# American Men & Women of Science

## 1998-99 • 20th Edition

The 20th edition of *AMERICAN MEN & WOMEN OF SCIENCE* was prepared by the R.R. Bowker Database Publishing Group in collaboration with the Publication Systems Department.


Senior Staff of the Database Publishing Group includes:

Senior Vice President & Chief Operating Officer, R.R. Bowker
**Neal Goff**


Publisher
**Nan Hudes**


Vice President, Database Publishing
**Leigh Yuster-Freeman**


**Editorial:**
Director: *Owen O'Donnell*
Managing Editor: *Karen Hallard*
Senior Editor: *Alison J. Butkiewicz*
Associate Editors: *Angela Krakow*
                 *Elizabeth McCarthy*

**Research:**
Director: *Judy Redel*
Senior Managing Editor: *Tanya Hurst*
Senior Editor: *Beverly Heath*

**Tampa Division:**
Director: *Valerie Harris*
Production Manager: *Debra Wilson*
Associate Coordinator: *Jennifer Rodgers*

# American Men & Women of Science

## 1998-99 • 20th Edition

**A Biographical Directory of Today's Leaders in Physical, Biological and Related Sciences.**

## Volume 7 • T-Z

**R.R. BOWKER**
A Unit of Reed Elsevier Business Information
New Providence, New Jersey

Published by R.R. Bowker, A Unit of Reed Elsevier Business Information

International Standard Book Number

| | |
|---|---|
| Set: | 0-8352-3748-6 |
| Volume 1: | 0-8352-3749-4 |
| Volume 2: | 0-8352-3775-3 |
| Volume 3: | 0-8352-3776-1 |
| Volume 4: | 0-8352-3778-8 |
| Volume 5: | 0-8352-3779-6 |
| Volume 6: | 0-8352-3781-8 |
| Volume 7: | 0-8352-3782-6 |
| Volume 8: | 0-8352-3783-4 |

International Standard Serial Number: 0192-8570
Library of Congress Catalog Card Number: 6-7326
Printed and bound in the United States of America.

8 Volume Set

ISBN 0 - 8352 - 3748 - 6

9 780835 237482

# Contents

# Advisory Committee

**Dr. Charles Henderson Dickens**
*Former Executive Secretary, Federal Coordinating Council for Science, Engineering & Technology*
Office of Science & Technology Policy

**Dr. Oscar Nicolas Garcia**
*NCR Distinguished Professor & Chair, Department of Computer Science & Engineering*
Wright State University

**Dr. Michael J. Jackson**
*Executive Director*
Federation of American Societies for Experimental Biology

**Dr. Shirley Mahaley Malcom**
*Head, Directorate for Education and Human Resources Programs*
American Association for the Advancement of Science

**Ms. Beverly Fearn Porter**
*Assistant to the Executive Director for Society Relations*
American Institute of Physics

**Dr. William Eldon Splinter**
*Former Vice Chancellor for Research*
University of Nebraska-Lincoln

**Dr. Dael Lee Wolfle**
*Professor Emeritus, Graduate School of Public Affairs*
University of Washington

**Dr. Ahmed H. Zewail**
*Linus Pauling Professor of Chemistry & Physics*
California Institute of Technology

# Preface

*American Men and Women of Science* remains without peer as a chronicle of North American and Canadian scientific endeavor and achievement. The present work is the twentieth edition since it was first compiled as *American Men of Science* by J. McKeen Cattell in 1906. In its ninety-two year history, *American Men and Women of Science* has profiled the careers of over 300,000 scientists and engineers. Since the first edition, the number of American scientists and the fields they pursue has grown immensely. This edition alone lists full biographies for 119,618 engineers and scientists, 4184 of which are listed for the first time. Although the book has grown, our stated purpose is the same as when Dr. Cattell first undertook the task of producing a biographical directory of active American scientists. It was his intention to record educational, personal and career data which would make "a contribution to the organization of science in America" and "make men [and women] of science acquainted with one another and with one another's work." It is our hope that this edition will fulfill these goals.

The biographies of engineers and scientists constitute seven of the eight volumes and provide birthdate, birthplace, field of specialty, education, honorary degrees, current position, professional and concurrent experience, awards, memberships, research information and addresses for each entrant when applicable. The eighth volume, the discipline index, organizes biographees by field of activity. This index, adapted from the National Science Foundation's Taxonomy of Degree and Employment Specialties, classifies entrants by 192 subject specialties listed in the table of contents of Volume 8. The index lists scientists and engineers by state within each subject specialty, allowing the user to easily locate a scientist in a given area. Also included are statistical information and charts showing the distribution of *AMWS* listees by age and discipline and and annotated listing of the recipients of the Nobel Prizes, the Craaford Prize, the Charles Stark Draper Prize, the National Medals of Science and Technology, the Fields Medal and the Alan T. Waterman Award since the last edition.

While the scientific fields covered by *American Men and Women of Science* are comprehensive, no attempt has been made to include all American scientists. Entrants are meant to be limited to those who have made significant contributions in their field. The names of new entrants were submitted for consideration at the editors' request by current entrants and by leaders of academic, government and private research programs and associations. Those included met the following criteria:

1. Distinguished achievement, by reason of experience, training or accomplishment, including contributions to literature, coupled with continuing activity in scientific work;

   or

2. Research activity of high quality in science as evidenced by publication in reputable scientific journals; or, for those whose work cannot be published due to governmental or industrial security, research activity of high quality in science as evidenced by the judgement of the individual's peers;

   or

3. Attainment of a position of substantial responsibility requiring scientific training and experience.

This edition profiles living scientists in the physical and biological fields, as well as public health scientists, engineers, mathematicians, statisticians, and computer scientists. The information is collected by means of direct communication whenever possible. All entrants receive forms for corroboration and updating. New entrants receive questionaires and verification proofs before publication. The information submitted by entrants is included as completely as possible within the boundaries of editorial and space restrictions. If an entrant does not return the form and his or her current location can be verified in secondary sources, the full entry is repeated. References to the previous edition are given for those who do not return forms and cannot be located, but who are presumed to be still active in science or engineering. Entrants known to be deceased are noted as such and a reference to the previous edition is given. Scientists and engineers who are not citizens of the United States or Canada are included if a significant portion of their work was performed in North America.

The information in *American Men & Women of Science* is available on magnetic tape. For information, contact Bowker Electronic Publishing (888-BOWKER-2). *American Men and Women of Science* is also available for online searching through Lexis®-Nexis® (800-227-4908) and through DIALOG, a service of Knight-Ridder Information, Inc. (800-334-2564). The online products allow fielded as well as key word searches of all elements of a record, including field of interest, experience, and location. An ERL-compliant CD-ROM is available through SilverPlatter Information (800-343-0064). Mailing lists are available through Reed Elsevier Business Information Lists (John Panza, Account Manager, Bowker Files, 245 W 17th St, New York, NY, 10011; 212-337-7164).

A project as large as publishing *American Men and Women of Science* involves the efforts of a great many people. The editors take this opportunity to thank the twentieth edition advisory committee for their guidance, encouragement and support. Appreciation is also expressed to the many scientific societies who provided their membership lists for the purpose of locating former entrants whose addresses had changed, and to the tens of thousands of scientists across the country who took time to provide us with biographical information. We also wish to thank Donna Brinkmann and Carol Carr of Reed Technology & Information Services, Inc. for their assistance in the successful production of this directory.

Comments, suggestions and nominations for the twenty-first edition are encouraged and should be directed to The Editors, *American Men and Women of Science*, R.R. Bowker, 121 Chanlon Road, New Providence, New Jersey, 07974.

Karen Hallard
Managing Editor

# Major Honors & Awards

### Nobel Prizes
Nobel Foundation, Royal Swedish Academy of Sciences &
Nobel Assembly of the Karolinska

*The Nobel Prizes were established in 1900 (and first awarded in 1901) to recognize those people who "have conferred the greatest benefit on mankind."*

#### 1995 Recipients

*Chemistry:*
Paul Josef Crutzen, Mario Jose Molina & Frank Sherwood Rowland
Awarded "for their work in atmospheric chemistry, particularly concerning the formation and decomposition of ozone."

*Physics:*
Martin Lewis Perl
Frederick Reines
Awarded to Perl "for the discovery of the tau lepton" and to Reines "for the detection of the nutrino."

*Physiology or Medicine:*
Edward B. Lewis, Christiane Nusslein-Volhard & Eric F. Wieschaus
Awarded "for their discoveries concerning the genetic control of early embryonic development."

#### 1996 Recipients

*Chemistry:*
Robert Floyd Curl, Harold Walter Kroto & Richard Errett Smalley
Awarded "for their discovery of fullerenes, carbon atoms bound in the form of a ball."

*Physics:*
David Morris Lee, Douglas Dean Osheroff & Robert Coleman Richardson
Awarded "for their discovery of superfluidity in helium-3."

*Physiology or Medicine:*
Peter Charles Doherty & Rolf Martin Zinkernagel
Awarded "for their discoveries of how the immune system recognizes virus-infected cells."

#### 1997 Recipients

*Chemistry:*
Paul Delos Boyer, Jens Christian Skou & John Ernest Walker
Awarded to Boyer & Walker "for their elucidation of the enzymatic mechanism underlying the synthesis of adenosine triphosphate (ATP)" and to Skou "for the first discovery of an ion-transporting enzyme, $NA^+$, $K^+$-ATPase."

*Physics:*
Claude Nessin Cohen-Tannoudji, Steven Chu & William Daniel Phillips
Awarded "for their development of methods to cool and trap atoms with laser light."

*Physiology or Medicine:*
Stanley Ben Prusiner
Awarded to Prusiner for his discovery of prions, a new genre of infectious agents.

### Crafoord Prize
Royal Swedish Academy of Sciences

*The Crafoord Prize was introduced in 1982 to award scientists in disciplines not covered by the Nobel Prize, namely mathematics, astronomy, geosciences and biosciences.*

#### 1995 Recipients

Willi Dansgaard & Nicholas John Shackleton
Awarded "for their fundamental work on developing and applying isotope geological analysis methods for the study of climatic variations during the Quaternary period."

#### 1996 Recipient

Robert McRedie May
Awarded to May "for his pioneering ecological research concerning theoretical analysis of the dynamics of populations, communities and ecosystems."

#### 1997 Recipients

Fred Hoyle & Edwin Ernest Salpeter
Awarded "for their pioneering contributions involving the study of nuclear reactions in stars and stars' development."

### Charles Stark Draper Prize
National Academy of Engineering

*The Draper Prize, awarded biennially, was introduced in 1989 to recognize engineering achievement.*

#### 1995 Recipients

John Robinson Pierce & Harold A. Rosen
Awarded for developing communications satellite technology.

#### 1997 Recipients
Vladimir Haensel
Awarded to Haensel for inventing "Platforming" — platinum reforming to convert petroleum into high-performance fuels.

## National Medal of Science
### National Science Foundation

*The National Medals of Science were established by the United States Congress in 1959 and have been awarded by the President of the United States since 1962. The National Science Foundation's selection criteria are based on the "total impact of an individual's work on the present state of physical, biological, mathematical, engineering, behavioral, or social sciences."*

### 1995 Recipients

Thomas Robert Cech
Hans Georg Dehmelt
Peter Goldreich
Hermann A(nton) Haus
Isabella Lugoski Karle
Louis Nirenberg
Alexander Rich
Roger N. Shepard

### 1996 Recipients

Wallace Broecker
Norman Ralph Davidson
James L(oton) Flanagan
Richard M. Karp
Chandra Kumar Naranbhai Patel
Ruth Patrick
Paul Anthony Samuelson
Stephen Smale

### 1997 Recipients

William K. Estes
Darleane Christian Hoffman
Harold Sledge Johnston
Marshall N. Rosenbluth
Martin Schwarzschild (deceased)
James Dewey Watson
Robert A. Weinberg
George West Wetherill
Shing-Tung Yau

## Fields Medal
### International Mathematical Union

*The Fields Medals were established in 1936 by Canadian mathematician John Fields to acknowledge outstanding research by young mathematicians. The medals are awarded every four years at the International Congress of Mathematicians.*

### 1994 Recipients

Jean Bourgain
Pierre Louis Lions
Jean-Christophe Yoccoz
Efim Isaakovich Zelmanof

Awarded to Bourgain for his insights into the geometry of infinite dimensional spaces. Awarded to Lions for advances in non-linear partial differential equations. Awarded to Yoccoz for analyzing the end results of complicated sequences of circle maps. Awarded to Zelmanov for solving the unrestricted Burnside problem.

## National Medal of Technology
### U.S. Department of Commerce

*The National Medals of Technology were created as part of the 1980 Stevenson-Wydler Technology Innovation Act and were first awarded in 1985. They are bestowed by the President of the United States to recognize individuals and companies for their development or commercialization of technology or for their contributions to the establishment of a technologically-trained workforce.*

### 1995 Recipients

Praveen Chaudhari
Jerome John Cuomo
Richard Joseph Gambino
Edward R. McCracken
Sam B. Williams
Alejandro Zaffaroni
Procter & Gamble Company
3 M

### 1996 Recipients

Charles Huron Kaman
Stephanie Louise Kwolek
James C. Morgan
Peter Henry Rose
Johnson & Johnson

### 1997 Recipients

Norman R. Augustine
Vinton Gray Cerf
Ray Milton Dolby
Robert Elliot Kahn
Robert Steven Ledley

## Alan T. Waterman Award
### National Science Foundation & National Science Board

*Established by the United States Congress in 1975, the Waterman Award is given annually to an outstanding researcher, aged 35 or younger, in any field of science or engineering supported by the National Science Foundation.*

### 1995 Recipient

Matthew P.A. Fisher
Awarded to Fisher "for his pioneering contributions to the theory of disordered superconductors."

### 1996 Recipient

Robert Mebane Waymouth
Awarded to Waymouth for discovering new ways to make polymers.

### 1997 Recipient

Eric Allin Cornell
Awarded to Cornell for creation of Bose-Einstein condensate (BEC).

# Statistics

Statistical distribution of entrants in *American Men & Women of Science* with U.S. mailing addresses is illustrated on the following five pages. The regional scheme for geographical analysis is diagrammed in the map below. A table enumerating the geographic distribution can be found on page xvi, following the charts. The statistics are compiled by tallying all occurrences of a major index subject. Each scientist may choose to be indexed under as many as four categories; thus, the total number of subject references is greater than the number of entrants in *AMWS*.

## All Disciplines

|  | Number | Percent |
|---|---|---|
| Northeast | 56,006 | 34% |
| Southeast | 41,313 | 25% |
| North Central | 19,699 | 12% |
| South Central | 12,169 | 7% |
| Mountain | 11,675 | 7% |
| Pacific | 25,703 | 15% |
| **TOTAL** | **166,565** | **100%** |

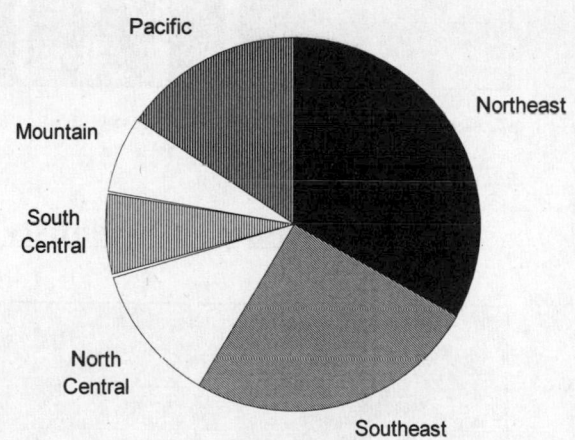

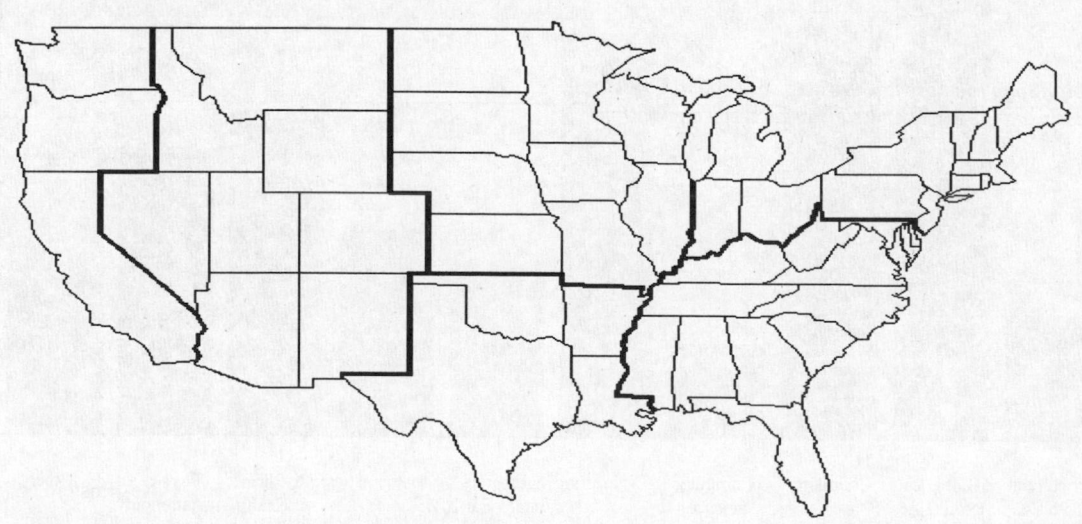

## Age Distribution of American Men & Women of Science

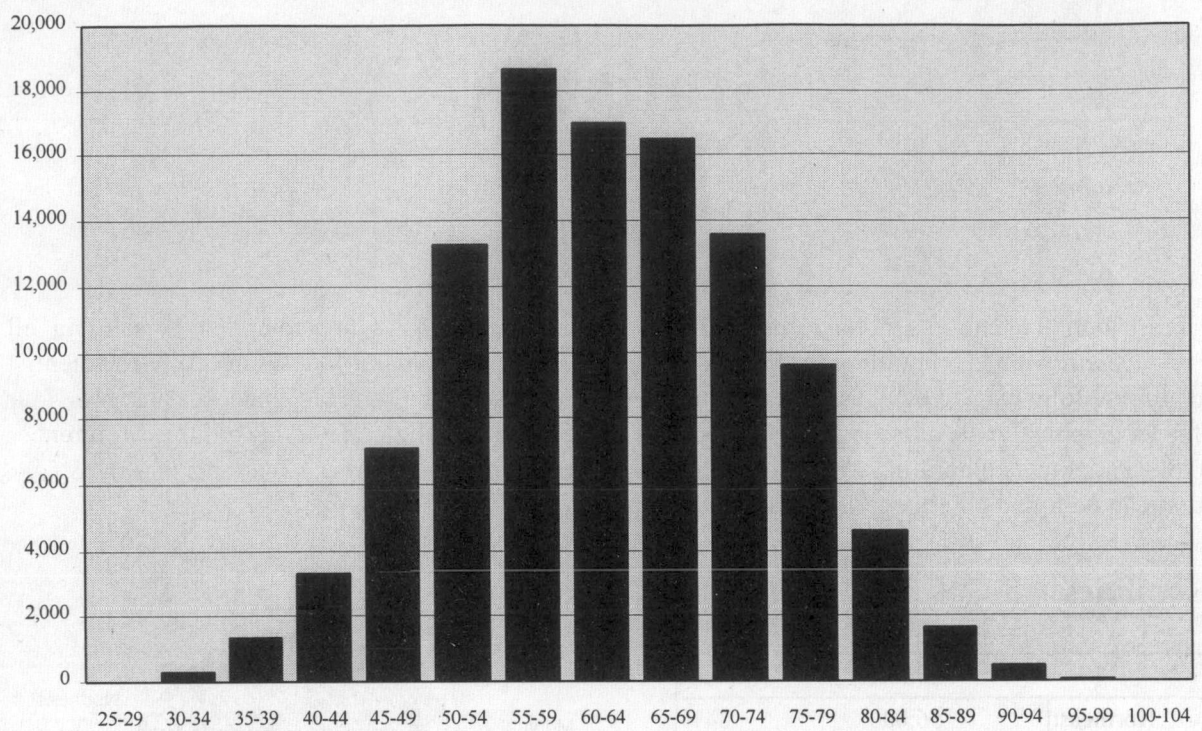

## Number of Scientists in Each Discipline of Study

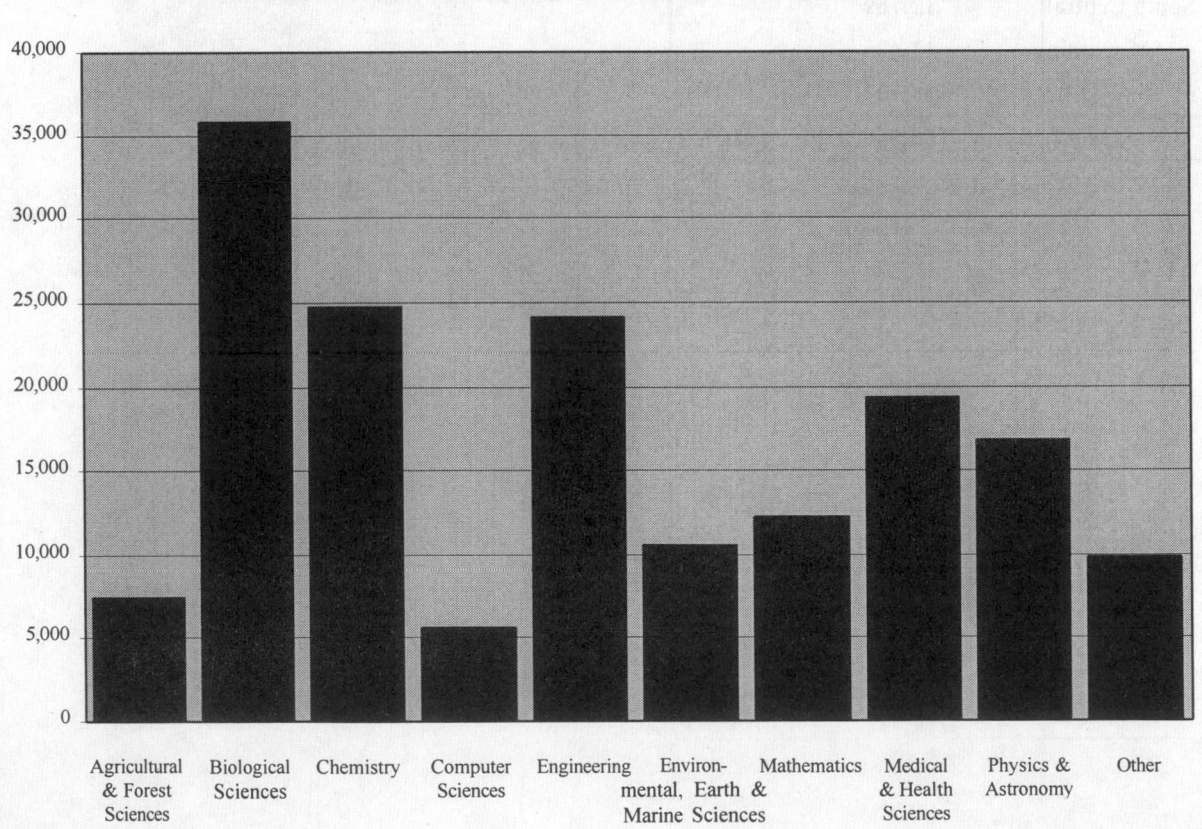

# Agricultural & Forest Sciences

|  | Number | Percent |
|---|---|---|
| Northeast | 1,585 | 21% |
| Southeast | 2,053 | 27% |
| North Central | 1,171 | 16% |
| South Central | 635 | 8% |
| Mountain | 739 | 10% |
| Pacific | 1,305 | 17% |
| **TOTAL** | **7,488** | **100%** |

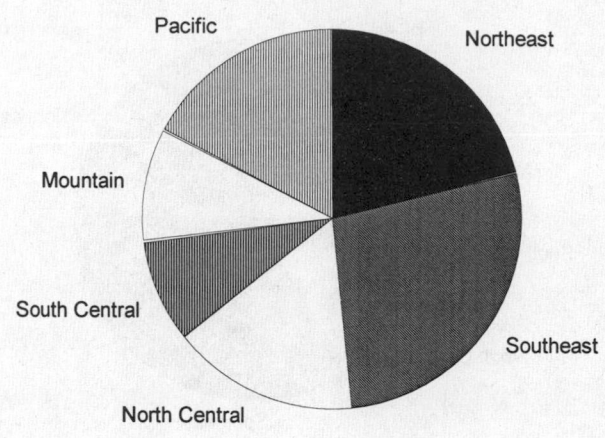

# Biological Sciences

|  | Number | Percent |
|---|---|---|
| Northeast | 11,671 | 33% |
| Southeast | 9,045 | 25% |
| North Central | 4,918 | 14% |
| South Central | 2,741 | 8% |
| Mountain | 2,125 | 6% |
| Pacific | 5,277 | 15% |
| **TOTAL** | **35,777** | **100%** |

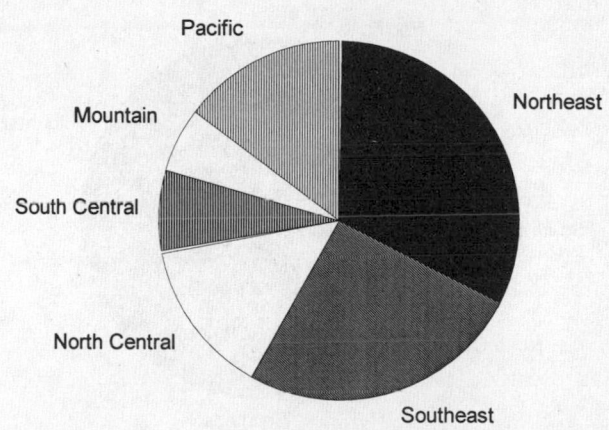

# Chemistry

|  | Number | Percent |
|---|---|---|
| Northeast | 9,296 | 38% |
| Southeast | 6,196 | 25% |
| North Central | 2,964 | 12% |
| South Central | 1,724 | 7% |
| Mountain | 1,381 | 6% |
| Pacific | 3,139 | 13% |
| **TOTAL** | **24,700** | **100%** |

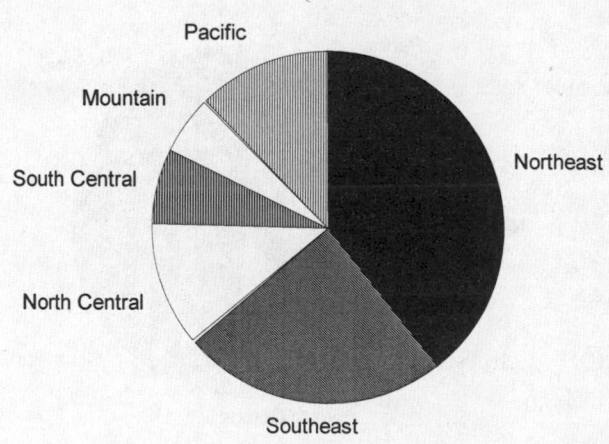

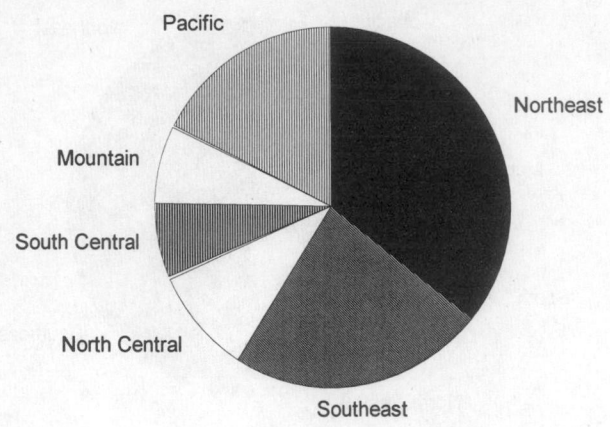

## Computer Sciences

|  | Number | Percent |
|---|---|---|
| Northeast | 1,983 | 35% |
| Southeast | 1,278 | 23% |
| North Central | 556 | 10% |
| South Central | 378 | 7% |
| Mountain | 423 | 7% |
| Pacific | 1,034 | 18% |
| **TOTAL** | **5,652** | **100%** |

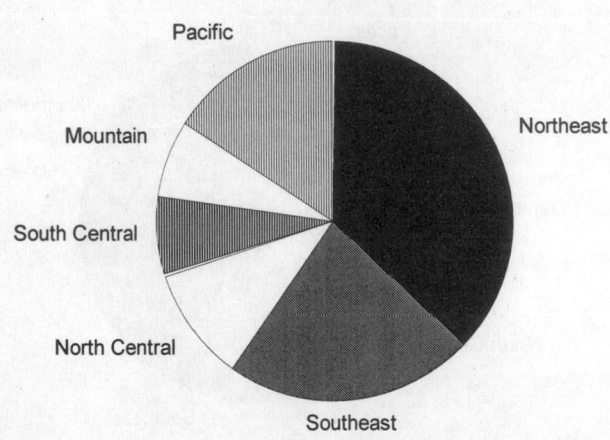

## Engineering

|  | Number | Percent |
|---|---|---|
| Northeast | 8,780 | 36% |
| Southeast | 5,487 | 23% |
| North Central | 2,501 | 10% |
| South Central | 1,742 | 7% |
| Mountain | 1,760 | 7% |
| Pacific | 3,883 | 16% |
| **TOTAL** | **24,153** | **100%** |

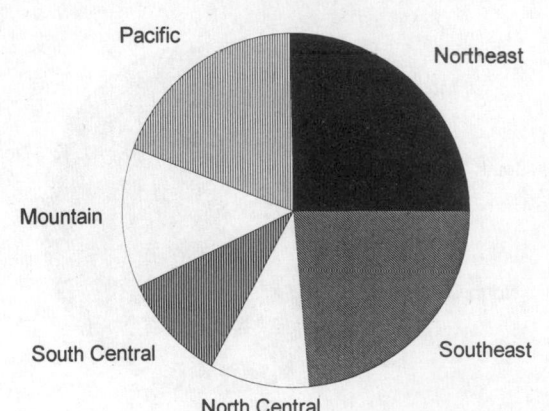

## Environmental, Earth & Marine Sciences

|  | Number | Percent |
|---|---|---|
| Northeast | 2,654 | 25% |
| Southeast | 2,507 | 24% |
| North Central | 984 | 9% |
| South Central | 1,008 | 10% |
| Mountain | 1,365 | 13% |
| Pacific | 2,008 | 19% |
| **TOTAL** | **10,526** | **100%** |

# Mathematics

|  | Number | Percent |
|---|---|---|
| Northeast | 4,292 | 35% |
| Southeast | 2,865 | 23% |
| North Central | 1,552 | 13% |
| South Central | 933 | 8% |
| Mountain | 760 | 6% |
| Pacific | 1,901 | 15% |
| **TOTAL** | **12,303** | **100%** |

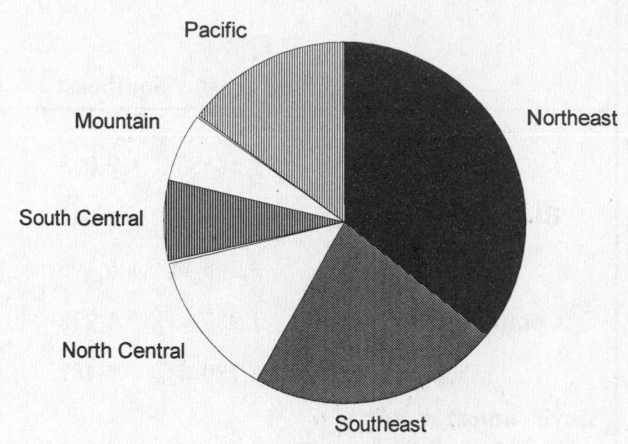

# Medical & Health Sciences

|  | Number | Percent |
|---|---|---|
| Northeast | 6,883 | 36% |
| Southeast | 5,139 | 27% |
| North Central | 2,471 | 13% |
| South Central | 1,494 | 8% |
| Mountain | 804 | 4% |
| Pacific | 2,501 | 13% |
| **TOTAL** | **19,292** | **100%** |

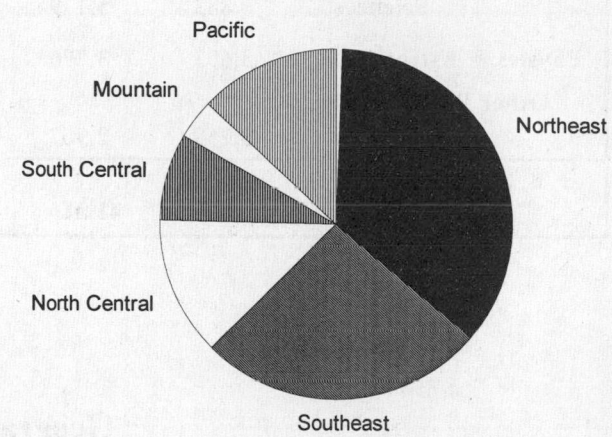

# Physics & Astronomy

|  | Number | Percent |
|---|---|---|
| Northeast | 5,603 | 33% |
| Southeast | 3,776 | 22% |
| North Central | 1,545 | 9% |
| South Central | 904 | 5% |
| Mountain | 1,674 | 10% |
| Pacific | 3,307 | 20% |
| **TOTAL** | **16,809** | **100%** |

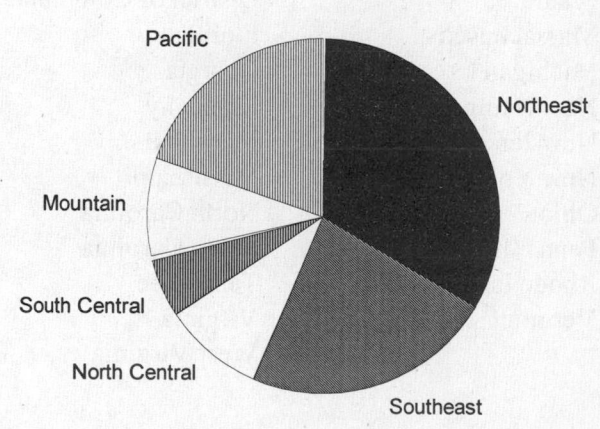

# Geographic Distribution of Scientists by Discipline

|  | Northeast | Southeast | North Central | South Central | Mountain | Pacific | TOTAL |
|---|---|---|---|---|---|---|---|
| **Agricultural & Forest Sciences** | 1,585 | 2,053 | 1,171 | 635 | 739 | 1,305 | **7,488** |
| **Biological Sciences** | 11,671 | 9,045 | 4,918 | 2,741 | 2,125 | 5,277 | **35,777** |
| **Chemistry** | 9,296 | 6,196 | 2,964 | 1,724 | 1,381 | 3,139 | **24,700** |
| **Computer Sciences** | 1,983 | 1,278 | 556 | 378 | 423 | 1,034 | **5,652** |
| **Engineering** | 8,780 | 5,487 | 2,501 | 1,742 | 1,760 | 3,883 | **24,153** |
| **Environmental, Earth & Marine Sciences** | 2,654 | 2,507 | 984 | 1,008 | 1,365 | 2,008 | **10,526** |
| **Mathematics** | 4,292 | 2,865 | 1,552 | 933 | 760 | 1,901 | **12,303** |
| **Medical & Health Sciences** | 6,883 | 5,139 | 2,471 | 1,494 | 804 | 2,501 | **19,292** |
| **Physics & Astronomy** | 5,603 | 3,776 | 1,545 | 904 | 1,674 | 3,307 | **16,809** |
| **Other Professional Fields** | 3,259 | 2,967 | 1,037 | 610 | 644 | 1,348 | **9,865** |
| **TOTAL** | **56,006** | **41,313** | **19,699** | **12,169** | **11,675** | **25,703** | **166,565** |

# Geographic Definitions

**Northeast**
Connecticut
Indiana
Maine
Massachusetts
Michigan
New Hampshire
New Jersey
New York
Ohio
Pennsylvania
Rhode Island
Vermont

**Southeast**
Alabama
Delaware
District of Columbia
Florida
Georgia
Kentucky
Maryland
Mississippi
North Carolina
South Carolina
Tennessee
Virginia
West Virginia

**North Central**
Illinois
Iowa
Kansas
Minnesota
Missouri
Nebraska
North Dakota
South Dakota
Wisconsin

**South Central**
Arkansas
Louisiana
Texas
Oklahoma

**Mountain**
Arizona
Colorado
Idaho
Montana
Nevada
New Mexico
Utah
Wyoming

**Pacific**
Alaska
California
Hawaii
Oregon
Washington

# Sample Entry

*American Men & Women of Science (AMWS)* is an extremely useful reference tool. The book is most often used in two ways: to find more information about a particular scientist and to locate a scientist in a specific field.

To locate information about an individual, the biographical section is most helpful. It encompasses the first seven volumes and lists scientists and engineers alphabetically by last name. The fictitious biographical listing shown below illustrates every type of information an entry may include.

The Discipline Index, volume 8, can be used to easily find a scientist in a specific subject specialty. This index is first classified by area of study; within each specialty entrants are divided further by state of residence.

Name — Field of Specialty — Current Position — Birthdate — Marriage/Spouse data — Children's Name(s) — Education — Honorary Degrees — Honors & Awards — Professional Experience — Concurrent Experience — Memberships — Research and Publications — Mailing Address — Fax Number — E-Mail Address

REED, SAMANTHA J(EAN), OCEANOGRAPHY, MARINE BIOLOGY. *Current Pos:* SR ASSOC OCEANOGRAPHER, DEPT NAVY, 86- *Personal Data:* b Brooklyn, NY, Nov 9, 42; m 67, James A. Mayer; c Steven C & Lillian M. *Educ:* Univ Notre Dame, BS, 63, MS, 65, Fla State Univ, PhD(oceanog), 70. *Hon Degrees:* DSc, Univ Calif, Davis, 79. *Honors & Awards:* Henry Bryant Bigelow Medal, Oceanog, 92; *Prof Exp:* Asst prof oceanog, 71-73, assoc prof oceanog & biol, Harvard Univ, 73-75. *Concurrent Pos:* Consult, New England Aquarium, 74-78; vis lect, Wash Univ, 77. *Mem:* AAAS, Am Soc Naval Engrs, Sigma Xi, Oceanog Soc (vpres 82-83). *Res:* Ocean pollution prevention, water treatment and analysis, ecology of marine plankton and sponges, author of 13 publications. *Mailing Address:* 121102 Smithfield Way, Boca Raton, FL 33431. *Fax:* 407-555-5939; *E-Mail:* sreed@usnavy.mil.fla

# Abbreviations

AAAS—American Association for the Advancement of Science
abnorm—abnormal
abstr—abstract
acad—academic, academy
acct—account, accountant, accounting
acoust—acoustic(s), acoustical
ACTH—adrenocorticotrophic hormone
actg—acting
activ—activities, activity
addn—addition(s), additional
Add—Address
adj—adjunct, adjutant
adjust—adjustment
Adm—Admiral
admin—administration, administrative
adminr—administrator(s)
admis—admission(s)
adv—adviser(s), advisory
advan—advance(d), advancement
advert—advertisement, advertising
AEC—Atomic Energy Commission
aerodyn—aerodynamic
aeronaut—aeronautic(s), aeronautical
aerophys—aerophysical, aerophysics
aesthet—aesthetic
AFB—Air Force Base
affil—affiliate(s), affiliation
agr—agricultural, agriculture
agron—agronomic, agronomical, agronomy
agrost—agrostologic, agrostological, agrostology
agt—agent
AID—Agency for International Development
Ala—Alabama
allergol—allergological, allergology
alt—alternate
Alta—Alberta
Am—America, American
AMA—American Medical Association
anal—analysis, analytic, analytical
analog—analogue
anat—anatomic, anatomical, anatomy
anesthesiol—anesthesiology
angiol—angiology
Ann—Annal(s)
ann—annual
anthrop—anthropological, anthropology
anthropom—anthropometric, anthropometrical, anthropometry

antiq—antiquary, antiquities, antiquity
antiqn—antiquarian
apicult—apicultural, apiculture
APO—Army Post Office
app—appoint, appointed
appl—applied
appln—application
approx—approximate(ly)
Apr—April
apt—apartment(s)
aquacult—aquaculture
arbit—arbitration
arch—archives
archaeol—archaeological, archaeology
archit—architectural, architecture
Arg—Argentina, Argentine
Ariz—Arizona
Ark—Arkansas
artil—artillery
asn—association
assoc(s)—associate(s), associated
asst(s)—assistant(s), assistantship(s)
assyriol—Assyriology
astrodyn—astrodynamics
astron—astronomical, astronomy
astronaut—astronautical, astronautics
astronr—astronomer
astrophys—astrophysical, astrophysics
attend—attendant, attending
atty—attorney
audiol—audiology
Aug—August
auth—author
AV—audiovisual
Ave—Avenue
avicult—avicultural, aviculture

b—born
bact—bacterial, bacteriologic, bacteriological, bacteriology
BC—British Colombia
bd—board
behav—behavior(al)
Belg—Belgian, Belgium
Bibl—Biblical
bibliog—bibliographic, bibliographical, bibliography
bibliogr—bibliographer
biochem—biochemical, biochemistry
biog—biographical, biography
biol—biological, biology
biomed—biomedical, biomedicine

biomet—biometric(s), biometrical, biometry
biophys—biophysical, biophysics
bk(s)—book(s)
bldg—building
Blvd—Boulevard
Bor—Borough
bot—botanical, botany
br—branch(es)
Brig—Brigadier
Brit—Britain, British
Bro(s)—Brother(s)
byrol—byrology
bull—Bulletin
bur—bureau
bus—business
BWI—British West Indies

c—children
Calif—California
Can—Canada, Canadian
cand—candidate
Capt—Captain
cardiol—cardiology
cardiovasc—cardiovascular
cartog—cartographic, cartographical, cartography
cartogr—cartographer
Cath—Catholic
CEngr—Corp of Engineers
cent—central
Cent Am—Central American
cert—certificate(s), certification, certified
chap—chapter
chem—chemical(s), chemistry
chemother—chemotherapy
chg—change
chmn—chairman
citricult—citriculture
class—classical
climat—climatological, climatology
clin(s)—clinic(s), clinical
cmndg—commanding
Co—County
Co—Companies, Company
co-auth—co-author
co-dir—co-director
co-ed—co-editor
co-educ—co-education, co-educational
col(s)—college(s), collegiate, colonel
collab—collaboration, collaborative
collabr—collaborator

xviii

Colo—Colorado
com—commerce, commercial
Comdr—Commander
commun—communicable, communication(s)
comn(s)—commission(s), commissioned
comndg—commanding
comnr—commissioner
comp—comparitive
compos—composition
comput—computation, computer(s), computing
comt(s)—committee(s)
conchol—conchology
conf—conference
cong—congress, congressional
Conn—Connecticut
conserv—conservation, conservatory
consol—consolidated, consolidation
const—constitution, constitutional
construct—construction, constructive
consult(s)—consult, consultant(s), consultantship(s), consultation, consulting
contemp—contemporary
contrib—contribute, contributing, contribution(s)
contribr—contributor
conv—convention
coop—cooperating, cooperation, cooperative
coord—coordinate(d), coordinating, coordination
coordr—coordinator
corp—corporate, corporation(s)
corresp—correspondence, correspondent, corresponding
coun—council, counsel, counseling
counr—councilor, counselor
criminol—criminological, criminology
cryog—cryogenic(s)
crystallog—crystallographic, crystallographical, crystallography
crystallogr—crystallographer
Ct—Court
Ctr—Center
cult—cultural, culture
cur—curator
curric—curriculum
cybernet—cybernetic(s)
cytol—cytological, cytology
Czech—Czechoslovakia, Czech Republic

DC—District of Columbia
Dec—December
Del—Delaware
deleg—delegate, delegation
delinq—delinquency, delinquent
dem—democrat(s), democratic
demog—demographic, demography
demogr—demographer
demonstr—demontrator
dendrol—dendrologic, dendrological, dendrology
dent—dental, dentistry
dep—deputy
dept—department
dermat—dermatologic, dermatological, dermatology

develop—developed, developing, development, developmental
diag—diagnosis, diagnostic
dialectol—dialectological, dialectology
dict—dictionaries, dictionary
Dig—Digest
dipl—diploma, diplomate
dir(s)—director(s), directories, directory
dis—disease(s), disorders
Diss Abst—Dissertation Abstracts
dist—district
distrib—distributed, distribution, distributive
distribr—distributor(s)
div—division, divisional, divorced
DNA—deoxyribonucleic acid
doc—document(s), documentary, documentation
Dom—Dominion
Dr—Drive

E—East
ecol—ecological, ecology
econ(s)—economic(s), economical, economy
economet—econometric(s)
ECT—electroconvulsive or electroshock therapy
ed—edition(s), editor(s), editorial
ed bd—editorial board
educ—education, educational
educr—educator(s)
EEG—electroencephalogram, electroencephalographic, electroencephalography
Egyptol—Egyptology
EKG—electrocardiogram
elec—electric, electrical, electricity
electrochem—electrochemical, electrochemistry
electroph—electrophysical, electrophysics
elem—elementary
embryol—embryologic, embryological, embryology
emer—emeriti, emeritus
employ—employment
encour—encouragement
encycl—encyclopedia
endocrinol—endocrinologic, endocrinology
eng—engineering
Eng—England, English
engr(s)—engineer(s)
enol—enology
Ens—Ensign
entom—entomological, entomology
environ—environment(s), environmental
enzym—enzymology
epidemiol—epidemiologic, epidemiological, epidemiology
equip—equipment
ERDA—Energy Research & Development Administration
ESEA—Elementary & Secondary Education Act
espec—especially
estab—established, establishment(s)
ethnog—ethnographic, ethnographical, ethnography
ethnogr—ethnographer

ethnol—ethnologic, ethnological, ethnology
Europ—European
eval—evaluation
Evangel—Evangelical
eve—evening
exam—examination(s), examining
examr—examiner
except—exceptional
exec(s)—executive(s)
exeg—exegeses, exegesis, exegetic, exegetical
exhib(s)—exhibition(s), exhibit(s)
exp—experiment, experimental
exped(s)—expedition(s)
explor—exploration(s), exploratory
expos—exposition
exten—extension

fac—faculty
facil—facilities, facility
Feb—February
fed—federal
fedn—federation
fel(s)—fellow(s), fellowship(s)
fermentol—fermentology
fertil—fertility, fertilization
Fla—Florida
floricult—floricultural, floriculture
found—foundation
FPO—Fleet Post Office
Fr—French
Ft—Fort

Ga—Georgia
gastroenterol—gastroenterological, gastroenterology
gen—general
geneal—genealogical, genealogy
geod—geodesy, geodetic
geog—geographic, geographical, geography
geogr—geographer
geol—geologic, geological, geology
geom—geometric, geometrical, geometry
geomorphol—geomorphologic, geomorphology
geophys—geophysical, geophysics
Ger—German, Germanic, Germany
geriat—geriatric
geront—gerontological, gerontology
Ges—Gesellschaft
glaciol—glaciology
gov—governing, governor(s)
govt—government, governmental
grad—graduate(d)
Gt Brit—Great Britain
guid—guidance
gym—gymnasium
gynec—gynecologic, gynecological, gynecology

handbk(s)—handbook(s)
helminth—helminthology
hemat—hematologic, hematological, hematology
herpet—herpetologic, herpetological, herpetology
HEW—Department of Health, Education & Welfare

# ABBREVIATIONS

Hisp—Hispanic, Hispania
hist—historic, historical, history
histol—histological, histology
HM—Her Majesty
hochsch—hochschule
homeop—homeopathic, homeopathy
hon(s)—honor(s), honorable, honorary
hort—horticultural, horticulture
hosp(s)—hospital(s), hospitalization
hq—headquarters
HumRRO—Human Resources Research Office
husb—husbandry
Hwy—Highway
hydraul—hydraulic(s)
hydrodyn—hydrodynamic(s)
hydrol—hydrologic, hydrological, hydrologics
hyg—hygiene, hygienic(s)
hypn—hypnosis

ichthyol—ichthyological, ichthyology
Ill—Illinois
illum—illuminating, illumination
illus—illustrate, illustrated, illustration
illusr—illustrator
immunol—immunologic, immunological, immunology
Imp—Imperial
improv—improvement
Inc—Incorporated
in-chg—in charge
incl—include(s), including
Ind—Indiana
indust(s)—industrial, industries, industry
Inf—Infantry
info—information
inorg—inorganic
ins—insurance
inst(s)—institute(s), institution(s)
instnl—institutional(ized)
instr(s)—instruct, instruction, instructor(s)
instrnl—instructional
int—international
intel—intellligence
introd—introduction
invert—invertebrate
invest(s)—investigation(s)
investr—investigator
irrig—irrigation
Ital—Italian

J—Journal
Jan—January
Jct—Junction
jour—journal, journalism
jr—junior
jurisp—jurisprudence
juv—juvenile

Kans—Kansas
Ky—Kentucky

La—Louisiana
lab(s)—laboratories, laboratory
lang—language(s)
laryngol—larygological, laryngology
lect—lecture(s)

lectr—lecturer(s)
legis—legislation, legislative, legislature
lett—letter(s)
lib—liberal
libr—libraries, library
librn—librarian
lic—license(d)
limnol—limnological, limnology
ling—linguistic(s), linguistical
lit—literary, literature
lithol—lithologic, lithological, lithology
Lt—Lieutenant
Ltd—Limited
m—married
mach—machine(s), machinery
mag—magazine(s)
maj—major
malacol—malacology
mammal—mammalogy
Man—Manitoba
Mar—March
Mariol—Mariology
Mass—Massachusetts
mat—material(s)
mat med—materia medica
math—mathematic(s), mathematical
Md—Maryland
mech—mechanic(s), mechanical
med—medical, medicinal, medicine
Mediter—Mediterranean
Mem—Memorial
mem—member(s), membership(s)
ment—mental(ly)
metab—metabolic, metabolism
metall—metallurgic, metallurgical, metallurgy
metallog—metallographic, metallography
metallogr—metallographer
metaphys—metaphysical, metaphysics
meteorol—meteorological, meteorology
metrol—metrological, metrology
metrop—metropolitan
Mex—Mexican, Mexico
mfg—manufacturing
mfr—manufacturer
mgr—manager
mgt—management
Mich—Michigan
microbiol—microbiological, microbiology
micros—microscopic, microscopical, microscopy
mid—middle
mil—military
mineral—mineralogical, mineralogy
Minn—Minnesota
Miss—Mississippi
mkt—market, marketing
Mo—Missouri
mod—modern
monogr—monograph
Mont—Montana
morphol—morphological, morphology
Mt—Mount
mult—multiple
munic—municipal, municipalities
mus—museum(s)
musicol—musicological, musicology
mycol—mycologic, mycology

N—North
NASA—National Aeronautics & Space Administration
nat—national, naturalized
NATO—North Atlantic Treaty Organization
navig—navigation(al)
NB—New Brunswick
NC—North Carolina
NDak—North Dakota
NDEA—National Defense Education Act
Nebr—Nebraska
nematol—nematological, nematology
nerv—nervous
Neth—Netherlands
neurol—neurological, neurology
neuropath—neuropathological, neuropathology
neuropsychiat—neuropsychiatric, neuropsychiatry
neurosurg—neurosurgical, neurosurgery
Nev—Nevada
New Eng—New England
New York—New York City
Nfld—Newfoundland
NH—New Hampshire
NIH—National Institute of Health
NIMH—National Institute of Mental Health
NJ—New Jersey
NMex—New Mexico
No—Number
nonres—nonresident
norm—normal
Norweg—Norwegian
Nov—November
NS—Nova Scotia
NSF—National Science Foundation
NSW—New South Wales
numis—numismatic(s)
nutrit—nutrition, nutritional
NY—New York State
NZ—New Zealand

observ—observatories, observatory
obstet—obstetric(s), obstetrical
occas—occasional(ly)
occup—occupation, occupational
oceanog—oceanographic, oceanographical, oceanography
oceanogr—oceanographer
Oct—October
odontol—odontology
OEEC—Organization for European Economic Cooperation
off—office, official
Okla—Oklahoma
olericult—olericulture
oncol—oncologic, oncology
Ont—Ontario
oper(s)—operation(s), operational, operative
ophthal—ophthalmologic, ophthalmological, ophthalmology
optom—optometric, optometrical, optometry
ord—ordnance
Ore—Oregon
org—organic

orgn—organization(s), organizational
orient—oriental
ornith—ornithological, ornithology
orthod—orthodontia, orthodontic(s)
orthop—orthopedic(s)
osteop—osteopathic, osteopathy
otol—otological, otology
otolaryngol—otolaryngological, otolaryngology
otorhinol—otorhinologic, otorhinology

Pa—Pennsylvania
Pac—Pacific
paleobot—paleobotanical, paleobotany
paleont—paleontology
Pan-Am—Pan-American
parasitol—parasitology
partic—participant, participating
path—pathologic, pathological, pathology
pedag—pedagogic(s), pedagogical, pedagogy
pediat—pediatric(s)
PEI—Prince Edward Islands
penol—penological, penology
periodont—periodontal, periodontic(s)
petrog—petrographic, petrographical, petrography
petrogr—petrographer
petrol—petroleum, petrologic, petrological, petrology
pharm—pharmacy
pharmaceut—pharmaceutic(s), pharmaceutical(s)
pharmacog—pharmacognosy
pharamacol—pharmacologic, pharmacological, pharmacology
phenomenol—phenomenologic(al), phenomenology
philol—philological, philology
philos—philosophic, philosophical, philosophy
photog—photographic, photography
photogeog—photogeographic, photogeography
photogr—photographer(s)
photogram—photogrammetric, photogrammetry
photom—photometric, photometrical, photometry
phycol—phycology
phys—physical
physiog—physiographic, physiographical, physiography
physiol—physiological, phsysiology
Pkwy—Parkway
Pl—Place
polit—political, politics
polytech—polytechnic(s)
pomol—pomological, pomology
pontif—pontifical
pop—population
Port—Portugal, Portuguese
Pos—Position
postgrad—postgraduate
PQ—Province of Quebec
PR—Puerto Rico
pract—practice
practr—practitioner
prehist—prehistoric, prehistory

prep—preparation, preparative, preparatory
pres—president
Presby—Presbyterian
preserv—preservation
prev—prevention, preventive
prin—principal
prob(s)—problem(s)
proc—proceedings
proctol—proctologic, proctological, proctology
prod—product(s), production, productive
prof—professional, professor, professorial
Prof Exp—Professional Experience
prog(s)—program(s), programmed, programming
proj—project(s), projection(al), projective
prom—promotion
protozool—protozoology
Prov—Province, Provincial
psychiat—psychiatric, psychiatry
psychoanal—psychoanalysis, psychoanalytic, psychoanalytical
psychol—psychological, psychology
psychomet—psychometric(s)
psychopath—psychopathologic, psychopathology
psychophys—psychophysical, psychophysics
psychophysiol—psychophysiological, psychophysiology
psychosom—psychosomatic(s)
psychother—psychoterapeutic(s), psychotherapy
Pt—Point
pub—public
publ—publication(s), publish(ed), publisher, publishing
pvt—private

Qm—Quartermaster
Qm Gen—Quartermaster General
qual—qualitative, quality
quant—quantitative
quart—quarterly
Que—Quebec

radiol—radiological, radiology
RAF—Royal Air Force
RAFVR—Royal Air Force Volunteer Reserve
RAMC—Royal Army Medical Corps
RAMCR—Royal Army Medical Corps Reserve
RAOC—Royal Army Ordnance Corps
RASC—Royal Army Service Corps
RASCR—Royal Army Service Corps Reserve
RCAF—Royal Canadian Air Force
RCAFR—Royal Canadian Air Force Reserve
RCAFVR—Royal Canadian Air Force Volunteer Reserve
RCAMC—Royal Canadian Army Medical Corps
RCAMCR—Royal Canadian Army Medical Corps Reserve
RCASC—Royal Canadian Army Service Corps

RCASCR—Royal Canadian Army Service Corps Reserve
RCEME—Royal Canadian Electrical & Mechanical Engineers
RCN—Royal Canadian Navy
RCNR—Royal Canadian Naval Reserve
RCNVR—Royal Canadian Naval Volunteer Reserve
Rd—Road
RD—Rural Delivery
rec—record(s), recording
redevelop—redevelopment
ref—reference(s)
refrig—refrigeration
regist—register(ed), registration
registr—registrar
regt—regiment(al)
rehab—rehabilitation
rel(s)—relation(s), relative
relig—religion, religious
REME—Royal Electrical & Mechanical Engineers
rep—represent, representative
Repub—Republic
req—requirements
res—research, reserve
rev—review, revised, revision
RFD—Rural Free Delivery
rhet—rhetoric, rhetorical
RI—Rhode Island
Rm—Room
RM—Royal Marines
RN—Royal Navy
RNA—ribonucleic acid
RNR—Royal Naval Reserve
RNVR—Royal Naval Volunteer Reserve
roentgenol—roentgenologic, roentgenological, roentgenology
RR—Railroad, Rural Route
Rte—Route
Russ—Russian
rwy—railway

S—South
SAfrica—South Africa
SAm—South America, South American
sanit—sanitary, sanitation
Sask—Saskatchewan
SC—South Carolina
Scand—Scandinavia(n)
sch(s)—school(s)
scholar—scholarship
sci—science(s), scientific
SDak—South Dakota
SEATO—Southeast Asia Treaty Organization
sec—secondary
sect—section
secy—secretary
seismog—seismograph, seismographic, seismography
seismogr—seismographer
seismol—seismological, seismology
sem—seminar, seminary
Sen—Senator, Senatorial
Sept—September
ser—serial, series
serol—serologic, serological, serology
serv—service(s), serving

ABBREVIATIONS

silvicult—silvicultural, silviculture
soc(s)—societies, society
soc sci—social science
sociol—sociologic, sociological, sociology
Span—Spanish
spec—special
specif—specification(s)
spectrog—spectrograph, spectrographic,
    spectrography
spectrogr—spectrographer
spectrophotom—spectrophotometer,
    spectrophotometric, spectrophotometry
spectros—spectroscopic, spectroscopy
speleol—speleological, speleology
Sq—Square
sr—senior
St—Saint, Street(s)
sta(s)—station(s)
stand—standard(s), standardization
statist—statistical, statistics
Ste—Sainte
steril—sterility
stomatol—stomatology
stratig—stratigraphic, stratigraphy
stratigr—stratigrapher
struct—structural, structure(s)
stud—student(ship)
subcomt—subcommittee
subj—subject
subsid—subsidiary
substa—substation
super—superior
suppl—supplement(s), supplemental,
    supplementary
supt—superintendent
supv—supervising, supervision
supvr—supervisor
supvry—supervisory
surg—surgery, surgical
surv—survey, surveying
survr—surveyor
Swed—Swedish
Switz—Switzerland
symp—symposia, symposium(s)
syphil—syphilology
syst(s)—system(s), systematic(s),
    systematical

taxon—taxonomic, taxonomy
tech—technical, technique(s)
technol—technologic(al), technology
tel—telegraph(y), telephone

temp—temporary
Tenn—Tennessee
Terr—Terrace
Tex—Texas
textbk(s)—textbook(s)
text ed—text edition
theol—theological, theology
theoret—theoretic(al)
ther—therapy
therapeut—therapeutic(s)
thermodyn—thermodynamic(s)
topog—topographic, topographical,
    topography
topogr—topographer
toxicol—toxicologic, toxicological,
    toxicology
trans—transaction(s)
transl—translated, translation(s)
translr—translator(s)
transp—transport, transportation
treas—treasurer, treasury
treat—treatment
trop—tropical
tuberc—tuberculosis
TV—television
Twp—Township

UAR—United Arab Republic
UK—United Kingdom
UN—United Nations
undergrad—undergraduate
unemploy—unemployment
UNESCO—United Nations Educational
    Scientific & Cultural Organization
UNICEF—United Nations International
    Childrens Fund
univ(s)—universities, university
UNRRA—United Nations Relief &
    Rehabilitation Administration
UNRWA—United Nations Relief & Works
    Agency
urol—urologic, urological, urology
US—United States
USAAF—US Army Air Force
USAAFR—US Army Air Force Reserve
USAF—US Air Force
USAFR—US Air Force Reserve
USAID—US Agency for International
    Development
USAR—US Army Reserve
USCG—US Coast Guard
USCGR—US Coast Guard Reserve

USDA—US Department of Agriculture
USMC—US Marine Corps
USMCR—US Marine Corps Reserve
USN—US Navy
USNAF—US Naval Air Force
USNAFR—US Naval Air Force Reserve
USNR—US Naval Reserve
USPHS—US Public Health Service
USPHSR—US Public Health Service
    Reserve
USSR—Union of Soviet Socialist Republics

Va—Virginia
var—various
veg—vegetable(s), vegetation
vent—ventilating, ventilation
vert—vertebrate
Vet—Veteran(s)
vet—veterinarian, veterinary
VI—Virgin Islands
vinicult—viniculture
virol—virological, virology
vis—visiting
voc—vocational
vocab—vocabulary
vol(s)—voluntary, volunteer(s), volume(s)
vpres—vice president
vs—versus
Vt—Vermont

W—West
Wash—Washington
WHO—World Health Organization
WI—West Indies
wid—widow, widowed, widower
Wis—Wisconsin
WVa—West Virginia
Wyo—Wyoming

Yearbk(s)—Yearbook(s)
YMCA—Young Men's Christian Associa-
    tion
YMHA—Young Men's Hebrew Association
Yr(s)—Year(s)
YT—Yukon Territory
YWCA—Young Women's Christian
    Association
YWHA—Young Women's Hebrew
    Association

zool—zoological, zoology

# AMERICAN MEN & WOMEN OF SCIENCE

# T

**TAAGEPERA, MARE,** PHYSICAL ORGANIC CHEMISTRY. *Current Pos:* FEL CHEM, UNIV CALIF, IRVINE, 71- *Personal Data:* b Narva, Estonia, May 16, 38; US citizen; m 61; c 3. *Educ:* Univ Del, BS, 60, MS, 63; Univ Pa, PhD(chem), 70. *Prof Exp:* Chemist, E I Du Pont de Nemours & Co, Inc, 62-64. *Mem:* Am Chem Soc; Sigma Xi; Asn Advan Baltic Studies. *Res:* Mechanisms of organic reactions; rate and equilibrium studies; mass and ion cyclotron resonance spectroscopy. *Mailing Add:* 19 Mayapple Way Irvine CA 92715-2714

**TAAM, RONALD EVERETT,** HYDRODYNAMICS, STELLAR STRUCTURE & EVOLUTION. *Current Pos:* from asst prof to assoc prof, 79-86, PROF PHYSICS & ASTRON, NORTHWESTERN UNIV, 86- *Personal Data:* b New York, NY, 48; m 74; c 2. *Educ:* Polytech Inst Brooklyn BS, 69; Columbia Univ, MA, 71, PhD(astron), 73. *Prof Exp:* Fel, Univ Calif, Santa Cruz, 73-76, vis prof astron, Berkeley, 76-78. *Mem:* Am Astron Soc; Royal Astron Soc; Am Phys Soc; Int Astron Union. *Res:* Application of fluid mechanics, radiation transfer, and nuclear physics to astrophysical problems; structure and evolution of close binary stars; high energy astrophysics. *Mailing Add:* Dept Physics & Astron Northwestern Univ Dearborn Observ Evanston IL 60208

**TABACHNICK, IRVING I A,** PHARMACOLOGY. *Current Pos:* RETIRED. *Personal Data:* b New York, NY, July 20, 24; m 51; c 2. *Educ:* Harvard Univ, AB, 48; Yale Univ, PhD(pharmacol), 53. *Prof Exp:* Pharmacologist & statistician, Baxter Labs, 53-55; pharmacologist, Schering Corp, 55-58, sr pharmacologist, 58-60, sect head, 60-61, head, Dept Biochem Pharm, 61-64, head, Dept Physiol & Biochem, 64-68, assoc dir, Biol Res Div, 68-70, dir, 70-72, sr dir biol res & develop, 72-77, vpres drug safety & metab, 77-89. *Mem:* AAAS; Am Soc Pharmacol & Exp Therapeut; Soc Exp Biol & Med; NY Acad Sci; Am Acad Allergy; Sigma Xi. *Res:* Histamine; diabetes; insulin; catecholamines; adrenergic receptors; anti-hormones; toxicology; drug metabolism. *Mailing Add:* 9 Woodland Ave North Caldwell NJ 07006

**TABACHNICK, JOSEPH,** RADIOIMMUNOASSAY. *Current Pos:* res biochemist, 52-59, sr res biochemist & assoc mem, Div Labs & head, Lab Exp Dermat, 59-78, HEAD, HORMONE RECEPTOR LAB, ALBERT EINSTEIN MED CTR, 78- *Personal Data:* b New York, NY, May 14, 19; m 61, Brunhild Stark; c Lysa & Maynard. *Educ:* Univ Calif, Berkeley, BS, 42, MS, 47, PhD(comp biochem), 50. *Prof Exp:* Res asst food technol, Univ Calif, Berkeley, 46-51, lab instr, 47-49; res chemist, Turner Hall Corp, NJ, 51-52. *Concurrent Pos:* Adj assoc prof, NY Med Col, 73- *Mem:* Sigma Xi; Clin Ligand Assay Soc; Am Asn Path; Radiation Res Soc. *Res:* Estrogen and progesterone receptors in human breast cancer; radiation biology and biochemistry of the skin; cytokinetics of repair in beta-irradiated skin; formation and metabolism of pyroglutamic acid and free amino acid in skin; suppression of radiation fibrosis. *Mailing Add:* 818 Asbury Terr Philadelphia PA 19126

**TABACHNICK, MILTON,** BIOCHEMISTRY. *Current Pos:* from asst prof to assoc prof, 61-69, dean Grad Sch Basic Med Sci, 71-80, PROF BIOCHEM, NEW YORK MED COL, 69- *Personal Data:* b New York, NY, June 25, 22; m 52, Elizabeth Svirnofsky. *Educ:* Univ Calif, AB, 47, MA, 49, PhD(biochem), 53. *Prof Exp:* Asst, Univ Calif, 49-52; Am Cancer Soc res fel biochem, Sch Med, Duke Univ, 52-53; instr, Inst Indust Med, Post-Grad Med Sch, NY Univ, 53-55; vis investr, Div Nutrit & Physiol, Pub Health Res Inst City New York, 55-57; res assoc chem, Mt Sinai Hosp, 57-59; res assoc, NY State Psychiat Inst, 59-60. *Mem:* Am Soc Biol Chem; Am Chem Soc; Endocrine Soc; Am Thyroid Asn; AAAS. *Res:* Protein chemistry; transport and mechanism of action of thyroid hormone; purification and characterization of thyroxine-binding globulin. *Mailing Add:* Dept Biochem New York Med Col Basic Sci Bldg Valhalla NY 10595

**TABACHNICK, WALTER J,** POPULATION GENETICS. *Current Pos:* RES SCIENTIST, AGR RES SERV, USDA, 87-, LAB DIR, 92- *Personal Data:* b Brooklyn, NY, June 14, 47; m 91, Darlene K Virchow. *Educ:* Brooklyn Col, City Univ New York, BS, 68; Rutgers Univ, MS, 71, PhD(zool), 74. *Prof Exp:* Asst prof genetics, Univ Wis-Parkside, 73-75; NIH fel, Yale Univ, 75-78; lectr biol & genetics, Univ Calif, Los Angeles, 78-79; res assoc genetics, Yale Univ, 79-82; prof biol, Loyola Univ, 82-85. *Concurrent Pos:* Nat Defense Educ Act Title IV fel, Rutgers Univ, 70-73; prin investr, Yale Univ, US Army, NIH res grants, 75-87, USDA res grants, 89- *Mem:* Entom Soc Am; Sigma Xi; Am Soc Study Evolution; Genetics Soc Am; Am Soc Trop Med & Hyg; US Animal Health Asn. *Res:* Studying the genetics and evolution of insect disease vectors with the goal of using this information to understand and control insect borne animal disease. *Mailing Add:* Arthropod-borne USDA-ARS PO Box 3965 Univ Sta Laramie WY 82071-3965

**TABADDOR, MAHMOOD M,** NONLINEAR MECHANICS. *Current Pos:* MEM TECH STAFF, LUCENT TECHNOL-BELL LABS, 96- *Educ:* Univ Akron, BS, 88; Univ Mich, MS, 90; Va Polytech Inst & State Univ, PhD(mech eng), 96. *Prof Exp:* Res engr, Goodyear Tire & Rubber Co, 90-96. *Mem:* Am Acad Mech; Am Soc Mech Engrs. *Res:* Non-linear mechanics of cable structures; manufacturing issues for high speed applications; finite element analysis; mechanics of coated fiber composites. *Mailing Add:* 2000 NE Expressway 1D36 Norcross GA 30071

**TABAK, DANIEL,** COMPUTER ARCHITECTURE. *Current Pos:* PROF ELEC & COMPUT ENG, GEORGE MASON UNIV, 85- *Personal Data:* b Wilna, Poland, June 16, 34; US citizen; m 60; c 2. *Educ:* Israel Inst Technol, BS, 59, MS, 63; Univ Ill, Urbana, PhD(elec eng), 68. *Prof Exp:* Asst nuclear sci, Israel Inst Technol, 61-63; elec engr, Univ Ill, Urbana, 63-66; guid & control systs engr, Missile & Space Div, Gen Elec Co, Pa, 66-68; sr consult, Wolf Res & Develop Corp, Md, 68-70; assoc prof systs eng, Rensselaer Polytech Inst, 70-72; assoc prof elec eng, Ben-Gurion Univ of the Negev, Israel, 72-76, chmn, Indust Eng Dept, 73-74, chmn, Elec Eng Dept, 76-77 & 79-83, prof elec eng, 76-85, Boston Univ, 79-85; chmn, Elec Eng Dept, Boston Univ, 83-85 & 79-83. *Concurrent Pos:* Consult, Missile & Space Div, Gen Elec Co, 66, Wolf Res & Develop Corp, 70-72; assoc ed, J Automatica, Int Fedn Automatic Control, 72-93; on leave, NRC sr res assoc, NASA Langley Res Ctr, 77-78 & vis prof elec eng, Univ Tex, Austin, 78-79. *Mem:* Sr mem Inst Elec & Electronics Engrs; Europ Micros Soc. *Res:* Digital systems; computer architecture; computer engineering. *Mailing Add:* Elec & Comput Sci Eng Dept MS 1G5 George Mason Univ 4400 University Dr Fairfax VA 22030-4444

**TABAK, MARK DAVID,** SOLID STATE PHYSICS, ELECTRICAL ENGINEERING. *Current Pos:* RETIRED. *Personal Data:* b Philadelphia, Pa, Dec 2, 37; m 61, Margaret; c Alison & Carolyn. *Educ:* Univ Pa, BS, 59; Princeton Univ, MA, 62, PhD(elec eng), 65. *Prof Exp:* Instr, Princeton Univ, 62-63; scientist xerographic sci, Res Labs Div, Xerox Res, 65-70, area mgr, 70-72, sect mgr, 72-73, mgr, Imaging Sci Lab, 73-77, mgr, Advan Marking Prog, Corp Res & Develop Group, 77-78, vpres & mgr, Webster Res Ctr, 78-84, vpres & mgr, Electronic Pub Bur, 84-85, vpres technol transfer, 85-87. *Concurrent Pos:* Mem, Advan Mgt Prog, Harvard Bus Sch, 82; consult & expert witness, xerography & non-impact printing. *Mem:* Am Phys Soc; Inst Elec & Electronics Engrs; Soc Imaging Sci & Technol. *Res:* Electrophotographic materials and systems; photoconductivity; electronic transport and photogeneration; amorphous semiconductors; xerography; non-impact printing technology. *Mailing Add:* 16244 Avenida Florencia Poway CA 92064. *Fax:* 619-451-9091; *E-Mail:* mark.d.tabak@worldnet.att.net

**TABAKIN, BURTON SAMUEL,** MEDICINE. *Current Pos:* from instr to assoc prof, Univ Vt, 54-67, dir Cardiopulmonary Lab, 54-80, dir Cardiol Univ, 72-80, actg chmn dept, 74-76, PROF, COL MED, UNIV VT, 67- *Personal Data:* b Philadelphia, Pa, July 6, 21; m 72; c 5. *Educ:* Univ Pa, AB, 43, MD, 47; Am Bd Internal Med, dipl, 55. *Prof Exp:* Fel physiol, Univ Vt & Trudeau Found, 51-52. *Concurrent Pos:* Attend physician, Mary Fletcher Hosp & DeGoesbriand Mem Hosp, Burlington, Vt, 60-66; fel coun clin cardiol, Am

Heart Asn. *Mem:* Fel Am Col Physicians; Am Heart Asn; Am Col Chest Physicians; Am Fedn Clin Res; fel Am Col Cardiol. *Res:* Clinical cardiopulmonary and exercise physiology; echocardiography. *Mailing Add:* 50 Northshore Dr Burlington VT 05401-1250

**TABAKIN, FRANK,** THEORETICAL PHYSICS. *Current Pos:* from asst prof to assoc prof, 65-74, PROF PHYSICS, UNIV PITTSBURGH, 74- *Personal Data:* b Newark, NJ, Sept 20, 35; m 63; c 2. *Educ:* Queens Col, NY, BS, 56; Mass Inst Technol, PhD(physics), 63. *Prof Exp:* Res assoc physics, Columbia Univ, 63-65. *Concurrent Pos:* Res visitor, Oxford Univ, 70. *Mem:* Am Phys Soc. *Res:* Nuclear forces and matter; three-body problems; properties of nuclei; meson physics; meson photoproduction; antiproton reactions. *Mailing Add:* Dept Physics Univ Pittsburgh Pittsburgh PA 15261. *Fax:* 412-624-9163

**TABAKOFF, BORIS,** NEUROPHARMACOLOGY, ALCOHOLISM. *Current Pos:* DIR, IRP, NAT INST ALCOHOL ABUSE & ALCOHOLISM/ALCOHOL, DRUG ABUSE & MENT HEALTH ADMIN/DEPT HEALTH & HUMAN SERV, 84- *Personal Data:* b Tien-Tsin, China, Sept 27, 42. *Educ:* Univ Colo, Boulder, BA & BPh, 66, PhD(pharmacol), 70. *Honors & Awards:* Vet Admin Award, 79. *Prof Exp:* Asst prof biochem, Chicago Med Sch, 71-73, assoc prof, 73-75; from assoc prof to prof, dept physiol, Med Ctr, Univ Ill, 75-84. *Concurrent Pos:* Bd trustees res award, Chicago Med Sch, 73; Hoffman LaRoche Found award & NIH-Swiss NSF award, 75; res award, Interstate Postgrad Med Asn NAm, 76; mem, NIH/Alcohol, Drug Abuse & Ment Health Admin Study Sect, Nat Inst Alcohol Abuse & Alcoholism, 78-81; res scientist, West Side Vet Admin Med Ctr, Chicago, 79-84; dir, Alcohol & Drug Abuse Res & Training Prog, Univ Ill Med Ctr, 80-84. *Mem:* Am Soc Pharmacol & Exp Therapeut; Am Soc Neurochem; Soc Neurosci; Res Soc Alcoholism; Int Soc Biomed Res Alcoholism; Am Col Neuropsychopharmacol. *Res:* Neurochemical and behavioral effects of alcohol and their contribution to development of tolerance and physical dependence; development of therapies to ameliorate tolerance and physical dependence. *Mailing Add:* Univ Colorado Dept Pharmacol 4200 E Ninth Ave PO Box C236 Denver CO 80262-0001. *Fax:* 303-270-7097

**TABAKOFF, WIDEN,** PROPULSION, GAS DYNAMICS. *Current Pos:* from instr to assoc prof, 58-66, PROF AEROSPACE ENG & APPL MECH, UNIV CINCINNATI, 67-, RES DIR, TURBOMACH EROSION LAB. *Personal Data:* b Stakevzi, Bulgaria, Dec 14, 19; US citizen; m 43, Gunhild Rombusch; c Irina Austin & Felicitas Singer. *Educ:* Prague Tech Univ, MS, 42; Univ Berlin, MS, 46, PhD(sci), 45. *Honors & Awards:* Award for Creative Develop Technol, NASA, 77 & 83; Res Award, Am Inst Aeronaut & Astronaut, 84; Fluid Mech Design A. *Prof Exp:* Asst instr, Univ Berlin, 42-46; designer, Aerotallers Argentinos, 48-50; tech dir prod, Helamet, Arg, 50-56; res dir, Knapsack Grisheim, Ger, 56-58. *Concurrent Pos:* Consult, Dept Defense, Dept Energy, NASA, Gen Elec Co, Rolls Royce, Allied Signal, Procter & Gamble, Praxair Technol, Sermatech, Mobile Tech Inc, Chromalloy Co, Sulzer Plasma Tech Inc, Garrett Turbine Co, US Army, Northrop Corp, Solar Turb Inc, Pimone Nuevo-Italy & Comatasu-Japan. *Mem:* Fel Am Inst Aeronaut & Astronaut; Am Soc Eng Educ; Am Soc Mech Engrs; Am Asn Univ Prof; Am Soc Testing & Mat. *Res:* Turbomachinery components, inlets, compressors, combustion chambers, turbine nozzles and exhaust engine nozzles; ramjet components; aerodynamic heating for hypersonic vehicles; internal gas dynamics flows; erosion problems in propulsion systems. *Mailing Add:* 9361 Bluewing Terr Cincinnati OH 45236. *Fax:* 513-556-5038; *E-Mail:* wtabakof@uceng.uc.edu

**TABARROK, B(EHROUZ),** MECHANICAL ENGINEERING. *Current Pos:* Ford found fel, 65-66, from asst prof to assoc prof, 66-87, PROF MECH ENG, UNIV TORONTO, 87- *Personal Data:* b Tehran, Iran, June 16, 38; m 63; c Alexander, Nicholas & Jeremy. *Educ:* Wolverhampton & Staffordshire Col Technol, BSc, 62; Oxford Univ, DPhil(struct dynamics), 65. *Honors & Awards:* Robert W Angus Medal, Can Soc Mech Eng, 85. *Concurrent Pos:* Alexander von Humboldt fel, Hannover Tech Univ, 69; sr res fel, Sci Res Coun, UK, 74; prof & chair, Dept Mech Eng, Univ Victoria, 87-97; pres, Can Soc Mech Eng, 93-94. *Mem:* Fel Can Soc Mech Engr; fel Eng Inst Can; Soc Automotive Engrs; Soc Eng Sci Inc; fel Am Acad Mech; Int Asn Comput Mech. *Res:* Applied mechanics, particularly in dynamics of structures; computational mechanics, variational principles in mechanics. *Mailing Add:* Dept Mech Eng Univ Victoria Victoria BC V8W 3P6 Can. *Fax:* 250-721-6051; *E-Mail:* bez.tabarrok@me.uvic.ca

**TABATA, SUSUMU,** PHYSICAL OCEANOGRAPHY. *Current Pos:* RETIRED. *Personal Data:* b Steveston, BC, Dec 9, 25; m 59, Barbara J McNally; c Susanne K, Ken D & Renee T. *Educ:* Univ BC, BA, 50, MA, 54; Univ Tokyo, DSc, 65. *Prof Exp:* Phys oceanogr, Pac Oceanog Group, Fisheries Res Bd Can, 52-70; res phys oceanogr, Ocean Physics Div, Inst Ocean Sci, 71-84, res scientist, 84-91. *Concurrent Pos:* Asst scientist, Pac Oceanog Group, Fisheries Res Bd Can, 52-58, assoc scientist, 59-65, sr scientist, 66-70. *Mem:* Am Soc Limnol & Oceanog; Am Meteorol Soc; Am Geophys Union; Can Meteorol & Oceanog Soc. *Res:* Circulation of inshore and offshore waters; processes affecting water properties; variability in the oceans; large-scale air-sea interactions; interpretation of satellite imagery; ocean climatology; ocean eddies; remote sensing. *Mailing Add:* Inst Ocean Sci Patricia Bay PO Box 6000 Sidney BC V8L 4B2 Can. *Fax:* 250-363-6746

**TABATABAI, LOUISA BRAAL,** BIOCHEMISTRY. *Current Pos:* Res assoc food technol, Iowa State Univ, 64-70, res assoc muscle biochem, 71-74, assoc biochem, 76-77, ASST PROF BIOCHEM, IOWA STATE UNIV, 85-; RES CHEMIST BIOCHEM, NAT ANIMAL DIS CTR, 77- *Personal Data:* b Oostvoorne, Neth, Dec 18, 39; US citizen; m 62; c 3. *Educ:* Univ Calif,

Berkeley, BA, 62; Iowa State Univ, MS, 66, PhD(biochem), 76. *Concurrent Pos:* Nat Res Coun fel, Nat Animal Dis Ctr, 77-78. *Mem:* Am Chem Soc; Am Soc Microbiol; AAAS; Protein Soc. *Res:* Virulence and pathogenicity of Brucella organisms; biochemical immunological properties of Brucella cell surface proteins, mechanism of action on host tissues; structure/function of Brucella proteins. *Mailing Add:* Nat Animal Dis Ctr USDA ARS 2300 Dayton Rd Ames IA 50010-0070. *Fax:* 515-239-8458

**TABATABAI, M ALI,** SOIL CHEMISTRY, SOIL BIOCHEMISTRY. *Current Pos:* Res assoc soil biochem, 66-72, from asst prof to assoc prof, 72-78, PROF SOIL CHEM & BIOCHEM, IOWA STATE UNIV, 78- *Personal Data:* b Karbala, Iraq, Feb 25, 34; US citizen; m 62; c 3. *Educ:* Univ Baghdad, BS, 58; Okla State Univ, MS, 60; Iowa State Univ, PhD(soil chem), 65. *Concurrent Pos:* Consult, Elec Power Res Inst, Palo Alto, Calif, 78-83. *Mem:* Am Soc Agron; Am Chem Soc; Am Soc Microbiol; AAAS; Int Soc Soil Sci. *Res:* Soil enzymology and chemistry of sulfur, nitrogen and phosphorus in soils; nutrient cycling in the environment. *Mailing Add:* Dept Agron Iowa State Univ Ames IA 50011-0061

**TABATABAI, MANOUCHEHR,** INTERFACE & SYSTEMS DESIGN, INFORMATION SEARCH STRATEGICS. *Current Pos:* ASSOC PROF COMPUT INFO SYSTS, FT HAYS UNIV, 92- *Personal Data:* b Tehran, Iran, Oct 31, 61. *Educ:* Calif State Univ, Hayward, BS(comput) & BS(mgt info systs), 84; Golden Gate Univ, MBA, 85; Ariz State Univ, PhD(comput info systs), 92. *Prof Exp:* Instr comput sci, Chabot Col, 85; instr comput info systs, Ariz State Univ, 86-91. *Concurrent Pos:* Consult comput info systs prog, Northeastern State Univ, 95; consult acct & mgt info systs prog, King Fahd Univ, 97. *Mem:* Decision Sci Inst; Int Bus Schs Comput Asn. *Res:* Experimental analysis of the effect of information channeling on decision performance when computer based decision support system is the only medium for information inquiry; computer assisted decision processes. *Mailing Add:* Dept Comput Info Systs Ft Hays State Univ Hays KS 67601-4099. *E-Mail:* butm@fhsu.edu

**TABB, DAVID LEO,** POLYMER SCIENCE. *Current Pos:* Res eng chem eng, 69-70, SR RES ENGR, POLYMER PRODS DEPT, SPECIALTY POLYMERS DIV, E I DU PONT DE NEMOURS & CO, INC, 74- *Personal Data:* b Louisville, Ky, Feb 8, 46; m 66; c 2. *Educ:* Univ Louisville, BChE, 69; Case Western Res Univ, MS, 72, PhD(polymer sci), 74. *Res:* Characterization of polymer structure and correlation to physical properties; thermoset and thermoplastic elastomers; polymer blends; polymer processing technology; Fourier transform infrared spectroscopy. *Mailing Add:* 2802 Bexley Ct Wilmington DE 19808

**TABBERT, ROBERT L,** GEOLOGY. *Current Pos:* RETIRED. *Personal Data:* b Ripon, Wis, Sept 6, 28; m 52; c 2. *Educ:* Univ Wis, BS, 52, MSc, 54. *Prof Exp:* Micropaleontologist, Magnolia Petrol Co, 54-59; micropaleontologist, Socony Mobil's Field Res Lab, 59-62; palynologist, Atlantic Richfield Co, 62-67, supvr palynology group, 67-73, dir struct & stratig res, 73-75, sr res assoc, Chevron Oil Field Res, 76-86. *Mem:* Soc Econ Paleont & Mineral; Am Asn Petrol Geologists; Am Asn Stratig Palynologists; Geol Soc Am; Asn Prof Geol Scientists. *Res:* Biostratigraphy of Cretaceous-Tertiary sediments of Alaska; regional correlations in Mesozoic and Tertiary sediments of Arctic; structural geology, stratigraphy and petroleum exploration of Arctic; exploration and geothermal energy of Western United States. *Mailing Add:* 211 Ursline Lafayette LA 70506

**TABBUTT, FREDERICK DEAN,** COMPUTER SIMULATIONS, CATASTROPHE THEORY. *Current Pos:* MEM FAC CHEM, EVERGREEN STATE COL, 70- *Personal Data:* b Philadelphia, Pa, Dec 28, 31; m 56; c 4. *Educ:* Haverford Col, BS, 53; Harvard Univ, MA, 55, PhD(chem), 58. *Prof Exp:* Instr, Reed Col, 57-59, asst prof to prof chem, 59-70. *Concurrent Pos:* NSF fac fel, Southhampton Univ, UK, 63-64, Univ Warwick, 74-75. *Mem:* Am Chem Soc. *Res:* Oscillating chemical reactions, particularly the Belousov-Zhabotinsky reaction; applications of castastrophe theory to oscillating systems; gas phase kinetics of unimolecular reactions; laser flash photolysis. *Mailing Add:* 3224 Cove Lane NW Olympia WA 98502-3934

**TABER, CHARLES ALEC,** ichthyology, for more information see previous edition

**TABER, DAVID,** ORGANIC CHEMISTRY. *Current Pos:* RETIRED. *Personal Data:* b New York, NY, July 14, 22; m 48; c Michael S, Jesse E & Alan L (deceased). *Educ:* NY Univ, AB, 48; Polytech Inst Brooklyn, PhD(chem), 53. *Prof Exp:* Jr chemist, Air Reduction Co, Inc, 48-49; res assoc indust med, Postgrad Med Sch, NY Univ, 53-55; chemist, Gen Aniline & Film Corp, 55-58; sr chemist, Koppers Co, Inc, 58-63; sect head, Org Chem, Armour Grocery Prod Co, 63-65, res mgr new chem, Household Prod Res & Develop Dept, 65-68, mgr biol & med progs, Armour-Dial, Inc, 68-69, asst res dir, 69-75; vpres & dir tech serv, Hollister, Inc, 75-77; dir regulatory affairs, Wesley-Jessen Inc, 77-84; vpres & dir regulatory affairs, Am Bioactive Colloids, Inc, 84-87; consult, David Taber & Assoc, 78-94; dir, Regulatory Affairs, Watson Labs, Inc, 87-94. *Mem:* Am Chem Soc; Soc Cosmetic Chemists; Sigma Xi. *Res:* Organic synthesis, germicides, microbiology; product safety; regulatory affairs; clinical testing; medical and hospital devices; quality assurance. *Mailing Add:* 2545 W Fitch Ave Chicago IL 60645

**TABER, DOUGLASS FLEMING,** ENANTIOSELECTIVE SYNTHESIS. *Current Pos:* asst prof, 82-84, assoc prof, 84-93, PROF ORG CHEM, UNIV DEL, 93- *Personal Data:* b Berkeley, Calif, Nov 11, 48; m 69, Susan Bahler; c John, Alan, Emma, Christina, Abigail & Robert. *Educ:* Stanford Univ, BS, 70; Columbia Univ, PhD(org chem), 74. *Prof Exp:* Res fel org chem, Univ Wis-Madison, 74-75; res instr, Dept Pharmacol, Vanderbilt Univ, 75-77, asst prof, 77-82. *Concurrent Pos:* Consult, Div Clin Pharmacol, Sch Med, Vanderbilt Univ, 82-; Alfred P Sloan Found fel, 83. *Mem:* Am Chem Soc; AAAS. *Res:* Development of new methods in synthetic organic chemistry; natural product synthesis; organometallics in organic synthesis; computational organometallic chemistry. *Mailing Add:* Dept Chem & Biochem Univ Del Newark DE 19716-0002. *Fax:* 302-831-6335; *E-Mail:* taberd@udel.edu

**TABER, ELSIE,** EMBRYOLOGY, REPRODUCTIVE PHYSIOLOGY. *Current Pos:* from asst prof to assoc prof, 48-65, PROF ANAT, MED UNIV SC, 65- *Personal Data:* b Columbia, SC, May 3, 15. *Educ:* Univ SC, BS, 35; Stanford Univ, MA, 36; Univ Chicago, PhD(zool), 47. *Prof Exp:* Teacher biol, Greenwood High Sch, SC, 36-38; instr, Lander Col, 38-41; instr, Univ Chicago, 44-48, asst dean students, Div Biol Sci, 47-48. *Mem:* AAAS; Am Soc Zool; Am Asn Anatomists; Am Inst Biol Sci; Soc Study Reproduction; Sigma Xi. *Res:* Developmental biology; endocrinology of reproductive systems. *Mailing Add:* 216 Molasses Lane Mt Pleasant SC 29464

**TABER, HARRY WARREN,** MICROBIOLOGY, MOLECULAR BIOLOGY. *Current Pos:* PROF MICROBIOL, DEPT MICROBIOL & IMMUNOL, ALBANY MED COL, UNION UNIV, 80- *Personal Data:* b Longview, Wash, Oct 30, 35; c 2. *Educ:* Reed Col, BA, 57; Univ Rochester, PhD(biochem), 63. *Prof Exp:* AEC fel, Univ Rochester, 62-64; USPHS fel, Nat Inst Neurol Dis & Stroke, Bethesda, Md, 64-66; USPHS spec fel, Photosynthesis Lab, Gif-sur-Yvette, France, 66-67; asst prof microbiol, Sch Med, Univ Rochester, 68-73, assoc prof, 73-79. *Concurrent Pos:* NIH res career develop award, 74-79, mem, study sect, 79-88. *Mem:* Am Soc Microbiol; Soc Gen Microbiol; AAAS; Am Asn Univ Professors. *Res:* Genetic regulation of respiratory chain components in bacteria; antibiotic transport by bacteria; biosynthesis of vitamin K. *Mailing Add:* David Axelrod Inst PO Box 22002 Albany NY 12201

**TABER, JOSEPH JOHN,** PETROLEUM ENGINEERING, OIL RECOVERY RESEARCH. *Current Pos:* from asst prof to prof chem, Grad Fac, NMex Inst Mining & Technol, 64-76, officer, Admin Dept, 64-76, adj assoc prof petrol eng, 67-72, prof petrol eng, 72-76, dir, NMex Petrol Recovery Res Ctr, 76-87, EMER DIR & ADJ PROF PETROL ENG, NMEX PETROLEUM RECOVERY RES CTR, NMEX INST MINING & TECHNOL, 87- *Personal Data:* b Adena, Ohio, Feb 6, 20; m 47, Catharine Holsinger; c Deborah, J John Jr, Thomas & Cathy. *Educ:* Muskingum Col, BS, 42; Univ Pittsburgh, PhD, 55. *Honors & Awards:* Enhanced Oil Recovery Pioneer Award, Soc Petrol Engrs, 90. *Prof Exp:* Asst prof naval sci, Ohio State Univ, 46; instr chem, Washington & Jefferson Col, 46-50; sr proj chemist, Gulf Res & Develop Co, 54-64. *Concurrent Pos:* Co-prin investr, res on carbon dioxide for enhanced oil recovery, 78-87; lectr, Int Energy Agency Workshops & Symp, enhanced oil recovery, 84; consult, Enhanced Recovery Comt, Interstate Oil Compact Comn, 80 & Argonne Nat Lab, 84-; tech auditor, Norway Oil Recovery Res, 86-91; mem adv bd, Sch Earth Sci, Stanford Univ, 89-91; consult, Greenhouse Gas Res & Develop Prog, Int Energy Agency. *Mem:* Am Chem Soc; Am Inst Mining, Metall & Petrol Engrs; AAAS; Sigma Xi; distinguished mem Soc Petrol Engrs. *Res:* Surface chemistry; liquid-liquid and liquid-solid interfaces; effect of interfacial energies on capillarity and fluid flow in porous media; new methods of petroleum recovery; effect of phase behavior on solvent displacement of oil from rocks; use of carbon dioxide and other gases for enhanced oil recovery; environmental problems of oil recovery; utilization and disposal of carbon dioxide to avert global warming. *Mailing Add:* NMex Petrol Recovery Res Ctr NMex Tech Socorro NM 87801

**TABER, RICHARD DOUGLAS,** WILDLIFE ECOLOGY. *Current Pos:* prof, 68-85, EMER PROF FOREST ZOOL, UNIV WASH, 85- *Personal Data:* b San Francisco, Calif, Nov 22, 20; m 46; c 3. *Educ:* Univ Calif, AB, 42, PhD, 51; Univ Wis, MS, 49. *Prof Exp:* Wildlife researcher & asst specialist, Univ Calif, 51-55, actg asst prof zool, 55-56; asst prof forestry, Univ Mont, 56-57, from assoc prof to prof, 58-68, assoc dir, Mont Forest & Conserv Exp Sta, 64-68. *Concurrent Pos:* US specialist forest-wildlife rels, Ger & Czech, 60 & Poland, 60 & 64; Fulbright res scholar, West Pakistan, 63-64; Guggenheim fel, 64; mem comn threatened deer, Int Union Conserv Nature, 73- *Mem:* Wildlife Soc; AAAS; Am Soc Mammal; Am Inst Biol Sci. *Res:* Biology and conservation of free-living birds and mammals; wildlife and human culture; ungulate biology and effects on ecosystem. *Mailing Add:* 625 Continental Way Missoula MT 59803-2203

**TABER, RICHARD LAWRENCE,** BIO-ORGANIC CHEMISTRY. *Current Pos:* From asst prof to assoc prof, 63-75, PROF CHEM, COLO COL, 75- *Personal Data:* b Pontiac, Mich, Nov 9, 35; m 57; c 2. *Educ:* Colo State Col, AB, 58; Univ NMex, PhD(org chem), 63. *Honors & Awards:* Meritorious Serv Award, Am Chem Soc, 69. *Mem:* Am Chem Soc; Sigma Xi. *Res:* Enzymology of dihydroorotate dehydrogenase; organic liquid scintillation solutes. *Mailing Add:* Chem Dept Colo Col Colorado Springs CO 80903-3294

**TABER, ROBERT IRVING,** PSYCHOPHARMACOLOGY, NEUROPHARMACOLOGY. *Current Pos:* BIOMED PROD DEPT, E I DU PONT DE NEMOURS & CO INC. *Personal Data:* b Perth Amboy, NJ, June 28, 36; m 60; c 3. *Educ:* Rutgers Univ, BS, 58; Med Col Va, PhD(pharmacol), 63. *Prof Exp:* Pharmacologist, Schering Corp, 62-66, sr pharmacologist, 66-71, mgr pharmacol, 71-74, dir biol res, 74-77, sr dir biol res, 77- *Mem:* AAAS; assoc Am Col Neuropsychopharmacol; Am Soc Pharmacol & Exp Therapeut; Acad Pharmaceut Sci; Am Pharmaceut Asn. *Res:* Analgesics; drug effects on learning and memory. *Mailing Add:* R&D Synaptic Pharmaceut Corp 215 College Rd Paramus NJ 07652-1431

**TABER, STEPHEN, III,** apiculture, for more information see previous edition

**TABER, WILLARD ALLEN,** microbiology, history & philosophy of science, for more information see previous edition

**TABI, RIFAT,** MECHANICAL ENGINEERING. *Current Pos:* asst prof mech eng technol, NY Inst Technol, 66-67, assoc prof, 67-70, prof, 70-72, PROF MECH, INDUST & AEROSPACE ENG & CHMN DEPT, NY INST TECHNOL, 72-, ASSOC DIR, CTR TECHNOL, 80- *Personal Data:* b Simferopol, Crimea, June 5, 38; US citizen; m 67; c 1. *Educ:* Aachen Tech Univ, BSME, 61, MSME, 62; Vienna Tech Univ, Dr Eng Sci (mech eng), 65; State Univ NY, PE, 72. *Prof Exp:* Sci res asst, Testing & Res Inst Mat, Vienna Tech Univ, 62-65; proj engr, Tech Ctr, Gen Motors Corp, Mich, 65-66. *Concurrent Pos:* Consult, pvt pract, 71-; qualified fallout shelter analyst & instr, Univ Hawaii, 68. *Res:* Materials-mechanics; fracture mechanics of materials and failure analysis. *Mailing Add:* 2 Lloyd Haven Dr Huntington NY 11743

**TABIBI, SEYED ESMAIL,** PHARMACEUTICAL SCIENCE, PHYSICAL & INDUSTRIAL PHARMACY. *Current Pos:* PROJ OFFICER, NAT CANCER INST, 93- *Personal Data:* Khoy, Iran, May 26, 45; US citizen; m 75, Shahnaz Rahaie; c Shahrzad, Shirazeh & Shabram. *Educ:* Univ Tabriz, Iran, BS, 67, DR, 69; Univ Md, PhD(pharmaceut), 82. *Prof Exp:* Dir res & develop, Micro Fluidics Int, 86-87, vpres, 87-90; vpres res & develop, Micro Vesicular Systs Inc, 90-93; assoc prof, Univ RI, 93. *Concurrent Pos:* Vis scientist, Univ Ariz, 89; adj assoc prof pharmaceut of indust pharm, Mass Col Pharm, 89-93; course dir & lectr, Technomic Pub Co, 89- *Mem:* Am Asn Pharmaceut Scientists; Controlled Release Soc; Am Pharmaceut Acad. *Res:* Novel drug delivery system with emphasis on the parenteral delivery of sparingly soluble drugs by means of colloidal systems including lipsomes, microemulsions and nanodispersion. *Mailing Add:* 14514 Bauer Dr Rockville MD 20853. *Fax:* 301-496-8333; *E-Mail:* tabibie@dtpepn.nci.nih.gov

**TABIBIAN, RICHARD,** POLYMER CHEMISTRY. *Current Pos:* CHEMIST, E I DU PONT DE NEMOURS & CO, INC, 55- *Personal Data:* b Detroit, Mich, June 1, 29; m 55; c 3. *Educ:* Wayne State Univ, BS, 51, MS, 54, PhD(chem), 56. *Mem:* Am Chem Soc. *Res:* Colloid chemistry; elastomers. *Mailing Add:* 105 Chipping Way Louisville KY 40222

**TABISZ, GEORGE CONRAD,** ATOMIC, MOLECULAR & OPTICAL PHYSICS. *Current Pos:* from asst prof to assoc prof, 70-80, PROF PHYSICS, UNIV MAN, 80- *Personal Data:* b New York, NY, Aug 28, 39; Can citizen; m 66, Ellen Clark; c Marie-Isabelle Edward. *Educ:* Univ Toronto, BASc, 61, MA, 63, PhD(physics), 68. *Prof Exp:* Nat Res Coun Can fel, High Pressure Lab, Nat Ctr Sci Res, France, 68-70. *Concurrent Pos:* Vis scientist, Univ Cambridge, 76-77, Nat Res Coun Can, Ottawa, 83-84, Joint Inst Lab Astrophys, Univ Colo, Boulder, 90-91. *Mem:* Optical Soc Am; Can Asn Physicists; Am Phys Soc. *Res:* Molecular interactions in gases and liquids; visible and infrared absorption spectroscopy; laser raman scattering; theory of spectral lineshapes; optical activity in molecules. *Mailing Add:* Dept Physics Univ Man Winnipeg MB R3T 2N2 Can. *Fax:* 204-269-8489; *E-Mail:* tabisz@ccu.umanitoba.ca

**TABITA, F ROBERT,** MICROBIAL BIOCHEMISTRY, PHOTOSYNTHETIC METABOLISM. *Current Pos:* from asst prof to assoc prof, 73-85, PROF MICROBIOL, UNIV TEX, AUSTIN, 85- *Personal Data:* b Bronx, NY, Oct 1, 43. *Educ:* St Johns Univ, BS, 65, MS, 67; Syracuse Univ, PhD(microbiol), 71. *Prof Exp:* NIH fel biochem, Wash State Univ, 71-73. *Concurrent Pos:* Panel mem, Biochem Study Sect, NIH, 76-77 & Microbiol, Physiol & Genetics Sect, 84-88; mem, Competitive Res Grants Panel, USDA, 81 & 84; asst dir, Ctr Appl Microbiol, Univ Tex Austin, 81- *Mem:* Am Soc Biol Chemists; Am Chem Soc; Am Soc Microbiol; AAAS; Am Soc Plant Physiologists; Int Soc Plant Microbiol. *Res:* Molecular basis and biochemistry of carbon dioxide fixation; regulation of biological nitrogen fixation; protection of nitrogenase from oxygen inactivation in vivo. *Mailing Add:* Dept Microbiol Ohio State Univ 484 W 12th Ave Columbus OH 43210-1292. *Fax:* 614-292-6337

**TABLER, RONALD DWIGHT,** HYDROLOGY. *Current Pos:* CONSULT SNOW & WIND ENG, TABLER & ASSOCS, 86- *Personal Data:* b Denver, Colo, May 18, 37; m 64, Alicia V Revollo; c Edward R & Alice A. *Educ:* Colo State Univ, BS, 59, PhD(watershed mgt), 65. *Honors & Awards:* USDA Super Serv Award, 76; D Grant Mickle Award, Nat Acad Sci, 79. *Prof Exp:* Res hydrologist, Rocky Mountain Forest & Range Exp Sta, US Forest Serv, 59-85. *Concurrent Pos:* Adj prof mech eng, Univ Wyo, 86-, adj prof range mgt, 86-; res affil, Univ Alaska, Fairbanks, 86-; vis scientist, Civil Eng Res Inst, Japan, 80-81. *Mem:* AAAS; Am Rwy Eng Asn; Am Geophys Union; Soil Conserv Soc; Am Water Resources Asn; Int Glaciol Soc. *Res:* Physics of snow transport by wind; design of snow fence systems for highway protection; management of snow in windswept areas to increase water yields; watershed management. *Mailing Add:* Tabler Assocs PO Box 483 Niwot CO 80544-0483

**TABOADA, JOHN,** PHYSICAL OPTICS, APPLIED PHYSICS. *Current Pos:* res physicist, Radiation Sci Div, Sch Aerospace Med, USAF, 68-80, res physicist, Data Sci Div, 80-84, RES PHYSICIST, CLIN SCI DIV, 84- *Personal Data:* b Tampico, Mex, Sept 8, 43; US citizen; m 68; c 1. *Educ:* Trinity Univ, BA, 66; Tex A&M Univ, MS, 68, PhD(physics), 73. *Honors & Awards:* Outstanding Tech Achievement Award, USAF Systs Command, 71, Outstanding Sci Achievement Award, 75. *Prof Exp:* Asst physics, Tex A&M Univ, 66-68. *Concurrent Pos:* Mem comt laser measurements, Am Nat Stand Inst, 76- *Mem:* Am Phys Soc; Optical Soc Am. *Res:* Biophysics of ultrashort pulsed lasers; laser spectroscopy; nonlinear optics; applied optics; robotics. *Mailing Add:* 12530 Elm Country San Antonio TX 78230

**TABOR, CELIA WHITE,** BIOCHEMISTRY. *Current Pos:* MEM STAFF, LAB BIOCHEM PHARMACOL, NAT INST ARTHRITIS, METAB & DIGESTIVE DIS & USPHS, 52- *Personal Data:* b Boston, Mass, Nov 15, 18; m 46; c 4. *Educ:* Radcliffe Col, BA, 40; Columbia Univ, MD, 43. *Prof Exp:* Intern med, Mass Gen Hosp, Boston, 44-45; asst resident, Univ Hosp, Vanderbilt Univ, 45-46; res assoc pharmacol, George Washington Univ, 47-49. *Mem:* AAAS; Am Soc Biol Chemists; Am Soc Pharmacol & Exp Therapeut. *Res:* Biochemistry; enzymatic and metabolic studies of the polyamines. *Mailing Add:* Nat Inst Diabetes & Digestive Kidney Dis NIH Bldg 8 Rm 221 Bethesda MD 20892-0830. *Fax:* 301-402-0240

**TABOR, CHRISTOPHER ALAN,** PLANT PHYSIOLOGY. *Current Pos:* res forester, 67-77, PLANT PHYSIOLOGIST, FOREST SERV, USDA, 77- *Personal Data:* b Frederick, Md, Jan 1, 37; div; c 1. *Educ:* NC State Univ, BS, 59, MS, 65; Univ Md, PhD, 82. *Prof Exp:* Mem staff bioprod res & develop, Dow Chem Co, 64-65. *Mem:* Am Soc Plant Physiologists. *Res:* Physiology of the effects of environmental stress on tree growth and development. *Mailing Add:* NE Forest Exp Sta PO Box 968 Burlington VT 05402-0968

**TABOR, DAVID,** PHYSICS. *Current Pos:* asst dir res, Cavendish Lab, Univ Cambridge, 46-64, reader physics, 64-73, head, Dept Physics & Chem Solids, 69-81, prof, 73-81, EMER PROF, CAVENDISH LAB, UNIV CAMBRIDGE, 81- *Personal Data:* b London, Eng, Oct 23, 13. *Educ:* Imp Col, BS, 34; Univ Cambridge, PhD, 39, ScD, 56. *Hon Degrees:* ScD, Univ Bath, 85. *Honors & Awards:* Nat Award, Am Soc Lubrication Engrs, 63; Wilson Award, Am Soc Metals, 69; Inaguaral Gold Medal Tribol, Inst Mech Engrs, 72, Donald Julius Groen Lectr, 91; Mayo D Hersey Award, Am Inst Mech Engrs, 74; Guthrie Medal, Inst Physics, 75; Royal Soc Gold Medal, 82. *Prof Exp:* Res asst, Commonwealth Sci & Indust Res Orgn, Melbourne, Australia, 40-45, actg head tribophysics sect, 45-46. *Concurrent Pos:* Fel, Stanford Res Inst, Calif, 55-56; vis fel, UNESCO, Israel, 60-61; supernumary fel, Gonville & Caius Col, 63; Russel, Springer vis prof, Berkeley, Calif, 70; GE sr vis fel, Schenectady, 79; vis prof, Imp Col, 81-89. *Mem:* Foreign assoc fel Nat Acad Eng; fel Royal Soc; fel Inst Physics. *Res:* Friction and lubrication of metals; structure of clean surfaces, surface forces, adhesion of clean surfaces; friction and transfer of polymers; friction of rubber; effect of hydrostatic pressure on the viscoelastic properties of polymers; shear properties of molecular films of long-chain organic molecules; hardness of solids. *Mailing Add:* Cavendish Lab Cambridge Univ Madingley Rd Cambridge CB3 0HE England

**TABOR, EDWARD,** VIROLOGY, CANCER ETIOLOGY. *Current Pos:* DIR, DIV TRANSFUSION, TRANSMITTED DIS, CTR BIOL EVAL & RES, FOOD & DRUG ADMIN, 95- *Personal Data:* b Washington, DC, Apr 30, 47; m 70; c 4. *Educ:* Harvard Univ, BA, 69; Columbia Univ, MD, 73. *Honors & Awards:* Commendation Medal, USPHS, 79, Unit Commendation, 85, Outstanding Serv Medal, 86; Outstanding Unit Commendation, USPHS, 87; Spec Citation, US Food & Drug Admin, 88. *Prof Exp:* Intern pediat, Columbia-Presby Med Ctr, New York, 73-74, resident, 74-75; sr med investr, Bur Biologics, FDA, 75-83, dir, Div Anti-Infective Drug Prods, FDA, 83-88; assoc dir biol careinogenesis, Nat Cancer Inst, NIH, 88-95. *Concurrent Pos:* Adj prof pediat, Georgetown Univ, 80-; asst clin prof child health & develop, George Washington Univ, 88-; guest lectr, Sch Pub Health, Harvard Univ, 93- *Res:* Hepatocellular carcinoma; hepatitis B virus; hepatitis C virus; oncogenes; tumor suppressor genes; growth factor genes. *Mailing Add:* Food & Drug Admin Ctr Biol Eval & Res 1401 Rockville Pike Rockville MD 20852-1448

**TABOR, HERBERT,** PHARMACOLOGY, BIOCHEMISTRY. *Current Pos:* chief, Lab Biochem Pharmacol, 43, NAT INST DIABETES, DIGESTIVE & KIDNEY DIS, NIH, 61-, CHIEF, SECT PHARMACOL. *Personal Data:* b New York, NY, Nov 28, 18; m 46, Celia White; c Edward, Richard & Marilyn(Stanley). *Educ:* Harvard Univ, AB, 37, MD, 41. *Honors & Awards:* Rose Award, Am Soc Biochem & Molecular Biol. *Prof Exp:* Biochem researcher, Harvard Med Sch, 41-42; intern med, New Haven Hosp, Conn, 42. *Concurrent Pos:* Field ed, J Pharmacol & Exp Therapeut, 60-68; assoc ed, J Biol Chem, 68-71, ed-in-chief, 71- *Mem:* Nat Acad Sci; Am Soc Pharmacol & Exp Therapeut; Am Soc Biol Chem; Am Chem Soc; Am Acad Arts & Sci. *Res:* Biochemistry of amino acids and amines. *Mailing Add:* Nat Inst Diabetes Digestive & Kidney Dis Bldg 8 Rm 223 Bethesda MD 20892. *E-Mail:* tabor@helix.nih.gov

**TABOR, JOHN MALCOLM,** BIOTECHNOLOGY, DRUG DEVELOPMENT OF BIOTHERAPEUTICS. *Current Pos:* sr scientist, Bristol-Myers Squibb Co, 82-84, dept head, 84-87, mgr, 87, asst dir, 87-90, ASSOC DIR, BRISTOL-MYERS SQUIBB CO, 90- *Personal Data:* b Harrisburg, Pa, May 30, 52. *Educ:* Elizabethtown Col, BS, 74; Kans State Univ, PhD(molecular biol), 78. *Prof Exp:* Postdoctoral, Roche Inst Molecular Biol, 79-80; postdoctoral, Mass Inst Technol, 80-81, vis scientist, 81-82, instr exp biol, 82. *Concurrent Pos:* Adj res asst prof, Biol Dept, Syracuse Univ, 82-83. *Mem:* Sigma Xi. *Res:* Planning genetic engineering support strategies for research discovery areas and development activities for the manufacture of recumbinant DNA and munoclonal antibody therapeutic products. *Mailing Add:* Biochem Div PO Box 4755 Syracuse NY 13221-4755

**TABOR, MARVIN WILSON,** ENVIRONMENTAL ANALYTICAL CHEMISTRY, MICROBIAL DEGRADATION OF HAZARDOUS WASTES. *Current Pos:* asst prof toxicol, 78-84, ASSOC PROF TOXICOL & ENVIRON CHEM, DEPT ENVIRON HEALTH, UNIV CINCINNATI, 84- *Personal Data:* b Bluefield, WVa, Nov 24, 44; c 2. *Educ:* Emory & Henry Col, BS, 66; Marshall Univ, MS, 68; Univ Cincinnati, PhD(biol chem), 74. *Honors & Awards:* Miguel Aleman Mem Award, Miguel Aleman Found, 90. *Prof Exp:* Res assoc biochem, Dept Obstet & Gynec, Univ Cincinnati Med Ctr, 76-78. *Concurrent Pos:* Course dir biochem, Dept Chem, Univ Cincinnati, 73-, dir mass spectrometry, Mass Spectrometry Facil, 81-, dir environ analytical chem, Inst Environ Health, 85-; sci adv/mentor, Int Vis Scientist Prog, World Health Orgn, 85-; vis scientist, Dept Environ Chem, Delft Tech Univ, Neth, 87; mem, Test & Eval Facil Tech Adv Coun, US Environ Protection Agency, 87-89; chmn bd trustees, Ohio River Basin Consortium for Res & Educ, 87-89; vis prof, Instituto Investigaciones Biomedicas, Universidad Nacional Autonoma Mex, 88; sci adv, Secretaria Desarrollo Urbano Y Ecolugia, Gov Mex, 88-, Secretaria Salud, 88-; adv & mem, Interagency Groundwater & Environ Adv Coun, State Ohio Gov Cabinet Cluster, 88- *Mem:* Am Chem Soc; Sigma Xi; Am Soc Microbiol; Int Soc Study Xenobiotics; Am Soc Mass Spectrometry; Am Waterworks Asn. *Res:* Identification and assessment of human exposure to environmental anthropogenic pollutants; development and assessment of microbial methods for the biodegradation, metabolism and detoxification of hazardous wastes. *Mailing Add:* 7930 Winterberry Pl Cincinnati OH 45241

**TABOR, ROWLAND WHITNEY,** GEOLOGY. *Current Pos:* GEOLOGIST, US GEOL SURV, 61- *Personal Data:* b Denver, Colo, June 10, 32; m 57, 70; c 2. *Educ:* Stanford Univ, BS, 54; Univ Wash, MS, 58, PhD(geol), 61. *Prof Exp:* Teaching asst geol, Univ Wash, 57-61. *Mem:* Fel Geol Soc Am. *Res:* Field mapping northwestern Washington, stratigraphy, igneous and metamorphic petrology and structure of Olympic and North Cascade Mountains; emphasis on geologic history and hazards; KAr geochronology; popular science writing. *Mailing Add:* US Geol Surv MS 975 345 Middlefield Rd Menlo Park CA 94025

**TABOR, SAMUEL LYNN,** NUCLEAR PHYSICS. *Current Pos:* from asst prof to assoc prof, 79-88, PROF PHYSICS, FLA STATE UNIV, 88- *Personal Data:* b Tylertown, Miss, June 10, 45; m 85, Michelle Boisseau. *Educ:* Tulane Univ, BS, 67; Stanford Univ, MS, 68, PhD(physics), 72. *Prof Exp:* Res assoc nuclear physics, Univ Pa, 72-75 & Argonne Nat Lab, 75-77; sr res assoc nuclear physics, Univ Md, 77-79. *Mem:* Am Phys Soc; Sigma Xi. *Res:* Nuclear structure and reactions. *Mailing Add:* Dept Physics Fla State Univ Tallahassee FL 32306. *E-Mail:* tabor@fsunuc.phy.fsu.edu

**TABOR, THEODORE EMMETT,** ORGANIC CHEMISTRY. *Current Pos:* prof mgr, 89-94, MGR COOP RES, DOW CHEM CO, 81- *Personal Data:* b Great Falls, Mont, Dec 28, 40; m 59, Jacqueline Lou Hart; c Lori, John & Lexi. *Educ:* Univ Mont, BA, 62; Kans State Univ, PhD(org chem), 67. *Prof Exp:* Res chemist, Spec Assignment Prog, Dow Chem Co, 67, res chemist, Prod Dept Lab, 67-72; res specialist, Halogens Res Lab, 72-75, mgr acad educ, 75-78, res leader org chem dept, 78-81. *Concurrent Pos:* Adj prof, Cent Mich Univ, Mt Pleasant, 79-83; co rep, Coun Chem Res, Dow Chem Co, 81-, Indust Res Inst, External Res Dirs Network, 91-, Am Chem Soc, Co Corp Assocs, 93- *Mem:* Am Chem Soc; Soc Res Adminr; AAAS; Nat Coun Univ Res Adminr Asn; Tech Transfer Soc. *Res:* Mechanisms of epoxide rearrangements; solvent processing of textiles; fire retardant chemicals for textiles and plastics; specialty organic chemicals product development. *Mailing Add:* Coop Res Dow Chem Co 1801 Bldg Midland MI 48674-0001

**TABORSKY, GEORGE,** PROTEIN CHEMISTRY. *Current Pos:* assoc prof biochem, Univ Calif, Santa Barbara, 70-72, chmn dept, 73-78, prof, 72-93, EMER PROF BIOCHEM, UNIV CALIF, SANTA BARBARA, 93- *Personal Data:* b Budapest, Hungary, Feb 12, 28; nat US; m 53, Eva Nemeth; c Peter & Andrea. *Educ:* Brown Univ, BS, 51; Yale Univ, PhD(biochem), 56. *Prof Exp:* Am Cancer Soc fel, Carlsberg Lab, Denmark, 56-57; from instr to assoc prof biochem, Yale Univ, 57-70, dir grad studies in biochem, 64-67. *Concurrent Pos:* Prin investr, NIH & NSF res grants, 63-93. *Mem:* Am Chem Soc; Biophys Soc; Am Soc Biochem & Molecular Biol; Am Inst Chemists; NY Acad Sci; Protein Soc. *Res:* Biochemistry of phosphoproteins; protein chemistry; biochemistry of egg yolk; phosphoprotein-metal interactions. *Mailing Add:* Dept Biol Sci Univ Calif Santa Barbara CA 93106

**TABORSKY, GERALD J, JR,** MEDICINE. *Current Pos:* Res assoc prof, 76-90, RES PROF, DEPT MED, UNIV WASH, 90- *Personal Data:* b Madison, Wis, Oct 26, 48; m; c 2. *Educ:* Marquette Univ, BS, 71; Univ Southern Calif, PhD(biomed eng), 76. *Mem:* Am Diabetes Asn; Am Physiol Soc; Endocrine Soc. *Res:* Pancreatic neuropeptides; neurocontrol of pancreatic islets. *Mailing Add:* Div Endocrinol & Metab 151 Vet Admin Pugent Sound Health Care Syst 1660 S Columbian Way Seattle WA 98108-1532

**TACHE, YVETTE FRANCE,** BRAIN-GUT INTERACTION. *Current Pos:* assoc prof res, 82-85, PROF MED, DIV DIGESTIVE DIS, UNIV CALIF, LOS ANGELES, 85- *Personal Data:* b Lyon, France, Feb 1, 45; US citizen; wid; c Stephanie & Veronique. *Educ:* Lycee Univ, BS, 65; Univ Claude Bernard, MS, 68, DEA, 69; Univ Montreal, PhD, 74. *Hon Degrees:* Dr, Univ Pecs, Hungary, 94. *Prof Exp:* Asst researcher, Univ Montreal, 77-78, from asst res prof to assoc res prof, 80-82; vis scientist, Salk Inst, 78-80. *Concurrent Pos:* Sr scientist award, NIMH, 88-; merit award, NIH, 96- *Mem:* Int Soc Psychoneuroendocrinol; Endocrine Soc; Soc Neurosci; Am Physiol Soc; Am Gastroenterol Soc; Hans Selye Found. *Res:* Brain-gut interactions and stress-related alterations of gastric intestinal motor function; role of neuropeptides in regulation of ingestive behavior. *Mailing Add:* W Los Angeles Med Ctr Bldg 115 Rm 203 1300 Welshire Blvd Los Angeles CA 90073. *Fax:* 310-268-4963; *E-Mail:* ytache@ucla.edu

**TACHIBANA, DORA K,** IMMUNOLOGY, MEDICAL MICROBIOLOGY. *Current Pos:* assoc prof, 70-75, PROF IMMUNOL & MICROBIOL, CALIF COL PODIATRIC MED, 75- *Personal Data:* b Cupertino, Calif, Dec 19, 34. *Educ:* San Jose State Col, BA, 56; Stanford Univ, MA, 62, PhD(immunol), 64. *Prof Exp:* Pub health microbiologist trainee, Calif State Dept Pub Health, 56-57; clin lab technician trainee, San Jose Hosp, Calif, 57; pub health microbiologist, Santa Clara Co Pub Health, 57-59; NIH fel immunol, Czech Acad Sci, 64-65; lab instr & res asst, Stanford Univ, 65-66; asst prof microbiol & immunol, San Francisco State Col, 66-69; res assoc med, Sch Med, Stanford Univ, 70. *Concurrent Pos:* Fac res award, San Francisco State Col, 68-69; clin lab dir, Calif Podiatry Hosp, San Francisco, 70-79; consult, Bur Med Devices-Immunol Div, Food & Drug Admin, 80-88. *Mem:* Am Soc Microbiol; Am Asn Immunol; Sigma Xi; Am Asn Univ Prof; AAAS. *Res:* Microbial flora of the foot. *Mailing Add:* Dept Basic Sci Calif Col Podiat Med 1210 Scott St San Francisco CA 94115-4000

**TACHIBANA, HIDEO,** PLANT PATHOLOGY. *Current Pos:* adj prof, 80-90, AFFIL PROF, IOWA STATE UNIV, 90- *Personal Data:* b Los Altos, Calif, June 30, 25; m 64, 84, Misa Takata; c Edward & Susanne. *Educ:* Univ Calif, Davis, BS, 57; Wash State Univ, PhD(plant path), 63. *Prof Exp:* Res plant pathologist, USDA, 63-90. *Mem:* Am Phytopath Soc; Int Soc Plant Path; Crop Sci Soc Am; AAAS; Am Soc Agr; Sigma Xi. *Res:* Soybean diseases; brown stem rot; breeding and screening for disease resistance; gene and pest management; prescription plant medicine. *Mailing Add:* 4024 Quebec St Ames IA 50014

**TACHIBANA, TAKEHIKO,** TUMOR IMMUNOLOGY, PSYCHONEUROIMMUNOLOGY. *Current Pos:* PROF TUMOR IMMUNOL, RES INST TUBERCULOSIS & CANCER, TOKYO UNIV, SENDAI, 74- *Personal Data:* b Toyana, Toyana, Apr 29, 28; m 55; c 2. *Educ:* Kanazawa Univ, BM, 52, DMS, 58. *Prof Exp:* Res assoc embryol, 2nd Dept Path, Med Sch, Kanazawa Univ, 53-59, instr tumor immunol 59-63; asst prof tumor immunol, Dept Cancer Prev, Res Inst Infect Dis, Tokyo Univ, 63-64; sect head tumor immunol, Virol Div, Nat Cancer Ctr Res Inst, Tokyo, 64-74. *Concurrent Pos:* Lectr, Fac Med, Tohoku Univ, 50- & Fac Pharmaceut, Kanazawa Univ, 78-81; res assoc immunochem, Dept Zool, Univ Mich, Ann Arbor, 57-59; vis investr tumor immunol, Dept Tumor Biol, Karolinska Inst, Stockholm, 68-69; lectr tumor immunol, Res Inst Med Sci, Tokyo Univ, 70-71, from assoc prof to prof, 71-76. *Mem:* Japan Cancer Asn; Japan Soc Allergol; Japan Immunol Asn; Japan Soc Cell Biol; Japan Soc Virol; Japan Soc Reticuloendothelial Syst. *Res:* Relationship between immunological responses in local tumor tissue and lymph-node metastasis of tumor cells; cellular and immunological properties of tumor cells metastasizing to the lymph node. *Mailing Add:* Japan Immunores Lab Co Ltd 351-1 Nishiyokote-cho Takasaki 370 Japan. *Fax:* 81-273-53-1770

**TACHMINDJI, ALEXANDER JOHN,** HYDRODYNAMICS. *Current Pos:* CONSULT, 89- *Personal Data:* b Athens, Greece, Feb 16, 28; US citizen; m 65, Diane Primeau. *Educ:* Durham Univ, BSc, 49, BSc(hons), 50; Mass Inst Technol, SM, 51. *Prof Exp:* Eng, Swann, Hunter & W Richardson, 45-46; res assoc naval archit, Mass Inst Technol, 50-51; mem res staff, Ship Div, David W Taylor Model Basin, US Navy, 51-54, head, Res & Propeller Br, 54-59; head tactical warfare group, Weapons Syst Eval Div, Inst Defense Analysis, 59-64, asst dir res & eng support div, 64-67, dep dir, Sci Technol Div, 67-69, dir, Systs Eval Div, 69-72; dir, Tactical Technol Off, Defense Advan Res Proj Agency, Dept Defense, 72-73, dep dir, Defense Advan Res Proj Agency, 73-75; chief scientist, Mitre Corp, 75-76, vpres, 76-84, gen mgr, 79-84, sr vpres, 84-89. *Concurrent Pos:* Consult, Am Bur Shipping, 56-59, Anti-Submarine Warfare Comt, Defense Sci Bd, 65-70 & Naval Surface Warfare Panel, 75; ed, J Defense Res, 69-91; mem finance comt, Am Inst Aeronaut & Astronaut. *Mem:* Fel AAAS; Soc Naval Architects & Marine Engrs; fel Am Inst Aeronaut & Astronaut; Opers Res Soc Am; fel Royal Inst Naval Architects. *Res:* Cavitation; super cavitation; potential theory; ship vibration and noise; systems analyses; hydroelasticity; granted one patent. *Mailing Add:* 5314 Falmouth Rd Bethesda MD 20816

**TACHOVSKY, THOMAS GREGORY,** IMMUNOLOGY, VIROLOGY. *Current Pos:* GEN PARTNER, MATCO ASSOCS. *Personal Data:* b Los Angeles, Calif, Feb 1, 47; m 68; c 2. *Educ:* Gonzaga Univ, BS, 68; Univ Rochester, PhD(microbiol), 74. *Prof Exp:* Lab technician microbiol, Sch Med, Univ Rochester, 71-74; fel immunol, 74-76, res asst, 76-77, asst prof neuroimmunol, Wistar Inst, 77-; mem tech staff, Cambridge Res Lab. *Mem:* Sigma Xi; Am Soc Microbiol; AAAS. *Res:* Neuroimmunology; multiple sclerosis; immunopathology of central nervous system diseases; neurovirology. *Mailing Add:* Dept Res & Develop Protyde Pharmaceut 39 Riverside Terr North Easton MA 02356-1360

**TACK, PETER ISAAC,** FISH BIOLOGY. *Current Pos:* instr zool, Mich State Univ, 40-43, asst prof & res asst, 43-46, assoc prof & res assoc, 46-50, prof fisheries & wildlife, 50-70, chmn dept, 50-69, prof fisheries, wildlife & zool, 70-78, EMER PROF FISHERIES & WILDLIFE, MICH STATE UNIV, 77- *Personal Data:* b Marion, NY, Apr 15, 11; m 37; c 2. *Educ:* Cornell Univ, BS, 34, PhD(agr), 39. *Prof Exp:* Asst biologist, State Conserv Dept, NY, 39-40, biologist, 40. *Concurrent Pos:* Mem, Governor's Botulism Control Comn, 64-65. *Mem:* Am Soc Limnol & Oceanog; Am Fisheries Soc; Am Soc Ichthyologists & Herpetologists; fel AAAS. *Res:* Pond fish culture; population fluctuations of whitefish in Northern Lake Michigan and effects of pumped storage generating facility on Lake Michigan ecology. *Mailing Add:* 2700 Marfitt Rd 106 East Lansing MI 48823

**TACKER, MARTHA MCCLELLAND,** BIOCHEMISTRY, SCIENCE WRITING & EDITING. *Current Pos:* BIOMED COMMUN CONSULT, 74- *Personal Data:* b Mineral Wells, Tex, Jan 16, 43; m 67, W A Jr; c 3. *Educ:* Concordia Col, MN(Chem), 64; Baylor Col Med, PhD(biochem), 69. *Honors & Awards:* Swanberg Award, Am Med Writers Asn. *Prof Exp:* Res assoc biochem, Baylor Col Med, 69-70; res asst gastroenterol, Mayo Grad Sch Med, Univ Minn & Mayo Found, 70-71; instr physiol, Baylor Col Med, 71-74. *Concurrent Pos:* Sci writer & ed, 74-; ed, CBE Views, 95- *Mem:* AAAS; Sigma Xi; fel Am Med Writers Asn (past-pres); Coun Biol Ed (past-pres); Soc Tech Commun; Europ Asn Sci Ed. *Mailing Add:* 704 228 NE Suite 623 Redmond WA 98053. *Fax:* 425-836-3284

**TACKER, WILLIS ARNOLD, JR,** CARDIOVASCULAR PHYSIOLOGY, MEDICAL EDUCATION. *Current Pos:* MEM FAC BIOMED ENG, PURDUE UNIV, WEST LAFAYETTE, 74-, EXEC DIR BIOMED ENG CTR. *Personal Data:* b Tyler, Tex, May 24, 42; m 67; c 3. *Educ:* Baylor Univ, BS, 64, MD & PhD(physiol), 70. *Prof Exp:* Intern med, Mayo Clin, 70-71; mem, Fac Physiol, Baylor Col Med, 71-74. *Mem:* Am Physiol Soc; Asn Advan Med Instrumentation. *Res:* Life-threatening arrhythmia therapy; new teaching techniques and devices; diagnostic and therapeutic devices development. *Mailing Add:* Biomed Eng Ctr Purdue Univ 1293AA Potter Bldg 204 West Lafayette IN 47907-1293

**TACKETT, JAMES EDWIN, JR,** ANALYTICAL CHEMISTRY. *Current Pos:* sr res chemist, 65-77, mgr, Analysis Dept, 77-83, SR RES CHEMIST, DENVER RES CTR, MARATHON OIL CO, 83- *Personal Data:* b Los Angeles, Calif, Oct 8, 37; m 62; c 3. *Educ:* Occidental Col, BA, 60; Univ Calif, Riverside, PhD(chem), 64. *Prof Exp:* Chemist, Union Carbide Corp, WVa, 64-65. *Mem:* Am Chem Soc; Sigma Xi. *Res:* Applied spectroscopy; thermal analysis; analytical separations; application of nuclear magnetic resonance and Fourier transform infrared to the study of aqueous polymer systems. *Mailing Add:* Denver Res Ctr Marathon Oil Co PO Box 269 Littleton CO 80160-0269

**TACKETT, JESSE LEE,** SOIL PHYSICS. *Current Pos:* assoc prof agr, 65-70, PROF AGR & DEAN SCH AGR & BUS, TARLETON STATE UNIV, 70- *Personal Data:* b Dublin, Tex, Sept 20, 35; m 55; c 3. *Educ:* Tex A&M Univ, BS, 57; Auburn Univ, MS, 61, PhD(soil physics), 63. *Prof Exp:* Instr agron, Tarleton State Col, 57-59; asst, Tex A&M Univ, 59-60; res soil scientist, Soil & Water Conserv Res Div, Agr Res Serv, USDA, 63-65. *Mem:* Am Soc Agron; Soil Sci Soc Am. *Res:* Soil aeration and strength; plant growth relations. *Mailing Add:* Dean Agr Tarleton State Univ Tarleton Sta Stephenville TX 76402-0001

**TACKETT, RANDALL LYNN,** CARDIOVASCULAR PHARMACOLOGY, VASCULAR BIOLOGY. *Current Pos:* from asst prof to assoc prof, Univ Ga, 81-95, dir grad studies & res, Col Pharm, 85-91, head, Dept Pharmacol & Toxicol, 91-95, PROF PHARMACOL & TOXICOL, UNIV GA, 95- *Personal Data:* b Jacksonville, Fla, Dec 7, 54; m 72, Ann Aspinwall; c Laura Marie & Allison Lynn. *Educ:* Jacksonville Univ, BS, 75; Auburn Univ, MS, 77; Univ Ga, PhD(pharmacol), 79. *Prof Exp:* Postdoctoral fel, Med Univ SC, 79-81. *Concurrent Pos:* Vis scientist, Fedn Am Soc Exp Biol, 94. *Mem:* Am Soc Pharmacol & Exp Therapeut; Am Heart Asn; fel Int Soc Hypertension Blacks. *Res:* Racial and gender differences in cardiovascular diseases and their treatment; activities also evaluate the abuse of alcohol and other drugs/substances. *Mailing Add:* Col Pharm Univ Ga Athens GA 30602-2356. *Fax:* 706-542-3398; *E-Mail:* rtackett@rx.uga.edu

**TACKETT, STANFORD L,** ANALYTICAL CHEMISTRY. *Current Pos:* RETIRED. *Personal Data:* b Virgie, Ky, Sept 5, 30; m 51, Elizabeth Anne Shode; c Keith, Bruce, Christopher & Neil. *Educ:* Ohio State Univ, BS, 57, PhD(chem), 62. *Prof Exp:* Instr chem, Ohio State Univ, 61-62; asst prof, Ariz State Univ, 62-66; assoc prof, Ind Univ, 66-69, chmn dept, 74-83, prof chem, 69-91. *Concurrent Pos:* Consult, Off Res Analysis, Holloman AFB, 63; NIH res grant, 64-66; vol scientist, Water Lab, Environ Protection Agency, 90 & 91. *Mem:* Am Chem Soc; Meteoritical Soc; Sigma Xi. *Res:* Analytical chemistry and electro-analytical techniques; chemistry of meteorites; chemistry of cyanocobalamin; environmental chemistry; chemistry of sewage sludge. *Mailing Add:* 109 Shady Dr Indiana Univ Pa Indiana PA 15701-3208

**TACKIE, MICHAEL N,** THERMOSETS, COMPOSITES PROCESSING. *Current Pos:* RES SCIENTIST, INDSPEC CHEM CO, 92- *Personal Data:* b Kumasi, Ghana, May 22, 58; US citizen. *Educ:* Yale Col, BS, 80; Syracuse Univ, MS, 83, PhD(chem eng), 89. *Prof Exp:* Staff scientist, Alcoa Tech Ctr, 87-92. *Mem:* Am Chem Soc; Soc Plastics Engrs; Soc Advan Mat & Process Eng. *Res:* Developing new monomers for exopy resins; modifying phenolic resins to improve fracture toughness. *Mailing Add:* 4969 Ludwig Rd Murrysville PA 15668-9757. *E-Mail:* 71046.1733@compuserve.com

**TADDEUCCI, TERRY N,** HIGH RESOLUTION NEUTRON POLARIMETRY TECHNIQUES. *Current Pos:* STAFF MEM, LOS ALAMOS NAT LAB, 86- *Educ:* Mich Technol Univ, Bs 76; Univ Va, PhD(physics), 80. *Prof Exp:* Res assoc, Ohio Univ, 80-84, Univ Md, 84-85; staff mem, Cyclotron Facil, Ind Univ, 85-86. *Res:* Proton in elastic and charge-exchange scattering, iso vector spin-flip strength distributions, effective nucleon-nucleon interactions, nuclear spin structure functions, high-resolution neutron polarimetry techniques. *Mailing Add:* Los Alamos Nat Lab Lansce 3 MSH855 Los Alamos NM 87545. *E-Mail:* taddeucci@lampf.lanl.gov

**TADEPALLI, ANJANEYULU S,** CARDIOVASCULAR PHARMACOLOGY, PHYSIOLOGY. *Current Pos:* SR RES SCIENTIST, BURROUGHS WELLCOME RES LABS, 80- *Educ:* Univ Pittsburgh, PhD(pharmacol), 72. *Mem:* Am Soc Pharmacol; Soc Neurosci; Int Soc Hypertension. *Mailing Add:* Dept Pharmacol Burroughs Wellcome Co Res Labs 3325 W Cornwallis Rd Durham NC 22705-5206

**TAEGTMEYER, HEINRICH,** CARDIOLOGY, MUSCLE PHYSIOLOGY. *Current Pos:* from asst prof to assoc prof, 82-91, PROF MED, UNIV TEX MED SCH, HOUSTON, 91- *Personal Data:* b Forst, Ger, Feb 14, 41; m 66; c 3. *Educ:* Univ Freiburg, MD, 68, Univ Oxford, PhD(biochem), 81. *Honors & Awards:* L B Johnson Award, Am Heart Asn, 83. *Prof Exp:* Clin fel med, Harvard Med Sch, 71-73, res fel, 73-76, instr, 76-79. *Mem:* Am Heart Asn; Am Col Cardiol; Am Col Physicians; Am Fedn Clin Res; Am Physiol Soc; Biochem Soc. *Res:* Metabolic regulation and control of energy metabolism in heart and skeletal muscle; glucose transport and phosphorylation; anaplerosis of the citric acid cycle; glycogen metabolism; metabolism and contraction; metabolic regulation. *Mailing Add:* Div Cardiol Univ Tex Med Sch Houston 6431 Fannin Houston TX 77030. *Fax:* 713-792-5187

**TAEUSCH, H WILLIAM,** PULMONARY DEVELOPMENT, PULMONARY SURFACTANT. *Current Pos:* DIR, DIV NEONATOLOGY, KING/DREW MED CTR, 87- *Educ:* West Res Med Sch, MD, 65. *Prof Exp:* From assoc prof to prof pediat, Sch Med, Harvard Univ, 74-87; scientist, Dept Neonatology, Brigham Women's Hosp, 80-87. *Concurrent Pos:* Vis scientist, Cardiovasc Res Inst, Univ Calif, San Francisco, 82-83. *Res:* Co-author of one book. *Mailing Add:* Dept Pediat Univ Calif-San Francisco San Francisco Gen Hosp Rm 6E 1001 Potrero San Francisco CA 94110. *Fax:* 415-206-3686

**TAFFE, WILLIAM JOHN,** COMPUTER SCIENCE EDUCATION. *Current Pos:* from asst prof to prof atmospheric physics, 71-81, PROF COMPUT SCI & CHMN DEPT, PLYMOUTH STATE COL, 81- *Personal Data:* b Albany, NY, Feb 3, 43; m 65, Betty Jo Miller; c 2. *Educ:* Le Moyne Col, NY, BS, 64; Univ Chicago, SM, 67, PhD(geophys), 68. *Prof Exp:* Res physicist, Air Force Cambridge Res Labs, 68-69; asst prof physics, Colby Col, 69-71. *Concurrent Pos:* Vis prof, Univ NH, Durham, 79 & Pontifical Cath Univ, Ecuador, 94-95; vis scientist, NH Ctr Atmospheric Res, 80; mem, NH Post Sec Educ Accreditation Teams, 82-88. *Mem:* Asn Comput Mach; Inst Elec & Electronics Engrs. *Res:* Computer science education. *Mailing Add:* Dept Comput Sci Plymouth State Col Plymouth NH 03264. *Fax:* 603-535-2282; *E-Mail:* wjt@oz.plymouth.edu

**TAFLOVE, ALLEN,** ELECTROMAGNETIC FIELDS & WAVES, NUMERICAL MODELING. *Current Pos:* assoc prof, 84-88, PROF ELEC ENG, NORTHWESTERN UNIV, 88- *Personal Data:* b Chicago, Ill, June 14, 49; m 77, Sylvia Friedman; c Michael & Nathan. *Educ:* Northwestern Univ, BS, 71, MS, 72, PhD(elec eng), 75. *Prof Exp:* Assoc engr, IIT Res Inst, Chicago, 75-77, res engr, 77-80, sr engr & group leader electronics, 80-84. *Concurrent Pos:* Prin investr, USAF Rome Air Develop Ctr, 77-81 & 82-84, Global Analysis, 81-82, Elec Power Res Inst, 81-83 & 84, Sci Appln Inc, 82-84, Lawrence Livermore Lab, 85-87, NASA, 85-87 & 90-94, NSF, 88-96, Lockheed Corp, 85-87, Off Naval Res, 88-96, Gen Dynamics, 88-91 & Northrop, 90-92, Cray Res, 93-95; consult, Lawrence Livermore Nat Lab, 85-87, Lockheed Corp, 85-87, Naval Res Lab, 87-95, MRJ, Inc, 87-90, City Wheaton, Ill, 91-92, Village Wilmette, Ill, 91-94, Mass Inst Technol Lincoln Lab, 92-93, Commonwealth Edison, 92-96 & Intec Group, 95-; guest ed, Wave Motion, 88; nat lectr, Antennas & Propagation Soc, Inst Elec & Electronics Engrs, 90-91. *Mem:* Sigma Xi; AAAS; fel Inst Elec & Electronics Engrs; NY Acad Sci; Int Union Radio Sci; Electromagnetics Acad. *Res:* Development and application of supercomputing computational electromagnetics models; numerical modeling of electromagnetic wave interactions with complex structures; first-principles computational modeling of ultrahigh-speed electronic and optical switching directly from Maxwell's equations; author and co-author of several books. *Mailing Add:* Dept Elec & Comput Eng McCormick Sch Eng Northwestern Univ Evanston IL 60208-3118. *Fax:* 847-491-4455

**TAFT, BRUCE A,** PHYSICAL OCEANOGRAPHY. *Current Pos:* AFFIL PROF, SCH OCEANOG, UNIV WASH, 95- *Personal Data:* b San Francisco, Calif, Jan 29, 30; m 61, Karen Handeverg; c Joshua. *Educ:* Stanford Univ, BS, 51; Univ Calif, San Diego, MS, 61, PhD(oceanog), 65. *Prof Exp:* Statistician, US Fish & Wildlife Serv, Calif, 55-58; grad res oceanogr, Scripps Inst, Univ Calif, 58-59; res asst, Johns Hopkins Univ, 59-60; grad res oceanogr, Scripps Inst Oceanog, Univ Calif, 60-65, asst res oceanogr, 65-68, asst prof oceanog, 68-73; from res assoc prof to res prof oceanog, Univ Wash, 73-83; supvry oceanogr, Pac Marine Environ Lab, Nat Oceanic & Atmospheric Admin, 81-89, WOCE Int Prof Off, IOS Deacon Lab, UK, 89-91, supvry oceanogr, Pac Marine Environ Lab, 91-95. *Concurrent Pos:* NSF grant, US-Japan Coop Sci Prog, 66-67; affil prof oceanog, Univ Wash, 83-89; chmn, CCCO Trop Pac Panel, sr fel, Joint Inst Study Atmosphere & Ocean, Wash & Joint Inst Marine Atmospheric Res, Hawaii; assoc ed, J Marine Res, 75-90. *Mem:* AAAS; Am Geophys Union; Oceanog Soc Japan; Am Meterol Soc. *Res:* Description of large scale oceanic circulation; velocity structure and distribution of properties in ocean currents. *Mailing Add:* 10580 NE South Beach Dr Bainbridge Island WA 98110. *Fax:* 206-526-6744

**TAFT, CHARLES KIRKLAND,** CONTROL ENGINEERING. *Current Pos:* prof, 67-91, chmn dept, 85-91, EMER PROF MECH ENG, UNIV NII, 91- *Personal Data:* b Cleveland, Ohio, July 24, 28; m 51; c Charles K Jr, Frederick D & Richard K. *Educ:* Amherst Col, BA, 51; Mass Inst Technol, BS, 53; Case Inst Technol, MS, 56, PhD(feedback control systs), 60. *Honors & Awards:* Charles Strosacker Award, Case Inst Technol, 66; Achievement Award, Nat Fluid Power Asn, 66; Rail Transp Award, Am Soc Mech Engrs, 80; Outstanding Innovator Award, Univ NH, 87. *Prof Exp:* Spec apprentice to res engr, Warner & Swasey, 53-58, chief servo engr, 60-61; from asst prof to assoc prof eng, Case Inst Technol, 61-67. *Mem:* Am Soc Mech Engrs; Inst Elec & Electronics Engrs. *Res:* Electromechanical systems; control system synthesis; digital and discontinuous control and fluidic systems. *Mailing Add:* Nato AWACS PSC 7 Box 656 APO AE 09104-5000

**TAFT, DAVID DAKIN,** POLYMER CHEMISTRY, TECHNICAL MANAGEMENT. *Current Pos:* CHIEF OPERATING OFFICER, LANDEC CORP, 93- *Personal Data:* b Cleveland, Ohio, Mar 27, 38; m 61, Sara Leonard; c 3. *Educ:* Kenyon Col, AB, 60; Mich State Univ, PhD(org chem), 63. *Prof Exp:* Sr res chemist, Archer Daniels Midland Co, 64-67; group leader, Resins, Ashland Chem Co, 67-70, mgr polymer chem, Ashland Oil, Inc, 70-72; asst to pres, Consumer & Spec Chem, Henkel Corp, 72-74, dir res & develop, 74-76, from vpres to exec vpres, 77-82; group mgr, Telecom Group, Raychem Corp, 83-86, vpres mfg, 86-93. *Concurrent Pos:* Vpres & gen mgr, Oxyplast, Inc, 74. *Mem:* Am Chem Soc; Indust Res Inst; Fedn Socs Paint Technol; Com Develop Asn; Asn Mfg Excellence. *Res:* Acrylic, polyester, epoxy, urethane coating and adhesive systems; water soluble coating and adhesive polymers; functional monomers; powder coatings; non-yellowing isocyanates; nylon polymers; hydrophilic polymers; surface active agents; specialty chemicals for cosmetics; consumer adhesive products; compounding of polymers; 24 US patents; medical devices. *Mailing Add:* 45 Melanie Lane Atherton CA 94027-6440. *Fax:* 650-368-0173

**TAFT, EARL J,** ALGEBRA. *Current Pos:* from asst prof to assoc prof, 59-66, PROF MATH, RUTGERS UNIV, 66- *Personal Data:* b New York, NY, Aug 27, 31; m 59, Hessy Levinsons; c Nina T (Plotkin) & Alexander. *Educ:* Amherst Col, BA, 52; Yale Univ, MA, 53, PhD(math), 56. *Prof Exp:* Instr math, Columbia Univ, 56-59. *Concurrent Pos:* NSF res grants, 63-67, 70-71, 73, 76 & 87; exec ed, Commun in Algebra, 74-, Exec Ed Monographs & Lectr Notes Math, Marcel Dekker Inc, New York. *Mem:* Am Math Soc; Math Asn Am. *Res:* Nonassociative algebras; Hopf algebras; rings; groups. *Mailing Add:* Dept Math Rutgers Univ New Brunswick NJ 08903. *E-Mail:* jcia@math.rutgers.edu

**TAFT, JAY LESLIE,** BIOLOGICAL OCEANOGRAPHY. *Current Pos:* Res assoc, 74, ASSOC RES SCIENTIST BIOL OCEANOG, CHESAPEAKE BAY INST, 74-; DIR ADMIN, DEPT ORGANISMIC & EVOLUTIONARY BIOL, HARVARD UNIV, 83- *Personal Data:* b Rockville Centre, NY, Mar 19, 44. *Educ:* Lafayette Col, BA, 67; Johns Hopkins Univ, MA, 73, PhD(biol oceanog), 74. *Mem:* AAAS; Am Soc Limnol & Oceanog. *Res:* Production and utilization of dissolved organic matter in estuaries and coastal ocean; nutrient cycling in estuaries. *Mailing Add:* 26 Oxford St Harvard Univ Cambridge MA 02138

**TAFT, KINGSLEY ARTER, JR,** FORESTRY, GENETICS. *Current Pos:* RETIRED. *Personal Data:* b Cleveland, Ohio, Nov 17, 30; m 55; c 3. *Educ:* Amherst Col, AB, 53; Univ Mich, BS, 57; NC State Univ, MS, 62, PhD(forestry, genetics), 66. *Prof Exp:* Forester, Nebo Oil Co, La, 57-59; res asst forestry, NC State, 59-63; forest geneticist, Div Forestry, Tenn Valley Authority, 63- 74, chief, Forest & Wildlife Resources Br, Fisheries & Wildlife Develop, 74-79, spec projs coordr & asst to dir, Div Land & Forest Resources, 79-88. *Mem:* Soc Am Foresters. *Res:* Hardwood tree improvement and genetics. *Mailing Add:* 325 Trossachs Ln NW Knoxville TN 37922

**TAFT, ROBERT WHEATON, JR,** PHYSICAL CHEMISTRY, ORGANIC CHEMISTRY. *Current Pos:* PROF CHEM, UNIV CALIF, IRVINE, 65- *Personal Data:* b Lawrence, Kans, Dec 17, 22; m 44; c 3. *Educ:* Univ Kans, BS, 44, MS, 46; Ohio State Univ, PhD(chem), 49. *Prof Exp:* Lab asst chem, Univ Kans, 44-46; asst, Ohio State Univ, 46-49; res assoc, Columbia Univ, 49-50; from asst prof to prof, Pa State Univ, 50-65. *Concurrent Pos:* Sloan fel, 55-57; Guggenheim fel, Harvard Univ, 58; consult, Sun Oil Co, 58- *Mem:* Am Chem Soc. *Res:* Kinetics; effect of molecular structure on reactivity; mechanisms of organic reactions; rate and equilibrium studies; fluorine nuclear magnetic resonance shielding. *Mailing Add:* Chem Univ Calif Irvine CA 92717-0001

**TAFURI, JOHN FRANCIS,** ENTOMOLOGY. *Current Pos:* from instr to assoc prof biol, 51-68, PROF BIOL, XAVIER UNIV, OHIO, 68- *Personal Data:* b St Barbara, Italy, Aug 4, 24; nat US; m 58; c 3. *Educ:* Fordham Univ, BS, 44, MS, 48, PhD, 51. *Prof Exp:* Lab instr comp anat, Fordham Univ, 47-48, lab instr entom, 48, instr comp anat, Sch Educ, 50-51. *Concurrent Pos:* Asst, Dept Animal Behav, Am Mus Natural Hist, NY, 48-51. *Mem:* AAAS; Sigma Xi. *Res:* Electrical changes in tissues; social behavior in insects; aging in cells and tissues. *Mailing Add:* 162 Ruskin Dr Cincinnati OH 45246

**TAG, PAUL MARK,** METEOROLOGY, ARTIFICIAL INTELLIGENCE. *Current Pos:* CONSULT METEOROLOGIST, 89- *Personal Data:* b Meyersdale, Pa, Sept 8, 45; m 84, Rebecca Dold. *Educ:* Pa State Univ, BS, 66, MS, 68, PhD(meteorol), 77. *Prof Exp:* Res meteorologist, Navy Weather Res Facil, 68-71 & Naval Environ Prediction Res Facil, 71-89. *Concurrent Pos:* Weather forecaster, Air Nat Guard, 70-76. *Mem:* Am Meteorol Soc. *Res:* Numerical weather prediction; cloud physics; atmospheric turbulence; boundary layer; atmospheric numerical modeling; artificial intelligence; satellite imagery interpretation. *Mailing Add:* Naval Res Lab Monterey CA 93943-5502. *Fax:* 408-656-4769; *E-Mail:* tag@nrlmry.navy.mil

**TAGER, IRA BRUCE,** CLINICAL EPIDEMIOLOGY, INFECTIOUS DISEASES. *Current Pos:* CHIEF INFECTIOUS DIS, VET ADMIN MED CTR, SAN FRANCISCO. *Personal Data:* US citizen. *Educ:* Colgate Univ, AB, 65; Univ Rochester, MD, 69; Harvard Med Sch, MPH, 73. *Prof Exp:* Res fel infectious dis, Harvard Med Sch, 72-73, instr med, 73-76, asst prof, 76- *Concurrent Pos:* Edward Elliot Trudeau fel, Am Lung Asn, 77-81; consult, Dept Health, Div Epidemiol, State of RI, 78- *Mem:* Am Thoracic Soc; Am Soc Microbiol; fel Infectious Dis Soc Am; fel Am Col Epidemiol. *Res:* Epidemiology chronic lung disease and identification of determinants; determinants interventions for hospital acquired infections. *Mailing Add:* Chief Infectious Dis Vet Admin Med Ctr 4150 Clement St San Francisco CA 94121-1598

**TAGGART, G(EORGE) BRUCE,** CONDENSED MATTER THEORY, TECHNICAL MANAGEMENT. *Current Pos:* PROG DIR, MAT THEORY, DIV MAT RES, NSF, 89- *Personal Data:* b Philadelphia, Pa, Apr 8, 42; div. *Educ:* Col William & Mary, BS, 64; Temple Univ, PhD(physics), 71. *Prof Exp:* Instr physics, Drexel Univ, 70; vis asst prof, Temple Univ, 70-71; asst prof, Va Commonwealth Univ, 71-76, assoc prof physics, 76-82, prof, 82-83; mgr mat sci technol, Advan Technol Div, BDM Corp, 83-90. *Concurrent Pos:* Consult, Temple Univ, 74, res assoc, 75; res assoc, Oak Ridge Nat Lab, 74; vis prof, Dept Theoret Physics, Oxford Univ, 78; vis assoc prof physics, Univ Ill, Urbana-Champaign, 78-79; guestworker, Thermophysics Div, Nat Bur Stand, Gaithersburg, Md, 78-88; vis prof physics, Fed Univ Pernambuco, Brazil, 80; res assoc, Semiconductor Br, Naval Res Lab, 82. *Mem:* AAAS; Am Phys Soc; Mat Res Soc. *Res:* Materials theory. *Mailing Add:* Div Mat Res NSF 4201 Wilson Blvd Arlington VA 22230. *Fax:* 703-306-0515; *E-Mail:* gtaggart@nsf.gov

**TAGGART, KEITH ANTHONY,** PHYSICS, COMPUTATIONAL PHYSICS. *Current Pos:* DIR, STRATEGIC DEFENSE TECHNOL, SCI APPLN INT CORP, 88- *Personal Data:* b Cleveland, Ohio, July 10, 44; m 68; c 3. *Educ:* Case Inst Technol, BS, 66, MS, 68; Case Western Res Univ, PhD(physics), 70. *Prof Exp:* Staff scientist plasma physics, Air Force Weapons Lab, 70-72; fel, Plasma Physics Lab, Princeton Univ, 73; staff mem, Laser Fusion, Los Almos Nat Lab, 73-79, staff mem, Computational Physics, 79-83, prog mgr, Strategic Defense Res, 83-85; dir countermeasures, Strategic Defense Initiative Orgn, 85-88. *Mem:* Am Phys Soc. *Res:* Laser fusion target simulation on digital computers; computational simulation of complex systems; computational fluid dynamics. *Mailing Add:* 4004 Patricia St Annandale VA 22003

**TAGGART, R(OBERT) THOMAS,** HUMAN GENETICS, MEDICAL GENETICS. *Current Pos:* DIR MOLECULAR BIOL RES, CAROLINAS MED CTR OB/GYN, 94- *Personal Data:* b Long Beach, Calif, July 14, 51. *Educ:* Univ Denver, BS, 73; Ind Univ, PhD(med genetics & molecular biol), 78. *Prof Exp:* Fel human genetics, Sch Med, Yale Univ, 78-80; asst prof med, Univ Calif, Los Angeles, 80-87; chief, Human Genetics, Vet Admin Med Ctr, Sepulveda, Calif, 81-87; assoc prof, dept molecular biol & genetics, Wayne State Univ Sch Med, 87-93. *Concurrent Pos:* Investr, Ctr Ulcer Res & Educ, Univ Calif, Los Angeles, 81-; mem, Jonsson Comprehensive Cancer Ctr, 81- & Inflammatory Bowel Dis Ctr, 84- *Mem:* AAAS; Am Soc Biol Chemists; Am Soc Human Genetics; Genetics Soc Am; Sigma Xi. *Res:* Molecular genetics analysis of gastrointestinal proteases, growth factors and hormones; chromosomal localization and isolation of the genes encoding specific proteins. *Mailing Add:* 26 Prestonwood Lane E Amherst NY 14051

**TAGGART, RAYMOND,** MECHANICAL ENGINEERING. *Current Pos:* from asst prof to prof, 59-91, EMER PROF MECH ENG, UNIV WASH, 91- *Personal Data:* b Bradford, Eng, July 9, 22; m 49. *Educ:* Univ London, BSc, 48; Queen's Univ, Belfast, PhD, 56. *Prof Exp:* Eng draftsman, Harland & Wolffe, Ltd, N Ireland, 38-43; instr mech eng, Col Technol, Belfast, 43-48, sr lectr, 48-56; lectr, Queen's Univ, Belfast, 56-57; Nat Res Coun Can fel metall, Univ Alta, 57-58, res assoc, 58-59. *Concurrent Pos:* Blair fel, London Co Coun, London, 57-58; consult, failure analysis, accident reconstruction, aircraft, helicopters, fracture & fatigue analysis, design analysis (mech), mat analysis & failure. *Mem:* Fel Am Soc Metals; Brit Inst Mech Engrs; Sigma Xi. *Res:* Fatigue of metals with reference to crack propagation; effects of microstructural changes and precipitate morphology on properties of materials, especially crack propagation; relation of constitution to mechanical properties in binary alloys; superconducting properties of zirconium and titanium base alloys. *Mailing Add:* 6445 NE 130th Pl Kirkland WA 98034

**TAHA, HAMDY ABDELAZIZ,** OPERATIONS RESEARCH. *Current Pos:* assoc prof, 69-75, PROF INDUST ENG, UNIV ARK, FAYETTEVILLE, 75- *Personal Data:* b Egypt, Apr 19, 37; US citizen; m 65; c 3. *Educ:* Univ Alexandria, BS, 58; Stanford Univ, MS, 62; Ariz State Univ, PhD(indust eng), 64. *Prof Exp:* Instr elec eng, Univ Assiut, 58-59; mgr planning, Suez Oil Co, Egypt, 64-67; asst prof indust eng, Univ Okla, 67-69. *Concurrent Pos:* Lectr, Cairo Univ, 64-67; consult, Tenneco Oil Co, Okla, 67, Sun Oil Co, Tex, 70, Ford Found, 72, Petromin, Saudi Arabia, 75 & Hylsa, SA, Puebla, Mex, 77-78; vis prof, Univ Americas, Puebla, Mex, 77-78. *Mem:* Am Inst Indust Engrs; Inst Mgt Sci; Opers Res Soc Am. *Res:* Mathematical programming with emphasis on integer programming. *Mailing Add:* 406 Lake Rd Springdale AR 72764

**TAHA, THIAB R,** SCIENTIFIC COMPUTING & SOFTWARE DEVELOPMENT, PARALLEL ALGORITHMS. *Current Pos:* from asst prof to assoc prof, 82-94, PROF, DEPT COMPUT SCI, UNIV GA, 94- *Personal Data:* b Jordan, Oct 21, 49; m 83, Eman A Zaidelkilani; c Nabil, Farah, Abir & Ruba. *Educ:* Univ Jordan, BS, 72, MSc, 77; Clarkson Univ, PhD(math & comput sci), 82. *Prof Exp:* Sec educ teacher, Jordan, 72-76; instr,

Teacher's Training Inst, Jordan, 76-78. *Concurrent Pos:* Vis prof, Col Sci & Technol, Jerusalem, 85-86; prin investr, Dept Energy, 90-93, NSF, 92-95; Fulbright scholar, Univ Jordan, Amman, 95-96. *Mem:* Asn Comput Mach; Soc Indust & Appl Math; Int Asn Math & Comput Simulation; Inst Elec & Electronics Engrs. *Res:* Scientific computing and related computer software developments for nonlinear partial differential equations; applied mathematics; discrete forms of nonlinear wave equations; parallel algorithms; symbolic computations. *Mailing Add:* Comput Sci Dept Univ Ga Athens GA 30602-7404. *Fax:* 706-542-2966; *E-Mail:* thiab@cs.uga.edu

**TAHILIANI, VASU H,** INSULATION, POWER QUALITY. *Current Pos:* proj mgr, 77-84, prog mgr, 84-90, SR PROG MGR, ELEC POWER RES INST, 91- *Personal Data:* b Baroda, India, Oct 26, 42; US citizen; m 70, Kiran Khushalani; c Mamta, Radhika & Diya. *Educ:* MS Univ Baroda, BE, 64; WVa Univ, MSEE, 70. *Prof Exp:* Dep engr, Gujarat Elec Bd, India, 64-65; design engr, Jyoti Elec Ltd, India, 65; engr, Power Syst Div, McGraw Edison, 66-71; sr engr, ITE Imp Corp, 71-74, proj mgr, 74-76. *Concurrent Pos:* Prin investr, High Temp Gas Insulated Cables, 74-76, 765 Kv Gas Insulated Substas, 75-77; proj mgr & chmn, ad hoc comt Gas Insulated Substas Technol, 78-80; chmn, SCV Chap, Power Eng Soc Inst Elec & Electronics Engrs. *Mem:* Sr mem Inst Elec & Electronics Engrs; Int Conf Large High Voltage Elect Systs. *Res:* Gas insulated substations technology; gas insulated cables; insulation coordination for electrical power systems; metal oxide varistor technology; distribution engineering; cable materials technology; distribution systems. *Mailing Add:* Inervision 1598 Dorcey Lane San Jose CA 95120

**TAHIR-KHELI, RAZA ALI,** THEORETICAL MAGNETISM. *Current Pos:* from asst prof to assoc prof, 66-71, PROF PHYSICS, TEMPLE UNIV, 71- *Personal Data:* b Hazara, West Pakistan, May 1, 36; m 62; c 1. *Educ:* Oxford Univ, BA, 58, DPhil(physics), 62. *Prof Exp:* Res assoc physics, Univ Pa, 62-64; sr sci officer, Pakistan AEC, 64-66. *Concurrent Pos:* Assoc, Exp Sta, E I Du Pont de Nemours & Co, Del, Inc, 67-70. *Mem:* Am Phys Soc; Sigma Xi. *Res:* Solid state physics; many body physics; magnetism; order-disorder phenomena; random magnetism; atomic diffusion; non-equilibrium thermodynamics. *Mailing Add:* 21 E New Field Way Bala Cynwyd PA 19004

**TAI, CHEN-TO,** ELECTRICAL ENGINEERING. *Current Pos:* PROF ELEC ENG, UNIV MICH, ANN ARBOR, 64- *Personal Data:* b Soochow, China, Dec 30, 15; US citizen; m 41, Chia Ming Shen; c Arthur, Bing, Julie, David & James. *Educ:* Tsinghua Univ, China, BS, 37; Harvard Univ, DSc(commun), 47. *Honors & Awards:* Centennial Award, Inst Elec & Electronics Engrs. *Prof Exp:* Res fel elec eng, Harvard Univ, 47-49; sr res engr, Stanford Res Inst, 49-54; assoc prof elec eng, Ohio State Univ, 54-56; prof electronics, Tech Inst Aeronaut, Brazil, 56-60; prof elec eng, Ohio State Univ, 60-64. *Concurrent Pos:* Mem, Comn B, Int Union Radio Sci, 62- *Mem:* Nat Acad Eng; fel Inst Elec & Electronics Engrs. *Res:* Electromagnetic and antenna theories. *Mailing Add:* Dept EECS Univ Mich Ann Arbor MI 48109

**TAI, DOUGLAS L,** RADIOLOGICAL PHYSICS. *Current Pos:* CHIEF PHYSICIST, DEPT RADIOL, BAPTIST MEM HOSP, MEMPHIS, 93- *Personal Data:* b Hong Kong, Nov 6, 40; m 70, Christine; c Stephanie & Oliver. *Educ:* Chinese Univ Hong Kong, BSc, 64; Cornell Univ, PhD(chem), 69; Univ Ky, MRD, 77. *Prof Exp:* Res assoc phys chem, Cornell Univ, 69-71; fac res assoc solid state chem, Ariz State Univ, 71-72, asst prof, 72-73; instr, Dept Chem, Univ Ky, 73-74 & Dept Physics & Astron, 75-77; instr & radiol physicist, Dept Radiol, Univ Miss Med Ctr, 77-79, asst prof & radiol physicist, 79-81; asst prof & radiol physicist, Dept Radiol, Univ Tenn, 81-93. *Mem:* Am Asn Physicists Med; Health Physics Soc; Am Endocrinether Soc; Am Col Med Physics. *Res:* Teletherapy and intracavitary dosimetry. *Mailing Add:* Dept Radiation & Oncol Univ Tenn 899 Madison Ave 266 Main Memphis TN 38146. *Fax:* 901-227-5021

**TAI, HAN,** ANALYTICAL CHEMISTRY. *Current Pos:* supvr pesticides monitoring lab, 70-80, CHEMIST, ENVIRON CHEM LAB, ENVIRON PROTECTION AGENCY, 80- *Personal Data:* b Yang Chow, China, Mar 20, 24; m 61, Doreen Y Wang; c Yolanda & Steven. *Educ:* Nanking Univ, BS, 49; Emory Univ, MS, 55, PhD(chem), 58. *Prof Exp:* Asst geol, Nat Taiwan Univ, Formosa, 51-54; res chemist, A E Staley Mfg Co, 58-66, head instrumental analytical lab, 66-67, group leader analytical labs, 67-70. *Mem:* Am Chem Soc; Soc Appl Spectros. *Res:* Chemical analysis of rocks and minerals, carbohydrates, polymers, pesticides; infrared spectroscopy; chromatography; environmental monitoring on inorganic and organic pollutants and pesticide residues. *Mailing Add:* Environ Chem Lab Environ Protection Agency Bay St Louis MS 39529

**TAI, JULIA CHOW,** CHEMISTRY. *Current Pos:* from asst prof to assoc prof, 69-79, PROF CHEM, UNIV MICH, DEARBORN, 79- *Personal Data:* b Shanghai, China, 1935; US citizen; m 60, Hung-chao; c Eve, Helen & Michael. *Educ:* Nat Taiwan Univ, BS, 57; Univ Okla, MS, 59; Univ Ill, Urbana, PhD(chem), 63. *Prof Exp:* Fels, Wayne State Univ, 63-68. *Concurrent Pos:* vis assoc prof, Nat Taiwan Univ, Taipei, Taiwan, 68-69. *Mem:* Am Chem Soc; Quantum Chem Prog Exchange; Coun Undergrad Res. *Res:* Molecular mechanics study of heterocyclic conjugated molecules; structural, spectral, and electronic properties. *Mailing Add:* Dept Natural Sci Univ Mich-Dearborn Dearborn MI 48128. *Fax:* 313-593-4937; *E-Mail:* jtai@cw-fl.umd.umich.edu

**TAI, PETER YAI-PO,** PLANT BREEDING. *Current Pos:* RES GENETICIST PLANT, AGR RES SERV, USDA, 77- *Personal Data:* b Chutung, Taiwan, July 6, 37; US citizen; m 64, Rosie Peng; c Robert H & Thomas H. *Educ:* Nat Taiwan Univ, BS, 61; Tex A&M Univ, MS, 66; Okla

State Univ, PhD(crop sci), 72. *Prof Exp:* Res assoc, Agr Exp Sta, Univ Ga, 72-75, instr plant breeding, 75-77. *Concurrent Pos:* Adj assoc prof, Univ Fla, Inst Food & Agr Sci. *Mem:* Am Soc Agron; Crop Sci Soc Am; Am Soc Sugar Cane Technol; AAAS. *Res:* Development of new breeding lines of sugarcane (Saccharum sp), improvement of cold tolerance in sugarcane and selection methodology; development of pollen storage techniques for Saccharum spontaneum. *Mailing Add:* Sugarcane Field Station Star Rte PO Box 8 USDA-ARS Canal Point FL 33438

**TAI, TSZE CHENG,** FLUID MECHANICS, COMPUTATIONAL AERODYNAMICS. *Current Pos:* res scientist, 68-84, SR RES SCIENTIST FLUID MECH, CARDEROCK DIV, NAVAL SURFACE WARFARE CTR, 84- *Personal Data:* b Shaoxiang, China, Apr 29, 33; US citizen; m 65, Thelma Sun; c Kuangheng, Kuangkai & Kuangshin. *Educ:* Air Force Inst Technol, Taiwan, dipl, 57; Clemson Univ, MS, 65; Va Polytech Inst, PhD(aerospace eng), 69. *Honors & Awards:* E N Brooks Award, David Taylor Res Ctr, 79. *Prof Exp:* Aircraft eng, Taoyuan Airbase, Taiwan, 58-63; res asst fluid mech, Clemson Univ, 63-65; teaching asst aerodyn, Va Polytech Inst, 65-67, instr aerospace eng, 67-68. *Concurrent Pos:* Chmn, Air Inlet & Diffusers Panel, Navy Aeroballistics Comt, 79-81; invited lectr, von Karman Inst Fluid Dynamics, Belg, 80; sci officer, Off Naval Res, 85-86; pres, David Taylor Sigma Xi Chap, 89-90. *Mem:* Assoc fel Am Inst Aeronaut & Astronaut; Sigma Xi. *Res:* Transonic aerodynamics; computational fluid dynamics; V-22 aerodynamics; three-dimensional flow separation. *Mailing Add:* Carderock Div Code 5300 Naval Surface Warfare Ctr Bethesda MD 20084-5000. *E-Mail:* tai@oasys.dt.navy.mil

**TAI, WILLIAM,** CYTOGENETICS, CROP BREEDING. *Current Pos:* CHIEF EXEC OFFICER, WILLIAM TAI & ASSOC INC. *Personal Data:* b Yangzhow, China, Mar 9, 34; m 63; c 4. *Educ:* Nat Chung Hsing Univ, BSc, 56; Utah State Univ, MSc, 64; Univ Utah, PhD(genetics), 67. *Prof Exp:* NIH fel biol sci, Stanford Univ, 67-69; from asst prof to prof bot & plant path, Mich State Univ, 69-82; prof plant sci, Univ Man, 82-88; prog dir, Mo Bot Gardens, 88-95. *Concurrent Pos:* Vis prof, Nat Chung-Hsing Univ, 75-76, Genetic Inst, Acad Sinica, Beijing, China; hon prof, Acad Sci China, Jiangsu Agr Col, China, Suchuan Univ Genetics Inst. *Mem:* Bot Soc Am; Am Inst Biol Sci; Genetic Soc Can; Am Soc Agron; Crop Sci Soc Am. *Res:* Plant cytogenetics; cytotaxonomy; plant breeding. *Mailing Add:* 865 Hollyridge Dr Ballwin MO 63011-3556

**TAIBLESON, MITCHELL H,** MATHEMATICS. *Current Pos:* From asst prof to assoc prof math, Wash Univ, 62-69, chmn dept, 70-73, res prof, Dept Phychiat, Med Sch, 73-75, PROF MATH, WASH UNIV, 69- *Personal Data:* b Oak Park, Ill, Dec 31, 29; m 49; c Judith, David & Michael. *Educ:* Univ Chicago, SM, 60, PhD(math), 62. *Concurrent Pos:* Mem, Inst Advan Study, 66-67; vis prof, Higher Normal Sch, Pisa, Italy, 80-81 & Nanjing Univ, People's Repub China, 85. *Mem:* Am Math Soc; Math Asn Am. *Res:* Several dimensional harmonic analysis on real and local fields; Lipschitz and potential spaces; special functions; Hardy spaces. *Mailing Add:* Dept Math Wash Univ Campus Box 1146 One Brookings Dr St Louis MO 63130-4899. *Fax:* 314-935-6839; *E-Mail:* mitch@prath.wustl.edu

**TAICHMAN, NORTON STANLEY,** PATHOLOGY, IMMUNOLOGY. *Current Pos:* RETIRED. *Personal Data:* b Toronto, Ont, May 27, 36; m 58; c 5. *Educ:* Univ Toronto, DDS, 61, PhD(immunopath), 67; Harvard Univ, dipl periodont, 64. *Hon Degrees:* MSc, Univ Pa, 72. *Honors & Awards:* Lindback Found Award, 77; Basic Sci Res Award, Int Asn Dent Res, 85. *Prof Exp:* Assoc dent, Fac Dent, Univ Toronto, 65-68, from lectr to asst prof path, 67-71; prof path & chmn dept, Sch Dent Med, Univ Pa, 72-95, assoc dean acad affairs, 91-95. *Concurrent Pos:* Assoc prof dent, Fac Dent, Univ Toronto, 68-72, assoc prof path, 71-72, mem, Inst Immunol, 70-72. *Mem:* Am Soc Exp Path; Am Soc Microbiol; Soc Leukocyte Biol; Int Asn Dent Res. *Res:* Inflammation, immunopathology, periodontal disease; angiogenesis. *Mailing Add:* Dept Path Univ Pa Sch Dent Med 4010 Locust St Philadelphia PA 19104-6002. *Fax:* 215-898-8380; *E-Mail:* taichman@research.dental.upenn.edu

**TAIGANIDES, E PAUL,** SANITARY ENGINEERING, ENVIRONMENTAL ENGINEERING. *Current Pos:* assoc prof, 65-69, prof agr eng, 69-76, EPT CONSULT, OHIO STATE UNIV, 87- *Personal Data:* b Polymylos, Greece, Oct 6, 34; m 61, Maro Liapaki; c Paul A, Tasps E & Katerina Sophia. *Educ:* Univ Maine, BS, 57; Iowa State Univ, MS, 60, PhD(environ eng), 63. *Honors & Awards:* Young Educator Award, Am Soc Agr Engrs, 74. *Prof Exp:* Asst prof agr eng, Iowa State Univ, 63-65; proj mgr & tech adv, Food & Agr Org, UN, 75-87. *Concurrent Pos:* Consult var indust & govt; proj mgr, US Feed Grains Coun, Tokyo, 73 & Food & Agr Orgn, UN, Singapore, 75-; chief tech adv & prog mgr, UN Develop Prog, Food & Agr Orgn, UN, Singapore & Malaysia, 75-87. *Mem:* Fel Am Soc Agr Engrs; Am Soc Eng Educ; Am Acad Environ Engrs. *Res:* Environmental engineering for food industry wastewater control. *Mailing Add:* 1800 Willow Forge Dr Columbus OH 43220. *Fax:* 614-451-0971; *E-Mail:* eptai@aol.com

**TAIGEN, THEODORE LEE,** PHYSIOLOGICAL ECOLOGY. *Current Pos:* ASST PROF ECOL, UNIV CONN, 81- *Personal Data:* b Seattle, Wash, Nov 22, 52; m 73; c 2. *Educ:* Colo State Univ, BS, 76, MS, 78; Cornell Univ, PhD(ecol), 81. *Mem:* Am Soc Ichthyologists & Herpetologists; Am Ornithologists Union; Am Soc Zoologists; Ecol Soc Am; Sigma Xi. *Res:* Ecological and behavioral correlates of metabolic characteristics of terrestrial vertebrates; physiological variables, including resting and activity metabolism, are analyzed for their association with foraging strategies, habitat selection, predator avoidance mechanisms and modes of locomotion. *Mailing Add:* Ecol Dept Univ Conn U-42 75 N Eagleville Storrs Manfield CT 06269-0002

**TAIMUTY, SAMUEL ISAAC,** PHYSICS. *Current Pos:* RETIRED. *Personal Data:* b West Newton, Pa, Dec 20, 17; m 53, 76, Rosalie Richards; c Matthew & Martha. *Educ:* Carnegie Inst Technol, BS, 40; Univ Southern Calif, PhD(physics), 51. *Prof Exp:* Asst res physicist, Am Soc Heat & Ventilating Eng Lab, 40-42; physicist, Philadelphia Naval Shipyard, 42-44 & Long Beach Naval Shipyard, 44-46; sr physicist, US Naval Radiol Defense Lab, 50-52 & Stanford Res Inst, 52-72; sr physicist, Lockheed Missiles & Space Co, 72-89. *Concurrent Pos:* Consult, 89- *Mem:* Am Phys Soc; Sigma Xi. *Res:* Heat transmission; magnetism; nuclear and radiation physics; radiation effects in solids; radiation dosimetry; industrial applications of radiation, ferroelectricity, thin films and organic dielectrics. *Mailing Add:* 3346 Kenneth Dr Palo Alto CA 94303-4217

**TAIT, JAMES SIMPSON,** FISH BIOLOGY. *Current Pos:* asst prof, 64-70, ASSOC PROF BIOL, YORK UNIV, 70- *Personal Data:* b Charlottetown, PEI, Feb 25, 30; m 58, Adrienne Boone; c Heather & Geoffrey. *Educ:* Dalhousie Univ, BSc, 50, MSc, 52; Univ Toronto, PhD(zool), 59. *Prof Exp:* Res scientist, Res Br, Ont Dept Lands & Forests, 58-64. *Concurrent Pos:* Consult, Res Br, Ont Dept Lands & Forests, 64-70. *Mem:* Am Fisheries Soc; Can Soc Zool. *Res:* Environmental physiology of fish particularly buoyancy regulation, behavioral thermoregulation, tolerance and avoidance of low oxygen and effects of insecticides on neuroendocrine systems; studies on stressed populations of salmonids. *Mailing Add:* Biol Sci York Univ 4700 Keele St North York ON M3J 1P3 Can

**TAIT, JOHN CHARLES,** NUCLEAR WASTE MANAGEMENT. *Current Pos:* RES CHEMIST PHYS CHEM, ATOMIC ENERGY CAN, LTD, 78- *Personal Data:* b Vancouver, BC, Sept 23, 45; m. *Educ:* Univ BC, BSc, 67, PhD(chem), 74. *Prof Exp:* Fel phys chem, Nat Res Coun Can, 74-77; res assoc, Univ BC, 77-78. *Mem:* Chem Inst Can. *Res:* Kinetics and dissolution properties of used fuel; surface adsorption; surface analysis by secondary ion mass spectrometry, electron spectroscopy for chemical analysis scanning electron microscopy, radiation chemistry. *Mailing Add:* Atomic Energy Can Ltd Whiteshell Lab Pinawa MB R0E 1L0 Can. *Fax:* 204-753-2455; *E-Mail:* taitj@wl.aecl.ca

**TAIT, KEVIN S,** APPLIED MATHEMATICS. *Current Pos:* RETIRED. *Personal Data:* b New York, NY, Nov 24, 33; m 59; c 4. *Educ:* Princeton Univ, AB, 55; Harvard Univ, PhD(appl math), 65. *Mem:* Soc Indust & Appl Math. *Mailing Add:* 21 Oakland St Lexington MA 02173

**TAIT, ROBERT JAMES,** CONTINUUM MATHEMATICS, WAVE MOTION. *Current Pos:* PROF MATH, UNIV ALTA, 82- *Personal Data:* b Glasgow, Scotland, Aug 28, 37. *Educ:* Univ Glasgow, PhD(math), 62. *Res:* Incompressible elastic materials and shock capturing techniques from a numerical point of view. *Mailing Add:* Dept Math Univ Alta Edmonton AB T6G 2G1 Can

**TAIT, WILLIAM CHARLES,** THEORETICAL SOLID STATE PHYSICS, ELECTROMAGNETIC THEORY. *Current Pos:* RETIRED. *Personal Data:* b Waterloo, Iowa, Feb 9, 32; m 54, Adele Witucki; c William Jr, Susan (Peterson), Samuel & George. *Educ:* Wabash Col, BA, 54; Cornell Univ, MA, 58; Purdue Univ, PhD, 62. *Prof Exp:* Teaching asst, Cornell Univ, 54-58; physicist, Res Lab, Bendix Corp, 58; instr physics, Wabash Col, 58-61; sr physicist, Cent Res, Minn Mining & Mfg Co, 62-66, res specialist, 67-68, supvr, 69-70, mgr cent res, 71-72, mgr duplicating prod, 72-75, sr res specialist, 75-93; physics consult, 93-94. *Mem:* Am Phys Soc; Sigma Xi. *Res:* Solid state and quantum field theory; semiconductor lasers; photoconductors; electrophotography; integrated optics. *Mailing Add:* 849 Autumn Way Stillwater MN 55082-7100

**TAIZ, LINCOLN,** PLANT PHYSIOLOGY. *Current Pos:* from asst prof to assoc prof, 73-83, PROF BIOL, UNIV CALIF, SANTA CRUZ, 83- *Personal Data:* b Philadelphia, Pa, Nov 5, 42; m 63; c 1. *Educ:* Univ Utah, BS, 67; Univ Calif, Berkeley, PhD(bot), 71. *Prof Exp:* Actg asst prof bot, Univ Calif, Berkeley, 72-73. *Concurrent Pos:* NSF fel, Univ Calif, 71-72. *Mem:* Am Soc Plant Physiologists; Bot Soc Am; AAAS. *Res:* The structure, function and evolution of the plant vacuolar ATPase; hormonal control of plant development. *Mailing Add:* Dept Biol Univ Calif Santa Cruz 1156 High St Santa Cruz CA 95064-1077

**TAJIMA, TOSHIKI,** PLASMAS PHYSICS. *Current Pos:* from asst prof to assoc prof, 80-89, PROF PHYSICS, UNIV TEX, AUSTIN, 90- *Personal Data:* b Nagoya, Japan, Jan 18, 48; m, Fumiko; c Mika & Yuhki. *Educ:* Univ Tokyo, BS, 71, MS, 73; Univ Calif, Irvine, PhD(physics), 75. *Honors & Awards:* Leadership Award, Japan Atomic Energy Res Inst, 93, Fac Res Award, 95. *Prof Exp:* Asst res physicist, Univ Calif, Los Angeles, 76-80, assoc res physicist, 80. *Concurrent Pos:* Consult, TRW, Inc, 78-81, Jaycor, 78-79, Toshiba, 79-80, Western Res Inc, 78-, FM Technol, 88-, SSC Lab, 89- & INEL, 91-; prin investr, NSF, 81-, Dept Energy, 83- & NASA, 85-; mem, Int Sci Radio Union/Nat Res Coun; vis scientist, Los Alamos, 83-85; co-ed, J Particle Accelerator, 85; group leader, Advan Sci Res Ctr, JAERI, 93- *Mem:* Fel Am Phys Soc; Am Geophys Union; fel Japan Soc Prom Sci; Am Astron Soc; Phys Soc Japan. *Res:* Physics of nuclear fusion, plasma physics, astrophysics, particle accelerators and computational physics; muon calalyzed fusion-fission hybrid reactor; direct energy conversion of x-ray to electricity; fusion reactor concept for muon fusion with magnetic-inertial confinement; author of one book. *Mailing Add:* Physics Dept Univ Tex Austin TX 78712. *E-Mail:* ttt@dino.ph.utexas.edu

**TAKACS, GERALD ALAN,** ATMOSPHERIC CHEMISTRY, PLASMA CHEMISTRY. *Current Pos:* vis asst prof phys chem, Rochester Inst Technol, 73-75, from asst prof to assoc prof, 75-82, PROF PHYS CHEM, ROCHESTER INST TECHNOL, 82- *Personal Data:* b Edmonton, Alta, Sept 10, 43; c 2. *Educ:* Univ Alta, Edmonton, BS, 65; Univ Wis-Madison, PhD(phys chem), 71. *Prof Exp:* Teaching asst chem, Univ Wis-Madison, 65-67, res asst phys chem, 67-71; fel phys chem, Rice Univ, 71-72; teaching intern & res assoc phys chem, Univ Ala, Huntsville, 72-73. *Concurrent Pos:* Sr res assoc, Nat Oceanic & Atmospheric Admin, Nat Res Coun, 82-83; prin investr, IBM, Endicott, NY, 84-; head, Dept Chem, Rochester Inst Technol, 85- *Mem:* Am Chem Soc; Am Vacuum Soc; Coun Undergrad Res. *Res:* Atmospheric chemistry; chem kinetics; photochemistry; physical chemistry; plasma chemistry. *Mailing Add:* Dept Chem Rochester Inst Technol Rochester NY 14623-5640

**TAKAGI, SHOZO,** CRYSTALLOGRAPHY. *Current Pos:* RES ASSOC, AM DENT ASN HEALTH FOUND RES UNIT, PAFFENBARGER RES CTR, NAT INST STAND & TECHNOL, 78- *Personal Data:* b Nishinomiya, Japan, Apr 2, 43; m 67, Hiroko Mito; c Keiko & Ken. *Educ:* Kwansei Gakuin Univ, BSc, 66; Univ Pittsburgh, PhD(crystallog), 71. *Prof Exp:* Res assoc chem, Vanderbilt Univ, 71-75; res assoc, Dept Chem, Brookhaven Nat Lab, 75-78. *Mem:* Int Asn Dent Res; Am Crystallog Asn. *Res:* To determine structures of components of importance to dental health by x-ray and neutron diffraction techniques; conduct research on topical fluoridation of tooth and calcium phosphate cement. *Mailing Add:* Am Dent Asn Health Found Paffenbarger Res Ctr Nat Inst Stand & Technol Gaithersburg MD 20899. *Fax:* 301-963-9143; *E-Mail:* shozo.takagi@nist.gov

**TAKAHASHI, AKIO,** POLYMER CHEMISTRY. *Current Pos:* VPRES TECHNOL, SUNKYONG AM, 88- *Personal Data:* b Andong, Korea, July 15, 32; m 64; c 4. *Educ:* Tokyo Col Sci, BS, 57; Tokyo Inst Technol, MS, 60, PhD(polymer chem), 63. *Prof Exp:* Sr chemist, Mitsui Chem Indust, Inc, 63-65; sr chemist, Gaylord Assocs, Inc, NJ, 65-67, sect mgr, 67-70; res assoc polymer chem, Hooker Chem & Plastics Co, 70-73, sr res assoc, 73-75, scientist & discipline/prog leader, 75-78; res mgr, Am Can Co, 78-83, Air Prods & Chem, 83-85 & Henkel Corp, 85-88. *Mem:* Am Chem Soc; Japanese Soc Polymer Sci. *Res:* Polymer-organic chemistry; polymerization by free radical, Ziegler-Natta and ionic catalysts; polymerization through charge-transfer complexes; polybutadiene; polyvinyl chloride; polyethers; graft copolymers. *Mailing Add:* Prides Crossing Flanders NJ 07836-9239

**TAKAHASHI, ELLEN SHIZUKO,** PHYSIOLOGICAL OPTICS, OPTOMETRY. *Current Pos:* RETIRED. *Personal Data:* b Berkeley, Calif; m 67, Clyde W Oyster. *Educ:* Univ Calif, Berkeley, BS, 52, MOpt, 53, PhD(physiol optics), 68. *Prof Exp:* Optometrist in pvt pract, 53-56; optometrist orthoptics, Stanford Univ Hosps, 56-62; clin instr & actg asst prof optom, Univ Calif, 62-67; NIH fel visual neurophysiol, Australian Nat Univ, 68-70; from asst prof to assoc prof, Univ Ala, 70-81, dir grad studies, Sch Optom, 74-76, prof physiol optics, 81-92. *Concurrent Pos:* Mem, Nat Adv Coun Health Prof Educ, 72-75, & Visual Sci B Study Sect, NIH, 79-82; mem, Papers Prog, Am Acad Optom, 81- *Mem:* Am Acad Optom; Asn Res Vision & Ophthal; Soc Neurosci. *Res:* Visual neurophysiology and anatomy; binocular vision. *Mailing Add:* 3517 Belle Meade Way Univ Ala Birmingham AL 35223

**TAKAHASHI, HIRONORI,** NUCLEAR FUSION. *Current Pos:* res staff mem, 80-85, res physicist, 85-96, PRIN RES PHYSICIST, PLASMA PHYSICS LAB, PRINCETON UNIV, 96- *Personal Data:* b Tokyo, Japan, June 5, 42; US citizen. *Educ:* Keio Univ, Japan, BEng, 65; Mass Inst Technol, MS, 67, DSc(aeronaut & astronaut), 70. *Prof Exp:* Fel plasma physics, Univ Stuttgart, 71-72, guest lectr, 72-73; res assoc, Plasma Physics Lab, Princeton Univ, 73-75, res staff mem, 75-79; group leader & co-prin investr, Nat Magnetic Lab, Mass Inst Technol, 79-80. *Mem:* Am Phys Soc. *Res:* Plasma physics in connection with controlled thermonuclear fusion research; magnetic diagnostics and operation of tokamaks; lower hybrid current drive. *Mailing Add:* Plasma Physics Lab Princeton Univ PO Box 451 Princeton NJ 08543-0451. *Fax:* 609-243-2418

**TAKAHASHI, HIROSHI,** ACCELERATOR BASED NUCLEAR REACTOR, MUON CATALIZED FUSION. *Current Pos:* res assoc, 59-61, physicist, 66-74, SR PHYSICIST NUCLEAR REACTOR PHYSICS, BROOKHAVEN NAT LAB, 77- *Personal Data:* b Kawaguchi, Saitama, Japan, Mar 4, 29; m 60, Yoshiko Ohama; c Mariko & Emiko. *Educ:* Waseda Univ, Batchelar, 52, Master, 55, PhD(nuclear reactor physics), 59. *Prof Exp:* Sr researcher nuclear physics, Japan Atomic Energy Res Inst, 57-66; prof, Tokyo Inst Technol, 74-77. *Concurrent Pos:* Qualified stagie, Joint Res Ctr, Euratom, Italy, 61-62. *Mem:* Am Phys Soc; Atomic Energy Soc Japan. *Res:* Application of accelerator to nuclear fuel cycle; acclerator based subcritical reactor for producing fissile material, transmuting high level waste and plutonium and production of tritium. *Mailing Add:* Setauket NY 11733. *Fax:* 516-282-2613

**TAKAHASHI, JOSEPH S,** CIRCADIAN RHYTHMS, MOLECULAR NEUROBIOLOGY & GENETICS. *Current Pos:* from asst prof to prof neurobiol, 83-91, ACTG ASSOC DIR, INST NEUROSCI, NORTHWESTERN UNIV, 88- *Personal Data:* b Dec 16, 51; m 85, Barbara (Pillsbury-Snook); c Erika S. *Educ:* Swarthmore Col, BA, 74; Univ Ore, Eugene, PhD(neurosci), 81. *Honors & Awards:* Honma Prize in Biol Rhythms, Honma Found, 86; 6th Ariens Kappers Award, 95. *Prof Exp:* Res assoc pharmacol, NIMH, 81-83. *Concurrent Pos:* Alfred P Sloan Award, 83-85; mem, adv bd, J Biol Rhythms, 84-, adv comt, Soc Res Biol Rhythms, 86-, NIMH Psychobiol & Behav Rev Comt, 88-92; Presidential young investr

award, 85-90; Searle scholar, 85-88; Bristol-Myers Unrestricted Award Neurosci Res, 95- *Mem:* AAAS; Soc Neurosci; Asn Res Vision & Ophthal; Soc Res Biol Rhythms; Int Mammalian Genome Soc. *Res:* Molecular biology and genetics of circadian rhythms; molecular neurobiology; signal transduction; photoreceptor gene expression and regulation. *Mailing Add:* Dept Neurobiol & Physiol Northwestern Univ 2153 N Campus Dr Evanston IL 60208. *Fax:* 847-491-5211

**TAKAHASHI, LOREY K,** DEVELOPMENTAL PSYCHOBIOLOGY, BEHAVIORAL NEUROENDOCRINOLOGY. *Current Pos:* asst scientist, 86-90, ASST PROF, DEPT PSYCHIAT, MED SCH, UNIV WIS, 90- *Personal Data:* b Honolulu, Hawaii, July 25, 53; m 82, Chirtana Y Yongnorasethkul; c Edwin A & Cyrus G. *Educ:* Univ Hawaii, Manoa, BA, 75, MA, 78; Rutgers Univ, NB, PhD(psychol), 82. *Prof Exp:* Undergrad teaching asst, Dept Psychol, Rutgers Univ, 78-82; NIMH trainee, Dept Biol, Princeton Univ, 82-83, fel, 83-85, res assoc, 85-86. *Concurrent Pos:* Clin asst prof, Dept Psychiat, Med Sch, Univ Wis, 89-90. *Mem:* Sigma Xi; AAAS; Am Psychol Asn; Soc Study Reproduction; Am Soc Zoologists; Animal Behav Soc; Soc Neurosci. *Res:* Neurobiology of emotional expression using animal models; combining neuroendocrine, neurochemical, neuroanatomical and ethological methods to study how brain processes influence the development of social and sexual patterns of behavior. *Mailing Add:* Dept Psychiat Univ Wis Medica 600 Highland Ave Madison WI 53792. *Fax:* 608-263-0265

**TAKAHASHI, MARK T,** PHYSICAL BIOCHEMISTRY. *Current Pos:* asst prof, 70-77, ASSOC PROF PHYSIOL, RUTGERS MED SCH, COL MED & DENT NJ, 77- *Personal Data:* b Holtville, Calif, Feb 26, 36; m 61; c 2. *Educ:* Oberlin Col, BA, 58; Univ Wis-Madison, PhD(phys chem), 63. *Prof Exp:* Res biochemist, Battelle Mem Inst, 64-67. *Concurrent Pos:* NIH fel, Univ Mass, Amherst, 67-70. *Mem:* AAAS; Biophys Soc; Am Soc Biol Chemists; Am Chem Soc. *Res:* Physical enzymology; membranes. *Mailing Add:* Dept Physiol & Biophys Univ Med & Dent NJ-R W Johnson Med Sch 675 Hoes Lane Piscataway NJ 08854-5635

**TAKAHASHI, PATRICK KENJI,** CHEMICAL ENGINEERING, ENERGY. *Current Pos:* asst prof eng, 71-75, ASSOC PROF CIVIL ENG, UNIV HAWAII, 75-, ACTG ASSOC DEAN ENG, 76-, ACAD ASST CHANCELLOR, 78-, PROF ENG, 82-, DIR, HAWAII NATURAL ENERGY INST, 84- *Personal Data:* b Honolulu, Hawaii, Sept 6, 40; m 62. *Educ:* Stanford Univ, BS, 62; La State Univ, Baton Rouge, MS, 69, PhD(chem eng), 71. *Prof Exp:* Sugar processing engr, C Brewer, 62-67; proj engr computerized optimization, Hawaiian Sugar Planters Asn, 67-68. *Concurrent Pos:* Consult, Lawrence Livermore Lab, Gen Tel & Electronics Corp, 77-; spec asst energy to Sen Spark Matsunaga, 79-82; dir, Hawaii Nat Energy Inst, Univ Hawaii, 84, vpres develop, 88. *Mem:* Am Chem Soc; Am Inst Chem Engrs. *Res:* Energy (biomass, geothermal, wind, solar); laser applications. *Mailing Add:* Hawaii Natural Energy Inst Univ Hawaii Manoa 2540 Dole St Honolulu HI 96822

**TAKAHASHI, TARO,** GEOCHEMISTRY, GEOPHYSICS. *Current Pos:* Res scientist, Lamont Geol Observ, 57-59, res assoc, 59-77, ADJ PROF, DEPT GEOL SCI & SR SCIENTIST, LAMONT-DOHERTY GEOL OBSERV, COLUMBIA UNIV, 77-, ASSOC DIR, 81-, DOHERTY SR SCIENTIST, 84- *Personal Data:* b Tokyo, Japan, Nov 15, 30; US citizen; m 66, Elaine Ache; c Timothy Taro & Suzanne E. *Educ:* Univ Tokyo, BEng, 53; Columbia Univ, PhD(geol), 57. *Concurrent Pos:* Lectr, Queens Col, NY, 58; res chemist, Scripps Inst Oceanog, Univ Calif, 59; asst prof, Col Ceramics, State Univ NY, Alfred, 59-62; vis prof, 63; assoc prof, Univ Rochester, 62-70, prof, 70; vis asst prof, Columbia Univ, 66; vis assoc prof, Calif Inst Technol, 71; distinguished prof, Queens Col, NY, 71-77; actg chief exec officer, Biosphere 2-Ctr Inc, Ariz, 96. *Mem:* Am Geophys Union; Geol Soc Am; Geochem Soc (secy, 81-84); Sigma Xi. *Res:* Thermodynamic and physical properties of metal oxides under extremely high pressures and temperatures; geochemistry of carbon dioxide in the ocean atmosphere system; thermodynamics of ore forming minerals. *Mailing Add:* 350 Hennessy St Haworth NJ 07641. *E-Mail:* taka@ldco.columbia.edu

**TAKAHASHI, YASUNDO,** mechanical engineering, for more information see previous edition

**TAKAHASHI, YASUSHI,** THEORETICAL PHYSICS. *Current Pos:* dir, Theoret Physics Inst, 69-85, PROF PHYSICS, UNIV ALTA, 68- *Personal Data:* b Osaka, Japan, Dec 12, 24; m 59; c 2. *Educ:* Nagoya Univ, BSc, 51, DSc(physics), 54. *Prof Exp:* Nat Res Coun Can fel, 54-55; res assoc physics, Iowa State Univ, 55-57; res scholar, Dublin Inst Advan Studies, 57, from asst prof to prof, 57-68. *Mem:* Fel Am Phys Soc; Royal Irish Acad; fel Royal Soc Can. *Res:* Quantization of relativistic fields; quantum electrodynamics and field theory; many-body theory. *Mailing Add:* Dept Physics Univ Alta Edmonton AB T6G 2J1 Can. *Fax:* 403-492-4256

**TAKAI, YASUYUKI,** CELLULAR IMMUNOLOGY, INTERNAL MEDICINE. *Current Pos:* HEAD, TAKAI NAIKA CLIN, 93- *Personal Data:* b Osaka, Japan, Aug 23, 51; m 82, Keiko Tsukiyama; c Toshikazu & Kenji. *Educ:* Osaka Univ, MD, 77, PhD(med), 84. *Prof Exp:* Fel immunol, Div Pediat Oncol, Dana-Farber Cancer Inst, 84-87; res fel immunol, Inst Cancer Res, Osaka Univ, 79-84, internal med, Second Dept Med, 79-90, asst prof, Biomed Res Ctr, 87-90; sr physician, Internal Med, Ikeda City Hosp, 90-93. *Mem:* Am Asn Immunologists; Fedn Am Socs Exp Biol. *Res:* Cellular immunology; clinical immunology. *Mailing Add:* 2-7-8 Toneyama Toyonaka Osaka 560 Japan. *Fax:* 81-6-846-3688

**TAKANO, MASAHARU,** CHEMICAL ENGINEERING, BIOTECHNOLOGY. *Current Pos:* CONSULT, TAKANO INT, 91- *Personal Data:* b Tainan, Taiwan, Jan 20, 35; nat US; m 65, Hiroko Takeshita; c Kentaro, Jojiro & Miwako. *Educ:* Hokkaido Univ, BSc, 57; Univ Tokyo, MSc, 59, DrSc(rheology), 63. *Prof Exp:* Nat Res Coun fel, McGill Univ, 63-65, fel, 65-67; res specialist, Corp Res Dept, Monsanto Agr Co, 67-75, sr res specialist & tech translator, 75-88, sr res consult, Animal Sci Div, 89-90. *Mem:* Am Chem Soc; AAAS; Am Phys Soc; Am Inst Chemists. *Res:* Rheology and physical chemistry of polymers and disperse systems; polymer and composite technologies; industrial process technologies; crystallization solvent extraction, reaction kinetics and purification formulation, bovine and porcine growth hormones from genetic engineered E Coli. *Mailing Add:* 13146 Roundstone Ct St Louis MO 63146-3642. *Fax:* 314-997-5143

**TAKARO, TIMOTHY,** MEDICINE. *Current Pos:* dir res & resident educ, 57-60, chief cardiovasc surg sect, 60-62, CHIEF SURG SERV, VET ADMIN MED CTR, ASHEVILLE, 62-, SR PHYSICIAN, 71-, CHIEF OF STAFF, 83- *Personal Data:* b Budapest, Hungary, Aug 30, 20; US citizen; m 49; c 4. *Educ:* Dartmouth Col, BA, 41; NY Univ, MD, 43; Univ Minn, MS, 50. *Prof Exp:* Dir surg, Wanless Tuberc Sanatorium, India, Presby Bd Foreign Missions, 54-57. *Concurrent Pos:* Exchange scientist, US-USSR Exchange Agreement, Moscow, 62; co-chmn, Vet Admin Coop Study of Surg for Coronary Arterial Occlusive Dis, 68-; assoc clin prof surg, Duke Univ Med Ctr, 68-80, clin prof, 80-; chmn, Cardiac Surg Adv Group, Vet Admin Cent Off, 70-; assoc ed, Annals Thoracic Surg, 70- *Mem:* Fel Am Col Surgeons; Am Asn Thoracic Surg; Soc Thoracic Surgeons; Soc Vascular Surg. *Res:* Pulmonary emphysema; coronary arterial occlusive disease. *Mailing Add:* Vet Admin Hosp Asheville NC 28805

**TAKASHIMA, SHIRO,** PHYSICAL BIOCHEMISTRY, MEMBRANE BIOPHYSICS. *Current Pos:* res assoc biomed eng, Univ Pa, 63-64, from asst prof to prof, 64-93, EMER PROF BIOMED ENG, UNIV PA, 93- *Personal Data:* b Japan, May 12, 23; m 53, Morita Yuki; c Nozomi & Makoto. *Educ:* Univ Tokyo, BS, 47, PhD(biochem), 55. *Prof Exp:* Res fel phys chem, Univ Minn, 55-57; res assoc biomed eng, Univ Pa, 57-59; from assoc prof to prof protein res, Osaka Univ, 59-62; vis scientist, Walter Reed Med Ctr, 62-63. *Mem:* Biophys Soc; Inst Elec & Electronics Engrs; NY Acad Sci; AAAS. *Res:* Dielectric relaxation of desoxyribonucleic acid; synthetic polynucleotides; polyamino acids and proteins; electrical properties of excitable and passive membranes. *Mailing Add:* Dept Bioeng Univ Pa 240 S 33rd St Philadelphia PA 19104-6392. *Fax:* 215-573-2071; *E-Mail:* takashim@eniac.seas.upenn.edu

**TAKASUGI, MITSUO,** CANCER, IMMUNOLOGY. *Current Pos:* RESEARCHER CANCER, DEPT SURG, UNIV CALIF, LOS ANGELES, 69- *Personal Data:* b Tacoma, Wash, Jan 28, 28; m 54; c 4. *Educ:* Univ Calif, Los Angeles, BA, 52, PhD(immunogenetics), 68; Univ Ore, MS, 62. *Prof Exp:* Sci teacher, Los Angeles City Schs, 53-64; fel, 53-64; Dept Tumor Biol, Karolinska Inst, Stockholm, Sweden, 68-69. *Mem:* AAAS; Am Asn Cancer Res; Am Asn Immunologists; Transplantation Soc. *Res:* Investigations into the cellular and humoral immune response to cancer. *Mailing Add:* 2482 Pesquera Dr Los Angeles CA 90049

**TAKATANI, SETSUO,** BIOENGINEERING, EXPERIMENTAL SURGERY. *Current Pos:* ASSOC PROF EXP SURG, BAYLOR COL MED, 89- *Personal Data:* b Hemeji, Japan, June 9, 46. *Educ:* Case Western Res Univ, PhD(tissue oxygenation), 78; Tokyo Med & Dent Univ, MD, 94. *Res:* Bioengineering; experimental surgery. *Mailing Add:* Dept Surg Baylor Col Med One Baylor Plaza Houston TX 77030

**TAKATS, STEPHEN TIBOR,** CYTOLOGY, GENETICS. *Current Pos:* from asst prof to assoc prof biol, 61-69, chmn dept, 69-75, PROF BIOL, TEMPLE UNIV, 69- *Personal Data:* b West Englewood, NJ, May 24, 30; m 60; c 3. *Educ:* Cornell Univ, BS, 52; Univ Wis, MS, 54, PhD(genetics), 58. *Prof Exp:* Asst genetics, Univ Wis, 52-55; res collabr & USPHS res fel, Biol Dept, Brookhaven Nat Lab, 57-60; USPHS res fel biochem, Univ Glasgow, 60-61, Med Res Coun grant, 61. *Mem:* Bot Soc Am; Am Soc Plant Physiol; Genetics Soc Am; Am Soc Cell Biol. *Res:* Biochemical cytology; control of DNA synthesis in plant development. *Mailing Add:* Dept Biol Temple Univ 1701 N Broad St Philadelphia PA 19122-2504

**TAKAYAMA, KUNI,** BIOCHEMISTRY, MICROBIOLOGY. *Current Pos:* assoc prof, 86-89, PROF BACT, UNIV WIS-MADISON, 90-; CHIEF RES CHEMIST, TUBERC RES LAB, VET ADMIN HOSP, MADISON, WIS, 74- *Personal Data:* b Wapato, Wash, Feb 28, 32; m 59, Masako Motoyoshi; c Karen & Janet. *Educ:* Ore State Univ, BS, 56; Univ Idaho, MS, 61, PhD(biochem), 64. *Prof Exp:* NIH grant, Inst Enzyme Res, Univ Wis-Madison, 64-65; proj assoc biochem of mycobact, Vet Admin Hosp, Madison, Wis, 65-67, res chemist, Tuberc Res Lab, 67-71, actg chief chemist, 68-69, chief chemist, 71-74. *Concurrent Pos:* Proj assoc, Inst Enzyme Res, Univ Wis-Madison, 65-67, asst prof, 67-85; NSF grants, Vet Admin Hosp & Univ Wis-Madison, 69-72, NIH grant, 73- *Mem:* AAAS; Am Soc Microbiol; Am Soc Biol Chem; Am Soc Cell Biol; Am Inst Biol Sci. *Res:* Biochemistry of mycobacteria; biological activity of lipopolysaccharides & lipid A; synthesis of lipids; mode of action of isoniazid; structure of lipopolysaccharides and lipid A; mechanism of septic shock. *Mailing Add:* Mycobact Lab Vet Admin Hosp 2500 Overlook Terr Madison WI 53705-2254

**TAKEDA, YASUHIKO,** PHYSIOLOGY, CLINICAL PATHOLOGY. *Current Pos:* RETIRED. *Personal Data:* b Nagano, Japan, Mar 16, 27; m 57; c 4. *Educ:* Shinshu Univ, 46-48; Chiba Univ, MD, 52; Am Bd Path, dipl, 70. *Prof Exp:* From instr to prof, Med Ctr, Univ Colo, Denver, 63-88. *Concurrent Pos:* Res fel, Div Lab Med, Med Ctr, Univ Colo, 58-60; Nat Res Coun Can res fel, McGill Univ, 60-63; Colo Heart Asn sr res fel med, Med Ctr, Univ Colo, Denver, 63-64; Am Heart Asn advan res fel, 64-66; NIH career develop award, 67-72; mem coun thrombosis, Am Heart Asn. *Mem:* AAAS; Am Physiol Soc; Am Soc Clin Path; Int Soc Thrombosis & Hemorrhagic Dis; Col Am Pathologists. *Res:* Regulation of plasma protein metabolism in health and disease; dynamics of thrombus formation and dissolution. *Mailing Add:* 635 Dexter St Denver CO 80220-5037

**TAKEMORI, AKIRA EDDIE,** OPIOID PHARMACOLOGY. *Current Pos:* from asst prof to assoc prof, 61-69, PROF PHARMACOL, HEALTH SCI CTR, UNIV MINN, MINNEAPOLIS, 69-, DIR GRAD STUDIES, 87- *Personal Data:* b Stockton, Calif, Dec 9, 29; m 58, Valerie Williams; c Tensho & Rima. *Educ:* Univ Calif, AB, 51, MS, 53; Univ Wis, PhD(pharmacol), 58. *Honors & Awards:* Vis Scientist Award, Japan Soc Prom Sci, 71; Alan Gregg Fel Med Educ, China Med Bd NY, 71; Nathan B Eddy Award, Col Probs Drug Dependence, 91. *Prof Exp:* Res asst pharmacol, Univ Calif, 51-53; teaching asst, Univ Wis, 55-57, Am Cancer Soc fel, Enzyme Inst, 58-59; instr pharmacol, State Univ NY Upstate Med Ctr, 59-61, asst prof, 61-63. *Concurrent Pos:* Mem, Pharmacol A Study Sect, NIH, 70-74; mem, Rev Panel on New Drug Regulation, Dept Health, Educ & Welfare, 76, bd sci counr, Addiction Res Ctr, Nat Inst on Drug Abuse, 82-86 & Comt on Probs Drug Dependence, 83-87. *Mem:* AAAS; Am Soc Pharmacol & Exp Therapeut; Soc Exp Biol & Med; Am Asn Univ Prof; fel Col Probs Drug Dependence; Am Col Neuropsychopharmacol. *Res:* Mechanism of action of opioid analgesics and opioid antagonists. *Mailing Add:* 5237 Wooddale Ave Edina MN 55424. *Fax:* 612-625-8408; *E-Mail:* takem001@maroon.tc.umn.edu

**TAKEMOTO, DOLORES JEAN,** CYCLIC NUCLEOTIDE METABOLISM. *Current Pos:* res assoc, 79-81, vis asst prof, 81-84, ASST PROF BIOCHEM, KANS STATE UNIV, 84- *Personal Data:* b Indianapolis, Ind, May 5, 49; m 73; c 2. *Educ:* Ball State Univ, BS, 71; Colo State Univ, MS, 73; Univ Southern Calif, PhD(molecular biol), 79. *Prof Exp:* Sr res technician physiol, Colo State Univ, 73-75; asst molecular biol, Univ Southern Calif, 75-79. *Concurrent Pos:* Prin investr, Nat Cancer Inst grant, 80-83; mem, Kans State Ctr Basic Cancer Res, 80-; prin investr, Nat Eye Inst grant, 85- *Mem:* Asn Res Vision & Ophthal; Am Soc Biol Chem; Am Asn Cancer Res. *Res:* Cyclic nucleotide metabolism in leukemic versus normal human lymphocytes; retinal biochemistry of dystrophies. *Mailing Add:* Dept Biochem Willard Hall No 103 DT Kans State Univ Manhattan KS 66506

**TAKEMOTO, JON YUTAKA,** MICROBIOLOGY, BIOCHEMISTRY. *Current Pos:* from asst prof to assoc prof, 75-85, PROF BIOL, UTAH STATE UNIV, 85-, DIR, MOLECULAR BIOL PROG, 89- *Personal Data:* b Chicago, Ill, Sept 13, 44; m 73, Lynnette; c Curtis & Ryan. *Educ:* Univ Calif, Los Angeles, BS, 67, PhD(microbiol), 73. *Prof Exp:* Fel biol & Maria Moor Cabot fel, Harvard Univ, 73-74. *Concurrent Pos:* NIH fel, Harvard Univ, 74; staff mem, Utah Agr Exp Sta, Logan, 75-; prin investr, NSF grants, Utah State Univ, 76-; vis prof biol, Freiburg Univ, WGer, 81-82, Alexander von Humboldt Found fel, 81-82; vis scientist, Hiroshima Univ, Japan, 88-89; Japan Soc Prom Sci fel, 88-89. *Mem:* Am Soc Microbiol; Sigma Xi; AAAS; Am Soc Plant Physiol. *Res:* Mechanisms of action, bacterial cyclic lipodepsipeptides; antifungal agents and syringomycin family lipopeptides. *Mailing Add:* Dept Biol Utah State Univ Logan UT 84322-5305. *Fax:* 435-750-1575; *E-Mail:* takemoto@cc.usu.edu

**TAKEMURA, KAZ H(ORACE),** ORGANIC CHEMISTRY. *Current Pos:* from asst prof to prof, 60-92, chmn dept, 70-73, EMER PROF CHEM, CREIGHTON UNIV, 93- *Personal Data:* b San Juan Bautista, Calif, Nov 2, 21; m 59, Nancy L Carlos; c Therese A, Michael F, John J, Peter J, Paul S, Thomas C & Katherine A. *Educ:* Univ Calif, Los Angeles, BS, 47; Univ Ill, MS, 48, PhD(chem), 50. *Prof Exp:* Res fel chem, Ohio State Univ, 50-52; res chemist, Univ Calif, Berkeley, 52-53; chemist southern regional res lab, USDA, La, 53-56; asst prof chem, Loyola Univ, La, 56-58 & Univ Tulsa, 58-59; chemist, Sahyun Labs, 59-60. *Concurrent Pos:* Vis prof, Univ Calif, Berkeley, 79. *Mem:* Royal Soc Chem; Am Chem Soc. *Res:* Organic synthesis and mechanisms. *Mailing Add:* 3417 S 127th Ave Omaha NE 68144

**TAKESAKI, MASAMICHI,** MATHEMATICS. *Current Pos:* PROF MATH, UNIV CALIF, LOS ANGELES, 70- *Personal Data:* b Sendai, Japan, July 18, 33; m 59, Kyoko Yamao; c 1. *Educ:* Tohoku Univ, Japan, MS, 58, DSc(math), 65. *Honors & Awards:* Fujiwara Sci Prize, 90. *Prof Exp:* Res asst math, Tokyo Inst Technol, 58-63; assoc prof, Tohoku Univ, Japan, 63-70. *Concurrent Pos:* Fel, Sakkokai Found, 65-68; vis assoc prof, Univ Pa, 68-69 & Univ Calif, Los Angeles, 69-70; vis prof, Univ Aix-Marseille, 73-74 & Univ Bielefeld, 75-76. *Mem:* Am Math Soc; Math Soc Japan. *Res:* Functional analysis; operator algebras; mathematical physics. *Mailing Add:* Dept Math 6356 Univ Calif Box 951555 Los Angeles CA 90095-1555

**TAKESHITA, TSUNEICHI,** PHYSICAL ORGANIC CHEMISTRY. *Personal Data:* b Tokyo, Japan, Sept 13, 26; m 56; c 3. *Educ:* Waseda Univ, Japan, BSEng, 50; Univ Del, PhD(org chem), 62. *Prof Exp:* Chemist, Cent Res Inst, Japan Monopoly Corp, Tokyo, 50-64; assoc prof catalysis, Res Inst Catalysis, Hokkaido Univ, 64-66; chemist, Elastomer Chem Dept, E I Du Pont de Nemours & Co, Inc, Wilminton, 66-80. *Mem:* Am Chem Soc; NY Acad Sci; Chem Soc Japan; Sigma Xi. *Res:* Catalytic studies in organic chemistry; polymer chemistry. *Mailing Add:* 2047 Nuuanu Ave Apt 1503 Honolulu HI 96817

**TAKETOMO, YASUHIKO,** PSYCHIATRY. *Current Pos:* assoc clin prof, 77-95, EMER CLIN PROF PSYCHIAT, 95- *Personal Data:* b Tokyo, Japan; US citizen; m 46, Haruko Kishimoto; c Masahiko & Toshihiko. *Educ:* First Col, Tokyo, BA, 42; Osaka Univ, MD, 45, DMedSc, 49; Columbia Univ, cert psychoanal med, 59; Univ State New York, MD, 81. *Honors & Awards:* Order of the Rising Sun, Emperor of Japan. *Prof Exp:* Spec res fel, Ministry Educ, Japanese Govt, Med Sch, Osaka Univ, 45-47, asst biochem & neuropsychiat, 47-50; asst resident neuropsychiat, Albany Med Col, 50-51; resident/asst res psychiatrist, Worcester State Hosp, 51-52; res psychiatrist/ sr res scientist, Res Facil, Rockland State Hosp, 52-64; res assoc neurol & psychiat, St Vincent's Hosp & Med Ctr, 64-67; asst prof psychiat, New York Med Col, 68-69; asst prof, Albert Einstein Col Med, 70-73, assoc prof psychiat, 73-77; clin prof psychiat, sr psychiatrist & assoc dir, Albert Einstein psychiat residency prog, Bronx Psychiat Ctr, 79-95. *Concurrent Pos:* Garioa scholar, US State Dept, Albany Med Col & Worcester State Hosp, 50-52; from res asst to res assoc, Col Physicians & Surgeons, Columbia Univ, 52-64; lectr, Med Sch, Osaka Univ, 54; vis scientist, NIH, 56; assoc, New York Sch Psychiat, 62-67; New York City Health Res Coun career scientist award, St Vincent's Hosp & New York Med Col, 64-69; mem acad fac, State Conn Dept Ment Health, 65-67; symp assoc, Ctr Res Math, Morphol & Psychol, 67-73; consult, Asn for Help of Retarded Children, 73-76; consult, Sch Med, Uniformed Serv Univ, 78; guest prof, Osaka Univ Med Sch, 84-91; acad chair, Japanese Ctr Qual Life Studies, Found Thanatology, Columbia Presby Med Ctr. *Mem:* Fel Am Psychiat Asn; fel Am Acad Psychoanalysis; Asn Psychoanalytical Med; Am Psychoanalysis Asn. *Res:* Psychopathology and treatment of psychiatric disorders of mental retardation; communicational behavior; cognitive and semiotic psychiatry; phenomenology of adaptational and existential crises; methodology of psychiatric research, especially the issue of temporality; transcultural psychiatry; creative tension between psychoanalysis and neuroscience; faith and psychotherapy. *Mailing Add:* 1198 Post Rd Scarsdale NY 10583

**TAKEUCHI, ESTHER SANS,** LITHIUM BATTERY DEVELOPMENT, IMPLANTABLE MEDICAL COMPONENT. *Current Pos:* sr chemist, 84-88, assoc dir res & develop, 88-91, DIR ELECTROCHEM RES, WILSON GREATBATCH LTD, 93- *Personal Data:* b Kansas City, Mo, Sept 8, 51; m 82, Kenneth. *Educ:* Univ Pa, BA, 75; Ohio State Univ, PhD(org chem), 81. *Honors & Awards:* Technol Award, Battery Div, Electrochem Soc. *Prof Exp:* Sr chemist, Union Carbide Corp, 81-82; researcher, Univ NC, 82-83, State Univ NY, Buffalo, 83-84. *Mem:* Electrochem Soc; Am Chem Soc. *Res:* Development of high technology batteries with a specialty in lithium implantable batteries for medical use; characterization and utilization of solid state materials for energy storage. *Mailing Add:* Wilson Greatbatch Ltd 10000 Wehrle Dr Clarence NY 14031. *Fax:* 716-759-5480; *E-Mail:* takeuchie@aol.com

**TAKEUCHI, KENJI,** engineering science, physics, for more information see previous edition

**TAKEUCHI, KIYOSHI HIRO,** BIOCHEMISTRY, CELL BIOLOGY. *Current Pos:* PROF, DEPT HUMANITIES, HOKKAI-GAKUEN UNIV, JAPAN, 92- *Personal Data:* b Furubira, Japan, Oct 20, 48; m 79; c 2. *Educ:* Hokkaido Univ, Japan, BS, 74; Tokyo Metrop Univ, Japan, PhD(biochem), 79. *Honors & Awards:* Deguchi Award, Sapporo, Japan, 90. *Prof Exp:* Res assoc, Dept Biochem, Molecular & Cell Biol, Northwestern Univ, Evanston, 79-83 & Dept Anat & Cell Biol, Northwestern Univ, Chicago, 83-84; cancer res scientist, Roswell Park Mem Inst, Buffalo, 84-88; asst investr, Dept Biomed Res, St Elizabeth's Hosp, Boston, 88-89; asst biochemist, Ralph Lowell Labs, 88-91. *Concurrent Pos:* Investr, Marine Biol Lab, Woods Hole, 82-83; asst prof, Dept Psychiat, Harvard Med Sch, 88-91. *Mem:* Am Soc Biochem & Molecular Biol; AAAS; Am Soc Cell Biol; NY Acad Sci; Int Soc Exp Hemat; Am Soc Neurochem. *Res:* Role of the proteolylysis in neurodegenerative diseases and aging, includng Alzheimer's disease; proteinase inhibitors in Chediak-Higashi (beige) neutrophils; embryo stem cells; developmental biology. *Mailing Add:* Hokkai-Gakuen Univ 4-1-40 Asahimachi Toyohiraki-ku Sapporo 062 Japan. *Fax:* 81-640-5247; *E-Mail:* drkt@jin.hokkai-s-u.ac.jp

**TAKEUTI, GAISI,** MATHEMATICAL LOGIC. *Current Pos:* PROF MATH, UNIV ILL, URBANA, 66- *Personal Data:* b Isikawa, Japan, Jan 25, 26; m 47; c 2. *Educ:* Univ Tokyo, PhD(math logic), 56. *Prof Exp:* Instr math, Univ Tokyo, 49-50; from asst prof to prof, Tokyo Univ Educ, 50-66. *Concurrent Pos:* Mem, Inst Advan Study, 59-60 & 66-68. *Mem:* Am Math Soc; Asn Symbolic Logic; Math Soc Japan; Japan Asn Philos Sci. *Res:* Proof-theory; set-theory. *Mailing Add:* Dept Math Univ Ill 1409 W Green St Urbana IL 61801-2917

**TAKHTADZHYAN, ARMEN LEONOVICH,** BOTANY. *Current Pos:* dir, 76-86, STAFF, KOMAROV INST BOT, 86- *Personal Data:* b June 6, 10; m, Alice. *Honors & Awards:* Hero Labor Medal, USSR, 90. *Prof Exp:* Prof bot, Leningrad Univ. *Concurrent Pos:* Guest taxon res, NY Bot Garden, NY. *Mem:* Foreign mem Nat Acad Sci; Russ Acad Sci. *Mailing Add:* Komarov Inst Bot Ulitsa Popova 2 St Petersburg 197022 Russia

**TAKMAN, BERTIL HERBERT,** chemistry, for more information see previous edition

**TAKVORIAN, KENNETH BEDROSE,** POLYMER CHEMISTRY, TEXTILE CHEMISTRY. *Current Pos:* RES CHEMIST, TEXTILE RES LAB, E I DU PONT DE NEMOURS & CO, INC, 69- *Personal Data:* b Philadelphia, Pa, Aug 24, 43; m 66; c 2. *Educ:* Philadelphia Col Textiles &

Sci, BS, 65; Clemson Univ, MS, 67, PhD(chem), 69. *Mem:* Am Chem Soc; Am Asn Textile Chemists & Colorists. *Res:* All areas of textile chemistry; dyeing, finishing, and textile technology; polymer synthesis and morphology; metal chelates and organic synthesis and mechanisms. *Mailing Add:* 732 Westcliff Wilmington DE 19803

**TALAAT, MOSTAFA E(ZZAT),** ELECTRICAL ENGINEERING. *Current Pos:* PROF MECH ENG, COL ENG, UNIV MD, COLLEGE PARK, 64- *Personal Data:* b Cairo, Egypt, May 16, 24; nat US; m 51; c 5. *Educ:* Cairo Univ, BSc, 46, MSc, 47; Univ Pa, PhD(elec eng), 51. *Honors & Awards:* Inst Elec & Electronics Engrs Awards, 56-58; Awards, Martin-Marietta Corp, 60-63. *Prof Exp:* Asst, Mass Inst Technol, 47-49; instr, Univ Pa, 51; proj engr, Westinghouse Elec Corp, 51-52; spec mach designer, Star Kimble Motor Div, Miehle Press, 53; sr res engr, Elliott Co Div, Carrier Corp, 53-59; mgr energy conversion & asst dir eng res, Nuclear Div, Martin-Marietta Corp, 59-64. *Concurrent Pos:* Consult. *Mem:* AAAS; Inst Elec & Electronics Engrs; Am Phys Soc; Am Inst Aeronaut & Astronaut. *Res:* Energy conversion, including magnetoplasma-dynamics, thermionic, thermoelectric and fuel cell energy conversion as well as biological power sources; solar-thermal energy storage and conversion. *Mailing Add:* Dept Mech Eng Univ Md College Park MD 20742. *Fax:* 301-314-9477

**TALALAY, PAUL,** MOLECULAR PHARMACOLOGY. *Current Pos:* John Jacob Abel prof pharmacol & exp therapeut & dir dept pharmacol, 63-75, JOHN JACOB ABEL DISTINGUISHED SERV PROF PHARMACOL & EXP THERAPEUT, SCH MED, JOHNS HOPKINS UNIV, 75- *Personal Data:* b Berlin, Ger, Mar 31, 23; nat US; m 53; c 4. *Educ:* Mass Inst Technol, SB, 44; Yale Univ, MD, 48. *Hon Degrees:* DSc, Acadia Univ, 74. *Honors & Awards:* Theobold Smith Award, AAAS, 57; Premio Int La Madonnina, Milan, 78. *Prof Exp:* Intern & asst resident, Surg Serv, Mass Gen Hosp, 48-50; asst prof, Ben May Lab Cancer Res, Univ Chicago, 50-57, from assoc prof to prof, Lab & Dept Biochem & Med, Univ, 57-63. *Concurrent Pos:* Am Cancer Soc scholar, 54-58; Am Cancer Soc res prof, 58-63; mem pharm B study sect, NIH, 63-67; mem, Nat Adv Cancer Coun, 67-71; ed-in-chief, Molecular Pharm, 68-71; mem bd sci consults, Sloan-Kettering Inst, 71-81; mem bd sci adv, Jane Coffin Childs Mem Fund for Med Res, 71-80; Guggenheim Mem fel, 73-74; Am Cancer Soc prof, 77-; bd overseers, Comt Visitation, Div Med Sci, Harvard Univ. *Mem:* Nat Acad Sci; Am Philos Soc; Am Soc Biol Chemists; Am Soc Pharmacol & Exp Therapeut; Am Soc Clin Invest; Am Cancer Soc; fel Am Acad Arts & Sci; fel AAAS. *Res:* Molecular pharmacology; biochemistry; chemoprotection against cancer; metabolism and mechanism of action of steroid hormones. *Mailing Add:* Dept Pharmacol Sch Med Johns Hopkins Univ Baltimore MD 21205

**TALAMANTES, FRANK,** ENDOCRINOLOGY. *Current Pos:* PROF ENDOCRINOL, DIV NATURAL SCI, THIMANN LABS, UNIV CALIF, SANTA CRUZ, 74- *Personal Data:* b July 8, 43. *Educ:* Univ St Thomas, Tex, BA, 66; Sam Houston State Univ, MA, 70; Univ Calif, Berkeley, PhD(endocrinol), 74. *Mem:* Sigma Xi; NY Acad Sci; Am Asn Anatomists; AAAS; Am Physiol Soc; Soc Exp Biol & Med. *Mailing Add:* Dept Biol Univ Calif-Santa Cruz Sinsheimer Labs Santa Cruz CA 95064. *Fax:* 408-459-3560

**TALAMO, BARBARA LISANN,** OLFACTION, PLASTICITY & SIGNALLING. *Current Pos:* asst prof, 80-83, dir, Grad Prog Neurosci, assoc prof neurol & physiol, 83-93, PROF NEUROSCI & PHYSIOL, MED SCH, TUFTS UNIV, 94-, CHAIR, DEPT NEUROSCI, 95- *Personal Data:* b Washington, DC, May 30, 39; m 58, 85, John S Kauer; c 3. *Educ:* Radcliffe Col, AB, 60; Harvard Univ, PhD(biochem), 72. *Prof Exp:* Tutor biochem sci, Harvard Col, 71-74; asst prof neurol & physiol chem, Med Sch, Johns Hopkins Univ, 74-80. *Concurrent Pos:* NSF fel neurobiol, Harvard Med Sch, 72-74; mem study sects, NIH, 79-83 & 94-98, prin investr, NIH grants, 76-, ad hoc mem, NSF study sect, 87-93. *Mem:* Soc Neurosci; Am Soc Neurochem; Int Soc Neurochem; Asn Chemoreception Sci; Soc Gen Physiologists; Asn Neurosci Depts & Progs (secy, 96-98). *Res:* Regulation and mechanism of neurotransmitter sensitivity; developmental regulation of mechanisms of secretion and second messenger systems; olfactory system; Alzheimer's disease and nerodegenerative diseases. *Mailing Add:* Dept Neurosci Tufts Med Sch 136 Harrison Ave Boston MA 02111. *Fax:* 617-956-7413; *E-Mail:* btalamo@ pearl.tufts.edu

**TALAPATRA, DIPAK CHANDRA,** FINITE ELEMENT ANALYSIS, STRUCTURAL DYNAMICS. *Current Pos:* aerospace engr, NASA, 80-83, mgr flight support syst, 83-85, mgr dynamic analysis, Goddard Space Flight Ctr, 85-87, tech prog mgt, Space Sta Prog Off, NASA Hq, 87-92, MGR, NASA LIAISON CAN, SPACE STA PROG, 92- *Personal Data:* b Bangladesh, Jan 20, 42; US citizen; m 73, Fischer; c 2. *Educ:* Indian Inst Technol, BTech, 63; McGill Univ, MEng, 68; Univ BC, PhD(mech eng),72. *Honors & Awards:* Merit Performance Award, NASA Goddard Space Flight Ctr, 84, 85, 86. *Prof Exp:* Sr scientist, Ensco Inc, 72-77; sr res engr, Gen Tire & Rubber Co, 77-80; mech engr, Dept Navy-Naval Ord Sta, 80. *Mem:* Am Soc Mech Engrs. *Res:* Structural mechanics investigation; fracture mechanics; finite element analysis; vibration testing; analysis of composites; modal analysis and testing; space systems engineering. *Mailing Add:* c/o Usembnasa PO Box 847 Champlain NY 12919-0847. *Fax:* 514-926-4948

**TALATY, ERACH R,** ORGANIC CHEMISTRY, ELECTROCHEMISTRY. *Current Pos:* from assoc chair to chair, Dept Chem, 91-94, RES PROF CHEM, WICHITA STATE UNIV, 69- *Personal Data:* b Nagpur, India, Oct 20, 26; nat US; m 60, Margaret Fisher. *Educ:* Univ Nagpur, BSc, 48, MSc, 49, PhD(electrochem), 54; Ohio State Univ, PhD(org chem), 57. *Prof Exp:* Lectr chem, Col Sci Univ Nagpur, 48-54; asst, Ohio State Univ, 56-57; sr res chemist, Columbia-Southern Chem Corp, 57-61, Bridesburg Labs, Rohm &

Haas Co, Pa, 61; fel, Harvard Univ, 61-62; assoc prof, Univ SDak, 62-64; res assoc, Iowa State Univ, 64-66; asst prof chem, La State Univ, New Orleans, 66-69. *Mem:* Am Chem Soc; Royal Soc Chem; Indian Chem Soc. *Res:* Isomerization of azobenzenes; electrodeposition of metals; phosgene chemistry; reactions of chloroformates and carbonates; addition and condensation polymers; acid chlorides; electron spin resonance; steroids; natural products; small-ring compounds; theoretical studies. *Mailing Add:* Dept Chem Wichita State Univ Wichita KS 67260-0051

**TALBERT, GEORGE BRAYTON,** AGING, ANATOMY. *Current Pos:* RETIRED. *Personal Data:* b Ripon, Wis, July 21, 21; m 47; c 2. *Educ:* Univ NDak, BS, 41; Univ Wis, MA, 42, PhD(zool), 50. *Prof Exp:* From res assoc to assoc prof, State Univ NY Downstate Med Ctr, 50-68, actg chmn, 82-85, prof anat & cell biol, Col Med, 68-88. *Concurrent Pos:* USPHS spec fel anat, Univ Birmingham, 63-64; USPHS res grant, Nat Inst Child Health & Human Develop, 66-76. *Mem:* Endocrine Soc; Am Asn Anatomists; Brit Soc Fertil; Geront Soc; Soc Study Reproduction. *Res:* Pituitary-gonadal relationship; sexual maturation; longevity; aging of reproductive system. *Mailing Add:* PO Box 33 Quinby VA 23423-0033

**TALBERT, JAMES LEWIS,** PEDIATRIC SURGERY, THORACIC SURGERY. *Current Pos:* assoc prof, 67-70, PROF SURG & PEDIAT, COL MED, UNIV FLA, 70- *Personal Data:* b Cassville, Mo, Sept 26, 31; m 58, Alice; c Alison & David. *Educ:* Vanderbilt Univ, BA, 53, MD, 57. *Prof Exp:* Intern surg, Johns Hopkins Hosp, 56-57, resident, 59-60 & 62-64, resident pediat surg, 64-65, instr surg, Sch Med, Johns Hopkins Univ, 65-66, asst prof surg & pediat surg, 66-67. *Concurrent Pos:* Sr asst surgeon, Nat Heart Inst, 60-62; Garrett scholar pediat surg, Sch Med, Johns Hopkins Univ, 65-66; consult surg, Univ Hosp Jacksonville & Vet Admin Hosp, Gainesville, 72- *Mem:* Am Surg Asn; Soc Pediat Res; Soc Univ Surgeons; Am Pediat Surg Asn; Am Pediat Soc. *Res:* Congenital anomalies; cancer in childhood; metabolic responses to surgical stress in infants and children. *Mailing Add:* Dept Surg Univ Fla Col Med J HIllis Miller Health Ctr PO Box 100286 Gainesville FL 32602-0286

**TALBERT, LUTHER M,** OBSTETRICS & GYNECOLOGY. *Current Pos:* From instr to assoc prof, 58-69, PROF OBSTET & GYNEC, SCH MED, UNIV NC, CHAPEL HILL, 69- *Personal Data:* b Abingdon, Va, Dec 30, 26; m 49; c 3. *Educ:* Emory & Henry Col, BA, 49; Univ Va, MD, 53; Am Bd Obstet & Gynec, dipl. *Mem:* Endocrine Soc; Soc Gynec Invest; Am Gynec Soc; Am Asn Obstet & Gynec; Am Fertil Soc; Am Col Obstet & Gynec. *Res:* Reproductive endocrinology and infertility. *Mailing Add:* Dept Obstet & Gynec Univ NC Med Sch 7570 McNider Chapel Hill NC 27599

**TALBERT, NORWOOD K(EITH),** CHEMICAL ENGINEERING, PHYSICAL CHEMISTRY. *Current Pos:* mgr com develop, Tex City Refinery, Agway Inc, 63-66, mgr nitrogen ctr, 66-67, mgr nitrogen div, 67-71, DIR ENVIRON QUAL, AGWAY INC, 71- *Personal Data:* b Felixville, La, July 29, 21; m 51; c 3. *Educ:* Tex A&M Univ, BS, 49. *Prof Exp:* Chem engr, Exp Sta, E I Du Pont de Nemours & Co, Del, 49-55; group leader & staff specialist, Chem Res Dept, Spencer Chem Co, 55-60, mgr new prod develop, Chemetron Corp, 60-63. *Mem:* Am Chem Soc; Am Inst Chem Engrs. *Res:* Chemical process studies and engineering development; economic evaluation and market appraisal; product and commercial development; management. *Mailing Add:* 14306 N Alamo Canyon Dr Tucson AZ 85737-9170

**TALBERT, PRESTON TIDBALL,** ORGANIC CHEMISTRY. *Current Pos:* from asst prof to assoc prof 59-70, assoc chmn dept, 66-87, PROF BIO-ORG CHEM, HOWARD UNIV, 70- *Personal Data:* b Washington, DC, Feb 17, 25; m 56. *Educ:* Howard Univ, BS, 50, MS, 52; Washington Univ, PhD(chem), 55. *Prof Exp:* Asst, Washington Univ, 51-52; res assoc, Univ Wash, 55-56, res instr, 56-59, NIH fel, 57-59. *Concurrent Pos:* Mem postdoc fel panel, Nat Res Coun, 80 & Ford Found, 83. *Mem:* Fel AAAS; fel Am Inst Chemists; Am Chem Soc; NY Acad Sci. *Res:* Mechanism of function, synthesis and degradation of biologically important compounds, especially nucleic, nucleosides, proteins and vitamins; enzyme function and mechanism of action. *Mailing Add:* 400 Old Stone Rd Silver Spring MD 20904-5958

**TALBERT, RONALD EDWARD,** AGRONOMY, WEED SCIENCE. *Current Pos:* from asst prof to assoc prof agron, 63-73, prof, 73-90, UNIV PROF AGRON, UNIV ARK, FAYETTEVILLE, 90- *Personal Data:* b Toulon, Ill, May 20, 36; m 55; c 3. *Educ:* Univ Mo, BS, 58, MS, 60, PhD(field crops), 63. *Prof Exp:* Instr field crops, Univ Mo, 60-63. *Mem:* AAAS; fel Weed Sci Soc Am; Am Soc Agron; Coun Agr Sci & Technol. *Res:* Use of herbicides in crops; behavior of herbicides in soils; physiological selectivity and action of herbicides. *Mailing Add:* Agron Univ Ark 115 Plant Sci Fayetteville AR 72701-1202

**TALBERT, WILLARD LINDLEY, JR,** NUCLEAR PHYSICS. *Current Pos:* SR SCIENTIST, AMPARO CORP, 94- *Personal Data:* b Casper, Wyo, Mar 8, 32; m 52, Mary A Williams; c Marc Allan, Kenneth Earl, Linda Sue (Canton) & Cynthia Lunette. *Educ:* Univ Colo, BA, 54; Iowa State Univ, PhD(physics), 60. *Prof Exp:* Res physicist, Ohio Oil Co, 59-62; from asst prof to prof physics, Iowa State Univ, 62-76; group leader, Los Alamos Nat Lab, 77-79 & 81-82, staff mem, 76-93. *Concurrent Pos:* Prog dir nuclear sci, Ames Lab, US Energy Res & Develop Admin, 74-76. *Mem:* Fel Am Phys Soc. *Res:* Experimental nuclear spectroscopy, especially shortlived isotopes using on-line isotope separator; development of targets to produce intense radioactive ion beams. *Mailing Add:* 1 E Sunrise Santa Fe NM 87501. *Fax:* 505-982-5710; *E-Mail:* willtalb@aol.com

**TALBOT, BERNARD,** MEDICAL SCIENCES. *Current Pos:* grants assoc, NIH, 70-71, med officer, Nat Cancer Inst, 71-75, spec asst intramural affairs, 75-78, spec asst to dir, 78-81, dep dir, Nat Inst Allergy & Infectious Dis, 81-87, MED OFFICER, NAT CTR RES RESOURCES, NIH, 87- *Personal Data:* b New York, NY, Oct 6, 37; m 63; c 2. *Educ:* Columbia Col, BA, 58; Columbia Univ, MD, 62; Mass Inst Technol, PhD(biol), 67. *Prof Exp:* Fel, Mass Inst Technol, 67-69 & Univ Rome, 69-70. *Mailing Add:* NIH Bldg RLK1 Rm 6124 Bethesda MD 20892. *Fax:* 301-480-3661; *E-Mail:* bernardt@ep.ncrr.nih.gov

**TALBOT, DONALD R(OY),** NUCLEAR ENGINEERING. *Current Pos:* RETIRED. *Personal Data:* b Bridgeport, Conn, Jan 23, 31; m 53; c 5. *Educ:* State Univ NY, BS, 52. *Honors & Awards:* Dept Defense Antarctica Serv Medal. *Prof Exp:* Test engr, Gen Elec Co, 52, engr, Knolls Atomic Power Lab, 53-56, proj engr, Atomic Power Equip Dept, 56-57, shift supvr, Vallecitos Atomic Lab, 57-58; mgr eng labs, Nuclear Div, Martin Co, 58-62, proj dir, Floating Nuclear Power Plant, 62-67, dir water resources progs, Chem Div, Martin Marietta Corp, NY, 67-69, dir spec studies, Corp Hq, 68-70, dir environ progs, Corp Res Lab, Md, 70-74, dir, Environ Technol Ctr, 74-84, gen mgr environ systs, Martin Marietta Corp, 84-87; vpres & gen mgr, Versar, Inc, 87-88. *Concurrent Pos:* Mem natural resources comt, US Chamber Com, 68-80; chmn environ steering comt, Ctr Int Mgt Studies, 73-82; mem bus & indust adv comt, Orgn Econ Coop & Develop, 73-; mem, Com Tech Adv Bd, Panel Proj Independence, Dept Com, 74- 75, Panel Energy Policy, 76-77, mem directorate, man & biosphere, UNESCO, 77-79; consult, Nat Comn Air Qual, 79-80; mem, Environ Protection Agency Task Force, Pres Pvt Sector Surv Cost Control, 83-84. *Mem:* Water Pollution Control Fedn; Air Pollution Control Asn. *Mailing Add:* 712 Hickory Lot Rd Baltimore MD 21286

**TALBOT, EUGENE L(EROY),** METALLURGY, MATERIALS ENGINEERING. *Current Pos:* supt mat develop, 63-75, MAT SPECIALIST, HERCULES INC, 75- *Personal Data:* b Ogden, Utah, Jan 18, 21; m 42; c 4. *Educ:* La State Univ, BS, 44; Univ Utah, BS, 47, MS, 48, PhD(metall), 50. *Prof Exp:* Chemist, Tri State Oil & Refining Co, 41-42; explosives, Ogden Ord Depot, 42; inorg applns leader, Minn Mining & Mfg Co, 50-63. *Concurrent Pos:* Lectr, Brigham Young Univ, 65 & Univ Utah, 67; adj prof, Univ Utah, 69- *Mem:* Soc Advan Mat & Process Eng (nat vpres, 73-75, nat pres, 75-76); Am Soc Metals; Soc Logistics Engrs. *Res:* Materials research; high temperature insulation; graphite; metals; stress corrosion; fractography; protective coatings; surface chemistry; adhesives; sealers; composite structures; ceramics; rocket motor systems. *Mailing Add:* 8670 Russell Park Rd Salt Lake City UT 84121

**TALBOT, FRANK HAMILTON,** MARINE RESEARCH. *Current Pos:* DIR, NAT MUS NATURAL HIST, SMITHSONIAN INST, WASHINGTON, 89- *Personal Data:* b Pletermaritzburg, Natal, Repub SAfrica, Jan 3, 30; m 53, Mabel S Logeman; c Helen C, Richard B, Jonathan C & Neil H. *Educ:* Univ Witwatersrand, SAfrica, BSc, 49; Univ Cape Town, SAfrica, MSc, 51, PhD, 59. *Prof Exp:* Fisheries res scientist, Brit Colonial Serv, Zanzibar, 54-57; marine biologist, SAfrican Mus, Cape Town, 58-59, asst dir, 60-63; cur fishes, Australian Mus, Sydney, 64-65, dir, 65-74; prof environ studies, MacQuarie Univ, Sydney, Australia, 75-81; exec dir, Calif Acad Sci, San Francisco, 82-88. *Mem:* Fel AAAS; Royal Zool Soc; Mus Asn Australia (pres, 73-74); Australian Marine Sci Asn (pres, 71-72); Explorers Club. *Res:* Marine science; environmental study. *Mailing Add:* 2737 Devonshire Pl NW Apt 103 Washington DC 20008

**TALBOT, JAMES LAWRENCE,** GEOLOGY, STRUCTURAL. *Current Pos:* vpres acad affairs, 76-84, PROF GEOL, WESTERN WASH UNIV, 84- *Personal Data:* b Epsom, Eng, Sept 6, 32; div; c 3. *Educ:* Cambridge Univ, BA, 54; Univ Calif, Berkeley, MA, 57; Univ Adelaide, PhD(geol), 63. *Prof Exp:* Lectr struct geol, Univ Adelaide, 58-63, sr lectr, 63-67; assoc prof geol, Lakehead Univ, 67-70; prof geol & chmn dept, 70-75, actg acad vpres, Univ Mont, 75-76. *Concurrent Pos:* Alexander von Humboldt Found fel, Univ Bonn, 63-64. *Mem:* Geol Soc Am; Sigma Xi. *Res:* Structural analysis of basement cover complexes; analysis of strain in metamorphic rocks; studies on rock cleavage and mylonites. *Mailing Add:* Geol Dept Western Wash Univ Bellingham WA 98225

**TALBOT, JOHN MAYO,** AEROSPACE MEDICINE, RADIOBIOLOGY. *Current Pos:* SR MED CONSULT, LIFE SCI RES OFF, FEDN AM SOCS EXP BIOL, 74- *Personal Data:* b Sebastopol, Calif, May 8, 13; m 46, Margaret Illingworth; c John M, Mark S & Neil C. *Educ:* Univ Ore, AB, 35, MD, 38. *Honors & Awards:* Theodore C Lyster Award, Aerospace Med Asn, 67. *Prof Exp:* Med officer, USAF, 39-45, res & develop, 46-56, med officer, 56-59, head, Biomed Sci Off, Secy Defense, 59-62, NASA liaison, 63-64, asst USAF surgeon gen, 67-70, SAC surgeon, 70-71, USAFE surgeon, 72-73; dir sci commun div, George Wash Univ Med Ctr, 73-74. *Concurrent Pos:* Consult aerospace med, NASA, 73-76; med consult, Environ Protection Agency, 73-75; pvt consult occup med, 78-80. *Mem:* Aerospace Med Asn (pres, 68-69); Int Acad Astronaut; Am Col Prev Med; Pan Am Med Asn; Air Force Asn. *Res:* General medical sciences and nutrition; investigations, reviews and reports in aerospace medicine; nutrition sciences, nutritional epidemiology and environmental toxicology. *Mailing Add:* 2509 Carrollton Rd Annapolis MD 21403

**TALBOT, LAWRENCE,** MECHANICAL ENGINEERING. *Current Pos:* Asst prof mech eng, Univ Calif, Berkeley, 52-58, assoc prof aeronaut sci, 58-63, prof mech eng, 63-91, vchmn dept, 70-74, PROF GRAD STUDIES, UNIV CALIF, BERKELEY, 91- *Personal Data:* b Brooklyn, NY, Dec 30, 25; m 59, Vivian C Pierce; c 2. *Educ:* Univ Mich, BS, 48, MS, 49, PhD(eng mech), 52. *Hon Degrees:* MA, Oxford Univ, Eng, 67. *Concurrent Pos:* Lectr &

consult, Adv Group Aeronaut Res & Develop, Europe, 56-57 & 67-68; Guggenheim fel & vis res fel, All Souls Col, Oxford Univ, 67-68. *Mem:* Fel Am Phys Soc; fel Am Inst Aeronaut & Astronaut; Sigma Xi; fel Am Soc Mech Engrs; fel AAAS. *Res:* Fluid mechanics; turbulent combustion. *Mailing Add:* 6173 Etcheverry Hall Univ Calif Berkeley CA 94720-1740. *Fax:* 510-642-6163

**TALBOT, LEE MERRIAM,** ECOLOGICAL BASIS FOR SUSTAINABLE DEVELOPMENT, NATIONAL & INTERNATIONAL ENVIRONMENTAL POLICY. *Current Pos:* SR ENVIRON ADV, WORLD BANK, 84-; SR PROF ENVIRON SCI ENT AFFAIRS & PUB POLICY, GEORGE MASON UNIV, FAIRFAX, 94- *Personal Data:* b New Beford, Mass, Aug 2, 30; m 59, Martha Hayne; c Lawrence H & Russell M. *Educ:* Univ Calif, AB, 53, MA & PhD(ecol & geog), 63. *Honors & Awards:* Wildlife Soc Award, 63; Albert Schweitzer Medal, Animal Welfare Inst, 75; Distinguished Serv Award, Am Inst Biol Sci, 79; Pierre Chaleur Prize, Fr Acad Sci, 93. *Prof Exp:* Field biologist, Arctic Res Lab, Alaska, 51; staff ecologist, UNESCO-Int Union Conserv, Belg, 54-56; ecologist & dir, EAfrican Wildlife & Wild Land Res Proj, Nat Acad Sci-Nat Res Coun, Rockefeller Found, NY Zool Soc & Govt Kenya, 59-63; dir, SE Asia Proj, Int Union Conserv, 64-65; field rep int affairs ecol & conserv & res ecologist, Smithsonian Inst, 66-70, sci coordr, Conserv Sect, Int Biol Prog, 66-70; sr scientist, President's Coun Environ Qual, 70-75, asst to chmn & dir, Int & Sci Affairs, 75-78; dir conserv & spec sci adv, World Wildlife Fund Int, 78-80; sr sci adv conserv & natural resources, Int Coun Sci Unions, 78-83; dir-gen, Int Union Conserv Nature & Natural Resources, 80-83; res fel, Environ & Policy Inst, East-West Ctr, Honolulu, 83-89; vis fel, World Resources Inst, Washington, DC, 84-89. *Concurrent Pos:* UNESCO lectr, Southeast Asia, 55, consult, 65-; leader, African wildlife exp, Wildlife Mgt Inst & Am Comt Int Wildlife Protection, 56; Taussig traveling fel, Univ Calif, 58-59; consult, var African, Am, Asian, Australian & Europ governments, 59-64; consult, UN Spec Fund, 62-63; Pac Sci Bd, Nat Acad Sci-Nat Res Coun, 64-65, Peace Corps, 66, Int Comn Nat Parks, 66-, Nat Park Serv, 68, AID, 69, WHO, 72, World Bank, 84-, Inter-Am Develop Bank, 87-90, UN Develop Prog, 88-, Asian Develop Bank, 90-; wildlife adv, UN Spec Fund & EAfrican Agr & Forestry Res Orgn, 63-64; assoc ecol, US Nat Zool Park, 66-; spec adv, Mus Natural Hist, Smithsonian Inst, 67-, res assoc, 74-; overseas consult, Fauna Preserv Soc, 67-; chmn, Am Comt Int Conserv, 74-78; vpres, Int Union Conserv Nature & Natural Resources, 75-78; Regent's lectr, Univ Calif, Santa Barbara, 85-86; adj prof ecol, Union Experimenting Col & Univs, 85-88; vpres, Fauna Soc, London, 86-; adj prof biol, George Mason Univ, 87-90; consult, UN Univ, 92-93, US Marine Mammal Comn, 92-; mem, US Nat Comt Probs Environ, Nat Res Coun, 93-96; pres, Lee Talbot Assocs Int, 91- *Mem:* Fel AAAS; Am Soc Mammal; Ecol Soc Am; Int Soc Ecol Econs; Wildlife Soc; Sigma Xi; fel Pop Ref Bur. *Res:* International conservation; wildlife, especially ecology and management; tropical land use and savannah ecology; conservation of renewable natural resources; methodology of ecological research and survey; environmental impact analysis; biodiversity and endangered species; incorporation environmental considerations into economic development; ecological basis of sustainable resource management. *Mailing Add:* 6656 Chilton Ct McLean VA 22101-4422

**TALBOT, NATHAN BILL,** pediatrics; deceased, see previous edition for last biography

**TALBOT, PIERRE J,** VIROLOGY, IMMUNOLOGY. *Current Pos:* from asst prof to assoc prof, 84-92, PROF VIROL, INST ARMAND-FRAPPIER, UNIV QUE, 92- *Personal Data:* b Quebec City, Que, July 11, 56; m 77, France Ouellet; c Natalie, Benoit & Dominic. *Educ:* Univ Laval, Ste-Foy, BSc, 77; Univ BC, Vancouver, PhD(biochem), 81. *Honors & Awards:* Fisher Sci Award, Can Soc Microbiologists, 87. *Prof Exp:* Teaching asst biochem, Univ BC, Vancouver, 78-79; res assoc virol, Scripps Clin & Res Found, La Jolla, 81-84. *Concurrent Pos:* Prog dir, PhD prog, Inst Armand-Frappier, Univ Que, 88-96; adj prof, Univ Montreal, 87- *Mem:* Am Soc Microbiol; Am Soc Virol; Can Soc Microbiologists; Fr-Can Asn Advan Sci; Can Soc Immunol; AAAS; Int Soc Neuroimmunol. *Res:* Molecular studies on viruses, especially neurotropic coronaviruses, and their relationship to the immune system and pathogenesis; research on viral proteins with the help of modern techniques of cellular fusion and recombinant DNA; research on viruses and multiple sclerosis. *Mailing Add:* Virol Res Ctr Inst Armand-Frappier 531 boul des Prairies Laval PQ H7V 1B7 Can. *Fax:* 514-686-5531; *E-Mail:* pierre__talbot@iaf.uquebec.ca

**TALBOT, PRUDENCE,** REPRODUCTIVE PHYSIOLOGY, CELL BIOLOGY. *Current Pos:* from asst prof to assoc prof, 81-86, PROF BIOL, UNIV CALIF, RIVERSIDE, 86- *Personal Data:* b Mass, June 9, 44; m 68. *Educ:* Wilson Col, BA, 66; Wellesley Col, MA, 68; Univ Houston, PhD(cell biol), 72. *Prof Exp:* Res assoc mammalian fertil, Univ Houston, 72-77. *Mem:* Am Soc Cell Biol; Am Soc Zoologists; Soc Study Reproduction; Sigma Xi. *Res:* Morphology, physiology and biochemistry of mammalian fertilization and the mechanism of mammalian ovulation; lobster reproductive biology. *Mailing Add:* Dept Biol Univ Calif-Riverside Riverside CA 92521-0001. *Fax:* 909-787-4286

**TALBOT, RAYMOND JAMES, JR,** IMAGE PROCESSING, ASTROPHYSICS. *Current Pos:* mem tech staff, 81-83, eng specialist, 83-90, DIR, AEROSPACE CORP, 90- *Personal Data:* b Portsmouth, Va, Sept 17, 41; m 68, Prue McCready. *Educ:* Mass Inst Technol, SB, 63, PhD(physics), 69. *Prof Exp:* Res assoc, Space Sci Physics & Astron, Rice Univ, 69-71, asst prof, 71-76, assoc prof, 76-81. *Mem:* Am Astron Soc; Sigma Xi. *Res:* Image processing. *Mailing Add:* 1927 Curtis Ave Redondo Beach CA 90278. *E-Mail:* raymond.talbot@aero.org

**TALBOT, RICHARD BURRITT,** toxicology; deceased, see previous edition for last biography

**TALBOT, T(HOMAS) F,** MECHANICAL ENGINEERING DESIGN, METALLURGY & ACCIDENT RECONSTRUCTION. *Current Pos:* from assoc prof to prof eng, Univ Ala, Birmingham, 67-70, dir continuing eng educ, 72-79, prof & chmn mech eng, 83-89, EMER PROF MECH ENG, UNIV ALA, BIRMINGHAM, 90- *Personal Data:* b Birmingham, Ala, July 31, 30; m 57, Donna Klinner; c Teresa (Pidgeon), Melanie (Markle) & Grace (Pate). *Educ:* Auburn Univ, BME, 52; Calif Inst Technol, MSME, 53; Ga Inst Technol, PhD(mech eng), 64. *Honors & Awards:* Triodyn Safety Award, Am Soc Mech Engrs. *Prof Exp:* Sr pract man, Tenn Coal & Iron Div, US Steel Corp, 56-58; asst prof mech eng, Ga Inst Technol, 58-65; assoc prof mat sci & mech design, Vanderbilt Univ, 65-67. *Concurrent Pos:* Consult, Humble Oil & Refining Co, 59, Chicago Bridge & Iron Co, 65 & Rust Eng Co, 66; chmn bd dirs, Am Alloy Prods, 77-96; mem, Bd Regist Prof Engrs & Land Survs, Ala, 85-; consult engr, 90- *Mem:* Am Soc Metals; Am Soc Mech Engrs; Am Soc Eng Educ; Am Welding Soc; Soc Automotive Engrs; Nat Coun Eng Examrs. *Res:* Machine design; materials processing; design aspects of automobile safety and accident reconstruction; design aspects of product liability. *Mailing Add:* 3837 Brook Hollow Lane Birmingham AL 35243-5935. *Fax:* 205-967-4550; *E-Mail:* ttalbot@eng.uab.edu

**TALBOTT, EDWIN M,** ELECTRONICS ENGINEERING, ENGINEERING MECHANICS. *Current Pos:* pres, Varigas Industs, Inc, 68-76, PRES, VARIGAS RES, INC, 77- *Personal Data:* b Baltimore, Md, Oct 3, 23; m 47; c 3. *Educ:* Johns Hopkins Univ, BE, 43; Univ Baltimore, JD, 50. *Prof Exp:* Engr, US Indust Chem Div, Airco, 46-50; engr & mgr, Bendix Corp, 50-60; prog mgr, Martin Marietta Corp, 60-64; pres, Chesapeake Systs Corp, 64-68. *Concurrent Pos:* Pres, Etalon Corp, 80-; mem, bd dirs, Sci Assocs, Inc, 81-85, Pneumatics, Inc, 84- *Mem:* Am Defense Preparedness Asn. *Res:* Energy economics; energy conservation; compressed air systems; powered hand tools; fluorescent lighting control. *Mailing Add:* 1314 Doves Cove Rd Baltimore MD 21286

**TALBOTT, RICHARD LLOYD,** ORGANIC CHEMISTRY. *Current Pos:* sr chemist, Cent Res Dept, 3M Co, 61-66, sr chemist, Indust Tape Div, 66-68, supvr adhesives res, 68-74, res mgr, Packing Systs Div, 74-84, CORP SCIENTIST, 3M CO, 84- *Personal Data:* b Chicago, Ill, July 15, 35; m 58; c 3. *Educ:* DePauw Univ, BA, 57; Univ Ill, PhD(org chem), 60. *Prof Exp:* NSF fel org chem, Mass Inst Technol, 60-61. *Mem:* Am Chem Soc; Tech Asn Pulp & Paper Indust. *Res:* Pressure-sensitive adhesives chemistry; chemistry of fluorinated oxidants and fluorinated peroxides; oriented plastic films. *Mailing Add:* 4398 Fisher Lane White Bear Lake MN 55110-3689

**TALBOTT, TED DELWYN,** REGISTRATIONS CHEMISTRY, RESOURCE MANAGEMENT. *Current Pos:* RETIRED. *Personal Data:* b Sudan, Tex, Oct 18, 29; m 55, Mildred C Adams; c Terri J & Thomas W. *Educ:* Univ NTex, BS, 51, MS, 55. *Prof Exp:* Indust chemist, E I Du Pont de Nemours & Co, Inc 55-57; analytical chemist, Res Ctr, US Rubber Co, 57-64; sr res chemist, Analytical Res Sect, Agr Div, Miles Inc, 64-92. *Mem:* Am Chem Soc. *Res:* Preparation and assembly of information on pesticides for product chemistry brochures for registrations of technicals and formulations in the United States and Canada; the development of a computer data-base for this information. *Mailing Add:* 6714 N Bales Kansas City MO 64119-1331

**TALBURT, JOHN RANDOLPH,** SYSTEMS ANALYSIS & SOFTWARE RE-ENGINEERING, SYSTEMS DOCUMENTATION. *Current Pos:* Assoc prof, 83-91, PROF COMPUT & INFO SCI, UNIV ARK, LITTLE ROCK, 91- *Personal Data:* m 89, Rebeca B Prince; c Caryn E, Alyssa L & Edgardo A. *Educ:* Ark State Univ, BS, 67; Univ Ark, MS, 69, PhD(math), 71. *Prof Exp:* From asst prof to assoc prof math & comput sci, Columbus Col, 71-77; owner, Data Mgt Serv, 77-80; mgr info systs, Carter, Mitchum & Co, 80-81; pres, Prof Comput Software, Inc, 81-83. *Concurrent Pos:* Comput modeling consult, US Army Infantry Ctr, 77; chair, Dept Comput & Info Sci, Univ Ark, Little Rock, 86-93, co-dir, Ctr Artificial Intel & Exp Systs, 89-91; res fel, Nat Ctr Toxicol Res, 89-92; vis researcher, Acxiom Corp, 93-94. *Mem:* Asn Comput Mach. *Res:* Applied computing research in the areas of systems analysis and software engineering directed at methods for re-engineering existing software systems to take advantage of new technologies. *Mailing Add:* 3222 Breckenridge Dr Little Rock AR 72227. *Fax:* 501-569-8144; *E-Mail:* jrtalburt@ualr.edu

**TALENT, DAVID LEROY,** ORBITAL DEBRIS STUDIES, ORBITAL DEBRIS MODELING. *Current Pos:* PRIN SCIENTIST, SOLAR SYST EXPLOR DEPT, LOCKHEED ENG & SCI CO, 86- *Personal Data:* b Springfield, Mo, Apr 1, 52; m 79, Virginia Garcia; c Daniel, Leslie, Aaron & Byron. *Educ:* Southwest Mo State Univ, BS, 74; Rice Univ, MS, 79, PhD(space physics), 81. *Prof Exp:* William Gaertner fel astron, Yerkes Observ, Univ Chicago, 80-82; asst prof physics, Abilene Christian Univ, 82-86. *Concurrent Pos:* Sci reporter, KRBC-TV, Abilene, Tex, 84-85; mem peer rev panel Int Ultraviolet Explorer Satellite, NASA, 85; chief scientist, Debris Collision Warning Sensor Proj, NASA, Lockheed, 86- *Mem:* Am Astron Soc; Astron Soc Pac; AAAS; Am Inst Aeronaut & Astronaut. *Res:* Observation and modeling of the earth orbital debris environment; design of a space shuttle payload known as the Debris Collision Warning Sensor (DCWS) experiment; author of numerous publications for science journals and one astronomy book. *Mailing Add:* Solar Syst Explor Dept Lockheed Eng & Sci Co Mail Code C-23 Houston TX 77058. *Fax:* 713-483-5347

**TALENT, LARRY GENE,** ECOLOGY, ZOOLOGY. *Current Pos:* asst prof, 80-85, ASSOC PROF ZOOL, OKLA STATE UNIV, 85- *Personal Data:* b Cerrogordo, Ark, May 4, 46; m 65; c 2. *Educ:* Calif State Univ, Fresno, BA, 70, MA, 73; Ore State Univ, PhD(wildlife), 80. *Prof Exp:* Instr biol, Hartnell Community Col, 73-74. *Mem:* Wildlife Soc; Wilson Ornith Soc; Am Ornithologists Union; Cooper Ornith Soc; Herpetologists League. *Res:* Vertebrate ecology; habitat use and competitive interactions of sympatric species. *Mailing Add:* Dept Zool Okla State Univ Stillwater OK 74078-0001

**TALESNIK, JAIME,** pharmacology, physiology; deceased, see previous edition for last biography

**TALHAM, ROBERT J,** APPLIED MATHEMATICS, ACOUSTICS. *Current Pos:* RETIRED. *Personal Data:* b Cohoes, NY, May 27, 29; m 56; c 4. *Educ:* State Univ NY Albany, BA, 55, MS, 56; Rensselaer Polytech Inst, PhD(appl math), 60. *Prof Exp:* Nat Acad Sci-Nat Res Coun res fel, Naval Res Lab, DC, 60-61; mem tech staff, Bell Tel Labs, NJ, 61-64; mgr undersea defense systs eng, Heavy Mil Electronics Dept, Gen Elec Co, 64-77, mgr oper planning, 77-89. *Mem:* Am Math Soc; Soc Indust & Appl Math; Acoust Soc Am. *Res:* Sonar systems; underwater acoustics; sound propagation in non-homogeneous medium; acoustic array design and development; signal processing. *Mailing Add:* 107 Old Powder Mill Rd Fayetteville NY 13066

**TALHOUK, RABIH SHAKIB,** EXTRACELLULAR MATRIX, EPITHELIAL. *Current Pos:* FEL CELL & MOLECULAR BIOL, LAWRENCE BERKELEY LAB, UNIV CALIF, BERKELEY & SAN FRANCISCO, 88- *Personal Data:* b Lebanon, Feb 20, 59; US citizen; m 83. *Educ:* Am Univ Beirut, BSc, 81, MSc, 83; Ohio State Univ, PhD(dairy sci), 88. *Honors & Awards:* Upjohn Ag/Vet Res Award, 83. *Mem:* Am Soc Cell Biol; Am Dairy Sci Asn. *Res:* Effect of extracellular matrix and extracellular matrix degrading proteinases on epithelial cell function; epithelial tissue growth and development. *Mailing Add:* Dept Biol Am Univ Beirut 850 Third Ave New York NY 10022. *Fax:* 212-478-1995

**TALIAFERRO, CHARLES M,** PLANT BREEDING, PLANT GENETICS. *Current Pos:* from asst prof to assoc prof, 68-76, PROF FORAGE BREEDING & GENETICS, OKLA STATE UNIV, 76- *Personal Data:* b Leon, Okla, Mar 1, 40; m 60; c 3. *Educ:* Okla State Univ, BS, 62; Tex A&M Univ, MS, 65, PhD(plant breeding & genetics), 66. *Prof Exp:* Res agronomist, Agr Res Serv, USDA, 65-68. *Mem:* Am Soc Agron; Am Genetic Asn. *Res:* Basic genetic and breeding studies involving forage crops. *Mailing Add:* Agron Okla State Univ Stillwater OK 74078-0001

**TALIAFERRO, STEVEN DOUGLAS,** MATHEMATICS. *Current Pos:* ASST PROF MATH, TEX A&M UNIV, 76- *Personal Data:* b Honolulu, Hawaii, Apr 4, 49. *Educ:* San Diego State Univ, BS, 71; Stanford Univ, PhD(math), 76. *Prof Exp:* Teaching asst math, Stanford Univ, 72-76. *Mem:* Am Math Soc. *Res:* Asymptotic behavior and stability of solutions of ordinary differential equations. *Mailing Add:* Dept Math Tex A&M Univ College Station TX 77843-3368

**TALKE, FRANK E,** precision engineering, tribology, for more information see previous edition

**TALL, FRANKLIN DAVID,** SET THEORY, SET THEORETIC TOPOLOGY. *Current Pos:* From asst prof to assoc prof, 69-80, PROF MATH, UNIV TORONTO, 80- *Personal Data:* b New York, NY, Apr 21, 44. *Educ:* Harvard Col, AB, 64; Univ Wis-Madison, PhD(math), 69. *Concurrent Pos:* Vis res prof, Dartmouth Col, 82-83 & 96; vis prof, Univ Sao Paulo, 97. *Mem:* Am Math Soc; Can Math Soc; Asn Symbolic Logic; Int Asn Neurolinguistic Prog. *Res:* Topology with emphasis on establishing that topological propositions are not decided by usual axioms for set theory; applications of neurolinguistic programmming to education and health. *Mailing Add:* Dept Math Univ Toronto Toronto ON M5S 3G3 Can. *Fax:* 416-978-4107

**TALL, JOANN,** ECOLOGY. *Honors & Awards:* Goldman Environ Prize, Goldman Environ Found, 93. *Mailing Add:* BIA Hwy 27 PO Box 47 Porcupine SD 57772

**TALLAL, PAULA,** EXPERIMENTAL PSYCHOLOGY, SPEECH SCIENCE. *Current Pos:* PROF & CO-DIR, CTR MOLECULAR & BEHAV NEUROSCI, RUTGERS UNIV, 88- *Personal Data:* b Austin, Tex, May 12, 47; m 72. *Educ:* NY Univ, BA, 69; Cambridge Univ, PhD(exp psychol), 73. *Honors & Awards:* Distinguished Young Scientist of the Year, Md Acad Sci, 76; President's Award, Notre Dame Col, 77. *Prof Exp:* Instr pediat, Sch Med, Johns Hopkins Univ, 74-75, asst prof neurol, 75-79; asst prof, Univ Calif, San Diego, 79-80, assoc prof psychiat, Sch Med, 80-86, prof, 86-88. *Concurrent Pos:* Prin investr, Nat Inst Neurol Dis & Stroke, NIH, 76-85, Nat Inst Neurol Dis, Commun Dis & Stroke/NIMH, 85- *Mem:* Int Neuropsychol Soc; Acoust Soc Am; Am Asn Phonetic Sci; Acad Aphasia; Am Speech-Lang-Hearing Asn; Soc Neurosci; Am Psychiat Asn. *Res:* Sensory, perceptual and cognitive function in normal and delayed language development; neural processing of nonverbal and verbal information in various sensory modalities. *Mailing Add:* Ctr Molecular & Behav Neurosci Rutgers Univ 197 University Ave Newark NJ 07102

**TALLAN, IRWIN,** GENETICS. *Current Pos:* RETIRED. *Personal Data:* b New York, NY, June 26, 27; m 59. *Educ:* Rutgers Univ, BA, 49; Ind Univ, PhD(genetics), 57. *Prof Exp:* Technician to H J Muller, Ind Univ, 50, asst to T M Sonneborn, 50-53; lectr zool, Univ Toronto, 56-58, from asst prof to prof zool, 58-95. *Mem:* Am Soc Zool; Brit Soc Gen Microbiol. *Res:* Genetics; nucleo-cytoplasmic interactions in protozoans; infectivity of kappa and other plasmids. *Mailing Add:* Dept Zool Univ Toronto Toronto ON M5S 3G5 Can

**TALLAN, NORMAN M,** MATERIALS SCIENCE, CERAMICS. *Current Pos:* Res physicist, Aerospace Res Labs, 59-61, supvr ceramic res, 61-70, dir, Metals & Ceramics Res Lab, 70-76, chief, Processing & High Temperature Mat Br, Air Force Mat Lab, 76-77, actg chief, Metals & Ceramics Div, 77-78, chief scientist, Mat Lab, 78-83, CHIEF, METALS & CERAMICS DIV, MAT LAB, WRIGHT-PATTERSON AFB, 83- *Personal Data:* b Newark, NJ, Sept 24, 32; m 58; c 4. *Educ:* Rutgers Univ, BSc, 54; Ohio State Univ, MS, 55; Alfred Univ, PhD(solid state ceramics), 59. *Honors & Awards:* Ross Coffin Purdy Award, 69. *Concurrent Pos:* Res asst, Israel Inst Technol, 66-67. *Mem:* Fel Am Ceramic Soc; Am Phys Soc. *Res:* Equilibrium point defect structure and the transport of charge and mass in metal oxides at high temperatures; physical and mechanical properties of ceramic materials. *Mailing Add:* 3743 Greenbay Dr Dayton OH 45415

**TALLARIDA, RONALD JOSEPH,** BIOMATHEMATICS, PHARMACOLOGY. *Current Pos:* asst prof, Temple Univ, 67-71, assoc prof pharmacol, 71-78, mem fac, 78-79, PROF PHARMACOL, TEMPLE UNIV, 79- *Personal Data:* b Philadelphia, Pa, May 26, 37; m 58; c 3. *Educ:* Drexel Inst, BS, 59, MS, 63; Temple Univ, PhD(pharmacol), 67. *Prof Exp:* Coop student, Philco Corp-Drexel Inst, 55-59; jr engr, Philco Corp, 59-60; from instr to asst prof math, Drexel Inst, 60-67. *Concurrent Pos:* Lectr, Philadelphia Col Pharm, 60, PMC Col, 61-62 & cardiovasc training grant prog, Med Sch, Temple Univ, 63-64; consult, Drexel Inst, 67- *Mem:* AAAS; Math Asn Am; Am Soc Pharmacol & Exp Therapeut. *Res:* Mathematical models for application to biology and medicine; drug receptor theory; pharmacology of vascular smooth muscle; pharmacology of morphine; drug induced disease. *Mailing Add:* Dept Pharmacol Temple Univ Sch Med 3420 N Broad St Philadelphia PA 19140-5104

**TALLEDO, OSCAR EDUARDO,** OBSTETRICS & GYNECOLOGY. *Current Pos:* resident, Med Col Ga, 58-60, fel, 60-61, from instr to assoc prof, 61-71, actg chmn, 81-82, PROF OBSTET & GYNEC, MED COL GA, 71-, CHIEF GYNEC SERV, 74- *Personal Data:* b Sullana, Peru, Aug 1, 29; US citizen; m 59; c 3. *Educ:* San Marcos Univ, Lima, BS, 48, MD, 55; Am Bd Obstet & Gynec, spec cert div gynec oncol, 75. *Prof Exp:* Intern, San Marcos Univ, Lima, 54-55; intern, Crawford W Long Hosp, Emory Univ, 56-57, resident obstet & gynec, 57-58. *Concurrent Pos:* Nat Heart Inst grant obstet & gynec, Med Col Ga, 65, NIH grant, 68, dir obstet/gynec residency training prog, 74-; consult, Cent State Hosp, Macon City Hosp, Greenville Mem Hosp & Mem Med Ctr, Univ Hosp & Humana Hosp, 69-, Vet Admin Med-Surg Ctr, 74- *Mem:* Fel Am Col Obstet & Gynec; Soc Gynec Invest; AMA; Am Fertil Soc; Soc Gynec Oncol; Gynec-Urol Soc; Gynec Laser Soc. *Res:* Physiology of pregnancy; vascular reactivity in pregnancy; fetal electrocardiography; uterine contractility studies; amniotic fluid; laser surgery and evaluation of chemotherapy in gynecological malignancies; vaginal flora in patients with abnormal Pap smears; urodynamics and cancer of the cervix. *Mailing Add:* PO Box 23089 Savannah GA 31403-3089

**TALLENT, WILLIAM HUGH,** BIOCHEMISTRY, ORGANIC CHEMISTRY. *Current Pos:* invests leader, Northern Regional Res Ctr, Agr Res Serv, USDA, 64-69, chief indust crops res, 69-75, dir, Northern Regional Res Ctr, 75-83, dep adminr, Northeastern Region, 83-84, asst adminr, 84-94, TECHNOL TRANSFER ADV, AGR RES SERV, USDA, WASHINGTON, DC, 94- *Personal Data:* b Akron, Ohio, May 28, 28; m 52; c 3. *Educ:* Univ Tenn, BS, 49, MS, 50; Univ Ill, PhD(biochem), 53. *Honors & Awards:* Distinguished Econ Botanist Award, Soc Econ Bot, 81; Technol 2002 Lifetime Achievement Award, NASA, 92. *Prof Exp:* Asst, Univ Tenn, 49-50 & Univ Ill, 50-53; asst scientist, Nat Heart Inst, 53-57; res chemist, G D Searle & Co, 57-64. *Concurrent Pos:* Assoc ed, J Am Oil Chemists Soc, 70-83. *Mem:* Am Chem Soc; Soc Econ Bot; AAAS. *Res:* Application of chromatographic and spectroscopic methods to analysis, biochemistry of fats and oils, isolation and structure determination of terpenes, plant lipids and natural insecticides; plant enzymes; useful derivatives and synthetic modifications of natural products; research management; technology transfer. *Mailing Add:* 6100 Westchester Park Dr L-2 College Park MD 20740

**TALLERICO, PAUL JOSEPH,** ELECTRICAL ENGINEERING. *Current Pos:* ASSOC GROUP LEADER, LOS ALAMOS NAT LAB, 68- *Personal Data:* b New York, NY, Nov 30, 38; m 62; Mary E Healy; c Catherine & Ellen. *Educ:* Mass Inst Technol, BS & MS, 61; Univ Mich, PhD(elec eng), 68. *Prof Exp:* Staff mem, Int Bus Mach Res Labs, 62-63. *Concurrent Pos:* Consult, var orgns, 79, 80, 88-90. *Mem:* Sigma Xi; Inst Elec & Electronics Engrs. *Res:* Microwave generation and amplification especially as applied to accelerator power sources. *Mailing Add:* 238 Loma del Escolar Los Alamos NM 87544-2526. *Fax:* 505-665-2818; *E-Mail:* tallerico@lanl.gov

**TALLEY, CHARLES PETER,** ORGANIC CHEMISTRY, POLYMER CHEMISTRY. *Current Pos:* CONSULT, RPM, 96- *Personal Data:* b New York, NY, Aug 15, 41; m 68, Dolores Woodland; c Christina & Peter. *Educ:* St Peter's Col, NJ, BS, 63; Polytech Inst New York, PhD(phys org chem), 74. *Prof Exp:* Sr res chemist, Merck Sharp & Dohme Res Labs, Div Merck & Co, 68-72; res chemist, Analytical Chem Div, Nat Bur Stand, 73; sr group leader analytical res, Calgon Corp, Subsid Merck & Co, Inc, 73-78; dir res & develop, Gaf Corp, 79-84, gen mgr int, 85-89; bus dir, Rhone Poulenc, 90; pres, Alan Motor Lines, 91-95. *Mem:* Am Chem Soc; AAAS. *Res:* Gas and high pressure liquid chromatography, especially as applied to the analysis of trace organics in biological, environmental and polymeric matrices. *Mailing Add:* 157 Pleasant Plains Ave Staten Island NY 10309-2725. *Fax:* 718-815-1328

**TALLEY, EUGENE ALTON,** agricultural chemistry; deceased, see previous edition for last biography

**TALLEY, JOHN HERBERT,** GROUND-WATER GEOLOGY. *Current Pos:* proj geologist, 72-74, scientist & hydrogeologist, 74-92, ASSOC DIR, DEL GEOL SURV, 92- *Personal Data:* b Wilmington, Del, Jan 16, 44; c 2. *Educ:* Univ Del, BA, 69; Franklin & Marshall Col, MS, 74. *Prof Exp:* Eng geologist, Geo-Del, Ltd, 71-72. *Mem:* Am Inst Prof Geologists; Asn Ground Water Scientist & Engrs. *Res:* Geologic mapping; subsurface stratigraphy and structural interpretation; hydrologic mapping; ground water exploration; ground water-surface water relationships; borehole geophysics. *Mailing Add:* Del Geol Surv Univ Del Newark DE 19716. *Fax:* 302-831-3579; *E-Mail:* john.talley@mvs.udel.edu

**TALLEY, JOHN J,** MEDICAL CHEMISTRY. *Current Pos:* SR RES FEL, G D SEARLE & CO, 96- *Personal Data:* m 96, Patricia E Kinamore; c Anne Elizabeth & Cynthia Marie. *Educ:* Univ Northern Iowa, BA, 74; Univ Minn, PhD(chem), 79. *Prof Exp:* Staff scientist, Gen Elec Res & Develop, 79-86; sr res specialist, Monsanto Co, 86-88, assoc fel, 88-91, res fel, 91-96. *Mem:* Am Chem Soc; Am Peptide Soc. *Res:* Medicinal chemistry efforts directed toward inhibition of HIV-protease and inhibition of cyclooxygenase-II; clinical candidates identified and developed based on both of the aforementioned research activities; granted 48 US patents. *Mailing Add:* G D Searle & Co 700 Chesterfield Pkwy N St Louis MO 63198. *Fax:* 314-737-7425; *E-Mail:* jjtall@ccmail.monsanto.com

**TALLEY, LYNNE DEBORAH,** PHYSICAL OCEANOGRAPHY. *Current Pos:* asst res oceanogr, 84-85, PROF PHYS OCEANOG, SCRIPPS INST OCEANOG, UNIV CALIF, SAN DIEGO, 85- *Educ:* Mass Inst Technol, PhD(phys oceanog), 82. *Prof Exp:* Postdoctoral fel, Ore State Univ, 82-83. *Concurrent Pos:* Mellon fel, 84; presidential young investr, NSF, 87. *Res:* General circulation of the oceans. *Mailing Add:* Scripps Inst Oceanog Univ Calif San Diego La Jolla CA 92093-0230

**TALLEY, ROBERT BOYD,** INTERNAL MEDICINE. *Current Pos:* RETIRED. *Personal Data:* b Scottsbluff, Nebr, 1931; m, Louise C. *Educ:* Colo Univ, MD, 56; Am Bd Internal Med, dipl. *Prof Exp:* Intern, Wayne Co Gen Hosp, 56-57; resident, Iowa Univ, 59-62, instr med, 62-63; physician internal med, Pvt Pract, Stockton, Calif, 63-96. *Concurrent Pos:* NIH fel, Div Gastroenterol, Univ Iowa, 62-63; consult gastroenterol, San Joaquin Co Hosp, 63-70; clin instr med, Med Ctr, Univ Calif, San Francisco, 65-70; chief staff, St Joseph's Hosp, Stockton, Calif, 71, chief med, 75-77, mem bd trustees, 84-86; mem, Community Serv Comt, Am Col Physicians, 71-81, Adv Comt Nat Health Ins, House Ways & Means Comt, US Cong, 78-80 & Tech Adv Comt, Group Health Asn Am, 82-85; vpres, United Found Med Care, 82-84, pres, 84-86; med dir & vpres, Concurrent Rev Technol, 87- *Mem:* Inst Med-Nat Acad Sci; fel Am Col Physicians. *Res:* Gastroenterology. *Mailing Add:* 1941 W Lincoln Rd Stockton CA 95207

**TALLEY, ROBERT LEE,** COMBUSTION, AEROSOL & BIOAEROSOL PHYSICS. *Current Pos:* PRIN PHYSICIST, TOPAZ 2000, INC, 96- *Personal Data:* b Eureka, Kans, Nov 25, 33; m 56, Ann Q Wallace; c Robert S, Christopher W, James Q & Timothy W. *Educ:* Kans Univ, BA, 55, MA, 56. *Prof Exp:* Res asst astrophys, Kans Univ, 54-56; res physicist, Cornell Aeronaut Lab, 61-67, head kinetics sect, 67-70, prod develop group physicist, Calspan Corp, 71-74; tech dir, Pelorex Corp, 74-75; sr res physicist, Falcon Res, 76-83; prin physicist, Veritay Technol, 83-96. *Concurrent Pos:* Consult magnetics, Pelorex Corp, 70-74, fiber optical sensors, Penn Va Corp, 85-86. *Mem:* Am Astron Soc; NY Acad Sci; Am Asn Physics Teachers; Inst Elec & Electronics Engrs. *Res:* Ignition, combustion and detonation processes in gases, liquids, solids and aerosols; liquid propellant gun combustion, atomization phenomena, high-speed diagnostics; break-through physics for space propulsion; gaseous electronics and plasmas; health and environmental instrumentation; bioaerosol instrumentation and analysis. *Mailing Add:* S 2221 Eastwood Rd East Aurora NY 14052. *Fax:* 716-775-0516

**TALLEY, ROBERT MORRELL,** INFRARED DETECTORS. *Current Pos:* vpres & mgr labs, 58-76, PRES, SANTA BARBARA RES CTR, 76- *Personal Data:* b Erwin, Tenn, Mar 13, 24; m 48; c 2. *Educ:* Univ SC, BS, 45; Univ Tenn, MS, 48, PhD(physics), 50. *Prof Exp:* Chief infrared br, US Naval Ord Lab, 51-57, chief solid state div, 57-58. *Mem:* Am Phys Soc; Optical Soc Am; Sigma Xi. *Res:* Infrared spectroscopy; intermetallic semiconductors; energy bands in solids; photodetectors; military infrared systems. *Mailing Add:* 1050 Via Los Padres Santa Barbara CA 93111

**TALLEY, SPURGEON MORRIS,** ANIMAL NUTRITION. *Current Pos:* RETIRED. *Personal Data:* b Atkins, Ark, May 6, 18; m 48; c 1. *Educ:* Agr, Mech & Norm Col, Ark, BSA, 47; Kans State Univ, MS, 53, PhD(nutrit), 66. *Prof Exp:* Asst prof poultry sci & prod mgr, Lincoln Univ, 54-66, assoc prof animal nutrit, 66-77, prof animal sci, 77-89, emer prof, 89. *Mem:* Poultry Sci Asn; Am Soc Animal Sci. *Res:* Monogastric animals; nutrition of poultry and swine; plant proteins as sources of protein for the avian species; level of dietary protein and phase feeding on esophagoulcerogenesis of market swine; metabolizable energy requirements of market-type swine. *Mailing Add:* 3303 College Ave Kansas City MO 64128

**TALLEY, THURMAN LAMAR,** PHYSICS. *Current Pos:* MEM STAFF, LOS ALAMOS NAT LAB, UNIV CALIF, 66- *Personal Data:* b Portales, NMex, July 26, 37; m 62; c 2. *Educ:* Eastern NMex Univ, BS, 59, MS, 60; Fla State Univ, PhD(physics), 68. *Prof Exp:* Instr eng sci, Fla State Univ, 64-65. *Concurrent Pos:* Chmn, Joint AEC-Dept Defense Working Group Safeguard Sprint Nuclear Vulnerability & Effects, 68-71. *Mem:* Am Phys Soc; Sigma Xi. *Res:* Nuclear reaction theory; nuclear weapons design; nuclear weapons effects; computer simulation of complex physical phenomena. *Mailing Add:* 606 Rim Rd Los Alamos NM 87544-2949

**TALLEY, WILSON K(INTER),** NUCLEAR ENGINEERING, APPLIED MATHEMATICS. *Current Pos:* from asst prof to prof, Univ Calif, Davis, 63-91, vchmn dept appl sci, 66-67, actg chmn, 68-69, 72-91, EMER PROF APPL SCI, UNIV CALIF, DAVIS, 91- *Personal Data:* b St Louis, Mo, Jan 27, 35; m 81, Helen Mazetis; c Donna, Steven, Elaine & Edward. *Educ:* Univ Calif, Berkeley, BS, 56, PhD(nuclear eng); 63; Univ Chicago, SM, 57. *Honors & Awards:* Except Civilian Serv Medal, US Army, 86. *Prof Exp:* Physicist, Lawrence Radiation Lab, 59. *Concurrent Pos:* Consult, Lawrence Livermore Lab, 63-91, asst to dir, 91-94, leader, Theoret Physics Div, 71 & Gov Select Comt, NY, 66-68; mem, Stanford Res Inst, 67-70; White House fel, Dept Health, Educ & Welfare, 69-70; consult, Hazardous Mat Adv Comt, Environ Protection Agency, 71-74; asst vpres acad planning, Univ Calif, 71-74; pres, Fannie & John Hertz Found, 72-; study dir, Comn Critical Choices Am, 74; asst admin res & develop, US Environ Protection Agency, Washington, DC, 74-77; mem, US Army Sci Bd, 78-86, 94-, chmn, 83-86, 95-96, Res Adv Bd, Johnson Controls Inc, 88-; dir, Helionetics, Inc, 81-86, chmn, 84-86. *Mem:* Am Phys Soc; AAAS. *Res:* Linear transport theory; peaceful uses of nuclear explosives; applications of radioisotopes; energy and environmental policy. *Mailing Add:* 4325 Terrabella Way Oakland CA 94619-3156. *Fax:* 510-373-6329; *E-Mail:* hertzwkt@aol.com

**TALLIAN, TIBOR E(UGENE),** TRIBOLOGY. *Current Pos:* TRIBOLOGY CONSULT, 85- *Personal Data:* b Budapest, Hungary, Oct 18, 20; nat US; m 50; c 2. *Educ:* Budapest Tech Univ, ME, 43. *Honors & Awards:* Nat Award, Am Soc Lubrication Engrs, 75. *Prof Exp:* Supvr eng & res, Ball Bearing Factories, Hungary, 52-56; supvr metrol, SKF Indust Inc, 57-58, mgr res lab, 58-68, vpres res, 68-73, vpres technol serv, 73-85. *Mem:* Fel Soc Tribologists & Lubrication Engrs; fel Am Soc Mech Engrs. *Res:* Tribology, fatigue of metals; applied mechanics of bearings; surface geometry and vibrations of rolling systems; mathematical statistics; random processes; electromechanical instrumentation; failure diagnosis; expert systems. *Mailing Add:* 36 Dunminning Rd Newtown Square PA 19073

**TALLITSCH, ROBERT BOYDE,** PHYSIOLOGY. *Current Pos:* asst prof, 75-83, PROF, BIOL DEPT, AUGUSTANA COL, 83- *Personal Data:* b Oak Park, Ill, June 3, 50; m 71. *Educ:* NCent Col, BA, 71; Univ Wis-Madison, MS, 72, PhD(physiol), 75. *Prof Exp:* Res fel, Wis Heart Asn, 74-75. *Concurrent Pos:* NIH res fel, 81 vis scientist, Geront Res Ctr, Nat Inst Aging, NIH, 81; mem hypertension coun, Am Heart Asn. *Mem:* Am Physiol Soc; Am Heart Asn; Int Soc Heart Res NAm Chap. *Res:* Ion transport in skeletal and cardiac muscle cells. *Mailing Add:* Dept Biol Augustana Col Rock Island IL 61201-2296. *Fax:* 309-794-7422

**TALLMADGE, J(OHN) A(LLEN), JR,** CHEMICAL ENGINEERING, ENVIRONMENTAL SCIENCE. *Current Pos:* actg head dept, 67 & 74, prof, 66-91, EMER PROF CHEM ENG, DREXEL UNIV, 91- *Personal Data:* b Allentown, Pa, Feb 19, 28; wid; c Jane, Beth, Susan, John & Robert. *Educ:* Lehigh Univ, BS, 48; Carnegie-Mellon Univ, MS, 50, PhD(chem eng), 54. *Honors & Awards:* Tallmadge Coating Award, Am Inst Chem Engrs. *Prof Exp:* Res engr process develop, E I du Pont de Nemours & Co, Inc 53-56; from asst prof to assoc prof chem eng, Yale Univ, 56-65,. *Concurrent Pos:* Fulbright prof, Univ NSW, Australia, 74; vis prof, Imp Col London, 65, Univ Colo, 72, Univ Calif, Berkeley, 82 & Univ Wash, 83. *Mem:* Am Chem Soc; Am Soc Eng Educ; Am Inst Chem Engrs; Sigma Xi. *Res:* Fluid dynamics; heat transfer; powder metallurgical atomization; industrial water treatment; mass transfer; packed beds; ion exchange; coating processes. *Mailing Add:* 511 Lexington Riddle Village Media PA 19063-6024

**TALLMAN, DENNIS EARL,** ELECTROCHEMISTRY, LABORATORY COMPUTERS. *Current Pos:* asst prof analytical chem, NDak State Univ, 70-73, assoc prof, 73-78, chmn dept, 77-79, PROF ANALYTICAL CHEM, NDAK STATE UNIV, 78- *Personal Data:* b Bellefontaine, Ohio, Apr 23, 42; m 92, Kathleen Maher; c 3. *Educ:* Ohio State Univ, BSc, 64, PhD(analytical chem), 68. *Prof Exp:* NIH fel chem, Cornell Univ, 68-70. *Concurrent Pos:* NAm ed, J Solid State Electrochem, 97- *Mem:* Electrochem Soc; Am Chem Soc; Soc Electroanal Chemists. *Res:* Electroanalytical chemistry; interfacial chemistry; environmental chemistry; polymer chemistry; corrosion; conducting polymers; materials science. *Mailing Add:* Dept Chem NDak State Univ Fargo ND 58105-5516. *Fax:* 701-231-8831; *E-Mail:* dtallman@plains.nodak.edu

**TALLMAN, J(OHN) C(ORNWELL),** CHEMICAL ENGINEERING. *Current Pos:* RETIRED. *Personal Data:* b Auburn, NY, June 12, 18; m 41; c 4. *Educ:* Cornell Univ, BCh, 39, ChemE, 40. *Prof Exp:* Jr Res engr, Ammonia Dept, Exp Sta, E I du Pont de Nemours & Co, Del, 40-41, WVa, 41-46, asst tech supt, 46-47, res engr, 47-52, econ studies supvr, Textile Fibers Dept, 52-56, indust mkt analyst, Develop Dept, 56-62, mgr mkt res, Latin Am Div, Int Dept, 62-69, mgr develop, Du Pont Do Brasil, 69-71, tech investr, Tech Div, Int Dept, 71-76, sr bus analyst, Finance Div, 77-81. *Concurrent Pos:* Abstractor, Chem Abstr, 47-75, sect ed, 59-62. *Mem:* Am Chem Soc; Chem Mkt Res Asn; Am Inst Chem Engrs. *Res:* Plastics; synthetic fibers; economic studies; market research; foreign exchange. *Mailing Add:* 119 Marcella Rd Wilmington DE 19803

**TALLMAN, JOHN FRANCIS,** PHARMACOLOGY, PSYCHIATRY. *Current Pos:* SCI DIR & EXEC VPRES, NEUROGEN CORP, 89- *Personal Data:* b New York, NY, Jan 24, 47; m 71. *Educ:* Georgetown Univ, BS, 68, PhD(biochem), 72. *Prof Exp:* Staff fel, Nat Inst Neurol & Commun Dis & Stroke, NIH, 72-74, sect chief, NIMH, Biol Psychiat Br, 74-83; assoc prof pharmacol & psychiat, Yale Univ Sch Med, 83-89. *Concurrent Pos:* Adj assoc prof pharmacol & psychiat, Yale Univ Sch Med, 89- *Mem:* Soc Neurosci; Am Soc Biochem & Molecular Biol; Am Soc Pharmacol & Exp Therapeut; Am Col Neuropsychopharmacol; Int Col Neuropsychopharmacol. *Res:* Gaba receptors; molecular biology and pharmacology of benzodiazepines. *Mailing Add:* Neurogen Corp 35 NE Industrial Rd Branford CT 06405

**TALLMAN, JOHN GARY,** GENETICS, BIOCHEMISTRY. *Current Pos:* from asst prof to assoc prof, 78-86, PROF BIOL & GENETICS, PEPPERDINE UNIV, 87- *Personal Data:* b Sistersville, WVa, Mar 20, 50. *Educ:* WLiberty State Col, AB, 71; WVa Univ, PhD(genetics), 76. *Prof Exp:* Res assoc biochem, Kans State Univ, 76-78. *Concurrent Pos:* Found fel genetics, WVa Univ, 71-75, Gulf Oil Found fel, 75-76; vis scholar, Stanford Univ, 86; vis res biologist, Univ Calif, Los Angeles, 94. *Mem:* Am Genetic Asn; Am Soc Plant Physiol; AAAS. *Res:* Heterosis; chromatin proteins; transcription; DNA tumor viruses; plant protoplasting and tissue culture; stomatal isolation and biochemistry; plant gas exchange; senescence of plant leaves. *Mailing Add:* Willamett Univ 900 State St Salem OR 97301. *Fax:* 310-456-4314; *E-Mail:* gtallman@pepperdine.edu

**TALLMAN, RICHARD DALE (JUNIOR),** CARDIOPULMONARY PHYSIOLOGY, VENTILATORY CONTROL. *Current Pos:* ASST PROF CARDIOPULMONARY RENOPHYSIOL, SCH MED, OHIO STATE UNIV, 79- *Educ:* Ohio State Univ, PhD(physiol), 79. *Res:* Extracortoreal oxygenation. *Mailing Add:* Dept Allied Med Professions Ohio State Univ Col Med 1583 Perry St Columbus OH 43210-1234

**TALLMAN, RICHARD LOUIS,** CORROSION. *Personal Data:* b Wheeling, WVa, Apr 24, 31; m 56, Joan Lacey; c Lisa (Helmle), Lynn (Furr) & Jane. *Educ:* Kenyon Col, AB, 53; Univ Wis, PhD(phys chem), 60. *Honors & Awards:* Res & Develop 100 Award, 88. *Prof Exp:* Sr chemist, Res Labs, Westinghouse Elec Corp, 59-73; sr res chemist, Gen Motors Res Labs, 73-76; assoc scientist, EG&G Idaho Inc, 77-80, scientist, 80-86. *Concurrent Pos:* Supvry res mat scientist, Mont Technol Cos, Inc, 89. *Mem:* Am Chem Soc; Am Nuclear Soc. *Res:* Corrosion; metal oxidation; combustion; crystallography; microscopy; gravimetry; radwaste leaching; ceramic joining; oxynitride glass making; hot isostatic pressing; pyrotechnics. *Mailing Add:* 1653 Halsey Idaho Falls ID 83401

**TALMAGE, DAVID WILSON,** TRANSPLANTATION, CANCER. *Current Pos:* chmn, Dept Microbiol, Univ Colo, 63-66, assoc dean, 66-68, actg dean, 68-69, dean, 69-71, dir, Webb-Waring Lung Inst, 73-83, assoc dean, 83-86, prof med, 59-87, prof microbiol, 60-87, DISTINGUISHED PROF MED & MICROBIOL, SCH MED, UNIV COLO, 87- *Personal Data:* b Kwangju, Korea, Sept 15, 19; US citizen; m 44, Laveryn M Hunicke; c Janet, Marilyn, David, Mark & Carol. *Educ:* Davidson Col, BS, 41; Washington Univ, MD, 44. *Hon Degrees:* DSc, Buena Vista Col, 69, Colo State Univ, 80. *Honors & Awards:* Sandoz Prize, 95. *Prof Exp:* USPHS res fel, Washington Univ, 50-51; asst res prof path, Sch Med, Univ Pittsburgh, 51-52; from asst prof to assoc prof med, Sch Med, Univ Chicago, 52-59. *Concurrent Pos:* Markle scholar med sci, 55-60; consult, Vet Admin Hosp, 59-71; ed, J Allergy, 63-67. *Mem:* Nat Acad Sci; AAAS; Am Soc Clin Invest; Am Asn Immunologists (pres, 78); Am Acad Allergy (pres, 65). *Res:* Effect of oxygen during culture on survival of mouse thyroid allografts; immunological tolerance in animals bearing cultured allografts. *Mailing Add:* Box C 321 Univ Colo 4200 E Ninth Ave Denver CO 80262. *Fax:* 303-270-8541

**TALMAGE, ROY VAN NESTE,** PHYSIOLOGY. *Current Pos:* dir orthop res & prof surg & pharmacol, 70-84, EMER PROF SURG & PHARMACOL, SCH MED, UNIV NC, CHAPEL HILL, 84- *Personal Data:* b Moppo, Korea, Feb 9, 17; US citizen; m 42; c 3. *Educ:* Maryville Col, AB, 38; Univ Richmond, MA, 40; Harvard Univ, PhD(endocrinol), 47. *Honors & Awards:* William Neuman Award, Am Soc Bone & Mineral Res, 84. *Prof Exp:* Instr biol, Univ Richmond, 40-41; asst, Harvard Univ, 41-42 & 46-47; from instr to prof, Rice Univ, 47-70, chmn dept, 56-64, master, Wiess Col, 57-70. *Concurrent Pos:* NIH res fel, State Univ Leiden, 64; mem, NIH Study Sects, 64-68 & 70-; gen chmn & co-chmn parathyroid confs, Houston, 60, Leiden, 64, Montreal, 67, Chapel Hill, 71, Oxford, Eng, 74, Vancouver, 77 & Denver, 80; staff biochemist, AEC, 69-70, mem nat adv dent res coun, Nat Inst Dent Res, 74-77; pres, Int Conf Calcium Regulatory Hormones, 79-81. *Mem:* AAAS; Orthop Res Soc; Am Soc Zoologists; Soc Exp Biol & Med; Am Physiol Soc; Endocrine Soc. *Res:* Calcium regulating hormones and ion transport processes in bone; osteoporosis and bone density in women. *Mailing Add:* PO Box 231 Montreat NC 28757. *Fax:* 704-669-8148

**TALMAN, JAMES DAVIS,** THEORETICAL PHYSICS. *Current Pos:* from asst prof to prof math, 60-67, chmn, 87-92, PROF APPL MATH, UNIV WESTERN ONT, 67- *Personal Data:* b Toronto, Ont, July 24, 31; m 57, Ragnhild B Nilssen; c Liv E, Stephen J, Marianne R & Eric A. *Educ:* Univ Western Ont, BA, 53, MSc, 54; Princeton Univ, PhD, 59. *Prof Exp:* Instr physics, Princeton Univ, 57-59; asst prof, Am Univ Beirut, 59-60. *Concurrent Pos:* Res asst, Univ Calif, Davis, 63-64; vis, Niels Bohr Inst, Copenhagen, Denmark, 69-70; vis prof physics & aeronomy, Univ Fla, Gainesville, 78-79. *Mem:* Am Phys Soc; Can Asn Physicists; Soc Indust & Appl Math; AAAS; Can Appl Math Soc; Can Math Soc. *Res:* Quantal many-body problem; atomic structure theory; numerical methods. *Mailing Add:* Dept Appl Math Univ Western Ont Western Sci Ctr 1151 Richmond St North London ON N6A 5B7 Can. *Fax:* 519-661-3523; *E-Mail:* jdtalman@uwo.ca

**TALMAN, RICHARD MICHAEL,** PHYSICS. *Current Pos:* From asst prof to assoc prof, 62-71, PROF PHYSICS, CORNELL UNIV, 71- *Personal Data:* b Toronto, Ont, Sept 24, 34; m 57; c 4. *Educ:* Univ Western Ont, BA, 56, MA, 57; Calif Inst Technol, PhD(physics), 63. *Mem:* Am Phys Soc. *Res:* Elementary and experimental particle physics; accelerator physics. *Mailing Add:* Lab Nuclear Study Cornell Univ Newman Lab Ithaca NY 14853

**TALNER, NORMAN STANLEY,** PEDIATRICS, CARDIOLOGY. *Current Pos:* from asst prof to assoc prof, 60-69, PROF PEDIAT, SCH MED, YALE UNIV, 69- *Personal Data:* b Mt Vernon, NY, Sept 28, 25; m 50; c 3. *Educ:* Univ Mich, Ann Arbor, BS, 45; Yale Univ, MD, 49. *Hon Degrees:* MA, Yale Univ, 69. *Prof Exp:* Intern & resident pediat, Kings Co Hosp, State Univ NY, 49-51; resident, Univ Hosp, Univ Mich, 51-52, instr, Med Sch, 54-56, Mich Heart Asn fel pediat cardiol, Hosp, 56-58, asst prof pediat, Univ, 58-60. *Concurrent Pos:* Attend physician, Yale-New Haven Hosp, 60-; USPHS career develop award, 62-72; examr, Sub-Bd Pediat Cardiol, Am Bd Pediat, 69-74; prog chmn, Am Heart Asn, 69-72; consult, Vet Admin, 72-; exam ed, Sub-Bd Pediat Cardiol. *Mem:* Soc Pediat Res (mem secy, 69-72); Am Pediat Soc; Am Col Cardiol (asst secy, 72-74); corresp mem Asn Europ Pediat Cardiol. *Res:* Cardiopulmonary physiology in infants and children. *Mailing Add:* Childrens Clin Res Ctr 333 Cedar St New Haven CT 06510-3289

**TALVACCHIO, JOHN,** SUPERCONDUCTIVITY, DEVICE PHYSICS. *Current Pos:* sr scientist, Cryogenic Electronics & Technol Dept, Westinghouse Res & Develop Ctr, 82-90, fel scientist, Superconducting Electronics Dept, Westinghouse Sci & Technol Ctr, 90-96, FEL SCIENTIST, NORTHROP GRUMMAN CORP, 96- *Personal Data:* b Cleveland, Ohio, Aug 11, 55. *Educ:* Case Western Res Univ, BS, 77; Stanford Univ, PhD(appl physics), 82. *Prof Exp:* Res asst, Condensed Matter Physics Group, Case Western Res Univ, 75-77; res asst, Hansen Lab, Stanford Univ, 77-82. *Concurrent Pos:* Vis scientist, NTT Ibaraki Lab, 87; mem Prog Comt Appl Superconductivity Conf; fel, NSF, 78-80. *Mem:* Am Phys Soc; Mat Res Soc. *Res:* Materials for applied superconductivity; author of over 100 publications in thin film growth and characterization, surface and interface science, electronic device development, and fundamental physics of superconductors. *Mailing Add:* Northrop Grumman Corp 1350 Beulah Rd Pittsburgh PA 15235-5080. *Fax:* 412-256-1190

**TALWANI, MANIK,** GEOPHYSICS. *Current Pos:* SCHLUMBERGER PROF GEOPHYS, RICE UNIV, 85-; DIR, GEOTECHNOL RES INST, HOUSTON ADVAN RES CTR, 85- *Personal Data:* b India, Aug 22, 33; m 58, Anni Fittler; c Rajeev, Indira & Sanjay. *Educ:* Univ Delhi, BSc, 51, MSc, 53; Columbia Univ, PhD(geol), 59. *Hon Degrees:* PhD, Univ Oslo, Norway, 81. *Honors & Awards:* Indian Geophys Union First Krishnan Medal, 65; James B Macelwane Award, Am Geophys Union, 67; NASA Except Sci Achievement Award, 73; Maurice Ewing Award, Am Geophys Union, 81; George Woollard Award, Geol Soc Am, 83; Sackler Distinguished lectr, Univ Tel Aviv, Israel, 88; UNESCO Toklen Award, Nat Inst Oceanog, India, 90; Alfred Wegener Medal, Europ Union Geosci, 93. *Prof Exp:* Mem staff, Lamont-Doherty Geol Observ, Columbia Univ, 57-81, prof geol, Univ, 70-82, dir, Observ, 73-81; dir, Ctr Crustal Studies, Gulf Res & Develop Co, 81-83, chief scientist, 83-85. *Concurrent Pos:* Mem ocean affairs bd & exec comt, Joint Oceanog Inst Deep Earth Sampling; mem, Ocean Policy Comt, Nat Acad Sci & Bd Gov Joint Oceanog Inst, Inc; Fulbright-Hays Fel, 73; Guggenheim fel, 74. *Mem:* Soc Explor Geophys; fel Am Geophys Union; Am Asn Petrol Geologists; fel Geol Soc Am; fel Norweg Acad Arts & Sci; Sigma Xi; foreign mem Russ Acad Natural Sci. *Res:* Marine geophysics; oceanography, geodesy; marine geophysical research in all the oceans of the world; instrumentaion for improving marine gravity measurements. *Mailing Add:* 1111 Hermann Dr Apt 10D Houston TX 77004-6929. *Fax:* 281-363-7924; *E-Mail:* manik@gtri4.harc.edu

**TAM, ANDREW CHING,** ATOMIC PHYSICS, MOLECULAR PHYSICS. *Current Pos:* res staff mem, 79-84, MGR, IBM RES DIV, 85- *Personal Data:* b Canton, China, Oct 13, 44; m 70; c 2. *Educ:* Univ Hong Kong, BSc, 68, MSc, 70; Columbia Univ, PhD(physics), 75. *Prof Exp:* Fac fel physics, Columbia Radiation Lab, Columbia Univ, 70-72, preceptor, 71-72, res asst, 72-74, asst prof, 75-77; mem tech staff, Bell Labs, 78-79. *Mem:* Fel Optical Soc Am; sr mem Inst Elec & Electronics Engrs; fel Am Phys Soc; Acoust Soc Am; Int Soc Optical Eng. *Res:* Atomic and molecular spectroscopy; optical pumping; lasers material processing; laser interaction with matter & surfaces; photoacoustics; photothermal sensors. *Mailing Add:* Dept K63-803 IBM Almaden Res Ctr San Jose CA 95120-6099. *E-Mail:* actam@almaden.ibm.com

**TAM, CHICK F,** AGING, IMMUNOLOGY. *Current Pos:* PROF NUTRIT, CALIF STATE UNIV, LOS ANGELES. *Personal Data:* b Toishan, China, Jan 17, 46. *Educ:* Univ Calif, Los Angeles, PhD(pub health), 74. *Mem:* Am Inst Nutrit; Sigma Xi; NY Acad Sci; Inst Food Technol; Am Dietetics Asn; Am Home Econ Asn. *Res:* Aging; nutrition; hibernation. *Mailing Add:* Dept Health & Nutrit Sci Calif State Univ 5151 State Univ Dr Rm FA255 Los Angeles CA 90032

**TAM, CHRISTOPHER K W,** FLUIDS, NOISE. *Current Pos:* assoc prof, 71-76, PROF MATH, FLA STATE UNIV, 76- *Personal Data:* US citizen; m 69, Delia Fung; c Brian & Tobey. *Educ:* McGill Univ, BEng, 62; Calif Inst Technol, MSc, 63, PhD(appl mech), 66. *Honors & Awards:* Aero Acoust Award, Am Inst Aeronaut & Astronaut, 87. *Prof Exp:* Res fel, Calif Inst Technol, 66-67; asst prof, Mass Inst Technol, 67-71. *Mem:* Fel Acoust Soc Am; Soc Indust & Appl Math; assoc fel Am Inst Aeronaut & Astronaut; fel Am Phys Soc. *Res:* Physics of noise generation and propagation in aeroacoustics, including jet noise; turbulence and hydrodynamic stability theory; applied mathematics, computational mathematics and computational fluid dynamics. *Mailing Add:* Dept Math Fla State Univ Tallahassee FL 32306-3027. *Fax:* 850-644-4053; *E-Mail:* tam@math.fsu.edu

**TAM, JAMES PINGKWAN,** MEDICINAL CHEMISTRY, BIOCHEMISTRY. *Current Pos:* PROF, DEPT MICROBIOL & IMMUNOL, VANDERBILT UNIV, 92- *Personal Data:* b Hong Kong, Mar 25, 47; m 72; c 2. *Educ:* Univ Wis, BS, 71, PhD(pharm), 76. *Prof Exp:* Fel, Rockefeller Univ, 76-77, res assoc, 77-79, from asst prof to assoc prof biochem, 80-82. *Concurrent Pos:* Counr, Am Peptide Soc. *Mem:* Am Chem Soc; NY Acad Sci; AAAS; Am Peptide Soc; Am Soc Biochem & Molecular Biol. *Res:* New synthetic methods; solution and solid phase peptide syntheses; hormonal, immunological peptides and enzyme inhibitors; design of novel vaccines; biologic functions of tumor growth factors; protein engineering. *Mailing Add:* Dept Microbiol & Immunol Vanderbilt Univ A5119MCN Nashville TN 37232-2363

**TAM, KWOK KUEN,** APPLIED MATHEMATICS. *Current Pos:* Asst prof, 65-69, assoc prof, 70-79, PROF APPL MATH, MCGILL UNIV, 80- *Personal Data:* b Hong Kong, Oct 30, 38; m 64; c 2. *Educ:* Univ Toronto, BASc, 62, MA, 63, PhD(appl math), 65. *Concurrent Pos:* Res fel, Harvard Univ, 71-72. *Mem:* Can Math Cong. *Res:* Fluid mechanics; construction of approximate solutions to some nonlinear boundary value problems. *Mailing Add:* Dept Math & Statist McGill Univ 805 Burnside Hall Montreal PQ H3A 2K6 Can

**TAM, KWOK-WAI,** MATHEMATICAL ANALYSIS, OPERATIONS RESEARCH. *Current Pos:* asst prof, 66-75, ASSOC PROF MATH, PORTLAND STATE UNIV, 75- *Personal Data:* b Hong Kong, Mar 16, 38; US citizen; m 68; c 3. *Educ:* Univ Wash, BS, 60, PhD(math), 67. *Prof Exp:* Teaching asst math, Univ Wash, 61-66. *Mem:* Am Math Soc. *Res:* Mathematical programming. *Mailing Add:* Dept Math Portland State Univ Box 751 Portland OR 97207-0751

**TAM, PATRICK YUI-CHIU,** BIOMEDICAL ENGINEERING FOR THIRD WORLD, TECHNOLOGY TRANSFER. *Current Pos:* PRIN, DANUBE INT, 89- *Personal Data:* b Canton, China, June 7, 48; US citizen; m 76; c 3. *Educ:* Mass Inst Technol, BS, 71, MS, 72; Univ Calif, Berkeley, PhD(mech eng), 78. *Prof Exp:* NIH fel bioeng, Univ Wash, 78-79, affil asst prof, 84-87; prog dir, Prog Appropriate Technol Health, 79-84; pres, Wash Res Found, 84-87 & Chemfet Int, 87-88; exec vpres, US Tech, 88-89. *Concurrent Pos:* Consult, WHO, 80-82; expert witness, US Senate Comt Sci & Technol, 86. *Mem:* NY Acad Sci; Biophys Soc; AAAS. *Res:* Physical properties of biological materials; technology transfer policy issues. *Mailing Add:* 6150 NE 192nd Seattle WA 98155. *Fax:* 425-486-1308; *E-Mail:* tam@alum.mit.edu

**TAM, SANG WILLIAM,** ANTIPSYCHOTICS, COGNITIVE ENHANCERS. *Current Pos:* assoc dir, 91-92, ACTG DIR, DUPONT MERCK PHARMACEUT CO, 92- *Personal Data:* US citizen; m, Coretta Chan; c Brian & Karen. *Educ:* Univ Wis, Oshkosh, BS, 74; Univ Nebr, MS, 76; State Univ NY, PhD(biochem), 79. *Prof Exp:* Teaching asst biochem, Univ Nebr, Lincoln, 74-76; res asst, Downstate Med Ctr, State Univ NY, 76-79; fel, Sch Med, Yale Univ, 79-81; res pharmacologist, E I du Pont de Nemours & Co, Inc, 81-86, sr res pharmacologist, 86-88, group leader, 88-89, sr group leader, 90-91. *Concurrent Pos:* Vis prof, Shanghai Med Univ, Shanghai, China, 87-88; mem, Biochem Subcomt, Nat Inst Drug Abuse, 93- *Mem:* Am Soc Pharmacol & Exp Therapeut; Soc Neurosci; Mid-Atlantic Pharmacol Soc; Soc Chinese Bioscientists Am. *Res:* Discovery of novel therapeutic agents for the treatment of central nervous system diseases; antipsychic, analgesic and cognitive enhancer research: biochemical pharmacology, behavior and molecular biology; author of 159 scientific papers and abstracts; granted several patents. *Mailing Add:* Dir Pharmacol Nitro Med Res Lab 801 Albany St Boston MA 02118. *Fax:* 302-695-3730

**TAM, WING YIM,** CHAOS, FRACTAL. *Current Pos:* ASST PROF TEACHING & RES, UNIV ARIZ, TUCSON, 88- *Personal Data:* b Hong Kong, Dec 12, 53; m 87; c 1. *Educ:* Univ Calif, Santa Barbara, PhD(physics), 85. *Prof Exp:* Res fel res, Univ Tex, Austin, 85-88. *Concurrent Pos:* Fel, IBM, 85-86; Sloan fel, Alfred P Sloan Found, 90-92. *Mem:* Am Phys Soc. *Res:* Nonlinear dynamics; chaos; fractal formation. *Mailing Add:* Physics Univ Ariz 1600 E University Blvd Tucson AZ 85721-0001

**TAM, WING-GAY,** PHYSICS. *Current Pos:* INDUST ADV, NAT RES COUN CAN, 87- *Personal Data:* Can citizen. *Educ:* Hong Kong Univ, BSc, 60; Univ BC, MSc, 64, PhD(physics), 67. *Prof Exp:* Nat Res Coun overseas fel theoret physics, Univ Nijmegan, Neth, 67-69; res assoc molecular physics, Laval Univ, Can, 69-72, asst prof, 72-74; defense scientist optical physics, Defense Res Estab, Valcartier, Que, 74-87. *Mem:* Optical Soc Am. *Res:* Atmospheric propagation of electromagnetic waves; energy transfer in molecular systems; atmospheric aerosols. *Mailing Add:* Nat Res Coun Inst Microstruct Scis Bldg M50 Montreal Rd Ottawa ON K1A 0R6 Can

**TAMANO, TERUO,** NUCLEAR FUSION, PLASMA PHYSICS. *Current Pos:* SCIENTIST, PLASMA RES CTR, UNIV TSUKUBA, JAPAN, 91- *Personal Data:* b Tokyo, Japan, Feb 13, 37; m 64; c 2. *Educ:* Univ Tokyo, BS, 61, MS, 63, PhD(physics), 66. *Prof Exp:* Res assoc physics, Univ Tokyo, 66-72; fel plasma physics, Plasma Physics Lab, Princeton Univ, 69-70; assoc scientist plasma physics, Gen Atomic Co, Gulf Oil Corp, 70, sr scientist, 70-74, dept mgr, 74-78, prog mgr plasma physics, 78-91. *Mem:* Fel Am Phys Soc; Phys Soc Japan. *Res:* Development of confinement concepts in nuclear fusion; plasma physics and manage experimental programs; investigation of the toroidal pinch concept, called OHTE. *Mailing Add:* 8908 Montrose Way San Diego CA 92122

**TAMAOKI, TAIKI,** BIOCHEMISTRY, PLANT PATHOLOGY. *Current Pos:* STAFF ONCOL RES GROUP, FAC MED, UNIV CALGARY. *Personal Data:* b Miki, Hyogo-Ken, Japan, Dec 3, 28; m 61; c 4. *Educ:* Univ Tokyo, BSc, 51; Purdue Univ, MS, 58; Univ Wis, PhD(plant path), 60. *Prof Exp:* Fel oncol, McArdle Lab, Univ Wis, 61-64; asst prof biochem, Cancer Res Unit, Univ Alta, 68-80; at Southern Alta Cancer Ctr, 80- *Mem:* AAAS; Am Chem Soc; Am Soc Biol Chem; Am Asn Cancer Res; Can Biochem Soc. *Res:* Regulation of protein and RNA synthesis in mammalian cells. *Mailing Add:* Dept Med Biochem Univ Calgary Fac Med 3330 Hosp Dr NW Calgary AB T2N 4N1 Can. *Fax:* 403-283-4740

**TAMAR, HENRY,** PROTOZOOLOGY, PHYSIOLOGY. *Current Pos:* assoc prof, 62-77, PROF ZOOL, IND STATE UNIV, TERRE HAUTE, 77- *Personal Data:* b Vienna, Austria, Sept 15, 29; nat US; m 55, Margaret Schweizer; c Earl, Allen & Mark. *Educ:* NY Univ, AB, 49, MS, 51; Fla State Univ, PhD(physiol), 57. *Prof Exp:* Researcher, Lebanon Hosp, NY, 51; asst physiol, Fla State Univ, 51-55; asst prof biol, Am Int Col, 55-57; prof & head div, Pembroke State Col, 57-62. *Concurrent Pos:* Vis prof, Stephen F Austin State Col, 59, NC State Col, 61-62, Marine Biol Labs, Woods Hole, 65, 72 & 74 & Marine Sci Ctr, Santa Catalina Island, 81. *Mem:* Am Micro Soc; Soc Protozool. *Res:* Principles of sensory physiology; locomotion, responses and structure of ciliates; jumping ciliates and their avoidance reactions. *Mailing Add:* Dept Life Sci Ind State Univ Terre Haute IN 47809. *Fax:* 812-237-4480; *E-Mail:* lstamar@scifac.indstate.edu

**TAMARELLI, ALAN WAYNE,** BATCH SYNTHESIS OF POLYMERS, CATALYTIC POLLUTION CONTROL. *Current Pos:* CHMN, DOCK RESINS CORP, 89- *Personal Data:* b Wilkinsburg, Pa, Aug 13, 41; m 63; c 2. *Educ:* Carnegie-Mellon Univ, BS, 63, MS, 65, PhD(chem eng), 66; NY Univ, MBA, 72. *Prof Exp:* Asst prof chem eng, Carnegie-Mellon Univ, 65-66; res engr, Exxon Corp, 66-70; sr vpres, Engelhard Corp, 70-83. *Concurrent Pos:* Pres, Linden Indust Asn, 90-; chmn, Chem Indust Coun NJ, 90-; chmn, Synthetic Org Chem Mfrs Asn, 91- *Mem:* Am Chem Soc; Am Inst Chem Engrs; Am Soc Safety Engrs; Fedn Socs Coatings Technol. *Res:* Chemical kinetics; catalysis; reactor engineering; polymerization; organic coatings applications. *Mailing Add:* 49 Wexford Way Basking Ridge NJ 07920. *Fax:* 908-862-4015

**TAMARI, DOV,** MATHEMATICS, DEVELOPMENTAL BIOLOGY & EMBRYOLOGY. *Current Pos:* prof, 63-81, chmn dept, 64-67, EMER PROF MATH, STATE UNIV NY, BUFFALO, 81- *Personal Data:* b Fulda, Ger, Apr 29, 11; m 48, Sara Slutzkai; c Doram, Tul & Yuval. *Educ:* Hebrew Univ, Israel, MSc, 39; Univ Paris, Dr Sc(math), 51. *Prof Exp:* Res fel math, Nat Ctr Sci Res, Paris, France, 49-53; sr lectr, Israel Inst Technol, 53-55, assoc prof, 55-59; prof, Univ Rochester, 59-60; mem, Inst Advan Study, 60-61; Orgn Am States vis prof, Univ Brazil, 61-62; res assoc, Univ Utrecht, 62; prof, Univ Caen, 62-63. *Concurrent Pos:* Vis prof, Hebrew Univ, Israel, 53-59, Israel Inst Technol, 75, State Univ Calif, Chico, 84 & Los Angeles, 86-87; mem, Inst Advan Study, 67-68. *Mem:* Am Math Soc; Math Asn Am; Asn Symbolic Logic. *Res:* Algebra; semi-group, group and ring theory; embedding and word problems; topological semi-groups, groups and fields; mathematical logic; binary relations; partial algebras; combinatorial analysis; associativity theory and the four-color-map problem; theory of lists and standard polyhedra with Whitney cycles and sets of lists applied to asynchronous embryonic cellgrowth by binary cell division. *Mailing Add:* 175 W 76th St Apt 1E New York NY 10023. *Fax:* 212-769-2558

**TAMARIN, ARNOLD,** ORAL BIOLOGY, HISTOLOGY. *Current Pos:* RETIRED. *Personal Data:* b Chicago, Ill, Mar 27, 23; m 45; c 2. *Educ:* Univ Ill, BS, 49, DDS, 51; Univ Wash, MSD, 60. *Prof Exp:* Assoc prof, Univ Wash, 66-69, prof oral biol, 69-89, adj prof, Dept Biol Struct, 74-89, emer prof, 89. *Concurrent Pos:* Hon res fel, Dept Anat & Embryol, Univ Col London, 82-; vis res prof, Middlesex Hosp Med Sch, 82-83. *Mem:* Fel Royal Micros Soc; Am Asn Anatomists; fel Zool Soc London; Am Soc Cell Biol; Pan-Am Anat Asn. *Res:* Comparative odontology; cell kinematics in the exocrine secretory process; exocrine collagen secretion in mytilus; ultrastructural morphology; embryological morphogenesis. *Mailing Add:* 10339 Lakeshore Blvd NE Seattle WA 98125

**TAMARIN, ROBERT HARVEY,** GENETICS, ECOLOGY. *Current Pos:* from asst prof to assoc prof, 71-83, PROF BIOL, BOSTON UNIV, 83-, DEPT CHMN, 90- *Personal Data:* b Brooklyn, NY, Dec 14, 42; m 68, Virginia M Londy; c David & Bonnie. *Educ:* Brooklyn Col, BS, 63; Ind Univ, PhD(zool), 68. *Prof Exp:* Comt Instnl Coop traveling scholar, Univ Wis, 67-68; USPHS fel genetics, Univ Hawaii, 68-70; Ford Found fel, Princeton Univ, 70-71. *Concurrent Pos:* NIH & NSF res grants; Howard Hughes Med Inst Educ grant. *Mem:* AAAS; Sigma Xi; Am Soc Mammal; Ecol Soc Am; Genetics Soc Am. *Res:* Population biology, including genetics, demography, reproductive physiology, behavior and general ecology of insular and mainland field mice to understand population regulation; tropical and radiation studies of field mice. *Mailing Add:* Dean Sci Univ Mass Lowell 1 University Ave Lowell MA 01854. *Fax:* 617-353-6340; *E-Mail:* tamarin@biology.by.edu

**TAMARO, GEORGE JOHN,** CIVIL ENGINEERING. *Current Pos:* PARTNER, MUESER RUTLEDGE CONSULT ENGRS, 80- *Personal Data:* b Weehawken, NJ, Mar 16, 37; m 61, Rosemary Ann Volta; c Peter Louis, Jean Marie, Paul Anthony & Mark Joseph. *Educ:* Manhattan Col, BCE, 59; Lehigh Univ, MCE, 61; Columbia Univ, MA, 69. *Honors & Awards:* Martin S Kapp Found Engr Award, Am Soc Civil Engrs, 87. *Prof Exp:* Staff engr, Port Authority NY & NJ, 61-71; vpres & chief engr, ICOS Corp Am, 71-80. *Concurrent Pos:* Adj asst prof, Manhattan Col. *Mem:* Nat Acad Eng;

fel UK Inst Civil Engrs; fel UK Inst Struct Engrs; fel Am Soc Civil Engrs; Int Soc Soil Mech & Found Engrs; Am Inst Steel Construct. *Res:* Slurry wall and tieback technology; conventional foundation and marine construction, sheeting, bracing and underpinning; granted patents in field and author of numerous articles. *Mailing Add:* Mueser Rutledge Consult Engrs 708 Third Ave 5th Floor New York NY 10017

**TAMASHIRO, MINORU,** INSECT PATHOLOGY. *Current Pos:* Asst entom, Univ Hawaii, 51-54, jr entomologist, 54-55, from asst prof entom & asst entomologist to prof entom & entomologist, 57-, EMER PROF ENTOM & ENTOMOLOGIST, UNIV HAWAII. *Personal Data:* b Hilo, Hawaii, Sept 16, 24; m 52. *Educ:* Univ Hawaii, BS, 51, MS, 54; Univ Calif, PhD, 60. *Concurrent Pos:* WHO consult, 63; NIH fel, 64-65. *Mem:* Entom Soc Am; Sigma Xi. *Res:* Microbial control; effect of pathogens and insecticides on biological control; termites, biology, ecology, control. *Mailing Add:* Dept Entom GIL 601 Univ Hawaii at Manoa 3050 Maile Way Honolulu HI 96822

**TAMBASCO, DANIEL JOSEPH,** THEORETICAL PHYSICS. *Current Pos:* Asst prof, 65-69, ASSOC PROF PHYSICS, MERRIMACK COL, 69- *Personal Data:* b Amsterdam, NY, Mar 10, 36; m 66, Geraldine Douvrain; c Myriam & Daniel. *Educ:* Union Col, BS, 58; Univ Iowa, PhD(physics), 65. *Mem:* Am Phys Soc. *Res:* Field theory theory; statistical mechanics. *Mailing Add:* Dept Physics Merrimack Col North Andover MA 01845

**TAMBORLANE, WILLIAM VALENTINE,** PEDIATRICS, DIABETOLOGY. *Current Pos:* fel pediat endocrinol, Yale Univ, 75-76, endocrinol & metab, 76-77, from asst prof to assoc prof, 77-86, PROF PEDIAT, YALE UNIV SCH MED, 86- *Personal Data:* b New York, NY, Aug 25, 46; m 69, Kathleen Blinn; c Melissa, Amy & James. *Educ:* Georgetown Univ, BS, 68, MD, 72. *Honors & Awards:* Mary Jane Kugel Award, Juv Diabetes Found Int, 85; Peter May Award, Am Diabetes Assoc, 85. *Prof Exp:* Resident pediat, Georgetown Univ. *Concurrent Pos:* Attend physician, Yale-New Haven Hosp, 77-; sect chief, Yale Univ Sch Med, 85; dir, Yale Childrens clin Res Ctr, 86-; assoc dir, Yale Diabetes Endocrinol Res Ctr, 92- *Mem:* Soc Pediat Res; Am Fedn Clin Res; Am Bd Pediat; Lawson Wilkens Pediat Endocrine Soc; Am Acad Pediat; Endocrine Soc; Am Soc Clin Invest. *Res:* Disorders of metabolism with special emphasis on diabetes mellitus in children; effect of treatment on diabetes control and diabetic complications currently under investigation. *Mailing Add:* Childrens Clin Res Ctr Yale Univ 333 Cedar St New Haven CT 06510. *Fax:* 203-785-7194

**TAMBORSKI, CHRIST,** ORGANIC CHEMISTRY, FLUORINE CHEMISTRY. *Current Pos:* CONSULT, 92- *Personal Data:* b Buffalo, NY, Nov 12, 26; m 92, Carolyn Olson; c 7. *Educ:* Univ Buffalo, BA, 49, PhD(org chem), 53. *Honors & Awards:* Jacobowitz Award, 52; US Dept Com Inventors Award; Outstanding Engrs & Scientist Award, 83. *Prof Exp:* Fel, Univ Buffalo, 53; sr scientist, Air Force Mat Lab, Wright-Patterson AFB, 55-86; pres, Fluidics Inc, 86-92. *Concurrent Pos:* Chmn, Fluorine Div, Am Chem Soc, 72; consult, Childrens Hosp Res Found, 74-, Sun Oil Co, 80- *Mem:* Am Chem Soc; Sigma Xi. *Res:* High temperature stable fluids and elastomers for advanced aerospace applications; synthesis of organometallic compounds, heterocyclic compounds, organoaliphatic and aromatic fluorine compounds, anti-oxidants; blood substitute compounds. *Mailing Add:* 2725 River Bluff Dr Spring Valley OH 45370

**TAMBURIN, HENRY JOHN,** INDUSTRIAL ORGANIC CHEMISTRY. *Current Pos:* group leader, CIBA-GEIGY Corp, 81-85, develop leader, 86-90, focus mgr, 91-93, plant support analysis QA team leader, 93-94, site dir, 95-96, TEAM LEADER, SAFETY ENVIRON AFFAIRS, CIBA-GEIGY CORP, 96- *Personal Data:* b Passaic, NJ, July 24, 44; m 68; c Jeffrey & Kevin. *Educ:* Seton Hall Univ, BS, 66; Univ Md, College Park, PhD(org chem), 71. *Prof Exp:* From teaching asst to instr org chem, Univ Md, College Park, 66-72; res & develop chemist, Toms River Chem Corp, 72-75, sr develop chemist, 75-77, actg group leader, 78-79, sr prod chemist, 79-81. *Mem:* Am Chem Soc. *Res:* Modern chemical and processing technology in the dyestuff manufacturing process. *Mailing Add:* 5807 Fleming Terr Rd Greensboro NC 27410. *E-Mail:* htamburin@aol.com

**TAMBURINO, LOUIS A,** OPTO-ELECTRONICS. *Current Pos:* MATH PHYSICIST, AVIONICS DIRECTORATE, WRIGHT LAB, USAF, 72-, WRIGHT LAB FEL, 91- *Personal Data:* b Pittsburgh, Pa, May 9, 36; m 58, Linda S Quinlivan; c Linda. *Educ:* Carnegie Inst Technol, BS, 57; Univ Pittsburgh, PhD(physics), 62. *Honors & Awards:* Outstanding Engr & Scientist Award, Affil Socs Coun, Eng & Sci Found, Dayton, Ohio, 91. *Prof Exp:* Res assoc, Syracuse Univ, 63-64; res physicist, Aerospace Res Labs, Wright-Patterson AFB, 64-72. *Concurrent Pos:* Adj assoc prof, Wright State Univ, Fairborn, Ohio, 88- *Mem:* Inst Elec & Electronics Engrs; Sigma Xi; Soc Photo Optical Instrumentation Engrs. *Res:* General relativity; airborne electronic terrain map and display systems; inertial navigation; pattern recognition; optics; image processing; neural networks and learning systems. *Mailing Add:* 2930 E Stroop Rd Kettering OH 45440

**TAMBURRO, CARLO HORACE,** INTERNAL MEDICINE, HEPATOLOGY. *Current Pos:* assoc prof med, Sch Med, Univ Louisville, 74-77, assoc oncol, Cancer Ctr, chief, Div Digestive Dis & Nutrit, & dir, Vinyl Chloride Proj, 74-80, prof commun health, 81-89, PROF MED, UNIV LOUISVILLE, 74-, PROF PHARMACOL & TOXICOL, 90- *Personal Data:* b Caserta, Italy, Jan 20, 36; US citizen; m 71; c 4. *Educ:* Georgetown Univ, BS, 58; Seton Hall Univ, MD, 62; Columbia Univ, MPH, 85. *Prof Exp:* Intern med, Jersey City Med Ctr, NJ, 62-63, resident, 63-64; asst, Sch Med, Tufts Univ, 64-65; instr med, NJ Med Sch, 67-68; asst prof, Col Med & Dent NJ,

Newark, 69-74; assoc prof, NJ Med Sch, 74. *Concurrent Pos:* Resident med, New Eng Ctr Hosp, Boston, 64-65; NIH fel hepatic dis, 65-68; assoc pediat, Sch Med, Univ Louisville, 77-, dir, Liver Res Ctr, 80-, chief, Div Occup Toxicol, 81-, assoc pharmacol & toxicol, 82-84. *Mem:* Int Asn Study Liver; Am Asn Study Liver Dis; Am Soc Human Genetics; Am Col Toxicol; Am Fedn Clin Res; Soc Toxicol; fel Am Col Physicians; fel Am Col Nutrit; Int Soc Environ Epidemiol; Am Col Epidemiol; AAAS; Am Col Occup Med; Am Pub Health Asn; Am Soc Parenteral & Enteral Nutrit. *Res:* Hepatic cancer; industrial chemical carcinogenesis, vinyl monomer; clinical toxicology; alcoholism, drug addiction, and withdrawal syndromes; viral hepatitis; liver disease and nutrition; vitamin metabolism and deficiency; liver regeneration and metabolism; hepatic collagen formation; immunology and liver injury. *Mailing Add:* Univ Louisville Sch Med 2301 S Third St Louisville KY 40292-0001

**TAMBURRO, KATHLEEN O'CONNELL,** PROTOZOOLOGY. *Current Pos:* admin assoc & grant coordr-med/ed, Div Digestive Dis & Nutrit, 76-80, sr med ed & admin assoc, Div Occup Dis, 80-95, RES FACILITATOR, SCH MED UNIV LOUISVILLE, 95- *Personal Data:* b New York, NY, Oct 30, 42; m 71; c 4. *Educ:* Marymount Manhattan Col, BA, 64; Fordham Univ, MS, 65, PhD(biol, protozool), 68. *Prof Exp:* From res asst to res assoc biochem & physiol protozoa, Haskins Labs, 65-74. *Mem:* AAAS; Sigma Xi; Soc Protozool; Am Soc Trop Med & Hyg; Am Soc Microbiologists. *Res:* Protozoa as pharmacological tools; chemotherapy of trypanosomatid parasites; nutrition; biochemistry and physiology of Trypanosomatidae. *Mailing Add:* 512 Brandon Rd Louisville KY 40207

**TAMERIUS, JOHN,** MICROBIOLOGY, IMMUNOLOGY. *Current Pos:* VPRES REGULATORY AFFAIRS QUAL ASSURANCE, QUIDEL CORP, 89- *Personal Data:* b Bremertown, Wash, June 27, 45. *Educ:* Univ Wash, PhD(microbiol & immunol), 76. *Prof Exp:* Vpres & dir res & develop, Cytotech, Inc, San Diego, 82-89. *Mailing Add:* Regulatory Affairs & Qual Assurance Quidel Corp 10165 McKellar Ct San Diego CA 92121-4299. *Fax:* 619-546-8955

**TAMHANE, AJIT C,** APPLIED STATISTICS, MATHEMATICAL STATISTICS. *Current Pos:* from asst prof to assoc prof, 75-87, PROF INDUST ENG & MGT SCI & STATIST, 87- *Personal Data:* b Bhiwandi, India, Nov 12, 46; m 75; c 2. *Educ:* Indian Inst Technol, Bombay, BTech(Hon), 68; Cornell Univ, MS, 73, PhD(statist), 75. *Honors & Awards:* W J Youdan Prize, 85. *Prof Exp:* Jr engr design, Larsen & Toubro Ltd, Bombay, 68-70. *Concurrent Pos:* Statist consult. *Mem:* Inst Math Statist; fel Am Statist Asn; Biomet Soc; Am Soc Qual Control. *Res:* Multiple comparisons; ranking and selection procedures; design of experiments; biostatistics; engineering statistics. *Mailing Add:* Dept Indust Eng McCormick Sch Eng & Appl Sci Northwestern Univ Evanston IL 60208-3119. *Fax:* 847-491-8005; *E-Mail:* ajit@iems.hwu.edu

**TAMIMI, YUSUF NIMR,** SOIL CHEMISTRY. *Current Pos:* Asst agronomist, Univ, 63-70, assoc soil scientist, 70-75, PROF SOIL SCI, AGR EXP STA, UNIV HAWAII, 75- *Personal Data:* b Nablus, Jordan, Nov 15, 31; m 63; c 3. *Educ:* Purdue Univ, BS, 57; NMex State Univ, MS, 60; Univ Hawaii, PhD(soil chem), 64. *Concurrent Pos:* Vis prof, Univ Hawaii, 70-71; prof & dept head, Dept Soil Sci & Irrig, Univ Jordan; sr soil scientist, Wash State Univ, Jordan, 85-87; consult, Wash State Univ, 88-90; state soil fertil ext specialist, Univ Hawaii, 90-96. *Mem:* Am Soc Agron; Int Soc Soil Sci; Am Soil Sci Soc; Sigma Xi; Am Soc Hort. *Res:* Chemistry of soil phosphorous; field crops, tropical pasture fertilization and forest tree nutrition; forest soils; nutrient management; calcium mobility in soils. *Mailing Add:* Agr Exp Sta Univ Hawaii 461 W Lanikaula St Hilo HI 96720. *Fax:* 808-959-3101; *E-Mail:* yusuf@hawaii.edu

**TAMIR, HADASSAH,** NEUROSCIENCE, BIOCHEMISTRY. *Current Pos:* SR RES SCIENTIST, DIV NEUROSCI, PSYCHIAT INST STATE NY, 71- *Personal Data:* b Haifa, Israel, Oct 5, 30; US citizen; m 49; c 2. *Educ:* Hebrew Univ, Jerusalem, MSc, 55; Israel Inst Technol, DSc(chem), 59. *Prof Exp:* Mem res staff, Princeton Univ, 65-67; res assoc, Med Sch, Columbia Univ, 67-71. *Concurrent Pos:* Res fel biochem, Pub Health Res Inst, City of New York, 59-63; res fel biochem & bact, Med Sch, NY Univ, 63-65. *Res:* Effects of drugs on release and uptake of biogenic amines in nerve endings and cell-free systems; storage and release of Serotinon in neurons and paraneurons (parafollicular cells of the thyroid); comparison with storage of the amines with non-neuronal cells such as platelets, mast cells and the enterochromaffin cells of the gut mucosa. *Mailing Add:* Div Neurosci Psychiat Inst State NY 722 W 168th St New York NY 10032-2603. *Fax:* 212-740-5329

**TAMIR, THEODOR,** ELECTROPHYSICS, OPTICS. *Current Pos:* res assoc, Polytech Univ, 58-62, from asst prof to assoc prof, 62-69, prof electrophys, 69-92, UNIV PROF, POLYTECH UNIV, 92- *Personal Data:* b Bucharest, Roumania, Sept 17, 27; m 49, Hadassah Cohen; c Jonathan & Yael J. *Educ:* Israel Inst Technol, BS, 53, Dipl Ing, 54, MS, 58; Polytech Inst Brooklyn, PhD(electrophys), 62. *Honors & Awards:* Inst Prem, Inst Elec Engrs, UK, 65; Spec Recognition, Antennas & Propagation Soc, Inst Elec & Electronics Engrs, 68; Citation Distinguished Res, Polytech Chap, Sigma Xi, 78. *Prof Exp:* Res engr, Sci Dept, Ministry Defense, Israel, 53-56; instr elec eng, Israel Inst Technol, 56-58. *Concurrent Pos:* Consult indust & govt labs; co-ed, Springer Ser in Optical Sci, 79-; adv ed, Optics Commun, 75-84; head, Dept Elec Eng, Polytech Inst NY, 74-79; NSF res grants. *Mem:* Fel Inst Elec & Electronics Engrs; Int Union Radio Sci; fel Optical Soc Am. *Res:* Electromagnetic wave propagation in non-uniform media and periodic structures; radiation and diffraction phenomena; properties of configurations supporting surface, leaky, lateral and other wave types; elastic and optical waves; integrated optics. *Mailing Add:* Dept Elec Eng Polytech Univ 100 Tech Pl Brooklyn NY 11201

**TAMLYN, DEBORAH LYNN,** PALLIATIVE CARE, HEALTH CARE LEADERSHIP. *Current Pos:* Asst dean, Fac Health Professions, Dalhousie Univ, 83-87, dir nursing, 86-93, assoc prof health admin, 95-97, ASSOC PROF NURSING, DALHOUSIE UNIV, 79- *Personal Data:* b Annapolis Royal, NS, Mar, 11, 53; c 3. *Educ:* McGill Univ, BN, 74; Ottawa Univ Med, 79; Dalhousie Univ, PhD(educ), 87. *Honors & Awards:* Can 125 Medal, 93. *Concurrent Pos:* Nursing consult, Queen Elizabeth II Health Sci Ctr, 95- *Mem:* Can Asn Univ Schs Nursing (pres, 91-93); Can Nurses Asn. *Res:* Education for health professionals; conducted research and published numerous articles in palliative care education and substance abuse; student empowerment and attitude change. *Mailing Add:* 0-158 Nursing Dalhousie Univ Halifax NS B3H 3J5 Can. *Fax:* 902-494-3487; *E-Mail:* deborah. tamlyn@dal.ca

**TAMM, IGOR,** virology, medicine; deceased, see previous edition for last biography

**TAMMEN, JAMES F,** PLANT PATHOLOGY. *Current Pos:* from asst prof to prof, Dept Plant Path, 56-65, dept head, 65-76, RES SCIENTIST ADVAN HORT SYSTS, PA STATE UNIV, UNIVERSITY PARK, 89-, ADJ PROF, 89- *Personal Data:* b Sacramento, Calif, Feb 27, 25; m, Marilyn L McDonald; c 2. *Educ:* Univ Calif, Berkeley, BS, 49, PhD, 54. *Concurrent Pos:* Jr plant pathologist, Calif Bur Plant Path, Riverside, Calif; plant pathologist, State Plant Bd Fla, Gainesville, chief, Plant Path Lab; dean, Col Agr, Minneapolis, 76-81; pres, Oglevee Assocs, Inc, 81-86; dir & res scientist, Tech Transfer Off, Inst Food & Agr Sci, Univ Fla, 86-89; consult plant path. *Mem:* Fel Am Phytopath Soc (pres, 72-75). *Res:* Plant pathology; agriculture; horticulture. *Mailing Add:* Dept Plant Path 207 Buckout Lab University Park PA 16802

**TAMMINGA, CAROL ANN,** SCHIZOPHRENIA, PSYCHOPHARMACOLOGY. *Current Pos:* assoc prof, 79-85, PROF PSYCHIAT, SCH MED, UNIV MD, 85-; CHIEF SCHIZOPHRENIA, INPATIENT RES PROG, 79-; DEP DIR, MD PSYCHIAT RES CTR, 94- *Personal Data:* b Grand Rapids, Mich, Jan 26, 46; c 2. *Educ:* Calvin Col, BS, 66; Vanderbilt Univ Sch Med, MD, 71. *Honors & Awards:* Sandoz Award Psychiat Res, Univ Chicago, 75; McAlpin Award, Nat Asn Ment Health, 79. *Prof Exp:* Chief res psychiat, Univ Chicago, 75-79, instr psychiat, 75-78, asst prof, 78-79; res fel schizophrenia, NIMH, 78-79; chief clin biochem, Exp Therapeut Br, Nat Inst Neurol & Commun Dis & Stroke, 79-85. *Concurrent Pos:* Villian Allen fel, Med Sch, Vanderbilt Univ, 68; mem, TDA rev comt, NIMH, 81-85; consult, Psychopharmacol Adv Comt, Food & Drug Admin, 82-85, Orphan Prod Develop, 83- & Dept Psychiat, Va Med Ctr, Baltimore, 85-; chair, Psychopharmacol Adv Comt, Food & Drug Admin, 91-95. *Mem:* Am Psychiat Asn; Am Col Neuropsychopharmacol; AAAS; Soc Neurosci. *Res:* Pathophysiology and new treatments for schizophrenia and hyperkinetic motor disorders. *Mailing Add:* Dept Psychiat Univ Md MPRC Box 21247 Baltimore MD 21228

**TAMOR, STEPHEN,** THEORETICAL PHYSICS. *Current Pos:* RETIRED. *Personal Data:* b New York, NY, Nov 29, 25; m 49; c 4. *Educ:* City Col NY, BS, 44; Univ Rochester, PhD, 50. *Prof Exp:* Physicist, Oak Ridge Nat Lab, 50-52; physicist, Radiation Lab, Univ Calif, 52-55; physicist, Res Lab, Gen Elec Co, NY, 55-66, Space Sci Lab, Pa, 66-71; physicist, Sci Appln Inc, 71-86; consult, 87-90. *Concurrent Pos:* Guggenheim fel, 63-64. *Mem:* Am Phys Soc; AAAS. *Res:* Meson theory; nuclear and plasma physics; reactor theory. *Mailing Add:* 1685 Caminito Asterisco La Jolla CA 92037

**TAMORRIA, CHRISTOPHER RICHARD,** CHEMISTRY. *Current Pos:* assoc dir, 84-87, SR ASSOC DIR, DRUG REGULATORY AFFAIRS, BOEHRINGER INGELHEIM PHARMACEUT, 87- *Personal Data:* b Washington, DC, June 20, 32; m 61, Eugenie Marshall; c John F. *Educ:* Georgetown Univ, BS, 54, MS, 58; Univ Md, PhD(med chem), 61. *Honors & Awards:* Gold Medal, Am Inst Chemists, 54. *Prof Exp:* Asst org chem, Georgetown Univ, 54-55; chemist, Food & Drug Admin, 55-56; asst org chem, Georgetown Univ, 56-57; asst inorg chem, Univ Md, 57-58; org chemist, Pharmaceut Prod Develop Sect, Lederle Labs, Am Cyanamid Co, 60-68, mgr regulatory agencies & info processing, Med Res Div, Cyanamid Int, 68-70; sr tech assoc, US Pharmacopeia, Md, 70-73; dir sci commun, Purdue Frederick Co & Affil, 73-77; mgr tech info, Toxicol Sect, Lederle Labs, 77; sr regulatory assoc, Drug Regulatory Affairs, Ayerst Labs, 78-80; dep dir, Drug Regulatory Affairs, Sterling Drug Inc, 80-84. *Mem:* Am Chem Soc; Am Pharmaceut Asn; fel Am Found Pharmaceut Educ; Am Inst Chemists; Regulatory Affairs Prof Soc; Drug Info Asn. *Res:* Partial synthesis of steroids; correlation of structure and biological activity, especially in the synthesis of new steroid homologs and tetracycline antibiotics. *Mailing Add:* 27 Maymont Lane Trumbull CT 06611

**TAMPAS, JOHN PETER,** RADIOLOGY. *Current Pos:* from asst prof to assoc prof, 62-69, PROF RADIOL & CHMN DEPT, UNIV VT, 70- *Personal Data:* b Burlington, Vt, May 18, 29; m 62; c 4. *Educ:* Univ Vt, BS, 51, MD, 54. *Prof Exp:* Teaching fel pediat radiol, Children's Hosp of Los Angeles, Univ Southern Calif, 60-61; NIH res fel cardiovasc radiol, Nat Heart Inst, 61-62. *Concurrent Pos:* James Picker Found scholar radiol res, Univ Vt, 62-65; from asst attend radiologist to attend radiologist, Mary Fletcher Hosp & DeGoesbriand Mem Hosp, 62-; physician-in-residence, Vet Admin Hosp, 72- *Mem:* AMA; fel Am Col Radiol; Soc Pediat Radiol; Am Roentgen Ray Soc; Radiol Soc NAm. *Res:* Basic and clinical problems in radiology; pediatric and cardiovascular radiology. *Mailing Add:* Dept Radiol Mary Fletcher Unit Med Ctr Hosp Vt Burlington VT 05401

**TAMPICO, JOSEPH,** ELECTRICAL ENGINEERING. *Current Pos:* mgr bus planning, Spacecraft Dept, Gen Elec Co, 65-72, mgr oper planning, Locomotive Dept, 72-76, strategic planning analyst, Locomotive Opers, 77-81, MGR MKT ANALYSIS, LOCOMOTIVE MKT, MKT DIV, GEN ELEC CO, 81- *Personal Data:* b Baltimore, Md, Apr 28, 16; div; c 3. *Educ:* Johns Hopkins Univ, BE, 37, Dr Eng, 41. *Prof Exp:* Mem staff, Lab Appl Physics, Johns Hopkins Univ, 45-54 & Hycon Mfg Co, 54-55; vpres, Assoc Missile Prod Corp, Am Mach & Foundry Co, 55-58; mgr independent res & develop, Marquardt Corp, 59-65. *Mem:* Assoc fel Am Inst Aeronaut & Astronaut; sr mem Inst Elec & Electronics Engrs. *Res:* Properties of dielectrics; resistance welding; jet propulsion engines; interfacial contact resistance; electronic test equipment; research administration; aerospace business planning. *Mailing Add:* 10850 Green Mountain Circle Apt 315 Columbia MD 21044

**TAMPLIN, MARK LEWIS,** ENVIRONMENTAL MICROBIOLOGY, MEDICAL MICROBIOLOGY. *Current Pos:* ASSOC PROF FOOD SAFETY, UNIV FLA, 90- *Personal Data:* b Rantoul, Ill, Feb 4, 55; m 79; c 2. *Educ:* Univ SFla, Tampa, BA, 78, MA, 81, PhD(med sci), 85. *Prof Exp:* Res assoc, Ctr Marine Biotechnol, Univ Md, 85-87, asst res scientist, 87; res microbiologist, Fishery Res Br, Food & Drug Admin, Dauphin Island, Ala, 87-90. *Concurrent Pos:* Consult, Jamaican Oyster Cult Prog, 82, Int Ctr Diarrheal Dis Res, 87 & Peruvian Govt Ministry Health, 91; comt chmn, Environ Panel, Food & Drug Admin Vibrio Vulnificus Workshop, 8; mem, Microbiol Comt, Interstate Shellfish Sanit Conf, 88-89, Depuration Comt, 88 & Vibrio Vulnificus Work Group, 89. *Mem:* Am Soc Microbiol; Nat Shellfisheries Asn. *Res:* Environmental influence on pathogenicity and epidemiology of water borne infections. *Mailing Add:* 425 NW 91st St Gainesville FL 32607

**TAMRES, MILTON,** PHYSICAL INORGANIC CHEMISTRY. *Current Pos:* from asst prof to assoc prof, 53-63, prof, 63-87, EMER PROF CHEM, UNIV MICH, ANN ARBOR, 87- *Personal Data:* b Warsaw, Poland, Mar 12, 22; US citizen; m 60; c 2. *Educ:* Brooklyn Col, BA, 43; Northwestern Univ, PhD(phys chem), 49. *Prof Exp:* Analytical chemist, Celanese Corp Am, Md, 43-44; asst, Northwestern Univ, 44-47; from instr to asst prof chem, Univ Ill, 48-53. *Concurrent Pos:* Guggenheim fel, 59-60; mem, Adv Coun Col Chem, 62-66; Am Chem Soc-Petrol Res Fund int fel, 66-67; vis scholar, Univ Tokyo, 74. *Mem:* Fel AAAS; Am Chem Soc; fel Am Inst Chemists. *Res:* Electron donor-acceptor interactions; basicities of cyclic compounds. *Mailing Add:* Univ Mich 3533 Chem Bldg Ann Arbor MI 48109-0105

**TAMSITT, JAMES RAY,** ZOOLOGY, MAMMALIAN SYSTEMATICS. *Current Pos:* INSTR BIOL, AUSTIN COMMUNITY COL, 88- *Personal Data:* b Big Spring, Tex, Nov 22, 28. *Educ:* Univ Tex, BA, 51, MA, 53, PhD(vert ecol), 58. *Prof Exp:* Lectr zool, Univ Man, 57-58; instr biol, ETex State Univ, 58-59; prof zool, Univ of the Andes, Colombia, 59-63; NIH fel med zool, Sch Med, Univ PR, San Juan, 65-67; assoc cur, Dept Mammal, Royal Ont Mus, 67-73, cur, 73-85; assoc prof zool, Univ Toronto, 69-85; lectr biol, Univ Tex, Austin, 86-88. *Concurrent Pos:* Vis prof biol, Pontificia Univ Javeriana, Colombia, 75, 82 & 85; sr Fulbright-Hays fel, 75 & 82; vis prof, Nat Univ Colombia, 82, 84 & 85, Univ Indust Santander, Colombia, 82; assoc ed, J Mammal, 68-70; ed, Royal Ont Mus Life Sci Publs, 71-73 & 81-84; resolutions comt, Am Soc Mammal, 70-72. *Mem:* Fel AAAS; Am Soc Mammalogists; fel Herpetologists' League. *Res:* Ecology, natural history, taxonomy and ectoparasites of Neotropical mammals. *Mailing Add:* 2903 Cedarview Dr Austin TX 78704-4608. *E-Mail:* tamsitt@acc.tx.us

**TAMSKY, MORGAN JEROME,** LABORATORY TECHNICAL DIRECTOR. *Current Pos:* Sr chemist, Cent Res Labs, 3M Co, 69-74, res specialist polymer physics, 74-77, supvr, 77-80, res mgr, 80-82, tech mgr, Com Tape Div, 82-84, lab mgr, Com Off Supply Div, 84-85, tech dir, Health Care Specialties Div, 87-89, TECH DIR, DISPOSABLE PROD DIV, 3M CO, 89- *Personal Data:* b St Louis, Mo, July 26, 42; m 66; c 2. *Educ:* Washington Univ, BA, 64; Univ Kans, PhD(chem), 70. *Mem:* Am Chem Soc; Adhesion Soc. *Res:* Surface phenomenon; adhesion; polymer physics; medical devices; pharmacentrical aerosol formulation filling; medical tapes. *Mailing Add:* Adhesive Technol Ctr 3M Bldg 201-15-12B St Paul MN 55144-1000

**TAMURA, ROY N,** MATHEMATICAL STATISTICS. *Current Pos:* Sr statistician, 84-89, res scientist, 89-95, SR RES SCIENTIST, LILLY RES LABS, 95- *Personal Data:* b New Haven, Conn, Oct 24, 56; m 84, Vipa Hemstapat. *Educ:* Oberlin Col, BA, 78; NC State Univ, MS, 80, PhD(statist), 84. *Mem:* Am Statist Asn; Inst Math Statist. *Res:* Applied statistics with concentration in experimental design; adaptive randomization methods in clinical trials and computer intensive experimental design; empirical Bayes methods in toxicology applications. *Mailing Add:* Lilly Res Labs Indianapolis IN 46285. *Fax:* 317-277-3220; *E-Mail:* tamura_roy_n@lilly.com

**TAMURA, TSUNENOBU,** PEDIATRICS. *Current Pos:* from asst prof to assoc prof, 82-92, PROF NUTRIT SCI, UNIV ALA, BIRMINGHAM, 92- *Personal Data:* b Tokyo, Japan, Dec 15, 38; m, Atsuko Ohnuma; c Yoshiko & Nobunori. *Educ:* Fukushima Med Col, MD, 64; Tohoku Univ, Dr Med Sci, 72. *Prof Exp:* Lectr, Tohoku Univ, 74-76; adj asst prof, Univ Calif, Davis, 78-82. *Mem:* Am Soc Clin Nutrit; Soc Exp Biol & Med; Am Soc Nutrit Sci. *Res:* Folate metabolism and nutrition; zinc nutrition; nutritional problems in various diseases. *Mailing Add:* Dept Nutrit Sci Univ Ala Birmingham AL 35294

**TAMURA, TSUNEO,** SOILS, WASTE MANAGEMENT. *Current Pos:* SR DEVELOP SCI, MARTIN MARIETTA ENERGY SYSTS, 90- *Personal Data:* b Hawaii, Nov 15, 25; div; c 3. *Educ:* Univ Hawaii, BS, 48; Univ Wis, MS, 51, PhD(soils), 52. *Prof Exp:* From asst soil scientist to assoc soil scientist, Conn Agr Exp Sta, 52-57; chemist, Westinghouse Elec Corp, 57; sr res staff mem, Oak Ridge Nat Lab, 57-77, earth sci sect head, 77-82, sr res adv, 82-90. *Mem:* Fel AAAS; fel Am Soc Agron; Am Chem Soc; Sigma Xi; fel Soil Sci Soc Am; fel Am Inst Chem; Clay Minerals Soc. *Res:* Soil chemistry and genesis; soil clay mineralogy; radioactive waste disposal; health physics; toxic metals in environment. *Mailing Add:* 8117 River Dr Oak Ridge TN 37830-3531

**TAN, AH-TI CHU,** CHEMISTRY, BIOCHEMISTRY. *Current Pos:* SR CONSULT, TAN & ASSOCS, 82-; PROF, CONCORDIA UNIV, MONTREAL. *Personal Data:* b Amoy, China, Sept 24, 35; Can citizen. *Educ:* Mapua Inst Technol, BSChem, 57; Adamson Univ, Manila, BSChE, 58; McGill Univ, MSc, 62, PhD(chem kinetics), 66. *Prof Exp:* Lectr phys chem, Adamson Univ, Manila, 58-60; res chemist, Bathurst Paper Co, 65-66; assoc biochem, Col Med, Univ Vt, 66-68, vis asst prof, 68-69; asst prof ophthal, Fac Med, McGill Univ, 69-72, asst prof anesthesia, 72-78; assoc prof, Fac Med, Univ Montreal, 78-79. *Concurrent Pos:* NIH grant biochem, Col Med, Univ Vt, 66-68; Que Med Res Coun grant ophthal, Fac Med, McGill Univ, 69-72; prof assoc anesthesia res, McGill Univ, 72-78. *Mem:* Am Chem Soc; Chem Inst Can; Can Biochem Soc; Soc Neurosci; AAAS; Sigma Xi. *Res:* Physicochemical studies of proteins; brain cell membranes; neurotransmitters; molecular mechanism of synaptic transmission; neuroendocrinology; molecular mechanism of depression. *Mailing Add:* 1951 de Maisonneuve E Apt 1108 Montreal PQ H2K 2C9 Can. *Fax:* 514-521-0187

**TAN, ARJUN,** IONOSPHERIC MODELLING, ORBITAL DEBRIS. *Current Pos:* from asst prof to assoc prof, 81-88, PROF PHYSICS, ALA A&M UNIV, 88- *Personal Data:* b Santiniketan, W Bengal, India, Aug 6, 43. *Educ:* Univ Calcutta, MSc, 65; Univ Fla, MS, 74; Univ Ala, Huntsville, PhD(physics), 79. *Prof Exp:* Instr phys sci, Visva-Bharati Univ, India, 66-67; lectr physics, Krishnagar Women's Col, India, 67-71; res assoc physics, Univ Ala, Huntsville, 79; assoc physics, Univ Fla, 79-80; instr math-physics, Newberry Col, 80-81. *Concurrent Pos:* Summer fac, Jadavpur Univ, India, 68, NASA Marshall Space Flight Ctr, 81, Arnold Air Force Sta, USAF, 86, NASA Johnson Space Ctr, 87, 88, US Army, Redstone Arsenal, 89 & USAF Kirtland AFB, 92 & 93; guest worker, Nat Oceanic & Atmospheric Admin Space Environ Lab, 77-79; lectr, Univ Ala, Huntsville, 81; physicist, US Army TMDE Lab, 82, 83 & 84, Lawrence Livermore Nat Lab, 85; prin investr, NSF grant, 83-85, 86-88, NASA grant, 87-91 & Air Force Off Sci Res sub contract, 92-93. *Mem:* Sigma Xi; Am Geophys Union; Am Asn Physics Teachers; Math Asn Am; Nat Coun Teachers Math; Am Phys Soc. *Res:* Planetary and space science; author of 90 articles which appeared in various journals. *Mailing Add:* PO Box 447 Normal AL 35762. *Fax:* 205-851-5622

**TAN, BARRIE,** CHEMICAL PROCESS RESEARCH & DEVELOPMENT, PHARMACOLOGY. *Current Pos:* asst prof analytical chem, 82-90, ADJ PROF FOOD SCI, UNIV MASS, AMHERST, 90-; VPRES, CAROTECH ASSOCS, 88- *Personal Data:* b Ipoh, Malaysia, Oct 7, 53; US citizen; m 90, Elizabeth Bachrach. *Educ:* Univ Otago, NZ, BS, 76, PhD(analytical chem), 79. *Prof Exp:* Res assoc fel environ toxicol, Auburn Univ, Ala, 79-81. *Mem:* Am Chem Soc; Am Oil Chem Soc; Inst Food Technol. *Res:* Molecular spectroscopic and luminescence detectors in high pressure liquid chromatography; bioanalytical techniques in cancer research (chemical carcinogenesis, bioanalytical/biochemical toxicology); analyses of lipid-soluble carotenoids, vitamins A and E from foods, plants and biological samples, carotenoid and vitamin E including tocotrienols metabolisms. *Mailing Add:* Dept Food Sci Univ Mass Amherst MA 01003-1410. *Fax:* 413-256-8665

**TAN, BOEN HIE,** BIOMEDICAL SCIENCE, MOLECULAR BIOLOGY. *Current Pos:* ANALYTICAL BIOCHEMIST, ALA DEPT ENVIRON MGT, MONTGOMERY, ALA, 92- *Personal Data:* b Padangan, Java, Indonesia, Dec 14, 26; US citizen. *Educ:* State Univ Leiden, Holland, BSc, 52, MSc, 55, DSc(pharmacol, toxicol, pharmaco & analytical biochem), 62. *Prof Exp:* Asst prof analytical pharmacol chem, Univ Leiden, Holland, 53-55 & 62-64; res fel analytical chem, Univ Minn, 55-61, res assoc analytical biochem, 64-68, res specialist analytical chem, 72-73; res fel phys biochem, Max Planck Inst, Ger, 61-62; res assoc analytical biochem, NY Hosp-Cornell Med Ctr, 68-72; res assoc pharmacol, Univ Groningen, Holland, 73-81; res assoc biochem, Univ SAla Med Col, Mobile, 82-92. *Mem:* Am Asn Clin Chem; Am Chem Soc; AAAS; Fedn Am Soc Exp Biol. *Res:* Purification, analysis, pharmacokinetic, pharmacological activities of anti-arrhythmic, new drugs; alpha-1-antitrypsin, plasma proteins, leucocyte-enzymes and liver functions; fibrin formation, inhibition and lysis; heart perfusions and type I, type II-diabetes; sulfhydryl, disulfides and protein denaturation-renaturations; vanadate-sulfhydryl complexes and PDE-activities; DNA damage and repair; clinical chemistry, nuclear medicine in diagnosis and the cure of diseases. *Mailing Add:* PO Box 230451 Montgomery AL 36123-0451. *Fax:* 334-272-8131

**TAN, CHARLOTTE,** CANCER. *Current Pos:* assoc prof, Med Sch, Cornell Univ, 70-78, prof pediat, 78-96, mem, Dept Pediat, Sloan Kettering Cancer Ctr, 84-96, EMER PROF, SLOAN KETTERING CANCER CTR, CORNELL UNIV, 96- *Personal Data:* b Kiang-Si, China, Apr 19, 23; US citizen; m 59; c 1. *Educ:* Hsiang-Ya Med Col, China, MD, 47; Am Bd Pediat, dipl, 54. *Prof Exp:* Resident & rotating intern, Nanking Cent Hosp, China, 47-48; rotating intern & gen residcnt, St Barnabas Hosp, Newark, NJ, 48-50; res resident hemat & pediat resident, Children's Hosp Philadelphia, 50-51; pediat resident, Philadelphia Gen Hosp, 52; res fel chemother, Sloan-Kettering Inst, 52-54, res assoc, 55-57, asst, 57-60, assoc mem, 60-84.

*Concurrent Pos:* Spec fel med, Mem Ctr, NY, 52-55, spec fel pediat, 55-57, clin asst, Pediat Serv, 57-58; instr med, Sloan-Kettering Div, Grad Sch Med Sci, Med Col, Cornell Univ, 54-55, instr med, Med Col, 55-57, instr pediat, 58-62; clin asst pediatrician, James Ewing Hosp, 57-58, from asst vis pediatrician to assoc vis pediatrician, 58-68; from asst attend pediatrician to assoc attend pediatrician, Mem Hosp, 58-70, attend pediatrician, 70-, assoc chmn chemother, 74-; vis prof, Nat Taiwan Univ Med Col, 66-67; assoc & attend pediatrician, NY Hosp, 78- *Mem:* Am Acad Pediat; Am Asn Cancer Res; Am Fedn Clin Res; AMA; Am Soc Clin Oncol; NY Acad Sci; Am Soc Hemat; Soc Surg Oncol; Int Soc Pediat Oncol. *Res:* Cancer chemotherapy. *Mailing Add:* Mem-Sloan-Kettering Res Ctr 1275 York Ave New York NY 10021-6007

**TAN, CHIN SHENG,** AGROMETEOROLOGY, IRRIGATION. *Current Pos:* RES SCIENTIST AGROMETEOROL & IRRIG, HARROW RES STA, CAN DEPT AGR, 78- *Personal Data:* b Taiwan, Mar 15, 47; Can citizen; m 73, Chun Chih; c Ivan & Kathy. *Educ:* Nat Chung-Hsing Univ, Taiwan, BSc, 69; Univ NH, MSc, 72; Univ BC, PhD(agrometeorol), 77. *Honors & Awards:* Carroll R Miller Award, Am Soc Hort Sci-Nat Peach Coun, 82 & 85; Hoechat Can Award, Can J Plant Sci, 86. *Prof Exp:* Vis scientist, Commonwealth Sci & Indust Res Orgn, Div Water Resources, Griffith, NSW Australia, 87-88. *Mem:* Am Soc Agron; Can Soc Hort Sci; Int Soc Hort Sci; Am Soc Agr Engrs. *Res:* Soil and plant water relations; water requirements of crops in relation to production; interrelationship of irrigation, climate, soil and crop management factors; evapotranspiration models for various crops; climatic model for scheduling irrigation; soil moisture effects on root growth; water table control on water quality. *Mailing Add:* Agr & Agr Food Can Greenhouse & Processing Crops Res Ctr 2585 Hwy 18 East Harrow ON N0R 1G0 Can. *Fax:* 519-738-2929

**TAN, CHOR-WENG,** MECHANICAL ENGINEERING. *Current Pos:* MANAGING DIR EDUC, AM SOC MECH ENGRS, 91- *Personal Data:* b Canton, China, Apr 20, 36; US citizen; m 63; c 2. *Educ:* Evansville Col, BS, 59; Univ Ill, MS, 61, PhD(mech eng), 63. *Prof Exp:* Prof mech eng, Cooper Union, 63-69, dean, Sch Eng, 76-87. *Concurrent Pos:* Prog dir, NSF; exec dir, Cooper Union Res Found; dir bd, Tround Int, Inc, Nomura Pac Basin Fund, Japan OTC Fund, Jakarta Growth Fund, UHT Corp, APT, Inc, Appl Biomed Asn; consult, 90- *Mem:* Am Soc Mech Engrs; Am Soc Eng Educ. *Res:* Thermodynamic and transport properties of partially ionized gases; magnetohydrodynamics; electrogasdynamics; environmental engineering. *Mailing Add:* 76 Echo Bay Dr New Rochelle NY 10805

**TAN, ENG M,** IMMUNOLOGY. *Current Pos:* DIR, W M KECK AUTOIMMUNE DIS CTR, SCRIPPS CLIN & RES FOUND, 82- *Personal Data:* b Malaysia, Aug 26, 26; US citizen; m 62; c 2. *Educ:* Johns Hopkins Univ, AB, 52, MD, 56. *Honors & Awards:* Dunlop-Dottridge Lectr, Can Rheumatism Asn, Ottawa, 80; Mclaughlin Lectr, Galveston, 81; Alexander von Humboldt Sr Sci Scientist Award, 86. *Prof Exp:* Res fel, Rockefeller Univ, 62-65; asst prof med, Wash Univ, 65-67; assoc mem, Dept Exp Path, Scripps Clin & Res Found, 67-70, head, Div Allergy & Immunol, 70-77; head, Div Rheumatic Dis, Univ Colo Med Ctr, 77-82. *Concurrent Pos:* Nesbitt vis prof, Minneapolis, 79; chmn, Allergy, Immunol & Transplantation Res Comt, NIH, 81; Macy Found fac scholar, 81. *Mem:* Asn Am Physicians; Am Soc Clin Invest; Am Asn Immunologists; Am Asn Pathologists; Am Rheumatism Asn (pres, 84-85). *Res:* Autoimmune diseases; immunological aspects of rheumatic diseases; antinuclear and other autoantibodies in systemic lupus erythematosus, rheumatoid arthritis, Sjogren's syndrome, scleroderma, dermatomyositis and polymyositis. *Mailing Add:* Scripps Res Inst 10666 N Torrey Pines Rd La Jolla CA 92037-1092

**TAN, FRANCIS C,** CHEMICAL OCEANOGRAPHY. *Current Pos:* RES SCIENTIST, DEPT FISHERIES & OCEANS, BEDFORD INST OCEANOG, CAN DEPT FISHERIES & OCEANS, 72- *Personal Data:* b Manila, Philippines, Sept 21, 39; m 71. *Educ:* Cheng Kung Univ, Taiwan, BSc, 61; McGill Univ, MSc, 65; Pa State Univ, PhD(geochem), 69. *Prof Exp:* NSF fel, Pa State Univ, 69-70; geochemist, Minn Geol Surv, Univ Minn, 70-72. *Concurrent Pos:* Hon res fel, Third Inst Oceanog, State Oceanic Admin, Xiamen, People's Repub China; hon res assoc, Dept Oceanog, Dalhousie Univ, Halifax, Can, 79-90. *Mem:* Am Geophys Union. *Res:* Stable isotope oceanography, marine geochemistry. *Mailing Add:* PO Box 1006 Bedford Inst Oceanog Dartmouth NS B2Y 4A2 Can. *Fax:* 902-426-6695; *E-Mail:* f__tan@bionet.bio.dfo.ca

**TAN, HENRY S I,** SYNTHETIC ORGANIC & NATURAL PRODUCTS CHEMISTRY. *Current Pos:* from asst prof to assoc prof pharm, 71-82, PROF PHARM CHEM, UNIV CINCINNATI, 82- *Personal Data:* b Bandung, Indonesia, Mar 26, 32; US citizen; m, Hetty G Liem. *Educ:* Univ Indonesia, BSPharm, 54, MSPharm, 56; Univ Ky, PhD(pharmaceut sci), 71. *Honors & Awards:* Ten-Year Serv Award & Twenty-Seven Year Serv Award, Chem Abstract Serv. *Prof Exp:* Instr & assoc prof, Bandung Inst Technol, 57-66. *Concurrent Pos:* Prin & co-investr funded grants; elected mem, USP, Comt Rev; consult, Merrell-Nat Labs, Hilltop Biolabs; chmn, Antibiotics Subcomt, US Pharacopeia, Comt Rev, 95-; mem, USP Drug Stand Exec Comt, 95- *Mem:* Am Asn Pharmaceut Scientists. *Res:* Development of analysis procedures for drugs in dosage forms, biological fluids, animal feed and cosmetic prepns. *Mailing Add:* 7335 Willowwood Dr Cincinnati OH 45241-3707. *E-Mail:* henry.tan@uc.edu

**TAN, JAMES CHIEN-HUA,** GENETICS, STATISTICS. *Current Pos:* from asst prof to assoc prof, 66-78, PROF BIOL, VALPARAISO UNIV, 78-, UNIV RES PROF, 80- *Personal Data:* b Nanchang, China, Oct 8, 35; m 65; c 2. *Educ:* Chung-Shing Univ, Taiwan, BS, 57; Mont State Univ, MS, 61; NC

State Univ, PhD(genetics), 68. *Prof Exp:* Asst prof biol, Slippery Rock State Col, 65-66. *Concurrent Pos:* Res fel, Roswell Park Mem Inst, 77; fel, O P Kretzemann Mem Wheat Ridge Found. *Mem:* AAAS; Am Genetics Soc; Environ Mutagen Soc; Genetics Soc Can. *Res:* Cytogenetics and statistical biology; mutagenicity and carcinogenicity testing. *Mailing Add:* Dept Biol Valparaiso Univ Valparaiso IN 46383-6493

**TAN, JULIA S,** POLYMER SCIENCE, PHYSICAL CHEMISTRY. *Current Pos:* res chemist, 70-77, RES ASSOC, RES LABS, EASTMAN KODAK CO, 77- *Personal Data:* b Taipei, Taiwan; US citizen. *Educ:* Nat Taiwan Univ, BA, 61; Wesleyan Univ, MA, 63; Yale Univ, PhD(chem), 66. *Prof Exp:* Asst prof chem, Wesleyan Univ, 66-69; res assoc biophys, Univ Rochester, 69-70. *Mem:* Am Chem Soc. *Res:* Solution properties of polyelectrolytes. *Mailing Add:* 437 True Hickory Dr Rochester NY 14615-1321

**TAN, KIM H,** TROPICAL AGRICULTURE, SOIL CHEMISTRY. *Current Pos:* asst prof soil sci, Dept Agron, 68-73, assoc prof agron, 73-77, PROF AGRON, UNIV GA, 77- *Personal Data:* b Djakarta, Indonesia, Mar 24, 26; US citizen; m 57; c 1. *Educ:* Univ Indonesia, MSc, 55, PhD(soil sci), 58. *Prof Exp:* Assoc prof soil sci fac agr, Univ Indonesia, 58-64, prof fac agr & agr acad, 64-67, head dept soil sci, 65-67; technician soil analytical nitrogen lab, Agr Res Serv, USDA, Colo, 67-68. *Concurrent Pos:* Rockefeller Found grant/fel, NC State Univ, 60-61 & Cornell Univ, 61; mem comt VIII, Southern Regional Coop Soil Surv, Soil Conserv Serv, USDA, 72- *Mem:* Clay Mineral Soc Am; fel Am Soc Agron; fel Soil Sci Soc Am; Int Soc Soil Sci. *Res:* Pedology; genesis and characterization of soils and organic matter in soils; effect of organic matter on soil properties and plant growth; chemistry and mineralogy of soils. *Mailing Add:* c/o Dr Suci Widayati Semampir Argorejo Sedayu Bantu Jateng IN 55759

**TAN, KOK-KEONG,** MATHEMATICS. *Current Pos:* from asst prof to assoc prof, 70-83, PROF MATH, DALHOUSIE UNIV, 83- *Personal Data:* b Shanghai, China, June 1, 43; m 69, Kwei-Ying Chan; c Chong-Jet, Chong-Chien, Chong-Feng & Chong-Yee. *Educ:* Nanyang Univ, BSc, 66; Univ BC, PhD(math), 70. *Prof Exp:* Teacher high sch, Malaysia, 66. *Concurrent Pos:* Vis res prof, Nat Tsing Hua Univ, Taiwan, 80-81; vis res expert, Acad Sinica, Taiwan, 81 & Nat Cent Univ, Taiwan, 84; vis res prof, Nat Cent Univ, Taiwan, 87; Ethel Raybound vis fel, Univ Queensland, Australia, 94. *Mem:* Am Math Soc; SE Asian Math Soc; Can Math Soc; Int Fedn Nonlinear Analysts. *Res:* Functional analysis and topology, in particular, fixed point theorems; convex analysis, in particular, minimax inequalities, variational inequalities mathematical economics, game theory. *Mailing Add:* Dept Math Statist & Comput Sci Dalhousie Univ Halifax NS B3H 3J5 Can. *Fax:* 902-494-5130; *E-Mail:* kktan@cs.dal.ca

**TAN, LIAT,** BIOCHEMISTRY, ORGANIC CHEMISTRY. *Current Pos:* from asst prof to assoc prof, 67-80, PROF BIOCHEM, UNIV SHERBROOKE, 80- *Personal Data:* b Semarang, Java, Apr 1, 29; div; c John E & Vincent. *Educ:* Univ Amsterdam, BSc, 53; Univ Munster, MSc, 55; Univ Freiburg, Dr rer nat, 58. *Prof Exp:* Res chemist, Steroid Res Lab, Leo Pharmaceut Prod, Denmark, 59-60; sr res chemist, Union Chimique Belge SA, 60-62; res fel org chem, Laval Univ, 62-63; examr steroid chem, Can Patent Off, 63-66; Welch res fel & instr biochem & nutrit, Med Br, Univ Tex, 66-67. *Concurrent Pos:* Vis scientist, Hormone Res Lab, Univ Calif, 76-77. *Mem:* AAAS; Am Chem Soc; NY Acad Sci; Can Biochem Soc. *Res:* Synthesis and biochemistry of anti-breast cancer steroids; steroid oxygenases, specificity and mechanism of action; physiologically active natural products; mechanism of biological oxidations at inactive sites in steroids; cytochrome P-450 aromatase; androgen synthetase; breast cancer; site-directed mutagenesis of CYP1g. *Mailing Add:* Dept Biochem Univ Sherbrooke Sherbrooke PQ J1K 2R1 Can. *Fax:* 819-564-5340

**TAN, MENG HEE,** INTERNAL MEDICINE, MEDICAL SCIENCES. *Current Pos:* MED DIR DIABETES DIS MGT, BECTON DICKINSON, 96- *Personal Data:* b Kuala Pilah, Malaysia, Mar 30, 42; Can citizen; m 70; c 3. *Educ:* Dalhousie Univ, BSc, 65, MD, 69; FRCP(C), 75; FACP, 78. *Prof Exp:* Lectr, Dalhousie Univ, 74-75, from asst prof to prof med, 75-96, head, Div Endocrinol, 81-96. *Concurrent Pos:* Res fel, Harvard Med Sch, 71-73, Cardiovasc Res Inst, San Francisco, 73-75; res fel, Med Coun Can, 71-74, centennial fel, 74-75. *Mem:* Am Col Physicians; Am Diabetes Asn; Am Fedn Clin Res; Royal Col Physicians & Surgeons Can; Int Diabetes Fedn (vpres). *Res:* Lipoprotein metabolism in secondary hyperlipidemia; triglyceride metabolism in diabetes mellitus; insulin receptors. *Mailing Add:* Med Dir Diabetes Dis Mgt Becton Dickinson 1 Beckton Dr Franklin Lakes NJ 07417-1883. *Fax:* 201-847-5865

**TAN, OWEN T,** ELECTRIC POWER ENGINEERING. *Current Pos:* from asst prof to prof, 67-94, EMER PROF ELEC ENG, LA STATE UNIV, BATON ROUGE, 95- *Personal Data:* b Indramaju, Indonesia, Aug 30, 31; US citizen; m 56, Martha Tan-Liem; c Joyce, Edward & Cindy. *Educ:* Bandung Technol Faculty, MSc, 55; Eindhoven Technol Univ, PhD(elec eng), 61. *Prof Exp:* Res & develop engr, Willem Smit & Co, Neth, 56-62; lectr elec eng, Bandung Technol Inst, 62-64; sr lectr, 64-66. *Concurrent Pos:* Res fel, Siemens Schuckert, WGer, 62, Eindhoven Univ Technol, 77 & Delft Univ Technol, 91. *Mem:* Inst Elec & Electronics Engrs; Neth Royal Inst Eng. *Res:* Energy conversion; power systems; artificial neural networks. *Mailing Add:* Dept Elec & Comput Eng La State Univ Baton Rouge LA 70803. *Fax:* 504-388-5200; *E-Mail:* tan@.ee.lsu.edu

**TAN, VICTOR,** POLYMER ENGINEERING, MATERIAL SCIENCE. *Current Pos:* SR ENGR, POLYMER PROCESSING INST, STEVENS INST TECHNOL, 81- *Personal Data:* b Manila, Philippines, Aug 8, 44; m 76. *Educ:* Adamson Univ, BS, 67; Univ Pittsburgh, MS, 70; Stevens Inst Technol, PhD(chem eng), 75. *Prof Exp:* Fel, McGill Univ, 74-76, res assoc chem eng, 78-81. *Mem:* Soc Plastics Engrs. *Res:* Polymer characterization and polymer processing; computer simulation of polymer processing; polymer physics. *Mailing Add:* 612 Park Ave Hoboken NJ 07030

**TAN, WAI-YUAN,** STATISTICS, PROBABILITY. *Current Pos:* RES PROF MATH, MEMPHIS STATE UNIV, 75- *Personal Data:* b China, Aug 14, 34; m 64, Shiow-Jen; c Emy & Eden. *Educ:* Taiwan Prov Col Agr, BA, 55; Nat Taiwan Univ, MS, 59; Univ Wis, MS(math) & MS(statist), 63, PhD(statist), 64. *Prof Exp:* Asst res fel biostatist, Inst Bot, Acad Sinica, Taiwan, 59-61, assoc res fel, 64-67 & res fel, 67-68; assoc prof statist, Nat Taiwan Univ, 65-67; from assoc prof to prof biostatist, Biol Res Ctr, Taiwan, 65-68; asst prof statist, Univ Wis-Madison, 68-72; assoc prof math, Wash State Univ, 73-75; Cancer Expert, Nat Cancer Inst, Bethesda, Md, 84-85. *Concurrent Pos:* Vis assoc prof, Tsing Hua Univ, Taiwan, 65-67; statist adv, Joint Inst Indust Res, Taiwan, 65-67; vis prof & consult, Dept Genetics, Univ Hawaii, Honolulu, 73, 74, 76; consult, Pig Res Inst, Taiwan, 75 & Fox Chase Cancer Ctr, Philadelphia, Pa, 83; sr res statistician, Oak Ridge Nat Lab, Tenn, 78, 79; cancer expert, Nat Cancer Inst, Bethesda, Md, 84-85; vis prof, Emory Univ, 90; math statistician, CDC, Atlanta, Ga, 90. *Mem:* Fel Am Statist Asn; Biomet Soc; Inst Math Statist; Royal Statist Soc; Chinese Statist Asn. *Res:* Statistical inferences; multivariate analysis; mathematical genetics and quantitative genetics; robust statistics; biostatistics; statistical methods for mutagenicity and carcinogenesis; cancer stochastic models; applied stochastic processes; robust procedures; AIDS stochastic models; risk assessment; published three books and over 130 papers. *Mailing Add:* Dept Math Memphis State Univ Memphis TN 38152. *Fax:* 901-678-2480; *E-Mail:* tanwy@msuvx1.memst.edu

**TAN, YEN T,** SOLID STATE PHYSICS, SURFACE PHYSICS. *Current Pos:* RES ASSOC, RES LABS, EASTMAN KODAK CO, 66-; SCI CONSULT. *Personal Data:* b Hong Kong, Feb 12, 40. *Educ:* Columbia Univ, BS, 62; Yale Univ, PhD(chem), 66. *Concurrent Pos:* Adj prof, Rochester Inst Technol, 74-75. *Mem:* Am Chem Soc; Am Inst Mining, Metall & Petrol Engrs; Am Vacuum Soc; Sigma Xi; fel Soc Imaging Sci. *Res:* Surface properties of solids; transport phenomena; thermodynamics; computational chemistry. *Mailing Add:* 437 True Hickory Dr Rochester NY 14615

**TAN, ZOILO CHENG HO,** MICROLITHOGRAPHY, ELECTRON-BEAM RESIST PROCESS. *Current Pos:* PRIN ENGR, ELEC SYSTS INC, 91- *Personal Data:* b Bulan, Philippines, Oct 18, 40; m 67, Bee Cheng Ang; c Irene, Kenneth & Joshua. *Educ:* Cheng Kung Univ, BS, 63; Univ Ark, MS, 66, Mass Inst Technol, PhD(nuclear chem), 69. *Honors & Awards:* Microwave Prize, Microwave Theory & Tech Soc Inst Elec & Electronics Engrs, 92. *Prof Exp:* Sr res chemist, Eastman Kodak Co, 69-84; Staff scientist, Synertek Inc, 84-85, Varian Assocs Inc, 86-90; sr staff res engr, Fairchild Semiconductors, 85-86; mem tech staff, Motorola, Inc, 90-91. *Res:* Resist process development for use in mask making of the 130 nanometer device generation; develop processes for electron-beam direct write and x-ray lithography. *Mailing Add:* 26460 Corporate Ave Hayward CA 94545. *Fax:* 510-786-9438; *E-Mail:* zoilo__tan@fc.etec.com

**TANABE, MASATO,** ORGANIC CHEMISTRY. *Current Pos:* sr org chemist, 57-72, DIR, DEPT BIO-ORG CHEM, SRI INT, MENLO PARK, 72- *Personal Data:* b Stockton, Calif, Jan 18, 25; m 55; c 3. *Educ:* Univ Calif, BS, 47, PhD(chem), 51. *Prof Exp:* Chemist, US Naval Radiation Defense Lab, 47-48; res chemist, Riker Labs, Inc, 51-57. *Concurrent Pos:* Fulbright res fel, Japan, 54-55. *Mem:* Am Chem Soc. *Res:* Medicinal chemistry; steroids; alkaloids; natural products; biosynthesis. *Mailing Add:* 972 Moreno St Palo Alto CA 94303-3733

**TANABE, MICHAEL JOHN,** HORTICULTURE, PLANT PHYSIOLOGY. *Current Pos:* PROF HORT, COL AGR, UNIV HAWAII, HILO, 75- *Personal Data:* b Keaau, Hawaii, Sept 15, 47; m 83, Nina Akahoshi; c Ashley. *Educ:* Univ Hawaii, Manoa, BS, 69, MS, 72, PhD(hort), 76. *Mem:* Am Soc Hort Sci; Sigma Xi; Tissue Cult Asn. *Res:* Determining regenerative capabilities of several tropical plant species by plant tissue culture; plant organ culture; in vitro triple indexing. *Mailing Add:* Col Agr 200 W Kawili St Hilo HI 96720-4051

**TANADA, TAKUMA,** PLANT PHYSIOLOGY. *Personal Data:* b Honolulu, Hawaii, Oct 30, 19; m 47; c Juliet T (Tanada-Vesely) & Chizuru Saito. *Educ:* Univ Hawaii, BS, 42, MS, 44; Univ Ill, PhD(bot), 50. *Prof Exp:* Asst soil chemist, Agr Exp Sta, Univ Hawaii, 42-44; sci consult natural resources sect, Supreme Comdr Allied Powers, US Army, Tokyo, 46-47; plant physiologist, Agr Res Serv, USDA, 50-57; agron res adv, Int Coop Admin, Ceylon, 57-60; res plant physiologist, sci & educ admin-agr res, USDA, 60-84. *Mem:* Am Soc Plant Physiol; Am Inst Biol Sci. *Res:* Photobiology; photosynthesis; mineral nutrition. *Mailing Add:* 19 Skycrest Way Napa CA 94558

**TANADA, YOSHINORI,** INSECT PATHOLOGY, INSECT VIROLOGY. *Current Pos:* RETIRED. *Personal Data:* b Puuloa, Oahu, Hawaii, June 8, 17; m 49; c 2. *Educ:* Univ Hawaii, BS, 40, MS, 45; Univ Calif, PhD(entom), 53. *Honors & Awards:* Founder's lect, Soc Invert Pathol, 84. *Prof Exp:* Asst zool, Univ Hawaii, 43-45, jr entomologist exp sta, 45-53, asst entomologist, 53-56, asst prof zool & entom, 54-56, assoc prof & assoc entomologist, 56; asst insect pathologist, Lab Insect Path, Univ Calif, Berkeley, 56-59, assoc insect pathologist, 59-64, lectr, 61-65, chmn, Div Invert Path, 64-65, insect pathologist, Exp Sta, 64-87, prof entom, 65-87. *Concurrent Pos:* Consult, US Army, Okinawa, 50, SPac Comn, Pac Sci Bd, Nat Res Coun, 59, UN Develop Prog, Western Samoa, 71 & Food & Agr Orgn, UN, Thailand, 71; Fulbright res scholar, Japan, 62-63; spec vis prof, Univ Tokyo, 80. *Mem:* Fel AAAS; Entom Soc Am; Soc Protozool; Soc Invert Path; Am Inst Biol Scientists; Am Soc Virol. *Res:* Insect virology; general insect pathology; epizootiology of diseases of insects. *Mailing Add:* 10 Truitt Lane Oakland CA 94618

**TANAKA, JOHN,** INORGANIC CHEMISTRY. *Current Pos:* from asst prof to assoc prof, 65-75, dir honors prog, 71-94, PROF CHEM, UNIV CONN, 75- *Personal Data:* b San Diego, Calif, June 18, 24; m 59; c 2. *Educ:* Univ Calif, Los Angeles, BA, 51; Iowa State Univ, PhD, 56. *Hon Degrees:* Dr, Univ Paul Sapatier, France. *Prof Exp:* From asst prof to assoc prof chem, SDak State Univ, 56-63; NASA fel, Univ Pittsburgh, 63-65. *Mem:* Am Chem Soc; Royal Soc Chem; fel Inst Elec & Electronics Engrs. *Res:* Synthesis and properties of ternary hydrides; materials for electrical insulation; reactions of boron hydrides; vacuum line syntheses. *Mailing Add:* Dept Chem U-60 Rm 151 Univ Conn 215 Glenbrook Rd Storrs CT 06269-3060

**TANAKA, KATSUMI,** PHYSICS. *Current Pos:* PROF PHYSICS, OHIO STATE UNIV, 64- *Personal Data:* b San Francisco, Calif, Mar 1, 25; m 53; c 1. *Educ:* Univ Calif, AB, 49, PhD(physics), 52. *Prof Exp:* Assoc physicist, Argonne Nat Lab, 52-64. *Concurrent Pos:* Vis prof, Univ Naples, 60-61. *Mem:* Fel Am Phys Soc. *Res:* Elementary particle physics. *Mailing Add:* Dept Physics Ohio State Univ Columbus OH 43210. *Fax:* 614-292-8261; *E-Mail:* tanaka@mps.ohio-state.edu

**TANAKA, KAY,** GENETICS, BIOCHEMISTRY. *Current Pos:* PROF HUMAN GENETICS, YALE UNIV, 82- *Personal Data:* b Osaka, Japan, Mar 2, 29; m, Tomoko Hasegawa; c Atau & Elly M. *Educ:* Univ Tokyo, Japan, MD, 56. *Hon Degrees:* MA, Yale Univ, 82. *Honors & Awards:* Merit Award, NIH. *Mem:* Am Soc Biol Chem; Am Soc Human Genetics. *Res:* Genetic metabolic disorders; molecular biology. *Mailing Add:* Dept Genetics 393 NSB SHM Yale Univ 333 Cedar St New Haven CT 06510-8005

**TANAKA, KOUICHI ROBERT,** MEDICINE, HEMATOLOGY. *Current Pos:* instr med & jr res hematologist, Univ Calif, Los Angeles, 57-59, asst prof med, Sch Med & asst res hematologist, Med Ctr, 59-61, assoc prof, 61-68, ATTEND PHYSICIAN, SCH MED, UNIV CALIF, LOS ANGELES, 58-, PROF MED, 68- CHIEF, DIV HEMAT, MED CTR, 61-, ASSOC CHMN, DEPT MED, 94- *Personal Data:* b Fresno, Calif, Dec 15, 26; m 65, Grace M Sakaguchi; c Anne, Nancy & Grace. *Educ:* Wayne State Univ, BS, 49, MD, 52. *Prof Exp:* Intern, Los Angeles Co Gen Hosp, 52-53; resident path, Detroit Receiving Hosp, Mich, 53-54, resident med, 54-57; actg chmn, Dept Med, Harbor-Univ Calif Med Ctr, Los Angeles, 71-72, 79-80, 92-94, assoc chmn, 70-79, 80-92. *Concurrent Pos:* Prog dir, Dept Med, Univ Calif, Los Angeles, 82-92; consult, St Mary Med Ctr, 67- *Mem:* AAAS; fel Am Col Physicians; Asn Am Physicians; Sigma Xi; Am Soc Clin Invest; Am Fedn Med Res. *Res:* Internal medicine; red cell metabolism; enzymopathies; hemolytic anemia; pyruvate kinase deficiency. *Mailing Add:* Dept Med Bin 400 Harbor-UCLA Med Ctr 1000 W Carson St Torrance CA 90509. *Fax:* 310-320-9688

**TANAKA, TOYOICHI,** BIOPHYSICS. *Current Pos:* Fel biophys, 72-75, from asst prof to assoc prof, 75-82, PROF PHYSICS, MASS INST TECHNOL, 82- *Personal Data:* b Nagaoka, Japan, Jan 4, 46; m 70, Tomoko; c Kazunori & Ayako. *Educ:* Univ Tokyo, BS, 68, MA, 70, DSc(physics), 72. *Honors & Awards:* Nishina Mem Prize, 85; Award Polymer Soc Japan, 86; Da Vinci Prize, 92; Inoue Prize, 94; Res & Develop 100 Award, 96; Discover Award, 96. *Concurrent Pos:* Res assoc med physics, Retina Found, 73-75; vis prof, Univ Louis Pasteur, 80-81. *Mem:* Am Phys Soc; Phys Soc Japan; Biophys Soc Japan. *Res:* Laser scattering spectroscopy; critical phenomena of macromolecular solutions with applications to cataract disease; critical phenomena and phase transition in polymers and gels; physics of molecular recognition and catalysis. *Mailing Add:* Mass Inst Technol Rm 13-2153 77 Massachusetts Ave Cambridge MA 02139

**TANAKA, YASUO,** OTORHINOLARYNGOLOGY. *Current Pos:* from assoc prof to prof, 79-96, EMER PROF, DOKKYO UNIV SCH MED, 96- *Personal Data:* b Kyoto, Japan, Mar 14, 31; m 60, Reiko Nakagawa; c Akio. *Educ:* Kyoto Prefecture Univ Med, MD, 56, PhD, 64. *Prof Exp:* Instr otolaryngol, Kyoto Perfecture Univ Med, 59-63, vis assoc prof, 67-75; instr physiol, Tokyo Med & Dent Univ, 63-65; asst res scientist, NY Univ, 65-67; vis assoc prof, Tsurumi Univ Sch Dent, 75-79. *Concurrent Pos:* Head, Dept Otolaryngol, Kaibara Red Cross Hosp, Hyogo Perfecture, 61, Yodogawa Christian Hosp, 61-63, Dokkyo Univ Koshigaya Hosp, 83-96; dir, Nagokakyo City Med Clin, 67-79. *Mem:* Japan Audiol Soc; Japan Otol Soc; Soc Practical Otolaryngol; Soc Otolaryngol Japan; Japan Bronch-esophagul Soc; Japan Soc Stomote-pharyngol. *Res:* Physiology of inner ear; clinical study of otoacoustic emissions; contributed articles to professional journals. *Mailing Add:* Tanaka ENT Clin Nagaokakyoshi 4-5 Takenodai Kytofu 617 Japan

**TANAKA, YASUO,** ASTRONOMY. *Current Pos:* RES DIR & PROF, INST SPACE ASTRON SCI SPACE RES. *Personal Data:* b Mar 18, 31. *Honors & Awards:* James Craig Watson Medal, Nat Acad Sci, 94; Nishina Prize, 94; Toray Prize, 94. *Mem:* Int Astron Union; Royal Dutch Acad. *Res:* X-ray astronomy; space science. *Mailing Add:* Inst Space Astron Sci Space Res 3-37-3 Hirayama Hino-Shi Tokyo 191 Japan

**TANAKA, YASUOMI,** FOREST ECOLOGY. *Current Pos:* FOREST NURSERY ECOLOGIST, WEYERHAEUSER FORESTRY RES CTR, 71- *Personal Data:* b Tokyo, Japan, Dec 5, 39; m 74; c 2. *Educ:* Tokyo Univ Educ, BS, 62; Duke Univ, MF, 67, PhD(forest ecol), 70. *Prof Exp:* Silviculturist, Agr Farm Monte D'Este, Brazil, 62-63; res fel forestry, Univ Sao Paulo, Brazil, 64-65; instr, Univ Parana, Brazil, 65-66; res assoc ecol, Ecol Sci Div, Oak Ridge Nat Lab, 70-71. *Mem:* Japanese Forestry Soc; Soc Am Foresters. *Res:* Physiological and ecological aspect of seedling production; seedling dormancy, growth, nutrition in the greenhouse and openbed nursery; seed technology. *Mailing Add:* 1111 N Washington Centralia WA 98531

**TANANBAUM, HARVEY DALE,** ASTROPHYSICS. *Current Pos:* ASTROPHYSICIST, SMITHSONIAN INST ASTROPHYS OBSERV, 73- *Personal Data:* b Buffalo, NY, July 17, 42; m 64; c 2. *Educ:* Yale Univ, BA, 64; Mass Inst Technol, PhD(physics), 68. *Honors & Awards:* Except Sci Achievement Medal, NASA, 80, Pub Serv Medal, 88. *Prof Exp:* Staff scientist, Am Sci & Eng, Inc, 68-73. *Concurrent Pos:* Assoc astron, Harvard Col Observ, Harvard Univ, 73-, lectr, dept astron, 80-; assoc dir, Harvard-Smithsonian Ctr Astrophys, 81-; mem, comt data mgt & comput, Space Sci Bd, 78-82, comt space astron & astrophys, 81-84, astron surv comt, Extragalactic Astron Working Group, 78-80, Res Briefing Panel Astron & Astrophys, Advan X-Ray Astrophys Facil Sci Working Group, 78-83, Astrophys Subcomt, NASA, 85-, Asn Univ Res Astron, Comt Future Directions, NOAO, 86-87, Space Sci & Applications Adv Comt, 88-, Automatic Planetary Sta Priorities Comt, 88, Astron & Astrophys Surv Comt, High Energy Panel, Nat Res Coun, 89- *Mem:* Fel AAAS; Am Astron Soc. *Res:* X-ray astronomy, especially discrete cosmic x-ray sources with satellite payloads. *Mailing Add:* 17 Lowe Circle Framingham MA 01701

**TANCIG, PETER,** ENGINEERING. *Current Pos:* MINISTER SCI & TECHNOL, 90- *Personal Data:* b Freudenstadt, Ger, 44; m 71, Simona; c Suna. *Educ:* Fac Elec Eng & Comput Sci, Ljubljana, BSc, MSc, PhD. *Prof Exp:* Vis scientist, Mass Inst Technol, 80-82; chmn, Sect Comput Ling, Slovenian Asn Appl Ling; head, Lab Lang & Speech Tech, Dept Comp Sci & Informatics, Josef Stefan Inst; prof comput sci, Fac Elec Eng & Comput Sci; nat coordr, EC Phare Prog Tech Assistance; pres coun, ZS Greens Slovenia. *Concurrent Pos:* Pres, Interministerial Coord Foreign Tech Assistance, Nat Com UNESCO, Interministerial Com Info Pub Admin. *Mem:* Inst Elec & Electronics Engrs; Am Asn Artificial Intel; Asn Comput Mach. *Mailing Add:* Ministry Sci & Technol Cankarjeva 5 Ljubljana 61000 Slovenia

**TANCRELL, ROGER HENRY,** PHYSICS, ELECTRICAL ENGINEERING. *Current Pos:* prin scientist med electronics, 68-82, HEAD TRANSDUCER GROUP, RAYTHEON RES, 82-, CONSULT SCIENTIST, 83- *Personal Data:* b Whitinsville, Mass, Feb 17, 35. *Educ:* Worcester Polytech Inst, BS, 56; Mass Inst Technol, MS, 58; Harvard Univ, PhD(appl physics), 68. *Honors & Awards:* Goddard Award, Worcester Polytech Inst, 91. *Prof Exp:* Mem staff digital electronics, Lincoln Labs, Mass Inst Technol, 56-60. *Mem:* Fel Inst Elec & Electronics Engrs; Acoust Soc Am. *Res:* Medical imaging systems including ultrasound, x-ray and nuclear; surface acoustic wave devices for filters and analog signal processing; sonar (naval) transducers; polymer transducers for underwater acoustics; ultrasonic sensors. *Mailing Add:* 7 Valyn Lane Wilmington MA 01887. *Fax:* 781-860-3195

**TANCZOS, FRANK I,** CHEMICAL PHYSICS. *Current Pos:* CONSULT, 80- *Personal Data:* b Northampton, Pa, Jan 2, 21. *Educ:* Moravian Col, BS, 39; Cath Univ, PhD(physics), 56. *Prof Exp:* Res chemist cent labs, Lehigh Portland Cement Co, Pa, 39-43; phys chemist, Bur Ord, 46-59, tech dir supporting res, Bur Naval Weapons, 59-66, tech dir res & technol, Air Systs Command, Dept Navy, 66-80. *Concurrent Pos:* Mem, NASA res adv comts, Chem Energy Processes, 59-60, mem chem energy systs, 60-61 & air-breathing propulsion systs, 62-; lectr grad sch eng, Cath Univ, 60-61. *Mem:* Am Chem Soc; Am Phys Soc; assoc fel Am Inst Aeronaut & Astronaut. *Res:* New cement composition chemistry; molecular vibrational relaxation theory; energy conversion; propellant chemistry and thermodynamics; rocket and air-breathing jet propulsion principles; hypersonic air-breathing propulsion principles. *Mailing Add:* 1500 Massachusetts Ave NW Apt 249 Washington DC 20005

**TANDBERG-HANSSEN, EINAR ANDREAS,** ASTRONOMY, PHYSICS. *Current Pos:* sr res scientist solar physics, 74-83, dep lab dir, 83-87, LAB DIR, NASA MARSHALL SPACE FLIGHT CTR, 87- *Personal Data:* b Bergen, Norway, Aug 6, 21; US citizen; m 51; c 2. *Educ:* Univ Oslo, PhD(astron), 60. *Prof Exp:* Res assoc astrophys, Univ Oslo, 50-57; mem sr res staff solar physics, High Altitude Observ, Boulder, Colo, 57-74. *Concurrent Pos:* Adj prof, Physics Dept, Univ Ala, Huntsville, 82- *Mem:* Int Astron Union; Am Astron Soc; Norweg Geophys Soc; Norweg Acad Soc. *Res:* Solar physics, particularly flare and prominence research; solar corona and interplanetary space. *Mailing Add:* 44 Revere Way Huntsville AL 35801

**TANDLER, BERNARD,** CYTOLOGY, ELECTRON MICROSCOPY. *Current Pos:* AFFIL PROF ORAL BIOL, SCH DENT, UNIV WASH, 91- *Personal Data:* b Brooklyn, NY, Feb 18, 33; wid, Helen Weisman; c Janice & Evan. *Educ:* Brooklyn Col, BS, 55; Columbia Univ, AM, 57; Cornell Univ, PhD(cytol), 61. *Prof Exp:* Res fel, Sloan-Kettering Inst, 61-62; instr anat, Sch Med, NY Univ, 62-63; assoc biol, Sloan-Kettering Inst Cancer Res, Cornell Univ, 63-67, asst prof, Grad Sch, Sloan-Kettering Div, 66-67; from assoc prof to prof oral biol & med, Sch Dent, Case Western Res Univ, 67-91, from assoc prof to prof anat, 67-91. *Concurrent Pos:* Lectr, Brooklyn Col, 61-63; vis prof anat, Univ Copenhagen, 73; vis assoc prof, Sch Med, Stanford Univ, 75; vis prof, Univ Cagliari, 83 & Col Med, Northeastern Ohio Univ, 81; actg chmn oral biol, Sch Dent, Case Western Res Univ, 87-88. *Mem:* Am Soc Cell Biol; Am Asn Anatomists; Electron Micros Soc Am; Int Asn Dent Res. *Res:* Mitochondrial biogenesis; ultrastructure of normal and neoplastic salivary glands; pulmonary ultrastructure. *Mailing Add:* Kyusttu Dent Col 2-6-1 Manazuru Kokurakita-Ku 803 Japan

**TANDON, SHIV R,** ULTRASTRUCTURAL STUDIES OF LEGUME ROOT NODULES, IMMUNOGOLD METHOD OF ENZYMES LOCALIZATION IN LEGUME ROOT NODULES. *Current Pos:* From asst prof to assoc prof, 68-80, PROF CELL BIOL & CHAIR, DEPT BOT, UNIV WIS-PLATTEVILLE, 80- *Personal Data:* m 71, Mahi Ziaian; c Shiv D & Sahun C. *Educ:* Panjab Univ, India, BS, 60, MS, 62; Univ SC, Columbia, PhD(bot), 67. *Res:* Ultrastructural studies of infected and unifected cells in legume root nodules; involvement of perotisomes in the ureides transporting legumes; immunogold labelling of enzymes found in infected and uninfected cells in legume root nodules. *Mailing Add:* Univ Wis Platteville One University Plaza Platteville WI 53818-3099

**TANEJA, VIDYA SAGAR,** MATHEMATICAL STATISTICS. *Current Pos:* assoc prof, 70-74, PROF MATH STATIST, WESTERN ILL UNIV, 74- *Personal Data:* b India, Sept 7, 31; m 62; c 2. *Educ:* Panjab Univ India, BA, 50, MA, 52; Univ Minn, MA, 63; Univ Conn, PhD(statist), 66. *Prof Exp:* Lectr math, Doaba Col, 53-59; instr, Univ Minn, Morris, 64-65; asst prof math statist, NMex State Univ, 66-70. *Concurrent Pos:* Vis prof, Ohio State Univ, 77-78. *Mem:* Inst Math Statist; Am Statist Asn. *Res:* Statistical methodology, statistical analysis, time series, ranking and selection; heteroscedastic methods; probability distributions. *Mailing Add:* 1418 Debbie Lane Macomb IL 61455

**TANENBAUM, BASIL SAMUEL,** BIOMEDICAL ENGINEERING, SCIENCE EDUCATION & ENGINEERING EDUCATION. *Current Pos:* PROF ENG, HARVEY MUDD COL, 75-, NORMAN F SPRAQUE JR PROF LIFE SCI, 96- *Personal Data:* b Providence, RI, Dec 1, 34; m 56, Carol Binder; c Laurie, Stephen & David. *Educ:* Brown Univ, BS, 56; Yale Univ, MS, 57, PhD(physics), 60. *Prof Exp:* Staff physicist res div, Raytheon Co, 60-63; prof eng, Case Western Res Univ, 63-75. *Concurrent Pos:* Vis scientist, Arecibo Observ, 67-68; Sigma Xi Res Award, 69; sci adv comt, Nat Astron & Ionospheric Ctr, 72-77; dean fac, Harvey Mudd Col, 75-93; vis scientist, Southern Calif Edison Co, 90, Beckman Laser Inst, Univ Calif, Irvine, 93-94. *Mem:* AAAS; Am Soc Eng Educ; Inst Elec & Electronics Engrs; Am Asn Univ Prof; Sigma Xi. *Res:* Laser applications in medicine; sound propagation; theory of turbulence; ionospheric physics; waves in plasmas; radiation in a plasma; kinetic theory of gas mixtures and plasmas; shock wave theory; energy conversion; electromagnetic fields; Laser applications in medicine. *Mailing Add:* 611 Delaware Dr Claremont CA 91711. *Fax:* 909-621-8967; *E-Mail:* sam__tanenbaum@hmc.edu

**TANENBAUM, MORRIS,** CHEMICAL PHYSICS, METALLURGY. *Current Pos:* RETIRED. *Personal Data:* b Huntington, WVa, Nov 10, 28; m 50, Charlotte M Silver; c Michael & Robin. *Educ:* Johns Hopkins Univ, AB, 49; Princeton Univ, Am, 51, PhD(phys chem), 52. *Hon Degrees:* DSc, NJ Inst Technol, 80, Seafoam Hall Univ, 81, Worcester Polytech Inst, 83, Lehigh Univ, 92; DE, Stevens Dist Technol, 82. *Prof Exp:* Asst, Princeton Univ, 49-50, instr, 50-51; mem tech staff, Bell Tel Labs, 52-56, subdept head, 56-60, asst metall dir, 60-62, dir solid state devices lab, 62-64; dir res & develop, Western Elec Co, Inc, 64-68, gen mgr eng, 68-71, vpres eng, 71-72, vpres, Transmission Equip Div, 72-75; exec vpres systems eng & develop, Bell Labs, 75-76; vpres eng & network serv, Am Tel & Tel Co, 76-78; pres, NJ Bell Tel Co, 78-80; exec vpres, AT&T, 80-84, chmn & chief exec officer, AT&T Commun, 84-86, vchmn & chief financial officer, 86-91. *Concurrent Pos:* Mem mat adv bd, Nat Res Coun-Nat Acad Sci; consult, Dept Defense, NASA & Nat Bur Stand; mem vis comts, Mass Inst Technol, Princeton Univ, Carnegie Inst Technol, Univ Pa & Lehigh Univ; Nat Res Coun Gov Bd. *Mem:* Nat Acad Eng; Am Chem Soc; fel Am Phys Soc; Am Inst Mining Metall & Petrol Engrs; fel Inst Elec & Electronics Engrs; fel AAAS; fel Am Acad Arts & Sci. *Res:* Chemistry and physics of solids; solid-state device physics; engineering research in manufacturing processes; pioneered the use of silicon in semiconductor devices. *Mailing Add:* 74 Falmouth St Short Hills NJ 07078

**TANENBAUM, STUART WILLIAM,** BIOCHEMISTRY, MICROBIOLOGY. *Current Pos:* dean, Sch Biol Chem & Ecol, 73-85, PROF BIOTECHNOL, COL ENVIRON SCI & FORESTRY, STATE UNIV NY, 85-; EMER PROF, UPSTATE MED CTR, 93- *Personal Data:* b New York, NY, July 15, 24; m 62; c 2. *Educ:* City Col New York, BS, 44; Columbia Univ, PhD, 51. *Honors & Awards:* Sigma Xi Fac Res Award, 86. *Prof Exp:* Instr chem, City Col New York, 48; Am Cancer Soc fel, Stanford Univ, 51-52; lectr bact, Univ Calif, 52; res assoc biol, Stanford Univ, 52-53; from res assoc to prof microbiol, Col Physicians & Surgeons, Columbia Univ, 53-73; adj prof microbiol, Upstate Med Ctr, 73-93. *Concurrent Pos:* Mem panel molecular biol, NSF, 62-63 & 72-73, resident prog dir molecular biol sect, 71-72; State Univ NY fac exchange scholar, 74-77; trustee, Forestry Found, Syracuse, NY, 74-; prog dir, Biomed Res Support Prog, State Univ NY Col Environ Seci & Forestry, 77-84; mem competitive res, NSF, 80-; chmn, oversight panel, molecular & genetic biosci, NSF, 82; vis prof, istituto superiore di sanita, Rome, 63-64. *Mem:* Am Soc Biol Chemists; Am Soc Microbiol; Am Chem Soc; Soc Indust Microbiol. *Res:* Fungal metabolism; antibiotic biosynthesis; bacterial physiology; immunochemistry; cell and molecular biology; biotechnology; cytoactive microbiol products; redox enzymes; biotechnology applications; extracellular amionic polysorbarides. *Mailing Add:* Chem Dept State Univ NY Col Environ Sci & Forestry Syracuse NY 13210

**TANFORD, CHARLES,** MEMBRANES & TRANSPORT. *Current Pos:* prof, 60-71, James B Duke prof, 71-88, EMER PROF, DUKE UNIV MED CTR, 88- *Personal Data:* b Halle, Ger, Dec 29, 21; nat US; div; c 3. *Educ:* NY Univ, BA, 43; Princeton Univ, MA, 44, PhD(phys chem), 47. *Honors & Awards:* Reilly Lectr, Univ Notre Dame, 79; Alexander von Humboldt Prize, 84; Am Soc Biochem & Molecular Biol, 92. *Prof Exp:* Asst, Princeton Univ, 43-44; chemist, Tenn Eastman Corp, 44-45; asst, Princeton Univ, 45-46; Lalor fel phys chem, Harvard Med Sch, 47-49; from asst prof to prof, Univ Iowa, 49-60. *Concurrent Pos:* Guggenheim fel, Yale Univ, 56-57; consult, USPHS, 59-63; USPHS res career award, 62; vis prof, Harvard Univ, 66; mem, Whitehead Med Res Inst, 77-81; George Eastman vis prof, Univ Oxford, 77-78; Walker-Ames prof, Univ Wash, 79. *Mem:* Nat Acad Sci. *Res:* Physical chemistry of proteins, especially transport proteins and related substances; structure and function of membranes. *Mailing Add:* Tarlswood Back Lane Easingwold York Y06 3BG England

**TANG, ALFRED SHO-YU,** ALGEBRA. *Current Pos:* Assoc prof, 66-80, PROF MATH, SAN FRANCISCO STATE UNIV, 80- *Personal Data:* b Shanghai, China, Sept 9, 34; US citizen; m 69; c 2. *Educ:* Univ Hong Kong, BSc, 56; Univ SC, MS, 60; Univ Calif, Berkeley, PhD(math), 69. *Mem:* AAAS; Am Math Soc; Math Asn Am. *Mailing Add:* 3236 Round Hill Dr Hayward CA 94542-2122

**TANG, ANDREW H,** PHARMACOLOGY. *Current Pos:* Res assoc, 64-70, SR RES SCIENTIST PHARMACOL, UPJOHN CO, 70- *Personal Data:* b Canton, China, Feb 10, 36; US citizen; m 64; c 2. *Educ:* Howard Col, BS, 60; Purdue Univ, MS, 62, PhD(pharmacol), 64. *Mem:* AAAS; Am Soc Pharmacol & Exp Therapeut. *Res:* Pharmacology of the central nervous system; spinal cord physiology; behavioral pharmacology. *Mailing Add:* Res Dept Upjohn Co 301 Henrietta St Kalamazoo MI 49001-0199

**TANG, CHA-MEI,** FREE-ELECTRON LASERS, FREE-EMITTER ARRAYS. *Current Pos:* res physicist, Plasma Physics Div, 81-85, head, Radiation & Accelerator Physics Sect, 85-93, SUPVRY RES PHYSICIST, NAVAL RES LAB, 93- *Personal Data:* b Taipei, Taiwan, Aug 9, 49; US citizen; m 71, Bertram Hai; c Jamie & Julie. *Educ:* Mass Inst Technol, BS, 71, MS, 73, ScD, 77. *Honors & Awards:* WISE Award Sci, Women Sci & Eng, 92. *Prof Exp:* Sr engr, Appl Physics Lab, Johns Hopkins Univ, 77-78; sr scientist, Jaycor, 78-81. *Concurrent Pos:* Vis scientist, Nat Inst Stand & Technol, 93-94. *Mem:* Fel Am Phys Soc; Inst Elec & Electronics Engrs; AAAS; Sigma Xi. *Res:* Analytical and numerical research on radiation sources in frequencies ranging from microwave to x-rays advanced electron accelerator concepts, accelerator instabilities, and fluid mechanics; field-emitter arrays, vacuum microelectronics and flat panel field emitter displays. *Mailing Add:* 11609 Lake Potomac Dr Potomac MD 20854. *E-Mail:* tang@ppd.nrl.navy.mil

**TANG, CHUNG LIANG,** PHYSICS. *Current Pos:* assoc prof elec eng, 64-68, SPENCER T OLIN PROF ENG, CORNELL UNIV, 68-; PRES, ITHACA RES CORP. *Personal Data:* b Shanghai, China, May 14, 34; US citizen; m 58; c 3. *Educ:* Univ Wash, BS, 55; Calif Inst Technol, MS, 56; Harvard Univ, PhD(appl physics), 60. *Prof Exp:* Res staff mem, Raytheon Co, 60-61, sr res scientist, 61-63, prin res scientist, 63-64. *Concurrent Pos:* Consult res div, Raytheon Co, 64-72; assoc ed, J Quantum Electronics, Inst Elec & Electronics Engrs, 69-76. *Mem:* Nat Acad Eng; fel Inst Elec & Electronics Engrs; fel Am Phys Soc; fel Optical Soc Am. *Res:* Quantum electronics; electromagnetic theory. *Mailing Add:* Sch Elec Eng Col Elec Eng 326 Phillips Hall Ithaca NY 14853. *Fax:* 607-255-5120; *E-Mail:* cltang@ee.cornell.edu

**TANG, CHUNG-MUH,** ATMOSPHERIC DYNAMICS. *Personal Data:* b Tungkang, Taiwan, Oct 20, 36; m 65, Lanling Mao; c Henry & Eugene. *Educ:* Nat Taiwan Univ, BS, 59; Univ Calif, Los Angeles, MA, 65, CPhil, 69, PhD(meteorol), 70. *Prof Exp:* Res asst, Taiwan Rain Stimulation Res Inst, 61-62; NSF grant & asst res meteorologist, Univ Calif, Los Angeles, 70; Defense Dept grant & res staff meteorologist, Yale Univ, 70-75; asst prof physics & atmospheric sci, Drexel Univ, 75-80; res scientist, Univ Space Res Asn, 80-82, consult, 82-88; fac, Villanova Univ, 89, asst prof physics, 90-91. *Mem:* Am Meteorol Soc. *Res:* Theoretical studies of large scale atmospheric motions; theoretical studies of shear-flow instability. *Mailing Add:* 241 Marple Rd Haverford PA 19041

**TANG, CHUNG-SHIH,** PLANT CHEMISTRY. *Current Pos:* from asst prof to assoc prof, 68-79, chmn, Dept Environ Biochem, 89-92, PROF ENVIRON BIOCHEM, UNIV HAWAII, 79- *Personal Data:* b China, Jan 8, 38; m 65, Wenjing Yang; c Annie, Nina & Michele. *Educ:* Taiwan Univ, BS, 60, MS, 62; Univ Calif, Davis, PhD(agr chem), 67. *Prof Exp:* Res chemist, Univ Calif, Davis, 67-68. *Concurrent Pos:* Hon res prof, SChina Inst Bot, Acad Sinica, Guangzhou, China, 87-, Kunming Inst Bot, Acad Sinica, Kunming, China, 88- *Mem:* Int Soc Chem Ecol; Am Chem Soc; Phytochem Soc NAm. *Res:* Bioactive plant secondary metabolite; allelopathy; rhizospheric chemistry. *Mailing Add:* Dept Biochem Univ Hawaii 1800 E W Rd Honolulu HI 96822-1888. *Fax:* 808-956-5037; *E-Mail:* tangcs@hawaii.edu

**TANG, DENNY DUAN-LEE,** MAGNETICS. *Current Pos:* Mem res staff, Int Bus Mach, 75-82, mgr, 82-89, mem tech planning staff, 89-90, MEM RES STAFF, IBM ALMADEN RES CTR, 90- *Personal Data:* b China; US citizen; m 71; c 3. *Educ:* Univ Mich, Ann Arbor, PhD(elec eng), 75. *Mem:* Fel Inst Elec & Electronics Engrs; Inst Elec & Electronics Engrs Electron Devices Soc. *Res:* Silicon bipolar technology; magnetic recording technology. *Mailing Add:* IBM Almaden Res Ctr 650 Harry Rd San Jose CA 95120

**TANG, DONALD T(AO-NAN)**, ELECTRICAL ENGINEERING. *Current Pos:* MEM RES STAFF, IBM CORP, 60- *Personal Data:* b China, May 9, 32; m 62; c 2. *Educ:* Nat Taiwan Univ, BS, 53; Univ Ill, PhD(elec eng), 60. *Prof Exp:* Instr elec eng, Univ Ill, 55-60. *Mem:* Inst Elec & Electronics Engrs; Sigma Xi. *Res:* Network theory, communication theory and information theory with applications to filter design, pattern recognition, error-correcting codes and data compaction. *Mailing Add:* 49 Fox Den Rd Mt Kisco NY 10549

**TANG, HOMER H(O)**, physical science, aeronautical engineering, for more information see previous edition

**TANG, HWA-TSANG**, LINEAR ALGEBRA, SET THEORY. *Current Pos:* ASSOC PROF MATH, CALIF STATE UNIV, HAYWARD, 69- *Personal Data:* b Shanghai, China, Nov 29, 37; US citizen; m 69. *Educ:* Univ Chicago, SM, 58, PhD(math), 65. *Prof Exp:* Asst prof math, Calif State Univ, Northridge, 59-61; asst prof math, Temple Univ, Philadelphia, 64-69. *Mem:* Am Math Soc. *Res:* Linear algebra; set theory; group theory; partial differential equations. *Mailing Add:* Dept Math Calif State Univ Hayward CA 94542-3092

**TANG, IGNATIUS NING-BANG**, AEROSOL SCIENCE, ATMOSPHERIC CHEMISTRY. *Current Pos:* CHEM ENGR, BROOKHAVEN NAT LAB, 64- *Personal Data:* b Nanking, China, July 7, 33; m 62, Carol Lin; c Marion & Alice. *Educ:* Nat Taiwan Univ, BS, 55; Univ NDak, MS(chem eng), 60; State Univ NY Stony Brook, MS, 75, PhD(appl math), 82. *Prof Exp:* Asst engr, Taiwan Fertilizer Corp, Taiwan, Repub of China, 56-58. *Mem:* Am Asn Aerosol Res; Am Chem Soc. *Res:* Thermodynamics of concentrated electrolyte solutions; mechanisms of gas-to-particle conversion and atmospheric nucleation phenomena; condensational growth and light scattering of atmospheric aerosols; gas phase reaction kinetics; mass transfer at gas-liquid interface. *Mailing Add:* PO Box 156 Shoreham NY 11786. *Fax:* 516-282-7905; *E-Mail:* intang@bnl.gov

**TANG, IRVING CHE-HONG**, NUMERICAL ANALYSIS. *Current Pos:* PROF MATH, OKLA STATE UNIV, 94- *Personal Data:* b Macau, China, Dec 29, 31; US citizen. *Educ:* Univ Calif, BS, 52; Univ Ill, MS, 53; Wash Univ, DSc, 65. *Prof Exp:* Design engr, Friden Calculators, 55-56; staff engr, IBM Corp, 56-66; postdoctoral fel, Univ Oslo, 66-68; head, Dept Math, NSW Inst Technol, 69-76; Hong Kong Polytech Inst, 77-89; prof math, Phillips Univ, 89-91, Rose State Col, Okla City Community Col, 91-94. *Mem:* Math Asn Am; Indust Math Soc; Sigma Xi; Brit Comput Soc; Hong Kong Math Soc (pres, 77-81). *Mailing Add:* PO Box 890773 Oklahoma City OK 73189. *Fax:* 405-945-9141; *E-Mail:* ictang@okway.okstate.edu

**TANG, JAMES JUH-LING**, APPLIED MECHANICS, HEAT TRANSFER. *Current Pos:* MGR CAN DEVELOP, CONTINENTAL CAN CO, OAK BROOK, IL, 87- *Personal Data:* b Tientsin, China, Mar 8, 37; US citizen; m 65; c 2. *Educ:* Nat Taiwan Univ, BS, 59; Univ Mo, Rolla, MS, 63; Yale Univ, PhD(appl mech), 70. *Prof Exp:* Engr, Weiskopf & Pickworth, 63-65; sr res engr, Am Can Co, Princeton, NJ, 70-75, res assoc, 75-77, supvr machine design, 77-78, supvr develop eng, 78-82, mgr eng & prod develop, Am Can Co, Barrington, Ill, 82-87. *Mem:* Am Soc Mech Engrs; Soc Rheology; Am Inst Physics. *Res:* Elastic-plastic material behavior; heat transfer of industrial processes; computerized process control; finite element analysis; computer-aided engineering. *Mailing Add:* 833 S Elm St Palatine IL 60067

**TANG, JORDAN J N**, BIOCHEMISTRY. *Current Pos:* res asst, Okla Med Res Found, 57-58, biochemist, 61-63, assoc biochem, 63-65, assoc prof, 65-69, head, Neurosci Sect & actg head, 70-71, HEAD, LAB PROTEIN STUDIES, OKLA MED RES FOUND, 71-; PROF BIOCHEM, SCH MED, UNIV OKLA, 71- *Personal Data:* b Foochow, China, Mar 23, 31; m 58; c 2. *Educ:* Taiwan Prov Col, BS, 53; Okla State Univ, MS, 57; Univ Okla, PhD(biochem), 61. *Prof Exp:* Res asst biochem, Okla State Univ, 55-57. *Concurrent Pos:* Res assoc biochem, Sch Med, Univ Okla, 62-63, asst prof & asst head dept, 63-67, assoc prof, 67-70; vis scientist, Lab Molecular Biol, Cambridge, Eng, 64-66; Guggenheim fel, 65; J G Puterbaugh chair med res, 85- *Mem:* AAAS; Am Chem Soc; Am Soc Biol Chemists. *Res:* Structure and function of proteins; structure of gastric, lysosomal and retroviral proteolytic enzymes. *Mailing Add:* Okla Med Res Found 825 NE 13th St Oklahoma City OK 73104

**TANG, KWONG-TIN**, PHYSICS, PHYSICAL CHEMISTRY. *Current Pos:* from asst prof to assoc prof, 67-72, chmn dept, 72-77, PROF PHYSICS, PAC LUTHERAN UNIV, 72- *Personal Data:* b Feb 24, 36; US citizen. *Educ:* Univ Wash, BS, 58, MA, 59; Columbia Univ, PhD(physics), 65. *Prof Exp:* Res assoc chem, Columbia Univ, 65-66; physicist, Collins Radio Co, 66-67. *Concurrent Pos:* Consult, Boeing Co, 70 & 72; vis lectr, Univ Wash, 71; Res Corp grant, Pac Lutheran Univ, 71-74. *Mem:* Am Phys Soc; Am Asn Physics Teachers. *Res:* Atomic and molecular collision; scattering theory; reaction rates; intermolecular forces; optical dispersion; lattice vibration. *Mailing Add:* Dept Physics Pac Lutheran Univ S Tacoma WA 98447

**TANG, MAN-CHUNG**, ENGINEERING. *Current Pos:* CHMN BD, T Y LIN INT. *Educ:* Tech Univ, Darmstadt, NSE, PhD(eng). *Honors & Awards:* Outstanding Civil Eng Achievement Award, Am Soc Civil Engrs; Outstanding Eng Achievement Award, Nat Soc Prof Engrs; Fed Design Achievement Award, Nat Endowmant Arts, 95. *Mem:* Nat Acad Eng; Am Concrete Inst; Am Soc Civil Engrs; Prestressed Concrete Inst; Nat Soc Prof Engrs; Asn Rational Environ Alternatives; Am Inst Steel Construct; Soc Sci Res Council; Int Asn Bridge & Struct Eng. *Res:* Sound and innovative techniques in the construction of bridges, especially long span bridges. *Mailing Add:* T Y Lin Int 825 Battery St San Francisco CA 94111

**TANG, PUQI PERRY**, COMPUTER NETWORKING, ANALYSIS OF COMPLEX VARIABLES. *Current Pos:* SOFTWARE ENGR, INTEL ARCHIT LABS, INTEL CORP, 96- *Personal Data:* m 87, Yihong Zhang. *Educ:* Peking Univ, China, Bach, 84, Master 87; Purdue Univ, PhD(math), 94, MS, 96. *Prof Exp:* Grad instr math, Purdue Univ, 87-96. *Res:* Quasiconformal transformation Cauchy-Riemann manifolds; quality of service of computer network. *Mailing Add:* 15703 NW Trakehner Way Portland OR 97229. *Fax:* 503-264-3483; *E-Mail:* ptang@juno.com

**TANG, RUEN CHIU**, FOREST PRODUCTS, WOOD COMPOSITES. *Current Pos:* PROF WOOD SCI, AUBURN UNIV, 78- *Personal Data:* b Kiangsu, China, Oct 31, 34; m 60; c 3. *Educ:* Nat Chung-Hsin Univ, Taiwan, BS, 57; NC State Univ, PhD(wood sci), 68. *Honors & Awards:* Excellence Award, Soc Am Foresters, 87. *Prof Exp:* Teacher, Kung Hua Sch Elec Technol, 56-57; wood technologist, Taiwan Forest Bur, 59-63; res asst, US Naval Res, NC State Univ, 63-66; teaching asst wood mech, Univ Wash, 66-67; State of Ky & USAF, res assoc, Inst Theoret & Appl Mech, Univ Ky, 68, State of Ky res assoc wood mech, Univ, 69, from asst prof to assoc prof wood sci, 74-77. *Mem:* Soc Wood Sci & Technol; Soc Exp Mech; Forest Prod Soc; AAAS; Am Soc Testing & Mat; Sigma Xi. *Res:* Anisotropic elasticity; composite materials; fiber mechanics; noise control; reliability in structural design; math modeling. *Mailing Add:* Dept Forestry Auburn Univ Auburn AL 36830

**TANG, SHIOW-SHIH**, NEPHROLOGY. *Current Pos:* asst prof med, 86-90, ASST PROF PEDIAT, HARVARD MED SCH, 90-; ASST BIOCHEMIST CHILDRENS SERV, MASS GEN HOSP, 90-, TECH DIR, PEDIAT RENAL LAB, 92- *Educ:* Nat Taiwan Univ, BPharm, 70, MPharmacol, 73; McGill Univ, PhD(physiol), 80. *Prof Exp:* Res fel, Hemat Div, Dept Internal Med, Univ Tex, Med Sch, 79-80; res assoc, Dept Biochem, Boston Univ Sch Med, 80-82, asst res prof biochem, 82-86; group leader biochem, Div Vascular Med, Dept Med, Brigham & Womens Hosp, 86-90, assoc biochemist, 86-90. *Concurrent Pos:* Lectr pharmacol, Kaohsiung Med Col, Taiwan, 73-74; prin investr, Taiwanese Nat Sci Res Coun, 73-74; Am Heart Asn, 84-86, NIH, 89-95, William F Milton Fund, 91-92, Dupont Merck, 91-94. *Mem:* Fel Am Heart Asn; fel Am Inst Chemists; AAAS; Am Chem Soc. *Res:* Nephrology; author of 31 publications. *Mailing Add:* 99 Laconia St Lexington MA 02173

**TANG, STEPHEN SHIEN-PU**, SYSTEMS ENGINEERING. *Current Pos:* proj engr space technol planning, 80-97, SR PROJ ENGR, AEROSPACE CORP, LOS ANGELES, 97- *Personal Data:* b Changsha, China, Nov 13, 35; m 72; c 2. *Educ:* Nat Taiwan Univ, BS, 59; Univ Cailf, Berkeley, MS, 64; Princeton Univ, PhD(aerosci), 69. *Prof Exp:* Res assoc molecular beams, Dept Appl Sci, Yale Univ, 68-71; vis assoc prof fluid mech, Nat Univ Taiwan, 71-72, vis assoc prof molecular beams, Tech Univ Hannover, Ger, 72-74; res scientist chem laser, Defense & Space Syst Group, TRW, Inc, 74-80. *Mem:* Am Inst Aeronaut & Astronaut; Am Phys Soc; Sigma Xi. *Res:* Molecular beams; gasdynamics and fluid mechanics; gas phase kinetics; gas-solid interactions; space technology planning; high power lasers; high beam energy particle beams; satellite systems and technologies. *Mailing Add:* 1611 Toscanini Dr Rancho Palos Verdes CA 90275

**TANG, TIAN-SHEN**, VERY-LARGE-SCALE INTEGRATED CIRCUIT DESIGN & COMPUTER-ASSISTED DESIGN, GLOBAL OPTIMIZATION & APPLICATIONS TO CIRCUIT DESIGN. *Current Pos:* LEAD DESIGN ENGR MEMORY CIRCUITS, LANSTAR SEMICONDUCTOR CORP, 97- *Personal Data:* b Tianjin, China, Jan 29, 57; m 86, Flora D Ho; c Winston R & Helen R. *Educ:* Nankai Univ, China, BS, 82; Tex A&M Univ, MS, 85, PhD(elec eng), 90. *Prof Exp:* From asst prof to assoc prof elec eng & comput sci, Tex A&M Univ, Kingsville, 90-97. *Concurrent Pos:* Leroy L Fouraker fel, Tex A&M Univ, 90; co-prin investr, NSF, 92-96 & Johnson Space Ctr, NASA, 92-; prin investr, Tex Advan Technol Prog, 93-96; partner, Reliance Technol, 93- *Mem:* Inst Elec & Electronics Engrs. *Res:* Developing radiation hardened complimentary metal-oxide silicon; very-large-scale integration design and computer-assisted design. *Mailing Add:* 3420 Woodside Dr Arlington TX 76016-2365. *Fax:* 817-469-1911; *E-Mail:* Internet Home Page: http://www.lesm.com

**TANG, TIN-WEI**, ELECTRICAL ENGINEERING, PLASMA PHYSICS. *Current Pos:* assoc prof elec eng, 68-74, PROF ELEC & COMPUT ENG, UNIV MASS, AMHERST, 74- *Personal Data:* b Taiwan, China, May 27, 34; m 63; c 2. *Educ:* Taiwan Univ, BSEE, 57; Brown Univ, MS, 61, PhD(eng), 64. *Prof Exp:* Teaching asst elec eng, Taiwan Univ, 57-59; res asst eng, Brown Univ, 59-63; instr elec eng, Univ Conn, 63-64, asst prof aerospace eng, 64-68. *Concurrent Pos:* NSF res initiation grant, 65-66, res grants, 66-68, 70-72, 74-76 & 76-78. *Mem:* Inst Elec & Electronics Engrs; Am Phys Soc. *Res:* Electromagnetic theory; nonlinear wave interactions in plasmas; antenna design; solid-state device modeling. *Mailing Add:* Dept Elec & Comput Eng Univ Mass Amherst 201 Marcus Hall Amherst MA 01003-5110

**TANG, VICTOR KUANG-TAO**, statistics, mathematics, for more information see previous edition

**TANG, WEN**, MOUNTAIN VALLEY CIRCULATION, MESO SCALE CIRCULATION. *Current Pos:* prof, 74-94, EMER PROF, UNIV MASS, LOWELL, 94- *Personal Data:* m 48, Tsuen-Kwong Hsu; c Cha-Mei, Cha-Kie, Cha-Min, Cha-Nan, Joyce & Jessamy. *Educ:* Nat Cent Univ, China, BS, 45; NY Univ, MS, 58, PhD(meteorol), 60. *Prof Exp:* Res scientist, GCA Corp, 60-68; from asst prof to assoc prof, Lowell Tech Inst, 68-74. *Mem:* Am Meteorol Soc. *Res:* General circulation on Mars and Venus; mountain-valley circulations; small scale circulations such as flow in the forests and agricultural fields; meso-scale circulations such as land and sea breezes; large scale atmospheric circulation of Asian monsoon season influenced by Tibet Plateau. *Mailing Add:* 9 Exbow Rd Lexington MA 02173

**TANG, WILLIAM MING-WU,** PLASMA PHYSICS. *Current Pos:* Res assoc, Princeton Plasma Physics Lab, 72-74, res staff, 74-76, res physicist, 76-79, PRIN RES PHYSICIST, PRINCETON PLASMA PHYSICS LAB, 79-, HEAD, THEORY DIV, 92-; PROF, DEPT ASTROPHYS SCI, PRINCETON UNIV, 79- *Personal Data:* b Chung-An, China, June 30, 44; US citizen; m, Mary; c Andrea. *Educ:* Univ San Francisco, BS, 66; Univ Calif, MS, 68, PhD(physics), 72. *Concurrent Pos:* Consult, Naval Res Lab, Washington, DC, 76-78, Sci Appln, Inc, La Jolla, Calif, 81-85; assoc prof astrophys sci, Princeton Univ, 76-79; mem, Nat Theory Coord Comt, 92- *Mem:* Fel Am Phys Soc. *Res:* Plasma physics with a special area of focus being kinetic theory of plasma dynamics relevant to confinement problems in fusion devices. *Mailing Add:* Plasma Physics Lab Princeton Univ Box 451 Princeton NJ 08543

**TANG, WILSON H,** RISK & RELIABILITY ANALYSIS, ENGINEERING EDUCATION. *Current Pos:* From asst prof to assoc prof, 69-80, assoc head, 89-91, PROF CIVIL ENG, UNIV ILL, URBANA-CHAMPAIGN, 80-; HEAD CIVIL ENG, HONG KONG UNIV SCI & TECHNOL, 96- *Personal Data:* b Hong Kong, Aug 16, 43; US citizen; m 69; c 2. *Educ:* Mass Inst Technol, BS, 66, MS, 67; Stanford Univ, PhD(civil eng), 69. *Honors & Awards:* State-of-the-Art Award, Am Soc Civil Engrs, 90. *Concurrent Pos:* Guggenheim fel, John S Guggenheim Found, 76; vis prof, Norweg Geotech Inst, Oslo, 76-77, Imp Col, London, 77 & Nat Univ Singapore, 83; prin investr, NSF & Am Petrol Inst, 79-; chmn, Offshore Reliability Comt, Am Soc Civil Engrs, 85-88; mem, Geotech Bd, Nat Res Coun; Co-chmn, Geotech Reliability Comt, Am Soc Civil Engrs, 93- *Mem:* Am Soc Civil Engrs; Am Soc Eng Educ; Int Soc Soil Mech & Found Eng; Int Geostatist Asn; Int Asn Struct Safety & Reliability; Int Asn Civil Eng Reliability & Risk Analysis. *Res:* Risk and reliability modeling and assessment in geotechnical, structural, hydraulic and offshore engineering. *Mailing Add:* Dept Civil Eng Hong Kong Univ Sci & Technol Clearwater Bay Kowloon Hong Kong People's Republic of China. *Fax:* 217-333-9464; *E-Mail:* wtang@civilgate.ce.uiuc.edu

**TANG, Y(U) S(UN),** HEAT TRANSFER, NUCLEAR WASTE MANAGEMENT. *Current Pos:* CONSULT ENG, 88- *Personal Data:* b Nanking, China, Oct 24, 22; US citizen; m 50, Lillian Mao; c Paul C, John C & Elaine (Lee). *Educ:* Nat Cent Univ, China, BSME, 44; Univ Wis, MS, 48; Univ Fla, PhD(chem eng), 52. *Prof Exp:* Sr process engr, Gen Chem Div, Allied Chem & Dye Corp, 52-54, sr proj engr, 54-56; sr develop engr, Steam Div, Westinghouse Elec Corp, 56-59; group leader heat transfer, Allison Div, Gen Motors Corp, 59-64, prin scientist, 64-66; adv engr, Astronuclear Lab, Westinghouse Elec Corp, 66-71, adv engr, Advan Reactors Div, 71-84; adj assoc prof energy res, Univ Pittsburgh, 84-86, res prof chem eng, 87-89, res prof mech eng, 89-90. *Concurrent Pos:* Lectr, Univ Pittsburgh, 67-68; chmn, Heat Transfer Res Comt, Am Inst Chem Engrs, 67-70, 80-83, Nuclear Energy Comt, 83-85; vis specialist, Nat Cent Univ, Taiwan, China, 84; vis prof, Nanyang Technol Inst, Singapore, 85, Nat Tsing Hua Univ, Taiwan, China, 86. *Mem:* Fel Am Inst Chem Engrs; Am Nuclear Soc; Am Soc Mech Engrs; fel AAAS. *Res:* Heat transfer and fluid flow; liquid metal boiling and two-phase flow; space power generation; liquid-metal fast breed reactor thermal analysis; nuclear waste management; radioactive waste management. *Mailing Add:* 1552 Holly Hill Dr Bethel Park PA 15102-3508. *Fax:* 412-854-5963

**TANG, YAU-CHIEN,** PHYSICS. *Current Pos:* assoc prof, 64-70, PROF PHYSICS, UNIV MINN, MINNEAPOLIS, 70- *Personal Data:* b China, Aug 7, 28; nat US; m 60; c 2. *Educ:* Univ Ill, PhD(physics), 58. *Honors & Awards:* Alexander von Humboldt Sr Scientist Award. *Prof Exp:* Res assoc, Fla State Univ, 58-62 & Brookhaven Nat Lab, 62-64. *Mem:* Am Phys Soc. *Res:* Low energy nuclear physics. *Mailing Add:* Sch Physics Univ Minn Minneapolis MN 55455

**TANG, YI-NOO,** PHYSICAL CHEMISTRY, RADIOCHEMISTRY. *Current Pos:* from asst prof to assoc prof, 67-77, PROF CHEM, TEX A&M UNIV, 77- *Personal Data:* b Hunan, China, Feb 28, 38; m 64; c 2. *Educ:* Chung Chi Col, Hong Kong, BA, 59; Univ Kans, PhD(chem), 64. *Prof Exp:* Fel, Univ Kans, 64-65; fel, Univ Calif, Irvine, 65-66, instr chem, 66-67. *Mem:* Am Chem Soc; Am Inst Physics. *Res:* Hot atom chemistry; unimolecular reactions; photochemistry; carbene chemistry; gas chromatography; silicon chemistry. *Mailing Add:* Dept Chem Tex A&M Univ College Station TX 77843

**TANG, YONG MING,** MOLECULAR BIOLOGY. *Current Pos:* SR STAFF FEL & PRIN INVESTR, DIV MOLECULAR EPIDEMIOL, NAT CTR TOXICOL RES, 95- *Personal Data:* m, Pei Ling Wang; c Michael. *Educ:* Fu Dan Univ, BS, 82; Academia Sinica, MS, 85; Purdue Univ, PhD(med chem & pharmacol), 92. *Prof Exp:* Res scientist, Shanghai Inst Cell Biol, Acad Sinica, 85-86; postdoctoral fel, Dept Pharmacol & Toxicol, Purdue Univ, 92-95. *Concurrent Pos:* Food & Drug Admin res grantee, Nat Ctr Toxicol Res, 97- *Mem:* Chinese Asn Cell Biol; Chinese Asn Biochem; Am Asn Cancer Res; Soc Chinese Bioscientists Am; Sino-Am Pharmaceut Asn. *Res:* Development, validation and clinical application of molecular biomarkers of carcinogen exposure and individual susceptibility in humans; role of cytochrome P450IB1 in drug metabolism and carcinogenesis. *Mailing Add:* Nat Ctr Toxicol Res 3900 NCTR Dr Jefferson AR 72079-9502. *Fax:* 780-543-7773; *E-Mail:* ytang@nctr.fda.gov

**TANG, YOU-ZHI,** ENVIRONMENTAL SAMPLING & ANALYSIS, GAS CHROMATOGRAPHY. *Current Pos:* proj scientist, Concord Environ, 89-90, SR SCIENTIST, BOVAR-CONCORD ENVIRON, 90- *Personal Data:* b Guangzhou, Guangdong, China, Dec 12, 59; Can citizen. *Educ:* Guangdong Inst Technol, BEng, 82; Dalhousie Univ, PhD(chem), 88. *Prof Exp:* Analytical chemist, Guangdong Environ Bur, China, 82; vis scientist, Environ Can, 87-89. *Concurrent Pos:* Adv, SChina Inst Environ Sci, 91-; adj assoc prof, Guangdong Inst Technol, 93- *Mem:* Air & Waste Mgt Asn. *Res:* Sampling and analysis of airborne pollutants; chemical instrumentation; gas chromatography; environmental monitoring; indoor air quality; environmental fate of chemicals. *Mailing Add:* 86 Madelaine Ave Scarborough ON M1L 2X7 Can. *Fax:* 416-630-0506

**TANGEL, O(SCAR) F(RANK),** METALLURGY. *Current Pos:* RETIRED. *Personal Data:* b Philadelphia, Pa, Jan 11, 10; m 36; c 3. *Educ:* Lafayette Col, BS, 32; Mont Sch Mines, MS, 34. *Prof Exp:* Mill supt & metall engr, Mont Coal & Iron Co, 35; metall engr, New Bonanza Mine, Nev, 36; mill supt & metall engr, Ambassador Gold Mines, Ltd, Nev, 36 & Goldfields of Am, Ltd, 36-37; metall engr, Fresnillo Co, Mex, 37-40, asst mill supt, 40-41; res engr, Battelle Mem Inst, 41-42, asst supvr, 45-53, div chief, 53-65, tech adv, 65-66; consult, Newmont Mining Corp, 66-67, chief metall engr, 68-71, vpres res & develop, 72-77; pvt consult, 78-91. *Concurrent Pos:* Plant shift boss, Lakeview Gold Mines, Mont, 35; assayer, King Solomon Gold Mines, Calif, 35-36; metall engr, Pan-Am Eng Co, Calif, 37; dir, Atlantic Cement Co, 67-85, Idarado Mining Co, 69-78, Newmont Explor Ltd, 69-, Foote Mineral Co, 74- & Magma Copper Co, 75-78; vpres, Newmont Explor Ltd, 69-78. *Mem:* Am Inst Mining, Metall & Petrol Engrs; Can Inst Mining & Metall. *Res:* Beneficiation of metallic and non-metallic ores. *Mailing Add:* 6428 Camino Viviente Goleta CA 93117-1524

**TANGHERLINI, FRANK R,** physics, for more information see previous edition

**TANG-MARTINEZ, ZULEYMA,** BEHAVIORAL ECOLOGY, SOCIAL BEHAVIOR. *Current Pos:* asst prof, 76-82, ASSOC PROF BIOL, UNIV MO, ST LOUIS, 82- *Personal Data:* b Ciudad Bolivar, Venezuela, Mar 9, 45; US citizen; div. *Educ:* St Louis Univ, BS, 67; Univ Calif, Berkeley, MA, 70, PhD(zool), 74. *Prof Exp:* NIMH fel ecol, Univ BC, 74-76. *Concurrent Pos:* Vis scholar, Psychol Dept, Univ Colo, Boulder, 83-84; chair, Div Animal Behav, Am Soc Zool, 89-91; vis assoc prof biol sci, Univ Kans, Lawrence, 90-91. *Mem:* Animal Behav Soc; Am Soc Zoologists; Am Soc Mammalogists; Int Soc Behav Ecol; Am Soc Icthiology & Herpet; Am Behav Soc (pres, 93-94). *Res:* Social behavior; dispersal and population dynamics; physiological correlates of social behavior; animal communication; chemical communication; kin recognition. *Mailing Add:* Dept Biol Univ Mo 8001 Natural Bridge Rd St Louis MO 63121. *E-Mail:* szthalp@umslvma.umsl.edu

**TANGNEY, JOHN FRANCIS,** HUMAN PATTERN RECOGNITION, VISUAL PSYCHOPHYSICS. *Current Pos:* PROG MGR, AIR FORCE SCI RES, 85-; DIV DIR, NAT RES COUN, 90- *Personal Data:* b Evanston, Ill, Aug 4, 49; m 85. *Educ:* Loyola Univ Chicago, BS, 71; State Univ NY Buffalo, PhD(psychol), 78. *Prof Exp:* Res asst, Parmly Hearing Inst, 73-74; fac res asst, Univ Md, Col Park, 79-80, fac res assoc, 81-85. *Concurrent Pos:* Co-prin investr, NIH grants, 80- *Mem:* Asn Res Vision & Ophthal; Acoust Soc Am; Optical Soc Am; Soc Neurosci. *Res:* Visual psychophysical experiments--to discriminate between models of human pattern recognition and to describe the dynamics and the interaction of neural structures that underlie vision. *Mailing Add:* Div Human Performance & Recognition AFOSR 110 Duncan Ave Suite B-115 Bolling AFB Washington DC 20332-0001

**TANGONAN, GREGORY LIGOT,** APPLIED PHYSICS, PHYSICS. *Current Pos:* Mem tech staff, 71-78, head, Integrated Optics Sect, Hughes Res Lab, 78-85, MGR, INFO NETWORK TECHNOLOGIES, HUGHES AIRCRAFT CO, 85-, CHIEF SCIENTIST, 92- *Personal Data:* b Springfield, Mass, Oct 26, 47; m, Gloria; c Cristina. *Educ:* Ateneo Manila Univ, BS, 69; Calif Inst Technol, MS, 72, PhD(appl physics), 75. *Mem:* Sigma Xi; Optical Soc Am. *Res:* Information network technologies for fiber connected systems with emphasis on multimedia networks using satellite, wireless and ground-based channels. *Mailing Add:* 141 Santa Rosa Ave Oxnard CA 93035-4475. *E-Mail:* tangonan@madmax.hrl.hac.com

**TANGORA, MARTIN CHARLES,** TOPOLOGY. *Current Pos:* asst prof, 70-72, ASSOC PROF MATH, UNIV ILL, CHICAGO, 72- *Personal Data:* b New York, NY, June 21, 36; m 73; c 2. *Educ:* Calif Inst Technol, BS, 57; Northwestern Univ, MS, 58, PhD(math), 66. *Prof Exp:* Instr math, Northwestern Univ, 66-67 & Univ Chicago, 67-69; temp lectr, Univ Manchester, 69-70. *Concurrent Pos:* Sr vis fel, Univ Oxford, 73-74. *Mem:* Am Math Soc; Math Asn Am. *Res:* Algebraic topology; homotopy theory; cohomological methods. *Mailing Add:* Dept Math m/c 249 Univ Ill 851 S Morgan Rm 322 Chicago IL 60607-7045

**TANGUAY, A(RMAND) R(ENE),** ELECTRICAL ENGINEERING. *Current Pos:* CONSULT, 83- *Personal Data:* b Can, Feb 1, 24; nat US; m 48; c 3. *Educ:* Univ Mass, BS, 50; Mass Inst Technol, MS, 51. *Prof Exp:* Asst comput lab, Mass Inst Technol, 50-51; sect head systs analysis, Cornell Aeronaut Lab, Inc, 51-57; dept head systs res, Res Div, Radiation, Inc, Fla, 57-60; dir advan systs, Ryan Aerolab, Aerolab Develop Co, 60-61; assoc mgr advan electronics & info systs div, Electro-Optical Systs, Inc, 61-63, mgr, 63, mgr energy conversion div, 64, mgr info systs div, 65-67; div mgr med diag opers, Xerox Corp, 67-70, mgr, Micrographics Progs Res & Eng Div, 70-71, mgr strategic tech planning info technol group, 72-80, tech specialist & prog mgr, 80-83. *Mem:* Sr mem Inst Elec & Electronics Engrs. *Res:* Systems and technology development and engineering in information sciences; automation; control systems; technical planning and program management; technology and systems planning and development management in digital and graphical information processing and management with specialties in micrographics and office information automation. *Mailing Add:* 5740 Barnes Rd Canandaigua NY 14424

**TANGUAY, ROBERT M,** CELLULAR & DEVELOPMENTAL BIOLOGY. *Current Pos:* from asst prof to assoc prof genetics, 71-83, dir, Dept Ontogenesis & Molecular Genetics, 81-86, PROF GENETICS, DEPT MED, LAVAL UNIV, 83-; DIR, LIFE & HEALTH SCI RES CTR, RSUS, 95- *Personal Data:* b Sherbrooke, Que, Dec 17, 44; m 67; c 2. *Educ:* Sherbrooke Sem, BA, 63; Sherbrooke Univ, BSc, 66; Laval Univ, DSc, 71. *Prof Exp:* Fel molecular biol, Karolinska Inst, Stockholm, 71-73. *Concurrent Pos:* Dir, Can Soc Cell Biol, 77-79 & Genetics Soc Can, 83-85; vis prof, Europ Molecular Biol Lab, Heidelberg, 80-81 & Inst Genetics, Munich, 88-89; pres, State Ministry Cult & Sci Develop, Can, 82-83; mem, Comt Terminol Genetic Eng, Med Res Coun, Can, 84-85, Human Genome Adv Comt, Can Network Centres Excellence; asst ed, Biochem & Cell Biol, 84-; hon vis prof, Tongji Med Univ, Wuhan, China, 90- *Mem:* Can Soc Cell Biol (treas, 86-89); Genetics Soc Can; Can Biochem Soc; NY Acad Sci. *Res:* Cellular and molecular biology of the heat shock response in Drosophila; biochemistry and function of the various heat shock proteins; regulation of gene activity during stress; study of the molecular basis of the hereditary disease, tyrosinemia (type 1). *Mailing Add:* Cellular Develop Genetics RSUS Pav Marchand Univ Laval Ste-Foy PQ G1V 7P4 Can. *Fax:* 418-656-7176; *E-Mail:* robert.tanguay@rsus.ulaval.ca

**TANI, SMIO,** THEORETICAL PHYSICS. *Current Pos:* assoc prof, 65-68, PROF PHYSICS, MARQUETTE UNIV, 68- *Personal Data:* b Tokyo, Japan, Feb 24, 25; US citizen; m 58; c 3. *Educ:* Univ Tokyo, BS, 46, ScD, 55. *Prof Exp:* Res assoc, Kyoto Univ, 51-54, Tokyo Univ Educ, 54-57, Case Western Res Univ, 57-59 & Wash Univ, 59-60; from res scientist to sr res scientist physics, NY Univ, 60-65. *Mem:* Am Phys Soc; Am Asn Physics Teachers. *Res:* Theory of scattering; canonical transformation in classical and quantum mechanics; atomic physics; elementary particle physics. *Mailing Add:* 4923 N Woodburn St Milwaukee WI 53217

**TANIGAKI, NOBUYUKI,** CANCER. *Current Pos:* RETIRED. *Personal Data:* b Tokyo, Japan, Oct 22, 29. *Educ:* Tokyo Univ, MD, 56. *Prof Exp:* Res fel path, Sch Med, Hokkaido Univ, 57-61, asst, 61-63, asst, Inst Cancer Immunopath, 63-66, instr, 66-67; asst prof, Cancer Res Inst, Kanazawa Univ, 67-68; sr cancer res scientist, Dept Biochem Res, Roswell Park Mem Inst, 69-72, assoc cancer res scientist, 72-75, prin cancer res scientist, 75- *Concurrent Pos:* Sloan-Kettering Inst Cancer Res fel, 63-64; cancer res scientist, Dept Biochem Res, Roswell Park Mem Inst, 64-66. *Mem:* Japanese Cancer Asn; Japanese Path Soc; Am Asn Immunologists. *Mailing Add:* Dept Molecular Immunol Roswell Park Mem Inst Elm & Carlton St Buffalo NY 14263

**TANIKELLA, MURTY SUNDARA SITARAMA,** PHYSICAL CHEMISTRY, POLYMER CHEMISTRY. *Personal Data:* b Amalapuram, India, Dec 5, 38; m 67; c 1. *Educ:* Osmania Univ, India, BSc, 57, MSc, 59; Princeton Univ, MA, 64; Univ Pittsburgh, PhD(phys, physico-org chem), 67. *Prof Exp:* Lectr chem, Osmania Univ, India, 59-62; fel with Prof K S Pitzer, Rice Univ, 67-68; fel, Nat Res Coun Can, 68-69; Nat Res Coun Can fel, Univ Calgary, 69-70; res chemist, Carothers Res Lab, 70-74, sr res chemist, 74-76, sr res chemist, Chattanooga Nylon Tech, 77-80, mem res staff, Feedstocks Div, Cent Res & Develop Dept, Exp Sta, 80-82, res assoc, Nomex Indust, appl res, 82-85, res assoc composites, Chestnut Run, Wilmington, Del, E I du Pont de Nemours & Co, Inc, 85-90. *Concurrent Pos:* Fulbright travel grant, 62. *Mem:* Am Chem Soc; Soc Advan Mat & Process Eng. *Res:* Thermodynamics of hydrogen bonding; spectroscopy; structure of water; problems in textile fibers chemistry; renewable resources; nomex and aromatic polyamides; composites, polyimides. *Mailing Add:* 314 Hampton Rd Wilmington DE 19803

**TANIMOTO, TAFFEE TADASHI,** MATHEMATICS, GEOMETRY. *Current Pos:* RETIRED. *Personal Data:* b Kobe, Japan, Dec 15, 17; nat US; m 46; c 4. *Educ:* Univ Calif, Los Angeles, AB, 42; Univ Chicago, MS, 46; Univ Pittsburgh, PhD(math), 50. *Prof Exp:* Instr math, Ill Inst Technol, 46-49; instr math, Allegheny Col, 49-51, asst prof, 51-54; mathematician, Int Bus Mach Corp, 54-61; head pattern recognition lab, Melpar, Inc, 61-63; staff mathematician, Honeywell, Inc, 63-65; prof math & chmn dept, Univ Mass, Boston, 65-90, dir grad progs, 75-76. *Mem:* Am Math Soc; Math Asn Am. *Res:* Geometry and analysis. *Mailing Add:* Univ Mass Boston Boston MA 02125-3393

**TANINO, KAREN KIKUMI,** PHYSIOLOGY, ENVIRONMENTAL STRESS. *Current Pos:* ASST PROF ENVIRON STRESS PHYSIOL, UNIV SASK, 89- *Personal Data:* b Toronto, Ont, Feb 15, 58; m 94, M P Nair; c Leela N. *Educ:* Univ Guelph, BSc, 81, MSc, 83; Ore State Univ, PhD(hort), 90. *Mem:* AAAS; Am Soc Plant Physiologists; Am Soc Hort Sci; Int Soc Hort Sci; Sigma Xi. *Res:* Environmental stress physiology; using whole plant and tissue culture systems to understand the role of abscisic acid in low temperature, drought, high temperature and salt stress resistance; examining the relationship between dormancy and stress resistance; latitudinal effects on plant growth and development. *Mailing Add:* Dept Hort Univ Sask Saskatoon SK S7N 0W0 Can. *Fax:* 306-966-8106; *E-Mail:* tanino@sask.usask.ca

**TANIS, ELLIOT ALAN,** COMPUTER ART, COMPUTERS IN EDUCATION. *Current Pos:* assoc prof, 65-71, interim dean natural sci, 93, PROF MATH, HOPE COL, 71- *Personal Data:* b Grand Rapids, Mich, Apr 23, 34; m 59, Elaine Buteyn; c Philip A, Joel E & Ellen M. *Educ:* Cent Col, Iowa, BA, 56; Univ Iowa, MS, 60, PhD(math), 63. *Honors & Awards:* Distinguished Serv Award, Mich Sect, Math Asn Am. *Prof Exp:* Lectr math, Univ Iowa, 63; asst prof math statist, Univ Nebr, 63-65. *Mem:* Am Math Soc; Sigma Xi; Math Asn Am; Am Statist Asn. *Res:* Writing educational materials in statistics-textbooks and computer based laboratory materials; developing computer programs for drawing artistic designs and repeating patterns; use of the computer in statistics. *Mailing Add:* Dept Math Hope Col Holland MI 49422-9000. *Fax:* 616-395-7123; *E-Mail:* tanis@math.hope.edu

**TANIS, JOHN ALLEN,** ATOMIC PHYSICS. *Current Pos:* asst prof, 80-82, assoc prof, 82-87, PROF, DEPT PHYSICS, WESTERN MICH UNIV, 87- *Personal Data:* b Nov 18, 45; US citizen; m 69, Patricia Mateer; c Derek, Kimberly & Kristin. *Educ:* Hope Col, BA, 67; Univ Iowa, MS, 69; New York Univ, PhD(physics), 76. *Prof Exp:* Mem tech staff, Bell Labs, 69-73; res asst, New York Univ, 73-75; res assoc, Univ NC, 75-77; vis asst prof, ECarolina Univ, 77-78; staff scientist, Lawrence Berkeley Lab, 79-80. *Concurrent Pos:* Vis scientist, Hahn-Meitner Inst, Ger, 86-87; chairperson, Dept Physics, Western Mich Univ, 89-93. *Mem:* Fel Am Phys Soc. *Res:* Experimental atomic physics. *Mailing Add:* Dept Physics Western Mich Univ Kalamazoo MI 49008

**TANIS, STEVEN PAUL,** SYNTHETIC ORGANIC CHEMISTRY. *Current Pos:* res scientist, 86-90, ASSOC DIR, MED CHEM RES, UPJOHN CO, 91- *Personal Data:* b Newport, RI, Sept 1, 52; m 79. *Educ:* Rutgers Univ, BA, 74; Columbia Univ, MA, 77, MPhil, 78, PhD(chem), 80. *Prof Exp:* NIH fel, Calif Inst Technol, 79-80; asst prof chem, Mich State Univ, 80-86. *Concurrent Pos:* Camille & Henry Dreyfuss award young fac chem, 80-84. *Mem:* Am Chem Soc. *Res:* Isolation; structure determination; synthesis of biologically active natural products; medicinal chemistry. *Mailing Add:* 7601 Farmington Ave Kalamazoo MI 49009-3807

**TANIUCHI, HIROSHI,** PROTEIN CHEMISTRY, CHEMICAL BIOLOGY. *Current Pos:* vis scientist, Lab Chem Biol, Nat Inst Arthritis & Metab Dis, 63-69, RES CHEMIST, LAB CHEM BIOL, NAT INST ARTHRITIS, DIABETES & DIGESTIVE & KIDNEY DIS, NIH, 69-, CHIEF PROTEIN CHEM & CONFORM, 85- *Personal Data:* b Japan, Apr 13, 30; US citizen; m 57, Yoshiko Tsurui; c Megumi & Erie (Michalopoulos). *Educ:* Kyoto Univ, MD, 62, PhD(biochem), 62. *Prof Exp:* Res assoc, Dept Med Chem, Kyoto Univ Fac Med, 61-63. *Concurrent Pos:* Res fel Dept Biol Chem, Harvard Med Sch, 63; chief sect protein conformation, lab chem biol, Nat Inst Arthritis, Diabetes & Digestive & Kidney Dis, NIH, 72-85. *Mem:* Am Soc Biochem & Molecular Biol. *Res:* Protein folding mechanism; antigen recognition mechanism; mechanism of long range interaction in proteins. *Mailing Add:* Protein Chem & Conformation Sect Nat Inst Diabetes & Digestive & Kidney Dis Bethesda MD 20892-0001

**TANK, DAVID W,** NEUROBIOLOGY. *Current Pos:* Fel mem tech staff, AT&T Bell Labs, 82-83, mem tech staff, 83-88, distinguished mem tech staff, 88-91, HEAD, BIOL COMPUT RES DEPT, AT&T BELL LABS, 91- *Personal Data:* b June 3, 53. *Educ:* Case Western Res Univ, BS, 76; Cornell Univ, PhD(physics), 82. *Honors & Awards:* Morris Prize, Case Western Res Univ, 76. *Concurrent Pos:* Biophys fel, Cornell Univ, 78-79, NIH fel, 80-81; co-dir, Marine Biol Lab, Mass, 92- *Mem:* Fel Am Phys Soc; Soc Neurosci; Biophys Soc; Int Soc Neuroethology. *Res:* Methods in computational neuroscience and biology. *Mailing Add:* Biol Comput Res Dept AT&T Bell Lab 600 Mountain Ave Rm 1C-427 Murray Hill NJ 07974. *E-Mail:* dwt@physics.att.com

**TANK, PATRICK WAYNE,** PATTERN FORMATION, REGENERATION. *Current Pos:* asst prof, 78-83, assoc prof anat, 83-89, PROF ANAT, UNIV ARK MED SCI, 89- *Personal Data:* b Charlotte, Mich, Jan 9, 50; m 73, Suzanne K Shaw. *Educ:* Western Mich Univ, BS, 72; Univ Mich, Ann Arbor, MS, 73, PhD(anat), 76. *Prof Exp:* Fel develop biol, Univ Calif, Irvine, 76-78. *Mem:* Am Asn Anatomists; Soc Develop Biol; Sigma Xi; Am Soc Zoologists; Am Asn Clin Anatomists. *Res:* Morphogenesis during development and regeneration in vertebrates; pattern formation during regeneration of the limbs of urodele amphibians; larval and embryonic systems. *Mailing Add:* Dept Anat 510 Univ Ark Med Sci 4301 W Markham Little Rock AR 72205

**TANKARD, ANTHONY JAMES,** hydrocarbon exploration, for more information see previous edition

**TANKERSLEY, DONALD,** IMMUNOCHEMISTRY. *Current Pos:* CHIEF, LAB PLASMA DERIVATIVES, CTR BIOL EVAL & RES, NIH, 84- *Personal Data:* b Stockton, Calif, Nov 29, 39. *Educ:* Calif State Univ, BS, 60; Univ Nev, MS, 62. *Mem:* Am Chem Soc; AAAS. *Mailing Add:* 14105 Heathfield Ct Rockville MD 20853-2760

**TANKERSLEY, ROBERT WALKER, JR,** VIROLOGY, BACTERIOLOGY. *Current Pos:* RETIRED. *Personal Data:* b Watsonville, Calif, June 18, 27; m 51; c 3. *Educ:* Stanford Univ, AB, 52, MA, 54, PhD(med microbiol), 56. *Prof Exp:* Instr virol, Med Sch, Univ Minn, 56-58, instr bact & virol, 58-60; from asst prof to assoc prof microbiol, Med Col Va, 60-68; dir microbiol res, A H Robbins Pharmaceut Co, 68-80, dir molecular biol, 80-90. *Concurrent Pos:* USPHS fel, Med Sch, Univ Minn, 56-58. *Mem:* Am Soc Microbiol. *Res:* Antiviral chemotherapy; cell-virus relationships. *Mailing Add:* 5011 Monument Ave Richmond VA 23230

**TANKIN, RICHARD S,** FLUID MECHANICS. *Current Pos:* from asst prof to assoc prof, 61-69, chmn dept, 72-77, PROF MECH ENG, NORTHWESTERN UNIV, EVANSTON, 70- *Personal Data:* b Baltimore, Md, July 14, 24; m 56; c 3. *Educ:* Johns Hopkins Univ, AB, 48, BS, 50; Mass Inst Technol, MS, 53; Harvard Univ, PhD(mech eng), 60. *Prof Exp:* Asst prof civil eng, Univ Del, 60-61. *Mem:* Am Soc Mech Engrs. *Res:* Hydrodynamic stability; plasma properties; combustion; two phase flow. *Mailing Add:* 820 Ridge Terr Evanston IL 60201-2970

**TANKINS, EDWIN S,** PHYSICAL METALLURGY. *Current Pos:* Jr engr air mat lab, Naval Air Eng Ctr, 54-55, res asst, 56-59, res metallurgist, 59, mat engr, 59-61, res metallurgist, 61-67, asst to chief scientist, 66-67, RES PHYS METALLURGIST, MAT LAB, AIRCRAFT & CREW SYSTS TECHNOL DIRECTORATE, NAVAL AIR WARFARE CTR, 67- *Personal Data:* b Midland, Pa, Sept 12, 27; m 55; c 3. *Educ:* Univ Wis, BS, 54; Univ Pa, MS, 57; Army War Col, grad, 77. *Concurrent Pos:* Adj prof, Eng Mgt Prog, Drexel Univ, 87-, Widener Univ, 91. *Mem:* AAAS; Am Soc Metals; Am Inst Mining, Metall & Petrol Engrs; Am Chem Soc; Sigma Xi. *Res:* Chemical metallurgy; neutron activation studies; yield and fracture stress of refractory metals as a function of temperature, grain, size and strain rate; equilibria of hydrogen and oxygen in iron group metals; binary and ternary alloys related to thermodynamic studies; gas analysis in metals; applied mathematics. *Mailing Add:* 1575 Revere Rd Morrisville PA 19067

**TANKSLEY, STEVEN D,** PLANT BREEDING. *Current Pos:* assoc prof, Dept Plant Breeding & Biomet, 85-91, prof, 91-94, LIBERTY HYDE BAILEY PROF PLANT BREEDING, CORNELL UNIV, 94- *Educ:* Colo State Univ, BS, 76; Univ Calif, Davis, PhD(genetics), 79. *Prof Exp:* Postdoctoral fel, Univ Calif, Davis, 79-81; asst prof, Dept Hart & Plant Genetic Eng Lab, NMex State Univ, 81-85. *Concurrent Pos:* Ed, Genetics, 88-92, Molecular Breeding, 96- *Mem:* Nat Acad Sci. *Mailing Add:* Dept Plant Breeding Cornell Univ 252 Emerson Ithaca NY 14853. *Fax:* 607-255-6683

**TANNAHILL, MARY MARGARET,** POLYMER CHEMISTRY. *Current Pos:* sr res chemist res & develop, 79, PROD & QUAL SUPVR, MOBIL CHEM CO, 80- *Personal Data:* b Weatherford, Tex, Apr 30, 44. *Educ:* Tex Tech Univ, BS, 66; Mich State Univ, PhD(phys chem), 73. *Prof Exp:* Asst chem, Mich State Univ, 66-72; trainee physiol, Univ Tex Med Br, Galveston, 72-73; res chemist, Union Carbide Corp, 74-75; dir mats control, High Density Polyethylene, Gulf Oil Chem Co, 75-79. *Mem:* Am Chem Soc; Soc Plastics Engrs. *Res:* Product development for polypropylene; catalyst preparation and testing; high density polyethylene. *Mailing Add:* 4406 Hyridge Dr Austin TX 78759-8056

**TANNEHILL, JOHN CHARLES,** COMPUTATIONAL FLUID DYNAMICS, AERODYNAMICS. *Current Pos:* from asst prof to assoc prof, 69-79, PROF AEROSPACE ENG & ENG MECH, IOWA STATE UNIV, 79-, MGR, COMPUT FLUID DYNAMICS CTR, 85- *Personal Data:* b Salem, Ill, Oct 14, 43; m 67, Marcia K George; c Michelle & Johnny. *Educ:* Iowa State Univ, BS, 65, MS, 67, PhD(aerospace eng & mech eng), 69. *Prof Exp:* Aerospace engr, Flight Res Ctr, NASA, 65; mem tech staff, Aerospace Corp, 68. *Concurrent Pos:* NASA-Am Soc Eng Educ fac fel, Ames Res Ctr, NASA, 70 & 71; consult, Eng Analysis, Inc, 75-84; pres, Eng Analysis, Inc, 84- *Mem:* Fel Am Inst Aeronaut & Astronaut; Am Soc Eng Educ. *Res:* Computational fluid dynamics; computation of a variety of flow fields using navier-stokes equations; computation of the flow around hypersonic vehicles. *Mailing Add:* Iowa State Univ 402 Town Eng Bldg Ames IA 50011. *Fax:* 515-294-8216; *E-Mail:* johnt@iastate.edu

**TANNEN, RICHARD L,** internal medicine, nephrology, for more information see previous edition

**TANNENBAUM, CARL MARTIN,** BIOCHEMISTRY. *Current Pos:* RES BIOLOGIST, PROCTER & GAMBLE CO, 78- *Personal Data:* b New York, NY, Apr 1, 40. *Educ:* City Col New York, BS, 60; Univ Ariz, MS, 68; Univ Nebr, PhD(chem), 74. *Prof Exp:* Chemist, Ciba Pharmaceut Co, 61-64; fel physiol, Med Sch, Yale Univ, 72-75; asst prof biochem, Swiss Fed Inst Technol, 75-78. *Mem:* Am Chem Soc. *Res:* Epithelial membrane transport of sugars and amino acids; characterization of the factors involved in transport. *Mailing Add:* 1941 S Staunton Dr Fairfield OH 45014

**TANNENBAUM, GLORIA SHAFFER,** NEUROENDOCRINOLOGY, GROWTH HORMONE. *Current Pos:* from asst prof to assoc prof, 78-89, PROF PEDIAT, NEUROL & NEUROSURG, MCGILL UNIV, 89- *Personal Data:* b Montreal, Que, July 9, 38; m 59, Allan; c Elyse, Rhonda, Caroline & Beth. *Educ:* McGill Univ, BSc, 59, MSc, 73, PhD(neuroendocrinol), 76. *Prof Exp:* Res fel neuroendocrinol, Montreal Gen Hosp, 76-78. *Concurrent Pos:* Dir, Neuropeptide Physiol Lab, McGill Univ-Montreal Children's Hosp Res Inst, 78-; mem, Assessment Panel, Can Coun Animal Care, 85- *Mem:* Am Endocrine Soc; Am Physiol Soc; Soc Neurosci; Can Soc Clin Invest; Can Soc Endocrinol & Metab; Int Brain Res Orgn. *Res:* Elucidation of the neuroendocrine control mechanisms governing the rhythmic secretion of growth hormone with particular focus on the roles of the hypothalamic hormones, somatostatin and growth hormone-releasing hormone. *Mailing Add:* Neuropeptide Physiol Lab McGill Univ Montreal Children's Hosp Res Inst 2300 Tupper St Montreal PQ H3H 1P3 Can. *Fax:* 514-934-4331; *E-Mail:* mcta@musica.mcgill.ca

**TANNENBAUM, HAROLD E,** SCIENCE EDUCATION. *Current Pos:* prof, 64-78, chmn dept curric & teaching, 68-72, EMER PROF SCI EDUC, HUNTER COL, 78- *Personal Data:* b New York, NY, Dec 31, 14; m 37; c 2. *Educ:* Columbia Univ, MA, 37, EdD, 50. *Prof Exp:* Teacher, Park Sch, Ohio, 37-42; head sci dept, Elisabeth Irwin High Sch, NY, 44-52; prof sci educ, State Univ NY Teachers Col, New Paltz, 52-61; chmn div curric & instruct, Grad Sch Educ, Yeshiva Univ, 61-64. *Concurrent Pos:* Sci Manpower Comt fel, Columbia Univ, 58-59; consult, State Educ Depts, NH, Va, NDak & NY. *Mem:* AAAS; Nat Sci Teachers Asn. *Mailing Add:* PO Box 295 Phoenicia NY 12464

**TANNENBAUM, HARVEY,** PHYSICAL CHEMISTRY. *Current Pos:* CONSULT, 88- *Personal Data:* b New York, NY, June 26, 23; m 46, Mildred Cohen; c David B, Mark S & Lynne E (Braverman). *Educ:* NY Univ, BS, 48. *Prof Exp:* Mem staff, CB Detection & Alarms Div, Chem Systs Lab, Edgewood Arsenal, 49-65; chief remote sensing, 65-79; prin staff engr, Chem Defense Ctr, Honeywell, Inc, Clearwater, Fla, 79-83; consult, Chem-Biol Defense Technol, 84-85; sr prog dir, SRI Int, Edgewood, Md, 87-88. *Concurrent Pos:* Partic, NATO Experts Panel Laser Remote Sensing of Atmosphere, 75-; mem, Joint Army Navy NASA Air Force Comt Propulsion Hazards, 75- *Mem:* Optical Soc Am; Sigma Xi. *Res:* Infrared physics; trace gas detection; pollution monitoring instrumentation; remote sensing instrumentation; electro-optical systems; spectroscopy. *Mailing Add:* 12611 Mt Laurel Ct Reisterstown MD 21136. *Fax:* 410-833-8737

**TANNENBAUM, IRVING ROBERT,** PHYSICAL CHEMISTRY. *Current Pos:* PRES & TECH DIR, CHEMATICS RES CORP, RESEDA, 65-; PROF CHEM, WLOS ANGELES COL, 79- *Personal Data:* b Spring Lake, NJ, Feb 24, 26; m 51; c 4. *Educ:* Va Polytech Inst, BS, 46, MS, 48; Univ Ill, PhD(phys chem), 51. *Prof Exp:* Instr math, Va Polytech Inst, 46-47; mem staff chem res, Los Alamos Sci Lab, Univ Calif, 51-56; sr phys chemist, Atomics Int Div, NAm Aviation, Inc, 56-61; scientist, Electro-Optical Systs, Inc, 61-63; sr scientist, Heliodyne Corp, 63-65; PRES & TECH DIR, CHEMATICS RES CORP, RESEDA, 65- *Concurrent Pos:* Adj prof, Univ Calif, Los Angeles, 58- *Mem:* Am Chem Soc; Sigma Xi. *Res:* Theory of liquid mixtures; inorganic and plutonium chemistry; hydrides; x-ray crystallography; chemical kinetics; re-entry physics. *Mailing Add:* 8354 Etiwanda Ave Northridge CA 91325

**TANNENBAUM, JANET,** CELL BIOLOGY, CYTOSKELETON. *Current Pos:* proj ed, 91-93, DEVELOP ED, W H FREEMAN & CO, 93- *Educ:* Brandeis Univ, BA, 69; Columbia Univ, PhD(microbiol), 75. *Prof Exp:* Fel, St Judes Childrens Res Hosp, 75-77, Inst Technol, 77-79; fel, Col Physicians & Surgeons, Columbia Univ, 79-80, asst prof path, 80-87; assoc ed, NY Acad Sci, 87-91. *Mem:* Am Soc Cell Biol; AAAS. *Res:* Textbook editor, college and graduate level, biological sciences. *Mailing Add:* 37 Nagle Ave Apt 3A New York NY 10040-1467

**TANNENBAUM, MICHAEL GLEN,** BIOLOGY. *Current Pos:* ASST PROF BIOL, NE MO STATE UNIV, 88- *Personal Data:* b New York, NY, July 19, 53; m 81; c 1. *Educ:* Cornell Univ, BS, 75; Clemson Univ, PhD(zool), 85. *Prof Exp:* Asst prof biol sci, Marshall Univ, 84-88. *Concurrent Pos:* Postdoctoral res assoc, Dept Cellular & Struct Biol, Univ Tex Health Sci Ctr, San Antonio, 86 & 87. *Mem:* AAAS; Am Soc Zoologists; Am Soc Mammalogists; Sigma Xi. *Res:* Endocrine changes underlying seasonal changes in function, behavior, and morphology in small wild rodents associated with overwinter survival. *Mailing Add:* Biol Dept Div Sci Truman State Univ Kirksville MO 63501

**TANNENBAUM, MICHAEL J,** HIGH ENERGY PHYSICS, RELATIVISTIC HEAVY ION PHYSICS. *Current Pos:* head planning & analysis, Isabelle Magnet Div, Brookhaven Nat Lab, 80-81, head superconductor procurement & magnet lamination physics, 81-82, physicist, Physics Dept, 82-87, SR PHYSICIST, BROOKHAVEN NAT LAB, 87- *Personal Data:* b Bronx, NY, Mar 10, 39; m 73, Barbara C Moshinsky; c Nina & Lisa. *Educ:* Columbia Univ, AB, 59, MA, 60, PhD(physics), 65. *Prof Exp:* Vis scientist, Europ Orgn Nuclear Res, 65-66; from asst prof to assoc prof physics, Harvard Univ, 66-71; assoc prof physics, Rockefeller Univ, 71-80. *Concurrent Pos:* Ernest Kempton Adams traveling fel from Columbia Univ, 65-66; NSF fel, 66; Alfred P Sloan Found fel, 67-69; mem prog adv comt, Fermi Nat Lab, 72-75; attache sci, Europ Orgn Nuclear Res, 73-80 & 91. *Mem:* Fel Am Phys Soc; fel AAAS; Sigma Xi. *Res:* Muon elastic and inelastic scattering; muon g-2; muon tridents; photoproduction with a tagged beam; single leptons, lepton pairs and high transverse momentum phenomena in proton-proton interactions; first direct measurement of the constituent scattering angular distribution; relativistic heavy ion collisions, spin at relativistic energies; superconductive magnetics; relativistic heavy ion physics. *Mailing Add:* Bldg 510C Physics Brookhaven Nat Lab PO Box 5000 Upton NY 11973-5000. *E-Mail:* mjt@bnl.gov

**TANNENBAUM, PETER,** MATHEMATICS, COMPUTER SCIENCE. *Current Pos:* assoc prof, 83-87, PROF MATH, CALIF STATE UNIV, FRESNO, 87- *Educ:* Univ Calif, Santa Barbara, BA, 69, MA, 71, PhD(math), 75. *Prof Exp:* Asst prof math & comput sci, Univ Simon Bolivar, Venezuela, 75-79; asst prof math, Univ Ariz, 79-83. *Concurrent Pos:* Regional dir, Math Diog Testing Proj, Univ Calif & Calif State Univ. *Mem:* Am Math Soc; Math Asn Am; Soc Indust & Appl Math; Asn Comput Math; AAAS. *Mailing Add:* Dept Math Calif State Univ Fresno CA 93740-0108

**TANNENBAUM, STANLEY,** INORGANIC CHEMISTRY. *Current Pos:* RETIRED. *Personal Data:* b New York, NY, Mar 1, 25; m 47, Pauline Yakirevitz; c 4. *Educ:* City Col New York, BS, 46; Ohio State Univ, PhD(chem), 49. *Prof Exp:* Res chemist, Nat Adv Comt Aeronaut, 50-53; res chemist, Reaction Motors Div, Thiokol Chem Corp, 53-59, sect head, 59-66, prod mgr, 66-69; mgr tech serv, Ronson Metals Corp, 69-76; sr scientist, Hazard Res Corp, 76-78; NJ Dept Agr, 79-95. *Mem:* Am Chem Soc. *Res:* Synthesis of silicon and boron containing chemicals; physical and thermochemical properties of materials; alteration of properties of rocket propellants; determination of fire and explosive hazards of chemicals and chemical processes. *Mailing Add:* 18 A Celtis Plaza Cranbury NJ 08512-3199

**TANNENBAUM, STEVEN ROBERT,** TOXICOLOGY. *Current Pos:* UNDERWOOD PROF & DIR, DIV TOXICOL, WHITAKER COL, 88-; PROF CHEM, DEPT CHEM, MASS INST TECHNOL, 88- *Personal Data:* b New York, NY, Feb 23, 37; m 59; c 2. *Educ:* Mass Inst Technol, BS, 58, PhD(food sci), 62. *Honors & Awards:* Samuel Cate Prescott Res Award, Inst Food Technologists, 70, Babcock Hart Award, 80. *Prof Exp:* From asst prof to assoc prof nutrit & food sci, Mass Inst Technol, 64-74, prof food chem, 74-88, prof toxicol, 81-88, regist & admis officer, Dept Appl Biol Sci, 82-88. *Concurrent Pos:* Consult, Inst Nutrit Cent Am & Panama, 68, Protein Adv Group, UN Develop Prog, 70-74, Food & Drug Admin, 71-73, Am Cancer Soc, 77-81 & Nat Cancer Inst-NIH, 78-82; mem, Comt Food Stand & Fortification Policy, Nat Res Coun, Nat Acad Sci, 70-73, Safe Drinking Water Comt, Comt Amines, Inst Food Technologists Expert Panel Food Safety & Nutrit, 71-73, co-chmn, 76-77, chmn, 77-78; vis prof, Hebrew Univ Jerusalem Fac Agr, 73-74; mem adv comt, Biochem & Chem Carcinogenesis, Am Cancer Soc, 77-81, Cancer Spec Prog Adv Comt, 79-82, Peer Rev Comt, Nat Toxicol Prog, 83-85, Frederick Cancer Fac Adv Comt, Nat Cancer Inst, 89- *Mem:* Inst Med-Nat Acad Sci; Am Chem Soc; fel Inst Food Technologists; Am Cancer Soc; Am Col Toxicol; Am Asn Cancer Res; Sigma Xi; AAAS; Am Inst Nutrition; Oxygen Soc. *Res:* Chemistry of nitrates, nitrites and nitrosamines; molecular dosimetry of carcinogens; analysis of cancer risk in human populations; formation distribution and metabolism of nitrate and N-nitroso compounds; over 350 research and review papers, 7 US patents. *Mailing Add:* Dept Chem Div Toxicol Rm 56-731 Mass Inst Technol 77 Massachusetts Ave Cambridge MA 02139-4307

**TANNENWALD, PETER ERNEST,** PHYSICS & QUANTUM ELECTRONICS. *Current Pos:* RETIRED. *Personal Data:* b Kiel, Ger, Mar 30, 26; nat US; div; c 1. *Educ:* Univ Calif, AB, 47, PhD(physics), 52. *Prof Exp:* Asst physics, Univ Calif, 47-51, Radiation Lab, 50-52; physicist, Mass Inst Technol, 52-59, asst group leader, 59-62, group leader, 62-63, asst div head, 63-65, assoc div head, 65-74, sr scientist, 74-86, consult, Solid State Div, Lincoln Lab, 86. *Mem:* Fel Am Phys Soc. *Res:* Solid state physics and quantum electronics; microwave resonance in ferrites; spin wave resonance in magnetic films; masers; millimeter waves; microwave ultrasonics; lasers; Raman and Brillouin spectroscopy; far infrared quantum electronics and submillimeter wave technology. *Mailing Add:* 225 Walden St Cambridge MA 02140

**TANNER, ALAN ROGER,** INDUSTRIAL ORGANIC CHEMISTRY, ELECTROCHEMISTRY. *Current Pos:* RES & DEVELOP CHEMIST, SOUTHWESTERN ANALYTICAL CHEM, INC, 71 - *Personal Data:* b Port Lavaca, Tex, Jan 2, 41; m 69; c 2. *Educ:* Univ Tex, Austin, BS, 64, PhD(org chem), 69. *Prof Exp:* Appln res chemist, Jefferson Chem Co, 69-71. *Concurrent Pos:* Instr org chem, St Edward's Univ, 74-75. *Mem:* Am Chem Soc; Electrochem Soc. *Res:* Conventional and electrochemical synthetic approaches to new and existing marketable products; electrochemical cell and plant design. *Mailing Add:* 1415 Fairfield Dr Austin TX 78758-7243

**TANNER, ALLAN BAIN,** GEOPHYSICS, GEOCHEMISTRY. *Current Pos:* Geophysicist, Theoret Geophys Br, US Geol Surv, DC, 54-69, geophysicist, Isotope Geol Br, 69-89, Sedimentary Processes Br, 89-90, EMER SCIENTIST, US GEOL SURV, 90- *Personal Data:* b New York, NY, May 27, 30; m 80, JoAnn Patnode; c Robert, Edward & Evan. *Educ:* Mass Inst Technol, SB, 52. *Concurrent Pos:* Comt mem, Nat Coun Radiation Protection & Measurements, 73-74 & 85-86; comt mem, Comt Radiation Res Policy Coord Sci Panel, Off Sci & Technol Policy, 84-90; US Dept Energy Grant, 90-93; consult radon & natural radionuclides, 90- *Mem:* Sigma Xi. *Res:* Behavior of radon isotopes in natural environments; nuclear geophysics and geochemistry; x-ray fluorescence; isotope geology; gamma-ray spectrometry; in situ neutron activation analysis; health physics. *Mailing Add:* 12125 Captira Ct Reston VA 20191-1204. *Fax:* 703-860-1033

**TANNER, CHARLES E,** IMMUNOLOGY, PARASITOLOGY. *Current Pos:* from asst prof to assoc prof parasitol, 58-71, PROF PARASITOL, INST PARASITOL, MACDONALD COL, McGILL UNIV, 71-, ASSOC MEM MICROBIOL, FAC AGR, 73- *Personal Data:* b Preston, Cuba, Sept 10, 32; Can citizen; m 57; c 2. *Educ:* Purdue Univ, BS, 53; McGill Univ, MS, 56, PhD, 57. *Prof Exp:* Teaching fel bact & immunol, McGill Univ, 55-57; Nat Res Coun Can overseas fel, 57-58. *Concurrent Pos:* Mem, Int Comn Trichinellosis, 73- *Mem:* AAAS; Am Soc Parasitologists; Can Soc Microbiol; Can Soc Immunol; Can Soc Zool; Sigma Xi. *Res:* Immunology of host-parasite relations; immunochemistry of parasite antigens. *Mailing Add:* Inst Parasitol Macdonald Col Ste Anne de Bellevue PQ H9X 3V9 Can

**TANNER, DANIEL,** HISTORY & PHILOSOPHY OF SCIENCE, SCIENCE EDUCATION. *Current Pos:* PROF EDUC & DIR, GRAD PROG CURRIC THEORY & DEVELOP, RUTGERS UNIV, 67- *Personal Data:* b New York, NY, Sept 22, 26; m 48. *Educ:* Mich State Univ, BS, 49, MS, 51; Ohio State Univ, PhD(educ), 55. *Honors & Awards:* John Dewey Mem lectr, 84; Raths Mem lectr, 84; Distinguished Achievement Award, Edpress Asn Am, 90. *Prof Exp:* Instr biol & dept chair, Galesburg Community Schs, Mich, 49-51; teaching asst sci educ, Mich State Univ, 51-52; instr biol sci & dept chair, State Univ NY Agr & Tech Inst, Morrisville, 52-53; asst prof sec educ, San Francisco State Univ, 55-60; assoc prof educ & coordr, Midwest Prog Airborne TV Instr, Purdue Univ, 60-62; assoc prof educ & assoc dir, Master Arts Teaching Prog, Northwestern Univ, 62-64, assoc dir, Int Prog Educ Leaders, 62-63; assoc prof educ res & dir Col Discovery & Develop Prog, City Univ New York, 64-66; prof educ & dir, Ctr Urban Educ, Univ Wis, Milwaukee, 66-67. *Concurrent Pos:* Vis lectr, Emory Univ, 58, Teachers Col, Columbia Univ, 66, State Univ NY, Binghamton, 68 & King Abdulaziz Univ, Jeddah, Saudi Arabia, 92; consult, US Off Educ, 65 & AT&T, 68-71; vis prof scholar, Univ London, 74-75; fel, Rutgers Res Coun, 74-75; distinguished

lectr, State Univ NY, Buffalo, 83; mem bd dirs, John Dewey Soc, 85-87, archivist, 89-; deleg leader people-to-people, Repub SAfrica, 96; consult, US Agency Int Develop, Czech Repub, 96-97. *Mem:* Fel AAAS; fel John Dewey Soc; Am Educ Res Asn; Soc Study Curric Hist. *Res:* Science in intellectual history; science and society; curriculum design and development for interdisciplinary science in school and college; philosophy of science. *Mailing Add:* Highwood Rd Somerset NJ 08873. *Fax:* 732-932-6803; *E-Mail:* piersant@rci.rutgers.edu

**TANNER, DAVID,** POLYMER CHEMISTRY, TECHNOLOGY MANAGEMENT. *Current Pos:* PRES, TANNERT ASSOC INC. *Personal Data:* b Brooklyn, NY, Aug 7, 28; m 53, Shirley Messenger; c Glenn, Allen, Michael & Philip. *Educ:* NY Univ, BA, 50; Brooklyn Polytech Inst, PhD(polymer chem), 54. *Prof Exp:* Res fel polymer chem, Univ Ill, 53-54; res chemist Dupont exp sta, Nylon Res Div, E I du Pont de Nemours & Co Inc, 54-59, res assoc, 59-62, supvr res, 62-63, sr supvr technol, Nylon Tech Div, 63-65, res mgr, Orlon-Lycra Res Div, 65-68, lab dir, Benger Lab, 68-69, tech mgr, Dacron Div, 70-72, tech mgr, Orlon-Acetate-Lycra Div, 72-76, res dir, Textile Fibers Dept, 76-80, mgr, Strategic Planning Div, 80-82, tech dir, Indust Fibers Div, 82-90, DuPont Ctr Creativity & Innovation, 90-91. *Mem:* Am Chem Soc; Asn Res Dirs; NAm Planning Soc; Asn Mgmt Innovation. *Res:* Organic polymer synthesis; radiation chemistry; fiber technology including polyesters, polyamides, acrylics, elastomers, aramids; creativity and innovation management. *Mailing Add:* 712 Hertford Rd Wilmington DE 19803-1618. *Fax:* 302-478-7497; *E-Mail:* daveeet.aol.com

**TANNER, DAVID BURNHAM,** PHYSICS. *Current Pos:* chmn, Dept Physics, 86-89, PROF PHYSICS, UNIV FLA, 82- *Personal Data:* b Norfolk, Va, Mar 12, 45; m 72, Marcia Haney; c James D & Michael G. *Educ:* Univ Va, BA, 66, MS, 67; Cornell Univ, PhD(physics), 72. *Prof Exp:* Assoc, Univ Pa, 72-74; asst prof physics, Ohio State Univ, 74-79, assoc prof physics, 79-82. *Concurrent Pos:* Consult, Xerox Webster Res Ctr, 78-; vis prof, Tech Univ Denmark, 85, McMaster Univ, 91; assoc dir, Microfabritech Prog, 86-87, interim co-dir, 88; affil prof chem, Univ Fla, 89- *Mem:* Fel Am Phys Soc; Sigma Xi. *Res:* Optical properties of solids: high-temperature superconductors, polymers and organic conductors, optical properties of organic conductors; axions; ultrafine metallic particles. *Mailing Add:* Dept Physics 215 Williamson Hall Univ Fla Gainesville FL 32611. *Fax:* 904-392-3591; *E-Mail:* uftanner@phys.ufl.edu

**TANNER, DENNIS DAVID,** ORGANIC CHEMISTRY. *Current Pos:* ann asst prof, 63-65, from asst prof to prof, 65-95, EMER PROF CHEM, UNIV ALTA, 95- *Personal Data:* b Montreal, Que, Mar 6, 30; US & Can citizen; m 60; c Martin E & Adrienne M. *Educ:* Univ Calif, Los Angeles, BSc, 53; Stanford Univ, MSc, 57; Univ Colo, PhD(chem), 61. *Prof Exp:* Asst, Stanford Univ, 56-57 & Univ Colo, 57-60; res fel chem, Columbia Univ, 61-63. *Mem:* Am Chem Soc; Chem Inst Can. *Res:* Mechanisms of free radical reactions; free radical and ionic rearrangement mechanisms. *Mailing Add:* Dept Chem Univ Alta Edmonton AB T6G 2G2 Can. *Fax:* 403-492-8231

**TANNER, GEORGE ALBERT,** RENAL FUNCTION. *Current Pos:* from asst prof to assoc prof, 67-78, PROF PHYSIOL, SCH MED, IND UNIV, INDIANAPOLIS, 78- *Personal Data:* b Vienna, Austria, Aug 2, 38; US citizen; m 62, Judith Shapiro; c Jonathan & Elizabeth. *Educ:* Cornell Univ, AB, 59; Harvard Univ, PhD(physiol), 64. *Prof Exp:* Nat Heart Inst res trainee physiol, Med Col, Cornell Univ, 64-67. *Concurrent Pos:* Vis prof, Heidelberg Univ, 74-75; sr postdoctoral fel, Yale Univ, 86-87; vis scientist, Heidelberg Univ, 96. *Mem:* Am Heart Asn; Int Soc Nephrology; Am Soc Nephrology; Am Physiol Soc. *Res:* Renal function. *Mailing Add:* Dept Physiol & Biophys MS Rm 339 635 Barnhill Dr Indianapolis IN 46202-5120. *Fax:* 317-274-3318; *E-Mail:* gtanner@iupui.edu

**TANNER, JAMES MERVIL,** THEORETICAL PHYSICS. *Current Pos:* RETIRED. *Personal Data:* b Jesup, Ga, Dec 29, 34; m 56; c 3. *Educ:* Ga Inst Technol, BS, 56, MS, 61, PhD(physics), 64. *Prof Exp:* Assoc scientist, Westinghouse Elec Corp, 56-58; instr physics, Ga Inst Technol, 58-62, asst prof, 64-65; assoc prof, Univ NC, Charlotte, 65-67; assoc prof physics, Ga Inst Technol, 67- *Mem:* Am Phys Soc; Am Asn Physics Teachers. *Res:* Mathematical physics. *Mailing Add:* 392 Big Canoe Jasper GA 30143

**TANNER, JAMES THOMAS,** RADIOCHEMISTRY. *Current Pos:* res chemist, 69-79, chief, Nutrient Surveillance Br, 79-93, SPEC ASST TO DIR, OFF SPEC NUTRITIONALS, FOOD & DRUG ADMIN, 93- *Personal Data:* b Franklin, Ky, Apr 23, 39; m 64, Bonnie O'Bryant. *Educ:* Eastern Ky State Col, BS, 61; Univ Ky, PhD(radiochem), 66. *Prof Exp:* Res chemist, Carnegie-Mellon Univ, 66-68, lectr chem, 67-69. *Mem:* Fel AAAS; fel Meteoritical Soc; Am Chem Soc; Sigma Xi; fel Am Nuclear Soc; fel Asn Off Analytical Chemists Int. *Res:* Neutron activation analysis; trace elements in meteorites; trace element distribution in foods, drugs and consumer products; nutrient content of foods; standard reference materials; 75 publications in refereed journals or books and 20 reports. *Mailing Add:* Off Spec Nutritionals HFS-451 Food & Drug Admin Washington DC 20204. *Fax:* 202-205-5295; *E-Mail:* jtt@fdacf.ssw.dhhs.gov

**TANNER, JOHN EYER, JR,** NUCLEAR CRITICALITY SAFETY. *Current Pos:* RETIRED. *Personal Data:* b Cleveland, Ohio, Apr 30, 30; m 66; c 3. *Educ:* Oberlin Col, AB, 51; Ind Univ, MS, 54; Univ Wis, PhD(phys chem), 66. *Prof Exp:* Res asst phys chem, Am Found Biol Res, Wis, 54-62; res fel, Pa State Univ, 66-68; res asst, Max Planck Inst Med Res, Ger, 68-69; fel, Sci Res Staff, Ford Motor Co, Mich, 69-71; res chemist, Naval Weapons Support Ctr, 71-79; sr res engr, Exxon Nuclear Idaho Co, 79-82; sr engr, Westinghouse

Idaho Nuclear Co, 82-96. *Mem:* Am Chem Soc; Am Nuclear Soc; Am Phys Soc. *Res:* Nuclear magnetic resonance; emission and absorption spectroscopy; thermodynamics; nuclear waste management; co-developer of the pulsed-field-gradient, nuclear-magnetic- resonance method of diffusion measurement; pioneered the application to viscous liquids, polymers, emulsions, plastic crystals, and biological cells. *Mailing Add:* 2175 Tasman Ave Idaho Falls ID 83404

**TANNER, LEE ELLIOT,** PHYSICAL METALLURGY. *Current Pos:* staff metallurgist, Mat Res Ctr, Allied Chem Corp, 73-78, sr metallurgist, ManLabs, Inc, 78-80, PRIN INVESTR, LAWRENCE LIVERMORE NAT LAB, 80- *Personal Data:* b Brooklyn, NY, May 28, 31; m 56; c 2. *Educ:* NY Univ, BS, 53; Univ Pa, MS, 58. *Honors & Awards:* Outstanding Sci Accomplishment in Metall & Ceramics Res, US Dept Energy, 88. *Prof Exp:* Res asst phys metall, Armour Res Found, 53, assoc metallurgist, 56-59; sr metallurgist, ManLabs, Inc, 59-63; sr res metallurgist, Ledgemont Lab, Kennecott Copper Corp, 63-73. *Mem:* AAAS; Am Soc Metals; Am Inst Mining, Metall & Petrol Engrs; Am Inst Physics; Electron Micros Soc Am. *Res:* Precipitation, ordering, martensitic transitions; relationships microstructure to physical properties; crystalline and amorphous; phase transformations, precipitation, ordering; relationships of microstructure to physical properties. *Mailing Add:* 769 Vicente Ave Berkeley CA 94707

**TANNER, LLOYD GEORGE,** geology; deceased, see previous edition for last biography

**TANNER, MARTIN ABBA,** SOFTWARE DEVELOPMENT. *Current Pos:* PROF, DEPT STATIST, NORTHWESTERN UNIV, 94- *Personal Data:* b Highland Park, Ill, Oct 19, 57; m 84, Anat; c Noam. *Educ:* Univ Chicago, BA, 78, MS, 81, PhD(statist), 82. *Honors & Awards:* Young Investr Award, NIH, 84; Mortimer Spiegelman Award, Am Pub Health Asn, 93. *Prof Exp:* Asst prof, Math Res Ctr, Univ Wis-Madison, 82-83, asst prof statist, 82-87, asst prof human oncol, 83-87, dir lab statist, 84-90, assoc prof statist, human oncol, 87-90; prof & chair, Dept Biostatist, Univ Rochester Med Ctr, 90-94. *Concurrent Pos:* Consult, Kirkland & Ellis, 80-82, Vet Admin, Dept Surg & Med, 82- & Bur Justice Statist, 83-; prin investr, NSF, 83-85 & tech reviewer, 84-; prin investr, reviewer, NIH, 86-, Standing Study Sect, 94-; assoc ed, J Am Stat Asn, 88- *Mem:* AAAS; fel Am Statist Asn; Sigma Xi; fel Royal Statist Soc. *Res:* Design and analysis of computational algorithms for Bayesian and conditional inference; design and analysis of clinical trials and laboratory experiments; development of statistical methodology for the analysis of missing data problems; development of statistical methodology for the analysis of agreement among raters; inferentia techniques for neural networks *Mailing Add:* Northwestern Univ 2006 Sheridan Rd Evanston IL 60208. *Fax:* 847-491-4939; *E-Mail:* matl32@nwu.edu

**TANNER, NOALL STEVAN,** pharmacology, pharmacognosy; deceased, see previous edition for last biography

**TANNER, RAYMOND LEWIS,** RADIOLOGICAL PHYSICS, HEALTH PHYSICS. *Current Pos:* assoc prof, Univ Tenn, 67-70, asst to chancellor for facil planning, 77-82, asst dean Grad Sch, 82-85, PROF MED PHYSICS, UNIV TENN, MEMPHIS, 70- *Personal Data:* b Memphis, Tenn, Dec 11, 31; m 68, Margaret Foster; c John W, Paul R & Rebecca L. *Educ:* Memphis State Univ, BS, 53; Vanderbilt Univ, MS, 55; Univ Calif, Los Angeles, PhD(med physics), 67. *Prof Exp:* Asst prof physics, Memphis State Univ, 55-62; vis physicist, Harbor Gen Hosp, Torrance, Calif, 63-64. *Concurrent Pos:* Consult self-radiation protection, 55-; chmn, Comn Physics, Am Col Radiol, 82-88. *Mem:* Am Asn Physicists in Med (pres, 73-74); Am Col Radiol; Sigma Xi. *Res:* Radiation dosimetry; x-ray quality control. *Mailing Add:* Univ Tenn 800 Madison Ave Memphis TN 38163. *Fax:* 901-448-5352; *E-Mail:* rltanner@utmem1.utmem.edu

**TANNER, ROBERT DENNIS,** CHEMICAL ENGINEERING, BIOCHEMICAL ENGINEERING. *Current Pos:* from asst prof to assoc prof, 72-84, PROF CHEM ENG, VANDERBILT UNIV, 84- *Personal Data:* b Detroit, Mich, Jan 17, 39; m 63, Ruth Kellman; c David S & Benjamin J. *Educ:* Univ Mich, BSE, 61 & 62, MSE, 63; Case Western Res Univ, PhD(chem eng), 67. *Prof Exp:* Engr, Diamond Shamrock Corp, 63; eng assoc res, Merck & Co, Inc, 67-72. *Concurrent Pos:* Chmn, Div Microbiol & Biochem Technol, 78-80; vis prof, Eidgenossiche Technische Hochschule, Zurich, 81-82; vis prof, Univ Sao Paulo, Brazil, 96. *Mem:* Am Inst Chem Engrs; Am Chem Soc; Sigma Xi; Int Orgn Biotechnol & Bioeng. *Res:* Fermentation modeling; enzyme kinetics; solid and semi-solid state fermentation processes in air fluidized beds; bubble and foam fractionation of proteins. *Mailing Add:* Dept Chem Eng Vanderbilt Univ Nashville TN 37235

**TANNER, ROBERT H,** NOISE CONTROL. *Current Pos:* ACOUST CONSULT, 75- *Personal Data:* b London, Eng, July 22, 15; m 40, Joan Garnham; c Christopher, Rosemary, Peter & David. *Educ:* Univ London, BSc, 36, MSc, 61. *Hon Degrees:* LLD, Concordia Univ, 89. *Honors & Awards:* McNaughton Medal, Inst Elec & Electronics Engrs, 74, Haraden Pratt Award, 81. *Prof Exp:* TV engr & res engr, Brit Broadcasting Corp, 36-47; from engr to mgr, Northern Elec Co, 47-70; dir info, Bell-Northern Res, 70-75. *Mem:* Fel Inst Elec & Electronics Engrs (pres, 72); fel Acoust Soc Am; fel Inst Elect Engrs; fel Eng Inst Can; Inst Noise Control Engrs. *Mailing Add:* 4051 Gulf Shore Blvd N Apt 701 Naples FL 34108. *Fax:* 941-261-1612

**TANNER, ROBERT MICHAEL,** INFORMATION SCIENCES. *Current Pos:* from asst prof to assoc prof info sci, 71-84, actg dean, Nat Sci, 88-89, PROF COMPUT & INFO SCI, UNIV CALIF, SANTA CRUZ, 84-, ACAD VCHANCELLOR, 89- *Personal Data:* b Spanish Fork, Utah, Mar 22, 46; m 65; c 2. *Educ:* Stanford Univ, BS, 66, MS, 67, PhD(elec eng). 71. *Prof Exp:* Asst prof elec eng, Tenn State Univ, 70-71. *Concurrent Pos:* Consult, Technol Commun Int, 71-79, Ford Aerospace, 85-89, Optimem, 82; vis assoc prof, Stanford, 81; vis scientist, IBM, 84. *Mem:* Inst Elec & Electronics Engrs. *Res:* Information theory, coding and complexity. *Mailing Add:* 523 Riverview Dr Capitola CA 95010

**TANNER, ROGER IAN,** engineering, rheology, for more information see previous edition

**TANNER, ROGER LEE,** ANALYTICAL & ATMOSPHERIC CHEMISTRY. *Current Pos:* asst chemist, Brookhaven Nat Lab, 73-75, assoc chemist, 75-77, head, Analytical Chem Group, 86-89, CHEMIST, ENVIRON CHEM DIV, BROOKHAVEN NAT LAB, 77-; RES PROF, DESERT RES INST, 89- *Personal Data:* b Union City, Pa, Sept 17, 43; c 4. *Educ:* Pa State Univ, BS, 64; Univ Ill, Urbana, PhD(analytical chem), 69. *Prof Exp:* Temp asst prof chem, Portland State Univ, 68-69; asst prof chem, Univ Okla, 69-71; res assoc chem, Univ Ill, Urbana, 72-73. *Concurrent Pos:* Consult, Sci Adv Bd, Environ Protection Agency, 77-81, sci rev panel, 87-; environ comt, NY Sect, Am Chem Soc, 82-86. *Mem:* Am Chem Soc; AAAS. *Res:* Trace analytical chemistry of environmental samples; chemistry of wet deposition processes; atmospheric chemistry of sulfur, nitrogen and carbon compounds; chemical speciation and source allocation of aerosols; real-time air monitoring instrumentation. *Mailing Add:* TVA Environ Res Ctr Chem Eng Bldg 2A PO Box 1010 Muscle Shoals AL 35662

**TANNER, WARD DEAN, JR,** WILDLIFE MANAGEMENT, ECOLOGY. *Current Pos:* from instr to prof, 53-84, EMER PROF BIOL, GUSTAVUS ADOLPHUS COL, 84- *Personal Data:* b Jacksonville, Fla, Dec 6, 18. *Educ:* Univ Minn, BS, 41; Pa State Univ, MS, 48; Iowa State Univ, PhD(zool), 53. *Prof Exp:* Asst wildlife mgt, Pa State Univ, 41, 46-48; refuge mgr, Bombay Hook Nat Wildlife Refuge, US Fish & Wildlife Serv, 48-50. *Mem:* Wildlife Soc; Sigma Xi. *Res:* Ecology of wildlife and ruffed grouse; botany; forestry; fisheries management. *Mailing Add:* 1407 18th Ave NE Minneapolis MN 55418

**TANNER, WILLIAM FRANCIS, JR,** SEDIMENT TRANSPORT, PALEOGEOGRAPHY. *Current Pos:* vis lectr geol, 54-56, from assoc prof to prof, 56-74, REGENTS PROF GEOL, FLA STATE UNIV, 74- *Personal Data:* b Milledgeville, Ga, Feb 4, 17; m 38, Julia Rigby; c William F III, Bruce R & Julianne (Talley). *Educ:* Baylor Univ, BA, 37; Tex Tech Col, MA, 39; Univ Okla, PhD(geol), 53. *Prof Exp:* Asst geol, Baylor Univ, 35-37 & Tex Tech, 37-39; oil ed, Amarillo Times, 39-41 & 45-46; asst prof geol & journalism, Okla Baptist Univ, 46-51; spec instr, Univ Okla, 51-54. *Concurrent Pos:* Geologist, Shell Oil Co, 54; ed, Coastal Res, 62-; NSF vis scientist, 65-66. *Mem:* Fel AAAS; fel Geol Soc Am; Soc Econ Paleontologists & Mineralogists; Int Asn Sedimentology; Am Geophys Union. *Res:* Sedimentology; stratigraphy; geomorphology; hydrodynamics; beach and shore processes; structural, areal, field and subsurface geology; rheology and deformation of materials; circular statistics; paleogeography; paleoclimatology; petroleum exploration and resources; other energy sources; suite statistics. *Mailing Add:* Dept Geol Fla State Univ Tallahassee FL 32306-3026. *Fax:* 850-644-4214

**TANNOCK, IAN FREDERICK,** MEDICAL ONCOLOGY, EXPERIMENTAL CANCER RESEARCH. *Current Pos:* Chief med, 90-96, SR SCIENTIST & STAFF PHYSICIAN, ONT CANCER INST & PRINCESS MARGARET HOSP, 78-; PROF MED & MED BIOPHYS, UNIV TORONTO, 89- *Personal Data:* b Hatfield, Eng, Nov 22, 43; Can citizen; m 67; c 3. *Educ:* Cambridge Univ, BA, 65; Inst Cancer Res, PhD(biophys), 68; Univ Pa, MD, 74. *Concurrent Pos:* Mem, Med Res Coun Panel, 86-88, chmn, 88-91. *Mem:* Am Soc Clin Oncol; Am Asn Cancer Res; Cell Kinetics Soc; Radiation Res Soc. *Res:* Laboratory-based research in biology and therapy of solid tumors; clinical trials methodology; clinical trials in genitouriary, head and neck, and breast cancer. *Mailing Add:* Ont Cancer Inst 610 University Ave Toronto ON M5G 2M9 Can

**TANNY, GERALD BRIAN,** POLYMER CHEMISTRY, MEMBRANE SCIENCE. *Current Pos:* CHIEF EXEC OFFICER, OSMOTEK, 91- *Personal Data:* b Montreal, Que, Dec 26, 45; m 68; c 3. *Educ:* McGill, BS, 66; PhD(polymer chem), 70. *Honors & Awards:* H Dudley Wright Award for Membrane Achievement. *Prof Exp:* fel, 70-72, scientist, 72-74, sr scientist, 74-77; assoc res dir, Gelman Sci Inc, 77-86, vpres, 86-90. *Concurrent Pos:* Managing dir, Gelman Sci Technol, 82-88. *Mem:* Am Chem Soc; Israel Chem Soc; Europ Membrane Soc. *Res:* Membrane science and technology; application of microporous membranes in crossflow microfiltration; UV curing for manufacturing microporous membranes; thermodynamics of membrane formation. *Mailing Add:* Osmotek PO Box 550 Rehovot Israel. *Fax:* 972-8-408759

**TANPHAICHITR, VICHAI,** HUMAN NUTRITION, ENTERAL & PARENTERAL NUTRITION. *Current Pos:* From asst prof to assoc prof, 75-80, PROF INTERNAL MED, FAC MED RAMATHIBODI HOSP, 81-, DIR RES CTR, MED RES, 88- *Personal Data:* b Bangkok, Thailand, Oct 5, 40; m 70; c 2. *Educ:* Univ Med Sci, MD, 64, MSc, 68; Vanderbilt Univ, PhD(biochem), 73. *Honors & Awards:* First Ajinomoto Award, Nat Res Coun Thailand, 85; First Govt Pharmaceut Orgn Thailand Award, Thailand,

91. *Concurrent Pos:* Lectr internal med, Fac Med, Ramathibodi Hosp, 66-74; mem, Int Glutamate Tech Comt, 83-; ed-in-chief, J Internal Med, Royal Col Physicians of Thailand, 85-; prin invesr, Bristol-Myers Squibb Unrestricted Nutrit Res Grant, 89-93; mem, Comt Functional Consequences of Vitamin Deficiency, 89-93. *Mem:* Am Soc Parenteral & Enteral Nutrit; Am Inst Nutrit; Am Col Physicians; Am Col Nutrit. *Res:* Nutrient requirements in tube feeding and parenteral nutrition; therapeutic nutrition in various diseases; thiamin, riboflavin, pyridoxine, vitamin A, carnitine, iron, and essential fatty acid metabolism in health and diseases; hyperlipoprotienemia. *Mailing Add:* Div Nutrit & Biochem Med Ramathibodi Hosp Rmam Six Rd Bangkok 4 Thailand

**TANQUARY, ALBERT CHARLES,** POLYMER SCIENCE. *Current Pos:* PRES, TANQUARY ASSOCS, 81-; PRES, TELESIS CORP, 90- *Personal Data:* b Columbus, Kans, Mar 9, 29; m 49, 80; c 5. *Educ:* Kans State Col, Pittsburg, BS, 50; Okla State Univ, MS, 52, PhD(chem), 54. *Prof Exp:* Sr chemist cent res dept, 3M Co, 54-55, group supvr, 55-58, res mgr, fibers dept, 59-61, mgr, 62-63; group leader res & develop div, Union Camp Corp, 63-65; assoc dir, Southern Res Inst, 66-80; dir, Gulf South Res Inst, 80-81; vpres, Res & Develop, Gulf Aviation Corp, 86-88; sr proj dir, Family Health Int, 88-90. *Mem:* Am Chem Soc; Controlled Release Soc; Licensing Exec Soc; Sigma Xi. *Res:* Polymer chemistry; characterization of polymers; mechanical properties of adhesives, fibers and films; fiber spinning; biomedical materials; microcapsules; membrane processes; controlled release systems. *Mailing Add:* 7504 Borkley Pl New Orleans LA 70126

**TANSEL, BERRIN,** HAZARDOUS WASTE MANAGEMENT & TREATMENT, CONTAMINATED SEDIMENT REMEDIATIONS. *Current Pos:* ASSOC PROF ENVIRON ENG, FLA INT UNIV, 90- *Personal Data:* m 82, Ibrahim; c Aylin & Derya. *Educ:* Middle East Tech Univ, BS, 78; Univ Wis-Madison, MS, 79, PhD(environ eng), 85. *Prof Exp:* Environ res engr, Tufts Univ, 86-87; sr proj eng, Peer Consults, Boston, Mass, 87-89; proj mgr, MWRA, Boston, Mass, 89-90. *Concurrent Pos:* Consult, Soap & Detergent Asn, 85, ERM-South, Miami, Fla & City Pompano Beach, Fla, 90-91, Metcalf & Eddy Inc, Miami, Fla, 92-94. *Mem:* Water Environ Fedn; Am Soc Civil Engrs. *Res:* Contaminant transport; oil-water separation; metal separation; solid waste management; ultrafiltration. *Mailing Add:* Dept Civil Eng Fla Int Univ Miami FL 33199. *Fax:* 305-348-2802; *E-Mail:* tansel@eng.fiu.edu

**TANSEY, MICHAEL RICHARD,** MYCOLOGY. *Current Pos:* NSF fel & res assoc microbiol, 70-71, asst prof, 71-77, ASSOC PROF BIOL, IND UNIV, BLOOMINGTON, 78- *Personal Data:* b Oakland, Calif, Mar 27, 43; m 63, 88, Janica Hooper; c Rowan & Sarah. *Educ:* Univ Calif, Berkeley, BA, 65, PhD(bot), 70. *Honors & Awards:* Weston Award, Mycol Soc Am, 96. *Mem:* AAAS; Mycol Soc Am; Brit Mycol Soc; Int Soc Human Animal Mycol; Am Inst Biol Sci; NAm Mycol Asn. *Res:* Biology of thermophilic fungi; heated habitats; medical mycology; anaerobic biology of Candida albicans. *Mailing Add:* Dept Biol Ind Univ Bloomington Bloomington IN 47405-6800. *Fax:* 812-855-6705; *E-Mail:* mtansey@indiana.edu

**TANSEY, ROBERT PAUL, SR,** PHARMACY. *Current Pos:* RETIRED. *Personal Data:* b Newark, NJ, Apr 27, 14; m 41; c 4. *Educ:* Rutgers Univ, BS, 38, MS, 50. *Prof Exp:* Control pharmacist, Res & Develop Labs, Burroughs Wellcome Co, Inc, 40-43; asst dept head prod & control, E R Squibb & Sons, 43-45; head, Pharmaceut Res & Develop Lab, Maltbie Labs, 45-50; assoc dept head, Merck & Co, 50-53; sect leader, Schering Co, Inc, 53-58; res coordr, Strong Cobb Arner Co, Inc, 58-62; regist pharmacist, Saywell Pharm, Ohio, 62-63; tech dir, Vet Labs, Inc, 63-70; consult, 88-91. *Mem:* Animal Health Inst; Am Pharmaceut Asn. *Res:* Pharmaceutical development; formulation and methods analysis; production processing techniques and control methods; pharmaceutical plant and equipment design; development of special techniques for control and sustained release medicinal forms; plant management. *Mailing Add:* 11141 Glen Arbor Rd Kansas City MO 64114

**TANSY, MARTIN F,** PHYSIOLOGY. *Current Pos:* from asst prof to assoc prof, 64-72, PROF PHYSIOL, SCHS DENT, PHARM & ALLIED HEALTH PROF, TEMPLE UNIV, 72-, CHMN DEPT, 64-, BASIC SCI COORDR, 79- *Personal Data:* b Wilkes Barre, Pa, Mar 8, 37; m 64; c 3. *Educ:* Wilkes Col, BA, 59; Jefferson Med Col, MS, 61, PhD(physiol), 64. *Prof Exp:* Res asst physiol, Jefferson Med Col, 59-61, fel, 62-64. *Mem:* Fel Am Col Nutrit; Soc Exp Biol & Med; Am Physiol Soc; Am Pharmaceut Asn; Am Fedn Clin Res. *Res:* Gastrointestinal and radiation physiology. *Mailing Add:* 412 Saint Davids Rd St Davids PA 19087-4322

**TAN-WILSON, ANNA L(I),** BIOCHEMISTRY, PLANT PHYSIOLOGY. *Current Pos:* from asst prof to assoc prof, 76-91, chair, Dept Biol Scis, 89-91, PROF BIOL, STATE UNIV NY, BINGHAMTON, 91- *Personal Data:* b Manila, Philippines, Mar 16, 46. *Educ:* Univ Philippines, BS, 66; Univ Col London, MSc, 67; State Univ NY, Buffalo, PhD(biochem), 73. *Prof Exp:* Instr chem, Univ Philippines, 67-69; res assoc biochem & immunol, State Univ NY, Buffalo, 73-75; res assoc biochem, Purdue Univ, 75-76. *Concurrent Pos:* Co-prin investr, NFS grant, 81-; proj dir undergrad educ grant, Howard Hughes Med Int, 92-97, 94-98; co-chair, Northeast Sect, Am Soc Plant Physiologists; co-proj dir, NSF educ grant, 96-98. *Mem:* Am Soc Plant Physiologists; AAAS; Am Chem Soc; Sigma Xi. *Res:* Structure, function and gene expression of proteelytic enzymes in cotyledous of legume seedlings. *Mailing Add:* Dept Biol Sci State Univ NY PO Box 6000 Binghamton NY 13902-6000. *E-Mail:* annatan@binghamton.edu

**TANZ, RALPH,** PHARMACOLOGY, PHYSIOLOGY. *Current Pos:* from assoc prof to prof, 69-90, EMER PROF PHARMACOL, SCH MED, ORE HEALTH SCI UNIV, 90- *Personal Data:* b New York, NY, Oct 10, 25; m 52; c 3. *Educ:* Univ Rochester, BA, 48; Univ Colo, PhD(pharmacol), 58. *Prof Exp:* Asst pharmacol, Sch Med, Univ Colo, 54-57; instr, Med Units, Univ Tenn, 57-59; sr instr, Sch Med, Western Res Univ, 59-62; asst prof pharmacol, New York Med Col, 62-63; head cardiovasc sect, Dept Pharmacol, Geigy Res Labs, NY, 63-69. *Concurrent Pos:* NIH career develop award, 61; chmn sect, Gordon Res Conf, 66; Fogarty sr int fel, Heart Res Labs, Dept Med, Univ Cape Town Med Sch, SAfrica, 76-77; Univ Melbourne & Univ Auckland, 84-85. *Mem:* AAAS; Am Soc Pharmacol & Exp Therapeut; Cardiac Muscle Soc (pres, 64); Am Heart Asn; Int Heart Res Soc. *Res:* Isolated cardiac tissue; effect of cardiac glycosides and catecholamines on cardiac muscle; antihypertensives; physiological and biochemical correlates of arrhythmogenesis and antiarrhythinic drugs. *Mailing Add:* Dept Pharmacol Sch Med L221 Ore Health Sci Univ 3181 SW Sam Jackson Park Rd Portland OR 97201-3098

**TANZER, CHARLES,** science education, medical microbiology; deceased, see previous edition for last biography

**TANZER, MARVIN LAWRENCE,** BIOCHEMISTRY. *Current Pos:* from asst prof to assoc prof biochem, 68-75, prof orthop surg & dir, Orthop Labs, 78-88, PROF BIOCHEM, HEALTH CTR, UNIV CONN, 75-, PROF BIOSTRUCT & FUNCTION, 86- *Personal Data:* b New York, NY, Jan 26, 35; m 54, Betsy Chernoff; c Laura, Andrew, Matthew & Jennifer. *Educ:* Mass Inst Technol, SB, 55; NY Univ, MD, 59. *Prof Exp:* Intern med, Johns Hopkins Hosp, Baltimore, 59-60, asst resident, 60-61; res fel, Mass Gen Hosp, Harvard Med Sch, 61-62 & 64-65, asst biologist, 65-68, assoc, 67-68. *Concurrent Pos:* Arthritis Found fel, Mass Gen Hosp, Boston, 61-62; Am Heart Asn fel, 64-66; Am Heart Asn estab investr, Mass Gen Hosp, Boston, 66-68 & Med Sch, Univ Conn, 68-71; investr, Marine Biol Lab, Woods Hole, 66-71; tutor biochem sci, Harvard Univ, 67-68; Josiah Macy, Jr Found fac scholar award, 74-75; vis prof dermat, Univ Liege, Belg, 74-75; NIH Study Sect, Biophys & Biophys Chem B, 76-80; vis prof, Univ Calif, Los Angeles, Bone Res Lab, 76; vis prof, Japanese Soc Prom Sci, Tokyo, 77, Univ Lund, Sweden, 81 & Univ Claude Bernard, Lyon, France, 85; mem, Breast Cancer Task Force comt, NIH, 82-86; prof & head, Dept Biostructure & Function, Univ Conn, 86-95; mem NIH study sect, pathobiochem, 86-90, chmn, 88-90; assoc ed, J Cellular Biochem, 90-; mem, Biochem Study Sect, Arthritis Found, 93-94. *Mem:* Am Soc Bone & Mineral Res; Orthop Res Soc; Am Soc Cell Biol; Am Chem Soc; Am Soc Biol Chemists; NY Acad Sci. *Res:* Properties, function and synthesis of connective tissue components. *Mailing Add:* Dept Biostruct & Function Univ Conn Health Ctr Farmington CT 06030. *Fax:* 860-679-2910; *E-Mail:* tanzer@panda.uchc.edu

**TAO, FU-MING,** INTERMOLECULAR FORCES, STRUCTURE & ENERGETICS OF VAN DER WAALS COMPLEXES. *Current Pos:* ASST PROF CHEM, CALIF STATE UNIV, FULLERTON, 95- *Personal Data:* b Suzhou, China, June 26, 60; m, Fuzhen Shi; c Li, Jim & Emily L. *Educ:* Univ Sci & Technol, China, BS, 82; Suzhou Univ, China, MS, 85; Boston Col, PhD(chem), 91. *Prof Exp:* Lectr chem, Suzhou Univ, China, 85-86; postdoctoral fel, Brown Univ, 91-92, Harvard Univ, 92-95. *Res:* Electronic structure of atoms and molecules; molecular structure and interactions in van der Waals molecules and hydrogen-bonded complexes; applications of ab initio quantum mechanical theory to atmospheric chemistry and biochemistry. *Mailing Add:* Dept Chem & Biochem Calif State Univ Fullerton CA 92834. *E-Mail:* ftao@fullerton.edu

**TAO, JINHLIA,** STOCHASTIC PROCESSES, RISK THEORY. *Current Pos:* asst prof, 92-96, ASSOC PROF MATH, CENT MO STATE UNIV, 96- *Personal Data:* b Shanghai, China, Dec 29, 61; m 87, Feng Zhang; c Kevin Z & Katie Z. *Educ:* Shanghai Jiao Tong Univ, BS, 84; Univ Wis-Madison, PhD(math), 92. *Prof Exp:* Assoc lectr math, Univ Wis Ctrs, 92. *Concurrent Pos:* Actuarial consult, Kans City Life Ins Co, 96. *Mem:* Math Asn Am; Soc Actuaries; Inst Math Statist. *Res:* Risk theory; mathematical finance with applications in the insurance area. *Mailing Add:* Dept Math Comput Sci Cent Mo State Univ Warrensburg MO 64093. *E-Mail:* tao@cmsuvmb.cmsu.edu

**TAO, L(UH) C(HENG),** CHEMICAL ENGINEERING. *Current Pos:* from assoc prof to prof, Univ Nebr, Lincoln, 59-70, Howard S Wilson prof chem eng, 70-86, chmn dept, 78-84, EMER PROF CHEM ENG, 86-, UNIV NEBR, LINCOLN, 86- *Personal Data:* b Wusih, China, Feb 6, 22; m 50; c 4. *Educ:* Univ Nanking, China, BS, 46; Univ Wis, MS, 49, PhD, 52. *Prof Exp:* Asst, Univ Nanking, 46-47; chem process engr, Singh Co, Ill, 52-55; res engr, Titanium Metals Corp Am, Nev, 55-59. *Mem:* AAAS; Am Chem Soc; Am Inst Chem Engrs; Am Soc Eng Educ; Sigma Xi. *Res:* Heat and mass transfer; phase equilibrium. *Mailing Add:* 701 Lakewood Dr Lincoln NE 68510

**TAO, LIANG NENG,** ENGINEERING. *Current Pos:* from asst prof to prof mech, 55-95, EMER PROF MECH, ILL INST TECHNOL, 95- *Personal Data:* b China, June 27, 27; nat US; m 57; c 3. *Educ:* Chiao Tung Univ, BS, 49; Univ Ill, MS, 50, PhD(mech eng), 53. *Prof Exp:* Res engr, Worthington Corp, 53-55. *Concurrent Pos:* Consult, Armour Res Found Am. *Mem:* Am Soc Eng Educ; Am Soc Mech Engrs; Am Inst Aeronaut & Astronaut; Am Asn Univ Prof; Sigma Xi. *Res:* Engineering sciences; applied mathematics; fluid mechanics; heat transfer; thermodynamics; lubrication; magnetohydrodynamics. *Mailing Add:* Dept Mech Eng Ill Inst Technol 10 West 32nd St Eng 1 Bldg Chicago IL 60616-3732

**TAO, LIXIU,** PARALLEL PROCESSING, COMBINATORIAL OPTIMIZATION. *Current Pos:* Asst prof, 88-93, ASSOC PROF COMPUT SCI, CONCORDIA UNIV, 93- *Personal Data:* b Wuxi, Jiangsu, Sept 23, 55; Can citizen; div; c Michael. *Educ:* Nanjing Inst Technol, BS, 78; Univ Pa, MS, 85, PhD(comput sci), 88. *Concurrent Pos:* Consult, Comput Res Inst Montreal, 91. *Mem:* Inst Elec & Electronics Engrs; Asn Comput Mach. *Res:* Design of parallel programming environments to support portable parallel programming and minimize CPU-load imbalance and inter-processor communication overhead. *Mailing Add:* Dept Comput Sci Concordia Univ 1455 de Maisonneuve Blvd W Montreal PQ H3G 1M8 Can. *Fax:* 514-848-2830; *E-Mail:* lixin@c.sconcordia.ca

**TAO, MARIANO,** ENZYMOLOGY, MEMBRANE BIOCHEMISTRY. *Current Pos:* actg head, 79-80, PROF BIOCHEM, UNIV ILL, CHICAGO, 70- *Personal Data:* b Davao City, Philippines, Mar 3, 38; US citizen; m 67, Pearl Koh; c Stephen & Kevin. *Educ:* Cheng Kung Univ, Taiwan, BS, 62; Univ Washington, Seattle, PhD(biochem), 67. *Prof Exp:* Sr fel biochem, Univ Wash, Seattle, 67-68; guest investr biochem, Rockefeller Univ, NY, 68-70. *Concurrent Pos:* Vis prof, Nat Taiwan Univ, 81; mem, Biochem Study Sect, NIH, 85-89. *Mem:* Am Chem Soc; AAAS; Am Soc Biochem & Molecular Biol. *Res:* Enzymology and control mechanisms; regulation of erythrocyte membrane cytoskeletal protein interactions and assembly by phosphorylation-dephosphorylation; structure-function relationships of protein kinases and the Fru-2,6-P2-regulated PPi-dependent phosphofructokinase. *Mailing Add:* 1305 Darien Club Dr Darien IL 60561-3671. *Fax:* 312-413-0364

**TAO, RONGJIA,** MATHEMATICAL PHYSICS, COMPUTATIONAL PHYSICS. *Current Pos:* ASST PROF PHYSICS, NORTHEASTERN UNIV, 85- *Personal Data:* b Shanghai, China, Jan 28, 47; m 77; c 2. *Educ:* Univ Sci & Technol China, BS, 70; Columbia Univ, MA, 80, MPhil & PhD(physics), 82. *Prof Exp:* Res assoc physics, Univ Wash, 82-84; asst prof physics, Univ Southern Calif, 84-85. *Concurrent Pos:* Vis scientist, Univ Cambridge, Eng, 83-84 & IBM Bergen Sci Ctr, 87. *Mem:* Am Phys Soc. *Res:* Properties of electron systems under strong magnetic fields; functional integration method in statistical mechanics; application of computer in physics; diffusion in disordered media; exact solution for physics models. *Mailing Add:* 902 S Valley Rd Carbondale IL 62901

**TAO, SHU-JEN,** NUCLEAR SCIENCE, PHYSICAL CHEMISTRY. *Current Pos:* SR STAFF SCIENTIST, NEW ENG INST MED RES, 65- *Personal Data:* b Soochow, China, Oct 7, 28; m 58; c 3. *Educ:* Amoy Univ, BSc, 49; Univ NSW, MEngSc, 61, PhD(nuclear chem), 64. *Prof Exp:* Scientist, Taiwan Rain Stimulation Res Inst, 51-59; res fel nuclear & radiation chem, Australian AEC, 60-61. *Mem:* AAAS; Am Phys Soc; Am Chem Soc; NY Acad Sci; Sigma Xi. *Res:* Positron physics; positronium chemistry; fast timing electronic instruments; applied statistics. *Mailing Add:* 12 Woodchuck Lane Wilton CT 06897-3427

**TAOKA, GEORGE TAKASHI,** ENGINEERING MECHANICS, CIVIL ENGINEERING. *Current Pos:* PROF CIVIL ENG, UNIV HAWAII, 65- *Personal Data:* b Honolulu, Hawaii, Feb 19, 35; m 25, Myrtle Hata. *Educ:* Ore State Univ, BS, 58; Univ Ill, MS, 60, PhD(mech), 64. *Prof Exp:* Struct engr, NAm Aviation, 58-59; instr mech, Univ Ill, 60-64; tech staff mech, Sandia Corp, 64-65. *Concurrent Pos:* NASA fel, Jet Propulsion Lab, 68; vis fel, Princeton Univ, 72-73; vis prof, Tokyo Inst Technol, 74. *Mem:* Am Acad Mech; Am Soc Civil Engrs; Soc Exp Stress Analysis; Inst Transp Engrs. *Res:* Traffic accident analysis; structural dynamics. *Mailing Add:* Dept Civil Eng Univ Hawaii at Manoa Honolulu HI 96822

**TAPAROWSKY, ELIZABETH JANE,** BIOLOGY. *Current Pos:* asst prof, 86-92, ASSOC PROF BIOL SCI, PURDUE UNIV, 92- *Personal Data:* b Worcester, Mass, Apr 12, 54; m 84, Stephen Francis Konieczny; c Matthew J & Peter F. *Educ:* Emmanuel Col, BA; 76; Brown Univ, PhD(biol), 82. *Honors & Awards:* Career Recognition Award, Women in Cell Biol, 91. *Prof Exp:* Fel, Cold Spring Harbor Lab, NY, 82-84, Univ Va Sch Med, 84-86. *Mem:* AAAS; Am Soc Cell Biol; Am Soc Microbiol. *Res:* Structure and function of genes involved in mammalian cell transformation; role of the ras oncoprotein in eukaryotic signal transduction; analysis of myc oncoprotein function. *Mailing Add:* Dept Biol Sci Purdue Univ West Lafayette IN 47907

**TAPE, GERALD FREDERICK,** SCIENCE ADMINISTRATION. *Current Pos:* from vpres to pres, Assoc Univs, Inc, 62-63, pres, 69-80, spec asst pres, 80-82, CONSULT, ASSOC UNIVS, INC, 82- *Personal Data:* b Ann Arbor, Mich, May 29, 15; m 39, Josephine Waffen; c Walter R, James W & Thomas G. *Educ:* Eastern Mich Univ, AB, 35; Univ Mich, MS, 36, PhD(physics), 40. *Hon Degrees:* DSc, Eastern Mich Univ, 64. *Honors & Awards:* Henry DeWolf Smyth Nuclear Statement Award, 78; Enrico Fermi Award, Dept Energy, 87. *Prof Exp:* Instr, Cornell Univ, 39-42; staff mem radiation lab, Mass Inst Technol, 42-46; from asst prof to assoc prof physics, Univ Ill, 46-50; asst to dir, Brookhaven Nat Lab, 50-51, dep dir, 51-62; comnr, US Atomic Energy Comn, 63-69. *Concurrent Pos:* Mem, President's Sci Adv Comn, 69-73; mem high energy adv panel, US Atomic Energy Comn, 69-74, sr tech adv Geneva IV, 71; mem, Defense Sci Bd, 70-74, chmn, 70-73; mem bd dirs, Atomic Indust Forum, 70-73; bd trustees, Sci Serv, 70-; mem sci adv comt, Int Atomic Energy Agency, 72-74, US rep, 73-77; mem gen adv comt, US Energy Res & Develop Admin, 75-77; mem, Univ Chicago Bd Gov, Argonne Nat Lab, 82-85. *Mem:* Nat Acad Eng; fel Am Phys Soc; fel Am Nuclear Soc; Am Astron Soc; AAAS. *Res:* Nuclear physics; particle physics; accelerator development; reactor development; applications of atomic energy; radioastronomy. *Mailing Add:* 4970 Sentinel Dr Apt 502 Bethesda MD 20816-3569. *Fax:* 301-229-6264

**TAPER, LILLIAN JANETTE,** TRACE MINERAL REQUIREMENTS. *Current Pos:* ASSOC PROF HUMAN NUTRIT, COL HUMAN RESOURCES, 76- *Educ:* Va Polytech Inst & State Univ, PhD(human nutrit), 76. *Mailing Add:* 311 Evaristus Hall Halifax NS B3M 2J6 Can. *Fax:* 540-231-7157

**TAPIA, FERNANDO,** PSYCHIATRY. *Current Pos:* prof, 72-89, CHIEF, MENT HEALTH SERV, UNIV HOSP & CLINS, UNIV OKLA, 72-, EMER PROF PSYCHIAT & BEHAV SCI, COL MED, 89- *Personal Data:* b Panama, Apr 8, 22; m 47; c 3. *Educ:* Univ Iowa, BA, 44, MD, 47; Am Bd Psychiat & Neurol, dipl psychiat, 60, dipl child psychiat, 66. *Prof Exp:* Intern, Santo Thomas Hosp, Panama, 48; dir, Boquette Sanit Unit-Panama, 48-54; resident psychiat, Barnes Hosp, Wash Univ, 54-57; asst dir out-patient clin, Malcolm Bliss Ment Health Ctr, 57-58; chief psychiatrist, Child Guid Clin, St Louis Co Health Ctr, 58-59, dir, Ment Health Div, 59-61; from asst prof to prof psychiat, Sch Med, Univ Mo, Columbia, 61-72, chief, Sect Child Psychiat, 61-72. *Concurrent Pos:* Instr, Wash Univ, 57-61; consult, St Louis Co Juv Court, 57-61 & Convent of the Good Shepherd, 57-61; dir children's serv, Mid-Mo Ment Health Ctr, 66-72. *Mem:* Fel Am Psychiat Asn; Sigma Xi. *Mailing Add:* 23029 N 94th St Scottsdale AZ 85255-4382

**TAPIA, M(OIEZ) A(HMEDALE),** ELECTRICAL ENGINEERING. *Current Pos:* ASST PROF ELEC ENG, UNIV MIAMI, 76- *Personal Data:* b Surat, India, Nov 17, 35; m 72. *Educ:* Univ Poona, BE, 60; Univ Ill, Urbana, MS, 62; Univ Notre Dame, PhD(elec eng), 66. *Prof Exp:* Asst lectr elec eng, Polytech Inst, India, 60-61; asst prof, Ga Inst Technol, 66-67 & Univ Miami, 67-68; asst prof, Ga Inst Technol, 68-76. *Concurrent Pos:* Jr engr, Koyna Elec, India, 60-61; Am Soc Eng Educ-Ford Found resident fel, NASA-Langley Res Ctr, 72-73; NASA grant fel prog comput sci, 72- *Mem:* Inst Elec & Electronics Engrs; Sigma Xi. *Res:* Computer engineering and science; network topology; communications; linear systems. *Mailing Add:* Elec Eng Dept Univ Miami Box 248294 Coral Gables FL 33124

**TAPIA, RICHARD,** NUMERICAL ANALYSIS, OPTIMIZATION. *Current Pos:* from asst prof to assoc prof, 70-76, PROF MATH SCI, RICE UNIV, 76- *Personal Data:* b Santa Monica, Calif, Mar 25, 39; m 60; c 3. *Educ:* Univ Calif, Los Angeles, BA, 61, MA, 66, PhD(math), 67. *Prof Exp:* Mathematician, Todd Shipyards, Calif, 61-63 & Int Bus Mach Corp, 63-65; actg asst prof math, Univ Calif, Los Angeles, 67-68; vis asst prof, US Army Math Res Ctr, Univ Wis-Madison, 68-70. *Mem:* Soc Indust & Appl Math; Inst Math Statist; Soc Advan Chicano & Native Am Scientists; Am Math Soc. *Mailing Add:* Dept Math Sci Rice Univ Houston TX 77005

**TAPIA, SANTIAGO,** astrophysics, technical management, for more information see previous edition

**TAPLEY, BYRON D(EAN),** AEROSPACE ENGINEERING, ASTRODYNAMICS. *Current Pos:* Asst prof aerospace eng & eng mech, Univ Tex, 60-64, assoc prof, 64-66, assoc prof aerospace eng, 66-68, chmn dept, 66-77, prof, 68-74, W R Woolrich prof aerospace eng & eng mech, 74-84, DIR, CTR SPACE RES, UNIV TEX, 82-, CLARE COCKRELL WILLIAMS CENTENNIAL CHAIR ENG, 84-, DIR, TEX SPACE GRANT CONSORTIUM, 89- *Personal Data:* b Charleston, Miss, Jan 16, 33; m 59; c 2. *Educ:* Univ Tex, BS, 56, MS, 58, PhD(eng mech), 60. *Honors & Awards:* Except Sci Achievement Medal, NASA, 83; Mech & Control of Flight Award, Am Inst Aeronaut & Astronaut, 87. *Concurrent Pos:* Ford Found fel, Univ Tex, 61-62; chmn, Comt Geodesy, Nat Res Coun, 78-82, mem, Aeronaut & Space Eng Bd, 81-85, mem, ad hoc comt, Space Sta Eng & Technol Develop, 84-85, chmn, Comt Earth Sci, 87-88, mem, Space Sci Bd, 87-88, Comt Earth Studies, 89-, Space Studies Bd, 89-, chmn, Geophys Study Comt, 90-; assoc ed, Celestial Mech J & J Guidance & Control; mem, Tech Panel on Dynamics of Artificial Satellites & Space Probes, Int Comt Space Res, 79- *Mem:* Nat Acad Sci; Am Astronaut Soc; fel Am Inst Aeronaut & Astronaut; Soc Eng Sci; fel AAAS; Am Soc Mech Engrs; fel Am Geophys Union; Am Acad Mech; Sigma Xi; Am Astron Soc. *Res:* Non-linear parameter estimation applied to orbit determination theory and applications of satellite tracking data to areas of satellite geodesy and satellite acanography. *Mailing Add:* 3100 Perry Lane Austin TX 78731-5327

**TAPLEY, DONALD FRASER,** INTERNAL MEDICINE. *Current Pos:* from asst prof to assoc prof, Columbia Univ, 56-72, actg dean fac med, 73-74, dean fac med, 74-84, PROF MED, COL PHYSICIANS & SURGEONS, COLUMBIA UNIV, 72-, ASSOC DEAN FAC AFFAIRS, 70-, SR DEP VPRES HEALTH SCI, 84-, ALUMNI PROF MED, 84- *Personal Data:* b Woodstock, NB, May 19, 27; nat US; m 57, Caroline Sorthall; c 3. *Educ:* Acadia Univ, BSc, 48; Univ Chicago, MD, 52. *Prof Exp:* Intern & asst resident, Presby Hosp, NY, 52-54; fel physiol chem, Johns Hopkins Univ, 54-56. *Concurrent Pos:* Fel physiol chem, Oxford Univ, 56-57; from asst attend physician to attend, Presby Hosp, 57- *Mem:* Am Soc Clin Invest; Am Thyroid Asn; Endocrine Soc; Harvey Soc. *Res:* Intermediary metabolism; thyroid physiology. *Mailing Add:* Columbia Univ 630 W 168th St Rm 2-401 New York NY 10032

**TAPLIN, LAEL BRENT,** MECHANICAL ENGINEERING, ELECTRICAL ENGINEERING. *Current Pos:* RETIRED. *Personal Data:* b Blackwell, Okla, Jan 5, 27; m 51; c 4. *Educ:* Ore State Col, BS, 48; Univ Ill, MS, 51. *Prof Exp:* Test engr, Gen Elec Co, 48-49; res asst theoret & appl mech, Univ, Ill, 49-50, res assoc, 50-51; sr engr, Vickers Inc, Sperry Rand Corp, 51-55, proj engr, 55-58; proj engr, Res Labs Div, Bendix Corp, 58-61, dept head, Lab Flight Controls, 61-64, mgr energy conversion & dynamic controls, 64-66, dir mech sci & controls lab, 66-74, consult scientist, Res Labs,

74-80; eng-advan tech & syst, Serry Vickers, 80-90. *Concurrent Pos:* Instr, Wayne State Univ, 57-58. *Mem:* Inst Elec & Electronics Engrs; Sigma Xi. *Res:* Dynamics of fluid power servovalves, motors and control systems; hot gas servos; pneumatic controls; gas generators and controls; pneumatic flight controls; fluidic elements, sensors and systems; fluidic circuit analysis; fuel management; electronic fuel injection; emissions control. *Mailing Add:* 8396 Golfside Dr Commerce Township MI 48382

**TAPP, CHARLES MILLARD,** ENGINEERING. *Current Pos:* tech staff mem radiation damage, Sandia Nat Labs, 64-66, div supvr vacuum tube physics & technol, 66-69, dept mgr vacuum tube devices, 69-71, dept mgr microelectronic components, 71-77, mgr, Info Systs Dept, 77-80, MGR, ELECTRONIC INSTRUMENTATION DEPT, SANDIA NAT LABS, 80- *Personal Data:* b Memphis, Tenn, Nov 9, 36; m 55, 78; c 3. *Educ:* Union Univ, BA, 58; Memphis State Univ, BS, 60; Univ Va, MS, 62, PhD(physics), 64. *Prof Exp:* Staff mem radiation calibration, Nat Bur Stand, 60, 62. *Concurrent Pos:* Ed, Transactions Components, Hybrids & Mfg Technol & gen chmn, Electronic Components Conf, Inst Elec & Electronics Engrs, 74- *Mem:* Sr mem Inst Elec & Electronics Engrs; Am Phys Soc. *Res:* Solid state electronics and circuits; microelectronic thin and thick film processes; vacuum tube design, development; radiation effects in devices; neutron sources. *Mailing Add:* 8731 Tierra Alegre Dr NE Albuquerque NM 87122-2643

**TAPP, WILLIAM JOUETTE,** ORGANIC CHEMISTRY. *Current Pos:* CONSULT, 81- *Personal Data:* b Quincy, Ill, July 26, 18; m 46, Hortense Ackerman; c William J III. *Educ:* Univ Ill, BS, 39; Cornell Univ, PhD(org chem), 43. *Prof Exp:* Asst chem, Cornell Univ, 40-41 & 41-43, Nat Defense Res Comt fel, 40-41; res & develop chemist, Union Carbide Corp, 43-46, proj leader, 46-54, staff asst, 55-56, patent adminr, 57-66, asst dir pharmaceut tech, 66-67, mgr admin, 67-81. *Mem:* Am Chem Soc. *Res:* Organic nitrogen and sulfur compounds; synthetic lubricants; industrial organic synthesis. *Mailing Add:* 1031 W Sterlington Pl Apex NC 27502

**TAPPEINER, JOHN CUMMINGS, II,** FOREST ECOLOGY, SILVICULTURE. *Current Pos:* PROF FORESTRY, SILVICULT & FOREST ECOL, ORE STATE UNIV, 81- *Personal Data:* b Los Angeles, Calif, Dec 15, 34; m 65; c 3. *Educ:* Univ Calif, Berkeley, BS, 57, MS, 61, PhD(forestry), 66. *Prof Exp:* Forester, US Forest Serv, 59-63; res asst forest ecol, Univ Calif, Berkeley, 63-66; Ford Found teaching fel forestry, Agr Univ Minas Gerais, 66-67; from asst prof to assoc prof, Forest Res Ctr, Univ Minn, St Paul, 68-73; regional silviculturist, US Forest Serv, 73-81. *Mem:* Soc Am Foresters; Ecol Soc Am. *Res:* Natural regeneration of Sierra Nevada Douglas fir and ponderosa pine; ecology of hazel and understory vegetation; biomass and nutrient content of shrubs and herbs; effect of mechanized harvesting of forest soils; ecology of shrubs and hardwood in forests of Oregon; regeneration, growth and autecology of forest plants, especially understory species; effects of shrubs and hardwoods on forest regeneration; development of sub-cultural systems for the production of wood and wildlife habitat, development of natural and managed forests. *Mailing Add:* Dept Forest Res & US Geol Surv BRD Ore State Univ Corvallis OR 97331. *Fax:* 541-750-7329

**TAPPEL, ALOYS LOUIS,** BIOCHEMISTRY. *Current Pos:* From instr to assoc prof, 51-61, PROF FOOD SCI & BIOCHEMIST, UNIV CALIF DAVIS, 61-, EMER PROF, 94- *Personal Data:* b St Louis, Mo, Nov 21, 26; m 51, Ardelle Fish; c Susan, Mary, Steve, Paul, Cathy & Liz. *Educ:* Iowa State Univ, BS, 48; Univ Minn, PhD(biochem), 51. *Honors & Awards:* Borden Award, Am Inst Nutrit, 73; Osborne & Mendel Award, 87. *Concurrent Pos:* Guggenheim fel, 65-66. *Mem:* Am Chem Soc; Am Oil Chem Soc; Am Soc Biol Chem; Am Inst Nutrit. *Res:* Oxidant molecular damage and biological protection systems. *Mailing Add:* Dept Food Sci & Technol Univ Calif-Davis Davis CA 95616-5224

**TAPPEN, NEIL CAMPBELL,** PHYSICAL ANTHROPOLOGY, PRIMATOLOGY. *Current Pos:* prof, 65-69, Earnest A Hooton prof, 69-90, EMER PROF ANTHROP, UNIV WIS, MILWAUKEE, 90- *Personal Data:* b Jacksonville, Fla, Feb 26, 20; m 52, Ardith Bennett; c Helen L & Martha J. *Educ:* Univ Fla, AB, 41; Univ Chicago, MA, 49, PhD(anthrop), 52. *Prof Exp:* Res assoc human biol, Univ Mich, 51-52; from assoc anthrop to instr, Univ Pa, 52-54; from instr to asst prof anat, Emory Univ, 54-59; assoc prof phys anthrop, Tulane Univ, 59-65. *Concurrent Pos:* NIH grants, Emory Univ, 55-59, Tulane Univ, 60-65 & Univ Wis, Milwaukee, 65-71; Fulbright sr res scholar, Makerere Col, Uganda, 56-57; NSF grant, Univ Wis, Milwaukee, 71-76. *Mem:* AAAS; Am Anthrop Asn; Am Asn Phys Anthropologists; Am Anat Asn; Int Primatological Soc. *Res:* Organization of bone; non-human primates and their relationship to human evolution; structure of bone in fossil hominids; problems of human evolution. *Mailing Add:* Dept Anthrop Univ Wis 2707 E Shorewood Blvd Milwaukee WI 53211

**TAPPER, DANIEL NAPHTALI,** NEUROPHYSIOLOGY. *Current Pos:* Asst physiol, Cornell Univ, 55-59, res assoc radiation biol, 59-61, from asst prof to prof, 61-97, EMER PROF RADIATION BIOL, CORNELL UNIV, 97- *Personal Data:* b Philadelphia, Pa, Dec 5, 29; m 59, 82, Judy Long. *Educ:* Rutgers Univ, BS, 51; Univ Pa, VMD, 55; Cornell Univ, PhD(physiol), 59. *Concurrent Pos:* NIH spec fel, Stockholm, 65-66; NIH spec fel, Rockefeller Univ, 72-73; adj prof, 73-74. *Mem:* AAAS; Soc Neurosci; Am Physiol Soc. *Res:* Behavior; receptor physiology; neurophysiology of skin sensibility. *Mailing Add:* NY State Col Vet Med Cornell Univ Ithaca NY 14853. *Fax:* 607-253-3851; *E-Mail:* dnt1@cornell.edu

**TAPPERT, FREDERICK DRACH,** PHYSICS. *Current Pos:* PROF APPL MARINE PHYSICS, 78- *Personal Data:* b Philadelphia, Pa, Apr 21, 40; m 79; c 2. *Educ:* Pa State Univ, BS, 62; Princeton Univ, PhD(physics), 67. *Prof Exp:* Mem tech staff, Bell Labs, 67-73; sr res scientist, Courant Inst Math Sci, NY Univ, 74-78. *Concurrent Pos:* Vis staff mem, Los Alamos Sci Lab, 74-; consult, Sci Applns, Inc, 74-; consult, Nat Oceanog & Atmospheric Admin, US Govt, 80- , Daubin Systs Corp, 82- , Naval Underwater Syst Cen, 83-84 & 89-90. *Mem:* Am Phys Soc; AAAS; Soc Indust & Appl Math; Am Geophys Union; fel Acoust Soc Am; Sigma Xi. *Res:* Theory and numerical simulation of wave propagation effects in plasmas, gases, liquids and solids. *Mailing Add:* 907 Jeronimo Dr Coral Gables FL 33146-1272

**TAPPHORN, RALPH M,** NUCLEAR PHYSICS. *Current Pos:* prin scientist, 87-90, sci supvr, 90-91, STAFF SCIENTIST, LOCKHEED ENG & SCI CO, 91- *Personal Data:* b Grinnell, Kans, July 26, 44; m 69, Karen L Johnson; c Janelle & Carolyn. *Educ:* Ft Hays Kans State Univ, BS, 66; Kans State Univ, PhD(physics), 70. *Honors & Awards:* Eagle Manned Mission Success Award, Nat Space Club, 90. *Prof Exp:* Res assoc nuclear physics, Ballistics Res Lab, Aberdeen Proving Ground, Md, 70-72; sr scientist nuclear physics, Schlumberger-Doll Res Ctr, 72-77; sr mem tech staff, Ball Aerospace Systs Div, 77-80, prog mgr, 80-82; bus mgr, Tapphorn Conserv, Ltd, 82-87. *Concurrent Pos:* Mem, Prin Innovative Technol, Inc. *Mem:* Am Phys Soc; Sigma Xi; Instrument Soc Am; Am Soc Nondestructive Testing. *Res:* Aerospace instrumentation of gamma-ray spectrometers for astrophysical studies; geophysical exploration with gamma-ray spectroscopy; nuclear detectors and instrumentation; radiation damage investigations; infrared fiber-optic sensors; flame combustion; Fourier transfer infrared combustion analysis spectroscopy; Laser induced combustion spectroscopy; flash X-ray radiography; neutron radiography and neutron activation analysis; ultrasonic imaging; aerospace instrumentation for materials testing; acoustic emission analysis. *Mailing Add:* 2200 Mars Ave Apt 11 Las Cruces NM 88012-8533. *E-Mail:* ralphmtapp@aol.com

**TAPPMEYER, WILBUR PAUL,** INORGANIC CHEMISTRY. *Current Pos:* from asst prof to assoc prof, 60-66, PROF CHEM, UNIV MO, ROLLA, 66- *Personal Data:* b Owensville, Mo, May 19, 22; m 47; c 5. *Educ:* Southeast Mo State Col, AB, 45; Univ Mo, BS, 47, PhD(inorg chem), 61. *Prof Exp:* Teacher high sch, Mo, 44-45; asst chem, Mo Sch Mines, 45-46; prof, Southwest Baptist Col, 47-60. *Mem:* Am Chem Soc. *Res:* Solid phase extraction of metal chelates; dimeric and polymeric properties of certain metal acetates and other alkonates. *Mailing Add:* 705 E Fifth St Rolla MO 65401-3417

**TAPSCOTT, ROBERT EDWIN,** OZONE DEPLETION, GLOBAL WARMING. *Current Pos:* from asst prof to assoc prof chem, 68-84, sr scientist, 84-91, DIR, CTR GLOBAL ENVIRON TECHNOL, UNIV NMEX, 91- *Personal Data:* b Terre Haute, Ind, June 10, 38; m 67, Mary F Summers; c 1. *Educ:* Univ Colo, BS, 64; Univ Ill, Urbana, PhD, 68. *Honors & Awards:* Stratospheric Ozone Protect Award, Environ Protect Agency, 93. *Concurrent Pos:* Vis prof, Univ NC, 78, prof chem, 84- *Mem:* Sigma Xi; AAAS; Royal Soc Chem; Am Chem Soc; Am Inst Chem Engrs; Air Pollution Control Asn. *Res:* Chemistry of combustion and extinguishment; environmental chemistry; hazardous materials; waste disposal technology; emissions from large fires; global environmental technologies; alternatives to ozone-depleting materials; halons; refrigeration. *Mailing Add:* Ctr Global Environ Technol 901 University Blvd SE Albuquerque NM 87106-4339. *Fax:* 505-272-7252; *E-Mail:* halons@hydra.unm.edu

**TARAGIN, MORTON FRANK,** nuclear experimental physics, for more information see previous edition

**TARAMAN, KHALIL SHOWKY,** MANUFACTURING PRODUCTIVITY, MANUFACTURING SYSTEMS. *Current Pos:* assoc dean eng & DIT endowed chmn, 86-89, DEAN ENG, LAWRENCE TECHNOL UNIV, 89- *Personal Data:* b Cairo, Egypt, July 9, 39; US citizen; m 69; c 3. *Educ:* Ain Shams Univ, Cairo, BSc, 64; MSc, 67; Univ Wis-Madison, MS, 69; Tex Tech Univ, Lubbock, PhD(indust eng), 71. *Prof Exp:* Instr prod eng, Ain Shams Univ, Cairo, 64-67; from asst prof to prof mfg eng, Univ Detroit, 70-86, dir, Mfg Eng Inst, 75-86, chmn dept, 77-86. *Concurrent Pos:* Sr tech consult, Ford, Gen Elec, Bendix & other co, 70-; chmn, Mat Removal Coun, Soc Mfg Engrs, 79-84, int dir, 82-87, chmn, Ref Publ Comt, 89-90, Publ & Ref Mgt Coun, 89-; dir, Mfg Div, Am Soc Eng Educ, 88-90; mem, Mfg Studies Bd, Nat Acad Engrs & Nat Res Coun, 89-90. *Mem:* Sr mem Soc Mfg Engrs; sr mem Am Inst Indust Engrs; Am Soc Mech Engrs; Am Soc Eng Educ. *Res:* Manufacturing engineering; author of numerous publications and two books. *Mailing Add:* Dept Mech Eng Lawrence Technol Univ 21000 W Ten Mile Rd Southfield MI 48075-1058

**TARANIK, JAMES VLADIMIR,** EXPLORATION GEOLOGY, PHOTOGEOLOGY. *Current Pos:* dean, MacKay Sch Mines, 82-87, PROF GEOL & GEOPHYS, DEPT GEOL SCI, UNIV NEV, RENO, 82-; DIR, COOP INST AEROSPACE SCI & TERRESTRIAL APPLNS, DESERT RES INST, UNIV NEV SYSTS, RENO, 86-, PRES, DESERT RES INST, 87-, ARTHUR BRANT CHAIR GEOL & GEOPHYS, 95- *Personal Data:* b Los Angeles, Calif, Apr 23, 40; m 71, Colleen; c Dan & Deb (Sterling). *Educ:* Stanford Univ, BS, 64; Colo Sch Mines, PhD(geol), 74. *Honors & Awards:* Except Sci Achievement Medal, NASA, 82, Group Achievement Award, OSTA-1, STS-2, 82; Johnson Space Ctr Group Achievement Award, STS-41G, 84; NASA Group Achievement Award, Shuttle Imaging Radar-B, STS-41G, 90; Merit Award, Am Soc Photogram & Remote Sensing, 94. *Prof Exp:* Chief remote sensing, Iowa Geol Surv, 71-74; prin remote sensing scientist, Earth Resources Observ Syst Data Ctr, US Geol Surv, 75-78; chief, Non-Renewable Resources Br, NASA HQ, Washington, DC, 79-82.

*Concurrent Pos:* Adj prof geol, Univ Iowa, 71-; vis prof civil eng, Iowa State Univ, 72-74; consult, Earth Resources Technol Satellite Follow on Eval Panel Geol, Goddard Space Flight Ctr, NASA, Synchronous Observ Satellite Prog Eval, Geol Applns, Active microwave Syst Eval Workshop Earth-Land Panel, Geol Landuse Water, Johnson Space Ctr, 74; adj prof Earth Sci, Univ SDak, 76-79; chmn working group on instrumentation for remote sensor data processing & analysis, Int Soc Photogram, 77-80; chmn, working group non-renewable resources, Int Soc Photogram & Remote Sensing; scientist, var space shuttle progs; chmn, Dept Com Working Group Commercialization & Weather Satellites, 82-84; chmn, NASA Space Applns Adv Comt, Subcomt Remote Sensing Earth, 86-88; mem, NASA Space Sci Ctr & Appln adv comt, 88-90, chmn subcomt Remote Sensing, NASA space applns adv comt, 86-89; comt Strategic Reloctable Targets, Air Force Studies Bd, NAS, 89-; prog dir, Space Grant Prog, Univ Nev Syst Space Grant Consortium, 91- *Mem:* Fel Geol Soc Am; Am Asn Petrol Geologists; Am Inst Aeronaut & Astronaut; Am Inst Prof Geologists; Soc Explor Geophysicists; fel AAAS; sr mem, Am Aeronaut & Astronaut; Am Astron Soc; Int Acad Astronaut. *Res:* Development of applications of remote sensing technology to mineral and mineral fuel exploration; assessment of environmental and engineering geologic aspects of mineral resource development; engineering geology and geohydrology of civil works site selection. *Mailing Add:* Desert Res Inst Univ Nev Syst PO Box 60220 Reno NV 89506. *Fax:* 702-673-7421; *E-Mail:* jtaranik@maxey.une.edu

**TARANTINE, FRANK J(AMES),** MECHANICAL ENGINEERING. *Current Pos:* From instr to assoc prof, 57-70, PROF MECH ENG, YOUNGSTOWN STATE UNIV, 70-, CHMN MECH ENG, 92- *Personal Data:* b Youngstown, Ohio, May 27, 35; m 57, Mary Mediate; c Frank, James, Anne & Jean. *Educ:* Youngstown Univ, BE, 57; Univ Akron, MS, 61; Carnegie Inst Technol, PhD(fluid dynamics), 65. *Concurrent Pos:* Engr, Com Sharing Inc, 53-56 & 59-63, Automatic Sprinkler Corp Am, 56-59; NSF sci fac fel, 64-65. *Mem:* Am Soc Mech Engrs; Am Soc Eng Educ; Sigma Xi. *Res:* Vibrations and experimental stress analysis; mechanical design; acoustics. *Mailing Add:* Mech Eng Youngstown State Univ 410 Wick Ave Youngstown OH 44555

**TARANTINO, LAURA M(ARY),** BIOCHEMISTRY. *Current Pos:* consumer safety officer, 87-92, CHIEF, BIOTECHNOL POLICY BR, FOOD & DRUG ADMIN, 92- *Personal Data:* b Exeter, Pa, Feb 6, 47. *Educ:* Col Misericordia, BS, 68; Cornell Univ, PhD(biochem), 75. *Prof Exp:* Assoc res scientist med, Col Physicians & Surgeons, Columbia Univ & Roosevelt Hosp, 75-78; asst prof biochem, Eastern Va Med Sch, 79-87. *Mem:* AAAS; Sigma Xi; NY Acad Sci; Am Chem Soc. *Res:* Enzyme regulation in the central nervous system; role and control of hexosemonophosphate shunt in cells; metabolic effects of insulin; diabetes. *Mailing Add:* Food & Drug Admin-HFS-206 200 C St SW Washington DC 20204-0001

**TARAPCHAK, STEPHEN J,** LIMNOLOGY, PHYCOLOGY. *Current Pos:* ECOLOGIST, 81-; IMMUNOTOXICOLOGY, MED SCH, UNIV MICH, 90- *Personal Data:* b Staten Island, NY, Mar 20, 42; m 65. *Educ:* Clarion State Col, BS, 64; Ohio Univ, MS, 66; Univ Minn, PhD(ecol), 73. *Prof Exp:* Res fel, Limnol Res Ctr, Univ Minn, Minneapolis, 73-74; res scientist biol oceanog, Great Lakes Environ Res Lab, Nat Oceanic & Atmospheric Admin, 74-90. *Concurrent Pos:* Consult, Environ Statements Syst Div, Argonne Nat Lab, 73-74. *Mem:* Am Phycol Soc; Am Soc Limnol & Oceanog; Int Limnol Soc; Int Asn Great Lakes Res. *Res:* Immunotoxicology; effects of environ contaminants, pesticides (organophosphorous) on human immune system at sentomolar level; resulting nullification of immune system. *Mailing Add:* 1803 Crestland Dr Ann Arbor MI 48104

**TARAS, MICHAEL ANDREW,** FOREST PRODUCTS, WOOD TECHNOLOGY. *Personal Data:* b Olyphant, Pa, Sept 6, 21; m 48, Jean Moyer; c Michael, Kenneth, Christopher & Steven. *Educ:* Pa State Univ, BS, 42, MF, 48; NC State Univ, PhD(wood technol), 65. *Prof Exp:* Forest prod technologist, Forest Prod Lab, US Forest Serv, 48-54 & Southeastern Forest Exp Sta, Forestry Sci Lab, 54-79; prof forestry, Clemson Univ, 79-82, dept head, 83-92. *Concurrent Pos:* Forest prod consult. *Mem:* Forest Prod Soc; Soc Wood Sci & Technol; Int Asn Wood Anat. *Res:* Forestry; wood anatomy related to wood identification, quality, seasoning and moisture movement through wood; in log and tree classification systems and wood weight-volume relationships; forest tree biomass prediction and evaluation. *Mailing Add:* 215 S Craggmore Dr Salem SC 29676

**TARAS, PAUL,** ELECTRO-WEAK PHYSICS & HIGH SPIN PHYSICS, RELATIVISTIC HEAVY ION PHYSICS. *Current Pos:* From asst prof to assoc prof, 65-76, PROF PHYSICS, UNIV MONTREAL, 76- *Personal Data:* b Tunisia, May 12, 41; Can citizen; m 63, Malinen Marja; c Lisa & Michele. *Educ:* Univ Toronto, BScEng Phys, 62, MSc, 63, PhD(nuclear physics), 65. *Concurrent Pos:* Vis prof, Univ Heidelberg, 71-72; attached staff, Chalk River Nuclear Labs, Atomic Energy Can Ltd, 78-89. *Mem:* Am Phys Soc; Can Asn Physicists. *Res:* Electro/weak physics, gas microstrip detectors research and development; high spin nuclear spectroscopy and reaction mechanisms via heavy ion induced reactions; CP violation. *Mailing Add:* Dept Physics Univ Montreal Montreal PQ H3C 3J7 Can. *Fax:* 514-343-6215; *E-Mail:* taras@lps.umontreal.ca

**TARASUK, JOHN DAVID,** THERMODYNAMICS, MECHANICAL ENGINEERING. *Current Pos:* mem fac mech eng, 68-89, HEAD, MECH ENGR DEPT, UNIV WESTERN ONT, 89- *Personal Data:* b St Walburg, Sask, Dec 24, 36; m 61; c 3. *Educ:* Univ Toronto, BASc, 59, MASc, 61; Univ Sask, PhD(mech eng), 69. *Prof Exp:* Demonstr thermodyn, Univ Toronto, 59-61; res & develop engr, John Inglis, Toronto, 61-62; asst prof heat transfer, NS Tech Col, 62-65; lectr thermodyn & heat transfer, Univ Sask, 65-68. *Concurrent Pos:* Consult, G Graner & Assoc, Toronto, 58-64; NSF grants, Okla State Univ, 63 & Univ Calif, Los Angeles, 64. *Res:* Natural convection; natural and forced convection; thermodynamic properties of engineering fluids. *Mailing Add:* Dept Mech Eng Univ Western Ont London ON N6A 5B9 Can

**TARASZKA, ANTHONY JOHN,** ANALYTICAL CHEMISTRY. *Current Pos:* Res assoc analytical res & develop, Upjohn Co, 62-63, head dept, 63-66, mgr control res & develop, 66-70, dir control, 70-74, vpres control, 74-80, CORP VPRES CONTROL, UPJOHN CO, 80- *Personal Data:* b Wallington, NJ, Feb 19, 35; m 60. *Educ:* Rutgers Univ, BS, 56, MS, 58; Univ Wis, PhD(pharmaceut chem), 62. *Mem:* Am Chem Soc; Am Pharmaceut Asn. *Res:* Trace component analysis; separation techniques; reaction mechanisms; pharmaceutical chemistry. *Mailing Add:* The Upjohn Co 7171 Portage Rd Kalamazoo MI 49001-0101

**TARBELL, DEAN STANLEY,** ORGANIC CHEMISTRY. *Current Pos:* Harvie Branscom distinguished prof, 75-76, distinguished prof chem, 67-81, EMER PROF CHEM, VANDERBILT UNIV, 81- *Personal Data:* b Hancock, NH, Oct 19, 13; m 42, Ann Tracy; c William, Linda & Theodore. *Educ:* Harvard Univ, AB, 34, MA, 35, PhD(org chem), 37. *Honors & Awards:* C H Herty Medal, Am Chem Soc, 73, Dexter Award, Hist Chem Div, 89; Fuson lectr, Univ Nev, 72. *Prof Exp:* Asst, Radcliffe Col, 36-37; fel, Univ Ill, 37-38; from instr to prof org chem, Univ Rochester, 38-60, Houghton prof chem, 60-66, chmn dept, 64-66. *Concurrent Pos:* Guggenheim fels, Oxford Univ, 46-47 & Stanford Univ, 61-62; mem, NIH study sects; consult, Walter Reed Army Inst Res, 72- *Mem:* Nat Acad Sci; Am Chem Soc; Am Acad Arts & Sci; The Chem Soc; Hist Sci Soc. *Res:* Reaction phenolic ethers; organic sulfur compounds; structure and synthesis of natural products; structural and theoretical organic chemistry; structure of antibiotics; history of organic chemistry in the United States. *Mailing Add:* 6033 Sherwood Dr Nashville TN 37215-5734

**TARBELL, JOHN M,** BIOMEDICAL ENGINEERING, BIOFOOD MECHANICS. *Current Pos:* PROF CHEM ENG, PA STATE UNIV, 87. *Personal Data:* b Malone, NY, June 20, 47. *Educ:* Rutgers Univ, BS, 69; Univ Del, MS, 72, PhD(chem eng), 75. *Prof Exp:* Vis scientist, Imp Col, 83-84. *Mem:* Biomed Eng Soc; Am Inst Chem Engrs; Am Soc Mech Engrs; AAAS; Sigma Xi. *Mailing Add:* 155 Fenske Lab Pa State Univ University Park PA 16802-4400

**TARBELL, THEODORE DEAN,** SOLAR PHYSICS, SPACE INSTRUMENT DESIGN. *Current Pos:* SR STAFF SCIENTIST ASTROPHYS, LOCKHEED PALO ALTO RES LAB, 76- *Personal Data:* b Rochester, NY, Nov 11, 50; m 73; c 1. *Educ:* Harvard Univ, AB, 71, Calif Inst Technol, PhD(astrophys), 76. *Concurrent Pos:* Co-investr on spacelab 2 mission, NASA Solar Optical Universal Polarimeter, 76-85, prin investr, Exp Sunlab Shuttle Mission, 85-, mem, Data Systs Users Working Group, 78-83, co-investr, Coord Instrument Package Orbiting Solar Lab, 80-, mem, Solar & Heliospheric Physics, 86-, mem, NSF Global Oscillations Network Group, 87-, mem, NAS Comt Solar & Space Physics, 87-, co-investr, Solar & Heliospheric Observ, 87-; prin investr, Air Force Geophys Lab Study Spectral Imaging, 80-85; mem, Max Steering Comt Flare Res, 87- *Mem:* Am Astron Soc; Am Phys Soc; Astron Soc Pac; Optical Soc Am. *Res:* Concentration on the structure of the sun and stars, first through theoretical modeling and more recently through observations of magnetohydrodynamic processes in the solar atmosphere; using spacecraft and mountain-top observation. *Mailing Add:* 1040 Los Altos Ave Los Altos CA 94022

**TARBY, THEODORE JOHN,** ANATOMY, NEUROPHYSIOLOGY. *Current Pos:* BARROW NEUROL INST, 80- *Personal Data:* b Auburn, NY, May 9, 41; m 64; c 1. *Educ:* Calif Inst Technol, BS, 64; Univ Calif, Los Angeles, PhD(anat), 68. *Prof Exp:* Asst prof anat, Med Ctr, Univ Colo, Denver, 68-80. *Concurrent Pos:* Milhelm Found Cancer Res grant, Med Ctr, Univ Colo, Denver, 71- *Mem:* AAAS; Am Asn Anat; Soc Neurosci. *Res:* Cerebral tissue impedance and extracellular space; blood-brain barrier; olfactory function in normal salmon; glial physiology. *Mailing Add:* 7710 N Hummingbird Lane Paradise Valley AZ 85253

**TARDIF, HENRI PIERRE,** MATERIALS TECHNOLOGY, ARMAMENT METALLURGY & DEFENSE SCIENCE. *Current Pos:* RETIRED. *Educ:* Univ Laval, BASc; Carnegie Inst Technol, MSc; Univ Birmingham, Eng, PhD, 53. *Prof Exp:* Head, Mat Lab, Defense Res Bd Can, Valcartier, Que, 56-65, dep chief Can Defense Res Staff, London, Eng, 66-68, dir, Armaments Div, Valcartier, Que, 69-72, asst chief, 73-77, dep chief, 77-84, chief, 84-90. *Concurrent Pos:* Nat Defense Col, Kingston, Ont, 72-73; mem, Can Coun Non-Destructive Testing Comt Aeronaut Struct & Mat, Nat Res Coun. *Mem:* Fel Inst Metals Eng; fel Am Soc Metals; Can Inst Mining & Metall; fel Can Aeronaut & Space Inst. *Res:* Application of materials technology to armaments; behavior of materials subjected to ballistic explosive and dynamic stresses; explosive forming of metals; dynamic properties of materials; determination of sabotage by explosives in airplane crashes; development of new alloys and their use in antiarmour munitions; more than 45 technical documents. *Mailing Add:* 1257 Jean Dequen Ave Ste-Foy PQ G1W 3H5 Can

**TARDIF, SUZETTE DAVIS,** REPRODUCTIVE BIOLOGY, PRIMATOLOGY. *Current Pos:* RES ASST PROF, DEPT ANTHROP, UNIV TENN, 86-, ASST PROF, 92- *Personal Data:* b Bay City, Tex, July 11, 55. *Educ:* Univ Okla, BS, 77; Mich State Univ, PhD(zool), 82. *Prof Exp:*

Scientist, Marmoset Res Ctr-Oak Ridge Assoc Univs, 83-92. *Concurrent Pos:* Fac mem, Ethology Prog, Univ Tenn, 93. *Res:* Comparative study of the reproductive strategies of neotropical primates, particularly marmosets and tamarins, examining the inter-relation of environment, physiology, and behavior. *Mailing Add:* Dept Anthrop Univ Tenn Knoxville 1345 Circle Park Knoxville TN 37996-0001. *Fax:* 423-974-2686; *E-Mail:* tardif@utkvs.utk.edu

**TARDIFF, ROBERT G,** TOXICOLOGY, ENVIRONMENTAL HEALTH. *Current Pos:* EXEC DIR TOXICOL & ENVIRON HEALTH, NAT ACAD SCI, 77-; DIR, RISK FOCUS DIV, BURSAR INC. *Personal Data:* b Lowell, Mass, Feb 1, 42; m 70; c 3. *Educ:* Merrimack Col, BA, 64; Univ Chicago, PhD(toxicol & pharmacol), 68. *Prof Exp:* Res toxicologist org contaminants, USPHS, 68-70; br chief toxicol assessments, Environ Protection Agency, 70-77. *Concurrent Pos:* USPHS fel, 64-68; assoc prof, Med Col Va, 79-; assoc prof, Georgetown Univ Sch Med, 87-90. *Mem:* Am Col Toxicol; Soc Toxicol; Environ Mutagen Soc; NY Acad Sci; Soc Risk Analysis. *Res:* Hazard assessment; interactions; metabolism; organic compounds in drinking water; mutagens; carcinogens; toxicology; pharmacology. *Mailing Add:* 1423 Tapline Ct Vienna VA 22182-1731

**TARDUNO, JOHN ANTHONY,** ARCTIC EARTH SCIENCES, PALEOMAGNETISM & PLATE TECTONICS. *Current Pos:* ASSOC PROF GEOPHYS, UNIV ROCHESTER, 96- *Personal Data:* b New York, NY, Jan 2, 61. *Educ:* Lehigh Univ, BS, 83; Stanford Univ, MS, 87, PhD(geophys), 87. *Prof Exp:* Postdoctoral fel, Stanford Univ, 88; NSF postdoctoral fel, ETH Zurich, 89. *Res:* Paleomagnetism and rock magnetism to study the rates of plate tectonic and hotspot motion, true polar wander, mantle plume volcanism, the fidelity of geomagnetic reversal records and applications of environmental magnetism. *Mailing Add:* Dept Earth & Environ Sci Univ Rochester Rochester NY 14627

**TAREN, JAMES A,** NEUROSURGERY. *Current Pos:* resident, Univ Mich, 55-57, from instr to assoc prof, 57-69, dir Neurobehav Sci Prog, 75-78, assoc dean, 78-87, dir, Med Ctr Info Technol Integration, 88-90, dir, Neuromodulation Prog, 90-96, PROF NEUROSURG MED SCH, UNIV MICH, ANN ARBOR, 69- *Personal Data:* b Toledo, Ohio, Nov 10, 24. *Educ:* Univ Toledo, BS, 48; Univ Mich, MD, 52; Am Bd Neurol Surg, dipl, 60. *Prof Exp:* Intern surg, Univ Hosp, Univ Mich, 52-53, resident, 53-54; teaching fel neurosurg, Harvard Med Sch, 54-55. *Concurrent Pos:* Res fel, Boston Children's Hosp, 54-55; asst surg, Peter Bent Brigham Hosp, Boston, 54-55; actg chief neurosurg, Vet Admin Hosp, Ann Arbor, 58-73; chief neurosurg, Wayne Co Gen Hosp, 58-72; vis fel, Karolinska Inst, Stockholm, 81; vis prof, Hosp Foch, Paris, 66, 73 & 80, Gumma Univ, Japan, 89, 90. *Mem:* AAAS; Asn Am Med Cols; Cong Neurol Surg; NY Acad Sci; Soc Neurosci; Am Neuromodulation Soc. *Res:* Central nervous system; stereotaxic neurosurgery; pain medecine. *Mailing Add:* Neurosurg Box 0338 1500 E Med Ctr Dr Ann Arbor MI 48106-0338

**TARESKI, VAL GERARD,** COMPUTER ENGINEERING, COMPUTER NETWORKS. *Current Pos:* asst prof, 71-83, ASSOC PROF, NDAK STATE UNIV, 83- *Personal Data:* b Bottineau, NDak, Dec 20, 41; m 66; c 3. *Educ:* NDak State Univ, BS, 63, MS, 69; Univ Ill, Urbana, PhD(comput sci), 73. *Prof Exp:* Engr, Collins Radio, 62; tech writer, AC Electronics Div, Gen Motors Corp, 63; asst elec eng, NDak State Univ, 63-64, instr, 64-67; res asst comput sci, Univ Ill, Urbana, 67-69 & 70-71; asst prog dir, NSF, 71-72, assoc prog dir, 72-74. *Concurrent Pos:* Instr, Moorhead State Col, 67 & NDak State Univ, 71-72; assoc prof, Univ Nebr, 72. *Mem:* Inst Elec & Electronics Engrs; Asn Comput Mach; Sigma Xi; Soc Indust & Appl Math. *Res:* Computer architecture; microcomputer systems; computer communications and networks. *Mailing Add:* Elec Eng Dept NDak State Univ Fargo ND 58105

**TARG, RUSSELL,** PHYSICS, PARAPSYCHOLOGY. *Current Pos:* sr res physicist, 82-86, PHYSICIST & SR STAFF SCIENTIST, DELPHI ASSOC, 86- *Personal Data:* b Chicago, Ill, Apr 11, 34; m 58, Joan Fischer; c Elisabeth, Alexander & Nicholas. *Educ:* Queens Col, NY, BS, 54. *Prof Exp:* Res asst physics, Columbia Univ, 54-56; engr, Sperry Gyroscope Co, 56-59; res assoc plasmas, Polytech Inst Brooklyn, 59; physicist, TRG, Inc, 59-62; eng specialist, Sylvania Elec Co, 62-72; sr res physicist, radio physics lab, Stanford Res Inst, 72-82. *Mem:* Am Phys Soc; Parapsychol Asn; Inst Elec & Electronics Engrs. *Res:* Electron beam-plasma interactions; gas laser research; laser detection; modulation and frequency control; research in extra sensory perception; laser remote sensing. *Mailing Add:* Lockheed Martin Res & Develop Lab Dept H152 3251 Hanover St Palo Alto CA 94304. *E-Mail:* targ@pacbell.net

**TARGETT, NANCY MCKEEVER,** CHEMICAL ECOLOGY. *Current Pos:* asst prof, 84-88, ASSOC PROF, UNIV DEL, 88- *Personal Data:* b Pittsburgh, Pa, Dec 23, 50; m 75; c 1. *Educ:* Univ Pittsburgh, BS, 72; Univ Miami, MS, 75; Univ Maine, PhD(oceanog), 79. *Prof Exp:* Res assoc, 80-82, asst res prof, Skidaway Inst Oceanog, 82-84. *Concurrent Pos:* Vis prof, Friday Harbor Lab, Univ Washington, 88. *Mem:* Am Chem Soc; Am Soc Limnol & Oceanog; Asn Women Sci; Int Soc Chem Ecol (secy, 87-90). *Res:* Chemical ecology, specifically the role of secondary metabolites in chemical-biological interactions among marine organisms; marine biofouling. *Mailing Add:* Univ Del 700 Pilottown Rd Lewes DE 19958-1298

**TARGETT, TIMOTHY ERWIN,** FISH ECOLOGY, TROPHIC ENERGETICS. *Current Pos:* assoc scientist, 84-86, asst prof, 86-90, ASSOC PROF, COL MARINE STUDIES, UNIV DEL, 91- *Personal Data:* b Farmington, Maine, Aug 1, 50; m 75, Nancy McKeever; c Katharine A. *Educ:* Univ Maine, BS, 72, PhD(zool), 79; Univ Miami, MS, 75. *Honors & Awards:*

Antarctica Serv Medal, NSF, 80. *Prof Exp:* Asst res prof, Skidaway Inst Oceanog, 80-84. *Concurrent Pos:* Adj asst prof, Dept Zool, Univ Ga, 81-84; US rep fish ecol, Biomass Working Party, 84; comnr, Atlantic States Marine Fisheries Comn, 87- *Mem:* Am Soc Ichthyologists & Herpetologists; Am Fisheries Soc; Estuarine Res Fedn. *Res:* Ecology of estuarine and coastal marine fishes; trophic biology of fishes (physiological ecology of feeding, digestion, assimilation and growth); energetics; food webs. *Mailing Add:* Grad Col Marine Studies Univ Del Lewes DE 19958. *Fax:* 302-645-4028; *E-Mail:* ttargett@udel.edu

**TARJAN, ARMEN CHARLES,** TERRESTRIAL & MARINE NEMATOLOGY. *Current Pos:* PROF NEMATOL, AGR RES & EDUC CTR, UNIV FLA, 55-, PROF DEPT ENTOM-NEMATOL, 78- *Personal Data:* b Cambridge, Mass, Dec 10, 20; m 45; c 2. *Educ:* Univ Mass, BS, 47; Univ Md, MS, 49, PhD(plant path), 51. *Prof Exp:* Asst nematologist, USDA, Md, 50-51; asst res prof plant path, Univ RI, 51-55. *Mem:* Soc Nematol; Europ Soc Nematol; Orgn Trop Am Nematol; Int Asn Meiobenthologists. *Res:* Biological control of plant nematodes; marine nematology; taxonomy and systematics. *Mailing Add:* 3426 SW 75th St Gainesville FL 32607

**TARJAN, ROBERT ENDRE,** COMPUTER SCIENCE. *Current Pos:* JAMES S MCDONNELL DISTINGUISHED UNIV PROF, DEPT COMPUT SCI, PRINCETON UNIV, 85- *Personal Data:* b Pomona, Calif, Apr 30, 48; div; c Alice, Zosia & Lily. *Educ:* Calif Inst Technol, BS, 69; Stanford Univ, MS, 71, PhD(comput sci), 72. *Honors & Awards:* Nevanlinna Prize Info Sci, 83; Nat Acad Sci Award, Initiatives in Res, 84; A M Turing Award, 86. *Prof Exp:* Asst prof, Cornell Univ, 72-74; asst prof, 74-77, assoc prof comput sci, Stanford Univ, 77-80; mem tech staff, AT&T Bell Labs, 80-90. *Concurrent Pos:* Miller fel, Univ Calif, Berkeley, 73-75; Guggenheim fel, Stanford Univ, 78-79; ed, numerous jours, 85-; mem comt, Math Sci: Status & Future Directions, Nat Res Coun, 89-90; mem, Comput Sci & Eng Peer Comt, Nat Acad Eng, 89-92; corresp, Math Intelligencer, 91- *Mem:* Nat Acad Sci; Nat Acad Eng; Am Acad Arts & Sci; fel AAAS; Am Philos Soc. *Res:* Analysis of algorithms; computational complexity; combinatorics; data structures. *Mailing Add:* Dept Comput Sci Princeton Univ 35 Olden St Princeton NJ 08544-2087

**TARKOY, PETER J,** GEOLOGY. *Current Pos:* GEOTECH & CONSTRUCT CONSULT, 71- *Personal Data:* b Budapest, Hungary, Nov 13, 41; m 83. *Educ:* City Col NY, BS, 64; Univ Tenn, Knoxville, MS, 67; Univ Urbana-Champaign, PhD(civil eng), 75. *Concurrent Pos:* Eng geologist, Ill Geol Surv, Champaign, 70-71, teaching & res asst, Univ Ill, Urbana-Champaign, 71-75; geotech consult, Perini Corp, Framingham, Mass, 75-78; vis assoc prof, Boston Univ, 79, Cornell Univ, 78; lectr, Univ Wis Exten, Milwaukee, 75- *Mem:* Am Soc Civil Engrs; Geol Soc Am; Int Asn Geologist; Asn Eng Geologists; Brit Tunnelling Soc; Tunnel Asn Can; Am Inst Mining Engrs. *Res:* Author of over 35 articles. *Mailing Add:* 17 Everett St Sherborn MA 01770

**TARLE, GREGORY,** PARTICLE ASTROPHYSICS, NON-ACCELERATOR HIGH ENERGY PHYSICS. *Current Pos:* asst prof, 83-87, ASSOC PROF PHYSICS, UNIV MICH, 80-; ASST RES PHYSICIST, SPACE SCI LAB, UNIV CALIF, BERKELEY, 78- *Personal Data:* b New York, NY, June 13, 51; m 72. *Educ:* Calif Inst Technol, BS, 72; Univ Calif, Berkeley, PhD(physics), 78. *Mem:* Am Phys Soc. *Res:* Composition of cosmic radiation; underground astrophysics. *Mailing Add:* 2306 Adare Rd Ann Arbor MI 48104

**TARLETON, GADSON JACK, JR,** RADIOLOGY. *Current Pos:* RADIOL, YORK VET ADMIN MED CTR, MURFREESBORO, TENN, 83- *Personal Data:* b Sumter, SC, Apr 29, 20; m 49; c Gadson Jack III & Rhea Therese. *Educ:* Morris Col, AB, 39; Meharry Med Col, MD, 44; Am Bd Radiol, dipl, 49. *Prof Exp:* Resident radiol & orthop, Hubbard Hosp & Meharry Med Col, 44, resident radiol, 45-48; assoc prof, Meharry Med Col, 49-52, chmn dept & dir tumor clin, 49-78, prof radiol, 52-78; asst chief, Dept Radiol, Vet Admin Med Ctr, Nashville, 79-83. *Concurrent Pos:* Fel radiother, Bellevue Hosp, NY, 48-49; vis scholar, Columbia Presby Hosp, NY, 49; guest examr, Am Bd Radiol, 71-76 & 78-87. *Mem:* Radiol Soc NAm; fel Am Col Radiol. *Mailing Add:* 1714 Windover Dr Nashville TN 37208

**TARLOV, ALVIN RICHARD,** INTERNAL MEDICINE, BIOCHEMISTRY. *Current Pos:* PROF MED, TUFTS UNIV, 90-; SR SCIENTIST, HEALTH INST, NEW ENG MED CTR, 90-, EXEC DIR HEALTH, 95- *Personal Data:* b South Norwalk, Conn, July 11, 29; m 56; c 5. *Educ:* Dartmouth Col, BA, 51; Univ Chicago, MD, 56. *Honors & Awards:* Alan Gregg Lectr, Asn Am Med Cols, 87; D Robert Glaser Award, Soc Gen Internal Med, 92. *Prof Exp:* Intern, Philadelphia Gen Hosp, 56-57; resident med, Univ Chicago, 57-58, res assoc, 58-62; res assoc biochem, Harvard Med Sch, 62-64; from asst prof to prof med, Univ Chicago, 64-85, chmn dept, 70-81, head gen internal med, 81-83; pres, Henry J Kaiser Family Found, 84-90. *Concurrent Pos:* USPHS res career develop award, 62-69; Markle scholar, 66-71; counr, Fed Coun Internal Med, 75-78, dir, Nat Study Internal Med Manpower Needs, 76-80, chmn, 78-79; chmn, Task Force Manpower Needs Internal Med, Asn Professors Med, 76-80, Grad Med Educ Nat Adv Comt, Health Resources Admin, US Dept Health & Human Serv, 77-81 & Comt Nat Agenda Prev Dis, Inst Med-Nat Acad Sci, 89-; mem, Comn Human Resources, Nat Res Coun, Nat Acad Sci, 80-82, Comt Plan Study Med Educ, Inst Med, 82-84, Comt Health Policy Agenda Am People, AMA, 83-86 & Res & Educ Adv Panel, US Gen Acct Off, 87-; prof health prom, Sch Pub Health, Harvard Univ, 90-; pres, chief exec officer & trustee, Med Outcome Trust, 93-; bd dir, Tobacco Control Resource Ctr, Inc, 94-; consult, physician performance, AMA. *Mem:* Inst Med-Nat Acad Sci; master Am Col

Physicians; Am Fedn Clin Res; Am Soc Hemat; Sigma Xi; Cent Soc Clin Res; Asn Am Physicians; Asn Prof Med (secy-treas, 75-78, pres-elect, 78-80, pres, 79-80). *Res:* Metabolism of red blood cells; inherited disorders of red cell metabolism; biochemistry of red cell membranes; health manpower, supply, productivity, needs. *Mailing Add:* Health Inst New Eng Med Ctr PO Box 345 750 Washington St Boston MA 02111

**TARN, TZYH-JONG,** MATHEMATICAL SYSTEMS THEORY. *Current Pos:* Res assoc control theory, Washington Univ, 68-69, asst prof chem eng, 69-72, assoc prof control systs, 72-77, PROF CONTROL SYSTS, WASHINGTON UNIV, 77-, DIR, CTR ROBOTICS & AUTOMATION, 87- *Personal Data:* b Szechwan, China, Nov 16, 37; m 67; c 2. *Educ:* Cheng Kung Univ, Taiwan, BSc, 59; Stevens Inst Technol, MEng, 65; Washington Univ, DSc(control systs), 68. *Concurrent Pos:* NSF grant, 70-85; assoc ed, Trans on Automatic Control, Inst Elec & Electronics Engrs, 86-89, tech ed, J Robotics & Automation, 88-; vpres, Inst Elec & Electronics Engrs Robotics & Automation Soc, 89-90. *Mem:* Soc Indust & Appl Math; Inst Elec & Electronics Engrs. *Res:* Control theory; stochastic systems; process optimization; robot arm control. *Mailing Add:* Washington Univ Campus Box 1040 St Louis MO 63130

**TARNEY, ROBERT EDWARD,** ORGANIC CHEMISTRY. *Current Pos:* RES CHEMIST, E I DU PONT DE NEMOURS & CO, INC, 57- *Personal Data:* b Hammond, Ind, Jan 8, 31; m 66; c 3. *Educ:* Purdue Univ, BS, 52; Univ Wis, PhD, 58. *Res:* Synthesis of monomers for and polymers of elastomeric materials. *Mailing Add:* 505 Summit Dr Hockessin DE 19707

**TARONE, ROBERT ERNEST,** SURVIVAL ANALYSIS, CATEGORICAL DATA ANALYSIS. *Current Pos:* MATH STATISTICIAN, NAT CANCER INST, 74- *Personal Data:* b Modesto, Calif, Sept 11, 46; m 76; c 2. *Educ:* Univ Calif, Davis, BS, 68, MS, 69, PhD(math), 74. *Concurrent Pos:* Assoc ed, Am Statist Asn, 78-83. *Mem:* Fel Am Statist Asn; Biomet Soc. *Res:* Analysis methods for censored survival data; categorical data analysis; empirical bayes methods for frequency data; multiple comparisons problems; methods for analyzing epidemiologic studies. *Mailing Add:* 14 Chantilly Ct Rockville MD 20850

**TARPLEY, ANDERSON RAY, JR,** PHYSICAL CHEMISTRY, SPECTROSCOPY. *Current Pos:* sr chemist analytical serv, Tenn Eastman Co, Eastman Kodak Co, 72-79, dir, P&A Div, Eastman Chem, 79-88, dir, Fiber Res Div, 88-96, VPRES CELLULAR TECHNOL, EASTMAN KODAK CO, 97- *Personal Data:* b New Orleans, La, Sept 19, 44; m 69, Susan Baker; c Treva Louise, Elizabeth (Baker) & Anderson Ray III. *Educ:* Ga Inst Technol, BS, 66; Emory Univ, MS, 70, PhD(phys chem), 71; Ga State Univ, MBA, 72. *Prof Exp:* Res chemist, Eastman Kodak Co, NY, 66-67; instr res, Emory Univ, 71-72. *Concurrent Pos:* NIH fel med chem, Emory Univ, 71. *Mem:* AAAS; Am Chem Soc; Am Inst Chem; Am Mgt Asn. *Res:* Nuclear magnetic resonance spectroscopy; technical management; uses of computers in science; molecular orbital calculations; mass spectrometry. *Mailing Add:* 1029 Hanover Ct Kingsport TN 37660-5840

**TARPLEY, JERALD DAN,** ATMOSPHERIC PHYSICS, REMOTE SENSING. *Current Pos:* physicist, Environ Res Labs, 70-73, PHYSICIST, SATELLITE RES LAB, NAT ENVIRON SATELLITE DATA & INFO SERV, NAT OCEANIC & ATMOSPHERIC ADMIN, 73- *Personal Data:* b Lubbock, Tex, July 13, 42; m 65; Hallie Pierce; c Sarah & Susannah. *Educ:* Tex Technol Col, BS, 64; Univ Colo, PhD(astrogeophys), 69. *Honors & Awards:* Silver Medal, US Dept Comm, 92. *Prof Exp:* Advan Study Prog fel, Nat Ctr Atmospheric Res, 69-70. *Mem:* Am Geophys Union; Am Meteorol Soc. *Res:* Remote sensing of the environment; atmospheric radiation. *Mailing Add:* Nat Environ Satellite Data & Info Serv Nat Oceanic & Atmospheric Admin Washington DC 20233. *E-Mail:* dtarpley@nesdis.noaa.gov

**TARPLEY, WALLACE ARMELL,** INSECT ECOLOGY. *Current Pos:* RETIRED. *Personal Data:* b Norwood, Ga, Feb 13, 34; m 59; c 2. *Educ:* Univ Ga, BSEd, 54, PhD(zool), 67; Clemson Univ, MS, 56. *Prof Exp:* Asst prof entom, Va Polytech Inst & State Univ, 60-64; assoc prof biol, ETenn State Univ, 64-91. *Mem:* AAAS; Entom Soc Am; Ecol Soc Am. *Res:* Ecological terminology, specifically the preparation of an ecological glossary; history of ecological terms; ecology of fresh water insects. *Mailing Add:* 2533 Cherokee Rd Johnson City TN 37604

**TARQUIN, ANTHONY JOSEPH,** SANITARY ENGINEERING, ENVIRONMENTAL ENGINEERING. *Current Pos:* Asst prof environ eng, Univ Tex, 69-73, asst dean eng, 76-79 & 87-89, assoc prof, 73-91, PROF CIVIL ENG, UNIV TEX, EL PASO, 91- *Personal Data:* b Follansbee, WVa, July 10, 41; m 65; c 2. *Educ:* WVa Univ, BSIE, 64, MSE, 65, PhD(environ eng), 69. *Concurrent Pos:* NSF & Environ Protection Agency grants. *Mem:* Water Pollution Control Fedn; Am Soc Civil Engrs. *Res:* Combined disposal of liquid and solid wastes; land disposal of wastewater and sludges; water treatment. *Mailing Add:* Dept Civil Eng Univ Tex 500 W Univ Ave El Paso TX 79968. *Fax:* 915-747-5616

**TARR, CHARLES EDWIN,** PHYSICS. *Current Pos:* from asst prof to assoc prof physics, Univ Maine, 68-78, assoc dean, Col Arts & Sci, 79-81, actg dean, grad sch, 81-87, actg vpres res, 84-87, PROF PHYSICS, UNIV MAINE, ORONO, 78-, DEAN GRAD SCH, 87- *Personal Data:* b Johnstown, Pa, Jan 14, 40; m 77. *Educ:* Univ NC, Chapel Hill, BS, 61, PhD(physics), 66. *Prof Exp:* Asst physics, Univ NC, Chapel Hill, 62-66, res assoc, summer 66 & Univ Pittsburgh, 66-68. *Mem:* Am Phys Soc; Inst Elec & Electronics Engrs. *Res:* Nuclear magnetic resonance; electron paramagnetic resonance; electronic instrumentation. *Mailing Add:* Dept Physics Univ Maine Winslow Hall Orono ME 04473

**TARR, DONALD ARTHUR,** INORGANIC CHEMISTRY. *Current Pos:* asst prof, 65-67, ASSOC PROF CHEM, ST OLAF COL, 67- *Personal Data:* b Norfolk, Nebr, Aug 1, 32; m 57; c 2. *Educ:* Doane Col, AB, 54; Yale Univ, MS, 56, PhD(chem), 59. *Prof Exp:* From instr to asst prof chem, Col Wooster, 58-65. *Concurrent Pos:* Danforth teaching fel, 58-; res assoc, Univ Colo, 64-65; vis res fel, Univ Kent, 72-73. *Mem:* Fedn Am Scientists; Am Asn Univ Professors; AAAS; Am Chem Soc. *Res:* Structure and stability of metal complexes; kinetics and mechanism of reaction of coordination compounds. *Mailing Add:* St Olaf Col 1520 St Olaf Ave Northfield MN 55057-1098

**TARR, JOEL ARTHUR,** HISTORY OF TECHNOLOGY & ENVIRONMENT. *Current Pos:* prof hist technol, 67-90, RICHARD S CALIGUIRI PROF URBAN STUDIES, CARNEGIE-MELLON UNIV, 90- *Personal Data:* b Jersey City, NJ, May 8, 34; m 78, Tova Brafman; c Michael, Joanna, Maya & Ilana. *Educ:* Rutgers Univ, BS, 56, MA, 57; Northwestern Univ, PhD(hist), 63. *Honors & Awards:* Abel Wolman Award, 89; Robert E Doherty Prize, Carnegie Mellon Univ, 92. *Prof Exp:* Asst prof hist, Calif State Univ, Long Beach, 61-66; vis asst prof, Univ Calif, Santa Barbara, 66-67. *Concurrent Pos:* Consult pollution hist & infrastructure hist. *Mem:* Am Soc Environ Hist; Soc Hist Technol; Sigma Xi; Orgn Am Historians; Urban Hist Asn. *Res:* The city and technology, interaction of the processes of urbanization and technological innovation; history of environmental pollution; wastewater systems; communication systems; transportation systems; energy systems; retrospective technology assessment. *Mailing Add:* Dept Hist Schenley Park Pittsburgh PA 15213. *Fax:* 412-268-1019; *E-Mail:* jt03@andrew.cmu.edu

**TARR, MELINDA JEAN,** immunopharmacology, comparative pathology, for more information see previous edition

**TARRANT, PAUL,** CHEMISTRY. *Current Pos:* from instr to assoc prof, 46-57, PROF CHEM, UNIV FLA, 57- *Personal Data:* b Birmingham, Ala, Nov 1, 14; m 37, 72; c 3. *Educ:* Howard Col, BS, 36; Purdue Univ, MS, 38; Duke Univ, PhD(chem), 44. *Prof Exp:* Instr, Ala Bd Educ, 38-40; chemist, Shell Develop Co, Calif, 40-41; asst, Duke Univ, 41-44; res chemist, Am Cyanamid Co, Conn, 44-46. *Concurrent Pos:* Chief investr, Off Naval Res Proj, 47-50 & 53-56; dir, Off Qm Gen Res Proj, 51-67; USAF Res Proj, 54-66 & 72-74, NSF, 68-71, NASA, 69-71 & Mass Inst Technol, 69-71; dir res, PCR, 53-66, vpres, 66-68; consult, Redstone Arsenal, US Dept Army & Naval Ord Lab, Calif; adv, Cotton Chem Lab, USDA; ed, Fluorine Chem Rev. *Mem:* Am Chem Soc. *Res:* Preparations and reactions of fluorine containing organic compounds and inert polymers. *Mailing Add:* 2211 NW 26th Terr Gainesville FL 32605

**TARRANTS, WILLIAM EUGENE,** SAFETY ENGINEERING, HUMAN FACTORS ENGINEERING. *Current Pos:* chief manpower develop div, US Dept Transp, 67-80, chief scientist, Off Prog & Demonstration Eval, 80-84, prog analyst, Off Occupant Protection, Hwy Safety, 84-87, PROG ANALYST, EVAL STAFF, HWY SAFETY, US DEPT TRANSP, 87- *Personal Data:* b Liberty, Mo, Dec 9, 27; m 52, 88, Lorna D Lundberg; c James T, Jennifer L, David M, Christine (Walls) & Janelle (McCrea). *Educ:* Ohio State Univ, BIE, 51, MSc, 59; NY Univ, PhD(indust safety), 63. *Prof Exp:* Chief, Ground Safety Div, USAF, 51-57; instr indust eng, Ohio State Univ, 58-59; instr & res assoc indust safety, NY Univ, 59-63, asst prof, 63-64; chief div accident res, Bur Labor Statist, US Dept Labor, 65-67. *Concurrent Pos:* Consult eval res, Indust Comn Ohio, 59; mem safety stand bd, Am Nat Stand Inst, 67-69; mem res proj comt, Nat Safety Coun, 73-76; chmn sci & tech info adv bd, Nat Hwy Traffic Safety Admin, 73-; mem comt planning & admin transp safety, Nat Acad Sci, 74-; chmn, Acad Accreditation Coun, Am Soc Safety Engrs, 78-; ed-in-chief, Traffic Safety Eval Res Rev, 83-; instr, Occup Safety & Health Mgt, Johns Hopkins Univ, Baltimore, Md, 84-; mem, Related Accreditation Comn, Accreditation Bd Eng & Technol, 93- *Mem:* AAAS; fel Am Soc Safety Engrs (pres, 77-78); sr mem Am Inst Indust Engrs; Human Factors Soc; Eval Res Soc; Soc Risk Analysis. *Res:* Measurement of safety performance; accident causation; psychological factors in accidents; risk acceptance; highway traffic safety; evaluation of safety programs; occupational safety and health; accident analysis and prevention. *Mailing Add:* 606 Woodsmans Way Crownsville MD 21032

**TARRIO, CHARLES,** EXTREME ULTRAVIOLET OPTICS. *Current Pos:* PHYSICIST, NAT INST STAND & TECHNOL, 91- *Personal Data:* b Middletown, Conn, Dec 20, 60; m 95, Danielle Partello. *Educ:* Bates Col, BS, 82; Univ Va, PhD(physics), 91. *Concurrent Pos:* Corresp, Synchrotron Radiation News, 95- *Mem:* Optical Soc Am; AAAS; Mat Res Soc. *Res:* Extreme ultraviolet spectroscopy & microscopy; Research, development & applications of multilayer optics. *Mailing Add:* Nat Inst Stand & Technol Bldg 245 Rm B102 Gaithersburg MD 20899. *E-Mail:* charles.tarrio@nist.gov

**TARSHIS, IRVIN BARRY,** parasitology, zoology; deceased, see previous edition for last biography

**TARTAGLIA, PAUL EDWARD,** ENGINEERING DESIGN. *Current Pos:* assoc prof & head mech eng dept, 77-86, head, Eng & Technol Div, 86-91, PROF MECH ENG, NORWICH UNIV, 91- *Personal Data:* b New York, NY, Sept 30, 44; div; c 3. *Educ:* Univ Detroit, BME, 67, DEng, 70; Northwestern Univ, Evanston, MSME, 68. *Prof Exp:* Engr, Space Div, Chrysler Corp, La, 64-65; test engr, Elec Boat Div, Gen Dynamics Corp, Conn, 65; proj engr, Eng Off, Chrysler Corp, Mich, 69-70; asst prof mech eng, Univ Mass, Amherst, 70-75; proj engr, Rodney Hunt Co, 75-76; chief engr, Computerized Biomech Analysis, Inc, 76-77. *Concurrent Pos:* NSF, Norton Co & Kollmorgen, Inc grants, Univ Mass, Amherst, 72-73. *Mem:* Am Soc

Mech Engrs; Am Soc Eng Educ. *Res:* Mechanical engineering; transportation; engineering systems design; automatic control systems; sports equipment design and analysis; biomechanics of sports. *Mailing Add:* Div Eng & Technol Norwich Univ Northfield VT 05663. *Fax:* 802-485-2580

**TARTER, CURTIS BRUCE,** ASTROPHYSICS, THEORETICAL PHYSICS. *Current Pos:* physicist, Lawrence Livermore Nat Lab, 67-69, group leader, 69-73, dep div leader, 73-78, div leader theoret physics, 78-84, dep assoc dir, 84-88, ASSOC DIR PHYSICS, LAWRENCE LIVERMORE NAT LAB, 88- *Personal Data:* b Louisville, Ky, Sept 26, 39; m 87; c 1. *Educ:* Mass Inst Technol, SB, 61; Cornell Univ, PhD(astrophys), 67. *Prof Exp:* Sr scientist, Aeronutronic Div, Philco-Ford Corp, 67. *Concurrent Pos:* Lectr, Dept Appl Sci, Univ Calif, Davis, 71- & Army Sci Bd, 89- *Mem:* Int Astron Union; Am Phys Soc; Am Astron Soc. *Res:* Theoretical description of the properties of matter at high temperatures and densities; theoretical astrophysics, particularly quasars, x-ray sources and stellar evolution. *Mailing Add:* 676 Old Jonas Hill Rd Lafayette CA 94549

**TARTER, DONALD CAIN,** ZOOLOGY. *Current Pos:* instr zool, 68-81, ASSOC PROF BIOL, MARSHALL UNIV, 81- *Personal Data:* b Somerset, Ky, July 22, 36; m 60; c 3. *Educ:* Georgetown Col, Ky, BS, 58; Miami Univ, Ohio, MAT, 62; Univ Louisville, PhD(zool), 68. *Prof Exp:* Teacher chem biol, Bradford High Sch, Ohio, 58-60 & Tipp City High Sch, Ohio, 60-64; teacher biol, Ky Southern Col, 64-68. *Mem:* Am Fisheries Soc; Am Entom Soc; Sigma Xi; Am Soc Ichthyologists & Herpetologists. *Res:* Taxonomy and ecology of fishes and aquatic insects. *Mailing Add:* 38 Lynn Marr Dr Huntington WV 25705

**TARTER, MICHAEL E,** BIOSTATISTICS. *Current Pos:* assoc prof, 70-76, PROF, UNIV CALIF, BERKELEY, 77- *Personal Data:* b New York, NY, Dec 20, 38; m 61; c 2. *Educ:* Univ Calif, Los Angeles, AB, 59, MA, 61, PhD(biostatist), 64. *Prof Exp:* From asst prof to assoc prof biostatist, Univ Mich, Ann Arbor, 64-67. *Concurrent Pos:* Consult, Upjohn Drug Co, Med Diag Corp, Regional Med Asn, Pac Med Ctr & Presch & Adolescent Proj; Calif State Health Dept, NIH Cancer & Heart, Lung & Blood Insts; FDA Comm on Neuropsyciatic Drugs; assoc prof, 68-78, prof biostat, Depts Med & Math, Univ Calif, Irvine, 78- *Mem:* Fel Am Statist Asn; Asn Comput Mach; Int Statist Inst. *Res:* Graphical biometry; computational aspects of statistical procedures; biostatistical consultation training; nonparametric density estimation; programmed and computer assisted instruction; sorting theory. *Mailing Add:* Sch Pub Health Univ Calif Berkeley Berkeley CA 94720-0001

**TARTOF, DAVID,** HUMAN CELLULAR IMMUNOLOGY. *Current Pos:* ASST PROF MED, UNIV CHICAGO, 80-; DIR, DIV RHEUMATOLOGY, MICHAEL REESE MED CTR. *Personal Data:* b Detroit, Mich, Sept 15, 45. *Educ:* Univ Mich, MD, 70; Univ Chicago, PhD(med), 78. *Concurrent Pos:* Attend physician, Michael Reese Med Ctr. *Mem:* Sigma Xi; Am Asn Immunol; fel Am Col Rheumatology. *Mailing Add:* Dept Rheumatology Michael Reese Med Ctr 2816 Adelbert Rd Chicago IL 60616-2907

**TARTOF, KENNETH D,** GENETICS. *Current Pos:* NIH res fel, Inst Cancer Res, 68-70, res assoc, 70-71, asst mem, 71-76, mem, 76-87, SR MEM, INST CANCER RES, 87- *Personal Data:* b Detroit, Mich, Dec 30, 41; m 67. *Educ:* Univ Mich, BS, 63, PhD(genetics), 68. *Mem:* AAAS; Genetics Soc Am. *Res:* Structure and function of genes; genetic control of gene redundancy; regulation of DNA and RNA metabolism. *Mailing Add:* Inst Cancer Res Rm 251 7701 Burholme Ave Philadelphia PA 19111

**TARTT, THOMAS EDWARD,** RESEARCH ADMINISTRATION. *Current Pos:* Indust engr, P H Glatfelter Co, 64-71, staff acct, 71-73, asst controller, 73-77, DIR INDUST ENGR, ECUSTA DIV, TECH DEPT, P H GLATFELTER CO, 77- *Personal Data:* b Martin, TN, July 3, 40; m 23; c 2. *Educ:* Auburn Univ, BS, 64. *Concurrent Pos:* Dir , Inst Indust Engrs, 74-76. *Mem:* Inst Indust Engrs. *Mailing Add:* Ridgewood Pl Brevard NC 28712

**TARUI, YASUO,** semiconductor devices, semiconductor material, for more information see previous edition

**TARVER, FRED RUSSELL, JR,** FOOD TECHNOLOGY, BACTERIOLOGY. *Current Pos:* RETIRED. *Personal Data:* b Knoxville, Tenn, Mar 7, 25; m 50, Aileen Ivin; c 3. *Educ:* Univ Tenn, BSA, 50, MA, 54; Univ Ga, PhD(food technol, bact), 63. *Prof Exp:* Mem staff, Security Mills, Inc, Tenn, 50-54; instr poultry, Univ Tenn, 54-56; asst prof, Univ Fla, 56-60, 62-63; exten assoc prof, NC State Univ, 63-75, exten prof food sci, 75-89. *Mem:* Inst Food Technol; Poultry Sci Asn; World Poultry Sci Asn; fel Inst Food Technologists. *Res:* Product development and marketing of new poultry and egg products; sanitation in processing plants, with emphasis on ecology; 4-H club activities connected with poultry and egg products. *Mailing Add:* 5501 Parkwood Dr Brookhaven Raleigh NC 27612-6230

**TARVER, HAROLD,** BIOCHEMISTRY, MEDICAL & HEALTH SCIENCES. *Current Pos:* from instr to prof, 41-75, EMER PROF BIOCHEM, SCH MED, UNIV CALIF, SAN FRANCISCO, 75- *Personal Data:* b Wigan, Eng, June 7, 08; nat US; m, Mitzie Fuduya; c Frank & Terry. *Educ:* Univ Alta, BS, 32, MSc, 35; Univ Calif, PhD(biochem), 39. *Prof Exp:* Asst, Univ Alta, 32-35; asst, Sch Med, Univ Calif, Berkeley, 36-39, fel, 39-41. *Mem:* AAAS; Am Soc Biol Chem. *Res:* Metabolism of sulfur and protein-isotopic studies. *Mailing Add:* Dept Biochem & Biophys Sch Med Univ Calif 1715 Wawona St San Francisco CA 94116-2925

**TARVIN, ROBERT FLOYD,** polymer application, research management, for more information see previous edition

**TARWATER, JAN DALTON,** ALGEBRA. *Current Pos:* from asst prof to assoc prof, Tex Tech Univ, 68-73, assoc chmn dept, 73-78, PROF MATH, TEX TECH UNIV, 73- *Personal Data:* b Ft Worth, Tex, Sept 30, 37; m 58; c 3. *Educ:* Tex Tech Col, BS, 59; Univ NMex, MA, 61, PhD(math), 65. *Prof Exp:* Asst prof math, Western Mich Univ, 65-67 & NTex State Univ, 67-68. *Mem:* Math Asn Am; Soc Indust & Appl Math. *Res:* Algebra, especially Abelian groups and homological algebra; graph theory; history of mathematics. *Mailing Add:* Dept Math Tex Tech Univ Lubbock TX 79409-2013

**TARWATER, OLIVER REED,** INTERNATIONAL MEDICAL RESEARCH. *Current Pos:* MGR, INT RES & DEVELOP PROJ, JAPAN, 91- *Personal Data:* b Chattanooga, Tenn, Mar 12, 44; m 66; c 2. *Educ:* Maryville Col, BS, 66; Purdue Univ, Lafayette, MS, 69, PhD(med chem), 70. *Prof Exp:* Res chemist, Personal Care Div, Gillette Co, Chicago, 70-74; sr chemist, Southern Res Inst, Birmingham, 74-76; sr chemist, Lilly Res Labs, Greenfield, Ind, 76-80, res scientist, 81-87, mgr pharmaceut proj, Lilly Corp Ctr, Indianapolis, 87-91. *Mem:* Am Chem Soc; Sigma Xi. *Mailing Add:* 331 Hickory Dr Greenfield IN 46140

**TASAKI, ICHIJI,** NEUROPHYSIOLOGY. *Current Pos:* mem staff, 61-66, CHIEF, LAB NEUROBIOL, NIMH, 66- *Personal Data:* b Fukushim-Ken, Japan, Oct 21, 10; nat US; c 2. *Educ:* Keio Univ, Japan, MD, 38. *Hon Degrees:* DS, Uppsala Univ, 72. *Prof Exp:* Privat-docent physiol, Keio Univ, 38-42, privat-docent physics & prof physiol, Med Col, 42-51; prof physiol, Nihon Univ, Tokyo, 51; res assoc, Cent Inst Deaf, St Louis, Mo, 51-53; chief, Spec Senses Sect, Lab Neurophysiol, Nat Inst Neurol Dis & Blindness, 53-61. *Concurrent Pos:* Mem, Marine Biol Lab, Woods Hole, Mass. *Mem:* Am Acad Neurol; Physiol Soc Japan. *Res:* Nerve and sense organs; electrophysiology. *Mailing Add:* Lab Neurobiol NIMH NIH Bldg 36 Rm 2D-16 Bethesda MD 20892

**TASCH, AL FELIX, JR,** ELECTRICAL ENGINEERING, SOLID STATE PHYSICS. *Current Pos:* COCKRELL FAMILY REGENTS CHAIR, UNIV TEX, 86- *Personal Data:* b Corpus Christi, Tex, May 12, 41; m 63; c 2. *Educ:* Univ Tex, Austin, BS, 63; Univ Ill, Urbana, MS, 65, PhD(physics), 69. *Honors & Awards:* J J Ebers Award, Inst Elec & Electronics Engrs, 88. *Prof Exp:* Res scientist & engr, Cent Res Labs, Tex Instruments Inc, 69-; dir res & develop, Motorola Inc. *Concurrent Pos:* Prof elec eng, Univ Tex, Austin. *Mem:* Electrochem Soc; Inst Elec & Electronics Engrs; Mat Res Soc. *Res:* Solid state device physics and silicon processing technology; process and device modeling; metal-oxide-silicon field effect transistors; charge-coupled devices. *Mailing Add:* Dept Elec Eng Univ Texas Austin 433 Ens Austin TX 78712

**TASCH, PAUL,** PALEOBIOLOGY, GEOLOGY. *Current Pos:* PROF GEOL, WICHITA STATE UNIV, 55-, DISTINGUISHED PROF NAT SCI, 77- *Personal Data:* b New York, NY, Nov 28, 10. *Educ:* City Col New York, BS, 48; Pa State Col, MS, 50; Iowa State Univ, PhD(geol), 52. *Honors & Awards:* Antarctic Serv Medal, US Cong, 70. *Prof Exp:* Instr geol, Pa State Col, 48-49; instr, Univ Conn, 52-53; asst prof, NDak Agr Col, 53-54; assoc prof, Moorhead State Univ, 54-55. *Concurrent Pos:* Chief investr earth sci grant, NSF, 56-73 & off polar progs, 66-76 & 77- *Mem:* Paleont Soc; fel Geol Soc Am; fel AAAS; fel Geol Soc India; fel Geol Soc London; Sigma Xi. *Res:* Non-marine fossil biotas of Antarctica and other Gondwana continents, especially conchostracans palynomorphs and spoor; geomicrobiology; evaporites; branchiopoda, fossil and living; history of science. *Mailing Add:* 1346 N Parkwood Lane Wichita KS 68208-2726

**TASCHEK, RICHARD FERDINAND,** PHYSICS. *Current Pos:* physicist, Los Alamos Nat Lab, 43-62, div leader exp physics, 62-70, asst dir res, 71-72, ASSOC DIR RES, LOS ALAMOS NAT LAB, 72- *Personal Data:* b Chicago, Ill, June 5, 15; m 42; c 4. *Educ:* Univ Wis, BA, 36, PhD(physics), 41; Univ Fla, MS, 38. *Prof Exp:* Teaching asst, Univ Wis, 38-40; res physicist, Oldbury Electro-Chem Co, NY, 41-42; Nat Defense Res Comt physicist, Princeton Univ, 42-43. *Concurrent Pos:* Mem nuclear cross sect adv group, AEC, 48-57, chmn, 53-57, mem tripartite nuclear cross sect comt, 56-61, chmn, 61; mem Euro-Am nuclear data comt, 57-72, chmn, 60-62; mem int nuclear data working group, 63-72; adv, Int Nuclear Data Comt, 63-73, ex-officio mem, 72-74; mem standing comt controlled thermonuclear reactions & ad hoc adv comt on Los Alamos meson proj; co-chmn, Vis Comt Lab Nuclear Sci, Mass Inst Technol, 67; mem adv comt neutron physics, Oak Ridge Nat Lab; mem, Nuclear Physics Panel, Physics Surv Comt, Div Phys Sci, Nat Res Coun; mem, Off Stand Ref Data Eval Panel, Nat Bur Stand, & Inst Basic Stand Eval Panel, 71-75; mem, Ctr Radiation Res, Nat Bur Stand Panel, 71-76, chmn, 72-; mem adv comt, Univ Alaska Geophys Inst, 73-76; mem, Numerical Data Adv Bd, US Nat Comt for CODATA, 73-, chmn, 74- *Mem:* Fel AAAS; fel Am Phys Soc; fel Am Nuclear Soc; Am Geophys Union; Sigma Xi. *Res:* Nuclear reactions and scattering; nuclear properties; neutron physics; accelerators and detectors; space physics; Vela satellite program; controlled thermonuclear reactions. *Mailing Add:* 2035 47th St Los Alamos NM 87544-1601

**TASCHNER, MICHAEL J,** ORGANIC CHEMISTRY. *Current Pos:* ASST PROF CHEM, UNIV AKRON, 82- *Personal Data:* b Milwaukee, Wis, Sept 5, 53; m 77; c 2. *Educ:* Univ Wis-Eau Claire, BSc, 76; Iowa State Univ, PhD(org chem), 80. *Prof Exp:* NIH fel chem, Univ Calif, Berkeley, 80-82. *Mem:* Am Chem Soc. *Res:* The total synthesis of natural products which possess biological activity; development of new synthetic methodology. *Mailing Add:* Dept Chem Univ Akron 190 E Buchtel Commons Akron OH 44325

**TASHIAN, RICHARD EARL,** MOLECULAR GENETICS. *Current Pos:* from res assoc to assoc prof, 57-70, PROF HUMAN GENETICS, MED SCH, UNIV MICH, ANN ARBOR, 70- *Personal Data:* b Cranston, RI, Oct 7, 22; m 68, Jeanne Fitzgerald; c Alexander. *Educ:* Univ RI, BS, 47; Purdue Univ, MS, 49, PhD(zool), 51. *Prof Exp:* Asst, Purdue Univ, 48-51; asst prof biol, Long Island Univ, 51-54, actg chmn dept, 54; sci assoc, Dept Trop Res, NY Zool Soc, 54-55; res assoc, Inst Study Human Variation, Columbia Univ, 56-57. *Concurrent Pos:* Vis scientist, dept chem, Carlsberg Lab, Copenhagen, Denmark, 68-69, 79. *Mem:* Fel AAAS; Am Soc Human Genetics; Am Soc Biochem & Molecular Biol; NY Acad Sci. *Res:* Structure-function relationships of carbonic anhydrase isozymes; organization, structure, expression, and evolution of carbonic anhydrase genes. *Mailing Add:* Dept Human Genetics 4708 MS II Box 0618 Univ Mich Med Sch Ann Arbor MI 48109-0618

**TASHIRO, HARUO,** ENTOMOLOGY. *Current Pos:* RETIRED. *Personal Data:* b Selma, Calif, Mar 24, 17; m 42; c 3. *Educ:* Wheaton Col, BS, 45; Cornell Univ, MS, 46, PhD(entom), 50. *Prof Exp:* Asst entom, Cornell Univ, 47-50; entomologist, USDA, 50-67; prof entom, Agr Exp Sta, Cornell Univ, 67-83. *Concurrent Pos:* Assoc prof, Cornell Univ, 58-63; res assoc, Univ Calif, Riverside, 63-67. *Mem:* Entom Soc Am. *Res:* Biology; biological and chemical control of turf insects; insects, ornamental plants, permanent plantings; insect pathology. *Mailing Add:* 31 Denton Ave Geneva NY 14456

**TASHJIAN, ARMEN H, JR,** ENDOCRINOLOGY, CELL BIOLOGY. *Current Pos:* Nat Found res fel, Harvard Univ, 61-63, from instr to assoc prof, 63-70, prof pharmacol, Sch Dent Med & Sch Med, 70-78, PROF TOXICOL, SCH PUB HEALTH & PROF BIOCHEM & MOLECULAR PHARMACOL, SCH MED, HARVARD UNIV, 78-, CHAIR, DEPT MOLECULAR CELL TOXICOL, SCH PUB HEALTH, 91- *Personal Data:* b Cleveland, Ohio, May 2, 32; m 55, Carol Miles; c Elizabeth, Amy & Victoria. *Educ:* Yale Univ, 50-53; Harvard Univ, MD, 57. *Honors & Awards:* H B Van Dyke Mem Award & Lectr, Columbia Univ, 77; Edwin B Astwood lectr, Endocrine Soc, 77. *Prof Exp:* Intern med, Harvard Serv, Boston City Hosp, 57-58, asst resident, 58-59; clin res assoc, Metab Dis Br, Nat Inst Arthritis & Metab Dis, 59-61. *Concurrent Pos:* Assoc ed, Metab, 70-80 & Cancer Res, 80-84; mem, Cell Biol Study Sect, Div Res Grants, NIH, 73-77; mem, Res Comt, Med Found Inc, 77-80; mem bd dirs, int confs calcium regulating hormones, 83-; Guggenheim fel, 84-85; vis prof biol chem, Hebrew Univ, Jerusalem, 84-85; vis fel commoner, Trinity Col, Cambridge Univ, 85. *Mem:* Fel AAAS; Am Soc Pharmacol & Exp Therapeut; Endocrine Soc; Am Soc Cell Biol; Tissue Cult Asn; Am Fedn Clin Res; fel NY Acad Sci; Norweg Acad Sci & Lett; Am Soc Bone & Mineral Res (pres, 89-90); Soc Toxicol. *Res:* Molecular mechanisms of action of protein and peptide hormones; hormone receptor transduction mechanisms and regulation of cell calcium; cell biology; establishment, control of function and growth of differentiated, clonal strains of animal and human cells in culture; biochemical mechanisms of action of tumor promoters; toxicology. *Mailing Add:* Dept Molecular & Cellular Toxicol Harvard Sch Pub Health 665 Huntington Ave Boston MA 02115-6021. *Fax:* 617-432-1780

**TASHJIAN, ROBERT JOHN,** veterinary medicine, for more information see previous edition

**TASI, JAMES,** MECHANICS. *Current Pos:* assoc prof, 66-72, PROF MECH ENG, STATE UNIV NY, STONY BROOK, 72-, CHMN, DEPT, 91- *Personal Data:* b New York, NY, Dec 6, 33; m 60, Nancy Nims; c Nancy Susan, Steven & Michael. *Educ:* NY Univ, BCE, 55; Univ Ill, MS, 56; Columbia Univ, PhD(mech), 62. *Prof Exp:* Engr, Martin Co, Md, 57-58, assoc res scientist, Colo, 61-65; fel mech, Johns Hopkins Univ, 65-66. *Mem:* Am Soc Mech Engrs; Sigma Xi; Am Phys Soc. *Res:* Acoustic vibrations of structures; thermoelastic dissipation in crystalline solids; wave propagation; stability; mechanical properties of solids; shock response of crystal lattices. *Mailing Add:* Dept Mech Eng State Univ NY Stony Brook NY 11794-2300

**TASKER, CLINTON WALDORF,** CHEMISTRY. *Current Pos:* RETIRED. *Personal Data:* b Syracuse, NY, Sept 14, 18; m 41; c 3. *Educ:* Syracuse Univ, BSc, 41, MSc, 44; McGill Univ, PhD(cellulose chem), 47. *Prof Exp:* Res chemist, Sylvania Indust Corp, Va, 41-43; lab asst pulp & paper technol, State Univ NY Col Forestry, Syracuse Univ, 43-44; lab demonstr org & inorg chem, McGill Univ, 44-46; sr res chemist, Sylvania Div, Am Viscose Corp, 47-53, tech supt, 53-59, mgr supt, 59-61; dir tech res & develop, Tenneco Inc, 61-65, vpres res & develop, 65-68, vpres & gen mgr, Filer Mill, Paperboard Div, 68-73, vpres corp res & develop, Packaging Corp Am, 73-86. *Mem:* Am Inst Chemists; NY Acad Sci; Am Chem Soc; Tech Asn Pulp & Paper Indust. *Res:* Alkaline chemical pulping processes; chemistry and structure of cellulose ethers; synthesis of plasticizers for cellulose; tosyl and iodo derivatives of some hydroxyethyl ethers. *Mailing Add:* 3075 Baker Park Dr SE Grand Rapids MI 49508

**TASKER, JOHN B,** VETERINARY MEDICINE, CLINICAL PATHOLOGY. *Current Pos:* RETIRED. *Personal Data:* b Concord, NH, Aug 28, 33; m 61, Grace E Elliott; c Sybil, Sarah & Sophia. *Educ:* Cornell Univ, DVM, 57, PhD(vet path), 63; Am Col Vet Path, dipl, 72. *Prof Exp:* Am Vet Med Asn fel, Cornell Univ, 61-63; from asst prof to assoc prof vet med, Colo State Univ, 63-67; assoc prof vet path, NY State Vet Col, Cornell Univ, 67-69, prof clin path, 69-78; prof clin path & assoc dean, Sch Vet Med, La State Univ, 78-84; prof path & dean, Col Vet Med, Mich State Univ, 84-93. *Mem:* Am Vet Med Asn; Am Soc Vet Clin Path. *Res:* Veterinary clinical pathology. *Mailing Add:* Rte 2 Box 238-C Delmar DE 19940. *Fax:* 517-336-1036; *E-Mail:* tasker@cvm.msu.edu

**TASKER, RONALD REGINALD,** NEUROSURGERY, CLINICAL NEUROPHYSIOLOGY. *Current Pos:* Asst physiol, Banting & Best Dept Med Res, Univ Toronto, resident fel neurosurg, Fac Med, 58-59, mem clin & res staff, 61-, Toronto Hosp, asst prof surg (neurosurg), assoc prof surg, 66-78, PROF SURG, FAC MED, UNIV TORONTO, 78- *Personal Data:* b Toronto, Ont, Dec 18, 27; m 55, Mary M Craig; c Moura, James, Ronald & Alison. *Educ:* Univ Toronto, BA, 48, MD, 52, MA, 54; FRCS(C), 59. *Honors & Awards:* Spiegel & Wycis Medal, World Soc Stereotactic & Functional Neurosurg; Distinguished Serv Award, Am Soc Stereotactic Functions Neurosurg, 95. *Concurrent Pos:* McLaughlin traveling fel, Mass Gen Hosp, 59 & Univ Wis, 60; Markle scholar, 61-66; mem grad fac, Inst Med Sci, 78- *Mem:* Am Soc Stereotactic & Functional Neurosurg (pres, 80-81); Int Asn Study Pain; World Soc Stereotactic & Functional Neurosurg (pres, 85-89); Am Acad Neurol Surg; Can Pain Soc (pres, 91-94); Brazil Neurosurg Soc; hon mem Japan Neurosurg Soc; hon mem Int Asn Study Pain. *Res:* Hyperkinetic disorders; dyskinesias and stereotatic surgery; sensory physiology and pain. *Mailing Add:* Toronto Western Hosp 399 Bathurst St 2 McL 431 Toronto ON M5T 2S8 Can. *Fax:* 416-369-5298

**TASLITZ, NORMAN,** NEUROANATOMY. *Current Pos:* assoc prof anat & prog dir human anat, 77-82, CHMN, DEPT ANAT & ASSOC DEAN ACAD AFFAIRS, NORTHEASTERN OHIO UNIVS COL MED, 82- *Personal Data:* b New York, NY, Feb 12, 29; m 56; c 3. *Educ:* NY Univ, BS, 51; Univ Pa, cert phys ther, 52; Stanford Univ, PhD(anat), 63. *Prof Exp:* Physical therapist, Univ Wis Hosps, Madison, 52-54 & Wis Neurol Found, Madison, 54-58; asst prof anat, Sch Phys Ther, Case Western Res Univ, 63-77, from instr to sr instr, Dept Anat, 63-67, asst prof, 68-76. *Concurrent Pos:* Adj prof, Sch Law, Case Western Res Univ, 77- *Mem:* Am Asn Anatomists; Sigma Xi; AAAS; Am Asn Univ Prof; Asn Advan Med Educ. *Res:* Development of biological models to demonstrate the hemodynamic, metabolic and electrophysiologic performance of intact central nervous system tissue under control conditions, at various subnormal temperature levels and following trauma or periods of circulatory arrest. *Mailing Add:* Dept Anat Northeastern Ohio Univs Col Med Rootstown OH 44272

**TASMAN, WILLIAM S,** OPHTHALMOLOGY. *Current Pos:* ASSOC RETINA SERV, RETINOVITREOUS ASSOC, 62-; OPHTHALMOLOGIST-IN-CHIEF, WILLS EYE HOSP, 85- *Personal Data:* US citizen; m 62; c 3. *Educ:* Haverford Col, BA, 51; Temple Univ, MD, 55. *Concurrent Pos:* Heed fel, 61-62; Retina Found fel, 62. *Mem:* Am Col Physicians; Am Col Surg; Am Ophthal Soc; Retina Soc; Am Bd Ophthal. *Res:* Retinal diseases in children; retinal detachment surgery; retinopathy of prematurity. *Mailing Add:* Wills Eye Hosp Ninth & Walnut Sts Philadelphia PA 19107

**TASSAVA, ROY A,** REGENERATION, DEVELOPMENTAL BIOLOGY. *Current Pos:* asst prof, 69-73, assoc prof, 73-76, PROF ZOOL, OHIO STATE UNIV, 76- *Personal Data:* b Ironwood, Mich, July 5, 37; m 61; c 3. *Educ:* Northern Mich Univ, BS, 59; Brown Univ, MAT, 65; Mich State Univ, PhD(zool), 68. *Prof Exp:* Pub sch teacher, 59-64; NIH res fel zool, Mich State Univ, 68-69. *Concurrent Pos:* Sigma Xi res award, 68. *Mem:* Am Inst Biol Sci; Am Soc Zoologists. *Res:* Role of nerves, wound epithelium and hormones in amphibian limb regeneration; pituitary, thyroid and adrenal hormone physiology in amphibians. *Mailing Add:* Molecular Genetics Ohio State Univ 484 W 12th Ave Columbus OH 43210-1214

**TASSELL, JON VAN,** OPTICAL ENGINEERING. *Current Pos:* OPTICAL ENGR, POLARIOD CORP. *Honors & Awards:* Eng Excellence Award, Optical Soc Am, 94. *Mailing Add:* Polariod Corp 730 Main St First Floor Cambridge MA 02139-3344

**TASSINARI, SILVIO JOHN,** NUCLEAR MEDICINE, RADIOCHEMISTRY. *Current Pos:* RETIRED. *Personal Data:* b New York, NY, June 2, 22; m 52; c 2. *Educ:* St Michael's Col, Vt, BS, 42, MS, 47; Int Univ, PhD(chem, nuclear med), 77. *Prof Exp:* Supv radiochemist, Brookhaven Nat Lab, 51-71; supv radiochemist, Vet Admin Med Ctr, Brooklyn, 71-72, supv radiochemist nuclear med, Northport, 72-84; pres & owner, Cert Hazardous Mat Mgt, Long Island Labs Inc, 80-90, Cert Hazard Mat Control Mgr, 84-90. *Concurrent Pos:* Consult, Cath Med Ctr Brooklyn & Queens, 73-83. *Mem:* Fel Am Inst Chemists; Radiation Res Soc; Health Physics Soc; Soc Nuclear Med; Am Soc Radiologic Technologists; fel NY Acad Sci. *Res:* Diagnostic nuclear medicine using new and innovative radioisotopes and radiopharmaceuticals; investigation of new procedures in organ and system dianosis; utilizing computer assistance such as computed-assisted diagnosis and computed-aided monitoring. *Mailing Add:* 47 Moriches Rd Nissequogue St James NY 11780-9711

**TASSOUL, JEAN-LOUIS,** STELLAR HYDRODYNAMICS, ROTATING STARS. *Current Pos:* from asst prof to prof, 68-93, RESEARCHER ASTROPHYS, UNIV MONTREAL, 94- *Personal Data:* b Brussels, Belg, Nov 1, 38; m 66. *Educ:* Free Univ Brussels, LSc, 61, DSc, 64. *Prof Exp:* Res fel, NSF, Belg, 65-66; res assoc, Univ Chicago, 66-67 & Princeton Univ, 67-68. *Mem:* Int Astron Union. *Res:* Stellar structure. *Mailing Add:* Dept Physics Univ Montreal PO Box 6128 Montreal PQ H3C 3J7 Can

**TASSOUL, MONIQUE,** ASTROPHYSICS. *Current Pos:* RESEARCHER ASTROPHYS, UNIV MONTREAL, 74- *Personal Data:* b Brussels, Belg, Sept 23, 42; m 66. *Educ:* Univ Brussels, Belg, LSc, 63; Univ Montreal, PhD(physics), 74. *Mem:* Int Astron Union. *Res:* Stellar structure and oscillations. *Mailing Add:* Dept Physics PO Box 6128 Montreal PQ H3C 3J7 Can

**TASWELL, HOWARD FILMORE,** IMMUNOHEMATOLOGY, LABORATORY MEDICINE. *Current Pos:* from instr to asst prof clin path, Univ Minn, 63-73, assoc prof lab med, 73-77, prof, 77-93, EMER PROF LAB MED, MAYO MED SCH, UNIV MINN, 93- *Personal Data:* b Paterson, NJ, July 21, 28; m 52; c 6. *Educ:* Harvard Col, AB, 49; New York Univ, MD, 53; Univ Minn, MS, 61; Am Bd Path, cert, anat & clin path, 61 & blood banking & immunohemat, 73. *Prof Exp:* Asst prof path, Hahnemann Med Sch, 61-63. *Concurrent Pos:* Assoc pathologist, Harrisburg Hosp, Pa, 61-63; NIH prin & co-investr, Nat Inst Arthritis & Metab Dis, 63-67, 66-71, 71-74 & 75-; dir blood bank, Mayo Clin, Rochester, Minn, 63-88; pres, Minn Asn Blood Banks, 69-70 & Minn Soc Clin Pathologists, 72-73; consult, Food & Drug Admin, Bur Biologics, 74-75; med fel, Bush Found, Univ Chicago. *Mem:* Am Asn Blood Banks; Col Am Path; AMA; Sigma Xi. *Res:* Clinical aspects of immunohematology, blood banking, blood transfusion and transfusion reactions; post-transfusion hepatitis; blood resource management and quality control; histocompatibility testing for tissue transplantation. *Mailing Add:* 2920 N Commonwealth Ave Apt 10A Chicago IL 60657

**TATA, PRAKASAM B S,** ENVIRONMENTAL PROBLEMS OF DEVELOPING COUNTRIES, TEACHING ENVIRONMENTAL ENGINEERING. *Current Pos:* proj mgr, 74-90, coordr tech serv, Environ Eng & Sci, 90-92, COORDR RES, METROP WATER RECLAMATION DIST GREATER CHICAGO, 92- *Personal Data:* b Vizianagram, AP, India, Jan 5, 36; US citizen; m 53, Padha Kopukvla; c Nagamani, Uma & Naroyan. *Educ:* MR Col, India, BS, 53; Nagpur Univ, India, MS, 55; Rutgers Univ, PhD(environ sci), 66. *Prof Exp:* Asst res officer, All India Inst Hyg & Pub Health, 55-59; jr sci officer, Cent Pub Health Eng Res Inst, India, 59-62; res asst, Rutgers Univ, NJ, 62-66; res assoc, Cornell Univ, Ithaca, NY, 66-70, sr res assoc & lectr, 70-74. *Concurrent Pos:* Mem comt, Water Pollution Control Fedn, stand methods, 72-80, res, 76-80, prog, 91; adj prof, dept environ eng, Ill Inst Technol, 74-; panel mem, Bostid, Nat Acad Sci, 74-76, adv, 78-84, consult, 85. *Mem:* Water Pollution Control Fedn; Air & Waste Mgt Asn; Int Asn Water Pollution Res & Control; Sigma Xi. *Res:* Sludge conditioning and dewatering, odor control activated sludge process performance optimization, nutrient control, anaerobic digestion and environmental pollution problems of developing countries; author of 80 publications and reports. *Mailing Add:* 7014 Richmond Ave Darien IL 60561. *Fax:* 708-780-6706; *E-Mail:* prakasam@mwrdgc.dst.il.us

**TATA, XERXES RAMYAR,** ELEMENTARY PARTICLE PHYSICS. *Current Pos:* assoc prof, 88-94, PROF PHYSICS, UNIV HAWAII, 94- *Personal Data:* b Bombay, India, Apr 27, 54; m 86, Kalpaua Kallianpur. *Educ:* Bombay Univ, BSc, 74; Indian Inst Technol, MSc, 76; Univ Tex Austin, PhD(physics), 81. *Prof Exp:* Res assoc physics, Univ Tex Austin, 81-83 & Univ Ore, Eugene, 83-84 & 85-86; sci assoc physics, Cern, Geneva, Switz, 84-85; asst scientist physics, Univ Wis-Madison, 86-88. *Concurrent Pos:* Vis scientist, Kek, Nat Lab High Energy Physics, Japan, 86-87. *Mem:* Am Phys Soc. *Res:* Fundamental and phenomenological studies in elementary particle physics; electroweak theory; supersymmetry; new particle searches at high energy colliders; unification of fundamental forces; model-building; search for physics beyond the standard model. *Mailing Add:* Physics Dept Univ Hawaii Manoa Honolulu HI 96822

**TATARCZUK, JOSEPH RICHARD,** NUCLEAR PHYSICS, COMPUTER ENGINEERING. *Current Pos:* CONSULT, 93- *Personal Data:* b Portland, Maine, June 15, 36; m 64; c 4. *Educ:* Col of the Holy Cross, BS, 58; Rensselaer Polytech Inst, MS, 61, PhD(physics), 65. *Prof Exp:* Res asst nuclear physics, Rensselaer Polytech Inst, 59-65; res assoc, Nuclear Physics Div, Max Planck Inst Chem, 65-66; res assoc neutron physics, Rensselaer Polytech Inst, 66-70, asst to dir Linac Opers & Support Serv, Linear Accelerator Lab, 70-83; assoc prof, Albany Med Col, 74-83. *Concurrent Pos:* Chief physicist, Nuclear Med Serv, Albany Vet Admin Hosp, 72-; adj prof nuclear eng & sci, Rensselaer Polytech Inst, 76-79, adj prof biomed eng, 80- *Mem:* Am Phys Soc. *Res:* Neutron physics; gamma ray spectroscopy; nuclear, accelerator and computer instrumentation. *Mailing Add:* 14 Indian Pipe Dr Wynantskill NY 12198

**TATARSKII, VALERIAN I,** WAVE PROPAGATION IN RANDOM MEDIA, TURBULENCE. *Current Pos:* SR RES ASSOC, UNIV COLO, BOULDER, 91- *Personal Data:* b Kharkov, USSR, Oct 13, 29; m 55, Maia S Granovskaia; c Viatcheslav. *Educ:* Moscow State Univ, MS, 52; USSR Acad Sci, PhD(physics & math), 57; Gorky State Univ, DSc, 64. *Honors & Awards:* USSR State Prize, Coun Ministers, USSR, 90; Max Born Award, Optical Soc Am, 94. *Prof Exp:* Researcher, Inst Atmospheric Physics, USSR Acad Sci, 53-59, sr researcher, 59-78, head lab, 78-90, head dept, Lebedev Phys Inst, 90-91. *Mem:* Foreign assoc Nat Acad Eng; USSR Acad Sci; fel Optical Soc Am. *Res:* Wave propagation in random (turbulent) media; acoustics; optics; wave scattering by rough surfaces, statistical optics, coherence theory, statistical mechanics; applications of wave propagation theory to geophysics. *Mailing Add:* NOAA/ERL/ETL 325 Broadway Boulder CO 80303. *Fax:* 303-497-6020; *E-Mail:* vit@etl.noaa.gov

**TATE, CHARLOTTE ANNE,** EXERCISE PHYSIOLOGY, CARDIOVASCULAR SCIENCES. *Current Pos:* fel biochem res muscle, 77-79, instr, 79-80, ASST PROF, BAYLOR COL MED, 80- *Personal Data:* b Mt Clemens, Mich, Sept 15, 44. *Educ:* Tex Woman's Univ, BS, 69; Southwest Tex State Univ, MA, 72; Univ Tex, Austin, PhD(phys educ & exercise physiol), 76. *Prof Exp:* Teacher adaptive phys educ, Northeast ISD, 69-72; teaching asst, Univ Tex, Austin, 72-76, res physiologist biochem, Inst Environ Stress, 76-77. *Concurrent Pos:* Res asst, Univ Res Coun, Univ Tex, Austin, 74-75; NIH trainee, Inst Environ Stress, 76-77 & NIH fel, Baylor Col Med, 77-79. *Mem:* Am Heart Asn; Am Col Sports Med; Am Physiol Soc; AAAS; NY Acad Sci; Biophys Soc. *Res:* Calcium fluxes in subcellular organelles of cardiac and skeletal muscle in normal and diseased states; biochemical adaptations to exercise and fatigue in muscle. *Mailing Add:* Dept Pharmacol Univ Houston Col Pharm Houston TX 77204-5515. *Fax:* 713-743-1229

**TATE, DAVID,** STERILE PROCESSING & DISTRIBUTION. *Current Pos:* DIR STUDENT SERV HEALTH SCI, PURDUE UNIV, 84-, EDUC COORDR CONTINUING EDUC, 88- *Personal Data:* b Lafayette, Ind, Feb 9, 46; m 72, Maureen Krug; c Ryan C. *Educ:* Purdue Univ, BS, 70, MS, 80. *Prof Exp:* Dir student serv, St Joseph's Col, 83-84. *Concurrent Pos:* Instr environ sci & med technol, Purdue Univ, 84-,; adj prof, Methodist Hosp, Ind, 84-; consult, Int Asn Healthcare Cent Serv & Mat Mgt, 86- *Res:* Ethylene oxide; hydrogen peroxide gas plasma. *Mailing Add:* Purdue Univ 1163 Civil Eng West Lafayette IN 47906

**TATE, DAVID PAUL,** ORGANIC & POLYMER CHEMISTRY. *Current Pos:* RETIRED. *Personal Data:* b Chicago, Ill, Dec 10, 31; m 53; c 3. *Educ:* Hamline Univ, BS, 53; Purdue Univ, MS, 55, PhD, 58. *Prof Exp:* Sr chemist, Stand Oil Co, Ohio, 57-63; mgr polymerization, Firestone Tire & Rubber Co, 63-71, asst dir res, 71-80, res assoc, 80-86; exec officer, Ctr Adhesives, Sealants & Coatings, Case Western Res Univ, 87-95. *Mem:* Am Chem Soc. *Res:* Lithium amine reductions; phosphorous compounds; organometallic chemistry; elastomer synthesis; inorganic polymers, phosphazene polymers. *Mailing Add:* 3420 Burwood Dr No 15 Richfield OH 44286-9690

**TATE, JEFFREY L,** BIOLOGY. *Current Pos:* SPEC ASST TO DIR, BIOL PROCESS TECH INST, UNIV MINN, 89- *Personal Data:* b Minneapolis, Minn, Dec 18, 57; m 89, Tracey J Benson. *Educ:* Univ Minn, BSc, 80, PhD(plant physiol), 85. *Prof Exp:* Staff scientist, Biol Process Tech Inst, Univ Minn, St Paul, 85-87; res assoc, Baltimore Univ, Univ Md, 87-89. *Concurrent Pos:* Secy & treas, Minn Biotech Asn, 91-93; distinguished dir, Democratic Farmer-Labor Party, Roseville, Minn, 92-; chmn, Coun Biotech Ctrs, 93- *Res:* Biology; plant pathology. *Mailing Add:* Univ Minn Biol Process Tech Inst 1479 Gortner Lab Biol Chem Rm 240 St Paul MN 55108

**TATE, JOHN T,** MATHEMATICS. *Current Pos:* PROF & SID W RICHARDSON CHAIR MATH, UNIV TEX, 90- *Personal Data:* b Minneapolis, Minn, Mar 13, 25; m 56; c 3. *Educ:* Harvard Univ, BA, 46; Princeton Univ, PhD(math), 50. *Honors & Awards:* Cole Prize in Number Theory, Am Math Soc, 56, Steele Prize Lifetime Achievement, 95. *Prof Exp:* Higgins res assoc & instr, Princeton Univ, 50-53; vis asst prof math, Columbia Univ, 53-54; from asst prof to prof, Harvard Univ, 54-90. *Concurrent Pos:* Sloan fel, 59-61; vis prof, Univ Calif, Berkeley, 63-, IHES, France, 68-69, Orsay, France, 80-81 & Univ Tex, 89-90; Guggenheim fel, IHES, France, 65-66. *Mem:* Nat Acad Sci; Am Math Soc; Math Asn Am; fel AAAS. *Res:* Algebra; algebraic number theory; diophantine algebraic geometry. *Mailing Add:* Univ Tex Dept Math RLM Hall 8-100 Austin TX 78712

**TATE, LAWRENCE GRAY,** INSECT TOXICOLOGY, INSECT PHYSIOLOGY. *Current Pos:* asst prof, 74-77, ASSOC PROF BIOL, UNIV SALA, 77- *Personal Data:* b Cambridge, Eng, Feb 10, 45; US citizen. *Educ:* Limestone Col, BS, 66; Univ SC, MS, 68, PhD(biol), 71. *Prof Exp:* USPHS res assoc insect toxicol, NC State Univ, 71-74. *Mem:* Sigma Xi. *Res:* Metabolism of xenobiotics in tissues of marine organisms; carbohydrate metabolism in insects. *Mailing Add:* Dept Biol Sci Univ SAla 307 Univ Blvd N Mobile AL 36688-0001

**TATE, R(OGER) W(ALLACE),** CHEMICAL ENGINEERING. *Current Pos:* RETIRED. *Personal Data:* b Chicago, Ill, Jan 31, 25; m 58; c 3. *Educ:* Ill Inst Technol, BS, 48; Univ Wis, MS, 48, PhD(chem eng), 50. *Honors & Awards:* Recognition & Appreciation Awards, Am Soc Testing & Mat, 83 & 91. *Prof Exp:* Chem engr, Stand Oil Develop Co, NJ, 50-54; staff engr, Kearney & Trecker Corp, Wis, 54-57; dir res, Delavan Inc, 57-90, eng consult, 90-96. *Concurrent Pos:* Adj prof, Newark Col Eng, 51-53. *Mem:* Am Inst Chem Engrs; Am Soc Testing & Mat. *Res:* Atomization and spray analysis; development of fuel injectors and spray nozzles. *Mailing Add:* 7901 Marilyn Dr Windsor Heights IA 50322

**TATE, ROBERT FLEMMING,** MATHEMATICAL STATISTICS. *Current Pos:* assoc prof, 65-67, prof, 67-86, EMER PROF MATH, UNIV ORE, 86- *Personal Data:* b Oakland, Calif, Dec 15, 21. *Educ:* Univ Calif, AB, 44, PhD(math statist), 52; Univ NC, MS, 49. *Prof Exp:* Lectr, Univ Calif, 51-53; from instr to assoc prof math, Univ Wash, Seattle, 53-65. *Concurrent Pos:* Mem, Math Inst & Inst Statist, Univ Vienna, 64. *Mem:* Sigma Xi; fel Inst Math Statist (assoc secy, 63-73); Am Statist Asn. *Res:* Theory of correlation and of estimation; multivariate analysis. *Mailing Add:* 3370 Potter St Eugene OR 97405-4267

**TATE, ROBERT LEE, III,** SOIL MICROBIOLOGY, ENVIRONMENTAL MICROBIOLOGY. *Current Pos:* from asst prof to assoc prof soil microbiol, Dept Soils & Crops, 81-90, ASSOC PROF SOIL MICROBIOL, DEPT ENVIRON SCI, RUTGERS UNIV, 90- *Personal Data:* b Victoria, Tex, Dec 1, 44; m 71, Ann C Sweezy; c Robert L IV & Geoffrey A. *Educ:* Univ Ariz, BS, 66, MS, 67; Univ Wis-Madison, PhD(bact), 70. *Prof Exp:* Scholar bact, Univ Calif, Los Angeles, 70-72, res assoc, Dept Agron, Cornell Univ, 72-75; asst prof microbiol, Agr Res & Educ Ctr, Univ Fla, 75-80, assoc prof, 80-81. *Concurrent Pos:* Consult, Brookhaven Nat Lab, 82-89; assoc ed, Soil Sci, 84-93, ed-in-chief, 93-; assoc ed, Soil Sci Soc Am J, 85-90. *Mem:* Am Soc Microbiol; Soil Sci Soc Am; Am Soc Agron. *Res:* Microbial interactions with soil organic matter; biogeochemical cycles in soils, nitrogen cycle, carbon cycle; behavior of xenobiotics in soil; denitrification; soil enzymes; soil quality. *Mailing Add:* Dept Environ Sci Rutgers Univ New Brunswick NJ 08903-0231. *Fax:* 732-932-8644; *E-Mail:* tate@aesop.rutgers.edu

**TATE, SURESH S,** PROTEIN CHEMISTRY, CELL BIOLOGY. *Current Pos:* ASSOC PROF BIOCHEM, MED COL, CORNELL UNIV, 78- *Personal Data:* b India, Dec 2, 36. *Educ:* London Univ, PhD(biochem), 63. *Mem:* Am Soc Biol Chemists; Harvey Soc; NY Acad Sci. *Mailing Add:* Dept Biochem Med Col Cornell Univ 1300 York Ave New York NY 10021-4896

**TATELMAN, MAURICE,** MEDICINE. *Current Pos:* RETIRED. *Personal Data:* b Omaha, Nebr, Dec 6, 17; m 61; c 2. *Educ:* Univ Nebr, AB, 40, MD, 42. *Prof Exp:* From asst prof to assoc prof, Col Med, Wayne State Univ, 50-61, prof radiol, 61-86. *Concurrent Pos:* Chmn, Dept Radiol, Sinai Hosp Detroit, 68-83; consult, Detroit Mem Hosp. *Mem:* Fel Am Col Radiol; Am Roentgen Ray Soc; Radiol Soc NAm; sr mem Am Soc Neuroradiol; Am Soc Head & Neck Radiol; Sigma Xi. *Res:* Clinical diagnostic radiology; neuroradiology. *Mailing Add:* 7525 E Gainey Ranch Rd No 150 Scottsdale AZ 85258-1607

**TATIC-LUCIC, SVETLANA,** SILICON MICROMACHINING, APPLICATIONS OF SILICON MICROMACHINING IN BIOLOGY & MEDICINE. *Current Pos:* RES ASST, CALIF INST TECHNOL, 89- *Personal Data:* b Belgrade, Yugoslavia, Nov 15, 61; m 89, Dragan Lucic. *Educ:* Univ Belgrade, dipl ing, 86; Calif Inst Technol, MS, 90. *Prof Exp:* Res engr, Inst Physics, Belgrade 86-89. *Mem:* Inst Elec & Electronics Engrs. *Res:* Fabricaton of silicon micromachined structures which are used for studies of live neural networks. *Mailing Add:* 2860 Woodland Hills 206 Colorado Springs CO 80918. *Fax:* 626-395-2944; *E-Mail:* ceca@cco.caltech.edu

**TATINA, ROBERT EDWARD,** PRAIRIE ECOLOGY. *Current Pos:* PROF BIOL, DAKOTA WESLEYAN UNIV, 76- *Personal Data:* b Chicago, Ill, May 18, 42; m 78, Geraldyne Sansone; c Thomas & Heather. *Educ:* Northern Ill Univ, BS, 65; Southern Ill Univ, MA, 71, PhD(bot), 81. *Prof Exp:* Teacher sci & math, Trewyn Jr High Sch, 65-66, biol, Evergreen Park Community High Sch, 66-69. *Mem:* Sigma Xi; Bot Soc Am; Am Biol Teachers Asn; Nat Sci Teachers Asn. *Res:* Flora of South Dakota; gradient analysis of mixed grass prairie. *Mailing Add:* Dept Biol Dakota Wesleyan Univ 1200 W University Ave Mitchell SD 57301. *Fax:* 605-995-2699

**TATINI, SITA RAMAYYA,** MICROBIOLOGY, FOOD SCIENCE. *Current Pos:* DEPT FOOD SCI & NUTRIT, UNIV MINN, MINNEAPOLIS. *Personal Data:* b Mortha, India, Oct 6, 35; m 54; c 3. *Educ:* Univ Madras, BVSc, 57; Univ Minn, MS, 66, PhD(food sci & indust), 69. *Prof Exp:* Vet asst surgeon, Andhra Animal Husb Dept, State of Andhra Pradesh, India, 58-61; res fel, 69, NIH-Food & Drug Admin res grant, 71-74, asst prof food microbiol, 69-77, prof food sci & nutrit, Univ Minn, St Paul, 77- *Mem:* AAAS; Inst Food Technol; Am Soc Microbiol; Am Dairy Sci Asn; Int Asn Milk, Food & Environ Sanit. *Res:* Growth, survival and production of enterotoxins by staphylococci in food products; developing rapid methods for assessment of psychrophilic bacteria in milk. *Mailing Add:* Dept Food Sci Univ Minn St Paul 225 Food Sci N Ctr 1334 Eckles Ave St Paul MN 55108-1040

**TATOMER, HARRY NICHOLAS,** CHEMICAL ENGINEERING. *Current Pos:* RETIRED. *Personal Data:* b Jersey City, NJ, Feb 13, 13; m 40; c 4. *Educ:* Univ Ill, BS, 37. *Prof Exp:* Develop engr, Olin Mathieson Chem Corp, 37-40, asst proj supvr, 40-43, proj supvr, 43-46, mgr pilot opers, 46-52, process develop, 52-57, tech asst prod, Energy Div, 57-60; tech asst prod, Chem Div, Union Carbide Corp, 60-64, admin assoc to dir rocket propulsion & staff coordr res & develop admin, SCharleston Tech Ctr, 64-77, chem eng, 77-78. *Mem:* Am Chem Soc; Am Inst Chem Engrs. *Res:* Pilot plant development of sodium chlorite; chlorine dioxide generation; sodium amalgam processes; hydrazine and derivatives; boron hydrides; high energy fuels; rocket propellants; government contract administration; research administration. *Mailing Add:* 2018 Weberwood Dr Charleston WV 25303

**TATOR, CHARLES HASKELL,** NEUROSURGERY. *Current Pos:* From assoc to asst prof, 69-74, assoc prof, 74-80, PROF SURG, UNIV TORONTO, 80-; SURGEON, DIV NEUROSURG, TORONTO WESTERN HOSP, 69- *Personal Data:* b Toronto, Ont, Aug 24, 36; m 60; c 3. *Educ:* Univ Toronto, MD, 61, MA, 63, PhD(neuropath), 65; FRCS(c); FACS. *Concurrent Pos:* Co-dir, Playfair Neurosci Unit, Univ Toronto. *Res:* Brain tumor research and spinal cord injury research. *Mailing Add:* Div Neurosurg Toronto Hosp Western Div 399 Bathurst St MCL 2-435 Toronto ON M5T 2S8 Can

**TATRO, CLEMENT A(USTIN),** MECHANICS. *Current Pos:* RETIRED. *Personal Data:* b Kingman Co, Kans, May 16, 24; m 46; c 2. *Educ:* Friends Univ, BA, 49; Purdue Univ, MS, 51, PhD(physics), 56. *Prof Exp:* Res asst, Purdue Univ, 49-56; asst prof appl mech, Mich State Univ, 56-60, assoc prof metall, mech & mat sci, 60-62; prof mech eng, Tulane Univ, 62-66; head mat eng sect, Dept Mech Eng, Lawrence Livermore Lab, Univ Calif, 66-77, res & advan develop engr, 77-90. *Mem:* Am Soc Testing & Mat; Am Phys Soc; Soc Exp Stress Analysis; Am Soc Nondestructive Testing; Inst Environ Sci (pres, 80-81); Sigma Xi. *Res:* Acoustic emission; wave propagation in solids; experimental stress analysis; material dynamics. *Mailing Add:* 384 Martin Ave Livermore CA 94550

**TATRO, PETER RICHARD,** PHYSICAL OCEANOGRAPHY, ACOUSTICS. *Current Pos:* CONSULT, 91- *Personal Data:* b Winthrop, Mass, Jan 20, 36; m 90; Linda J Locke; c Peter, Susan, Scott, Benjamin & Christopher. *Educ:* Ga Inst Technol, BME, 57; Mass Inst Technol, PhD(oceanog), 66. *Honors & Awards:* Navy Achievement Medal; Navy Expeditionary Medal. *Prof Exp:* Res oceanogr, Fleet Numerical Weather Ctr, Calif, 66-69; spec asst for ocean sci, Off Naval Res, Washington, DC, 69-72,

head, Acoust Environ Support Detachment, Arlington, 72-75, spec asst oceanogr of the Navy, 75-76; mgr, Ocean Sci Div, Sci Appln Int Corp, 77-80, sr vpres, Ocean Sci Dept, McLean, Va, 80-91. *Concurrent Pos:* Consult, Int Decade Ocean Explor, NSF, 72-75. *Mem:* Acoust Soc Am; fel Marine Technol Soc; Oceanog Soc. *Res:* Application of advanced digital technology to the problem of predicting the acoustic characteristics of the oceans. *Mailing Add:* 717 Oyster Cove Dr Grasonville MD 21635

**TATSUMOTO, MITSUNOBU,** geochemistry, geochronology, for more information see previous edition

**TATTAR, TERRY ALAN,** FOREST PATHOLOGY, SHADE TREE PATHOLOGY. *Current Pos:* from asst prof to assoc prof, 73-84, PROF SHADE TREE PATH, UNIV MASS, 85- *Personal Data:* b Port Chester, NY, May 9, 43; m 69; c 2. *Educ:* Northeastern Univ, BA, 67; Univ New Hampshire, PhD(bot), 71. *Prof Exp:* Plant pathologist forest path, USDA Forest Serv, 71-73. *Concurrent Pos:* Consult, Tree Health, 75- *Mem:* Am Phytopath Soc; Sigma Xi; Am Soc Consult Arborists. *Res:* Determining the effects of vascular wilt pathogens on trees; developing diagnostic techniques for early detection of diseases of trees; detection of hazard trees. *Mailing Add:* 6 Pine Tree Circle Amherst MA 01002

**TATTER, DOROTHY,** MEDICINE, PATHOLOGY. *Current Pos:* From instr assoc prof, 49-83, EMER PROF PATH, SCH MED, UNIV SOUTHERN CALIF, 83- *Personal Data:* b Chicago, Ill, Apr 11, 22; m 49, Richard B Newton; c 3. *Educ:* Rosary Col, BS, 43; Univ Ill, MD, 47. *Concurrent Pos:* Resident path, Los Angeles Co Gen Hosp, 49-52, head physician, Autopsy Dept Labs, 52-83. *Mem:* Sigma Xi. *Res:* Pathology; autopsy. *Mailing Add:* 555 Madeline Dr Pasadena CA 91105-2839

**TATTERSALL, IAN,** PALEO ANTHROPOLOGY, PRIMATOLOGY & SYSTEMATICS. *Current Pos:* From asst cur to assoc cur, 71-81, CUR PHYS ANTHROP, AM MUS NATURAL HIST, 81-, CHMN ANTHROP, 90- *Personal Data:* b Paignton, Devon, Eng, May 10, 45; US citizen. *Educ:* Cambridge Univ, BA, 67, MA, 70; Yale Univ, MPhil, 70, PhD(geol), 71. *Honors & Awards:* Achievement Award, Inst Human Origins, 93. *Concurrent Pos:* Vis lectr, Grad Fac, New Sch Social Res, 71-72; adj asst prof, Lehman Col, City Univ New York, 71-74; adj assoc prof, Columbia Univ, 78-79, adj prof, 92-; adj prof, City Univ NY Grad Sch, 91-; exhib consult, Gunma Mus Nat Hist, 94-97. *Mem:* Am Asn Phys Anthropologists; Soc Vert Paleont; Am Soc Primatology; Int Primatology Soc; AAAS; Sigma Xi. *Res:* Evolution, functional anatomy, ecology and behavior of the primates, particularly of the Malagasy lemurs; human evolution; primate systematics; evolutionary theory in relation to phylogenetic reconstruction and other systematic applications. *Mailing Add:* Dept Anthrop Am Mus Natural Hist Cent Park W at 79th St New York NY 10024-5192

**TATUM, CHARLES MARIS,** BIOCHEMISTRY, ORGANIC CHEMISTRY. *Current Pos:* sr scientist, Explor Agr Res, Rohm & Haas Co, 79-82, res sect mgr, 82-84, res dept mgr, 84-90, VPRES, CORP DIR RES, ROHM & HAAS CO, 90- *Personal Data:* b Philadelphia, Pa, Oct 10, 47; m 70; c 2. *Educ:* Amherst Col, BA, 69; Pa State Univ, PhD(org chem), 76. *Prof Exp:* Biochemist clin chem, Gen Rose Mem Hosp, 70-72; asst prof chem, Middlebury Col, 76-79. *Mem:* Am Chem Soc. *Res:* Strategic planning, agricultural applications of genetic engineering and pesticide biochemistry; pesticide synthesis; pesticide biology. *Mailing Add:* 475 W Prospect Ave North Wales PA 19454-2629

**TATUM, JAMES PATRICK,** PHYSICAL CHEMISTRY. *Personal Data:* b Dallas, Tex, July 6, 38. *Educ:* Rice Univ, BA, 61; Fla State Univ, PhD(phys chem), 66. *Prof Exp:* Res assoc chem, Univ Ill, 66-68; from asst prof to prof chem, Ind State Univ, Terre Haute, 68-82. *Concurrent Pos:* Vis prof quantum theory proj, Univ Fla, Gainesville, 78. *Mem:* Am Phys Soc. *Res:* Theoretical chemistry. *Mailing Add:* Dept Chem Ind State Univ Terre Haute IN 47809. *E-Mail:* chtatum@scitec.indstate.edu

**TATUM, WILLIAM EARL,** ORGANIC CHEMISTRY. *Current Pos:* RETIRED. *Personal Data:* b Ft Payne, Ala, Sept 13, 33; m 52; c 4. *Educ:* Chattanooga Univ, BS, 55; Univ Tenn, PhD(chem), 58. *Prof Exp:* Res chemist, Exp Sta, E I Du Pont de Nemours & Co Inc, 58-61, tech rep, Venture Develop Sect, 61-63, staff scientist, Yerkes Res Lab, 63-64, res supvr, Circleville Res Lab, Ohio, 64-67, develop supvr, Circleville Plant, 67-68, tech supt, Florence Plant, SC, 68-70, cellophane prod mgr, Del, 70-71, dir, Prod & Tech Div, 71-73, venture mgr, 73-74, dir, Specialty Mkt Div, 75-76, dir, Packaging Films Div, 76-78, dir, Fluoropolymers Div, Polymer Prod Dept, 78-80, dir safety, health & environ affairs, 80-81, gen mgr, Energy & Mat Dept, 81-82, vpres, Mat & Logistics, Dept, 82-84, vpres Int Dept, 84-85, sr vpres, Mat & Logistics Dept, 85- *Concurrent Pos:* Mem steering comt, Bus Roundtable, Off Technol Assessment, US Cong, Conserv Found & Nat Environ Develop Asn; mem, Environ Assessment Coun. *Mem:* Am Chem Soc. *Res:* Polymer chemistry and engineering; synthetic organic chemistry. *Mailing Add:* 13839 Silkvine Lane Jacksonville FL 32224

**TATYREK, ALFRED FRANK,** POLYMER MATERIALS IDENTIFICATION. *Current Pos:* CONSULT, 96- *Personal Data:* b Hillside, NJ, Jan 23, 30. *Educ:* Seton Hall Univ, BS, 54. *Prof Exp:* Res chemist polymer synthesis, Bakelite Div, Union Carbide Corp, 53-58; res chemist polymer res & appln, US Radium Corp, 59-62; analytical chemist chem items, US Army, NY, 62-64, res chemist chemiluminescent & pyrotechnics, Armament Res & Develop Ctr, 64-73, chem engr environ, 73-84, mats eng & chem, 84-95.

*Concurrent Pos:* Pres, Picatinny Chap, Sigma Xi, 74-75, 79-80, 85-86, lectr, 81- *Mem:* Sigma Xi; Nat Soc Inventors. *Res:* Experimental exploratory research on new polymers and their synthesis, analysis and applications as structural materials, adhesives and coatings; developing electroluminescent light emiting cells based upon highly polar polymer systems; chemical reaction methods of generating colored smokes; kinetics and mechanism of thermal decomposition of explosives; applications and chemical reactions useful for increasing the light yield of chemiluminescent compounds; development and engineering on new industrial systems for the control and disposal of hazardous wastes generated at Army ammunition plants; analytical investigations into the composition of organic materials using FTIR infrared spectrometry, thermal analysis and mechanical analysis; design of an innovative vacuum crankcase system for internal combustion engines for control of air pollution and engine oil contamination; 6 US patents. *Mailing Add:* 27 Orchard Rd Maplewood NJ 07040. *Fax:* 973-724-2864

**TAUB, AARON M,** PHARMACY. *Current Pos:* mgr & dir qual control, Fisons Corp, 72-81, dir regulatory affairs, 81-83, dir proj mgt, 83-88, DIR NEW PROD COORD, FISONS CORP, 89- *Personal Data:* b Jersey City, NJ, Dec 21, 35; m 67, Rosemary Dessel; c Michael & Debbie. *Educ:* Wagner Col, BS, 60; State Univ NY Buffalo, PhD(biol), 65. *Prof Exp:* Asst prof zool, Pa State Univ, 64-68; asst prof anat, Ont Vet Col, Univ Guelph, 68-69; mgr med serv, Fisons (Can) Ltd, 68-72. *Concurrent Pos:* Chmn, Med Awareness Subcomt, Internation Pharmaceut Aerosol Corp, 90-94. *Mem:* Sigma Xi; NY Acad Sci. *Res:* Pharmaceutical drug delivery/aerosol systems. *Mailing Add:* 5 Glencannon Trail Pittsford NY 14534. *Fax:* 716-272-3906

**TAUB, ABRAHAM,** PHARMACEUTICAL CHEMISTRY. *Current Pos:* From instr to prof chem, 22-65, distinguished serv prof, 65-69, EMER DISTINGUISHED SERV PROF CHEM, COL PHARMACEUT SCI, COLUMBIA UNIV, 69- *Personal Data:* b New York, NY, Sept 21, 01. *Educ:* Columbia Univ, BS, 22, AM, 27. *Hon Degrees:* ScD, Columbia Univ, 76. *Honors & Awards:* Rusby Award, 62; Man of Year Award, Nat Asn Pharmaceut Mfrs, 72. *Concurrent Pos:* Asst, Revision Comt, US Pharmacopeia, 20-30; consult chemist, 22-; asst, Nat Formulary, 37; consult, Nat Asn Pharmaceut Mfrs, 70-86. *Mem:* AAAS; Am Chem Soc; Am Pharmaceut Asn; fel Am Inst Chem; NY Acad Sci. *Res:* Quantitative color standards; deterioration of medicinals; development of analytical methods; stability of parenteral solutions; chromatography; radioisotope tracer techniques. *Mailing Add:* 1080 Fifth Ave New York NY 10128-0102

**TAUB, ABRAHAM HASKEL,** MATHEMATICS. *Current Pos:* dir, Comput Ctr, 64-68, prof, 64-78, EMER PROF MATH, UNIV CALIF, BERKELEY, 78- *Personal Data:* b Chicago, Ill, Feb 1, 11; m 33, Cecilia Vaslow; c Mara, Nadine & Haskell. *Educ:* Univ Chicago, BS, 31; Princeton Univ, PhD(math physics), 35. *Honors & Awards:* Pres Cert Merit, 46. *Prof Exp:* Asst, Princeton Univ, 34-35 & Inst Adv Study, 35-36 & 40-41; from instr to prof math, Univ Wash, Seattle, 36-48; res prof appl math, Univ Ill, Urbana, 48-64, head, Digital Comput Lab, 61-64. *Concurrent Pos:* Theoret physicist, Div 2, Nat Defense Res Comt, Princeton Univ, 42-45; mem, Guggenheim Post-Serv, 47-48 & Guggenheim fel, 53 & 58; mem, Appl Math Adv Coun, Nat Bur Stand, 49-54, chmn adv panel, Appl Math Div, 51-60; mem comt on training & res in math, Nat Res Coun, 52-54; mem rev comt, Appl Math Div, Argonne Nat Lab, 60-62. *Mem:* Fel AAAS; Am Math Soc; fel Am Phys Soc; Math Asn Am; fel Am Acad Arts & Sci. *Res:* Relativity; interaction of shock waves; gravitational waves; general relativistic hydrodynamics; cosmology. *Mailing Add:* Dept Math Univ Calif Berkeley CA 94720-0001

**TAUB, ARTHUR,** NEUROLOGY, NEUROPHYSIOLOGY. *Current Pos:* dir, neurosurg res lab, Yale Univ, 69-75, dir pain clin, 71-75, asst prof, 68-72, assoc prof neurophysiol & neurol, 72-75, prof clin anesthesiol & dir sect study & treatment of pain, 75-76, CLIN PROF, DEPT ANESTHESIOL, SCH MED, YALE UNIV, 76- *Personal Data:* b New York, NY, Jan 4, 32; m 63; c 1. *Educ:* Yeshiva Univ, BA, 52; Mass Inst Technol, SM, 53, PhD(neurophysiol), 64; Yale Univ, MD, 57; Am Bd Psychiat Neurol, dipl, 75. *Prof Exp:* NIH fel neurophysiol, Mass Inst Technol, 64-66, res assoc, 66-68. *Concurrent Pos:* NIH res career develop award, Mass Inst Technol & Yale Univ, 66-73; resident neurol, Sch Med, Yale Univ, 69-72; assoc neurologist, Yale New Haven Hosp, 71-75, attend neurologist, 75-; Royal Soc Med Found traveling fel, UK, 72. *Mem:* Am Asn Study Headache; Am Acad Neurol; Am Soc Function Stereot Neurosurg; Soc Neurosci; Int Asn Study Pain; Am Pain Soc; Am Soc Regional Anesthesia. *Res:* Pain; application of basic scientific approach to modalities for control; neuropharmacology; computer applications medicolegal studies; clinical control by medical, surgical and anesthesiological means. *Mailing Add:* 468 Prince St No 203 New Haven CT 06519-1604

**TAUB, DAVID,** PHARMACEUTICAL CHEMISTRY. *Current Pos:* RETIRED. *Personal Data:* b New York, NY, Nov 13, 19; m 44; c 2. *Educ:* City Col NY, BS, 40; Harvard Univ, AM, 46, PhD, 50. *Prof Exp:* Chemist, Manhattan Proj, Kellex Corp, 42-46; USPHS fel, Harvard Univ, 49-51; sr chemist, Merck Sharp & Dohme Res Labs, 51-65, sect head process res, 65-68, sr res fel, 68-77, sr investr, 77-90. *Mem:* Am Chem Soc. *Res:* Organic synthesis; natural products; synthetic medicinals. *Mailing Add:* 54 Wistar Ave Metuchen NJ 08840

**TAUB, DENNIS DANIEL,** CHEMOKINES, T CELL CLONES. *Current Pos:* Sr staff fel, Nat Cancer Inst, 91-93, scientist, 93-97, SECT CHIEF, LAB IMMUNOL, NAT INST AGING, NIH, 97- *Personal Data:* b Norfolk, Va, Sept 27, 64; m 95, Deborah J Gunton. *Educ:* Pa State Univ, BS, 85; Temple Univ Sch Med, PhD(microbiol & immunol), 91. *Prof Exp:* Res assoc, Hahnemann Med Sch, 91. *Concurrent Pos:* Outstanding investr award, Clin

Immunol Soc, 93; assoc investr, Nat Cancer Inst, 94-97. *Mem:* Am Asn Immunol; Am Soc Med Technologists; Am Asn Clin Pathologists; Int Cytokine Soc. *Res:* Examination of t-cell activation and differentiations; various inflammatory mediators which mediate lymphocyte migrations; development of cancer-specific vaccines; developing clinical/research trials in cancer patients and elderly. *Mailing Add:* 16A Elm St Thurmont MD 21788. *Fax:* 410-558-8284; *E-Mail:* ddtaub@concentric.net, taubd@grc.nia.nih.gov

**TAUB, EDWARD,** PHYSIOLOGICAL PSYCHOLOGY. *Current Pos:* PROF PSYCHOL, UNIV ALA, BIRMINGHAM, 86- *Personal Data:* b Brooklyn, NY, Oct 22, 31; m 59, Mildred Allen. *Educ:* Brooklyn Col, BA, 53; Columbia Univ, MA, 59; NY Univ, PhD(psychol), 70. *Honors & Awards:* Distinguished Res Award, Biofeedback Soc Am, 88; Pioneering Res Contrib Award, Asn Appl Psychophysiol & Biofeedback, 89. *Prof Exp:* Res asst psychol, Columbia Univ, 56; res asst, Dept Exp Neurol, Jewish Chronic Dis Hosp, 57-60, res assoc, 60-68; chief, Behav Biol Ctr, Inst Behav Res, 68-83, dir, Feedback Res Ctr, 83-87. *Concurrent Pos:* Asst prof, Sch Med, Johns Hopkins Univ, 70-82; Guggenheim fel, 83-84; mem, Am Psychol Asn, Exec Comt Div 6, Steering Comt Sect Nervous Syst, Am Physiol Soc. *Mem:* Fel Am Psychol Asn; Soc Neurosci; Biofeedback Soc Am (pres, 79); Am Physiol Soc; fel Behav Med Soc; fel AAAS; fel Am Psychol Soc. *Res:* The role of somatosensory feedback and spinal reflexes in movement and learning; biofeedback and self-regulation of human hand temperature; rehabilitation of movement; diagnosis of functional gastrointestinal disorders. *Mailing Add:* Dept Psychol Univ Ala Birmingham 415 Campbell Hall Birmingham AL 35294-0001. *Fax:* 205-975-6110

**TAUB, FRIEDA B,** ECOLOGY, POLLUTION. *Current Pos:* Fisheries biologist, Univ Wash, 59-61, biologist, Inst Food Sci, 61-62, from res asst prof to res assoc prof, 62-71, PROF FISHERIES, SCH FISHERIES, UNIV WASH, 71- *Personal Data:* b Newark, NJ, Oct 11, 34; m 54; c 3. *Educ:* Rutgers Univ, BA, 55, MA, 57, PhD(zool), 59. *Concurrent Pos:* Res grants, 61-91; sr assoc, Nat Res Coun, 90-91. *Mem:* Fel AAAS; Ecol Soc Am; Am Soc Limnol & Oceanog; Sigma Xi; Am Fisheries Soc; Am Soc Testing & Mat; Soc Environ Toxicol & Chem; Am Soc Microbiol; Am Inst Fisheries Res Biologists; Soc Int Limnol. *Res:* Aquatic food chains; ecosystems; closed ecological systems; environmental risk; genetically engineered organisms. *Mailing Add:* Sch Fisheries Univ Wash Box 355100 Seattle WA 98195-0001

**TAUB, HASKELL JOSEPH,** SURFACE PHYSICS. *Current Pos:* from asst prof to assoc prof, 75-84, PROF PHYSICS, DEPT PHYSICS & ASTRON, UNIV MO, COLUMBIA, 84- *Personal Data:* b Princeton, NJ, June 8, 45; m 72; c 1. *Educ:* Stanford Univ, BS, 66. *Prof Exp:* Assoc res scientist, Dept Physics, New York, Univ, 71-73; asst physicist, Dept Physics, Brookhaven Nat Lab, 73-75. *Concurrent Pos:* Vis prof, Fr Nat Comt Physics, Univ d'Aix-Marseille II, 81-82; res assoc, Ames Lab, 82-84; vis assoc prof, Sch Appl & Eng Physics, Cornell Univ, 82. *Mem:* Am Phys Soc; AAAS. *Res:* Experimental surface physics; studies of the structure and dynamics of adsorbed films by neutron scattering, low-energy electron diffraction and x-ray scattering techniques; structural and magnetic phase transitions in bulk condensed matter and films. *Mailing Add:* 506 Edgewood Ave Columbia MO 65203

**TAUB, HERBERT,** ELECTRICAL ENGINEERING. *Current Pos:* tutor, 44-46, from instr to assoc prof, 47-59, PROF ELEC ENG, CITY COL NEW YORK, 60- *Personal Data:* b New York, NY, Dec 23, 18; m 43; c 3. *Educ:* City Col New York, BS, 40; Columbia Univ, MA, 43, PhD, 49. *Prof Exp:* Tutor, Dept Physics, City Col New York, 40-43; elec engr, Nat Defense Res Proj, Princeton Univ, 43-44. *Concurrent Pos:* Elec engr, Allen B Du Mont, Inc, NJ, 41; consult, Gen Tel & Electronics, Inc, NY, 69-70; Bell Labs, 72-83 & Paine-Webber Inc, 84-86. *Mem:* Sr mem Inst Elec & Electronics Engrs; Sigma Xi. *Res:* Determination of nuclear magnetic moments by molecular beam methods; electronics, especially pulse circuitry. *Mailing Add:* Dept Elec Eng City Col New York New York NY 10031

**TAUB, IRWIN A(LLEN),** FOOD PRESERVATION, FOOD IRRADIATION. *Current Pos:* supvry chemist & chief, Cobalt Br, Radiation Sources Div, US Army Natick Res, Develop & Eng Ctr, 69-80, chief plant prod group, develop labs, 80-84, chief, Technol Acquisition & Develop Br, Food Technol Div, 84-91, SR RES SCIENTIST, US ARMY NATICK RES, DEVELOP & ENG CTR, 91- *Personal Data:* b Brooklyn, NY, July 18, 34; m 59, Barbara Cohen; c Mitchell & Sarah. *Educ:* Queens Col, NY, BS, 55; Univ Minn, PhD(inorg chem), 61. *Prof Exp:* Resident res assoc, Argonne Nat Lab, 61-63; fel, Carnegie-Mellon Univ, 63-69. *Concurrent Pos:* Radiation consult, 85- *Mem:* Am Chem Soc; Sigma Xi; AAAS; Inst Food Technologists; Int Inst Refrig. *Res:* Radiation chemistry; free radical kinetics; food irradiation; inorganic fast reactions; protein and lipid radicals; myoglobin radiolysis; food dehydration and extrusion; protein-carbohydrate crosslinking; food structure and glass transitions; intrinsic chemical markers of thermoprocessive; nutrients and performance enhancement. *Mailing Add:* 29 William J Heights Framingham MA 01702-6133. *Fax:* 508-233-5274; *E-Mail:* itaub@natick—emh2.army.mil

**TAUB, JAMES M,** NUCLEAR ENGINEERING, MATERIALS SCIENCE. *Current Pos:* RETIRED. *Personal Data:* b Cleveland, Ohio, July 26, 18; m 43, Selma S Pearlman; c Janet B & Judith A. *Educ:* Case Western Res Univ, BS, 40, MS, 43. *Honors & Awards:* E O Lawrence Award, AEC, 65. *Prof Exp:* Group leader, Los Alamos Nat Lab, 45-75; consult, AEC, Dept Energy, 75-79. *Mem:* Fel Am Soc Metals Int; Am Nuclear Soc. *Mailing Add:* 5686 N Camino de la Noche Tucson AZ 85718

**TAUB, JESSE J,** ELECTRICAL ENGINEERING, PHYSICS. *Current Pos:* CHIEF SCIENTIST, AIL SYSTS INC, 75- *Personal Data:* b New York, NY, Apr 27, 27; m 55; c 3. *Educ:* City Col New York, BEE, 48; Polytech Inst Brooklyn, MEE, 49. *Honors & Awards:* Centennial Medal, Inst Elec & Electronics Engrs, 84. *Prof Exp:* Engr, US Naval Mat Lab, 49-51, group leader, 51-55; engr, AIL Div, Eaton Corp, 55-58, group leader, 58, sect head, 58-60, dept consult, 60-66, div consult, 66-75. *Concurrent Pos:* Mem staff, Grad Sch, City Col New York, 59-61. *Mem:* Fel Inst Elec & Electronics Engrs; Sigma Xi; Asn Old Crows. *Res:* Microwave device development; millimeter and submillimeter techniques; mixers and mixer diodes; multimode power measurements; microwave network synthesis; gallium arsenide integrated circuits. *Mailing Add:* AIL Systs Inc Commack Rd Deer Park NY 11729

**TAUB, JOHN MARCUS,** PSYCHOPHYSIOLOGY. *Personal Data:* b Chicago, Ill, July 26, 47. *Educ:* Univ Calif, Santa Cruz, AB, 69, MS & PhD(biopsychol), 72. *Prof Exp:* Res biopsychologist, Univ Calif, Santa Cruz, 72-73; fel neurosci, Brain Res Inst, Univ Calif, Los Angeles, 73-75; dir, Sleep & Dream Lab & asst prof psychiat & psychol, Sch Med, Univ Va, 75-78; assoc res prof & dir, Sleep & Performance Lab, St Louis Univ, 78-83. *Concurrent Pos:* NIMH fel, Univ Calif, Los Angeles Brain Res Inst & Dept Psychiat,73-75. *Mem:* AAAS; Sleep Res Soc; Soc Neurosci. *Res:* Investigations on the behavioral and psychophysiological effects of acute and chronic variations in the length and time of sleep in young adults; biological rhythms; sleep and human performance. *Mailing Add:* 7323 Hoover Ave Apt B3 Richmond Heights MO 63117

**TAUB, MARY L,** ANIMAL CELL CULTURE, ENDOCRINOLOGY. *Current Pos:* asst prof, 79-85, ASSOC PROF BIOCHEM, SCH MED, STATE UNIV NY BUFFALO, 85- *Personal Data:* b Chicago, Ill, Sept 26, 48. *Educ:* Univ Calif, San Diego, BA, 71, Santa Barbara, MA, 75, PhD(biol), 76. *Prof Exp:* Teaching fel biochem & cell biol, Dept Biol, Univ Calif, San Diego, 76-79. *Mem:* Am Soc Cell Biol; AAAS; Am Women Sci. *Res:* Mechanisms by which hormones and other regulatory factors control animal cell growth and expression of differentiated function; kidney cell culture, serum free medium; somatic genetics; primary cell culture. *Mailing Add:* Dept Biochem 140 Farber Hall State Univ NY Buffalo Health Sci Ctr 3435 Main St Buffalo NY 14214-4028. Fax: 716-829-2725

**TAUB, ROBERT NORMAN,** ONCOLOGY, HEMATOLOGY. *Current Pos:* co-dir, Comprehensive Cancer Ctr, 81-85, PROF CLIN MED, COL PHYSICIANS & SURGEONS, COLUMBIA UNIV, 81- *Personal Data:* b Brooklyn, NY, Apr 21, 36; m 68; c 1. *Educ:* Yeshiva Univ, AB, 57; Yale Univ, MD, 61; Univ London, PhD(biol), 69. *Honors & Awards:* Emil Conason Mem Res Award, Mt Sinai Sch Med, 71. *Prof Exp:* Intern med, New Eng Med Ctr Hosps, Boston, 61-62; intern path, Sch Med, Yale Univ, 62-63; clin & res fel hemat, New Eng Med Ctr Hosps, 63-65, asst resident med, 65-66; NIH res fel immunol, Nat Inst Med Res, London, 66-68; assoc hemat, Mt Sinai Sch Med, 68-69, asst prof med, 69-72, assoc prof med, 72-76, head transplantation immunol lab, Mt Sinai Hosp, 70-76; prof & chmn, Med Col Va, Richmond, 76-81, assoc dir, Va Commonwealth Univ Cancer Ctr, 77-81. *Concurrent Pos:* Res fel path, Sch Med, Yale Univ, 62-63; Leukemia Soc Am scholar award, 68-73; attend physician, Mt Sinai Hosp, 69-70; USPHS res career develop award, 75-; Am Cancer Soc prof clin oncol, 77-; co-dir, Columbia Comprehensive Cancer Ctr, 81- *Mem:* Transplantation Soc; Am Soc Clin Invest; Am Soc Hemat; Am Asn Immunologists; Am Soc Exp Path; Am Soc Clin Oncol; Am Asn Cancer Res. *Res:* Cancer cell biology; immunology of cancer and leukemia. *Mailing Add:* Dept Med Columbia Univ 630 W 168th St New York NY 10032-3702

**TAUB, STEPHAN ROBERT,** COMPUTER, APPLICATIONS IN BIOLOGY. *Current Pos:* chmn dept, 74-77, PROF BIOL, GEORGE MASON UNIV, FAIRFAX, 74- *Personal Data:* b Jamaica, NY, Nov 30, 33; m 63; c 2. *Educ:* Rochester Univ, AB, 55; Univ Ind, PhD(zool), 60. *Prof Exp:* Instr biol, Harvard Univ, 60-63; asst prof, Princeton Univ, 63-69; from asst prof to assoc prof, Richmond Col, City Univ New York, 69-74. *Mem:* AAAS; Genetics Soc Am; Am Soc Cell Biol. *Res:* Extra-chromosomal and developmental genetics; population genetics, trends in amair populations. *Mailing Add:* Dept Biol George Mason Univ 4400 University Dr Fairfax VA 22030-4443

**TAUBE, HENRY,** INORGANIC CHEMISTRY. *Current Pos:* prof chem, Stanford Univ, 62-86, chmn dept, 72-74 & 78-79, Marguerite Blake Wilbur Endowed prof, 76-88, EMER MARGUERITE BLAKE WILBUR PROF CHEM, STANFORD UNIV, 86- *Personal Data:* b Neudorf, Sask, Nov 30, 15; nat US; m 40, 52; c 4. *Educ:* Univ Sask, BS, 35, MS, 37; Univ Calif, PhD(chem), 40. *Hon Degrees:* LLD, Univ Sask, 73; DSc, Univ Chicago, 83, Polytech Inst NY, 84, State Univ NY, 85, Univ Guelph, 87, Seton Hall Univ, 88, Lajos Kossuth Univ, Hungary, 88 & Northwestern Univ, 90; HD, Univ Athens, 93. *Honors & Awards:* Nobel Prize in Chem, 83; Award, Am Chem Soc, 55, Howe Award, 60; Chandler Award, Columbia Univ, 64; Kirkwood Award, Yale Univ & Am Chem Soc, 66; Monsanto Co, 81; Nat Medal of Sci, 77; Chem Sci Award, Nat Acad Sci, 83; Baylor Medal, Univ Ill, 83; Robert A Welch Found Award, 83; Priestly Medal, Am Chem Soc, 85; Distinguished Achievement Award, Int Precious Metals Inst, 86. *Prof Exp:* Instr chem, Univ Calif, 40-41; from instr to asst prof, Cornell Univ, 41-46; res assoc, Nat Defense Res Comt, 44-45; from asst prof to prof chem, Univ Chicago, 46-61, chmn dept, 55-59. *Concurrent Pos:* Guggenheim fel, 49 & 55; corresp mem, Acad Arts & Sci PR, 85; consult, Catalytica Assocs, Inc, Mountain View, Calif. *Mem:* Nat Acad Sci; Am Chem Soc; Am Acad Arts & Sci; Am Philos Soc; hon mem Hungarian Acad Sci; hon mem Can Chem Soc; Sigma Xi; Royal Danish Acad Sci & Lett; foreign mem Finnish Acad Sci & Lett; corresp mem Brazilian Acad Sci; hon fel Royal Soc Chem; hon fel Indian Chem Soc;

foreign mem Royal Soc; foreign assoc Eng Acad Sci; hon mem Chem Soc Japan. *Res:* Chemistry of complex ions; new aquo ions, nitrogen as a ligand; mechanisms of atom and electron transfer reactions; mixed valence molecules; charge transfer as affecting properties including the reactivity of ligands; basic chemistry of osmium and nuthenium; over 375 scientific articles and a book published. *Mailing Add:* Dept Chem Stanford Univ Stanford CA 94305

**TAUBE, SHEILA EFRON,** CANCER DIAGNOSIS, DEVELOPMENTAL RESEARCH. *Current Pos:* PROG DIR BIOCHEM & GENETICS, NAT CANCER INST, NIH, 83-, BR CHIEF CANCER DIAG PROG, 86- *Personal Data:* b New York, NY, Aug 5, 41; m 65; c 2. *Educ:* Brandeis Univ, BA, 63; Univ Pittsburg, PhD(microbiol), 70. *Honors & Awards:* Dir's Award, NIH. *Prof Exp:* Assoc human genetics, Yale Univ Sch Med, 71-73; from instr to asst prof microbiol, Univ Conn Med Sch, 73-81; prog dir genetics, NSF, 81-82; grants assoc, NIH, 82-83. *Concurrent Pos:* Prin investr, NIH, 76-79 & Univ Conn res found grant, 79- 80. *Mem:* Am Asn Cancer Res; Am Soc Human Genetics; AAAS; Am Women Sci. *Res:* Direct program to develop improved approaches to cancer diagnosis and prognosis. *Mailing Add:* Nat Cancer Inst Exec Plaza N Rm 700 Bethesda MD 20852

**TAUBENECK, WILLIAM HARRIS,** PETROLOGY. *Current Pos:* From instr to prof, 51-84, EMER PROF GEOL, ORE STATE UNIV, 84- *Personal Data:* b Marshall, Ill, Aug 27, 23. *Educ:* Ore State Col, BS, 49, MS, 50; Columbia Univ, PhD(geol), 55. *Concurrent Pos:* NSF fel, 59-61; Guggenheim fel, 63-64. *Mem:* AAAS; Geol Soc Am; Mineral Soc Am. *Res:* Layering in igneous rocks; petrogenesis of granite rocks; Columiba River basalt group including feeder dikes; general geology of northeastern Oregon and western Idaho; evolution of the Pacific Northwest. *Mailing Add:* Dept Geosci Wilkinson Hall 104 Ore State Univ Corvallis OR 97331-5506

**TAUBER, ALFRED IMRE,** NEUTROPHIL BIOCHEMISTRY, CELL BIOLOGY. *Current Pos:* assoc res prof biochem, Boston Univ, 82-86, assoc prof med, 82-86, assoc prof path, 85-86, PROF MED, SCH MED, BOSTON UNIV, 86-, PROF PATH, 87- *Personal Data:* b Washington, DC, June 24, 47; m 66, Swerdlow; c Joel, Dylan, Benjamin & Hana. *Educ:* Tufts Univ, BS, 69, MD, 73. *Prof Exp:* From instr to asst prof med, Med Sch, Harvard Univ, 78-82; jr assoc, Peter Bent Brigham Hosp-Brigham & Women's Hosp, 79-82. *Concurrent Pos:* Consult, US Pub Serv Hosp, Brighton, Mass, 80-82, Boston Vet Admin Hosp, 83-; consult, US Pub Serv Hosp, Brighton, Mass, 80-82, Boston Vet Admin Hosp, 83-; assoc physician, Boston City Hosp, 82-, chief hemat/one sect, 82-91, dir labs, 84-91; assoc staff, Univ Hosp, 83-; dir, Boston Univ Sch Med-Hebrew Univ Exchange Prog, 85-87. *Mem:* Am Fedn Clin Res; Am Soc Hemat; Am Col Physicians; Soc Free Radical Res; Am Soc Biol Chemists; Am Soc Clin Invest; Am Soc Cell Biol; Am Asn Immunol; Asn Am Physicians. *Res:* Elucidation of the mechanisms of oxidative microbial killing by human neutrophil; cell activation pathways; oxidative enzymology; chemistry of the oxygen-derived reactive species. *Mailing Add:* Boston Univ Sch Med 80 E Concord St Boston MA 02118

**TAUBER, ARTHUR,** CHEMISTRY, MAGNETISM. *Current Pos:* CONSULT, 87- *Personal Data:* b New York, NY, June 2, 28; m 56; c 3. *Educ:* NY Univ, BA, 51, MA, 52; Polytech Inst Brooklyn, MS, 59, PhD, 72. *Honors & Awards:* Meritorious Civilian Serv Medal, US Dept Army, 63. *Prof Exp:* Phys chemist, Sig Corps Eng Labs, 52-56, res phys scientist, Electronics Res & Develop Labs, 56-63; electronics command, US Army, 63-75, electronic res & develop command, ET&D Lab, 75-80, res phys scientist supvr, electronic res develop command, ET&D, Lab, 80-85, res phys scientist supvr, Labcom, ET&D Lab, 85-87. *Concurrent Pos:* Res & Develop Award, US Army, 63 & 83. *Mem:* Am Chem Soc; Inst Elec & Electronics Engrs; Am Crystallog Asn; Am Asn Crystal Growth. *Res:* Synthesize and characterize polycrystalline and single crystal microwave/millimeter wave ferrites; samarium cobalt permanent magnets; amorphous magnetics; intermetallic hydrogen absorbers; high Tc superconductors. *Mailing Add:* 927 Woodgate Ave Elberon NJ 07740

**TAUBER, CATHERINE A,** BIOSYSTEMATICS, INSECT SEASONALITY. *Current Pos:* NIH res fel, 67-69, res assoc, 69-76, SR RES ASSOC, CORNELL UNIV, 66- *Personal Data:* b San Francisco, Calif. *Educ:* Univ Calif, Berkeley, BS, 62, MS, 64, PhD(entom), 67. *Mem:* Entom Soc Am; Soc Study Evolution; Soc Syst Zoologists; Sigma Xi. *Res:* Seasonal adaptations, evolutionary diversification and speciation of insects with special emphasis on the Neuroptora. *Mailing Add:* Dept Entom Comstock Hall Cornell Univ Ithaca NY 14853-0901

**TAUBER, MAURICE JESSE,** ENTOMOLOGY. *Current Pos:* Chmn dept, 81-86, PROF ENTOM, CORNELL UNIV, 66- *Personal Data:* b Cracow, Can, Oct 21, 37; m 66, Catherine Ann; c Paul, Michael & Agatha. *Educ:* Univ Man, BS, 58, MS, 59; Univ Calif, Berkeley, PhD, 66. *Mem:* Fel AAAS; Am Soc Zool; Animal Behav Soc; Ecol Soc Am; Am Inst Biol Sci; Sigma Xi; fel Entom Soc Can; Soc Study Evolution. *Res:* Insect behavior; biological control; insect phenology. *Mailing Add:* Dept Entom Comstock Hall Cornell Univ Ithaca NY 14853-0901. Fax: 607-255-0939; E-Mail: mjt4@cornell.edu

**TAUBER, RICHARD NORMAN,** SEMICONDUCTOR DEVICE TECHNOLOGY, VERY LARGE SCALE & ULTRA LARGE SCALE INTEGRATION DEVICE PROCESSING. *Current Pos:* DIR STRATEGIC TECHNOL, APPL MAT, INC, 93- *Personal Data:* b New York, NY, Apr 7, 40; m 63; c Steven C & Laura R. *Educ:* NY Univ, BA & BMetE, 61, MS, 64, PhD(mat sci), 66. *Prof Exp:* Asst prof mat sci, Lehigh Univ, 66-69; mem tech staff, Bell Tel Labs, 69-74; mgr, Gould Inc, 74-75,

Xerox Corp, 75-77 & Hughes, 77-78; chief scientist, TRW, 78-89; pres, Microelectronics Educ Assocs, 89-93. *Mem:* Inst Elec & Electronics Engrs; Sigma Xi. *Res:* Microelectronics industry; ultra large scale integration technology and manufacturing; technological issues; process equipment; manufacturing issues; marketing directions and seminar development; author of one book. *Mailing Add:* 2661 Pescara Ct Campbell CA 95008. *Fax:* 408-986-2826; *E-Mail:* RichT69989@aol.com

**TAUBER, SELMO,** APPLIED MATHEMATICS. *Current Pos:* RETIRED. *Personal Data:* b Shanghai, China, Aug 24, 20; nat US; m 50; c 1. *Educ:* Beirut Sch Eng, Lebanon, dipl, 43; Univ Lyons, France, Lices-Sc, 47; Univ Vienna, Austria, DrPhil, 50. *Prof Exp:* Head sci dept, High Sch, Lebanon, 51-55; design engr, 56-57; from instr to asst prof, Univ Kans, 57-59; assoc prof, Portland State Univ, 59-63, prof math, 63-90. *Res:* Engineering structural problems; finite differences; differential equations; combinatorial analysis; system analysis; mathematical models in air pollution; mathematical models in physiology. *Mailing Add:* 2839 SW Fairmont Blvd Portland OR 97201-1442

**TAUBERT, KATHRYN ANNE,** CARDIOVASCULAR PHYSIOLOGY. *Current Pos:* SR SCI CONSULT, NAT OFF, AM HEART ASN, 85- *Personal Data:* b Lufkin, Tex, Jan 3, 45. *Educ:* Stephen F Austin State Univ, BS, 65, MS, 66; Univ Tex Southwestern Med Sch, PhD(physiol), 75. *Prof Exp:* Res asst cardiol, Univ Tex Southwestern Med Sch, 66-68; physiologist, Dallas Vet Admin Hosp, 68-75; instr, Univ Tex Southwestern Med Sch, 75-77; asst prof physiol, Univ Calif, Riverside, 77-80; assoc prof physiol & pharmacol, Sch Pharm, Univ Pac, 80-85. *Concurrent Pos:* Fel, Univ Tex Health Sci Ctr, 75; NIH investr, Univ Calif, Riverside, 77-80; prin investr, Calif Heart Asn, 78-81 & 81-85; adj assoc prof physiol, Univ Tex Southwestern Med Sch, 85- *Mem:* Am Heart Asn; Am Fedn Clin Res; Am Physiol Soc; Int Soc Heart Res; Int Soc Hypertension Blacks; Sigma Xi; Am Soc Microbiol. *Res:* Diagnosis, treatment, and prevention of infectious diseases of the heart, including rheumatic fever, endocarditis, and kawasaki disease. *Mailing Add:* Am Heart Asn 7320 Greenville Ave Dallas TX 75231-4596. *Fax:* 214-373-0268

**TAUBES, CLIFFORD H,** GEOMETRY. *Current Pos:* PROF MATH, HARVARD UNIV. *Honors & Awards:* Oswald Veblen Geom Prize, Am Math Soc, 91. *Mem:* Nat Acad Sci. *Mailing Add:* Dept Math Harvard Univ Cambridge MA 02138

**TAUBLER, JAMES H,** MICROBIOLOGY. *Current Pos:* asst prof, 69-71, PROF BIOL, ST VINCENT COL, 71-, CHMN DEPT, 85- *Personal Data:* b Cokeville, Pa, Mar 30, 35; m 59, 80; c 3. *Educ:* St Vincent Col, BA, 57; Cath Univ, MS, 59, PhD(microbiol), 65. *Prof Exp:* Microbiologist, Philadelphia Gen Hosp, 59-69. *Concurrent Pos:* Lectr, Holy Family Col, Pa, 66-; dir, Delmont Labs, Swarthmore, 66-; Environ Protection Agency grant, 75-77; mem, Pa State Task Force, health care needs AIDS patients. *Mem:* NY Acad Sci. *Res:* Staphylococcal alpha toxin and its relationship to pathogenesis; delayed hypersensitivity and its effects in staphylococcal infections. *Mailing Add:* Dept Biol St Vincent Col 300 Fraser Purchase Latrobe PA 15650-2667

**TAUBMAN, MARTIN ARNOLD,** IMMUNOLOGY, ORAL BIOLOGY. *Current Pos:* from asst clin prof to assoc clin prof, Dept Oral Biol & Pathophysiol, Harvard Sch Dent Med, 76-97, PROF, DEPT ORAL BIOL, SCH DENT MED, HARVARD MED SCH, 97-; HEAD, DEPT IMMUNOL, FORSYTH DENT CTR, 72-, SR MEM STAFF, 80- *Personal Data:* b New York, NY, July 10, 40; m 65, Joan P Mikelbank; c Ben & Joel. *Educ:* Brooklyn Col, BS, 61; Columbia Univ, DDS, 65; State Univ NY Buffalo, PhD(immunol/oral biol), 70. *Honors & Awards:* Merit Award, NIH, 91; Oral Biol Award, Int Asn Dent Res, 91. *Prof Exp:* Asst mem staff, Immunochem Sect, Forsyth Dent Ctr, Boston, 70-74, assoc mem staff & head, 74-80. *Concurrent Pos:* USPHS res career develop award, 71-76, Nat Inst Dent Res grant, Forsyth Dent Ctr, 72-; mem, Oral Biol & Med Study Sect, 80-84; pres, Am Asn Dent Res, 87-91. *Mem:* Am Asn Immunologists; Int Asn Dent Res; Am Soc Microbiol; Soc Mucosal Immunol. *Res:* Secretory immunoglobulins; effect of secretory antibodies on oral microorganisms; immune regulation and T cells in periodontal diseases; dental caries vaccine. *Mailing Add:* Forsyth Dent Ctr 140 Fenway Boston MA 02115. *Fax:* 617-262-4021; *E-Mail:* mtaubman@forsyth.org

**TAUBMAN, ROBERT EDWARD,** PSYCHIATRY, PSYCHOLOGY. *Current Pos:* assoc prof, 64-70, PROF PSYCHIAT, MED SCH, UNIV ORE, 70- *Personal Data:* b New York, NY, Jan 12, 21; m 43; c 3. *Educ:* City Col New York, BA, 41; Columbia Univ, MS, 42, PhD(psychol), 48; Univ Nebr, MD, 60. *Prof Exp:* Chief psychol serv, Hastings State Hosp, Nebr, 52-56; resident physician psychiat, Ore State Hosp, Salem, 61-64. *Concurrent Pos:* NIMH fel ment retardation, Letchworth Village, Thiells, NY, 62; consult, Ore Fairview Home, Div Voc Rehab, Marion Co Juv Dept, 62-64; pvt pract, 64-; attend physician, Vet Admin Hosp, Portland, Ore, 64-; psychiat dir, Physicians Inst, Ore Acad Family Physicians, 65- *Mem:* Am Pyschiat Asn; AMA; Soc Teachers Family Med. *Res:* Aging; dying; death; self growth among physicians and other professionals; emotional components of life-threatening diseases; psychiatry for non-psychiatric physicians. *Mailing Add:* 5242 SW Humphrey Blvd Portland OR 97221

**TAUBMAN, SHELDON BAILEY,** immunology, pathology, for more information see previous edition

**TAUC, JAN,** AMORPHOUS SEMICONDUCTORS. *Current Pos:* L Herbert Ballou prof, 70-92, dir, Mat Res Lab, 83-88, EMER L HERBERT BALLOU PROF ENG & PHYSICS, BROWN UNIV, 92- *Personal Data:* b Pardubice, Czech, Apr 15, 22; m 47, Vera Koubelova; c Elena (Kokta) & Jan Jr. *Educ:* Czech Tech Univ, IngDr, 49; Czech Acad Sci, DrSc(physics), 56; Charles Univ, Prague, RNDr, 56. *Honors & Awards:* Nat Prize for Sci, Czech Govt, 55 & 69; Alexander von Humboldt US Sr Scientist Award, 81; Isakson Prize, Am Phys Soc, 82; D Adler Lect Award, Am Phys Soc, 88; Hlavka Medal, Czech Acad Sci, 92; Silver Medal, Union Czech Mathematicians & Physicists, 92. *Prof Exp:* Scientist microwave res, Sci & Tech Res Inst, Tanvald & Prague, Czech, 49-52; dept head inst solid state physics, Czech Acad Sci, 53-69; prof exp physics, Charles Univ, Prague, 64-69; dir inst physics, 68-69; mem tech staff, Bell Labs, 69-70. *Concurrent Pos:* UNESCO res fel, Harvard Univ, 61-62; vis prof, Univ Paris, 69 & Stanford Univ, 77; consult, Bell Labs, 70-78; vis scientist, Max Planck Inst Solid State Res, Stuttgart, WGer, 82. *Mem:* Nat Acad Sci; fel Am Phys Soc; fel AAAS. *Res:* Optical properties and electronic states of crystalline and amorphous solids; picosecond spectroscopy of amorphous semiconductors; real time studies of ultra-high frequency phonons. *Mailing Add:* Div Eng Brown Univ Providence RI 02912. *Fax:* 401-863-1157; *E-Mail:* Jan_Tauc@brown.edu

**TAUCHERT, THEODORE R,** SOLID MECHANICS. *Current Pos:* assoc prof, 70-76, PROF ENG MECH, UNIV KY, 76-, CHMN, DEPT ENG MECH, 80-84 & 89- *Personal Data:* b New York, NY, Sept 3, 35; m 58, Ann Bradlee; c Amy, Charles, Sarah, Rebecca & Macy. *Educ:* Princeton Univ, BSE, 57; Yale Univ, MEng, 60, DEng(solid mech), 64. *Prof Exp:* Struct engr, Sikorsky Aircraft Div, United Aircraft Corp, 57-61; res assoc & lectr solid mech, Princeton Univ, 64-65, asst prof, 65-70. *Mem:* Am Soc Eng Educ; Sigma Xi; Am Soc Civil Engrs; Am Soc Mech Engrs; Soc Eng Sci. *Res:* Composite materials; thermal stresses. *Mailing Add:* Dept Eng Mech Univ Ky Lexington KY 40506-0001. *Fax:* 606-257-3342; *E-Mail:* tauchert@ukcc.uky.edu

**TAUER, JANE E,** RHEOLOGY, ASPHALT RESEARCH. *Current Pos:* PRIN RES SCIENTIST, WESTERN RES INST, 90- *Personal Data:* b Teaneck, NJ, Sept 13, 52; m 78, Victor Lawnicki. *Educ:* Fairleigh Dickenson Univ, BS, 74. *Prof Exp:* Mem tech staff, Hughes Aircraft, 78-81; sr test engr, Ford Aerospace, 81-82, Northrup Corp, 82-84, Precision Monlithics Inc, 84-87; consult, 87-90. *Mem:* Am Phys Soc. *Res:* Asphalt and asphalt mix rheology; asphalt and crumb rubber interactions. *Mailing Add:* Western Res Inst PO Box 3395 Laramie WY 82071-3395. *Fax:* 307-721-2300

**TAUER, KENNETH J,** PHYSICAL CHEMISTRY, CHEMICAL PHYSICS. *Current Pos:* MEM RES STAFF, MAT RES AGENCY LAB, US ARMY MAT & MECH RES CTR, 57- *Personal Data:* b Minn, Apr 5, 23; m 44; c 4. *Educ:* Univ Minn, PhD, 51. *Prof Exp:* Researcher, Gen Elec Co, Wash, 51-53; asst prof chem, Boston Col, 53-56. *Mem:* Am Chem Soc; Am Phys Soc. *Res:* Electronics structure of transition metals and alloys; magnetism; electronic transport; magnetoresistance; Hall effect. *Mailing Add:* 23 Old Tavern Rd Cochituate MA 01778-5034

**TAULBEE, CARL D(ONALD),** MECHANICAL ENGINEERING, NUCLEAR ENGINEERING. *Current Pos:* SR MECH ENGR, RUBY & ASSOCS, 93- *Personal Data:* b Detroit, Mich, Oct 18, 28; div; c Carl R & Gale A. *Educ:* Wayne State Univ, BSME, 53, MSME, 59. *Prof Exp:* Engr, Studebaker-Packard Corp, 53-56; suprvy engr, Res Lab Div, Bendix Corp, 56-73; spec proj mgr, Door-Man Mfg Co, 73-79; pres, Am Indust Doors, 79-89; sr mech engr, Mult Dynamics, 90-93. *Mem:* Am Welding Soc; Am Nuclear Soc; Am Soc Mech Engrs; Nat Soc Prof Engrs. *Res:* Nuclear power plant products; earth resources; radiation effects; nuclear power and propulsion and gas turbine technologies; nuclear power plant aging. *Mailing Add:* 26 Oakland Park Blvd Pleasant Ridge MI 48069

**TAULBEE, DALE B(RUCE),** AEROSPACE & ENGINEERING SCIENCE. *Current Pos:* DEPT MECH, AEROSPACE ENG, 79- *Personal Data:* b Detroit, Mich, Nov 17, 36; m 58; c 2. *Educ:* Mich State Univ, BS, 58, MS, 60; Univ Ill, PhD(appl mech), 64. *Prof Exp:* Asst prof aerospace eng, State Univ NY, Buffalo, 63-70, assoc prof eng sci, 70-79. *Concurrent Pos:* Tech consult, Bell Aerosysts Co, 66- *Mem:* Am Inst Aeronaut & Astronaut; Am Soc Mech Engrs; Sigma Xi. *Res:* Fluid mechanics, laminar and turbulent boundary layers; gas dynamics, high speed viscous flows. *Mailing Add:* 30 Harbour Pointe Common Buffalo NY 14202

**TAUNTON-RIGBY, ALISON,** BIOTECHNOLOGY, PROTEIN SCIENCE. *Current Pos:* PRES & CHIEF EXEC OFFICER, MITOTIX, INC, 93- *Personal Data:* b Barnsley, Eng, Apr 23, 44; m 66; c Jon, Roy, Josie & Liz. *Educ:* Bristol Univ, BSc, 65, PhD(chem), 68. *Prof Exp:* Vpres res & develop, Collab Res Inc, 69-83; vpres bus develop, Biogen Inc, 83-84; vpres & gen mgr, Vivotech Inc, 84-86; health industs mgr, Arthur D Little Co, 86-87; sr vpres therapeut, Genzyme Corp, 87-93. *Concurrent Pos:* Dir, Asn Biotechnol Co, 84-88, Centaur Inc, 85-87; New Eng Brit Bus Asn, 86-90, Mass Biotech Coun, 90-, Coastal Corp, 92-93 & Synoptic Pharmaceut, 93-; trustee, Worcester Found Exp Biol. *Mem:* AAAS; Am Chem Soc. *Res:* Molecular biology; recombinant DNA; immunology; microbiology; cell biology; glycoproteins; enzymology; biopolymers; carbohydrate chemistry. *Mailing Add:* Farrar Rd Lincoln MA 01773

**TAUROG, ALVIN,** BIOCHEMISTRY, PHYSIOLOGY. *Current Pos:* from assoc prof to prof, 59-87, EMER PROF PHARMACOL, UNIV TEX SOUTHWESTERN MED CTR, DALLAS, 87- *Personal Data:* b St Louis, Mo, Dec 5, 15; wid; c Avraham H & Joel D. *Educ:* Univ Calif, Los Angeles,

BA, 37, MA, 39; Univ Calif, Berkeley, PhD(physiol), 43. *Prof Exp:* Asst chem, Univ Calif, Los Angeles, 37-38; asst physiol, Univ Calif, Berkeley, 42-43, chemist, Radiation Lab, 44-45, res assoc physiol, 46-59. *Concurrent Pos:* Career res award, USPHS, 63-87; distinguished lectr, Am Thyroid Asn, 80. *Mem:* AAAS; Am Chem Soc; Am Soc Biol Chem; Endocrine Soc; Am Thyroid Asn; Sigma Xi. *Res:* Thyroid physiology and biochemistry; iodine metabolism. *Mailing Add:* Dept Pharmacol Univ Tex Southwestern Med Ctr 5323 Harry Hines Blvd Dallas TX 75235-9041

**TAUSSIG, ANDREW,** MICROBIOLOGY, BIOCHEMISTRY. *Current Pos:* BACTERIOLOGIST, MICROBIOL LAB, 69- *Personal Data:* b Budapest, Hungary, Dec 6, 29; Can citizen; m 59, Margaret Peto; c Robert, Peter & Karen. *Educ:* McGill Univ, BSc, 52, PhD(biochem), 55. *Prof Exp:* Res fel biochem, McGill Univ, 55-61; from asst bacteriologist to bacteriologist, Jewish Gen Hosp, 61-67; vis scientist, Dept Biochem, McGill Univ, 67-70. *Concurrent Pos:* Bacteriologist, Bellechasse Hosp, Montreal, 73-84, Jewish Convalescent Hosp, Chomedey & Mt Sinai Hosp, Cote St Luc, Que; dir labs, Mt Sinai Hosp, Cote St Luc, Que, 74-; mem exec coun, Can Col Microbiologists. *Mem:* Am Soc Microbiol; Can Col Microbiolists. *Res:* Nucleic acids of bacteria and bacteriophage; induced enzyme synthesis in bacteria; diagnostic bacteriology. *Mailing Add:* Microbiol Lab 5845 Cote de Neiges Rd Montreal PQ H3S 1Z4 Can

**TAUSSIG, STEVEN J,** INDUSTRIAL MICROBIOLOGY, ENZYMOLOGY. *Current Pos:* RETIRED. *Personal Data:* b Timisoara, Rumania, June 2, 14; US citizen; m 65; c 1. *Educ:* Univ Prague, Czech, Chem Eng, 37; Bucharest Polytech Inst, PhD(biochem), 58. *Prof Exp:* Chemist, Solventul SA, Timisoara, 37-48; asst prof, Polytech Inst Timisoara, 48-57; res fel, Agr Res Inst, Timisoara, 57-59; mgr plant & equip sales, Int Chem Corp, NY, 60-61; tech dir, Pac Labs, Inc, Honolulu, 61-62 & Pac Enzyme Prod, 62-63; res biochemist, Dole Co, Inc, 63-64, dir lab serv, 64-73; pres, Chem Consults Int Inc, Honolulu, 73-94. *Concurrent Pos:* Tech consult, Pac Labs, Inc & Pac Biochem Co, 63- & Monsanto Co, Mo, 64-65. *Mem:* AAAS; Am Chem Soc; Soc Indust Microbiol; Inst Food Technologists. *Res:* Fermentations; bacterial and other hydrolytic enzymes; chemical equilibria in esterification reactions; cancer research; study of effects of Bromelain on cancer. *Mailing Add:* 469 Ena Rd Apt 3212 Honolulu HI 96815-1728

**TAUSSKY, OLGA,** algebraic number theory, integral matrices; deceased, see previous edition for last biography

**TAUTVYDAS, KESTUTIS JONAS,** BIOPROCESSING. *Current Pos:* supvr biol screening & biochem, 79-85, BIOTECHNOL SUPVR, 3M CO, 85- *Personal Data:* b Telsiai, Lithuania, Jan 1, 40; US citizen; m 62; c 4. *Educ:* Univ Md, BS, 63; Cornell Univ, MS, 65; Yale Univ, PhD(cell & molecular develop biol), 69. *Prof Exp:* Res assoc cell biol, Univ Colo, 69-71; asst prof plant physiol, Marquette Univ, 71-79. *Mem:* Am Soc Microbiol. *Res:* Biotransformations. *Mailing Add:* 8182 Hidden Bay Trail Lake Elmo MN 55042

**TAUXE, WELBY NEWLON,** NUCLEAR MEDICINE, CLINICAL PATHOLOGY. *Current Pos:* prof nuclear med & clin path, 72-77, PROF DIAG RADIOL & PATH, COL MED, UNIV ALA, BIRMINGHAM, 77- *Personal Data:* b Knoxville, Tenn, May 24, 24; c 4. *Educ:* Univ Tenn, Knoxville, BS, 44, MD, 50; Univ Minn, Minneapolis, MS, 58. *Prof Exp:* Mayo Found fel, Mayo Clin, 54-58, chief nuclear med dept, 58-72. *Concurrent Pos:* Consult, AEC, 62-70; treas, Am Bd Nuclear Med, 71; consult, Am Nat Stand Inst, 72. *Mem:* Am Soc Clin Path; Soc Nuclear Med. *Res:* Copper kinetics in Wilson's disease; use of radioactive materials in diagnosis. *Mailing Add:* Dept Radiol Univ Pittsburgh Sch Med Pittsburgh PA 15261-0001

**TAVANO, DONALD C,** PUBLIC HEALTH EDUCATION, MEDICAL EDUCATION. *Current Pos:* from asst prof to assoc prof community med, 66-83, PROF, MED EDUC RES & DEVELOP, MICH STATE UNIV, 83- *Personal Data:* b Newark, NY, Aug 26, 36; m 58; c 2. *Educ:* State Univ NY Col Cortland, BS, 60; Univ Ill, MS, 61; Univ Mich, MPH, 63; Mich State Univ, PhD(educ), 71. *Prof Exp:* Instr health educ, State Univ NY Col Cortland, 61-62; dir health educ, Saginaw City & Co Health Depts, 63-65; consult health educ, Mich Dept Pub Health, 65-66. *Concurrent Pos:* Vis lectr, Sch Pub Health, Univ Mich, 72; consult, Mich Dept Educ, 66-, Gov Off Health & Med Affairs & Nat Bd Examrs Osteop Physicians & Surgeons Inc, 75. *Mem:* Soc Pub Health Educ; Am Pub Health Asn; Asn Behav Sci Med Educ; Asn Teachers Prev Med. *Res:* Patient education; the impact of patient education on health care cost containment, patient compliance and treatment outcomes. *Mailing Add:* 2020 Northwest Ave Lansing MI 48906

**TAVARES, ISABELLE IRENE,** MYCOLOGY, LICHENOLOGY. *Current Pos:* Sr lab technician protozool, Univ Calif, 49-52, from herbarium botanist to sr herbarium botanist, 52-68, assoc specialist bot, 68-84, specialist, 84-93, RES ASSOC, UNIV CALIF, BERKELEY, 94- *Personal Data:* b Merced, Calif, Oct 6, 21. *Educ:* Univ Calif, PhD(bot), 59. *Mem:* Mycol Soc Am; Am Bryological & Lichenological Soc; Brit Lichenology Soc; Int Asn Lichenology. *Res:* Laboulbeniales; Usnea. *Mailing Add:* Univ Herbarium 1001 Valley Life Sci Bldg No 2465 Univ Calif Berkeley CA 94720-2465

**TAVARES, STAFFORD EMANUEL,** ELECTRICAL ENGINEERING, CRYPTOGRAPHY & DATA SECURITY. *Current Pos:* asst prof, 70-74, assoc prof, 74-80, PROF ELEC ENG, QUEEN'S UNIV, ONT, 80- *Personal Data:* b Kingston, Jamaica, WI, May 11, 40; Can citizen. *Educ:* McGill Univ, BEng, 62, PhD(elec eng), 68; Calif Inst Technol, MS, 64. *Prof Exp:* Jr res off

elec eng, Nat Res Coun Can Labs, Ottawa, 62-65, asst res off, 65-70. *Concurrent Pos:* Lectr, Carleton Univ, 68-70; Natural Sci & Eng Res Coun Can res grants, Queen's Univ, Ont, 71-; vis assoc prof, Stanford Univ, 77-78; prin invstr, Proj Secure Wireless Commun; sponsor, Telecommunication Res Inst Ont. *Mem:* Inst Elec & Electronics Engrs; Int Asn Cryptologic Res. *Res:* Computer communications; digital communications; error-correcting codes; data encryption and security in computer communications networks. *Mailing Add:* Dept Elec Eng Queen's Univ Walter Light Hall Kingston ON K7L 3N6 Can. *E-Mail:* tavares@ee.queensu.ca

**TAVE, DOUGLAS,** AQUACULTURE, FISH BREEDING. *Current Pos:* CO-OWNER, URANIA UNLIMITED. *Personal Data:* b Oxford, Eng, Dec 13, 49; US citizen; m 78, Katherine Bruner; c Kai S. *Educ:* Coe Col, BA, 71; Univ Ill, MS, 73; Auburn Univ, PhD(aquacult), 79, MEd, 85. *Prof Exp:* Fel fish breeding, Dept Fisheries & Allied Aquacult, Auburn Univ, 74-80, asst prof, 80-81; asst prof aquacult, Dept Entom, fisheries & wildlife, Univ Minn, 81-84; vis scientist, Dept Fisheries & Allied Aquacult, Auburn Univ, 84-89; assoc prof, Dept Aquacult, Univ Ark, Pine Bluff, 89- *Concurrent Pos:* Peace Corps, 75-76. *Mem:* Sigma Xi; World Aquacult Soc. *Res:* Quantitative and mendelian genetic research on tropical and temperate food fish: tilapia, catfishes and baitfishes. *Mailing Add:* 586 N Second St Coos Bay OR 97420

**TAVEL, JUDITH FIBKINS,** INTRODUCTORY COLLEGE-LEVEL SCIENCE EDUCATION. *Current Pos:* From asst prof to assoc prof, 76-88, PROF PHYSICS, DUTCHESS COMMUNITY COL, 88-, HEAD, DEPT MATH, PHYS & COMPUT SCI, 88- *Personal Data:* m 69, Morton; c Phillip A. *Educ:* Vassar Col, BA, 69; State Univ NY, Albany, MS, 71, PhD(physics), 78. *Mem:* Am Asn Physics Teachers. *Res:* Physical science and mathematics education at the introductory college level with an emphasis on retraining the technical workforce and educating the adult learner. *Mailing Add:* 437 Hillside Lake Rd Wappingers Falls NY 12590. *E-Mail:* tavel@sunydutchess.edu

**TAVEL, MORTON,** THEORETICAL PHYSICS. *Current Pos:* from asst prof to assoc prof, 67-74, PROF PHYSICS, VASSAR COL, 74- *Personal Data:* b Brooklyn, NY, June 14, 39; m 69, Judith Fibkins; c Phillip A. *Educ:* City Col New York, BS, 60; Stevens Inst Technol, MS, 62; Yeshiva Univ, PhD(physics), 64. *Prof Exp:* Res assoc, Brookhaven Nat Lab, 64-66, asst scientist, 66-67. *Mem:* Inst Elec & Electronics Engrs; Am Phys Soc. *Res:* Quantum field theory; plasma physics; transport theory. *Mailing Add:* Dept Physics Vassar Col Poughkeepsie NY 12604. *E-Mail:* motavel@vassar.edu

**TAVERAS, JUAN M,** RADIOLOGY. *Current Pos:* RADIOLOGIST-IN-CHIEF, MASS GEN HOSP, BOSTON, 71-; PROF RADIOL, HARVARD MED SCH, 71- *Personal Data:* b Dominican Repub, Sept 27, 19; nat US; m 47; c 3. *Educ:* Norm Sch Santiago, Dominican Repub, BS, 37; Univ Santo Domingo, MD, 43; Univ Pa, MD, 49. *Hon Degrees:* MA, Harvard Univ, 71; DSc, Univ Pedro Henriquez, 87. *Honors & Awards:* Gold Medal, Am Col Radiol; Gold Medal, Am Roentgen Ray Soc; Gold Medal, Radiol Soc NAm, 80; Gold Medal, Asn Univ Radiol. *Prof Exp:* Instr radiol, Col Physicians & Surgeons, Columbia Univ, 50-52, from asst prof to prof, 52-65; prof radiol & chmn dept, Sch Med, Wash Univ, radiologist-in-chief, Barnes & Allied Hosps, Univ Med Ctr & dir, Mallinckrodt Inst Radiol, 65-71; RADIOLOGIST-IN-CHIEF, MASS GEN HOSP, BOSTON, 71- *Concurrent Pos:* Dir radiol, Neurol Inst, New York, 52-65; from asst to attend radiologist, Presby Hosp, New York, 50-65; mem neurol study sect, Nat Inst Neurol Dis & Stroke, 64-68; consult, US Marine Hosp, Staten Island, NY, Bronx Vet Admin Hosp, St Barnabas Hosp Chronic Dis, New York, Morristown Mem Hosp, NJ, St Louis City Hosp & Jewish Hosp, St Louis, 65-71; hon prof med, Univ Santo Domingo & Univ Chile. *Mem:* AMA; Am Neurol Asn; fel Am Col Radiol; Am Roentgen Ray Soc; Am Soc Neuroradiol (pres, 62-64); Radiol Soc NAm; Asn Univ Radiol. *Res:* Radiologic aspect of neurological science, especially cerebral angiography and cerebral vascular disease. *Mailing Add:* Dept Radiol Mass Gen Hosp Fruit St Boston MA 02114

**TAVES, MILTON ARTHUR,** ORGANIC CHEMISTRY. *Current Pos:* CONSULT, 81- *Personal Data:* b Aberdeen, Idaho, Aug 14, 25; m 45, Kathleen M Davies; c Marsha A (Paulson) & Donald E. *Educ:* Univ Utah, BS, 45; Mass Inst Technol, PhD(org chem), 48. *Prof Exp:* Lab asst chem, Univ Utah, 43-45; asst, Mass Inst Technol, 45-46; res chemist, Res Ctr, Hercules, Inc, 48-54, res supvr, 54-60 & 62-64, tech asst to dir res, 60-62, res mgr, Synthetic Res Div, 64-77, new technol coordr, 77-81. *Mem:* Am Chem Soc; Sigma Xi. *Res:* Heterocyclics; hydrogen peroxide; hydroperoxide chemistry; auto-oxidation and catalytic oxidation of organic compounds; terpenes; condensation polymers; resins; plasticizers; chemicals via fermentation; immobilized enzyme technology; process development; agricultural chemicals. *Mailing Add:* 210 N Spring Valley Rd Wilmington DE 19807-2427

**TAVILL, ANTHONY SYDNEY,** GASTROENTEROLOGY, HEPATOLOGY. *Current Pos:* PROF MED & NUTRIT, CASE WESTERN RES UNIV, 75-; MATHILE & MORTON STONE CHAIR DIGESTIVE & LIVER DIS, MT SINAI MED CTR, CLEVELAND, 91- *Personal Data:* b Manchester, Eng, July 15, 36; m 59, Anne Rayburn; c Leanore, Michael & Stephanie. *Educ:* Univ Manchester, MB & ChB, 60, MD, 70; Royal Col Physicians London, MRCP, 63, FRCP, 78, FACP, 96. *Prof Exp:* Med Res Coun travelling fel med, Albert Einstein Col Med, 66-68; lectr, Royal Free Hosp, Sch Med, Univ London, 68-71; sr clin scientist, Div Clin Invest, Med Res Coun Clin Res Ctr, Eng, 71-72, consult gastroenterol & liver dis, 72-75. *Mem:* Fel Am Col Physicians; Brit Soc Gastroenterol; Am Col Gastroenterol; Am Asn Study Liver Dis; Int Asn Study Liver; Am Gastroenterol Asn. *Res:*

Control mechanisms in hepatic protein metabolism in gastrointestinal and renal disease, homeostasis of plasma transport proteins and metabolic interrelationships between iron transport and storage proteins of the liver; hepatotoxicity of iron; hemochromatosis. *Mailing Add:* Friedman Ctr Digestive & Liver Dis Mt Sinai Med Ctr Cleveland OH 44106. *Fax:* 216-421-5789

**TAVLARIDES, LAWRENCE LASKY,** SEPARATIONS, KINETICS. *Current Pos:* chmn, Dept Chem Eng & Mat Sci, 81-85, assoc dean, Grad Affairs & Res, Col Eng & Comput Sci, 95-96, PROF CHEM ENGR, SYRACUSE UNIV, 85- *Personal Data:* b Wilkinsburg, Pa, Jan 8, 42; m 65, Alexandra Pappas; c Muostula & Phaedra (Honz). *Educ:* Univ Pittsburgh, BSChE, 63, MS, 64, PhD(chem eng), 68. *Prof Exp:* Engr, Mobay Chem Co, 62; chem engr, Gulf Res & Develop Co, 64-66 & 68; fel photochem reactions, Delft Univ Technol, 68-69; from asst prof to prof, Ill Inst Technol, 69-81. *Concurrent Pos:* Consult, CPC Int, Inc, 70-78, Res Inst, Ill Inst Technol, 73-77 & Exxon, 84-; NSF res grants, 71-72, 75, 77, 78, 82, 83, 85, 86-87, 87-88 & 91-93; Dept Energy grants, 79-86; Dept Defense, Naval Surface Weapons Ctr, 85-87; NY State Ctr Hazardous Waste Mgt, 88-91; NY State Energy & Res Develop Authority, 89-91; Nat Inst Environ Health & Sci, 90-91; ed, Solvent Extraction & Ion Exchange; affil staff scientist, Pac Northwest Labs, 94-97. *Mem:* AAAS; fel Am Inst Chem Engrs; Am Chem Soc. *Res:* Metal extraction in liquid dispersions; droplet rate processes in liquid dispersions; mixing in liquid dispersions; kinetics of metal extraction; Fischer-Tropsch kinetics; chemical reaction engineering; plasma reactors and reactions; supercritical extraction and supercritical wet oxidation for soils remediation; supercritical fluid technology; synthesis of inorganic chemically active supports for metal ion separations from aqueous streams. *Mailing Add:* Dept Chem Eng & Mat Sci 334 Hinds Hall Syracuse Univ Syracuse NY 13244

**TAVOULARIS, STAVROS,** FLUID MECHANICS, EXPERIMENTAL TECHNIQUES. *Current Pos:* from asst prof to assoc prof, 80-83, PROF MECH ENG, UNIV OTTAWA, 88- *Personal Data:* b Athens, Greece, June 16, 50; Can citizen; m 78, Sofia Hashemi; c Christina & Jason. *Educ:* Nat Tech Univ Greece, dipl eng, 73; Va Polytech Inst & State Univ, MSc, 74; Johns Hopkins Univ, PhD(fluid mech), 78. *Prof Exp:* Assoc res scientist, Dept Chem Eng, Johns Hopkins Univ, 79-80. *Concurrent Pos:* Chmn, Dept Mech Eng, Univ Ottawa, 87-90; dir, Ottawa-Carleton Inst Mech & Aerospace Eng, 90-96. *Mem:* Am Phys Soc; Sigma Xi. *Res:* Fluid mechanics, especially turbulent flows; structure of turbulent shear flows; turbulent diffusion and mixing; flow in nuclear reactor rod bundles; hemodynamics of cardiac assist devices; pulsatile flows; aerodynamics. *Mailing Add:* Dept Mech Eng Univ Ottawa 770 King Edward Ave Ottawa ON K1N 6N5 Can. *Fax:* 613-562-5177; *E-Mail:* tav@eng.uottawa.ca

**TAX, ANNE W,** IMMUNOLOGY. *Current Pos:* PVT PRACT, 91-; LECTR NURSING CTR ADVAN CARE & SERIOUS ILLNESS, NURSING SCH, UNIV PA, 92- *Personal Data:* b New York, NY, May 7, 44; m 68; c 2. *Educ:* Rutgers Univ, BA, 66; Cornell Univ, PhD(microbiol), 71; Temple Univ, MEd, 87; Union Inst, PhD(psych/clin), 92. *Prof Exp:* Head radioimmunoassay lab, Meloy Labs, 71-73; asst prof tumor immunol, Wistar Inst, 73-86. *Mem:* AAAS; Am Asn Immunologists; Am Asn Cancer Res. *Res:* Immunology to produce and utilize monoclonal antibodies to detect cell surface antigens; virology; tumor viruses; molecular biology. *Mailing Add:* 9733 Bustleton Ave Suite 2N Philadelphia PA 19115

**TAYA, MINORU,** APPLIED MECHANICS, MATERIALS SCIENCE. *Current Pos:* assoc prof, 86-89, PROF MECH ENG, UNIV WASH, 90- *Personal Data:* b Yokosuka, Japan, Sept 19, 44; m 76; c 3. *Educ:* Univ Tokyo, BS, 68; Northwestern Univ, MS, 73, PhD(ductile fracture), 77. *Prof Exp:* Design engr stress analysis, Sumitomo Heavy Industs Co Ltd, Japan, 68-71 & 73-76; fel mech property of porous media, Northwestern Univ, 77-78; from asst prof to assoc prof, Univ Del, 83-86. *Mem:* Am Acad Mech; Am Soc Mech Engrs; Am Inst Mineral Eng; Am Ceramic Soc. *Res:* Solid mech; thermo-mechanical properties of composite materials; manufacturing process of composite materials; impact physics; electrical packaging materials. *Mailing Add:* Dept Mech Eng Box 352600 Univ Wash Seattle WA 98195

**TAYAMA, HARRY K,** HORTICULTURE, FLORICULTURE. *Current Pos:* from asst prof to assoc prof, 64-67, PROF HORT, OHIO AGR RES & DEVELOP CTR, OHIO STATE UNIV, 70- *Personal Data:* b Los Angeles, Calif, May 26, 35; m 61; c 2. *Educ:* Univ Ill, BS, 58, MS, 59; Ohio State Univ, PhD(hort), 63. *Honors & Awards:* Kenneth Post Award, 66. *Prof Exp:* Asst prof hort, Pa State Univ, 63-64. *Concurrent Pos:* Exec dir & ed, Ohio Florists' Asn Bull, 77- *Mem:* Am Soc Hort Sci. *Res:* Ecological factors affecting growth and flowering of florist crops; plant growth regulators. *Mailing Add:* 1318 Carron Dr Columbus OH 43220

**TAYBACK, MATTHEW,** PUBLIC HEALTH. *Current Pos:* from asst prof to assoc prof, 52-65, PROF HYG & PUB HEALTH, SCH MED, UNIV MD, BALTIMORE CITY, 65-; ADJ PROF, JOHNS HOPKINS UNIV, 83- *Personal Data:* b Tarrytown, NY, June 30, 19; m 45, Anita Moffat; c Robert, Gordan & Sheila. *Educ:* Harvard Univ, AB, 39; Columbia Univ, AM, 40; Johns Hopkins Univ, ScD(biostatist), 53. *Prof Exp:* Res assoc, NY State Psychiat Inst, 40-42; res statistician, NY State Health Dept, 46-48, dir, Bur Biostatist, Baltimore, 48-53, dir, Statist Sect, 53, asst comnr health, 57-63, dep comnr health, 63-69, asst secy, Health & Ment Hyg & Sci Affairs, 69-73. *Concurrent Pos:* Lectr, Johns Hopkins Univ, 51-; vis prof, Univ Philippines, 57; consult, US Army, 57-, WHO, 60- & USAID, 61-; vchmn, State Comn on Aging, Md, 61-75; chmn, State Adv Bd Price Comn, 72-74; chmn, State Emp Ret Rev Bd, 74-; hon prof community med, Pahlavi Univ, Iran, 78; state

dir on aging, 74-83; vis prof, Univ Jordan Fac Med, 88- *Mem:* Am Pub Health Asn. *Res:* Epidemiology; demography; health services administration; geriatrics clinical trials. *Mailing Add:* Dept Med Mason F Lord Bldg Johns Hopkins Bayview Med Ctr 5200 Eastern Ave Baltimore MD 21224. *Fax:* 301-550-1310

**TAYLOR, A,** METALLURGY, PHYSICS. *Current Pos:* PRES, A&R TAYLOR TRANSL & SCI CONSULT SERV, 73- *Personal Data:* b Manchester, Eng, Aug 20, 11. *Educ:* Manchester Univ, BSc, 33, MSc, 34, PhD(physics), 36. *Hon Degrees:* DSc, Manchester Univ, 67. *Prof Exp:* Sr physicist, Mond Nickel Co, 47-52; sr fel engr, Westinghouse Res Lab, 54-73. *Mem:* Am Phys Soc; Inst Phys Soc Eng. *Mailing Add:* 2415 Beechwood Blvd Pittsburgh PA 15217

**TAYLOR, ALAN D,** SET THEORIST, MATHEMATICAL POLITICAL SCIENCE. *Current Pos:* From asst prof to assoc prof, 75-82, chmn, 85-88, PROF MATH, UNION COL, 82- *Personal Data:* b Melrose, Mass, Oct 27, 47. *Educ:* Dartmouth Col, PhD(math), 75. *Mailing Add:* Dept Math Union Col Schenectady NY 12308-2311

**TAYLOR, ALAN G,** SEED BIOLOGY, SEED TECHNOLOGY. *Current Pos:* Asst prof, 81-87, assoc prof, 87-96, PROF SEED SCI & TECHNOL, CORNELL UNIV, 97- *Personal Data:* b Detroit, Mich, Nov 22, 53; m 77, Betty; c Ryan & Andrew. *Educ:* Heidelberg Col, BS, 75; Mich State Univ, MS, 77; Okla State Univ, PhD(crop sci), 81. *Concurrent Pos:* Vis fac, Ore State Univ, 90-91; assoc ed, Am Soc Hort Sci, 95- *Mem:* Am Soc Hort Sci; Agron Soc Am; Crop Sci Soc Am. *Res:* Physiological, biochemical and biophysical markers to predict seed viability; seed coating technologies for application of materials including pesticides. *Mailing Add:* Dept Hort Sci Cornell Univ Geneva NY 14456. *Fax:* 315-787-2320; *E-Mail:* agti@cornell.edu

**TAYLOR, ALAN H,** PLANT ECOLOGY, ENVIRONMENTAL MANAGEMENT-CONSERVATION. *Current Pos:* asst prof, 90-93, ASSOC PROF GEOG, PA STATE UNIV, 93- *Personal Data:* m 83, Kristin A Brusits; c Kendra & Erik. *Educ:* Calif State Univ, Hayward, BS, 77; Ore State Univ, MS, 79; Univ Colo, PhD(geog), 87. *Prof Exp:* Teaching asst geog, Ore State Univ, 77, res asst geog, 78-79, teaching asst range sci, 81-82; botanist, Nature Conservancy, 80; environ scientist, US Environ Protection Agency, 80-81; res asst, Univ Colo, 82-83, lectr geog, 86-87; plant ecologist, World Wildlife Fund, 84-85; asst prof geog, Univ Md, Baltimore, 87-90. *Concurrent Pos:* Consult, World Wide Fund Nature, 84-; prin investr-cooperator, USDA Forest Serv, 89-; chair, Biogeog Specialty Group, Asn Am Geographers, 91-93; prin investr, US Dept Int, Nat Park Serv, 93- *Mem:* Asn Am Geographers; Ecol Soc Am; Am Bot Soc; Torrey Bot Club; Int Soc Vegetation Scientists. *Res:* Dynamics of vegetation over time scales of decades to centuries; what mechanisms promote species coexistence and ultimately control diversity of biological communities. *Mailing Add:* Dept Geog Penn State Univ 302 Walker Bldg University Park PA 16802-5011. *Fax:* 814-863-7943; *E-Mail:* ahti@psuvm.psu.edu

**TAYLOR, ALAN NEIL,** ANATOMY, PHYSIOLOGY. *Current Pos:* from assoc prof to prof, 77-85, PROF & CHMN, DEPT ANAT, BAYLOR COL DENT & GRAD SCH, BAYLOR UNIV, 85- *Personal Data:* b Franklin, NY, Sept 10, 34; m 55; c 2. *Educ:* Ohio State Univ, BS, 57; Cornell Univ, MS, 60, PhD(phys biol), 69. *Prof Exp:* Res assoc mineral metab, NY State Vet Col, Cornell Univ, 60-66, NIH traineeship, 66-69, sr res assoc membrane transport, 69-75. *Mem:* AAAS; Am Inst Nutrit; Am Asn Anatomists; Soc Exp Biol & Med; Int Asn Dent Res. *Res:* Mineral metabolism; membrane transport; mechanisms of vitamin D action; biochemistry. *Mailing Add:* Baylor Col Dent Dallas TX 75246-2097. *Fax:* 214-828-8346

**TAYLOR, ALBERT WILLIAM,** PHYSIOLOGY, KINESIOLOGY. *Current Pos:* dean fac phys educ & hon prof, Dept Physiol, 82-91, dean, Fac Kinesiology, 91-97, PROF, FAC HEALTH SCI, UNIV WESTERN ONT, 97- *Personal Data:* b Brantford, Ont, Sept 18, 39; m 74, Carole June; c Mary-Jill, Andrew S, Taryn-Lise & Edward T. *Educ:* Univ Western Ont, BA, 62, HBA, 63; Univ BC, MSc, 64; Wash State Univ, PhD(appl physiol), 67. *Hon Degrees:* DSc, London Inst Appl Res, 72, Univ Sherbrooke, 93 & Ukrainian State Univ Phys Educ & Sports, 95. *Honors & Awards:* Merit Award, Can Asn Health, Phys Educ & Recreation, 75; Hon Award, Can Asn Sports Sci, 86. *Prof Exp:* Res assoc, Dept Nat Health & Welfare, 67; from asst prof to assoc prof phys educ, Univ Alta, 70-73; prof, Dept Phys Educ, Univ Montreal, 74-77, prof titulaire, 78-81; reader, Dept Human Movement Studies, Univ Queensland & res assoc, Dept Anat, 81-82. *Concurrent Pos:* Res assoc, Surg/Med Res Inst, Univ Alta, 70-74; vis prof, Karolinska Hosp, Stockholm, 73-74, Univ Western Ont, 75 & Univ Calif, Los Angeles, 78; hon prof, Sch Phys & Occup Ther, McGill Univ, 78-81, Dept Physiol, Fac Med, Univ Western Ont, 87- *Mem:* Can Asn Health, Phys Educ & Recreation; Am Col Sports Med; Can Physiol Soc; Can Fedn Biol Sci; Int Biochem Exercise Group; Can Asn Sports Sci; Can Soc Ex Physiol. *Res:* Skeletal muscle enzyme analysis and morphology; contributed more than 300 articles to professional journals. *Mailing Add:* Fac Kinesiology-R 118 TH Univ Western Ont London ON N6A 3K7 Can. *Fax:* 519-661-2008

**TAYLOR, ALLEN,** CATARACT REMEDIATION, ENZYMOLOGY. *Current Pos:* PROF BIOCHEM & NUTRIT, TUFTS UNIV, 83-, DIR, LAB NUTRIT & VISION RES, USDA HUMAN NUTRIT RES CTR ON AGING, 83- *Personal Data:* b New York, NY, Jan 11, 46; m 77; c 1. *Educ:* City Col New York, BS, 67; Rutgers Univ, PhD(chem & biochem), 73. *Prof Exp:* Fel biochem, Univ Calif, Berkeley, 73-75, lectr, 76; asst prof chem & nutrit, Williams Col, 77-81, fel, 81-83. *Concurrent Pos:* NIH fel, 74, res grant,

78-94; vis scientist, Harvard Univ, 81-83; consult, Biogen USA Consult Capacities Group, 83-; Guggenheim fel, 86-88. *Mem:* Am Chem Soc; Sigma Xi; NY Acad Sci; Asn Res Vision Ophthal; Am Soc Biochem & Molecular Biol. *Res:* Use of nutrition to delay the onset of cataracts and other visual disorders; molecular and structural studies on leucine aminopeptidase; relationships between aging, antioxidant function and proteolytic capability; investigation of the ubiquitin and energy requirement for proteolytic activity in the aging eye lens; development of alternatives to surgery for cataract victims. *Mailing Add:* Lab Nutrit & Vision Res USDA Human Nutrit Res Ctr Aging Tufts Univ 711 Washington St Boston MA 02111-1525. *Fax:* 617-556-3344

**TAYLOR, ANDREW RONALD ARGO,** BOTANY. *Current Pos:* from asst prof to assoc prof biol, Univ NB, 46-62, prof, 62-87, actg dean sci, 74-75, EMER PROF BOT, UNIV NB, FREDERICTON, 87- *Personal Data:* b Ottawa, Ont, July 6, 21; m 47; c 4. *Educ:* Univ Toronto, BA, 43, PhD(bot), 55. *Prof Exp:* Asst bot, Univ Toronto, 43-46. *Concurrent Pos:* Asst biologist, Fisheries Res Bd Can, 48-60; hon lectr, Univ St Andrews, 60-61, 76; vis prof, Univ Adelaide, 75-76; hon res assoc, Univ Western Australia, 82-83; vpres, Can Bot Asn, 83-84. *Mem:* Int Phycol Soc (treas, 77-82); Phycol Soc Am; Brit Phycol Soc. *Res:* Developmental morphology, ecology and taxonomy of marine algae and sea grasses. *Mailing Add:* Dept Biol Univ NB Fredericton NB E3B 5A3 Can

**TAYLOR, ANDREW T, JR,** DEVELOPMENT & CLINICAL APPLICATIONS OF RENAL RADIOPHARMACEUTICALS, RADIONUCLIDE THERAPY. *Current Pos:* PROF RADIOL & CO-DIR, DIV NUCLEAR MED, EMORY UNIV SCH MED, 86- *Personal Data:* b Jackson, Tenn, Jan 14, 42; m 80, Naomi Parver; c Rebecca M. *Educ:* Rice Univ, BA, 64; Duke Univ, MD, 68. *Honors & Awards:* Alexander D Langmuir Award, Epidemic Intel Serv, Ctrs Dis Control, 73. *Prof Exp:* From asst prof to assoc prof radiol, Univ Calif, San Diego, 74-81; from assoc prof to prof & dir nuclear med, Univ Utah, Salt Lake City, 81-86, adj prof internal med, 84-86. *Concurrent Pos:* Staff assoc med, Emory Univ, 71-72; staff physician nuclear med, Vet Admin Med Ctr, San Diego, 74-79, Salt Lake City, 84-86, Grady Hosp, Atlanta, 86-; consult, Vet Admin Hosp, Salt Lake City, 81-83. *Mem:* Soc Nuclear Med; Asn Univ Radiologists; Am Col Nuclear Physicians; Am Col Nuclear Med; Radiol Soc NAm; Europ Asn Nuclear Med. *Res:* Nuclear medicine. *Mailing Add:* Dept Radiol Emory Univ Hosp 1364 Clifton Rd NE Atlanta GA 30322. *Fax:* 404-727-3488

**TAYLOR, ANGUS ELLIS,** MATHEMATICS. *Current Pos:* univ provost & chancellor, Univ Calif, Santa Cruz, 76-77, EMER PROF, UNIV CALIF, LOS ANGELES & BERKELEY, EMER UNIV PROVOST & EMER CHANCELLOR, SANTA CRUZ, 77- *Personal Data:* b Craig, Colo, Oct 13, 11; m 36; c 3. *Educ:* Harvard Univ, SB, 33; Calif Inst Technol, PhD(math), 36. *Prof Exp:* Instr math, Calif Inst Technol, 36-37; Nat Res Coun fel, Princeton Univ, 37-38; from instr to prof math, Univ Calif, Los Angeles, 38-66; vpres acad affairs, Univ Calif Systemwide Admin, 65-75, Univ provost, 75-77. *Concurrent Pos:* Fulbright res fel, Univ Mainz, 55. *Mem:* Am Math Soc; Math Asn Am. *Res:* Theory of functions; linear operators and spectral theory; history of mathematics. *Mailing Add:* 82 Norwood Ave Kensington CA 94707-1150

**TAYLOR, ANNA NEWMAN,** PHYSIOLOGY, ANATOMY. *Current Pos:* asst res anatomist, 67-68, from asst prof to assoc prof, 68-79, PROF ANAT, UNIV CALIF, LOS ANGELES, 79-; CHIEF, ALCOHOL RES LAB, US VET ADMIN, BRENTWOOD, LOS ANGELES, 79- *Personal Data:* b Vienna, Austria, Oct 28, 33; US citizen; m 59. *Educ:* Western Res Univ, AB, 55, PhD(physiol), 61. *Prof Exp:* Am Heart Asn res fel physiol, Western Res Univ, 61-63, instr, 62-63; Am Heart Asn adv res fel, Lab Neurophysiol, Henri-Rousselle Hosp, Paris, France, 63-64; asst prof physiol, Western Res Univ, 64-65; asst prof anat, Dept Anat & Psychiat, Col Med, Baylor Univ, 65-67. *Concurrent Pos:* USPHS fel, 61; res specialist, Houston State Psychiat Inst, 65-67; NIMH res scientist develop award, 72-77; mem biomed panel, Nat Insts Drug Abuse Res Review Comt, 77-81; US Vet Admin Alcohol res award, 79-81. *Mem:* Fel AAAS; Am Physiol Soc; Endocrine Soc; Am Asn Anat; Soc Neurosci. *Res:* Neuroendocrinology; central nervous system regulation of pituitary-adrenal function; central actions of hormones; developmental and long-term effects of perinatal exposure to hormones, drugs of abuse and alcohol. *Mailing Add:* Dept Anat 73-235 Univ Calif-Los Angeles Sch Med 405 Hilgard Ave Los Angeles CA 90024-1763. *Fax:* 310-393-1929

**TAYLOR, ANTHONY BOSWELL,** SPECIALIZED METALLURGICAL ANALYSIS FOR LOW LEVEL ELEMENTS. *Current Pos:* CHIEF CHEMIST, CHUTE CHEM CO, 90- *Personal Data:* b London, UK, Nov 28, 40. *Educ:* London Univ, BSc, 66, MSc, 68; Royal Inst Chem, GRIC, 67. *Prof Exp:* Chief chemist, Lucas Aerospace, 76-86; res consult, Univ Maine, 86-89. *Res:* Chemistry of acidification of New England lakes using a watershed manipulation model. *Mailing Add:* 233 Bomarc Rd Bangor ME 04401

**TAYLOR, ARCHER S,** ELECTRONICS ENGINEERING. *Current Pos:* ENGR & SR VPRES ENG, MALARKEY-TAYLOR ASSOC, 65- *Personal Data:* b Longmont, Colo, Feb 14, 16; m 44, LaVerne Wise; c David, Lawrence, Kenneth & Margaret. *Educ:* Antioch Col, BS, 38. *Honors & Awards:* Matti S Siukola Award, Inst Elec & Electronics Engrs. *Prof Exp:* Physicist & engr, Nat Bur Stand, 38-43; engr, Paul F Godley Co, Montclaire, NJ, 44-47; engr, Missoula, Mont, 47-64. *Concurrent Pos:* Technician & instr, Mont State Univ, Missola, 50-62. *Mem:* Fel Inst Elec & Electronics Engrs; Soc Motion Picture & TV Eng; fel Soc Cable Telecommun Eng. *Mailing Add:* Strategis Group Inc 1130 Connecticut Ave NW Suite 325 Washington DC 20036

**TAYLOR, ARDELL NICHOLS,** PHYSIOLOGY. *Current Pos:* dean sch related health sci, Chicago Med Sch, 67-69, pres, 69-76, EMER PRES, UNIV HEALTH SCI-CHICAGO MED SCH, 76- *Personal Data:* b Terral, Okla, Jan 19, 17; m 43; c 2. *Educ:* Tex Tech Col, BS, 39; Univ Tex, MA, 41, PhD(zool sci), 43. *Hon Degrees:* DSc, Lincoln Col, 71. *Honors & Awards:* Distinguished Serv Award. *Prof Exp:* Tutor zool, Univ Tex, 39-42, from instr to asst prof physiol, Sch Med, 43-46; from asst prof to assoc prof, Sch Med, Univ Okla, 46-51, prof, chmn dept & assoc dean, 51-60; assoc secy, Coun Med Educ & dir, Dept Allied Med Prof & Serv, AMA, 60-67. *Concurrent Pos:* Ord Episcopal priest, 70, assoc rector, Christ Church, 70- *Mem:* Soc Exp Biol & Med; Am Physiol Soc; Am Math Asn; Am Asn Med Rec Librn. *Res:* Nucleic acid metabolism in ova; nerve conduction and facilitation; hypertension; experimental vascular physiology; dynamics of circulation; medical education. *Mailing Add:* 503 Hawthorn Winnetka IL 60093

**TAYLOR, AUBREY ELMO,** PHYSIOLOGY, BIOPHYSICS. *Current Pos:* PROF PHYSIOL & CHMN DEPT, UNIV SALA, 77- *Personal Data:* b El Paso, Tex, June 4, 33; m 54, Mary J Davis; c Audrey J (Hildebrand), Lenda S (Brown) & Mary A (Smith). *Educ:* Tex Christian Univ, AB, 60; Univ Miss, PhD(physiol, biophys), 64. *Honors & Awards:* Landis Award, Microcirculatory Soc; Wiggers Award, Am Physiol Soc, 87; C Drinker Award NAm Soc Lymphol, 88; Dickinson Richards Award, Am Heart Asn, 88, Distinguished Achievement Award; Philip Dow lectr; John Whitney lectr; A Guyton lectr; Merit Award, Nat Heart Lung & Blood Inst. *Prof Exp:* Res asst learning theory, Bell Helicopter Co, Tex, 59-60; prof math, Exten Ctr, Univ Miss, 60-65, from asst prof physiol & biophys to prof, Med Ctr, 71-77. *Concurrent Pos:* Fel, Harvard Med Sch Biophys Lab, 64-67; assoc ed, J Appl Physiol; ed, J Critical Care; bd dirs, Fed Am Soc Exp Biol, NAS & Int Physiol Unit. *Mem:* Am Physiol Soc (counr & pres, 88-89); Microcirculatory Soc (pres & counr); Biophys Soc; fel AAAS; NY Acad Sci; Europ Microcirculatory Soc; NAm Soc Lymphol (pres, 88-); Int Lymphol Soc; fel Royal Soc Med; Int Pathophysiol Soc (vpres). *Res:* Irreversible thermodynamics and membrane biophysics applied to mammalian physiology, especially in fields of cardio-pulmonary, intestinal dynamics and capillary exchange of fluid and protein; author or co-author of over 700 publications and 7 textbooks. *Mailing Add:* Dept Physiol Univ SAla Mobile AL 36688. *Fax:* 334-460-6464

**TAYLOR, AUSTIN LAURENCE,** BACTERIAL GENETICS, BACTERIOPHAGE GENETICS. *Current Pos:* asst prof, 65-70, ASSOC PROF MICROBIOL, SCH MED, UNIV COLO, DENVER, 70- *Personal Data:* b Vancouver, BC, Jan 23, 32; US citizen; m 56; c 2. *Educ:* Western Md Col, BS, 54; Univ Calif, Berkeley, PhD(bact), 61. *Prof Exp:* Res assoc bact genetics, Brookhaven Nat Lab, 61-62; res microbiologist, NIH, 62-65. *Concurrent Pos:* Prin investr, USPHS res grant, 66- *Mem:* AAAS; Genetics Soc Am; Am Soc Microbiol. *Res:* Molecular genetic studies on the mechanism of bacteriophage Mu DNA replication and transposition. *Mailing Add:* Dept Microbiol Univ Colo Health Sci 4200 E Ninth Ave Denver CO 80220-3706

**TAYLOR, B GRAY,** ONCOLOGY, SURGERY. *Current Pos:* ASST CONSULT PROF SURG, DUKE UNIV MED CTR, 86-; CHIEF OF STAF, VA MED CTR, FAYETTEVILLE, NC, 86- *Personal Data:* b Booneville, Miss, Aug 11, 24; m 49; c 2. *Educ:* Harvard Med Sch, MD, 48. *Prof Exp:* From intern to resident surg, Grady Mem Hosp, Atlanta, Ga, 48-50; resident, Hosp, Emory Univ, 50-51; resident, Mem Ctr Cancer & Allied Dis, New York, 53-57; instr surg, 57-61, assoc prof clin surg, 64-72, assoc prof surg, 72-74, prof surg, La State Univ Med Ctr, New Orleans, 74-86. *Concurrent Pos:* Spec fel head & neck surg with Dr Hayes Martin, Mem Ctr Cancer & Allied Dis, New York, 57; chief surg, Vet Admin Hosp, New Orleans, 64-, sr physician, 72-; consult, USPHS Hosp, New Orleans, 64-81; active staff, Touro Infirmary, New Orleans, 64-86; sr vis surgeon, Charity Hosp, New Orleans, 64-86; assoc staff, St Charles Hosp, New Orleans, 72-86. *Mem:* James Ewing Soc; Soc Head & Neck Surg; fel Am Col Surg. *Res:* Oncologic and head and neck surgery; physical and chemical properties of human cadaver blood; clincial studies of ameloblastoma of the mandible and carotid body tumors; clinical studies on carcinoma of the male breast, the parotid salivary gland and the larynx. *Mailing Add:* 2300 Ramsey St Fayetteville NC 28301-3856

**TAYLOR, BARNEY EDSEL,** EXPERIMENTAL SOLID STATE PHYSICS. *Current Pos:* STAFF, DEPT PHYSICS, WRIGHT STATE UNIV. *Personal Data:* b Elizabethton, Tenn, Dec 10, 51; m 71. *Educ:* ETenn State Univ, BS, 73; Clemson Univ, PhD(physics), 78. *Prof Exp:* Asst prof physics, Denison Univ, 78-79; asst prof physics, Jackson State Univ, 79- *Mem:* Am Phys Soc; Am Asn Physics Teachers. *Res:* Transport studies in ionic solids by means of electrical conductivity; ionic thermocurrents and radiotracer diffusion. *Mailing Add:* 807 Marcia Dr Trenton OH 45067

**TAYLOR, BARRIE FREDERICK,** MICROBIOLOGY, BIOCHEMISTRY. *Current Pos:* PROF MARINE & ATMOSPHERIC CHEM DIV, ROSENSTIEL SCH MARINE & ATMOSPHERIC SCI & PROF BIOCHEM & MOLECULAR BIOL, SCH MED, UNIV MIAMI, 80- *Personal Data:* b Nottingham, Eng, Nov 21, 39; m 65, Kathleen Norwood; c David & Karen. *Educ:* Univ Leeds, BSc, 62, PhD(biochem), 65. *Prof Exp:* Postdoctoral, Rutgers Univ, 65-67; res assoc microbiol, Univ Tex, Austin, 67-69; asst prof marine sci, Biol & Living Resources Div, Sch Marine & Atmospheric Sci, Univ Miami, 70-74, assoc prof, 74-78; prof biol & living resources, Univ Miami, Coral Gables, 78-80. *Concurrent Pos:* NSF res grants, 70-72 & 73-81, 86-89 & 90-93; NIH grant, 74-77 & 81-84; ed, Appl & Environ Microbiol, Am Soc Microbiol, 90- *Mem:* Fel AAAS; Am Soc Microbiol; Soc Gen Microbiol; fel Am Acad Microbiol. *Res:* Microbial biochemistry; autotrophic and lithotrophic micro-organisms; aromatic degradation by microbes. *Mailing Add:* Mac-RSMAS-UM 4600 Rickenbacker Causeway Miami FL 33149. *Fax:* 305-361-4689; *E-Mail:* btaylor@rsmas.miami.edu

**TAYLOR, BARRY EDWARD,** SOLID STATE CHEMISTRY. *Current Pos:* chemist, Dupont Electronics, 73-74, res chemist, exp sta, 74-78, sr res chemist, 78-81, res assoc, Photo EMD, E I Du Pont de Nemours & Co, Inc, Niagara Falls, NY, 81-87, res assoc, Dupont Japan Tech Ctr, 87-88, sr res assoc, 88-92, RES FEL, DUPONT ELECTRONICS, RTP, NC, 92- *Personal Data:* b Potsdam, NY, July 7, 47; m 87, Peggy Pascoe; c Jerome. *Educ:* State Univ NY Col Fredonia, BS, 69; Brown Univ, PhD(chem), 74. *Prof Exp:* Teaching asst chem, State Univ NY Col Fredonia, 66-67, res asst, 68-69; teaching assoc chem, Brown Univ, 69-73. *Mem:* Am Chem Soc; Int Soc Hybrid Microelectronics; Am Ceramic Soc. *Res:* Preparative solid state chemistry; crystallographic and physical properties of oxides, halides and sulfides; chemistry of alkali metal compounds; study of ionic conductivity in solids; thick film technology of resistors, conductors, dielectrics and solder compositions; best practices and root cause analysis. *Mailing Add:* Dupont Electronics 14 Alexander Dr PO Box 13999 Research Triangle Park NC 27709-4425. *Fax:* 919-248-5715

**TAYLOR, BARRY L,** MICROBIOLOGY, BACTERIOLOGY. *Current Pos:* From asst prof to assoc prof, 76-83, PROF BIOCHEM, LOMA LINDA UNIV, 83-, PROF & CHMN MICROBIOL & MOLECULAR GENETICS, 88- *Personal Data:* b Sydney, Australia, May 7, 37; m 61, Desmyrna R Tolhurst; c Lyndon J, Nerida R & Darrin M. *Educ:* Avondale Col, Australia, BA, 59; Univ NSW, Australia, BSc, 66; Case Western Res Univ, PhD(biochem), 73. *Concurrent Pos:* Res assoc, Univ Calif, Berkeley, 73-75; vis fel, Australian Nat Univ, 75-76; vis scientist biol, Univ Utah, 82-83; interim dir, Ctr Molecular Biol, Loma Linda Univ, 89-93 & 96- *Mem:* Am Soc Microbiol; Am Soc Biochem & Molecular Biol; AAAS. *Res:* Bacterial chemotaxis by pathways that are independent of receptor methylation; mechanism by which oxygen chemoreceptors detect changes in oxygen concentration; oxygen receptores in bacteria are used as a model system. *Mailing Add:* Dept Microbiol & Molecular Genetics Loma Linda Univ Sch Med Loma Linda CA 92350. *Fax:* 909-824-4035; *E-Mail:* bltaylor@ccmail.llu.edu

**TAYLOR, BARRY NORMAN,** FUNDAMENTAL CONSTANTS, PRECISION MEASUREMENTS. *Current Pos:* chief, Absolute Elec Measurements Sect, Nat Bur Stand, 70-74, chief, Elec Div, 74-88, MGR, FUNDAMENTAL CONSTANTS DATA CTR, NAT INST STAND & TECHNOL, 88- *Personal Data:* b Philadelphia, Pa, Mar 27, 36; m 58, Sheila A Cohen; c Deborah, David & Denise. *Educ:* Temple Univ, AB, 57; Univ Pa, MS, 60, PhD(physics), 63. *Honors & Awards:* RCA Outstanding Achievement Award in Sci, 69; John Price Wetherill Medal, Franklin Inst, Wash, Philadelphia & Silver Medal Award, Dept Com, 75, Gold Medal Award, 89. *Prof Exp:* From instr to asst prof physics, Univ Pa, 63-66; physicist, RCA Labs, NJ, 66-70. *Concurrent Pos:* Consult, Philco Corp, 64-65; instr math, Rider Col, 69-70; mem, Nat Acad Sci-Nat Res Coun-Nat Acad Eng Adv Comt Fundamental Constants & Stand, 69-87, mem adv panel, Elec Div, Inst Basic Stand, Nat Bur Stand, 69, mem, Comt Data Sci & Technol Task Group on Fundamental Constants, 76-; Nat Bur Stand deleg, 14th session Comt Consult Elec, Comt Int Poids & Measures, Paris, France, 75, deleg 15th Session, 78, 16th Session, 83, 17th Session, 86, 18th Session, 88, 19th Session, 92 & 20th Session, 95; adminr, Precision Measurement Grants Prog, Nat Inst Stand & Technol, 75-, rep, Int Electrotech Comn, TC 25, Working Group 1, 89- US Tech Adv Group, Int Orgn Standardization TC 12, 89-, ISO TAG 4/WG3, Metrol, 89-, ISO TAG 4/WG1 Int Vocab Metrol, 89-, Int Adv Panel, ISO TC 12, 89-, Subcomt Stand & Metric Practices Metrication Operating Comt, Interagency Comt Metric Policy, 89-, Comt E-43 SI Pract, Am Soc Testing & Mat, 89-, authorized off interpretation, Int Syst Units US, 89-; mem, NSF Interagency Atomic & Molecular Physics Group, 76-83; ed, Metrologia, 76-84 & 88-; charter mem, Sr Exec Serv, US Govt, 79-; vchmn, Topical Group on Fundamental Constants & Precise Tests of Phys Laws, Am Phys Soc, 88-90, chmn, 90-92; mem, Nat Conf Stand Labs, Com Uncertainty, 92-; tech adv TC 25, US Nat Comt, Int Electrotech Comn, 89-; mem & chair, Stand Coord Comt 14, Inst Elec & Electronics Engrs, 89-; chief ed, J Res Nat Inst Stand & Technol, 89- *Mem:* Fel Am Phys Soc; fel Inst Elec & Electronics Engrs; Sigma Xi. *Res:* Precision measurement and fundamental constants; data analysis; quantities and units; absolute electrical measurements; measurement uncertainty; metric system. *Mailing Add:* Nat Inst Stand & Technol Bldg 225 Rm B161 Gaithersburg MD 20899-0001

**TAYLOR, BENJAMIN JOSEPH,** PHYSICS, ASTRONOMY. *Current Pos:* ASST PROF PHYSICS & ASTRON, BRIGHAM YOUNG UNIV, 80- *Personal Data:* b Pasadena, Calif, July 5, 42; m 70; c 6. *Educ:* Pasadena City Col, AA, 62; Univ Calif, Berkeley, BA, 64, PhD(astron), 69. *Prof Exp:* Res assoc, Princeton Univ, 69-71; res assoc, Univ Wash, 71-73, instr astron, 74; Nat Res Coun assoc, Ames Res Ctr, NASA, 74-76, assoc, 77-80. *Concurrent Pos:* Instr physics & astron, San Jose State Univ, 77-80. *Mem:* Astron Soc Pac. *Res:* Spectrophotometry of secondary standards and solar analogs; differential broad-band photometry of clusters for blanketing analyses; spectrophotometry of K giants for abundance analyses. *Mailing Add:* Dept Physics & Astron 296 ESC Brigham Young Univ Provo UT 84602-1022

**TAYLOR, BERNARD FRANKLIN,** VIROLOGY, SERODIAGNOSIS. *Current Pos:* from virologist to chief virologist, 60-79, DIR, PUB HEALTH LAB SERV DIAG MICROBIOL, NJ STATE DEPT HEALTH, 79- *Personal Data:* b Charles Town, WVa, Mar 21, 30; m 57; c 2. *Educ:* Storer Col, Harpers Ferry, WVa, BS, 52; Mich State Univ, MS, 58; Rutgers Univ, New Brunswick, NJ, PhD(microbiol), 72; Rider Col, Lawrenceville, NJ, MA, 80. *Honors & Awards:* Ella Stewart Biol Award. *Prof Exp:* Bacteriologist I virol, Mich State Dept Health, 52-54, virologist II, 56-59; instr sci, Elizabeth City State Col, NC, 59-60. *Concurrent Pos:* Med technician, Helene Fuld Hosp, Trenton, NJ, 61-64; adj prof biol, Trenton State Col, NJ, 72-; Nat Defense exec reservist, Fed Emergency Mgt Agency Reg III, Philadelphia, Pa, 84-87 & 87-90; mem, Med Technician Adv Comn, Mercer Co Community Col, Trenton, NJ, 84-87. *Mem:* Theobald Smith Soc; Nat Soc Biol Teachers; Conf Pub Health Admin; NY Acad Sci; Sigma Xi. *Res:* Development of cost-effective serodiagnostic techniques which are specific, sensitive and yield rapid results. *Mailing Add:* 438 Walnut Ave Trenton NJ 08609-1534

**TAYLOR, BEVERLEY ANN PRICE,** PHYSICS, QUANTUM FIELD THEORY. *Current Pos:* FAC, DEPT PHYSICS, MIAMI UNIV, OHIO, 84- *Personal Data:* b Kingsport, Tenn, Nov 24, 51; m 71. *Educ:* ETenn State Univ, BS, 73; Clemson Univ, PhD(physics), 78. *Prof Exp:* asst prof physics, Denison Univ, 78-79; asst prof physics, Jackson State Univ, 79-84. *Mem:* Am Phys Soc; Am Asn Phys Teachers; Sigma Xi. *Res:* Intrinsically nonlinear quantum field theories; elementary school science curriculum and instruction. *Mailing Add:* Physics Dept Miami Univ 1601 Peck Blvd Hamilton OH 45011-3316

**TAYLOR, BRUCE CAHILL,** BIOMEDICAL ENGINEERING, INSTRUMENTATION. *Current Pos:* res assoc prof, 81-88, dir, Dept Biomed Eng Res, 85-88, ASSOC PROF BIOENG, UNIV AKRON, 88-, ASSOC PROF ELEC ENG, 92- *Personal Data:* b Cleveland, Ohio, June 5, 42; div; c 4. *Educ:* Hiram Col, BA, 64; Kent State Univ, MA, 66, PhD(physiol), 71. *Prof Exp:* Assoc dir res, Vascular Res Lab, Akron City Hosp, 71-75; sr res scientist, Abcor, Inc, 75-76; dir dept med eng, Akron City Hosp, 78-84. *Concurrent Pos:* Biomed consult, 75-; prog dir, Proj Hope, People's Repub China, 84-85; developer, Biomed Eng Support Serv. *Mem:* Am Soc Artifical Internal Organs; Asn Advan Med Instrumentation; Inst Elec & Electronics Engrs; Eng Med & Biol Soc. *Res:* Design and development of new types of medical instrumentation; blood pressure monitoring; computer modeling and simulation. *Mailing Add:* Dept Biomed Eng Univ Akron Akron OH 44325

**TAYLOR, C(HARLES) E(DWIN),** OPTIC METHODS OF STRESS ANALYSIS. *Current Pos:* prof, 81-91, EMER PROF ENG SCI, UNIV FLA, 91- *Personal Data:* b West Lafayette, Ind, Mar 24, 24; m 46, Lucile Nitsche; c Gary A & Glenn C. *Educ:* Purdue Univ, BSME, 46, MS, 48; Univ Ill, PhD(theoret & appl mech), 53. *Honors & Awards:* M M Frocht Award, Soc Exp Stress Analysis, 69, M Hetenyi Award, 70 & 73; F G Tatnall Award, 83. *Prof Exp:* Instr eng mech, Purdue Univ, 46-48; from instr to asst prof theoret & appl mech, Univ Ill, Urbana, 48-52, from asst prof to prof, 54-80; struct res engr, David Taylor Model Basin, DC, 52-54. *Concurrent Pos:* Vis prof, India, 66, 69 & Univ Calif, Berkeley, 68. *Mem:* Nat Acad Eng; fel Am Soc Mech Engrs; Am Soc Eng Educ; fel Soc Eng Sci (pres, 77-78); hon mem Soc Exp Stress Analysis (pres, 66-67); fel Am Acad Mech (pres, 93-94). *Res:* Three-dimensional photoelasticity; applications of lasers to experimental mechanics; shell theory; holography; image processing. *Mailing Add:* 8322 SW Fifth Pl Gainesville FL 32607

**TAYLOR, C P(ATRICK) S(TIRLING),** BIOPHYSICS. *Current Pos:* from asst prof to prof, 68-95, EMER PROF BIOPHYS, UNIV WESTERN ONT, 95- *Personal Data:* b Toronto, Ont, May 11, 30; m 55, Elizabeth; c 4. *Educ:* Univ BC, BA, 52; Oxford Univ, BA, 54, MA, 57; Univ Pa, PhD(biophys), 60. *Prof Exp:* Childs Mem Fund fel biophys, Cambridge Univ, 60-61; asst prof physics, Univ BC, 61-67. *Mem:* Sigma Xi. *Res:* Mathematical modelling. *Mailing Add:* Dept Med Biophys Univ Western Ont London ON N6A 5C1 Can

**TAYLOR, CARL ERNEST,** PREVENTIVE MEDICINE, EPIDEMIOLOGY. *Current Pos:* EMER PROF, DEPT INT HEALTH, JOHNS HOPKINS UNIV, 84- *Personal Data:* b Mussoorie, India, July 26, 16; m 43; c 3. *Educ:* Muskingum Col, BS, 37; Harvard Univ, MD, 41, MPH, 51, DrPH, 53; FRCP(C), 45; Am Bd Prev Med, dipl, 52. *Hon Degrees:* DSc, Muskingum Col, 62; DHL, Towson State Univ, Baltimore, 78. *Honors & Awards:* Edward M Ryan Prize Contrib to Int Nutrit Narangwal Proj, 74; Int Health Leadership Award, Nat Coun Int Health, 80; Int Health Sect Career Award Distinguished Serv & Leadership, Am Pub Health Asn, 91; Award for Sustained Work to Protect Children Around World, US Pres, 93. *Prof Exp:* Med officer, Gorgas Hosp, 41-44; chief med serv, USPHS Marine Hosp, Pittsburgh, 44-46; hosp supt, Fatehgarh, India, 47-50; instr, Sch Pub Health, Harvard Univ, 51-53; prof prev med, Christian Med Col, India, 53-56; assoc prof prev med & pub health & dir prog for teachers, Sch Pub Health, Harvard Univ, 56-61; prof & chair, Dept Int Health, Sch Hyg & Pub Health, Johns Hopkins Univ, 61-84; US rep, Unicer, China, 84-87. *Concurrent Pos:* Hon prof, Tongji Univ Med Col, China, 88, Pei Union Med Col, China, 92. *Mem:* Inst Med-Nat Acad Sci; Asn Teachers Prev Med; Am Pub Health Asn; Royal Soc Trop Med & Hyg; Am Soc Trop Med & Hyg. *Res:* International health; health planning in developing countries; population dynamics; medical education; epidemiology of leprosy and nutrition and infections; integration of health and family planning. *Mailing Add:* Johns Hopkins Univ Sch Hyg & Pub Health 615 N Wolfe St Baltimore MD 21205

**TAYLOR, CARSON WILLIAM,** ELECTRICAL POWER ENGINEERING, CONTROL ENGINEERING. *Current Pos:* elec engr, 69-89, PRIN ENGR, BONNEVILLE POWER ADMIN, 89- *Personal Data:* b Superior, Wis, May 24, 42; m 66, Gudrun R Leistner; c Natasha M (Tiffany). *Educ:* Univ Wis, BS, 65; Rensselaer Polytech Inst, MS, 69. *Prof Exp:* Elec engr, US Bur Reclamation, 67-68. *Concurrent Pos:* Adj prof, Univ Portland, 82-86; working group chmn, Inst Elec & Electronic Engrs, 82-, mem, Int Conf Large High Voltage Elec Systs, 82-; prin, Carson Taylor Seminars, 86-; mem, Interconnection Dynamics WG, NAm Elec Reliability Coun, 90- *Mem:* Fel Inst Elec & Electronics Engrs; Int Conf Large High Voltage Elec Systs. *Res:* Innovative control and protection methods to ensure reliability of large electric power systems. *Mailing Add:* 252 NW Seblar Ct Portland OR 97210. *E-Mail:* cwtaylor@bpa.gov

**TAYLOR, CHARLES BRUCE,** pathology; deceased, see previous edition for last biography

**TAYLOR, CHARLES ELLETT,** POPULATION GENETICS, ARTIFICIAL LIFE. *Current Pos:* assoc prof, 80-87, PROF BIOL, UNIV CALIF, LOS ANGELES, 87- *Personal Data:* b Chicago, Ill, Sept 9, 45; m 69, Minna Glushien; c Amy. *Educ:* Univ Calif, Berkeley, AB, 68; State Univ NY, Stony Brook, PhD(ecol & evolution), 73. *Prof Exp:* Asst prof biol, Univ Calif, Riverside, 74-79. *Concurrent Pos:* Co-dir, cognitive sci res prog, Univ Calif, Los Angeles. *Mem:* Genetics Soc Am; Soc Study Evolution. *Res:* Population genetics and ecology; artificial life. *Mailing Add:* Dept Biol Univ Calif Los Angeles CA 90095. *Fax:* 310-206-3987; *E-Mail:* taylor@ca.ucla.edu

**TAYLOR, CHARLES EMERY,** NUCLEAR MAGNETIC RESONANCE, ZERO GRAVITY MATERIALS SCIENCE. *Current Pos:* From asst prof to assoc prof, 67-80, PROF PHYSICS, ANTIOCH COL, 80- *Personal Data:* b White Plains, NY, Mar 2, 40; m 96, Meicheng Chiang; c Brendan. *Educ:* Williams Col, BA, 61, MA, 63; Mich State Univ, PhD(physics), 67. *Concurrent Pos:* NSF fac fel, 75-76, grantee, 91; dir, Sci Inst, 82-86 & 90-96. *Mem:* Am Phys Soc; Am Solar Energy Asn; Am Asn Physics Teachers. *Res:* Holography; holaesthetics; solar energy and alternative energy sources; zero gravity experiments, for future shuttle flight, on solidification; use of multi-media in physics education. *Mailing Add:* Dept Physics Inst Sci Antioch Col 795 Livermore St Yellow Springs OH 45387. *E-Mail:* ctaylor@antioch-college.edu

**TAYLOR, CHARLES JOEL,** PHYSICS. *Current Pos:* RETIRED. *Personal Data:* b Portland, Ore, Apr 12, 19; m 52; c 3. *Educ:* Univ Ill, BS, 40, MS, 48, PhD(physics), 51. *Prof Exp:* Asst nuclear physics, Univ Ill, 50-51; physicist, NAm Aviation, Inc, 51-52; physicist, Lawrence Livermore Nat Lab, Univ Calif, 52-85, tech mgt systs analysis nuclear weapons, 75-81, asst assoc dir, 81-85. *Concurrent Pos:* Consult, US Deleg, conf disarmament, Geneva, Switz, 79, 80. *Mem:* Am Phys Soc. *Res:* Scintillation counters; neutron physics; nuclear weapons design; systems analysis. *Mailing Add:* 4275 Cornell Way Livermore CA 94550-4906

**TAYLOR, CHARLES RICHARD,** comparative physiology, environmental physiology; deceased, see previous edition for last biography

**TAYLOR, CHARLES WILLIAM,** ORGANIC CHEMISTRY. *Current Pos:* Sr chemist, 3M Co, 57-72, res specialist, 72-81, sr res specialist, Med Prod Div, Cent Res Dept, 81-87, DIV SCIENTIST, 3M CO, 87- *Personal Data:* b Duluth, Minn, Sept 26, 30; m 53; c 4. *Educ:* Univ Minn, BA, 52; Univ Wis, PhD(chem), 57. *Mem:* Am Chem Soc; Sigma Xi; Adhesion Soc. *Res:* Fluorocarbon chemistry; biomedical materials; thermosetting acrylics; pressure sensitive adhesives. *Mailing Add:* 4677 Birchbark Trail N Lake Elmo MN 55042-9527

**TAYLOR, CHRISTOPHER E,** IMMUNOLOGY, NUTRITION. *Current Pos:* ASST PROF IMMUNOL, MED COL PA, 83- *Educ:* Johns Hopkins Univ, ScD, 81. *Mailing Add:* DMID NIAID NIH 6003 Executive Blvd Rm 3B01 MSC 7630 Bethesda MD 20892-7630

**TAYLOR, CLAYBORNE D,** ELECTROMAGNETICS. *Current Pos:* prof elec eng, 72-74, PROF ELEC ENG & PHYSICS, MISS STATE UNIV, 74-86 & 88-, ASSOC DEAN GRAD AFFAIRS, 91- *Personal Data:* b Kokomo, Miss, July 15, 38; m 63, Jean B Taylor; c 3. *Educ:* Miss State Univ, BS, 61; NMex State Univ, MS, 64, PhD(physics), 65. *Prof Exp:* Staff mem, Sandia Corp, 65-67; from asst prof to assoc prof physics, Miss State Univ, 67-71; prof elec eng, Univ Miss, 71-72. *Concurrent Pos:* Var consult activ & short course instr; Stocker vis prof & chair, Ohio Univ, 86-88; consult, USAF; teaching emp, R&B Enterprises, Praxis Int; Herrin Hess prof, Miss State Univ, 90-91 & 91-92. *Mem:* Nat Soc Prof Engrs; Inst Elec & Electronics Engrs; Int Radio Union Radio Sci; Am Soc Eng Educ. *Res:* Field and antenna theories; electromagnetic boundary value problems. *Mailing Add:* Assoc Dean Grad Affairs Miss State Univ PO Drawer DE Mississippi State MS 39762. *Fax:* 601-325-8573; *E-Mail:* ctaylor@engr.msstate.edu

**TAYLOR, CLIVE ROY,** PATHOLOGY. *Current Pos:* chmn path, 83, PROF & CHMN PATH, UNIV SOUTHERN CALIF, LOS ANGELES, 76- *Personal Data:* b Cambridge, Eng, July 24, 44; m 67; c 4. *Educ:* Cambridge Univ, MBBChir, 69, MD, 80; Oxford Univ, PhD(immunol), 74. *Prof Exp:* Lectr path, Univ Oxford, 70-75; fel cancer res, UK Res Coun, 75-76. *Res:* Immunopathology, immunohistology and cancer diagnosis, with particular reference to leukemia & lymphoma. *Mailing Add:* Dept Path Univ Southern Calif Med Sci Ctr 2025 Zonal Ave HMR 204 Los Angeles CA 90033-1054. *Fax:* 213-342-3314

**TAYLOR, CONSTANCE ELAINE SOUTHERN,** ECOLOGY, SYSTEMATIC BOTANY. *Current Pos:* from instr to assoc prof, 70-85, PROF BIOL, SOUTHEASTERN OKLA STATE UNIV, 85- *Personal Data:* b Washington, DC, Nov 14, 37; m 59; c 3. *Educ:* Univ Okla, BS, 59, MS, 61, PhD(plant ecol & syst bot), 75. *Prof Exp:* Teacher pub schs, Okla, 63-64. *Mem:* Am Soc Plant Taxonomists; Nat Wildlife Fedn. *Res:* The genus Solidago and Euthamia, goldenrods, Oklahoma vascular plants, endangered and rare species. *Mailing Add:* Dept Biol Southeastern Okla State Univ Box 4027 Sta A Durant OK 74701-0609

**TAYLOR, D DAX,** ANATOMIC PATHOLOGY, CLINICAL PATHOLOGY. *Current Pos:* MED DIR, QUEST DIAG, 87- *Personal Data:* b Chicago, Ill, Oct 10, 37; m 61; c 3. *Educ:* Amherst Col, AB, 59; Univ Mo, Columbia, MD, 63; Am Bd Path, dipl & cert anat path & clin path, 68. *Prof Exp:* Resident path, Sch Med, Univ Mo, Columbia, 63-68, instr, 68-69, asst prof path & asst dean sch med, 69-72; assoc prof & assoc dean med educ, Southern Ill Univ, Springfield, 72-76, prof path & assoc dean acad affairs, Sch Med, 76-79, exec assoc dean, 79-80; vpres, Eval Prog, Nat Bd Med Examiners, 80-87. *Mem:* Asn Am Med Cols; Am Soc Clin Path; Col Am Pathologists. *Res:* Medical education, student and curriculum evaluation; platelet patho-physiology. *Mailing Add:* Quest Diagnostics 1355 Mittel Blvd Wood Dale IL 60191

**TAYLOR, D(OROTHY) JANE,** BIOLOGY. *Current Pos:* RETIRED. *Personal Data:* b Waco, Tex. *Educ:* Rice Univ, BA, 43; Iowa State Univ, MS, 47; George Washington Univ, PhD(biol), 57. *Honors & Awards:* Super Serv Award, Dept Health & Human Serv, Pub Health Serv, 81. *Prof Exp:* Tech asst, Synthetic Rubber Lab, Humble Oil Co, 43-45; lab instr zool, biol & physiol, Iowa State Univ, 45-47; parasitologist, Lab Trop Dis, NIH, 47-58; head endocrine-related tumor syst sect, Cancer Chemother Nat Serv Ctr, 58-69, head, Gen Lab & Clin, 64-73; head exp biol proj sect, Breast Cancer Prog Coord Br, Nat Cancer Inst, NIH 73-82, chief, Breast Cancer Prog Coord Br, Div Cancer Biol & Diag & Exec Secy, Breast Cancer Task Force Comt, 75-82; sci adminr, Stehlin Found Cancer Res, Houston, Tex, 82-88; consult, Breast Cancer Res, Rose Joan Gordon Ctr, Houston, Tex, 90-93. *Concurrent Pos:* Mem bd, Nat Alliance Breast Cancer Orgn, New York, NY, 87-; mem adv bd, Cancer Fighter's of Houston, 89-, Rose Mammography Ctr, Houston, Tex, 90. *Mem:* Fel AAAS; Am Asn Cancer Res; Sigma Xi. *Res:* Experimental biology of breast cancer; malaria and amebiasis; in vitro cultivation; experimental chemotherapy; nutritional aspects; endocrine tumors; host-tumor biology and therapy; chemotherapy of human tumors in athymic mice; immune competence of women with stage one breast cancer. *Mailing Add:* 5001 Woodway Dr No 605 Houston TX 77056-1718

**TAYLOR, D LANSING,** CELL BIOLOGY. *Current Pos:* PROF BIOL, CARNEGIE-MELLON UNIV, 82- *Personal Data:* b Baltimore, Md, Dec 26, 46; m 69; c 3. *Educ:* Univ Md, BS, 68; State Univ NY, Albany, PhD(biol), 73. *Prof Exp:* Fel biophys, Marine Biol Labs, 73-74; asst prof biol, Harvard Univ, 74-78, assoc prof, 78-82. *Concurrent Pos:* Ed, J Cell Biol & J Cell Motility, 81- *Mem:* Am Soc Cell Biol; Biophys Soc; NY Acad Sci. *Res:* Molecular basis of amoeboid movements, utilizing biochemical, cell biological and biophysical approaches and fluorescence spectroscopy. *Mailing Add:* NSF Sci/Tech Ctr Dept Biol Sci Carnegie-Mellon Univ 4400 Fifth Ave Pittsburgh PA 15213-2863. *Fax:* 412-268-6571

**TAYLOR, DALE FREDERICK,** CORROSION, ELECTROCHEMISTRY. *Current Pos:* Staff scientist battery res, 70-73, mgr personnel admin, 74, STAFF SCIENTIST, MAT LABS, GEN ELEC CORP RES & DEVELOP, 75- *Personal Data:* b Evansville, Ind, June 16, 44; m 67, Heather Denning; c Sarah & James. *Educ:* Univ Toronto, BSc, 66, MSc, 68, PhD(chem), 70. *Mem:* Electrochem Soc. *Res:* Corrosion of boiling water reactor fuel cladding and structural materials. *Mailing Add:* Gen Elec Res & Develop Ctr PO Box 8 Schenectady NY 12301. *Fax:* 518-387-7007; *E-Mail:* taylord@crd.ge.com

**TAYLOR, DAVID COBB,** ELECTROCHEM, COMPUTER TECHNIQUES. *Current Pos:* From asst prof to assoc prof, 68-83, PROF CHEM, SLIPPERY ROCK UNIV, 83- *Personal Data:* b Portland, Maine, June 7, 39; m 71, Elaine. *Educ:* Bowdoin Col, AB, 61; Wesleyan Univ, MA, 63; Univ Conn, PhD(chem), 70. *Concurrent Pos:* Consult analytical methods & environ systs eng; dir, Oil Well Automation Co, Inc. *Mem:* AAAS; Am Chem Soc; fel Am Inst Chemists. *Res:* Electroanalytical chemistry and multicomponent systems in the realm of industrial methods development. *Mailing Add:* Dept Chem Slippery Rock Univ Slippery Rock PA 16057-1326. *E-Mail:* david.taylor@sru.edu

**TAYLOR, DAVID JAMES,** FAULT TOLERANCE, DISTRIBUTED SYSTEMS. *Current Pos:* Asst prof, 77-87, assoc prof, 87-96, PROF COMPUT SCI, UNIV WATERLOO, 96- *Personal Data:* b Ottawa, Ont, May 12, 51. *Educ:* Univ Sask, BSc, 72; Univ Waterloo, MSc, 74, PhD(comput sci), 77. *Concurrent Pos:* SERC vis fel, Comput Lab, Univ Newcastle upon Tyne, 83-84; vis scholar, Ctr Advan Studies, IBM Can, Toronto, 91-92. *Mem:* Asn Comput Mach; Inst Elec & Electronics Engrs. *Res:* Software fault tolerance particularly robust storage structures; software structure for distributed computer systems. *Mailing Add:* Dept Comput Sci Univ Waterloo Waterloo ON N2L 3G1 Can. *Fax:* 519-885-1208; *E-Mail:* dtaylor@uwaterloo.ca

**TAYLOR, DAVID NEELY,** INFECTIOUS DISEASES. *Current Pos:* EPIDEMIOLOGIST ENTERIC DIS, CTR DIS CONTROL, WALTER REED ARMY INST RES, 80- *Personal Data:* b Ann Arbor, Mich, July 31, 48; m 80. *Educ:* Kenyon Col, BA, 70; Dartmouth Med Sch, DMS, 72; Harvard Med Sch, MD, 74; London Sch Hyg & Trop Med, MSc, 78. *Prof Exp:* Med resident, State Univ NY, Buffalo, 74-77; res fel geog med, Sch Med, Johns Hopkins Univ, 78-80. *Concurrent Pos:* Consult, Gorga's Hosp, Panama, 78-80 & Chilalongkorn Hosp, Thailand, 83- *Mem:* Am Soc Microbiol; Am Soc Trop Med & Hyg. *Res:* Epidemiologic studies in infectious causes of diarrheal disease, including studies in salmonella, typhoid, campylobacter and intestinal parasites; development of rapid diagnostic methods to detect enteric disease agents. *Mailing Add:* Ctr Vaccine Develop 10 S Pine St Baltimore MD 21201-1192

**TAYLOR, DAVID WARD,** THEORETICAL PHYSICS, SOLID STATE PHYSICS. *Current Pos:* from asst prof to assoc prof, 67-77, assoc chmn, Physics Dept, 80-84, PROF THEORET SOLID STATE PHYSICS, MCMASTER UNIV, 77- *Personal Data:* b Chesterfield, Eng, Aug 18, 38; m 65; c 2. *Educ:* Oxford Univ, BA, 61, MA, 65, PhD(physics), 65. *Prof Exp:*

Mem tech staff, Bell Tel Labs, NJ, 64-67. *Mem:* Can Phys Soc; Am Phys Soc. *Res:* Dynamics of disordered crystals; calculations of phonons and phonon dependent properties of metals and alloys. *Mailing Add:* Dept Physics McMaster Univ Hamilton ON L8S 4M1 Can. *E-Mail:* taylordw@mcmaster. ca

**TAYLOR, DEAN PERRON,** ACTINOMYCETE MOLECULAR GENETICS, HETEROLOGUS GENE EXPRESSION. *Current Pos:* sci proj mgr, 89-90, dir biotechnol, 90-91, DIR AM/ASIA BIOTECHNOL, PANLABS, INC, 91- *Personal Data:* b Cordova, Alaska, Nov 19, 47; m 72, JoBess HineLine; c Matthew P & Mark L. *Educ:* Univ Wash, Seattle, BS, 70; Univ Wis, PhD(molecular biol), 76. *Honors & Awards:* Kitasato Medal, Kitasato Inst, 92. *Prof Exp:* Fel, Dept Genetics, Stanford Univ, 76-79; assoc sr investr, Dept Microbiol, Smith Kline & Fr Labs, 79-81, sr investr, 81-82, sr investr, Dept Nat Prod Pharmacol, 82-83, Dept Molecular Genetics, 83-85, asst dir, 85-89. *Concurrent Pos:* Teaching asst cellular biol, Univ Wis, 71-72; fel, Am Cancer Soc, 76-78, Bank Am-Giannini Found, 78-79; lectr, Univ Pa, 81-85. *Mem:* AAAS; Am Soc Microbiol; Sigma Xi; Soc Indust Microbiol. *Res:* Expression of heterologous gene products in streptomyces; cloned actinomycete genes for antibiotic biosynthesis, protease inhibitors; cloned human PDE IV gene; described physical map for bacterial photosynthesis genes; studied plasmid replication and developed cloning vectors. *Mailing Add:* 17419 151st Ave NE Woodinville WA 98072. *Fax:* 425-487-3787; *E-Mail:* taylod@aol.com

**TAYLOR, DERMOT BROWNRIGG,** PHARMACOLOGY. *Current Pos:* chmn dept, 53-68, PROF PHARMACOL, UNIV CALIF, LOS ANGELES, 53- *Personal Data:* b Ireland, Mar 30, 15; US citizen; m 45, 65; c 1. *Educ:* Trinity Col, Dublin, MD, 37, MB, BCh & BAO, 38. *Prof Exp:* Asst physiol, Trinity Col, Dublin, 38-39; lectr, King's Col, Univ London, 39-45, lectr pharmacol, 45-50; assoc prof, Univ Calif, San Francisco, 50-53. *Concurrent Pos:* Univ London traveling fel, Yale Univ, 48. *Mem:* Am Soc Pharmacol & Exp Therapeut; Brit Physiol Soc; Royal Soc Chem; Brit Biochem Soc; Brit Pharmacol Soc. *Res:* Mode of action of neuromuscular blocking agents. *Mailing Add:* Neurosci Res Inst Univ Calif-Santa Barbara Santa Barbara CA 93106-0001

**TAYLOR, DIANE WALLACE,** TROPICAL MEDICINE, HYBRIDOMA TECHNOLOGY. *Current Pos:* assoc prof, 82-93, PROF, DEPT BIOL, GEORGETOWN UNIV, WASHINGTON, DC, 93- *Personal Data:* b Covina, Calif; m. *Educ:* Univ Hawaii, BA, 68, MS, 70, PhD(zool), 75. *Prof Exp:* Instr biol, Sch Med, Univ Hawaii, 70-73, fel trop med, 75-78; fel immunol, Lab Microbiol Immunol, NIH, 78-82. *Mem:* Am Soc Trop Med & Hyg; Sigma Xi; Am Soc Microbiologists. *Res:* Immune studies of parasitic infections with special emphasis on malaria. *Mailing Add:* 10233 Holly Hill Pl Potomac MD 20854-5025

**TAYLOR, DONALD CURTIS,** MATHEMATICS. *Current Pos:* assoc prof, 73-77, PROF MATH, MONT STATE UNIV, 77- *Personal Data:* b London, Ky, June 16, 39; m 67; c 1. *Educ:* Univ Ky, BS, 61, MS, 64, PhD(math), 67. *Prof Exp:* Elec eng, Westinghouse Elec Corp, 61-62; assoc prof math, Univ Mo Columbia, 67-73. *Concurrent Pos:* Fel, La State Univ, Baton Rouge, 69-70. *Mem:* Am Math Soc. *Res:* Functional analysis. *Mailing Add:* Dept Math Mont State Univ Bozeman MT 59717

**TAYLOR, DONALD JAMES,** ASTRONOMY. *Current Pos:* ASSOC PROF PHYSICS, UNIV NEBR, LINCOLN, 71- *Personal Data:* b Dayton, Ohio, Mar 6, 33; m 55, 85, Mary Martin; c Brook & Glenn. *Educ:* Calif Inst Technol, BS, 55, MS, 58; Univ Wis, PhD(astron), 63. *Prof Exp:* Proj assoc space astron lab, Univ Wis, 63-65; asst prof astron, Univ Ariz, 65-71. *Mem:* Int Astron Union; Am Astron Soc; Astron Soc Pac. *Res:* Planetary astronomy; astronomical instrumentation; pulsars; nebulae. *Mailing Add:* 116 Brace Lab Univ Nebr Lincoln NE 68588-0111. *E-Mail:* dtaylor@unlinto.unl.edu

**TAYLOR, DOUGLAS HIRAM,** ETHOLOGY, ECOLOGY. *Current Pos:* from asst prof to assoc prof, 71-78, PROF ZOOL, 78-, CHAIR, 92- *Personal Data:* b Doddsville, Miss, Dec 15, 39; m 61; c 2. *Educ:* Univ Dayton, BS, 66, MS, 68; Miss State Univ, PhD(zool), 70. *Prof Exp:* NSF fel, Univ Notre Dame, 70-71. *Concurrent Pos:* Res biologist, US Environ Protection Agency. *Mem:* AAAS; Am Soc Zoologists; Animal Behav Soc; Ecol Soc Am; Sigma Xi; Soc Study Amphibians & Reptiles. *Res:* Animal behavior, ecology and orientation; agonistic behavior; behavioral aspects of ecology of vertebrates; behavioral toxicology. *Mailing Add:* Dept Zool Miami Univ 500 E High St Oxford OH 45056-1618

**TAYLOR, DUANE FRANCIS,** DENTAL MATERIALS. *Current Pos:* RETIRED. *Personal Data:* b Iowa City, Iowa, Sept 30, 25; m 50; c 7. *Educ:* Univ Mich, BSE, 49, MSE, 50; Georgetown Univ, PhD(biochem), 61. *Prof Exp:* Head dept dent mat, Sch Dent, Washington Univ, St Louis, 50-54; phys metallurgist, Dent Sect, Nat Bur Stand, 54-61; dir mat res, CMP Industs, 61-63; prof, Sch Dent, Univ NC, Chapel Hill, 63-74, prof oper dent-dent sci, Dent Res Ctr, 74-97. *Concurrent Pos:* Consult, US Army, 67- & NIH, 69- *Mem:* AAAS; Am Soc Metals; Int Asn Dent Res. *Res:* Dental amalgams; cobalt-chromium alloys; denture base materials; polymerization mechanisms; properties of multiphase solids; materials for implant prosthesis. *Mailing Add:* 1405 Heron Pond Dr Chapel Hill NC 27516

**TAYLOR, DUNCAN PAUL,** NEUROPHARMACOLOGY. *Current Pos:* ASSOC DIR, BUS DEVELOP, PHARMACIA & UPJOHN, 96- *Personal Data:* b Bremerton, Wash, Feb 4, 49; m 72, Jeanne Damgaard; c Aubrey. *Educ:* Calif Inst Technol, BS, 71; Ore State Univ, PhD(biochem), 77. *Honors & Awards:* Nat Res Serv Award, Nat Inst Drug Abuse. *Prof Exp:* Technician, Anal Serv, Carnation Co Res Labs, 67-70; vol, US Peace Corps, 71-73; res asst, Dept Biochem & Biophys, Ore State Univ, 73-77; res assoc, Sect Biochem & Pharmacol, NIMH, 77-79; scientist & neuropharmacologist, Mead Johnson & Co, 79-80, res assoc & neuropharmacologist, 80, sr scientist & neuropharmacologist biol res, Pharmaceut Div, 80-82; sr scientist, Bristol-Myers Squibb Co, 82-83, sr res scientist, 83-85, res fel, 85-89, sr res fel, Cent Nervous Syst Neuropharmacol Dept, Pharmaceut Res Inst, 89-94; dir pharmacol, Symphony Pharmaceut, 94-95; instr biol sci, Univ Hartford, 95; free-lance med writer, 95-96. *Concurrent Pos:* Res fel, Comt Advan Sci Training, NSF, 65 & 70; teaching asst, Dept Biochem & Biophys, Ore State Univ, 74; partic, Advan Study Inst Cyclic Nucleotides, NATO, 77. *Mem:* Am Chem Soc; AAAS; fel Am Inst Chemists; Am Soc Pharmacol Exp Ther; Soc Neurosci. *Res:* Receptors in nervous tissue membranes; receptor coupling to second messengers; linkage of changes in receptors to pathology behavior; author or coauthor of over 50 publications. *Mailing Add:* 8722 West F Ave Kalamazoo MI 49009-8895. *Fax:* 616-833-9507; *E-Mail:* duncan.p.taylor@ am.pnu.com

**TAYLOR, EDITH L,** PALEOBOTANY, PLANT ANATOMY. *Current Pos:* PROF BOT, UNIV KANS, 95-, SR CUR, UNIV KANS, NATURAL HIST MUS, 95- *Personal Data:* b Ft Worth, Tex, Aug 21, 51; div; c 1. *Educ:* Ohio State Univ, BSc, 76, MSc, 78, PhD(bot), 83. *Honors & Awards:* Antarctic Medal US, 85. *Prof Exp:* Teaching asst & res asst bot, Dept Bot, Ohio State Univ, 77-82; fel, Am Asn Univ Women, 82-83; asst prof biol, Hope Col, 83-86; sr res assoc, Ohio State Univ, 87-88, res scientist, Byrd Polar Res Ctr, 88-95. *Concurrent Pos:* Teaching assoc bot, Dept Bot, Univ Tex, 79; researcher, Inst Polar Studies, Ohio State Univ, 85-86; adj asst prof, Dept Bot, Ohio State Univ, 87-89, adj assoc prof plant biol & geol sci, 89-; NAm rep, Int Orgn Paleobot, 93- *Mem:* Bot Soc Am; Int Orgn Paleobot; Int Asn Wood Anatomists; fel AAAS; fel Linnean Soc; Asn Women Sci; Geol Soc Am. *Res:* Phloem anatomy of Paleozoic and Mesozoic plants; investigation of Permian and Triassic silicified plants from the Central Transantarctic Mountains, Antarctica; fossil tree-rings and paleoclimate; adaptations of high-latitude fossil floras; structure and phylogenetic trends of fossil plants. *Mailing Add:* Dept Bot Univ Kans Haworth Hall Lawrence KS 66045-2106. *Fax:* 614-292-6345; *E-Mail:* eltaylor@osu.edu

**TAYLOR, EDWARD CURTIS,** ORGANIC CHEMISTRY. *Current Pos:* from asst prof to assoc prof, 54-64, chmn dept chem, 74-79, PROF CHEM, PRINCETON UNIV, 64-, A BARTON HEPBURN PROF ORG CHEM, 66- *Personal Data:* b Springfield, Mass, Aug 3, 23; m 46, Virginia D Crouse; c Edward N & Susan R (Spielman). *Educ:* Cornell Univ, AB, 46, PhD(org chem), 49. *Hon Degrees:* DSc, Hamilton Col, 69. *Honors & Awards:* Res Awards, Smith Kline & Fr Found, 55, Hoffmann-La Roche Found, 64 & 65, S B Penick Found, 69, 70, 71 & 72 & Ciba Pharmaceut Co, 71; Creative Work Award, Am Chem Soc, 74; H J Backer lectr, Univ Groningen, 71; 5th Int Award in Heterocyclic Chem, 89; Gowland Hopkins Medal, 93. *Prof Exp:* Merck fel, Zurich Tech Univ, 49-50; Du Pont fel, Univ Ill, 50-51, instr chem, 51-53, asst prof org chem, 53-54. *Concurrent Pos:* NSF sr fac fel, Harvard Univ, 59; Fulbright scholar, 60; vis prof inst org chem, Stuttgart Tech Univ, 60; vis lectr, Weizmann Inst, 60; mem, Chem Adv Comt, Air Force Off Sci Res, 62-70; consult, Eastman Kodak Co, 65-82, Eli Lilly & Co, 70-, Tenn Eastman Co, 71-82, Burroughs-Wellcome Co, 83-95, DuPont Merck Pharmaceut Co, 85-; distinguished vis prof, Univ Buffalo, 69; ed org chem, Wiley Intersci, Inc, 69-; vis prof, Univ E Anglia, 69 & 72; ed, Advances in Org Chem; co-ed, Gen Heterocyclic Chem & Chem of Heterocyclic Compounds; Guggenheim Mem fel, 79-80; Alexander von Humboldt sr US scientist award, 84-85; A C Cope scholar, Am Chem Soc, 94. *Mem:* AAAS; Am Chem Soc; fel NY Acad Sci; Royal Soc Chem; Ger Chem Soc. *Res:* Organic synthesis; heterocyclic chemistry, particularly pyrimidines, purines and pteridines; organothallium chemistry; natural products; photochemistry; medicinal chemistry. *Mailing Add:* Frick Chem Lab Princeton Univ Princeton NJ 08540. *Fax:* 609-258-1368; *E-Mail:* sunup@chemvax. princeton.edu

**TAYLOR, EDWARD DONALD,** PHYSICS & CHEMISTRY. *Current Pos:* PROF CHEM, ODESSA COL, 68- *Personal Data:* b Clifton, Tex, Sept 30, 40; m 65; c 1. *Educ:* Univ Tex, Austin, BS, 63; Tex Tech Univ, PhD(chem), 67. *Honors & Awards:* Eastman Fel, Eastman Kodak Co, 68. *Prof Exp:* Asst prof & fel chem, Fla State Univ, 67-68. *Concurrent Pos:* Fel, Tex A&M Univ, 71. *Mem:* Am Chem Soc. *Res:* Investigations of thermoluminescence via electron paramagnetic resonance to understand the mechanism of the process. *Mailing Add:* Odessa Col 201 W Univ Odessa TX 79764-7105

**TAYLOR, EDWARD MORGAN,** GEOLOGY, PETROLOGY. *Current Pos:* asst prof geol, 66-71, assoc prof, 71-, PROF GEOSCI, ORE STATE UNIV. *Personal Data:* b Rapid City, SDak, Dec 27, 33; m 58; c 2. *Educ:* Ore State Univ, BS, 57, MS, 60; Wash State Univ, PhD(geol), 67. *Prof Exp:* Instr geol, Ore State Univ, 62-63 & Wash State Univ, 64-65. *Mem:* Geol Soc Am; Mineral Soc Am; Am Geophys Union. *Res:* Volcanic petrology of Cascade Range of California, Oregon and Washington. *Mailing Add:* Dept Geol Ore State Univ Wilkinson 130 Corvallis OR 97331

**TAYLOR, EDWARD STEWART,** OBSTETRICS & GYNECOLOGY. *Current Pos:* Prof obstet & gynec & head dept, Univ Colo, 47-76, dir, Am Bd Obstet & Gynec, 60-69, clin prof, 77-80, EMER PROF OBSTET & GYNEC, MED CTR, UNIV COLO, DENVER, 80- *Personal Data:* b Hecla, SDak, Aug 20, 11; m 40; c 3. *Educ:* Univ Iowa, BA, 33, MD, 36; Am Bd Obstet &

Gynec, dipl, 46. *Honors & Awards:* Distinguished Serv Award, Am Col Obstet & Gynec, 84. *Concurrent Pos:* Consult Surgeon Gen, US Dept Air Force; coun mem, Nat Inst Child Health & Human Develop; ed, Obstet & Gynec Surv, 67-76. *Mem:* Am Gynec Soc; Am Asn Obstet & Gynec; Am Col Surg; Am Col Obstet & Gynec; Am Gynec & Obstet Soc. *Res:* Cancer of the cervix; physiology of pregnancy. *Mailing Add:* 80 Dexter St Denver CO 80222

**TAYLOR, EDWIN FLORIMAN,** PHYSICS. *Current Pos:* dir, Educ Video Resources, 79-91, EMER PROF, MASS INST TECHNOL, 91-; RES PROF RELATIVITY, BOSTON UNIV, 91- *Personal Data:* b Oberlin, Ohio, June 22, 31; m 55; c 3. *Educ:* Oberlin Col, AB, 53; Harvard Univ, MA, 54, PhD(physics), 58. *Prof Exp:* Asst prof physics, Wesleyan Univ, 56-64; vis assoc prof, Educ Res Ctr, Mass Inst Technol, 64-66, sr res scientist, 66-73; ed, Am J Physics, 73-78. *Mem:* Am Phys Soc; Am Asn Physics Teachers. *Res:* Solid state physics; educational writing and research in mechanics, special relativity and quantum physics; computer-assisted learning. *Mailing Add:* Physics Dept Rm 255 Boston Univ 590 Commonwealth Dr Boston MA 02215. *E-Mail:* eftalo@mit.edu

**TAYLOR, EDWIN WILLIAM,** BIOPHYSICS. *Current Pos:* from instr to prof biophys, 59-74, PROF BIOPHYS & THEORET BIOL, UNIV CHICAGO, 74-, MASTER BIOL SCI, COL DIV & ASSOC DEAN, 76- *Personal Data:* b Toronto, Ont, June 8, 29; m 56; c 3. *Educ:* Univ Toronto, BA, 52; McMaster Univ, MSc, 55; Univ Chicago, PhD(biophys), 57. *Prof Exp:* Instr physics, Ont Agr Col, 52-53; res assoc biol, Mass Inst Technol, 57-59. *Mem:* Biophys Soc. *Res:* Mechanochemical systems; muscle; flagella; protoplasmic streaming; mechanism of cell division; physical protein chemistry. *Mailing Add:* Dept Molecular Genetics-Cell Biol/CLSC 339 Univ Chicago 920 E 58th St Chicago IL 60637

**TAYLOR, ELIZABETH BEAMAN HESCH,** MATHEMATICS. *Current Pos:* RETIRED. *Personal Data:* b Sumter, SC, Oct 27, 21; m 48, 77, Jackson J; c Thomas C Hesch. *Educ:* Winthrop Col, BA, 43; Duke Univ, MA, 46; Columbia Univ, PhD, 55. *Prof Exp:* Instr math, Winthrop Col, 43; teacher pub schs, SC, 43-45; asst prof, Radford Col, 46-52 & Westhampton Col, 52-70; from assoc prof to prof math, Univ Richmond, 70-85. *Mem:* Math Asn Am. *Res:* Nature of mathematical evidence and its significance for the teaching of secondary school mathematics. *Mailing Add:* 2431 Swathmore Rd Richmond VA 23235

**TAYLOR, ELLISON HALL,** PHYSICAL CHEMISTRY. *Current Pos:* RETIRED. *Personal Data:* b Kalamazoo, Mich, Sept 6, 13; wid; c Laurence R & William E. *Educ:* Cornell Univ, BChem, 35; Princeton Univ, MA, 37, PhD(phys chem), 38. *Honors & Awards:* S C Lind lectr. *Prof Exp:* Instr chem, Univ Utah, 38-40; instr chem eng, Cornell Univ, 40-42; res chemist, Div War Res, Columbia Univ, 42-45; res chemist, Clinton Labs, Tenn, 45-48, asst dir chem div, 46-48; actg dir, Chem Div, Oak Ridge Nat Lab, 48, prob leader, 48-49, from assoc dir to dir, Chem Div, 49-51, asst dir res, 51-54, dir, Chem Div, 54-75, sr res staff mem, 75-84. *Concurrent Pos:* Vis prof, Cornell Univ, 65; consult, 84- *Mem:* AAAS; Am Chem Soc; Am Phys Soc. *Res:* Heterogeneous catalysis; chemical problems related to isotope separations; radiation chemistry; chemical kinetics; molecular beams in chemistry; trace element analysis by resonance ionization. *Mailing Add:* 143 Orchard Lane Oak Ridge TN 37830

**TAYLOR, ERIC ROBERT,** BIOPHYSICS. *Current Pos:* ASST PROF BIOCHEM, UNIV SOUTHWESTERN LA, 84- *Personal Data:* b Quincy, Mass, Oct 31, 47; m 74; c 1. *Educ:* Ohio State Univ, BS, 72; Rutgers Univ, PhD(biochem), 81. *Prof Exp:* Res asst, Dept Chem, Renesselaer Polytech Inst, 81-84. *Mem:* NY Acad Sci; Sigma Xi; AAAS. *Res:* Computer modeling of DNA drug interactions. *Mailing Add:* Dept Chem Univ Southwestern La PO Box 44370 Lafayette LA 70504

**TAYLOR, EUGENE M,** PHYSIOLOGY, PHARMACOLOGY. *Current Pos:* HEALTH EFFECTS SPECIALIST, OFF WATER, US ENVIRON PROTECTION AGENCY, 94- *Personal Data:* b Cheyenne, Wyo, Dec 25, 32; m 78, Marilyn Johston; c Corey, Matthew, Mitchell, Mark & Cameron. *Educ:* Idaho State Col, BS, 58; Univ Wash, MS, 59, PhD(physiol & psychol), 64. *Prof Exp:* Res asst prof rehab med, Sch Med, Univ Wash, 72-74; investr physiol, Va Mason Res Ctr, 74-77, assoc mem sci staff physiol, 77-81; lectr psychol, Univ Wash, 81-82; res scientist, Dept Hemat/Oncol, Children's Hosp & Med Ctr, Seattle, 82-91. *Concurrent Pos:* Consult, Vet Admin Hosp, Phoenix, Ariz, 68-72; fel, Dept Bioeng, Univ Wash, 71-72; affil assoc prof, Dept Otolaryngol, 76-82, res affil, Regional Primate Res Ctr, 77-80, res assoc, Dept Pediat, 85-91; affil investr, Virginia Mason Res Ctr, 71-74. *Res:* Evaluation of chemical contamination of drinking water; development of drinking water standards and regulation. *Mailing Add:* OW-136 US Environ Protection Agency 1200 Sixth Ave Seattle WA 98101. *E-Mail:* taylorgenem@epamail.epa.gov

**TAYLOR, FLETCHER BRANDON, JR,** INTERNAL MEDICINE. *Current Pos:* OKLA MED RES FOUND. *Personal Data:* b Aug 24, 29; m 54; c 4. *Educ:* Stanford Univ, BS, 52; Univ Calif, San Francisco, MD, 56. *Hon Degrees:* MS, Univ Pa, 71. *Honors & Awards:* Cochems Prize Cardiovasc Res, 68; Louis Pasteur Lectr Award, Univ Paris, 69. *Prof Exp:* Intern, Southern Pac Hosp, San Francisco, 56-57; resident surg, 57-58; res assoc protein chem, London Hosp, Eng, 58-59; mem res staff thrombosis, Cardiovasc Res Inst, San Francisco, 59-65; from asst prof to assoc prof med, Hosp Univ Pa, Philadelphia, 65-74, co-chmn div allergy & immunol, 68-74; prof path & med & dir div exp path & med, Health Sci Ctr, Univ Okla, 74- *Concurrent Pos:*

Resident med, Univ Calif Hosp, San Francisco, 59-62; consult hemat, NASA Manned Space Flight Ctr, 68-; mem thrombosis coun, Am Heart Asn, 71-; head, Am Acad Allergy Post-Grad Educ Comt; clin prof res med, Okla Univ Health Sci Ctr, prof res biochem, head sect exp path & med; dir clin hemat serv, Univ Hosp, Oklahoma City; dir, Oklahoma City Children's Mem Hosp Coagulation Lab. *Mem:* Int Soc Thrombosis & Haemostasis; Am Asn Immunol; Am Soc Clin Invest; Am Physiol Soc; Am Fedn Clin Res; Sigma Xi. *Res:* Thrombosis and protein chemistry. *Mailing Add:* Cardiovasc Biol Res Dept Okla Med Res Found 825 NE 13th St Oklahoma City OK 73104-5097. *Fax:* 405-271-7890

**TAYLOR, FLOYD HECKMAN,** MATHEMATICS. *Current Pos:* RETIRED. *Personal Data:* b North Versailles, Pa, May 6, 26; m 55; c 2. *Educ:* Bucknell Univ, BS, 49; Univ Pittsburgh, MS, 53, ScD, 63. *Prof Exp:* Asst proj engr math, Sperry Gyroscope Co, NY, 53-54; instr, Hood Col, 54-56; mathematician, Atlantic Div, Aerojet Gen Corp Div, Gen Tire & Rubber Co, 56-57 & US Army Biol Labs, 57-64; asst prof biostatist, Grad Sch Pub Health & asst prof prev med, Sch Med, Univ Pittsburgh, 64-70, assoc prof community med, 70-75, res prof community med, Sch Med, 75-87. *Concurrent Pos:* Instr, Frederick Community Col, 57-61. *Mem:* Sigma Xi; Am Statist Soc; Biomet Soc. *Res:* Numerical analysis; applications of mathematics to digital computers; mathematical models as applied to biology; biostatistics. *Mailing Add:* 5023 Frew St Pittsburgh PA 15213

**TAYLOR, FRANCIS B,** MATHEMATICS. *Current Pos:* From instr to assoc prof, 47-65, head dept, 64-72, PROF MATH, MANHATTAN COL, 65- *Personal Data:* b New York, NY, June 15, 25. *Educ:* Manhattan Col, BA, 44; Columbia Univ, AM, 47, PhD(math educ), 59. *Concurrent Pos:* Lectr, Col Mt St Vincent, 53-56; NSF fac fel, 57-58; lectr, Sch Gen Studies, Hunter Col, 59-60. *Mem:* Math Asn Am; Am Statist Asn; Inst Math Statist; Nat Coun Teachers Math; Sigma Xi. *Res:* Mathematical statistics. *Mailing Add:* Dept Math & Comput Sci Manhattan Col Bronx NY 10471

**TAYLOR, FRANK EUGENE,** EXPERIMENTAL HIGH ENERGY PHYSICS. *Current Pos:* SR RES SCIENTIST, MASS INST TECHNOL, 83- *Personal Data:* b Richmond, Va, Apr 1, 42; m 68; c 3. *Educ:* Mich State Univ, BS, 64; Cornell Univ, PhD(exp high energy physics), 70. *Prof Exp:* Res assoc exp high energy physics, Lab Nuclear Studies, Cornell Univ, 70-71, Deutsches Elektronen Synchrotron-Hamburg, Ger, 71-72; from asst prof to assoc prof exp high energy physics, 77-83, prof physics, Northern Ill Univ, 83-87. *Concurrent Pos:* Prin physicist, Dept Energy grant, 78-83. *Mem:* Am Phys Soc. *Res:* Experiment and phenomenology of inclusive reactions in strong interactions; experimental high energy neutrino physics; electron-positron collisions at ZO pole. *Mailing Add:* Mass Inst Technol Bldg 24 5th Floor Cambridge MA 02139

**TAYLOR, FRANK JOHN RUPERT (MAX),** MARINE BIOLOGY, PROTISTOLOGY. *Current Pos:* from asst prof to assoc prof, 65-75, PROF BIOL & OCEANOG, DEPT OCEANOG, UNIV BC, 75- *Personal Data:* b Cairo, Egypt, July 17, 39; m 63; c 3. *Educ:* Univ Cape Town, BSc, 59, Hons, 60, PhD(marine bot), 65. *Prof Exp:* Res asst marine phytoplankton, Inst Oceanog, Univ Cape Town, 60-64. *Concurrent Pos:* Can-France Exchange fel, France, 72; vis scientist, Phuket Marine Biol Ctr, Thailand, 73; res assoc, Int Develop Res Ctr, Bellairs Res Inst, Barbados, 79-80, Plant Sci, Univ Oxford, 86-87; Christensen fel, Oxford Univ, UK, 86; I W Killam sr fel, Univ BC, 87. *Mem:* Hon mem Int Soc Evolutionary Protistology (pres, 79-81); fel Royal Soc Can; Int Soc Study Harmful Algae. *Res:* Taxonomy and distributional ecology of unicellular marine organisms, principally diatoms and dinoflagellates; undergraduate biology; marine phytoplankton ecology; red tides; intracellular symbiosis; evolution, especially origin of eukaryotes and protist evolution. *Mailing Add:* Oceanog Dept Earth & Ocean Sci Univ BC Vancouver BC V6T 1Z4 Can

**TAYLOR, FRED M,** PEDIATRICS. *Current Pos:* RETIRED. *Personal Data:* b Chanute, Kans, Aug 21, 19; m 42; c 5. *Educ:* Stanford Univ, AB, 41, MD, 44. *Prof Exp:* From instr to prof pediat, Baylor Col Med, 48-69; prof, Med Sch, Univ Tex, San Antonio, 69-72, from asst dean to assoc dean acad develop, 69-72; dir, Off Continuing Educ, Baylor Col Med, 72-78, prof pediat, 72-85, spec asst to exec vpres & dean, 78-80, exec asst to pres, 80-85, emer prof & adv to pres, 85- *Mem:* AAAS; Am Acad Pediat; Soc Res Child Develop. *Res:* Infant nutrition and feeding; developmental behavior of infants, children and adolescents. *Mailing Add:* 810 Alhambra Sugar Land TX 77478-4003

**TAYLOR, FRED WILLIAM,** WOOD SCIENCE & TECHNOLOGY. *Current Pos:* prof wood sci & technol & asst dir, Miss Forestry Prod Utilization Lab, 65-97, EMER PROF WOOD SCI, MISS STATE UNIV, 97- *Personal Data:* b Springcreek, WVa, Jan 17, 32; m 54; c 4. *Educ:* Va Polytech Inst, BS, 53; NC State Col, MWT, 54, PhD(wood sci & technol), 65. *Prof Exp:* Asst prof forestry, Univ Vt, 54-55; asst timber buyer, J B Belcher Lumber Co, 55-56; wood technologist, Pulaski Veneer & Furniture Co, 56-59; res asst, NC State Univ, 59-62; wood utilization exten specialist, Univ Mo, 63-65. *Concurrent Pos:* Coun Sci & Indust Res grant, SAfrica, 71-72. *Mem:* Forest Prod Res Soc; Soc Wood Sci & Technol; Int Asn Wood Anatomists; Inst Wood Sci. *Res:* Natural variation in the anatomical structure of angiosperm xylem, especially genetic implications of property variations. *Mailing Add:* Miss State Univ Box 9820 Mississippi State MS 39762

**TAYLOR, FREDRIC WILLIAM,** ATMOSPHERIC PHYSICS. *Current Pos:* HEAD, DEPT ATMOSPHERIC PHYSICS, OXFORD UNIV, 79- *Personal Data:* b Amble, Eng, Sept 24, 44; m 69. *Educ:* Univ Liverpool, BSc, 66; Oxford Univ, DPhil(atmospheric physics), 70. *Honors & Awards:* Except Sci Achievement Award Rank Prize, NASA, 89. *Prof Exp:* Res scientist tech staff atmospheric physics, Jet Propulsion Lab, Calif Inst Technol, 71-79. *Concurrent Pos:* Founder, Smith Inst Indust Math, New Sun Found, World Meteorol Orgn. *Mem:* Fel Royal Meteorol Soc; Am Meteorol Soc; Optical Soc Am; assoc Am Astron Asn; fel Royal Soc Arts. *Res:* Physics of the atmospheres of the Earth and planets, specializing in atmospheric radiation, remote sensing techniques and infrared observational methods. *Mailing Add:* Dept Physics Clarendon Lab Oxford Univ Parks Rd Oxford 0X1 3PU England. *Fax:* 44-1865-272924

**TAYLOR, FREDRICK JAMES,** ELECTRICAL ENGINEERING, COMPUTER SCIENCE. *Current Pos:* PROF, UNIV FLA, 83- *Personal Data:* b Wisconsin Rapids, Wis, Apr 28, 40; m 68; c 3. *Educ:* Milwaukee Sch Eng, BS, 65; Univ Colo, MS, 66, PhD(elec eng), 69. *Prof Exp:* Researcher elec eng, Tex Instruments, Dallas, 69-70; assoc prof, Univ Tex, El Paso, 70-75; prof elec eng, Univ Cincinnati, 75-83. *Concurrent Pos:* Prin investr, US Army Atmospheric Sci Lab grant, 73-75, Eng Found grant, 77-78 & NSF grant, 78- *Mem:* Inst Elec & Electronics Engrs. *Res:* Digital systems; digital signal processing; medical signal analysis; ultrasound; finite mathematics. *Mailing Add:* Dept Elec & Comput Eng Univ Fla 435 NEB Gainesville FL 32611

**TAYLOR, G DON,** COMPUTER SIMULATION, LOGISTICS. *Current Pos:* asst prof, 90-94, ASSOC PROF INDUST ENG, UNIV ARK, 94-; PRES, DON TAYLOR CONSULT SERV, 91- *Personal Data:* b Anchorage, Alaska, Mar 25, 60; m 87, Jo Ellen Gibson; c D Alex & Caroline F. *Educ:* Univ Tex, Arlington, BS, 83, MS, 85; Univ Mass, PhD(indust eng & opers res), 90. *Honors & Awards:* Doctor Theo Williamson Award, Integrated Mfg Systs, 95. *Prof Exp:* Mfg engr & supvr, Tex Instruments, 83-86; process engr, Digital Equipment Corp, 87-89. *Concurrent Pos:* Prin investr, Univ Ark, 90-; vis prof decision sci & eng systs, Rensselaer Polytech Inst, 96-97. *Mem:* Am Soc Eng Educ; Inst Indust Engrs. *Res:* Operations management and logistics with an emphasis on applied research using discrete event system simulation; author of more than 80 technical publications. *Mailing Add:* Univ Ark 4207 Bell Eng Ctr Fayetteville AR 72701. *Fax:* 501-575-8431; *E-Mail:* gdt@engr.uark.edu

**TAYLOR, G JEFFREY,** PLANETARY SCIENCE. *Current Pos:* PROF, HAWAII INST GEOPHYS & PLANETOL, UNIV HAWAII, MENOA, 90- *Personal Data:* b Port Jefferson, NY, June 27, 44; m 65; c 5. *Educ:* Colgate Univ, AB, 66; Rice Univ, MA, 68, PhD(geol), 70. *Honors & Awards:* Nininger Meteorite Prize, Ctr Meteorite Studies, Ariz State Univ, 69. *Prof Exp:* Smithsonian Res Found res fel, lunar mineral & petrol, Smithsonian Astrophys Observ, 70-72, res assoc, 72-73; asst prof, Wash Univ, 73-76; sr res assoc, Inst Meteoritics, Univ NMex, 76-90. *Concurrent Pos:* Assoc, Harvard Univ, 70-; vis scientist, Lunar Sci Inst, 74-76. *Mem:* Am Geophys Union; Geochem Soc; Meteoritical Soc; AAAS. *Res:* Petrologic and chemical nature of the moon, meteorites and earth, with emphasis on their origins and thermal histories. *Mailing Add:* Hawaii Inst Geophys & Planetol 2525 Correa Rd Honolulu HI 96822

**TAYLOR, GARY,** PLASMA PHYSICS, MICROWAVE & FAR-INFRARED MEASUREMENTS. *Current Pos:* Res assoc, Princeton Univ, 77-79, staff res physicist, Plasma Physics Lab, 79-85, res physicist, 85-94, PRIN RES PHYSICIST, PRINCETON UNIV, 94- *Personal Data:* b London, Eng, Sept 23, 52; US citizen; m 83, Wendy Collins. *Educ:* Univ Manchester, BSc, 74; Oxford Univ, MSc, 75, DPhil(plasma physics), 77. *Mem:* Am Phys Soc. *Res:* Application of microwave and far-infrared techniques to high temperature plasma confinement in Tokamak magnetic fusion machines. *Mailing Add:* Princeton Plasma Physics Lab Princeton Univ PO Box 451 Princeton NJ 08543. *Fax:* 609-243-2665; *E-Mail:* gtaylor@pppl.gov

**TAYLOR, GARY N,** organic chemistry, for more information see previous edition

**TAYLOR, GENE WARREN,** PHYSICAL CHEMISTRY, MATERIALS SCIENCE. *Current Pos:* staff mem chem, 72-91, INTEL ANALYST NON-PROLIFERATION INT SECURITY, LOS ALAMOS NAT LAB, 91- *Personal Data:* b Abilene, Tex, Nov 9, 36; m 64, Barbara J Anderson; c Tom. *Educ:* Tex Western Col, BS, 63; NMex State Univ, PhD(phys chem), 69. *Honors & Awards:* Withens Award for Weapons Res. *Prof Exp:* Mem staff chem, El Paso Natural Gas Prod, 63-65; teacher math, Ysleta Independent Schs, 64-65; mem fac chem, Kans State Univ, 69-72. *Concurrent Pos:* Mem staff, Schlesinger Res Found, 64-65; fel, Kans State Univ, 69-72. *Mem:* Am Chem Soc. *Res:* Rare gas, metastable atom flowing afterglow reactions for chemical analysis; gas phase chemical kinetics, and solid phase thermal decomposition reaction kinetics; composite materials; export controls-nonproliferation-technical assessment. *Mailing Add:* 69 Futura Los Alamos NM 87544. *Fax:* 505-667-3690

**TAYLOR, GEOFF W,** DEVICE PHYSICS, MATERIAL PHYSICS & PHYSICS OF OPTICAL DEVICES. *Current Pos:* PROF, UNIV CONN, 94- *Educ:* Queens Univ, Kingston, Ont, BASc, 66; Univ Toronto, MASc, 68 & PhD(elec eng), 72. *Prof Exp:* Mem tech staff, Honeywell, 74-76; mem tech staff, AT&T Bell Labs, Murray Hill, 76-86, mem tech staff, AT&T Bell Labs, Holmdel, 86-87. *Concurrent Pos:* Comt mem, Device Res Conf, 80-85, tech prog chmn, 85 & conf chmn, 86- *Mem:* Sr mem Inst Elec & Electronics Engrs; Optical Soc Am; Soc Photo-Optical Instrumentation Engrs. *Res:* Integrated opto-electronics using transistors, lasers, detectors, and integrated optics components. *Mailing Add:* Dept Elec & Systs Eng Univ Conn 260 Greenbrook Rd MS U-157/204 Storrs CT 06269

**TAYLOR, GEORGE EVANS, JR,** EVOLUTIONARY BIOLOGY. *Current Pos:* MEM STAFF, BIOL SCI CTR, DESERT RES INST, 90- *Personal Data:* b Richmond, Va, June 3, 49; m 72; c 2. *Educ:* Randolph-Macon Col, BS, 71; Emory Univ, PhD(biol), 76. *Prof Exp:* Instr biol, Agnes Scott Col, 76-77; res assoc bot, Nat Acad Sci, Nat Res Coun, 77-80; mem staff, Oak Ridge Nat Lab, 80-90. *Mem:* Am Soc Plant Physiologist; Bot Soc Am; Am Chem Soc; AAAS; Sigma Xi. *Res:* Plant stress physiology; evolutionary biology of plant populations including genetics, physiological ecology and population biology; rapid microevolutionary events in response to man generated stesses. *Mailing Add:* Environ Res Studies Dept 1000 Valley Rd Reno NV 89512

**TAYLOR, GEORGE STANLEY,** SOIL PHYSICS. *Current Pos:* from asst prof to assoc prof, 51-61, prof agron, 61-85, EMER PROF AGRON, OHIO STATE UNIV, 85- *Personal Data:* b Jackson, NC, Nov 29, 20; m 47; c 3. *Educ:* NC State Col, BS, 43, MS, 48; Iowa State Univ, PhD(soil physics), 50. *Prof Exp:* Asst, NC State Col, 47-48 & Iowa State Univ, 49-50. *Concurrent Pos:* Vis assoc prof, Univ Calif, 58-59; consult, US Agency Int Develop, Punjab, India, 68 & 70; UN Univ, Nigeria, 85. *Mem:* Am Soc Agron; Am Soc Agr Engrs; Am Geophys Union; Soil Sci Soc Am. *Res:* Water flow in porous media; land drainage; two-dimensional modeling of heat and water flow in porous media by numerical techniques; disposal wastes in soil. *Mailing Add:* 1387 Friar Lane Columbus OH 43221

**TAYLOR, GEORGE THOMAS,** DEVELOPMENTAL BIOLOGY, ZOOLOGY. *Current Pos:* RES ASSOC, DEPT BIOL SCI, FLA INT UNIV, 88-; DIR, ELECTRON MICROS LAB, 91- *Personal Data:* b Asheboro, NC, July 18, 35. *Educ:* Guilford Col, AB, 57; Univ NC, Chapel Hill, MA, 64; Univ Mass, Amherst, PhD(zool), 70. *Prof Exp:* Instr zool, Atlantic Christian Col, 62-65; asst prof human anat, Col Osteop Med & Surg, 69-73; asst prof physiol, Southern Ill Univ, 73-77; asst prof dept biol sci & dir electron micros lab, Am Univ, Caribbean, 77-82, assoc prof anat, 84-85. *Mem:* AAAS; Am Soc Cell Biol; Am Soc Zoologists; Soc Develop Biol; Am Ornithologists Union. *Res:* Cytochemical and cytological aspects of oocyte differentiation and early development in marine invertebrates; special interest in changes in subcellular morphology and function during embryonic cytodifferentiation. *Mailing Add:* 19510 SW 87th Ave Miami FL 33157. *Fax:* 305-348-1986

**TAYLOR, GEORGE WILLIAM,** SOLID STATE PHYSICS, ELECTRICAL ENGINEERING. *Current Pos:* vpres res & eng, Princeton Mat Sci Inc, 71-75, PRES, PRINCETON RESOURCES INC, 75- & PRINCETON RES ASSOCS, 77- *Personal Data:* b Perth, Australia, June 16, 34; US citizen; m 57; c 4. *Educ:* Western Australia Univ, BE, 57, DEng, 81; London Univ, PhD(ferroelec), 61. *Hon Degrees:* DSc, Don Pedag Inst, USSR, 89. *Honors & Awards:* Fisk Prize, IRE, 56; Achievement Award, RCA Labs, 66. *Prof Exp:* Group engr, telecommun, Australian Post Off, 61; lectr elec eng, Sydney Univ, 61-62; mem tech staff comput res, RCA Corp Labs, 62-70. *Concurrent Pos:* Ed, Int J Ferroelectrics, 70-, Int J Ferroelectrics Lett, 82- emer ed, Electronic Display World; prof elec eng, Rutgers Univ, 76-77; travel fel, US NSF, 76. *Mem:* Sr mem Inst Elec & Electronics Engrs; fel Australian Inst Eng; Am Phys Soc; fel Brit Inst Elec Eng. *Res:* Properties, synthesis, applications of ferroelectric materials; computer memories; displays and electro-optics; piezoelectric and pyroelectric materials and devices; author of two books. *Mailing Add:* PO Box 211 Princeton NJ 08542-0211

**TAYLOR, GERALD C,** BACTERIOLOGY, VIROLOGY. *Current Pos:* asst, Lab Br, Commun Dis Ctr, USPHS, 55-57, lab supvr & unit chief, Tissue Cult Unit, 57-71, LAB SUPVR & UNIT CHIEF, LAB BR & CHIEF, CELL CULT & MEDIA SECT, SCI SERV DIV, CTR DIS CONTROL, USPHS, 71- *Personal Data:* b Oregon, Mo, Sept 10, 19; m 50; c 4. *Educ:* Univ Kans, BA, 49, MA, 51, PhD(bact), 55. *Prof Exp:* Lab instr bact & virol, Univ Kans, 50-52; asst rickettsiae, 52-55. *Mem:* AAAS; Am Soc Microbiol; Sigma Xi. *Res:* Human and animal virology; development of tissue culture in the field of virology. *Mailing Add:* 2855 Hollywood Dr Decatur GA 30333-5020

**TAYLOR, GERALD REED, JR,** PHYSICS. *Current Pos:* assoc prof physics, Madison Col, 69-80, PROF PHYSICS, JAMES MADISON UNIV, HARRISONBURG, VA, 80- *Personal Data:* b Bloxom, Va, Apr 17, 37; m 60; c 2. *Educ:* Va Polytech Inst & State Univ, BS, 59, MS, 61; Univ Va, PhD(physics), 67. *Honors & Awards:* J Shelton Horsley Res Award, Va Acad Sci, 62. *Prof Exp:* Assoc physicist, Texaco Exp Inc, 60-62; res physicist solid state physics, Linde Div, Union Carbide Corp, 67-69. *Concurrent Pos:* Dir, Vis Scientists Prog, Va Acad Sci, 77-79. *Mem:* Am Phys Soc; Am Asn Physics Teachers; Sigma Xi. *Res:* Low Temperature solid state physics; ferromagnetism; magneto-thermal conductivity; resistivity; physics education and instruction; plasma physics and plasma diagnostics. *Mailing Add:* Dept Physics James Madison Univ Miller Hall Harrisonburg VA 22807

**TAYLOR, GLADYS GILLMAN,** FOUNDATION & PHILOSOPHY OF MATHEMATICS. *Current Pos:* RETIRED. *Personal Data:* b Bloomfield, NJ, Dec 6, 26; div; c John G, Steven G & Jill B. *Educ:* Skidmore Univ, BA, 48; Radcliffe Univ, MA, 52; Ind Univ, PhD(hist & philos sci), 80. *Prof Exp:* From asst prof to prof math, Ind State Univ, 65-89. *Mem:* Philos Sci Asn. *Res:* Logic and set theory; realism, nominalism and conceptualism in the foundations of mathematics. *Mailing Add:* 2711 Wilson Dr Terre Haute IN 47803

**TAYLOR, HAROLD ALLISON, JR,** HUMAN GENETICS, BIOCHEMISTRY. *Current Pos:* DIR LABS, GREENWOOD GENETIC CTR, 75- *Personal Data:* b Richmond, Va, Oct 18, 42; m 65; c 2. *Educ:* Univ Tenn, BS, 65, MS, 67, PhD(zool), 71. *Prof Exp:* Fel pediat, Sch Med, Johns

Hopkins Univ, 71-73, instr, 73-75; asst dir, Genetics Lab, John F Kennedy Inst, Baltimore, 73-75. *Mem:* AAAS; Am Soc Human Genetics. *Res:* Lysosomal storage diseases; inborn errors of metabolism; genetics of mental retardation. *Mailing Add:* Greenwood Genetics Ctr 1 Gregor Mendel Circle Greenwood SC 29646

**TAYLOR, HAROLD EVANS,** PLASMA PHYSICS, SPACE PHYSICS. *Current Pos:* from asst prof to prof, 71-88, prof astrophys, 88-90, PROF PHYSICS, RICHARD STOCKTON COL, 90- *Personal Data:* b Philadelphia, Pa, Sept 13, 39; m 64, 84, Suzanne Rie; c Laura, Peter, Amy, Jeremy, Bernard & Doren. *Educ:* Haverford Col, BA, 61; Mass Inst Technol, MS, 62; Univ Iowa, PhD(physics), 66. *Prof Exp:* Res assoc physics, Univ Iowa, 66; Nat Acad Sci assoc, Goddard Spaceflight Ctr, NASA, 66-68; res assoc plasma physics, Princeton Univ, 68-71. *Concurrent Pos:* Consult, Los Alamos Sci Labs, Princeton Univ, 86-87, vis res scientist, 86-87, vis prof mech eng, Univ Pa, 78; vis res scientist, Princeton Univ, 94- *Mem:* Am Asn Phys Teachers; Fedn Am Sci; Int Solar Energy Soc; Am Phys Soc; Inst Elec & Electronics Engrs; Royal Astron Soc Can. *Res:* Energy conservation in buildings; space plasma physics, including physics of the magnetosphere; physics of the interplanetary medium; cosmic rays; solar and wind energy devices; astronomical photometry; personal computer hardware; pulsars. *Mailing Add:* Fac Natural Sci & Math Richard Stockton Col Pomona NJ 08240. *Fax:* 609-748-5515; *E-Mail:* hal@riverfarm.org

**TAYLOR, HAROLD LELAND,** BIOCHEMISTRY. *Current Pos:* RETIRED. *Personal Data:* b Cambridge, Kans, May 3, 20; m 43; c 1. *Educ:* Southwestern Col, Kans, AB, 42; Univ Kans, PhD(biochem), 55. *Hon Degrees:* DSc, Southwestern Col, Kans, 73. *Prof Exp:* Res assoc, Harvard Univ, 42-46; biochemist, State Health Dept, Mich, 46-51 & 53-56; mgr, Immunochem Dept, Pitman-Moore Div, Dow Chem Co, 56-63, tech asst to dir biol labs, 63-64, res chemist, Dow Res Labs, Zionsville, 64-72, clin monitor, Med Dept, 72-74, clin investr, Merrell Dow Pharmaceut, 74-92. *Mem:* Am Chem Soc; Sigma Xi; NY Acad Sci; Am Soc Clin Pharmacol & Therapeut. *Res:* Fractionation of human blood plasma; physiological effects of antithyroid drugs in rats; isolation of immune fraction from hyperimmune canine plasma; control of biologicals production; drug metabolism; serum cholesterol lowering drugs. *Mailing Add:* 799 W 750 S Hebron IN 46341-9739

**TAYLOR, HAROLD MELLON,** ORGANIC CHEMISTRY. *Current Pos:* RETIRED. *Personal Data:* b Lucama, NC, May 14, 29; m 53; c 3. *Educ:* Univ NC, AB, 51, PhD(org chem), 59. *Prof Exp:* Researcher, Eli Lilly & Co, 59-80, res adv, 80-91. *Concurrent Pos:* Sr adv, Dow Elanco, 91- *Res:* Discovery and development of new agricultural pesticides. *Mailing Add:* 7459 Steinmeier Dr Indianapolis IN 46250

**TAYLOR, HAROLD NATHANIEL,** CHEMISTRY. *Current Pos:* PRES, HAGERSTOWN LEATHER GOODS CO, 53- *Personal Data:* b Baltimore, Md, May 18, 21; m 42; c 3. *Educ:* Johns Hopkins Univ, BE, 42, MS, 45; Cornell Univ, PhD(phys chem), 49. *Prof Exp:* Jr chem engr, Tenn Valley Authority, Wilson Dam, Ala, 42-43; jr instr chem eng, Johns Hopkins Univ, 43-44, asst, Off Rubber Res, 44 & Manhattan Proj, SAM Labs, Columbia Univ, 44-45; res chemist, Manhattan Proj, Carbide & Carbon Chem Co, 45-46 & Ammonia Dept, Exp Sta, E I du Pont de Nemours & Co, 49-53. *Concurrent Pos:* Dir, Cent Chem Co, 70- & Antietam Bank Co, 74- *Mem:* AAAS; Am Chem Soc. *Res:* Polymer chemistry; polymerization; plastic applications. *Mailing Add:* 13220 Fountain Head Rd Hagerstown MD 21740

**TAYLOR, HARRY ELMER,** ELECTRICAL ENGINEERING. *Current Pos:* Mem tech staff, 58-68, SUPVR, INTEGRATED CIRCUIT DESIGN GROUP, BELL TEL LABS, 68- *Personal Data:* b Easton, Pa, July 1, 31; m 53; c 3. *Educ:* Okla State Univ, BS, 57, MS, 58. *Res:* Transistor applications in Bell System use; consult and advise circuit designers desiring custom integrated circuits for Bell System use. *Mailing Add:* Bell Tel Labs 555 Union Blvd Allentown PA 18103

**TAYLOR, HARRY WILLIAM,** nuclear spectroscopy; deceased, see previous edition for last biography

**TAYLOR, HENRY L,** EXPERIMENTAL PSYCHOLOGY, TRAINING & SIMULATION HUMAN FACTORS. *Current Pos:* actg head, Aviation Res Lab, 81-84, DIR, INST AVIATION & DIR COM OPERS, WILLARD AIRPORT & PROF AVIATION, UNIV ILL, URBANA-CHAMPAIGN, 80-, PROF, DEPT PSYCHOL, 81-, INTERIM HEAD PILOT TRAINING, INST AVIATION, 93- *Personal Data:* b Tallassee, Ala, Nov 1, 33; m 3, Mary C Garrison; c Kenneth H, Gregory L & Barry C. *Educ:* Auburn Univ, BS, 56, MS, 57; Fla State Univ, PhD(psychol), 65. *Honors & Awards:* Raymond F Longacre Award, Aerospace Med Asn, 92; Franklin V Taylor Award, Div 21, Am Psychol Asn, 94; Hanson Award, Aerospace Human Factors Asn, 96. *Prof Exp:* Staff scientist & dep chief, Div Comp Psychol, 6571st Aeromed Res Lab, Holloman, AFB, NMex, 65-67; instr & navigator, C-130-E 345th Tactical Airlift Squadron, CCK, Taiwan, 67-69; prog monitor, Human Resources Lab, Andrews AFB, Md, 69-72; mil asst, Off Secy Defense, Washington, 72-78. *Concurrent Pos:* Drug res coordr, Dept Defense, 72-75; chmn, Internal Affairs Comt, Ill Pub Airports Asn, 84-86; mem, Ill Task Force Compatible Land Use, 86-91, Strategic Oversight Comt, Nat Aviation Training Maintenance & Tech Ctr, 89-90, Comt Intermodal Transp Ctr, 91-; bd dirs, Ill Pub Airports Asn, 80-90, pres, 86-88, past pres, 88-90; rep, Am Psychol Coun, 95. *Mem:* Fel Am Psychol Asn (secy, 84-88, pres, 88, past pres, 89-90); fel Am Psychol Soc; fel Human Factors & Ergonomics Soc; fel Aerospace Human Factors Asn (pres, 91-92, past pres, 92-93); Asn Aviation Psychologists; Image Soc; Soc Automotive Engrs; Sigma Xi; AAAS; Am Inst Aeronaut & Astronaut. *Res:* Aerospace psychology; aviation; training devices and simulators; transfer of training. *Mailing Add:* Univ Ill Willard Airport Inst Aviation Urbana IL 61801. *Fax:* 217-248-8761; *E-Mail:* h-taylor@uiuc.edu

**TAYLOR, HERBERT LYNDON,** PHYSICS, ELECTRICAL ENGINEERING. *Current Pos:* VPRES ENG, VERY BRITE TECHNOL INC, 91- *Personal Data:* b Van Alstyne, Tex, Aug 11, 31; m 56, Barbara Luther; c Karen (Hook) & Harmon. *Educ:* Austin Col, BA, 51; Rice Inst, MA, 52, PhD(physics), 55. *Prof Exp:* Mem tech staff res & develop, Tex Instruments Inc, 55-63; vis lectr, Univ Tex, Austin, 63-65, assoc prof, 65-80; failure analyst, Mostek, 80-81; consult engr, 81-83; component engr, Rockwell, Int, 83-91. *Mem:* Am Phys Soc; Inst Elec & Electronics Engrs; Am Vacuum Soc; Electrochem Soc. *Res:* Semiconductors; solid state devices; solid surfaces and interfaces; telecommunications defect analysis; optical systems; fiber optics. *Mailing Add:* 7014 Mason Dells Dr Dallas TX 75230

**TAYLOR, HOWARD EDWARD,** MATHEMATICS. *Current Pos:* Callaway prof, 69-87, EMER PROF MATH, STATE UNIV W GA, 87- *Personal Data:* b Ft Worth, Tex, Feb 1, 22; m 44; c 3. *Educ:* Rice Univ, BA, 42, MA, 48, PhD(math), 50; Calif Inst Technol, MS, 43. *Prof Exp:* Instr meteorol, Calif Inst Technol, 43-44; asst math, Rice Inst, 46-50; from instr to assoc prof, Fla State Univ, 50-69. *Concurrent Pos:* Vis assoc prof, Univ Chicago, 57-58; assoc chmn, Dept Math, Fla State Univ, 64-69; mem comt, Math Achievement Test, Col Entrance Exam Bd, 70-80, chmn, 75-80, mem, Math Adv Comt, 76-80. *Mem:* Am Meteorol Soc; Math Asn Am. *Res:* Functions of a complex variable; analysis. *Mailing Add:* 145 E Greenwood Dr Carrollton GA 30117

**TAYLOR, HOWARD LAWRENCE,** APPLIED MATHEMATICS, RESEARCH ADMINISTRATION. *Current Pos:* GEOPHYS CONSULT, ARAMCO, 85- *Personal Data:* b Kansas City, Mo, May 23, 38; m 60; c 2. *Educ:* Austin Col, AB, 59; Univ Kans, MA, 62, PhD(math), 68. *Prof Exp:* Lab asst physics, Austin Col, 57-59; asst math, Univ Kans, 59-67; mathematician, Sun Oil Co, 60-70, mgr res, 70-77, mgr geophys, 77-78, consult, 78-85. *Concurrent Pos:* Lectr, Univ Tex, Arlington & Univ Dallas. *Mem:* Math Asn Am; Soc Indust & Appl Math; Soc Petrol Engrs; Soc Explor Geophysicists; Europ Asn Explor Geophysicists; Asn Comput Mach. *Res:* Development of mathematical methods to analyze geophysical data and solve reservoir engineering problems; simulation models and inverse problems; deconvolution with the li norem. *Mailing Add:* 32 Fir Hl Akron OH 44304-1333

**TAYLOR, HOWARD MILTON, III,** APPLIED PROBABILITY, STATISTICS. *Current Pos:* PROF MATH SCI, UNIV DEL, 95- *Personal Data:* b Baltimore, Md, May 9, 37; m 95, B Florence Newman. *Educ:* Cornell Univ, BME, 60, MIndustEng, 61; Stanford Univ, PhD(math, statist), 65. *Prof Exp:* Res assoc & lectr appl probability, Stanford Univ, 64-65; from asst prof to prof opers res, Cornell Univ, 65-95. *Concurrent Pos:* NSF fel & vis asst prof, Univ Calif, Berkeley, 68-69; on leave at Math Inst, Oxford Univ, 72-73; grad fac rep, Cornell Univ, 74-77. *Mem:* Fel Inst Math Statist; Am Math Soc; Math Asn Am. *Res:* Applied probability; stochastic modeling. *Mailing Add:* 21142 Schooner Bay Rd Onancock VA 23417

**TAYLOR, HOWARD S,** PHYSICAL MATHEMATICS, MECHANICS, THEORETICAL CHEMISTRY & DYNAMICS. *Current Pos:* from asst prof to prof, 61-74, Humboldt prof, 74-75, PROF CHEM & PHYSICS, UNIV SOUTHERN CALIF, 75- *Personal Data:* b New York, NY, Sept 17, 35; m 59, Harriet Aune; c 3. *Educ:* Columbia Univ, BA, 56; Univ Calif, Berkeley, PhD(chem physics), 59. *Honors & Awards:* Max Planck Res Award for Atomic & Molecular Physics, 92. *Prof Exp:* NSF fel chem, Free Univ Brussels, 59-61. *Concurrent Pos:* Consult, Jet Propulsion Lab, Calif Inst Technol, 60-, NAm Aviation Inc, 65-66, Lawrence Livermore Nat Lab & Los Alamos Sci Lab; guest prof, Univ Freiburg, 67; staff scientist, Los Alamos Nat Lab, 73; vis prof, Freiberg Univ, 67-68, Univ Munich, 74-75 & Univ Amsterdam, 83-84. *Mem:* Am Chem Soc; fel Am Phys Soc. *Res:* Atomic and molecular physics; lasers; dynamics; spectroscopy; chaotic phenomena; theoretical chemistry and dynamics; atomic and molecular physics; theoretical and computational research is done into the nature of the dynamics and states of small molecules; special emphasis is given to situations where chaos is present; mathematical methods are developed for these subjects; interpretive and mathematical methods are developed. *Mailing Add:* Dept Chem Univ Southern Calif Los Angeles CA 90089. *Fax:* 213-740-4118

**TAYLOR, HUGH P, JR,** ORE DEPOSITS, ISOTOPE GEOCHEMISTRY. *Current Pos:* from asst prof to prof, 62-82, ROBERT P SHARP PROF GEOL, CALIF INST TECHNOL, 82- *Personal Data:* b Holbrook, Ariz, Dec 27, 32; m 59. *Educ:* Calif Inst Technol, BS, 54, PhD(geochem), 59; Harvard Univ, AM, 55. *Honors & Awards:* Arthur C Day Medal, Geol Soc Am, 93; Ure Medal, Europ Asn Geochem, 95. *Prof Exp:* Asst prof geol, Calif Inst Technol, 59-61; asst prof geochem, Pa State Univ, 61-62. *Mem:* Nat Acad Sci; fel AAAS; fel Geol Soc Am; fel Am Geophys Union; fel Mineral Soc Am; Am Acad Arts & Sci. *Res:* Oxygen, hydrogen, carbon and silicon isotopic compositions of igneous and metamorphic minerals and rocks, meteorites and the moon; ore deposits and hydrothermal alteration; ultramafic rocks of southeast Alaska. *Mailing Add:* Div Geol & Planetary Sci Calif Inst Technol Pasadena CA 91125

**TAYLOR, IAIN EDGAR PARK,** PLANT PHYSIOLOGY, PLANT BIOCHEMISTRY & BIOPHYSICS. *Current Pos:* from asst prof to assoc prof, 68-86, PROF BOT, UNIV BC, 86-, DEPT HEAD, 94- *Personal Data:* b Chester, Eng, Aug 18, 38; m 67, Sylvia Cadd; c Jennet. *Educ:* Univ Liverpool, BSc, 61, PhD(bot), 64. *Honors & Awards:* Mary Elliott Award, Can Bot Asn, 89. *Prof Exp:* Teacher, Blundell's Sch, Tiverton, Eng, 64-66; res assoc bot, Univ Tex, Austin, 67-68, vis asst prof, 68. *Concurrent Pos:* Ed, Can J Bot, 89-; asst ed-in-chief, Nat Res Coun Can Res J. *Mem:* Am Soc Plant Physiol; Can Bot Asn (pres, 85-86); Can Soc Plant Physiol; Brit Biochem Soc; Brit Inst Biol. *Res:* Biophysics and biochemistry of plant cell wall structure and growth; research ethics in life sciences; scientific publication ethics. *Mailing Add:* Dept Bot Univ BC Vancouver BC V6T 1Z4 Can. *Fax:* 604-822-6089; *E-Mail:* canjbot@unixg.ubc.ca

**TAYLOR, ISAAC MONTROSE,** MEDICINE. *Current Pos:* RETIRED. *Personal Data:* b Morganton, NC, June 15, 21; m 46, 79; c 6. *Educ:* Univ NC, AB, 42; Harvard Univ, MD, 45. *Prof Exp:* Intern, Mass Gen Hosp, 45-46, resident physician, 47; asst med adv, Harvard Med Sch, 48; chief med res, Mass Gen Hosp, 51; from asst prof to assoc prof, Sch Med, Univ NC, Chapel Hill, 52-64, dean sch med, 64-71, prof med, 64-78, res prof, Dept Community Med, 78-80; dep dir admin, Hubert H Humphrey Cancer Res Ctr, Boston Univ, 80-93, adj prof med, Sch Med, 81-93. *Concurrent Pos:* Nat Res Coun fel, Harvard Med Sch, 48-50; Markle scholar, 54-61; manpower consult, Tristate Regional Med Prog, 71-72, assoc dir manpower, 72-74. *Mem:* AMA; Am Fedn Clin Res. *Res:* Metabolism of electrolytes. *Mailing Add:* 9 Charles River Sq Boston MA 02114-3202

**TAYLOR, J(AMES) HERBERT,** BIOLOGY, GENETICS. *Current Pos:* assoc dir, Fla State Univ, 72-90, prof biol sci, 64-83, dir, Inst Molecular Biophys, 80-85, Robert O Lawton distinguished prof, 83-90, EMER PROF, FLA STATE UNIV, 90- *Personal Data:* b Corsicana, Tex, Jan 14, 16; m 46, Shirley Hoover; c Lynne S, Lucy D & Michael W. *Educ:* Southeastern State Col, BS, 39; Univ Okla, MS, 41; Univ Va, PhD(biol), 44. *Prof Exp:* Teacher high sch, Okla, 39-40; asst prof plant sci, Univ Okla, 46-47; assoc prof bot, Univ Tenn, 47-51; from asst prof to assoc prof, Columbia Univ, 51-58, prof cell biol, 58-64. *Concurrent Pos:* Guggenheim Found fel, Calif Inst Technol, Pasadena, 58-59. *Mem:* Nat Acad Sci; Am Soc Cell Biol (pres, 70-71); Genetics Soc Am. *Res:* Autoradiographic studies of nucleic acid and protein synthesis at the cellular level; chromosome duplication and structure; mechanisms of DNA replication in chromosomes; molecular organization of chromosomes; cloning origins of replication and modifications of DNA (methylation). *Mailing Add:* 1414 Hill Top Dr Tallahassee FL 32303. *Fax:* 850-385-7862

**TAYLOR, JACK ELDON,** OPTICS. *Current Pos:* RETIRED. *Personal Data:* b Emporia, Kans, Jan 16, 26; m 48; c 2. *Educ:* Univ Wis, PhB, 46, MS, 49, PhD(physics), 51. *Prof Exp:* Asst physics, Univ Wis, 47-51; res assoc, Gen Elec Co, 51-61; sr res staff mem, Gen Dynamics/Electronics, 61-71; prin engr, Stromberg Carlson Corp, 71-81; prin engr, Eastman Kodak Apparatus Div, Eastman Kodak Res Lab, 81-86, sr res staff, 86-91. *Concurrent Pos:* Consult, semiconductor mfg, 79-82; adj prof, Rochester Inst Technol, 80-82. *Mem:* Am Phys Soc; Inst Elec & Electronics Engrs; sr mem Optical Soc Am; Sigma Xi. *Res:* Ultra high vacuum techniques; gas lasers; optical communication systems; atmospheric optical transmission; solid state devices; LSI logic arrays; switching matrices; material and manufacturing problems. *Mailing Add:* 31 Old Pond Rd Rochester NY 14625-1541

**TAYLOR, JACK HOWARD,** PHYSICS. *Current Pos:* assoc prof, 56-60, PROF PHYSICS, SOUTHWESTERN MEMPHIS, 60-, PRIN INVESTR INFRARED, AIR FORCE CAMBRIDGE RES CTR CONTRACT, 59-, DIR LAB ATMOSPHERIC & OPTICAL PHYSICS, 64- *Personal Data:* b Memphis, Tenn, July 7, 22; m 44; c 4. *Educ:* Southwestern Memphis, BS, 44; Johns Hopkins Univ, PhD(physics), 52. *Prof Exp:* Physicist, US Naval Res Lab, 44-46; instr physics, Southwestern Memphis, 46-47; asst, Radiation Lab, Johns Hopkins Univ, 48-50; physicist, Exp Sta, E I du Pont de Nemours & Co, 52-53; asst prof physics, Univ South, 53-54; consult infrared, US Naval Res Lab, 54-56. *Concurrent Pos:* Consult, Electro-Optics Group, Pan Am World Airways, Inc & Patrick AFB, Fla, 63- *Mem:* Fel AAAS; Am Phys Soc; fel Optical Soc Am; Am Asn Physics Teachers; Sigma Xi. *Res:* Physics and military applications of infrared; atmospheric physics and transmission in infrared; time-dependent infrared phenomena and infrared techniques. *Mailing Add:* 671 East Dr Memphis TN 38112

**TAYLOR, JACKSON JOHNSON,** PHYSICS. *Current Pos:* From instr to assoc prof, Univ Richmond, 48-69, chmn, Div Sci, 55-72, chmn, Dept Physics, 51-54, 55-58 & 63-69, prof, 69-86, EMER PROF PHYSICS, UNIV RICHMOND, 86- *Personal Data:* b Winnabow, NC, Nov 20, 18; m 51; c 3. *Educ:* Univ Richmond, BS, 42; Cornell Univ, MS, 48. *Concurrent Pos:* Assoc prof, Sch Pharm, Med Col Va, 51-61. *Mem:* Am Phys Soc; Am Asn Physics Teachers. *Res:* Evaporation of chlorine atoms from silver chloride crystals; teaching undergraduate physics, especially lecture demonstrations and curriculum development; computer-assisted instruction in introductory physics. *Mailing Add:* 2431 Swathmore Rd Richmond VA 23235

**TAYLOR, JAMES A,** BIOCHEMISTRY, PHARMACOLOGY. *Current Pos:* PRES, TAYLOR ASSOC, 93- *Personal Data:* b Woonsocket, RI, 1939; m 60, Irene Legendre; c 3. *Educ:* Providence Col, BS, 60; Purdue Univ, MS, 63, PhD(biochem), 66. *Prof Exp:* Resident res assoc, Div Biol & Med, Argonne Nat Lab, 65-67; sr res scientist, Med Res Labs, Pfizer Inc, 67-75, liaison officer, Food & Drug Admin, Pfizer Cent Res, 75-79; mgr, New Drug Affairs, ICI Americas, 79-80, dir, Drug Regulatory Affairs Dept, 80-83; vpres regulatory affairs, Carter-Wallace Inc, 83-87; pres & chief regulatory officer, Immunogen Inc, 87-93. *Mem:* Am Soc Pharmacol & Exp Therapeut; Sigma Xi; Regulatory Affairs Prof Soc; Drug Info Asn. *Res:* Drug metabolism and pharmacokinetics; biopharmaceutical development. *Mailing Add:* Taylor Assoc 11048 Ipai Ct San Diego CA 92127-1382. *Fax:* 619-675-0808

**TAYLOR, JAMES EARL,** RESEARCH ADMINISTRATION. *Current Pos:* CONSULT, 83- *Personal Data:* b Beverly, Ohio, Sept 7, 16; m 45, Theresa Angello; c 3. *Educ:* Western Res Univ, AB, 38, MS, 40; Univ Pa, PhD(physics), 43. *Prof Exp:* Asst physics, Western Res Univ, 38-40 & Univ Pa, 40-42; physicist, Norden Labs Corp, 43-44, head res & develop sect, 44-50; from supvr electronics group & dir exp lab to lab dir, M Ten Bosch, Inc, 50-63; mem tech planning dept, Xerox Corp, 63-66, mgr res, Tech Planning Off, 66-69 & commun & educ, 69-70, tech staff specialist, 70-74, mgr res tech staff, 74-85. *Mem:* Am Phys Soc; Am Radio Relay League. *Res:*

Ultrasonic studies; mass spectrometry; isotope separation; ordnance research and development; antenna development; research and development management; education. *Mailing Add:* 1257 Wildflower Dr Webster NY 14580

**TAYLOR, JAMES H(OBERT),** SOIL COMPACTION BY MACHINERY. *Current Pos:* RETIRED. *Personal Data:* b Tishomingo, Miss, Jan 28, 29; m 51; c 2. *Educ:* Miss State Univ, BS, 51; Auburn Univ, PhD(agr eng), 64. *Prof Exp:* Jr engr, Int Harvester Co, 51-52, asst zone mgr farm equip, 54-59; asst agr eng, Auburn Univ, 59-62; res agr engr, USDA, 62-72, res leader, traction res, Nat Tillage Mach Lab, Agr Res, 72-85, nat tech adv, traction & controlled traffic, 82-91. *Concurrent Pos:* Res lectr, Grad Fac, Auburn Univ, 68- *Mem:* Am Soc Agr Engrs; Int Soc Terrain-Vehicle Systs; Soc Automotive Engrs; Am Soc Testing & Mat. *Res:* Terrain vehicle systems; off-road-locomotion; soil-machine systems; mobility; force-deformation relationships; systems analysis; soil dynamics; traffic-induced soil compaction. *Mailing Add:* 463 Cary Dr Auburn AL 36830

**TAYLOR, JAMES HUGH,** nonlinear systems theory, expert systems, for more information see previous edition

**TAYLOR, JAMES KENNETH,** WETLANDS ECOLOGY, CONSERVATION. *Current Pos:* RETIRED. *Personal Data:* b Fall River, Mass, July 28, 29; m 53, Barbara Gray; c Sherry & Keith. *Educ:* State Teachers Col Bridgewater, BScEd, 51; Columbia Univ, MA, 55. *Honors & Awards:* Distinguished Serv Conserv Award, Trout Unlimited, 86. *Prof Exp:* Teacher pub schs, Mass, 51-56; from instr to assoc prof, Westfield State Col, 56-85, chmn dept, 74-89, prof biol, 85- *Concurrent Pos:* Chmn, Westfield Conserv Comn, 62-; consult, Rand-McNally Publ Co, 72-83 & D C Heath Publ Co, 83-90. *Mem:* Nat Asn Biol Teachers; Ecol Soc Am; Nat Sci Teachers Asn. *Res:* Ecological basis of conservation; dissemination of ecological principles and their applications to solution of local problems; acid rain monitoring. *Mailing Add:* 8 Graylock St Westfield MA 01085

**TAYLOR, JAMES LEE,** HORTICULTURE. *Current Pos:* Prof hort & exten specialist, 60-89, EMER PROF HORT, MICH STATE UNIV, 89- *Personal Data:* b Berkey, Ohio, Jan 6, 31; m 58; c 2. *Educ:* Ohio State Univ, BS, 53; Mich State Univ, MS, 57; Univ Ill, PhD(bot), 60. *Mem:* Am Hort Soc; Am Soc Hort Sci; Nat Jr Hort Asn. *Res:* Nut tree culture and physiology. *Mailing Add:* 6132 Shoeman Rd Haslett MI 48840

**TAYLOR, JAMES VANDIGRIFF,** FORENSIC ANTHROPOLOGY. *Current Pos:* from asst prof to assoc prof, 67-84, PROF ANTHROP, LEHMAN COL, CITY UNIV NEW YORK, 84- *Personal Data:* b New York, NY, Dec 27, 31; m 55; c 1. *Educ:* Columbia Univ, BS, 57, PhD(anthrop), 68. *Prof Exp:* Lectr anthrop, Hunter Col, City Univ New York, 64-65; lectr anthrop, New York Univ, 66-67. *Concurrent Pos:* Prin investr res award, City Univ New York, 75-76, co-prin investr, 80-81, prin investr, 79-; dir Metrop Forensic Anthrop Team, Lehman Col, City Univ New York, 79- *Res:* Identification of human skeletal and dental remains in a forensic context. *Mailing Add:* 250 Bedford Park Blvd W Bronx NY 10468

**TAYLOR, JAMES WELCH,** ANALYTICAL CHEMISTRY. *Current Pos:* from asst prof to assoc prof, 66-70, PROF CHEM, UNIV WIS-MADISON, 70- *Personal Data:* b Newton, Miss, Sept 17, 35; m 57; c 2. *Educ:* Vanderbilt Univ, BA, 56; Ga Inst Technol, MS, 58; Univ Ill, Urbana, PhD(chem), 64. *Prof Exp:* Develop chemist, Mobil Oil Co, 58-61; asst prof chem, Tulane Univ, La, 64-66. *Mem:* Am Chem Soc; Chem Soc; Sigma Xi. *Res:* Photoionization mass spectrometry; photoelectron spectroscopy; isotope kinetics; rates and mechanisms of reactions; analytical instrumentation. *Mailing Add:* Dept Chem Univ Wis 1101 University Ave Madison WI 53706

**TAYLOR, JAVIN MORSE,** ELECTRICAL ENGINEERING, COMPUTER ENGINEERING. *Current Pos:* dept head, Elec & Comput Eng, 87-89, PROF ELEC & COMPUT ENG, NMEX STATE UNIV, 76- *Personal Data:* b Lancaster, Wis, Jan 20, 36; m 59; c 4. *Educ:* Univ Ill, Urbana, BS, 57; Univ Southern Calif, MS, 62; Univ Wyo, PhD(elec eng), 70. *Prof Exp:* Field engr, Hughes Aircraft Co, 57-59; engr, Ramo-Wooldridge Div, TRW, Inc, 59-61, TRW Comput Div, 61-62; eng specialist, Guid & Control Systs Div, Litton Industs, 62-66; instr & res engr, Natural Resources Res Inst, Univ Wyo, 66-69; res engr, Autonetics Div, NAm Rockwell, Inc, 69-70; from asst prof to assoc prof elec eng, Univ Mo-Rolla, 70-76. *Concurrent Pos:* Consult, TRW Comput Div, TRW, Inc, 63, Guid & Control Systs Div, Litton Industs, 66-68 & John S Bereman & Co Eng Consult, 68-69; lectr, Calif State Univ, Los Angeles, 70; consult, Instrumentation Directorate, White Sands Missile Range, 77-80; elec & comput eng prog evaluator, Accrediting Bd Eng & Tech. *Mem:* Inst Elec & Electronics Engrs; Inst Elec & Electronics Engrs Comput Soc; Inst Elec & Electronics Engrs Educ Soc; Am Soc Eng Educ. *Res:* Computer architecture and design; digital communication networks; computer networks; digital signal processing. *Mailing Add:* Dept Elec Eng NMex State Univ Box 3-0 Las Cruces NM 88003

**TAYLOR, JAY EUGENE,** CHEMISTRY. *Current Pos:* from assoc prof to prof, 60-84, RES PROF CHEM, KENT STATE UNIV, 84- *Personal Data:* b Stayton, Ore, Feb 2, 18; m 48, Carol Cartier; c Barbara, Janet (Lehman), Pamela (Pierce) & Leann (Whyte). *Educ:* Ore State Col, BA, 40; Univ Wis, MS, 43; Purdue Univ, PhD, 47. *Prof Exp:* Instr chem, Univ Wis, 46-48; asst prof chem, Miami Univ, 48-52; fel phys chem, Ohio State Univ, 52-54; asst prof, Univ Nebr, 54-60. *Mem:* Am Chem Soc; Sigma Xi. *Res:* Mechanisms of oxidation and decomposition reactions; flow techniques applied to kinetic studies of both liquid and gaseous systems; homogeneous versus heterogeneous gas-phase pyrolysis studies using wall-less and homogeneous front reactors. *Mailing Add:* Dept Chem Kent State Univ Kent OH 44242. *Fax:* 330-672-3816

**TAYLOR, JEAN ELLEN,** GEOMETRIC MEASURE THEORY, SOME ASPECTS OF THEORETICAL METALLURGY. *Current Pos:* from asst prof to assoc prof, 73-82, prof math, 82-87, PROF II MATH, RUTGERS UNIV, 87- *Personal Data:* b San Mateo, Calif, Sept 17, 44; wid; c 3. *Educ:* Mt Holyoke Col, BA, 66; Univ Calif, Berkeley, MSc, 68 & Univ Warwick, 71; Princeton Univ, PhD(math), 73. *Prof Exp:* Instr math, Mass Inst Technol, 72-73. *Concurrent Pos:* Prin investr grants, 73-, Air Force Off Sci Res grants, 88-90; mem, Inst Adv Study, 74-75, 77-78 & 85; Alfred P Sloan Found fel, 76-78; mem, Nominating Comt, Am Math Soc, 77-78, coun, 84-88, exec comt, 85-88 & chair, Nat Prog Comt; mem, Comt Appl Math Training, Nat Acad Sci/Nat Res Coun, 77-78, Comt Math Sci Appl Mat Sci, 92-93; vis, Princeton Univ, 80-81, Stanford Univ, 89; fac, Geom Ctr, Univ Minn, 89-; consult, Nat Inst Stand & Technol, 90-; mem bd dirs, AAAS, 95- *Mem:* Am Math Soc (vpres, 94-97); Math Asn Am; Asn Women Math; fel AAAS; Mat Res Soc; Soc Indust & Appl Math. *Res:* Crystal growth problems involving anisotropic surface energy and/or mobility are investigated. *Mailing Add:* Dept Math Rutgers Univ New Brunswick NJ 08903. *E-Mail:* taylor@math.rutgers.edu

**TAYLOR, JEAN MARIE,** TOXICOLOGY, PHARMACOLOGY. *Current Pos:* RETIRED. *Personal Data:* b Protection, NY, Nov 21, 32. *Educ:* Keuka Col, BA, 54; Univ Rochester, MS, 56, PhD(pharm), 59. *Prof Exp:* Res assoc pharm, Atomic Energy Proj, Univ Rochester, 54-59; pharmacologist, US Food & Drug Admin, 59-71, actg chief, Chronic Toxicol Br, Div Toxicol, 71-89. *Mem:* Soc Toxicol; Sigma Xi. *Res:* Toxicity of flavoring agents; hepatotoxins. *Mailing Add:* 941 Broadview Dr Harrisonburg VA 22801-4956

**TAYLOR, JERRY DUNCAN,** MATHEMATICS. *Current Pos:* PROF MATH, CAMPBELL UNIV, NC, 62- *Personal Data:* b Plumerville, Ark, June 5, 38; m 64; c 3. *Educ:* State Col Ark, BA, 60; Univ Ark, MS, 64; Fla State Univ, PhD(math educ), 69. *Concurrent Pos:* Co-auth, Prentice-Hall Encyl Math, 83. *Mem:* Math Asn Am. *Res:* New methods of extending the field of rational numbers to the field of real numbers. *Mailing Add:* Box 396 Buies Creek NC 27506-0396

**TAYLOR, JERRY LYNN,** INTERFERON, VIROLOGY. *Current Pos:* fel virol, Med Col Wis, Milwaukee, 77-79, from instr to asst prof microbiol, 79-84, asst prof microbiol & ophthal, 81-84, assoc prof microbiol & ophthal, 84-90, PROF MICROBIOL & OPHTHAL, MED COL WIS, MILWAUKEE, 90- *Personal Data:* b Warrenton, Mo, Jan 12, 47; m 71. *Educ:* Univ Mo, BA, 69, MA, 71; Southern Ill Univ, Carbondale, PhD(microbiol), 76. *Prof Exp:* Asst prof virol, Calif State Univ, Long Beach, 76-77. *Mem:* Am Soc Microbiol; Am Soc Virol; Int Soc Antiviral Res; Asn Res Vision & Ophthal; AAAS; Sigma Xi. *Res:* Actions of antiviral agents including nucleoside analogues, interferons and interferon inducers on viral diseases especially herpes simplex virus keratitis; effects of interferons on cellular differentiation. *Mailing Add:* Dept Microbiol Med Col Wis 8701 Watertown Plank Rd Milwaukee WI 53226. *Fax:* 414-257-8427

**TAYLOR, JOCELYN MARY,** ZOOLOGY. *Current Pos:* RETIRED. *Personal Data:* b Portland, Ore, May 30, 31; wid. *Educ:* Smith Col, BA, 52; Univ Calif, Berkeley, MA, 53, PhD(zool), 59. *Honors & Awards:* Hartley H T Jackson Award, Am Soc Mammalogists. *Prof Exp:* Asst zool, Conn Col, 53-54; Fulbright grantee, Australia, 54-55; assoc zool, Univ Calif, 59; from instr to asst prof, Wellesley Col, 59-65; from assoc prof to prof zool, Univ BC, 65-82; dir, Cowan Vertebrate Mus, 65-82; collab scientist, Ore Regional Primate Res Ctr, 83-87; courtesy prof, Ore State Univ, 84-94; adj prof biol, Case Western Res Univ, 87-96; dir, Cleveland Mus Natural Hist, 87-96. *Concurrent Pos:* Sigma Xi grant, 61-62; Lalor Found grant, 62-63; NSF grants, 63-71 & Australia, 63-64 & 65; Nat Res Coun Can res grants, 66-84, travel grant, Div Animal Physiol, Commonwealth Sci & Indust Res Orgn, Australia, 71-72; Killiam Sr fel, 78-79; assoc ed, J Mammalog, 81-82; mem rodent specialist group, endangered species, Int Union Conserv Nature & Natural resources, 80-; bd dirs, Am Soc Mammalogists, 84- *Mem:* Sigma Xi; Am Soc Mammalogists (vpres, 78-82, pres, 82-84); Cooper Ornithol Soc; Australian Mammal Soc; Soc Women Geogrs. *Res:* Reproductive biology of mammals; evolution of Australasian murid rodents; marsupial placentation. *Mailing Add:* 2718 SW Old Orchard Rd Portland OR 97201. *E-Mail:* jmtaylor@earthworld.com

**TAYLOR, JOHN CHRISTOPHER,** PROBABILITY. *Current Pos:* from asst prof to assoc prof, 63-74, PROF MATH, MCGILL UNIV, 74- *Personal Data:* b Chelmsford, Eng, Jan 17, 36; Can citizen; m 69, Brenda Macgibban; c Stephanie, Jeremy & Jonathan. *Educ:* Acadia Univ, BSc, 55; Queen's Univ, Ont, MA, 57; McMaster Univ, PhD(math), 60. *Prof Exp:* J F Ritt instr math, Columbia Univ, 60-63. *Mem:* Am Math Soc; Can Math Cong. *Res:* symmetric spaces; Potential theory; probability theory; boundary theory. *Mailing Add:* Dept Math McGill Univ 805 Sherbrooke St W Montreal PQ H3A 2K6 Can. *E-Mail:* taylor@math.mcgill.ca

**TAYLOR, JOHN DIRK,** CANCER BIOLOGY. *Current Pos:* from asst prof to assoc prof, Wayne State Univ, 68-75, assoc prof comp med, 72-75, chmn, Dept Biol, 74-87, dep dean, Lib Arts, 83-84, PROF BIOL, WAYNE STATE UNIV, 75-, PROF RADIATION ONCOL, SCH MED, 80- *Personal Data:* b Mecca, Calif, Mar 31, 39; m 63; c 2. *Educ:* Univ Ariz, BS, 62, PhD(biol), 67. *Prof Exp:* NSF, US-Japan Coop Sci Prog fel biol, Keio Univ, Japan, 67-68.

*Concurrent Pos:* Asian Found guest lectr, Univs in Seoul, Korea, 68. *Mem:* Fel AAAS; Am Soc Cell Biol; Am Soc Zool; Soc Develop Biol. *Res:* Biochemical and ultrastructural aspects of developmental processes with particular emphasis on intracellular movements and metastasis. *Mailing Add:* Wayne State Univ 210 Sci Hall Wayne State Univ Detroit MI 48202-3919

**TAYLOR, JOHN EDGAR,** RANGE SCIENCE, PLANT ECOLOGY. *Current Pos:* From instr to prof, 63-89, EMER PROF RANGE SCI, MONT STATE UNIV, 91- *Personal Data:* b Cheyenne, Wyo, Oct 17, 31; wid; c Diana, Hillary & David. *Educ:* Idaho State Univ, BS, 58 & Wash State Univ, 60; Mont State Univ, MS, 67; NDak State Univ, PhD(bot & plant ecol), 76. *Mem:* Fel Soc Range Mgt. *Res:* Rangeland analysis and measurements; remote sensing of natural resources. *Mailing Add:* 508 Holter Helena MT 59601

**TAYLOR, JOHN GARDINER VEITCH,** PHYSICS. *Current Pos:* RETIRED. *Personal Data:* b Toronto, Ont, Sept 22, 26; m 55, Doreen Trevoy. *Educ:* McMaster Univ, BSc, 50; Univ Sask, MSc, 52. *Prof Exp:* Res physicist photonuclear reactions, Univ Sask, 53; res physicist atomic mass measurements, McMaster Univ, 54-55; res physicist radioactivity stand, Atomic Energy Can, Ltd, 56-76, head, Counter Develop Sect, 76-82, head, Nuclear Detectors & Metrol Sect, 82-91. *Concurrent Pos:* Ed, Int J Appl Radiation Isotopes, 68-88; chmn, Sect II (Measure of Radionuclides), Consult Comt Stand Measure Ionizing Radiation, Int Bur Weights & Measures, 85-91. *Mem:* Am Phys Soc; Can Asn Physicists; AAAS; Int Comt Radionuclide Metrol. *Res:* Radioactivity; radiation detectors. *Mailing Add:* 75 Rutherford Ave PO Box 43 Deep River ON K0J 1P0 Can

**TAYLOR, JOHN JOSEPH,** MATHEMATICS. *Current Pos:* NUCLEAR ENERGY CONSULT, 95- *Personal Data:* b Hackensack, NJ, Feb 27, 22; m 43, Lorraine Crowley; c John, Nancy & Susan. *Educ:* St John's Univ, NY, BS, 42; Univ Notre Dame, MS, 46. *Hon Degrees:* DSc, St John's Univ, NY, 74. *Honors & Awards:* Westinghouse Award of Merit, 57; George Westinghouse Gold Medal Award, Am Soc Mech Engrs, 90; Walter Zinn Award, Am Nuclear Soc, 93. *Prof Exp:* Appl mathematician, Bendix Aviation Corp, 46-47; scientist, Physics Dept, Kellex Corp, NY, 47-50; vpres, Nuclear Power Div, Elec Power Res Inst, 85-95; sr scientist, Bettis Atomic Power Lab, Westinghouse Elec Corp, 50-52, mgr shielding physics, 52-55, mgr surface ship proj, Physics Dept, 55-58, mgr reator develop, 58-65, mgr mat develop, 65-67, mgr eng, Atomic Power Div, 67, eng mgr, Power Plant Div, 67-70, gen mgr, Breeder Reactor Div, 70-74, vpres, Advan Nuclear Systs, 74-76, vpres & gen mgr, Water Reactor Bus Unit, 76-81. *Concurrent Pos:* Mem bd dirs, Am Nuclear Soc, 71-74, Advan Reactor Corp, 81-91, Inst Nuclear Power Opers Adv Coun, 88-95, Vis Comt Dept Nuclear Eng, Brookhaven Nat Lab; consult, US Govt Acct Off, 74-81. *Mem:* Nat Acad Eng; fel AAAS; fel Am Phys Soc; fel Am Nuclear Soc. *Res:* Nuclear reactors; shielding and reactors for atomic submarines; digital computer techniques in reactor design; nuclear fuel development. *Mailing Add:* PO Box 10412 Elec Power Res Inst Palo Alto CA 94303

**TAYLOR, JOHN JOSEPH,** anatomy, electron microscopy; deceased, see previous edition for last biography

**TAYLOR, JOHN LANGDON, JR,** medical education; deceased, see previous edition for last biography

**TAYLOR, JOHN MARSTON,** VIROLOGY. *Current Pos:* CHIEF CHEMIST, GLADSTONE FEDN LABS, SAN FRANCISCO. *Personal Data:* b Melbourne, Australia, Sept 10, 41; m 60; c 2. *Educ:* Univ Melbourne, BSc, 62, MSc, 64; Univ Toronto, PhD(cell biol), 68. *Prof Exp:* Mem staff, Inst Cancer Res, 74- *Res:* Virus replication; cell biology; carcinogenesis. *Mailing Add:* Univ Calif-San Francisco Gladstone Inst PO Box 419100 2550 23rd St San Francisco CA 94141-9100. *Fax:* 415-285-5632

**TAYLOR, JOHN ROBERT,** THEORETICAL PHYSICS. *Current Pos:* from asst prof to assoc prof, 66-72, PROF PHYSICS, UNIV COLO, BOULDER, 72- *Personal Data:* b London, Eng, Feb 2, 39; m 62; c 2. *Educ:* Cambridge Univ, BA, 60; Univ Calif, Berkeley, PhD(physics), 63. *Honors & Awards:* Distinguished Serv Citation, Am Asn Physics Teachers, 89. *Prof Exp:* NATO fel physics, Cambridge Univ, 62-64; instr, Princeton Univ, 64-66. *Mem:* Am Asn Physics Teachers. *Res:* Quantum theory; quantum theory of scattering. *Mailing Add:* Dept Physics Univ Colo Box 390 Boulder CO 80309-0390

**TAYLOR, JOHN WILLIAM,** ANALYTICAL & PHARMACEUTICAL CHEMISTRY. *Current Pos:* REVIEWING CHEMIST RX DRUGS, DIV GENERIC DRUG MONOGRAPHS, BUR DRUGS, FOOD & DRUG ADMIN, HEW, 74- *Personal Data:* b Austin, Tex, Dec 14, 46; m 68; c 2. *Educ:* Univ Cincinnati, BS, 69; Duke Univ, PhD(analytical chem), 78. *Mem:* Sigma Xi; Asn Off Analytical Chemists; Am Chem Soc. *Res:* Prediction of ion exchange selectivities in mixed solvents; isotope separations; polymorphism and bioavailability. *Mailing Add:* 215 White Meadow Rd Rockaway NJ 07866-1106

**TAYLOR, JOSEPH HOOTON, JR,** RADIO ASTRONOMY, PULSARS. *Current Pos:* prof, 80-86, JAMES S MCDONNELL DISTINGUISHED PROF PHYSICS, PRINCETON UNIV, 86- *Personal Data:* b Philadelphia, Pa, Mar 29, 41; m 63, Marietta Bisson; c 4. *Educ:* Haverford Col, BA, 63; Harvard Univ, PhD(astron), 68. *Hon Degrees:* DSc, Univ Chicago, 85, Univ Mass, 94. *Honors & Awards:* Nobel Prize Physics, 93; Dannie Heineman

Prize, Am Astron Sci, 80; George Darwin Lectr, Royal Astron Soc, 80; Morris Leob Lectr, Harvard Univ, 84; Henry Draper Medal, Nat Acad Sci, 85; Tomalla Found Prize Gravitation & Cosmology, Tomalla Found, 87; Magellanic Premium, Am Philos Soc, 90; John J Carty Award Advan Sci, US Nat Acad Sci, 91; Einstein Prize Laureate, Albert Einstein Soc, 91; Wolf Prize, 92. *Prof Exp:* Lectr astron & res fel, Harvard Col Observ, Harvard Univ, 68-69; from asst prof to prof, Univ Mass, 69-81. *Concurrent Pos:* Grant, Res Corp, Univ Mass, 68-69, NSF, 69-82 & NASA, 71-72; consult, Mass Gen Hosp, 71-73; counr, High Energy Astrophys Div, Am Astron Soc, 76-78, coun soc, 85-88; vis comt, Nat Radio Astron Observ, Kitt Peak Nat Observ & Cerro Tololo Inter-Am Observ, 80-83; vchmn, Astrophys Div, Am Phys Soc, 85-86, chmn, 86-87; mem, Radio Astron Panel, Astron Surv Comt, Nat Acad Sci, 89-90. *Mem:* Nat Acad Sci; Am Astron Soc; Int Sci Radio Union; Int Astron Union; fel Am Phys Soc; fel Am Acad Arts & Sci. *Res:* Radio astronomy; pulsars; experimental gravitation; design and development of radio telescopes and information processing systems. *Mailing Add:* Dept Physics Jadwin Hall Princeton Univ PO Box 708 Princeton NJ 08544-0708

**TAYLOR, JOSEPH LAWRENCE,** MATHEMATICAL ANALYSIS. *Current Pos:* from asst prof to assoc prof, Univ Utah, 65-71, chmn dept, 79-82, dean sci, 85-87, acad vpres, 87-90, PROF MATH, UNIV UTAH, 71- *Personal Data:* b Apr 7, 41; US citizen; m 59; c 3. *Educ:* La State Univ, BS, 63, PhD(math), 64. *Honors & Awards:* Steele Prize, Am Math Soc, 75. *Prof Exp:* Instr math, Harvard Univ, 64-65. *Concurrent Pos:* Sloan fel. *Mailing Add:* Dept Math Univ Utah Salt Lake City UT 84112

**TAYLOR, JULIUS DAVID,** BIOCHEMISTRY, TOXICOLOGY. *Current Pos:* RETIRED. *Personal Data:* b Erie, Pa, Dec 18, 13; m 38; c 1. *Educ:* Univ Pittsburgh, BS, 36; Univ Rochester, PhD(biochem), 40. *Prof Exp:* Instr biochem, Sch Med & Dent, Univ Rochester, 40-41; res org chemist, Distillation Prod, Inc, NY, 41-43; res biochemist, Eaton Labs, Inc, 43-47; chem pharmacologist, Abbott Labs, 48-60, from asst dept head to dept head pharmacol, 60-64, drug eval specialist, Dept Drug Regist, 65-69 & Div Regulatory Affairs, 69-70, data specialist, Dept Exp Biomet, 70-77, control record coordr, 78-79. *Concurrent Pos:* Lectr, Med Sch, Northwestern Univ, Chicago, 59-62; lectr, Sch Med, Univ Chicago, 62-65. *Mem:* AAAS; Am Soc Pharmacol & Exp Therapeut; Soc Toxicol. *Res:* Drug enzymology, metabolism and kinetics; pharmacology; toxicology; bionics; simulation. *Mailing Add:* 905 Baldwin Ave Apt A8 Waukegan IL 60085-2375

**TAYLOR, KATHLEEN C,** PHYSICAL CHEMISTRY. *Current Pos:* assoc sr res chemist, Gen Motors Corp, 70-74, sr res chemist, 74-75, asst dept head, 75-83, DEPT HEAD, PHYSICS & PHYS CHEM DEPT, DIV GEN MOTORS RES DEVELOP CTR, 83- *Personal Data:* b Cambridge, Mass, Mar 16, 42. *Educ:* Rutgers Univ, New Brunswick, AB, 64; Northwestern Univ, Evanston, PhD(phys chem), 68. *Honors & Awards:* Garvan Medal, Am Chem Soc. *Prof Exp:* Fel, Univ Edinburgh, 68-70. *Mem:* Nat Acad Eng; Catalysis Soc; Royal Chem Soc; Mat Res Soc; Soc Automotive Engrs; Am Chem Soc. *Res:* Surface chemistry; heterogeneous catalysis; catalytic control of automobile exhaust emissions. *Mailing Add:* 1646 Fairway Birmingham MI 48009. *Fax:* 810-986-3091; *E-Mail:* ktaylor@notes.gmr.com

**TAYLOR, KEITH EDWARD,** BIOCHEMISTRY. *Current Pos:* from asst prof to assoc prof, 76-96, PROF BIOCHEM, UNIV WINDSOR, 96- *Personal Data:* b Toronto, Ont, Dec 21, 46; m 68, Barbara Heartwell; c Justine & Alexis. *Educ:* Univ Toronto, BSc, 69; PhD(bioorg chem), 74. *Prof Exp:* Fel enzymatic stereochem, Lab Org Chem, Swiss Fed Inst Technol, 73-76; fel protein chem, Harvard Univ, 76. *Concurrent Pos:* Sabbaticant, Lab Biochem, Switz Fed Inst Technol, 84-85. *Mem:* Am Chem Soc; Chem Inst Can; Tech Asn Pulp Paper Indust. *Res:* Protein chemistry enzymology; glycoproteins; immobilized enzymes; enzyme-based reactors; wastewater treatment. *Mailing Add:* Dept Chem & Biochem Univ Windsor Windsor ON N9B 3P4 Can. *Fax:* 519-973-7098; *E-Mail:* taylor@uwindsor.ca

**TAYLOR, KENNETH BOIVIN,** BIOCHEMISTRY, ENZYMOLOGY. *Current Pos:* ASSOC PROF BIOCHEM, UNIV ALA, BIRMINGHAM, 70- *Personal Data:* b Columbus, Ohio, Aug 7, 35; m 58; c 2. *Educ:* Oberlin Col, AB, 57; Case Western Res Univ, MD, 61; Mass Inst Technol, PhD, 67. *Prof Exp:* Res assoc, Mass Inst Technol, 64-67, asst prof biol, 67-70. *Concurrent Pos:* Dir, Fermentation Facil, Univ Ala, Birmingham, 83- *Mem:* Am Soc Biochem & Molecular Biol; Am Chem Soc; AAAS; Am Soc Microbiol. *Res:* Enzyme mechanisms & kinetics; genetic engineering in plants; biotechnology-fermentation, purification. *Mailing Add:* Dept Biochem Univ Ala Birmingham AL 35294-0001

**TAYLOR, KENNETH DOYLE,** BIOENGINEERING & BIOMEDICAL ENGINEERING, ELECTRICAL ENGINEERING. *Current Pos:* VPRES RES & DEVELOP, VALLEYLAB, INC, 93- *Personal Data:* b Hartford, Conn, Nov 5, 49; m 72, M Jane; c Jerome. *Educ:* Univ Conn, BS, 71, MS, 74, PhD(biol eng), 81; Rensselaer Polytech Inst, MBA, 88. *Prof Exp:* Coordr, Res Lab, St Francis Hosp & Med Ctr, 71-73, mgr, 74-79; design engr, Nuclear & Ultrasound Div, Picker Corp, 73-74; sr proj engr, United Technologies Res Ctr, 79-90; asst dir technol assessment, Pfizer Hosp Prod Group, 90-92, dir, 92-93. *Concurrent Pos:* Lectr, Univ Conn, 77-82; adj asst prof, Hartford Grad Ctr, 80-; spec asst to dir, Div Heart & Vascular Dis, Nat Heart, Lung & Blood Inst, 85-86; adj prof, Trinity Col, 88-90. *Mem:* Inst Elec & Electronics Engrs; Sigma Xi; Asn Advan Med Instrumentation; Asn Univ Technol Mgrs. *Res:* Development of medical devices using electronic and/or electro-optic technology particularly RF and ultrasonic systems for tissue ablation, cutting and coagulation. *Mailing Add:* ValleyLab Inc 5920 Longbow Dr Boulder CO 80301. *Fax:* 303-530-6277; *E-Mail:* taylor@pfizer.com

**TAYLOR, KENNETH GRANT,** ORGANIC CHEMISTRY. *Current Pos:* from asst prof to assoc prof, Univ Louisville, 66-73, chmn dept, 78-87, assoc dean, Col Arts & Sci, 91-97, PROF CHEM, UNIV LOUISVILLE, 73- *Personal Data:* b Paterson, NJ, May 12, 36; m 61, Carla M Rydell; c Koren, Kevin & Kaylyn J. *Educ:* Calvin Col, AB, 57; Wayne State Univ, PhD(org chem), 63. *Prof Exp:* Res assoc, Mass Inst Technol, 63-64; sr res assoc chem, Wayne State Univ, 64-66. *Concurrent Pos:* Assoc prof, Univ Nancy I, France, 74-75, 82-83; vis prof, Univ Lund, Sweden, 91. *Mem:* Am Chem Soc; fel AAAS. *Res:* Synthesis of strained carbocyclic and heterocyclic compounds; carbohydrate chemistry; cycloaddition reactions. *Mailing Add:* Dept Chem Univ Louisville Louisville KY 40292-0001. *Fax:* 502-852-8149; *E-Mail:* kgtayl01@ulkyvm.louisville.edu

**TAYLOR, KENNETH J W,** RADIOLOGY. *Current Pos:* assoc prof radiol, 75-79, PROF DIAG IMAGING, YALE UNIV, 79- *Personal Data:* b Essex, Gt Brit, Mar 8, 39; m 75; c 2. *Educ:* London Univ, BSc, 61, MB & BS, 64, MD, 75, PhD(biophys), 73; Yale Univ, MA, 79. *Prof Exp:* Lectr anat, London Univ, 67-72; sr fel nuclear med, Royal Hosp, 73-75. *Concurrent Pos:* Chmn Bd Clin Diag US, 76-; vis prof, Bristol Univ, 82-83; co-dir, Ctr Sonics & Ultrasonics, Yale Univ, 83-; prin investr, NIH, 88- *Mem:* Am Inst Ultrasound Med (bd govs, 79-82); Am Roentgen Ray Soc; Radiol Soc Am; Royal Col Surgeons. *Res:* Applications of ultrasound in medicine; imaging techniques; doppler investigation of flow 7 physiologic function. *Mailing Add:* Diag Radiol Yale Univ Sch Med PO Box 208042 New Haven CT 06520-8042

**TAYLOR, KENNETH LAPHAM,** HISTORY OF MODERN SCIENCE, HISTORY OF GEOLOGY. *Current Pos:* From asst prof to assoc prof, 67-72, chmn dept hist sci, 79-92, PROF HIST SCI, UNIV OKLA, 85- *Personal Data:* b Los Angeles, Calif, May 16, 41; m 69, Melva L Johnson; c Melissa L (Hyde), Benjamin D & Nathaniel J. *Educ:* Harvard Univ, AB, 62, AM, 65, PhD(hist sci), 68. *Concurrent Pos:* Fel, Alexandre Koyre Ctr, Ecole Pratique des Hautes Etudes, 73-74; mem, Gov Coun, Hist Sci Soc, 79-81, Dibner vis historian sci, 90-91; mem, Int Comn Hist Geol Sci, 84-; chmn, US Nat Comt Hist Geol, 90-93. *Mem:* Hist Sci Soc; Hist Earth Sci Soc (treas, 85-91, pres, 97-98); Soc Hist Technol; Brit Soc Hist Sci; Soc Hist Natural Hist. *Res:* History of geology in 18th & early 19th centuries; history of science in 18th century. *Mailing Add:* Dept Hist Sci Univ Okla Phys Sci No 622 Norman OK 73019-0315. *Fax:* 405-325-2363; *E-Mail:* ktaylor@ou.edu

**TAYLOR, KIRMAN,** ANALYTICAL CHEMISTRY, CLINICAL CHEMISTRY. *Current Pos:* PRES, KIRMAN ASSOCS, TECH & MKT CONSULTS, 80- *Personal Data:* b Yorkshire, Eng, Sept 30, 20; nat US; m 41, Lillian Thorsen; c Kirman R & Diane L. *Educ:* Queen's Col, NY, BS, 41; Polytech Inst Brooklyn, MS, 43. *Prof Exp:* Instr, Polytech Inst Brooklyn, 46; res chemist, Celotex Corp, 47-48; res chemist & group leader, Westvaco Chem Div, Food Machinery & Chem Corp, 48-52; res assoc, George Washington Univ, 52-54; group leader, Diamond Alkali Co, 54-65, proj mgr, 65-67, assoc dir res dept, 68-75, dir res admin, res ctr, Diamond Shamrock Corp, 76-79. *Concurrent Pos:* Lectr, Wagner Col, 49-52 & Lake Erie Col, 60-67. *Mem:* Am Chem Soc; NY Acad Sci; AAAS. *Res:* Building materials technology; inorganic phosphates; coordination compounds; inorganic polymers; plastic and metal coatings; nuclear fuels; water chemistry; electroless and electrolytic plating; research administration; hydrometallurgy; management of analytical environmental chemical facilities. *Mailing Add:* 512 Whisperwood Dr Greenville TN 37743-6646. *E-Mail:* slowkt@greene.xtn.net

**TAYLOR, LARRY THOMAS,** POLYMER CHEMISTRY, ANALYTICAL CHEMISTRY. *Current Pos:* from asst prof to assoc prof, 67-78, PROF CHEM, VA POLYTECH INST & STATE UNIV, 78- *Personal Data:* b Woodruff, SC, Dec 31, 39; m 60; c 2. *Educ:* Clemson Univ, BS, 62, PhD(chem), 65. *Prof Exp:* Res assoc chem, Ohio State Univ, 65-67. *Mem:* Am Chem Soc; Sigma Xi. *Res:* Supercritical fluid chromatography; fourier transform infrared spectrometry; liquid chromatography; surface analysis; modification of polymers by metal ion addition. *Mailing Add:* 2101 Walnut Dr Blacksburg VA 24060-1812

**TAYLOR, LAURISTON SALE,** MEDICAL & RADIOLOGICAL PHYSICS, BIOPHYSICS. *Current Pos:* pres, 64-77, HON PRES, NAT COUN RADIATION PROTECTION & MEASUREMENT, 77-; RADIATION PHYSICS CONSULT, 77- *Personal Data:* b Brooklyn, NY, June 1, 02; m 25, 73, Robena Harper; c Lauriston, Nelson, Christine, Carolyn, Constance & Cynthia. *Educ:* Cornell Univ, AB, 26. *Hon Degrees:* DSc, Univ Pa, 60 & St Procopius Col, 65. *Honors & Awards:* Bronze Star, USAF, 45; Sylvanus Thompson Medal, Brit Inst Radiol, 50; Lester Medal Lectr, Soc Nondestructive Testing, 54; Janeway Medal, Am Radium Soc, 56; Gold Medal, Am Col Radiol; Edward Bennett Rosa Award, Nat Bur Stand; Failla Mem lectr, Health Physics Soc NY; Gold Medal, Royal Swed Acad Sci & 13th Int Cong Radiol, Madrid, 73; Landauer Award, Am Asn Physicists Med & Health Physics Soc, 79; Sievert Award, Int Radiol Protection Agency, 79; Antoine Beclere Prize & Gold Medal, Int Soc Radiol, 81; Launiston S Taylor lectr, Nat Coun Radiation Protection & Measurement, 77; Gold Medal, Am Roentgen Ray Soc, 92. *Prof Exp:* Asst, Heckscher Found, Cornell Univ, 24-27; from asst physicist to assoc physicist, Nat Bur Stand, 27-35, sr physicist & chief, X-ray Sect, 35-41, chief proving ground group, 40-43, chief x-ray sect, 42-43, 46-49, asst chief, Atomic Physics Div, 47-51, chief, Radiol Physics Lab, 49-51, Atomic & Radiation Physics Div, 51-60 & Radiation Physics Div, 60-62, assoc dir, 62-64; spec asst to pres, Nat Acad Sci, 65-69, exec dir adv comt emergency planning, 65-71. *Concurrent Pos:* Mem, Int Comn Radiol Protection, 28-69, secy, 37-50, emer mem, 69-; mem, Int Comn Radiol Units & Measurements 28-69, secy, 34-50, chmn, 53-69, hon chmn & emer mem, 69-; chmn, Nat Coun Radiation Protection & Measurements, 29-64, chmn subcomt regulation of radiation exposure, 53-57, subcomt permissible exposure under emergency conditions, 55-59; dir, Pan-Am Cancer Union, 39; mem sect E, div A, Nat Defense Res Comt, Off Sci Res & Develop, 42; nuclear comt Z-54, safety code, indust use of radiation, Am Nat Sta; chief opers res, Eigth Fighter Command, 43 & Ninth Air Force, 43-45, consult, Air Force Opers Analysis Div, Dept Defense, 47-52, mem, guided missiles countermeasures panel, Res & Develop Bd, 47-52, adv comt radiol defense, 48-51, comt weapons systs eval with Nat Acad Sci, 53-55, consult, Weapons Systs Eval Group, Joint Chiefs of Staff, 54-65, mem interagency comt biomed weapons effects tests, 57, consult, Inst Defense Analysis, 57-67, mem ad hoc sci adv comt, Armed Forces Radiobiol Res Facil & chmn panel radiol instruments, 62-65, mem nuclear weapons effects res med adv group, 65-71, chmn rev comt, Armed Forces Radiobiol Res Inst, 66; chief biophys br, AEC, 48-49; mem subcomt radiobiol, Comt Nuclear Sci, Nat Acad Sci-Nat Res Coun, 49-54, consult comt med & surg, 54, comt radiol, 54, mem adv comt civil defense, 54-65, chmn, 57-65; sr consult, Civil Serv Bd Expert Exam, Civil Serv Comn, 52-58, chmn, 62-65. *Mem:* Am Asn Physicists Med; fel Am Phys Soc; Am Roentgen Ray Soc; fel Am Col Radiol; hon mem Ger Roentgen Soc; Health Physics Soc (pres, 58-59); Radiation Res Soc; Radiol Soc NAm; Sigma Xi; hon mem Nippon Soc Radiol; hon fel Am Col Dentists. *Res:* Development of radiation measurement standards and means and standards for protection against harmful effects of ionizing radiation. *Mailing Add:* 10450 Lottsford Rd Unit 3011 Mitchellville MD 20721-2734

**TAYLOR, LAWRENCE AUGUST,** GEOCHEMISTRY, PETROLOGY. *Current Pos:* mem fac, dept geol sci, 73, PROF GEOL SCI, UNIV TENN, KNOXVILLE, 73-, DIR PLANETARY GEOSCI INST, 93- *Personal Data:* b Paterson, NJ, Sept 14, 38; m 93, Dong-Hwa Shin; c Jeffrey & Kelly. *Educ:* Ind Univ, Bloomington, BS, 61, MS, 63; Lehigh Univ, PhD(geochem), 68. *Honors & Awards:* Sci Achievement Award, NASA, 78 & 83; Chancellor's Scholar, Univ Tenn, 81; Pres Medal Space Res Activ, Fr Govt. *Prof Exp:* Instr geol, Univ Del, 63-64; fel geochem, Geophys Lab, Carnegie Inst Wash, 68-70; Fulbright fel, Max Planck Inst Nuclear Physics, Heidelberg, 70-71; asst prof, Purdue Univ, West Lafayette, 71-73. *Concurrent Pos:* Res grants, Geochem Sect, NSF; prin investr, Lunar Sample Prog, NASA, 72-; co-investr, Max Planck Inst Nuclear Physics; prin investr, NASA Planetary Mat Prog, NASA Meteorite Prog, mem, Lunar Sample Rev Panel, 74-75, Lunar & Planetary Rev Panel, 75-76, Lunar Sample Analytical Prog Team, 76-78, Lunar & Planetary Sample Team, 78-81, NASA meteorite steering comt, 81-82, mem, Lunar & Planetary Sci Conf Prog Comt, 79-87, chmn, Lunar & Planetary Sample Team, 82-86, Lunar & Planetary Rev Panel, 82-84, Geosci Rev Panel, 84-85, Planetary Geosci Working Group, 84-86, Planetary Meetings Steering Comt, 84-86, Lunar Base Comt, 86-,Lunar Base Site Selection Comt, NASA Space Indignous Mat Res Utilization, 89-; discipline scientist & prog mgr, Solar Syst Explor, NASA, Washington, DC, 81-82; assoc ed, Proc Lunar & Planetary Sci Conf, 75, 77-79 & 81, J Geophys Res, 82-86; rev panel, lunar & planetary geosci, NASA, 91-92; curation & analytical planning team, Extraterrestrial Mats, 93- *Mem:* Fel Mineral Soc Am; Mineral Asn Can; Am Geophys Union; fel Meteoritical Soc; Int Mineral Asn; Geochem Soc. *Res:* Geochemistry and petrology into the stability relations of sulfide, oxide and silicate compounds at low and high pressures within natural mineral and rock systems; mineralogy, petrology and geochemistry of lunar rocks, meteorites, Kimberlites and mantle xenoliths; resource utilization at lunar & martian basis. *Mailing Add:* Dept Geol Sci 057949970 306 G&G Bldg Knoxville TN 37996-1410. *Fax:* 423-974-2368; *E-Mail:* lataylor@utkvx.utk.edu

**TAYLOR, LAWRENCE DOW,** GLACIOLOGY, GEOMORPHOLOGY. *Current Pos:* from asst prof to assoc prof geol, 64-76, chmn dept, 64-85, PROF GEOL, ALBION COL, 77- *Personal Data:* b Boston, Mass, Oct 6, 32; m 55, Jean Ryland; c Charles & Keith. *Educ:* Dartmouth Col, BA, 54, MA, 58; Ohio State Univ, PhD(geol), 62. *Honors & Awards:* Congressional Medal for Antarctic Serv; Antarctica Geog feature named in honor, Taylor Hills. *Prof Exp:* Geologist, US Geol Surv, Greenland, 54-55; res assoc, Northwest Greenland Glaciol, Dartmouth Col & Air Force Cambridge Res Labs, 57-58; res assoc, Southeast Alaska Glaciol, Inst Polar Studies, Ohio State Univ, 59-62; chief glaciologist, SPole Traverse, US Antarctic Res Prog, NSF, 62-63; asst prof geol, Col Wooster, 63-64. *Concurrent Pos:* NSF res grants, 60-61 & 62-63, field inst grant, Can Rockies, 68; Kellogg Found res & teaching grant, 71-72; Hewlett-Mellow Found res grant, 81, Pew Sci Prog grant, 91; pres, E Cent Sect, Nat Asn Geol Teachers, 84-85. *Mem:* AAAS; fel Geol Soc Am; Int Glaciological Soc; Nat Asn Geol Teachers; Arctic Inst NAm; Sigma Xi. *Res:* Glacial geology of Michigan; structure of lake ice, Greenland; structure and flow of Alaskan glaciers; snow stratigraphy, Antarctica; microparticles in Antarctic ice. *Mailing Add:* Dept Geol Sci Albion Col Albion MI 49224. *E-Mail:* ltaylor@albion.edu

**TAYLOR, LEONARD S,** ELECTRICAL ENGINEERING, BIOELECTROMAGNETICS. *Current Pos:* prof, radiol oncol, 67-96, EMER PROF ELEC ENG, UNIV MD, COLLEGE PARK, 96- *Personal Data:* b New York, NY, Dec 28, 28; m 54; c 2. *Educ:* Harvard Univ, AB, 51; NMex State Univ, MS, 56, PhD(physics), 60. *Prof Exp:* Electronics engr, Raytheon Mfg Co, 51-54; electronics scientist, White Sands Missile Range, 54-59; theoret physicist, Gen Elec Co, 60-64; assoc prof eng, Case Western Res Univ, 64-67. *Concurrent Pos:* Sr Fulbright lectr, Univ Madrid, 62-63; consult, Ford Found & vis prof, Ford Found prog, Ctr Adv Res & Studies, Nat Polytech Inst, Mex, 64-65; mem, Comn VI, US Nat Comt/Int Union Radio Sci, 71-, US Nat Comn, Int Sci Radio Union, 78-82 & Eng Adv Coun, Coun Int Exchange Scholars, 92-; assoc ed, Bioelectromagnetics J, 83-85, Inst Elec & Electronics Engrs-Biomed Electronics, 86-87; panelist, Nat Res Coun, 89-; distinguished lectr, Inst Elec & Electronics Engrs Biomed Eng Soc, 92- *Mem:* Fel Inst Elec & Electronics Engrs; fel Am Soc Laser Med & Surg; Am Phys Soc; Bioelectromagnetics Soc; Optical Soc Am. *Res:* Biological effects of microwaves; microwave surgery and hyperthermia; optical and radio communication systems; remote sensing; microwave engineering. *Mailing Add:* Dept Elec Eng Univ Md College Park MD 02181

**TAYLOR, LINCOLN HOMER,** AGRONOMY. *Current Pos:* RETIRED. *Personal Data:* b Wolsey, SDak, Oct 26, 20; m 46; c 5. *Educ:* SDak State Col, BS, 42; Iowa State Univ, MS, 49, PhD, 51. *Prof Exp:* From asst prof to assoc prof agron, Univ Maine, 51-55; prof agron, Va Polytech Inst & State Univ, 55-86. *Concurrent Pos:* Grass breeding consult. *Mem:* Crop Sci Soc Am; Am Soc Agron. *Res:* Forage crop and turfgrass breeding; genetics. *Mailing Add:* 1100 Westover Dr Blacksburg VA 24060

**TAYLOR, LLOYD DAVID,** OTHER CHEMISTRY. *Current Pos:* PRES, CHEMSOCIATES, INC, 93- *Personal Data:* b Boston, Mass, Jan 11, 33; m 57, Marianne Cassie; c Lloyd III, Julianne & Lisa. *Educ:* Boston Col, BS, 54; Mass Inst Technol, PhD(org chem), 58. *Prof Exp:* Res assoc, Mass Inst Technol, 57-58; scientist, Polaroid Corp, Cambridge, 58-65, res group leader, 65-68, mgr polymer res lab, 68-78, tech dir polymer sci, 78-80, dir chem res, 80-83, sr res fel & corp officer, 80-93. *Mem:* AAAS; Am Chem Soc; Soc Photog Sci & Eng; NY Acad Sci. *Res:* Polymer chemistry; photographic chemistry; syntheses of novel monomers and polymers; plastics; solubility and diffusional phenomena; critical temperature behavior; chemistry of molecular switches activated by heat or light; molecular recognition. *Mailing Add:* 1 Maureen Rd Lexington MA 02173-2103. *Fax:* 781-862-0358

**TAYLOR, LYLE HERMAN,** LASERS. *Current Pos:* sr scientist, 67-84, FEL SCIENTIST, WESTINGHOUSE RES LABS, 84- *Personal Data:* b Paton, Iowa, Oct 23, 36; m 59; c 5. *Educ:* Iowa State Univ, BS, 58; NMex State Univ, MS, 61; Univ Kans, PhD(physics), 68. *Prof Exp:* Asst physicist, White Sands Missile Range, 58-61; assoc physicist, Midwest Res Inst, 61-64, tech consult, 64-67. *Mem:* Am Phys Soc. *Res:* Laser pumps; holographic strain analysis; gas laser computer simulation; laser radar; inertial confinement fusion studies; molecular spectroscopy; acoustic-optic devices. *Mailing Add:* 3317 Benden Dr Murrysville PA 15668

**TAYLOR, MALCOLM HERBERT,** ENVIRONMENTAL PHYSIOLOGY, ENDOCRINOLOGY. *Current Pos:* res assoc marine sci, Col Marine Studies, 71-73, asst prof biol sci, 73-79, ASSOC PROF BIOL, UNIV DEL, 79- *Personal Data:* b Annapolis, Md, Apr 7, 42; m 65; c 4. *Educ:* Franklin & Marshall Col, BA, 64; Johns Hopkins Univ, PhD(physiol), 69. *Prof Exp:* NIH fel physiol, Med Sch, Univ Pittsburgh, 69-71. *Concurrent Pos:* Joint appt, Col Marine Studies, Univ Del, 77- *Mem:* Am Soc Zoologists; Am Fisheries Soc. *Res:* Environmental control of reproduction in fish. *Mailing Add:* Dept Biol Univ Del 117A Wolf Hall Newark DE 19716

**TAYLOR, MARTHA LOEB,** NUTRITION. *Current Pos:* ASST PROF HUMAN NUTRIT, UNIV MD, COLLEGE PARK, 85- *Personal Data:* b Birdsboro, Pa, May 9, 49; m 72; c 1. *Educ:* Univ Del, Newark, BS, 71; Univ Md, College Park, MS, 72, PhD(nutrit sci), 77. *Prof Exp:* Proj coordr & res asst, Ohio State Univ, Columbus, 77-81; asst prof human nutrit, Drexel Univ, 81-85. *Mem:* AAAS; Sigma Xi; Am Dietetic Asn; Am Col Nutrit; Am Inst Nutrit; Soc Nutrit Educ. *Res:* Growth, development and nutritional status of children with developmental disabilities; nutritional status of individuals with chronic health problems. *Mailing Add:* Dept Food Nutrit Food Serv Mgt Univ NC Greensboro Greensboro NC 27412-5001. *Fax:* 919-334-3009

**TAYLOR, MARY LOWELL BRANSON,** MICROBIAL PHYSIOLOGY. *Current Pos:* res assoc biol, 61-77, assoc prof environ sci & resources, 77-95, PROF BIOL & ENVIRON SCI, PORTLAND STATE UNIV, 95- *Personal Data:* b Coeur d'Alene, Idaho, Nov 24, 32. *Educ:* Univ Idaho, BS, 54; Univ Ill, PhD(bact), 59. *Prof Exp:* Asst, Univ Ill, 54-57; res assoc, Emory Univ, 57-59; USPHS fel, Oak Ridge Nat Lab, 59-61. *Mem:* Am Soc Microbiol; Am Soc Plant Physiol. *Res:* Bacterial physiology; alcohol oxidation; natural products oxidation; enzyme biosynthesis; role of metals and metaloids in microbial; aromatic assimilation and bioremediation. *Mailing Add:* 16565 SW Upper Boones Ferry Rd Tigard OR 97224

**TAYLOR, MERLIN GENE,** PHYSICS. *Current Pos:* asst prof, 69-71, assoc prof, 71-81, PROF PHYSICS, BLOOMSBURG STATE COL, 81- *Personal Data:* b Zanesville, Ohio, May 11, 36; m 63; c 2. *Educ:* Muskingum Col, BS, 58; Brown Univ, MSc, 65, PhD(physics), 67. *Prof Exp:* Res asst, High Energy Physics Lab, Brown Univ, 58-66; asst prof physics, Wilkes Col, 66-67 & Am Univ Cairo, 67-69. *Mem:* Am Phys Soc; Am Asn Physics Teachers. *Res:* Use of computers in physics teaching; nuclear physics; activation analysis. *Mailing Add:* Dept Physics Bloomsburg Univ Bloomsburg PA 17815

**TAYLOR, MICHAEL ALAN,** NEUROPSYCHIATRY. *Current Pos:* dir residency training, Chicago Med Sch, 76-89, chmn, Dept Psychiat & Behav Sci, 77-80, actg chmn, 86-87, PROF PSYCHOL, CHICAGO MED SCH, 77-, PROF PSYCHIAT & BEHAV SCI, 76- *Personal Data:* b New York, NY, Mar 6, 40; m 63; c 2. *Educ:* Cornell Univ, BA, 61; New York Med Col, MD, 65. *Honors & Awards:* A E Bennett Clin Res Award, Soc Biol Psychiat, 69; First Prize Clin Res, NY Acad Med, 69; Morris L Parker Award, Chicago Med Sch, Univ Health Sci, 78. *Prof Exp:* Residency psychiat, New York Med Col, 69, asst prof & chief acute treatment univ, 71-73; assoc prof & dir residency training, State Univ NY, Stony Brook, 73-76. *Concurrent Pos:* Consult, Pilgrim Psychiat Ctr, West Brentwood, NY, 73-76, Kings Park Psychiat Ctr, Kings Park, NY, 74-76, South Oaks Hosp, Amityville, NY, 74-76 & Psychiat Serv, North Chicago Vet Admin Hosp, North Chicago, Ill, 76-; mem res subcomt, Prov Ment Health Adv Coun, Alta, Can, 76-80; mem psychiat adv bd, Ill Dept Ment Health & Deviation Dis, Springfield, Ill, 77-; actg chmn, Dept Psychol, Sch Grad & Postdoctoral Studies, Chicago Med Sch, Univ Health Sci, 77-80. *Mem:* Am Psychiat Asn; Am Psychopath Asn; Psychiat Res Soc; AAAS; Int Neuropsychol Soc. *Res:* Validity of diagnoses of schizophrenia and manic depressive illness by relating clinical phenomenology of these groups to demographic, family illness, cerebral lateralization of cortical dysfunction, neuropsychological and treatment response variables; functional relationships between neuronal groups and behavior utilizing neuropsychological techniques; genetics of major psyches. *Mailing Add:* Dept Psychiat & Behav Sci Univ Health Sci Chicago Med Sch Bldg 50 3333 Greenbay Rd North Chicago IL 60064

**TAYLOR, MICHAEL DEE,** MATHEMATICS. *Current Pos:* Asst prof, 68-72, ASSOC PROF MATH, UNIV CENT FLA, 72- *Personal Data:* b New York, NY, Dec 17, 40; m 70. *Educ:* Univ Fla, BA, 63; Fla State Univ, MS, 65, PhD(math), 69. *Mem:* Math Asn Am; Am Math Soc. *Res:* Nondeterministic analysis and cellular automata. *Mailing Add:* Dept Math Univ Cent Fla Orlando FL 32816-1364

**TAYLOR, MICHAEL E,** GEOLOGICAL RESEARCH. *Current Pos:* RES GEOLOGIST, US GEOL SURV, 69- *Personal Data:* b Salt Lake City, Utah, Aug 28, 39; m 64, Julia H Taylor; c Sarah. *Educ:* Utah State Univ, BS, 62 & MS, 64; Univ Calif, Berkeley, PhD(paleontol), 71. *Honors & Awards:* G K Gilbert Award, US Geol Surv. *Concurrent Pos:* Guest scientist, Acad Sinica, Peoples Repub China, 84 & 86, Russ & Kuzatehstanian Acad Sci, Russ & Kuzatehstan, 85, 87, 90 & 92. *Mem:* Geol Soc Am; Soc Sedimentary Geol; AAAS; Paleont Soc; Am Asn Petrol Geologists; Inst Cambrian Studies. *Res:* Lower Paleozoic stratigraphy and paleontology; paleoncological and geological studies in North America and Republic of Kuzatehstan. *Mailing Add:* US Geol Surv Mail Stop 919 PO Box 25046 Fed Ctr Denver CO 80225. *Fax:* 303-236-5690; *E-Mail:* 73611.2771@compuserve.com

**TAYLOR, MICHAEL LEE,** ANALYTICAL & ENVIRONMENTAL CHEMISTRY, DEVELOPMENT OF TECHNOLOGY FOR DETOXIFYING HAZARDOUS CHEMICALS & HAZARDOUS WASTES. *Current Pos:* dir res & develop & sr tech assoc, 87-91, DIR SCI TECHNOL & DISTINGUISHED TECH ASSOC, IT CORP, CINCINNATI, 91- *Personal Data:* b Rockville, Ind, May 27, 41; m 65; c 2. *Educ:* Purdue Univ, Lafayette, BS, 63, MS, 65, PhD(med chem), 67. *Prof Exp:* Nat Res Coun resident res assoc, Chem Lab, Aerospace Res Labs, Wright-Patterson AFB, Ohio, 70-71, res scientist analytical mass spectros, 71-75; res assoc prof chem, Wright State Univ, 75-87, assoc prof pharmacol & assoc dir, Brehm Lab, 78-87. *Mem:* Air & Waste Mgt Asn; Am Chem Soc; Soc Toxicol. *Res:* Use of ultrasensitive mass spectral techniques to assess relationships between molecular structure and elicited toxicological and pharmacological response and to determine environmental distribution and the fate of toxic chemicals; develop bench, pilot and full scale processes for detoxifying hazardous chemicals and chemically contaminated soil and debris. *Mailing Add:* IT Corp 11499 Chester Rd Cincinnati OH 45246-4098. *Fax:* 513-782-4807; *E-Mail:* mtaylor@atcrp.com

**TAYLOR, MILTON WILLIAM,** GENETICS, MOLECULAR BIOLOGY. *Current Pos:* from asst prof to assoc prof, 67-75, PROF MICROBIOL & GENETICS, IND UNIV, BLOOMINGTON, 75- *Personal Data:* b Glasgow, Scotland, Dec 10, 31; US citizen; m 57, Miriam Reifer; c Yuval & Jonathan. *Educ:* Cornell Univ, BS, 61; Stanford Univ, PhD(biol), 66. *Prof Exp:* NIH fel virol, Univ Calif, Irvine, 66-67. *Concurrent Pos:* Vis prof, Univ Rome, Italy, 83-84; Fogarty Int fel, NIH, 83-84; consult, Amgen Corp, 89-, TKT, 92-, Cell Genesys, 92-94. *Mem:* AAAS; Am Soc Microbiol; Am Soc Biol Chemists; Am Soc Virol; Int Soc Interferon Res; Am Acad Microbiol. *Res:* Cancer research; recombinant DNA and gene cloning; somatic cell genetics; purine metabolism; microbiology; interferon; virology; gene therapy. *Mailing Add:* Dept Biol Ind Univ Bloomington IN 47405. *Fax:* 812-855-6705; *E-Mail:* taylor@indiana.edu

**TAYLOR, MORRIS CHAPMAN,** INSTRUMENTATION. *Current Pos:* PRES & CHIEF EXEC OFFICER, NAT BUS CONTROL SYSTS, 86- *Personal Data:* b Fulton, Ky, May 28, 39; m 60, Glenda Ricker; c Susan & Jennifer. *Educ:* Univ Tenn, BS, 62; Univ Calif, Los Angeles, MS, 64; Rice Univ, MA, 66, PhD(physics), 68. *Prof Exp:* Lab technician, Oak Ridge Nat Lab, 61-62; mem tech staff, Hughes Aircraft Co, 62-64; asst prof physics, St Louis Univ, 68-69; mem staff, Columbia Sci Res Inst, Houston, 69-71; AEC & State of Tex joint sr fel, Rice Univ & Univ Tex M D Anderson Hosp & Tumor Inst, 71; chief scientist, Columbia Sci Industs, 72-76, dir eng, 76-82; pres & chief exec officer, Sci Measurement Syst, 82-86. *Mem:* Am Soc Testing & Mat; Air Pollution Control Asn; Instrument Soc Am; Am Phys Soc. *Res:* Experimental nuclear physics; radiological physics; air quality monitoring; nondestructive elemental analysis. *Mailing Add:* 11102 Aerie Cove Austin TX 78759. *Fax:* 512-834-3654

**TAYLOR, MORRIS D,** SCIENCE EDUCATION, PHYSICAL CHEMISTRY. *Current Pos:* from asst prof to prof chem & educ, 63-70, PROF CHEM, EASTERN KY UNIV, 70- *Personal Data:* b Mitchell, Ind, Apr 14, 34; m 56; c 3. *Educ:* Purdue Univ, BS, 56, PhD(sci educ), 66. *Prof Exp:* Instr physics & educ, Purdue Univ, 60-63. *Mem:* AAAS; Nat Sci Teachers Asn. *Mailing Add:* Dept Chem Eastern Ky Univ Richmond KY 40475

**TAYLOR, NORMAN FLETCHER,** BIOCHEMISTRY, CARBOHYDRATE METABOLISM & TRANSPORT. *Current Pos:* prof, 73-93, ADJ PROF BIOCHEM, UNIV WINDSOR, 93- *Personal Data:* b Newcastle Upon Tyne, Eng, Mar 4, 28; m 84, Edna Blackburne; c Adam & Matthew. *Educ:* Univ Oxford, BA, 53, MA, 56, DPhil(biochem), 56; FRSC. *Prof Exp:* Exchange vis scientist, Dept Pharmacol, Univ Calif, Los Angeles, 57-59; Sci Res Coun fel, Dept Biochem, Univ Oxford, 59-60; sr lectr chem, Bristol Col Sci & Technol, Eng, 62-65; reader & head biochem, Univ Bath, Eng, 65-73. *Concurrent Pos:*

Vis prof, Dept Chem, Temple Univ, 67, Dept Biochem, Univ Cambridge, UK, Weizmann Ins Sci, Israel, 83 & Dept Biochem, Univ WI, Trinidad, 92-; fel, Canterbury Col, Ont, 74- *Mem:* Am Soc Biochem & Molecular Biol; Can Biochem Soc; Brit Biochem Soc; Brit Chem Soc. *Res:* Microbial and mammalian metabolism of synthetic fluorinated carbohydrates and related compounds; mechanism of transport across biological membranes; insect biochemistry (locusta migratoria). *Mailing Add:* Dept Chem & Biochem Univ Windsor Windsor ON N9B 3P4 Can. *Fax:* 519-973-7098; *E-Mail:* ntaylor@server.uwindsor.ca

**TAYLOR, NORMAN LINN,** AGRONOMY. *Current Pos:* Asst agronomist, 53-56, assoc prof, 56-66, ASSOC AGRONOMIST, UNIV KY, 56-, PROF AGRON, 66- *Personal Data:* b Augusta, Ky, July 18, 26; m 51; c 5. *Educ:* Univ Ky, BS, 49, MS, 51; Cornell Univ, PhD(plant breeding), 53. *Mem:* AAAS; fel Crop Sci Soc Am; fel Am Soc Agron; Am Genetic Asn; Genetics Soc Can. *Res:* Forage crops genetics and breeding; interspecific hybridization in the genus Trifolium. *Mailing Add:* Agron Univ Ky 500 S Limestone St Lexington KY 40506-0001

**TAYLOR, OLIVER CLIFTON,** HORTICULTURE. *Current Pos:* horticulturist, Univ Calif, 53, horticulturist, Statewide Air Pollution Res Ctr, 53-89, lectr plant sci, 74-76, EMER PROF PLANT SCI, UNIV CALIF, RIVERSIDE, 89. *Personal Data:* b Hallett, Okla, Nov 29, 18; m 40; c 3. *Educ:* Okla Agr & Mech Col, MS, 51; Mich State Col, PhD, 53. *Prof Exp:* Asst co agent, Okla Exten Serv, 47-49; instr agr, Northeast Okla Agr & Mech Col, 50-51. *Mem:* AAAS; Air Pollution Control Asn; Am Soc Hort Sci. *Res:* Citriculture; biological effects of air pollutants and plant physiological responses to air pollutants. *Mailing Add:* 4762 Windsor Rd Riverside CA 92507

**TAYLOR, PALMER WILLIAM,** MOLECULAR BIOLOGY, MOLECULAR PHARMACOLOGY. *Current Pos:* assoc prof, 74-78, prof & head, Div Pharmacol, 78-86, PROF & CHMN, DEPT PHARMACOL, SCH MED, UNIV CALIF, SAN DIEGO, 87-, SANDRA & MONROE TROUT CHAIR PHARMACOL. *Personal Data:* b Stevens Point, Wis, Oct 3, 38; m 65, Susan Serota; c Tasha, Ashton & Palmer A. *Educ:* Univ Wis-Madison, BS, 60, PhD(pharm), 64. *Prof Exp:* Res assoc pharmacol, NIH, Bethesda, Md, 64-68; NIH vis fel, Molecular Pharmacol Res Unit, Cambridge Univ, 68-70. *Mem:* Am Soc Biol Chemists; Am Soc Pharmacol & Exp Therapeut; Am Asn Med Sch Pharmacol; AAAS. *Res:* Cholinergic neurotransmission; cholinergic receptors; acetylcholinesterase; regulation of gene expression in the cholinergic nervous system; signal transduction; drug design. *Mailing Add:* Med/Sch Med Univ Calif San Diego 9500 Gilman Dr La Jolla CA 92093-0636

**TAYLOR, PATRICK TIMOTHY,** GEOMAGNETICS. *Current Pos:* geophysicist, US Naval Oceanog Off, 66-76, Naval Ocean Res & Develop Activity, 76-78, GEOPHYSICIST, GEODYNAMICS BR, GODDARD SPACE FLIGHT CTR, NASA, 78- *Personal Data:* b Mt Vernon, NY, Mar 20, 38; m 73, Mary Kelley; c 2. *Educ:* Mich State Univ, BS, 60; Pa State Univ, MS, 62; Stanford Univ, PhD(geophys), 65. *Honors & Awards:* Kaminiski Award, Sci Res Soc Am, 70. *Prof Exp:* Res asst marine geophys, Lamont-Doherty Earth Observ, Columbia Univ, 65-66. *Concurrent Pos:* Assoc prof lectr, George Washington Univ; adj prof, Univ Md. *Mem:* Am Geophys Union; Geol Soc Am; Soc Explor Geophys. *Res:* Interpretation of satellite derived geophysical data, such as gravity and magnetics with supporting geophysical and geological information, for example petrology, remotely sensed photographs, seismicity and heat flow. *Mailing Add:* Code 921 NASA Greenbelt MD 20771. *Fax:* 301-286-1616; *E-Mail:* f8ptt@gibbs.gsfc.nasa.gov

**TAYLOR, PAUL DUANE,** CHEMISTRY & FIRE CHEMICAL CATALYSIS, POLYMERS. *Current Pos:* dir chem & process res, GAF Corp, Wayne, NJ, 85-92, VPRES & GEN MGR, ISP FINE CHEM, COLUMBUS, OHIO, 92- *Personal Data:* b Warren, Ohio, July 8, 40; m 65; c 4. *Educ:* Ind Inst Technol, BS, 62; Long Island Univ, MS, 64; Univ Cincinnati, PhD(inorg chem), 69. *Prof Exp:* Teaching asst, Long Island Univ, 62-64; res chemist, Res & Eng Develop Dept, M W Kellogg Co, 64-66; teaching asst, Univ Cincinnati, 66-68; from res chemist to sr res chemist, Celanese Res Co, 69-74, res supvr, 74-77, sect leader, Celanese Chem Co, Tex, 77-78; res mgr, Oxirane Int, 78-81; mgr catalysis develop, Arco Chem Co, Pa, 81-82; mgr planning, Lummus, 82-83; mgr com develop, PQ Corp, 83-85. *Concurrent Pos:* Chmn, NY Catalysis Soc, 76-77. *Mem:* Com Develop Asn; Am Chem Soc; Chem Mkt Res Asn; Am Semio Chem Asn (treas, 94-); Indust Res Inst. *Res:* Research and management of catalysis; speciality chemicals and speciality polymers; fire chemicals; business management. *Mailing Add:* PO Box 1333 Dublin OH 43017-6333

**TAYLOR, PAUL JOHN,** ANALYTICAL CHEMISTRY. *Current Pos:* lectr, 78-81, PROF, UNIV WIS, LA CROSSE, 81- *Personal Data:* b Chicago, Ill, Jan 30, 39; m 60; c Peter. *Educ:* Northern Ill Univ, BS, 64, PhD(analytical chem), 71. *Prof Exp:* US AEC fel, Purdue Univ, Lafayette, 70-72; from asst prof to assoc prof chem, Wright State Univ, 72-78. *Concurrent Pos:* Dir, Nuclear Med Technol Prog, Univ Wis, La Crosse, 94- *Mem:* Am Chem Soc; Sigma Xi. *Res:* Coordination compounds and their analytical applications, gas chromatography; computers and their applications to analytical chemistry; liquid crystals and mass spectroscopy. *Mailing Add:* Dept Chem Univ Wis La Crosse WI 54601

**TAYLOR, PAUL M,** PEDIATRICS, PHYSIOLOGY. *Current Pos:* RETIRED. *Personal Data:* b Baltimore, Md, June 26, 27; m 55; c 4. *Educ:* Johns Hopkins Univ, AB, 47, MD, 51. *Prof Exp:* Res fel, Sch Med, Univ Pittsburgh, 54-56, from instr to prof, 56-91, emer prof pediat, 91- *Concurrent Pos:* USPHS fel, Nuffield Inst Med Res, Oxford Univ, 59-60; dir, Div Neonatology & chief, Dept Pediat, Magee-Women's Hosp, 65-; vis prof, Inst Path, Univ Geneva, 71-72. *Mem:* Soc Pediat Res; Am Physiol Soc. *Res:* Physiology of the newborn infant; development of parent-infant attachment. *Mailing Add:* 820 College Ave Pittsburgh PA 15232

**TAYLOR, PAUL PEAK,** PEDIATRIC DENTISTRY. *Current Pos:* Prof grad pedodontics & chmn dept, 60-86, EMER PROF PEDODONTICS, COL DENT, BAYLOR UNIV, 86- *Personal Data:* b Childress, Tex, May 11, 21; m 45; c Scott V & Anne J. *Educ:* Baylor Univ, DDS, 44; Univ Mich, MS, 51. *Prof Exp:* Dir training & chief, Children's Med Ctr, 60-87, dir dent, 66-87. *Concurrent Pos:* Staff, Tex Scottish Rite Hosp for Crippled Children, Dallas, Tex, 60-97 & Denton State Sch, 64-87; proctor, Am Bd Pedodont, 66; exam mem, Am Bd Pedodont, 77-84. *Mem:* Fel Am Col Dent; Am Acad Pedodont; Am Dent Asn; Am Soc Dent Children. *Res:* Physiological responses of pulp tissues and the testing of patient responses to dental stimuli. *Mailing Add:* 2615 Briarcove Plano TX 75074

**TAYLOR, PETER,** INORGANIC CHEMISTRY, CRYSTALLOGRAPHY. *Current Pos:* fel, 75-77, RES OFFICER STRUCT INORG CHEM, RES CHEM BR, WHITESHELL NUCLEAR RES ESTAB, ATOMIC ENERGY CAN LTD, 77- *Personal Data:* b Warkworth, Eng, Sept 12, 49; m 73; c 1. *Educ:* Univ Birmingham, BSc, 69, PhD(inorg chem), 72. *Prof Exp:* Fel struct inorg chem, Univ NB, 72-75. *Mem:* Chem Inst Can. *Res:* Structural chemistry, phase relations, agueous and surface chemistry of inorganic oxide systems; radioactive waste management. *Mailing Add:* AECL Whiteshell Lab Pinawa MB R0E 1L0 Can

**TAYLOR, PETER ANTHONY,** PHYSICAL CHEMISTRY, TEXTILE ENGINEERING. *Current Pos:* PROJ MGR, PHILLIPS FIBERS CORP, 66- *Personal Data:* b Liverpool, Eng, June 9, 32; m 68; c 2. *Educ:* Liverpool Col Technol, Eng, ARIC, 56; Univ Manchester, PhD(chem), 63. *Prof Exp:* Jr asst analyst, Liverpool City Pub Health Dept, 49-52; analyst, Distillers Co (Biochem), Ltd, 52-56, res chemist, 58-60 & Fibers Div, Allied Chem Corp, 63-66. *Mem:* Royal Inst Chem; Am Chem Soc. *Res:* Polymerization kinetics, free radical and condensation; man-made fiber rheology, processing and dyeing; polymer pigmentation; textile and fiber finishing; spin finish development. *Mailing Add:* 29 Fieldstone Pl Greenville SC 29615-3822

**TAYLOR, PETER BERKLEY,** MARINE ECOLOGY. *Current Pos:* PROF OCEANOG, EVERGREEN STATE COL, 71- *Personal Data:* b Yonkers, NY, Dec 1, 33; m 58; c 3. *Educ:* Cornell Univ, BS, 55; Univ Calif, Los Angeles, MS, 60; Univ Calif, San Diego, PhD(marine biol), 64. *Prof Exp:* NSF res fel, 63-64; asst prof oceanog, Univ Wash, 64-71. *Res:* Coastal and estuarine benthic ecology; ecology of marine fishes; venomous marine animals. *Mailing Add:* Lab One Evergreen State Col 2700 Evergreen Pkwy W Olympia WA 98505

**TAYLOR, PETER D,** POPULATION MODELING, GENETIC MODELS. *Current Pos:* From asst prof to assoc prof math, 69-75, PROF MATH & BIOL, QUEENS UNIV, 81- *Personal Data:* b Vancouver, BC, Dec 7, 42. *Educ:* Queens Univ, BSc, 64; Harvard Univ, PhD(math), 69. *Mem:* AAAS; Can Math Soc; Math Asn Am. *Res:* Mathematics education. *Mailing Add:* Dept Math & Statist Queens Univ Kingston ON K7L 3N6 Can

**TAYLOR, PHILIP CRAIG,** CRYSTALLINE & AMORPHOUS SEMICONDUCTORS. *Current Pos:* PROF PHYSICS, UNIV UTAH, 82-, CHMN, 89- *Personal Data:* b Paterson, NJ, March 17, 42; m 69, Muriel Allison; c Allison L & Heather M. *Educ:* Carleton Col, BA, 64; Brown Univ, PhD(physics), 69. *Prof Exp:* Nat Acad Sci res assoc, Naval Res Lab, 69-71, res physicist, 71-80, supvr res physicist, 80-82. *Concurrent Pos:* Vis prof, Heriot-Watt Univ, Edinburgh & Cambridge Univ, 76-77; adj prof, Mat Sci Eng Dept, Univ Utah, 85-, assoc dir, Laser Inst, 87- *Mem:* Fel Am Phys Soc; AAAS; Mat Res Soc; Am Asn Physics Teachers. *Res:* Optical, electronic and structural properties of crystalline and amorphous semiconductors including localized electronic states in amorphoys semiconductors, metastabilities in disordered solids and electronic properties of very thin layered structures. *Mailing Add:* Dept Physics Univ Utah Salt Lake City UT 84112. *Fax:* 801-581-4801; *E-Mail:* craig@mail.physics.utah.edu

**TAYLOR, PHILIP LIDDON,** PHYSICS OF POLYMERS. *Current Pos:* Magnavox res fel mat sci, 62-64, from asst prof to prof physics, 64-88, PROF MACROMOLECULAR SCI, CASE WESTERN RES UNIV, 77-, PERKINS PROF PHYSICS, 88- *Personal Data:* b London, Eng, Oct 17, 37; m 66, Sarah L Butler; c Camilla (Bronwen) & Imogen R. *Educ:* Univ London, BSc, 59; Cambridge Univ, PhD(physics), 62. *Concurrent Pos:* Mem, comt recommendations for US Army basic sci res, Nat Res Coun Assembly Math & Phys Sci. *Mem:* Fel Am Phys Soc; fel AAAS. *Res:* Theoretical solid state physics. *Mailing Add:* Dept Physics Case Western Res Univ Cleveland OH 44106. *Fax:* 216-368-4671; *E-Mail:* plt@po.cwru.edu

**TAYLOR, PHILLIP R,** CANCER RESEARCH. *Current Pos:* actg dep br chief, NIH, 83-86, sr investr, Cancer Prev Studies Br, Cancer Prev Res Prog, Div Cancer Prev & Control, 83-87, actg br chief, 86-87, BR CHIEF, NAT CANCER INST, USPHS, DEPT HEALTH & HUMAN SERV, NIH, 87- *Personal Data:* b Mason City, Iowa, Feb 20, 48; m 74; c 3. *Educ:* Iowa State Univ, BS, 69; Univ Iowa, MD, 73; Harvard Sch Pub Health, SM, 82, ScD, 88; Am Bd Internal Med, cert, 76. *Prof Exp:* Intern, Vanderbilt Univ Med Ctr, Nashville, 73-74, resident, 74-76; med epidemiologist, Field Serv Div, Bur Epidemiol, Ctr Dis Control, USPH, Dept HEW, Acute Commun Dis Control, Los Angelas, Calif, Calif, 76-78, Spec Studies Br, Chronic Dis Div, Bur Epidemiol, Div Epidemiol, NY State Dept Health, Albany, 78-80, Indust Wide Studies Br, Div Surveillance, Hazard Eval & Field Studies, Nat Inst Occup Safety & Health, 80-81; grad student, Dept Epidemiol, Harvard Sch Pub Health, Boston, 81-83. *Concurrent Pos:* Co-prin investr, Nutrit Intervention Studies, Esophageal Cancer, Linxian, China, co-investr, Isotretinoin Basal Cell Carcinoma Prev Trial, Alpha-Tocopherol Beta Carotene Lung Prev Trial & Lung Cancer Intervention Feasibility Study Among Yunnan Tin Miners. *Mem:* Am Pub Health Asn; Soc Epidemiol Res; AAAS; Am Col Epidemiol; Am Soc Prev Oncol. *Res:* Nutrition and cancer; nutritional intervention studies; clinical nutrition/metabolic studies; environmental epidemiology. *Mailing Add:* NIH Nat Cancer Inst Cancer Prev Studies Br Exec Plaza N Rm 211 Bethesda MD 20892-7326

**TAYLOR, R(AYMOND) JOHN,** PLANT TAXONOMY. *Current Pos:* RETIRED. *Personal Data:* b Ada, Okla, Jan 20, 30; m 59; c 3. *Educ:* ECent State Col, BSEd, 54; Univ Okla, MNS, 61, PhD(plant ecol), 67. *Prof Exp:* Teacher high sch, Okla, 54-55 & Okla City Pub Sch Syst, 55-61; asst prof biol, Southeastern State Col, 61-63; asst bot, Univ Okla, 63-65; from assoc prof to prof biol, Southeastern State Univ, 74-91. *Concurrent Pos:* Grants, Southeastern State Col Res Found, 68 & NIH, 72. *Mem:* Am Soc Plant Taxonomists. *Res:* Dauphine Island, Oklahoma, Alaska, Costa Rica and Alabama plants; aquatic macrophytes; endangered plant species. *Mailing Add:* Rte 1 PO Box 157 Durant OK 74701

**TAYLOR, RALPH DALE,** HIGH ENERGY PULSE MEASUREMENTS, ADMINISTRATION OF RESEARCH & DEVELOPMENT. *Current Pos:* chief engr, 74-91, DIR ENG, DIT-MCO, 91- *Personal Data:* b Boonville, Mo, Dec 24, 45; m 92, Cynthia C Cavanaugh; c Jennifer & Nathan. *Educ:* Univ Mo, Rolla, BS, 68; Univ Mo, Columbia, MS, 70; Univ Mo, Kansas City, MBA, 78. *Prof Exp:* Sr engr, Bendix, 68-74. *Concurrent Pos:* Adj prof logic, Univ Mo, Columbia, 74-78. *Mem:* Inst Elec & Electronics Engrs. *Res:* Basic design and development of large computer directed test equipment. *Mailing Add:* 1120 Sampson Lees Summit MO 64081. *Fax:* 816-444-9737

**TAYLOR, RALPH WILSON,** FIELD BIOLOGY, MALACOLOGY. *Current Pos:* from asst prof to assoc prof, 72-84, PROF BIOL, MARSHALL UNIV, 84-, ASSOC DEAN, COL SCI, 90- *Personal Data:* b Whitesburg, Ky, June 1, 37. *Educ:* Murray State Univ, BS, 60; Univ Louisville, MS, 68, PhD(herpet), 72. *Prof Exp:* Pub sch teacher biol, Durrett High Sch, Louisville, Ky, 60-66; instr, Spalding Col, 69-70. *Concurrent Pos:* Pres, WVa Acad Sci, 86-87 *Mem:* Am Malacological Union; Sigma Xi. *Res:* Ecology, taxonomy, and distribution of freshwater and terrestrial mollusks of West Virginia and surrounding states. *Mailing Add:* Dept Biol Sci Marshall Univ 400 Halgreer Blvd Huntington WV 25755-0001. *Fax:* 304-696-3333

**TAYLOR, RAYMOND DEAN,** LOW TEMPERATURE PHYSICS, MOSSBAUER SPECTROSCOPY. *Current Pos:* assoc group leader, 73-86, mcm staff, 54-90, CONSULT, LOS ALAMOS NAT LAB, 90- *Personal Data:* b Okemah, Okla, Aug 18, 28; m 61, Janis Dexter; c Scott E & Kay (Miller). *Educ:* Pittsburg State Univ, BS, 50; Rice Univ, PhD(phys chem), 54. *Prof Exp:* Asst, Rice Inst, 51-52. *Concurrent Pos:* Humble Res fel, 52-54. *Mem:* Am Chem Soc; Am Phys Soc. *Res:* Low temperature calorimetry; cryogenics; transport and state properties of liquid helium; Mossbauer effect; superconductivity; magnetism; high pressures. *Mailing Add:* Los Alamos Nat Lab MST-10 MSK-764 Los Alamos NM 87545. *Fax:* 505-665-7652; *E-Mail:* RDT@LANL.Gov

**TAYLOR, RAYMOND ELLORY,** THERMOPHYSICAL PROPERTIES, HEAT TRANSFER. *Current Pos:* assoc sr researcher & assoc prof, Thermophys Properties Res Ctr, 67-75, SR RESEARCHER & DIR, THERMOPHYS PROPERTIES RES LAB, SCH MECH ENG, PURDUE UNIV, 75- *Personal Data:* b Ames, Iowa, Oct 19, 29; m 52; c 2. *Educ:* Iowa State Univ, BS, 51; Univ Idaho, MS, 56; Pa State Univ, PhD(solid state technol), 67. *Honors & Awards:* Thermal Conductivity Award, Int Thermal Conductivity Conf, 77; Cert Recognition, NASA, 82 & 84; Europ Thermophys Award, Europ Conf Thermophys, 90. *Prof Exp:* Chemist, Gen Elec, Richland, Wash, 51-56; sr res engr, Atomic Int, 57-64; res fel, NAm Rockwell, 64-67. *Concurrent Pos:* Consult numerous industs, 74-91; mem, exec bd, E-37 Thermal Analysis, Am Soc Testing & Mat, 75-91; chmn, Int Thermal Conductivity Conf, 86-90, mem, Head Placement Comt & By-Laws Comt; ed, Rev Sci Instruments, 86-89. *Mem:* Am Soc Testing & Mat; Int Thermal Conductivity Conf (secy, 90-). *Res:* Thermophysical properties of solids, especially at elevated temperatures; thermal conductivity; thermal diffusivity; specific heat capacity; thermal expansion; emissivity. *Mailing Add:* Thermophys Properties Res Lab Purdue Univ 2595 Yeager Rd West Lafayette IN 47906. *Fax:* 765-463-5235; *E-Mail:* rtaylor@tprl.com

**TAYLOR, RAYMOND L,** LASERS, CHEMICAL PHYSICS. *Current Pos:* CONSULT, 96- *Personal Data:* b Providence, RI, July 3, 30; m 55; c 5. *Educ:* Brown Univ, ScB, 55; Calif Inst Technol, PhD(chem), 60. *Honors & Awards:* Silver Combustion Medal, Combustion Inst, 68. *Prof Exp:* Asst, Calif Inst Technol, 55-59; prin res scientist, Avco Everett Res Lab, Inc, 59-73; prin scientist & mem bd dirs, Phys Sci Inc, 73-78, mgr laser devices, 78-80; mem staff, Res & Laser Tech Inc, 80-82; vpres res & eng, CVD, Inc, 82-96. *Concurrent Pos:* Chmn, Atomic Physics Res Comt, Avco Everett Res Lab, Inc, 70-73; mem, Comt Stratospheric Chem, Dept Transp, 73-75. *Mem:* Am Chem Soc; Am Phys Soc; Combustion Inst; Sigma Xi. *Res:* Radiation and energy transfer processes in gases; optical experiments and instrumentation; molecular gas laser device research and development; laser applications. *Mailing Add:* 223 Puritan Rd Swampscott MA 01907

**TAYLOR, RHODA E,** GENETIC TOXICOLOGY, MARINE BIOLOGY. *Current Pos:* assoc prof, 67-80, dept chmn, 84-89, PROF BIOL, SLIPPERY ROCK UNIV, 80- *Personal Data:* b Hartford City, Ind, Feb 20, 36; div; c 2. *Educ:* Asbury Col, BA, 57; Purdue Univ, MS, 63, PhD(physiol), 65. *Prof Exp:* Asst prof biol, Ind Univ, Kokomo, 65-67. *Concurrent Pos:* Cong affairs specialist, Intergovt Personnel Agreement, Appt Nat Oceanic & Atmospheric Admin, 80-83; NSF pre-col teacher develop sci prog grants, 79 & 80. *Res:* Mutagenesis and aneuploidy induction; reproductive physiology and behavior; maternal behavior. *Mailing Add:* Dept Biol Slippery Rock Univ Slippery Rock PA 16057. *E-Mail:* rhoda.taylor@sru.edu

**TAYLOR, RICHARD EDWARD,** PARTICLE PHYSICS. *Current Pos:* staff mem, Stanford Univ, 62-68, assoc prof, 68-70, assoc dir, Stanford Linear Accelerator Ctr Res, 82-86, PROF PHYSICS, STANFORD UNIV, 70- *Personal Data:* b Medicine Hat, Alta, Nov 2, 29; m 50, Rita J Bonneau; c N Edward. *Educ:* Univ Alta, BSc, 50, MSc, 52; Stanford Univ, PhD(physics), 62. *Hon Degrees:* Dr, Univ Paris, 80; LLD, Univ Calgary, 93, Univ Lethbridge, 93, Univ Victoria, 94. *Honors & Awards:* Nobel Prize in Physics, 90; Alexander von Humboldt Award, 82; W K H Panofsky Award, Am Phys Soc, 89. *Prof Exp:* Boursier, Ecole Normale Superiere, Paris, 58-61; physicist, Lawrence Radiation Lab, Univ Calif, 61-62. *Concurrent Pos:* Guggenheim fel, 71. *Mem:* Foreign assoc Nat Acad Sci; Can Asn Physicists; fel Royal Soc Can; Am Phys Soc; Am Acad Arts & Sci. *Res:* Particle physics, interactions of electrons and photons with matter; high energy electron scattering; gamma rays in space; graitational waves. *Mailing Add:* Stanford Linear Accelerator Ctr MS 96 Stanford Univ PO Box 4349 Stanford CA 94309

**TAYLOR, RICHARD G,** CELL BIOLOGY, ELECTRON MICROSCOPY. *Current Pos:* ELECTRON MICROSCOPIST, UNIV ARIZ, TUCSON, 90- *Personal Data:* b Rochester, Minn, Nov 9, 52; div; c 1. *Educ:* Mont State Univ, BS, 75; Wake Forest Univ, MS, 84, PhD(path), 87. *Prof Exp:* Instr path, Bowman Gray Sch Med, NC, 88-90. *Mem:* Am Soc Cell Biol; Fedn Am Socs Exp Biol; Am Heart Asn; Electron Micros Soc Am. *Res:* Cell biology of smooth muscle, skeletal muscle, and blood platelets; electron microscopy and activities involving ultrastructional examination, enzyme cytochemistry and immunolocalization. *Mailing Add:* Muscle Biol Group Univ Ariz Univ Ariz Tucson AZ 85721-0001. *Fax:* 520-621-1396

**TAYLOR, RICHARD L,** CIVIL ENGINEERING, SANITARY & ENVIRONMENTAL ENGINEERING. *Current Pos:* from asst prof to assoc prof civil eng technol, NCent Campus, 68-86, actg head, 84-86, HEAD, TECH ENG DEPT, PURDUE UNIV, 86- *Personal Data:* b South Bend, Ind, Aug 11, 39; m 61; c 2. *Educ:* Purdue Univ, BS, 63, MS, 65. *Prof Exp:* Jr engr sanit eng, Clark-Dietz & Assoc, 65-67; design engr sanit eng, Boyd E Phelps & Assoc, 67-68. *Concurrent Pos:* Consult, 67-80. *Res:* Anaerobic sludge digestion; land surveying relocation problems. *Mailing Add:* NCent Campus Dept Eng & Technol Purdue Univ Westville IN 46391

**TAYLOR, RICHARD MELVIN,** AGRONOMY, PLANT PHYSIOLOGY. *Current Pos:* RETIRED. *Personal Data:* b Salt Lake City, Utah, Aug 19, 29; m 55; c 4. *Educ:* Utah State Univ, BS, 58, MS, 59; Iowa State Univ, PhD(agron, plant physiol), 64. *Prof Exp:* Instr agron, Iowa State Univ, 59-64; assoc prof agron, Tex A&M Univ, 64-89, consult, 89. *Mem:* Am Soc Agron; Crop Sci Soc Am; Am Soc Hort. *Res:* Effects of soluble salts and temperature upon the germination and emergence of seeds and fruiting patterns of cotton; production and management; root physiology, native plant domestication and vegetable production. *Mailing Add:* 3429 Aberdeen El Paso TX 79925

**TAYLOR, RICHARD N,** SOFTWARE ENGINEERING, ENVIRONMENTS. *Current Pos:* from asst prof to assoc prof, 82-91, PROF, DEPT INFO & COMPUT SCI, UNIV CALIF, IRVINE, 91- *Personal Data:* b Denver, Colo, Dec 11, 52. *Educ:* Univ Colo, Denver, BS, 74; Univ Colo, Boulder, MS, 76, PhD(comput sci), 80. *Prof Exp:* Analyst & programmer, US Bur Reclamation, Denver, Colo, 74-76; teaching asst, Dept Comput Sci, Univ BC, 76-77; sr software engr, Boeing Comput Serv, Seattle, 77-79; res asst, Univ Colo, Boulder, 79-80; asst prof, Dept Comput Sci, Univ Victoria, 81-83. *Concurrent Pos:* Consult, Boeing Comput Serv Co, Seattle, Wash, 79-82, Joint Syst Develop Corp, Tokyo, Japan, 83, Res Triangle Inst, Res Triangle Park, NC, 83, ITT Adv Technol Ctr, Stratford, Conn, 84, Aerospace Corp, El Segundo, Calif, 83-88, GSI-TECSI Indust, Paris, France, 87-88, Inst Defense Analysis, Arlington, Va, 88, TRW, Redondo Beach, Calif, 88, Telesoft, San Diego, Calif, 88-89, Nimble Comput Corp, Encino, Calif, 89-90, IBM, 91-94; grants, Pres Nat Sci & Eng Res Coun, Res Prog, 81-82, operating, 82-83, 83-84, Microelectronics Innovation & Comput Sci Res Prog, Univ Calif, 85-86 & 86-87, Alcoa Found, 85-87, ARPA, 87-94; presidential young investr, NSF, 85; exec comt, Inst Elec & Electronics Engrs Comput Soc Tech Comt, Software Eng, 85-86; conf prog comt, Sixth Int Conf Distrib Comput Systs, 86, Comput Languager, Inst Elec & Electronics Engrs, 86; vchair, Asn Comput Mach SIGSOFT, 89-93, chair, 89-93, prog chair, 90; comt, Asn Comput Mach Software Syst Award, 90- *Res:* Software engineering environments; user interface systems; software technologies to support teams and their processes; concurrent systems analysis and testing. *Mailing Add:* Dept Info & Comput Sci Univ Calif Irvine CA 92717. *Fax:* 714-856-4056; *E-Mail:* taylor@ics.uci.edu

**TAYLOR, RICHARD TIMOTHY,** ORGANIC CHEMISTRY. *Current Pos:* ASST PROF ORG CHEM, MIAMI UNIV, 78- *Personal Data:* b Coatesville, Pa, June 12, 50. *Educ:* Univ Del, BS, 72; Ohio State Univ, PhD(chem), 77. *Prof Exp:* Asst chem, Ohio State Univ, 73-75, fel, 75-77; NIH fel org chem, Cornell Univ, 77-78. *Mem:* Am Chem Soc; Sigma Xi. *Res:* Synthetic aspects of organosilicon chemistry; synthesis of strained ring compounds. *Mailing Add:* Chem Dept Miami Univ Oxford OH 45046-1618

**TAYLOR, ROBERT BURNS, JR,** ORGANIC CHEMISTRY, INFORMATION SCIENCE. *Current Pos:* RETIRED. *Personal Data:* b Downingtown, Pa, Oct 13, 20; m 45, 71, Phoebe Carson; c Kathryn T Walters. *Educ:* Swarthmore Col, AB, 41; Ohio State Univ, MSc, 42; Pa State Col, PhD(org chem), 45. *Prof Exp:* Instr chem, Pa State Col, 45-46; res chemist, E I DuPont de Nemours & Co, Inc, 46-53, res supvr, 53-56, sr patent chemist, 56-60, from supvr to sr supvr textile fibers patent div, 60-71, mgr cent patent index, 71-76, asst to div mgr, info syst dept, 76-82. *Mem:* Sigma Xi. *Res:* Synthetic antimalarials; synthetic fibers; patents. *Mailing Add:* 1306 Grayson Rd Wilmington DE 19803

**TAYLOR, ROBERT CLEMENT,** PHYSIOLOGY, ZOOLOGY. *Current Pos:* RETIRED. *Personal Data:* b Mankato, Minn, Dec 2, 35; m 57; c 6. *Educ:* Mankato State Col, BS, 57; Univ SDak, MS, 61; Univ Ariz, PhD(physiol), 66. *Prof Exp:* From asst prof to assoc prof zool, Univ Ga, 77-91. *Mem:* AAAS; Am Soc Zoologists. *Res:* Comparative physiology; neurophysiology. *Mailing Add:* PO Box 1331 Hartwell GA 30643

**TAYLOR, ROBERT COOPER,** PHYSICAL CHEMISTRY, MOLECULAR SPECTROSCOPY. *Current Pos:* from instr to assoc prof, Univ Mich, Ann Arbor, 49-62, actg chmn, 66, prof, 62-87, assoc chmn, 67-87, EMER PROF CHEM, UNIV MICH, ANN ARBOR, 87- *Personal Data:* b Colorado Springs, Colo, May 5, 17; m 42, Evelyn L Seeley; c David R & Donald C. *Educ:* Kalamazoo Col, AB, 41; Brown Univ, PhD(phys chem), 47. *Prof Exp:* Asst chem, Brown Univ, 41-42, res chemist, Manhattan Proj, 42-46, instr phys chem, 47-49. *Concurrent Pos:* Nat Res Coun fel, 46-47; consult, W J Barrow Res Lab, 74-77; vis staff mem, Los Alamos Nat Lab, 75-85. *Mem:* Fel AAAS; Am Chem Soc; Am Phys Soc; Am Crystallog Asn. *Res:* Molecular spectroscopy and structure; boron hydride derivatives; Lewis complexes; hydrogen bonded substances; uranium chemistry. *Mailing Add:* Dept Chem Univ Mich Ann Arbor MI 48109-1055. *Fax:* 313-647-4865; *E-Mail:* rcprtylr@umich.edu

**TAYLOR, ROBERT CRAIG,** INORGANIC CHEMISTRY. *Current Pos:* ASSOC PROF CHEM, OAKLAND UNIV, 72- *Personal Data:* b Franklin, Pa, Jan 26, 39; m 66; c 1. *Educ:* Col Wooster, BA, 60; Princeton Univ, MA, 62, PhD(chem), 64. *Prof Exp:* NATO fel, Imp Col, Univ London, 64-65; asst prof chem, Univ Ga, 65-72. *Mem:* Am Chem Soc; Royal Soc Chem; Sigma Xi; Am Asn Univ Prof; NY Acad Sci. *Res:* Transition metal chemistry; organophosphorous chemistry; lanthanide shift reagents; transition metal catalyzed stereospecific polymerizations of diolefins; transition metal complexes as antitumor agents; role of molybdenum in enzymes; Nuclear magnetic resonance and electrochemistry of metal clusters. *Mailing Add:* Dept Chem Oakland Univ Rochester MI 48309-4401

**TAYLOR, ROBERT DALTON,** MICROBIOLOGY OF CLOSED SYSTEMS, RISK ASSESSMENT. *Current Pos:* SYSTS SCIENTIST, MITRE CORP, 92- *Personal Data:* b Greenville, Ala, June 29, 50; m 83, Patricia Dunhardt. *Educ:* Southeastern La Univ, BS, 72, MS, 73; La State Univ, PhD(microbiol), 79. *Prof Exp:* Fel, Nat Cancer Inst, 79-82; asst prof microbiol, Dept Microbiol, Univ Southern Miss, 82-83, from asst prof to assoc prof, Dept Biol Sci, 83-87; environ microbiologist, Microbiol Lab, Johnson Space Ctr, NASA, 87-89, group mgr, Biomed Opers & Res Group, 89-91. *Concurrent Pos:* NIH fel, 79-82; consult, US Army, Camp Shelby, Miss, 84-86 & Nat Marine Fisheries Serv, 85-88. *Mem:* Am Soc Microbiol; AAAS; Inst Food Technol; NY Acad Sci; Proj Mgt Inst. *Res:* Potential health effects resulting from bio remediation. *Mailing Add:* PO Box 35514 San Antonio TX 78235-0514. *Fax:* 210-536-4335; *E-Mail:* rtaylor@mitre.org

**TAYLOR, ROBERT E,** PHYSIOLOGY, BIOPHYSICS. *Current Pos:* RETIRED. *Personal Data:* b Havelock, Nebr, July 24, 20; div; c 3. *Educ:* Univ Ill, BS, 42; Univ Rochester, PhD(physiol), 50. *Prof Exp:* Mem staff, Radiation Lab, Off Sci Res & Develop, Mass Inst Technol, 42-45; Merck fel physiol, Univ Chicago, 50-51, Nat Heart Inst fel, 51-52; asst prof neurophysiol, Col Mcd, Univ Ill, 52-53; NSF fel, Physiol Lab, Cambridge Univ, 53-54, Nat Inst Neurol Dis & Blindness fel, 54-55 & Univ Col, Univ London, 55-56; physiologist, lab biophys, nat inst neurol & commun dis & stroke, 56-88. *Mem:* Am Physiol Soc; Biophys Soc; NY Acad Sci; Soc Gen Physiol; hon mem Chilean Biol Soc. *Res:* Properties of natural excitable membranes; muscle contraction activation. *Mailing Add:* 20 Harbor Hill Rd Woods Hole MA 02543-1215

**TAYLOR, ROBERT EMERALD, JR,** endocrinology, for more information see previous edition

**TAYLOR, ROBERT GAY,** MICROBIOLOGY, ENVIRONMENTAL SCIENCES. *Current Pos:* from asst prof to assoc prof microbiol, 69-86, dir, Sch Natural Sci, 77-80, PROF MICROBIOL, EASTERN NMEX UNIV, 87- *Personal Data:* b Cleveland, Ohio, July 8, 40. *Educ:* Wittenberg Univ, BS, 63; John Carroll Univ, MS, 66; Tex A&M Univ, PhD(environ studies), 69. *Honors & Awards:* Outstanding Res Award, Nat Air Pollution Control Asn, 67. *Prof Exp:* Sr bacteriologist, Cleveland Dept Pub Health, 63-65. *Concurrent Pos:* Dept Interior, Water Resources Res Inst grant, Eastern NMex Univ, 71-72; vis scientist, Lawrence Berkeley Lab, Univ Calif, 72; consult, Dept Civil Eng, Univ Tex, El Paso, 72-74; pest mgt specialist, NMex State Univ, 80-97; peanut dis specialist, 80-97. *Mem:* AAAS; Am Chem Soc. *Res:* Biomedical biochemical mechanisms; environmental microbiology with respect to water treatment and contamination; agricultural consulting peanut diseases. *Mailing Add:* PO Box 2296 Portales NM 88130. *Fax:* 505-562-2192; *E-Mail:* taylorr@ziavmis.enmu.edu

**TAYLOR, ROBERT JOE,** POPULATION ECOLOGY. *Current Pos:* PRES, ENDANGERED SPECIES GROUP, 96- *Personal Data:* b Pomona, Calif, May 1, 45; m 67; c 2. *Educ:* Stanford Univ, AB, 67; Univ Calif, Santa Barbara, MS, 70, PhD(biol), 72. *Prof Exp:* Res assoc ecol, Princeton Univ, 71-72; asst prof, Univ Minn, St Paul, 72-78; assoc prof zool, Clemson Univ, 78-85; assoc prof fisheries & wildlife, Utah State Univ, 85-92; dir wildlife ecol, Calif Forestry Assocs, 92-96. *Mem:* Ecol Soc Am; Brit Ecol Soc; Soc Pop Ecol. *Res:* The influence of predatory behavior upon population in space and time; artificial intelligence models in ecology. *Mailing Add:* Endangered Species Group PO Box 228 Orangevale CA 95662. *Fax:* 916-989-9383; *E-Mail:* rtaylor@ns.net

**TAYLOR, ROBERT JOSEPH,** PHYSICS, ELECTROMAGNETISM. *Current Pos:* RETIRED. *Personal Data:* b Salt Lake City, Utah, Dec 10, 41; m 67; c 6. *Educ:* Univ Utah, BA, 67; Cornell Univ, PhD(appl physics), 71. *Prof Exp:* Scientist metall, Res Ctr, Kennecott Copper Co, 67; scientist acoust, Interand Corp, 71-72; physicist, Appl Physics Lab, Johns Hopkins Univ, 72-91. *Concurrent Pos:* Teaching & consult. *Mem:* Am Geophys Union. *Res:* Electromagnetic wave propagation through the ionosphere for global dissemination of submicrosecond time from satellites; tropospheric propagation and radio frequency ducting; acoustics; impact of ultrasound on colonial hydroids; infrared propagation. *Mailing Add:* Appl Physics Lab Johns Hopkins Univ Johns Hopkins Rd Laurel MD 20723-6099

**TAYLOR, ROBERT LEE,** medical mycology, for more information see previous edition

**TAYLOR, ROBERT LEE,** MATHEMATICS, STATISTICS. *Current Pos:* PROF STATIST, UNIV GA, 83-, DEPT HEAD, 89- *Personal Data:* b Tenn, July 23, 43; m 68. *Educ:* Univ Tenn, Knoxville, BS, 66; Fla State Univ, MS, 69, PhD(statist), 70. *Prof Exp:* Teaching asst math, Univ Tenn, Knoxville, 66-67; asst prof math & statist, Univ SC, 71-74, assoc prof math, 74-80, prof, 80-83. *Mem:* Math Asn Am; Am Statist Asn; Inst Math Statist. *Res:* Probability; probabilistic functional analysis and statistical applications. *Mailing Add:* Dept Statist Univ Ga Athens GA 30602-1952. *Fax:* 706-542-3381; *E-Mail:* bob@stat.uga.edu

**TAYLOR, ROBERT LEROY,** CIVIL ENGINEERING. *Current Pos:* from asst prof to prof, 62-96, EMER PROF CIVIL ENG, UNIV CALIF, BERKELEY, 72- *Personal Data:* b Riverside, Calif, July 14, 34; m 63; c 5. *Educ:* Univ Calif, Berkeley, BS, 56, MS, 58, PhD(civil eng), 63. *Hon Degrees:* Hon fel, Univ Wales, UK, 88. *Concurrent Pos:* Founder & dir solid mech, Centric Eng Systs, Inc, 90- *Mem:* Nat Acad Eng; Am Soc Civil Engrs; Int Asn Comput Mech; Soc Comput Mech. *Res:* Development of finite methods and software for problems in solid and structural mechanics; non-linear applications. *Mailing Add:* Dept Civil & Environ Eng Univ Calif 721 Davis Hall Berkeley CA 94720

**TAYLOR, ROBERT MORGAN,** ANALYTICAL CHEMISTRY, ELECTROCHEMISTRY. *Current Pos:* VPRES PROD, CAPITAL CONTROLS CO, 93- *Personal Data:* b Orange, NJ, May 13, 41; m 65; c 2. *Educ:* Williams Col, BA, 63; Pa State Univ, PhD(chem), 68; Drexel Univ, MBA, 74. *Prof Exp:* From scientist to corp scientist, Leeds & Northrup Co, 68-84, dir res, Tech Ctr, 85-93. *Mem:* Am Chem Soc; Electrochem Soc; Inst Elec & Electronics Engrs; Instrument Soc Am. *Res:* Potentiometric and voltammetric analysis; high temperature electrochemistry; molten and solid electrolytes; thermometric analysis; chemical instrumentation. *Mailing Add:* Capital Controls Co 3000 Advance Lane Colmar PA 18915

**TAYLOR, ROBERT THOMAS,** BIOCHEMISTRY. *Current Pos:* RES BIOCHEMIST, BIOMED SCI DIV, LAWRENCE LIVERMORE NAT LAB, 68- *Personal Data:* b Harrison, Ark, Sept 14, 36; m 58; c 2. *Educ:* Univ Calif, Los Angeles, BA, 59; Univ Calif, Berkeley, PhD(biochem), 64. *Prof Exp:* USPHS res fel, Nat Heart Inst, 64-66, staff res fel, 66-68. *Mem:* Inter-Am Photochem Soc; Soc Environ Geochem & Health; Am Soc Biol Chem; AAAS; Environ Mutagen Soc; Am Chem Soc; Inst Food Technologists. *Res:* Enzymatic methylation, folate one carbon cell mutants and metabolism; mammalian cell mutagenesis, especially auxotrophic reversion mutagenesis; methanol fuel related genotoxicity; mechanisms of mutagenic heterocyclic amine formation during cooking of meat; metal alkylation and mutagenesis; microbiol sulfur and selenium metabolism. *Mailing Add:* Biomed Sci Div L-452 308 Stonework Ct Roseville CA 95747

**TAYLOR, ROBERT TIECHE,** MEDICAL ENTOMOLOGY. *Current Pos:* sr scientist, 65-72, SCIENTIST DIR ENTOM, PARASITIC DIS DIV, CTR INFECTIOUS DIS, USPHS, 72- *Personal Data:* b San Diego, Calif, June 29, 32; m 64; c 2. *Educ:* Okla State Univ, BS, 54, MS, 57, PhD(entom), 60. *Prof Exp:* Asst prev med officer, US Army, Ft Stewart, Ga, 54-56; malaria specialist, Pan Am Health Orgn, 60-61; spec asst wood preserv & entom, Are Pub Works Off, Chesapeake, US Navy, 61-63; malaria specialist, Malaria Eradication Prog, Port-au-Prince, Haiti, 63-65. *Concurrent Pos:* Consult, WHO, Pan Am Health Orgn & USAID. *Mem:* Am Soc Trop Med & Hyg; Royal Soc Trop Med & Hyg; Entom Soc Am; Am Mosquito Control Asn. *Res:* Conducting and supervising investigations on chemical control of mosquitoes, triatomidae and simuliidae. *Mailing Add:* 635 Grecken Green Peachtree City GA 30269

**TAYLOR, ROBERT WALTER,** SOIL PHYSICAL CHEMISTRY, ENVIRONMENTAL CHEMISTRY. *Current Pos:* assoc prof, 81-92, PROF SOIL & ENVIRON CHEM, ALA A&M UIV, 92- *Personal Data:* b Jamaica, WI, Mar 1, 47; m 73, Beverly Ann Redfield; c Derrick C & Theniece R. *Educ:* Tuskegee Univ, BS, 70; Mich State Univ, MS, 72, PhD(soil chem), 77. *Honors & Awards:* Int Biog Roll Honor, 85. *Prof Exp:* Sr agronomist & soil scientist, Ministry Agr, Bahamas, 77-79; co-investr, Tenn State Univ, 79-81. *Concurrent Pos:* Panel mem air, water & soils small bus innovative res, Coop State Res Serv, USDA, 92 & 93; consult, Environ Sci Prog, Spelman Col, 97. *Mem:* Am Soc Agron; Soil Sci Soc Am; Int Soc Soil Sci; AAAS; NY Acad Sci. *Res:* Pesticide transport in the vadose zone; kinetics and mechanisms of toxic metals retenion/release in geochemical processes in the soil; wetland biogeochemistry. *Mailing Add:* PO Box 1208 Normal AL 35762. *Fax:* 205-851-5429; *E-Mail:* aambrobol@asnaam.aamu.edu

**TAYLOR, ROBERT WILLIAM,** COMPUTER SCIENCE, RESEARCH MANAGEMENT. *Current Pos:* dir, Systs Res Ctr, 83-96, CONSULT, DIGITAL EQUIP CORP, 96- *Personal Data:* b Dallas, Tex, Feb 10, 32; m 55; c 3. *Educ:* Univ Tex, Austin, BA, 57, MA, 64. *Honors & Awards:* Cert Appreciation, Advan Res Projs Agency, Off Secy Defense, 69. *Prof Exp:* Res scientist psychoacoust, Defense Res Lab, Univ Tex, Austin, 55-59; teacher math, Howey Acad, Fla, 59-60; systs engr systs design, Martin Co, Fla, 60-61; sr res scientist man-mach systs res, ACF Electronics, Md, 61-62; res mgr electronics & control, Off Advan Res & Technol, NASA Hq, Washington, DC, 62-65; res dir comput sci, Advan Res Projs Agency, Off Secy Defense, 65-69; res dir, Info Res Lab, Univ Utah, 69-70; prin scientist & assoc mgr, Xerox Palo Alto Res Ctr, 70-77, mgr, Comput Sci Lab, 77-83. *Concurrent Pos:* Mem comts vision & bioacoust, Nat Res Coun, 62-65; mem, Comput Sci & Eng Bd, Nat Acad Sci, 67-69; mem, Electronic Data Processing Adv Bd, Dept Defense, 68-69; mem, Comput Sci Adv Bd, Stanford Univ, 71-81 & chmn, 78-79; lectr, NSF, 75-; mem, Comput Sci Adv Comt, 78-81 & Univ Calif, Berkeley, 80- *Mem:* Nat Acad Eng; Inst Elec & Electronics Engrs; Asn Comput Mach. *Res:* Interactive information processing and communications systems; central nervous system; computer graphics; artificial intelligence; research and development management. *Mailing Add:* Digital Equip Corp Syst Res Ctr 130 Lytton Ave Palo Alto CA 94301. *E-Mail:* taylor@ta.dec.com

**TAYLOR, ROGER LEE,** MATHEMATICS, COMPUTER SCIENCE. *Current Pos:* TEACHER MATH & COMPUT MATH, AIEA HIGH SCH, 97- *Personal Data:* b Newton, NJ, May 3, 46; c Stacy. *Educ:* Fla State Univ, PhD(math), 73. *Prof Exp:* Teacher math, Cent Tex Col, 87-90; teacher math & comput math, Waianae High Sch, 90-97. *Mailing Add:* PO Box 1542 Aiea HI 96701. *Fax:* 808-486-9910; *E-Mail:* rogert@pixi.com

**TAYLOR, RONALD,** BOTANY, GENETICS. *Current Pos:* Asst prof bot, 64-68, assoc prof biol, 68-72, PROF BIOL, WESTERN WASH UNIV, 72- *Personal Data:* b Victor, Idaho, Oct 16, 32; m 55; c 2. *Educ:* Idaho State Univ, BS, 56; Univ Wyo, MS, 60; Wash State Univ, PhD(bot, genetics), 64. *Concurrent Pos:* Environ consult. *Mem:* AAAS; Bot Soc Am; Genetics Soc Am; Am Soc Plant Taxon; Sigma Xi; Torrey Bot Club. *Res:* Chemotaxonomy and evolution of selected higher plant taxa; biosystematics of Taraxacum; biosystematics of North American/Mexican Picea. *Mailing Add:* Dept Biol Western Wash Univ Bellingham WA 98225-9160

**TAYLOR, RONALD D,** SCIENCE POLICY, NAVAL SCIENCE & TECHNOLOGY. *Current Pos:* from prog officer to sr prog officer, bd physics & astron, 91-94, assoc dir, 94-95, DIR, NAVAL STUDIES BD, NAT ACAD SCI, 95- *Personal Data:* b Baltimore, Md, Dec 16, 50. *Educ:* Johns Hopkins Univ, BA, 72; Col William & Mary, MS, 74, PhD(physics), 79. *Prof Exp:* Instr physics, Embry-Riddle Aeronaut Univ, 75-77; res assoc, Dept Chem, Univ Toronto, 79-83; asst prof physics, Villanova Univ, 83-84; staff scientist, Berkeley Res Assocs, 84-90. *Mem:* Am Phys Soc. *Res:* Atomic and molecular collision theory; atomic processes in plasmas; science policy. *Mailing Add:* Nat Acad Sci 2101 Constitution Ave NW Washington DC 20418. *Fax:* 202-334-3695; *E-Mail:* rtaylor1@nas.edu

**TAYLOR, RONALD PAUL,** BIOPHYSICAL CHEMISTRY, IMMUNE COMPLEX CHEMISTRY. *Current Pos:* from asst prof to assoc prof, 73-83, PROF BIOCHEM, SCH MED, UNIV VA, 83- *Personal Data:* b Oct 18, 45; m 82; c 3. *Educ:* City Col NY, BS, 66; Princeton Univ, PhD(chem), 70. *Prof Exp:* Fel, Univ Minn, 71-73. *Concurrent Pos:* Consult, NIH, NSF, Vet Admin & Toxicol Div, Environ Protection Agency; consult & ad hoc reviewer, Can Arthritis Asn; fel rev comt, Arthritis Found; Fogert fel, US-USSR Health Scientist Exchange. *Mem:* Am Rheumatism Asn; Am Chem Soc; Biophys Soc; Union Concerned Scientists; Am Soc Biol Chemists; Fedn Am Scientists. *Res:* Lupus pathogenesis; complement and complement receptors; immunochemistry; red blood cell-complement receptor heterocomplexes in immunotherapy. *Mailing Add:* Dept Biochem Univ Va Charlottesville VA 22908

**TAYLOR, ROSS,** SEPARATION PROCESS SIMULATION, MULTICOMPONENT MASS TRANSFER. *Current Pos:* From asst prof to assoc prof, 80-93, PROF CHEM ENG, CLARKSON UNIV, 89- *Personal Data:* b Welwyn Garden City, Eng, Oct 25, 54; m 79, Elizabeth Hirst; c Julie, Jeremy, Andrew & Claudia. *Educ:* Univ Manchester Inst Sci & Technol, BSc, 76, MSc, 78, PhD(chem eng), 80. *Concurrent Pos:* Vis prof, Onderzoek Sch Process Technol, Neth. *Mem:* Am Inst Chem Engrs. *Res:* Mathematical modeling of multicomponent mass transfer rate governed processes like distillation, absorption and condensation; development of algorithms for solving process models equations; applications of computer algebra in engineering. *Mailing Add:* Dept Chem Eng Clarkson Univ Potsdam NY 13699-5705. *Fax:* 315-268-6654; *E-Mail:* taylor@sun.soe.clarkson.edu

**TAYLOR, ROY LEWIS,** PLANT TAXONOMY. *Current Pos:* PRES & CHIEF EXEC OFFICER, CHICAGO HORT SOC, 85-; DIR, CHICAGO BOT GARDEN, 85- *Personal Data:* b Olds, Alta, Apr 12, 32; m 79, Janet R Stein. *Educ:* Sir George Williams Univ, BSc, 57; Univ Calif, Berkeley, PhD(bot), 62. *Honors & Awards:* Queen's Silver Jubilee Medal, 77; Mary E Elliott Serv Award, Can Bot Asn, 83; Award Merit, Am Asn Bot Gardens & Arboreta, 87; Award Merit, Am Asn Mus, Washington, DC, 91. *Prof Exp:* Teaching bot, Univ Calif, Berkeley, 58-60, assoc, 61-62; res officer, Plant Res Inst, Can Dept Agr, 62-65, chief taxon sect, 65-68; prof plant sci & dir Bot Garden, Univ BC, 68-85. *Concurrent Pos:* Mem gov bd, Biol Coun Can, 66-69, secy, 69-72, from vpres to pres, 72-74; mem exec comt & coun, Pac Sci Asn, 79-83; mem accreditation comn, Am Asn Mus, 80-91, chmn, 85-91, chmn, Ethics Comn, 91-93; trustee, Bot Gardens Conserv Int, London. *Mem:* Am Soc Plant Taxon; Can Bot Asn (secy, 65-66, vpres, 66-67, pres, 67-68); Am Asn Bot Gardens & Arboretums (vpres, 73-75, pres, 75-77); Bot Soc Am. *Res:* Systematic botany of western North American vascular plants; systematics and cytotaxonomy of the vascular plants of British Columbia. *Mailing Add:* Rancho Santa Ana Bot Garden 1500 N College Ave Claremont CA 91711-3157

**TAYLOR, RUSSELL JAMES, JR,** CLINICAL PHARMACOLOGY. *Current Pos:* sr med assoc, 80-85, asst dir clin res, 85-87, ASST DIR PROF SERV, MILES PHARMACEUT, 87- *Personal Data:* b Rockville, Conn, Mar 8, 35. *Educ:* Bates Col, BS, 57; Ohio State Univ, MSc, 62, PhD(biochem), 64. *Prof Exp:* Res chemist, Parke, Davis & Co, Mich, 57-59; asst biochem, Ohio State Univ, 59-64; res biochemist, Lederle Labs, Am Cyanamid Co, NY, 64-69; sr res biochemist, McNeil Labs, Inc, 69-70, group leader biochem, 70-79, asst dir med res, 79-80. *Mem:* Am Soc Clin Pharmacol & Therapeut; Am Chem Soc; NY Acad Sci; Am Med Writers Asn; AAAS; Am Soc Pharmacol & Exp Therapeut. *Res:* Clinical pharmacology; cardiovascular drugs. *Mailing Add:* 92 Eramo Terr Hamden CT 06518-2013

**TAYLOR, SAMUEL EDWIN,** PHARMACOLOGY. *Current Pos:* ASSOC PROF, DEPT ORAL MAXILLOFACIAL SURG & PHARMACOL, TEX A&M UNIV SYST-BAYLOR COL DENT, 96-, GRAD FAC, 96- *Personal Data:* b Tuskegee, Ala, Oct 19, 41; m 61, Ouida Oswalt; c Samuel E & Leslie A. *Educ:* Univ Ala, Tuscaloosa, BS, 63; Univ Ala, Birmingham, PhD(pharmacol) , 71. *Prof Exp:* NIH trainee pharmacol, Univ Tenn Med Units, 71-72; asst prof, Sch Dent, Univ Ore Health Sci Ctr, 72-77; from asst prof to assoc prof, Pharmacol Dept, Col Dent, Baylor Univ, 77-96, grad fac, 80-96, staff, Salivary Dysfunction Clin, 93-96. *Mem:* Am Soc Pharmacol & Exp Therapeut; Am Asn Dent Res; Soc Exp Biol & Med; Sigma Xi. *Res:* Receptor/signal transduction; calcium signaling; salivary function; autonomic pharmacology. *Mailing Add:* Baylor Col Dent Dept Oral Surg & Pharmacol 3302 Gaston Ave Dallas TX 75246. *Fax:* 214-828-8466; *E-Mail:* se.taylor@tambcd.edu

**TAYLOR, SAMUEL G, III,** ONCOLOGY. *Current Pos:* dir cancer ctr planning, Rush Presby-St Luke's Med Ctr, 72-75, assoc dir, Rush Cancer Ctr, 75-78, prof, Rush Univ, 71-78, EMER PROF MED, RUSH UNIV, 78- *Personal Data:* b Elmhurst, Ill, Sept 2, 04; m 38, 80; c 3. *Educ:* Yale Univ, BA, 27; Univ Chicago, MD, 32. *Prof Exp:* Dir steroid tumor clin, Univ Ill, 47-71. *Concurrent Pos:* Assoc attend physician, Presby Hosp, 48-60; from asst prof to prof, Univ Ill Col Med, 48-72; rep dept med, Tumor Coun, Univ Ill, 48-72; mem consult staff, Lake Forest Hosp, 54-61; from attend physician to sr attend physician, Presby-St Luke's Hosp, Chicago, 61-78, head sect oncol, 61-71, consult, Sect Oncol, 71-; consult, Cancer Control Prog, USPHS, 59-63; dir, Ill Cancer Coun Comprehensive Cancer Ctr, 73-78. *Mem:* Endocrine Soc; Am Asn Cancer Res; Am Col Physicians; Am Radium Soc; Soc Surg Oncol. *Res:* Systematic therapy for cancer. *Mailing Add:* PO Box 646 Lake Forest IL 60045

**TAYLOR, SAMUEL JAMES,** MATHEMATICS. *Current Pos:* chmn dept, 86-89, Whyburn prof, 84-95, EMER WHYBURN PROF MATH, UNIV VA, CHARLOTTESVILLE, 95- *Personal Data:* b Carrickferbus, Northern Ireland, Dec 13, 29; m; c Richard, Charles, Jonathan & Helen. *Educ:* Queens Univ, Belfast, Northern Ireland, BSc, 50; Cambridge Univ, PhD, 54. *Prof Exp:* Bye fel Peterhouse, Cambridge Univ, Eng, 53-55; lectr, Birmingham Univ, Eng, 55-62; prof, London Univ, 62-75, Liverpool Univ, Eng, 75-83; vis prof, Univ BC, Vancouver, Can, 83-84. *Concurrent Pos:* Procter vis fel, Princeton Univ, NJ, 52. *Mem:* Fel Cambridge Philos Soc; Inst Math Statist; Am Math Soc. *Res:* Mathematics; philosophy. *Mailing Add:* Dept Math Univ Va Math & Astron Bldg Charlottesville VA 22903-3145. *E-Mail:* sjt4k@aol.com

**TAYLOR, SNOWDEN,** PARTICLE PHYSICS, TECHNICAL EDUCATION FOR DISADVANTAGED STUDENTS. *Current Pos:* from instr to prof, 58-90, EMER PROF PHYSICS, STEVENS INST TECHNOL, 91- *Personal Data:* b New York, NY, June 25, 24; m 49, Alice Anne Jones; c Timothy, Dean, David, Rolf, Nancy & Mary. *Educ:* Stevens Inst Technol, ME, 50; Columbia Univ, AM, 57, PhD(physics), 59. *Honors & Awards:* Ottens Res Award, 63; STEP Award, 75 & 82; Arthur Schomberg Award, Asn Equality & Excellence Educ, 87. *Prof Exp:* Fac, Oak Ridge Sch Reactor Technol, 51-52; asst & lectr physics, Columbia Univ, 52-58. *Mem:* Am Phys Soc; Fedn Am Scientists; Union Concerned Scientists. *Res:* Horology; particle physics; technical education for minority and disadvantaged students. *Mailing Add:* 318 Western Hwy Tappan NY 10983. *Fax:* 914-359-3278

**TAYLOR, STEPHEN KEITH,** INDUSTRIAL CHEMISTRY, ORGANIC CHEMISTRY. *Current Pos:* assoc prof, 85-93, PROF CHEM, HOPE COL, 93- *Personal Data:* b Los Angeles, Calif, Mar 28, 44; m 69, Nancy Thomson; c Daniel & Melissa. *Educ:* Pasadena Col, BA, 69; Univ Nev, Reno, PhD(org chem), 74. *Prof Exp:* Res chemist, E I du Pont de Nemours & Co, Inc, 73-78,

sr res chemist, 78; from asst prof to prof chem, Olivet Nazarene Col, 78-85. *Mem:* Am Chem Soc; Sigma Xi; Soc Photog Scientist & Engrs; Coun Undergrad Res. *Res:* Influence of metal ions in organic reactions; reactions of epoxides; stereoselective reactions; enzymes in organic synthesis. *Mailing Add:* Dept Chem Hope Col Holland MI 49422-9000

**TAYLOR, STEPHEN LLOYD,** FOOD TOXICOLOGY, FOOD SAFETY. *Current Pos:* PROF & HEAD DEPT FOOD SCI & TECHNOL & DIR, FOOD PROCESSING CTR, UNIV NEBR, LINCOLN, 87- *Personal Data:* b Portland, Ore, July 19, 46; m 73, Susan Kerns; c Amanda & Andrew. *Educ:* Ore State Univ, BS, 68, MS, 69; Univ Calif, Davis, PhD(biochem), 73. *Prof Exp:* Chief, Food Toxicol Lab Letterman Army Inst Res, 75-78; from asst prof to assoc prof, Univ Wis Food Res Inst, 78-87. *Concurrent Pos:* Fel environ toxicol, Nat Inst Environ Health Sci, 73-74; consult food safety, 78-; chair, Food Chemicals Codex Comt, Nat Acad Sci, 90-, mem, Food Nutrit Bd, 91- *Mem:* Fel Inst Food Technologists; Am Acad Allergy & Immunol; Am Chem Soc; Int Asn Milk, Food & Environ Sanitarians; Am Peanut Res & Educ Soc. *Res:* Safety evaluation of food ingredients and naturally occurring toxicants in food, especially allergic reactions to proteins in foods. *Mailing Add:* Univ Neb Dept Food Sci H C Filley Hall Lincoln NE 68583

**TAYLOR, STUART ROBERT,** PHYSIOLOGY, BIOPHYSICS. *Current Pos:* asst prof physiol, Univ Minn, 71-75, asst prof biophys, 75-79, assoc prof physiol & pharmacol, 75-80, PROF BIOPHYS, PHYSIOL & PHARMACOL, GRAD SCH MED, UNIV MINN, 80-, PROF PHYSIOL & BIOPHYS, PHARMACOL, MAYO MED SCH, UNIV MINN, 78-, CONSULT, 71- *Personal Data:* b Brooklyn, NY, July 15, 37; m 63; c 3. *Educ:* Cornell Univ, BA, 58; Columbia Univ, MA, 61; NY Univ, PhD(physiol), 66. *Prof Exp:* Lab asst zool, Columbia Univ, 59-60, lectr, 60-61; res asst physiol, Inst Muscle Dis, Inc, 62-67; Dept Health, Educ & Welfare rehab res fel, Univ Col, Univ London, 67-69; from instr to asst prof pharmacol, State Univ NY Downstate Med Ctr, 69-71. *Concurrent Pos:* Mem res allocations comt, Minn Heart Asn, 72-74, mem bd dirs, 73-75; mem physiol study sect, Div Res Grants, NIH, 73-77; estab investr, Am Heart Asn, 74-79; adv panel gen prof educ of the physician, Asn Am Med Col, 81-84; guest prof, State of Baden-Wurttemberg, Univ Ulm, 83-85; adv panel, Cellular Physiol Prog, NSF, 85-88, Physiol Processes/Physiol & Behav Prog, 90-94, Instrumentation & Instrument Develop Prog, Biol Instrumentation & Resources Div, 92-96; bd sci counr, NIH & Nat Inst Neurol Commun Dis & Stroke, 87-91, chmn, 90-91; asst ed, New Physiol Sci, 88-94, assoc ed, 94-97. *Mem:* Am Physiol Soc; Biophys Soc; sr mem Inst Elec & Electronics Engrs; assoc dir Phys Soc; NY Acad Sci; Int Soc Optical Eng; fel AAAS. *Res:* Physiology of stimulus-response coupling in contractile cells; computerized image analysis of rapid cellular events; excitation-contraction coupling; electronic imaging microscopy; signal transduction and calcium-binding proteins; forces involved in stabilization of the cytoskeleton. *Mailing Add:* 711D Guggenheim Bldg Mayo Clin Rochester MN 55905-0001. *Fax:* 507-284-9111; *E-Mail:* taylor@mayo.edu

**TAYLOR, SUSAN SEROTA,** BIOCHEMISTRY. *Current Pos:* NIH fel, Univ Calif, 71-72, asst prof, 72-79, assoc prof, 79-85, PROF CHEM, UNIV CALIF, SAN DIEGO, 85- *Personal Data:* b Racine, Wis, June 20, 42; m 65, Palmer William; c Tasha, Katherine, Ashton, David & Palmer Andrew. *Educ:* Univ Wis-Madison, BA, 64; Johns Hopkins Univ, PhD(biochem), 68. *Honors & Awards:* Eli Lilly Lectr, Mich State Univ, 91; Leslie Hellerman Mem Lectr, Sch Med, Johns Hopkins Univ, 92. *Prof Exp:* NIH fel, Med Res Coun Lab Molecular Biol, Cambridge Univ, 68-70. *Concurrent Pos:* NIH career develop award & res grant, Univ Calif, San Diego, 72-77; NIH biochem study sect, 78-82; Fogarty fel, Cambridge Univ, 80-81; Am Cancer Soc Rev Group, 83-; counr, Am Soc Biochem & Molecular Biol, 88, co-chair, 91; Burroughs-Welcome vis prof pharmacol, Rochester Univ, 92; fac distinguished lectr, Sch Med, Univ Calif, San Diego, 92; clin invest award, Am Chem Soc, 93-96. *Mem:* Nat Acad Sci; Inst Med-Nat Acad Sci; Am Soc Biol Chemists; Am Chem Soc; fel AAAS; Am Soc Biochem & Molecular Biol (pres, 95-96). *Res:* Protein chemistry; cAMP-dep protein kinase; LDH; amino acid sequencing; structure-function relationships; regulation of kinase genes; signal transduction; contributed numerous articles to professional journals. *Mailing Add:* Dept Chem & Biochem 0654 Univ Calif-San Diego 9500 Gilman Dr La Jolla CA 92093-0654. *Fax:* 619-534-8193; *E-Mail:* staylor@ucsd.edu

**TAYLOR, THEODORE BREWSTER,** APPLIED PHYSICS. *Current Pos:* INDEPENDENT CONSULT, 89- *Personal Data:* b Mexico City, Mex, July 11, 25; nat US; m 48, Caro Arnim; c Clare (Hastings), Katherine (Robertson), Christopher, Robert & Jeffrey. *Educ:* Calif Inst Technol, BS, 45; Cornell Univ, PhD(theoret physics), 54. *Hon Degrees:* DSc, Carleton Col, 81. *Honors & Awards:* Lawrence Mem Award, Atomic Energy Comn, 65; Boris Pregel Award, NY Acad Sci, 81. *Prof Exp:* Physicist, Radiation Lab, Univ Calif, 46-49, theoret physicist, Los Alamos Sci Lab, 49-56; nuclear physicist, High Energy Fluid Dynamics Dept & chmn, Gen Atomic Div, Gen Dynamics Corp, 56-64; dep dir, Defense Atomic Support Agency, 64-66; chmn bd, Int Res & Tech Corp, 67-76; prof mech & aerospace eng, Princeton Univ, 76-80; pres, Nova, Inc, Wellsville, NY, 80-89. *Concurrent Pos:* Consult, Govt & Indust, 56-; pres, Appropriate Solar Technol Inst, Damascus, Md, 80-87; lectr, San Diego State Col, 57, Univ Calif, Santa Cruz, 88- *Mem:* AAAS; Am Phys Soc; Solar Energy Soc. *Res:* Renewable energy systems; controlled environment agriculture; international control and development of nuclear energy; nuclear explosives and effects of nuclear explosions; space propulsion; pollution control; technology assessment; energy conservation. *Mailing Add:* PO Box 662 Wellsville NY 14895. *Fax:* 716-593-6347

**TAYLOR, THOMAS NEWTON,** SURFACE PHYSICS. *Current Pos:* STAFF PHYSICIST, LOS ALAMOS NAT LAB, 75- *Personal Data:* b Cedar Rapids, Iowa, June 21, 44. *Educ:* Iowa State Univ, BS, 66; Brown Univ, MS & PhD(physics), 73. *Prof Exp:* Fel surface physics, Lawrence Berkeley Lab & Lawrence Livermore Lab, 73-75. *Concurrent Pos:* Guest scientist, FOM-Inst Atomic & Molecular Physics, Amsterdam, Holland, 88. *Mem:* Am Chem Soc; Am Vacuum Soc. *Res:* Surface properties of metallic and ceramic advanced materials; emphasis on interface growth and corrosion; low energy electron diffraction; ion scattering; Auger electron spectroscopy and allied techniques. *Mailing Add:* Los Alamos Nat Lab MS J565 CST-2 Los Alamos NM 87545

**TAYLOR, THOMAS NORWOOD,** PALEOBOTANY. *Current Pos:* DISTINGUISHED PROF BOT & SR CUR, DEPT BOT, NATURAL HIS MUS & BIOL DIV, UNIV KANS, 95- *Personal Data:* b Lakewood, Ohio, June 14, 37; m 59; c 5. *Educ:* Miami Univ, AB, 60; Univ Ill, Urbana, PhD(bot), 64. *Honors & Awards:* Merit Award, Bot Soc; Alexander Von Humboldt Sr Scientist Award. *Prof Exp:* NSF res fel, Yale Univ, 64-65; from asst prof to prof biol sci, Univ Ill, Chicago Circle, 65-72, dir, Scanning Electron Microscope Lab, 67-72; prof bot, Ohio Univ, 72-74. *Concurrent Pos:* NSF res grants, 64-; NSF res grants paleobot, 65-78; res assoc, Geol Dept, Field Mus Natural Hist, Chicago, 67-; Ill Acad Sci res grants, 70-72; vis prof, Univ Alta, Edmonton, Can, 83, Univ Tex, Austin; chmn dept, Ohio State Univ, 74-78, prot bot, 74-95, prof, Dept Geol Sci, 79-95, res scientist, Byrd Polar Res Ctr, 89-95. *Mem:* Nat Acad Sci; Brit Paleont Asn; Int Orgn Paleobot; Mycol Soc Am; Am Asn Stratig Palynologists; Latin-Am Asn Paleobot & Palinol; Bot Soc Am. *Res:* Structure and evolution of Paleozoic vascular plants; electron microscopy of fossil pollen and spores; morphology of extant vascular plants; Antarctica fossil plants; fossil fungi; origin of land plants; biostratigraphy of Antarctica; Mesozoic seed plants; origin of flowering plants. *Mailing Add:* Dept Bot Univ Kans Kansas City KS 66045. *Fax:* 785-864-5321; *E-Mail:* ttaylor@falcon.cc.ukans.edu

**TAYLOR, THOMAS TALLOTT, SR,** PHYSICS. *Current Pos:* from asst prof to prof, 63-80, chmn dept, 67-77, EMER PROF PHYSICS, LOYOLA MARYMOUNT UNIV, LOS ANGELES, 80- *Personal Data:* b Montpelier, Ind, Apr 18, 21; m 58; c 2. *Educ:* Purdue Univ, BS, 42; Calif Inst Technol, MS, 53, PhD(physics), 58. *Prof Exp:* Engr, Gen Elec Co, 42-46; res physicist, Hughes Aircraft Co, 46-54; asst prof physics, Univ Calif, Riverside, 58-63. *Concurrent Pos:* Instr, Engr Exten, Univ Calif, Los Angeles, 47-50 & 57-58. *Mem:* Am Phys Soc; fel Inst Elec & Electronics Engrs; Am Asn Physics Teachers. *Res:* Electromagnetic theory; antennas; lattice sums in crystals. *Mailing Add:* 6622 W 87th St Los Angeles CA 90045

**TAYLOR, TIMOTHY H,** AGRONOMY. *Current Pos:* assoc agronomist, Agr Exp Sta, 55-60, from assoc prof to prof 60-84, EMER PROF AGRON, 84- *Personal Data:* b Sawyer, Ky, July 4, 18; m 45, Andree Ererra; c Richard J. & Kathyryn (Thompson). *Educ:* Univ Ky, BS, 48, MS, 50; Pa State Univ, PhD(agron), 55. *Prof Exp:* Asst agronomist, Va Agr Exp Sta, 49-55. *Concurrent Pos:* Consult, 59-; vis scientist, Am Soc Agron; vis biologist, Am Inst Biol Sci. *Mem:* Fel Am Soc Agron; fel Crop Sci Am; Am Forage & Grassland Coun; Sigma Xi. *Res:* Ecology of humid temperate grasslands; forage crop ecology and physiology; ecology of cultivated grasslands. *Mailing Add:* He 84 Box 555 Parker Lake KY 42634

**TAYLOR, TONY S,** PLASMA PHYSICS. *Current Pos:* HEAD, STABILITY PHYSICS GROUP, GEN ATOMICS. *Honors & Awards:* Excellence in Plasma Physics Res Award, Am Phys Soc, 94. *Mailing Add:* Gen Atomics PO Box 85608 San Diego CA 92186-9784

**TAYLOR, WALTER FULLER,** MATHEMATICS. *Current Pos:* From asst prof to assoc prof, 67-77, NSF grants, 69-74 & 76-79, PROF MATH, UNIV COLO, 77- *Personal Data:* b Boston, Mass, Dec 5, 40; m 67. *Educ:* Swarthmore Col, AB, 62; Harvard Univ, MA, 63, PhD(math), 68. *Concurrent Pos:* Fulbright Found sr res fel, Univ NSW, Australia, 75; vis prof, Univ Hawaii, 77-78; ed, Algebra Universalis, 77- *Mem:* Am Math Soc; Sigma Xi. *Res:* Model theory, universal algebra and topology. *Mailing Add:* Campus Box 426 Boulder CO 80309-0426

**TAYLOR, WALTER HERMAN, JR,** MICROBIAL PHYSIOLOGY. *Current Pos:* from asst prof to assoc prof, 61-69, PROF BIOL & HEAD DEPT, PORTLAND STATE UNIV, 69- *Personal Data:* b Laurens, SC, July 5, 31; m 55; c 2. *Educ:* Duke Univ, MA, 54; Univ Ill, PhD(bact), 59. *Prof Exp:* Asst bact, Univ Ill, 54-57 & Emory Univ, 57-59; res assoc biol div, Oak Ridge Nat Lab, 59, USPHS fel, 59-61. *Mem:* AAAS; Am Soc Microbiol; Brit Soc Gen Microbiol; Am Chem Soc. *Res:* Bacterial physiology; carbohydrate metabolism; protein biosynthesis; pyrimidine metabolism in microorganisms. *Mailing Add:* Dept Biol Portland State Univ PO Box 751 Portland OR 97207-0751

**TAYLOR, WALTER KINGSLEY,** ORNITHOLOGY, VERTEBRATE ECOLOGY. *Current Pos:* from asst prof to assoc prof, 69-82, PROF BIOL, UNIV CENT FLA, 82- *Personal Data:* b Calhoun, Ky, Nov 12, 39; m 68, Karin Satter; c Anna R. *Educ:* Murray State Univ, BS, 62; La Tech Inst, MS, 64; Ariz State Univ, PhD(zool), 67. *Prof Exp:* Asst, La Tech Univ, 62-64 & Ariz State Univ, 64-67. *Mem:* Am Ornith Union; Wilson Ornith Soc; Cooper Ornith Soc; Sigma Xi; Nat Wildflower Res Ctr. *Res:* Breeding biology; migratory biology; population ecology of birds; vocalizations of birds; Florida wildflowers; biology of wildflowers. *Mailing Add:* Dept Biol Univ Cent Fla PO Box 25000 Orlando FL 32816. *Fax:* 407-823-2917; *E-Mail:* wtaylor@pegasus.cc.ucf.edu

**TAYLOR, WARREN EGBERT,** METROLOGY. *Current Pos:* RETIRED. *Personal Data:* b Colorado Springs, Colo, Nov 15, 20; m 47; c 3. *Educ:* Kalamazoo Col, BA, 47; Ohio State Univ, PhD(physics), 52. *Prof Exp:* Mem tech staff, Sandia Nat Labs, 52-70, proj leader, Vacuum Metrol Group, 70-86. *Mem:* Am Phys Soc; Am Vacuum Soc; Sigma Xi. *Res:* Vacuum technology; nuclear radiation measurements; health physics. *Mailing Add:* 5123 Royene Ave NE Albuquerque NM 87110. *E-Mail:* wtatalb@juno.com

**TAYLOR, WELTON IVAN,** CLINICAL MICROBIOLOGY, FOOD POISONING. *Current Pos:* RETIRED. *Personal Data:* b Birmingham, Ala, Nov 12, 19; m 45, Jayne Kemp; c Karyn & Shelley. *Educ:* Univ Ill, Urbana, AB, 41, MS, 47, PhD(bact), 48; Am Bd Med Microbiol, dipl, 68. *Honors & Awards:* Bacteria named in honor of, Enterobacter taylorae. *Prof Exp:* From instr to asst prof bact, Univ Ill Col Med, 48-54; res bacteriologist, Swift & Co, 54-59; supvr clin microbiol, Children's Mem Hosp, 59-64; bacteriologist in chief, WSuburban Hosp, Oak Park, Ill, 64-69; assoc prof microbiol, Med Ctr, Univ Ill, 61-87. *Concurrent Pos:* Consult microbiol, Northwest Community Hosp, Arlington Heights, Ill, 63-70, Jackson Park, 64-81, Englewood Hosps, Chicago, 64-88, Armour & Co, 66-68, Resurrection Hosp, Chicago, 67-92, Grant Hosp, Chicago, 69-75, St Mary Nazareth Hosp Ctr, Chicago, 73-80 & Swed Covenant Hosp, Chicago, 74-88; Nat Inst Allergy & Infectious Dis spec res fel, Inst Pasteur, France & Cent Pub Health Lab, Eng, 61-62; bd sci adv, Am Asn Bioanalysts, 70-82, bd dirs, 73-82; Am Bd Bioanal Dept Army res contract, 71-73; pres & owner, Micro-Palettes, Inc, 77-88. *Mem:* Fel Am Soc Microbiol; fel Am Acad Microbiol. *Res:* Detection of Vibrio parahemolyticus in routine stool analysis; methods for detection of Salmonella and Shigella with minimal laboratory facilities; rapid indentification procedures for non-enteric pathogens, enteric pathogens, anaerobes, and sexually-transmitted diseases. *Mailing Add:* 7621 S Prairie Ave Chicago IL 60619

**TAYLOR, WESLEY GORDON,** MEDICINAL CHEMISTRY, PESTICIDE CHEMISTRY. *Current Pos:* RES SCIENTIST PESTICIDE CHEM, RES BR, RES STA, AGR CAN, 76- *Personal Data:* b Melfort, Sask, Mar 29, 47; m 69. *Educ:* Univ Sask, BSP, 69; PhD(pharm), 73. *Prof Exp:* Fel pharm, Dept Med Chem & Pharmacog, Sch Pharm & Pharm Sci, Purdue Univ, 73-75. *Mem:* Am Chem Soc; Chem Inst Can. *Res:* Biological alkylating agents; organic synthesis; drug metabolism; pesticide toxicology. *Mailing Add:* Saskatoon Res Ctr 107 Sci Pl Saskatoon SK S7N 0X2 Can

**TAYLOR, WILLIAM CLYNE,** PEDIATRICS. *Current Pos:* RETIRED. *Personal Data:* b Aberdeen, Scotland, Mar 26, 24; Can citizen; m 54; c 3. *Educ:* Aberdeen Univ, MB & ChB, 45; Univ London, DCH, 50; FRCP(C), 58. *Prof Exp:* Prof pediat, Univ Alta, 57- *Concurrent Pos:* Mead Johnson res fel, Univ Alta, 58-59; Brit Commonwealth grant, UK, 66; Schering traveling fel, Africa, Australia & NZ, 66-67. *Mem:* Can Soc Clin Invest; Am Acad Pediat; Can Pediat Soc. *Res:* Evaluation of undergraduate and postgraduate medical education; delivery of health care in the Northwest Territories of Canada. *Mailing Add:* Dept Pediat 2C300 Univ Alta Edmonton AB T6G 2R7 Can

**TAYLOR, WILLIAM DANIEL,** DNA REPAIR, MUTAGENESIS. *Current Pos:* asst prof biophys, Pa State Univ, 63-68, assoc prof, 68-71, head dept, 71-75, chmn molecular biol prog, 84-89, assoc dean, Col Sci, 89-91, actg dir, Mat Res Lab, 93-96, actg dean, Grad Sch, 95, PROF BIOPHYS, PA STATE UNIV, UNIVERSITY PARK, 71- *Personal Data:* b Cardiff, Gt Brit, May 25, 34; m 73, Andrea M Mastro. *Educ:* Univ Manchester, BSc, 56, PhD(phys chem), 59. *Prof Exp:* Fel physics, Pa State Univ, 59-61; res fel chem, Univ Manchester, 61-63. *Mem:* AAAS; Radiol Res Soc; Biophys Soc; Fedn Am Sci; The Chem Soc; Am Soc Photobiol. *Res:* Biophysical chemistry; chemical carcinogenesis; nucleic acids; radiation biology. *Mailing Add:* Intercol Res Prog Pa State Univ 205 Kern Grad Bldg University Park PA 16802-6003

**TAYLOR, WILLIAM DAVID,** LIMNOLOGY, PROTOZOOLOGY. *Current Pos:* fel, 78-80, assoc prof, 81-94, PROF, DEPT BIOL, UNIV WATERLOO, 94-, CHAIR, 96- *Personal Data:* b Toronto, Can, Feb 2, 50; m, Carol C Gonsalves; c Christine, David & Kenneth. *Educ:* Univ Toronto, BSc, 73, PhD(zool), 78. *Honors & Awards:* Chandler-Misener Award, Int Asn Great Lakes Res, 93. *Prof Exp:* Vis fel, Nat Water Res Inst, 80-81. *Mem:* Can Soc Limnologists; Int Asn Great Lakes Res; Am Soc Limnol Oceanog; Int Soc Limnol. *Res:* Plankton microbiology, especially the ecology of planktonic Ciliophora, the phosphorus cycle in lakes and streams, and lake food webs. *Mailing Add:* Dept Biol Univ Waterloo Waterloo ON N2L 3G1 Can. *Fax:* 519-746-0614; *E-Mail:* wdtaylor@sciborg.uwaterloo.ca

**TAYLOR, WILLIAM F,** BIOSTATISTICS. *Current Pos:* head med res statist sect, 67-76, MEM FAC, DEPT MED STATIST & EPIDEMIOL, MAYO CLIN, 76- *Personal Data:* b Cincinnati, Ohio, Oct 14, 21; m 43, 81; c 3. *Educ:* Univ Calif, PhD(math statist), 51. *Prof Exp:* Instr biostatist, Univ Calif, 50-51; chief dept biometrics, Sch Aviation Med, USAF, 51-58; assoc prof biostatist, Sch Pub Health, Univ Calif, Berkeley, 58-63, prof, 63-67. *Mem:* Biomet Soc; fel Am Pub Health Asn; fel Am Statist Asn; Sigma Xi. *Res:* Design of clinical trials; sequential analysis in medicine; reference value problems. *Mailing Add:* 1524 Wilshire Dr NE Rochester MN 55906

**TAYLOR, WILLIAM FRANCIS,** FUEL TECHNOLOGY, PETROLEUM ENGINEERING. *Current Pos:* res engr, Exxon Res & Eng Co, 57-71, sr res engr, 71-75, eng assoc, 75-80, SR ENGR ASSOC, EXXON RES & ENG CO, 80- *Personal Data:* b Washington, DC, Apr 20, 31; m 61, Marianne Fazzini; c Patricia C, Barbara (Schuszler) & Margaret (Lane). *Educ:* Cath Univ Am, BChE, 53; Ohio State Univ, MS, 57; Rutgers Univ, MS, 62; Stevens Inst

Technol, ScD(chem eng), 67. *Prof Exp:* Chem engr, Goodyear Tire & Rubber Co, Ohio, 53-54. *Concurrent Pos:* Mem, coord res coun, Am Soc Testing & Mat. *Mem:* Am Inst Chem Engrs; Am Chem Soc; Sigma Xi. *Res:* Aviation fuels product quality; jet fuel thermal stability; synthetic fuels; heterogeneous kinetics and catalysis. *Mailing Add:* 1598 Brookside Rd Mountainside NJ 07092. *Fax:* 908-474-2085

**TAYLOR, WILLIAM GEORGE,** CELL BIOLOGY. *Current Pos:* RES BIOLOGIST, NAT CANCER INST, NIH, 70- *Educ:* Univ Ill, PhD(microbiol), 70. *Mailing Add:* Lab Cell & Molecular Biol Nat Cancer Inst NIH 9000 Rockville Park Bldg 37 Rm 1C-09 Bethesda MD 20892-0001. *Fax:* 301-496-8479

**TAYLOR, WILLIAM H, II,** SOLID STATE PHYSICS. *Current Pos:* GEN PARTNER, TAYLOR & TURNER, VENTURE CAPITAL, 79- *Personal Data:* b Philadelphia, Pa, Dec 17, 38; m 57; c 2. *Educ:* Johns Hopkins Univ, BES, 60; Princeton Univ, MSE, 61, AM, 61, PhD(solid state sci), 64. *Prof Exp:* Staff mem, Redstone Arsenal Res Div, Rohm & Haas Co, Ala, 63-64; chief, Solid State Br, Explosives Lab, Picatinny Arsenal, 66-68; vpres, Data Sci Ventures, Inc, 68-72, White, Weld & Co, Inc, 72-73 & Crocker Capital Corp, 73-79. *Mem:* Am Phys Soc. *Res:* Investment banking, venture capital financing of technology companies; point defects in solids; properties of solid explosives; soft contact lens materials. *Mailing Add:* 2452 Francisco St San Francisco CA 94123. *Fax:* 415-346-5488

**TAYLOR, WILLIAM IRVING,** ORGANIC CHEMISTRY. *Current Pos:* CONSULT, 88- *Personal Data:* b NZ, July 23, 23; m 52, Giuliana Valsangiacomo; c John S, Frank W & Mark A. *Educ:* Univ Auckland, PhD(chem), 48, DSc, 68. *Honors & Awards:* Res Achievement Award Natural Prod, Am Pharmaceut Asn, 68. *Prof Exp:* Nat Res Coun scholar, Switz, 48-49; Nat Res Coun Can fel, 50; Imp Chem Industs fel, Cambridge Univ, 51-52; assoc prof chem, Univ NB, 52-55; chemist, Ciba Pharmaceut Co, 55-62, dir natural prod, 63-67, dir biochem res, 67-68; dir fragrance res, Int Flavors & Fragrances, Inc, 68-71, vpres res & develop, 71-88, dir, chem synthesis & develop, 72-88, vpres, 78-88. *Concurrent Pos:* Guest investr, Rockefeller Univ, 66-67. *Mem:* Am Chem Soc; NY Acad Sci. *Res:* Synthesis and structural elucidation of natural products, especially in field of flavor and aroma chemicals. *Mailing Add:* 4 Hickory Hill Radford VA 24141. *E-Mail:* tiwtiw@aol.com

**TAYLOR, WILLIAM JAPE,** internal medicine, cardiology, for more information see previous edition

**TAYLOR, WILLIAM JOHNSON,** THEORETICAL CHEMISTRY, PHYSICAL CHEMISTRY. *Current Pos:* spectros & low-temperature res, Cryogenic Lab, 47-50, from asst prof to prof chem, 50-85, EMER PROF CHEM, OHIO STATE UNIV, 85- *Personal Data:* b Chengdu, China, Dec 3, 16; US citizen; m 49; c 4. *Educ:* Denison Univ, AB, 37; Ohio State Univ, PhD(phys chem), 42. *Prof Exp:* Instr chem, Univ Calif, Berkeley, 41-42; sr res assoc, Thermochem Sect, Nat Bur Stand, 42-47. *Concurrent Pos:* Vis prof, Lab Molecular Struct & Spectra, Univ Chicago, 63. *Mem:* Am Chem Soc; Am Phys Soc; AAAS; Am Asn Univ Prof. *Res:* Statistical and quantum mechanics; statistics of long-chain molecules; molecular vibrations; dipole moments; localized molecular orbitals; configuration interaction method and correlation energy; quantum integrals; applications of group theory. *Mailing Add:* Dept Chem Ohio State Univ 120 W 18th Ave Columbus OH 43210

**TAYLOR, WILLIAM L,** METEOROLOGY, ELECTROMAGNETISM. *Current Pos:* PHYSICIST, CIMMS, UNIV OKLA, 84- *Personal Data:* b Corsicana, Tex, Oct 17, 26; m 50, Norma Koester; c 3. *Educ:* Okla State Univ, BS, 50. *Prof Exp:* Physicist, Nat Bur Stand, Washington, DC, 50-51, Alaska, 51-52 & Colo, 52-65; physicist, Inst Telecommun Sci & Aeronomy, Environ Sci Serv Admin, US Dept Com, 65-70, physicist, Environ Res Labs, Nat Oceanic & Atmospheric Admin, 70-84. *Mem:* AAAS; Am Geophys Union; Sigma Xi; Int Union Radio Sci; Am Meteorol Soc. *Res:* Radio propagation between the earth and ionosphere in the lower frequency bands, using lightning discharges as the source; measurement of radio noise from severe thunderstorms and tornadoes; lightning discharge characteristics at all radio frequencies; relationships between thunderstorm precipitation, windfields, turbulence and lightning. *Mailing Add:* 4300 Brookline Pl Norman OK 73072

**TAYLOR, WILLIAM ROBERT,** ENGINEERING, APPLIED STATISTICS. *Current Pos:* asst prof, 69-77, ASSOC PROF INDUST & MGT ENG, MONT STATE UNIV, 77-, US FOREST SERV GRANT, 71- *Personal Data:* b Borger, Tex, Oct 25, 39; m 59; c 2. *Educ:* Okla State Univ, BS, 63; Univ Ark, Fayetteville, MS, 67, PhD(eng), 69. *Prof Exp:* Indust engr, Southwestern Bell Tel Co, Okla, 63-65; teaching asst, Univ Ark, Fayetteville, 68-69. *Concurrent Pos:* Consult, Morrison-Knudsen Co, Inc, 72- *Mem:* Am Inst Indust Engrs; Am Soc Eng Educ. *Res:* Operations research applications for harvesting timber; application of management science principles to hospital systems; application of engineering principles in designing disease diagnostic equipment. *Mailing Add:* Dept Indust Eng Mont State Univ Bozeman MT 59717

**TAYLOR, WILLIAM WALLER,** LIMNOLOGY, FISHERIES BIOLOGY. *Current Pos:* ASST PROF, DEPT FISHERIES & WILDLIFE, MICH STATE UNIV, 80- *Personal Data:* b Rochester, NY, Nov 20, 50; c 1. *Educ:* Hartwick Col, BA, 72; WVa Univ, MS, 75; Ariz State Univ, PhD(zool), 78. *Prof Exp:* Asst prof fisheries, Univ Mo, Columbia, 78-80. *Concurrent Pos:* Vis scientist, Hydrobiol Inst, Lake Ohrid, Yugoslavia, Smithsonian Inst, 76-

*Mem:* AAAS; Am Fisheries Soc; Am Soc Limnol & Oceanog; Int Asn Theoret & Appl Limnol; Sigma Xi. *Res:* Biological limnology; population dynamics and production of heterotrophs; ecosystem structure and function. *Mailing Add:* Dept Fish & Wildlife Mich State Univ East Lansing MI 48824

**TAYLOR, WILLIAM WEST,** PHARMACY. *Current Pos:* RETIRED. *Personal Data:* b Northampton Co, NC, Dec 4, 23; m 53; c 4. *Educ:* Univ NC, BS, 47, PhD(pharm), 62. *Prof Exp:* Intern hosp pharm, Duke Hosp, Durham, NC, 46-47, staff pharmacist, 48; chief pharmacist, Strong Mem Hosp, Rochester, NY, 48; instr, Univ NC, Chapel Hill, 52-62, asst prof hosp pharm, Div Pharmaceut, 62-83. *Concurrent Pos:* Chief pharmacist, NC Mem Hosp, 52-68, assoc dir, Div Pharm Serv, 68-74, spec formulations pharmacist, 75- *Mem:* Am Pharmaceut Asn; Am Soc Hosp Pharmacists; Am Asn Cols Pharm. *Res:* Hospital pharmacy; drug control; special compounding and dosage preparation; purification and formulation of dyes for clinical purposes. *Mailing Add:* 200 Westminister Dr Apt 30C Chapel Hill NC 27514

**TAYLOR-CADE, RUTH ANN,** ENGINEERING, COMPUTER SCIENCE. *Current Pos:* asst prof math, 68-75, assoc prof comput sci, 75-83, PROF CONSTRUCT & ARCHIT ENG TECH, UNIV SOUTHERN MISS, 83-, DIR, SCH ENG TECHNOL, 89- *Personal Data:* b Yazoo City, Miss, Nov 17, 37; m 74; c 1. *Educ:* Miss State Univ, BS, 63; Univ Ala, MA, 68, PhD(eng), 69. *Prof Exp:* Chem engr, Southern Res Inst, 63-64; instr eng mech, Univ Ala, 67-68. *Mem:* Am Soc Eng Educ. *Res:* Women in science and engineering. *Mailing Add:* Dept Archit Eng Tech Univ Southern Miss PO Box 5137 Hattiesburg MS 39406-5137

**TAYSOM, ELVIN DAVID,** ANIMAL HUSBANDRY. *Current Pos:* from asst prof to prof, 53-82, EMER PROF ANIMAL SCI, ARIZ STATE UNIV, 82- *Personal Data:* b Rockland, Idaho, Aug 5, 17; m 39, Myrtle Hall; c David W, Jay W & Rex E. *Educ:* Univ Idaho, BS, 40; Utah State Univ, MS, 50; Wash State Univ, PhD, 61. *Prof Exp:* Asst animal sci, Utah State Univ, 49-50; asst, Wash State Univ, 50-53, sheep specialist, 53. *Concurrent Pos:* Asst dir, Int Stockmen's Sch, Ariz & Tex, 63-81, Ag-Tech Sch, Kiev, Ukrain, 93, Stavropol, Russia, 93; livestock consult, N Yemen, 82. *Mem:* Am Soc Animal Sci. *Res:* Mineral metabolism and its relation to the formation to urinary calculi and hormone functions in the body. *Mailing Add:* 2028 S College Ave Tempe AZ 85282

**TAZUMA, JAMES JUNKICHI,** CHEMISTRY. *Current Pos:* RETIRED. *Personal Data:* b Seattle, Wash, July 17, 24; m 54; c 2. *Educ:* Univ Wash, BSc, 48, PhD(org chem), 53. *Prof Exp:* Parke Davis Co fel, Wayne State Univ, 52-53; res chemist, Henry Ford Hosp, 53-54 & Food Mach & Chem Corp, NJ, 55-58; sr res chemist, Goodyear Tire & Rubber Co, 58-65, sect head spec assignment, 65-79, res scientist, 79-90. *Mem:* Am Chem Soc. *Res:* Petroleum chemistry; catalysis; reaction mechanism; process development; polymer additives; monomers; rubber chemicals development. *Mailing Add:* 15800 Village Green Dr Unit 5 Mill Creek Bothell WA 98012-1299

**TCHAO, RUY,** CELL BIOLOGY. *Current Pos:* asst prof path, 72-76, ASSOC PROF PATH, MED COL PA, 76- *Personal Data:* b China. *Educ:* Univ Nottingham, BSc, 60; Univ Manchester, PhD(biochem), 64. *Prof Exp:* Res fel, Inst Cancer Res, Chester Beatty Inst, London, 64-66, from mem res staff to sr biochemist, 66-72. *Concurrent Pos:* Vis assoc prof, Med Col, Nat Taiwan Univ, 69; vis prof, Institut fur Zellforschungszentrum, Heidelberg, Ger, 77; res fel, Int Agency Res Cancer, Lyon, France, 80-81. *Mem:* Int Soc Differentiation; Europ Tissue Cult Asn; NY Acad Sci; Am Asn Cancer Res. *Res:* Tumor cell differentiation, invasion. *Mailing Add:* Dept Pharmacol & Toxicol Philadelphia Col Pharm & Sci 600 S 43rd St & Woodland Ave Philadelphia PA 19104

**TCHEN, TCHE TSING,** biochemistry, for more information see previous edition

**TCHERTKOFF, VICTOR,** PATHOLOGY. *Current Pos:* assoc prof, 61-67, PROF PATH, DEPT PATH, NY MED COL, 67-, ACTG CHMN, 88-; DIR PATH LABS, METROP HOSP, 67- *Personal Data:* b Lausanne, Switz, Aug 7, 19; US citizen; m 42; c 2. *Educ:* City Col New York, BS, 40; New York Med Col, MD, 43; Am Bd Path, dipl anat, 61. *Prof Exp:* Asst pathologist, Metrop Hosp, NY, 57-60. *Concurrent Pos:* Pathologist-in-charge, Metrop Hosp, 61-66. *Mem:* Col Am Path; Am Soc Clin Path; Int Acad Path. *Mailing Add:* Metrop Hosp 1901 First Ave New York NY 10029-7418

**TCHEUREKDJIAN, NOUBAR,** PHYSICAL CHEMISTRY. *Current Pos:* Sr res chemist, S C Johnson & Son, Inc, 63-80, res assoc, 80-82, sect mgr, 82, sr group leader, 82-89, mgr, 89-96, MGR, PHYS SCI & MICROBIOL, S C JOHNSON & SON, INC, 96- *Personal Data:* b Beirut, Lebanon, Jan 4, 37; m 71, Hourig Derderian; c Lucene & Haig. *Educ:* Ill Inst Technol, BS, 58; Lehigh Univ, MS, 60, PhD(phys chem), 63. *Mem:* Am Chem Soc; Soc Rheology; Sigma Xi; Int Asn Colloid & Surface Scientists. *Res:* Colloid and surface chemistry; personal care; chemical specialties; aerosol technology. *Mailing Add:* Phys Res S C Johnson & Son Inc Racine WI 53403-5011. *Fax:* 414-260-4015; *E-Mail:* ntcheure@scj.com

**TCHOBANOGLOUS, GEORGE,** ENVIRONMENTAL ENGINEERING, SOLID WASTE MANAGEMENT. *Current Pos:* assoc prof, 70-76, PROF CIVIL ENG, UNIV CALIF, DAVIS, 76- *Personal Data:* b Patterson, Calif, May 24, 35; m 57; c 3. *Educ:* Univ of the Pac, BS, 58; Univ Calif, Berkeley, MS, 60; Stanford Univ, PhD(sanit eng), 69. *Honors & Awards:* Gordon

Masken Fair Medal, Water Pollution Control Fedn; Thomas R Camp lectr, Boston Civil Engrs. *Prof Exp:* Res engr, Univ Calif, Berkeley, 60-62 & Water Resources Engrs, Inc, 62-63; actg asst prof sanit eng, Stanford Univ, 66-70. *Concurrent Pos:* Consult, Nolte & Assoc, 81- *Mem:* AAAS; Water Pollution Control Fedn; Am Soc Civil Engrs; Am Geophys Union; Am Water Works Asn. *Res:* Physical processes in water and wastewater treatment; small treatment systems; solid waste management; aquatic treatment systems; construction of wetland systems. *Mailing Add:* 662 Diego Pl Davis CA 95616-0123

**TCHOLAKIAN, ROBERT KEVORK,** BIOCHEMISTRY, REPRODUCTIVE BIOLOGY & ENDOCRINOLOGY. *Current Pos:* from asst prof to assoc prof reproductive med & biol, 71-83, assoc prof obstet, gynec & reproductive sci, 83-95, ASSOC PROF INTEGRATIVE BIOL, PHARMACOL & PHYSIOL, MED SCH, UNIV TEX, 96- *Personal Data:* b Apr 26, 38; US citizen; M 79, Alitz Boynerian; c Talar, Talin & Tamar. *Educ:* Berea Col, BS, 58; Fla State Univ, MS, 63; Med Col Ga, PhD(physiol, biochem), 67. *Prof Exp:* NIH fels, Steroid Biochem Inst, Univ Utah, 67-68 & Univ Southern Calif, 68-69; instr reproduction, Univ Southern Calif, 69-70; asst prof endocrinol, M D Anderson Hosp & Tumor Inst, 70-71. *Concurrent Pos:* Assoc mem, Grad Sch Biomed Sci, Univ Tex, Houston, 77- *Mem:* AAAS; Am Soc Zoologists; Soc Study Reproduction; Am Soc Andrology; Endocrine Soc. *Res:* Reproductive biology and steroid biochemistry as related to action of hormones; endocrine and paracrine regulation of testicular testosterone synthesis and the role of endocrine disruptors in human and wildlife. *Mailing Add:* Dept Integrative Biol Pharmacol & Physiol Houston TX 77030. *Fax:* 713-500-7455; *E-Mail:* rtchol@farmr1.med.uth.tmc.edu

**TEABEAUT, JAMES ROBERT, II,** PATHOLOGY. *Current Pos:* assoc prof, 59-69, PROF PATH, MED COL GA, 69- *Personal Data:* b Fayetteville, NC, Aug 27, 24. *Educ:* Duke Univ, MD, 47; Am Bd Path, dipl, 53. *Prof Exp:* Intern path, Duke Hosp, Durham, NC, 48, intern internal med, 49; Rockefeller res fel legal med, Harvard Med Sch, 49-51; chief div forensic path, Armed Forces Inst Path, 51-54; asst prof path, Sch Med, Univ Tenn, 54-59; coroner, Shelby Co, Tenn, 55-59. *Concurrent Pos:* Lederle med fac award, 54-55; med examr, State of Ga, 59-; consult, Vet Admin Hosp, Augusta, Ga, 59- & US Army Hosp, Ft Gordon, Ga, 60-, lectr, Mil Police Sch, 63-, hon mem staff, 66- *Mem:* Col Am Path; Am Soc Clin Path; AMA; Int Acad Path; Int Acad Forensic Sci. *Res:* Forensic pathology; pathology of human cardiovascular disease. *Mailing Add:* 721 Montrose Ct Augusta GA 30904

**TEACH, EUGENE GORDON,** ORGANIC CHEMISTRY. *Current Pos:* RES ASSOC, STAUFFER CHEM CO, 57-, SUPVR, 74- *Personal Data:* b Hayward, Calif, Oct 27, 26; m 54; c 1. *Educ:* St Mary's Col, Calif, BS, 51; Univ Notre Dame, PhD(chem), 53. *Prof Exp:* Res assoc, Univ Calif, Los Angeles, 53-54, res chemist, USDA, 54-57; res assoc, ICI Americas, 87-91. *Mem:* Am Chem Soc. *Res:* Actylene-allene chemistry; high temperature polymers; fluorine chemistry; agricultural chemistry. *Mailing Add:* 1929 Downey Pl El Cerrito CA 94530-1827

**TEAF, CHRISTOPHER MORRIS,** TOXICOLOGY, ENVIRONMENTAL RISK ASSESSMENT. *Current Pos:* Res staff, Hazardous Waste Mgt Prog, Fla State Univ, 79-81, res assoc, Ctr Biomed & Toxicol Res, 81-83, res asst, Nat Ctr Toxicol Res, 82-85, ASSOC DIR, CTR BIOMED & TOXICOL RES, FLA STATE UNIV, 85- *Personal Data:* b Philadelphia, Pa, May 5, 53; m 81, Patricia Heaton; c Andrew & Patrick. *Educ:* Pa State Univ, BS, 75; Fla State Univ, MS, 80; Univ Ark, PhD(toxicol), 85. *Concurrent Pos:* Chair, Toxic Substances Adv Comt, Dept Labor. *Mem:* Soc Toxicol; Soc Risk Analysis; AAAS; Sigma Xi; Nat Asn Underwater Instrs; Soc Environ Toxicol & Chem. *Res:* Risk assessment; modulation of mutagenic processes; reproductive toxicology; establishment of acceptable concentrations of toxic contaminants in water, soil and air. *Mailing Add:* Ctr Biomed & Toxicol Res Fla State Univ 2035 Dirac Dr 226 HMB Tallahassee FL 32310. *Fax:* 850-574-6704; *E-Mail:* cteaf@res.fsu.edu

**TEAFORD, MARGARET ELAINE,** BIOCHEMISTRY, CLINICAL CHEMISTRY. *Current Pos:* RETIRED. *Personal Data:* b Union Star, Mo, Feb 2, 28. *Educ:* Northwest Mo State Col, BS, 50; Univ Mo, Columbia, MS, 59, PhD(biochem), 64; Am Bd Clin Chemists, dipl. *Prof Exp:* Med technologist, Methodist Hosp, St Joseph, Mo, 51-52, chief med technol, 52-56; NIH traineeship, Univ Wash, 64-66; tech dir lab med, Allen Med Labs, Ltd, 66-78, assoc dir, 78-83. *Mem:* AAAS; Am Asn Clin Chemists; assoc Am Soc Clin Path; hon mem Sigma Xi. *Res:* Methodology in clinical chemistry and establishing normal values for the various biochemical parameters in the human. *Mailing Add:* 1964 Dougherty Ferry St Louis MO 63122

**TEAGER, HERBERT MARTIN,** ELECTRICAL ENGINEERING, BIOMEDICAL ENGINEERING. *Current Pos:* From asst prof to assoc prof, 59-66, RES PROF MED & CHIEF BIOMED ENG, SCH MED, BOSTON UNIV, 66- *Personal Data:* b Canton, Ohio, Mar 20, 30; m 53; c 2. *Educ:* Mass Inst Technol, SB, 52, ScD(control eng), 55. *Concurrent Pos:* Consult, President's Sci Adv, Sprague Elec Co, Elec Boat Div, Gen Dynamics Corp, Am Optical Co & Compagnie Europeene D'Automatisme Electronique; lectr elec eng, Mass Inst Technol, 66- *Mem:* AAAS; sr mem Inst Elec & Electronics Engrs; Asn Comput Mach; NY Acad Sci; Am Soc Acoust. *Res:* Application of information processing techniques to the collection and analysis of diagnostic information from machine perceived sonic, tactile and visual information; instrumentation; computer design and man-machine interaction; physiology and pathology of speech production and hearing; diagnostic uses of sound (passive) and vibration; speech recognition. *Mailing Add:* 58 Edgemoor Rd Belmont MA 02178

**TEAGUE, ABNER F,** CHEMICAL ENGINEERING. *Current Pos:* RETIRED. *Personal Data:* b Gainesville, Tex, May 25, 19; m 46, 71, Nora K Henderson; c Barbara J (Hollman), Julie A (Youngsren), James A & C D Janes. *Educ:* Tex Tech Col, BS, 43; Univ Southern Calif, MS, 69. *Prof Exp:* Chemist, Naval Ord Test Sta, 46-48, res chemist, 48-51; unit head, Bur Ord, US Navy, Washington, DC, 51-56; proj engr, Astrodyn, McGregor, Tex, 56-58; engr, TRW Space Tech Labs, 59-63, proj mgr, TRW Systs, Inc, 63-65, proj engr, 65-67, mgr propulsion subproj, TRW, Inc, 67-71; engr, Naval Weapons Eng Support Activ Navy Space Projs-Fleet Commun Satellite Proj, Naval Electronic Systs Command, 71-77, head, Mech Systs Br & dir missile develop, Joint Cruise Missile Projs Off Cruise Missile, Navy Mat Command, Washington, DC, 77-83 & ORI 83-84; pres, A Teague Assoc, Eng & Mkt Consult, 84-86. *Mem:* NY Acad Sci; Am Inst Chem Engrs; Nat Geog Soc. *Res:* Developing hydrazine propulsion systems for satellite attitude control and station keeping; development and processing of solid propellant rockets; head of cruise missile mechanical systems including booster and pyrotechnic pneumatic systems for tomahawk cruise missile. *Mailing Add:* PO Box 626 Hamilton TX 76531

**TEAGUE, CLAUDE EDWARD, JR,** CHEMISTRY. *Current Pos:* RETIRED. *Personal Data:* b Sanford, NC, Sept 9, 24; div; c Penny, Brian & Ted. *Educ:* Univ NC, AB, 47, PhD(chem), 50. *Prof Exp:* Res chemist, Am Viscose Corp, 50-51; res chemist, R J Reynolds Tobacco Co, 52-60, mgr chem res, 60-70, asst dir res, 70-75, planning mgr, 76-77, dir corp res, R J Reynolds Indust, 78-81, dir res & develop admin, 81-87. *Mem:* Am Chem Soc; Sigma Xi; NY Acad Sci. *Res:* Synthetic organic chemistry; research planning; polymers and synthetic fibers; tobacco chemistry. *Mailing Add:* 716 Archer Rd Winston-Salem NC 27106

**TEAGUE, DAVID BOYCE,** APPLIED MATHEMATICS. *Current Pos:* ASSOC PROF MATH, WESTERN CAROLINA UNIV, 68- *Personal Data:* b Franklin, NC, May 17, 37; m 64, 85; c 2. *Educ:* NC State Col, BSEE, 59, MS, 61; NC State Univ, PhD(appl math), 65. *Prof Exp:* Instr math, NC State Univ, 64-65; asst prof, Univ NC, Charlotte, 65-68. *Concurrent Pos:* Vis assoc prof comput sci, UTK 82. *Mem:* Asn Comput Mach; Sigma Xi. *Res:* Elasticity; mathematical theory of elasticity; mixed boundary value problems in elasticity; computer science; operating systems. *Mailing Add:* 151 Wike Cemetary Rd Cullowhee NC 28723

**TEAGUE, HAROLD JUNIOR,** ORGANIC CHEMISTRY. *Current Pos:* Assoc prof, 70-77, PROF CHEM, PEMBROKE STATE UNIV, 77- *Personal Data:* b Fayetteville, NC, Nov 5, 41; m 70. *Educ:* Methodist Col, NC, BS, 64; NC State Univ, MS, 67, PhD(org chem). 70. *Mem:* Am Chem Soc. *Res:* Mechanistic rearrangement studies of sulfur containing ring compounds; biochemical mechanisms. *Mailing Add:* 109 Elmhurst Dr Lumberton NC 28358-7731

**TEAGUE, LAVETTE COX,** SYSTEMS ANALYSIS & DESIGN. *Current Pos:* PROF COMPUT INFO SYSTS, CALIF STATE POLYTECH UNIV, 80- *Personal Data:* b Birmingham, Ala, Oct 8, 34. *Educ:* Mass Inst Technol, BA, 57, MS, 65, PhD(civil eng systs), 68. *Prof Exp:* Archit designer, Carroll C Harmon, Architect, 57, Fred Renneker, Architect, 58-59; architect, Rust Eng Co, 59-62, Synergetics, Inc, 62-64; res liaison, Rust Eng Co, 64-68; dir comput serv, Skidmore, Owings & Merrill, 68-74; consult, Lavette Cox Teague, 74-80. *Concurrent Pos:* Res asst, Mass Inst Technol, 64-67, instr, 67-68, res assoc, 68; fel archit & urban planning, Univ Calif, Los Angeles, 72; adj assoc prof archit & civil eng, Carnegie-Mellon Univ, 73-74; lectr info systs, Calif State Polytech Univ, 80, asst chmn, Comput Info Systs, 89-91, chmn, 91-93. *Mem:* Asn Comput Mach; Sigma Xi. *Res:* Information systems analysis and design, system development methods. *Mailing Add:* 1696 N Altadena Dr Altadena CA 91001-3623. *E-Mail:* lcteague@csupomona.edu

**TEAGUE, MARION WARFIELD,** PHYSICAL INORGANIC CHEMISTRY. *Current Pos:* ASSOC PROF CHEM, HENDRIX COL, 70- *Personal Data:* b Arkadelphia, Ark, July 6, 41; m 62; c 3. *Educ:* Ouachita Baptist Col, BS, 63; Purdue Univ, MS, 68, PhD(chem), 71. *Prof Exp:* Res chemist, Aberdeen Res & Develop Ctr, 68-70. *Mem:* AAAS; Am Chem Soc. *Res:* Non-coplanar aromatic systems; electron transfer mechanism. *Mailing Add:* Dept Chem Hendrix Col Conway AR 72032

**TEAGUE, PERRY OWEN,** IMMUNOLOGY. *Current Pos:* REAL ESTATE. *Personal Data:* b Marshall, Tex, July 13, 36; m 64; c 2. *Educ:* NTex State Univ, BA, 58, MA, 61; Univ Okla, PhD(immunol), 66. *Prof Exp:* Res assoc immunol, Univ Southern Calif, 66; res fel, Univ Minn, 66-68; from asst prof to assoc prof path, Med Sch, Univ Fla, 73-84; lab dir, NW Labs, Oklahoma City, 84-89; tech dir, Nat Health Labs, Winston-Salem, NC, 90-92, Damon Labs, Berwyn, Ill, 92-93; exec vpres & gen mgr, Clinistatickin, Vermont Hills, Ill, 93-94. *Concurrent Pos:* NIH fel pediat, Univ Minn, 67-68. *Mem:* Am Asn Immunol; Soc Exp Biol & Med; assoc Am Soc Clin Path. *Res:* Age-associated and early decline of thymus dependent lymphocyte function; diagnostic clinical immunology. *Mailing Add:* 1235 Hollingswood Ave Naperville IL 60564

**TEAGUE, PEYTON CLARK,** ORGANIC CHEMISTRY. *Current Pos:* from assoc prof to prof, 50-82, assoc dean grad sch, 66-68, DISTINGUISHED EMER PROF CHEM, UNIV SC, 82- *Personal Data:* b Montgomery, Ala, June 26, 15; m 37, Patricia Lamb; c Norah T (Grimball). *Educ:* Auburn Univ, BS, 36; Pa State Univ, MS, 37; Univ Tex, PhD(org chem, biochem), 42. *Prof Exp:* Res chemist, Am Agr Chem Co, NJ, 37-39; instr chem, Auburn Univ, 41-42; res chemist, US Naval Res Lab, DC, 42-45; asst prof chem, Univ Ga, 45-48 & Univ Ky, 48-50. *Concurrent Pos:* Vis prof, Univ Col, Dublin, 63-64 & 77. *Mem:* Am Chem Soc; Phytochem Soc NAm (pres, 69-70). *Res:* Chemistry and stereochemistry of flavonoids. *Mailing Add:* Dept Chem Univ SC Columbia SC 29208-0001

**TEAGUE, TOMMY KAY,** DATA COMPRESSION, GROUP THEORY. *Current Pos:* mgr operating systs, 85-87, consult programmer, 87-88, CONSULT SOFTWARE ENGR, UNISYS, 88- *Personal Data:* b Crossett, Ark, July 11, 43; m 65, Mary J Crum; c Jennifer. *Educ:* Hendrix Col, AB, 65; Univ Kans, MA, 67; Mich State Univ, PhD(math), 71. *Prof Exp:* Asst prof math, Gustavus Adolphus Col, 71; asst prof math, Hendrix Col, 71-76, coordr comput syst & serv, 75-76; systs rep, Burroughs, 76-77, sr syst rep, 77-79, systs specialist, 79-80, sr systs specialist, 80-84; vpres, Fed Home Loan Bank Dallas, 84-85. *Mem:* Am Math Soc; Math Asn Am. *Res:* Varieties of groups; embeddings of groups; operating systems; data compression. *Mailing Add:* 22942 Luciana Mission Viejo CA 92691-2106. *Fax:* 714-472-6341; *E-Mail:* tkteague@aol.com

**TEAL, GORDON KIDD,** PHYSICAL-INORGANIC CHEMISTRY. *Current Pos:* RETIRED. *Personal Data:* b Dallas, Tex, Jan 10, 07; m 31; c 3. *Educ:* Baylor Univ, AB, 27; Brown Univ, ScM, 28, PhD(phys-inorg chem), 31. *Hon Degrees:* LLD, Baylor Univ, 69; ScD, Brown Univ, 69. *Honors & Awards:* Inventor of the Year Award, Patent, Trademark & Copyright Res Inst, George Washington Univ, 66; Golden Plate Award, Am Acad Achievement, 67; Cert Appreciation & Honor Scroll, Nat Bur Stand & US Dept Com, 67; Medal of Honor, Inst Elec & Electronics Engrs, 68; Creative Invention Award, Am Chem Soc, 70; Inst Elec & Electronics Engrs Centennial Medal, 84; Semmy Award, Semiconductor Mat & Equip Inst, 84. *Prof Exp:* Chem solid state physicist, Bell Tel Labs Inc, 30-53; asst vpres & dir mat & components res, Tex Instruments, Dallas, 53-55, asst vpres & dir, Cent Res Labs, 55-61, asst vpres res & eng, 61-63, asst vpres & int tech dir, London, Paris, Rome, 63-65; first dir, Inst Mat Res, Nat Bur Stand, Washington, DC, 65-67; asst vpres tech develop, Equip Group, Tex Instruments, Dallas, 67-68, vpres & chief scientist, 68-72; consult indust & govt, 72-78. *Concurrent Pos:* Res assoc, Columbia Univ, 32-35; consult, Dept Defense, 56-64, 70-72, NASA, 70-72, Nat Bur Stand, 72-73, Tex Instruments, 72-77; mem, Panel Selenium, Nat Acad Sci-Nat Res Coun, 56, Panel Semiconductors, 57, Mat Adv Bd, 60-64, Ad Hoc Comt Mat & Processes Electronic Devices, 70-71; mem, Mat Panel, Adv Group Electronic Parts, Off Asst Secy Defense, 56-59; dir at large, Inst Radio Eng, 59 & 62; mem adv panels, Nat Acad Sci, Nat Acad Eng & Nat Res Res Coun to Inst Appl Technol, Nat Bur Stand, 69-75, consult, Comt Electronic Technol Issues Study, 72-73, chmn, Panel Evaluate Electronic Technol Div, 72-75; mem, US-India Nat Acad Sci Workshop Indust Res Mgt, 70; trustee, Brown Univ, 69-74, emer trustee, 74-, chmn, Corp Comt Comput Educ, 71-75, mem, 76-81; chmn, US Nat Acad Sci deleg to Ceylon, Indust Res Mgt Workshop, 70; mem, Nat Acad Eng Comn Int Activ, 70-71; mem, Aeronaut & Space Eng Bd, Nat Acad Eng, 70-72; trustee, Baylor Univ, 70-79, Med Ctr, Dallas, 70-79; mem adv coun, Col Arts & Sci, Univ Tex, Austin, 72-78, Col Educ, 77-, Col Nat Sci, 79-; contribr, Comt Surv Mat Sci & Eng, Nat Acad Sci, 72-75; mem US Nat Acad Sci deleg to Joint Repub China-US Workshop Indust Innovation & Prod Develop, Taiwan, 75; chmn panel, Nat Acad Sci-Nat Res Coun, res facil & sci opportunities in use of low energy neutrons, 77-78. *Mem:* Nat Acad Eng; fel AAAS; fel Inst Elec & Electronics Engrs; fel Am Inst Chem; Am Chem Soc; Am Phys Soc; Electrochem Soc; emer mem Indust Res Inst; Sigma Xi. *Res:* Raman spectra deuterium isotopic effects; photoelectric and secondary emission phenomena; pyrolytically deposited hard or semiconducting films; microwave attenuator materials; silicon carbide varistors; germanium and silicon single crystals; transistors; junction transistor; recipient of 64 patents from US and abroad. *Mailing Add:* 5515 Glen Lakes Dr Walnut Place 632 Dallas TX 75231

**TEAL, JOHN MOLINE,** COASTAL & WETLANDS ECOLOGY. *Current Pos:* assoc scientist, 61-71, sr scientist, 71, EMER SCIENTIST, WOODS HOLE OCEANOG INST. *Personal Data:* b Omaha, Nebr, Nov 9, 29; m 50, 79, Susan B Peterson; c 2. *Educ:* Harvard Univ, AB, 51, MA, 52, PhD, 55. *Prof Exp:* Asst prof zool, Marine Inst, Univ Ga, 55-59; asst zool & oceanog, Inst Oceanog, Dalhousie Univ, 59-61. *Mem:* AAAS; Am Soc Limnol & Oceanog; Ecol Soc Am; Soc Wetland Sci; Estuarine Res Fedn. *Res:* Ecology, chemical cycling, waste treatment productivity of coastal wetlands; hydrocarbon biogeochemistry; coastal pollution; salt marsh restoration. *Mailing Add:* Woods Hole Oceanog Inst Woods Hole MA 02543. *Fax:* 508-457-2169; *E-Mail:* steal@whoi.edu

**TEAL, PETER E A,** ISOLATION & IDENTIFICATION OF INSECT HORMONES & SEX PHEROMONES. *Current Pos:* RES PHYSIOLOGIST, USDA, 90- *Personal Data:* m 82, Kathleen J. *Educ:* Univ Ottawa, BSc, 76, MSc, 78; Univ Fla, PhD(entom), 81. *Prof Exp:* Asst prof, Univ Guelph, 83-86; assoc res scientist, Univ Fla, 86-90. *Mem:* Am Chem Soc; Am Entom Soc; Can Entom Soc. *Res:* Isolation indentification and modes of action of hormones that regulate the induction and termination of sex pheromone biosynthesis in insects. *Mailing Add:* Vet Entom USDA Agr Res Serv PO Box 14565 Gainesville FL 32604-2565

**TEANEY, DALE T,** SOLID STATE PHYSICS, ACOUSTICS. *Current Pos:* PRES, SYNCHROVOICE INC, 90- *Personal Data:* b Monrovia, Calif, May 19, 33; div; c 3. *Educ:* Pomona Col, BA, 55; Univ Calif, Berkeley, PhD(physics), 60. *Prof Exp:* Res assoc physics, Atomic Energy Res Estab, Eng, 60-62; res staff mem, Watson Res Ctr, IBM Corp, 62-83; prof elec eng, NJ Inst Tech, 83-90. *Concurrent Pos:* Staff scientist, Nat Acad Sci Phys Surv Comt, 70-71; hon res fel, Univ Col, London, 80-81; Voice Found Fel, 80-81. *Mem:* AAAS; fel Am Phys Soc; NY Acad Sci. *Res:* Magnetic resonance; calorimetry; liquid crystals; lipid bilayers; acoustic spectroscopy; voice science. *Mailing Add:* PO Box No 506 400 Harrison Ave Harrison NJ 07029

**TEARE, IWAN DALE,** INTEGRATED PEST MANAGEMENT. *Current Pos:* RETIRED. *Personal Data:* b Moscow, Idaho, July 24, 31; m 52, Claudia J Patterson; c Steven M, Bradley L, Kurtis B & Kelly M (Boynton). *Educ:* Univ Idaho, BS, 53; Wash State Univ, MS, 59; Purdue Univ, PhD(crop physiol, ecol), 63. *Prof Exp:* Co agent, Idaho, 56-57; instr agron, Purdue Univ, 61-63; asst prof, Wash State Univ, 63-69; assoc prof agron, Kans State Univ, 69-77, prof, 77-79; prof agr & dir, Agr Res & Educ Ctr, Univ Fla, Quincy-Marianna, 79-82, res scholar & scientist, NFla Res & Educ Ctr, Quincy, 82-96. *Concurrent Pos:* Vis prof, Duke Univ, 78-79; assoc ed, Agron J, 79-85, tech ed, 85-92; bio-space technol training prog, Univ Va, 69. *Mem:* Crop Sci Soc Am; fel Am Soc Agron; Sigma Xi; Entom Soc Am. *Res:* Modeling crop responses to insect and disease pests, the microclimate and the soil-plant-air continuum; developing hardware and software for conducting integrated pest and crop management research. *Mailing Add:* 420 Maxwell Dr Cairo GA 31728. *Fax:* 850-627-9236; *E-Mail:* qui@gnv.ifas.ufl.edu

**TEARNEY, RUSSELL JAMES,** HYPERTENSION. *Current Pos:* ADJ ASSOC PROF, UNIV DIST COLUMBIA. *Personal Data:* b Aug 10, 38; m; c 3. *Educ:* Howard Univ, PhD(physiol), 73. *Prof Exp:* DIR PHYSIOL LABS, MED SCH, HOWARD UNIV, 80- *Mem:* Porter fel Am Physiol Soc; Am Col Sports Med; Am Hypertension Soc. *Res:* Vascular dispensibility in hypertensive subjects. *Mailing Add:* 1515 Menlee Dr Silver Spring MD 20904-2732

**TEAS, HOWARD JONES,** GENETICS. *Current Pos:* PROF BIOL, UNIV MIAMI, 67- *Personal Data:* b Rolla, Mo, Sept 4, 20; m 42; c 4. *Educ:* La State Univ, AB, 42; Stanford Univ, MA, 46; Calif Inst Technol, PhD(genetics), 47. *Prof Exp:* Asst genetics, Carnegie Inst, 42-43; biologist, Oak Ridge Nat Lab, 47-48; res fel, Calif Inst Technol, 48-49, sr res fel, 50-53; plant physiologist, USDA, 53-56; assoc prof biochem, Univ Fla, 56-60; head agr bio-sci div, Nuclear Ctr, Univ PR, 60-62; prog dir, NSF, 62-64; chmn div biol sci, Univ Ga, 64-67. *Concurrent Pos:* Mem bd dirs, Orgn Trop Studies, 67-72. *Mem:* AAAS; Ecol Soc Am; Am Soc Plant Physiol; Am Soc Biol Chem; Radiation Res Soc. *Res:* Plant physiology; tropical biology; physiological ecology. *Mailing Add:* 417 E Ridge Village Dr Miami FL 33157

**TEASDALE, JOHN G,** PHYSICS. *Current Pos:* from asst prof to assoc prof physics, 56-62, PROF PHYSICS, SAN DIEGO STATE UNIV, 62- *Personal Data:* b Utah, June 11, 13; m 42; c 3. *Educ:* Univ Calif, Los Angeles, AB, 36, PhD(physics), 50. *Prof Exp:* Physicist, US Navy Radio & Sound Lab, 41 & Manhattan Proj, Radiation Lab, Univ Calif, 42-45; res fel, Calif Inst Technol, 50-52, sr res fel, 52-56. *Concurrent Pos:* Consult, Convair Div, Gen Dynamics Corp, 60. *Mem:* Am Phys Soc; Am Inst Physics; Am Asn Physics Teachers; Sigma Xi. *Res:* Nuclear physics. *Mailing Add:* 23732 Villena Mission Viejo CA 92692-1817

**TEASDALE, WILLIAM BROOKS,** ORGANIC CHEMISTRY. *Current Pos:* Prod chemist, Eastman Kodak Co, 61-62, develop chemist, 62-73, sr develop chemist, 73-76 & Dept Tech Staff, 76-77, SR DEVELOP CHEMIST, DIV TECH STAFF, EASTMAN KODAK CO, 77- *Personal Data:* b Brownsville, Pa, July 19, 39; m 63; c 3. *Educ:* Geneva Col, BS, 61. *Mem:* Am Chem Soc; Soc Photog Scientists & Engrs. *Res:* Organic chemical processes to be used in the production of photographic chemicals. *Mailing Add:* 104 Paddy Hill Dr Rochester NY 14616-1138

**TEATE, JAMES LAMAR,** FOREST ECOLOGY. *Current Pos:* DIR & PROF, SCH FORESTRY, LA TECH UNIV, 76- *Personal Data:* b Moultrie, Ga, Mar 4, 32; m 53; c 3. *Educ:* Univ Ga, BS, 54, MF, 56; NC State Univ, PhD(forestry, ecol), 67. *Prof Exp:* Info & educ forester, Fla Forest Serv, 56-58; instr forestry & res assts, Auburn Univ, 58-60; instr & asst forest, Miss State Univ, 60-62; asst prof forestry, Wis State Univ-Stevens Point, 65-67; assoc prof forest recreation, Okla State Univ, 67-76; res specialist, Okla Agr Exp Sta, 67-76. *Concurrent Pos:* Proj consult statewide comprehensive outdoor recreation plan, Okla Indust Develop & Parks Dept, 69-70; chmn, Southern Regional Educ Comt, mem, Nat Educ Comt, Nat Asn Prof Forestry Schs & Cols, 88-89. *Mem:* Fel Soc Am Foresters; Forest Farmers Asn; Sigma Xi; Am Forestry Asn; Int Soc Trop Foresters. *Mailing Add:* Sch Forestry La Tech Univ 305 Wisteria St Ruston LA 71272-0001

**TEATER, ROBERT WOODSON,** AGRONOMY. *Current Pos:* dir, Sch Natural Resources, 71-74, chmn & prof, Dept Natural Resources & prof agron, 73-74, ASSOC DEAN, COL AGR & HOME ECON, OHIO STATE UNIV, 69- *Personal Data:* b Ky, Feb 27, 27; m 52; c 4. *Educ:* Univ Ky, BS, 51; Ohio State Univ, MS, 55, PhD(agron), 57. *Prof Exp:* Asst prof agron, Ohio State Univ & Agr Exp Sta, 57; exec asst to dir, Ohio Dept Natural Resources, 61-63, asst dir, 63-69; dir, Ohio Dept Natural Resources, 75-83. *Concurrent Pos:* Pres, Robert W Teater & Assocs, 83- *Mem:* Am Soc Agron; Soil Conserv Soc Am. *Res:* Soil fertility; plant nutrition; conservation; natural resources; nature conservancy; environmental science. *Mailing Add:* 286 W Wisheimer Rd Columbus OH 43214

**TEAYS, TERRY JOHN,** PULSATING VARIABLE STARS, ULTRAVIOLET ASTRONOMY. *Current Pos:* Resident astronr, Int Ultraviolet Explorer Observ, Goddard Space Flight Ctr/Comput Sci Corp, 87-89, data analysis facil astronr, 89-90, supvr telescope opers, 90-93, DIR, CTR SCI RES, COMPUT SCI CORP, 93- *Personal Data:* b St Louis, Mo, Aug 4, 50; m 72, Carol Riggs. *Educ:* Univ Calif, Santa Cruz, BA, 73; Univ Hawaii, Manoa, MS, 76; Univ Nebr, Lincoln, PhD(physics), 86. *Concurrent Pos:* Prin investr, Int Ultraviolet Explorer, NASA, 87-93. *Mem:* Int Astron Union; Am Astron Soc. *Res:* Pulsating variable stars and what they reveal about stellar evolution, atmospheres and distances; satellite astronomy, especially in the ultraviolet. *Mailing Add:* 8811 Magnolia Dr Lanham MD 20706. *Fax:* 301-459-4482; *E-Mail:* teays@iuegtc.gsfc.nasa.gov

**TEBBE, DENNIS LEE,** ELECTRICAL ENGINEERING, STATISTICS. *Current Pos:* sr prin engr, 82-88, PROG MGR, GCS DIV, HARRIS CORP, 89- *Personal Data:* b St Louis, Mo, Oct 21, 42; m 64, Patricia Mitchell; c Paul & Leanne. *Educ:* Univ Mo, Columbia, BS, 64, MS, 65, PhD(elec eng, statist), 68. *Prof Exp:* Asst prof elec eng, Univ Mo, Columbia, 68-74; scientist, Geometric Data, Div Smithkline Corp, 74-82. *Mem:* Inst Elec & Electronics Engrs; AAAS. *Res:* Communication systems; neural networks; digital signal processing; automatic pattern recognition. *Mailing Add:* Harris Corp GCS Div PO Box 91000 Melbourne FL 32902. *E-Mail:* dtebbe@harris.com

**TEBBENS, SARAH F,** MARINE GEOPHYSICS. *Current Pos:* ASST PROF, UNIV SFLA, 94- *Personal Data:* m 91, Christopher Cramer Barton; c William N & Katherine L. *Educ:* Vassar Col, AB, 87; Columbia Univ, MA, 92, PhD(marine geol & geophys), 94. *Concurrent Pos:* Prin investr, US Geol Surv, 94-97. *Mem:* AAAS; Am Geophys Union; NY Acad Sci; Sigma Xi. *Res:* Plate tectonic evolution with an emphasis on major plate boundary reorganizations, the role of microplates and triple junction migration; probalistic forecasting of tsunami run up; role of estuaries of the geology of the West Florida continental shelf. *Mailing Add:* Univ SFla DMS 140 Seventh Ave S St Petersburg FL 33701. *Fax:* 813-553-3966; *E-Mail:* tebbens@marine.usf.edu

**TEBBS, RICHARD RAY,** TECHNOLOGY IN MATHEMATICS EDUCATION, LEARNING THEORY. *Current Pos:* from asst prof to assoc prof, 65-91, PROF MATH & COMPUT SCI, SOUTHERN UTAH UNIV, 91- *Personal Data:* m 62, Irene Henrie; c Marilyn, Christine, Kathryn, Barbara, Holly, Bruce R, Robert N & Brian R. *Educ:* Brigham Young Univ, BS, 62, MS, 64. *Prof Exp:* Instr math, Brigham Young Univ, 62-65. *Concurrent Pos:* Mathematician, Hercules Powder Co, 62; instr math, Linn-Benton & Lane Community Cols, 70-72; guest consult, Univ Mo, Rolla, 71; res assoc, Univ Ore, 72-75. *Mem:* Math Asn Am (pres, 79-82); Am Math Soc; Nat Coun Teachers Math; Sigma Xi. *Res:* Flow through pouris media and heat transfer. *Mailing Add:* Southern Utah Univ Cedar City UT 84720. *Fax:* 435-865-8051; *E-Mail:* tebbs@suu.edu

**TE BEEST, DAVID ORIEN,** PLANT PATHOLOGY. *Current Pos:* res assoc, 75-78, from asst prof to assoc prof, 78-85, PROF, UNIV ARK, FAYETTEVILLE, 85- *Personal Data:* b Baldwin, Wis, Nov 9, 46; m 72; c 2. *Educ:* Univ Wis-Stevens Point, BS, 68, Univ Wis-Madison, MS, 71, PhD(plant path), 74. *Honors & Awards:* Super Serv in Res, USDA, 90. *Prof Exp:* Res asst plant path, Univ Wis-Madison, 68-74. *Mem:* Am Phytopath Soc; Int Soc Plant Path; Sigma Xi; Am Soc Microbiol. *Res:* Biological control of weeds with plant pathogens; ecological epidemiology; physiology of plant disease. *Mailing Add:* Dept Plant Path Univ Ark 217 Plant Sci Fayetteville AR 72701-1202

**TEBO, HEYL GREMMER,** ANATOMY. *Current Pos:* prof anat, 62-84, chmn gross anat, 78-84, EMER PROF ANAT SCI, UNIV TEX HEALTH SCI CTR, HOUSTON, 84- *Personal Data:* b Atlanta, Ga, Oct 17, 16; m 40, Ruth Davidson. *Educ:* Oglethorpe Univ, AB, 37, MA, 39; Emory Univ, DDS, 47. *Prof Exp:* Instr anat, Oglethorpe Univ, 38-39; teaching fel oral surg & anat, Univ Tex Dent Br Houston, 47-48, instr anat & surg, 48-50; asst prof diag & radiol, Sch Dent, Univ Ala, Birmingham, 50-52; asst chief dent serv, Vet Admin Hosp, Houston, Tex, 52-61. *Concurrent Pos:* Clin assoc prof, Univ Tex Dent Br Houston, 52-61; consult, Vet Admin Hosp, Houston, Tex, 62- *Mem:* Fel AAAS; Am Asn Anat; Int Asn Dent Res; Am Acad Dent Radiol; Am Asn Phys Anthrop. *Res:* Osteology of head; radiographic anatomy; personality characteristics of patients; oral pathology related to radiography of head. *Mailing Add:* 5822 Queensloch Dr Houston TX 77096-3917

**TECHO, ROBERT,** INFORMATION SCIENCE, DATA COMMUNICATIONS. *Current Pos:* assoc prof, 69-74, PROF INFO SYSTS, GA STATE UNIV, 74- *Personal Data:* b New York, NY, Jan 1, 31; m 55; c 3. *Educ:* Ga Inst Technol, BChE, 53, MS, 58, PhD(chem eng), 61. *Prof Exp:* Sr res engr, Eng Exp Sta, Ga Inst Technol 59-65. *Concurrent Pos:* Consult chem eng & comput analysis, 65- *Mem:* Am Chem Soc; Am Inst Chem Eng; Asn Comput Mach. *Res:* Computer applications of engineering problems, including systems analysis for pipeline operations and hydraulic transients; computer science, including teleprocessing information systems, data communications design and computer communication networks. *Mailing Add:* 4 Cristina Lane Hartwell GA 30643

**TECKLENBURG, HARRY,** chemical engineering; deceased, see previous edition for last biography

**TECOTZKY, MELVIN,** INORGANIC CHEMISTRY. *Current Pos:* PVT CONSULT, 91- *Personal Data:* b Chicago, Ill, Feb 17, 24; m 56; c 2. *Educ:* Univ Ill, BS, 48, PhD(chem), 53. *Prof Exp:* Res asst inorg chem, Univ Ill, 51-53, fel, 53-54; res chemist, Diversey Corp, 54-56; sr chemist, W R Grace & Co, 56-59; res chemist & proj leader, FMC Corp, 59-61; staff scientist, Missiles & Space Div, Lockheed Aircraft Corp, Calif, 61-68; dir res, Chem Prod Div, Radium Corp, 68-80; vpres, Optonix Inc, Hackettstown, NJ, 80-84; vpres, Digirad Corp, Palo Alto, Calif, 84-88, consult, AGFA, 88-91. *Mem:* Electrochem Soc; Soc Info Display. *Res:* Rare earths; solid state chemistry; luminescence; chelates; thorium; uranium; sulfides; hydrazine; phosphates; transition elements; electronic materials; magnetic materials; non-aqueous solvents. *Mailing Add:* 27 N Linden Lane Mendham NJ 07945

**TEDESCHI, DAVID HENRY,** PHARMACOLOGY. *Current Pos:* dir biosci res, 78-88, STAFF SCIENTIST BIOSCI, 3M CO, 89- *Personal Data:* b Newark, NJ, Feb 20, 30. *Educ:* Rutgers Univ, BSc, 52; Univ Utah, PhD(pharmacol), 55. *Honors & Awards:* Philemon Hommell Prize Pharmacol, 52; Am Pharmaceut Asn Found Award in Pharmacodynamics, 69. *Prof Exp:* A0st pharmacol, Univ Utah, 52-54; assoc dir pharmacol, Smith Kline & Fr Labs, Pa, 55-68; dir pharmacol, Geigy Pharmaceut, NY, 68-70, dir pharmacol & dep dir biol res, Ciba-Geigy Corp, 70-72; dir cent nerv syst dis ther, Res Sect, Lederle Labs Div, Am Cyanamid Co, 72-77; dir res, Biobasics, 77-78. *Mem:* Am Col Neuropsychopharmacol; Am Soc Pharmacol & Exp Therapeut; Soc Exp Biol & Med; Int Col Neuropsychopharmacol; Int Soc Biochem Pharmacol. *Res:* Neuropsychopharmacology; site and mechanism of action of drugs on central nervous system. *Mailing Add:* 62 Deer Hills Ct North Oaks MN 55127

**TEDESCHI, HENRY,** CELL BIOLOGY. *Current Pos:* chairperson, Dept Biol Sci, 82-85, PROF BIOL, STATE UNIV NY, ALBANY, 65- *Personal Data:* b Novara, Italy, Feb 3, 30; nat US; m 57, Terry L Kershner; c Alexander, Devorah & David. *Educ:* Univ Pittsburgh, BS, 50; Univ Chicago, PhD(physiol), 55. *Prof Exp:* Res assoc & instr, Univ Chicago, 55-57, asst prof, 57-60; from asst prof to assoc prof physiol, Univ Ill Col Med, 60-65. *Concurrent Pos:* NIH sr res fel, Oxford Univ, 71-72. *Mem:* Biophys Soc; Am Soc Cell Biol; Am Physiol Soc; Soc Gen Physiol. *Res:* Cell physiology; structural and functional organization of the cell; intracellular membranes. *Mailing Add:* Dept Biol Sci State Univ NY 1400 Washington Ave Albany NY 12222. *Fax:* 518-442-4761

**TEDESCHI, RALPH EARL,** PHARMACOLOGY. *Current Pos:* RETIRED. *Personal Data:* b Newark, NJ, Nov 20, 27; m 51; c 2. *Educ:* Rutgers Univ, BS, 51; Med Col Va, PhD(pharmacol), 54. *Prof Exp:* Resident pharmacol, Oxford Univ, 54-55; res assoc, Div Metab Res, Jefferson Med Col, 55-56; assoc dir pharmacol, Smith Kline & Fr Labs, 56-69; head, Dept Pharmacol, Wm S Merrell Co, Ohio, 69-71; head dept, Dow Chem Co,\Zionsville, 71-72, dir clin pharmacol, 72-73, dir develop, 73-74, tech asst to dir pharmaceut res & develop, 74-85, tech asst to med dir, Human Health Res & Develop Labs & group dir clin res, Marion-Merrell Dow, 75-93. *Mem:* Am Soc Pharmacol & Exp Therapeut. *Res:* Neuropharmacology; pharmacology of the autonomic nervous system; cardiovascular pharmacology; atherosclerosis. *Mailing Add:* 11507 Applejack Ct Cincinnati OH 45249

**TEDESCHI, ROBERT JAMES,** ORGANIC & ACETYLENE CHEMISTRY, SPECIALTY CHEMICALS. *Current Pos:* PRES, TEDESCHI & ASSOCS, 80- *Personal Data:* b Woodside, NY, July 25, 21; m 52; c 3. *Educ:* Cornell Univ, AB, 44, MS, 45, PhD(org chem), 47. *Prof Exp:* Microanalytical chemist, Wyeth Inst, Pa, 46; res chemist, Calco Chem Div, Am Cyanamid Co, NJ, 47-53; sect head, Cent Res Labs, Air Reduction Co, 53-59, proj leader, Air Prod & Chem Co, 59-64, supvr, Chem Div, Airco Chem & Plastics Div, 64-69, supvr org chem, 69-71, dir res & develop, Acetylenic Chem Div, 71-74, assoc dir res, Air Prod & Chem, Inc, Middlesex, 74-79. *Concurrent Pos:* Invited lectr acetylene chem, USSR Acad Sci, Irbutok, Siberia, 87. *Mem:* Am Chem Soc; fel Am Inst Chem; NY Acad Sci. *Res:* Acetylene chemistry; high pressure synthesis; catalytic reactions; organic chemicals development; industrial applications for acetylenic chemicals; organo metallics; chelates and complexes; corrosion inhibitors; perfumery intermediates; agricultural chemicals; acetylenic surfactants; specialty monomers and polymers. *Mailing Add:* 2F Mar Val Terr Bldg F Winslow ME 04901

**TEDESCO, FRANCIS J,** GASTROENTEROLOGY. *Current Pos:* assoc prof, 78-81, PROF, MED COL GA, 81- *Personal Data:* b Derby, Conn, March 8, 44; m 70, Luann L Ekern; c Jennifer N. *Educ:* Fairfield Univ, BS, 65; St Louis Univ Sch Med, MD, 69. *Honors & Awards:* Eddie Palmer Award Gastrointestinal Endoscopy, 83; Rudolph Schindler Award, 93. *Prof Exp:* Asst instr, Hosp Univ Pa, 71-72; fel gastroenterol, Wash Univ Sch Med, 72-74; asst prof, Wash Univ Sch Med, 74-75; from asst prof to assoc prof, Univ Miami, 75-78, co-dir clin res, 76-78. *Concurrent Pos:* Chief gastroenterol, Med Col Ga, 78-88, actg vpres clin activ, 84, vpres clin activ, 84-88, interim dean, 86-88, pres, 88; gastroenterol spec study sect, NIH, 82- *Mem:* Am Soc Gastrointestinal Endoscopy (treas, 81-84, pres, 85-86); Am Col Physicians; Am Col Gastroenterol; AMA. *Res:* Gastroenterology. *Mailing Add:* Pres Off Med Col Ga Augusta GA 30912-7600

**TEDESCO, THOMAS ALBERT,** HUMAN GENETICS, REPRODUCTION. *Current Pos:* from asst prof to assoc prof, Col Med, Univ SFla, 74-90, dir pediat labs, 85-92, PROF PEDIAT, COL MED, UNIV SFLA, 90-; DIR, MEDIGEME INC, 92- *Personal Data:* b York, Pa, Dec 5, 35. *Educ:* Franklin & Marshall Col, BS, 60; Univ Pa, PhD(biol, genetics), 69. *Prof Exp:* Res technician pediat, Univ Pa, 60-61, res asst, 61-62, res assoc genetics, 62-65, from instr to asst prof pediat, Sch Med, 65-72, asst prof pediat & med genetics, 72-74; dir, Embryol & Andrology Labs, IVF/GIFT Prog, Univ S Fla/Humana Womens Hosp, Tampa, Fla, 85-91. *Concurrent Pos:* Prin investr, NIH grant; prog dir, Nat Found-March Dimes Med Serv grant; co-dir, Regional Genetics Prog, Childrens Med Serv, Dept Health & Rehab Serv, State Fla. *Mem:* NY Acad Sci; AAAS; Am Soc Human Genetics; Am Chem Soc; Am Genetics Asn; Am Fertil Soc. *Res:* Inborn errors in metabolism; early embryonic development; prenatal and preimplantation genetic diagnosis. *Mailing Add:* Dept Pediat Univ SFla Col Med 12901 Bruce B Downs Tampa FL 33612-4742. *Fax:* 813-971-2427

**TEDESKO, ANTON,** structural & civil engineering; deceased, see previous edition for last biography

**TEDFORD, RICHARD HALL,** VERTEBRATE PALEONTOLOGY, STRATIGRAPHY. *Current Pos:* assoc cur vert paleont, 66-69, CUR VERT PALEONT, AM MUS NATURAL HIST, 69-, CHMN DEPT, 77- *Personal Data:* b Los Angeles, Calif, Apr 25, 29; m 54. *Educ:* Univ Calif, Los Angeles, BS, 51; Univ Calif, Berkeley, PhD(paleont), 60. *Prof Exp:* Instr geol, Univ Calif, Riverside, 59-60, lectr, 60-61, from asst prof to assoc prof, 61-66. *Mem:* Australian Mammal Soc; Soc Vert Paleont; Paleont Soc; Am Soc Mammal; Sigma Xi. *Res:* Phylogeny, geographic distribution and paleoecology of Carnivora, Marsupials and other mammals; stratigraphy and chronology of Cenozoic rocks. *Mailing Add:* Dept Vert Paleont Am Mus Nat Hist Central Park W & 79th St New York NY 10024

**TEDLOCK, DENNIS,** ANTHROPOLOGY. *Current Pos:* JAMES H MCNULTY PROF, DEPT ENG, STATE UNIV NY, BUFFALO, 87- *Personal Data:* b St Joseph, Mo, June 19, 39. *Educ:* Univ NMex, BA, 61; Tulane Univ, PhD(anthrop), 68. *Honors & Awards:* Victor Turner Prize, 91. *Prof Exp:* Asst prof anthrop, Iowa State Univ, 66-67; asst prof rhetoric, Univ Calif, Berkeley, 67-69; res assoc, Sch Am Res, 69-70; asst prof anthrop, Brooklyn Col, 70-71; asst prof, Yale Univ, 72-73; assoc univ prof anthrop & relig, Boston Univ, 73-82. *Concurrent Pos:* Vis asst prof, Wesleyan Univ, 71-72; adj prof, Univ NMex, 80-81; mem, Inst Advan Study, 86-87; Guggenheim fel, 86. *Res:* Anthropology; literature; religion. *Mailing Add:* State Univ NY Buffalo Clemens Hall Buffalo NY 14260-0001

**TEDMON, CRAIG SEWARD, JR,** METALLURGY, ELECTROCHEMISTRY. *Current Pos:* HEAD, CORP RES & DEVELOP, ASEA BROWN BOVER CO, GENEVA, 94- *Personal Data:* b Pueblo, Colo, Jan 19, 39; m 59; c 3. *Educ:* Mass Inst Technol, SB, 61, MS, 62, ScD(metall), 64. *Prof Exp:* Instr metall, Mass Inst Technol, 63-64; res metallurgist, Gen Elec Co, 64-70, mgr, Surfaces & Reactions Br, Gen Elec Res & Develop Ctr, 70-94. *Concurrent Pos:* Mem adj staff, Union Col NY, 66- *Mem:* AAAS; Electrochem Soc; Am Soc Metals; Am Inst Mining, Metall & Petrol Engrs; Brit Inst Metals. *Res:* Metallurgy of high-field superconductors; high-temperature oxidation; diffusion in metals and oxides; high temperature electrochemistry. *Mailing Add:* ABB Ltd PO Box 8131 Zurich 8050 Switzerland

**TEDROW, JOHN CHARLES FREMONT,** SOILS. *Current Pos:* from instr to prof, 47-84, EMER PROF SOILS, RUTGERS UNIV, NEW BRUNSWICK, 84- *Personal Data:* b Rockwood, Pa, Apr 21, 17; m 43; c 2. *Educ:* Pa State Univ, BS, 39; Mich State Univ, MS, 40; Rutgers Univ, PhD, 50. *Honors & Awards:* Antarctic Serv Medal. *Prof Exp:* Jr soil surveyor, Soil Conserv Serv, USDA, 41, soil scientist, 46-47. *Concurrent Pos:* Sr pedologist, Arctic Soil Invests, 53; consult indust & govt; prin investr, Arctic Inst NAm, 55-67; Antarctic pedologic investr, NSF, 61-63; ed-in-chief, Soil Sci, 69-79; Lindback res award, Rutgers Univ. *Mem:* Fel Soil Sci Soc Am; Am Arbit Asn; Am Geophys Union; fel Am Soc Agron; Sigma Xi; fel Arctic Inst NAm. *Res:* Soil morphology; genesis and survey; soils of the Arctic and Alpine regions. *Mailing Add:* 5 Bluebird Ct Edison NJ 08820

**TEDROW, PAUL M,** ELECTRON TUNNELING. *Current Pos:* RES SCIENTIST, NAT MAGNET LAB, MASS INST TECHNOL, 67- *Personal Data:* b Ware, Mass, 1940; m 70, Prabha Kumbhare; c Usha, Paul & John. *Educ:* Mass Inst Technol, BS, 61; Cornell Univ, PhD(physics), 66. *Mem:* Fel Am Phys Soc. *Res:* Experimental study of superconducting and magnetic thin films in intense magnetic fields; low temperature physics. *Mailing Add:* Mass Inst Technol Rm NW14-3107 77 Massachusetts Ave Cambridge MA 02139. *Fax:* 617-253-5405; *E-Mail:* tedrow@slipknot.mit.edu

**TEEBOR, GEORGE WILLIAM,** CARCINOGENESIS, DNA REPAIR MECHANISMS. *Current Pos:* PROF PATH, NY UNIV MED CTR, 65- *Personal Data:* b Vienna, Austria, July 22, 35; US citizen; m 58; c 3. *Educ:* Yale Univ, BS, 56; Yeshiva Univ, MD, 61. *Concurrent Pos:* Merit Award, NCI-NIH, 88. *Mem:* Am Asn Cancer Res; Am Asn Pathologists; Am Chem Soc; Radiation Res Soc. *Res:* Mammalian DNA repair enzymology; characterization of DNA damage. *Mailing Add:* NY Univ Sch Med 550 First Ave New York NY 10016-6481

**TEEGARDEN, BONNARD JOHN,** ASTROPHYSICS. *Current Pos:* PHYSICIST ASTROPHYS, NASA GODDARD SPACE FLIGHT CTR, 63- *Personal Data:* b Elizabeth, NJ, Aug 23, 40; m 62; c 2. *Educ:* Mass Inst Technol, BS, 62; Univ Md, PhD(physics), 67. *Mem:* Am Phys Soc; Am Astron Soc. *Res:* Gamma-ray astronomy. *Mailing Add:* NASA Goddard Space Flight Ctr Code 661 Greenbelt MD 20771

**TEEGARDEN, DAVID MORRISON,** MONOMER & POLYMER SYNTHESIS. *Current Pos:* RES ASSOC, EASTMAN KODAK CO, 86- *Personal Data:* b Dayton, Ohio, Jan 10, 41; m 66; c 3. *Educ:* Ohio Wesleyan Univ, AB, 63; Univ Mich, MS, 65, PhD(org chem), 72. *Prof Exp:* Asst prof chem, Univ Wis, Platteville, 69-73; from asst prof to prof chem, John Fisher Col, 73-86; mem res staff, Xerox Webster Res Ctr, 80-82. *Concurrent Pos:* Fel, Xerox Webster Res Ctr, 79-80. *Mem:* Am Chem Soc. *Res:* Synthesis and characterization of functional monomers and polymers; polymer blends; polymer coatings. *Mailing Add:* 159 Village Lane Rochester NY 14610. *E-Mail:* 125770@ovmail.kodak.com

**TEEGARDEN, KENNETH JAMES,** PHYSICS. *Current Pos:* Res assoc, Univ Rochester, 54-58, asst prof, 58-59, sr res assoc, 60-61, assoc prof, 61-66, PROF OPTICS, INST OPTICS, UNIV ROCHESTER, 66-, DIR, INST OPTICS, 81-, DIR, CTR ADV OPTICAL TECHNOL, 83- *Personal Data:* b Chicago, Ill, May 13, 28; m 59. *Educ:* Univ Chicago, AB, 47, BS, 50; Univ Ill, MS, 51, PhD, 54. *Concurrent Pos:* Alfred P Sloan Found fel, Univ Rochester, 59-63. *Mem:* Fel Am Phys Soc; fel Optical Soc Am. *Res:* Electronic properties of ionic solids and the solid rare gases. *Mailing Add:* 82 Westland Ave Rochester NY 14618

**TEEGUARDEN, DENNIS EARL,** FORESTRY ECONOMICS. *Current Pos:* asst specialist, Agr Exp Sta, Univ Calif, Berkeley, 58-63, actg asst prof, Sch Forestry, 63, from asst prof to assoc prof, 64-73, chmn, Dept Forestry & Resource Mgt, 78-86, actg dir, Forest Prod Lab, 87-88, prof, Sch Forestry, 73-93, assoc dean acad affairs, Col Nat Resources, 90-93, EMER PROF FORESTRY, UNIV CALIF, BERKELEY, 93- *Personal Data:* b Gary, Ind, Aug 21, 31; m 54; c 3. *Educ:* Mich Tech Univ, BS, 53; Univ Calif, Berkeley, MF, 58, PhD(agr econ), 64. *Prof Exp:* Res asst, Pac Southwest Forest & Range Exp Sta, US Forest Serv, Berkeley, Calif, 57. *Mem:* Fel Soc Am Foresters. *Res:* Application of operations research techniques to problems of resource allocation in public and private forestry enterprises. *Mailing Add:* 145 Mulford Hall Univ Calif Berkeley CA 94720-3114

**TEEKELL, ROGER ALTON,** METABOLISM, BIOCHEMISTRY. *Current Pos:* head, Dept Poultry Sci, Va Polytech Inst & State Univ, Blacksburg, 76-79, assoc dean to dean, Grad Sch, 79-82 & 79-90, PROF POULTRY SCI, VA POLYTECH INST & STATE UNIV, BLACKSBURG, 90- *Personal Data:* b Elmer, La, Mar 3, 30; m 53; c 4. *Educ:* La State Univ, BS, 51, MS, 55, PhD(nutrit, biochem), 58. *Prof Exp:* Asst, La State Univ, 54-58; res scientist, Agr Res Lab, Univ Tenn-AEC, 58-61; res chemist, Dow Chem Co, Tex, 61-63; from assoc prof to prof physiol, La State Univ, Baton Rouge, 63-67, prof poultry sci, 67-76. *Mem:* Am Inst Biol Sci; Sigma Xi; Poultry Sci Asn; World Poultry Sci Asn. *Res:* Intermediary metabolism of amino acids and lipids using labeled compounds. *Mailing Add:* Poultry Sci Dept La State Univ Baton Rouge Baton Rouge LA 70803-0001

**TEELE, THURSTON FERDINAND,** ECONOMICS. *Current Pos:* PRES & CHIEF EXEC OFFICER, CHEMONICS INT, 75- *Personal Data:* b New Rochelle, NY, Mar 27, 34; m, Barbara Mangrum Carmichael; c Edward B, Stacia L, Kristy A & Allen F. *Educ:* Amhurst Col, BA, 56; Tufts Univ, MA, 62; Georgetown Univ, PhD, 64. *Prof Exp:* Foreign serv officer, US Dept State, 56-64; consult economist & chief party, Checchi Co, 64-75. *Concurrent Pos:* Vchmn, Prof Serv Coun, AID Task Force, 92. *Mailing Add:* 2231 Q St NW Washington DC 20008-2825

**TEER, FAYE P,** BUSINESS, INFORMATION SYSTEMS. *Current Pos:* from asst prof to assoc prof, 86-96, asst dean, Col Bus, 89-92, PROF INFO SYSTS, JAMES MADISON UNIV, 96- *Educ:* Southern La Univ, BA, 69; Loyola Univ, New Orleans, MEd, 73; La Tech Univ, DBA, 85. *Prof Exp:* Bus teacher, Chalmette High Sch, 69-73, Pelahatchie High Sch, 73-74; prog head & instr, Manpower Training & Develop Act, 74-76; instr, Hinds Jr Col, 76-78; from asst prof to assoc prof, Ft Lewis Col, Colo, 81-86. *Concurrent Pos:* Dept chairperson, Voc Bus & Off, Hinds Jr Co, Miss, 77-78. *Mem:* Asn Info Systs; Am Asn Artificial Intel; Int Bus Schs Comput Asn. *Mailing Add:* Info & Decision Sci Dept James Madison Univ Harrisonburg VA 22807

**TEER, JAMES G,** ZOOLOGY. *Current Pos:* DIR, WELDER WILDLIFE FOUND. *Honors & Awards:* Aldo Leopold Mem Award, Wildlife Soc, 94. *Mailing Add:* Welder Wildlife Found PO Box 1400 Sinton TX 78387

**TEERI, JAMES ARTHUR,** ECOLOGY, POLAR BIOLOGY. *Current Pos:* DIR, CHASE SANBORN PRESERVE, UNIV MICH, ANN ARBOR, 87-, BIOSTA, 87-, GLOBAL CHANGE PROJ, 92- *Personal Data:* b Exeter, NH, Feb 28, 44; m 67. *Educ:* Univ NH, BS, MS, 68; Duke Univ, PhD(bot), 72. *Prof Exp:* Asst prof biol, Univ Chicago, 72-88, chmn evolution prog, 79-86, assoc dean, 82-85, chmn, Biol Dept, 85-87. *Concurrent Pos:* Assoc ed, Paleobiol, 74-; mem, Comn Optical Radiation Measurement, 74; actg chmn, Comt Evolution Biol, 78. *Mem:* Fel AAAS; Sigma Xi; Ecol Soc Am; Am Inst Biol Sci; Arctic Inst NAm. *Res:* Evolution of plant growth responses to environmental fluctuation; evolutionary biology. *Mailing Add:* 1911 Mershion Dr Ann Arbor MI 48103

**TEETER, JAMES WALLIS,** MICROPALEONTOLOGY, PALEOECOLOGY. *Current Pos:* From asst prof to prof, 65-94, EMER PROF GEOL, UNIV AKRON, 94- *Personal Data:* b Hamilton, Ont, Mar 14, 37; m 60; c 3. *Educ:* McMaster Univ, BSc, 60, MSc, 62; Rice Univ, PhD(paleont), 66. *Concurrent Pos:* Fac res grants, Univ Akron, 69, 73, 74, 78 & 83. *Mem:* Paleont Soc; Sigma Xi; Geol Soc Am; Int Oceanog Found; Soc Econ Paleont & Mineral. *Res:* Post Pleistocene depositional history, San Salvador Island, Bahamas; Key Largo limestone facies; Ordovician Nautiloid touchmarks; Ostracoda and environments of Caloosahatchee Formation; living Pelecypod behavior; marine Ostracoda dispersal. *Mailing Add:* Dept Geol Univ Akron 302 Buchtel Common Akron OH 44325-4101

**TEETER, MARTHA MARY,** PROTEIN CRYSTALLOGRAPHY, BIOPHYSICS. *Current Pos:* vis asst prof phys chem, Dept Chem, Boston Univ, 77-78, instr life sci chem, 78-80, res asst prof, 80-86, ASSOC PROF, DEPT CHEM, BOSTON COL, 86- *Personal Data:* b Boston, Mass, Oct 15, 44; m 88, Curtis J DuRand; c 2. *Educ:* Wellesley Col, BA, 66; Pa State Univ, PhD(inorg chem), 73. *Prof Exp:* Res scientist, Rohm & Haas, 73-74; Nat Cancer Inst fel, Dept Biol, Mass Inst Technol, 74-76, Naval Res Lab, 76-77. *Concurrent Pos:* Vis scientist, Dept Biol, Mass Inst Technol, 77-86. *Mem:* Am Chem Soc; Am Crystallog Asn; Biophys Soc; AAAS; Protein Soc. *Res:* High resolution protein crystal structure determination (x-ray and neutron) as well as molecular dynamics; protein structure; water structure around proteins; molecular modeling; membrane-active plant toxins. *Mailing Add:* Dept Chem Boston Col Chestnut Hill MA 02167. *Fax:* 617-552-2705

**TEETER, RICHARD MALCOLM,** MASS SPECTROMETRY. *Current Pos:* RETIRED. *Personal Data:* b Berkeley, Calif, Feb 24, 26; div; c 2. *Educ:* Univ Calif, BS, 49; Univ Wash, PhD(chem), 54. *Prof Exp:* From res chemist to sr res chemist, Chevron Res Co, 54-68, sr res assoc, 68-86. *Concurrent Pos:* Pres, PCMASPEC, owner, 89- *Mem:* Am Chem Soc; Am Soc Mass Spectrometry. *Res:* Analytical mass spectrometry; preparation of derivatives to aid analysis; reaction mechanisms in mass spectrometry; application of computers to mass spectrometry. *Mailing Add:* 1925 Cactus Ct No 2 Walnut Creek CA 94595

**TEETERS, NANCY HAYS,** ECONOMICS. *Current Pos:* TRUSTEE & BD DIRS, PRUDENTIAL MUTUAL FUNDS, 85- *Personal Data:* b Marion, Ind, July 29, 30; m 52, Robert Duane; c Ann, James & John. *Educ:* Oberlin Col, AB, 52; Univ Mich, MA, 54. *Hon Degrees:* LLD, Oberlin Col, 79, Bates Col, 81, Univ Mich, 83, Mt Holyoke Col, 83. *Prof Exp:* Teaching fel, Univ Mich, 54-55, postgrad & instr, 56-57; instr, Univ Md Overseas, Ger, 55-56; staff economist, Govt Finance Sect, Bd Gov Fed Res Syst, 57-66, mem bd, 78-84; economist, Coun Econ Adv, 62-63, Bur Budget, 66-70; sr fel, Brookings Inst, 70-73; sr specialist, Cong Res Serv, Libr Cong, 73-74; asst dir & chief economist, House Reps Comt Budget, 74-78; vpres & chief economist, IBM, 84-90. *Concurrent Pos:* Bd dirs, Inland Steel Industs. *Mem:* Nat Economists Club (vpres, 73-74, pres, 74-75); Am Econ Asn. *Res:* Contributed various articles to professional publications. *Mailing Add:* 243 Willowbrook Ave Stamford CT 06902-7020

**TEGGE, B(RUCE) R(OBERT),** CHEMICAL ENGINEERING. *Current Pos:* RETIRED. *Personal Data:* b Haddon Heights, NJ, May 31, 17; m 40; c Judith (Printillo), Bruce R Jr, William L & Susan (Browne). *Educ:* Pa State Univ, BS, 38, MS, 40, PhD(chem eng), 42. *Prof Exp:* Asst petrol ref, Pa State Col, 40; sr eng assoc, Exxon Res & Eng Co, 42-86. *Mem:* Am Textile Inst; Am Inst Chem Engrs; Am Chem Soc; Soc Plastics Engrs. *Res:* Equilibrium relationships between sulfur dioxide and pure binary hydrocarbon mixtures; performance of solvent extraction equipment; butyl rubber; paraxylene; petroleum resins; synthetic polymer plants; polypropylene; synthetic textile fibers; synthetic fertilizers; organic fungicides; polyesters; mastics and polyisobutylenes; detergents. *Mailing Add:* 68 Prospect St Madison NJ 07940-2642

**TEGGINS, JOHN E,** INORGANIC CHEMISTRY, CHEMISTRY FOR DISABLED STUDENTS. *Current Pos:* from asst prof to assoc prof, 66-75, PROF CHEM, AUBURN UNIV, MONTGOMERY, 75-, HEAD DEPT, 81- *Personal Data:* b Wallasey, Eng, Jan 6, 37; m 60; c 3. *Educ:* Univ Sheffield, BSc, 58; Boston Univ, AM, 60, PhD(chem), 65. *Prof Exp:* Res chemist, Courtaulds Can, Ltd, 60-62; res assoc radiochem, Iowa State Univ, 65-66, Liverpool Univ, 83. *Mem:* Am Chem Soc; sr mem Chem Inst Can. *Res:* Determination of thermodynamic and kinetic data for coordination complexes in aqueous solution; accessible laboratories for disabled. *Mailing Add:* 4425 Shamrock Lane Montgomery AL 36106-3534

**TEGNER, MIA JEAN,** ZOOLOGY. *Current Pos:* Res asst develop biol, 71-74, RES BIOLOGIST MARINE BIOL, SCRIPPS INST OCEANOG, UNIV CALIF, SAN DIEGO, 74- *Personal Data:* b Santa Monica, Calif, July 7, 47; m 80; c 1. *Educ:* Univ Calif, San Diego, BA, 69, PhD(marine biol), 74. *Concurrent Pos:* Researcher, Sea Grant, 74-, Develop Multispecies Mgt Kelp Bed Resources, 77-81 & Exp Abalone Enhancement Prog, 77-87; chairperson, Joint Univ Calif Sea Grant Col & Calif Dept Fish & Game Exp Abalone Enhancement Prog, 77-81. *Mem:* AAAS; Am Soc Limnol & Oceanog; Am Soc Zoologists. *Res:* Kelp forest community ecology; living marine resources of the nearshore environment; how man's activities have affected the structure and dynamics of this community. *Mailing Add:* Scripps Inst Oceanog Univ Calif San Diego 9500 Gilman Dr La Jolla CA 92093-0201

**TEGTMEYER, CHARLES JOHN,** angiography & interventional radiology; deceased, see previous edition for last biography

**TEH, HUNG-SIA,** IMMUNOLOGY. *Current Pos:* from asst prof to assoc prof, 77-90, actg dir, Biomed Res Ctr, 92-94, PROF MICROBIOL, UNIV BC, VANCOUVER, 90- *Personal Data:* b Telok Intan, Malaysia, Oct 2, 45; Can citizen; m 69, Soo-Jeet Chai; c Siow-Ping & Sun-Kai. *Educ:* Univ Alta, BSc, 69, PhD(biochem), 75. *Prof Exp:* Res fel immunol, Ont Cancer Inst, Toronto, 75-77. *Concurrent Pos:* Mem, Basel Inst Immunol, 81-82; counr, Can Soc Immunol, 85-88; vis scientist, Basel Inst Immunol, 88. *Mem:* Can Soc Immunol; Am Asn Immunologists. *Res:* Cellular immunology; transgenic mice; T cell development; T cell tolerance; T cell activation. *Mailing Add:* Dept Microbiol & Immunol Univ BC 6174 University Blvd Rm 300 Vancouver BC V6T 1Z3 Can. *Fax:* 604-822-6041

**TEH, THIAN HOR,** GOAT, CASHMERE MEAT & MOHAIR. *Current Pos:* DIR & RES PROF, LANGSTON UNIV, 90- *Personal Data:* b Kelang, Malaysia, Sept 29, 53; US citizen; m 80, Valerie D Barrett; c Jelena M & Telena P. *Educ:* Berea Col, BS, 76; Univ Ky, MS, 79; PhD(animal sci), 82. *Prof Exp:* Res scientist, Prairie View A&M Univ, 82-87, res leader, 87-90. *Concurrent Pos:* Consult, Int Agr Consults, 93-; adj prof, Okla State Univ, 93- *Mem:* Int Goat Asn; Am Dairy Sci Asn; Am Soc Animal Sci; Int Dairy Fedn; Am Registry Prof Animal Scientists; Coun Agr Sci & Technol. *Res:* Nutrition and management of dairy, cashmere, angora and meat type goats; investigation on nutrient requirements of goats; physiological control of fiber growth; nutritional influence on milk production, growth and fiber quantity and quality. *Mailing Add:* 5709 Parkhurst Rd Edmond OK 73034

**TEHON, STEPHEN WHITTIER,** PIEZOELECTRICITY. *Current Pos:* STAFF SCIENTIST, GMK CONSULT SERV, 87- *Personal Data:* b Shenandoah, Iowa, Oct 20, 20; m 42, Betty I Albright; c 5. *Educ:* Univ Ill, BS, 42, MS, 47, PhD(elec eng), 58. *Prof Exp:* Sr engr, Curtiss-Wright Corp, 47; instr elec eng, Univ Ill, 47-52; engr, Electronics Lab, Gen Elec Co, 52-60, consult engr, 60-66; res elec engr, Res Lab, Tecumseh Prod Co, 66-67; consult scientist, Gen Elec Co, 67-80, prin staff scientist, Electronics Lab, 80-87. *Concurrent Pos:* Adj prof, Univ Mich, 66-67 & Syracuse Univ, 76-; vis prof, Clarkson Col Technol, Potsdam, NY, 79. *Mem:* Fel Inst Elec & Electronics Engrs; Acoust Soc Am; Sigma Xi. *Res:* Ultrasonic transducers; nondestructive testing; ultrasonic medical imaging; digital sensors. *Mailing Add:* 6056 Pine Grove Rd Cicero NY 13039

**TEICH, MALVIN CARL,** QUANTUM OPTICS, PHOTONICS. *Current Pos:* PROF, DEPT ELEC & COMPUT ENG, BIOMED ENG, COGNITIVE & NEURAL SYSTS, BOSTON UNIV, 95-; EMER PROF ENG SCI, COLUMBIA UNIV, 96- *Personal Data:* b New York, NY, May 4, 39. *Educ:* Mass Inst Technol, SB, 61; Stanford Univ, MS, 62; Cornell Univ, PhD(quantum electronics), 66. *Honors & Awards:* Browder J Thompson Mem Prize Award, Inst Elec & Electronics Engrs, 69, Morris E Leeds Award, 97; John Simon Guggenheim Award, 73; Inst Sci Info Citation Classic Award, 81; Mem Gold Medal, Palacky Univ, Czech Repub, 92. *Prof Exp:* Res scientist, Lincoln Lab, Mass Inst Technol, 66-67; prof eng sci, Columbia Univ, 67-96, mem, Radiation Lab, 77-96, chmn, Dept Elec Eng & Comput Sci, 78-80. *Mem:* Fel Am Phys Soc; fel Inst Elec & Electronics Engrs; fel Optical Soc Am; fel Acoust Soc Am; fel AAAS; Asn Res Otolaryngol; Sigma Xi. *Res:* Quantum imaging; photonics; fractal point processes; information transmission in biological sensory systems; co-author of book on photonics. *Mailing Add:* Dept Elec Comput Eng Boston Univ Boston MA 02215. *Fax:* 212-932-9421; *E-Mail:* mct2@columbia.edu

**TEICHBERG, SAUL,** EPITHELIAL CELL BIOLOGY, GASTROINTESTINAL STRUCTURE. *Current Pos:* instr, Med Col, Cornell Univ, 73-76, asst prof pediat, 76-83, assoc prof clin pediat, 83-86, ASSOC PROF CELL BIOL PEDIAT, MED COL, CORNELL UNIV, 86-; HEAD, ELECTRON MICROSCOPE LAB, NORTH SHORE UNIV MED COL, 73- *Personal Data:* b New York, NY, Apr 19, 38; m 79, Lora Weiselberg; c Lisa, Glenn & Jonathan. *Educ:* City Col NY, BS, 67; Columbia Univ, PhD(biol), 72. *Prof Exp:* NIMH trainee, Albert Einstein Col Med, 72-73. *Mem:* Am Soc Cell Biol; Histochem Soc; Am Inst Nutrit; Soc Exp Biol & Med; AAAS. *Res:* Structure of small intestine epithelium in relation to absorptive-secretory functions; development and maintenance of the intestinal antigen barrier. *Mailing Add:* North Shore Univ Hosp Manhasset NY 11030. *E-Mail:* sault@nshs.edu

**TEICHER, HARRY,** FOOD SCIENCE & TECHNOLOGY. *Current Pos:* PRIN, TEICHER CONSULT SERV, 92- *Personal Data:* b Middle Village, NY, Jan 11, 27; m 51, Charlotte Leavy; c 3. *Educ:* Queens Col, NY, BS, 48; Syracuse Univ, MS, 50, PhD(chem), 53. *Prof Exp:* Asst chem, Syracuse Univ, 49-53; res chemist, Monsanto Co, 53-56, res group leader, 56-81, res mgr, Res & Develop Dept, 81-85, tech serv mgr, 86-88, mkt tech serv prin, 88-92. *Mem:* Am Chem Soc; Sigma Xi; Am Asn Cereal Chemists; Inst Food Technol. *Res:* Silica; food technology; consulting on applications of phosphates in food industry; use of sorbates for food preservation. *Mailing Add:* Teicher Consult Serv 9512 Laguna Dr St Louis MO 63132

**TEICHER, HENRY,** MATHEMATICAL STATISTICS, PROBABILITY. *Current Pos:* PROF MATH STATIST, RUTGERS UNIV, NEW BRUNSWICK, 68- *Personal Data:* b Jersey City, NJ, July 9, 22; m, Anne Severin; c Rikke. *Educ:* Univ Iowa, BA, 46; Columbia Univ, MA, 47, PhD(math statist), 50. *Prof Exp:* Asst prof math, Univ Del, 50-51; from asst prof to prof math statist, Purdue Univ, 51-67; vis prof, Columbia Univ, 67-68. *Concurrent Pos:* Vis asst prof, Stanford Univ, 55-56; vis assoc prof & mem inst math sci, NY Univ, 60-61. *Mem:* Am Math Soc; fel Inst Math Statist. *Res:* Probability and mathematical statistics, especially stopping rules, limit distributions and mixtures of distributions; law of the iterated logarithms. *Mailing Add:* Dept Statist Rutgers Univ New Brunswick NJ 08903-2101

**TEICHER, JOSEPH D,** psychiatry, for more information see previous edition

**TEICHERT, CURT,** GEOLOGY, PALEONTOLOGY. *Current Pos:* ADJ PROF GEOL SCI, UNIV ROCHESTER, 77- *Personal Data:* b Koenigsberg, Prussia, May 8, 05; m 28. *Educ:* Univ Koenigsberg, PhD(geol), 28; Univ Western Australia, DSc, 44. *Honors & Awards:* David Syme Prize, Univ Melbourne, 49; Raymond Cecil Moore Medal, Soc Econ Paleontologists & Mineralogists, 82; Paleont Soc Medal, 84. *Prof Exp:* Asst, Freiburg Univ, 27-29; Rockefeller fel geol, 30; res fel, Univ Copenhagen, 33-37; res lectr, Univ Western Australia, 37-46; asst chief govt geologist, Victoria Mines Dept, 46-47; sr lectr, Univ Melbourne, 47-53; prof geol, NMex Inst Mining & Technol, 53-54; geologist, US Geol Surv, 54-64, chief petrol geol lab, 54-58, staff geologist, 58-61, geol adv, US AID, Pakistan, 61-64; regents distinguished prof geol, Univ Kans, 64-75. *Concurrent Pos:* Fulbright traveling scholar, 51-52; guest prof, Univs Gottingen, Bonn & Freiburg, 58, Univ Tex, 61 & Free Univ Berlin, 74; consult, Caltex, 40-41, Stand Vacuum, 48-50, Australian Bur Mineral Resources, 48-51 & Shell Oil Co, 53-54; mem, Danish Exped, Greenland, 31-32; US coordr, Cento Treaty Orgn Stratig Working Group, 63-76. *Mem:* Fel Geol Soc Am; fel AAAS; Paleont Soc (pres, 71-72); hon corresp Australian Geol Soc (secy, 51-53); Am Asn Petrol Geol; Int Paleont Asn (pres, 76-80); Sigma Xi; hon fel Geol Soc London; hon mem Geol Soc Belg; hon mem Royal Soc Western Australia; Soc Econ Paleontologists & Mineralogists; foreign assoc Geol Soc France; foreign mem Danish Acad Sci; hon mem Ger Paleont Soc; foreign corresp Senckenberg

Natural Sci Soc; foreign corresp Paleont Soc India. *Res:* Paleozoic stratigraphy and paleontology; stratigraphy of southwestern Asia; ancient and modern coral reefs; fossil cephalopods; sedimentation; paleoecology. *Mailing Add:* 737 Highland Ave Rochester NY 14620

**TEICHLER ZALLEN, DORIS,** HUMAN GENETICS, BIOETHICS. *Current Pos:* assoc prof humanities, 83-90, assoc prof, 90-97, PROF, SCI STUDIES & HUMANITIES, VA POLYTECH INST & STATE UNIV, 97- *Personal Data:* b Brooklyn, NY, Mar 7, 41; m 64, Richard; c Jennifer & Avram. *Educ:* Brooklyn Col, BS, 61; Harvard Univ, AM, 63, PhD(biol), 66. *Honors & Awards:* Prog Excellence Award, Choices & Challenges Proj, Nat Univ Continuing Educ Asn, 88. *Prof Exp:* NIH fel biol, Univ Rochester, 66-69, asst prof, 69-70; asst prof, Nazareth Col, Rochester, 77-83. *Concurrent Pos:* Asst prof biol, Univ Rochester, 74, res fel pediat, Genetics Div, Sch Med, 77-83; interim assoc dir, Ctr Progs in Humanities, Va Polytech Inst & State Univ, 86-87, dir, Choices & Challenges Proj, 84-, adj biochem & nutrit, 88-; mem, Subcomt Human Gene Ther, NIH, 89-91; acad vis, Imp Col Sci, Technol & Med, London, 91; hon res fel, Wellcome Inst Hist Med, London, 91. *Mem:* AAAS; Am Soc Human Genetics; Sigma Xi; Hist Sci Soc. *Res:* Development of new methods of prenatal detection of genetic disorders; genetic and biomedical basis of chloroplast development; social and ethical issues arising in genetic and reproductive technologies; history of genetics. *Mailing Add:* 233 Lane Hall Va Polytech Inst & State Univ Blacksburg VA 24061-0227. *Fax:* 540-231-7013; *E-Mail:* dtzallen@vt.edu

**TEICHMANN, THEODOR,** applied physics, for more information see previous edition

**TEICHOLZ, PAUL M,** CIVIL ENGINEERING. *Current Pos:* PROF CIVIL ENG, STANFORD UNIV, CALIF, 88-, DIR, CTR INTEGRATED FACIL ENG, 88- *Personal Data:* b New York, NY, May 24, 37; m 59, Susan Swire; c Marc, Nina & Leslie. *Educ:* Cornell Univ, BS, 59; Stanford Univ, MCE, 60, PhD, 63. *Prof Exp:* Consult partner, Jacobs Assocs, San Francisco, 63-68; dir mgt info syst & strategic planning, Guy F Atkinson, Co, South San Francisco, 68-88. *Concurrent Pos:* Dir develop, Col Prep Sch, Oakland, Calif, 85-90; regist prof civil engr, Calif. *Mem:* Am Soc Civil Engrs; Optical Res Soc Am. *Res:* Civil engineering. *Mailing Add:* Stanford Univ Ctr Integrated Facil Eng Terman Eng Ctr Stanford CA 94305-4020

**TEICHROEW, DANIEL,** MATHEMATICS. *Current Pos:* chmn dept, 68-73, PROF INDUST ENG, UNIV MICH, ANN ARBOR, 68-; PRES, ISDOS, INC, 83- *Personal Data:* b Can, Jan 5, 25; nat US; m 50; c 1. *Educ:* Univ Toronto, BA, 48, MA, 49; Univ NC, PhD(statist), 53. *Prof Exp:* Res assoc, Univ NC, 51-52; mathematician, Nat Bur Stand, DC & Inst Numerical Analysis, Univ Calif, Los Angeles, 52-55; sr electronics appln specialist, Nat Cash Register Co, 55, spec rep prod develop, 55-56, head bus systs analysis, 56-57; from assoc prof to prof mgt, Grad Sch Bus, Stanford Univ, 57-64; prof orgn sci & head div, Case Western Res Univ, 64-68. *Concurrent Pos:* Lectr, Sch Bus Admin, Univ Southern Calif, 56-57; ed sci & bus appln sect, Commun, Asn Comput Mach, 63- *Mem:* Asn Comput Mach; Inst Mgt Sci (vpres, 67-); Opers Res Soc Am; Inst Math Statist; Am Math Soc; Soc Mgt Info Systs (pres, 76). *Res:* Development and application of scientific techniques to organizational problems, particularly operations research, management science and computer techniques; computer-aided tools and techniques for system development and software engineering; problem statement languages and analyzers. *Mailing Add:* Dept Indust Eng Univ Mich 110 IOE Bldg Ann Arbor MI 48109

**TEIGER, MARTIN,** PHYSICS, ASTRONOMY. *Current Pos:* from asst prof to assoc prof, 66-75, chmn dept, 69-79, PROF PHYSICS, LONG ISLAND UNIV, 75- *Personal Data:* b New York, Dec 30, 36; m 64; c 1. *Educ:* Columbia Univ, AB, 58, MA, 60, PhD(physics), 65. *Prof Exp:* Lectr physics, City Col New York, 61-65, instr, 65-66. *Mem:* AAAS; Am Phys Soc; Am Pub Health Asn; NY Acad Sci. *Res:* Planetary atmospheres and surface environments; radiative transfer theory; numerical methods for computers; environmental management. *Mailing Add:* 6633 Yellowstone Blvd Forest Hills NY 11375

**TEITEL, ROBERT J(ERRELL),** METALLURGY. *Current Pos:* PRES, ROBERT J TEITEL ASSOCS, 76- *Personal Data:* b Indianapolis, Ind, Aug 4, 22. *Educ:* Purdue Univ, BS, 44; Mass Inst Technol, ScD(metall), 48. *Prof Exp:* Assoc metallurgist, Brookhaven Nat Labs, 48-53, metallurgist, 53-55; group leader, Nuclear & Basic Res Lab, Dow Chem Co, Mich, 55-60; sr tech specialist, Rocketdyne Div, NAm Aviation, Inc, 60-61; prin scientist, Douglas Aircraft Co, 61-72; head mat eng dept, KMS Fusion, Inc, Ann Arbor, Mich, 72-76. *Concurrent Pos:* Civilian with AEC, 44. *Mem:* AAAS; Am Soc Metals; fel Am Nuclear Soc. *Res:* Material sciences; nuclear fission and fusion reactor materials and design; nuclear fuel cycles; missile materials; space nuclear power plants; hydrogen production and storage systems; fossil fuel systems; metallurgical thermodynamics; liquid metal corrosion; alloy phase diagrams. *Mailing Add:* 5025 Santorini Way Oceanside CA 92056-5858

**TEITELBAUM, CHARLES LEONARD,** ANALYTICAL CHEMISTRY. *Current Pos:* ADJ ASST PROF, NY CITY UNIV, 88- *Personal Data:* b Brooklyn, NY, June 14, 25; m 50. *Educ:* Brooklyn Col, BA, 45; Purdue Univ, MS, 48, PhD(org chem), 51. *Prof Exp:* Res chemist, Heyden Chem Corp, 50-53; prin chemist, Battelle Mem Inst, 53-58; chemist, Coty, Inc Div, Chas Pfizer & Co, 58-65 & Florasynth, Inc, 65-66; res specialist, Gen Foods Corp, 66-86. *Mem:* Am Chem Soc. *Res:* Analysis of natural products relating to odor and flavor. *Mailing Add:* 85-46 Midland Pkwy Jamaica NY 11432-2222

**TEITELBAUM, MICHAEL STEWART,** ECONOMICS, POPULATION. *Current Pos:* CONSULT, 92- *Personal Data:* b St Louis, Mo, Jan 21, 44; m 69, Vivien Stewart; c Emma, Abigail Clare & Justin Andrew. *Educ:* Reed Col, BA, 66; Oxford Univ, PhD, 70, MA, 75. *Prof Exp:* Asst prof & res assoc, Princeton Univ, 69-73; prog officer, Ford Found, 73-74 & 80-81; fel & lectr demography, Nuffield Col & Oxford Univ, 74-78; staff dir select comt pop, US House Reps, 78-80; sr assoc, Carnegie Endowment Int Peace, 81-83; prog officer, Alfred P Sloan Found, 83-92. *Concurrent Pos:* Comnr, US Comn Study Int Migration & Coop Econ Develop, 87-90. *Mem:* AAAS; Coun Foreign Rels; Soc Study Social Biol (pres, 84-90); Pop Asn Am (vpres, 91-92); Int Union Sci Study Pop. *Res:* Author of several books. *Mailing Add:* Alfred P Sloan Found 630 Fifth Ave Rm 2550 New York NY 10111

**TEITELBAUM, PHILIP,** NEUROSCIENCE, PHYSIOLOGICAL PSYCHOLOGY. *Current Pos:* DISTINGUISHED GRAD RES PROF PSYCHOL, UNIV FLA, 85- *Personal Data:* b Brooklyn, NY, Oct 9, 28; c 5. *Educ:* City Col New York, BS, 50; Johns Hopkins Univ, MA, 52, PhD, 54. *Honors & Awards:* Distinguished Sci Contrib Award, Am Psychol Asn. *Prof Exp:* Instr, Harvard Univ, 54-56, asst prof physiol psychol, 56-59; assoc prof, Univ Pa, 59-63, prof, 63-73; prof psychol, Univ Ill, Champaign, 73-85, prof, Ctr Advan Study, 80-85. *Concurrent Pos:* Fel behav sci, Ctr Advan Study, Stanford Univ, 75-76; Fulbright fel, Dept Zool, Tel Aviv Univ, 78-79; Guggenheim fel, 84-85. *Mem:* Nat Acad Sci; Am Physiol Soc; Am Psychol Soc (pres, 77); Soc Exp Psychologists. *Res:* Movement analysis to help Parkinson's disease patients walk better. *Mailing Add:* Dept Psychol Univ Fla Gainesville FL 32611. *Fax:* 352-392-7985; *E-Mail:* teilelb@webb.psych.ufl.edu

**TEITLER, SIDNEY,** THEORETICAL PHYSICS. *Current Pos:* RETIRED. *Personal Data:* b New York, NY, July 1, 30. *Educ:* Long Island Univ, BS, 51; Univ Ill, MS, 53; Syracuse Univ, PhD(physics), 57. *Prof Exp:* Physicist, Elec Sci & Tech Div, US Naval Res Lab, 57- *Mem:* Sigma Xi; fel Am Phys Soc. *Mailing Add:* 5505 Seminary Rd 2211 N Falls Church VA 22041

**TEIXEIRA, ARTHUR ALVES,** FOOD ENGINEERING, AGRICULTURAL ENGINEERING. *Current Pos:* assoc prof, 82-89, PROF FOOD ENG, UNIV FLA, 89- *Personal Data:* b Fall River, Mass, Jan 30, 44; m 84, Marjorie St John; c Allan, Scott & Marjorie St John. *Educ:* Univ Mass, BS, 66, MS, 68, PhD, 71. *Prof Exp:* Proj leader res, Ross Div, Abbott Labs, 71-73, group leader mgt, 73-77; sr consult, Arthur D Little Inc, 77-82. *Concurrent Pos:* Sr guest fel, NATO, Portugal, 88 & 89; Fulbright scholar, Portugal, 90; consult food engr. *Mem:* Inst Food Technologists; fel Am Soc Agr Engrs; Inst Thermal Process Specialists; Am Inst Chem Engrs; Am Soc Eng Educ; Coun Agr Sci & Technol. *Res:* Thermal processing of canned foods; food product and process development; applications of energy-saving technologies in food processing; computer simulation and control of food processing operations. *Mailing Add:* Agr Eng Dept Frazier-Rogers Hall Univ Fla PO Box 110570 Gainesville FL 32611-0570. *Fax:* 904-392-4092; *E-Mail:* atex@agen.ufl.edu

**TEJA, AMYN SADRUDDIN,** PHASE EQUILIBRIA, CRITICAL PROPERTIES & SEPARATIONS. *Current Pos:* assoc prof, 80-84, prof chem eng, 84-90, REGENTS PROF, GA INST TECHNOL, 90- *Personal Data:* b Zanzibar, Tanzania, May 11, 46; UK citizen; m 71, Carole R Thurlow; c Kerima A & Adam R. *Educ:* Imp Col London, BSc, & ACGI, 68, PhD(chem eng) & DIC, 72. *Honors & Awards:* David Spurr Medal, 67; Hinchley Medal, 68; Sustained Res Award, Sigma Xi, 87. *Prof Exp:* Vis assoc prof chem eng, Ohio State Univ, 80; res fel, Loughborough Univ, Eng, 71-74, lectr, 74-80; vis assoc prof, Univ Del, 78-79. *Concurrent Pos:* Assoc ed, Chem Eng J, 73-; tech dir, Fluid Properties Res, Inc, 85- *Mem:* Am Inst Chem Engrs; Am Soc Eng Educ; Sigma Xi; Am Chem Soc. *Res:* Measurement, correlation and prediction of the thermodynamic and transport properties of mixtures with emphasis on the critical region and on mixtures of technological interest; bioseparations using supercritical fluids. *Mailing Add:* Sch Chem Eng Ga Inst Technol Atlanta GA 30332-0100. *Fax:* 404-894-2866; *E-Mail:* amyn_teja@chemeng.gatech.edu

**TEJWANI, GOPI ASSUDOMAL,** OPIOID RECEPTORS & PEPTIDES, ANESTHETICS. *Current Pos:* clin asst prof, 76-78, asst prof, 78-88, ASSOC PROF PHARMACOL, COL MED, OHIO STATE UNIV, 88- *Personal Data:* b Dadu, India, March 1, 46; m 73, Sarla Tejwani; c Samir. *Educ:* Nagpur Univ, India, BS, 66, MS, 68; All-India Inst Med Sci, PhD(biochem), 73. *Prof Exp:* Fel enzyme, Sch Med, St Louis Univ, 73-74 & Roche Inst Molecular Biol, 74-76. *Concurrent Pos:* Vis prof, Univ Sao Paulo, Brazil, 78 & Moscow State Univ, 81; lectr, Univ Chile, 78, Univ Wroclaw, Poland, 81 & Univ Ioannina, Greece, 81; consult, Immunobiol Res Inst, NJ, 80; prin investr, numerous res grants biochem pharmacol, 78- *Mem:* AAAS; Am Soc Biochem & Molecular Biol; Soc Neurosci; Am Soc Pharmacol & Exp Therpeut. *Res:* Regulation of key enzymes involved in glycolysis and gluconegenesis; role of endorphins in obesity and cardiovascular diseases; role of stress in facilitation of mammary tumorigenesis; modulation of opioid receptors by anesthetics; pharmacologic effects of nicotine and neurotoxins. *Mailing Add:* Dept Pharmacol Ohio State Univ 333 W Tenth Ave Columbus OH 43210-1239. *Fax:* 614-292-7232; *E-Mail:* tejwani.1@osu.edu

**TEKEL, RALPH,** ORGANIC CHEMISTRY. *Current Pos:* RETIRED. *Personal Data:* b New York, NY, May 27, 20; m 60, Lillian Toll; c Linda (Beelitz) & Billie (Elias). *Educ:* Polytech Inst NY, BS, 41; Purdue Univ, MS, 47, PhD(chem), 49. *Prof Exp:* Asst tech dir, Vitamins Inc, Ill, 48-49; res assoc, Carter Prod, NJ, 49-51; mgr pilot plant, Nat Drug Co, 51-60; asst to mgr, Chem Div, Wyeth Labs, 60-63; dir org res, Betz Lab, 63-65; from asst prof to assoc prof org chem, La Salle Col, 65-74, assoc prof chem, 74-85. *Concurrent Pos:* Lectr, Holy Family Col, Pa, 66-67; consult, Am Electronic

Labs, 66- & Dermascis, 80-81. *Mem:* AAAS; fel Am Inst Chem; Am Chem Soc; NY Acad Sci. *Res:* Medicinals; biochemicals; halogen chemicals; pilot plant development; continuous thin layer chromatography. *Mailing Add:* 21 Linden Dr Breyer Woods Elkins Park PA 19027

**TEKELI, SAIT,** VETERINARY MEDICINE, PATHOLOGY. *Current Pos:* SR RES PATHOLOGIST, ABBOTT LABS, 69- *Personal Data:* b Samsun, Turkey, June 14, 32; m 59; c 1. *Educ:* Univ Ankara, DVM, 54, DSc(path), 58; Univ Wis-Madison, MS, 62, PhD(avian leukosis), 64. *Prof Exp:* Dist vet, Dept Agr, Samsun, Turkey, 54-55; res asst animal path, Univ Ankara, 55-60; res asst vet sci, Univ Wis-Madison, 60-64, res asst bovine leukosis, 66-67; res pathologist, Norwich Pharmacal Corp, 67-69. *Mem:* Soc Toxicol; Int Acad Path; Soc Toxicol Pathologists; Sigma Xi. *Res:* Drug toxicity; drug-induced lesions as well as chemical carcinogens. *Mailing Add:* 4083 Harper Ave Gurnee IL 60031

**TELANG, VASANT G,** MEDICINAL CHEMISTRY. *Current Pos:* mem staff, Col Pharm, 74-80, assoc dean, 80-96, ASSOC PROF BIOMED CHEM, HOWARD UNIV, 80-, INTERIM DEAN, SCH PHARM, 96- *Personal Data:* b Kumta, India, July 18, 35. *Educ:* Univ Bombay, BS, 56, MS, 64; Univ RI, PhD(pharmaceut chem), 68. *Prof Exp:* Lab instr pharmaceut chem, Univ Bombay, 59-62, asst prof pharm, 62-63; teaching asst pharmaceut chem, Col Pharm, Univ RI, 63-68; NIH res specialist, Col Pharm, Univ Minn, Minneapolis, 68-74. *Concurrent Pos:* Consult, Suneeta Labs, India, 70- *Mem:* Indian Pharmaceut Asn; Am Chem Soc. *Res:* Mechanism of action of narcotic analgesics and their antagonists. *Mailing Add:* Col Pharm Howard Univ 2300 Fourth St NW Washington DC 20059

**TELEB, ZAKARIA AHMED,** toxicology, for more information see previous edition

**TELEGDI, VALENTINE LOUIS,** PARTICLE PHYSICS, WEAK INTERACTIONS. *Current Pos:* ADJ PROF, UNIV CALIF, SAN DIEGO, 97- *Personal Data:* b Budapest, Hungary, Jan 11, 22; nat US; m 50, Lidia Leonardi. *Educ:* Univ Lausanne, MSc, 46; Swiss Fed Inst Technol, PhD(physics), 50. *Hon Degrees:* DHC, Louvain, Belg, 89, Univ Budapest, 90, Univ Chicago, 92. *Honors & Awards:* Grand Prize, ETH, 50; Page Lectr, Yale Univ; Schitt lectr, Stanford Univ; Wolf Prize Physics, 91; Lilienfeld Prize, Am Phys Soc, 95. *Prof Exp:* Asst physics, Swiss Fed Inst Technol, 47-50; from instr to prof, Univ Chicago, 50-71, Enrico Fermi distinguished serv prof, 71-76; prof, Swiss Fed Inst Technol, 76-89. *Concurrent Pos:* Vis mem, H H Wills Lab, Univ Bristol, 48; lectr, Northwestern Univ, 53-54; vis res fel, Calif Inst Technol, 53; Ford fel & NSF vis scientist, Europ Orgn Nuclear Res, Geneva, 59; Loeb vis prof, Harvard Univ, 66; univ lectr, NY Univ, 67; vis prof, Calif Inst Technol, 78-92; Sherman Fairchild distinguished scholar; Humboldt fel. *Mem:* Nat Acad Sci; Am Acad Arts & Sci; Acad Sci; Torino Acad Sci; Acad Nat Lincei; Hungarian Acad Sci. *Res:* Nuclear emulsion technique; experiment and theory of interaction of nuclei with photons; Compton effect of proton; symmetry properties of weak interactions; muon decay and absorption; decay of free neutron; magnetic properties of the muon; hypernuclei; long-lived strange particles; parity violation in atoms; spin motion. *Mailing Add:* CERN PPE Div Geneva 1211 Switzerland. *Fax:* 41-22-7827558; *E-Mail:* val.telegdi@cern.ch

**TELEN, MARILYN JO,** HEMATOLOGY, IMMUNOHEMATOLOGY. *Current Pos:* fel hemat & immunohemat, Duke Univ, 80-83, assoc med, 83-85, asst prof, 85-92, ASSOC PROF MED, DUKE UNIV, 92- *Personal Data:* b New York, NY, Nov 30, 47; m 73, Henry Greene; c Samuel Greene & Benjamin Greene. *Educ:* Vassar Col, AB, 69; NY Univ, MD, 77. *Prof Exp:* Intern-resident, State Univ NY, Buffalo, 77-80. *Concurrent Pos:* Assoc med dir, Transfusion Serv, Duke Univ, 87-, asst prof path, 91-, dir, Hemat & Oncol Fel Prog, 91- *Mem:* Am Soc Clin Invest; Am Soc Hemat; Am Asn Blood Banks. *Res:* Biochemical and genetic basis of blood group antigens, including the functional roles of proteins involved in antigen expression and the effects of antigen-related polymorphism on protein function. *Mailing Add:* Duke Univ Med Ctr Box 3387 Durham NC 27710. *Fax:* 919-681-7688

**TELFAIR, RAYMOND CLARK, II,** FISH & WILDLIFE SCIENCES. *Current Pos:* CONSERV SCIENTIST & CERT WILDLIFE BIOLOGIST, WILDLIFE DIV, TEX PARKS & WILDLIFE DEPT, 86- *Personal Data:* b Ennis, Tex, Mar 5, 41. *Educ:* NTex State Univ, BA, 65, MA, 67; Tex A&M Univ, PhD(wildlife & fisheries sci), 79. *Prof Exp:* Instr, NTex State Univ, 65-68; instr wildlife & fisheries sci biol, Tex A&M Univ, 72-84. *Mem:* Am Ornithologists' Union; Am Soc Zoologists; Sigma Xi; Wildlife Soc; Soc Conserv Biol; Soc Ecol Restoration. *Res:* Biology and ecology of colonial waterbirds with emphasis on the Cattle Egret, Bubulcus ibis; evaluate various project impacts on fish-wildlife; review environmental documents; provide guidelines on construction, reclamation and mitigation; develop data bases-reports; serve as expert witness. *Mailing Add:* 11780 S Hill Creek Rd Whitehouse TX 75791-9601. *Fax:* 903-566-2178

**TELFER, NANCY,** MEDICINE, NUCLEAR MEDICINE. *Current Pos:* RETIRED. *Personal Data:* b San Francisco, Calif, Apr 15, 30. *Educ:* Stanford Univ, AB, 51; Med Col Pa, MD, 56; Am Bd Internal Med, dipl, 63 & 77; Am Bd Nuclear Med, dipl, 72. *Prof Exp:* Intern, Los Angeles Co-Univ Southern Calif Med Ctr, 56-57, resident internal med, 57-60; instr med, Ctr Health Sci, Univ Calif, Los Angeles, 60-61, asst prof, 62-67; from asst prof to assoc prof radiol & med, Los Angeles Co-Univ Southern Calif Med Ctr, 67-84. *Concurrent Pos:* Los Angeles Co Heart Asn res fel, Isotope Lab Med, Cantonal Hosp, Geneva, Switz, 61-62; Kate Meade Hurd fel, Woman's Med Col Pa, 61-62; vis assoc prof nuclear med, Beth Israel Hosp-Harvard Med Sch,

81-82. *Mem:* Fel Am Col Physicians; fel Am Col Nuclear Physicians. *Res:* Body electrolyte composition using radioactive tracers and the dilution principle; computer analysis of radionuclide cardiac and pulmonary function studies; soft tissue deposition of 99m technetium diphorphonate; red blood cell 86 rubidium uptake. *Mailing Add:* PO Box 3142 Warrenton VA 22186

**TELFER, WILLIAM HARRISON,** REPRODUCTIVE BIOLOGY, DEVELOPMENTAL BIOLOGY. *Current Pos:* from asst prof to prof biol, Univ Pa, 54-73, chmn grad group, 60-70, prof zool & chmn, Dept Biol, 73-77, PROF BIOL, UNIV PA, 78- *Personal Data:* b Seattle, Wash, June 21, 24; m 50; c 2. *Educ:* Reed Col, BA, 48; Harvard Univ, MS, 49, PhD(biol), 52. *Prof Exp:* Jr fel, Harvard Soc Fels, 52-54. *Concurrent Pos:* Guggenheim fel, Stanford Univ, 60-61; NSF sr fel, Univ Miami, 68-69; staff mem, NIH training prog in fertilization & gamete physiol, Marine Biol Lab, Woods Hole, Mass, 71-; res assoc biochem, Univ Ariz, 81-82. *Mem:* Am Soc Zool; Soc Develop Biol. *Res:* Physiology and developmental aspects of egg formation and blood proteins in insects. *Mailing Add:* Dept Biol Univ Pa Philadelphia PA 19104

**TELFORD, IRA ROCKWOOD,** ANATOMY. *Current Pos:* VIS PROF ANAT, UNIFORMED SERV UNIV, 78- *Personal Data:* b Idaho Falls, Idaho, May 6, 07; m 33; c 4. *Educ:* Univ Utah, AB, 31, AM, 33; George Washington Univ, PhD(anat), 42. *Prof Exp:* Sch teacher, Idaho, 33-37; from instr to assoc prof anat, Sch Med, George Washington Univ, 41-47, prof anat, Schs Med, 53-72; prof & chmn dept, Sch Dent, Univ Tex, 47-53; prof anat, Sch Med & Dent, Georgetown Univ, 72-78. *Mem:* Soc Exp Biol & Med; Am Asn Anat; Am Acad Neurol. *Res:* Histology, muscle and nerve studies in vitamin E deficiency; vitamins; cancer in dietary deficiencies; muscular dystrophy. *Mailing Add:* 3424 Garrison St NW Washington DC 20008-2037

**TELFORD, JAMES WARDROP,** ATMOSPHERIC PHYSICS, COMPUTER SCIENCE. *Current Pos:* PRES, DIR RES, ATMOSPHERIC CONCEPTS INC, RENO, 95- *Personal Data:* b Merbein, Australia, Aug 16, 27; m 54, Mary Billing; c David J, Susan G & Catriona A. *Educ:* Univ Melbourne, BSc, 50, DSc(atmospheric convection), 70; Univ Sydney, dipl numerical analysis automatic comput, 62. *Prof Exp:* Sr res scientist, Radiophys Div, Commonwealth Sci & Indust Res Orgn, 50-65; vis scientist, Dept Cloud Physics, Imp Col, Univ London, 65-66; sr res scientist, Radiophys Div, Commonwealth Sci & Indust Res Orgn, 66-67; dep dir lab atmospheric physics & res prof, Des Res Inst, Univ Nev Syst, Reno, 67-78, dir air motion lab & res prof, 78-95. *Concurrent Pos:* Dept Defense res contract, Atmospheric Sci Ctr, Desert Res Inst, Reno, 67-88, NSF res grants, 70-88, lectr, Univ Nev, Reno, 78; NASA res contracts, 75-88. *Mem:* Fel Am Meteorol Soc; fel Royal Meteorol Soc; Sigma Xi; fel AAAS; Am Geophys Union. *Res:* Experimental and theoretical work on stochastic coalescence mechanisms in warm clouds; marine boundary layer, airborne observations and theory; observations and theory of clear air and cloudy air convection; airborne air motion measuring system; thunderstorm theory. *Mailing Add:* 1975 Fallen Leaf Ct Reno NV 89509. *Fax:* 702-829-0658

**TELFORD, SAM ROUNTREE, JR,** EPIZOOTIOLOGY. *Current Pos:* int assoc cur, Fla State Mus, Univ Fla, 70, asst cur, 70-73, asst prof biol sci & zool, 70-73, FIELD RES ASSOC & ADJ CUR, FLA STATE MUS, UNIV FLA, 73- *Personal Data:* b Winter Haven, Fla, Aug 25, 32; m 57, Michiko Miyazawa; c Sam R III, Randolph S & Robert M. *Educ:* Univ Va, BA, 55; Univ Fla, MS, 61; Univ Calif, Los Angeles, PhD(zool), 64. *Prof Exp:* Lectr zool, Univ Calif, Los Angeles, 64-65; Nat Inst Allergy & Infectious Dis res fel parasitol, Inst Infectious Dis, Univ Tokyo, 65-67; mem staff, Gorgas Mem Lab, CZ, 67-70. *Concurrent Pos:* Med zoologist, WHO, Geneva, Switz, 73, Chagas Dis Vector Res Unit, Acarigua, Venezuela, 73-75 & Vertebrate Pest Control Ctr, Karachi, Pakistan, 75-77; WHO Spec Prog for Res & Training in Trop Dis-Div Malaria, Geneva, Switz, 77-78; Rodent Control Demonstration Unit, WHO, Rangoon, Burma, 78-80; proj leader, Denmark-Tanzania Rodent Control, Morogoro, 81-85; WHO consult med zool, Govt Zaire, 81; res assoc entom & nematol, 85-87 & Dept Infectious Dis, Col Vet Med, Univ Fla, 89-91; res assoc, Fla Mus Natural Hist, 87-88; consult pub health vector-borne & parasitic dis, Govt Ecuador Inter-Am Develop Bank Trop Res & Develop, Gainesville, Fla, 88; consult upland ecol & endangered species, Wetlands Mgt, Inc, Jensen Beach, Fla, 88-89; field zoologist, Fla Natural Areas Inventory Nature Conserv, Tallahassee, 91; consult upland ecol, Gainesville, Fla, 92- *Mem:* Am Soc Parasitol. *Res:* Herpetology; parasitology; ecology; population dynamics of reptilian host-parasite associations; lower vertebrate parasitology; ecology and systematics of reptiles and amphibians; saurian malaria; zoonotic disease; rodent control-biology. *Mailing Add:* 1712 NW 49th Terr Gainesville FL 32605

**TELFORD, SAM ROUNTREE, III,** BIOLOGY OF LYME DISEASE & OTHER TICKBORNE ZOONOSES. *Current Pos:* grad res asst, 84-90, res fel, 90-92, LECTR, TROP PUB HEALTH, HARVARD UNIV, 92- *Personal Data:* b Gainesville, Fla, Aug 29, 61. *Educ:* Johns Hopkins Univ, BA, 83; Harvard Univ, MS, 87, DSc(parasitol), 90. *Prof Exp:* Curatorial asst, Mus Comp Zool, 84-86. *Concurrent Pos:* Consult, Trop Dis Diag, Becton Dickinson Co, 88-92, Smith Kline Beecham Biol, 92-; NIH first award, Nat Inst Allergy & Infectious Dis, 95-, NIH grant, 96- *Mem:* Soc Study Evolution; Soc Study Amphibians & Reptiles; Herpetologists League; Am Soc Trop Med & Hyg; Am Soc Parasitologists; Am Soc Mammalogists. *Res:* Medical zoology; parasite ecology; evolutionary theory. *Mailing Add:* Dept Trop Pub Health Harvard Univ 665 Huntington Ave Boston MA 02115. *Fax:* 617-738-4914; *E-Mail:* stelford@hsph.harvard.edu

**TELIONIS, DEMETRI PYRROS,** AERODYNAMICS, APPLIED MATHEMATICS. *Current Pos:* asst prof aerospace eng, 70-74, assoc prof eng mech, 74-78, PROF ENG MECH, VA POLYTECH INST & STATE UNIV, 78- *Personal Data:* b Athens, Greece, Mar 17, 41; m 67. *Educ:* Nat Tech Univ Athens, dipl, 64; Cornell Univ, MS, 69, PhD(aerospace eng), 70. *Honors & Awards:* Soc Eng Res Award, AmSoc Eng Educ, 87. *Prof Exp:* Mech engr, Royal Greek Navy Shipyards, 64-67. *Concurrent Pos:* Consult, Commun Orgn of Greece, 67 & Hellenic Air Force, 77- *Mem:* Assoc fel Am Inst Aeronaut & Astronaut; Sigma Xi; Tech Chamber Greece; Am Soc Mech Engrs. *Res:* Incompressible and compressible aerodynamics; viscous flows; boundary-layer theory; acoustics; applied mechanics; turbulent flows; unsteady aerodynamics; experimental fluid mechanics. *Mailing Add:* 3138 Indian Meadow Dr Blacksburg VA 24060-8838

**TELKES, MARIA,** SOLAR ENERGY CONVERSION, THERMAL ENERGY STORAGE. *Current Pos:* CONSULT, 80- *Personal Data:* b Budapest, Hungary, Dec 12, 00; nat US. *Educ:* Univ Budapest, BA, 20, PhD(phys chem), 24. *Hon Degrees:* DSc, St Joseph Col, Conn, 57. *Honors & Awards:* C G Abbot Award, Am Solar Energy Soc, 77. *Prof Exp:* Instr physics, Univ Budapest, 23-24; biophysicist, Cleveland Clin Found, 26-37; engr, Res Dept, Westinghouse Elec & Mfg Co, 37-39; res assoc, Mass Inst Technol, 39-53; proj dir solar energy prog, Res Div, NY Univ, 53-58; res dir, Solar Energy Lab, Curtiss-Wright Corp, 58-60; dir res, Cryo-Therm, Inc, Pa, 60-64; mgr, Thermodyn Lab, Melpar Inc, Westinghouse Air Brake Co, 64-69; sr res specialist, Nat Ctr Energy Mgt & Power, Univ Pa, 69-72; sr scientist, Inst Energy Conversion, Univ Del, 72-77; dir solar thermal storage develop, Am Technol Univ, 77-80. *Mem:* Am Chem Soc; Solar Energy Soc; Soc Women Engrs. *Res:* Solar-thermal storage materials used in solar heated and cooled buildings; thermoelectric generators; semiconductors; phase-change thermal control of terrestrial and space applications. *Mailing Add:* 1475 NE 125th Terr Suite 414 North Miami FL 33161-5265

**TELL, BENJAMIN,** PHYSICS. *Current Pos:* RETIRED. *Personal Data:* b Philadelphia, Pa, Dec 11, 36; m 66; c 2. *Educ:* Columbia Univ, BA, 58; Univ Mich, Ann Arbor, MS, 60, PhD(physics), 63. *Prof Exp:* Mem tech staff, Bell Tel Labs, 63-93. *Concurrent Pos:* Vis mem staff, Philips Industs N V Philips Res Lab, Eindhoven Holland, 76. *Mem:* Am Phys Soc. *Res:* Optical and electrical properties of semiconductors; ion implantation and III-V devices; visible vertical cavity surface emitting lasers and long wavelength photonic integrated circuits. *Mailing Add:* 36 Infield Lane Matawan NJ 07747

**TELLE, JOHN MARTIN,** LASERS. *Current Pos:* RES SCIENTIST, PHILLIPS AIR FORCE LAB, UNIV NMEX, 95- *Personal Data:* b Akron, Ohio, Nov 3, 47; m 68; c 3. *Educ:* Univ Colo, BS, 69; Cornell Univ, MS, 72, PhD(physics), 75. *Prof Exp:* Res scientist laser physics, Los Alamos Nat Lab, 75-95. *Mem:* Am Phys Soc; Optical Soc Am. *Res:* Optically pumped infrared gas lasers. *Mailing Add:* 126 Shady Oak Circle Tijeras NM 87059-7400

**TELLEP, DANIEL M,** MECHANICAL ENGINEERING, FLUIDS. *Current Pos:* RETIRED. *Personal Data:* b Forest City, Pa, Nov 20, 31. *Educ:* Univ Calif, Berkeley, BS, 54, MS, 55. *Honors & Awards:* Lawrence B Sperry Award, Am Inst Aeronaut & Astronaut, 64, Missile Syst Award, 86 & Syst Award, 86. *Prof Exp:* Sr scientist, Lockheed Missiles & Space Co, 55-57, head thermal res, 58-61, mgr missile thermodyn, 63-66, chief Poseidon reentry systs eng, asst chief engr develop & chief engr, Missile Systs Div, 66-75, vpres & asst gen mgr, Advan Systs Div, 75-83, exec vpres, 83-84, pres, 84-87, group pres, Lockheed Missiles & Space Systs, 86-87, pres, Lockheed Corp, 88-89, chmn bd, Lockheed Martin Corp, 89-96, chief exec officer, 89-95. *Concurrent Pos:* Mem bd dirs, Lockheed Missiles & Space Systs, 87- *Mem:* Nat Acad Eng; Sigma Xi; fel Am Inst Aeronaut & Astronaut; fel Am Astronaut Soc. *Mailing Add:* Lockheed Martin Corp 6801 Rockledge Dr Bethesda MD 20817

**TELLER, AARON JOSEPH,** ENVIRONMENTAL & CHEMICAL ENGINEERING. *Current Pos:* SR VPRES TECHNOL, AWT, 92- *Personal Data:* b Brooklyn, NY, June 30, 21; m 46; c 1. *Educ:* Cooper Union, BChE, 43; Polytech Inst Brooklyn, MChE, 49; Case Western Res Univ, PhD(chem), 51. *Honors & Awards:* Ann Lectr Award, Am Inst Chem Engrs, 72; Valeur Award, 75; Sensebaugh Award, 91. *Prof Exp:* Res engr chem eng, Columbia Univ-Manhattan Proj, 42-44 & Martin Labs, 44-45; develop engr, City Chem Corp, 45-47; chmn, Dept Chem Eng, Cleveland State Univ, 47-56; res prof chem eng & chmn dept, Univ Fla, 56-61; vpres eng, Colonial Iron-Patterson Industs, 61-63; dean, Col Eng & Sci, Cooper Union, 63-70; pres, Teller Environ Systs Inc, 70-86; consult, Res Cottrell Co, 86-89, sr tech adv & vpres technol, 86-92. *Concurrent Pos:* Consult, Davy Power Gas, Bechtel, C F Braun, Borden Co, Am Cyanamide, Exxon & Tenn Valley Authority, 56-70; mem, Nat Adv Comt Air Pollution Technol, Environ Protection Agency, 68-71. *Mem:* Am Inst Chem Engrs; Am Chem Soc. *Res:* Environmental-chemical engineering; diffusional operations, packing; nucleation; chromatographic absorption; dioxin recovery, fine particulate recovery, bioscrubbing processes. *Mailing Add:* 47 St James Dr Palm Beach Gardens FL 33418

**TELLER, CECIL MARTIN, II,** NONDESTRUCTIVE EVALUATION, FATIGUE & FRACTURE. *Current Pos:* pres, 88-89, CHIEF ENGR, TEX RES INT/APPL RES & TECHNOL, INC, 89-; CORP SCI OFFICER, TEX RES INT, INC, 89- *Personal Data:* b Galveston, Tex, Oct 25, 39; m 66; c 2. *Educ:* Univ Tex Austin, BS, 64, MS, 66 & PhD(mat sci & eng), 71. *Prof Exp:* Mgr, Tracor Inc, 72-74; br chief, US Govt, 74-77; mgr, Southwest Res Inst, 77-83; tech dir, Tex Res Inst Inc, 83-85, vpres, 85-88. *Concurrent Pos:* Chief engr, Tex Res Inst Inc, 89- *Mem:* Am Soc Mech Engrs; Am Soc Metals Int; Am Soc Nondestructive Testing. *Res:* Research and development of new nondestructive evaluation methods for metals and composites; bonded structures and thick composites. *Mailing Add:* 2201 Lakeway Blvd Apt 34 Austin TX 78734

**TELLER, DAVID CHAMBERS,** PHYSICAL BIOCHEMISTRY. *Current Pos:* Asst prof, 65-70, ASSOC PROF BIOCHEM, UNIV WASH, 70- *Personal Data:* b Wilkes-Barre, Pa, July 25, 38; m 60; c 1. *Educ:* Swarthmore Col, BA, 60; Univ Calif, Berkeley, PhD(biochem), 65. *Concurrent Pos:* Consult, Spinco Div, Beckman Instruments, 66. *Mem:* Am Soc Biol Chem; Sigma Xi. *Res:* Physical chemistry and equilibria of proteins; non-covalent association. *Mailing Add:* Dept Biochem Univ Wash Seattle WA 98195-0001

**TELLER, DAVID NORTON,** NEUROCHEMISTRY, PSYCHOPHARMACOLOGY. *Current Pos:* assoc prof, 76-79, PROF, DEPT PSYCHIAT & BEHAV SCI, MED SCH, UNIV LOUISVILLE, 79- *Personal Data:* b New York, NY, Oct 1, 36; m 59. *Educ:* Brooklyn Col, BS, 57; NY Univ, MS, 60, PhD(cytochem), 64. *Prof Exp:* Biologist, Fine Organics, Inc, 56-57; res asst hemat & nutrit, New York Med Col, 57-59; sr res scientist, NY State Ment Hyg, Manhattan State Hosp, NY State Res Inst, 59-66, assoc res scientist, 66-76. *Concurrent Pos:* Lectr, Dept Psychiat, New York Med Col, 66-67 & Grad Div, Fairleigh Dickinson Univ, 68-71. *Mem:* Am Chem Soc; Am Soc Neurochem; Am Soc Pharmacol & Exp Therapeut; Am Soc Testing & Mat; Int Col Neuropsychopharmacol; Biochem Soc Brit. *Res:* Drug binding and transport; subcellular particle preparation; molecular pharmacology; evaluation of medical education. *Mailing Add:* Dept Psychiat Univ Louisville Med Sch Louisville KY 40292-0001

**TELLER, DAVIDA YOUNG,** VISION, VISUAL DEVELOPMENT. *Current Pos:* Res asst prof psychol, Univ Wash, 65-67, actg asst prof, 67-68, from asst prof to assoc prof psychol & physiol, 68-74, PROF PSYCHOL, PHYSIOL & BIOPHYS, UNIV WASH, 74- *Personal Data:* b Yonkers, NY, July 25, 38; m 90; c 2. *Educ:* Swarthmore Col, BA, 60; Univ Calif, Berkeley, PhD(psychol), 65. *Honors & Awards:* Glenn Fry Award, Am Acad Optom, 82. *Concurrent Pos:* Nat Inst Neurol Dis & Blindness res grant, 68-71; Nat Eye Inst res grants, 71-; mem comt vision, Nat Res Coun, 71-80; mem vision res & training comt, Nat Eye Inst, 72-76; affil, Regional Primate Res Ctr, 73- & Child Develop & Ment Retardation Ctr, 75-; NSF res grant, 75-85; mem, Vision B Study Sect, NIH, 81-85, chair, 83-85. *Mem:* Fel AAAS; fel Optical Soc Am; Asn Res Vision & Ophthal; Asn Women Sci; Sigma Xi; fel Coun Am Asn Advan Sci. *Res:* Development of vision in human infants; philosophical aspects of visual sciences; visual psychophysics. *Mailing Add:* 2301 Fairview Ave E Apt 416 Seattle WA 98102-3361

**TELLER, EDWARD,** PHYSICS. *Current Pos:* prof, 53-60, univ prof, 60-75, EMER PROF PHYSICS, UNIV CALIF, BERKELEY, 75-; SR RES FEL, HOOVER INST WAR, PEACE & REVOLUTION, STANFORD UNIV, 75- *Personal Data:* b Budapest, Hungary, Jan 15, 08; nat US; m 34; c 2. *Educ:* Univ Leipzig, PhD, 30. *Hon Degrees:* Many from var cols & univ in US, 54-64. *Honors & Awards:* Priestley Mem Award, Dickinson Col, 57; Einstein Award, 59; Gen Donovan Mem Award, 59; Award, Midwest Res Inst, 60; Living Hist Award, Res Inst Am, 60; Golden Plate Award, 61; White & Fermi Awards, 62; Robins Award Am, 63; Leslie R Groves Gold Medal Award, 74; Harvey Prize, Technion Inst, Israel, 75; Albert Einstein Award, Inst Israel, 77; Gold Medal, Am Col Nuclear Med, 80 & Am Acad Achievement, 82; A C Eringen Award, Soc Eng Sci, Inc, 80; Nat Medal Sci for 1982, Pres Ronald Reagan, 83; Sylvanus Thayer Award, 86. *Prof Exp:* Res assoc, Univ Leipzig, 29-31 & Univ Gottingen, 31-33; Rockefeller fel, Copenhagen, 34; lectr, Univ London, 34-35; prof physics, George Washington Univ, 35-41 & Columbia Univ, 41-42; physicist, Manhattan Eng Dist, Univ Chicago, 42-43 & Los Alamos Sci Lab, 43-46; prof, Univ Chicago, 46-52. *Concurrent Pos:* Asst dir, Los Alamos Sci Lab, 49-52; consult, Lawrence Radiation Lab, Livermore, 52-53, assoc dir, Lawrence Livermore Lab, Univ Calif, 54-58 & 72-, dir, 58-60; dir, Thermo Electron Corp; consult, Comn Critical Choices of Americans, 74-; emer bd mem, Defense Intel Sch; hon trustee, Asn Unmanned Space Vehicle Systs; consult, Defense Sci Bd, Undersecy Defense. *Mem:* Nat Acad Sci; fel Am Nuclear Soc; fel Am Phys Soc; Am Ord Asn; fel Am Acad Arts & Sci; fel AAAS; Am Defense Preparedness Asn; Am Geophys Union; Int Platform Asn; Scientists & Engrs Secure Energy. *Res:* Chemical, molecular and nuclear physics; quantum theory. *Mailing Add:* Hoover Inst Stanford CA 94305-6010

**TELLER, JAMES TOBIAS,** GEOLOGY. *Current Pos:* from asst prof to assoc prof, 70-81, PROF GEOL, UNIV MAN, 81- *Personal Data:* b Evanston, Ill, Aug 1, 40; m 63; c 2. *Educ:* Univ Cincinnati, BS, 62, PhD(geol), 70; Ohio State Univ, MS, 64. *Honors & Awards:* Stillwell Medal, Geol Soc Australia, 87. *Prof Exp:* Field geologist, Inst Polar Studies, 64-65; petrol geologist, Atlantic Richfield Co, 65-67. *Concurrent Pos:* Nat Sci & Eng Res Coun Can grants, Univ Man, 70-75 & 77-89, Geol Surv Can grants, 71-72 & 81-83; geol consult sand, gravel & petrol, 75-; vis assoc prof geol, Univ Cincinnati, 76; res fel, Australian Nat Univ, 77; assoc ed, Geosci Can, 79-; vis scientist, Univ Cape Town, 83; mem, NAm Comn Stratig Nomenclature, 84-87, Can Nat Comm INQUA, 88-92; mem sedimentation, paleohydrology, & hist of Assiniboine Delta & Valley Syst of Lake Agassiz, NSERC, Geol Surv Can, 89-92, hist, paleohydrology & sediment of glacial Lake Agassiz inflow & outflow, 92-95; mem, AMQUA coun, 90-94; chmn working group, ITCP253, 90-95; panel, Geol Soc Am Quat Geol Geomorphol Div, 93-95. *Mem:* Am Asn Quaternary Res; Soc Econ Paleont & Mineral; Can Quaternary Asn; Int Asn Sedimentologists; Am Geophys Union; Geol Soc Am. *Res:* Quaternary geology; sedimentology; history of lacustrine, glacial and fluvial deposits mainly in central North America, including Lake Agassiz. *Mailing Add:* Dept Geol Sci Univ Man Winnipeg MB R3T 2N2 Can

**TELLER, JOHN ROGER,** ALGEBRA. *Current Pos:* ASSOC PROF MATH, GEORGETOWN UNIV, 65- *Personal Data:* b Cincinnati, Ohio, June 30, 32; m 60; c 2. *Educ:* Univ Cincinnati, BS, 55, MA, 59; Tulane Univ, PhD(math), 64. *Prof Exp:* Asst prof math, Univ NH, 64-65. *Mem:* Am Math Soc; Math Asn Am. *Res:* Mathematical research in partially ordered groups. *Mailing Add:* Dept Math Georgetown Univ 37th & O Sts NW Washington DC 20057-0002

**TELLERIA, CARLOS MARCELO,** REPRODUCTIVE ENDOCRINOLOGY, OVARIAN PHYSIOLOGY. *Current Pos:* POSTDOCTORAL RES ASSOC, DEPT PHYSIOL & BIOPHYS, UNIV ILL, 95- *Personal Data:* b Los Toldos, Argentina, Sept 24, 64; m, Alicia Goyeneche; c Nahuel & Micaela. *Educ:* Nat Univ San Luis, Argentina, MSc, 86; Idem, MSc, 89, PhD(reproductive endocrinol), 93. *Honors & Awards:* Perkins Mem Award, Am Physiol Soc, 96. *Prof Exp:* Postdoctoral fel, Nat Res Coun Argentina, 94-95 & Fogarty Int Ctr, NIH, 95-97. *Mem:* AAAS; Soc Study Reproduction; Endocrine Soc. *Res:* Expression and mechanism of action of steroid and peptide hormones in the ovary, particularly at the corpus luteum level. *Mailing Add:* Dept Physiol & Biophys Univ Ill 835 S Wolcott Ave M/C 901 Chicago IL 60612-7340. *Fax:* 312-996-1414; *E-Mail:* carlosmt@uic.edu

**TELLINGHUISEN, JOEL BARTON,** MOLECULAR SPECTROSCOPY, MOLECULAR PHYSICS. *Current Pos:* from asst prof to assoc prof, 75-83, PROF CHEM, VANDERBILT UNIV, 83- *Personal Data:* b Cedar Falls, Iowa, May 27, 43; m 72; c 2. *Educ:* Cornell Univ, AB, 65; Univ Calif, Berkeley, PhD(chem), 69. *Prof Exp:* Res assoc chem, Univ Canterbury, 69-71; res assoc physics, Univ Chicago, 71-73; Nat Res Coun res assoc, Nat Oceanic & Atmospheric Admin, Boulder, Co, 73-75. *Mem:* Am Chem Soc; Am Phys Soc. *Res:* Molecular and atomic physics; optical spectroscopy; lasers. *Mailing Add:* Dept Chem Vanderbilt Univ PO Box 1668 Nashville TN 37235

**TELSCHOW, KENNETH LOUIS,** PHYSICS, MATERIALS SCIENCE. *Current Pos:* ASST PROF PHYSICS, SOUTHERN ILL UNIV, 77-; CONSULT SCIENTIST, IDAHO NAT ENG LAB, 93- *Personal Data:* b St Paul, Minn, Jan 4, 47; m 74; c 1. *Educ:* Univ Calif, Los Angeles, BS, 69, PhD(physics), 73. *Prof Exp:* Adj asst prof physics, Univ Calif, Los Angeles, 74-75; lectr, Univ Mass, Amherst, 75-77. *Concurrent Pos:* Teaching fel physics, Univ Calif, Los Angeles, 69-73; fel, Univ Mass, Amherst, 75-77; prin investr, Res Corp res grant, 77-79; prin investr, NSF res grant, 79-81. *Mem:* Am Phys Soc; Acoust Soc Am. *Res:* Low temperature physics; liquid helium; acoustics; quantum fluids and solids. *Mailing Add:* Idaho Nat Eng Lab Lockheed Martin Idaho Technol Inc PO Box 1625 Idaho Falls ID 83415

**TELSER, ALVIN GILBERT,** BIOCHEMISTRY, CELL BIOLOGY. *Current Pos:* asst prof, 71-77, ASSOC PROF ANAT & CELL BIOL, MED SCH, NORTHWESTERN UNIV, CHICAGO, 77- *Personal Data:* b Chicago, Ill, May 11, 39; m 67; c 2. *Educ:* Univ Chicago, BS, 61, PhD(biochem), 68. *Prof Exp:* Helen Hay Whitney Found fel develop biol, Brandeis Univ, 68-70; Helen Hay Whitney Found fel cell biol, Yale Univ, 70-71. *Mem:* AAAS; Soc Develop Biol; Am Soc Cell Biol; NY Acad Sci; Sigma Xi. *Res:* Biochemical aspects of differentiation and development in eukaryotic systems with emphasis on understanding regulatory mechanisms at a molecular level. *Mailing Add:* Dept Cell Molecular & Struct Biol Northwestern Univ Med Sch 303 E Chicago Ave Chicago IL 60611-3008. *Fax:* 312-503-7912

**TEMARES, M LEWIS,** MANAGEMENT TECHNOLOGY, TELECOMMUNICATIONS. *Current Pos:* adj prof mkt & comput info systs, 80-92, vpres info resources & chief info officer, 80-94, PROF COMPUT & INFO SYSTS, UNIV MIAMI, 92-, VPRES INFO TECHNOL & DEAN, COL ENG, 94- *Personal Data:* b New York, NY, Feb 5, 41; m, Louise; c Scott, Stacy, Christy & Jenny. *Educ:* City Col NY, New York, BBA, 62, MBA, 64; Columbia Univ, MS, 69; City Univ NY, PhD(statist), 80. *Prof Exp:* Proj dir, Bernard M Baruch Col, 62-71, asst dean admin, 71, registr, 71-77; dir & asst to provost, Hunter Col, 77-80. *Concurrent Pos:* Lectr statist, Bernard M Baruch Col, 62-78. *Mem:* Sr mem Inst Elec & Electronics Engrs; Soc Info Mgt. *Res:* Statistical sampling in the area of operations research and auditing; management and leadership in information technology. *Mailing Add:* PO Box 248294 Coral Gables FL 33124-0620. *Fax:* 305-284-3815; *E-Mail:* mtemares@miami.edu

**TEMES, CLIFFORD LAWRENCE,** ELECTRICAL ENGINEERING. *Current Pos:* SR SCIENTIST, SENTEL CORP, 94- *Personal Data:* b Jersey City, NJ, Feb 4, 30; m 63, Vivian Newman; c David, Lisa & Joel. *Educ:* Cooper Union, BEE, 51; Case Inst Technol, MS, 54; Columbia Univ, EE, 60; Polytech Inst Brooklyn, PhD(elec eng), 65. *Honors & Awards:* Qual Award, Naval Res Lab, 78. *Prof Exp:* Electronic scientist instrumentation, Nat Adv Comt Aeronaut, 51-54; lab supvr radar systs, Electronics Res Lab, Columbia Univ, 56-60; sr proj engr elec eng, Fed Sci Corp, 60-65; mem tech staff, Gen Res Corp, 65-74; mem dept staff, Mitre Corp, 74-77; head, Search Radar Br, Naval Res Lab, 77-94. *Concurrent Pos:* Consult, Electronics Res Lab, Columbia Univ, 60-65; reviewer, Inst Elec & Electronics Engrs, 60-75; Prentice-Hall, 68-69. *Mem:* Sigma Xi; sr mem Inst Elec & Electronics Engrs. *Res:* Radar systems and technology; signal processing and wave form design; surveillance and tracking radar; clutter rejection; pulse compression and high resolution systems. *Mailing Add:* 8321 Cherry Valley Lane Alexandria VA 22309

**TEMES, GABOR CHARLES,** ELECTRICAL ENGINEERING, COMPUTER SCIENCES. *Current Pos:* chmn dept elec sci & eng, 75-80, PROF ELEC ENG, UNIV CALIF, LOS ANGELES, 69- *Personal Data:* b Budapest, Hungary, Oct 14, 29; Can citizen; m 54; c 2. *Educ:* Budapest Tech Univ, Dipl Ing, 52; Eotvos Lorand Univ, Budapest, dipl phys, 54; Univ Ottawa, PhD(elec eng), 61. *Honors & Awards:* Darlington Award, Inst Elec & Electronics Engrs, Circuits & Systs Soc, 69, 81 & Centennial Medal, 84. *Prof Exp:* Asst prof elec eng, Budapest Tech Univ, 52-56; proj engr, Measurement Eng Ltd, 57-59; dept head networks, Northern Elec Co Ltd, 59-64; group leader light electronics, Stanford Linear Accelerator Ctr, 64-66; corp consult networks, Ampex Corp, Calif, 66-69. *Concurrent Pos:* Ed, Trans on Circuit Theory, 69-71; consult, TRW, Rockwell Int, 75-, Am Microsysts, Inc, 78- & Xerox Corp, 80- *Mem:* Fel Inst Elec & Electronics Engrs. *Res:* Integrated circuit design, filters and digital signal processing. *Mailing Add:* Rm 202 Elec & Comput Eng Bldg Ore State Univ Corvallis OR 97331

**TEMEYER, KEVIN BRUCE,** BIOLOGICAL CONTROL OF INSECTS, PLASMID BIOLOGY. *Current Pos:* res microbiologist, 82-89, RES MOLECULAR BIOLOGIST, AGR RES SERV, USDA, KERRVILLE, TEX, 90- *Personal Data:* b Independence, Iowa, July 15, 51. *Educ:* Iowa State Univ, BS, 73; Univ Mo, MA, 77, PhD(biol sci), 82. *Honors & Awards:* Young Investr Award, Am Soc Microbiol, 84; Fed Consortium Technol Transfer Award, Fed Lab Consortium, 93. *Prof Exp:* Res asst, Vet Med Res Inst, Iowa State Univ, Ames, Iowa, 73; teaching asst gen biol, Univ Mo, Columbia, Mo, 75-78 & 80-82, res asst, 78-82. *Mem:* Soc Invert Path; Soc Indust Microbiol; Southwestern Asn Parasitol. *Res:* Molecular genetics, physiology, plasmid biology and toxicology of entomopathogenic bacteria, particularly Bacillus thuringiensis; nutritional physiology and microecology of horn fly larvae; molecular phylogeny of ectoparasitic Dipteran insects. *Mailing Add:* US Livestock Insects Lab USDA Agr Res Serv 2700 Fredericksburg Rd Kerrville TX 78028. *Fax:* 830-792-0314; *E-Mail:* ktemeyer@ktc.com

**TEMIN, RAYLA GREENBERG,** GENETICS. *Current Pos:* Proj assoc, Univ Wis-Madison, 63-72, asst scientist med genetics & genetics, 72-82, adj assoc prof, 82-88, ADJ PROF, UNIV WIS-MADISON, 88- *Personal Data:* b New York, NY, May 4, 36; m 62, Howard M Temin; c 2. *Educ:* Brooklyn Col, BS, 56; Univ Wis, MS, 58, PhD(genetics), 63. *Concurrent Pos:* Fulbright scholar, Inst Animal Genetics, Edinburgh, 59-60. *Mem:* Genetics Soc Am. *Res:* Studies of major modifiers of the segregation distorter, a meiotic drive gene in Drosophila melanogaster; teaching of undergraduate genetics. *Mailing Add:* Dept Genetics 118 Genetics Univ Wis Madison 445 Henry Mall Madison WI 53706-1577. *Fax:* 608-262-2976

**TEMIN, SAMUEL CANTOR,** POLYMER CHEMISTRY. *Current Pos:* CONSULT, 85- *Personal Data:* b Washington, DC, Nov 4, 19; m 47, Esther H Crowell; c Harriet (Collins) & Thomas. *Educ:* Wilson Teachers Col, BS, 39; Univ Md, MS, 43, PhD(org chem), 49. *Prof Exp:* Res chemist, Army Chem Ctr, Md, 42-44; asst gen org chem & biochem, Univ Md, 46-48; res chemist, Indust Rayon Corp, Ohio, 49-53, res supvr, 53-58; mgr polymer chem group, Explor Sect, Koppers Co, Inc, 58-65; asst dir, Fabric Res Labs, Inc, Mass, 65-72; sect head polymer chem, Lexington Lab, Kendall Co, Colgate-Palmolive Co, Lexington, 72-83, sr scientist, 83-85. *Concurrent Pos:* Lectr, Pa State Univ, 63-65, Northeastern Univ, 66-77, Tufts Univ, 78 & Fla Atlantic Univ, 88, 90. *Mem:* Am Chem Soc; Fiber Soc; Int Asn Dent Res; Soc Plastics Engrs. *Res:* Polymer synthesis and structural relationships, adhesives, dental materials, monomer synthesis. *Mailing Add:* 5297 Brookview Dr Boynton Beach FL 33437

**TEMKIN, AARON,** ATOMIC PHYSICS. *Current Pos:* SR SCIENTIST, LAB ASTRON & SOLAR PHYSICS, GODDARD SPACE FLIGHT CTR, NASA, 60- *Personal Data:* b Morristown, NJ, Aug 15, 29; wid; c Philip H & Jean M. *Educ:* Rutgers Univ, BS, 51; Mass Inst Technol, PhD(physics), 56. *Honors & Awards:* Goddard Except Performance Award, NASA, 71. *Prof Exp:* Fulbright fel, Ger, 56-57; physicist, US Naval Res Lab, 57-58. *Mem:* Fel Am Phys Soc. *Res:* Scattering of electrons from atoms, molecules, polarized orbitals, nonadiabatic theory; oxygen, hydrogen; threshold law for electron-atom impact ionization; symmetric Euler angle decomposition of three body problem; calculation of autoionization states; resonance projection operators; fixed-nuclei, adiabatic-nuclei and hybrid theories of electron-molecule scattering; non-iterative numerical technique for solution of elliptic partial differential equations. *Mailing Add:* Code 682 NASA-Goddard Space Flight Ctr Greenbelt MD 20771. *Fax:* 301-286-1753

**TEMKIN, OWSEI,** HISTORY OF MEDICINE & SCIENCE. *Current Pos:* assoc, Johns Hopkins Univ, 32-35, from assoc prof to prof, 35-58, William H Welch prof & dir dept, 58-68, EMER WILLIAM H WELCH PROF HIST MED, JOHNS HOPKINS UNIV, 68- *Personal Data:* b Minsk, Belarus, Oct 6, 02; US citizen; wid; c 2. *Educ:* Univ Leipzig, MD, 27. *Hon Degrees:* LLD, Johns Hopkins Univ, 73; DSc, Med Col Ohio, 75. *Honors & Awards:* William H Welch Medal, Am Asn Hist Med, 52; Sarton Medal, Hist Sci Soc, 60; Hideyo Noguchi lectr, Johns Hopkins Univ, 69; Messenger lectr, Cornell Univ, 70; Prize Distinguished Scholar Humanities, Am Coun Learned Soc, 62. *Prof Exp:* Intern, St Jacob Hosp, Leipzig, Ger, 27-28; asst hist med, Univ Leipzig, 28-32, pvt dozent, 31-33. *Concurrent Pos:* Actg ed & ed, Bull Hist Med, 48-68. *Mem:* Nat Acad Sci; Am Philos Soc; Am Acad Arts & Sci; Am Asn Hist Med (pres, 58-60); Hist Sci Soc. *Res:* Life and work of Hippocrates and Galen. *Mailing Add:* 830 W 40th St Baltimore MD 21211

**TEMKIN, RICHARD JOEL,** LASERS, PLASMA PHYSICS. *Current Pos:* staff mem physics, Francis Bitter Nat Magnet Lab, Mass Inst Technol, 74-79, asst group leader, 79, group leader, 80-85, DIV HEAD, PLASMA FUSION CTR, MASS INST TECHNOL, 86-, SR SCIENTIST, PHYS DEPT, 86- *Personal Data:* b Boston, Mass, Jan 8, 45; m 72; c 3. *Educ:* Harvard Col, BA, 66; Mass Inst Technol, PhD(physics), 71. *Prof Exp:* Res fel physics, Harvard Univ, 71-74. *Concurrent Pos:* IBM Corp fel, 72-74; assoc ed, Int J Infrared & Millimeter Waves, Trans Electron Devices, Inst Elec & Electronics Engrs, prog comt, Conf Infrared & Millimeter Waves. *Mem:* Am Phys Soc; Fusion Power Asn; Inst Elec & Electronics Engrs. *Res:* Submillimeter lasers, both theory and experiment; laser breakdown and heating of gases; optical and submillimeter diagnostics of plasmas; plasma heating; cyclotron resonance masers and gyrotrons, free electron lasers. *Mailing Add:* Sci & Plasma Fusion Ctr MIT-NW16 Cambridge MA 02139

**TEMKIN, SAMUEL,** FLUID DYNAMICS, ACOUSTICS. *Current Pos:* from asst prof to assoc prof eng, Rutgers Univ, NB, 67-73, grad prog dir mech & aerospace engr, 76-89, chmn, Dept Mech & Aerospace Eng, 80-89, PROF MECH ENG, RUTGERS UNIV, NB, 73-, ASSOC PROVOST ACAD AFFAIRS SCI, 92- *Personal Data:* b Mexico City, Mex, Jan 10, 36; m 65, Judith C Olchak; c David & Michael. *Educ:* Univ Nuevo Leon, ME, 60; Brown Univ, ScM, 64, PhD(eng), 66. *Honors & Awards:* Victor & Erna Hasselblad Found Award, Sweden, 86. *Prof Exp:* Sr scientist acoust, Bolt Beranek & Newman, Inc, 66-67. *Concurrent Pos:* Consult, US Army Ballistic Res Labs, 69-73 & Naval Res Lab, Washington, DC, 86-89; vis prof, Israel Inst Technol, 74-75, Royal Inst Technol, Stockholm, Sweden, 89, Univ Twente, Enschede, Neth, 90 & Inst Acoust, Consejo Super de Investigaciones Cientificas, Madrid, Spain, 92 & 93; vis scientist, Inst Transuranium Elements, Karlsruhe, Ger, 90. *Mem:* Am Phys Soc; Acoust Soc Am; fel Am Soc Mech Engrs. *Res:* Acoustic wave propagation; fluid dynamics of aerosols; droplet dynamics; bubble dynamics. *Mailing Add:* PO Box 909 Piscataway NJ 08855-0909. *Fax:* 732-932-8184; *E-Mail:* temkin@jose.rutgers.edu

**TEMME, DONALD H(ENRY),** ELECTRICAL ENGINEERING. *Current Pos:* assoc group leader, 58-76, GROUP LEADER, LINCOLN LAB, MASS INST TECHNOL, 76- *Personal Data:* b Winside, Nebr, Jan 12, 28; m 55; c 2. *Educ:* Univ Nebr, BS, 49; Mass Inst Technol, MS, 55. *Prof Exp:* Asst physics, Univ Nebr, 49-51. *Mem:* Inst Elec & Electronics Engrs. *Res:* Phased array radar components. *Mailing Add:* Mass Inst Technol Lincoln Lab 244 Wood St PO Box 73 Lexington MA 02173

**TEMMER, GEORGES MAXIME,** NUCLEAR PHYSICS. *Current Pos:* dir, Nuclear Physics Lab, 63-85, from prof to univ prof, 63-91, EMER PROF PHYSICS, RUTGERS UNIV, NB, 91- *Personal Data:* b Vienna, Austria, Apr 10, 22; nat US; m 43, 79. *Educ:* Queens Col, NY, BS, 43; Univ Calif, MA, 44, PhD(physics), 49. *Honors & Awards:* Lindback Award for Excellence in Res, Rutgers Univ, 73; Alexander von Humboldt Prize, 84. *Prof Exp:* Asst physics, Univ Calif, 43-44 & 46-49; res assoc, Univ Rochester, 49-51; physicist, Nat Bur Stand, 51-53; mem staff terrestrial magnetism, Carnegie Inst, 53-63; prof physics, Fla State Univ, 60-63. *Concurrent Pos:* Guest investr, Cryogenic Sect, Nat Bur Stand, 53-55; Guggenheim mem fel, Paris & Copenhagen, 56-57; vis prof, Univ Md, 59; Rutgers Res Coun fac fel, 68-69 & 75; Nat Acad Sci sr exchange scholar, People's Repub China, 80. *Mem:* Fel Am Phys Soc. *Res:* Nuclear reaction mechanisms; very short lifetimes; scattering; angular correlation; low temperature nuclear alignment; gamma-ray spectroscopy; Coulomb excitation; polarized particle sources; electron channeling radiation; beam-foil spectroscopy; nuclear arms race concerns. *Mailing Add:* Skillman Rd Skillman NJ 08558. *Fax:* 732-932-4343; *E-Mail:* temmer@rutphy

**TEMPEL, GEORGE EDWARD,** CARDIOVASCULAR, AUTONOMIC. *Current Pos:* ASSOC PROF PHYSIOL, MED UNIV SC, 78- *Personal Data:* b Feb 14, 44; m 68; c 2. *Educ:* Ind Univ, PhD(physiol), 72. *Mem:* Am Physiol Soc; Sigma Xi. *Mailing Add:* Dept Physiol Med Univ SC 171 Ashley Ave Charleston SC 29425-2258

**TEMPELIS, CONSTANTINE H,** IMMUNOLOGY. *Current Pos:* from asst res immunologist to assoc res immunologist, Univ Calif, Berkeley, 58-66, lectr, 60-66, assoc prof-in-residence immunol, 67-70, assoc prof, 70-72, prof immunol, Sch Pub Health, 72-95 PROF GRAD SCH, UNIV CALIF, BERKELEY, 96- *Personal Data:* b Superior, Wis, Aug 27, 27; m 55, Nancy L Foster; c William H & Daniel S. *Educ:* Univ Wis-Superior, BS, 50; Univ Wis-Madison, MS, 53, PhD(med microbiol), 55. *Prof Exp:* Proj assoc immunol, Univ Wis, 55-57; instr microbiol, Sch Med, Univ WVa, 57-58. *Concurrent Pos:* NIH career develop award, 65-70; vis scientist, Wellcome Res Labs, Eng, 77-78, gen & exp path, Univ Innsbruck, Austria, 85, 90, 91 & 92; Fogarty Sr Int Fel, 77-78. *Mem:* AAAS; Am Asn Immunol; NY Acad Sci; Sigma Xi; Fedn Am Soc Exp Biol. *Res:* Studies of immune regulation in the chicken and host-parasite interactions. *Mailing Add:* Sch Pub Health Univ Calif Berkeley CA 94720. *Fax:* 510-642-6350; *E-Mail:* miyuki@uclink3.berkeley.edu

**TEMPERLEY, JUDITH KANTACK,** WEAPONS SYSTEMS ANALYSIS. *Current Pos:* Res physicist, US Army Ballistic Res Lab, 65-84, chief, Air Defense Systs Br, 84-86, chief, Ballistic Weapons Systs Eng Br, 86-92, CHIEF, WEAPONS ANALYSIS BR, US ARMY RES LAB, 92- *Personal Data:* b Meriden, Conn, Feb 12, 36; wid. *Educ:* Univ Rochester, BS, 57; Univ Ore, MS, 59, PhD(physics), 65. *Mem:* Am Phys Soc; Sigma Xi. *Res:* Engineering analysis and effectiveness studies of new concepts in weapon systems; computer simulation methodology. *Mailing Add:* 31 Neptune Dr Joppa MD 21085. *E-Mail:* temper@arl.army.mil

**TEMPERO, KENNETH FLOYD,** PHARMACEUTICAL, PHARMACOLOGY. *Current Pos:* CONSULT, 96- *Personal Data:* b Morrisville, Vt, Sept 30, 39; m 80, Jeanne M Smith; c Suzelle J & Gavin K. *Educ:* Univ Nebr, BSc, 61; Northwestern Univ, MSc, 64, PhD, 66, MD, 67. *Hon Degrees:* MBA, Fairleigh Dickinson Univ, 81. *Prof Exp:* Med intern, Cincinnati Gen Hosp, 67-68; resident internal med, Univ Minn Hosps, 68-69 & 71-72; dir clin pharm, Merck/MSDRL, Rahway, NJ, 73-75, sr dir, 75-78, exec dir clin res, 78-83; sr vpres clin res & med affairs, G D Searle & Co, Skokie, Ill, 83-87; chmn & chief exec officer, MGI Pharma, Inc, 87-96. *Concurrent Pos:* Instr & NIH spec res fel, Univ Minn, 72-73; vis physician, Rockefeller Univ, New York, 74-85; assoc prof, Drew Med Sch, Los Angeles, 85-87; treas, Villa Turicum Asn, Lake Forest, Ill, 85. *Mem:* Am Col Physicians; Am Soc Clin Pharmaceut & Therapeut; Drug Info Asn. *Res:* Pharmacology; therapeutics. *Mailing Add:* 1290 Frencie Creek Dr Wayzata MN 55391-9102

**TEMPERO, MARGARET ANN,** GASTROINTESTINAL ONCOLOGY. *Current Pos:* Asst prof, 83-87, ASSOC PROF MED, UNIV NEBR MED CTR, 87- *Personal Data:* b Urbana, Ill, Dec 9 47,; m, Richard; c Rick & Michael. *Educ:* Creighton Univ, BS, 74; Univ Nebr Med Ctr, MD, 77. *Concurrent Pos:* Consult, Methodist Hosp, 83-, St Anthonys Regional Hosp, 83-, St Francis Med Ctr, 83-, Bishop Clarkson Hosp, 90-; chief oncol, Omaha Vet Med Ctr, 83-; med dir, University East Hosp, 92- *Mem:* Fel Am Col Physicians; Am Soc Clin Oncol; Am Asn Clin Res; Am Fedn Clin Res; Am Gastroenterol Asn; Sigma Xi. *Res:* Focus is on novel therapy for advanced gastrointestinal cancers; role of radio labeled antibodies for therapy of metastatic cancer. *Mailing Add:* 717 Hackleberry Rd Omaha NE 68198-3330

**TEMPEST, BRUCE DEAN,** INFECTIOUS DISEASES. *Current Pos:* CLIN DIR SURVEILLANCE PROJ, GALLUP INDIAN MED CTR, 71-, CHIEF INTERNAL MED, 82- *Personal Data:* b Catasauqua, Pa, Nov 3, 35; m 59; c 3. *Educ:* Lafayette Col, AB, 57; Univ Pa, MD, 61; Am Bd Internal Med, cert, 68 & 74. *Prof Exp:* Resident med, Philadelphia Gen Hosp, 61-65; fel allergy & immunol, Univ Pa Hosp, 65-67; chief internal med, Dept Health, Educ & Welfare, USPHS, Tuba City, 67-70 & Gallup Indian Med Ctr, 70-71. *Concurrent Pos:* Clin asst prof, Dept Med, Sch Med, Univ NMex, 73-78, clin assoc prof, 78-; clin dir, Pneumococcal Surveillance Proj, 71-76, dep chief internal med, 75-82. *Mem:* Fel Am Col Physicians. *Res:* Epidemiology of pneumonia, especially pneumococcal pneumonia and the study of clinical manifestations; efficacy of vaccines in pneumonia prevention. *Mailing Add:* 1127 Boggio Dr Gallup NM 87301

**TEMPLE, AUSTIN LIMIEL, (JR),** APPLIED MATHEMATICS. *Current Pos:* asst prof, 70-75, ASSOC PROF MATH, NORTHWESTERN STATE UNIV, 75- *Personal Data:* b Leesville, La, Nov 3, 40; m 62; c 2. *Educ:* Centenary Col La, BS, 62; La State Univ, Baton Rouge, MA, 64; George Peabody Col, PhD(math), 71. *Prof Exp:* Instr math, Northwestern State Univ, 64-65, asst prof, 67-69; instr, Vanderbilt Univ, 69-70. *Mem:* Math Asn Am. *Res:* Mathematics education, in-service curriculum for elementary school teachers; develop and standardize tests for college freshmen math courses; develop computer statistical library. *Mailing Add:* 937 Harling Lane Natchitoches LA 71457

**TEMPLE, CARROLL GLENN,** ORGANIC CHEMISTRY, MEDICINAL CHEMISTRY. *Current Pos:* Assoc chemist, Southern Res Inst, 55-59, res chemist, 60-64, sr chemist, 64-80, HEAD, PHARMACEUT CHEM DIV, SOUTHERN RES INST, 81-, DIR, ORG CHEM RES DEPT, 91- *Personal Data:* b Hickory, NC, Mar 7, 32; m 56, Felton Newell; c Laura F & Sara L. *Educ:* Lenoir-Rhyne Col, BS, 54; Birmingham-Southern Col, MS, 58; Univ NC, PhD(org chem), 62. *Mem:* Am Chem Soc. *Res:* Synthesis of potential antimalarian and anticancer drugs. *Mailing Add:* 2224 Lynnchester Circle Birmingham AL 35216

**TEMPLE, DAVIS LITTLETON, JR,** MEDICINAL CHEMISTRY. *Current Pos:* sr investr, 70-80, DIR CHEM RES, MEAD JOHNSON & CO, DIV BRISTOL-MYERS CO, 80- *Personal Data:* b Tupelo, Miss, June 10, 43; m 66. *Educ:* Univ Miss, BS, 66, PhD(med chem), 69. *Prof Exp:* Res assoc, La State Univ, New Orleans, 69-70. *Concurrent Pos:* Mem, Bio-Org & Nat Prod Study Sect, NIH, 81; adv bd, Advan Develop Chem Ser, Am Chem Soc. *Mem:* AAAS; Am Chem Soc; Soc Neurosci; hon mem Brit Brain Asn; NY Acad Sci. *Res:* Central nervous system, cardiovascular and respiratory drugs; chemistry and biology. *Mailing Add:* 1016 Durham Rd Wallingford CT 06492

**TEMPLE, KENNETH LOREN,** GEOENVIRONMENTAL SCIENCE. *Current Pos:* RETIRED. *Personal Data:* b St Paul, Minn, Mar 22, 18; m 43; c 3. *Educ:* Middlebury Col, AB, 40; Univ Wis, MS, 42; Rutgers Univ, PhD(microbiol), 48. *Prof Exp:* Chemist, US Naval Res Lab, DC, 42-45; instr bact, Univ RI, 48; assoc res specialist, Eng Exp Sta, WVa Univ, 48-53; microbiologist, Tex Co, 53-55; assoc prof microbiol, Agr Exp Sta, Mont State Univ, 55-61; sr res specialist, Commonwealth Sci & Indust Res Orgn, Australia, 61-63; prof microbiol, Mont State Univ, 64-83. *Res:* Autotrophic bacteria; microbiology of thermal waters; coal mines; geomicrobiology. *Mailing Add:* 6950 Tepee Ridge Rd Bozeman MT 59715-8631

**TEMPLE, PETER LAWRENCE,** SOLAR ENERGY. *Current Pos:* CONSULT, PETER TEMPLE & ASSOC, 82- *Personal Data:* b Springfield, Mass, Dec 13, 46; m 78; c 1. *Educ:* Dartmouth Col, AB, 69. *Prof Exp:* Instr physics, Mount Holyoke Col, 70-73; instr physics eng, Holyoke Community Col, 76-77; sr res engr, res & develop solar energy, Total Environ Action, Inc, 77-82. *Concurrent Pos:* Tech ed, Solar Age, Solar Vision Inc, 77- *Mem:* Int Solar Energy Soc. *Res:* Solar energy system design; building energy analysis; solar materials science; appropriate technology for developing countries; innovative solar product development; photovoltaics; passive solar systems. *Mailing Add:* Box 65 Harrisville NH 03450-0065

**TEMPLE, ROBERT DWIGHT,** ORGANIC CHEMISTRY. *Current Pos:* RES CHEMIST, PROCTER & GAMBLE CO, 66-, SECT HEAD, 72- *Personal Data:* b Des Moines, Iowa, July 1, 41; div; c 4. *Educ:* Clemson Col, BS, 62; Fla State Univ, PhD(chem), 66. *Prof Exp:* Chemist, E I du Pont de Nemours & Co, 62. *Mem:* Am Chem Soc. *Res:* Physical organic chemistry. *Mailing Add:* 1421 Hillcrest Rd Cincinnati OH 45224

**TEMPLE, ROBERT JAY,** INTERNAL MEDICINE. *Current Pos:* med officer, Div Endocrine & Metab Drug Prod, 72-74, asst to dir, Bur Drugs, 74-76, DIR, DIV CARDIO-RENAL DRUG PROD, BUR DRUGS, FOOD & DRUG ADMIN, 76-, MED POLICY ASSOC DIR, CTR DRUG EVAL

& RES. *Personal Data:* b New York, NY, July 18, 41; m 63; c 1. *Educ:* Harvard Col, BA, 63; NY Univ, MD, 67. *Honors & Awards:* Award of Merit, Food & Drug Admin, 78. *Prof Exp:* Intern med, Columbia-Presby Med Ctr, 67-68, asst resident, 68-69; clin assoc, Clin Endocrinol Br, Nat Inst Arthritis, Metab & Digestive Dis, 69-72. *Concurrent Pos:* Mem, Coop Studies Rev Comt, Vet Admin, 77- *Mem:* Am Soc Clin Pharmacol & Therapeut; AAAS; Am Fedn Clin Res. *Mailing Add:* Ctr Drug Eval & Res Food & Drug Admin 1451 Rockville Pike Rm HFD10 Rockville MD 20855

**TEMPLE, STANLEY,** RESIROMETRY, FLUOROCARBON CHEMISTRY. *Current Pos:* CONSULT CHEMIST, 93- *Personal Data:* b New York, NY, Aug 17, 30; m 83, Romaine; c Ellen J & Amy S. *Educ:* NY Univ, AB, 52, PhD(org chem), 58. *Prof Exp:* Res fel cancer steroids, Med Sch, Univ Va, 58-60; res chemist, Plant Tech Sect, Org Chem Dept, E I Du Pont de Nemours & Co, Inc, 60, res chemist, Process Dept, 60-61, res chemist, Res & Develop Div, Org Chem Dept, 61-74, sr res chemist, Jackson Labs, Chambers Works, 74-93. *Mem:* Sigma Xi; Royal Soc Chem; NY Acad Sci. *Res:* Fluorochemicals; fluorinated polymers; surface active agents; bio-organic chemistry; cosmetics; environmental chemistry; pollution control; water treatment; food processing. *Mailing Add:* 214 East Ct Wilmington DE 19810. *E-Mail:* stemple998@aol.com

**TEMPLE, STANLEY A,** CONSERVATION BIOLOGY, ENDANGERED SPECIES. *Current Pos:* from asst prof to assoc prof, 76-84, PROF WILDLIFE ECOL, UNIV WIS-MADISON, 84-, BEERS-BASCOM PROF CONSERV, 80- *Personal Data:* b Cleveland, Ohio, Sept 26, 46; m 80, Anita J Buck. *Educ:* Cornell Univ, BS, 68, MS, 70, PhD(vert zool), 73. *Honors & Awards:* Distinguished Achievement Award, Soc Conserv Biol, 89. *Prof Exp:* Teaching asst ecol, Cornell Univ, 67-72; res biologist, World Wildlife Fund, 72-75; res assoc ornith, Cornell Univ, 75-76. *Concurrent Pos:* Dir, Int Coun Bird Preserv, 76-78, secy, 78-, dir, 80-; comt mem, Nat Acad Sci, 86-87 & 89-91; vis prof, Univ Wis, 94-95. *Mem:* Fel Am Ornithologists Union; Soc Conserv Biol (pres, 91-93); Nature Conserv; Int Coun Bird Preserv; Wildlife Conserv Int. *Res:* Conservation biology; wildlife ecology; endangered species and species that have declined because of human actions; bird populations and communities. *Mailing Add:* Dept Wildlife Ecol 226 Russell Lab Univ Wis 1630 Linden Dr Madison WI 53706-1520. *Fax:* 608-262-6099

**TEMPLE, VICTOR ALBERT KEITH,** SOLID STATE PHYSICS. *Current Pos:* DIR, HARRIS SEM-I CONDUCTOR, LATHAM, NY, 93- *Personal Data:* b Winnipeg, Man, Apr 3, 44. *Educ:* Univ Man, BSc, 67; MacMaster Univ, MEng, 69, PhD(physics), 72. *Prof Exp:* Physicist, Res & Develop Ctr, Gen Elec, 74-93. *Concurrent Pos:* Nat Adv Coun fel, MacMaster Univ, 72-74; consult, 93- *Mem:* Inst Elec & Electronics Engrs. *Res:* Physics of power semiconductor carriers and the design, fabrication and development of new and improved power semiconductor devices. *Mailing Add:* Harris Sem-I Conductor 3 N Way Lane N Latham NY 12110

**TEMPLEMAN, GARETH J,** PHYSICAL CHEMISTRY, ANALYTICAL CHEMISTRY. *Current Pos:* GROUP DIR, SCI SERV, NABISCO FOODS GROUP, 86- *Personal Data:* b Little Falls, NY, Apr 21, 37; m 70; c 1. *Educ:* Ohio Wesleyan Univ, BA, 60; State Univ NY, Buffalo, PhD(chem), 70. *Prof Exp:* Res fel phys org chem, State Univ NY, Buffalo, 69-70; scientist, Pillsbury Co, 70-71, group leader instrumentation, Corp Res, 71-78; mgr appl res, Pepsico Inc, 78-80; dir analytical serv, Stand Brands, Inc, 80-81; group dir, Res Serv, Nabisco Brands, Inc, 81-84, group dir sci res, 85-86. *Mem:* Am Chem Soc; Inst Food Technologists; Am Asn Cereal Chemists. *Res:* Nuclear magnetic resonance; mass spectrometry; analytical robotics; flavors; perception; food chemistry; microwave heating; fats and oils; food analysis; beverage technology; emulsions; chemical kinetics; food chemistry; food microbiology; cereal chemistry; polymer chemistry; sensory analysis; information science and systems. *Mailing Add:* 2 Natures Way Sparta NJ 07871

**TEMPLER, DAVID ALLEN,** POLYMER CHEMISTRY. *Current Pos:* Sr chemist, 68-75, lab head, Latin Am oper, 75-78, RES & DEVELOP MGR, INDUST CHEMS, LATIN AM REGION, TECH SERV LAB, ROHM & HAAS, 78- *Personal Data:* b Chicago, Ill, July 23, 42; m 65; c 1. *Educ:* Northwestern Univ, Evanston, BS, 64; Ind Univ, Bloomington, PhD(org chem), 68. *Mem:* AAAS; Am Chem Soc; Royal Soc Chem. *Res:* Polymer synthesis and characterization with regard to applications in the area of organic coatings; medicinal chemistry; leather chemistry; textile chemistry; ion exchange. *Mailing Add:* 1899 Nicole Dr Dresher PA 19025-1430

**TEMPLETON, ALAN ROBERT,** EVOLUTIONARY GENETICS, GENETIC EPIDEMIOLOGY. *Current Pos:* assoc prof, 77-81, PROF, DEPT BIOL, WASH UNIV, 81- *Personal Data:* b Litchfield, Ill, Feb 28, 47; m 69, Bonnie Altman; c Jeremy A & Jeffrey A. *Educ:* Wash Univ, AB, 69; Univ Mich, MA, 72, PhD(human genetics), 72. *Honors & Awards:* Edward Bean Award, Am Asn Zool Parks & Aquaria, 84 & 89. *Prof Exp:* Jr fel, Soc Fels Univ Mich, 72-74; vis scholar, Dept Genetics, Univ Hawaii, 74; asst prof, Dept Zool, Univ Tex Austin, 74-77; vis asst prof, Dept Biol, Univ Sao Paulo, Brazil, 76. *Concurrent Pos:* Genetics study sect, NIH, 83-87; vis prof, Dept Human Genetics, Univ Mich, 85 & distinguished vis scientist, Mus Zool, 86; prin investr, NSF & NIH, 86-; mem, Biodiversity, Task Force State Mo, 90-92; fac, Conserv Acad Am Asn Zool Parks & Aquaria, 91-93; vis fel, Merton Col, Oxford, UK, 92; consult, St Louis Zool Garden, 79, Nat Zool Park, Washington, DC, 83-89; res assoc, Mo Bot Garden, 80-; mem, Comt Human Genome Diversity Proj, Nat Res Coun, 96-97. *Mem:* AAAS; Soc Study Evolution (vpres, 82, pres, 06-97); Genetics Soc Am; Soc Conserv Biol; Nature Conservancy. *Res:* Molecular genetics, mathematical and statistical theory and computer programming to apply evolutionary genetics to a wide variety of problems including, genetic epidemiology, conservation biology, the meaning and origin of species, ecological genetics and the reconstruction of evolutionary history of a variety of species including humans. *Mailing Add:* Dept Biol Wash Univ St Louis MO 63130-4899. *Fax:* 314-935-4432; *E-Mail:* temple—a@biodec.wustl.edu

**TEMPLETON, ARCH W,** medicine, radiology, for more information see previous edition

**TEMPLETON, CHARLES CLARK,** PHYSICAL CHEMISTRY. *Current Pos:* RETIRED. *Personal Data:* b Houston, Tex, Oct 4, 21; m 44; c 4. *Educ:* La Polytech Inst, BS, 42; Univ Wis, MS, 47, PhD(chem), 48. *Prof Exp:* Jr res chemist, Shell Oil Co, 42; res chemist, Univ Wis, 46-48; instr, Univ Mich, 48-50; staff res chemist, Bellaire Res Ctr, Shell Develop Co, 50-80. *Mem:* Am Chem Soc; Soc Petrol Engrs; Am Inst Mech Engrs. *Res:* Solvent extraction; phase equilibria; electrochemistry; multiphase fluid flow; petroleum production. *Mailing Add:* 6119 Reamer St Houston TX 77074-7543

**TEMPLETON, DAVID HENRY,** PHYSICAL CHEMISTRY. *Current Pos:* res chemist, Radiation Lab, Univ Calif, 46-47, from instr to assoc prof, Univ, 47-58, dean, Col Chem, 70-75, PROF CHEM, UNIV CALIF, BERKELEY, 58- *Personal Data:* b Houston, Tex, Mar 2, 20; m 48, Lieselotte Kamm; c Diana & Alan. *Educ:* La Polytech Inst, BS, 41; Univ Tex, MA, 43; Univ Calif, PhD(chem), 47. *Hon Degrees:* Fil Dr, Univ Uppsala, 77. *Honors & Awards:* Patterson Award, Am Crystallog Asn, 87. *Prof Exp:* Instr chem, Univ Tex, 42-44; res chemist, Metall Lab, Univ Chicago, 44-46. *Concurrent Pos:* Guggenheim mem fel, 53; lectr, Univ Lausanne, 82. *Mem:* Fel AAAS; Am Chem Soc; Am Crystallog Asn (pres, 85). *Res:* Properties of radioactive isotopes; nuclear reactions; structures of crystals; anomalous scattering of x-rays. *Mailing Add:* 1244 Brewster Dr El Cerrito CA 94530-2524

**TEMPLETON, FREDERIC EASTLAND,** RADIOLOGY. *Current Pos:* prof & exec officer, Univ Wash, 47-53, clin prof, 53-68, prof, 68-75, EMER PROF RADIOL, MED SCH, UNIV WASH, 75- *Personal Data:* b Portland, Ore, May 11, 05; m 36, 75; c 2. *Educ:* Washington Univ, BS, 27; Univ Ore, MD, 31. *Prof Exp:* Univ Chicago fel radiol, Univ Stockholm, 33-34; from instr to assoc prof roentgenol, Univ Chicago, 35-43; head dept radiol, Cleveland Clin, 43-45. *Mem:* Am Gastroenterol Asn; Am Roentgen Ray Soc (1st vpres, 54); fel AMA; Radiol Soc NAm; hon mem Mex Soc Radiol & Phys Ther; Sigma Xi. *Res:* Radiologic gastroenterology. *Mailing Add:* PO Box 103 Medina WA 98039-0103

**TEMPLETON, GEORGE EARL,** PLANT PATHOLOGY. *Current Pos:* from asst prof to prof, 58-85, univ prof plant path, 85-91, DISTINGUISHED PROF, UNIV ARK, FAYETTEVILLE, 91- *Personal Data:* b Little Rock, Ark, June 27, 31; m 58; c George E, Gary L, Patricia J & Larry E. *Educ:* Univ Ark, BS, 53, MS, 54; Univ Wis, PhD(plant path), 58. *Honors & Awards:* Excellence Award, Weed Sci Soc Am, 73; John White Award Excellence Agr Res, 79; Super Serv Award, USDA, 90; Ruth Allen Award, Am Phytopath Soc, 91. *Prof Exp:* Asst, Univ Wis, 56-58. *Concurrent Pos:* Joint planning & eval staff, US Dept Agr, Sci & Educ Admin, 80; Underwood fel, UK Agr Res Coun, 83; vis scholar, Univ Guelph, Ont, Can, 85. *Mem:* Fel Am Phytopath Soc; Mycol Soc Am; Sigma Xi; Weed Sci Soc Am; Brit Mycol Soc. *Res:* Physiology of parasitism; diseases of rice; biological control of weeds with plant pathogen. *Mailing Add:* Plant Pathol Univ Ark 1217 Plant Sci Fayetteville AR 72701-1202. *Fax:* 501-575-7601; *E-Mail:* gt27488@uafsysb. uark.edu

**TEMPLETON, GORDON HUFFINE,** PHYSIOLOGY. *Current Pos:* instr, 70-71, asst prof, 71-77, ASSOC PROF PHYSIOL, UNIV TEX SOUTHWESTERN MED SCH, DALLAS, 78- *Personal Data:* b Edowah, Tenn, July 17, 40; m 64; c 1. *Educ:* Univ Tenn, Knoxville, BS, 63; Southern Methodist Univ, MS, 68; Univ Tex Southwestern Med Sch Dallas, PhD(biophys), 70. *Prof Exp:* Instrumentation engr, Gen Dynamics Corp, Tex, 63-66. *Mem:* Am Heart Asn; Inst Elec & Electronics Engrs; Am Fedn Clin Res; Am Physiol Soc. *Res:* Muscle mechanics; detection of ventricular asynergy by three-dimensional imaging. *Mailing Add:* Dept Physiol Univ Tex Southwestern Med Sch 5323 Harry Hines Blvd Dallas TX 75235-7200

**TEMPLETON, IAN M,** METAL PHYSICS, LOW TEMPERATURE PHYSICS. *Current Pos:* RETIRED. *Personal Data:* b Rugby, Eng, July 31, 29; m 56, Elsa Wood; c Nicola J & Jennifer J. *Educ:* Oxford Univ, MA, 50, DPhil(physics), 53. *Prof Exp:* Fel physics, Nat Res Coun Can, 53-54; mem staff, Res Lab, Assoc Elec Industs, Rugby, 55-57; from asst res officer to sr res officer, Physics Div, Nat Res Coun Can, 57-71, prin res officer, 71-94. *Mem:* Fel Brit Inst Physics; fel Royal Soc Can; Can Asn Physicists. *Res:* Noise in semiconductors; superconductive devices; thermoelectricity; fermi surfaces; focused ion beams. *Mailing Add:* Nat Res Coun Inst Microstruct Sci Ottawa ON K1A 0R6 Can. *Fax:* 613-957-8734; *E-Mail:* imt@nrcphy1.phy. nrc.ca

**TEMPLETON, JOE WAYNE,** IMMUNOLOGY, GENETICS. *Current Pos:* assoc prof vet med & surg, 75-80, genetics & vet pathobiol, 80-87, PROF GENETICS & VET PATHOBIOL, COL VET MED, TEX A&M UNIV, 87- *Personal Data:* b Loraine, Tex, July 18, 41; m 62; c 1. *Educ:* Abilene Christian Col, BS, 64; Ore State Univ, PhD(genetics), 68. *Prof Exp:* Res fel genetics, Ore State Univ, 65-68; asst prof med genetics, Med Sch, Univ Ore, 68-75; asst prof microbiol & immunol, Baylor Col Med, Houston, 75-78. *Mem:* Genetics Soc Am; Am Genetic Asn. *Res:* Immunogenetics of organ transplantation, especially in the dog; general canine genetics. *Mailing Add:* 8400 Spring Creek College Station TX 77845

**TEMPLETON, JOHN CHARLES,** INORGANIC CHEMISTRY. *Current Pos:* Asst prof, 70-76, ASSOC PROF CHEM, WHITMAN COL, 76- *Personal Data:* b Buffalo, NY, June 7, 43; m 67; c 2. *Educ:* Col Wooster, BA, 65; Wesleyan Univ, MA, 67; Univ Colo, Boulder, PhD(inorg chem), 70. *Concurrent Pos:* NSF grant, Whitman Col, 71-73. *Mem:* Am Chem Soc; Sigma Xi (vpres, 72-73, pres, 73-74). *Res:* Studies of transition-metal complex ions in concentrated acid solutions, correlations with acidity functions; reaction kinetics and mechanisms; ultraviolet-visible spectroscopy. *Mailing Add:* Dept Chem Whitman Col Walla Walla WA 99362-2083

**TEMPLETON, JOHN Y, III,** SURGERY, CARDIOTHORACIC SURGERY. *Current Pos:* RETIRED. *Personal Data:* b Portsmouth, Va, July 1, 17; m 43, Dorothy E Fraley; c Mary B, Frances E, Dorothy A & Richard B. *Educ:* Davidson Col, BS, 37; Jefferson Med Col, MD, 41. *Hon Degrees:* DSc, Davidson Col, 87; LLD, Thomas Jefferson Univ, 87. *Prof Exp:* Clin prof surg, Jefferson Med Col, 57-64; prof surg, Univ Pa, 65-67; Samuel D Gross prof & head dept, Jefferson Med Col, 67-70, prof, 70-87, emer prof surg, 87- *Concurrent Pos:* Am Cancer Soc clin fel, Jefferson Hosp, 50-51, Runyon fel, 51-52. *Mem:* Am Surg Asn; Am Asn Thoracic Surg; Am Col Surg; Soc Vascular Surg; Int Soc Surg; Sigma Xi. *Res:* General, cardiac and gastrointestinal surgery. *Mailing Add:* 311 Airdale Rd Bryn Mawr PA 19010

**TEMPLETON, JOSEPH LESLIE,** EARLY TRANSITION METALS, METAL CLUSTERS. *Current Pos:* asst prof, 76-81, assoc prof inorg, 81-86, PROF, UNIV NC, CHAPEL HILL, 86-, ACTG ASSOC DEAN, 95- *Personal Data:* b Knoxville, Iowa, Nov 3, 48; m 71; c 2. *Educ:* Calif Inst Technol, BS, 71; Iowa State Univ, PhD(chem), 75. *Prof Exp:* NATO fel, Imp Col Sci & Technol, 75-76. *Mem:* Am Chem Soc. *Res:* Reactions of ligands bound to early transition metals off both regio and stereo control; small molecule activation, ligand coupling reactions and enantio selective catalysis. *Mailing Add:* Dept Chem CB 3290 Univ NC Chapel Hill NC 27599-3290

**TEMPLETON, MCCORMICK,** ANATOMY. *Current Pos:* RETIRED. *Personal Data:* b Cincinnati, Ohio, May 12, 23; m 54, Anne Ross; c 2. *Educ:* Columbia Univ, AB, 48; Univ Kans, PhD(anat), 58. *Prof Exp:* Asst zool, Columbia Univ, 48-49, asst oncol & path, Med Ctr, Univ Kans, 49-51, instr anat, 51-54, asst neuroembryol, 54-57; instr anat, Med Sch, Northwestern Univ, 57-65; asst prof, Sch Dent, Univ Southern Calif, 65-69, actg chmn dept, 71-76, chmn dept, 76-80, assoc prof anat, 69-88, co-dir temporomandibular joint & orofacial pain clin, 78-88. *Mem:* AAAS; Am Asn Anat; Biol Stain Comn; Am Soc Cell Biol. *Res:* Medical anatomy; histochemistry and microchemistry of nervous system of embryo and adult vertebrates; electrophoresis of esterases in blood and digestive tract. *Mailing Add:* 4529 Valdina Pl Los Angeles CA 90043

**TEMPLETON, WILLIAM LEES,** RADIOLOGICAL ASSESSMENT, MARINE DUMPING. *Current Pos:* RETIRED. *Personal Data:* b London, Eng, Apr 15, 26; m 52, Muriel H Williamson; c David, Andrew & Paul. *Educ:* Univ St Andrews, BSc, 50, Hons, 51. *Prof Exp:* Sr biologist, UK Atomic Energy Authority, Windscale, Eng, 51-65; sr res scientist radioecol, Pac Northwest Labs, 65-68, mgr aquatic ecol, 68-69, assoc dept mgr ecosysts, 69-85, sr staff scientist, Earth & Environ Sci Dept, 85-86, mgr Nepa & Radiol Protection, Off Hanford Environ, 86-94; proj mgr, ONR Arctic Naval Waste Assessment Prog, 94-96. *Concurrent Pos:* Consult, Int Atomic Energy Agency, 60-; mem panel radioactivity in marine environ, Nat Acad Sci-Nat Res Coun, 68-72, mem panel energy & environ, 75-78; chmn, Exec Comt Coord Res & Environ Surveillance Prog, Orgn Econ Coop & Develop/ Nuclear Energy Agency, 80-85; mem coun, Nat Coun Radiation Protection & Measurements, 85-97; consult, 94- *Mem:* Fel AAAS; Marine Biol Asn UK; UK Freshwater Biol Asn. *Res:* Waste management practice as related to radioecology and limnology of fresh and marine waters; effects of low level chronic pollution; radiological assessment. *Mailing Add:* 2331 Enterprise Dr Richland WA 99352. *E-Mail:* envassess@aol.com

**TENAZA, RICHARD REUBEN,** ETHOLOGY, ECOLOGY. *Current Pos:* ASST PROF BIOL, UNIV PAC, 77- *Personal Data:* b San Mateo, Calif, Mar 22, 39. *Educ:* San Francisco State Univ, BA, 64; Univ Calif, Davis, PhD(zool), 74. *Prof Exp:* Asst prof biol, Univ Pac, 75-76; res scientist wildlife biol, Sci Applns, Inc, 76-77. *Concurrent Pos:* Consult wildlife biol, Sci Applns, Inc, 77- *Mem:* AAAS. *Res:* Primatology; behavioral ecology; animal communication; marine birds and mammals; environmental impacts of oil development. *Mailing Add:* Dept Biol Sci Univ Pac 3601 Pacific Ave Stockton CA 95211-0110

**TENBRINK, NORMAN WAYNE,** QUATERNARY GEOLOGY. *Current Pos:* chmn dept, 83-85, dir, Fac Teaching & Learning Ctr, 95-96, PROF GEOL, GRAND VALLEY STATE COL, 73- *Personal Data:* b Shelby, Mich, May 17, 43; m 67, Shirley Bishop; c Andrew & Ryan. *Educ:* Univ Mich, Ann Arbor, BS, 66; Franklin & Marshall Col, MS, 68; Univ Wash, PhD(geol), 71. *Prof Exp:* Contract geologist, Geol Surv Greenland, 69-71; res fel geol, Inst Polar Studies & Dept Geol, Ohio State Univ, 71-72, asst dir, Inst Polar Studies, 72-73. *Concurrent Pos:* Field leader NSF grant, Univ Wash, 70-71; prin investr NSF grants, Ohio State Univ, 72-74 & 73-75; consult geohydrologist, Environ Protection Agency, 76-77; prin investr, Nat Park Serv & Nat geog grants, Grant Valley State Col & Univ Alaska, 77-83 & Alaska Geol Surv grants, 82-83; vis prof, SIll Univ, 79-80 & Univ Colo, 87; consult geologist, Woodward-Clyde consults, 80-81. *Mem:* Am Quaternary Asn; fel Arctic Inst NAm; Geol Soc Am. *Res:* Glacial geology and geomorphology of Arctic, Antarctic and alpine areas. *Mailing Add:* Dept Geol Grand Valley State Univ One Campus Dr Allendale MI 49401-9401. *E-Mail:* tenbrinn@gusu.edu

**TENBROEK, BERNARD JOHN,** ZOOLOGY. *Current Pos:* RETIRED. *Personal Data:* b Grand Rapids, Mich, Mar 29, 24; m 48; c 4. *Educ:* Calvin Col, BA, 49; Univ Colo, MA, 55, PhD(zool), 60. *Prof Exp:* From instr to assoc prof, Calvin Col, 55-66, chmn dept, 61-73, prof biol, 66-86. *Mem:* AAAS; Am Soc Zool; Sigma Xi. *Res:* Studies on thyroid and pituitary function in neotenic forms of Ambystoma tigrinum. *Mailing Add:* 2307 Edgewood St SE Grand Rapids MI 49546

**TENCA, JOSEPH IGNATIUS,** ENDODONTICS. *Current Pos:* PROF & CHMN ENDODONTICS DEPT, SCH DENT MED, 75-, DIR, ADVAN EDUC, TUFTS UNIV, 83- *Personal Data:* b Bay Shore, NY, Mar 6, 29; m 55; c 3. *Educ:* Holy Cross Col, AB, 50; Georgetown Univ, DDS, 54; George Washington Univ, MA, 74; Am Bd Endodontics, dipl. *Prof Exp:* Captain dent, US Navy, 53-75. *Concurrent Pos:* Dir, secy-treas & pres, Am Bd Endodontics, 79-85; chmn & dir grad educ, Nat Naval Dent Ctr, Md, 71-75; prof & lectr oral biol, Grad Sch George Washington Univ, 71-75; consult, Nat Naval Dent Ctr, 76- & Comn Dent Accreditation, Am Dent Asn, 80-; vis lectr, Dept Restorative Dent, Sch Clin Dent, Univ Sheffield, UK, 85-86. *Mem:* Int Asn Dent Res; Am Asn Endodontists; Am Dent Asn; Am Asn Dent Schs; fel Int Col Dentists. *Res:* Clinical endodontics, more specifically in radiographic interpretation and reliability of various endodontic instruments, filling materials; restoration of endodontically treated teeth. *Mailing Add:* 230 ACA Pesket Rd East Falmouth MA 02536

**TEN CATE, ARNOLD RICHARD,** ANATOMY, DENTISTRY. *Current Pos:* prof anat & dent, Univ Toronto, 68-71, chmn div, 71-77, prof biol sci & dean fac dent, 77-89, VPROVOST, HEALTH SCI, UNIV TORONTO, 89- *Personal Data:* b Accrington, Eng, Oct 21, 33; m 56; c 3. *Educ:* Univ London, BDS, 60, BSc, 55, PhD(anat), 58. *Hon Degrees:* DSc, McGill, 89, Univ Western Ont, 89. *Honors & Awards:* Colyer Prize, Royal Soc Med, 62; Milo Hellman Award, Am Asn Orthod, 75; Isaac Schour Mem Award, Int Asn Dent Res, 78. *Prof Exp:* Sr lectr dent sci, Royal Col Surgeons Eng, 61-63; sr lectr anat in dent, Guy's Hosp Med Sch, Univ London, 63-68. *Mem:* Int Asn Dent Res (vpres, 82, pres-elect, 83, pres, 84). *Res:* Dental histology; development of periodontium and connective tissue remodeling. *Mailing Add:* Dent Dept Univ Toronto 124 Edward St Toronto ON M5S 1A1 Can. *Fax:* 416-979-4910

**TENCER, MICAL STEFAN,** ELECTRONICS MATERIALS & RELIABILITY. *Current Pos:* SR SCI STAFF MEM, NORTEL TECHNOL, 91- *Personal Data:* b Warsaw, Poland, May 5, 48; Can citizen; c Daniel. *Educ:* Warsaw Univ Technol, MSc, 70; Polish Acad Sci, PhD(phys org chem), 75. *Prof Exp:* Res officer, Inst Nuclear Res, Poland, 75-81. *Concurrent Pos:* Postdoctoral fel, Mem Univ Nfld, 77-78; res assoc, Swiss Fed Inst Technol, 91-92, Univ Toronto, 93-96, Lehigh Univ, 96-98. *Mem:* Am Chem Soc. *Res:* Material science and applied chemistry as related to reliability and design of electronic equipment especially in area of telecommunications; materials for electronics. *Mailing Add:* PO Box 3511 Ottawa ON K1Y 4H7 Can. *E-Mail:* mtencer@ortel.ca

**TENCZA, THOMAS MICHAEL,** ORGANIC CHEMISTRY. *Current Pos:* DIR PROD DEVELOP, BRISTOL-MYERS CO, HILLSIDE, 60- *Personal Data:* b Wallington, NJ, July 8, 32; m 59. *Educ:* Columbia Univ, AB, 54; Seton Hall Univ, MS, 64, PhD(chem), 66; Fairleigh Dickinson Univ, MBA, 71. *Prof Exp:* Res chemist, S B Penick Co, 57-60. *Mem:* Am Chem Soc; Am Pharmaceut Asn; Am Mgt Asn; Soc Cosmetic Chemists. *Res:* Research and development management; product development; rearrangement reactions of small ring compounds; botanical drugs. *Mailing Add:* 31 Wagner Ave Wallington NJ 07057-1638

**TENDAM, DONALD JAN,** NUCLEAR PHYSICS. *Current Pos:* Asst, Purdue Univ, West Lafayette, 40-42, from instr to prof, 42-82, assoc head dept, 66-82, EMER PROF PHYSICS, PURDUE UNIV, WEST LAFAYETTE, 82- *Personal Data:* b Hamilton, Ohio, May 28, 16; m 39; c 3. *Educ:* Miami Univ, AB, 40; Purdue Univ, MS, 42, PhD(physics), 49. *Mem:* AAAS; Am Phys Soc; Am Asn Physics Teachers. *Res:* Particle accelerators; radioactive tracers; nuclear reactions; deuteron-bombarded semiconductors. *Mailing Add:* 332 Meridian St West Lafayette IN 47906

**TENDLER, MOSES DAVID,** MICROBIOLOGY. *Current Pos:* From instr to assoc prof, 52-63, asst dean, 56-59, PROF BIOL, YESHIVA UNIV, 63-, PROF TALMUD, 65- & PROF MED ETHICS, 86- *Personal Data:* b New York, NY, Aug 7, 26; m 48; c 8. *Educ:* NY Univ, BA, 47, MA, 51; Columbia Univ, PhD, 57. *Honors & Awards:* Maimonides Award, 87. *Concurrent Pos:* Consult, Eli Lilly & Co, 59-61 & Hoffmann-La Roche Inc, 63-; res dir, Thermobios Pharmaceut Corp, 63-; mem res adv coun, NY Cancer Res Inst, 65-71; vchmn, Kashruth Adv Bd, NY State Dept Agr, 68- *Mem:* AAAS; Am Soc Microbiol; Asn Orthodox Jewish Scientists; NY Acad Sci. *Res:* Nutrition of thermophilic actinomycetes; antibiotic and antitumor agents proliferated by thermophilic organisms; physiological problems of thermophily; discoverer of Anthramycin, an antitumor antibiotic. *Mailing Add:* Dept Natural Sci Yeshiva Univ 500 W 185th St New York NY 10033-3201

**TEN EICK, ROBERT EDWIN,** CARDIAC CELLULAR ELECTROPHYSIOLOGY, PHARMACOLOGY. *Current Pos:* from asst prof to assoc prof, 68-81, PROF PHARMACOL, MED SCH, NORTHWESTERN UNIV, CHICAGO, 81- *Personal Data:* b Portchester, NY, Oct 14, 37; m 62, Marisa Costa; c Matthew E & Andrew P. *Educ:* Columbia Univ, BS, 63, PhD(pharmacol), 68. *Prof Exp:* Guest investr cardiac electrophysiol, Rockefeller Univ, 68. *Concurrent Pos:* NIH trainee cardiac electrophysiol, Rockefeller Univ, 68; vis prof II, Physiol Inst, Univ Saarland,

WGer, 74-75; NIH res career develop award, 75-80; consult, Heart, Lung & Blood Inst & Physiol & Cardiovasc Study Sect, Pharmacol Study Sect, NIH, 88-92; Warren McDonald int scholar, Australian Heart Coun, Nat Heart Found, 90; vis prof, Royal NShore Hosp, Sydney, Australia, 90. *Mem:* Am Physiol Soc; Am Heart Asn; Am Soc Pharmacol & Exp Therapeut; Cardiac Muscle Soc; Int Soc Heart Res. *Res:* Regulation of ion channel function in cardiac cells; cellular electrophysiology of the heart; myocardial membrane currents and their relation to cardiac electrical activity during cardiac hypertrophy. *Mailing Add:* Dept Pharmacol Northwestern Univ Med Sch 303 E Chicago Ave Chicago IL 60611. *Fax:* 312-503-5349; *E-Mail:* r__teneick@nwu.edu

**TENENBAUM, JOEL,** DYNAMIC METEOROLOGY, COMPUTER GRAPHICS. *Current Pos:* asst prof, State Univ NY Col Purchase, 71-76, actg dean, Natural Sci, 78 & 79, assoc prof physics, 76-89, PROF PHYSICS & SCI COMPUT, STATE UNIV NY COL PURCHASE, 89- *Personal Data:* b Brooklyn, NY, Dec 17, 40; m 67, Elizabeth C Brody; c Jessica, David & Elena. *Educ:* Calif Inst Technol, BS, 62; Harvard Univ, AM, 63, PhD(physics), 69. *Prof Exp:* Res assoc physics, Stanford Linear Accelerator Ctr, 68-71. *Concurrent Pos:* Consult, Inst Space Studies, NASA Goddard Space Flight Ctr, 72-75; vis assoc prof meteorol, Mass Inst Technol, 80-82; vis scholar meteorol, Harvard, 80-82. *Mem:* AAAS; Am Phys Soc; Am Asn Physics Teachers; Am Meteorol Soc. *Res:* Modeling of large scale processes in dynamic meteorology; computer graphics representations of atmospheric phenomena. *Mailing Add:* Div Natural Sci State Univ NY Col Purchase NY 10577-1400. *E-Mail:* joel@purvid.purchase.edu

**TENENBAUM, MICHAEL,** BASIC OXYGEN FURNACE STEELMAKING TECHNOLOGY. *Current Pos:* RETIRED. *Personal Data:* b St Paul, Minn, July 23, 13; m 41; c 2. *Educ:* Univ Minn, BS, 36, MS, 37, PhD(metall, phys chem), 40. *Hon Degrees:* DSc, Northwestern Univ, 74. *Honors & Awards:* Nat Open Hearth Comt Award, Am Inst Mining, Metall & Petrol Engrs, 47 & 48, Raymond Award, 49, Hunt Award, 50 & Fairless Award, 75; Bessemgr Medal, Brit Metal Soc, 80. *Prof Exp:* Raw mat res TC&I RR, 39-40; metallurgist, Metall Dept, Inland Steel Co, 41-50, asst supt qual control, 50-56, supt, Metall Dept, 56-59, asst gen mgr tech serv, 59-61, gen mgr res & qual control, 61-66, vpres res, 66-68, vpres, Steel Mfg, 68-71, pres, 71-78, dir, 71-85. *Concurrent Pos:* Dir, Blast Furnace Res, Inc, 64-69; US rep, Int Iron & Steel Inst; dir, Paxall Ind, Cont Ill Bank, 72-80. *Mem:* Nat Acad Eng; distinguished mem Am Inst Mining, Metall & Petrol Engra; Metall Soc (pres, 68); distinguished mem Am Soc Metals; Am Iron & Steel Inst; Asn Iron & Steel Engrs; Brit Inst Metals. *Res:* Metallurgy and chemistry of iron and steel manufacture. *Mailing Add:* 4049 220 Pl SE Issaquah WA 98029

**TENENBAUM, SAUL,** MICROBIOLOGY. *Current Pos:* RETIRED. *Personal Data:* b New York, NY, Nov 3, 17; m 41; c 3. *Educ:* Wash State Univ, BS, 43; Long Island Univ, MS, 64. *Prof Exp:* Jr seafood inspector, US Food & Drug Admin, 42-44; asst chemist, US Maritime Comn, 44-45; sr biochemist, Stand Brands, 45-46; bacteriologist, Atlantic Yeast Co, 46-48; chief bacteriologist, Premo Pharmaceut Lab, 48-57; group leader, Revlon Res Ctr, 57-65, mgr, 65-67, asst dir microbiol, 67-79, dir res microbiol, 79-84. *Concurrent Pos:* Lectr, Fairleigh-Dickinson Univ, 51-56; adj assoc prof pharmaceut sci, Sch Pharm, St John's Univ, 73-85; course dir, Ctr Continuing Educ, 77-84. *Mem:* Soc Indust Microbiol; Am Soc Microbiol; Soc Cosmetic Chemistry; NY Acad Sci. *Res:* Development and evaluation of biostatic and biocidal agents; pseudomonads; preservation; microbial content; skin microbiology; immunology; hypersensitive state and agents; mutagenicity, topical and ocular infection; clinical evaluation of irritants and allergens; sterilization, disinfection and antisepsis; phototoxicity. *Mailing Add:* 2143 Sunhaven Circle Fairfield CA 94533

**TENENHOUSE, ALAN M,** BIOCHEMISTRY, ENDOCRINOLOGY. *Current Pos:* DIR, METAB BONE CTR, MONTREAL GEN HOSP. *Personal Data:* b Montreal, Que, Aug 8, 35; m 61; c 2. *Educ:* McGill Univ, BSc, 55, PhD(biochem), 59, MD & CM, 62. *Prof Exp:* Asst prof, McGill Univ, 68-77, assoc prof pharmacol & therapeut, 78- *Concurrent Pos:* Fel biochem, Univ Wis, 63-65 & Univ Pa, 65-68; NIH fel, 64-66; plan scholar, Univ Pa, 65-68. *Mem:* Endocrine Soc; Can Biochem Soc; Can Pharmacol Soc. *Res:* Mechanism of hormone action with emphasis on role of 3' 5' AMP and calcium in hormone action; biochemistry and physiology of parathyroid hormone and calcitonin. *Mailing Add:* Montreal Gen Hosp 1650 Cedar Ave Rm L8136 Montreal PQ H3G 1B4 Can

**TENENHOUSE, HARRIET SUSIE,** GENETICS. *Current Pos:* Lectr pediat, 77-81, from asst prof to assoc prof, 81-93, PROF PEDIAT, MCGILL CTR HUMAN GENETICS, MCGILL UNIV, 93- *Personal Data:* b Montreal, Que, Apr 15, 40; m 61; c 2. *Educ:* McGill Univ, BSc, 61, MSc, 63, PhD(biochem), 72. *Mem:* Am Soc Biol Chemists; Am Soc Bone & Mineral Res; Can Biochem Soc; Am Soc Nephrology. *Res:* The regulation of renal phosphate, calcium and vitamin D metabolism; the nature of the primary mutation in a mouse model (Hyp) of X-linked hypophosphatemic rickets in man; molecular genetics of renal phosphate transport and vitamin D metabolism. *Mailing Add:* Med Res Coun Genetics Group Montreal Children's Hosp 2300 Tupper St Montreal PQ H3H 1P3 Can

**TENER, GORDON MALCOLM,** BIOCHEMISTRY. *Current Pos:* RETIRED. *Personal Data:* b Vancouver, BC, Nov 24, 27. *Educ:* Univ BC, BA, 49; Univ Wis, MS, 51, PhD(biochem), 53. *Honors & Awards:* Merck Sharp & Dohme Award, Chem Inst Can, 64. *Prof Exp:* Rockefeller fel biochem, Inst Phys-Chem Biol, Paris, France, 53-54; res scientist, BC Res Coun, Vancouver, 54-60; from asst prof to prof, Univ BC 60-92, emer prof biochem & molecular biol, 93-95. *Mem:* Am Chem Soc; Am Soc Biol Chem; Can Biochem Soc; Royal Soc Chem; AAAS. *Res:* Purification and properties of transfer ribonucleic acids; gene localization in Drosophila; gene structure; recombinant DNA; molecular biology of aging. *Mailing Add:* 504-4665 W Tenth Ave Vancouver BC V6R 2J4 Can. *E-Mail:* gtener@unixg.ubc.ca

**TEN EYCK, EDWARD H(ANLON), JR,** CHEMICAL ENGINEERING, INDUSTRIAL & MANUFACTURING ENGINEERING. *Current Pos:* INDUST CONSULT, 85- *Personal Data:* b Pearl River, NY, Sept 6, 23; m 52, Joreen Stewart; c Karen & Gregory. *Educ:* Syracuse Univ, BChE, 43; Polytech Inst Brooklyn, MChE, 48, DChE, 50. *Prof Exp:* Chem engr, Johns Manville Corp, 44; from asst tech supt to lab adminr, E I du Pont de Nemours Co, Inc, Wilmington, 49-71, prog mgr, 71-76, mfg mgr plastics develop, 76-85. *Mem:* Am Chem Soc; Am Inst Chem Engrs; Sigma Xi. *Res:* Polymerization and plasticizers; phase relations of petroleum hydrocarbons; process development; organic chemicals; energy economics. *Mailing Add:* PO Box 3656 Greenville DE 19807-0656. *Fax:* 610-388-1478; *E-Mail:* ed@teneyck.com

**TENFORDE, THOMAS SEBASTIAN,** BIOPHYSICS, SCIENCE ADMINISTRATION. *Current Pos:* chief scientist, Health Div, 88-97, CHIEF SCIENTIST, ENVIRON TECHNOL DIV, BATTELLE-PAC NW LABS, 97- *Personal Data:* b Middletown, Ohio, Dec 15, 40; m 79, Susan Daniels; c Adam & Mark. *Educ:* Harvard Univ, AB, 62; Univ Calif, Berkeley, PhD(biophys), 69. *Prof Exp:* Fel, Univ Calif, Berkeley, 69-73; biophysicist, Lawrence Berkeley Lab, Univ Calif, 73-87, sr scientist, 82-87, group leader, Radiation Biophys Group, 81-82, dept dir, Donner Lab, Biol & Med Div, 82-83, group leader, Environ Physiol Group, 83-87. *Concurrent Pos:* Mem, Comt SC-67, Nat Coun Radiation Protection & Measurements, 81-; mem, Tech Panel Magnetic Fusion Energy, Energy Res Adv Bd, US Dept Energy, 83-84; mem, Physiol Working Group Comt 95.4, Am Nat Stand Inst, 83-90; mem, Fla Sci Adv Comn Elec & Magnetic Fields, 84-85; mem, Comt Biol & Human Health Effects Extremely Low Frequency Fields, Am Inst Biol Sci, 84-85; mem, Adv Comt Biol Effects Elec & Magnetic Fields, Elec Power Res Inst, 85-93; mem, Energy Eng Bd, Comt Energy Conserv Res, Nat Res Coun, 85-86; mem, Comt Man & Radiation, Inst Elec & Electronics Engrs, 88-91; coun mem, Nat Coun Radiation Protection & Measurements, 88-, chmn, Comt SC-89 & Comt SC-1, 92-; mem, Bd Radiation Effects Res, Nat Res Coun, 89-95; Phys Agents Comt, Am Conf Govt Indust Hygienists, 88-, bd dir, Nat Coun Radiation Protection & Measurements, 91-96; chmn, Comt Health Effects Ground Wave Emergency Network, Nat Res Coun, 90-93; mem, Int Comn Nonionizing Radiation Protection, 92-; mem, Adv Comt Electromagnetic Fields & Human Health, Harvard Ctr Risk Analysis, 94-; sci vpres, Nat Coun Radiation Protection & Measurements, 95- *Mem:* AAAS; Bioelectromagnetics Soc (pres 87-88); Biophys Soc; NY Acad Sci; Radiation Res Soc; Am Conf Govt Indust Hygienists. *Res:* Radiation biology; biological effects of electromagnetic fields; surface chemistry of normal and cancer cells; medical applications of radioisotopes. *Mailing Add:* Environ Technol Div P7-52 Battelle-Pac NW Labs PO Box 999 Richland WA 99352-0999. *E-Mail:* ts__tenforde@pnl.gov

**TENG, CHING SUNG,** REPRODUCTIVE BIOLOGY, BIOCHEMISTRY. *Current Pos:* PROF ANAT & PHYSIOL, NC STATE UNIV, 81- *Personal Data:* b Amoy, Fukien, Nov 20, 37; US citizen; m 64; c 2. *Educ:* Tunghai Univ, Taiwan, BS, 60; Univ Tex, Austin, MS, 64, PhD(biochem), 67. *Prof Exp:* Res assoc biochem, Univ Tex, Austin, 67-69; guest investr, Rockefeller Univ, 69-71; asst prof develop biol, State Univ NY Stony Brook, 71-73; assoc prof cell biol, Baylor Col Med, 73-80. *Concurrent Pos:* NIH res fel, Cancer Inst, 69-70, NIH spec res fel, 70-71, NIH grant award, 73-; NSF grant award, 82-; Rockefeller Found grant award, 83- *Mem:* Am Soc Cell Biol; Endocrine Soc; Sigma Xi. *Res:* Steroid hormone-controlled sex organ differentiation. *Mailing Add:* Dept Anat Physiol Sci & Radiol NC State Univ 4700 Hillsborough St Raleigh NC 27606-1428. *Fax:* 919-829-4465

**TENG, CHOJAN,** NONCOOPERATIVE TARGET RECOGNITION, RADAR & TARGET CLASSIFICATION,. *Current Pos:* mem tech staff, 78-80 & 83-96, LEAD STAFF, MITRE CORP, 96- *Personal Data:* b Taipei, Taiwan, Aug 31, 47; m 83; c 3. *Educ:* Nat Taiwan Univ, BS, 69; Wash State Univ, MS, 72; Univ Wis-Madison, MS, 76, PhD(elec eng), 78. *Prof Exp:* Mem staff, Lincoln Lab, Mass Inst Technol, 80-83. *Concurrent Pos:* Adj prof, Univ Lowell, 85- *Mem:* Inst Elec & Electronics Engrs; Sigma Xi; Appl Computational Electromagnetic Soc; Int Soc Optical Eng. *Res:* Noncooperative target recognition techniques including radar signal modulation, neural network, inverse SAR, high range resolution, laser radar detection of vibration signatures; radar system design and analysis; digital signal processing; numerical analysis; applied mathematics. *Mailing Add:* Mitre Corp MS M225 Burlington Rd Bedford MA 01730-0208. *E-Mail:* cteng@mitre.org

**TENG, CHRISTINA WEI-TIEN TU,** GENE REGULATION. *Current Pos:* expert, 83-97, sr staff fel, 91-93, HEAD, GENE REGULATION GROUP, NAT INST ENVIRON HEALTH SCI, NIH, 93- *Personal Data:* b Kuming, Yunnan, China, July 23, 42; m 64, Ching Sung; c Janet & Peggy. *Educ:* Tunghai Univ, Taiwan, BS, 63; Univ Tex, Austin, PhD(biol), 69. *Prof Exp:* Guest investr cell biol, Rockefeller Univ, 69-71; sr res assoc med, Brookhaven Nat Lab, 71-73; asst prof cell biol, Baylor Col Med, 73-81. *Concurrent Pos:* Adj prof, Univ NC, Chapel Hill, 95- *Mem:* Am Soc Cell Biol; Sigma Xi; Endocrince Soc. *Res:* Hormone controlled sex organ differentiation; study of the regulatory mechanism for gene activation in mammalian system; human lactoferrin structure and function relationship. *Mailing Add:* Nat Inst Environ Health Sci NIH PO Box 12233 E201 Research Triangle Park NC 27709-2233. *Fax:* 919-541-0696

**TENG, EVELYN LEE,** NEUROPSYCHOLOGY. *Current Pos:* from asst prof to assoc prof, 72-95, PROF NEUROL, SCH MED, UNIV SOUTHERN CALIF, 95- *Personal Data:* b Chungking, China, Feb 8, 38; m 63, Ta-liang; c Frances & Frank. *Educ:* Taiwan Univ, BS, 59; Stanford Univ, MA, 60, PhD(psychol), 63. *Honors & Awards:* Res Award Psychogeriat, Int Phychogeriat Asn, 93; B S Schoenburg Int Award, Am Acad Neurol, 94. *Prof Exp:* Res fel psychobiol, Calif Inst Technol, 63-69, sr res fel, 69-72. *Concurrent Pos:* Lectr neuroepidemiol, Am Acad Neurol, 94. *Mem:* Am Psychol Asn; Int Neuropsychol Soc; Geront Soc Am. *Res:* Functional relationship between brain and behavior; higher cognitive functions; cultural issues in cognitive assessment; dementia. *Mailing Add:* 1474 Rose Villa St Pasadena CA 91106. *Fax:* 213-226-5869; *E-Mail:* eteng@hsc.usc.edu

**TENG, JAMES,** ENGINEERING. *Current Pos:* res proj mgr, Anheuser Busch Co, 68-75, res mgr advan prod, 75-78, mgr, Process Optimization Ctr, 78-83, DIR, PROCESS DEVELOP & OPTIMIZATION CTR, ANHEUSER BUSCH CO, 83-, SR DIR, TECHNOL PLANNING. *Personal Data:* b Hong Kong, Dec 4, 29; US citizen; m 57; c 2. *Educ:* Tri-State Col, BS, S2; Case Western Res Univ, MS, 61, PhD(org chem), 67. *Prof Exp:* Chem engr, Radio Receptor Co, 52-53; process engr, Nylonge Corp, 53-56, res supvr, 56-61, tech supvr, 61-66; fel, Purdue Univ, 66-67. *Mem:* AAAS; Am Inst Chem; NY Acad Sci; Am Chem Soc; Master Brewers Asn Am. *Res:* Carbohydrate chemistry; regenerated cellulose; cellulose derivatives; starch derivatives; carbohydrates in brewing; brewing process. *Mailing Add:* 107 Frontenac Forest St Louis MO 63131-3259

**TENG, JON IE,** STEROID CHEMISTRY, NATURAL PRODUCTS CHEMISTRY. *Current Pos:* res biochemist, 70-75, RES SCIENTIST, UNIV TEX MED BR, GALVESTON, 75- *Personal Data:* b Kienow, China, Oct 19, 30; m 58; c 2. *Educ:* Nat Taiwan Univ, BS, 55; SDak State Univ, MS, 62; Univ Fla, PhD(agr biochem), 65. *Prof Exp:* Agr scientist, Taiwan Sugar Corp, Inc, 56-60; res assoc nitrogen metab in hort plants, Univ Ill, Urbana, 65-66; res chemist, Am Crystal Sugar Co, 66-68; NIH fel steroid biochem, Med Sch, Univ Minn, 68-69, res assoc pharmacol, 69-70. *Mem:* Am Chem Soc; Inst Am Chemists; Sigma Xi. *Res:* Steroid biosynthesis and metabolism; drug metabolism; plant nutrition and biochemistry; steroid biochemistry; cholesterol metabolism in mammalian liver, kidney, brain and aortal tissues. *Mailing Add:* 3101 Ave P Galveston TX 77550

**TENG, LEE CHANG-LI,** ACCELERATOR PHYSICS. *Current Pos:* head accelerator theory sect, Fermi Nat Accelerator Lab, Synchrotron Radiation Res Ctr, 67-72, assoc head, Accelerator Div, 72-75, head adv proj sect, 75-83, dir, Synchrotron Radiation Res Ctr, Taiwan, 83-85, dirs off spec assignment, 87-89, BD DIRS, SYNCHROTRON RADIATION RES CTR, 85-; HEAD ACCELERATOR PHYSICS, ADVAN PHOTON SOURCE PROJ, ARGONNE NAT LAB, 89- *Personal Data:* b Peiping, China, Sept 5, 26; nat US; m 61, Nancy Huang; c Michael N. *Educ:* Fu Jen Univ, China, BS, 46; Univ Chicago, MS, 48, PhD(physics), 51. *Honors & Awards:* Gold Medal of Achievement, Chinese Ministry Educ, 56. *Prof Exp:* Cyclotron asst, Univ Chicago, 49-51; lectr physics, Univ Minn, 51-52, asst prof, 52-53; assoc prof, Univ Wichita, 53-55; assoc physicist, Particle Accelerator Div, Argonne Nat Lab, 55-61, head theory group, 56-62, sr physicist, 61-67, dir, 62-67. *Concurrent Pos:* Hon prof, Beijing Normal Univ, 83; Argonne fel, Argonne Nat Lab, 84-89. *Mem:* Fel Am Phys Soc; Am Asn Univ Prof. *Res:* High energy accelerators and instrumentation; high energy and nuclear physics; research and development in accelerator physics; design and construction of particle accelerators. *Mailing Add:* Argonne Nat Lab 9700 S Cass Ave Argonne IL 60439. *Fax:* 630-252-4732; *E-Mail:* teng@aps.anl.gov

**TENG, LINA CHEN,** DRUG METABOLISM. *Current Pos:* sr res chemist, 73-78, res assoc, 78-84, SR RES ASSOC, A H ROBINS CO, 84- *Personal Data:* b Fukien, China, Dec 8, 39; US citizen; m 65. *Educ:* Nat Taiwan Univ, BS, 63; Utah State Univ, PhD(org chem), 67. *Prof Exp:* Res chemist, Philip Morris Inc, 67-71. *Mem:* Am Chem Soc; Sigma Xi; AAAS. *Res:* Studies of the metabolism, mainly isolation and identification of the metabolites, of the existing or research drugs in animals and human beings; synthesis of radiolabelled compounds for drug research. *Mailing Add:* 7638 Redbud Rd Richmond VA 23235-5235

**TENG, MAO-HUA,** COMPUTER SIMULATION & PROGRAMMING, NANOPHASE MATERIALS. *Current Pos:* FEL, NORTHWESTERN UNIV, 92- *Personal Data:* b Taipei, Taiwan, Oct 27, 58; m 87, Hsiao-Wei Chang; c Lin-Chieh. *Educ:* Nat Taiwan Univ, BS, 81, MS, 84; Northwestern Univ, PhD(mat sci), 92. *Mem:* Am Ceramic Soc; Mat Res Soc; Minerals Metals & Mat Soc; Sigma Xi. *Res:* Synthesis and processing nanophase nickel-based materials. *Mailing Add:* CCMS Nat Taiwan Univ 1 Roosevelt Rd Taipei Taiwan. *Fax:* 886-2-363-6095; *E-Mail:* mhteng@ccms.ntu.edu.tw

**TENG, MICHELLE HSIAO TSING,** OCEAN & COASTAL ENGINEERING, HYDRAULIC ENGINEERING. *Current Pos:* ASST PROF FLUID MECH, UNIV HAWAII, MANOA, 92- *Educ:* Qinghua Univ, Beijing, BS, 85; Calif Inst Technol, MS, 87, PhD(eng sci), 90. *Prof Exp:* Staff scientist, Calif Inst Technol, 90-92. *Concurrent Pos:* Res assoc, Hong Kong Univ Sci & Technol, 91-92; chmn, Energy & Ocean Tech Comt, Am Soc Civil Eng, Hawaii, 93-94; vis scholar, Hong Kong Univ Sci & Technol, 94. *Mem:* Am Phys Soc; Am Soc Civil Engrs; Soc Indust & Appl Math; Am Geophys Union. *Res:* Nonlinear water wave modeling; modeling of coastal current, ocean internal waves, wind generated waves, flood in rivers, sediment transport. *Mailing Add:* Dept Civil Eng Univ Hawaii 2540 Dole St Holmes Hall 337 Honolulu HI 96822. *Fax:* 808-956-5014; *E-Mail:* michelle@manoa.eng.hawaii.edu

**TENG, TA-LIANG,** GEOPHYSICS. *Current Pos:* from asst prof to assoc prof geophys, 67-74, assoc prof, 74-77, PROF GEOL SCI, UNIV SOUTHERN CALIF, 78- *Personal Data:* b China, July 3, 37; m 63; c 2. *Educ:* Univ Taiwan, BS, 59; Calif Inst Technol, PhD(geophys, appl math), 66. *Prof Exp:* Res fel geophys, Seismol Lab, Calif Inst Technol, 66-67. *Mem:* AAAS; Am Geophys Union; Seismol Soc Am. *Res:* Elastic wave propagations; observational and theoretical seismology; elastic and anelastic properties of the earth and planetary interiors. *Mailing Add:* Geol Univ Southern Calif 3651 Trousdale Pkwy Los Angeles CA 90089-0016

**TENGERDY, ROBERT PAUL,** APPLIED MICROBIOLOGY & IMMUNOLOGY. *Current Pos:* asst prof chem & microbiol, Colo State Univ, 61-64, assoc prof biochem & microbiol, 64-71, prof, 71-92, EMER PROF MICROBIOL, COLO STATE UNIV, 92- *Personal Data:* b Budapest, Hungary, Dec 17, 30; US citizen; m 53, Catherine Kokeny; c Thomas & Peter. *Educ:* Tech Univ, Budapest, Dipl Chem Eng, 53; St John's Univ, NY, PhD(microbial biochem), 61. *Prof Exp:* Asst prof biochem eng, Tech Univ, Budapest, 53-56; res biochemist, Chas Pfizer & Co, NY, 57-61. *Concurrent Pos:* Europ Molecular Biol Orgn fel, Pasteur Inst Paris, 68; Humboldt fel, Max Planck Inst, Univ Goettingen, 68; vis prof, USSR, 80 & 83, Hungary, 91, 92, 93, 94, 95 & 96; Fulbright fel, Peru, 85, Hungary, 91-92. *Mem:* Soc Indust Microbiol; Am Soc Microbiol. *Res:* Agricultural biotechnology; nutritional aspects of immunology; applied microbiology; waste conversion by microbes; vaccine development; bioconversion of agricultural residues into animal feed or fuel using combined enzymatic hydrolysis and ensiling, solid substrate fermentation by fungi; fluidized bed technology development of vitamin E adjuvant vaccines for veterinary use. *Mailing Add:* Dept Microbiol Colo State Univ Ft Collins CO 80523. *E-Mail:* rteng@lamar.colostate.edu

**TENHOVER, MICHAEL ALAN,** catalysis, for more information see previous edition

**TENN, JOSEPH S,** MODERN HISTORY ASTRONOMY. *Current Pos:* from asst prof to assoc prof, 70-80, PROF, PHYSICS & ASTRON, SONOMA STATE UNIV, 80- *Personal Data:* b Los Angeles, Calif, May 11, 40; m 67; c 2. *Educ:* Stanford Univ, BS, 62; Univ Wash, Seattle, MS, 66, PhD(physics), 70. *Prof Exp:* Teacher physics & math, US Peace Corps, Ethiopia, 62-64; assoc res, Univ Wash, 66-70; res scientist physics, NASA Ames Res Ctr, 65. *Concurrent Pos:* Postgrad res astronr, Lick Obser, 75-76; adj prof, physics & astron, Univ Mass, Amherst, 84-85; chmn, Hist Comt, Astron Soc Pac, 93- *Mem:* Am Phys Soc; Am Asn Physics Teachers; Am Astron Soc; Astron Soc Pac. *Res:* Astronomy, history of astronomy. *Mailing Add:* Dept Phys & Astron Sonoma State Univ Rohnert Park CA 94928-3609. *E-Mail:* joe.tenn@sonoma.edu

**TENNANKORE, KANNAN NAGARAJAN,** CHEMICAL ENGINEERING, TECHNICAL MANAGEMENT. *Current Pos:* eng res analyst flow mass & heat transfer enclosures, Whiteshell Nuclear Res Estab, Atomic Energy Can Ltd Res, 78-83, head, Combustion Sect, 83-88, actg mgr, High Temperature Chem Br, 88-90, mgr, Containment Analysis Br, 90-93, dir, Eng & Design Div, 93-94, Eng Sci Div, 94-95, DIR ENG PROD & SERV, CHALK-RIVER LAB, ATOMIC ENERGY CAN LTD RES, 96- *Personal Data:* b Madras, India, Oct 30, 46; m 71, K V Lakshim; c Dhenuka & Karthik. *Educ:* Univ Madras, BSc, 65; Indian Inst Technol, Madras, BTech, 68, MTech, 70; Univ NB, PhD(chem eng), 75. *Prof Exp:* Asst eng design & develop distillation columns, Engrs India Ltd, India, 70-71; fel combustion, Univ NB, 75-77, res assoc dispersion of aerial sprays, 77-78. *Mem:* Can Nuclear Soc; Combustion Inst Can. *Res:* Experimental study and modeling of flow, heat and mass transfer in enclosures. *Mailing Add:* Atomic Energy Can Ltd Chalk River Lab Chalk River ON K0J 1J0 Can. *E-Mail:* tennankorek@aecl.ca

**TENNANT, BUD C,** VETERINARY MEDICINE, GASTROENTEROLOGY. *Current Pos:* PROF COMP GASTROENTEROL, NY STATE COL VET MED, CORNELL UNIV, 72- *Personal Data:* b Burbank, Calif, Nov 10, 33; m 63; c 3. *Educ:* Univ Calif, BS, 57, DVM, 59. *Prof Exp:* Intern, Sch Vet Med, Univ Calif, 59, from asst prof to assoc prof, 62-72; res assoc, Dept Surg, Albert Einstein Col Med, 62; res fel, Gastrointestinal Unit, Mass Gen Hosp, 6869. *Mem:* Am Col Vet Internal Med; Am Gastroenterol Asn; Am Inst Nutrit; Am Vet Med Asn; Soc Exp Biol Med. *Res:* Diseases of the gastrointestinal tract and liver of domestic animals; pathogenesis of viral hepatitis; mechanisms of hepatic injury. *Mailing Add:* Cornell Univ Col Vet Med 4 Sunny Knoll Ithaca NY 14853-6401. *Fax:* 607-253-3289

**TENNANT, DONALD L,** FISH BIOLOGY, LIMNOLOGY. *Current Pos:* RETIRED. *Personal Data:* b Mt Gilead, Ohio, Jan 27, 27; m 56; c 3. *Educ:* Ohio State Univ, BS, 52. *Honors & Awards:* Fisheries Scientist Award, Am Fisheries Soc, 68. *Prof Exp:* Fish mgt supvr, Ohio Div Wildlife, 52-57; fishery res biologist, US Fish & Wildlife Serv, 57-59, fishery biologist, 59-67, fish & wildlife biologist, 67- *Mem:* Am Fisheries Soc; fel Am Inst Fishery Res Biologists. *Res:* In stream flow regimens for fish, wildlife, recreation and related environmental resources; reservoir, lake and pond limnology and management; artificial propagation of muskellunge and fish hybridization. *Mailing Add:* 1809 Darlene Ave Billings MT 59102

**TENNANT, RAYMOND WALLACE,** GENETIC TOXICOLOGY, CARCINOGENESIS. *Current Pos:* CHIEF, LAB ENVIRON CARCINOGENESIS & MUTAGENESIS, NAT TOXICOL PROG, NAT INST ENVIRON HEALTH SCI, RESEARCH TRIANGLE PARK, NC, 80- *Personal Data:* b West Frankfort, Ill, Sept 19, 37; m 60, Mary Jenkins; c

Steven, Stephanie L, Mary C & Gregory. *Educ:* St Joseph's Col, BS, 59; Univ Notre Dame, MS, 61; Georgetown Univ, PhD(microbiol), 63. *Honors & Awards:* Dirs Award, NIH. *Prof Exp:* Virologist, Dept Virus Res, Microbiol Assocs, Inc, Md, 61-65; USPHS fel replication DNA viruses, Albert Einstein Med Ctr, 65-66; sr staff scientist, Biol Div, Oak Ridge Nat Lab, 66-80. *Concurrent Pos:* Mem adv comt, Am Cancer Soc. *Mem:* Environ Mutagen Soc; Am Asn Cancer Res. *Res:* Cancer biology; RNA tumor virus cell biology and genetics; cellular transformation; genetic toxicology; chemical carcinogenesis; transgenic mice. *Mailing Add:* 1420 Acres Way Raleigh NC 27614. *Fax:* 919-541-1460

**TENNANT, WILLIAM EMERSON,** SOLID STATE PHYSICS, MATERIALS SCIENCE ENGINEERING. *Current Pos:* Mem tech staff physics, Rockwell Int Sci Ctr, 73-79, mgr, Infrared Detector Mat Group, 79-86, prin scientist, Electronic Imaging Function, 86-88, dir, imaging, 88-94, PRIN SCIENTIST, ELECTRON DEVICES LAB, ROCKWELL INT SCI CTR, 94- *Personal Data:* b Washington, DC, Oct 8, 45; m 68, Margaret Aris Hinman; c Jessica (Faris), Elizabeth (Ashton) & Richard Shelton. *Educ:* Harvard Univ, AB, 67; Univ Calif, Berkeley, PhD(solid state physics), 74. *Honors & Awards:* Leviwstein Award, 93. *Mem:* Am Phys Soc; Sigma Xi; sr mem Inst Elec & Electronics Engrs. *Res:* Infrared detectors and imagers; semiconductor devices; collective excitations in solids; optical nondestructive evaluation methods; radiation damage; crystal alloys and defects; solar energy collection. *Mailing Add:* Rockwell Int Sci Ctr 1049 Camino Dos Rios Thousand Oaks CA 91360. *E-Mail:* wetennan@scimail.risc.rockwell.com

**TENNENT, DAVID MADDUX,** BIOCHEMISTRY, SCIENCE ADMINISTRATION. *Current Pos:* RETIRED. *Personal Data:* b Bryn Mawr, Pa, Oct 2, 14; m 45, Martha A Meloy; c Blythe, Meredith (Conway), David L & Charles M. *Educ:* Yale Univ, AB, 36, PhD(org chem), 40. *Prof Exp:* Asst appl physiol, Yale Univ, 40-42; biochemist, Merck Inst Therapeut Res, 42-60; asst dir res, Hess & Clark Div, Richardson-Merrell Inc, 60-63; dir res & develop, 63-69, vpres & dir res & develop, 69-75; consult, Vet Affairs, Rhodia Inc, 75-79. *Concurrent Pos:* Fel, Coun Arteriosclerosis, Am Heart Asn. *Mem:* Fel AAAS; Am Chem Soc; Am Soc Biol Chem; Soc Exp Biol & Med. *Res:* Pharmacology of drugs; bacterial pyrogens; cholesterol metabolism and experimental atherosclerosis; medications to improve performance and health of production animals; FDA applications. *Mailing Add:* 981 TWP Rd 1546 Ashland OH 44805

**TENNENT, HOWARD GORDON,** ORGANOMETALLIC CHEMISTRY. *Current Pos:* SR SCIENTIST, HYPERION CATALYSIS INT, LEXINGTON, MASS, 85- *Personal Data:* b Quebec, Que, Feb 29, 16; US citizen; m 48; c 4. *Educ:* Rensselaer Polytech Inst, BS, 37, MS, 39; Univ Wis, PhD(phys chem), 42. *Prof Exp:* Res chemist, Hercules, Inc, 42-47, mgr res, Div Cellulose Prod, 47-51, exp sta, 52, cent res div, 53-57, res assoc, 58-66, sr res assoc, 66-81. *Mem:* Am Chem Soc; Sci Res Soc Am. *Res:* Synthesis and applications of carbon fibrils. *Mailing Add:* 301 Chandler Mill Rd Kennett Square PA 19348-2613

**TENNER, THOMAS EDWARD, JR,** CARDIOVASCULAR PHARMACOLOGY. *Current Pos:* from asst prof to assoc prof, 78-90, PROF DEPT PHARMACOL, TEX TECH UNIV HEALTH SCI CTR, 90- *Personal Data:* b Pittsburgh, Pa, June 2, 49; m 72; c 3. *Educ:* Univ Dallas, BA, 71; Univ Tex Health Sci Ctr, PhD(pharmacol), 76. *Prof Exp:* Fel, Fac Pharmaceut Sci, Univ BC, 76-78. *Concurrent Pos:* Vis scientist, Holland Lab, Am Red Cross, Md. *Mem:* Am Soc Pharm & Exp Therapeut; Am Heart Asn. *Res:* Drug-induced modulation of sensitivity and responsiveness of the cardiovascular system in particular reserpine and propranolol withdrawal induced supersensitivity phenomena. *Mailing Add:* Tex Tech Univ Health Sci Ctr Dept Pharmacol & Therapeut 3601 Fourth St Lubbock TX 79430-0001. *Fax:* 806-743-2744

**TENNESSEN, KENNETH JOSEPH,** FRESH WATER ECOLOGY, ODONATA SYSTEMATICS. *Current Pos:* BIOLOGIST ECOL EFFECTS AQUATIC INSECTS & MOSQUITOES, TENN VALLEY AUTHORITY, 75- *Personal Data:* b Ladysmith, Wis, June 10, 46; m 67; c 2. *Educ:* Univ Wis, BS, 68; Univ Fla, MS, 73, PhD(entom), 75. *Honors & Awards:* Hammer Award, VPres Al Gore, 95. *Mem:* Dragonfly Soc Am (pres); NAm Benthological Soc; Int Soc Odontol; Am Entom Soc. *Res:* Biology, ecology and identification of mosquitoes regarding nuisance and disease potential; use of aquatic insects in stream/lake quality assessment; identification of Chironomidae. *Mailing Add:* Water Mgt CTR 2P-M Tenn Valley Authority Muscle Shoals AL 35660

**TENNEY, AGNES,** THEORETICAL PHYSICAL CHEMISTRY. *Current Pos:* ASST PROF CHEM, UNIV PORTLAND, 77- *Personal Data:* b Boston, Mass. *Educ:* Regis Col, AB, 68; Ind Univ, PhD(chem), 75. *Prof Exp:* Assoc instr chem, Ind Univ, 68-73, syst analyst comput sci, 73-76, vis asst prof, 76-77. *Concurrent Pos:* Fac res grant, Univ Portland, 78-79. *Mem:* Am Chem Soc; Am Phys Soc; Int Asn Hydrogen. *Res:* Theory, particularly, electron atom molecule scattering in the intermediate energy range; renewable energy storage via hydrogen; computer controlled experiments. *Mailing Add:* 5000 N Williamette Blvd Portland OR 97203-5750

**TENNEY, ALBERT SEWARD, III,** PHYSICAL CHEMISTRY. *Current Pos:* DIR RES DEVELOP & ENG, GOW-MAC INSTRUMENT CO, 92- *Personal Data:* b Lakewood, NJ, Mar 31, 43; m 66, Jocelyn Farguhan; c Laura & Alan. *Educ:* Rutgers Univ, AB, 65, PhD(phys chem), 71. *Prof Exp:* Phys chemist mat sci, Gen Elec Co, 69-74; group leader solar cells, SES, Inc, 74-76; prin scientist temp measurement, Leeds & Northrup Co, 76-80, prin scientist

sensor develop, 80-91; mgr res develop & eng, TBI Bailey, 91-92. *Mem:* Am Chem Soc; Instrument Soc Am. *Res:* Materials research on molten salts, thin films, glasses and semiconductors; temperature measurement; development of light-emitting diodes, solar cells, temperature measuring instruments, analytical sensors, particle size analyzing and chromatography detectors. *Mailing Add:* 801 E Walnut St North Wales PA 19454-2823. *Fax:* 610-954-0599

**TENNEY, MARK W,** environmental health engineering, civil engineering, for more information see previous edition

**TENNEY, STEPHEN MARSH,** PHYSIOLOGY. *Current Pos:* prof, Dartmouth Med Sch, 56-74, chmn dept, 56-77, Nathan Smith prof, 74-88, NATHAN SMITH EMER PROF PHYSIOL, DARTMOUTH MED SCH, 88- *Personal Data:* b Bloomington, Ill, Oct 22, 22; m 47; c 3. *Educ:* Dartmouth Col, AB, 43; Cornell Univ, MD, 46. *Hon Degrees:* DSc, Univ Rochester, 84. *Honors & Awards:* Pres Award, Phorasic Soc, 88. *Prof Exp:* Asst prof physiol, Dartmouth Med Sch, 51-54; from asst prof to assoc prof physiol & med, Sch Med & Dent, Univ Rochester, 52-56. *Concurrent Pos:* Markle scholar, 54-59. *Mem:* Inst Med-Nat Acad Sci; Am Acad Arts & Sci; Am Physiol Soc; Am Soc Clin Invest; AAAS. *Res:* Physiology of circulation and respiration. *Mailing Add:* Dept Physiol Borwell Bldg Dartmouth Hitchcock Med Ctr Lebanon NH 03756

**TENNEY, WILTON R,** PLANT PATHOLOGY. *Current Pos:* from asst prof to assoc prof, 57-71, PROF BIOL, UNIV RICHMOND, 71- *Personal Data:* b Buckhannon, WVa, July 2, 28; m 51. *Educ:* WVa Wesleyan Col, BS, 50; Univ WVa, MS, 52, PhD(plant path), 55. *Prof Exp:* Plant scientist, Chem Res & Develop Labs, Army Chem Ctr, Md, 57. *Mem:* Sigma Xi. *Res:* Physiology of fungi; host-parasite relations in fungus diseases of plants; toxicity of freshwater bryozoans. *Mailing Add:* 1507 Cutshaw Pl Richmond VA 23226

**TENNILLE, AUBREY WAYNE,** SOIL FERTILITY, SOIL MICROBIOLOGY. *Current Pos:* RETIRED. *Personal Data:* b Baker Co, Ga, Feb 4, 29; m 53; c 2. *Educ:* Univ Ga, BSA, 50; Okla State Univ, MSA, 55; Univ Fla, PhD(soils), 59. *Prof Exp:* Lab asst soil microbiol, Univ Fla, 58-59; asst co agent, Coop Exten, Univ Ga, 59-60, exten specialist, 60-62; from asst prof to prof agron, Ark State Univ, 62-88. *Mem:* Am Soc Agron; Soil Sci Soc Am; Soil Conserv Soc Am. *Res:* Fertility research on zinc and manganese of rice soils of Arkansas and soil salt problems of eastern Arkansas. *Mailing Add:* 355 Crockett Rd Higden AR 72067

**TENNYSON, RODERICK C,** AEROSPACE SCIENCE. *Current Pos:* Chmn, Dept Eng Sci, 82-85, PROF, INST AEROSPACE STUDIES, UNIV TORONTO, 74-, DIR, 85- *Personal Data:* b Toronto, Ont, June 7, 37; m 61, Judith G Williams; c Shan, Marc & Kristin. *Educ:* Univ Toronto, BA, 60, MA, 61, PhD, 65. *Concurrent Pos:* Dir, Ctr Excellence, Inst Space & Terrestrial Sci; chmn, Can Found, Inst Space Univ; Can experimenter on space shuttle flights; consult. *Mem:* Fel Can Aeronaut & Space Inst. *Res:* Aerospace science; aeronautics. *Mailing Add:* Inst Aerospace Studies Univ Toronto 4925 Dufferin St Downsview ON M3H 5T6 Can

**TENORE, KENNETH ROBERT,** BIOLOGICAL OCEANOGRAPHY. *Current Pos:* PROF & DIR, CHESAPEAKE BIOL LAB, CTR ENVIRON SCI, UNIV MD, SOLOMONS, 84- *Personal Data:* b Boston, Mass, Mar 22, 43. *Educ:* St Anselm Col, AB, 65; NC State Univ, MS, 67, PhD(zool), 70. *Prof Exp:* Investr biol oceanog, Woods Hole Oceanog Inst, 70-72, asst scientist, 72-75; asst prof biol oceanog, Skidaway Inst Oceanog, 75-77, mem fac, 80-83; adj prof, Grad Sch Oceanog, Univ RI, 78-80. *Mem:* Am Soc Limnol & Oceanog; Estuarine Res Fedn; Ecol Soc Am; AAAS. *Res:* Bioenergetics of detrital food chains in marine benthic communities. *Mailing Add:* Univ Md Ctr Environ Sci Chesapeake Biol Lab PO Box 38 Solomons MD 20688-0038

**TENOSO, HAROLD JOHN,** immunology, medical microbiology, for more information see previous edition

**TENSMEYER, LOWELL GEORGE,** PHYSICAL CHEMISTRY. *Current Pos:* RETIRED. *Personal Data:* b Pocatello, Idaho, Feb 21, 28; m 54, Virgina; c Kermit, Lisa, Richard & John. *Educ:* Univ Utah, BA, 52, PhD(combustion), 57. *Prof Exp:* Asst prof chem, Ohio Univ, 56-57 & Utah State Univ, 57-59; Petrol Inst fel ceramics, Pa State Univ, 59; res scientist, Linde Div, Union Carbide Corp, 60-63; sr phys chemist, Eli Lilly & Co, 63-72, res scientist, 72-92. *Mem:* Am Chem Soc; Am Phys Soc; Coblentz Soc. *Res:* Molecular spectroscopy; adsorption; crystal growth and purification; lasers; photochemistry and photobiology. *Mailing Add:* 35 W 59th St Indianapolis IN 46208

**TENZER, RUDOLF KURT,** MAGNETIC MATERIALS, X-RAY ANALYSIS. *Current Pos:* OWNER & CONSULT, TENZER ASSOCS, 84- *Personal Data:* b Jena, Ger, Oct 9, 20; nat US; m 47; c 4. *Educ:* Univ Frankfurt, Dipl & Dr rer nat, 50. *Prof Exp:* Scientist radiation temperature measurements, Hartmann & Braun Co, Ger, 48-53; scientist magnetics; Ind Gen Corp, 53-65, mgr res, 65-69; mgr res, Electronic Memories & Magnetics Corp, 69-74, mgr res & mfg eng, 74-76, tech dir, IGC Div, 76-84. *Mem:* Inst Elec & Electronics Engrs; Am Phys Soc; Am Ceramic Soc. *Res:* Permanent magnets; magnetization process; domain theory; ferrites; high temperature properties; temperature measurements by radiation; color pyrometers; magnetic bubble memories bias field assemblies. *Mailing Add:* 1643 Brookdale Dr Martinsville NJ 08836

**TEPAS, DONALD IRVING,** PHYSIOLOGICAL PSYCHOLOGY, NEUROSCIENCE. *Current Pos:* PROF PSYCHOL & DIR, DIV INDUST & ORGN PSYCHOL, UNIV CONN, 85- *Personal Data:* b Buffalo, NY, Apr 7, 33; m; c 2. *Educ:* Univ Buffalo, BA, 55; State Univ NY Buffalo, PhD(psychol), 63. *Prof Exp:* Instr psychol, Univ Buffalo, 58-59; res scientist neuropsychiat, Walter Reed Army Inst Res, 59-62; sr res scientist human factors, Honeywell, Inc, 62-66; prof psychol, St Louis Univ, 66-78; prof, Ill Inst Technol, 78-85, chmn dept, 78-81. *Concurrent Pos:* Asst prof ophthal res, Univ Minn, 63-66; prin investr, USAF, NSF, NIMH, Nat Inst Occup Safety & Health grants, exchange scientist, Nat Acad Sci, Czech, 67; mem, Sci Comt on Night & Shift Work, Int Comn Occup Health, 79-, Comt Outer Continental Shelf Safety Info & Analysis, Nat Res Coun, 82-84, exec comt, Sleep Res Soc, 84-87; US ed, Shiftwork Int Newslett, 85-, NAm ed, Work & Stress, 88- *Mem:* Fel Am Psychol Asn; fel AAAS; Psychonomic Soc; Soc Neurosci; Soc Comput Psychol (pres, 72-73); Sleep Res Soc; Human Factors Soc; Int Comn Occup Health; fel Am Psychol Soc. *Res:* Shiftwork; ergonomics; occupational safety and health; human electrophysiology; human factors aspects of computer hardware and software USC. *Mailing Add:* 47 Elizabeth Rd Mansfield Center CT 06250

**TE PASKE, EVERETT RUSSELL,** BIOLOGY, ANIMAL BEHAVIOR. *Current Pos:* RETIRED. *Personal Data:* b Sheldon, Iowa, Sept 15, 30; m 51; c 4. *Educ:* Westmar Col, AB, 51; State Col Iowa, MA, 57; Okla State Univ, PhD(zool), 63. *Prof Exp:* Teacher pub schs, Iowa, 52-61; from asst prof to prof biol, Univ Northern Iowa, 63-89. *Mem:* AAAS; Animal Behav Soc; Nat Asn Biol Teachers; Mammal Soc. *Res:* Morphology and taxonomy of Chiroptera; breeding behavior in the Japanese quail; social behavior in chickens. *Mailing Add:* 411 N Francis St Cedar Falls IA 50613

**TEPFER, SANFORD SAMUEL,** PLANT MORPHOLOGY. *Current Pos:* from asst prof to prof, Univ Ore, 55-83, co-chmn dept, 68-71, head dept, 72-78, EMER PROF BIOL, UNIV ORE, 84- *Personal Data:* b Brooklyn, NY, Mar 24, 18; m 42, Bertha Fliess; c David A, Mark G, Gary E & Fred L. *Educ:* City Col New York, BS, 38; Cornell Univ, MS, 39; Univ Calif, PhD(bot), 50. *Prof Exp:* Asst bot, Univ Calif, 47-50; instr, Univ Ariz, 50-53, res assoc agr, 53-54; instr biol, Ore Col Educ, 54-55. *Concurrent Pos:* NSF sci fac fel, 65; Fulbright lectr, Univ Paris, 71-72, vis prof, 71-72 & 78-79. *Mem:* AAAS; Bot Soc Am. *Res:* Developmental studies of shoot apex and flowers; culture of floral buds; floral morphogenesis. *Mailing Add:* 2011 Elk Ave Eugene OR 97403. *E-Mail:* stepfer@oregon.uoregon.edu

**TEPHLY, THOMAS R,** PHARMACOLOGY, TOXICOLOGY. *Current Pos:* PROF PHARMACOL, UNIV IOWA, 71- *Personal Data:* b Norwich, Conn, Feb 1, 36; m 60, Joan Clifcorn; c Susan, Linda & Annette. *Educ:* Univ Conn, BS, 57; Univ Wis, PhD(pharmacol), 62; Univ Minn, MD, 65. *Honors & Awards:* John J Abel Award, Am Soc Pharmacol & Exp Therapeut, 71; Kenneth Dubois Award, Soc Toxicol. *Prof Exp:* Instr pharmacol, Univ Wis, 62; from asst prof to assoc prof, Univ Mich, Ann Arbor, 65-71. *Concurrent Pos:* Am Cancer Soc res scholar, 62-65. *Mem:* Am Soc Pharmacol & Exp Therapeut; Am Soc Biochem & Molecular Biol; Soc Toxicol; Res Soc Alcoholism. *Res:* Biochemical pharmacology and toxicology; drug metabolism; methanol and ethanol metabolism; heme biosynthesis. *Mailing Add:* Dept Pharmacol BSB2-452 Univ Iowa Iowa City IA 52240

**TEPLEY, NORMAN,** MEDICAL PHYSICS, NEUROSCIENCE. *Current Pos:* assoc prof, 69-77, chmn dept, 83-96, PROF PHYSICS, OAKLAND UNIV, 77- *Personal Data:* b Denver, Colo, Dec 14, 35; m 68; c 3. *Educ:* Mass Inst Technol, SB, 57, PhD(physics), 63. *Prof Exp:* Asst prof physics, Wayne State Univ, 63-69. *Concurrent Pos:* Vis prof, Dept Physics, Univ Lancaster, 70; sci dir, Neuromagnetism Lab, Henry Ford Hosp, 88- *Mem:* AAAS; Am Phys Soc. *Res:* Magnetic fields arising from living systems; neuromagnetism; physics of metals; ultrasonic studies of Fermi surfaces; electronic structures of metals; properties of superconductors. *Mailing Add:* Oakland Univ Rochester MI 48309

**TEPLICK, JOSEPH GEORGE,** MEDICINE, RADIOLOGY. *Current Pos:* clin assoc prof radiol, Hahnemann Med Col, 63-69, clin assoc prof diag radiol, 69-71, prof radiol, 71-90, dir, Div Gen Diag, 74-90, EMER PROF RADIOL, HAHNEMANN MED COL, 90- *Personal Data:* b Philadelphia, Pa, Sept 29, 11; m 37; c 3. *Educ:* Univ Pa, AB, 31, MS, 32, MD, 36, MSc, 42. *Prof Exp:* Assoc radiol, Jefferson Med Col, 43-48; chief & dir radiol, Kensington Hosp, 49-63. *Concurrent Pos:* Dir, Curtis X-ray Dept, Jefferson Med Col, 45-48; chief radiol, Albert Einstein Med Ctr, 50-53; vis radiologist, Philadelphia Gen Hosp, 60-; assoc, Sch Med, Univ Pa, 60-; mem staff, Hahnemann Hosp, 63-; expert in medico legal litigation. *Mem:* Fel Am Col Radiol; Radiol Soc NAm; Roentgen Ray Soc; Am Thoracic Soc; NY Acad Sci. *Res:* Hapato-splenography; intravenous and parenteral radiopaque emulsions; computed tomography of the spine. *Mailing Add:* Medico Legal Cons 130 Spruce St Philadelphia PA 19106

**TEPLITZ, VIGDOR LOUIS,** ASTROPHYSICS. *Current Pos:* chair, Physics Dept, 90-95, PROF PHYSICS, SOUTHERN METHODIST UNIV, 95- *Personal Data:* b Cambridge, Mass, Feb 5, 37; m 61; c 2. *Educ:* Mass Inst Technol, SB, 58; Univ Md, PhD(physics), 62. *Prof Exp:* Physicist, Lawrence Radiation Lab, Univ Calif, Berkeley, 62-64; NATO fel physics, Europ Orgn Nuclear Res, 64-65; from asst prof to assoc prof, Mass Inst Technol, 65-73; head dept, Va Polytech Inst & State Univ, 73-77, prof physics, 73-78; phys sci officer, US Arms Control & Disarmament Agency, 78-80, dep div chief, 81-90. *Concurrent Pos:* Coun mem, Fedn Am Scientists, 72-76; coun mem forum on physics & soc, Am Phys Soc, 77-79; mem, US ASAT deleg, 78-79, START deleg, 90; prog dir theoret physics, NSF, 87-88. *Mem:* Fel Am Phys Soc; Fedn Am Sci; Am Astron Soc. *Res:* Elementary particle theory; phenomenology and data analysis; applications of particle theory to cosmology and astrophysics. *Mailing Add:* Physics Dept Southern Methodist Univ PO Box 0175 Dallas TX 75275

**TEPLY, LESTER JOSEPH,** BIOCHEMISTRY. *Current Pos:* ADJ PROF, NY MED COL, 85- *Personal Data:* b Muscoda, Wis, Apr 22, 20; m 50; c 3. *Educ:* Univ Wis, BA, 40, MS, 44, PhD(biochem), 45. *Prof Exp:* Asst biochem, Univ Wis, 40-45; tech secy, Food Composition Comt, Nutrit Biochemist Coord, Nat Res Coun, 45; biochemist, USPHS, 45-46; res biochemist, Columbia Univ, 46-48; res biochemist, Enzyme Inst, Univ Wis, 48-51, asst dir labs, Wis Alumni Res Found, 51-55, dir lab projs, 55-60; sr nutritionist, UNICEF, NY, 60-85. *Concurrent Pos:* Chmn, Int Vitamin A Consult Group. *Mem:* Am Chem Soc; Inst Food Tech; Am Pub Health Asn; Am Inst Nutrit. *Res:* Nutrition; vitamins; enzymes; animal nutrition; microbiological nutrition and metabolism; B-complex vitamins; food technology. *Mailing Add:* 32 Colonial Ave Larchmont NY 10538

**TEPLY, MARK LAWRENCE,** ALGEBRA. *Current Pos:* PROF MATH, UNIV WIS-MILWAUKEE, 85- *Personal Data:* b Lincoln, Nebr, Jan 11, 42; m 68, 83, Nancy L Wilkowske; c David, Stephanie, Andrew & Grant. *Educ:* Univ Nebr, BA, 63, MA, 65, PhD(math), 68. *Prof Exp:* From asst prof to prof math, Univ Fla, 68-85. *Concurrent Pos:* Ed, Commun in Algebra, 81-; investr NSF grants, 73, 77, 78; vis assoc prof, Fla State Univ, 76; US Dept Educ grant, 90-93 & 94-97. *Mem:* Am Math Soc; Math Asn Am; Sigma Xi. *Res:* Noncommutative rings and their modules; torsion theories; filters of ideals; direct sum decompositions of modules; idealizer subrings; semigroup rings; graded rings. *Mailing Add:* Univ Wis Milwaukee WI 53201

**TEPPER, BYRON SEYMOUR,** MICROBIOLOGY. *Current Pos:* RETIRED. *Personal Data:* b New Bedford, Mass, Apr 12, 30; m 55; c 2. *Educ:* Northeastern Univ, BS, 51; Univ Mass, MS, 53; Univ Wis, PhD(microbiol), 57. *Prof Exp:* Res assoc biochem, Univ Ill Col Med, 57-59; asst prof, Johns Hopkins Univ, 60-68, assoc prof pathobiol, Sch Hyg, 68-77, exec secy, Comt Use Infectious Agents & Biohazardous Mats, 78-90, assoc prof, environ health, 78-, dir, Off Safety & Environ Health, 90-95. *Concurrent Pos:* Assoc biochemist, Leonard Wood Mem Leprosy Res Lab, Baltimore, 59-65, microbiologist, 65-74; biohazards safety officer, Johns Hopkins Med Insts, 74-77. *Mem:* AAAS; Am Soc Microbiol; Soc Gen Microbiol; Int Leprosy Asn; Am Acad Microbiol. *Res:* Host dependent microorganisms; human and murine leprosy; mycobacterial physiology; photobiology. *Mailing Add:* 8504 Southfields Circle Lutherville MD 21093

**TEPPER, FREDERICK,** PHYSICAL CHEMISTRY, METALLURGY. *Current Pos:* GEN MGR, CATALYST RES CORP, 70-, VPRES, 71-; PRES, ARGONIDE CORP, 97- *Personal Data:* b Brooklyn, NY, Apr 9, 34; m 54, Sheila Schron; c Joi & Cindi. *Educ:* NY Univ, BA, 54. *Prof Exp:* Chemist, Turner-Hall Corp, 54-55; phys chemist, Radiation Res Corp, 55-56; metallurgist, Atomic Energy Div, Sylvania-Elec Corp, 56-57; phys chemist, Mine Safety Appliances Res Corp, 57-60, sect head mat res, 60-69, dir res, 69-70, gen mgr, Instrument Div, Mine Safety Appliance 6, 83-96, vpres, 84-96. *Mem:* Electrochem Soc; Instrument Soc Am; Am Chem Soc. *Res:* Alkali metals; physical, thermodynamic and chemical properties; phase diagrams; production and purification techniques; corrosive effects on structural materials; gas sorption phenomena by activated carbon, metal oxides and ion exchange resins; molten salt electrochemistry; batteries; gas analysis; nanosize metal powders; propellants; pyrotechnics. *Mailing Add:* 4985 Fawn Ridge Pl Sanford FL 32771. *E-Mail:* fredtepper@aol.com

**TEPPER, HERBERT BERNARD,** PLANT GROWTH & DEVELOPMENT. *Current Pos:* from instr to assoc prof, 62-67, PROF FOREST BOT, STATE UNIV NY, COL ENVIRON SCI & FORESTRY, SYRACUSE, 67- *Personal Data:* b Brooklyn, NY, Dec 25, 31; m 84, Sirpa Jorassma; c 2. *Educ:* State Univ NY Col Forestry, Syracuse Univ, BS, 53, MS, 58; Univ Calif, Davis, PhD(bot), 62. *Prof Exp:* Res asst forest bot, State Univ NY, Col Forestry, Syracuse Univ, 56-58; res forester, US Forest Serv, 58-59; res asst, Univ Calif, Davis, 59-62. *Mem:* AAAS; Bot Soc Am; Int Soc Plant Morphol; Sigma Xi; Tissue Cult Asn. *Res:* Morphogenesis in the shoot apex; seed germination; bud and cambial reactivation. *Mailing Add:* Environ Sci Bot State Univ NY Syracuse NY 13210

**TEPPER, LLOYD BARTON,** TOXICOLOGY, OCCUPATIONAL HEALTH. *Current Pos:* CORP MED DIR, AIR PROD & CHEM, INC, 76-; ADJ PROF ENVIRON MED, UNIV PA, 77- *Personal Data:* b Los Angeles, Calif, Dec 21, 31; m 57; c 2. *Educ:* Dartmouth Col, AB, 54; Harvard Univ, MD, 57, MIH, 60, ScD(occup med), 62; Am Bd Prev Med, dipl, 64. *Prof Exp:* Fel, Mass Gen Hosp, 58-60, Mass Inst Technol, 59-61; physician, Eastman Kodak Co, 61-62 & AEC, 62-65; assoc dir occup med & inst environ health, Kettering Lab, Univ Cincinnati, 65-72, assoc prof environ health, Univ, 65-71, prof, 71-72, assoc prof med, 69-72; assoc comnr sci, Food & Drug Admin, 72-76. *Concurrent Pos:* Ed, J Occup Med, 79-91; vchmn, Am Bd Prev Med, 86-94. *Mem:* Am Acad Occup Med (pres, 80-81); Am Col Occup Environ Med. *Res:* Industrial and environmental toxicology, especially as related to toxicology of beryllium, lead and other industrial metals; environmental and medical standards. *Mailing Add:* Air Prod & Chem Inc Allentown PA 18195-1501. *Fax:* 610-481-8951

**TEPPER, MORRIS,** METEOROLOGY, SCIENCE ADMINISTRATION. *Current Pos:* RETIRED. *Personal Data:* b Palestine, Mar 1, 16; nat US; m, Sandra Levin; c Andrew S & Bradford M. *Educ:* Brooklyn Col, BA, 36, MA, 38; Johns Hopkins Univ, PhD(fluid mech), 52. *Honors & Awards:* Meissinger Award, Am Meteorol Soc, 50; Except Serv Medal, NASA, 66; Gold Medal, Nat Ctr Space Studies, France, 72; Am Meteorol Soc Spec Award, 78; Nordberg Mem Award, Comt Space Res, 79. *Prof Exp:* Qualifications analyst & chief, Phys Sci Unit, US Civil Serv Comn, 39-43; chief, Severe Local Storms Res Unit, US Weather Bur, 46-59; dir meteorol prog, NASA, 59-65, dep dir space applications progs & dir meteorol, 66-69, dep dir earth observs progs

& dir meteorol, 69-78, head, Spec Proj Off, Goddard Space Flight Ctr, 78-79; prof math physics, Capitol Col, Md, 79-90; consult, Dept Energy, 87-90. *Concurrent Pos:* Mem staff, USDA Grad Sch, 52-79; mem, US Nat Comt Int Hydrol Decade & chmn work group remote sensing in hydrol, Nat Acad Sci, 71-75, liaison rep, US Comt Global Atmospheric Res Prog, mem, Comt Int Environ Progs, US Interagency Comts; chmn, Working Group 6, Comt Space Res, Int Coun Sci Unions; mem, Int Comn Space Sci Bd, 65-79; consult, Systs Gen Corp, 83-90. *Mem:* Fel Am Meteorol Soc. *Res:* Satellite meteorology; mesometeorology; severe local storms; space applications; earth observation satellites; remote sensing; global atmospheric research; climate; education. *Mailing Add:* 107 Bluff Terr Silver Spring MD 20902

**TEPPERMAN, BARRY LORNE,** MEDICAL SCIENCES. *Current Pos:* asst prof, 77-82, ASSOC PROF PHYSIOL, UNIV WESTERN ONT, 82- *Personal Data:* b Toronto, Ont, Jan 29, 47; m 72; c 2. *Educ:* Univ Toronto, BSc, 69, MSc, 72; Univ Calgary, PhD(physiol), 75. *Prof Exp:* Fel physiol, Univ Tex, Houston, 75-77. *Mem:* Am Gastroenterol Asn; Can Physiol Soc. *Res:* Factors regulating the integrity of gastrointestinal mucosa, specifically prostaglandins and prostaglandin receptors and salivary gland factors; role of gastrointestinal peptides of central origin in the regulation of gastrointestinal function. *Mailing Add:* Dept Physiol Fac Med Univ Western Ont London ON N6A 5C1 Can

**TEPPERMAN, HELEN MURPHY,** PHYSIOLOGICAL CHEMISTRY. *Current Pos:* from instr to prof, 46-85, EMER PROF PHARMACOL, STATE UNIV NY UPSTATE MED CTR, 85- *Personal Data:* b Hartford, Conn, Jan 9, 17; m 43; Jay; c 3. *Educ:* Mt Holyoke Col, BA, 38; Yale Univ, PhD(physiol chem), 42. *Hon Degrees:* DSc, State Univ NY, 87, Mt Holyoke Col, 91. *Prof Exp:* Asst, Mem Hosp, NY, 42-43 & Yale Univ, 43-44; pharmacologist, Med Res Lab, Edgewood Arsenal, Md, 44-45. *Mem:* Am Physiol Soc; Endocrine Soc. *Res:* Endocrinology and metabolism. *Mailing Add:* Dept Pharmacol 750 E Adams St State Univ NY Health Sci Ctr Syracuse NY 13210-2375

**TEPPERMAN, JAY,** MEDICINE. *Current Pos:* RETIRED. *Personal Data:* b Newark, NJ, Mar 23, 14; m 43; c 3. *Educ:* Univ Pa, AB, 33; Columbia Univ, MD, 38. *Hon & Awards:* DSc, 87. *Honors & Awards:* Purkinje Medalist, Czech Med Soc. *Prof Exp:* Intern, Bassett Hosp, NY, 38-40; hon fel, Sch Med, Yale Univ, 40-41, Coxe fel, 41-42, asst, Aeromed Unit, Dept Physiol, 42-44; assoc prof pharmacol, 46-53, prof exp med, Col Med, State Univ NY Upstate Med Ctr, 53-85. *Concurrent Pos:* Mem metab study sect, NIH & physiol comt, Nat Bd Med Examr, 63-67, mem pharmacol comt, 72-75; consult, Vet Admin, DC, 64-67 & Food & Drug Admin, 69-; fac exchange scholar, State Univ NY. *Mem:* Soc Exp Biol & Med; Am Physiol Soc; Endocrine Soc; Am Soc Pharmacol & Exp Therapeut; Am Soc Biol Chem. *Res:* Endocrinology and metabolism. *Mailing Add:* Dept Pharmacol State Univ NY Health Sci Ctr Syracuse 7684 Stonehedge Lane Manlius NY 13104

**TEPPERMAN, KATHERINE GAIL,** CELLULAR PHYSIOLOGY, BIOINORGANIC CHEMISTRY. *Current Pos:* asst prof, 76-83, ASSOC PROF BIOL, UNIV CINCINNATI, 83- *Personal Data:* b Syracuse, NY, May 31, 47; m 79; c 2. *Educ:* Middlebury Col, BA, 68; Univ Conn, PhD(develop biol), 73. *Prof Exp:* From instr to asst prof biol, Middlebury Col, Vt, 72-74; fel, Dept Embryol, Carnegie Inst, 74-76. *Mem:* Am Soc Cell Biol. *Res:* Metal based drugs and interactions of metal ions in biological systems; gold based antiarthritis drugs, effects of silver drugs and electrochemically generated silver on tissue culture cells and renal damage induced by platinum anti-cancer drugs. *Mailing Add:* Dept Biol Univ Cincinnati 2600 Clifton Ave Cincinnati OH 45220-2872

**TEPPING, BENJAMIN JOSEPH,** mathematical statistics, applied statistics; deceased, see previous edition for last biography

**TERADA, KAZUJI,** INORGANIC CHEMISTRY. *Current Pos:* RETIRED. *Personal Data:* b Honolulu, Hawaii, Jan 4, 27. *Educ:* Univ Hawaii, BA, 52, MS, 54; Univ Utah, PhD, 61. *Prof Exp:* Chemist, Res & Develop, Rocky Flats Div, Rockwell Int, Golden, 60-88. *Mem:* Am Chem Soc. *Mailing Add:* 1443 NW Beach Rd Oak Harbor WA 98277

**TERAMURA, ALAN HIROSHI,** PHYSIOLOGICAL ECOLOGY, ENVIRONMENTAL STRESS PHYSIOLOGY. *Current Pos:* DEAN, COL NATURAL SCI, UNIV HAWAII, MANOA, 94- *Personal Data:* b Los Angeles, Calif, Dec 26, 48; m 74, Karen L McKnight; c Kevin & Kai. *Educ:* Calif State Univ, Fullerton, BA, 71, MA, 73; Duke Univ, PhD(physiol ecol), 78. *Prof Exp:* Fel photobiol, Univ Fla, 77-78; from asst prof to assoc prof ecol, Univ Md, 79-88, prof & chmn, 88-93. *Concurrent Pos:* Vis prof ecol, Utah State Univ, 79-; consult, Environ Protection Agency, 80-, Nat Acad Sci, 84 & 88; guest prof photobiol, Univ Karlsruhe, Fed Repub Ger, 82-83; vis prof, Univ Hawaii, 87 & 88; chmn, Sci Adv Bd, Ctr Global Chg, Univ Md, 89-93. *Mem:* Ecol Soc Am; Am Soc Plant Physiologists; Scand Soc Plant Physiol; Bot Soc Am; AAAS. *Res:* The effects of environmental stress on plant growth, physiology, and ecology; adaptive strategies of widespread, weedy plants; the effects of global climate change on plant productivity. *Mailing Add:* Off Dean Col Natural Sci Univ Hawaii Manoa Honolulu HI 96822. *Fax:* 808-956-9111; *E-Mail:* teramura@hawaii.edu

**TERANGO, LARRY,** AUDIOLOGY, SPEECH & LANGUAGE PATHOLOGY. *Current Pos:* RETIRED. *Personal Data:* b Clarksburg, WVa, Nov 30, 25; m 58, Stella Sally Herron; c Eileen Rebecca & Laura Renee. *Educ:* Kent State Univ, BA, 50, MA, 54; Case Western Res Univ, PhD(speech lang path & audiol), 66. *Prof Exp:* Clinician, Painesville City Schs, 52-59; instr speech path & audiol, Kent State Univ, 61-62; asst prof, San Jose State Col, 62-63; instr speech path & audiol, Kent State Univ, 63-64; instr speech & dir speech & hearing clin, Ohio State Univ, 64-66; assoc prof speech & dir speech & hearing clin, Univ Wyo, 66-68; prof, chmn dept spec educ & dir speech & hearing clin, ETenn State Univ, 68-74; prof health sci & dir speech & hearing ctr, Western Carolina Univ, 74-78; prof spec educ & coordr commun prog, Eastern Ky Univ, 78-91. *Concurrent Pos:* Vpres, Wyo Cleft Palate Eval Team, 66-68; audiologist & hearing aid consult, 78- *Mem:* Am Speech & Hearing Asn; Coun Except Children; Nat Educ Asn; Am Cleft Palate Asn; fel Am Speech, Hearing & Lang Asn. *Res:* Vocal characteristics in the male voice; language dysfunction; multidisciplinary approach to study of neurological disturbances, deterioration of educational quality in our educational institutions-degree and grade inflation. *Mailing Add:* 2265 Stone Garden Lane Lexington KY 40513-1394

**TERANISHI, ROY,** ORGANIC CHEMISTRY. *Current Pos:* RES CHEMIST, USDA, 54- *Personal Data:* b Stockton, Calif, Aug 1, 22; m 44. *Educ:* Univ Calif, BS, 50; Ore State Col, PhD, 54. *Hon Degrees:* Dr Agr Sci, Univ Gent, Belg. *Prof Exp:* Instr chem, Portland State Col, 53-54. *Mem:* Am Chem Soc; hon fel Japan Soc Prom Sci. *Res:* Gas chromatography; flavor chemistry. *Mailing Add:* 89 Kingston Rd Kensington CA 94707-1321

**TERASAKI, MARK RYO,** cell biology, for more information see previous edition

**TERASAKI, PAUL ICHIRO,** IMMUNOLOGY. *Current Pos:* Res asst zool, Univ Calif, Los Angeles, 52-54, res asst, Atomic Energy Proj, 54-55, res zoologist, Dept Surg, 55-56, jr res zoologist, 56-57, asst res zoologist, 58-61, assoc res zoologist, 61-62, assoc prof surg, 62-66, PROF SURG, CTR HEALTH SCI, UNIV CALIF, LOS ANGELES, 66- *Personal Data:* b Los Angeles, Calif, Sept 10, 29; m 56; c 4. *Educ:* Univ Calif, Los Angeles, BA, 50, MA, 52, PhD(zool), 56. *Honors & Awards:* Modern Med Award Distinguished Achievement. *Concurrent Pos:* Res fel zool with Prof P B Medawar, Univ Col, Univ London, 57-58; USPHS career develop award, 63-; mem, Transplantation & Immunol Adv Comt, NIH, 67-70; mem, Nomenclature Comt Leukocyte Antigens, WHO. *Mem:* Am Soc Cell Biol; Am Asn Immunol; Soc Cryobiol; Am Soc Immunol; Int Transplantation Soc. *Res:* Transplantation immunology; homotransplantation; leucocyte typing. *Mailing Add:* Tissue Typing Lab Univ Calif-Los Angeles 950 Veteran Ave Los Angeles CA 90024-1652. *Fax:* 310-206-3216

**TERASAWA, EI,** NEUROENDOCRINOLOGY, REPRODUCTIVE PHYSIOLOGY. *Current Pos:* assoc scientist, 73-80, SR SCIENTIST, PHYSIOL, PRIMATE RES CTR, UNIV WIS-MADISON, 80- *Personal Data:* b Ihda City, Japan, Apr 8, 38; m 75, Robert L Grilley; c Juneko E Grilley. *Educ:* Univ Tokyo, BS, 61; Yokohama City Univ, PhD(physiol), 66. *Prof Exp:* Res physiologist anat, Dept Physiol, Univ Calif, Berkeley, 66-67; res fel physiol, Dept Anat, Univ Calif, Los Angeles, 67-68; instr, Dept Physiol, Med Sch, Yokohama City Univ, 68-70, asst prof, 70-73. *Concurrent Pos:* NIHDRG mem Reproductive Biol Study Sect, 87-91, Behav Neurosci Study Sect, 91- *Mem:* Soc Study Reproduction; AAAS; Soc Neurosci; Am Physiol Soc; Endocrine Soc. *Res:* Integral function of the hypothalamus in control of the pituitary-gonadal system; development and function of luteinizing hormone-releasing hormone (LHRH) neurons in primates, mechanisms of action of steroid hormones in the brain; developmental neurobiology. *Mailing Add:* Regional Primate Res Ctr Univ Wis 1223 Capitol Ct Madison WI 53715-1299. *Fax:* 608-263-4031; *E-Mail:* terasawa@primate.wisc.edu

**TERASMAE, JAAN,** GEOLOGY, PALYNOLOGY. *Current Pos:* prof, 68-91, chmn, Dept Geol Sci, 69-75, EMER PROF GEOL, BROCK UNIV, 91- *Personal Data:* b Estonia, May 28, 26; nat Can; m 54, Vaike Jurima. *Educ:* Univ Uppsala, Fil Kand, 51; McMaster Univ, PhD, 55. *Honors & Awards:* W A Johnston Medal, 90. *Prof Exp:* Asst, Palynological Lab Stockholm, 50-51; geologist, Geol Surv Can, 55-68. *Mem:* Geol Soc Can; Int Glaciol Soc; Int Limnol Soc; Royal Soc Can; Geol Soc Am; Am Asn Stratig Palynologist. *Res:* Pleistocene chronology, geology and stratigraphy; paleobotany of Pleistocene deposits. *Mailing Add:* Dept Geol Sci Brock Univ St Catherines ON L2S 3A1 Can. *Fax:* 905-682-9020

**TERBORGH, JOHN J,** POPULATION BIOLOGY, PLANT PHYSIOLOGY. *Current Pos:* Ruth F Devarney prof, 89-93, dir, Ctr Trop Conserv, 91-96, JAMES B DUKE PROF NATURAL SCI, DUKE UNIV, 93-, CO-DIR, CTR TROP CONSERV, 96- *Personal Data:* b Washington, DC, Apr 16, 36. *Educ:* Harvard Univ, AB, 58, AM, 60, PhD(biol), 63. *Honors & Awards:* Daniel Giraud Elliot Medal, Nat Acad Sci, 96. *Prof Exp:* Staff scientist, Tyco Labs, Inc, 63-65; asst prof bot, Univ Md, 65-71; from assoc prof to prof biol, Princeton Univ, 71-89. *Concurrent Pos:* Res grants, Am Philos Soc, Am Mus Natural Hist & Nat Geog Soc, 64-67; NSF res grants, 68- *Mem:* Nat Acad Sci; Am Soc Naturalists; Soc Study Evolution; Ecol Soc Am; fel AAAS. *Res:* Tropical ecology; population biology of birds. *Mailing Add:* Ctr Trop Conserv Duke Univ Box 90381 Durham NC 27708

**TERDIMAN, JOSEPH FRANKLIN,** BIOMEDICAL ENGINEERING. *Current Pos:* asst to dir, Med Methods Res, 80-90, SR INVESTR, KAISER-PERMANENTE, 90- *Personal Data:* b New York, NY, Feb 14, 40; m 65; c 2. *Educ:* Cornell Univ, BEngPhys, 61; NY Univ, MD, 65; Univ Ill Med Ctr, PhD(physiol), 72. *Prof Exp:* Res scientist pop exposure studies, Nat Ctr Radiol Health, 67-69; med info scientist, Kaiser Found Res Inst, 69-79. *Concurrent Pos:* Lectr, Univ Ill, Chicago Circle, 65-67 & Sch Optom, Univ Calif, Berkeley, 69-78; NIH special fel, 67-69; clin asst prof, Sch Optom, Univ

Calif, Berkeley, 79- *Mem:* AAAS; Soc Advan Med Systs; Biomed Eng Soc. *Res:* Development of medical information systems for hospital automation; patient monitoring, diagnosis and therapy; integration of computers and engineering methods with classical neurophysiological techniques; neurophysiology. *Mailing Add:* 30 Oak Mountain Ct San Rafael CA 94903

**TERENZI, JOSEPH F,** PLASTICS ENGINEERING, CHEMICAL & ENVIRONMENTAL ENGINEERING. *Current Pos:* RETIRED. *Personal Data:* b Marlboro, NY, Aug 21, 32; m 54, Tamara Smishkoff; c Mark, Charles & Tania. *Educ:* Rensselaer Polytech Inst, BS, 53; Princeton Univ, MS, 55, PhD, 58. *Prof Exp:* Mem staff res & develop, Am Cyanamid Co, 58-65, tech mgr, Plastics Div, 65-71, mgr mfg, 71-75, dir mfg technol, 75-80, dir environ toxicol, 80-90; vpres, Safety Health & Environ, 91-94. *Concurrent Pos:* Mem fac, Dept Chem Eng, Univ Conn, 64; lectr, Princeton Univ, Columbia Univ, Pa State Univ & Lowell Tech Inst; bd trustees, Polymer Processing Inst, Stevens Inst Technol, 90- *Mem:* Am Inst Chem Engrs; Sigma Xi; Soc Plastics Eng. *Res:* Study of the extent of hydrogen bonding in polymers of the polyamide and polyurethane types; kinetics and novel process designs for polyaery lamides and polymethyl methacrylates. *Mailing Add:* 688 King Rd Franklin Lakes NJ 07417

**TERENZIO, JOSEPH V,** PUBLIC HEALTH. *Current Pos:* RETIRED. *Personal Data:* b New Haven, Ct, Feb 4, 18; m 45; c 3. *Educ:* Yale Univ, BA, 39; Fordham Univ Law Sch, JD, 47; Columbia Univ Sch Pub Health, MS, 52. *Prof Exp:* Exec vpres admin, Brooklyn Cumberland Med Ctr, New York, 60-66; commr hosp, Dept Hosps, New York, 66-70; exec vpres, Evanston Hosp, Ill, 70-72; pres, United Hosp Fund at New York, 75-83; chmn bd, Meta Health Technol Inc, 83-86. *Concurrent Pos:* Spec adv to pres, Columbia Univ, 72-80, adj prof, Pub Health Admin, 72- *Mem:* Nat Acad Sci; fel Am Pub Health Asn; hon fel Am Health Care Execs. *Mailing Add:* 1 Grove Isle Dr Miami Beach FL 33133

**TERESA, GEORGE WASHINGTON,** BACTERIOLOGY. *Current Pos:* RETIRED. *Personal Data:* b Osceola, Ark, Nov 23, 23; m 54. *Educ:* Ark Agr & Mech Col, BS, 52; Univ Ark, MS, 55; Kans State Univ, PhD(microbiol), 59. *Prof Exp:* Asst prof bact, Auburn Univ, 59-61 & Univ RI, 61-62; assoc prof biol, Wichita State Univ, 62-68; from asst prof to assoc prof bact & biochem, Univ Idaho, 68-81, prof bact, 81-89. *Mem:* AAAS; Am Soc Microbiol; Sigma Xi. *Res:* Immunology and pathogenic bacteriology; immunology and pathogenic mechanism of Gram anaerobes. *Mailing Add:* 2400 Princeton Ct Apt 1 Bellingham WA 98226-8865

**TERESHKOVICH, GEORGE,** HORTICULTURE. *Current Pos:* assoc prof hort, 68-74, PROF & ASSOC CHAIRPERSON, DEPT AGR-HORT-ENTOM, TEX TECH UNIV, 75- *Personal Data:* b New York, NY, Mar 18, 30; m 55; c 1. *Educ:* La Tech Univ, BS, 52; Univ Ga, MS, 57; La State Univ, PhD(hort, agron), 63. *Prof Exp:* Res asst, Univ Ga, 52-54, asst prof hort, 54-60; res assoc, La State Univ, 60-63; asst prof (hort), Univ Ga, 63-68. *Mem:* Am Soc Hort Sci. *Res:* Cultural and adaptability studies with vegetable and ornamental crops. *Mailing Add:* 3801 55th St Lubbock TX 79413

**TERESI, JOSEPH DOMINIC,** BIOCHEMISTRY, HEALTH PHYSICS. *Current Pos:* RETIRED. *Personal Data:* b San Jose, Calif, Aug 18, 15; m 47, Margaret Kohake; c Jeanne, Geraldine, Paul, Sallie, Marci & Connie. *Educ:* San Jose State Col, AB, 38; Univ Wis, PhD(biochem), 43. *Prof Exp:* Res assoc, Manhattan Proj, Chicago, 43, Clinton Labs, Tenn, 44, & Univ Chicago, 45; res assoc, Stanford Univ, 47-51, actg instr, 48-50, actg asst prof, 50-51; chemist, US Naval Radiol Defense Lab, 51-69; sr biochemist, Stanford Res Inst, 69-71; sr scientist, San Francisco Bay Marine Res Ctr, 71-73; res assoc div nuclear med, Stanford Univ, 73-74; sr eng, Advan Reactor Systs Dept, Gen Elec Co, 74-80. *Mem:* Fel AAAS; Am Chem Soc; Health Physics Soc. *Res:* Analysis of radionuclides in biological materials; radiation effects; aerospace nuclear safety; radiation protection; radiation ecology and internal emitters; bay sediment analysis; radiological assessment; nuclear reactor safety analysis. *Mailing Add:* 1395 Villa Dr Los Altos CA 94024-5338

**TERHAAR, CLARENCE JAMES,** toxicology, for more information see previous edition

**TER HAAR, GARY L,** INORGANIC CHEMISTRY. *Current Pos:* Res assoc, 62-76, DIR TOXICOL & INDUST HYG, ETHYL CORP, 76-, VPRES, HEALTH & ENVIRON, 85- *Personal Data:* b Zeeland, Mich, May 2, 36; m 56; c 2. *Educ:* Hope Col, BA, 58; Univ Mich, MS, 60, PhD(chem), 62. *Mem:* Am Chem Soc; Soc Toxicol. *Res:* Environmental research. *Mailing Add:* Albemarle Corp 451 Florida St Baton Rouge LA 70801-1779

**TERHUNE, ROBERT WILLIAM,** QUANTUM ELECTRONICS. *Current Pos:* CONSULT. *Personal Data:* b Detroit, Mich, Feb 7, 26; m 47; c 2. *Educ:* Univ Mich, BS, 47 & PhD(physics), 57; Dartmouth Col, Ma, 48. *Honors & Awards:* Sci & Eng Award, Drexel Inst Technol, 64; Ives Medal, Optical Soc Am, 92. *Prof Exp:* Supvr, Digital Comput & Logic Des Sect, Willow Run Labs, Univ Mich, 51-54, res physicist, 54-59, mgr, Solid State Physics Lab, 59-60; res physicist, Sci Lab, Ford Motor Co, Dearborn, Mich, 60-65, mgr, Physics Electronics Dept, 65-75; vis scholar, Stanford Univ, 75-76; sr staff scientist, Eng & Res Staff, Ford Motor Co, 76-87; sr mem tech staff, JPL-Calif Tech, 88-95. *Concurrent Pos:* Ed, Optics Let J, 77-83, J Ont Soc Am, Optical Soc Am, 84-87. *Mem:* Optical Soc Am; Am Phys Soc; Inst Elec & Electronic Engrs. *Res:* Quantum electronics; nonlinear optics; optical properties of solids and surfaces; molecular spectroscopy; advanced instrumentation. *Mailing Add:* 4002 Tall Oaks Dr Blacksburg VA 24060

**TER KUILE, BENNO HERMAN,** CELL PHYSIOLOGY, PARASITOLOGY. *Current Pos:* assoc, 92-93, res assoc, 93-95, ASST PROF, ROCKEFELLER UNIV, 95- *Personal Data:* b Amsterdam, Neth, July 9, 56; m 83, Nurit Herschkowitz; c Hagar. *Educ:* Univ Groningen, BSc, 80, MSc, 83; Hebrew Univ Jerusalem, PhD(protozool), 89. *Prof Exp:* Fel, Int Inst Cellular & Molecular Path, 89-92. *Mem:* Am Soc Microbiol; Soc Protozoologists; Neth Inst Biologists. *Res:* Intracellular interactions using energy metabolism in eukaryotic microorganisms as a model; elucidate how cellular processes are coordinated to form a living cell. *Mailing Add:* Rockefeller Univ 1230 York Ave New York NY 10021. *Fax:* 212-327-7974; *E-Mail:* terkuil@rockvax

**TERMAN, CHARLES RICHARD,** ANIMAL ECOLOGY, ANIMAL BEHAVIOR. *Current Pos:* from asst prof to assoc prof, 63-69, PROF BIOL, COL WILLIAM & MARY, 69- *Personal Data:* b Mansfield, Ohio, Sept 8, 29; m 51; c 2. *Educ:* Albion Col, AB, 52; Mich State Univ, MS, 54, PhD(behav pop dynamics), 59. *Prof Exp:* Assoc prof biol, Taylor Univ, 61-63, actg dir res, 62-63. *Concurrent Pos:* NIMH fel, Sch Hyg & Pub Health, Johns Hopkins Univ, 59 & Penrose Res Lab, 59-61; NIH career develop award, 70-74; NATO sr sci fel, eng & exchange scientist, US & Polish Nat Acads Sci, 74. *Mem:* Fel AAAS; Animal Behav Soc; Am Sci Affil; Am Soc Mammal; Am Soc Nat. *Res:* Population dynamics; socio-biological factors influencing the growth and physiology of populations; reproductive physiology; behavioral ecology. *Mailing Add:* Dept Biol Col William & Mary PO Box 8795 Williamsburg VA 23187-8795

**TERMAN, LEWIS MADISON,** ELECTRONICS, SOLID STATE TECHNOLOGY DEVICES. *Current Pos:* Res staff mem, IBM Corp, 61-63, mgr read only storage res, 63-65, mgr integrated memory circuit res, 65-70, mgr semiconductor storage-circuits & systs, 70-75, res staff mem, 75-79, mem & dir res tech planning staff, 79-80, mgr, very-large-scale integration circuits, 80-82, mgr very large scale integration logic & memory, 82-91, sr mem, tech planning staff, 91-93, mgr VLSI processor design, 93-94, PROG MGR, IBM CORP, 94- *Personal Data:* b San Francisco, Calif, Aug 26, 35; m 58, Barbara Chertok. *Educ:* Stanford Univ, BS, 56, MS, 58, PhD(elec eng), 61. *Honors & Awards:* Solid State Circuits Tech Field Award, Inst Elec & Electronics Engrs, 95, Electron Devices Distinguished Serv Award, 96. *Concurrent Pos:* Ed, J Solid State Circuits, 74-77; mem, Circuits & Systs Admin Comt, Inst Elec & Electronics Engrs, 81-83 & Electron Devices Soc Admin Comt, 84-90; chmn, Int Solid-State Circuits Conf, 83; chmn, Symp Very Large Scale Integration Technol, 85-86 & Symp Very Large Scale Integration Circuits, 88-89; vpres, Inst Elec & Electronics Engrs Electron Devices Soc, 88-89, pres, 90-91; treas, Solid-State Circuits Coun, Inst Elec & Electronics Engrs, 88-89, vpres, 96-97, treas, Tech Activ Bd, 95-97. *Mem:* Nat Acad Eng; fel Inst Elec & Electronics Engrs; fel AAAS. *Res:* Integrated circuits, memory systems and semiconductor device research and development; logic design; design of high performance processors for reduced instruction set computer and complex instruction set computer systems, including circuit design, chip design, system organization, design methodologies and tools. *Mailing Add:* IBM Res Ctr PO Box 218 Yorktown Heights NY 10598

**TERMAN, MAX R,** ECOLOGY, ETHOLOGY. *Current Pos:* PROF BIOL, TABOR COL, 69- *Personal Data:* b Mansfield, Ohio, Apr 15, 45; m 68; c 2. *Educ:* Spring Arbor Col, BA, 67; Mich State Univ, MS, 69, PhD(zool), 73. *Concurrent Pos:* Consult, Environ Land Use. *Mem:* Ecol Soc Am; Am Soc Mammalogists; Animal Behav Soc; Am Inst Biol Sci; Sigma Xi. *Res:* Interspecific competition between rodents; ecosystem ecology; rodent population dynamics; behavior of rodents and birds; earth-sheltered housing; golf course design-ecological aspects; author of two books. *Mailing Add:* RR 2 Box 78B Hillsboro KS 67063

**TERMINE, JOHN DAVID,** BIOCHEMISTRY, MOLECULAR BIOLOGY. *Current Pos:* exec dir, Osteoporosis/Osteoarthritis Res, 91-95, VPRES, LILLY RES LABS, ELI LILLY & CO, INDIANAPOLIS, IND, 95- *Personal Data:* b Brooklyn, NY, Sept 25, 38; m 61, Virginia A Galvin; c Mary, John C, Theresa & Anne. *Educ:* St John's Univ, NY, BS, 60; Univ Md, MS, 63; Cornell Univ, PhD(biochem), 66. *Honors & Awards:* NIH Dir Award, 83; Biol Mineralization Res Award, Int Asn Dent Res, 88. *Prof Exp:* Teaching asst chem, Univ Md, 60-63; from asst res scientist to assoc res scientist, Hosp Spec Surg, New York, 63-66; from instr to asst prof biochem, Med Col, Cornell Univ, 66-70; spec res fel, NIH, 70-73, res biochemist, Molecular Struct Sect, 73-80, chief, Skeletal Matrix Biochem Sect, Lab Biol Struct, 80-83, Bone Res Br, Nat Inst Dent Res, 83-91. *Concurrent Pos:* Counr, Am Soc Bone & Mineral Res, 84-87; assoc ed, Calcified Tissue Int, 86-; mem bd dirs, Int Conf Calcium Regulating Hormones & Bone Metab, 87- *Mem:* AAAS; Int Asn Dent Res; Am Chem Soc; Biophys Soc; Am Soc Biochem & Molecular Biol; Am Soc Bone & Mineral Res; Orthop Res Soc; Am Soc Cell Biol. *Res:* Molecular and cellular biology of bone and tooth; molecular biology; protein biochemistry; osteoporosis and osteoarthritis research. *Mailing Add:* Lilly Res Labs Lilly Corp Ctr Eli Lilly & Co Indianapolis IN 46285

**TERNAY, ANDREW LOUIS, JR,** ORGANIC CHEMISTRY, MEDICINAL CHEMISTRY. *Current Pos:* assoc prof, 70-76, PROF CHEM, UNIV TEX, ARLINGTON, 77-, DIR, MED CHEM RES, 88- *Personal Data:* b New York, NY, Aug 29, 39; m 61, Marilyn Kranepool; c 2. *Educ:* City Col New York, BS, 59; NY Univ, MS, 62, PhD(chem), 63. *Prof Exp:* NSF fel & res assoc chem, Univ Ill, 63-64; instr, Case Western Res Univ, 64-65, asst prof, 65-69. *Concurrent Pos:* Grants, Nat Cancer Inst, Dept Chem, Case Western Res Univ, 66-69 & Welch Found, Univ Tex, 72-; consult, Arbrook, Inc, 71-; adj prof med chem, Univ Houston, 81; US Army Med Res & Develop Command, 84- *Mem:* AAAS; Am Chem Soc; Royal Soc Chem; Sigma Xi. *Res:* Drug design; molecular spectroscopy; application of stereochemistry to synthesis of new drugs, especially psychoactive materials; radioprotective drugs and chemical defense; organosulfur chemistry. *Mailing Add:* Dept Chem Univ Tex Box 19065 Arlington TX 76019-0065. *Fax:* 817-273-3808

**TERNBERG, JESSIE L,** MEDICAL EDUCATION, PEDIATRIC SURGERY. *Current Pos:* res fel, Dept Surg, 57-58, from instr to assoc prof, 59-71, PROF SURG, SCH MED, WASHINGTON UNIV, 71-, PROF PEDIAT SURG, 75-, CHIEF, DIV PEDIAT SURG, DEPT SURG, 72- *Personal Data:* b Corning, Calif, May 28, 24. *Educ:* Grinnell Col, AB, 46; Univ Tex, PhD(biochem), 50; Washington Univ, MD, 53. *Hon Degrees:* DSc, Grinnell Col, 72 & Univ Mo-St Louis, 81. *Honors & Awards:* Horatio Alger Award. *Prof Exp:* Intern med, Boston City Hosp, 53-54; asst resident surg, Barnes Hosp, St Louis, 54-57, chief & admin resident surg, 58-59. *Concurrent Pos:* Pediat surgeon-in-chief, St Louis Children's Hosp, 74-; chmn surg sect, pediat oncol group, US Food & Drug Admin. *Mem:* Fel Am Col Surgeons; Am Pediat Surg Asn; Soc Surg Alimentary Tract; Soc Pelvic Surgeons; Brit Asn Pediat Surg. *Res:* Formation of neo-mucosa of the intestine; nutritional aspects of short gut. *Mailing Add:* Washington Univ 4960 Childrens Pl St Louis MO 63110-1002

**TERNER, CHARLES,** BIOCHEMISTRY. *Current Pos:* prof, 59-87, EMER PROF BIOL, BOSTON UNIV, 87- *Personal Data:* b Lublin, Poland, Apr 30, 16; nat US; m 45, Ruth Cohn; c 3. *Educ:* Univ London, BSc, 44, DSc(biochem), 69; Univ Sheffield, PhD(biochem), 49. *Prof Exp:* Mem staff, Med Res Coun Unit for Res Cell Metab, Dept Biochem, Univ Sheffield, 47-50; sr sci officer, Dept Physiol, Nat Inst Res in Dairying, Eng, 50-55; mem staff, Worcester Found Exp Biol, 55-59. *Concurrent Pos:* Vis scientist, Pop Coun, Rockefeller Univ, 72. *Mem:* AAAS; Am Soc Biochem & Molecular Biol; Biochem Soc (Gt Brit); Soc Exp Biol & Med; Soc Study Reproduction. *Res:* Biochemistry of male reproductive tissues; control of male fertility; embryonic development of fish. *Mailing Add:* Biol Sci Ctr Boston Univ 5 Cummington St Boston MA 02215

**TERNER, JAMES,** RESONANCE RAMAN SPECTROSCOPY, HEME ENZYMES. *Current Pos:* Asst prof, 81-86, ASSOC PROF CHEM, VA COMMONWEALTH UNIV, 86- *Personal Data:* b Reading, Eng, Mar 27, 51; US citizen; m 79, Ellen C Shapiro; c Steven, Jeremy, Benjamin & Zachary. *Educ:* Brandeis Univ, BA, 73; Univ Calif Los Angeles, PhD(chem), 79. *Concurrent Pos:* Alfred P Sloan Found fel, 85. *Mem:* Am Chem Soc; Biophys Soc; AAAS. *Res:* Resonance Raman spectroscopy of transient species; intermediates and excited states of photochemical and biological significance. *Mailing Add:* Chem Dept Va Commonwealth Univ 1001 Main St Richmond VA 23284-2006. *Fax:* 804-828-8599; *E-Mail:* jterner@saturn.vcu.edu

**TER-POGOSSIAN, MICHEL MATHEW,** medical physics; deceased, see previous edition for last biography

**TERRAGLIO, FRANK PETER,** ENVIRONMENTAL SCIENCE, CHEMISTRY. *Current Pos:* from asst prof to assoc prof, 66-72, PROF APPL SCI, PORTLAND STATE UNIV, 72- *Personal Data:* b Portland, Ore, May 19, 28; m 64. *Educ:* Univ Portland, BS, 49; Rutgers Univ, MS, 62, PhD(environ sci), 64. *Prof Exp:* Chemist, Ore State Bd Health, 49-50 & Ore Air Pollution Authority, 52-56; asst instr air pollution, Rutgers Univ, 56-63; res chemist, Calif Dept Pub Health, 63-64; asst prof civil eng, Ore State Univ, 64-66. *Mem:* Am Chem Soc; Air Pollution Control Asn; Am Water Works Asn; Water Pollution Control Fedn; Am Indust Hyg Asn; Sigma Xi. *Res:* Reactions of atmospheric sulfur dioxide. *Mailing Add:* 3809 SW Dakota St Portland OR 97221-3329

**TERRANOVA, ANDREW CHARLES,** ENTOMOLOGY, TOXICOLOGY. *Current Pos:* RETIRED. *Personal Data:* b Cleveland, Ohio, Aug 29, 35. *Educ:* Ohio State Univ, BSc, 60, MSc, 61, PhD(entom), 65. *Prof Exp:* Insect physiologist, Metab & Radiation Res Lab, USDA, 65-76, res entomologist, Sci & Educ Admin-Agr Res, 76-90. *Mem:* AAAS; Entom Soc Am; Am Chem Soc. *Res:* Metabolism and mode of action of insect chemosterilants; biochemistry and physiology of insect reproduction; population genetics. *Mailing Add:* 911 Oak Ave Sanford FL 32771

**TERRAS, AUDREY ANNE,** NUMBER THEORY, ANALYSIS. *Current Pos:* from asst prof to assoc prof, 72-83, PROF MATH, UNIV CALIF, SAN DIEGO, 83- *Personal Data:* b Wash, DC, Sept 10, 42; div. *Educ:* Univ Md, College Park, BS, 64; Yale Univ, MA, 66, PhD(math), 70. *Prof Exp:* Instr math, Univ Ill, Urbana, 68-70; asst prof, Univ PR, Mayaguez, 70-71 & Brooklyn Col, 71-72. *Concurrent Pos:* NSF prin investr, 74-88; vis assoc prof, Mass Inst Technol, 83; mem, Inst Advan Study, Princeton, NJ, 84. *Mem:* Am Math Soc; Math Asn Am; Am Women Math; Soc Indust & Appl Math; fel AAAS; Asn Women Sci. *Res:* Zeta functions; automorphic forms of matrix argument; harmonic analysis on homogeneous spaces; fundamental domains of discrete transformation groups; spectra of Cayleg graphs of finite matrix groups; Selberg's trace formula. *Mailing Add:* Dept Math Univ Calif San Diego 0112 La Jolla CA 92093-0112

**TERREAULT, BERNARD J E J,** SURFACE PHYSICS, ION IMPLANTATION. *Current Pos:* assoc prof, 72-77, PROF ENERGY & MAT SCI, ENERGY CTR, NAT INST SCI RES, UNIV QUE, 77- *Personal Data:* b Montreal, Que, Mar 29, 40; div; c 2. *Educ:* Univ Montreal, BSc, 60, MSc, 62; Univ Ill Urbana-Champaign, PhD(physics), 68. *Prof Exp:* Fel, Lab High Energy Physics, Polytech Sch, Paris, 69-70; res assoc high energy physics, Ohio Univ, 70-71, asst prof, 71-72. *Concurrent Pos:* Foreign scientist, Fr Atomic Energy Comn, 82-83. *Mem:* Am Phys Soc; Can Asn Physicists; Am Vacuum Soc; Mat Res Soc. *Res:* Surface modification of materials by ion beams and plasmas. *Mailing Add:* Energy Ctr Nat Inst Sci Res Univ Que CP 1020 Varennes PQ J3X 1S2 Can. *Fax:* 514-449-8102; *E-Mail:* terreau@inrs-ener.uquebec.ca

**TERREL, RONALD LEE,** CIVIL ENGINEERING, CONSTRUCTION MATERIALS. *Current Pos:* from asst prof to prof, 67-75, EMER PROF CIVIL ENG, UNIV WASH, 85-; OWNER, TERREL RES, 86- *Personal Data:* b Klamath Falls, Ore, Sept 2, 36; m 59, 81, Alice Blanchard; c Douglas S, Nancy D & Janet L. *Educ:* Purdue Univ, Lafayette, BSCE, 60, MSCE, 61; Univ Calif, Berkeley, PhD(civil eng), 67. *Honors & Awards:* Walter Emmons Award, Asn Asphalt Paving Technologists, 83 & 95, Award of Merit, 91. *Prof Exp:* Estimator, J H Pomeroy & Co, Inc, 55-56; mat engr, US Bur Reclamation, Denver, 61-64; proj engr, J H Pomeroy & Co, Inc, 64-65; res asst, Univ Calif, Berkeley, 65-67; dir, Wash State Transp Ctr, 81-83; head transp div, Dept Civil Eng, Seattle Eng Int, Inc, 76-80, vpres, 80-82. *Concurrent Pos:* Chmn, Triaxial Inst Struct Pavement Design, 71-73; pres, Pavements Systs, Inc, 72-80; vpres, Pavement Technol, Inc, 85-86; prof civil eng, Oregon State Univ, 89-94; vpres, Hydrogenesis, Inc, 91-; mem trans res bd, Nat Acad Sci; consult eng res & develop, gov & pvt indust, States, Fed Hwy Admin, UN; chmn & chief exec officer, RL Technologies, Ltd, 96- *Mem:* Asn Soc Civil Engrs; Am Soc Testing & Mat; Int Soc Asphalt Pavements. *Res:* Pavement and construction materials technology including asphalt, polymer modified asphalt, concrete, aggregates, waste materials such as sulphur, lignin, ash, and recycled pavement materials for highway and airports; construction methods, equipment, engineering and management; systems for environmental storage of solid waste. *Mailing Add:* 9703 241st Pl SW Edmonds WA 98020-6512. *Fax:* 206-542-6159; *E-Mail:* rterrel@u.washington.edu

**TERRELL, C(HARLES) W(ILLIAM),** NUCLEAR ENGINEERING, ENGINEERING EDUCATION. *Current Pos:* SR TECHNOLOGIST, PHILLIPS LAB, KIRKLIN AFB, 87- *Personal Data:* b Louisville, Ky, May 10, 27; m 52; c 2. *Educ:* Purdue Univ, BSEE, 52, PhD(nuclear eng), 70; NC State Univ, Raleigh, BS, 54, MS, 55. *Prof Exp:* Res engr, Bendix Res Labs, Mich, 52-54; mem res & teaching staff physics, NC State Univ, Raleigh, 54-57; supvr reactor opers, Armour Res Found, 57-59, mgr reactor res, 59-61, mgr nuclear res, 61-63; asst dir physics res, IIT Res Inst, 63-65, dir physics res div, 65-67; assoc prof nuclear eng & supvr comput opers, Purdue Univ, 69-70; dist mgr appl sci & mkt support, Comput Sci Corp, Ill, 70-72; pres, Ind Inst Technol, 72-77; prof nuclear eng, Univ Okla, 77-87. *Mem:* Am Nuclear Soc; Am Soc Eng Educ; sr mem Inst Elec & Electronics Engrs. *Res:* Higher education administration; nuclear engineering education; research management. *Mailing Add:* 10 Bridal Lane Tijeras NM 87059

**TERRELL, CHARLES R,** MARINE BIOLOGY. *Current Pos:* nat water qual specialist, 80-93, NAT ENVIRON COORDR, SOIL CONSERV SERV, WASHINGTON, DC, 94- *Personal Data:* b Waltham, Mass, June 20, 43; m 67, Sandra J Sturtevant; c Julia A & Alicia J. *Educ:* Boston Univ, BA, 65; Northeastern Univ, MS, 68. *Prof Exp:* Asst prof & lab dir biol sci, Salem State Col, 67-74; dir, Coastal Rev Ctr, Coastal Zone Mgt, 75-76; assoc, Conserv Found, 76-77; actg sect chief, Environ Protection Agency, 77-80. *Concurrent Pos:* Mem, Shellfish Adv Comn, 69-74; consult ecologist, Edwards & Kelcey Inc, 71-72; legis fel, US Senate, 85 & 86. *Mem:* Fed Water Qual Asn (secy, 89-91, vpres, 91-92, pres-elect, 92-93, pres, 93-94); Water Pollution Control Fed; Am Inst Biol Sci; Am Water Resources Asn. *Res:* Establish national technical policies on abating agricultural pollution; water conservation; environmental problems; numerous publications and audio-visuals. *Mailing Add:* 13211 Pressmont Lane Fairfax VA 22033

**TERRELL, EDWARD EVERETT,** PLANT TAXONOMY. *Current Pos:* RETIRED. *Personal Data:* b Wilmington, Ohio, Oct 6, 23; m 50, Bessie Zimmerly; c Stephen (deceased), Jonathan & Susanna. *Educ:* Wilmington Col, AB, 47; Cornell Univ, MS, 49; Univ Wis, PhD, 52. *Prof Exp:* Muellhaupt scholar bot, Ohio State Univ, 52-53; assoc prof biol & head, Dept Sci, Pembroke State Col, 54-56; assoc prof biol, Guilford Col, 56-60; botanist, Agr Res Serv, USDA, 60-85. *Concurrent Pos:* Vis prof bot, Univ Md, 86 & 93-94, res assoc bot, 86-91 & 95-97. *Mem:* Bot Soc Am; Am Soc Plant Taxon; Int Asn Plant Taxon. *Res:* Plant taxonomy and ecology; taxonomy of Hedyotideae (Rubiaceae); taxonomy of grasses. *Mailing Add:* 14001 Wildwood Dr Silver Spring MD 20905

**TERRELL, GLEN EDWARD,** NUCLEAR PHYSICS. *Current Pos:* Asst prof, 66-74, ASSOC PROF PHYSICS, UNIV TEX, ARLINGTON, 74- *Personal Data:* b Humble, Tex, Nov 17, 39; m 59; c 2. *Educ:* Univ Tex, Austin, BS, 62, MA, 64, PhD(physics), 66. *Mem:* Am Phys Soc. *Res:* Computer-assisted instruction; low energy nuclear physics; polarization of protons elastically scattered by several nuclei; gamma ray directional correlation. *Mailing Add:* Dept Physics Univ Tex Arlington Box 19059 Arlington TX 76019-0001

**TERRELL, MARVIN PALMER,** INDUSTRIAL ENGINEERING, OPERATIONS RESEARCH. *Current Pos:* from asst prof to assoc prof, 66-77, PROF INDUST ENG, OKLA STATE UNIV, 77- *Personal Data:* b Pine Bluff, Ark, May 19, 34; m 59; c 2. *Educ:* Univ Ark, Fayetteville, BSIE, 57, MSIE, 60; Univ Tex, Austin, PhD(opers res), 66. *Prof Exp:* Instr indust eng, Univ Ark, Fayetteville, 57-60; mfg engr, Gen Elec Co, 60-63; indust engr, Tex Instruments Co, 63-64; asst eng & Ford Found & Alcoa fels, Univ Tex, Austin, 64-66, Nat Tau Beta Pi-Ford fel, 65-66. *Concurrent Pos:* Consult, Continental Oil Co, 67, NAm Rockwell Corp, 68-69, Phillips Petrol Co, 72 & Bray Truck Lines, 79-82. *Mem:* Am Inst Indust Engrs; Opers Res Soc Am; Inst Mgt Sci; Am Soc Eng Educ. *Res:* Mathematical programming; optimization theory; combinatorics; operations modeling and analysis; management science; quality control and reliability. *Mailing Add:* 522 N Skyline Lane C22 N Skyline Ln Stillwater OK 74075

**TERRELL, N(ELSON) JAMES,** PHYSICS, ASTROPHYSICS. *Current Pos:* staff mem, 51-89, assoc, Los Alamos Nat Lab, 89-94, AFFIL, UNIV CALIF, 94- *Personal Data:* b Houston, Tex, Aug 15, 23; m 45, Elizabeth Pearson; c Anne (deceased), Barbara & Jean. *Educ:* Rice Univ, BA, 44, MA, 47, PhD(physics), 50. *Prof Exp:* Res asst physics, Rice Univ, 50; asst prof, Case Western Res Univ, 50-51. *Concurrent Pos:* USAEC fel, 48-50; vis prof, Highlands Univ, Las Vegas, 59; vis scientist, Univ Calif, Lawrence Berkeley Lab, 63. *Mem:* Fel AAAS; fel Am Phys Soc; Am Astron Soc; Sigma Xi; Int Astron Union. *Res:* Astrophysics; relativity; fission; diffraction; Fourier analysis; x-ray and gamma-ray astronomy; quasars. *Mailing Add:* Los Alamos Nat Lab Mail Stop D436 Group NIS-2 Los Alamos NM 87545. *Fax:* 505-665-4414; *E-Mail:* terrell@lanl.gov

**TERRELL, TERRY LEE TICKHILL,** aquatic ecology, for more information see previous edition

**TERRES, GERONIMO,** IMMUNOBIOLOGY. *Current Pos:* from assoc prof to prof, 69-91, EMER PROF PHYSIOL, SCH MED, TUFTS UNIV, 91- *Personal Data:* b Santa Barbara, Calif, July 1, 25; m 47; c 5. *Educ:* Univ Calif, BA, 50; Stanford Univ, MA, 51; Calif Inst Technol, PhD(biol), 56. *Honors & Awards:* Yamagiwa-Yoshida Fel Award, 79. *Prof Exp:* Asst, Calif Inst Technol, 52-55; assoc scientist microbiol, Brookhaven Nat Lab, 55-60; asst prof human physiol, Sch Med, Stanford Univ, 60-69. *Concurrent Pos:* NIH sr res fel, 60-62; USPHS res career develop award, 62-69; vis asst prof, Harvard Med Sch, 67-68; vis scientist, Mass Inst Technol, 75-76, Swiss Inst Allergy & Asthma Res, Davos, 89; res collabr, Swiss Inst Exp Cancer Res, Lausanne, Switz, 79; vis assoc, Calif Inst Technol, 81; mem, Basel Inst Immunol, Switz, 82-83; fel, DNAX, 91-93. *Mem:* AAAS; Am Asn Immunol; Soc Exp Biol & Med; Am Physiol Soc; Radiation Res Soc; Sigma Xi. *Res:* Immune degradation; tumor (leukemias) cell rejection; T cell hybridization; acquired immune tolerance in mice; initiation and control of the immune response. *Mailing Add:* 335 Iris Way Palo Alto CA 94303. *Fax:* 650-856-2340

**TERRIERE, ROBERT T,** GEOLOGY. *Current Pos:* RETIRED. *Personal Data:* b Seattle, Wash, July 17, 26; m 58; c 2. *Educ:* Calif Inst Technol, BS, 49; Pa State Col, MS, 51; Univ Tex, PhD(geol), 60. *Prof Exp:* Geologist, US Geol Surv, 51-58; res geologist, Cities Serv Oil Co, 58-70, res assoc, 70-78, sr geol assoc, 78-80, region geologist, Cities Serv Co-Petrol Explor, 80-83, sr geol assoc, 83-85. *Mem:* Fel Geol Soc Am; Am Asn Petrol Geol. *Res:* Physical stratigraphy; sedimentary petrography; petroleum geology. *Mailing Add:* 2618 S Allison St Denver CO 80227

**TERRILE, RICHARD JOHN,** PLANETARY SCIENCE. *Current Pos:* physicist, Trend Western Tech Corp, 78-80, sr scientist, 80-81, MEM TECH STAFF, JET PROPULSION LAB, 81- *Personal Data:* b New York, NY, Mar 22, 51; m 81. *Educ:* State Univ NY, Stony Brook, BS, 72; Calif Inst Technol, MS, 73, PhD(planetary sci), 78. *Honors & Awards:* Except Sci Achievement Medal, NASA, 88. *Prof Exp:* Res asst, Calif Inst Technol, 72-78, assoc scientist, 78. *Concurrent Pos:* Mem, Voyager Target Selection Working Group, 78-; planetary astron prin investr, NASA grant, 78-, planetary atmospheres prin investr, 79-; guest investr, Voyager Imaging Sci Team, 78-80. *Mem:* Am Astron Soc; Am Geophys Union; Int Astron Union; Sigma Xi. *Res:* Ground-based planetary astronomy; planetary atmospheres; comparative geology; photographic interpretation of spacecraft data and the study of planetary ring systems. *Mailing Add:* 2121 Woodlyn Rd Pasadena CA 91104

**TERRILL, CLAIR ELMAN,** ANIMAL BREEDING. *Current Pos:* COLLABR, 81- *Personal Data:* b Rippey, Iowa, Oct 27, 10; m 32; c 2. *Educ:* Iowa State Col, BS, 32; Univ Mo, PhD, 36. *Honors & Awards:* Achievement Award, Ital Exp Inst & Ital Soc Advan Zootech; Distinguished Achievement Award, Sheep Indust Develop; Distinguished Serv Award, Am Soc Animal Sci. *Prof Exp:* Asst animal husb, Univ Mo, 32-36; asst animal husbandman, Exp Sta, Univ Ga, 36; asst animal husbandman, Sheep Exp Sta, Bur Animal Indust, Idaho, 36-37, assoc animal husbandman, Western Sheep Breeding Lab & Sheep Exp Sta, Agr Res Serv, 53-55, chief sheep & fur animal res br, Animal Husb Res Div, 55-72, nat prog staff scientist for sheep & other animals, Agr Res Serv, USDA, 72-80. *Concurrent Pos:* Dir, Am Forage & Grass Land Coun, 63-65; mem, World Asn Animal Prod Coun, 63- *Mem:* Fel AAAS; Genetics Soc Am; hon fel Am Soc Animal Sci (secy-treas, 60-62, vpres, 63, pres, 64); Am Meat Sci Asn; Am Genetic Asn (vpres, 69, pres, 70). *Res:* Animal genetics; reproductive physiology; sheep, goat and fur animal breeding and production. *Mailing Add:* USDA Agr Res Serv Rm 12 Bldg 005 Barc-W Beltsville MD 20705

**TERRIS, JAMES MURRAY,** HYPERTENSION, COMPARATIVE KIDNEY PHYSIOLOGY. *Current Pos:* ASSOC PROF KIDNEY PHYSIOL, UNIFORMED SERV, UNIV HEALTH SCI, F EDWARD HERBERT SCH MED, 78- *Personal Data:* b May 6, 41; m; c 3. *Educ:* Mich State Univ, PhD(physiol), 74. *Mem:* Am Physiol Soc; Am Chem Soc; AAAS. *Res:* Hypertension; renal physiology. *Mailing Add:* Dept Physiol Uniformed Serv Univ Health Sci Sch Med 4301 Jones Bridge Rd Bethesda MD 20814-4799. *Fax:* 301-295-3566

**TERRIS, MILTON,** EPIDEMIOLOGY. *Current Pos:* RETIRED. *Personal Data:* b New York, NY, Apr 22, 15; m 41, 71; c 2. *Educ:* Columbia Col, AB, 35; NY Univ, MD, 39; Johns Hopkins Univ, MPH, 44. *Prof Exp:* Intern, Harlem Hosp, NY, 39-41 & Bellevue Psychiat Hosp, NY, 41-42; apprentice epidemiologist, State Dept Health, NY, 42-43, asst dist health officer, 44-46; med assoc subcomt on med care, Am Pub Health Asn, 46-48, staff dir, 48-51; assoc prev med & pub health, Sch Med, Univ Buffalo, 52-54, from asst prof to assoc prof, 54-58; prof epidemiol, Sch Med, Tulane Univ, 58-60; head chronic dis unit, Div Epidemiol, Pub Health Res Inst NY, 60-64; prof prev med, New York Med Col, 64-80, chmn dept community & prev med, 68-80. *Concurrent Pos:* Asst dean post-grad educ, Univ Buffalo, 51-58. *Mem:* Am Pub Health Asn (pres, 66-67); Soc Epidemiol Res (pres, 67-69); Am Epidemiol Soc; Asn Teachers Prev Med (pres, 61-62); Int Epidemiol Asn. *Res:* Epidemiology of cancer; cirrhosis of liver; prematurity; heart disease. *Mailing Add:* Journal Pub Health Policy 208 Meadowood Dr South Burlington VT 05403-7401

**TERRY, DAVID LEE,** SOIL SCIENCE. *Current Pos:* COORDR FERTILIZER REGULATORY PROG, UNIV KY, 74- *Personal Data:* b Burkley, Ky, Mar 22, 36; div; c 3. *Educ:* Univ Ky, BS, 58, MS, 61; NC State Univ, PhD(soil sci), 68. *Prof Exp:* Agronomist, Univ Ky, 59-60; from instr to asst prof soil sci, NC State Univ, 71-74. *Mem:* Asn Am Plant Food Control Officials; Am Soc Agron. *Res:* Soil fertility; fertilizer control in state of Kentucky. *Mailing Add:* 3521 Coltneck Lane Lexington KY 40502

**TERRY, FRED HERBERT,** ELECTRICAL ENGINEERING, BIOENGINEERING. *Current Pos:* Asst prof, Christian Bros Col, 67-69, head elec eng, 69-72, assoc prof, 70-80, dean eng, 72-92, PROF ELEC ENG, CHRISTIAN BROS COL, 80- *Personal Data:* b Bedford, Ind, July 29, 40; m 80, Dorothy S Jones; c Mike & Laura. *Educ:* Rose-Hulman Inst Technol, BS, 62, MS, 64; Case Western Res Univ, PhD(eng), 67. *Concurrent Pos:* Instr med units, Univ Tenn, 67-; gen res eng, Memphis Vet Admin Hosp, 75-78. *Mem:* Inst Elec & Electronics Engrs; Am Soc Eng Educ; Nat Soc Prof Engrs; Sigma Xi. *Res:* Computer acquisition and analysis of electrophysiological data; linear electrical properties of canine purkinje tissue; modeling of cardiac conduction abnormalities; electrical safety. *Mailing Add:* 4237 Moonfall Way Memphis TN 38141. *Fax:* 901-722-0494

**TERRY, JAMES LAYTON,** ATOMIC & HIGH TEMPERATURE PHYSICS. *Current Pos:* RES STAFF PHYSICS, MASS INST TECHNOL, 78- *Personal Data:* b Peoria, Ill, Apr 8, 51. *Educ:* Denison Univ, BS, 73; Johns Hopkins Univ, MA, 75, PhD(physics), 78. *Mem:* Am Phys Soc. *Res:* Diagnostics of high temperature plasmas. *Mailing Add:* Mass Inst Technol Bldg NW17-176 Cambridge MA 02139

**TERRY, LEON CASS,** NEUROENDOCRINOLOGY, NEUROSCIENCE. *Current Pos:* CHMN & PROF NEUROL, MED COL WIS, 89-, PROF PHYSIOL, 89-, ASSOC DEAN, AMBULATORY CARE, 96-, CHIEF STAFF, FROEDTERT HOSP, 97- *Personal Data:* b Northville, Mich, Dec 22, 40; m 64, Suzanne Martin; c Kristin & Sean. *Educ:* Univ Mich, Dr Pharm, 64; Marquette Univ, MD, 69; McGill Univ, PhD(neuroendocrinol), 82; Univ SFla, MBA, 94. *Prof Exp:* Med intern, Univ Rochester, NY, 69-70; staff assoc, Nat Inst Arthritis, Diabetes & Digestive & Kidney Dis, NIH, 70-72; resident neurol, McGill Univ, 72-75, fel neuroendocrinol, 75-78; assoc prof neurol, Ctr Health Sci, Univ Tenn, 78-81; assoc prof, Univ Mich, 81-84, assoc prof physiol, 83-89, prof neurol, 84-89. *Concurrent Pos:* Consult, Baptist Hosp, Memphis, Tenn, 79-81 & Methodist Hosp, 80-81; prin investr, Vet Admin Merit Ref Res grants, 80-, NIH res grants, 81-; staff physician, Vet Admin Med Ctr, Memphis, 80-81, clin investr, 81, asst chief, Ann Arbor, 82-85; co-investr, NIH res grants, 80-; actg chief neurol, Vet Admin Med Ctr, Ann Arbor, 85-89. *Mem:* Am Soc Clin Invest; Am Neurol Asn; Endocrine Soc; Am Acad Neurol. *Res:* Neural regulation of anterior pituitary hormone secretion focussing on hypothalamic regulation of endocrine rhythms; neurotransmitter and neuropeptide regulation of growth hormone secretion; effects of cocaine on the central nervous system; clinical drug studies on multiple sclerosis. *Mailing Add:* Dept Neurol Froedtert Hosp 9200 W Wis Ave Milwaukee WI 53226. *Fax:* 414-259-0469; *E-Mail:* cass@execpc.com

**TERRY, LUCY IRENE,** insect ecology, for more information see previous edition

**TERRY, NORMAN,** PLANT PHYSIOLOGY. *Current Pos:* asst specialist plant physiol, Dept Soils & Plant Nutrit, 68-72, from asst prof to assoc prof, 72-84, PROF PLANT BIOL, UNIV CALIF, BERKELEY, 84- *Personal Data:* b Maidstone, Eng, Sept 5, 39; m 68; c 4. *Educ:* Southampton Univ, BSc, 61; Nottingham Univ, MSc, 63, PhD(plant physiol), 66. *Prof Exp:* Res fel plant physiol, Div Biosci, Nat Res Coun Can, 66-68. *Mem:* Am Soc Plant Physiologists; AAAS; Crop Sci Soc Am; Brit Soc Exp Biol. *Res:* Environmental and internal factors involved in the regulation of photosynthesis; chloroplast development; mineral nutrition and salinity effects on plant function. *Mailing Add:* Dept Plant Biol Univ Calif Berkeley 345 Mulford Hall Berkeley CA 94720-0001

**TERRY, PAUL H,** ORGANIC & ANALYTICAL CHEMISTRY. *Current Pos:* RETIRED. *Personal Data:* b Fall River, Mass, June 22, 28. *Educ:* Southeastern Mass Univ, BS, 51; Univ Mass, MS, 59, PhD(org chem), 63. *Prof Exp:* Chemist, Dept Geront, Wash Univ, 52-53; res chemist, Insect Chemosterilants Lab, Agr Environ Qual Inst, USDA, Beltsville, Md, 63-79, res chemist, Plant Hormone Lab, Plant Physiol Inst, Agr Res Serv, 79-88. *Concurrent Pos:* Chmn, Chem Soc Washington, 87; counr, Am Chem Soc, 97- *Mem:* Sigma Xi; Am Chem Soc; Am Inst Chem. *Res:* Synthesis of compounds to sexually sterilize insects; analysis of plant hormones, especially abscisic acid and indole-3-acetic acid, in plants; comparison of hormone levels with plant stress; physiological responses of plants to various stress factors. *Mailing Add:* 3102 Craiglawn Rd Beltsville MD 20705-3437

**TERRY, PAUL WILLIS,** PLASMA TURBULENCE, TURBULENT TRANSPORT. *Current Pos:* from asst prof to assoc prof, 88-94, PROF PHYSICS, UNIV WIS-MADISON, 94- *Personal Data:* b Salt Lake City, Utah, Apr 2, 52. *Educ:* Mass Inst Technol, BS, 76; Univ Tex, Austin, PhD(physics), 81. *Prof Exp:* Res fel, Inst Fusion Studies, Univ Tex, Austin, 81-83, res assoc, 83-87, res scientist, 87-88. *Concurrent Pos:* Vis scientist, Free Univ, Brussels, 80, Culham Lab, UK Atomic Energy Agency, 89; lectr, Culham Summer Sch Plasma Physics, 89, Transp Task Force Summer Schs, 91 & 93; prin investr, Dept Energy, Univ Wis-Madison, 89-; assoc ed, Physics Fluids B, 90-92. *Mem:* Fel Am Phys Soc. *Res:* Theory of turbulence and turbulent transport in fusion, astrophysical plasmas and neutral fluids; spectral energy transfer, intermittency and coherent structures; direct numerical simulation; flow shear effects in turbulence, fluid models of plasma microturbulence; codiscoverer of flow shear-induced transport suppression in turbulence principle. *Mailing Add:* 1150 University Ave Madison WI 53706

**TERRY, RAYMOND DOUGLAS,** MATHEMATICS. *Current Pos:* asst prof, 74-78, ASSOC PROF MATH, CALIF POLYTECH STATE UNIV, SAN LUIS OBISPO, 78- *Personal Data:* b Southampton, NY, Apr 19, 45; m 81. *Educ:* State Univ NY, Stony Brook, BS, 66; Mich State Univ, MS, 68, PhD(math), 72. *Prof Exp:* Teaching asst math, Mich State Univ, 66-72; instr math, Ga Inst Technol, 72-74. *Concurrent Pos:* Vis assoc prof, Mich State Univ, 81-82. *Mem:* Am Math Soc; Math Asn Am; Soc Indust & Appl Math. *Res:* Higher-order delay and functional differential equations. *Mailing Add:* Dept Math Calif Polytech State Univ San Luis Obispo CA 93407

**TERRY, RICHARD D,** oceanography, space sciences, for more information see previous edition

**TERRY, RICHARD ELLIS,** SOIL BIOCHEMISTRY, SOIL MICROBIOLOGY. *Current Pos:* assoc prof, 80-86, PROF AGRON, BRIGHAM YOUNG UNIV, 86- *Personal Data:* b Rigby, Idaho, Feb 8, 49; m 72; c 3. *Educ:* Brigham Young Univ, BS, 72; Purdue Univ, MS, 74, PhD(soil Sci), 76. *Prof Exp:* Asst soil sci, Purdue Univ, 74-75, res asst, 72-76; asst prof soil biochem, Univ Fla, 77-80. *Mem:* Am Soc Agron; Soil Sci Soc Am; Int Humic Substances Soc. *Res:* Microbial oxidation of soil organic matter; subsidence of organic soils; nitrogen transformations in soils and sediments; denitrification in terrestrial and aquatic systems; soil iron nutrition. *Mailing Add:* Dept Agron Brigham Young Univ 275 WIDB Provo UT 84602-1049

**TERRY, ROBERT DAVIS,** NEUROPATHOLOGY. *Current Pos:* PROF NEUROSCI & PATH, UNIV CALIF, SAN DIEGO, 84- *Personal Data:* b Hartford, Conn, Jan 13, 24; m 52, Patricia Blech; c Nicolas S. *Educ:* Williams Col, BA, 46; Union Univ, MD, 50. *Hon Degrees:* DSc, Williams Col, 91. *Honors & Awards:* Potamkin Prize, Am Acad Neurol, 88; Distinguished Serv Award, Am Asn Neuropathologists, 89; Metrop Life Found Award, 91. *Prof Exp:* Asst pathologist, Montefiore Hosp, 55-59; from assoc prof to prof path, Einstein Col Med, 59-84, chmn dept, 69-84. *Concurrent Pos:* Res fel cancer, Inst Cancer Res, 65-66; mem, Med & Sci Adv Bd, Alzheimer Dis & Related Dis, 78-88. *Mem:* Fel AAAS; Am Neurol Asn; Am Asn Neuropathologists (pres, 69-70); Int Soc Neuropath (vpres, 82-84); Am Asn Neurologists; Am Acad Neurol; Am Asn Pathologists. *Res:* Morphological and quantitative studies of the brain in Alzheimer disease. *Mailing Add:* Dept Neurosci Univ Calif La Jolla CA 92093-0064. *Fax:* 619-534-6232

**TERRY, ROGER,** SURGICAL PATHOLOGY. *Current Pos:* head surg pathologist, Los Angeles Co, 69-82, prof, 69-82, EMER PROF PATH, MED CTR, UNIV SOUTHERN CALIF, 82- *Personal Data:* b Waterville, NY, May 8, 17; m 42, Eleanor V Wallace; c Robin (deceased) & Orrin. *Educ:* Colgate Univ, AB, 39; Univ Rochester, MD, 44. *Prof Exp:* Intern path, Med Ctr, Univ Rochester, 44-45, instr, 45-51; from asst prof to prof, 51-69. *Concurrent Pos:* Actg pathologist, Park Ave Hosp, Rochester, NY, 45-47; resident, Med Ctr, Univ Rochester, 45-51; actg pathologist, Genesee Hosp, Rochester, 47-50 & Highland Hosp, 49-51; co-exec dir, Calif Tumor Tissue Registry, Los Angeles, 69-82; pathologist, San Gabriel Valley Med Ctr, 82- *Mem:* Am Soc Clin Path; Am Soc Invest Path; Col Am Pathologists; Int Acad Path; AMA; Am Soc Cytol; Int Soc Dermatopath. *Res:* Metabolic bone diseases. *Mailing Add:* 2841 Shakespeare Dr San Marino CA 91108-2230. *Fax:* 626-457-7112

**TERRY, STUART LEE,** COMMERCIAL DEVELOPMENT, APPLICATIONS TECHNOLOGY. *Current Pos:* DIR TECHNOL, SONOCO, 89- *Personal Data:* b Chicago, Ill, Apr 8, 42; m 80, Mary A Stames; c Robin Andrews, Mark Andrews, Marc Terry & Robin Terry. *Educ:* Cornell Univ, BChemE, 65, PhD(chem eng), 69; Rensselaer Polytech Inst, MS, 74. *Honors & Awards:* Alvin J Huss Award, Am Forest & Paper Asn, 93. *Prof Exp:* NSF trainee polymer chem, Cornell Univ, 64-68 & asst, 65-68; sr res chemist, Monsanto Co, 68-75, group leader polymer synthesis, 75-78, prod develop, 78-82, mgr, com develop, 82-84, bus develop, 85, technol planning, 86-87, mgr technol acquisition, 87-89. *Mem:* Soc Plastic Engrs; Tech Trans Soc; Tech Asn Pulp & Paper Indust; Futures Soc. *Res:* Identification of product opportunities and preparation of polymeric materials with morphologies required for industrial and consumer end use performance; development of technology and products in paper, plastics and adhesion for the industrial and consumer packaging markets. *Mailing Add:* Sonoco Second St Hartsville SC 29550

**TERRY, THOMAS MILTON,** BIOPHYSICS, MICROBIOLOGY. *Current Pos:* asst prof microbiol & biol, 77-81, ASSOC PROF MOLECULAR & CELL BIOL, UNIV CONN, 81- *Personal Data:* b Knoxville, Tenn, Apr 2, 39; m 76; c 2. *Educ:* Yale Univ, BA, 61, MS, 63, PhD(molecular biophys), 67. *Prof Exp:* USPHS fel biophys, Univ Geneva, 67; asst prof microbiol, Albert Einstein Col Med, 68-69. *Mem:* AAAS; Am Soc Microbiol. *Res:* Biological membrane structure and function; molecular biology of mycoplasma; ultrastructure of bacteria. *Mailing Add:* Dept Molecular & Cell Biol Univ Conn U-44 75 N Eaglevil Rd Storrs CT 06269

**TERRY, WILLIAM DAVID,** IMMUNOLOGY. *Current Pos:* SR VPRES & GEN MGR ADMIN, DAMON BIOTECH INC, 88- *Personal Data:* b New York, NY, Oct 22, 33; m 66; c 4. *Educ:* Cornell Univ, BA, 54; State Univ NY Downstate Med Ctr, MD, 58. *Prof Exp:* Intern, Jewish Hosp Brooklyn, NY, 58-59, asst resident, 59-61; NIH trainee, Sch Med, Univ Calif, San Francisco, 61-62; res assoc, Immunol Sect, Gen Labs & Clins, Nat Cancer Inst, 62-64, sr investr, 64-71, br chief, 71-87, assoc dir immunol, Div Cancer Biol & Diag, 73-87. *Concurrent Pos:* Adminr, Cancer Ctrs Prog, Nat Cancer Inst, 78-81, Cancer Control Prog, 79-80, ctrs & community activ, Div Resources, 80-81. *Mem:* Am Asn Immunol; Am Fedn Clin Res; Am Soc Clin Invest; Am Asn Cancer Res. *Res:* Nature of the immune response, particularly as it relates to the recognition of and reaction against tumors by the tumor bearing host. *Mailing Add:* Brigham & Women's Hosp 75 Francis St PBB-3 Boston MA 02115-6195. *Fax:* 617-732-5343

**TERSOFF, JERRY DAVID,** THEORETICAL MATERIALS PHYSICS, SURFACES & INTERFACES. *Current Pos:* RES STAFF MEM, IBM THOMAS J WATSON RES CTR, 84- *Personal Data:* b Washington, DC, June 12, 55; m 89, Deborah S Franzblau. *Educ:* Swarthmore Col, BA, 77; Univ Calif, Berkeley, PhD(physics), 82. *Honors & Awards:* Peter Mark Mem Award, Am Vacuum Soc, 88; Mat Res Soc Medal, 96. *Prof Exp:* Fel, Bell Labs, 82-84. *Mem:* Fel Am Phys Soc; Mat Res Soc; Am Vacuum Soc. *Res:* Electronic and structural properties of surfaces and interfaces; theory of epitaxial growth; theory of scanning tunnelling microscopy; semiconductor heterojunction band lineups; Schottky barriers. *Mailing Add:* IBM Thomas J Watson Res Ctr PO Box 218 Yorktown Heights NY 10598

**TERSS, ROBERT H,** ORGANIC CHEMISTRY. *Current Pos:* MGT CONSULT, 86- *Personal Data:* b East St Louis, Ill, Sept 13, 25; m 55, Eugenia Lozos. *Educ:* Wash Univ, AB, 49; Univ Kans, PhD(chem), 53. *Prof Exp:* Asst instr chem, Univ Kans, 49-51; res chemist, Dept Org Chem, E I Du Pont de Nemours & Co, Inc, 53-57, res supvr dyes, 57-58, head div dyes, 59-63, patents & intel, 63-65, photochem, 65-70, supt dyes & chem qual control, 70-71, supt dye mfg, 71-73, div head dyes process, 73-75, div head patents, 76-77, mem, Res & Develop Staff Serv, 76-79, mem, Personnel Develop, Employee Relations Dept. *Concurrent Pos:* Adj fac, Master's Prog, Wilmington Col, Del. *Mem:* Am Chem Soc; Am Soc Training & Develop. *Res:* Dyes; heterocycles; photochemistry; information handling systems; photographic materials. *Mailing Add:* 708 Ambleside Dr Westminster Wilmington DE 19808-1503

**TERWEDOW, HENRY ALBERT, JR,** medical entomology, agricultural entomology, for more information see previous edition

**TERWILLIGER, DON WILLIAM,** COMPUTER SCIENCE. *Current Pos:* MGR COMPUT RES, TEKTRONIX LABS, 76- *Personal Data:* b Klamath Falls, Ore, Mar 27, 42; m 70. *Educ:* Calif Inst Technol, BS, 64; Univ Ore, MA, 66, PhD(physics), 70. *Prof Exp:* Asst prof physics, Middlebury Col, 70-75. *Mem:* Inst Elec & Electronics Engrs; Comput Soc; Comput Applns & Instrumentation. *Res:* Low temperature physics; electron scattering from imperfections in metals; Fermi surface studies. *Mailing Add:* 14120 SW Barlow Rd Beaverton OR 97005

**TERWILLIGER, JAMES PAUL,** chemical engineering, for more information see previous edition

**TERWILLIGER, NORA BARCLAY,** RESPIRATORY PROTEINS, COMPARATIVE BIOCHEMISTRY & MARINE SCIENCES. *Current Pos:* res assoc, 81-89, ASSOC PROF, DEPT BIOL, INST MARINE BIOL, UNIV ORE, 89- *Personal Data:* b Hartford, Conn, Oct 9, 41; wid; c Kelly J & Robert B. *Educ:* Univ Vt, BS, 63; Univ Wis, MS, 65; Univ Ore, PhD(biol), 81. *Prof Exp:* Res asst, Boston Univ, 67-69, lectr embryol, 68; res asst, Inst Marine Biol, Univ Ore, 71-78; instr biol, Southwestern Ore Community Col, Coos Bay, 80-81. *Concurrent Pos:* Instr marine biol, Div Continuing Educ, State of Ore, 74-75; consult, Coos Bay Sch Dist, Ore, 75-76; vis scientist, Marine Biol Asn Lab, Plymouth, UK, 83-84; vis prof, Univ Mainz, Ger, 94. *Mem:* AAAS; Am Soc Zoologists; Crustacean Soc. *Res:* Comparative biochemistry, physiology and ontogeny of respiratory proteins; structure and function of invertebrate hemoglobins, hemocyanins and hemerythrins; marine biology. *Mailing Add:* Ore Inst Marine Biol Univ Ore Charleston OR 97420

**TERWILLIGER, PAUL M,** COMBINATORICS & FINITE MATHEMATICS, ALGEBRA. *Current Pos:* asst prof, 85-89, ASSOC PROF MATH, UNIV WIS, 89- *Personal Data:* b Ann Arbor, Mich, June 24, 55; m 82. *Educ:* Univ Mich, BS, 77; Univ Ill, PhD(math), 82. *Prof Exp:* Instr math, Ohio State Univ, 82-85. *Mem:* Am Math Soc; Math Asn Am. *Res:* Combinatorics and graph theory. *Mailing Add:* Dept Math Van Vleck Hall Univ Wis 480 Lincoln Dr Madison WI 53706-1388

**TERZAGHI, MARGARET,** CANCER. *Current Pos:* RES ASSOC CANCER RES, OAK RIDGE NAT LAB, 75- *Personal Data:* b Boston, Mass, May 7, 41. *Educ:* Boston Univ, AB, 64, MS, 69; Harvard Univ, MS, 70, DSc(radiation biol, physiol), 74. *Prof Exp:* Res asst cancer res, Harvard Univ, 70-75, res assoc, 75. *Mem:* Sigma Xi. *Res:* An examination of possible in vitro models of in vivo carcinogenesis induced by chemical carcinogens and/or radiation. *Mailing Add:* 107 Orkney Rd Oak Ridge TN 37830-3806

**TERZAKIS, JOHN A,** DERMATOPATHOLOGY, ELECTRON MICROSCOPY. *Current Pos:* CHIEF SURG PATH, LENOX HILL HOSP, NEW YORK,86-, ATTEND PATHOLOGIST, 76- *Personal Data:* b Bridgeport, Conn, Sept 13, 35; m 61; c 3. *Educ:* New York Univ, MD, 61. *Mem:* Am Soc Cell Biol; NY Acad Sci. *Res:* Morphologic ultrastructure of human tissues, normal and diseased; x-ray microanalysis of diseased human tissue. *Mailing Add:* Dept Path Lenox Hill Hosp 100 E 77th St New York NY 10021-1882

**TERZIAN, YERVANT,** ASTRONOMY. *Current Pos:* Res assoc radio astron, Cornell Univ Ctr Radiophys & Space Res & Arecibo Ionospheric Observ, 65-67, from asst prof to assoc prof, 67-77, asst dir, Ctr Radiophys & Space Res, 68-74, grad fac rep, 74-79, PROF ASTRON, CORNELL UNIV, 77-, CHMN, DEPT ASTRON, 79-, DIR, PEW SCI EDUC NY PROG, 88-, JAMES A WEEKS PROF PHYS SCI, 90- *Personal Data:* b Feb 9, 39; m 66, Araxy Hovsepian; c 2. *Educ:* Am Univ Cairo, BSc, 60; Univ Ind, MA, 63, PhD(astron), 65. *Hon Degrees:* DSc, Ind Univ, 89, Yerevan State Univ, Armenia, 94, Aristotle Univ, Ressaloniki, Greece, 97. *Concurrent Pos:* Vis prof, Univs Montreal, Thessaloniki & Florence; assoc ed, Astrophys J; dir, NASA NY Space Grant. *Mem:* Int Union Radio Sci; Int Astron Union; Am Astron Soc; foreign mem Armenian Acad Sci. *Res:* Radio astronomical studies of interstellar matter; radio properties of galaxies and other radio sources; radio emission from planetary nebulae; pulsars; author of numerous scientific publications and editor of 5 books. *Mailing Add:* Dept Astron Space Sci Bldg Cornell Univ Ithaca NY 14853. *Fax:* 607-255-9817

**TERZUOLI, ANDREW JOSEPH,** MATHEMATICS. *Current Pos:* prof, 46-86, EMER PROF MATH, POLYTECH INST BROOKLYN, 86- *Personal Data:* b Brooklyn, NY, Oct 5, 14; m 42; c 4. *Educ:* Brooklyn Col, BA, 36; NY Univ, MS, 48. *Concurrent Pos:* Consult statist. *Mem:* AAAS; Am Math Soc; Am Meteorol Soc; Math Asn Am; Inst Math Statist. *Res:* Probability; mathematical statistics. *Mailing Add:* 2481 Stuart St Brooklyn NY 11229

**TERZUOLO, CARLO A,** NEUROSCIENCES. *Current Pos:* RETIRED. *Personal Data:* b Acqui, Italy, Sept 2, 25; nat US; m 54, Margherita Ertallini; c Eric R. *Educ:* Univ Torino, MD, 49. *Prof Exp:* Asst, Univ Torino, 48-49; Ital Res Coun fel, 50-51; asst prof, Free Univ Brussels, 51-53; asst, Univ Calif, Los Angeles, 54-56, res assoc, 57-59; prof physiol, Univ Minn, Minneapolis, 59-93. *Concurrent Pos:* Mult Sclerosis Soc fel, 56-57; Fulbright res fel, Univ Pisa, 66-67. *Mem:* Am Physiol Soc; Soc Neurosci. *Res:* Nerve cell and receptor physiology; dynamic characteristics of neuronal systems controlling movements; vestibular, cerebellar and segmental reflex mechanisms; motor control. *Mailing Add:* 1235 Yale Pl 407 Minneapolis MN 55403

**TESAR, DELBERT,** MECHANICAL ENGINEERING. *Current Pos:* assoc prof, 64-69, PROF MECH ENG & ENG SCI, UNIV FLA, 69- *Personal Data:* b Beaver Crossing, Nebr, Sept 2, 35; m 57; c 4. *Educ:* Univ Nebr, BSc, 58, MSc, 60; Ga Inst Technol, PhD(mech eng), 64. *Prof Exp:* Instr eng mech, Univ Nebr, 57-59 & appl mech, Kans State Univ, 59-61; lectr mech eng, Ga Inst Technol, 61-64. *Concurrent Pos:* Chief investr, US Army Res Off res grant, 61; NSF res grants, 64, 69-71 & 72-74; NSF-NATO fel, Vienna Tech Univ, 64-65; consult, Procter & Gamble Co, Ohio, 66-; vis prof, Wash State Univ, 67; consult, Wayne S Colony Co, Fla, 71- & Deering Milliken Res Corp, SC, 72-; vis res prof, Liverpool Polytech, Eng, 71-72; mem, Sci Adv Bd Air Force, 82-; dir & founder, Ctr Intelligent Machines & Robotics. *Mem:* Am Soc Eng Educ; Am Soc Mech Engrs. *Res:* Kinematic synthesis; dynamic analysis and synthesis; vibrations; machine design; lubrication; experimental stress analysis; strength of materials; continuum mechanics. *Mailing Add:* 8005 Two Coves Dr Austin TX 78730

**TESAR, MILO B,** PLANT BREEDING & GENETICS. *Current Pos:* From asst prof to assoc prof, Mich state Univ, 49-58, actg chmn dept, 64-66, prof crop sci, 58-88, EMER PROF, MICH STATE UNIV, 88- *Personal Data:* b Nebr, Apr 7, 20; m 44; c 4. *Educ:* Univ Nebr, BS, 41; Univ Wis, MS, 47, PhD(agron), 49. *Hon Degrees:* DSc, Univ Nebr, 89. *Honors & Awards:* Agron Achievement Award, Am Soc Agron, 84; Career Award, Crop Sci Soc Am, 88. *Concurrent Pos:* NATO fel, Grassland Res Inst, Eng, 59-60; consult, Univ Ryukus, 67 & Univ Federale Ro Grande do Sul, Brazil, 76; mem, Int Grassland Cong, USA, 52, 81, Australia, 70, Russia, 74, Japan, 85, Europ Grassland Fedn, 77; mem, USSR Forage Surv, 74 & AID, Somalia Mission, 78; lectr, Inner Mongolia, China, 85. *Mem:* Crop Sci Soc Am; fel Am Soc Agron; Sigma Xi. *Res:* Forage physiology, management, and digestibility; maximum yield of alfalfa; legume seeding establishment; no-till pasture renovation; alfalfa breeding; autotoxicity/allelopathy in alfalfa; alfalfa to reduce effluent damage to environment; USDA patentee webfoot alfalfa. *Mailing Add:* 2379 Emerald Forest Circle East Lansing MI 48823

**TESCHAN, PAUL E,** MEDICINE, NEPHROLOGY. *Current Pos:* PROF MED & ASSOC PROF UROL & BIOMED ENG, VANDERBILT UNIV, 69- *Personal Data:* b Milwaukee, Wis, Dec 15, 23; m 48; c 2. *Educ:* Univ Minn, BS, 46, MD & MS, 48; Am Bd Internal Med, dipl, 55. *Prof Exp:* Intern, Res & Educ Hosp, Univ Ill, 48-49, resident internal med, Presby Hosp, Chicago, 49-50, ward officer, Metab Ward, Dept Hepatic & Metab Dis, Walter Reed Army Inst Res, 50-53, resident internal med, Barnes Hosp, St Louis, Mo, 53-54, chief renal br, Surg Res Unit, Brooke Army Med Ctr, Ft Sam Houston, Tex, 54-60, asst commandant, Walter Reed Army Inst Res, Walter Reed Army Med Ctr, 60-63, dep dir div basic surg res, 64-65, dep dir div surg, 65-66, chief dept metab & dir div med, 66-69. *Concurrent Pos:* Med Corps, US Army, 48-69; fel cardiorenal dis, Peter Bent Brigham Hosp, Boston, 50; chief renal insufficiency ctr, Korea, 52-53; consult, Surgeon Gen, US Army, 60-69; chief dept surg physiol, Walter Reed Army Inst Res, Walter Reed Army Med Ctr, 61-66, dep dir div basic surg res, 62-63, chief renal-metab serv, Walter Reed Gen Hosp, 66-69; chief US Army med res team, Vietnam, 63-64; dir, Tenn Mid-South Regional Med Prog, 69-72. *Mem:* Am Fedn Clin Res; fel Am Col Physicians; Soc Artificial Internal Organs; Am Physiol Soc; Int Soc Nephrology. *Res:* Pathogenesis and prevention of acute renal failure; prophylactic dialysis; uremia; prevention of progression in chronic renal failure. *Mailing Add:* 2710 Hemingway Dr Nashville TN 37215-4014

**TESH, ROBERT BRADFIELD,** MICROBIOLOGY. *Current Pos:* PROF PATH, MICROBIOL & IMMUNOL, UNIV TEX MED BR, 95- *Personal Data:* b Wilmington, Del, Jan 22, 36; m 93, Hilda Guzman; c Diana, Carolyn & Natalia. *Educ:* Franklin & Marshall Col, BS, 57; Jefferson Med Col, MD, 61; Tulane Univ, MS, 67. *Hon Degrees:* MS Yale Univ, 88- *Prof Exp:* Intern, San Francisco Gen Hosp, Calif, 61-62; resident pediat, Gorgas Hosp, 62-63; physician, USPHS, Peace Corps, Recife, Brazil, 63-65; NIH fel infectious dis, Depts Pediat & Epidemiol, Sch Med, Tulane Univ, 65-67; epidemiologist, Mid Am Res Unit, NIH, 67-72, Pac Res Sect, 72-80; prof, Dept Epidemiol & Pub Health, Yale Univ Sch Med, 80-85. *Mem:* Fel AAAS; Am Soc Trop Med & Hyg; Am Soc Microbiol; Royal Soc Trop Med & Hyg; Entom Soc Am; Soc Vector Ecol. *Res:* Entomology; microbiology; epidemiology; virology. *Mailing Add:* Univ Tex Med Br Galveston TX 77555-0609. *Fax:* 409-747-2429; *E-Mail:* rtesh@mspo6.med.utmb.edu

**TESK, JOHN ALOYSIUS,** STANDARDS & REFERENCE MATERIALS, TEST METHODS. *Current Pos:* gen phys scientist, Nat Bur Stand, 78-83, leader dent & med mats, 83-94, COORDR, BIOMAT PROG, NAT INST STAND & TECHNOL, 94- *Personal Data:* b Chicago, Ill, Oct 19, 34; m, Regina S Budzyn; c John. *Educ:* Northwestern Univ, BS, 57, MS, 60, PhD(mat sci), 63. *Honors & Awards:* Grainger Award, 64; Bronze Medal, Nat Bur Stand, 87. *Prof Exp:* Asst prof metall, Univ Ill, Chicago, 64-68; asst metallurgist, Metall Div, Argonne Nat Lab, 68-70; asst mgr res & develop, How-Medica, Inc, Chicago, 70-71; dir res & develop, Dent Div, 71-77; dir educ serv, Inst Gas Technol, Chicago, 77-78. *Concurrent Pos:* Consult, Argonne Nat Lab, 64-67, Dentsply Int, 77-78; pres, Wash Chap, Int Asn Dent Res, 84-85, treas, DMG, 87- *Mem:* Int Asn Dent Res; Am Inst Metall Engrs; Am Soc Metals; Soc Biomat; Sigma Xi; fel Acad Dent Mat; Am Phys Soc. *Res:* Radiation damage in metals at low temperature; point defects in metals; dental and medical materials and devices; biomaterials. *Mailing Add:* 6759 Cortina Dr Highland MD 20777. *Fax:* 301-963-9143; *E-Mail:* john.tesk@nist.gov

**TESKA, WILLIAM REINHOLD,** ECOLOGY, MAMMALOGY. *Current Pos:* PROF BIOL, FURMAN UNIV, 77- *Personal Data:* b Chicago, Ill, Oct 11, 50. *Educ:* Univ Idaho, BS, 72; Mich State Univ, MSc, 74, PhD(zool), 78. *Concurrent Pos:* Vis prof biol, Univ Andes, Bogota, Colombia, 91. *Mem:* Am Soc Mammalogists; Wildlife Soc; Sigma Xi. *Res:* Mammalian ecology; population ecology; vertebrate ecology; tropical biology and conservation. *Mailing Add:* Dept Biol Furman Univ Greenville SC 29613-0001. *Fax:* 864-294-2058; *E-Mail:* teska@frmnvax1

**TESKE, RICHARD GLENN,** ASTRONOMY. *Current Pos:* From instr to assoc prof, McMath-Hulbert Observ, 61-77, PROF ASTRON, UNIV MICH, ANN ARBOR, 77- *Personal Data:* b Cleveland, Ohio, Aug 16, 30; m 75. *Educ:* Bowling Green State Univ, BS, 52; Ohio State Univ, MA, 56; Harvard Univ, PhD, 61. *Concurrent Pos:* Dir, Mich Dartmouth MIT Observ, 88-91. *Mem:* Int Astron Union; Am Astron Soc. *Res:* Supernova remnants; solar physics; x-rays from supernova remnants. *Mailing Add:* 2759 Antietam Ct Ann Arbor MI 48105

**TESKE, RICHARD H,** VETERINARY MEDICINE, TOXICOLOGY. *Current Pos:* RETIRED. *Personal Data:* b Christiansburg, Va, July 22, 39; m 61; c 2. *Educ:* Va Polytech Inst, BA, 62; Univ Ga, DVM, 65; Univ Fla, MS, 66; Am Bd Vet Toxicol, dipl. *Prof Exp:* Asst prof vet sci, Univ Fla, 67; dir toxicol, Hill Top Res, Inc, Ohio, 67-70; vet med officer, Ctr Vet Med, Food & Drug Admin, 70-97. *Mem:* Fel Am Acad Vet & Comp Toxicol; fel Am Acad Vet Pharm & Therapeut. *Res:* Comparative pharmacology and toxicology. *Mailing Add:* 6712 Lumsden St McLean VA 22101

**TESKEY, HERBERT JOSEPH,** ENTOMOLOGY, SYSTEMATICS. *Current Pos:* RETIRED. *Personal Data:* b Grande Prairie, Alta, June 9, 28; m 53; c 2. *Educ:* Univ Alta, BSc, 51; Univ Toronto, MSA, 56; Cornell Univ, PhD(entom), 67. *Prof Exp:* Res scientist entom, Can Dept Agr, Guelph, 51-67; res scientist entom, Biosyst Res Inst, Agr Can, 67-86. *Mem:* Entom Soc Can. *Res:* Systematics of the Diptera, especially of the lower Brachycera and of the immature stages of Diptera. *Mailing Add:* 569 Brierwood Ottawa ON K2A 2H6 Can

**TESMER, IRVING HOWARD,** STRATIGRAPHY, PALEONTOLOGY. *Current Pos:* from asst prof to assoc prof, 57-63, chmn dept, 66-69, PROF GEOL, STATE UNIV NY COL BUFFALO, 63- *Personal Data:* b Buffalo, NY, May 31, 26; m 64; c 2. *Educ:* Univ Buffalo, BA, 46, MA, 48; Syracuse Univ, PhD(geol), 54. *Prof Exp:* From instr to asst prof geol, Univ NH, 50-55; instr, Rutgers Univ, 55-57. *Concurrent Pos:* Mem, Paleont Res Inst; res assoc geol, Buffalo Mus Sci, 70- *Mem:* Fel AAAS; fel Geol Soc Am; Am Asn Petrol Geol; Paleont Soc. *Res:* Devonian stratigraphy and paleontology; geology of western New York; history of geology of Western New York. *Mailing Add:* 127 Fayette Ave Buffalo NY 14223-2707

**TESMER, JOSEPH RANSDELL,** EXPERIMENTAL NUCLEAR PHYSICS. *Current Pos:* MEM STAFF NUCLEAR PHYSICS, LOS ALAMOS NAT LAB, 75- *Personal Data:* b Lafayette, Ind, Sept 9, 39; m 62; c 2. *Educ:* Purdue Univ, BS, 62; Univ Wash, PhD(nuclear physics), 71. *Prof Exp:* Engr, Boeing Co, 62-64; res assoc nuclear physics, Purdue Univ, 71-73; asst scientist physics, Univ Wis, 73-75. *Mem:* Am Phys Soc; AAAS. *Res:* Stripping of high energy negative hydrogen beams, and negative hydrogen beam production; accelerator development; accelerator based mass spectrometry. *Mailing Add:* 408 Rover Blvd White Rock Los Alamos NM 87544

**TESORIERO, JOHN VINCENT,** CELL BIOLOGY, BIOLOGY OF AGING. *Current Pos:* RETIRED. *Personal Data:* b Brooklyn, NY, Feb 10, 41; m 64; c 2. *Educ:* Fairfield Univ, BS, 63; Adelphi Univ, MS, 68; State Univ NY, Downstate Med Sch, PhD(anat), 76. *Prof Exp:* Asst prof basic sci & edùc, NE Med Sch, Univ Med & Dent NJ, 75-91. *Mem:* Am Asn Anatomists; Am Soc Cell Biol. *Res:* Cell biology of mammalian oogenesis with particular emphasis on age related changes in maturing oocytes; age related changes of the tubulin-microtubular system in mammalian oocytes. *Mailing Add:* 1 Sutton Pl Florham Park NJ 07932

**TESORO, GIULIANA C,** ORGANIC POLYMER CHEMISTRY. *Current Pos:* RES PROF, POLYTECH UNIV, 82- *Personal Data:* b Venice, Italy, June 1, 21; nat US; m 43, Victor; c Claudia M & Andrew J. *Educ:* Yale Univ, PhD(org chem), 43. *Honors & Awards:* Olney Medal, Am Asn Textile Chem & Colorists; Achievement Award, Soc Women Engrs. *Prof Exp:* Res chemist, Calco Chem Co, NJ, 34-44; res chemist, Onyx Oil & Chem Co, 44-46, head org synthesis dept, 46-55, asst dir res, 55-57, assoc dir, 57-58; asst dir org res, Cent Res Lab, J P Stevens & Co, Inc, 58-68; sr scientist, Textile Res Inst, NJ, 68-69; sr scientist, Burlington Industs, Inc, 69-71, dir chem res, 71-72. *Concurrent Pos:* Vis prof, Mass Inst Technol, 72-76; adj prof & sr res scientist, 76-82; mem comt on fire safety aspects of polymeric materials, Nat Acad Sci, 72-78, mem nat mat adv bd, 76-78; mem comt military personnel supplies, Nat Res Coun, 79-81, comt toxicol combustion prod, 84-89. *Mem:* Am Chem Soc; Am Asn Textile Chem & Colorists; Fiber Soc (pres, 74); Am Inst Chemists; AAAS. *Res:* Synthesis of pharmaceuticals; textile chemicals; germicides; polymers; chemical modification of fibers; synthesis and rearrangement of glycols in the hydrogenated naphthalene series; polymer flammability and flame retardants; polymers for electronics; thermally stable polymers and coupling agents in composites; recovery of polymeric materials (recycling), recoverable thermosets. *Mailing Add:* 278 Clinton Ave Dobbs Ferry NY 10522-3007. *Fax:* 914-693-7399

**TESS, ROY WILLIAM HENRY,** COATINGS, SOLVENTS. *Current Pos:* INDEPENDENT CONSULT, 79- *Personal Data:* b Chicago, Ill, Apr 25, 15; m 44, Marjorie Kohler; c Steven & Roxanne (Daneri). *Educ:* Univ Ill, BS, 39; Univ Minn, PhD(org chem), 44. *Honors & Awards:* Roon Award, Fedn Soc Coatings Technol, 56, Heckel Award, 78; Distinguished Serv Award, Polymeric Mat Div, Am Chem Soc, 93. *Prof Exp:* Lab asst, Underwriters Labs, Inc, Ill, 36-37; asst chem, Univ Minn, 39-44; chemist, Shell Develop Co, 44-59, res supvr, Shell Chem Co, 59-62 & 64-67, Royal Dutch Shell Plastics Lab, Holland, 62-63, tech planning supvr, Coatings, Shell Chem NY, 67-70, Tex, 70-73, tech supvr solvents bus ctr, 73-78, consult solvents & resin prod, 78-79. *Concurrent Pos:* Mem air qual comt, Nat Paint & Coatings Asn, 68-79; trustee, Paint Res Inst, 71-79, pres, 73-76; ed, Solvents Theory & Pract, 73, Appl Polymer Sci, 75 & Appl Polymer Sci Second Ed, 85; dir, Fedn Soc Coatings Technol, 73-76; chmn div org coating & plastic chem, Am Chem Soc, 78, exec com, div polymeric mats, 77- *Mem:* Fedn Soc Coatings Technol; fel Am Inst Chem; Am Chem Soc; AAAS. *Res:* Epoxy, alkyd, polyester and hydrocarbon resins; surface coatings; varnishes and drying oils; polyols; polar and hydrocarbon solvents; high polymer latexes; atmospheric chemistry; polymer chemistry; writer on applied polymer science. *Mailing Add:* 1615 Chandelle Lane Fallbrook CA 92028-1707

**TESSEL, RICHARD EARL,** NEUROPHARMACOLOGY, PSYCHOPHARMACOLOGY. *Current Pos:* ASST PROF PHARMACOL, SCH PHARM, UNIV KANS, 75-, ASSOC TOXICOL, 81- *Personal Data:* b Cincinnati, Ohio, June 9, 44. *Educ:* Univ Calif, Los Angeles, BA, 66; Univ Ill, Chicago Circle, MA, 69; Univ Mich, PhD(pharmacol), 74. *Prof Exp:* Nat Inst Drug Abuse fel pharmacol, Sch Med, Univ Colo, 74-75. *Res:* Role of biogenic amine disposition in brain in modulating the reinforcing, locomotor-stimulant, stereotypic and operant-schedule effects of amphetamines and its congeners. *Mailing Add:* Dept Pharmacol & Toxicol Univ Kans Sch Pharm 5040 Mal Lawrence KS 66045-0001. *Fax:* 785-864-5219

**TESSER, HERBERT,** PHYSICS. *Current Pos:* CHMN COMPUT SCI & SOFTWARE DEVELOP, MARSHALL UNIV, 93- *Personal Data:* b Jersey City, NJ, Mar 25, 39; m 61; c 2. *Educ:* Polytech Inst Brooklyn, BS, 60; Stevens Inst Technol, MS, 63, PhD(physics), 68. *Prof Exp:* Metrol engr, Kearfott Corp, 60-62; res asst physics, Stevens Inst Technol, 64-67; from assoc prof to prof physics, Pratt Inst, 81-85. *Concurrent Pos:* Res consult, NRA, Inc, 71-72, Procedyne, 73-74 & Stevens Inst, 75-78. *Mem:* Am Phys Soc. *Res:* Electrodynamics; statistical mechanics; relativity; plasma physics. *Mailing Add:* 15 Briar Oaks Huntington WV 25704

**TESSIER, ANDRE,** GEOCHEMISTRY OF TRACE ELEMENTS IN LAKES, REACTIONS TO SEDIMENT-WATER INTERFACE. *Current Pos:* From asst prof to assoc prof, 70-80, PROF AQUATIC CHEM, NAT INST SCI RES-EAU, UNIV QUE, 80- *Personal Data:* b Que, Oct 21, 40; m 65, Charlotte Ste-Marie; c Anne, Philippe & Alex. *Educ:* Laval Univ, BSc, 65, PhD(chem), 70. *Honors & Awards:* Michel Jurdant Prize Environ Sci, Can-Fr

Asn Advan Sci, 89. *Concurrent Pos:* Prof geol, McMaster Univ, 83- *Mem:* Assoc mem, Int Union Pure & Appl Chem; Can Soc Chem. *Res:* In situ trace element reactions in recent sediments with particular reference to sorption on diagenetic material, then predict trace element partitioning between water, sediments and benthic organisms. *Mailing Add:* Univ Que INRS-EAU Ste Foy PQ G1V 4C7 Can. *Fax:* 418-654-2600

**TESSIER, CLAIRE ADRIENNE,** SYNTHETIC INORGANIC & ORGANOMETALLIC CHEMISTRY. *Current Pos:* asst prof, 90-96, ASSOC PROF INORG CHEM, UNIV AKRON, 96- *Personal Data:* b Staten Island, NY, Oct 24, 53; m 78; c 1. *Educ:* Univ Vt, BS, 75; State Univ NY, Buffalo, PhD(chem), 82. *Prof Exp:* Res assoc, Northwestern Univ, 80-82; vis asst prof gen chem, Univ RI, 82-83; vis asst prof org chem, Case Western Res Univ, 83-85, sr instr, 85-86, sr res assoc, 86-90. *Concurrent Pos:* Vis prof, Chem Dept, Univ Wis-Madison, 91; adj prof, Chem Dept, Case Western Res Univ, 91-93. *Mem:* Am Chem Soc; AAAS. *Res:* Organosilicon chemistry; silicon containing oligomers and polymers; main-group chemistry; catalysis. *Mailing Add:* Dept Chem Univ Akron 190 E Buchetel Commons KNCL 111 Akron OH 44325-3601. *Fax:* 330-972-7370; *E-Mail:* tessier@atlas.chemistry. uakron.edu

**TESSIERI, JOHN EDWARD,** RESEARCH ADMINISTRATION. *Current Pos:* RETIRED. *Personal Data:* b Vineland, NJ, Sept 3, 20; m 43; c 3. *Educ:* Pa State Univ, BS, 42, MS, 47; Stanford Univ, PhD(org chem), 50. *Prof Exp:* Chemist & asst to asst dir res, Texaco, Inc, NY, 49, group leader, 55, asst supvr lubricants res, 55, Tex, 55-56, supvr chem res, 56-57, asst dir res, 57-60, dir fuels & chem res, 60-62, vpres, Texaco Exp Inc, Va, 62-63, exec vpres, 63-65, pres, 65-66, mgr sci planning, Texaco Inc, 67-68, asst to pres, 68-69, staff coordr strategic planning group exec off, 69-70, gen mgr strategic planning, 70-71, vpres Res Environ & Safety Dept, Texaco, Inc, 71-81. *Mem:* Am Chem Soc; Indust Res Inst; AAAS; Sci Res Soc Am; Dirs Indust Res. *Res:* Product and process development, including petrochemicals, fuels and lubricants; exploration and production research; coal beneficiation, gasification and liquefaction. *Mailing Add:* 27 Lincoln Dr Poughkeepsie NY 12601

**TESSLER, ARTHUR NED,** UROLOGY. *Current Pos:* Investr, USPHS grant, 59-62, PROF CLIN UROL, SCH MED, NY UNIV, 72- *Personal Data:* b New York, NY, Feb 21, 27; m 53, Roslyn Chinitz; c Daniel, Marc, Jonathan & Sara. *Educ:* NY Univ, AB, 48, MD, 52; Am Bd Urol, dipl. *Honors & Awards:* Carl Hartman Award, Am Fertil Soc, 63. *Concurrent Pos:* Consult, Vet Admin Hosp, NY, 70- *Mem:* AMA; Am Fertil Soc; Am Col Surg. *Res:* Beta naphtholamine metabolites; effects of vaucerele in fertility; management of renal tumors. *Mailing Add:* Dept Urol NY Univ Sch Med 550 First Ave New York NY 10016-6481

**TESSLER, GEORGE,** PHYSICS. *Current Pos:* FEL SCIENTIST, BETTIS ATOMIC POWER LAB, WESTINGHOUSE ELEC CORP, 63- *Personal Data:* b Brooklyn, NY, Mar 7, 36; m 69; c 2. *Educ:* Brooklyn Col, BS, 57; Univ Pa, MS, 59, PhD(physics), 64. *Mem:* Am Phys Soc; AAAS; NY Acad Sci; Am Nuclear Soc. *Res:* Acquisition of neutron cross section data for use in reactor design; nuclear reactor design. *Mailing Add:* 284 Ben Til Dr Pittsburgh PA 15236-4306

**TESSLER, MARTIN MELVYN,** ORGANIC CHEMISTRY, POLYSACCHARIDE CHEMISTRY. *Current Pos:* proj supvr, Nat Starch & Chem Corp, 68-72, res assoc, 72-81, sr res assoc, 81-83, assoc dir, 83-85, DIR NATURAL POLYMER RES, NAT STARCH & CHEM CORP, BRIDGEWATER, 85- *Personal Data:* b Brooklyn, NY, Sept 12, 37; m 62, Marilyn Moskovitz; c David & Jacqueline. *Educ:* Brooklyn Col, BS, 58; Univ Kans, PhD(chem), 62. *Prof Exp:* Chemist, Enjay Chem Intermediates Lab, Esso Res & Eng Co, 65-68. *Mem:* AAAS; Am Chem Soc; Am Asn Cereal Chemists. *Res:* Starch chemistry; biodegradable polymers. *Mailing Add:* 507 Darwin Blvd Edison NJ 08820

**TESSMAN, IRWIN,** MICROBIOLOGY, MOLECULAR BIOLOGY. *Current Pos:* PROF BIOL, PURDUE UNIV, 62- *Personal Data:* b New York, NY, Nov 24, 29; wid; c Adam. *Educ:* Cornell Univ, AB, 50; Yale Univ, MS, 51, PhD(physics), 54. *Honors & Awards:* Gravity Res Found Prize, 53; Sigma Xi Res Award, Purdue Univ, 66. *Prof Exp:* NSF fel, Cornell Univ, 54-55, Am Cancer Soc fel, 55-57; fel, Mass Inst Technol, 57-58, res assoc biol, 58-59; assoc prof biophys, Univ Calif, Irvine, 59-62, prof biochem & molecular biol, 70-72. *Concurrent Pos:* NSF sr fel, Harvard Med Sch, 67; prof molecular biol, Univ Calif, 69-72. *Mem:* Am Soc Biochem & Molecular Biol; AAAS; Genetics Soc Am; Am Soc Microbiol. *Res:* Molecular genetics; reproduction of bacterial viruses; molecular studies of repair, mutation, recombination and function of genetic material. *Mailing Add:* Dept Biol Sci Purdue Univ West Lafayette IN 47907. *Fax:* 317-494-0876; *E-Mail:* itessman@purdue.edu

**TESSMER, CARL FREDERICK,** PATHOLOGY. *Current Pos:* RETIRED. *Personal Data:* b North Braddock, Pa, May 28, 12; m 39; c 2. *Educ:* Univ Pittsburgh, BS, 33, MD, 35; Am Bd Path, dipl, 41. *Honors & Awards:* Hektoen lectr, 60. *Prof Exp:* Resident path, Presby Hosp, Pittsburgh, 36-37; fel, Mayo Clin, 37-38; resident pathologist, Queen's Hosp, Honolulu, Hawaii, 39-40; chief lab, Tripler Gen Hosp, Honolulu, Med Corps, US Army, 42-45, chief, Radiologic Safety, Bikini, 46, pathologist, US Naval Med Res Inst, 46-48, dir, Atomic Bomb Casualty Comn, Nat Res Coun, 48-51, commanding officer, Army Med Res Lab, Ft Knox, Ky, 51-54, chief, Basic Sci Div & Radiation Path Br, Armed Forces Inst Path, Walter Reed Army Med Ctr, DC, 54-60, commanding officer, 406th Med Gen Lab, Japan, 60-62, pathologist, Walter Reed Army Inst Res, 62-63; chief, Exp Path Sect, Univ Tex M D

Anderson Hosp & Tumor Inst Houston, 63-71, prof path, 63-73; chief lab serv, Vet Admin Ctr, Temple, Tex, 73-85. *Concurrent Pos:* Armed Forces Inst Path Centennial lect, 62; mem grad fac, Univ Tex Grad Sch Biomed Sci, 63-73, path coordr, Univ Tex Med Sch, Houston, 71-73; consult, Walter Reed Army Med Ctr, 64-; mem, USPHS Adv Comt, Collab Radiol Health Animal Res Lab, 65-70; mem, Subcomt 34, Nat Comt Radiation Protection, 70-76; consult, Radiation Bioeffects & Epidemiol Adv Comn, Food & Drug Admin, Dept Health, Educ & Welfare, 72-75. *Mem:* Emer fel Am Soc Clin Path; emer mem Radiation Res Soc; emer mem Am Asn Path & Bact; emer fel Col Am Path; emer mem Int Acad Path. *Res:* Morphologic and experimental radiation pathology; trace elements; copper metabolism. *Mailing Add:* Rte 5 Box 5291 Belton TX 76513-9303

**TEST, CHARLES EDWARD,** MEDICINE. *Current Pos:* RETIRED. *Personal Data:* b Indianapolis, Ind, Jan 10, 16; m 38; c 4. *Educ:* Princeton Univ, AB, 37; Univ Chicago, MD, 41. *Prof Exp:* Instr med, Univ Chicago, 49-51; from asst prof to prof, Sch Med, Ind Univ, Indianapolis, 53-89. *Mem:* Endocrine Soc; Am Diabetes Asn; fel Am Col Physicians. *Res:* Endocrinology; metabolism. *Mailing Add:* 4430 N Meridian St Indianapolis IN 46208-3571

**TEST, FREDERICK L(AURENT),** MECHANICAL ENGINEERING. *Current Pos:* RETIRED. *Personal Data:* b Philadelphia, Pa, June 15, 25; m 47; c 3. *Educ:* Mass Inst Technol, SB, 45, SM, 47; Pa State Univ, PhD(mech eng), 56. *Prof Exp:* Res engr, Mass Inst Technol, 47-48; instr mech eng, Northeastern Univ, 48-49; from instr to assoc prof, Univ RI, 49-72, chmn dept, 72-76, prof, 72- *Concurrent Pos:* NSF fac fel, 59-60; consult, US Navy, 60-66; Fulbright res fel, Neth, 66-67. *Mem:* Am Soc Mech Engrs; Am Inst Aeronaut & Astronaut; Sigma Xi. *Mailing Add:* 258 Blackberry Hill Dr Wakefield RI 02879

**TESTA, ANTHONY CARMINE,** PHYSICAL CHEMISTRY, PHOTOCHEMISTRY. *Current Pos:* from asst prof to assoc prof, 63-71, PROF CHEM, ST JOHN'S UNIV, NY, 71- *Personal Data:* b New York, NY, Nov 19, 33; m 62, Helga Kittlinger. *Educ:* City Col New York, BS, 55; Columbia Univ, MA, 58, PhD(chem), 61. *Prof Exp:* Res chemist, Cent Res Div, Lever Bros Co, 61-63. *Concurrent Pos:* Res leave, Max-Planck Inst Spectros, Goettingen, 70-71. *Mem:* Am Chem Soc; InterAm Photochem Soc. *Res:* Photochemistry and flash photolysis of molecules in solution; luminescence spectroscopy; fluorescence and phosphorescence. *Mailing Add:* Dept Chem St John's Univ Jamaica NY 11439

**TESTA, DOUGLAS,** MICROBIOLOGY. *Current Pos:* exec dir, Interferon Sci Inc, 81-84, vpres res, 84-87, vpres res & develop, 87-93, RES DIR, INTERFERON SCI INC, 84-, VPRES RES, DEVELOP & CLIN AFFAIRS, 93- *Personal Data:* Concord, Mass, May 22, 44; m; c 2. *Educ:* City Univ New York, BS, 67, MS, 71, PhD(microbiol), 76. *Prof Exp:* Chmn, Sci Dept, Intermediate Sch 201, 67-70; lectr & lab course coordr principles in biol course, Hunter Col, 70-76, adj asst prof biol, 78-81; fel & res assoc cell biol, Roche Inst Molecular Biol, 76-79; proj leader, Dept Virol, Ortho Diag Res & Develop, 79-80; asst dir biologics, Hydron Labs, 80-81. *Concurrent Pos:* Adj assoc prof, Dept Biol Sci, Rutgers Univ, 85-88; ed, Cancer Ther & Control, 90- *Mem:* Am Inst Biol Sci; Am Inst Chemists; Am Soc Biochem & Molecular Biol; Am Soc Microbiol; Am Soc Testing & Mat; Am Soc Virol; Int Soc Hemat; Int Soc Biol Stand; NY Acad Sci; Soc Indust Microbiol; Sigma Xi; Protein Soc. *Mailing Add:* Interferon Sci Inc 19 Edgewood Dr Neshanic Station NJ 08853

**TESTA, RAYMOND THOMAS,** MICROBIOLOGY, BIOCHEMISTRY. *Current Pos:* mem staff, Med Res Div, Am Cyanamid Co, 77-, SECT DIR INFECTIOUS RES, WYETH-AYERST. *Personal Data:* b New Haven, Conn, Dec 21, 37; m 62; c 3. *Educ:* Providence Col, BS, 59; Syracuse Univ, MS, 64, PhD(microbiol), 66. *Prof Exp:* Res asst microbiol, Syracuse Univ, 64-66; scientist, Schering Corp, 66-68, sr scientist, 68-72, prin microbiologist, 72-74, mgr, Antibiotics Screening & Fermentation Dept, 74-77. *Concurrent Pos:* Counr, NY Acad Sci, 88-; chair-elect, Div A, Am Soc Microbiol, 91-92. *Mem:* Am Soc Microbiol; Soc Indust Microbiol (secy, 76-79, pres elec, 79-80, pres, 80-81); NY Acad Sci. *Res:* Clinical microbiology; antibiotics; resistance mechanisms; factors affecting the production and biosynthesis of antibiotics; spore formation. *Mailing Add:* Wyeth-Ayerst Labs Antiinfective Res 401 N Middletown Rd Pearl River NY 10965

**TESTA, RENE B(IAGGIO),** CIVIL ENGINEERING, ENGINEERING MECHANICS. *Current Pos:* From asst prof to assoc prof, 63-75, dir, Robert A W Carleton Mat Lab, 65-92, PROF CIVIL ENG & ENG MECH, COLUMBIA UNIV, 75-, CHMN, 95- *Personal Data:* b Montreal, Can, May 30, 37; m 59; c 4. *Educ:* McGill Univ, BEng, 59; Columbia Univ, MS, 60, Eng ScD(eng mech), 63. *Concurrent Pos:* Pres, Tegja Inc. *Mem:* Am Soc Mech Engrs; Am Soc Civil Engrs; Am Soc Testing & Mat; Struct Stability Res Coun. *Res:* Solid mechanics; experimental mechanics of materials and structures; damage mechanics. *Mailing Add:* Dept Civil Eng Columbia Univ 500 W 120th St New York NY 10027

**TESTA, STEPHEN M,** GEOLOGY, HYDROGEOLOGY. *Current Pos:* PRES, APPL ENVIRON SERV, 90- *Personal Data:* b Fitchburg, Mass, July 17, 51; m 86; c 1. *Educ:* Calif State Univ, Northridge, BS, 76, MS, 78. *Honors & Awards:* Presidential Cert of Merit, Am Inst Prof Geologists, 87. *Prof Exp:* Engr geologist, R T Franklian & Assocs, 76-78; geologist & chief petrologist, Bechtel Inc, 78-80; proj geologist, Converse Consults, Wash, 80-82; chief hydrologist ecol & environ, Wash, 82-83; proj mgr & hydrogeologist, Dames & Moore, 83-86; vpres west coast opers, Eng Enterprises, Inc, 86-90.

*Concurrent Pos:* Adv bd trustee, Geol Soc Am; co-chmn, Am Asn Engr Geologists, Wash State Sect, 86; mem, Nat Comt Hydrogeol & Waste Mgt, 89-90; instr geol, mineral, geochem & hazardous waste mgt, Calif State Univ, Fullerton; mem, Nat Comt Prof Develop, Nat Comt Continuing Educ & Nat Comt Ann Meeting, Am Inst Prof Geologists. *Mem:* AAAS; Am Asn Petrol Geologists; Am Inst Prof Geologists; Mineral Soc Can; Mineral Soc Am; Nat Water Well Asn; Asn Eng Geologists; Geol Soc Am; Hazardous Mat Control Res Inst; Sigma Xi. *Res:* Environmental science; fate and transport of contaminants in geologic and hydrogeologic systems; remediation design and methods; public policy issues; environmental law; igneous and metamorphic petrology; historical development of applied geosciences. *Mailing Add:* 31831 S Camino Capistrano San Juan Capistrano CA 92675

**TESTARDI, LOUIS RICHARD,** SOLID STATE PHYSICS. *Current Pos:* PROF PHYSICS, FLA STATE UNIV, 85- *Personal Data:* b Philadelphia, Pa, Sept 23, 30; m 57; c 4. *Educ:* Univ Calif, Berkeley, AB, 56; Univ Pa, MS, 60, PhD(physics), 63. *Prof Exp:* Res physicist, Elec Storage Battery Co, 57-58 & Franklin Inst Labs, 58-62; res asst, Univ Pa, 63; res physicist, Bell Tel Labs, 63-80; dir mat processing in space, NASA Hq, 80-82; chief, Metall Div, Nat Bur Stand, Gaithersburg, MD, 82-85. *Mem:* Fel Am Phys Soc. *Res:* Transport, optical, magnetic and ultrasonic properties of solids; low temperature physics; superconductivity. *Mailing Add:* 1803 Sageway Dr Tallahassee FL 32303

**TESTER, CECIL FRED,** BIOCHEMISTRY, BIOTECHNOLOGY. *Current Pos:* RES CHEMIST, BELTSVILLE AGR RES CTR, AGR RES SERV, USDA, 75- *Personal Data:* b Boone, NC, May 23, 38; m 67; c 3. *Educ:* Appalachian State Univ, BS, 60; Univ Ga, PhD(biochem), 67. *Honors & Awards:* Super Serv Award, USDA, 77. *Prof Exp:* Teacher city schs, NC, 60-61; res asst biochem, Univ Ga, 64-65, teaching asst, 65-66; AEC fel, Purdue Univ, Lafayette, 67-68; res chemist & USDA grant, NC State Univ, 68-75. *Concurrent Pos:* Prof leader org matter transformations & mineral nutrit. *Mem:* Am Soc Agron; Soil Sci Soc; Crop Sci Soc. *Res:* Biochemistry of rhizosphere plant-microbial interactions; characterization and use of monodonial antibodies for genetic determinants. *Mailing Add:* 11402 Westview Ct Beltsville MD 20705

**TESTER, JEFFERSON WILLIAM,** CHEMICAL ENGINEERING, PHYSICAL CHEMISTRY. *Current Pos:* from assoc prof to prof, 80-96, dir, Sch Chem Eng Pract, 80-90, DIR, ENERGY LAB, MASS INST TECHNOL, 89-, H P MEISSNER PROF CHEM ENG, 96- INST TECHNOL, 80-, PROF CHEM ENG, 88-, DIR, ENERGY LAB, 89- *Personal Data:* b New York, NY, Mar 27, 45; m 67, Sue Kelsey; c Kelsey Alison. *Educ:* Cornell Univ, BS, 66, MS, 67; Mass Inst Technol, PhD(chem eng), 71. *Prof Exp:* Fel, Los Alamos Sci Lab, Univ Calif, 71-72; asst prof chem eng & dir, Sch Chem Eng Pract at Oak Ridge Nat Lab, Mass Inst Technol, 72-74; group leader-geothermal technol, Los Alamos Sci Lab, 74-80. *Concurrent Pos:* Vis staff mem, Los Alamos Sci Lab, Univ Calif, 72-74; adj prof chem eng, Univ NMex, 75-80; consult, Los Alamos Nat Lab & Sandia Nat Labs, 88-; mem, Nat Res Coun Comt on Geothermal Energy Technol, 86-87, Indust Waste Reduction & Utilization, 90- *Mem:* Am Inst Chem Engrs; Am Chem Soc; Soc Petrol Engrs; Geothermal Resources Coun. *Res:* Applied thermodynamics; physical chemistry of supercritical fluids; transport and chemical reaction in supercritical water; environmental control technology; alternative energy systems; geothermal energy technology. *Mailing Add:* 19 Liberty Rd Hingham MA 02043. *Fax:* 617-253-8013; *E-Mail:* testere@mit.edu

**TESTER, JOHN ROBERT,** ECOLOGY, WILDLIFE SCIENCE. *Current Pos:* asst scientist ecol, Mus Natural Hist, 56-60, from instr to assoc prof, 60-70, head dept, 73-76, PROF ECOL, EVOLUTION & BEHAV, UNIV MINN, ST PAUL, 70- *Personal Data:* b New Ulm, Minn, Nov 18, 29; m 60; c 2. *Educ:* Univ Minn, BS, 51; Colo State Univ, MS, 53; Univ Minn, PhD(wildlife ecol), 60. *Prof Exp:* Res asst wildlife biol, Colo Game & Fish Dept, 51-53; game biologist, Minn Div Game & Fish, 54-56. *Concurrent Pos:* NSF fel, Aschoff Div, Max Planck Inst Physiol of Behav & Aberdeen Univ, 69-70; mem behav sci training comt, NIH; Nat Acad Sci exchange scientist, 82; hon fel, Aberdeen Univ, Scotland; dir, Cedar Creek Nat Hist Area, 84-91. *Mem:* Fel AAAS; Ecol Soc Am; Am Soc Mammal; Wildlife Soc. *Res:* Population ecology; biotelemetry; wildlife management; behavioral ecology; fire ecology; landscape ecology. *Mailing Add:* Dept Ecol Evolution & Behav Univ Minn St Paul MN 55108. *E-Mail:* teste001@maroon.tc.umn.edu

**TESTERMAN, JACK DUANE,** STATISTICS, COMPUTER SCIENCE. *Current Pos:* MGT CONSULT, 97- *Personal Data:* b Marietta, Okla, Dec 13, 33; m 53; c Ken, Sherri & Jay. *Educ:* Okla State Univ, BS, 55, MS, 57; Univ Tex, PhD, 72. *Prof Exp:* Res statistician, Jersey Prod Res Co, 57-63 & Phillips Petrol Co, 63; assoc prof, Univ Southwestern La, 63-69, registr, 65-70, prof math & statist, 69-84, dir instnl res, 70-84, vpres univ relations, 73-84; consult, 84-87; prof mgt, Southeastern Okla State Univ, 86-96. *Concurrent Pos:* Chmn, Inst Studies & Opers Analysis Comt. *Mem:* Am Statist Asn; Asn Comput Mach; Am Mgt Asn. *Res:* Application of statistics; data analysis and use of computers; management and marketing. *Mailing Add:* Rte 1 Box 436 Marietta OK 73448

**TESU, ION CONSTANTIN,** ANALOG & DIGITAL INTEGRATED CIRCUITS DESIGN, SIMULATION & MODELING OF ELECTRONIC CIRCUITS & SYSTEMS. *Current Pos:* DESIGN ENGR, CRYSTAL SEMICONDUCTOR, 95- *Personal Data:* b Pipirig, Romania, Oct 30, 57; m 92, Gabriela, Vasiliu; c Tudor Ion. *Educ:* Tech Univ Iasi, MS, 81, PhD(elec eng), 94. *Prof Exp:* Design engr, Aerofira, Bucharest, 81-83; prof, Iasi Tech Univ, 83-94; vis researcher, Univ Tex, Austin, 94-95. *Mem:* Inst Elec &

Electronics Engrs. *Res:* Modeling and simulation of analog integrated circuits and devices; design of analog integrated circuits for disk drive. *Mailing Add:* Crystal Semiconductor 4209 S Industrial Dr Austin TX 78744-1076. *E-Mail:* tesu@crystal.cirrus.com

**TETENBAUM, MARVIN,** PHYSICAL CHEMISTRY. *Current Pos:* CHEMIST, ARGONNE NAT LAB, 59- *Personal Data:* b Brooklyn, NY, June 27, 21; m 54; c 3. *Educ:* NY Univ, BChE, 42; Polytech Inst Brooklyn, MChE, 47, PhD(chem), 54. *Honors & Awards:* Award for significant contribution in field of Nuclear Technol, Am Nuclear Soc. *Prof Exp:* Res asst, Metall Lab, Univ Chicago, 42-43; res engr sam labs, Columbia Univ, 43-44; chem engr, Ballistics Res Lab, Ord Dept, US Dept Army, 47-48; radio chemist, US Naval Res Lab, 48-56; sr engr, Aircraft Nuclear Propulsion Dept, Gen Elec Co, Ohio, 56-59. *Concurrent Pos:* Mem staff, Atomic Energy Res Estab, Harwell, Eng, 66-67; vis scientist, Europ Inst Transuranium Elements, Karlsruhe, WGer, 83-84. *Mem:* Am Nuclear Soc; fel Am Ceramic Soc; AAAS; Am Chem Soc; Sigma Xi; Mat Res Soc. *Res:* High temperature chemistry; superconductivity. *Mailing Add:* Chem Technol Div Argonne Nat Lab Bldg 205 9700 S Cass Ave Argonne IL 60439

**TETERIS, NICHOLAS JOHN,** OBSTETRICS & GYNECOLOGY. *Current Pos:* Asst prof, 65-67, assoc prof & asst dean col med, 67-70, PROF OBSTET & GYNEC, COL MED, OHIO STATE UNIV, 70- *Personal Data:* b Martins Ferry, Ohio, Jan 14, 29; m 61; c 2. *Educ:* Washington & Jefferson Col, BA, 50; Ohio State Univ, MD, 54, MSc, 61; Am Bd Obstet & Gynec, dipl, 65. *Concurrent Pos:* Cancer fel obstet & gynec, Col Med, Ohio State Univ, 62-64; consult, USAF Hosps, Wright-Patterson & Lockborne AFB, 62; asst dir, Ohio State Univ Hosps, 62- *Mem:* AMA; Am Col Obstet & Gynec; Am Col Surg. *Res:* Fetology; gynecologic cancer; obstetrical emergencies. *Mailing Add:* Ohio State Univ S 407RH 410 W 10th Ave Columbus OH 43210

**TETLOW, NORMAN JAY,** CHEMICAL ENGINEERING. *Current Pos:* process syst specialist, 68-79, PROCESS ENG MGR, TEX DIV, DOW CHEM CO, 79- *Personal Data:* b Downs, Kans, Dec 9, 34; m 57; c 2. *Educ:* Kans State Univ, BS, 57, MS, 59; Tex A&M Univ, PhD(chem eng), 66. *Prof Exp:* Chem engr, Mason & Hanger, Silas Mason Co, 57-58 & 59-60; res & develop engr, Dow Chem Co, 60-63 & Tex Instruments, Inc, 66-68. *Mem:* Am Inst Chem Engrs; Am Chem Soc. *Res:* Application of computers and numerical methods to chemical process engineering and process control. *Mailing Add:* 120 Clover Lake Jackson TX 77566-4606

**TETRAULT, ROBERT CLOSE,** ENTOMOLOGY. *Current Pos:* RETIRED. *Personal Data:* b Walhalla, NDak, Nov 25, 33; m 58; c 4. *Educ:* NDak State Univ, BS, 58, MS, 63; Univ Wis, PhD(entom), 67. *Prof Exp:* From asst prof to assoc prof entom, Pa State Univ, University Park, 71-86. *Mem:* Entom Soc Am. *Res:* Taxonomy of Coleoptera, especially the family Helodidae. *Mailing Add:* PO Box 63 Walhalla ND 58282

**TETTENHORST, RODNEY TAMPA,** MINERALOGY. *Current Pos:* From asst prof to assoc prof, 60-75, PROF MINERAL, OHIO STATE UNIV, 75- *Personal Data:* b St Louis, Mo, Feb 1, 34; m 60; c 3. *Educ:* Wash Univ, BS, 55, MA, 57; Univ Ill, Urbana, PhD(mineral), 60. *Mem:* Clay Minerals Soc; Mineral Soc Am; Mineral Soc Gt Brit & Ireland. *Res:* Clay mineralogy; x-ray diffraction and physical properties of small crystalline particles. *Mailing Add:* Dept Geol 125 S Oval Mall Ohio State Univ Columbus OH 43210-1308

**TEUBER, LARRY ROSS,** PLANT BREEDING, POLLINATION BIOLOGY. *Current Pos:* from asst prof to assoc prof plant breeding, 77-91, PROF PLANT BREEDING & AGRON, UNIV CALIF, DAVIS, 91- *Personal Data:* b Prescott, Ariz, July 8, 51; m 83. *Educ:* NMex State Univ, BS, 73, MS, 74; Univ Minn, PhD(plant breeding), 78. *Concurrent Pos:* Agronomist, Calif Agr Exp Sta, 77-; mem, NAm Alfalfa Improv Conf. *Mem:* Crop Sci Soc Am; Am Soc Agron; Int Comn Bee Bot; Sigma Xi. *Res:* Alfalfa breeding and genetics; pollinator activity and seed production; forage yield and quality; nitrogen fixation, disease and insect resistance including: Colletotrichum, Stagnospora, and Stemphylium lygos and silver leaf whitefly. *Mailing Add:* Dept Agron & Range Sci Univ Calif Davis CA 95616-5224. *Fax:* 530-752-4361; *E-Mail:* lrteuber@ucdavis.edu

**TEUKOLSKY, SAUL ARNO,** THEORETICAL ASTROPHYSICS, RELATIVITY. *Current Pos:* from asst prof to assoc prof physics, 74-83, PROF PHYSICS & ASTRON, CORNELL UNIV, 83- *Personal Data:* b Johannesburg, SAfrica, Aug 2, 47; m 71; c 2. *Educ:* Univ Witwatersrand, BSc Hons(physics) & BSc Hons(appl math), 70; Calif Inst Technol, PhD(physics), 73. *Prof Exp:* Res assoc physics, Calif Inst Technol, 73-74. *Concurrent Pos:* Alfred P Sloan Found res fel, 75-77; John Simon Guggenheim Mem fel, 81-82. *Mem:* Am Phys Soc; Am Astron Soc. *Res:* General relativity and relativistic astrophysics. *Mailing Add:* 608 Space Sci Bldg Cornell Univ Ithaca NY 14853

**TEUSCHER, GEORGE WILLIAM,** DENTISTRY. *Current Pos:* From instr to assoc prof, Northwestern Univ, 31-45, dean, Dent Sch, 53-72, prof, 45-72, EMER PROF PEDODONTICS, DENT SCH, NORTHWESTERN UNIV, 72- *Personal Data:* b Chicago, Ill, Jan 11, 08; m 34; c 2. *Educ:* Northwestern Univ, DDS, 29, MSD, 36, MA, 40, PhD(educ), 42. *Hon Degrees:* ScD, NY Univ, 65. *Concurrent Pos:* Regent, Nat Libr Med; ed, J Am Soc Dent Children, 68- *Mem:* Am Soc Dent Children; Am Dent Asn; Am Acad Pedodontics; fel Am Col Dent; Int Asn Dent Res. *Res:* Dental caries; reactions of dental pulp in children; sodium fluoride; prevention in clinical dentistry for children; principles of dental education. *Mailing Add:* Am Soc Dent Children 875 N Michigan Ave Suite 4040 Chicago IL 60611-1901

**TEVAULT, DAVID EARL,** INORGANIC CHEMISTRY. *Current Pos:* US ARMY CHEM RES, DEVELOP & ENG CTR, 87- *Personal Data:* b Evansville, Ind, July 23, 48; m 73, Judy Keith; c Neil & Nancy. *Educ:* Univ Evansville, BA, 70; Univ Va, PhD(chem), 74. *Honors & Awards:* Berman Award, Naval Res Lab, 81. *Prof Exp:* Fel chem, Marquette Univ, 74-76; fel chem, Naval Res Lab, 76-78, staff scientist, 78-87. *Mem:* Am Chem Soc; Sigma Xi. *Res:* Mechanisms and kinetics of atmospheric, combustion related, heterogeneous catalysis, and infrared laser promoted chemical reactions by cryogenic spectroscopic methods; air purification. *Mailing Add:* 802 Hayden Ct Bel Air MD 21014-2788

**TEVEBAUGH, ARTHUR DAVID,** NUCLEAR CHEMISTRY, INORGANIC CHEMISTRY. *Current Pos:* RETIRED. *Personal Data:* b Knox Co, Ind, Nov 25, 17; m 43, Ruth O Donohue; c Joyce & Jean. *Educ:* Purdue Univ, BS, 40; Iowa State Univ, PhD(phys chem), 47. *Prof Exp:* Asst chem, Iowa State Univ, 40-42; res chemist, Manhattan Proj, 42-47; res chemist, Knolls Atomic Power Lab, Gen Elec Co, 47-55; supvr reactor chem unit, Gen Elec Co, 50-54, actg mgr chem & chem eng sect, 54-55, sr res chemist, Res & Develop Lab, 55-63; sr chemist & sect mgr chem eng div, Argonne Nat Lab, 63-69, assoc dir div, 69-72, dir lab prog planning off, 72-73, dir coal progs, 73-77, assoc dir chem div, 77-81. *Mem:* Am Chem Soc. *Res:* Analytical, nuclear and soil chemistry; production and handling of fluorine; chemical problems related to development and operation of nuclear reactors and reactor fuel reprocessing; polymer research; thermoelectric materials; fuel cells and batteries; electrochemistry; nuclear reactor safety. *Mailing Add:* 21 Rte 152 RMC No 280 Sellersville PA 18960-1699. *E-Mail:* knoxco@fast.net

**TEVEROVSKY, ALEXANDER,** QUALITY CONTROL, RELIABILITY PHYSICS. *Current Pos:* ENGR, UNISYS, 94- *Personal Data:* b Moscow, Russia, Oct 15, 45; m 69, Nadezhda Krikunehix; c Yelena & Julia. *Educ:* Moscow Inst Electronics, MS, 68, PhD(elec eng), 72. *Prof Exp:* Asst prof, Moscow Inst Electronics, 73-75, researcher, 75-80, res group leader, 80-93. *Concurrent Pos:* Lectr, Moscow Inst Electronics, 73-93, prin investr, 80-93. *Res:* Reliability physics of semiconductor devices encapsulated in plastics; quality control of encapsulating materials; author of more than 50 articles; holder of 11 patents. *Mailing Add:* 5503 April Journey Columbia MD 21044. *Fax:* 301-731-8603; *E-Mail:* alexander.a.teverovsky.1@gsfc.nasa.gov

**TEVETHIA, MARY JUDITH (ROBINSON),** MOLECULAR BIOLOGY, GENETICS. *Current Pos:* STAFF MEM, DEPT MICROBIOL, PA STATE UNIV. *Personal Data:* b Ft Wayne, Ind, Feb 25, 39; m 65; c 2. *Educ:* Mich State Univ, BS, 60, MS, 62, PhD(microbiol), 64. *Prof Exp:* Fel microbiol, Emory Univ, 64-65; fel biol, Univ Tex, M D Anderson Hosp & Tumor Inst, Houston, 65-72, asst biologist & asst prof biol, 72-73; asst prof path, Sch Med, Tufts Univ, 73- *Concurrent Pos:* NIH fels, 64-65, 65- *Mem:* Am Soc Microbiol; Am Soc Virol. *Res:* Genetic studies on simian papova virus SV4O; human cytomegalovirus. *Mailing Add:* Dept Microbiol Pa State Univ Col Med PO Box 850 Hershey PA 17033-0850

**TEVETHIA, SATVIR S,** VIROLOGY, IMMUNOLOGY. *Current Pos:* PROF MICRO BIOL, COL MED, PA STATE UNIV, 78- *Personal Data:* b Buland Shahr, India, Aug 5, 36; m 65; c 1. *Educ:* Agra Univ, BSc, 54, BVSc, 58; Mich State Univ, MS, 62, PhD(microbiol), 64. *Prof Exp:* Vet asst surg, Indian Govt, 58-59; res asst microbiol, Mich State Univ, 60-64; from asst prof to assoc prof virol, Baylor Col Med, 71-73; assoc prof path, Sch Med, Tufts Univ, 73-77, prof, 77-78. *Concurrent Pos:* Fel virol, Baylor Col Med, 64-66; Nat Cancer Inst res career develop award, 67-71. *Mem:* AAAS; Am Soc Microbiol; Am Asn Cancer Res. *Res:* Tumor viruses and immunology. *Mailing Add:* Dept Microbiol & Immunol Col Med Pa State Univ 500 University Dr Rm C6467D Hershey PA 17033-0850. *Fax:* 717-531-6522

**TEVIOTDALE, BETH LUISE,** TREE FRUITS & NUTS. *Current Pos:* EXTEN SPECIALIST PLANT PATH, KEARNEY AGR CTR, UNIV CALIF, 75- *Personal Data:* b Long Beach, Calif, July 17, 40; div. *Educ:* Pomona Col, BA, 62; Univ Calif, Davis, MS, 70, PhD(plant path), 74. *Prof Exp:* Lab technician bot, Calif Inst Technol, 62-63; lab technician immunol, Univ Calif, Los Angeles, 65-68. *Mem:* Sigma Xi; Am Phytopath Soc; AAAS. *Res:* Epidemiology and control of fungal and bacterial diseases of deciduous nut and fruit trees. *Mailing Add:* Kearney Agr Ctr Univ Calif 9240 S Riverbend Ave Parlier CA 93648

**TEW, JOHN GARN,** IMMUNOLOGY, MICROBIOLOGY. *Current Pos:* from asst prof to assoc prof, 72-82, PROF MICROBIOL, VA COMMONWEALTH UNIV, 82- *Personal Data:* b Mapleton, Utah, Oct 26, 40; m 65; c 6. *Educ:* Brigham Young Univ, BS, 66, MS, 67, PhD(microbiol), 70. *Prof Exp:* NIH fel, Case Western Res Univ, 70-72. *Concurrent Pos:* Vis prof, Walter & Elizabeth Hall Inst Med Res, Melbourne, Australia, 77-78. *Mem:* Am Soc Microbiol; Am Asn Immunologists; Reticuloendothelial Soc; Sigma Xi. *Res:* Role of persisting antigen and follicular dendritic cells in the induction maintenance and regulation of the humoral immune response; role of beta-lysin in innate immunity; immunobiology of periodontal disease. *Mailing Add:* Dept Microbiol Med Col Va PO Box 980678 Richmond VA 23298-0678. *Fax:* 804-786-9946

**TEW, KENNETH DAVID,** CANCER CHEMOTHERAPY, DRUG RESISTANCE. *Current Pos:* CHMN PHARMACOL, FOX CHASE CANCER CTR, PHILADELPHIA, 85- *Personal Data:* b Dumbarton, Scotland, Apr 20, 52; US citizen; m 87. *Educ:* Univ London, PhD(biochem pharmacol), 76, DSc(molecular pharmacol), 96. *Prof Exp:* Asst prof med & pharmacol, Sch Med, Georgetown Univ, Washington, DC, 81-85. *Concurrent Pos:* Adj prof pharmacol, Univ Pa, 85-90, adj prof, 90-; mem, Study Sect ET

1, NIH, 88-, chmn, 90-92; chmn, Gordon Conf Chemother Cancer, 89; mem, Subcomt Space Sta Pharmacodynamics, NASA/ACS, 88-; vis prof, Nat Cancer Inst, Tokyo, 88-89. *Mem:* Am Soc Pharmacol & Exp Therapeut; Am Assoc Cancer Res; Am Soc Cell Biol; AAAS. *Res:* Focused upon understanding the mechanisms of action of alkylating agent classes of anticancer drugs, with special emphasis on determinants of tumor cell resistance to these agents. *Mailing Add:* Chmn Dept Pharmacol Fox Chase Cancer Ctr 7701 Burholme Rd Philadelphia PA 19111

**TEWARI, SUJATA LAHIRI,** MOLECULAR BIOLOGY, NEUROCHEMISTRY. *Current Pos:* asst researcher neurochemist step III, Univ Calif, Irvine, 70-72, asst researcher neurochemist step IV, 72, asst prof res III, 72-76, asst prof res IV, 76-78, ASSOC PROF, DEPT PSYCYHIAT & HUMAN BEHAV, UNIV CALIF, IRVINE, 78- *Personal Data:* b Murshidabad, India, July 1, 38; m 64, Krishna K; c Krishnansu & Devansu T. *Educ:* Agra Univ, BSc, 55; Univ Lucknow, MS, 57; McGill Univ, PhD(biochem), 62. *Honors & Awards:* Res Career Develop Award, Type II, Nat Inst Alcohol, Abuse & Alcoholism. *Prof Exp:* Neurochemist co-investr brain protein synthesis & neurotransmitters, Vet Admin Hosp, City of Hope, Sepulveda, Calif, 66-70. *Concurrent Pos:* UGC fel biochem, Lucknow Univ, India, 63-64; NSF res proj grant, 75; prin investr, Nat Inst Alcohol Abuse & Alcoholism, 76-, NIMH grant, 78-, NSF grant, UCI Focussed Res Prog; mem, Pub Comt Alcoholism, Clin & Exp Res, 77- & biomed panel Calif state supported ctr, 78-; sponsor, Nat Inst Alcohol Abuse & Alcoholism, Ronald L Alkana & Eugene Fleming fel, 78-; sci dir, Nat Inst Alcohol Abuse & Alcoholism, Alcohol Res Ctr grant, 78-; co-prin investr, UCI Success & FIPSE Proj, Dept Educ; fel, Coun Sci Indust Res. *Mem:* AAAS; Biochem Soc; Int Soc Neurochem; Res Soc Alcoholism; Int Soc Biomed Res Alcoholism; Am Soc Neurochem; Am Pub Health Asn; NY Acad Sci; Neurobehav Terotology Soc. *Res:* Neurobiology combining the disciplines of molecular biology, neurochemistry and neuropharmacology; special emphasis on biomedical research in alcoholism and psychoactive drugs; neuroimmunological studies focussing on astrocytes dysfunctions and susceptibility to retroviral infection of prenatally alcohol exposed brain. *Mailing Add:* Biol Chem Univ Calif Irvine Irvine CA 92717-0001. *Fax:* 714-856-7012

**TEWARSON, REGINALD P,** BIOMATHEMATICS. *Current Pos:* from asst prof to prof, 64-89, actg chmn, 83-84, LEADING PROF APPL MATH, STATE UNIV NY, STONY BROOK, 89-, LEADING PROF PHYSIOL & BIOPHYS, 94- *Personal Data:* b Pauri, India, Nov 17, 30; div; c Anita & Monique. *Educ:* Univ Lucknow, BSc, 50; Agra Univ, MSc, 52; Boston Univ, PhD(appl math), 61. *Prof Exp:* Lectr physics, Messmore Col, India, 50-51; lectr math, Univ Lucknow, 52-57; sr mathematician, Honeywell Inc, 60-64. *Concurrent Pos:* Vis prof, Oxford Univ, 70-71. *Mem:* Am Math Soc; Soc Indust & Appl Math; Soc Math Biol. *Res:* Sparse matrices; linear algebra; numerical analysis; mathematical modelling in biology. *Mailing Add:* 22 Night Heron Dr Stony Brook NY 11790-1108. *Fax:* 516-632-8490; *E-Mail:* tewarson@ams.sunysb.edu

**TEWELL, JOSEPH ROBERT,** ADVANCED PROGRAMS, PROJECT DEVELOPMENT. *Current Pos:* sr res scientist, Martin Marietta Corp, 65-72, mgr, Space Teleopers, 73-75, Space Lab, 76-77, Space Vehicles, 78-79, Advan Progs, 79-86 & Launch Systs, 87-90, mgr comput aided prod, 90-96, MGR SYST ENG, MARTIN MARIETTA CORP, 96- *Personal Data:* b Albany, NY, May 19, 34; m 60, Barbara A Johnson; c Patricia A, Donna L & Joseph R III. *Educ:* Rensselaer Polytech Inst, BEE, 55, MEE, 60. *Honors & Awards:* Achievement Award, NASA, 74, New Technol Award, 76. *Prof Exp:* Instr elec eng, Rensselaer Polytech Inst, 55-64. *Concurrent Pos:* Res engr, NAm Aviation, Inc, 55; assoc res engr, Lockheed Aircraft Corp, 56; consult, Redford Corp, 61-62. *Mem:* Am Inst Aeronaut & Astronaut; Unmanned Vehicle Syst Asn; fel Explorers Club; Smithsonian Inst; Air & Space Mus. *Res:* Astronaut space maneuvering units; spacecraft docking and retrieval mechanisms; on-orbit teleoperators; launch vehicle design; stereo visual systems for space and undersea systems; atmospheric re-entry systems; solar power satellites; launch system technology requirements; author of over 35 publications. *Mailing Add:* 619 Legendre Dr Slidell LA 70460

**TEWHEY, JOHN DAVID,** HYDROGEOCHEMISTRY, HYDROGEOLOGY. *Current Pos:* PRES, TEWHEY ASSOCS, 87- *Personal Data:* b Lewiston, Maine, Feb 14, 43; m 65; c 3. *Educ:* Colby Col, BA, 65; Univ SC, MS, 68; Brown Univ, PhD(geol), 75. *Prof Exp:* Geologist, Lawrence Livermore Lab, Univ, Calif, 74-80; mgr, E C Jordan, Co, 81-87. *Concurrent Pos:* Mem geosci fac, Chabot Col, Livermore, Calif, 73-80, Univ Southern Maine, Gorham, 87-89. *Mem:* Geol Soc Am; Am Geophys Union; Am Chem Soc; Asn Groundwater Scientists & Engrs; Am Inst Hydrol; Asn Eng Geologists. *Res:* Evaluation of contamination in ground water; evaluation of the geochemical controls of soil-water interaction; radionuclide migration; geological applications to engineering. *Mailing Add:* Tewhey Assocs 500 Southborough Dr South Portland ME 04106-6903

**TEWINKEL, G CARPER,** PHOTOGRAMMETRY. *Current Pos:* RETIRED. *Personal Data:* b Lamona, Wash, Jan 20, 09. *Educ:* Wash State Univ, BSc, 32; Syracuse Univ, MCE, 40. *Honors & Awards:* Fairchild Award, Am Soc Photogram, 71; Schwidefsky Award, Int Soc Photogram, 88. *Prof Exp:* Draftsman cartog, US Soil Conserv Serv, 35-40; gen engr photogram, Nat Ocean Surv, US Nat Oceanic, Atmospheric Admin, Rockville, Md, 40-72. *Concurrent Pos:* Instr Math, George Washington Univ, 45-48; ed in chief, Am Soc Photogram, 65-75. *Mem:* Am Soc Photogram (pres, 60); Am Cong Surv & Mapping; Am Soc Civil Engrs; Inst Soc Photogram (vpres, 68-72). *Res:* Development of a computational system and a computer program called Analytic Aerotriangulation which greatly improved the accuracy of aerial mapping and enabled a reduction of costs for applications to nautical and aeronautical charting. *Mailing Add:* 2013 Rainbow Lane Wenatchee WA 98801

**TEWKSBURY, CHARLES ISAAC,** RUBBER CHEMISTRY. *Current Pos:* RETIRED. *Personal Data:* b Portsmouth, NH, Feb 26, 25; m 49; c 3. *Educ:* Univ NH, BS, 48, MS, 49; Princeton Univ, PhD(chem), 53. *Prof Exp:* Lab asst, Univ NH, 48-49; asst, Princeton Univ, 49-53; phys chemist, Nat Res Corp, 53-54, proj mgr, 54-57, sr chemist, 57-59; res chemist, Monsanto Chem Co, 59; group leader, Cabot Corp, 59-61; asst assoc dir new prod res, 61-63; res dir, Odell Co, 63-; treas, Fay Specialties, Inc, 71-74, pres, 74-79. *Mem:* Am Chem Soc. *Res:* Gas kinetics; hydrocarbon oxidation; heterogeneous catalysis; metals; high temperature phenomena; radiation chemistry; polymerization; polymer characterization; elastomers; adhesives. *Mailing Add:* Tall Pines Rd Chocorua NH 03817-0338

**TEWKSBURY, DUANE ALLAN,** BIOCHEMISTRY. *Current Pos:* Res biochemist, 64-80, SR RES BIOCHEMIST, MARSHFIELD MED FOUND, 80- *Personal Data:* b Osceola, Wis, Oct 4, 36; div; c 2. *Educ:* St Olaf Col, BA, 58; Univ Wis, MS, 60, PhD(biochem), 64. *Mem:* Am Chem Soc; Am Soc Biol Chemists; Inter-Am Soc Hypertension; Am Heart Asn. *Res:* Biochemical studies of peptide hormone systems; isolation and characterization of the protein components of the renin-angiotensin system. *Mailing Add:* Marshfield Med Found 1000 N Oak Ave Marshfield WI 54449

**TEWKSBURY, L BLAINE,** INDUSTRIAL RESEARCH, EDUCATION. *Current Pos:* RETIRED. *Personal Data:* b Boston, Mass, Sept 1, 17; m 49; c Marie, Jan, Debbie, Frances, Lyndon, Rachel, Julie & Sydney. *Educ:* Yale Univ, BS, 38, PhD(org chem), 41. *Prof Exp:* Chief chemist, Tom's of Maine Inc, 72-90. *Mem:* Sigma Xi; Am Chem Soc. *Res:* Rubber latex chemistry; mechanism of the formation of thyroxine from criodotyrosins; chemistry of adduct rubber odor production. *Mailing Add:* RR 1 Box 4990 Wayne ME 04284-9801

**TEWKSBURY, STUART K,** SYSTEMS DESIGN & SYSTEMS SCIENCE. *Current Pos:* PROF COMPUT ENG, WVA UNIV, 90- *Personal Data:* b Manchester, NH, Apr 22, 42; m 65; c 2. *Educ:* Univ Rochester, NY, BS, 64, PhD(physics), 69. *Prof Exp:* Mem res staff, AT&T Bell Labs, 69-90. *Mem:* Sr mem Inst Elec & Electronics Engrs; Am Inst Physics; Int Soc Optical Eng. *Res:* Integrated electronic systems with emphasis on limits facing present device/system technologies, new emerging technologies and enabled new system architectures/organizations. *Mailing Add:* Dept Elec & Comput Eng WVa Univ Eng Sci Bldg 827 Morgantown WV 26506. *Fax:* 304-293-7486; *E-Mail:* skt@msrc.wvu.edu

**TEWS, JEAN KRING,** BIOCHEMISTRY. *Current Pos:* proj assoc physiol, Univ Wis-Madison, 55-62, res assoc, 63-66, res assoc biochem, 67-77, ASSOC SCIENTIST BIOCHEM, UNIV WIS-MADISON, 77- *Personal Data:* b Ogdensburg, NY, May 21, 28; m 56; c 1. *Educ:* St Lawrence Univ, BS, 49; Univ Wis, MS, 52, PhD(biochem), 54. *Prof Exp:* Asst biochem, Univ Wis, 50-54; biochemist, Galesburg State Res Hosp, 54-55. *Concurrent Pos:* Acad vis, Inst Psychiat, London, 85. *Mem:* Int Soc Neurochem; Am Inst Nutrit; Am Soc Neurochem. *Res:* Enzyme activities and nutrition; neurochemistry; factors influencing chemical components of brain; amino acids; amino acid transport. *Mailing Add:* 5445 Lake Mendota Dr Madison WI 53705-1246

**TEWS, LEONARD L,** BOTANY, MYCOLOGY. *Current Pos:* from instr to assoc prof, 64-75, PROF BIOL, UNIV WIS-OSHKOSH, 75- *Personal Data:* b Rush Lake, Wis, May 28, 34; m 60; c 4. *Educ:* Wis State Univ, Oshkosh, BS, 56; Ind Univ, MA, 58; Univ Wis, PhD(bot, mycol), 65. *Prof Exp:* Teaching asst bot, Ind Univ, 56-58; teacher high sch, 58-61; res asst mycol, Univ Wis, 61-63. *Concurrent Pos:* Water Resources res grant, Water Resources Ctr, 69-70; vis prof, Univ RI, 83. *Mem:* Mycol Soc Am; Brit Mycol Soc. *Res:* Vesicular-arbuscular endomycorrhizal fungi. *Mailing Add:* Dept Biol Univ Wis Oshkosh 800 Algoma Blvd Oshkosh WI 54901-3551

**TEXON, MEYER,** MEDICINE, CARDIOVASCULAR DISEASE. *Current Pos:* RETIRED. *Personal Data:* b New York, NY, Apr 23, 09; m 41, Ami Gold; c Stephen J & Sylvia T (Rogers). *Educ:* Harvard Univ, AB, 30; NY Univ, MD, 34; Am Bd Internal Med & Am Bd Cardiovasc Dis, dipl, 44. *Honors & Awards:* Hektoen Silver Medal, AMA, 58. *Prof Exp:* From asst prof to assoc prof forensic med, Sch Med, NY Univ, 57-96. *Concurrent Pos:* Asst med examr, City of New York, 57-; sr clin asst med, Mt Sinai Hosp; consult cardiovasc dis, Bur Hearings & Appeals, Social Security Agency, Dept Health, Educ & Welfare; fel, Coun Clin Cardiol & Coun Atherosclerosis, Am Heart Asn; attend physician, NBeth Israel Hosp; pres, NY Co Med Soc, 82-83. *Mem:* AMA; Am Heart Asn; Am Col Physicians; fel Am Col Cardiol; NY Acad Med. *Res:* Cardiovascular disease; internal medicine; atherosclerosis; hemodynamics; heart disease and industry; role of vascular dynamics in the development of atherosclerosis; forensic med - can the cardiac stand trial!. *Mailing Add:* 365 West End Ave New York NY 10024. *Fax:* 212-737-5135

**TEXTER, E CLINTON, JR,** medical education, gastroenterology; deceased, see previous edition for last biography

**TEXTER, JOHN,** PHYSICAL & COLLOID CHEMISTRY, BIOPHYSICS. *Current Pos:* res chemist, Emulsion Phys Chem Lab, Eastman Kodak Co, 78-80, sr res scientist, Dispersion Tech Lab, 80-90, sr res scientist, Color Paper Mat Lab, 90-92, RES ASSOC, ANALYTICAL TECHNOL DIV, EASTMAN KODAK CO, 93- *Personal Data:* b Lancaster, Pa, Aug 9, 49; m 84, Melanie Martin; c Kurt & Grace. *Educ:* Lehigh Univ, BSEE, 71, MS, 73, MS, 76, PhD(chem), 76. *Prof Exp:* Instr chem, Lafeyette Col, 73-74; assoc physiologist, Biophys Spectros Lab, Univ Calif, Irvine, 76-77; res assoc, Chem Dept, State Univ NY, Binghamton, 77-78. *Concurrent Pos:* Consult, Strider Res Corp, 87-; dir, Montessori Sch Rochester, 94-96; vchair, Div Colloid & Surface Chem, Am Chem Soc, 96, chair-elect, 97; chair, Chem Interfaces Gordon Conf, 96. *Mem:* Am Phys Soc; Sigma Xi; Inst Elec & Electronics Engrs; Am Chem Soc; Int Asn Colloid Interface Scientists; Am Inst Chem Engrs; Soc Photo Sci Engrs. *Res:* Heterogeneous chemistry of image dye formation in photographic coupler dispersions; reaction-diffusion kinetics in colloidal systems; oil/water interfacial structure and trans-interfacial transport; microemulsion polymerization; stabilization of pigment dispersions; electrochemistry; colloid chemistry. *Mailing Add:* Res Lab Eastman Kodak Co Rochester NY 14650-2109. *Fax:* 716-722-5411; *E-Mail:* texter@kodak.com

**TEXTOR, ROBIN EDWARD,** MATHEMATICS. *Current Pos:* COMPUT APPLN ANALYST, OAK RIDGE NAT LAB, UNION CARBIDE CORP, 72-, SECT HEAD, 73- *Personal Data:* b Detroit, Mich, Mar 19, 43; m 65; c 2. *Educ:* Tenn Polytech Inst, BS, 64; Univ Tenn, Knoxville, MS, 68; Drexel Univ, PhD(math), 72. *Prof Exp:* Comput appln programmer, Comput Technol Ctr, Union Carbide Corp, Tenn, 64-69; asst prof math, Univ SC, 71-72. *Mem:* Math Asn Am; Am Math Soc; Soc Indust & Appl Math. *Res:* Singular hyperbolic partial differential equations; numerical solution of fluid flow problems and partial differential equations. *Mailing Add:* 119 Montana Ave Oak Ridge TN 37830

**TEXTORIS, DANIEL ANDREW,** GEOLOGY. *Current Pos:* from asst prof to assoc prof, Univ NC, Chapel Hill, 65-73, asst dean res admin, 68-74, assoc dean res admin, 74-83, PROF GEOL, UNIV NC, CHAPEL HILL, 73- *Personal Data:* b Cleveland, Ohio, Jan 19, 36; m 59; c 3. *Educ:* Case Western Res Univ, BA, 58; Ohio State Univ, MS, 60; Univ Ill, PhD(geol), 63. *Prof Exp:* Asst prof geol, Univ Ill, 63-65. *Concurrent Pos:* Geologist, Diamond Alkali Co, 57-60; consult, Southern Ill-Pa Coal, 61-65; coord NSF sci develop prog, 67-74, Carbonate dredging, 68-70 & Chevron, Texaco & Exxon, 82-; sr assoc, Dept Energy, 78-, consult, 79-81. *Mem:* AAAS; Geol Soc Am; Soc Econ Paleont & Mineral; Am Asn Petrol Geol. *Res:* Sedimentary geology; carbonate petrography; diagenesis of sediments; petrology and geochemistry of volcanic tuff; interpretation of ancient carbonate environments; paleoecology; geology of fossil fuels. *Mailing Add:* 1609 Jones Ferry Rd Chapel Hill NC 27516

**TEYKER, ROBERT HENRY,** genetic variation, genotype by environment interactions in root development, for more information see previous edition

**TEYLER, TIMOTHY JAMES,** NEUROSCIENCES. *Current Pos:* assoc prof, 77-81, PROF NEUROBIOL, COL MED, NORTHEASTERN OHIO UNIV, 81- *Personal Data:* b Portland, Ore, Nov 25, 42; m 66; c 1. *Educ:* Ore State Univ, BS, 64; Univ Ore, MS, 68, PhD(psychol), 69. *Prof Exp:* Asst prof psychol, Univ Southern Calif, 68-69; lectr psychobiol, Univ Calif, Irvine, 69-72, assoc res psychobiologist, 73-74; lectr psychol, Harvard Univ, 74-75, assoc prof, 75-77. *Concurrent Pos:* NIMH fel, Univ Calif, Irvine, 70-72; NSF sr fel & Fulbright scholar, Inst Neurophysiol, Univ Oslo, 73-74. *Mem:* Soc Neurosci; Psychonomic Soc. *Res:* Neurobiological correlates of behavioral plasticity; neurolinguistics; magnetoencephalography; neuroendocrinology. *Mailing Add:* Neurobiol Northwestern Ohio Univ Col Med 4209 State Rte 44 Box 95 Rootstown OH 44272-9698

**TEZAK, EDWARD G,** ASTRODYNAMICS, NON-LINEAR VIBRATIONS. *Personal Data:* b Steelton, Pa, Oct 16, 40. *Educ:* US Mil Acad, BS, 63; Univ Calif, Los Angeles, MS, 67, Va Poly Tech Inst & State Univ, 79. *Prof Exp:* Instr statist & dyn, Dept Mech, US Mil Acad, 69-79, asst prof space mech, 70-72, assoc prof statist, dyn & strength vibrations, 76-88, exec officer & dir, Admin Mgt Div, Off Dean, 79-81, assoc dean, 89-93; dean, Sch Info Systs & Eng Technol, State Univ NY, Utica/Rome, 93-97. *Concurrent Pos:* Chair, Prof Interest Coun III & bd dirs, Am Soc Eng Educ, 93-95. *Mem:* Am Soc Eng Educ; Am Soc Mech Engrs; Soc Am Mil Engrs. *Res:* Non-linear vibrations. *Mailing Add:* 6 Crown Lane Whitesboro NY 13492

**THACH, ROBERT EDWARDS,** PROTEIN BIOSYNTHESIS, VIROLOGY. *Current Pos:* assoc prof biol chem, Washington Univ, 70-72, dir, Ctr Basic Cancer Res, 72-77, dir, Grad Prog Molecular Biol, 74-77, chmn, Dept Biol, 77-81, PROF BIOL CHEM, WASHINGTON UNIV, 72-, PROF BIOL, 77-, DEAN, GRAD SCH ARTS & SCI, 93- *Personal Data:* b Oklahoma City, Okla, Feb 2, 39; m 68; c 3. *Educ:* Princeton Univ, BA, 61; Harvard Univ, PhD(biochem), 64. *Prof Exp:* Res fel biochem & molecular biol, Harvard Univ, 64-66, from asst prof to assoc prof, 66-70. *Concurrent Pos:* Fel, Guggenheim Mem Found, 69-; mem, res grant rev comt, United Cancer Coun, Inc, 77-79; inst biosafety Comt, Monsanto Co, 80-83; biochem rev panel, NSF, 80-81. *Mem:* Am Soc Biol Chem; Am Soc Virol; NY Acad Sci; AAAS; Sigma Xi. *Res:* Mech and regulation of protein biosynthesis; viral replication and effects on host cells. *Mailing Add:* Dept Biol Wash Univ 1 Brookings Dr St Louis MO 63130-4899

**THACH, WILLIAM THOMAS,** NEUROPHYSIOLOGY, NEUROLOGY. *Current Pos:* assoc prof, 75-80, PROF NEUROBIOL & NEUROL, SCH MED, WASH UNIV, 80-, DIR, IWJ REHAB INST, 91- *Personal Data:* b Oklahoma City, Okla, Jan 3, 37; div; c 3. *Educ:* Princeton Univ, AB, 59; Harvard Med Sch, MD, 64. *Prof Exp:* Intern & resident med & neurol, Mass Gen Hosp, 64-66, 69-71; staff assoc neurophysiol, NIMH, 66-69; from asst prof to assoc prof physiol & neurol, Med Sch, Yale Univ, 71-75. *Concurrent Pos:* Prin investr, Nat Inst Neurol Dis & Stroke res grant, 71-; neurologist,

Barnes Hosp, Jewish Hosp & St Louis Regional Hosp, 75- *Mem:* Soc Neurosci; Am Physiol Soc; Am Acad Neurol; Am Neurol Asn; Am Asn Neurol Rehab. *Res:* Physiology of behavior; cerebellar control of posture and movement; mechanisms of neurorehabilitation. *Mailing Add:* Dept Anat & Neurobiol Wash Univ Sch Med 660 Euclid Ave St Louis MO 63110

**THACHER, HENRY CLARKE, JR,** COMPUTER SCIENCE, NUMERICAL ANALYSIS. *Current Pos:* prof, 71-84, EMER PROF COMPUT SCI, UNIV KY, 84- *Personal Data:* b New York, NY, Aug 8, 18; m 42; c 5. *Educ:* Yale Univ, AB, 40; Harvard Univ, MA, 42; Yale Univ, PhD(phys chem), 49. *Prof Exp:* Instr chem, Yale Univ, 46-48; asst prof, Ind Univ, 49-54; task scientist, Aeronaut Res Lab, Wright Air Develop Ctr, USAF, Ohio, 54-58; assoc chemist, Argonne Nat Lab, 58-66; prof comput sci, Univ Notre Dame, 66-71. *Concurrent Pos:* Consult, Argonne Nat Lab, 66-77. *Mem:* AAAS; NY Acad Sci. *Res:* Numerical approximation and computer programming; computation and approximation of special functions. *Mailing Add:* 4342 Randolph St San Diego CA 92103-1348

**THACHER, PHILIP DURYEA,** METROLOGY. *Current Pos:* STAFF MEM, SANDIA NAT LABS, 65- *Personal Data:* b Palo Alto, Calif, Jan 13, 37; m 63, Aija; c Nara & Jeffrey. *Educ:* Calif Inst Technol, BS, 58; Cornell Univ, PhD(physics), 65. *Mem:* AAAS; Am Phys Soc. *Res:* Optical effects in ferroelectric ceramics and crystals; laser energy; radiometry; 14 MeV neutron detection. *Mailing Add:* 524 Camino Del Bosque NW Albuquerque NM 87114

**THACKER, CHARLES P,** DIGITAL EQUIPMENT, COMPUTERS. *Current Pos:* RETIRED. *Educ:* Univ Calif, BA, 67. *Prof Exp:* Engr, Univ Calif Berkeley, 67-68; proj leader, Berkeley Comput Corp, 69-71; mem res staff, Xerox Palo Alto Res Ctr, 71-75, mgr processor archit, Syst Develop Div, 75-77, mgr digital processor develop, Electronics Div, 77-79, prin engr, 79-80, res fel, 80-82, sr res fel, 82-83; sr consult engr, Syst Res Ctr, Digital Equip Corp, 83-89, corp consult engr, 89-97. *Mem:* Nat Acad Eng; Inst Elec & Electronics Engrs; Asn Comput Mach. *Res:* Digital computer development. *Mailing Add:* Digital Equip Corp 130 Lytton Ave Palo Alto CA 94301

**THACKER, HARRY B,** high energy physics, particle physics, for more information see previous edition

**THACKER, JOHN CHARLES,** STATISTICAL ANALYSIS. *Personal Data:* b Clinton, Okla, Oct 29, 43; m 68; c 2. *Educ:* Cornell Univ, BS, 66; Brown Univ, PhD(appl math), 74. *Prof Exp:* Mem tech staff statist, Aerospace Corp, 74-91, prin dir systs analysis sub syst, Eng Div Eng Group, 91-93. *Mem:* Am Math Soc; Inst Math Statist; Am Statist Asn; Soc Indust & Appl Math. *Res:* Statistical inference on stochastic processes; time series analysis; stochastic point processes; application of statistical techniques to air and water pollution problems. *Mailing Add:* 411 San Domingo Way Los Altos CA 94022

**THACKER, RAYMOND,** ELECTROCHEMISTRY, PHYSICAL CHEMISTRY. *Current Pos:* RETIRED. *Personal Data:* b Ashton-U-Lyne, UK, May 9, 32. *Educ:* Univ Manchester, BSc, 52, MSc, 53, PhD(phys chem), 55. *Prof Exp:* Sci officer, UK Atomic Energy Authority Indust Group, 55-58; res assoc electrode kinetics, Univ Pa, 58-60; staff res scientist, Res Labs, Gen Motors Corp, 60-90. *Mem:* Electrochem Soc; Royal Soc Chem. *Res:* Thermodynamic properties of nonelectrolyte solutions; electrochemistry of surfaces; fuel cell electrode processes; batteries. *Mailing Add:* PO Box 250075 Franklin MI 48025

**THACKER, STEPHEN BRADY,** TECHNOLOGY ASSESSMENT, PUBLIC HEALTH SURVEILLANCE. *Current Pos:* Chief, consolidated surveillance & commun activ, Epidemiol Prog Off, Ctr Dis Control, 78-83, dir, Div Surveillance & Epidemiol Studies, 83-86, asst dir sci, Ctr Environ Health & Injury Control, 86-89, DIR, EPIDEMIOL PROG OFF, CTR DIS CONTROL, 89-, ACTG DIR, NAT CTR ENVIRON HEALTH, 93- *Personal Data:* b Independence, Mo, Dec 30, 47; m 76; c 2. *Educ:* Princeton Univ, NJ, AB, 69; Mt Sinai Sch Med, NY, MD, 73; London Sch Hyg & Trop Med, MSc, 84. *Honors & Awards:* Mosby Bood Award for Excellence, 73; Saul Horowitz Jr Mem Award, 90; Supvry Award for Contrib to the Advan of Women, 91. *Concurrent Pos:* Mem steering comt, Asn Behav Sci Med Educ, 71-74; Robert Wood Johnson Found Clin scholar, 74-75; assoc, Dept Community Med, Med Ctr, Duke Univ, Durham, NC, 75-76; lectr, Dept Community Med, Mt Sinai Sch Med, NY, 78- & Sch Med, Emory Univ, Atlanta, Ga, 85-86; consult epidemiol, Arab Rep Egypt, 79-91; clin asst prof community health, Sch Med, Emory Univ, 86- *Mem:* Am Epidemiol Soc; Am Pub Health Asn. *Res:* Published broad range of fields in epidemiology including public health surveillance; infectious disease; environmental health; alcohol abuse; health care delivery; meta-analysis; technology assessment. *Mailing Add:* Ctr Dis Control & Prev CO8 1600 Clifton Rd Atlanta GA 30333

**THACKRAY, ARNOLD,** HISTORY OF SCIENCE, TECHNOLOGY & BUSINESS. *Current Pos:* JOSEPH PRIESTLEY EMER PROF, UNIV PA; PRES, CHEM HERITAGE FOUND. *Personal Data:* b Eng, July 30, 39; c Helen, Gillian & Timothy. *Educ:* Bristol Univ, Eng, BSc, 60; Cambridge Univ, Eng, MA, 65, PhD(hist sci), 66. *Honors & Awards:* Dexter Award, Am Chem Soc, 83; George Sarton Mem lectr, AAAS, 84. *Prof Exp:* Res fel, Churchill Col, Cambridge Univ, 65-68. *Concurrent Pos:* Vis lectr, Harvard Univ, 67-68, nat lectr, Sigma Xi, 76; ed, Isis, 78-85 & Osiris, 85-94; mem bd dir & treas, Am Coun Learned Soc, 85-96; mem bd dir, Am Coun Educ, 85-86. *Mem:* Fel AAAS; fel Royal Hist Soc; fel Royal Soc Chem; Soc Social Studies Sci (pres,

82-84); Hist Sci Soc; fel Am Acad Arts & Sci. *Res:* History of chemical science and chemical technology; historography; research administration; science policy. *Mailing Add:* Chem Heritage Found 315 Chestnut St Philadelphia PA 19106

**THACKSTON, EDWARD LEE,** ENVIRONMENTAL ENGINEERING, WATER RESOURCES ENGINEERING. *Current Pos:* from asst prof to assoc prof sanit & water resources eng, 66-76, prof environ & water resources eng, 76-80, PROF CIVIL & ENVIRON ENG & CHMN DEPT, VANDERBILT UNIV, 80- *Personal Data:* b Nashville, Tenn, Apr 29, 37; m 61, Betty Tucker; c Carol (Nixon) & Leah (Hawkins). *Educ:* Vanderbilt Univ, BE, 61, PhD(environ & water resources eng), 66; Univ Ill, Urbana, MS, 63. *Honors & Awards:* Z Cartter Patten Award, 83. *Prof Exp:* City engr, Lebanon, Tenn, 58-59; design engr, City of Nashville, 61-62. *Concurrent Pos:* Consult engr, Vanderbilt Univ, 66-; on leave as staff asst environ affairs, Gov State of Tenn, 72-73; mem, bd trust, Cumberland Univ, Lebanon, Tenn. *Mem:* Am Soc Civil Engrs; Am Water Works Asn; Water Pollution Control Fedn; Asn Environ Eng Prof. *Res:* Mixing and reaeration in streams; effects of impoundments on water quality; environmental policy; dredged material disposal. *Mailing Add:* 2010 Priest Rd Nashville TN 37215. *Fax:* 615-322-3365; *E-Mail:* elt@vuse.vanderbilt.edu

**THACORE, HARSHAD RAI,** VIROLOGY. *Current Pos:* asst prof, 74-79, ASSOC PROF MICROBIOL, STATE UNIV NY BUFFALO, 79- *Personal Data:* b Ahmedabad, India, Dec 1, 39; US citizen; m 65; c 1. *Educ:* Univ Lucknow, BSc, 58, MSc, 60; Duke Univ, PhD(microbiol), 65. *Prof Exp:* Fel virol, Ohio State Univ, 65-67; res assoc, Univ Pittsburgh, 67-69, instr, 69-71, asst res prof, 71-74. *Mem:* Am Soc Microbiol; Am Soc Virol; Int Soc Interferon Res. *Res:* Interferon, especially mechanism and induction of; rescue of interferon sensitive virus by poxviruses; persistent viral infections, especially initiation and maintenance of. *Mailing Add:* Dept Microbiol Sch Med & Biomed Sci State Univ NY Buffalo NY 14214-3078. *Fax:* 716-829-2158; *E-Mail:* hthacore@ubmedf.buffalo.edu

**THADDEUS, PATRICK,** PHYSICS, ASTROPHYSICS. *Current Pos:* PROF ASTRON & APPL PHYSICS, HARVARD UNIV, 86- *Personal Data:* b June 6, 32; US citizen; m 63, Janice Farrar; c Eva & Michael. *Educ:* Univ Del, BSc, 53; Oxford Univ, MA, 55; Columbia Univ, PhD(physics), 60. *Honors & Awards:* Alexander von Humboldt Award, WGer, 73; Lindsey Mem Award, 76; Medal Except Sci Achievement, NASA, 70 & 85. *Prof Exp:* Res physicist, Radiation Lab, Columbia Univ, 60-61; Nat Acad Sci fel astrophys, 61-64, res physicist, Goddard Inst, Space Studies, 64-86. *Concurrent Pos:* Fulbright fel, 53-55; adj asst prof, Columbia Univ, 64-66, adj prof, 71-; adj assoc prof, NY Univ, 63-; vis assoc prof, State Univ NY, Stony Brook, 66-; mem, Space Sci Adv Comt, NASA, 79 & Astron Surv Comt, 78-80 & 88-90; sr vis fel, Univ Cambridge, 83. *Mem:* Nat Acad Sci; Am Phys Soc; Am Astron Soc; Sigma Xi; Int Astron Union; Am Acad Arts & Sci. *Res:* Radio astronomy; interstellar molecules; microwave spectroscopy. *Mailing Add:* 58 Garfield St Cambridge MA 02138

**THAELER, CHARLES SCHROPP, JR,** ZOOLOGY. *Current Pos:* RETIRED. *Personal Data:* b Philadelphia, Pa, Jan 9, 32; m 57; c 3. *Educ:* Earlham Col, AB, 54; Univ Calif, Berkeley, MA, 60, PhD(zool), 64. *Prof Exp:* Actg instr zool, Univ Calif, Berkeley, 63-64, actg asst cur, Mus Vert Zool, 63-64; asst prof, South Bend Campus, Ind Univ, 64-66; from asst prof to prof biol, NMex State Univ, 66-93. *Concurrent Pos:* NSF res grants, 68-70 & 72-74. *Mem:* Fel AAAS; Am Soc Mammal; Soc Study Evolution; Ecol Soc Am; Soc Syst Zool; Sigma Xi. *Res:* Mammalian systematics and cytogenetics; evolution and ecology, especially taxonomy; evolution, cytogenetics and distribution of geomyids; taxonomy of microtine rodents. *Mailing Add:* PO Box 6114 Roswell NM 88202-6114

**THAGARD, NORMAN E,** ELECTRICAL ENGINEERING. *Current Pos:* FAC, COL ENG, FLA A&M UNIV-FLA STATE UNIV, 96- *Personal Data:* b Marianna, Fla, July 3, 43; m, Rex Kirby Johnson; c Norman G, James R & Daniel C. *Educ:* Fla State Univ, BS, 65, MS, 66; Univ Tex SW Med Sch, MD, 77. *Hon Degrees:* DHL, Fla Atlantic Univ, 96. *Honors & Awards:* Melbourne W Bointon Award, Am Astronaut Soc; Hubertus Strughold Award, Aerospace Med Asn; Jeffries Award, Am Inst Aeronaut & Astronaut. *Prof Exp:* Intern internal med, Med Univ SC, 77-78; astronaut, NASA, 78-96, mission specialist, Space Shuttle Challenger Flight STS-7, NASA, 83, Spacelab-3 Mission STS-51B, 85, Space Shuttle Atlantis Flight STS-30, 89, payload comdr, Space Shuttle Discovery Flight STS-42 Int Microgravity Lab-1 Module Exp, 92, crew mem, Space Station MIR-18, 95. *Mem:* Am Inst Aeronaut & Astronaut; Aerospace Med Asn; Soc Human Performance Extreme Environ. *Res:* Contributed various articles to professional journals. *Mailing Add:* Col Eng Fla A&M Univ-Fla State Univ 2525 Pottsdamer St Tallahassee FL 32310-6046. *Fax:* 850-487-6486; *E-Mail:* nthagard@eng.fsu.eng

**THAKAR, JAY H,** NEUROPHARMACOLOGY. *Current Pos:* SR STAFF FEL, NIH, BETHESDA, MD, 96- *Personal Data:* b Bombay, India, Dec 4, 40; Can citizen; m 73; c 2. *Educ:* Univ Bombay, BSc Hons, 62, MSc, 64; Univ Man, PhD(biochem), 73. *Prof Exp:* Sci officer, Bhabha Atomic Res Ctr, Bombay, India, 64-68; fel animal sci, Univ Calif, Davis, 74-76; prof asst biochem, Univ Western Ont, 76-78; clin chemist, Civic Hosp, Ottawa, 78-80; chief, Neuropharmacol Lab, Royal Ottawa Hosp, 80-84; chief, Neuropharmacol Lab, Ottawa Civic Hosp, 85; assoc investr, St Jude's Children's Hosp, 85-96. *Res:* Neuropsychopharmacology of psychiatric disorders; normal and abnormal functions of muscle organelle; animal models of muscular dystrophy; Parkinson's Disease and movement disorders. *Mailing Add:* 5558 Massey Station Rd Memphis TN 38134

**THAKKAR, AJIT JAMNADAS,** INTERMOLECULAR FORCES, SCATTERING THEORY. *Current Pos:* assoc prof, 84-88, PROF CHEM, UNIV NB, 88-, CHMN, 93- *Personal Data:* b Poona, India, Oct 23, 50; Can citizen; m 81, Baukje Miedema; c Aroon & Niels. *Educ:* Queen's Univ, Can, BSc, 73, PhD(chem), 76. *Honors & Awards:* Noranda lectr, Can Soc Chem, 91. *Prof Exp:* Fel chem, Univ Waterloo, 76-78; res assoc, Queen's Univ, Can, 78-79, asst prof, 79-80; asst prof, Univ Waterloo, 80-84. *Concurrent Pos:* Hon adj prof, Dalhouse Univ, 89- *Mem:* Fel Chem Inst Can; Can Soc Chem; Can Asn Theoret Chemists (treas, 94-95, pres, 96); Am Asn Physics Teachers. *Res:* Theoretical studies of polarizabilities; dispersion coefficients; intermolecular forces; electronic momentum densities; x-ray and high energy electron scattering; generalized oscillator strengths; electron pair densities; correlation holes, density matrices and density functionals. *Mailing Add:* Dept Chem Univ NB Fredericton NB E3B 6E2 Can. *Fax:* 506-453-4981; *E-Mail:* ajit@unb.ca

**THAKKAR, ARVIND LAVJI,** PHYSICAL PHARMACY. *Current Pos:* sr pharmaceut chemist, 67-75, RES SCIENTIST, RES LABS, ELI LILLY & CO, 75- *Personal Data:* b Karachi, Pakistan, Apr 19, 39; c 3. *Educ:* Univ Bombay, BPharm, 61; Columbia Univ, MS, 64; Univ Wash, PhD(phys pharm), 67. *Prof Exp:* Tcaching asst col pharm, Columbia Univ, 61-63; col pharm, Univ Wash, 64-66. *Mem:* Am Pharmaceut Asn; Acad Pharmaceut Sci; NY Acad Sci. *Res:* Surface activity of drugs; micellar solubilization; drug absorption; controlled release of drugs; solubility. *Mailing Add:* Lilly Res Labs Dept MC 741 307 E McCarty St Indianapolis IN 46285

**THAKKAR, RAJ B,** FATIGUE OF METALS & STRUCTURES, VIBRATION ANALYSIS. *Current Pos:* PROJ MGR, TOWER AUTOMOTIVE, 96- *Personal Data:* m 68, Heena Kakad; c Reena & Rupin. *Educ:* MS Univ Baroda, India, BS, 60; Univ Wis, MS, 62; Iowa State Univ, PhD(eng mech), 72. *Prof Exp:* Assoc reliability engr, Allis Chalmers Mfg Co, 62-64; sr advan engr, A O Smith Automotive, 65-68, sr advan engr, 73-79, supvr prod eng, 79-96, proj mgr advan prods, 96-97. *Concurrent Pos:* Adj lectr mech eng, Univ Wis-Milwaukee, 89-94. *Mem:* Soc Exp Mech; Soc Automotive Engrs. *Res:* Derived mathematical relationship to predict fatigue life of steel structures from strain measurements made on polyvinyl chloride scale model; effect of stress concentration due to geometry, welding, manufacturing process; correlating modes of vibration measured on polyvinyl chloride to those of steel prototype; correlating fatigue life predictions. *Mailing Add:* 3533 N 27th St Milwaukee WI 53216

**THAKKER, DHIREN R,** DRUG METABOLISM, CHEMICAL CARCINOGENESIS. *Current Pos:* SR INVESTR, NIH, 83- *Personal Data:* b Broach, India, Jan 25, 49. *Educ:* Univ Kans, PhD(biochem), 76. *Mem:* Am Chem Soc; Am Asn Cancer Res; Am Soc Pharmaceut & Exp Therapeut. *Mailing Add:* Univ NC Sch Pharm Beard Hall CB7360 Chapel Hill NC 27599-7360. *Fax:* 919-990-5652

**THAKOR, NITISH VYOMESH,** BIOMEDICAL COMPUTING, MEDICAL INSTRUMENTATION. *Current Pos:* ASSOC PROF BIOMED ENG, JOHNS HOPKINS SCH MED, 84- *Personal Data:* b Bombay, India, Feb 19, 52; m, Ruchira; c Mitali & Milan. *Educ:* Indian Inst Technol, BTech, 74; Univ Wis-Madison, MS, 78, PhD(elec eng), 81. *Honors & Awards:* Presidential Young Investr Award, NSF; Res Career Develop Award, NIH. *Prof Exp:* Electronics engr instrument design & mkt, Philips India, Ltd, 74-76; res asst biomed eng, Univ Wis-Madison, 77-81; asst prof elec & comput eng, Northwestern Univ, 81-83. *Concurrent Pos:* Assoc ed, Inst Elec & Electronics Engrs Trans Biomed Eng, J Ambulatory Monitoring & J Biol Syst. *Mem:* Inst Elec & Electronics Engrs Comput Soc; Inst Elec & Electronics Engrs Biomed Soc; Sigma Xi; Biomed Eng Soc. *Res:* Medical instrumentation and computer applications in medical care, including microprocessors, very large scale integration, and supercomputers modeling and signal/information processing in the heart and the brain; advanced instrumentations for cardiac and neurological monitoring and therapy; biomedical signal processing. *Mailing Add:* 12010 Misty Rise Ct Clarksville MD 21029. *Fax:* 410-955-0549; *E-Mail:* nthakor@eureka.wbme.jhu.edu

**THAKORE, YATIN B,** INTERNET WEB SITE DESIGN, TECHNOLOGY TRANSFER FOR CHEMISTRY & BIOMEDICAL RELATED FIELDS. *Current Pos:* PRES & CHIEF EXEC OFFICER, SOURCE INDIA INC, 96- *Personal Data:* b Bombay, India, Aug 11, 51; US citizen. *Educ:* Indian Inst Technol, Bombay, India, BTech, 74; Univ Utah, ME, 81, PhD(mat sci), 81. *Prof Exp:* Mem tech staff, Bendix Advan Tech Ctr, 81-83; vpres res & develop, Kingston Technologies Inc, 83-93. *Concurrent Pos:* Sr assoc, Kyle Assocs Inc, 94- *Res:* Creating and promoting websites for technology companies; bringing trade publications from India online; technology transfer. *Mailing Add:* 11 Rues Lane East Brunswick NJ 08816

**THAKUR, MADHUKAR L,** RADIOPHARMACEUTICALS. *Current Pos:* PROF & DIR RADIOPHARMACEUT RES, DIV NUCLEAR MED, DEPT RADIATION THER & NUCLEAR MED, 82-, PROF DIAG RADIOL, THOMAS JEFFERSON UNIV HOSP, 91- *Personal Data:* m, Lalita; c Netra & Neil. *Educ:* Bombay Univ, BS, 61; Univ London, MS, 69, PhD(radiochem), 73. *Honors & Awards:* Maurice R Chamberland Award, Am Cancer Soc, 80; Paul Aebersold Award, Soc Nuclear Med, 92. *Prof Exp:* Sci asst, Isotope Div, Bhabha Atomic Res Ctr, 61-67; sci staff, Med Res Coun, Cyclotron Unit, Hammersmith Hosp, Eng, 67-77; res assoc, Chem Dept, Brookhaven Nat Lab, Washington Univ Sch Med, 77-83. *Concurrent Pos:* Vis prof, Mallinckrodt Inst Radiol, Washington Univ Sch Med, 75-76; assoc prof diag radiol, Yale Univ Sch Med, 77-82; numerous consults at univs & private insts in US & abroad; numerous vis professorships in US & abroad. *Mem:* Soc Nuclear Med; Am Heart Asn; Am Chem Soc; Radiation Res Soc; AAAS;

Sigma Xi; NY Acad Sci; Indo-Am Soc Nuclear Med; Am Inst Chemists; Am Col Nuclear Physicians. *Res:* Production and isolation of many medically useful reactor produced radionuclides; production and isolation of many medically useful cyclotron produced radionuclides; development of analytical and radiochemical techniques; development and evaluation of a variety of radioactive labeled compounds of medical potential; development of agents for diagnosis of infectious diseases and thronbolitic disorders. *Mailing Add:* Thomas Jefferson Univ 359 JAH Philadelphia PA 19107. *E-Mail:* thakurl@ jeflin.tju.edu

**THAKUR, PRAMOD CHANDRA,** PRODUCTION OF COALBED METHANE & CONTROL, RESPIRABLE DUST-HEALTH ASPECTS & ENGINEERING CONTROL. *Current Pos:* RES ASSOC, CONSOL INC, 90- *Personal Data:* b Bhagalpur, Bihar, India, Jan 4, 39; US citizen; m 58, Meera Pathak; c Gautam C & Anand C. *Educ:* Indian Sch Mines, AISM & BSC, 61; Pa State Univ, MS, 71, MA, 74, PhD(mining eng), 74. *Prof Exp:* Engr & asst mine mgr, Andrew Yule & Co, 61-64, sr engr, 64-69; res asst, Pa State Univ, 69-74; res engr, Conoco Inc, 74-76, res supvr, 76-77, res group leader, 77-90. *Concurrent Pos:* Chmn, NAm Coalbed Methane Forum, 85- *Mem:* Soc Petrol Engrs. *Res:* Mine ventilation design; coalbed methane production and control; health impact and control of respirable particulates in mines; detection, prevention and control of mine fires; hydraulic stowing of sand/waste in mines for ground support. *Mailing Add:* Rte 1 Box 119 Morgantown WV 26505-9799

**THALACKER, VICTOR PAUL,** POLYMER SCIENCE & ENGINEERING, TECHNICAL MANAGEMENT. *Current Pos:* Sr chemist org chem, 3M, 67-77, res supvr, 77-80, tech mgr, 80-84, LAB MGR, 3M, 84- *Personal Data:* b Muscatine, Iowa, Apr 21, 41; m 70, Connie Meininger; c Paul & Jason. *Educ:* Wis State Univ-Stevens Point, BS, 63; Univ Ariz, PhD(org chem), 68. *Concurrent Pos:* Mem, Polymer Div, Am Chem Soc & Rad Tech Intl. *Mem:* Am Chem Soc; Soc Plastics Engrs. *Res:* Radiation curing; radiation curable coatings and adhesives; lasers, microstructures; reactive processes; polymer processing; extrusion; plant culture; abrasives; polymer morphology; solventless processing, adhesives. *Mailing Add:* 3M Co Bldg 208-1 3M Ctr St Paul MN 55144. *Fax:* 612-733-3304; *E-Mail:* vpthalacker@mmm.com

**THALE, THOMAS RICHARD,** PSYCHIATRY. *Current Pos:* from instr to assoc prof, St Louis Univ, 50-90, prof, Med Sch & assoc prof social work, Sch Social Serv, 70-90, clin prof, 80-95, EMER PROF PSYCHIAT, ST LOUIS UNIV, 95- *Personal Data:* b Indianapolis, Ind, June 4, 15; m 41; c 5. *Educ:* Loyola Univ Chicago, BSM, 38, MD, 39. *Prof Exp:* Resident psychiat, Manteno State Hosp, Ill, 39 & Norwich State Hosp, Conn, 39-43; instr psychol, Univ Conn, 42-45; instr psychiat & pub health, Yale Univ, 43-45; instr psychiat, Wash Univ, 45-50. *Concurrent Pos:* Med adv, Bur Hearings & Appeals, Social Security Admin, 67-; consult, Family & Childrens Soc Greater St Louis & Vet Admin Asn Retarded Children. *Mem:* AMA, fel Am Psychiat Asn; Am Group Psychother Asn. *Res:* Psychological evaluation chemotherapy. *Mailing Add:* 351 Meadowbrook Dr Ballwin MO 63011-2414

**THALER, ALVIN ISAAC,** COMPUTATIONAL MATHEMATICS, ALGEBRA. *Current Pos:* prog dir algebra & number theory, NSF, 71-81, prog dir spec projs math sci, 81-86, prog mgr expres, 86-89, prog dir computational math, 89-93, PROG DIR STRATEGIC ACTIV & SPEC PROJS, NSF, 93- *Personal Data:* b New York, NY, Aug 26, 38; m, Gail Mello; c Adam & Jonathan. *Educ:* Columbia Univ, AB, 59; Johns Hopkins Univ, PhD(math), 66. *Prof Exp:* Assoc math appl physics lab, Johns Hopkins Univ, 62-64; instr, Col Notre Dame, Md, 64-66; asst prof, Univ Md, 66-71. *Mem:* Am Math Soc; Math Asn Am. *Res:* Algebraic number theory; algebraic geometry. *Mailing Add:* NSF Div Math Sci 4201 Wilson Blvd Arlington VA 22230. *E-Mail:* thaler@nsf.gov

**THALER, BARRY JAY,** ADVANCED ELECTRONIC PACKAGING DEVELOPMENT, CERAMICS DEVELOPMENT. *Current Pos:* MEM TECH STAFF, RCA LAB, 79- *Personal Data:* b Brooklyn, NY, June 10, 50; m 82; c 2. *Educ:* State Univ NY, Stony Brook, BS, 72; Mich State Univ, MS, 74, PhD(physics), 77. *Prof Exp:* Fel, Northwestern Univ, 77-79. *Concurrent Pos:* Vis scientist, Argonne Nat Lab, 78-79. *Mem:* Am Phys Soc; Inst Elec & Electronics Engrs. *Res:* Insulating properties of organic and inorganic; electronic packaging applications. *Mailing Add:* SRI Int David Sarnoff Res Ctr CN 5300 Princeton NJ 08543. *Fax:* 609-734-2221

**THALER, DAVID SOLOMON,** MOLECULAR MECHANISMS OF MUTATION & RECOMBINATION, ANTIBIOTIC RESISTANCE. *Current Pos:* ASST PROF, LAB MOLECULAR GENETICS & INFORMATICS, ROCKEFELLER UNIV, 91- *Personal Data:* b Parishville, NY, Sept 14, 53. *Educ:* State Univ NY, BA, 72; Univ Mass, MS, 79; Univ Ore, PhD(molecular biol), 86. *Prof Exp:* Anna Fuller & Helen Hay Whitney res assoc, Univ Utah, 88-91. *Concurrent Pos:* Lectr, Dept Biol, Univ Mass, 77-79, genetics, Univ Ore, 85; vis scientist, McMaster Univ, 80, Univ Paris, 88. *Res:* Study the ways by which living cells change in a hereditary manner, in particular mechanisms by which DNA repair, mutation and recombination can be focused in time (meiosis/sos) and space (differential repair in the genome). *Mailing Add:* Lab Molecular Genetics & Informatics Rockefeller Univ 1230 York Ave Box 400 New York NY 10021

**THALER, ERIC RONALD,** SYNOPTIC METEOROLOGY. *Current Pos:* Meteorologist & forecaster, 82-90, SCI & OPERS OFFICER, NAT WEATHER SERV, 90- *Personal Data:* b Denver, Colo, May 19, 60; m 83; c 2. *Educ:* Univ Utah, BS, 82; Colo Sch Mines, MS, 89. *Concurrent Pos:* Mem, Atmospheric Technol Comt, Nat Weather Asn, 90- *Mem:* Am Meteorol Soc; Nat Weather Asn. *Res:* Finding ways to use new observational and theoretical advances to improve weather forecasts; numerical modelling using advanced datasets. *Mailing Add:* Nat Weather Serv 10230 Smith Rd Denver CO 80239

**THALER, G(EORGE) J(ULIUS),** ELECTRICAL ENGINEERING. *Current Pos:* from asst prof to prof, 51-76, DISTINGUISHED PROF ELEC ENG, NAVAL POSTGRAD SCH, 76- *Personal Data:* b Baltimore, Md, Mar 15, 18; m 44; c 4. *Educ:* Johns Hopkins Univ, BE, 40, DrEng, 47. *Prof Exp:* Instr & asst elec eng, Johns Hopkins Univ, 42-47; asst prof, Univ Notre Dame, 47-51. *Mem:* Am Soc Eng Educ; Inst Elec & Electronics Engrs. *Res:* Theory of automatic control, particularly discontinuous and nonlinear systems. *Mailing Add:* Dept Elec Eng US Naval Postgrad Sch Monterey CA 93943

**THALER, JON JACOB,** EXPERIMENTAL HIGH ENERGY PHYSICS. *Current Pos:* ASST PROF PHYSICS, UNIV ILL, URBANA, 77- *Personal Data:* b Richland, Wash, Feb 3, 47; m 68; c 1. *Educ:* Columbia Univ, BA, 67, MA, 69, PhD(physics), 72. *Prof Exp:* From instr to asst prof physics, Princeton Univ, 71-77. *Mem:* Am Phys Soc. *Res:* Investigation of high energy processes as tests of the Quark-Parton model, scaling, and the possible existence of new quantum numbers. *Mailing Add:* Dept Physics Loomis Lab Physics Univ Ill 1110 W Green St Urbana IL 61801. *Fax:* 217-333-4990

**THALER, M MICHAEL,** PEDIATRICS, DEVELOPMENTAL BIOLOGY. *Current Pos:* from instr to assoc prof, 67-76, PROF PEDIAT, SCH MED, UNIV CALIF, SAN FRANCISCO, 77- *Personal Data:* Can citizen; m 66; c 2. *Educ:* Univ Toronto, MD, 58. *Prof Exp:* Intern, Mt Zion Hosp, San Francisco, 58-59; jr pediat resident, Children's Hosp, Detroit, 59-60; sr resident, Boston City Hosp, Mass, 60-61; asst resident path, Hosp Sick Children, Toronto, 61-62; res fel pediat path, Univ Toronto, 62; vis resident, Hosp St Antoine, Paris, 63; res fel path chem, Hosp Sick Children, Toronto, 63-65; res fel develop biochem, Harvard Med Sch, 65-67. *Concurrent Pos:* Vis scientist, Wash Univ, 64 & Weizmann Inst Sci, Israel; Josiah Macy Jr Found fac scholar, 74-75. *Mem:* Soc Pediat Res; Am Soc Clin Invest; Am Soc Biol Chemists; Am Asn Study Liver Dis; Int Asn Study Liver. *Res:* Liver disease of newborn infants; perinatal and developmental aspects of hepatic metabolism; bilirubin metabolism; pediatric gastrointestinal function and pathology. *Mailing Add:* Dept Pediat Univ Calif San Francisco Med Sch 500 Parnassus MO4-E San Francisco CA 94143-0136

**THALER, OTTO FELIX,** psychiatry, psychoanalysis; deceased, see previous edition for last biography

**THALER, RAPHAEL MORTON,** theoretical physics, for more information see previous edition

**THALER, WARREN ALAN,** ORGANIC CHEMISTRY. *Current Pos:* Res assoc, 60-77, SR CORP RES LAB, EXXON RES & ENG CO, 77- *Personal Data:* b New York, NY, Jan 7, 34; m 56; c 1. *Educ:* City Col New York, BS, 56; Columbia Univ, MA, 58, PhD(chem), 61. *Mem:* Am Chem Soc. *Res:* Free radical chemistry; sulfur chemistry; additive substitution reactions; stereochemistry of free radical reactions; cationic polymerization; elastomer chemistry. *Mailing Add:* 5 Pleasant View Way Flemington NJ 08822

**THALER, WILLIAM JOHN,** PHYSICS. *Current Pos:* PHYSICIST, US OFF NAVAL RES, 51-; PROF PHYSICS, GEORGETOWN UNIV, 60- *Personal Data:* b Baltimore, Md, Dec 4, 25; m 51; c 2. *Educ:* Loyola Col, BS, 47; Cath Univ, MS, 49, PhD(physics), 51. *Prof Exp:* Physicist, Baird Assocs, Inc, 47; instr physics, Cath Univ, 47-48, asst, 48-51. *Concurrent Pos:* Chief scientist, Off Telecommun Policy, Exec Off Pres, 76-77, dir, 77-78. *Mem:* Am Phys Soc; Acoust Soc Am. *Res:* Ultrasonic studies of relaxation phenomena in gases; propagation of shock waves in liquids, solids and gases; effects of ultrasonics on biological media; laser research. *Mailing Add:* 5532 Summit St Centreville VA 20120

**THALL, PETER FRANCIS,** MATHEMATICAL STATISTICS, PROBABILITY. *Current Pos:* DEPT MATH, M D ANDERSON CANCER CTR, UNIV TEX. *Personal Data:* b Stillwater, Okla, Aug 5, 49. *Educ:* Mich State Univ, BS, 71; Fla State Univ, MS, 73, PhD(statist & probability), 75. *Prof Exp:* Asst prof prog math sci, Univ Tex, 75-80; from asst prof to assoc prof, Dept Statist, George Washington Univ, 80-84; statistician, Nat Coop Gallstone Study, 82, Diabetes Control & Complications Trial, Biostatist Ctr, Dept Statist, NIH, Nat Inst Arthritis, Diabetes & Digestive Kidney Dis, 83 & Dept Radiation Oncol, 85. *Concurrent Pos:* Sci corres, Hazardous Waste & Pollution Adv Lett, Bur Bus Pract, Prentice Hall Publ Co, 82-83; statistician, Nat Coop Gallstone Study, 82, Diabetes Control & Complications Trial, Biostatist Ctr, Dept Statist, NIH, Nat Inst Arthritis, Diabetes & Digestive Kidney Dis, 83 & Dept Radiation Oncol, 85. *Mem:* Am Statist Asn; Inst Math Statist; Soc Clin Trials. *Res:* Biostatistics; clinical trials; stochastic point processes and random measures; reliability theory. *Mailing Add:* 2708 Carolina Way Houston TX 77005

**THALMANN, ROBERT H,** NEUROSCIENCE. *Current Pos:* STAFF MEM, BAYLOR COL MED, 69-, ASSOC PROF, 84- *Personal Data:* b San Antonio, Tex, Nov 14, 39. *Educ:* Univ Tex, BA, 61; Univ Mich, MA, 64, PhD(psychol), 67. *Prof Exp:* USPHS fel, Emory Univ, 67-69. *Concurrent Pos:* Vis asst prof, Univ Calif, Irvine, 78; res vis, AT&T Bell Labs, 85-86. *Mem:* Soc Neurosci; AAAS. *Res:* Neurophysiology of neurotransmitters. *Mailing Add:* Dept Cell Biol Baylor Col Med 1 Baylor Plaza Houston TX 77030-3411

**THAM, MIN KWAN,** CHEMICAL ENGINEERING, PHYSICAL CHEMISTRY. *Current Pos:* tech adv, 83-88, SR SCI ADV, NAT INST PETROL & ENERGY RES, 88- *Personal Data:* b Rangoon, Burma, July 29, 39; US citizen; m 70; c 2. *Educ:* Rangoon Univ, BSc, 62; Univ Fla, MSE, 68,

PhD(chem eng), 70. *Prof Exp:* Asst lectr chem eng, Rangoon Inst Technol, 63-66; fel, Univ Fla, 70-72, res assoc, 72-74, asst engr, 74-76; chem engr, Bartlesville Energy Technol Ctr, US Dept Energy, 76-83. *Concurrent Pos:* Hon tech adv, Sci Res Inst Petrol Explor & Develop, People's Repub China. *Mem:* Am Inst Chem Engrs; Soc Petrol Engrs. *Res:* Statistical thermodynamics; fuel cells and batteries research; physical and chemical aspects of tertiary oil recovery; interfacial phenomena, adsorptions, mass transfer. *Mailing Add:* 837 SE Belmont Rd Bartlesville OK 74006

**THAMER, B(URTON) J(OHN),** NUCLEAR ENGINEERING, CHEMISTRY. *Current Pos:* RETIRED. *Personal Data:* b Kitchener, Ont, June 22, 21; nat US. *Educ:* Univ Calif, BS, 43; Iowa State Col, PhD(chem), 50; Univ Ariz, MS, 73. *Prof Exp:* Asst chemist, Manhattan Proj Calif, 43-44, Clinton Labs, 44 & Hanford Eng Works, 44-45; asst chem, Inst Atomic Res, Iowa State Univ, 46-50; mem staff, Los Alamos Sci Lab, NMex, 50-71; metallurgist, Magma Copper Co, Ariz, 73-77; nuclear engr, Ford, Bacon & Davis, Utah, 77-84; chemist, USA Dugway Proving Ground, Utah, 85-86; consult, 86-90. *Mem:* Am Chem Soc; Am Nuclear Soc. *Res:* Chemistry of nuclear reactors, management of radioactive waste, chemical equilibria; diffusion of radon. *Mailing Add:* 7548 Hollaran Ct Las Vegas NV 89128

**THAMES, HOWARD DAVIS, JR,** BIOMATHEMATICS. *Current Pos:* Proj investr, 70-71, from asst prof to assoc prof, 71-83, PROF BIOMATH, UNIV TEX M D ANDERSON CANCER CTR, HOUSTON, 84- *Personal Data:* b Monroe, La, Aug 3, 41; m 66; c 2. *Educ:* Rice Univ, BA, 63, PhD(chem), 70. *Mem:* Radiation Res Soc; Brit Inst Radiol. *Res:* Experimental design analysis in radiology. *Mailing Add:* Dept Biomath Univ Tex M D Anderson Cancer Ctr 1515 Holcomb Houston TX 77030

**THAMES, JOHN LONG,** WATERSHED MANAGEMENT. *Current Pos:* from assoc prof to prof, 67-86, prof chmn, 75-86, EMER PROF, WATERSHED HYDROL UNIV ARIZ, 86- *Personal Data:* b Richmond, Va, Sept 29, 24; wid; c John L III, Janna M, Robert M & Anne J. *Educ:* Univ Fla, BSF, 50; Univ Miss, MS, 59; Univ Ariz, PhD, 66. *Prof Exp:* Res forester, US Forest Serv, 50-67. *Concurrent Pos:* Consult, Argonne Nat Lab, Am Smelting & Refining Co & Shelly Loy, USAID. *Mem:* Soil Sci Soc Am; Soc Am Foresters; Sigma Xi; Am Geophys Union. *Res:* Plant-soil-water relations; hydrologic modeling; decision analyses; hydrology of surface mined lands. *Mailing Add:* 5470 N Cumberland Dr Tucson AZ 85704

**THAMES, MARC,** CARDIOLOGY. *Current Pos:* CHIEF CARDIOL, VET ADMIN MED CTR, RICHMOND, VA, 82- *Personal Data:* b Houston, Tex, Sept 25, 44. *Educ:* Va Commonwealth Univ, MD, 70. *Prof Exp:* PROF & CHIEF INTERNAL MED, MED COL VA, 82- *Mailing Add:* 11100 Eucliud Ave Cleveland OH 44106-2602. *Fax:* 216-844-8954

**THAMES, SHELBY FRELAND,** POLYMER CHEMISTRY, ORGANIC CHEMISTRY. *Current Pos:* From instr to assoc prof chem, Univ Southern Miss, 60-70, dean col sci, 71-74, dean col sci & technol, 74-77, PROF POLYMER SCI, UNIV SOUTHERN MISS, 70-, VPRES ADMIN & REGIONAL CAMPUSES, 77-, DISTINGUISHED UNIV RES PROF POLYMER SCI, 86- *Personal Data:* b Hattiesburg, Miss, Aug 10, 36; m 54; c 3. *Educ:* Univ Southern Miss, BS, 59, MS, 61; Univ Tenn, PhD(org chem), 64. *Honors & Awards:* Mattiello Lectr, Fedn Soc Coatings Technol. *Concurrent Pos:* Res grants, Walter Reed Inst Res, 64-68; Diamond-Shamrock Corp, 66-68, Inst Copper Res Asn, NASA, Masonite Corp, Stand Paint & Varnish Co & Dept Defense, USDA; Petrol Res Fund fel award, 68-69; dir, Southern Inst Surface Coatings, 68-70; exec vpres, Southern Inst Surface Coatings, 80-96; chmn, New Uses Coun, 93-94. *Mem:* Am Chem Soc; Am Inst Chem; Fedn Socs Coatings Technol; Sigma Xi; Am Oil Chemists Soc; Soc Plastics Engrs. *Res:* Organic coatings, waterborne, high-solid, powder and solvent systems, organosilanes, high performance polymers, emulsion polymerization solventless emulsions, structure-property relationships in the utility of ag materials as industrial raw materials for the polymer industry. *Mailing Add:* Dept Polymer Sci Univ Southern Miss Box 10037 Southern Sta Hattiesburg MS 39406. *Fax:* 601-266-5880; *E-Mail:* sfthames@whale.st.usm.edu

**THAMES, WALTER HENDRIX, JR,** NEMATOLOGY. *Current Pos:* assoc prof, 59-68, prof, 68-80, EMER PROF PLANT NEMATOL, TEX A&M UNIV, 80- *Personal Data:* b Richmond, Va, July 29, 18; m 43; c 2. *Educ:* Univ Fla, BSA, 47, MS, 48, PhD, 59. *Prof Exp:* Asst entomologist, Everglades Exp Sta, Univ Fla, 48-55, asst soil microbiol, 57-59. *Concurrent Pos:* Prin instr, Nematode Identification Short Course, Clemson Univ, 81-88. *Mem:* Soc Nematol. *Res:* Biology and control of nematodes; plant nematology. *Mailing Add:* 705 Pershing St College Station TX 77840

**THANASSI, JOHN WALTER,** BIOCHEMISTRY. *Current Pos:* from asst prof to assoc prof, 67-78, PROF BIOCHEM, COL MED, UNIV VT, 78- *Personal Data:* b St Louis, Mo, Oct 2, 37; m 64; c 3. *Educ:* Lafayette Col, BA, 59; Yale Univ, PhD(biochem), 63. *Prof Exp:* Fel chem, Cornell Univ, 63-64; fel, Univ Calif, Santa Barbara, 64-65; staff fel, Lab Chem, NIH, 65-67. *Concurrent Pos:* USPHS res grants, 68-71, 72-76 & 78-, NASA res grant, 74-75. *Mem:* AAAS; Am Soc Biol Chem; Am Inst Nutrit; Am Asn Univ Prof; Am Asn Cancer Res. *Res:* Vitamin B6 metabolism. *Mailing Add:* Dept Biochem Given Bldg Univ Vt Col Med Burlington VT 05405-0068

**THANGAM, SIVA,** MECHANICAL ENGINEERING, THERMO SCIENCE. *Current Pos:* From asst prof to assoc prof, 80-90, PROF, STEVENS INST TECHNOL, 90- *Personal Data:* b India, 1950. *Educ:* Madras Univ, India, BS, 71; Indian Inst Technol, MS, 73; Rutgers Univ, PhD(mech eng), 80. *Concurrent Pos:* Dir, NJ Space Grant Consortium, 93- *Mem:* Am Phys Soc; Sigma Xi; Asian-Indian Women Am; Am Soc Mech Engrs; Am Inst Aeronaut & Astronaut; Am Soc Eng Educ. *Res:* Computational fluid mechanics; heat and mass transfer; modeling of fluid turbulence; analysis of turbomachinery; analysis, simulation and modeling of industrial thermal systems. *Mailing Add:* Dept Mech Eng Castle Point Sta Hoboken NJ 07030

**THANGARAJ, SANDY,** TECHNICAL ACTIVITIES, NEW PRODUCT RESEARCH IN RUBBER. *Current Pos:* VPRES, TECH & LAB MGR, RUBBER INDUSTS INC, SHAKOPEE, MINN, 88- *Personal Data:* b Madras, India, Dec 3, 34; m, Jaroslava K; c Neena & Paula M (Castano). *Educ:* Univ Madras, India, BS, 54, MS, 56, dipl rubber technol, 57, PhD(chem eng), 60. *Prof Exp:* Plant mgr & chief tech officer, Plastics & Rubber Industs, Nairobi, Kenya, EAfrica, 65-71; mgr res & develop, Globe Super Prod, 71-72; tech dir & chief chemist, Avon Sole Co & Subsid, 72-75; mgr res & develop rubber, Teknon Apex Co, 75-78; dir tech & mfg, Industs Modernon LTDA, Colombia, SAm, 79-80; mgr res & develop, Int Shoe Co, Tex, 80-82; mgr res & develop prod, O'Sullivan-Vulcan Corp, Tenn, 82-87. *Concurrent Pos:* Tech consult, footwear prods & mfg int level. *Mem:* Am Chem Soc; Am Inst Chemists; Am Chem Soc Rubber Div; Int Union Pure & Appl Chem; Am Soc Testing & Mat. *Res:* Setting standards for products especially rubber and plastics; product developments formulations for rubber products; equipments research for rubber products; specialized in making products from tire recycled material; tire recycle process. *Mailing Add:* Rubber Industs Inc 200 Cavanaugh Dr Shakopee MN 55379. *Fax:* 612-445-7934

**THANSANDOTE, ARTNARONG,** HEALTH EFFECTS OF ELECTROMAGNETIC FIELDS, INSTRUMENTATION & MEASUREMENTS. *Current Pos:* RES SCIENTIST, ELECTROMAGNETICS UNIT, HEALTH CAN, 91- *Personal Data:* b Chumphon, Thailand, Dec 16, 50; Can citizen; m 76, Pimprapha Netirungsivachara; c Maythee L & Puttinee P. *Educ:* Khon Kaen Univ, Thailand, BEng, 73, Univ Man, MSc, 76; Carleton Univ, PhD(elec eng), 82. *Prof Exp:* Lectr, Khon Kaen Univ, Thailand, 73-83, asst prof elec eng, 83-86, assoc prof, 86-88; res assoc, Univ Ottawa, 88-91. *Concurrent Pos:* Fel, Univ Ottawa, Can, 82, Can Int Develop Agency/Natural Sci & Eng Res Coun, 88, Can vis scientist, 91; assoc head, Elec Eng Dept, Khon Kaen Univ, 83-85, dep dir, Comput Ctr, 84-85; Japan Soc Prom Sci vis scientist, Tohoku Gakuin Univ, Japan, 87; actg head, Electromagnetics Unit, Health Can, 91-, head, Electromagnetics Unit, 94- *Mem:* Sr mem Inst Elec & Electronics Engrs; Inst Elec & Electronics Engrs Instrumentation & Measurements Soc; Inst Elec & Electronics Engrs Antennas & Propagation Soc; Inst Elec & Electronics Engrs Electromagnetic Compatability Soc; Bioelectromagnetics Soc. *Res:* Health effects from exposure to 60-Hz magnetic fields; occupational exposure assessment for transient electromagnetic fields; energy absorption in humans due to radio frequency fields from portable radio tranceivers; design, development, building and testing of transient magnetic field sensors. *Mailing Add:* Health & Welfare Can Bur Rad Med Dev Rm 66 775 Brookfield Rd Ottawa ON K1A 1C1 Can

**THAPAR, MANGAT RAI,** SEISMOLOGY, GEOPHYSICS. *Current Pos:* PRES, INT GEOPHYS CO, 85- *Personal Data:* b Khanna, India, Apr 10, 39; m 68; c 2. *Educ:* Indian Sch Mines, Dhanbad, BSc, 61, MSc & AISM, 62; Univ Western Ont, PhD(geophys), 68. *Prof Exp:* Sr sci officer seismol, Coun Sci & Indust Res, New Delhi, 62-64; teaching fel seismol & geophys, Univ Western Ont, 68-71; NSF res fel seismol, Univ Pittsburgh, 71-72; chief res engr, Seismograph Serv Corp, 72; analyst seismol, Phillips Petrol Co, 72-74; geophys assoc, Cities Serv Co, 74-80, sr geophys assoc, 80-85. *Concurrent Pos:* Lectr, Univ Pittsburgh, 71-72. *Mem:* Am Geophys Union; Soc Exp Geophys; Indian Soc Earthquake Technol; Europ Asn Exp Geophysicists. *Res:* Applied geophysics; experimental, theoretical, model earthquake and lunar seismology; digital data processing techniques; geophysical exploration techniques; seismic interpretation research; seismic wave propagation; 2-dimensional digital seismic modeling; color processing of seismic data. *Mailing Add:* 6810 E 50th Pl Tulsa OK 74145

**THAPAR, NIRWAN T,** VETERINARY PATHOLOGY, VETERINARY MEDICINE. *Current Pos:* PRIN, BLADENSBURG ANIMAL HOSP, 93- *Personal Data:* b Raikot, India, Jan 26, 38; US citizen; m 67; c 2. *Educ:* Punjab Univ FSc, 57; Punjab State Vet Col, India, BVScAH, 61; Univ SDak, Brookings, MS, 64. *Prof Exp:* Instr, Punjab State Vet Col, 61-62; grad res fel, SDak State Univ, 62-64; res asst, Univ Wis-Madison, 64-66; veterinarian, Norwich Pharmaceut Co, 66-68 & Toxicol Path Sect, Wis Alumni Res Found, 68-69; instr path & neuropath, Dept Path, Univ Wis-Madison, 69-72; vet pathologist, San Diego Co, Calif, 72-77; dir, State Animal Health Diag Lab, Centreville, Md, 77-87; vet pathologist, Animal Health Lab, Md Dept Agr, 87-93. *Concurrent Pos:* Rockefeller travel fel award, 62-64; res fel, Univ SDak, 62-64 & Univ Wis, 64-66, teaching fel, 69-72; monitor, study site review prog vet path, C L Davis Found Southern Calif, 72; veterinarian-in-charge, Meat Inspection Plant, Wis State Dept Agr, 71. *Mem:* Sigma Xi; Am Vet Med Asn; Soc Pharmacol & Environ Pathologists; Asn Indian Vet Am (pres, 90-). *Res:* Experimental pathology; diagnostic and toxicologic pathology. *Mailing Add:* 841 Meadow Heights Lane Arnold MD 21012

**THARIN, JAMES COTTER,** GEOLOGY. *Current Pos:* assoc prof, 67-74, PROF GEOL, HOPE COL, 74-, CHMN DEPT, 67-80 & 88- *Personal Data:* b West Palm Beach, Fla, Mar 22, 31; m 55, Joanne Febel; c James & Catherine. *Educ:* St Joseph's Col, Ind, BS, 54; Univ Ill, Urbana, MS, 58, PhD(geol), 60. *Prof Exp:* Instr phys sci, Univ Ill, Urbana, 59-61; petrol geologist, Chevron Oil Co, 61-63; asst prof geol, Wesleyan Univ, 63-67. *Mem:* AAAS; Geol Soc Am; Soc Econ Paleont & Mineral; Sigma Xi. *Res:* Sedimentation; Pleistocene geology; glacial geology and clay mineralogy; textural studies of glacial drift in northwestern Pennsylvania, Calgary area, Alberta and Connecticut Valley; petroleum exploration in Mississippi Delta. *Mailing Add:* Dept Geol Hope Col Holland MI 49423

**THARP, A G,** INORGANIC CHEMISTRY. *Current Pos:* RETIRED. *Personal Data:* b Franklinton, Ky, Jan 6, 27. *Educ:* Univ Ky, BS, 51; Purdue Univ, PhD, 57. *Prof Exp:* Asst, Purdue Univ, 51-54; asst res engr, Univ Calif, 54-55, res engr, 59; res chemist, Oak Ridge Nat Lab, 56-59; from asst prof to prof inorg chem, Calif State Univ, Long Beach, 59-74, prof chem, 74-88. *Mem:* Am Chem Soc. *Res:* Structural investigations of high melting silicides, germanides and carbides; thermodynamic properties of high melting inorganic compounds. *Mailing Add:* 52 John St Multinational Village Paranaque Metro 1708 Manila Philippines

**THARP, GERALD D,** VERTEBRATE PHYSIOLOGY. *Current Pos:* from asst prof to assoc prof, 67-76, PROF PHYSIOL, UNIV NEBR, LINCOLN, 76- *Personal Data:* b Wahoo, Nebr, Aug 9, 32; m 57; c 4. *Educ:* Univ Nebr, BS, 58, MS, 61; Univ Iowa, PhD(physiol), 65. *Prof Exp:* Instr physiol, Univ Iowa, 64-65; asst prof, Wis State Univ, Oshkosh, 65-67. *Mem:* Am Physiol Soc; Am Col Sports Med. *Res:* Exercise and stress physiology especially the effects of training. *Mailing Add:* Sch Life Sci Univ Nebr 213 Manter Hall Lincoln NE 68588-0001

**THARP, VERNON LANCE,** VETERINARY MEDICINE. *Current Pos:* instr vet surg & clin, Ohio State Univ, 42-47, from asst prof to prof vet med, 47-83, dir vet clin, 47-71, chmn dept vet clin sci, 60-71, dir equine res ctr, 65-71, dir food animal res ctr, 70-71, assoc dean, 72-83, EMER PROF VET MED, COL VET MED, OHIO STATE UNIV, 83- *Personal Data:* b Hemlock, Ohio, Mar 13, 17; m 40; c 6. *Educ:* Ohio State Univ, DVM, 40. *Prof Exp:* Field vet, US Bur Animal Indust, 40-42. *Concurrent Pos:* Harness Tracks Am, NY Racing Asn & New York Jockey Club grants equine res col vet med, Ohio State Univ, 65-72; consult, Am Holstein-Friesian Asn, 82-; comnr, Ohio Racing Comn, 83- *Mem:* World Vet Asn (vpres, 79-); Am Asn Bovine Practitioners (pres, 76); Am Vet Med Asn (pres, 78-79); Am Asn Vet Clinicians (secy-treas, 62-72); World Equine Vet Asn (secy-treas, 85-). *Res:* Funding, administration and performance of research in environmental health, nutrition, reproduction and diseases of domestic and laboratory animals. *Mailing Add:* 7762 Roberts Rd Hilliard OH 43026

**THATCHER, C(HARLES) M(ANSON),** CHEMICAL ENGINEERING. *Current Pos:* DISTINGUISHED PROF CHEM ENG, UNIV ARK, FAYETTEVILLE, 70- *Personal Data:* b Milwaukee, Wis, Apr 4, 22; m 46; c 2. *Educ:* Univ Mich, BSE, 43, MSE, 50, PhD(chem eng), 55. *Honors & Awards:* Western Elec Award, 67; Burlington Northern Award, 87. *Prof Exp:* From instr to asst prof chem eng & metall eng, Univ Mich, 47-58; prof chem eng & chmn dept, Pratt Inst, 58-63, dean, Sch Eng & Sci, 63-70. *Mem:* Am Chem Soc; Am Inst Chem Engrs; Nat Soc Prof Engrs. *Res:* Computer systems programming and data processing; mathematical modelling and computer simulation; educational methods. *Mailing Add:* PO Box 925 Friendswood TX 77546-0925

**THATCHER, ROBERT CLIFFORD,** FOREST ENTOMOLOGY. *Current Pos:* RETIRED. *Personal Data:* b Boonville, NY, Jan 11, 29; m 49; c 4. *Educ:* State Univ NY, BS, 53, MS, 54; Auburn Univ, PhD, 71. *Prof Exp:* Biol aide, Southern Forest Exp Sta, USDA, La, 54, entomologist, 54-68, asst br chief forest insects, 68-73, proj leader, 73-74, prog mgr, Off Secy, Southern Pine Beetle Prog, 74-80, prog mgr, Integrated Pest Mgt, Res Develop & Appln Prog, Southern Forest Exp Sta, 81-85, asst sta dir, Southeast Forest Exp Sta, US Forest Serv, 85-89. *Concurrent Pos:* Instr, Stephen F Austin State Univ, 57 & 63. *Mem:* Soc Am Foresters; Entom Soc Am. *Res:* Forest ecology; interdisciplinary research and development activities relating to southern pine beetle pest management. *Mailing Add:* 12 Bevlyn Dr Asheville NC 28803-3331

**THATCHER, WALTER EUGENE,** ANALYTICAL CHEMISTRY. *Current Pos:* RES SPECIALIST, CENT RES LABS, 3M CO, 54- *Personal Data:* b Evanston, Ill, Jan 22, 27; m 49; c 11. *Educ:* Northwestern Univ, BS, 50; Univ Ill, PhD(chem), 55. *Mem:* Am Chem Soc; Am Crystallog Asn. *Res:* Analytical chemistry in x-ray diffraction and fluorescence. *Mailing Add:* 7024 Dakota Ave S Chanhassen MN 55317-9582

**THATCHER, WAYNE RAYMOND,** SEISMOLOGY. *Current Pos:* chief, Br Tectonophys, 84-89, GEOPHYSICIST, OFF EARTHQUAKE STUDIES, US GEOL SURV, 71-84, 89- *Personal Data:* b Montreal, Que, May 23, 42; m 79, Mary E Farwell; c Iain. *Educ:* McGill Univ, BSc, 64; Calif Inst Technol, MS, 67, PhD(geophys), 72. *Honors & Awards:* Bradley lectr, Geol Div Western Region, US Geol Surv, 84. *Concurrent Pos:* Vis prof, Stanford Univ, 72-76; mem, comt on geodesy, Nat Acad Sci, 76-78; assoc ed, Geophys Res Lett, 77-79 & J Geophys Res, 81-83; pres-elect, Tectonophys Sect, Am Geophys Union, 88-90, pres, 90-92. *Mem:* Fel Am Geophys Union; Seismol Soc Am. *Res:* Aspects of earthquake source mechanism; crustal deformation and earthquake hazard assessment; crustal structure; microearthquakes. *Mailing Add:* Off Earthquake Studies MS 977 US Geol Surv 345 Middlefield Rd Menlo Park CA 94025. *E-Mail:* thatches@thepub.wr.usgs.gov

**THATCHER, WILLIAM WATTERS,** REPRODUCTIVE PHYSIOLOGY, REPRODUCTION ENDOCRINOLOGY. *Current Pos:* from asst prof to assoc prof, 69-78, PROF REPRODUCTIVE PHYSIOL & ENDOCRINOL, UNIV FLA, 78-, GRAD RES PROF, 88- *Personal Data:* b Baltimore, Md, Jan 12, 42; m 78, Marie-Joelle Duchantre; c 3. *Educ:* Univ Md, BS, 63, MS, 65; Mich State Univ, PhD(dairy sci), 68. *Honors & Awards:* Physiol Award, Am Dairy Sci Asn, 81, Borden Award, 92; Phycol & Endocrin Award, Am Soc Animal Sci, 85. *Prof Exp:* NIH fel, Mich State Univ, 68-69. *Concurrent Pos:* Sabbaticals, France, 77 & 85. *Mem:* Am Dairy Sci Asn; Soc Study Reproduction; Am Soc Animal Sci; Int Embryo Transfer Soc. *Res:* Embryos; uterus; corpus luteum; pregnancy; post partum; Follide. *Mailing Add:* 6520 NW 44th Pl Gainesville FL 32606-4264. *Fax:* 904-392-5595

**THAU, FREDERICK E,** ELECTRICAL ENGINEERING. *Current Pos:* assoc prof, 76-78, PROF, DEPT ELEC ENG, CITY COL NEW YORK, 78- *Personal Data:* b Bronx, NY, Dec 2, 38; m 62; c 2. *Educ:* NY Univ, BEE, 59, MEE, 61, DEngSc(modern control theory), 64. *Prof Exp:* Mem tech staff digital systs, Bell Labs, NY, 59-65; sr staff scientist modern control theory, Kearfott Div, Singer Co, NJ, 65-69; asst prof, City Col New York, 69-76. *Concurrent Pos:* City Univ New York fac res grant, 70-71. *Mem:* Inst Elec & Electronics Engrs. *Res:* Modern control theory and applications to process control; biological control problems; power systems; large space structures; adaptive signal processing. *Mailing Add:* Dept Elec Eng City Col New York New York NY 10031

**THAU, ROSEMARIE B ZISCHKA,** IMMUNOLOGY, ENDOCRINOLOGY. *Current Pos:* scientist, 72-87, SR SCIENTIST, DIR CONTRACEPTIVE DEVELOP, POP COUN, ROCKEFELLER UNIV, 87- *Personal Data:* b Vienna, Austria, Mar 15, 36; m 70. *Educ:* Univ Vienna, BS, 54, PhD(chem), 63. *Prof Exp:* Res assoc exp surg med ctr, Duke Univ, 63-65; instr pediat, State Univ NY Downstate Med Ctr, 67-70, asst prof, 67-72. *Mem:* Sigma Xi; Endocrine Soc; Am Soc Immunol Reproduction. *Res:* Contraceptive development, endocrinology of reproduction, antifertility vaccines. *Mailing Add:* 400 Central Park W No 7-C New York NY 10025-5831

**THAW, RICHARD FRANKLIN,** BOTANY, NATURAL HISTORY. *Current Pos:* from assoc prof to prof, 59-83, EMER PROF BIOL & NATURAL SCI, SAN JOSE STATE UNIV, 83- *Personal Data:* b Denver, Colo, Nov 13, 20; m 42; c 1. *Educ:* Ore State Col, BS, 43, MEd, 47, MS, 53, EdD(gen sci, sci educ), 58. *Prof Exp:* Teacher high sch, Ore, 47-58; sci coordr, San Diego Co Schs, Calif, 58-59. *Concurrent Pos:* Crown-Zellerbach fel, 54. *Mem:* Nat Sci Teachers Asn; Nat Audubon Soc. *Res:* Plant taxonomy; science teaching methods. *Mailing Add:* 1010 Creekside Ct Morgan Hill CA 95037-6209

**THAWLEY, DAVID GORDEN,** EPIDEMIOLOGY, VETERINARY MEDICINE. *Current Pos:* asst prof, 76-79, ASSOC PROF VET MED, UNIV MO, 80- *Personal Data:* b Hastings, NZ, Oct 4, 46; m 71; c 2. *Educ:* Massey Univ, NZ, BVSc, 70; Univ Guelph, PhD(vet prevent med), 75; Am Col Vet Prev Med, dipl, 78. *Prof Exp:* Vet pvt pract, Huntly Vet Club, 69-70, Morrinsville Club, 70-71; asst vet med, Univ Guelph, 71-75; clin teaching fel, Massey Univ, 75. *Concurrent Pos:* Coop investr epidemiologist, US Dept Agr, 78-; prin investr, USPHS-NIH, 78-80, Mo Pork Producers & Nat Pork Producers, 78- *Mem:* Am Vet Med Asn; US Animal Health Asn; Am Acad Vet Prev Med; Asn Teachers Vet Pub Health & Prev Med. *Res:* Investigation of pseudorabies epidemiology and strategies for control; investigation of interactions among heavy metals and the resulting toxicities produced; general infectious disease epidemiology. *Mailing Add:* 32 E Oaks Rd St Paul MN 55127

**THAXTON, GEORGE DONALD,** NUCLEAR PHYSICS, SOLID STATE PHYSICS. *Current Pos:* RETIRED. *Personal Data:* b Richmond, Va, Feb 28, 31; m 54; c 4. *Educ:* Richmond Univ, BS, 59; Univ NC, PhD(physics), 65. *Prof Exp:* Res assoc physics, Fla State Univ, 64-66; from asst prof to assoc prof physics, Auburn Univ, 66- *Mem:* Am Phys Soc; Am Asn Physics Teachers. *Res:* Theory of direct nuclear reactions; theory of band structure of solids. *Mailing Add:* 910 Cherokee Rd Auburn AL 36830

**THAXTON, JAMES PAUL,** AVIAN PHYSIOLOGY. *Current Pos:* DIR RES & DEVELOP, EMBREX, INC, RALEIGH, NC, 85- *Personal Data:* b Longview, Miss, Sept 6, 41; m 65; c 3. *Educ:* Miss State Univ, BS, 64, MS, 66; Univ Ga, PhD(physiol), 71. *Honors & Awards:* Poultry Sci Assoc Res Award, Poultry Sci Asn, 74; Res Award, Sigma Xi. *Prof Exp:* Instr biol, Northeast La Univ, 66-67; from asst prof to prof poultry sci, NC State Univ, 71-85. *Concurrent Pos:* Consult, Nat Inst Environ Health Sci, 74-84. *Mem:* AAAS; Poultry Sci Asn; World Poultry Sci Asn; Sigma Xi; Soc Develop & Comp Immunol. *Res:* Effects of environmental parameters, such as temperatures, toxins and heavy metals, on the immunological responsiveness of the avian species. *Mailing Add:* Dept Poultry Sci Miss State Univ Box 9665 Mississippi State MS 39762-9665

**THAYER, CHARLES WALTER,** INVERTEBRATE PALEONTOLOGY, PALEOECOLOGY. *Current Pos:* Asst prof, 71-78, ASSOC PROF GEOL, UNIV PA, 78- *Personal Data:* b Springfield, Vt, May 18, 44; c 2. *Educ:* Dartmouth Col, BA, 66; Yale Univ, MPhil, 69, PhD(geol), 72. *Concurrent Pos:* Res assoc, Acad Natural Sci, Philadelphia, 78- *Mem:* AAAS; Paleont Soc; Sigma Xi. *Res:* Pattern and process of evolution; marine ecology; sedimentary environments. *Mailing Add:* Dept Geol Univ Pa Philadelphia PA 19104

**THAYER, CHESTER ARTHUR,** MOLECULAR PHOTOPHYSICS, LASER ISOTOPE SEPARATION. *Current Pos:* Res chemist, E I Du Pont de Nemours & Co, Inc, Victoria, Tex, 74-78, asst div supt, 78-80, res supvr, Savannah River Lab, 80-83, res assoc, E I Du Pont Exp Sta, 83-92, SR RES ASSOC, E I DU PONT DE NEMOURS & CO, INC, 92- *Personal Data:* b Stillwater, Okla, July 30, 48; m 69; c 2. *Educ:* Okla State Univ, BS, 70; Univ Ill, PhD(phys chem), 74. *Concurrent Pos:* Instr, Victoria Col, 77-80. *Mem:* Am Chem Soc; Sigma Xi. *Res:* Development of flexible printed circuit materials for the electronics industry; photophysics of laser excited molecules; industrial synthesis of nylon intermediates. *Mailing Add:* 123 Parrish Lane Shipley Woods Wilmington DE 19810-3457

**THAYER, DONALD WAYNE,** MICROBIOLOGY, BIOCHEMISTRY. *Current Pos:* RES LEADER, FOOD SAFETY RES, AGR RES SERV, USDA, 81- *Personal Data:* b Kansas City, Mo, Jan 15, 37; m 69. *Educ:* Kans State Univ, BS, 62, MS, 63; Colo State Univ, PhD(microbiol), 66. *Prof Exp:* Nat Acad Sci, Nat Res Coun resident res assoc, Naval Med Res Inst, 66-67, res chemist, 66-69; from asst prof to prof biol, Tex Tech Univ, 69-79; prog mgr appl biol, NSF, 78-81. *Concurrent Pos:* Lectr, Soc Sigma Xi-Sci Res Soc Am regional lect exchange prog, 71; indust consult, 77-79; rep Interdept Man & Biosphere Task Force, NSF, 79 & Interagency Integrated Pest Mgt Task Force for Pub Health, 80-81; mem Adv Panel Biotechnol, NSF, 83; mem subj-matter expert rating panel life sci, Agr Res Serv, 83-85; US deleg, Food & Agr Orgn working group, health impact & control methods of irradiated foods, Neuhrberg, 86; adv bd, Food Res Inst, Univ Wis, 88-; US deleg, harmonization regulations food irradiation, Inter-Am meeting, Int Atomic Energy Agency, 89; US deleg, Int Consult Group, food irradiation-irradiation as quarantine treatment, 90. *Mem:* Am Soc Microbiol; Am Chem Soc; Soc Indust Microbiol; Sigma Xi; Inst Food Technol; fel Am Acad Microbiol; Asn Milk Food Environ Sanitarians. *Res:* Single-cell protein and carbohydrate metabolism; food borne microorganisms; microbiological, chemical and nutritional safety of foods treated with ionizing radiation. *Mailing Add:* ERRC/USDA/ARS-ERRC Food Safety 600 E Mermaid Lane Wyndmoor PA 19038

**THAYER, DUANE M,** METALLURGICAL ENGINEERING. *Current Pos:* From instr to assoc prof, 59-70, PROF METALL ENG, MICH TECHNOL UNIV, 70-, ADMIN ASST, 66- *Personal Data:* b Kingsford, Mich, June 15, 34; m 87, Mary P Jukkala; c Cecile, Martha, Mary, Terese & Susan. *Educ:* Mich Tech Univ, BS, 59, MS, 62. *Mem:* Am Inst Mining Metall & Petrol Engrs. *Res:* Mineral processing; flotation and agglomeration of iron oxides; fine particle flotation; reclamation of industrial wastes. *Mailing Add:* Dept Metall Eng Mich Technol Univ Rm 201 1400 Townsend Dr Houghton MI 49931

**THAYER, GORDON WALLACE,** WETLAND ECOLOGY, WETLAND RESTORATION ECOLOGY. *Current Pos:* Fishery biologist, Southeast Fisheries Ctr, 68-77, RES TEAM LEADER, BEAUFORT LAB, NAT MARINE FISHERIES SERV, NAT OCEANIC & ATMOSPHERIC ADMIN, 77- *Personal Data:* b Weymouth, Mass, Feb 28, 40; m 63; c 2. *Educ:* Gettysburg Col, BA, 62; Oberlin Col, MA, 64; NC State Univ, PhD(zool), 69. *Concurrent Pos:* Habitat coordr, Nat Marine Fisheries Serv; sci coordr, Restoration Ctr, Nat Oceanic & Atmospheric Admin. *Mem:* Estuarine Res Fedn; Sigma Xi. *Res:* Ecology of seagrass; wetland habitat use; dynamics of zooplankton and estuarine fishery populations; influence of detritus in invertebrate and vertebrate food webs; restoration ecology. *Mailing Add:* Beaufort Lab Nat Oceanic & Atmospheric Admin Beaufort NC 28516. *Fax:* 919-728-8784; *E-Mail:* gordon.thayer@noaa.gov

**THAYER, JOHN STEARNS,** INORGANIC CHEMISTRY, ORGANOMETALLIC CHEMISTRY. *Current Pos:* from asst prof to assoc prof, 66-88, PROF CHEM, UNIV CINCINNATI, 89- *Personal Data:* b Glen Ridge, NJ, Apr 1, 38. *Educ:* Cornell Univ, BA, 60; Univ Wis, PhD(chem), 64. *Prof Exp:* Asst prof chem, Ill Inst Technol, 64-66. *Concurrent Pos:* Frederick Gardner Cottrell grant, 67-73; vis res assoc prof, Chesapeake Biol Lab, 80-84; guest worker, Nat Bur Stand, 83-90; vis res prof, Leicester Polytech, UK, 87 & 89. *Mem:* AAAS; Am Chem Soc. *Res:* Transalkylation of metals in aqueous media; biological aspects of organometallic chemistry; reactions of zerovalent metals with aqueous alkyl halides. *Mailing Add:* Dept Chem Univ Cincinnati Cincinnati OH 45221. *Fax:* 513-556-9239; *E-Mail:* thayer@ucmodl.che.uc.edu

**THAYER, KEITH EVANS,** DENTISTRY. *Current Pos:* From instr to assoc prof, 56-63, head dept, 60-80, PROF FIXED PROSTHODONTICS, COL DENT, UNIV IOWA, 63- *Personal Data:* b Lime Springs, Iowa, Feb 5, 28; m 53; c 4. *Educ:* Cornell Col, BA, 51; Univ Iowa, DDS, 55, MS, 56. *Concurrent Pos:* Attend dentist, Vet Admin Hosp, Iowa City; vis Fulbright prof, Univ Singapore, 68-69; consult, Am Dent Asn Vietnam Educ Proj, 72; consult, Vet Admin Hosp. *Mem:* Int Dent Fedn; Int Asn Dent Res; Am Dent Asn; Sigma Xi. *Res:* Rubber base and silicone impression materials; gingival retraction agents and their effect on oral tissues; occlusion. *Mailing Add:* 5 Longview Knolls NE Iowa City IA 52240

**THAYER, MARGARET KATHRYN,** SYSTEMATICS, BIOGEOGRAPHY. *Current Pos:* vis asst cur, 88-92, RES ASSOC, FIELD MUS NATURAL HIST, 86- *Personal Data:* b Oakland, Calif, June 14, 52; m, Alfred F Newton Jr. *Educ:* Brown Univ, ScB, 73; Harvard Univ, PhD(biol), 85. *Prof Exp:* Curatorial assoc, Mus Comp Zool, Harvard Univ, 76-80; teaching fel entom & biol, Harvard Univ, 82-84. *Mem:* Coleopterists Soc (treas, 87-91, pres elect, 93-94, pres, 95-96); Entom Soc Am; Am Asn Zool Nomenclature; Sigma Xi; Soc Syst Biologists. *Res:* Systematics, evolution, biology and historical biogeography of rove beetles (Staphylinidae) with special interest in the southern hemisphere temperate fauna. *Mailing Add:* Zool-Insects Field Mus Natural Hist Roosevelt Rd at Lakeshore Dr Chicago IL 60605. *Fax:* 312-663-5397; *E-Mail:* thayer@fmnh785.fmnh.org

**THAYER, PAUL ARTHUR,** MARINE GEOLOGY, SEDIMENTOLOGY. *Current Pos:* from asst prof to assoc prof marine sci res, 70-78, prof geol, 78-82, PROF GEOL, UNIV NC, WILMINGTON, 86- *Personal Data:* b New York, NY, Apr 30, 40; m 66, Carolyn King; c Christopher B. *Educ:* Rutgers Univ, BA, 61; Univ NC, PhD(geol), 67. *Prof Exp:* Develop geologist, Calif Co Div, Chevron Oil Co, 67-68; asst prof geol, Tex A&M Univ, 68-70, Amoco Prod Co, 82-85 & Mobil Oil, 86. *Concurrent Pos:* Tex A&M Univ fac res grants, 68-69 & 69-70; Soc Sigma Xi grant, 69; petrol geologist, BP Alaska Explor Inc, 75-; instrnl sci equipment prog award, NSF, 72-74 & 75-77; res grant, AEC, 74; consult, E I du Pont, SC Water Resources Comn, Sci Appl Int Corp, Westinghouse Environ Co, Ohio, Westinghouse Savannah River Co, US Geol Surv, US Dept Energy, Law Environ & Eng, Inc, US Army CEngrs, USAF Weapons Lab & Va Div Mineral Resources. *Mem:* AAAS; Geol Soc Am; Int Asn Sedimentol; Soc Econ Paleont & Mineral; Am Asn Petrol Geol. *Res:* Petrology of clastic sedimentary rocks; reconstruction of depositional environments within ancient sedimentary rocks; Triassic nonmarine stratigraphy; provenance, dispersal and origin of modern and ancient terrigenous sediments; sedimentology of modern carbonate sediments. *Mailing Add:* Dept Earth Sci Univ NC Wilmington 601 S College Rd Wilmington NC 28403-3297. *Fax:* 910-395-3550; *E-Mail:* thayer@vxc.uncwil.edu

**THAYER, PAUL LOYD,** PLANT PATHOLOGY. *Current Pos:* RETIRED. *Personal Data:* b Centralia, WVa, Feb 25, 28; m 53; c 3. *Educ:* Marietta Col, BS, 52; Ohio State Univ, MS, 55, PhD, 58. *Prof Exp:* Asst plant pathologist, Everglades Exp Sta, Univ Fla, 58-65; plant pathologist, Eli Lilly & Co, Greenfield, 65-72, northeastern regional plant sci res mgr, 72-80, head crop protection res, 80-87. *Mem:* Am Phytopath Soc. *Res:* Bacterial and fungus diseases of vegetable crops; fungicide and nematocide evaluation. *Mailing Add:* 4145 NW 67th Terr Gainesville FL 32606

**THAYER, ROLLIN HAROLD,** poultry nutrition; deceased, see previous edition for last biography

**THAYER, THOMAS P,** CHROMIUM GEOLOGY. *Current Pos:* RETIRED. *Personal Data:* b Scarsdale, NY, May 22, 07. *Educ:* Univ Ore, BS, 29, Northwestern Univ, MS, 31; Calif Inst Technol, PhD(geol), 34. *Prof Exp:* Geologist, Mineral Resources Br, US Geol Surv, 35-77. *Mem:* Geol Soc Am; AAAS. *Mailing Add:* 3211 W Maritana St Petersburg Beach FL 33706

**THAYER, WALTER RAYMOND, JR,** MEDICINE, GASTROENTEROLOGY. *Current Pos:* assoc prof, 66-70, PROF MED, BROWN UNIV, 70-; CHIEF GASTROENTEROL, RI HOSP, 66- *Personal Data:* b Providence, RI, Apr 16, 29; m 55; c 3. *Educ:* Providence Col, BS, 50; Tufts Univ, MD, 54. *Hon Degrees:* MA, Brown Univ, 66. *Prof Exp:* Resident gastroenterol, Sch Med, Yale Univ, 61-62, instr med, 60-62, asst prof, 62-66. *Concurrent Pos:* Fel clin gastroenterol, Sch Med, Yale Univ, 59-60; NSF fel, Wenner-Gren Inst, Stockholm, 71-72. *Mem:* Am Soc Clin Invest; Am Gastroenterol Asn. *Res:* Immunology in gastrointestinal diseases; gastric secretion. *Mailing Add:* RI Hosp Providence RI 02902

**THAYER, WILLIAM,** BIOENERGETICS, BIOCHEMICAL PHARMACOLOGY. *Current Pos:* Asst prof, 77-83, ASSOC PROF BIOCHEM, HAHNEMANN UNIV, 83- *Personal Data:* b Plymouth, In, Sept 23, 48; m 78. *Educ:* Ind Univ, BS, 70; Cornell Univ, PhD(biochem), 75. *Honors & Awards:* Res Scientist Develop Award, Nat Inst Alcohol Abuse & Alcoholism, 87. *Mem:* Am Chem Soc; Am Soc Biochem & Molecular Biol; Am Asn Pharmaceut Scientists; Oxygen Soc; AAAS; NY Acad Sci. *Res:* Bioenergetic aspects of alcohol consumption; role of oxygen radicals and peroxides in cardiomyopathy; biochemical toxicology; membrane biochemistry and biophysics. *Mailing Add:* NIM Inc 3624 Market St Suite 508 Philadelphia PA 19104. *Fax:* 215-246-5836

**THAYNE, WILLIAM V,** EXPERIMENTAL DESIGN. *Current Pos:* instr animal sci, WVa Univ, 67-70, asst prof statist & comput sci, 73-75, from asst prof to assoc prof animal sci, 70-85, PROF STATIST & COMPUT SCI, WVA UNIV, 85- *Personal Data:* b Binghamton, NY, July 23, 41; m 63; c 3. *Educ:* Cornell Univ, BS, 63; Univ Ill, MS, 67, PhD(dairy sci), 71. *Prof Exp:* Res asst dairy sci, Univ Ill, 63-67. *Mem:* Biomet Soc; Am Genetic Asn. *Res:* Statitical applications and agriculture. *Mailing Add:* Dept Statist & Comput Sci WVa Univ Knapp Hall Morgantown WV 26506-0001

**THEDFORD, ROOSEVELT,** ORGANIC BIOCHEMISTRY, MOLECULAR BIOLOGY. *Current Pos:* assoc prof, Clark Col, 74-84, PROF CHEM, CLARK ATLANTA UNIV, 84- *Personal Data:* b Greene Co, Ala, Apr 16, 37; m 60; c 5. *Educ:* Clark Col, BS, 59; Univ Buffalo, MA, 62; State Univ NY, Buffalo, PhD(biochem), 73. *Prof Exp:* Cancer res scientist, Roswell Park Mem Inst, 61-69 & 72-74. *Mem:* Am Chem Soc; Sigma Xi. *Res:* Study of the physicochemical and biological properties of alkylated synthetic homopoly ribonucleotides and determination of the functions of strategically located modified nucleosides as found in transfer RNA. *Mailing Add:* Dept Chem Clark Atlanta 223 James Brawley Atlanta GA 30314-4358

**THEEUWES, FELIX,** PHYSICAL CHEMISTRY, PHARMACY. *Current Pos:* res scientist pharm chem, 70-74, PRIN SCIENTIST, ALZA CORP, 74-, VPRES PROD, RES & DEVELOP, 80- *Personal Data:* b Duffel, Belg, May 25, 37; m 62; c 3. *Educ:* Cath Univ Louvain, Licentiaat physics, 61, DrSc(physics), 66. *Honors & Awards:* Louis Busse lectr, Dept Pharmacol, Univ Wis, 81. *Prof Exp:* Res assoc chem, Univ Kans, 66-68, asst prof, 68-70. *Concurrent Pos:* High sch teacher, St Vincent Sch, Westerlo, Belg, 61-64.

*Mem:* Acad Pharmaceut Sci; NY Acad Sci; Am Chem Soc. *Res:* Osmosis, diffusion; solid state physics; cryogenics; high pressure; thermodynamics; pharmacology; pharmacokinetics; calorimetry. *Mailing Add:* 950 Page Mill Rd Palo Alto CA 94304-1012

**THEIL, ELIZABETH,** BIOCHEMISTRY, MOLECULAR & DEVELOPMENTAL BIOLOGY. *Current Pos:* res assoc, 67-69, from instr to prof, 69-88, UNIV PROF BIOCHEM, NC STATE UNIV, 88- *Personal Data:* b Jamaica, NY, Mar 29, 36; div; c 2. *Educ:* Cornell Univ, BS, 57; Columbia Univ, PhD(biochem), 62. *Honors & Awards:* O Max Gardener Award, 88. *Prof Exp:* Res assoc chem, Fla State Univ, 64-66. *Concurrent Pos:* NIH merit grant, 87. *Mem:* Sigma Xi; Am Chem Soc; Soc Develop Biol; Am Soc Biol Chemists. *Res:* Molecular biology of ferritin; cell-specificity of gene expression; developmental changes in gene expression; memory RNA structure/function (translational control of protein synthesis); biophysics of iron proteins (x-ray absorption spectroscopy fine structure). *Mailing Add:* Dept Biochem Box 7622 NC State Univ Raleigh NC 27695-7622. *E-Mail:* elizabeth_theil@ncsu.edu

**THEIL, MICHAEL HERBERT,** POLYMER CHEMISTRY. *Current Pos:* from asst prof to assoc prof, 66-80, PROF TEXTILE CHEM, NC STATE UNIV, 80- *Personal Data:* b Brooklyn, NY, Nov 2, 33; div; c 2. *Educ:* Cornell Univ, AB, 54; Polytech Inst Brooklyn, PhD(chem), 63. *Prof Exp:* Sr res chemist, Res Ctr Tex, US Chem Co, 62-64; res assoc chem, Fla State Univ, 64-66. *Mem:* Am Chem Soc; Am Phys Soc; Sigma Xi; Fiber Soc. *Res:* Phase transitions of polymers; polymerization mechanisms; copolymer statistics. *Mailing Add:* Dept Textile Box 8301 NC State Univ Raleigh NC 27695-8301

**THEILEN, GORDON H,** VETERINARY MEDICINE. *Current Pos:* lectr vet med, Sch Vet Med, Univ Calif, Davis, 56-57, from instr to asst prof, 57-62, from asst prof to prof clin sci, 62-74, PROF SURG, SCH VET MED, UNIV CALIF, DAVIS, 74- *Personal Data:* b Montevideo, Minn, May 29, 28; m 53; c 3. *Educ:* Univ Calif, BS, 53, DVM, 55. *Honors & Awards:* Alexander von Humboldt Sr Scientist Award, WGer Govt, 79-80; Small Animal Res Award, Ralston Purina, 82. *Prof Exp:* Pvt pract, Ore, 55-56. *Concurrent Pos:* Spec fel, Leukemia Prog, Nat Cancer Inst, 64-65; NY Cancer Res Inst fel tumor immunol, with Chester Beatty, Univ London, 72-73; mem sci & rev comt & bd dirs, Leukemia Soc Am, 71-76; World Comt mem, Int Asn Comp Res Leukemia & Related Dis, 90- 94. *Mem:* Am Vet Med Asn; Am Asn Cancer Res; Am Asn Vet Clin; Int Asn Comp Res Leukemia & Related Dis. *Res:* Leukemia-sarcoma and myeloproliferative disease complex and subjects dealing with clinical oncology, particularly tumor biology. *Mailing Add:* Dept Surg Sch Vet Med Univ Calif Davis CA 95616

**THEILHEIMER, FEODOR,** MATHEMATICS. *Current Pos:* RETIRED. *Personal Data:* b Gunzenhausen, Ger, June 18, 09; nat US; m 48; c 1. *Educ:* Berlin Univ, PhD(math), 36. *Prof Exp:* From instr to asst prof math, Trinity Col, 42-48; mathematician, Naval Ord Lab, 48-53, Naval Ship Res & Develop Ctr USN, Bethesda, Md, 53-78. *Mem:* Am Math Soc; Math Asn Am; Soc Indust & Appl Math; Asn Comput Mach. *Res:* Numerical analysis; fluid dynamics. *Mailing Add:* 2608 Spencer Rd Chevy Chase MD 20815-3825

**THEILHEIMER, WILLIAM,** ORGANIC CHEMISTRY. *Current Pos:* consult, 48-59, lit chemist sci info dept, 59-63, RESIDENT CONSULT, HOFFMANN-LA ROCHE, INC, 64- *Personal Data:* b Augsburg, Ger, Oct 11, 14; nat US; wid; c 1. *Educ:* Basel Univ, PhD(org chem), 40. *Honors & Awards:* Herman Skolnik Award, 87. *Prof Exp:* Asst, Basel Univ, 40-47. *Concurrent Pos:* Ed, Synthetic Methods Org Chem, 44-81. *Mem:* Am Chem Soc. *Res:* Synthetic methods. *Mailing Add:* 318 Hillside Ave Nutley NJ 07110-1116

**THEIMER, EDGAR E,** ANALYTICAL CHEMISTRY, PHARMACEUTICAL CHEMISTRY. *Current Pos:* CONSULT, 87- *Personal Data:* b Newark, NJ, June 29, 15; m 58; c 1. *Educ:* Polytech Inst Brooklyn, BChE, 36; NY Univ, MS, 39. *Prof Exp:* Chief chemist, Metrop Labs, Inc, 40-58; chief chemist, Pharmich Div, Mich Chem Corp, 58-61; staff chemist, Int Flavors & Fragrances, Inc, 61-64; head analytical chem sect res & develop, Smith, Miller & Patch, Inc, 64-72; head analytical chem sect prod develop, Cooper Labs, Inc, 72-78; sr sci assoc, US Pharmacopeial Conv, Inc, Rockville, Md, 78-87. *Mem:* Am Chem Soc. *Res:* Analytical methods development. *Mailing Add:* 3919 Brooke Meadow Lane Olney MD 20832-1303

**THEIS, JEROLD HOWARD,** MEDICAL MICROBIOLOGY, PARASITOLOGY. *Current Pos:* from asst prof to assoc prof, 70-86, PROF MED MICROBIOL, SCH MED, UNIV CALIF, DAVIS, 86- *Personal Data:* b Richmond, Calif, July 29, 38; m 67; c 2. *Educ:* Univ Calif, Berkeley, AB, 60; Univ Calif, Davis, DVM, 64, PhD(comp path), 72. *Honors & Awards:* Grand Prize, Int Med Film Festival, Brussels, Belg, 72. *Prof Exp:* Asst res vet, George Williams Hooper Found, Univ Calif, San Francisco Med Ctr & Repub Singapore, 64-67. *Concurrent Pos:* USPHS fel, Univ Calif, Davis, 67-69; consult, Sacramento Med Ctr, Calif, 71- & Primate Res Ctr, Davis, 72-; consult, Environ Health Proj Camp Dresser & McKee Int Inc, 96. *Mem:* Int Soc Travel Med; Am Soc Trop Med & Hyg; Calif Vet Med Asn. *Res:* Mechanisms of transmission of arthropod borne disease agents at the host-arthropod interface; epidemiology of parasitic agents; forensic science. *Mailing Add:* Dept Med Microbiol Univ Calif Sch Med Davis CA 95616. *Fax:* 530-752-8692

**THEIS, RICHARD JAMES,** ORGANIC POLYMER CHEMISTRY, POLYESTER & POLYIMIDE FILMS IN ELECTRICAL END USES. *Current Pos:* TECH CONSULT, 87- *Personal Data:* b Cincinnati, Ohio, Nov 30, 37; m 61, Frances A Witte; c Maria, Laura & Eric. *Educ:* Xavier Univ, BS, 60, MS, 62; Univ Cincinnati, PhD(chem), 66. *Prof Exp:* Res Chemist, E I du Pont de Nemours & Co, Inc, 66-72, staff scientist, Electronics Dept, 73-87. *Concurrent Pos:* Mem, Comt Magnet Wire Insulation, Am Soc Testing & Mat; lectr, Elec & Electronics Insulation Conf. *Mem:* Am Chem Soc; Am Soc Testing & Mat. *Res:* Barrier coatings for films; films for packaging uses; adherable films; filled films; polyester films for capacitors; polyester films for printed circuits and membrane switches; polyimide films for magnet wire insulation. *Mailing Add:* E I du Pont de Nemours & Co Inc PO Box 89 Circleville OH 43113

**THEISEN, CYNTHIA THERES,** ORGANIC CHEMISTRY. *Current Pos:* Assoc ed org chem, 67-75, sr assoc ed, 75-81, SR ED ORG CHEM, CHEM ABSTR SERV, 81- *Personal Data:* b Dearborn, Mich. *Educ:* Siena Heights Col, BS, 60; Purdue Univ, Lafayette, MS, 63; St John's Univ, PhD(org chem), 67. *Mem:* Am Chem Soc. *Mailing Add:* 2450 Sherwood Villa Columbus OH 43221

**THEISEN, WILFRED ROBERT,** HISTORY OF SCIENCE, PHYSICS. *Current Pos:* PROF PHYSICS & HIST SCI, ST JOHN'S UNIV, MINN, 55- *Personal Data:* b Sept 5, 29; US citizen. *Educ:* St John's Univ, BA, 52; Univ Colo, MS, 63; Univ Wis, PhD(hist of sci), 72. *Res:* Medieval optical manuscripts of Euclid; alchemy. *Mailing Add:* Physics Dept St John's Univ Collegeville MN 56321-3000

**THEISS, JEFFREY CHARLES,** GENETIC TOXICOLOGY, CELLULAR TOXICOLOGY. *Current Pos:* dir genetic toxicol, 85-90, DIR MOLECULAR TOXICOL, WARNER LAMBERT CO, 90- *Personal Data:* b Stamford, Conn, Aug 29, 46; m 68; c 2. *Educ:* Univ RI, BS, 68; Brown Univ, PhD(med sci), 73. *Honors & Awards:* Nat Res Award, Am Soc Hosp Pharm Res & Ed Found. *Prof Exp:* Res assoc biochem pharmacol, Roger Williams Gen Hosp & Brown Univ, 71-73; res fel biochem pharmacol, Univ Calif, San Diego & L C Strong Res Found, 73-75; asst res sci pharmacol & toxicol, Univ Calif, San Diego, 75-77, asst prof res community med, 77-80; assoc prof environ health, Sch Pub Health, Univ Tex, 80-85. *Mem:* Sigma Xi; AAAS; Am Asn Cancer Res; Soc Toxicol; Environ Mutagen Soc. *Res:* Mechanistic studies in chemical mutagenesis, carinogenesis and cocarcinogenesis; screening of chemicals for carcinogenic potency by the A mouse lung tumor bioassy; testing of chemicals and body fluids for mutagenic activity. *Mailing Add:* Warner Lambert Co Parke Davis Div 2800 Plymouth Rd Ann Arbor MI 48105

**THEKDI, ARVIND C,** COMBUSTION ENGINEERING, HEAT TRANSFER. *Current Pos:* VPRES, INDUGAS, 87- *Personal Data:* b Ahmedabad, India, Aug 5, 41; US citizen. *Educ:* Gujarat Univ, India, BS, 63; Indian Inst Sci, Bangalore, MS, 65; Pa State Univ, PhD(fuel sci), 70. *Prof Exp:* Res engr, Surface Combustion, Midland-Ross Corp, 70-73, mgr thermal systs, 73-77, mgr thermal & mech eng, 78-80, asst dir develop, 80-84, dir res & develop, Tech Ctr, 84-87. *Concurrent Pos:* Res asst, Pa State Univ, 67-70; instr, Toledo Univ, 72-74. *Mem:* Am Soc Mech Engrs; Combustion Inst; Air Pollution Control Asn. *Res:* Energy conservation and conversion; combustion heat transfer; heat recovery; process development in carbon and graphite industry. *Mailing Add:* 7756 Shaftsbury Dr Sylvania OH 43560

**THELEN, CHARLES JOHN,** ORGANIC CHEMISTRY, AEROSPACE TECHNOLOGY. *Current Pos:* TECH ADV, PROPULSION DIV, ATLANTIC RES CORP, 85- *Personal Data:* b Cedar Rapids, Nebr, Mar 2, 21; m 47; c 1. *Educ:* Univ Iowa, BS, 42, PhD(org chem), 49. *Honors & Awards:* L T E Thompsin Award, 80. *Prof Exp:* Chemist, B F Goodrich Co, 42; asst, Univ Iowa, 47-49; fel, Univ Calif, Los Angeles, 49-50; res chemist, US Naval Ord Test Sta, Naval Weapons Ctr, 50-58, head explosives & pyrotech div, 58-60, head propellants div, 60-68, missile propulsion technol adminr, 69-80, air weaponry technol adminr, 80-82, weapons cookoff prog adminr, 82-85. *Concurrent Pos:* Michelson Lab fel mgt, Naval Weapons Ctr, 72; mem bd dirs, Ridgecrest Community Hosp, 76-85 & 88- *Mem:* Am Chem Soc; Sigma Xi. *Res:* Missile propulsion technology and high polymers. *Mailing Add:* 344 E Monte Vista Ave Ridgecrest CA 93555-7708

**THELEN, THOMAS HARVEY,** GENETICS. *Current Pos:* from asst prof to assoc prof, 70-82, PROF BIOL, CENT WASH UNIV, 82- *Personal Data:* b Albany, Minn, Aug 11, 41; m 64, Sally; c Gretchen & Paul. *Educ:* St John's Univ, Minn, BS, 64; Univ Minn, PhD(genetics), 69. *Prof Exp:* Cytogeneticist, Minn Dept Health, 69-70. *Res:* Behavioral genetics, population modeling. *Mailing Add:* Dept Biol Cent Wash Univ Ellensburg WA 98926

**THELIN, JACK HORSTMANN,** chemistry; deceased, see previous edition for last biography

**THELIN, LOWELL CHARLES,** TECHNICAL MANAGEMENT. *Current Pos:* HEALTH PHYSICS CONSULT, 96- *Personal Data:* b Plainfield, NJ, July 31, 46; m 71, Ellen; c Alyson & Alexandra. *Educ:* Muhlenberg Col, AB, 68; Rutgers Univ, MS, 73; Fairleigh-Dickinson Univ, BSEE, 90. *Prof Exp:* Radiation safety officer, Cambridge Nuclear Radiopharmaceut Corp, NL Industs, 73-74, Indust Reactor Labs, Inc, 74-75 & Sterling Forest Res Ctr, Union Carbide Corp, 75-87; staff health physicist, Cintichem Inc, Subsid Hoffman-Laroche Inc, 87-94. *Concurrent Pos:* Appointee, Comprehensive Cert Panel Examr, Am Bd Health Physics, 85-88. *Mem:* Health Physics Soc.

*Res:* Technical analysis for decommissioning plan of major hot laboratory and nuclear research reactor facility; noble gas effluent dosimetry; beta dosimetry; fission product internal dose assessment; nuclear worker radiation protection program. *Mailing Add:* 126 Greenlawn Ave Clifton NJ 07013

**THELLMANN, EDWARD L,** METALLURGY. *Current Pos:* RETIRED. *Personal Data:* b Cleveland, Ohio. *Educ:* Cleveland State Univ, BS, 59. *Honors & Awards:* Am Soc Metals Award; John C Valler Award; IR-100 Award. *Prof Exp:* Mgr, Appl Mat Technol, Gould, Inc, 59-87. *Mem:* Fel Am Soc Metals; Am Powder Metall Inst. *Res:* Ten patents; milestone advances in titanium powder metallurgy; fuel cells; author of numerous technical papers. *Mailing Add:* Village Walton Hills Munic Bldg 7595 Walton Rd Walton Hills OH 44146

**THELMAN, JOHN PATRICK,** PAPER CHEMISTRY. *Current Pos:* chief res proj chemist, Scott Paper Co, Philadelphia, 77-81, chief develop assoc, 81-87, chief technologist, 87-96, CHIEF TECHNOLOGIST, KIMBERLY CLARK, WIS, 96- *Personal Data:* b Richmond Hill, NY, Dec 25, 42; m 65; c 3. *Educ:* State Univ NY, Stony Brook, BS, 64; State Univ NY, Buffalo, PhD(org chem), 69. *Prof Exp:* Res chemist, ITT Rayonnier Inc, Whippany, NJ, 68-71, res group leader, Acetate Sect, 71-74, res supvr, Acetate Sect, Eastern Res Div, 74-77. *Mem:* Tech Asn Pulp & Paper Indust. *Res:* Papermaking; product development. *Mailing Add:* 1038 N Lake St Neenah WI 54956-1431

**THEMELIS, NICKOLAS JOHN,** CHEMICAL ENGINEERING, INDUSTRIAL ECOLOGY. *Current Pos:* chmn, Henry Krumb Sch Mines, 85-87, PROF MINERAL ENG, COLUMBIA UNIV, 80-, HEAD, EARTH ENG CTR & STANLEY THOMPSON PROF CHEM METALL, 91- *Personal Data:* b Athens, Greece, Apr 25, 33; US citizen; m 91, Liliana Nikolich; c 3. *Educ:* McGill Univ, BEng, 56, PhD(chem eng), 61. *Honors & Awards:* ERCO Award, Minerals, Metals & Mats Soc, 71, 72 & 75, McConnell Award, 87. *Prof Exp:* Engr, Pulp & Paper Res Inst Can, 56-57; res consult, Strategic Mat Corp, 60-62; head, Dept Chem Eng, Noranda Res Ctr, Can, 62-66, mgr, Eng Div, 67-72; vpres res & eng, Metal Mining Div, Kennecott Copper Corp, 72-79, vpres technol, 79-80. *Mem:* Nat Acad Eng; Can Inst Mining & Metall; Can Soc Chem Engrs; Am Inst Mining Metall & Petrol Engrs; fel Metall Soc. *Res:* Process metallurgy; rate phenomena; process design. *Mailing Add:* Henry Krumb Sch Mines Columbia Univ New York NY 10027

**THEOBALD, CHARLES EDWIN, JR,** ELECTRICAL ENGINEERING, OPERATIONS RESEARCH. *Current Pos:* ENG CONSULT, 74- *Personal Data:* b Hackensack, NJ, Aug 14, 27; m 52, Theresa A LeBlanc; c Marc, Amy & Carl. *Educ:* Columbia Univ, AB, 47, AM, 48; Mass Inst Technol, SM, 59. *Prof Exp:* Aerodynamicist, Curtiss-Wright Corp, NJ, 49-56; sr aerodynamicist, Kaman Aircraft Corp, Conn, 56-58; teaching asst instrumentation & control, Mass Inst Technol, 58-59; sr scientist, Syst Develop Corp, 59-67; prin engr, Systs Electronics Lab, Raytheon Co, 67-74. *Concurrent Pos:* Engr, H H Aerospace Design Co, 77- *Res:* Adaptive learning and optimal control; statistical decision theory; queueing theory; reliability theory; stability and control of fixed and rotary wing aircraft; public transit operations; railroad track dynamics and geometry. *Mailing Add:* 37 Old Billerica Rd Bedford MA 01730

**THEOBALD, J KARL,** physics, for more information see previous edition

**THEOBALD, WILLIAM L,** systematic botany, horticulture, for more information see previous edition

**THEODORE, JOSEPH M, JR,** PHARMACY. *Current Pos:* assoc prof, 66-74, PROF PHARM, OHIO NORTHERN UNIV, 74- *Personal Data:* b Fall River, Mass, Apr 29, 31; m 55; c 5. *Educ:* New Eng Col Pharm, BS, 55; Univ Wis, MS, 58; Mass Col Pharm, PhD(pharm), 65. *Prof Exp:* Instr pharm, New Eng Col Pharm, 58-61; from instr to asst prof, Northeastern Univ, 62-66. *Mem:* Am Pharmaceut Asn; Am Col Apothecaries; Am Soc Hosp Pharmacists. *Res:* Spectrofluorometric analysis of drugs; solid state reactions occurring in certain tablet formulations. *Mailing Add:* Dept Pharm Ohio Northern Univ 525 S Main St Ada OH 45810-1555

**THEODORE, TED GEORGE,** ECONOMIC GEOLOGY. *Current Pos:* GEOLOGIST, US GEOL SURV, 67- *Personal Data:* b Los Angeles, Calif, Aug 19, 37; m 61; c 2. *Educ:* Univ Calif, Los Angeles, AB, 61, PhD(geol), 67. *Mem:* AAAS; Geol Soc Am; Soc Econ Geol. *Res:* Genesis of porphyrytype, molybdenum and copper deposits; geochemistry of base-metal ore deposits; fabrics of metamorphic terranes. *Mailing Add:* 2015 Camino De Los Robles Menlo Park CA 94025

**THEODORE, THEODORE SPIROS,** MICROBIAL PHYSIOLOGY. *Current Pos:* MEM STAFF, LAB STEPOCOCCAL DIS, NAT INST ALLERGY & INFECTIOUS DIS, NIH, 76- *Personal Data:* b Braddock, Pa, Nov 6, 33; m 57; c 3. *Educ:* Univ Pittsburgh, BSc, 55, MSc, 57, PhD(bact), 62. *Prof Exp:* Asst bact, Univ Pittsburgh, 57-62; staff fel, NIH, 62-65, res microbiologist, 65-76. *Mem:* AAAS; Am Soc Microbiol. *Res:* Bacterial physiology and nutrition; intermediary and mineral metabolism; biochemical genetics. *Mailing Add:* 1136 Pipestem Pl Rockville MD 20854

**THEODORE, WILLIAM H,** NEUROLOGY. *Current Pos:* Sr investr, 79-86, CHIEF, CLIN EPILEPSY SECT, NIH, 86- *Personal Data:* b New York, NY, July 26, 47. *Educ:* Harvard Univ, BA, 69; Columbia Univ, MD, 74. *Honors & Awards:* Clin Investr Award, Am Epilepsy Soc, 90. *Mem:* Am Epilepsy Soc; Am Neurol Asn; Am Acad Neurol. *Mailing Add:* NIH Clin Epilepsy Sect Bldg 10 Rm 5 N250 Bethesda MD 20892. *Fax:* 301-402-2871

**THEODORIDES, VASSILIOS JOHN,** DRUG TOXICOLOGY. *Current Pos:* sr microbiologist parasitologist, SmithKline & Fr Labs, 65-66, group leader microbiol, 66-68, group leader, Animal Health Dept, 68, assoc dir res chemother, 68-73, mgr parasitol, SmithKline Corp, 73-82, DIR TOXICOL, SMITHKLINE & BEECHAM AH, 82- *Personal Data:* b Konstantia, Greece, Feb 20, 31; US citizen; m 58; c 3. *Educ:* Univ Thessaloniki, DVM, 56; Boston Univ, MA, 60, PhD(parasitol), 63. *Prof Exp:* Asst to prof clins vet sch, Univ Thessaloniki, 56-57; teaching fel microbiol, Boston Univ, 58-62; lectr micros anat, 62-63; res parasitologist, Charles Pfizer & Co, Inc, 63-65. *Concurrent Pos:* Adj prof, Sch Vet Med, Univ Pa, 72- *Mem:* Am Soc Microbiol; Am Vet Med Asn; Am Soc Parasitol; Am Soc Trop Med & Hyg; NY Acad Sci. *Res:* Morphology, physiology and electron microscopy of Trichomonas; development of chemotherapeutic agents for the control of gastrointestinal nematodes of domestic animals; toxicologic evaluvation of potential animal drugs. *Mailing Add:* 1632 Herron Lane West Chester PA 19380

**THEODORIDIS, GEORGE CONSTANTIN,** BIOMEDICAL ENGINEERING. *Current Pos:* ASSOC PROF BIOMED ENG, UNIV VA, 70- *Personal Data:* b Braila, Romania, Dec 3, 35; US citizen; m 75, Lilly K Hyman; c Alexander. *Educ:* Nat Tech Univ Athens, dipl elec eng, 59. *Hon Degrees:* ScD, Mass Inst Technol, 64. *Prof Exp:* Res assoc biol, Mass Inst Technol, 64; sr scientist space res, Am Sci Eng, Mass, 64-68; assoc prof physiol optics, Univ Calif, Berkeley, 68-70. *Concurrent Pos:* Prof, Univ Patras, Greece, 76-83; consult, Food & Drug Admin, 77-78 & Appl Physics Lab, Johns Hopkins Univ, 78. *Mem:* Biomed Eng Soc; Am Phys Soc; Inst Elec & Electronics Engrs; Am Geophys Union; NY Acad Sci. *Res:* Speech perception; evolution; space physics. *Mailing Add:* Dept Biomed Eng Univ Va Charlottesville VA 22908. *Fax:* 804-982-3870; *E-Mail:* gct@virginia.edu

**THEODOROU, DOROS NICOLAS,** computer modeling of matter, polymer science & engineering, for more information see previous edition

**THEOFANOUS, THEOFANIS GEORGE,** MULTIPHASE FLOW, RISK ASSESSMENT & MANAGEMENT. *Current Pos:* PROF CHEM & NUCLEAR ENG, UNIV CALIF, SANTA BARBARA, 85-, PROF MECH & ENVIRON ENG, 94- *Personal Data:* b Athens, Greece, May 21, 42; m 69; c 2. *Educ:* Nat Tech Univ Athens, dipl, 65; Univ Minn, Minneapolis, PhD(chem eng), 69. *Honors & Awards:* E O Lawrence Medal. *Prof Exp:* Instr chem eng, Univ Minn, Minneapolis, 68-69; from asst prof to prof nuclear eng, Purdue Univ, 69-85. *Concurrent Pos:* Dir, Ctr Risk Studies & Safety, Univ Calif, Santa Barbara. *Mem:* Fel Am Nuclear Soc; Am Inst Chem Engrs. *Res:* Transport phenomena in turbulent and multiphase systems with particular emphasis on nuclear and chemical reactor safety applications. *Mailing Add:* Dept Chem Eng Univ Calif Santa Barbara CA 93106-0001. *E-Mail:* theo@theo.ucsb.edu

**THEOFILOPOULOS, ARGYRIOS N,** IMMUNOLOGY. *Current Pos:* MEM, DEPT IMMUNOL, SCRIPPS CLIN & RES FOUND, 73- *Educ:* Univ Athens, Greece, MD, 70. *Mailing Add:* Dept Immunol IMM3 Scripps Clin & Res Found 10666 N Torrey Pines Rd La Jolla CA 92037-1092. *Fax:* 619-554-6229

**THEOKRITOFF, GEORGE,** PALEONTOLOGY. *Current Pos:* from assoc prof to prof, 67-94, EMER PROF GEOL, RUTGERS UNIV, NEWARK, 94- *Personal Data:* b Eng, Apr 7, 24; US citizen; m, Elizabeth A Briere. *Educ:* Univ London, BSc, 45, MSc, 48, PhD(geol), 61. *Prof Exp:* Instr geol, Mt Holyoke Col, 54-56 & Bucknell Univ, 56-60; asst prof, Univ NH, 60-61; assoc prof, St Lawrence Univ, 64-67. *Mem:* Geol Soc Am; Geol Soc London; Paleont Soc. *Res:* Cambrian paleontology and stratigraphy, including morphology, taxonomy and evolution of Cambrian trilobites; ecology of Cambrian organisms; biogeography and biostratigraphy of North Atlantic region. *Mailing Add:* Dept Geol Rutgers Univ Newark NJ 07102

**THEOLOGIDES, ATHANASIOS,** INTERNAL MEDICINE, ONCOLOGY. *Current Pos:* From instr to assoc prof, 65-74, Nat Cancer Inst grant, Med Ctr, 69-75, PROF MED, MED SCH, UNIV MINN, MINNEAPOLIS, 74- *Personal Data:* b Ptolemais, Greece, Feb 5, 31; US citizen; m 65, Maria Mystakidou; c Stergios & Evangelia. *Educ:* Aristoteles Univ, MD, 55; Univ Minn, Minneapolis, PhD(med & biochem), 67. *Mem:* Am Asn Cancer Res; Am Fedn Clin Res; Am Soc Clin Oncol; Soc Exp Biol & Med; Am Soc Hemat. *Res:* Medical oncology; tumor-host metabolic interrelationships; hematology. *Mailing Add:* Sta 13/3506 Minn Mutual Life Ins Co 400 Robert St N St Paul MN 55101-2098

**THEON, JOHN SPERIDON,** SPACEBORNE OBSERVATIONS OF EARTH. *Current Pos:* CONSULT, CHIEF SCIENTIST, INST GLOBAL ENVIRON STRATEGIES, 95- *Personal Data:* b Wash, DC, Dec 12, 34; m 65, Joanne Edens; c Christopher J & Catherine. *Educ:* Univ Md, BS, 57; Pa State Univ, BS, 59, MS, 62; Univ Tenn, PhD(eng sci & mech), 85. *Honors & Awards:* Losey Medal, Am Inst Aeronaut & Astronaut, 86; Silver Snoopy Award, 85; Radio Wave Award, Ministry Posts & Telecom Japan, 95. *Prof Exp:* Aeronaut eng, Douglas Aircraft Co, 57-58; weather officer, USAF, 58-60; mech engr, US Naval Ord Lab; res meteorologist, Goddard Space

Flight Ctr, NASA, 62-74, head, Meteorol Br, 74-77, asst chief, Lab Atmospheric Sci, 77-78, mgr, Global Weather Res, Earth Sci Div, 78-82, chief, Atmosphere Dynamics & Radiation, 82-91, chief, Atmosphere Dynamics, Radiation & Hydrol, Earth Sci Div, 91-93, chief, Phys Climate Res Br, Mission To Planet Earth Sci Div, 93-94, sr scientist, MTPE Sci Div, 94-95; consult, Orbital Sci Corp, 95-96. *Concurrent Pos:* Proj scientist, Nimbus 5 & Nimbus 6 projs, Goddard Space Flight Ctr, 72-78; prog scientist, Spacelab 3 Prog, NASA Hq, 78-86 & Trop Rainfall Measuring Mission Prog, 88-95; mem, Laser in-Space Tech Prog, 82-95; chmn, Atmospheric Environ Tech Comn, Am Inst Aeronaut & Astronaut, 86-89; instrument scientist, EOS Prog, 88-93, EOS PM Prog Scientist, 93-95. *Mem:* Am Meteorol Soc; Am Geophys Union. *Res:* Explored the meteorology of the mesosphere using sounding rockets; investigation of circulation, noctilucent clouds, gravity waves and turbulence; developed techniques to observe precipitation from space using passive microwave radiometry; broad research program in remote sensing and climate change; focused on spaceborn observations on earth. *Mailing Add:* 6801 Lupine Lane McLean VA 22101. *Fax:* 703-875-8635; *E-Mail:* jtheon@erols.com

**THEOPOLD, KLAUS HELLMUT,** MATERIALS SCIENCE. *Current Pos:* assoc prof, 90-95, PROF, DEPT CHEM & BIOCHEM & CHEM ENG, UNIV DEL, 95- *Personal Data:* b Berlin, Ger, Apr 18, 54; c Beatina E, Jessica G & Nikolas M. *Educ:* Univ Hamburg, vordiplom, 77; Univ Calif, Berkeley, PhD(chem), 82. *Honors & Awards:* Presidential Young Investr Award, 85. *Prof Exp:* Assoc fel, Mass Inst Technol, 82-83; asst prof inorg chem, Cornell Univ, 83-90. *Concurrent Pos:* Alfred P Sloan res fel, 92. *Mem:* Am Chem Soc; Ger Chem Soc; Mat Res Soc; fel AAAS. *Res:* Structure and reactivity of organometallic and inorganic compounds; models for catalysis; semiconductor clusters. *Mailing Add:* Dept Chem & Biochem Univ Del Newark DE 19716. *Fax:* 302-831-6335; *E-Mail:* theopold@udel.edu

**THERIAULT, GILLES P,** OCCUPATIONAL CANCER EPIDEMIOLOGY, OCCUPATIONAL MEDICINE. *Current Pos:* assoc prof, 82-89, CHAIR, DEPT OCCUP HEALTH, MCGILL UNIV, 83-, PROF OCCUP HEALTH & EPIDEMIOL, 89- *Personal Data:* b Montreal, Que, Jan 26, 41; m 65, Helene Garceau; c Valerie & Sarah. *Educ:* Col St-Joseph, Trois-Rivieres, BA, 62; Univ Laval, MD, 66; Harvard Univ, MIH, 71, DrPH, 73. *Prof Exp:* Teacher human biol, Centre des Hautes etudes collegiales de Trois-Rivieres, 68-70; teaching fel health & environ, Harvard Univ, 72; course supvr occup health, Univ Laval, 73-77, from asst prof to assoc prof, 77-82. *Concurrent Pos:* Consult specialist, Gen Hosp Montreal, 82- & Hosp Sacre-Coeur, Montreal, 88- *Res:* Occupational cancer epidemiology; epidemiology of occupational diseases; exposure to electromagnetic fields and cancer; poly aromatic hydrocarbons and cancer. *Mailing Add:* Joint Depts Epidemiol Biostatist & Occup Health McGill Univ 1020 Pine Ave W Montreal PQ H3A 1A2 Can. *Fax:* 514-398-7435

**THERIOT, EDWARD DENNIS, JR,** PHYSICS. *Current Pos:* CONSULT, 94- *Personal Data:* b Baton Rouge, La, Mar 19, 38; m 60; c 2. *Educ:* Duke Univ, BS, 60; Yale Univ, MS, 61, PhD(physics), 67. *Prof Exp:* NATO vis scientist fel physics, Europ Orgn Nuclear Res, Geneva, Switz, 67-68; res fel, Los Alamos Sci Lab, 68-69; physicist, Fermi Nat Accelerator Lab, 69-93, head, Neutrino Dept, 76-78, dept head collider detector, 81-88, assoc dir, 89-93. *Mem:* Am Phys Soc. *Res:* Elementary particle physics, particularly relating to weak and electromagnetic interactions; neutrino interactions; hyperon decays; particle production; positronium; proton-antiproton colliding beams. *Mailing Add:* 445 N Shore Rd Longboat Key FL 34228

**THERIOT, KEVIN JUDE,** POLYALPHAOLEFIN. *Current Pos:* Sr res & develop specialist, 94-96, ADVISOR, ALBEMARLE CORP, 96- *Personal Data:* b Houma, La, June 16, 58; m 91. *Educ:* NE La Univ, BSc, 80; La State Univ, PhD(chem), 89. *Prof Exp:* Sr res & develop chemist, Ethyl Corp, 89-92, res & develop specialist, 92-94. *Mem:* Am Chem Soc. *Res:* Polyalphaolefins; synthetic lubricants; organopalladium compounds; organoplatinum compounds; pharmaceutical compounds. *Mailing Add:* 8000 GSRI Ave Baton Rouge LA 70820

**THERIOT, LEROY JAMES,** INORGANIC CHEMISTRY. *Current Pos:* from asst prof to assoc prof, 65-80, PROF CHEM, NTEX STATE UNIV, 80- *Personal Data:* b Port Arthur, Tex, Apr 11, 35; m 58; c 3. *Educ:* Southwestern La Univ, BS, 57; Tulane Univ, PhD(chem), 62. *Prof Exp:* Chemist, Ethyl Corp, 62-63; fel, Harvard Univ, 63-64 & Univ Tex, 64-65. *Mem:* Am Chem Soc. *Res:* Preparation and electronic structure of metal complexes. *Mailing Add:* Dept Chem NTex State Univ PO Box 5068 Denton TX 76203-0068

**THERN, ROYAL EDWARD,** ACCELERATOR PHYSICS. *Current Pos:* SR PHYSICS ASSOC, BROOKHAVEN NAT LAB, 79- *Personal Data:* b Winona, Minn, May 11, 42; m 71; c 3. *Educ:* St Olaf Col, BA, 64; Mass Inst Technol, PhD(physics), 72. *Prof Exp:* Res specialist, Univ Pa, 72-79. *Mem:* Am Phys Soc. *Res:* Accelerator physics; beam lines; instrumentation. *Mailing Add:* Accelerator Dept Bldg 911B Brookhaven Nat Lab Upton NY 11973

**THERRIEN, CHESTER DALE,** MYCOLOGY, CYTOCHEMISTRY. *Current Pos:* From asst prof to assoc prof biol, 65-87, ASSOC PROF BIOL & PLANT PATH, PA STATE UNIV, 87- *Personal Data:* b Coos Bay, Ore, June 18, 36; m 83; c 4. *Educ:* St Ambrose Col, BA, 62; Univ Tex, PhD(bot), 66. *Mem:* Bot Soc Am; Genetics Soc Am. *Res:* Cytology and genetics of phytophthora infestans. *Mailing Add:* Dept Biol NC Wesleyan Coll 3400 N Wesleyan Blvd Rocky Mount NC 27804-8677

**THET, LYN AUNG,** BIOCHEMISTRY, PATHOLOGY. *Current Pos:* ASSOC PROF MED, UNIV WIS, 90- *Educ:* Inst Med, Burma, MD, 71. *Prof Exp:* Asst prof med, Sch Med, Duke Univ, 80-90. *Mailing Add:* Dept Med Univ Wis Med Sch H-6-380 Clin Sci Ctr 600 Highland Ave Madison WI 53792-3240

**THEUER, PAUL JOHN,** TECHNOLOGY TRANSFER-MANAGEMENT. *Current Pos:* SR VPRES, SHELADIA ASSOCS, INC, ROCKVILLE, MD, 91- *Personal Data:* b Hoboken, NJ, Jan 9, 36; m 60, Doris J Kenny; c Paul J Jr & Judyth M. *Educ:* St Peter's Col, BS, 57; Iowa State Univ, BS, 66; Pa State Univ, MEng, 73; Army War Col, dipl, 80. *Prof Exp:* Comput programmer, Nat Coun Compensation Ins, 57; reliability engr missiles, Douglas Aricraft Co, 57-58; comd & staff assignments, US Army, 58-68, comdr construct mgt, 808th Eng Battalion, 68-69, chief opers log mgt, US Army Support Command, Cam Ranh Bay, SVietnam, 69-70, commandant of cadets, Mil Sci, Pa State Univ, 70-73, div chief construct mgt, US Army Eng Command, Europe, 73-74, exec chief staff, Off Eng, HQ US Army, Europe, 74-76, rep hq, Staff HQ, US Army, Europe, 76-78, asst dir construct mgt, HQ US Army CEngrs, 78-83, comdr & dir, US Army Construct Eng Res Lab, 83-86, vpres, Stanley Consults, Inc, Washington, DC, 86-91. *Concurrent Pos:* Consult, HP Gauff Engrs, Inc, Frankfurt, WGer, 80-83; pres, Theuer Consults, Commodities Mgt, Eng Serv, 86- *Mem:* Am Soc Civil Engrs; Sigma Xi; Am Consult Engrs Coun; Soc Am Mil Engrs. *Res:* Construction engineering and facilities management; solid waste management and disposal; solid-liquid fuel boiler combustion and conversion; industrial sanitary-environmental facilities design; technology transfer; systems maintenance management. *Mailing Add:* 2 Chester Mill Ct Silver Spring MD 20906. *Fax:* 301-948-7174

**THEUER, RICHARD C,** NUTRITION. *Current Pos:* vpres res & develop, 83-86, pres, 86-89, VPRES RES & DEVELOP, BEECHNUT NUTRIT CORP, 89- *Personal Data:* b Hoboken, NJ, June 15, 39; m 62; c 3. *Educ:* St Peter's Col, NJ, BS, 60; Univ Wis-Madison, MS, 62, PhD(biochem), 65; Ind State Univ, MBA, 73. *Prof Exp:* Res asst biochem, Univ Wis, 60-65; sr scientist, Mead Johnson Res Ctr, 65-67, group leader, 67-68, sect leader, 68-70, dir dept nutrit res, 70-75; dir nutrit bus develop, Int Div, Bristol-Myers Co, 76-80; asst vpres nutrit serv, Nestec, 80-83, vpres res & develop, 83-86, 89-, PRES, BEECHNUT NUTRIT CORP, 86-89. *Mem:* Am Chem Soc; Am Inst Nutrit. *Res:* Infant nutrition; research and development of nutritional specialty products. *Mailing Add:* Res & Develop Beech-Nut Nutrit Corp 800 Market St St Louis MO 63101. *Fax:* 314-982-1679

**THEUER, WILLIAM JOHN,** ORGANIC CHEMISTRY. *Current Pos:* res chemist, Celanese Res Co, 67-68, sr res chemist, Celanese Fibers Co, 68-71, group leader, Celanese Fibers Mkt Co, 71-74, tech mgr, 74-76, prod mgr, 76-77, tech dir resins, 78, TECH DIR RESINS DIV, CELANESE POLYMER-SPECIALTIES CO, 79-, BUS MGR, BASF, 85- *Personal Data:* b New York, NY, Nov 27, 35; m 61; c 3. *Educ:* Queens Col, BS, 57; Univ Del, PhD(chem), 65. *Prof Exp:* Sr scientist, Sandoz Pharmaceut, 65-67. *Mem:* Am Chem Soc; Am Asn Textile Chemists & Colorists; Int Disposable & Nonwoven Asn; Sigma Xi. *Res:* Heterocyclic chemistry; photochemistry; cellulose and fiber chemistry; spinning research; pharmaceutical chemistry; industrial fibers; textile polymer chemistry. *Mailing Add:* 1 Pine Knoll Dr Lake Wylie SC 29710-9245

**THEURER, CLARK BRENT,** ANIMAL NUTRITION. *Current Pos:* assoc prof, 64-71, head, Dept Animal Sci, 81-88, PROF ANIMAL SCI, UNIV ARIZ, 71- *Personal Data:* b Logan, Utah, Oct 17, 34; m 56, Cheri Peterson; c Cindy, Michael, Jeff & Alan. *Educ:* Utah State Univ, BS, 56; Iowa State Univ, MS, 60, PhD(animal nutrit), 62. *Honors & Awards:* Indust Serv Award, Am Soc Animal Sci, 91. *Prof Exp:* Asst prof animal sci, Va Polytech Inst, 62-64. *Concurrent Pos:* Mem, Bd Dir, Am Soc Animal Sci, 79-81. *Mem:* Fel Am Soc Animal Sci (pres, pres-elect, secy-treas, 83-88); Am Dairy Sci Asn; Am Inst Nutrit; Fedn Am Soc Food Animal Sci (pres & vpres, 89-91); Coun Agr Sci & Technol. *Res:* Starch and protein metabolism in ruminants; role of splanchnic tissues in partitioning nutrients for increased efficiency of animal protein production. *Mailing Add:* Dept Animal Sci Univ Ariz Agr Sci Bldg 38 Rm 208 Tucson AZ 85721-0001. *Fax:* 520-621-9435

**THEURER, JESSOP CLAIR,** PLANT GENETICS, PLANT BREEDING. *Current Pos:* res agronomist, USDA, 62-63, geneticist, Crops Res Div, 63-89, Sugarbeet res geneticist & res leader, Agr Res Serv, 89-93, ADJ RES GENETICIST, USDA, 93- *Personal Data:* b Logan, Utah, Sept 4, 28; m 53; c Michael, Scott, Bruce & David. *Educ:* Utah State Univ, BS, 53, MS, 57; Univ Minn, PhD(plant genetics), 62. *Honors & Awards:* Meritorious Serv Award, Am Soc Sugar Beet Technologists, 91. *Prof Exp:* Res fel oats radiation, Univ Minn, 61-62. *Concurrent Pos:* Int farm youth exchange student, Lebanon & Syria, 52; assoc ed, Crop Sci Soc Am, 70-72; actg nat prog leader, Hort & Sugar Crops, Beltsville, Md, 91. *Mem:* Am Soc Agron; Am Soc Sugar Beet Technol; Crop Sci Soc Am. *Res:* Agronomy; cytology; plant pathology; breeding, genetics, male sterility, plant architecture and disease resistance of sugar beets. *Mailing Add:* Crop & Soil Sci Mich State Univ East Lansing MI 48824

**THEUSCH, COLLEEN JOAN,** NUMBER THEORY, OPERATIONS RESEARCH. *Current Pos:* sr applns analyst, 89-91, APPLNS DEVELOP SPECIALIST, AM GREETINGS, 91- *Personal Data:* b Milwaukee, Wis, Dec 18, 32. *Educ:* Col Racine, Wis, BEd, 61; Univ Detroit, MA, 66; Mich State Univ, PhD(math), 71. *Prof Exp:* Instr math, Col Racine, 70-71; mathematician, Res & Develop Dept, Richman Bros Co, 71-84, sr res assoc, 84-89; sr res assoc, Laser Cam, 84-89. *Concurrent Pos:* Instr, Cleveland State Univ & Cuyahoga Community Col, 71-72. *Mem:* Am Math Soc. *Res:*

Development of grading and marker making system and numerically controlled cutting via laser cutters in men's clothing manufacturing; software for laser cutters; CAD systems; customize mac graphics programs. *Mailing Add:* 22962 Maple Ridge Rd North Olmsted OH 44070-1471

**THEWALT, MICHAEL L W,** SEMICONDUCTOR PHYSICS, OPTICAL PROPERTIES OF SEMICONDUCTORS. *Current Pos:* PROF PHYSICS, SIMON FRASER UNIV, 80- *Personal Data:* b Karlsruhe, Ger, Dec 5, 49; Can citizen; m 82, Jennifer; c Eric. *Educ:* McMaster Univ, BSc, 72; Univ BC, Msc, 75, PhD(physics), 77. *Honors & Awards:* Rutherford Medal, Royal Soc Can, 94. *Prof Exp:* Res fel, T J Watson Res Lab, IBM Corp, 78-80. *Mem:* Fel Am Phys Soc; Can Asn Physicists; Mat Res Soc. *Res:* Optical properties of semiconductors, especially involving excitons as defects; semiconductor and defect characterization; photoluminenescence, Raman scattering and optical absorption spectroscopy. *Mailing Add:* Dept Physics Simon Fraser Univ Burnaby BC V5A 1S6 Can. *Fax:* 604-291-3592; *E-Mail:* thewalt@.sfu.ca

**THEWS, ROBERT L(EROY),** THEORETICAL PHYSICS. *Current Pos:* from asst prof to assoc prof, 70-80, PROF PHYSICS, UNIV ARIZ., 80- *Personal Data:* b Fairmont, Minn, June 13, 39; c 2. *Educ:* Mass Inst Technol, SB, 62, PhD(physics), 66. *Prof Exp:* Physicist, Lawrence Berkeley Lab, Univ Calif, 66-68; res assoc & asst prof physics, Univ Rochester, 68-70. *Mem:* Am Phys Soc. *Res:* Theoretical high energy elementary particle physics. *Mailing Add:* 7037 N Chimney Rock Pl Tucson AZ 85718. *Fax:* 520-621-4721

**THIBAULT, LAWRENCE L,** ENGINEERING. *Honors & Awards:* Melville Medal, Am Soc Mech Engrs, 95. *Mailing Add:* 2406 Fitlers Walk Philadelphia PA 19103

**THIBAULT, ROGER EDWARD,** ECOLOGY. *Current Pos:* ASST PROF BIOL, BOWLING GREEN STATE UNIV, 75- *Personal Data:* b Salem, Mass, June 28, 47; m 70; c 1. *Educ:* Univ Wis, BS, 69; Univ Conn, PhD(ecol), 74. *Prof Exp:* NDEA fel ecol, Univ Conn, 71-74; instr zool, Iowa State Univ, 74-75. *Mem:* Am Soc Ichthyol & Herpet; Ecol Soc Am; Soc Study Evolution; Sigma Xi; AAAS. *Res:* Aquatic ecology; aquatic entomology and ichthyology; evolution of unisexual vertebrates. *Mailing Add:* Dept Biol Sci Bowling Green State Univ 1001 E Wooster St Bowling Green OH 43403-0001

**THIBAULT, THOMAS DELOR,** ORGANIC CHEMISTRY. *Current Pos:* RES SCIENTIST, DOWELANCO, 89⁻ *Personal Data:* b Claremont, NH, Aug 14, 42; m 69; c 4. *Educ:* Providence Col, BS, 64; Mass Inst Technol, PhD(org chem), 69. *Prof Exp:* Sr org chemist, Eli Lilly & Co, 69-74, res scientist, 74-89. *Mem:* Am Chem Soc. *Res:* Synthesis of biologically active structures; reaction mechanisms; new synthetic reactions. *Mailing Add:* 1520 N Franklin Rd Indianapolis IN 46219-3918

**THIBEAULT, JACK CLAUDE,** COLLOID CHEMISTRY, POLYMER CHEMISTRY. *Current Pos:* res chemist, 74-93, RES FEL, ROHM & HAAS CO, 93- *Personal Data:* b Lowell, Mass, June 23, 46; div; c Patrick. *Educ:* Lowell Technol Inst, BS, 67; Calif Inst Technol, PhD(inorg chem), 72. *Prof Exp:* Fel theoret chem, Cornell Univ, 72-74. *Concurrent Pos:* Vis fel, Princeton Univ, 93. *Mem:* Am Chem Soc. *Res:* Physical chemistry and rheology of polymer colloids and solutions. *Mailing Add:* Res Div Rohm & Haas Co 727 Norristown Rd Spring House PA 19477. *E-Mail:* rssjct@rohmhaas.com

**THIBERT, ROGER JOSEPH,** CLINICAL CHEMISTRY. *Current Pos:* Lectr chem, Univ Windsor, 53-56, from asst prof to assoc prof, 57-67, assoc dean arts & sci, 64-70, div head, Clin Chem Lab, 71-94, dir clin chem, 72-94, PROF CHEM & BIOCHEM, UNIV WINDSOR, 67-, EMER PROF, CLIN CHEM LAB, DETROIT RECEIVING HOSP, UNIV HEALTH CTR, 94- *Personal Data:* b Tecumseh, Ont, Aug 29, 29; m 54, Audrey M Wissler; c Mark R & Robert F. *Educ:* Univ Western Ont, BA, 51; Univ Detroit, MS, 54; Wayne State Univ, PhD(biochem), 58. *Honors & Awards:* Union Carbide Award, Chem Inst Can, 78; SmithKline Clin Labs Award, 80; Ames Award, Can Soc Clin Chemists, 88; Beckman Educ Excellence Award, Can Soc Clin Chemists, 92. *Concurrent Pos:* Instr sch nursing, Grace Hosp, 54-73; res assoc sch med, Wayne State Univ, 71-72, prof path, 72-94. *Mem:* Fel AAAS; fel Nat Acad Clin Biochem; fel Chem Inst Can; fel Can Acad Clin Biochem; Am Asn Clin Chem; Can Soc Clin Chemists; Am Soc Biochem & Molecular Biol; Am Chem Soc; Sigma Xi. *Res:* Clinical biochemistry; development of new reagents or methods for the measurement of phospholipids, hydrogen peroxide, glycated proteins, carbamylated proteins, lipoproteins and oxalates. *Mailing Add:* Dept Chem & Biochem Univ Windsor Windsor ON N9B 3P4 Can

**THIBODEAU, GARY A,** PHYSIOLOGY, PHARMACOLOGY. *Current Pos:* from asst prof to prof entom-zool, 65-80, vpres, 80-85, PROF BIOL, SDAK STATE UNIV, 80-; CHANCELLOR, UNIV WIS, RIVER FALLS, 85- *Personal Data:* b Sioux City, Iowa, Sept 26, 38; m 64; c 2. *Educ:* Creighton Univ, BS, 62; SDak State Univ, MS, 67, MS, 70, PhD(physiol), 71. *Prof Exp:* Mem prof serv staff, Baxter Labs, Inc, 63-65. *Mem:* AAAS; Am Inst Biol Sci; Am Pub Health Asn. *Res:* Animal physiology; pharmacology of hypolipedemic agents; pathological dyslipemias; thyroid physiology; vascular morphology; anatomy. *Mailing Add:* 439 River Hills Rd N River Falls WI 54022-2936

**THIBODEAUX, LOUIS J,** ENGINEERING. *Current Pos:* PROF CHEM ENG, LA STATE UNIV, BATON ROUGE, 84- *Personal Data:* b Church Point, La, Nov 14, 39; m 59; c 2. *Educ:* La State Univ, BS, 62, MS, 66, PhD(ionic diffusion), 68. *Prof Exp:* Engr, E I du Pont de Nemours & Co, 62-64, Uniroyal, Inc, 64 & Nat Coun Air Stream Improv, 64-68; from asst prof to prof chem eng, Univ Ark, Fayetteville, 68-84. *Concurrent Pos:* Consult to numerous chem companies; consult, Ga Kraft Co, 69 & Int Paper Co, 70- *Mem:* AAAS; Am Inst Chem Engrs; Am Chem Soc; Sigma Xi (pres, 77-78). *Res:* Movement of chemicals in the environment, environmental chemistry and interphase mass transfer; fate, life-time, transport rates, direction of movement, chemodynamics of trace chemicals in the natural environment. *Mailing Add:* 3449 Tezcucco Dr Baton Rouge LA 70808-5012

**THICH, JOHN ADONG,** AEROSPACE LUBRICANTS. *Current Pos:* LAB DIR, ROYAL LUBRICANTS CO, INC, NJ, 79- *Personal Data:* b London, Eng, Nov 16, 48; US citizen; m 74. *Educ:* Temple Univ, Pa, BA, 70; Rutgers Univ, NJ, PhD(inorg chem), 75. *Prof Exp:* Res fel chem, Calif Inst Technol, 75-77; scientist, Rohm & Haas Co, Pa, 77-79. *Mem:* Am Chem Soc; Am Soc Lubrication Engrs; Am Soc Testing & Mat; Soc Automotive Engrs. *Res:* Development of high performance fluids and lubricants for the aerospace industry and the United States military. *Mailing Add:* 210 William St Boonton NJ 07005-0474

**THICKSTUN, WILLIAM RUSSELL, JR,** MATHEMATICS. *Current Pos:* ASSOC PROF MATH, ST LAWRENCE UNIV, 76- *Personal Data:* b Washington, DC, Oct 14, 22; m 54. *Educ:* Univ Md, BSc, 47, MA, 49, PhD, 52. *Prof Exp:* Mathematician, US Naval Ord Lab, Md, 53-68; assoc prof math, Clarkson Col Technol, 68-76 & Univ Petrol & Mineral, Saudi Arabia, 76-78. *Mem:* Am Math Soc; Soc Indust & Appl Math; Am Inst Aeronaut & Astronaut. *Res:* Applied mathematics; fluid dynamics. *Mailing Add:* 143 Henlopen Ave Rehoboth Beach DE 19971-1634

**THIEBAUX, H JEAN,** APPLIED STATISTICS, STOCHASTIC MODELING OF GEOPHYSICAL PROCESSES. *Current Pos:* RES MATH STATIST, NAT OCEANIC & ATMOSPHERIC ADMIN/NAT WEATHER SERV/NAT METEOROL CTR, 88- *Personal Data:* b Washington, DC, Aug 17, 35; c 5. *Educ:* Reed Col, BA, 57; Univ Ore, MA, 60; Stanford Univ, PhD(statist), 64. *Prof Exp:* Res asst econ & indust, Ivan Block & Assoc, Econ & Indust Consult, 58; statist analyst, Med Sch, Univ Ore, 60; asst pub health analyst, Calif Dept Pub Health, 61; res assoc, Hanson Physics Labs, Stanford Univ, 63-64; asst prof statist, Univ Conn & Univ Mass, Amherst, 64-71; lectr, Univ Colo, Boulder, 72-73; consult & vis scientist, Nat Ctr Atmospheric Res, 72-74; from assoc prof to prof, Dalhousie Univ, 75-87. *Concurrent Pos:* NSF vis prof, Pa State Univ, 90-91; NSF prog dir, Math Sci, 92-94. *Mem:* Fel Royal Meteorol Soc; Am Statist Asn; Am Geophys Union. *Res:* Statistical modelling, analysis and estimation of spatially coherent systems; applications to atmospheric and ocean sciences, including interfacing models and reality, with data assimilation and validation. *Mailing Add:* 9708 Old Allentown Rd Ft Washington MD 20744. *Fax:* 301-763-8545; *E-Mail:* thiebaux@sun1.wwb.noaa.gov

**THIEBERGER, PETER,** EXPERIMENTAL NUCLEAR PHYSICS. *Current Pos:* res asst, Brookhaven Nat Lab, 65-67, from asst physicist to physicist, 67-74, head Tandem Van De Graaff Facil Opers, 71-75, GROUP LEADER, TANDEM VAN DE GRAAFF FACIL OPERS & DEVELOP GROUP, 75-, HEAD, TANDEM VAN DE GRAAFF RES, 85-, SR PHYSICIST, BROOKHAVEN NAT LAB, 74- *Personal Data:* b Vienna, Austria, Sept 19, 35; m 63, Gloria Rey; c Eduardo. *Educ:* Balseiro Inst Physics, Argentina, MS, 59; Univ Stockholm, Fil lic, 61, Fil Dr(physics), 62. *Prof Exp:* Physicist, Bariloche Atomic Ctr, Argentine AEC, 62-65. *Concurrent Pos:* Asst prof, Balseiro Inst Physics, 62-63, prof, 63-65; vis scientist, Res Inst Physics, Stockholm, Sweden, 68-69; consult, Tennelec Instrument Co, 67-71, Arg AEC, 77- & Techint SACI, Arg, 78-80; NSF grant for coop res with Latin Am, 76-85; dep mgr, heavy ion transfer line proj prod relativistic heavy ions, 84-87; Yale Univ A W Wright Nuclear Struct Lab, 85-87. *Mem:* Fel Am Phys Soc. *Res:* Nuclear structure; measurements of half-lives and g-factors of nuclear states; development of nuclear instruments and methods; nuclear reactions with heavy ions; accelerator development and operation; applied uses of accelerators and nuclear techniques. *Mailing Add:* Physics Dept Brookhaven Nat Lab Upton NY 11973. *Fax:* 516-344-4583; *E-Mail:* pt@bnl.gov

**THIEDE, EDWIN CARL,** MMW-IR SENSORS, SIGNAL PROCESSING. *Current Pos:* SR ENGR FEL, ALLIANT TECHSYSTEMS, 90- *Personal Data:* b Richland Co, Wis, Nov 11, 37; m 64. *Educ:* Univ Wis-Madison, BS, 59; Univ Calif, Los Angeles, MS, 64; Stanford Univ, PhD(elec eng), 68. *Prof Exp:* Dynamics engr, Gen Dynamics/Astronaut, 59-62; tech staff engr, Hughes Aircraft Co, 63-65; res asst radar astron, Stanford Electronics Lab, 65-68; asst prof elec eng, Univ Minn, Minneapolis, 68-73; sr prin scientist, Honeywell-SRC, 73-84, sr staff engr, Honeywell-PWO, Minneapolis, 84-89. *Concurrent Pos:* Consult, Univac Defense Systs Div, 72-74; instr, Hennepin Co Vo-Tech, 74-80; lectr, Technol Training Corp, 89-92, Univ Minn, 95- *Mem:* Inst Elec & Electronics Engrs. *Res:* Multisensor fusion, target detection and classification, infrared and radar signal processing in surveillance and guided missiles, digital filtering, optimal filtering, statistical communication theory. *Mailing Add:* 12510 Hilloway Rd Way Hopkins MN 55305

**THIEDE, HENRY A,** OBSTETRICS & GYNECOLOGY. *Current Pos:* PROF & CHMN DEPT OBSTET & GYNEC, OBSTETRICIAN & GYNECOLOGIST-IN-CHIEF, UNIV ROCHESTER MED SCH, 77- *Personal Data:* b Rochester, NY, Oct 2, 26; m 51; c 2. *Educ:* Univ Buffalo, MD, 49. *Prof Exp:* Intern surg, Buffalo Gen Hosp, 49-50; asst resident obstet

& gynec, Genesee & Strong Mem Hosps, Rochester, 52-54; resident, Genesee Hosp, 54-56; from instr to assoc prof, Sch Med, Univ Rochester, 57-66; prof obstet & gynec & chmn dept, Sch Med, Univ Miss, 67-77, asst dean, Sch Med, 70-73, assoc dean, 73-77. *Mem:* Am Col Obstet & Gynec; Soc Gynec Invest; Am Gynec & Obstet Soc; Am Gynec Club; Am Fertil Soc. *Res:* Biology of reproduction and reproduction wastage. *Mailing Add:* Univ Rochester Obgyn Rochester NY 14642-0001

**THIEL, FRANK L(OUIS),** FIBER OPTICS, OPTICAL WAVEGUIDES. *Current Pos:* DIR, TECHNOL TRANSFER, 93- *Personal Data:* b Buffalo, NY, July 22, 42; m 63, Patricia E Plunkett; c Frank L & Karl A. *Educ:* Rensselaer Polytech Inst, BEE, 64, MEE, 65, PhD(electrophys), 69. *Prof Exp:* Instr elec eng, Rensselaer Polytech Inst, 65-69; sr physicist, Corning Glass Works, 69-71, sr res physicist, 71-75, mgr, 75-80; chief engr & tech mgr, Optical Fibres, Deeside, Clwyd, Wales, UK, 80-84; mgr, Corning Glass Works, 84-87; dir technol, Corning Japan KK, Japan, 87-93. *Concurrent Pos:* Lectr optical waveguide courses, Univ Colo, 74-76 & George Washington Univ, 74-75; mem working group, Brit Stand Inst, 83-84; mem, High Technol & Res & Develop Comts, Am Chambers Com, Japan, 87-93; mem bd dirs, Alfred Technol Resources, Inc, 93- *Mem:* Inst Elec & Electronics Engrs; Am Phys Soc; Am Ceramic Soc; Optical Soc Am. *Res:* Electronic materials; physical electronics; opto-electronics; optical waveguides and associated components and processes; liquid crystal displays. *Mailing Add:* Corning Inc Sullivan Park SP-FR-02-11 Corning NY 14831. *Fax:* 607-974-3298; *E-Mail:* thiel_fl@corning.com

**THIEL, PATRICIA ANN,** SURFACE CHEMISTRY. *Current Pos:* from asst prof to assoc prof, 83-91, PROF CHEM, AMES LAB, IOWA STATE UNIV, 91- *Personal Data:* b Adrian, Minn, Feb 20, 53. *Educ:* Macalester Col, BA, 75; Calif Inst Technol, PhD(chem), 81. *Prof Exp:* Assoc scientist, Control Data Corp, 75-76; scientist, Sandia Nat Lab, Livermore, 81-83. *Concurrent Pos:* Sloan award, Alfred P Sloan Found, 84; NSF presidential young investr, 85; Dreyfus teacher scholar, Camille & Henry Dreyfus Found, 86; prog dir mat chem, Ames Lab, 88-; NSF fac awardee women in sci & eng, 91. *Mem:* Am Vacuum Soc; Am Chem Soc; Mat Res Soc; AAAS; Am Phys Soc. *Res:* Surface chemistry; gas-solid interactions; metal film growth; metal oxidation; surface properties of quasicrystals. *Mailing Add:* Ames Lab & Dept Chem Iowa State Univ Ames IA 50011-0061

**THIEL, THOMAS J,** applied computer science, soil physics, for more information see previous edition

**THIELE, ELIZABETH HENRIETTE,** BIOCHEMISTRY. *Current Pos:* RETIRED. *Personal Data:* b Portland, Ore, Apr 26, 20. *Educ:* Univ Wash, BS, 42; Univ Pa, MS, 43, PhD(bact), 51. *Prof Exp:* Technician, Merck Sharp & Dohme, 43-44, res assoc, Merck Inst Therapeut Res, 44-78. *Mem:* Am Soc Microbiol; Reticuloendothelial Soc. *Res:* Enzymology; immunology. *Mailing Add:* 18755 W Bernardo Dr Apt 1332 San Diego CA 92127-3015

**THIELE, ERNEST,** chemical engineering; deceased, see previous edition for last biography

**THIELE, GARY ALLEN,** ANTENNAS, ELECTROMAGNETISM. *Current Pos:* assoc dean eng grad studies, 80-91, TAIT PROF, UNIV DAYTON, 91- *Personal Data:* b Cleveland, Ohio, May 5, 38; m 60; c 3. *Educ:* Purdue Univ, BSEE, 60; Ohio State Univ, MSc, 64, PhD(elec eng), 68. *Prof Exp:* Elec engr, Gen Elec Co, 60-61; res assoc, Ohio State Univ, 63-68, from asst prof to assoc prof elec eng, 68-80. *Concurrent Pos:* Consult, numerous orgns; NATO res award, 77. *Mem:* Int Union Radio Sci; fel Inst Elec & Electronics Engrs; Sigma Xi; Am Inst Aeronaut & Astronaut. *Res:* Electromagnetics; radiation and scattering problems via numerical methods; microwave techniques; propagation of electromagnetic waves; antennas; radar cross section. *Mailing Add:* Box 0227 300 Col Park Ave Dayton OH 45469-0226

**THIELEN, LAWRENCE EUGENE,** ORGANIC CHEMISTRY, EDITING RESEARCH REPORTS ENVIRONMENTAL INSPECTIONS. *Current Pos:* CONSULT, THIELEN INC, 87- *Personal Data:* b Chicago, Ill, Sept 2, 21; m 50; c 2. *Educ:* Loyola Univ, Ill, BS, 42. *Prof Exp:* Chemist, Kankakee Ord Works, E I du Pont de Nemours & Co, 42; res chemist, Pure Oil Co, 43 & 46, G D Searle & Co, 46-56, Nalco Chem Co, 56-58 & Abbott Labs, 58-62; group leader polymer & org chem, R R Donnelley & Sons Co, 62-76; safety & health dir, Printing Ink Technol, Inmont Corp, Chicago, 76-87. *Concurrent Pos:* Mem bd dirs, Chicago Sect, Am Chem Soc; mem bd dirs & vpres, Salt Creek Sanit Dist, Dupage Co. *Mem:* Am Chem Soc (treas, 93-). *Res:* Pharmaceuticals; synthesis of plastics and pharmaceuticals; inks; coatings; printing process technology. *Mailing Add:* 110 E Madison St Villa Park IL 60181

**THIELGES, BART A,** FOREST GENETICS. *Current Pos:* ASSOC DEAN RES, COL FORESTRY, ORE STATE UNIV, 90- *Personal Data:* b Chicago, Ill, June 16, 38; m 60, Judy McMullen; c Bart C, Jon & Patrick. *Educ:* Southern Ill Univ, BS, 63; Yale Univ, MF, 64, MPhil, 67, PhD(forest genetics), 67. *Prof Exp:* Res asst plant anat, Southern Ill Univ, 62-63; res asst forest genetics, Yale Univ, 63-67; asst prof, Ohio Agr Res & Develop Ctr, 67-71; assoc prof, Sch Forestry & Wildlife Mgt, La State Univ, Baton Rouge, 71-76; proj leader, US Forest Serv, Starkville, Miss, 76-77; prof & chmn, Dept Forestry, Univ Ky, 77-90. *Concurrent Pos:* Vis prof, Univ Oxford, Eng, 83-84; res prog mgr, USDA, 85-86. *Mem:* Soc Am Foresters; Forest Prod Soc; AAAS. *Res:* Breeding of forest trees; natural variation studies; genetics of disease resistance; management of research; host-parasite coevolution. *Mailing Add:* Col Forestry Ore State Univ Corvallis OR 97331-5704. *Fax:* 541-737-2906; *E-Mail:* thielgeb@ccmail.orst.edu

**THIELMANN, VERNON JAMES,** ANALYTICAL CHEMISTRY. *Current Pos:* from asst prof to assoc prof, 74-82, head dept, 84-90, PROF CHEM, SOUTHWEST MO STATE UNIV, 82- *Personal Data:* b Hastings, Minn, June 4, 37; m 63, Anita Walior; c Russell & Brian. *Educ:* Northern State Col, BS, 63; Univ SDak, MNS, 68; Baylor Univ, PhD(chem), 74. *Prof Exp:* Teacher pub schs, SDak & Iowa, 63-69; asst prof chem, Morningside Col, 69-72. *Mem:* Am Chem Soc; Sigma Xi; Clay & Clay Mineral Soc. *Res:* Preparation of complex cation exchanged montmorillonite clays and subsequent study of their structure, thermal stability, surface area and effectiveness for use as gas chromatographic packing materials; clay and clay minerals. *Mailing Add:* Dept Chem Southwest Mo State Univ Springfield MO 65804-0089. *Fax:* 417-836-6934

**THIELSCH, HELMUT,** MECHANICAL ENGINEERING. *Current Pos:* PRES, THIELSCH ENG, INC, CRANSTON, RI, 84-, PRES HITECH REALITY ASSOC, INC. *Personal Data:* b Berlin, Ger, Nov 16, 22; nat US; m 52, Margaret E McKenna; c Barbara A, Donald K, Deborah L & Helmut J Jr. *Educ:* Auburn Univ, BS, 43. *Honors & Awards:* Freeman Award, Am Bd Forensic Examiners, 85; Third Ann Safety Award & Medal, Nat Bd Boiler & Pressure Vessel Inspection, 90; Adms Lect Award, 92; Comfort A Adams Lectr Award, Am Welding Soc, 92. *Prof Exp:* Res engr, Allis Chalmers Co, Milwaukee, Wis, 45-46; metall engr, Black, Sivalls & Bryson, Inc, Kansas City, Mo, 46-47; res engr, Lukens Steel Co, Coatsville, Pa, 48-49; engr, Welding Res Coun, NY, 49-52; dir res, develop & eng, Eutectic Welding Alloys Co, NY, 52-53; vpres & dir res, develop & eng, ITT Grinnell Corp, Providence, 54-84. *Concurrent Pos:* Consult on mat eng, failure analysis to indust, pub utilities, chem indust, equip builders, 54-; lectr, confs on failures & failure prev, var univ; mem, Component Tech Comt, Argonne Nat Lab, Ill; mem, Comt Am Soc Testing & Mat, E-7 Comt, Nondestructive Testing & Tech Coun; mem, Fabrication, Inspection & Testing Comt, Am Soc Mech Engrs; chmn, Metall Eng Comt, Pipe Fabrication Inst; consult, Adv Comt, Reactor Safeguards Nuclear Regulatory Comn. *Mem:* Fel Am Soc Mech Engrs; Am Soc Testing & Mat; fel Am Soc Nondestructive Testing; Nat Asn Corrosion Engrs; Tech Asn Pulp & Paper Indust; fel Am Soc Metals; fel Am Welding Soc; Am Chem Soc; Am Nuclear Soc; Am Soc Qual Control; Nat Soc Prof Engrs; Am Soc Prof Engrs. *Res:* Failure analysis; materials evaluation; quality assurance; author of various publications; granted ten patents. *Mailing Add:* 195 Frances Ave Cranston RI 02910-2211

**THIEME, CORNELIS LEO HANS,** SUPERCONDUCTORS, COMPOSITE MATERIALS. *Current Pos:* RES STAFF MAT SCI, FRANCES BITTER MAGNET LAB & PLASMA FUSION CTR, MASS INST TECHNOL, 81- *Personal Data:* b Arnhem, Neth, Dec 7, 48. *Educ:* Twente Univ Technol, Neth, BEngSc, 73, MEngSc, 75. *Prof Exp:* Res staff, Twente Univ Technol, Neth, 75-80. *Mem:* Neth Ceramic Soc. *Res:* Development of multifilamentary ductile superconductor materials. *Mailing Add:* 21 Mill Rd Westborough MA 01581

**THIEME, MELVIN T,** SHOCK HYDRODYNAMICS, COMPUTER SCIENCE. *Current Pos:* RETIRED. *Personal Data:* b Decatur, Ind, Oct 27, 25; m 49, Loretta Luke; c Ellen, Rita & Randall. *Educ:* Purdue Univ, BS, 49, MS, 51, PhD(nuclear physics), 55. *Prof Exp:* Staff mem, Lawrence Livermore Lab, 63-64; staff mem, Los Alamos Nat Lab, 55-63, 64-72 & 76-86, asst group leader, 72-76. *Concurrent Pos:* Teacher, Pima Community Col, Tucson, Az & Northern NMex Community Col, Esponola, NMex. *Mem:* Am Phys Soc. *Res:* Beta-ray spectroscopy; nuclear weapon design and development with specialization in shock hydrodynamics. *Mailing Add:* 7205 Gettysburg Rd NE Albuquerque NM 87109

**THIEN, LEONARD B,** EVOLUTION, SYSTEMATICS. *Current Pos:* from asst prof to assoc prof ecol, 71-81, PROF BIOL, TULANE UNIV, 81- *Personal Data:* b Breese, Ill, Nov 11, 38; m 67; c 2. *Educ:* Southern Ill Univ, BS, 59; Washington Univ, MS, 61; Univ Calif, Los Angeles, PhD(bot), 68. *Prof Exp:* Asst prof cytol & systs, Dept Bot, Univ Wis-Madison, 67-71. *Concurrent Pos:* Hormel & NSF fel, Univ Minn, 75. *Mem:* Bot Soc Am; AAAS; Int Asn Plant Taxonomists; Soc Study Evolution; Asn Trop Biol; Soc Study Species Biol. *Res:* plant-insect relationships; productivity of marshes. *Mailing Add:* Cell & Molecular Biol Dept Tulane Univ New Orleans LA 70118-5698. *E-Mail:* lthien@mailhost.tcs.tulane.edu

**THIEN, STEPHEN JOHN,** AGRONOMY. *Current Pos:* from asst prof to assoc prof, 70-81, PROF AGRON, KANS STATE UNIV, 81- *Personal Data:* b Clarence, Iowa, Apr 11, 44; m 66; c 2. *Educ:* Iowa State Univ, BS, 66; Purdue Univ, Lafayette, MS, 68, PhD(agron), 71. *Prof Exp:* Asst agron, Purdue Univ, 66-70. *Concurrent Pos:* Danforth assoc. *Mem:* Fel Am Soc Agron; Soil Sci Soc Am. *Res:* Soil fertility; plant nutrition and physiology; soil management; soil biochemistry. *Mailing Add:* Dept Agron 2004 Throck Morton Hall Kans State Univ Manhattan KS 66506-5501

**THIENE, PAUL G(EORGE),** PHYSICAL ELECTRONICS. *Current Pos:* RETIRED. *Personal Data:* b Pasadena, Calif, Dec 10, 19; m 46; c 3. *Educ:* Calif Inst Technol, BS, 43, PhD(phys electronics), 52. *Prof Exp:* Asst physicist, Calif Inst Technol, 43-45, res engr, Jet Propulsion Lab, 46-47; dep chief & res adminr, Western Div, Off Sci Res, USAF, 52-55, consult, Air Tech Intel Ctr, 55-57; sr physicist, Res Lab, Giannini Plasmadyne Corp, 58-62; sr staff scientist, MHD Res Inc, 62-66; supvr, Optical Physics Sect, Res Lab, Aeronutronic Div, Philco-Ford Corp, 66-72. *Concurrent Pos:* Consult, Litech, Inc, P W Webster Co, Surg Mech Res, Inc & Curt Deckert Assocs, 73-88; consult, 72- *Mem:* Am Phys Soc. *Res:* Electromedical technology, laser technology; semiconductor devices; superconductivity; plasma physics; magneto gas dynamics; electro-optics; microwave spectroscopy and radiometry. *Mailing Add:* 24833 Outlook Ct Carmel CA 93923

**TIIIER, SAMUEL OSIAH,** HEALTH SCIENCE POLICY. *Current Pos:* PRES & CHIEF EXEC OFFICER, PARTNERS HEALTH CARE SYST INC, 97- *Personal Data:* b Brooklyn, NY, June 23, 37; m 58; c 3. *Educ:* State Univ NY, Syracuse, MD, 60; Am Bd Internal Med, dipl, 67, recert, 74. *Hon Degrees:* MA, Univ Pa, 71 & Yale Univ, 75; DSc, State Univ NY, 87, Tufts Univ & George Washington Univ, 88, City Univ NY & Hahnemann Univ, 89; LHD, Rush Univ, 89, Brandeis Univ, Dartmouth Col, Mt Sinai Sch Med. *Honors & Awards:* Helen & Payne Whitney Lectr, Cornell Univ, 76; E Stanley Emery Jr Mem Lectr, Brigham & Women's Hosp, 81; Gunnar Lectr, Univ Ill, 81; Blankenhorn Lectr, Univ Cincinnati, 85; Michael & Irene Karl Master Sci Ser Lectr, Washington Univ, 86; John E Franklin Lectr, Cornell Univ, 87; Moshe Prywes Lectr, Ben-Gurion Univ, 87; Heller Lectr, Mt Sinai Hosp, 87; Martin E Rehfuss Lectr, Thomas Jefferson Univ, 87; Thomas M Durant Mem Lectr, Temple Univ, 87; Donald P Shiley Lectr, Scripps Clin & Res Found, 88; Jacob Yules Lectr, Tufts Univ, 88; Ralph Major Lectr, Univ Kans, 88; Florence Mahoney Lectr, NIH, 88; Ernest J & Elena B Bruno Mem Lectr, Lenox Hill Hosp, 88. *Prof Exp:* Instr med, Harvard Med Sch, 67, assoc, 67-68, asst prof, 69; from assoc prof to prof, Sch Med, Univ Pa, 69-74; prof internal med & chmn dept, Sch Med, Yale Univ, 75-85, chief med, Yale-New Haven Hosp, 75-85; pres, Inst Med-Nat Acad Sci, 86-91; pres, Brandeis Univ, 91-94; pres, Mass Gen Hosp, 94-97. *Concurrent Pos:* Asst med & chief, Renal Unit, Mass Gen Hosp, 67-69; assoc dir med serv, Univ Pa Hosp, 69-74; vchmn med, Sch Med, Univ Pa, 71-74; mem bd dirs, Hospice Inc, 76-82 & Yale-New Haven Hosp, 78-85; vis prof & lectr, numerous univs, 76-90; mem, Comt Study Airline Pilot Age, Health & Performance, Inst Med, Nat Acad Sci, 82, chmn, Bd Health Sci Policy, 83, mem, Comt Study Orgn Struct, NIH, 85; chmn, Am Bd Internal Med, 84. *Mem:* Inst Med-Nat Acad Sci; master Am Col Physicians; Am Fedn Clin Res (pres, 76); Asn Am Med Cols; Am Physiol Soc; Am Soc Nephrology; fel Am Acad Arts & Sci. *Res:* Amino acid transport in the kidney. *Mailing Add:* Partners Health Care Syst Inc Prudential Tower 800 Boylston St Suite 1150 Boston MA 02199-8001

**THIERET, JOHN WILLIAM,** BOTANY. *Current Pos:* chmn, Dept Biol Sci, 73-80, prof, 73-92, EMER PROF BOT, NORTHERN KY UNIV, 92- *Personal Data:* b Chicago, Ill, Aug 1, 26; m 50, Mildred A Wolf; c Robert G, Nancy L, Richard L, Jeffrey G & Jennifer L. *Educ:* Utah State Univ, BS, 50, MS, 51; Univ Chicago, PhD(bot), 53. *Prof Exp:* Cur econ bot, Field Mus Natural Hist, 53-62; from assoc prof to prof biol, Univ Southwestern La, 62-73, Edwin Lewis Stephens prof sci, 72-73. *Concurrent Pos:* Adv, Encycl Britannica, 59-; ed, Econ Bot, 87-90. *Mem:* Soc Econ Bot. *Res:* Flora of central and southeastern United States; taxonomy of Gramineae; economic botany. *Mailing Add:* Dept Biol Sci Northern Ky Univ Highland Heights KY 41099-7010

**THIERMAN, VERNON,** ENGINEERING. *Current Pos:* RETIRED. *Honors & Awards:* John B Stirling Medal, Eng Inst Can, 95. *Mem:* Eng Inst Can. *Mailing Add:* 8324 120th St Edmonton AB T6G 1X2 Can

**THIERMANN, ALEJANDRO BORIES,** VETERINARY MEDICINE, EPIDEMIOLOGY. *Current Pos:* nat prog leader animal health, Agr Res Serv, 87-89, DEP ADMINR INT SERV, USDA, 89- *Personal Data:* b Valparaiso, Chile, July 15, 47; US citizen; m 73; c 2. *Educ:* Univ Chile, Santiago, DVM, 71; Wayne State Univ, PhD(microbiol, immunol), 79. *Prof Exp:* Vet small animals, pvt pract, 71-72; med ecologist pub health, Lockheed Elec Co, NASA, Houston, 72-73; instr, Lab Animal Med, Sch Med, Wayne State Univ, 73-79; res leader leptospirosis & mycobacteriosis, Nat Animal Dis Ctr, 79-87. *Concurrent Pos:* Mem, Am Leptospirosis Res Conf, 74-, chmn epidemiol sect, 77-, pres, 84, secy-treas, 85-; mem biohazards comt, Wayne State Univ, mem recombinant DNA subcomt, 77-79; res leader, Leptospirosis & Mycobacteriosis Labs & Nat Leptospirosis Ref Ctr, 85-87. *Mem:* Am Soc Microbiologists; Sigma Xi; Am Vet Med Asn; US Animal Health Asn; Am Asn Vet Lab Diagnosticians; Wildlife Dis Asn. *Res:* Leptospirosis, its epidemiology, pathogenesis and molecular biology; paratuberculosis, its pathogenesis and molecular biology. *Mailing Add:* USDA/APHIS/IS FAF-USEU PSC 82 Box 002 APO AE 09724

**THIERRIN, GABRIEL,** MATHEMATICS, COMPUTER SCIENCE. *Current Pos:* prof, 70-87, EMER PROF MATH, UNIV WESTERN ONT, 87- *Personal Data:* b Surpierre, Switz, Dec 22, 21; m 51; c 2. *Educ:* Univ Fribourg, DSc, 51; Univ Paris, DSc, 54. *Prof Exp:* Sci assoc, Nat Ctr Sci Res, France, 52-54 & NFS Res, Switz, 54-57; prof math, Inst Higher Studies, Tunisia, 57-58 & Univ Montreal, 58-70. *Res:* Algebra; theories of rings and semi-groups; systems theory; theory of automata and languages; theory of cooles; DNA computing. *Mailing Add:* Dept Math Middlesex Col Univ Western Ont London ON N6A 5B7 Can

**THIERS, BRUCE HARRIS,** DERMATOLOGY. *Current Pos:* from asst prof to assoc prof, 80-93, FAC, SCH GRAD STUDIES, MED UNIV SC, 83-, PROF DERMAT, 94- *Personal Data:* b New York, NY, June 15, 49; m 87, Halette Resnick. *Educ:* Brooklyn Col, BA, 70; State Univ NY, Buffalo, MD, 74. *Prof Exp:* Asst prof dermat, State Univ NY, Buffalo, 79-80. *Concurrent Pos:* Attend physician dermat, Buffalo Gen Hosp, Buffalo, NY & Erie Co Med Ctr, Buffalo, NY, 79-80 & Med Univ SC Hosp, Charleston, SC, 80-; chief, Dermat Serv, Vet Admin Med Ctr, Buffalo, NY, 79-80 & Charleston, SC, 80-; prin investr, Ortho Pharmaceut Corp, 87-88 & 88-89, Pfizer Inc, 94-95, Ligand Pharmaceut, 96-97 & Bristol-Myers Squibb, 96-97; assoc ed, J Am Acad Dermat. *Mem:* Am Acad Dermat; Am Dermat Asn; Soc Investigative Dermat; Dermat Found. *Res:* Advances in dermatologic therapeutics. *Mailing Add:* Dept Dermat Med Univ SC 171 Ashley Ave Charleston SC 29425. *Fax:* 803-792-9157; *E-Mail:* thiersb@musc.edu

**THIERS, EUGENE ANDRES,** PRICE FORMATION MECHANISMS, ROBUSTNESS ANALYSIS. *Current Pos:* dir, Metals Ctr, 79-83, SR CONSULT, SRI INT, 75- *Personal Data:* b Santiago, Chile, Aug 25, 41; US citizen; m 83; c 1. *Educ:* Univ Chile, Santiago, BS, 59; Columbia Univ, MS, 65, DESc(mineral eng), 70. *Prof Exp:* Mgr, Minbanco Corp, 66-70; sr engr, Battelle Mem Inst, 70-72, dir, 72-75. *Concurrent Pos:* Consult prof, Stanford Univ, 82-; mgr inorganics, SRI Int, 90- *Mem:* Fel AAAS; Am Inst Mining, Metall & Petrol Engrs. *Res:* Mineral economics, particularly price formation mechanisms in industrial minerals and metals; competitive analysis of resource industries. *Mailing Add:* 426 27th Ave San Mateo CA 94403. *Fax:* 650-859-6434

**THIERS, HARRY DELBERT,** MYCOLOGY. *Current Pos:* assoc prof, 59-63, PROF BIOL, SAN FRANCISCO STATE UNIV, 63- *Personal Data:* b Ft McKavett, Tex, Jan 22, 19; m 53; c 1. *Educ:* Schreiner Inst, AB, 38; Univ Tex, BA, 41, MA, 47; Univ Mich, PhD, 55. *Prof Exp:* Asst, Univ Tex, 39-41, tutor bot, 45-47, instr bot & mycol, Tex A&M Univ, 47-50, asst biol, 50-55, assoc prof, 55-59. *Concurrent Pos:* Assoc plant pathologist, USDA, 48. *Mem:* Bot Soc Am; Mycol Soc Am; Am Bryol & Lichenological Soc. *Res:* Taxonomy of fleshy fungi of California and West Coast of North America. *Mailing Add:* Dept Biol San Francisco State Univ 1600 Holloway Ave San Francisco CA 94132

**THIERSTEIN, GERALD E,** CROP PROTECTION, CONSERVATION TILLAGE. *Current Pos:* RETIRED. *Personal Data:* b Whitewater, Kans, Apr 30, 31; m 76, Samia Shehadeh. *Educ:* Kans State Univ, BS, 57, MS, 63. *Honors & Awards:* Jyoti Award, Indian Soc Agr Engrs; Kishida Int Award, Am Soc Agr Engrs. *Prof Exp:* Asst prof agr eng, WVa Univ, 62-67; res assoc, McGill Univ, 67-71; sr lectr, Makerere Univ, Kampala, 71-73; vis assoc prof, Agr Mechanization, Fac Agr Sci, Am Univ-Beirut, 73-76; prin scientist agr eng, Int Crops Res Inst Semi-Arid Tropics, India, 76-84; assoc prof & res engr, Dept Agr Eng, Kans State Univ, Manhattan, 84-93. *Concurrent Pos:* Adj prof, Agr Eng Dept, Univ Fla, Gainesville, 84. *Mem:* Sigma Xi. *Res:* Conservation tillage; crop protection; surface irrigation. *Mailing Add:* 2525 Baxter Pl Ft Collins CO 80526-5360. *Fax:* 970-224-3458

**THIERSTEIN, HANS RUDOLF,** GEOLOGY, MICROPALEONTOLOGY. *Current Pos:* asst prof, 76-80, ASSOC PROF GEOL, SCRIPPS INST OCEANOG, UNIV CALIF, SAN DIEGO, 80- *Personal Data:* b Zurich, Switz, May 27, 44; m 69; c 2. *Educ:* Univ Zurich, dipl geol, 69, DrPhil, 72. *Prof Exp:* Teaching asst geol, Eidgenoessische Tech Hochschule, Zurich, Switz, 69-71, res asst, 71-73; fel, Swiss NFS, 73-76. *Mem:* Geol Soc Am; Swiss Geol Soc; Am Geophys Union. *Res:* Paleoceanography, calcareous nannoplankton, biostratigraphy, sedimentology, geochemistry. *Mailing Add:* Geol Inst ETH Centrum CH 8092 Zurich Switzerland. *E-Mail:* thierstein@erdw.ethz.ch

**THIERY, JEAN PAUL,** MOLECULAR EMBRYOLOGY. *Current Pos:* Sr researcher, 68-82, DIR RES, NAT CTR SCI RES, PARIS, 82- *Personal Data:* b Remiremont, France, Apr 25, 47. *Educ:* Nancy Univ, Baccalaureate, 64; Paris Univ, Docteur d'Etat(biochem), 74. *Honors & Awards:* Karger Prize, 90. *Concurrent Pos:* Dir, Lab Physiopath Develop, Nat Ctr Sci Res & Ecole Normale Super, 87- *Mem:* Am Soc Cell Biol; Int Soc Develop Biol; Europ Molecular Biol Orgn. *Res:* Molecular embryology, cell recognition, cell migration and pattern formation; cancer invasion and metastasis; molecular immunology, hematopoietic precursors; adhesion molecules; growth factors and receptors. *Mailing Add:* Res Div CNRS Inst Curie 26 rue d'Ulm Cedex 05 Paris 75248 France. *Fax:* 33-1-43269026

**THIES, RICHARD WILLIAM,** SYNTHESIS, HIGH PERFORMANCE POLYMERS. *Current Pos:* from asst prof to assoc prof, 68-87, PROF ORG CHEM, ORE STATE UNIV, 88- *Personal Data:* b Detroit, Mich, Sept 16, 41; m 76, D Diane Rich; c Jeffrey, Michael & Timothy. *Educ:* Univ Mich, BS, 63; Univ Wis, PhD(org chem), 67. *Prof Exp:* NIH fel org chem, Univ Calif, Los Angeles, 67-68. *Concurrent Pos:* NATO sr scientists fel, 79-80; prog officer synthetic, org & natural prod chem, NSF, 83-84, asst dean sci, 87-89, assoc dean, 89- *Mem:* Am Chem Soc; Royal Soc Chem. *Res:* Medium sized ring chemistry; carbonium ion chemistry; thermal rearrangements; synthesis of hormone analogs; polymers. *Mailing Add:* Dept Chem Gilbert Hall 153 Ore State Univ Corvallis OR 97331-4003. *Fax:* 541-737-1009; *E-Mail:* thiesr@ccmail.orst.edu

**THIES, ROBERT SCOTT,** GROWTH & DIFFERENTIATION FACTORS, RECEPTORS & SIGNAL TRANSDUCTION. *Current Pos:* staff scientist II, 89-93, PRIN SCIENTIST, GENETICS INST INC, 93- *Personal Data:* b St Louis, Mo, Feb 9, 57. *Educ:* Univ Miami, BS, 79; Duke Univ, PhD(physiol), 83. *Prof Exp:* Fel, Dept Biol Chem, Univ Calif, Los Angeles Med Ctr, 84-87, Dept Endocrinol, Univ Calif, San Diego Med Ctr, 87-89. *Mem:* Endocrine Soc; Am Soc Cell Biol. *Res:* Effects of growth and differentiation factors on cell function; mechanisms by which these factors mediate biological effects. *Mailing Add:* Dept Tissue Growth & Repair Genetics Inst Inc 87 Cambridge Park Dr Cambridge MA 02140

**THIES, ROGER E,** NEUROPHYSIOLOGY. *Current Pos:* assoc prof, 67-97, MED CTR, ASSOC PROF BIOL PSYCHOL, HEALTH SCI CTR, UNIV OKLA 72-, PROF PHYSIOL, 97- *Personal Data:* b Bronxville, NY, June 30, 33; m 85, Emily McEwen; c Eric, David, Douglas, Laura & Molly. *Educ:* Bates Col, BS, 55; Harvard Univ, AM, 57; Rockefeller Univ, PhD(physiol), 61; Univ Okla, MA, 75. *Prof Exp:* Guest investr neurophysiol & NIH fel, Rockefeller Univ, 60-61; from instr to asst prof physiol, Sch Med, Wash Univ, 61-65; lectr, Makerere Univ Col, Uganda, 65-67. *Concurrent Pos:* Hon res asst & NIH spec fel, Univ Col, Univ London, 64-65. *Mem:* Am Physiol Soc; Soc Neurosci. *Res:* Etiology of myopia; effect of vagal activity on relay of cardiac pain to the brain; affective education and innovative teaching, especially problem solving for health professional and minority students. *Mailing Add:* Dept Physiol Health Sci Ctr Univ Okla PO Box 26901 Oklahoma City OK 73190. *Fax:* 405-271-3181; *E-Mail:* roger-thies@uokhsc.edu

**THIESFELD, VIRGIL ARTHUR,** BOTANY, PLANT PHYSIOLOGY. *Current Pos:* asst prof, 65-68, assoc prof biol, 68-76, CHMN DEPT, UNIV WIS-STEVENS POINT, 68-, PROF BIOL, 76- *Personal Data:* b Glencoe, Minn, Oct 26, 37; m 59; c 2. *Educ:* Luther Col, Iowa, BA, 59; Univ SDak, Vermillion, MA, 63; Univ Okla, PhD(bot), 65. *Prof Exp:* Teacher high sch, Iowa, 59-60 & Minn, 60-62; res asst bot, Univ Okla, 63-65. *Concurrent Pos:* Res grant, Univ Wis-Stevens Point, 68-69. *Mem:* Am Soc Plant Physiol; Sigma Xi. *Res:* Plant growth regulators. *Mailing Add:* Dept Biol Univ Wis Stevens Point 2100 Main St Stevens Point WI 54481-3871

**THIESSEN, HENRY ARCHER,** ELEMENTARY PARTICLE PHYSICS, ACCELERATOR PHYSICS. *Current Pos:* STAFF MEM MEDIUM ENERGY PHYSICS, LOS ALAMOS NAT LAB, 66- *Personal Data:* b Teaneck, NJ, Nov 8, 40; m 62; c 1. *Educ:* Calif Inst Technol, BS, 61, MS, 62, PhD(physics), 67. *Mem:* Fel Am Phys Soc. *Res:* Design of accelerators for medium energy physics; nuclear physics with kaon, pion and high energy proton beams; elementary particle physics. *Mailing Add:* Los Alamos Nat Lab PO Box 1663 MS H846 Los Alamos NM 87545

**THIESSEN, JACOB WILLEM,** research administration, for more information see previous edition

**THIESSEN, REINHARDT, JR,** BIOCHEMISTRY. *Current Pos:* RETIRED. *Personal Data:* b Kiel, Wis, Oct 20, 13; m 38; c 2. *Educ:* Univ Pittsburgh, BS, 34. *Prof Exp:* Asst, Univ Pittsburgh, 35-37; head chemist res & control lab, Repub Yeast Corp, NJ, 37-41; proj leader cent labs, Gen Foods Corp, 42-46, head biol sect, 46-48, head nutrit sect, 48-55, from asst lab dir to lab dir, 55-62, sr res specialist, Tech Ctr, 62-69, res assoc & area mgr nutrit sci, 69-72, corp res mgr, 72-81, prin scientist nutrit sci, Tech Ctr, 81-82. *Mem:* AAAS; Am Pub Health Asn; Am Chem Soc; Inst Food Technol; Am Inst Nutrit. *Res:* Nutrition; toxicology; bacteriology; protein nutrition; carbohydrate nutrition; cacao chemistry; tracers in nutrition and toxicology; food chemistry; dental caries. *Mailing Add:* 3340 Hearthstone Ct Holiday FL 34691-2543

**THIESSEN, RICHARD E,** MATHEMATICS EDUCATION, INTEGRATION OF MATHEMATICS & SCIENCE. *Current Pos:* PROF MATH EDUC & DIR, GRAD MATH/SCI PROG, FRESNO PAC COL, 87- *Personal Data:* b Hutchison, Kans, Nov 18, 38; m 60, Evelyn Jean Langenegger; c David, Mark & John. *Educ:* Friends Univ, BA, 62; Univ Okla, MNS, 67, PhD(math educ), 71. *Prof Exp:* From asst prof to prof, Oral Roberts Univ, 73-87. *Concurrent Pos:* Pres elect, Calif Math Coun, pres, Cent Sect. *Mem:* Nat Coun Math; Math Asn Am. *Res:* Writing of middle school curriculum materials in mathematics. *Mailing Add:* 5263 E Townsend Fresno CA 93727. *Fax:* 209-255-6396; *E-Mail:* rethiess@fresno.edu

**THIESSEN, WILLIAM ERNEST,** ORGANIC CHEMISTRY, CALORIMETRY. *Current Pos:* CONSULT, 90- *Personal Data:* b Kansas City, Mo, Sept 17, 34; m 60, 85, Kathleen Moore; c Karl. *Educ:* Univ Calif, Berkeley, BS, 56, PhD(chem), 60. *Prof Exp:* Instr chem, Univ Wash, 60-62; asst prof, Univ Calif, Davis, 62-68; NIH spec fel, 68-70, res chemist, Chem Div, Oak Ridge Nat Lab, 70-90. *Mem:* Am Chem Soc; Am Crystallog Asn. *Res:* Structure elucidation of complex natural products and accurate molecular geometry of organic compounds by x-ray and neutron diffraction; development of expert systems for planning complex organic synthesis; enthalpies of dilution of electrolyte solutions at elevated temperature and pressure. *Mailing Add:* 108 Olney Lane Oak Ridge TN 37830. *E-Mail:* wethiessen@aol.com

**THIGPEN, J(OSEPH) J(ACKSON),** MECHANICAL ENGINEERING. *Current Pos:* RETIRED. *Personal Data:* b Ruston, La, Feb 4, 17; m 41; c 2. *Educ:* La Polytech Inst, BS, 36; US Mil Acad, BS, 41; Univ Tex, MS, 51, PhD(mech eng), 59. *Prof Exp:* From asst prof to prof mech eng, La Tech Univ, 47-75, head dept, 53-75, assoc dean, 76, dean col eng, 76-82. *Concurrent Pos:* Consult, Opers Res Off, Johns Hopkins Univ, 48-50. *Mem:* Am Soc Mech Engrs; Am Soc Eng Educ; Nat Soc Prof Engrs; Sigma Xi. *Res:* Thermodynamics; heat transfer. *Mailing Add:* 1116 Carey Ave Ruston LA 71270

**THILENIUS, OTTO G,** PEDIATRIC CARDIOLOGY, PHYSIOLOGY. *Current Pos:* Resident, Univ Chicago, 57-59, instr, 61-62, asst prof pediat & physiol, 64-69, assoc prof pediat, 69-72, PROF PEDIAT, UNIV CHICAGO, 72- *Personal Data:* b Bad Soden, Ger, July 7, 29; US citizen; m 56; c 3. *Educ:* Univ Frankfurt, MD, 53; Univ Chicago, PhD(physiol), 62. *Concurrent Pos:* USPHS fel physiol, Univ Chicago, 59-61; fel cardiol, Harvard Univ, 62-64. *Mem:* Am Acad Pediat; Am Col Cardiol. *Mailing Add:* Dept Pediat Christ Hosp & Med Ctr 4440 W 95th St Oak Lawn IL 60453-2600

**THILL, DONALD CECIL,** WEED SCIENCE, PLANT PROTECTION. *Current Pos:* ASSOC PROF WEED SCI, UNIV IDAHO, 80- *Personal Data:* b Colfax, Wash, Aug 30, 50; m 71; c 5. *Educ:* Wash State Univ, BS, 72, MS, 76; Ore State Univ, PhD(crop sci), 79. *Prof Exp:* Plant physiologist, Agr Res Serv, USDA, 75-79; biochem field specialist, PPG Industs, Inc, 79-80. *Concurrent Pos:* Prin investr, Weed Control Systs, Univ Idaho, 81- *Mem:* Weed Sci Soc Am; Sigma Xi. *Res:* Develop cultural and herbicidal weed control tactics for use in small grains; herbicide mode and mechanism of action experiments; weed biology; herbicide resistance. *Mailing Add:* 2641 Weymouth St Moscow ID 83843

**THILL, RONALD E,** RANGE-WILDLIFE INTERACTIONS. *Current Pos:* Range scientist, Forest Ser, USDA, 77-86, RES WILDLIFE BIOLOGIST, SFOREST EXP STA, 86- *Personal Data:* b Tonopah, Nev, Oct 22, 44; m 66; c 2. *Educ:* Humboldt State Col, Calif, BS, 67; SDak State Univ, MS, 69; Univ Ariz, PhD(range mgt), 81. *Mem:* Soc Range Mgt; Wildlife Soc. *Res:* Deer and cattle interactions; riparian zone wildlife; effects of forest management practices on wildlife; forest management effects (spacing and site preparation) on cattle and deer forage resources; radiotelemetry, deer behavior. *Mailing Add:* 4124 Raguet St Nacogdoches TX 75961

**THIMANN, KENNETH VIVIAN,** plant physiology, plant hormones; deceased, see previous edition for last biography

**THIND, GURDARSHAN S,** HYPERTENSION, INTERNAL MEDICINE. *Current Pos:* assoc prof, 76-85, DIR, HYPERTENSION SECT, UNIV LOUISVILLE, 76-, PROF MED, 85- *Personal Data:* b Lyallpore, India, Oct 17, 40; m 67, Rajinder K Sekhon; c Gurpreet K & Gurbir S. *Educ:* Punjab Univ, MD, 62; Univ Pa, MS, 66. *Prof Exp:* Assoc & instr, Univ Pa, 65-70, asst prof med, 70-72; asst prof & dir, Cardiovasc Sect, Cochran Div, Vet Admin Hosp, St Louis, Mo, 72-76. *Concurrent Pos:* Head, Chair Heart Res, Univ Louisville, 77-82. *Mem:* Fel Am Col Physicians; fel Am Col Cardiol; Am Physiol Soc; NY Acad Sci; Am Heart Asn; AAAS; Am Soc Hypertension. *Res:* Hypertension and hypertensive cardio-renal diseases. *Mailing Add:* Hypertension Sec Dept Med Div Cardiol Univ Louisville Sch Med Ambul Care Bldg A3G12 Louisville KY 40292-0001. *Fax:* 502-852-7147

**THIO, ALAN POO-AN,** MEDICINAL CHEMISTRY, PESTICIDE CHEMISTRY. *Current Pos:* assoc med chem, Col Pharm, 67-70, REGULATORY SPECIALIST, DIV REGULATORY SERV, UNIV KY, 70- *Personal Data:* b Jatinegara, Indonesia, Jan 17, 31; US citizen; m 57, Tatty H Lim; c Amy, Nirmayati & Susanti. *Educ:* Univ Indonesia, BS, 54, MS, 57; Univ Ky, PhD(org chem), 61. *Prof Exp:* Assoc prof org chem, Bandung Inst Technol, 60-67. *Concurrent Pos:* Abstractor, Chem Abstr Serv, 66-94. *Mem:* Am Chem Soc. *Res:* Development of analytical procedures for the quantitative determination of a pesticide residues in feeds, fertilizers and soils; amino acids in feeds. *Mailing Add:* 242 Aberdeen Dr Lexington KY 40517-1302. *E-Mail:* apthio@hotmail.com

**THIRION, JEAN PAUL JOSEPH,** SOMATIC CELL & HUMAN GENETICS, RECOMBINANT DNA. *Current Pos:* From asst prof to assoc prof, 72-80, PROF MICROBIOL, UNIV SHERBROOKE, 80- *Personal Data:* b Metz, France, July 30, 39; Can citizen; m 67, Ouei Nancy; c Daniel & Philippe. *Educ:* Univ Nancy, France, BS, 60; ENSic, 63; Univ Wis-Madison, PhD(biochem), 66; Pasteur's Inst, France, Doct d'etat, 69. *Prof Exp:* Attache genetics, Nat Ctr Sci Res, Pasteur's Inst, 67-68, charge, 68-72. *Concurrent Pos:* Fulbright fel, 63-67. *Mem:* Am Genetics Soc. *Res:* Genetic analysis of gene regulation. *Mailing Add:* Dept Microbiol Chu-Univ Sherbrooke Sherbrooke PQ J1H 5N4 Can. *Fax:* 819-564-5392

**THIRKILL, JOHN D,** CHEMICAL ENGINEERING. *Current Pos:* RETIRED. *Personal Data:* b Soda Springs, Idaho, Apr 26, 29; m 50; c 3. *Educ:* State Col Wash, BS, 53. *Prof Exp:* Chem engr, E I du Pont de Nemours & Co, Inc, 53; proj engr, Thiokol Chem Corp, Md, 55-58, dept head Rocket Eng, Wasatch Div, 58-60, preliminary design & analysis, 60-63, div mgr, 63-64, proj eng, 64-67, div mgr, 68-71, dep dir space shuttle prog, 71-78, dir eng, 78-89. *Concurrent Pos:* Adv, NASA Internal Comt Design Criteria for Chem Propulsion, 66-68. *Mem:* Am Ord Asn; Am Inst Aeronaut & Astronaut. *Res:* Rocket propulsion, design and development of solid propellant propulsion systems. *Mailing Add:* 5292 S 1300 E Ogden UT 84403

**THIRUMALAI, DEVARAJAN,** STATISTICAL MECHANICS, THEORY OF LIQUIDS GLASSES & POLYMERS. *Current Pos:* from asst prof to assoc prof, 85-93, PROF, STATIST MECH, INST PHYS SCI & TECHNOL, UNIV MD, COLLEGE PARK, 93- *Personal Data:* b Madras, India, June 6, 56; m 82. *Educ:* Indian Inst Technol, Kanpur, India, MSc, 77; Univ Minn, PhD(theoret chem), 82. *Honors & Awards:* Presidential Young Investr Award. *Prof Exp:* Res assoc statist mech, Columbia Univ, 82-85. *Concurrent Pos:* Guest worker, Nat Inst Stand & Technol. *Mem:* Am Phys Soc. *Res:* Equilibrium and non-equilibrium statistical mechanics; theory of disordered systems; protein sciences; biophysics. *Mailing Add:* Inst Phys Sci & Technol Univ Md College Park MD 20742

**THIRUVATHUKAL, JOHN VARKEY,** GEOPHYSICS, OCEANOGRAPHY. *Current Pos:* from asst prof to assoc prof, 70-88, geosci coordr, 85-94, PROF GEOL, MONTCLAIR STATE COL, 88- *Personal Data:* b Shertallay, India, Aug 4, 39; m 71, Teresa Kailath; c George J & Christina E. *Educ:* St Louis Univ, BS, 61; Mich State Univ, MS, 63; Ore State Univ, PhD(geophys), 68. *Prof Exp:* Res asst geophys, Ore State Univ, 63-67; from instr to asst prof geol, DePauw Univ, 67-70. *Concurrent Pos:* Consult,

Bd Earth Sci, Nat Acad Sci, 69-87; adj prof, Fairleigh Dickinson Univ, 71-75. *Mem:* Am Geophys Union; Soc Explor Geophys. *Mailing Add:* Dept Earth & Environ Studies Montclair State Univ 1 Normal Ave Upper Montclair NJ 07043-1624. *E-Mail:* thir@pegasus.montclair.edu

**THIRUVATHUKAL, KRIS V,** ZOOLOGY, MORPHOLOGY. *Current Pos:* chmn dept, 68-71, PROF BIOL, LEWIS UNIV, 68- *Personal Data:* b Shertallay, Kerala, India, May 1, 25; div; c George K, Maria K & Cheryl K. *Educ:* Univ Kerala, BSc, 53; Boston Col, MS, 56; St Louis Univ, PhD(biol, histol), 60. *Prof Exp:* Instr zool, anat, histol & animal tech, Duquesne Univ, 59-60; asst prof zool & histol, Aquinas Col, 60-62; asst prof biol, Gonzaga Univ, 62-65 & Canisius Col, 65-68. *Mem:* Am Micros Soc; Soc Syst Zool; Indian Soc Animal Morphol & Physiol; Am Soc Zoologists; Am Asn Univ Profs (secy, 75-). *Res:* Histology and morphology of reptiles; vertebrate zoology; coelacanth morphology; research in reptilia and coelacanth. *Mailing Add:* 2213 Arden Pl Joliet IL 60435

**THISSEN, WIL A,** SYSTEMS ANALYSIS & MODELING, POLICY ANALYSIS. *Current Pos:* assoc prof, 86-92, PROF SYSTS & POLICY ANALYSIS, DELFT UNIV TECHNOL, 92- *Personal Data:* Neth citizen. *Educ:* Eindhoven Univ Technol, MEng, 73, PhD(systs & control eng), 78. *Prof Exp:* Asst prof systs & control eng, Eindhoven Univ Technol, 73-78; asst prof & sr scientist, Univ Va, 78-80; head, Policy Analysis Div, Rykswaterstaat, Dutch Pub Works Dept, 80-85. *Mem:* Inst Elec & Electronics Engrs, Systs Man & Cybernet Soc; Asn Pub Policy Analysis & Mgt; Inst Mgt Sci; Int Asn Impact Assessment. *Res:* Systems engineering and policy analysis methodology, specifically applied to integrated water resource management, transportation and infrastructures; environmental problems. *Mailing Add:* Delft Univ Technol PO Box 5015 Dept Systs & Policy Analysis Delft 2600 GA Netherlands

**THISTED, RONALD AARON,** BIOSTATISTICS, COMPUTATIONAL STATISTICS. *Current Pos:* From asst prof to assoc prof statist, 76-92, assoc prof anesthesia & critical care, 89-92, PROF STATIST, ANESTHESIA & CRITICAL CARE, UNIV CHICAGO, 92-, PROF HEALTH STUDIES, 96- *Personal Data:* b Los Angeles, Calif, Mar 2, 51; m 72, Linda Soder; c Walker C. *Educ:* Pomona Col, BA, 72; Stanford Univ, MS, 73, PhD(statist), 77. *Concurrent Pos:* Vis lectr, Soc Indust & Appl Math, 79-80; assoc ed, J Am Statist Asn, 79-85. *Mem:* Fel Am Statist Asn; Inst Math Statist; Asn Comput Mach; Am Pub Health Asn; fel AAAS. *Res:* Statistical computation; development of algorithms; pharmacoepidemiology; biostatistics; clinical trials. *Mailing Add:* Dept Statist Univ Chicago 5734 University Ave Chicago IL 60637. *E-Mail:* r-thisted@uchicago.edu

**THISTLE, DAVID,** BENTHIC ECOLOGY, ECOLOGY OF MEIOFAUNA. *Current Pos:* Asst prof, 77-88, PROF OCEANOG, FLA STATE UNIV, 88- *Personal Data:* b Lowell, Mass, Oct 1, 49. *Educ:* Harvard Univ, AB, 71; Scripps Inst Oceanog, PhD(oceanog), 77. *Mem:* Ecol Soc Am; Am Geophys Union; Am Soc Limmologists & Oceanogrs; Int Asn Meiobenthologists (treas, 88-90). *Res:* Soft bottom communities from shallow water to the deep sea, particularly the organizing role of physical disturbance; deep seal ecology. *Mailing Add:* Oceanog Fla State Univ 600 W College Ave Tallahassee FL 32306-1096

**THODE, E(DWARD) F(REDERICK),** INDUSTRIAL CHEMISTRY, MATERIALS. *Current Pos:* prof chem eng & head dept, NMex State Univ, 63-84, assoc dir eng exp sta, 65-66, actg dir, Ctr Bus Res & Serv, 77, prof mgt, 74-86, EMER PROF, CHEM ENG & MGT, NMEX STATE UNIV, 86- *Personal Data:* b New York, NY, May 31, 21; m 44, Isobel Zoeller; c Karen E (O'Neil), Stephen F & Jonathan E. *Educ:* Mass Inst Technol, SB, 42, SM, 43, ScD(chem eng), 47. *Prof Exp:* Chem engr, Boston Woven Hose & Rubber Co, Mass, 43-45; from asst prof to assoc prof chem eng, Univ Maine, 47-54; chem engr, Cent Res Dept, Minn Mining & Mfg Co, 54-55; res assoc phys chem, Inst Paper Chem, 55-57; chem eng, 57-59, chief pulping & papermaking sect, 59-60, adminr eng & tech sect, 60-61, coordr info processing, 61-63. *Concurrent Pos:* Affil, Los Alamos Nat Lab, 65-90; consult, Gen Elec Co, 64-66 & Bell Tel Labs, 66-70. *Mem:* Sigma Xi; Am Inst Chem Engrs; Am Soc Eng Educ. *Res:* Technico-economic studies of energy alternatives; environmental control technology; management science; production/operations management. *Mailing Add:* 905 Conway 45 Las Cruces NM 88005-3775. *E-Mail:* ethode@nmsu.edu

**THODE, HENRY GEORGE,** geochemistry; deceased, see previous edition for last biography

**THODE, LESTER ELSTER,** PLASMA PHYSICS, CHARGED PARTICLE BEAM PHYSICS. *Current Pos:* Staff mem, 73-78, alt group leader, 78-79, GROUP LEADER INTENSE PARTICLE BEAM PHYSICS, LOS ALAMOS NAT LAB, 79- *Personal Data:* b Alameda, Calif, Apr 8, 43; m 67; c 3. *Educ:* Univ Calif, Berkeley, BS, 69; Cornell Univ, PhD(appl physics), 74. *Mem:* Am Phys Soc. *Res:* Collective behavior of particle beams. *Mailing Add:* X-DOT B218 Los Alamos Nat Lab Box 1663 Los Alamos NM 87545. *Fax:* 505-665-4080

**THODOS, GEORGE,** CHEMICAL ENGINEERING. *Current Pos:* from asst prof to prof chem eng, 47-77, WALTER P MURPHY PROF, TECH INST NORTHWESTERN UNIV, EVANSTON, 77- *Personal Data:* b Chicago, Ill, Sept 15, 15. *Educ:* Armour Inst Technol, BS, 38, MS, 39; Univ Wis, PhD(chem eng), 43. *Prof Exp:* Jr chem engr, Stand Oil Co Ind, 39-40 & Phillips Petrol Co, Okla, 40-41, chem engr, 43-46; chem engr, Pure Oil Co,

Ill, 46-47. *Mem:* Am Chem Soc; Am Inst Chem Engrs. *Res:* Petroleum processing; mass transfer studies; vapor pressures and critical constants of hydrocarbons; transport properties of substances; vapor-liquid equilibrium studies. *Mailing Add:* Dept Tech Chem Eng Bldg Northwestern Univ Evanston IL 60201

**THOE, ROBERT STEVEN,** ATOMIC PHYSICS. *Current Pos:* CONSULT, 75- *Personal Data:* b Pensacola, Fla, Aug 19, 45; m 68; c 1. *Educ:* Baylor Univ, BS, 68; Univ Conn, MS, 70, PhD(physics), 73. *Prof Exp:* Asst res prof physics, Univ Tenn, 73-76, asst prof, 76-80. *Mem:* Am Phys Soc. *Res:* The study of atomic collision phenomena, primarily by the detection and measurement of the non-characteristic radiations emitted during violent ion-atom collisions. *Mailing Add:* 2622 Crater Rd Livermore CA 94550

**THOENE, JESS GILBERT,** CLINICAL BIOCHEMICAL GENETICS, PEDIATRICS. *Current Pos:* from asst prof to assoc prof pediat, 77-86, asst prof biochem, 84-87, ASSOC PROF BIOCHEM, UNIV MICH, 87-, PROF PEDIAT, 86- *Personal Data:* b Bakersfield, Calif, Aug 4, 42; m 65. *Educ:* Stanford Univ, BS, 64; Johns Hopkins Univ, MD, 68. *Honors & Awards:* Pub Health Serv Award Outstanding Achievement Orphan Prod Develop, 86. *Prof Exp:* Asst clin prof pediat, Univ Calif, San Diego, 75-77. *Concurrent Pos:* Dir, Mich Dept Ment Health Genetic Screening Lab, 77-89 & Pediat Clin Res Ctr, 86; Welcome Found Travel Grant, 84; vchmn, Nat Comn Orphan Dis, 86-89, chair, 89; Kennedy Found Fel, 88-89. *Mem:* Soc Pediat Res; Am Soc Clin Invest; Am Soc Human Genetics; Am Chem Soc; Nat Orgn Rare Dis (pres, 85-93); Am Pediat Soc; Am Soc Biochem & Molecular Biol. *Res:* Orphan drug research; lysosomol physiology. *Mailing Add:* Dept Pediat 2612 SPHI Univ Mich Med Ctr 300 N1B 1182 SE Ann Arbor MI 48109-0408

**THOENEN, HANS,** NEUROSCIENCE. *Current Pos:* dir, 79-96, EMER DIR, DEPT NEUROCHEM, MAX PLANCK INST PSYCHIAT, 96- *Personal Data:* b May 5, 28; m 55, Sonja Amstutz; c Andreas & Gert. *Educ:* Univ Bern, MD, 54. *Hon Degrees:* Dr, Univ Zurich, 92. *Honors & Awards:* Feldberg Prize, 80; Cloetta Prize, 85; Wakeman Award, Duke Univ, 88; Ipsen Prize Neuronal Plasticity, 94; Charles A Dana Award Pioneering Achievements in Health, Inst Med-Nat Acad Sci, 94; Ralph W Gerard Prize Neurosci, 95; Bristol-Myers Squibb Award Distinguished Achievement Neurosci Res, 97. *Prof Exp:* Staff mem, Dept Path, Univ Bern, Switz, 54-55, Dept Internal Med, Univ Basel, Switz, 55-59, Inst Exp Geront, 60-61; staff scientist, Dept Exp Med, Hoffmann-LaRoche & Co, Basel, 61-68 & 69-71; vis scientist, Lab Julius Axelrod, NIMH, 68-69; head, Neurobiol Res Group, Biocenter, Univ Basel, 72-78. *Concurrent Pos:* Hon prof, Ludwig-Maximilians-Univ Munich, Ger, 81. *Mem:* Assoc mem Nat Acad Sci; Europ Molecular Biol Orgn; Acad Europaea. *Res:* Molecular neurobiology, in particular neurotrophic factors, structure/function relationship, physiological function including therapeutic perspectives. *Mailing Add:* Max Planck Inst Psychiat Dept Neurochem Am Klopferspitz 18A 82152 Martinsried Germany

**THOENNESSEN, MICHAEL,** RADIOACTIVE NUCLEAR BEAMS, GIANT RESONANCES. *Current Pos:* asst prof, 90-95, ASSOC PROF PHYSICS, MICH STATE UNIV, 95- *Personal Data:* b Cologne, Ger, Aug 23, 59. *Educ:* Univ Cologne, Ger, dipl, 85; State Univ NY, Stony Brook, PhD(exp nuclear physics), 88. *Prof Exp:* Res assoc, Joint Inst Heavy Ion Res, Tenn, 88-90. *Mem:* Am Phys Soc. *Res:* Structure and decay of properties of exotic nuclei using radioactive beams; fission and fusion dynamics of hot nuclei by measuring the decay of the giant dipole resonance. *Mailing Add:* Cyclotron Lab Mich State Univ East Lansing MI 48824

**THOLEN, ALBERT DAVID,** CIVIL ENGINEERING, METROLOGY. *Current Pos:* dep dir Stand Analysis Div, 77, CHIEF, OFF WEIGHTS & MEASURES, NAT BUR STAND US DEPT COM, 77- *Personal Data:* b Philadelphia, Pa, Aug 23, 27; m 56; c 4. *Educ:* Drexel Univ, BSCE, 49. *Prof Exp:* Vpres opers res, Gen Res Corp, 62-77. *Concurrent Pos:* Adv comt mem, Int Legal Metrol, US Dept Com, 78- *Mem:* Fel AAAS; Opers Res Soc Am. *Res:* Measurement science; electronics; microprocessing. *Mailing Add:* 7121 Thomas Branch Dr Bethesda MD 20817

**THOM, RONALD MARK,** MARINE BENTHIC ALGAE, MARINE POLLUTION. *Current Pos:* RES SCIENTIST, BATTELLE, 90- *Personal Data:* b Long Beach, Calif, June 6, 48; m 71; c 1. *Educ:* Calif State Col, Dominguez Hills, BA, 71; Calif State Univ, Long Beach, MA, 76; Univ Wash, PhD(phycol), 78. *Prof Exp:* Biologist, Co Sanitation Dist, Los Angeles, 71-74 & US Army Corps Engrs, 79-82; res scientist, Univ Wash, 82-90; instr oceanog, Chapman Col, 85- *Concurrent Pos:* Consult, City of Seattle, 82-; adv, Off Puget Sound, US Environ Protection Agency, 84-90. *Mem:* AAAS; Ecol Soc Am; Phycol Soc Am; Am Soc Limnol & Oceanog; Estuarine Res Fedn. *Res:* Marine algal ecology; nearshore marine systems ecology; primary productivity of seaweed dominated systems; pollution effects on nearshore marine systems; wetland construction. *Mailing Add:* 34 Wild Rose Lane Sequim WA 98382

**THOMA, GEORGE EDWARD,** INTERNAL MEDICINE, NUCLEAR MEDICINE. *Current Pos:* RETIRED. *Personal Data:* b Dayton, Ohio, Aug 9, 22; m 49; c 8. *Educ:* Univ Dayton, BS, 43; St Louis Univ, MD, 47. *Prof Exp:* From instr assoc prof internal med, St Louis Univ, 51-76, head, Sect Nuclear Med, 59-73, asst to vpres 62-67, asst vpres, Med Ctr, 67-73, vpres, Med Ctr, 73-, prof internal med, 76- *Concurrent Pos:* Dir radioisotopes lab, Med Ctr, St Louis Univ, 49-51 & 54-73; consult, Health Physics Div, Oak Ridge Nat Lab, 54-, Lockheed Aircraft Corp, 54-, US Army, 56-, Med Div, Oak Ridge Inst Nuclear Studies, 58-, Div Radiol Health, USPHS, 60-, Div

Compliance, US Nuclear Res Coun, 62- & Am Pub Health Asn, 62-; ed, J Nuclear Med, 59-70. *Mem:* Soc Nuclear Med; Radiation Res Soc; Health Physics Soc; Am Thyroid Asn; Am Soc Internal Med. *Res:* Radiobiology; thyroid function; clinical application of radioisotopes. *Mailing Add:* 5 Georgian Acres St Louis MO 63131

**THOMA, GEORGE RANJAN,** ELECTRICAL ENGINEERING, COMMUNICATIONS ENGINEERING. *Current Pos:* SR ELECTRONICS ENGR & CHIEF COMMUN ENG, NAT LIBR MED, 74- *Personal Data:* b India, Mar 1, 44; US citizen. *Educ:* Swarthmore Col, BS, 65; Univ Pa, MS, 67, PhD(elec eng), 71. *Honors & Awards:* Qual Serv Award, 83; Fed 100 Award, 95. *Prof Exp:* Ford Found fel, 65-67; res assoc, Moore Sch Elec Eng, Univ Pa, 68-71; systs engr, AII Systs, Moorestown, NJ, 71-73, Gen Elec Co, 73-74. *Concurrent Pos:* Consult, NSF & var industs, Nat Endowment Humanities & Nat Inst Stand & Technol. *Mem:* Inst Elec & Electronics Engrs; Am Soc Info Sci; Soc Photo-Optical & Instrumentation Engrs. *Res:* Telecommunications; signal processing; satellite aided video and voice communications; satellite aided radio navigation; digital image processing; video disc and optical disk technologies; electronic document storage and retrieval; information science and systems; digital xray image processing; information science and systems. *Mailing Add:* Nat Libr Med 8600 Rockville Pike Bethesda MD 20894. *Fax:* 301-402-0341; *E-Mail:* thoma@nlm.nih.gov

**THOMA, JOHN ANTHONY,** BIOCHEMISTRY. *Current Pos:* PROF CHEM, UNIV ARK, 70- *Personal Data:* b Springfield, Ill, Dec 6, 32; m 58; c 4. *Educ:* Bradley Univ, AB, 54; Iowa State Univ, PhD(biochem), 58. *Prof Exp:* Asst prof, Ind Univ, 60-66. *Concurrent Pos:* Vis fel, Univ Sydney, 72; vis scholar, Univ Calif, Los Angeles, 77-78. *Mem:* Am Chem Soc; Sigma Xi; Am Asn Biol Chemists. *Res:* Anti-viral substances; enzymology; theory and practice of chromatography. *Mailing Add:* Chem Univ Ark 114 Chem Bldg Fayetteville AR 72701-1202

**THOMA, RICHARD WILLIAM,** CHEMICAL & INDUSTRIAL SAFETY, REGULATORY COMPLIANCE. *Current Pos:* PRES, ST LUCIE BIO-TECH, 93- *Personal Data:* b Milwaukee, Wis, Dec 7, 21; m 52; c 4. *Educ:* Univ Wis, BSc, 47, MSc, 49, PhD(biochem), 51. *Prof Exp:* Res assoc sect microbiol, Squibb Inst Med Res, 51-61, res supvr microbiol develop, 62-68, asst dir biol process develop, 68-79, sr res fel, biol process develop, E R Squibb & Sons, 79-82; dir, process develop, New Brunswick Sci Co, Inc, 82-84; pres, Thoma Consult, Inc, 84-93; safety officer, Harbor Br Oceanog Inst Inc, 88-96. *Concurrent Pos:* Consult, Chem Health & Safety, Hazardous Mat Mgt, Regulatory Compliance, 88- *Mem:* Am Chem Soc; NY Acad Sci; Am Soc Safety Engrs; Sigma Xi; Am Soc Microbiol; Soc Indust Microbiol. *Res:* Fermentation process research and development. *Mailing Add:* 3772 Outrigger Ct Ft Pierce FL 34946. *Fax:* 561-465-2446

**THOMA, ROY E,** INORGANIC CHEMISTRY, ENVIRONMENTAL ASSESSMENTS. *Current Pos:* RETIRED. *Personal Data:* b San Antonio, Tex, May 12, 22; m 53; c 2. *Educ:* Univ Tex, MA, 48. *Prof Exp:* Assoc prof, Sam Houston State Col, 48-51; asst prof, Tex Tech Col, 51-52; chemist, Oak Ridge Nat Lab, 52-60, proj chemist, Molten Salt Reactor Progs, 64-71, task group dir, 71-78, tech asst to assoc dir admin, 78-80, environ assessments analyst, 80-85, prin investr, Environ Health & Safety, Synfuel Proj, 85-86. *Concurrent Pos:* Mem bd dirs, Environ Systs Corp, 73-77; mem, environ qual adv bd, City of Oak Ridge, 85-88. *Mem:* Am Chem Soc; Sigma Xi; fel Am Ceramic Soc; Am Nuclear Soc; fel AAAS. *Res:* Physical chemistry of inorganic fused salts, particularly determinations of phase equilibria and interrelationships of crystal structures in condensed systems of these materials; environmental effects of nuclear and synfuels facilities. *Mailing Add:* 119 Underwood Rd Oak Ridge TN 37830

**THOMAN, CHARLES JAMES,** MODEL MEMBRANE TRANSPORT, SYNTHESIS OF ANTIVIRALS. *Current Pos:* chair, 89-94, PROF CHEM, PHILADELPHIA COL PHARM & SCI, 89- *Personal Data:* b Wilkes-Barre, Pa, Nov 4, 28; m 82, Grace U Garrett; c Robert Miller & Catherine Miller. *Educ:* Spring Hill Col, BS, 53; Fordham Univ, MS, 56; Woodstock Col, STB, 59, STM, 60; Univ Mass, Amherst, PhD(org chem), 66. *Prof Exp:* Instr chem, Univ Scranton, 53-55, from asst prof to prof, 66-82, chmn chem, 78-82; res assoc toxicol, Sch Med, La State Univ, Shreveport, 82-83; vis prof chem, Univ Ala, Tuscaloosa, 83-84; prof, Univ Scranton, 84-87; prof & chair, Stephen F Austin State Univ, 87-89. *Concurrent Pos:* Chair, Philadelphia Sect, Am Chem Soc, 95, past-chair, 96. *Mem:* Am Chem Soc; Sigma Xi. *Res:* Chemistry and biochemistry of polysorbate 80; chemistry of n-nitrosoketimines; sydnone chemistry. *Mailing Add:* Chem Dept Philadelphia Col Pharm & Sci Philadelphia PA 19104

**THOMAN, MARILYN LOUISE,** CELLULAR IMMUNOLOGY. *Current Pos:* ASST MEM IMMUNOL DEPT, SCRIPPS CLIN & RES FOUND, 84- *Educ:* Univ Calif, Berkeley, PhD(molecular biol), 78. *Mailing Add:* Dept Immunol Scripps Clin & Res Found 10666 N Torrey Pines Rd La Jolla CA 92037-1092. *Fax:* 619-554-6705

**THOMANN, GARY C,** ELECTRIC UTILITY TRANSMISSION SYSTEMS. *Current Pos:* SR ENGR, POWER TECHNOL, INC, 87- *Personal Data:* b Burlington, Iowa, July 23, 42. *Educ:* Univ Kans, BS, 65, MS, 67, PhD(elec eng), 70. *Prof Exp:* Res engr, Univ Kans, 67-70; prin investr, NASA, 70-75; from asst prof to assoc prof elec eng, Wichita State Univ, 75-87. *Mem:* Inst Elec & Electronics Engrs; Sigma Xi; Am Soc Eng Educ. *Res:* Electric utility transmission systems. *Mailing Add:* Power Technol Inc 1482 Erie Blvd Schenectady NY 12301-1058. *Fax:* 518-346-2777

**THOMANN, ROBERT V,** CIVIL ENGINEERING, OCEANOGRAPHY. *Current Pos:* PROF CIVIL ENG, MANHATTAN COL, 66- *Personal Data:* b New York, NY, Sept 1, 34; m 57; c 7. *Educ:* Manhattan Col, BCE, 56; NY Univ, MCE, 60, PhD(oceanog), 63. *Prof Exp:* Engr, Delaware River & Bay Study, USPHS, 56-59, engr in charge Narragansett Bay Study, 59-60; tech dir estuary water qual mgt, Fed Water Pollution Control Admin, 62-66. *Concurrent Pos:* Consult. *Mem:* Am Chem Soc; Am Soc Limnol & Oceanog; Am Soc Civil Engrs; Water Pollution Control Fedn; Sigma Xi. *Res:* Interrelationships of environment on waste water discharge, water quality and water use. *Mailing Add:* 326 N Maple Ave Ridgewood NJ 07450

**THOMAS, ABDELNOUR SIMON,** MATHEMATICS. *Current Pos:* FOUNDER & DIR RES ACTIV, A S THOMAS, INC, 55- *Personal Data:* b Kharhoune, Lebanon, Oct 25, 13; m 51, Eva M Ballings; c Robert F, David C, Paul J, Simon S, Mary E & John T. *Educ:* Holy Cross Col, BS, 37; Boston Univ, MEd, 39, PhD, 50. *Concurrent Pos:* Regist prof engr, Mass; prof math & math statist; vis prof, Mass Inst Technol. *Res:* Co-development of theory of graded and hybrid absorber materials; theory of modulated surface wave antennas; re-entry vehicle antennas; characterization of radar cross section of metallic, coated metallic and non-metallic bodies. *Mailing Add:* Thomas A S Inc 355 Providence Hwy Westwood MA 02090

**THOMAS, ADRIAN WESLEY,** RISK STRATEGIES, HYDROLOGIC MODELING. *Current Pos:* Res scientist, Agr Res Serv, USDA, Tifton, Ga, 65-69, Ft Collins, Colo, 69-72, Watkinsville, Ga, 72-78, res leader, Watkinsville, Ga, 78-89, LAB DIR, AGR RES SERV, USDA, TIFTON, GA, 89- *Personal Data:* b Edgefield, SC, June 23, 39; m 64, Martha E McAllister; c Wesley A & Andrea E. *Educ:* Clemson Univ, BSAE, 62, MSAE, 65; Colo State Univ, PhD(agr eng), 72. *Concurrent Pos:* Acad fac, Colo State Univ, Ft Collins, 69-72; adj prof, Univ Ga, Athens, 73- *Mem:* Am Soc Agr Engrs; Am Soc Agron; Soil & Water Conserv Soc; Soil Sci Soc Am; Sigma Xi. *Res:* Development of technologies that will integrate soil, water and climate resources for optimization of conservation and environmental strategies in agricultural systems for the Southeast. *Mailing Add:* USDA-Agr Res Serv PO Box 946 Tifton GA 31793. *Fax:* 912-386-7215; *E-Mail:* sewrl@tifton.cpes. peachnet.edu

**THOMAS, ALAN R,** OCEANOGRAPHY. *Current Pos:* ACTG ASST ADMINR, OCEANIC & ATMOSPHERIC RES, NAT OCEANIC & ATMOSPHERIC ADMIN, 96- *Personal Data:* b Utica, NY, July 2, 39. *Educ:* Hamilton Col, PhD. *Mailing Add:* Nat Oceanog & Atmospheric Admin 1315 East-West Hwy Rm 11627 Silver Spring MD 20910-3279

**THOMAS, ALBERT LEE, JR,** electronics; deceased, see previous edition for last biography

**THOMAS, ALEXANDER,** PSYCHIATRY. *Current Pos:* From instr to assoc prof, 48-66, PROF PSYCHIAT, SCH MED, NY UNIV, 66- *Personal Data:* b New York, NY, Jan 11, 14; m 38; c 4. *Educ:* City Col New York, 32; NY Univ, MD, 36; Am Bd Psychiat & Neurol, dipl, 48. *Honors & Awards:* Ittleson Award, Am Psychiat Asn; Baum Award, NY Ment Health Asn. *Concurrent Pos:* Dir, Psychiat Div, Bellevue Hosp, NY, 68-78; assoc attend psychiatrist, Bellevue & Univ Hosps, 58-68; attend psychiatrist, 68- *Mem:* Fel Am Psychiat Asn; Sigma Xi. *Res:* Longitudinal study of child development; psychosomatic medicine. *Mailing Add:* 275 W 96th St No 23B Sch Med NY Univ 550 First Ave New York NY 10025

**THOMAS, ALEXANDER EDWARD, III,** ORGANIC CHEMISTRY, ANALYTICAL CHEMISTRY. *Current Pos:* RETIRED. *Personal Data:* b Chicago, Ill, May 3, 30; m 56; c 3. *Educ:* Univ Ill, BS, 55; DePaul Univ, MS, 61. *Prof Exp:* Res chemist, Cent Org Res Lab, Glidden Co, 55-58, sect head analytical chem, Durkee Foods Group, 58-66, mgr, Chem Res Dept, 66-71, mgr chem res, Dwight P Joyce Res Ctr, 71-78, mgr applns res, Glidden-Durkee Div, 71-78, assoc dir appl sci, Dwight P Joyce Res Ctr, Durkee Div, SCM Corp, 78-85, tech consult, 86-90. *Mem:* Am Chem Soc; Am Oil Chem Soc. *Res:* Analytical chemistry of glycerides, surfactants and protective coatings; chromatographic and instrumental methods; synthesis of organic azides. *Mailing Add:* 16335 Ramona Dr Cleveland OH 44130

**THOMAS, ALFORD MITCHELL,** MEDICINAL PROCESS RESEARCH & DEVELOPMENT, PEPTIDE CHEMISTRY. *Current Pos:* SR RES INVESTR, GLAXO WELLCOME, INC. *Personal Data:* b Bunnlevel, NC, July 24, 42; m 70, Elizabeth Wadsworth; c Edward B. *Educ:* Campbell Col, NC, BA, 64; Univ NC, Chapel Hill, PhD(org chem), 69. *Prof Exp:* NIH fel, Univ Va, 69-71, res assoc org chem, 71-72; sr chemist, Abbott Labs, 72-77, res investr, 78-91; sr chemist, Burroughs Wellcome Co, 91- *Mem:* Am Chem Soc; AAAS; Sigma Xi. *Res:* Synthesis of biological peptides; process development of pharmaceutically. *Mailing Add:* 1326 Red Twig Rd Apex NC 27502

**THOMAS, ALVIN DAVID, JR,** PHYSICAL METALLURGY. *Current Pos:* RETIRED. *Personal Data:* b Gary, Ind, Nov 3, 28; m 52; c 3. *Educ:* Case Inst Technol, BS, 40; Purdue Univ, MS, 59, PhD(metall eng), 61. *Prof Exp:* Res engr, Repub Steel Res Ctr, 60-63; asst prof mech eng, Univ Tex, 63-67; head mat res sect, Tracor, Inc, 67-72, dep dir, Environ & Phys Sci Div, 72-76; dir, Mat Sci Div, Radian Corp, 76-91. *Mem:* Am Inst Mining, Metall & Petrol Engrs; Am Soc Metals; Am Soc Testing & Mat. *Res:* Mechanisms in precipitation hardening; strengthening mechanisms in steels; properties of Invar and Elinvar type alloys; resistance welding; composite materials; failure analysis and accident prevention. *Mailing Add:* 23 W W Hill Rd Maple Dale Farm Winsted CT 06098

**THOMAS, ANTHONY,** MECHANICAL ENGINEERING, ENGINEERING PHYSICS. *Current Pos:* RETIRED. *Personal Data:* b May 3, 31; US citizen; c 2. *Educ:* Univ Mich, BS, 54, MS, 63. *Prof Exp:* Res proj engr aerial photog, Chicago Aerial Industs, 57-61; group leader Bubble Chamber, Argone Nat Lab, 61-78, prog mgr ocean thermal energy conversion, 78-, sect magr exp systs eng, 80-, mgr, Thermal Technol Prog, 87- *Concurrent Pos:* Mem, US Bubble Chamber Working Group, 77-78; chmn, Deep Ocean Environ, Workshop on Conserv Related Heat Transfer Res, 87. *Res:* Design and operation of cryogenic devices; devices for energy conservation, conversion and efficiency enchancement. *Mailing Add:* Argonne Nat Lab ES-Bldg 362 Rm E365 9700 S Cass Ave Argonne IL 60439

**THOMAS, ARTHUR L,** CHEMISTRY. *Current Pos:* ABSTRACTOR, AM PETROL INST, NEW YORK, 88- *Personal Data:* b New York, NY, July 24, 28; m 77, Charlotte B Harriau. *Educ:* Columbia Col, AB, 51; Princeton Univ, PhD, 56. *Prof Exp:* Engr photo prod, E I du Pont de Nemours & Co, Inc, 55-58, res supvr, 58-59; chem engr, Stand Ultramarine & Color Co, 60-65 & MHD, Inc & Plasmachem Inc, 65-68; from instr to asst prof chem, Calif State Polytech Col, San Luis Obispo, 69-72; vis asst prof immunochem, Columbia Univ, 73; sci ed, Ronald Press Co, 74-77; ed, Chem Mkt Res, Hull & Co, 78-87. *Mem:* AAAS; Sigma Xi; NY Acad Sci. *Res:* Pigments; high temperature reactions. *Mailing Add:* 2 Putnam Park Greenwich CT 06830-5747

**THOMAS, ARTHUR NORMAN,** SURGERY, THORACIC SURGERY. *Current Pos:* resident, Univ Hosp, 60-62, clin instr, Sch Med, 63-68, from asst prof to assoc prof, 68-83, PROF SURG, SCH MED, UNIV CALIF, SAN FRANCISCO, 83-; CHIEF THORACIC SURG, SAN FRANCISCO GEN HOSP, 70- *Personal Data:* b Los Angeles, Calif, Jan 27, 31; m 50; c 5. *Educ:* Stanford Univ, BS, 53; Univ BC, MD, 57. *Prof Exp:* Intern surg, San Francisco Gen Hosp, 57-58, resident, 58-59. *Concurrent Pos:* NIH res fel, Univ Hosp, Univ Calif, San Francisco, 59-60, NIH fel, Cardiovasc Res Inst, 63-65; asst chief surg, Vet Admin Hosp, San Francisco, 66-70, attend physician thoracic surg, 70- *Mem:* Soc Thoracic Surg; Samson Thoracic Surg Soc; Am Asn Thoracic Surg. *Res:* Thoracic surgery; cardiopulmonary research. *Mailing Add:* 1001 Potrero Ave San Francisco CA 94110-3518

**THOMAS, AUBREY STEPHEN, JR,** TISSUE CULTURE, PHYSIOLOGICAL ECOLOGY. *Current Pos:* From asst prof to assoc prof bot & ecol, Merrimack Col, 67-87, chmn, Dept Biol, 75-81, actg dean, Div Sci & Eng, 84-85, from asst to actg assoc dean, Col Arts & Sci, 85-86, PROF BOT & ENVIRON SCI, MERRIMACK COL, 87- *Personal Data:* b Wolfeboro, NH, Nov 4, 33; m 56, Satoko Nagaoka. *Educ:* Keene State Col, BEd, 62; Univ NH, MS, 64, PhD(bot), 67. *Concurrent Pos:* Adj vis scientist, Citrus Res & Educ Ctr, Univ Fla, Lake Alfred, 88. *Mem:* Sigma Xi; Am Soc Plant Physiologists; Bot Soc Am; Am Soc Hort Sci; Nat Asn Biol Teachers; Am Inst Biol Sci. *Res:* Botany; tissue culture; physiological ecology; alletopathy; climatology. *Mailing Add:* Dept Biol Merrimack Col Turnpike St North Andover MA 01845. *Fax:* 978-837-5222; *E-Mail:* athomas@merrimack.edu

**THOMAS, BARRY,** ZOOLOGY, ENVIRONMENTAL EDUCATION. *Current Pos:* asst prof, 72-75, PROF ENVIRON EDUC, CALIF STATE UNIV, FULLERTON, 75- *Personal Data:* b Eng, Dec 31, 41; US citizen. *Educ:* Calif State Univ, Fullerton, BA, 67, MA, 68; Univ BC, PhD(zool), 71. *Prof Exp:* Lectr ecol, Univ Calgary, 71-72. *Concurrent Pos:* Pres, BioReCon, 71-; dir, Tucker Wildlife Sanctuary, 72- *Mem:* Am Soc Mammal; Audubon Soc. *Res:* Karyotaxonomy of island rodents; urbanization effects on wild animal populations; biological impact statements. *Mailing Add:* Dept Biol Sci Calif State Univ 800 N State Col Fullerton CA 92631-3547

**THOMAS, BARRY HOLLAND,** BIOCHEMISTRY, PHARMACOLOGY. *Current Pos:* RES SCIENTIST, HEALTH PROTECTION BR, DEPT NAT HEALTH, 69- *Personal Data:* b Lancaster, Eng, June 1, 39; m 66; c 2. *Educ:* Univ Liverpool, BSc, 62, PhD(pharmacol), 65. *Prof Exp:* Asst lectr pharmacol, Univ Liverpool, 65-67, lectr, 67-69. *Concurrent Pos:* Assoc ed, Can J Physiol Pharmacol, 80-86. *Mem:* Soc Toxicol Can (pres, 86-87); Pharmacol Soc Can; Soc Toxicol USA. *Res:* Role of drug metabolism in the toxicity of drugs; toxicity of drug interactions. *Mailing Add:* PO Box 51 Kars ON K0A 2E0 Can

**THOMAS, BILLY SEAY,** THEORETICAL PHYSICS. *Current Pos:* RETIRED. *Personal Data:* b Tenn, Dec 31, 26; m 53; c 1. *Educ:* Wayne State Univ, BS, 53; Vanderbilt Univ, MS, 55, PhD(physics), 59. *Prof Exp:* Nat Res Coun fel, Argonne Nat Lab, 58-59; asst prof physics, Vanderbilt Univ, 59-60; asst prof physics, Univ Fla, 60-77, assoc prof, 77-94. *Mem:* Am Phys Soc. *Res:* Atomic and molecular scattering; elementary particle physics. *Mailing Add:* Dept Physics Univ Fla 215 Williamson Hall Gainesville FL 32611-2002

**THOMAS, BRUCE ROBERT,** EXPERIMENTAL PHYSICS, ELECTRONICS. *Current Pos:* from asst prof to assoc prof, 67-77, PROF PHYSICS, CARLETON COL, 77- *Personal Data:* b Guthrie Center, Iowa, Jan 1, 38; m 60, Alice A Miller; c Lise, Valerie & Megan. *Educ:* Grinnell Col, BA, 60; Cornell Univ, PhD(theoret physics), 65. *Prof Exp:* Asst prof physics, Grinnell Col, 65-67. *Concurrent Pos:* Guest asst prof, Univ Heidelberg, Ger, 74-75. *Mem:* Am Phys Soc; Am Asn Physics Teachers. *Res:* Experimental atomic physics. *Mailing Add:* Dept Physics & Astron Carleton Col Northfield MN 55057-4025. *E-Mail:* bthomas@carleton.edu

**THOMAS, CECIL OWEN, JR,** NUCLEAR POWER, PLANT SAFETY. *Current Pos:* proj mgr, Div Proj Mgt, US Nuclear Regulatory Comn, 75-80, prin systs eng, Div Systs Integration, 80-81, tech coordr, 81, sect leader, Clinch River Breeder Reactor Prog Off, 81-82, chief, Stand & Spec Proj Br, 82-85, chief, Reactor Systs Br, 85-87, proj dir, Integrated Safety Assessment Proj Directorate, 87, chief, Policy Develop & Tech Support Br, 87-89, dep dir, Div Reactor Controls & Human Factors, 89-94, BR CHIEF, HUMAN FACTORS ASSESSMENT BR, US NUCLEAR REGULATORY COMN, 94- *Personal Data:* b East Cleveland, Ohio, Sept 6, 42. *Educ:* Univ Tenn, Knoxville, BS, 64, MS, 66, PhD(nuclear eng), 71. *Prof Exp:* Res technician biomed res, Mem Res Ctr & Hosp, Univ Tenn, Knoxville, 63-64; asst, Univ, 67-68; Oak Ridge fel, Savannah River Lab, E I Du Pont de Nemours & Co, Inc, 68-71; nuclear engr, Nuclear Eng Br, Tenn Valley Authority, 71-75. *Mem:* Am Nuclear Soc. *Res:* Nuclear instrumentation and control systems. *Mailing Add:* US Nuclear Regulatory Comn MS 09H15 Washington DC 20555

**THOMAS, CECIL WAYNE,** BIOMEDICAL ENGINEERING, VISUAL PERCEPTION. *Current Pos:* PROF BIOENG, CASE WESTERN RES UNIV, 73- *Personal Data:* b Dry Ridge, Ky, May 17, 41; m 63; c 2. *Educ:* Univ Ky, BS, 63, MS, 65; Univ Tex, PhD(bioeng), 74. *Prof Exp:* Res engr electronics, Martin Marietta Corp, 65-69. *Concurrent Pos:* Consult, Proj Hope, 82; vis prof, Cairo Univ, Egypt, 82 & Australian Nat Univ, 90. *Mem:* Inst Elec & Electronics Engrs; Psychomet Soc. *Res:* Imaging; visual perception; biomedical signals; computer pattern recognition; intelligent systems; biological applications. *Mailing Add:* Dept Biomed Eng Case Western Res Univ 10900 Euclid Ave Wickendon Hall Rm 504 Cleveland OH 44106

**THOMAS, CHARLES ALLEN, JR,** BIOPHYSICAL CHEMISTRY. *Current Pos:* FOUNDER, DIR, HELICON FOUND, 81- *Personal Data:* b Dayton, Ohio, July 7, 27; m 51; c 2. *Educ:* Princeton Univ, AB, 50; Harvard Univ, PhD(phys chem), 54. *Prof Exp:* Res scientist, Eli Lilly & Co, Ind, 54-55; Nat Res Coun fel physics, Univ Mich, 55-56 , instr, 56-57; from asst prof to prof biophys, Johns Hopkins Univ, 57-67; prof biol chem, Harvard Med Sch, 67-77; mem & chmn, Dept Cellular Biol, Scripps Clin & Res Found, 77-81. *Concurrent Pos:* NSF sr fel, Weizmann Inst, 65; ed bd, Plasmid, Mechanisms Aging & Develop. *Mem:* Am Acad Arts & Sci; Genetics Soc Am; Am Soc Biol Chemists. *Res:* Molecular anatomy of viral and bacterial chromosomes; genetic recombination, organization and function of higher chromosomes; role of free radicals in cellular aging. *Mailing Add:* Helicon Found 4622 Santa Fe St San Diego CA 92109-1601

**THOMAS, CHARLES CARLISLE, JR,** NUCLEAR SAFETY, NUCLEONICS. *Current Pos:* RETIRED. *Personal Data:* b Rochester, NY, Aug 18, 25; m 45, Marilyn Smith; c Charles C III, Frank C, Jeffery C & Jonathan C. *Educ:* Univ Iowa, BS, 47; Univ Rochester, MS, 50. *Prof Exp:* Nuclear chemist, US Bur Mines, Okla, 50-51; sr engr, Bausch & Lomb Optical Co, NY, 51-52; tech engr, Aircraft Nuclear Propulsion Dept, Gen Elec Co, Ohio, 52-53; prin chemist, Battelle Mem Inst, 53-55; fel engr, Westinghouse Elec Corp, Pa, 55-60; proj leader radiation chem, Quantum, Inc, 60-62; res mgr, Western NY Nuclear Res Ctr, Inc, 62-72; actg dir, Nuclear Sci & Technol Fac, State Univ NY, Buffalo, 72-74, dir, 74-78; mem staff, Los Alamos Nat Lab, Univ Calif, 78-90; instr, Northern NMex Community Col, 85-90. *Concurrent Pos:* Int Atomic Energy Agency vis prof, Tsing Hua, China, 64-65; adj assoc prof eng sci, aerospace & nuclear eng, State Univ NY Buffalo, 73-78; consult, 90- *Mem:* Am Chem Soc; fel Am Nuclear Soc; Sigma Xi; Health Physics Soc. *Res:* Nuclear materials production, safety; neutron activation analysis; reactor technology; environmental analysis; radiation effects on materials; hazards analysis of non-reactor nuclear facilities. *Mailing Add:* 3373 La Avenida de San Marcos Santa Fe NM 87505. *Fax:* 505-471-9048; *E-Mail:* chath.@roadrunner.com

**THOMAS, CHARLES HILL,** POULTRY SCIENCE, GENETICS. *Current Pos:* Asst prof poultry husb, Miss State Univ & asst poultry husbandman, Agr Exp Sta, 56-58, assoc prof & assoc poultry husbandman, 58-66, prof poultry sci, Miss State Univ & Poultry Geneticist, Agr Exp Sta, 66-87, prof sci basic to med, Col Vet Med, 77-86, EMER PROF, MISS STATE UNIV, 87- *Personal Data:* b Dexter, Ga, Jan 31, 22; m 45, Inez Myers; c Diane C. *Educ:* Univ Ga, BSA, 52, MSA, 53; NC State Univ, PhD(genetics), 56. *Concurrent Pos:* Coordr genetic interdisciplinary prog, Miss State Univ, 66-87. *Mem:* Am Poultry Sci Asn; Am Genetic Asn. *Res:* Inheritance of resistance to insecticides in Drosophila melanogaster. *Mailing Add:* Dept Poultry Sci Miss State Univ Box 298 Mississippi State MS 39762-0298

**THOMAS, CHARLES L(AMAR),** PETROLEUM, CHEMISTRY. *Current Pos:* RETIRED. *Personal Data:* b Hendersonville, NC, Oct 13, 05; m 30; c 2. *Educ:* Univ NC, BS, 28, MS, 29; Northwestern Univ, PhD, 31. *Prof Exp:* Fel, Northwestern Univ, 29-31; res chemist & assoc dir res, Universal Oil Prods Co, 31-45; dir, res & develop, Great Lakes Carbon Corp, 45-51; staff asst, Sun Oil Co, 51-52, mgr, chem res lab, 52-53, assoc dir, dept res & develop, 53-57, dir, 57-59, sci adv, dept res eng, 59-68. *Mem:* Am Chem Soc; Soc Automotive Eng; fel Inst Chem; Inst Chem Eng. *Res:* Thermal and catalytic reactions of hydrocarbons; catalysts; heterogeneous catalysis; chemistry and physics of solid carbons. *Mailing Add:* 2625 E Southern Ave C-290 Tempe AZ 85282-7601

**THOMAS, CLAUDE EARLE,** SCIENCE ADMINISTRATION, PHYTOPATHOLOGY. *Current Pos:* Res plant pathologist, Subtrop Res Lab, 66-82, US Veg Lab, 82-90, LAB DIR, US VEG LAB, AGR RES SERV, USDA, CHARLESTON, SC, 90- *Personal Data:* b Spartanburg, SC, Dec 4, 40; m 60; c 3. *Educ:* Wofford Col, AB, 62; Clemson Col, MS, 64; Clemson

Univ, PhD(plant path), 66. *Concurrent Pos:* Assoc ed, Plant Dis, 86-88; adj prof, Clemson Univ, 83- *Mem:* Am Phytopath Soc. *Res:* Identification, characterization and genetics of resistance to foliar fungal diseases in vegetable crops. *Mailing Add:* US Veg Lab Agr Res Serv USDA 2875 Savannah Hwy Charleston SC 29414

**THOMAS, CLAUDEWELL SIDNEY,** PSYCHIATRY, PUBLIC HEALTH. *Current Pos:* prof & vchmn, 83-93, prof psychiat, Dept Psychiat & Biobehav Sci, 83-93, PROF PSYCHIAT, DREW MED SCH, UNIV CALIF, LOS ANGELES, 83-, EMER PROF PSYCHIAT & BIOBEHAV SCI, 93- *Personal Data:* b New York, NY, Oct 5, 32; m 68, Carolyn Puzansky; c Jeffrey F, Julieanne E & Jessica D. *Educ:* Columbia Univ, BA, 52; State Univ NY, MD, 56; Am Bd Psychiat, dipl, 62; Yale Univ, MPH, 64. *Prof Exp:* Chief emergency treatment serv, Ment Health Ctr, New Haven, Conn, 65-67; educ dir psychiat emergency serv, Yale Univ, 67-68, dir social & community psychiat training, 68-73; dir div ment health prog, NIMH, 73-74; chmn dept psychiat, Col Med & Dent, NJ Med Sch, 76-83; chmn, Dept Psychiat & Human Behav, Chas Drew Med Sch, 83-93. *Concurrent Pos:* Consult, Compass Club, New Haven, 63-65; consult psychiatrist, Div Alcoholism, State of Conn, 63-65; vol consult, Caribbean Fed Ment Health, NY, 64; dir Hill-West Haven div & chief unit III, Conn Ment Health Ctr, 67-68; mem ad hoc comt minority admin, Yale Univ, 68-70; soc sci mem, Nat Ctr Health Res & Develop, 69-71; mem assembly behav & soc sci, Nat Acad Sci; consult, Wash Sch Psychiat, A K Rice Inst Wash, 70-77; vis prof sociol, Rutgers Univ, 73-80; attend psychiatrist, Harrison Martland Hosp, Newark; consult, Carrier Clin Belle Mead, St Joseph's Hosp, Patterson, 73-83; chief serv psychiat, Martin Luther King Hosp, Los Angeles, Calif; dep dir ment health, Los Angeles Co Dept Ment Health, Los Angeles Co Super Ct Panel Psychiatrists & Psychologists. *Mem:* Fel Am Psychiat Asn; fel Am Pub Health Asn; fel Royal Soc Health; fel NY Acad Med; fel NY Acad Sci. *Res:* Application of theory and concepts in the areas of social and community psychiatry to further the understanding of mental health needs of individuals and groups. *Mailing Add:* Dept Psychiat & Human Behav Charles Drew Postgrad Med School 1720 E 120 St Los Angeles CA 90059. *Fax:* 310-519-9274; *E-Mail:* cysid32@ucla.edu

**THOMAS, CLAYTON LAY,** MEDICINE. *Current Pos:* med dir, Tampax Inc, 58-70, vpres med affairs, 69-87, EMER DIR MED AFFAIRS & CONSULT, TAMBRANDS INC, 87- *Personal Data:* b Metropolis, Ill, Dec 23, 21; m 50, Margaret Gellner; c Robert, Clayton, Wendy & Gwynne. *Educ:* Univ Ky, BS, 44; Med Col Va, MD, 46; Harvard Univ, MPH, 58. *Prof Exp:* Intern med, Montreal Gen Hosp, 46-47; instr, US Naval Sch Aviation Med, 53-54; instr, Col Med, Univ Utah, 54-56. *Concurrent Pos:* Clin asst, Harvard Med Serv, Boston City Hosp, 56-57; res fel path, Mallory Inst Path, 56-57; consult, Flight Safety Found, 57-58 & Parachutes, Inc, Mass, 60; consult, Dept Pop Sci, Sch Pub Health, Harvard Univ, fel epidemiol, 57-58; mem med & training serv comt, US Olympic Comt, 66-73; pres, Balloon Sch Mass, Inc, 70-; Fed Aviation Admin pilot exam-lighter-than-air-free balloon, 72-; pres, Pop Res Found, 74-; mem, Med Dept Vis Comt, Mass Inst Technol, 75-78; mem, Med & Training Serv Comt, US Olympic Comt Sports Med, 78-80. *Mem:* Am Col Physicians; Aerospace Med Asn. *Res:* Medical ecology; physiology of menstruation; medical aspects of sport parachuting and hot air ballooning; aerospace medicine; epidemiology; medical lexicography; sports medicine; health and sex education; physiology of reproduction. *Mailing Add:* Dingley Dell 14 Sotcliffe Rd Brimfield MA 01010

**THOMAS, COLIN GORDON, JR,** SURGERY. *Current Pos:* from asst prof to prof, Sch Med, Univ NC, Chapel Hill, 52-84, chmn dept, 66-84, chief gen surg, 84-89, PROF SURG, SCH MED, UNIV NC, CHAPEL HILL, 89- *Personal Data:* b Iowa City, Iowa, July 25, 18; m 46; c 4. *Educ:* Univ Chicago, BS, 40, MD, 43. *Prof Exp:* Assoc surg, Col Med, Univ Iowa, 50-51, asst prof, 51-52. *Mem:* Am Col Surgeons; Am Asn Cancer Res; Am Thyroid Asn; Am Surg Asn; Soc Surg Alimentary Tract; Am Asn Endocrine Surgeons; Int Asn Endocrine Surgeons. *Res:* Thyroid cancer; gastrointestinal disorders; biological characeristics of thyroid neoplasms related to the influence of thyroid-stimulating hormone on their genesis, growth, function and management. *Mailing Add:* Dept Surg Univ NC Sch Med 136 Burnett Womack Bldg Campus Box 7210 Chapel Hill NC 27599-7210

**THOMAS, CRAIG EUGENE,** ROLE OF OXIDATIVE DAMAGE IN ATHEROSCLEROSIS, BIOCHEMICAL MECHANISMS OF TOXICITY. *Current Pos:* sr res biochemist, 89-90, assoc scientist, 90-92, SR ASSOC SCIENTIST, MARION MERRELL DOW RES INST, 92- *Personal Data:* b Clearfield, Pa, Apr 30, 58; m 85, Jean Cascaddan; c 2. *Educ:* Pa State Univ, BS, 80, MS, 82; Mich State Univ, PhD(biochem & environ toxicol), 86. *Prof Exp:* Nat Inst Environ Health Sci fel biochem/environ health sci, Ore State Univ, 86-88; sr biochem toxicol, Rohm & Haas Co, 88-89. *Mem:* Fedn Am Socs Exp Biol; Am Soc Biochem & Molecular Biol; Oxygen Soc. *Res:* Study of cell death resulting from oxidative damage to biomolecules; role of low density lipoprotein oxidation in atherosclerosis; contribution of oxygen radicals to cerebral ischemic/reperfusion injury; oxidative injury in the central nervous system. *Mailing Add:* Eli Lilly PO Box 708 Greenfield IN 46140. *Fax:* 513-948-6439

**THOMAS, DAN ANDERSON,** PHYSICS. *Current Pos:* RETIRED. *Personal Data:* b Ooltewah, Tenn, Oct 1, 22; m 44; c 2. *Educ:* Univ Chattanooga, BS, 45; Vanderbilt Univ, PhD(physics), 52. *Prof Exp:* Asst prof physics, Univ of the South, 49-51; res physicist, US Naval Ord Lab, 51-52; from assoc prof to prof physics, Rollins Col, 52-63; prof physics & dean faculties, Jacksonville Univ, 63-80, vpres, 67-80, trustee prof, 80-87. *Concurrent Pos:* Consult, US Naval Underwater Sound Ref Lab, 53-63. *Mem:* Fel AAAS; Am Phys Soc; Acoust Soc Am; Am Asn Physics Teachers. *Res:* Beta ray spectroscopy; underwater acoustics; wave motion in solids; vibration of plates. *Mailing Add:* 1990 River Bluff Rd N Jacksonville FL 32211

**THOMAS, DAVID ALDEN,** MATERIALS SELECTION, FAILURE ANALYSIS. *Current Pos:* from assoc prof to prof metall & mat sci, Lehigh Univ, 68-94, assoc dir, Mat Res Ctr, 68-83, dean grad studies, 87-90, EMER PROF MAT SCI, LEHIGH UNIV, 94- *Personal Data:* b Baltimore, Md, Sept 8, 30; m 56, Anne Horsfall; c James, Bruce & Margaret. *Educ:* Cornell Univ, BMetE, 53; Mass Inst Technol, ScD(metall), 58. *Prof Exp:* From instr to assoc prof metall, 53-63; chief mat sci res, Ingersoll-Rand Co, 63-68. *Mem:* AAAS; Am Soc Metals Int; Sigma Xi; Tin Mining Soc. *Res:* Structure and mechanical properties of metals, polymers and composites, polymer blends; materials applications; electronmicroscopy. *Mailing Add:* 2067 Pleasant Dr Bethlehem PA 18015. *E-Mail:* dat1@lehigh.edu

**THOMAS, DAVID BARTLETT,** MEDICINE, EPIDEMIOLOGY. *Current Pos:* assoc prof, 75-81, PROF EPIDEMIOL, UNIV WASH, 81- *Personal Data:* b Butte, Mont, Sept 8, 37; m 61, Mary C Mitchell; c Rachel S & Douglas D. *Educ:* Univ Washington, MD, 63; Johns Hopkins Univ, DrPH(epidemiol), 72. *Prof Exp:* From asst prof to assoc prof epidemiol, Johns Hopkins Univ, 71-75. *Concurrent Pos:* Mem epidemiol, Fred Hutchinson Cancer Res Ctr, 75-; consult epidemiol, WHO, 78-79. *Mem:* Soc Epidemiol Res; Am Pub Health Asn; AAAS; Am Epidemiol Soc; fel Am Col Epidemiol; Int Asn Cancer Registries; Int Epidemiol Asn; Int Asn Breast Cancer Res; Am Soc Prev Oncol; Physicians Social Responsibility. *Res:* Epidemiologic studies of the etiology and prevention of gynecologic and breast cancers; studies of the potential carcinogenic effects of steroid contraceptives. *Mailing Add:* Fred Hutchinson Cancer Res Ctr 1100 Fairview Ave N MP 474 PO Box 19024 Seattle WA 98109-1024. *Fax:* 206-667-4787; *E-Mail:* dbthomas@cdin.fherc. org

**THOMAS, DAVID DALE,** MOLECULAR BIOPHYSICS. *Current Pos:* ASST PROF BIOCHEM, DEPT BIOL, SCH MED, UNIV MINN, 80- *Personal Data:* b Lansing, Mich, Sept 18, 49; m 75. *Educ:* Stanford Univ, BS, 71, PhD(biophys), 76. *Prof Exp:* Res asst physics, High Energy Physics Lab, Stanford Univ, 70; res asst, Dept Genetics, Stanford Univ, 71; fel biophys, Dept Muscle Res, Boston Biomed Res Inst, 76-77; mem fac, Dept Biophys, Stanford Univ, 77-80. *Concurrent Pos:* NSF fel, 71; fel, Muscular Dystrophy Asns Am, Inc, 76-77. *Mem:* AAAS; Fedn Am Scientists; Biophys Soc. *Res:* Molecular dynamics in muscle contraction as studied by spectroscopic probe methods; electron paramagnetic resonance studies of spin-labeled muscle proteins, such as actin and myosin. *Mailing Add:* Dept Biochem 4-225 Millard Univ Minn Med Sch 435 Delaware St SE Minneapolis MN 55455. *Fax:* 612-624-0632

**THOMAS, DAVID GLEN,** hydrodynamics, chemical engineering; deceased, see previous edition for last biography

**THOMAS, DAVID LEE,** ANIMAL BREEDING, ANIMAL PRODUCTION. *Current Pos:* PROF ANIMAL SCI, UNIV WIS, 91- *Personal Data:* b Dodgeville, Wis, May 22, 49; m 71; c 3. *Educ:* Univ Wis-Madison, BS, 71; Okla State Univ, Stillwater, MS, 75, PhD(animal breeding), 77. *Prof Exp:* Asst prof, Ore State Univ, 77-81; from asst prof to assoc prof animal sci, Univ Ill, 81-91. *Concurrent Pos:* US Peace Corps, Kenya, 71-73. *Mem:* Am Soc Animal Sci; Am Genetic Asn; Sigma Xi. *Res:* Animal breeding research with sheep and sheep production with primary emphasis on improvement of reproductive efficiency. *Mailing Add:* 438 Animal Sci Bldg Univ Wis 1675 Observatory Dr Madison WI 53706

**THOMAS, DAVID TIPTON,** ELECTRICAL ENGINEERING. *Current Pos:* CONSULT ENGR, 83- *Personal Data:* b Barnesville, Ohio, Dec 13, 37; m 66; c 2. *Educ:* Carnegie Inst Technol, BS, 59, MS, 60; Ohio State Univ, PhD(elec eng), 62. *Prof Exp:* Res assoc elec eng, Antenna Labs, Ohio State Univ, 61-62, assoc supvr & asst prof, 62-63; asst prof elec eng, Carnegie-Mellon Univ, 63-68; mem tech staff, Radio Transmission Lab, Bell Tel Labs, 68-73; prin engr, Electromagnetic Systs Div, Raytheon Corp, 73-78, mgr Antenna & Microwave Eng, 78-83. *Concurrent Pos:* NSF grant, Carnegie-Mellon Univ, 66-68. *Mem:* Inst Elec & Electronics Engrs. *Res:* Electromagnetic field theory; computer solutions in electromagnetics; scattering, antennas and radiation. *Mailing Add:* Raytheon Co Electromagnetics Systs 6380 Hollister Ave Goleta CA 93017

**THOMAS, DAVID WARREN,** ANTIGEN PRESENTATION, T-LYMPHOCYTE ACTIVATION. *Current Pos:* PROF IMMUNOL, UNIV MICH, 85- *Educ:* Univ Colo, PhD(microbiol & immunol), 75. *Prof Exp:* Asst prof immunol, Wash Univ, 77-85. *Mailing Add:* Dept Cell Biol & Immunol Res Biogen Inc 12 Cambridge Ctr Cambridge MA 02142-1481. *Fax:* 617-252-9616

**THOMAS, DON WYLIE,** VETERINARY SCIENCE, ANIMAL SCIENCE. *Current Pos:* RETIRED. *Personal Data:* b Spanish Fork, Utah, Aug 8, 23; m 52; c 6. *Educ:* Utah State Univ, BS, 49; Iowa State Univ, DVM, 53. *Prof Exp:* Vet pathologist, Calif State Dept Agr, 53-54; prof vet & animal sci & exten vet, Utah State Univ, 54-86. *Concurrent Pos:* State del nat plans conf, USDA, 56, 58 & 62; vchmn, Utah Herd Health & Mastitis Comt, 58- *Mem:* Am Asn Exten Vet; Am Asn Vet Nutritionists. *Res:* Prevention of diseases in cattle, sheep, horses and poultry. *Mailing Add:* 234 E Center St Box 98 Hyde Park UT 84318

**THOMAS, DONALD CHARLES,** MICROBIOLOGY, PATHOLOGY. *Current Pos:* RETIRED. *Personal Data:* b Cincinnati, Ohio, Sept 26, 36; m 57; c 3. *Educ:* Xavier Univ, BS, 57; Univ Cincinnati, MS, 59; St Louis Univ, PhD(microbiol & virol), 68. *Prof Exp:* Asst dir, Dept Surg, Surg Bact Labs,

Univ Cincinnati, 59-61; instr, Dept Biol, Villa Madonna Col, 61-63; grad student, Dept Microbiol & Molecular Virol Inst, St Louis Univ, 63-68; instr, Dept Med Microbiol & Pediat, Col Med, Ohio State Univ, 68-69, asst prof, 69-72, assoc dir, Prog Develop Asst Div, 72-77; dir contracts & grants mgt, Wright State Univ, 77-78, asst dean res, Sch Grad Studies, 79-80, actg dean & assoc dean res & dir, Univ Res Serv, 80-83, dean & assoc vpres for res, 83-90, assoc prof, Dept Path & assoc prof, Dept Microbiol & Immunol, Sch Med & Col Sci & Math, 78-93. Concurrent Pos: Adj asst prof, Dept Med Microbiol & Pediat, Col Med, Ohio State Univ, 72-77; admin adv, Nat Reyes Syndrome Found, Ohio, 75-; lab consult, Vet Admin Ctr, Ohio, 78-; fed liaison rep, Am Coun Educ, Wright State Univ, 79-; Reagents Adv Comt Grad Studies, 83-90, chmn, 88-89; Governor's Technol Task Force, 82. Mem: Am Soc Microbiol; AAAS; Fedn Am Scientists; Licensing Execs Soc. Res: Diagnostic virology; molecular aspects of virus replication, pathogenesis of virus diseases and developments in tumor viruses. Mailing Add: 1360 Heritage Rd Dayton OH 45459-3303

THOMAS, DONALD E(ARL), MATERIALS SCIENCE ENGINEERING. Current Pos: RETIRED. Personal Data: b Pittsburgh, Pa, Oct 27, 18; m 42; c 3. Educ: Carnegie Inst Technol, BS, 42, MS, 49; DSc, 50. Honors & Awards: Eng Mat Achievement Award, Am Soc Metals, 72; Outstanding Achievement Award, Am Nuclear Soc, 85. Prof Exp: Asst phys metall, Carnegie Inst Technol, 46-47; supvry scientist corrosion & phys metall, Atomic Power Div, Westinghouse Elec Corp, 49-58, mgr naval reactor metall, 58-59, mgr mat dept, Astronuclear Lab, 59-66, eng mgr systs & technol, 66-71, consult scientist, Res Labs, 71-82. Concurrent Pos: Instr, Carnegie Inst Technol, 51-52. Mem: Fel Am Nuclear Soc; Am Inst Mining, Metall & Petrol Engrs; fel Am Soc Metals. Res: Materials research and development. Mailing Add: Dept Elec & Comput Eng Carnegie Mellon Univ Schenley Park PA 15213

THOMAS, DONALD H(ARVEY), COMPUTER AIDED INSTRUCTION. Current Pos: From instr to asst prof, Drexel Univ, 56-61, assoc prof mech eng, 65-88, chmn mech eng, 70-73, assoc dir, Ctr Teaching Innovation, 74-84, assoc dean eng, 80-88, PROF MECH ENG, DREXEL UNIV, 88- Personal Data: b Phoenixville, Pa, Dec 1, 33; div; c 2. Educ: Drexel Inst, BSME, 56, MSME, 59; Case Inst Technol, PhD(design eng), 65. Honors & Awards: Fred Merryfield Design Award, Am Soc Eng Educ, 86. Concurrent Pos: Consult, 59- Mem: Sigma Xi; Am Soc Mech Engrs; Am Soc Eng Educ; Soc Automotive Engrs. Res: Medical engineering; innovative teaching in engineering; biomechanics; product design liability; system dynamics and control; vehicle dynamics; computer-aided design engineering. Mailing Add: Dept Mech Eng Drexel Univ 32nd & Chestnut Sts Philadelphia PA 19104

THOMAS, EDWARD DONNALL, INTERNAL MEDICINE, ONCOLOGY. Current Pos: prof, 63-90, head, Div Oncol, 63-85, EMER PROF MED, SCH MED, UNIV WASH, 90- Personal Data: b Mart, Tex, Mar 15, 20; m 42; c 3. Educ: Univ Tex, BA, 41, MA, 43; Harvard Med Sch, MD, 46; Am Bd Internal Med, dipl, 53. Hon Degrees: MD, Univ Cagliart, Sardinia, 81, Univ Verona, Italy, 91, Univ Parma, Italy, 92, Nat Acad Med, Mex, 94, Univ Barcelona, Spain, 94, Univ Warsaw, Poland, 96. Honors & Awards: Nobel Prize Med, 90; var named lectureships, 74-85; Nat Award Basic Sci, Am Cancer Soc, 80; Kettering Prize, Gen Motors Cancer Res Found, 81; Robert Roesler de Villiers Award, Leukemia Soc Am, 83; Karl Lansteiner Mem Award, 87; Nat Medal of Sci, 90; Terry Fox Award, Can, 90. Prof Exp: From intern to sr asst resident med, Peter Bent Brigham Hosp, Boston, 46-52, chief med res, 52-53, hematologist, 53; res assoc, Cancer Res Found, Children's Med Ctr, 53-55; hematologist & asst physician, Mary Imogene Bassett Hosp, 55-56; assoc clin prof med, Col Physicians & Surgeons, Columbia Univ, 56-63. Concurrent Pos: Fel med, Mass Inst Technol, 50-51; instr, Harvard Med Sch, 53-55; physician-in-chief, Mary Imogene Bassett Hosp, 56-63; clin prof, Albany Med Col, 58-63; attending physician, Univ Wash Hosp, 63-90, Harborview Med Ctr, 63-90, Vet Admin Hosp, 63-90, Providence Med Ctr, 73-90, Swed Hosp, 75-; consult physician, Children's Orthop Hosp & Med Ctr, 63-90; mem, Fred Hutchinson Cancer Res Ctr, Seattle, 74-, dir med oncol, 74-89, assoc dir, Clin Res Progs, 82-89. Mem: Nat Acad Sci; Am Soc Clin Invest; Am Asn Cancer Res; Am Soc Hemat (pres, 88); Exp Hemat Soc; Transplantation Soc; Belg Royal Acad Med; Am Asn Physicians; Am Fed Clin Res; Am Soc Clin Oncol; hon mem Swed Soc Hemat; Int Soc Hemat; Soc Exp Biol & Med; Swiss Soc Hermat; Western Asn Physicians. Res: Marrow biochemistry and transplantation; irradiation effects; hematology. Mailing Add: Fred Hutchinson Cancer Res Ctr 1124 Columbia St Seattle WA 98104

THOMAS, EDWARD SANDUSKY, JR, MATHEMATICS. Current Pos: from assoc prof to prof, 69-85, chmn, Dept Math & Statist, DISTINGUISHED TEACHING PROF MATH, STATE UNIV NY, ALBANY, 85- Personal Data: b Kansas City, Mo, Jan 11, 38; m 60. Educ: Whittier Col, BA, 59; Univ Wash, MS, 61; Univ Calif, Riverside, PhD(math), 64. Prof Exp: Asst prof math, Univ Mich, Ann Arbor, 65-69. Mem: Am Math Soc. Res: Topology, dynamical systems; differential equations. Mailing Add: Dept Math & Statist State Univ NY ES Bldg Albany NY 12222-0001

THOMAS, EDWARD WILFRID, PHYSICS. Current Pos: Asst res physicist, Ga Inst Technol, 64-65, from asst prof to assoc prof, 65-73, dir, Sch Physics, 82-91, PROF PHYSICS, GA INST TECHNOL, 73- Personal Data: b Croydon, Eng, May 9, 40; m, Carol Hayler; c Graham, Shona & Robin. Educ: Univ London, BSc, 61, PhD(physics), 64. Concurrent Pos: Consult, Oak Ridge Nat Lab, 65- Mem: Am Phys Soc; Am Soc Eng Educ. Res: Collisions between atomic, ionic and molecular systems, particularly on the formation of excited states; surface & materials analysis by SIMS; sputtering; particle-wall interactions in fusion devices. Mailing Add: Sch Physics Ga Inst Technol Atlanta GA 30332-0430. Fax: 404-894-9958; E-Mail: edward. thomas@physics.gatech.edu

THOMAS, EDWIN LEE, BIOCHEMISTRY. Current Pos: ASSOC MEM STAFF BIOCHEM, ST JUDE CHILDREN'S HOSP & ASST PROF, UNIV TENN, 72- Personal Data: b Sandusky, Ohio, Nov 30, 43. Educ: Miami Univ, BA, 65; Univ Mich, PhD(biochem), 70. Prof Exp: Fel biochem, Roche Inst Molecular Biol, 70-72. Concurrent Pos: Prin investr, Dent Res Inst, NIH, 76- Mem: Am Soc Microbiol; AAAS; Am Soc Biol Chemists. Res: Biological membrane structure and function; mechanisms of resistance to infection. Mailing Add: Dent Res Ctr Univ Tenn 210 Nash Bldg 894 Union Ave Memphis TN 38163-0001. Fax: 901-528-6517

THOMAS, EDWIN LORIMER, POLYMER SCIENCE, MATERIALS ENGINEERING. Current Pos: PROF MAT SCI & ENGR, MASS INST TECHNOL, 89- Personal Data: b Attleboro, Mass, June 14, 47; m 70; c 3. Educ: Univ Mass, BS, 69; Cornell Univ, PhD(mat sci), 73. Honors & Awards: Young Polymer Chemist Award, Am Chem Soc, 85; Fiber Soc Distinguished Award, 86; Ford Prize Polymer Physics, Am Phys Soc, 91. Prof Exp: Asst prof chem engr, Univ Minn, 73-77; assoc prof, Univ Mass, 77-82, prof, 82-88, head dept, 85-88. Concurrent Pos: Humboldt fel, Univ Freiburg, Ger, 81; vis prof, Univ Minn, 83 & Cambridge Univ, 84. Mem: Am Chem Soc; Electron Micros Soc Am; Mat Res Soc; Royal Micros Soc; fel Am Phys Soc. Res: Polymer physics and engineering; application of electron microscopy; electron and x-ray diffraction to materials characterization; structure property relationships. Mailing Add: Mass Inst Technol Rm 13-5098 77 Massachusetts Ave Cambridge MA 02139-4307

THOMAS, ELIZABETH WADSWORTH, ANALYTICAL CHEMISTRY, BIOPHARMACEUTICS. Current Pos: DIR, ANALYTICAL DEVELOP, AAI, WILMINGTON, NC, 96- Personal Data: b Washington, DC, May 23, 44; m 70, Alford M; c Edward B. Educ: ECarolina Univ, BS, 66; Univ Va, PhD(phys & org chem), 70. Prof Exp: Res assoc pharmacol, Med Sch, Univ Va, 70-72; lectr, Univ Wis, Parkside, 73-74; analytical chemist, Abbott Labs, 75-79, pharmacologist, 80-86, group leader & sr scientist, 87-88, mgr, 89-91; assoc dept head, Burroughs Wellcome Co, 91-95. Concurrent Pos: Pres, Abbott Chap, Sigma Xi, 82-83; chair, Abbott's Tech Adv Bd, 89-90. Mem: Am Chem Soc; Am Asn Pharmaceut Sci; Sigma Xi. Res: Created and validated stability assays for bulk chemicals and formulated products; directed animal studies for evaluation of new drug formulations; determined pharmacokinetics from animal/human data; develop analytical methods for new drug delivery systems; established department that offered unique drug delivery capabilities; monitor quality compliance for clinical diagnostic products; analytical support for new drug products data used in global regulatory filings. Mailing Add: 125 Hallbrook Farms Circle Wilmington NC 28405

THOMAS, ELMER LAWRENCE, food science, for more information see previous edition

THOMAS, ELVIN ELBERT, RUMINANT NUTRITION, ANIMAL NUTRITION. Current Pos: RES SCIENTIST, ELI LILLY & CO, 89- Personal Data: b Osceola, Iowa, Nov 23, 44; m 69, Jean McClurg; c James A, Lyn E, Sara J & Matthew E. Educ: Iowa State Univ, BS, 68, MS, 74, PhD(animal nutrit), 77. Prof Exp: Voc agr instr, Newell Providence Community Schs, 68-71; instr animal sci, Iowa State Univ, 73-76; assoc prof animal sci, Auburn Univ, 77-87; beef & dairy nutritionist, Vigortone Agr Prods, Iowa, 87-89. Mem: Am Soc Animal Sci; Am Dairy Sci Asn. Res: Improvement in efficiency of meat and milk production. Mailing Add: Box 708 Greenfield IN 46140

THOMAS, ERIC OWEN, PHYSIOLOGICAL ECOLOGY. Current Pos: ASST PROF BIOL, UNIV PAC, 91- Personal Data: b Saudi Arabia, Aug 14, 62; US citizen. Educ: Univ Calif, Riverside, BS, 84, MA, 87; Univ Calif, Berkeley, PhD(zool), 91. Mem: Am Soc Zoologists; Am Soc Ichthyologists & Herpetologists; Am Sci Affil. Res: Studying the physiology and endocrinology of amphibians and reptiles with a special interest in mating-courtship pheromones. Mailing Add: Dept Biol Univ Pac 3601 Pacific Ave Stockton CA 95211-0110

THOMAS, ESTES CENTENNIAL, III, PETROPHYSICS, CORE ANALYSIS. Current Pos: chemist, Shell Oil Co, 67-72, sr engr, 75-82, sr staff engr, 82-86, PETRO PHYS ADV, SHELL OIL CO, 86- Personal Data: b Plaquemine, La, Dec 13, 40; m 64, Brenda; c Eric, Carl & Scott. Educ: La State Univ, Baton Rouge, BS, 62; Stanford Univ, PhD(phys chem), 66. Prof Exp: Fel, Princeton Univ, 66-67. Mem: Soc Prof Well Log Analysts; Soc Petrol Engrs; Sigma Xi; Soc Core Analysts. Res: Physical characteristics and responses to transport of energy through interstices of subterranean earthen formations, particularly those containing hydrocarbons; analysis of these data to deduce volume and type of hydrocarbons with subterranean strata and their propensity to expel hydrocarbons. Mailing Add: Shell E&D Technol Co PO Box 481 Houston TX 77001-0481

THOMAS, EVERETT DAKE, FARM MANAGEMENT. Current Pos: Exten Agronomist, Cornell Univ, 69-81, AGRONOMIST & VPRES, W H MINER AGRICULT RES INST, 81- Personal Data: b Stamford, Conn, Jan 24, 43; m 66; c 3. Educ: Univ Conn, BS, 65; Cornell Univ, MS, 67. Prof Exp: Agr Exten agent, Coop Exten Asn Clinton Co, 66-69. Concurrent Pos: Consult, US Holstein Asn, 84-; adj fac, Univ Vt, 82-, State Univ NY Col, Plattsburgh, 82- Mem: Am Soc Agron; Soil Sci Soc; Forage & Grassland Coun. Res: Soil fertility and crop management; author of articles writes for regional and national magazines on a variety of agricultural crop subjects and edits a small newsletter. Mailing Add: 820 Peasleville Rd Schuyler Falls NY 12985

**THOMAS, FORREST DEAN, II,** INORGANIC CHEMISTRY. *Current Pos:* From asst prof to assoc prof, 59-73, PROF CHEM, UNIV MONT, 73- *Personal Data:* b Provo, Utah, Dec 27, 30; m 52; c 2. *Educ:* Brigham Young Univ, BS, 55; Pa State Univ, PhD(chem), 59. *Mem:* Am Chem Soc. *Res:* Organic and inorganic synthesis; preparation of coordination compounds. *Mailing Add:* Chem Univ Mont Missoula MT 59812-0001

**THOMAS, FRANCIS T,** THORACIC SURGERY. *Current Pos:* CHIEF TRANSPLANTATION SURG, DIR RESIDENT RES TRAINING & SURG RES LAB & PROF SURG, ECAROLINA UNIV SCH MED, 79- *Personal Data:* b Minneapolis, Minn, June 24, 39; m 68; c 3. *Educ:* Univ Minn, BS, 62 & MD, 64. *Prof Exp:* Fel thoracic surg, Case Western Res Univ, 69-71; instr surg, Med Col Va, 71-72, from asst prof to assoc prof, 71-79. *Concurrent Pos:* Wangensteen fel foreign study, Birmingham, Eng, 64; mem, Comt Issues, Assoc Acad Surg, 76-79, Human Biol Coun; chmn, Va State Comt Brain Death, Am Soc Transport Surgeon, 78-79, mem prog & publ comt, 88; Adv Bd, Dialysis & Transplantation; mem, Bd Dirs, Kidney Found NC, planning & info comt, NC Kidney Coun, Carolina Orgn Procurement Agency; med, Adv Bd, Nat Kidney Found NC, 81-84; ad hoc sci consult, Nat Heart, Lung & Blood Inst, Nat Inst Allergy & Infectious Dis & NIH res ctr grants; mem, Bd Dirs, Sci Proj & Publ Comt, Southeastern Organ Procurement Found; mem, Coun Transplantation, Pan-Am Med Asn; reviewer, Am J Kidney Dis, 83-84; ad hoc site reviewer, Transplant Training Prog, Tumor Registr Asn NC; comt publ, Coun Nominating Comt, Soc Univ Surgeons; guest lectr, Rutgers Med Sch & Univ Calif Los Angeles, 75, Univ Fla, Gainesville & Univ Wash, 76, Cornell Med Sch & Bowman-Gray Sch Med, 77, Med Col Pa & Naval Med Res Ctr, 78, Va Med Soc & Marshfield Clin, 79, Int Conf Immunol Monitoring, Neth & Int Transplant Soc, Mass, 80, Barnes Hosp & Univ Minn, Minneapolis, 81, 9th Int Cong Transplantation Soc, Brighton, UK & Am Col Surgeons, Chicago, 82, Int Cong Kidney Transplantation, Ger & Am Col Surgeons, Atlanta, 83, Lenoir-Green Med Soc, NC & 10th Int Cong Transplantation Soc, 84 & other var univ & conf, 85-88; adv comt cardiac transplant, Pitt Co Mem Hosp, med dir ECU Transplantation & Procurement, human organ transplantation comt, nursing liaison comt, renal care comt & rep End Stage Res Dis Coun SE; dir resident res activ & surg res lab, dept surg exec, chmn liver transplantation comt & ad hoc comt fac tenure, ECarolina Sch Med; physician's comt comput-based hosp info syst. *Mem:* AAAS; Am Asn Immunologists; Am Asn Tissue Banks; Am Asn Univ Prog; fel Am Cancer Soc; fel Am Col Surgeons; Am Diabetes Asn; AMA; Am Soc Microbiol; Am Soc Nephrology. *Res:* Cinical and experimental organ transplantation, immunology, surgery, kidney, pancreas and heart transplantation. *Mailing Add:* 728 Lyons Harrison Bldg Univ Ala Birmingham 701 S 19th St Birmingham AL 35294-0016. *Fax:* 919-816-3542

**THOMAS, FRANK BANCROFT,** HORTICULTURE, FOOD TECHNOLOGY. *Current Pos:* food processing exten specialist, NC State Univ, 58 61, exten assoc prof, 61-66, exten prof food sci, 66-, EMER PROF, NC STATE UNIV. *Personal Data:* b Camden, Del, June 14, 22; m 60; c 2. *Educ:* Univ Del, BS, 48; Pa State Univ, MS, 49, PhD(hort), 55. *Honors & Awards:* Earl P McFee Award. *Prof Exp:* From instr to asst prof hort, Pa State Univ, 49-58. *Concurrent Pos:* Vis fel food technol, Mass Inst Technol, 54-55; consult cryogenic foods, 63-64; mem, NC Gov Comn Com Fisheries, 64-65, mem, Com & Sport Fisheries Adv Comt, 75-76; sabbatical, Dept Food Sci & Technol, Univ Hawaii, 68; partic, Food & Agr Orgn Conf Fish Qual & Inspection, Halifax, Can, 69 & Conf Fishery Prod Technol, Japan, 73; prog leader, Food Sci Seafood Adv Serv, NC Sea Grant Prog, 70- *Mem:* Inst Food Technologists. *Res:* Post-harvest physiology of fruits and vegetables; food processing; chemical and microbiological changes in seafoods; flavor and color evaluation; extension and applied research on seafood utilization. *Mailing Add:* 4712 Quail Hollow Dr Raleigh NC 27609

**THOMAS, FRANK J(OSEPH),** ENGINEERING, NUCLEAR PHYSICS. *Current Pos:* pres, Pac Sierra Res Corp, Los Angeles, 71-94, DIR RES, PAC-SIERRA RES CORP, SANTA MONICA, CALIF, 94- *Personal Data:* b Pocatello, Idaho, Apr 15, 30; m 49, Carol Jones; c Dale, Wayne & Keith. *Educ:* Univ Idaho, BS, 52; Univ Calif, Berkeley, MS, 57. *Honors & Awards:* Master Design Award, Prod Eng Mag, 63; Meritorious Civilian Serv Award, Secy Defense, 67. *Prof Exp:* Staff mem advan studies, Sandia Corp, 52-56; prog mgr mobile reactors, Aerojet-Gen Nucleonics Div, 57-61, mgr eng, 61-63, dep mgr appl sci div, 63-64; staff specialist res & eng, Off Secy Defense, 64-65, asst dir res & eng, Nuclear Progs, 65-67; phys scientist, Rand Corp, Calif, 67-71. *Concurrent Pos:* Lectr, Exten Div, Univ Calif, Berkeley, 57-58; adv, Sci Adv Comt, Defense Intel Agency, 66-73; consult, US Arms Control & Disarmament Agency, 72-76; chair, Panel for Hydrotest Assess, US Dept Energy, 91-92. *Mem:* Am Inst Aeronaut & Astronaut; AAAS; Sigma Xi. *Res:* Explore and develop means to verify arms-control agreements, particularly nuclear test bans. *Mailing Add:* 2901 28th St Suite 300 Santa Monica CA 90405. *Fax:* 310-314-2323; *E-Mail:* frank%mgate@psrv.com

**THOMAS, GAIL B,** clinical microbiology, chlamydia, for more information see previous edition

**THOMAS, GARETH,** PHYSICAL METALLURGY, MATERIALS SCIENCE. *Current Pos:* from asst prof to assoc prof, Univ Calif, Berkeley, 60-66, Miller res prof, 64, assoc dean, Grad Div, 68-69, asst chancellor & actg vchancellor acad affairs, 69-72, chmn fac, Col Eng, 77-78, sci dir, Nat Ctr Electron Micros, Lawrence Berkeley Lab, 81-93, PROF METALL, UNIV CALIF, BERKELEY, 66- *Personal Data:* b Maesteg, Gt Brit, Aug 9, 32; m 94, Annelies; c Julian. *Educ:* Univ Wales, BSc, 52; Cambridge Univ, PhD(metall), 55, ScD, 69. *Hon Degrees:* DSc, Lehigh Univ, 96. *Honors & Awards:* Nat Award Phys Sci, Electron Micros Soc, 65, 75-76 & 80-81; Electron Micros Soc Am Prize, 65; Curtis-McGraw Res Award, Am Soc Eng Educ, 66; Rosenhain Medal, Brit Metals Soc, 77; Ernest O Lawrence Award, US Dept Energy, 78. *Prof Exp:* Imp Chem Industs Fel metall, Cambridge Univ, 56-59. *Concurrent Pos:* Consult, Exxon; vis scientist, Alcoa Res Labs, 59; Guggenheim fel, Cambridge Univ, 71-72; Alexander von Humboldt sr scientist award, Max Planck Inst, Ger, 81 & IFW Dresden, 96. *Mem:* Nat Acad Sci; Nat Acad Eng; Electron Micros Soc Am(pres,75); Am Phys Soc; Am Inst Mining, Metall & Petrol Engrs; Brit Inst Metals; fel Am Soc Metals; fel Metall Soc; fel Royal Micros Soc. *Res:* Electron microscopy; investigations of the relation of structure to properties; alloy design. *Mailing Add:* Dept Mat Sci & Mineral Eng Univ Calif 561 Evans Hall Berkeley CA 94720-1760. *Fax:* 510-643-0965; *E-Mail:* garth@uclink2.berkeley.edu

**THOMAS, GARLAND LEON,** NUCLEAR ENGINEERING. *Current Pos:* RETIRED. *Personal Data:* b Topeka, Kans, Aug 29, 20; m 48; c 3. *Educ:* Drury Col, BS, 42; Univ Mo, AM, 48, PhD(physics), 54. *Prof Exp:* Fel engr, Atomic Power Dept, Westinghouse Elec Corp, 53-59; assoc prof physics, Drury Col, 59-66 & Fla Inst Technol, 66-71; mem staff, Fla Planning Dept, Brevard Co, 71-79; prin engr, Planning Res Corp, Kennedy Space Ctr, 79-85, aerospace engr, NASA Safety Eng Off, 85-97. *Mem:* Biophys Soc; Am Phys Soc; Am Asn Physics Teachers; Am Nuclear Soc. *Res:* Remote sensing; nuclear reactor physics; ultrasonic cavitation. *Mailing Add:* 1208 E River Dr No 102 Melbourne FL 32901

**THOMAS, GARTH JOHNSON,** BEHAVIORAL NEUROBIOLOGY. *Current Pos:* prof, 66-82, dir, 70-77, EMER PROF, CTR BRAIN RES, UNIV ROCHESTER, 82- *Personal Data:* b Pittsburg, Kans, Sept 8, 16; m 45; c 2. *Educ:* Kans State Teachers Col Pittsburg, AB, 38; Univ Kans, MA, 40; Harvard Univ, AM, 43, PhD(exp psychol), 48. *Prof Exp:* Asst instr, Univ Kans, 38-41; tutor, Harvard Univ, 41-43 & 47-48; from instr to asst prof psychol, Univ Chicago, 48-54; res assoc & assoc prof, Neuropsychiat Inst, Col Med, Univ Ill, 54-57, res prof, Biophys Res Lab, Dept Elec Eng & Dept Physiol & Biophys, 57-66. *Concurrent Pos:* Dept Defense NIMH & NSF res grants, Univ Chicago, Univ Ill & Univ Rochester, 51-77; mem psychol sci fel rev panel, NIMH, 64-69 & psychobiol rev panel NSF, 68-71; consult ed, behav neurosci; assoc ed, J Comp & Physiol Psychol, 69-74, ed, 75-81. *Mem:* AAAS; Am Physiol Soc; Psychonomic Soc; Soc Exp Psychol; Soc Neurosci; Am Psychol Asn; Animal Behav Soc. *Res:* Brain function; studies of behavioral effects of central nervous system lesions; spatial behavior; animal memory. *Mailing Add:* Dept Neurobiol & Anat Box 603 Med Ctr Univ Rochester Rochester NY 14642

**THOMAS, GARY E,** ATMOSPHERIC PHYSICS. *Current Pos:* assoc prof astro-geophys, 67-74, PROF, DEPT ATMOSPHERIC & PLANETARY SCI, UNIV COLO, BOULDER, 74- *Personal Data:* b Lookout, WVa, Oct 25, 34; m 61, Susan Cherup; c 2. *Educ:* NMex State Univ, BS, 57; Univ Pittsburgh, PhD(physics), 63. *Prof Exp:* Res assoc, Aeronomy Serv, Nat Ctr Sci Res, France, 62-63; mem tech staff, Space Physics Lab, Aerospace Corp, 65-67. *Concurrent Pos:* Distinguished vis prof, Univ Adelaide, Australia, 95. *Mem:* Am Geophys Union; Int Comn Middle Atmosphere Sci. *Res:* Theoretical study of upper atmosphere; radiative transfer; application of spectroscopic remote sensing data to study of atmospheric structure; radiative and photochemical processes in the stratosphere and mesosphere; noctilucent clouds. *Mailing Add:* Dept Atmospheric & Planetary Sci Univ Colo Boulder CO 80309

**THOMAS, GARY LEE,** FISHERIES ACOUSTICS, ECOSYSTEM CONSERVATION. *Current Pos:* PRES & DIR, PRINCE WILLIAM SOUND SCI CTR, 90-, DIR, PRINCE WILLIAM SOUND OIL SPILL RECOVERY INST, 92- *Personal Data:* b El Paso, Tex, Feb 27, 47; m 70, Mariola; c Melanie, Jeremy, Emily & Heather. *Educ:* Calif Western Univ, BS, 71; San Diego State Univ, MS, 73; Univ Wash, PhD(fisheries), 78. *Honors & Awards:* Outstanding Serv Award, US Fish & Wildlife Serv, 90. *Prof Exp:* Res assoc, Scripps Inst Oceanog, Univ Calif, 71-73; res fac, Univ Wash, 79-89. *Concurrent Pos:* Prin investr, Fisheries Res Inst, 79- *Mem:* Am Fisheries Soc; AAAS; Am Fisheries Res Biologists. *Res:* Applications of new measurement technologies to assess fish and aquatic resources to enable the conservation of natural stocks and their habitats. *Mailing Add:* PO Box 1331 Cordova AK 99574. *Fax:* 907-424-5820

**THOMAS, GARY LEE,** ELECTRICAL ENGINEEERING, SOLID STATE PHYSICS. *Current Pos:* vpres, 80-90, PROVOST & SR VPRES, ACAD AFFAIRS, NJ INST TECHNOL, 90- *Personal Data:* b Willows, Calif, May 12, 37; m 77; c 3. *Educ:* Univ Calif, Berkeley, BSc, 60, MA, 62, PhD(elec eng), 67. *Prof Exp:* Ed officer elec sci, Accra Polytech Inst, 62-64; instr elec eng, Univ Calif, Berkeley, 67; from asst prof to prof elec eng, State Univ NY, Stony Brook, 67-79, chmn dept, 75-79. *Concurrent Pos:* NSF grants, 72-; AAAS cong fel, 74-75; mem mat prog, Off Technol Assessment, 74-75; secy bd dir, Kessler Corp, 90- *Mem:* Am Phys Soc; Inst Elec & Electronics Engrs; AAAS; Am Asn Univ Prof. *Res:* Solid state electronics; laser annealing; magnetoelastic surface wave. *Mailing Add:* Off Provost NJ Inst Technol 323 Martin Luther King Blvd Newark NJ 07012

**THOMAS, GEORGE B,** RADIATION CURING. *Current Pos:* DIR RES & DEVELOP, ROPPE CORP, 91- *Personal Data:* b Madras, India, Feb 26, 41; US citizen; m 70, Geetha Mary Antony; c 3. *Educ:* Univ Kerala, India, BSc, 61, MSc, 63; Indian Inst Technol, Kharagpur, dipl high polymer & rubber technol, 64; Polytech Inst NY, MS, 66, PhD(polymer chem), 71. *Prof Exp:* Res chemist, Polymer Res Corp Am, 71-74; group leader, Floor Prod Res Lab, GAF Corp, 74-81; sr res chemist, Res Div, Gencorp, 81-87; sr res chemist, Gen Tire Co, 87-90, res scientist, 90-91. *Mem:* Am Chem Soc. *Res:* Ultraviolet curable coatings; EB cure of rubber; vulcanization chemistry; adhesive systems; structure-property relationships of polymers; rubber and vinyl floor products. *Mailing Add:* Roppe Corp PO Box 1158 Fostoria OH 44830-1158

**THOMAS, GEORGE BRINTON, JR,** MATHEMATICS. *Current Pos:* RETIRED. *Personal Data:* b Boise, Idaho, Jan 11, 14; m 36, 75, 80, Thais Waldron; c Georgia Fay (Bakhru), Jean Heath & James Hardin. *Educ:* State Col Wash, AB, 34, AM, 36; Cornell Univ, PhD(math), 40. *Prof Exp:* Instr math, Cornell Univ, 37-40; from instr to prof math, Mass Inst Technol, 44-78, asst elec eng, 43-45, exec officer dept math, 50-59. *Mem:* Am Math Soc; Math Asn Am (1st vpres, 58-59). *Res:* Calculus and analytic geometry. *Mailing Add:* 500 E Marylyn Ave No G-106 State College PA 16801-6270

**THOMAS, GEORGE HOWARD,** PEDIATRICS. *Current Pos:* asst pediat, Sch Med, John F Kennedy Inst, 65-67, instr, 67-68, asst prof pediat & med, Sch Med & dir, Genetics Lab, 68-76, assoc prof, 76-, PROF PEDIAT, JOHNS HOPKINS HOSP, JOHNS HOPKINS UNIV. *Personal Data:* b Minerva, Ohio, Apr 27, 36; m 60; c 3. *Educ:* Western Md Col, AB, 59; Univ Md, PhD, 63. *Prof Exp:* Instr biochem, Sch Med, Univ Md, 63. *Mem:* AAAS; Am Soc Human Genetics; Soc Inherited Metab Dis; Soc Pediat Res. *Res:* Human genetics. *Mailing Add:* Dept Pediat & Med Kennedy Inst 707 N Broadway Suite 500I Baltimore MD 21205

**THOMAS, GEORGE JOSEPH, JR,** MACROMOLECULAR ASSEMBLY, STRUCTURAL BIOLOGY. *Current Pos:* CURATORS PROF & HEAD, DIV CELL BIOL & BIOPHYS, SCH BIOL SCI, UNIV MO, KANSAS CITY, 87- *Personal Data:* b New Bedford, Mass, Dec 24, 41; m 66, Martha A Sheehan; c Elizabeth A, George J III & Jeanine M. *Educ:* Boston Col, BS, 63; Mass Inst Technol, PhD(phys chem), 67. *Honors & Awards:* Coblentz Award, Coblentz Soc & Soc Appl Spectros. *Prof Exp:* From asst prof to prof chem, 68-87, head dept, Univ Mass, Dartmouth, 74-80. *Concurrent Pos:* Prin investr, NIH & NSF grants, 70-; sr res fel, US-Japan Coop Sci Prog, Inst Protein Res, Osaka Univ, Japan, 75-76; mem adv comt, NIH, 79-83; vis scientist, Dept Biol, Mass Inst Technol, Cambridge, 83-84; ed, Biopolymers, 84-; adj prof anesthesiol, St Luke Hosp, Kansas City; mem, major res instrumentation, NSF Panel, 97- *Mem:* Biophys Soc; AAAS; Sigma Xi; Am Chem Soc; Am Soc Biochem & Molecular Biol; Asn Med Sch Microbiol. *Res:* Raman and infrared spectroscopy; structure and function of biological molecules; nucleic acid and protein interactions and structures; virus structure and assembly. *Mailing Add:* Dept Cell Biol & Biophys Sch Biol Sci Univ Mo 5100 Rockhill Rd Kansas City MO 64110-2499. *Fax:* 816-235-1503

**THOMAS, GEORGE RICHARD,** ORGANIC CHEMISTRY. *Current Pos:* RETIRED. *Personal Data:* b Bethlehem, Pa, Feb 1, 20; m 55; c 4. *Educ:* Bowdoin Col, BS, 41; Northwestern Univ, PhD(chem), 48; Harvard Univ, adv mgt prog, 62. *Prof Exp:* Res fel, Univ Ill, 48-49 & Harvard Univ, 49-50; proj dir, Boston Univ, 50-54; dyestuffs res sect, Qm Res & Eng Command, Natick Labs, US Army, 54-56, asst chief res & develop, Chem & Plastics Div, 56-58, chief, 58-62, assoc dir & dir res, Clothing & Org Mat Lab, 62-68, chief, Mat Res Labs, 68-72, Org Mat Lab, 72-86, chief scientist, Army Mat & Mech Res Ctr, 86-89. *Concurrent Pos:* Pres, Thomason Chem, Inc, 54-60; vis prof, Boston Univ, 63-65; sr exec fel, Kennedy Sch Gov, Harvard Univ, 80; vis scientist, Univ Mass Dartmouth, 89-; consult, 89- *Mem:* Fel Am Inst Chemists; fel AAAS; Am Chem Soc; Sigma Xi. *Res:* Military applications of polymers as fibers, films, foams, elastomers and rigid and reinforced plastics; materials research; polymer research; operations and management research; business administration; automation in manufacturing. *Mailing Add:* 18 Cabot St Winchester MA 01890-3502

**THOMAS, GERALD ANDREW,** RADIOCHEMISTRY. *Current Pos:* RETIRED. *Personal Data:* b Birmingham, Ala, Oct 8, 11; m 40; c 4. *Educ:* Birmingham-Southern Col, BS & MS, 32; Univ Fla, PhD(chem), 52. *Prof Exp:* Teacher pub schs, Ala, 32-39; asst, Johns Hopkins Univ, 39-40; res chemist, Niagara Alkali Co, 40-45; from instr to assoc prof chem, Univ Fla, 46-57; chmn div sci, math & eng, San Francisco State Univ, 57-63, prof chem, 57-77. *Concurrent Pos:* NSF fel, 54-56; lectr & scientist, US AEC Latin-Am Prog, Atoms in Action, 65-68; consult, Oak Ridge Assoc Univs, 63-80. *Mem:* Am Chem Soc; Am Nuclear Soc. *Res:* Physical properties of organic compounds; nucleonics; radioisotopes. *Mailing Add:* 410 Hillcrest Blvd Millbrae CA 94030-2346

**THOMAS, GERALD H,** SOFTWARE SYSTEMS, THEORETICAL PHYSICS. *Current Pos:* mem tech staff, 81-84, SUPVR, AT&T BELL LABS, 84- *Personal Data:* b Salt Lake City, Utah, Sept 3, 42; m; c 1. *Educ:* Calif Inst Technol, BS, 64; Univ Calif, Los Angeles, MS, PhD(physics), 69. *Prof Exp:* NATO fel physics, Europ Orgn Nuclear Res, 69-70; res assoc, Univ Helsinki, 70-71; postdoctoral physicist, Argonne Nat Lab, 71-73, asst physicist, 73-75, physicist, 75-81. *Mem:* Am Phys Soc; Inst Elec & Electronics Engrs Comput Soc; Asn Comput Mach; NY Acad Sci; AAAS; Math Asn Am. *Res:* Planning and development of large software systems, particularly switching systems. *Mailing Add:* 939 W Winona No 1E Chicago IL 60640. *Fax:* 847-632-4275

**THOMAS, GORDON ALBERT,** EXPERIMENTAL SOLID STATE PHYSICS. *Current Pos:* MEM TECH STAFF PHYSICS, BELL LABS, 72- *Personal Data:* b Kingston, Pa, June 8, 43; m 66, Deborah Allen; c Allen M. *Educ:* Brown Univ, ScB, 65; Univ Rochester, PhD(physics), 71. *Prof Exp:* Fel physics, Univ Rochester, 71-72. *Concurrent Pos:* Vis prof, Univ Tokyo, 81; vis scholar, Harvard Univ, 85-86. *Mem:* Fel Am Phys Soc. *Res:* Studies of optical properties of new materials of technological interest. *Mailing Add:* Bell Labs Lucent Technol 1D238 Murray Hill NJ 07974-0636. *E-Mail:* gat@bell-labs.com

**THOMAS, GRAHAM HAVENS,** COMPUTERIZED SIGNAL PROCESSING & IMAGE ANALYSIS. *Current Pos:* GROUP LEADER, LAWRENCE LIVERMORE NAT LAB, 90- *Personal Data:* b Summit, NJ, Mar 26, 51; m 80; c 2. *Educ:* Drexel Univ, BS, 74, MS, 75, PhD(mech eng), 79. *Prof Exp:* Sr mem tech staff, Sandia Nat Labs, 79-90. *Mem:* Fel Am Soc Nondestructive Testing; Int Soc Optical Eng. *Res:* Application of signal processing and pattern recognition techniques to ultrasonic nondestructive evaluation; weld flaw detection and sizing; bond strength determination in adhesive and solid state bonds; material characterizations. *Mailing Add:* 1679 Quail Ct Livermore CA 94550

**THOMAS, GRANT WORTHINGTON,** SOIL CHEMISTRY. *Current Pos:* PROF AGRON, UNIV KY, 68- *Personal Data:* b Washington, DC, Feb 23, 31; m 51; c 5. *Educ:* Brigham Young Univ, BS, 53; NC State Univ, MS, 56, PhD(soils), 58. *Prof Exp:* Asst prof agron, Va Polytech Inst, 58-60, assoc prof, 60-64; prof soils, Tex A&M Univ, 64-68. *Concurrent Pos:* Vis prof, Univ Calif, Riverside, 62-63; vis fel, St Cross Col, Univ Oxford, 76. *Mem:* Fel Am Soc Agron; fel Soil Sci Soc Am. *Res:* Reactions and movement of solutes in soils and no-tillage cropping. *Mailing Add:* Agron Univ Ky 500 S Limestone St Lexington KY 40506-0001

**THOMAS, H RONALD,** PHOTOELECTRON SPECTROSCOPY, SURFACE CHEMISTRY. *Current Pos:* SR RES SCIENTIST, MINERALS, PIGMENTS & METALS DIV, PFIZER, INC, 82- *Personal Data:* b Auburn, Ind, June 9, 42. *Educ:* Univ Durham, MSc, 75, PhD(surface chem), 77. *Prof Exp:* Chemist, Xerox Webster Res Ctr, 67-74, assoc scientist, 77-79, scientist, 79-82. *Concurrent Pos:* Instr, Intensive Short Course Photoelectron Spectros, 79-; adj prof chem eng, Univ Wash, 82- *Mem:* Am Chem Soc; Am Phys Soc; Am Vacuum Soc. *Res:* Surface studies on organic polymeric and metallic materials using photoelectron spectroscopy; radio frequency plasma chemistry; laser assisted chemical vapor deposition; interface studies; conducting and semiconducting polymers. *Mailing Add:* 217 Wiley Rd Apt 40 Carneys Point NJ 08069

**THOMAS, HAROLD A(LLEN), JR,** CIVIL ENGINEERING. *Current Pos:* RETIRED. *Personal Data:* b Terre Haute, Ind, Aug 14, 13; m 35; c 3. *Educ:* Carnegie Inst Technol, BS, 35; Harvard Univ, MS, 37, ScD(sanit eng), 38. *Honors & Awards:* R E Horton Medal, Am Geophys Union, 78. *Prof Exp:* From instr to assoc prof sanit eng, Harvard Univ, 38-56, Gordon McKay prof civil & sanit eng, 56-80. *Concurrent Pos:* Consult, Nat Acad Sci-Nat Res Coun, 43-, Dept Health, Educ & Welfare, 49- & US Dept Defense, 52-58. *Mem:* Nat Acad Eng; fel Am Acad Arts & Sci; Am Geophys Union; Am Soc Civil Engrs. *Res:* Fluid mechanics; hydrology; mathematical statistics; water supply and treatment; systems analysis for water resource development; sanitary and environmental engineering. *Mailing Add:* 61 Cotuit Rd Sandwich MA 02563

**THOMAS, HAROLD LEE,** MATHEMATICS, STATISTICS. *Current Pos:* from asst prof to assoc prof, 64-69, PROF MATH, PITTSBURG STATE UNIV, 69- *Personal Data:* b Westphalia, Kans, July 2, 34; m 56; c 3. *Educ:* Kans State Col Pittsburg, BS, 58, MS, 59; Okla State Univ, PhD(statist), 64. *Prof Exp:* Instr math, Kans State Col Pittsburg, 59-60; asst, Okla State Univ, 60-64. *Mem:* Math Asn Am; Am Statist Asn. *Res:* Factorial experiments in experimental designs. *Mailing Add:* 2011 S Homer St Pittsburg KS 66762

**THOMAS, HAROLD TODD,** PHOTOCHEMISTRY, OPTICAL DISC MATERIALS. *Current Pos:* sr res chemist, Eastman Kodak Co, 70-79, res assoc, 79-84, tech assoc, 84-96, SR TECH ASSOC, EASTMAN KODAK CO, 96- *Personal Data:* b Seattle, Wash, Feb 3, 42; c 1. *Educ:* Calif Inst Technol, BS, 64; Wesleyan Univ, MA, 66; Princeton Univ, PhD(chem), 70. *Prof Exp:* Res chem, Bell Tel Labs, 69-70. *Mem:* Am Chem Soc. *Res:* Photochemistry of ordered systems; spectroscopy and photochemistry of adsorbed molecules; photoresists; optical disc materials. *Mailing Add:* 60 Wintergreen Way Rochester NY 14618. *Fax:* 716-588-2624

**THOMAS, HAZEL JEANETTE,** organic chemistry, medicinal chemistry, for more information see previous edition

**THOMAS, HERIBERTO VICTOR,** PREVENTIVE MEDICINE, PUBLIC HEALTH & EPIDEMIOLOGY. *Current Pos:* CONSULT, 80- *Personal Data:* b Panama City, Repub Panama, Mar 17, 17; US citizen; m 50; c Lesbia Marcia & Fermin Alejandro. *Educ:* Univ Southern Calif, AB, 50, MS, 60; Univ Calif, Los Angeles, MPH, 64; Univ Calif, Berkeley, PhD. *Honors & Awards:* Macgee Award, Am Oil Chem Soc, 63. *Prof Exp:* Res fel pharmacol & biochem, Univ Southern Calif, 53-56, res assoc, Sch Med, 57-61; res assoc physiol & biochem, St Joseph Hosp, Burbank, 61-64; res chemist, Calif State Dept Health, 64-66, res specialist, 66-72, coordr, Sickle Cell Anemia Prog, 72-74, chief genetic dis, 74-80; sr lectr health & med sci, Univ Calif, Berkeley, 73-81. *Concurrent Pos:* Reviewer & consult sci, AAAS & NSF, 72-80 & Nat Heart, Lung & Blood Inst, NIH, Rev Br, 75-81; mem, Med Qual Rev Comt No 5, State Med Bd Calif, 80-93. *Mem:* AAAS; Am Chem Soc; Am Soc Human Genetics; Sigma Xi. *Res:* Physiological chemistry of air pollutants and their health effects; lipid metabolism; structural changes in lung tissue as a consequence of adverse ambient conditions; prenatal diagnosis of disabling genetic diseases; genetic counseling as a method of prevention. *Mailing Add:* PO Box 9062 Berkeley CA 94709

**THOMAS, HERMAN H,** ROCK MAGNETISM, TRACE ELEMENT. *Current Pos:* GEOPHYSICIST GEOCHEM, GODDARD SPACE FLIGHT CTR, NASA, 66- *Personal Data:* b Raleigh, NC, Dec 26, 31; m 81, Gretchen E Dickinson; c Sheila A, Carla A & Scott B. *Educ:* Lincoln Univ, Pa, BA, 58; Univ Pa, PhD(geochem), 73. *Prof Exp:* Chemist, US Geol Surv, 58-64, Fairchild-Hiller Corp, 64-65 & Melpar Corp, 65-66. *Mem:* Am Geophys Union. *Res:* Composition of the Earth; geophysical analysis of Earth's lithosphere; composition and age of the solar system. *Mailing Add:* Goddard Space Flight Ctr NASA Code 921 Greenbelt MD 20771

**THOMAS, HOWARD H,** PARASITOLOGY, BIODIVERSITY OF CENTRAL AMERICA. *Current Pos:* PROF & CHMN, DEPT BIOL, FITCHBERG STATE COL, 81- *Personal Data:* b Schenectady, NY, Nov 28, 48; m 79, Phaedra Prior; c Gregory Kurt & Scott Wesley. *Educ:* Geneseo State Col, BS, 72; Adelphi Univ, MS, 74; Northeastern Univ, PhD (biol), 82. *Prof Exp:* Marine biologist, Grumman Ecosysts Corp, 73-74; instr, Northeastern Univ, 78-80. *Concurrent Pos:* Wetlands wildlife consult, Personal Consult Firm, 87-; assoc res mammals, Mus Comp Zool, Harvard Univ, 96- *Mem:* Am Soc Mammalogists; Soc Vector Ecologists; Sigma Xi. *Res:* Understanding mammal evolution by means of zoogeographic patterns, morphological patterns and differences in ectodyte faunas. *Mailing Add:* 310 Legate Hill Rd Leominster MA 01453. *Fax:* 978-665-3578; *E-Mail:* hthomas@fsc.edu

**THOMAS, HOWARD MAJOR,** PHYSICAL CHEMISTRY. *Current Pos:* RETIRED. *Personal Data:* b Elwood, Nebr, Feb 14, 18; m 43, Mary E; c Patricia, Donna, Barbara, David, Theresa & Margaret. *Educ:* Nebr State Teachers Col, 42; Univ Iowa, PhD(chem), 49. *Prof Exp:* Asst prof chem & head dept, St Ambrose Col, 49-52; from assoc prof to prof, Univ SDak, 53-58; prof chem, Univ Wis, Superior, 58-82, chmn dept, 58-79. *Concurrent Pos:* Vis prof, Univ Wis, 64-65; Fulbright lectr phys chem, Univ Col Cape Coast, Ghana, 68-69. *Mem:* AAAS; Am Chem Soc; Sigma Xi. *Res:* Chemical kinetics; azeotropic solution; audio-visual aids for chemistry teaching. *Mailing Add:* RFD 9 Box 9240 Hayward WI 54843. *E-Mail:* elchymist@aol.com

**THOMAS, HUBERT JON,** DIGITAL SYSTEM SIMULATION, CONTROL SYSTEM ANALYSIS. *Current Pos:* SR ENG SPECIALIST, PERFORMANCE SEMI-CONDUCTOR, SUNNYVALE, 96- *Personal Data:* b Philadelphia, Pa, June 14, 40; m 81. *Educ:* Pa State Univ, BS, 62, MS, 64, PhD(elec eng), 69. *Prof Exp:* Asst prof elec eng, Rochester Inst Technol, 69-71; asst prof eng, Calif State Univ, Los Angeles, 71-73; res engr, Zenith Radio Corp, 73-77; res engr, Litton Mat Serv Ctr, 77-92, sr eng specialist, 92-96. *Mem:* Inst Elec & Electronics Engrs. *Res:* Analog and hybrid computation; logical design and switching theory; system simulation and identification; stochastic optimal controls. *Mailing Add:* 4455 Park Bristol Pl San Jose CA 95136

**THOMAS, J EARL,** MELT GROWTH OF CRYSTALS, SEMICONDUCTOR SURFACE PHYSICS. *Current Pos:* RETIRED. *Personal Data:* b Seattle, Wash, Sept 7, 18; m 77, Margaret Johnston; c Richard, Jacob, John, James, Denise & Jeff. *Educ:* Johns Hopkins Univ, AB, 39; Calif Inst Technol, PhD(physics), 43. *Prof Exp:* Group leader, Calif Inst Technol, 42-45, Manhattan Projs Los Alamos, 45-46; asst prof elec eng, Mass Inst Technol, 46-55; chmn, Physics Dept, Wayne State Univ, Detroit, 55-59; develop mgr, IBM, Poughkeepsie, 62-64; Gen Instruments, 64-67, Victor Comptometer, 71-75, NCR Corp, 75-84; vpres, Carmen Sapphire Co, 67-70; consult, Warnecke Div Northrup, 70-71. *Concurrent Pos:* Mem tech staff, Bell Tel Lab, 51-52; group leader, Lincoln Lab, 52-55; chair, Electron Device Panel, Dept Defense, 56-62, Inst Elec & Electronics Engrs, Electron Device Soc, 64-66. *Mem:* Fel Inst Elec & Electronics Engrs; Sigma Xi. *Res:* Semiconductor surface physics; applied physics. *Mailing Add:* 323 Savage Farm Dr Ithaca NY 14850-6503. *E-Mail:* mjt22@cornell.edu

**THOMAS, JACK WARD,** WILDLIFE BIOLOGY. *Current Pos:* RETIRED. *Personal Data:* b Ft Worth, Tex, Sept 7, 34; m 57, F Margaret Schinaler; c Britt W & Scranton G. *Educ:* Tex A&M Univ, BS, 57; WVa Univ, MS, 69; Univ Mass, PhD, 73. *Honors & Awards:* Ore Chapter Award, Wildlife Soc, 79; Einarsen Award, Northwest Sect, Wildlife Soc, 81; Gulf Conserv Award, 84; Earle A Chiles Award, 85; Nat Wildlife Fedn Award, 91. *Prof Exp:* Biologist, Tex Game & Fish Comn, 57-62; res biologist, Tex Parks & Wildlife Dept, 62-67; wildlife res biologist, Forestry Sci Lab, Northeastern Forest Exp Sta, US Forest Serv, 67-71, proj dir environ forestry res, Pinchot Inst Environ Forestry, 71-73, chief res biologist, 80-93, proj leader, Range & Wildlife Habitat Res, Pac Northwest Forest Exp Sta, 73-96, chief, 93-96. *Concurrent Pos:* Adj prof, Wash State Univ, Ore State Univ, Univ Idaho, Eastern Ore State Col & WVa Univ. *Mem:* Sigma Xi; Wildlife Soc; Wilson Ornith Soc; Am Ornith Union; Am Soc Mammal; fel Soc Am Foresters. *Res:* Mobility and home range management of deer and turkeys; population dynamics of deer; disease impact on deer and antelope populations; wildlife habitat research; sociobioeconomic implications of game habitat manipulation; habitat requirements for wildlife in urbanizing areas; relationships of wild and domestic ungulates to forested ranges; non-consumptive utilization of wildlife; forestry-wildlife relationships. *Mailing Add:* USDA Forest Serv 14th & Independence Washington DC 20024

**THOMAS, JAMES,** COMPUTER SCIENCE, COMPUTER GRAPHICS. *Current Pos:* Chief scientist, Environ & Molecular Sci Lab, 87-91, COMPUT SCI TECHNOL LAB, BATTELLE PAC NORTHWEST LABS, 91- *Personal Data:* b Spokane, Wash, 1946. *Educ:* Eastern Wash Univ, BS, 68; Wash State Univ, MS, 71. *Concurrent Pos:* Chair, Spec Interest Group Comput Graphics, Asn Comput Mach, 89- *Mem:* Inst Elec & Electronics Engrs; Asn Comput Mach; Human Factors Soc. *Mailing Add:* Battelle Pac Northwest Labs PO Box 999 MS K7-02 Richland WA 99352

**THOMAS, JAMES ARTHUR,** OXIDATIVE STRESS, ENZYMES. *Current Pos:* from asst prof to assoc prof, 69-87, PROF BIOCHEM, IOWA STATE UNIV, 88- *Personal Data:* b International Falls, Minn, Apr 22, 38; m 61; c 2. *Educ:* St Olaf Col, BA, 60; Univ Wis, MS, 63, PhD(biochem), 66. *Prof Exp:* USPHS fel biochem, Univ Minn, 67-69. *Mem:* Am Soc Biochem & Molecular Biol; Am Chem Soc; Am Soc Biol Chemists; Sigma Xi; Oxygen Soc. *Res:* Protein S-thiolation; oxidative stress and proteins in intact cells. *Mailing Add:* Dept Biochem Iowa State Univ 375 C Gilman Ames IA 50011-0001. *Fax:* 515-294-0453

**THOMAS, JAMES E,** PHYSICS. *Current Pos:* assoc prof, 63-65, PROF PHYSICS, PITTSBURG STATE UNIV, 65-, ACTG CHAIR, 90- *Personal Data:* b Marshall, Mo, May 17, 26; m 52; c 2. *Educ:* Mo Valley Col, BS, 50; Univ Mo-Rolla, MS, 55; Univ Mo-Columbia, PhD(physics), 63. *Prof Exp:* Teacher high sch, Mo, 50-52; instr math, Univ Mo-Rolla, 52-55; assoc prof physics, Mo Valley Col, 55-61. *Mem:* Am Phys Soc; Am Asn Physics Teachers. *Res:* Small angle x-ray diffraction; particle size and structure determination, solid state; radiation damage in perfect crystals; thin films growth and characterization; vapor crystal growth. *Mailing Add:* Dept Physics Pittsburg State Univ Pittsburg KS 66762

**THOMAS, JAMES H,** PLANT BREEDING, GENETICS. *Current Pos:* DIR, USDA REGIONAL RES, INDIA, 90- *Personal Data:* b Cardston, Alta, Jan 9, 36; m 59; c 4. *Educ:* Utah State Univ, BSc, 61, MS, 63; Univ Alta, PhD(genetics), 66. *Prof Exp:* Res asst agron, Utah State Univ, 60-63; teacher sci, Taber Sch Div, Alta, 63-64; res asst genetics, Univ Alta, 64-66; res officer, Can Dept Agr, 66-67 & Rudy Patrick Seed Co, 67-69; seed specialist & adv, Utah State Univ-AID, Bolivia, 69-72, assoc prof plant sci & int progs, Utah State Univ, 72-74, dryland farming adv, Tehran, Iran, 74-76, int progs coordr, 76-80, chief party & dir res, Lapaz, Bolivia, 80-82, forage res adv, Egypt, 82-84, dir int progs, 84-90. *Mem:* Am Soc Agron; Crop Sci Soc Am; Am Inst Biol Sci. *Res:* Administrator international programs. *Mailing Add:* Dept Plant Sci Utah State Univ Logan UT 84322-4800

**THOMAS, JAMES H,** HEAVY ION PHYSICS, WEAK INTERACTIONS. *Current Pos:* physicist, 89-91, group leader heavy ion physics, 92-96, STAR DEP PROJ DIR, LAWRENCE LIVERMORE NAT LAB, 96- *Personal Data:* b Waltham, Mass, Mar 4, 55; m 81, Mary J Bartholomew; c Jonathan & Gwendolyn. *Educ:* Wash State Univ, BS, 76; Yale Univ, MS, 77, MPhil, 79, PhD(physics), 82. *Prof Exp:* Millikan fel, Calif Inst Technol, 83-85, mem res facil, 86-88. *Mem:* Am Phys Soc; Sigma Xi. *Res:* Relativistic heavy ion physics; weak interaction physics; beta decay; nuclear physics; gravitational physics. *Mailing Add:* Lawrence Berkeley Nat Lab MS 70A-3307 Berkeley CA 94720. *E-Mail:* jhthomas@lbl.gov

**THOMAS, JAMES WARD,** RHEUMATOLOGY, DIABETES. *Current Pos:* PROF MED, VANDERBILT MED CTR, VANDERBILT UNIV, 89- *Educ:* Univ Tenn, Memphis, MD, 73. *Prof Exp:* Asst prof med microbiol & immunol, Baylor Col Med, 81-89. *Mailing Add:* Dept Med Vanderbilt Med Ctr N Vanderbilt Univ MCN T3219 21st & Garland Nashville TN 37232-2681

**THOMAS, JAMES WILLIAM,** MATHEMATICS. *Current Pos:* assoc prof, 72-77, PROF MATH, COLO STATE UNIV, 77- *Personal Data:* b Ironwood, Mich, Nov 11, 41; m 67; c 4. *Educ:* Mich Technol Univ, BS, 63; Univ Ariz, MS, 65, PhD(math), 67. *Prof Exp:* Asst prof math, Univ Wyo, 67-72. *Concurrent Pos:* NSF sci develop grant, Univ Ariz, 70-71. *Mem:* Am Math Soc; Soc Indust & Appl Math. *Res:* Applied mathematics; hydrodynamics; nonlinear functional analysis and application; numerical solution of partial differential equations. *Mailing Add:* Colo State Univ Ft Collins CO 80523

**THOMAS, JEROME FRANCIS,** AIR & WATER POLLUTION, COMBUSTION. *Current Pos:* Res chemist, 50-55, assoc prof, 55-72, PROF SANIT ENG, UNIV CALIF, BERKELEY, 72-, CHMN, DIV HYDRAUL & SANIT ENG, 73-, EMER PROF, 87- *Personal Data:* b Chicago, Ill, Jan 8, 22; m, Rosemary Renner; c Jerrie, Nicki, Peter, Kathie, Michelle, Mike, Pat, Sean & Jeff. *Educ:* DePaul Univ, BS, 43; Univ Calif, PhD(chem), 50. *Concurrent Pos:* Consult, Energy Res Develop Agency 69- & Nat Acad Sci, 73-; adj prof, Environ Protection Agency, 70- *Mem:* Am Chem Soc; Am Soc Eng Educ; Soc Appl Spectros; Am Water Works Asn. *Res:* Sanitary chemistry; chemical aspects applied to air, water pollution and quality control; applied organic chemistry. *Mailing Add:* Davis Hall Univ Calif Berkeley CA 94720. *Fax:* 510-848-1776

**THOMAS, JOAB LANGSTON,** BOTANY. *Current Pos:* PRES, PA STATE UNIV, 90- *Personal Data:* b Holt, Ala, Feb 14, 33; m 54; c 4. *Educ:* Harvard Univ, AB, 55, AM, 57, PhD, 59. *Hon Degrees:* DSc, Univ Ala, 81; LLD, Stillman Col, 87. *Honors & Awards:* Carleton K Butler Award, 75. *Prof Exp:* Cytotaxonomist, Arnold Arboretum Harvard Univ, 59-61; from asst prof to prof biol, Univ Ala, 61-76, asst dean, Col Arts & Sci, 65, dean students & vpres students affairs, 69-76; chancellor, NC State Univ, Raleigh, 76-81; pres, Univ Ala, 81-88. *Concurrent Pos:* Dir, Herbarium, Univ Ala, 61-76, dir arboretum, 64-76. *Mem:* Am Soc Plant Taxon; Bot Soc Am; Int Asn Plant Taxon; Sigma Xi. *Res:* Systematics and cytogenetics of higher plants. *Mailing Add:* 1 Fairmont Woods Tuscaloosa AL 35405-1711

**THOMAS, JOE ED,** electrical engineering, for more information see previous edition

**THOMAS, JOHN A,** PHARMACOLOGY, TOXICOLOGY. *Current Pos:* VPRES ACAD SERV, UNIV TEX HEALTH SCI CTR, 88- *Personal Data:* b La Crosse, Wis, Apr 6, 33; m 57; c 2. *Educ:* Univ Wis-La Crosse, BS, 56; Univ Iowa, MA, 58, PhD(physiol), 61. *Honors & Awards:* Sci Recognition, Environ Protection Agency; DuBois Award Toxicol. *Prof Exp:* Instr physiol, Univ Iowa, 60-61; asst prof pharmacol, Sch Med, Univ Va, 61-64; assoc prof, Sch Med, Creighton Univ, 64-67; prof pharmacol, Sch Med, WVa Univ, 67-82, asst dean, 73-75, assoc dean, 75-82; vpres corp res, Baxter Int, 82-88. *Concurrent Pos:* Adj prof, Northwestern Univ, Univ Ill, Rush-Presby, Chicago Med, Univ Chicago, 83-88 & Med Col Wis, 83-; prof pharmacol, Div Toxicol, Univ Tex, Health Sci Ctr, San Antonio, 88- *Mem:* Am Soc Pharmacol & Exp Therapeut; Endocrine Soc; Soc Toxicol; Pharmacol Soc Can; Am Col Toxicol; Am Acad Vet Pharmacol & Therapeut; Teratology Soc; Soc Basic Urol Res. *Res:* Endocrine pharmacology, mechanism of action of androgens; prostate gland neoplasms; pesticides and reproduction; reproductive toxicology; phthalate acid esters; genetic engineering and biotechnology. *Mailing Add:* Univ Tex Health Sci Ctr 7703 Floyd Curl Dr San Antonio TX 78284-0001

**THOMAS, JOHN ALVA,** BIOCHEMISTRY. *Current Pos:* from asst prof to assoc prof, 70-84, PROF BIOCHEM, SCH MED, UNIV SDAK, 85- *Personal Data:* b Berwyn, Ill, May 9, 40; m 65, Loretta Cihak; c Richard & Wendy. *Educ:* DePauw Univ, AB, 62; Univ Ill, Urbana, PhD(biochem), 68. *Prof Exp:* NIH fel, Univ Pa, 68-70. *Concurrent Pos:* Vis prof, Cornell Univ, 77-78, Bowman Gray Sch Med & Wake Forest Univ, 93. *Mem:* AAAS; Biophys Soc; Am Soc Biochem & Molecular Biol; Sigma Xi; Soc Gen Physiologists. *Res:* Bioenergetics and oxidative phosphorylation; enzyme kinetics; intracellular pH; anoxia and cell death. *Mailing Add:* Dept Biochem Univ SDak Sch Med Vermillion SD 57069. *Fax:* 605-677-5109; *E-Mail:* jthomas@sundance.usd.edu

**THOMAS, JOHN B(OWMAN),** ELECTRICAL ENGINEERING. *Current Pos:* RETIRED. *Personal Data:* b New Kensington, Pa, July 14, 25; m 44; c 6. *Educ:* Gettysburg Col, AB, 44; Johns Hopkins Univ, BS, 52; Stanford Univ, MS, 53, PhD(elec eng), 55. *Prof Exp:* Elec engr, Koppers Co, Inc, 46-51, asst chief engr, 51-52; from asst prof to assoc prof elec eng, Princeton Univ, 55-62, prof, 62- *Concurrent Pos:* NSF sr fel, 67-68. *Mem:* Fel Inst Elec & Electronics Engrs. *Res:* Communication and information theory; random processes; corona discharge; high voltage rectification. *Mailing Add:* 3651 Las Pilitas Rd Santa Margarita CA 93453

**THOMAS, JOHN HOWARD,** SOLAR ASTROPHYSICS, FLUID DYNAMICS. *Current Pos:* dean grad studies, 83-91, PROF MECH & AEROSPACE SCI, UNIV ROCHESTER, 81-, PROF ASTRON, 86- *Personal Data:* b Chicago, Ill, Apr 9, 41; m 62, Lois Moffit; c Jeffrey & Laura. *Educ:* Purdue Univ, BS, 62, MS, 64, PhD(eng sci), 66. *Prof Exp:* NATO fel appl math, Cambridge Univ, 66-67; from asst prof to assoc prof mech & aerospace sci, Univ Rochester, 67-81, assoc dean grad studies, 81-83, assoc, C E K Mees Observ, 72-85. *Concurrent Pos:* Vis scientist, Max Planck-Inst Physics & Astrophys, Munich, 73-74; High Altitude Observ, Boulder, Colo, 85, Nat Solar Observ, Sunspot, NMex; vis prof theoret physics, Univ Oxford, 87-88, vis fel, Worcester Col, Oxford, 87-88; affil sci, High Altitude Observ, Boulder, Colo, 89-; Guggenheim fel, 93-94; sci ed, Astrophys J, 93- *Mem:* Am Phys Soc; Am Astron Soc; Int Astron Union; Am Geophys Union; AAAS; Sigma Xi. *Res:* Astrophysical fluid dynamics; magnetohydrodynamics; solar physics; physics of sunspots; solar observations; stellar dynamos. *Mailing Add:* 223 Hopeman Univ Rochester River Campus Rochester NY 14627

**THOMAS, JOHN HUNTER,** PLANT SYSTEMATICS. *Current Pos:* From asst cur to cur, 58-72, assoc prof, 69-77, DIR DUDLEY HERBARIUM, STANFORD UNIV, 72-, PROF BIOL SCI, 77- *Personal Data:* b Beuthen, Ger, Mar 26, 28; US citizen. *Educ:* Calif Inst Technol, BS, 49; Stanford Univ, AM, 49, PhD, 59. *Concurrent Pos:* Cur, Dept Bot, Calif Acad Sci, 69- *Mem:* Am Soc Plant Taxon; Bot Soc Am; Soc Study Evolution; Am Fern Soc. *Res:* Flora of central and lower California and Alaska; management of systematic collections; information storage and retrieval in systematic collections; botanical history. *Mailing Add:* Dept Biol Sci Stanford Univ Gilbert Hall Stanford CA 94305-9991

**THOMAS, JOHN JENKS,** GEOLOGY. *Current Pos:* From asst prof to assoc prof, 68-82, PROF GEOL, SKIDMORE COL, 82-, CHAIR, DEPT GEOL, 93- *Personal Data:* b Boston, Mass, Dec 15, 36; m 65, Barbara R Rasmussen; c Rebecca B & Hannah J. *Educ:* Williams Col, BA, 61; Northwestern Univ, MS, 65; Univ Kans, PhD(geol), 68. *Mem:* AAAS; Geol Soc Am; Nat Asn Geol Teachers; Sigma Xi. *Res:* Structural geology; tectonics; metamorphic petrology; earth science education. *Mailing Add:* Geol Skidmore Col Saratoga Springs NY 12866-1661. *Fax:* 518-584-3023; *E-Mail:* jthomas@scott.skidmore.edu

**THOMAS, JOHN KERRY,** PHYSICAL CHEMISTRY. *Current Pos:* prof chem, 70-83, JULIUS NIEUWLAND PROF CHEM, UNIV NOTRE DAME, 83- *Personal Data:* b Llanelly, South Wales, Gt Brit, May 16, 34; m 59, June; c 3. *Educ:* Univ Manchester, BSc, 54, PhD(chem), 57, DSc, 69. *Hon Degrees:* DSc, Univ Manchester, Eng, 69. *Honors & Awards:* Res Award, Radiation Res Soc, 72; Colloids & Surfaces Award, Am Chem Soc. *Prof Exp:* Nat Res Coun Can fel chem, 57-58; sci off, Atomic Energy Res Estab, Eng, 58-60; res assoc, Argonne Nat Lab, 60-62, assoc chemist, 62-70. *Mem:* Radiation Res Soc; Am Chem Soc; fel Royal Soc Chem; Photobiol Soc. *Res:* Photo-induced reactions in organized media, including micellas, zeolites, microemulsions, P stymes and colloidal semiconductors; techniques used in rapid laser spectroscopy; colloid chemistry; polymer radiation chemistry; photochemistry. *Mailing Add:* Dept Chem Univ Notre Dame Notre Dame IN 46556. *Fax:* 219-631-6852

**THOMAS, JOHN M,** BIOMETRICS, ECOLOGY. *Current Pos:* STAFF, WASH STATE UNIV, 96- *Personal Data:* b Wilmar, Calif, Sept 17, 36; m 57, Patsy C McCarty; c Shelly, Sheryl & Steven. *Educ:* Calif State Polytech Col, BS, 58; Wash State Univ, MS, 60; Univ Ariz, PhD(biochem), 65. *Prof Exp:* Instr avian physiol, Calif State Polytech Col, 60-61; res assoc biochem, Univ Ariz, 61-65; sr res scientist, Pac Northwest Labs, Battelle Mem Inst, 61-71; gen ecologist, Div Biol & Med, Energy Res & Develop Admin, 71-72; res assoc, Battelle Mem Inst, 72-76, mem staff, Environ Sci Dept, Pac Northwest Div, 76-95; African Nazarene Univ, 95-96. *Concurrent Pos:* Mem task group, Int Comt Radiation Protection, 74-; adj prof & coordr biol prog, Wash State Univ, 77- *Mem:* Soc Environ Toxicol & Chem; Am Statist Asn; Biomet Soc. *Res:* Biology and ecology; methods development for field surveys and the prediction of effects of various insults on humans based on laboratory animal data; ecological effects; environmental impacts; bioassessment of hazardous chemical waste sites; dam bypass studies. *Mailing Add:* 5222 E Rail Ct Richland WA 99352. *Fax:* 509-372-2748; *E-Mail:* jthomas@tricity.wsu.edu

**THOMAS, JOHN MARTIN,** PEDIATRICS. *Current Pos:* from asst prof to prof, 49-83, asst prof rehab, 66-83, EMER PROF PEDIAT, UNIV NEBR, MED CTR, OMAHA, 83-; STAFF PHYSICIAN, GLENWOOD STATE HOSP-SCH, 83- *Personal Data:* b Omaha, Nebr, Oct 17, 10; m 36; c 4. *Educ:* Grinnell Col, AB, 32; Yale Univ, MD, 37. *Prof Exp:* From instr to asst prof pediat, Col Med, Creighton Univ, 40-49. *Mem:* AMA; Am Acad Pediat. *Mailing Add:* Glenwood State Hosp Sch Glenwood IA 51534

**THOMAS, JOHN MEURIG,** CHEMISTRY. *Current Pos:* PROF CHEM, DIR & RESIDENT PROF, DAVY FARADAY RES LAB, ROYAL INST GT BRIT, 86- *Personal Data:* b Llanelli, Wales, Dec 15, 32; m 59, Margaret Edwards; c 2. *Educ:* Univ Col Swansea, MA; Queen Mary Col, PhD. *Hon Degrees:* Several from foreign univs, 84-95. *Prof Exp:* Sci officer UK Atomic Energy Authority, 57-58, from asst lectr to lectr, 58-65, reader, 65-69; prof & head, Dept Chem, Univ Col Wales, 69-78; prof & head, Dept Phys Chem & fel King's Col, Univ Cambridge, 78-86. *Concurrent Pos:* Vis prof, Tech Univ, Neth, 62, Pa State Univ, 63-67, Tech Univ Karlsruhe, Fed Repub Ger, 66, Wiezmann Inst, Israel, 69, Univ Florence, Italy, 72, Am Univ, Cairo, 73, IBM Res Ctr, 77, Queen Mary Col, 86-, Imp Col, London, 86- & Acad Sinica, Beijing Inst Ceramic Sci, 86-; mem, Chem Comt, Sci Res Coun, 76-78, Radioactive Waste Mgmt Comt, 78-80, Royal Inst, 78-80, main comt, Sci & Eng Res Coun, 86-; distinguished vis lectr, London Univ, 80, Univ Western Ont, 83, Tex A&M Univ, 84, Univ Notre Dame, 86; Winegard vis prof, Guelph Univ, 82; chmn, Chemrawn, Int Union Pure & Appl Chem, 87-93. *Mailing Add:* Royal Inst 21 Albemarle St London W1X 4BS England

**THOMAS, JOHN OWEN,** BIOPHYSICAL CHEMISTRY, ELECTRON MICROSCOPY. *Current Pos:* asst prof biochem, 75-82, RES ASSOC PROF, MED SCH, NY UNIV, 82- *Personal Data:* b Los Angeles, Calif, Nov 1, 46; c 2. *Educ:* San Diego State Univ, BS, 68; Cornell Univ, PhD(biochem), 72. *Prof Exp:* Fel, Biochem Dept, Stanford Univ, 72-75. *Concurrent Pos:* Fel, Damon Runyon Mem Fund, 72-74; Am Cancer Soc Sr Fel, 74-75. *Mem:* NY Acad Sci. *Res:* Nucleic acid-protein interactions; structures of large nucleoprotein complexes; electron microscopy of macromolecules; RNA metabolism. *Mailing Add:* Dept Biochem NY Univ Sch Med 550 First Ave New York NY 10016-6481. *Fax:* 212-263-8166

**THOMAS, JOHN PELHAM,** MATHEMATICS. *Current Pos:* RETIRED. *Personal Data:* b Ashby, Ala, Apr 18, 22; m 45; c 6. *Educ:* Auburn Univ, BS, 46; Univ Va, MAT, 61; Univ SC, PhD(math), 65. *Prof Exp:* Asst co agt, Agr Exten Serv, Auburn, 46-53; farmer, 53-54; jr & high sch teacher, Ala, 55-60; asst prof math, Univ NC, 64-67; head dept, Western Carolina Univ, 67-75, prof math, 67-84. *Mem:* Math Asn Am. *Res:* Maximal topological spaces; separation axioms; properties preserved under strengthening and weakening of topologies. *Mailing Add:* 78 Medallion Dr Cullowhee NC 28723

**THOMAS, JOHN RICHARD,** PHYSICAL CHEMISTRY. *Current Pos:* RETIRED. *Personal Data:* b Anchorage, Ky, Aug 26, 21; m 44, Beatrice Davidson; c Richard G & Jonnie T (Jacobs). *Educ:* Univ Calif, BS, 43, PhD(phys chem), 47. *Honors & Awards:* Earl B Barnes Award, Am Chem Soc, 90. *Prof Exp:* Asst Nat Defense Res Comt, Univ Calif, 43-44, Manhattan Proj, 44-47; res assoc, US AEC Contract, Gen Elec Co, 47-48; res chemist, Calif Res Corp, 48-49; asst chief chem br, US AEC, 49-51; sr res scientist, Calif Res Corp, 51-67, mgr res & develop, Ortho Div, Chevron Chem Co, 67-68, asst secy, Stand Oil Co Calif, 68-70, pres, Chevron Res Co, 70-83, vpres, Chevron Corp, 83-86. *Mem:* Am Chem Soc. *Res:* Free radicals 250 Beatrice Davidson; oxidation kinetics; electron spin resonance; petroleum technology; synthetic fuels. *Mailing Add:* 847 Mcellen Way Lafayette CA 94549

**THOMAS, JOHN WILLIAM,** ANIMAL NUTRITION, DAIRY SCIENCE. *Current Pos:* prof, 60-87, EMER PROF DAIRY SCI, MICH STATE UNIV, 87- *Personal Data:* b Spanish Fork, Utah, Mar 25, 18; m 45; c 4. *Educ:* Utah State Univ, BS, 40; Cornell Univ, PhD(nutrit), 46. *Honors & Awards:* Am Feed Mfrs Asn Award, 53; Borden Award, Am Dairy Sci Asn, 74. *Prof Exp:* Res assoc, Nat Defense Res Comt, Northwestern Univ, 42-45 & Carnegie Inst Technol, 45; nutritionist & biochemist, Bur Dairy Indust, USDA, 46-53 & dairy husb res br, 53-60. *Concurrent Pos:* Exten specialist dairy, 79- *Mem:* Fel AAAS; fel Am Soc Animal Sci; Am Dairy Sci Asn; Am Inst Nutrit; Sigma Xi. *Res:* Mineral and vitamin requirements and functions in feeding of dairy cattle; forage evaluation and preservation; thyroid active stimulants for cattle; rumen functions; calf nutrition. *Mailing Add:* Dept Animal Sci Anthony Hall Mich State Univ East Lansing MI 48824. *Fax:* 517-353-1699

**THOMAS, JOHN XENIA, JR,** PHYSIOLOGY. *Current Pos:* res assoc, 76-78, asst prof, 78-84, ASSOC PROF PHYSIOL, STRITCH SCH MED, LOYOLA UNIV, CHICAGO, 84- *Personal Data:* b Birmingham, Ala, July 25, 50; m 74; c 1. *Educ:* Birmingham-Southern Col, BS, 72; Univ Miss Med Ctr, PhD(physiol), 76. *Prof Exp:* Res assoc, Dept Physiol & Biophys, Univ Miss, 72-76. *Concurrent Pos:* Res fel, Chicago Heart Asn, 77-78; instr nursing physiol, Hinds Jr Col, 75-76; Schweppe Found career develop award, 78-82; chmn, Cardiovasc Inst, 85- *Mem:* Am Heart Asn; Am Physiol Soc; AAAS. *Res:* Cardiac metabolism; cardiac dynamics; coronary circulation; nervous control of circulation. *Mailing Add:* Dept Physiol Loyola Univ Med Ctr 2160 S First Ave Maywood IL 60153

**THOMAS, JOSEPH CALVIN,** SCIENCE EDUCATION, ORGANIC CHEMISTRY. *Current Pos:* asst prof sci, Univ NAla, 61-65, chmn chem dept, 63-74, assoc dean Sch Arts & Sci, 79-81, dean, 81-87, dean, fac & instr, 87-90, PROF CHEM, UNIV NALA, 65-, VPRES ACAD AFFAIRS & PROVOST, 90- *Personal Data:* b Churubusco, Ind, May 2, 33; m 55; c 1. *Educ:* Asbury Col, AB, 54; Univ Ky, MA, 55, EdD(sci educ, chem), 61. *Prof Exp:* Instr chem, Asbury Col, 54-59 & Jessamine Co High Sch, 59-60. *Concurrent Pos:* Sci consult local pub sch systs, 63- *Mem:* AAAS; Am Chem Soc; Nat Sci Teachers Asn. *Res:* Preparation and continued education of secondary school science teachers, particularly their preparation in the physical sciences. *Mailing Add:* Box 5041 Univ NAla Florence AL 35632-0001. *Fax:* 205-760-4329

**THOMAS, JOSEPH CHARLES,** MATHEMATICS. *Current Pos:* Instr, 68-70, ASST PROF MATH, LOCK HAVEN STATE COL, 72-; PROF MATH, KUTZTOWN UNIV. *Personal Data:* b Mt Union, Pa, Oct 16, 45; m 65; c 2. *Educ:* Shippensburg State Col, BS, 66; Pa State Univ, MA, 68; Kent State Univ, PhD(math), 75. *Res:* Torsion theories generated by ideals; global dimension of associative rings with identity. *Mailing Add:* Dept Math Kutztown Univ Kutztown PA 19530

**THOMAS, JOSEPH ERUMAPPETTICAL,** APPLIED PSYCHOPHYSIOLOGY, HYPNOTHERAPY. *Current Pos:* DIR CLIN PSYCHOL, INST BEHAV HEALTH, 80- *Personal Data:* b Piravom, Kerala State, India, Feb 11, 37; m 64, Chinnamma Kavatt; c Joseph, Kurian & Elizabeth. *Educ:* Univ Kerala, India, BA, 57, MA, 60, PhD(psychol), 69. *Prof Exp:* Res asst, Univ Kerala, 63-66, lectr psychol, 66-70; intern clin psychol, Northwestern Univ Med Sch, 71-72; psychologist drug abuse res, Univ Chicago, 72-74; psychologist, Inst Psychiat, Northwestern Univ, 74-76; psychologist chronic pain mgt, Rehab Inst Chicago, 76-80. *Concurrent Pos:* Postdoctoral fel, Northwestern Univ Med Sch, 72, asst prof, Dept Psychiat & Behav Sci, 77-; consult, Michael Reese Hosp, Chicago, Ill, 80-85, NIH, 84-; dir, Psychiat Unit, Ment Health Ctr, La Salle, Ill, 74; pres, Biofeedback Soc Ill, 85; consult psychologist, DuPage Ment Health Serv Ltd, Ill, 94-, Block Med Ctr & Res Found, 95- *Mem:* Am Psychol Asn; Am Soc Clin Hypnosis; Asn Appl Psychophysiol & Biofeedback. *Res:* Treatment of chronic anxiety using electroencephalogram feedback; multi-cultural self; psychophysiologic management of attention deficit disorders; psychoneuro-immunology and the behavioral management of cancer patients. *Mailing Add:* 16 W 731 89th Pl Hinsdale IL 60521. *Fax:* 630-887-1842

**THOMAS, JOSEPH FRANCIS, JR,** MATERIALS ENGINEERING, MATERIALS PROCESSING. *Current Pos:* from asst prof to assoc prof eng & physics, Wright State Univ, 72-83, prog dir, Mat Sci & Eng, 76-84, dept chair Mech & Mat Eng, 84-90, PROF MAT SCI & ENG, WRIGHT STATE UNIV, 83-, DEAN, SCH GRAD STUDIES & ASSOC PROVOST RES, 90- *Personal Data:* b Chicago, Ill, Feb 29, 40; m 67; c 3. *Educ:* Cornell Univ, BEP, 63; Univ Ill, Urbana, MS, 65, PhD(physics), 68. *Prof Exp:* Res asst physics, Univ Va, 67-72. *Concurrent Pos:* Prog Dir Metall, NSF, 83-84. *Mem:* Am Soc Metals Int; Am Phys Soc; Minerals, Metals & Mat Soc; Am Soc Mech Engrs; Am Soc Eng Educ. *Res:* Plastic deformation; applications to metal forming; material constitutive equations. *Mailing Add:* Grad Studies & Res Wright State Univ Colonel Glenn Hwy Dayton OH 45435-0001. *E-Mail:* thomas@wright.edu

**THOMAS, JOSEPH JAMES,** BIOCHEMISTRY. *Current Pos:* TECH PULP, PAPER & CHEM CONSULT, 73- *Personal Data:* b Columbia, Pa, Sept 10, 09; m 32, 51; c 7. *Educ:* Pa State Univ, BS, 30, MS, 32, PhD(biochem), 35. *Prof Exp:* Asst res, NY Exp Sta, Geneva, 30; instr agr biochem, Pa State Univ, 31-36; biochemist, Rohm & Haas, 36-41; from asst dir to dir res, S D Warren Co, 42-68, vpres res, 68-72; tech consult, Edward C Jordan Co, Inc, 73-76. *Concurrent Pos:* Tech adv, Int Exec Serv Corps, 80. *Mem:* Am Chem Soc; Tech Asn Pulp & Paper Indust. *Res:* Synthetic resins; functional uses of pulp and paper. *Mailing Add:* 16234 N 111th Ave Sun City AZ 85351-1098

**THOMAS, JUDITH M,** TRANSPLANTATION IMMUNOLOGY. *Current Pos:* Assoc prof, 79-84, DIR TRANSPLANT IMMUNOL, ECAROLINA UNIV, 80-, PROF SURG, 84- & DIR HLA LAB, SCH MED. *Personal Data:* b Lynn, Mass, Jan 4, 44; m, Francis T; c Scott, David & Jason. *Educ:* Manhattanville Col, BA, 65; NY Univ, MS, 69, PhD(biol immunol), 72. *Concurrent Pos:* Adj prof microbiol & biol, Sch Med, ECarolina Univ, 84- *Mem:* Am Asn Immunol; Int Transplantation Soc; Am Soc Histocompatibility & Immunogenetics; Sigma Xi; Nat Soc Med Res; AAAS. *Mailing Add:* Div Surg Transplantation Ctr & Dir Immunolbiol Dept Surg Suite 802 Univ Ala Birmingham 18088 7th Ave S Boshell Bldg Birmingham AL 35294-0016

**THOMAS, JULIAN EDWARD, SR,** MICROBIAL PHYSIOLOGY. *Current Pos:* assoc prof, 73-77, PROF BIOL, TUSKEGEE INST, 77-, HEAD, BIOL DEPT, 79-, ASSOC DIR, CARVER RES FOUND, 79- *Personal Data:* b Yazoo City, Miss, Aug 1, 37; m 56; c 3. *Educ:* Fisk Univ, AB, 59; Atlanta Univ, MS, 67, PhD(biol), 71; Southern Univ, MST, 68. *Prof Exp:* Teacher pub schs, Ga, 59-65; instr biol & chem, SC State Col, 67-69; fel microgenetics, Argonne Nat Lab, 71-73. *Concurrent Pos:* Consult, Argonne Ctr Educ Affairs, 75-76. *Mem:* Sigma Xi; Fedn Am Scientists; AAAS; Am Soc Microbiol. *Res:* Involvement of transfer RNA in the regulation of enzyme synthesis by repression, and derepression, control. *Mailing Add:* 2306 George St Tuskegee AL 36088

**THOMAS, KENNETH ALFRED, JR,** PROTEIN CHEMISTRY & CRYSTALLOGRAPHY, GROWTH FACTORS. *Current Pos:* DIR GROWTH FACTOR RES, MERCK SHARP & DOHME RES LABS, MERCK INST, 79- *Personal Data:* b Oklahoma City, Okla, Nov 28, 46; m 73, Theresa Behrens; c Kenneth, Christopher & Katharine. *Educ:* Univ Del, BS, 69; Duke Univ, PhD(biochem), 74. *Prof Exp:* Res fels, Duke Univ, 74-75, NIH, 75-77 & Wash Univ, 77-79. *Mem:* Protein Chem Soc; AAAS; Am Soc Biol Chemists. *Res:* Protein growth factors; blood vessel growth control; tumor metastasis; the structure and function of proteins; endocrinology; biotechnology. *Mailing Add:* Dept Pharmacol Rm V42-300 Merck Res Labs Sunneytown Pike PO Box 4 West Point PA 19486-0004

**THOMAS, KENNETH EUGENE, III,** INORGANIC CHEMICAL SEPARATIONS. *Current Pos:* Resident, 79-80, MEM STAFF, LOS ALAMOS NAT LAB, 80- *Personal Data:* b Hammond, La, Jan 31, 54; m 79. *Educ:* Southeastern La Univ, BS, 75; Univ Calif, Berkeley, PhD(chem), 80. *Mem:* Am Chem Soc. *Res:* Production and isolation of large quantities of various radionuclides for use in the fields of medicine, chemistry, and physics; development of chemical separation processes applicable to hot cell handling of highly radioactive target materials. *Mailing Add:* 376 Catherine Los Alamos NM 87544-3565

**THOMAS, KEVIN ANTHONY,** ORTHOPAEDIC SURGERY RESEARCH, BIOMECHANICS & BIOMATERIALS. *Current Pos:* Asst prof, 91-96, ASSOC PROF, DEPT ORTHOP SURG, MED CTR, LA STATE UNIV, 96- *Personal Data:* b New Orleans, La, Oct 22, 59; m 82, Kathleen Liuzza; c Samuel T & Philip M. *Educ:* Tulane Univ, BSE, 81, MS, 83, PhD(biomed eng), 85. *Concurrent Pos:* Adj asst prof biomed eng, Tulane Univ, 90- *Mem:* Soc Biomat; Orthop Res Soc; Biomed Eng Soc. *Res:* Orthopaedic biomechanics and biomaterials research; mechanical evaluation of fracture fixation, spinal instrumentation and bone implant interfaces; bioactive implant materials. *Mailing Add:* La State Univ Med Ctr 2025 Gravier St Suite 400 New Orleans LA 70112. *Fax:* 504-568-4466; *E-Mail:* kthoma@lsumc.edu

**THOMAS, KIMBERLY W,** NUCLEAR CHEMISTRY, NUCLEAR PHYSICS. *Current Pos:* Staff scientist chem, Los Alamos Nat Lab, 78-85, asst group leader, 85-87, sect leader, 87-89, dep group leader, 89-92, prog mgr, 92-94, PHYSICS DIV CHIEF-OF-STAFF, LOS ALAMOS NAT LAB, 94- *Personal Data:* b Albany, NY, July 3, 52; m 79, Kenneth E III; c Scott & Brent. *Educ:* Middlebury Col, AB, 73; Univ Calif, Berkeley, MBioradiol, 78, PhD(nuclear chem), 78. *Honors & Awards:* Achievement Award, Am Inst Chemists. *Mem:* Am Chem Soc; Asn Women Sci; Am Phys Soc. *Res:* Radiochemistry; radioactive waste management; isotope synthesis and isolation; applications of radiochemistry to biology and medicine; chemical separations. *Mailing Add:* Physics Div MS-D434 Los Alamos Nat Lab Los Alamos NM 87545. *Fax:* 505-665-3644; *E-Mail:* kwthomas@lanl.gov

**THOMAS, LARRY EMERSON,** APPLIED MATHEMATICS. *Current Pos:* Asst prof, 70-72, ASSOC PROF MATH, ST PETER'S COL, NJ, 72-, COORDR PRE-ENG PROG, 76- *Personal Data:* b Indianapolis, Ind, Dec 27, 43. *Educ:* Rose Polytech Inst, BS, 66; Rensselaer Polytech Inst, MS, 68, PhD(math), 70. *Mem:* Math Asn Am; Soc Indust & Appl Math. *Res:* Differential equations. *Mailing Add:* Dept Math St Peter's Col 92 Highland Ave Jersey City NJ 07306

**THOMAS, LAWRENCE E,** PROBABILITY, REAL ANALYSIS. *Current Pos:* from asst prof to assoc prof, 74-81, PROF MATH, UNIV VA, 81- *Personal Data:* b Columbus, Ohio, Mar 15, 42. *Educ:* Yale Univ, BS, 64, PhD(physics), 70. *Prof Exp:* Res asst, Fed Inst Technol, Zurich, Switz, 70-72; res asst, Univ Geneva, 72-74. *Mem:* Am Phys Soc; Am Math Soc; Int Asn Math Physics. *Res:* Work and theory Shrodinger operators, statistical mechanics, and stocastic processes. *Mailing Add:* Kerchof Hall Cabell Dr Univ Va Charlottesville VA 22903-3145

**THOMAS, LAZARUS DANIEL,** PHYSICAL CHEMISTRY. *Current Pos:* RETIRED. *Personal Data:* b Toledo, Ohio, Oct 21, 25; m 50; c 5. *Educ:* Univ Mich, BS, 48, MS, 49. *Prof Exp:* Teaching fel, Univ Mich, 49-50; res supvr, Libbey-Owens-Ford Co, 51-88. *Mem:* Electrochem Soc; Am Electroplaters Soc; Am Chem Soc; Am Ceramic Soc. *Res:* Films on glass; semiconductors; surface chemistry of glass; electrochemistry. *Mailing Add:* 263 Varsity Sq Bowling Green OH 43402-4738

**THOMAS, LEE W(ILSON),** CHEMICAL ENGINEERING. *Current Pos:* PRIN CONSULT, CECON GROUP INC, 85- *Personal Data:* b Boswell, Pa, Oct 31, 26; m 50; c 2. *Educ:* Univ Pittsburgh, BS, 49. *Prof Exp:* Chem analyst, Jones & Laughlin Steel Co, 49-50; process engr, Bethlehem Steel Co, 50-52; field engr, Eng Dept, E I du Pont de Nemours & Co, Inc, 52-63, res engr,

Pigments Dept, 63-67, sr res engr, Newport, 67-72, tech serv rep, Pigments Dept, 72-85. *Mem:* Am Inst Chem Engrs; Am Chem Soc. *Res:* Development work in particle processes including extreme temperature ranges. *Mailing Add:* 122 Cardinal Circle Wilmington DE 19808

**THOMAS, LEO ALVON,** PARASITOLOGY, MEDICAL MICROBIOLOGY. *Current Pos:* RETIRED. *Personal Data:* b Gifford, Idaho, Mar 19, 22; c 2. *Educ:* Univ Idaho, BS, 49; Univ Mich, MS, 50; Tulane Univ, PhD(parasitol, med microbiol), 55. *Prof Exp:* Staff, Virus Labs, Rockefeller Found, NY, 55-57; med bacteriologist, Rocky Mountain Lab, USPHS, 57-80, res microbiologist, 80-85. *Res:* Ecology and classification of arthropod-borne viruses; biological and chemical characterization of Coxiella burnetii antigens. *Mailing Add:* 810 S Third St Hamilton MT 59840

**THOMAS, LEO JOHN,** CHEMICAL ENGINEERING. *Current Pos:* RETIRED. *Personal Data:* b Grand Rapids, Minn, Oct 30, 36; m 58; c 4. *Educ:* Univ Minn, BS, 58; Univ Ill, MS, 60, PhD(chem eng), 62. *Hon Degrees:* Dr, Worcester Polytech Inst, 88. *Honors & Awards:* Presidential Proclamation, Soc Motion Picture & Television Engrs, 95. *Prof Exp:* Chmn, Sterling Drug Inc, 88-89; res chemist, Color Photog Div, Res Labs, Eastman Kodak Inc, 61-67, head, Color Physics & Eng Lab, 67-70, asst div head, 70-72, tech asst to dir, 72-75, asst dir, Res Labs, 75-77, vpres, 77-78, sr vpres & dir, 78-84, gen mgr, Life Sci Div, 84-88, group vpres & gen mgr, Health Group, 89-91, group vpres & pres imaging, 91-96. *Concurrent Pos:* Mem, Bd Chem Sci & Technol, Nat Res Coun, 84; mem, Resource Develop Comt, Dept Chem Eng, Univ Ill; mem bd dirs, Rochester Tel Corp & John Wiley & Sons, Inc. *Mem:* Nat Acad Eng; Am Acad Arts & Sci; fel Am Inst Chem Engrs; AAAS; hon mem Soc Imaging Sci & Technol; fel Am Inst Med & Biol Eng. *Res:* Photographic science; chemical engineering kinetics. *Mailing Add:* Gladbrook Rd Pittsford NY 14534. *Fax:* 716-724-6770

**THOMAS, LEONARD WILLIAM, SR,** ELECTROMAGNETIC COMPATIBILITY. *Current Pos:* ELECTRONICS ENGR, THOMAS ENG CO, 70- *Personal Data:* b Birmingham, Ala, May 11, 09; m 34; c 3. *Educ:* Ala Polytech Inst, BS, 31. *Honors & Awards:* LG Cumming Award, Electromagnetic Compatibility Soc, Inst Elec & Electronics Engrs, 79. *Prof Exp:* Radio eng, radiostation WAPI, Birmingham, 32-39 & Columbia Broadcasting Syst, Washington, DC, 39-42. *Mem:* Inst Elec & Electronics Engrs; Soc Automotive Engrs; Nat Soc Prof Engrs; Am Soc Naval Engrs; Am Nat Stand Comt. *Res:* Development of measurement instruments; instrument specifications and standards; radiated and conducted measurement techniques. *Mailing Add:* 1604 Buchanan St NE Washington DC 20017

**THOMAS, LEWIS EDWARD,** ORGANIC CHEMISTRY. *Current Pos:* RETIRED. *Personal Data:* b Lima, Ohio, May 18, 13; m 40; c 4. *Educ:* Ohio Northern Univ, BS, 35; Purdue Univ, MS, 37. *Prof Exp:* Asst chem, Purdue Univ, 35-39; from instr to asst prof, Va Mil Inst, 40-45; develop engr, 45-50, tech serv & lab supvr, 50-70, asst mgr lab, 70-73, mgr lab, Sun Oil Co, 74-78. *Concurrent Pos:* Vis scientist, Ohio Acad Sci, NSF vchmn bd trustees, Univ Toledo & Toledo-Lucas Co Libr Syst. *Mem:* Nat Soc Prof Engrs; Am Chem Soc; Am Inst Chem Engrs; Sigma Xi. *Res:* Chlorination of aliphatic hydrocarbons; selective solvents for olefin and diolefin purification; pyrolysis of chlorinated aliphatic hydrocarbons; esterification of alcohol ethers. *Mailing Add:* 4148 Deepwood Lane Toledo OH 43614

**THOMAS, LEWIS JONES, JR,** BIOMEDICAL COMPUTING, QUANTITATIVE BIOMEDICAL IMAGING. *Current Pos:* asst prof anesthesiol, Sch Med, Washington Univ, 64-74, asst prof physiol & biophys, 70-74, asst prof biomed eng, 72-74, assoc dir, Biomed Comput Lab, 72-75, assoc prof, Inst Biomed Comput, 85-89, actg dir, 91-92, ASSOC PROF ANESTHESIOL, PHYSIOL/BIOPHYS & BIOMED ENG, SCH MED, WASHINGTON UNIV, 74-, ELEC ENG, 78-, PROF, INST BIOMED COMPUT, 89- *Personal Data:* b Philadelphia, Pa, Dec 13, 30; m 55, Jane Priem; c Lewis III & Sarah. *Educ:* Haverford Col, BS, 53; Wash Univ, MD, 57; Am Bd Anesthesiol, dipl, 63. *Honors & Awards:* Borden Award. *Prof Exp:* Intern med, Bronx Munic Hosp, NY, 57-58; USPHS res fel, Sch Med, Washington Univ, 58-60; resident anesthesiol, Barnes Hosp, St Louis, Mo, 60-62; staff anesthesiologist, Clin Ctr, NIH, 62-64. *Concurrent Pos:* Dir, Biomed Comput Lab, Sch Med, Washington Univ, 75-, assoc dir, Inst Biomed Comput, 83-91 & 92-; USPHS res career develop award, 66, consult, 80- *Mem:* AAAS; Am Physiol Soc; NY Acad Sci; Am Bd Anes. *Res:* Respiratory physiology; biomedical computer applications. *Mailing Add:* Biomed Comput Lab Sch Med Washington Univ 700 S Euclid St Louis MO 63110-1012. *Fax:* 314-362-0234; *E-Mail:* ljt@wubcl.wustl.edu

**THOMAS, LLYWELLYN MURRAY,** NEUROSURGERY. *Current Pos:* Assoc prof, Wayne State Univ, 65-68, asst chmn dept, 65-70, assoc dean hosp affairs, 72-81, PROF NEUROSURG & CHMN DEPT, SCH MED, WAYNE STATE UNIV, 70- *Personal Data:* b Detroit, Mich, Sept 23, 22; m 47; c 6. *Educ:* Wayne State Univ, BA, 49, MD, 52. *Concurrent Pos:* Sr attend, Detroit Gen Hosp, 65- & Grace Hosp, Detroit, 70-; consult, Harper Hosp, 71- & Children's Hosp Mich, 71- *Mem:* Am Asn Neurol Surg; Am Col Surg; AMA; Cong Neurol Surg. *Res:* Head injury. *Mailing Add:* Wayne State Univ 4201 St Antoine St No 6E Detroit MI 48201-2194

**THOMAS, LOUIS BARTON,** PATHOLOGY. *Current Pos:* RETIRED. *Personal Data:* b Medicine Lodge, Kans, June 8, 19; m 44; c 3. *Educ:* Col Idaho, AB, 40; Univ Chicago, MD, 45; Am Bd Path, dipl, 52. *Prof Exp:* Resident path, Univ Minn, 48-51; spec fel neuropath, Mayo Clin, 51-52; resident, Mem Ctr Cancer & Allied Dis, New York, 52-53; head, Surg Path & Post-Mortem Serv, Clin Ctr, NIH, 53-69; chief lab path, Nat Cancer Inst,

69- *Concurrent Pos:* Clin prof, Schs Med & Dent, Georgetown Univ, 72- *Mem:* Am Asn Path & Bact; fel Col Am Path; Am Asn Cancer Res; Am Soc Exp Path; Int Acad Path. *Res:* Diagnostic and research pathology, particularly cancer; leukemia and malignant lympomas. *Mailing Add:* 2107 Essex Ct Ft Collins CO 80526-1615

**THOMAS, LUCIUS PONDER,** ELECTRONICS ENGINEERING. *Current Pos:* RETIRED. *Personal Data:* b Easley, SC, June 30, 25; m 52; c 2. *Educ:* Clemson Univ, BS, 47. *Prof Exp:* Engr, RCA Corp, 47-61, leader eng TV, 61-69, mgr advan prod develop, 69-71, mgr black & white TV, 71-78, mgr eng prod safety, 78-87. *Mem:* Sr mem Inst Elec & Electronics Engrs. *Res:* Design, development and supervision in television receiver development. *Mailing Add:* 7311 N Lesley Ave Indianapolis IN 46250

**THOMAS, MCCALIP JOSEPH,** chemistry, safety & efficacy testing of products; deceased, see previous edition for last biography

**THOMAS, MARLIN ULUESS,** STOCHASTIC MODELING, RELIABILITY & MAINTENANCE PLANNING. *Current Pos:* PROF & HEAD, SCH INDUST ENG, PURDUE UNIV, WEST LAFAYETTE, INC, 93- *Personal Data:* b Middlesboro, Ky, June 28, 42; m 63, Susan; c Pamela C & Martin P. *Educ:* Univ Mich, BS, 67, MS, 68, PhD(indust & oper eng), 71. *Prof Exp:* From asst to assoc prof oper res, Naval Postgrad Sch, 71-76; assoc prof syst design, Univ Wis-Milwaukee, 76-78; mgr tech plan & analytical vehicle reliability, Chrysler Corp, 76-79; prof indust eng, Univ Mo, Columbia, 79-82; prof & chmn, dept indust eng, Cleveland State Univ, 82-88 & Lehigh Univ, 88-93. *Concurrent Pos:* Actg dir, Advan Mfg Ctr, Cleveland State Univ, 84-85; prog dir, Div Elec Commun & Syst Engr, NSF, 87-88; area ed, Mil Appln, Oper Res Soc Am, 88-93. *Mem:* Oper Res Soc Am; fel Inst Indust Engrs; Am Statist Asn; Am Soc Eng Educ; Am Soc Qual Control; Soc Am Mil Engrs. *Res:* Mathematical modeling of logistics and distribution planning for manufacturing and service systems; development of methods and techniques for the analysis and evaluation of reliability, warranties and maintenance replacement strategies and plans for products and systems. *Mailing Add:* 1287 Grissom Hall Purdue Univ West Lafayette IN 47907-1287. *E-Mail:* muthomas@ecn.purdue.edu

**THOMAS, MARTHA JANE BERGIN,** ANALYTICAL CHEMISTRY, PHYSICAL CHEMISTRY. *Current Pos:* RETIRED. *Personal Data:* b Boston, Mass, Mar 13, 26; m 55; c 4. *Educ:* Radcliffe Col, AB, 45; Boston Univ, AM, 50, PhD(chem), 52; Northeastern Univ, MBA, 81. *Honors & Awards:* Nat Achievement Award, Soc Women Engrs, 65; Golden Plate, Am Acad Achievement, 66; Centennial Alumni Award, Boston Latin Acad, 78. *Prof Exp:* Sr engr in chg chem lab, Gen Tel & Electronics Corp, Danvers, Mass, 45-59, group leader lamp mat eng labs, Lighting Prod Div, 59-66, sect head chem & phosphor lab, Sylvania Lighting Ctr, 66-72, mgr test anal labs, GTE Sylvania lighting prod group, Sylvania Elec Prod, Inc, 72-81, tech dir, Tech Serv Labs, 81-83, dir, Tech Qual Control, 83-93. *Concurrent Pos:* Instr eve div, Boston Univ, 52-70; adj prof chem, Univ RI, 74- *Mem:* Am Chem Soc; Electrochem Soc; fel Am Inst Chemists; Soc Women Engrs. *Res:* Phosphors; photoconductors; ion exchange membranes; complex ions; instrumental analysis. *Mailing Add:* 18 Cabot St Winchester MA 01890-3502

**THOMAS, MARTIN LEWIS HALL,** BIOLOGY. *Current Pos:* asst prof, 70-74, assoc prof, 70-79, PROF BIOL, UNIV NB, ST JOHN, 79- *Personal Data:* b Feb 9, 35; Can citizen; m 56; c 3. *Educ:* Univ Durham, BSc, 56; Univ Toronto, MSA, 62; Dalhousie Univ, PhD, 70. *Prof Exp:* Assoc scientist, Biol Sta, Fisheries Res Bd Can, Ont, 56-62; scientist, Biol Sub-Sta, 62-70. *Concurrent Pos:* Mem, Int Oceanog Found, 55-; bd dir, Huntsman Marine Lab, 77-80. *Mem:* Hon mem NY Acad Sci; Nat Shellfisheries Asn; Marine Biol Asn UK; Brit Ecol Soc. *Res:* Ecology of larval lampreys; estuarine ecology; marine benthic ecology; marine intertidal ecology; mangrove biology. *Mailing Add:* Dept Biol Univ NB PO Box 5050 St John NB E2L 4L5 Can

**THOMAS, MARY BETH,** INVERTEBRATE CYTOLOGY. *Current Pos:* PROF BIOL, UNIV NC, CHARLOTTE, 80- *Personal Data:* b Sewanee, Tenn, Mar 2, 41. *Educ:* Agnes Scott Col, BA, 63; Univ NC, Chapel Hill, MA, 70, PhD(zool), 71. *Prof Exp:* Vis asst prof biol, Wake Forest Univ, 71-72, asst prof, 72-76, assoc prof, 76-79. *Mem:* Am Soc Zoologists; Am Micros Soc. *Res:* Invertebrate embryology and cytology; cnidarian ultrastructure; turbellarian ultrastructure and phylogeny. *Mailing Add:* Dept Biol Univ NC Charlotte 9201 University City Charlotte NC 28223-0001. *Fax:* 704-547-3128; *E-Mail:* mbthomas@unccvm.uncc.edu

**THOMAS, MICHAEL CHARLES,** SYSTEMATICS. *Current Pos:* taxon entomologist, 88-93, ENTOM ADMINR, DIV PLANT INDUST, FLA DEPT AGR, 93- *Personal Data:* b Miami, Fla, May 5, 48; m 70, Sheila McCuiston; c Andrea L & Erin J. *Educ:* Univ SFla, BA, 70; Univ Fla, MS, 81, PhD(entom), 85. *Prof Exp:* Taxon entomologist, WVa Dept Agr, 86-88. *Concurrent Pos:* Ed, Insecta Mundi, 88- *Mem:* Entom Soc Am; Coleopterists Soc. *Res:* Biology and systematics of Cucujidae, Silvanidae and related families of cucujoid Coleoptera; phylogeny and evolution of Cucujoidea. *Mailing Add:* PO Box 147100 Gainesville FL 32614-7100. *Fax:* 352-955-2301; *E-Mail:* mct@delphi.com

**THOMAS, MICHAEL DAVID,** GEOPHYSICS. *Current Pos:* RES SCIENTIST, GEOL INTERPRETATION OF GRAVITY & MAGNETIC DATA, GEOL SURV CAN, 86- *Personal Data:* b Merthyr Tydfil, Wales, Jan 2, 42; m; c 2. *Educ:* Univ Wales, BS, 64, PhD(geol), 68. *Prof Exp:* Geol interpretation magnetic data, Geol Surv Can, 68-69; geophysicist, Survair Ltd, 69-71; res scientist gravity interpretation, Earth Physics Br, Dept Energy, Mines & Resources, Can, 72-86. *Res:* Geological interpretation of gravity and magnetic anomalies over the Canadian landmass and territorial waters with a particular interest in the plate tectonic evolution of the crust since early Precambrian time. *Mailing Add:* Continental Geosci Div Geol Surv Can 1 Observatory Crescent Ottawa ON K1A 0Y3 Can

**THOMAS, MICHAEL E(DWARD),** OPERATIONS RESEARCH. *Current Pos:* prof & dir, Sch Indust & Systs Eng, 78-91, PROVOST & EXEC VPRES, GA INST TECHNOL, 91- *Personal Data:* b Monahans, Tex, May 10, 37; m 59; c 3. *Educ:* Univ Tex, BS, 60, MS, 63; Johns Hopkins Univ, PhD(opers res), 65. *Prof Exp:* Prod engr, Union Carbide Corp, 60-61; res asst optimization, Univ Tex, 61-62; jr instr chem eng, Johns Hopkins Univ, 62-63, res asst opers res, 63-64, instr, 64-65; from asst prof to prof indust & systs eng, Univ Fla, 65-78, chairperson dept, 73-78. *Concurrent Pos:* Consult, US Army Corps Engrs, 70-77, MAPS, Inc, 74-78 & Hewlett Packard, Inc, 80-81; opers res analyst, Nat Bur Sci, 71-72. *Mem:* Opers Res Soc Am (secy, 80-83, pres, 84-85); Inst Mgt Sci; fel Am Inst Indust Engrs; Sigma Xi. *Res:* Optimization techniques, including decomposition techniques for nonlinear programming problems and optimal control theory. *Mailing Add:* Pres Off 225 N Ave Carnegie Bldg Atlanta GA 30332-0325

**THOMAS, MIRIAM MASON HIGGINS,** NUTRITION. *Current Pos:* RETIRED. *Personal Data:* b Chicago, Ill, June 22, 20; wid; c Brian K. *Educ:* Bennett Col, NC, BS, 40; Univ Chicago, MS, 42. *Prof Exp:* Res assoc food chem, Div Biol Sci, Univ Chicago, 42-45; res chemist nutrit, Sci & Adv Tech Lab, Biol Sci Div, US Army Natick Res & Develop Labs, 45-85. *Concurrent Pos:* Vis fac lectr, Dept Nutrit & Food Sci, Mass Inst Technol, 74-83; Dept Defense Sec Army fel, 75-76. *Mem:* AAAS; Soc Nutrit Educ; Asn Vitamin Chemists; Inst Food Technol; Sigma Xi. *Res:* Chemical aspects of protein and amino acid metabolism; bioavailability of nutrients; effects of processing and storage on the nutritive quality of military rations and vitamin fortification of ration components. *Mailing Add:* 57 Eaton Rd Framingham MA 01701

**THOMAS, MITCHELL,** RADIATIVE TRANSFER, INFLATABLE STRUCTURES. *Current Pos:* PRES, THOMAS DYNAMICS MODELING, INC, 96- *Personal Data:* b Terre Haute, Ind, Nov 25, 36; m 70, Helen Morris; c Mitchell H, Sheri H (Winters) & Deborah M. *Educ:* Harvard Univ, AB, 58; Univ Ill, Urbana, MS, 59; Calif Inst Technol, PhD(radiative transfer), 64. *Prof Exp:* Engr, McDonnell Douglas Corp, 59-61, eng consult, 62, sect chief appl res, 64-68, br chief, Advan Systs & Technol, 68-75; dir res & develop, L'Garde Inc, 75-76, pres, 76-96. *Mem:* Am Inst Aeronaut & Astronaut; AAAS. *Res:* Ablation, reentry and midcourse physics, especially radiative transfer through gases; calculation of transport properties of high-temperature gases; inflatable structures; modeling of motion dynamics. *Mailing Add:* Thomas Dynamics Modeling Inc 9691 Villa Woods Dr Villa Park CA 92861. *Fax:* 714-637-8856; *E-Mail:* tdmi@ix.netcom.com

**THOMAS, MONTCALM TOM,** PHYSICS. *Current Pos:* MEM STAFF, BATTELLE PAC NORTHWEST LABS, 74- *Personal Data:* b Brooklyn, Conn, Feb 5, 36; m 62; c 1. *Educ:* Univ Conn, BA, 57, MS, 59; Brown Univ, PhD(physics), 66. *Prof Exp:* Mem tech staff, Bell Tel Labs, NJ, 65-68; asst prof physics, Wash State Univ, 68-74. *Mem:* Am Phys Soc; Am Vacuum Soc. *Res:* Solid state, atomic and molecular physics; surface structure and kinetics of solids; thin films in solid state physics; photoelectric phenomena; low energy electron diffraction; high vacuum techniques. *Mailing Add:* Phys Sci Bldg Battelle Pac NW Labs PO Box 999 K2-18 Richland WA 99352. *Fax:* 509-375-6916

**THOMAS, MORLEY KEITH,** METEOROLOGY, CLIMATOLOGY. *Current Pos:* RETIRED. *Personal Data:* b Middlesex Co, Ont, Aug 19, 18; m 42, Clara McCandless; c Stephen & John. *Educ:* Univ Western Ont, BA, 41; Univ Toronto, MA, 49. *Honors & Awards:* Patterson Distinguished Serv Medal Can Meteorol, 80; Thomas Award Vol Weather Observers Estab, 83; Massey Medal Outstanding Achievement in Climat, 85. *Prof Exp:* Meteorologist, Atmospheric Environ Serv, Can, 41-51 & dir bldg res, Nat Res Coun Can, 51-53; supt climat opers, Atmospheric Environ Serv, 53-72, dir, Meteorol Applns Br, 72-75, dir gen, Cent Servs, 76-80, dir gen, Can Climate Ctr, 80-83, consult & hist meteorol proj, 83- *Concurrent Pos:* Assoc, Comt Snow & Ice Mech, Nat Res Coun Can, 59-65 & Subcomt Meteorol & Atmospheric Sci, 67-70; mem working group on climatic atlases, World Meteorol Orgn, 60-65, chmn, 65-69; mem, Nat Adv Comt Geog Res, 65-70; pres, Comn Climatol & Appln Meteorol, World Meteorol Orgn, 78-82. *Mem:* Fel Am Meteorol Soc; Royal Meteorol Soc (treas, Can Br, 50-51, secy, 64-66, vpres, 66-67); Can Meteorol Soc (vpres, 67-68, pres, 68-70); Can Asn Geog; fel Royal Can Geog Soc. *Res:* Atlases; urban climates; climatic change; climatological services; meteorological applications; history of meteorology and climatology; history of Canadian meteorology. *Mailing Add:* Atmospheric Environ Can Attn: Libr 4905 Dufferin St Downsview ON M3H 5T4 Can

**THOMAS, NORMAN RANDALL,** DENTISTRY, PHYSIOLOGY. *Current Pos:* prof dent & hons prof med, 68-89, EMER PROF, UNIV ALTA, 89- *Personal Data:* b Caerphilly, Wales, Dec 22, 32; m 54; c 5. *Educ:* Bristol Univ, BDS, 57 & 58, PhD(dent), 65, Am Bd Oral Path, cert, FRCD(C), 86. *Prof Exp:* Med Res Coun sci asst path res, Royal Col Surgeons, Eng, 60-62; lectr dent med, Bristol Univ, 62-66, lectr anat, 66-68. *Mem:* Can Dent Asn; Can Asn Anat; Int Asn Dent Res; fel Int Col Craniomandibolar Orthop; Am Asn Oral Path. *Res:* Collagen formation and maturation in tooth eruption; neurophysiology of orofacial complex; TMJ dysfunction. *Mailing Add:* 5412 142 St Edmonton AB T6H 4B8 Can

**THOMAS, OWEN PESTELL,** poultry nutrition; deceased, see previous edition for last biography

**THOMAS, PAUL A V,** ELECTRICAL ENGINEERING. *Current Pos:* RETIRED. *Personal Data:* b Guernsey, Channel Islands, Europe, Oct 6, 25; m 53; c 3. *Educ:* London Univ, BSc, 50; Glasgow Univ, PhD(elec eng), 61. *Prof Exp:* Res asst mech, Royal Col Sci & Technol, Scotland, lectr, Glasgow Univ, 53-62; from assoc prof to prof elec eng, Univ Windsor, 63-75, head dept, 64-68; dept chmn, Brock Univ, 75-78 & 80-85, prof comput sci & info processing, 75-90. *Mem:* Sr mem Inst Elec & Electronics Engrs; Brit Comput Soc; Brit Inst Elec Eng; Asn Comput Mach; Can Info Processing Soc. *Res:* Electronic computers and graphics systems. *Mailing Add:* 421-1 Jacksway Crescent London ON N5X 3T5 Can

**THOMAS, PAUL CLARENCE,** PLANT BREEDING, VEGETABLE CROPS. *Current Pos:* DIR RES, PETOSEED CO, INC, 58-, SR VPRES, 78- *Personal Data:* b Watsonville, Calif, Nov 26, 28; m 56, Mary A Stewart; c Rodney S. *Educ:* Col Agr, Univ Calif, BS, 50. *Prof Exp:* Veg breeder, W Atlee Burpee Co, 50-58. *Concurrent Pos:* Mem bd dirs, All Am Selections; comnr, Calif Pepper Comn. *Mem:* Fel Am Soc Hort Sci. *Res:* Management of quality assurance and stock seed production programs of vegetable hybrid parents in northern and southern hemispheres. *Mailing Add:* 4 Juniper Ct Woodland CA 95695

**THOMAS, PAUL DAVID,** ORGANIC CHEMISTRY, PATENT LAW. *Current Pos:* RETIRED. *Personal Data:* b Bellwood, Pa, Mar 8, 26; m 51; c 4. *Educ:* Rutgers Univ, BA, 49; Univ Ill, PhD(org chem), 54. *Prof Exp:* Chemist, Fries Bros Chem Mfg Co, 49-51; res chemist, Tidewater Assoc Oil Co, 51; res chemist, Pfizer Inc, 54-71, res supvr org chem res & develop, 71-73, registered patent agent, 78-87. *Concurrent Pos:* Pvt consult, 87- *Mem:* Am Chem Soc; Inst Food Technol. *Res:* Food additives and flavors. *Mailing Add:* 271 Plant St Groton CT 06340

**THOMAS, PAUL EMERY,** NUMBER THEORY. *Current Pos:* from asst prof to prof, 56-91, EMER PROF MATH, UNIV CALIF, BERKELEY, 91- *Personal Data:* b Phoenix, Ariz, Feb 15, 27; m 58; c 2. *Educ:* Oberlin Col, BA, 50; Oxford Univ, BA, 52; Princeton Univ, PhD(math), 55. *Prof Exp:* Res instr, Columbia Univ, 55-56. *Concurrent Pos:* NSF fel, 58-59; Guggenheim Mem Found fel, 61; prof, Miller Inst, 66-67; ed, Proc, Am Math Soc, 68-71; mem, Div Math Sci, Nat Res Coun, 70-72; trustee, Am Math Soc, 80-84; dep dir, Math Sci Res Inst, 87-90; exec dir, Miller Inst Basic Res Sci, 87-89. *Mem:* Am Math Soc. *Res:* Number theory. *Mailing Add:* Dept Math 970 Evans Hall Univ Calif Berkeley CA 94720

**THOMAS, PAUL MILTON,** IMMUNOBIOLOGY, ICHTHYOLOGY. *Current Pos:* chmn dept, 69-85, prof, 68-90, EMER PROF BIOL, EDINBORO UNIV PA, 90- *Personal Data:* b Sligo, Pa, Dec 1, 29; m 51; c 1. *Educ:* Allegheny Col, BS, 58; Univ Mich, MA, 59, MS, 62, PhD(sci admin, ichthyol), 64; Drew Univ, DMin, 80. *Prof Exp:* Instr biol, Houghton Col, 59-62; teacher high sch, Mich, 62-64; from asst prof to assoc prof biol, Pasadena Col, 64-67; res fel, Calif Inst Technol, 67-68. *Concurrent Pos:* Res fel radiation biol, Cornell Univ, 66-67. *Mem:* Am Fisheries Soc. *Res:* Fish anesthetics; effects of industrial pollution of fish; radiation effects on elasmobranch antibody response; sexual dimorphism in fish; artificial fish shelters; administrative effects on science education; gamma globulin synthesis in fish; Lake Erie fishery; death education; acid rain and aquatic habitats. *Mailing Add:* 87 W High Union City PA 16438

**THOMAS, PETER,** GLYCOPROTEIN METABOLISM, CANCER MARKERS. *Current Pos:* from assoc med to prin assoc med, 79-85, asst prof surg biochem, 85-90, ASSOC PROF SURG BIOCHEM, HARVARD MED SCH, 90-; SR SCIENTIST, DEACONESS HOSP, 90- *Personal Data:* b Bridgend, UK, Apr 25, 46; m 80, Wendy S Judith; c Bethan, Marie & Michael J. *Educ:* Univ Wales, BSc, 67, PhD(biochem), 71. *Prof Exp:* A K fel chem, Inst Cancer Res, London, 71-79; sr res assoc, Mallory Gastrointestinal Res Lab, Mallory Inst Path, Boston City Hosp, 79-86; assoc mem, Cancer Res Inst, New Eng Deaconess Hosp, 85-90. *Mem:* Biochem Soc; Am Soc Biochem & Molecular Biol; Am Gastroenterol Asn; Am Asn Study Liver Dis; Protein Soc; Am Asn Cancer Res. *Res:* The metabolism of glycoproteins especially carcinoembryonic antigen; interactions between the Kupffer cell and hepatocyte in glycoprotein handling; mechanism of transfer of proteins from blood to bile; tumor cell surfaces' relationship to development of hepatic metasteses especially from colorectal cancer. *Mailing Add:* Lab Cancer Biol Shields Warren Radiation Lab New Eng Deaconess Hosp 50 Binney St Boston MA 02115-6086. *Fax:* 617-738-9188

**THOMAS, QUENTIN VIVIAN,** ANALYTICAL CHEMISTRY, MASS SPECTROMETRY. *Current Pos:* Appln chemist mass spectrometry, Finnigan Instrument Div, 76-78, sr instr analytical chem, 78-80, MGR TRAINING, FINNIGAN INST, 80- *Personal Data:* b Glendale, Calif, Apr 13, 49; m 69; c 2. *Educ:* Ore State Univ, BS, 71; Purdue Univ, MS, 74, PhD(chem), 76. *Mem:* Am Chem Soc; Am Soc Mass Spectrometry. *Res:* Negative ion mass spectrometry; application of computers in the chemical laboratory. *Mailing Add:* 1574 Christine Dr Fairfield OH 45014

**THOMAS, R E,** ELECTRICAL ENGINEERING. *Current Pos:* RETIRED. *Personal Data:* b Austin, Tex, Apr 12, 30; m 51; c 3. *Educ:* NMex State Univ, BS, 51 & 52; Stanford Univ, MS, 53; Univ Ill, PhD(elec eng), 59. *Prof Exp:* Consult engr, Wright Air Develop Ctr, USAF, 53-57, from instr to prof astronaut, USAF Acad, 59-65, prof elec eng & head dept, 66-79; sr scientist, Kaman Sci Corp, Colorado Springs, 79-82 & Mission Res Corp, 82-84; prin engr, Motorola Inc, 84-85; pres, Thomas Consult Serv, 85-94. *Mem:* Inst Elec & Electronics Engrs. *Res:* Control system analysis and synthesis; active network synthesis; linear systems synthesis; servomechanism analysis and synthesis. *Mailing Add:* 10685 E Ironwood Dr Scottsdale AZ 85258

**THOMAS, R HAYES, III,** COMPUTER SOFTWARE. *Current Pos:* ACCT EXEC, PROG INTEL CORP, 86- *Personal Data:* b El Paso, Tex, May 21, 60. *Educ:* Wake Forest Univ, BA, 82; Harvard Univ, BA, 82. *Honors & Awards:* D R Fulkerson Award, Am Math Soc, 94. *Prof Exp:* Opers analyst Data Gen Corp, 78-81; mkt rep, Bay State Bus Inc, 83-85. *Concurrent Pos:* Bd dirs, Businessware Assocs Inc, 89- *Mailing Add:* Prog Intell 3295 River Exchange Dr Norcross GA 30092-4220

**THOMAS, R NOEL,** ENGINEERING. *Current Pos:* MGR, RES & DEVELOP CTR, WESTINGHOUSE ELEC CORP, PITTSBURGH, PA, 62- *Personal Data:* b Caernarfon, NWales, Dec 25, 36. *Educ:* Univ Col NWales, UK, Bsc, 58; Univ Cambridge, Eng, PhD(physics), 61. *Mem:* Fel Inst Elec & Electronics Engrs; Am Phys Soc. *Res:* Melt growth of large denominator of element of compound semi-conductors. *Mailing Add:* R & D Center Westinghouse Sci & Tech Ctr 1310 Beulah Rd Pittsburgh PA 15235. *Fax:* 412-256-1348

**THOMAS, RALPH HAROLD,** HEALTH PHYSICS. *Current Pos:* head, Hazards Control Dept, 90-93, EMER PARTIC GUEST, SPEC PROJ DIV, LAWRENCE LIVERMORE NAT LAB, 93-; ADJ PROF, SCH PUB HEALTH, UNIV CALIF, BERKELEY, 90- *Personal Data:* b Reading, Eng, Nov 27, 32; m 58, Mavis Waldegrave; c Simon, Shelagh & Susan. *Educ:* Univ Col, London, BSc, 55, PhD(nuclear physics), 59, DSc, 79; Am Bd Health Physics, cert, 69; Univ Calif Sch Pub Health, MPH, 82. *Hon Degrees:* MA, Oxon, 85. *Prof Exp:* Res physicist, Assoc Elec Industs, UK, 58-59; prin sci officer, Rutherford High Energy Lab, Sci Res Coun, UK, 59-68; sr health physicist, Stanford Univ, 68-70; var app, Lawrence Berkeley Nat Lab, 70-87, div head, Occup Health Div, 88-90. *Concurrent Pos:* Lectr, Reading Col Technol, 55-63; vis scientist, Lawrence Berkeley Lab, Univ Calif, 63-65, Europ Orgn Nuclear Res, Geneva, Switz, 66, Brookhaven Nat Lab, 70 & KEK Nat Lab High-Energy Physics, Oho-Machi, Japan, 77; mem working group, Int Comn Radiol Protection, 66-70; chmn adv panel accelerator radiation safety, USAEC, 69-72; mem, Comt High Energy & Space Dosimetry, Int Comn Radiation Units, 73-78; mem comt 3, Int Comn Radiol Protection, 78-85, mem comt 2, 85-93; mem, comt int syst units, Nat Coun Radiation Protection & Measurement, 90-96; mem int comn, Radiation Units & Measurements Comt, Dose Equivalent Determination, 80-; vis fel, Keble Col, Oxford Univ, 85-86; vis scholar, Radcliffe Sci Libr, Univ Oxford; coun mem, Nat Coun Radiation Protection & Measurements, 90-; chmn, Sci Comt, 90- *Mem:* Fel Health Physics Soc (treas, 77-79); Radiol Res Soc; fel Brit Inst Physics; fel Royal Soc Health; fel Soc Radiol Protection; hon mem Australian Radiation Protection Soc. *Res:* Accelerator radiation problems; high energy dosimetry; radiological protection standards. *Mailing Add:* 7 Carey Ct Moraga CA 94556

**THOMAS, RALPH HENRY, SR,** PACKAGE ENGINEERING, INTERNATIONAL PACKAGE RESEARCH. *Current Pos:* PRES, THOMAS PACKAGING CONSULTS, 81- *Personal Data:* b Brooklyn, NY, July 7, 31; m 44; c 4. *Educ:* State Univ NY, BS, 79. *Prof Exp:* Dept head, Packaging Res, E R Squibb & Sons, 53-55; proj leader, Packaging Res, Gen Foods Corp, 54-55 & Colgate Palmolive Co, 55-57; packaging res engr, Bristol-Myers Co, 49-53, dir, 57-81. *Concurrent Pos:* Instr packaging technol, Columbia Univ, Upsala Col, Ctr Prof Educ, Felician Col, Packaging Inst & Am Mgt Asn. *Mem:* Am Soc Mech Engrs; Am Mgt Asn; Soc Plastic Engrs; Packaging Inst. *Res:* Package production and manufacturing; author of 78 publications and six books; awarded 38 patents. *Mailing Add:* 2204 Morris Ave Suite LL6 Union NJ 07083

**THOMAS, RAYE EDWARD,** SOLID STATE ELECTRONICS, ELECTRICAL ENGINEERING. *Current Pos:* PRES, DARENTEK CORP, KEMPTVILLE, ONT, 88-, CHMN, 94-; PRES & CHMN, MEGASOL CORP, KEMPTVILLE, ONT, 93- *Personal Data:* b Cross Creek, NB, June 5, 38; m 63; c 2. *Educ:* Univ NB, BScEE, 61; Imp Col, Univ London, PhD(elec eng), 66. *Prof Exp:* Mem sci staff solid state devices, Res & Develop Labs, Northern Elec Co Ltd, 66-69, mgr physics devices, 69; from asst prof to prof, Carleton Univ, 69-84; pres, TPK Solar Systs Inc, 79-88. *Concurrent Pos:* Consult, Microsysts Int Ltd, 69-70; Bell-Northern Res, 73-84 & Mitel Corp, 79-63; adj prof eng, Carleton Univ, 84- *Mem:* Sr mem Inst Elec & Electronics Engrs; Solar Energy Soc Can; Int Solar Energy Soc. *Res:* Solid state device physics; discrete device and integrated circuit design, fabrication and characterization; device modeling; solar energy conversion-photovoltaics. *Mailing Add:* 5 Frederick Pl Ottowa ON K1S 3G1 Can

**THOMAS, (JOHN) (PAUL) RICHARD,** vertebrate systematics, for more information see previous edition

**THOMAS, RICHARD ALAN,** LOW TEMPERATURE PHYSICS. *Current Pos:* Asst physicist, 77-80, PHYSICS ASSOC I, BROOKHAVEN NAT LAB, 77- *Personal Data:* b Smithville, Mo, Mar 14, 48. *Educ:* William Jewell Col, BA, 70; Stanford Univ, PhD(appl phys), 77. *Mem:* Am Phys Soc; Inst Elec & Electronics Engrs; Asn Comput Mach. *Res:* Superconducting power transmission, polymeric insulation, dielectric properties of helium, automatic monitoring and control of large-scale low-temperature systems, quantum mechanical tunneling in dielectrics; particle acclerators. *Mailing Add:* Bldg 902b Brookhaven Nat Lab Upton NY 11973-5000

**THOMAS, RICHARD CHARLES,** ORGANIC CHEMISTRY, MEDICINAL CHEMISTRY. *Current Pos:* sr res scientist chem, 77-93, ASSOC DIR, MED CHEM RES, UPJOHN CO, 93- *Personal Data:* b Syracuse, NY, July 22, 49; m 71. *Educ:* Univ Rochester, BS, 71; Univ Calif, Los Angeles, PhD(chem), 76. *Prof Exp:* Fel chem, Mass Inst Technol, 76-77. *Mem:* Am Chem Soc; Royal Soc Chem. *Res:* Chemical synthesis and modification of antibiotics; antivirals. *Mailing Add:* Med Chem Res 7246-300-601 Pharmacia & Upjohn Kalamazoo MI 49001-0199

**THOMAS, RICHARD DEAN,** TOXICOLOGY, PATHOLOGY. *Current Pos:* DIR HUMAN TOXICOL & RISK ASSESSMENT, NAT ACAD SCI, NAT RES COUN, 82- *Personal Data:* b Payson, Utah, Feb 14, 47; m 70, Mary J Wells; c Austin, Sterling, Joel, Carmen & Cameron. *Educ:* Utah State Univ, BS, 71; Colo State Univ, PhD(med chem), 74. *Prof Exp:* Sr metab chemist agr chem, Biochem Dept, Agr Div, Ciba-Geigy Corp, 74-76; toxicologist & criteria doc mgr, Ctr Occup & Environ Safety & Health, Stanford Res Inst, 76-78; sr environ systs scientist toxicol, Dept Environ Chem & Biol, Metrek Div, The Mitre Corp, 78-80; staff, Borriston Labs Inc, 80-82. *Concurrent Pos:* Adv & consult, Environ Protection Agency, Food & Drug Admin, Dept Energy, WHO, Int Agency Res Cancer, Justice Dept, CDC & UN. *Mem:* Am Chem Soc; AAAS; Am Inst Chemists; Am Soc Appl Spectros; Am Col Toxicol; Am Pub Health Asn; Environ Mutagen Soc; Environ Health Inst; Genetic Tox Asn; NY Acad Sci; Soc Toxicol; US Acad Path. *Res:* Investigation into the toxicology, metabolism and environmental impact of chemicals; physiological impairment and potential for cancer and disease production related to chemical exposure; setting tolerances as they relate to health and regulation of chemicals; risk assessment. *Mailing Add:* Thomas & Thomas Tech Inc 7511 Blaise Trail McLean VA 22102-2101. *Fax:* 202-334-2752; *E-Mail:* rthomas@nas.edu

**THOMAS, RICHARD EUGENE,** aerospace engineering, for more information see previous edition

**THOMAS, RICHARD GARLAND,** PHYSICS. *Current Pos:* PROF PHYSICS & HEAD DEPT, PRAIRIE VIEW AGR & MECH COL, 68- *Personal Data:* b Houston, Tex, June 23, 23; m 71. *Educ:* Hampton Inst, BS, 43; Columbia Univ, MA, 50; Univ Calif, Berkeley, PhD(physics), 59. *Prof Exp:* Sr scientist physics, Gen Elec Co, 59-63 & Lawrence Livermore Lab, 63-68. *Mem:* AAAS; Am Phys Soc; Am Asn Physics Teachers; Sigma Xi. *Res:* Low energy nuclear physics; x-ray spectroscopy. *Mailing Add:* Dept Physics Prairie View AHM Univ Box 519 Prairie View TX 77446-0519

**THOMAS, RICHARD H,** LINGUISTICS. *Current Pos:* PROF, LING & INTELLIGENT SYST DEPT, UNIV PITTSBURGH, 72- *Personal Data:* b Chicago, Ill, Oct 5, 39. *Educ:* Yale Univ, PhD(philos), 65. *Mailing Add:* Ling & Intelligent Systs Dept Univ Pittsburgh Pittsburgh PA 15260

**THOMAS, RICHARD JOSEPH,** WOOD TECHNOLOGY. *Current Pos:* RETIRED. *Personal Data:* b Wilkes-Barre, Pa, Nov 29, 28; m 51; c 2. *Educ:* Pa State Univ, BS, 54; NC State Univ, MWT, 55; Duke Univ, DF, 67. *Prof Exp:* Tech rep, Nat Casein NJ, 55-57, sales mgr, 57; from asst prof to assoc prof, Sch Forest Resources, NC State Univ, 57-71, prof wood & paper sci, 71-, head dept, 78- *Concurrent Pos:* Sci fac fel, NSF. *Mem:* Forest Prods Res Soc (vpres, 83, pres elect, 84, pres, 85); Int Asn Wood Anat; Soc Wood Sci & Technol (pres elect, 81, pres, 82). *Res:* Study of wood ultrastructure, particularly relationships of ultrastructure to physical properties and function within the plant; investigations of differentiation of cell wall and cell wall markings; distribution of major chemical constituents throughout cell wall. *Mailing Add:* Dept Wood & Paper Sci Sch Forest Resources NC State Univ Box 8005 Raleigh NC 27695-8005

**THOMAS, RICHARD NELSON,** stellar atmospheres, nonequilibrium thermodynamics; deceased, see previous edition for last biography

**THOMAS, RICHARD SANBORN,** SOIL MICROBIOLOGY, MICROSCOPY. *Current Pos:* res physicist, 60-90, COLLABR, WESTERN REGIONAL RES CTR, USDA, 90- *Personal Data:* b Madison, Wis, June 14, 27; m 57; c 2. *Educ:* Oberlin Col, BA, 49; Univ Calif, Berkeley, PhD(biophys), 55. *Prof Exp:* Am Cancer Soc fel cancer res & NSF fel cytochem, Carlsberg Lab, Denmark, 55-57; asst res biophysicist, Virus Lab, Univ Calif, Berkeley, 58-60. *Concurrent Pos:* USPHS spec fel, Dept Gen Bot, Swiss Fed Inst Technol, 67-68; consult micros & biosci appln plasma chem, Tegal Corp, Richmond, Calif, 72-79. *Mem:* AAAS; Electron Micros Soc Am; Soil Sci Soc Am; Biophys Soc; Microbeam Analytical Soc; Am Soc Agron. *Res:* Biological ultrastructure and fine cytochemistry; development of techniques for electron microscopic cytochemistry and electron probe microanalysis, especially by plasma etching; intracellular mineral deposits, bacterial spores, keratin, microfibrillar proteins, virus particles; plant tissues; cereal products; effects of endomycorrhizal fungi on host plants and soils; microscopy of microorganisms in soil. *Mailing Add:* 10 Windsor Ave Berkeley CA 94708

**THOMAS, ROBERT,** CRYSTALLOGRAPHY, PHYSICAL CHEMISTRY. *Current Pos:* AEC res assoc, 66-68, assoc scientist chem, 68-77, SCIENTIST CHEM, BROOKHAVEN NAT LAB, 77- *Personal Data:* b Atlanta, Ga, Aug 27, 34; m 69, Birgit M Hansen. *Educ:* Boston Univ, AB, 55, PhD(phys chem), 65. *Prof Exp:* NIH res assoc chem, Univ Colo, 64-66. *Mem:* Sigma Xi; Am Crystallog Asn; Am Chem Soc. *Res:* Crystal structure determination by x-ray and neutron diffraction; study of phase transitions, ferroelectrics and critical phenomena. *Mailing Add:* Off Educ Progs Bldg 438 Brookhaven Nat Lab PO Box 5000 Upton NY 11973-5000. *Fax:* 516-344-5832; *E-Mail:* thomas@bnlarm.bnl.gov

**THOMAS, ROBERT E,** PHYSIOLOGY, BIOCHEMISTRY. *Current Pos:* from asst prof to assoc prof, 66-74, PROF BIOL SCI, CALIF STATE UNIV, CHICO, 74- *Personal Data:* b Salineville, Ohio, Feb 17, 36; m 62, Judith Visintainer; c Elizabeth & Susan. *Educ:* Kent State Univ, BS, 61, MA, 63, PhD(biol sci), 66. *Honors & Awards:* Charles Y Conkle Publ Award, Nat Oceanic & Atmospheric Admin, US Dept Com, 84. *Prof Exp:* Instr biol sci, Kent State Univ, 63-64. *Concurrent Pos:* Res physiologist, Nat Marine Fisheries Serv, 73- *Mem:* AAAS; Am Inst Biol Sci; Sigma Xi. *Res:* Sublethal effects of pollutants on marine life. *Mailing Add:* Dept Biol Sci Calif State Univ Chico CA 95929-0001

**THOMAS, ROBERT EUGENE,** PSYCHIATRY. *Current Pos:* RETIRED. *Personal Data:* b Iowa, Oct 15, 19; m 43; c 4. *Educ:* Univ Southern Calif, AB, 42, MD, 51; Johns Hopkins Univ, MPH, 55. *Prof Exp:* Intern, Santa Fe Coastlines Hosp, Los Angeles, Calif, 50-51; psychiat resident, Vet Admin Hosp, Perry Point & Baltimore, Md, 51-53; chief div ment health, Wash Co Dept Health, Hagerstown, 53; from instr to asst prof pub health admin, Sch Hyg, Johns Hopkins Univ, 54-58; regional ment health adminr, Calif Dept Ment Hyg, 58-68, regional ment health dir, div local progs, 68-69; dir, Hemet Valley Community Ment Health Ctr, 69-85. *Concurrent Pos:* Chief div ment health, State Dept Health, Md, 54-60; mem, Gov Comn Ment Health, 54; lectr, Sch Pub Health & asst clin prof, Dept Psychiat, Sch Med, Univ Calif, Los Angeles, 60-70; third year psychiat resident ment health admin in pub health, Sch Hyg, Johns Hopkins Univ; assoc clin prof, Dept Psychiat, Loma Linda Sch Med. *Mem:* Fel Am Psychiat Asn; AMA; fel Am Pub Health Asn; fel Am Orthopsychiat Asn. *Res:* Mental health administration in public health; administration of alcoholism programs. *Mailing Add:* 475 E Cypress Ave Redlands CA 92373

**THOMAS, ROBERT GLENN,** RADIOBIOLOGY, BIOPHYSICS. *Current Pos:* PROG COORDR, ARGONNE NAT LAB, 90- *Personal Data:* b Watertown, NY, Oct 9, 26; m 49, Lanny R; c Carol, Glenn & Paula. *Educ:* St Lawrence Univ, BS, 49; Univ Rochester, PhD(radiation biol), 55. *Prof Exp:* From instr to asst prof radiation biol, Univ Rochester, 55-61; from sect head to dept head radiobiol, Lovelace Found Med Educ & Res, 61-74; group leader mammalian biol, Los Alamos Nat Lab, 74-79, health div off, 79-84; prog mgr, US Dept Energy, 84-90. *Concurrent Pos:* Mem task group, Biol Effects Radiation on Lung Comt 1, Int Comn Radiol Protection, 68-69; ed, Health Physics J, 76-80; mem, site restoration & clean-up, Nat Acad Sci, 91-; mem, Stand Comt, Am Nuclear Soc, 92- *Mem:* Am Radiation Res Soc; Health Physics Soc; Reticuloendothelial Soc; Am Indust Hyg Asn; AAAS; NY Acad Sci. *Res:* Toxicity of inhaled radioactive materials; application of experimental results to practical hazards evaluation in nuclear industry; toxicity of inhaled fossil fuel products; dose reconstruction; decommissioning & decontamination; risk assessment. *Mailing Add:* PO Box 279 Bigfork MT 59911. *Fax:* 406-837-3759

**THOMAS, ROBERT JAMES,** BOTANY, DEVELOPMENTAL PHYSIOLOGY. *Current Pos:* From asst prof to assoc prof, 75-88, chmn dept, 82-93, PROF BIOL, BATES COL, 88- *Personal Data:* b Flint, Mich, July 5, 49; m 91, Carol Frechette; c Emile Allan. *Educ:* Univ Mich, Flint, AB, 71; Univ Calif, Santa Cruz, PhD(biol), 75. *Mem:* Bot Soc Am; Am Soc Plant Physiologists; Am Bryol & Lichenol Soc; Brit Bryol Soc; Sigma Xi. *Res:* Plant growth and development; physiology, biochemistry and development of bryophytes. *Mailing Add:* Dept Biol Bates Col Lewiston ME 04240. *E-Mail:* rthomas@bates.edu

**THOMAS, ROBERT JAY,** COMPUTER SCIENCES, HUMAN SEXUALITY. *Current Pos:* RETIRED. *Personal Data:* b Harvey, Ill, Mar 30, 30; m 53; c 2. *Educ:* Oberlin Col, BA, 52; Ind Univ, MS, 54; Univ Ill, MS, 58, PhD(math), 64. *Prof Exp:* Dir recreational ther, Cent State Ment Hosp, Indianapolis, Ind, 54-55; adv, 3-2 combined eng prog, DePauw Univ, 62-72, dir, Comput Ctr, 63-66, from instr to prof math, 58-91, prof comput sci, 76-91. *Concurrent Pos:* Pace res appointment, Argonne Nat Lab, 67, comput consult, 67-71; bd dirs, Sex Info & Educ Coun US, 83. *Mem:* AAAS; Asn Comput Mach; Am Asn Sex Educrs & Counrs; Sex Info & Educ Coun US. *Res:* Pattern recognition; determination of cell motility by computer; human sexuality. *Mailing Add:* Dept Math & Comput Sci DePauw Univ Locust St Greencastle IN 46135

**THOMAS, ROBERT JOSEPH,** CHEMISTRY. *Current Pos:* RETIRED. *Personal Data:* b Lowell, Mass, July 13, 12; m 42, Rita V Kirk; c Elizabeth M (Gamble), Robert J Jr, Gertrude J (Kasianchuk) & James M. *Educ:* Lowell Textile Inst, BTC, 34; Univ Notre Dame, MS, 37, PhD(org chem), 39. *Prof Exp:* Textile chemist, Apponaug Co, RI, 34-36; res chemist, Tech Lab, E I du Pont de Nemours & Co, Inc, 39-42, Jackson Lab, 42-43, Manhattan Proj, Chambers Works, 43-44 & Tech Lab, 44-50, supvr dyeing develop div, 50-65, interdept liaison, Tech Lab, 65-77; consult textile chem & dyeing, 77-80. *Concurrent Pos:* Adj prof textiles, Clemson Univ, 77-80. *Mem:* Am Chem Soc; Am Asn Textile Chem & Colorists. *Res:* Dye application to textile fibers; textile chemistry. *Mailing Add:* 12 Sack Ave Penns Grove NJ 08069

**THOMAS, ROBERT L,** APPLIED PHYSICS. *Current Pos:* res assoc physics, Wayne State Univ, 65-66, from asst prof to assoc prof, 66-76, asst chmn, 81-86, PROF PHYSICS, WAYNE STATE UNIV, 76-, DIR, INST MFG RES, 86- *Personal Data:* b Dover-Foxcroft, Maine, Oct 10, 38; m 62; c 1. *Educ:* Bowdoin Col, AB, 60; Brown Univ, PhD(physics), 65. *Prof Exp:* Res asst physics, Brown Univ, 60-65. *Concurrent Pos:* Sr vis fel, Bedford Col, Univ London, 73-74. *Mem:* Fel Am Phys Soc; Sigma Xi; Inst Elec & Electronics Engrs. *Res:* Ultrasonics; thermal wave imaging. *Mailing Add:* Dept Physics 281 Physics Wayne State Univ 666 W Hancock Detroit MI 48202. *E-Mail:* bob@thermal.physics.wayne.edu

**THOMAS, ROBERT SPENCER DAVID,** MATHEMATICS, APPLICATIONS & PHILOSOPHY. *Current Pos:* from asst prof to assoc prof comput sci, 70-78, assoc prof, 78-85, PROF APPL MATH, UNIV MAN, 85- *Personal Data:* b Toronto, Ont, July 29, 41; m 65, Mary E Wright; c Hugh & Michael. *Educ:* Univ Toronto, BSc, 64; Univ Waterloo, MA, 65; Univ Southampton, PhD(math), 68. *Prof Exp:* Lectr math, Univ Waterloo, 65-66 & Univ Zambia, 68-70. *Concurrent Pos:* Managing ed, Utilitas Math, 71-82; ed, Philosophia Mathematica, 92-; adj prof philos, 96- *Mem:* Can App Math Soc; Inst Math & Appln; Can Soc Hist & Philos Math (pres, 96-); Can Math Soc; Am Math Soc; Math Asn Am. *Res:* Philosophy of mathematics; application of mathematics. *Mailing Add:* Dept Appl Math Univ Man Winnipeg MB R3T 2N2 Can. *Fax:* 204-275-0019; *E-Mail:* thomas@cc. umanitoba.ca

**THOMAS, ROBIN,** MATHEMATICS. *Current Pos:* PROF MATH, GAS INST TECHNOL. *Mailing Add:* Math Dept Ga Inst Technol 225 N Ave NW Atlanta GA 30332

**THOMAS, ROGER DAVID KEEN,** PALEOECOLOGY. *Current Pos:* asst prof, Franklin & Marshall Col, 75-80, assoc prof geol & assoc dean acad affairs, 80-91, prof & dept chair, 91-97, JOHN WILLIAMSON NEVIN PROF GEOSCI, FRANKLIN & MARSHALL COL, 97- *Personal Data:* b Maidstone, Kent, Eng, Oct 5, 42; m 70, Anna L Stefanelli; c Andrea E & David J. *Educ:* Imp Col Univ London, BSc, 63, ARCS, 63; Harvard Univ, AM, 65, PhD(geol), 70. *Prof Exp:* Asst prof geol, Harvard Univ, 70-75. *Concurrent Pos:* Allston Burr sr tutor, Quincy House, Harvard Univ, 70-75, asst cur invert paleont, Mus Comp Zool, Harvard Univ, 70-75; Wissenschaftlich Angestellte Palokologie Universitat Tubingen, 73-74; prin investr, NSF grants, 77-79, 81-82, 83 & 85; vis scientist, Field Mus Natural Hist, Chicago, 82; vis prof, Univ Tubingen, 84; proj dir, Howard Hughes Med Inst grant, 89-91. *Mem:* Paleont Soc; Int Palaeont Asn; Geol Soc Am; AAAS; Soc Sedimentary Geol; Geol Soc London. *Res:* Paleobiology, design of animal skeletons; interaction of mechanical function, growth patterns and evolutionary history in the determination of organic form; paleoecology, functional morphology and the evolution of fossil bivalves. *Mailing Add:* Dept Geosci Franklin & Marshall Col Lancaster PA 17604-3003. *Fax:* 717-291-4186; *E-Mail:* r_thomas@acad.fandm.edu

**THOMAS, ROGER JERRY,** SOLAR PHYSICS, ASTROPHYSICS. *Current Pos:* Nat Acad Sci-Nat Res Coun resident res assoc solar physics, Goddard Space Flight Ctr, NASA, 70-71, proj scientist orbiting solar observ satellite prog, 76-83, actg dep chief, Off Solar & Heliospheric Physics, 83-84, ASTROPHYSICIST, GODDARD SPACE FLIGHT CTR, NASA, 71- *Personal Data:* b Detroit, Mich, July 3, 42; m 66; c 1. *Educ:* Univ Mich, Ann Arbor, BS, 64, MS, 66, PhD(astron), 70. *Mem:* Int Astron Union; Am Astron Soc. *Res:* Solar x-ray and extreme ultraviolet astronomy; solar activity; solar flares; solar corona; x-ray and EUV optics. *Mailing Add:* Code 682-1 Goddard Space Flight Ctr NASA Greenbelt MD 20771

**THOMAS, RONALD EMERSON,** MATHEMATICAL STATISTICS, OPERATIONS RESEARCH. *Current Pos:* RETIRED. *Personal Data:* b Ont, Can, Apr 19, 30; m 62; c 3. *Educ:* Queen's Univ, Ont, BA, 52, MA, 58; Univ NC, PhD(math statist), 62. *Prof Exp:* Actuarial asst, Excelsior Life Inst Co, 52-57; mem tech staff, Bell Labs, 62-68, supvr, Appl Probability Group, 68-75, opers res methods, 75-80, supvr field performance studies, 80-84 & data networks bus planning, 84-86, supvr & systs engr, AT&T Info Prods, 86-90. *Concurrent Pos:* Adj prof, Fairleigh Dickinson Univ, 64-65; assoc ed, Networks J, 79-87. *Mem:* Opers Res Soc Am; Am Statist Asn. *Res:* Mathematical studies of probability; statistical methodology; graph theory and network design. *Mailing Add:* 3640 Bal Harbor Blvd No 333 Punta Gorda FL 33950

**THOMAS, RONALD LESLIE,** AGRONOMY. *Current Pos:* From asst prof to assoc prof, 63-71, PROF SOIL SCI, UNIV GUELPH, 71- *Personal Data:* b Edmonton, Alta, Can, June 29, 35; m 59; c 3. *Educ:* Univ Alta, BSc, 57, MSc, 59; Ohio State Univ, PhD(soils), 63. *Mem:* Am Soc Agron; Can Soc Soil Sci. *Res:* Soil organic matter chemistry, the reactions, nature and importance of organic matter and its decomposition. *Mailing Add:* 11 Carnaby Circle Guelph ON N1G 2W1 Can

**THOMAS, ROY DALE,** PLANT TAXONOMY. *Current Pos:* Assoc prof, 66-76, CUR HERBARIUM, NORTHEAST LA UNIV, 74-, PROF BIOL, 76- *Personal Data:* b Sevier Co, Tenn, Nov 12, 36; m 59, Barbara Gilliam; c Steven, Scott & Suzanne. *Educ:* Carson-Newman Col, BS, 58; Southeastern Baptist Theol Sem, BD, 62; Univ Tenn, PhD(plant taxon), 66. *Mem:* Am Soc Plant Taxon; Bot Soc Am; Int Soc Plant Taxon; Soc Econ Bot; Am Fern Soc; Soc Wetland Scientists. *Res:* Vegetation and flora of Chilhowee Mountain in east Tennessee; flora of Louisiana; Ophioglossaceae of the Gulf South. *Mailing Add:* Dept Biol Northeast La Univ Monroe LA 71209-0502. *Fax:* 318-342-1755; *E-Mail:* bithomas@alpha.nlu.edu

**THOMAS, ROY ORLANDO,** ANIMAL NUTRITION, DAIRY HUSBANDRY. *Current Pos:* RETIRED. *Personal Data:* b Oneida, Tenn, Dec 15, 21; m 45; c 1. *Educ:* Berea Col, BS, 46; Univ Tenn, MS, 52; Mich State Univ, PhD(animal nutrit), 64. *Prof Exp:* Teacher, Lewis Co, Ky Bd Educ, 46 & Scott Co, Tenn Bd Educ, 46-51; cow tester exten serv, Univ Tenn, 52; fieldman, Nashville Milk Producers, Inc, 52-53; asst dairy husbandman, Univ Tenn, 53-61; res asst animal nutrit, Mich State Univ, 61-64; from asst prof to assoc prof dairy sci, WVa Univ, 64-87, dairy scientist, 72-87. *Mem:* AAAS; Am Dairy Sci Asn; Am Soc Animal Sci. *Res:* Evaluation of feed materials, methods of feeding and the effect of these materials and methods on production and well-being of animals; design of free stalls and sequential exposure of animals to stalls and feed. *Mailing Add:* Div Animal Sci WVa Univ Morgantown WV 26506

**THOMAS, RUTH BEATRICE,** BOTANY. *Current Pos:* RETIRED. *Personal Data:* b Ringgold, La. *Educ:* Northwestern State Col, La, BS, 40; George Peabody Col, MA, 44; Vanderbilt Univ, PhD(biol), 51. *Prof Exp:* Pub sch teacher, La, 40-44; instr, Sullins Col, 44-46; instr, George Peabody Col, 46-48; asst prof biol, Millikin Univ, 51-54; prof, Eastern NMex Univ, 54-63; assoc prof, Sam Houston State Univ, 64-70, prof biol, 70-91. *Mem:* Fel AAAS; Bot Soc Am; Nat Asn Biol Teachers. *Res:* Gymnosperm gametophyte development; descriptive morphology. *Mailing Add:* Dept Biol Sam Houston State Univ PO Box 1440 Huntsville TX 77342

**THOMAS, RUTHANNE DETRICK,** ORGANOLITHIUM CHEMISTRY, NUCLEAR MAGNETIC RESONANCE SPECTROSCOPY. *Current Pos:* assoc prof, 88-93, CHAIR, DEPT CHEM, UNIV NTEX, 93- *Personal Data:* b Bellefontaine, Ohio, Feb 13, 52; m 76, Clifford; c Gwen. *Educ:* Denison Univ, BS, 74; Wayne State Univ, PhD(chem), 81. *Prof Exp:* Res chemist, Battelle Columbus Labs, 74-76; asst prof chem, NTex State Univ, 81-88. *Mem:* Am Chem Soc. *Res:* Development of nuclear magnetic resonance techniques and their application to main group organometallic compounds; synthesis and characterization of organolithium compounds and the elucidation of the reaction mechanisms. *Mailing Add:* Dept Chem PO Box 5068 Denton TX 76203. *E-Mail:* rthomas@unt.edu

**THOMAS, SAMUEL GABRIEL,** RESEARCH MANAGEMENT. *Current Pos:* analytical chemist, Ethyl Corp, 76-80, sr analytical chemist, 80-81, actg supvr, 81-84, supvr analytical chem, 84-89, mgr res & develop, 89-90, struct & activ testing dir, 90-92, chem res & develop dir, 92-93, RES & DEVELOP DRI FLAME RETARDANTS, ETHYL CORP, 92- *Personal Data:* b Youngstown, Ohio, Dec 20, 46; m 68; c 3. *Educ:* Youngstown State Univ, BS, 68; Univ Cincinnati, PhD(chem), 73; Mich State Univ, MBA, 82. *Prof Exp:* Teaching fel phys chem, Drexel Univ, 73-74; instrument chemist analytical chem, Amerada Hess Corp, 74-76. *Mem:* Am Chem Soc. *Res:* Separation and indentification of complex hydrocarbon mixtures; separation by high performance liquid chromatography and identification of gas chromatography-mass spectrometry; applications research for materials, surfactants and lubricants; flame retardants and bromine chemicals. *Mailing Add:* Ethyl Corp PO Box 14799 Baton Rouge LA 70898

**THOMAS, SARAH NELL,** PHYSIOLOGY, RADIATION BIOLOGY. *Current Pos:* assoc prof, 70-75, PROF BIOL & CHMN DEPT NATURAL SCI, LANGSTON UNIV, 75- *Personal Data:* b Gainesville, Ga. *Educ:* Brenau Col, BA, 48; Univ Denver, MS, 57; Tex Woman's Univ, PhD(radiation biol), 70. *Prof Exp:* Teacher & head dept sci, Pub Schs, Ga, 48-60; assoc prof biol & chmn dept, Brenau Col, 60-67; instr, Tex Woman's Univ, 70. *Concurrent Pos:* NSF traineeship, 67-69. *Mem:* AAAS; Am Inst Biol Sci; Nat Asn Biol Teachers. *Res:* Gonad development in male rats irradiated the first day of postnatal life. *Mailing Add:* Appl Sci Langston Univ Langston OK 73050

**THOMAS, SETH RICHARD,** METALLURGY. *Current Pos:* dir metall serv, 77-81, dir plating & finishing & dir tech servs, 87-96, VPRES TECHNOL, THOMAS STEEL STRIP CORP, 96- *Personal Data:* b Torrington, Conn, May 5, 41; m 63; c 4. *Educ:* Lehigh Univ, BA, 63, BS, 64, MS, 66. *Prof Exp:* Process engr, Tex Instruments, 65-68; tech dir, Teledyne Rodney Metals, 68-77. *Mem:* Fel Am Soc Metals Int; Sigma Xi; Am Soc Testing & Mat; Am Soc Qual Control. *Res:* Crystallographic orientation of unidirectionally-solidified lamellar eutectics, reverse martensitic transformations in stainless steel and continuous electroplating of low carbon steel strip. *Mailing Add:* 7505 Hillbrook Brecksville OH 44141

**THOMAS, STANISLAUS S(TEPHEN),** MECHANICAL ENGINEERING, INDUSTRIAL ENGINEERING. *Current Pos:* CONSULT, 86- *Personal Data:* b Barberton, Ohio, Nov 1, 19; m 46; c 5. *Educ:* Univ Akron, BME, 50; Cornell Univ, MS, 55; Purdue Univ, PhD, 67. *Prof Exp:* Chief resident inspector, Pittsburgh Chem Warfare Procurement Dist, Pa, 40-45; sr draftsman, Goodyear Tire & Rubber Co, Ohio, 46-51; engr, Army Chem Ctr, Md, 51-52; instr mach design, Sibley Sch Mech Eng, Cornell Univ, 52-55; asst prof mech eng, Notre Dame Univ, 55-60; mech engr, Midwestern Univs Res Asn, 60-61; instr, Sch Civil Eng, Purdue Univ, 65; eng mgr, Midwest Appl Sci Corp, Ind, 67-71; asst chmn dept indust & mgt eng, NJ Inst Technol, 71-83, assoc dean eng technol, 83-85. *Concurrent Pos:* Assoc fac, Grad Sch Mgt, Rutgers Univ; vis prof, Purdue Univ, 85-86. *Mem:* Am Soc Mech Engrs; Am Soc Eng Educ; Am Soc Metals; Am Inst Indust Engrs; Int Mat Handling Soc; Soc Mfg Engrs. *Res:* Design of mechanisms and machines; quality control in manufacturing processes; reliability of engineering systems. *Mailing Add:* 2311 Covenanter Dr Bloomington IN 47401

**THOMAS, STEVEN P,** BAT FLIGHT PHYSIOLOGY, EXERCISE PHYSIOLOGY. *Current Pos:* PROF BIOL, DUSQUESNE UNIV, 82- *Personal Data:* b Lancaster, Pa, July 30, 43. *Educ:* Ind Univ, Bloomington, PhD(physiol), 71. *Mailing Add:* Dept Biol Sci Dusquesne Univ Pittsburgh PA 15282-1502

**THOMAS, TELFER LAWSON,** ORGANIC CHEMISTRY, SOFTWARE SYSTEMS. *Current Pos:* CONSULT, ASTRA ARCUS, USA, 94- *Personal Data:* b Montreal, Que, June 1, 32; m 56; c 3. *Educ:* McGill Univ, BS, 53, PhD(org chem), 57. *Prof Exp:* Res chemist, Imp Oil Ltd, 57-59 & Gen Aniline & Film Co, 59-62; prin investr, Pharmaceut Div, Pennwalt Corp, 62-94. *Mem:* Am Chem Soc. *Res:* Synthesis of new compounds for discovery of useful drugs; micro/mini computer operating systems; database management systems. *Mailing Add:* 17 Candle Wood Dr Pittsford NY 14534-2868. *E-Mail:* tthomas@vivanet.com

**THOMAS, TERENCE MICHAEL,** SURFACE-INTERFACE CHEMISTRY, INORGANIC BONDING THEORY. *Current Pos:* SR CHEMIST, BRUSH WELLMAN INC, 87- *Personal Data:* b Ft Dix, NJ, Apr 13, 52; m 75, Anita Betzen; c Edmund, Elizabeth, Karen & Anna. *Educ:* Benedictine Col, BA, 74; Colo State Univ, MS, 76; Univ Tenn, Knoxville, PhD(inorg chem), 80. *Prof Exp:* Tech asst, phys chem lab, Colo State Univ, 74-76; surface chemist, Oak Ridge Nat Lab, 76-80, electro chemist, 78; staff chemist surface-interface mat res, Solar Energy Res Inst, 80-87. *Concurrent Pos:* Tech asst, gen chem lab, Univ Tenn, Knoxville, 76-80. *Mem:* Am Chem Soc; Am Vacuum Soc. *Res:* Perform XPS, ISS, SIMS and Auger spectroscopies on advanced materials; identify the physical and chemical processes which degrade the performance of advanced materials or increase the lifetime of manufactured components. *Mailing Add:* Brush Wellman Inc 17876 St Clair Ave Cleveland OH 44110

**THOMAS, THOMAS DARRAH,** PHYSICAL CHEMISTRY. *Current Pos:* chmn, 81-85, dir, Ctr Advan Mat Res, 86-91, PROF CHEM, ORE STATE UNIV, 71-, DISTINGUISHED PROF CHEM, 89- *Personal Data:* b Glen Ridge, NJ, Apr 8, 32; m 56; c 4. *Educ:* Haverford Col, BS, 54; Univ Calif, PhD(chem), 57. *Prof Exp:* From instr to asst prof chem, Univ Calif, 57-59; vis assoc chemist, Brookhaven Nat Lab, 59-60, assoc chemist, 60-61; from asst prof to assoc prof chem, Princeton Univ, 61-71. *Concurrent Pos:* Consult, Los Alamos Sci Lab, 65; Guggenheim fel, Univ Calif, Berkeley, 69; fel, Univ Liverpool, 84-85. *Mem:* Fel AAAS; Am Chem Soc; fel Am Phys Soc. *Res:* electron spectroscopy. *Mailing Add:* Dept Chem Gilbert Hall 153 Ore State Univ Corvallis OR 97331-4003. *E-Mail:* thomast@ccmail.orst.edu

**THOMAS, TIMOTHY FARRAGUT,** PHYSICAL CHEMISTRY, CHEMICAL DYNAMICS. *Current Pos:* asst prof, 66-73, ASSOC PROF CHEM, UNIV MO-KANSAS CITY, 73- *Personal Data:* b Cleveland, Ohio, June 15, 38; m 63; c 3. *Educ:* Oberlin Col, AB, 60; Univ Ore, PhD(chem kinetics), 64. *Prof Exp:* Res assoc chem, Brandeis Univ, 64-66. *Concurrent Pos:* Nat Res Coun sr res assoc, Air Force Cambridge Res Lab, 75-76; univ resident res prog vis prof, Air Force Geophys Lab, 81-83. *Mem:* Am Chem Soc; Am Phys Soc; Am Soc Mass Spectrometry; Royal Soc Chem; Inter-Am Photochem Soc; Sigma Xi. *Res:* Unimolecular reaction kinetics; photochemistry of gases; fluorescence lifetimes and quantum yields; mass spectrometric appearance potentials; photodissociation spectra of gaseous ions. *Mailing Add:* Dept Chem Univ Mo 5009 Rockhill Rd Kansas City MO 64110

**THOMAS, TUDOR LLOYD,** physical chemistry; deceased, see previous edition for last biography

**THOMAS, VERA,** CHEMISTRY, TOXICOLOGY. *Current Pos:* asst prof, 67-77, assoc prof, 77-81, PROF DRUG METAB, SCH MED, UNIV MIAMI, 81- *Personal Data:* b Prague, Czech, May 2, 28; US citizen; m 67. *Educ:* Charles Univ, Prague, MS, 52; Czech Acad Sci, PhD(chem), 62. *Prof Exp:* Res assoc indust toxicol, Inst Indust Hyg & Occup Dis, Prague, Czech, 49-67. *Concurrent Pos:* Secy comt maximum allowable concentration toxic compounds, Czech Ministry Health, 62-67; consult, WHO, Chile & Venezuela, 67. *Mem:* NY Acad Sci; Am Conf Govt Indust Hygienists. *Res:* Uptake, distribution, metabolism and excretion of drugs, especially of volatile compounds; pesticides distribution. *Mailing Add:* Dept Anesthesiol Sch Med Univ Miami PO Box 012410 Miami FL 33101

**THOMAS, VIRGINIA LYNN,** medical microbiology; deceased, see previous edition for last biography

**THOMAS, WALTER DILL, JR,** FORESTRY, HORTICULTURE. *Current Pos:* RETIRED. *Personal Data:* b St Louis, Mo, July 3, 18; m 84, Nancy Masters; c Sandra, Arthur D & Pat (McCarthy). *Educ:* Colo State Univ, BS, 39; Univ Minn, MS, 43, PhD(phytopath), 47. *Prof Exp:* Instr bot, Colo State Univ, 39-41; asst phytopath, Univ Minn, 41-44, 46; from asst prof plant path & asst plant pathologist to prof & plant pathologist, Agr Exp Sta, 46-54; dir res, Arboricult Serv & Supply Co, Colo, 54-55; lead res biologist, Ortho Div, Chevron Chem Co, 55-66, tech asst to mgr res & develop, 66-67; forestry specialist, 67-70; pres, Forest & Environ Protection Serv, 70-71; vpres, Natural Resouces Mgt Corp & mem bd dir, Environ Home & Garden Serv, 72-74; pres, Forest-Agr Corp, 74-86; consult, dendro-pathologist, 86-97. *Concurrent Pos:* Mem, Calif Forest Stewardship Comt, Calif Dept Forestry & Fire Control, 90-96. *Mem:* Am Phytopath Soc; fel AAAS; Soc Am Foresters; Asn Consult Foresters; Am Soc Consult Arborists; Int Soc Arboricult; Am Forestry Asn; Am Bd Forensics Examrs. *Res:* Disease of potatoes, beans, onions and ornamental plants; forest diseases; agricultural pesticides; mycorrhizae; air pollution damage to plants; remote sensing of forest diseases and insects. *Mailing Add:* 2435 Heatherleaf Lane Martinez CA 94553

**THOMAS, WALTER E,** MANUFACTURING ENGINEERING, ENGINEERING TECHNOLOGY. *Current Pos:* RETIRED. *Personal Data:* b West Lafayette, Ind, Dec 19, 22; m 43; c 4. *Educ:* Purdue Univ, Lafayette, BSME, 48, MSIE, 53. *Prof Exp:* Instr, Sch Eng, Purdue Univ, Lafayette, 48-53; design supvr, Chrysler Grad Inst, Mich, 53-54; asst prof, Sch Eng, Univ Mich, Ann Arbor, 54-57; asst chief draftsman, Fla Res & Develop Ctr, Pratt & Whitney Aircraft, 57-62; mgr eng serv, Atlantic Res Corp, Va, 62-63; sr design engr, Fla Res & Develop Ctr, Pratt & Whitney Aircraft, 63-64; prof mech eng & head dept, Mfg Technol, Purdue Univ, Lafayette, 64-73; prof & assoc dean, Sch Technol, Fla Int Univ, 73-76; prof & dean, Sch Technol & Appl Sci, Western Carolina Univ, 76-90. *Concurrent Pos:* Design engr, HydroPower Inc, Ohio, 50-52; consult, Altamil Corp, Ind,

70-; chmn eng technol comt, Engrs Coun Prof Develop, 77-78. *Mem:* Soc Mfg Engrs; Am Soc Eng Educ. *Res:* Updating of manufacturing processes in the machine tool area and in the foundry area. *Mailing Add:* Dean Sch Engr Technol Univ Ark 33 & Univ Ave Little Rock AR 72204

**THOMAS, WARREN H(AFFORD),** INDUSTRIAL ENGINEERING, OPERATIONS RESEARCH. *Current Pos:* from asst prof to assoc prof, State Univ NY, Buffalo, 63-77, chmn dept, 69-87, distinguished prof, 77-97, assoc dean indust eng, 87-97, EMER PROF, STATE UNIV NY, BUFFALO, 97- *Personal Data:* b Portsmouth, Ohio, July 15, 33; m 57; c 2. *Educ:* Case Inst Technol, BSME, 55; Purdue Univ, MSIE, 61, PhD(indust eng), 64. *Prof Exp:* Instr indust eng, Purdue Univ, 62-63. *Concurrent Pos:* Vis sr res fel, Dept Oper Res, Univ Lancaster, 70-71; vis prof, Univ Nottingham, 81. *Mem:* Inst Indust Engrs; Am Soc Eng Educ. *Res:* Manufacturing systems; computer simulation; design of production control systems. *Mailing Add:* Dept Indust Eng State Univ NY 342 Bell Hall Buffalo NY 14260-0001

**THOMAS, WILBUR ADDISON,** PATHOLOGY. *Current Pos:* CYRUS STRONG MERRILL PROF PATH & CHMN DEPT, ALBANY MED COL, 59- *Personal Data:* b Louisville, Miss, June 26, 22; m 49; c 2. *Educ:* Univ Miss, BA, 41; Univ Tenn, MD, 46; Am Bd Path, dipl. *Prof Exp:* Intern, Baptist Hosp, Memphis, Tenn, 46-47, asst resident path, 49-50; asst resident & resident, Mass Gen Hosp, Boston, 50-52; instr, Harvard Med Sch, 52-53; from instr to assoc prof, Sch Med, Wash Univ, 53-59. *Mem:* Am Soc Exp Path; Am Asn Path & Bact; AMA; Col Am Path. *Res:* Arteriosclerosis. *Mailing Add:* 8 Locust Lane Loudonville NY 12211-1620

**THOMAS, WILLIAM ALBERT,** CELL-CELL ADHESION, NEURONAL GUIDANCE. *Current Pos:* ASST PROF NATURAL SCI, COLBY-SAWYER COL, NEW LONDON, NH, 91- *Personal Data:* b Washington, DC, Apr 25, 50; m 76; c 1. *Educ:* Hamilton Col, BA, 72; Princeton Univ, PhD(develop biol), 79. *Prof Exp:* Asst prof biochem & develop biol, Dept Biol, Wake Forest Univ, 83-91. *Mem:* Am Soc Cell Biol; AAAS. *Res:* Use of immunological and cell biological techniques to investigate the possible role of specific cell surface adhesion molecules in guiding cell rearrangements characteristic of early avian development. *Mailing Add:* Dept Natural Sci Colby-Sawyer Col New London NH 03257

**THOMAS, WILLIAM ANDREW,** GEOLOGY. *Current Pos:* PROF GEOL & CHMN DEPT, UNIV KY, 91- *Personal Data:* b Berea, Ky, July 23, 36; m 57, Rachel Leach; c 2. *Educ:* Univ Ky, BS, 56, MS, 57; Va Polytech Inst, PhD(geol), 60. *Prof Exp:* Geologist, Calif Co, 59-63; from assoc prof to prof geol, Birmingham-Southern Col, 63-70, chmn dept, 67-70; assoc prof, Queens Col, NY, 70-72, chmn dept, 71-72; prof geol & chmn dept, Ga State Univ, 72-79; prof geol, Univ Ala, 79-90. *Concurrent Pos:* Ed, Geol Soc Am Bull, 82-88; vis scientist, Cornell Univ, 87. *Mem:* Geol Soc Am; Am Asn Petrol Geol; Soc Econ Paleontologists & Mineralogists; Asn Earth Sci Ed. *Res:* Tectonics and tectonic framework of sedimentation; stratigraphic and structural continuity of Appalachian and Ouachita Mountains; stratigraphy and structure of Gulf Coastal Plain; Appalachian structure and stratigraphy; thrust-belt structure; intracratonic basement faults. *Mailing Add:* Dept Geol Univ Ky 500 S Limestone St Lexington KY 40506-0001. *Fax:* 606-323-1938

**THOMAS, WILLIAM CLARK, JR,** INTERNAL MEDICINE, ENDOCRINOLOGY. *Current Pos:* from asst prof to assoc prof med, Univ Fla, 57-63, chief, Div Postgrad Educ, 57-60 & Endocrine Div, 57-70, dir, Clin Res Ctr, 62-68, prof, 63-96, EMER PROF MED, UNIV FLA, 96- *Personal Data:* b Bartow, Ga, Apr 7, 19; m 46. *Educ:* Univ Fla, BS, 40; Cornell Univ, MD, 43. *Prof Exp:* Intern med, New York Hosp, 44, asst resident med, 46-49; pvt pract, 49-54; NIH fels, Johns Hopkins Univ, 54-57. *Concurrent Pos:* Chief med serv, Vet Admin Hosp, Gainesville, Fla, 68-73, assoc chief of staff for res, 73-85; hon res fel, Univ Manchester, 69-70; dir, Geriat Res Ed Clin Ctr & Vet Admin Med Ctr, Gainesville, Fla, 85-, chief staff, 92-96. *Mem:* AAAS; Am Clin & Climat Asn; Am Diabetes Asn; Endocrine Soc; Am Fedn Clin Res. *Res:* Mineral metabolism; clinical research; factors affecting renal calculus formation. *Mailing Add:* Med Serv Vet Admin Hosp Gainesville FL 32601

**THOMAS, WILLIAM ERIC,** neurochemistry, for more information see previous edition

**THOMAS, WILLIAM GRADY,** AUDIOLOGY. *Current Pos:* From instr to asst prof, 61-70, ASSOC PROF, DEPT SURG, MED SCH, UNIV NC, CHAPEL HILL, 70-, DIR HEARING & SPEECH, 61-, DIR, AUDITORY RES LAB, 68-, ASSOC PROF, DIV SPEECH & HEARING SCI, 70- *Personal Data:* b Charlotte, NC, Mar 21, 34; m 55; c 3. *Educ:* Appalachian State Univ, BS, 57; Wash Univ, MA, 61; Univ Fla, PhD(auditory physiol), 68. *Honors & Awards:* Cert of Recognition, Am Speech & Hearing Asn, 69; Cert of Appreciation, Am Speech & Hearing Soc. *Concurrent Pos:* Fac res grant, Univ NC, Chapel Hill, 68-69, Off Naval Res grants, 69-79, NIH grant, 72-75; consult, Exp Diving Unit, Dept Navy, 69- & Nat Inst Environ Health Sci, 72-; Rockefeller Found grant, 75-80; NIH grant, 75-80; res scientist, Child Develop Inst, 76-; adj prof, Dept Commun & Theater, Univ NC, Greensboro, 81-86; pvt pract, 86- *Mem:* Fel Am Speech & Hearing Asn; Acoust Soc Am. *Res:* Auditory physiology and psychoacoustics, particularly the effects of drugs and environmental conditions on the ear; basic electrophysiology of the auditory system. *Mailing Add:* 4002 Barrett Dr Suite 101 Raleigh NC 27609

**THOMAS, WILLIAM HEWITT,** BIOLOGICAL OCEANOGRAPHY, LIMNOLOGY. *Current Pos:* RETIRED. *Personal Data:* b Riverside, Calif, Dec 25, 26; m 56, Sara Sussman; c Ann M & Alan K. *Educ:* Pomona Col, BA, 49; Univ Md, MS, 52, PhD, 54. *Prof Exp:* Lab asst, Regional Salinity Lab, USDA, 46-47, lab asst plant physiol, 48; lab asst plant physiol, Citrus Exp Sta, Univ Calif, 49-50 & Univ Md, 51-54; jr res biologist, Scripps Inst Oceanog, Univ Calif, San Diego, 54-56, asst res biologist, 56-64, assos res biologist, 64-75, res biologist, 75-88, emer res biologist, 88- *Mem:* AAAS; Am Soc Limnol & Oceanog; Phycol Soc Am; Int Phycol Soc. *Res:* Mineral nutrition and nitrogen metabolism of algae; primary production in the ocean; cultural requirements of marine phytoplankton; marine and freshwater pollution; desert and mountain algae. *Mailing Add:* Scripps Inst Oceanog Univ Calif San Diego La Jolla CA 92093

**THOMAS, WILLIAM J,** TISSUE CULTURE, FREEZE-DRYING. *Current Pos:* RETIRED. *Personal Data:* b Sharon, Pa, Oct 11, 24; m 49; c 2. *Educ:* Westminster Col, Pa, BS, 48; Univ Md, MS, 51; Univ Pa, PhD(med micro), 59. *Prof Exp:* Sect leader, Wistar Inst, Ft Detrick, Md, 50-55, res assoc, 55-58; group leader, Merrell Nat Labs, 58-78; dir prod, Gov Serv Div, Salk Inst, 78-93. *Concurrent Pos:* Pres, Mt Pocono Munic Authority, 70-72 & Burnley Workshop, Pa, 78-84. *Mem:* Tissue Cult Asn; Soc Cryobiol. *Res:* Developer of certified tissue culture cell systems for vaccine propagation; studies on stabilizers for freeze drying attenuated vaccines such as Junin and Rift Valley Fever; preparation of diagnostic reagents. *Mailing Add:* Gov Serv Div Salk Inst PO Box 250 Swiftwater PA 18370

**THOMAS, WILLIAM ROBB,** FOOD SCIENCE, DAIRY BACTERIOLOGY. *Current Pos:* RETIRED. *Personal Data:* b Toronto, Kans, Dec 17, 26; m 54, Eleanor McCord; c Michael K. *Educ:* Okla State Univ, BSc, 50; Ohio State Univ, MSc, 52; Iowa State Univ, PhD(dairy bact), 61. *Prof Exp:* Asst dairy tech, Ohio State Univ, 50-52; mem sanit stand staff, Evaporated Milk Asn, Ill, 52-53; asst prof dairy mfg, Univ Wyo, 53-59; res asst, Iowa State Univ, 59-61; assoc prof dairy mfg, Univ Wyo, 61-65; exten food technologist, Univ Calif, Davis, 65-68; assoc dean & dir resident instr, Col Agr Sci, Colo State Univ, 69-89, interim dean, 84-85. *Concurrent Pos:* Appointee, Int Sci & Educ Coun, 74-77. *Mem:* Nat Asn Col & Teachers Agr (pres, 75-76); Am Dairy Sci Asn; Inst Food Technol; Int Asn Milk, Food & Environ Sanit. *Res:* Dairy technology; thermoduric bacteria; lipolytic enzymes of milk; consumer and market analysis of dairy products; dairy plant operation analysis. *Mailing Add:* 2017 Stover St Ft Collins CO 80525

**THOMAS, WINFRED,** AGRONOMY. *Current Pos:* RETIRED. *Personal Data:* b Geneva, Tex, June 6, 20; m 43; c 1. *Educ:* Prairie View State Col, BS, 43; Cornell Univ, MS, 47; Ohio State Univ, PhD(agron), 54. *Prof Exp:* Instr agron, Ala Agr & Mech Col, 47-51; asst, Ohio State Univ, 51-53; agronomist, Ala A&M Univ, 53-81, dean, Sch Agr & Environ Sci, 73-82, prof agron, 81-82. *Mem:* Am Soc Agron; Soil Sci Soc Am. *Res:* Effect of foliar applied fertilizers on growth and composition of corn; plant population-nitrogen relationships of corn; nitrogen-sulfur-protein relationships of corn. *Mailing Add:* 2041 Winchester Rd NE Huntsville AL 35811

**THOMASIAN, ARAM JOHN,** ELECTRICAL ENGINEERING, STATISTICS. *Current Pos:* PROF ELEC ENG & STATIST, UNIV CALIF, BERKELEY, 56- *Personal Data:* b Boston, Mass, Aug 12, 24; m 53; c 3. *Educ:* Brown Univ, BSc, 49; Harvard Univ, MA, 51; Univ Calif, PhD(math statist), 56. *Mem:* Inst Elec & Electronics Engrs. *Res:* Information theory; probability; electroencephatography. *Mailing Add:* Dept Elec Eng & Comput Sci Univ Calif Berkeley CA 94720

**THOMASON, BERENICE MILLER,** microbiology; deceased, see previous edition for last biography

**THOMASON, DAVID MORTON,** POULTRY SCIENCE. *Current Pos:* dir tech serv, Am Soybean Asn, 81-85, tech dir, 85-87, regional dir, 87-89, CONSULT, AM SOYBEAN ASN, SINGAPORE, 90-; INSTR NATURAL SCI, ART INST FT LAUDERDALE, 91- *Personal Data:* b Martinsville, Va, May 28, 47; m 77. *Educ:* Va Polytech Inst, BS, 69, MS, 71, PhD(genetics), 74. *Prof Exp:* Res asst, Va Polytech Inst, 69-73; res assoc, Duck Res Lab, Cornell Univ, 74-76; exten poultry scientist, Coop Exten Serv, Univ Ga, 76-79; tech training dir, Mathtech, Inc, 79-81. *Concurrent Pos:* Adj assoc prof genetics, Southampton Col Long Island Univ, 75; consult, Delight Menues, Baltimore Md, 78, Pinecrest Duck Farm, 78, Govt Egypt thru Mathtec, 79, Int Develop Assoc, 81 & Poultry & Egg Facs, 81. *Mem:* Poultry Sci Asn; World Poultry Sci. *Res:* Practical poultry processing technology; economical and physiological evaluation of the reproductive performance of turkeys under different environmental conditions; soybean meal use in animal nutrition. *Mailing Add:* Art Inst Ft Lauderdale 1799 SE 17th St Ft Lauderdale FL 33316

**THOMASON, DONALD BRENT,** MUSCLE PHYSIOLOGY, CARDIOVASCULAR PHYSIOLOGY. *Current Pos:* asst prof physiol, 90-95, ASSOC PROF PHYSIOL, HEALTH SCI CTR, UNIV TENN, 95- *Personal Data:* b Richland, Wash, Oct 15, 57. *Educ:* Univ Va, BS, 80; Univ Calif, Irvine, PhD(physiol), 86. *Mem:* AAAS; Am Chem Soc; Am Physiol Soc. *Res:* Mechanisms of gene expression in muscle in response to functional demand; effects of exercise and gravitation. *Mailing Add:* Dept Physiol & Biophys Univ Tenn Health Sci Ctr 894 Union Ave Memphis TN 38163. *Fax:* 901-448-7126; *E-Mail:* thomason@physio1.utmem.edu

**THOMASON, IVAN J,** PLANT NEMATOLOGY, PLANT PATHOLOGY. *Current Pos:* jr nematologist, Citrus Res Ctr, Agr Exp Sta, 54-56, from asst nematologist to nematologist, 54-89, chmn, dept nematol, 63-70, prof nematol, 67-89, prof plant path, 73-89, EMER PROF NEMATOL & PLANT PATH, UNIV CALIF, RIVERSIDE, 89- *Personal Data:* b Burney, Calif, June 27, 25; m 50; c 5. *Educ:* Univ Calif, BS, 50; Univ Wis, MS, 52, PhD(plant path), 54. *Prof Exp:* Res asst plant path, Univ Wis, 50-54. *Concurrent Pos:* Mem, subcomt nematodes, Agr Bd, Nat Acad Sci-Nat Res Coun, 64-67; mem, Univ Calif-AID Pest Mgt Study Team, Southeast Asia, 71; mem, agr pest control adv comt, Calif State Dept Agr, 72- & pest control advisors comt, Dir, adv comt on APCA, Calif Dept Food & Agr, 74-76; asst dir, Pest & Dis Mgt Prog, Coop Exten, Univ Calif, 76-81, asst dir, Agr Exp Sta & dir, Statewide Pest Mgt Proj, 78-81. *Mem:* Fel Am Phytopath Soc; fel Soc Nematologists (pres, 75-76); Soc Europ Nematol; Org Trop Am Nematologists. *Res:* Biology and control of nematodes attacking field and vegetable crops; efficacy of nematicides; nematode resistance in crop plants. *Mailing Add:* 4686 Holyoke Pl Riverside CA 92507

**THOMASON, ROBERT WAYNE,** algebraic geometry & topology; deceased, see previous edition for last biography

**THOMASON, STEVEN KARL,** MATHEMATICAL LOGIC. *Current Pos:* From asst prof to assoc prof, 66-78, PROF MATH, SIMON FRASER UNIV, 78- *Personal Data:* b Salem, Ore, June 2, 40; m 60; c 2. *Educ:* Univ Ore, BS, 62; Cornell Univ, PhD, 66. *Concurrent Pos:* Vis asst prof, Univ Calif, Berkeley, 68-69. *Mem:* Am Math Soc; Can Math Cong; Asn Symbolic Logic. *Res:* Nonclassical logic, especially modal logic. *Mailing Add:* Dept Math Simon Fraser Univ Burnaby BC V5A 1S6 Can

**THOMASON, WILLIAM HUGH,** PHYSICAL CHEMISTRY, CORROSION. *Current Pos:* Res scientist, 75-80, res group leader Phys Chem & Corrosion Res & Develop, 80-93, SR SCIENTIST, CONOCO, INC, 93- *Personal Data:* b Hampton, Ark, Apr 4, 45; m 69; c 1. *Educ:* Hendrix Col, BA, 67; La State Univ, Baton Rouge, PhD(phys chem), 75. *Mem:* Am Chem Soc; Soc Petrol Engrs; Nat Asn Corrosion Engrs. *Res:* Corrosion problems in oil production, particularly those caused by hydrogen sulfide; water treating and scale problems. *Mailing Add:* 61 Stonerridge Ponca City OK 74604

**THOMASSEN, DAVID GEORGE,** carcinogenesis, for more information see previous edition

**THOMASSEN, KEITH I,** PLASMA PHYSICS. *Current Pos:* MFTF Prog leader, Univ Calif, Livermore, 77-83, asst assoc dir, 83-87, MTX Prog leader, 87, DEP ASSOC DIR, UNIV CALIF, LIVERMORE, 88-, PROF IN RESIDENCE, NUCLEAR ENG, BERKELEY, 89- *Personal Data:* b Harvey, Ill, Nov 22, 36; m 57; c 2. *Educ:* Chico State Col, BS, 58; Stanford Univ, MS, 60, PhD(elec eng), 63. *Prof Exp:* Res assoc plasma physics, Stanford Univ, 62-63, NATO fel, 63-64, res assoc, 64-65, lectr, 64-68, res physicist, 65-68; from asst prof to assoc prof elec eng, Mass Inst Technol, 68-73; asst ctr div leader, Los Alamos Sci Lab, 73-74, assoc ctr div leader, 74-77. *Concurrent Pos:* Consult, Lincoln Labs, Lexington, Mass, 68-74. *Mem:* Fel Am Phys Soc; Am Nuclear Soc. *Res:* Fusion reactor design; component development; plasma research, energy storage and transfer. *Mailing Add:* 9030 Doubletree Lane Livermore CA 94550

**THOMASSON, CLAUDE LARRY,** PHARMACY. *Current Pos:* assoc prof, 66-92, EMER PROF PHARM, AUBURN UNIV, 92- *Personal Data:* b Blue Grass, Va, Mar 6, 32; m 57; c 3. *Educ:* Univ Cincinnati, BS, 54; Univ Fla, PhD(pharm), 57. *Prof Exp:* Assoc prof pharm, Southern Col Pharm, Mercer, 57-61, prof & chmn dept, 61-64; assoc prof, WVa Univ, 64-66. *Mem:* Am Pharmaceut Asn; Acad Pharmaceut Sci; AAAS. *Res:* Dispensing and clinical pharmacy. *Mailing Add:* Dept Clin Pharmacol Auburn Univ Auburn University AL 36849-3501

**THOMASSON, JOHN ALEXANDER,** AGRICULTURAL ENGINEERING. *Current Pos:* RES ENGR, AGR RES SERV, USDA, 89- *Personal Data:* b Galveston, Tex, Apr 9, 63; m 84, Tanya M Millisan; c John A Jr, Andrea M, Ian A & Samuel W. *Educ:* Tex Tech Univ, BS, 87, La State Univ, MS, 89; Univ Ky, PhD(agr eng), 97. *Concurrent Pos:* Chair, Spec Crops Processing Comt, Am Soc Agr Engrs, 92, Cotton Eng Comt, 93; lt, Res Detachment 510, US Naval Res, 95- *Mem:* Am Soc Agr Engrs. *Res:* Crop processing; development of processing equipment, sensors for quality measurement, value-added utilization of processing by-products; precision agriculture. *Mailing Add:* PO Box 3340 Mississippi State MS 39762-3340

**THOMASSON, JOSEPH R,** PALEOBOTANY, PLANT SYSTEMATICS. *Personal Data:* b Hayden, Colo, June 6, 46; m 67, Nadine Giebler; c Russell, Heather & Scott. *Educ:* Ft Hays State Univ, BS, 68;Iowa State Univ, PhD(bot), 76. *Prof Exp:* Assoc prof bot, Black Hill State Col, 76-81; prof bot, Ft Hays State Univ, 82-87; distinguished vis prof bot, USAF Acad, 88-90. *Concurrent Pos:* Prin investr, NSF grants, 78-85 & Nat Geog Soc grants, 78-86, Legacy Found grants, 91-94. *Res:* Investigations of fossil and living grasses in order to elucidate the origins and evolution of grasses. *Mailing Add:* Dept Biol Ft Hays State Univ Hays KS 67601. *E-Mail:* bijo@fhsuvm.fhsu.edu

**THOMASSON, M RAY,** GEOLOGY, PETROLEUM EXPLORATION USING PLAY CONCEPT. *Current Pos:* PRES, THOMASSON PARTNER ASSOC, INC, 85- *Personal Data:* b Columbia, Mo, Sept 3, 30; m 90, Merrill Shields; c Julie (King), Laura (St Gemme) & Mary (Justice). *Educ:* Univ Mo, BA, 53, MA, 54; Univ Wis, PhD(geol), 59. *Prof Exp:* Geologist, Shell Oil Co, La, 59-68, mgr geol dept, Shell Develop Co, Tex, 68-70, div explor mgr, Shell Oil Co, La, 70-72, mgr forecasting, planning & econ, 72-74, mem staff, Shell Int Petrol Co, Ltd, London, 74-76, chief geologist, Shell Oil Co, Houston, 76-77; vpres explor, McCormick Oil & Gas Corp, 77-80; pres, Spectrum Oil & Gas, 80-82; pres, Pend Orielle Oil & Gas, 83-85. *Mem:* Geol Soc Am; Soc Econ Paleont & Mineral; Am Asn Petrol Geol. *Res:* Paleogeography and sedimentation of western North America; paleocurrent and basin studies; general stratigraphy and stratigraphic paleontology; seismic stratigraphy in carbonates; integrated visualization in exploration; surface exploration technology in petroleum. *Mailing Add:* Thomasson Partner Assoc Inc 1100 Stout Suite 1400 Denver CO 80204

**THOMBORSON, CLARK D(AVID),** very large scale integrated circuits theory, computer-aided design, for more information see previous edition

**THOMEIER, SIEGFRIED,** TOPOLOGY, ALGEBRAIC TOPOLOGY. *Current Pos:* PROF MATH, MEM UNIV NFLD, 68- *Personal Data:* b Aussig, Czech, Dec 19, 37; Can citizen; m 61; c 2. *Educ:* Univ Frankfurt, Dipl Math, 62, Dr Phil Nat(math), 65. *Prof Exp:* Sci asst math, Frankfurt Univ, 63-65; assoc prof, Math Inst, Aarhus, Denmark, 65-68. *Concurrent Pos:* Nat Res Coun Can res grant, Mem Univ Nfld, 69-; vis prof math, Univ Konstanz, Ger, 75-76. *Mem:* Can Math Soc; Math Asn Am; London Math Soc; Ger Math Soc; NY Acad Sci; Can Soc Hist & Philos Math. *Res:* Homotopy theory; homotopy groups of special topological spaces; homology theory; homological and categorical algebra; topological fixed point theory; applications of topology and error-correcting codes. *Mailing Add:* Dept Math Mem Univ Nfld St John's NF A1B 3X7 Can

**THOMERSON, JAMIE E,** ICHTHYOLOGY, ZOOLOGY. *Current Pos:* from asst prof to assoc prof, 65-77, PROF ZOOL, SOUTHERN ILL UNIV, EDWARDSVILLE, 77- *Personal Data:* b Ft McKavett, Tex, May 7, 35; m 57; c 2. *Educ:* Univ Tex, BS, 57; Tex Tech Col, MS, 61; Tulane Univ, PhD(zool), 65. *Prof Exp:* High sch teacher, 58-59. *Mem:* Am Soc Ichthyologists & Herpetologists; Am Fisheries Soc; Asn Trop Biol; Soc Syst Zool. *Res:* Fish systematics, ecology, behavior and genetics. *Mailing Add:* Dept Biol Southern Ill Univ Edwardsville IL 62026-1651

**THOMFORDE, C(LIFFORD) J(OHN),** ELECTRICAL ENGINEERING. *Current Pos:* asst prof, 47-55, chmn dept, 55-75, PROF ELEC ENG, UNIV NDAK, 55-; CONSULT ENG. *Personal Data:* b Crookston, Minn, Dec 15, 17; m 41; c 3. *Educ:* Univ NDak, BS, 41; Iowa State Univ, MSEE, 51. *Prof Exp:* Engr, Fed Commun Comn, 41-42 & Collins Radio Co, 42-47. *Mem:* Am Soc Eng Educ; Inst Elec & Electronics Engrs. *Res:* Radio communications, particularly in the field of radio and television broadcasting. *Mailing Add:* 2615 Fourth Ave N Grand Forks ND 58201

**THOMMES, ROBERT CHARLES,** ZOOLOGY. *Current Pos:* From instr to assoc prof, 56-67, chmn dept, 68-70, PROF BIOL, DE PAUL UNIV, 67- *Personal Data:* b Chicago, Ill, Aug 31, 28. *Educ:* De Paul Univ, BS, 50, MS, 52; Northwestern Univ, PhD, 56. *Mem:* AAAS; Soc Zool; Soc Develop Biol; Soc Exp Biol & Med; Endocrine Soc; Poultry Sci Soc. *Res:* Developmental endocrinology. *Mailing Add:* 2621 Tanglewood Dr Sarasota FL 34239

**THOMOPOULOS, NICK TED,** OPERATIONS RESEARCH, STATISTICS. *Current Pos:* PROF, STEWARD SCH BUS, ILL INST TECHNOL. *Personal Data:* b Chicago, Ill, Aug 21; m 64; c 1. *Educ:* Univ Ill, BS, 53, MA, 58; Ill Inst Technol, PhD(indust eng), 66. *Prof Exp:* Supvr opers res, Int Harvester Co, 58-66; sr scientist, IIT Res Inst, 66-68; assoc prof indust eng, Ill Inst Technol, 68-96. *Mem:* Inst Mgt Sci; Opers Res Soc Am. *Res:* Manufacturing and assembly methods; uncertainty in mathematical models; statistical analysis; production and inventory control. *Mailing Add:* 15 W 459 60th Pl Hinsdale IL 60521

**THOMPKINS, LEON,** PHARMACEUTICAL CHEMISTRY. *Current Pos:* RETIRED. *Personal Data:* b Augusta, Ga, Nov 4, 36; div; c Deidra L & Walden P. *Educ:* Morehouse Col, BS, 61; Univ Calif, San Francisco, PhD(pharmaceut chem), 68. *Prof Exp:* Chemist, Hyman Labs, Fundamental Res Co, Inc, 62-63; sr pharmaceut chemist, Eli Lilly & Co, 68-76, res scientist, 76-93. *Mem:* Am Chem Soc; Sigma Xi; AAAS; NY Acad Sci. *Res:* Development and bioavailability of human drug dosage forms. *Mailing Add:* 1948 Adams St Indianapolis IN 46218

**THOMPSON, ALAN BRUCE,** GEOLOGY, EARTH SCIENCES. *Current Pos:* PROF, EIDGENOSSICHE TECH SCH, 77-, UNIV ZURICH, 78- *Personal Data:* b Newcastle upon Tyne, UK, May 1, 47; div; c Alexis B & Ishbel V. *Educ:* Manchester Univ, BSc, 68, PhD(geol), 71. *Honors & Awards:* N L Bowen Award, Am Geophys Union, 94. *Prof Exp:* Lectr geol, Manchester Univ, 70-73; asst prof, Harvard Univ, 73-76. *Mem:* Fel Mineral Soc Am; Europ Union Geosci (vpres, 88-94); Europ Asn Geochem (pres, 90-93); fel Japan Acad Prom Sci; Am Geophys Union. *Mailing Add:* Eidgenossiche Tech Sch Sonneggstrasse 5 Zurich 8092 Switzerland. *Fax:* 41-1-632-1008

**THOMPSON, ALLAN LLOYD,** PHYSICAL CHEMISTRY, ENGINEERING. *Current Pos:* RETIRED. *Personal Data:* b Lccds, Que, Mar 4, 20; m 43; c 3. *Educ:* Bishop's Univ, Can, BA, 40; McGill Univ, PhD(chem), 43. *Prof Exp:* Res chemist, Nat Res Coun Can, 43-46; res assoc chem, Radiation Lab, McGill Univ, 46-85, assoc prof mech eng, 58-85.

*Concurrent Pos:* From sci consult to assoc dir, Gas Dynamics Lab, McGill Univ, 53-58. *Mem:* Sigma Xi. *Res:* Engineering science; chemical kinetics; analytical, nuclear and high temperature chemistry; cyclotron chemical problems; ignition and corrosion studies; vacuum engineering; combustion; road safety; collision investigations; pollution control of vehicles. *Mailing Add:* Dept Mech Eng McGill Univ 817 Sherbrooke St W Montreal PQ H3A 2M5 Can

**THOMPSON, ALLAN M,** PETROLOGY, SEDIMENTOLOGY. *Current Pos:* Asst prof, 67-72, ASSOC PROF GEOL, UNIV DEL, 72- *Personal Data:* b Ithaca, NY, May 22, 40; c Cynthia & Susan. *Educ:* Carleton Col, BA, 62; Brown Univ, ScM, 64, PhD(stratig), 68. *Mem:* Geol Soc Am; Am Asn Petrol Geologists; Sigma Xi. *Res:* Sedimentology, plutonic petrology and structure; stratigraphy, structure and petrology of Appalachian orogen. *Mailing Add:* Dept Geol Univ Del Newark DE 19711. *E-Mail:* allan.thompson@back.udel educ

**THOMPSON, ALONZO CRAWFORD,** ORGANIC CHEMISTRY, PHARMACEUTICAL CHEMISTRY. *Current Pos:* RETIRED. *Personal Data:* b Tifton, Ga, June 4, 28; m 55; c 3. *Educ:* Berry Col, AB, 53; Univ Miss, MS, 55, PhD(chem), 62. *Prof Exp:* Prof chem, Miss Delta Jr Col, 55-56 & Southern State Col, 56-58; res chemist, Boll Weevil Res Lab, USDA, 62-89. *Concurrent Pos:* Adj asst prof biochem, Miss State Univ, 74-89. *Mem:* Am Chem Soc; Am Inst Chemists. *Res:* Pharmaceutical synthesis; natural products; insects and plant stimulants. *Mailing Add:* 50365 Old Hwy 25 Aberdeen MS 39730

**THOMPSON, ALVIN JEROME,** GASTROENTEROLOGY. *Current Pos:* RETIRED. *Personal Data:* b Washington, DC, Apr 5, 24; m 50; c 5. *Educ:* Howard Univ, MD, 46; Am Bd Internal Med, dipl, 53. *Prof Exp:* Intern, St Louis City Hosp, Mo, 46-47, resident, 47-51; physician & gastroenterologist, Vet Admin Hosp, Seattle, 53-57; founder & dir, Gastroenterol Lab, Providence Hosp, Seattle, 63-77, chief med, 72-74; clin prof med, Sch Med, Univ Wash, 72-74; pvt med pract internal med & gastroenterol, 57-94. *Concurrent Pos:* Med adv, Draft Bd, 67-72; co-chmn phys health task force, King Co Comprehensive Health Planning Coun, 68, vpres, 73-; mem adv bd, King Co Med Serv Bur, 69-70; consult, Div Educ & Res Fac, NIH, 70-72. *Mem:* Inst Med-Nat Acad Sci; Nat Med Asn; AMA; fel Am Col Physicians; Am Gastroenterol Asn; Am Soc Gastrointestinal Endoscopy; Am Soc Internal Med. *Mailing Add:* 8222 Avalon Dr Mercer Island WA 98040

**THOMPSON, ANSEL FREDERICK, JR,** ENVIRONMENTAL ENGINEERING, ENGINEERING MANAGEMENT. *Current Pos:* RETIRED. *Personal Data:* b Birmingham, Ala, Oct 19, 41; m 63, Susan; c Angel, Jennifer & Melissa. *Educ:* Pa State Univ, BS, 63; Calif Inst Technol, MS, 65, PhD(environ health eng), 68. *Prof Exp:* Proj engr & scientist, Roy F Weston Inc, 67-70, prin engr, Weston Europe Spa, 70-73, proj mgr, 73-75, vpres, Eng Design, 75-80, qual assurance/finance, 80-87, exec vpres, 87-89, vchmn, 89-91, chmn, 91-97. *Concurrent Pos:* Dipl, Am Acad Environ Engrs. *Mem:* Am Water Works Asn; Water Environ Fedn; Am Soc Civil Engrs; Am Acad Environ Engrs; Prof Serv Mgt Asn. *Res:* Thermodynamics and ultrafiltration of salt-polyelectrolyte solutions; automatic control of biological treatment processes; Monte Carlo methods in analysis of treatment systems; systems analysis. *Mailing Add:* 656 St Matthews Rd Chester Springs PA 19425

**THOMPSON, ANSON ELLIS,** plant breeding, plant genetics; deceased, see previous edition for last biography

**THOMPSON, ANTHONY RICHARD,** RADIO ASTRONOMY INSTRUMENTATION, ELECTROMAGNETIC COMPATIBILITY. *Current Pos:* VLA proj engr, Nat Radio Astron Observ, dep mgr VLA proj, 75-81, systs engr & frequency coordr VLA proj, 81-84, head, electronics div VLBA proj, 84-92, dep mgr, VLBA proj, 87-92, DEP HEAD, CENT DEVELOP LAB, NAT RADIO ASTRON OBSERV, 92- *Personal Data:* b Hull, Eng, Apr 7, 31; m 63, Sheila M Press; c Sarah L. *Educ:* Univ Manchester, BSc, 52, PhD, 56. *Prof Exp:* Electronic engr, Elec & Musical Instruments Ltd, Eng, 55-57; res assoc, Harvard Col Observ, 57-61, res fel, 61-62; radio astronr, Stanford Univ, 62-70, sr res assoc, 70-72. *Concurrent Pos:* Vis sr res fel, Calif Inst Technol, 66-71, vis assoc, 71-72; mem, US Study Group 7, Int Telecommun Union, 79-; chmn, Radio Astron Subcomt, Comt on Radio Frequencies, Nat Acad Sci, 80-86; mem, Comt on Radio Frequencies, 80-; sec, Interunion Comn Allocation Frequencies Radioastronomy & Space Sci, 82-88, mem, 91- *Mem:* Int Astron Union; Int Union Radio Sci; fel Inst Elec & Electronics Engrs; Am Astron Soc. *Res:* Design of radio telescopes; theory and practice of radio interferometry; electromagnetic compatibility and frequency protection of radio astronomy instruments; structure of cosmic radio sources; co-author of 1 book and more than 50 scientific papers. *Mailing Add:* Nat Radio Astron Observ 520 Edgemont Rd Charlottesville VA 22903

**THOMPSON, ANTHONY W,** METALLURGY, MATERIALS SCIENCE. *Current Pos:* STAFF, LAWRENCE BERKELEY LAB. *Personal Data:* b Burbank, Calif, Mar 6, 40; m 63, Mary Cummings; c Campbell & Michael. *Educ:* Stanford Univ, BS, 62; Univ Wash, MS, 65; Mass Inst Technol, PhD(metall, mat sci), 70. *Prof Exp:* Res engr, Jet Propulsion Lab, 62-63; mem tech staff, Sandia Labs, 70-73, Rockwell Int Sci Ctr, 73-77; assoc prof metall, Carnegie Mellon Univ, 77-79, prof metall, 80-94, dept head, Metall Eng & Mat Sci Dept, 87-90. *Concurrent Pos:* Overseas fel, Churchill Col, Cambridge, UK, 82-83; ed, Metall Trans, 83-88. *Mem:* AAAS; fel Am Soc Metals; Am Inst Mech Engrs; Sigma Xi; Mat Res Soc. *Res:* Relation between microstructure of materials and mechanical behavior, particularly strength and fracture; including environmental effects and grain size effects on polycrystal behavior; fatigue and fracture toughness of engineering materials. *Mailing Add:* Lawrence Berkeley Lab MS-62-603 Berkeley CA 94720

**THOMPSON, ARTHUR HOWARD,** SOLID STATE PHYSICS. *Current Pos:* sr res physicist, Exxon Res & Eng Co, Linden, 71-76, group head, Linden, NJ, 76-81, GROUP HEAD & RES ADV, EXXON PROD RES CO, HOUSTON, 81- *Personal Data:* b Salt Lake City, Utah, Mar 3, 42; m 65, Caroly Galbraith; c Peter. *Educ:* Ohio State Univ, BSc & MSc, 66; Stanford Univ, PhD(physics), 70. *Prof Exp:* Fel, Stanford Univ, 70; group leader physics, Syva Co, Calif, 70-71. *Concurrent Pos:* Vis prof, Earth, Atmospheric & Planetary Sci Dept, Mass Inst Technol, 93. *Mem:* Fel Am Phys Soc; AAAS; Am Geophys Union; Soc Explor Geophys. *Res:* Super conductivity; semiconductors; transport and magnetic properties; geophysics. *Mailing Add:* PO Box 2189 Exxon Prod Res Co Houston TX 77252. *Fax:* 713-966-6360

**THOMPSON, ARTHUR ROBERT,** NUCLEAR MAGNETIC RESONANCE SPECTROSCOPY. *Current Pos:* CHEMIST, NCAUR, AGR RES SERV, USDA, 88- *Personal Data:* b Washington, DC, May 8, 59; m 86, Laura Pittman; c Carol. *Educ:* Valparaiso Univ, BS, 81; Univ Ill, PhD(phys chem), 87. *Prof Exp:* Fel, Argonne Nat Lab, 86-88. *Mem:* Am Chem Soc. *Res:* Multinuclear nuclear magnetic resonance to study materials which do not lend themselves to easy interpretation by solution nuclear magnetic resonance; solid state nuclear magnetic resonance of plant polymers. *Mailing Add:* NCAUR Agr Res Serv USDA 1815 N University St Peoria IL 61604

**THOMPSON, AYLMER HENRY,** METEOROLOGY. *Current Pos:* prof, 60-88, EMER PROF METEOROL, TEX A&M UNIV, 88- *Personal Data:* b Ill, Sept 11, 22; m 41; c 3. *Educ:* Univ Calif, Los Angeles, MA, 48, PhD(meteorol), 60. *Prof Exp:* Lectr meteorol, Univ Calif, Los Angeles, 48-52; asst prof, Univ Utah, 52-60. *Concurrent Pos:* Sci adv, Found Glacier & Environ Res, Wash; sci consult, 55-; vis prof, Geophys Inst, Univ Alaska, 67-68 & 71-72. *Mem:* Am Meteorol Soc; Am Geophys Union; Royal Meteorol Soc; Int Glaciol Soc; Sigma Xi. *Res:* Synoptic meteorology of sub-tropics; satellite meteorology; inversions; meteorology of glaciated regions. *Mailing Add:* PO Box 1948 Port Angeles WA 98362-0406

**THOMPSON, BOBBY BLACKBURN,** MEDICINAL CHEMISTRY, ORGANIC CHEMISTRY. *Current Pos:* Asst prof, 60-70, ASSOC PROF MED CHEM, SCH PHARM, UNIV GA, 70- *Personal Data:* b Lumber City, Ga, May 15, 33; m 59; c 1. *Educ:* Berry Col, BA, 55; Univ Miss, MS, 56, PhD(org med chem), 63. *Mem:* Am Chem Soc; Am Pharmaceut Asn. *Res:* Synthesis of organic and heterocyclic compounds of potential medicinal value; structural elucidation by chemical and instrumental means. *Mailing Add:* 375 Pinewood Circle Athens GA 30606

**THOMPSON, BONNIE CECIL,** SOLID STATE PHYSICS. *Current Pos:* asst prof, 65-74, ASSOC PROF, UNIV TEX, ARLINGTON, 74-, ASSOC CHMN PHYSICS, 87- *Personal Data:* b Baird, Tex, Dec 18, 35; m 59; c 2. *Educ:* NTex State Univ, BA, 57, MA, 58; Univ Tex, PhD(physics), 65. *Prof Exp:* Instr physics, NTex State Univ, 58-60; teaching asst, Univ Tex, Austin, 60-61, res scientist, 61-65. *Mem:* Am Phys Soc. *Res:* Nuclear spin-lattice relaxation processes in solids; nuclear magnetic resonance of biological molecules. *Mailing Add:* 2809 Augusta Lane Arlington TX 76012-2110

**THOMPSON, BRIAN J,** OPTICS. *Current Pos:* dir, Inst Optics, Univ Rochester, 68-75, prof optics, 68-95, dean col eng & appl sci, 75-84, provost, 84-94, DISTINGUISHED UNIV PROF & EMER PROVOST, UNIV ROCHESTER, 94- *Personal Data:* b Glossop, Eng, June 10, 32; m 56; c 2. *Educ:* Univ Manchester, BScTech, 55, PhD(appl physics), 59. *Honors & Awards:* Presidents Award, 67; Kingslake Medal & Pezuto Award, Soc Photo-Opitcal Instrumentation Engrs, 78, Gold Medal, 86. *Prof Exp:* Demonstr physics fac tech, Univ Manchester, 55-56, asst lectr, 56-59; lectr, Leeds Univ, 59-62; sr physicist, Tech Opers, Inc, 63-65, mgr, Phys Optics Dept, 65-66, dir, Optics Dept, 66-67; mgr tech opers west & tech dir, Beckman & Whitley Div, 67-68. *Concurrent Pos:* Adj prof, Northeastern Univ, 66-67. *Mem:* Am Phys Soc; fel Optical Soc Am; fel Brit Inst Physics & Phys Soc; fel Soc Photo-Optical Instrumentation Engrs (pres, 74-75, 75-76). *Res:* Diffraction; interference; partial coherence; holography; application to particle sizing; optical data processing. *Mailing Add:* Provost 200 Admin Bldg Univ Rochester Rochester NY 14627. *Fax:* 716-244-2629

**THOMPSON, BUFORD DALE,** HORTICULTURE, VEGETABLE CROPS. *Current Pos:* Asst prof veg crops & asst horiculturist, Univ Fla, 49-60, assoc prof & assoc horiculturist, 60-66, prof veg crops & horticulturist, 66-80, EMER PROF, VEG-CROPS & ASST HORTICULTURIST, UNIV FLA, 80- *Personal Data:* b Lake Wales, Fla, Oct 22, 22; m 44, Margaret V Cody; c 3. *Educ:* Univ Fla, BSA, 48, MSA, 49, PhD(hort), 54, JD, 76. *Honors & Awards:* Vaughan Award, Am Soc Hort Sci, 62. *Concurrent Pos:* Atty agr law, agr legal consult, US Army, 80. *Mem:* Am Soc Plant Physiol. *Res:* Biological and chemical changes involved in the post harvest handling, transportation and storage of horticultural crops; agricultural law. *Mailing Add:* 3920 NW 29th Lane Gainesville FL 32606-6671

**THOMPSON, CARL EUGENE,** ANIMAL BREEDING, ANIMAL GENETICS. *Current Pos:* asst prof, 74-77, assoc prof, 77-81, PROF BEEF CATTLE BREEDING, CLEMSON UNIV, 81- *Personal Data:* b Lucinda, Pa, June 14, 41; m 64; c 4. *Educ:* Pa State Univ, University Park, BS, 63, MS,

68; Va Polytech Inst & State Univ, PhD(animal breeding & genetics), 71. *Prof Exp:* Asst co agr agent, Agr Exten Serv, Pa State Univ, 63-66; asst prof animal sci, Ft Hays State Univ, 71-73. *Mem:* Am Soc Animal Sci; Am Genetics Asn; Sigma Xi. *Res:* Beef cattle breeding and genetics; cross-breeding; genetic-environmental interaction; reproductive physiology. *Mailing Add:* Animal & Vet Sci Dept Clemson Univ B108 Poole Agr Ctr Clemson SC 29634-0361

**THOMPSON, CHARLES,** NONLINEAR & CHAOTIC SYSTEMS, FLUID MECHANICS. *Current Pos:* assoc dean, 94-96, PROF ELEC ENG & CO-DIR, CTR ADVAN COMPUT & TELECOMMUN, UNIV MASS, LOWELL, 87- *Personal Data:* b Tachiakawa, Japan, Jan 15, 54; US citizen; m 75, Tita Bersamira; c Danielle, Lara & Charles. *Educ:* NY Univ, BS, 76; Polytech Univ, MS, 78; Mass Inst Technol, PhD, 82. *Prof Exp:* Asst prof appl mech, Va Polytech Inst & State Univ, 82-87. *Concurrent Pos:* Analog Devices prof, Analog Devices, 87; exec bd, AT&T Res Fel, 91 & Lucent Technol Fel; Blackwell scholar, Univ Mass, 94; ed, Telecomm Res & Develop Mass, 94 & 95. *Mem:* Acoust Soc Am; Am Phys Soc; Inst Elec & Electronics Engrs; Soc Mfg Engrs. *Res:* Theoretical and computational modeling of fluid and electronic systems; control theory; applied mathematics; telecommunications; signal processing; acoustics. *Mailing Add:* Dept Elec Eng Ctr Advan Comput & Telecommun Univ Mass Lowell MA 01854. *Fax:* 978-934-3027; *E-Mail:* thompsonc@woods.uml.edu

**THOMPSON, CHARLES CALVIN,** ORAL PATHOLOGY. *Current Pos:* RETIRED. *Personal Data:* b Los Angeles, Calif, May 4, 35; m 60; c 2. *Educ:* St Martin's Col, BA, 57; Univ Ore, DMD, 62; Emory Univ, MSD, 68; Am Bd Oral Path, dipl; Nat Bd Forensic Dent, dipl. *Prof Exp:* Pvt dent pract, Ore, 64-66; resident path, Dent Sch, Emory Univ, 66-68; asst prof oral diag & med, Dent Sch, Univ Calif, Los Angeles, 68-69; assoc prof path, Dent Sch & Ore Health Sci Univ, 69-96. *Concurrent Pos:* Nat Inst Dent Res fel, Emory Univ, 66-68; attend consult, Wadsworth Vet Admin Hosp, Los Angeles, 68-69; oral pathologist & clin consult, 71-; instr, Mt Hood Community Col, 72-73. *Mem:* Fel Am Acad Oral Path; Int Soc Forensic Odontol-Stomatol. *Res:* Oncology, chemical, physical carcinogenesis; teratology, induction of developmental defects and explanation; forensic odontology; bone, especially effects of dimethyl sulfoxide on bone. *Mailing Add:* 11525 SW Vacuna Ct Portland OR 97219

**THOMPSON, CHARLES DENISON,** CORROSION. *Current Pos:* CORROSION ENGR, KNOLLS ATOMIC POWER LAB, LOCKHEED MARTIN, 73- *Personal Data:* b Niagara Falls, NY, May 4, 40. *Educ:* Oberlin Col, BA, 62; Am Univ, MS, 68, PhD(chem), 71. *Prof Exp:* Chemist, US Army Environ Hyg Agency, 63-65; chemist biochem, Aldridge Assocs, 69; Welch fel, Rice Univ, 71-72. *Mem:* Electrochem Soc. *Res:* High temperature materials corrosion and electrochemistry. *Mailing Add:* 50 Hill St Alplaus NY 12008

**THOMPSON, CHARLES FREDERICK,** POPULATION ECOLOGY, ORNITHOLOGY. *Current Pos:* asst prof, 78-82, assoc prof, 82-88, PROF ECOL, ILL STATE UNIV, 88- *Personal Data:* b Dayton, Ohio, Oct 1, 43; m 67. *Educ:* Ind Univ, BA, 67, MA, 70, PhD(zool), 71. *Prof Exp:* Res fel ecol, Univ Ga, 71-72, asst prof zool, 72-73; teaching fel zool, Miami Univ, 73-75; asst prof biol, State Univ NY Col Geneseo, 75-78. *Concurrent Pos:* Vis asst prof zool, Ind Univ, 74; vis scientist, DSIR Ecol Div, NZ, 84, Edward Grey Inst, Oxford Univ, 85, 91. *Mem:* Ecol Soc Am; Brit Ecol Soc; Am Ornithologists Union; Brit Ornithologists Union; Neth Ornithologists Union. *Res:* Regulation and dynamics of bird populations; avian breeding adaptations; structure and evolution of avian social organization; evolution of avian life-history traits. *Mailing Add:* Dept Biol Sci Ill State Univ Campus Box 4120 Normal IL 61790-0001

**THOMPSON, CHARLES WILLIAM NELSON,** INDUSTRIAL ENGINEERING, MANAGEMENT SCIENCE. *Current Pos:* assoc prof, 68-77, PROF INDUST ENG & MGT SCI, TECHNOL INST, NORTHWESTERN UNIV, 77- *Personal Data:* b Bethlehem, Pa; m 48; c 3. *Educ:* Kutztown Univ, BS, 43; Harvard Law Sch, LLB, 49; Ohio State Univ MBA, 56; Northwestern Univ, PhD(indust eng), 69. *Prof Exp:* Chief electronic reconnaissance sect, Wright Air Develop Ctr, USAF, 52-58; dir eng serv, Govt Electronics Div, Admiral Corp, 58-64. *Concurrent Pos:* Consult exp technol prog, Nat Bur Stand, 75-80. *Mem:* Inst Elec & Electronics Engrs; Inst Mgt Sci; Am Inst Indust Engrs; Sigma Xi. *Res:* Theory and methodology of unstructured problems in organizations and systems, with particular emphasis on field research, including administrative experiments. *Mailing Add:* 240 Randolph St Glencoe IL 60022-2131

**THOMPSON, CHESTER RAY,** BIOCHEMISTRY. *Current Pos:* RETIRED. *Personal Data:* b Storrs, Utah, May 27, 15; m 40, Margaret Hill; c Lorin, Bruce, Russell & Sharen. *Educ:* Utah State Univ, BS, 38; Univ Wis, MS, 41, PhD(biochem), 43. *Prof Exp:* Chemist, Rocky Mountain Packing Corp, Utah, 36-39; biochemist, Univ Wis, 39-43, Forest Prods Lab, US Forest Serv, 43 & Purdue Univ, 44-45; plant biochemist, Univ Chicago, 45-49; head forage invest, Field Crops Lab, Western Utilization Res & Develop Div, USDA, 49-60; proj leader, Statewide Air Pollution Res Ctr, Agr Air Res Prog, Univ Calif, Riverside, 60-67, res biochemist, 67-85. *Mem:* Fel AAAS; Am Soc Plant Physiol; Am Chem Soc; Air Pollution Control Asn. *Res:* Chemical stabilization of carotene in alfalfa; occurrence of anti-oxidants in natural products; carotenoids in green plants; saponins and estrogens in forages; effects of air pollution on plants and human beings. *Mailing Add:* Statewide Air Pollution Res Ctr Univ Calif Riverside CA 92521

**THOMPSON, CHRISTOPHER WILLIAM,** ornithology, physiological ecology, for more information see previous edition

**THOMPSON, CLARENCE HENRY, JR,** veterinary medicine, for more information see previous edition

**THOMPSON, CLIFTON C,** PHYSICAL CHEMISTRY, COMPUTATIONAL CHEMISTRY. *Current Pos:* RETIRED. *Personal Data:* b Franklin, Tenn, Aug 16, 39; m 59, 78, Sarah E Gaunt; c Brenda & Vickie. *Educ:* Middle Tenn State Univ, BS, 61; Univ Miss, PhD(phys & inorg chem), 64. *Prof Exp:* Res assoc, Univ Tex, 64-65; asst prof spectrochem, Rutgers Univ, 65; asst prof chem, Marshall Univ, 65-66; assoc prof, Mid Tenn State Univ, 66-68; from asst prof to assoc prof, Memphis State Univ, 68-74; dean, Sch Sci & Technol, SW Mo State Univ, 74-84, dean, Col Sci & Math, 84-87, dir, Ctr Sci Res, 87-89, assoc vpres grad studies & res, 89-90, prof chem, 74-, head, Dept Chem, 90-97. *Concurrent Pos:* Lectr, Kanawha Valley Grad Ctr, WVa Univ, 66; NSF acad year exten grant, 66-68; mem, Med Technol Rev Comt, 74-80. *Mem:* Am Chem Soc; Royal Soc Chem; AAAS; Sigma Xi. *Res:* Spectral, thermodynamic and kinetic studies of molecular complexes; quantum chemistry; computer applications to physical systems; radioactivity in the environment. *Mailing Add:* 1010 Highland Mt Pleasant MI 48858. *Fax:* 417-836-6934; *E-Mail:* cct500f@smsvma

**THOMPSON, CRAYTON BEVILLE,** ORGANIC CHEMISTRY. *Current Pos:* RES & DEVELOP CHEMIST, EASTMAN KODAK CO, 49- *Personal Data:* b Paris, Tex, Dec 28, 20; m 55; c 1. *Educ:* Univ Tex, BS, 42; Univ Ill, MS, 47, PhD(chem), 49. *Prof Exp:* Chem engr, Freeport Sulphur Co, 42-46; lab asst chem, Univ Ill, 47-49. *Mem:* Am Chem Soc. *Res:* Synthesis of amino acids; antihalation backings for photographic films; abrasion resistant and anitstatic applications for plastics; adhesion. *Mailing Add:* 505 Wanda Ridge Durham NC 27712-2751

**THOMPSON, D(ONALD) W(ILLIAM),** CHEMICAL ENGINEERING. *Current Pos:* assoc prof, 67-77, PROF CHEM ENG, UNIV BC, 77- *Personal Data:* b Gosport, Eng, Mar 16, 33; m 57; c 2. *Educ:* Univ Birmingham, BSc, 54, PhD(chem eng), 58. *Honors & Awards:* Jr Moulton Medal, Brit Inst Chem Eng, 61. *Prof Exp:* Res fel chem eng, Univ BC, 58-60; engr, Shell Develop Co, Calif, 60-67. *Mem:* Am Inst Chem Engrs; Chem Inst Can; Brit Inst Chem Eng. *Res:* Adsorption and chromatographic processes; cyclic separation processes; membrane separations; flow visualization; optimization methods. *Mailing Add:* Dept Chem Eng Univ BC 2216 Main Hall Rm 306 Vancouver BC V6T 1Z4 Can

**THOMPSON, DANIEL JAMES,** TERATOLOGY, REPRODUCTIVE TOXICOLOGY. *Current Pos:* Res specialist, 66-80, res leader, Dow Chem Co, 80-82, SR RES TOXICOLOGIST, MARION MERRELL DOW INC, 82- *Personal Data:* b Terre Haute, Ind, Feb 10, 42; m 65; c 2. *Educ:* Ind State Univ, BS, 64, MA, 66; Am Bd Toxicol, dipl, 81. *Concurrent Pos:* Adj assoc prof, Purdue Univ. *Mem:* Teratology Soc; Environ Mutagen Soc; Soc Toxicol. *Res:* Reproductive physiology; perinatal toxicology. *Mailing Add:* Hoechst Marion Roussel PO Box 9627 H4M2-2110 Marion Merrell Dow Inc 10236 Marion Park Dr Kansas City MO 64134-0627

**THOMPSON, DANIEL QUALE,** WILDLIFE ECOLOGY, CONSERVATION. *Current Pos:* CONSULT/WRITER FISH & WILDLIFE SCI, 86- *Personal Data:* b Madison, Wis, Oct 3, 18; m 53, Edith J Bond; c 4. *Educ:* Univ Wis-Madison, BS, 42, MS, 50; Univ Mo, PhD(field zool), 55. *Prof Exp:* Instr field zool, Univ Mo, 50-54; from asst prof to assoc prof biol, Ripon Col, 55-62; wildlife res biologist, US Fish & Wildlife Serv & leader, NY Coop Wildlife Res Unit, Cornell Univ, 62-75; wildlife ed, Colo State Univ, US Fish & Wildlife Serv, 75-85. *Concurrent Pos:* Mem, Grad Fel Panel, NSF, 71-72; ed, J Wildlife Mgt, 73-74. *Mem:* Wilderness Soc; Wildlife Soc. *Res:* Wildlife conservation; ecology of terrestrial vertebrates. *Mailing Add:* 623 Del Norte Pl Ft Collins CO 80521

**THOMPSON, DAVID A(LFRED),** ERGONOMICS. *Current Pos:* actg instr indust eng, Stanford Univ, 56-58, actg asst prof, 58-61, res assoc rehab med, 58-64, from asst prof to prof, 61-83, assoc chmn dept, 72-83, EMER PROF INDUST ENG, STANFORD UNIV, 83-; PRES, PORTOLA ASSOCS, PALO ALTO, CALIF. *Personal Data:* b Chicago, Ill, Sept 9, 29; wid; c 5. *Educ:* Univ Va, BME, 51; Univ Fla, BIE, 55, MSE, 56; Stanford Univ, PhD(indust eng), 61. *Prof Exp:* Asst eng & indust, Exp Sta, Univ Fla, 55-56. *Concurrent Pos:* Consult. *Mem:* Am Inst Indust Engrs; Human Factors Soc; Inst Elec & Electronics Engrs; Am Soc Eng Educ; Sigma Xi. *Res:* Analysis and design of man-machine systems, especially the physiological, neurological and psychological information processing in man. *Mailing Add:* 2600 El Camino Real Stuite 414 Palo Alto CA 94306

**THOMPSON, DAVID A,** INFORMATION STORAGE TECHNOLOGY, APPLIED MAGNETISM. *Current Pos:* dir, Compact Storage Lab, IBM, T J Watson Res Ctr, 87-92, dir, Magnetic Rec Inst, 87-92, FEL, IBM RES, IBM ALMADEN RES CTR, 80-, DIR, ADV MAGNETIC REC LAB, IBM, T J WATSON RES CTR, 92- *Personal Data:* b Devils Lake, NDak, Dec 17, 40. *Educ:* Carnegie Inst Technol, BS, 62, MS, 63, PhD(elec eng), 66. *Prof Exp:* Asst prof elec eng, Carnegie Inst Technol, 65-68; res staff mem, IBM, T J Watson Res Ctr, 68-80. *Concurrent Pos:* Admin comt, Inst Elec & Electronics Engrs Magnetics Soc, 76-; adv comt, Ctr Magnetic Rec Res, Univ Calif San Diego & Magnetic Tech Ctr, Carnegie-Mellon Inst. *Mem:* Nat Acad Eng; fel Inst Elec & Electronics Engrs. *Res:* Information storage technology; applied magnetism; magnetic recording systems; sensors and measurement systems; servo mechanisms. *Mailing Add:* IBM Almaden Res Ctr 650 Harry Rd K01 802 San Jose CA 95120. *Fax:* 408-927-4055; *E-Mail:* davidt@almodew.ibm.com

**THOMPSON, DAVID ALLAN,** ENGINEERING PHYSICS, MATERIALS SCIENCE ENGINEERING. *Current Pos:* from asst prof to assoc prof, 73-81, chmn dept, 81-87, PROF ENG PHYSICS, MCMASTER UNIV, 81-, DIR, CENTRE ELECTRO PHOTONIC MAT & DEVICES, 87- *Personal Data:* b Oxford, Eng, Apr 28, 42; Can citizen; m 64, Elizabeth A Hart; c Michael, Jennifer & Susan. *Educ:* Reading Univ, UK, BSc, 63, PhD(physics), 67. *Prof Exp:* Mgr process res & develop, Westinghouse Can, 67-72. *Concurrent Pos:* Consult various orgn. *Mem:* Mat Res Soc; Inst Elec & Electronics Engrs; Boehmische Phys Soc; Inst Physics UK. *Res:* Atomic collisions in solids; ion beam processing of solids; ion beam analysis; device technology; molecular beam epitaxy. *Mailing Add:* Dept Eng Physics McMaster Univ Hamilton ON L8S 4L7 Can. *Fax:* 905-527-8409; *E-Mail:* dathomp@mcmaster.ca

**THOMPSON, DAVID ALLEN,** INORGANIC CHEMISTRY, GLASS CHEMISTRY. *Current Pos:* Res chemist, Corning Glass Works, 76-80, supvr explor res, 80-84, mgr, optical waveguide res, 84-86, optical component res, 86-90, MGR COMPONENT TECHNOL, CORNING GLASS WORKS, 91- *Personal Data:* b Gallipolis, Ohio, July 10, 50; m 72; c 2. *Educ:* Ohio State Univ, BS, 72; Univ Mich, MS, 73, PhD(chem), 77. *Mem:* Am Chem Soc; Am Ceramic Soc; Optical Soc Am. *Res:* Glass chemistry research including composition, durability, diffusion and melting of glass. *Mailing Add:* Corning Inc MP-HQ-E1-45 Corning NY 14831-0001

**THOMPSON, DAVID BRIAN,** SURFACE WATER HYDROLOGY, GROUND WATER HYDROLOGY. *Current Pos:* ASST PROF CIVIL ENG, TEX TECH UNIV, 93- *Personal Data:* b Van Nuys, Calif, May 31, 53; m 73, Janet Kay McMinn; c Rebecca, Jacob & Michael. *Educ:* Univ Mo, Rolla, BSCE, 80, MSCE, 83, PhD(civil eng), 89. *Prof Exp:* Staff hydrologist, Law Eng Testing Co, 82-83; hydrologist, Dept Int, US Geol Surv, 89-93. *Concurrent Pos:* Consult hydrologist, 80- *Mem:* Am Soc Civil Engrs. *Res:* Modeling and analysis of surface water and ground water hydrologic processes; hydraulics of pipelines; mitigation of scale resistance in potable water transport pipelines; water shed modeling; global climate change/hydrologic modeling. *Mailing Add:* Dept Civil Eng Tex Tech Univ Lubbock TX 79409-0001. *Fax:* 806-742-3449; *E-Mail:* thompson@cam203g.le.ttu.edu

**THOMPSON, DAVID CHARLES,** LASER PHYSICS, DESIGN OF LARGE-SCALE ICF LASER SYSTEMS. *Current Pos:* res assoc, 87-88, RES ASSOC, DEPT ELEC ENG, UNIV ALTA, 90- *Personal Data:* b Toronto, Ont, Sept 5, 55. *Educ:* Univ Toronto, BSc, 77, MSc, 80, PhD(physics), 85. *Prof Exp:* Fel, Dept Physics, Univ Toronto, 86; res scientist, Laser Fusion Proj, Alterra Laser Technol, Edmonton, Alta, 89-90. *Concurrent Pos:* Vis scientist, Los Alamos Nat Lab, 91- *Mem:* Can Asn Physicist; Optical Soc Am. *Res:* Development of KrF lasers as inertial confinement fusion drivers, including laser physics and system issues; use of LIDAR for remote sensing applications. *Mailing Add:* Los Alamos Nat Lab Chem Sci & Technol Mail Stop E548 Los Alamos NM 87545. *Fax:* 505-665-4026; *E-Mail:* dcthomp@lanl.gov

**THOMPSON, DAVID DUVALL,** internal medicine; deceased, see previous edition for last biography

**THOMPSON, DAVID FRED,** EMISSIONS CONTROL, SPECIALTY MATERIALS. *Current Pos:* MGR TECH DEVELOP, ZIRCOA PROD, CORNING GLASS WORKS, 74-, SR DEVELOP ASSOC, CORNING, INC. *Personal Data:* b Columbus, Ohio, Mar 6, 41; m 66; c 4. *Educ:* Ohio State Univ, BSc, 64, MSc, 64, PhD(ceramic eng), 68. *Prof Exp:* Proj engr, Edward Orton Jr Ceramic Found, 62-68; sect head, GTE Sylvania, 68-74. *Mem:* Am Ceramic Soc; Am Soc Testing & Mat; Am Soc Metals; Soc Automotive Engrs. *Res:* Zirconia ceramics; solid electrolytes; processing technology; optimization of ceramic material properties; physical property measurement; test development; emissions control. *Mailing Add:* Corning Inc Sullivan Park Corning NY 14831

**THOMPSON, DAVID J,** GENETICS, PLANT BREEDING. *Current Pos:* Co-geneticist, Ferry-Morse Seed Co, 60-63, res dir genetics & plant breeding, 63-76, vpres, Res Div, 76-85, pres, 86-90, SR BREEDER, FERRY-MORSE SEED CO, 91- *Personal Data:* b Danville, Ind, Apr 17, 34; m 68, Sharon Louise McElroy; c David Alan & Beth Ann. *Educ:* Univ Idaho, BS, 54, MS, 56; Cornell Univ, PhD(plant breeding), 60. *Mem:* Int Soc Hort Sci; Am Soc Hort Sci. *Res:* Genetics, cytology and physiology of male-sterility and self-incompatibility in plants. *Mailing Add:* PO Box 937 San Juan Bautista CA 95045

**THOMPSON, DAVID JEROME,** MINERAL NUTRITION. *Current Pos:* RETIRED. *Personal Data:* b Sand Creek, Wis, July 21, 37; m 62; c 2. *Educ:* Univ Wis-Madison, BS, 60, MS, 61, PhD(biochem), 63; Univ Chicago, MBA, 75. *Prof Exp:* Res assoc biochem, Univ Wis-Madison, 63-64; res biochemist, Int Minerals & Chem Corp, 64-69, mgr tech serv, 69-78, dir tech serv, 78-79, regional sales mgr, 79-81, vpres, sci & technol, 81-84, vpres & gen mgr, Sterwin Div, 84-86, vpres planning & develop, 87-89; dir tech planning & eval, Pitman-Moore Inc, 89-92. *Concurrent Pos:* Mem, Mineral Toxic Animals Subcomt, Nat Res Coun, Nat Acad Sci, 76-80; mem, Nutrit Sci External Adv Comt, Univ Ill, 85-91. *Mem:* NY Acad Sci; Am Chem Soc; AAAS; Coun Agr Sci & Technol. *Res:* Mineral nutrition of animals. *Mailing Add:* 826 Fair Way Libertyville IL 60048

**THOMPSON, DAVID JOHN,** ASTROPHYSICS, GAMMA RAY ASTRONOMY. *Current Pos:* ASTROPHYSICIST, GODDARD SPACE FLIGHT CTR, NASA, 73- *Personal Data:* b Cincinnati, Ohio, Jan 11, 45; m 72, Carlynn J Grumbles; c Lessa A & Kira J. *Educ:* Johns Hopkins Univ, BA, 67; Univ Md, PhD(physics), 73. *Prof Exp:* Res assoc physics, Univ Md, 73. *Concurrent Pos:* Co-investr, Energetic Gamma Ray Exp Telescope, Gamma Ray Observ, 78-; NASA High Energy Astrophys Mgt Opers Working Group, 90-92, Gamma Ray Astrophys Prog Working Group, 95-97. *Mem:* Am Astron Soc; Am Phys Soc. *Res:* Gamma ray astronomy and its relationship to cosmic ray physics and other aspects of astrophysics; high energy gamma ray detectors. *Mailing Add:* Code 661 Goddard Space Flight Ctr NASA Greenbelt MD 20771. *E-Mail:* djt@egret.gsfc.nasa.gov

**THOMPSON, DAVID RUSSELL,** ENGINEERING, FOOD SCIENCE. *Current Pos:* prof & head, Agr Eng Dept, 85-91, PROF & ASSOC DEAN INSTR & EXTEN, COL ENG, ARCHIT & TECH OKLA STATE UNIV, STILLWATER, 91- *Personal Data:* b Cleveland, Ohio, Apr 4, 44; m 66, Janet A Schall; c Devin M, Darin M & Colleen M. *Educ:* Purdue Univ, West Lafayette, BS, 66, MS, 67; Mich State Univ, PhD(agr eng), 70. *Honors & Awards:* Young Researcher Award, Am Soc Agr Engrs, 83. *Prof Exp:* From asst prof to prof food eng, Univ Minn, St Paul, 70-85. *Concurrent Pos:* NSF grant, 72-73; sabbatical leave to work for Green Giant (Pillsbury) Co, LeSueur, Minn, 78-79; mem rev team, Dept Defense Food Res Develop, Test & Eng Prog, Nat Res Coun, 80. *Mem:* Fel Am Soc Agr Engrs; Inst Food Technol; Am Soc Eng Educ; Am Soc Heating, Refrig & Air Conditioning Engrs; Nat Soc Prof Engrs. *Res:* Food processing; modeling heat and mass transfer reaction kinetics of changes in nutrition; microbiological populations and organoleptic characteristics in food systems during heating and cooling processes; energy conservation in food systems. *Mailing Add:* Col Eng Archit & Tech 111 Engr N Stillwater OK 74078-7545. *Fax:* 405-744-7545; *E-Mail:* dthomps@okway.okstate.edu

**THOMPSON, DAVID WALKER,** SPACE TECHNOLOGY. *Current Pos:* CHMN BD, PRES & CHIEF EXEC OFFICER, ORBITAL SCI CORP, 82- *Personal Data:* b Philadelphia, Pa, Mar 21, 54. *Educ:* Mass Inst Technol, BS; Harvard Bus Sch, MBA; Calif Inst Technol, MS. *Honors & Awards:* Nat Medal Technol, 91; Lawrence Sperry Award, Am Inst Aeronaut & Astronaut, 88; Lloyd V Brucker Award, Am Astronaut Soc, 89. *Prof Exp:* Proj mgr & engr, Marshall Space Flight Ctr, NASA; spec asst to pres, Missile Systs Group, Hughes Aircraft Co. *Concurrent Pos:* Dir, Am Astron Soc, Space Found, Nat Space Club, Found for Space Bus Res & Aurora Flight Sci Corp; mem, Com Prog Adv Comt, NASA; vchmn, Com Space Transp Adv Comt, Dept Transp; consult, Defense Sci Bd. *Mem:* Fel Am Astronaut Soc; assoc fel Am Inst Aeronaut & Astronaut. *Res:* Commercial space technology; develop, manufacture and market space transportation systems; commercial satellite applications. *Mailing Add:* Orbital Sci Corp 21700 Atlantic Blvd Dulles VA 20166

**THOMPSON, DAVID WALLACE,** INORGANIC CHEMISTRY, ORGANOMETALLIC CHEMISTRY. *Current Pos:* Asst prof, 67-70, ASSOC PROF CHEM, COL WILLIAM & MARY, 70- *Personal Data:* b Chicago, Ill, Jan 27, 42; m 63; c 2. *Educ:* Wheaton Col, BS, 63; Northwestern Univ, Evanston, PhD(chem), 68. *Mem:* Am Chem Soc. *Res:* Coordination chemistry of group IV elements; use of transition elements to catalyze organic reactions. *Mailing Add:* Dept Chem William & Mary Col Williamsburg VA 23185-3647

**THOMPSON, DONALD B,** NUTRIENT BIOAVAILABILITY, INGREDIENT FUNCTIONALITY. *Current Pos:* ASST PROF FOOD SCI, PA STATE UNIV, 84- *Personal Data:* b Camden, NJ, Oct 27, 48; m 71; c 3. *Educ:* Haverford Col, BA, 70; Univ Ill, MS, 80, PhD(food sci), 84. *Prof Exp:* Food scientist, R T French Co, 80-81. *Mem:* Inst Food Technologists; Am Chem Soc; assoc Am Inst Nutrit. *Res:* Influence of food processing on bioavailability of minerals, especially iron and zinc; functionality of hydrocolloid materials in food systems. *Mailing Add:* Dept Food Sci 111 Borland Lab Pa State Univ University Park PA 16802-0001. *Fax:* 814-863-6132

**THOMPSON, DONALD LEO,** PHYSICAL CHEMISTRY. *Current Pos:* PROF CHEM, OKLA STATE UNIV, 83- *Personal Data:* b Keota, Okla, Dec 31, 43; m 65; c 3. *Educ:* Northeastern Okla State Univ, BS, 65; Univ Ark, Fayetteville, PhD(phys chem), 70. *Prof Exp:* Res assoc theoret chem, Univ Calif, Irvine, 70-71; mem staff theoret chem, Los Alamos Nat Lab, 71-83. *Concurrent Pos:* Vis assoc prof physics, Univ Miss, 75-76; vis prof chem, Okla State Univ, 80-81. *Mem:* Am Chem Soc. *Res:* Theoretical molecular dynamics; reaction kinetics and intermolecular energy transfer. *Mailing Add:* Dept Chem Okla State Univ Stillwater OK 74078

**THOMPSON, DONALD LEROY,** HEALTH PHYSICS. *Personal Data:* b Highland Park, Mich, Nov 15, 32; m 62; c 1. *Educ:* City Col New York, BS, 61; Long Island Univ, MS, 66; St Johns Univ, PhD(phys chem), 72, cert health physics, 81. *Prof Exp:* Sr scientist med physics, Radiation Physics Lab, State Univ NY Downstate Med Ctr, 62-65, asst dir, 65-69, co-dir, 69-72; health physicist, Bur Radiol Health, 72-74, actg dep dir, Div Radioactive Mat Br, 75-78, dep chief nuclear med, 78-82. *Concurrent Pos:* Instr radiol, State Univ NY, 65-69, asst prof radiol sci, 69-72; instr, Found Advan Educ Sci, 73-81. *Mem:* Am Asn Physicists in Med; Health Physics Soc. *Res:* Radiation exposures related to medical and consumer products. *Mailing Add:* Ctr Devices & Radiol Health 5600 Fishers Lane Rockville MD 20857

**THOMPSON, DONALD LORAINE,** AGRONOMY. *Current Pos:* RETIRED. *Personal Data:* b SDak, Feb 10, 21; m 49; c 1. *Educ:* SDak State Col, BS, 47, MS, 49; Iowa State Col, PhD(corn breeding), 53. *Prof Exp:* Asst small grain breeding, SDak State Col, 47-49; corn breeding, Iowa State Col, 49-52; prof crop sci & res agronomist, USDA, NC State Univ, 52-83. *Mem:* Am Soc Agron. *Res:* Practical and theoretical aspects of corn breeding relating to quantitative genetics; disease resistance; relationships among economic traits; maximum production; forage evaluation. *Mailing Add:* 1613 Pineview Dr Raleigh NC 27606

**THOMPSON, DONALD OSCAR,** SOLID STATE PHYSICS, NONDESTRUCTIVE EVALUATION. *Current Pos:* dir, 79-87, PROF AEROSPACE ENG & ENG MECH, IOWA STATE UNIV, 79-, PRIN SCIENTIST & PROG DIR, AMES LAB, 79-, EMER DIR, CTR NONDESTRUCTIVE EVAL, 97- *Personal Data:* b Clear Lake, Iowa, Feb 27, 27; m 46, Barbara Newell; c James, Stephen & John. *Educ:* Univ Iowa, BA, 49, MS, 50, PhD(physics), 53. *Prof Exp:* Group leader elastic & anelastic effects & mem, Radiation Effects Group, Solid State Physics Div, Oak Ridge Nat Lab, 54-64; mgr tech staff & dir, Struct Mat Dept, Rockwell Int Sci Ctr, 64-79. *Mem:* Nat Acad Eng; Am Inst Mech & Mining Engrs; fel Inst Elec & Electronics Engrs; Sigma Xi; Am Soc Nondestructive Testing; fel Am Phys Soc. *Res:* Radiation damage in metals, particularly interaction of radiation-produced defects and dislocations; anharmonic and nonlinear effects in solids; materials research in support of nondestructive testing; nondestructive testing apparatus. *Mailing Add:* Ctr Nondestructive Eval Appl Sci Complex II Scholl Rd Iowa State Univ 1915 Scholl Rd Ames IA 50011. *Fax:* 515-294-7771; *E-Mail:* dthompson@cnde.iastate.edu

**THOMPSON, DUDLEY,** chemical engineering; deceased, see previous edition for last biography

**THOMPSON, EARL RYAN,** METALLURGICAL ENGINEERING, MATERIALS SCIENCE. *Current Pos:* sr res scientist high temp alloy res, 65-74, mgr mat sci, 74-85, DIR MAT & STRUCT, UNITED TECHNOL RES CTR, 85- *Personal Data:* b Lenoir, NC, Jan 9, 39; m 60, Sylvia Ransdell; c Ashley, Amy & Brian. *Educ:* NC State Univ, BS, 60, MS, 62; Univ VA, DSc, 66. *Honors & Awards:* Grossman's Auth Award, Am Soc Metals, 70. *Prof Exp:* Res scientist metal, Reynolds Metals Co, 61-62. *Concurrent Pos:* Newcomb fel, Univ Va, 64; mem, Solid State Sci Panel, Nat Res Coun, 76-79; mem, Nat Mat Adv Comt, 90-, Int Mat Rev Comt; mem adv bd mat proj, Energy Conversion & Utilization Technol Prog, Dept Energy, 84-87, adv comt, Metals & Ceramics Div, Oak Ridge Nat Lab, 87- *Mem:* Fel Am Soc Metals; Am Inst Mining, Metall & Petrol Engrs; Am Ceramic Soc; Sigma Xi; Am Soc Testing & Mat; AAAS. *Res:* High temperature alloy research and development; composite materials; directional solidification; ceramics for gas turbine use; rapidly solidified alloys; high temperature coatings; plasma spray processing; machinery and tribology. *Mailing Add:* United Technol Res Ctr Silver Lane East Hartford CT 06108. *Fax:* 860-727-7879; *E-Mail:* ert@utrc.utc.com

**THOMPSON, EDWARD IVINS BRADBRIDGE,** CELL GENETICS, HORMONES & CANCER. *Current Pos:* PROF & CHMN, DEPT HUMAN BIOL CHEM & GENETICS & PROF INTERNAL MED, UNIV TEX MED BR, 84-, INTERIM DIR, SEALY CTR MOLECULAR SCI, 96- *Personal Data:* b Burlington, Iowa, Dec 20, 33; m 57, Lynn Parsons; c Edward E & Elizabeth L. *Educ:* Rice Inst, BA, 55; Harvard Med Sch, MD, 60. *Prof Exp:* Intern & resident med, Presby Hosp, Col Physicians & Surgeons, Columbia Univ, 60-62; res assoc neurochem, Lab Clin Sci, NIMH, 62-64, res scientist molecular biol, Lab Molecular Biol, Nat Inst Arthritis & Metab Dis, 64-69, sr res scientist molecular & cell biol, 69-73, head, Sect Biochem Gene Expression, Lab Biochem, Nat Cancer Inst, 73-84. *Concurrent Pos:* Corresp ed, J Steroid Biochem; sci adv biotechnol, Am Cancer Soc Rev Bd; assoc ed, Cancer Res; ed-in-chief, Molecular Endocrinol, 85-92; coun res, Am Cancer Soc, 89-93; bd sci overseers, Pennington Nutrit Ctr, La State Univ. *Mem:* Endocrine Soc; Am Soc Cell Biol; Am Soc Biochem & Molecular Biol; Am Asn Cancer Res; Am Soc Microbiol; Am Col Med Genetics. *Res:* Endocrinology; regulation of gene expression in eukaryotic cells; mechanism of steroid hormone action; effects of steroids in malignant cells; cholesterol regulation; steroids; hormones and AIDS; programmed cell death. *Mailing Add:* Dept Human Biol Chem & Genetics Univ Tex Med Br Galveston TX 77555-0645. *Fax:* 409-772-5159; *E-Mail:* bthompso@mspo1.med.utmb.edu

**THOMPSON, EDWARD OTIS,** USEOF TECHNOLOGY, MATHEMATICS TEACHING EDUCATION. *Current Pos:* PROF MATH, WESTERN MONT COL, UNIV MONT, 79- *Personal Data:* b Rural Madison Co, Mont, Feb 8, 44; m 65, Darylene Jo Stroud; c David L & Shelley L. *Educ:* Western Mont Col, BS, 66; Mont State Univ, MS, 68, DEd, 92. *Prof Exp:* Prof math, Flathead Valley Community Col, 69-79. *Mem:* Math Asn Am; Nat Coun Teachers Math; Consortium Math & Appls. *Res:* How students learn mathematics and the effects technology has on the learning process instruction of high school and college mathematics courses. *Mailing Add:* Western Mont Col 710 S Atlantic Dillon MT 59725-3598. *E-Mail:* o_thompson@wmc.edu

**THOMPSON, EDWARD VALENTINE,** POLYMER MATERIAL SCIENCE, MEMBRANE TECHNOLOGY. *Current Pos:* PROF CHEM ENG, UNIV MAINE, ORONO, 66- *Personal Data:* b Sharon, Conn, Feb 6, 35; m 56; c 2. *Educ:* Cornell Univ, AB, 56; Polytech Inst Brooklyn, PhD(phys chem), 62. *Prof Exp:* Chemist, Am Cyanamid Co, 56-57, res chemist, 61-66. *Mem:* Am Chem Soc; Am Inst Chem Engrs. *Res:* Polymer composite structures; membrane separation processes; flow and compressibility characteristics of porous media. *Mailing Add:* Dept Chem Eng Univ Maine Jenness Hall Orono ME 04469

**THOMPSON, EDWARD WILLIAM,** ELECTRON MICROSCOPY, CARDIAC SURGERY. *Current Pos:* RES ASSOC, HORMEL INST, UNIV MINN, 84-, MGR, ELECTRON MICRO LAB, 84- *Personal Data:* b Twin Falls, Idaho, June 26, 51; m 75; c 3. *Educ:* Macalester Col, BA, 73; Med Col Wis, PhD(anat), 82. *Prof Exp:* Res fel anat & cardiol, Sch Med, Temple Univ, 82-84, res instr anat, 83-84. *Concurrent Pos:* Mem, Adv Comt & Selection Comt, Am Asn Anatomists, 84-88; instr anat, Mayo Clinic, 89- *Mem:* Am Asn Anatomists; Am Heart Asn; Am Soc Cell Biol; Electron Micros Soc Am; Soc Exp Biol Med. *Res:* Stereologic, ultrastructural and biochemical anlysis of myocardium in diabetic cardiomyopathy, obesity and hypertrophy induced by pressure or volume overloading. *Mailing Add:* Dept Biol Winona State Univ PO Box 5838 Winona MN 55987-5838. *Fax:* 507-437-9606

**THOMPSON, ELIZABETH ALISON,** GENETIC EPIDEMIOLOGY OF COMPLEX TRAITS, STATISTICAL INFERENCE OF POPULATION STRUCTURE OF ENDANGERED SPECIES. *Current Pos:* PROF STATIST & BIOSTATIST, UNIV WASH, 85- *Personal Data:* b Oxford, Eng, May 22, 49. *Educ:* Univ Cambridge, BA(Hons) 70, dipl 71, MA, 74, PhD(statist), 74, ScD, 88. *Prof Exp:* Sci Res Coun-NATO fel, Stanford Univ, 74-75; res fel, Kings Col, Cambridge, 75-76; lectr, math statist, Univ Cambridge, 76-85. *Concurrent Pos:* Vis res consult, Univ Utah, 75, 76, 78; vis scholar, Univ Mich, 75, 77; fel & financial tutor, Kings Col, 78-81; fel & dir studies, Newnham Col, 81-85; prin investr, NSF, 86-, USDA, 88-90 & NIH, 91-; consult, DMS Inc, 87-88; vis prof, Rutgers Univ, 91-92. *Mem:* Royal Statist Soc; Biomet Soc; Int Statist Inst. *Res:* Development of methods for the statistical analysis of genetic data both in the area of genetic epidemiology and also the conservation genetics of highly endangered species. *Mailing Add:* Dept Statist GN-22 Univ Wash 3900 Seventh Ave NE Seattle WA 98195-0001. *Fax:* 206-685-7419; *E-Mail:* thompson@stat.washington.edu

**THOMPSON, EMMANUEL BANDELE,** PHARMACOLOGY. *Current Pos:* RETIRED. *Personal Data:* b Zarla, Nigeria, Mar 15, 28. *Educ:* Rockhurst Col, BS, 55; Univ Mo-Kansas City, BS, 59; Univ Nebr, Lincoln, MS, 63; Univ Wash, PhD(pharmacol), 66. *Prof Exp:* Hosp pharmacist, Univ Kans Med Ctr, 59-60; retail pharmacist, Cundiff Drug Store, 61; sr res pharmacologist, Baxter Labs Inc, Ill, 63-66; asst prof, Med Ctr, Univ Ill, 69-73, assoc prof pharmacol, Col Pharm, 73-97. *Concurrent Pos:* Univ Ill Grad Col grant, 69-70 & Exten, 70-71; prin res investr & consult, West Side Vet Admin Hosp, Chicago, 71-; USPHS grant, 72-74. *Mem:* NY Acad Sci; Am Asn Cols Pharm; Am Pharmaceut Asn. *Res:* Cardiovascular pharmacology. *Mailing Add:* Dept Pharmacodynamics M/C 865 Univ Ill Health Sci 833 S Wood St Chicago IL 60612-4324

**THOMPSON, EMMETT FRANK,** FOREST ECONOMICS. *Current Pos:* head dept, 77-84, PROF FORESTRY, AUBURN UNIV, 77-, DEAN, SCH FORESTRY, 85- *Personal Data:* b El Reno, Okla, Nov 6, 36; m 61, ViAnn Brown; c Julia, Charles & Meri. *Educ:* Okla State Univ, BS, 58; NC State Univ, MS, 60; Ore State Univ, PhD(forest econ), 66. *Prof Exp:* From asst prof to prof forestry, Va Polytech Inst, 62-73; prof forestry & head dept, Miss State Univ, 73-77. *Mem:* Fel Soc Am Foresters; Forest Products Res Soc. *Res:* Economics of forest resource management. *Mailing Add:* Sch Forestry Auburn Univ Auburn AL 36849-5418

**THOMPSON, ERIC DOUGLAS,** SOLID STATE PHYSICS, SOLID STATE ELECTRONICS. *Current Pos:* Chandler-Weaver prof & chmn, 83-86, PROF COMPUT SCI & ELEC ENG, LEHIGH UNIV, 86- *Personal Data:* b Buffalo, NY, Mar 24, 34; m 60; c 3. *Educ:* Mass Inst Technol, SB & SM, 56, PhD(physics), 60. *Prof Exp:* NSF res fel, 62-63; from asst prof to assoc prof, Case Western Res Univ, 63-69, prof eng, 69-83. *Concurrent Pos:* Sr res assoc, Jet Propulsion Lab, 72-73; prog dir, NSF, 81-82. *Mem:* Fel Am Phys Soc; sr mem Inst Elec & Electronics Engrs. *Res:* Theory of magnetism; solid state microwave active devices; Josephson Junction devices; thermal atomic scattering; cryogenic electronics; optical mixing. *Mailing Add:* 2042 Hilltop Rd Bethlehem PA 18015

**THOMPSON, ERIK G(RINDE),** ENGINEERING MECHANICS. *Current Pos:* assoc prof, 68-76, PROF CIVIL ENG, COLO STATE UNIV, 76- *Personal Data:* b Dallas, Tex, May 3, 34; m 59; c 3. *Educ:* Southern Methodist Univ, BS, 57; Univ Tex, MS, 59, PhD(eng mech), 65. *Prof Exp:* From asst prof to assoc prof eng sci, Univ Idaho, 64-68. *Mem:* Am Soc Eng Educ; Am Acad Mech; Sigma Xi. *Res:* Plasticity and creep in engineering materials; finite element method; metal forming analysis. *Mailing Add:* 1812 Yorktown Ft Collins CO 80526-1659

**THOMPSON, ERNEST AUBREY, JR,** BIOCHEMISTRY, MOLECULAR BIOLOGY. *Current Pos:* assoc prof, 87-89, PROF BIOL CHEM, UNIV TEX, 89- *Personal Data:* b Tyler, Tex, Nov 17, 45; m 67; c 2. *Educ:* Southern Methodist Univ, BS, 68; Univ Tex, Dallas, PhD(biochem), 74. *Prof Exp:* Fel biochem, Med Ctr, Univ Calif, San Francisco, 74-77; from asst prof to assoc prof biol, Univ SC, 77-87. *Concurrent Pos:* Fel, Am Cancer Soc 74-75, res prof; NIH fel, 76-77, grant, 78- *Res:* Hormonal control of cellular proliferation. *Mailing Add:* Dept Human Biol Univ Tex Med Sch Rte 0645 301 Univ Blvd Galveston TX 77550-0645

**THOMPSON, EVAN M,** PHYSICAL ORGANIC CHEMISTRY. *Current Pos:* from asst prof to assoc prof, 65-74, dean, Sch Natural Sci, 70-76, PROF CHEM, CALIF STATE UNIV, STANISLAUS, 74- *Personal Data:* b Payson, Utah, Aug 7, 33; m 59, Norene Schumann; c Bryan, Cheryl, Alan, Ethan & Devan. *Educ:* Brigham Young Univ, BA, 60, PhD(org chem), 65. *Prof Exp:* Charles F Kettering & Great Lakes Cols Asn teaching fel chem, Antioch Col, 64-65. *Mem:* Am Chem Soc. *Res:* Organic reaction mechanisms; kinetics; chemical education. *Mailing Add:* 661 Meadowlark Dr Turlock CA 95382. *E-Mail:* evan@chem.csustan.edu

THOMPSON, FAY MORGEN, OCCUPATIONAL HEALTH, ENVIRONMENTAL CHEMISTRY. *Current Pos:* instr occup health, Sch Pub Health, 70-78, occup health chemist, Environ Health & Safety, 74-82, ASST PROF ENVIRON HEALTH, SCH PUB HEALTH, UNIV MINN, 78-, ASST DIR, ENVIRON HEALTH & SAFETY, 82- *Personal Data:* b St Paul, Minn, Dec 13, 35; m 55; c 2. *Educ:* Univ Minn, BA, 63, PhD(org chem), 70; Am Bd Indust Hyg, cert, 77. *Prof Exp:* Instr chem, Macalester Col, 67-68. *Concurrent Pos:* Mem adv comt hazardous waste, Minn Waste Mgt Bd, 80-; mem, Comt Hazardous Substances in Lab, Nat Res Coun, 81-83; mem bd dirs, Am Lung Asn, 84- *Mem:* Am Indust Hyg Asn; Am Chem Soc; Am Conf Govt Indust Hygienists; Am Acad Indust Hyg; Sigma Xi; Air Pollution Control Asn. *Res:* Collection and analysis of selected air contaminants; waste minimization; hazardous waste disposal; laboratory safety; laboratory use of carcinogens. *Mailing Add:* Pub Health Box 197 Mayo Univ Minn 420 Delaware St SE Minneapolis MN 55455-0374

THOMPSON, FRANCIS TRACY, ELECTRICAL ENGINEERING. *Current Pos:* RETIRED. *Personal Data:* b New York, NY, Nov 22, 30; m 55, Gloria Gray; c Nancy, Robert & Mark. *Educ:* Rensselaer Polytech Inst, BSEE, 52; Univ Pittsburgh, MS, 55, PhD(elec eng), 64. *Honors & Awards:* B G Lamme Award. *Prof Exp:* Develop engr, Res Labs, Westinghouse Elec Corp, 53-57, fel engr, New Prod Lab, 57-61, supvry engr, Res Labs, 61-64, mgr info & control circuitry, elec systs & power conditioning, 64-69, dir instrumentation & systs res, 69-72, dir, electronics & electromagnetics res, 72-74, dir, elec sci res, 74-77, mgr Electronics Technol. 77-78, gen mgr, Eng Technol Div, 87-91. *Concurrent Pos:* Mem bd dir, Siliconix, 80-88. *Mem:* Fel Inst Elec & Electronics Engrs; Instrument Soc Am. *Res:* Digital computer development; control systems; instrumentation; television systems; solid-state circuitry; magnetic and mechanical systems; power electronic systems. *Mailing Add:* 3482 Treeline Dr Murrysville PA 15668

THOMPSON, FRED C, ELECTRONICS ENGINEERING. *Current Pos:* RETIRED. *Personal Data:* b Snow Shoe, Pa, Feb 26, 28; m 52; c 4. *Educ:* Pa State Univ, BS, 50, MS, 58. *Prof Exp:* Engr, Martin Co, Md, 52-54; engr, HRB-Singer, Inc, 54-58, div mgr receiving systs, 58-60, staff engr, 60-63, lab dir countermeasures equip, 63-66, staff asst to tech vpres, 66-69; vpres, Locus, Inc, 68-80, pres, 80-89. *Mem:* Sr mem Inst Elec & Electronics Engrs. *Res:* Very high frequency-ultra high frequency receiving systems; microwave devices. *Mailing Add:* 1440 Willowbrook Dr Boalsburg PA 16827

THOMPSON, FRED GILBERT, MALACOLOGY. *Current Pos:* interim assoc cur, 66-71, assoc cur malacol, 71-81, CUR MALACOL & PROF ZOOL, FLA STATE MUS, UNIV FLA, 81- *Personal Data:* b Cleveland, Ohio, Nov 13, 34; m 57; c 1. *Educ:* Univ Mich, BS, 58; Wayne State Univ, MA, 61; Univ Miami, PhD(zool), 64. *Prof Exp:* Res scientist, Univ Miami, 64-66. *Concurrent Pos:* NIH res grant systs Amnicolidae, 64-67. *Mem:* Am Malacol Union; Asn Syst Malacologists. *Res:* Systematics, ecology, land and freshwater mollusks. *Mailing Add:* Fla Mus Nat Hist Museum Rd Gainesville FL 32611

THOMPSON, FREDERICK NIMROD, JR, REPRODUCTIVE ENDOCRINOLOGY. *Current Pos:* asst prof, 73-90, PROF PHYSIOL, UNIV GA, 90- *Personal Data:* b Newport News, Va, Dec 9, 39; m 62, Judith; c Gregory & Alison. *Educ:* Wake Forest Univ, BS, 61; Univ Ga, DVM, 65; Iowa State Univ, PhD(physiol), 73. *Prof Exp:* Instr physiol, Iowa State Univ, 67-73. *Mem:* Soc Study Reproduction; Sigma Xi; Am Vet Med Asn; Am Soc Animal Sci. *Res:* Bovine fescue toxicosis. *Mailing Add:* Dept Physiol & Pharmacol Col Vet Med Univ Ga Athens GA 30602. *Fax:* 706-542-3015; *E-Mail:* thompson.f@calc.vet.uga.edu

THOMPSON, GARY GENE, GEOLOGY, PALYNOLOGY. *Current Pos:* assoc prof, 83-89, SEAGER PROF GEOL, ROCKY MOUNTAIN COL, 89- *Personal Data:* b Beach, NDak, Oct 18, 40; div; c Erica. *Educ:* Univ NDak, BS, 62; Mich State Univ, PhD(geol), 69. *Prof Exp:* Geologist, Shell Develop Co, 68-69 & Shell Oil Co, 69-70; from asst prof to assoc prof geol, Salem State Col, 71-81. *Mem:* Soc Econ Paleontologists & Mineralogists; Am Asn Stratig Palynologists. *Res:* Cretaceous, tertiary and quaternary palynomorph biostratigraphy and paleoecology. *Mailing Add:* Dept Geol Rocky Mountain Col 1511 Poly Dr Billings MT 59102. *E-Mail:* ggthomps@rocky.edu

THOMPSON, GARY HAUGHTON, PHYSICAL CHEMISTRY, INORGANIC CHEMISTRY. *Current Pos:* PROG MGR, EG&G ROCKY FLATS, INC, 90- *Personal Data:* b Long Beach, Calif, Mar 25, 35; div; c 3. *Educ:* Univ Colo, Boulder, BS, 60; Univ Utah, PhD(chem), 69. *Prof Exp:* Engr, Hercules Powder Co, 60-63; res chemist, Savannah River Lab, E I du Pont de Nemours & Co, Inc, 69-75; group leader, Rocky Flats Plant, Rockwell Int Corp, 76-81; process oper mgr, 81-86, prog mgr, 86-90. *Mem:* Am Nuclear Soc; Am Chem Soc; Sigma Xi. *Res:* Chromatography, including gas, liquid and ion exchange; radioiodine sorption, gas-solid and gas-liquid systems; radioactive waste management and solvent extraction processes. *Mailing Add:* 10729 Varese Lane Denver CO 80234

THOMPSON, GEOFFREY, GEOCHEMISTRY, OCEANOGRAPHY. *Current Pos:* asst scientist, 65-70, assoc scientist, 70-78, SR SCIENTIST & CHMN, DEPT CHEM, WOODS HOLE OCEANOG INST, 78- *Personal Data:* b Stockton-on-Tees, Durham, Eng, Oct 18, 35; m 61; c 3. *Educ:* Univ Manchester, BSc, 61, PhD(geochem), 65. *Prof Exp:* Res chemist, Imp Chem Industs, UK, 58-59; geologist, Transvaal Gold Mines, SAfrica, 60. *Concurrent Pos:* Res assoc dept mineral sci, Smithsonian Inst, 70-; assoc ed, Geochimica et Cosmochmica Acta, 73- & J Marine Res, 74- *Mem:* AAAS; Geochem Soc; Am Geophys Union; Soc Appl Spectros. *Res:* Origin, evolution and geochemistry of oceanic crust; geochemistry of ocean sediments and marine organisms. *Mailing Add:* Dept Chem Woods Hole Oceanog Inst Woods Hole MA 02543

THOMPSON, GEORGE ALBERT, GEOPHYSICS, GEOLOGY. *Current Pos:* actg instr, Stanford Univ, 47-48, lectr, 48-49, from asst prof to prof, 49-60, chmn, Dept Geophys, 67-86, chmn, Dept Geol, 79-82, Otto N Miller prof earth sci, 80-89, dean, Sch Earth Sci, 87-89, PROF GEOPHYS, STANFORD UNIV, 60- *Personal Data:* b Swissvale, Pa, June 5, 19; m 44, Anita Kimmell; c Albert J, Dan A & David C. *Educ:* Pa State Col, BS, 41; Mass Inst Technol, MS, 42; Stanford Univ, PhD(geol), 49. *Honors & Awards:* George P Woollard Award, Geol Soc Am, 83. *Prof Exp:* Geologist, US Geol Surv, 42-44; US Navy (lt jg), 44-46. *Concurrent Pos:* Geologist & geophysicist, US Geol Surv, 46-76; NSF fel, 56-57; Guggenheim fel, 63-64; G K Gilbert award seismic geol, 64; consult, Adv Comt Reactor Safeguards, Nuclear Reg Comn, 72-94; mem, Geodynamics Comt, Nat Res Coun, 75-78; coun mem, Geol Soc Am, 83-86; mem bd, Earth Sci, Nat Res Coun, 86-88; co-chmn, Sci planning & rev comt, Edge Deep Seismic Reflection Prog, 86-92; sr external events rev group, Lawrence Livermore Nat Lab, 90-92; exec comt, Inc Res Inst Seismol (IRIS), 90-92; coun, Continental Sci Drilling, Nat Acad Sci, 90-; panel coupled processes, Yucca Mt, Nat Res Coun, 90-92; consult, Los Alamos Nat Lab, 92-96; chair, Nat Res Coun Comt, Ward Valley, Calif, 94-95; mem, Panel Probabalistic Volcanic Hazard Anal, Geometrix Cons, 95-96. *Mem:* Nat Acad Sci; Soc Explor Geophys; fel Geol Soc Am (vpres, 96, pres, 97); fel Am Geophys Union; fel AAAS; Seismol Soc Am. *Res:* Structure and geophysics of Basin Range Province; crust-mantle structure from deep seismic reflection and refraction measurements; lunar traverse gravity experiment; geophysics of ultramafic rocks; coupled magmatic-tectonic processes. *Mailing Add:* Dept Geophys Stanford Univ Stanford CA 94305-2215. *Fax:* 650-725-7344; *E-Mail:* thompson@pangea.stanford.edu

THOMPSON, GEORGE REX, TOXICOLOGY, PHARMACOLOGY. *Current Pos:* CHIEF EXEC OFFICER, COMPLIANCE INNOVATIONS, 83- *Personal Data:* b Oakley, Idaho, July 24, 43; m 63; c 4. *Educ:* Ore State Univ, BS, 65, PhD(toxicol & pharmacol), 69. *Prof Exp:* Res asst toxicol & pharmacol, Ore State Univ, 66-69; researcher toxicol, Mason Res Inst, Mass, 69-72; supvr toxicol, Biomed Res Lab, ICI Am Inc, 72-73; head, Sect Gen Toxicol, Abbott Labs, 73-77; mgr prod safety systs, Int Flavors & Fragrances Inc, 77-80, dir corp safety assurance, 80-83. *Mem:* Soc Toxicol; Am Soc Pharmacol & Exp Therapeut; Environ Mutagen Soc; Inst Food Technol. *Res:* Toxicity of marihuana or tetrahydrocannabinol, cyclamate/cyclohexylamine, new drugs, anticancer compounds and pesticides; delineation of normal physiological parameters via the utilization of toxic materials; safety criteria for flavors and fragrance; computerized safety evaluations; employee health and safety; environmental protection. *Mailing Add:* Compliance Innovations 706 Rte 15 S Suite 207 Lake Hopatcong NJ 07849

THOMPSON, GEORGE RICHARD, INTERNAL MEDICINE, RHEUMATOLOGY. *Current Pos:* resident, Hosp, 55-58, from instr to prof, 62-92, EMER PROF INTERNAL MED, MED SCH, UNIV MICH, ANN ARBOR, 92- *Personal Data:* b Ann Arbor, Mich, Apr 2, 30; m 57, Ruth M Payne; c David, Nancy & Susan. *Educ:* Univ Mich, Ann Arbor, BS, 50, MD, 54. *Prof Exp:* Intern, Ohio State Univ Hosp, 54-55; dir, Rheumatology Sect, Wayne Co Gen Hosp, Eloise, 63-84; Vet Admin Hosp, Ann Arbor, 84-87. *Concurrent Pos:* USPHS fel rheumatology, Rackham Arthritis Res Unit, Univ Mich Hosp, Ann Arbor, 60-62, assoc physician, 63- *Mem:* Fel Am Col Rheumatology; fel Am Col Physicians; Am Fedn Clin Res; Cent Soc Clin Res. *Res:* Arthritis; mucopolysaccharide metabolism; gout and urate excretion; rubella-associated arthritis. *Mailing Add:* Dept Internal Med Univ Mich 3918 Taubman 1500 E Med Ctr Dr Ann Arbor MI 48109

THOMPSON, GERALD LEE, ORGANIC CHEMISTRY. *Current Pos:* sr org chemist, Eli Lilly & Co, 74-79, res scientist, 80, head chem res div, 80-84, head cancer res, 84-86, head process res, 86-89, DIR CHEM PROCESS RES & DEVELOP, ELI LILLY & CO, 89- *Personal Data:* b Swea City, Iowa, Mar 16, 45; m 90; c 3. *Educ:* Iowa State Univ, BS, 68; Ohio State Univ, PhD(chem), 72. *Prof Exp:* NIH fel, Harvard Univ, 72-74. *Mem:* Am Chem Soc. *Res:* Antitumor drug design; alkaloid synthesis; general medicinal chemistry. *Mailing Add:* Dept IC742 Bldg 110/1 Lilly Corp Ctr Indianapolis IN 46285-2524

THOMPSON, GERALD LUTHER, COMBINATORIAL OPTIMIZATION. *Current Pos:* IBM PROF SYSTS & OPER RES, GRAD SCH INDUST ADMIN, CARNEGIE MELLON UNIV, 59- *Personal Data:* b Rolfe, Iowa, Nov 25, 23; m 54, Dorothea Mosley; c Allison M, Emily A & Abigail E. *Educ:* Iowa State Col, BS, 44; Mass Inst Technol, SM, 48; Univ Mich, PhD(math), 53. *Prof Exp:* Instr math, Princeton Univ, 51-53; asst prof, Dartmouth Col, 53-58; prof, Ohio Wesleyan, 58-59. *Concurrent Pos:* Consult, Princeton Univ, Int Bus Mach Corp, Sandia Corp, Beth Steel Corp, Timken Co, Westinghouse Elec Co & McKinsey & Co, Gen Motors, PPG Co; Inst Mgt Sci rep, Math Div, Nat Res Coun, 71-73; mem, Sealift Readiness Comt, Nat Acad Sci, 74-75. *Mem:* Am Math Soc; Inst Mgt Sci; Math Asn Am; Opers Res Soc Am; Math Prog Soc. *Res:* Applications of mathematics to management; mathematical economics; optimal control theory; graph theory and combinatorial problems; game theory; combinatorial optimization. *Mailing Add:* Grad Sch Indust Carnegie Mellon Univ Pittsburgh PA 15213

THOMPSON, GORDON WILLIAM, epidemiology, for more information see previous edition

THOMPSON, GRANT, PROPELLANT CHEMISTRY. *Current Pos:* RETIRED. *Personal Data:* b Ogden, Utah, Feb 26, 27; m 49; c 6. *Educ:* Univ Utah, BA, 50, PhD(chem), 53. *Prof Exp:* Res chemist, E I du Pont de Nemours & Co, 53-58; proj chemist, Thiokol Corp, 58-59, sr chemist, 59-60, supvr new propellants sect, 60-62, mgr propellant develop dept, Wasatch Div,

63-75, mgr, Res & Develop Labs, Wasatch Div, 75-85, dir, Res & Develop Labs, Advan Technol, 85-92. *Mem:* Am Chem Soc. *Res:* Mechanism of propellant cure; curing agents and catalysts for hydrocarbon propellants; mechanism of hydrocarbon propellant aging; high energy oxidizers and propellants. *Mailing Add:* 121 N 600 E Brigham City UT 84302-2227

**THOMPSON, GRANVILLE BERRY,** AGRICULTURAL RESEARCH ADMINISTRATION, ANIMAL NUTRITION & MANAGEMENT. *Current Pos:* AGR CONSULT, 96- *Personal Data:* b Sedalia, Mo, June 18, 29; m 58, Gertrude Stabely Alexander; c Mark G, Matt W & Dan A. *Educ:* Univ Mo, BS, 51, MS, 55, PhD(animal nutrit), 58. *Prof Exp:* Asst exten agent, Mo Agr Exten Serv, 51-55; grad asst animal sci, Univ Mo, 53-55, from instr to prof, 55-76; resident dir res & prof animal sci, Tex A&M Univ, 76-96, assoc dir, 93-96. *Mem:* Sigma Xi; Am Soc Animal Sci; Am Forage & Grassland Coun; Am Registry Prof Animal Scientists; Coun Agr & Technol; Acad Vet Consults. *Res:* Beef cattle nutrition and management; beef production systems; research administration. *Mailing Add:* 4243 Coats Lane Columbia MO 65203. *Fax:* 573-446-7411

**THOMPSON, GUY A, JR,** BIOCHEMISTRY. *Current Pos:* assoc prof, 67-74, PROF BOT, UNIV TEX, AUSTIN, 74-, DEPT CHMN, 96- *Personal Data:* b Rosedale, Miss, May 31, 31; m 60; c 3. *Educ:* Miss State Univ, BS, 53; Calif Inst Technol, PhD(biochem), 59. *Prof Exp:* NSF res fel chem, Univ Manchester, 59-60; res assoc biochem, Univ Wash, 60-62, from instr to asst prof, 62-67. *Concurrent Pos:* NIH res career develop award, 63-67. *Mem:* Fel AAAS; Am Soc Biol Chem; Am Oil Chem Soc; Am Chem Soc; Sigma Xi. *Res:* Lipid metabolism; biochemistry of membranes. *Mailing Add:* Dept Bot Univ Tex Austin TX 78724

**THOMPSON, H BRIAN,** ENGINEERING, FIBER PRODUCTS. *Current Pos:* sr vpres corp develop, 81-85, pres, Mid-Atlantic Div, Arlington Va, 85-87, EXEC VPRES, MCI COMMUN CORP, 87- *Personal Data:* b Buffalo, NY, Mar 24, 39; m, Mary Ann Selby; c Christiana & Brandon. *Educ:* Univ Mass, BS, 60; Harvard Bus Sch, MBA, 68. *Prof Exp:* Res engr, Kendall Co, 60-62, Monsanto Res Corp, 66; consult, McKinsey & Co, 68-77; sr vpres planning & mkt, Resource Sci Corp, 77-79; exec vpres, Gelman Sci, 79; pres, Subscription TV Am, 79-81. *Res:* Granted patent for non-woven fiber products. *Mailing Add:* 3636 Trinity Dr Alexandria VA 22304-1841

**THOMPSON, HANNIS WOODSON, JR,** ELECTRICAL ENGINEERING, SOLID STATE PHYSICS. *Current Pos:* PROF ELEC ENG, PURDUE UNIV, 63-, ASST HEAD EDUC, SCH ELEC ENG, 84- *Personal Data:* b Salisbury, NC, Sept 3, 28; m 51; c 2. *Educ:* NC State Univ, BS, 53, MS, 59; Purdue Univ, PhD(elec eng), 63. *Prof Exp:* Engr missile systs, Western Elec Co, 53-57. *Concurrent Pos:* Sr scientist, Navy Electronics Lab, 63, 64; consult, electronics & solid state, CTS Microelectronics, 62, 65- *Mem:* Inst Elec & Electronics Engrs; Am Phys Soc; Sigma Xi. *Res:* Solid state devices, oxide deposition, thin film and silicon technology. *Mailing Add:* 215 Timbercrest Rd West Lafayette IN 47906-8504

**THOMPSON, HARTWELL GREENE, JR,** NEUROLOGY. *Current Pos:* PROG DIR, DEPT NEUROL, HARTFORD HOSP, 76- *Personal Data:* b Hartford, Conn, Aug 30, 24; m 55; c 4. *Educ:* Yale Univ, BA, 46; Cornell Univ, MD, 50. *Prof Exp:* From asst to assoc neurol, Col Physicians & Surgeons, Columbia Univ, 57-59; from asst prof to assoc prof, Univ Wis, 59-64; prof & chmn dept, Sch Med, WVa Univ, 64-69; prof & assoc dean student affairs, Sch Med, Univ Pa, 69-73; prof neurol & dean, Charleston Div, WVa Univ Med Ctr, 73-76. *Concurrent Pos:* Consult, Vet Admin Hosp, Clarksburg, WVa, 64- *Mem:* AMA; Am Acad Neurol; Sigma Xi. *Res:* Neurology training programs and undergraduate education in neurology; multiple sclerosis; motor neuron disease. *Mailing Add:* 12 Mountain Rd West Hartford CT 06107-2913

**THOMPSON, HARVEY E,** AGRONOMY. *Current Pos:* RETIRED. *Personal Data:* b Valders, Wis, Oct 30, 20; m 53; c 2. *Educ:* Univ Wis, BS, 47, MS, 48, PhD(agron, econ entom), 51. *Prof Exp:* Enten agronomist, Iowa State Univ, 50-83. *Mem:* Am Soc Agron. *Res:* Forage and grain crop production. *Mailing Add:* 2200 Hamilton Dr Ames IA 50014

**THOMPSON, HAZEN SPENCER,** plant pathology, for more information see previous edition

**THOMPSON, HENRY JOSEPH,** BIOLOGY. *Current Pos:* CONSULT, 83- *Personal Data:* b Mamaroneck, NY, Sept 5, 21; m 47; c 3. *Educ:* Whittier Col, AB, 47; Stanford Univ, MA, 48, PhD, 52. *Prof Exp:* Instr biol, Whittier Col, 48-49; actg instr, Stanford Univ, 51-52; instr bot, Univ Calif, Los Angeles, 52-54, from asst prof to prof, 54-83. *Mem:* Am Soc Plant Taxon; Soc Study Evolution. *Res:* Systematics and evolution. *Mailing Add:* Lab Nutrit Res AMC Cancer Res Ctr 1600 Pierce St Lakewood CO 80214-1897. *Fax:* 303-233-9562

**THOMPSON, HERBERT BRADFORD,** STRUCTURAL CHEMISTRY. *Current Pos:* RETIRED. *Personal Data:* b Detroit, Mich, Apr 22, 27; m 49, Jane E Lang. *Educ:* Olivet Col, BS, 48; Oberlin Col, AM, 50; Mich State Col, PhD(chem), 53. *Prof Exp:* Res instr chem, Mich State Univ, 53-55; from asst prof to assoc prof, Gustavus Adolphus Col, 55-63; res assoc, Inst Atomic Res, Iowa State Univ, 63-65; res assoc, Univ Mich, 65-67; prof chem, Univ Toledo, 67-90, chmn dept, 68-69 & 74-75; scholar in residence chem & physics, Gustavus Adolphus Col, 90-94. *Mem:* Am Chem Soc; Am Phys Soc; Asn

Comput Mach. *Res:* Molecular structure and geometry; conformational analysis; data acquisition and computer applications in chemistry; dipole moments; models of the chemical bond. *Mailing Add:* 1604 Riverview Rd St Peter MN 56082

**THOMPSON, HERBERT STANLEY,** OPHTHALMOLOGY, NEUROLOGY. *Current Pos:* From instr to prof, 67-97, EMER PROF OPHTHAL, UNIV IOWA, 97- *Personal Data:* b China, June 12, 32; nat US; m 55; c 5. *Educ:* Univ Minn, BA, 53, MD, 61; Univ Iowa, MS, 66. *Concurrent Pos:* Nat Inst Neurol Dis & Blindness spec fel clin neuro-ophthal, Univ Calif, San Francisco, 66-67; Nat Inst Neurol Dis & Blindness res career develop award, 68; coun mem, Int Neuro-Ophthal Soc, 76-; assoc ed, 81-84, book rev ed, Am J Ophthal, 84-; dir, Am Bd Ophthal, 89- *Mem:* Asn Res Vision & Ophthal; Ophthal Soc UK; France Soc Ophthal; Am Acad Ophthal; Am Ophthal Soc; Int Neuro-Ophthal Soc. *Res:* Neuro-ophthalmology, especially of the autonomic nervous system. *Mailing Add:* Dept Ophthal Univ Iowa Hosps Iowa City IA 52242

**THOMPSON, HOLLY ANN,** BIOTECHNOLOGY, CELLULAR & DEVELOPMENTAL BIOCHEMISTRY. *Current Pos:* MGR RES & DEVELOP, CHROMATOCHEM, INC, 87- *Personal Data:* US citizen. *Educ:* Univ Del, BA, 76; Kans State Univ, PhD(cell & develop biol), 82. *Prof Exp:* Fel, NIH, 82-84; vis asst prof biochem, Univ Mont, 84-86. *Mem:* Am Soc Cell Biol. *Res:* Affinity chromatography, analytical immunoaffinity chromatography, novel quantitative solid phase assays, proteoglycan biosynthesis, extracellular matrix and morphogenesis, and mammalian development. *Mailing Add:* Dept Chem Univ Mont Missoula MT 59812. *Fax:* 406-728-5924

**THOMPSON, HOWARD DOYLE,** GAS DYNAMICS, LASER VELOCIMETRY. *Current Pos:* Asst eng sci, Purdue Univ, 61-62, asst mech eng, 62-65, from asst prof to assoc prof, 65-74, PROF MECH ENG, PURDUE UNIV, WEST LAFAYETTE, 74- *Personal Data:* b Cedar City, Utah, Apr 17, 34; m 56, Patricia A Frei; c Tamra, Kimberly (Smith), Shauna (Bigham), Trisha (Weeks) & Stephanie (Yorgason). *Educ:* Univ Utah, BS, 57; Purdue Univ, MS, 62, PhD(mech eng), 65. *Concurrent Pos:* Consult, Dynetics, Inc, 66-72, Detroit Diesel Allison, 74-76, Univ Dayton, 78-80, McDonnell-Douglas, 80-85, Air Force Wright Aeronaut Lab, 80-, Arnold Eng Develop Ctr, 81-85 & Ballistic Missile Div, Redstone Arsenal, Ala; assoc res scientist, Pratt & Whitney Aircraft, 69-70; sr mech engr, Arnold Eng Develop Ctr, 80-81; vis scientist, WL/POP, Wright-Patterson AFB, 90-91. *Mem:* Assoc fel Am Inst Aeronaut & Astronaut; Am Soc Mech Engrs; Laser Inst Am. *Res:* Propulsion gas dynamics; nozzle design; three-dimensional supersonic flows; optimization of aerodynamic shapes; transonic and annular flows; laser doppler velocimetry; experimental and numerical fluid mechanics; fluid mechanics in turbomachinery. *Mailing Add:* Sch Mech Eng Purdue Univ West Lafayette IN 47907

**THOMPSON, HOWARD K, JR,** internal medicine, for more information see previous edition

**THOMPSON, HUGH ALLISON,** MECHANICAL ENGINEERING. *Current Pos:* from instr to assoc prof mech eng, 63-71, PROF MECH ENG, TULANE UNIV, 71-, DEAN, 76- *Personal Data:* b Chattanooga, Tenn, Mar 24, 35; m 57; c 1. *Educ:* Auburn Univ, BS, 56; Tulane Univ, MSc, 62, PhD(mech eng), 64. *Prof Exp:* Process engr, Mobil Oil Corp, 56-60. *Mem:* Am Soc Mech Engrs; Inst Elec & Electronics Engrs. *Res:* Dynamic response of bus conductor structures to short circuit loads, of pole-mounted electric transmission lines to hurricane winds and of transformer coils to through faults. *Mailing Add:* Tulane Univ New Orleans LA 70118

**THOMPSON, HUGH ANSLEY,** CAPILLARY ENGINEERING, TEXTILES. *Current Pos:* PRIN, THOMPSON ENG, 82- *Personal Data:* b Olympia, Wash, Feb 22, 36; m 66, Grace Hilton. *Educ:* Mass Inst Technol, BS & MS, 63. *Prof Exp:* Develop engr, Procter & Gamble Co, 63-72, inventor-scientist, 73-94. *Mem:* Sigma Xi; Int Solar Energy Soc; Acad Appl Sci; Am Soc Mech Engrs. *Res:* Invention and development of microengineered capillary networks, textiles and related materials; absorbent products; solar and renewable energy development; 19 US patents. *Mailing Add:* 5777 Windermere Lane Fairfield OH 45014

**THOMPSON, HUGH ERWIN,** ENTOMOLOGY. *Current Pos:* RETIRED. *Personal Data:* b Newport, RI, Aug 4, 17; m 46; c 4. *Educ:* Univ RI, BS, 47; Cornell Univ, PhD(entom), 54. *Prof Exp:* Asst state entomologist, State Dept Agr & Conserv, RI, 47-48; entomologist, State Dept Agr, Pa, 53-56; from asst prof to prof entom, Kans State Univ, 56-86. *Mem:* Int Soc Arboricult; Arboricult Res & Educ Acad (pres, 78-79); Sigma Xi; Entom Soc Am; Soc Am Foresters. *Res:* Biology and control of insects attacking shade trees and ornamental plants; insect transmission of tree diseases. *Mailing Add:* 244 Summit Ave Manhattan KS 66502-3835

**THOMPSON, HUGH WALTER,** ORGANIC CHEMISTRY. *Current Pos:* from asst prof to assoc prof, 64-72, PROF CHEM, RUTGERS UNIV, NEWARK, 72- *Personal Data:* b New York, NY, Dec 7, 36; m 64; c 1. *Educ:* Cornell Univ, AB, 58; Mass Inst Technol, PhD(org chem), 63. *Prof Exp:* NIH res fel, Columbia Univ, 62-64. *Mem:* Am Chem Soc. *Res:* Mechanisms and stereochemical courses of organic reactions; compounds of unusual symmetry and stereochemistry; electronically crowded molecules; hydrogen bonding in keto carboxylic acids. *Mailing Add:* Dept Chem Rutgers Univ Newark NJ 07102. *Fax:* 973-648-1264

**THOMPSON, J G,** MATHEMATICS. *Current Pos:* EMER PROF, MATH DEPT, UNIV CAMBRIDGE, 95- *Mem:* Nat Acad Sci. *Mailing Add:* Math Dept Univ Cambridge Cambridge CB2 1SB England

**THOMPSON, JAMES ARTHUR,** ENVIRONMENTAL & INDUSTRIAL HYGIENE MANAGEMENT. *Current Pos:* res chemist analytical div, Alcoa Res Lab, 59-61, sr chemist, Warrick Opers, Ind, 61-70, chief chemist, Wenatchee Works, 70-75, NORTHWEST ENVIRON & INDUST HYG MGR, ALUMINUM CO AM, 75- *Personal Data:* b Sturgeon Bay, Wis, Aug 15, 31; m 55; c 3. *Educ:* St Olaf Col, BA, 55; Iowa State Univ, MS, 58. *Prof Exp:* Analytical chemist, Ames Lab, AEC, 55-59. *Mem:* AAAS; Am Chem Soc; Air Pollution Control Asn; Sigma Xi; Am Indust Hyg Asn. *Res:* Instrumental analysis; industrial hygiene; air and water pollution. *Mailing Add:* 1600 Washington St Wenatchee WA 98801-2559

**THOMPSON, JAMES BURLEIGH, JR,** PETROLOGY, GEOCHEMISTRY. *Current Pos:* instr petrol, Harvard Univ, 49-50, asst prof petrog, 50-55, assoc prof mineral, 55-60, prof, 60-77, STURGIS HOOPER PROF GEOL, HARVARD UNIV, 77- *Personal Data:* b Calais, Maine, Nov 20, 21; m 57, Eleanora Mairs; c 1. *Educ:* Dartmouth Col, AB, 42; Mass Inst Technol, PhD, 50. *Hon Degrees:* DSc, Dartmouth Col, 75. *Honors & Awards:* A L Day Medal, Geol Soc Am, 64; Roebling Medal, Mineral Soc Am, 78; V M Goldschmidt Medal, Geochem Soc, 85. *Prof Exp:* Instr geol, Dartmouth Col, 42; asst, Mass Inst Technol, 46-47, instr, 47-49. *Concurrent Pos:* Ford Found fel, 52-53; Guggenheim fel, 63; adj prof geol, Dartmouth Col, 92- *Mem:* Nat Acad Sci; AAAS; fel Geol Soc Am; fel Mineral Soc Am; fel Am Acad Arts & Sci; Geochem Soc. *Res:* Metamorphic petrology; geology of New England; coastal chemistry of rock-forming minerals. *Mailing Add:* Dept Earth & Planetary Sci Harvard Univ Cambridge MA 02138

**THOMPSON, JAMES CHARLES,** SURGERY, PHYSIOLOGY. *Current Pos:* prof, 70-86, JOHN WOODS HARRIS PROF SURG, UNIV TEX MED BR GALVESTON, 86-, CHMN DEPT & CHIEF SURG HOSP, 70- *Personal Data:* b San Antonio, Tex, Aug 16, 28; c 5. *Educ:* Agr & Mech Col Tex, BS, 48; Univ Tex, MD, 51, MA, 52; Am Bd Surg, dipl. *Honors & Awards:* Merit Award, NIH, 86. *Prof Exp:* Intern, Univ Tex Med Br Galveston, 51-52; asst resident surg, Hosp, Univ Pa, 52-54 & 56-58, chief resident, 58-59; from asst surgeon to assoc surgeon, Pa Hosp, 59-63; head physician, Harbor Gen Hosp, 63-67, chief surg, 67-70. *Concurrent Pos:* Fel, Harrison Dept Surg Res, Sch Med, Univ Pa, 52-54 & 56-57, Albert & Mary Lasker fel, 57-59; John A Hartford Found grants, 60-; NIH grants, 60-; asst instr surg, Sch Med, Univ Pa, 53-54 & 56-58, from instr to assoc instr, 58-61, asst prof, 61-63; from assoc prof to prof, Sch Med, Univ Calif, Los Angeles, 63-70. *Mem:* AAAS; Am Surg Asn; Am Physiol Soc; Am Gastroenterol Asn; Endocrine Soc; Soc Univ Surgeons. *Res:* Metabolism of regulatory peptides of gut; effect of aging on gut function and gastrointestinal hormones; gut hormones and growth (normal and neoplastic); signal transduction and molecular biology of gut hormones. *Mailing Add:* Dept Surg Univ Tex Med Br Galveston TX 77550-1220. *Fax:* 409-772-6368

**THOMPSON, JAMES CHARLTON,** INORGANIC CHEMISTRY. *Current Pos:* from asst prof to assoc prof chem, Univ Toronto, 67-93, assoc chmn dept, 74-77 & 82-94, actg chmn, 79-80, PROF CHEM & CHAIR PHYS SCI, UNIV TORONTO, SCARBOROUGH. *Personal Data:* b Leeds, UK, Jan 4, 41; div; c 2. *Educ:* Cambridge Univ, BA, 62, PhD(chem), 65. *Prof Exp:* Fel, Rice Univ, 65-67. *Mem:* Chem Inst Can. *Res:* Studies on the synthesis, structures and properties of silicon compounds, particularly those with fluorine or hydrogen bound to silicon. *Mailing Add:* Div Phys Sci Univ Toronto 1265 Military Trail Scarborough ON M1C 1A4 Can

**THOMPSON, JAMES CHILTON,** PHYSICS. *Current Pos:* From asst prof to assoc prof, 56-67, PROF PHYSICS, UNIV TEX, AUSTIN, 67- *Personal Data:* b Ft Worth, Tex, June 14, 30; m 55; c 3. *Educ:* Tex Christian Univ, BA, 52; Rice Inst, MA, 54, PhD(physics), 56. *Mem:* Am Phys Soc. *Res:* Transport coefficients in solid and liquid metals; metal-ammonia solutions; metal-nonmetal transition; electrode-electrolyte interfaces. *Mailing Add:* Dept Physics RLM14 218 Univ Tex Austin TX 78712

**THOMPSON, JAMES EDWIN,** ORGANIC CHEMISTRY. *Current Pos:* CHEMIST, PROCTER & GAMBLE CO, 61- *Personal Data:* b Maryville, Mo, Feb 2, 36; m 65; c 2. *Educ:* Cent Methodist Col, AB, 56; Univ Mo, PhD(chem cyclopropanes), 61. *Mem:* Am Chem Soc. *Res:* Electronic effects in cyclopropanes; synthetic lipid and phospholipid, organo-phosphorus and organo-sulfur chemistry; radiochemical synthesis. *Mailing Add:* 11790 Tennyson Dr Cincinnati OH 45241

**THOMPSON, JAMES JARRARD,** IMMUNOLOGY. *Current Pos:* actg head, 81-83, from asst prof to assoc prof, 74-90, PROF, DEPT MICROBIOL, LA STATE, UNIV MED CTR, NEW ORLEANS, 90- *Personal Data:* b Des Moines, Iowa; m 69, Harriet Willis; c Mark, Neil & Julliette. *Educ:* Univ Iowa, BA, 65, MS, 68, PhD(microbiol), 70. *Prof Exp:* Instr microbiol & immunol, Dept Microbiol, Univ Iowa, 70-71; instr, Temple Univ, 71-72, asst prof, 72-74. *Concurrent Pos:* Prin investr, NSF, 75-77, Am Heart Asn, 77-78, Arthritis Found, 78-79, NIH, 80- *Mem:* Am Asn Immmunologists; Am Soc Microbiol; AAAS; Sigma Xi; Am Asn Univ Prof. *Res:* Immmunoassay of apolipoproteins; structure and function of apolipoproteins; humoral immune responses in periodontal diseases; mechanisms of complement activation; humoral mediators of adaptive host responses. *Mailing Add:* Dept Microbiol & Immunol La State Univ Med Ctr 1901 Perdido St New Orleans LA 70112-1393

**THOMPSON, JAMES JOSEPH,** RADIATION SAFETY, RADIOACTIVE WASTE MANAGEMENT. *Current Pos:* DIR & RADIATION SAFETY OFFICER, UNIV UTAH, 94-, ADJ ASSOC PROF CIVIL & ENVIRON ENG, 96- *Personal Data:* b Waterbury, Conn, Oct 1940; m 63, Jeanette Gurule; c James T, Bruce E & Seth J. *Educ:* Univ NMex, BA, 62; Purdue Univ, MS, 70, PhD(bionucleonics), 72. *Prof Exp:* Dir health & safety, Lovelace Biomed & Environ Res Inst, 72-94. *Concurrent Pos:* Fac affil, Dept Environ Health, Colo State Univ, 85- *Mem:* Health Physics Soc; Am Nuclear Soc; Am Indust Hyg Asn. *Res:* Applied radiation protection problems; radioactive and mixed waste management; personnel radiation dosimetry; radioactive materials packaging and transportation. *Mailing Add:* 850 S Donner Way Salt Lake City UT 84108. *Fax:* 801-581-4206; *E-Mail:* jjthompson@rso.utah.edu

**THOMPSON, JAMES LAURENCE, JR,** AERONAUTICAL & ASTRONAUTICAL ENGINEERING. *Current Pos:* tech dir, Washington Off, 83-90, SR SCIENTIST SYSTEMS ENG AERO RADAR, LOGICON RDA, 90- *Personal Data:* b Union City, Tenn, Feb 20, 33; m 55, Jean G Danforth; c Tamara, Tara, Trisa & Tryna. *Educ:* US Naval Acad, BS, 55; USAF Inst Technol, MS, 62; Stanford Univ, PhD(aeronaut & astronaut eng), 73. *Prof Exp:* 2nd Lt through Col (fighter pilot), USAF, 55-76; tech dir, Washington Off, Res & Develop Assoc, 76-83. *Res:* Research in military and civilian employment of superconducting magnetic energy storage systems. *Mailing Add:* 2307 Rockwood Rd Accokeek MD 20607. *E-Mail:* jthompson@logicon.com

**THOMPSON, JAMES LOWRY,** APPLIED MATHEMATICS, ENGINEERING SCIENCE. *Current Pos:* mech engr, 74-82, chief, Survival Technol Br, 82-93, chief, Armor & Damage Reduction Div, US Army Tank Automotive Command, 93-95, ASSOC DIR SURVIVABILITY, US ARMY TANK AUTOMOTIVE RES & DEVELOP CTR, 95- *Personal Data:* b Syracuse, NY, Oct 5, 40; m 63, Carolyn Williams; c 2. *Educ:* Brown Univ, AB, 62; Johns Hopkins Univ, PhD(mech), 68. *Prof Exp:* Asst prof math & eng sci, State Univ NY, Buffalo, 68-74. *Concurrent Pos:* NSF res grant, State Univ NY, Buffalo, 71-73. *Mem:* AAAS; Am Math Soc; Soc Natural Philos; Soc Indust & Appl Math; Asn Comput Mach. *Res:* Analysis and optimization of complex systems; continuum mechanics. *Mailing Add:* 1448 Anita Ave Grosse Pointe Woods MI 48236-1476. *Fax:* 313-574-6674; *E-Mail:* jlthompson@acm.org

**THOMPSON, JAMES MARION,** plant breeding, plant genetics, for more information see previous edition

**THOMPSON, JAMES NEAL, JR,** GENETICS. *Current Pos:* asst prof, 75-79, ASSOC PROF ZOOL, UNIV OKLA, 79-, CHMN DEPT ZOOL, 84- *Personal Data:* b Lubbock, Tex, May 24, 46. *Educ:* Univ Okla, BS, 68, BA, 68; Univ Cambridge, PhD(genetics), 73. *Prof Exp:* Fel genetics, Univ Cambridge, 73-75. *Concurrent Pos:* Marshall scholar, Univ Cambridge, 70-73. *Mem:* Genetics Soc Am; Genetical Soc Gt Brit; Sigma Xi; Soc Study Evolution. *Res:* Development and genetics of quantitative characters; genetic determination of patterns; hybrid dysgenesis and mutator genes in natural populations. *Mailing Add:* Dept Zool Univ Okla 900 Asp Ave Norman OK 73019-4050

**THOMPSON, JAMES R,** SOLID STATE PHYSICS, HIGH TEMPERATURE SUPERCONDUCTIVITY. *Current Pos:* RES & DEVELOP SCIENTIST, SOLID STATE DIV, OAKRIDGE NAT LAB, 88- *Personal Data:* b Charlotte, NC, Sept 14, 42. *Educ:* Davidson Col, BS, 64; Duke Univ, PhD(physics), 69. *Prof Exp:* From asst prof to prof physics, Univ Tenn, Dept Physics, 71-88. *Mem:* Am Phys Soc; Sigma Xi; Mat Res Soc. *Res:* Experimental aspects of high temperature super conductors. *Mailing Add:* Dept Phys Univ Tenn Knoxville TN 37996-0001. *Fax:* 423-574-6263

**THOMPSON, JAMES ROBERT,** MATHEMATICS, STATISTICS. *Current Pos:* assoc prof, 70-77, PROF MATH SCI, RICE UNIV, 77-, PROF STATIST, 87- *Personal Data:* b Memphis, Tenn, June 18, 38; m 67. *Educ:* Vanderbilt Univ, BE, 60; Princeton Univ, MA, 63, PhD(math), 65. *Honors & Awards:* Wilkes Medal for Appl Statist. *Prof Exp:* Asst prof, Vanderbilt Univ, 64-67; asst prof math, Ind Univ, Bloomington, 67-70. *Concurrent Pos:* Adj prof, Univ Tex, M D Anderson Cancer Ctr, 77-, Baylor Col Med, 88-, Univ Tex, Sch Pub Health, 90- *Mem:* Am Math Soc; fel Inst Math Statist; fel Am Statist Asn; fel Int Statist Inst. *Res:* Biomathematics; modelling; statistical process control. *Mailing Add:* Dept Statist Rice Univ PO Box 1892 Houston TX 77251-1892. *E-Mail:* thomp@rice.edu

**THOMPSON, JAMES ROBERT, JR,** AERONAUTICAL ENGINEERING. *Current Pos:* CONSULT, 92- *Personal Data:* b Greenville, SC, Mar 6, 36; m 58, 89, Sherry K Gray; c James R III, Susan P (Rowe) & Scott A. *Educ:* Ga Inst Technol, BS, 58; Univ Fla, MSMechE, 63. *Hon Degrees:* PhD, Univ Ala, 88. *Honors & Awards:* Meritorious Sr Govt Exec Award, US Pres, 82 & 87; Holley Medal, Am Soc Mech Engrs, 91. *Prof Exp:* Performance analysis engr, Pratt & Whitney, 60-63; mech engr, Advan Propulsion Sect, Res & Develop Lab, Marshall Space Flight Ctr, NASA, 63-66, aerospace technologist liquid propulsion systs, 66-68, chief, Space & Nuclear Eng Sect, Propulsion & Vehicle Eng Lab, Res & Develop Directorate, 68-70, chief, Man/Systs Integration Br, Astro Lab, Sci & Eng Directorate, 70-74, mgr main engine proj, Shuttle Projs Off, 74-82, assoc dir eng, Sci & Eng Directorate, 82-83, dir ctr, Marshall Space Flight Ctr, 86-92. *Concurrent Pos:* Dep dir tech opers, Plasma Physics Lab, Princeton Univ, 86. *Mem:* Assoc fel Am Inst Aeronaut & Astronaut; Sigma Xi; Nat Space Club. *Res:* Rocket engine nozzle skirt with transpiration cooling. *Mailing Add:* 416 Randolph Ave Huntsville AL 35801

**THOMPSON, JEFFERY SCOTT,** INORGANIC CHEMISTRY. *Current Pos:* CHEMIST, E I DU PONT DE NEMOURS & CO INC, 80- *Personal Data:* b Hartford, Conn, Mar 20, 52; m 74. *Educ:* Trinity Col, BS, 74; Northwestern Univ, PhD(chem), 79. *Prof Exp:* Fel biochem, Med Sch, Harvard Univ, 78-80. *Mem:* Am Chem Soc. *Res:* Investigation of the role of metal ions in biological processes, through the study of both native and model systems. *Mailing Add:* CR & D Dept Du Pont Co Exp Sta Wilmington DE 19880-0328

**THOMPSON, JEFFREY MICHAEL,** BIOLOGY, NEUROSCIENCES. *Current Pos:* asst prof, 88-93, ASSOC PROF, DEPT BIOL, CALIF STATE UNIV, SAN BERNARDINO, 93- *Personal Data:* b Eau Claire, Wis, May 10, 50. *Educ:* Mich State Univ, BS, 72; Fla State Univ, PhD(molecular biophys), 76. *Prof Exp:* Staff fel res, Nat Heart, Lung & Blood Inst, 77-78; staff fel res, Nat Inst Aging, 79-81, sr staff fel res, 81-82; asst prof, Dept Anat Sci, Col Med, Univ Ill, 82-88. *Mem:* Int Soc Develop Neurosci; Soc Neurosci. *Res:* Mechanisms and specificity of synapse formation and their development patterns; synapse formation of isolated cells in culture detected by electrophysiological recording; neurochemical correlates of synapse behavior; treatment of Parkinsons disease with fetal brain grafts. *Mailing Add:* Dept Biol Calif State Univ San Bernardino CA 92407. *E-Mail:* jthompso@wiley.csasb.edu

**THOMPSON, JERRY NELSON,** GENETICS, BIOCHEMISTRY. *Current Pos:* asst prof, 72-77, assoc prof biochem & pediat, 77-91, PROF BIOCHEM & MOLECULAR GENETICS, MED CTR, UNIV ALA, BIRMINGHAM, 91-, DIR, GRAD PROG MED GENETICS, 96- *Personal Data:* b Cincinnati, Ohio, Apr 2, 39; m 65, Jean Welz; c Amy, Riley & Marc W. *Educ:* Univ Cincinnati, BS, 64; Ind Univ, PhD(med genetics), 70. *Prof Exp:* Res asst teratology, Cincinnati Children's Hosp Res Found, 61-64. *Concurrent Pos:* USPHS fel, Univ Chicago, 70-72; Nat Found March Dimes Basil O'Connor starter res grant, Med Ctr, Univ Ala, Birmingham, 74-76; mem bd dirs, Am Col Med Genetics, 91-94. *Mem:* Am Soc Human Genetics; Am Soc Biol Chemists; fel Am Col Med Genetics. *Res:* Biochemical and genetic studies of genetic lysosomal storage diseases. *Mailing Add:* Dept Med Genetics Univ Ala Sch Med Univ Sta Birmingham AL 35294. *Fax:* 205-934-1078; *E-Mail:* jthompson@bmg.bhs.uab.edu

**THOMPSON, JESSE CLAY, JR,** systematics, for more information see previous edition

**THOMPSON, JESSE ELDON,** SURGERY, VASCULAR SURGERY. *Current Pos:* from asst prof to assoc prof, 54-68, CLIN PROF SURG, UNIV TEX HEALTH SCI CTR, DALLAS; CHIEF CONSULT PERIPHERAL VASCULAR SURG, BAYLOR UNIV MED CTR, DALLAS, 68-, CHIEF SURG, 82- *Personal Data:* b Laredo, Tex, Apr 7, 19; m 44; c 4. *Educ:* Univ Tex, BA, 39; Harvard Univ, MD, 43. *Prof Exp:* Instr surg, Boston Univ, 51-54. *Concurrent Pos:* Rhodes scholar physiol & Fulbright fel, Oxford Univ, 49-50; chief surg & vascular surg, Baylor Univ Med Ctr, Dallas, Tex, 82-86. *Mem:* Int Soc Surg; Soc Vascular Surg; Am Surg Asn; Am Col Surgeons; AMA; Int Soc Cardiovasc Surg; Southern Surg Asn; Sigma Xi. *Res:* Vascular surgery; clinical investigation of hypertension, gastric physiology, peripheral vascular diseases and strokes; surgical management of vascular diseases. *Mailing Add:* 712 N Washington Ave Suite 509 Dallas TX 75246-1635

**THOMPSON, JOE DAVID,** SOLID STATE PHYSICS, LOW TEMPERATURE PHYSICS. *Current Pos:* Fel, Los Alamos Nat Lab, 75-77, staff mem condensed matter & thermal physics, 77-89, dep group leader condensed matter & thermal physics, 89-92, STAFF MEM, AFFIL CTR MAT SCI, LOS ALAMOS NAT LAB, 84-, GROUP LEADER CONDENSED MATTER & THERMAL PHYSICS, 92- *Personal Data:* b Columbus, Ind, Oct 28, 47; m 67; c 2. *Educ:* Purdue Univ, BS, 69; Univ Cincinnati, MS, 71, PhD(physics), 75. *Honors & Awards:* Japan Soc for the Promotion of Sci Award, 90; Award for Sustained Outstanding Res in Solid State Physics, Dept Energy, 91. *Concurrent Pos:* Counr, Div Condensed Matter Physics, Am Phys Soc, 95-98; mem, Sci Prog Comt, Nat High Magnetic Field Lab, 95- *Mem:* Fel Am Phys Soc; AAAS; Sigma Xi. *Res:* Superconducting and magnetic materials; high pressure physics, heavy electron physics and correlated electron behavior. *Mailing Add:* MS K764 Los Alamos NM 87544. *Fax:* 505-665-7652

**THOMPSON, JOE FLOYD,** COMPUTATIONAL FLUID DYNAMICS. *Current Pos:* from asst prof to prof, 64-88, DISTINGUISHED PROF AEROSPACE ENG, MISS STATE UNIV, 88- *Personal Data:* b Grenada, Miss, Apr 13, 39; m 74, Emilie Wilson; c Douglass & Mardi. *Educ:* Miss State Univ, BS, 61, MS, 63; Ga Inst Technol, PhD(aerospace eng), 71. *Honors & Awards:* Res Award, Am Soc Eng Educ, 75; Aerodynamics Award, Am Inst Aeronaut & Astronaut, 92. *Prof Exp:* Aerospace engr, NASA Marshall Space Flight Ctr, 63-64. *Concurrent Pos:* Consult, Numerical Grid Generation; assoc ed, Numerical Heat Transfer, J Comput Physics; founding dir, NSF Eng Res Ctr, 90-95. *Mem:* Am Inst Aeronaut & Astronaut; Soc Indust & Appl Math; Inst Elec & Electronics Engrs. *Res:* Numerical grid generation; computational fluid dynamics. *Mailing Add:* NSF Eng Res Ctr Box 9627 Miss State Univ Mississippi State MS 39762. *Fax:* 601-825-7692; *E-Mail:* joe@erc.msstate.edu

**THOMPSON, JOHN,** chemical engineering, chemistry, for more information see previous edition

**THOMPSON, JOHN ALEC,** DRUG METABOLISM, TOXICOLOGY. *Current Pos:* asst prof, 77-80, ASSOC PROF MED CHEM, SCH PHARM, UNIV COLO, 80- *Personal Data:* b Newton, Mass, Nov 27, 42. *Educ:* Clark Univ, BA, 64; Univ Calif, Los Angeles, PhD(org chem), 69. *Prof Exp:* Fel chem, Univ Calif, Irvine, 69-70 & Syntex Corp, Mexico City, 70-71; res chemist, pharmacol, Vet Admin Hosp, Minneapolis, 71-73; res assoc pharmacol, Univ Colo Med Ctr, 73-76. *Concurrent Pos:* Res grants, NIH, 79-85, 86-89; Coun for Tobacco Res, 79-86; Chemex Pharmaceut Res Fel, 86-88. *Mem:* Am Chem Soc; Am Soc Mass Spectrometry; Am Soc Pharmacol & Exp Therapeut; Soc Toxicol. *Res:* Chemical and biochemical aspects of the metabolism of drugs and other xenobiotics; application of gas chromatographic/mass spectrometric techniques to studies in pharmacology and toxicology; studies of enzyme mechanisms. *Mailing Add:* Sch Pharm Univ Colo 4200 E Ninth Ave Box C-238 Denver CO 80262. *Fax:* 303-270-6281

**THOMPSON, JOHN C, JR,** ENVIRONMENTAL HEALTH. *Current Pos:* RETIRED. *Personal Data:* b Thomas, WVa, Oct 4, 30; m 54; c 3. *Educ:* Va Polytech Inst, BS, 51, MS, 58; Cornell Univ, PhD(agr econ), 62. *Prof Exp:* Res assoc phys biol, Cornell Univ, 61-65, asst prof environ radiation biol, 65-68, assoc prof environ radiation biol, 68-90. *Concurrent Pos:* Instr, NY State Drinking Driver Prog. *Mem:* Health Physics Soc. *Res:* Radioactive contamination of the food chain, sampling techniques, controlled human studies, radionuclide deposition and cycling, world wide evaluation of fallout; biological costs of energy production; comparative environmental analyses and energy options; animal health and veterinary economics. *Mailing Add:* 792 Ridge Rd Lansing NY 14882

**THOMPSON, JOHN CARL,** CIVIL ENGINEERING, ENGINEERING MECHANICS. *Current Pos:* Res asst prof, 69-70, asst prof to assoc prof, 70-96, ADJ ASSOC PROF CIVIL ENG, UNIV WATERLOO, 96- *Personal Data:* b Toronto, Ont, Nov 28, 41. *Educ:* Univ Toronto, BSc, 63, Univ Ill, MS, 65, PhD(civil eng), 69. *Honors & Awards:* Robert T McGrutton Lit Award, Am Soc Mech Engrs. *Mem:* Soc Exp Mech; Can Soc Civil Eng; Prof Engrs Ont. *Res:* Optimization of experimental and numerical stress analysis techniques for stress concentration regions with or without cracks, including shape optimization; forensic engineering; experimental mechanics. *Mailing Add:* Dept Civil Eng Univ Waterloo Waterloo ON N2L 3G1 Can. *Fax:* 519-888-6197

**THOMPSON, JOHN DARRELL,** PHYSICS, MOLECULAR BIOPHYSICS. *Current Pos:* From instr to assoc prof, 57-78, PROF PHYSICS, AUGUSTANA COL, SDAK, 78- *Personal Data:* b Mitchell, SDak, Sept 13, 33; m 57; c 4. *Educ:* Augustana Col, SDak, BA, 55; Iowa State Univ, MS, 62; Univ Wis, PhD(biophys), 67. *Mem:* AAAS; Am Asn Physics Teachers. *Res:* Structure and function of Escherichia coli ribosomes; hormonal control of protein synthesis in the chick embryo; microcomputers in the laboratory. *Mailing Add:* Dept Physics Augustana Col 29th St & S Summit Ave Sioux Falls SD 57197

**THOMPSON, JOHN EVELEIGH,** BIOCHEMISTRY, PLANT PHYSIOLOGY. *Current Pos:* asst prof biol, 68-72, assoc prof, 72-77, PROF BIOL, UNIV WATERLOO, 77- *Personal Data:* b Toronto, Ont, May 30, 41; m 65. *Educ:* Univ Toronto, BSA, 63; Univ Alta, PhD(plant biochem), 66. *Prof Exp:* Fel med biochem, Univ Birmingham, 66-67. *Mem:* Can Soc Plant Physiol; Am Soc Plant Physiol. *Res:* Membrane biochemistry and molecular biology; the molecular basis of membrane deterioration in aging tissues; plant membrane-hormone interactions; comparative aspects of senescence and stress including the role of hormones and the involvement of free radicals; molecular cloning of genes involved in senescence and stress. *Mailing Add:* Dept Biol Univ Waterloo Waterloo ON N2L 3G1 Can. *Fax:* 519-746-2543

**THOMPSON, JOHN FANNING,** PLANT BIOCHEMISTRY. *Current Pos:* from instr to asst prof bot, 50-55, ASSOC PROF BOT, CORNELL UNIV, 55-; PLANT PHYSIOLOGIST, PLANT, SOIL & NUTRIT LAB, USDA, 52- *Personal Data:* b Ithaca, NY, May 24, 19; m 43; c 5. *Educ:* Oberlin Col, AB, 40; Cornell Univ, PhD(biochem), 44. *Prof Exp:* Instr biochem, Cornell Univ, 44-45; res assoc bot, Univ Chicago, 46-47; NIH fel, Univ Rochester, 47-49, res assoc, 49-50. *Concurrent Pos:* NSF sr fel, 59-60. *Mem:* Am Soc Plant Physiol; Am Chem Soc; Am Soc Biol Chem; Sigma Xi; AAAS. *Res:* Nitrogen and sulfur metabolism and mineral nutrition of plants; chromatographic techniques; control mechanisms; seed storage proteins. *Mailing Add:* US Plant Soil & Nutrit Lab USDA Tower Rd Ithaca NY 14853-0001. *Fax:* 607-255-2459; *E-Mail:* jft3@cornell.edu

**THOMPSON, JOHN FREDERICK,** FORENSIC PHARMACOLOGY, MEDICAL TOXICOLOGY. *Current Pos:* asst prof, 75-90, ASSOC PROF CLIN PHARMACOL, UNIV SOUTHERN CALIF, 90- *Personal Data:* b Los Angeles, Calif, Mar 19, 47; m 80, Carol A; c Chelsea A & Collin A. *Educ:* Calif State Univ, Los Angeles, BSc, 69; Univ Southern Calif, PharmD, 73. *Honors & Awards:* George F Archambalt, Am Soc Consult Pharm. *Prof Exp:* Resident clin pharmacol, Wadsworth Vet Admin Med Ctr, Los Angeles, 73-74; clin pharmacist, Los Angeles Co-Univ Southern Calif Med Ctr, 74-75; asst clin prof, Med Sch, Loma Linda Univ, 80-83. *Concurrent Pos:* Pres, Pharmanal Assoc, Inc, 78-; prin investr, Univ Southern Calif, 80-83; consult, Peer Stand Rev Orgn, Pasadena, 80-83. *Mem:* Am Col Clin Pharmacol. *Res:* Detection and analysis of adverse drug reactions and interactions; prescribing habits of physicians: analysis, and the appropriateness of drug therapy prescribing. *Mailing Add:* 1601 NW 12th Ave D-820 1985 Zonal Ave Miami FL 33136. *Fax:* 909-594-8956

**THOMPSON, JOHN HAROLD, JR,** parasitology; deceased, see previous edition for last biography

**THOMPSON, JOHN LESLIE,** ENVIRONMENTAL SCIENCES. *Current Pos:* RETIRED. *Personal Data:* b New Castle, Pa, July 11, 17; m 42; c 2. *Educ:* Slippery Rock State Teachers Col, BS, 40; Univ Wis, MS, 48, PhD(geog), 56. *Prof Exp:* Teacher gen sci, Sharpsville High Sch, Pa, 40-41; from asst prof to assoc prof geog, Miami Univ, 49-61, prof, 61-84. *Mem:* Asn Am Geog; Am Geog Soc; Nat Coun Geog Educ; Conserv Educ Asn. *Res:* Social aspects of environmental problems. *Mailing Add:* 6073 Conteras Rd Oxford OH 45056

**THOMPSON, JOHN N,** EVOLUTIONARY ECOLOGY, COEVOLUTION. *Current Pos:* from asst prof to assoc prof, 78-87, PROF BOT & ZOOL, WASH STATE UNIV, 87-, EDWARD MEYER DISTINGUISHED PROF, COL SCI, 94- *Personal Data:* b Pittsburgh, Pa, Nov 15, 51; m 73. *Educ:* Washington & Jefferson Col, BA, 73; Univ Ill, Urbana, PhD(ecol), 77. *Prof Exp:* Vis asst prof entom, Univ Ill, 77-78. *Concurrent Pos:* Fulbright sr scholar, Australia, 91-92. *Mem:* Fel AAAS; Brit Ecol Soc; Ecol Soc Am; Soc Study Evolution; Am Soc Naturalists (vpres, 98). *Res:* Coevolution of animals and plants; theory on the evolution of interspecific interactions. *Mailing Add:* Dept Zool & Bot Wash State Univ Pullman WA 99164

**THOMPSON, JOHN R,** agronomy; deceased, see previous edition for last biography

**THOMPSON, JOHN ROBERT,** PULSED POWER. *Current Pos:* PRIN SCIENTIST, MAXWELL TECHNOL INC, 85- *Personal Data:* b San Francisco, Calif, Dec 15, 51; m 74; c 2. *Educ:* Univ Calif, San Diego, BA, 73, PhD, 85. *Mem:* Am Inst Physics; Inst Elec & Electronics Engrs. *Res:* Research involving opening switch technology used in inductive energy storage based pulsed power systems. *Mailing Add:* 812 Temple St San Diego CA 92106

**THOMPSON, JOHN S,** INTERNAL MEDICINE, IMMUNOLOGY. *Current Pos:* PROG MED & ASSOC CHIEF STAFF RES, VA MED CTR, LEXINGTON, KY, 90- *Personal Data:* b Lincoln, Nebr, Oct 29, 28; m 54, 72; c 5. *Educ:* Univ Calif, Berkeley, BA, 49; Univ Chicago, MD, 53. *Prof Exp:* Intern, Univ Chicago Hosps, 53-54; jr asst resident, Presby Hosp, New York, 54-55; sr asst resident med, Univ Chicago Hosps, 57-58, resident, 58-59; from instr to assoc prof, Sch Med, Univ Chicago, 59-69; vchmn vet affairs, Univ Iowa, 69-71, chmn dept, 71-77, prof med, 69-80; prof & chmn med, Univ Ky, 80-90. *Concurrent Pos:* Nat Cancer Inst res fel, 58-60; Lederle med fac award, 66-68; chief med & chief sect allergy & clin immunol, Vet Admin Hosp, Iowa City. *Mem:* Fel Am Col Physicians; fel Am Acad Allergy; Transplantation Soc; Am Asn Immunologists; Sigma Xi. *Res:* HLA- and B-cell typing and genetics; natural monoclonal antibodies for immunotherapy and diagnosis. *Mailing Add:* ACOS Res Albert Chandler Med Ctr Univ Ky 800 Rose St Lexington KY 40536. *Fax:* 606-281-4989

**THOMPSON, JOHN STEWART,** technical management & technology forecasting, for more information see previous edition

**THOMPSON, JON H,** DIFFERENTIAL EQUATIONS & APPLICATIONS. *Current Pos:* From asst prof to assoc prof, 70-81, PROF MATH, UNIV NB, 81- *Personal Data:* b NB, Can, Jan 30, 42. *Educ:* Univ Toronto, PhD(math), 70. *Mailing Add:* Dept Math Univ NB Fredericton NB E3B 5A3 Can

**THOMPSON, JOSEPH GARTH,** MECHANICAL ENGINEERING, AUTOMATIC CONTROLS. *Current Pos:* PROF MECH ENG, KANS STATE UNIV, 71-, DIR, CTR RES COMPUT CONTROLLED AUTOMATION, 81- *Personal Data:* b Logan, Utah, Aug 15, 35; m 60, Barbara Coates; c Nathan, Anthony, Heidi (Klinefelter), Julie, Aaron, Jeremy & Jessica (Bailey). *Educ:* Brigham Young Univ, BES, 60; Purdue Univ, MSME, 62, PhD(mech eng), 67. *Prof Exp:* Design engr, Space Tech Labs, Thompson, Ramo, Wooldridge, Inc, 61-62; instr mech eng, Purdue Univ, 62-66; asst prof, Univ Tex, 66-71. *Mem:* Am Soc Mech Engrs; Nat Soc Prof Engrs; Am Soc Eng Educ; Am Soc Heating, Refrig & Air Conditioning Engrs. *Res:* Modeling, design and compensation of nonlinear dynamic systems; design of regulator and feedback control systems; simulation and optimization of dynamic systems; application of microprocessors to automatic control. *Mailing Add:* Dept Mech Eng Kans State Univ Manhattan KS 66506. *E-Mail:* jgt@ksu.edu

**THOMPSON, JOSEPH KYLE,** PHYSICAL INORGANIC CHEMISTRY. *Current Pos:* RETIRED. *Personal Data:* b Columbus, Ohio, Oct 2, 20; m 56; c John, James & Jeffrey. *Educ:* Sterling Col, BA, 42; Univ Kans, MA, 49, PhD, 50. *Hon Degrees:* DSc, Sterling Col, 67. *Prof Exp:* Chemist, US Naval Res Lab, 42-46 & 50-86. *Mem:* Am Chem Soc; Sigma Xi. *Res:* Kinetics and mechanisms of adsorption and filtration, particularly air cleaning devices; oxides of alkali and alkaline earth metals; nuclear magnetic resonance. *Mailing Add:* 6905 Vista Dr Frederick MD 21702

**THOMPSON, JOSEPH LIPPARD,** RADIOCHEMISTRY. *Current Pos:* LOS ALAMOS SCI LAB, 82- *Personal Data:* b Newport News, Va, May 12, 32; m 72, Lois; c 5. *Educ:* Va Polytech Inst, BS, 54; Pa State Univ, MS, 59, PhD(chem), 63. *Prof Exp:* Nat Res Coun res asst, Nat Bur Stand, Washington, DC, 63-64; from asst prof to assoc prof, 64-78, prof chem, 78-82. *Mem:* Am Chem Soc. *Res:* Radionuclide transport in the environment. *Mailing Add:* Los Alamos Nat Lab CST-7 MS J514 Los Alamos NM 87545. *E-Mail:* joet@lanl.gov

**THOMPSON, JULIA ANN,** ELEMENTARY PARTICLE PHYSICS, HIGH ENERGY PHYSICS. *Current Pos:* from asst prof to assoc prof, 72-86, PROF PHYSICS, UNIV PITTSBURGH, 86- *Personal Data:* b Little Rock, Ark, Mar 13, 43; m 64, 76, David E Kraus; c Diane Elizabeth, Vincent Szewczyk & Larry Lynch. *Educ:* Cornell Col, BA, 64; Yale Univ, MS, 66, PhD(physics), 69. *Prof Exp:* Res assoc physics, Brookhaven Nat Lab, 69-71; res assoc & assoc instr, Univ Utah, 71-72. *Concurrent Pos:* Counr, Soc Physics Students, Am Phys Soc, 86-89, mem exec comt, Forumon Physics & Soc, 92-96; Nat Acad Sci exchange, Novosibirsk, USSR, 89-90. *Mem:* Am Phys Soc. *Res:* Direct photon and lepton production; classification of hadronic jets; strange particle interactions and decays. *Mailing Add:* Dept Physics & Astron Allen Hall 107 Univ Pittsburgh Pittsburgh PA 15260

**THOMPSON, KENNETH DAVID,** MICROBIOLOGY, IMMUNOLOGY. *Current Pos:* ASSOC PROF PATH, UNIV CHICAGO, 93- *Personal Data:* b Wimbeldon, NDak, Apr 13, 40; m 65; c 3. *Educ:* Univ NDak, BS, 63; MS, 67, PhD(microbiol), 70. *Prof Exp:* NIH fel, Temple Univ, 70-72, instr, 72-73, asst prof microbiol & immunol, Health Sci Ctr, 73-78; assoc prof path, Med Ctr, Loyola Univ, 78-93. *Mem:* Am Soc Microbiol; NY Acad Sci; Sigma Xi. *Res:* Tumor immunology and clinical immunology; molecular virology; human cytomegalovirus. *Mailing Add:* Univ Chicago Pritzker Sch Med 5841 Maryland Ave Chicago IL 60637-1463. *Fax:* 773-702-2315; *E-Mail:* thompson@midway.uchicago.edu

**THOMPSON, KENNETH LANE,** OPERATING SYSTEMS, NETWORKS. *Current Pos:* DISTINGUISHED STAFF MEM, LUCENT TECHNOL, 66- *Personal Data:* b New Orleans, La, Feb 4, 43; m 67; c 1. *Educ:* Univ Calif, Berkeley, BS, 65, MS, 66. *Honors & Awards:* Vis Mackay Lectr Comput Sci, Univ Calif, Berkeley, 75-76; Piorie Award, Inst Elec & Electronics Engrs, 82 & Hamming Award. *Mem:* Nat Acad Sci; Nat Acad Eng; Asn Comput Mach. *Res:* Operating systems for telephone switching; computer chess. *Mailing Add:* Lucent Technol 700 Mountain Ave Murray Hill NJ 07974. *Fax:* 908-582-5857; *E-Mail:* ken@plan9.bell-labs.com

**THOMPSON, KENNETH O(RVAL),** mechanical engineering, aeronautical engineering, for more information see previous edition

**THOMPSON, LANCELOT CHURCHILL ADALBERT,** INORGANIC CHEMISTRY. *Current Pos:* from asst prof to assoc prof inorg chem, Univ Toledo, 58-66, asst dean, Col Arts & Sci, 64-66, vpres, Student Affairs, 68-88, prof chem & dean, Student Serv, 66-88, EMER PROF CHEM, UNIV TOLEDO, 88- *Personal Data:* b Jamaica, WI, Mar 3, 25; US citizen; m 52, Naomi E Sims; c Lancelot C Jr, Carol L & Angela M *Educ:* Morgan State Col, BS, 52; Wayne State Univ, PhD(inorg chem), 56. *Prof Exp:* Instr chem, Wolmers Boys Sch, Jamaica, 55-56; Int Nickel Co fel, Pa State Univ, 57. *Concurrent Pos:* Consult, Owens-Ill Glass Co, Ohio, 62-64. *Mem:* AAAS; Am Chem Soc. *Res:* Determination of structure of coordination compounds; coordination polymers; solubility of hydrous oxides. *Mailing Add:* Dept Chem Univ Toledo Toledo OH 43606

**THOMPSON, LARRY CLARK,** INORGANIC CHEMISTRY. *Current Pos:* From asst prof to assoc prof, 60-68, head dept, 72-84, PROF CHEM, UNIV MINN, DULUTH, 68- *Personal Data:* b Hoquiam, Wash, June 13, 35; m 55, Frances E Dressel; c Martha E & Whitney K. *Educ:* Willamette Univ, BS, 57; Univ Ill, MS, 59, PhD(inorg chem), 60. *Concurrent Pos:* Vis prof, Univ Sao Paulo, 69, Fed Univ Ceara, 73 & 74, Fed Univ Pernambuco, 77, 93 & 96, Aroraguara, 95. *Mem:* Am Chem Soc; Sigma Xi. *Res:* Coordination chemistry of the rare earth elements; high coordination numbers; ligands with unusual steric requirements. *Mailing Add:* Dept Chem Univ Minn Duluth MN 55812. *Fax:* 218-726-7394; *E-Mail:* lthompso@madonna.d.umn.edu

**THOMPSON, LARRY DEAN,** PHYSICAL METALLURGY, MATERIALS SCIENCE. *Current Pos:* ASSOC PROF MECH ENG, SAN DIEGO STATE UNIV, 81- *Personal Data:* b Warren, Ohio, Oct 16, 51; m 73; c 2. *Educ:* Youngstown State Univ, BE, 73; Univ Calif, Berkeley, MS, 76, PhD(mat sci & eng), 78. *Honors & Awards:* Achievement Award, Am Soc Metals, 77. *Prof Exp:* Res asst mat sci, Lawrence Berkeley Lab, 73-77; sr scientist mat sci, Gen Atomic Co, 77-81; pres, PSI Met, 81-89. *Concurrent Pos:* Lectr, San Diego State Univ, 81- *Mem:* Am Soc Metals; Am Inst Mining, Metall & Petrol Engrs. *Res:* Structural instability of high-temperature alloys and superalloys; high-temperature gaseous corrosion of metals; phase transformations in austenitic stainless steels; alloy design of stainless steels, fracture/mechanical properties of structural materials. *Mailing Add:* Dept Mech Eng San Diego State Univ 5500 Campanile Dr San Diego CA 92182-1323

**THOMPSON, LARRY FLACK,** POLYMER CHEMISTRY. *Current Pos:* VPRES RES & DEVELOP, INTEGRATED SOLUTIONS INC, 95- *Personal Data:* b Union City, Tenn, Aug 31, 44; m 64; c 2. *Educ:* Tenn Technol Univ, BS, 66, MS, 68; Univ Mo, Rolla, PhD(chem), 71. *Honors & Awards:* Award, Semi Conductor Equip Mat Int, 96. *Prof Exp:* Mem tech staff chem & thin films, Bell Labs, 70-78, head org mat & chem eng, 78-95. *Concurrent Pos:* Guest prof, Rutgers Univ, 72. *Mem:* Nat Acad Eng; Am Chem Soc; AAAS; Inst Elec & Electronics Engrs; Soc Photo-Optical Instrumentation Engrs; Am Inst Chem Engrs. *Res:* Electron beam polymer resist studies for microfabrication of integrated electronics; thin polymer films for use in microelectronic fabrication; materials and processes for optical fiber fabrication. *Mailing Add:* 309 Comet Austin TX 78734. *E-Mail:* thompson@austin.insol.com

**THOMPSON, LAWRENCE HADLEY,** DNA REPAIR, MUTAGENESIS. *Current Pos:* SR BIOMED SCIENTIST, LAWRENCE LIVERMORE NAT LAB, UNIV CALIF, SAN FRANCISCO, 73-, ADJ PROF, DEPT RADIATION ONCOL, SCH MED, 90- *Personal Data:* b Tyler, Tex, July 22, 41; m 93, Heather A Galick; c Benjamin & Larissa. *Educ:* Univ Tex, Austin, BS, 63, MS, 67, PhD(biophys), 69. *Prof Exp:* Fel cell biol, Ont Cancer Inst, 69-71, staff physicist, 71-73. *Concurrent Pos:* Counr, Environ Mutagen Soc, 85-88. *Mem:* Radiation Res Soc; Environ Mutagen Soc; AAAS. *Res:* Study mechanisms of somatic cell mutation and DNA repair by characterizing mammalian DNA repair genes and their encoded proteins; develop DNA-repair deficient transgenic mice. *Mailing Add:* Lawrence Livermore Nat Lab PO Box 808 Livermore CA 94551. *Fax:* 510-422-2282

**THOMPSON, LEE P(RICE),** MECHANICS. *Current Pos:* RETIRED. *Personal Data:* b Pastura, NMex, June 29, 13; m 36; c 4. *Educ:* Ind Univ, BA, 36; Agr & Mech Col, Tex, MS, 38, PhD(eng), 49. *Prof Exp:* Asst, Agr & Mech Col, Tex, 36-38, from instr to prof mech eng, 38-55; prof eng, Ariz State Univ, 55-83, dean, Col Eng & Appl Sci, 55-83 & dir, Sch Eng, 55-83. *Concurrent Pos:* Mgr, Res & Testing Lab, AiResearch Corp, 44-46; partic, Am Soc Eng Educ-NSF vis engr prog. *Mem:* Am Soc Eng Educ; Am Inst Aeronaut & Astronaut. *Res:* Applied mechanics; aircraft cabin pressure systems; aircraft electronic equipment cooling research; vibrations; heat and mass transfer by electrical analogy; math studies for application of computers to solution of missile-satellite problems. *Mailing Add:* 10426 S 159th St Gilbert AZ 85234

**THOMPSON, LEIF HARRY,** REPRODUCTIVE PHYSIOLOGY. *Current Pos:* EXTEN SPECIALIST ANIMAL PHYSIOL, UNIV ILL, 78- *Personal Data:* b Chadron, Nebr, Dec 6, 43; c 1. *Educ:* Univ Nebr, BS, 67; NC State Univ, MS, 70, PhD(animal sci), 72. *Prof Exp:* Asst prof reproductive physiol, Tex Tech Univ, 72-77. *Mem:* Am Soc Animal Sci; Soc Study Fertil; Soc Study Reproduction. *Res:* Influence of environment, nutrition, development, hormonal therapy and selection on reproductive efficiency in swine, beef cattle and sheep and hormonal regulation of growth of feedlot animals. *Mailing Add:* Dept Animal Sci Mumford Hall Univ Ill Urbana IL 61801

**THOMPSON, LEITH STANLEY,** ENTOMOLOGY, PLANT PATHOLOGY. *Current Pos:* RETIRED. *Personal Data:* b Margate, PEI, Aug 22, 34; m 58; c 4. *Educ:* McGill Univ, BSc, 56; Cornell Univ, PhD(entom), 61. *Prof Exp:* Res scientist entom, Agr Can, 56-90, asst dir, Sect Entom & Admin, 77-90. *Mem:* Entom Soc Can; Entom Soc Am. *Res:* Forage insect studies; biological control of insects; potato insect studies. *Mailing Add:* 35 Ash Dr Sherwood PE C1A 6X4 Can

**THOMPSON, LEWIS CHISHOLM,** NUCLEAR PHYSICS. *Current Pos:* RETIRED. *Personal Data:* b Brechenridge, Tex, Jan 18, 26; m 55; c 2. *Educ:* Rice Univ, BA, 50, MA, 52, PhD(physics), 54. *Prof Exp:* Physicist, Naval Res Lab, 54-56; sr nuclear engr, Gen Dynamics/Convair, 56-59; asst prof physics, Univ Ga, 59-63; assoc prof, La Sierra Col, 65-70; prof, Loma Linda Univ, 70-77; prof physics, Oakwood Col, 77-91. *Mem:* Am Asn Physics Teachers. *Res:* Energy levels of light nuclei; nuclear instruments; nuclear shielding; low energy particle accelerators. *Mailing Add:* 447 Meadowlands Ct Martinez GA 30907-9591

**THOMPSON, LILIAN UMALE,** DIET & CANCER ANTINUTRIENTS. *Current Pos:* from asst prof to assoc prof, 69-88, PROF NUTRIT SCI, UNIV TORONTO, 88- *Personal Data:* b Cavinti, Philippines; m 68, Walter; c Sylvan & Rhyna. *Educ:* Mapua Instit Technol, BSc, 60; Univ Philippines, MSc, 64; Univ Wis, PhD(food sci), 69. *Prof Exp:* Chemist, Inhelder Lab Inc, 61; res instr, chem, Univ Philippines, 64-65; res asst, Univ Wis, 65-69. *Concurrent Pos:* Chmn, Nutrit Interest Group, Can Inst Food, 85-86; mem, Expert Comt Plant Prods, Can Comt Food, Agr, 81-84; chmn, Acad Panel, Ont grad scholarship, Ont Ministry Cols & Univ, 86-87; mem, Operating Grant Selection Comm, Nat Sci & Eng Res Coun, 86-90, Strategic Grant Selection Comt, 90-92. *Mem:* Am Inst Nutrit; Can Soc Nutrit Sci; Am Assoc Cereal Chemists; Inst Food Technologists; Can Inst Food Sci Technol. *Res:* Bioavailability-digestibility of nutrients; diet and cancer; protein isolation and functionality; dietary fiber properties and health effects; health benefits of antinutrients. *Mailing Add:* Dept Nutrit Sci Fac Med Univ Toronto 150 College St Toronto ON M5S 1A8 Can. *Fax:* 416-978-5882

**THOMPSON, LOUIS JEAN,** CIVIL ENGINEERING, SOIL MECHANICS. *Current Pos:* RETIRED. *Personal Data:* b Big Spring, Tex, Apr 26, 25; m 46; c 4. *Educ:* Tex A&M Univ, BSCE, 49, MSCE, 51; Univ Va, DSc(civil eng), 66. *Prof Exp:* Engr, Lockwood & Andrews, Tex, 51-52; partner, Benson-Thompson-Nash, Engrs-Architects, 52-61; asst prof civil eng, Univ NMex, 61-64; assoc prof, Tex A&M Univ, 66-80, prof civil eng, 80- *Concurrent Pos:* Consult, Sandia Corp, NMex, 63- *Mem:* Am Soc Civil Engrs; Am Soc Eng Educ; Int Asn Bridge & Struct Eng; Sigma Xi. *Res:* High rate of deformation of earth materials; earth penetration; wave propagation in soils and rock; earth impact; cratering; drilling; tunnelling and design of earth structures. *Mailing Add:* 1901 Bee Creek Dr College Station TX 77840-6821

**THOMPSON, LYELL,** SOILS. *Current Pos:* assoc prof agron, 58-69, PROF AGRON, UNIV ARK, FAYETTEVILLE, 69- *Personal Data:* b Rock Island, Ill, May 10, 24; m 46; c 5. *Educ:* Okla State Univ, BS, 48; Ohio State Univ, PhD(soils), 52. *Prof Exp:* Asst prof, Ohio State Univ, 51-53; soil scientist, Noble Found, Okla, 53-58. *Mem:* Am Soc Agron; Soil Sci Soc Am; Sigma Xi. *Res:* Effect of soil fertility, trace element availability and soil acidity upon crop production; increase of food production. *Mailing Add:* Dept Agron Univ Ark 115 Plant Sci Fayetteville AR 72703

**THOMPSON, LYNNE CHARLES,** FOREST ENTOMOLOGY, BIOLOGICAL CONTROL. *Current Pos:* from asst prof to assoc prof, 80-91, PROF, SCH FOREST RESOURCES, UNIV ARK 91- *Personal Data:* b St Paul, Minn, Jan 30, 44; m, Joyce Brown; c Pat, Keith & Jennifer. *Educ:* Kans State Univ, BS, 70; Univ Minn, MS, 73, PhD(entom), 76. *Prof Exp:* Res assoc forest entom, Univ Minn, 76-77; asst prof, Kans State Univ, 77-80. *Mem:* Entom Soc Am; Ecol Soc Am; Sigma Xi; Soc Am Foresters. *Res:* Conduct research on the biology and control of forest insects. *Mailing Add:* Forest Resources Univ Ark Monticello AR 71655-3468

**THOMPSON, MAJOR CURT,** INORGANIC CHEMISTRY. *Current Pos:* ADV SCIENTIST, WESTINGHOUSE, SAVANNAH RIVER CO, 89- *Personal Data:* b Cullman, Ala, May 25, 37; m 62; c 2. *Educ:* Birmingham-Southern Col, BS, 59; Ohio State Univ, MS, 61, PhD(inorg chem), 63. *Prof Exp:* Res assoc, Atomic Energy Div, Savannah River Lab, E I du Pont de Nemours & Co, Inc, 63-89. *Mem:* Am Chem Soc; Sigma Xi. *Res:* Synthesis of binary compounds of actinide elements which are stable at high temperature; complexes of the actinides and lanthanides; solvent extraction. *Mailing Add:* 126 Idlewind Dr Aiken SC 29803-5360

**THOMPSON, MALCOLM J,** ORGANIC CHEMISTRY. *Current Pos:* RETIRED. *Personal Data:* b Baldwin, La, Feb 15, 27; m 53, Mary Barze; c Eileen M, Malcolm J Jr & Michele A. *Educ:* Xavier Univ, La, BS, 50, MS, 52. *Honors & Awards:* Hillebrand Award, 87. *Prof Exp:* Instr chem, Xavier Univ, La, 52-54; chemist, US Bur Mines, 54-55; org chemist, NIH, 55-60; res org chemist, Chem Warfare Labs, Army Chem Ctr, Md, 60-62; res chemist, Insect & Nematode Hormone Lab, USDA, 62-88. *Mem:* Fel AAAS; Am Chem Soc; NY Acad Sci. *Res:* Chemistry of steroids, sapogenins and natural products; synthesis and structural elucidations; insect hormones, isolation and structural elucidation of insect molting hormones; feeding stimulants; synthesis of compounds with insect hormonal activity and inhibitors of insect development and reproduction. *Mailing Add:* 3607 Cedardale Rd Baltimore MD 21215-7305

**THOMPSON, MARGARET DOUGLAS,** GEOLOGY. *Current Pos:* assoc prof geol, 76-92, PROF GEOL, WELLESLEY COL, 92- *Personal Data:* b Wilmington, Del, May 12, 47; m 83; c 2. *Educ:* Smith Col, BA, 69; Harvard Univ, MA, 74, PhD(geol sci), 76. *Concurrent Pos:* Brachman-Hoffman fel, Wellesley Col, 81-83. *Mem:* Geol Soc Am; Sigma Xi. *Res:* U-Pb zircon geochromology stratigraphy and structure of the Southeastern New England Avalon Zone. *Mailing Add:* Geol Dept Wellesley Col Wellesley MA 02181. *Fax:* 781-283-3642; *E-Mail:* mthompson@wellesby.edu

**THOMPSON, MARGARET WILSON,** HUMAN & MEDICAL GENETICS. *Current Pos:* res assoc pediat & lectr zool, Univ Toronto, 63-64, asst prof pediat & zool, 64, assoc prof zool, 65-70, from assoc prof to prof pediat, 66-85, assoc prof med cell biol, 69-72, prof med genetics, 73-85, EMER PROF, UNIV TORONTO, 85- *Personal Data:* b Northwich, Eng, Jan 7, 20; Can citizen; wid; c Gordon & Bruce. *Educ:* Univ Sask, BA, 43; Univ Toronto, PhD(human genetics), 48. *Honors & Awards:* Pres Award, Genetics Soc Can, 86; Founders Award, Can Col & Med Geneticist, 92; First Ann Award Excellence Human Genetics Educ, Am Soc Human Genetics, 95. *Prof Exp:* Lectr zool, Univ Toronto, 47-48 & Univ Western Ont, 48-50; lectr, Univ Alta, 50-59, asst prof human genetics, 59-62; vis investr, Jackson Lab, 62-63. *Concurrent Pos:* Res fel, Muscular Dystrophy Asn Can, 62-63; sr staff geneticist, Hosp for Sick Children, Toronto, 63-88, consult genetics, 88-; mem bd dirs, Am Soc Human Genetics, 75-78; mem bd trustees, Res Dis Children, Queen Elizabeth II Res Fund, 72-; hon res assoc, Dept Human Genetics & Biomet, Univ Col London, 77-78; Saul Lehman vis prof, Downstate Med Ctr, State Univ, NY, 81. *Mem:* Am Soc Human Genetics; fel Can Col Med Genetics (pres, 83-85); Genetics Soc Can (pres, 72-73). *Res:* Human and medical genetics; muscular dystrophy genetics; co-author of textbooks. *Mailing Add:* Dept Genetics Hosp Sick Children Toronto ON M5G 1X8 Can. *Fax:* 416-813-5345

**THOMPSON, MARK EWELL,** NEW PRODUCT DISCOVERY & SCALEUP INTELLECTUAL PROPERTY MANAGEMENT. *Current Pos:* Res chemist, DuPont Agr Prods, 81-90, res suprv, 90-93, tech group mgr, Du Pont Lycra, 93-96, TECH GROUP MGR, DUPONT AGR PROD, E I DUPONT DE NEMOURS & CO, 96- *Personal Data:* b Morocco, Nov 9, 55; US citizen; m 80, E Maria Lopez; c Phillip & David. *Educ:* Duke Univ, BS, 77; Yale Univ, PhD(org chem), 81. *Mem:* Am Chem Soc. *Res:* Total synthesis of natural products, development of new synthetic methodology, design and synthesis of biologically active molecules, process development and scaleup. *Mailing Add:* Du Pont Agr Prod Exp Sta Wilmington DE 19880-0402. *E-Mail:* mthomp1015@aol.com

**THOMPSON, MARSHALL RAY,** CIVIL ENGINEERING. *Current Pos:* res asst, 60-63, from instr to prof, 63-96, EMER PROF CIVIL ENG, UNIV ILL, URBANA, 96- *Personal Data:* b Monterey, Ill, July 22, 38; m 60; c 2. *Educ:* Univ Ill, Urbana, BS, 60, MS, 62, PhD(civil eng), 64. *Honors & Awards:* A W Johnson Mem Award, Hwy Res Bd, 70; Huber Res Prize, Am Soc Civil Engrs, 70. *Prof Exp:* Field engr, McCann & Co, Inc, 57-60. *Concurrent Pos:* Spec consult, Mil Asst Command, US Navy, Vietnam, 69-70; consult engr, Construct Eng Res Lab, US Army Corps Engrs, Caterpillar Tractor Co & var indust and govt agencies, 72-; Sect J comt rep, chmn Lime Stabilization Comt & mem, Cement Stabilization Comt, Hwy Res Bd, Nat Acad Sci-Nat Res Coun. *Mem:* Am Soc Testing & Mat; Am Soc Eng Educ; Am Concrete Inst; Am Soc Civil Engrs; Sigma Xi. *Res:* Soil stabilization; highway materials; surficial soils; pavements. *Mailing Add:* Univ Ill 205 N Mathews Urbana IL 61801

**THOMPSON, MARTIN LEROY,** INORGANIC CHEMISTRY. *Current Pos:* From instr to assoc prof, 62-78, PROF CHEM, LAKE FOREST COL, 79- *Personal Data:* b Kindred, NDak, Jan 8, 35; m 63, Ann Switzer; c Paige, Niels, Kurt & Cole. *Educ:* Concordia Col, Moorhead, Minn, BA, 56; Ind Univ, PhD(inorg chem), 64. *Mem:* Am Chem Soc; Sigma Xi. *Res:* Inorganic chemistry of silicon boron and phosphorus compounds; organometallic chemistry. *Mailing Add:* 513 E Ryan Pl Lake Forest IL 60045-2449. *Fax:* 847-735-6291

**THOMPSON, MARVIN P,** BIOCHEMISTRY. *Current Pos:* Biochemist, Eastern Regional Res Ctr, 60-71, chief, Milk Properties Lab, 71-74, res chemist, Dairy Lab, 74-80, res leader, Plant Sci Lab, 80-85, lead scientist, Plant & Soil Biophys, LEAD SCIENTIST MILK COMPONENTS, EASTERN REGIONAL RES CTR, 87- *Personal Data:* b Troy, NY, June 22, 33; m 53; c 3. *Educ:* Kans State Univ, BS, 56, MS, 57; Mich State Univ, PhD(food sci), 60. *Honors & Awards:* Borden Award, 70; Arthur S Flemming Award, 71; Super Serv Award, USDA, 71; Fed Lab Corsortium Award, 87. *Concurrent Pos:* Prof, Pa State Univ, 65- *Mem:* Am Chem Soc; Am Dairy Sci Asn; Am Soc Biol Chem; AAAS; Am Soc Plant Physiol; Inst Food Technol. *Res:* Isolation and properties of milk proteins; genetic polymorphism of milk proteins; structure of casein micelles; calcium binding proteins. *Mailing Add:* Dept Allied Health St Augustines Col 2941 New Bern Ave Raleigh NC 27610

**THOMPSON, MARVIN PETE,** WILDLIFE ECOLOGY, MAMMALOGY. *Current Pos:* From asst prof to assoc prof, 68-80, PROF BIOL, EASTERN KY UNIV, 80-, FAC RES GRANTS, 69- *Personal Data:* b Mackville, Ky, Sept 28, 41; m 62; c 4. *Educ:* Univ Ky, BS, 63; Kans State Univ, MS, 67; Southern Ill Univ, Carbondale, PhD(zool), 71. *Mem:* Wildlife Soc; Am Soc Mammal; Nat Wildlife Fedn. *Res:* Woodchuck ecology and physiology; ecology of pest mammals; wildlife restoration. *Mailing Add:* Dept Biol Sci Eastern Ky Univ 521 Lancaster Ave Richmond KY 40475-3100

**THOMPSON, MARY E,** PHYSICAL INORGANIC CHEMISTRY. *Current Pos:* lab instr, Col St Catherine, 53-56, from asst prof to assoc prof, 64-78, chmn dept, 69-90, PROF CHEM, COL ST CATHERINE, 78- *Personal Data:* b Minneapolis, Minn, Dec 21, 28. *Educ:* Col St Catherine, BA, 53; Univ Minn, MS, 58; Univ Calif, Berkeley, PhD(chem), 64. *Prof Exp:* Instr sci & math, Derham Hall High Sch, 53-57 & 58-59; res asst chem, Lawrence Radiation Lab, Calif, Berkeley, 61-64. *Concurrent Pos:* Consult-Evaluator, NCent Asn, 84-; chmn, Women Chemists Comt, Am Chem Soc, 92-94. *Mem:* AAAS; Am Chem Soc; Chem Soc; Sigma Xi; Nat Sci Teachers Asn. *Res:* Hydrolytic polymerization in aqueous solutions; kinetics; magnetic susceptibility of solutions of transition metal polymers. *Mailing Add:* Dept Chem Col St Catherine 2004 Randolph Ave St Paul MN 55105. *E-Mail:* methompson@alex.stkate.edu

**THOMPSON, MARY ELEANOR,** GEOCHEMISTRY. *Current Pos:* RETIRED. *Personal Data:* b Cleveland, Ohio, Nov 5, 26. *Educ:* Boston Univ, BA, 48; Harvard Univ, MA, 63, PhD(geol), 64. *Prof Exp:* Mineralogist, US Geol Surv, 48-57; electrode chemist, EPSCO, Inc, Mass, 62-63; res assoc geochem, Dept Geol, Univ SC & electrode chem, Dept Geol & Sch Med, Stanford Univ, 64-67; res scientist & mgr chem limnol, Can Ctr Inland Waters, 67- *Concurrent Pos:* Co-recipient, NSF grant, Univ SC, 65-66; res assoc, Dept Geol, McMaster Univ, 68-69. *Mem:* Int Asn Hydrol Sci; Geochem Soc; AAAS. *Res:* Low temperature aqueous geochemistry; specific-ion electrodes; chemical limnology; aquatic effects of acid precipitation. *Mailing Add:* 110 Regis Rd East Falmouth MA 02536

**THOMPSON, MARY ELINORE,** STATISTICS. *Current Pos:* From lectr to assoc prof, 69-80, PROF STATIST, UNIV WATERLOO, 80- *Personal Data:* b Winnipeg, Man, Sept 9, 44; m 68; c 3. *Educ:* Univ Toronto, BSc, 65; Univ Ill, MS, 66, PhD(math), 69. *Mem:* Am Math Soc; Can Math Soc; Inst Math Statist; Statist Soc Can; fel Am Statist Asn; Int Statist Inst. *Res:* Survey sampling; estimation theory. *Mailing Add:* Statist & Act Sci Univ Waterloo Waterloo ON N2L 3G1 Can

**THOMPSON, MAX CLYDE,** ORNITHOLOGY, ORCHIDOLOGY. *Current Pos:* INSTR BIOL, SOUTHWESTERN COL, 67-; RES ASSOC, UNIV KANS, 70- *Personal Data:* b Winfield, Kans, Jan 10, 36. *Educ:* Southwestern Col, BA, 57; Univ Kans, MA, 64. *Prof Exp:* Zoologist, Univ Kans, 58 & USPHS, 58-60; ornithologist, Bernice P Bishop Mus, 62-63 & Univ Md, 63; cur res, Smithsonian Inst, 64-67. *Mem:* Am Ornithologists Union; Wilson Ornith Soc; Cooper Ornith Soc; Brit Ornithologists Union; Am Hort Soc; Am Orchid Soc. *Res:* Migration and systematics of birds, particularly shorebirds, of Mexico, Argentina, Africa, Southeast Asia, Australia and the United States. *Mailing Add:* Dept Natural Sci Southwestern Col 100 College St Winfield KS 67156-2443

**THOMPSON, MAXINE MARIE,** GENETICS, HORTICULTURE. *Current Pos:* res assoc hort, Ore State Univ, 64-67, asst prof bot, 66-68, from asst prof to prof, 68-86, EMER PROF HORT, ORE STATE UNIV, 86- *Personal Data:* b Bloomington, Ill, Nov 3, 26; m 53; c 2. *Educ:* Univ Calif, BS, 48, MS, 51, PhD(genetics), 60. *Prof Exp:* Jr specialist viticulture, Univ Calif, Davis, 62-63; asst prof biol, Wis State Univ, Oshkosh, 63-64. *Concurrent Pos:* Res horticulturist, Nat Clonal Germplasm Repository, USDA, Corvallis, Ore, 92-94. *Mem:* Am Soc Hort Sci. *Res:* Cytological and botanical studies related to horticultural problems, especially horticultural breeding; fruit breeding and genetics; rubus cytology. *Mailing Add:* Dept Hort Ore State Univ Rm 4017 Corvallis OR 97331-7304

**THOMPSON, MAYNARD,** MATHEMATICAL MODELING. *Current Pos:* Lectr, Ind Univ, 62-64, from asst prof to prof, 64-73, chmn dept, 74-77, assoc dean, Grad Sch, 81-84, assoc dean, 84-88, PROF MATH, IND UNIV, BLOOMINGTON, 73-, DEAN, BUDGETARY ADMIN, 88-, VCHANCELLOR, 90- *Personal Data:* b Michigan City, Ind, Sept 8, 36; m 55; c 2. *Educ:* DePauw Univ, AB, 58; Univ Wis, MS, 59, PhD(math), 62. *Concurrent Pos:* Res assoc, Univ Md, 70-71; sr res scientist, Gen Motors Res Labs, 78. *Mem:* Am Math Soc; Math Asn Am; Soc Indust & Appl Math. *Res:* Approximation theory; complex analysis; mathematical biology. *Mailing Add:* Dept Math Ind Univ Bloomington IN 47405-4703. *Fax:* 812-855-1871; *E-Mail:* thompson@indiana.edu

**THOMPSON, MICHAEL BRUCE,** EMBRYOLOGY. *Current Pos:* Head dept biol, 70-74, asst prof, 69-76, chmn div sci & math, 74-84, ASSOC PROF BIOL, MINOT STATE COL, 76- *Personal Data:* b Kansas City, Mo, Aug 25, 39; m 67; c 2. *Educ:* Baker Univ, BS, 63; Kans State Univ, MS, 67, PhD(biol), 69. *Mem:* Soc Study Reproduction; Sigma Xi. *Res:* Developmental placentation. *Mailing Add:* Biol Dept Minot State Univ 500 University Ave W Minot ND 58707

**THOMPSON, MICHAEL MCCRAY,** HOMOGENEOUS CATALYSIS, HETEROGENEOUS CATALYSIS. *Current Pos:* LEAD CHEMIST, CHEVRON CHEM CO, 90- *Personal Data:* m 88, Jacqueline L Williams; c Mollee M. *Educ:* DePauw Univ, BA, 77; Ind State Univ, MA, 80; Southern Ill Univ, PhD(chem), 85. *Prof Exp:* Fel, Dept Energy, 85; chemist III, Allied-Signal, 86-90. *Mem:* Am Chem Soc. *Res:* Synthesis and modification of catalysts for high density polyethylene. *Mailing Add:* Chevron Chem Co FM 1006 Orange TX 77630

**THOMPSON, MILTON AVERY,** ENVIRONMENTAL MANAGEMENT. *Current Pos:* RETIRED. *Personal Data:* b Salem, Ore, July 5, 29; m 57; c 3. *Educ:* San Jose State Col, BA, 51; Ore State Univ, MS, 53, PhD(phys chem), 57. *Prof Exp:* From chemist to sr chemist, Dow Chem Co, 57-61, res supvr, 62-65, sr res mgr, 66-68, dir chem res & develop, 69-70, mgr environ sci, 70-74; mgr environ sci & waste control, Rockwell Int, 75-78; environ scientist, Stearns-Roger Inc, 78-79, Cyprus Mines Corp, 79-80; prin licensing engr & dir mining serv, Harding-Lawson Assoc, 81-82; mgr, Breckenridge Sanit Dist, 82-93. *Mem:* Am Chem Soc; Sigma Xi; Am Nuclear Soc. *Res:* Plutonium chemistry; plutonium processing, recovery and corrosion; nonaqueous plutonium chemistry, environmental management, mining licenses and permits. *Mailing Add:* 4280 Woody Creek Lane Ft Collins CO 80524

**THOMPSON, MILTON ORVILLE,** aeronautical engineering; deceased, see previous edition for last biography

**THOMPSON, NANCY LYNN,** MEMBRANE BIOPHYSICS, FLUORESCENCE MICROSCOPY. *Current Pos:* from asst prof to assoc prof chem, 85-93, FRANCIS STUART CHAPIN PROF, UNIV NC, CHAPEL HILL, 93- *Personal Data:* b Charlotte, NC, Sept 28, 56. *Educ:* Guilford Col, BS(physics) & BS(math), 77; Univ Mich, Ann Arbor, MS, 80, PhD(physics), 82. *Honors & Awards:* Presidential Young Investr Award, NSF, 86; Margaret Oakley Dayhoff Award, Biophys Soc, 89. *Prof Exp:* Res fel chem, Stanford Univ, Damon Runyon-Walter Winchell Cancer Fund, 82-85. *Mem:* Biophys Soc; Am Phys Soc; Am Chem Soc; AAAS. *Res:* Cell membrane biophysics and cell-surface immunology; fluorescence microscopy and spectroscopy. *Mailing Add:* Dept Chem Venable Hall CB No 3290 Univ NC Chapel Hill NC 27599-3290. *Fax:* 919-962-2388; *E-Mail:* thompson@uncvx1.oit.unc.edu

**THOMPSON, NEAL PHILIP,** PLANT PHYSIOLOGY, PLANT ANATOMY. *Current Pos:* Asst prof plant physiol & asst plant physiologist, Univ Fla, 65-72, assoc prof plant physiol & assoc plant physiologist, 72-77, asst dean res, 80-86, assoc dean res, 87-93, PROF PLANT PHYSIOL & PLANT PHYSIOLOGIST, UNIV FLA, 77- *Personal Data:* b Brooklyn, NY, July 18, 36; m 58, Beverly Godhsall; c 5. *Educ:* Wheaton Col, Ill, BS, 57; Miami Univ, Ohio, MA, 62; Princeton Univ, PhD(biol), 65. *Mem:* Am Chem Soc. *Res:* Developmental structure of higher plants; translocation of materials, exogenously applied or endogenous, in higher plants, their effects on anatomical structure and their metabolism; pesticides in the environment, particularly as related to birds and fish. *Mailing Add:* 6510 NW 16th Pl Gainesville FL 32605

**THOMPSON, NOEL PAGE,** BIOMEDICAL ENGINEERING. *Current Pos:* CONSULT ASSOC PROF ENG, STANFORD UNIV, 61- *Personal Data:* b San Francisco, Calif, Oct 22, 29; m 54; c 2. *Educ:* Stanford Univ, BA, 51, MS, 61; Univ Calif, Los Angeles, MD, 55. *Prof Exp:* Intern med, Univ Hosps, Univ Wis, 55-56; chief bioeng & physiol div, Palo Alto Med Res Found, 58-73; chief, Med Instrumentation Lab, Palo Alto Med Clin, 64-92; mem staff, Physician Med Inst, 77-92. *Concurrent Pos:* Consult assoc prof, Stanford Univ, 61- & Univ Santa Clara, 62-68. *Mem:* AMA; Am Inst Ultrasonics in Med; Am Acad Family Physicians; sr mem Inst Elec & Electronics Engrs. *Res:* Theoretical and applied biomedical engineering; mathematics and electronic instruments as applied to research and in the practice of medicine. *Mailing Add:* Physician Med Inst Dept Elec Eng Stanford Univ Stanford CA 94305

**THOMPSON, NORMAN STORM,** CHEMISTRY OF RADICALS, POLYSACCHARIDE CHEMISTRY. *Current Pos:* CONSULT, 85- *Personal Data:* b Ft William, Ont, Nov 10, 23; m 51; c 4. *Educ:* Univ Man, BSc, 50, MSc, 52; McGill Univ, PhD(wood chem), 54. *Hon Degrees:* MSc,

Lawrence Univ, 87. *Prof Exp:* Res chemist, Rayonier, Inc, Wash, 53-60; res assoc, Inst Paper Chem, 60-69, prof chem & sr res assoc, 69-86. *Mem:* AAAS; Am Chem Soc; Sigma Xi; Can Pulp & Paper Asn. *Res:* Location and composition of the constituents of wood and their behavior during pulping. *Mailing Add:* 6042 Rosewood Dr Appleton WI 54915-9591

**THOMPSON, OWEN EDWARD,** METEOROLOGY, ATMOSPHERIC PHYSICS. *Current Pos:* from asst prof to assoc prof, 68-82, PROF METEOROL, UNIV MD, COLLEGE PARK, 82- *Personal Data:* b St Louis, Mo, Nov 20, 39; m 72; c 1. *Educ:* Univ Mo-Columbia, BS, 61, MS, 63, PhD(atmospheric sci), 66. *Prof Exp:* Instr physics & math, Stephens Col, 64-66; instr atmospheric sci, Univ Mo-Columbia, 66-68. *Concurrent Pos:* Wallace Eckert vis scientist, IBM Thomas J Watson Res Ctr, Yorktown Heights, NY, 75-76; asst provost, Div Math & Phys Sci & Eng, Univ Md, 78-79; comnr educ & manpower, Am Meterol Soc, 80-86; dir educ affairs, Univ Corp Atmospheric Res, Boulder, Colo, 86-87. *Mem:* Am Meteorol Soc; Am Geophys Union. *Res:* Dynamical and physical meteorology; atmospheric waves and oscillations; micrometeorology and boundary layer studies; forest environment; satellite meteorology; meteorological instrumentation; science education. *Mailing Add:* Meteorol Univ Md College Park MD 20742-0001

**THOMPSON, PATRICK W,** RESEARCH ON LEARNING & TEACHING MATHEMATICS, RESEARCH ON USES OF TECHNOLOGY IN MATHEMATICS EDUCATION. *Current Pos:* asst prof, 90- PROF MATH, SAN DIEGO STATE UNIV, 90- *Personal Data:* m 77; c 2. *Educ:* Cent Wash State Univ, BS, 72; Univ Ga, MEd, 77, EdD, 82. *Prof Exp:* Assoc prof math, Ill State Univ, 85-90. *Concurrent Pos:* Prin investr, Mult Representations Proj, 87-89, Quant Reasoning Prog, 89-93. *Mem:* Am Educ Res Asn; Math Asn Am; Nat Coun Teachers Math; Int Group Psychol Math Educ. *Res:* Investigations of imagery and mental operations in students construction of mathematical and scientific concepts with special emphasis on concepts of quantity, change and relational complexity. *Mailing Add:* 6475 Alvarado Rd No 206 San Diego CA 92120. *Fax:* 619-594-1581; *E-Mail:* pthompson@sciences.sdsu.edu

**THOMPSON, PAUL DEVRIES,** BIOMEDICAL ENGINEERING, AGRICULTURAL EQUIPMENT. *Current Pos:* prod mgr, 78-80, vpres, 80-82, PRES, DAIRY EQUIP CO, 82- *Personal Data:* b Glen Cove, NY, Dec 6, 39; m; c 4. *Educ:* Cornell Univ, BEE, 62; Univ Pa, PhD(biomed eng), 70. *Prof Exp:* Electronics engr, Mastitis Res, Agr Res Serv, USDA, 71-78. *Mem:* Am Inst Ultrasonics in Med; Am Soc Agr Engrs; Am Dairy Sci Asn; Inst Elec & Electronics Engrs; Am Solar Energy Soc; Human Factors Soc; Farm & Indust Equip Inst. *Res:* Biological flow measurements using electromagnetic and ultrasonic techniques; applications to blood flow in all species and to milk flow in cows. *Mailing Add:* Bou-Matic PO Box 8050 Madison WI 53708

**THOMPSON, PAUL O,** PSYCHOACOUSTICS, BIOACOUSTICS. *Current Pos:* RETIRED. *Personal Data:* b Stoughton, Wis, Feb 12, 21; m 77; c 2. *Educ:* St Olaf Col, BA, 43; Univ Southern Calif, MA, 50. *Prof Exp:* Res psychologist, US Navy Electronics Lab, 48-67; res psychologist, Naval Ocean Systs Ctr, 67-82; consult, 82. *Mem:* Acoust Soc Am. *Res:* Speech intelligibility, intensity and pitch sensation and perception; thresholds; bioacoustics of marine mammals, particularly whales. *Mailing Add:* 3845 Falcon St San Diego CA 92103-2917

**THOMPSON, PAUL WOODARD,** chemistry, wetlands & studies of ecological communities; deceased, see previous edition for last biography

**THOMPSON, PETER ALLAN,** PHYTOPLANKTON ECOLOGY. *Current Pos:* LECTR, DEPT AQUACULT, UNIV TAZMANIA, 97- *Personal Data:* b Perth, Western Australia, Jan 16, 56; Can citizen; m 78, Elizabeth Chepesulk; c Michael, Andrew & Katharine. *Educ:* Univ BC, BSc, 81, PhD(oceanog), 91; Univ Toronto, MA, 83. *Prof Exp:* Vis scientist, Dept Fisheries & Oceans, 91-92; res scientist, Commonwealth Sci & Indust Re Org, Australia, 93-96. *Res:* Phytoplankton physiology and ecology; adaptations to light, temperature and nutrients by phytoplankton; lipids, fatty acids, carbon 13 in plankton; biochemical markers in ecology. *Mailing Add:* Dept Aquacult PO Box 1214 Launceston 7250 Tas Australia

**THOMPSON, PETER ERVIN,** GENETICS. *Current Pos:* prof zool, 68-96, head dept, 72-81, EMER PROF CELLULAR BIOL, UNIV GA, 96- *Personal Data:* b Urbana, Ill, Mar 20, 31; m 60; c Philip & Hilary. *Educ:* Purdue Univ, BS, 54, MS, 56; Univ Tex, PhD(genetics), 59. *Prof Exp:* NIH fel zool, Univ Calif, Berkeley, 59-60; res assoc biol, Oak Ridge Nat Lab, 60-61; from asst prof to assoc prof genetics, Iowa State Univ, 61-68. *Concurrent Pos:* Vis lectr, Univ Wis, 63, 64 & 66. *Mem:* Genetics Soc Am; Am Soc Nat. *Res:* Invertebrate and primate genetics; genetic control of protein synthesis; developmental regulation of gene activities; hemoglobin structures and evolution. *Mailing Add:* Dept Cellular Biol Univ Ga Athens GA 30602-4066

**THOMPSON, PETER TRUEMAN,** PHYSICAL CHEMISTRY. *Current Pos:* from instr to prof, 58-95, chmn dept, 71-72, 77-78 & 81-86, EMER PROF CHEM, SWARTHMORE COL, 95- *Personal Data:* b Palmerton, Pa, Oct 15, 29; m 54, Margaret Tucker; c Trueman S, Susan T, Barbara C (Amann) & Joseph C. *Educ:* Johns Hopkins Univ, AB, 51; Univ Pittsburgh, PhD(phys chem), 57. *Prof Exp:* Res asst, Univ Pittsburgh, 51-56, res assoc & instr, 56-58. *Concurrent Pos:* NSF sci fac fel, Cambridge Univ, 65-66; vis adj prof, Univ Del, 73-74, 76-77 & 93-94; vis scientist, Nat Bur Stand, 85. *Mem:* Am Chem Soc; Sigma Xi. *Res:* Physical chemistry of solutions both aqueous and non-aqueous; computer simulations of aqueous systems. *Mailing Add:* Dept Chem Swarthmore Swarthmore PA 19081. *Fax:* 610-328-7355; *E-Mail:* pthomps1@swarthmore.edu

**THOMPSON, PHEBE KIRSTEN,** ENDOCRINOLOGY, GERIATRICS. *Current Pos:* RETIRED. *Personal Data:* b Glace Bay, NS, Sept 5, 97; nat US; wid; c 4. *Educ:* Dalhousie Univ, MD, CM, 23. *Honors & Awards:* Thewlis Award, Am Geriat Soc, 66; Cert of Appreciation, Am Thyroid Asn, 66. *Prof Exp:* Asst biochem, Sch Pub Health, Harvard Univ, 24-26; res fel med, Thyroid Clin, Mass Gen Hosp, 26-29; asst endocrinol, metab dept, Rush Med Col, Univ Chicago & Ctr Free Dispensary, Chicago, 30-46; med ed & writing, 46-53; ed, J Am Geriat Soc, 54-82. *Concurrent Pos:* Managing ed, J Clin Endocrinol & Metab, Endocrine Soc, 54-61; consult ed, J Clin Endocrinol & Metab, 61-65 & Endocrinol, 61-65; freelance ed & writer, 61- *Mem:* Fel Am Med Writers' Asn; Am Pub Health Asn; fel Am Geriat Soc; fel Geront Soc Am; Am Genetic Asn; Endocrine Soc; AAAS. *Res:* Medical writing and editing. *Mailing Add:* c/o Donald M Thompson 55 W Monroe Suite 750 Chicago IL 60603

**THOMPSON, PHILIP A,** FLUID MECHANICS, THERMODYNAMICS. *Current Pos:* RETIRED. *Personal Data:* b Galesburg, Ill, Sept 10, 28; m 46; c 3. *Educ:* Rensselaer Polytech Inst, BS, 57, MS, 58; Mass Inst Technol, ScD(mech eng), 61. *Honors & Awards:* Alexander von Humboldt Award, WGer, 75. *Prof Exp:* From asst prof to prof mech eng, Rensselaer Polytech Inst, 60-91. *Concurrent Pos:* Ford Found resident, Large Steam Turbine-Generator Dept, Gen Elec Co, 64-65; Alexander von Humboldt sci grant, 75; vis scientist, Max-Planck Inst Stromungsforschung, 75-78 & 81 & 88; prog mgr conserv, US Dept Energy, 78-80. *Mem:* Nat Acad Eng; fel Am Soc Mech Engrs; Am Inst Aeronaut & Astronaut; Am Chem Soc; Sigma Xi; Am Phys Soc. *Res:* Fundamental gas dynamics; mechanics of dense fluids; fast phase changes in liquid-vapor states; thermodynamics of real gases; author of various publications; granted one patent. *Mailing Add:* 79 Cole Lane Troy NY 12180

**THOMPSON, PHILLIP EUGENE,** SOLID STATE PHYSICS, MOLECULAR BEAM EPITAXIAL. *Current Pos:* head, Vacuum Deposition Sect, 88-90, RES PHYSICIST, NAVAL RES LAB, 81-, HEAD, MOLECULAR BEAM EPITAXIAL GROWTH & CHARACTERIZATION SECT, 90- *Personal Data:* b York, Pa, Nov 14, 46; m 73, Eileen McGrath; c Patrick H & Elizabeth C. *Educ:* Lebanon Valley Col, BS, 68; Univ Del, PhD(physics), 75. *Prof Exp:* Asst engr, York Div, Borg-Warner Corp, 69-70; asst prof physics, Lebanon Valley Col, 74-81. *Concurrent Pos:* Consult physics educ, Annville-Cleona High Sch, 80-81; prof, NVa Community Col, 82-84. *Mem:* Am Phys Soc; Am Inst Elec & Electronics Engrs; Mat Res Soc; Metals Soc. *Res:* Molecular beam epitaxial growth of Si and SiGe for electrical and electro-optical devices; ion implantation and activation of dopants in semiconductors. *Mailing Add:* Code 6812 Naval Res Lab 4555 Overlook Ave SW Washington DC 20375. *Fax:* 202-404-7194; *E-Mail:* thompson@estd.nrl.navy.mil

**THOMPSON, PHILLIP GERHARD,** INDOOR AIR QUALITY, HAZARDOUS WASTE MANAGEMENT. *Current Pos:* RETIRED. *Personal Data:* b Eagle Grove, Iowa, Jan 28, 30; m 55; c 2. *Educ:* St Olaf Col, BA, 54; Cornell Univ, PhD(inorg chem), 59. *Prof Exp:* Fulbright scholar & Ramsay fel, Cambridge Univ, 59; sr chemist, Cent Res Labs, 3M Co, 59-64, sr res chemist, Contract Res Lab, Cent Res, 64-68, sr res scientist, Magnetic Prod Div, 68-70; tech dir & consult, Thompson Assocs, 70-77, pres, 84-92; patent adminr, Univ Minn, 77-83, assoc prof indoor air qual, 87-92. *Concurrent Pos:* Mem, Metrop Coun Comprehensive Health Planning Bd, Metrop Coun, 68-70; 3M Indust lectr, 3M Co, 68-70; vis Ramsay res fel, Dept Physics & Chem, St Olaf Col, 70-71; mem & secy, St Paul Environ Qual Bd, 70-72; comprehensive environ health fel, Dept Environ Health, Sch Pub Health, Univ Minn, 72 & 73; comnr, St Paul Water Bd, 72-80, vpres, 74-80; consult, Environ Health & Safety, Univ Minn, 74, vis lectr, 74-77; dir, Minn Acad Sci, 76-80, consult, 77-; dir, Inventors & Technol Transfer Corp, 84-87; ed, Soc Univ Patent Admin, 85-86. *Mem:* Air Pollution Control Asn; AAAS; Am Chem Soc; Am Indust Hyg Asn; Am Water Works Asn; Am Soc Heating, Refrig & Air Conditioning Engrs. *Res:* Environmental chemistry; air and respirable mass sampling; water quality; trace contaminants; transformation of environmental pollutants; new synthetic techniques; unusual oxygen fluorine compounds; propellants; high performance sealants; ferrites; Mossbauer spectroscopy; university-industry technology transfer; environmental law and regulations; laboratory fume hoods; cold climate housing moisture and indoor air quality problems; radon; statewide information center and data base for industrial air quality in residential housing; hazardous waste treatment methods and facilities; audio-visual training programs. *Mailing Add:* 1492 Dora Lane St Paul MN 55106

**THOMPSON, RALPH J,** PHYSICAL CHEMISTRY. *Current Pos:* assoc prof, 65-70, PROF CHEM, EASTERN KY UNIV, 70- *Personal Data:* b Greenville, Tex, Apr 11, 30; m 59; c 2. *Educ:* ETex State Col, BS & MS, 54; Univ Tex, Austin, PhD(chem), 63. *Prof Exp:* Asst prof chem, Univ Tex, Arlington, 55-59; fel, Ind Univ, 63-65. *Mem:* Am Chem Soc. *Res:* Nuclear magnetic resonance of boron; nucleic acid research as related to brain function. *Mailing Add:* 205 Stratford Dr Richmond KY 40475

**THOMPSON, RALPH J, JR,** SURGERY. *Current Pos:* From instr to assoc prof, 64-77, PROF SURG, SCH MED, LOMA LINDA UNIV, 77- *Personal Data:* b Los Angeles, Calif, Jan 27, 28; m 48; c 3. *Educ:* La Sierra Col, BS, 50; Loma Linda Univ, MD, 51; Am Bd Surg, dipl, 61. *Concurrent Pos:* Fel cancer surg, Mem Sloan-Kettering Cancer Ctr, 60-61. *Mem:* Am Soc Surg Oncol; James Ewing Soc; Am Soc Clin Oncol. *Res:* Cancer surgery. *Mailing Add:* Loma Linda Univ Med Ctr Loma Linda CA 92354

**THOMPSON, RALPH LUTHER,** PLANT TAXONOMY, PLANT GEOGRAPHY. *Current Pos:* asst prof, 80-85, ASSOC PROF BOT & PLANT TAXON, DEPT BIOL, BEREA COL, 85- *Personal Data:* b Niangua, Mo, Feb 6, 43; m 70. *Educ:* Southwest Mo State Univ, BS, 71, MA, 75; Northeast La Univ, MEd, 72; Southern Ill Univ, PhD(bot), 80. *Prof Exp:* Instr bot, Dept Life Sci, Southwest Mo State Univ, 74-75; spec asst, Dept Bot, Southern Ill Univ, 76-80. *Concurrent Pos:* Vis asst prof, Ohio State Univ, 80. *Mem:* Sigma Xi; AAAS. *Res:* Floristic and descriptive studies of the vascular flora of Kentucky; taxonomy and distributional history of nonindigenous plants of the United States; revisionary studies in the subfamily Mimosoideae of the fabaceae (Leguminosae); vegetation of coal surface mines. *Mailing Add:* Dept Biol Berea Col 101 Chestnut St Berea KY 40404-0001

**THOMPSON, RALPH NEWELL,** CHEMICAL ENGINEERING. *Current Pos:* RETIRED. *Personal Data:* b Boston, Mass, Mar 4, 18; m 42; c 3. *Educ:* Mass Inst Technol, BS, 40. *Honors & Awards:* Goodreau Medal, Goodreau Mem Fund, 36. *Prof Exp:* Res engr paper mfg, Middlesex Prod, 40-42, tech dir, Falulah Paper Co, 45-48; staff engr paper chem, Calgon Corp, 48-54, res mgr water treat spec chem, 55-57, mgr res & develop, 58-63, dir res & eng, 63-67, vpres & gen mgr, Spec Chem Div, 67-70; vpres corp develop polymers, Pa Indust Chem Corp, 70-74; gen mgr, Chem Div, Thiokol Corp, 74-76; group vpres spec chem, 76-83. *Mem:* Tech Asn Pulp & Paper Indust; Soc Chem Indust; NY Acad Sci; fel Am Inst Chemists. *Res:* Colloid chemistry; polymer chemistry; industrial water treatment; chemical engineering. *Mailing Add:* 1006 Lehigh Dr Yardley PA 19067-2908

**THOMPSON, RAYMOND G,** JOINING OF MATERIALS. *Current Pos:* asst prof to assoc prof mat eng, 81-89, PROF MAT SCI & ENG, UNIV ALA BIRMINGHAM, 89- *Personal Data:* b Birmingham, Ala, Dec 5, 52; m 72; c 3. *Educ:* Univ Ala Birmingham, BSE, 74, MSE, 75; Vanderbilt Univ, PhD(mat sci), 79. *Honors & Awards:* Adams Award, Am Welding Soc, 86. *Prof Exp:* Asst prof mat eng, Clemson Univ, 78-81. *Concurrent Pos:* Res fac, Am Soc Eng Educ, 79 & 81; prin investr, Nat Aeronaut & Space Admin, 80-85 & NSF, 85-88 & 87-92. *Mem:* Am Welding Soc; Am Soc Metals; Metall Soc, Am Inst Mining Engrs. *Res:* Surface atomic structure and chemistry and their effects on material properties and processing. *Mailing Add:* Dept Mat Eng Univ Ala 1150 Tenth Ave S Birmingham AL 35294-4461

**THOMPSON, RICHARD BRUCE,** MATHEMATICS. *Current Pos:* Asst prof, 67-70, ASSOC PROF MATH, UNIV ARIZ, 70- *Personal Data:* b Fargo, NDak, Oct 12, 39; m 61; c 2. *Educ:* Univ Northern Iowa, BA, 61; Univ Wis, MS, 63, PhD(topology), 67. *Concurrent Pos:* NSF res grants, 68-71. *Mem:* Am Math Soc; Math Asn Am. *Res:* Topological fixed point theory, particularly semicomplexes, quasi-complexes and local and global fixed point indices. *Mailing Add:* Dept Math Univ Ariz Tucson AZ 85721

**THOMPSON, RICHARD CLAUDE,** INORGANIC CHEMISTRY. *Current Pos:* from asst prof to assoc prof, 67-77, PROF CHEM, UNIV MO-COLUMBIA, 77- *Personal Data:* b Kansas City, Mo, Mar 12, 39. *Educ:* Univ Chicago, BS, 61; Univ Md, PhD(chem), 65. *Prof Exp:* Resident res assoc, Chem Div, Argonne Nat Lab, 65-66; asst prof chem, Ill Inst Technol, 66-67. *Concurrent Pos:* Consult, Argonne Nat Lab, 66-75. *Mem:* Am Chem Soc. *Res:* Kinetics and mechanisms of inorganic reactions. *Mailing Add:* Dept Chem Univ Mo Columbia MO 65211-0001

**THOMPSON, RICHARD DAVID,** ANALYTICAL METHODS DEVELOPMENT. *Current Pos:* Analytical chemist, 64-72, pharmaceut analyst, 73-84, RES CHEMIST, US FOOD & DRUG ADMIN, 85- *Personal Data:* b Ely, Minn, Nov 30, 36; m 62, Shirley Solberg; c David. *Educ:* Mankato State Univ, BA, 64; Univ Minn, MS, 72. *Concurrent Pos:* Consult, Vet Admin Res Lab, 73. *Mem:* Am Chem Soc; fel Asn Off Analytical Chemists; NY Acad Sci. *Res:* Analytical methods development related to problems involving foods, pharmaceuticals, pesticides and germicides; application of recent analytical technology including high-performance liquid chromatography and capillary electrophoresis. *Mailing Add:* US Food & Drug Admin 240 Hennepin Ave Minneapolis MN 55401

**THOMPSON, RICHARD E(UGENE),** PROCESS DESIGN. *Current Pos:* from asst prof to assoc prof, Univ Tulsa, 62-95, prof, 75-95, chmn dept, 77-79 & 89-94, EMER PROF CHEM ENG, UNIV TULSA, 95- *Personal Data:* b Parsons, Kans, Oct 15, 29; m 51, Marilyn Short; c Gary D & Julia (Christman). *Educ:* Okla State Univ, BS, 51, PhD(chem eng), 63; Colo Sch Mines, MS, 59. *Prof Exp:* Reactor engr, Atomic Energy Div, Phillips Petrol Co, 51-53; process engr, Tex Div, Dow Chem Co, 53-54. *Concurrent Pos:* Consult, Crest Eng, Inc, 64-82; sr consult, BWT Furlow-Philbeck Assocs, Inc, 75-82; instr, Oil & Gas Consults, Int, 87- *Mem:* Am Inst Chem Engrs; Soc Petrol Engrs; Sigma Xi; Gas Processors Asn. *Res:* Equilibrium-stage processes; oil and gas processing; computer simulation; computer-aided design. *Mailing Add:* Dept Chem Eng Univ Tulsa 600 S College Tulsa OK 74104. *Fax:* 918-631-3268

**THOMPSON, RICHARD EDWARD,** BIOCHEMISTRY, BIOMETRICS-BIOSTATISTICS. *Current Pos:* RES & DEVELOP MGR, ABBOTT LABS, 83- *Personal Data:* b Wichita, Kans, Oct 17, 46; m 71; c 2. *Educ:* Wichita State Univ, BS, 68, MS, 69; Okla State Univ, PhD(biochem), 74. *Prof Exp:* Fel biochem, Univ Cincinnati, 74-77; asst prof biochem, N Tex State Univ, 77-83. *Concurrent Pos:* Adj assoc prof biochem, Tex Col Osteop Med, 77-83; NIH fel, Univ Cincinnati, 75-77. *Mem:* Am Chem Soc; Sigma Xi; Am Asn Clin Chem. *Res:* Physical biochemistry; enzymology; regulation of cholesterol biosynthesis; analytical biochemistry; clinical chemistry; computational chemistry. *Mailing Add:* 1616 Pleasant Ct Libertyville IL 60048-4431

**THOMPSON, RICHARD FREDERICK,** BEHAVIORAL NEUROSCIENCE, LEARNING & MEMORY. *Current Pos:* KECK PROF PSYCHOL & BIOL SCI, UNIV SOUTHERN CALIF, 87-, DIR NEUROSCI PROG, 89-, PROF NEUROL, 91- *Personal Data:* b Portland, Ore, Sept 6, 30; m 60; c 3. *Educ:* Reed Col, BA, 52; Univ Wis, MS, 53, PhD(physiol psychol), 56. *Honors & Awards:* Commonwealth Award, 66; Distinguished Sci Contrib Award, Am Psychol Asn, 77; Warren Medal, Soc Exp Psychologists, 89. *Prof Exp:* NIH fel physiol, Univ Wis, 56-59; from asst prof to prof med psychol, Med Sch, Univ Ore, 59-67; prof psychobiol, Univ Calif, Irvine, 67-73 & 75-80; prof psychol, Harvard Univ, 73-75; prof psychol & Bing prof human biol, Stanford Univ, 80-87. *Concurrent Pos:* NIMH res career award, 62-73; mem res scientist rev comt, 69-74; mem adv panel psychobiol, NSF, 67-70, mem overview comt neurosci, 83; mem comt biol bases soc behav, Social Sci Res Coun, 72-80; mem US Nat Comt, Int Brain Res Orgn, 75-78; mem comt substance abuse & habitual behav, Nat Res Coun, 77-80, mem res task panel, Preident's Comt Ment Health, 77-80, exec comt Assembly Behav & Social Sci, 77-85, USA Nat Comt Int Brain Res Orgn, 78-80; neural & cog sci rev comt, Off Naval Res & Naval Studies Bd, 88-89, Comt Nat Needs Biomed & Behav Res Personnel, Nat Acad Sci, Nat Res Coun, 93-95. *Mem:* Nat Acad Sci; Soc Neurosci; Am Psychol Asn; fel AAAS; fel Am Physiol Soc (pres, 95); fel Am Acad Arts & Sci; Coun Sci Soc (pres, 95-97); Soc Exp Psychologists; Psychonomic Soc. *Res:* Neurophysiology brain substrates of learning and memory; roles of cerebellum hippocampus, cerebral cortex in memory; neurol substrates of habituation and sensitization. *Mailing Add:* Neurosci Prog Hedco Neurosci Bldg Univ Southern Calif Los Angeles CA 90089-2520

**THOMPSON, RICHARD JOHN,** ANALYTICAL CHEMISTRY, AIR POLLUTION. *Current Pos:* RETIRED. *Personal Data:* b Chapman Ranch, Tex, Aug 9, 27; div; c 2. *Educ:* Univ Tex, BS, 52, MA, 56, PhD(inorg chem), 59. *Prof Exp:* Asst prof chem, Lamar State Col, 57-58 & NTex State Univ, 59-68; from asst prof to assoc prof, Tex Tech Col, 62-68; chief metals & adv analytical unit, Air Qual & Emission Data Prog & supvry res chemist, Nat Air Pollution components and sampling of large quantities of sized respirable air-borne particulate matter serv br, Div Air Qual & Emissions Data, Bur Criteria & Stand, 69-71; chief, Air Qual Analytical Lab Br, Div Atmospheric Surveillance, Environ Protection Agency, 71-73, chief, Qual Assurance & Environ Monitoring Lab, 73-75, chief, Analytical Chem Br, 75-78, actg dir, Environ Monitoring Div, 78-79, chief adv, Analytical Tech Br, Environ Monitoring Support Lab, Environ Res Ctr, 80; prof, Sch Pub Health, Univ Ala, Birmingham, 81-86; res sci & adj prof chem & civil eng, Arlington Univ, 86-88; training specialist, Tex A&M Univ, 88-89. *Concurrent Pos:* Res grants, Res Corp, 60-, Welch Found, 61-69 & NSF, 64-68, 74-75; adj prof, NC State Univ, 74-; consult, Lawrence Livermore Lab, 70-72, World Meteorol Orgn, 74-80, environ, prog assessment & develop, training & litigation support, indust hyg area; chair, bd dir, Tex Registry Environ Prof; exec secy, Intersoc Comt. *Mem:* Air & Waste Mgt Asn; Am Chem Soc; Sigma Xi; Soc Appl Spectros; fel Am Inst Chem; Am Indust Hyg Asn; Am Bd Indust Hyg. *Res:* Development of methods for collection and analysis of atmospheric pollutants, including analysis of trace elements, organics, non-metals inorganics, and precipitation components. *Mailing Add:* Rte 1 Box 42A Harwood TX 78632

**THOMPSON, RICHARD MICHAEL,** BIOCHEMISTRY, ANALYTICAL CHEMISTRY. *Current Pos:* DEPT HEAD, MARION MERRELL DOW INC, 87- *Personal Data:* b Thief River Falls, Minn, May 30, 45; m 67, Ricki A Spelbrink; c Zachary & Zachlyn. *Educ:* Univ Minn, BChem, 67; Univ Wis, PhD(biochem), 71. *Prof Exp:* Asst prof pediat, Sch Med, Ind Univ, Indianapolis, 73-78; prin res scientist, Columbus Div, Battelle Mem Inst, 78-84, projs mgr 84-87. *Concurrent Pos:* NIH trainee, Baylor Col Med, 71-72, Nat Heart Inst res associateship, 72-73. *Mem:* Am Soc Mass Spectrometry; Sigma Xi. *Res:* Drug metabolism; bioanalytical chemistry/drug metabolism. *Mailing Add:* Hoechst Marion Roussel PO Box 9627 Kansas City MO 64134-0627

**THOMPSON, RICHARD SCOTT,** SUPERCONDUCTIVITY. *Current Pos:* asst prof, 70-72, ASSOC PROF PHYSICS, UNIV SOUTHERN CALIF, 72- *Personal Data:* b Lubbock, Tex, May 24, 39; m 67, Nina Fainberg; c Andrew & Paul. *Educ:* Calif Inst Technol, BS, 61; Harvard Univ, AM, 62, PhD(physics), 65. *Prof Exp:* NSF fel, Ctr Nuclear Res, France, 66; mem, Inter-Acad Exchange Prog, Inst Theoret Physics, Moscow, 66-67 & 74-75; vis foreign scientist, Ctr Nuclear Res, France, 67-68; asst physicist, Brookhaven Nat Lab, 68-70. *Concurrent Pos:* Vis scientist, Univ Dortmund, Ger, 75-76. *Mem:* Am Phys Soc. *Res:* Superconductivity. *Mailing Add:* Dept Physics Univ Southern Calif University Park MC0484 Los Angeles CA 90089. *Fax:* 213-740-6653; *E-Mail:* rsthom@physics.usc.edu

**THOMPSON, ROBERT ALAN,** MECHANICAL & PRODUCTION ENGINEERING. *Current Pos:* mech engr appl mech unit, 66-70, MECH ENGR CORP RES & DEVELOP, PROCESS TECHNOL PROG, GEN ELEC CO, SCHENECTADY, 70- *Personal Data:* b Catskill, NY, July 16, 37; m 71; c 3. *Educ:* Bucknell Univ, BS, 60; Rensselaer Polytech Inst, MS, 62; Univ Rochester, PhD(mech & aerospace sci), 66. *Honors & Awards:* Blackall Machine Tool & Gage Award, Am Soc Mech Engrs. *Prof Exp:* Engr trainee truck develop, Ford Motor Co, Mich, 61-62; mech engr advan energy systs, Pratt & Whitney Aircraft Co, Conn, 62-63. *Mem:* Fel Am Soc Mech Engrs. *Res:* Mechanical analysis of processes for process optimization and process automation; manufacturing process conception, process equipment design and development; technical areas: machine tool dynamics, flame hardening, residual stress, ceramic manufacturing process, shot peening and thermal barrier coating. *Mailing Add:* PO Box 44 Quaker Street NY 12141. *Fax:* 518-387-6232

**THOMPSON, ROBERT BRUCE,** NON-DESTRUCTIVE EVALUATION, ULTRASONICS. *Current Pos:* dir metall & ceramics div, 86-89, SR SCIENTIST, AMES LAB, IOWA STATE UNIV, 80-, PROF MAT SCI, ENG & MECH, 86-, ASSOC DIR, AMES LAB, 89-, PROF AEROSPACE ENG & ENG MECH & DEP DIR, CTR NONDESTRUCTIVE EVAL, 96- *Personal Data:* b Bryan, Tex, July 18, 41; m 67, Ann Dunkle; c Amy A (Roberts) & Robert K. *Educ:* Rice Univ, BA, 64; Stanford Univ, MS, 65, PhD(appl physics), 71. *Prof Exp:* Mem tech staff, Rockwell Int Sci Ctr, 70-75, group leader, 75-80. *Concurrent Pos:* Vchmn, Nondestructive Eval Working Group, 77-; consult, var indust & acad orgns, 80-; ed, J Nondestructive Eval, 87-; vis fel, Wolfson col, Oxford Univ, 87. *Mem:* Fel Inst Elec & Electronics Engrs; Am Soc Mech Engrs; Soc Eng Sci; Am Soc Mat; Mat Res Soc; Mat Soc. *Res:* Development of new ultrasonic techniques for characterizing the structure of materials and their flaws; specialties include the characterization of stresses and preferred grain orientation in metals; strengths of solid state metallic bonds; the prediction of the reliability of flaw detection. *Mailing Add:* 311 TASF Iowa State Univ Ames IA 50011

**THOMPSON, ROBERT CHARLES,** mathematics; deceased, see previous edition for last biography

**THOMPSON, ROBERT GENE,** PHYSICAL ORGANIC CHEMISTRY. *Current Pos:* RETIRED. *Personal Data:* b Hiddenite, NC, Dec 23, 31; m 53; c 2. *Educ:* Univ NC, BS, 52; Univ Tenn, MS, 54, PhD(chem), 56. *Prof Exp:* Res chemist, E I Du Pont de Nemours & Co, Inc, 56-60, sr res chemist, 60-61, supvr res, 61-63, tech, 63-64, sr supvr, 64-66, tech supt, 66-71, res mgr, 71-76, bus coordr, 76-78, mfg mgr, 78-86, tech mgr, 78-92. *Concurrent Pos:* Consult, 92- *Mem:* Am Chem Soc; Sigma Xi. *Res:* Vinyl and condensation polymers; synthetic textile fibers. *Mailing Add:* 1013 Weldin Circle Wilmington DE 19803

**THOMPSON, ROBERT HARRY,** MATHEMATICS, COMPUTER SCIENCE. *Current Pos:* RETIRED. *Personal Data:* b Columbus, Ohio, May 2, 24; m 47, Barbara Dietz. *Educ:* Sterling Col, BS, 45, DSc, 69; Univ Kans, MA, 51. *Prof Exp:* Prof math, Sterling Col, 47-67; assoc prof math, Washburn Univ, Topeka, 67-89. *Mem:* Math Asn Am. *Res:* General mathematics. *Mailing Add:* 1300 NE 16th Ave No 538 Portland OR 97232-1481

**THOMPSON, ROBERT JAMES,** CRYPTOGRAPHY. *Current Pos:* RETIRED. *Personal Data:* b Dayton, Ohio, Sept 21, 30; m 56, Shirley Hendershot; c Eric & Kurt. *Educ:* Ohio State Univ, BSc, 52, MSc, 54, PhD(math), 58. *Prof Exp:* Asst math, Ohio State Univ, 52-53, from asst instr to instr, 53-58; mem staff, Sandia Nat Lab, 58-65, supvr appl math div II, 65-72, supvr numerical analysis div, 72-75, supvr appl math div, 75-90, distinguished mem tech staff, 90-94. *Mem:* Am Math Soc; Math Asn Am. *Res:* Applied mathematics; numerical analysis; cryptography. *Mailing Add:* 12500 Loyola Ave NE Albuquerque NM 87112. *Fax:* 505-844-5081

**THOMPSON, ROBERT JOHN, JR,** PHYSICAL CHEMISTRY, RESEARCH ADMINISTRATION & TECHNICAL MANAGEMENT. *Current Pos:* RETIRED. *Personal Data:* b San Francisco, Calif, Nov 10, 17; m 45, Nancy Marmer; c William A, John E & Anne G (Welch. *Educ:* Univ Calif, Los Angeles, BS, 40; Univ Rochester, PhD(phys chem), 46. *Prof Exp:* Control chemist, Eastman Kodak Co, 37-41; res assoc, George Washington Univ, 43-46; sr res engr, M W Kellogg Co Div, Pullman, Inc, 46-53 & Bendix Aviation Corp, 53-54; vpres & dir res div, Rocketdyne Div, NAm Aviation, Inc, Calif, 54-71, vpres & gen mgr, Rocketdyne Solid Rocket Div, 71-72, sr staff scientist, Rocketdyne Div, NAm Rockwell Corp, 72-73; spec asst to dir, Appl Physics Lab, Johns Hopkins Univ, 74-80, supvr tech, info, 80-85, prin prof staff, 85-95. *Concurrent Pos:* Mem subcomt rocket engines, NASA, 51-54 & subcomt aircraft fuels, 58, mem res adv comt energy processes, Md Gov Sci Adv Coun, 59-; staff mem, Whiting Sch Eng, Johns Hopkins Univ; mem, Combustion Inst. *Mem:* Fel AAAS; Am Chem Soc; assoc fel Am Inst Aeronaut & Astronaut; Am Inst Chem Engrs. *Res:* Guided missiles; rocket and jet propulsion; propellants and fuels; combustion; heat transfer and fluid flow; chemical processes, thermodynamics and kinetics; radiation and spectra; space science; energy processes, systems and applications. *Mailing Add:* 12912 Ruxton Rd Silver Spring MD 20904-5278

**THOMPSON, ROBERT L,** EXPERIMENTAL PSYCHOLOGY, LEARNING, BEHAVIOR ANALYSIS & CONDITIONING, COMPARATIVE BIOPSYCHOLOGY OF ANIMAL COGNITION. *Current Pos:* from assoc prof to prof, 66-92, EMER PROF PSYCHOL, HUNTER COL & CITY UNIV NY, 92- *Personal Data:* b Queens, NY, Dec 6, 26; div. *Educ:* Columbia Univ, BS, 46, MA, 53, PhD(exp psychol), 59. *Prof Exp:* Chem engr & chemist, Monsanto Chem Co, 46-47; asst chem, Columbia Univ, 47-49, instr psychol, 57-58, res assoc neurol, 58-46; chemist, Colgate-Palmolive-Peet Co, 49-51. *Concurrent Pos:* Adj assoc prof exp psychol, Hunter Col, 64-66, City Univ NY, 66-68, doctoral fac, Grad Sch, 66-, prog head biopsychol, 68-81 & 87-92; adj assoc prof exp psychol, Columbia Univ, 66-68. *Mem:* Am Psychol Asn; Am Psychol Soc; Animal Behav Soc; fel NY Acad Sci; Psychonomic Soc; Soc Neurosci. *Res:* Experimental analysis of behavior: conditioning, comparative cognition, motivation in primates, cats, rodents, electric fish; basal ganglia of brain, avoidance learning, sandbathing in chinchillas and mirror-mediated self-recognition in primates. *Mailing Add:* PO Box 393 Ridgefield NJ 07657-0393. *Fax:* 212-772-5620

**THOMPSON, ROBERT LEE,** AGRICULTURAL POLICY, INTERNATIONAL TRADE. *Current Pos:* PRES, WINROCK INT, MORRILTON ARK, 93- *Personal Data:* b Canton, NY, Apr 25, 45; m 68; c 2. *Educ:* Cornell Univ, BS, 67; Purdue Univ, MS, 69, PhD(agr econ), 74. *Honors & Awards:* Qual of Commun Award, Am Agr Econ Asn, 79 & 91. *Prof Exp:* From asst prof to assoc prof, Purdue Univ, 74-83, prof agr econ, 83-, dean agr, 87-93. *Concurrent Pos:* Vol agriculturist, Int Vol Serv, Laos, 68-70; vis prof agr econ, Fed Univ Vicosa, Brazil, 72-73 & Econ Res Serv, USDA, 79-80; res scholar, Int Inst Appl Systs Anal, Austria, 83; sr staff economist, President's Coun Econ Adv, 83-85; asst secy econ, USDA, 85-87; mem, Nat Comn Agr Trade & Export Policy, 85-86, Bd Agr, Nat Res Coun & Int Policy Coun Agr & Trade, 88-; chair adv coun, Nat Ctr Food & Agr Policy, 89- *Mem:* Fel AAAS; Am Agr Econ Asn; Am Econ Asn; Int Asn Agr Economists (pres-elect); Sigma Xi. *Res:* Agricultural trade policy; US agricultural policy; world agricultural development. *Mailing Add:* Winrock Int 38 Winrock Dr Morrilton AR 72110-9537

**THOMPSON, ROBERT POOLE,** developmental biology, for more information see previous edition

**THOMPSON, ROBERT QUINTON,** BIOANALYTICAL CHEMISTRY, FORENSIC CHEMISTRY. *Current Pos:* asst prof to assoc prof chem, 82-96, chmn, 93-96 & 97-98, PROF OBERLIN COL, 96- *Personal Data:* b Morristown, NJ, Nov 3, 55; m 81, Janis Grocock; c Paul, Ben & Cassie. *Educ:* Col Wooster, BA, 78; Mich State Univ, PhD(analytical chem), 82. *Concurrent Pos:* Prin investr, NSF grant, 85-87 & Petrol Res Fund grant, 88-91; appointee, Comt Prof Status, Am Chem Soc, 88-91; vis prof, Dept Chem, Univ Tenn, 89 & Dept Chem, Univ Cincinnati, 89-90; secy, Div Analytical Chem, Am Chem Soc, 96-; vis scientist Fed Bur Invest Res Lab, 97. *Mem:* Am Chem Soc; Sigma Xi. *Res:* Analysis of explosive residues by liquid chromatography coupled to selective detectors; biomolecule-based determinations of clinical and environmental analytes. *Mailing Add:* Dept Chem Kettering Hall Oberlin Col Oberlin OH 44074. *E-Mail:* robertqthompson@oberlin.edu

**THOMPSON, ROBERT RICHARD,** ORGANIC GEOCHEMISTRY. *Current Pos:* res group supvr, 71-75, res sect dir, 75-86, RES CONSULT, AMOCO PROD CO, 86- *Personal Data:* b Springfield, Mo, Mar 30, 31; m 55; c 2. *Educ:* Drury Col, BS, 53; Wash Univ, St Louis, 55-56, PhD(org chem), 57. *Prof Exp:* Sr res engr, Pan Am Petrol Corp, Stand Oil Co, Ind, 57- 61, tech group supvr, 61-65, staff res scientist, 65-71. *Mem:* Am Chem Soc; Geochem Soc. *Res:* Organic geochemistry; origin of oil; geochemical prospecting. *Mailing Add:* 5617 S Quebec Tulsa OK 74135-4231

**THOMPSON, RODGER IRWIN,** ASTROPHYSICS. *Current Pos:* Asst prof optical sci, Univ Ariz, 70-71, asst prof astron, 71-74, assoc prof, 74-81, PROF ASTRON, STEWARD OBSERV, UNIV ARIZ, 81- *Personal Data:* b Texarkana, Tex, Aug 9, 44; div; c 2. *Educ:* Mass Inst Technol, SB, 66, PhD(physics), 70. *Mem:* Am Phys Soc; Am Astron Soc. *Res:* Theoretical astrophysics including molecular physics, stellar evolution and star formation; observational infrared and dispersive spectroscopy with Fourier transform spectrometers; principal investigator for an infrared instrument for the Hubble Space Telescope. *Mailing Add:* Steward Observ Univ Ariz Tucson AZ 85721

**THOMPSON, ROGER KEVIN RUSSELL,** ANIMAL COGNITION, COMPARATIVE PSYCHOLOGY. *Current Pos:* Asst prof psychol, 76-77, ASST PROF BIOL & PSYCHOL, FRANKLIN & MARSHALL COL, 77- *Personal Data:* b Eng, Dec 12, 45; m 68; c 2. *Educ:* Univ Auckland, BA, 70, MA, 71; Univ Hawaii, PhD(psychol), 76. *Mem:* AAAS; Animal Behav Soc; Am Primatological Soc; Am Asn Univ Prof; Sigma Xi. *Res:* Comparative analysis of animal memory and related cognitive processes; animal auditory and tonic immobility. *Mailing Add:* Dept Biol Franklin & Marshall Col PO Box 3003 Lancaster PA 17604-3003

**THOMPSON, RONALD G,** SOLUTION INTERACTIONS BETWEEN SURFACE ACTIVE POLYMERS & SUSPENDED INORGANIC PARTICLES, PARTICLE CHARACTERIZATION. *Current Pos:* ADVAN CHEMIST, PETROL TECHNOL CTR, MARATHON OIL CO, 87- *Personal Data:* b Texas City, Tex, Mar 15, 60; m 78, Linde J Cain; c Margaret. *Educ:* Abilene Christian Univ, BS, 82; Colo State Univ, PhD(chem), 87. *Mem:* Am Chem Soc; Sigma Xi. *Res:* Investigation of mechanisms of interaction between surface active polyelectrolytes and suspended inorganic particles in aqueous fluids; controlled release systems for delivery of surface active agents in field applications. *Mailing Add:* 1616 12th Ave Greeley CO 80631

**THOMPSON, RONALD HALSEY,** PHYSIOLOGY. *Current Pos:* ASSOC PROF MAT SCI, PASCO-HERNANDO COMMUNITY COL, 85- *Personal Data:* b Brooklyn, NY, Apr 29, 26; m 51; c 2. *Educ:* Adelphi Col, BA, 50; Columbia Univ, MA, 51; Univ Pa, PhD, 59. *Prof Exp:* Technician, Cornell Univ, 51-53 & Univ Pa, 53-55; physiologist, Nat Insts Health, 55-75, Sci Dir, 68-75; teacher, Northern Va Community Col, 74-80, asst prof mat sci, 80-85. *Mem:* AAAS; Am Physiol Soc. *Res:* Temperature regulation; environmental physiology; instrumentation for physiology. *Mailing Add:* Pasco-Hernando Community Col 9753 Lakeside Lane Port Richey FL 34668

**THOMPSON, RONALD HOBART,** NUCLEAR CHEMISTRY. *Current Pos:* from asst prof to assoc prof chem, 72-82, PROF CHEM ENG, LA TECH UNIV, 82-, DIR, NUCLEAR CTR & RADIATION SAFETY OFFICER, 86- *Personal Data:* b Memphis, Tenn, Feb 21, 35; m 60; c 4. *Educ:* La Tech Univ, BS, 61, MS, 68; Univ Ark, PhD(chem), 72. *Prof Exp:* Chemist, Western Elec Corp, 68-70. *Mem:* Am Chem Soc; AAAS; Am Nuclear Soc; Am Health Physic Soc. *Res:* Cosmology; concentration of trace elements on the earth; migration rates of radionuclides in soils; medical applications of radioisotopes; radiation dosimetry. *Mailing Add:* La Tech Univ PO Box 3015 Ruston LA 71272-0046

**THOMPSON, ROSEMARY ANN,** MARINE & FRESHWATER BIOLOGY, MITIGATION PLANNING. *Current Pos:* PRES, SWIFT'S ENVIRON ANALYSIS, 85-; SR BIOLOGIST, SCI APPLNS INT CORP, 89- *Personal Data:* b San Diego, Calif, May 15, 45; m 67, John Joseph; c 1. *Educ:* Univ Mo, Columbia, BA, 67; Univ Calif, San Diego, PhD(marine biol), 72. *Prof Exp:* Res assoc marine biol, Univ Southern Calif, 72-73; sr biologist, Henningson, Durham & Richardson, 74-84 & URS Consults, 84-89. *Concurrent Pos:* Consult environ scientist, EG&G Co, 74; consult, Hinningson, Durham & Richardson, 74 & 84. *Mem:* Sigma Xi; Am Fisheries Soc; Desert Fishes Coun. *Res:* Marine terrestrial and aquatic biology impact assessment; preparation of environmental reports; field surveys; expert witness; wetland delineation, endangered species protection; habitat restoration. *Mailing Add:* Swift's Environ Analysis 4634 Mint Lane Santa Barbara CA 93110-1936. *Fax:* 805-564-6061; *E-Mail:* rosemary.a.thompson@cpmx.saic.com

**THOMPSON, ROY CHARLES, JR,** RADIATION BIOLOGY, BIOCHEMISTRY. *Current Pos:* CONSULT, 85- *Personal Data:* b Kansas City, Mo, June 19, 20; m 76; c 4. *Educ:* Univ Tex, BA, 40, MA, 42, PhD(biochem), 44. *Honors & Awards:* Distinguished Sci Achievement Award, Health Physics Soc, 85. *Prof Exp:* Tutor, Univ Tex, 40-41, instr, 41-43, res assoc biochem, 43-44, asst prof chem, 47-50; res chemist, Manhattan Dist, US Army Engrs Plutonium Proj, Metall Lab, Univ Chicago, 44-46; res chemist, Radiation Lab, Univ Calif, 46-47; res chemist, Gen Elec Co, Washington, 50-65; staff scientist, Biol Dept, Pac Northwest Lab, Battelle Mem Inst, 65-85. *Concurrent Pos:* Mem comt int exposure, Int Comn Radiol Protection, 69-85; mem, Nat Coun Radiation Protection & Measurements, 76-88; assoc ed, Radiation Res, 80-83; hon mem, Nat Coun Radiation Protection & Measurements, 88- *Mem:* AAAS; Radiation Res Soc; Health Physics Soc. *Res:* Radiochemical study of biochemical processes; evaluation of hazards from internally deposited radioisotopes; especially plutonium and other transuranium elements. *Mailing Add:* 10820 W Court St Pasco WA 99352

**THOMPSON, ROY LLOYD,** AGRONOMY, AGRICULTURAL EXPERIMENT STATION DEVELOPMENT & MANAGEMENT. *Current Pos:* RETIRED. *Personal Data:* b Minn, Apr 29, 27; m 54, Blythe Parriot; c Bradley J, Barbara K (Kirkpatrick) & Curtis E. *Educ:* Univ Minn, BS, 51, MS, 59; Pa State Univ, PhD(agron), 67. *Prof Exp:* Field supvr, Minn Crop Improv Asn, 49-51; agronomist, Univ Minn, Morris, 56-67 & Rockefeller Found, 67-72; exten agronomist, Univ Minn, St Paul, 72-78, asst dir, Minn Arg Exp Sta, 78-91. *Concurrent Pos:* Consult, agr exp stat develop. *Mem:* Am Soc Agron; Crop Sci Soc Am. *Res:* Applied crop physiology in the management of field crops for the development and improvement of crop production systems; council of agriculture, science and technology. *Mailing Add:* 2521 Snelling Curve Roseville MN 55113-3111. *E-Mail:* rlthomps@maroon.tc.umn.edu

**THOMPSON, SAMUEL, III,** PETROLEUM GEOLOGY, STRATIGRAPHY. *Current Pos:* RES ASSOC, DEPT GEOL SCI, UNIV TEX. *Personal Data:* b Dallas, Tex, Aug 12, 32. *Educ:* Southern Methodist Univ, BS, 53; Univ NMex, MS, 55. *Prof Exp:* Petrol geologist, Exxon Corp, 54-74; petrol geologist, NMex Bur Mines & Mineral Resources, 74- *Mem:* Am Asn Petrol Geologists. *Res:* Regional evaluation of the potential for petroleum exploration in southwestern New Mexico; system for analysis of sedimentary units; physico-stratigraphy, chronostratigraphy and eustatic geochronology. *Mailing Add:* Geol Sci Univ Tex El Paso TX 79968-0555

**THOMPSON, SAMUEL LEE,** THEORETICAL PHYSICS. *Current Pos:* TECH STAFF MEM, SANDIA CORP, 66- *Personal Data:* b Hopkinsville, Ky, Oct 24, 41; m 59; c 2. *Educ:* Murray State Univ, BS, 62; Univ Ky, PhD(physics), 66. *Mem:* Am Phys Soc. *Res:* Equation of state; hydrodynamics; radiation transport; molecular relaxation. *Mailing Add:* 1201 Arizona NE Albuquerque NM 87110. *Fax:* 505-844-3321

**THOMPSON, SHELDON LEE,** CHEMICAL ENGINEERING. *Current Pos:* Res engr, Sun Oil Co, 62-69, assoc engr, 69-70, chief, Eng Res Lab, 70-72, res prog mgr, Eng Res, 72-74, mgr, Venture Eng, Sun Ventures, 74-77, mgr chem, 77-80, dir, Appl Res & Develop Dept, 80-, SR VPRES & CHIEF ADMIN OFFICER, SUN CO. *Personal Data:* b Minneapolis, Minn, Oct 7, 38; m 62; c 3. *Educ:* Univ Minn, Minneapolis, BS, 60, MS, 62. *Mem:* Am Inst Chem Engrs; Am Petrol Inst; Ind Res Inst. *Res:* Process engineering research and appropriate computer simulation leading to the design of new petroleum and chemical plants; analytical risk-related economic studies; petroleum product development. *Mailing Add:* Sun Co Ten Penn Ctr 1801 Market St Philadelphia PA 19103

**THOMPSON, SHIRLEY JEAN,** NOISE-EFFECTS EPIDEMIOLOGY, REPRODUCTIVE EPIDEMIOLOGY. *Current Pos:* ASSOC PROF EPIDEMIOL, SCH PUB HEALTH, UNIV SC, 77- *Personal Data:* b Danville, Va, Dec 19, 37. *Educ:* Med Col Va, BS, 60; Univ NC, Chapel Hill, MS, 65, PhD(epidemiol), 72. *Prof Exp:* Instr nursing, Roanoke Mem Hosp, 60-61; staff nurse & supvr, IVNA-CNS, Richmond, Va, 61-63; asst prof community health, Med Col Va, 65-67; res assoc epidemiol, Univ NC, Chapel Hill, 69-70; assoc prof edidemiol & nursing, Med Col Va, 72-76. *Concurrent Pos:* Mem, Int Comn Biol Effects Noise. *Mem:* Am Col Epidemiol; Soc Epidemiol Res; Am Pub Health Asn; Geront Soc Am; Aerospace Med Asn; Biol Res Units Intensive Treatment Noise; Int Soc Environ Epidemiol; Soc Pediat Epidemiol Res. *Res:* Epidemiology of noise-related health effects and communicative disorders as they relate to aging; perinatal reproductive epidemiology. *Mailing Add:* Epidemiol Univ SC Columbia SC 29208-0001. *Fax:* 803-777-4783

**THOMPSON, SHIRLEY WILLIAMS,** MATHEMATICAL STATISTICS. *Current Pos:* ASST PROF MATH, MOREHOUSE COL, ATLANTA, 80- *Personal Data:* b Laurens, SC, Oct 12, 41; m 69; c 3. *Educ:* Johnson C Smith Univ, BS, 63; Univ NC, MAEd, 71; Ga State Univ, PhD(career & math develop), 80. *Prof Exp:* Comput prog, Celanese Corp, Charlotte, NC, 67, Wyoming Hosp Med Serv, 68-69; instr math, C A Johnson High, Columbia, SC, 63-65; instr math, East Mechlenburg High, Charlotte, NC, 69-71, Cent Piedmont Community Col, 70, De Kalb Community Col, Ga, 75-80 & Ga State Univ, Atlanta, 76-77. *Concurrent Pos:* Math consult, Proj Opportunity, Univ NC, 70, Richmond County Sch Syst, Augusta, Ga, 75-76. *Mem:* Math Asn Am; Nat Coun Teachers Math. *Res:* Testing the effects of career education awareness in mathematics on the career maturity, attitude toward mathematics and mathematics achievement of students in beginning algebra at a community college. *Mailing Add:* 3161 Weslock Circle Decatur GA 30034

**THOMPSON, STARLEY LEE,** CLIMATOLOGY, CLIMATE MODELING. *Current Pos:* Fel, 82-83, SCIENTIST, NAT CTR ATMOSPHERIC RES, 83- *Personal Data:* b Victoria, Tex, Jan 16, 54. *Educ:* Tex A&M Univ, BS, 76, MS, 77; Univ Wash, PhD(atmospheric sci), 83. *Mem:* Am Meterol Soc; Am Geophys Union. *Res:* Climate theory and numerical simulation of global climate; paleoclimatic theory; impact of man-made influences on future climates. *Mailing Add:* Nat Ctr Atmospheric Res 1815 Table Mesa Dr Boulder CO 80307

**THOMPSON, STEVEN RISLEY,** ZOOLOGY, GENETICS. *Current Pos:* asst prof, 68-73, ASSOC PROF GENETICS, ITHACA COL, 73- *Personal Data:* b Hermiston, Ore, Dec 3, 38; m 68. *Educ:* Portland State Col, BS, 61; Ore State Univ, MS, 64, PhD(zool), 66. *Prof Exp:* Res assoc genetics, Univ Notre Dame, 66-68. *Mem:* Nat Asn Biol Teachers; Nat Sci Teachers Asn. *Res:* General and population genetics of Drosophila melanogaster; Canalizina selection. *Mailing Add:* Dept Biol 177 New Sci Bldg Ithaca Col Ithaca NY 14850-7278

**THOMPSON, SUE ANN,** CLEFT LIP & PALATE, WOUND HEALING. *Current Pos:* assoc histol & anat, 75-78, asst prof anat, 78-90, RES BIOLOGIST, DEPT SURG, UNIV IOWA, 90-, ASST RES SCIENTIST, DEPT OTOLARYNGOL, UNIV HOSP. *Personal Data:* b New Orleans, La, March 26, 38. *Educ:* Univ Ala, BS, 59; La State Univ Med Ctr, MS, 71, PhD(physiol), 75. *Prof Exp:* Assoc biologist, Southern Res Inst, 59-65; res biologist, Med Sch, Tulane Univ, 65-82. *Mem:* Am Cleft Palate/Cranofacial Asn. *Res:* Effect of growth factors on wound healing in a ofital mouse palate model, in vitro. *Mailing Add:* Otolaryngol Dept Rm 10 Med Res Coun Univ Iowa Iowa City IA 52242

**THOMPSON, THOMAS EATON,** SOLID STATE PHYSICS. *Current Pos:* mem tech staff, 89-93, SR MEM TECH STAFF, APPL MAT, 94- *Personal Data:* b San Mateo, Calif, Aug 10, 38; m, Linda Lubin; c 4. *Educ:* Univ Calif, Berkeley, AB, 60; Univ Pa, MS, 62, PhD(physics), 69. *Prof Exp:* Asst prof solid state electronics, Univ Pa, 70-76; sr res physicist, SRI Int, 77-83; tech dir, Genus, Inc, 83-85; res & develop mgr, A G Assoc, 85-88. *Mem:* Am Phys Soc. *Res:* Electronic properties of metals and semiconductors; graphite intercalation compounds; photovoltaic materials; magnetic quantum effects in solids; ultrasonics; surface acoustic waves; semiconductor production equipment. *Mailing Add:* 446 Los Altos Ave Los Altos CA 94022-1603

**THOMPSON, THOMAS EDWARD,** BIOPHYSICS. *Current Pos:* chmn dept, 66-76, PROF BIOCHEM, SCH MED, UNIV VA, 66-, HARRY FLOOD BYRD, JR PROF BIOCHEM, 83- *Personal Data:* b Cincinnati, Ohio, Mar 15, 26; m 53; c 4. *Educ:* Kalamazoo Col, BA, 49; Harvard Univ, PhD(biochem), 55. *Honors & Awards:* K C Cole Award, Biophys Soc, 80; Alexander von Humboldt Prize, 86. *Prof Exp:* From asst prof to assoc prof physiol chem, Sch Med, Johns Hopkins Univ, 58-66. *Concurrent Pos:* NIH res fel biochem, Harvard Univ, 55-57; Swed-Am exchange fel, Am Cancer Soc, LKB-Produkter Fabrikasaktiebolog, Sweden, 57-58; hon res fel, Birmingham, Eng, 58; ed, Biophys J, 88. *Mem:* Am Chem Soc; Biophys Soc (pres, 76); Am Soc Biol Chemists; Sigma Xi. *Res:* Physical chemistry of proteins; lipid protein interactions; biological membrane structure. *Mailing Add:* Dept Biochem Univ Va Sch Med Charlottesville VA 22908-0001

**THOMPSON, THOMAS LEO,** bacterial physiology, for more information see previous edition

**THOMPSON, THOMAS LUMAN,** GEOLOGY. *Current Pos:* PRES, GEO-DISCOVERY INC, 81- *Personal Data:* b Boulder, Colo, Dec 25, 27; m 56, Nancy; c Warren G, Dorothy J (Thackrey), Jennie A, Nancy S, Julie L, Amy E & Heidi A. *Educ:* Univ Colo, BA, 50; Stanford Univ, PhD(geol), 62. *Prof Exp:* Geologist, Phillips Petrol Corp, 50-51; staff res scientist, Amoco Prod Co, 62-76; prof geol & geophys, Univ Okla, 76-81. *Mem:* Geol Soc Am; Am Asn Petrol Geol; Am Geophys Union. *Res:* World tectonics; structure of continental margins; deep water petroleum and mineral exploration. *Mailing Add:* 580 Euclid Ave Boulder CO 80302-7161

**THOMPSON, THOMAS LUTHER,** GEOLOGY. *Current Pos:* GEOLOGIST, MO GEOL SURV & WATER RESOURCES, 65-, CHIEF AREAL GEOL & STRATIG, 71- *Personal Data:* b Houston, Tex, Feb 28, 38. *Educ:* Univ Kans, BS, 60, MS, 62; Univ Iowa, PhD(geol), 65. *Mem:* Geol Soc Am; Paleont Soc; Soc Econ Paleont & Mineral; Int Paleont Union; Pander Soc. *Res:* Stratigraphy; biostratigraphy; micropaleontology; correlation of Paleozoic strata through the use of paleontology. *Mailing Add:* 10955 Thompson Dr Rolla MO 65401-7735

**THOMPSON, THOMAS WILLIAM,** SPACE PHYSICS. *Current Pos:* MEM TECH STAFF, JET PROPULSION LAB, CALIF INST TECHNOL, 81- *Personal Data:* b Canton, Ohio, May 25, 36; m 66; c 2. *Educ:* Case Inst Technol, BS, 58; Yale Univ, ME, 59; Cornell Univ, PhD(elec eng), 66. *Honors & Awards:* Except Serv Award-Magellan, NASA, 92. *Prof Exp:* Engr, Sylvania Elec Prod, 59-61; res asst radar astron, Arecibo Observ, Cornell Univ, 63-64, 66-69; mem tech staff, Jet Propulsion Lab, Calif Inst Technol, 69-76; staff scientist, Planetary Sci Inst, Pasadena, Calif, 77-81. *Concurrent Pos:* Dep proj mgr, Geosar. *Mem:* Am Geophys Union; Am Astron Soc; Int Astron Union; Int Union Radio Sci; Inst Elec & Electronics Engrs. *Res:* Radar astronomy; mapping of lunar radar echoes; resolution of the delay-Doppler ambiguity. *Mailing Add:* 3043 Cloudcrest Rd La Crescenta CA 91214

**THOMPSON, TIMOTHY J,** RADIO ASTRONOMY. *Current Pos:* MEM TECH STAFF, JET PROPULSION LAB, 84- *Personal Data:* b Alhambra, Calif, Dec 1, 49. *Educ:* Calif State Univ, Los Angeles, BS, 78, MS, 85. *Prof Exp:* Mem tech staff, Ball Aerospace Corp, 82-84. *Mem:* AAAS; Am Phys Soc. *Res:* Primarily planetary radio astronomy; outer planet atmospheres and magnetic fields. *Mailing Add:* 1947 E Huntington Dr Apt C Duarte CA 91010

**THOMPSON, TOMMY BURT,** ECONOMIC GEOLOGY, PETROLOGY. *Current Pos:* assoc prof, 73-81, PROF GEOL, COLO STATE UNIV, 81- *Personal Data:* b Tucumcari, NMex, Apr 3, 38; m 58; c 4. *Educ:* Univ NMex, BS, 61, MS, 63, PhD(geol), 66. *Prof Exp:* From asst prof to assoc prof geol, Okla State Univ, 66-73. *Mem:* Geol Soc Am; Am Inst Mining, Metall & Petrol Engrs; Soc Econ Geologists. *Res:* Conceptual models for exploration of metallic resources; mineral resources of Colorado; igneous petrology; hydrothermal alteration of igneous rocks; exploration for gold in sedimentary and igneous rocks. *Mailing Add:* Earth Sci Colo State Univ Ft Collins CO 80523-0001

**THOMPSON, TOMMY EARL,** PLANT GENETICS, PLANT BREEDING. *Current Pos:* res geneticist flax genetics, Agr Res Serv, NDak, 74-76, res geneticist sunflower genetics, Agr Res Ser, 76-79, RES GENETICIST PECAN GENETICS, AGR RES SERV, USDA, 79- *Personal Data:* b Dublin, Tex, June 18, 44; m 72, Elaine Menschel; c Travis, Andrea & Aaron. *Educ:* Tex A&M Univ, BS, 66, MS, 70; Purdue Univ, West Lafayette, PhD(genetics & plant breeding), 73. *Prof Exp:* Field researcher agr econ, Tex A&M Univ, 65, res asst plant breeding, 66-67 & 69-70; res asst plant genetics, Purdue Univ, West Lafayette, 70-73, asst prof forage breeding, 73-74. *Concurrent Pos:* Sci adv, Flax Inst US, 74-76; nat tech adv sunflower prod, Sci & Educ Admin-Fed Res, USDA, 77-79; instr advan plant breeding, WTex State Univ, 78-79. *Mem:* Am Soc Hort Sci; Am Genetic Asn. *Res:* Genetics; pecan research; yieldability of pecans; heritability of yield traits; heritability of dichogamy; insect resistance; disease resistance of pecans. *Mailing Add:* USDA Pecan Genetics Rte 2 Box 133 Somerville TX 77879

**THOMPSON, TRAVIS,** PSYCHOLOGY, DEVELOPMENTAL DISABILITIES. *Current Pos:* PROF & DIR, JOHN F KENNEDY CTR, VANDERBILT UNIV, 91- *Personal Data:* b Minneapolis, Minn, July 20, 37; m 70, Anna Leyens; c Rebecca L, Jennifer E, Andrea L & Peter E. *Educ:* Univ Minn, BA, 58, MA & PhD, 61. *Honors & Awards:* Don Hake Award, Am Psychol Asn, 90. *Prof Exp:* NSF fel, Univ Md, College Park, 61-63; from asst prof to prof, Univ Minn, Minneapolis, 63-91, dir, Inst Disabilities Studies, 87-91. *Concurrent Pos:* Consult to numerous co s, 63-; vis fel, Cambridge Univ, 68-69; vis scientist, Nat Inst Drug Abuse, 79-80; comt mem, Nat Inst Child Health; prog chair behav pharmacol & toxicol, Am Asn Behav Anal, 84 & 85; mem, Human Develop 3 Res Rev Comt, NIH, 88-91. *Mem:* Fel Am Psychol Asn; fel Col Probs Drug Abuse; Am Acad Ment Retardation; Asn Advan Behav Ther; Am Col Pharmacol; Am Asn Behav Anal; Nat Asn Dual Diag; Behav Pharmacol Soc; Europ Behav Pharmacol Soc. *Res:* Co-discoverer of technique for screening abuse; behavioral pharmacology of developmental disabilities; behavior and architecture. *Mailing Add:* Vanderbilt Univ 2201 W End Ave Nashville TN 37240-0001. *Fax:* 615-322-8236; *E-Mail:* thompst@ctrvax.vanderbilt.edu

**THOMPSON, TRUET B(RADFORD),** electrical engineering, electrical safety; deceased, see previous edition for last biography

**THOMPSON, VINTON NEWBOLD,** EVOLUTIONARY GENETICS, ECOLOGICAL GENETICS. *Current Pos:* asst prof to assoc prof biol, 80-95, chair, Dept Biol, 91-93, DIR, SCH SCI & MATH, ROOSEVELT UNIV, 93-, PROF BIOL, 95- *Personal Data:* b Mt Holly, NJ, July 24, 47; m 75, Ruth Moscovitch; c Isaiah & Owen. *Educ:* Harvard Univ, AB, 69; Univ Chicago, PhD(genetics), 74. *Prof Exp:* Indust hygienist, Ill Dept Labor, 75 & Occup Safety & Health Admin, US Dept Labor, 75-77; instnl res assoc, City Coll Chicago, 88-90. *Mem:* Soc Study Evolution. *Res:* Mathematical models of frequency-dependent selection; ecological genetics and ecology of spittlebugs. *Mailing Add:* Roosevelt Univ Sch Sci & Math 430 S Michigan Ave Chicago IL 60605. *Fax:* 312-341-3680; *E-Mail:* vthompso@acfsysu.roosevelt.edu

**THOMPSON, W P(AUL),** CHEMICAL PHYSICS. *Current Pos:* Mem tech staff, Aerophys Dept, Aerospace Corp, 61-67, sect head, Exp Aerophys, Aerodyn & Propulsion Lab, 67-68, dir countermeasures, Reentry Systs Div, 68-74, assoc prin dir technol develop, Reentry Systs Div, 74-79, prin dir space technol planning, 79-81, dir, Aerophys Lab, 81-89, prin scientist, Develop Group, 89-93, PRIN DIR, OFFICE STRATEGIC PLANNING, AEROSPACE CORP, 93- *Personal Data:* b Elmira, NY, June 3, 34; m 77, Anne S Coons; c Helen, Bruce, Leila & Judy. *Educ:* Yale Univ, BS, 55; Lehigh Univ, MS, 57, PhD(physics), 63. *Concurrent Pos:* Instr physics, Moravian Co,

57-58; astron, Los Angeles Trade-Tech Col, 67. *Mem:* Am Phys Soc; assoc fel Am Inst Aeronaut & Astronaut; Sigma Xi. *Res:* Shock tube gasdynamics; gas kinetics; microwave-plasma interactions; reentry physics; electronic and optical countermeasures; system engineering; space systems technology. *Mailing Add:* Aerospace Corp PO Box 92957 Mail Sta M1-016 Los Angeles CA 90009. *Fax:* 310-336-1091; *E-Mail:* thompsonw@courier2.aero.org

**THOMPSON, WALTER ROLPH,** EXERCISE PHYSIOLOGY. *Current Pos:* PROF & DIR, APPL PHYSIOL LAB, UNIV SOUTHERN MISS, 85- *Personal Data:* b Ridgewood, NJ, Mar 8, 56; m 78, Deon Lee; c Jessica A & Walter A. *Educ:* Wake Forest Univ, BS, 78, MA, 79, Ohio State Univ, PhD(exercise physiol), 83. *Prof Exp:* Adminr, Swedish Covenant Hosp, 80-85. *Concurrent Pos:* Adj asst prof physiol, Northeastern Ill Univ, Chicago, 80-83, George Williams Col, 83-85. *Mem:* Fel Am Physiol Soc; fel Am Col Sports Med; fel Am Alliance Health Phys Educ Recreation & Dance. *Res:* Cardiovascular physiology and control mechanisms during periods of physical stress. *Mailing Add:* Ctr Sports Med Ga State Univ University Plaza Atlanta GA 30303-3083. *Fax:* 601-266-4445; *E-Mail:* walt_thompson@bull.cc.usm.edu

**THOMPSON, WARREN CHARLES,** COASTAL GEOMORPHOLOGY & PROCESSES. *Current Pos:* assoc prof aerol & oceanog, 53-59, prof, 59-81, EMER PROF OCEANOG, NAVAL POSTGRAD SCH, 81- *Personal Data:* b Santa Monica, Calif, May 22, 22; m 48, Dorothy Stanley; c Craig W, Diana T (Gibeau), Forrest S & Laurel T (Hotten). *Educ:* Univ Calif, Los Angeles, BA, 43; Univ Calif, San Diego, MS, 48; Agr & Mech Col Tex, PhD, 53. *Prof Exp:* Asst, Scripps Inst, Univ Calif, San Diego, 46-47, 47-48; proj dir, Tex A&M Res Found, 50-52. *Concurrent Pos:* Assoc petrol engr, Humble Oil & Ref Co, La, 47; sci liaison officer, London Br, US Off Naval Res, 60-61; vpres, Oceanog Serv Inc, Santa Barbara, 65-66; consult, 50-92. *Mem:* AAAS; Geol Soc Am; Soc Econ Paleont & Mineral; Am Meteorol Soc; Oceanog Soc; Sigma Xi. *Res:* Coastal geomorphology. *Mailing Add:* 830 Dry Creek Rd Monterey CA 93940-4211

**THOMPSON, WARREN ELWIN,** SCIENCE ADMINISTRATION, PHYSICAL CHEMISTRY. *Current Pos:* GUEST RESEARCHER, NAT INST STAND & TECHNOL, GAITHERSBURG, MD, 88- *Personal Data:* b Joliet, Ill, June 15, 30; m 62, Ellen Coon; c Barbara & Douglas. *Educ:* Univ Wis, BS, 51; Harvard Univ, AM, 53, PhD(chem), 56. *Prof Exp:* Fulbright scholar, Kamerlingh Onnes Lab, Univ Leiden, 55-57; instr & asst prof chem, Univ Calif, Berkeley, 57-59; asst prof, Case Western Res Univ, 59-65; prog mgr, Div Int Progs, NSF, 65-76, 77-83, policy analyst, Div Policy Res & Analysis, 76-77, sr prog mgr, Div Int Progs, 83-91. *Mem:* Am Chem Soc. *Res:* Molecular spectroscopy; photochemistry; chemical studies related to astronomy. *Mailing Add:* 4509 Amherst Lane Bethesda MD 20814-4007

**THOMPSON, WARREN SLATER,** WOOD SCIENCE & TECHNOLOGY. *Current Pos:* prof wood sci & technol & head dept, 74-83, DIR, FOREST PROD LAB, MISS STATE UNIV, 64-, DEAN, SCH FOREST RESOURCES, 83- *Personal Data:* b Utica, Miss, Aug 19, 29; m 53; c 4. *Educ:* Auburn Univ, BS, 51, MS, 55; NC State Univ, PhD, 60. *Honors & Awards:* Fred Gottschalk Mem Award, Forest Prod Res Soc. *Prof Exp:* Asst forester, Miss State Univ, 53-54; wood technologist, Masonite Corp, 57-59; asst & assoc prof forestry, La State Univ, 59-64. *Mem:* Forest Prod Res Soc; Soc Wood Sci & Technol; Am Soc Testing & Mat; Am Wood-Preservers' Asn. *Res:* Wood pathology and preservation. *Mailing Add:* Dean Forest Res Miss State Univ Mississippi State MS 39762-9999. *Fax:* 601-325-8726; *E-Mail:* wst@sfr.msstate.edu

**THOMPSON, WAYNE JULIUS,** SYNTHESIS. *Personal Data:* b Chicago, Ill, Oct 18, 52; m; c 2. *Educ:* Ill Inst Technol, BS, 74; Calif Inst Technol, PhD(chem), 78. *Prof Exp:* NIH fel, Mass Inst Technol, 79-80. *Concurrent Pos:* Asst prof, Univ Calif, Los Angeles. *Mem:* Am Chem Soc. *Res:* Design and synthesis of pharmaceutical agents. *Mailing Add:* 2291 Locust Dr Lansdale PA 19446-5885

**THOMPSON, WESLEY JAY,** NEUROMUSCULAR DEVELOPMENT. *Current Pos:* from asst prof to assoc prof, 79-92, PROF ZOOL, UNIV TEX, 92- *Personal Data:* b Alice, Tex, Dec 10, 47; m 86, Mary Ann Rankin; c Anne. *Educ:* NTex State Univ, BS, 70, MA, 71; Univ Calif, Berkeley, PhD(molecular biol), 75. *Honors & Awards:* Res Career Develop Award, NIH. *Prof Exp:* Fel neurobiol, Univ Oslo, 75-77; fel, Sch Med, Wash Univ, 77-78. *Concurrent Pos:* Muscular Dystrophy Asn fel, 75-76; NATO fel, 76-77; Searle scholar. *Mem:* AAAS; Soc Neurosci. *Res:* The formation and maintenance of synaptic connections at the neuromuscular junction; role of glial cells in the maintenance and repair of synaptic structure. *Mailing Add:* Dept Zool Univ Tex Austin TX 78712-1064

**THOMPSON, WILEY ERNEST,** ELECTRICAL & SYSTEMS ENGINEERING. *Current Pos:* asst prof, 68-72, assoc prof, 72-80, PROF ELEC ENG, NMEX STATE UNIV, 80- *Personal Data:* b Murphysboro, Ill, June 30, 41; m 62; c 2. *Educ:* Southern Ill Univ, Carbondale, BS, 63; Mich State Univ, MS, 64, PhD(elec eng), 68. *Prof Exp:* Design engr, Olin Mathieson Chem Corp, 63; asst elec eng, Mich State Univ, 63-64, res asst systs, 64-68, asst prof elec eng & systs, 68. *Concurrent Pos:* Consult, White Sands Missile Range, 69-; NSF initiation grant, NMex State Univ, 70-72. *Mem:* Inst Elec & Electronics Engrs; Am Soc Eng Educ; Sigma Xi. *Res:* Systems optimization, stability; mathematical modeling; computer-aided analysis and design; systems structure; guidance and control; stochastic systems; ecological systems. *Mailing Add:* Dept Elec & Comput Eng NMex State Univ University Park Las Cruces NM 88003

**THOMPSON, WILLIAM, JR,** ACOUSTICS, ELECTROACOUSTIC TRANSDUCERS. *Current Pos:* res asst transducer studies, 66-72, from asst prof to assoc prof acoust mech, Appl Res Lab, 72-80, assoc prof, 80-85, PROF ENG SCI, APPL RES LAB & DEPT ENG SCI & MECH, PA STATE UNIV, 85- *Personal Data:* b Hyannis, Mass, Dec 4, 36; m 59, Martha M Cate; c Melanie A, Sharon E, Jennifer L & Keith W. *Educ:* Mass Inst Technol, BS, 58; Northeastern Univ, MS, 63; Pa State Univ, PhD(eng acoust), 71. *Prof Exp:* Jr engr, Raytheon Co, 58-60; sr engr, Cambridge Acoust Assocs, Inc, 60-66. *Mem:* Fel Acoust Soc Am; Inst Elec & Electronics Engrs; Soc Eng Sci. *Res:* Electroacoustic transducer design, construction and calibration; acoustic radiation and scattering; underwater acoustics. *Mailing Add:* 601 Glenn Rd State College PA 16803-3475. *Fax:* 814-863-7967; *E-Mail:* w1tesm@engr. psu.edu

**THOMPSON, WILLIAM A,** SOLID STATE PHYSICS. *Current Pos:* RETIRED. *Personal Data:* b Moorestown, NJ, Oct 25, 36; m 61; c Aimee. *Educ:* Drexel Inst Tech, BS, 59; Univ Pittsburgh, PhD(physics), 64. *Prof Exp:* res staff mem physics, Thomas J Watson Res Ctr, IBM Corp, 64-91. *Mem:* Am Phys Soc. *Res:* Electron tunneling properties of superconductors and magnetic semiconductors. *Mailing Add:* 1 Rivermore Apt G Alger Court Bronxville NY 10708

**THOMPSON, WILLIAM BALDWIN,** GEOPHYSICS. *Current Pos:* MGR, AM TEL & TEL LONG LINES, 77- *Personal Data:* b Meriden, Conn, Mar 28, 35; m 60; c 3. *Educ:* Mass Inst Technol, BS & MS, 58, PhD(geophys), 63. *Prof Exp:* Mem tech staff, Bellcomm, Inc, 63-72; head dept, Bell Labs, 72-75; dir, Am Bell Int, Inc, 75-77. *Mem:* Am Geophys Union. *Res:* Electromagnetic cavity resonance phenomena in the earth's atmosphere; physical properties of lunar and planetary surfaces and atmospheres; scientific mission planning for Apollo lunar exploration and planetary missions; economic analyses of telephone network costs and investment; business economics. *Mailing Add:* 6 Oak Knoll Rd Mendham NJ 07945

**THOMPSON, WILLIAM BELL,** plasma physics; deceased, see previous edition for last biography

**THOMPSON, WILLIAM BENBOW, JR,** OBSTETRICS & GYNECOLOGY. *Current Pos:* asst prof, Univ Calif, 66-73, assoc dean med student serv, 69-73, actg chmn, 73-77, ASSOC PROF OBSTET & GYNEC & DIR, GYNEC DIV, COL MED, UNIV CALIF, 77- *Personal Data:* b Detroit, Mich, July 26, 23; m 47, 58; c 3. *Educ:* Univ Southern Calif, AB, 47, MD, 51; Am Bd Obstet & Gynec, dipl. *Prof Exp:* Intern, Harbor Gen Hosp, Los Angeles, 51-52; resident obstet & gynec, Galliinger Munic Hosp, Washington, DC, 52-53; from resident to sr resident, George Washington Univ Hosp, 53-55; asst, La State Univ, 55-56; clin instr, Univ Calif, Los Angeles, 56-62, asst clin prof, 62-64; assoc prof, Calif Col Med, 64-66. *Concurrent Pos:* Dir obstet & gynec, Orange Co Med Ctr, Orange, 67- *Mem:* Fel Am Col Obstetricians & Gynecologists; fel Am Col Surgeons. *Res:* Techniques in tubal sterilization. *Mailing Add:* US Irvine Med Ctr 101 The City Dr Orange CA 92668-2901

**THOMPSON, WILLIAM FRANCIS, III,** MOLECULAR GENETICS, PLANT DEVELOPMENT. *Current Pos:* UNIV PROF BOT & GENETICS, NC STATE UNIV, 86- *Personal Data:* b Seattle, Wash, Jan 21, 45; m 65, Pamela Whitehall; c Nicholas & Peter. *Educ:* Princeton Univ, AB, 66; Univ Wash, PhD(plant physiol), 70. *Prof Exp:* NSF fel biol, Harvard Univ, 70-72; asst prof bot, Univ Mass, 72-74; mem staff plant biol, Carnegie Inst Wash, 74-86. *Concurrent Pos:* Adj assoc prof, Univ Mass, 74-79; vis scientist, Plant Breeding Inst, Cambridge, UK, 82-83; asst-assoc prof by courtesy, Stanford Univ, 74-86. *Mem:* Am Soc Plant Physiologists; Genetics Soc Am; Int Soc Plant Molecular Biol; fel AAAS. *Res:* Control of plant gene expression; plant molecular genetics. *Mailing Add:* Dept Bot NC State Univ Raleigh NC 27695. *Fax:* 919-515-3436; *E-Mail:* wftb@ncsu.edu

**THOMPSON, WILLIAM HORN,** CHEMICAL ENGINEERING. *Current Pos:* RETIRED. *Personal Data:* b Somerville, NJ, Feb 9, 37; m 60; c 3. *Educ:* Pa State Univ, BS, 61, MS, 62, PhD(chem eng), 66. *Prof Exp:* Res asst, Dept Chem Eng, Pa State Univ, 62-65, instr, 65-66; engr, Petrol Processing Dept, Shell Develop Co, Calif, 66-68; group leader, Technol Dept, Wood River Refinery, Shell Oil Co, 68-69, asst mgr, Lube Oil Dept, 69-70, mgr, Refinery Lab, 70-71 & Catalytic Cracking Dept, 71-72, supt opers light oil processing, 72-73, sr staff engr, 73-74, mgr, supply & qual lube, 74-75, mfg oper, 75-77, fuels logistics, 77-78, mgr, Gasoline Bus Ctr, 78-80; supt, Deer Park Mfg Complex, 80-82, complex mgr, 82-85, mgr, Mfg Mgt Systs, 85-96. *Mem:* Am Inst Chem Engrs. *Res:* Physical thermodynamic and transport properties of hydrocarbons and related substances. *Mailing Add:* 14762 Carolcrest St Houston TX 77079

**THOMPSON, WILLIAM LAY,** VERTEBRATE ZOOLOGY. *Current Pos:* From asst prof to assoc prof, 59-71, PROF BIOL, WAYNE STATE UNIV, 71- *Personal Data:* b Austin, Tex, Feb 16, 30; m 58; c 3. *Educ:* Univ Tex, BA, 51, MA, 52; Univ Calif, Berkeley, PhD(zool), 59. *Mem:* Fel AAAS; Animal Behav Soc; Am Ornith Union; Wilson Ornith Soc. *Res:* Animal behavior, especially communication and habitat selection in birds. *Mailing Add:* 37 Wellesley Dr Pleasant Ridge MI 48069-1241

**THOMPSON, WILLIAM OXLEY, II,** MATHEMATICAL STATISTICS, TECHNICAL MANAGEMENT. *Current Pos:* DIR & PROF BIOSTATIST, MED COL GA, 86- *Personal Data:* b Richmond, Va, Apr 25, 41; m 63, Joan E Homel; c Elaine E & Lorin A III. *Educ:* Univ Va, BA, 63;

Va Polytech Inst & State Univ, PhD(statist), 68. *Prof Exp:* Teacher high sch, Va, 63-64; asst prof & assoc prof statist, Univ Ky, 67-75; mgr statist serv group, Tech Serv Div, Agr Mkt Serv, USDA, 74-76, dir, Tech Serv Div, 76-79, statist & systs coordr res, Forest Serv, 79-82; corp mgr math sci, Gen Foods Corp, 82-86. *Concurrent Pos:* Consult, Clin Res Ctr, NIMH, 68-71, consult, Addiction Res Ctr, 70-72, math statistician, 72-74; adj prof statist, Va Polytech Inst & State Univ, 78-80; adj assoc prof statist, Univ SC, 92- *Mem:* Am Statist Asn; Sigma Xi; Soc Behav Med. *Res:* Experimental designs and analysis for estimating linear and nonlinear models; estimation of variance components; development of statistical methodology in fields of application; biostatistics; research management. *Mailing Add:* 4260 Quail Springs Circle Augusta GA 30907. *Fax:* 706-721-6294; *E-Mail:* billt@stat. mcg.edu

**THOMPSON, WILMER LEIGH,** STRATEGIC PLANNING, HEALTH INFORMATICS. *Current Pos:* CHIEF EXEC OFFICER, PROFOUND QUAL RESOURCES LTD, 95- *Personal Data:* b Shreveport, La, June 25, 38; m 57, Maurice E Horne; c Mary L (Peters). *Educ:* Col Charleston, BS, 58; Med Univ SC, MS, 60, PhD(pharmacol), 63; Johns Hopkins Univ, MD, 65; Am Bd Internal Med, dipl, 71. *Hon Degrees:* ScD, Med Univ SC, 94. *Prof Exp:* Intern, Osler Med Serv, Johns Hopkins Hosp, 65-66, resident, 66-67 & 69-70; asst prof med & pharmacol, Sch Med, Johns Hopkins Univ, 70-74; assoc prof med & pharmacol, Sch Med, Case Western Res Univ, 74-80, prof, 80-82; dir, Eli Lilly & Co, 82, exec dir, 82-87, vpres, 87-89, group vpres, 89-91, exec vpres, 91-93, chief sci officer, 93-94. *Concurrent Pos:* Fels med, Sch Med, Johns Hopkins Univ, 65-67 & 69-70; staff assoc, Nat Cancer Inst, 67-69; asst physician & dir med intensive care unit, Johns Hopkins Hosp, 70-74; physician & dir clin pharmacol prog, Univ Hosps Cleveland, 74-82; adj prof, Sch Libr Sci, Case Western Res Univ, 74-82; adj assoc prof, Dept Pharmacol, Col Med, Ohio State Univ, 75-82; Burroughs Wellcome scholar clin pharmacol, 75-80; prof med, Ind Univ, 82-94. *Mem:* Am Soc Pharmacol & Exp Therapeut; Hon life mem Soc Critical Care Med (pres, 81-82); fel Am Col Critical Care Med; fel Am Col Physicians; Am Soc Pharmacol & Exp Therapeut. *Res:* Management of shock; artificial bloods; treatment of poisoning; new druug development; decision analysis in drug research; health informatics. *Mailing Add:* 54 King St Charleston SC 29401-2731. *Fax:* 803-577-8940; *E-Mail:* leight@awod.com

**THOMPSON, WYNELLE DOGGETT,** BIOCHEMISTRY, ORGANIC CHEMISTRY. *Current Pos:* from asst prof to prof, 55-76, EMER PROF CHEM, BIRMINGHAM-SOUTHERN COL, 76- *Personal Data:* b Birmingham, Ala, May 25, 14; m 38, David H; c Carolyn, Helen (Kohl), Cynthia C & David H Jr. *Educ:* Birmingham-Southern Col, BS, 34, MS, 35; Univ Ala, MS, 56, PhD(biochem), 60. *Prof Exp:* Instr chem, Birmingham-Southern Col, 35-36; high sch instr gen sci, Ala, 36-37; jr chemist, Bur Home Econ, USDA, Washington, DC, 37-38; high sch instr gen sci, Ala, 40-41; instr chem, Birmingham-Southern Col, 41-44; instr, Exten Ctr, Univ Ala, 50-52 & 53-55. *Concurrent Pos:* Adj prof biochem, Med Col, Univ Ala, Birmingham, 76-78; adj prof chem, Jeff State Jr Col, Birmingham, 80-87. *Mem:* Am Chem Soc; Sigma Xi. *Res:* Protozoa growth and culture; enzymes, structure of and assays techniques; allosteric effects; fluorescence produced; circular dichroism. *Mailing Add:* 1237 Berwick Rd Hoover Birmingham AL 35242-7124

**THOMS, RICHARD EDWIN,** PALEONTOLOGY. *Current Pos:* asst prof, 64-70, assoc prof, 70-80, PROF GEOL, PORTLAND STATE UNIV, 80- *Personal Data:* b Olympia, Wash, June 5, 35; m 67. *Educ:* Univ Wash, Seattle, BS, 57, MS, 59; Univ Calif, PhD(paleont), 65. *Prof Exp:* Teaching asst paleont, Univ Calif, 60-64. *Mem:* Paleont Soc. *Res:* West coast marine Tertiary biostratigraphy; ichnology. *Mailing Add:* Dept Geol Portland State Univ PO Box 751 Portland OR 97207-0751

**THOMSEN, DONALD LAURENCE, JR,** MATHEMATICS. *Current Pos:* PRES, SOCIETAL INST MATH SCI, CONN, 73- *Personal Data:* b Stamford, Conn, Apr 21, 21; m 58, Linda R Leach; c Melinda R, Katherin (Love) & Donald L III. *Educ:* Amherst Col, BA, 42; Mass Inst Technol, PhD, 47. *Prof Exp:* Teaching fel, Mass Inst Technol, 42, instr, 43-47; from instr to asst prof, Haverford Col, Pa, 47-50; from res fel to res engr, Jet Propulsion Lab, Calif Inst Technol, 50-52; asst prof, Pa State Univ, 52-54; staff, IBM Corp, 54-72, spec asst dir educ, 61-62, dir prof activ, 63-66, corp dir eng educ, 67-72. *Concurrent Pos:* Chmn trustees, Soc Indust & Appl Math, 60-72; chmn, Educ Comt, Am Fedn Info Processing Soc, 65-66; US Comt, Int Fedn Info Processing Congress, 66-69, bd dirs, 69-77, exec comt, 75-77; mem vis comt, Col Sci, Drexel Inst Technol, 69-71; prin investr res studies environ pollution & human exposure, 73-; AIDS researcher, 88- *Mem:* AAAS; Am Math Soc; Am Statist Asn; Math Asn Am; Soc Indust & Appl Math (pres, 59); Am Fedn Info Processing Socs; Asn Comput Mach; Int Fedn Info Processing; Int Soc Exposure Analysis. *Res:* Author 3 books and articles in professional journals. *Mailing Add:* Societal Inst Math Sci 97 Parish Rd S New Canaan CT 06840-4424

**THOMSEN, HARRY LUDWIG,** GEOLOGY, OIL & GAS RESOURCE APPRAISAL. *Current Pos:* RETIRED. *Personal Data:* b Boise, Idaho, June 14, 11; wid; c Katherine A (Wood) & Barbara J (Sample) & Elinor J (Boldus). *Educ:* Oberlin Col, AB, 32, MA, 34. *Honors & Awards:* Unit Award, Excellence of Serv, US Dept Interior, 76. *Prof Exp:* Seismic party chief, Shell Oil Co, Calif, 35-38, seismologist, 38-41, div geophysicist, Calif & Rocky Mt area, 41-48, dist geologist, Colo, 48-51, area geologist, Okla, 51-53; spec assignment, Bataafse Petrol Maatschappij NV, Holland, 53-54; div explor mgr, Shell Oil Co, Mont, 54-60, mgr, explor econ, NY, 60-66, sr staff geologist, Shell Develop Co, Tex, 66-69, spec asst to vpres explor, Shell Oil Co, 69-70; geol consult, 70-74; geophysicist, US Geol Surv, 74-76, geol consult, 76-77; geol consult, Colo Sch Mines, 81-85. *Concurrent Pos:* Pres,

Rocky Mt Sect, Am Asn Petrol Geol, 59-60, mem, Exec Adv Comt & vchmn, Indust & Acad Relations Comt, 64-65, mem, Energy Minerals Comt, 71-75, Petrol Resources Estimation Proj, 76-77; guest lectr, Univ Houston, 70 & Colo Sch Mines Grad Sch, 72. *Mem:* Am Asn Petrol Geol; Sr fel Geol Soc Am; Soc Explor Geophys; Am Inst Prof Geologists. *Res:* Exploration for oil and gas; development and application of methods for evaluating petroleum exploration opportunities; estimation of undiscovered oil and gas resources. *Mailing Add:* 13717 E Marina Dr No B Aurora CO 80014-3775

**THOMSEN, JOHN STEARNS,** ATOMIC PHYSICS, CLASSICAL THERMODYNAMICS. *Current Pos:* res scientist, Johns Hopkins Univ, 54-55, asst prof mech eng, 55-61, res scientist, 62-70, FEL BY COURTESY PHYSICS, JOHNS HOPKINS UNIV, 70- *Personal Data:* b Baltimore, Md, June 10, 21; m 52, Helen C Steuart; c Mary H (Davisson), Steuart H, Alice T (Bockman) & John M. *Educ:* Johns Hopkins Univ, BE, 43, PhD(physics), 52. *Prof Exp:* Elec engr, Gen Elec Co, 43-45; asst prof physics, Univ Md, 50-51; res staff asst, Radiation Lab, Johns Hopkins Univ, 51-52, res scientist, 52-53; asst prof, Stevens Inst Technol, 53-54. *Concurrent Pos:* Mem comt fundamental constants, Nat Res Coun, 61-72, chmn, 69-71. *Mem:* Fel Am Phys Soc; Am Asn Physics Teachers. *Res:* Thermodynamics; irreversible processes; nonlinear electrical circuits; heat conduction with temperature dependent properties; statistical evaluation of atomic constants; x-ray wave lengths and precision experiments. *Mailing Add:* Dept Physics & Astron Johns Hopkins Univ Baltimore MD 21218. *E-Mail:* 74004.2223@compuserve.com

**THOMSEN, KURT O,** DATA COLLECTION PROCEDURES, APPLIED ENVIRONMENTAL METHODS. *Current Pos:* DIR PRC ENVIRON TRAINING CTR, PRC ENVIRON MGT, 90-, VPRES, GEOSCI, 94- *Personal Data:* b Chicago, Ill, Sept 26, 40; m 72, Sheila M Hardenstein; c Emily M, Kurt O II & Max G. *Educ:* Northeastern Ill Univ, BA, 70, MS, 74, PhD(environ eng), 84. *Prof Exp:* Hydrogeol consult, Qutub & Assocs, Inc, 70-74; res environ chemist, Ill Inst Technol, 74-76; partner & environ chemist, Best Environ Inc, 76-78; proj hydrogeologist, Dames & Moore, 78-84; proj mgr, Wang Eng Inc, 84-85. *Concurrent Pos:* Adj prof hydrogeol, Northeastern Ill Univ, 76-; environ consult, DePaul & Assocs, Inc, 90- *Mem:* Am Chem Soc; Am Inst Prof Geologists; Asn Ground Water Scientists & Engrs; Hazardous Mat Control Res Inst; Soc Am Mil Engrs; Water Resources Fedn. *Res:* Developing training methods to provide hands-on, on the job training of environmental methods and data collection techniques. *Mailing Add:* PRC Environ Mgt 200 E Randolph Dr Suite 4700 Chicago IL 60601-5518. *Fax:* 312-938-0118

**THOMSEN, LEON,** ROCK PHYSICS, EXPLORATION GEOPHYSICS. *Current Pos:* RES ASSOC GEOPHYS, AMOCO CORP, 86-, SPEC RES ASSOC, 91- *Personal Data:* b Tulsa, Okla, Oct 22, 42; m 65. *Educ:* Calif Inst Tech, BS, 64; Columbia Univ, PhD(geophys), 69. *Honors & Awards:* Fessenden Award, Soc Explor Geophys, 93. *Prof Exp:* Sr researcher, Ctr Nat Recherche Sci, 69-70; res fel, Calif Inst Tech, 70-72; from asst prof to assoc prof geophys, State Univ NY, 72-80; sr res scientist & staff res scientist, Amoco Corp, 80-86. *Concurrent Pos:* Prof, Scuola Int Fisica Enrico Fermi, 70; consult, IBM, 70-72; vis res fel, Australian Nat Univ, 79; mem, Mineral Phys Comt, Am Geophys Union, 83-; mem, External Eval Comt, Div Earth Sci, Laurence-Berkeley Lab, 86-88; mem res comt, Soc Explor Geophys, 87- *Mem:* Am Geophys Union; Soc Explor Geophys; Am Physics Soc; AAAS. *Res:* Application of rock & mineral physics to exploration for hydrocarbons; anisotropic wave propagation in the sedimentary crust. *Mailing Add:* 12707 Melvern Ct Houston TX 77009

**THOMSEN, MICHELLE FLUCKEY,** SPACE PLASMA PHYSICS. *Current Pos:* STAFF SCIENTIST, LOS ALAMOS NAT LAB, 81- *Personal Data:* b Burlington, Colo, June 25, 50; m 73; c 2. *Educ:* Colo Col, BA, 71; Univ Iowa, MS, 74, PhD(physics), 77. *Hon Degrees:* DSc, Colo Col, 92. *Prof Exp:* Res assoc, Univ Iowa, 77-80; res fel, Max Planck Inst Aeronomy, 80-81. *Mem:* Am Geophys Union. *Res:* Physics of planetary magnetospheres and their interaction with the solar wind; kinetic instabilities and wave-particle interactions in space plasmas; ion and electron heating and acceleration at collisionless shocks. *Mailing Add:* NIS-1 Mail Stop D466 Los Alamos Nat Lab Los Alamos NM 87545. *E-Mail:* mthomsen@lanl.gov

**THOMSEN, ROBERT HAROLD,** cardiovascular pharmacology, drug & product development, for more information see previous edition

**THOMSON, ALAN,** GEOLOGY. *Current Pos:* RETIRED. *Personal Data:* b Passaic, NJ, July 1, 28; m 53, Sally Whelan; c Michael, John, Maris, Judith & James. *Educ:* WVa Univ, BS, 52, MS, 54; Rutgers Univ, PhD(geol), 57. *Prof Exp:* Asst geol, WVa Univ, 52-54; petrogr, Shell Oil Co, 57-65, sr geologist, 65, res geologist, 65-67, res assoc, 67-72, staff res geologist, 72-73, from staff geologist to sr staff geologist, 73-82, geol adv, 82-85. *Concurrent Pos:* Instr, Odessa Col, 58-62; geol consult & adj prof geol, Univ New Orleans, 85- *Mem:* Sr fel Geol Soc Am; Soc Econ Paleont & Mineral; Int Asn Sedimentol; Am Petrol Geologists; Soc Petrol Engrs. *Res:* Petrology of sedimentary rocks; determination of depositional environments; provenance of sandstones, sandstone diagenesis. *Mailing Add:* 212 Coffee St Mandeville LA 70448

**THOMSON, ALAN B R,** GASTROENTEROLOGY. *Current Pos:* from asst prof to assoc prof, 75-82, PROF MED, UNIV ALTA, EDMONTON, 82- *Personal Data:* b Toronto, Ont, May 29, 43; c 4. *Educ:* Queen's Univ, BA, 65, MD, 67, MSc, 70, PhD, 71; FRCP(C), 74 & 75. *Prof Exp:* Asst prof med, Southwestern Med Sch, Dallas, 74-75. *Concurrent Pos:* Mem, Med Adv Bd, Can Found Ileitis & Colitis, 77-82, med, Adv Bd Exec Comt, 78-82; secy,

Med Staff Adv Bd, Univ Alta Hosp, 81-82. *Mem:* Royal Soc Med; Can Asn Gastroenterol (vpres, 85-86); Am Gastroenterol Asn; NY Acad Sci; Am Geriat Soc; Can Physiol Soc; Can Soc Clin Pharmacol; Am Physiol Soc. *Res:* Mechanisms of intestinal adaptation in health and disease; alterations in intestinal transport, morphology and brush border membrane composition, following abdominal radiation, intestinal resection, chronic ethanol indigestion, aging, and in response to dietary manipulation. *Mailing Add:* Div Gastroenterol 519 Robert Newton Res Bldg Univ Alta Edmonton AB T6G 2C2 Can. *Fax:* 403-492-7964

**THOMSON, ALAN JOHN,** ECOLOGY, LANDSCAPE MANAGEMENT. *Current Pos:* RES SCIENTIST BIOL SYST ANALYSIS, PAC FORESTRY CTR, CAN FOREST SERV, 76- *Personal Data:* b Nov 4, 46; Brit & Can citizen; m 67, Catherine M Johnston; c Craig & Elizabeth. *Educ:* Glasgow Univ, BSc, 68; McMaster Univ, PhD(ecol), 72. *Prof Exp:* Res fel physiol ecol, Inst Animal Resource Ecol, Univ BC, 72-76. *Concurrent Pos:* Killam res scholar, Univ BC, 74-76. *Mem:* Can Entom Soc; Am Asn Artificial Intel; Artificial Intel Res Environ Sci. *Res:* Develop decision support systems for natural resource management, using artificial intelligence and computer simulation; stakeholder modeling and knowledge-base development to represent environmental values and ethical systems. *Mailing Add:* Pac Forestry Ctr Can Forest Serv 506 W Burnside Rd Victoria BC V8Z 1M5 Can. *Fax:* 250-363-0775; *E-Mail:* athomson@pfc.forestry.ca

**THOMSON, ASHLEY EDWIN,** MEDICINE, PHARMACOLOGY. *Current Pos:* Prof med pharmacol & therapeut, 65-89, EMER PROF MED, UNIV MAN, 89- *Personal Data:* b Regina, Sask, June 6, 21; m 47; c 7. *Educ:* Univ Sask, BA, 43; Univ Man, MD, 45, MSc, 48; FRCPS(C). *Mem:* Can Soc Nephrology; Am Soc Nephrology; Int Soc Nephrology; Am Physiol Soc; Can Soc Clin Invest. *Res:* Hemodialysis and transplantation. *Mailing Add:* 172 Harvard Ave Winnipeg MB R3M 0K5 Can

**THOMSON, BRUCE M,** HAZARDOUS & RADIOACTIVE WASTE MANAGEMENT, GROUNDWATER ENGINEERING. *Current Pos:* PROF, DEPT CIVIL ENG, UNIV NMEX, 78- *Personal Data:* b Mar 13, 50; m 76, Phyllis H Taylor; c Elizabeth & Blake. *Educ:* Univ Calif, Davis, BS, 71; Rice Univ, MS, 74, PhD(environ eng), 79. *Prof Exp:* Environ engr, US Environ Protection Agency Region IX, San Francisco, Calif, 73-74; vis prof, Dept Environ Eng, Rice Univ, 77-78. *Concurrent Pos:* Vis prof, USAF Environics Lab, 85-86. *Mem:* Am Chem Soc; Am Soc Civil Engrs; Nat Ground Water Asn; Asn Environ Eng Professors; fel NATO. *Res:* Remediation of soils and ground water contaminated with radioactive and hazardous wastes. *Mailing Add:* Dept Civil Eng Univ NMex Albuquerque NM 87131. *Fax:* 505-277-1988; *E-Mail:* bthomson@unm.edu

**THOMSON, DALE S,** DEVELOPMENTAL BIOLOGY. *Current Pos:* assoc prof, 67-74, PROF BIOL, MALONE COL, 74-, CHMN, DIV SCI & MATH, 69- *Personal Data:* b Cleveland, Ohio, Feb 12, 34; m 56; c 3. *Educ:* Cedarville Col, AB, 56; Ohio State Univ, MS, 62, PhD(zool), 65. *Prof Exp:* Teacher, Miami Christian Sch, 56-57; from asst prof to assoc prof biol, Cedarville Col, 57-67. *Mem:* Am Sci Affil. *Res:* Developmental biology, especially cellular ultrastructure with respect to gland development in the chick. *Mailing Add:* Math & Sci Malone Col 515 25th St NW Canton OH 44709-3823

**THOMSON, DAVID JAMES,** UNDERWATER ACOUSTICS. *Current Pos:* DEFENCE SCIENTIST, DEFENCE RES ESTAB PAC, 74- *Personal Data:* b Victoria, BC, June 25, 44; m 76. *Educ:* Univ Victoria, BS, 66, PhD(geophys), 73. *Prof Exp:* Fel physics, Univ Victoria, BC, 72-73 & Univ Alta, 73-74. *Mem:* Can Asn Physicists. *Res:* Geomagnetism; modelling of electric currents induced in non-uniform conductors; underwater acoustics; numerical modelling of underwater sound propagation in horizontally stratified and range dependent environments. *Mailing Add:* 733 Lommax Rd Victoria BC V8X 3W9 Can

**THOMSON, DAVID M P,** CANCER IMMUNOLOGY. *Current Pos:* Assoc physician, 72-82, SR PHYSICIAN, MONTREAL GEN HOSP, 83-, RES ASSOC, RES INST, 72- *Personal Data:* b Nov 4, 39; m 63, Janice E Simpson; c Tracey & Sally. *Educ:* Univ Western Ont, MD, 64; Univ London, Eng, PhD(immunol), 73. *Honors & Awards:* Med medal, Royal Col Physicians & Surgeons, 71; Presidential Award, New Eng Cancer Soc, 81. *Concurrent Pos:* From asst prof to assoc prof med, McGill Univ, 72-81, prof med, 81-, res assoc, McGill Cancer Ctr, 78- *Mem:* Can Soc Clin Invest; Am Asn Immunologists; Am Clin Immunol & Allergies; Am Asn Cancer Res. *Res:* Human immune response to cancer; purification, definition and sequencing of putative tumor antigen; characterization of leukocytes responding to cancer antigens; assays of cytokines in biological immune responses. *Mailing Add:* 1650 Cedar Ave Rm A6-149 Montreal PQ H3G 1A4 Can. *Fax:* 514-933-7146

**THOMSON, DENNIS WALTER,** ENVIRONMENTAL EARTH & MARINE SCIENCES. *Current Pos:* from asst prof to assoc prof, 70-78, PROF METEOROL, COL EARTH & MINERAL SCI, PA STATE UNIV, UNIVERSITY PARK, 78-, HEAD DEPT, 92- *Personal Data:* b New York, NY, Mar 14, 41; m 65, Joan Schurch; c Erik & Heather. *Educ:* Univ Wis-Madison, BS, 63, MS, 64, PhD(meteorol), 68. *Prof Exp:* Ger Acad Exchange Serv fel, Univ Hamburg, 68-69. *Concurrent Pos:* Consult var industs & govt; res aviation panel, Nat Ctr Atmospheric Res, 71-77, Nat Sci Eval Comt, Univ Corp Atmospheric Res, 76, 81 & Nat Ocean Agency Hq, Environ Res Lab, 76, 85-; vis sci, Risoe Nat Lab, Denmark, 77-78; vist asst prof metorol, Univ Wis-Madison, 69-70; rev comt, Environ Res Div, Argonne Nat Lab, 85-87, 90-; G J Haltiner res chair prof, Naval Postgrad Sch,

Monterey, Calif, 86; IPA sci officer, Off Chief Naval Res, Arlington, Va, 89-91; mem, boundary layer dyn workshop, Nat Res Coun. *Mem:* Fel Am Meteorol Soc; Sigma Xi. *Res:* Indirect atmospheric sounding; meteorological measurements and instrumentation systems; marine meteorology; dynamical systems. *Mailing Add:* Dept Meteorol Pa State Univ 502 Walker Bldg University Park PA 16802-5013. *Fax:* 814-865-3663

**THOMSON, DONALD A,** MARINE ECOLOGY, ICHTHYOLOGY. *Current Pos:* From asst prof to assoc prof zool, 63-77, PROF ECOL & EVOLUTIONARY BIOL, UNIV ARIZ, 77-, CUR FISHES, 66-, CHMN MARINE SCI PROG, ECOL & EVOLUTIONARY BIOL DEPT, 73- *Personal Data:* b Detroit, Mich, Apr 9, 32; m 57; c 4. *Educ:* Univ Mich, BS, 55, MS, 57; Univ Hawaii, PhD(zool), 63. *Concurrent Pos:* Coordr, Ariz-Sonora Marine Sci Prog, 64-66; prin investr, Off Naval Res, 65-69; chief scientist, R/V Te Vega, Stanford Exped 16, 67; assoc investr, Off Saline Water, 68. *Mem:* Am Soc Naturalists; Am Soc Ichthyol & Herpet; Asn Syst Collections; Ecol Soc Am. *Res:* Community ecology, species diversity and stability of marine shore fishes in the Gulf of California. *Mailing Add:* Dept Ecol & Evolutionary Biol Univ Ariz Tucson AZ 85721

**THOMSON, GEORGE HERBERT,** PHYSICAL & THERMODYNAMIC PROPERTIES OF CHEMICALS, CHEMICAL INFORMATION. *Current Pos:* CONSULT, PRECISE PROPERTIES, 92- *Personal Data:* b Philadelphia, Pa, Sept 35; m 55; c 2. *Educ:* Okla State Univ, BS, 56; Univ Chicago, PhD(phys chem), 63. *Prof Exp:* NSF, Nat Res Coun fel, Nat Bur Stand, 63-64; res chemist, E I du Pont de Nemours & Co, Inc, 64-65; Babcock & Wilcox Co, 65-68; from asst prof to assoc prof, Gen Motors Inst, 68-75; sr systs specialist, Phillips Petrol Co, 75-92. *Concurrent Pos:* Liaison Comt Chair, Design Inst Phys Property Data, Am Inst Chem Engrs, 89-96, vtech dir, 92-96, long range planning comt chair, 93-96, tech dir, 96- *Mem:* Am Chem Soc; Am Inst Chem Engrs. *Res:* Development and use of old and new methods for the estimation and correlation of thermophysical and thermodynamic properties of organic and inorganic chemicals. *Mailing Add:* 356 Fleetwood Dr Bartlesville OK 74006. *Fax:* 918-335-3201; *E-Mail:* ghthomason@compuserv.com

**THOMSON, GERALD EDMUND,** INTERNAL MEDICINE, NEPHROLOGY. *Current Pos:* chief div nephrology, 70-71, DIR MED, HARLEM HOSP CTR, 71-; LAMBERT PROF MED, COLUMBIA UNIV, 72-, SR ASSOC DEAN, COL PHYSICIANS & SURG, 90- *Personal Data:* b New York, NY, June 6, 32; m 58, Carolyn W Thomson; c 2. *Educ:* Queens Col, BS, 55; Howard Univ, MD, 59. *Prof Exp:* Clin dir, Dialysis Unit, Kings Co Hosp, Downstate Med Ctr, State Univ NY, 65-67; assoc dir med, Coney Island Hosp, Brooklyn, 67-70. *Concurrent Pos:* NY Heart Asn fel renal dis, Downstate Med Ctr, State Univ NY, 65-65; mem med adv bd, NY Kidney Found, 71-; mem, Health Res Coun City of New York, 72-75; mcm, Health Res Coun State Subsurface Injection; oilwell hypertension info comt & mem educ adv comt, NIH, 73; mem bd dirs, NY Heart Asn, 73- & chmn, Comt High Blood Pressure, 75-; chief of staff & exec vpres, Columbia-Presby Med Ctr, 85-90; chmn, Am Bd Internal Med, 90-91. *Mem:* Inst Med-Nat Acad Sci; Am Col Physicians (pres, 95-96); Am Soc Nephrology. *Res:* Hypertension. *Mailing Add:* Col Physicians & Surgeons Columbia Univ 630 W 168th St New York NY 10032

**THOMSON, GORDON BENNETT,** EXPERIMENTS STUDYING K MESONS, WEAK INTERACTION PHYSICS. *Current Pos:* from asst prof to assoc prof, 80-96, PROF PHYSICS, RUTGERS UNIV, 96- *Educ:* Ill Inst Technol, BS, 65; Harvard Univ, MA, 68, PhD(physics), 72. *Prof Exp:* Res assoc, Case Western Res Univ, 72-74, Mich State Univ, 74-76; asst scientist, Univ Wis, 76-80. *Concurrent Pos:* Vis res assoc, Univ Chicago, 77-80. *Mem:* Am Phys Soc. *Res:* Symmetry principles of the weak interaction, particularly on the charge-parity and charge-parity-time symmetries, by studying the decays of K Mesons. *Mailing Add:* 201 S Second Ave No 23 Highland Park NJ 08904. *E-Mail:* thomson@ruthep.rutgers.edu

**THOMSON, GORDON MERLE,** BIOSTATISTICS. *Current Pos:* STATISTICIAN, RALSTON PURINA CO, 71-, MGR BIOL SERV, RES 900, 75- *Personal Data:* b Madison, Wis, May 3, 41; m 63; c 2. *Educ:* Cornell Univ, BS, 63; Iowa State Univ, MS, 66, PhD(animal breeding statist), 68. *Prof Exp:* Assoc statist & comput sci, Iowa State Univ, 68-71. *Mem:* Am Statist Asn; Am Dairy Sci Asn; Am Soc Animal Sci; Sigma Xi. *Res:* Application of statistics to biological research data; conduct of biological experiments in the areas of toxicology and efficacy of feed additives. *Mailing Add:* 143 Gray Ave St Louis MO 63119

**THOMSON, JAMES ALAN,** RESEARCH ADMINISTRATION. *Current Pos:* vpres, 81-89, PRES & CHIEF EXEC OFFICER, RAND CAPITOL CORP, 89- *Personal Data:* b Boston, Mass, Jan 21, 45; m, Darlene; c Kristen Ann & David Alan. *Educ:* Univ NH, BS, 67; Purdue Univ, MS, 70, PhD, 72. *Prof Exp:* Res fel, Univ Wis-Madison, 72-74; systs analyst, Off Secy Defense, US Dept Defense, 74-77; staff mem, Nat Security Coun, White House, 77-81. *Mem:* Int Inst Strategic Studies. *Res:* Contributed various articles to professional journals. *Mailing Add:* Rand Capitol Corp 1700 Main St Santa Monica CA 90407-2138

**THOMSON, JAMES DOUGLAS,** POLLINATION BIOLOGY, BEE BIOLOGY. *Current Pos:* PROF ECOL & EVOL, STATE UNIV NY, STONY BROOK, 80- *Personal Data:* b Chicago, Ill, Feb 18, 50; m 70, Barbara A Fowler. *Educ:* Univ Chicago, AB, 72; Univ Wis-Madison, MS, 75, PhD(zool), 78. *Prof Exp:* Researcher, Univ Toronto, 79-80. *Concurrent Pos:* Consult, Educ Testing Serv, 88-91; coun men, Soc Study Evol, 88-91. *Mem:*

Soc Study Evol; fel AAAS; Ecol Soc Am; Bot Soc Am; Am Soc Naturalists; Int Soc Behav Ecol. *Res:* Behavior and ecology of pollinating bees and their consequencs for pollination success, floral evolution, and plant communities. *Mailing Add:* Dept Ecol & Evol State Univ NY Stony Brook NY 11794-5245. *Fax:* 516-632-7627; *E-Mail:* jt@sbbioym.bitnet

**THOMSON, JOHN ANSEL ARMSTRONG,** HORTICULTURAL IMPROVEMENTS WITH CARBON-HYDROGEN-OXYGEN COMPLEXES. *Current Pos:* RETIRED. *Personal Data:* b Detroit, Mich, Nov 23, 11; m 38, June A Hummel; c Sheryll L, Patricia D & Robert R. *Educ:* Univ Southern Calif, AB, 57. *Hon Degrees:* BS, Calif Polytech State Univ, San Luis Opispo, 61. *Honors & Awards:* Sci & Indust Gold Medal, World Fair, 40. *Prof Exp:* Biochemist & owner, Vitapure Labs, Vitamin Inst, 39. *Concurrent Pos:* Voc educ instr, US War Manpower Comn, 43-44. *Mem:* Int Soc Hort Sci; Am Inst Biol Sci; NY Acad Sci; Soc Nutrit Educ; AAAS; Am Hort Soc. *Res:* Biochemistry; vigorous longevity; nutrients' behavior-normalization; formulation, processing and utilization of products supplying life process substances, especially carbon-hydrogen-oxygen molecular groups for horticulture and environment improvements; human physical and mental health improvements through optimization of nutrients and of interference with their metabolism by adverse exposures; sole originator of over 100 products. *Mailing Add:* 8054 St Clair Ave North Hollywood CA 91605-1321. *Fax:* 818-766-8482

**THOMSON, JOHN OLIVER,** PHYSICS. *Current Pos:* from asst prof to assoc prof, 58-72, PROF PHYSICS, UNIV TENN, KNOXVILLE, 72- *Personal Data:* b Cleveland, Ohio, Feb 2, 30; m 55; c 3. *Educ:* Williams Col, AB, 51; Univ Ill, MS, 53, PhD, 56. *Prof Exp:* Fulbright grant, Univ Rome, 56-57 & Univ Padua, 57-58. *Concurrent Pos:* Consult, Physics Div, Oak Ridge Nat Lab, 58-; assoc prof, Memphis State Univ, 66-68. *Mem:* Am Phys Soc. *Res:* Solid state and low temperature physics. *Mailing Add:* 1144 Keowee Ave Knoxville TN 37919

**THOMSON, KEITH A,** FISHERIES OCEANOGRAPHY, BIOPHYSICAL MODELS. *Current Pos:* RES ASSOC DEPT OCEANOG, UNIV BC, 90- *Educ:* Royal Roads Mil Col, BSc, 77; Univ BC, PhD(phys oceanog), 86. *Prof Exp:* Scientist, Dobrocky Seatech Ltd, 86, Seaconsult Ltd, 87-90. *Res:* Biophysical controls of fish migration and production individual based models. *Mailing Add:* Fisheries Ctr Univ BC 2204 Main Mall Hut B8 Vancouver BC V6T 1Z4 Can. *Fax:* 604-822-8934; *E-Mail:* userckat@mtsg.ubc.ca

**THOMSON, KEITH STEWART,** ZOOLOGY, PALEONTOLOGY. *Current Pos:* pres, Acad Natural Sci, 87-95, UNIV DISTINGUISHED SCIENTIST-IN-RESIDENCE, NEW SCH SOC RES, PHILADELPHIA, 96- *Personal Data:* b Heanor, Eng, July 29, 38; m 63, Linda Price; c Jessica A & Elizabeth R. *Educ:* Univ Birmingham, Eng, BSc, 60; Harvard Univ, Am, 61, PhD(biol), 63. *Hon Degrees:* AM, Yale Univ, 76. *Honors & Awards:* Golden Trilobite Award, Paleont Soc Am, 95. *Prof Exp:* NATO sci fel & temp lectr zool, Univ Col, Univ London, 63-65; asst prof & asst cur vert zool, Peabody Mus Natural Hist, Yale Univ, 65-70, assoc cur vert zool & assoc prof biol, 70-76, dir, 77-79, prof biol & cur vert zool, Peabody Mus Natural Hist, Yale Univ, 76-87, dir, Sears Found Marine Res & Oceanog Hist, 77-88, dean, Grad Sch Arts & Sci, 79-86. *Concurrent Pos:* Bd mem & trustee, Wetlands Inst, 75-, Woods Hole Oceanog Inst, 81-, Wistar Inst & Cent Philadelphia Develop Corp, 87-95. *Mem:* Soc Nautical Res; fel Linnean Soc London; fel Zool Soc London; Soc Vert Paleont; Sigma Xi. *Res:* Vertebrate biology, especially of lower vertebrates; coelacanths, lungfishes, origin of tetrapods; origin of adaptations and of major groups; morphogenesis; history of science, Darwinism; popular science writing. *Mailing Add:* 41 Summit St Philadelphia PA 19118

**THOMSON, KENNETH CLAIR,** ECONOMIC GEOLOGY, PETROGRAPHY. *Current Pos:* from asst prof to assoc prof, 68-78, PROF GEOL, SOUTHWEST MO STATE UNIV, 78- *Personal Data:* b Gunnison, Utah, Mar 5, 40; m 61, Edda M Noon; c Rick, Lauri, Jennifer & Elysia. *Educ:* Univ Utah, BS, 63, PhD, 70. *Prof Exp:* Illustr-geologist, Utah Geol Surv, 59-68. *Concurrent Pos:* Pres, Mo Speleol Surv, Inc. *Mem:* Fel Nat Speleol Soc; Am Inst Prof Geologists. *Res:* Karst hydrogeology; speleology; stratigraphy of Southwestern Missouri. *Mailing Add:* Dept Geog Geol & Planning Southwest Mo State Univ 901 S Nat Springfield MO 65804-0089

**THOMSON, KERR CLIVE,** GEOPHYSICS, SEISMOLOGY. *Current Pos:* PROF PHYSICS, BRYAN COL. *Personal Data:* b Toronto, Ont, Mar 2, 28; US citizen; m 55; c 2. *Educ:* Univ BC, BA, 52; Colo Sch Mines, DSc(geophys), 65. *Prof Exp:* Seismologist, Seismograph Serv Corp, Okla, 52-54; seismologist, Stand Oil Co Calif, 54-55, seismic party chief, 55-58; instr physics, Colo Sch Mines, 58-61; res physicist, Air Force Cambridge Res Labs, 61-65, br chief seismol, 65-75, dir terrestrial sci lab, 75- *Concurrent Pos:* Lectr, Gordon Col, 66-69 & Boston Col, 72. *Mem:* Seismol Soc Am; Am Geophys Union; Soc Explor Geophys; Europ Asn Explor Geophys; Am Sci Affil. *Res:* Earthquake focal mechanism; theoretical seismology; model seismology; wave propagation in absorptive media; seismic radiation in tectonically stressed media; nuclear test detection; structural vibration; terrestrial gravity. *Mailing Add:* 260 Fairview Lane Dayton TN 37321

**THOMSON, NEIL R,** CIVIL ENGINEERING. *Current Pos:* PROF CIVIL ENG, UNIV WATERLOO. *Honors & Awards:* Horst Leiphole Medal, Can Soc Civil Eng, 92. *Mailing Add:* Dept Civil Eng Univ Waterloo Waterloo ON N2L 3G1 Can

**THOMSON, QUENTIN ROBERT,** ENGINEERING. *Current Pos:* RETIRED. *Personal Data:* b Lake Charles, La, Nov 14, 18; m 42; c 8. *Educ:* Ga Inst Technol, BS, 40; Univ Ariz, MS, 53; Calif Western Univ, PhD(eng econ), 75. *Honors & Awards:* Ralph Teetor Award, Soc Automotive Engrs, 76; Am Soc Heating, Refrig & Air Conditioning Engrs Award, 76. *Prof Exp:* Exp test engr, Pratt & Whitney Aircraft Co, 40-41; engr & inspector, US Vet Admin, 51-53; consult engr, 81-93. *Concurrent Pos:* Chief engr, Krueger Mfg Co, 63-67, consult, Krueger Div, Lear-Siegler, Inc, 67- & Shipley & Assoc. *Mem:* Am Soc Mech Engrs; Am Soc Heating, Refrig & Air Conditioning Engrs; Am Mgt Asn; Soc Automotive Engrs. *Res:* Performance of gasoline as related to octane and distillation in automobiles. *Mailing Add:* 4730 Camino Luz Tucson AZ 85718

**THOMSON, RICHARD EDWARD,** PHYSICAL OCEANOGRAPHY. *Current Pos:* RES SCIENTIST, INST OCEAN SCI, FISHERIES & OCEANS CAN, 71- *Personal Data:* b Comox, BC, Apr 14, 44. *Educ:* Univ BC, BS, 67, PhD(physics & oceanog), 71. *Concurrent Pos:* Vis scientist, Monash Univ, Australia, 74; vis researcher, Australian Inst Marine Sci, 82; vis lectr, Univ NSW, Australia, 88. *Mem:* Can Meteorol & Oceanog Soc; Am Geophys Union; Am Soc Limnol & Oceanog; AAAS; Can Geophys Union; fel Royal Soc Chem. *Res:* Wave propagation in random media; energetics of planetary waves and internal gravity waves; vorticity mixing and redistribution in the ocean; baroclinic tides and inertial currents; generation and propagation of shelf waves; long-term sea level fluctuations; vortex streets in the atmosphere; rectilinear leads in arctic ice; mesoscale eddies; hydrothermal vents; tidal rectification; ocean climate. *Mailing Add:* Inst Ocean Sci 9860 W Saanich Rd PO Box 6000 Sidney BC V8L 4B2 Can. *Fax:* 250-363-6479; *E-Mail:* rick@ios.bc.ca

**THOMSON, ROBB M(ILTON),** MATERIALS SCIENCE, SOLID STATE PHYSICS. *Current Pos:* sr res scientist, 71-95, EMER FEL, NAT INST STAND & TECHNOL, 95- *Personal Data:* b El Paso, Tex, Feb 4, 25; m 48; c 4. *Educ:* Univ Chicago, MS, 50; Syracuse Univ, PhD(physics), 53. *Prof Exp:* Res assoc physics, Univ Ill, Urbana, 53-56, from asst prof to assoc prof metall, 56-60, prof physics & metall, 60-68; prof mat sci & chmn dept, State Univ NY Stony Brook, 68-71. *Concurrent Pos:* Dir mat sci, Adv Res Projs Agency, US Dept Defense, 65-68. *Mem:* Am Phys Soc; AAAS. *Res:* Theory of imperfections in solids; mechanical properties of solids. *Mailing Add:* Mat Sci & Eng Lab Nat Inst Stand & Technol Gaithersburg MD 20899

**THOMSON, ROBERT FRANCIS,** metallurgical engineering, for more information see previous edition

**THOMSON, STANLEY,** GEOTECHNICS, ENGINEERING GEOLOGY. *Current Pos:* From asst prof to prof, 61-84, EMER PROF CIVIL ENG, UNIV ALTA, 84- *Personal Data:* b Toronto, Ont, Dec 23, 23; m 46; c 5. *Educ:* Univ Toronto, BASc, 50; Univ Alta, MSc, 55, PhD(soil mech, found), 63, BSc, 71. *Honors & Awards:* Eng Medal, Can Pac Rwy, 90. *Concurrent Pos:* Nat Res Coun Can oper res grants, 65-91. *Mem:* Eng Inst Can; Can Geotech Soc. *Res:* Foundation engineering; slope stability in highly over-consolidated soils; influence of geology in soil mechanics. *Mailing Add:* Dept Civil Eng Univ Alta Edmonton AB T6G 2G7 Can

**THOMSON, TOM RADFORD,** PHYSICAL ORGANIC CHEMISTRY, THEORETICAL CHEMISTRY. *Current Pos:* from assoc prof to prof, 61-81, EMER PROF CHEM, ARIZ STATE UNIV, 81- *Personal Data:* b Hachiman, Japan, Nov 7, 18; nat US; m 46, June Tucker; c Belle R, Gina M, Marcus T, Channing L & Warren L. *Educ:* Univ Calif, BS, 39; Kans State Univ, MS, 40, PhD(chem), 45. *Prof Exp:* Asst chem, Kans State Univ, 39-40, instr, 42, chemist, 42-47; from assoc prof to prof chem, Adams State Col, 47-61, head dept, 47-61. *Concurrent Pos:* Sigma Xi res grant, 54; res assoc, Univ Calif, 54; vis scholar, Utah, 59; Res Corp grant, 59-60; resident author, Addison-Wesley Publ Co, Calif, 67-68; chem consult, 81- *Mem:* Am Chem Soc. *Res:* Carbohydrates; starch chemistry; chemical education; relationship of structure to physical properties; theoretical chemistry; water-soluble polymers. *Mailing Add:* 65 Ramon Sonoma CA 95476. *Fax:* 707-935-1033

**THOMSON, WILLIAM JOSEPH,** CHEMICAL ENGINEERING. *Current Pos:* DEPT CHEM ENG, WASH STATE UNIV. *Personal Data:* b New York, NY, May 15, 39; m 64; c 4. *Educ:* Pratt Inst, BChE, 60; Stanford Univ, MS, 62; Univ Idaho, PhD(chem eng), 69. *Prof Exp:* Asst scientist, Avco Res & Advan Develop Div, 61-62; assoc prof, 69-75, prof chem eng, Univ Idaho, 75- *Mem:* Am Inst Chem Engrs; Am Chem Soc. *Res:* Catalytic kinetics; chemical reactor development; fluidization. *Mailing Add:* Dept Chem Eng Wash State Univ Pullman WA 99163

**THOMSON, WILLIAM TYRRELL,** ENGINEERING. *Current Pos:* prof mech eng & chmn dept, 66-76, EMER PROF MECH ENG, UNIV CALIF, SANTA BARBARA, 76- *Personal Data:* b Kyoto, Japan, Mar 24, 09; US citizen; m 41, Patricia Inglis; c Sharon, Roger & Hugh. *Educ:* Univ Calif, BS, 33, MS, 34, PhD(elec eng), 38. *Honors & Awards:* Den Hartog Award, Am Soc Mech Engrs, 89. *Prof Exp:* Instr mech, Kans State Col, 37-41; res engr, Boeing Airplane Co, Wash, 41; asst prof mech, Cornell Univ, 41-44; head vibration & flutter, Ryan Aeronaut Co, Calif, 44-46; from assoc prof to prof mech, Univ Wis, 46-51; prof eng, Univ Calif, Los Angeles, 51-66. *Concurrent Pos:* Consult, Space Technol Labs, 55-; Fulbright res prof, Kyoto Univ, 57-58; Guggenheim fel, Ger, 61-62. *Mem:* Fel Am Soc Mech Engrs; assoc fel Am Inst Aeronaut & Astronaut. *Res:* Applied mathematics; vibrations; dynamics. *Mailing Add:* Dept Mech Eng Col Eng Univ Calif Santa Barbara CA 93106

**THOMSON, WILLIAM WALTER,** BOTANY, CYTOLOGY. *Current Pos:* Asst res botanist, Air Pollution Res Ctr, 63-64, from asst prof to assoc prof, 64-74, PROF BIOL, UNIV CALIF, RIVERSIDE, 74- *Personal Data:* b Chico, Calif, Oct 11, 30; c 3. *Educ:* Sacramento State Col, BA, 53, MA, 60; Univ Calif, Davis, PhD(bot), 63. *Mem:* Am Soc Plant Physiol; Bot Soc Am. *Res:* Ultrastructure of chloroplasts and plant membranes as related to development, physiology and stress conditions. *Mailing Add:* Dept Bot & Plant Sci Univ Calif Riverside 900 University Ave Riverside CA 92521-0101

**THOMULKA, KENNETH WILLIAM,** MICROBIAL PHYSIOLOGY, ENVIRONMENTAL MICROBIOLOGY. *Current Pos:* ASST PROF MICROBIOL, PHILADELPHIA COL PHARM, 72- *Personal Data:* b Mt Holly, NJ, Sept 28, 42; m 66, Piontkowski; c Andrew, Jenny, Tom & Richard. *Educ:* Hahneman Univ, PhD(microbiol), 70. *Concurrent Pos:* Adj prof anat, physiol & microbiol, Camden Co Col, 76- *Mem:* Am Soc Microbiol. *Res:* Developed a bioluminescence-reduction assay to detect biohazardous substances in the environment using Vibrio harvegi. *Mailing Add:* Biol Sci Dept Philadelphia Col Pharm Sci 600 S 43rd St Philadelphia PA 19104

**THONAR, EUGENE JEAN-MARIE,** CARTILAGE BIOCHEMISTRY, CARBOHYDRATE BIOCHEMISTRY. *Current Pos:* from asst prof to assoc prof, 80-88, PROF BIOCHEM & INTERNAL MED, RUSH PRESBY, ST LUKE'S MED CTR, 88-, GEORGE W STUPPY PROF ARTHRITIS, 90-, ASSOC CHMN, DEPT BIOCHEM, 94-, PROF ORTHOP SURG, 96- *Personal Data:* b Liege, Belg, Oct 4, 45; m 82, Jennifer Neuman; c Benjamin & Alexandra. *Educ:* Witwatersrand Univ, BSc, 69, BSc(hons), 70, PhD(biochem), 77. *Honors & Awards:* Carol Nachman Prize Rheumatology, 87. *Prof Exp:* Res asst orthop surg, Witwatersrand Univ, 73-76, res officer, 77-79; vis assoc biochem, Nat Inst Dent Res, 79-80. *Concurrent Pos:* Prin investr, William Noble Lane, MRO, 80-88; specialist lectr, Cook Co Grad Sch Med, 82-; consult, NIH Pathobiochem Study Sect, 85, CIBA-Geigy Corp, 86-90, Eisai Co, 92- *Mem:* Am Soc Biol Chemists & Molecular Biol; Orthop Res Soc; Sigma Xi; AAAS; Am Col Rheumatology. *Res:* Biochemistry of cartilage; proteoglycans of cartilage matrix in health and disease; age-related changes in structure and metabolism of proteoglycans; blood assays for assessing cartilage and corneal disease. *Mailing Add:* Dept Biochem Rush-Presby-St Luke's Med Ctr 1653 W Cong Pkwy Chicago IL 60612-3864. *Fax:* 312-942-3053; *E-Mail:* 75122,2151@compuserve.com

**THONNARD, NORBERT,** ATOMIC PHYSICS, ASTROPHYSICS. *Current Pos:* dir technol, 83-85, vpres res & develop, 85-89, PRES, ATOM SCI, INC, 89- *Personal Data:* b Berlin, Ger, Jan 22, 43; US citizen; m 64; c 4. *Educ:* Fla State Univ, BA, 64; Univ Ky, MS, 69, PhD(physics), 71. *Prof Exp:* Physicist, US Army Engr Res & Develop Labs, 64-66; consult astrophys, Battelle Pac Northwest Labs, Battelle Mem Inst, 72; fel, Carnegie Inst, 70-72, staff mem, Dept Terrestrial Magnetism, 72-84. *Concurrent Pos:* Mem Users Comt, Nat Radio Astron Observ, 78-81; vis scientist, Kapteyn Lab, Univ Groningen, Neth, 82. *Mem:* Am Phys Soc; Am Astron Soc; AAAS; Int Astron Union; Am Chem Soc. *Res:* Development of laser-based ultra-sensitive element analysis techniques and instrumentation; analysis application developement of resonance ionization spectroscopy; application of one-atom detection; galaxy studies from Z1-cm and optical observations; development of instrumentation for radio and optical astronomy; observational cosmology. *Mailing Add:* Inst Rare Isotope Mea 10521 Research Dr No 300 Knoxville TN 37932-2573

**THOR, EYVIND,** FOREST GENETICS, SILVICULTURE. *Current Pos:* Asst prof forestry res, 59-65, from assoc prof to prof, 65-82, EMER PROF FORESTRY, UNIV TENN, 82- *Personal Data:* b Oslo, Norway, Nov 24, 28; US citizen; m 56; c 3. *Educ:* Univ Wash, Seattle, BS, 54, MS, 56; NC State Univ, PhD(forestry), 61. *Concurrent Pos:* Elwood L Demmon res award, 61; US Forest Serv res grant, 66-68; grant, Inland Container Corp, 75-76. *Mem:* Soc Am Foresters. *Res:* Population genetics; breeding of trees for timber production (pines and hardwoods), Christmas trees (pine and spruce) and disease resistance (American chestnut). *Mailing Add:* 310 Wesley Rd Knoxville TN 37909

**THOR, KARL BRUCE,** PHARMACOLOGY. *Current Pos:* sr pharmacologist, 90-93, RES SCIENTIST, LILLY RES LABS, 94- *Personal Data:* b Pittsburgh, Pa, Mar 30, 54; m 81; c 2. *Educ:* Pa State Univ, BS, 76; Univ Pittsburgh, PhD(pharmacol), 85. *Prof Exp:* Pharmacol fel, Uniformed Serv Univ, 85-88; sr staff fel neurophysiol, Nat Inst Neurol Dis & Stroke, NIH, 88-90. *Concurrent Pos:* Grant reviewer, Am Heart Asn, 87-90, Paralyzed Vet Am, 90-; adj asst prof pharmacol, Uniformed Serv Univ, 88-90, Ind Univ Med Sch, 91-93, adj asst prof urol, 91-93; adj assoc prof pharmacol & urol, Ind Univ Med Sch, 93-96; mem, Neurol B Study Sect, NIH; adj assoc prof surg, obstet & gynec, Duke Univ. *Mem:* Soc Neurosci; Soc Basic Urol Res; Int Continence Soc; Urodynamics Soc. *Res:* Central control of lower urinary tract function; use of electrophysiology, neuroanatomy, receptor autoradiography and immunohistochemistry to determine neurotransmitter systems that regulate lower urinary tract function in adults, neonates and paraplegic patients. *Mailing Add:* Div CNS Res Lilly Res Labs Indianapolis IN 46285. *Fax:* 317-276-5546; *E-Mail:* thor_karl_b@lilly.com

**THORBECKE, GEERTRUIDA JEANETTE,** IMMUNOLOGY, EXPERIMENTAL PATHOLOGY. *Current Pos:* from res assoc to assoc prof, 57-70, PROF PATH, SCH MED, NY UNIV, 70- *Personal Data:* b Neth, Aug 2, 29; m 57; c Best, Steven & Neal. *Educ:* State Univ Groningen, MD, 50, PhD, 54. *Prof Exp:* Asst path, State Univ Leiden, 56-57. *Concurrent Pos:* Foreign Opers Mission to Neth scholar, Lobund Inst, Ind, 54-56; USPHS res grants, 59-, USPHS res career develop award, 61-71; career scientist award, Health Res Coun, City of New York, 71-72; corresp mem, Royal Dutch Acad

Sci, 80; coun, Am Asn Immunol, 84-91, pres, 89-90; coun, Fed Am Socs Exp Biol Bd, 89-91; mem, Coun Int Union Immunol Soc, 89-92; consult, Schering Corp, 75-, Repligen, 87-89, Merck, 89-90; bd sci counr, Nat Cancer Inst, 71-75, Nat Inst Allergy & Infectious Dis, 78-84. *Mem:* Am Soc Exp Path; Soc Exp Biol & Med; fel NY Acad Sci; Reticuloendothelial Soc; Brit Soc Immunol; Am Asn Cancer Res. *Res:* Antibody formation; lymphoid tissues and lymphoid cell interaction; immunological tolerance; tumor immunity; effect of aging on immune response; immunoglobin D, germinal centers and antoimmunity. *Mailing Add:* Dept Path NY Univ Sch Med 550 First Ave MSB 523 New York NY 10016-6402

**THORESEN, ASA CLIFFORD,** ORNITHOLOGY. *Current Pos:* RETIRED. *Personal Data:* b Blenheim, NZ, Sept 9, 30; nat US; m 52; c 2. *Educ:* Emmanuel Missionary Col, BA, 54; Walla Walla Col, MA, 58; Ore State Col, PhD, 60. *Prof Exp:* Vis prof biol, Biol Sta, Walla Walla Col, 60, 70; from asst prof to assoc prof, Andrews Univ, 60-67, chmn dept, 63-83, prof, 67- *Concurrent Pos:* Leader biol expeds Peru, 64-65, 68 & SPac & Australia, 72, 82, 85; NSF grant, NZ, 66-67. *Mem:* Electron Micros Soc Am; Cooper Ornith Soc; Am Ornith Union. *Res:* Life history and behavioral studies of oceanic birds, particularly of the family Alcidae; ultrastructural studies of avian tissues. *Mailing Add:* 885 Eckman Ct McMinnville OR 97128

**THORGEIRSSON, SNORRI S,** CARCINOGENESIS RESEARCH. *Current Pos:* WEISBERG PROF, COMP SCI, CHMN COMP SCI & SOFTWARE DEVEL, MARSHALL UNIV, 93- *Personal Data:* b Iceland, Dec 1, 41; nat US. *Educ:* Univ Iceland, MD, 68; Univ London, PhD, 71. *Prof Exp:* Intern, Univ Hosp, Reykjavik, Iceland, 68-69; registr & res fel, Dept Clin Pharmacol, Royal Postgrad Med Sch, London, Eng, 69-71; assoc prof, Pratt Inst, 67-81, prof physics, 81-85. *Concurrent Pos:* Mem, Chem Selection Working Group, 78-82, Comt Occup Carcinogenesis, 79, Comt Amines, Nat Acad Sci; preceptor, Pharmacol Res Assoc Prog, Nat Inst Gen Med Sci, NIH, 77-; Nat Cancer Inst rep, Subcomt Testing & Test Method Validation Comt Coord Environ Health & Related Prog, 91- *Mem:* AAAS; Am Chem Soc; Am Asn Cancer Res; Am Soc Cell Biol; Am Soc Microbiol; Am Soc Pharmacol & Exp Therapeut; NY Acad Sci; Soc Toxicol. *Res:* Cellular and molecular biology of hepatocarcinogenesis; regulation and role of the multidrug resistance gene family; genetic control of growth and differentiation during normal and neoplastic development. *Mailing Add:* Nat Cancer Inst Div Cancer Etiol NIH Lab Exp Carcinogenesis Bldg 37 Rm 3C28 Bethesda MD 20892-4255

**THORINGTON, RICHARD WAINWRIGHT, JR,** BIOLOGY. *Current Pos:* chmn, Dept Vert Zool, 87-92, CUR PRIMATES, BIOL PROG, SMITHSONIAN INST, 69- *Personal Data:* b Philadelphia, Pa, Dec 24, 37; m 67, Caroline Miller; c Ellen (Moffat) & Katherine (Kimball). *Educ:* Princeton Univ, BA, 59; Harvard Univ, MΛ, 63, PhD(biol), 64. *Prof Exp:* Primatologist, New Eng Regional Primate Res Ctr, 64-69, assoc mammal, Mus Comp Zool, 64-69. *Mem:* AAAS; Am Soc Mammal; Soc Study Evolution; Int Primatology Soc; Sigma Xi; Am Soc Primatology. *Res:* Form and function of mammals; thermoregulation and thermal effects on development; primate ecology and taxonomy. *Mailing Add:* 7714 Old Chester Rd Bethesda MD 20817-6278. *Fax:* 202-357-4779; *E-Mail:* mnhvz049@sivm.si.edu

**THORLAND, RODNEY HAROLD,** SOLID STATE PHYSICS. *Current Pos:* SR, HONEYWELL CO, 82- *Personal Data:* b Lake Mills, Iowa, Feb 16, 41. *Educ:* Luther Col, BA, 64; Emory Univ, MSc, 69, PhD(physics), 71. *Prof Exp:* Vol, US Peace Corps, 64-67; asst prof physics, Kennesaw Jr Col, 71-72; res assoc physics, Emory Univ, 72-73; from asst prof to prof physics, Vol State Community Col, 73-81. *Mem:* AAAS; Am Phys Soc; Am Asn Physics Teachers; assoc Sigma Xi. *Res:* Nuclear magnetic resonance, electron paramagnetic resonance and far infrared spectroscopy. *Mailing Add:* 5723 Pond Dr St Paul MN 55126-4832

**THORLEIFSON, LEONARD HARVEY,** CENTRAL NORTH AMERICA GLACIAL GEOLOGY, DIAMOND EXPLORATION METHODS. *Current Pos:* RES SCIENTIST, GEOL SURV CAN, 86- *Personal Data:* b Man, Apr 6, 57. *Educ:* Univ Winnipeg, BA, 80; Univ Manitoba, MSc, 83; Univ Colo, PhD(geol), 89. *Mem:* Geol Soc Am; Geol Asn Can; Am Quaternary Asn; Can Quaternary Asn; Can Inst Mining & Metall. *Res:* Quaternary history of central North America; glacial history and geology, geomorphology, hydrogeology and indicator minerals. *Mailing Add:* Geol Surv Can 601 Booth St Ottawa ON K1A 0E8 Can. *Fax:* 613-992-0190; *E-Mail:* thorleifson@gsc.nrcan.gc.ca

**THORMAN, CHARLES HADLEY,** GEOLOGY. *Current Pos:* GEOLOGIST, US GEOL SURV, 71- *Personal Data:* b Albany, Calif, June 14, 36; m 57; c 2. *Educ:* Univ Redlands, BS, 58; Univ Wash, MS, 60, PhD(geol), 62. *Prof Exp:* Geologist, Humble Oil & Ref Co, 62-65 & Olympic Col, Wash, 65-68; vis asst prof geol, Univ Ore, 68-71. *Mem:* Am Asn Petrol Geol; Geol Soc Am. *Res:* Tectonics of the eastern basin and range; structure of Liberia; tectonics of southwest Arizona and southeast New Mexico. *Mailing Add:* 12464 W Second Dr Lakewood CO 80228-5011

**THORMAR, HALLDOR,** VIROLOGY, SLOW VIRUS INFECTIONS. *Current Pos:* PROF BIOL, UNIV ICELAND, 86- *Personal Data:* b Iceland, Mar 9, 29; m 62, Lilja Asbjornsdottir; c Sigridur, Asdis B & Olina M. *Educ:* Copenhagen Univ, PhD(cell physiol), 56, DrPhil(virol), 66. *Prof Exp:* Res scientist, State Serum Inst, Copenhagen, Denmark, 60-62; from res scientist to assoc res scientist, Inst Exp Path, Keldur, Iceland, 62-67; chief res scientist virol, NY State Inst Basic Res Develop Disabilities, Staten Island, NY, 67-86.

*Concurrent Pos:* Investr virol, Sci Res Inst, Caracas, Venezuela, 65-66; vis prof, Free Univ Brussels, Belgium, 75; vis scientist, Catholic Univ, Leuven, Belgium, 92, 95, Chinese Acad Med Sci Beijing, 92. *Mem:* Am Soc Microbiol; Icelandic Acad Sci. *Res:* Virucidal effect of lipid compounds on enveloped viruses; effect of antiviral agents on lentivirus infections in vitro and in vivo. *Mailing Add:* Inst Biol Univ Iceland Grensasvegur 12 Reykjavik Iceland. *Fax:* 354-525-4069; *E-Mail:* halldort@rhi.hi.is

**THORN, CHARLES BEHAN, III,** THEORETICAL PHYSICS. *Current Pos:* PROF PHYSICS, UNIV FLA, 80- *Personal Data:* b Washington, Ind, Aug 14, 46; m 79, Mary A Furman; c Alexandra M & Jessica S. *Educ:* Mass Inst Technol, BS, 68; Univ Calif, Berkeley, MA, 69, PhD(particle theory), 71. *Prof Exp:* Res assoc, Europ Orgn Nuclear Res, NSF, 72; res assoc physics, Mass Inst Technol, 73, from asst prof, to assoc prof, 73-80. *Concurrent Pos:* Alfred P Sloan fel, 74; vis, Dept Appl Math & Theoret Physics, Cambridge Univ, 76 & 91; invited prof, Ecole Normal Superieure, Paris, 85; mem, Inst Advan Study, Princeton, 86-87; John Simon Guggenheim fel, 86-87. *Mem:* Fel Am Phys Soc. *Res:* Theory of elementary particles; theory of strongly interacting particles; theory of relativistic strings. *Mailing Add:* Dept Physics Univ Fla PO Box 118440 Gainesville FL 32611-8440. *E-Mail:* thorn@quark.phys.ufl.edu

**THORN, DONALD CHILDRESS,** MICROWAVE DEVICES. *Current Pos:* CONSULT, 58-; EMER PROF, UNIV AKRON, 87- *Personal Data:* b Ft Worth, Tex, June 2, 29; m 53, Margaret Landers; c Sharon L, Michael L & Carla L (Guinn). *Educ:* Tex A&M Univ, BS, 51; Univ Tex, Austin, MS, 55, PhD(elec eng), 58. *Prof Exp:* Asst prof elec eng, Univ Tex, Austin, 56-58; from asst prof to prof, Univ NMex, 58-67; prof, Univ Akron, 67-87. *Mem:* Sigma Xi; Nat Soc Prof Engrs; Nat Acad Forensic Engrs. *Res:* Microwave devices; microwave propagation in the atmosphere and other media. *Mailing Add:* PO Box 90045 San Antonio TX 78209-9045

**THORN, GEORGE W,** ENDOCRINOLOGY. *Current Pos:* prof, 42-72, EMER PROF, HOWARD MED SCH, 72- *Personal Data:* b Buffalo, NY, Jan 15, 06; m 31; c 1. *Educ:* Univ Buffalo, MD, 29. *Hon Degrees:* Numerous from foreign & US univs, 42-87. *Prof Exp:* Asst med, Univ Buffalo, 32-34; assoc prof med, Johns Hopkins Med Sch, 38-42. *Concurrent Pos:* Physician, Johns Hopkins Hosp, Baltimore, 40-42; physician-in-chief, Peter Bent Brigham Hosp, Boston, 42-72, emer physician-in-chief, 72-; emer chmn bd, Howard Hughes Med Inst; emer corp mem, Mass Inst Technol. *Mem:* Asn Am Physicians; Endocrine Soc; Clin & Climat Soc; Am Acad Arts & Sci. *Res:* Endocrinology, studies of the adrenal gland; kidney, development of dialysis and kidney transplant. *Mailing Add:* Harvard Med Sch Howard Hughes Med Inst 320 Longwood Ave Enders 661 Boston MA 02115. *Fax:* 617-730-0408

**THORNBER, CARL RICHARD,** MANTLE PETROLOGY, EXPERIMENTAL IGNEOUS PETROLOGY. *Current Pos:* Geologist, Br Exp Geochem & Mineral, US Geol Surv, Reston, Va, 77-82, geologist/chief mineralogist, Saudi Arabian Mission, Jeddah, 82-86, geologist, Br Igneous & Geothermal Processes, Denver, Colo, 86-94, GEOLOGIST, HAWAIIAN VOLCANO OBSERV, US GEOL SURV, 94- *Personal Data:* b New Bedford, Mass, Sept 26, 53; m 71, Mary A Love; c Wendi L, Andrew R, Spencer A & Timothy S. *Educ:* Univ Mass, Amherst, BS, 76; Queens Univ, MSC, 78; Univ Colo, Boulder, PhD(geol), 92. *Mem:* Mineral Soc Am; Am Geophys Union. *Res:* Lunar and terrestrial experimental igneous petrology; petrologic, geochemical and isotopic systematics of continental rift volcanism and mantle evolution; metallogenesis in rifted deep crustal environments; Hawaiian volcanism. *Mailing Add:* US Geol Surv Hawaiian Volcano Observ PO Box 51 Hawaii National Park HI 96718

**THORNBER, JAMES PHILIP,** PLANT BIOCHEMISTRY. *Current Pos:* asst prof bot, Univ Calif, 70-72, assoc prof biol, 72-75, chmn dept, 81-86, PROF BIOL, UNIV CALIF, LOS ANGELES, 75- *Personal Data:* b Hebden Bridge, Eng, Dec 22, 34; m 60, 83, Elaine M Tobin; c 4. *Educ:* Cambridge Univ, BA, 58, MA, 61, PhD(biochem), 62. *Prof Exp:* Sci off plant biochem, Twyford Labs Ltd, Arthur Guinness, Son & Co, Ltd, 61-67; res assoc biol, Brookhaven Nat Lab, 67-69, asst scientist, 69-70. *Concurrent Pos:* NSF grant, Univ Calif, Los Angeles, 71-93; Guggenheim mem fel, 76-77; USDA grant, 78- *Mem:* Am Soc Biol Chem; Am Soc Plant Physiol. *Res:* Photosynthesis; organization of chlorophyll in plants and bacteria; chlorophyll-protein complexes; photochemical reaction centers; membrane composition, structure and biogenesis. *Mailing Add:* Dept Biol Univ Calif 2337 Veteran Ave Los Angeles CA 90024-2107. *Fax:* 310-206-4386; *E-Mail:* ibb9tho@uclamvs.bitnet

**THORNBER, NORA S,** QUANTUM ELECTRODYNAMICS. *Current Pos:* instr, 87-92, ASSOC PROF MATH, RARITAN VALLEY COMMUNITY COL, 97- *Personal Data:* b Palo Alto, Calif, Apr 7, 40; m 67, Karen & Carol. *Educ:* Univ Calif, Riverside, AB, 62; Calif Inst Technol, PhD(physics), 67. *Prof Exp:* Postdoctoral, Linear Accelerator Ctr, Stanford Univ, 67-68, Univ Bristol, Eng, 68-69; asst prof math, Newark Col Eng, 68-71. *Concurrent Pos:* Adj prof physics, Mont State Univ, 95- *Mem:* Math Asn Am; Am Asn Physics Teachers; Am Phys Soc; Sigma Xi. *Res:* Exact solution to the coupled non-linear equations of massless (non-2nd-quantized) quantum electrodynamics, in three plus one dimensions. *Mailing Add:* Math Dept Raritan Valley Community Col PO Box 3300 Somerville NJ 08876

**THORNBERRY, HALBERT HOUSTON,** PLANT PATHOLOGY. *Current Pos:* from asst prof to prof, 38-71, EMER PROF PLANT PATH, UNIV ILL, URBANA, 71- *Personal Data:* b Corydon, Ky, Dec 28, 02; m 46, Kathryn K Winder; c Martha L. *Educ:* Univ Ky, BS, 25, MS, 26; Univ Minn, PhD(plant path), 34. *Prof Exp:* Asst plant path, Univ Minn, 26-28 & Univ Ill, 28-31; fel, Rockefeller Inst Med Res, 31-35; jr plant pathologist, Citrus Exp Sta, Univ Calif, 35-36; asst pathologist, Univ Ky, 36-37; pathologist, Bur Plant Indust, USDA, 37-38. *Concurrent Pos:* Res award, Soc Am Florists, 68; consult plant health & mgt, 71- *Mem:* AAAS; Am Phytopath Soc; Am Soc Microbiol; Am Chem Soc. *Res:* Phytovirology; chemopathology; antibiotics; bacterial diseases. *Mailing Add:* 1602 S Hillcrest St PO Box 128 Urbana IL 61801

**THORNBOROUGH, JOHN RANDLE,** NEUROBIOLOGY, NEUROENDOCRINOLOGY. *Current Pos:* res med, NY Med Col, 72-73, instr, 73-74, asst prof, 74-80, ADJ ASSOC PROF PHYSIOL, NY MED COL, 80-; ASSOC PROF PHYSIOL, MT SINAI SCH MED, 87- *Personal Data:* b Columbus, Ohio, Feb 2, 39; m 87, Janice N McLean; c 2. *Educ:* Ohio State Univ, BA, 60, MA, 61; NY Med Col, PhD(physiol), 72. *Prof Exp:* Instr biol, Denison Univ, 61-67; assoc med prof physiol, City Col NY-Sophie Davis Sch Biomed Educ, 80-86, dir acad affairs, 80-84. *Concurrent Pos:* Adj prof physiol, Sarah Lawrence Col, 73-77; assoc prof med educ, Mt Sinai Sch Med, 87-, assoc dean academic affairs, 88-92. *Mem:* Soc Neurosci. *Res:* Hypothalamic control of sodium and water metabolism. *Mailing Add:* Dept Physiol Mt Sinai Sch Med 1 Gustave Levy Pl Box 1218 New York NY 10029. *E-Mail:* jrt@ilocinc.com

**THORNBURG, DONALD RICHARD,** PHYSICAL METALLURGY, MAGNETISM. *Current Pos:* sr engr magnetics, 58-73, FEL ENGR MAGNETICS, RES & DEVELOP CTR, WESTINGHOUSE ELEC CORP, 73- *Personal Data:* b Pittsburgh, Pa, Oct 16, 33; m 71; c 3. *Educ:* Rensselaer Polytech Inst, BMetE, 55; Carnegie Inst Technol, MS, 63; Carnegie-Mellon Univ, PhD(metall), 72. *Prof Exp:* Navigator, US Air Force, 55-57. *Mem:* AAAS; Am Soc Metals; Am Inst Mining, Metall & Petrol Engrs; Sigma Xi. *Res:* Development of magnetic materials; calculation of texture development using crystal plasticity theory; methods for improving the properties of magnetic materials; corrosion and mechanical properties of zirconium-based materials. *Mailing Add:* 387 Barclay Ave Pittsburgh PA 15221

**THORNBURG, JOHN ELMER,** CLINICAL PHARMACOLOGY, TOXICOLOGY. *Current Pos:* Fel pharmacol, 70-72, ASST PROF PHARMACOL, DEPT PHARMACOL, TOXI-FAMILY MEDICINE COL & FAMILY MED, MICH STATE UNIV, 77- *Personal Data:* b Syracuse, Ind, Apr 15, 42; m 70; c 2. *Educ:* Purdue Univ, BS, 65, MS, 68, PhD(pharmacol), 70; Mich State Univ, DO, 76. *Mem:* Soc Neurosci; AAAS; Am Osteop Asn. *Res:* Perinatal toxicity of organophosphates; sympathetic nervous system and platelet alpha adrenergic receptors in hypertensive subjects. *Mailing Add:* Dept Pharmacol & Toxicol Mich State Univ East Lansing MI 48824-0001

**THORNBURGH, DALE A,** FOREST ECOLOGY. *Current Pos:* from asst prof to assoc prof forest ecol, 64-74, chmn dept, 77-80, PROF FOREST ECOL, HUMBOLDT STATE UNIV, 74- *Personal Data:* b Tiffin, Ohio, Dec 1, 31; m 61; c 3. *Educ:* Univ Wash, BS, 59, PhD(forestry), 69; Univ Calif, Berkeley, MS, 62. *Prof Exp:* Lectr silviculture, Univ Wash, 63-64. *Mem:* Ecol Soc Am; Soc Am Foresters. *Res:* Carrying capacity of subalpine meadows in wilderness areas; development of forest habitat types and successional models. *Mailing Add:* Dept Forestry Humboldt State Univ 1 Harps St Arcata CA 95521-8299

**THORNBURGH, GEORGE E(ARL),** mechanical engineering, for more information see previous edition

**THORNBURN, THOMAS H(AMPTON),** soils, engineering; deceased, see previous edition for last biography

**THORNBURY, JOHN R,** radiology, for more information see previous edition

**THORNDIKE, EDWARD HARMON,** ELEMENTARY PARTICLE PHYSICS. *Current Pos:* from asst prof to assoc prof, 61-72, PROF PHYSICS, UNIV ROCHESTER, 72- *Personal Data:* b Pasadena, Calif, Aug 2, 34; m 55, Elizabeth Wenger; c 3. *Educ:* Wesleyan Univ, AB, 56; Stanford Univ, MS, 57; Harvard Univ, PhD(physics), 60. *Prof Exp:* Res fel physics, Harvard Univ, 60-61. *Concurrent Pos:* NSF sr fel, Univ Geneva & Europ Orgn Nuclear Res, 70; fel, Guggenheim Found, 87-88. *Mem:* Am Phys Soc. *Res:* Nucleon-nucleon interactions; few nucleon problems; electron-positron colliding beam phenomena; energy and environment; high energy photoproduction processes; b-quark decay. *Mailing Add:* Dept Physics Univ Rochester Rochester NY 14627

**THORNE, BILLY JOE,** NON LINEAR SYSTEMS OF PARTIAL DIFFERENTIAL EQUATIONS. *Current Pos:* staff mem, 81-82 dept, mgr, 82-85, DISTINGUISHED MEM TECH STAFF, SANDIA NAT LABS, 85- *Personal Data:* b Chanute, Kans, Aug 19, 37; m 59, Linda Kay Gammon; c 4. *Educ:* Phillips Univ, AB, 59; Kans State Univ, MA, 61; Univ NMex, PhD(math), 68. *Prof Exp:* Staff mem, Sandia Nat Labs, 61-66; instr math, Smith Col, Northampton, Mass, 67-68; staff mem, Sandia Nat Labs, 68-74; div mgr, Civil Eng Res Facil, Univ NMex, 74-77; vpres, Civil Systs Inc, Subsid Sci Appl Inc, 77-80, pres, 80-81. *Concurrent Pos:* Asst vpres, Sci Appl Inc, 80-81. *Res:* The use of computational techniques for the solution of a wide range of physical and engineering problems, usually involving the numerical solution off non-linear systems of partial differential equations. *Mailing Add:* 7412 Gladden Ave NE Albuquerque NM 87110

**THORNE, CHARLES JOSEPH,** APPLIED MATHEMATICS. *Current Pos:* RETIRED. *Personal Data:* b Pleasant Grove, Utah, May 28, 15; m 42, Margaret Lien; c Charles L & Joseph O. *Educ:* Brigham Young Univ, AB, 36; Iowa State Col, MS, 38, PhD(math physics), 41. *Prof Exp:* Asst math, Iowa State Col, 38-41; instr, Univ Mich, 41-43; asst prof, La State Univ, 43-44; develop engr, Curtiss-Wright Corp, 44-45; from asst prof to prof math, Univ Utah, 45-55; res scientist, Res Dept, US Naval Ord Test Sta, 55-60, sr res scientist & head math div, 60-61; supvry mathematician, Pac Missile Range, Pac Missile Test Ctr, 61-65, sr opers res analyst, Naval Missile Ctr, 65-76, head assessment div, 75-79, head mgt systs div, 79-82. *Concurrent Pos:* Assoc prof, Univ Calif, Los Angeles, 48-49, lectr, 56-68; sr investr, US Navy Projs, 49-51; dir & prin investr, US Army Ord Projs, 51-55. *Mem:* Am Math Soc; Am Soc Mech Engrs; Math Asn Am; Soc Indust & Appl Math. *Res:* Differential equations; boundary value problems; elasticity; analysis; operations research; numerical analysis. *Mailing Add:* 1447 Sunrise Ct Camarillo CA 93010

**THORNE, CHARLES M(ORRIS),** ENGINEERING, QUALITY ENGINEERING. *Current Pos:* RETIRED. *Personal Data:* b Seattle, Wash, June 27, 21; m 47, Marge Myers; c Karen & Jill. *Educ:* Univ Wash, BSEE, 50. *Prof Exp:* Design engr, Boeing Airplane Co, 50; proj engr, Naval Undersea Warfare Eng Sta, 51-52, sr proof engr, 52-56, head, Electronics Div, Weapons Qual Eng Ctr, 56-60, dir eng, 60-63, tech dir, 64-81. *Mem:* Inst Elec & Electronics Engrs; Am Soc Qual Control. *Res:* Testing and evaluation of underwater missiles; proximity fuzes, high energy batteries, pyrotechnics; environmental testing; non-destructive testing; metrology and functional testing. *Mailing Add:* 1499 NW Bucklin Hill Rd Bremerton WA 98311

**THORNE, CURTIS BLAINE,** microbial genetics, for more information see previous edition

**THORNE, JAMES MEYERS,** PHYSICAL CHEMISTRY. *Current Pos:* PROF CHEM, BRIGHAM YOUNG UNIV, 66- *Personal Data:* b Logan, Utah, June 3, 37; m 60; c 2. *Educ:* Utah State Univ, BS, 61; Univ Calif, Berkeley, PhD(chem), 66. *Concurrent Pos:* Vis staff, Laser Div, Los Alamos Sci Lab, Univ Calif, 72- *Mem:* Am Chem Soc; Sigma Xi. *Res:* Applications of lasers to nuclear fusion, nonlinear optics; magneto and electrooptics. *Mailing Add:* Brigham Young Univ 218 ESC Provo UT 84601

**THORNE, JOHN CARL,** PLANT BREEDING, GENETICS. *Current Pos:* plant breeder, 69-79, SOYBEAN RES DIR, NORTHRUP, KING & CO, 79- *Personal Data:* b Ft Dodge, Iowa, Feb 24, 43; m 70, Helen Gilbert; c Mary & Sandra (Abbott). *Educ:* Augustana Col, Ill, BA, 65; Iowa State Univ, MS, 67, PhD(plant breeding), 69. *Prof Exp:* Res assoc soybean breeding, Iowa State Univ, 67-69. *Concurrent Pos:* Dir & past pres, Nat Coun Com Plant Breeders, 85-91; bd mem, Nat Plant Germplasm Resources Bd, 90-92; vchmn, Soybean Genetics Crop Adv Comt, 90-96. *Mem:* Am Soc Agron; Am Soybean Asn; Crop Sci Soc Am; Am Phytopath Soc. *Res:* Plant breeding and genetics related to soybean variety development. *Mailing Add:* Novartis Seeds Inc PO Box 949 Washington IA 52353. *Fax:* 319-653-4609

**THORNE, KIP STEPHEN,** ASTROPHYSICS, GRAVITATION & THEORETICAL PHYSICS. *Current Pos:* res fel physics, Calif Inst Technol, 66-67, assoc prof, 67-70, prof theoret physics, 70-91, William R Kenan Jr Prof, 81-91, FEYNMAN PROF THEORET PHYSICS, CALIF INST TECHNOL, 91- *Personal Data:* b Logan, Utah, June 1, 40; m 62, 84, Carolee J Winstein; c Kares A & Bret C. *Educ:* Calif Inst Technol, BS, 62; Princeton Univ, AM, 63, PhD(theoret physics), 65. *Hon Degrees:* DSc, Ill Col, 79; DHC, Moscow Univ, 81. *Honors & Awards:* Sci Writing Award, Am Inst Physics-US Steel Corp, 69-94; John Danz Lectr, Univ Wash, 81; Silliman Lectr, Yale Univ, 84; Karl Herzfeld Lectr, Cath Univ, 85; Hans Bethe Lectr, Cornell Univ, 86; Sigma Xi Centenial lectr, 86; Bart Bok Mem Lectr, Astron Soc Pac, 87; Richtmeyer Mem Lectr, Am Asn Phys Teachers, 92; PAM Dirac Mem Lectr, Univ Cambridge, 95; Lillienfeld Prize, Am Phy Soc, 96; Karl Schwarzchild Medal, Astron Soc Ger, 96. *Prof Exp:* NSF fel physics, Princeton Univ, 65-66. *Concurrent Pos:* Lectr, Enrico Fermi Int Sch Physics, Varenna, Italy, 65, 68; Fulbright lectr, Sch Theoret Physics, Les Houches, France, 66; Alfred P Sloan res fel, 66-70; Guggenheim fel, Inst Astrophys, Paris, France, 67-68; vis assoc prof, Univ Chicago, 68; vis prof, Moscow State Univ, 69, 75, 78, 81, 86, 88 & 90; gov comt, Div High Energy Astrophys, Am Astron Soc, 70-72; mem, Int Comt Gen Relativity & Gravitation, 71-80; adj prof, Univ Utah, 71-; vis sr res assoc, Cornell Univ, 77, Andrew D White Prof, 86-; mem comt, US-USSR Coop in Physics, 78-79; mem adv bd, Inst Theoret Physics, Univ Calif, Santa Barbara, 78-80, mem, 81-82, 93, mem, Space Sci Bd, 80-84; chair, Topical Group Gravity, Am Phys Soc, 97-98. *Mem:* Nat Acad Sci; fel Am Acad Arts & Sci; fel Am Phys Soc; Sigma Xi; fel AAAS; Am Astron Soc. *Res:* Theoretical physics; theoretical and relativistic astrophysics; gravitation physics. *Mailing Add:* Calif Inst Technol 130-33 Pasadena CA 91125

**THORNE, MARLOWE DRIGGS,** AGRONOMY. *Current Pos:* prof, 63-74, head dept, 63-70, EMER PROF AGRON, UNIV ILL, URBANA, 74- *Personal Data:* b Perry, Utah, Nov 4, 18; m 41; c 4. *Educ:* Utah State Agr Col, BS, 40; Iowa State Col, MS, 41; Cornell Univ, PhD, 48. *Prof Exp:* Soil physicist & head, Dept Agron, Pineapple Res Inst, Univ Hawaii, 47-54; soil scientist & irrig work proj leader, Eastern Soil & Water Mgt Sect, Soil & Water Conserv Res Br, Agr Res Serv, US Dept Agr, 55-56; prof agron & head dept, Okla State Univ, 56-63. *Concurrent Pos:* Water technol adv, G B Pant Univ, Pantnagar, India, 70-72; team leader, Inst Agr & Animal Sci, Rampur Nepal, 82-84. *Mem:* Soil Sci Soc Am; Am Soc Agron (pres, 77); Soil Conserv Soc Am. *Res:* Irrigation; mulching; tillage. *Mailing Add:* 2009 E Michigan Urbana IL 61802

**THORNE, MELVYN CHARLES,** epidemiology, for more information see previous edition

**THORNE, RICHARD EUGENE,** FISHERIES, HYDROACOUSTICS. *Current Pos:* SR SCIENTIST, BIOSONICS, INC, 88-, VPRES, 95- *Personal Data:* b Aberdeen, Wash, Apr 12, 43; m 64; c 2. *Educ:* Univ Wash, BS, 65, MS, 68, PhD(fisheries), 70. *Honors & Awards:* Cert for Outstanding Res & Professionalism, Am Fisheries Soc, 86. *Prof Exp:* Sr res assoc, Fisheries Res Inst, Univ Wash, 70-75, res assoc prof, 76-80, res prof fisheries, 81-88. *Concurrent Pos:* Acoust expert, Food & Agr Orgn, UN, 71-78; prog coordr, Div Marine Resources, Univ Wash, 73-86, sr scientist, Appl Physics Lab, 78-86. *Mem:* Acoust Soc Am; Am Fisheries Soc; Marine Technol Soc; Am Soc Limnol & Oceanog. *Res:* Hydroacoustic techniques of fish detection and abundance estimation; ecology of fishes. *Mailing Add:* 4027 Leary Way NW Seattle WA 98107-5045

**THORNE, RICHARD MANSERGH,** SPACE PHYSICS, PLASMA PHYSICS. *Current Pos:* Asst prof meteorol, 68-71, assoc prof atmospheric physics, 71-75, PROF ATMOSPHERIC PHYSICS, UNIV CALIF, LOS ANGELES, 75- *Personal Data:* b Birmingham, Eng, July 25, 42; c 2. *Educ:* Univ Birmingham, BSc, 63; Mass Inst Technol, PhD(physics), 68. *Concurrent Pos:* NSF grants, 71-; mem nat comt, Int Union Radio Sci, 71-; consult, Jet Propulsion Lab, Calif Inst Technol & Aerospace Corp; chmn atmospheric sci, Univ Calif, Los Angeles, 76-79; vis fel, St Edmunds Col, Cambridge, 86-87 & 92. *Mem:* Am Geophys Union; Int Union Radio Sci; Planetary Soc. *Res:* Structure and stability of radiation belts; magnetosphere-ionosphere interactions; wave propagation in anisotropic media; space plasma physics. *Mailing Add:* Dept Atmospheric Sci Univ Calif Los Angeles CA 90095. *Fax:* 310-206-5219; *E-Mail:* rmt@jupiter.atmos.ucla.edu

**THORNE, ROBERT FOLGER,** systematics, biogeography, for more information see previous edition

**THORNER, JEREMY WILLIAM,** GENE REGULATION, CELL BIOLOGY. *Current Pos:* asst prof, Univ Calif, 74-80, from assoc prof to prof microbiol, 80-85, prof biochem, 85-89, PROF BIOCHEM & MOLECULAR BIOL, UNIV CALIF, BERKELEY, 89- *Personal Data:* b Quincy, Mass, Jan 18, 46; m. *Educ:* Harvard Col, BA, 67; Harvard Univ, PhD(biochem), 72. *Prof Exp:* Fel biochem, Sch Med, Stanford Univ, 72-74. *Concurrent Pos:* Prin investr res grant, Nat Inst Gen Med Sci, 75-; consult, Chron Corp, Berkeley, Calif, 82-, Syntex Corp, Palo Alto, Calif, 88-; Merit Award, NIH, 89- *Mem:* Am Soc Biol Chemists; Am Soc Microbiol; Am Chem Soc; AAAS; NY Acad Sci; Genetic Soc Am; Protein Soc. *Res:* Molecular and cellular basis of the interactions that control the conjugation response of the yeast Saccharomyces cerevisiae to provide information about the mechanisms of developmental gene regulation and morphogenic control in eukaryotic cells. *Mailing Add:* Div Biochem & Molecular Biol Rm 401 Univ Calif Barker Hall Berkeley CA 94720-3202

**THORNER, MICHAEL OLIVER,** ENDOCRINOLOGY, NEUROENDOCRINOLOGY. *Current Pos:* assoc prof internal med, 77-82, PROF MED, MED CTR, UNIV VA, 82-, DIR, CLIN RES CTR, 84-, HEAD, DIV ENDOCRINOL & METAB, 86-; ASSOC DIR, CTR BIOL TIMING, NSF, 89- *Personal Data:* b Beaconsfield, Bucks, UK, Jan 14, 45; US citizen; m 66; c 2. *Educ:* Univ London, BS, 70 & DSc, 88; Royal Col Physicians, London, MRCP(med), 72. *Hon Degrees:* FRCP, Royal Col Physicians, London, 84. *Honors & Awards:* Albion O Bernstein Award, NY Med Soc, 84; Edwin B Astwood, Award, Endocrine Soc, 92. *Prof Exp:* Lectr chem path, St Bartholomew's Hosp, London, 74, lectr internal med, 75-77. *Concurrent Pos:* Mem, Med Adv Bd, Nat Hormone & Pituitary Prog, 84-86; mem, Endocrinol & Metab Drugs Adv Comn, 84-88; mem, Biochem Endocrinol Study Sect, NIH, 85-89. *Mem:* Fel Royal Col Physicians; Endocrine Soc; Am Physiol Soc; Am Soc Clin Invest; Soc Neurosci; Asn Am Physicians. *Res:* Neuroendocrinology, basic and clinical aspects of hypothalamic pituitary functions with particular emphasis on the regulation of prolactin secretion and regulation of growth hormone secretion by growth hormone releasing hormone. *Mailing Add:* Med Ctr Univ Va PO Box 511-66 Health Ctr McKim Hall Charlottesville VA 22908. *Fax:* 804-979-4967

**THORNGATE, JOHN HILL,** PHYSICS. *Current Pos:* PHYSICIST, LAWRENCE LIVERMORE LAB, 78- *Personal Data:* b Eau Claire, Wis, Dec 23, 35; m 56; c 3. *Educ:* Ripon Col, BA, 57; Vanderbilt Univ, MS, 61, PhD, 76. *Prof Exp:* Inspector health physics, Oak Ridge Opers Off, US Atomic Energy Comn, 59; res group leader radiation dosimetry, Health Physics Div, Oak Ridge Nat Lab, 64-75, asst sect chief, 73-75, health physicist, 60-78. *Mem:* Health Physics Soc; Am Phys Soc; Sigma Xi; Inst Elec & Electronics Engrs. *Res:* Radiation dosimetry and spectrometry. *Mailing Add:* 5480 Arlene Way Livermore CA 94550. *Fax:* 510-423-3090

**THORNHILL, JAMES ARTHUR,** ENDOCRINOLOGY, NEUROPHYSIOLOGY. *Current Pos:* asst prof, 80-83, ASSOC PROF ENDOCRINOL, UNIV SASK, 83- *Personal Data:* b London, Ont, Feb 11, 51; m 76. *Educ:* Univ Western Ont, BSc, 74, MSc, 75, PhD(pharmacol), 78. *Prof Exp:* Fel, Univ Calgary, 78-80. *Concurrent Pos:* Med Res Coun Fel, 78-80. *Mem:* Am Physiol Soc; Can Physiol Soc; Can Pharmacol Soc; Soc Neurosci; AAAS; Can Soc Neurosci. *Res:* Possible physiological role that endogenous opioid peptides (endorphins or enkephalins) have on feeding and temperature regulation; cardiovascular mechanisims of action of opiates and opioids. *Mailing Add:* Dept Physiol Col Med Univ Sask Saskatoon SK S7N 5E5 Can

**THORNHILL, PHILIP G,** METALLURGY. *Current Pos:* RETIRED. *Personal Data:* b Maidstone, Eng, July 7, 18; Can citizen; m 45; c 3. *Educ:* Univ Toronto, BASc, 50, MASc, 51. *Honors & Awards:* Technol Medal, Metall Soc, 74; Airey Award, Can Inst Mining & Metall, 76. *Prof Exp:* Res engr, Falconbridge Nickel Mines Ltd, 51-53, res metallurgist, 54-59, supvr metall res, 60-68, mgr process metall, 68-69, dir metall res, 69-82, process consult, 82- *Concurrent Pos:* Pres, Lakefield Res Can Ltd, 81-82. *Mem:* Am Inst Mining, Metall & Petrol Engrs; Electrochem Soc; Can Inst Mining & Metall; The Chem Soc. *Res:* Hydrometallurgical processes for extraction and refining of nickel. *Mailing Add:* 330 Second St Newmarket ON L3Y 3W6 Can

**THORNTHWAITE, JERRY T,** ONCOLOGY. *Current Pos:* SCI DIR, ONCOL RES LABS, CEDARS MED CTR, 83- *Personal Data:* b Huntsville, Ala, Aug 16, 48. *Educ:* Fla State Univ, PhD(chem), 77. *Mem:* Soc Anal Cytol; Histochem Soc; Am Asn Immunologists. *Res:* Solid tumors. *Mailing Add:* 7880 SW 139th Terr Miami FL 33158

**THORNTON, ARNOLD WILLIAM,** BIOMEDICAL DEVICE INDUSTRY. *Current Pos:* VPRES PROD DEVELOP, IOTEK INC, MINNEAPOLIS, MINN, 94- *Personal Data:* b Hull, Eng, Apr 20, 43; m 73; c 3. *Educ:* Oxford Univ, Eng, BA, 64, MA, 68, DPhil, 68. *Prof Exp:* Res scientist, Dept Metall & Mat Sci, Univ Denver, Colo, 68-73; proj engr, Uniroyal Corp, Detroit, Mich, 73-75; dir res, Cardiac Pacemakers Inc, St Paul, Minn, 75-82; dir prod develop & prod assurance, Medtronic, Minneapolis, Minn, 83-90, dir leads technol, 90-91; dir balloon catheter res & develop, Sci Med Life Systs, Minneapolis, Minn, 91-94. *Concurrent Pos:* Lectr polymer & ceramic sci, Dept Metall & Mat Sci, Univ Denver, Colo, 70-73; mem adv bd, Dept Appl Math, Univ St Thomas, St Paul, Minn. *Res:* Application of polymer, ceramic and metallurgical science to the design and implementation of implantable devices for electrically stimulating the heart; devices for treating heart disease; drug delivery systems for urological/gynecological applications. *Mailing Add:* 1258 Willow Lane Roseville MN 55113

**THORNTON, C G,** SEMICONDUCTORS, MICROELECTRONICS. *Current Pos:* PVT CONSULT, 96- *Personal Data:* b Detroit, Mich, Aug 3, 25; m 49, Gloria Fuchs; c Richard S, Susan C (Webb). *Educ:* Univ Mich, BS, 49, MS, 50, PhD(phys chem). 52. *Honors & Awards:* Res & Develop Achievement Award, 76; Crozier Award; Gold Medal Award, Air Force Commun & Electronics Asn, 83; Centennial Medal, Inst Elec & Electronics Engrs, 84, Eng Leadership Award, 94. *Prof Exp:* Proj engr, Sylvania Elec Co, 51-52; from sect head to dir, Semiconductors Div, Philco Corp, 52-60, dir, Res & Develop, 60-72; dir, Elec Technol & Devices Lab, 72-92, Dept Army Directorate Exec, Electronics & Power Sources Directorate, Army Res Lab, 92-95. *Concurrent Pos:* Chmn, numerous gov comts, task groups & studies. *Mem:* Fel Inst Elec & Electronics Engrs; AAAS; Armed Forces Commun & Electronics Asn; Inst Elec & Electrics Engrs Electron Devices soc (past pres); Inst Elec & Electronics Engrs Eng Mgrt Soc. *Res:* Research in semiconductor devices, microelectronics, semiconductor processing; emphasis on high frequency devices and circuits and microfabrication techniques; very high speed integrated circuits and monolithic microwave/millimeter integrated circuits displays; frequency control and acoustic wave devices; power sources including pulse power; technology transfer expertise; global enterprise research and development; technology management. *Mailing Add:* Attn AMSRL-EP US Army Electronics & Power Sources Directorate Ft Monmouth NJ 07703-5601. *Fax:* 732-946-3088; *E-Mail:* cthornton@monmouth.com

**THORNTON, CHARLES H,** STRUCTURAL MECHANICS. *Current Pos:* CHMN, THORTON-TOMASAETTI ENGRS. *Educ:* Manhattan Col, BCE, 61; NY Univ, MCE, 63, PhD(struct & eng mech), 66. *Honors & Awards:* Civil Engr Yr, Met Sect, Am Soc Civil Engrs, 90; Leader Indust Award, Concrete Indust Bd, 91; Gold Award, Pedestrian Bridges Connecting Copley Pl Develop in Boston, James F Lincoln Arc Welding Found, 86, United Airlines Terminal at Chicago O'Hare Airport, 88. *Concurrent Pos:* Adj prof civil eng, Cooper Union, NY, 67, Manhattan Col, 81; vis distinguished prof, Pratt Inst, NY, 86-96, Manhattan Col, 90-96; vis lectr, Princeton Univ, 96. *Mem:* Nat Acad Eng; Am Soc Civil Engrs; Am Soc Testing & Mats; Am Inst Steel Construct; Am Concrete Inst; fel Soc Mil Engrs. *Res:* Involvement in the design and construction of hundreds of millions of dollars worth of projects; published author. *Mailing Add:* Thornton-Tomasaetti Engrs 641 Avenue of Americas New York NY 10011. *Fax:* 212-645-9236

**THORNTON, CHARLES PERKINS,** PETROLOGY. *Current Pos:* assoc prof, 63-69, PROF GEOL, PA STATE UNIV, UNIVERSITY PARK, 69- *Personal Data:* b Indianapolis, Ind, Jan 1, 27; m 54; c 2. *Educ:* Univ Va, AB, 49; Yale Univ, MS, 50, PhD(geol), 53. *Prof Exp:* Field geologist, State Geol Surv, Va, 50-52; from instr to asst prof petrog, Pa State Univ, 52-61; asst prof geol, Bucknell Univ, 61-63. *Mem:* Geol Soc Am. *Res:* Geology of central Shenandoah Valley, Virginia; petrography and petrology of volcanic rocks; volcanology. *Mailing Add:* Dept Geosci Pa State Univ 403 Deike Bldg Rm 536 University Park PA 16802-2713

**THORNTON, DONALD CARLTON,** ANALYTICAL CHEMISTRY. *Current Pos:* asst prof chem, 77-84, res scholar, 84-86, RES ASSOC PROF, DREXEL UNIV, 86- *Personal Data:* b Baltimore, Md, Apr 16, 47. *Educ:* Univ Va, BS, 69; Pa State Univ, MS & PhD(chem), 76. *Prof Exp:* Res assoc chem, Univ Fla, 76-77. *Mem:* AAAS; Am Chem Soc; Sigma Xi; Am Geophys Union. *Res:* Measurements of sulfur compounds in the atmosphere; sulfur biogeochemical cycle; development of analytical instrumentation and techniques applicable to atmospheric chemistry. *Mailing Add:* Dept Chem Drexel Univ Philadelphia PA 19104

**THORNTON, EDWARD RALPH,** ORGANIC CHEMISTRY, BIOLOGICAL CHEMISTRY. *Current Pos:* from asst prof to assoc prof, 61-69, PROF CHEM, UNIV PA, 69- *Personal Data:* b Syracuse, NY, July 19, 35; m 69, Elizabeth D Kaplan; c Cara E. *Educ:* Syracuse Univ, BA, 57; Mass Inst Technol, PhD(org chem), 59. *Hon Degrees:* MA, Univ Pa, 71. *Honors & Awards:* Ninth Philadelphia Sect Award, Am Chem Soc, 70. *Prof Exp:* NIH fel, Mass Inst Technol, 59-60 & Harvard Univ, 60-61. *Mem:* Fedn Am Sci; Am Chem Soc; Royal Soc Chem; Am Soc Biochem & Molecular Biol; Protein Soc. *Res:* Molecular interactions and selectivity: stereoselectivity, recognition, transition state structure, receptor design, molecular devices. *Mailing Add:* Dept Chem Univ Pa Philadelphia PA 19104-6323

**THORNTON, ELIZABETH K,** PHYSICAL ORGANIC CHEMISTRY. *Current Pos:* asst prof, 68-75, curric coordr, Sci Div, 87-93, ASSOC PROF CHEM, WIDENER UNIV, 75-, CHAIR, DEPT CHEM, 93- *Personal Data:* b Brooklyn, NY, June 4, 40. *Educ:* Mt Holyoke Col, AB, 61; Univ Pa, PhD(org chem), 66. *Honors & Awards:* Lindback Award, 86. *Prof Exp:* Teaching asst chem, Univ Pa, 61-62, NIH fel org chem, 63-66; NATO fel, Swiss Fed Inst Technol, 66-68. *Mem:* AAAS; Fedn Am Sci; Sigma Xi; Am Chem Soc. *Res:* Kinetic isotope effects and reaction mechanisms; organic and biochemistry. *Mailing Add:* Dept Chem Widener Univ Chester PA 19013. *E-Mail:* thornton@popi.science.widener.edu

**THORNTON, GEORGE DANIEL,** SOILS. *Current Pos:* RETIRED. *Personal Data:* b Elberton, Ga, Aug 10, 10; m 39. *Educ:* Univ Ga, BS, 36, MS, 38; Iowa State Col, PhD(soil fertility), 47. *Prof Exp:* Co agr agent, Ga Exten Serv, 36; asst soil survr, Ga State Col, 36, instr agron, 37-40; asst agronomist, Exp Sta, Univ Ga, 40-41; asst prof soils & asst soil microbiologist, Col Agr, Univ Fla, 41-45; asst, Iowa State Col, 45-47; assoc prof soils & assoc soil microbiology, Col Agr, Univ Fla, 47-51, prof soils, 51-71, soil microbiologist, 51-56, asst dean col, 56-71, emer prof soils, 71. *Mem:* Fel Am Soc Agron; Soil Sci Soc Am. *Res:* Soil microbiology. *Mailing Add:* PO Box 833 Venice FL 34284

**THORNTON, GEORGE FRED,** internal medicine, infectious diseases; deceased, see previous edition for last biography

**THORNTON, HUBERT RICHARD,** CERAMIC ENGINEERING, METALLURGY. *Current Pos:* assoc prof, 67-77, ASSOC PROF MECH ENG, TEX A&M UNIV, 77- *Personal Data:* b Van Etten, NY, Nov 15, 32; m 59; c 2. *Educ:* Alfred Univ, BS, 54, MS, 57; Univ Ill, PhD(ceramic eng), 63. *Prof Exp:* Res engr, Nat Bur Standards, 56-59; res assoc ceramic eng, Univ Ill, 59-63; proj standards engr, Gen Dynamics, Ft Worth, 63-67. *Mem:* Am Ceramic Soc; Am Soc Metals; Soc Aerospace Mat & Process Eng; Am Soc Mech Engrs; fel Am Inst Chem. *Res:* Explosive forming; fracture mechanics; failure modes in materials; fracture analysis; design optimization; teaching of materials and materials in design. *Mailing Add:* 2505 Willow Bend Dr Bryan TX 77802-2461

**THORNTON, J RONALD,** PHYSICS & MATHEMATICS. *Current Pos:* DIR, SOUTHERN TECH APPLNS CTR, UNIV FLA, 79- *Personal Data:* b Fayetteville, Tenn, Aug 19, 39; m 64, 76, 86, Bernice McKinney; c Nancy C, Trey & Paul L. *Educ:* Berry Col, BS, 61; Wake Forest Univ, MS, 64. *Prof Exp:* Res physicist, Brown Eng Co, 63-66; sr staff engr, Martin Marietta Corp, Orlando, 66-75; dep dir, NASA, 76-77; exec asst, Congressman Louis Frey Jr, Orlando, 78; pres, Tens Tec Inc, 78-79. *Concurrent Pos:* Mem, Light Wave Tech Comt, Fla High Technol & Indust Coun, Tallahassee, 86-; Javits fel, 86-91. *Mem:* Inst Elec & Electronics Engrs; Tech Transfer Soc. *Res:* Engineering physics. *Mailing Add:* Southern Tech Applns Ctr 17829 NW 20th Ave Newberry FL 32615

**THORNTON, JANICE ELAINE,** NEUROENDOCRINOLOGY, BEHAVIORAL ENDOCRINOLOGY. *Current Pos:* ASST PROF NEUROSCI & BIOL, OBERLIN COL, OHIO, 90- *Personal Data:* b Vancouver, Wash, Apr 5, 52; m 85, Michael D Loose; c Katherine J. *Educ:* Portland State Univ, BS, 76; Univ Wis-Madison, MS, 79, PhD(physiol, psychol), 83. *Prof Exp:* Postdoctoral fel, Rockefeller Univ, New York, NY & Rutgers Univ, Newark, NJ, 83-86; postdoctoral fel, Ore Health Sci Univ, Portland, Ore, 87-89; asst scientist, Ore Regional Primate Res Ctr, 89-90. *Mem:* Soc Neurosci; Soc Study Reproduction; AAAS; Sigma Xi. *Res:* Organizational and activational effects of gonadal hormones on brain and behavior, noradrenergic system and neuropeptides in the control of female reproductive behavior and ovulation. *Mailing Add:* Dept Obstet/Gynec Univ Wash Sch Med Box 356460 Seattle WA 98195-6460. *Fax:* 440-775-8960; *E-Mail:* fthornton@ocvaxa.cc.oberlin.edu

**THORNTON, JOHN IRVIN,** FORENSIC CHEMISTRY. *Current Pos:* from asst prof to assoc prof forensic sci, 74-82, vchmn, Dept Biomed & Environ Health Sci, 81-84, PROF FORENSIC SCI, SCH PUB HEALTH, UNIV CALIF, BERKELEY, 82- *Personal Data:* b Sacramento, Calif, Jan 11, 41; m 75; c 4. *Educ:* Univ Calif, Berkeley, BS, 62, MCriminalistics, 68, DCriminalistics, 74. *Honors & Awards:* Paul Kirk Award, Am Acad Sci. *Prof Exp:* Criminologist, Contra Costa Count Sheriff's Dept, 63-72. *Concurrent Pos:* Mem proj adv comt, Nationwide Crime Lab Proficiency Testing Proj, Forensic Sci Found, 74-82. *Mem:* Am Chem Soc; Am Acad Forensic Sci; Forensic Sci Soc Gt Brit; Sigma Xi. *Res:* Analysis, identification, and interpretation of physical evidence; author or coauthor of over 150 publications. *Mailing Add:* Sch Pub Health Univ Calif Berkeley CA 94720-0001

**THORNTON, JOHN WILLIAM,** ZOOLOGY, CYTOLOGY. *Current Pos:* From asst prof to assoc prof, 60-74, prof, 74-, EMER PROF ZOOL, OKLA STATE UNIV. *Personal Data:* b Shawnee, Okla, Apr 21, 36; m 57; c 3. *Educ:* Okla State Univ, BS, 58; Univ Wash, PhD(zool), 64. *Concurrent Pos:* USPHS res grant, 65-68; staff biologist, Comn Undergrad Educ Biol Sci, 70-71; mem adv comt, Purdue Minicourse Proj. *Mem:* AAAS; Am Soc Zoologists; Am Inst Biol Sci. *Res:* Cellular ultrastructure; cell and tissue culture; undergraduate curricular improvement; investigative laboratories. *Mailing Add:* Dept Zool 430 Life Sci W Okla State Univ Stillwater OK 74078-3052

**THORNTON, JOSEPH SCOTT,** MATERIALS SCIENCE. *Current Pos:* PRES, TEX RES INT, INC, 75- *Personal Data:* b Sewickley, Pa, Feb 6, 36; c 2. *Educ:* Univ Tex, BS, 57; Carnegie Inst Technol, MS, 62; Univ Tex, Austin, PhD(mat sci), 69. *Prof Exp:* Design engr, Walworth Co, 57; res engr, Westinghouse Elec Co, 61-64; instr metall, Univ Tex, Austin, 64-66; group leader metals & composites, Tracor, Inc, 67-69; mgr mat, Horizons Inc, 67-73; dir appl sci, Tracor, Inc, 73-75. *Mem:* Am Soc Metals; Am Soc Testing & Mat; Am Soc Mech Engrs; Adhesion Soc. *Res:* Contract research administration; development and characterization of engineering materials; reliability of devices in adverse environments; failure analysis; accelerated life test development; recovery techniques for hazardous materials spills. *Mailing Add:* 9063 Bee Caves Rd Austin TX 78733-6201

**THORNTON, KATHRYN C,** PHYSICS. *Current Pos:* PROF & DIR, CTR SCI, MATH & ENG, UNIV VA. *Personal Data:* b Montgomery, Ala, Aug 17, 52; m, Stephen T; c Carol E, Laura L & Susan A. *Educ:* Auburn Univ, BS, 74; Univ Va, MS, 77, PhD, 79. *Prof Exp:* NATO fel, Max Planck Inst Nuclear Physics, Ger, 79-80; physicist, US Army Foreign Sci & Technol Ctr, Charlottesville, Va, 80-84; staff mem, NASA, 84-, astronaut, Lyndon B Johnson Space Ctr, 85-, mission specialist, Space Shuttle Discovery, 89, astronaut, Space Shuttle Endeavor, 92. *Mem:* AAAS; Am Phys Soc; Sigma Xi. *Res:* Astrophysics. *Mailing Add:* Sch Eng & Appl Sci Thornton Hall Univ Va Charlottesville VA 22903

**THORNTON, KENT W,** AQUATIC ECOLOGY, SYSTEMS SCIENCE. *Current Pos:* SYSTS ECOLOGIST, WATERWAYS EXP STA, US ARMY ENGRS, 74- *Personal Data:* b Ames, Iowa, Apr 29, 44; m 66; c 1. *Educ:* Univ Iowa, BA, 67, MS, 69; Okla State Univ, PhD(ecol), 72. *Prof Exp:* Teaching asst zool, Univ Iowa, 68-69; lectr environ systs theory, Okla State Univ, 72; asst prof biol, Bowling Green State Univ, 73-74. *Concurrent Pos:* NSF fel, Ctr Systs Sci, Okla State Univ, 72-73; mem methods ecosyst anal, Nat Comn Water Qual, 74; actg br chief, Waterways Exp Sta, US Army Engrs, 75. *Mem:* AAAS; Am Inst Biol Sci; Ecol Soc Am; NAm Benthological Soc; Int Soc Limnol. *Res:* Systems theoretical approach to the conceptualization, analysis and application of mathematical ecosystem models for watershed-reservoir planning and management; sampling theory approach to dynamic systems. *Mailing Add:* 3 Inwood Circle Little Rock AR 72211

**THORNTON, MELVIN CHANDLER,** MATHEMATICS. *Current Pos:* asst prof, 69-73, ASSOC PROF MATH, UNIV NEBR, LINCOLN, 73- *Personal Data:* b Sioux City, Iowa, July 2, 35; m 58; c 4. *Educ:* Univ Nebr, BS, 57; Univ Ill, MS, 61, PhD(math), 65. *Prof Exp:* Asst prof math, Univ Wis, 65-69. *Mem:* Am Math Soc; Math Asn Am. *Res:* General topology. *Mailing Add:* Dept Math Univ Nebr 835 Oldfather Hall Lincoln NE 68588-0323

**THORNTON, MELVIN LEROY,** BOTANY. *Current Pos:* RETIRED. *Personal Data:* b Billings, Mont, Nov 7, 28; m 52; c 2. *Educ:* Univ Denver, BA, 52; Tufts Univ, MA, 58; Univ Mont, PhD(bot), 69. *Prof Exp:* NSF fel, Birkbeck Col, Univ London, 69-70; from asst prof to assoc prof bot, Univ Mont, 71-80. *Mem:* Sigma Xi. *Res:* Dispersal of fungi; ecology of zoosporic fungi. *Mailing Add:* PO 1678 Sultan WA 98294-1678

**THORNTON, PAUL A,** PHYSIOLOGY, NUTRITION. *Current Pos:* RETIRED. *Personal Data:* b Campbell Co, Ky, June 29, 25; m 45; c 2. *Educ:* Univ Ky, BS, 49, MS, 53; Mich State Univ, PhD(nutrit), 56. *Prof Exp:* Asst & assoc prof nutrit, Colo State Univ, 56-62, assoc prof physiol, 63-64; vis prof, Univ Ky, 62-63, assoc prof physiol, 64-77, prof, 77-; res physiologist, Vet Admin Hosp, Lexington, 64-92. *Mem:* Soc Exp Biol & Med; Am Inst Nutrit; Am Physiol Soc; Geront Soc. *Res:* Skeletal physiology and the influence of age on bone tissue change; endocrinological and other environmental factors which affect bone. *Mailing Add:* 464 Lamont Dr Lexington KY 40503

**THORNTON, RICHARD D(OUGLAS),** ELECTRICAL ENGINEERING, COMPUTER SCIENCE. *Current Pos:* From asst prof to assoc prof, 57-68, PROF ELEC ENG & COMPUT SCI, MASS INST TECHNOL, 68- *Personal Data:* b New York, NY, Sept 24, 29; m 59; c 3. *Educ:* Princeton Univ, SB, 51; Mass Inst Technol, MS, 54, ScD(elec eng), 57. *Honors & Awards:* Baker Award, Inst Radio Eng, Inst Elec & Electronics Engrs, 59. *Concurrent Pos:* Chmn, Thornton Assocs, Inc. *Mem:* Inst Elec & Electronics Engrs. *Res:* Maglev transportation systems; electronic circuits and computer aided engineering design; microcomputer controlled electromechanical systems. *Mailing Add:* Mass Inst Technol Rm 36-361 77 Massachusetts Ave Cambridge MA 02139

**THORNTON, ROBERT KIM,** POTATO FERTILITY & PHYSIOLOGY RESEARCH, STATISTICAL ANALYSIS WITH EMPHASIS ON SOIL-PLANT RELATIONS. *Current Pos:* rcs specialist, 81-84, corn & potato variety specialist, 84-87, DIR RES & AGRON, AGRINORTHWEST, INC, 87- *Personal Data:* b Moscow, Idaho, May 9, 57. *Educ:* Wash State Univ, BS, 79, MS, 81; Ore State Univ, PhD(crop sci), 94. *Prof Exp:* Pesticide applicator, Columbia River Farms, 77; field scout, Hammond Farms, 78; greenhouse worker, Wash State Univ, 79-81. *Concurrent Pos:* Consult, ABC Consults, 85-; mem, Nat Anti-Bruise Comt, 86-; dir, Physiol/Prod Mgt Sect, Potato Asn Am, 88-90 & 90-92. *Mem:* Potato Asn Am. *Res:* Potato and corn fertility; growth and development measurements; internal disorder manipulation in potatoes; corn variety evaluations; correlative data on field soil and petiole tissue analysis versus tuber yield, size and quality. *Mailing Add:* Agrinorthwest Inc 2810 Clearwater Ave Kennewick WA 99336. *Fax:* 509-735-6471

**THORNTON, ROBERT MELVIN,** BIOLOGY, PLANT PHYSIOLOGY. *Current Pos:* from asst prof to assoc prof, 68-81, SR LECTR BOT, UNIV CALIF, DAVIS, 81- *Personal Data:* b Auburn, Calif, Nov 14, 37; m 57, 71; c 2. *Educ:* Calif Inst Technol, BS, 59; Harvard Univ, MA, 61, PhD(biol), 66. *Prof Exp:* Sr scientist, Biol/Eng, Appl Sci Corp, Calif, 61-63; instr, Ojai Valley Sch, 63-64; instr biol, Univ Calif, Santa Cruz, 66-67, asst prof, 67-68. *Concurrent Pos:* NSF res grant, Univ Calif, Davis, 69-72. *Mem:* AAAS; Am Soc Plant Physiol; Bot Soc Am. *Res:* Regulatory mechanisms in morphogenesis of plants and fungi; educational research on critical thinking limitations with particular attention to memory management. *Mailing Add:* Dept Plant Biol Univ Calif Davis CA 95616-5200

**THORNTON, ROGER LEA,** ORGANIC CHEMISTRY. *Current Pos:* RETIRED. *Personal Data:* b Wilmington, Del, Mar 9, 35; m 58; c 3. *Educ:* Univ Del, BS, 57; Mass Inst Technol, PhD(org chem), 61. *Prof Exp:* Res chemist, E I DuPont de Nemours & Co, Inc, Del, 61-65, Va, 65-67, sr res chemist, 67-86, licensing assoc, Del, 86-96. *Res:* Vapor-phase catalytic reactions; thermally stable condensation polymers; emulsion polymerization; fluorinated compounds. *Mailing Add:* 2323 Kennwynn Rd Wilmington DE 19810

**THORNTON, ROY FRED,** ELECTROCHEMICAL ENGINEERING, ELECTROCHEMISTRY. *Current Pos:* Chem eng, Battery Bus Dept, 67-69, STAFF MEM ADV ENG SYST, GEN ELEC CO CORP RES & DEVELOP, 69- *Personal Data:* b Upper Darby, Pa, Feb 27, 41; m 66; c 2. *Educ:* Johns Hopkins Univ, BS, 63, PhD(chem eng), 67. *Mem:* Am Inst Chem Engrs; Electrochem Soc. *Res:* Development of processes and systems for pollution prevention and waste minimization. *Mailing Add:* Corp Res & Develop Bldg K1 Rm 4B30 Gen Elec Co PO Box 8 Schenectady NY 12301

**THORNTON, STAFFORD E,** EDUCATION ADMINISTRATION. *Current Pos:* from asst prof to prof civil eng, WVa Inst Technol, 63-86, head dept, 64-77, asst dean, 77-86, dir, Tech Assistance Ctr, 87-96, ASSOC DEAN ENG, WVA INST TECHNOL, 97- *Personal Data:* b Campbell Co, Va, July 29, 34; m 63, Josephine Whittle; c Suzanne (Garrett), William S & Rives W. *Educ:* Univ Va, BCE, 59, MCE, 62. *Honors & Awards:* Roy D Koch Award, 86. *Prof Exp:* Instr civil eng, Univ Va, 60-61, res engr, 62-63. *Concurrent Pos:* City Engr, Montgomery, WVa, 77-; mem, WVa Regist Bd, 79-90; United Eng Trust Trustee, 83-97; bd mem, Accreditation Bd Eng & Technol, 95- *Mem:* Am Soc Civil Engrs (dir, 79-81, vpres, 82-84, pres-elect, 93-94, pres, 94 & 95); Am Soc Eng Educ. *Res:* Structural design; concrete and steel; foundations; city planning; stress analysis of rotating disks and cylinders. *Mailing Add:* Col Eng WVa Univ Inst Technol Montgomery WV 25136. *Fax:* 304-442-3307; *E-Mail:* sethor@wvit.wvnet.edu

**THORNTON, STEPHEN THOMAS,** EXPERIMENTAL NUCLEAR PHYSICS, PHYSICS & SCIENCE EDUCATION. *Current Pos:* asst prof, 68-72, assoc prof, 72-82, PROF PHYSICS, UNIV VA, 82- *Personal Data:* b Kingsport, Tenn, Oct 2, 41; m 61, 79, Kathryn Cordell; c Kenneth, Michael, Carol, Laura & Susan. *Educ:* Univ Tenn, Knoxville, BS, 63, MS, 64, PhD(physics), 67. *Prof Exp:* Us AEC fel, Univ Wis-Madison, 67-68. *Concurrent Pos:* Consult, Physics Div, Oak Ridge Nat Lab, 72-77; Fulbright-Hays sr fel, Max Planck Inst, Heidelberg, 73-74 & 79-80. *Mem:* AAAS; Am Phys Soc; Sigma Xi; Am Asn Physics Teachers; Nat Sci Teachers Asn. *Res:* Electromagnetic nuclear physics; science education; textbook author. *Mailing Add:* Dept Physics Univ Va Charlottesville VA 22903. *E-Mail:* stt@virginia.edu

**THORNTON, WILLIAM ALOYSIUS,** STRUCTURAL MECHANICS OF CONNECTIONS FOR STEEL STRUCTURES. *Current Pos:* CHIEF ENGR, CIVES STEEL CO, ROSWELL, GA, 79-, PRES, CIVES ENG CORP, 87- *Personal Data:* b New York, NY, Sept 8, 38; m 63, Joan Garvol Kossoff; c William & Michael. *Educ:* Manhattan Col, BCE, 60; Case Western Res Univ, MSEM, 64, PhD(eng mech), 67. *Honors & Awards:* T R Higgins lectr, 95. *Prof Exp:* Asst prof civil eng, Clarkson Col Technol, 67-72, assoc prof civil & environ eng, 72-79. *Concurrent Pos:* Lectr, AISC Regional Lect Ser, 84- *Mem:* Fel Am Soc Civil Engrs; Am Soc Testing & Mat; Am Welding Soc; Am Soc Mech Engrs; Res Coun Struct Connections. *Res:* Behavior, analysis and design of structural connections for steel structures. *Mailing Add:* 9475 Martin Rd Roswell GA 30076. *Fax:* 770-692-1755; *E-Mail:* bthornton@civcs.com

**THORNTON, WILLIAM ANDRUS, JR,** COLOR VISION, COLORIMETRY. *Current Pos:* PRES, PRIME-COLOR, INC, 83- *Personal Data:* b Buffalo, NY, June 16, 23; wid; c 4. *Educ:* Univ Buffalo, BA, 48; Yale Univ, MS, 49, PhD(physics), 51. *Prof Exp:* Res assoc labs, Gen Elec Co, 51-56; sr res engr, Westinghouse Elec Corp, Bloomfield, 56-59, fel res engr, 59-65, mgr phosphor res, 65-67, res eng consult, 67-83. *Mem:* Fel Illum Eng Soc; Int Soc Color Coun. *Res:* Light and color; human color vision; international colorimetry system. *Mailing Add:* 27 Harvard Rd Cranford NJ 07016

**THORNTON, WILLIAM EDGAR,** MEDICINE, ASTRONAUTICS. *Current Pos:* CHMN, DEPT CRIMINAL JUSTICE, LOYOLA UNIV, NEW ORLEANS. *Personal Data:* b Faison, NC, Apr 14, 29; c 2. *Educ:* Univ NC, BS, 52, MD, 63. *Honors & Awards:* NASA Except Sci Achievement Award, 74. *Prof Exp:* Chief engr, Electronics Div, Del Mar Eng Labs, Calif, 55-59; intern, Wilford Hall Hosp, Lackland AFB, US Air Force, Tex, 64, assigned to Aerospace Med Div, Brooks AFB, 65-67; scientist-astronaut, Johnson Space Ctr, NASA, 67- *Concurrent Pos:* Instr, Dept Med, Univ Tex Med Br, Galveston. *Res:* Physics; biomedical instrumentation; cardiovascular; principle investigator on sky lab experiments including mass measurements in space, musculo-skeletal and cardiovascular investigations. *Mailing Add:* Loyola Univ 6363 St Charles Ave PO Box 55 New Orleans LA 70118

**THOROUGHGOOD, CAROLYN A,** MARINE SCIENCES. *Current Pos:* Asst prof food sci & nutrit, Univ Del, 68-72, assoc prof, 72-74, dir, Marine Adv Serv, 74-76, assoc dir, Del Sea Grant Col Prog, 76-78, assoc prof marine studies, food sci & nutrit, 78-84, assoc dean, 80-84, DEAN & PROF, COL MARINE STUDIES, UNIV DEL, 84- *Personal Data:* b Sept 1, 43; m 64; c 1. *Educ:* Univ Del, BS, 65; Univ Md, MS, 66, PhD(nutrit), 68. *Concurrent Pos:* Exec dir, Del Sea Grant Col Prog, Col Marine Studies, Univ Del, 78-84; chair, Nat Coun Sea Grand Dirs, 80-81, exec comt mem, 81-; dir, Del Sea Grant Col Prog, 84-; mem, Governor's Task Force Aquacult, 90- *Mem:* AAAS; Sigma Xi; Marine Technol Soc; Am Chem Soc. *Res:* Nutritional biochemistry of bivalve molluscs; aquaculture of bivalves; lipid biochemistry of marine organisms; marine education and the development of policy and materials required to enhance the general public's marine literacy. *Mailing Add:* PO Box 3693 Greenville DE 19807-0693

**THORP, BENJAMIN A,** FLUIDS, MATHEMATICS STATISTICS. *Current Pos:* VPRES ENG, JAMES RIVER CORP, RICHMOND, VA, 86- *Personal Data:* b Albany, NY, May 31, 38; m 87; c 1. *Educ:* Univ Md, BS, 64. *Prof Exp:* Mkt mgr, Huyck Formex Div, Huyck Corp, 71-74, vpres & gen mgr, 74-76, vpres & gen mgr, Huytech Systs Div, 76-80, vpres & dir res, 80-81; pres, Benjamin A Thorp Inc, 81-83 & Poyry-Bek Inc, Raleigh, NC, 83-85; vpres eng, B E & K Inc, Birmingham, Ala, 85-86. *Mem:* Fel Tech Asn Pulp & Paper Indust; Paper Indust Mgt Asn; Exp Aircraft Asn. *Res:* Impact and relationship between human systems and hi-tech systems; development of high performance work systems. *Mailing Add:* 3800 Cogbill Rd Richmond VA 23234

**THORP, EDWARD O,** MATHEMATICS. *Current Pos:* PRES & DIR RES, EDWARD O THORP & ASSOC, 89- *Personal Data:* b Chicago, Ill, Aug 14, 32; m 56, Vivian Sinetar; c Jeffrey, Raun & Karen. *Educ:* Univ Calif, Los Angeles, BA, 53, MA, 55, PhD(math), 58. *Prof Exp:* Instr math, Univ Calif, Los Angeles, 58-59; C L E Moore instr, Mass Inst Technol, 59-61; from asst prof to assoc prof, NMex State Univ, 61-65; assoc prof, Univ Calif, Irvine, 65-67, prof math & finance, 67-82, adj prof, Grad Sch Mgt, 82-83; managing gen partner, Princeton Newport Partners, 69-89, pres & chmn, Oakley Sutton Mgt Corp, 72-90. *Concurrent Pos:* Res grants, NSF, 62-64 & USAF Off Sci Res, 64-74; gen partner, Midas Advisors, 87-90; vis prof finance, Anderson Grad Sch Mgt, Univ Calif, Los Angeles, 90-91, regents prof, Irvine, 93; portfolio mgr, Glenwood Balanced Fund, 92-94. *Mem:* Sigma Xi. *Res:* Functional analysis; probability theory; game theory; statistics; mathematical finance. *Mailing Add:* 21 Ridgeline Dr Newport Beach CA 92660-6825. *E-Mail:* eothorp@ix.netcom.com

**THORP, FRANK KEDZIE,** PEDIATRICS, METABOLISM DIABETES. *Current Pos:* from instr to asst prof, 65-72, ASSOC PROF PEDIAT, UNIV CHICAGO, 72- *Personal Data:* b Denver, Colo, Apr 29, 36; m 65, Nina Terry; c Alexander & Nicholas. *Educ:* Mich State Univ, BA, 55; Univ Chicago, MD, 60, PhD(biochem), 62. *Honors & Awards:* Outstanding Contrib Diabetes & Camping Award, Am Diabetes Asn, 90. *Prof Exp:* Intern pediat, Univ Chicago, 61-62; resident, Children's Hosp Med Ctr, Boston, 62-63. *Concurrent Pos:* NIH res fel biochem, Children's Hosp Med Ctr, Boston, 63-65; Joseph P Kennedy, Jr scholar, 66-; Am Acad Pediat grant, 69-; dir, Ment Develop Clin, Joseph P Kennedy, Jr Ment Retardation Res Ctr, 71-74; dir, Clin Serv, Wyler Children's Hosp, 77-81; mem, Am Bd Pediat, 80-93; mem, Comt Human Nutrit & Nutrit Biol, 81-; bd dirs, Am Diabetes Asn, 89-92, chmn, N Cent Regional Prog, 91-93. *Mem:* Am Acad Pediat; Sigma Xi; NY Acad Sci; Am Diabetes Asn; Am Soc Perenteral & Enteral Nutrit. *Res:* Teaching and clinical work in pediatrics; metabolic and nutritional diseases of children; development of nutrition training and nutrition education programs; genetics and management of diabetes in children. *Mailing Add:* Univ Chicago Dept Pediat MC6051 5841 S Maryland Ave Chicago IL 60637-1463

**THORP, JAMES HARRISON, III,** AQUATIC ECOLOGY, COMMUNITY ECOLOGY. *Current Pos:* PROF BIOL & DIR WATER RESOURCES LAB, UNIV LOUISVILLE, 88- *Personal Data:* b Kansas City, Mo, July 23, 48; m 70; c 2. *Educ:* Univ Kans, BA, 70; NC State Univ, MS, 73, PhD(zool), 75. *Concurrent Pos:* Dir, Calder Conserv & Ecology Ctr, Fordham Univ, 85-88; educ prog dir, Savannah River Ecol Lab, 77-80; assoc ed, Freshwater Invertebrate Biol, 81-84; prin investr, numerous grants, ecology & education; proj dir, Indust Fac Res Partic, NSF grant, 79. *Mem:* Ecol Soc Am; NAm Benthological Soc Am; Soc Int Limnol; AAAS. *Res:* Experimental field studies of factors regulating structure in benthic macroinvertebrate communities within freshwater rivers and lakes; behavioral ecology and competitive interactions among crustaceans. *Mailing Add:* Biol Dept Univ Louisville Louisville KY 40292-0001

**THORP, JAMES SHELBY,** ELECTRICAL ENGINEERING. *Current Pos:* From asst prof to assoc prof, 62-75, PROF ELEC ENG, CORNELL UNIV, 75-, DIR, SCH ELEC ENG, 94- *Personal Data:* b Kansas City, Mo, Feb 7, 37; m 59; c 2. *Educ:* Cornell Univ, BEE, 59, MS, 61, PhD(elec eng), 62. *Concurrent Pos:* Consult, ADCOM, Mass, 62, Gen Elec Co, 64 & Am Elec Power Serv Corp, 77- *Mem:* Nat Acad Eng; Sigma Xi; Inst Elec & Electronics Engrs. *Res:* Control systems and optimal control; power systems. *Mailing Add:* Cornell Univ 224 Phillips Hall Ithaca NY 14850. *Fax:* 607-255-1001; *E-Mail:* thorp@ee.cornell.edu

**THORP, JAMES WILSON,** DIVING MEDICINE, PEDIATRICS. *Current Pos:* DIR, NEWBORN MED, BROCKTON HOSP. *Personal Data:* b Cohocton, NY, Mar 17, 42; m 65; c 3. *Educ:* Cornell Univ, BS, 63; Iowa State Univ, PhD(nutrit), 67; Georgetown Univ, MD, 75. *Prof Exp:* Res physiologist radiobiol, Armed Forces Radiobiol Res Inst, Bethesda, Md, 67-71; resident pediat, Naval Hosp, Bethesda, Md, 75-78; fel neonatology, Childrens Hosp, Washington, DC, 78-80; staff physician neonatology, Naval Hosp, Bethesda, Md, 80-87; res physician diving med, Naval Med Res Inst, Bethesday, Md, 87-93. *Concurrent Pos:* Assoc prof pediat, Uniformed Serv, Univ Health Sci, Bethesda, Md, 80-93; staff neonatologist, Naval Hosp, Bethesda, Md, 87-93; asst ed, Am J Clin Nutrit, 86-92; clin assoc prof pediat, Brown Univ, Providence, RI, 93- *Mem:* Am Soc Clin Nutrit; Am Acad Pediat; AMA. *Res:* Metabolism and nutrition requirements of humans working under hyperboric conditions and effects of extreme cold or heat; nutrition in pediatrics. *Mailing Add:* Dept Pediat Brockton Hosp 680 Center St Brockton MA 02402-3395. *E-Mail:* james_thorpe_md@brown.edu

**THORP, ROBBIN WALKER,** INSECT TAXONOMY, ECOLOGY. *Current Pos:* asst apiculturist, 64-72, assoc prof entom & assoc apiculturist, 72-78, PROF ENTOM & APICULTURIST, UNIV CALIF, DAVIS, 78- *Personal Data:* b Benton Harbor, Mich, Aug 26, 33; m 54, 67; c 3. *Educ:* Univ Mich, BS, 55, MS, 57; Univ Calif, Berkeley, PhD(entom), 64. *Prof Exp:* Jr specialist, Univ Calif, Berkeley, 62-63, asst specialist, 63-64, asst res entomologist, 64. *Mem:* AAAS; Ecol Soc Am; Soc Syst Zool; Entom Soc Am; Soc Study Evolution; Sigma Xi. *Res:* Pollination ecology, especially bee and flower relationships; ecology and systematics of bees and ecology of their biotic enemies; coevolution and coadaptation of pollinating insects and entomophilous angiosperms. *Mailing Add:* 1021 Vassar Dr Davis CA 95616

**THORPE, BERT DUANE,** IMMUNOLOGY, WILDLIFE DISEASES. *Current Pos:* prof microbiol, 68-77, prof zool, 77-88, EMER PROF, NORTHERN COLO, 88- *Personal Data:* b Spanish Fork, Utah, Sept 21, 29; m 55; c 6. *Educ:* Univ Utah, BS(chem) & BS(bact), 58, PhD(microbiol), 63. *Prof Exp:* Res bacteriologist, Epizool Lab, 58-61, Res Inst Ecol & Epizool, 61-63, dir, Epizool Lab, 61-68, from asst res prof to assoc res prof, 63-68, clin lectr microbiol, 67-68. *Concurrent Pos:* Lectr, Brigham Young Univ, 65-66; consult, Dept Defense, 67-; vpres nat comt, Int Northwestern Conf Dis Man. *Mem:* Am Chem Soc; Am Asn Immunol; Am Soc Microbiol; Am Soc Trop Med & Hyg; Soc Exp Biol & Med. *Res:* Host mechanisms of resistance to infectious diseases; new methods of detection and isolation of microorganisms; zoonoses; animal infections and human diseases; natural and acquired immunity. *Mailing Add:* 4920S 1065 E Salt Lake City UT 84117

**THORPE, COLIN,** FLAVOPROTEINS, FLAVINS. *Current Pos:* from asst prof to assoc prof, 78-89, PROF BIOCHEM, DEPT CHEM & BIOCHEM, UNIV DEL, 89- *Personal Data:* b Grantham, Eng, May 1, 47; m 75; c 2. *Educ:* Univ Cambridge, UK, BA, 69; Univ Kent, UK, PhD(chem), 72. *Prof Exp:* Fel biochem, Dept Biol Chem, Univ Mich, 72-78. *Mem:* Am Chem Soc; Biochem Soc; Am Soc Biochem & Molecular Biol. *Res:* Structure, function and mechanism of action of flavoproteins involved in fatty acid oxidation. *Mailing Add:* Dept Chem Univ Del Newark DE 19716-0002

**THORPE, JAMES F(RANKLIN),** MECHANICAL ENGINEERING. *Current Pos:* RETIRED. *Personal Data:* b Sandusky, Ohio, Oct 2, 26; m 49; c 3. *Educ:* Univ Cincinnati, ME, 52; Univ Ky, MS, 55; Univ Pittsburgh, PhD(mech eng), 60. *Prof Exp:* Proj engr, E W Buschman Co, Ohio, 52-53; instr mech eng, Univ Ky, 53-55; engr, Bettis Atomic Power Lab, Westinghouse Elec Corp, 55-57, sr instr reactor eng, 57-59, sr engr, 60-61; assoc prof mech eng, Univ Ky, 61-67; head dept, Univ Cincinnati, 70-79, prof mech eng, 67-93. *Concurrent Pos:* Consult numerous co, govt & univs, 61-; Nat Endowment for Humanities Ethics fel, 78. *Mem:* Am Soc Mech Engrs; Am Soc Eng Educ; Nat Soc Prof Engrs. *Res:* Fluid mechanics; non-traditional machining; vibrations; mechanical design; product liability and product safety. *Mailing Add:* 6537 Chesapeake Run Cincinnati OH 45248

**THORPE, JOHN A(LDEN),** GEOMETRY. *Current Pos:* PROF MATH, PROVOST & SR VPRES ACAD AFFAIRS, QUEENS COL CITY UNIV NEW YORK, 97- *Personal Data:* b Lewiston, Maine, Feb 29, 36; m 59, Marilyn Austin; c Kendall & Steven. *Educ:* Mass Inst Technol, SB, 58; Columbia Univ, AM, 59, PhD(math), 63. *Prof Exp:* Instr math, Columbia Univ, 63; C L E Moore instr, Mass Inst Technol, 63-65; asst prof, Haverford Col, 65-68; from assoc prof to prof, State Univ NY, Stony Brook, 68-87, prof, vprovost & dean, Buffalo, 87-93. *Concurrent Pos:* Mem, Inst Adv Study, 67-68; prog dir, NSF, 84-86, dep div dir, 86-87; bd govs, Math Asn Am, 84-87, chair, Sci Policy Comt, 87-89. *Mem:* Am Math Soc; Math Asn Am; Am Asn Higher Educ. *Res:* Differential geometry; general relativity. *Mailing Add:* Queens Col City Univ New York 1104 Kiely Hall Flushing NY 11367-1597. *Fax:* 718-997-5879; *E-Mail:* provost@mkh1.qc.edu

**THORPE, MARTHA CAMPBELL,** physical organic chemistry, for more information see previous edition

**THORPE, MICHAEL FIELDING,** THEORETICAL PHYSICS, CONDENSED MATTER. *Current Pos:* from assoc prof to prof, 76-96, DISTINGUISHED PROF PHYSICS, MICH STATE UNIV, 97- *Personal Data:* b Bromley, Eng, Mar 12, 44; m 68, Angela Frith; c Amanda K & Wendy R. *Educ:* Univ Manchester, BSc, 65; Oxford Univ, DPhil(physics), 68. *Hon Degrees:* DSc, Oxford Univ, 92. *Prof Exp:* Res assoc physics, Brookhaven Nat Lab, 68-70; from asst prof to assoc prof physics, Yale Univ, 70-77. *Concurrent Pos:* Yale jr fac fel & guest scientist, Max Planck Inst Solids, Stuttgart, 72-73; sr res fel, Oxford Univ, 78 & 82; vis prof, Brazil, Japan, Australia & Eng; NAm ed, J Physics: Condensed Matter. *Mem:* Fel Am Phys Soc; fel Brit Inst Physics; Sigma Xi. *Res:* Theoretical condensed matter physics, including low temperature excitations, amorphous solids, glasses and networks. *Mailing Add:* Dept Physics & Astron Mich State Univ East Lansing MI 48824. *Fax:* 517-353-0690; *E-Mail:* thorpe@pa.msu.edu

**THORPE, NEAL OWEN,** BIOCHEMISTRY. *Current Pos:* sr prog officer 89-95, EXEC DIR & TRUSTEE, MURDOCK TRUST, 96- *Personal Data:* b Wausau, Wis, Sept 8, 38; m 60; c 3. *Educ:* Augsburg Col, BA, 60; Univ Wis, Madison, PhD(physiol chem), 64. *Prof Exp:* USPHS fel, 65-66; Am Heart Asn adv res fel, 66-67; assoc prof biol, Augsburg Col, 67-80, prof, 80-89. *Concurrent Pos:* Res Corp grant & Am Heart Asn grant, 69-71; regional dir grants, Res Corp, 73-74. *Mailing Add:* 703 Broadway St Suite 710 Vancouver WA 98660

**THORPE, RALPH IRVING,** ECONOMIC GEOLOGY, ISOTOPE GEOCHEMISTRY. *Current Pos:* RES SCIENTIST MINERAL DEPOSITS, GEOL SURV CAN, 65- *Personal Data:* b Halls Harbour, NS, Feb 29, 36; m 68; c 2. *Educ:* Acadia Univ, BSc, 58; Queen's Univ, Ont, MSc, 63; Univ Wis-Madison, PhD(econ geol), 67. *Mem:* Mineral Asn Can; Can Inst Mining & Metall; Geol Asn Can; Geochem Soc. *Res:* Genesis of metalliferous ore deposits; lead isotope interpretations; ore mineralogy; zircon geochronology; develop lead evolution models. *Mailing Add:* Mineral Deposits Sect Geol Surv Can 601 Booth St Rm 520 Ottawa ON K1A 0E8 Can. *Fax:* 613-996-9820; *E-Mail:* thorpe@gsc.emr.ca

**THORPE, RODNEY WARREN,** APPLIED MATHEMATICS, OPERATIONS RESEARCH. *Current Pos:* RETIRED. *Personal Data:* b Boston, Mass, Sept 27, 35. *Educ:* Harvard Col, AB, 59, SM, 65, PhD(appl math), 70. *Prof Exp:* Programmer, Ling Proj, Dept Environ Syst, Harvard Univ, 59-65, comput programmer, 71-72; dir environ syst, Appl math, Qei, Inc, 72-85. *Mem:* Sigma Xi. *Res:* Mathematical modeling of transportation problems; pollution problems; simulation operations research. *Mailing Add:* 58 Bradford St Needham MA 02192

**THORPE, TREVOR ALLEYNE,** PLANT PHYSIOLOGY. *Current Pos:* from asst prof to assoc prof, 69-78, asst dean fac arts & sci, 74-76, PROF BOT, UNIV CALGARY, 78- *Personal Data:* b Barbados, WI, Oct 18, 36; m 63; c 2. *Educ:* Allahabad Agr Inst, BScAgr, 61; Univ Calif, Riverside, MS, 64, PhD(plant sci & physiol), 68. *Prof Exp:* Nat Res Coun fel & res plant physiologist, Fruit & Vegetable Chem Lab, US Dept Agr, Calif, 68-69. *Concurrent Pos:* Convener, panel on plant biol & technol, Int Cell Res Organ, UNESCO, 79-85; adj prof, Forestry Sci, Univ Alta, 86-; affiliated scientist, Nat Res Coun Can, Plant Biotechnol Inst, Sask, 87-; head biol sci, 88-89. *Mem:* Can Soc Plant Physiol; Am Soc Plant Physiol; Japanese Soc Plant Physiol; Scand Soc Plant Physiol; Tissue Cult Asn; Int Soc Plant Morphologists; Int Asn Plant Tissue Cult (chmn, 74-78). *Res:* Experimental plant morphogenesis; cytology, physiology and biochemistry of organ formation in tissue culture systems; plant propagation of conifers and selection of salt-tolerant variants by tissue culture methods. *Mailing Add:* Dept Biol Sci Univ Calgary Calgary AB T2N 1N4 Can

**THORSELL, DAVID LINDEN,** PHYSICAL CHEMISTRY. *Current Pos:* asst prof chem, 74-79, actg dean, Sch Sci & Eng, 80-81, CHMN, DEPT CHEM, SEATTLE UNIV, 76-, ASSOC PROF CHEM, 79- *Personal Data:* b July 6, 42; US citizen. *Educ:* Univ Minn, Duluth, BA, 60; Ohio State Univ, PhD(phys chem), 71. *Prof Exp:* Lectr & fel chem, Ohio State Univ, 72-74. *Mem:* AAAS; Am Chem Soc; Inter-Am Photochem Soc. *Res:* Electron paramagnetic reasonance of organic and inorganic single crystal systems; photochemistry; atmospheric chemistry. *Mailing Add:* Seattle Univ Seattle WA 98122

**THORSEN, ARTHUR C,** EXPERIMENTAL SOLID STATE PHYSICS. *Current Pos:* RETIRED. *Personal Data:* b Portland, Ore, July 27, 34; c Jennifer & Melissa. *Educ:* Reed Col, BA, 56; Rice Inst, MA, 58, PhD(physics), 60; Calif Lutheran Col, MBA, 81. *Prof Exp:* Res physicist, Atomics Int Div, NAm Rockwell Corp, 60-63, mem tech staff, Sci Ctr, 63-67, Autonetics Div, 67-70, Res & Technol Div, Anaheim, Calif, 70-73, mem tech staff, 73-74, prog mgr independent res & develop, 74-78, dir, Corp Res Progs, 78-84, dir mat synthesis & processing, 84-87, sr res exec, Rockwell Int Sci Ctr, 87-90. *Res:* Low temperature solid state physics; electronic structure of metals; transport properties of semiconductors; thin films; superconductivity. *Mailing Add:* 3263 W Sierra Dr Thousand Oaks CA 91360

**THORSEN, RICHARD STANLEY,** THERMAL SCIENCES, SOLAR ENERGY. *Current Pos:* PROF & HEAD, DEPT MECH & AEROSPACE ENG, POLYTECH INST NY, 74-, DIR, SOLAR ENERGY APPLNS CTR, 77-, VPRES RES & ADVAN PROG, 93- *Personal Data:* b New York, NY, Oct 6, 40; m 62; c 2. *Educ:* City Univ New York, BS, 62; NY Univ, PhD(mech eng), 67. *Concurrent Pos:* Consult, Grumman Aerospace Corp, 68-; vpres inst & alumni rels, Polytech Inst NY. *Mem:* Am Soc Mech Engrs; Am Inst Aeronaut & Astronaut; Int Solar Energy Soc; Am Soc Eng Educ. *Res:* Multi-phase heat transfer; solar energy. *Mailing Add:* Dept Instr & Alumni Rels Polytech Univ NY 6 MetroTech Ctr Brooklyn NY 11201

**THORSETT, EUGENE DELOY,** SYNTHETIC ORGANIC & NATURAL PRODUCTS CHEMISTRY, NEUROSCIENCES. *Current Pos:* DIR CHEM, ATHENA NEUROSCI, 91- *Personal Data:* b Wadena, Minn, Nov 28, 48; m 70, Ruth Kehir; c 3. *Educ:* Univ Minn, BA, 70; Colo State Univ, PhD(org chem), 73. *Prof Exp:* Res assoc, Rice Univ, 73-75; sr res chemist, Merck, Sharp & Dohme Res Lab, Merck & Co, Inc, 75-88; sr scientist, Genentech, Inc, 88-91. *Mem:* Am Chem Soc; AAAS. *Res:* Organic synthesis; peptidomimetic drug design; enzyme inhibitor design. *Mailing Add:* PO Box 963 Moss Beach CA 94038-0963

**THORSETT, GRANT OREL,** MOLECULAR BIOLOGY. *Current Pos:* From asst prof to assoc prof, 67-79, chmn dept, 84-96, PROF BIOL, WILLAMETTE UNIV, 79- *Personal Data:* b Shelton, Wash, Jan 25, 40; m 63, Karen Smith; c Stephen, David & Jeffrey. *Educ:* Wash State Univ, BS, 62; Yale Univ, MS, 65, PhD(molecular biophys), 69. *Concurrent Pos:* Instr, Proj Newgate, Ore State Penitentiary, 71-72; NSF res partic, Willamette Univ, 71-73. *Mem:* Am Inst Biol Sci. *Res:* Bacterial transformation; biochemical systematics; bacterial biochemistry; use of computers in undergraduate curricula. *Mailing Add:* Dept Biol Willamette Univ Salem OR 97301. *Fax:* 503-375-5425; *E-Mail:* gthorset@willamette.edu

**THORSETT, STEPHEN ERIK,** RADIO ASTRONOMY, PULSAR PHYSICS. *Current Pos:* ASST PROF PHYSICS, PRINCETON UNIV, 94- *Personal Data:* b New Haven, Conn, Dec 3, 64; m 94, Rachel Dewey; c Laura Alice. *Educ:* Carleton Col, BA, 87; Princeton Univ, MA, 89, PhD(physics), 91. *Honors & Awards:* Ernest Fullam Award. *Prof Exp:* Millikan fel physics, Calif Inst Technol, 91-94. *Mem:* Am Astron Soc; Int Astron Union. *Res:* Search for and observations of binary radio pulsars, especially for tests of general relativity, and multi-wavelength observations of gamma ray bursters. *Mailing Add:* Dept Physics Princeton Univ Princeton NJ 08544. *E-Mail:* steve@pulsar.princeton.edu

**THORSON, JAMES A,** GERONTOLOGY, THANATOLOGY. *Current Pos:* from asst prof to prof geront, Omaha, 77-89, assoc prof adult educ, Lincoln, 79-84, DIR GERONT, UNIV NEBR, OMAHA, 79-, PROF ADULT EDUC, LINCOLN, 84-, ISAACSON PROF, 89- *Personal Data:* b Chicago, Ill, Oct 8, 46; m 66; c 2. *Educ:* Northern Ill Univ, Dekalb, BS, 67; Univ NC, Chapel Hill, MEd, 71; Univ Ga, Athens, EdD(adult educ), 75. *Honors & Awards:* John Tyler Mauldin Award Serv Aging. *Prof Exp:* Asst, Exten Div, Univ NC, Chapel Hill, 70-71; from instr to asst prof adult educ, Univ Ga, Athens, 71-77. *Concurrent Pos:* Prin investr, Career Training Prog, US Admin Aging, 78-81; adj assoc prof, Dept Theol Studies, St Louis Univ, 79; vis assoc prof, Dept Educ, Concordia Univ, Montreal, 80; co-leader, US Sci Deleg, People's Repub China, 82-; trainer, Ghost Ranch Ctr, Abiquiu, NMex, 84, Nebr Scholars' Inst, Lincoln, 85-; ed consult, Prentice Hall, Univ Southern Calif Geront Ctr, 85; mem, Comn Prof Adult Educ; expert witness, numerous retirement home tax cases. *Mem:* Fel Geront Soc Am. *Res:* Psychology of aging and spiritual well-being of the elderly; training and adult learning; attitudes toward the aged; death anxiety, personality, death education, nursing and social worth of the aged; aging in China; suicide; humor and death; lethal behaviors. *Mailing Add:* 430 N 61st St Omaha NE 68132

**THORSON, JOHN WELLS,** NEUROPHYSIOLOGY, BIOPHYSICS. *Current Pos:* AFFIL, MAX PLANCK INST, 79- *Personal Data:* b Detroit, Mich, Feb 25, 33; m 64, Marguerite Biederman. *Educ:* Rensselaer Polytech Inst, BS, 55, MS, 58; Univ Calif, Los Angeles, PhD(zool), 65. *Prof Exp:* Physicist, Gen Elec Co, 55-60; NIH trainee biophys, Univ Calif, Los Angeles, 60-65; NSF fel physiol, Max Planck Inst Biol, 65-66 & Oxford Univ, 66-67; asst prof neurosci, Univ Calif, San Diego, 67-68, res scientist, 68-69; vis lectr zool, Oxford Univ, 69-70; res fel, Max Planck Inst Physiol of Behav, 70-72; affil zool, Oxford Univ, 72-79. *Concurrent Pos:* Mass Inst Technol Neurosci Res Prog fel, Univ Colo, 66; prin investr, Air Force Off Sci Res grants, 67-69 & 69-70; consult, Max Planck Inst, 75-, Univ Calif, San Diego, 80 & J W Goethe Univ, Frankfurt, 80-85. *Mem:* Sigma Xi. *Res:* Experimental and theoretical analysis of the dynamics of biological systems; visual movement perception; macromolecular basis of muscle contraction; mathematics of distributed relaxation processes; computers in physiological analysis and control of experiments; methodology in behavioral experiments identifying mechanisms of sensory recognition. *Mailing Add:* The Old Marlborough Arms Combe Witney Oxon OX88NQ England

**THORSON, THOMAS BERTEL,** zoology; deceased, see previous edition for last biography

**THORSON, WALTER ROLLIER,** theoretical chemistry, for more information see previous edition

**THORSTENSEN, THOMAS CLAYTON,** INDUSTRIAL EFFLUENT TREATMENT. *Current Pos:* CONSULT TO PRES, THORSTENSEN LAB, 59- *Personal Data:* b Milwaukee, Wis, Nov 29, 19; c 3. *Educ:* Univ Minn, BS, 42; Lehigh Univ, MS, 47, PhD, 49. *Prof Exp:* Chemist, S B Foot Tanning Co, 42-44; asst, Lehigh Univ, 46-49, res assoc, 49-51; res chemist, J S Young Co, 51-55; proj dir, Res Found, Lowell Technol Inst, 55-59. *Concurrent Pos:* Vis prof, Lowell Technol Inst, 60-; consult aid to underdeveloped nations, UN & Dept State. *Mem:* Am Chem Soc; Am Leather Chem Asn (pres, 74). *Res:* Mineral tannages; chromium; iron; aluminum and zirconium; theory of mineral tannages; synthetic tanning agents; chemical waste streams. *Mailing Add:* 20 Summer St Chelmsford MA 01824

**THORUP, OSCAR ANDREAS, JR,** MEDICINE. *Current Pos:* RETIRED. *Personal Data:* b Washington, DC, Mar 12, 22; m 44; c 1. *Educ:* Univ Va, BA, 44, MD, 46; Am Bd Internal Med, dipl, 55. *Prof Exp:* From asst resident to resident internal med, Hosp, Univ Va, 50-52, asst to dean, Sch Med, 53-67, dir teacher's preventorium, 53-54, from instr to assoc prof internal med, 53-66; prof & head dept, Univ Ariz, 66-74. *Concurrent Pos:* Fel internal med, Hosp, Univ Va, 50; res fel, Univ NC, 52-53; AMA coun on continuing physician educ. *Mem:* AMA; Am Fedn Clin Res; fel Am Col Physicians; Am Clin & Climat Asn; Sigma Xi. *Res:* Hematology, particularly red blood cell enzymes and proteins. *Mailing Add:* 208 Colthurst Dr Charlottesville VA 22901-2038

**THORUP, RICHARD M,** SOIL FERTILITY, PLANT NUTRIENT MANAGEMENT. *Current Pos:* ADJ PROF AGRON, BRIGHAM YOUNG UNIV, 87-; CONSULT, 88- *Personal Data:* b Salt Lake City, Utah, Dec 20, 30; m 57, 80, Evelyn McKinney; c Teria (Tribett), Richard T, Troy W, Christine (Lydon), Deanna (Weeks) & Margaret (Katz). *Educ:* Brigham Young Univ, BA, 55; NC State Univ, MS, 57; Univ Calif, Davis, PhD(soil sci, plant nutrit), 62. *Honors & Awards:* Award Hon, Am Soc Agron. *Prof Exp:* Agronomist, Chevron Chem Co, 60-61, field agronomist, 61-67, regional agronomist, 67-75, nat mgr agron, 75-83, chief agronomist, 83-86. *Concurrent Pos:* Consult, Spain & Mex; bd dirs, Am Registry Cert Prof Agron, Crops & Soils, 78-81, chmn agron sub-bd, 80-81. *Mem:* Am Soc Agron; Soil Sci Soc Am. *Res:* Chemistry of phosphates in the soil, including solubility and interrelationships with soil moisture; maximum fertility studies with field and tree crops; micronutrients; effect of fertilizers on environment; fertilizer response studies on numerous crops. *Mailing Add:* 1741 N 1500 E Provo UT 84604

**THOULESS, DAVID JAMES,** TAPOLOGICAL QUANTUM NUMBERS. *Current Pos:* PROF PHYSICS, UNIV WASH, 80-, UEHLING DISTINGUISHED SCHOLAR, 88- *Personal Data:* b Bearsden, Scotland, Sept 21, 34; m 58, Margaret Scrase; c Michael, Christopher & Helen. *Educ:* Cambridge Univ, BA, 55, ScD, 86; Cornell Univ, PhD(theoret physics), 58. *Honors & Awards:* Maxwell Medal, Inst Physics, 73; Paul Dirac Prize, 93; Holweck Medal, Fr Soc Physics, 81; Fritz London Award, Int Conf Low Temperature Physics, 84; Wolf Prize Physics, 90. *Prof Exp:* Physicist, Lawrence Berkeley Lab, 58-59; res fel, Univ Birmingham, 59-61; lectr, Cambridge Univ, 61-65; prof math physics, Univ Birmingham, 65-78; prof appl sci, Yale Univ, 79-80. *Concurrent Pos:* Prof, Queens Univ, Kingston, Ont, 78; royal soc res prof, Cambridge Univ, 83-85. *Mem:* Nat Acad Sci; Fel Am Acad Arts & Sci; fel Am Phys Soc; fel Royal Soc. *Res:* Statistical mechanics and critical phenomena; theory of disordered electron systems; quantum hall effect; quantized vortices. *Mailing Add:* Dept Physics Box 351560 Univ Wash Seattle WA 98195. *Fax:* 206-685-0635; *E-Mail:* thouless@phys.washington.edu

**THOURET, WOLFGANG E(MERY),** PHYSICS, ELECTRICAL ENGINEERING. *Current Pos:* assoc dir eng, 57-71, DIR ENG, DURO-TEST CORP, 71- *Personal Data:* b Berlin, Ger, Aug 27, 14; US citizen; m 62. *Educ:* Tech Univ, Berlin, MS, 36; Univ Karlsruhe, D Ing, 52. *Prof Exp:* Physicist, Res Dept, OSRAM Corp, Ger, 36-40, sect mgr, 40-48; lab mgr, Quartz Lamp Soc, Germany, 49-52; develop engr, Lamp Div, Westinghouse Elec Corp, NJ, 52-57. *Mem:* Fel Am Illum Eng Soc; Am Phys Soc; NY Acad Sci; Inst Elec & Electronics Engrs; Soc Motion Picture & TV Engrs. *Res:* Gaseous discharges; spectroscopy; optical equipment, high intensity light and radiation sources; compact arc high pressure lamps; incandescent lamps; halogen quartz incandescent lamps; metal vapor additive lamps; alumina and sapphire metal vapor lamps. *Mailing Add:* 1 Claridge Dr Verona NJ 07044

**THRAILKILL, JOHN,** HYDROGEOLOGY, GEOCHEMISTRY. *Current Pos:* RETIRED. *Personal Data:* b San Diego, Calif, Aug 31, 30; m 52, Lavine Zauche. *Educ:* Univ Colo, AB, 53, MS, 55; Princeton Univ, PhD(geol), 65. *Prof Exp:* Geologist, Continental Oil Co, 55-61; from asst prof to prof geol, Univ Ky, 65-92, chmn dept, 74-77. *Mem:* AAAS; Nat Speleol Soc; Geol Soc Am; Geochem Soc; Am Geophys Union; Sigma Xi. *Res:* Hydrogeology and geochemistry of limestone terrains. *Mailing Add:* 1093 A1A Beach Blvd No 348 St Augustine Beach FL 32084

**THRALL, ROBERT MCDOWELL,** MATHEMATICS. *Current Pos:* prof & chmn, Dept Math Sci, 69-78, Noah Harding prof, 78-84, EMER PROF MATH, RICE UNIV, HOUSTON, 84- *Personal Data:* b Toledo, Ill, Sept 23, 14; m 36, Natalie Hunter; c Charles A, James H & Mary Emily. *Educ:* Ill Col, BA, 35; Univ Ill, MA, 35, PhD(math), 37. *Hon Degrees:* ScD, Ill Col, 60. *Prof Exp:* Instr math, Univ Mich, 37-42, from asst prof to prof, 42-69, prof oper anal, 56-69, head opers res dept, 57-60; mem, Inst Advan Study, 40-42; from asst prof to prof math, Univ Mich, Ann Arbor, 42-69; prof math sci & chmn dept, Rice Univ, 69-85. *Concurrent Pos:* Res mathematician appl math group, Nat Defense Res Coun, Columbia Univ, 44-45; mem staff radiation lab & sect chief & ed-in-chief, Mars, Mass Inst Technol, 44-46; prof opers anal, Univ Mich, Ann Arbor, 56-69, head opers res dept, 57-60, res mathematician inst sci & technol, 60-69; consult, Rand Corp, 51-74; US Army OCRD, 58-78, Holt, Rinehart & Winston, Inc, 61-76, Gen Elec Corp, 63-69, Dow Chem Co, 65-69, Comshare Co, 67-69, Gen Motors Corp, 67-69, Nat Water Comm, 70-71; ed-in-chief, Mgt Sci, 61-69; adj prof biomath, Baylor Sch Med, Univ Tex, 69-, Comput Sci Inst, 71-75, Sch Pub Health, 71-; pres, Robert M Thrall & Assoc, Inc; lectr, Soc Indust & Appl Math, 70-72; vis prof quant methods, Univ Houston & sr scientist NSF Industs Studies, 74-75. *Mem:* AAAS; Am Math Soc; Soc Indust & Appl Math; Inst Opers Res & Mgt Sci; Math Asn Am; Inst Mgt Sci (pres, 69-70); Sigma Xi; Am Asn Univ Prof; Econometric Soc; Am Psychometric Soc. *Res:* Representations of groups; rings and lie rings; operations research linear and nonlinear programming and game theory; theory of application of mathematical models. *Mailing Add:* 12003 Pebble Hill Dr Houston TX 77024-6208

**THRASHER, GEORGE W,** ANIMAL NUTRITION. *Current Pos:* asst dir animal health prod res, 64-80, DIR ANIMAL HEALTH RES, PFIZER INC, 80- *Personal Data:* b Bloomington, Ind, July 8, 31; m 53; c 1. *Educ:* Purdue Univ, BS, 52, MS, 54, PhD, 58. *Prof Exp:* Asst animal nutrit, Chas Pfizer & Co, 54; voc agr teacher, Morgan County Schs, Ind, 54-56; asst animal nutrit, Purdue Univ, 56-58, exten swine specialist, 58-59; res animal nutritionist, Com Solvents Corp, 59-64. *Mem:* Am Soc Animal Sci; Sigma Xi. *Res:* Antibiotics; hormones; anthelmintics; antimicrobials; chemotherapeutics; minerals; vitamins. *Mailing Add:* US Animal Health Pfizer Inc 1107 S Missouri Dr 291 Lees Summit MO 64063

**THRASHER, JACK D,** TOXICOLOGY & IMMUNOTOXICOLOGY OF SOLVENTS & PESTICIDES. *Current Pos:* CONSULT & EXPERT WITNESS, THRASHER & ASSOCS, 76- *Personal Data:* b Nashville, Kans, Aug 13, 36; m, Diane Walton; c Jon, Traci & Kristen. *Educ:* Long Beach State Univ, Calif, BS, 59; Univ Calif, Los Angeles, PhD(anat & cell biol), 64. *Prof Exp:* Asst prof anat, Univ Colo, 64-66, Univ Calif, Los Angeles, 66-72; appln specialist, Millipone Corp, 73-75; regulatory affairs, Am Technol, 78-80. *Concurrent Pos:* Chief exec officer, Int Inst Res Chem Hypersensitivity, 91-95; fac chem, Eastern NM Univ, 93-96; ed-in-chief, Informed Consent, 93-95. *Res:* Effects of solvents and pesticides on the human immune system: phenotype alterations and autoimmunity. *Mailing Add:* PO Box 879 Alto NM 88312. *Fax:* 505-336-8427

**THRASHER, L(AWRENCE) W(ILLIAM),** MECHANICAL ENGINEERING. *Current Pos:* RETIRED. *Personal Data:* b Ind, Dec 30, 22; m 52; c 2. *Educ:* Purdue Univ, BSME, 43, MSME, 49, PhD(mech eng), 54. *Prof Exp:* Engr aircraft heating & vent systs, Martin Co, 46-47; oil field prod facilities, Arabian Am Oil Co, 49-50; res facil nuclear res, Calif Res & Develop Corp, 52, sect supvr prod tech oil field res, 54-65; sect supvr, Chevron Res Co, Chevron Oil Field Res Co, 65-68, mgr, Opers Technol Div, 68-74, vpres prod res, 74-83. *Concurrent Pos:* Chmn, Coord Subcomt for Study, Enhanced Oil Recovery, Nat Petrol Coun, 75-76. *Mem:* AAAS; assoc Am Soc Mech Engrs; Soc Petrol Engrs. *Res:* Oil field production; well drilling and stimulation; fluid mechanics; ocean wave forces; dynamics of anchored vessels; enhanced oil recovery. *Mailing Add:* 2424 E Clark Ave Fullerton CA 92631-4318

**THRASHER, TERRY NICHOLAS,** PHYSIOLOGY, NEUROSCIENCE. *Current Pos:* ASST PROF PHYSIOL, UNIV CALIF, SAN FRANCISCO, 76- *Educ:* Univ Fla, PhD(physiol), 76. *Mailing Add:* Univ Maryland 10 S Pine St Rm 400 Baltimore MD 21201. *Fax:* 415-476-4929

**THREADGILL, ERNEST DALE,** BIOLOGICAL ENGINEERING. *Current Pos:* assoc prof & head Dept Agr Eng, 75-87, PROF & CHMN, DIV AGR ENG, COASTAL PLAIN EXP STA, UNIV GA, 87- *Personal Data:* b Tallassee, Ala, June 26, 42; m 67; c 2. *Educ:* Auburn Univ, BS, 64, PhD(agr eng), 68. *Prof Exp:* From asst prof to assoc prof agr & biol eng, Miss State Univ, 68-75. *Mem:* Am Soc Agr Engrs. *Res:* Soil erosion and drainage; pesticide applications; plant microclimate; irrigation; soil tillage; chemigation. *Mailing Add:* 1100 Riverside Dr Watkinsville GA 30677

**THREADGILL, W(ALTER) D(ENNIS),** CHEMICAL ENGINEERING. *Current Pos:* RETIRED. *Personal Data:* b Huron, Tenn, Mar 17, 22; m 59. *Educ:* Vanderbilt Univ, BE, 50; Univ Mo, PhD(chem eng), 54. *Prof Exp:* Asst instr chem eng, Univ Mo, 50-52, asst & chem engr, Eng Exp Sta, 52-53; from asst prof to prof chem eng, Vanderbilt Univ, 54-87, actg head dept, 56-57, head dept, 60-72, chmn dept, 75-80. *Mem:* Am Soc Eng Educ; Am Inst Chem Engrs. *Res:* Thermodynamics; chemical engineering unit operations. *Mailing Add:* 24 N Meadow Dr Lexington TN 38351

**THREEFOOT, SAM ABRAHAM,** CARDIOVASCULAR DISEASES. *Current Pos:* prof med, 76-91, EMER PROF MED, TULANE UNIV, 91-, EMER ADJ PROF, SCH PUB HEALTH & TROP MED, 93- *Personal Data:* b Meridian, Miss, Apr 10, 21; m 54, Virginia Rush; c Ginny R (Lindberg), Tracy (Esenstad), Shelley (Cowan) & Barbara (Mattingly). *Educ:* Tulane Univ, BS, 43, MD, 45; Am Bd Internal Med, dipl, 53. *Honors & Awards:* Honors Achievement Award, Angiol Res Found, 68; Award of Merit, Am Heart Assoc, 76. *Prof Exp:* Intern, Michael Reese Hosp, Chicago, 45-47; from instr to prof med, Tulane Univ, 48-70; prof med & asst dean, Med Col Ga, 70-76; chief staff, Forest Hills Div, Vet Admin Hosp, Augusta, 70-76; assoc chief staff res, Vet Admin Hosp, New Orleans, 76-79, chief of staff, 79-91. *Concurrent Pos:* Fel med, Sch Med, Tulane Univ, 47-49; from asst vis physician to sr vis physician, Charity Hosp La, New Orleans, 47-69, consult, 69-70 & 76-; consult, Lallie Kemp Charity Hosp, Independence, Mo, 51-53, Vet Admin Med Ctr, New Orleans, 91-; clin asst, Touro Infirmary, 53-56, dir res & med studies, 53-63, jr staff mem, 56-60, sr assoc, 60-63, sr dept med, 63-70, dir res, Touro Res Inst, 53-70; mem exec comt, Coun on Circulation, Am Heart Asn, 68-75, from vchmn to chmn, 71-75, chmn credentials comt, 72-73; mem bd consult, Int Soc Lymphology, 70-76; mem bd dirs, Am Heart Asn, 66-70 & 72-75, mem exec comt, 69-70 & 73-75. *Mem:* Am Fedn Clin Res; fel Am Col Physicians; Am Heart Asn (vpres,67-68); fel Am Col Cardiol; Sigma Xi. *Res:* Electrolyte turnover in congestive heart failure; anatomy and physiology of lymphatics as a transport system and their role in pathogenesis of disease; lymphology. *Mailing Add:* 347 Millaudon St New Orleans LA 70118. *E-Mail:* s3fta@mailhost.tcs.tulane.edu

**THREET, RICHARD LOWELL,** GEOLOGY. *Current Pos:* prof, 68-80, EMER PROF GEOL, SAN DIEGO STATE UNIV, 80- *Personal Data:* b Browns, Ill, Nov 17, 24; m 46; c 4. *Educ:* Univ Ill, BS & AB, 47, AM, 49; Univ Wah, Seattle, PhD(geol), 52. *Prof Exp:* From instr to asst prof geol, Univ Nebr, 51-57; asst prof, Univ Utah, 57-61; from asst prof to assoc prof, Calif State Univ, San Diego, 61-68,. *Concurrent Pos:* Vis prof, Ohio State Univ, 53, 63, 66-70 & 72-73, Col Southern Utah, 54-55 & Univ Ill, 57; chmn dept geol, San Diego State Univ, 72-73; vis prof, Western Washington State Univ, 80-82. *Mem:* Fel Geol Soc Am. *Res:* Colorado plateau geology; geomorphology; structural geology; photogeology. *Mailing Add:* 2801 17th St Anacortes WA 98221

**THRELFALL, WILLIAM,** parasitology, ornithology, for more information see previous edition

**THRELKELD, STEPHEN FRANCIS H,** BIOLOGY, GENETICS. *Current Pos:* RETIRED. *Personal Data:* b Watford, Eng, Dec 27, 24; m 52; c 2. *Educ:* Univ Alta, BSc, 57, MSc, 58; St Catharine's Col, Cambridge, PhD(bot), 61. *Prof Exp:* From asst prof to prof genetics, McMaster Univ, 61-90, chmn res unit biochem, biophys & molecular biol, 64-68, assoc chmn dept biol, 66-68, chmn, Dept Biol, 77-83 & 86-90. *Mem:* Am Soc Naturalists; Genetics Soc Am; Genetics Soc Can; Chem Inst Can; Can Soc Cell Biol. *Res:* Neurospora; recombination; Drosophila behavioral genetics; insecticide resistance. *Mailing Add:* Dept Biol 1280 Main St W McMaster Univ Hamilton ON L8S 4K1 Can

**THRIFT, FREDERICK AARON,** ANIMAL BREEDING. *Current Pos:* Assoc prof, 67-78, PROF ANIMAL SCI, UNIV KY, 78- *Personal Data:* b St George, Ga, Oct 6, 40; m 67; c 2. *Educ:* Univ Fla, BSA, 62; Univ Ga, MS, 65; Okla State Univ, PhD(animal breeding), 68. *Mem:* Biomet Soc; Am Soc Animal Sci. *Res:* Beef cattle and sheep breeding research. *Mailing Add:* Animal Sci Univ Ky 500 S Limestone St Lexington KY 40506-0001

**THRO, MARY PATRICIA,** PHYSICS, MATHEMATICS. *Current Pos:* asst prof physics, 73-77, ASSOC PROF PHYSICS & MATH, MARYVILLE UNIV, 77-, CHAIRPERSON DEPT, 74- *Personal Data:* b St Charles, Mo, Mar 14, 38. *Educ:* Maryville Col, BA, 61; Fordham Univ, MS, 67; Wash Univ, PhD(educ), 76. *Honors & Awards:* Fulbright lectr, Philippines, 90-91. *Prof Exp:* Teacher math, Villa Duchesne Elem & Sec Schs, St Louis, 61-64; instr physics, Maryville Univ, 67-69; team mem admin, Relig of Sacred Heart, 69-73. *Concurrent Pos:* NSF grants, New Orleans, 69-71, Kansas City, 72-73 & Memphis, 78-79; eval chairperson, Acad Sacred Heart, 76; mem bd joint grad educ prog, Wash Univ-Maryville Univ, 77-79; co-dir, Mo Jr Acad Sci, 77-; publ, J Educ Psychol, 78. *Mem:* AAAS; Sigma Xi; Am Asn Physics Teachers; Am Educ Res Asn. *Res:* Relationships between associative and content structure of physics concepts; chemical abundance of elements in the cosmos determined by analysis of ion damage recorded on meteorite crystals; spectral analysis of compounds. *Mailing Add:* Maryville Univ 13550 Conway Rd St Louis MO 63141-7232. *Fax:* 314-542-9085; *E-Mail:* c19208@umslvma.umsl.edu

**THROCKMORTON, ANN ELIZABETH,** POPULATION & PLANT ECOLOGY, LIMNOLOGY. *Current Pos:* ASST PROF BIOL, WESTMINSTER COL, 90- *Personal Data:* b Hastings, Nebr, Apr 30, 60. *Educ:* Hastings Col, BA, 82; Fort Hays State Univ, 87; Fla State Univ, PhD(pop ecol), 90. *Mem:* Ecol Asn Am; Etomological Asn Am; Am Asn Univ Women. *Res:* Host plant choice by parasitic plants; population dynamics of dodder, Cuscuta spp. *Mailing Add:* Dept Biol Westminster Col New Wilmington PA 16172. *E-Mail:* athrock@westminster.edu

**THROCKMORTON, GAYLORD SCOTT,** COMPARATIVE ANATOMY, BIOMECHANICS. *Current Pos:* from asst prof to assoc prof, 75-96, PROF HUMAN ANAT, UNIV TEX HEALTH SCI CTR, 96- *Personal Data:* b Kansas City, Kans, Aug 7, 46; m 67, Linda Sue Reger; c 3. *Educ:* Univ Kans, BA, 68; Univ Chicago, PhD(evolutionary biol), 74. *Prof Exp:* Asst prof human anat, Col Dent, Univ Ill Med Ctr, 73-75. *Concurrent Pos:* Prin investr, NSF, 78-81; co-investr, NIH, 80-83, Am Asn Oral & Maxillofacial Surgeons, 90-95; cur, Anat Teaching Mus, Univ Tex Southwestern Med Ctr, 79-; reviewer, Systs & Ecol Prog, NSF, 81- *Mem:* Am Soc Biomech; Int Asn Dent Res. *Res:* Form and function of the vertebrate feeding apparatus including biomechanical modeling of mandibular forces, mechanisms controlling mastication, and the effect of orthognatic surgery on function of the jaw muscles in humans. *Mailing Add:* Dept Cell Biol & Neurosci Univ Tex Southwestern Med Ctr Dallas TX 75235-9039. *Fax:* 214-648-8950; *E-Mail:* throckmo@utsw.swmed.edu

**THROCKMORTON, JAMES RODNEY,** PESTICIDE CHEMISTRY. *Current Pos:* Sr chemist, Imaging Res Lab, 64-66, Contract Res Lab, 66-71, RES SPECIALIST, 3M CO, 74- *Personal Data:* b St John, Wash, Sept 4, 36; m 58; c 3. *Educ:* Univ Idaho, BS, 58, MS, 60; Univ Minn, PhD(org chem), 64. *Mem:* Am Chem Soc. *Res:* Organic fluorochemicals; imaging technology. *Mailing Add:* 7149 Aberdeen Curve Woodbury MN 55125-1667

**THROCKMORTON, LYNN HIRAM,** ZOOLOGY. *Current Pos:* RETIRED. *Personal Data:* b Loup City, Nebr, Dec 20, 27. *Educ:* Univ Nebr, BS, 49, MS, 56; Univ Tex, PhD(zool), 59. *Prof Exp:* Instr zool, Univ Nebr, 56; spec instr, Univ Tex, 59-60; vis asst prof, Univ Calif, 60-61; res assoc, Univ Chicago, 61-62, from instr to prof biol, 62-89. *Mem:* AAAS; Am Genetics Soc; Soc Syst Zool; Am Inst Biol Sci; Sigma Xi. *Res:* Taxonomy; phylogeny and biogeography of Drosophila and other Drosophilids; biochemical evolution and speciation of Drosophila; utilization and evaluation of computer methods in taxonomy. *Mailing Add:* 1451 E 55th Apt 927 Chicago IL 60615

**THROCKMORTON, MORFORD C,** POLYMER CHEMISTRY. *Current Pos:* RETIRED. *Personal Data:* b Waynesburg, Pa, July 28, 19. *Educ:* Grove City Col, BS, 40; Western Res Univ, MS, 41, PhD(phys chem), 44. *Prof Exp:* Res chemist, Texaco, Inc, 43-54, group leader, 54-59; sr res chemist, Firestone Tire & Rubber Co, 60-63; sr res chemist, Goodyear Tire & Rubber Co, 64-68, res scientist, 68-86. *Mem:* Am Chem Soc. *Res:* Catalysis; synthetic fuels; development of synthetic rubber; stereoregular polymerization; petrochemicals. *Mailing Add:* 967 Newport Rd Akron OH 44303-1319

**THROCKMORTON, PETER E,** TRANSITION METAL CATALYSIS. *Current Pos:* RETIRED. *Personal Data:* b St Paul, Minn, Jan 20, 27; m 48; c 3. *Educ:* Univ Minn, BCHE, 48, MS, 55; Kans State Univ, PhD, 60. *Prof Exp:* Asst res engr, Tainton Co, 48-49; res engr, Glenn L Martin Aircraft Co, 49-52; chemist, Gen Mills Co, 52-56; asst, Kans State Univ, 56-59; assoc chemist, Midwest Res Inst, 59-65; sr res chemist, Archer, Daniels, Midland, 65-67; sr res chemist II, Ashland Chem Co, 67-86; consult, Throckmorton Consult, 86-96. *Concurrent Pos:* China-US Sci Exchange, China Asn Sci & Technol, 84; consult, Teltech Tech Knowledge Serv, Minneapolis, Minn, 91- *Mem:* Am Chem Soc; emer mem Sigma Xi; fel Am Inst Chemists. *Res:* Heterocyclic sulfer and organometallic compounds; synthesis; selective catalytic oxidations; author of 44 technical publications, 17 US patents; new radiation-resistant plastics and new processes for catalytic oxidation. *Mailing Add:* 114 Colchester Dr Normal IL 61761

**THRODAHL, MONTE C(ORDEN),** RESEARCH MANAGEMENT, ENVIRONMENTAL MANAGEMENT. *Current Pos:* CONSULT, 84- *Personal Data:* b Minneapolis, Minn, Mar 25, 19; m 48; c 2. *Educ:* Iowa State Univ, BS, 41. *Prof Exp:* Res chemist, Org Res Dept, Monsanto Co, 41-45, group leader, 45-50, asst res dir, 50-52, mgr, Rubber Chem Sect, Org Develop Dept, 52-54, asst dir develop, 54-56, dir develop, 56-60, dir res, Org Res Dept, 60-62, dir mkt, 62-64, asst gen mgr, Int Div, 64, gen mgr, 64-66, vpres technol & dir, 66-77, group vpres & sr vpres environ policy, 77-84. *Mem:* Nat Acad Eng; fel AAAS; Com Develop Asn; fel Am Inst Chem Engrs; Soc Chem Indust. *Mailing Add:* 20 South Central Rm 210 St Louis MO 63166

**THRON, JONATHAN LOUIS,** NUCLEON DECAY EXPERIMENTS, NEUTRINO OSCILLATIONS. *Current Pos:* Postdoctoral, 83-85, asst physicist, 85-90, PHYSICIST, ARGONNE NAT LAB, 90- *Personal Data:* b Boulder, Colo, Nov 21, 54; m 87. *Educ:* Carleton Col, BA, 77; Yale Univ, MPhil, 79, PhD(physics), 83. *Mem:* Am Phys Soc. *Res:* Data analysis of the Soudan 2, high resolution, tracking calorimeter nucleon decay experiment; preparation for the Minos long baseline neutrino oscillation experiment. *Mailing Add:* Argonne Nat Lab 9700 S Cass Ave HEP Bldg 362 Argonne IL 60439-4815. *E-Mail:* jlt@hep.anl.gov

**THRON, WOLFGANG JOSEPH,** MATHEMATICS. *Current Pos:* from assoc prof to prof, 54-85, EMER PROF MATH, UNIV COLO, BOULDER, 85- *Personal Data:* b Ribnitz, Ger, Aug 17, 18; US citizen; wid; c Jonathan, Penelope, Peter, Karin & Rajinder. *Educ:* Princeton, AB, 39; Rice Inst, MA, 42, PhD(math), 43. *Honors & Awards:* Kongl Norske Videnskabers Selskab, 80, Univ Colo Medal, 85. *Prof Exp:* Instr math, Harvard Univ, 43-44; from instr to assoc prof, Washington Univ, St Louis, 46-54. *Concurrent Pos:* Vis prof, Free Univ Berlin, 51, Philippines, 66-67, Univ Erlangen, 70-71, Punjab Univ, India, 74-75 & Univ Trondheim, 78-79 & 82-83; res grant, Air Force Off Sci Res, Ger, 57-58; vis prof & Fulbright lectr, India, 62-63. *Mem:* Am Math Soc; Math Asn Am; Kongl Norske Videnskabers Selskab. *Res:* Complex variables, analysis of convergence and truncation errors of infinite processes in particular continued fractions; general topology, lattice of topologies, proximity, contiguity and nearness spaces, extensions of spaces. *Mailing Add:* Dept Math Univ Colo Campus Box 395 Boulder CO 80309-0395

**THRONE, JAMES EDWARD,** SIMULATION MODELING, INTEGRATED PEST MANAGEMENT. *Current Pos:* RES ENTOMOLOGIST, STORED PROD INSECTS RES & DEVELOP LAB, AGR RES SERV, USDA, 85- *Personal Data:* b Calembrone, Italy, Sept 10, 54; US citizen; m 85, Janet H Van Kirk; c Evan. *Educ:* Southeastern Mass Univ, BS, 76; Wash State Univ, MS, 78; Cornell Univ, PhD(entom), 83. *Prof Exp:* Res fel, NC State Univ, 83-85. *Mem:* Entom Soc Am; Sigma Xi. *Res:* Bionomics and management of agricultural pests; simulation modelling to optimize pest management strategies. *Mailing Add:* 1525 Westwind Manhattan KS 66502

**THRONE, JAMES LOUIS,** CHEMICAL ENGINEERING, POLYMER ENGINEERING. *Current Pos:* eng consult, 85-86, PRES, SHERWOOD TECHNOL, INC, HINCKLEY, OHIO, 91- *Personal Data:* b Cleveland, Ohio, July 10, 37; m 59, Jean; c 2. *Educ:* Case Inst Technol, BS, 59; Univ Del, MChE, 61, PhD(chem eng), 64. *Prof Exp:* Res engr, Eng Res Labs, E I du Pont de Nemours & Co, Inc, 63-64; assoc prof chem eng, Ohio Univ, 64-68; supvr plastics processing, Am Stand, NJ, 68-71; assoc prof energetics, Univ Wis-Milwaukee, 71-72; dir plastics res, Beloit Corp, Wis, 72-74; res assoc plastics processing, Amoco Chem Corp, 74-85; prof eng, Univ Akron, 86-89; fel, BF Goodrich, Avon Lake, Ohio, 89-91. *Concurrent Pos:* Vis prof chem eng, Univ Cincinnati, 65; adj prof plastics processing, Newark Col Eng, 68-71; prof food eng, Orgn Am States, Brazil, 72; consult, Sherwood Tech Serv, Beloit, Wis, 72-74; Am Soc Eng Educ fel, NASA, Hampton, Va, 88-89. *Mem:* Polymer Processing Soc; Soc Rheology; fel Brit Plastics & Rubber Inst; fel Soc Plastics Engrs; Soc Advan Mat & Process Eng; Soc Mfg Engrs. *Res:* Plastics process engineering, with emphasis in thermoforming, rotational molding, foam processing and comparative process economics; materials engineering. *Mailing Add:* 158 Brookside Blvd Hinckley OH 44233-9676. *Fax:* 330-273-6463; *E-Mail:* throne@apk.net

**THRONEBERRY, GLYN OGLE,** PLANT PHYSIOLOGY. *Current Pos:* asst prof biol, 55-57, from asst prof to assoc prof, 57-67, PROF BOT & ENTOM, NMEX STATE UNIV, 67- *Personal Data:* b Rule, Tex, Nov 1, 27; m 48; c 1. *Educ:* NMex State Univ, BS, 50; Iowa State Col, MS, 52, PhD(plant physiol), 53. *Prof Exp:* Plant physiologist, Kans State Col, USDA, 54-55. *Mem:* AAAS; Am Soc Plant Physiol; Am Phytopath Soc; Sigma Xi. *Res:* Plant host-pathogen relationships; intermediary metabolism; fungus physiology; plant biochemistry. *Mailing Add:* 1778 Imperial Ridge St Las Cruces NM 88011-4810

**THRONER, GUY CHARLES,** TERMINAL BALLISTICS, WEAPON SYSTEMS ENGINEERING. *Current Pos:* PRES, G C THRONER & ASSOC-TECH & MGT CONSULTS, 86- *Personal Data:* b Minneapolis, Minn, Sept 14, 19; m 43, Jean W Holt; c Richard, Carol A & Steven. *Educ:* Oberlin Col, AB, 43. *Honors & Awards:* IR-100 Award, 72; Bronze Medallion, Am Defense Preparedness Asn, 74, Simon Silver Medal, 85; Distinguished Inventor's Medallion, Battelle Mem Inst, 83; Commendation, US Cong, 85. *Prof Exp:* Mgr res & develop, Ordnance Div, Aerojet Gen, 53-63, mgr res & develop, Tactical Weapon Systs Div, Aerojet Gen Corp, 63-64; vpres & div gen mgr res & develop, FMC Corp, 64-74; dir res & develop, Vacu-Blast & Tronic Corp, 76-78; vpres prod eng, Dahlman Inc, 78-79; sect mgr res & develop, Columbus Labs, 79-86. *Concurrent Pos:* Vpres & gen mgr res & develop, Steel Prod Div, FMC Corp, 64-74; exec vpres res & develop, Am Vidionetics Corp, 76-78; mem, Air Armament Bd, Bomb & Warhead Steering Comt & Underwater Weapons Steering Comt. *Mem:* Sigma Xi; Sci Res Soc Am; Am Defense Preparedness Asn; Am Inst Aeronaut & Astronaut. *Res:* Metal forming; high speed instrumentation; medical devices; oil field equipment; agri-machinery; weapon and space technology; author or coauthor of over 80 publications; granted 26 patents. *Mailing Add:* 17992 Jayhawk Dr Penn Valley CA 95946-9206

**THRONSON, HARLEY ANDREW, JR,** STAR FORMATION, INTERSTELLAR MEDIUM. *Current Pos:* from asst prof to assoc prof, 81-91, PROF ASTRON, DEPT PHYSICS, UNIV WYO, 91-, PLANETARIUM DIR, 81- *Personal Data:* b Madison, Wis, Oct 13, 48; m 78, Cristina Hodge; c Katherine & Evan. *Educ:* Univ Calif, Berkeley, BS, 71; Univ Chicago, MS, 73, PhD(astrophys), 78. *Prof Exp:* Res assoc, astron, Steward Observ, Univ Ariz, 77-81. *Mem:* Int Astron Union; Am Astron Soc. *Res:* Formation of stars in the Milky Way and other galaxies; evolution of the interstellar medium in galaxies; history and sociology of astronomy. *Mailing Add:* 1902 Beaufort Laramie WY 82070. *Fax:* 307-766-2652; *E-Mail:* thronson@uwyo.edu

**THROOP, LEWIS JOHN,** ANALYTICAL CHEMISTRY. *Current Pos:* CONSULT ANALYTICAL CHEMIST, 95- *Personal Data:* b Detroit, Mich, June 18, 29; m 54; c 1. *Educ:* Wayne State Univ, BS, 54, MS, 56, PhD(analytical chem), 57. *Prof Exp:* Chemist, Syntex, SA, Mex, 57-59; group leader anal chem, Mead Johnson & Co, 59-64; head dept, Syntex Corp, 64-71, asst dir anal chem, Inst Org Chem, 71-78, dir anal res, 78-85, vpres & dir anal & environ res, 85-93; design engr, Turner Designs Inst, 93-95. *Mem:* Am Chem Soc. *Res:* Electrochemistry; organic structure characterization; laboratory automation. *Mailing Add:* 27272 Byrne Park Lane Los Altos Hills CA 94022. *Fax:* 650-941-8242; *E-Mail:* lthroop@aol.com

**THROW, FRANCIS EDWARD,** SCIENCE COMMUNICATIONS, GENERAL PHYSICS. *Current Pos:* RETIRED. *Personal Data:* b Ottumwa, Iowa, Oct 4, 12; wid; c Carol E (McCoy), Jeannette E (Bacon) & Edward R. *Educ:* Park Col, BA, 33; Univ Mich, MS, 36, PhD(physics), 40. *Prof Exp:* Instr physics, Milwaukee State Teachers Col, 39; instr physics & math, Polytech Inst PR, 40-41; instr physics, Altoona Undergrad Ctr, 41-42; ground sch instr math, physics & theory of flight, US Navy Pre-Flight Sch, Iowa Univ, 42-44; prof physics & head dept, Cornell Col, 44-52; chmn dept physics, Wabash Col, 52-56; asst dir physics div, Argonne Nat Lab, 56-73, asst dir radiol & environ res div, 73-77. *Concurrent Pos:* Consult, tech ed & writer, report on electronic control, Borg-Warner, 78, annual brochures, Argonne Univ Asn, 80, 81 & 82. *Mem:* Am Phys Soc; Am Asn Physics Teachers. *Mailing Add:* 3131 Simpson St Apt GW-206 Evanston IL 60201-1933

**THROWER, PETER ALBERT,** PHYSICS, MATERIALS SCIENCE. *Current Pos:* PROF MAT SCI, PA STATE UNIV, UNIVERSITY PARK, 69- *Personal Data:* b Norfolk, Eng, Jan 9, 38; m 85, Carol A Black. *Educ:* Cambridge Univ, BA, 60, MA, 63, PhD(physics), 69. *Prof Exp:* Sci officer, Atomic Energy Res Estab, Eng, 60-65, sr sci officer, 65-69. *Concurrent Pos:* Ed, Chem & Physics of Carbon, ed-in-chief, Carbon J. *Mem:* Am Soc Metals Int; Am Carbon Soc. *Res:* Structure and properties of carbon and graphite; irradiation damage to graphite; electron microscopy; mineral microstructures. *Mailing Add:* 1659 S Cherry Hill Rd State College PA 16803. *Fax:* 814-865-2917

**THRUPP, LAURI DAVID,** INFECTIOUS DISEASES, MICROBIOLOGY. *Current Pos:* assoc prof & head div, 68-77, PROF MED, DIV INFECTIOUS DIS, UNIV CALIF, IRVINE, 77- *Personal Data:* b Sask, Nov 30, 30; US citizen; m 52; c 4. *Educ:* Stanford Univ, AB, 51; Univ Wash, MD, 55. *Prof Exp:* Asst chief & chief polio surveillance, Epidemiol Br, Nat Commun Dis Ctr, 56-58; resident physician & fel, Boston City Hosp, Thorndike Serv & Harvard Med Sch, 58-63; jr staff physician, Harvard Serv, 61-63; asst prof med & med microbiol, Sch Med, Univ Southern Calif, 63-66, asst prof med, 66-68. *Concurrent Pos:* Life Ins Med Res Found res fel med & bact, Boston City Hosp & Harvard Med Sch, 60-63; asst chief commun dis, Los Angeles Co Gen Hosp, 63-64, attend physician, 63-, med microbiologist, 64-65; consult, Los Angeles County Health Dept, 64- & Calif State Health Dept, 66-; chief infectious dis serv, Orange Co Med Ctr, 68- *Mem:* Am Fedn Clin Res; Am

Soc Microbiol; Am Pub Health Asn; Infectious Dis Soc Am; NY Acad Sci. *Res:* Clinical and experimental pyelonephritis, pathogenesis and immune response, role of bacterial L-forms; gram-negative hospital-acquired infections; meningitis, clinical and immunological; bacteriology. *Mailing Add:* Infectious Dis Univ Calif Sch Med Irvine CA 92717-0001

**THRUSTON, ALFRED DORRAH, JR,** ANALYTICAL CHEMISTRY. *Current Pos:* RES CHEMIST, ATHENS ENVIRON RES LAB, ENVIRON PROTECTION AGENCY, 66- *Personal Data:* b Greenville, SC, Nov 3, 34; m 64; c 2. *Educ:* Ga Inst Technol, BS, 57. *Prof Exp:* Chemist, US Food & Drug Admin, 59-66. *Mem:* Am Chem Soc. *Res:* Liquid chromatographic, mass spectrometric and gas chromatographic analysis of water pollutants. *Mailing Add:* US Environ Protection Agency Environ Res Lab College Station Rd Athens GA 30613

**THUAN, TRINH XUAN,** FORMATION AND EVOLUTION OF DWARF GALAXIES, ASTROPHYSICS. *Current Pos:* assoc prof, 76-90, PROF ASTRON, UNIV VA, 90- *Personal Data:* b Hanoi, Vietnam, Aug 20, 48. *Educ:* Calif Inst Technol, BS, 70; Princeton Univ, PhD(astrophys), 74. *Honors & Awards:* Henri Chretien Award, Am Astron Soc, 92. *Prof Exp:* Res fel astrophys, Calif Inst Technol, 74-76. *Concurrent Pos:* Vis fel, Inst d'Astrophys, Paris, 78 & 87; vis prof, Ctr d'Etudes Nucleaires de Saclay, Paris, 81 & 87; Fulbright res scholar, 87; vis prof, Univ Paris, France, 93-94; vis astronr, Observ Riendon, France, 95. *Mem:* Am Astron Soc; Int Astron Union. *Res:* Study of the formation, clustering and evolution of galaxies; observational cosmology. *Mailing Add:* Dept Astron Univ Va PO Box 3818 Univ Sta Charlottesville VA 22903-3199. *Fax:* 804-924-3104; *E-Mail:* txt@virginia.edu

**THUBRIKAR, MANO J,** HEART VALVE PROSTHETICS, ATHEROSCLEROSIS. *Current Pos:* HEINEMAN RES PROF, HEINEMAN MED RES CTR, 91- *Personal Data:* b Nagpur, India, Aug 27, 47; m 73; c 2. *Educ:* Nagpur Univ, BE, 69; NY Univ, MS, 71, PhD(biomed eng), 75. *Prof Exp:* From asst prof to assoc prof, Univ Va, 75-91. *Concurrent Pos:* Res career develop award, NIH, 80-85; dir surg res, Univ Va, 87-91, res prof, Div Atherosclerosis. *Mem:* Biomed Eng; Am Soc Artificial Internal Organs; Eng Med & Biol; Soc Cardiac Biol Implants. *Res:* Mechanism of atherogenesis; mechanics of arterial tissue; heart valve function; designing bioprosthetic and prosthetic heart valves. *Mailing Add:* 4703 Avonwood Lane Charlotte NC 28270

**THUENTE, DAVID JOSEPH,** OPERATIONS RESEARCH, COMPUTER SCIENCE. *Current Pos:* asst prof math, 74-79, assoc prof math & comput sci, 80-89, PROF COMPUT SCI, IND UNIV-PURDUE UNIV, FT WAYNE, 89- *Personal Data:* b Decorah, Iowa, Mar 17, 45; m 67, Mary H Ernst; c Michael P & Daniel D. *Educ:* Loras Col, BS, 67; Univ Kans, MA, 69, PhD(math), 74. *Prof Exp:* Systs analyst transp, Jewel Co, Inc, 67; instr math, Univ Kans, 70-74; mem fac res staff nonlinear prog, Argonne Nat Lab, 76-77, 80, 83. *Concurrent Pos:* Res grant, Purdue Univ, 75 & 80; fac res grant, Argonne Nat Lab, 76-77, 80 & 83, consult, 80-81; mem tech staff, Mitre Corp, 81-82; comput lit grant, 84-; sr software engr, Magnavox Electronic Systs Co, 88- *Mem:* Soc Indust & Appl Math; Opers Res Soc Am; Math Prog Soc; Sigma Xi; Asn Comput Mach; Inst Elec & Electronics Engrs Comput Soc. *Res:* Simulation for distributed processing; simulation languages and applications; nonlinear programming; optimization and mathematical modeling; software engineering. *Mailing Add:* 2820 Knightsbridge Pl Ft Wayne IN 46815-8503. *Fax:* 219-481-6880; *E-Mail:* thuente@cvax.ipfw.indiana.edu

**THUERING, GEORGE LEWIS,** INDUSTRIAL ENGINEERING. *Current Pos:* RETIRED. *Personal Data:* b Milwaukee, Wis, Sept 2, 19; m 45, 75; c 1. *Educ:* Univ Wis, BS, 41, ME, 54; Pa State Univ, MS, 49. *Prof Exp:* Mfg engr, Lockheed Aircarft Corp, Calif, 41-47, supvr plant layout & space control dept, Ga Div, 51-52; from instr to assoc prof, Pa State Univ, 47-56, dir, Dept Mgt Engr, 62-77, prof, 56-, emer prof indust eng. *Concurrent Pos:* Consult. *Mem:* Am Inst Indust Engrs; Am Soc Eng Educ; Am Soc Mech Engrs (vpres, 82-84); Sigma Xi. *Res:* Manufacturing science. *Mailing Add:* 436 Homan Ave State College PA 16801

**THUESEN, GERALD JORGEN,** INDUSTRIAL ENGINEERING. *Current Pos:* from assoc prof to prof, 68-96, EMER PROF INDUST ENG, GA INST TECHNOL, 96- *Personal Data:* b Oklahoma City, Okla, July 20, 38; m 60, 82, Harriett Mathis; c Karen E & Dyan L (Thuesen). *Educ:* Stanford Univ, BS, 60, MS, 61, PhD(indust eng), 68. *Honors & Awards:* Eugene L Grant Award, Am Soc Eng Educ, 77, 89; Wellington Award, Inst Indust Engrs, 89, Outstanding Inst Indust Engrs Publ Award, 90. *Prof Exp:* Engr, Pac Tel Co, 61-62; mgt engr comput systs, Atlantic Refining Co, 62-63; asst prof indust eng, Arlington State Col, 63-64 & Univ Tex, Arlington, 67-68. *Mem:* Fel Inst Indust Engrs; fel Am Soc Eng Educ; Sigma Xi. *Res:* Decision analysis; engineering economy; capital budgeting; statistical decision theory. *Mailing Add:* 4440 Paces Battle NW Atlanta GA 30327. *Fax:* 404-894-2301; *E-Mail:* gthuesen@isye.gatech.edu

**THUESON, DAVID OREL,** IMMUNOPHARMACOLOGY, DRUG DESIGN. *Current Pos:* VPRES, COSMEDERM TECHNOL INC, 93- *Personal Data:* b Twin Falls, Idaho, May 9, 47; m 69, Sherrie L Lowe; c Sean, Kirsten, Eric, Ryan & Todd. *Educ:* Brigham Young Univ, BS, 71; Univ Utah, Salt Lake City, PhD(pharmacol), 76. *Prof Exp:* Res scientist, Univ Tex Med Br, 76-77, asst prof immunol & pharmacol, 77-82; sr res assoc res, Parke-Davis Pharmaceut Res, 82-88; dept dir pharmacol, Immunetech Pharmaceut, 88-90; dept dir immunopharmacol, Tanabe Res Labs, USA,

90-93. *Concurrent Pos:* Postdoctoral fel, Univ Tex Med Br, 75-77, asst prof, Grad Fac, Biomed Sci, 77-82; young investr award, NIH, 78. *Mem:* Am Acad Allergy & Clin Immunol; Am Asn Immunologists; Am Thoracic Soc; Am Acad Dermat. *Res:* Drug discovery development of clinical agents for arthritis, autoimmune diseases, asthma and allergies; regulation of cell activation and mechanisms of inflammation; inhibition of mediator production/release from inflammatory effector cells. *Mailing Add:* Dept Discovery Cosmederm Technol 3252 Holiday Ct Suite 226 La Jolla CA 92037. *Fax:* 619-550-7075

**THUILLIER, RICHARD HOWARD,** METEOROLOGY. *Current Pos:* SR METEOROLOGIST, PAC GAS & ELEC, SAN FRANCISCO, 80- *Personal Data:* b New York, NY, Apr 3, 36; wid; c Stephen, David, Lawrence & Daniel. *Educ:* Fordham Univ, BS, 59; NY Univ, MS, 63. *Honors & Awards:* Outstanding Contrib to Advan of Appl Meteorol Award, Am Meteorol Soc, 93. *Prof Exp:* Instr, State Univ NY, 63-66; dir res, Weather Engrs Panama Inc, 66-68; meteorologist & chief res & planning, Bay Area Air Qual Mgt, San Francisco, 68-76; sr res meteorologist, SRI Int, 76-80. *Concurrent Pos:* Lectr, Hunter Col, 65-66, Univ Calif, Berkeley, 73-74 & San Jose State Univ, 84-91; consult meteorologist, 68- *Mem:* Am Meteorol Soc; hon mem Sigma Xi. *Res:* Meteorology. *Mailing Add:* 1139 Sunnyhills Rd Oakland CA 94610-1862

**THUM, ALAN BRADLEY,** MARINE ECOLOGY. *Personal Data:* b Washington, DC, May 30, 43; m 66; c 2. *Educ:* Univ Redlands, BS, 65; Univ Pac, MS, 67; Ore State Univ, PhD(marine ecol), 71. *Prof Exp:* Lectr invert zool, Univ Cape Town, 71-75; sr scientist & Environ consult, Lockheed Marine Biol Lab, Lockheed Aircraft Serv, 75-84; Kinetic Labs, Inc, 84-90. *Concurrent Pos:* Consult, Bur Land Mgt, Univ Southern Calif, 76- *Mem:* Ecol Soc Am; Am Soc Limnol & Oceanog; Int Asn Meiobenthologists; Royal Soc SAfrica. *Res:* Ecology of interstitial meiofauna; ecology and systematics of turbellaria; reproductive ecology of marine benthic invertebrates; aquatic toxicology. *Mailing Add:* 1392 Peachwood Dr Encinitas CA 92024

**THUMANN, ALBERT,** ELECTRICAL & ENERGY ENGINEERING. *Current Pos:* EXEC DIR, ASN ENERGY ENGRS, 77- *Personal Data:* b New York, NY, Mar 12, 42; m 66; c 1. *Educ:* City Col New York, BEE, 64; NY Univ, MSEE, 67, MSIE, 70. *Prof Exp:* Proj mgr eng construct, Bechtel, 64-77. *Concurrent Pos:* Adj prof, Univ Louisville & lectr, Sch Continuing Educ, NY Univ, 76- *Mem:* Nat Soc Prof Engrs; Asn Energy Engrs (pres, 77); Am Soc Asn Execs; Am Soc Assoc Execs; Coun Eng; Sci Soc Execs. *Res:* Noise control; energy. *Mailing Add:* 931 Smoketree Dr Tucker GA 30084

**THUMM, BYRON ASHLEY,** ANALYTICAL CHEMISTRY. *Current Pos:* RETIRED. *Personal Data:* b Malden, WVa, Jan 2, 23; m 56. *Educ:* Morris Harvey Col, BS, 45; Duke Univ, PhD(chem), 51. *Prof Exp:* Res chemist, Am Viscose Div, FMC Corp, 51-63; emer prof chem, State Univ NY Col, Fredonia, 63-87. *Mem:* Am Chem Soc. *Res:* Solution kinetics and equilibrium; rayon spinning process; water analysis; formaldehyde complexes. *Mailing Add:* 24 Maple Ave Fredonia NY 14063

**THUN, MICHAEL JOHN,** CANCER EPIDEMIOLOGY. *Current Pos:* DIR, ANALYTIC EPIDEMIOL, AM CANCER SOC, 89- *Personal Data:* b Sinking Spring, Pa, Sept 29, 44; m 75, Patricia L Moody; c Nicholas, Lupe & Haley. *Educ:* Harvard Col, BA, 70; Univ Pa, MD, 75; Harvard Sch Pub Health, MS, 83. *Prof Exp:* Med intern, Shands Teaching Hosp, Univ Fla, 75-76, resident internal med, 76-77; med officer, NJ State Health Dept, 78-80; epidemic intel serv, Ctr Dis Control, Nat Inst Occup Safety & Health, 80-82; career develop award, Harvard Sch Pub Health, 82-83; supvr med officer, Nat Inst Occup Safty & Health, 83-84, chief epidemiol, Section II, 84-89. *Concurrent Pos:* Clin assoc prof epidemiol & biostatist, Emory Univ Sch Pub Health, 90-, environ & occup health, 92- *Mem:* Am Pub Health Asn; Soc Epidemiol Res; Physicians Social Responsibility; Am Soc Prev Oncol; Am Asn Career Res. *Res:* Cancer epidemiology; aspirin in prevention of colon and digestive tract tumors; diet in prevention of colon cancer; smoking and mortality; occupational and environmental risk factors. *Mailing Add:* Am Cancer Soc 1599 Clifton Rd NE Atlanta GA 30329. *Fax:* 770-322-4669

**THUN, RUDOLF EDUARD,** engineering management, microelectronics; deceased, see previous edition for last biography

**THUN, RUDOLF PAUL,** ELEMENTARY PARTICLE PHYSICS. *Current Pos:* from asst prof to assoc prof, 74-82, PROF, UNIV MICH, 82- *Personal Data:* b Ger, July 22, 44; US citizen. *Educ:* Princeton Univ, AB, 65; State Univ NY, Stony Brook, PhD(physics), 72. *Prof Exp:* Fel, State Univ NY, Stony Brook, 72-74. *Mem:* Fel Am Phys Soc; Sigma Xi. *Res:* Elementary particle physics. *Mailing Add:* Physics Dept Univ Mich Ann Arbor MI 48109-1120. *Fax:* 313-936-1817

**THUNING-ROBERSON, CLAIRE ANN,** CANCER CHEMOTHERAPY, ONCOGENIC VIRUSES. *Current Pos:* res assoc, Goodwin Inst Cancer Res, 74-87, assoc dir, 88-90, dir, 90-, CHIEF SCI OFFICER, GOODWIN INST CANCER RES. *Personal Data:* b Cincinnati, Ohio, Nov 17, 45; m 84. *Educ:* St Mary-of-the-Woods Col, BA, 67; Nova Univ, MS, 77, PhD(biol), 82. *Prof Exp:* Sr res assoc, St Vincent Charity Hosp, 69-74. *Concurrent Pos:* Dir grad studies, Goodwin Inst Cancer Res, 81- *Mem:* AAAS; Am Soc Clin Path; Am Asn Cancer Res. *Res:* Investigating the control of cancer using combined hyperthermia and chemotherapy; the use of oxygen immunosuppression in promoting xenogeneic tumor growth and blocking autoimmune disease; properties of recombinant herpes virus strains. *Mailing Add:* Goodwin Inst Cancer Res 1850 NW 69th Ave Plantation FL 33313

**THURBER, CLIFFORD HAWES,** SEISMOLOGY, VOLCANOLOGY. *Current Pos:* assoc prof, 89-92, PROF GEOPHYS, UNIV WIS-MADISON, 92- *Personal Data:* b Doylestown, Pa, Aug 3, 54; m 76; c 2. *Educ:* Cornell Univ, AB, 75; Mass Inst Technol, PhD(geophys), 81. *Prof Exp:* From asst prof to assoc prof geophys, State Univ NY, Stony Brook, 81-89. *Concurrent Pos:* Secy, Inc Res Insts Seismol, 86-88; exec comt, Inc Res Inst Seismol, 89-90. *Mem:* Am Geophys Union; Seismol Asn Am; Sigma Xi. *Res:* Seismic imaging of earth structure, methods for earthquake location and seismic wave propagation; seismotectonics; volcanic earthquakes and magma transport; regional and global geophysical studies, especially gravity, stress and tectonics; seismic verification. *Mailing Add:* Geol 225 Weeks Hall Univ Wis 1215 W Dayton St Madison WI 53706-1692

**THURBER, DAVID LAWRENCE,** GEOCHEMISTRY. *Current Pos:* assoc prof, 66-70, PROF GEOL, QUEENS COL, NY, 70- *Personal Data:* b Oneonta, NY, Dec 29, 34; m 64; c 1. *Educ:* Union Col, NY, BS, 56; Columbia Univ, MA, 58, PhD(geol), 63. *Prof Exp:* Res asst geochem, Lamont Geol Observ, Columbia Univ, 56-63, res scientist, 63-64, res assoc, 64-66. *Concurrent Pos:* Am Geophys Union vis lectureship, 64; lectr, Queens Col, NY, 65-66; vis res assoc, Lamont Geol Observ, 66-70, vis sr res assoc, Lamont-Doherty Geol Observ, 70-74; vis prof, Fed Univ Bahia, 74-78. *Mem:* AAAS; Am Geophys Union; Geochem Soc. *Res:* General geochemistry; stable and radioisotope geochemistry; geochronology; hydrochemistry; soil chemistry. *Mailing Add:* 59 W Forest Ave Teaneck NJ 07666

**THURBER, JAMES KENT,** APPLIED MATHEMATICS. *Current Pos:* PROF MATH, PURDUE UNIV, LAFAYETTE, 69- *Personal Data:* b Utica, NY, Oct 29, 33. *Educ:* Brooklyn Col, BS, 55; NY Univ, PhD, 61. *Prof Exp:* Asst appl math, NY Univ, 57-61; asst prof math, Adelphi Univ, 61-64; assoc math, Brookhaven Nat Lab, 64-66, mathematician, 66-69. *Mem:* Am Math Soc; Am Nuclear Soc; Math Asn Am; Soc Indust & Appl Math; NY Acad Sci. *Res:* Neutron transport; kinetic theory of gases; asymptotic analysis; mathematical programming; applications of nonstandard analysis. *Mailing Add:* 1808 Charles St West Lafayette IN 47904-1430

**THURBER, ROBERT EUGENE,** PHYSIOLOGY, BIOPHYSICS. *Current Pos:* PROF PHYSIOL & CHMN DEPT, SCH MED, ECAROLINA UNIV, 70- *Personal Data:* b Bayshore, NY, Oct 11, 32; m 53, 84, Linda Boyd; c 4. *Educ:* Col of the Holy Cross, BS, 54; Adelphi Univ, MS, 61; Univ Kans, PhD(physiol), 65. *Prof Exp:* Res assoc radiation biol, Brookhaven Nat Lab, Assoc Univs Inc, 56-61; from instr to assoc prof physiol, Med Col Va, Va Commonwealth Univ, 64-69; assoc prof, Jefferson Med Col, Thomas Jefferson Univ, 69-70. *Concurrent Pos:* Consult, US Vet Admin, Va State Bd Med Examr & NASA, Va, 66-69; US Naval Hosp, Portsmouth, 68-69 & Psychol Consult Inc, 68-70; mem bd dirs, NC Heart Asn, 72-, pres elect, 78-79, pres, 79-80; mem, Comt Regional & Nat Res, Am Heart Asn, 81-82. *Mem:* AAAS; Am Physiol Soc; NY Acad Sci; Sigma Xi; Asn Chmn Dept Physiol. *Res:* Nonequilibrium transfer and distribution of electrolytes; renal transport; radiation biology and carbohydrate metabolism. *Mailing Add:* Dept Physiol Sch Med ECarolina Univ Greenville NC 27858-4354. *Fax:* 919-816-3460

**THURBER, WALTER ARTHUR,** ORNITHOLOGY. *Current Pos:* RETIRED. *Personal Data:* b East Worcester, NY, Nov 27, 08; m 34, 81, Amanda Villeda; c David L & Robert N. *Educ:* Union Col NY, BS, 33; NY State Col Teachers, MS, 38; Cornell Univ, PhD(nature study), 41. *Prof Exp:* Teacher NY schs, 26-29, 33-38; asst ed, Cornell Univ, 38-39; instr physics & phys sci, State Univ NY Teachers Col, Cortland, 40-43; asst prof physics & phys & earth sci, 43-48, prof sci, 48-58; vis prof sci educ, Syracuse Univ, 58-61, adj prof, 61-72; textbook writer, 61-80. *Concurrent Pos:* Consult, NY State Educ Dept, 43-55, NY pub schs, 47-52, Orgn Cent Am States, 66-79, Ministry of Educ, 72 & Gen Direction Natural Resources, El Salvador, 74-79; lab assoc, Lab Ornith, Cornell Univ, 70-85; vis prof, Nat Univ El Salvador, 71-79. *Mem:* Fel AAAS; NY Acad Sci; Am Ornith Union; Wilson Ornith Soc; Cooper Ornith Soc; Sigma Xi. *Res:* Elementary and secondary science education; organization of syllabuses and textbooks; distribution and life histories Central American birds. *Mailing Add:* PO Box 16918 Temple Terrace FL 33687

**THURBER, WILLIAM SAMUELS,** ORGANIC CHEMISTRY. *Current Pos:* RETIRED. *Personal Data:* b Ann Arbor, Mich, Mar 6, 22; m 43; c 4. *Educ:* Mich State Univ, BS, 46, MS, 48. *Prof Exp:* Asst dir styrene polymerization lab, Dow Chem Co, 54-57, dir, Strosackers Res & Develop Group, 57-61, plant supt, 61-64, tech dir, Saginaw Bay Res Dept, 64-68, admin asst to div dir res, 68-70, sect mgr process develop & eng, 70-76, mgr, 76-81, mgr Equal Opportunity Employ Progs, Dow Chem USA, 81-83. *Mem:* Am Chem Soc. *Res:* Styrene polymers; antioxidants; polyglycols; surface active agents. *Mailing Add:* 106 Belmont Ct Southern Pines NC 28387-2945

**THURBER, WILLIS ROBERT,** SEMICONDUCTORS, MATERIALS SCIENCE. *Current Pos:* Res physicist, Solid State Physics Sect, Nat Bur Standards, 62-66, res physicist, Electron Devices Div, 66-80, res physicist, semiconductors, Semiconductor Mat & Processes Div, 80-85, SEMICONDUCTOR ELECTRONICS DIV, NAT BUR STANDARDS, 85- *Personal Data:* b Butte, Nebr, July 10, 38; m 65, Carolyn Bowen; c Karen & Kent. *Educ:* Nebr Wesleyan Univ, AB, 60; Univ Md, MS, 63. *Mem:* Am Soc Testing & Mat. *Res:* Electrical and optical properties of semiconductors, particularly silicon, including Hall effect, resistivity, mobility, lifetime, infrared transmission and absorption; deep level transient spectroscopy. *Mailing Add:* 17616 Mill Creek Dr Derwood MD 20855. *Fax:* 301-948-4081

**THURBERG, FREDERICK PETER,** PHYSIOLOGY, MARINE BIOLOGY. *Current Pos:* PHYSIOLOGIST, NAT MARINE FISHERIES SERV, NAT OCEANIC & ATMOSPHERIC ADMIN, 71- *Personal Data:* b Weymouth, Mass, Aug 31, 42; m 64; c 2. *Educ:* Univ Mass, BA, 64, MEd, 66; Univ NH, MS, 69, PhD(zool, physiol), 72. *Prof Exp:* Teacher pub schs, Mass, 64-67. *Mem:* Estuarine Res Fedn; Am Soc Zoologists; Nat Shellfisheries Asn. *Res:* Physiological ecology; effects of pollutants on marine organisms; invertebrate physiology; marine biotoxins; red tides. *Mailing Add:* 30 Alden Dr Guilford CT 06437

**THURESON-KLEIN, ASA KRISTINA,** BIOLOGY, PHARMACOLOGY. *Current Pos:* res assoc, 65-68, asst prof, 69-74, assoc prof, 74-78, PROF PHARMACOL, MED CTR, UNIV MISS, 78- *Personal Data:* b Sweden, May 31, 34; m 61; c 2. *Educ:* Univ Stockholm, MA, 58, PhD(biol), 68. *Prof Exp:* Instr bot, Univ Stockholm, 58-64. *Concurrent Pos:* Pharmaceut Mfrs Asn Found fel pharmacol & morphol, Med Ctr, Univ Miss, 71-73; vis prof, Dept Physiol, Karolinska Inst, Sweden, 83 & 85. *Mem:* Am Soc Pharmacol & Exp Therapeut; Scand Soc Physiol; Soc Neurosci; Sigma Xi. *Res:* Effects of pharmacological agents on neurotransmitter release using combined biochemical and morphological methods; non-synaptic exocytosis from large neuropeptide containing vesicles; effects of leukotrienes B4 and C4 on the microcirculation. *Mailing Add:* 724 Shore Dr Destin FL 32541-3947

**THURLBECK, WILLIAM MICHAEL,** PULMONARY PATHOLOGY, PEDIATRIC PATHOLOGY. *Current Pos:* PROF PATH, UNIV BC, 80- *Personal Data:* b Johannesberg, Transvaal, SAfrica, Sept 7, 29; Can citizen; m 55; c 3. *Educ:* Univ Cape Town, BSc, 50, MB, ChB, 53. *Honors & Awards:* Medallist, Am Col Chest Physicians, 76; Sommer Mem Lectr, Univ Ore, 81. *Prof Exp:* From asst prof to prof path, McGill Univ, 61-73; sr investr path, Midhurst Med Res Inst, 73-75; prof path & head dept, Univ Man, 75-80. *Concurrent Pos:* Adj prof, dept anat, Univ Calif, Davis, 84. *Mem:* Can Thoracic Soc (pres, 84); Am Asn Pathologists; Int Acad Path; Can Soc Clin Invest; Am Thoracic Soc; corresp mem Brit Thoracic Soc. *Res:* Human lung growth; manipulation and control of experimental lung growth; pathology and pathophysiology of chronic airflow obstruction. *Mailing Add:* Dept Path Fac Med Univ BC 2211 Wesbrook Mall Vancouver BC V6T 1W5 Can

**THURLIMANN, BRUNO,** STRUCTURAL ENGINEERING, MASONRY. *Current Pos:* res asst, 46-48, prof struct eng, 60-90, EMER PROF, SWISS FED INST TECHNOL, 90- *Personal Data:* b Gossau, Switz, Feb 6, 23; Swiss & US citizen; m 53, Susi Gimmel; c Christoph, Peter & Elisabeth. *Educ:* Swiss Fed Inst Technol, Zurich, Dipl, 46; Lehigh Univ, PhD(civil eng), 51. *Hon Degrees:* Dr, Univ Stuttgart, Fed Repub Ger, 83; DrEng, Univ Glasgow, UK, 97. *Honors & Awards:* Res Prize, Am Soc Civil Engrs, 60; Norman Medal, 63; Moisseff Award, 64; Howard Award, 86; A Ostenfeld Gold Medal, Tech Univ Denmark, 91; Prix Albert Caquot, Fr Asn Construct, 93; Alfred E Lindau Award, Am Concrete Inst, 96. *Prof Exp:* Res asst struct eng, Lehigh Univ, 49-50, res prof, 53-60; res assoc, Brown Univ, 51-52. *Mem:* Nat Acad Eng; hon mem Am Soc Civil Engrs; Swiss Engrs & Architects Soc; Swiss Acad Tech Sci; Int Asn Bridge & Struct Eng (hon pres); hon mem Am Concrete Inst. *Res:* Concrete shell structures, plastic design of steel structures, stability, plate girders, composite construction; design of static and fatigue testing installation; plastic design of concrete structures; prestressed and partially prestressed structures; shear, torsion and combined actions; structural analysis; masonry construction. *Mailing Add:* Pfannenstiel-Str 56 Zurich CH-8132 EGG Switzerland

**THURMAIER, ROLAND JOSEPH,** ORGANIC CHEMISTRY, POLYMER CHEMISTRY. *Current Pos:* ASST PROF ORG CHEM, UNIV WIS-STEVENS POINT, 66- *Personal Data:* b Chicago, Ill, June 25, 28; m 55; c 4. *Educ:* Bradley Univ, BS, 50; Univ Iowa, MS, 58, PhD(org chem), 60. *Prof Exp:* Plant chemist, Corn Prod Ref Corp, 51-55; res chemist, E I du Pont de Nemours & Co, 60-66. *Concurrent Pos:* Mem, Stevens Point Transit Comn, 70; mem, Study Comt Mass Transit, 72 & Environ Coun, Univ Wis, Stevens Point, 73-74. *Mem:* Am Chem Soc; Sigma Xi. *Res:* Polymers; stabilizers for polyurethanes. *Mailing Add:* 1926 Center St Stevens Point WI 54481-3740

**THURMAN, GARY BOYD,** LYMPHOKINES, CELL MEDIATED IMMUNITY. *Current Pos:* VIS SCHOLAR, DEPT BIOCHEM, VANDERBILT UNIV, 90- *Personal Data:* b 1941; c 4. *Educ:* Univ Utah, PhD(radiation biol), 71. *Prof Exp:* Assoc sci dir, Biotherapeut, 85-89. *Mem:* Am Asn Immunologists; Am Asn Cancer Res. *Mailing Add:* Dept Biochem Vanderbilt Univ Sch Med Nashville TN 37232-0146. *Fax:* 615-322-4349

**THURMAN, HENRY L, JR,** ENGINEERING. *Current Pos:* Instr tech archit construct, Southern Univ, Baton Rouge, 48-52, dir div indust technol, 53-56, dir technol & eng, 56-59, dean col eng, 59-72, PROF ARCHIT ENG, SOUTHERN UNIV, BATON ROUGE, 72- *Personal Data:* b Lawrenceville, Va, Jan 14, 27; m 52; c 1. *Educ:* Hampton Inst, BS, 47; Univ Ill, MS, 49. *Concurrent Pos:* Mem bd dirs, Comn Eng Educ, 67- *Mem:* Am Soc Eng Educ. *Res:* Structural and architectural design; shelter analysis. *Mailing Add:* 2845 79th Ave Baton Rouge LA 70807

**THURMAN, LLOY DUANE,** PLANT ECOLOGY. *Current Pos:* from asst prof to assoc prof biol, 67-72, chmn dept natural sci, 69-73, PROF BIOL, ORAL ROBERTS UNIV, 72- *Personal Data:* b Oconto, Nebr, Sept 3, 33; m 57, B Joan Patterson; c Sonya R, Daniel K, Linda M & Bryan P. *Educ:* Univ Nebr, BS, 59, MS, 61; Univ Calif, Berkeley, 66. *Prof Exp:* Asst prof biol, Southern Calif Col, 65-67. *Mem:* Sigma Xi; Soc Col Sci Teachers; fel Am Sci Affil; Nat Sci Teachers Asn. *Res:* Ecology of Orthocarpus; curricula and teaching methods in biology; computers in biology and nutrition; creation versus evolution controversy. *Mailing Add:* Biol Dept Oral Roberts Univ 7777 S Lewis Tulsa OK 74171-0003

**THURMAN, RICHARD GARY,** CHEMISTRY. *Current Pos:* MEM STAFF, UNION CAMP, 77- *Personal Data:* b Wichita, Kans, Mar 1, 40; m 70. *Educ:* NMex State Univ, BS, 62, MS, 65; Univ Ariz, PhD(chem), 71. *Prof Exp:* Asst prof chem, Univ Ariz, 70-71; from asst prof to assoc prof chem, Univ Nebr-Omaha, 71-77. *Mem:* Am Chem Soc. *Res:* Liquid and gas chromatography-study of the separation processes; computer-controlled chemical instrumentation; use of computers in chemical education. *Mailing Add:* 2028 Old York Rd Burlington NJ 08016-9767

**THURMAN, ROBERT ELLIS, II,** PHYSICS. *Current Pos:* from instr to assoc prof, 66-80, PROF PHYSICS, SOUTHWEST MO STATE UNIV, 80- *Personal Data:* b Springfield, Mo, Oct 15, 39; m 62, Dorothy Joslyn; c Robert, Elizabeth, Natalie & Susannah. *Educ:* Mo Sch Mines, BS, 62; Univ Wis, MS, 64; Univ Mo-Rolla, PhD(physics), 77. *Prof Exp:* Res asst physics, Univ Wis, 63-66. *Concurrent Pos:* Physicist, US Forest Prod Lab, 63-64; NSF sci fac fel, 70-71; res asst physics, Univ Mo-Rolla, 71-72; sabbatical leave, Cloud Physics Ctr, Univ Mo-Rolla, 81-82. *Mem:* AAAS; Am Asn Physics Teachers; Sigma Xi. *Res:* Atmospheric physics; electrical mobility of water molecule cluster ions; aerosol evolution. *Mailing Add:* 1851 S Maryland Ave Springfield MO 65807-2745. *E-Mail:* ret359f@smsvma.bitnet

**THURMAN, RONALD GLENN,** BIOCHEMISTRY, PHARMACOLOGY. *Current Pos:* ASSOC PROF PHARMACOL, UNIV NC, CHAPEL HILL, 77- *Personal Data:* b Carbondale, Ill, Nov 25, 41. *Educ:* St Louis Col Pharm, BS, 63; Univ Ill, PhD(pharmacol), 68. *Prof Exp:* Asst prof biophys & phys biochem, Johnson Res Found, Univ Pa, 71-77. *Concurrent Pos:* Fel, Johnson Res Found, Univ Pa, 67-69; NATO fel, Inst Physiol Chem, Munich, Ger, 69-70; Alexander von Humboldt fel, 70-71; NIMH career develop award, 71-82. *Mem:* AAAS; Am Pharmaceut Soc. *Res:* Drug and alcohol metabolism. *Mailing Add:* Lab Hepatobiol & Toxicol Dept Pharmacol Univ NC at Chapel Hill FLOB Bldg Chapel Hill NC 27599-7365. *Fax:* 919-966-1893

**THURMAN, WAYNE LAVERNE,** SPEECH PATHOLOGY. *Current Pos:* RETIRED. *Personal Data:* b Detroit, Mich, June 11, 23. *Educ:* SE Mo State Col, BA & BSE, 48; State Univ Iowa, MA, 49; Purdue Univ, PhD(speech path), 53. *Prof Exp:* Instr speech, SE Mo State Col, 49-51; prof speech path & chmn dept, Eastern Ill Univ, 53-84. *Mem:* Fel Am Speech-Lang-Hearing Asn. *Res:* Voice quality disorders severity scales; voice therapy procedures. *Mailing Add:* 238 El Caminito Carmel Valley CA 93924

**THURMAN, WILLIAM GENTRY,** PEDIATRICS, ONCOLOGY. *Current Pos:* PROF PEDIAT & PRES, OKLA MED RES FOUND, 79- *Personal Data:* b Jacksonville, Fla, July 1, 28; m 49; c Andrew, Anne, Allison & Stephanie. *Educ:* Univ NC, BS, 49; McGill Univ, MD & CM, 54. *Prof Exp:* Asst prof pediat, Tulane Univ, 60-61; assoc prof, Emory Univ, 61-62; prof, Cornell Univ, 62-64; prof & chmn dept, Sch Med, Univ Va, 64-73, dir, Ctr Delivery Health Care, 69-73; dean sch med, Tulane Univ, 73-75; prof pediat & provost, Univ Okla Health Sci Ctr, 75-79. *Concurrent Pos:* Fel hemat & oncol, 58-60; Markle scholar acad med, 59-64; consult, USAF, 59-; Comn on Cancer, 63- & Comn on Pediat Hemat, 65-; chmn dept pediat, Mem Sloan-Kettering Cancer Ctr, 62-64; prog consult, Nat Found, 64-; prog consult pediat, VI, 66-; mem, Nat Rev Comt Regional Med Prog. *Mem:* Soc Pediat Res; Am Soc Hemat; Am Soc Human Genetics; Am Asn Cancer Res; Am Pediat Soc. *Res:* Immunologic abnormalities associated with malignancy in children; clinical management of children with malignancy; evaluation of various drugs; methods and models for delivery of health care. *Mailing Add:* Okla Med Res Found 825 NE 13th St Oklahoma City OK 73104. *Fax:* 405-271-3980

**THURMON, JOHN C,** VETERINARY ANESTHESIOLOGY. *Current Pos:* From instr to asst prof vet med, 62-70, assoc prof vet anesthesiol, 71-76, assoc prof physiol & pharmacol, 75-76, HEAD DIV, COL VET MED, UNIV ILL, URBANA, 71-, PROF VET ANESTHESIOL, VET ANAT, PHYSIOL & PHARMACOL, 76-, ASSOC PROF BIOENG, COL ENG, 72- *Personal Data:* b Redford, Mo, Mar 4, 30; m 56; c 1. *Educ:* Univ Mo, BS, 60, DVM, 62, MS, 67. *Concurrent Pos:* Nat Heart Inst fel, Baylor Col Med, 69; vis prof anesthesiol, Col Med, Univ Ill, Chicago, 70; consult, Bristol Labs, Syracuse, NY, 70-74, Affil Labs, Whitehall, Ill, 72-74, Bay Vet Corp, Shawnee Mission, Kans, 73-, Norden Labs, Lincoln, Nebr, 74- & Dept Med Sci, Southern Ill Univ, 75- *Mem:* Am Soc Vet Anesthesiol (pres elect, 73, pres, 74); Am Soc Anesthesiologists; Int Anesthesia Res Soc; Am Col Vet Anesthesiologists (pres, 75-77); Sigma Xi. *Res:* General anesthesia and its effects on homeostatic mechanisms of domestic and wild animals; development and design of equipment for use in veterinary anesthesia. *Mailing Add:* 2003 Cureton Dr Urbana IL 61801-6225

**THURMON, THEODORE FRANCIS,** MEDICAL GENETICS. *Current Pos:* assoc prof, 69-77, prof pediat & dir, Pediat Genetics Div, New Orleans, 77-86, PROF PEDIAT & DIR MED GENETICS, MED SCH, LA STATE UNIV, SHEEVEPORT, 86- *Personal Data:* b Baton Rouge, La, Oct 20, 37; m 92, Suzanne Greenwood; c Penelope, Suzanna, Sarah & Amanda. *Educ:* La State Univ, Baton Rouge, BS, 60; La State Univ, New Orleans, MD, 62. *Prof Exp:* Intern, Naval Hosp, Pensacola, Fla, 62-63, resident, Philadelphia, Pa, 63-65, pediatrician, cytogeneticist & cardiologist, St Albany, NY, 65-68. *Concurrent Pos:* Fel med genetics, Johns Hopkins Hosp, Baltimore, 68-69; consult, La State Dept Hosps, 70- *Mem:* AAAS; Am Soc Human Genetics; Human Biol Coun; NY Acad Sci. *Res:* Genetic regulation; genetic epidemiology; diagnostic techniques. *Mailing Add:* Dept Pediat La State Univ 1501 Kings Hwy Shreveport LA 71130. *Fax:* 318-675-6089; *E-Mail:* thurm@lsumc.edu

**THURMOND, JOHN TYDINGS,** VERTEBRATE PALEONTOLOGY, ENVIRONMENTAL GEOLOGY. *Current Pos:* ASSOC PROF EARTH SCI, UNIV ARK, LITTLE ROCK, 77-, CHAIRPERSON DEPT, 78- *Personal Data:* b Dallas, Tex, Oct 22, 41; m 69; c 3. *Educ:* St Louis Univ, BS, 63; Southern Methodist Univ, MS, 67, PhD(geol), 69. *Prof Exp:* Res asst to pres, Inst Study Earth & Man, Southern Methodist Univ, 70; asst prof geol, Birmingham-Southern Col, 70-77. *Concurrent Pos:* Vis prof fac chem sci & pharm, San Carlos Univ, Guatemala, 71; geologist, Harbert Construct Co, Ala, 71-72; asst cordr coop univ upper-div prog, Univ Ala, Gadsden, 72. *Mem:* AAAS; Paleont Soc; Soc Vert Paleont. *Res:* Paleoecology, functional morphology, taxonomy of Mesozoic/Cenozoic fishes; Pleistocene paleoecology; Cretaceous marine reptiles; environmental geology; data retrieval in paleontology. *Mailing Add:* Earth Sci Univ Ark 2801 S University Ave Little Rock AR 72204-1000

**THURMOND, WILLIAM,** DEVELOPMENTAL PHYSIOLOGY. *Current Pos:* from instr to prof zool, 76, PROF BIOL SCI, CALIF POLYTECH STATE UNIV, SAN LUIS OBISPO, 76- *Personal Data:* b Lodi, Calif, Apr 11, 26; m 49; c 2. *Educ:* Univ Calif, Berkeley, AB, 48, MA, 50, PhD(zool), 57. *Prof Exp:* Instr zool, San Mateo Community Col, Calif, 49-50. *Concurrent Pos:* Vis prof, Univ Frankfort, 69-70. *Mem:* Fel AAAS; Am Soc Zool; Am Inst Biol Sci; Sigma Xi. *Res:* Development of the pituitary and the developmental interdependance with other endocrine glands and the hypothalamus. *Mailing Add:* Dept Biol Sci Calif Polytech State Univ 368 Lincoln St San Luis Obispo CA 93405-2332

**THURNAUER, HANS,** CERAMICS. *Current Pos:* RETIRED. *Personal Data:* b Nurnberg, Ger, June 11, 08; nat US; m 35; c Peter, Marion & Dorothy. *Educ:* Tech Univ Berlin, Dipl, 31, DrEng, 58; Univ Ill, MS, 32. *Prof Exp:* Ceramic engr, Steatite-Magnesia Co, Ger, 32-33; ceramic lab asst, Steatite & Porcelain Prod, Ltd, Eng, 33-35; dir res & vpres, Am Lava Corp, Tenn, 35-55; head ceramic dept, Minn Mining & Mfg Co, 55-66; consult & tech adv, Int Exec Serv Corps, Coors Procelain Co, 67-74. *Concurrent Pos:* Dir, Israel Ceramic & Silicate Inst, Haifa, 64-66; consult mat comts, US Dept Defense & NASA. *Mem:* AAAS; fel Am Ceramic Soc; Electrochem Soc (pres, 57); Am Chem Soc. *Res:* Technical ceramics; solid state devices; refractory and abrasion resistant materials; nuclear ceramics. *Mailing Add:* 440 College Ave Boulder CO 80302

**THURNAUER, MARION CHARLOTTE,** PHOTOSYNTHESIS, MAGNETIC RESONANCE. *Current Pos:* fel, Argonne Nat Lab, 74-77, asst scientist, 77-81, scientist chem, 81-91, SR SCIENTIST, ARGONNE NAT LAB, 91-, DIR CHEM DIV, 95- *Personal Data:* b Chattanooga, Tenn; m 67, Alexander D. *Educ:* Univ Chicago, BA, 68, MS, 69, PhD(chem), 74. *Mem:* Am Chem Soc; Biophys Soc; Sigma Xi; Asn Women Sci. *Res:* Electron paramagnetic resonance studies (continuous wave and pulsed) of radicals, radical pairs and triplet state; magnetic resonance studies of photosynthetic systems; time resolved magnetic resonance studies; pulsed electron paramagnetic resonance studies of photosynthetic systems; magnetic resonance; semi-conduction colloids. *Mailing Add:* Argonne Nat Lab 9700 S Cass Ave Argonne IL 60439-4831. *Fax:* 630-252-9289; *E-Mail:* thurnauer@anlchm.chm.anl.gov

**THURNER, JOSEPH JOHN,** INORGANIC CHEMISTRY. *Current Pos:* RETIRED. *Personal Data:* b Middletown, NY, Oct 26, 20; m 48, Jean King; c John & Laura. *Educ:* Hartwick Col, BS, 49; Harvard Univ, MA, 51. *Prof Exp:* From instr to assoc prof, Colgate Univ, 51-69, chmn dept, 67-70, dir, Div Natural Sci & Math, 70-74, prof chem, 74-87. *Concurrent Pos:* Consult, Indium Corp Am, 52-62. *Mem:* AAAS; Am Chem Soc; Sigma Xi. *Res:* Organometallic compounds of germanium; organometallic and inorganic compounds; alloys of indium; synthesis and analysis of indium-bearing substances. *Mailing Add:* 50 Broad St Hamilton NY 13346

**THUROW, GORDON RAY,** ZOOLOGY, ANATOMY. *Current Pos:* ASSOC PROF BIOL, WESTERN ILL UNIV, 66- *Personal Data:* b Aurora, Ill, Feb 13, 29; m 55; c 5. *Educ:* Univ Chicago, PhB, 48, BS, 50, MS, 51; Ind Univ, PhD, 55. *Prof Exp:* Asst zool & ornith, Ind Univ, 52 & 54, tech adv ed film, 55; assoc prof natural sci, Newberry Col, 57-59; fel anat, Med Col SC, 59-61; asst prof, Univ Kans, 61-66. *Mem:* Am Soc Ichthyologists & Herpetologists; Soc Study Amphibians & Reptiles; Soc Study Evolution; Ecol Soc Am; Am Asn Anat; Sigma Xi. *Res:* Morphological, physiological and behavioral adaptations of vertebrates; transplantation; herpetology; ecology. *Mailing Add:* Dept Biol-Sci Western Ill Univ Macomb IL 61455

**THURSTON, EARLE LAURENCE,** BOTANY, CELL BIOLOGY. *Current Pos:* ASSOC PROF CELL BIOL & COORDR, ELECTRON MICROS CTR, TEX A&M UNIV, 70- *Personal Data:* b New York, NY, Jan 17, 43; m 62; c 3. *Educ:* State Univ NY, Geneseo, BS, 64; Iowa State Univ, MS, 67, PhD(bot), 69. *Prof Exp:* NSF fel cell res inst, Univ Tex, Austin, 69-70. *Mem:* Bot Soc Am; Electron Micros Soc; Am Soc Cell Biol. *Res:* Developmental morphology and ultrastructure; electron microprobe analysis. *Mailing Add:* 4905 Atton Oaks Dr College Station TX 77845

**THURSTON, GAYLEN AUBREY,** ENGINEERING MECHANICS. *Current Pos:* RETIRED. *Personal Data:* b Garwin, Iowa, May 15, 29; m 51; c 5. *Educ:* Iowa State Col, BS, 50; Ohio State Univ, MS, 51; Cornell Univ, PhD(eng mech), 56. *Prof Exp:* Shell struct specialist, Jet Engine Dept, Gen Elec Co, 55-63; res scientist mech, Denver Div, Martin Marietta Corp, 63-69; prof, Univ Denver, 69-75; assoc prof mech, Univ Colo, Denver, 75-80. *Mem:* Sigma Xi; Am Soc Eng Educ. *Res:* Nonlinear mechanics; shell structures. *Mailing Add:* 5850 S Sherman Way Littleton CO 80121-1131

**THURSTON, GEORGE BUTTE,** BIOMEDICAL ENGINEERING, RHEOLOGY. *Current Pos:* PROF MECH ENG & BIOMED ENG, UNIV TEX, AUSTIN, 68- *Personal Data:* b Austin, Tex, Oct 8, 24; m 47, Carol McWharter; c John & Mary. *Educ:* Univ Tex, BS, 44, MA, 48, PhD(physics), 52. *Honors & Awards:* Alexander von Humboldt US Sr Scientist Award, WGer, 75. *Prof Exp:* Res scientist, Defense Res Lab, Tex, 49-52; asst prof physics, Univ Wyo, 52-53 & Univ Ark, 53-54; from assoc prof to prof, Okla State Univ, 54-68. *Concurrent Pos:* Consult, US Naval Ord Test Sta, 54-55; res physicist, Univ Mich, 58-59; NSF fel, Macromolecules Res Ctr, Strasbourg, 63-64; vis prof, Helmholtz Inst, Rhineland-Westphalian Tech High Sch, Aachen, WGer, 75-76; guest prof, Nat Ctr Sci Res, CRM, Strasbourg, France, 83-84. *Mem:* Fel Am Phys Soc; fel Acoust Soc Am; Soc Rheology; Int Soc Biorheology; Brit Soc Rheology; Int Soc Clin Hemorheology. *Res:* Acoustics; rheology; polymer science; macromolecules; optical and electrical properties of solutions. *Mailing Add:* Dept Mech Eng Univ Tex Austin TX 78712. *E-Mail:* thurston@mail.utexas.edu

**THURSTON, HERBERT DAVID,** PLANT PATHOLOGY. *Current Pos:* PROF PLANT PATH, CORNELL UNIV, 67- *Personal Data:* b Sioux Falls, SDak, Mar 24, 27; m 51; c 3. *Educ:* Univ Minn, MS, 53, PhD(plant path), 58. *Prof Exp:* Asst plant path, Univ Minn, 50-53, instr, 53-54; asst plant pathologist, Rockefeller Found, Colombia, 54-56; instr plant path, Univ Minn, 56-57; from assoc plant pathologist to plant pathologist, Rockefeller Found, Colombia, 58-67. *Mem:* Am Phytopath Soc; Potato Asn Am. *Res:* Diseases of potatoes; tropical plant pathology; nature of resistance to fungus diseases. *Mailing Add:* Dept Plant Path 334 Plant Sci Bldg Cornell Univ Ithaca NY 14853-0001

**THURSTON, JAMES N(ORTON),** ELECTRICAL ENGINEERING. *Current Pos:* RETIRED. *Personal Data:* b Murphysboro, Ill, May 6, 15; m 40, Agnes Wallner; c Anita, Paul, Eric & Peter. *Educ:* Ohio State Univ, BEE, 36; Mass Inst Technol, SM, 43, ScD(elec eng), 50. *Prof Exp:* Test engr, Gen Elec Co, 36-38; geophysicist, Mott-Smith Corp, 38-40; from asst to asst prof elec eng, Mass Inst Technol, 40-49; assoc prof, Univ Fla, 49-52 & Calif Inst Technol, 52-54; prof & head dept, Clemson Univ, 54-66, alumni prof elec eng, 66-80. *Concurrent Pos:* Consult, Ruge-Deforest, 45-49, Firestone Tire & Rubber Co, 53- & Nat Coun Eng Examr, 73-88. *Mem:* Am Soc Eng Educ; sr mem Inst Elec & Electronics Engrs. *Res:* Electronic measurement and control systems; communications systems. *Mailing Add:* 322 Woodland Way Clemson SC 29631

**THURSTON, JOHN ROBERT,** BACTERIOLOGY, IMMUNOLOGY. *Current Pos:* LEAD SCIENTIST, NAT ANIMAL DIS LAB, USDA, 61- *Personal Data:* b Maumee, Ohio, May 6, 26; m 53; c 2. *Educ:* Ohio State Univ, BSc, 49, MSc, 51, PhD(bact), 55. *Prof Exp:* Res microbiologist, Ohio Tuberc Hosp, Columbus, 55-57; microbiologist, Trudeau Found, Inc, NY, 57-61. *Mem:* Am Asn Vet Immunol. *Res:* Serologic investigations of mycobacteria; serologic diagnosis in tuberculosis; intradermal tuberculin testing of cattle; glycoprotein changes in tuberculous cattle; serology of nocardiosis and aspergillosis; effect of mycotoxins on the immune system; atrophic rhinitis. *Mailing Add:* 632 20th St Ames IA 50010-4928

**THURSTON, M(ARLIN) O(AKES),** ELECTRICAL ENGINEERING. *Current Pos:* PRES, THURSTON-BELL ASSOCS, INC, 82- *Personal Data:* b Denver, Colo, Sept 20, 18; m 42; c 3. *Educ:* Univ Colo, BA, 40, MS, 46; Ohio State Univ, PhD(elec eng), 55. *Prof Exp:* Assoc prof elec eng & actg head dept, Air Force Inst Technol, 46-52; res assoc, Ohio State Univ, 52-55, from assoc prof to prof elec eng, 55-82, chmn dept, 65-77, dir, Electron Device Lab, 77-82. *Concurrent Pos:* Elec eng ed, Marcel Dekker, Inc, 75-; chmn bd, Nat Eng Consortium, Inc, 77-79; vpres, Neoprobe Corp, 83- *Mem:* Fel Inst Elec & Electronics Engrs; Am Phys Soc; Am Soc Eng Educ. *Res:* Solid state electron devices; biomedical engineering. *Mailing Add:* Dept Elec Eng Ohio State Univ 2015 Neil Ave Columbus OH 43210

**THURSTON, ROBERT NORTON,** WAVE PROPAGATION, ELECTROMECHANICAL INTERACTIONS. *Current Pos:* mem tech staff, Bell Tel Labs, Murray Hill, 52-83, BELL COMMUN RES, HOLMDEL, NJ, 84- *Personal Data:* b Kilbourne, Ohio, Dec 31, 24; m 49, Jessica J Morrison; c Barcey (Levy), Sandra S, Nancy (Lang) & Anne A. *Educ:* Ill Inst Technol, BS, 45; Ohio State Univ, MS, 48, PhD(physics), 52. *Prof Exp:* Teacher high sch, Ohio, 46-47; instr aeronaut eng, Ohio State Univ, 49-50. *Concurrent Pos:* Vis lectr thermodyn, Dept Mech & Aerospace Eng, Rutgers Univ, 91-93. *Mem:* Am Phys Soc; fel Acoust Soc Am; Inst Elec & Electronics Engrs; Soc Natural Philos; Soc Eng Sci; Optical Soc Am. *Res:* Mechanics; crystal physics; communications science; liquid crystals; guided waves and optoelectronics; physical acoustics; nonlinear propagation. *Mailing Add:* 40 Squire Terr Colts Neck NJ 07722

**THURSTON, RODNEY SUNDBYE,** MECHANICAL ENGINEERING. *Current Pos:* assoc group leader, 59-76, PROJ MGR, LOS ALAMOS SCI LAB, 76- *Personal Data:* b Brooklyn, NY, Sept 17, 33; m 55; c 5. *Educ:* Columbia Univ, AB, 55, BS, 56, MS, 58; Univ NMex, PhD(mech eng), 66. *Prof Exp:* Jr engr, Am Elec Power Co, NY, 56-57; teaching asst mech eng, Columbia Univ, 57-58 & Cornell Univ, 58-59. *Mem:* Am Soc Mech Engrs; Sigma Xi. *Res:* Heat transfer; shock wave propagation; material damage induced by photon and neutron deposition. *Mailing Add:* 5 Dakota Lane Pa Los Alamos NM 87544

**THURSTON, WILLIAM P,** GEOMETRY. *Current Pos:* PROF, MATH DEPT, UNIV CALIF, DAVIS, 96- *Personal Data:* b Washington, DC, Oct 30, 46; m 93, Karen. *Educ:* New Col, Sarasota, BA, 67; Univ Calif, Berkeley, PhD, 72. *Hon Degrees:* Dr, Univ Paris-Sud, Orsay, 87. *Honors & Awards:* Oswald Veblen Prize in Geom, Am Math Soc, 76; Alan T Waterman Award, NSF, 79; Fields Medal, Int Math Union, 82. *Prof Exp:* Asst prof, Mass Inst Technol, 73; prof, Dept Math, Princeton Univ, 74-93; prof, Math Dept, MSRI, Berkeley, 93-96. *Concurrent Pos:* Alfred P Sloan fel, 74; Ulam vis prof math, Univ Colo, 80-81; coun mem, Am Math Soc, 81-84. *Mem:* Fel Nat Acad Sci; fel Am Acad Sci; Am Math Soc (vpres, 87-88); Math Asn Am; Soc Indust & Appl Math; fel Am Acad Arts & Sci. *Res:* Three-dimensional geometry and topology; dynamical systems; theory of groups and symmetry; visualization of mathematics with the aid of computer graphics. *Mailing Add:* Math Dept Kerr Hall Univ Calif Davis CA 95616. *E-Mail:* wpt@math.ucdavis.edu

**THURSTON, WILLIAM R,** GEOLOGY & SCIENCE ADMINISTRATION. *Current Pos:* RETIRED. *Personal Data:* b New York, NY, Nov 1, 15; m 37, Sherry Cunningham; c Thomas C. *Educ:* Columbia Univ, AB, 38, AM, 43, PhD, 52. *Prof Exp:* Asst geologist, Cuban-Am Manganese Corp, Cuba, 38-39; asst geol, Brown Univ, 39-40; trustees asst, Columbia Univ, 40-42; geologist, US Geol Surv, 42-51, mining co, Mex, 51-52 & Nicaro Nickel Co, Cuba, 52-54; assoc prof, Sch Eng, La Polytech Inst, 54-55; exec secy div earth sci, Nat Acad Sci-Nat Res Coun, 55-59; staff geologist, US Geol Surv, 59-67; asst to sci adv, US Dept Interior, 67-70, spec asst to dir, US Geol Surv, 70-76; staff officer, Nat Acad Sci-Nat Res Coun, 76-77; consult geologist, 77-85. *Concurrent Pos:* Mem & nat del, Int Geol Cong, 64, 68 & 72. *Mem:* Fel AAAS; Geol Soc Am; Soc Econ Geol. *Res:* Economic geology; geology of pegmatites and fluorspar. *Mailing Add:* 200 Alhambra Sedona AZ 86336

**THURSTONE, ROBERT LEON,** ELECTRICAL ENGINEERING. *Current Pos:* RETIRED. *Personal Data:* b Chicago, Ill, July 29, 27; m 66, Betty Bass. *Educ:* Ill Inst Technol, BS, 51; Univ Mo, MS 53; NC State Univ, PhD(elec eng), 65. *Prof Exp:* Instr elec eng, Duke Univ, 53-57 & NC State Univ, 57-61; from asst to assoc prof elec eng, Univ Ala, Huntsville, 65-87, chmn dept, 72-81. *Res:* Energy transfer through biological tissue. *Mailing Add:* 1401 Toney Dr Huntsville AL 35802

**THUT, PAUL DOUGLAS,** PSYCHOPHARMACOLOGY. *Current Pos:* ASSOC PROF PHARM, SCH DENT, UNIV MD, 74- *Personal Data:* b Exeter, NH, Feb 1, 43; m 66; c 3. *Educ:* Hamilton Col, AB, 65; Univ RI, MS, 68; Dartmouth Col, PhD(pharmacol), 71. *Prof Exp:* Asst prof pharmacol, Col Med, Univ Ariz, 70-74. *Concurrent Pos:* Pharmaceut Mfrs Found grant, 72-73; consult, Vet Admin Hosp, Tucson, 72- *Mem:* Soc Neurosci; Am Soc Pharmacol & Exp Therapeut; Sigma Xi. *Res:* Psychomotor effects of l-dehydroxphenylalanine; competitive neuromuscular antagonists. *Mailing Add:* Dept Pharmacol Univ Md Sch Dent Baltimore MD 21201. *Fax:* 410-706-3028

**THWAITES, THOMAS TURVILLE,** NUCLEAR PHYSICS. *Current Pos:* RETIRED. *Personal Data:* b Madison, Wis, Aug 21, 31; m 53; c 2. *Educ:* Univ Wis, BS, 53; Univ Rochester, MA, 56, PhD(physics), 59. *Prof Exp:* Physicist, Stromberg Carlson Div, Gen Dynamics Corp, 55-56; from asst prof to assoc prof physics, Pa State Univ, University Park, 59- *Mem:* Am Phys Soc. *Res:* Scattering of 200 million electron volts polarized protons; radioactive decay schemes; radiative capture of charged particles; scattering of charged particles. *Mailing Add:* 1113 Centre Lane State College PA 16801

**THWAITES, WILLIAM MUELLER,** GENETICS, SCIENCE EDUCATION. *Current Pos:* RETIRED. *Personal Data:* b Madison, Wis, July 10, 33; m 55; c 3. *Educ:* Univ Wis, BS, 55; Univ Mich, MS, 62, PhD(genetics), 65. *Prof Exp:* From asst prof to assoc prof biol, San Diego State Univ, 65-95. *Concurrent Pos:* Prin investr, NSF res grant, 66-68 & 76-78; fel, Battelle Mem Inst, Richland, Washington, 72-73; vis prof, Instituto de Investigaciones Biomedicas, Mexico City, 73-74. *Mem:* Genetics Soc Am; AAAS. *Res:* General, microbial and biochemical genetics; evolution education. *Mailing Add:* 6001 Fourth St NW Tillamook OR 97141. *E-Mail:* wthwaite@sunstroke.sdsu.edu

**THWEATT, JOHN G,** ORGANIC CHEMISTRY. *Current Pos:* res chemist, Tenn Eastman Co, 60-63, sr res chemist, Res Labs, 63-75, sr chemist, Develop Dept, 75-76, tech staff, Dyes Dept, 76-83, tech staff, develop dept, 83-87, DEVELOP ASSOC, DEVELOP DEPT, ORG CHEM DIV, TENN EASTMAN CO, 87- *Personal Data:* b Norton, Va, Nov 21, 32; m 54; c 2. *Educ:* Ga Inst Technol, BS, 54, PhD(org chem), 61. *Prof Exp:* Instr chem, Ga Inst Technol, 57-59. *Mem:* Am Chem Soc. *Res:* Chemistry of enamines and other electron rich olefins; process development, photographically active compounds; process improvement; hydrogenation and other high pressure reactions. *Mailing Add:* 3416 Lakeshore Dr Kingsport TN 37663-3370

**THYAGARAJAN, B S,** ORGANIC CHEMISTRY. *Current Pos:* dir earth & phys sci div, 74-77, PROF CHEM, UNIV TEX, SAN ANTONIO, 74- *Personal Data:* b Tiruvarur, India, July 14, 29; m 56; c 3. *Educ:* Loyola Col, Madras, India, MA, 51; Presidency Col, Madras, MSc, 53, PhD(chem), 56. *Honors & Awards:* Intrasci Res Award, 66. *Prof Exp:* Fel, Northwestern Univ, 56-58; fel, Univ Wis, 58-59; reader org chem, Madras Univ, 60-68; prof, Univ Idaho, 69-74. *Mem:* Fel Am Inst Chemists; NY Acad Sci; The Chem Soc; Sigma Xi; Soc Cosmetic Chemists. *Res:* Heterocyclic chemistry; aromaticity; molecular migrations; synthesis of organosulphur pesticides; novel reactions in sulphur chemistry; mass spectral rearrangements in organo-sulphur molecules. *Mailing Add:* 6119 Amble Trail San Antonio TX 78249-2108

**THYE, FORREST WALLACE,** NUTRITION & EXERCISE. *Current Pos:* ASSOC PROF NUTRIT & ENERGY METAB, VA POLYTECH INST & STATE UNIV, 81- *Personal Data:* b Burlington, Iowa, Aug 24, 40; m 68; c 2. *Educ:* Cornell Univ, PhD(nutrit), 69. *Mem:* Am Inst Nutrit. *Res:* Effect of diet on blood lipids and mineral balance. *Mailing Add:* Dept Human Nutrit & Foods Va Polytech Inst & State Univ Col Human Resources Blacksburg VA 24061. *Fax:* 540-231-7157

**THYER, NORMAN HAROLD,** METEOROLOGY, SURVEYING ENGINEERING. *Current Pos:* RETIRED. *Personal Data:* b Gloucester, Eng, Sept 3, 29; m 65, Anna Rempel; c Anita, Linda & David. *Educ:* Univ Birmingham, BSc, 57; Univ Wash, Seattle, PhD(meteorol), 62; BC Inst Technol, dipl, 83; Univ Calgary, MSc, 87. *Honors & Awards:* Intera Kenting Award, Can Inst Surv & Mapping, 89. *Prof Exp:* Meteorol asst, Air Ministry, UK, 49-50 & Falkland Islands Dependencies Surv, 50-53; tech asst aeronaut eng, Gloster Aircraft Co, 54; micrometeorologist, Univ Wash, Seattle, 60, meteorol training expert, World Meteorol Orgn, 62-63; asst prof meteorol & physics, Univ BC, 63-66; from asst prof to assoc prof, Notre Dame Univ, Nelson, 68-77. *Concurrent Pos:* Res assoc meteorol, McGill Univ, 68-77; climatologist, 79-80; vis prof, Univ Vercruzana, Mex, 80-82; jr surv eng, Geodetic Surv Can, 88-89; forecaster, Oceanroutes (UK) Ltd, Aberdeen, Scotland, 89. *Res:* Local winds near valleys and convectional storms; surveying engineering. *Mailing Add:* 6115 Sproule Creek Rd RR 2 S22 C7 Nelson BC V1L 5P5 Can. *E-Mail:* nthyer@web.net

**THYGESEN, KENNETH HELMER,** EXPERIMENTAL SOLID STATE PHYSICS & SURFACE PHYSICS. *Current Pos:* assoc prof, 67-77, chmn dept, 76-87, PROF PHYSICS, STATE UNIV NY, COL POTSDAM, 77-, CHMN DEPT, 95- *Personal Data:* b Cambridge, NY, June 30, 37; m 55, Catherine J Marley; c K Wayne & Cathy D. *Educ:* Washington & Lee Univ, 58; Clarkson Col Technol, MS, 60, PhD(physics), 67. *Prof Exp:* Instr physics, Clarkson Col Technol, 59-65. *Mem:* Am Phys Soc; Sigma Xi. *Res:* Atomic and molecular physics low energy ion implantation simulations; surface physics: x-ray standing wave studies of semiconductor-metal interfaces. *Mailing Add:* 26 Cedar St Potsdam NY 13676. *E-Mail:* thygeskh@potsdam.edu

**THYGESON, JOHN R(OBERT), JR,** CHEMICAL ENGINEERING. *Current Pos:* RETIRED. *Personal Data:* b Boston, Mass, Sept 25, 24. *Educ:* Drexel Inst, BS, 47; Univ Pa, MS, 55, PhD(chem eng), 61. *Prof Exp:* Res engr, Proctor & Schwartz, Inc, 47-58; asst prof, Drexel Univ, 61-63, assoc prof chem eng, 63- *Concurrent Pos:* Consult, Proctor & Schwartz, Inc, 63- *Mem:* Am Inst Chem Engrs; Am Chem Soc. *Res:* Transport phenomena; mechanisms of the reaction of hydrogen with carbon steels; simultaneous heat and mass transfer in packed beds of particulate solids. *Mailing Add:* Dept Chem Eng Drexel Univ Philadelphia PA 19104-4360

**THYR, BILLY DALE,** PLANT PATHOLOGY, MYCOLOGY. *Current Pos:* CONSULT, 83- *Personal Data:* b Kansas City, Kans, June 1, 32; m 58, 83, Sally L Myers; c Gregory D, Amy S & Sara A. *Educ:* Univ Ottawa, Kans, BA, 59; Wash State Univ, PhD(plant path), 64. *Prof Exp:* Res plant pathologist, Agr Res Serv, USDA, 63-86, alfalfa res leader, 80-83. *Concurrent Pos:* Owner & operator, Plant Health Servs. *Mem:* Am Soc Agron; Am Phytopath Soc; Crop Sci Soc Am; Soc Nematologists. *Res:* Bacterial diseases of tomato and other vegetables; control of bacterial diseases through host resistance; alfalfa diseases; interaction of organisms infecting alfalfa; interaction of water relations and alfalfa disease. *Mailing Add:* 2230 King Edward Dr Reno NV 89503

**THYSEN, BENJAMIN,** LABORATORY MEDICINE, GYNECOLOGY. *Current Pos:* asst prof, 71-86, DIR, ENDOCRINE LABS, ALBERT EINSTEIN COL MED, 71-, ASSOC PROF OBSTET & GYNEC, 86- *Personal Data:* b Bronx, NY, July 27, 32; m 75; c Julie & Greg. *Educ:* City Col New York, BS, 54; Univ Mo, MS, 63; St Louis Univ, PhD(biochem), 67. *Prof Exp:* Res asst obstet & gynec & biochem, Albert Einstein Col Med, 59-61; asst biochem, Sch Med, Univ Mo, 61-63; instr, St Louis Univ, 67-68; sr res scientist, Technicon Corp, 68-69, group leader, 69-70. *Concurrent Pos:* Mem, Spec Study Sect, Core Ctr Grants, Nat Inst Environ Health Sci, 86. *Mem:* AAAS; Endocrine Soc; Am Chem Soc; Am Asn Clin Chemists; Soc Study Reproduction; Sigma Xi. *Res:* Estrogen metabolism; testes; laboratory medicine; toxicology; methodology; reproductive endocrinology. *Mailing Add:* Dept Obstet & Gynec Albert Einstein Col Med 1635 Poplar St Bronx NY 10461. *Fax:* 718-829-2625; *E-Mail:* thysen@aecom.yu.edu

**THYVELIKAKATH, GEORGE,** ORGANIC CHEMISTRY, CANCER RESEARCH. *Current Pos:* CHMN & PROF, CHEM DEPT, ORAL ROBERTS UNIV, 77- *Personal Data:* b Kerala, India, Apr 29, 43. *Educ:* Kerala Univ, BS, 65; Univ SW La, MS, 71; Okla State Univ, PhD(cancer res), 75. *Prof Exp:* Fel, Univ Ark, 75-77. *Mem:* Am Chem Soc; Am Inst Chem. *Mailing Add:* Sci Dept Oral Roberts Univ 777 S Lewis St Tulsa OK 74171-0002

**TIAB, DJEBBAR,** PETROLEUM ENGINEERING. *Current Pos:* from asst prof to assoc prof, 77-88, PROF PETROL ENG, UNIV OKLA, 88- *Personal Data:* b Ain Beida, Algeria, Sept 23, 50; m 75; c 1. *Educ:* NMex Inst Mining & Technol, BSc, 74, MSc, 75; Univ Okla, PhD(petrol eng), 76. *Honors & Awards:* Kerr-McGee Distinguished Lectr, 85. *Prof Exp:* Chief technician petrol geol, Alcore, Inc, Algeria, 69-71; res assoc petrol eng, NMex Inst Mining & Technol, 70-76, asst prof, 76-77. *Concurrent Pos:* NSF res scientist, 78-80; pres, United Petrol Tech, 79-83; sr res eng, Core Labs, 88-89; Halliburton Lectureship Award, 87-92. *Mem:* Assoc Soc Petrol Engrs. *Res:* Reservoir mechanics of enhanced oil recovery; well testing; natural gas technology; reservoir engineering; horizontal wells; rock properties; petrophysics. *Mailing Add:* 3709 Windover Dr Norman OK 73072

**TIAN, GANG,** DIFFERENTIAL GEOMETRY. *Current Pos:* prof, 95-96, SIMONS PROF MATH, MASS INST TECHNOL, 96-; PROF MATH, COURANT ISNT MATH SCI, NY UNIV, 92- *Personal Data:* b People's Repub China, Nov 24, 58. *Educ:* Nanking Univ, BS, 82; Peking Univ, MS, 84; Harvard Univ, PhD, 88. *Honors & Awards:* 19th Alan T Waterman Award, 94; Bergmann Mem Lectr, Stanford Univ, 94; Oswald Veblen Prize, 96. *Prof Exp:* Asst prof math, Princeton Univ, NJ, 88-90; assoc prof, State Univ NY, Stony Brook, 90-91 & Courant Inst Math Sci, NY Univ, 91-92. *Concurrent Pos:* Alfred P Sloan Found Doctoral Dissertation fel, 87; vis mem, Inst Advan Study, Princeton, NJ, 88-89; prof, Math Inst, Academia Sinica, China, 88- & Peking Univ, Beijing, China, 91-; NSF res grant, 89-91, 91-93 & 93-98; National Sci Found res grants, 89-98; vis mem, Inst Hautes Etudes Sci, Paris, 91; Alfred P Sloan res fel, 91-93; ed, Pac J Math, 94-, Geom & Topology, 96; assoc ed, J Am Math Soc, 95-; Courant Lect, NY Univ, 96; distinguished vis lect, Univ Wis-Madison, 96. *Mem:* Am Math Soc. *Res:* Differential geometry; geometric analysis; partial differential equations; algebraic geometry; complex analysis. *Mailing Add:* Dept Math Rm 2-172 Mass Inst Technol 77 Massachusetts Ave Cambridge MA 02139-4307. *Fax:* 617-253-4358; *E-Mail:* tian@math.mit.edu

**TIAO, GEORGE CHING-HWUAN,** MATHEMATICAL STATISTICS, ECONOMIC STATISTICS. *Current Pos:* assoc prof, 66-68, prof statist & bus, 68-81, BASCOM PROF STATIST & BUS, UNIV WIS-MADISON, 81- *Personal Data:* b London, Eng, Nov 8, 33; Chinese citizen; m 58; c 4. *Educ:* Nat Taiwan Univ, BA, 55; NY Univ, MBA, 58; Univ Wis-Madison, PhD(econ), 62. *Prof Exp:* Asst prof statist & bus, Univ Wis-Madison, 62-65; vis assoc prof statist, Harvard Bus Sch, 65-66. *Concurrent Pos:* Vis lectr, Post Col Prof Educ, Carnegie Mellon Univ, 66-73; statist consult to var indust co, 66-; vis prof, Univ Essex, 70-71; chmn dept statist, Univ Wis-Madison, 73-75; vis prof, Nat Taiwan Univ, 75-76; assoc ed, J Am Statist Asn, 76-81; vis Ford Found prof, Univ Chicago, Ill, 80-81. *Mem:* Fel Royal Statist Soc; fel Am Statist Asn; fel Inst Math Statist; AAAS; Int Statist Inst. *Res:* Bayesian methods in statistics; time series analysis; statistical analysis of environmental data; economic and business forecasting. *Mailing Add:* 1445 E 56th St Chicago IL 60637

**TIBBALS, HARRY FRED, III,** DATA SYSTEMS ENGINEERING, SIMULATION ANALYSIS. *Current Pos:* PRES, BIODIGITAL TECHNOL, INC, 89- *Personal Data:* b Jacksonville, Tex, Apr 7, 43; m 66; c 2. *Educ:* Baylor Univ, BS, 65; Univ Houston, PhD(chem), 70. *Prof Exp:* Appln consult phys sci & comput sci, Univ Glasgow, 72-74; acad staff, Comput Unit, Durham Univ, UK, 74-79; asst prof anal chem, NTex State Univ, 78-79; mem staff, Advan Anal Dept, Collins Commun Systs Div, Rockwell Int, 79-89. *Concurrent Pos:* Sci Res Coun fel chem, Univ Leicester, 70-72; mem, Commun Coord Group, Scottish Regional Comput Org, 72-74; fel, & partic var advan study insts, NATO & Comn Sci & Technol, 73-78; systs programmer & adv nonnumerical appln, Comput Unit, Univ Durham, Eng, 74-; analyst, Commun Proj, NUmbrian Multi-Access Comput Org, UK, 75-78; tutor & counr, Technol Fac, Open Univ, Eng, 76-78; consult, Delta Mgt & Software Systs, 78-79; prin design engr, Mostek; transputer prod mgr, Inmos. *Mem:* Am Chem Soc; Asn Comput Mach; Inst Elec & Electronics Engrs; Brit Comput Soc; Royal Soc Chem. *Res:* Applications of computer systems to problems in chemical analysis; analysis of complex systems; communications, measurement and control systems; simulation; real-time interactive man-machine systems. *Mailing Add:* 616 W Virginia St McKinney TX 75069-4542

**TIBBETTS, CLARK,** VIROLOGY, MOLECULAR GENETICS. *Current Pos:* assoc prof, 82-87, PROF MICROBIOL, SCH MED, VANDERBILT UNIV, 88- *Personal Data:* b Hartford, Conn, Feb 18, 47; m 67, 82; c 4. *Educ:* Amherst Col, BA, 68; Calif Inst Technol, PhD(biophysics), 72. *Prof Exp:* Fel microbiol, Wallenberg Lab, Univ Uppsala, Sweden, 72-74; asst prof, Sch Med, Univ Conn, 74-80, assoc prof, 80-82. *Mem:* Am Soc Biol Chemists; Am Soc Virologists; Am Soc Microbiol; AAAS. *Res:* Structure and function of viral DNA sequences which regulate gene expression; viral DNA encapsidation to transfer novel genes or arrangements of genes to animal cells in culture; large scale automated DNA sequencing technology. *Mailing Add:* Vanderbilt Univ Sch Med 21st Ave S & Garland Nashville TN 37232-0001

**TIBBETTS, GARY GEORGE,** PHYSICS. *Current Pos:* SR RES PHYSICIST, GEN MOTORS RES LABS, 69-, SR STAFF RES SCIENTIST, 85- *Personal Data:* b Omaha, Nebr, Oct 12, 39; m 64; c Margaret, Elizabeth & Katherine. *Educ:* Calif Inst Technol, BS, 61; Univ Ill, Urbana, MS, 63, PhD(physics), 67. *Honors & Awards:* John M Campbell, GM REs Labs, 88; Graffin Lectr, Am Carbon Soc, 90. *Prof Exp:* Ger Res Asn grant, vis scientist, Munich Tech Univ, 67-69. *Mem:* Am Phys Soc; Am Carbon Soc; Mat Res Soc. *Res:* Surface physics; plasma-surface interactions; adsorption of gases on surfaces; electronic and chemical properties of surfaces; carbon fibers; growth of whiskers; inorganic fibers; composite materials. *Mailing Add:* Physics Dept Gen Motors R&D Ctr Warren MI 48090-9055. *Fax:* 810-986-3091; *E-Mail:* gtibbett@dewey.ph.gmr.com

**TIBBETTS, MERRICK SAWYER,** ORGANIC CHEMISTRY. *Current Pos:* RETIRED. *Personal Data:* b Keene, NH, Dec 30, 25; m 50, Elizabeth H Edson; c 4. *Educ:* Univ NH, BS, 48, MS, 51; Stevens Inst Technol, PhD(org chem), 66. *Prof Exp:* Plant chemist, Rubber Div, Eberhard Faber Pencil Co, 51-53; sr chemist, Bendix Corp, 53-62; proj leader synthetic org chem, Int Flavors & Fragrances, 66-69; sr res chemist, Florasynth, Inc, 69-70; sr res scientist, Pepsico Inc, Long Island City, NY, 70-81; asst prof chem, St Joseph's Col, Brooklyn, NY, 86-88. *Concurrent Pos:* Vis prof chem, Monmouth Col, 85-87; adj prof chem, Dept Math & Sci, Pratt Inst, 81-88. *Mem:* Am Chem Soc; Sigma Xi. *Res:* Conformational analysis; organic synthesis; subjective-objective correlation; carbohydrate chemistry. *Mailing Add:* 16 N Cherry Lane Rumson NJ 07760

**TIBBITS, DONALD FAY,** SPEECH PATHOLOGY. *Current Pos:* PROF SPEECH PATH, CENT MO STATE UNIV, WARRENSBURG. *Personal Data:* b May 7, 43; US citizen. *Educ:* Univ Ark, BS, 64, MS, 68; Univ Mo-Columbia, PhD(speech path), 73. *Prof Exp:* Speech pathologist, Pub Schs, Ark, 63-70; teaching asst, Univ Mo-Columbia, 70-73; asst prof, Univ Ark, Fayetteville, 73-76; asst prof commun dis, Univ Tex, Dallas, 76- *Concurrent Pos:* Mem, Coun Except Children. *Mem:* Am Speech & Hearing Asn; Asn Children Learning Disabilities. *Res:* Language acquisition and development in children and adolescents; langauge disabilities in children; gestural communications. *Mailing Add:* Dept Speech Path & Audiol Cent Mo State Univ Warrensburg MO 64093

**TIBBITTS, FORREST DONALD,** embryology; deceased, see previous edition for last biography

**TIBBITTS, THEODORE WILLIAM,** ENVIRONMENTAL PHYSIOLOGY, LIFE SUPPORT IN SPACE. *Current Pos:* From asst prof to assoc prof, 55-71, dir biotron, 87-92, PROF HORT, UNIV WIS-MADISON, 71- *Personal Data:* b Melrose, Wis, Apr 10, 29; m 55, 75, 86, Mary Olmsted; c Scott & Tia A. *Educ:* Univ Wis, BS, 50, MS, 52, PhD(hort, agron), 53. *Honors & Awards:* Marion Meadows Award, Am Soc Hort Sci, 68, fel Award, 79. *Concurrent Pos:* Res engr space biol, NAm Aviation, Inc, Calif, 65-66; bot adv, Manned Space Craft Ctr, Tex, 68-69; mem NASA rev panel, Skylab Biol Exps, 70-71 & Space Shuttle Biol Exp, 78; res leave, Lab Plant Physiol Ond, Neth, 74 & Climate Lab, Dept Sci & Indust Res, NZ, 81; vis scientist, Guelph, Can, 81; assoc ed, Am Soc Hort Sci, 87-90; co-prin investr, Commercialization Ctr Space Automation & Robotics, NASA, 87-, mem, Closed Ecol Life Support Syst, Disciple Working Group, 89-; chmn, CIE TC6-22 Comt Light Terminology Plants. *Mem:* AAAS; fel Am Soc Hort Sci; Am Soc Plant Physiol; Int Soc Hort Sci; Am Inst Biol Sci; Am Soc Gravitation & Space Biol. *Res:* Environmental physiology of vegetable crops; bioregenerative life support systems for space; optimization of growth; air pollution and contaminants in enclosed environments; geophysical environment of plants; standardization in plant growth chambers; physiological breakdowns. *Mailing Add:* 1575 Linden Dr Univ Wis Madison WI 53706. *Fax:* 608-262-4743; *E-Mail:* twt@facstaff.wisc.edu

**TIBBLES, JOHN JAMES,** FISHERIES. *Current Pos:* RETIRED. *Personal Data:* b Toronto, Ont, Mar 16, 24; m 51; c 2. *Educ:* Ont Agr Col, BSA, 51; Univ Wis, MS, PhD(fisheries), 56. *Prof Exp:* Assoc scientist, Fisheries Res Bd Can, Can Dept Fisheries & Oceans, 56-65, dir, Sea Lamprey Control Ctr, Pacific & Freshwater Fisheries, 66-86. *Mem:* Am Fisheries Soc. *Res:* Sea lamprcy control. *Mailing Add:* 72 Bainbridge Sault Ste Marie ON P6C 2H1 Can

**TIBBS, JOHN FRANCISCO,** PROTOZOOLOGY. *Current Pos:* From asst prof to assoc prof zool, 68-77, DIR BIOL STA, UNIV MONT, 70-, PROF ZOOL, 77-, CHMN, ZOOL DEPT. *Personal Data:* b Pacific Grove, Calif, Oct 12, 38; m 66. *Educ:* Fresno State Col, BA, 60; Univ Southern Calif, MS, 64, PhD(biol), 68. *Mem:* AAAS; Soc Protozool. *Res:* Ecology of Arctic and Antarctic protozoans and marine invertebrates; taxonomy of the Phaeodarina; ecology of the Sarcodina. *Mailing Add:* Dept Biol Sci Univ Mont Missoula MT 59812-0001

**TIBBS, NICHOLAS H,** ENVIRONMENTAL GEOLOGY. *Current Pos:* from asst prof to assoc prof, 78-88, PROF GEOL, SOUTHEAST MO STATE UNIV, 88-, CHMN, EARTH SCI DEPT, 85- *Personal Data:* b Windsor, Eng, May 31, 45; US citizen; m 68; c 3. *Educ:* Univ Mo-Rolla, BS, 66, MS, 69, PhD(geol), 72. *Prof Exp:* Res fel environ geol, Univ Mo-Rolla, 72-73; asst prof geol, Paducah Community Col, Univ Ky, 73-75; geologist environ geol, Nuclear Raw Mat Br, Tenn Valley Authority, 75-78. *Mem:* Sigma Xi; Geol Soc Am; Nat Asn Geol Teachers; Am Geophys Union. *Res:* Environmental geology primarily in southeast Missouri. *Mailing Add:* 6345 US Hwy 61 Jackson MO 63755-7147. *Fax:* 573-651-2223

**TICE, DAVID ANTHONY,** THORACIC SURGERY, CARDIOVASCULAR SURGERY. *Current Pos:* res asst, NY Univ, 60-62, from instr to asst prof, 60-67, from asst attend to assoc attend, NY Univ, 60-68, assoc prof, Sch Med, 67-73, PROF SURG, SCH MED, NY UNIV, 73- *Personal Data:* b Brooklyn, NY, Dec 31, 29; m 52, 85; c 4. *Educ:* Columbia Univ, BA, 51; NY Univ, MD, 55; Am Bd Surg, dipl, 61; Bd Thoracic Surg, dipl, 65. *Prof Exp:* Intern, Third Surg Div, Bellevue Hosp, 55-56, asst resident, 56-59; resident, Bellevue Hosp & asst surg, NY Univ, 59-60. *Concurrent Pos:* NY Heart Asn fel, Sch Med, NY Univ, 60-62; asst attend surg, Methodist Hosp Brooklyn, 60-63; from asst vis physician to assoc vis physician, Bellevue Hosp, 60-66, vis physician, 66-; consult cardiovasc surg, NY State Dept Health, 62 & Lutheran Med Ctr, 70; asst med examr, City of New York, 62-73; attend cardiovasc surg, New York Vet Admin Hosp, 63-66, attend thoracic surg, 64-66, chief surg serv, 67-74, chief thoracic & cardiovasc surg, 67-; attend surg, NY Univ Hosp, 68-; mem, Vet Admin Res & Educ Coun, Washington, DC, 72-73. *Mem:* Am Asn Thoracic Surg; fel Am Col Cardiol; fel Am Col Surgeons; Soc Univ Surgeons; Transplantation Soc; Soc Vascular Surg. *Res:* Thoracic and cardiovascular physiology and disease; surgery for acquired heart disease. *Mailing Add:* Dept Surg Va Med Ctr 408 First Ave New York NY 10010

**TICE, LINWOOD FRANKLIN,** PHARMACEUTICAL CHEMISTRY. *Current Pos:* asst prof, Philadelphia Col Pharm, 38-40, dean, 59-75, dir, Sch Pharm, 40-71, asst dean, 41-56, assoc dean, 56-59, prof pharm, 40-75, EMER DEAN, PHILADELPHIA CLL PHARM, 75-; CONSULT, MEDICO-LEGAL, 75- *Personal Data:* b Salem, NJ, Feb 17, 09; m 29, 86; c 2. *Educ:* Philadelphia Col Pharm, BS, 33, MSc, 35; St Louis Col Pharm, DSc, 54. *Honors & Awards:* Remington Honor Medal, Am Pharmaceut Asn, 71. *Prof Exp:* Res fel, Wm R Warner & Co, 31-35; res fel, Edible Mfrs Res Soc, 35-38. *Concurrent Pos:* Res fel, Sharp & Dohme, 38-40; ed, Am J Pharm, 40-77; tech ed, El Farmaceutico, 41-59 & Pharm Int, 47-59; mem revision comt, US Pharmacopoeia, 40-60, bd trustees, 60-70, 70-75; dir, Am Found Pharmaceut Ed, 54-59; mem Am Coun Pharmaceut Ed, 60-66; mem, Philadelphia Med-Pharmaceut Sci, 63- *Mem:* AAAS (vpres, 71-72); Am Chem Soc; Am Pharmaceut Asn (pres elect, 65-66, pres, 66-67); Asn Cols Pharm (pres, 55-56); fel Am Inst Chem. *Res:* Pharmaceuticals; surfactants; proteins; emulsions. *Mailing Add:* Philadelphia Col Pharm & Sci 600 S 43rd St & Kingsessing Ave Philadelphia PA 19104

**TICE, RAYMOND RICHARD,** GENETIC TOXICOLOGY, CYTOGENETICS. *Current Pos:* dir genetic toxicol, 90-92, dir, Environ Health Div, 92-93, VPRES RES & DEVELOP, INTEGRATED LAB SYSTS. *Personal Data:* b Bridgeport, Conn, Jan 22, 47; m 88, Carol A Smith; c Kevin. *Educ:* Univ Calif, San Diego, BA, 69; San Diego State Univ, MS, 72; Johns Hopkins Univ, PhD(human genetics), 76. *Prof Exp:* Res assoc, Brookhaven Nat Lab, 76-78, asst scientist, 78-81, assoc scientist, 81-84, scientist, Dept Med, 85-90. *Concurrent Pos:* Training grant, Dept Med, Brookhaven Nat Lab, 76-78; coordr InVivo Sister Chromatid Exchange Group, WHO. *Mem:* Gene toxicity & Environ Mutagen Soc; Environ Mutagen Soc. *Res:* Examination of mechanisms of cytogenetic manifestations of genotoxic damage in vivo, genetic toxicological evaluation of environmental pollutants; detection of individuals at minimal risk to genotoxic agents; molecular epidemiology. *Mailing Add:* Integrated Lab Systs PO Box 13501 Research Triangle Park NC 27709. *Fax:* 919-544-0380

**TICE, RUSSELL L,** PHYSICAL CHEMISTRY. *Current Pos:* from asst prof to assoc prof, 65-75, PROF CHEM, CALIF POLYTECH STATE UNIV, 75- *Personal Data:* b Parkersburg, WVa, Dec 5, 32; m 56; c 4. *Educ:* Marshall Col, BS, 60; Univ Calif, Los Angeles, PhD(chem), 65. *Prof Exp:* Res asst chem, Univ Calif, Los Angeles, 62-65. *Concurrent Pos:* NSF fel, Ind Univ, 66; vis prof, Purdue Univ, 76-77. *Mem:* Am Chem Soc. *Res:* Investigation of electron-atom and electron-molecule collision cross sections by cyclotron resonance; electron spin resonance of radicals. *Mailing Add:* Chem Dept Calif Polytech State Univ San Luis Obispo CA 93407

**TICE, THOMAS E(ARL),** ELECTRICAL ENGINEERING. *Current Pos:* PROF ELEC ENG & CHMN DEPT, ARIZ STATE UNIV, 67- *Personal Data:* b Florence, Ala, Jan 24, 24; m 49; c 2. *Educ:* Ohio State Univ, BEE, 47, MSc, 48, PhD(elec eng), 51. *Prof Exp:* Asst eng, Marshall Col, 43; asst math, Ohio State Univ, 47, asst elec eng, 47-48, res assoc & proj engr, Antenna Lab, 48-54, dir, 54-61, from asst prof to prof, 52-61; chief engr, Antenna & Microwave Group, Motorola, Inc, 61-67. *Mem:* Fel Inst Elec & Electronics Engrs; Sigma Xi. *Res:* Antennas; electronics; radar; microwave reflection and refraction. *Mailing Add:* 545 N Miller St Mesa AZ 85203-7227

**TICE, THOMAS ROBERT,** CONTROLLED RELEASE, MICROENCAPSULATION. *Current Pos:* res scientist microencapsulation res & develop, 79-82, sect head, 82-84, div head controlled release res & develop, 84-, DIR, PHARM FORMUL, SOUTHERN RES INST, 95- *Personal Data:* b Rochester, NY. *Educ:* Syracuse Univ, BS, 70, PhD(biophy), 75. *Prof Exp:* Postdoctoral res, Univ Ala Birmingham, 75-79. *Concurrent Pos:* Prin investr, NIH & Dept Defense, 82-; lectr, Ctr Prof Advan, 82- & Thomas Alva Edison Sci Found, 84-86; bd gov, Controlled Release Soc, 86-89; NIH, Study Sect, 86-; dir, CRS-APV Joint Workshop, 90. *Mem:* Am Asn Pharmaceut Scientists; Controlled Release Soc. *Res:* Microencapsulation and controlled-release technology as used for pharmaceutical, specialty chemicals, cosmetics, and consumer products; injectable LHRH microspheres to treat prostate and other cancers; author of various publications; granted several patents. *Mailing Add:* Southern Res Inst 2000 Ninth Ave S Birmingham AL 35205

**TICHAUER, ERWIN RUDOLPH,** OCCUPATIONAL HEALTH & BIOMECHANICS. *Current Pos:* res prof, 67-68, prof biomech & dir div, Ctr Safety & Inst Rehab Med, Med Ctr, 68-77, PROF BIOMECH & DIR PROGS ERGONOMICS & BIOMECH, DEPT OCCUP HEALTH & SAFETY, NY UNIV, 77- *Personal Data:* b Berlin, Ger, Apr 27, 18; m 46. *Educ:* Technische Hochschule, dipl, 38; Albertus Univ, ScD(phys sci), 40. *Honors & Awards:* Gilbreth Medal, Soc Advan Mgt; Golden Plate Award; Metrop Life Award, Nat Safety Coun. *Prof Exp:* Dep dir area team 1065, UNRRA, 46-47; engr in-chg trainiing & res, FAMIC Ltda, Chile, 47-50; works mgr design & develop, PMS Pty Ltd, Australia, 50-53; specialist lectr eng, Univ Queensland, 53-56; expert productivity, UN Tech Assistance Admin, 56-59; sr lectr indust eng, Univ New SWales, 60-64; prof, Tex Tech Univ, 64-67. *Concurrent Pos:* Distinguished vis prof, San Marcos Univ, Lima, 58; hon consult, Royal S Sidney Hosp, 60-64; consult, UNICEF, 61, Major Corp, 64- & Waterbury Hosp, Conn, 69-; vis assoc prof, Tex Tech Univ, 63; mem, Australian Coun Rehab of Disabled, 64-; guest lectr, USPHS, 67; chmn subcomt biomech, Comt Z-94, Am Nat Stand Inst, 68-75; Am Soc Mech Engrs rep, US Nat Comt Eng, Med & Biol, Nat Acad Eng-Nat Res Coun, 69-72; mem bd trustees comt, NJ Inst Technol, 69-; chmn biomed eng, NY Acad Med, 71-72; mem comt prosthetics res in Vet Admin, Nat Res Coun, 75-77. *Mem:* Fel NY Acad Sci; fel Royal Soc Health; fel Am Soc Mech Engrs; Am Inst Indust Engrs; Am Soc Eng Educ; Sigma Xi. *Res:* Occupational biomechanics, ergonomics; anatomy; medical education; medical thermography; preventive occupational medicine, safety and traumatology; functional anatomy and physiology applied to design of tasks, tools and equipment for both healthy and disabled workers; work stress on women. *Mailing Add:* 330 E 33 St Apt 12J New York NY 10016

**TICHENOR, ROBERT LAUREN,** PHYSICAL CHEMISTRY. *Current Pos:* RETIRED. *Personal Data:* b Ft Atkinson, Wis, Sept 1, 18; m 43; c 4. *Educ:* Mont State Univ, BS, 39; Harvard Univ, AM, 41, PhD(phys chem), 43. *Prof Exp:* Res chemist, Tenn Eastman Corp, 42-45; sect head, Thomas A Edison, Inc, 45-51; sr res chemist, E I du Pont de Nemours & Co, Inc, 51-85. *Mem:* AAAS; Electrochem Soc. *Res:* Durability of organic polymers to weathering; electrochemistry of alkaline iron and nickel oxide electrodes; development of acrylic textile fibers. *Mailing Add:* 437 Walnut Ave Waynesboro VA 22980

**TICHO, HAROLD KLEIN,** PARTICLE DETECTORS. *Current Pos:* vchancellor acad affairs, 83-89, PROF PHYSICS, UNIV CALIF, SAN DIEGO, 83- *Personal Data:* b Brno, Czech, Dec 21, 21; nat US. *Educ:* Univ Chicago, PhD(physics), 49. *Prof Exp:* Asst, Univ Chicago, 42-48; from asst prof to prof physics, Univ Calif, Los Angeles, 48-83, chmn dept, 67-71, dean, Div Phys Sci, 74-83. *Concurrent Pos:* Guggenheim fel, 66-67, 73-74. *Mem:* Fel Am Phys Soc; Sigma Xi. *Res:* High energy nuclear physics; elementary particles. *Mailing Add:* Dept Physics 0319 Univ Calif San Diego La Jolla CA 92093. *Fax:* 619-534-0173

**TICHY, ROBERT J,** reliability based structural design, total quality education, for more information see previous edition

**TICKLE, ROBERT SIMPSON,** NUCLEAR PHYSICS. *Current Pos:* From instr to assoc prof, 60-68, PROF PHYSICS, UNIV MICH, ANN ARBOR, 68- *Personal Data:* b Norfolk, Va, July 31, 30; m 55, 86; c 1. *Educ:* US Mil Acad, BS, 52; Univ Va, MS, 58, PhD(nuclear physics), 60. *Mem:* Am Phys Soc; Am Asn Physics Teachers. *Res:* Measurement of photonuclear cross sections; accelerator design and development; study of nuclear structure with charged particle experiments; study of reaction mechanisms using heavy ions. *Mailing Add:* 4534 W Liberty Rd Ann Arbor MI 48103

**TICKNOR, LELAND BRUCE,** PHYSICAL CHEMISTRY. *Current Pos:* RETIRED. *Personal Data:* b Centralia, Wash, May 9, 22; m 52, Gail Cowan. *Educ:* Univ Wash, BS, 44; Mass Inst Technol, PhD(phys chem), 50. *Prof Exp:* Mem staff, dept metall, Mass Inst Technol, 50-52; instr chem, Swarthmore Col, 52-54; phys chemist & sect leader, Res & Develop Dept, Viscose Div, FMC Corp, 54-65; sr res chemist, Appl Res Lab, US Steel Corp, 65-68; sr res chemist, BASF Corp, 68-75, group leader, Acrylic Fibers Res Dept, Fibers Div, 75-85; instr chem, William & Mary Col, 85-88. *Mem:* Am Chem Soc. *Res:* Thermodynamics of solutions; retained energies of cold working in metals; cellulose chemistry; cellulose fibers; metal coatings; acrylic fibers. *Mailing Add:* 1202 Pinehurst Rd Staunton VA 24401

**TICKNOR, ROBERT LEWIS,** ORNAMENTAL HORTICULTURE. *Current Pos:* assoc prof, 59-69, PROF HORT, ORE STATE UNIV, 69- *Personal Data:* b Portland, Ore, Oct 26, 26; m 50; c 3. *Educ:* Ore State Univ, BS, 50; Mich State Univ, MS, 51; PhD(pomol), 53. *Honors & Awards:* Gold Medal, Am Rhododendron Soc, 70; Jackson Dawson Gold Medal, Mass Hort Soc, 83; C J Alley Award, Int Plant Propagators Soc, 85. *Prof Exp:* Asst hort, Mich State Univ, 50-53; from asst prof to assoc prof nursery culture, Univ Mass, 53-59. *Mem:* Am Rhododendron Soc (sec-treas, 64-71, pres, 71-73); Weed Sci Soc Am; Int Plant Propagators Soc; Am Hort Soc. *Res:* Chemical weed control; plant nutrition, propagation, breeding and materials. *Mailing Add:* 844 N Holly Canby OR 97013

**TICKU, MAHARAJ K,** PHARMACOLOGY. *Current Pos:* ASST PROF PHARMACOL, UNIV HEALTH SCI CTR, SAN ANTONIO, 78-, ASST PROF PSYCHIAT, 81- *Personal Data:* b India, March 19, 48. *Educ:* Birla Inst Technol & Sci, India, BS, 69; Univ Okla, MS, 72; State Univ NY, Buffalo, PhD(biochem), 76. *Prof Exp:* Teaching asst pharmacol, Univ Okla, 71-72; grad asst, State Univ NY, Buffalo, 72-75; fel, Univ Calif, Riverside, 76-78. *Concurrent Pos:* Res starter grant, Pharmaceut Mfg Asn, 79; travel award, NSF, 81. *Mem:* Am Soc Pharmacol & Exp Therapeut; Soc Neurosci; Europe Brain & Behav Soc; Brit Brain Res Asn; Sigma Xi. *Res:* Molecular pharmacology of synaptic transmission; molecular mechanisms of depressant and convulsant drugs; y-aminobutyic acid synaptic pharmacology; y-aminobutyic acid pharmacology; experimental hypertension; drug receptor studies. *Mailing Add:* Dept Pharmacol Univ Tex Health Sci Ctr 7703 Floyd Curl Dr San Antonio TX 78284-7764

**TIDBALL, CHARLES STANLEY,** INFORMATION RETRIEVAL, DATABASE DEVELOPMENT & RESEARCH IN HIGHER EDUCATION. *Current Pos:* asst res prof, George Washington Univ, 59-63, from assoc prof to prof, 63-65, from actg chmn to chmn dept, 63-71, dir comput assisted educ, 73-78, res prof med, 72-80, Henry D Fry Prof physiol, 65-84, prof educ, Sch Educ, 81-84, prof comput med, 84-92, prof neurol surg, 90-92, EMER PROF COMPUT MED & NEUROL SURG, GEORGE WASHINGTON UNIV, 92- *Personal Data:* b Geneva, Switz, Apr 15, 28; US citizen; m 52, Elizabeth Peters. *Educ:* Wesleyan Univ, BA, 50; Univ Rochester, MS, 52; Univ Wis, PhD(physiol), 55; Univ Chicago, MD, 58. *Hon Degrees:* LHD, Wilson Col, 94. *Prof Exp:* Asst physiol, Univ Wis, 52-55; res asst surg, Univ Chicago, 55-56, asst physiol, 56-58, res asst, 57; intern, Madison Gen Hosp, Wis, 58-59; physician, Mendota State Hosp, 59. *Concurrent Pos:* USPHS fel, 60-61, USPHS res career develop award, 61-63; consult to var hosp, indust, col & govt orgn, 60-; distinguished res scholar, Hood Col, 94-, co-dir, Tidbau Ctr Study Educ Environ, 94-; mgr, Info Syst Prog, Wash Nat Cathedral. *Mem:* Asn Am Univ Prof; emer mem Am Physiol Soc. *Res:* Computer assisted education; medical education; computer literacy; small college database; cathedral art information database. *Mailing Add:* 4100 Cathedral Ave NW Washington DC 20016-3584. *Fax:* 202-363-5704; *E-Mail:* ctidball@gwis2.circ.gwu.edu

**TIDBALL, M ELIZABETH PETERS,** SCIENCE EDUCATION, EDUCATIONAL ENVIRONMENTS. *Current Pos:* assoc physiol, George Washington Univ, 60-62, asst res prof pharmacol, 62-64, assoc res prof physiol, 64-70, res prof, 70-71, prof physiol, 71-94, EMER PROF, GEORGE WASHINGTON UNIV, 94-; DISTINGUISHED RES SCHOLAR & CO-DIR, TIDBALL CTR STUDY EDUC ENVIRON, HOOD COL, 94- *Personal Data:* b Anderson, Ind, Oct 15, 29; m 52, Charles S. *Educ:* Mt Holyoke Col, BA, 51; Univ Wis, MS, 55, PhD(physiol), 59; Wesley Theological Sem, MTS, 90. *Hon Degrees:* ScD, Wilson Col, 73; DSc, Trinity Col, 74, Cedar Crest Col, 77, Univ of the South, 78 & Goucher Col, 79; LHD, Mt Holyoke Col, 76, Skidmore Col, 84, Marymount Col, Tarrytown, 85, Converse Col, 85 & Mt Vernon Col, 86; HHD, St Mary's Col, 77, Hood Col, 82; DLitt, Regis Col, 80, Col St Catherine, 80 & Alverno Col, 89; LLD, St Joseph Col, 83; DSc, St Mary of the Woods Col, 86. *Prof Exp:* Asst physiol, Univ Wis, 52-55, 58-59; asst histochem, Univ Chicago, 55-56, physiol, 56-58; USPHS fel, Nat Heart Inst, 59-61; staff pharmacologist, Hazelton Labs, Inc, 61-62. *Concurrent Pos:* Shattuck fel, 55-56; Mary E Woolley fel, Mt Holyoke Col, 58-59; postdoctoral fel, USPHS, 59-61; consult, Hazelton Labs, Inc, 62-63; assoc sci coordr, Food & Drug Admin, Sci Assocs Training Prog, 66-67; consult, Food & Drug Admin, 66-68; trustee, Mt Holyoke Col, 68-73, vchmn, 72-73, trustee fel, 88-; nat adv comt, NIH training progs & fels, Nat Acad Sci, 72-75; exec secy, 74-75, vchmn, 77-82, NAS-Nat Res Coun comn on human resources in comt educ & employment of women in sci & eng; consult, inst res, Wellesley Col, 74-75 & Woodrow Wilson Nat Fel Found, 74-; chmn task force on women, Am Physiol Soc, 73-80; consult & chmn rev panels, NSF, 74-; trustee, 79-85, chmn bd, 83-85, scholar in residence, Col Preachers, 89; mem gov bd, exec comt, Washington Cathedral Found, 83-85; Lucie Stern distinguished vis trustee prof natural sci, Mills Col, 80; nat panelist, Am Coun Educ, 83-90; assoc res, Nat Resource Ctr, Girls Clubs Am, 83-; consult ed, J Higher Educ, 84-; distinguished scholar in residence, Southern Methodist Univ, 85, Salem Col, 85, Wesley Theol Sem, 92-93; founder & dir, Summer Sem for Women, 87-95. *Mem:* AAAS; Am Physiol Soc; Am Asn Higher Educ; Sigma Xi. *Res:* Environments for the education of women in science, engineering and medicine; institutional research; science literacy; human resources development. *Mailing Add:* 4100 Cathedral Ave NW Washington DC 20016. *Fax:* 202-363-5703

**TIDMAN, DEREK ALBERT,** PLASMA MASS LAUNCH TECHNOLOGY. *Current Pos:* PRES, SLINGATRON TECH INC, 95- *Personal Data:* b London, Eng, Oct 18, 30; US citizen; m 59; c 2. *Educ:* London Univ, BSc, 52, PhD(physics), 56. *Prof Exp:* Res fel cosmic radiation, Sydney Univ, Australia, 56-57; asst prof plasma physics, Fermi Inst, Univ Chicago, 57-60; res assoc prof, Inst Phys Sci & Technol, Univ Md, 61-64, res prof, 64-80; pres, GT-Devices, Subsid Gen Dynamics, 80-95. *Concurrent Pos:* Consult, Goddard Space Flight Ctr, NASA, 61-69 & Lawrence Livermore Lab, 77-80; vis scientist, Harvard Col Observ, 66; mem, Assoc Eval Comt, Nat Acad Sci, 66-69; assoc ed, Physics Fluids, 70-72 & J Math Physics, 72-74; prin investr, GT-Devices, Subsid Gen Dynamics, 89- *Mem:* Fel Am Phys Soc; Inst Elec & Electronics Engrs. *Res:* Plasma-driven mass launchers including both electrothermal and electromagnetic launchers; plasma physics generally including kinetic theory, turbulence, shock waves, instabilities, and applications to space physics and thermonuclear plasmas; co-author of three books and over 80 journal publications; granted ten US patents. *Mailing Add:* 6801 Benjamin St McLean VA 22101. *Fax:* 703-642-9146

**TIDMORE, F EUGENE,** ANALYSIS, LINEAR OPTIMIZATION. *Current Pos:* assoc prof, 71-79, PROF MATH, BAYLOR UNIV, 80- *Personal Data:* b Ballinger, Tex, Oct 1, 40. *Educ:* Okla State Univ, PhD(math), 68. *Prof Exp:* Asst prof math, Tex Tech, 67-71. *Mailing Add:* Dept Math Baylor Univ Waco TX 76798-0001

**TIDOR, BRUCE,** MOLECULAR RECOGNITION, RATIONAL DESIGN. *Current Pos:* ASST PROF, MASS INST TECHNOL, 94- *Educ:* Harvard Univ, AB, 83, PhD(biophysics), 90; Univ Oxford, MSc, 85. *Prof Exp:* Whitehead fel, Whitehead Inst Biomed Res, 90-94. *Res:* Biophysical chemistry; molecular recognition and stability of biopolymers; continuum electrostatic and molecular dynamics simulation methodology; protein-nucleic acid interactions; rational molecular design. *Mailing Add:* Dept Chem Mass Inst Technol Cambridge MA 02139-4307

**TIDWELL, EUGENE DELBERT,** INSTRUMENTATION, OPTICS. *Current Pos:* GEN ENGR HIGH ENDOATMOSPHERIC INTERCEPTOR, US ARMY STRATEGIC DEFENSE COMMAND, 85- *Personal Data:* b Lehi, Utah, Sept 5, 26; m 48, Leah Call; c Michael, Thomas, Anthony, Julia, Christopher, David, Bruce & Marietta. *Educ:* Brigham Young Univ, BS, 51. *Prof Exp:* Asst gas chemist copper smelt, Kennecott Copper Corp, 44-45 & 47-52; staff physicist spectros, Nat Bur Standards, 52-63; staff engr instrumentation, Aro, Inc, 63-85. *Concurrent Pos:* Prog mgr flying optical platform, Infrared Instrumentation Syst. *Res:* Theoretical spectral analysis of light gases; environmental erosion research for aeroballistics and space engineering; missile boost and reentry phases infrared and visible signature data research. *Mailing Add:* 13002 Astalot Dr SE Huntsville AL 35803

**TIDWELL, THOMAS TINSLEY,** ORGANIC REACTION MECHANISMS, SYNTHETIC METHODS. *Current Pos:* assoc prof, Scarborough Col, Univ Toronto, 72-77, assoc dean, 79-82, actg chmn phys sci, 88-89, assoc chmn chem, 91-93, PROF CHEM, UNIV TORONTO, 77- *Personal Data:* b Atlanta, Ga, Feb 20, 39; m 71, Sarah Huddleston. *Educ:* Ga Inst Technol, BS, 60; Harvard Univ, AM, 63, PhD(reaction mechanisms), 64. *Honors & Awards:* Lemieux Award, Can Soc Chem. *Prof Exp:* NIH fel, Univ Calif, San Diego, 64-65; asst prof chem, Univ SC, 65-72. *Concurrent Pos:* Vis prof, Stanford Univ, 79; Nato fel, Turkey, 81-82, France, 85-86, Italy, 88-92,

Romania, 93-94; vis fel, Syntex Corp, 82-83; Nat Acad Sci fel, Bulgaria, 83, USSR, 89; Nat Sci & Eng Res Coun fel, Italy, 88; fel, Japan Soc Prom Sci, 89; mem, Comn Phys Org Chem, Int Union Pure & Appl Chem, 92-93, chair, 94- *Mem:* Am Chem Soc; fel Chem Inst Can; fel AAAS. *Res:* Steric strain; peroxides; enolates; carbonium ions; ketenes; fluorocarbons; oil from wood; organic conductors; radiochemistry. *Mailing Add:* Dept Chem Univ Toronto Toronto ON M5S 3H6 Can. *Fax:* 416-287-7204; *E-Mail:* tidwell@scar.utoronto.ca

**TIDWELL, WILLIAM LEE,** MICROBIOLOGY. *Current Pos:* asst prof biol, San Jose State Univ, 55-58, assoc prof bact, 58-62, chmn, Microbiol Area, 78-82, chmn, Dept Biol Sci, 83-85, prof, 62-88, EMER PROF MICROBIOL, SAN JOSE STATE UNIV, 88- *Personal Data:* b Greenville, SC, Jan 14, 26; m 46, Louise Van Hollebeke; c Paul L. *Educ:* Univ SC, BS, 45; Univ Hawaii, MS, 48; Univ Calif, Los Angeles, PhD(microbiol), 51. *Prof Exp:* Asst bact, Univ Hawaii, 46-48 & Univ Calif, Los Angeles, 48-51; asst prof biol, Agr & Mech Col, Tex, 51-55, asst res bact, Eng Exp Sta, 52-55. *Concurrent Pos:* Consult, State Col Affairs, Calif State Employees Asn, 66-68; vpres, Calif Fac Asn, 81-85. *Mem:* Am Soc Microbiol; NY Acad Sci; Sigma Xi; Nat Parks Conserv Asn. *Res:* General bacteriology; water and sewage bacteriology. *Mailing Add:* 40649 Crystal Dr Three Rivers CA 93271-9736

**TIECKELMANN, HOWARD,** BIO-ORGANIC CHEMISTRY. *Current Pos:* from instr to prof, 46-61, chmn dept, 70-74, DISTINGUISHED TEACHING PROF CHEM, STATE UNIV NY, BUFFALO, 75- *Personal Data:* b Chicago, Ill, Oct 29, 16; m 42; c 5. *Educ:* Carthage Col, BA, 42; Univ Buffalo, PhD(org chem), 48. *Prof Exp:* Chemist, Armour Res Found, Ill, 46. *Concurrent Pos:* Lectr, Inst Teknologi Mara, Malaysia, 88-91. *Mem:* AAAS; Royal Soc Chem; Am Inst Chemists; Am Chem Soc. *Res:* Heterocyclic compounds; pyridines; pyrimidines, alkylations and rearrangements; natural products. *Mailing Add:* 59 Chaumont Dr Williamsville NY 14221-3509

**TIEDCKE, CARL HEINRICH WILHELM,** chemistry, toxicology; deceased, see previous edition for last biography

**TIEDEMANN, ALBERT WILLIAM, JR,** QUALITY ASSURANCE. *Current Pos:* RETIRED. *Personal Data:* b Baltimore, Md, Nov 7, 24; m 53, Mary T Sellmayer; c Marie, Donna, Albert W III & David. *Educ:* Loyola Col, Md, BS, 47; NY Univ, MS, 49; Georgetown Univ, PhD(chem), 58. *Prof Exp:* Instr chem, Mt St Agnes Col, 50-55; sr res chemist, Emerson Drug Co, 55-56, chief chemist, Emerson Drug Co Div, Warner-Lambert Pharmaceut Co, 56-60; supvr anal group, Allegany Ballistic Lab, Hercules, Inc, 61-68, supt tech serv, Radford Army Ammunition Plant, 68-72; dir, Consol Labs, Commonwealth, Va, 72-92. *Concurrent Pos:* Mem drinking water lab working group, US Environ Protection Agency, 76-77 & 86-88; chmn, Sci & Technol Comt, Asn Food & Drug Officials, 82-85, secy-treas, 85-87; lectr, Lab Qual Assurance, Asn Off Anal Chemists, 84-87, bd dirs, 86-90; exec bd, Cent Atlantic States Asn Food & Drug Officials, 77-84, vpres, 81-82, pres, 82-83; consult, 92- *Mem:* Am Soc Qual Control; fel Am Inst Chemists; Asn Food & Drug Officials (secy-treas, 85-87); Asn Official Anal Chemists; Anal Lab Mgr Asn. *Res:* Development of analytical methods. *Mailing Add:* 10511 Cherokee Rd Richmond VA 23235-1008

**TIEDEMANN, HERMAN HENRY,** electrochemistry, petrochemicals; deceased, see previous edition for last biography

**TIEDEMANN, WILLIAM HAROLD,** ELECTROCHEMICAL ENGINEERING. *Current Pos:* assoc dir res, 79-85, DIR CHEM & MAT RES, JOHNSON CONTROLS, INC, 85-, VPRES ADVAN BATTERY RES, 91- *Personal Data:* b June 3, 43; c 3. *Educ:* Univ Calif, Los Angeles, BS, 66, MS, 68, PhD(electro chem eng), 71. *Prof Exp:* Sr electrochemist, Globe Union, Inc, 71-76, mgr electrochem res, 76-79. *Mem:* Electrochem Soc. *Res:* Theoretical mathematical modeling; experimental investigations of a variety of electrochemical systems; system simulation and scale-up. *Mailing Add:* 5757 N Green Bay Ave Milwaukee WI 53201

**TIEDERMAN, WILLIAM GREGG, JR,** MECHANICAL ENGINEERING, FLUID MECHANICS. *Current Pos:* CHMN, DEPT MECH ENG, UNIV FLA, 93- *Personal Data:* b Tulsa, Okla, Jan 29, 38; m 63; c 3. *Educ:* Stanford Univ, BS, 60, MS, 61, PhD(mech eng), 65. *Prof Exp:* Engr, Shell Develop Co, 65-68; from asst prof to prof mech eng, Okla State Univ, 68-78; prof mech eng, Purdue Univ, West Lafayette, 78-93, asst dean eng, 89-93. *Mem:* Am Soc Mech Engrs; Am Phys Soc; Sigma Xi; Am Inst Aeronaut & Astronaut. *Res:* Turbulence; viscous fluid mechanics; laser velocimetry; solid-liquid and liquid-liquid separation; drag reduction. *Mailing Add:* Dept Mech Eng Univ Fla PO Box 116300 Gainesville FL 32611-6300

**TIEDJE, J THOMAS,** CONDENSED MATTER PHYSICS, OPTOELECTRONICS. *Current Pos:* assoc prof, 87-89, PROF, DEPT PHYSICS & ASTRON, UNIV BC, 89-, DEPT ELEC & COMPUT ENG & DIR, ADVAN MAT & PROCESS ENG LAB. *Personal Data:* b Sarnia, Ont, Feb 11, 51; m 77, Glenna; c 3. *Educ:* Univ Toronto, BASc, 73; Univ BC, MSc, 75, PhD(solid state physics), 77. *Honors & Awards:* Herzberg Prize, Can Asn Physicists, 89. *Prof Exp:* From res physicist to group head, Corp Res Lab, Exxon Res & Eng Co, Annandale, NJ, 77-87. *Concurrent Pos:* Steacie fel, Natural Sci & Eng Res Coun, 90-92; mem, Asn Prof Engrs BC. *Mem:* Can Asn Physicists; fel Am Phys Soc. *Res:* Molecular beam epitaxy growth of III-V semiconductor materials and optoelectronic devices; scanning tunneling microscopy studies of surfaces in UHV; synchrotron radiation studies of surfaces. *Mailing Add:* Advan Mat & Processing Eng Lab Univ BC 2355 E Mall Vancouver BC V6T 1Z4 Can. *Fax:* 604-822-4750

**TIEDJE, JAMES MICHAEL,** MICROBIAL ECOLOGY, SOIL MICROBIOLOGY. *Current Pos:* From asst prof to assoc prof, 68-78, PROF MICROBIAL ECOL, MICH STATE UNIV, 78-; DIR, SCI & TECHNOL CTR MICROBIAL ECOL, NSF, 88- *Personal Data:* b Newton, Iowa, Feb 9, 42; m 65; c 3. *Educ:* Iowa State Univ, BS, 64; Cornell Univ, MS, 66, PhD(soil microbiol), 68. *Honors & Awards:* Res Award, Soil Sci Soc Am. *Concurrent Pos:* Eli Lilly career develop grant, 74; vis assoc prof, Univ Ga, 74-75; ed, Appl Microbiol, 74-, ed in chief, 80-; consult, NSF, 74-77; vis prof, Univ Calif, Berkeley, 81-82; Sigma Xi jr res award, 81; mem, Biotech Sci Adv Comt, GPA, 86-89, chair, Sci Adv Panel, GPA, 88-90; fel Int Inst Biotechnol. *Mem:* Am Soc Microbiol; fel Am Soc Agron; Soil Sci Soc Am; fel AAAS; Sigma Xi; Ecol Soc Am. *Res:* Denitrification; microbial metabolism of organic pollutants; molecular microbiol ecology. *Mailing Add:* Dept Crop & Soil Sci Mich State Univ East Lansing MI 48824

**TIEFEL, RALPH MAURICE,** BOTANY. *Current Pos:* RETIRED. *Personal Data:* b Brazil, Ind, Sept 3, 28; m 66. *Educ:* Cent Mo State Col, BS, 53; Univ Mo, MA, 55, PhD(bot), 57. *Prof Exp:* From assoc prof to prof biol, Carthage Col, 57-95. *Mem:* Soc Econ Bot; Torrey Bot Club. *Res:* Soil and plant relationships; meristems; history of science. *Mailing Add:* PO Box 208 Waterford WI 53185

**TIEFENTHAL, HARLAN E,** organic chemistry; deceased, see previous edition for last biography

**TIEH, THOMAS TA-PIN,** MINERALOGY. *Current Pos:* asst prof, 66-71, assoc prof, 71-81, PROF GEOL, TEX A&M UNIV, 81- *Personal Data:* b Peking, China, May 2, 34; US citizen; m 62; c 4. *Educ:* Univ Ill, Urbana, BS, 58; Stanford Univ, MS, 60, PhD(geol), 65. *Prof Exp:* Geologist, Bear Creek Mining Co, 60; res assoc geol, Univ Hawaii, 62-63; asst cur mining & petrol, Stanford Univ, 65-66. *Concurrent Pos:* Welch Found grant, Tex A&M Univ, 69-72. *Mem:* Brit Mineral Soc; Soc Econ Paleontologists & Mineralogists. *Res:* Petrology and geochemistry. *Mailing Add:* Geol Tex A&M Univ College Station TX 77843-0100

**TIELEMAN, HENRY WILLIAM,** FLUID MECHANICS. *Current Pos:* Asst prof eng mech, 69-72, from assoc prof to prof, 72-96, EMER PROF ENG SCI & MECH, VA POLYTECH INST & STATE UNIV, 97- *Personal Data:* b Rotterdam, Neth, May 26, 33; Can citizen; m 62; c 2. *Educ:* Ont Agr Col, BSA, 61; Univ Toronto, BAS, 62; Univ Iowa, MS, 64; Colo State Univ, PhD(civil eng), 69. *Mem:* Am Soc Mech Engrs; Sigma Xi. *Res:* Fluid mechanics; turbulent boundary layers; theory of turbulence; turbulence measurements. *Mailing Add:* PO Box 109 Riner VA 24149

**TIEMAN, SUZANNAH BLISS,** DEVELOPMENTAL NEUROBIOLOGY, VISION. *Current Pos:* res assoc, 77-90, SR RES ASSOC, NEUROBIOL RES CTR, STATE UNIV NY, ALBANY, 90- *Personal Data:* b Washington, DC, Oct 10, 43; m 69, David G. *Educ:* Cornell Univ, AB, 65; Stanford Univ, PhD(psychol), 74. *Prof Exp:* Nat Eye Inst fel, Dept Anat, Univ Calif Med Ctr, San Francisco, 74-77. *Concurrent Pos:* From adj asst prof biol to adj assoc prof, State Univ NY, Albany, 77-87, res assoc prof, 87-90, res prof, 90-; prin investr, Nat Eye Inst res grant, 79-83; NSF res grants, 83-86, 88-92, 92-97; assoc prof biomed sci, State Univ NY, Albany, 88-95, prof, 95- *Mem:* Am Asn Anatomists; Asn Res Vision & Ophthal; AAAS; Soc Neurosci; Asn Women in Sci. *Res:* Structure and function of the visual system; anatomical and behavioral effects of restricted early visual experience; neural development; visual neurotransmitters. *Mailing Add:* Neurobiol Res Ctr State Univ NY 1400 Washington Ave Albany NY 12222. *Fax:* 518-442-4767; *E-Mail:* tieman@albany.edu

**TIEMANN, JEROME J,** APPLIED MATHEMATICS, SOLID STATE PHYSICS. *Current Pos:* PHYSICIST, RES & DEVELOP CTR, GEN ELEC CO, 57- *Personal Data:* b Yonkers, NY, Feb 21, 32; m 57. *Educ:* Mass Inst Technol, ScB, 53; Stanford Univ, PhD(physics), 60. *Prof Exp:* Asst, Stanford Univ, 53-55 & 56-57. *Concurrent Pos:* Consult, Radiation Lab, Univ Calif, 55-57; Coolidge fel, Gen Elec Corp Res & Develop Ctr. *Mem:* Nat Acad Eng; fel Inst Elec & Electronics Engrs. *Res:* Quantum mechanics; electronics; solid state electronic device phenomena; electronic circuit and system design; signal processing circuit and system design. *Mailing Add:* Gen Elec Co MS KWC 1307 PO Box 8 Schenectady NY 12301

**TIEMEIER, DAVID CHARLES,** PHARMACEUTICAL LICENSING & BUSINESS DEVELOPMENT, NEW TECHNOLOGY RESEARCH & DEVELOPMENT. *Current Pos:* SR DIR LICENSING, G D SEARLE CO, 92- *Personal Data:* b Cincinnati, Ohio, Feb 18, 47; m 72, Shawn Murata; c Brian, Tracy & Kelly. *Educ:* Univ Notre Dame, BS, 69; Univ Calif, Berkeley, PhD(biochem), 75. *Prof Exp:* Fel Res, Inst Child Health & Human Develop, 73-77; asst prof, Univ Calif, Irvine, 77-80; fel & sr fel, Monsanto, 80-87; sr dir, Immunoinflammatory & Infectious Dis, L D Searle, 87-92. *Concurrent Pos:* Mem adv bd, Searle/Monsanto Res Prog, Univ Wash, 82-92, Fogarty Int Ctr, NIH, 90-92. *Mem:* AAAS; Am Soc Biochem & Molecular Biol; Licensing Exec Soc. *Res:* Organization of mammalian genes and the control of their expression; development and application of animal cell vector systems and bacterial gene cloning systems; control of immunoinflammatory and infectious diseases. *Mailing Add:* 5200 Old Orchard Rd Skokie IL 60077. *E-Mail:* dctiem@searle.monsanto.com

**TIEN, C(HANG) L(IN),** HEAT TRANSFER, HEAT RADIATION. *Current Pos:* Actg asst prof mech eng, Univ Calif, Berkeley, 59-60, from asst prof to assoc prof, 60-68, chmn, Thermal Systs Div, 69-71, Dept Mech Eng, 74-81, vchancellor res, 83-85, chancellor, 90-97, PROF MECH ENG, UNIV CALIF, BERKELEY, 68-, A MARTIN BERLIN PROF, 87-88 & 90-, CHANCELLOR, 90- *Personal Data:* b Wuhan, China, July 24, 35; nat US; m 59, Di-Hwa Liu; c Norman C, Phyllis C & Christine C. *Educ:* Nat Taiwan Univ, BS, 55; Univ Louisville, MME, 57; Princeton Univ, MA & PhD(mech eng), 59. *Hon Degrees:* Dr, Univ Louisville, 91, Univ Notre Dame, 92, Hong Kong Univ Sci & Technol, 93, Univ Conn, 94, Univ Waterloo, 95, Univ Ill, 95, Ohio State Univ, 96, Hong Kong Baptist Univ, 96 & Ariz State Univ, 96. *Honors & Awards:* Heat Transfer Mem Award, Am Soc Mech Engrs, 74, Gustus L Larson Mem Award, 75 & Max Jakob Mem Award, 81; Thermophysics Award, Am Inst Aeronaut & Astronaut, 77; US Sci Award, Alexander von Humboldt Found, 79; Prince Distinguished Lectr, Ariz State Univ, 83; Hawkins Mem Lectr, Purdue Univ, 87; Most Distinguished Chinese Scholar, Soc Hong Kong Scholars, 89; Woodruff Distinguished lectr, Ga Inst Technol, 92; Li Ka Shing Distinguished Lectr, Univ Hong Kong, 94; Gordon Wu Distinguished Lectr, Princeton Univ, 95; Martin Martel Lectr, Brown Univ, 96. *Concurrent Pos:* Consult, Lockheed Missile & Space Co, 63-80 & Gen Elec Co, 72-80; Guggenheim fel, 65-; res assoc prof, Miller Inst Basic Res Sci, Univ Calif, 67-68; assoc ed, J Quant Spectros & Radiative Transfer, 71-; sr US scientist fel, Japan Soc Prom Sci, 80; chmn, exec comt, Int Ctr Heat & Mass Transfer, 80-82, Am Soc Mech Engrs Heat Transfer Div, 80-81; hon res prof, Inst Thermophys, Chinese Acad Sci, 81-; vis Viola D Hank chair prof, Univ Notre Dame, 83; distinguished lectr, Am Soc Mech Engrs, 87-89; mem, Int Affairs Adv Comt, Nat Acad Eng, 87-90 & Mech Eng Peer Comt, 87-90, chair, 88-90; bd dir, AAAS, 92-; Nat Adv Coun, Am Soc Eng Educ, 93-; chmn, Int Adv Panel, Univ Tokyo, Inst Indust Sci, 95; bd trustees, US Comt Econ Develop, 94. *Mem:* Fel Nat Acad Sci; Nat Acad Eng; fel Am Inst Aeronaut & Astronaut; hon mem Am Soc Mech Engrs; fel AAAS; fel Am Acad Arts & Sci; Chinese Acad Sci. *Res:* Heat transfer; radiative heat transfer; thermal insulation and enclosure convection; reactor safety heat transfer; microscale thermal phenomena. *Mailing Add:* Univ Calif Off Chancellor 200 California Hall No 1500 Berkeley CA 94720

**TIEN, CHI,** CHEMICAL ENGINEERING. *Current Pos:* assoc prof, 63-66, PROF CHEM ENG, SYRACUSE UNIV, 66-, CHMN, DEPT CHEM ENG & MAT SCI, 70- *Personal Data:* b Peking, China, Oct 8, 30; US citizen; m 60; c 2. *Educ:* Nat Taiwan Univ, BSc, 52; Kans State Univ, MSc, 54; Northwestern Univ, Evanston, PhD(chem eng), 58. *Prof Exp:* Asst prof chem eng, Univ Tulsa, 57-59; from asst prof to assoc prof, Univ Windsor, 59-63. *Concurrent Pos:* Expert, US Army Cold Regions Res & Eng Lab, Hanover, NH, 59-64 & 69- *Mem:* AAAS; Am Inst Chem Engrs; Chem Inst Can. *Res:* Advanced treatment of waste water, especially by filtration and adsorption; heat transfer with phase change. *Mailing Add:* 318 Roe Ave Syracuse NY 13210

**TIEN, H TI,** BIOPHYSICS, MEMBRANES. *Current Pos:* PROF BIOPHYS & CHMN DEPT, MICH STATE UNIV, 66- *Personal Data:* b Peking, China, Feb 1, 28; US citizen; m, Angelica Leitmannova; c 4. *Educ:* Univ Nebr, BS, 53; Temple Univ, MA, 60, PhD(chem), 63. *Prof Exp:* Proj engr, Allied Chem Corp, 56-57; med scientist, Eastern Pa Psychiat Inst, 57-63; assoc prof chem, Northeastern Univ, 63-66. *Concurrent Pos:* Grants, Res Corp, 64-65, NIH, 64-, Off Saline Water, US Dept Interior, 68-71, Dept Energy, 80-82, NSF, USAR, USAID & Off Naval Res; hon prof, Academia Sinica. *Mem:* AAAS; Am Chem Soc; Biophys Soc. *Res:* Physical chemical investigations of membranes, particularly bilayer lipid membranes; photosynthesis and vision; solar energy conversion; specific electrodes; ion-exchange equilibria; bilayer lipid membranes as models of biological membranes; biomolecular electronics devices. *Mailing Add:* Dept Physiol Mich State Univ East Lansing MI 48824. *Fax:* 517-355-5125; *E-Mail:* tien@psl.msu.edu

**TIEN, JAMES SHAW-TZUU,** COMBUSTION, PROPULSION. *Current Pos:* Res assoc, 70-71, from asst prof to assoc prof, 71-82, PROF ENG, CASE WESTERN RES UNIV, 82- *Personal Data:* b China, Mar 8, 42; m 67; c 2. *Educ:* Nat Taiwan Univ, BS, 63; Purdue Univ, Lafayette, MS, 66; Princeton Univ, PhD(aeronaut & mech eng), 71. *Mem:* Combustion Inst; Am Inst Aeronaut & Astronaut; Am Soc Mech Engrs. *Res:* Combustion and chemically-reacting flows; propulsion and fire research. *Mailing Add:* 434 Leverett Lane Cleveland OH 44143-3722

**TIEN, MING,** ENZYMOLOGY. *Current Pos:* from asst prof to assoc prof, 85-93, PROF BIOCHEM, PA STATE UNIV, 93- *Personal Data:* b Taipei, Taiwan, Oct 6, 53; US citizen; m, Mary L Balatti; c Leland M. *Educ:* Univ Mich, BA, 75; Mich State Univ, PhD(biochem), 82. *Honors & Awards:* Presidential Young Investr, NSF, 87. *Prof Exp:* Res chemist, Forest Prods Lab, 83-85. *Mem:* Am Soc Biochem & Molecular Biol; Am Chem Soc. *Res:* Biochemical mechanism of fungal lignin degradation. *Mailing Add:* Dept Molecular & Cell Biol 303 Althouse Lab Pa State Univ University Park PA 16802-4503. *Fax:* 814-863-8616; *E-Mail:* mxt3@psuvm.psu.edu

**TIEN, P(ING) K(ING),** MICROWAVE TECHNOLOGY, HIGH SPEED ELECTRONICS. *Current Pos:* mem tech staff, Bell Tel Labs, Inc, 52-59, head, Dept Electron Physics Res, 59-84, head, Dept High Speed Electronics, 85-91, FEL, PHOTONICS RES LAB, BELL TEL LABS, INC, 91- *Personal Data:* b China, Aug 2, 19; m 52, Nancy N Chen; c 2. *Educ:* Nat Cent Univ, China, BS, 42; Stanford Univ, MS, 48, PhD, 51. *Honors & Awards:* Monis N Lieberman Award, Inst Elec & Electronics Engrs, 79. *Prof Exp:* Res assoc, Stanford Univ, 51-52. *Concurrent Pos:* Ed-in-chief, Int J High Speed Electronics. *Mem:* Nat Acad Sci; Nat Acad Eng; Am Inst Physics; fel Inst Elec & Electronics Engrs; fel Optical Soc Am. *Res:* Device physics; microwave electronics; electron dynamics; wave propagation; noise; ferrites; acoustics in solids; gas lasers; superconductivity; integrated optics. *Mailing Add:* Bell Tel Labs Inc Holmdel NJ 07733. *Fax:* 732-949-8988; *E-Mail:* prt@bell-labs.com

**TIEN, REX YUAN,** ORGANIC CHEMISTRY. *Current Pos:* SR CHEMIST, AM HOECHST CORP, 68- *Personal Data:* b Hupei, China, Aug 4, 35; c 3. *Educ:* Chung Hsing Univ, Taiwan, BS, 58; Univ RI, PhD(chem), 68. *Prof Exp:* NSF fel chem, State Univ NY Albany, 67-68. *Mem:* Am Chem Soc. *Res:* Applied chemistry, dyes and pigments; photochemistry; organometallic chemistry, kinetics and instrumentation. *Mailing Add:* 129 Sturbridge Dr Warwick RI 02886-8630

**TIEN, TSENG-YING,** CERAMICS. *Current Pos:* assoc prof, 66-73, PROF MAT, UNIV MICH, ANN ARBOR, 73- *Personal Data:* b Hopei, China, June 28, 24; US citizen; m 48, Chin-Kai Chang; c 5. *Educ:* Pa State Univ, MS, 60, PhD(ceramics), 65. *Hon Degrees:* DSc, Swiss Fed Inst Technol, Zurich, 92. *Prof Exp:* Sr scientist, Westinghouse Res Labs, 60-66. *Mem:* Fel Am Ceramic Soc. *Res:* Structure and physical properties of solid ceramics materials. *Mailing Add:* Dept Mat Sci & Eng Univ Mich N Campus Ann Arbor MI 48109

**TIER, CHARLES,** ASYMPTOTIC METHODS, QUEUEING THEORY. *Current Pos:* PROF MATH, UNIV ILL, CHICAGO, 76- *Personal Data:* b Albany, NY, Sept 25, 47; m 74; c 2. *Educ:* Rensselaer Polytech Inst, BS, 69, MS, 71; NY Univ, PhD(appl math), 76. *Prof Exp:* Instr math, NY Univ, 72-76. *Concurrent Pos:* Vis asst prof, Northwestern Univ, 81-82, res fel, 83-84. *Mem:* Soc Indust & Appl Math; AAAS; Asn Comput Mach. *Res:* Application of applied mathematics methods to analysis of stochastic models arising in queueing systems; biological models; chemical systems. *Mailing Add:* 1635 Linden Ave Highland Park IL 60035

**TIERNAN, ROBERT JOSEPH,** PHYSICS, CERAMICS. *Current Pos:* ENGR/SCIENTIST ADVAN RES & DEVELOP, GTE/SYLVANIA, 76- *Personal Data:* b Boston, Mass, Dec 14, 35; m 59; c 4. *Educ:* Boston Col, AB, 57, MS, 59; Mass Inst Technol, PhD(ceramics), 69. *Prof Exp:* Res asst accelerators, Grad Sch, Boston Col, 57-59; solid state physicist, Naval Res Lab, 59-62; atomic physicist, Nat Bur Stand, 63; develop engr, Sylvania, 63-64; AEC res asst, Grad Sch, Mass Inst Technol, 64-69; sr res scientist, Raytheon Co, Waltham, 69-74. *Concurrent Pos:* Res assoc, Argonne Nat Lab, 75. *Mem:* Am Ceramic Soc; Int Soc Optical Engrs; Sigma Xi. *Res:* Solid state physics; electronic, optical and magnetic properties of ceramics; diffusion in ceramics; mechanical properties; sodium reaction in HID lamps; emissivity of alumina; thermal shock of alumina. *Mailing Add:* 224 North St Stoneham MA 02180-2143

**TIERNAN, THOMAS ORVILLE,** ANALYTICAL & ENVIRONMENTAL CHEMISTRY, CHEMICAL PHYSICS. *Current Pos:* dir, Brehm Lab, 76-87, PROF CHEM, WRIGHT STATE UNIV, 75-, DIR, TOXIC CONTAMINANT RES PROG, 87- *Personal Data:* b Chattanooga, Tenn, July 22, 36; m 61, Marlene Gerstner; c Margaret Ann (Reidy). *Educ:* Univ Windsor, BSc, 58; Carnegie Inst Technol, MS, 60, PhD(chem), 66. *Prof Exp:* Ohio State Univ Res Found res chemist, Wright-Patterson AFB, 60-61, res chemist, Off Aeronaut Space Res, Aerospace Labs, 61-67, group leader high energy chem kinetics, 67-75. *Concurrent Pos:* Extensive consulting on environ issues; pres, Anal Innovations, Inc, Dayton, OH, 92- *Mem:* Am Soc Mass Spectrometry; Am Chem Soc; Am Phys Soc; Am Soc Lubrication Engrs; fel Am Inst Chemists. *Res:* Mass spectrometry; gas phase kinetics; ion and electron impact-phenomena; plasma characterization and diagnostics; lasers; gaseous electronics; analytical methods development; environmental monitoring, materials characterization; environmental reservation technology. *Mailing Add:* 6532 Senator Lane Dayton OH 45459. *Fax:* 937-775-3807

**TIERNEY, DONALD FRANK,** PHYSIOLOGY, MEDICINE. *Current Pos:* assoc prof, 68-75, PROF MED, UNIV CALIF, LOS ANGELES, 75- *Personal Data:* b Butte, Mont, May 24, 31; m 54; c 2. *Educ:* Univ Calif, Berkeley, BA, 53; Univ Calif, San Francisco, MD, 56. *Prof Exp:* Intern, Philadelphia Gen Hosp, 57; asst resident, Univ Pa, 58; asst resident, Univ Calif, San Francisco, 59, asst prof physiol, 65-68. *Concurrent Pos:* USPHS fels, Univ Calif, San Francisco, 59-65; mem, Pulmonary Dis Adv Comt, Nat Heart & Lung Inst, 73-76; chief, Palmonary Div, Univ Calif, Los Angeles Hosp; chmn Study Sect, Pediat Specialized Ctr Res, Nat Heart Lung & Blood Inst, NIH, 80-81; mem, Pulmonary Dis Adv Comt, NHLB, 74-78, appl physiol study sect, NIH, 87-91. *Mem:* Am Physiol Soc; Am Thoracic Soc (vpres, 76-77, pres, 78-79); Am Soc Clin Invest; Asn Am Physicians. *Res:* Pulmonary physiology, biochemistry and metabolism. *Mailing Add:* Dept Med Pulmonary Univ Calif-Los Angeles Los Angeles CA 90095-1690

**TIERNEY, JOHN W(ILLIAM),** CHEMICAL ENGINEERING, SEPARATION SYSTEMS. *Current Pos:* assoc prof, 60-62, PROF CHEM ENG, UNIV PITTSBURGH, 62- *Personal Data:* b Oak Park, Ill, Dec 29, 23. *Educ:* Purdue Univ, BS, 47; Univ Mich, MS, 48; Northwestern Univ, PhD(chem eng), 51. *Prof Exp:* Res engr, Pure Oil Co, 48-50, 51-54; asst prof chem eng, Purdue Univ, 54-56; dept mgr, Res Div, Univac Div, Sperry Rand Corp, 56-60. *Concurrent Pos:* Lectr, Univ Minn, 58-59; vis prof, Santa Maria Univ, Chile, 60-62; Fulbright lectr, Univ Barcelona, 68-69. *Res:* Application of computer techniques to chemical engineering; reaction engineering; distillation; direct and indirect coal liquefaction. *Mailing Add:* 1330 Sheridan Ave Pittsburgh PA 15206-1760

**TIERNEY, WILLIAM JOHN,** TOXICOLOGY, PHARMACOLOGY. *Current Pos:* PRES, TIERNEY & ASSOCS, 89- *Personal Data:* b New York, NY, Aug 17, 44; m 77; c 2. *Educ:* Columbia Univ, BS, 68; St John's Univ, MS, 74, PhD(pharmacol), 77; Am Bd Toxicol, dipl, 81. *Prof Exp:* Toxicologist, Bio/Dynamics, Inc, 77-80, asst dir toxicol, 80-84, dir res, 84-89. *Concurrent*

*Pos:* Asst prof, St John's Univ, 80-82. *Mem:* Soc Toxicol; Europ Soc Toxicol; Am Col Toxicol; Int Soc Study Xenobiotics. *Res:* Preclinical safety evaluations of foods, drugs, chemicals, pesticides and cosmetics. *Mailing Add:* 687 County Rd 579 Pittstown NJ 08867

**TIERNO, PHILIP M, JR,** CLINICAL MICROBIOLOGY. *Current Pos:* asst dir, Goldwater Mem Hosp, 70-75, dir, 75-81, DIR MICROBIOL, TISCH-UNIV HOSP, NEW YORK UNIV MED CTR, 81- *Personal Data:* b Brooklyn, NY, June 5, 43; m 67, Josephine Martine; c Alexandra & Meredith. *Educ:* Brooklyn Col Pharm-Long Island Univ, BS, 65; New York Univ, MS, 74, PhD(microbiol), 77. *Prof Exp:* Clin microbiologist, Lutheran Med Ctr, 65-66; chief res microbiologist, US Vet Admin Hosp, 66-70. *Concurrent Pos:* Asst prof microbiol, City Univ New York, 74-76 & Bloomfield Col Sch Nursing, 75-82; consult microbiologist, Maimonides Med Ctr, 70-79; assoc prof microbiol & path, New York Univ Sch Med, 81-; co-founder & chmn bd, Found Sci Res Pub Interest, 85- *Mem:* Am Acad Microbiol; Am Soc Microbiol; AAAS; Am Pub Health Asn; Am Asn Univ Prof. *Res:* Clinical application of enzymic reactions to microorganisms especially as they relate to indentifications and typing systems; microbial ecology and epidemiology; role of staphylococci in human health and disease; toxic shock syndrome; acquired immune deficiency syndrome. *Mailing Add:* 30 Carter St Norwood NJ 07648

**TIERS, GEORGE VAN DYKE,** ORGANIC MATERIALS SCIENCE, ORGANIC FLUORINE CHEMISTRY. *Current Pos:* chemist, 51-65, CORP SCIENTIST, CORP RES LABS, 3M CO, 65- *Personal Data:* b Chicago, Ill, Mar 23, 27; m 50, Jane E Hanafin; c Jerrold S. *Educ:* Univ Chicago, SB, 46, SM, 50, PhD(chem), 56. *Honors & Awards:* Carbide Award, Am Chem Soc, 59. *Prof Exp:* Asst pharmacol, Univ Chicago, 45-46, chemist, Ord Res Proj, 48-49. *Mem:* Am Chem Soc; NAm Thermal Anal Soc. *Res:* Nuclear magnetic resonance spectroscopy; fluorine, dye, organic, polymer and physical-organic chemistry; duplicating and imaging technology; non-linear-optical materials; materials science of organic compounds; differential scanning calorimetry; coatings and surface treatments. *Mailing Add:* 3M Sci Res Lab 201-2S-14 PO Box 33221 St Paul MN 55133-3221. *Fax:* 612-733-0648

**TIERSTEN, HARRY FRANK,** APPLIED MECHANICS. *Current Pos:* PROF MECH, RENSSELAER POLYTECH INST, 68- *Personal Data:* b Brooklyn, NY, Jan 4, 30; m 53; c 2. *Educ:* Columbia Univ, BS, 52, MS, 56, PhD(appl mech), 61. *Prof Exp:* Stress analyst, Grumman Aircraft Eng Corp, 52-53; struct designer, J G White Eng Corp, 53-56; instr civil eng, City Col New York, 56-60; res asst appl mech, Columbia Univ, 60-61; mem tech staff, Bell Tel Labs, 61-68. *Mem:* Am Phys Soc; Acoust Soc Am; Am Soc Mech Engrs; Soc Natural Philos; Inst Elec & Electronics Engr; Sigma Xi. *Res:* Elasticity, couple stress elasticity; electromagnetism; electrostriction; piezoelectricity; magnetism; magnetoelasticity; waves; vibrations. *Mailing Add:* 2288 Pinehaven Dr Schenectady NY 12309-2607

**TIERSTEN, MARTIN STUART,** PHYSICS. *Current Pos:* Tutor physics, 57-62, from instr to assoc prof, 62-83, PROF PHYSICS, CITY COL NEW YORK, 83- *Personal Data:* b Aug 7, 31; US citizen; m 53; c 2. *Educ:* Queens Col, NY, BA, 53; Columbia Univ, AM, 58, PhD(theoret solid state physics), 62. *Mem:* Am Phys Soc; Am Asn Physics Teachers. *Res:* Theoretical physics. *Mailing Add:* Dept Physics City Col New York Convent at 138th St New York NY 10031

**TIESZEN, LARRY L,** PLANT PHYSIOLOGY, PLANT ECOLOGY. *Current Pos:* from asst prof to assoc prof, 66-75, PROF BIOL, AUGUSTANA COL, SDAK, 75-, CHMN DEPT, 77- *Personal Data:* b Marion, SDak, Mar 2, 40; m 59; c 2. *Educ:* Augustana Col, SDak, BA, 61; Univ Colo, PhD(bot), 65. *Prof Exp:* Kettering fel biol, Albion Col, 65-66; asst prof, Univ Minn, Duluth, 66. *Concurrent Pos:* Res grants, Sigma Xi, 65-67, Arctic Inst NAm, 66-68 & NSF, 70-82; NSF vis prof, Univ Nairobi, Kenya, 75; prog assoc, NSF, 78-79; Fulbright fel, Univ Nairobi, 82; consult, Int Agencies. *Mem:* AAAS; Am Soc Plant Physiol; Ecol Soc Am; Arctic Inst NAm; Can Soc Plant Physiol. *Res:* Photosynthesis and pigments in arctic and alpine grasses; environmental influence of photosynthesis; growth under extreme conditions; physiological adaptation; United States tundra biome program; photosynthesis and water stress in finger millet and other tropical grasses; C3 and C4 photosynthesis; stable isotope ecology; tropical ecology; paleoecology; agroforestry. *Mailing Add:* Dept Biol Augustana Col 2001 S Summit Ave Sioux Falls SD 57197-0001

**TIETHOF, JACK ALAN,** INORGANIC CHEMISTRY, SURFACE SCIENCE. *Current Pos:* proj leader prod develop, 74-78, group leader new bus res, 78-81, GROUP LEADER CATALYST RES, ENGELHARD MINERALS & CHEM CORP, 81- *Personal Data:* b Grand Rapids, Mich, July 23, 43; div; c 3. *Educ:* Western Mich Univ, BS, 67, PhD(inorg chem), 71. *Prof Exp:* Res assoc inorg chem, Ohio State Univ, 71-73, lectr gen chem, 73-74. *Concurrent Pos:* Nat Defense Educ Act fel, Western Mich Univ, 67-70; fel, Grad Sch, Ohio State Univ, 71-72. *Mem:* Am Chem Soc; Clay Mineral Soc. *Res:* Development of new catalysts for petroleum refining, particularly in fluidized bed cracking reforming catalysts; material research include zeolites and supported precious metals. *Mailing Add:* Englehard Ctr Tech Inc 6489 Calle Real Goleta CA 93117

**TIETJEN, JAMES JOSEPH,** PHYSICAL CHEMISTRY. *Current Pos:* Mem tech staff mat sci, 63-69, group head, 69-70, Dir Mat Res, RCA Labs, 70-77, STAFF VPRES, MAT & COMPONENTS RES, RCA CORP, 77- *Personal Data:* b New York, NY, Mar 29, 33; m 58; c 2. *Educ:* Iona Col, BS, 56; Pa State Univ, MS, 58, PhD(chem), 63. *Honors & Awards:* David Sarnoff

Outstanding Achievement Awards, 67 & 70. *Concurrent Pos:* Assoc ed, Mat Res Bull, 71; mem Solid State Sci Adv Panel, Nat Acad Sci, 73-; mem, NASA Space Systs & Technol Adv Comt, 78- *Mem:* Am Chem Soc; Am Inst Mining Metall & Petrol Engrs; Electrochem Soc; Sigma Xi. *Res:* Displays, semiconductor materials and devices; insulators; metallic systems; optical phenomena; electron optics; negative electron affinity effects; luminescent materials; videodisc systems. *Mailing Add:* 3 De Hart Dr Belle Mead NJ 08502-5419

**TIETJEN, JOHN H,** MARINE BIOLOGY, INVERTEBRATE ZOOLOGY. *Current Pos:* from asst prof to assoc prof, 66-75, PROF BIOL, CITY COL NEW YORK, 75-; RES ASSOC, AM MUS NATURAL HIST, 92- *Personal Data:* b Jamaica, NY, June 19, 40; m 68, Theresa Martin; c Theresa & Mary. *Educ:* City Col New York, BS, 61; Univ RI, PhD(oceanog), 66. *Prof Exp:* Dir, Inst Marine & Atomspheric Sci, City Univ New York, 78-89. *Concurrent Pos:* Consult, Northeast Utilities, 68-, SW Res Inst, 78-79, other pvt & govt consult; res grants, NSF, 68-88, Nat Oceanic & Atmospheric Admin, 73-82, Off Naval Res, 80-82 & Brookhaven Nat Lab, 84-86; chmn biol, City Col New York, 81-87; vis scientist, Aust Inst Marine Sci, 87-88; res grants, Nat Acad Sci/Nat Res Coun, 96, Earthwatch, 95-96. *Mem:* Int Asn Meiobenthologist; Sigma Xi. *Res:* Estuarine ecology; physiological ecology of meiofauna; ecology; pollution ecology of benthos. *Mailing Add:* Dept Biol City Col New York New York NY 10031. *Fax:* 212-650-8585; *E-Mail:* jhtcc@cunyvm.cuny.edu

**TIETJEN, WILLIAM LEIGHTON,** AQUATIC ECOLOGY. *Current Pos:* from asst prof to assoc prof, 67-78, PROF & CHMN BIOL DEPT, GA SOUTHWESTERN COL, 78- *Personal Data:* b Americus, Ga, Jan 3, 37; m 68, Mildred Campbell; c William C. *Educ:* Univ Ga, BS, 58; Univ Tenn, PhD(radiation biol), 67. *Prof Exp:* Res asst marine biol, Marine Inst, Univ Ga, 60. *Concurrent Pos:* Actg dean, Sch Arts & Scis, Southwestern Col, 96-97. *Mem:* AAAS; Am Inst Biol Sci; Am Soc Limnol & Oceanog; Ecol Soc Am; Entom Soc Am; NAm Beuthological Soc. *Res:* Arthropod metabolism and energy flow; environmental effects on physiology of arthropods; wetland ecology; nutrient flux in streams and lakes. *Mailing Add:* Dept Biol Ga Southwestern State Univ Americus GA 31709. *Fax:* 912-931-2734; *E-Mail:* wtietjen@gsw1500.gsw.peachnet.edu

**TIETZ, NORBERT W,** CLINICAL CHEMISTRY. *Current Pos:* DIR CLIN CHEM, UNIV KY MED CTR & PROF PATH, COL MED, 76- *Personal Data:* b Stettin, Ger, Nov 13, 26; US citizen; m 59; c 4. *Educ:* Stuttgart Tech Univ, PhD(natural sci), 50. *Honors & Awards:* Clin Chemist Award, Am Asn Clin Chemists, 71, Award Outstanding Efforts Educ & Training, 76, Steuben Bowl Award, 78, Bernard F Gerulat Award, 88, Donald D Van Slyke Award, 89, Award Outstanding Contrib Clin Chem, 89. *Prof Exp:* Res fel biochem, Univ Munich, 51-54; res fel clin chem, Rockford Mem Hosp, 54-55 & Univ Chicago, 55-56; head div biochem, Reid Mem Hosp, Richmond, Ind, 56-59; assoc path, Chicago Med Sch-Univ Health Sci, 59-64, from asst prof to assoc prof clin path, 64-69, prof clin chem, 69-76. *Concurrent Pos:* Dir clin chem, Mt Sinai Hosp Med Ctr, 59-76; consult, Dept Health, State of Ill, 67-76, Vet Admin Hosp, Hines, Ill, 74-76 & Bet Admin Hosp Lexington, Ky, 76- *Mem:* Fel AAAS; Am Asn Clin Chem; Am Chem Soc; Am Soc Clin Path; fel Am Inst Chemists; Sigma Xi; Acad Clin Lab Physicians & Scientists. *Res:* Methodology related to clinical chemistry; enzyme chemistry; writing and editing in clinical chemistry. *Mailing Add:* Dept Path & Clin Chem Vet Admin Med Ctr Lab SCVS 9113 3350 La Jolla Village Dr San Diego CA 92161

**TIETZ, THOMAS E(DWIN),** physical metallurgy; deceased, see previous edition for last biography

**TIETZ, WILLIAM JOHN, JR,** NEUROPHYSIOLOGY, ANIMAL-HUMAN DISEASE EPIZOOLOGY. *Current Pos:* prof vet specialties & pres, 77-90, EMER PRES, MONT STATE UNIV, 90- *Personal Data:* b Chicago, Ill, Mar 6, 27; div; c Karyn E, William J III & Julia W (Samuel). *Educ:* Swarthmore Col, BA, 50; Univ Wis, MS, 52; Colo State Univ, DVM, 57; Purdue Univ, PhD(physiol), 61. *Hon Degrees:* DSc, Purdue Univ, 82. *Prof Exp:* Instr physiol, Purdue Univ, 57-59, from instr to assoc prof physiol, 59-64; sect leader, Collab Radiol Health Lab, Colo State Univ, 64-67, assoc prof physiol & biophys, Univ, 64-67, chmn dept & prof physiol & biophys, 67-70, vpres student-univ rels, relations, 70-71, prof physiol & biophys, 67-77, dean, Col Vet Med & Biomed Sci, 71-77; pub serv fel, Va Polytech Univ, 91; vpres & chief operating officer, Deaconess Res Inst, Billings Mont, 92-95. *Concurrent Pos:* Trustee, Yellowstone Asn, 81-, chmn, 87-; mem, Mont Sci & Technol Alliance, 85-88; mem, Gov Trade Comn, 85 & 90; steering comt, Wild Trout Dis Lab. *Mem:* Am Physiol Soc; Am Vet Med Asn; Conf Res Workers Animal Dis. *Res:* Radiation biology; veterinary neurophysiology and neurosurgery; effects of ionizing radiation on early embryogenesis; development of nantavirus; development of wild trout research. *Mailing Add:* 10030 Happy Acres Bozeman MT 59718. *Fax:* 406-586-3023

**TIETZE, FRANK,** BIOCHEMISTRY. *Current Pos:* RETIRED. *Personal Data:* b Manila, Philippines, Aug 19, 24; nat US; m 54; c 4. *Educ:* Trinity Col, Conn, BS, 45; Northwestern Univ, MS, 47, PhD(biochem), 49. *Prof Exp:* USPHS fel, Duke Univ, 49-50; USPHS fel, Univ Wash, 50-51, instr biochem, 51-52; instr, Univ Pa, 52-56; res biochemist, Nat Inst Diabetes & Digestive & Kidney Dis, 56-94. *Res:* Inherited disorders of lysosomal transport. *Mailing Add:* 17404 Park Mill Dr Derwood MD 20855

**TIFFANY, CHARLES F,** ENGINEERING. *Current Pos:* RETIRED. *Personal Data:* b Aitkin, Minn, Nov 23, 29; m 52; c 3. *Educ:* Univ Minn, BCE & BS, 52. *Honors & Awards:* Spirit of St Louis Aeronaut Award, Am Soc Mech Engrs, 93. *Prof Exp:* Spec tech adv, airframe & propulsion syst struct, aeronaut systs div, USAF, 72-79; vpres res & eng, Boeing Mil Airplane Co, 79-84, advan systs, 84-87, exec vpres prog & technol, 87-90. *Mem:* Nat Acad Eng; fel Am Inst Aeronaut & Astronaut; Am Defense Preparedness Asn; Unmanned Vehicle Soc. *Mailing Add:* 4160 E Via Del Cuculin Tucson AZ 85718. *Fax:* 520-299-6514; *E-Mail:* ctiffany@aol.com

**TIFFANY, LOIS HATTERY,** PLANT PATHOLOGY, MYCOLOGY. *Current Pos:* From instr to assoc prof, Iowa State Univ, 50-65, prof bot, 65-94, chmn dept, 92-96, DISTINGUISHED PROF, IOWA STATE UNIV, 94- *Personal Data:* b Collins, Iowa, Mar 8, 24; m 45; c Ray, Jean & David. *Educ:* Iowa State Univ, BS, 45, MS, 47, PhD, 50. *Honors & Awards:* William H Weston Award, Mycol Soc Am, 80. *Mem:* Am Phytopath Soc; Mycol Soc Am; Bot Soc Am; Sigma Xi. *Res:* Soil fungi and parasitic fungi of prairie plants; ascomycetes. *Mailing Add:* Dept Bot Iowa State Univ Ames IA 50011. *Fax:* 515-294-1337

**TIFFANY, OTHO LYLE,** PHYSICS. *Current Pos:* CONSULT, 80- *Personal Data:* b Flint, Mich, Nov 26, 19; m 42; c 5. *Educ:* Univ Mich, BS, 43, MS, 46, PhD(physics), 50. *Prof Exp:* Mem staff, Radiation Lab, Mass Inst Technol, 43-45; res engr, Willow Run Res Ctr, Mich, 49-58; chief scientist, Aerospace Systs Div, Bendix Corp, 58-70, dir space & earth sci, 70-80. *Mem:* Am Phys Soc; Am Geophys Union; Inst Elec & Electronics Engrs. *Res:* Space sciences, geophysics, oceanography, environmental research. *Mailing Add:* 1828 Vinewood Blvd Ann Arbor MI 48104

**TIFFNEY, BRUCE HAYNES,** PLANT EVOLUTION, PALEOBIOLOGY. *Current Pos:* ASSOC PROF GEOL, DEPT GEOL SCI, UNIV CALIF, 86- *Personal Data:* b Sharon, Mass, July 3, 49. *Educ:* Boston Univ, BA, 71; Harvard Univ, PhD(biol), 77. *Prof Exp:* Assoc prof paleobiol, dept biol, Yale Univ, 77-86. *Concurrent Pos:* Cur Herbarium, Paleobotanical Collections, Peabody Mus Natural Hist, 77-86. *Mem:* Bot Soc Am; fel Geol Soc Am; Int Asn Plant Taxonomists; Soc Study Evolution; Asn Trop Biol; Soc Syst Zool. *Res:* The fossil record and evolution of angiosperms with emphasis on the study of their fossilized fruiting remains; patterns and processes involved in the evolution of land plants as a group. *Mailing Add:* Dept Geol Sci Univ Calif 552 University Ave Santa Barbara CA 93106-0002

**TIFFT, WILLIAM GRANT,** GALAXIES, COSMOLOGY. *Current Pos:* assoc prof, 64-73, PROF ASTRON, UNIV ARIZ, 73- *Personal Data:* b Derby, Conn, Apr 5, 32; m 65; Janet A Lindner Homewood; c William J, Jennifer G, Amy K (Sloan), Hollis R Homewood, Susan F (Burke) & Patricia A (Byer). *Educ:* Harvard Univ, AB, 54; Calif Inst Technol, PhD, 58. *Prof Exp:* Hon res fel astron, Australian Nat Univ, 58-60; res assoc astron & physics, Vanderbilt Univ, 60-61; astronr, Lowell Observ, 61-64. *Concurrent Pos:* NSF fel, 58-60, grant, 84-87; vis scientist, Inst Astron, Bologna, Italy, 78-79, Max-Planck Inst Radioastron, Bonn, Ger, 87, Nat Radio Astron Observ, Green Bank, WVa, 88, 96-97. *Mem:* Am Astron Soc; Int Astron Union. *Res:* Optical stellar astronomy; galactic structure and extragalactic problems; interpretation of the redshift in galaxies; pairs and clusters of galaxies; precision of 21 cm redshifts; large scale structure, superclusters; large scale gravitation; nature and structure of time. *Mailing Add:* Dept Astron Univ Ariz Tucson AZ 85721. *Fax:* 520-621-1532; *E-Mail:* wtifft@as.arizona.edu

**TIGCHELAAR, EDWARD CLARENCE,** vegetable crops, plant breeding; deceased, see previous edition for last biography

**TIGCHELAAR, PETER VERNON,** PHYSIOLOGY. *Current Pos:* assoc prof, 75-79, PROF BIOL, CALVIN COL, 79- *Personal Data:* b Chicago, Ill, May 15, 41; m 63; c 2. *Educ:* Calvin Col, AB, 63; Univ Ill, Urbana, MS, 66, PhD(physiol), 69. *Prof Exp:* NIH fel endocrinol, Univ Ill, 70-71; asst prof physiol, Sch Med, Ind Univ-Purdue Univ, Indianapolis, 71-75. *Concurrent Pos:* NIH fel endocrinol, 69-70. *Mem:* AAAS; Endocrine Soc; Am Physiol Soc. *Res:* Mammalian reproductive physiology; synthesis, control and effects of mammalian gonadotrophic hormones. *Mailing Add:* Dept Biol Calvin Col 3201 Burton St SE Grand Rapids MI 49546-4349

**TIGER, LIONEL,** BIOLOGICAL ANTHROPOLOGY, SOCIAL STRUCTURE. *Current Pos:* assoc prof anthrop, Livingston Col, Rutgers Univ, 68-70, assoc prof, fac grad studies & dir grad progs, 70-72, prof anthrop, 72-90, CHARLES DARWIN PROF ANTHROP, GRAD SCH, RUTGERS UNIV, 90- *Personal Data:* b Montreal, Que, Feb 5, 37; c 3. *Educ:* McGill Univ, BA, 57, MA, 59; London Sch Econ, PhD(polit sociol), 63. *Prof Exp:* Asst prof sociol, Univ BC, 63-68. *Concurrent Pos:* Can Coun spec award soc sci & Nat Res Coun Assoc Comt Exp Psychol, 66-67; Can Coun-Killam bequest & Guggenheim fel, 68; co-sr investr human aggress, Guggenheim Found, 72-, consult & res dir, 72-84. *Mem:* Am Sociol Asn; Can Sociol & Anthrop Asn; Asn Study Animal Behav; Royal Anthrop Inst Gt Brit & Ireland; Am Anthrop Asn. *Res:* Human evolution; nature and expression of sex differences; male groups; theoretical implications of biosociological research; evolution of ethics and the industrial system; the anthropology of gender and of male behavior. *Mailing Add:* Anthrop Dept Rutgers Univ New Brunswick NJ 08903

**TIGERTT, WILLIAM DAVID,** pathology; deceased, see previous edition for last biography

**TIGGES, JOHANNES,** NEUROANATOMY. *Current Pos:* neuroanatomist, Yerkes Regional Primate Res Ctr, 66-71, sr neuroanatomist, 71-79, from asst prof to assoc prof, 67-78, PROF ANAT, EMORY UNIV, 78-, PROF, DEPT OPHTHAL, 81-, RES PROF & CHIEF, DIV NEUROBIOL, YERKES REGIONAL PRIMATE RES CTR, 79- *Personal Data:* b Rietberg, Ger, July 7, 31; m 59; c 2. *Educ:* Univ Munster, PhD(zool), 61. *Prof Exp:* Res assoc neuroanat, Max Planck Inst Brain Res, 61-62; res assoc vision in primates, Yerkes Primate Labs, Fla, 62-63; res assoc neuroanat & physiol, Max Planck Inst Brain Res, 63-65. *Mem:* Asn Am Anatomists; Int Primatological Soc; Soc Neurosci; Asn Res Vision & Opthal; Am Soc Primatologists; Int Brain Res Orgn; Cajal Club. *Res:* Light and electron microscopy of primate visual system; anatomical correlates of aging in primate brain. *Mailing Add:* Yerkes Regional Primate Res Ctr Emory Univ Atlanta GA 30322

**TIGNER, JAMES ROBERT,** WILDLIFE BIOLOGY. *Current Pos:* ENVIRON IMPACT STUDY TEAM LEADER, BUR LAND MGT, DEPT INTERIOR, 81- *Personal Data:* b El Paso, Tex, June 17, 36; m 57; c 2. *Educ:* Colo State Univ, BS, 58, MS, 60; Univ Colo, PhD(biol), 72. *Prof Exp:* Wildlife biologist, US Fish & Wildlife Serv, 60-61, proj leader, 62-70, sta leader animal damage control res, 73-81. *Mem:* Wildlife Soc; Sigma Xi. *Res:* Animal damage control, especially coyote. *Mailing Add:* 104 E Kendrick St Rawlins WY 82301

**TIGNER, MAURY,** HIGH ENERGY PHYSICS. *Current Pos:* Res assoc, 63-68, sr res assoc physics, 68-77, PROF PHYSICS & MEM STAFF, LAB ATOMIC & SOLID STATE PHYSICS, CORNELL UNIV, 77- *Personal Data:* b Middletown, NY, Apr 22, 37; m 60; c 2. *Educ:* Rensselaer Polytech Inst, BS, 58; Cornell Univ, PhD(physics), 63. *Mem:* Nat Acad Sci; Am Vacuum Soc; Am Phys Soc; Am Acad Arts & Sci. *Res:* Design and development of new particle accelerators and improvement of existing designs. *Mailing Add:* Lab Nuclear Studies Cornell Univ Ithaca NY 10021. *E-Mail:* tiger@ins62.ins.cornell.edu

**TIHANSKY, DIANE RICE,** THEORY, SOFTWARE SYSTEMS. *Current Pos:* ENGR COMPUT SYSTS, ELECTRONIC DATA SYSTS, 89- *Personal Data:* b Kansas City, Mo, Feb 20, 48; div; c 2. *Educ:* Marygrove Col, Detroit, Mich, BS, 69; Harvard Univ, MS, 72. *Prof Exp:* Programmer-analyst, City Alexandria, Va, 72 & US Dept Treas, 72-74; instr comput sci & math, Fla Int Univ, Miami, 77-78; instr, St Mary's Col, Orchard Lake, Mich, 83-84, chmn, Dept Math & Comput Sci, 84-89. *Mem:* Math Asn Am; Am Math Soc. *Res:* Mathematics and computer anxiety; computer-assisted instruction for bilingual education and language learning. *Mailing Add:* 266 Woodside Ct Rochester Hills MI 48307

**TIHEN, JOSEPH ANTON,** ZOOLOGY. *Current Pos:* from asst prof to prof, 61-87, EMER PROF BIOL, UNIV NOTRE DAME, 87- *Personal Data:* b Harper, Kans, Nov 20, 18; m 40; c 7. *Educ:* Univ Kans, AB, 40; Univ Rochester, PhD(zool), 45. *Prof Exp:* Asst instr zool, Univ Kans, 40-41; asst instr, Univ Rochester, 41-44, res assoc mouse genetics unit, Manhattan Proj, 44-46; asst prof zool, Tulane Univ, 46-47; asst prof, Univ Fla, 50-57, res assoc, AEC Proj, Sch Med, 57-58; asst prof zool, Univ Ill, 58-61. *Mem:* Am Soc Zool; Soc Study Amphibians & Reptiles; Soc Vert Paleont; Am Soc Ichthyologists & Herpetologists; Sigma Xi. *Res:* Systematics, Cenozoic paleontology and phylogeny of reptiles and amphibians. *Mailing Add:* 13290 Medinah Circle W Ft Myers FL 33907

**TIHON, CLAUDE,** pathobiology, biochemistry, for more information see previous edition

**TIKOO, MOHAN L,** EXTENSION THEORY, DYNAMICAL SYSTEMS. *Current Pos:* from asst prof to assoc prof, 84-93, PROF MATH, SE MO STATE UNIV, CAPE GIRADEAU, 93- *Personal Data:* b Sringagar, Kashmir, India, Feb 15, 43; m 69; Jai Kishuri; c Sonia T. *Educ:* Univ Kashmir, BA, 60, MA, 63; Univ Kans, MA, 81, PhD(math), 84. *Honors & Awards:* Florence Black Award, Univ Kans, 82. *Prof Exp:* Asst prof math, Univ Kashmir, 66-78; asst instr, Univ Kans, 78-84. *Concurrent Pos:* Reviewer, Math Rev; reviewer, Zentralblatt Math; May Lanois fel, Univ Kans, 81. *Mem:* Am Math Soc; Math Asn Am; Planetary Soc; Nat Geog Soc; Int Platform Soc. *Res:* Topology; functional analysis; zeros of polynomials. *Mailing Add:* Dept Math SE Mo State Univ Cape Girardeau MO 63701. *Fax:* 573-651-2223; *E-Mail:* cg93scm@semovm.semo.edu

**TIKSON, MICHAEL,** MATHEMATICS. *Current Pos:* RETIRED. *Personal Data:* b Campbell, Ohio, Nov 22, 24; m 57; c 4. *Educ:* Youngstown Univ, BS, 48; Lehigh Univ, MA, 49; Mass Inst Technol, MS, 56. *Prof Exp:* Instr math, Lehigh Univ, 49-50; guest worker, Nat Bur Stand, DC, 51-52; sr mathematician, Wright Air Develop Div, USAF, Res & Develop Command, 52-56, chief, Anal Sect, Digital Comput Br, 56-58, br chief, 58-60; consult & head, Digital Comput Ctr, Battelle Mem Inst, 60-66, assoc mgr, Systs & Electronics Dept, Columbus Labs, 66-70, mgr comput systs & applications, 70-74, mgr, Comput & Info Systs Dept, 74-88. *Mem:* Simulation Coun; Asn Comput Mach. *Res:* Management of research and operations in computer and information systems. *Mailing Add:* 845 Lookout Point Dr Columbus OH 43235

**TIKU, MOTI,** RHEUMATOLOGY & IMMUNOLOGY. *Current Pos:* ASST PROF RHEUMATOLOGY, DIV RHEUMATOLOGY, UNIV ILL IIOSP, CHICAGO. *Res:* Hematology. *Mailing Add:* Dept Med & Dent NJ-R W Johnson Med Sch 1 Robert Johnson Pl CN-19 New Brunswick NJ 08903-0019. *Fax:* 732-418-8238

**TILBROOK, BRONTE DAVID,** OCEANOGRAPHY. *Current Pos:* RES SCIENTIST, COMMONWEALTH SCI & INDUST RES MARINE LABS, 90-; FEL, COOP RES CTR ANTARCTIC & S OCEAN EQUIP, 93- *Personal Data:* b Minlanton, Australia, July 6, 55; m 93, Tracey M Lincoln. *Educ:* Univ Hawaii, MS, 82, PhD, 92. *Concurrent Pos:* Newcomb Cleveland Prize, AAAS, 91. *Mem:* Am Geophys Union; Am Soc Limnol & Oceanog; Geochem Soc. *Mailing Add:* Commonwealth Sci & Indust Res 8 B Trumpeter St Battery Point Tas 7004 Australia

**TILBURY, ROY SIDNEY,** RADIOCHEMISTRY, BIOPHYSICS. *Current Pos:* PROF CHEM, NUCLEAR MED, UNIV TEX SYST CANCER CTR, HOUSTON, 81- *Personal Data:* b Ealing, Eng, Aug 7, 32; US citizen; m 61; c 2. *Educ:* Univ London, BSc, 55; McGill Univ, PhD(radiochem), 63. *Prof Exp:* Asst exp officer chem, UK Atomic Energy Res Estab, 55-59; res scientist, Union Carbide Corp, 63-67; assoc biophys, Mem Sloan-Ketterring Cancer Ctr, 67-74, assoc mem, 74-81. *Concurrent Pos:* Asst prof biophys, Grad Sch Med Sci, Cornell Univ, 67-74, assoc prof, 74-81; adj prof med chem, Col Pharm, Univ Ky, 78-88; assoc ed, J Nuclear Med, 85-89. *Mem:* Am Chem Soc; Soc Nuclear Med; Sigma Xi; AAAS. *Res:* Radiochemicals and labeled compounds for use in medical research, especially cyclotron produced short-lived radionuclides. *Mailing Add:* 5702 Jason St Houston TX 77096

**TILDON, J TYSON,** BIOCHEMISTRY. *Current Pos:* res asst prof biochem & pediat, 68-71, dir pediat res, 70-83, assoc prof pediat, 71-74, assoc prof biochem, 72-82, PROF PEDIAT, SCH MED, UNIV MD, BALTIMORE CITY, 74-, PROF BIOCHEM, 82- *Personal Data:* b Baltimore, Md, Aug 7, 31; m 88, Sania Amr; c Levia, Jay, Sharon & Sania. *Educ:* Morgan State Col, BS, 54; Johns Hopkins Univ, PhD(biochem), 65. *Prof Exp:* Res asst chem, Sinai Hosp, Baltimore, Md, 54-59; asst prof, Goucher Col, 67-68. *Concurrent Pos:* Fulbright scholar, Univ Paris, 59-60; Helen Hay Whitney fel biochem, Brandeis Univ, 65-67; lectr, Antioch Col, Baltimore Campus, 72-; Josiah Macy, Jr Fac Scholar, State Univ Groningen, Neth, 75-76. *Mem:* AAAS; Am Soc Biol Chemists; Am Soc Neurochem; Am Chem Soc; Tissue Cult Asn. *Res:* Developmental biochemistry and metabolic control processes. *Mailing Add:* Dept Pediat Univ Md Med 655 W Baltimore St Rm 14-021 BRB Baltimore MD 21201-1559. *Fax:* 410-706-0020

**TILFORD, SHELBY G,** ATMOSPHERIC SCIENCES, EARTH & ENVIRONMENTAL SCIENCES. *Current Pos:* space scientist solar physics, NASA Hq, 76, discipline chief upper atmosphere, 76-78, br chief atmospheric processes, 78-81, div of environ opers, 81-84, div dir earth sci & appln, 84-94, CHIEF SCIENTIST, ORBITAL SCI, NASA HQ, 95- *Personal Data:* b Grayson Co, Ky, Jan 11, 37; m 56; c 2. *Educ:* Western Ky Univ, BS, 58; Vanderbilt Univ, PhD(phys chem), 62. *Prof Exp:* Res assoc spectros, Naval Res Lab, 61-63, res chemist, 63-66, spectros consult physicist, 66-72, sect head extreme ultraviolet spectros, 72-76. *Concurrent Pos:* Vis prof, Univ Md, 69-76. *Res:* High resolution vacuum ultra violet spectroscopy of atoms and molecules of atmospheric, laser and astrophysical interest; mesospheric research; tropospheric and stratospheric air quality; upper atmospheric research; oceanic processes. *Mailing Add:* 8805 Church Field Lane Laurel MD 20708-2428

**TILGHMAN, SHIRLEY MARIE,** DEVELOPMENTAL BIOLOGY, EMBRYOLOGY. *Current Pos:* prof biol, 86-, HOWARD A PRIOR PROF LIFE SCI, PRINCETON UNIV, 86-, PRIN INVESTR, HOWARD HUGHES MED INST, 86- *Educ:* Temple Univ, PhD(biochem), 75. *Mem:* Foreign assoc Nat Acad Sci; Inst Med-Nat Acad Sci. *Mailing Add:* Lewis Thomas Lab Princeton Univ HHMI Washington Rd Princeton NJ 08544. *Fax:* 609-258-3345

**TILL, CHARLES EDGAR,** ENGINEERING PHYSICS. *Current Pos:* asst physicist, Argonne Nat Lab, 63-65, assoc physicist, 65-66, sect head, Exp Develop Sect, 66-68, head, Critical Exp Anal Sect, 68-72, mgr, Zero Power Reactor Prog, 68-72, assoc dir, Appl Physics Div, 72-73, dir appl physics, 73-80, ASSOC LAB DIR, ENG RES, ARGONNE NAT LABS, 80- *Personal Data:* b Can, June 14, 34; m; c 3. *Educ:* Univ Sask, BE, 56, MSc, 58; Univ London, PhD(reactor physics), 60. *Prof Exp:* Jr res officer physics, Nat Res Coun Can, 56-58; reactor physicist, Can Gen Elec, 61-63. *Mem:* Nat Acad Eng; Am Nuclear Soc; Nat Acad Res. *Res:* Fast reactor research. *Mailing Add:* Bldg 208 9700 S Cass Ave Argonne IL 60439. *Fax:* 603-252-5318; *E-Mail:* ctill@abk.gov

**TILL, JAMES EDGAR,** BIOPHYSICS, MEDICAL & HEALTH SCIENCES. *Current Pos:* assoc dean grad studies, 81-84, PROF MED BIOPHYS, UNIV TORONTO, 65-, UNIV PROF, 84-; SR SCIENTIST, ONT CANCER INST, 82- *Personal Data:* b Lloydminster, Sask, Aug 25, 31; m 59, Joyce Sinclair; c David T, Karen (Condon) & Susan (Sopchek). *Educ:* Univ Sask, BA, 52, MA, 54; Yale Univ, PhD(biophys), 57. *Honors & Awards:* Gairdner Found Award, 69; Robert L Noble Prize, Nat Cancer Inst Can, 93. *Prof Exp:* Biophysicist, Ont Cancer Inst, 57-69, head, Biores Div, 69-82. *Concurrent Pos:* Res fel microbiol, Connaught Med Res Labs, 56-57. *Mem:* Can Bioethics Soc; fel Royal Soc Can; Order Can. *Res:* Various aspects of cancer research; research on judgment and decision problems in health care settings; public health; epidemiology; bioethics. *Mailing Add:* 182 Briar Hill Ave Toronto ON M4R 1H9 Can. *E-Mail:* till@oci.utoronto.ca

**TILL, MICHAEL JOHN,** PEDIATRIC DENTISTRY. *Current Pos:* chmn dept, 70-90, PROF PEDODONTICS, UNIV MINN, MINNEAPOLIS, 70-, PROF PEDIAT DENT, DEPT PEDIAT DENT, 84- *Personal Data:* b Independence, Iowa, July 30, 34; m 67; c 2. *Educ:* Univ Iowa, DDS, 61, MS, 63; Univ Pittsburgh, MEd & PhD(higher educ), 70. *Prof Exp:* Instr pedodontics, Univ Iowa, 61-63; pedodontist, Eastman Inst, Stockholm, Sweden, 63-64; asst prof, Royal Dent Col, Denmark, 64-66; asst prof, Univ Pittsburgh, 66-70. *Concurrent Pos:* Pres, Minn Dent Asn, 88-89; dir, Proj Hope, Portugal, 89-90. *Mem:* Am Dent Asn; Int Asn Dent Res; Am Educ Res Asn; Am Soc Dent Children; Am Acad Pedodont. *Res:* Dental educational research; pedodontics. *Mailing Add:* 4725 Isabel Ave Minneapolis MN 55406

**TILLAY, ELDRID WAYNE,** INORGANIC CHEMISTRY. *Current Pos:* from asst prof to assoc prof, 60-72, PROF CHEM, PAC UNION COL, 72-, HEAD DEPT, 74- *Personal Data:* b Yerington, Nev, Feb 26, 25; m 53; c 2. *Educ:* Pac Union Col, BA, 50; Stanford Univ, MS, 52; La State Univ, PhD(inorg chem), 67. *Prof Exp:* Res asst chem, Stanford Univ, 52-57; instr, Sacramento City Col, 57-60. *Mem:* Am Chem Soc. *Res:* Organometallic chemistry and bio-inorganic chemistry. *Mailing Add:* 160 Cold Springs Rd Angwin CA 94508-9654

**TILLER, CALVIN OMAH,** PHYSICS. *Current Pos:* RETIRED. *Personal Data:* b Richmond, Va, June 22, 25; m 52; c 2. *Educ:* Col William & Mary, BS, 48; Syracuse Univ, MS, 50. *Honors & Awards:* J Sheldon Horsley Award, Va Acad Sci, 60; IR-100 Award, Indust Res, Inc, 72. *Prof Exp:* Qual engr, Eastman Kodak Co, 50-51; supvr, Optical Eng Dept, Otis Elevator Co, 51-55; physicist, Titmus Optical Co, 55-56; sr res physicist, Va Inst Sci Res, 56-68; res scientist, Res & Develop Ctr, Philip Morris, Inc, 68-88. *Mem:* NAm Thermal Analytical Soc; Am Phys Soc. *Res:* Solid state physics of thin metallic films; electron microscopy and diffraction; physical optics; thermal analysis of tobacco. *Mailing Add:* 1561 King William Woods Rd Midlothian VA 23113

**TILLER, F(RANK) M(ONTEREY),** SOLID & LIQUID SEPARATION, FILTRATION, CLARIFICATION, THICKENING, CENTRIFUGATION, FLOW THROUGH COMPACTIBLE & POROUS MEDIA. *Current Pos:* prof chem & elec eng & dean eng, Univ Houston, 55-63, dir int affairs, 63-67, Latin Am, 66-67, dir, Ctr Study Higher Educ, Latin Am, 68-73, M D ANDERSON PROF CHEM & CIVIL & ENVIRON ENG, UNIV HOUSTON, 63- *Personal Data:* b Louisville, Ky, Feb 26, 17; m 82, Martha R Browder; c Fay (Bryan) & Richard B. *Educ:* Univ Louisville, BChE, 37; Univ Cincinnati, MS, 39, PhD(chem eng), 46. *Hon Degrees:* Dr, Univ Brazil, 62 & State Univ Rio de Janeiro, 67. *Honors & Awards:* Streng Award, Univ Louisville, 37; Colburn Award, Am Inst Chem Engrs, 50, Founder's Award, 87; Phillips lectr, Okla State Univ, 77; Gold Medal, Filtration Soc, 78; Frank Tiller Tech Award, Am Filtration & Separations Soc. *Prof Exp:* Technician, Charles R Long, Jr Co, 34-35; chemist, Durkee Famous Foods Div, Glidden Co, 36 & Colgate-Palmolive-Peet Co, 37; civil engr, US Corps Engrs, Ky, 39; chem engr, C M Hall Lamp Co, 40; instr chem eng, Univ Cincinnati, 40-42; from asst prof to assoc prof, Vanderbilt Univ, 42-51; dean eng, Lamar State Col, 51-55. *Concurrent Pos:* Indust consult, 43-; dir, Gupton-Jones Col Mortuary Sci, 45-51; vis prof, Inst Oleos, Rio de Janeiro, 52, Rice Univ, 72-73, Fed Univ, Rio de Janeiro & Sergipe, 79 & Univ PR, 85; lectr, Humble Oil Col, 58, Esso Res Labs, 62 & Nat Taiwan Univ, 82; Fulbright prof, Univ Guayaquil & Univ Cent Equador, 58; hon prof, Cent Univ Ecuador, Univ Guayaquil, 58, Pontifical Cath Univ, Rio de Janeiro, 63, Fed Univ Santa Mairi, 69, Fed Univ Espirito Santo, 72, Autonomous Univ Guadalajara, 75; Aid Univ Contract dir, Univ Guayaquil, 60-64, consult, 64-67; mem, President's Sci Adv Comt, 61, Latin Am Sci Bd/Nat Acad Sci, 63-65 & Int Exchange Persons Comt, Conf Bd, Assoc Res Coun, 67; consult, Int Coop Admin Mission, Ecuador, 61; titular prof, Cath Univ Rio de Janeiro, 62; grants, Orgn Am States, Univ Brazil, 62-63, NATO sr fac, Univ Col London, 69-70 & Japanese Soc Prom Sci, Nagoya Univ, 82-83; dir, univ contracts, Univ Brazil & Cath Univ Rio de Janeiro, 63-70 & Coun Rectors Brazilian Univs, 66-72; adv, Autonomous Univ Guadalajara, 64-67; consult, Union Tex Petrol contract, Univ Costa Rica, 64-68; joint prog study univ admin & finances, Off Cult Affairs, US Dept State-Gulerpe, 66-67; pres, Int Consortium Filtration Res Groups, 71-76; hon pres, First World Cong Filtration, 73; vis prof, Nagoya Univ, 82 & 86, vis res, Commonwealth Sci & Indust Res Orgn, Canberra, Melbourne, 86; ed, Fluid/Particle Separation J, 88-92. *Mem:* Fel Am Inst Chem Engrs; Am Filtration Soc; Am Soc Eng Educ; Int Consortium Filtration Res Groups; Sigma Xi; hon mem Filtration Soc Belg; Water Environ Fedn; Int Asn Water Qual. *Res:* Flow through porous media; solid-liquid separation; thickening, filtration, centrifugation and expression; particle science; agricultural fibers. *Mailing Add:* Dept Chem Eng Univ Houston Houston TX 77204-4792. *Fax:* 713-743-4323, 649-5403; *E-Mail:* tiller@jetson.uh.edu

**TILLER, RALPH EARL,** pediatrics, for more information see previous edition

**TILLER, WILLIAM ARTHUR,** PHYSICS, PHYSICAL METALLURGY. *Current Pos:* exec head, Dept Mat Sci, 66-71, prof, 64-92, EMER PROF MAT SCI, STANFORD UNIV, 92- *Personal Data:* b Toronto, Ont, Sept 18, 29; m 52, Jean E Ackroyd; c Andrea & Jeffery. *Educ:* Univ Toronto, BASc, 52, MASc, 53, PhD(phys metall), 55. *Prof Exp:* Res engr, Res Lab, Westinghouse Elec Corp, 55-57, adv physicist, 57-59, sect mgr crystallogenics, 59-64. *Concurrent Pos:* Guggenheim fel, Oxford Univ, 70-71; distinguished vis prof, Univ Del, 81-82. *Mem:* Fel AAAS. *Res:* Solidification and crystal growth; physics of metals; surfaces; properties of materials; solid state physics; biomaterials; psychoenergetics; semiconductor processing. *Mailing Add:* Dept Mat Sci Stanford Univ Stanford CA 94305-2205. *Fax:* 650-725-4034

**TILLERY, BILL W,** SCIENCE EDUCATION. *Current Pos:* assoc prof, 73-75, PROF PHYSICS, ARIZ STATE UNIV, 75- *Personal Data:* b Muskogee, Okla, Sept 15, 38; m 59, 81, Patricia Northrop; c Tonya, Lisa & Elizabeth. *Educ:* Northeastern Okla State Univ, BS, 60; Univ Northern Colo,

MA, 65, EdD(sci educ), 67. *Prof Exp:* Teacher pub schs, Okla & Colo, 60-64; res assoc sci, Univ Northern Colo, 66-67; asst prof sci educ, Fla State Univ, 67-69; assoc prof & dir sci ctr, Univ Wyo, 69-73. *Mem:* Nat Sci Teachers Asn; Asn Educ Teachers Sci; Nat Asn Res Sci Teaching. *Res:* Physical science textbook and curriculum writer; energy education; science for nonscience students. *Mailing Add:* Dept Physics & Astron Ariz State Univ Tempe AZ 85287-1504. *Fax:* 602-965-7331; *E-Mail:* tillery@phyast.la.asu.edu

**TILLERY, MARVIN ISHMAEL,** AEROSOL PHYSICS, INHALATION TOXICOLOGY. *Current Pos:* staff scientist, Los Alamos Nat Lab, 71-72, sect leader aerosol technol, 72-83, staff scientist, Indust Hyg Group, 83-91, SECT LEADER INDUST/HYG FIELD SUPPORT, LOS ALAMOS NAT LAB, 91- *Personal Data:* b Idabel, Okla, Oct 10, 36; m 61, Patricia MacNerny; c Stephen, Anne & Denise. *Educ:* Univ NMex, BS, 67; Univ Rochester, MS, 71; Colo State Univ, PhD, 92. *Prof Exp:* Aerosol physicist, Inhalation Toxicol Res Inst, Albuquerque, NMex, 67-68; tech assoc aerosol technol, Univ Rochester, 68-70. *Mem:* Am Indust Hyg Asn; Am Asn Aerosol Res; Ger Inst Aerosol Res; Am Acad Indust Hyg. *Res:* Aerosol coagulation; generation and characterization instrumentation; aerosol filtration; development of inhalation chambers for toxicology studies; characterization of inhalation hazards; industrial hygiene; respirators; personal protective equipment. *Mailing Add:* MS K499 Los Alamos Nat Lab PO Box 1663 Los Alamos NM 87545. *E-Mail:* tillerym@lanl.gov

**TILLES, ABE,** ELECTRICAL ENGINEERING, FORENSIC ENGINEERING. *Current Pos:* CONSULT ENGR, 73- *Personal Data:* b New York, NY, Mar 9, 07; m 30; c 2. *Educ:* Univ Calif, BS, 28, MS, 32, PhD(elec eng), 34. *Honors & Awards:* Recipient, Founder Socs Alfred Noble Prize, 36. *Prof Exp:* Elec tester, Los Angeles Bur Power & Light, 28-30; jr testing engr, State Hwy Testing & Res Labs, Calif, 30; assoc elec eng, Univ Calif, 30-32, from instr to asst prof, 32-45, lectr, Exten Div, 31 & 38, instr defense training, 41, sr elec engr, Manhattan Proj, Radiation Lab, 44-45; asst transmission engr, Pac Gas & Elec Co, 45-54; prof elec eng, Israel Inst Technol, 54-56; consult, R W Thomas & Assocs, Calif, 56-57; sr electronic engr, Lawrence Livermore Lab, Univ Calif, 58-73. *Concurrent Pos:* Jr elec engr, Los Angeles Bur Power & Light, 36; elec designer, Pac Gas & Elec Co, 37-38; with L S Ready, 39; assoc elec engr, Mare Island Navy Yard, 41; chief elec design engr, Southwest Eng Co, 42; develop engr, Richmond Shipyard, Kaiser Co, 42-44; ed, San Francisco Engr, 47-49; chmn, San Francisco Eng Coun, 53; consult engr, 58- *Mem:* Am Soc Eng Educ; fel Inst Elec & Electronics Engrs; Sigma Xi. *Res:* Sparkover; high voltage cable; steel shaft quality; specialized electromagnetic instruments; nuclear science; continuing engineering education; forensic engineering. *Mailing Add:* c/o Kreith 43236 E Oakside Pl Davis CA 95616

**TILLES, HARRY,** ORGANIC CHEMISTRY. *Current Pos:* RETIRED. *Personal Data:* b Buffalo, NY, Mar 22, 23; m 48, Elizabeth Holzapfel; c David Alan, Susan Elsbeth, Nanci Louise & Mark Daniel. *Educ:* Univ Buffalo, BA, 48; Univ Calif, PhD(org chem), 51. *Prof Exp:* Res chemist org synthesis, Nat Aniline Div, Allied Chem & Dye Corp, 51-53; res chemist, Stauffer Chem Co, 53-59, group leader indust chem group, 59-62, proj officer, Nat Cancer Inst contract, 62-64, sr res chemist, 64-68, res assoc, Western Res Ctr, 68-74, sr res assoc, De Guigne Tech Ctr, 74-86. *Mem:* Sigma Xi. *Res:* Synthesis of organic chemicals for agricultural screening; optimization of chemical synthesis processes. *Mailing Add:* 703 Balra Dr El Cerrito CA 94530. *E-Mail:* lrtilles@earthlink.net

**TILLEY, BARBARA CLAIRE,** BIOMETRICS, BIOSTATISTICS. *Current Pos:* div head, Div Biostatist, Res Epidemiol & Comput, 83-97, DEPT HEAD, HENRY FORD HOSP, DETROIT, MICH, 97- *Personal Data:* b San Rafael, Calif, Apr 26, 42. *Educ:* Calif State Univ, Northridge, BA, 72; Univ Wash, MS, 75; Univ Tex, PhD(biometry), 81. *Prof Exp:* Biostatistician, Child Develop & Ment Retardation Ctr, 73-74; Mayo Clin, 74-77; fac assoc, Syst Cancer Ctr, Univ Tex, 78-80; asst prof biomath, cancer prev & biometry, 80-82. *Concurrent Pos:* Mem, policy adv bd, Div Cancer Biol & Diag, Nat Cancer Inst Data Monitoring Group, Minn Colon Cancer Screening Study, 86-; adj assoc prof, Univ Mich, Ann Arbor, 88- *Mem:* Biometrics Soc; Am Statist Asn; Am Pub Health Asn; Am Women Sci. *Res:* Developing and improving a subset selection algorithm for categorical data analysis; carrying out biostatistical research relating to cancer prevention; clinical trials health services. *Mailing Add:* Dept Biostatist Henry Ford Health Sci Ctr 1 Ford Pl Suite 3E Detroit MI 48202

**TILLEY, BRIAN JOHN,** ELECTRICAL ENGINEERING. *Current Pos:* SECT HEAD, HUGHES AIRCRAFT CO, CULVER CITY, 71- *Personal Data:* b Croydon, Eng, Apr 28, 36; m 63; c 3. *Educ:* Univ Wales, BSc, 61, PhD(elec eng), 65. *Prof Exp:* Technician, Marconis Wireless Tel Co Ltd, Eng, 54-56, jr engr, 56-58; mem sci staff, RCA Res Labs, Montreal, Que, 65-68; mem sci staff, Semiconductor Div, TRW Inc, 68-70, mem sci staff, Systs Microwave Div, 70-71. *Mem:* Inst Elec & Electronics Engrs. *Res:* Process and materials; large scale integrated circuits; high-speed, low-power and low-noise transistors; high reliability passive elements. *Mailing Add:* 29026 Indian Valley Rd Rancho Palos Verdes CA 90274

**TILLEY, DAVID RONALD,** RADIATIVE CAPTURE, NUCLEAR DATA. *Current Pos:* assoc prof, 66-72, PROF PHYSICS, NC STATE UNIV, 72- *Personal Data:* b Fuquay Springs, NC, Mar 10, 30; m 65; c 1. *Educ:* Univ NC, BS, 52; Vanderbilt Univ, MS, 54; Johns Hopkins Univ, PhD(nuclear physics), 58. *Prof Exp:* Jr instr physics, Johns Hopkins Univ, 53-58; res assoc nuclear physics, Duke Univ, 58-61, asst prof, 61-66. *Concurrent Pos:* Staff physicist, Triangle Univs Nuclear Lab, 64- *Mem:* Am Phys Soc; AAAS; Sigma Xi. *Res:* Radiative capture; gamma ray spectroscopy; nuclear reactions. *Mailing Add:* Dept Physics NC State Univ Box 8202 Raleigh NC 27695

**TILLEY, DONALD E,** PHYSICS. *Current Pos:* RETIRED. *Personal Data:* b Flushing, NY, July 6, 25; Can citizen; m 48, Margaret E Torrance; c James, Peggy & Peter. *Educ:* McGill Univ, BSc, 48, PhD(physics), 51. *Hon Degrees:* DSc, Royal Mil Col Can, 88. *Prof Exp:* Res assoc physics, Radiation Lab, McGill Univ, 51-52; from asst prof to prof physics, Col Mil Royal, Quebec, 52-78, head dept, 61-71, dean sci & eng, 69-78; prin, Royal Mil Col Can, Kingston, 78-84. *Mem:* Am Phys Soc; Can Asn Physicists. *Res:* Physics of dielectrics; nuclear reactions; radioactive isotopes. *Mailing Add:* 44 Faircrest Blvd Kingston ON K7L 4V1 Can. *E-Mail:* tilley-d@rmc.ca

**TILLEY, JEFFERSON WRIGHT,** ORGANIC CHEMISTRY, MEDICINAL CHEMISTRY. *Current Pos:* Sr chemist, Hoffman-La Roche, Inc, 72-80, group chief, 80-85, res leader, 85-93, DISTINGUISHED RES LEADER, HOFFMAN-LA ROCHE, INC, 93- *Personal Data:* b Detroit, Mich, Dec 13, 46; m 70, Katherine Mighell; c Molly & Jennifer. *Educ:* Harvey Mudd Col, BS, 68; Calif Inst Technol, PhD(chem), 72. *Mem:* Am Chem Soc; NY Acad Sci; Sigma Xi. *Res:* Heterocyclic chemistry; peptide mimetics; design and synthesis of antiallergy agents such as PAF antagonists and leukotriene antagonists; design of novel drugs based on peptide hormones and proteins as lead compounds. *Mailing Add:* 19 Evergreen Dr North Caldwell NJ 07006. *Fax:* 973-235-7122; *E-Mail:* tilleyj@ruche.com

**TILLEY, JOHN LEONARD,** MATHEMATICS. *Current Pos:* assoc prof, Miss State Univ, 64-69, prof math, 69-88, dir S D Lee hons prog, 69-81, actg head dept math, 71-72, EMER PROF MATH, MISS STATE UNIV, 88- *Personal Data:* b New York, NY, June 4, 28; m 51; c Dolores M Cope. *Educ:* Univ Pa, BS, 50; Univ Fla, MEd, 54, PhD(math), 61. *Honors & Awards:* Cert Meritorious Serv, Math Asn Am, 89. *Prof Exp:* Teacher high sch, Fla, 54-56 & St Petersburg Jr Col, 56-58; instr math, Univ Fla, 60-61; from asst prof to assoc prof, Clemson Univ, 61-64. *Concurrent Pos:* Secy-Treas & Newsletter Ed, La-Miss Sect, Math Asn Am, 78-89. *Mem:* Math Asn Am. *Res:* Classical methods of applied mathematics. *Mailing Add:* PO Box 391 Mississippi State MS 39762-0391

**TILLEY, SHERMAINE ANN,** MOLECULAR IMMUNOLOGY, VIROLOGY. *Current Pos:* res asst prof path, 85-94, RES ASSOC PROF PATH, NY UNIV MED CTR, 94- *Personal Data:* b Shawnee, Okla, Feb 22, 52. *Educ:* Okla City Univ, BA, 73; Johns Hopkins Univ, PhD(biochem), 80. *Honors & Awards:* James A Shannon Directors Award, NIH, 91. *Prof Exp:* Fel cell biol, Albert Einstein Col Med, 80-85. *Concurrent Pos:* Nat Arthritis Found fel, 82-85; asst mem, Dept Develop & Struct Biol, Pub Health Res Inst, 85-93, bd dirs, 93-95, assoc mem, 94-; prin investr, Life & Health Ins Med Res Fund grant, 86-89, NIH, Pub Health Serv grants, 88-, Stopping Aids Together, 91-92, Aaron Diamond Found Res grants, 91-93 & 94-95, Lucille P Markey Charitable Trust, 94-95; fac mem, Sackler Inst Grad Biomed Sci, NY Univ Sch Med, 88-; comt mem, Spec Rev Comt, NIH, 95. *Mem:* Am Asn Immunologists; AAAS; Am Soc Metals. *Res:* Isolation and structural and biological characterization of human & chimpanzee mabs raised against HIV-1 envelope during viral infection; use of Abs as tools to identify neutralization and ADCC epitopes important in HIV-1 infection and as probes of HIV-1 envelope structure. *Mailing Add:* Pub Health Res Inst 455 First Ave Rm 1133 New York NY 10016. *Fax:* 212-578-0804; *E-Mail:* tilley@phri.nyu.edu

**TILLEY, STEPHEN GEORGE,** HERPETOLOGY. *Current Pos:* From asst prof to assoc prof, 70-82, chmn dept, 77-80, PROF BIOL SCI, SMITH COL, 83- *Personal Data:* b Lima, Ohio, July 21, 43; div; c 2. *Educ:* Ohio State Univ, BS, 65; Univ Mich, Ann Arbor, MS, 67, PhD(zool), 70. *Mem:* Soc Study Evolution; Am Soc Ichthyol & Herpet; Soc Study Amphibians & Reptiles; AAAS; Ecol Soc Am. *Res:* Population biology and evolution of amphibians, especially desmognathine salamanders; genetic structures of populations; speciation in plethodontid salamanders. *Mailing Add:* Dept Biol Sci Smith Col Northampton MA 01063. *Fax:* 413-585-3786; *E-Mail:* stilley@smith.edu

**TILLEY, T(ERRY) DON,** COORDINATION POLYMERIZATIONS. *Current Pos:* from asst prof to assoc prof, 83-90, PROF INORG CHEM, UNIV CALIF, SAN DIEGO, 90- *Personal Data:* b Norman, Okla, Nov 22, 54; m 85; c 2. *Educ:* Univ Tex, Austin, BS, 77; Univ Calif, Berkeley, PhD(chem), 82. *Prof Exp:* Inorg chem, Swiss Fed Inst Technol, 82-83. *Concurrent Pos:* Alfred P Sloan Found award, 88; consult, Exxon Res & Develop Labs, 90- *Mem:* Am Chem Soc; Royal Soc Chem; Mat Res Soc; Sigma Xi; AAAS. *Res:* Synthetic, mechanistic and catalytic problems in inorganic and organometallic chemistry; coordination polymerizations and silicon-containing polymers; organometallic precursors to solid state materials. *Mailing Add:* Dept Chem Univ Calif Berkeley CA 94720

**TILLING, ROBERT INGERSOLL,** GEOLOGY, VOLCANOLOGY. *Current Pos:* Geologist, US Geol Surv, Va, 62-72, Hawaiian Volcano Observ, 72-75, scientist-in-chg, Hawaiian Volcano Observ, 75-76, chief off geochem & geophys, Geol Div, 76-81, geologist/volcanologist, 82-95, CHIEF SCIENTIST VOLCANO HAZARDS TEAM, US GEOL SURV, 96- *Personal Data:* b Shanghai, China, Nov 26, 35; US citizen; m 62; c 2. *Educ:* Pomona Col, BA, 58; Yale Univ, MS, 60, PhD(geol), 63. *Mem:* Geol Soc Am; Am Geophys Union; Int Asn Volcanology & Chem Earth's Interior. *Res:* Igneous petrology and volcanology. *Mailing Add:* US Geol Sur Mail Stop 910 345 Middlefied Rd Menlo Park CA 94025. *Fax:* 650-329-5235; *E-Mail:* rtilling@mojave.wr.usgs.gov

**TILLINGHAST, JOHN AVERY,** ELECTRICAL ENGINEERING. *Current Pos:* CHIEF EXEC OFFICER, BAY CORP HOLDINGS LTD, DOVER, NH, 97- *Personal Data:* b New York, NY, Apr 30, 27; m 48; c 3. *Educ:* Columbia Univ, BS, 48, MS, 49. *Prof Exp:* Mem staff, Am Elec Power Serv Corp, 49-67, exec vpres eng & construct, 67-72, sr exec vpres, 72-75, vchmn eng & construct, 75-79; sr vpres technol, Wheelabrator-Frye Inc, 79-81, chmn, Wheelabrator Utility Serv Inc, 81-86; pres, Teltec Inc, Portsmouth, NH, 86-94; sr vpres sci applns, Int Corp, 86-88; chief exec officer, Great Bay Power Corp, Dover, NH, 94-97. *Mem:* Nat Acad Eng; fel Am Soc Mech Engrs; Edison Elec Inst; Inst Elec & Electronics Engrs. *Res:* Generating unit control system. *Mailing Add:* Bay Corp Holdings 100 Main St Dover NH 03820

**TILLMAN, FRANK A,** INDUSTRIAL ENGINEERING. *Current Pos:* from asst prof to assoc prof, 65-69, head dept, 66-87, PROF INDUST ENG, KANS STATE UNIV, 69- *Personal Data:* b Linn, Mo, July 22, 37; m 59; c 3. *Educ:* Univ Mo, BS, 60, MS, 61; Univ Iowa, PhD(indust eng), 65. *Prof Exp:* Instr indust eng, Univ Mo, 60-61; oper res analyst, Stand Oil Ohio, 61-63; instr indust eng, Univ Iowa, 63-65. *Concurrent Pos:* Pres, Systs Res Corp, 68-; dir prog control, Price Comn, Exec Off of the Pres & consult, 72; consult, USDA; vpres, IBES, HIX, Int, 86, chief exec officer, 87. *Mem:* Fel Am Inst Indust Engrs; Sigma Xi. *Res:* Operations research; engineering statistics and the applications of multiple criteria decision methods and optimization to a wide variety of applications. *Mailing Add:* 1328 Sharingbrook Dr Manhattan KS 66509-7527

**TILLMAN, J(AMES) D(AVID), JR,** ELECTRICAL ENGINEERING. *Current Pos:* RETIRED. *Personal Data:* b Evansville, Ind, July 4, 21; m 56; c 3. *Educ:* Univ Tenn, BS, 47, MS, 50; Auburn Univ, PhD, 68. *Prof Exp:* From instr to prof elec eng, Univ Tenn, Knoxville, 47-, dir antenna projs, 56- *Concurrent Pos:* Researcher, Eng Exp Sta, Univ Tenn, Knoxville, 50-51 & Navy & Air Force Projs, 51-64. *Mem:* Am Soc Eng Educ; Inst Elec & Electronics Engrs. *Res:* Antenna systems and arrays, especially circular symmetry; propagation studies; electronic scanning systems; scattering of pulses from long wires; transient response of antennas. *Mailing Add:* 8200 Fox Run Lane Knoxville TN 37919

**TILLMAN, LARRY JAUBERT,** ANATOMY. *Current Pos:* ASST PROF ANAT, MED CTR, UNIV MISS, 78- *Personal Data:* b Bay St Louis, Miss, Aug 20, 48; m 70; c 1. *Educ:* Univ Miss, BA, 70, MS, 72, PhD(histol, electron micros), 74. *Prof Exp:* Chief electron micros, Dept Path, Brooke Army Med Ctr, 74-77. *Concurrent Pos:* Clin appointee, Dept Anat, Micros Anat Sect, Univ Tex Health Sci Ctr & Med Sch, San Antonio, 75-77. *Mem:* Soc Armed Forces Med Lab Scientists; Electron Micros Soc Am; AAAS. *Res:* Correlation of the fine structure of the cells comprising the uriniferous tubules of Gallus domesticus to their function; use of transmission and scanning electron microscopy in the diagnosis of renal and tumor disease. *Mailing Add:* Dept Phys Ther Univ Tenn 615 McCallie Ave Chattanooga TN 37403-2504

**TILLMAN, RICHARD MILTON,** ORGANIC CHEMISTRY. *Current Pos:* CONSULT, 88- *Personal Data:* b Muskogee, Okla, Sept 7, 28; m 48; c 2. *Educ:* Southern Methodist Univ, BS, 52, MS, 53. *Prof Exp:* From asst res chemist to sr res chemist, Continental Oil Co, 53-61, res group leader, 61-63, tech asst, 63-64, supvry res scientist, 64-67, mgr, Plant Foods Res Div, 67-72, assoc mgr, Petrol Prod Div, Res & Develop, 72-75, mgr, Res Serv Div, Res & Develop, 75-88. *Mem:* Sr mem Am Chem Soc. *Res:* Hydrocarbon fuels; petroleum-based specialties; plant foods; phosphate rock; analytical chemistry; laboratory safety and fire protection; environmental chemistry. *Mailing Add:* 2400 Wildwood Ponca City OK 74604-4144

**TILLMAN, ROBERT ERWIN,** WILDLIFE ECOLOGY, ENVIRONMENTAL ASSESSMENT. *Current Pos:* SR ENVIRON SPECIALIST, WORLD BANK, 89- *Personal Data:* b Hammondsport, NY, June 29, 37; m 86, Marie Edward; c Henry C & Franz R. *Educ:* State Univ NY, Albany, AB, 59, MA, 61; Cornell Univ, PhD(environ educ), 72. *Prof Exp:* Teacher biol, Dundee Cent Sch, NY, 59-65; asst prof biol, Dutchess Community Col, 66-69, assoc prof nat res, 71-73; coordr wildlife res, Cary Arboretum, 71-78, chmn environ assessment, NY Bot Garden, 78-82; human settlements officer, UN Ctr Human Settlement, 82-84; environ adv, USAID-Peru, 84-85; sr environ scientist, ARD Inc, 85-87; Jubba environ & social surv, Somalia, 87-88. *Mem:* Wildlife Soc; Soc Am Foresters; Inst Trop Forestry. *Res:* Powerline ecology, including vegetation management on powerline rights of way; hydroelectric generation sites, including transmission line rights of way; environmental assessment-Africa region. *Mailing Add:* 1971 Beach Rd Rock Stream NY 14878. *Fax:* 202-473-8185; *E-Mail:* rtillman@worldbank.org

**TILLMAN, RODERICK W,** SILICLASTIC SEDIMENTOLOGY, SEQUENCE STRATIGRAPHY. *Current Pos:* CONSULT SEDIMENTOLOGIST/STRATIGRAPHER, 85- *Personal Data:* b Macomb, Ill, Feb 24, 34; m 57, 76, Carol Howard; c 4. *Educ:* Univ Wis, BS, 57, MS, 60; Univ Colo, PhD, 67. *Prof Exp:* Explor geologist, Conoco, 60-62; res geologist, Sinclair Oil Co, 67-69; res assoc, Cities Serv Oil & Gas Corp, 69-85. *Concurrent Pos:* Comt mem, Soc Petrol Engrs, 87; adj prof, Colo Sch Mines. *Mem:* Am Asn Petrol Geologists; hon mem Soc Sedimentary Geol (pres, 90-91); fel Geol Soc Am; Soc Petrol Engrs; Europ Asn Geologists & Engrs. *Res:* Petroleum reservoir geologic and production description and modeling; sequence stratigraphy of silicastic deep water, shelf, shoreline, estuarine and valley fill sandstones. *Mailing Add:* 2121 E 51st St Suite 112 Tulsa OK 74105-5862

**TILLMAN, STEPHEN JOEL,** MATHEMATICS. *Current Pos:* asst prof, 70-75, ASSOC PROF MATH, WILKES COL, 75- *Personal Data:* b Springfield, Mass, Mar 31, 43; m 65; c 2. *Educ:* Brown Univ, ScB, 65, PhD(math), 70; Lehigh Univ, MS, 78. *Prof Exp:* Instr math, Brown Univ, 69-70. *Mem:* Am Math Soc; Math Asn Am; Opers Res Soc Am. *Res:* Teaching and developing additional courses in operations research and related areas. *Mailing Add:* Dept Math & Comput Sci Wilkes Univ Wilkes-Barre PA 18766

**TILLOTSON, JAMES E,** FOOD SCIENCE. *Current Pos:* DIR, FOOD POLICY INST, SCH NUTRIT, TUFTS UNIV, 89-, PROF, FOOD POLICY, 89- *Personal Data:* b Cambridge, Mass, Feb 9, 29; m 56; c 2. *Educ:* Harvard Univ, AB, 53; Boston Univ, MA, 56; Mass Inst Technol, PhD(food sci), 64; Univ Del, MBA, 69. *Prof Exp:* Teacher, Manter Hall Sch, 57-63; res asst nutrit & food sci, Mass Inst Technol, 61-63; training fel, Nat Inst Health, Mass Inst Technol, 63-64; res chemist indust & biochem dept, E I du Pont de Nemours & Co, 64-66, tech rep, Agr Tech Develop, 66-69; dir res & develop, Ocean Spray Cranberries Inc, 69-77, vpres tech res & develop, 77-89. *Mem:* Fel Am Inst Chem; Am Chem Soc; prof mem Inst Food Technol; Soc Nutrit Educ; Nat Food Processors Asn; Grocery Mfg Am. *Res:* Commercial development of food products and agricultural chemicals; research management; technical forecasting; government regulation of agribusiness. *Mailing Add:* 240 Forest Rd Cohasset MA 02025-1154

**TILLOTSON, JAMES GLEN,** ELECTRONICS. *Current Pos:* RETIRED. *Personal Data:* b Brandon, Man, July 20, 23; m 48; c James W, Joy G & Shirley M. *Educ:* Univ Man, BSc, 45; Univ Western Ont, MSc, 47. *Prof Exp:* Asst prof physics, Univ NB, 47-53; dir appl physics sect, Can Armament Res & Develop Estab, 53-55; prof physics, Acadia Univ, 55-89. *Concurrent Pos:* Consult, NB Dept Health, 51-52; Defence Res Bd Can grant, 57-59. *Mem:* Inst Elec & Electronics Engrs. *Res:* Acoustic radiation. *Mailing Add:* RR 2 Comp C3 Site 8 Wolfville NS B0P 1X0 Can

**TILLOTSON, JAMES RICHARD,** INFECTIOUS DISEASES, INTERNAL MEDICINE. *Current Pos:* from assoc prof to prof, 70-86, head, Div Infectious Dis, 70-86, CLIN PROF, ALBANY MED COL & MED CTR HOSP, 86- *Personal Data:* b Berkeley, Calif, Oct 3, 33; m 82; c 2. *Educ:* Lehigh Univ, BA, 55; Univ Calif, San Francisco, MD, 59; State Univ NY, Albany, EDD. *Prof Exp:* Instr med, Med Sch, Harvard Univ, 67-68; asst prof, Sch Med, Univ Mich, 68-70. *Concurrent Pos:* Clin res fel, Sch Med, Wayne State Univ, 64-66 & Med Sch, Harvard Univ-Boston City Hosp, 66-68; chief, Div Infectious Dis, Wayne County Gen Hosp, 68-70; consult, Albany Vet Admin Hosp & head, Div Infectious Dis, Albany Med Ctr Hosp, 70-86; adj prof, Albany Med Col & Med Ctr Hosp, 84-; hon sr res fel, Centre Med Educ, Dundee, Scotland, 84. *Mem:* Am Fedn Clin Res; Am Soc Microbiol; fel Infectious Dis Soc Am; fel Am Col Clin Pharmacol; Asn Am Med Cols; Asn Study Med Educ. *Res:* Pneumonia, especially gram-negative bacillary; prostatitis; antimicrobial activity of anti-tumor drugs; antimicrobial synergy; other areas of clinical microbiology and infectious diseases; medical education, especially instructional methods and decision making. *Mailing Add:* 14221 Headlands Dr Mendocino CA 95460

**TILLSON, HENRY CHARLES,** RUBBER CHEMISTRY, POLYMER CHARACTERIZATION. *Current Pos:* RETIRED. *Personal Data:* b Philadelphia, Pa, Sept 16, 23; m 50, Helen Hannah; c Ruth (Stanczak) & Clare (Corridori). *Educ:* Mass Inst Technol, SB, 44; Pa State Univ, MS, 48, PhD(org chem), 51. *Prof Exp:* Res chemist, Res Ctr, Hercules Inc, 50-52, tech rep, 52-54, res chemist, Res Ctr, 54-86. *Mem:* AAAS; Am Chem Soc. *Res:* Organic nitrogen compounds-nitramines; emulsion polymerization vinyl and condensation polymers, especially protective coatings; rubber compounding and crosslinking; polymer fractionation, mainly polyolifins. *Mailing Add:* 2808 Applewood Dr Freehold NJ 07728

**TILMAN, G DAVID,** RESOURCE COMPETITION THEORY, PLANT ECOLOGY. *Current Pos:* Lectr, 75-76, from asst prof to assoc prof, 76-84, PROF ECOL, UNIV MINN, 84- *Personal Data:* b Aurora, Ill, July 22, 49; m 71; c 4. *Educ:* Univ Mich, BS, 71, PhD(zool), 76. *Honors & Awards:* W S Cooper Award, Ecol Soc Am, 89. *Concurrent Pos:* Ed, Limnol & Oceanog, 78-81; mem, bd dirs, Orgn Trop Studies, 80-82 & Ecol Panel, NSF, 89-90; prin investr, Long Term Ecol Res, 81-; John Simon Guggenheim Found fel, 84-85; adv, Theoret Ecol, Lund Univ, Sweden, 85. *Mem:* Ecol Soc Am; Brit Ecol Soc; Am Soc Naturalists; Am Soc Limnol & Oceanog; fel AAAS. *Res:* Mechanistic models designed to predict the biodiversity, species composition and dynamics of ecological communities; role of environmental constraints; quantitative tradeoffs organisms face in dealing with several constraints. *Mailing Add:* Univ Minn St Paul 1445 Gortner Ave St Paul MN 55108-1095

**TILNEY, LEWIS GAWTRY,** ELECTROMICROSCOPY. *Current Pos:* PROF BIOL, UNIV PA, 62- *Educ:* Cornell Univ, PhD(biol), 64. *Mailing Add:* Dept Biol Univ Pa Philadelphia PA 19104-6018. *Fax:* 215-898-8780

**TILNEY, NICHOLAS LECHMERE,** KIDNEY TRANSPLANTATION. *Current Pos:* PROF SURG, SCH MED, HARVARD UNIV & SURGEON, BRIGHAM & WOMEN'S HOSP, BOSTON, 73- *Educ:* Cornell Univ, MD, 62. *Res:* Peripheral vascular disease. *Mailing Add:* Dept Surg Brigham & Women's Hosp 75 Francis St Boston MA 02115-6195

**TILSON, BRET RANSOM,** MATHEMATICS, COMPUTER SCIENCE. *Current Pos:* asst prof, 74-77, ASSOC PROF MATH, QUEEN'S COL, NY, 77- *Personal Data:* b Yuba City, Calif, May 19, 37. *Educ:* Mass Inst Technol, BS, 60; Univ Calif, Berkeley, PhD(math), 69. *Prof Exp:* Asst prof math, Columbia Univ, 69-74. *Concurrent Pos:* Dir res & develop, Comarc Design Systs, San Francisco, 80-81. *Res:* Decomposition and complexity of finite semigroups; automata theory. *Mailing Add:* 1517 Holly St Berkeley CA 94703-1036

**TILSON, HUGH ARVAL,** BEHAVIORAL NEUROSCIENCE & TOXICOLOGY. *Current Pos:* DIR, NEUROTOXICOL DIV, US ENVIRON PROTECTION AGENCY, 89- *Personal Data:* b Plainview, Tex, July 24, 46; m 81. *Educ:* Tex Tech Univ, BA, 68; Univ Minn, PhD, 72. *Prof Exp:* Head, Behav Neurosci, Nat Inst Environ Health Sci, 77-88. *Mem:* Am Soc Pharm & Exp Therapeut; Sigma Xi; Int Neurotoxicol Asn; Soc Neurosci; Soc Toxicol. *Res:* Compensatory and modulatory processes associated with progressive degeneration. *Mailing Add:* Neurotoxicol Div US Environ Protection Agency MD-74B Research Triangle Park NC 27711-0001. *Fax:* 919-541-4849

**TILSWORTH, TIMOTHY,** GENERAL ENVIRONMENTAL SCIENCES, WATER RESOURCES. *Current Pos:* asst prof environ health eng, Univ Alaska, Fairbanks, 70-74, head prog, 71-76, asst to pres, 76-77, assoc prof environ qual eng & civil eng, 74-84, PROF ENVIRON QUAL ENG & CIVIL ENG, UNIV ALASKA, FAIRBANKS, 84- *Personal Data:* b Norfolk, Nebr, Apr 6, 39; m 84; c 2. *Educ:* Univ Nebr-Lincoln, BS, 66, MS, 67; Univ Kans, PhD(environ health eng), 70. *Prof Exp:* Lab technician, Nitrogen Div, Allied Chem & Dye Corp, 60-61; civil engr technician, Scott Eng, 61-62; asst city engr, Norfolk, Nebr, 62-64; instr civil eng, Univ Nebr, 67. *Concurrent Pos:* Spec consult, Philleo Eng & Archit Serv, 71- & Hill, Ingman & Chase & Co, 71-74; owner, Tilsworth & Assoc, 72-85, Alaska Arctic Environ Serv, 85- & DJT's Shelties Delight, 85-; proj mgr, State of Alaska Proposal for Superconducting Super Collider, 87; head, Dept Civil Eng, Univ Alaska, 89-, chmn, Grad Coun, Univ Alaska Chancellor Search Comt, 89- *Mem:* Am Soc Civil Engrs; Asn Prof Environ Eng; Water Pollution Control Fedn; Am Water Works Asn. *Res:* Environmental health engineering; pollution control; solid waste management; biological waste water treatment; physical and chemical treatment; water quality; air pollution control; environmental impact assessment. *Mailing Add:* 1900 Raven Dr Fairbanks AK 99709

**TILTON, GEORGE ROBERT,** GEOCHEMISTRY. *Current Pos:* prof geochem, 65-91, EMER PROF, UNIV CALIF, SANTA BARBARA, 91- *Personal Data:* b Danville, Ill, June 3, 23; m 48, Elizabeth Foster; c Linda, Helen, David & John. *Educ:* Univ Ill, BS, 47; Univ Chicago, PhD(chem), 51. *Hon Degrees:* DSc, Swiss Inst Technol, Zurich, 84. *Honors & Awards:* Alexander von Humboldt Sr Scientist Award, 89. *Prof Exp:* Asst, Univ Chicago, 47-51; mem staff, Dept Terrestrial Magnetism, Carnegie Inst, 51-56, phys chemist, Geophys Lab, 56-65. *Concurrent Pos:* Assoc ed, Geochimica Cosmochimica Acta, 74-80; guest prof, Swiss Fed Inst Technol, Zurich, 71-72. *Mem:* Nat Acad Sci; Geochem Soc (pres, 80-81); fel Am Geophys Union; fel Geol Soc Am; Meteoritical Soc; fel AAAS. *Res:* Geochemical studies applied to origin of volcanic and plutonic rocks, and the evolution of the Earth's crust and mantle; isotopic composition of lead in terrestrial and meteoritic materials; geologic age of minerals. *Mailing Add:* Dept Geol Sci Univ Calif Santa Barbara CA 93106. *Fax:* 805-893-2314

**TILTON, ROBERT DAYMOND,** POLYMER SURFACTANTS & ADSORPTION, INTERFACE SCIENCE. *Current Pos:* DuPont asst prof, 92-95, asst prof, 95-97, ASSOC PROF, CARNEGIE-MELLON UNIV, 97- *Personal Data:* b Summit, NJ, Sept 2, 64; m 95. *Educ:* Univ Del, BChE, 86; Stanford Univ, MS, 87, PhD, 91. *Honors & Awards:* Victor K La Mer Award, Am Chem Soc, 93; Career Award, NSF, 96. *Prof Exp:* Vis scientist, Inst Surface Chem & Royal Inst Technol, Sweden, 91-92. *Mem:* Am Inst Chem Engrs; Am Chem Soc; Sigma Xi. *Res:* Surface diffusion and intermolecular forces in protein adsorption; polymer adsorption phenomena; adsorption from mixtures of polymers and surfactants; colloidal forces. *Mailing Add:* Dept Chem Eng Carnegie-Mellon Univ Pittsburgh PA 15213. *E-Mail:* tilton@andrew.cmu.edu

**TILTON, VARIEN RUSSELL,** plant bioengineering, for more information see previous edition

**TIMASHEFF, SERGE NICHOLAS,** PHYSICAL BIOCHEMISTRY. *Current Pos:* PROF BIOCHEM, BRANDEIS UNIV, 66- *Personal Data:* b Paris, France, Apr 7, 26; nat US; m 53; c 1. *Educ:* Fordham Univ, BS, 46, MS, 47, PhD(chem), 51. *Hon Degrees:* Dr, Univ Aix-Marseille, France, 90. *Honors & Awards:* Am Chem Soc Award, 63 & 66, Arthur H Flemming Award, 64; Frances Stone Burns Award, Am Can Soc, 74; Kelly lectr, Purdue Univ, 85; Humboldt Res Award for Sr US Scientists. *Prof Exp:* Instr chem, Fordham Univ, 47-49, lectr, 49-50; res fel, Calif Inst Technol, 51 & Yale Univ, 51-55; prin phys chemist, Eastern Regional Res Lab, USDA, Pa, 55-66, head, Pioneering Res Lab, Mass, 66-73. *Concurrent Pos:* NSF sr res fel, Macromolecule Res Ctr, France, 59-60; head phys-chem invest, Milk Properties Lab, Eastern Regional Res Lab, USDA, 61-66, adj prof, Drexel Inst Technol, 63-64; vis prof, Univ Ariz, 66; mem, Fordham Univ Coun, 68-; mem, Biophys-Phys Biochem Study Sect, NIH, 68-72; exec ed, Archives Biochem & Biophys, 70-86, volume ed, Methods Enzym; Guggenheim fel, Univ Molecular Biol, Paris, 72-73; vis prof, Univ Paris, 72-73; co-ed, Biol Macromolecules; vis prof, Duke Univ, 77, Univ Tech de Lille, 80, Pierre et Marie Curie Univ de Paris, 82-83, Univ de Paris, Orsay, 86-87, Univ Aix-Marseille II, 92-93; distinguished lectr, Univ Maine, 79; sr int fel, Fogarty Int Ctr, NIH, 86-87. *Mem:* Fel AAAS; Am Chem Soc; Am Soc Biol Chemists;

Biophys Soc; Sigma Xi; Am Soc Biochem & Molecular Biol. *Res:* Structure and interactions of proteins and nucleic acids; physical methods of high polymer studies; solution thermodynamics of macromolecules; author of 226 research publications. *Mailing Add:* Brandeis Univ Grad Dept Biochem 415 South St Waltham MA 02254-9110

**TIMBERLAKE, JACK W,** ORGANIC CHEMISTRY. *Current Pos:* from asst prof to assoc prof, 68-78, PROF ORG CHEM, UNIV NEW ORLEANS, 78- *Personal Data:* b Middletown, Ohio, May 26, 40; m 62; c 2. *Educ:* Univ Ill, MS, 65, PhD, 67. *Prof Exp:* Fel org chem, Univ Calif, Irvine, 67-68. *Concurrent Pos:* Petrol Res Found grant, Am Chem Soc, 75-77 & 76-79; Army Res Off grant, 76-78; consult med prog, Sch Med, Tulane Univ, 76-79; Diamond Shamrock crop grant, 77-79. *Mem:* Am Chem Soc; Sigma Xi. *Res:* Physical and synthetic organic chemistry; free radical reactions; small ring heterocycles; synthesis and screening of new anti-convulsants. *Mailing Add:* Dept Chem Univ New Orleans New Orleans LA 70148

**TIMBERLAKE, JOSEPH WILLIAM,** CLINICAL BIOCHEMISTRY. *Current Pos:* dir, 77-79, dir, Statist Lab, 79-82, CONSULT, LATTIMORE FINK LAB, KANS, 82- *Personal Data:* b Kansas City, Kans, Sept 5, 40; m 67. *Educ:* Univ Mo-Kansas City, BA, 63, MS, 69; Univ Kans Med Ctr, Kansas City, PhD(biochem), 74. *Prof Exp:* Technologist clin chem, Res Hosp & Med Ctr, 63-65; develop chemist, Univ Kans Med Ctr, Kansas City, 66-69; lab dir, Statlabs of Kans, Inc, 73-75; clin biochemist, Kansas City Gen Hosp, Univ Mo Med Sch, 75-77. *Mem:* Am Asn Clin Chemists. *Res:* Developmental clinical biochemistry. *Mailing Add:* 8312 Lakewood Circle Wichita KS 67207

**TIMBERLAKE, WILLIAM EDWARD,** MICROBIOLOGY, MYCOLOGY. *Current Pos:* VPRES RES, MILLENIUM PHARMACEUT, CAMBRIDGE, MASS, 93- *Personal Data:* b Washington, DC, May 2, 48; m 69; c 2. *Educ:* State Univ NY Col Forestry, BS, 70; State Univ NY Col Environ Sci & Forestry, MS, 72, PhD(biol), 74. *Prof Exp:* Assoc, Univ Geneva, 74; asst prof biol, Wayne State Univ, 74-79, assoc prof, 79-81; prof plant path, Univ Calif, Davis, 81-86; prof genetics & plant path, Univ Ga, Athens, 86-90, dir, Ctr Plant Cellular & Molecular Biol, 88-91, res prof, Dept Genetics, 90-93. *Concurrent Pos:* Adj prof, Dept Genetics, Univ Ga, Athens, 93- *Mem:* AAAS; Genetics Soc Am; Mycol Soc Am; Sigma Xi; Am Soc Microbiol; Int Soc Plant Molecular Biol; Soc Develop Biol. *Res:* Genetic regulation of development in fungi; genetic engineering of fungi; antifungal drug discovery. *Mailing Add:* Millenium Pharmaceut 1 Kendall S Bldg 300 Cambridge MA 02139

**TIMBERS, GORDON ERNEST,** FOOD SCIENCE. *Current Pos:* Res scientist, 64-82, SR SCIENTIST, ENG & STATIST RES INST, CAN DEPT AGR, 83-, HEAD, FOOD ENG SECT, 80-; FOOD COORDR, AGR CAN, 91- *Personal Data:* b Regina, Sask, Sept 14, 40; c 1. *Educ:* Univ BC, BSA, 62, MSA, 64; Rutgers Univ, New Brunswick, PhD(food sci), 71. *Honors & Awards:* Prix Innovation Technique, Indust Alimentaires et Agricole for Cryogran, 72; Royal Gordon Maybee Award, CIFST, 84; Inst Award, Can Inst Food Sci & Technol, 88. *Concurrent Pos:* Adj prof, Univ Man, Univ Guelph, McDonald Col & McGill Univ. *Mem:* Can Inst Food Sci & Technol (pres, 82-83); Inst Food Technologists. *Res:* Food engineering; development of new processes and equipment for food processing; unit operations; thermal properties of food products. *Mailing Add:* 5 Dallas Pl Ottawa ON K2G 3E2 Can

**TIMBIE, PETER T,** COSMOLOGY, DETECTOR DEVELOPMENT. *Current Pos:* ASSOC PROF PHYSICS, UNIV WIS, 97- *Personal Data:* b Hartford, Conn, Aug 19, 57; m 89, Patricia A Rosenmeyer; c Daniel R. *Educ:* Harvard Univ, BA, 79; Princeton Univ, PhD(physics), 85. *Prof Exp:* Postdoctoral fel physics, Princeton Univ, 85-87 & Univ Calif, Berkeley, 87-90; from asst prof to assoc prof, Brown Univ, 90-97. *Concurrent Pos:* NSF presidential young investr, 90. *Mem:* Am Phys Soc; Am Astron Soc. *Res:* Cosmic microwave background radiation and its anisotropy through the development of sensitive microwave and infrared detectors. *Mailing Add:* Dept Physics Univ Wis 1150 Univ Ave Madison WI 53706. *E-Mail:* timbie@wisp.physics.wisc.edu

**TIMBLIN, LLOYD O, JR,** WATER RESOURCES ENGINEERING, PHYSICAL SCIENCE. *Current Pos:* WATER RESOURCES CONSULT, 91- *Personal Data:* b Denver, Colo, June 25, 27; m 50, Barbara H McNiel; c Carol L. *Educ:* Univ Colo, BS, 50; Univ Denver, MS, 67. *Honors & Awards:* Meritorious Serv Award, US Dept Interior, 77. *Prof Exp:* Physicist, US Bur Reclamation, 50-58, head, Spec Invests Lab Sect, 58-63, chief, Chem Eng Br, 63-70, chief, Appl Sci Br, Res & Lab Serv Div, 70-91. *Concurrent Pos:* Mem Colo adv coun, Sem Environ Arts & Sci; chmn US team, US/USSR Joint Study Plastic Films & Soil Stabilizers, 75-85; accredited corrosion specialist, Nat Asn Corrosion Engrs, 76-; mem, Nat Sanit Found Comt on Flexible Membrane Liners, 79-87; chmn, Comt Mat Embankment Dams, USCOLD, 81-86, Comt Environ Effects, 88-; chmn, Tech Prog Int Symp Geomembranes, Denver, Colo, 84; mem, Int Comn Large Dams Comt Environ, 86-; mem, US Comt Large Dams; US tech coordr, Sci & Tech Coop Study Water Resources, US Bur Reclamation & Ministry Agr, Israel; mem, ICOLD Study Team Environ 3 Gorges Dam, China, 87. *Mem:* Am Phys Soc; Am Water Works Asn; Nat Asn Corrosion Engrs; NAm Lake Mgt Soc; Sigma Xi; Am Soc Testing & Mat. *Res:* Water resources development and management; corrosion engineering; cathodic protection; radioisotopes applications; water quality and pollution control; reservoir and river ecology; materials analysis and development; water treatment and desalting; aquatic weed control; remote sensing; global climate change. *Mailing Add:* 355 Martin Dr Boulder CO 80303-3444. *Fax:* 303-449-0906; *E-Mail:* timblinl@netone.com

**TIMELL, TORE ERIK,** ORGANIC CHEMISTRY. *Current Pos:* RETIRED. *Personal Data:* b Stockholm, Sweden, Mar 31, 21; nat US; m 47,67, Anna; c Anna, Britta & Marie. *Educ:* Royal Inst Technol, Sweden, ChemE, 46, lic, 48, DrTech(cellulose chem), 50. *Honors & Awards:* Anselme Payen Award, Am Chem Soc, 71. *Prof Exp:* Chief asst, Royal Inst Technol, Sweden, 46-50; res assoc chem, McGill Univ, 50-51; res assoc, State Univ NY Col Forestry, Syracuse, 51-52; Hibbert Mem fel, McGill Univ, 52, res assoc, 53-62; prof forest chem, State Univ NY Col, environ sci & forestry, Syracuse, 62-95. *Concurrent Pos:* Chemist, Pulp & Paper Res Inst Can, 53-59, res group leader, 60-62. *Mem:* Am Chem Soc; Int Acad Wood Sci; Int Asn Wood Anat. *Res:* Chemistry of wood and bark; ultrastructure, cytology and physiology of wood and bark; reaction wood. *Mailing Add:* State Univ NY Col Environ Sci & Forestry Syracuse NY 13210

**TIMIAN, ROLAND GUSTAV,** PLANT VIROLOGY. *Current Pos:* RETIRED. *Personal Data:* b Langdon, NDak, Mar 5, 20; m 49; c 5. *Educ:* NDak Agr Col, BS, 49, MS, 50; Iowa State Col, PhD(plant path), 53. *Prof Exp:* Asst bot, NDak Agr Col, 47-49, fed agent pathologist, 49-50; path res asst, Iowa State Col, 50-53; res plant pathologist, Agr Res, NDak State Univ, USDA, 53-86. *Concurrent Pos:* Tech adv barley, NCent Region, Agr Res Serv, USDA, 73-80, mem, Nat Barley Improv Comt, 78-83; plant pathol consult, NDak State Univ, USDA, 86- *Mem:* Am Phytopath Soc; Sigma Xi. *Res:* Cereal virus diseases; diseases in barley, especially virus diseases; serology; host-virus interaction. *Mailing Add:* 2305 Tenth St N Fargo ND 58102-1882

**TIMIRAS, PAOLA SILVESTRI,** DEVELOPMENTAL PHYSIOLOGY, NEUROENDOCRINOLOGY. *Current Pos:* asst physiologist, 55-58, from asst prof to assoc prof, 58-67, PROF PHYSIOL & CHMN DEPT, UNIV CALIF, BERKELEY, 67- *Personal Data:* b Rome, Italy, July 21, 23; nat US; m 46; c 2. *Educ:* Univ Rome, MD, 47; Univ Montreal, PhD(exp med, surg), 52. *Prof Exp:* Asst prof exp med & surg, Univ Montreal, 50-51, asst physiol, 51-53; asst prof pharmacol, Univ Utah, 54-55. *Mem:* AAAS; Endocrine Soc; Am Soc Pharmacol & Exp Therapeut; Am Physiol Soc; Geront Soc; Int Soc Develop Neurosci. *Res:* Endocrinology; environmental physiology; aging. *Mailing Add:* Dept Molecular & Cell Biol Univ Calif Berkeley 410 Barker Hall Berkeley CA 94720-3202. *Fax:* 510-643-6791

**TIMKO, JOSEPH MICHAEL,** ORGANIC CHEMISTRY. *Current Pos:* RES CHEMIST ORG CHEM, UPJOHN CO, 77- *Personal Data:* b Danville, Ill, May 20, 49. *Educ:* Univ Ill, Urbana, BS, 71; Univ Calif, Los Angeles, PhD(chem), 75. *Prof Exp:* Fel org chem, Univ Wis-Madison, 75-77. *Concurrent Pos:* NIH fel, Univ Wis-Madison, 76-77. *Mem:* AAAS; Am Chem Soc. *Res:* Development of synthesis and transformations of medicinally important compounds. *Mailing Add:* 12368 Sprinkle Vicksburg MI 49097-9429

**TIMKOVICH, RUSSELL,** BIOCHEMISTRY. *Current Pos:* PROF, CHEM DEPT, UNIV ALA. *Personal Data:* b East Chicago, Ind. *Educ:* Mich State Univ, BS, 70; Calif Inst Technol, PhD(chem), 74. *Prof Exp:* Fel, Calif Inst Technol, 74-75; asst prof, 75-80, assoc prof, Ill Inst Technol, 80- *Mem:* Am Chem Soc; Am Soc Biol Chemists; Biophys Soc. *Res:* Biochemistry and biophysics of electron transport proteins and enzymes; bacterial electron transport systems. *Mailing Add:* Dept Chem Univ Ala Tuscaloosa PO Box 870336 Tuscaloosa AL 35487-0336

**TIMM, DELMAR C,** CHEMICAL ENGINEERING. *Current Pos:* from asst prof to assoc prof, 67-75, PROF CHEM ENG, UNIV NEBR, LINCOLN, 75- *Personal Data:* b Muscatine, Iowa, Aug 19, 40; m 62; c 3. *Educ:* Iowa State Univ, BS, 62, MS, 65, PhD(chem eng), 67. *Prof Exp:* Chem engr, Esso Res & Eng Co, 62-63. *Mem:* Am Chem Soc; Am Inst Chem Engrs. *Res:* Crystallization from solution; kinetics of polymerization; molecular characterization thermosets. *Mailing Add:* 2933 Jackson Dr Lincoln NE 68502-5037

**TIMM, GERALD WAYNE,** BIOMEDICAL ENGINEERING, NEURO-UROLOGIC DEVICES. *Current Pos:* PRES, CHMN & CHIEF EXEC OFFICER, DACOMED CORP, 80- *Personal Data:* b Brandon, Minn, Dec 9, 40; m 75; c 4. *Educ:* Univ Minn, Minneapolis, BEE, 63, MS, 65, PhD(elec eng), 67. *Honors & Awards:* Gold Medal, Urol Div AMA, 74. *Prof Exp:* Assoc prof neurol, Med Sch, Univ Minn, Minneapolis, 67-76, adj assoc prof mech eng, 78-83; exec vpres, Am Med Systs, Inc, 76-79; founder & chmn, Timmo Uro-Care Inst, 89. *Concurrent Pos:* Res fel elec eng, Univ Minn, Minneapolis, 67, NIH trainee, 70-72, prin investr, NIH grant, 74-76; mem grad fac, Univ Minn, 71-76; consult, Baylor Col Med, 72-76, Purdue Univ, 74- & Long Beach, Vet Admin Med Ctr, res assoc neurol, 83-85. *Mem:* AAAS; Inst Elec & Electronics Engrs; sr mem Instrument Soc Am; NY Acad Sci. *Res:* Lower urinary tract and male erectile function; investigations of instrumentation systems and devices to diagnose and treat impaired genito-urinary and gastrointestinal function. *Mailing Add:* Urohealth Systs Inc 1701 E 79th St Suite 17 Minneapolis MN 55425

**TIMM, RAYMOND STANLEY,** ELECTRONICS ENGINEERING, OPERATIONS RESEARCH. *Current Pos:* RETIRED. *Personal Data:* b Bay City, Mich, Nov 28, 18; m 44; c 8. *Educ:* Lawrence Inst Technol, BSc, 42. *Prof Exp:* Assoc sect head electronic systs, Naval Res Lab, 42-48; sr engr naval res, Off Naval Res, 48-51; asst to pres component res, Balco Corp, 51-55; sr analyst electronic systs, Westinghouse Elec Corp, 55-57; br head systs anal, Melpar Corp, 57-58; div mgr systs anal, Anal Serv Inc, 58-81, consult MIT Systs, 81-86. *Mem:* Inst Elec & Electronics Engrs; sr mem Opers Res Soc Am. *Res:* Analysis of electronic aides to navigation; research and development of antenna filter networks. *Mailing Add:* 9803 Singleton Dr Bethesda MD 20817

**TIMMA, DONALD LEE,** chemistry, for more information see previous edition

**TIMME, ROBERT WILLIAM,** APPLIED PHYSICS. *Current Pos:* head Mat Res Sect, 73-79, RES PHYSICIST, NAVAL RES LAB, 71-, HEAD, TRANSDUCER BR, 79- *Personal Data:* b Victoria, Tex, July 22, 40; m 62; c 2. *Educ:* Tex A&M Univ, BS, 62; Rice Univ, MA, 69, PhD(physics), 70. *Honors & Awards:* NASA Achievement Awards, Manned Spacecraft Ctr, 66 & Hq, 73; Res Publ Award, Naval Res Lab, 76, 79 & 80, Performance Awards, 74, 78 & 80. *Prof Exp:* Res physicist, Ames Res Lab, NASA, 62-65, aerospace engr, Manned Spacecraft Ctr, 65-66; res assoc solid state physics, Rice Univ, 66-70; prin engr electromagnetics, Lockheed Electronics Co, Inc, 70-71. *Concurrent Pos:* Mem, Transducer Mat Comt, Naval Sea Systs Command, 73-; mem oceanology adv group, Naval Res Lab, 75-78; prof oceanology, Fla Inst Technol, 75-78; program manager, Sonar Transducer Reliability Improvement Program, 78- *Mem:* Am Phys Soc; Acoust Soc Am. *Res:* Characterization of the effects of stress, temperature and time on the piezoelectric, magnetostrictive, elastic and acoustic properties of materials applicable to sonar systems; development of long life, reliable sonar transducers. *Mailing Add:* 4001 Luray Dr Orlando FL 32812

**TIMMERHAUS, K(LAUS) D(IETER),** CHEMICAL ENGINEERING. *Current Pos:* from asst prof to prof, 53-61, assoc dean eng & dir Eng Res Ctr, 63-86, PROF CHEM ENG, UNIV COLO, BOULDER, 61- *Personal Data:* b Minneapolis, Minn, Sept 10, 24; m 52, Jean; c Carol. *Educ:* Univ Ill, BS, 48, MS, 49, PhD(chem eng), 51. *Honors & Awards:* S C Collins Award, 67; G Westinghouse Award, Am Soc Eng Educ, 68, F Merryfield Award, 92; Founders Award, Am Inst Chem Engrs, 78, Eminent Chem Eng Award, 83, W K Lewis Award, 87, F J Van Antwerpen Award, 91; W T Pentzer Award, Int Inst Refrig, 89; R Teetor Award, Soc Automotive Engrs, 91. *Prof Exp:* Process design engr, Calif Res Corp, Stand Oil Co, Calif, 52-53. *Concurrent Pos:* Lectr, Exten, Univ Calif, 53 & Univ Calif, Los Angeles, 61-62, 67, 70 & 78-85; ed, Advan in Cryogenic Eng, 54-81; consult numerous govt & indust orgn, 55-; mem & secy-treas, Cryogenic Eng Conf Bd, 56-66, 70-; co-ed, Int Cryogenic Monogr Ser; sect head, NSF, Washington, DC, 72-73; 3-M lectr award, Am Soc Eng Educ, 80; dir, Sigma Xi, 80-86 & Am Soc Eng Educ, 86-88; presidential teaching scholar, Univ Colo, Boulder, 89-; inst lectr, Am Inst Chem Engrs, 95. *Mem:* Nat Acad Eng; fel Am Inst Chem Engrs (vpres & pres); fel Am Soc Eng Educ; Am Astronaut Soc; Austrian Acad Sci; fel AAAS; Am Acad Environ Engrs; Sigma Xi (pres elect, pres 86); Am Soc Heating Refrig & Air Conditioning Engrs; Int Inst Refrig (vpres, 79-87, pres, 87-95). *Res:* Cryogenic processes; heat transfer; distillation; thermodynamic properties; cryocooler development. *Mailing Add:* Eng Ctr Campus Box 424 Univ Colo Boulder CO 80309. *Fax:* 303-492-4341

**TIMMERMANN, BARBARA NAWALANY,** NATURAL PRODUCTS CHEMISTRY. *Current Pos:* res assoc, Univ Ariz, 81-85, asst res scientist, 85-87, asst prof, 87-90, ASSOC PROF, UNIV ARIZ, 90- *Personal Data:* b Suffolk, Eng, May 30, 47; div; c 2. *Educ:* Univ Nacional de Cordoba, Arg, BA, 70; Univ Tex, Austin, MA, 77, PhD(bot), 80. *Prof Exp:* Res asst, Univ Nacional de Cordoba, 67-70; res asst, Univ Tex, Austin, 70-72, teaching asst biol, 70-72, instr, 80. *Mem:* Phytochem Soc NAm; Am Soc Pharmcognosy; Bot Soc Am; Europ Phytochem Soc; Int Soc Chem Ecol. *Res:* Chemical studies of North and South American desert plants, including the isolation and identification of natural products and evaluation of their potential uses as alternate sources of energy and chemical feedstocks; biocides and antitumor and antiviral agents. *Mailing Add:* 1019 N Bedford Dr Tucson AZ 85710

**TIMMERMANN, DAN, JR,** botany, crop breeding, for more information see previous edition

**TIMMINS, ROBERT STONE,** CHEMICAL ENGINEERING. *Current Pos:* PRES & CHIEF EXEC OFFICER, ORGANON TEKNIKA, 88- *Personal Data:* b Dallas, Tex, Aug 25, 33; m 55; c 3. *Educ:* Univ Tex, BS, 55; Mass Inst Technol, SM, 57, ScD, 59. *Prof Exp:* Sr engr prod res, Sun Oil Co, 59-61, group leader reservoir anal, 61-62; sect chief energy transfer & nuclear effects, Avco Corp, 62-63, asst mgr, Mat Dept, 63-64, mgr, Mat Sci Dept, 64-66; vpres res & develop, Abcor, Inc, 66-70, exec vpres, 70-71, pres, 72-77; sr vpres, Cobe Labs, Inc, 77-88. *Mem:* Am Inst Chem Engrs; Am Chem Soc. *Res:* Separation and purification; materials; high temperature chemistry. *Mailing Add:* 4201 Champaign Dr Durham NC 27707

**TIMMIS, GERALD C,** CARDIOLOGY. *Current Pos:* CLIN PROF HEALTH SCI & MED PHYSICS, OAKLAND UNIV, 85- *Personal Data:* b Apr 23, 30. *Educ:* Univ Detroit, BS, 51; Wayne State Univ, MD, 55; Am Bd Internal Med, cert, 62 & 65. *Prof Exp:* Intern, Harper Hosp, 55-56, resident internal med, 56-58; fel, Dept Med & Cardiol, Wayne State Univ, 58-60; chief cardiovasc serv, US Army Med Corps, Ft Belvoir, Va, 60-62; asst prof, Wayne State Univ Sch Med, 62-67, clin asst prof, Dept Pediat, 67- *Concurrent Pos:* Co-dir, Cardiovasc Lab, Children's Hosp Mich, 61-67, attend staff, Cardiol Dept, 61-75; co-dir, Cardiovasc Lab, Harper Hosp, Detroit, Mich, 67-73 & Div Cardiovasc Dis, William Beaumont Hosp, Royal Oak, Mich, 67-87; assoc med dir res, William Beaumont Res Inst, Royal Oak, Mich, 77-83, dir, Cardiovasc Lab, Hosp, 80-, dir cardiovasc res, 87-, consult staff, Div Cardiol, Troy, Mich, 78-89; clin prof health sci & internal med, Oakland Univ, 83-84. *Mem:* Fel Am Col Cardiol; fel Am Col Angiol; sr fel Soc Cardiac Angiography; fel Am Col Physicians; fel Am Col Chest Physicians; Am Heart Asn; AMA; Am Fedn Clin Res; Am Col Nuclear Cardiol. *Res:* Author of numerous articles, books and chapters in the field of cardiovascular studies. *Mailing Add:* William Beaumont Hosp 3601 W Thirteen Mile Rd Royal Oak MI 48073-6700

**TIMMONS, DARROL HOLT,** NUCLEAR ENGINEERING. *Current Pos:* sr engr, Exxon Nuclear Co, 79, mgr neutronics develop, 79-81, mgr Incore Monitoring, 81-83, staff engr, 83-85, MGR INCORE MONITORING SOFTWARE DEVELOP, EXXON NUCLEAR CO, 85- *Personal Data:* b Little River, Kans, July 7, 40; m 62; c 2. *Educ:* Kans State Univ, BS, 63, MS, 66, PhD(nuclear eng), 69. *Prof Exp:* Instr nuclear eng, Kans State Univ, 67-68; asst prof nuclear eng, Univ Mo-Columbia, 68-74, assoc prof, 74-79. *Concurrent Pos:* Am Soc Eng Educ/Ford Found Eng Residency Prog partic, Commonwealth Edison Co, Ill, 71-72. *Mem:* Am Nuclear Soc. *Res:* Nuclear reactor physics, fuel management and incore monitoring. *Mailing Add:* 2521 Davison Ave Richland WA 99352

**TIMMONS, RICHARD B,** PHYSICAL CHEMISTRY. *Current Pos:* chmn dept, 77-90, PROF CHEM, UNIV TEX, ARLINGTON, 77- *Personal Data:* b Sherbrooke, Que, June 23, 38; US citizen; m 63, Philomena C Liscio; c Kevin M, Gregory P & Brenda C. *Educ:* St Francis Xavier Univ, BS, 58; Cath Univ Am, PhD(chem), 62. *Prof Exp:* Fel chem kinetics, Brookhaven Nat Lab, 62-64; asst prof chem, Boston Col, 64-65; from asst prof to prof chem, Cath Univ Am, 65-77. *Mem:* Am Chem Soc. *Res:* Chemical kinetics; kinetic isotope effects on reaction rates; heterogeneous catalysis; plasma chemistry. *Mailing Add:* Dept Chem Box 19065 Univ Tex Arlington TX 76019-0065

**TIMMONS, THOMAS JOSEPH,** FISHERIES BIOLOGY, ICHTHYOLOGY. *Current Pos:* PROF BIOL, MURRAY STATE UNIV, 82- *Personal Data:* b Webster City, Iowa, Sept 4, 48; m 78, Kathryn Hartzog; c Glenn T & David J. *Educ:* Iowa State Univ, BS, 72; Tenn Tech Univ, MS, 75; Auburn Univ, PhD(fisheries & aquacult), 79. *Prof Exp:* Asst prof fisheries, Auburn Univ, 79-82. *Concurrent Pos:* Pres, Sigma Xi Chap, Murray State Univ, 89 & Ky Chap, Am Fisheries Soc, 91. *Mem:* Am Fisheries Soc; Am Soc Ichthyologists & Herpetologists; Sigma Xi. *Res:* Life history and population dynamics of freshwater fishes in lakes and streams of the southeastern United States. *Mailing Add:* Hancock Biol Sta Po Box 9 Murray State Univ Murray KY 42071-0009

**TIMON, WILLIAM EDWARD, JR,** MATHEMATICAL STATISTICS. *Current Pos:* EMER PROF, ROWAN STATE COL NJ, 88- *Personal Data:* b Natchitoches, La, Jan 13, 24; m 46, 56, Katherine Muse; c 6. *Educ:* Northwestern State Col La, BS, 50; Tulane Univ, MS, 51; Okla State Univ, PhD, 62. *Prof Exp:* Chief comput, Western Geophys Co, 45-46; instr, Tulane Univ, 50-51; mathematician, Esso Stand Oil Co, 51-53; instr math, La State Univ, 53-54; asst prof, Northwestern State Col La, 54-56 & Southwestern La Inst, 56-57; from asst prof to prof, Northwestern State Col La, 57-65, head dept, 62-65; prof, Parsons Col, 65-74, chmn dept, 67-74; prof math, Glassboro State Col, 74-88. *Res:* Analysis of the slipped-block design. *Mailing Add:* 209 Lakeside Dr Natchitoches LA 71457

**TIMONY, PETER EDWARD,** ORGANIC CHEMISTRY, TECHNICAL MANAGEMENT. *Current Pos:* DIR CHEM TECHNOL, LONZA, INC, 90- *Personal Data:* b Orange, NJ, Dec 30, 43; m 66, Pamela Logan; c Susan, Kacey, Kristen & Jennifer. *Educ:* Fairleigh Dickinson Univ, BA, 67; Univ Notre Dame, PhD(org chem), 72. *Prof Exp:* Res chemist, Stauffer Chem Co, 71-75, sr res chemist, 75-76, supvr prod develop, 76-79, asst to dir, 79-81, mgr functional fluids, 81-82, mgr org res, 82-88; dir res, Alcolac, 88-90. *Mem:* Am Chem Soc; Am Soc Lubrication Engrs; Am Oil Chemists Soc. *Res:* Mechanistic organoboron chemistry; synthetic lubricants; organic synthesis; funtional monomers; specialty organic chemicals. *Mailing Add:* 446 Alder Trail Crownsville MD 21032-1624. *Fax:* 908-730-1546

**TIMOSHENKO, GREGORY STEPHEN,** ELECTRICAL & ELECTRONIC MEASUREMENTS OF PHYSICAL PHENOMENA. *Current Pos:* from asst prof to prof, 39-71, head dept, 46-68, EMER PROF ENG, UNIV CONN, STORRS, 71- *Personal Data:* b St Petersburg, Russia, Nov 1, 04; nat US; m 34, Iris Airey; c 2. *Educ:* Tech Univ, Berlin (Ger), Dipl Ing, 29; Univ Mich, PhD(elec eng), 32. *Prof Exp:* Instr elec eng, Mass Inst Technol, 34-39. *Concurrent Pos:* Res & consult engr, Pratt & Whitney Aircraft, East Hartford, Conn, 42-46. *Mem:* Fel Am Phys Soc; fel Inst Elec & Electronics Engrs; Soc Eng Educ; NY Acad Sci; Illuminating Eng Soc; Sigma Xi. *Res:* Conduction of electricity in gases, liquids and solids applied to aircraft ignition systems, arc reignition, ion sources, cathode sputtering and lasers; illuminating engineering applied to US air defense systems and to habitability of submarines. *Mailing Add:* Univ Conn Storrs CT 06268

**TIMOTHY, DAVID HARRY,** PLANT GENETICS, PLANT BREEDING. *Current Pos:* assoc prof, 61-66, prof crop sci, 66-93, EMER PROF CROP SCI, BOT & GENETICS, NC STATE UNIV, 93- *Personal Data:* b Pittsburgh, Pa, June 9, 28; m 53, Marian C Whiteley; c Marjory J, M Elisabeth & David W. *Educ:* Pa State Univ, BS, 52, MS, 55; Univ Minn, PhD(plant genetics), 56. *Honors & Awards:* Frank N Meyer Medal for Plant Genetic Resources, 94. *Prof Exp:* Asst geneticist, Rockefeller Found, 56-58, assoc geneticist, 58-61. *Concurrent Pos:* Consult, Latin Am Sci Bd, Nat Acad Sci, 64-65; mem, Adv Comt, Orgn Trop Studies, 68-70; mem, Exec Comt, Southern Pasture & Forage Crop Improv Conf, 68-72, chmn, 71; mem, Nat Cert Grass Variety Rev Bd, 68-74 & Nat Found Seed Proj Planning Conf, 64-68; mem germplasm task force, Nat Plant Germ Plasm Syst, US Dept Agr, 81 & Germplasm Resources Info Prog Coord Comt, 81 & 82; assoc ed, Crop Sci, 82-84; consult, World Bank, 82; mem policy adv comt, Sci & Educ Res Grants Prog, USDA, 82-83; crop adv comt, Forage Grasses, 82-86; consult, Off Int Coop & Develop, US Agency Int Develop, 84-86; chief scientist, Compctitive Rcs Grants Prog, USDA, Fiscal, 85, 86; mem bd dirs, exec comt & treas, Genetic Resources Commun Systs Inc, 85-93, pres, 92-93; comt managing global genetic resource, agr imperatives, Nat Plant Germplasm Syst Working Group, Bd Agr, Nat Res Coun, 87-90; mem, Nat Plant Genetic

Resources Bd, 88-90, vchmn, 91- *Mem:* Fel AAAS; Asn Trop Biol; fel Am Soc Agron; fel Crop Sci Soc Am; Am Inst Biol Sci. *Res:* Origin, race inter-relationships and evolution of maize; corn and forage grass breeding; germ plasm resources; evaluation and improvement methods in the Gramineae; cytotaxonomy; evolution in domesticated grasses and their wild relatives. *Mailing Add:* 13 Furches St Raleigh NC 27607

**TIMOTHY, JOHN GETHYN,** SPACE PHYSICS. *Current Pos:* PROF PHYSICS, CTR SPACE SCI, STANFORD UNIV. *Personal Data:* b Ripley, Eng, Sept 23, 42. *Educ:* Univ London, BS, 63, PhD(space physics), 67. *Prof Exp:* Res asst space physics, Mullard Space Sci Lab, Univ Col London, 67-71; physicist, Harvard Col Observ, 71-72, sr physicist, 73-78; res assoc, lab atmospheric & space physics, Univ Colo, 78- *Mem:* Optical Soc Am; Am Geophys Union; Int Astron Union; Am Astron Soc. *Res:* Space astronomy; instrumentation for photometric measurements at extreme ultraviolet and soft x-ray wavelengths; photoelectric detector systems, imaging and nonimaging, for use at visible, ultraviolet and soft x-ray wavelengths. *Mailing Add:* Appl Physics ERL/CSSA HePL Stanford University ERL 314 Stanford CA 94305-4045

**TIMOURIAN, HECTOR,** DEVELOPMENTAL BIOLOGY. *Current Pos:* BIOLOGIST, LAWRENCE LIVERMORE LAB, UNIV CALIF, 65- *Personal Data:* b Mex, Aug 24, 33; US citizen; m 58; c 2. *Educ:* Univ Calif, Los Angeles, BA, 55, PhD(zool), 60. *Prof Exp:* Commonwealth Sci & Indust Res Orgn res fel immunol, Queensland Univ, 60-61; res zoologist, Univ Calif, Los Angeles, 61-62; NIH res fel biol, Calif Inst Technol, 62-64; asst prof biol, Calif State Univ, Northridge, 64-65. *Mem:* AAAS; Sigma Xi. *Res:* Sperm morphology, activity and fertilization; environmental toxicology; genetic toxicology of effluents and products from energy technologies; science education. *Mailing Add:* 935 Lynn St Livermore CA 94550-3522

**TIMOURIAN, JAMES GREGORY,** MATHEMATICS. *Current Pos:* from asst prof to assoc prof, 69-77, PROF MATH, UNIV ALTA, 77- *Personal Data:* b New York, NY, May 5, 41. *Educ:* Syracuse Univ, PhD(math), 67. *Prof Exp:* Asst prof math, Univ Tenn, 67-69. *Mem:* Sigma Xi. *Res:* Differential topology; singularities of maps on manifolds. *Mailing Add:* PO Box 9137 Edmonton AB T5P 4K2 Can

**TIMS, EUGENE F(RANCIS),** ELECTRICAL ENGINEERING. *Current Pos:* CONSULT ENGR, 83- *Personal Data:* b Madison, Wis, Oct 31, 21; m 49; c 4. *Educ:* La State Univ, BS, 43, MS, 49; Wash Univ, DSc(elec eng), 55. *Prof Exp:* From instr to asst prof elec eng, La State Univ, 46-50; lectr, Wash Univ, 51-55; engr sr staff, Appl Phys Lab, Johns Hopkins Univ, 55-58; sect chief engr, Martin Co, Fla, 58-59; staff engr, Fla Aero Div, Honeywell Inc, 59-60, from proj engr to prin staff engr, 60-64; prof elec eng, La State Univ, Baton Rouge, 64-83. *Concurrent Pos:* Pres, Nocon Corp, 70-89. *Mem:* AAAS; Inst Elec & Electronics Engrs; Inst Noise Control Eng; Acoust Soc Am; Nat Acad Forensic Engrs; Am Acad Forensic Sci; Int Asn Arson Investrs. *Res:* Noise control engineering; acoustics. *Mailing Add:* 4840 Newcomb Dr Baton Rouge LA 70808-4746

**TIMS, GEORGE B(ARTON), JR,** industrial engineering; deceased, see previous edition for last biography

**TIMUSK, JOHN,** CIVIL ENGINEERING. *Current Pos:* Demonstr, 58-60, lectr, 60-63, from asst prof to assoc prof, 65-76, PROF CIVIL ENG, UNIV TORONTO, 76-, ASSOC, SYSTS BLDG CTR, 72- *Personal Data:* b Narva, Estonia, Jan 2, 35; Can citizen; m 58; c 1. *Educ:* Univ Toronto, BASc, 58, MASc, 61; Univ London, PhD(civil eng), 69. *Mem:* Am Concrete Inst. *Res:* Creep and shrinkage of portland cement concrete; development of materials for thermal insulation; plaster casts for orthopedic applications. *Mailing Add:* Dept Civil Eng Galbraith Bldg Univ Toronto 35 St George St Toronto ON M5S 1A1 Can

**TIMUSK, THOMAS,** PHYSICS. *Current Pos:* from asst prof to assoc prof, 65-73, PROF PHYSICS, MCMASTER UNIV, 74- *Personal Data:* b Estonia, June 3, 33; Can citizen; m 57; c 2. *Educ:* Univ Toronto, BA, 57; Cornell Univ, PhD(physics), 61. *Prof Exp:* Res assoc physics, Cornell Univ, 61-62; asst, Univ Frankfurt, 62-64; res asst prof, Univ Ill, Urbana, 64-65. *Concurrent Pos:* Sloan fel, 66-68; vis scientist, Univ Calif, Berkeley, 79; adj prof, Univ Fla, 88; consult, AT&T Bell Labs, 88. *Mem:* Fel Am Phys Soc; Can Asn Physicists. *Res:* Solid state physics; localized vibrations; far infrared spectroscopy; excitons and electron-hole drops; superconductivity; quasi crystals. *Mailing Add:* Dept Physics McMaster Univ 1280 Main St W Hamilton ON L8S 4M1 Can ABB258. *Fax:* 905-546-1252; *E-Mail:* timusk@mcmaster.ca

**TIN, HLA NGWE,** ALTERNATIVE ENERGY & RENEWABLE ENERGY RESOURCES, HAZARDOUS MATERIAL MANAGEMENT. *Current Pos:* PRES & CHIEF EXEC OFFICER, GENOTECH INDUSTS, INC, 89-; PRES & CHIEF EXEC OFFICER, PHARM CHEM, INC, 93- *Personal Data:* b Yesagyo, Myanmar, Apr 8, 42; US citizen; m 80, Khin Khin; c Michael E. *Educ:* Rangoon Univ, Burma, BS, 63; Univ Ark, MS, 65; Univ Calif, PhD(physics), 70. *Prof Exp:* NSF fel, St Francis Xavier Univ, 70-71; prog develop dir, Res Div, Nat Tech Systs, 80-83; pres & chief exec officer, Halo Technol Inc, 83-87; vpres, Kettenbauer, 88-89. *Concurrent Pos:* Prin investr, Nat Technol Systs Inc, 80-83. *Res:* Alternative energy resources, holographic applications, hazardous materials management and pharmaceutical racemic mixture separations. *Mailing Add:* 2281 Golden Circle Newport Beach CA 92660. *Fax:* 714-645-6919

**TINANOFF, NORMAN,** pediatric dentistry, for more information see previous edition

**TINARI, PAUL DENIS,** ENVIRONMENTAL PHYSICS, CONTAMINATED SITE REMEDIATION. *Current Pos:* DIR, PAC INST ADVAN STUDY, 89- *Personal Data:* b New Haven, Conn, Oct 16, 57. *Educ:* Queens Col, BSc, 81, MEng, 84; Von Karman Inst, PhD(environ fluid mech), 89. *Honors & Awards:* Hon mention, Int Rolex Awards Innovation, 93. *Prof Exp:* Res engr, Von Karman Inst Fluid Mech, 85-89. *Concurrent Pos:* Vis prof, Univ BC & Univ Toronto, 94-; prin investr, Ore Grad Inst, 95-96, BC Hydro Authority, 96-97; consult, Nat Comt Air Technologies, Can, 96-, BC Inst Technol, 97- *Mem:* Can Asn Physicists; Nat Groundwater Asn; World Future Soc. *Res:* Contaminated site remediation; clean-up of superfund sites; heavy metals contaminated sites; clean-up of crude oil spills; advanced technology biofiltration; remediation of contaminated groundwater. *Mailing Add:* 936 Thermal Dr Coquitlam BC V3J 6R8 Can. *Fax:* 604-469-3552; *E-Mail:* pacific@imag.net

**TINCHER, WAYNE COLEMAN,** PHYSICAL CHEMISTRY. *Current Pos:* assoc prof textile chem, 71-77, PROF TEXTILE ENG, A FRENCH TEXTILE SCH, GA INST TECHNOL, 77- *Personal Data:* b Frankfort, Ky, Jan 15, 35; m 57; c 3. *Educ:* David Lipscomb Col, BA, 56; Vanderbilt Univ, PhD(chem), 60. *Prof Exp:* Res chemist, Chemstrand Res Ctr, Monsanto Co, 60-65, group leader spectros, 65-71. *Mem:* AAAS; Am Chem Soc; Am Asn Textile Chemists & Colorists; Sigma Xi. *Res:* Nuclear magnetic resonance spectra and structure of polymers; mechanics of polymer degradation; fiber and fabric flammability; textile process water pollution control. *Mailing Add:* Textile & Fiber Engr Ga Inst Technol A French Textile Sch Atlanta GA 30332-0001

**TINDALL, CHARLES GORDON, JR,** FORENSIC SCIENCE, TOXICOLOGY. *Current Pos:* CHIEF FORENSIC SCIENTIST, NJ STATE POLICE. *Personal Data:* b Trenton, NJ, Sept 3, 42; m 64; c 3. *Educ:* Col Wooster, BA, 64; Ohio State Univ, MS, 67, PhD(org chem), 70. *Prof Exp:* Fel med chem, Nucleic Acid Res Inst, Int Chem & Nuclear Corp, 70-72. *Concurrent Pos:* Adj prof, Stockton State Col, 74- & Ocean Co Col, 75- *Mem:* Am Chem Soc; Am Soc Crime Lab Dirs; Am Acad Forensic Sci. *Res:* Detection of accelerants in arson investigation; characterization of hair; toxicology and detection of drugs and poisons in blood and urine. *Mailing Add:* 283 Chicagami Trail Medford Lakes NJ 08055-2137

**TINDALL, DONALD J,** ANDROGEN ACTION, PROSTATE CANCER. *Current Pos:* PROF, MAYO CLIN-FOUND, 89- *Personal Data:* b Columbia, SC, May 16, 44; m 67; c 4. *Educ:* Univ SC, BS, 66; Clemson Univ, MS, 70; Univ NC, PhD(biochem), 73. *Prof Exp:* Postdoctoral, Baylor Col Med, 74-76, from instr to assoc prof, 76-88. *Concurrent Pos:* Consult, Mayo Clin-Found, 89-; assoc ed, Cancer Res, 91. *Mem:* Am Soc Biol Chemists; Endocrine Soc; Am Soc Androl; Am Asn Cancer Res; Am Soc Cell Biol. *Res:* Mechanism of androgen action in prostate cancer. *Mailing Add:* Dept Urol & Molecular Biol Mayo Clin 17 Guggenheim 200 First St SW Rochester MN 55905-0001. *Fax:* 507-284-0762

**TINDALL, DONALD R,** MARINE TOXINS, MARINE & FRESHWATER ECOLOGY. *Current Pos:* from asst prof to assoc prof, 66-78, chmn, 79-86, PROF BOT, SOUTHERN ILL UNIV, 78-, PROF PLANT BIOL, 79-, ASSOC DEAN, COL SCI, 86- *Personal Data:* b Shelby County, Ky, June 29, 37; m 63; c 2. *Educ:* Georgetown Col, BS, 59, Univ Louisville, MS, 62 & PhD(bot), 66. *Prof Exp:* Instr bot, Univ Louisville, 60-61, researcher, 61-65; fel bot, Ind Univ, 65-66. *Concurrent Pos:* Proj dir ciguatera res, dept bot, Southern Ill Univ, 78- *Mem:* Sigma Xi; Phycol Soc Am; Int Phycol Soc. *Res:* Identification, culture and ecology of ciguatoxigenic dinoflagellates and the extraction, purification and characterization of toxins responsible for ciguatera. *Mailing Add:* Dept Bot Southern Ill Univ Carbondale IL 62901-4399

**TINDALL, GEORGE TAYLOR,** NEUROSURGERY. *Current Pos:* PROF NEUROSURG, SCH MED, EMORY UNIV, 73- *Personal Data:* b Magee, Miss, Mar 13, 28; m 47; c 4. *Educ:* Univ Miss, AB, 48; Johns Hopkins Univ, MD, 52. *Prof Exp:* Intern gen surg, Johns Hopkins Univ, 52-53; resident neurosurg, Med Ctr, Duke Univ, 55-61, from asst prof to assoc prof, 61-68; chief, Neurosurg Serv, Vet Admin Hosp, 61-68; prof neurosurg & chief div, Univ Tex Med Br, Galveston, 68-73. *Mem:* Cong Neurol Surgeons; Soc Neurol Surgeons; Soc Univ Neurosurgeons (pres, 65). *Res:* Hypophysectomy and neuroendocrinology; measurement of the cerebral circulation; physiologic changes induced by increases in intracranial pressure, hemorrhage and effect of various pharmacologic agents; cranial aneurysms. *Mailing Add:* Emory Clin Neuro Surg Emory Univ 1365 Clifton Rd NE Atlanta GA 30307-1013

**TINDELL, RALPH S,** DISTRIBUTED SYSTEMS, GRAPH THEORY. *Current Pos:* assoc prof, 70-78, prof math, 78-84, PROF COMPUTER SCI, STEVENS INST TECHNOL, 84- *Personal Data:* b Tampa, Fla, Jan 16, 42; div; c 2. *Educ:* Univ SFla, BA, 63; Fla State Univ, MS, 65, PhD(math), 67; Stevens Inst Technol, MEng, 84. *Prof Exp:* Res assoc math, Univ Ga, 66; asst prof, Univ Ga, 67-70. *Concurrent Pos:* Vis mem & grantee, Inst Advan Study, 66-67, res assoc, 69-70; vis prof, Univ der Saavlandes, 76 & Univ SFla, 82 & 84-85. *Mem:* Am Math Soc; Asn Mems Inst Advan Study; Asn Comput Mach. *Res:* Graph theory; theoretical computer science. *Mailing Add:* Castle Point Terr Hoboken NJ 07030. *E-Mail:* tindell@gauss.stevens-tech.edu

**TINDER, RICHARD F(RANCHERE),** MATERIALS SCIENCE. *Current Pos:* From asst prof to assoc prof metall, 61-70, assoc prof elec eng, 70-73, PROF ELEC ENG, WASH STATE UNIV, 73- *Personal Data:* b Long Beach, Calif, Dec 17, 30; m 69; c 4. *Educ:* Univ Calif, Berkeley, BS, 57, MS, 58,

PhD(metall), 62. *Concurrent Pos:* Vis assoc prof mech eng, Univ Calif, Davis, 72-73. *Res:* Initiation of plastic flow in crystals; mechanism of surface ionization of heated filaments; shock studies of single crystals; peizothermoelectric effects in crystals; tensor properties of solids; direct energy conversion. *Mailing Add:* 640 SW Winter Circle Pullman WA 99163

**TING, CHIH-YUAN CHARLES,** HIGH PERFORMANCE LIQUID & GAS CHROMATOGRAPHY. *Current Pos:* DIR, PENEDERM INC, 97- *Personal Data:* b Tsingtao, China, Feb 1, 47; m 71, Margaret A; c Michelle & Michael. *Educ:* Fu-Jen Univ, Taiwan, BS, 70; Wilkes Univ, MS, 73; Pa State Univ, PhD(anal chem), 78. *Prof Exp:* Res specialist, Monsanto Co, 77-83; res scientist, G D Searle, 84-87; sr scientist, Calif Biotechnol, Inc, 88-92; group leader, Abaxis, 92-93; assoc dir, Anal Develop, Sequus Pharmaceut Inc, 93-97. *Mem:* Am Chem Soc; Sigma Xi. *Res:* Electrochemistry of biological compounds; automated chromatographic instrumentation analysis of trace level of herbicide and waste effluents; product quality control of herbicides; peptide, protein and amino acid analysis; industrial hygiene; analytical specifications of biopharmaceuticals; analytical phospholipids; immunoassay of biopharmaceuticals in manufacturing process and serum. *Mailing Add:* 320 Lakeside Dr Suite A Foster City CA 94404

**TING, CHOU-CHIK,** IMMUNOLOGY, PATHOLOGY. *Current Pos:* spec fel, 68-70, staff fel, 71-74, SR INVESTR IMMUNOL, NAT CANCER INST, NIH, 74- *Personal Data:* b Fu-Yang, An-Hweir, China, Jan 7, 39; US citizen; m 68, Kai-Li Hsia; c Ray & Nan. *Educ:* Nat Taiwan Univ Med Sch, MD, 62. *Prof Exp:* Resident path, NY Med Col, Metrop Hosp, 63-64; resident path, Albert Einstein Col Med, Bronx Munic Hosp, 64-67, chief resident, 67-68. *Concurrent Pos:* China scholar, Nat Acad Sci, 81; adj prof, Dept Path, Uniformed Serv Univ Health Sci, 90- *Mem:* Am Asn Immunologists; Am Asn Cancer Res. *Res:* Tumor immunology to study specific humoral and cell mediator immunity to tumor associated antigens in animals; activation of killer cells by anti-T cell receptor antibody and cytokines and to determine the mechanism of activation and its implication in immunotherapy of cancer. *Mailing Add:* Nat Cancer Inst NIH Bldg 10 Rm 4B17 Bethesda MD 20892-0001

**TING, FRANCIS TA-CHUAN,** GEOLOGY. *Current Pos:* assoc prof, 74-79, PROF GEOL, WVA UNIV, 79- *Personal Data:* b Tsingtao, China, Apr 26, 34; US citizen; m 66; c 2. *Educ:* Nat Taiwan Univ, BS, 57; Univ Minn, MS, 62; Pa State Univ, PhD, 67. *Prof Exp:* Fel, Pa State Univ, 67-68; asst prof geol, Macalester Col, 68-69; res assoc coal petrol, Pa State Univ, 69-70; from asst prof to assoc prof geol, Univ NDak, 70-74. *Concurrent Pos:* Fel, Univ Minn, 68-69; NATO sr fel, 73. *Mem:* Sigma Xi; Geol Soc Am; Bot Soc Am; Soc Econ Paleont & Mineral; Geochem Soc; Am Asn Petrol Geologists. *Res:* Coal petrology and chemistry; paleobotany. *Mailing Add:* 129 Bakers Dr Morgantown WV 26505

**TING, IRWIN PETER,** PLANT PHYSIOLOGY, METABOLISM. *Current Pos:* plant physiologist, 65-66, from asst prof to assoc prof plant physiol & metab, 66-72, PROF BIOL, UNIV CALIF, RIVERSIDE, 72- *Personal Data:* b San Francisco, Calif, Jan 13, 34; m 52, Coleen D; c 1. *Educ:* Univ Nev, BS, 60, MS, 61; Iowa State Univ, PhD(plant physiol, biochem), 64. *Prof Exp:* NSF fel, 64-65. *Concurrent Pos:* Vis fel, Australian Nat Univ, 72; exchange prof, Univ Paris, 74; orgn & coop develop fel, France; prof, Nat Univ Cata Marca, Arg; chair bot & plant sci, Univ Calif, Riverside, 82-88. *Mem:* Bot Soc Am; Am Soc Plant Physiologists. *Res:* Gas transfer between plant surfaces and environment; carbon dioxide metabolism; plant isoenzymes; crassulacean acid metabolism; photosynthesis. *Mailing Add:* Dept Bot & Plant Sci Univ Calif 900 University Ave Riverside CA 92521

**TING, LU,** APPLIED MATHEMATICS. *Current Pos:* prof aeronaut & astronaut, 64-68, PROF MATH, NY UNIV, 68- *Personal Data:* b China, Apr 18, 25; nat US; div; c Luke, Diana & Mary. *Educ:* Chiao Tung Univ, China, BS, 46; Mass Inst Technol, SM, 48; Harvard Univ, MS, 49; NY Univ, ScD, 51. *Prof Exp:* Res assoc aerodyn, NY Univ, 51-52; spec design engr, Foster Wheeler Corp, 52-55; res prof aerodyn, Polytech Inst Brooklyn, 55-64. *Concurrent Pos:* Consult, Inst Comput Appln Sci & Eng NASA Langley Res Ctr, 77-79, 86-; Humboldt Res Award, Alexander von Humboldt Found, Bonn, Ger, 96- *Mem:* Soc Indust & Appl Math; Am Inst Aeronaut & Astronaut; Am Phys Soc; NY Acad Sci. *Res:* Shock deflections; boundary layer theory; supersonic wing-body interference; space mechanics; nonlinear wave propagations; perturbation methods; aeroacoustics. *Mailing Add:* Dept Math NY Univ Washington Sq New York NY 10012. *Fax:* 212-995-4121

**TING, MINGFANG,** CLIMATE DYNAMICS & CLIMATE VARIABILITY, EL NINO & SOUTHERN OSCILLATION. *Current Pos:* ASST PROF ATMOSPHERIC SCI, UNIV ILL, 93-, FAC, COMPUT SCI & ENG PROG, 95- *Personal Data:* b Yi Xim, China, Oct 26, 63; m 86, Xin Tao; c Connie Tao & Conrad Tao. *Educ:* Peking Univ, BS, 83, MS, 85; Princeton Univ, PhD(atmospheric sci), 90. *Honors & Awards:* Career Award, NSF, 95. *Prof Exp:* Res assoc, Univ Colo, 90-92. *Mem:* Am Meteorol Soc; Am Geophys Union. *Res:* Understanding how ocean sea surface temperature influences atmospheric circulation and its climate anomalies, such as drought, floods, severe winter storms and hurricane activities. *Mailing Add:* 105 S Gregory Ave Urbana IL 61801. *Fax:* 217-244-4393; *E-Mail:* ting@uiuc.edu

**TING, ROBERT YEN-YING,** RHEOLOGY, APPLIED MECHANICS. *Current Pos:* mech engr surface chem, Chem Div, 71-76, sect head polymer mech, 77-80, HEAD MAT RES, UNDERWATER SOUND REFERENCE DIV, NAVAL RES LAB, 80- *Personal Data:* b Kwei-Yang, China, March 8, 42; US citizen; m 67, Teresa Yen-chun Chen; c Paul H & Peggy Y. *Educ:* Nat

Taiwan Univ, BS, 64; Mass Inst Technol, MS, 67; Univ Calif, San Diego, PhD(eng sci), 71. *Prof Exp:* Res staff, Aerophys Lab, Mass Inst Technol, 67-68. *Concurrent Pos:* Assoc prof lectr, George Washington Univ, 75; lectr appl rheology, Kent State Univ, 76-80; translation ed, Chinese Physics, Am Inst Physics, 81-92; mem, Comt Composite Technol Transfer, Soc Plastics Indust, 77-81. *Mem:* Fel Acoust Soc Am; Am Res Soc; Sigma Xi. *Res:* Research and management in underwater acoustical materials and transducers including piezoelectrics and ferroelectrics, elastomers, plastics, optical fibers, fluids, composites and sonar transducer development. *Mailing Add:* Naval Res Lab PO Box 568337 Orlando FL 32856-8337. *Fax:* 407-857-5202

**TING, SAMUEL C C,** PARTICLE PHYSICS. *Current Pos:* assoc prof, 67-69, PROF PHYSICS, MASS INST TECHNOL, 69-, THOMAS DUDLEY CABOT INST PROF, 77- *Personal Data:* b Ann Arbor, Mich, Jan 27, 36; m 60; c 2. *Educ:* Univ Mich, BSE(physics) & BSE(math), 59, MS, 60, PhD(physics), 62. *Hon Degrees:* ScD, Univ Mich, 78, Chinese Univ Hong Kong, 87, Univ Bologna, 8, Columbia Univ & Univ Sci & Technol, China, 90, Moscow State Univ, 91, Univ Bucharest, 93. *Honors & Awards:* Nobel Prize in Physics, 76; Ernest Orlando Lawrence Award, US Dept Energy, 76; Eringen Medal, Soc Eng Sci, 77; DeGasperi Award Sci, Govt Italy, 88; Golden Leopard Award for Excellence, 88; Gold Medal Sci, 88; Forum Engelberg Prize, 96. *Prof Exp:* Ford Found fel, Europ Coun Nuclear Res, Switz, 63-64; instr physics, Columbia Univ, 64-65, asst prof, 65-67. *Concurrent Pos:* Ground leader, Deutches Electronen Synchrotronen, Hamburg, Ger, 66; assoc ed, Nuclear Physics B, 70; hon prof, Beijing Normal Col, China, 84 & Jiatong Univ, 87. *Mem:* Nat Acad Sci; Europ Phys Soc; Ital Phys Soc; fel Am Phys Soc; fel AAAS; fel Am Acad Arts & Sci; foreign mem Pakistan Acad Sci; foreign mem Soviet Acad Sci. *Res:* Experimental particle physics; quantum electrodynamics; interactions of photons with matter. *Mailing Add:* Dept Phys Mass Inst Technol Bldg 44 Rm 114 51 Vassar St Cambridge MA 02139

**TING, SHIH-FAN,** CHEMISTRY. *Current Pos:* from assoc prof to prof, 69-83, EMER PROF CHEM, MILLERSVILLE STATE COL, 83- *Personal Data:* b Changteh, China, Sept 27, 17; US citizen; m 47; c 1. *Educ:* Univ Chekiang, BS, 41; Univ Ala, MS, 57, PhD(chem), 60. *Prof Exp:* Asst prof chem, Fisk Univ, 60-65; fel, Duquesne Univ, 65-66. *Concurrent Pos:* NSF grant, 63-65. *Mem:* Am Chem Soc. *Res:* High-frequency titration; rhenium chemistry; coordination compounds; nuclear magnetic resonance studies of hydrogen bonding. *Mailing Add:* 777 E Valley Blvd No 102 Alhambra CA 91801-5240

**TING, SIK VUNG,** HORTICULTURE. *Current Pos:* RETIRED. *Personal Data:* b Shanghai, China, Mar 3, 18; nat US; m 46; c 3. *Educ:* Mich State Univ, BS, 41; Ohio State Univ, MS, 43, PhD(hort), 52. *Prof Exp:* Asst, Ohio State Univ, 41-43 & 49-52, Agr Exp Sta, 43-45; assoc prof hort, Nanking Univ, 47-49; asst horticulturist, Citrus Exp Sta, Fla State Citrus Comn, 52-60, assoc biochemist, 60-68, res biochemist, 68-83; prof biochem, Univ Fla, 68-83. *Concurrent Pos:* Consult, 83- *Mem:* Am Soc Hort Sci; Am Chem Soc; Inst Food Technologists. *Res:* Biochemistry of horticultural plants, especially chemical components of citrus fruit. *Mailing Add:* 620 Mathews 210 Ft Collins CO 80524-3040

**TING, THOMAS C(HI) T(SAI),** APPLIED MATHEMATICS, MECHANICS. *Current Pos:* from asst prof to assoc prof, 65-70, PROF APPL MECH, UNIV ILL, CHICAGO CIRCLE, 70- *Personal Data:* b Taipei, Taiwan, Feb 9, 33; m 62, Romana T K Li; c 2. *Educ:* Nat Taiwan Univ, BSc, 56; Brown Univ, PhD(appl math), 62. *Prof Exp:* Res asst appl math, Brown Univ, 59-62, res assoc eng, 62-63, asst prof, 63-65. *Concurrent Pos:* Assoc mem, Ctr Advan Study, Univ Ill, 67-68; vis prof, Stanford Univ, 72-73; assoc ed, J Appl Mech, Am Soc Mech Engrs, 75-82. *Mem:* Math Asn Am; fel Am Soc Mech Engrs; Soc Indust & Appl Math; fel AAAS; Sigma Xi. *Res:* Continuum mechanics; viscoelasticity and viscoplasticity; wave propagations; numerical analysis; partial differential equations; anisotropic elasticity. *Mailing Add:* Univ Ill Chicago 842 W Taylor St M/C246 Chicago IL 60607-7023

**TING, TSUAN WU,** MATHEMATICS. *Current Pos:* prof math, 66-, EMER PROF MATH, UNIV ILL, URBANA. *Personal Data:* b Anking, Anhwei, China, Oct 10, 22; nat US; m 57; c 2. *Educ:* Nat Cent Univ, China, BS, 47; Univ RI, MS, 56; Ind Univ, MS, 59, PhD(math), 60. *Prof Exp:* Technician, China 60th Arsenal, 47-49, assoc engr, 49-53; res asst eng, Univ RI, 54-56; math, Ind Univ, 56-59; sr mathematician, Gen Motors Res Labs, 60-61; asst prof mech, Univ Tex, 61-63; vis mem, Courant Inst Math Sci, NY Univ, 63-64; assoc prof math, NC State Univ, 64-66. *Mem:* Soc Indust & Appl Math; Tensor Soc; Am Math Soc; Soc Natural Philos. *Res:* Theory of partial differential equations; mathematical physics; principles of continuum mechanics and differential geometry. *Mailing Add:* Dept Math Univ Ill 1409 W Green St Urbana IL 61801-2917

**TING, YU-CHEN,** PLANT CYTOLOGY, PLANT GENETICS & TISSUE CULTURE. *Current Pos:* from asst prof to assoc prof biol, 62-67, prof,67-91, EMER PROF BIOL, BOSTON COL, 91- *Personal Data:* b Honan, China, Oct 3, 20; m 60, Jovina Chen; c Andrew Claire S (Mantis). *Educ:* Nat Honan Univ, China, BS, 44; Cornell Univ, MSA, 52; La State Univ, PhD(hort genetics), 54. *Prof Exp:* Asst bot, Nat Honan Univ, 44-47; res fel, Harvard Univ, 54-62. *Concurrent Pos:* Hon prof, Genetics Inst, Beijing, China & Honan Univ, Honan, China; sr res fel, Nat Acad Sci, 79. *Mem:* AAAS; Genetics Soc Am; Am Genetic Asn; Bot Soc Am; Am Soc Hort Sci. *Res:* Cytology and genetics of Ipomoea batatas and related species; flower induction and site of synthesis of pigments in sweet potato plants; cytogenetics and tissue culture of maize and its relatives. *Mailing Add:* 230 Bonad Rd Chestnut Hill MA 02167. *Fax:* 617-552-2011; *E-Mail:* tingy@hermid.bc.edu

**TINGA, JACOB HINNES,** HORTICULTURE, PLANT PHYSIOLOGY. *Current Pos:* PROF HORT, UNIV GA, 68- *Personal Data:* b Wilmington, NC, Mar 9, 20; m 57; c 2. *Educ:* NC State Col, BS, 42; Cornell Univ, MS, 52, PhD, 56. *Prof Exp:* Assoc prof hort, Va Polytech Inst, 55-68. *Mem:* Am Soc Hort Sci. *Res:* Effect of environment on growth of horticultural crops; ornamental and greenhouse crops; winter protection; container production; propagation of large cuttings of woody plants; nursery economics. *Mailing Add:* 190 Springtree Rd Athens GA 30605

**TING-BEALL, HIE PING,** CELL PHYSIOLOGY, BIOPHYSICS. *Current Pos:* res assoc physiol & pharm, Duke Univ Med Ctr, 72-74, asst med res prof physiol, 75-83, asst med res prof anat, 75-88, asst med res prof, cell biol, 88-89, res assoc, 89-91, ASST RES PROF, MECH ENG & MAT SCI, SCH ENG, DUKE UNIV, 92- *Personal Data:* b Sibu, Malaysia, Dec 15, 40; US citizen; m 70, Harry C Beall; c Allen. *Educ:* Greensboro Col, BS, 63; Tulane Univ, MS, 65, PhD(physiol), 67. *Prof Exp:* NIH fel biophys, Mich State Univ, 67-69, res assoc biochem, 70-72; NIH trainee phys biochem, Johnson Res Found, Univ Pa, 69-70. *Concurrent Pos:* K E Osserman fel, Myasthenia Gravis Found, 73-74; NIH res grants, 82-88. *Mem:* Biophys Soc; Sigma Xi; Electron Micros Soc Am. *Res:* Structure and function of cell membranes; biophysics of bimolecular lipid membranes; ultrastructure of sodium, potassium-ATPase and calcium-ATPase; cell mechanics; cell culture of hybridomas; neutrophil adhesion and activation. *Mailing Add:* Dept Mech Eng & Mat Sci Sch Eng Duke Univ Durham NC 27708-0300. *Fax:* 919-660-8963; *E-Mail:* beallall@acpub.duke.edu

**TINGELSTAD, JON BUNDE,** PEDIATRICS, PEDIATRIC CARDIOLOGY. *Current Pos:* PROF PEDIAT, SCH MED, ECAROLINA UNIV, 76-, CHMN DEPT, 77- *Personal Data:* b McVille, NDak, Jan 15, 35; m 60; c 3. *Educ:* Univ NDak, BA, 57, BS, 58; Harvard Univ, MD, 60. *Prof Exp:* From asst prof to assoc prof pediat, Med Col Va, 67-76. *Concurrent Pos:* Intern pediat, Children's Hosp Med Ctr, Boston, 60-61, jr asst resident, 61-62; chief resident, Med Ctr, Univ Colo-Denver, 62-63; fel pediat cardiol, Children's Hosp, Buffalo, NY, 65-67. *Mem:* Am Acad Pediat; Am Col Cardiol; Am Inst Ultrasound Med; Ambulatory Pediat Asn. *Res:* Pediatric echocardiography and education. *Mailing Add:* Dept Pediat ECarolina Univ Sch Med Greenville NC 27858-4354

**TINGEY, DAVID THOMAS,** PLANT PHYSIOLOGY, AIR POLLUTION. *Current Pos:* PLANT PHYSIOLOGIST, ENVIRON PROTECTION AGENCY, CORVALLIS ENVIRON RES LAB, 73- *Personal Data:* b Salt Lake City, Utah, Jan 30, 41; m 68; c 5. *Educ:* Univ Utah, BA, 66, MA, 68; NC State Univ, PhD(plant physiol), 72. *Prof Exp:* Plant physiologist, US Environ Protection Agency, NC State Univ, 68-73. *Concurrent Pos:* Asst prof bot, Ore State Univ, 74-80, assoc prof, 80-87, prof, 88- *Mem:* Am Soc Plant Physiol; Scand Soc Plant Physiol. *Res:* Studying the effects of atmospheric pollutants on plant physiology. *Mailing Add:* 425 NW Merrie Dr Corvallis OR 97330

**TINGEY, GARTH LEROY,** NUCLEAR BYPRODUCTS, NUCLEAR GRAPHITE. *Current Pos:* sr res scientist, 65-66, unit mgr mat, 66-70, RES ASSOC, PAC NORTHWEST LABS, BATTELLE MEM INST, 70- *Personal Data:* b Woodruff, Utah, Apr 14, 32; m 53; c 8. *Educ:* Brigham Young Univ, BS, 54, MS, 59; Pa State Univ, PhD(phys chem), 63. *Prof Exp:* Sr scientist, Gen Elec Corp, 63-65. *Mem:* Am Chem Soc; Sigma Xi. *Res:* Radiation chemical studies of gaseous mixtures; inert gas sensitized radiolysis reactions; chemical kinetics; chemical studies of carbon and graphite; high temperature gas cooled nuclear reactor technology; food irradiation; nuclear waste management; nuclear graphite. *Mailing Add:* 1213 Oxford Ave Richland WA 99352

**TINGEY, WARD M,** ENTOMOLOGY. *Current Pos:* asst prof entom, 74-80, assoc prof, 80-87, PROF ENTOM, CORNELL UNIV, 87- *Personal Data:* b Brigham City, Utah, Apr 9, 44; m 68; c 2. *Educ:* Brigham Young Univ, BS, 66, MS, 68; Univ Ariz, PhD(entom), 72. *Prof Exp:* Asst res entomologist, Univ Calif, Davis, 72-74. *Mem:* Entom Soc Am; AAAS; Potato Asn Am. *Res:* Genetic resistance of crop plants to insect pests; plant defense mechanisms against insects; pest management. *Mailing Add:* Dept Entom Cornell Univ 162 Comstock Hall Ithaca NY 14853-2601. *E-Mail:* ward_tingey@cornell.edu

**TING KAI, LI,** FERROELECTRIC & DIELECTRIC MATERIALS FOR FRAM DRAW APPLICATION. *Current Pos:* STAFF SCIENTIST, EMCORE CORP, 95- *Personal Data:* b Changsha, China, Jan 21, 48; m 80, Zhen Zhong; c Qintfeng Li. *Educ:* Univ Technol, Wuhan, BS, 81; Hunan Univ, MS, 84; Zhejiang Univ, PhD(ceramic eng), 87. *Honors & Awards:* Nat Award II, NSF, China, 84. *Prof Exp:* Assoc prof, Zhejiang Univ, 87-90; res scientist, Va Polytech Inst & State Univ, 90-95. *Concurrent Pos:* Vis prof, Ctr Theoretical Physics, Italy, 89-; postdoctoral fel, Va State, 90-93. *Mem:* Mat Res Soc; Am Ceramic Soc; Am Vacuum Soc. *Res:* Investigation and development of advanced micro processes, equipment and thin film materials; design of CVO machine and CVO thin films, semiconductor, optics thin film, and dielectricmaterials and thin film characterization; author of 60 scientific publications and granted 4 US patents. *Mailing Add:* 53 Nostrand Rd Somerville NJ 08876. *Fax:* 732-271-9686; *E-Mail:* tingli@emcore.com

**TINGLE, AUBREY JAMES,** VIROLOGY, ARTHRITIS. *Current Pos:* from asst prof to assoc prof, 74-86, PROF, DEPT PEDIAT & PATH, UNIV BC, 86-, ASST DEAN, RES FAC MED, 92-; DIR RES, BC CHILDRENS HOSP, 92-; DIR RES, BC RES INST CHILD & FAMILY HEALTH, 94- *Personal Data:* b St Paul, Alta, June 28, 43; m 68, Valerie J Anderson; c

Heather L & Brian J. *Educ:* Univ Alta, MD, 67; McGill Univ, PhD(immunol), 73; FRCP(c), 74. *Concurrent Pos:* Coun mem, Western Soc Pediat Res, 86-90; interim dir res, Tzu Chi Inst Complementary & Alternative Med, 96- *Mem:* Fel Soc Pediat Res; Western Soc Pediat Res; fel Royal Col Physicians & Surgeons Can; fel Can Soc Clin Invest. *Res:* The role of persistent virus infections in the induction of autoimmune or connective tissue disorders; rubella virus infection is used as a model system for study of viral-induced arthritis and diabetes. *Mailing Add:* BC Res Inst Child & Family Health 950 28th Ave Vancouver BC V5Z 4H4 Can

**TINGLE, FREDERIC CARLEY,** INSECT BEHAVIOR, INSECT-HOST PLANT INTERACTIONS. *Current Pos:* RES ENTOMOLOGIST, BOLL WEEVIL RES LAB, AGR RES SERV, USDA, 64- *Personal Data:* b Meridian, Mass, Jan 28, 40. *Educ:* Miss State Univ, BS, 62, MS, 64. *Mem:* Int Soc Chem Ecol; Entom Soc Am; Sigma Xi. *Res:* Developing pest management strategies for Heliothis spp and other economic insect pests with emphasis on identification of the biological mechanisms that drive the mating process, host selection and oviposition behavior. *Mailing Add:* PO Box 1500 Lake Placid FL 33862

**TINGLE, MARJORIE ANNE,** MICROBIOLOGY. *Current Pos:* health scientist adminr, 75-86, CHIEF DIR, BIOMED RES SUPPORT PROG, NAT CTR RES RESOURCES, NIH, 82- *Personal Data:* b Far Rockaway, NY, Oct 5, 38. *Educ:* Brown Univ, AB, 60; Univ Wis-Madison, MS, 63, PhD(bacteriol), 66. *Prof Exp:* NIH trainee bacteriol, Univ Wis, 62-66; NIH fel, Dept Biol Sci, Purdue Univ, 67-68; Am Cancer Soc fel, Lab Enzymol, Nat Ctr Sci Res, France, 68-70; res assoc, Rosenstiel Ctr, Brandeis Univ, 71-75. *Mem:* Am Soc Microbiol; AAAS; Genetics Soc Am; NY Acad Sci. *Res:* Microbial physiology; regulation of gene expression; health administration. *Mailing Add:* Nat Ctr Res Resources Westwood Bldg Rm 848 5333 Westbard Ave Bethesda MD 20892

**TINGLE, WILLIAM HERBERT,** GENERAL INSTRUMENTATION, MANUFACTURING PROCESS MEASUREMENT & CONTROL. *Current Pos:* CONSULT, 82- *Personal Data:* b Parnassus, Pa, Aug 31, 17; m 45, Annetta Johnson; c William H & Susan J (Krumpe). *Educ:* Univ Pittsburgh, BS, 49. *Honors & Awards:* H V Churchill Award Meritorious Serv Spectro-Chem Anal, Am Soc Testing & Mat, 77. *Prof Exp:* Instr eng physics, Univ Pittsburgh, 49-50; spectroscopist anal chem, 51-62, sect head anal chem, 63-72, sci assoc equip develop, Alcoa Labs, 73-81. *Concurrent Pos:* Chmn subcomt, Am Soc Testing & Mat, 62-73; secretariat, Int Stand Orgn, 70-79. *Mem:* Sigma Xi; Optical Soc Am; Soc Appl Spectros; Am Chem Soc; Am Inst Physics. *Res:* Evaluating principles of measurement and control in chemical and metallurgical processes, atomic emission spectroscopy, plasma excitation, and optical instrumentation; administering of research projects. *Mailing Add:* 3104 Leechburg Rd Lower Burrell PA 15068

**TINGLEY, ARNOLD JACKSON,** MATHEMATICS. *Current Pos:* head dept, Dalhousie Univ, 66-73, secy senate, 75-80, from asst prof to prof math, 53-85, registr, 73-85, bd gov, 80-86, EMER PROF, DALHOUSIE UNIV, 86- *Personal Data:* b Point de Bute, June 9, 20; m 46; c 2. *Educ:* Mt Alison Univ, BA, 49; Univ Minn, PhD(math), 52. *Prof Exp:* Instr math, Univ Nebr, 52-53. *Mem:* Can Math Soc. *Res:* Analysis. *Mailing Add:* Dept Math Statist & Comput Sci Dalhousie Univ Halifax NS B3H 3J5 Can. *E-Mail:* tingley@cs.dal.ca

**TINKER, DAVID OWEN,** BIOCHEMISTRY, PHYSICAL CHEMISTRY. *Current Pos:* from asst prof to assoc prof, 66-82, PROF BIOCHEM, UNIV TORONTO, 82- *Personal Data:* b Toronto, Ont, Jan 25, 40; m 62, Sheila Wilcox; c Nicholas, Timothy, Michael & Katherine. *Educ:* Univ Toronto, BSc, 61; Univ Wash, PhD(biochem), 65. *Prof Exp:* Nat Res Coun Can fel, Univ London, 65-66. *Concurrent Pos:* Assoc ed, Can J Biochem, 74-82. *Mem:* Sigma Xi; Can Biochem Soc; Biophys Soc; NY Acad Sci; Inst Elec & Electronics Engrs Comput Soc. *Res:* Computer applications in biochemistry; lipid-protein interactions. *Mailing Add:* Dept Biochem Fac Med Univ Toronto Toronto ON M5S 1A8 Can. *Fax:* 416-978-8548; *E-Mail:* dtinker@blunile.guild.org

**TINKER, H(ORALD) BURNHAM,** CHEMISTRY. *Current Pos:* tech dir, 81-90, VPRES RES & DEVELOP, MOONEY CHEMS, INC, 91- *Personal Data:* b St Louis, Mo, May 16, 39; m 65, Barbara A Lydon; c Michael B, Mary K & Ann E. *Educ:* St Louis Univ, BS, 61; Univ Chicago, MS, 64, PhD(chem), 66. *Prof Exp:* Sr res chemist, Monsanto, 66-69, res specialist, 69-73, res group leader, 73-77, res mgr, 77-81. *Mem:* Am Chem Soc. *Res:* Chemistry. *Mailing Add:* Corp Develop 3800 Terminal Tower Cleveland OH 44113

**TINKER, JOHN FRANK,** CHEMISTRY, INFORMATION SCIENCE. *Current Pos:* RETIRED. *Personal Data:* b Wis, Mar 25, 22; m 48, Mary Russell. *Educ:* Univ Va, BS, 43; Harvard Univ, PhD(chem), 51. *Prof Exp:* Instr chem, Harvard Univ, 50-52; info scientist, Eastman Kodak Co, 52-84. *Res:* Chemical information. *Mailing Add:* 9843 47th Ave SW Seattle WA 98136-2717

**TINKER, SPENCER WILKIE,** ichthyology, conchology & cetology, for more information see previous edition

**TINKHAM, MICHAEL,** SUPERCONDUCTIVITY. *Current Pos:* chmn dept physics, 75-78, prof physics, 66-80, GORDON MCKAY PROF APPL PHYSICS, HARVARD UNIV, 66-, RUMFORD PROF PHYSICS, 80- *Personal Data:* b Green Lake Co, Wis, Feb 23, 28; m 61, Mary Merin; c Jeffrey M & Christopher G. *Educ:* Ripon Col, AB, 51; Mass Inst Technol, MS, 51, PhD(physics), 54. *Hon Degrees:* ScD, Ripon Col, 76; MA, Harvard Univ, 66. *Honors & Awards:* Buckley Prize, Am Phys Soc, 74. *Prof Exp:* NSF fel, Clarendon Lab, Oxford Univ, 54-55; res physicist, Univ Calif, Berkeley, 55-57, lectr, 56-57, from asst prof to prof physics, 57-66. *Concurrent Pos:* Guggenheim fel, 63-64; NSF sr fel, Cavendish Lab, Cambridge Univ, 71-72; Humboldt sr scientist, Univ Karlsruhe, 78-79; vis Miller res prof, Univ Calif, Berkeley, 87; mem, Briefing Panel, High Temperature Superconductivity, Nat Acad Sci, 87; vis prof, Delft Univ Technol, 93. *Mem:* Nat Acad Sci; fel Am Acad Arts & Sci; fel Am Phys Soc; fel AAAS. *Res:* Superconductivity: energy gap, fluxoid quantization and macroscopic quantum interference, fluctuation effects, Josephson junctions, nonequilibrium effects including charge imbalance, and energy imbalance and macroscopic quantum tunneling, charging energy effects; microwave and far-infrared magnetic resonance. *Mailing Add:* Dept Physics Harvard Univ Cambridge MA 02138

**TINKLER, JACK D(ONALD),** CHEMICAL ENGINEERING. *Current Pos:* RETIRED. *Personal Data:* b Topeka, Kans, Apr 12, 36; m 60; c 2. *Educ:* Univ Ill, BS, 58; Univ Del, MChE, 61, PhD(chem eng), 63. *Prof Exp:* Res engr, Res & Develop Dept, Sun Oil Co, 63-70, chief eng fundamentals, Corp Res Dept, 70-77; vpres eng, Occidental Res Corp, 77-80, Occidental Chem Co, 81-82, Occidental Petrol Corp, 83-85; mgr, Process Develop, Pennwalt Corp, 85-87, gen mgr, Cent Eng, 87-89; vpres tech, Atochem NA, 90- *Mem:* Am Inst Chem Engrs; Am Chem Soc. *Res:* Kinetics; simulation; model building; process design and evaluation; technical economics. *Mailing Add:* 498 Meadow Lane King of Prussia PA 19406

**TINLINE, ROBERT DAVIES,** PLANT PATHOLOGY. *Current Pos:* RETIRED. *Personal Data:* b Moose Jaw, Sask, Aug 4, 25; m 48, June Brackenbury; c Jennifer, Judith, Robert, John & Ross. *Educ:* Univ Sask, BA, 48; Univ Wis, MS, 52, PhD(plant path), 54. *Prof Exp:* From tech officer I to tech officer II, Agr Can, 48-51, agr res officer, 51-67, res scientist, 67-94. *Mem:* Mycol Soc Am; Am Phytopath Soc; fel Can Phytopath Soc (pres, 77-78); Agr Inst Can. *Res:* Root and leaf diseases of cereals; variability and genetics of plant pathogenic fungi. *Mailing Add:* 523 Garrison Crescent Saskatoon SK S7H 2Z9 Can

**TINNEY, FRANCIS JOHN,** MEDICINAL CHEMISTRY. *Current Pos:* res assoc, Warner-Lambert/Parke-Davis & Co, 78-87, sr patent atty, 87-89, asst patent coun, 89-92, assoc patent coun, 92-95, coun patents, 95, SR COUN, PHARMACEUT PATENTS, 95- *Personal Data:* b Brooklyn, NY, July 31, 38; m 74, Kathleen Dickson; c Michael, Kathryn, Kristen & Francis. *Educ:* St John's Univ, NY, BS, 59, MS, 61; Univ Md, PhD(aza steroids), 65; Univ Toledo, JD, 85; Wayne State Univ, LLM, 92. *Prof Exp:* Ortho Res Found fel chem, Univ Md, 65-66; assoc res chemist, Parke Davis & Co, 66-69, res chemist, 69-70, sr res chemist, 70-78. *Mem:* Am Chem Soc; Am Pharmaceut Asn; NY Acad Sci; Am Intellectual Property. *Res:* Organic medicinal chemistry; steroids; heterocyclic steroids; heterocyclics; organic nitrogen containing compounds; peptides; antiallergy compounds. *Mailing Add:* Warner-Lambert/Parke-Davis & Co 2800 Plymouth Rd Ann Arbor MI 48105. *Fax:* 313-996-1553

**TINNEY, WILLIAM FRANK,** ELECTRIC POWER SYSTEMS. *Current Pos:* INDEPENDENT CONSULT, 79- *Personal Data:* b Portland, Ore, May 5, 21; m 48; c 2. *Educ:* Stanford Univ, BS, 48, MS, 49. *Prof Exp:* Elec engr, Bonneville Power Admin, 50-63, head methods anal, 63-79. *Mem:* Fel Inst Elec & Electronics Engrs. *Res:* Development of solution methods for large scale electric power network problems, energy management systems, optimal operation & control. *Mailing Add:* 9101 SW Eighth Ave Portland OR 97219

**TINNIN, ROBERT OWEN,** PLANT ECOLOGY. *Current Pos:* From asst prof to assoc prof, 69-80, PROF BIOL, PORTLAND STATE UNIV, 80- *Personal Data:* b Santa Barbara, Calif, Sept 6, 43; m 65; c 1. *Educ:* Univ Calif, Santa Barbara, BA, 65, PhD(ecol), 69. *Mem:* Ecol Soc Am. *Res:* Host-parasite interactions and their effect on plant communities; natural systems under study are coniferous forest sites infected by arceuthobium species. *Mailing Add:* Dept Biol Portland Univ PO Box 751 Portland OR 97207

**TINOCO, IGNACIO, JR,** PHYSICAL CHEMISTRY. *Current Pos:* from instr to assoc prof, 56-66, chmn dept, 79-82, PROF CHEM, UNIV CALIF, BERKELEY, 66- *Personal Data:* b El Paso, Tex, Nov 22, 30; m 51; c 1. *Educ:* Univ NMex, BS, 51, DSc, 72; Univ Wis, PhD(chem), 54. *Honors & Awards:* Calif Sect Award, Am Chem Soc, 65. *Prof Exp:* Res fel chem, Yale Univ, 54-56. *Concurrent Pos:* Guggenheim fel, 64. *Mem:* Nat Acad Sci; Am Chem Soc; Am Phys Soc; Biophys Soc; Am Soc Biol Chemists. *Res:* Biophysical chemistry. *Mailing Add:* Dept Chem Univ Calif Berkeley CA 94720

**TINOCO, JOAN W H,** LIPID METABOLISM. *Current Pos:* RETIRED. *Personal Data:* b Nome, Alaska, Oct 14, 32. *Educ:* Univ Calif, Berkeley, BS, 58, PhD(nutrit), 62. *Prof Exp:* Technician II lipid res, Dept Home Econ, Univ Calif, Berkeley, 58-59, res asst, 59-61, res fel, Dept Nutrit Sci, 61-67, asst res biochemist, 67-73, res fel, Dept Chem, 73-75, assoc res biochemist, Dept Nutrit Sci, 75-85. *Concurrent Pos:* Res fel, Dept Path, Cambridge Univ, Eng, 64; actg asst prof biochem, Ore State Univ, Corvallis, 70-71. *Mem:* Am Soc Nutrit Sci; AAAS; Sigma Xi. *Res:* Functions of lipids; metabolism of cholesterol, fatty acids, and phospholipids; dietary requirements for essential fatty acids, especially n-3 fatty acids; behavior of cholesterol and phospholipids in monomolecular films (membrane model). *Mailing Add:* 1035 Spruce St Berkeley CA 94707

**TINSLEY, BRIAN ALFRED,** SPACE PHYSICS, ATMOSPHERIC ELECTRICITY. *Current Pos:* PROF, UNIV TEX, DALLAS, 88- *Personal Data:* b Wellington, NZ, Apr 23, 37; m 61; c Alan, Teresa, W Walter & E Waverly. *Educ:* Univ Canterbury, BSc, 58, MSc, 61, PhD(physics), 63. *Prof Exp:* Res assoc atmospheric & space sci, Univ Tex, Dallas, 63-65, res scientist, 65-67, from asst prof to prof physics, 67-86; aeronomy prog dir, NSF, 86-88. *Concurrent Pos:* Chmn, Div II, Int Asn Geomog & Aeronomy, 73-79; mem, Comn Solar Terrestrial Physics, Nat Acad Sci, 75-79; assoc ed, J Geophys Res, 74-78 & Rev Geophys, 88-92; Orson Anderson scholar, Los Alamos Nat Lab, 95-96. *Mem:* Am Geophys Union. *Res:* Optical observations of airglow and low latitude aurorae; design of optical instruments for measurement of airglow and aurorae; theoretical studies of atmospheres of earth and planets; effects of solar variability and atmospheric electricity on weather and climate. *Mailing Add:* Physics Prog F022 Univ Tex-Dallas PO Box 830688 Richardson TX 75083-0688. *E-Mail:* tinsley @utdallas.edu

**TINSLEY, IAN JAMES,** BIOCHEMISTRY. *Current Pos:* from asst prof to assoc prof, 57-70, PROF BIOCHEM, ORE STATE UNIV, 70- *Personal Data:* b Sydney, Australia, Sept 23, 29; m 55; c 2. *Educ:* Univ Sydney, BSc, 50; Ore State Univ, MS, 55, PhD(food sci), 58. *Honors & Awards:* Florasynth Award, Inst Food Technologists, 55. *Prof Exp:* Res officer, Commonwealth Sci & Indust Res Orgn, Australia, 50-53. *Mem:* Am Inst Nutrit; Am Oil Chem Soc; Am Chem Soc. *Res:* Lipid metabolism; essential fatty acid nutrition; biochemical effects of pesticide ingestion; interactions of pesticides with lipids. *Mailing Add:* Dept Agr Chem Ore State Univ Weniger Hall 339 Corvallis OR 97331-7301

**TINSLEY, SAMUEL WEAVER,** ORGANIC CHEMISTRY. *Current Pos:* RETIRED. *Personal Data:* b Hopkinsville, Ky, July 15, 23; m 45, Jeane Payne; c Samuel III, Kathryn & Kristen. *Educ:* Western Ky State Col, BS, 44; Northwestern Univ, PhD(org chem), 50. *Prof Exp:* Asst prof chem, Tex Tech Col, 49-50; res chemist, Union Carbide Corp, 50-60, asst dir org res, 60-64, assoc dir res & develop, 64-67, mgr new chem, 67-71, mgr corp res, 71-74, dir corp res, 74-77, dir corp technol, 77-85. *Mem:* Am Chem Soc; Indust Res Inst; Com Develop Asn. *Res:* Aromatic synthesis; peracids; epoxides. *Mailing Add:* 1739 Irish Blvd Sanford NC 27330

**TINSMAN, JAMES HERBERT, JR,** PHYSICAL ANTHROPOLOGY. *Current Pos:* RETIRED. *Personal Data:* b Philadelphia, Pa, Apr 22, 30; m 56; c 4. *Educ:* Univ Pa, AB, 56, AM, 60; Univ Colo, MA, 66, PhD(anthrop), 71. *Prof Exp:* From instr to assoc prof philos & econ, Kutztown State Col, 59-71, prof anthrop, 71-74, chmn, Dept Soc Sci, 74-77, chmn, Dept Anthrop & Sociol, 85-86; pres, Asn Pa State Col & Univ Faculties, 86-92. *Concurrent Pos:* Lectr anthrop, Univ Colo, 69-71; co-ed, Newsletter Pa Anthropologists; NSF fel, 64, 65-66 & 68-71. *Mem:* Fel Am Anthrop Asn; Soc Study Social Biol; Am Asn Phys Anthrop. *Res:* Contemporary human variation, anthropometric, anthroscopic and serological, as relates to human genetics, population structure and, ultimately, human evolution. *Mailing Add:* 431 Caloric Circle Topton PA 19562

**TINT, HOWARD,** BIOCHEMISTRY, BIOLOGICALS. *Current Pos:* RETIRED. *Personal Data:* b Philadelphia, Pa, Jan 22, 17; m 41; c 2. *Educ:* Univ Pa, AB, 37, PhD(mycol, plant path), 43. *Prof Exp:* Leader scouting crews, Bur Entom & Plant Quarantine, USDA, Washington, DC, 39-40, biol tech aide, Bur Plant Indust, 41, physiologist, Bur Agr & Indust Chem, 43-45; biochemist, Wyeth Inc, 45-50, sr res biochemist, 50-56, supvr, Biologics Lab, Wyeth Labs, 56-60, dir, Prod Develop Div, 60-63, dir, Biol & Chem Develop Div, 63-82. *Concurrent Pos:* Microbiologist, Off Sci Res & Develop, Johnson Found, Univ Pa, 45. *Mem:* Am Chem Soc; Sigma Xi; NY Acad Sci. *Res:* Microbiology; physiology; virology; tissue culture; cancer immunology; chemical development and pilot-plant; fine-chemicals production. *Mailing Add:* 33 Deep Well Lane Los Altos CA 94022

**TINTI, DINO S,** PHYSICAL CHEMISTRY. *Current Pos:* from asst prof to assoc prof, 70-81, PROF CHEM, UNIV CALIF, DAVIS, 81- *Personal Data:* b San Bernardino, Calif, Feb 20, 41; m 62, Diana Campbell; c Katrina, Laura & Lisa. *Educ:* Univ Calif, Riverside, BA, 62; Calif Inst Technol, PhD(chem), 68. *Prof Exp:* Res chemist, Univ Calif, Los Angeles, 67-70. *Concurrent Pos:* Sloan fel, 74-78. *Mem:* Am Chem Soc. *Res:* Electronic and magnetic resonance spectroscopy of excited electronic states. *Mailing Add:* Chem Dept Univ Calif Davis CA 95616-5224. *E-Mail:* dstinti@ucdavis.edu

**TINTINALLI, JUDITH ELLEN,** EMERGENCY MEDICINE. *Current Pos:* PROF, CHMN & RESIDENCY PROG DIR, DEPT EMERGENCY MED, UNIV NC, CHAPEL HILL, 91- *Personal Data:* b Detroit, Mich, Mar 6, 43. *Educ:* Wayne State Univ, MD, 69; Univ Mich, MS, 91; Am Bd Internal Med, dipl, 74; Am Bd Emergency Med, dipl, 81. *Prof Exp:* Intern, Detroit Gen Hosp, 69-70; resident, Univ Mich Med Ctr, 71-74; instr, Dept Internal Med, Wayne State Univ, 74-81, Dept Community Med, 75-84, asst prof, Dept Surg, Div Emergency Med, 79, assoc prof, 79-84; emergency med residency prog dir, William Beaumont Hosp, Mich, 84-91, clin dir, Dept Emergency Med, 84-91. *Concurrent Pos:* Attending physician, Emergency Dept, Detroit Receiving Hosp, 74-77, vchief & residency prog dir, 77-84; dir, Am Bd Emergency Med, 82-91, secy-treas, 87-88, pres-elect, 88-89, pres, 89-90; clin asst prof surg, Univ Mich, 86-91; attending physician, Emergency Dept, Univ Mich Med Ctr, 88-91; chmn, Sect Emergency Med Residency Dirs, Am Col Emergency Physicians, 89-91. *Mem:* Inst Med-Nat Acad Sci; fel Am Col Emergency Physicians; Soc Acad Emergency Med. *Mailing Add:* Dept Emergency Med Univ NC Sch Med CB 7594 Chapel Hill NC 27599-7594

**TINUS, RICHARD WILLARD,** PLANT PHYSIOLOGY, FORESTRY. *Current Pos:* Plant physiologist, Agr Res Serv, 65-68, proj leader, 68-93, PRIN PHYSIOLOGIST, US FOREST SERV, USDA, 68- *Personal Data:* b Orange, NJ, Mar 26, 36; m 58; c 2. *Educ:* Wesleyan Univ, BA, 58; Duke Univ, MF, 60; Univ Calif, Berkeley, PhD(plant physiol), 65. *Concurrent Pos:* Chmn working party, cold & drought hardiness, Int Union Forestry Res Orgn, ex-chmn working party, nursery opers; adv ed, Tree Planters Notes. *Mem:* Am Soc Plant Physiologists; Int Plant Propagators Soc; Soc Am Foresters; Sigma Xi. *Res:* Development of greenhouse container systems for tree seedling production; vegetative propagation of pine; cold and drought resistance of trees. *Mailing Add:* Southern Res Sta Forestry Sci Lab 2500 S Pine Knoll Dr Flagstaff AZ 86001. *Fax:* 520-556-2130

**TIN-WA, MAUNG,** MEDICINAL CHEMISTRY, PHARMACOGNOSY. *Current Pos:* PRES BIOSCI, ANPRA INC, 88- *Personal Data:* b Rangoon, Burma, May 12, 40; US citizen; m 79. *Educ:* Univ Rangoon, Burma, BSc, 61; Ohio State Univ, Columbus, MSc, 65, PhD(pharmacog & natural prods), 69. *Prof Exp:* Teaching asst chem, Univ Rangoon, 61-62; teaching asst pharmacog, Univ Pittsburgh, 69; NSF fel plant sci, Univ Calif, Riverside, 70-71; NIH res assoc natural anticancer agents, Univ Ill Med Ctr, 71-72, asst prof pharmacog, 73-75; res dir, Res & Consult Assocs, 75-79; dir biosci, Sci Innovations, 80-87. *Concurrent Pos:* Sr investr, Nat Cancer Inst, 72-74; dir, Nortech Labs Ltd, 82-87; chief tech dir, Pharm Chem Inc, 93- *Mem:* Inst Food Technologists; Am Soc Pharmacog. *Res:* Development of synthetic and natural products with potential use for the treatment of cancer, immunodeficiency and cardiovascular diseases; ethnopharmacology and economic botany; food products; natural products chemistry. *Mailing Add:* Anpra Inc 30 Arroyo Way San Francisco CA 94127. *Fax:* 415-239-4245

**TIO, CESARIO O,** ORGANIC SYNTHESIS, PHARMACOKINETICS. *Current Pos:* res chemist II, 65-67, res chemist III, 67-78, UNIT SUPVR, WYETH-AYERST RES LABS, 65-, RES SCIENTIST, 86- *Personal Data:* b Cebu, Philippines, Aug, 30, 32; m 62; c 2. *Educ:* Univ Santo Tomas, Philippines, BS, 56; Georgetown Univ, Wash, MS, 61. *Prof Exp:* Res asst, Georgetown Univ Hosp, 78-86. *Res:* Drug disposition and metabolism; methods development for drug analysis; radiotracer synthesis; isolation and characterization of drug metabolites; synthesis of metabolites of drugs and pharmacokinetics. *Mailing Add:* Wyeth-Ayerst Res Labs Inc CN 8000 Princeton NJ 08543-8000

**TIPANS, IGORS O,** ELECTRICAL ACTIVITY IN A HEART, OSCILLATIONS IN MECHANICAL & BIOLOGICAL SYSTEMS. *Current Pos:* researcher, Riga Tech Univ, 76-79, asst prof mech, 82-87, sr lectr, 87-88, ASSOC PROF MECH, RIGA TECH UNIV, LATVIA, 90- *Personal Data:* b Riga, Latvia, Feb 7, 53; m 82, Indra Vitolina; c Marcis & Zane. *Educ:* St Peterburg Polytech Inst, Russia, Eng-phys, 76; Biophys Inst, Moscow, Cand phys-math sci, 85; Riga Tech Univ, Dr sci ing, 93. *Concurrent Pos:* Fel, Duke Univ, 88-89 UTC Compiegne, France, 96; consult, UN Develop Prog, 93-; mem, Latian Nat Mech Comt. *Mem:* Sr mem Biomed Eng Soc; Latvian Scientist Union. *Res:* Mathematical modelling of electrical excitation in heart cells; action potentials of sinoatrial node pacemaker cells; modelling of calcium blocking drugs action mechanisms. *Mailing Add:* Riga Tech Univ Kalku St 1A Riga LV-1658 Latvia. *Fax:* 371-7820094; *E-Mail:* igors@cfp.edu.lv

**TIPEI, NICOLAE,** TRIBOLOGY, FLIGHT MECHANICS. *Current Pos:* RETIRED. *Personal Data:* b Calarasi, Romania, Apr 19, 13; US citizen; m 41, Letitia I Radulescu; c Sever. *Educ:* Polytech Inst, Bucharest, MD, 36; Romanian Acad, DrEng, 68. *Honors & Awards:* Mayo D Hersey Award, Am Soc Mech Engrs, 80. *Prof Exp:* Asst prof airports & airplane oper, Polytech Inst, Bucharest, Romania, 36-48, assoc prof flight mech & rocket dynamics, 48-64, emer prof flight mech, rocket dynamics & aerodyn, 64-71; head solid & fluid mech, Gen Mech Div, Inst Appl Mech, Romanian Acad, 49-67, head tribology, Lubric Div, Inst Fluid Mech, 67-69; head, Tribology Div, Inst Sci Creation & Technol, Bucharest, 69-71; res fel engr res fluid mech, Gen Motors Corp Res Labs, 72-85. *Concurrent Pos:* Chief engr locomotive overhaul, Romanian Rwy, 37-38; chief engr airplane aerodyn & maintenance, Romanian Airlines, Romanian Air Transp, 38-39; pres, Nicolae Tipei Mech Trade Co, 39-43; chief engr, Romanian Mech & Chem Indust, 45-49; consult engr, Elec France & Total Co, 71-72. *Res:* General mechanics; aerodynamics and flight mechanics; rocket dynamics and space flight; lubrication-tribology; fluid mechanics. *Mailing Add:* 105 Flora Dr Champaign IL 61821

**TIPLER, FRANK JENNINGS, III,** GLOBAL GENERAL RELATIVITY, COSMOLOGY. *Current Pos:* assoc prof, 81-87, PROF MATH & PHYSICS, TULANE UNIV, 87- *Personal Data:* b Andalusia, Ala, Feb 1, 47; m 84, Jolanta Rokicka; c Allison A & Caroline N. *Educ:* Mass Inst Technol, SB, 69; Univ Md, PhD(physics), 76. *Prof Exp:* Res mathematician, Univ Calif, Berkeley, 76-79; sr res fel, Oxford Univ, 79; res assoc, Univ Tex, Austin, 79-81. *Concurrent Pos:* Vis fel, Astron Ctr, Univ Sussex, UK, 85, 87; vis prof, Univ Berne, Switz, 88, Univ Liege, Belg, 88 & Univ Vienna, Austria, 92. *Mem:* Am Phys Soc; Royal Astron Soc; Sigma Xi; Int Soc Gen Relativity & Gravitation; Int Astron Union. *Res:* Structure of singularities in classical general relativity; quantum cosmology omega point theory; extraterrestrial intelligent life; future evolution of universe; anthropic principle; wave function interpretation. *Mailing Add:* Depts Math & Physics Tulane Univ New Orleans LA 70118. *E-Mail:* frank.tipler@tulane.edu

**TIPLER, PAUL A,** NUCLEAR PHYSICS. *Current Pos:* CONSULT, 82- *Personal Data:* b Antigo, Wis, Apr 12, 33; div; c 2. *Educ:* Purdue Univ, BS, 55; Univ Ill, PhD(physics), 62. *Prof Exp:* Asst prof physics, Wesleyan Univ, 61-62; from asst prof to prof ohysics, Oakland Univ, 62-82. *Mem:* Am Phys Soc; Am Asn Physics Teachers. *Res:* Low energy nuclear physics. *Mailing Add:* 1329 Arch St Berkeley CA 94708

**TIPPENS, DORR E(UGENE) F(ELT),** CHEMICAL ENGINEERING. *Current Pos:* OWNER, DNE NO-LOAD MUTUAL FUND ADV SERV, 82- *Personal Data:* b Grand Rapids, Mich, Dec 28, 23; m 43, Doris R Willsey; c 3. *Educ:* Purdue Univ, BS, 48. *Prof Exp:* Engr in training, Oper Dept, Am Sugar Co, 49-50, asst supt Refining Dept, Baltimore Refinery, 50-53, refining supt, 53-56, asst to refining mgr, 56-58, process design engr, NY, 58-59, dept head New Food Prod Develop, Res & Develop Div, 59-64, dir Process Develop, 64-68, sr chem engr, 68-76, proj mgr, Amstar Corp, 76-82. *Mem:* Am Chem Soc; Sugar Indust Tech; Am Inst Chem Engrs. *Res:* New process development in sugar refining and new food product development, directing and administrating. *Mailing Add:* Box 5 Gibson Island MD 21056-0665. *E-Mail:* aul@dne__mfas

**TIPPER, DONALD JOHN,** MICROBIOLOGY, MOLECULAR BIOLOGY. *Current Pos:* chmn dept, 71-80, PROF MICROBIOL & MOLECULAR GENETICS, MED SCH, UNIV MASS, 71- *Personal Data:* b Birmingham, Eng, July 21, 35; m 65; c 3. *Educ:* Univ Birmingham, BSc, 56, PhD(chem), 59. *Honors & Awards:* Frankland Prize, 59. *Prof Exp:* Res assoc immunochem, Dept Surg Res, St Luke's Hosp, 59-60; chemist, Guinness's Brewery, Dublin, Ireland, 60-62; res asst pharmacol, Washington Univ, 62-64; res asst, Univ Wis-Madison, 64-65, from asst prof to assoc prof, 65-71. *Concurrent Pos:* USPHS career develop award, 68-71. *Mem:* Am Soc Microbiol; Brit Soc Gen Microbiol; Genetics Soc Am; Am Soc Biochem & Molecular Biol. *Res:* Structure and biosynthesis of bacterial cell walls; mode of action of penicillins; mechanism of membrane protein insertion; yeast dsRNA-coded killer system; G-protein coupled signal transduction in yeast. *Mailing Add:* Dept Molecular Genetics & Microbiol Univ Mass Med Ctr Worcester MA 01655

**TIPPER, RONALD CHARLES,** BIOLOGICAL OCEANOGRAPHY, ARCTIC SYSTEM SCIENCE. *Current Pos:* sci officer environ qual div, US Naval Oceanog Off, 71-72, aide & exec asst oceanog res & develop, 72-74, dir oceanic biol prog, Off Naval Res, 74-76 & Naval Ocean Res & Develop Activity, 76-77, cmndg officer, Oceanog Unit One, 77-78, dir oceanic biol prog, Off Naval Res, 78-81, dir ocean surv prog, 81-83, res prog mgr, Off Naval Res, 83-86, off asst secy, Navy Res & Systs, 86-87, cmndg officer, Polar Oceanog Ctr, 87-89, dir, Naval Requirements D & D Hydrographic & Topographic Ctr, 89-94, DIR SATELLITE PROG, JOINT OCEANOG INST, INC, US NAVAL OCEANOG OFF, 91- *Personal Data:* b Sacramento, Calif, July 17, 42; m 64; c 2. *Educ:* Ore State Univ, BS, 64, PhD(biol oceanog), 68. *Prof Exp:* Antisubmarine warfare officer, USS Coontz DLG-9, San Diego, Calif, 68-70; res plans officer oceanog res, US Naval Oceanog Off, 70-71. *Concurrent Pos:* Affil prof oceanog, Dept Oceanog, Seattle, Wash, 94- *Mem:* Sigma Xi; Am Geophys Union; AAAS; Oceanog Soc. *Res:* Oceanic biology; marine biodeterioration; distribution and abundance of Micronekton and Zooplankton; benthic ecology; geophysics; cartography; navigation; arctic system science. *Mailing Add:* 9819 Summerday Dr Burke VA 22015

**TIPPETT, JAMES T,** COMPUTER SCIENCE, ELECTRONICS ENGINEERING. *Current Pos:* ELECTRONIC ENGR, NAT SECURITY AGENCY, 55- *Personal Data:* b Oxford, NC, May 11, 31; m 65; c 2. *Educ:* NC State Col, BSEE, 54, EE, 55. *Mem:* AAAS; Inst Elec & Electronics Engrs; Asn Comput Mach. *Res:* Ultra high speed computer circuits; software techniques; computer languages; networks of computers; computer security; software engineering; telecommunications; general computer sciences. *Mailing Add:* Dept Defense Nat Security Agency 9800 Savage Rd Ft George G Meade MD 20755

**TIPPING, RICHARD H,** MOLECULAR PHYSICS. *Current Pos:* PROF PHYSICS & ASTRON, UNIV ALA, 82- *Personal Data:* b Abington, Pa, Aug 31, 39. *Educ:* Pa State Univ, BSc, 63, MSc, 66, PhD(physics), 69. *Prof Exp:* From asst prof to assoc prof, mem Univ Nfld, 69-77; assoc prof physics, Univ Nebr, Omaha, 77-81, prof, 80. *Mem:* Am Phys Soc; Sigma Xi. *Res:* Molecular spectral line shapes; intensities and spectroscopic constants of diatomic molecules. *Mailing Add:* 4 Wenza Pl Northport AL 35476. *Fax:* 205-348-5051; *E-Mail:* rtipping@ua1vm.ua.edu

**TIPPLES, KEITH H,** CEREAL CHEMISTRY. *Current Pos:* Nat Res Coun Can res fel, 63-64, res scientist, 64-79, DIR, GRAIN RES LAB, CAN GRAIN COMN, 79- *Personal Data:* b Cambridge, Eng, Feb 4, 36; m 62, Maureen N Mannall; c 3. *Educ:* Univ Birmingham, BSc, 59, PhD(appl biochem), 62. *Honors & Awards:* C W Brabender Award, 75; Gold Medal, Czechoslovak Acad Agr, 82; William F Leddes Mem Award, 91. *Mem:* Fel Am Asn Cereal Chem. *Res:* Basic and applied research on the quality of cereal grains and oilseeds aimed at understanding the chemistry and technology of end-use quality and development of improved methods for quality assessment. *Mailing Add:* Grain Res Lab Can Grain Comn 1404-303 Main St Winnipeg MB R3C 3G8 Can. *Fax:* 204-983-0724; *E-Mail:* ktipples@cgc.ca

**TIPSWORD, RAY FENTON,** PHYSICS. *Current Pos:* asst prof, 63-68, assoc prof, 68-81, PROF PHYSICS, VA POLYTECH INST & STATE UNIV, 81- *Personal Data:* b Beecher City, Ill, Sept 9, 31; m 52; c 2. *Educ:* Eastern Ill Univ, BSEd, 53; Southern Ill Univ, MS, 57; Univ Ala, PhD(physics), 62. *Prof Exp:* Instr physics, Mo Sch Mines, 57-59; fel, Univ Ala, 62-63. *Res:* Nuclear magnetic resonance and low temperature physics. *Mailing Add:* 1827 E Ridge Dr Blacksburg VA 24060

**TIPTON, C(LYDE) R(AYMOND), JR,** SCIENCE COMMUNICATIONS. *Current Pos:* sr consult, 87-89, PRES COMMUN DEVELOP, QUEST INT, 89- *Personal Data:* b Cincinnati, Ohio, Nov 13, 21; m 42, Marian G Beushausen; c Marian (Page) & Robert B. *Educ:* Univ Ky, BS, 46, MS, 47. *Prof Exp:* Asst, Univ Ky, 46-47; res engr, Battelle Mem Inst, 47-49; phys metallurgist, Los Alamos Sci Lab, 49-51; from asst div chief to sr tech adv, Physics Dept, Battelle Mem Inst, 51-62; dir res, Basic, Inc, 62-64; from staff mgr to asst dir, Pac Northwest Labs, 64-69, coordr corp commun, 69-73, vpres commun, 73-75, pres & trustee, Battelle Commons Co, 75-78, asst pres, 78-80, vpres & corp dir commun & pub affairs, Battelle Mem Inst, 80-87. *Concurrent Pos:* Consult, Atomic Energy Comn, 58-61; secy, US Deleg 2nd UN Int Conf Peaceful Uses Atomic Energy, Geneva, Switz, 58; sr fel, Otterbein Col, 78; chmn, Prof Engrs Ind, 88-89. *Mem:* Am Soc Metals; Nat Soc Prof Engrs (pres, 95-96); Sigma Xi. *Res:* Reactor materials; technical and scientific information handling; industrial research. *Mailing Add:* 6475 Strathaven Ct W Worthington OH 43085. *Fax:* 614-846-4059

**TIPTON, CARL LEE,** BIOCHEMISTRY. *Current Pos:* Assoc & instr, 61-62, from asst to assoc prof, 62-78, PROF BIOCHEM, IOWA STATE UNIV, 78- *Personal Data:* b Collins, Iowa, July 26, 31; m 57; c 3. *Educ:* Univ Nebr, BS, 54, MS, 57; Univ Ill, PhD, 61. *Concurrent Pos:* NIH sr fel, Univ Calif, Davis, 69-70. *Mem:* AAAS; Am Chem Soc; Am Soc Biochem & Molecular Biol. *Res:* Cholesterol metabolism. *Mailing Add:* Dept Biochem & Biophys Iowa State Univ Ames IA 50011-0001

**TIPTON, CHARLES M,** EXERCISE PHYSIOLOGY, SPACE PHYSIOLOGY. *Current Pos:* RETIRED. *Personal Data:* b Evanston, Ill, Nov 29, 27; m 53, Betty Jane; c Teresa, Paula, Barbara & Mary E. *Educ:* Springfield Col, BS, 52; Univ Ill, MS, 53, PhD(physiol), 62. *Prof Exp:* High sch teacher, Ill, 53-55; teaching asst health educ, Univ Ill, 55-57, instr, 57-58, asst physiol, 58-61; asst prof, Springfield Col, 61-63; from asst prof to assoc prof physiol, Univ Iowa, 63-73, prof, 73-84; prof & head, Dept Exercise & Sports Sci, Univ Ariz, 84-91, dir, Sch Health Related Professions, 87-91, prof physiol, 95, prof surg, 87-96. *Concurrent Pos:* Chmn study sect appl physiol & bioeng, NIH, 73-76; ed, Med Sci Sports Exercise, 79-84, Am Inst Biol Sci, 80-90. *Mem:* Am Physiol Soc; fel Am Heart Asn; Am Col Sports Med (pres, 74-75). *Res:* Exercise physiology, including bradycardia of training, mechanisms of cardiac hypertrophy, ligamentous strength, diabetes, endocrines and training; exercise testing; hypertension; pharmacological differences and training; animal models for simulated microgravity; making weight by scholastic wrestlers. *Mailing Add:* Dept Physiology Univ Ariz INA E Gittings Bldg Tucson AZ 85721-0093

**TIPTON, KENNETH WARREN,** PLANT GENETICS, AGRONOMY. *Current Pos:* assoc dir, 79-89, VCHANCELLOR & DIR, LA AGR EXP STA, AGR CTR, LA STATE UNIV, 89- *Personal Data:* b Belleville, Ill, Nov 14, 32; m 57, Barbara Adds; c Kenneth W Jr & Nancy (O'Neal). *Educ:* La State Univ, BS, 55, MS, 59; Miss State Univ, PhD(agron, genetics), 69. *Prof Exp:* Teaching asst, 58-59, from asst prof to prof agron, Agr Exp Sta, La State Univ, Baton Rouge, 59-75; prof & supt, Red River Valley Agr Exp Sta, Bossier City, 75-79. *Concurrent Pos:* Chmn, Comt Nine, 88, Exp Sta Comt Policy, 89-91. *Mem:* Am Soc Agron; Crop Sci Soc Am; Coun Agr Sci & Technol; Sigma Xi. *Res:* Varietal evaluation and adaptation of grain sorghum; varietal evaluation, breeding and genetics of small grains. *Mailing Add:* Sch Archit La State Univ Baton Rouge LA 70803-0001

**TIPTON, MERLIN J,** GEOLOGY. *Current Pos:* Geologist, 56-62, from asst state geologist to assoc state geologist, 62-82, STATE GEOLOGIST, SDAK GEOL SURV, 82-; LECTR EARTH SCI, UNIV SDAK, 76- *Personal Data:* b Watertown, SDak, Mar 23, 30; m 54; c 3. *Educ:* Univ SDak, BA, 55, MA, 58. *Mem:* Fel Geol Soc Am. *Res:* Pleistocene geology and hydrogeology. *Mailing Add:* 1545 Crestview Dr Vermillion SD 57069

**TIPTON, VERNON JOHN,** PARASITOLOGY, MEDICAL ENTOMOLOGY. *Current Pos:* RETIRED. *Personal Data:* b Springville, Utah, July 12, 20; m 43; c 5. *Educ:* Brigham Young Univ, BS, 48, MS, 49; Univ Calif, PhD, 59. *Prof Exp:* Entomologist, Walter Reed Army Inst Res, Med Serv Corps, US Army, 49-52, Calif, 52-54, commanding officer, 37th Prev Med Co, Korea, 54-55, chief entom sect, 5th Army Med Lab, St Louis, Mo, 56-59, chief environ health br, Off Surgeon, Ft Amador, CZ, 57-62, chief entom br dept prev med, Med Field Serv Sch, Ft Sam Houston, Tex, 62-66, chief dept entom, 406th Med Lab, 66-68; from assoc prof to prof zool, Brigham Young Univ, 68-86, dir, Ctr Health Environ Studies, 75-86. *Res:* Siphonaptera; mesostigmatid mites; systematics; bionomics. *Mailing Add:* 346 S Canyon Ave Springville UT 84663

**TIRMAN, ALVIN,** PHYSICAL CHEMISTRY, MATHEMATICS. *Current Pos:* From asst prof to assoc prof, 69-88, PROF MATH, KINGSPORT UNIV CTR, E TENN STATE UNIV, 88- *Personal Data:* b Brooklyn, NY, Nov 27, 31. *Educ:* Hofstra Col, AB, 53; Bowling Green State Univ, MA, 65; Carnegie-Mellon Univ, PhD(chem), 70. *Mem:* Math Asn Am; Sigma Xi. *Res:* History of mathematics; geometry; number theory. *Mailing Add:* 548 Brandonwood Rd Kingsport TN 37660-2927

**TIRRELL, MATTHEW VINCENT,** POLYMER SCIENCE, CHEMICAL ENGINEERING. *Current Pos:* From asst prof to assoc prof, 77-85, Shell distinguished chair chem eng, 86-91, PROF CHEM ENG, UNIV MINN, MINNEAPOLIS, 85-, EARL E BAKKEN PROF BIOMED ENG, 93-, DIR, BIOMED ENG INST, 95-, HEAD CHEM ENG & MAT SCI, 95- *Personal Data:* b Phillipsburg, NJ, Sept 5, 50; m 95, Pamela la Vigne. *Educ:* Northwestern Univ, BSChE, 73; Univ Mass, PhD(polymer sci & eng), 77.

*Honors & Awards:* Allan P Coburn Award, Am Inst Chem Engrs, 85; John H Dillon Medal, Am Phys Soc, 87; Prof Progress Award, Am Inst Chem Engrs, 94, Charles M A Stine Award, 96. *Concurrent Pos:* Vis prof, Univ Nacional, Argentina, 79, Univ Guadalajara, 80, Inst Francais du Petrole, 81, Ecole Superieure de Physique Chimie, 81 & Australian Nat Univ, 82. *Mem:* Nat Acad Eng; Am Inst Chem Engrs; fel Am Phys Soc; AAAS; Controlled Release Soc; Mat Res Soc; Soc Biomat; Soc Polymer Sci; Am Chem Soc. *Res:* Engineering applications of chemistry and physics of macromolecules; polymerization reactor design; flow-induced conformational and structural changes; rheology; diffusion and interfacial properties of polymers. *Mailing Add:* Dept Chem Eng & Mat Sci Univ Minn 151 Amundson Hall 421 Washington Ave SE Minneapolis MN 55455

**TISCHENDORF, JOHN ALLEN,** APPLIED STATISTICS, DATA ANALYSIS. *Current Pos:* RETIRED. *Personal Data:* b Lincoln City, Ind, July 22, 29; m 59, Norma Sies; c Lisa K, Diana J & John E. *Educ:* Evansville Col, AB, 50; Purdue Univ, MS, 52, PhD(math statist), 55. *Prof Exp:* Mem tech staff, Bell Tel Labs, 57-59, supvr, reliability & Statist Studies, Allentown, 59-64, supvr statist appln, 64-78, supvr eng data anal, Holmdel, 78-83; supvr eng data anal, AT&T-IS, 83-85; supvr, Prod Qual & Reliability, 85-89; mgr, Nat Tech Support Ctr, 89-92. *Concurrent Pos:* Vis lectr, Rutgers Univ, 66 & 67 & Stanford Univ, 68-69. *Mem:* Am Statist Asn; Am Soc Qual Control. *Res:* Statistics applied to engineering and management problems; data analysis; statistical consulting; mathematical modeling; reliability; sampling; order statistics; market analysis; data base management; quality assurance. *Mailing Add:* 7798 Oakview Pl Castle Rock CO 80104-8868

**TISCHER, FREDERICK JOSEPH,** ELECTROPHYSICS, COMMUNICATIONS. *Current Pos:* RETIRED. *Personal Data:* b Plan, Austria, Mar 14, 13; US citizen; m 42. *Educ:* Prague Tech Univ, MSc, 36, PhD(elec eng), 38. *Prof Exp:* Fel physics, Univ Berlin, 38; res assoc, Telefunken, Berlin, 38-42; owner, Tischer Phys Lab, Austria, 42-47; lectr microwaves, Royal Inst Technol, Sweden, 47-54; br chief, Guid Lab, Ord Missile Lab, Ala, 54-56; assoc prof electromagnetics, Ohio State Univ, 56-62; asst dir, Res Inst, Univ Ala, Huntsville, 62-64; prof electromagnetics, NC State Univ, 64-78, emer prof, 78-79. *Concurrent Pos:* Vis lectr, Helsinki Inst Technol, 52; consult, Chance Vought Aircraft Co, Tex, 59-61 & Harry Diamond Labs, DC, 60-74; consult, NASA Hq, 62-63; expert consult, NASA-Goddard Space Flight Ctr, Md, 62; fel plasma physics, Princeton Univ, 62; consult, 76-; vis distinguished prof, Naval Postgrad Sch, 78-79; vis prof, Univ Bern, Switz, 80, Swiss Fed Inst Technol, Zurich, 81 & Sheffield, Eng, 83. *Mem:* Fel Inst Elec & Electronics Engrs; Optical Soc Am; Am Phys Soc; Sigma Xi. *Res:* Microwaves, waveguides, plasma physics, space communications; holography; millimeter waves; satellite communications. *Mailing Add:* 114 Springmoor Dr Raleigh NC 27615

**TISCHER, RAGNAR P(ASCAL),** PHYSICAL CHEMISTRY, METALLURGY. *Current Pos:* RETIRED. *Personal Data:* b Berlin, Ger, Apr 30, 22; m 61, Barbara A Mathews; c Sandra A (Ingalls) & Dirk P. *Educ:* Univ Goettingen, dipl phys, 53; Stuttgart Tech Univ, Dr rer nat(phys chem), 57. *Prof Exp:* Res assoc electrochem, Dept Chem, Univ Ill, 57-59; asst metall, Gebr Boehler A G, Edelstahlwerk Dusseldorf, Ger, 59-60; res assoc electrochem, Inst Phys Chem, Bonn, 61-63; sr res chemist, Electrochem Dept, Res Labs, Gen Motors Corp, 63-66; prin res scientist assoc, Ford Motor Co, 66-68; staff scientist, res staff, 68-88. *Mem:* Electrochem Soc; Sigma Xi. *Res:* Electrode kinetics in aqueous solutions and in fused salts; fuel cells; corrosion of binary alloys; battery electrodes and metal deposition in organic solvents. *Mailing Add:* 1449 Suffield Ave Birmingham MI 48009-1041

**TISCHER, THOMAS NORMAN,** PHOTOGRAPHIC CHEMISTRY. *Current Pos:* RES ASSOC, EASTMAN KODAK CO, 61- *Personal Data:* b Milwaukee, Wis, Apr 21, 34. *Educ:* Marquette Univ, BS, 56, MS, 58; Univ Wis, PhD(anal chem), 61. *Mem:* Am Chem Soc. *Res:* Photographic patent liaison; organic chemistry; materials science engineering; thermal-dye imaging and research. *Mailing Add:* 115 Heritage Circle Rochester NY 14615

**TISCHFIELD, JAY ARNOLD,** SOMATIC CELL GENETICS. *Current Pos:* PROF MED & MOLECULAR GENETICS & DIR, DIV MOLECULAR GENETICS, IND UNIV SCH MED, 87- *Personal Data:* b New York, NY, June 15, 46; m 78, Donna M Mitchell; c Max A, Samuel E & David J. *Educ:* Brooklyn Col, BS, 67; Yale Univ, MPhil, 69, PhD(biol), 73. *Prof Exp:* Asst prof biol, genetics & pediat, Case Western Res Univ, 72-78; prof anat, cell & molecular biol & pediat, Med Col Ga, 78-87. *Concurrent Pos:* Fel, Univ Calif, San Francisco, 72-73; prin investr, US Pub Health grant, 73- & NSF grant, 82- *Mem:* Genetics Soc Am; Am Bd Med Genetics; Am Col Med Genetics; Am Soc Microbiol; Am Soc Human Genetics. *Res:* Human medical genetics and mammalian somatic cell genetics, especially the effects of mutations on all levels of gene expression; biotechnology and transgenic animals. *Mailing Add:* Dept Med Genetics Ind Univ Med Ctr 975 W Walnut St Indianapolis IN 46202-5251. *E-Mail:* jay@medgen.iupui.edu

**TISCHIO, JOHN PATRICK,** BIO-PHARMACEUTICALS. *Current Pos:* SCIENTIST, DRUG METAB, IMMUNO BIOL RES INST, 88- *Personal Data:* b Newark, NJ, Mar 17, 42; m 66, 88; c 2. *Educ:* Fairleigh Dickinson Univ, BS, 65; Univ Rochester, PhD(biochem), 71. *Prof Exp:* Asst prof biochem, Philadelphia Col Pharm & Sci, 70-77; scientist, drug metab, Ortho Pharm Corp, 77-78. *Concurrent Pos:* Lectr, Wagner Free Inst Sci, 71-77, Philadelphia Community Col, 76-77, Raritan Valley Community Col, 89- *Mem:* AAAS; Am Chem Soc; Sigma Xi; Am Pharmaceut Asn; Am Asn Pharmaceut Scientists. *Res:* Biotransformation and disposition of drugs; methods development for drugs in biological fluids; radio immune assay technology; bioavailability and pharmacokinetics in animals and humans. *Mailing Add:* 17 Meadow Ave Manasquan NJ 08736

**TISCHLER, HERBERT,** INVERTEBRATE PALEONTOLOGY. *Current Pos:* chmn, Dept Earth Sci, 65-90, PROF GEOL, UNIV NH, 65- *Personal Data:* b Detroit, Mich, Apr 28, 24; m 54, Annette Zeidman; c Michael A & Robert D. *Educ:* Wayne State Univ, BS, 50; Univ Calif, Berkeley, MA, 55; Univ Mich, PhD(geol), 61. *Prof Exp:* Instr geol, Wayne State Univ, 56-58; assoc prof earth sci, Northern Ill Univ, 58-65. *Concurrent Pos:* NSF sci fac fel, Columbia Univ, 64-65. *Mem:* Fel Geol Soc Am. *Res:* Paleoecology of marine invertebrates; ecology of benthic foraminifera; carbonate petrology; stratigraphy. *Mailing Add:* Dept Earth Sci James Hall Univ NH Durham NH 03824-4724

**TISCHLER, MARC ELIOT,** INTERMEDIARY METABOLISM, HORMONAL REGULATION. *Current Pos:* from asst prof to assoc prof, 79-90, PROF BIOCHEM, UNIV ARIZ, 90- *Personal Data:* b New York, NY, Nov 10, 49; m 79; c 2. *Educ:* Boston Univ, BA, 71; Univ SC, MS, 73; Univ Pa, PhD(biochem), 77. *Prof Exp:* Fel, Med Sch, Harvard Univ, 77-79. *Concurrent Pos:* Estab investr, Am Heart Asn, 82-87. *Mem:* Am Physiol Soc; Am Soc Biol Chemists; Am Soc Gravitational & Space Biol (vpres, 89-90, pres, 90-91). *Res:* Regulation of muscle metabolism and responses to physiologic perturbations such as fasting, trauma and muscle disuse; regulation and role of insect protein turnover. *Mailing Add:* Dept Biochem Univ Ariz Col Med Tucson AZ 85724-0001. *Fax:* 520-626-2110

**TISCHLER, OSCAR,** PROCESSING OF THIN FILMS, SUBSTRATES FOR THIN FILM DEPOSITION. *Current Pos:* RETIRED. *Personal Data:* b New York, NY, Oct 7, 23; m 50; c 3. *Educ:* Cooper Union, BChE, 51; Newark Col Eng, MS, 58. *Prof Exp:* Engr, Balco Corp, 51-56 & Daven Corp, 56-58; staff engr, Kearfott Div, KDI Electronics, 58-60, dir res, Pyrofilm Div, 60- *Mem:* Am Chem Soc; Am Ceramics Soc; Mat Res Soc; Am Vacuum Soc. *Res:* Techniques used to deposit thin films of metals and alloys and non-metals or insulators; study of the properties and uses of these films. *Mailing Add:* 32 Park Terr Caldwell NJ 07006

**TISDALE, GLENN E(VAN),** ELECTRICAL ENGINEERING. *Current Pos:* gen mgr sea technol dept, 65, MGR INFO TECHNOL AEROSPACE DIV, WESTINGHOUSE ELEC CORP, 66- *Personal Data:* b Madison, Wis, July 4, 24; m 60; c 2. *Educ:* Yale Univ, BE, 44, MEng, 47, PhD(elec eng), 49. *Prof Exp:* Jr engr, Raytheon Mfg Co, 49; engr, Servo Corp Am, NY, 50 & Perkin-Elmer Corp, 51-52; sr res engr, Electro-Mech Res, Inc, 53-57, mgr systs eng dept, 57-63; pres, Sea Technol Corp, 63-64. *Concurrent Pos:* Consult, Spencer-Kennedy Labs, 49-52. *Mem:* Inst Elec & Electronics Engrs; Sigma Xi. *Res:* Recognition logic; signal processing; data transmission systems; design of equipment for aerospace and underseas missions. *Mailing Add:* 13 Windward Dr Severna Park MD 21146-2441

**TISE, FRANK P,** ORGANIC PHOTOCHEMISTRY. *Current Pos:* RES SCIENTIST, RES CTR, HERCULES, INC, 81- *Personal Data:* b Washington, DC, Dec 4, 51; m 81; c 1. *Educ:* Univ Md, BS, 73; Univ NC, PhD(org chem), 80. *Mem:* Am Chem Soc. *Res:* Integrated circuit photoresists; phenolic-modified ink resins. *Mailing Add:* 5907 Stone Pine Rd Wilmington DE 19808-1015

**TISHKOFF, GARSON HAROLD,** MEDICINE, HEMATOLOGY. *Current Pos:* RETIRED. *Personal Data:* b Rochester, NY, Aug 8, 23; m 59. *Educ:* Univ Rochester, BS, 44, PhD(pharmacol), 51, MD, 53. *Prof Exp:* AEC assoc, Univ Rochester, 46-52; instr med, Med Sch, Tufts Univ, 56-57 & Harvard Med Sch, 57-60; from asst prof to assoc prof, Sch Med, Univ Calif, Los Angeles, 60-71; prof med, Mich State Univ & dir, Great Lakes Regional Blood Prog, Am Red Cross, 71- *Concurrent Pos:* Nat Acad Sci-Nat Res Coun fel, New Eng Ctr Hosp, Tufts Univ, 55-56; assoc, Beth Israel Hosp, Boston, 57-60. *Mem:* AAAS; Am Soc Hemat; Int Soc Hemat; Int Soc Thrombosis & Haemostasis; Int Soc Blood Transfusion. *Res:* Internal medicine; hemolytic anemia; blood coagulation; blood transfusion. *Mailing Add:* 4000 N Mich Rd 139 Dimondale MI 48821-9744

**TISHLER, PETER VERVEER,** MEDICAL GENETICS. *Current Pos:* ASSOC CHIEF STAFF EDUC, VET ADMIN MED CTR, BROCKTON & WEST ROXBURY, MASS, 80- *Personal Data:* b Boston, Mass, July 18, 37; m 60, Sigrid A Lemlein; c Jordan L & Alison J. *Educ:* Harvard Univ, AB, 59; Yale Univ, MD, 63. *Prof Exp:* Staff assoc, Nat Inst Arthritis & Metab Dis, 66-68; house officer internal med II & IV, Harvard Med Serv, 63-66, res fel med, Thorndike Mem Lab & Channing Lab, 68-69, staff mem med & genetics, Channing Lab, Boston City Hosp & Harvard Med Sch, 69-77 & Peter Bent Hosp & Harvard Med Sch, 77- *Concurrent Pos:* Francis Weld Peabody fel med, Harvard Univ, 69-75; asst physician, Dept Pediat, Boston City Hosp, assoc vis physician, Dept Med, 71-77; assoc, Ctr Human Genetics, Harvard Med Sch, 71, asst prof med, 72; assoc med, Peter Bent Brigham Hosp, 76, assoc prof med, 83- *Mem:* AAAS; NY Acad Sci; Am Soc Human Genetics; Am Fedn Clin Res; Int Soc Twin Studies. *Res:* Genetics of chronic disease; biochemistry of diseases of porphyrin metabolism. *Mailing Add:* Vet Admin Med Ctr 1400 VFW Pkwy West Roxbury MA 02132. *Fax:* 617-363-5549; *E-Mail:* tishler.peter@forum.va.gov

**TISON, RICHARD PERRY,** ELECTROCHEMISTRY. *Current Pos:* Chem engr plant eng, Gen Motors Truck & Coach Div, 68-69, STAFF RES ENGR ELECTROCHEM, GEN MOTORS RES LABS, GEN MOTORS CORP, 69- *Personal Data:* b Pontiac, Mich, June 23, 44; m 63; c 3. *Educ:* Gen Motors Inst, BME, 68; Rensselaer Polytech Inst, MS, 68. *Mem:* Am Electroplaters' Soc. *Res:* Stress-strain analysis; adhesion failure of plated plastic automotive parts; methods for electrophoretic analysis of concentrated suspensions; improved methods for electrochemical recovery of metals from industrial process streams. *Mailing Add:* 1655 Nancy G Lane Lake Orion MI 48359

**TISONE, GARY C,** ATMOSPHERIC PHYSICS. *Current Pos:* STAFF MEM, SANDIA CORP, 67- *Personal Data:* b Boulder, Colo, Dec 24, 37; m 59; c 4. *Educ:* Univ Colo, BS, 59, PhD(physics), 67. *Prof Exp:* Physicist, Vallecitos Atomic Lab, Gen Elec Co, 59-61; physicist, Nat Bur Standards, 61-62; res assoc atomic physics, Univ Colo, 66-67. *Mem:* Am Phys Soc. *Res:* Electron-negative ion collisions; photodetachment of negative ions; gaseous electronics; physics of the upper atmosphere; gas laser research; particle beam fusion. *Mailing Add:* 10212 Chapala Pl NE Albuquerque NM 87111

**TISSUE, BRIAN MAX,** LANTHANIDE SPECTROSCOPY, MASS SPECTROMETRY. *Current Pos:* ASST PROF CHEM, VA POLYTECH INST & STATE UNIV, 93- *Personal Data:* b Fayetteville, NC, Jan 11, 61. *Educ:* Johns Hopkins Univ, BA, 83; Univ Wis-Madison, PhD(chem), 88. *Honors & Awards:* Career Award, NSF, 95; Cottrell Award, Res Corp, 96. *Prof Exp:* Postdoctoral assoc, Univ Ga, 88-91; postdoctoral fel, Los Alamos Nat Lab, 91-93. *Concurrent Pos:* Pres, Sci Hypermedia, Inc, 96- *Mem:* Am Chem Soc; Mat Res Soc. *Res:* Laser spectroscopy of nanocrystalline phosphors; time-of-flight mass spectrometry; chemical education hypermedia. *Mailing Add:* Dept Chem Va Polytech Inst & State Univ Blacksburg VA 24061-0212. *E-Mail:* tissue@vt.edu

**TISSUE, ERIC BRUCE,** TEST EVALUATION, VERIFICATION & VALIDATION. *Current Pos:* STAFF MATHEMATICIAN, SOLIPSYS CORP, 87- *Personal Data:* b Hagerstown, Md, Feb 7, 55; m 80, Nancy A Tschiember; c Jonathan & Nicholas. *Educ:* Towson State Univ, BS, 77; Mich State Univ, MS, 82. *Prof Exp:* Sr prog analyst, Syscon Corp, Div Logicon, 83-87. *Concurrent Pos:* Sr lectr, Dept Math, Towson State Univ, 85- *Mem:* Soc Indust & Appl Math; Int Test Eval Asn. *Res:* Simulation and modeling in performing test and evaluation of complex systems, including computer software, and verification and validation activities over the software development life-cycle. *Mailing Add:* 1687 King Richard Rd Eldersburg MD 21784-6265

**TISUE, GEORGE THOMAS,** ENVIRONMENTAL CHEMISTRY, ANALYTICAL CHEMISTRY. *Current Pos:* assoc prof, 82-91, PROF CHEM, CLEMSON UNIV, 91- *Personal Data:* b Carroll, Iowa, Nov 25, 40; c 4. *Educ:* Beloit Col, BS, 61; Yale Univ, PhD(org chem), 66. *Prof Exp:* Res chemist, Tech Ctr, Celanese Chem Co, Tex, 66 & 68; NIH fel plant biochem, Univ Freiburg, 66-67; from asst prof to assoc prof chem, Beloit Col, 68-74; chemist, Argonne Nat Lab, 74-81; res assoc, Ctr Great Lakes Studies, Univ Wis-Milwaukee, 81. *Concurrent Pos:* Vis prof, Dept Chem, Univ Wis-Milwaukee, 81, Shaw vis prof, 88. *Mem:* AAAS; Am Chem Soc; Int Asn Environ Anal Chem; Int Asn Great Lakes Res. *Res:* Biogeochemical cycling and effects of heavy metal pollutants in the Great Lakes and coastal waters; fluxes at the sediment-water interface. *Mailing Add:* Dept Chem Clemson Univ PO Box 341905 Clemson SC 29634-1905

**TISZA, LASZLO,** PHYSICS. *Current Pos:* from instr physics to prof physics, 41-73, EMER PROF PHYSICS, MASS INST TECHNOL, 73- *Personal Data:* b Budapest, Hungary, July 7, 07; nat US; m 73. *Educ:* Univ Budapest, PhD(physics), 32. *Prof Exp:* Res assoc, Phys Tech Inst, Kharkov, 35-37; res assoc, Col France, 37-40. *Concurrent Pos:* Guggenheim fel, 62-63; vis prof, Univ Paris, 62-63. *Mem:* Fel Am Phys Soc; fel Am Acad Arts & Sci; fel AAAS. *Res:* Theoretical physics; foundations of quantum mechanics; statistical thermodynamics. *Mailing Add:* Dept Physics Mass Inst Technol 77 Man Ave Cambridge MA 02139. *Fax:* 617-253-8000

**TITCHENER, EDWARD BRADFORD,** BIOCHEMISTRY. *Current Pos:* from asst prof to assoc prof, 58-74, PROF BIOCHEM, UNIV ILL COL MED, 74- *Personal Data:* b Cambridge, Mass, July 15, 27; m 52; c 2. *Educ:* Univ Mich, BS, 51; Ohio State Univ, MS, 54, PhD(physiol chem), 56. *Prof Exp:* Asst biochem, Ohio State Univ, 53-56. *Concurrent Pos:* NIH trainee, Enzyme Inst, Univ Wis, 56-58. *Mem:* AAAS; Am Chem Soc; Am Soc Biol Chemists; NY Acad Sci; Sigma Xi. *Res:* Transfer RNA. *Mailing Add:* 1225 60th Pl Downers Grove IL 60516

**TITCHENER, JAMES LAMPTON,** PSYCHIATRY, PSYCHOANALYSIS. *Current Pos:* from instr to assoc prof, 54-68, PROF PSYCHIAT, MED CTR, UNIV CINCINNATI, 68-; MEM FAC PSYCHOANAL, CINCINNATI PSYCHOANAL INST, 74- *Personal Data:* b Binghamton, NY, Apr 9, 22; c 4. *Educ:* Princeton Univ, AB, 46; Duke Univ, MD, 49; Chicago Psychoanal Inst, cert psychoanal, 64. *Prof Exp:* Intern psychiat, Walter Reed Gen Hosp, 49-50; resident, Cincinnati Gen Hosp, 50-54. *Concurrent Pos:* Career investr, USPHS, 55-60 & NIMH, 57-62; training & supv analyst, Cincinnati Psychoanal Inst, 74-; attend physician, Cincinnati Gen Hosp. *Mem:* Fel AAAS; fel Am Psychiat Asn; Am Psychosom Soc; Am Psychoanal Asn; Sigma Xi. *Res:* Study of the effects of physical trauma on personality functioning; family and marital dynamics and marital therapy; psychological trauma resulting from disasters such as the Buffalo Creek disaster and Beverly Hills fire. *Mailing Add:* 3529 Elland Ave Cincinnati OH 45229

**TITELBAUM, SYDNEY,** ANIMAL PHYSIOLOGY. *Current Pos:* PROF BIOL, FROMM INST, UNIV SAN FRANCISCO, 78- *Personal Data:* b Luck, Russia, Apr 24, 13; US citizen; m 39, Olga Adler; c Daniel E. *Educ:* Univ Chicago, PhB, 33, PhD(physiol), 38, JD, 42. *Honors & Awards:* Award, Asn Off Racing Chem, 60. *Prof Exp:* Teaching asst physiol, Univ Chicago, 34-38; chief physiologist, Chicago Biol Res Lab, 39-59; lectr forensic med, Sch Med, Loyola Univ Chicago, 46-64; prof biol, City Cols Chicago, 60-77. *Concurrent Pos:* Ed, Asn Off Racing Chem Jour, 56-58; consult-examr, NCent Asn Cols & Sec Schs, 66-78; dean, Bogan Col, 67-68. *Mem:* AAAS; Am Inst Biol Sci; Asn Off Racing Chem (pres, 57). *Res:* Physiology of sleep; history of science. *Mailing Add:* 3628 Fillmore St San Francisco CA 94123-1602

**TITELER, MILT,** PHARMACOLOGY, BIOCHEMISTRY. *Current Pos:* AT DEPT PHARMACOL & NEUROSCI, ALBANY MED COL. *Personal Data:* b Lakewood, NJ, Nov 8, 49. *Educ:* State Univ NY, Buffalo, BS, 72, MSc, 76; Univ Toronto, PhD(pharmacol), 78. *Prof Exp:* Res asst biochem, Univ Buffalo, 73-76; from res asst to res assoc pharmacol, Univ Toronto, 76-79, asst prof, 79- *Mem:* Soc Neurosci. *Res:* Neuronal receptor pharmacology; biological psychiatry; neurochemistry. *Mailing Add:* Dept Pharmacol & Neurosci Albany Med Col 47 New Scotland Ave Albany NY 12208-3479. *Fax:* 518-445-5199

**TITKEMEYER, CHARLES WILLIAM,** ANATOMY, BACTERIOLOGY. *Current Pos:* RETIRED. *Personal Data:* b Rising Sun, Ind, Jan 14, 19; m 47; c 2. *Educ:* Ohio State Univ, DVM, 49; Mich State Univ, MS, 51, PhD, 56. *Prof Exp:* From instr to prof anat, Mich State Univ, 49-65; prof vet anat & head dept, Sch Vet Med, La State Univ, Baton Rouge, 69-85. *Concurrent Pos:* Consult vet, Univ Ky Contract Team, Bogor, Indonesia, 60-62; prof & head dept vet sci, Univ Nigeria, 66-68. *Mailing Add:* 1148 Aurora Pl Baton Rouge LA 70806

**TITLEBAUM, EDWARD LAWRENCE,** ELECTRICAL ENGINEERING. *Current Pos:* from asst prof to assoc prof, 64-85, PROF ELEC ENG, UNIV ROCHESTER, 85- *Personal Data:* b Boston, Mass, Mar 23, 37; c 2. *Educ:* Northeastern Univ, BSEE, 59; Cornell Univ, MS, 63, PhD(elec eng), 65. *Prof Exp:* Engr, Avco Res & Adv Develop Labs, 59-61. *Concurrent Pos:* Consult, Gen Dynamics Corp, 64-65; vis assoc prof, Johns Hopkins Univ, 70-71. *Mem:* AAAS; Inst Elec & Electronics Engrs. *Res:* Communication systems and signals; radar; sonar; echo-location systems in nature, acoustics and hearing; bat and dolphin sonar systems. *Mailing Add:* Dept Elec Eng Univ Rochester River Campus CSB 419 Rochester NY 14627

**TITLEY, SPENCER ROWE,** GEOLOGY, GEOCHEMISTRY. *Current Pos:* from asst prof to assoc prof, 60-67, PROF GEOL, UNIV ARIZ, 67- *Personal Data:* b Denver, Colo, Sept 27, 28; m 51; c 3. *Educ:* Colo Sch Mines, GeolE, 51; Univ Ariz, PhD(geol), 58. *Honors & Awards:* Thayer Lindsley Distinguished lectr, Soc Econ Geol, 85-86; Fulbright Sr Lectr, Fed Univ Para, Brazil, 86. *Prof Exp:* Geologist, NJ Zinc Co, 51 & 53-55, explor geologist, 58-60; geologist, US Geol Surv, 63-73. *Concurrent Pos:* Consult occidental minerals, Placer prospecting, Cerro de Pasco, Australia & ConZincRioTinto Homestake Mining Co, 73-84; consult, NSF Adv Comt Appl Sci & Eng, 78-80. *Mem:* Soc Econ Geol; fel Geol Soc Am; Soc Explor Geophys; Am Inst Mining, Metall & Petrol Engrs; Am Geophys Union; Australasian Inst Mining & Metall. *Res:* Mineral deposit geology, regional geology and tectonics; metallogenesis; geochemistry and petrology of hydrothermal ore systems. *Mailing Add:* Dept Geosci Univ Ariz 1600 E University Blvd Tucson AZ 85721-0001

**TITMAN, PAUL WILSON,** BOTANY. *Current Pos:* RETIRED. *Personal Data:* b Lowell, NC, Aug 30, 20. *Educ:* Belmont Abbey Col, BS, 39; Univ NC, AB, 41, MA, 49; Harvard Univ, PhD(biol), 52. *Prof Exp:* Instr bot, Univ NC, 48-49; asst prof, Univ Louisville, 52-53; instr, Univ Conn, 53-55; from assoc prof to prof bot, Chicago State Univ, 55-88. *Concurrent Pos:* Res resident, Harvard Univ, 54; chmn coun faculties, Ill State Bd Cols & Univs; consult. *Mem:* Bot Soc Am; fel Royal Hort Soc. *Res:* Morphogenesis; systematic anatomy; microbiology; paleontology. *Mailing Add:* 1453 E 54th Chicago IL 60615

**TITMAN, RODGER DONALDSON,** WATERFOWL ECOLOGY. *Current Pos:* asst prof, 73-79, ASSOC PROF WILDLIFE BIOL, MACDONALD COL, MCGILL UNIV, 79- *Personal Data:* b Montreal, Que, Can, Aug 26, 43; m 74, Elise Aitken; c Stephanie & Andrew R. *Educ:* McGill Univ, BSc, 65; Bishops Univ, MSc, 69; Univ NB, PhD(wildlife ecol), 73. *Prof Exp:* Asst dir, Delta Waterfowl Res Sta, 69-70; lectr wildlife biol, Univ NB, 72-73. *Concurrent Pos:* Exec, Wildlife Biologists Sect, Can Soc Zoologists, 78-83; chmn, Dept Renewable Resources, McGill Univ, 83-88, assoc dean, 90-91; trustee, Nature Conservancy Can; vpres, Falcon-Duck Enterprises. *Mem:* Wildlife Soc; Am Ornithologists Union; Cooper Ornith Soc; Wilson Ornith Soc; Sigma Xi; Soc Field Ornithologists. *Res:* Waterfowl ecology, behavior and energetics, particularly social systems in breeding ducks and waterfowl post-breeding and wintering ecology; avian groups; marsh ecology; vertebrate pest interaction with agriculture. *Mailing Add:* Dept Natural Resource Sci Macdonald Campus McGill Univ 21111 Lakeshore Rd Ste Anne de Bellevue PQ H9X 3V9 Can. *Fax:* 514-398-7990; *E-Mail:* titman@nrs.mcgill.ca

**TITS, JACQUES LEON,** CHEMISTRY. *Current Pos:* assoc prof chem, 73-74, PROF GROUP THEORY, COL FRANCE, 75- *Personal Data:* b Uccle, Belg, Aug 12, 30. *Honors & Awards:* Wettrens Prize, Acad Belg, 58; Sci, Math & Physics Prize, Acad Sci, 76; Wolf Math Prize, 93. *Prof Exp:* Asst prof, Univ Brussels, 56-64; prof, Univ Benn, 64-74. *Mem:* Inst Med-Nat Acad Sci; AAAS; Royal Neth Soc Arts & Sci; London Math Soc; Acad Europ. *Mailing Add:* Col de France 11 pl Marcelin-Berthelot 75231 Paris Cedex 05 France

**TITTEL, FRANK K(LAUS),** PHYSICS, ELECTRICAL ENGINEERING. *Current Pos:* assoc prof, 67-72, PROF ELEC ENG, RICE UNIV, 72-, CHAIR, 92- *Personal Data:* b Berlin, Ger, Nov 14, 33; US citizen; m 65, Maria H; c Mark H & Alexander M. *Educ:* Oxford Univ, BA, 55, PhD(physics), 59. *Hon Degrees:* DSc, Tate Univ, Szeged, Hungary, 93. *Prof Exp:* Physicist, Gen Elec Co, 59-65; assoc prof physics, Am Univ Cairo, 65-67. *Mem:* Fel Am Phys Soc; fel Optical Soc Am; fel Inst Elec & Electronics Engrs; Int Soc Optical Eng. *Res:* Precision measurements of atomic constants; quantum electronics; laser development; laser spectroscopy; nonlinear optics. *Mailing Add:* 1111 Hermann Dr Houston TX 77004

**TITTERTON, PAUL JAMES,** ELECTROOPTICS. *Current Pos:* SR TECHNOLOGIST, GTE INC, 66- *Personal Data:* b Copiague, NY, Feb 23, 40; m 63; c 3. *Educ:* Boston Col, BS, 61; Brandeis Univ, MS, 63, PhD(physics), 67. *Mem:* Optical Soc Am; Am Phys Soc. *Res:* Atmospheric effects on laser beams; precise optical ranging techniques; optimum optical communication methodology; sensitive optical receiver research. *Mailing Add:* 1412 Hamilton Ave Palo Alto CA 94301

**TITTLE, CHARLES WILLIAM,** operations research; deceased, see previous edition for last biography

**TITTMAN, JAY,** PETROPHYSICS, WELL LOGGING. *Current Pos:* CONSULT, JAY TITTMAN TECH CONSULT SERV, 83- *Personal Data:* b Bayonne, NJ, Dec 28, 22; m 44, Eleanor Gelber; c Carol S, Nancy T (Keefe) & Barbara T (Markusson). *Educ:* Drew Univ, BA, 44; Columbia Univ, MA, 48, PhD(physics), 51. *Honors & Awards:* Gold Medal for Tech Achievement, Soc Prof Well Log Analysts, 93. *Prof Exp:* Physicist, Schlumberger-Doll Res Ctr, 51-54, sect head nuclear physics, 54-66, sr staff scientist, 66-67, dept head physics res, 67-72, sci consult to dir res, 81-83, dept head eng physics, Schlumberger Well Serv, Houston, 72-78, dir develop eng, 78-81. *Concurrent Pos:* Adj prof phys sci, New Eng Inst, Ridgefield, Conn, 70-72. *Mem:* Sigma Xi; fel Am Phys Soc; AAAS; Soc Petrol Engrs; hon mem Soc Prof Well Log Analysts. *Res:* Physical methods and instruments for subsurface geophysical exploration, borehole or well logging, in particular the application of neutron and gamma-ray physics and instruments to this field. *Mailing Add:* 11 Tanglewood Dr Danbury CT 06811. *E-Mail:* neutronman@aol.com

**TITTMANN, BERNHARD R,** SOLID STATE PHYSICS, ACOUSTICS. *Current Pos:* BAYARD KUNCLE PROF ENG SCI & MECH, PA STATE UNIV, UNIVERSITY PARK, PA, 89- *Personal Data:* b Moshi, Tanzania, Sept 15, 35; US citizen; m 66, Katharine Shower; c Christine M, Heidi E, Raymond J, Monica M & Brian P. *Educ:* George Washington Univ, BS, 57; Univ Calif, Los Angeles, PhD(solid state physics), 65. *Honors & Awards:* Rockwell IR&D Award. *Prof Exp:* Mem tech staff, Res & Develop Aerospace & Systs Group, Hughes Aircraft Co, 57-61; res asst solid state physics, Univ Calif, Los Angeles, 61-65, asst prof & fel, 65-66; mem tech staff, Rockwell Int, 66-79, mgr, Earth & Planetary Sci Group, 79-84, mgr, Mat Characterization Dept, Sci Ctr, 84-90. *Concurrent Pos:* Vis prof physics, Univ Paris VII, Paris, France, 77-78; res grantee, Ecole Normale Superior, Paris, France, 82-83; prin invest award, NASA; mem, Nat Res Coun, 90-93; Schell chair prof eng. *Mem:* Am Phys Soc; Am Geophys Union; fel Inst Elec & Electronics Engrs; Sigma Xi; Soc Explor Geophys. *Res:* Non-destructive evaluation and acoustic surface waves; acoustic properties of lunar and terrestrial rock; ultrasonic absorption of type I and type II superconductors; dislocation-electron interaction; superconductivity in high pressure polymorphs of semiconductors; ferromagnetic modes in epitaxial single crystal yttrium iron garnet; microwave conformal array antennas. *Mailing Add:* 2466 Sassafras Ct State College PA 16803-3366. *Fax:* 814-865-3626; *E-Mail:* brtesm@engr.psu.edu

**TITUS, CHARLES JOSEPH,** MATHEMATICS. *Current Pos:* RETIRED. *Personal Data:* b Mt Clemens, Mich, June 23, 23; m 49; c 2. *Educ:* Univ Detroit, BSc, 44; Brown Univ, ScM, 45; Syracuse Univ, PhD(math), 48. *Prof Exp:* Instr math, Syracuse Univ, 48; from instr to prof math, Univ Mich, Ann Arbor, 49- *Concurrent Pos:* Vis prof, Univ Calif, 58-59; mem, Inst Defense Anal, 60-61. *Mem:* Am Math Soc. *Res:* Complex variables and generalizations; transformation semigroups; qualitative theory of differential equations; communications; geometric analysis; differential topology. *Mailing Add:* 1210 Arlington Blvd Ann Arbor MI 48104

**TITUS, CHARLES O,** OPHTHALMOLOGY. *Current Pos:* RETIRED. *Personal Data:* b Augusta, Maine, Jan 26, 27; m 54; c 7. *Educ:* Univ Ottawa, BA & BSc, 51, MD, 55. *Prof Exp:* Chief ophthal, Travis AFB, 59-63 & USAF Hosp Weisbaden, 63-66; pvt pract, Chevy Chase, Md, 66-74; corp dir med affairs, Bausch & Lomb, 74-94. *Mem:* Am Acad Ophthal; Am Soc Contemp Ophthal; Am Acad Med Dirs; fel Am Col Surgeons. *Res:* Contact lens of ophthalmology. *Mailing Add:* 12 Niblick Ct Penfield NY 14526

**TITUS, DONALD DEAN,** INORGANIC CHEMISTRY. *Current Pos:* Asst prof, 71-77, ASSOC PROF CHEM, TEMPLE UNIV, 77- *Personal Data:* b Worland, Wyo, Mar 22, 44; m 66; c 2. *Educ:* Univ Wyo, BS, 66; Calif Inst Technol, PhD(chem), 71. *Concurrent Pos:* Am Chem Soc Petrol Res Fund grant, 71-74. *Mem:* Am Chem Soc; Am Crystallog Asn. *Res:* Transition-metal complexes, non-rigidity in hydrides, the trans-influence and selenium complexes; x-ray crystal structures. *Mailing Add:* Dept Chem Temple Univ 1701 N Broad St Philadelphia PA 19122-2504

**TITUS, DUDLEY SEYMOUR,** FOOD TECHNOLOGY. *Current Pos:* RETIRED. *Personal Data:* b Ithaca, NY, Mar 18, 29; m 54, May Cormack. *Educ:* Cornell Univ, BS, 52; State Col Wash, MS, 54; Univ Ill, PhD(food tech), 57. *Prof Exp:* Asst food technol, State Col Wash, 52-54; food technologist, Merck & Co, Inc, 57-67; head food technol sect, Mallinckrodt Chem Works, 67-72, res & develop scientist, 72, mkt res specialist, Mallinckrodt, Inc, 72-77, dir planning, food, flavor & fragrance group, 77-86; consult, 86-96. *Mem:* Am Asn Cereal Chem; Int Nutrit Anemia Consultative Group; Inst Food Technol. *Res:* Food microbiology and preservation; human nutrition; cereal products canned and frozen foods; dairy products; food additives; fragrances and olfaction. *Mailing Add:* 8343 Ardsley Dr St Louis MO 63121

**TITUS, ELWOOD OWEN,** ORGANIC CHEMISTRY. *Current Pos:* SR SCI CONSULT, LIFE SCI RES OFF, FED AM SOCS EXP BIOL, 90- *Personal Data:* b Rochester, NY, Sept 20, 19; m 51, Doris E Walz; c Elizabeth & David. *Educ:* Williams Col, BA, 41; Columbia Univ, PhD(chem), 47. *Prof Exp:* Asst antimalarials, Div War Res, Columbia Univ, 43-46; res assoc antibiotics & metab prod, Squibb Inst Med Res, 46-50; chemist, Chem Pharmacol Lab, Nat Heart & Lung Inst, 50-77; dir, Div Drug Biol, Bur Drugs, Food & Drug Admin, 77-86. *Concurrent Pos:* Mem, Nat Res Coun, 66-74; vis prof, Dept Pharmacol, Univ Bern, Switz, 86, Dept Clin Pharmacol, Karolinska Inst, Stockholm, Sweden, 87, Dept Physiol, Uniformed Serv Univ of the Health Sci, Bethesda, MD, 88-90. *Mem:* Am Chem Soc; Am Soc Biol Chem; Am Soc Pharmacol & Exp Therapeut; NY Acad Sci; Biophys Soc. *Res:* Organic synthesis; biochemistry; metabolism of biologically active compounds; application of counter-current distribution to metabolic studies on 4-amino-quinoline antimalarials; mechanism of action of steroids and catecholamines; lipid metabolism; biochemistry of cell membranes. *Mailing Add:* 5519 Rockville Pike Bethesda MD 20817-3781

**TITUS, HAROLD,** SYSTEMS DESIGN, CONTROL ENGINEERING. *Current Pos:* PROF ELEC ENG, US NAVAL POSTGRAD SCH, 62- *Personal Data:* b Detroit, Mich, Jan 10, 30; m 55; c 3. *Educ:* Univ Kans, BS, 52; Stanford Univ, MS, 57, PhD(eng mech), 62. *Concurrent Pos:* Consult, US Naval Ord Test Sta, 65-97, Stanford Res Inst & US Naval Air Develop Ctr, 66-97. *Mem:* Inst Elec & Electronics Engrs; Sigma Xi. *Res:* Optimum filtering, identification and control applications to naval weapons problems. *Mailing Add:* Dept Electronic & Comput Eng Naval Postgrad Sch Code EC/TS Monterey CA 93940

**TITUS, JACK L,** CARDIOVASCULAR PATHOLOGY. *Current Pos:* DIR REGISTRY CARDIOVASC DIS, UNITED HOSP, ST PAUL, MINN, 87- *Personal Data:* b South Bend, Ind, Dec 7, 26; m 49, Beverly J Harden; c Jack L, Elizabeth A (Engelbrecht), Michael N, Matthew D & Joan M (Davis). *Educ:* Univ Notre Dame, BS, 48; Wash Univ, MD, 52; Univ Minn, PhD(path), 62. *Honors & Awards:* Billings Gold Medal, AMA, 68, Hoektoen Gold Medal, 69; Distinguished Achievement Award, Soc Cardiovasc Path, US-Can Acad Path, 93. *Prof Exp:* Physician, Rensselaer, Ind, 53-57; assoc prof path, Mayo Grad Sch Med, Univ Minn, 61-72, prof, Mayo Clin, 71-72; prof path & chmn dept, Baylor Col Med, 72-87. *Concurrent Pos:* Fel path, Mayo Grad Sch Med, Univ Minn, 57-61; chief path serv, Methodist Hosp, 72-87; pathologist-in-chief, Harris County Hosp Dist, 72-87. *Mem:* AMA; Am Asn Pathologists; Am Soc Clin Path; Int Acad Path; Col Am Pathologists; Sigma Xi. *Res:* Cardiac conduction system; cardiac anomalies; valvular heart disease; ischemic heart disease; atherosclerosis. *Mailing Add:* 4274 Pond View Dr White Bear Lake MN 55110. *Fax:* 612-220-7114

**TITUS, JOHN ELLIOTT,** PLANT ECOLOGY. *Current Pos:* ASSOC PROF BIOL, STATE UNIV NY, BINGHAMTON, 77- *Personal Data:* b Iowa City, Iowa, July 24, 49; m 73; c 2. *Educ:* Oberlin Col, BA, 71; Univ Wis, MA, 73, PhD(bot), 77. *Concurrent Pos:* Prin investr, NSF, 78-82, 85-89, Environ Protection Agency, 81-84. *Mem:* Am Soc Limnol & Oceanog; Am Inst Biol Sci; Sigma Xi; Ecol Soc Am; Torrey Bot Club. *Res:* Comparative physiological ecology of submersed macrophytes; importance of physico-chemical environment, especially acidic conditions, as determinants of plant distribution and abundance; community compositional change. *Mailing Add:* Dept Biol Sci Binghamton Univ PO Box 6000 Binghamton NY 13902-6000. *Fax:* 607-777-6521

**TITUS, JOHN S,** POMOLOGY. *Current Pos:* RETIRED. *Personal Data:* b Mich, Apr 19, 23; m 46; c 4. *Educ:* Mich State Col, BS, 46, MS, 47; Cornell Univ, PhD(pomol), 51. *Honors & Awards:* Gourley Award, Am Soc Hort Sci, 74. *Prof Exp:* Instr hort, Mich State Col, 46-48; asst, Cornell Univ, 49-51; from instr to prof pomol, Dept Hort, Univ Ill, Urbana, 51-87. *Concurrent Pos:* Res assoc, Univ Calif, Davis, 62-63; Fulbright-Hays lectr, Univ Col, Dublin, 71-72. *Mem:* Fel AAAS; Am Soc Hort Sci; Am Soc Plant Physiol; Soc Exp Biol & Med. *Res:* Mineral nutrition of deciduous fruit trees; soil fertility requirements of fruit trees; soil morphology in relation to fruit tree performance; translocation in woody plants; amino acid synthesis in higher plants. *Mailing Add:* 805 W Nevada St Univ Ill Urbana IL 61801

**TITUS, RICHARD LEE,** ORGANIC CHEMISTRY. *Current Pos:* from asst prof to assoc prof, 67-73, PROF CHEM, UNIV NEV, LAS VEGAS, 73- *Personal Data:* b Dayton, Ohio, Aug 6, 34. *Educ:* DePauw Univ, BA, 56; Mich State Univ, PhD(chem), 64. *Prof Exp:* From instr to asst prof chem, Univ Toledo, 62-67. *Mem:* AAAS; Am Chem Soc; Sigma Xi. *Res:* Synthesis of heterocyclic compounds. *Mailing Add:* Dept Chem Univ Nev Las Vegas NV 89154-4003

**TITUS, ROBERT CHARLES,** INVERTEBRATE PALEONTOLOGY. *Current Pos:* PROF GEOL, HARTWICK COL, 74- *Personal Data:* b Paterson, NJ, Aug 9, 46. *Educ:* Rutgers Univ, BS, 68; Boston Univ, AM, 71, PhD(geol), 74. *Prof Exp:* Instr geol, Windham Col, 73-74. *Mem:* Sigma Xi; Paleont Soc; Paleont Asn; Geol Soc Am; Soc Econ Paleontologists & Mineralogists. *Res:* Paleontology of Middle Ordovician fossil invertebrate benthic communities. *Mailing Add:* Dept Geol Hartwick Col Oneonta NY 13820

**TITUS, WILLIAM JAMES,** LOW TEMPERATURE & COMPUTATIONAL PHYSICS, STATISTICAL MECHANICS. *Current Pos:* from asst prof to assoc prof, 70-85, PROF PHYSICS, CARLETON COL, 85- *Personal Data:* b Oakland, Calif, Dec 13, 41; m 67; c 1. *Educ:* Univ Calif, Davis, BS, 63; Stanford Univ, MS, 65, PhD(physics), 68. *Prof Exp:* Res assoc physics, Univ Minn, 68-70. *Mem:* Am Phys Soc; Am Asn Physics Teachers; Sigma Xi. *Mailing Add:* Dept Physics Carleton Col Northfield MN 55057

**TITZE, INGO ROLAND,** VOICE ACOUSTICS, BIOMECHANICS OF THE LARYNX. *Current Pos:* assoc prof, 79-84, DISTINGUISHED PROF SPEECH SCI & VOICE, UNIV IOWA, 79-; EXEC DIR, WILBUR JAMES GOULD VOICE RES CTR, DENVER CTR PERFORMING ARTS, 83- *Personal Data:* b Hirschberg, Ger, July 8, 41; US citizen; m 69, Katherine; c Karin, Michael, Jason & Gregory. *Educ:* Univ Utah, BSEE, 63, MS, 65; Brigham Young Univ, PhD(physics), 72. *Honors & Awards:* Jacob Javits Neurosci Invest Award, NIH, 84; Gould Award, William & Harriot Gould Found, 84; Claude Petter Award, 89; Quintant Award, Voice Found, 90; Am Laryngological Asn Award. *Prof Exp:* Res engr, NAm Aviation, 65-66 & Boeing Co, 68-69; instr physics, Brigham Young Univ, 72-73; lectr, Calif State Polytech Univ, 73-74; asst prof, Univ Petrol & Minerals, Saudi Arabia, 74-76; asst prof speech commun, Gallaudet Col, 76-79. *Concurrent Pos:* Mem, Tech Comt Musical Acoust, Acoust Soc Am, 73-82; consult speech sci, Bell Labs, 77-78; prin investr, NIH, 78-; dir publ, Int Asn Res in Singing, 82-; assoc ed, Nat Asn Teachers Singing J, 85-; panelist & site visitor, Nat Res Coun, Nat Acad Sci, 84-; pres, Voice Consults, 85-; mem, Collegium Medicorum Teatri, 88-; prin investr res award, Toward Standards for Voice Anal & Recording, NIH, 87- & Naturalness in Speech Synthesis, US West Advan Technol, 88; adj prof, Westminster Choir Col, Princeton, 89-; dir, Nat Ctr Voice & Speech, 90- *Mem:* Fel Acoust Soc Am; Nat Asn Teachers Singing; Am Speech, Hearing & Lang Asn; Am Asn Phonetic Sci; Int Asn Res in Singing; Int Asn Logopedics & Phoniatrics. *Res:* Acoustics and biomechanics of voice production understanding the physical and physiologic mechanisms by which voice is produced; voice characteristics of actors, singers, public speakers; effects of environment, fatigue, drugs, aging on human voice. *Mailing Add:* 330 SHC Univ Iowa Iowa City IA 52242. *Fax:* 319-335-8851; *E-Mail:* titze@shc.uiowa.edu

**TIUS, MARCUS ANTONIUS,** SYNTHETIC ORGANIC CHEMISTRY. *Current Pos:* Asst prof, 80-84, ASSOC PROF CHEM, UNIV HAWAII, MANOA, 84- *Personal Data:* b Izmir, Turkey, Apr 18, 53; US citizen. *Educ:* Dartmouth Col, BA, 75; Harvard Univ, MS, 77, PhD(chem), 80. *Concurrent Pos:* Alfred P Sloan Fel, 87-89. *Mem:* Am Chem Soc. *Mailing Add:* Univ Hawaii Manoa Chem Dept 2545 The Mall Honolulu HI 96822-1888

**TIWARI, SURENDRA NATH,** AEROSPACE ENGINEERING, ENVIRONMENTAL SCIENCES. *Current Pos:* assoc prof thermal eng, 71-77, prof mech eng & mech, 77-79, EMINENT PROF MECH ENG & MECH, OLD DOMINION UNIV, 79-, EMINENT SCHOLAR, 89- *Personal Data:* b Gorakhpur, India, Jan 1, 38; c 1. *Educ:* Univ Allahabad, BS, 59; Univ Maine, MS, 62 & 64; State Univ NY, Stony Brook, PhD(eng sci), 69. *Honors & Awards:* NASA Achievement Award. *Prof Exp:* Syst analyst, Implements Factory, India, 55-57, res engr, 57-60; res asst agr eng, Univ Maine, 60-62, instr mech eng, 62-64; instr eng, State Univ NY, Stony Brook, 64-69, res assoc radiation, 69-70, asst prof eng, 70-71. *Concurrent Pos:* Consult, Grumman Aerospace Corp, NY, 69-71; NASA grant, Old Dominion Univ, 71-, dir, Inst Comput & Appl Mech, 83-; res consult, Langley Field, NASA, Va, 71- *Mem:* Fel Am Inst Aeronaut & Astronaut; fel Am Soc Mech Engrs; AAAS; Am Soc Eng Educ; Am Asn Univ Professors. *Res:* Radiation gas dynamics; boundary layer flows; multi-phase flows; combustion processes and flow of chemically reacting and radiating gases; high temperature gas kinetics; atmospheric radiation; computational fluid mechanics; planetary entry heating, hypersonics. *Mailing Add:* Dept Mech Eng Old Dominion Univ 238 KDH Norfolk VA 23529

**TIZARD, IAN RODNEY,** IMMUNOLOGY, WOUND HEALING. *Current Pos:* prof & head, Dept Vet Microbiol & Parasitol, 82-90, PROF, DEPT PATHOBIOL, TEX A&M UNIV, COLLEGE STATION, 90- *Personal Data:* b Belfast, Northern Ireland, Oct 27, 42; m 69; c 2. *Educ:* Univ Edinburgh, BVMS, 65, BSc, 66; Cambridge Univ, PhD(immunol), 69. *Prof Exp:* Med Res Coun Can fel, Univ Guelph, 69-71; vet res officer, Animal Dis Res Asn, 71-72; from asst prof to prof vet immunol, Univ Guelph, 72-82. *Mem:* Wound Healing Soc; Am Asn Immunologists. *Res:* Veterinary immunology; effect of immunomodulators on wound healing. *Mailing Add:* Dept Vet Pathobiol Tex A&M Univ Col Vet Med College Station TX 77843

**TJEPKEMA, JOHN DIRK,** NITROGEN FIXATION, NITROGEN CYCLE. *Current Pos:* from asst prof to assoc prof, 82-89, PROF PLANT PHYSIOL, UNIV MAINE, 89- *Personal Data:* b Madison, Wis, June 14, 43. *Educ:* Univ Mich, BA, 65, MA, 67, PhD(bot), 71. *Prof Exp:* Res assoc, Wash Univ, 72-73, Univ Wis, 73-74 & Ore State Univ, 74-75; res fel, EMBRAPA, Rio de Janeiro, 76; asst & assoc prof soil biol, Harvard Univ, 76-82. *Mem:* Am Soc Plant Physiologists; Bot Soc Am. *Res:* Physiology and ecology of nitrogen fixation by nodulated plants and their symbiotic bacteria; associative nitrogen fixation; nitrogen cycle of ecosystems, especially exchange of nitrogenous compounds with the atmosphere. *Mailing Add:* Dept Plant Biol & Path Univ Maine Orono ME 04469-5722. *Fax:* 207-581-2969; *E-Mail:* tjepkema@maine.maine.edu

**TJIAN, ROBERT TSE NAN,** MOLECULAR BIOLOGY, BIOCHEMISTRY. *Current Pos:* PROF BIOCHEM, UNIV CALIF, BERKELEY, 79- *Personal Data:* b Hong Kong, Sept 22, 49; Brit citizen; m 76. *Educ:* Univ Calif, Berkeley, AB, 71; Harvard Univ, PhD(molecular biol), 76. *Prof Exp:* Staff investr molecular virol, Cold Spring Harbor Lab, 76. *Concurrent Pos:* Robertson fel, Cold Spring Harbor Lab, 78. *Mem:* Nat Acad Sci. *Res:* Oncogenic viruses and their interactions with the host cell; control of gene expression; simian virus 40, a small DNA containing oncogenic virus, tumor antigen, its structure and function. *Mailing Add:* Dept MCB Univ Calif 401 Barker Hall Berkeley CA 94720. *Fax:* 510-643-9547

**TJIO, JOE HIN,** CYTOGENETICS. *Current Pos:* res biologist, 59-78, CHIEF CYTOGENETICS SECT LAB EXP PATH, NAT INST ARTHRITIS & METAB DIS, 74- *Personal Data:* b Java, Indonesia, Feb 11, 19; US citizen; m 48; c 1. *Educ:* Univ Colo, PhD(biophys, cytogenetics), 60; Univ Zaragosa, Spain, Dr, 81. *Hon Degrees:* Dr, Univ Claude Bernard, France, 74, Sci-Univ, Zaragosa, Spain, 81. *Honors & Awards:* Joseph P Kennedy Jr Found Award, 62. *Prof Exp:* Head cytogenetics, Estacion Exp de Aula Dei, 48-59. *Concurrent Pos:* Vis scientist, Univ Lund, Sweden, 47-59, res assoc, Genetics Inst, 59-; res collabr, Univ Berkeley, 79-, Albany Med Col, 85-; fel award, Japan Soc Prom Sci, 84. *Mem:* Genetics Soc Am; Am Soc Human Genetics; Am Genetic Asn; Am Soc Nat. *Res:* Plant, animal and human cytogenetics; mammalian cytogenetics and immunology. *Mailing Add:* 120 Center Dr No 411 Bethesda MD 20814

**TJIOE, DJOE TJHOO,** MAMMALIAN PHYSIOLOGY, PHARMACOLOGY. *Current Pos:* ASSOC PROF PHYSIOL, CALIF STATE UNIV, LONG BEACH, 70- *Personal Data:* b Medan, Indonesia, Oct 1, 37; US citizen; m 64; c 2. *Educ:* Sioux Falls Col, BSc, 65; Univ Wis, MSc, 67, PhD(physiol), 70. *Prof Exp:* Teaching asst physiol, Univ Wis, 65-70. *Concurrent Pos:* Consult, Concept Media, 74-78. *Mem:* AAAS; Am Physiol Soc; Fedn Am Socs Exp Biol. *Res:* Cardiovascular, neuro and respiratory physiology. *Mailing Add:* 410 Daroca Ave Long Beach CA 90803

**TJIOE, SARAH ARCHAMBAULT,** PHARMACOLOGY. *Current Pos:* Instr, 72-75, ASST PROF PHARMACOL, COL MED, OHIO STATE UNIV, 75- *Personal Data:* b Philadelphia, Pa, Oct 12, 44; m 67; c 1. *Educ:* Univ Pa, BA, 66, PhD(pharmacol), 71. *Concurrent Pos:* NIH training grant pharmacol, Col Med, Ohio State Univ, 71-72, Pharmaceut Mfrs Asn Found fel pharmacol-morphol, 72-74. *Mem:* Am Soc Pharmacol & Exp Therapeut; Soc Neurosci. *Res:* Neuropharmacology; neurochemistry. *Mailing Add:* Dept Pharmacol Ohio State Univ Col Med 333 W Tenth Ave Columbus OH 43210-1218

**TJOSTEM, JOHN LEANDER,** MICROBIOLOGY, PLANT PHYSIOLOGY. *Current Pos:* assoc prof, 68-80, PROF BIOL, LUTHER COL, IOWA, 80-, BIOL DEPT HEAD, 88- *Personal Data:* b Sisseton, SDak, June 6, 35; m 62; c 3. *Educ:* Concordia Col, Moorhead, Minn, BA, 59; NDak State Univ, MS, 62, PhD(bot), 68. *Prof Exp:* Instr biol, Luther Col, Iowa, 62-65; assoc prof, Concordia Col, Moorhead, Minn, 67-68. *Mem:* Am Soc Microbiol; Am Biol Teachers. *Res:* Metabolic pathways of certain carbohydrates in algae; groundwater pollution. *Mailing Add:* Dept Biol Luther Col 700 College Dr Decorah IA 52101-1039

**TKACHEFF, JOSEPH, JR,** PHARMACY. *Current Pos:* RETIRED. *Personal Data:* b Waterbury, Conn, Feb 13, 26; m 54; c 2. *Educ:* RI Col Pharm, BSc, 46; Philadelphia Col Pharm, MSc, 47. *Prof Exp:* Pharmacist, E M Altman & Waterbury Drug Co, Conn, 45-46; control chemist, G F Harvey Co, 47-49, res & develop chemist, 49-50, plant chemist, 50-51, prod mgr, 51-58; sr res pharmacist, group leader & sect head, Pharmaceut Sci Prod Develop, Sterling-Winthrop Res Inst, 58-88. *Mem:* Am Chem Soc; Am Pharmaceut Asn; Acad Pharmaceut Sci. *Res:* Pharmaceutical chemistry; physiological biochemistry; pharmaceutical sciences, product development and technical services; pilot plant and product transfer to manufacturing sites. *Mailing Add:* 13 Russell Rd Greenfield Center NY 12833-1318

**TKACHUK, RUSSELL,** CHEMISTRY. *Current Pos:* RES SCIENTIST, GRAIN RES LAB, CAN GRAIN COMN, 59- *Personal Data:* b Redwater, Alta, Dec 25, 30; m 57; c 3. *Educ:* Univ BC, BA, 54, MSc, 56; Univ Sask, PhD(chem), 59. *Concurrent Pos:* Adj prof, Univ Man; fel, St Vincent's Sch Med Res, Melbourne, Australia, 68-69. *Mem:* Am Asn Cereal Chem; Am Chem Soc; fel Chem Inst Can; Can Inst Chem; Sigma Xi. *Res:* Chemistry of amino acids and proteins in wheat; near infrared reflectance spectroscopy. *Mailing Add:* Gen Delivery Grain Res Lab Rm 1404 Roberts Creek BC V0N 2W0 Can

**TKACZ, JAN S,** ANTIBIOTICS & NATURAL PRODUCTS. *Current Pos:* sr res fel, 87-93, DIR, MERCK RES LABS, 93- *Personal Data:* b Kittery, Maine, Oct 24, 44; m 78, Mary A Talle. *Educ:* Univ NH, BA, 66; Rutgers Univ, PhD(microbiol), 71. *Prof Exp:* Fel biochem, Med Sch, Harvard Univ, 71-73; res assoc, M S Hershey Med Ctr, Pa State Univ, 73-74; asst res prof microbiol, Rutgers Univ, 75-78, asst prof microbiol, Waksman Inst Microbiol, 78-81; sr res investr, Dept Microbiol, The Squibb Inst Med Res, 81-87. *Concurrent Pos:* NSF res fel, Dept Biol Chem, Lab Carbohydrate Res, Med Sch, Harvard Univ, 71-72; vis prof microbiol, Rutgers Univ. *Mem:* Am Soc Microbiol; Am Chem Soc; AAAS. *Res:* Biosynthesis of cell wall and membrane constituents in eukaryotic microorganisms, antibiotics and natural products of fungi. *Mailing Add:* Merck & Co Inc PO Box 2000 R80Y 215 Rahway NJ 07065-0900. *Fax:* 732-594-1399; *E-Mail:* jan_tkacz@merck.com

**TLALKA, JACEK,** APPLICATION OF MATHEMATICS IN TECHNICAL SCIENCE. *Current Pos:* PROF MATH, LIVINGSTONE COL, 83- *Personal Data:* b Krosno, Poland, Dec 16, 37; Polish & US citizen; c Marek & Irena. *Educ:* Jagiellonian Univ, Cracow, Poland, MS, 60; Mining & Metall Univ, Cracow, PhD(appl math), 71. *Prof Exp:* Teacher math & physics, Tech High Sch, Cracow, Poland, 60-63; asst prof math, Mining & Metall Univ, Cracow, 63-71; teacher math, Gordon Tech High Sch, 82-83. *Mem:* Math Asn Am; Nat Coun Teachers Math. *Res:* Applications of mathematics in technical science and economics; author of 17 publications. *Mailing Add:* 1003 Terrace Dr Salisbury NC 28146

**TLSTY, THEA DOROTHY,** MOLECULAR PATHOLOGY OF NEOPLASIA, GENOMIC INSTABILITY. *Current Pos:* asst prof, 85-92, MEM, LINEBERGER COMPREHENSIVE CANCER CTR, UNIV NC, 85-, ASSOC PROF PATH, 92- *Personal Data:* b Mobile, Ala, Jan 28, 52. *Educ:* Univ SFla, BS, 73; Wash Univ, PhD(molecular & cellular biol), 80. *Prof Exp:* Res asst, Dept Chem, Univ SFla, 73-74; fel & sr res assoc, Stanford Univ, 81-85. *Concurrent Pos:* Fel microbiol, Wash Univ, 80; sr res assoc, Stanford Univ, 84; vis scholar, Univ Zimbabwe, 92; lectr, Univ Nebr Med Ctr, Univ Calif, San Francisco, Salk Inst & Stanford Univ, 93, Duke Univ, 94. *Mem:* AAAS; Am Soc Microbiol; Asn Women Sci; Am Asn Cancer Res; Am Soc Biochem & Molecular Biol; Women Cancer Res. *Res:* Regulation of genomic fluidity; study of cellular systems which respond to DNA damage cell cycle checkpoints; regulation of gene amplification and the formation of other chromosomal abnormalities; chemical carcinogenesis. *Mailing Add:* Univ Calif Dept Path Box 6006 San Francisco CA 94413-0506. *Fax:* 919-966-3015

**TOBA, H(ACHIRO) HAROLD,** APHID VECTORS, POTATO VIRUSES. *Current Pos:* RETIRED. *Personal Data:* b Puunene, Hawaii, Aug 24, 32; m 58, Matsuko; c Wynne, Rhonda & Luanne. *Educ:* Univ Hawaii, BS, 57, MS, 61; Purdue Univ, PhD(entom), 66. *Honors & Awards:* IR-4 Meritorious Serv Award. *Prof Exp:* Res entomologist, Agr Res Serv, USDA, 65-96. *Mem:* AAAS; Entom Soc Am; Sigma Xi; Entom Soc Brit Col. *Res:* Elucidate vector-virus-plant host relationships of potato viruses and develop management strategies of aphid vectors for virus control. *Mailing Add:* 5230 Konnowack Pass Rd Wapato WA 98951. *Fax:* 509-454-5646

**TOBACH, ETHEL,** COMPARATIVE PSYCHOLOGY. *Current Pos:* assoc cur, Am Mus Natural Hist, 64-69, cur, Dept Animal Behav, 69-81, cur, Dept Mammal, 81-90, EMER CUR, AM MUS NATURAL HIST, 90- *Personal Data:* b Miaskovka, Russia, Nov 7, 21; nat US; wid. *Educ:* Hunter Col, BA, 49; NY Univ, MA, 52, PhD(comp psychol, physiol psychol), 57. *Hon Degrees:* DSc, Long Island Univ, 75. *Honors & Awards:* Kurt Lewin Award; Gustavus Meyer Fund, 96. *Prof Exp:* Res assoc, Payne Whitney Psychiat Clin, New York, 49-53 & Pub Health Res Inst NY, Inc, 53-56; res fel comp & physiol psychol, Am Mus Natural Hist, 57-61; asst prof comp physiol & exp psychol, Sch Med, NY Univ, 61-65. *Concurrent Pos:* Adj prof biol & psychol & develop psychol, City Univ New York, 69- *Mem:* AAAS; fel Am Psychol Asn; fel Animal Behav Soc; Int Soc Comp Psychol. *Res:* Development and evolution of behavior; emotional behavior; social behavior; racism; sexism; genetic determinism. *Mailing Add:* Am Mus Nat Hist Cent Park West at 79th St New York NY 10024-5192. *Fax:* 212-769-5233; *E-Mail:* etthc@cunyvm

**TOBACK, F(REDERICK) GARY,** NEPHROLOGY, EPITHELIAL CELL GROWTH. *Current Pos:* from asst prof to assoc prof, 74-85, PROF MED & CELL PHYSIOL, SCH MED, UNIV CHICAGO, 85- *Personal Data:* b Brooklyn, NY, Oct 23, 41; m 68, Phyllis Brooks; c David, Alison & Jonathan. *Educ:* Columbia Col, AB, 63; New York, Univ, MD, 67; Boston Univ, PhD(biochem), 74; Am Bd Int Med, dipl, 74; Am Bd Nephrol, dipl, 76. *Prof Exp:* Internship internal med, Cleveland Metrop Gen Hosp, 67-68, residency, 68-69; lt med, US Navy Med Corps, 69-70; res assoc med & nephrol, Sch Med, Boston Univ, 70-73; clin fel nephrol, Harvard Med Sch, Beth Israel Hosp, 74. *Concurrent Pos:* Am Cancer Soc scholar, Salk Inst Biol Studies, 79-80; estab investr, Am Heart Asn, 80-85 & sci councils; co-chmn, Nat Inst Diabetes & Digestive & Kidney Dis, Workshop on Control of Renal Growth, mem, Spec Grants Rev Comt. *Mem:* Am Physiol Soc; Cent Soc Clin Res; Am & Int Soc Nephrol; Am Soc Clin Invest; Am Asn Physicians; Am Fedn Clin Res. *Res:* Growth of kidney cells in physiological and pathological states: regeneration after acute renal failure; potassium depletion nephropathy; kidney autocrine growth factors, signal transduction in growing kidney cells; urinary crystal-renal cell interactions. *Mailing Add:* Dept Med Univ Chicago Pritzker Sch Med 5841 S Maryland Ave MC 5100 Chicago IL 60637-1463

**TOBE, STEPHEN SOLOMON,** INVERTEBRATE ENDOCRINOLOGY, REPRODUCTIVE PHYSIOLOGY. *Current Pos:* from asst prof to assoc prof, Univ Toronto, 74-82, assoc dean sci, 88-93, vdean, Fac Arts & Sci, 95-96, PROF ZOOL & PHYSIOL, DEPT ZOOL, UNIV TORONTO, 82- *Personal Data:* b Niagara-on-the-Lake, Ont, Can, Oct 11, 44; m 69, Martha Reller. *Educ:* Queen's Univ, Kingston, Que, BSc, 67; York Univ, Downsview, Ont, MSc, 69; McGill Univ, Montreal, Ont, PhD(parasitol), 72. *Honors & Awards:* C Gordon Hewitt Award, Entom Soc Can, 82, Gold Medal, 90; Pickford Medal Comp Endocrinol, Int Fedn Comp Endocrinol Soc, 93. *Prof Exp:* Res fel invert endocrinol, Agr Res Coun, Univ Sussex, 72-74. *Concurrent Pos:* Ed Bull Can Soc Zoologists, 79-82; vis prof, Dept Entom Sci, Univ Calif, Berkeley, 81, Dept Zool, Nat Univ Singapore, 87 & 93-94, Pac Biomed Res Ctr, Univ Hawaii, 88; E W R Steacie Mem fel, Nat Sci & Eng Res Coun Can, 82-84; res dir, Insect Biotech Can, 93- *Mem:* fel Royal Entom Soc; Soc Exp Biol; AAAS; fel Royal Soc Can; Entomol Soc Am. *Res:* Invertebrate endocrinology; regulation of hormone biosynthesis, particularly juvenile hormone; molecular biology of invertebrate neuropeptides; hormonal control of metamorphosis and reproduction in insects; mode of action of hormone agonists and antagonists. *Mailing Add:* Univ Toronto Dept Zool 25 Harbord St St George Campus Toronto ON M5S 3G5 Can. *E-Mail:* stephen.tobe@utoronto.ca

**TOBERMAN, RALPH OWEN,** analytical chemistry; deceased, see previous edition for last biography

**TOBES, MICHAEL CHARLES,** CARDIOLOGY, HEART FAILURE. *Current Pos:* FEL, DIV CARDIOVASC MED, HENRY FORD HOSP, DETROIT, MICH, 93- *Personal Data:* b Detroit, Mich, Oct 7, 48; m 79, Carol; c 2. *Educ:* Mich State Univ, BS, 70; Univ Mich, MS, 72, PhD(biol

chem), 76; Univ Miami, MD, 90. *Prof Exp:* Scholar, Dept Internal Med, Univ Mich, Ann Arbor, 76-79, res investr, 79-81, dir, Biochem Res Unit, 79-85, asst res scientist, 81-85; mem tech staff, AT&T Bell Labs, Middletown, NJ, 85-88; resident internal med, Milton S Hershey Med Ctr, Hershey, Pa, 90-93. *Mem:* AMA. *Res:* Heart failure; management of heart failure-physiologic changes; post cardiac trasplantation. *Mailing Add:* 30755 Old Stream Southfield MI 48076

**TOBEY, ARTHUR ROBERT,** APPLIED PHYSICS. *Current Pos:* RETIRED. *Personal Data:* b Portland, Ore, Aug 4, 20; m 77; c 3. *Educ:* Yale Univ, BS, 42, MS, 46, PhD(physics), 48. *Prof Exp:* Mem staff, Radiation Lab, Mass Inst Technol, 42-45; asst cosmic ray proj, Off Naval Res, Yale Univ, 47-48; asst prof physics, State Col Wash, 48-50; supvr physics, Armour Res Found, 50-52; sr scientist, 52-53; supvr TV res, Stanford Res Inst, SRI Int, 53-56, group head video systs lab, 56-59, staff scientist, Eng Div, 59-88. *Mem:* Am Phys Soc; Sigma Xi. *Res:* Radar and radar-type systems; neutron component of cosmic rays; electromechanical and electro-optical devices; electronic instrumentation; communication theory; man-computer systems; satellite systems modelling. *Mailing Add:* 527 Valencia Dr Los Altos CA 94022

**TOBEY, FRANK LINDLEY, JR,** VISION, PHOTOMETRY. *Current Pos:* ASST PROF SPECTROS VISION, MED SCH, UNIV FLA, 74- *Personal Data:* b Coeur d'Alene, Idaho, Aug 28, 23; m 57; c 1. *Educ:* Univ Mich, BSCh, 47, MSCh, 48, MS, 50, PhD(physics), 62. *Prof Exp:* Res assoc physics, Univ Mich, 50-60; res physicist, Cornell Aeronaut Lab, 62-64; fel lab astrophys, Harvard Col Observ, 64-65; fel shocktube physics, McDonnell-Douglas Corp, 66-69; res instr spectros of vision, Med Sch, Wash Univ, 70-74. *Concurrent Pos:* Asst prof physics & astron, Southern Ill Univ, Edwardsville, 70. *Mem:* AAAS; Am Phys Soc; Asn Res Vision & Ophthal; Sigma Xi. *Res:* Measurement of transition probabilities; atomic and molecular parameters; plasma diagnostics; optical properties of the retina and retinal receptors; spectroscopy; experimental determination of receptor waveguide properties; physics of vision. *Mailing Add:* 4114 NW 19th Pl Gainesville FL 32605-3528

**TOBEY, ROBERT ALLEN,** CELL BIOLOGY, CANCER. *Current Pos:* RETIRED. *Personal Data:* b Owosso, Mich, May 26, 37; m 60; c 2. *Educ:* Mich State Univ, BS, 59; Univ Ill, PhD, 63. *Prof Exp:* Staff mem, Genetics Group, Los Alamos Nat Lab, 64-91. *Concurrent Pos:* Los Alamos Nat Lab Fel, 83. *Mem:* AAAS; Am Soc Cell Biol; Am Soc Biochem & Molecular Biol. *Res:* Factors controlling traverse of the life cycle; sequential biochemical markers in the mammalian cell cycle; control of mammalian cell proliferation; mechanisms of action and effects on mammalian cell growth and division of anticancer drugs; mammalian cell synchronization. *Mailing Add:* 102 Rover Blvd Los Alamos NM 87544

**TOBEY, STEPHEN WINTER,** PHARMACEUTICAL CHEMISTRY. *Current Pos:* res chemist, Eastern Res Lab, 65-68, sr res chemist, 68-70, res dir, 70-74, dir chem lab, 73-75, mgr chem process develop, 75-76, mgr pharmaceut, process develop, 76-84, sr assoc scientist, 78-84, RES SCIENTIST, MICH DIV, DOW USA, 84- *Personal Data:* b Chicago, Ill, Jan 9, 36; m 53; c 4. *Educ:* Ill Inst Technol, BS, 57; Univ Wis, MS, 59, PhD(inorg chem), 65. *Prof Exp:* Instr phys chem, WVa Wesleyan Col, 59-61; asst prof inorg chem, Purdue Univ, 64-65. *Concurrent Pos:* Vis prof, Harvard Univ, 65 & Saginaw Valley State Col, 83 & 84. *Mem:* Am Chem Soc. *Res:* Pharmaceutical product development; water soluble polymers. *Mailing Add:* 4201 Congress St Midland MI 48642

**TOBIA, ALFONSO JOSEPH,** PHARMACOLOGY. *Current Pos:* EXEC VPRES, VINRX PHARMACEUT. *Personal Data:* b Brooklyn, NY, June 19, 42; m 70; c 2. *Educ:* St Louis Col Pharm, BS, 65; Purdue Univ, MS & PhD(pharmacol), 69. *Prof Exp:* Asst prof pharmacol, Univ Ga, 69-74; sr investr pharmacol, Smith Kline & French Labs, 74-77; group leader, Ortho Pharmaceut Corp, 77-81, sect head, 82-84, asst dir cardiovascular immunopharmacol dermato-pharmacol, 85, dir pharmacol, 85-89; sr dir pharmacol, drug discovery res, R W Johnson PRI, 90- *Concurrent Pos:* Ga Heart Asn res grant, Univ Ga, 71-72, Nat Heart & Lung Inst res grant hypertension, 71-74, mem, Coun High Blood Pressure Coun Circulation & Coun Basic Sci, Am Heart Asn. *Mem:* Am Soc Pharmacol & Exp Therapeut; Sigma Xi, Am Heart Asn; NY Acad Sci; Soc Exp Biol Med; Am Chem Soc. *Res:* Drug discovery and development; cardiovascular, gastrointestinal, micro biology and biochemical pharmacology. *Mailing Add:* VINRX Pharmaceut 2751 Centerville Rd Suite 210 Wilmington DE 19808

**TOBIAN, LOUIS,** INTERNAL MEDICINE. *Current Pos:* assoc prof, 54-64, PROF MED, SCH MED, UNIV MINN, MINNEAPOLIS, 64- *Personal Data:* b Dallas, Tex, Jan 26, 20; m 51. *Educ:* Univ Tex, BA, 40; Harvard Med Sch, MD, 44. *Honors & Awards:* Ciba Award, 78; Karger Award, 79; Volhard Award, 88. *Prof Exp:* House officer med, Peter Bent Brigham Hosp, Boston, 44; asst resident, Univ Hosp, Univ Calif, 44-45 & Parkland Hosp, Tex, 45-46; asst prof med, Univ Tex Southwestern Med Sch Dallas, 54. *Concurrent Pos:* Res fel med, Univ Tex Southwestern Med Sch Dallas, 46-51; res fel biochem, Harvard Med Sch, 51-54; estab investr, Am Heart Asn, 51-56, mem coun arteriosclerosis, 56-, chmn, Coun High Blood Pressure Res, 72; George Brown lectureship, 69; chmn task force hypertension, Nat Heart & Lung Inst, 72-73; mem adv comt hypertension res ctrs, 72-74; chmn comt hypertension & renal vascular dis, NIH Kidney Res Surv Group, 74-75. *Mem:* Am Clin & Climat Asn; Asn Am Physicians; Am Soc Clin Invest; Am Physiol Soc; fel NY Acad Sci. *Res:* Hypertension; renal circulation; sodium excretion. *Mailing Add:* Hypertension Sect Dept Internat Med Univ Minn Hosp & Sch Med Box 285 Univ Minn Health Ctr 420 Delaware St SE Minneapolis MN 55455-0374. *Fax:* 612-626-4866

**TOBIAS, CHARLES W,** electrochemistry, chemical engineering; deceased, see previous edition for last biography

**TOBIAS, CORNELIUS ANTHONY,** BIOPHYSICS. *Current Pos:* prof radiol, San Francisco, 77-90, EMER PROF, UNIV CALIF, BERKELEY, 90- *Personal Data:* b Budapest, Hungary, May 28, 18; nat US; m 43, Ida Lanning; c 2. *Educ:* Univ Calif, Berkeley, MA, 40, PhD(nuclear physics), 42. *Honors & Awards:* Lawrence Mem Award, 63; Annual Award, Aerospace Div, Am Nuclear Soc, 72. *Concurrent Pos:* Fel med physics, Univ Calif, Berkeley, 45-47; Guggenheim fel, Karolinska Inst, Sweden, 56-57; vis prof, Harvard Univ, 60; mem subcomt, Nat Res Coun, mem, Comt Radiol, Nat Acad Sci-Nat Res Coun; mem, Radiation Study Sect, NIH, 60-63; pres, Radiation Biophys Comn, Int Union Pure & Appl Physics, 69-72, coun mem, Int Union Pure & Appl Biophys, 69-75; Alexander von Humboldt US sr scientist award, 81; res assoc, BC Cancer Res Ctr, 85. *Mem:* Am Asn Physicists in Med; NY Acad Sci; Am Phys Soc; Radiation Res Soc (pres, 62-63); Biophys Soc. *Res:* Biological effects of radiation; cancer research; space medicine. *Mailing Add:* 4395 Mill St Eugene OR 97405-3444

**TOBIAS, GEORGE S,** chemical engineering; deceased, see previous edition for last biography

**TOBIAS, JERRY VERNON,** PSYCHOACOUSTICS. *Current Pos:* AT AUDITORY & COMMUN SCI DEPT, NAVAL SUBMARINE MED RES LAB. *Personal Data:* b St Louis, Mo, Oct 14, 29; c 2. *Educ:* Univ Mo, AB, 50; Univ Iowa, MA, 54; Western Reserve Univ, PhD(audition), 59. *Prof Exp:* Asst, Univ Iowa, 53-54; instr speech path & audiol, Ball State Teachers Col, Ind, 54-56; res assoc audition, Western Reserve Univ, 56-59; res scientist psychophys, Defense Res Lab & vis asst prof psychol, Univ Tex, 59-61; assoc prof psychol, Univ Okla, 63-71, prof, 71-80; chmn commun processes, Civil Aeromedical Inst, Fed Aviation Admin, 77-80; at Indust Audiol, 80- *Concurrent Pos:* Mem comt hearing, bioacoust & biomech, Nat Acad Sci-Nat Res Coun; supvry psychologist, Civil Aeromed Inst, Fed Aviation Admin, 61-77. *Mem:* Fel Acoust Soc Am; Sigma Xi; fel Am Speech & Hearing Asn. *Res:* Physiological and psychological acoustics; audition; experimental phonetics; physiological psychology; psychophysics; sensation and perception; auditory time constants; binaural audition; noise hazards and control. *Mailing Add:* 6 Huntington Way Ledyard CT 06339

**TOBIAS, PHILIP E,** OPTICS. *Current Pos:* PRES, TOBIAS ASSOC, INC, IVYLAND, PA, 56- & COMPUSTATICS, INC, PA, 73- *Personal Data:* b Harrison, NJ, July 15, 19; m 46; c 4. *Educ:* Cooper Union Inst Technol, BChE, 39, Polytechnic Inst, MChE, 41. *Hon Degrees:* ChE, Cooper Union Inst Tech, 46. *Honors & Awards:* Tech Asn Graphic Arts Honors Award, 80. *Prof Exp:* Civil serv examr, US Civil Serv Comn, 39-40; asst res eng, Nat Bur Standards, 40-42; head, instrument lab, Publicker Indust, 42-46; dir res eng, Edward Stern & Co, 45-56. *Concurrent Pos:* Graphic arts consult, self employed, Philadelphia, 56-59. *Mem:* Tech Asn Graphic Arts (vpres, 58-59, pres 59-60); Am Chem Soc; fel Am Inst Chemists; Sigma Xi; Graphic Arts Tech Found. *Res:* Developer of quality control approaches and devices used in the printing industry. *Mailing Add:* 50 Industrial Dr Ivyland PA 18974. *Fax:* 215-322-1504

**TOBIAS, RUSSELL LAWRENCE,** MICROCOMPUTER DESIGN. *Current Pos:* VPRES, TOBIAS ASSOC, PA, 93- *Personal Data:* b Upper Darby, Pa, Dec 18, 48. *Educ:* Temple Univ, AB, 70; Univ Md, MS, 75, PhD(physics), 78. *Prof Exp:* Res asst physics, Dept Physics & Astron, Univ Md, 75-78; res analyst, Compustatics, Inc, 78-93. *Res:* Instrumentation design and development in graphic arts and radiology; management information system design and administration. *Mailing Add:* PO Box 2699 Warminster PA 18974-0347

**TOBIASON, FREDERICK LEE,** PHYSICAL CHEMISTRY, POLYMER CHEMISTRY. *Current Pos:* from asst prof to assoc prof, 66-91, PROF PHYS CHEM, PAC LUTHERAN UNIV, TACOMA, 92- *Personal Data:* b Pe Ell, Wash, Sept 15, 36; m 61; c 3. *Educ:* Pac Lutheran Univ, BA, 58; Mich State Univ, PhD(phys chem), 63. *Prof Exp:* Res assoc nuclear magnetic resonance spectros, Emory Univ, 63-64; res chemist, Benger Lab, E I du Pont de Nemours & Co, Inc, 64-66. *Concurrent Pos:* Consult, Reichhold Chem, Inc, 67-; chmn, Chem Dept, Pac Lutheran Univ, 73-76 & regency prof, 75-76; vis res prof, Univ Wash, 76, Univ Helsinki, 76, La State Univ, 82, Univ Sci & Technol, Lille, France, 91-93 & 96; consult, Bennett Lab, Inc, 80-82, US Commodotoes, 85; vis lectr, Japan, 83, Yugoslavia, 87-; vis prof, Chengdu Univ Sci & Technol, China, 89-91; vis scholar, Dnepropetrovsk, Ukraune, 91. *Mem:* Am Chem Soc. *Res:* Molecular structure; nuclear magnetic resonance spectroscopy; electric dipole moments; molecular characterization of polymers; wood chemistry; adhesives; polymer chain configuration calculations; phenolic resins; quantum mechanical calculations. *Mailing Add:* Dept Chem Pac Lutheran Univ Tacoma WA 98447-0001. *Fax:* 253-536-5355; *E-Mail:* tobiasfl@plu.edu

**TOBIESSEN, PETER LAWS,** PLANT ECOLOGY. *Current Pos:* From asst prof to assoc prof, 77-83, PROF BIOL, UNION COL, NY, 83- *Personal Data:* b Philadelphia, Pa, Mar 30, 40; m 68. *Educ:* Wesleyan Univ, BA, 63; Pa State Univ, University Park, MS, 66; Duke Univ, PhD(bot), 71. *Mem:* Ecol Soc Am. *Res:* Physiological plant ecology. *Mailing Add:* 1377 Dean St Schenectady NY 12309-5233

**TOBIN, ALBERT GEORGE,** PHYSICAL METALLURGY. *Current Pos:* STAFF SCIENTIST, GRUMMAN AEROSPACE CORP, 69-; SR RES SCIENTIST, NORTHROP GRUMMAN CORP, 72- *Personal Data:* b Boston, Mass, June 7, 38; m 63. *Educ:* Mass Inst Technol, BS, 60, MS, 63; Columbia Univ, PhD(metall), 68. *Prof Exp:* Staff metallurgist, Nuclear Metals Inc, 60-62; res asst metall, Mass Inst Technol, 62-63 & Columbia Univ, 63-68; res metallurgist, Union Carbide Corp, 68-69. *Mem:* Am Soc Metals; Am Ceramic Soc. *Res:* Magnetic and dielectric materials; high temperature properties of materials; fracture and fatigue properties of titanium alloys; hydrogen embrittlement; application of materials to fusion reactors; metal matrix composites; radiation damage in ceramics; surface physics and chemistry; ceramic matrix composites; ceramic metal composites. *Mailing Add:* Northrup Grumman South Oyster Bay Rd Bethpage NY 11714

**TOBIN, ALLAN JOSHUA,** MOLECULAR NEUROBIOLOGY. *Current Pos:* asst prof, 75-81, assoc prof, 81-84, PROF, UNIV CALIF, LOS ANGELES, 84-, CHAIR, INTERDEPARTMENTAL PROG NEUROSCI, 89- *Personal Data:* b Manchester, NH, Aug 22, 42; m 81; c 2. *Educ:* Mass Inst Technol, BS, 63; Harvard Univ, PhD(biophys), 69. *Prof Exp:* USPHS fels, Weizman Inst Sci, 69-70 & Mass Inst Technol, 70-71; asst prof biol, Harvard Univ, 71-74. *Concurrent Pos:* Sci dir, Hereditary Dis Found, 79- *Mem:* AAAS; Soc Develop Biol; Am Soc Neurochem; Soc Neurosci. *Res:* Molecular neurobiology. *Mailing Add:* Dept Biol Univ Calif 10833 Le Conte Ave CHS Box 951761 Los Angeles CA 90095-1761

**TOBIN, ELAINE MUNSEY,** PLANT DEVELOPMENT, MOLECULAR BIOLOGY. *Current Pos:* from asst prof to assoc prof, 75-85, PROF BIOL, UNIV CALIF, LOS ANGELES, 85- *Personal Data:* b Louisville, Ky, Dec 23, 44; m 83, J Philip Thornber; c David M & Adam M. *Educ:* Oberlin Col, BA, 66; Harvard Univ, PhD(biol), 72. *Prof Exp:* Fel biol, Brandeis Univ, 73-75. *Concurrent Pos:* Mem grant rev panel, USDA & NIH. *Mem:* Am Soc Plant Physiologists; AAAS; Int Soc Plant Molecular Biol. *Res:* Control of plant development by light. *Mailing Add:* Dept Biol Univ Calif Los Angeles CA 90095. *E-Mail:* ibb9toe@mvs.oac.ucla.edu

**TOBIN, GORDON ROSS,** PLASTIC & RECONSTRUCTIVE SURGERY, MEDICAL RESEARCH. *Current Pos:* From instr to assoc prof, 77-86, PROF SURG, UNIV LOUISVILLE, 86- *Personal Data:* b Twin Falls, Idaho, Jan 6, 41; m 68; c 2. *Educ:* Whitman Col, AB, 65; Univ Calif, San Francisco, MD, 69. *Concurrent Pos:* Prin investr, Paralyzed Vets Am, 75-76; mem var comts, Am Soc Plastic & Reconstruct Surgeons, 81-91; prin investr, Jewish Hosp Heart & Lung Inst, 91- *Mem:* Soc Univ Surgeons; Am Col Surgeons; Am Asn Plastic Surgeons; Plastic Surg Res Coun; Am Soc Plastic & Reconstruct Surgeons; Sigma Xi. *Res:* Tissue repair and wound healing; spinal cord wound healing and regeneration; muscle and skin anatomy and flap physiology; skin tissue culture and burn resurfacing; bone and soft tissue reconstruction. *Mailing Add:* Dept Surg Univ Louisville Health Sci Ctr Louisville KY 40292

**TOBIN, JAMES,** ECONOMICS. *Current Pos:* from assoc prof to Sterling prof, 50-88, EMER PROF ECON, YALE UNIV, 88- *Personal Data:* b Champaign, Ill, Mar 5, 18; m 46, Elizabeth F Ringo; c Margaret, L Michael, Hugh & Roger G. *Educ:* Harvard Univ, AB, 39, MA, 40, PhD, 47. *Hon Degrees:* Numerous from US & foreign cols & univs, 67-96. *Honors & Awards:* Nobel Prize in Econs, 81; John Bates Clark Medal, Am Econ Asn, 55; Grand Cordon Order of the Sacred Treasure, Japan, 88. *Prof Exp:* Teaching fel econs, Harvard Univ, 46-47, Harvard Soc Fellows, 47-50, Dept Appl Econ, Univ Cambridge, 49-50. *Concurrent Pos:* Fac fel, Soc Sci Res Coun, 51-54; mem, Coun Econ Advisers, 61-62; vis, Univ Nairobi, Kenya, 72-73; chair, Dept Econ, Yale Univ; dir, Cowles Found. *Mem:* Nat Acad Sci; fel Econometric Soc (pres, 58); fel Am Statist Asn; corresp fel Brit Acad; Am Philos Soc; Am Econ Asn (vpres, 64, pres, 71); Acad Sci Portugal; fel Am Acad Arts & Sci. *Res:* Macroeconomics, theory and policy; financial markets and their relation to economic activity; author of 15 books. *Mailing Add:* 117 Alden Ave New Haven CT 06515-2109

**TOBIN, JOHN ROBERT, JR,** INTERNAL MEDICINE, CARDIOLOGY. *Current Pos:* chmn dept, 69-82, prof med, 62-87, dean, 82-87, EMER PROF MED & DEAN, STRITCH SCH MED, LOYOLA UNIV, CHICAGO, 87- *Personal Data:* b Elgin, Ill, Dec 18, 16; wid; c Mary Catherine. *Educ:* Univ Notre Dame, BS, 38; Univ Chicago, MD, 42; Univ Minn, MS, 50; Am Bd Internal Med, dipl, 52; Am Bd Cardiovasc Dis, dipl, 66. *Hon Degrees:* DSc, Loyola Univ, 93. *Prof Exp:* Intern med & surg, Presby Hosp, Chicago, 42-43; resident path, Univ Chicago Clins, 46-47; asst staff, Mayo Clin, 51; staff, Rockwood Clin, Spokane, Wash, 51-55; sr physician, Med Educ Div, 55-59, dir adult cardiol, Cook Co Hosp, Ill, 59-69. *Concurrent Pos:* Fel med, Mayo Found, 47-50, NIH spec fel physiol, 63-64; assoc & attend staff med, 55-69, Cook Co Hosp, chief of staff, 67-69; physician-in-chief, Loyola Hosp, 69-82. *Mem:* Fel Am Col Physicians; fel Am Col Cardiol. *Res:* Cardiovascular physiology and disease. *Mailing Add:* Loyola Med Ctr 2160 S First Ave Maywood IL 60153-5500

**TOBIN, MARTIN JOHN,** REGULATION OF RESPIRATION, PULMONARY MECHANICS. *Current Pos:* PROF MED & DIR, DIV PULMONARY & CRITICAL CARE MED, LOYOLA UNIV SCH MED, CHICAGO, 90- *Personal Data:* b Kilkenny, Ireland, Apr 23, 51; m 77; c 3. *Educ:* Fac Med, Univ Col, Dublin, MB(med), BCh(surg) & BAO(obstet), 75; Am Bd Internal Med, dipl, 83, dipl pulmonary dis, 84, dipl critical care med, 88. *Prof Exp:* Registr, Med Professorial Unit, Univ Col-St Vincent's Hosp, Dublin, 78-79; Brit Thoracic Asn res fel, King's Col Hosp, London, 79-80, res & clin fel, div pulmonary dis, Mt Sinai Med Ctr, Miami Beach, 80-82 & Critical Care Training Prog, Presby-Univ Hosp, Univ Health Ctr, Pittsburgh, 82-83; from asst prof to assoc prof internal med, Div Pulmonary Med, Univ Tex Health Sci Ctr, Houston, 83-90. *Concurrent Pos:* Assoc ed, Am J Respiratory & Critical Care Med, Intensive Care Med. *Mem:* Am Physiol Soc; Am Thoracic Soc; Am Col Chest Physicians; Soc Critical Care Med; Brit Thoracic Soc; Royal Col Physicians Ireland; Am Soc Clin Invest. *Res:* Neuromuscular control of breathing; respiratory monitoring; mechanical ventilation; critical care medicine. *Mailing Add:* Div Pulmonary Med Loyola Univ Med Ctr 2160 S First Ave Maywood IL 60153. *Fax:* 708-531-7982

**TOBIN, RICHARD BRUCE,** PHYSIOLOGY. *Current Pos:* assoc prof med, 66-68, assoc prof physiol, 67-68, PROF MED & BIOCHEM, UNIV NEBR MED CTR, OMAHA, 68-; STAFF PHYSICIAN, VET ADMIN HOSP, OMAHA, 68- *Personal Data:* b Buffalo, NY, Mar 6, 25; m 47, H Jean McNair; c 5. *Educ:* Union Univ, NY, BS, 45; Univ Rochester, MD, 49. *Prof Exp:* Instr physiol & med, Sch Med & Dent, Univ Rochester, 54-59, asst prof & asst physician, 59-63. *Concurrent Pos:* USPHS fel biochem, Univ Amsterdam, 63-65. *Mem:* Am Physiol Soc; Endocrine Soc; Am Inst Nutrit; fel Am Col Physicians; Am Diabetes Asn. *Res:* Cellular energetics; thyroid hormone regulation of intermediary metabolism. *Mailing Add:* Univ Nebr Med Ctr 600 S 42nd St Omaha NE 68105. *Fax:* 402-559-6205

**TOBIN, ROGER LEE,** ECONOMICS, TRANSPORTATION RESEARCH. *Current Pos:* mem tech staff, Dept Econ & Statist, 85-91, Network Planning Methods Dept, 91-95, CUSTOMER SERV, PROCESSES DEPT, GTE LABS, 95- *Personal Data:* b Grand Rapids, Mich, Oct 11, 40; m 85, Barbara Payne; c Anna & Thomas. *Educ:* Univ Mich, BSE, 64, MSE, 69, MA, 72, PhD(indust eng), 73. *Prof Exp:* Sr indust & process engr, Hoover Ball & Bearing, 64-68; sr res engr transp & traffic sci, Gen Motors Res Labs, Gen Motors Corp, 73-80; environ systs engr, Environ Res Div, Argonne Nat Lab, 80-85. *Concurrent Pos:* Adj assoc prof, Dept Civil Eng, Univ Pa, 83-90. *Mem:* Opers Res Soc Am; Inst Mgt Sci; Math Prog Soc; Regional Sci Asn Int. *Res:* Mathematical modeling of business processes; development of decision support tools; transportation logistics and mathematical programming. *Mailing Add:* 29 Oxford St Arlington MA 02174

**TOBIN, SARA L,** CONTRACTILE PROTEIN GENETICS, MOLECULAR GENETICS. *Current Pos:* asst prof, 83-89, ASSOC PROF, DEPT BIOCHEM & MOLECULAR BIOL, HEALTH SCI CTR, UNIV OKLA, 89- *Personal Data:* b Springfield, Mass, Apr 27, 46; div. *Educ:* Univ Wash, Seattle, BS, 68 & PhD(develop biol), 77; Univ Okla, MSW, 93. *Prof Exp:* Fel, Dept Genetics, Univ Calif Berkeley, 78-82, Dept Biochem & Biophys, Univ Calif, San Francisco, 78-81; asst res geneticist, Dept Genetics, Univ Calif Berkeley, 81-82; muscular dystrophy fel, 78-79; NIH fel, 79-81; sr fel, Calif Div, Am Cancer Soc, 81-82. *Concurrent Pos:* Prin investr, NIH, 81, Am Heart Asn, 85; vis assoc prof & except prin investr, Univ Calif, Berkeley, 93-; vis professorship for women awardee, NSF, 93- *Mem:* Am Soc Cell Biol; Sigma Xi; Am Soc Biochem & Molecular Biol; AAAS; Asn Women Sci. *Res:* Expression of individual actin genes during development of Drosophila melanogaster; structure, function and expression of the single Drosophila calmodulin gene in visual transduction; use of baculoviruses to test promoters in lepidopteran insects. *Mailing Add:* Dept Biochem & Molecular Biol Univ Okla Health Sci Ctr PO Box 26901 Oklahoma City OK 73126-0901. *Fax:* 405-271-3139; *E-Mail:* sara.tobin@cclink.net.uokhsc.edusltobin@nature.berkeley.edu

**TOBIN, SIDNEY MORRIS,** OBSTETRICS & GYNECOLOGY. *Current Pos:* Clin lectr, 61-71, ASST PROF OBSTET & GYNEC, UNIV TORONTO, 71-; PVT PRACT. *Personal Data:* b Toronto, Ont, Jan 18, 23; m 49; c 4. *Educ:* Univ Toronto, MD, 46; FRCS(C), 51. *Concurrent Pos:* Chmn, Res Adv Comt, Res Dept, Mt Sinai Hosp, Toronto, 70- *Mem:* Can Med Asn; Soc Obstetricians & Gynecologists Can; Royal Col Physicians & Surgeons Can; Can Oncol Soc; Can Fel Travel Soc. *Res:* Studies to elucidate the role of herpes simplex virus type II as a carcinogen or co-carcinogen in the etiology of squamous cell carcinoma of the cervix in humans. *Mailing Add:* 99 Avenue Rd Suite 206 Toronto ON M5R 2G5 Can

**TOBIN, THOMAS,** TOXICOLOGY, PHARMACOLOGY. *Current Pos:* assoc prof vet sci, 75-78, prof vet sci & toxicol, 78-90, GRAD DIR, GRAD CTR TOXICOL, UNIV KY, 90- *Personal Data:* b Dublin, Ireland, Aug 7, 41; US citizen; div. *Educ:* Univ Col Dublin, DVM, 64; Univ Guelph, MSc, 66; Univ Toronto, PhD(parmacol), 69; Am Bd Toxicol, cert, 80. *Prof Exp:* Res assoc pharmacol, Univ Toronto, 66-70; asst prof, Mich State Univ, 71-75. *Concurrent Pos:* NIH grant, 73-76; NSF grant, 74-76; Ky Equine Drug Res grant, 75-; consult equine medication & drug detection, 75- *Mem:* Am Col Vet Pharmacol & Therapeut; Am Soc Pharmacol & Exp Therapeut; Am Col Vet Toxicol; Equine Vet Asn Eng. *Res:* Equine medication; doping; drug analysis; drug disposition; pharmacokinetics; molecular pharmacology; toxicology. *Mailing Add:* 1242 Sommet Dr Lexington KY 40502. *Fax:* 606-258-1059

**TOBIN, THOMAS VINCENT,** BIOLOGY. *Current Pos:* from instr to asst prof, King's Col, 52-62, chmn, Div Natural Sci, 71-76, chmn, Dept Biol, 85-90, ASSOC PROF BIOL, KING'S COL, 62-, CHIEF HEALTH PROFESSIONS ADV, 89- *Personal Data:* b Plymouth, Pa, Apr 8, 26; m 47, Dolores Chewey; c Cynthia. *Educ:* King's Col, BS, 51; Boston Col, MS, 53. *Prof Exp:* Asst biol, Boston Col, 51-52. *Concurrent Pos:* Dir, Clin Lab Sci Prog, Kings Col, 90. *Res:* Chemoreception and proprioception in the crayfish; cold acclimitization; influence of drugs on animal behavior. *Mailing Add:* Dept Biol King's Col Wilkes-Barre PA 18711-0801. *Fax:* 717-825-5937

**TOBIS, JEROME SANFORD,** MEDICINE, GERIATRIC MEDICINE. *Current Pos:* RETIRED. *Personal Data:* b Syracuse, NY, July 23, 15; m 38; c 3. *Educ:* City Col New York, BS, 36; Chicago Med Sch, MD, 43. *Prof Exp:* Consult phys med & rehab, Vet Admin Hosp, Bronx, NY, 48-53; prof phys med & rehab & dir, NY Med Col, 52-70; chief phys med & rehab, Montepore Hosp & Med Ctr, Bronx, NY, 61-70; prof, Albert Einstein Col Med, 62-70; chmn dept, Univ Calif, Irvine-Calif Col Med, 70-82, prof phys med & rehab, 70-86, dir dept, med ctr, 70-82, dir prog genetic med, 80-86. *Concurrent Pos:* Baruch fel, Columbia Univ, 47; dir phys med & rehab, Metrop Hosp, 52-70 & Bird S Coler Hosp, 52-70; consult, City Hosp, 48 & Bur Handicapped Children, New York City Dept Health, 53-70; ed, Arch Phys Med & Rehab, 59-73; chief rehab med, Montefiore Hosp Med Ctr, 61-70; dir dept phys med & rehab, Orange County Med Ctr, 70-77; distinguished clinician, Am Acad Phys Med & Rehab, 93. *Mem:* AAAS; AMA; Am Pub Health Asn; Am Cong Rehab Med; Am Acad Phys Med & Rehab. *Res:* Hemiplegia; cardiac rehabilitation; rehabilitation of handicapped children; geriatrics. *Mailing Add:* Dept Phys Med & Rehab Univ Calif Irvine CA 92668

**TOBISCH, OTHMAR TARDIN,** STRUCTURAL GEOLOGY. *Current Pos:* from asst prof to assoc prof, 69-78, PROF EARTH SCI, UNIV CALIF, SANTA CRUZ, 78- *Personal Data:* b Berkeley, Calif, June 18, 32; m 64; c 1. *Educ:* Univ Calif, Berkeley, BA, 58, MA, 60; Univ London, PhD(struct geol), 63. *Prof Exp:* Fulbright fel, Innsbruck, Austria, 63-64; res geologist, US Geol Surv, 64-69. *Mem:* Geol Soc Am; fel Geol Soc London. *Res:* Polyphase deformation in orogenic belts; quantitative strain determination of deformed rocks; genesis of orogenic belts. *Mailing Add:* Dept Earth Sci Earth & Marine Sci Univ Calif Bldg Rm A232 Santa Cruz CA 95064

**TOBKES, MARTIN,** ORGANIC CHEMISTRY, ANTIBIOTICS & STEROIDS. *Current Pos:* RETIRED. *Personal Data:* b New York, NY, Feb 8, 28; m 52, Elizabeth Somers; c Nancy (Lunt) & Carol S. *Educ:* City Col New York, BS, 48; Polytech Inst Brooklyn, MS, 54, PhD(org chem), 63. *Prof Exp:* Res & develop chemist, Nopco Chem Co, 49-54 & Charles Bruning Co, 54-56; res org chemist, Ethicon, Inc, 56-58; res fel org chem, Polytech Inst Brooklyn, 59-63; prin res chemist fermentation develop, Lederle Labs, Am Cyanamid Co, 63-90. *Mem:* Am Chem Soc; Sigma Xi. *Res:* Vitamin synthesis and stability; Perkin condensations; corrosion; light sensitive coatings; medicinal synthesis; polymers; antibiotics; steroids; fermentation derived products. *Mailing Add:* 98 Sutin Pl Chestnut Ridge NY 10977

**TOBKES, NANCY J,** PROTEIN CHEMISTRY. *Current Pos:* PHD, REGENERATION PHARMACEUT. *Personal Data:* b Somerville, NJ, Feb 12, 58; m 86. *Educ:* Brandeis Univ, BA, 80; Columbia Univ, MA, 81, MPhil, 83, PhD(biochem), 86. *Prof Exp:* Fel cell biol, NY Univ Med Ctr, 86-89; sr scientist protein biochem, Hoffmann-La Roche, Inc, 89- *Mem:* Protein Soc; Am Soc Cell Biol; Am Chem Soc; AAAS. *Res:* Structure and function relationships in membrane proteins; purifying and characterizing different recombinant forms of the human immunoglobulin E receptor and immunoglobulin E fragments to study their interactions. *Mailing Add:* 3 Fairfield Ct Danbury CT 06811-0001

**TOBOCHNIK, JAN,** THERMAL PHYSICS. *Current Pos:* ASSOC PROF PHYSICS & COMPUT SCI, KALAMAZOO COL, 85- *Personal Data:* b Philadelphia, Pa, July 31, 53. *Educ:* Amherst Col, BA, 75; Cornell Univ, PhD(physics), 80. *Prof Exp:* Res assoc, Rutgers Univ, 80-82; asst prof physics, Worcester Polytech Inst, 82-83. *Concurrent Pos:* Adj prof physics, Clark Univ, 85; vis prof, McGill Univ, 91-92. *Mem:* Am Phys Soc; Am Asn Physics Teachers. *Res:* Computer simulation of condensed matter and other complex systems focusing on phase transitions. Examples include phospholipid bilayers, porous media, two-dimensional systems and binary fluids. *Mailing Add:* 2400 Bruce Dr Kalamazoo MI 49008. *E-Mail:* jant@kzoo.edu

**TOBOCMAN, WILLIAM,** THEORETICAL NUCLEAR PHYSICS, INVERSE THEORY. *Current Pos:* assoc prof, 60-66, PROF PHYSICS, CASE WESTERN RES UNIV, 66- *Personal Data:* b Detroit, Mich, Mar 14, 26; m 50; c 2. *Educ:* Mass Inst Technol, SB, 50, PhD(physics), 53. *Prof Exp:* Res assoc, Cornell Univ, 53-54; mem, Inst Adv Study, 54-56; NSF fel, Univ Birmingham, 56-57; asst prof physics, Rice Univ, 57-60. *Concurrent Pos:* Sloan Found fel, 61-64; res fel, Weizmann Inst, 63-64. *Mem:* Am Phys Soc. *Res:* Theory of nuclear reactions; quantum mechanical many-body problem; classical wave scattering, inverse scattering; medical imaging. *Mailing Add:* Dept Physics Case Western Res Univ University Circle Cleveland OH 44106. *Fax:* 216-368-4671

**TOBUREN, LARRY HOWARD,** ATOMIC & MOLECULAR PHYSICS, ATOMIC COLLISIONS & RADIATION DOSIMETRY. *Current Pos:* PROF, DEPT PHYSICS, E CAROLINA UNIV, 95- *Personal Data:* b Clay Center, Kans, July 9, 40; m 62, Lana L Henry; c Debra & Tina. *Educ:* Emporia State Univ, BA, 62; Vanderbilt Univ, PhD(physics), 68. *Prof Exp:* Sr res scientist, Pac Northwest Labs, Battelle Mem Inst, 67-80, mgr radiol physics sect, 80-93; sr staff officer, Nat Res Coun/Nat Acad Scis, 93-95. *Concurrent Pos:* Adj assoc prof radiol sci, Univ Wash, 81-93. *Mem:* Fel Am Phys Soc; Radiation Res Soc; AAAS; Int Radiation Physics Soc; Sigma Xi. *Res:* Atomic and molecular collision processes; Auger electron studies; measurement of inner and outer shell ionization cross sections and continuum electron distributions resulting from charged particle impact. *Mailing Add:* Dept Physics E Carolina Univ Greenville NC 27858. *Fax:* 919-328-6314; *E-Mail:* phtobure@ecuvm.cis.ecu.edu

**TOBY, SIDNEY,** PHYSICAL CHEMISTRY. *Current Pos:* from instr to assoc prof, 57-69, PROF CHEM, RUTGERS UNIV, NEW BRUNSWICK, 69- *Personal Data:* b London, Eng, May 30, 30; m 53; c 2. *Educ:* Univ London, BSc, 52; McGill Univ, PhD, 55. *Prof Exp:* Fel photochem, Nat Res Coun, Can, 55-57. *Mem:* AAAS; Am Chem Soc. *Res:* Kinetics of gaseous reactions; photochemistry; chemiluminescence. *Mailing Add:* Dept Chem Ritgers Univ PO Box 939 Piscataway NJ 08855-0939

**TOCCI, PAUL M,** BIOCHEMISTRY, GENETICS. *Current Pos:* DIR, BIOCHEM GENETICS LAB, UNIV MIAMI, 64-, ASSOC PROF PEDIAT, SCH MED, 67- *Personal Data:* b Brooklyn, NY, Nov 11, 33; m 68; c Dominick, Nina, Angelo, Paul, Todd, Michael & Michelle. *Educ:* Johns Hopkins Univ, BA, 55; Univ Md, PhD(biochem), 64. *Mem:* AAAS; Am Asn

Clin Chemists; fel Am Inst Chemists; Am Soc Human Genetics; Am Fedn Clin Res; Int Fedn Clin Chem; NY Acad Sci. *Res:* Amino acid metabolism; inborn errors of metabolism; human genetics. *Mailing Add:* Dept Pediat R131 Univ Miami Sch Med 1600 NW Tenth Ave Miami FL 33101

**TOCCO, DOMINICK JOSEPH,** BIOCHEMISTRY, PHARMACOLOGY. *Current Pos:* RETIRED. *Personal Data:* b New York, NY, Jan 25, 30; m 52; c 4. *Educ:* St John's Univ, BS, 51, MS, 53; Georgetown Univ, PhD(chem), 60. *Prof Exp:* Biochemist, US Army Chem Ctr, Md, 53-55, Nat Heart Inst, 55-60, Merck Inst Therapeut Res, 60-66, Shell Develop Co, 66-70, Merck, Sharp & Dohme Res Labs, 70-93. *Mem:* Am Soc Pharmacol & Exp Therapeut. *Res:* Transport of drugs and natural substances across biological membranes; drug metabolism; pharmacodynamics; experimental enzyme kinetics. *Mailing Add:* c/o Kathleen Jordan Merck & Co PO Box 100 Whitehouse Station NJ 08889

**TOCHER, RICHARD DANA,** PLANT PHYSIOLOGY. *Current Pos:* asst prof, 66-70, ASSOC PROF BIOL, PORTLAND STATE UNIV, 70- *Personal Data:* b Oakland, Calif, Oct 8, 35; m 61; c 3. *Educ:* Stanford Univ, AB, 57; Univ Wash, Seattle, MS, 63, PhD(bot), 65. *Prof Exp:* Nat Res Coun Can fel marine bot, Atlantic Regional Lab, 65-66. *Mem:* Am Soc Plant Physiol; Soc Econ Bot. *Res:* Plant physiology and biochemistry, especially marine algae and parasitic angiosperms. *Mailing Add:* Dept Biol Portland State Univ Box 751 Portland OR 97207-0751

**TOCK, RICHARD WILLIAM,** CHEMICAL ENGINEERING, POLYMER SCIENCE. *Current Pos:* vis assoc prof, 74-75, assoc prof, 75-85, PROF, CHEM ENG, TEX TECH UNIV, 85- *Personal Data:* b Centerville, Iowa, July 13, 40; m 65, Phoebe L Hewlett; c Christine L, Jennifer A & Jese T. *Educ:* Univ Iowa, BS, 63, MS, 64, PhD(chem eng), 67. *Honors & Awards:* Ralph R Teetor Award, Soc Automotive Engrs, 80; Student Chap Counr Award, Am Inst Chem Eng, 80. *Prof Exp:* From instr to asst prof chem eng, Univ Iowa, 65-67; res engr, Monsanto Co, 68-70; asst prof chem eng, Univ Iowa, 70-74. *Concurrent Pos:* Consult engr, 80- *Mem:* Am Inst Chem Engrs; Soc Plastics Engrs; Am Soc Eng Educ; Am Leather Chemists Asn; Soc Am Mil Engrs. *Res:* Membrane separation processes; polymer science, engineering materials and properties; biomass conversion; oxidations with ozone; fuel catalysts; waste treatment. *Mailing Add:* Dept Chem Eng Tex Tech Univ PO Box 43121 Lubbock TX 79409-3121. *E-Mail:* tock@cdei.coe.ttu.edu

**TOCZEK, DONALD RICHARD,** ENTOMOLOGY, BOTANY. *Current Pos:* PROF BIOL, HILLSDALE COL, 67- *Personal Data:* b LaPorte, Ind, Nov 21, 38; m 72; c 3. *Educ:* Purdue Univ, BS, 61; NDak State Univ, MS, 63, PhD(entom), 67. *Prof Exp:* Res asst entom, NDak State Univ, 61-67. *Mem:* Entom Soc Am; Ecol Soc Am; Sigma Xi. *Res:* Basic botany; invertebrate zoology. *Mailing Add:* Dept Biol Hillsdale Col 33 E College St Hillsdale MI 49242-1205

**TODARO, GEORGE JOSEPH,** CANCER. *Current Pos:* CHMN & PROF, DEPT PATHOBIOL, SCH PUB HEALTH & COMMUNITY MED, UNIV WASH, SEATTLE, 91- *Personal Data:* b New York, NY, July 1, 37; m 62, Jane Lehu; c Wendy C, Thomas M & Anthony A. *Educ:* Swarthmore Col, BA, 58; NY Univ, MD, 63. *Honors & Awards:* Super Serv Award, HEW, 71; Gustav Stern Award for Virol, 72; Parke-Davis Award, Am Soc Exp Path, 75; Walter Hubert Lectr, Brit Cancer Soc, 77; Solomon A Bernson Med Achievement Award, 81. *Prof Exp:* Intern path, NY Univ Sch Med, 62-63, fel, 64-65; asst prof, 65-67; chief, Molecular Biol Sect, Viral Carcinogenesis Br, Nat Cancer Inst, NIH, Bethesda, 67-70, chief, Viral Leukemia & Lymphoma Br, 70-83, chief, Lab Viral Carcinogenics, 76-83; sci dir, Oncogen, Seattle, 83-87; exec vpres & sci dir, Genetics Systs Corp, 87-88; pres & sci dir, Oncogen, 88-90; sr vpres, Pharmaceut Res Inst, Bristol-Myers Squibb, Princeton, NJ, 90. *Concurrent Pos:* Career develop award, USPHS, 67; affil prof path, Sch Med, Univ Wash, Seattle, 83-, adj prof, 91-; spec lectr, Japanese Cancer Asn, 85; vis scientist, Fred Hutchinson Cancer Res Ctr, 90-; staff mem, CNI, 97- *Mem:* Nat Acad Sci; Am Asn Cancer Res; Soc Exp Biol & Med; Am Soc Microbiol; Am Soc Biol Chemists; Am Soc Clin Invest; Am Physic Pluto Soc; Am Asn Pathologists; NY Acad Sci. *Res:* Virus, growth and genetic factors, oncogenes and growth inhibitors in cancer etiology; diagnostic tests for retroviral infections and for cancer susceptibility; viral genes and vaccines; population based and public health related effects of infectious disease and cancer in health care. *Mailing Add:* Dept Pathobiol Univ Wash Box 357238-7238 Seattle WA 98195

**TODARO, MICHAEL P,** POPULATION ECONOMICS, DEVELOPMENT ECONOMICS. *Current Pos:* PROF ECON, NY UNIV, 78-; SR ASSOC, RES DIV, POP COUN, 78- *Personal Data:* b NY, May 14, 42; m 74, Donna Crickenberger; c 1. *Educ:* Haverford Col, BA, 64; Yale Univ, MPhil, 66, PhD(econ), 67. *Prof Exp:* Lectr econ, Mararere Univ, Uganda, 64-65; sr lectr econ, Univ Nairobi, Kenya, 68-70; assoc dir, Rockefeller Found, 70-74; vis prof econ, Univ Nairobi, Kenya, 74-76 & Univ Calif, Santa Barbara, 76. *Concurrent Pos:* Mem, Coun Foreign Rel. *Mem:* Am Econ Asn; Int Union Sci Study Pop; Pop Asn Am. *Res:* Determinants and consequences of population movements in the international economy; economic problems of underdeveloped countries; interrelationships between population and development. *Mailing Add:* 48 Indian Trail York ME 03909

**TODD, AARON RODWELL,** LINEAR TOPOLOGICAL SPACES, TOPOLOGY. *Current Pos:* ASSOC PROF MATH, BARUCH COL, CITY UNIV NY, 86- *Personal Data:* b El Portal, Fla, Dec 25, 42; m 85, Sheree A Neese; c Joshua, Clara & Julian. *Educ:* Univ Mich, BS, 64; Univ Leeds, MSc, 68; Univ Fla, PhD(math), 72. *Prof Exp:* Asst prof math, Univ PR, 72-74;

Brooklyn Col, 74-78; from asst prof to assoc prof math, St John's Univ, NY, 78-87. *Concurrent Pos:* Vchmn, Sect Math, NY Acad Sci, 83-85, chair, 86-87. *Mem:* Am Math Soc; NY Acad Sci; Asn Comput Mach; Asn Women Math. *Res:* Functional analysis and especially properties related to the Baire category theorem; algorithms; numerical analysis. *Mailing Add:* Baruch Col City Univ New York 17 Lexington Ave New York NY 10010-5585. *E-Mail:* artbb@cunyum.bitnet

**TODD, ALEXANDER ROBERTUS,** organic chemistry; deceased, see previous edition for last biography

**TODD, BETH ANN,** ORTHOPEDIC BIOMECHANICS, ASSISTIVE TECHNOLOGY RELATED TO WHEELED MOBILITY & SEATING. *Current Pos:* ASST PROF MECH ENG, UNIV ALA, 92- *Personal Data:* b Greensburg, Pa, Aug 31, 59. *Educ:* Pa St Univ, BS, 81; Univ Va, MS, 86, PhD(mech & aerospace eng), 92. *Prof Exp:* Assoc engr, Westinghouse Elec Corp, 81-83; res asst, Rehab Eng Ctr, Univ Va, 83-90; instr mech eng, GMI Eng & Mgt Inst, 90-92. *Mem:* Am Soc Mech Engrs; Nat Soc Prof Engrs; Am Soc Eng Educ; Soc Women Engrs; Rehab Eng Soc NAm. *Res:* Problems related to the human body as a structure and their solution with computational techniques; problems of wear resulting in tissue necrosis, fracture and trauma due to accidental impact. *Mailing Add:* Dept Mech Eng Box 870276 Univ Ala Tuscaloosa AL 35487-0276

**TODD, DAVID BURTON,** CHEMICAL ENGINEERING, POLYMER ENGINEERING. *Current Pos:* PRES, TODD ENG, 89- *Personal Data:* b Chester, Pa, Dec 21, 25; m 50, Mary Boekhoff; c Rebecca, Brian, Raymond & Clifford. *Educ:* Northwestern Univ, BS, 46, MS, 48; Princeton Univ, PhD(chem eng), 52. *Honors & Awards:* Int Award Eng & Technol, Soc Plastics Engrs, 93. *Prof Exp:* Engr, Shell Develop Co, Calif, 52-62, supvr develop, 62-63; mgr eng, Podbielniak Div, Dresser Indust, Ill, 63-67; tech dir, Baker Perkins, Inc, 67-87; vpres tech, APV Chem Mach Inc, 87-88. *Concurrent Pos:* Fulbright fel, Delft Tech Univ, 50-51; mem adv comt eng & technol, Saginaw Valley State Col, 77-; mem indust advt comt, Mich Molecular Inst, 78-87; lectr, Ctr Prof Advan & Plastics Inst Am, 80-83 & Polymer Processing Inst, 82; adj prof, Stevens Inst Technol, 89- *Mem:* AAAS; fel Am Inst Chem Engrs; Am Chem Soc; Am Soc Safety Engrs; fel Soc Plastics Engrs. *Res:* Liquid-liquid extraction; fluidization; polymerization; catalysis; acid treating; equipment design; mixing; polymer extrusion. *Mailing Add:* 35-H Chicopee Dr Princeton NJ 08540. *Fax:* 201-216-8243

**TODD, DAVID KEITH,** CIVIL ENGINEERING, HYDROLOGY & WATER RESOURCES. *Current Pos:* from instr to assoc prof, PROF CIVIL ENG, UNIV CALIF, 62- *Personal Data:* b Lafayette, Ind, Dec 30, 23; m 48, Caroline Lark; c Stuart & Brian. *Educ:* Purdue Univ, BS, 48; NY Univ, MS, 49; Univ Calif, Berkeley, PhD(civil eng), 53. *Honors & Awards:* Res Prize, Am Soc Civil Engrs, 60. *Prof Exp:* Hydraul engr, US Bur Reclamation, 48-50. *Concurrent Pos:* NSF fel, 57-58; NSF sr fel, 64-65; centennial prof, Am Univ Beirut, 67; pres, David Keith Todd Consult Engrs, Inc, 78- *Mem:* Am Soc Civil Engrs; Am Geophys Union; Am Water Works Asn; Am Meteorol Soc; AAAS; Nat Ground Water Asn. *Res:* Water resources planning, development and management; surface water and groundwater hydrology; precipitation; runoff and floods; saline water intrusion underground; groundwater pollution. *Mailing Add:* c/o Todd Eng 2200 Powell St Suite 225 Emeryville CA 94608

**TODD, DONALD FREDERICK,** GEOLOGY. *Current Pos:* STAFF, CONSTELLATION GROUP. *Honors & Awards:* Michel T Halbouty Human Needs Award, Am Asn Petrol Geologists, 92. *Mailing Add:* Constellation Group 1700 Broadway Suite 420 Denver CO 80290

**TODD, EDWARD PAYSON,** ATMOSPHERIC PHYSICS, SCIENCE ADMINISTRATION. *Current Pos:* RETIRED. *Personal Data:* b Newburyport, Mass, Jan 26, 20; m 50, Barbara Adams Wright; c Glendon G, Nathaniel A & Charles P. *Educ:* Mass Inst Technol, BS, 42; Univ Colo, PhD(physics), 54. *Honors & Awards:* Distinguished Serv Award, NSF, 71. *Prof Exp:* Res physicist, United Shoe Mach Corp, Mass, 46-49; supvr appl res, Pitney-Bowes, Inc, Conn, 54-57; mem res staff physics, Univ Colo, 57-59, tech dir upper air lab, 59-63; assoc prog dir atmospheric sci sect, NSF, 60-61, prog dir aeronomy, 63-65; actg sect head atmospheric sci sect, 63-64, spec asst to assoc dir res, 65-66, dep assoc dir res, 66-70, dep asst dir res, 70-75, dep asst dir astron, atmospheric, earth & ocean sci, 75-77, actg dir, Atmospheric Sci Div, 75-76, dir, Div Polar Progs, 77-84. *Concurrent Pos:* Mem, Fed Comt Meteorol Serv & Supporting Res, 70-77, chmn, Interdept Comt Atmospheric Sci, 73-78, chmn, Interagency Arctic Res Coord Comt, 77-78. *Mem:* Am Geophys Union; Am Meteorol Soc; Antarctican Soc (pres, 84-86); Oceanog Soc. *Mailing Add:* 312 N Van Buren St Falls Church VA 22046-3655

**TODD, ERIC E(DWARD),** CHEMICAL ENGINEERING. *Current Pos:* RETIRED. *Personal Data:* b Marlow, Eng, Apr 27, 06; nat US; m 36; c 3. *Educ:* Univ BC, BASc, 29, MASc, 30; Stanford Univ, PhD(chem, physics), 34. *Prof Exp:* Chemist, B C Cement Co, Can, 28; chemist metall assays, Consol Mining & Smelting, 29; chemist petrol, Union Oil Co, Calif, 31-32; res chemist, Mich Alkali Co, Calif, 34-35; head chemist, Calif Testing Labs, 36-39; res chemist frozen foods, Calif Consumers Corp, 39-47; tech dir packaged foods, Lady's Choice Foods, Inc, 47-48; chem engr, Ventura Farms Frozen Foods, Inc, 48-59; res chemist, Milo Harding Co, 59-80. *Concurrent Pos:* Consult chem engr, M M H Corp, 48-, Oxnard Frozen Foods Coop & H L Hunt Foods, 59-80, Gen Elec Co & Case Swayne Co, 69-81. *Mem:* AAAS; Am Chem Soc; Nat Soc Prof Engrs; Inst Food Technol. *Res:* Frozen and specialty foods; chemistry; physics. *Mailing Add:* 28730 Grayfox St Malibu CA 90265-4251

**TODD, EWEN CAMERON DAVID,** MICROBIOLOGICAL METHODS OF SURVEILLANCE OF FOODBORNE DISEASE, SEAFOOD TOXINS. *Current Pos:* res scientist, 68-70, head, Methodol Sect Food Microbiol, 71-73, HEAD, CONTAMINATED FOODS SECT, BUR MICROBIAL HAZARDS, HEALTH PROTECTION BR, DEPT NAT HEALTH & WELFARE, 74-, CHMN, FOOD-BORNE DIS REPORTING CTR, 77- *Personal Data:* b Glasgow, Scotland, Dec 25, 39; m 67, Zora I Carson; c Andrew, Amanda, Natasha & Alexander. *Educ:* Glasgow Univ, BSc, 63, PhD(bact taxon), 68. *Honors & Awards:* Citation Award, Int Asn Milk, Food & Environ Sanitarians, 92. *Prof Exp:* Asst lectr bact, Glasgow Univ, 65-68. *Mem:* Int Asn Milk, Food, & Environ, Sanitarians. *Res:* Development of methods for food microbiology; public health aspects of food; foodborne disease statistics; costs of foodborne disease and food spoilage; microbiol risk assessment. *Mailing Add:* Res Div Bur Microbial Hazards Health Can Health Protection Br Ottawa ON K1A 0L2 Can. *Fax:* 613-941-0280; *E-Mail:* ewen__todd@isdtcp3.hwc.ca

**TODD, FRANK ARNOLD,** VETERINARY MEDICINE. *Current Pos:* RETIRED. *Personal Data:* b Merrill, Iowa, Sept 11, 11; m 36; c 2. *Educ:* Iowa State Col, DVM, 33; Yale Univ, MPH, 35; Am Bd Vet Pub Health, dipl. *Prof Exp:* Secy res & develop bd, Off Secy Defense, US Army, 49-51; consult vet serv, Fed Civil Defense Admin, 51-54; asst to adminstr, Agr Res Serv, USDA, 54-65; Wash rep, Am Vet Med Asn, 65-75. *Mem:* Am Vet Med Asn; Am Pub Health Asn; NY Acad Sci. *Res:* Epidemiology and epizootiology of animal diseases; exotic animal diseases; biological and chemical warfare defense; atomic energy. *Mailing Add:* 145 S Aberdeen St Arlington VA 22204

**TODD, GLEN CORY,** PATHOLOGY. *Current Pos:* RETIRED. *Personal Data:* b Crawfordsville, Ind, May 10, 31; m 54; c 4. *Educ:* Ind Cent Col, BA, 54; Univ Pa, VMD, 58; Cornell Univ, PhD(path), 65; Am Col Vet Path, dipl. *Prof Exp:* Vet, Agr Res Serv, USDA, 58-62; teaching assoc path, Cornell Univ, 62-65; pathologist, Agr Res Serv, USDA, 65-66 & Vet Res Div, Food & Drug Admin, 66-67; sr pathologist, Lilly Res Labs, Eli Lilly & Co, 67-92. *Mem:* Am Vet Med Asn; NY Acad Sci; Int Acad Path. *Res:* Physiopathology of vitamin E and selenium; nutritional hepatic necrosis; aflatoxicosis in animals; induced myopathies; developmental and neoplastic diseases. *Mailing Add:* RR 4 Box 74 Crawfordsville IN 47933-9130

**TODD, GLENN WILLIAM,** plant physiology, for more information see previous edition

**TODD, GORDON LIVINGSTON,** ANATOMY, ELECTRON MICROSCOPY. *Current Pos:* ASSOC PROF ANAT & PREV & STRESS MED, UNIV NEBR MED CTR, 75- *Personal Data:* b Princeton, WVa, Mar 17, 44; m 68; c 3. *Educ:* Kenyon Col, AB, 66; Med Col Ga, MS, 69, PhD(anat), 72. *Prof Exp:* Asst prof anat, Sch Med, Creighton Univ, 72-75. *Concurrent Pos:* Nebr Heart Asn grant, Univ Nebr Med Ctr, 75-76, 77-78 & 78-79, Nat Heart, Lung & Blood Inst grant, 80-84, Marion Labs grant, 83-85. *Mem:* Int Soc Heart Res; Am Asn Anat; Sigma Xi; Am Heart Asn; NY Acad Sci; Electron Micros Soc Am. *Res:* Cardiac pathology; cardiac physiology; stress; catecholamines; electron microscopy; lymphatics; autonomic innervation. *Mailing Add:* Dept Cell Biol & Anat Univ Nebr Med Ctr 600 S 42nd St Omaha NE 68198-6395

**TODD, HAROLD DAVID,** chemistry, for more information see previous edition

**TODD, HARRY FLYNN, JR,** anthropology, medical anthropology, for more information see previous edition

**TODD, HOLLIS N,** PHOTOGRAPHY, PHYSICS. *Current Pos:* Prof, 46-77, EMER PROF PHYSICS, ROCHESTER INST TECHNOL, 77- *Personal Data:* b Glens Falls, NY, Jan 28, 14; m 84; Thelma Lerch; c H Schuyler. *Educ:* Cornell Univ, BA, 34, MEd, 35. *Res:* Photographic physics, science and engineering. *Mailing Add:* 3213 Bay Berry Terr Sarasota FL 34237

**TODD, JAMES S,** SURGERY. *Current Pos:* EXEC VPRES, AMA, 93- *Personal Data:* b Hyannis, Mass, 1931. *Prof Exp:* Intern, Presby Hosp, New York, 57-58, resident surg, 59-63; resident surg, Delafield Hosp, New York, 63; resident obstet & gynec, Sloane Women's Hosp, New York, 58-59; resident, Valley Hosp, Ridgewood, NJ; clin asst prof surg, Univ Med & Dent NJ, Newark. *Mailing Add:* AMA 515 N State St Chicago IL 60610-4320

**TODD, JAMES WYATT,** ECONOMIC ENTOMOLOGY, HOST PLANT RESISTANCE. *Current Pos:* CONSULT, 90- *Personal Data:* b Houston Co, Ala, Dec 16, 42; m 64; c 2. *Educ:* Auburn Univ, BS, 66, MS, 68; Clemson Univ, PhD(entom), 73. *Honors & Awards:* Bailey Award, Am Peanut Res & Educ Soc. *Prof Exp:* From field res asst to res asst entom, Auburn Univ, 64-68; from asst prof to prof res entom, Univ Ga, 68-97. *Concurrent Pos:* Sr examr, Pest Mgt Rev Bd, Am Registry Prof Entomologists; peer panelist, Competitive Grants Prog, USDA; regional coordr, Pesticide Impact Assessment, 87-88; pres, Southeastern Br, Entom Soc Am, 90. *Mem:* Entom Soc Am; Am Peanut Res & Educ Soc. *Res:* Development of peanut insect pest management systems including multiple pest resistance; plant viruses and insect vector relations; virus epidemiology and thrips phenology; utilization of natural control agents; cultural control practices; pest complexes; thysanoptera. *Mailing Add:* Entom Univ Ga Coastal Plain Exp Sta Tifton GA 31793. *E-Mail:* todd@tifton.cpes.peachnet.edu

**TODD, JERRY WILLIAM,** ANALYTICAL CHEMISTRY. *Current Pos:* RETIRED. *Personal Data:* b La Crosse, Wis, Jan 7, 30; m 56, Geraldine Brooks; c Susan J. *Educ:* Wis State Univ, Platteville, BS, 51; Univ Wis, PhD(anal chem), 60. *Prof Exp:* Teacher high sch, Wis, 51-52; chemist, Liberty Powder Defense Corp, Olin Mathieson Chem Corp, 52-56; sr chemist, Cent Res Lab, 3M Co, 60-69, sr res specialist, Agrichem Anal Lab, 69-83, sr res specialist, Magnetic Media Anal Lab, 83-96, div scientist, 92-96. *Mem:* Am Chem Soc. *Res:* Gas and liquid chromatography; ur-vis-IR spectroscopy; titrimetry; analytical method development and write up. *Mailing Add:* 2297 E County Rd F White Bear Lake MN 55110

**TODD, JOHN,** NUMERICAL ANALYSIS. *Current Pos:* PROF MATH, CALIF INST TECHNOL, 57- *Personal Data:* b Carnacally, Ireland, May 16, 11; nat US; m 38. *Educ:* Queen's Univ, Belfast, BSc, 31. *Prof Exp:* Lectr, Queen's Univ, Belfast, 33-37 & King's Col, London, 37-49; expert appl math, Nat Bur Stand, 47-48, chief comput lab, 49-54, numerical anal, 54-57. *Concurrent Pos:* Scientist, Brit Admiralty, 40-46; Fulbright prof, Univ Vienna, 65. *Mem:* Am Math Soc; Soc Indust & Appl Math; Math Asn Am. *Res:* Mathematical analysis; algebra. *Mailing Add:* Caltech 253-37 Pasadena CA 91125

**TODD, KENNETH S, JR,** VETERINARY PARASITOLOGY. *Current Pos:* from asst prof to prof, 67-94, EMER PROF VET PARASITOL, UNIV ILL, URBANA, 94-, ACTG DEPT HEAD & DIR GRAD EDUC, 94- *Personal Data:* b Three Forks, Mont, Aug, 25, 36. *Educ:* Mont State Univ, BS, 62, MS, 64; Utah State Univ, PhD(zool), 67. *Honors & Awards:* Beecham Res Excellence Award, 85. *Prof Exp:* Asst zool, Utah State Univ, 64-67. *Concurrent Pos:* Chairperson, div vet parasitol, Univ Ill, Urbana, 83-90, prof vet progs in agr, 84-90, from asst head to actg head, 87-88, head, Dept Vet Pathbiol, 90-; affil prof scientist, natural hist surv, Urbana, Ill. *Mem:* Am Soc Parasitol; Am Vet Med Asn; Am Soc Trop Med & Hyg; Am Heartworm Soc; Am Asn Vet Parasitologists; Sigma Xi; Soc Protozoologists. *Res:* Parasites of wildlife and domestic animals; ecology of parasitism. *Mailing Add:* 6957 Bristol Dr Bozeman MT 59715-9506. *Fax:* 217-333-4628; *E-Mail:* todd%up%cum@vetmed.cvm.uiuc.edu

**TODD, LEE JOHN,** BORON CHEMISTRY, SOLID STATE CHEMISTRY. *Current Pos:* assoc prof, 68-74, PROF CHEM, IND UNIV, BLOOMINGTON, 74- *Personal Data:* b Denver, Colo, Nov 8, 36; m 79; c 3. *Educ:* Univ Notre Dame, BS, 58; Fla State Univ, MS, 60; Ind Univ, PhD(chem), 63. *Prof Exp:* Res assoc chem, Mass Inst Technol, 63-64; asst prof inorg chem, Univ Ill, Urbana, 64-68. *Mem:* Am Chem Soc. *Res:* Synthetic chemistry of boron-containing materials; NMR; boron neutron capture therapy; propellants; biological activity of boron compounds; organometallic chemistry; coal chemistry; solid state chemistry. *Mailing Add:* Dept Chem Ind Univ Bloomington IN 47405

**TODD, LEONARD,** THEORETICAL MECHANICS. *Current Pos:* PROF APPL MATH, LAURENTIAN UNIV, 69- *Personal Data:* b Glasgow, Scotland, Feb 7, 40. *Educ:* Strathclyde Univ, BSc, 61; Cambridge Univ, PhD(appl math), 64. *Prof Exp:* C L E Moore instr appl math, Mass Inst Technol, 64-66; lectr, Strathclyde Univ, 66-69. *Concurrent Pos:* Nat Res Coun Can res grants, 69- *Res:* Theoretical fluid mechanics; asymptotic expansions with emphasis on applications. *Mailing Add:* Dept Math & Comput Sci Laurentian Univ Ramsey Lake Rd Sudbury ON P3E 2C6 Can

**TODD, MARY ELIZABETH,** ANATOMY, EMBRYOLOGY. *Current Pos:* sessional lectr oral biol & zool, 72-73, asst prof, 73-75, ASSOC PROF ANAT, UNIV BC, 75- *Personal Data:* b Kingston, Ont; m 72. *Educ:* Univ BC, BA, 57, MSc, 59; Univ Glasgow, PhD(zool), 62. *Prof Exp:* Lectr & head biol dept, United Col, Man, 62-63; from lectr to sr lectr anat, Univ Glasgow, 62-71; vis asst prof anat, Univ BC, 70-71; asst prof anat, Univ Western Ont, 72. *Mem:* Anat Soc Gt Brit; Can Asn Anatomists; Am Asn Anatomists; Sigma Xi. *Res:* Ultrastructure of vascular tissues; specifically developmental studies on components of the walls of vessels and on vasomotor innervation; morphometrics of vascular tissues from computer assisted reconstructions using serial sections; smooth muscle cell dimensional parameters in hypertension. *Mailing Add:* Dept Anat Univ BC 2177 Wesbrook Mall Vancouver BC V6T 1Z3 Can

**TODD, MICHAEL JEREMY,** MATHEMATICAL PROGRAMMING & ANALYSIS. *Current Pos:* from asst prof to prof opers res, 73-88, dir, Ctr Appl Math, 86-89, LEON C WELCH PROF ENG, CORNELL UNIV, 88- *Personal Data:* b Chelmsford, Eng, Aug 14, 47; m 71, Marina Bandidos; c Jonathan. *Educ:* Cambridge Univ, Eng, BA, 68; Yale Univ, PhD(admin sci), 72. *Honors & Awards:* Dantzig Prize, Math Prog Soc & Soc Indust Appl Math, 88. *Prof Exp:* Asst prof opers res, Univ Ottawa, 72-73. *Concurrent Pos:* Prin investr, NSF, 74-76, 77-79, 79-82, 82-85 & 89-; assoc ed, Math Opers Res, 78-, co-ed, Math Prog, 80-86, ed-in-chief, 86-89, assoc ed, 90-; sr vis, Dept Appl Math & Theoret Physics, Cambridge Univ, Eng, 80-81; Guggenheim fel, 80-81; Sloan fel, 81-85. *Mem:* Opers Res Soc Am; Sigma Xi; Math Prog Soc; Soc Indust Appl Math. *Res:* Mathematical programming; combinatorial optimization; mathematical economics. *Mailing Add:* Sch Opers Res Cornell Univ Ithaca NY 14853-3801. *E-Mail:* miketodd@orie.cornell.edu

**TODD, NEIL BOWMAN,** genetics, for more information see previous edition

**TODD, PAUL WILSON,** CELL BIOPHYSICS, BIOCHEMICAL ENGINEERING. *Current Pos:* RES PROF CHEM ENG, UNIV COLO, BOULDER, 92- *Personal Data:* b Bangor, Maine, June 15, 36; m 57, Judith Stow (Blackmer); c Kevin, Dana, Trevor & Andrea. *Educ:* Bowdoin Col, BA, 59; Mass Inst Technol, SB, 59; Univ Rochester, MS, 60; Univ Calif, Berkeley, PhD(biophys), 64. *Honors & Awards:* R & D 100 Award, 90. *Prof Exp:* Lectr med physics, Univ Calif, Berkeley, 64-66; from asst prof to prof biophys, Pa State Univ, 66-86, chmn, Grad Prog Genetics, 73-78,; dir, Bioprocessing & Pharmaceut Res Ctr, Philadelphia, 84-87; physicist, Nat Inst Stand & Technol, 88-91. *Concurrent Pos:* Eleanor Roosevelt Int Cancer res fel, 67-68; mem biomed steering comt, Los Alamos Meson Physics Facil, 70-77, chmn, 73-74 & vis staff mem, Los Alamos Sci Lab, 74, mem bd dir, Los Alamos Meson Physics Facil Users Group, 76-77; vis fel, Princeton Univ, 71-72; mem biol comt, Argonne Univ Asn, 73-75 & chmn, 75; consult, Oak Ridge Nat Lab, 75-85; assoc ed, Radiation Res, 76-79, Cell Biophys, 78-, Cytometry, 81-88, Anal Quant Cytol, 81-86; vis scientist, J Biochem & Biophys Methods, 82-, Electrophoresis, 85-89 & Theoret & Appl Electrophoresis, 90-95; vis prof med physics, Univ Calif, 79; mem, Discipline Working Group in Microgravity & Biotechnol, Univs Space Res Asn, 78-86, chmn, 82-85; vis scientist, Univ Uppsala, 79, 84 & Oncol Sci Ctr, Moscow, 79; low level radiation expert, NIH, 80-83; mem, Health & Environ Res Adv Comt, Dept Energy, 83-87 & adv comt, Bevalac Biomed Prog, Lawrence Berkeley Lab, 83-87; mem, Space Appln Bd, Nat Res Coun, Nat Acad Sci, 85-88 & Lifesat Working Group, NASA, 90-92. *Mem:* Am Soc Eng Educ; Am Inst Chem Engrs; Tissue Cult Asn; Radiation Res Soc; Am Soc Gravitational & Space Biol; Am Chem Soc. *Res:* Bioseparations; aqueous two-phase partitioning; membrane-based separations; cellular radiation biology; mammalian cell culture; electrophoresis; low-gravity technology; laser light scattering and interferometry; space biophysics and bioprocessing; flow cytometry. *Mailing Add:* 2595 Vassar Dr Boulder CO 80303. *Fax:* 303-492-4341; *E-Mail:* todd@spot.colorado.edu

**TODD, PETER JUSTIN,** ION OPTICS. *Current Pos:* STAFF SCIENTIST, OAK RIDGE NAT LAB, 80- *Personal Data:* b Lackawanna, NY, June 26, 49; m 72; c 1. *Educ:* Rensselaer Polytech Inst, BS, 71; Cornell Univ, MS, 77, PhD(chem), 80. *Mem:* Am Chem Soc; Am Soc Mass Spectrometry; Sigma Xi. *Res:* Organic mass spectrometry, particularly in design and construction of spectrometers; collision and fragmentation of high energy polyatomic ions. *Mailing Add:* Oak Ridge Nat Lab PO Box 2008 MS 6365 Bldg 5510 Oak Ridge TN 37831-6365

**TODD, ROBIN GRENVILLE,** ENTOMOLOGY. *Current Pos:* ENTOMOLOGIST, INSECT CONTROL & RES, INC, 80- *Personal Data:* b Devon, Eng, July 24, 48; m 78. *Educ:* Univ Lancaster, BA, 71; Univ Reading, PhD(entom), 79. *Prof Exp:* Res asst entom mosquito res & control, Grand Cayman Brit W Duties Unit, 79-80. *Mem:* Am Mosquito Control Asn; Entom Soc Am; Inst Biol. *Res:* Minnows as potential control agents of mosquiotes in Caribbean; evaluation of pesticides against household and medically important insects and arachnids. *Mailing Add:* 1330 Dillon Heights Ave Baltimore MD 21228

**TODD, TERRY RAY,** FUEL TECHNOLOGY & PETROLEUM ENGINEERING, ANALYTICAL CHEMISTRY. *Current Pos:* MGR, SYST ENG, UOP GUIDED WAVE, 92- *Personal Data:* b De Kalb, Ill, Oct 9, 47; m 78; c 3. *Educ:* Northern Ill Univ, BS, 69; Pa State Univ, MS, 72, PhD(physics), 76. *Prof Exp:* Nat Bur Stand-Nat Res Coun fel physics, Gaithersburg, 76-78; staff scientist physics, Laser Anal Inc, 78-80; staff physicist, Exxon Res & Eng Co, 80-91. *Concurrent Pos:* Pres, T R Todd Enterprises, Inc, 91- *Mem:* Optical Soc Am; Soc Appl Spectros; Int Soc Optical Eng; Instrument Soc Am. *Res:* High resolution molecular spectroscopy in the infrared region; optics; radiation thermometry; industrial applications of near infrared spectroscopy; infrared physics. *Mailing Add:* UOP Guided Wave 5190 Golden Foothill Pkwy El Dorado Hills CA 95762

**TODD, WILLIAM MCCLINTOCK,** medical microbiology, virology, for more information see previous edition

**TODHUNTER, JOHN ANTHONY,** TOXICOLOGY, BIOCHEMISTRY. *Current Pos:* PRES, SRS INT, 90- *Personal Data:* b Cali, Colombia, Oct 9, 49; US citizen; m 72, 86, D Holli Wilson; c Jennifer, Julia & Jacque. *Educ:* Univ Calif, Los Angeles, BS, 71; Calif State Univ, Los Angeles, MS, 73; Univ Calif, Santa Barbara, PhD(chem), 76; Am Bd Toxicol, dipl, 87; Am Bd Forensic Examiners, 95. *Prof Exp:* Instr, Dept Chem, Calif State Univ, Los Angeles, 72-73; teaching asst, Univ Calif, Santa Barbara, 74, res asst biochem, 74-76; fel, Roche Inst Molecular Biol, Hoffman-La Roche, Nutley, 76-78; asst prof biol & chmn prog biochem, Cath Univ Am, 78-81; asst adminr, pesticides & toxic substances, Environ Protection Agency, 81-83; Todhunter Assocs, 83-89. *Concurrent Pos:* Consult, Arral Industs, Encino, 72-; assoc, Andrulis Res Corp, Bethesda, 78-; mem, Hazardous Waste Siting Bd, State Md, 80-81; consult, WHO, 85. *Mem:* Am Chem Soc; NY Acad Sci; fel Am Inst Chemists; Soc Toxicol; Soc Risk Anal; Am Col Forensic Examiners. *Res:* Mechanisms of drug and toxicant action; dynamic behavior of biochemical systems; risk assessment; safety testing of drugs and biologicals; exposure assessment; analysis of chemically induces injury; safety of investigational drugs, biologicals and devices. *Mailing Add:* 1625 K St NW Suite 1000 Washington DC 20006. *Fax:* 202-835-8970; *E-Mail:* todhunter@srsinternational.com

**TODREAS, NEIL EMMANUEL,** NUCLEAR ENGINEERING EDUCATION. *Current Pos:* from asst prof to assoc prof nuclear eng, 70-75, head dept, 81-89, PROF NUCLEAR ENG, MASS INST TECHNOL, 75- *Personal Data:* b Peabody, Mass, Dec 17, 35; m 58, Carol Sue Schonberg; c Ian & Timothy. *Educ:* Cornell Univ, BS, 58, MS, 58; Mass Inst Technol, ScD(nuclear eng), 66. *Honors & Awards:* Tech Achievement Award, Thermal-Hydraulic Div, Am Nuclear Soc, 94, Arthur Holly Compton Award, 95. *Prof Exp:* Reactor engr, Div Reactor Develop & Technol, US Atomic Energy Comn, Washington, DC, 58-62, sr reactor engr, 65-70. *Concurrent Pos:* Vis asst prof, Tech Univ Berlin, 72-; vis prof, Univ Hong Kong, 92; chmn, EG&G Accident Anal Indust Rev Group, 83-88, Nuclear Safety Res Rev Comt, Nuclear Regulatory Comn, 88-90, Peer Rev Group Code Scaling, Applicability & Uncertainty Methodology, 88, Brookhaven Nat Lab, Nuclear Energy Vis Comt, 90-94, Argonne Nat Lab, Univ Chicago Rev Comt, 90-91 & Inst Nuclear Powers Opers, Adv Coun, 95-; mem numerous comts, Nat Acad Sci, Nat Acad Eng, Dept Energy, 86-92. *Mem:* Nat Acad Eng; fel Am Nuclear Soc; fel Am Soc Mech Engrs. *Res:* Nuclear power reactor design and safety analysis with emphasis on thermal and hydraulics activity. *Mailing Add:* Dept Nuclear Eng 24-219 Mass Inst Technol 77 Massachusetts Ave Cambridge MA 02139-4307

**TODSEN, THOMAS KAMP,** SCIENCE ADMINISTRATION, BOTANY. *Current Pos:* res assoc, 77-79, ASST PROF, NMEX STATE UNIV, 79- *Personal Data:* b Pittsfield, Mass, Oct 21, 18; m 39, Margaret Dorsey; c Thomas A & William L. *Educ:* Univ Fla, BS, 39, MS, 42, PhD(org chem), 50. *Prof Exp:* Asst & instr, Univ Fla, 47-50; instr, NMex Col Agr & Mech Arts, 50-51; chief chemist, White Sands Missile Range, 51-53, chief warheads engr, 53-58, sci adv off, 58-59, land combat systs eval, 59-66, dir test opers, 66-69, dir SSMPO, 69-72, tech dir army missile test & eval, 72-78. *Concurrent Pos:* Consult, Planning Res Corp, 80-84, Sci-Tech, 93- *Mem:* AAAS; Am Chem Soc; Sigma Xi; Am Soc Plant Taxonomists; Asn Trop Biol. *Res:* Naturally occurring plant constituents; plant taxonomy; plant distribution. *Mailing Add:* 2000 Rose Lane Las Cruces NM 88005

**TODT, WILLIAM LYNN,** CELL BIOLOGY. *Current Pos:* ASST PROF BIOL, CONCORDIA COL, MOOREHEAD, MINN, 90- *Personal Data:* b Columbus, Ohio, Dec 31, 54; m 78, Rebecca West; c Kirsten, Benjamin, Michael, Annalisa & Priscilla. *Educ:* Berea Col, Ky, BA, 80; Univ Wis-Madison, PhD(anat), 87. *Prof Exp:* Researcher, Univ Calif, Irvine, 87-90. *Mem:* AAAS; Soc Develop Biol; Am Soc Zoologists; Sigma Xi. *Res:* Cellular and tissue interactions that lead to the development of pattern formation and differentiation; vertebrate embryos. *Mailing Add:* Biol Dept Concordia Col Moorhead MN 56562. *E-Mail:* todt@gloria.cord.edu

**TOENISKOETTER, RICHARD HENRY,** ENVIRONMENTAL SCIENCES, INDUSTRIAL HYGIENE. *Current Pos:* CONSULT, 93- *Personal Data:* b St Louis, Mo, Mar 21, 31; m 53; c 6. *Educ:* Univ St Louis, BS, 52, MS, 56, PhD(chem), 58. *Honors & Awards:* Sci Merit Award, Am Foundrymen's Soc, 84. *Prof Exp:* Res chemist, Union Carbide Corp, 57-67; sr res chemist, ADM Chem Co Div, Ashland Oil Co, 67-68, group leader, Ashland Chem Co, 68-70, mgr inorg chem res, 70-73, foundry res, 73-78, environ occup safety, 78-88, health & safety, 88-89, dir health & safety, 89-91, dir prod safety & health, 91- 93. *Mem:* Am Chem Soc; Am Foundrymen's Soc; Sigma Xi. *Res:* Organic and inorganic polymer chemistry; coordination and fluorine compounds; boron hydrides; materials and foundry products research; environmental science; industrial hygiene; safety and product safety; toxicology. *Mailing Add:* 6771 Masefield St Worthington OH 43085

**TOENNIES, JAN PETER,** MOLECULAR PHYSICS, SURFACE PHYSICS. *Current Pos:* Asst, 57-67, docent, 67-71, HON PROF, INST PHYSICS, UNIV BONN, 71-; DIR, MAX PLANCK INST FLUID DYNAMICS, 69-, PROF PHYSICS. *Personal Data:* b Philadelphia, Pa, May 3, 30; m 66, Monika Zelesnick; c 2. *Educ:* Brown Univ, PhD(chem), 57. *Honors & Awards:* Physics Prize, Acad Sci, 64; Gold Heyrovsky Medal, Czech Acad Sci, 91; Hewlett-Packard Europhysics Prize, 92; Max-Planck-Prize, Ger Res Soc & Alexander von Humboldt & Found, 92. *Concurrent Pos:* Guest docent, Gothenburg Univ, 66-75; apl prof, Univ Goettingen, 72- *Mem:* Fel Am Phys Soc; Ger Phys Soc; Europ Phys Soc; Ger Acad Natural Scientists. *Res:* Molecular beam investigations of elastic, inelastic and reactive collisions; theory of inelastic scattering; chemical reactions in shock waves; molecular beam investigations of structure and dynamics of crystal surfaces. *Mailing Add:* Max Planck Inst Fluid Dynamics Bunsenstrasse 10 37073 Goettingen Germany. *Fax:* 495515176607

**TOENNIESSEN, GARY HERBERT,** ENVIRONMENTAL SCIENCES. *Current Pos:* Prog assoc, 71-72, asst dir natural & environ sci, 72-78, asst dir, 78-84, ASSOC DIR AGR SCI, ROCKEFELLER FOUND, 84- *Personal Data:* b Lockport, NY, July 9, 44; m 67. *Educ:* State Univ NY, Buffalo, BA, 66; Univ NC, MS, 68, PhD(microbiol), 71. *Mem:* Am Soc Microbiol; Int Soc Plant Molecular Biol. *Res:* Plant molecular and cellular biology; plant breeding and environmental problems associated with agriculture. *Mailing Add:* 17 Fenimore Dr Harrison NY 10528-1412

**TOENSING, C(LARENCE) H(ERMAN),** METALLURGY, PHYSICAL CHEMISTRY. *Current Pos:* RETIRED. *Personal Data:* b St Paul, Minn, Aug 23, 15; m 45; c 1. *Educ:* Macalester Col, AB, 37; Mont Sch Mines, MS, 39; Carnegie Inst Technol, ScD(phys chem), 47. *Prof Exp:* Instr chem, Mont Sch Mines, 37-39; asst, Carnegie Inst Technol, 39-44, instr, 44-49; sr technologist, US Steel Corp, 44-50; asst to mgr opers, Brush Beryllium Co, Ohio, 50, res engr, Brush Electronics Co, 50-51; res & develop engr, Lamp Metals & Components Dept, Gen Elec Co, 51-59; dir res, Firth Sterling, Inc, 59-64, dir tech serv, Carmet Co, 64-69; plant mgr, Valeron Corp, 69-81. *Mem:* Am Chem Soc; Am Soc Metals. *Res:* Gas-metal reactions; chemistry and metallurgy of tungsten and molybdenum; refractory carbides and materials. *Mailing Add:* 702 Via Zapata Riverside CA 92507

**TOEPFER, ALAN JAMES,** PULSED POWER, FUSION. *Current Pos:* ASST VPRES, SCI APPL INT CORP, 85- *Personal Data:* b Chicago, Ill, Oct 20, 41. *Educ:* Marquette Univ, BA, 62; Univ Southern Calif, MS, 64, PhD(physics), 68. *Prof Exp:* Res asst, Royal Inst Technol, Stockholm, 64-65; tech staff, Aerospace Corp, 65-66; tech staff, Sandia Labs, 68-75, supvr, 75-79; dir, 79-81, vpres & dir, Res & Develop, Physics Int Co, 81-85. *Mem:* Am Phys Soc; AAAS; Am Inst Aeronaut & Astronaut. *Res:* Inertial confinement fusion; pulsed power; intense relativistic electron beams; electromagnetic armor; radiation effects of nuclear weapons; neutral particle beams. *Mailing Add:* 623 Cedar Hill Rd NE Albuquerque NM 87122

**TOEPFER, RICHARD E, JR,** DATA PROCESSING, CONTROL SYSTEMS. *Current Pos:* DIR PROG MGT, KUBOTA PAC COMPUT, INC, 91- *Personal Data:* b Chicago, Ill, Oct 9, 34; m 65, M Elizabeth Henderson; c R Elizabeth, Maria C & John F. *Educ:* Univ Ill, BSEE, 56, MSEE, 57, PhD(elec eng), 62. *Prof Exp:* Mem tech staff, Aerospace Corp, 61-63; res specialist, Autonetics Div, NAm Aviation, Inc, 63-64; adv engr, IBM Corp, Calif, 65-69; chief systs engr, Measurex Corp, 68-69; proj mgr, Data Systs Develop Div, Hewlett Packard, 70-71; sect mgr, 71-76, prod eng mgr, Data Systs Div, 76-80; opers mgr, Spectra Physics, 80-81; vpres mfg, Magnuson Comput, 81-82; mfg mgr, Convergent, Inc, 82-84, dir pilot mfg, 84-88, technol dir, Distrib Ctr, 87-88; vpres develop & opers, Lasa Inc, San Jose, 88-90; dir mfg technol, Unisys, Comput Systs Prod Group, San Jose, Calif, 90-91. *Concurrent Pos:* Mem & subcomt chmn, Tech Adv Comt on Comput Systs, Bur East-West Trade, US Dept Com, 73-75; mem bd dirs, Asst Technol Inc, San Jose, 84-86. *Mem:* Inst Elec & Electronics Engrs; Soc Indust & Appl Math; Sigma Xi. *Res:* Data processing systems; process control systems; control systems theory; video systems design. *Mailing Add:* 16300 Los Serenos Robles Los Gatos CA 95030-3026. *Fax:* 408-748-6301; *E-Mail:* toepfer@kpc.com

**TOETZ, DALE W,** FISH BIOLOGY, LIMNOLOGY. *Current Pos:* from asst prof to assoc prof, 65-79, PROF ZOOL, OKLA STATE UNIV, 80- *Personal Data:* b Milwaukee, Wis, Sept 23, 37; m, Charlotte Wall; c Mark & Eric. *Educ:* Univ Wis, BS, 59, MS, 61; Ind Univ, PhD(zool), 65. *Prof Exp:* Actg instr zool, Univ Wis, Milwaukee, 61-62; teaching asst, Ind Univ, 62-65. *Concurrent Pos:* Assoc res biologist, Scripps Inst Oceanog, 74; tech consult, US Environ Protection Agency, 77; res affil, Inst Arctic & Alpine Res, 88-91; res assoc, Kellogg Biol Sta, 93. *Mem:* Am Fisheries Soc; Ecol Soc Am; Am Soc Limnol & Oceanog; Int Soc Theoret & Appl Limnol; NAm Lake Mgt Soc; NAm Benthological Soc. *Res:* Limnology of nitrogen; stable isotopes; nutrients in streams; lake restoration. *Mailing Add:* Zool Dept Okla State Univ Stillwater OK 74078-0001. *Fax:* 405-744-7074

**TOEWS, ARREL DWAYNE,** NEUROCHEMISTRY, BIOCHEMICAL NEUROPATHOLOGY. *Current Pos:* From res instr to res assoc prof, 77-94, RES SCIENTIST, NEUROSCI CTR, UNIV NC, CHAPEL HILL, 79-, RES PROF BIOCHEM, 86- *Personal Data:* b Enid, Okla, July 22, 48; m 71, Kathleen Kay Neufeld; c Erin L & Laura K. *Educ:* Tabor Col, BA, 70; Ohio State Univ, PhD(physiol chem), 74. *Mem:* Int Soc Neurochem; Am Soc Neurochem; Soc Hist Alchemy & Chem. *Res:* Neurochemistry; neurotoxicology; altered gene expression during toxic neuropathies; molecular biology of demyelination, remyelination & axon-Schwann cell interactions; molecular biology of cholesterol metabolism in the nervous system. *Mailing Add:* Neurosci Ctr CB 7250 Univ NC Chapel Hill NC 27599-7250. *Fax:* 919-966-9605; *E-Mail:* arrel@css.unc.edu

**TOEWS, CORNELIUS J,** ENDOCRINOLOGY, BIOCHEMISTRY. *Current Pos:* ASST PROF BIOCHEM & MED, MCMASTER UNIV, MED SCH, 71-, ASSOC PROF. *Personal Data:* b Altona, Man, Mar 22, 37; m 61; c 3. *Educ:* Univ Man, BSc & MD, 63; Queen's Univ, Ont, PhD(biochem), 67; FRCPS(C), 69. *Concurrent Pos:* Med Res Coun Can Centennial res fel med, Joslin Res Lab, Harvard Univ, 68-71; jr assoc med, Peter Bent Brigham Hosp, Boston, 70-71; instr, Harvard Univ, Med Sch, 70-71. *Mem:* Can Soc Clin Invest; Can Biochem Soc; Am Diabetes Asn; Can Diabetes Asn. *Res:* Regulation of gluconeogenesis in the liver; regulation of glycolysis and intermediary metabolism in skeletal muscle. *Mailing Add:* 180 Vine St Suite 201 St Catherine ON L2R 7P3 Can

**TOEWS, DANIEL PETER,** ANIMAL PHYSIOLOGY. *Current Pos:* assoc prof, 71-80, PROF BIOL, ACADIA UNIV, 80- *Personal Data:* b Grande Prairie, Alta, Dec 18, 41; m 64; c 3. *Educ:* Univ Alta, BSc, 63, MSc, 66; Univ BC, PhD(zool), 69. *Prof Exp:* Asst prof zool, Univ Alta, 69-71. *Concurrent Pos:* NSERC Grant Selection Comt. *Mem:* Can Soc Zool; Brit Soc Exp Biol. *Res:* Comparative respiration and circulation in fishes and amphibians. *Mailing Add:* Dept Biol Acadia Univ Wolfville NS B0P 1X0 Can

**TOFE, ANDREW JOHN,** NUCLEAR MEDICINE. *Current Pos:* MGR NUCLEAR MED, BENEDICT NUCLEAR PHARMACEUT, 81- *Personal Data:* b New York, NY, May 6, 40. *Educ:* Univ Dayton, BS, 63; Fla State Univ, PhD(nuclear chem), 69. *Prof Exp:* Gen mgr/sr vpres, Procter & Gamble Co, 70-72, scientist nuclear med, 72-80. *Mem:* Soc Nuclear Med; Am Chem Soc. *Res:* Manufacture and sales of radioisotopes for use in early detection of human disease or abnormalities. *Mailing Add:* 2195 Urban Dr Lakewood CO 80215

**TOFFEL, GEORGE MATHIAS,** CHEMISTRY. *Current Pos:* from asst prof to assoc prof, 47-77, EMER ASSOC PROF CHEM, UNIV ALA, TUSCALOOSA, 77- *Personal Data:* b Greensburg, Pa, Jan 28, 11; m 38; c 4. *Educ:* Vanderbilt Univ, BA, 35, MS, 36. *Prof Exp:* Instr chem, Vanderbilt Univ, 34-36; teacher high sch, Ga, 36-37; head sci dept, Marion Inst, 37-47.

*Concurrent Pos:* Vis prof, Univ Hawaii, 64-65. *Mem:* Am Chem Soc; fel Am Inst Chem; AAAS. *Res:* Electro-organic chemistry; free radicals; resistor research; magnetic alloys of manganese; reaction mechanism studies with carbon-14 fatty acid esters; ketonization of fatty acids. *Mailing Add:* 303 Queen City Ave Tuscaloosa AL 35401

**TOGASAKI, ROBERT K,** PLANT PHYSIOLOGY, CELL BIOLOGY. *Current Pos:* from asst prof to assoc prof plant sci, 68-83, PROF BIOL, IND UNIV, BLOOMINGTON, 83- *Personal Data:* b San Francisco, Calif, July 24, 32; m 59. *Educ:* Haverford Col, BA, 56; NIH fel & PhD(biochem), Cornell Univ, 64. *Prof Exp:* Res fel biol, Harvard Univ, 67, lectr, 67-68. *Concurrent Pos:* NIH fel, 65-67. *Mem:* Am Soc Plant Physiol; Am Soc Cell Biol; Phycol Soc Am; Japan Soc Plant Physiol. *Res:* Photosynthetic carbon metabolism and its regulation; biochemical and genetic analysis of photosynthetic mechanisms and its regulation in Chlamydomonas reinhardi, a model eukaryotic photosynthetic organism. *Mailing Add:* Dept Biol Ind Univ Bloomington IN 47405-3680. *Fax:* 812-855-6705

**TOGURI, JAMES M,** CHEMISTRY. *Current Pos:* assoc prof, 66-69, chmn dept, 76-81, PROF METALL & MAT SCI, UNIV TORONTO, 69-; CHAIR CHEM PROCESS METALL, INCO/NSERC, 88- *Personal Data:* b Vancouver, BC, Sept 22, 30; m 57, Elsie Y Iwasaki; c Robert, John, Jamie, David & Joel. *Educ:* Univ Toronto, BASc, 55, MASc, 56, PhD(metall), 58. *Honors & Awards:* Alcan Award, 79; Extractive Metall Sci Award, Am inst Mining, Metall & Petrol Engrs, 81; Silver Medal, Can Inst Mining Metall, 86; Can Metall Chem Award, 90. *Prof Exp:* Nat Res Coun Can fel metall, Imp Col Sci & Technol, Univ London, 58-59; fel inorg chem, Tech Univ Norway, 59-61; res assoc chem, Inst Metals, Univ Chicago, 61-62; group leader, Noranda Res Ctr, Que, 62-63, head dept, 63-66. *Concurrent Pos:* Royal Norweg Sci Coun fel, 60-61; grants, Nat Res Coun Can & Defence Res Bd Can, 66-; ed-in-chief, Can Metall Quart, 67-86. *Mem:* Am Inst Mining, Metall & Petrol Engrs; fel Can Inst Mining & Metall; fel Am Soc Metals; fel Royal Soc Can; fel Norweg Acad Tech Sci. *Res:* High temperature chemistry; thermodynamic properties; kinetics high temperature; fused salt chemistry; nonferrous pyrometallurgy; recycling. *Mailing Add:* Dept Metall & Mat Sci Univ Toronto Toronto ON M5S 3E4 Can. *Fax:* 416-978-4155; *E-Mail:* toguri@mms.utoronto.ca

**TOHLINE, JOEL EDWARD,** MULTIDIMENSIONAL HYDRODYNAMICS. *Current Pos:* ASST PROF PHYSICS & ASTRON, LA STATE UNIV, 82- *Personal Data:* b Crowley, La, July 15, 53; m 74; c 1. *Educ:* Centenary Col La, BS, 74; Univ Calif, Santa Cruz, PhD(astron), 78. *Prof Exp:* J W Gibbs instr astron, Yale Univ, 78-80; fel astrophys, Los Alamos Nat Lab, 80-82. *Mem:* Am Astron Soc; Int Astron Union. *Res:* Computer modeling of multidimensional, hydrodynamic flows in astrophysical phenomena; star formation and gas dynamics in galaxies. *Mailing Add:* 381 Bancroft Way Baton Rouge LA 70808

**TOHVER, HANNO TIIT,** PHYSICS. *Current Pos:* asst prof, 68-71, ASSOC PROF PHYSICS, UNIV ALA, BIRMINGHAM, 71- *Personal Data:* b Tartu, Estonia, Dec 18, 35; Can citizen. *Educ:* Queen's Univ, Ont, BS, 57, MS, 59; Purdue Univ, PhD, 68. *Prof Exp:* Asst, Purdue Univ, 60-67. *Mailing Add:* Dept Physics Campbell Hall 310 Univ Ala 1300 University Blvd Birmingham AL 35294

**TOIDA, SHUNICHI,** ELECTRICAL ENGINEERING. *Current Pos:* PROF COMPUT SCI, OLD DOMINION UNIV, 82- *Personal Data:* b Shizuoka, Japan, Jan 8, 37; m 67; c 4. *Educ:* Univ Tokyo, BS, 59; Univ Ill, Urbana, MS, 66, PhD(elec eng), 69. *Prof Exp:* Comput engr, Mitsubishi Elec Co, 59-63; from asst prof to assoc prof, Systs Design, Univ Waterloo, 69-82. *Concurrent Pos:* Nat Res Coun Can grant, 69-71 & 73-81; vis prof, Univ Dortmund, WGer, 75-76. *Mem:* Inst Elec & Electronics Engrs. *Res:* Linear graph theory and its applications; fault diagnosis of logic circuits; automatic reasoning. *Mailing Add:* Dept Comput Sci Old Dominion Univ Norfolk VA 23508

**TOIVOLA, PERTTI TOIVO KALEVI,** MEDICAL PHYSIOLOGY, NEUROENDOCRINOLOGY. *Current Pos:* ASST SCIENTIST, REGIONAL PRIMATE RES CTR, UNIV WIS, 73-, PROF PHYSIOL, SCH MED, 74- *Personal Data:* b Pori, Finland, Aug 15, 46; US citizen; m 73. *Educ:* Univ Wash, BA, 68, PhD(physiol & biophys), 73. *Prof Exp:* Res asst physiol, Regional Primate Res Ctr, Univ Wash, 68-69, sr fel endocrinol, Dept Med, 73. *Mem:* Endocrine Soc; Int Soc Neuroendocrinol; Am Physiol Soc. *Res:* Central nervous system regulation of the endocrine system. *Mailing Add:* 13028 Ninth Ave NW Seattle WA 98177-4102

**TOKAR, MICHAEL,** CERAMICS, METALLURGY. *Current Pos:* sr ceramist, US Nuclear Regulatory Comn, 75-80, sr reactor fuels engr, 80-83, waste mgt mat engr, 83-85, sect leader, 85-, SECT CHIEF, US NUCLEAR REGULATORY COMN, 85- *Personal Data:* b Elizabeth, NJ, Apr 27, 37; m 61, Inga Pratt; c Jeffrey M, John A & Jennifer S. *Educ:* Univ Mich, BS, 61; Stevens Inst Technol, MS, 64; Rutgers Univ, PhD(ceramics), 68. *Prof Exp:* Metall trainee, Nat Castings Co, Ill, 61-62; res asst res & develop high temperature mat, Am Stand Corp Res Lab, 62-65; res asst ceramic sci, Rutgers Univ, 65-67; staff mem, Los Alamos Sci Lab, Univ Calif, 67-75. *Mem:* Am Ceramics Soc. *Res:* Analysis and evaluation of reactor fuel systems design; fabrication of ceramic nuclear fuels; measurement of physical and mechanical properties of ceramic materials; permanent magnet ferrites; high temperature oxidation-resistant coatings; radioactive waste management. *Mailing Add:* US Nuclear Regulatory Comn Washington DC 20555. *Fax:* 301-415-5370; *E-Mail:* mst@nrc.gov

**TOKAY, ELBERT,** BIOLOGY. *Current Pos:* instr, 41-43, from asst prof to assoc prof, 47-58, prof physiol, 58-77, PROF BIOL, VASSAR COL, 77- *Personal Data:* b Brooklyn, NY, May 27, 16; m 40; c 2. *Educ:* City Col New York, AB, 36; Univ Chicago, PhD(physiol), 41. *Prof Exp:* Asst physiol, Univ Chicago, 39-41. *Mem:* AAAS; Sigma Xi. *Res:* Drugs and other factors affecting central nervous potentials and metabolism. *Mailing Add:* Dept Biol Vassar Col Box 475 Poughkeepsie NY 12601

**TOKAY, F HARRY,** AUDIOLOGY. *Current Pos:* RETIRED. *Personal Data:* b St Paul, Minn, July 30, 36. *Educ:* St Cloud State Col, BS, 60; Mich State Univ, MA, 62, PhD(audiol), 66. *Prof Exp:* Asst prof audiol, Cent Mich Univ, 65-66 & Univ Mass, Amherst, 67-74; assoc prof audiol, Univ NH, 74-77, assoc prof commun dis, 77-, chmn, Commun Dis Prog, 74- *Mem:* Am Speech & Hearing Asn; Acoust Soc Am. *Res:* Audiology with children. *Mailing Add:* Smith Garrison Rd Newmarket NH 03857

**TOKES, LASZLO GYULA,** ORGANIC CHEMISTRY. *Current Pos:* fel, 66-67, dept head spectros, 67-79, ASST DIR ANALYSIS & ENVIRON RES, SYNTEX RES, SYNTEX CORP, 79- *Personal Data:* b Budapest, Hungary, July 7, 37; US citizen. *Educ:* Univ Southern Calif, BA, 61; Stanford Univ, PhD(chem), 65. *Prof Exp:* Nat Ctr Sci Res, France fel, Univ Strasbourg, 65-66. *Concurrent Pos:* Chmn award comt, Am Chem Soc, 73-74. *Mem:* Am Chem Soc; Am Soc Mass Spectrometry. *Res:* Mass spectrometric fragmentation mechanisms; isotope labeling studies; structure elucidations by using advanced spectroscopic methods; natural product chemistry with special interest in marine chemistry; environmental contaminants. *Mailing Add:* 4133 Thain Way Palo Alto CA 94306

**TOKES, ZOLTAN ANDRAS,** BIOCHEMISTRY, DEVELOPMENTAL BIOLOGY. *Current Pos:* asst prof, 74-80, assoc prof & dir, Cell Membrane & Cell Cult Labs, Univ Southern Calif Cancer Ctr, 80-92, PROF BIOCHEM & VCHMN MOLECULAR BIOL, UNIV SOUTHERN CALIF, 92- *Personal Data:* b Budapest, Hungary, May 14, 40; m 72; c Geza T & Anahid K. *Educ:* Univ Southern Calif, BSc, 64; Calif Inst Technol, PhD(biochem), 70. *Prof Exp:* Lectr biochem, Univ Malaya, 70-71; res immunol, Basel Inst Immunol, Hoffmann-LaRoche, Inc, 71-74. *Concurrent Pos:* Consult biotechnol; res grants, NIH, Nat Cancer Inst & Nat Inst Aging. *Mem:* Am Soc Biol Chemists; Am Asn Pathologists; Am Asn Cancer Res; Int Soc Differentiation; Am Soc Cell Biologists; Soc Neurosci. *Res:* Recognition of cell surface changes with differentiation; cell-cell interactions, tumor markers and drug delivery. *Mailing Add:* Dept Biochem & Cancer Ctr Univ Southern Calif Sch Med 13 N Mission Rd Rm 102 Los Angeles CA 90033-1020

**TOKITA, NOBORU,** PHYSICS. *Current Pos:* SR STAFF MEM, CABOT CORP, 90- *Personal Data:* b Sapporo, Japan, Feb 20, 23; m 53. *Educ:* Hokkaido Univ, BS, 47, DrSci, 56. *Prof Exp:* Res mem, Kobayashi Inst Physics, Japan, 47-52; asst prof physics, Waseda Univ, Japan, 52-57; res assoc polymer sci, Duke Univ, 57-60; sr res physicist, Uniroyal Inc, 60-68, res assoc, Res Ctr, 68-90. *Mem:* Am Chem Soc; Soc Rheology. *Res:* Polymer physics; vibration and sound; rheology of elastomer and plastics; tire technology. *Mailing Add:* Cabot Corp Billerica Tech Ctr Concord Rd Billerica MA 01821

**TOKSOZ, MEHMET NAFI,** GEOPHYSICS. *Current Pos:* from asst prof to assoc prof, 65-71, PROF GEOPHYS, MASS INST TECHNOL, 71-, DIR, GEORGE WALLACE JR GEOPHYS OBSERV, DEPT EARTH & PLANETARY SCI, 75-, DIR, EARTH RESOURCES LAB, 82- *Personal Data:* b Antakya, Turkey, Apr 18, 34. *Educ:* Colo Sch Mines, GpE, 58; Calif Inst Technol, MS, 60, PhD(geophys, elec eng), 63. *Prof Exp:* Res fel geophys, Calif Inst Technol, 63-65. *Mem:* AAAS; Am Geophys Union; Seismol Soc Am; Soc Explor Geophys; Soc Prof Well Log Analysts; Geol Soc Am; Am Asn Petrol Geologists; Royal Astron Soc. *Res:* Seismology; borehole geophysics; well logging; rock physics. *Mailing Add:* Dept Earth Sci Lab Mass Inst Technol 77 Massachusetts Ave E34-440 Cambridge MA 02139

**TOKUDA, SEI,** IMMUNOLOGY, MICROBIOLOGY. *Current Pos:* from asst prof to prof, 66-97, chair, 92-97, EMER PROF IMMUNOL, SCH MED, UNIV NMEX, 97-, EMER CHAIR MICROBIOL, 97- *Personal Data:* b Ewa, Hawaii, Aug 17, 30; m 55, Miyoko M Yoshina; c David S, Kathleen L & Ray S. *Educ:* Univ Hawaii, BS, 53; Univ Wash, PhD(microbiol), 60. *Prof Exp:* Trainee microbiol, Univ Wash, 59-60, res instr immunol, 62-63; asst prof immunol & microbiol, Univ Vt, 63-66. *Concurrent Pos:* Res fel immunochem, Calif Inst Technol, 60-62; NIH fel, 61-62, NIH res grant, 64-; Am Cancer Soc res grant, 64; coun mem, Midwinter Conf Immunologists, 67-72, Am Soc Microbiol, 82-87; USPHS career develop award, 68-73; regional ed, Life Sci, 68-73; consortium, NIH Minority Biomed Res Prog Dirs, 75-77; mem, Cancer Res Manpower Rev Comt, Nat Cancer Inst, 76-80; assoc ed, J Immunol, 79-81. *Mem:* AAAS; Am Asn Immunologists; Am Soc Microbiol; Transplantation Soc; Sigma Xi. *Res:* Immune responses of mice against syngeneic tumors; transplantation immunity; hormonal regulation of the immune response; neuroimmuno endocrinology. *Mailing Add:* Dept Microbiol Univ NMex Sch Med Albuquerque NM 87131-5276

**TOKUHATA, GEORGE K,** EPIDEMIOLOGY, PUBLIC HEALTH. *Current Pos:* RES DIR, DIV RES & BIOSTATIST, PA STATE DEPT HEALTH, 67- *Personal Data:* b Matsue, Japan, Aug 25, 24; US citizen; m 49. *Educ:* Keio Univ, Japan, BA, 50; Miami Univ, MA, 53; Univ Iowa, PhD(behav sci), 56; Johns Hopkins Univ, DPH(epidemiol), 62. *Prof Exp:* Res assoc ment health, Mich State Dept Ment Health, 56-59; spec asst div chief, Div Chronic Dis, USPHS, 59-62, prin epidemiologist, 62-63; assoc prof prev med, Col Med, Univ Tenn & chief epidemiol, St Jude Children's Res Hosp, 63-67. *Concurrent Pos:* USPHS fel, Med Ctr, Johns Hopkins Univ, 59-60, NIH fel, 60-61; Mary

Reynold Babcock Found res grant, 59-61; Food & Drug Admin res grant; US Consumer Prod Safety Comn grant, 73-74; Maternal & Child Health Serv grant, 74-; Nat Ctr Health Statist grant, 74-; prof epidemiol & biostatist, Grad Sch Pub Health, Univ Pittsburgh; assoc prof community med, Col Med, Temple Univ. *Mem:* Fel Am Pub Health Asn; fel Am Sociol Asn; fel Am Col Epidemiol. *Res:* Genetics aspects of cancer and other chronic diseases in adults and children; epidemiology of chronic diseases; environ health evaluation of public health programs research and development. *Mailing Add:* 410 Rupley Rd Camp Hill PA 17011

**TOKUNAGA, ALAN TAKASHI,** PLANETARY SCIENCE, INTERSTELLAR MEDIUM. *Current Pos:* asst astronr, 79-83, assoc astronr, 83-90, ASTRONR, UNIV HAWAII, 90- *Personal Data:* b Puunene, Hawaii, Dec 17, 49; m 75, Cheryl. *Educ:* Pomona Col, BS, 71; State Univ NY, Stony Brook, MS, 73, PhD(astron), 76. *Prof Exp:* Res assoc, Ames Res Ctr, NASA, 76-77; res assoc, Steward Observ, Univ Ariz, 77-79. *Concurrent Pos:* Mem, Kuiper Airborne Obs Time Allocation Comt, 88-90; mem planetary & optical panels, Astron & Astrophys Surv Comt, 89-90; mem, Div Planetary Sci Comt, Am Astron Soc, 90-93; Comt Planetary & Lunar Explor, 94- *Mem:* Am Astron Soc; Astron Soc Pac; Int Astron Union. *Res:* Spectroscopy of comets, planetary satellites and interstellar medium; construction of ground-based infrared instrumentation. *Mailing Add:* 2232 Halekoa Dr Honolulu HI 96821. *Fax:* 808-988-3893; *E-Mail:* tokunaga@galileo.ifa.hawaii.edu

**TOKUYASU, KIYOTERU,** CELL BIOLOGY, DEVELOPMENTAL BIOLOGY. *Current Pos:* assoc res pathologist, Univ Calif, San Diego, 64-69, assoc res biologist, 69-73, res biologist, 73-77, prof-in-residence, 77-91, EMER PROF CELL BIOL, UNIV CALIF, SAN DIEGO, 91- *Personal Data:* b Nagasaki, Japan, Oct 16, 25; US citizen; m 57, Suzuko Kumagai; c Setsu & Taku. *Educ:* Kyushu Univ, Japan, BS, 49, PhD(med sci), 57. *Prof Exp:* Assoc prof histol, Med Sch, Kurume Univ, Japan, 56-58; chief designer electron microscope, Hitachi Naka Works, Japan, 58-63. *Mem:* Am Soc Cell Biol; Micros Soc Am; Histochem Soc Am; AAAS. *Res:* Developmental, cell biological and molecular biological aspects of embryonic heart development; immunocytochemistry and autoradiography at the light and electron microscopic levels; further development of cryoultramicrotomy and its contribution to cell biology. *Mailing Add:* Dept Biol B-0322 Univ Calif-San Diego La Jolla CA 92093-0322. *Fax:* 619-534-7151; *E-Mail:* ktokuyasu@ucsd.edu

**TOLAN, DEAN RICHARD,** GENETICS & MOLECULAR BIOLOGY OF HEREDITARY FRUCTOSE INTOLERANCE, ENZYMOLOGY OF ALDOLASE. *Current Pos:* from asst to assoc prof, 87-93, ASSOC PROF BIOL, BOSTON UNIV, 93-, ASSOC PROF & ASSOC DIR MOLECULAR BIOL, CELLULAR BIOL & BIOCHEM, 96-, ASST DIR, 96- *Personal Data:* b Denver, Colo, Apr 24, 53; c Victoria. *Educ:* Univ Colo, Boulder, BA, 75; Univ Calif, Davis, PhD(biochem), 81. *Prof Exp:* Nat Res Serv Award fel, Univ Calif, Berkeley, 81-83, asst specialist biochemist, 84-86. *Concurrent Pos:* Prin investr, Nat Inst Diabetes & Digestive & Kidney Dis, NIH, 87- & March of Dimes, 90-92; vis prof biophys, Univ Regensburg, Ger, 96-97. *Mem:* Soc Inherited Metab Dis; Protein Soc; Am Soc Biochem & Molecular Biol; Am Soc Human Genetics; Am Chem Soc; AAAS. *Res:* Biochemical causes to hereditary diseases that arise from mutations in the human aldolase genes; work on hereditary fructose intolerance and enzyme structure and catalytic mechanisms for the aldolases. *Mailing Add:* Dept Biol Boston Univ Boston MA 02215. *Fax:* 617-353-6340; *E-Mail:* tolan@bio.bu.edu

**TOLBERT, BERT MILLS,** BIOCHEMISTRY, NUTRITION. *Current Pos:* assoc prof, 57-61, PROF CHEM, UNIV COLO, 61- *Personal Data:* b Twin Falls, Idaho, Jan 15, 21; m 59; c 4. *Educ:* Univ Calif, Berkeley, BS, 42, PhD(chem), 45. *Prof Exp:* Teaching asst, Univ Calif, Berkeley, 42-44, res chemist, Lawrence Radiation Lab, 44-57. *Concurrent Pos:* USPHS fel, 52-53; Int Atomic Energy Agency vis prof, Univ Buenos Aires, 62-63; biophysicist, US AEC, Washington, DC, 67-68; vis staff, Los Alamos Sci Lab, 70-80; consult, Surgeon Gen Off, US Army. *Mem:* Am Chem Soc; Am Soc Biochem & Molecular Biol; Am Inst Nutrit; Radiation Res Soc; Soc Exp Biol Med; AAAS. *Res:* Metabolism and function of ascorbic acid; radiation chemistry of proteins; catabolism of labeled compounds; application of C-14 and H-3 to biochemistry; instrumentation in radiochemistry; synthesis of labeled compounds; use of stable isotopes. *Mailing Add:* 444 Kalmia Ave Boulder CO 80304-1732

**TOLBERT, CHARLES RAY,** ASTRONOMY, EDUCATION. *Current Pos:* res assoc, Ctr Advan Studies, 67-69, from asst prof to assoc prof, 69-80, PROF, UNIV VA, 80- *Personal Data:* b Van, WVa, Nov 14, 36; m 67; c 3. *Educ:* Univ Richmond, BS, 58; Vanderbilt Univ, MS, 60, PhD(physics, astron), 63. *Prof Exp:* Res assoc, Kapteyn Astron Lab, Neth, 63-67. *Concurrent Pos:* Educ officer, Am Astron Soc, 85-91. *Mem:* Am Astron Soc; Int Astron Union; Int Union Radio Sci; fel AAAS; Soc Sci Explor; Sigma Xi. *Res:* Photoelectric photometry; 21 centimeter radio-astronomical studies. *Mailing Add:* Dept Astron Univ Va PO Box 3818 Charlottesville VA 22903-3199

**TOLBERT, DANIEL LEE,** NEUROSCIENCES. *Current Pos:* from asst prof to assoc prof, 78-88, DIR, MURPHY NEUROANAT RES LAB, ST LOUIS UNIV, 78-, ASST PROF, DEPT SURG, 78-, PROF, DEPT ANAT, 88- *Personal Data:* b Fairview Heights, Ill, Oct 16, 46; m 72; c 2. *Educ:* Quincy Col, BS, 68; St Louis Univ, MS, 72, PhD, 75. *Prof Exp:* Fel, Dept Neurosurg, Univ Minn, 75-78. *Mem:* Am Asn Anatomists; Soc Neurosci. *Res:* Anatomical and neurophysiological study of the development of the brain. *Mailing Add:* Dept Anat Sch Med St Louis Univ 1402 S Grand Blvd St Louis MO 63104-1004

**TOLBERT, LAREN MALCOLM,** ORGANIC SYNTHESIS, ORGANIC ELECTRONIC MATERIAL. *Current Pos:* PROF CHEM, GA INST TECHNOL, 85- *Personal Data:* b New Orleans, La, Sept 30, 49; m 68; c 4. *Educ:* Tulane Univ, BA, 70; Univ Wis, Madison, PhD(org chem), 75. *Prof Exp:* Res fel, Harvard Univ, 75-76; asst prof chem, Univ Ky, 76-81, assoc prof, 81-85. *Mem:* Am Chem Soc; AAAS. *Res:* Organic photochemistry, particularly of anions; photodehalogenation and radicalnucleophile interactions; organic polymer chemistry. *Mailing Add:* Ga Inst Technol 706 State St Atlanta GA 30332-0400

**TOLBERT, MARGARET A,** GEOCHEMISTRY. *Current Pos:* PROF, DEPT CHEM, UNIV COLO, BOULDER. *Honors & Awards:* James B Macelwane Young Investr Medal, Am Geophys Union, 93. *Mailing Add:* Dept Chem Univ Colo Campus Box 215 Boulder CO 80309-0215

**TOLBERT, MARGARET ELLEN MAYO,** BIOCHEMISTRY, ANALYTICAL CHEMISTRY. *Current Pos:* DIR, DIV EDUC PROGS, ARGONNE NAT LAB, 94- *Personal Data:* b Suffolk, Va, Nov 24, 43; c Lawson K. *Educ:* Tuskegee Inst, BS, 67; Wayne State Univ, MS, 68; Brown Univ, PhD(biochem), 74. *Honors & Awards:* Award Sci & Med; Carver Res Asn Cert, Carver Res Found Fel. *Prof Exp:* Instr, Opportunities Industrialization Ctr, 71-72; instr math, Tuskegee Inst, 69-70, res technician biochem, 69, asst prof chem, 73-76; assoc prof pharmaceut chem & assoc dean, Sch Pharm, Fla A&M Univ, 77-78; prof chem & dir, Assoc Provost Res & Develop, Carver Res Found, Tuskegee Univ, 79-87; sr budgets & control analyst & sr planner, BP Res; dir, Res Improv Minority Inst, NSF; interim exec secy, Comt Educ & Training, Fed Coord Coun Sci, Eng & Technol; consult scientist, Howard Hughes Med Inst, 94. *Concurrent Pos:* NIH fel, 78-79; vis res scientist, Int Inst Cellular & Molecular Path, Cath Univ Louvain, Brussels, Belg & Brown Univ, RI; partic, Biomed Summer Inst, Lawrence Livermore Lab, 74. *Mem:* Sigma Xi; Am Chem Soc; Soc Environ Toxicol & Chem; fel AAAS. *Res:* Signal transduction in isolated hepatocytes. *Mailing Add:* Educ Progs Div Argonne Nat Lab 9700 S Cass Ave Argonne IL 60439. *Fax:* 630-252-3193; *E-Mail:* tolbert@dep.anl.gov

**TOLBERT, NATHAN EDWARD,** BIOCHEMISTRY, PLANT SCIENCES. *Current Pos:* prof, 58-90, EMER PROF BIOCHEM, MICH STATE UNIV, 90- *Personal Data:* b Twin Falls, Idaho, May 19, 19; m 52; c 3. *Educ:* Univ Calif, BS, 41; Univ Wis, MS, 48, PhD(biochem), 50. *Prof Exp:* Asst chem, Dept Viticult, Col Agr, Univ Calif, 41-43, biochemist, Radiation Lab, 50; res admin, US AEC, 50-52; sr biochemist, Oak Ridge Nat Lab, 52-58. *Mem:* Nat Acad Sci; Am Chem Soc; Am Soc Biol Chem; Am Soc Plant Physiol. *Res:* Plant biochemistry and plant growth substances; glycolic acid metabolism, biosynthesis and function; photosynthesis and relation to plant growth; microbodies and peroxisomes. *Mailing Add:* Dept Biochem Mich State Univ East Lansing MI 48823

**TOLBERT, ROBERT JOHN,** PLANT ANATOMY. *Current Pos:* assoc prof, 63-65, PROF BIOL, MOORHEAD STATE UNIV, 65- *Personal Data:* b Pelican Rapids, Minn, Apr 16, 28; m 53; c 2. *Educ:* Moorhead State Univ, BS & BA, 55; Rutgers Univ, PhD(bot), 59. *Prof Exp:* From asst prof to assoc prof biol, Univ WVa, 59-63. *Mem:* AAAS; Bot Soc Am; Sigma Xi. *Res:* Anatomical investigation of vegetative shoot apices; comparative studies of shoot apices in the order Malvales. *Mailing Add:* 3306 Village Green Blvd Moorhead MN 56560

**TOLBERT, THOMAS WARREN,** PHYSICAL CHEMISTRY, MOLECULAR SPECTROSCOPY. *Current Pos:* proj mgr res & develop, Springs Industs, 85-88, DIR, NEW VENTURES PRODS, RES & DEVELOP, 89-, DIR, AUTOMATION GROUP. *Personal Data:* b Greenwood, SC, Dec 1, 45; m 78; c 1. *Educ:* Wofford Col, BS, 67; State Univ NY Binghamton, PhD(chem), 74. *Prof Exp:* Asst prof chem, Wofford Col, 72-74; proj scientist, 74-75; lab supvr, Parke-Davis Med Surg Div, 75-77, proj mgr res & develop, Parke Davis Deseret Div, 77-81; dir res & develop, Flexible Tubing Div, Automation Industs, 81-85. *Mem:* Am Chem Soc. *Res:* Interaction characteristics of reacting molecules; industrial and manfacturing engineering; issued four patents. *Mailing Add:* Springs Industs Inc PO Box 70 Ft Mill SC 29715-0070

**TOLBERT, VIRGINIA ROSE,** AQUATIC ECOLOGY, HYDROLOGY & WATER RESOURCES. *Current Pos:* res assoc, 79-85, RES STAFF, ENVIRON SCI DIV, OAK RIDGE NAT LAB, TENN, 85- *Personal Data:* b Scottsboro, Ala, July 16, 48; m 72; Wayne; c Rebecca. *Educ:* ETenn State Univ, BS, 70; Univ Tenn, Knoxville, MS, 72, PhD(ecol), 78. *Prof Exp:* Fel, Dept Zool, Univ Tenn, Knoxville, 78-79. *Mem:* Ecol Soc Am; NAm Benthological Soc (treas, 88-); Asn Women Sci; Sigma Xi. *Res:* Effects of coal surface mining on aquatic communities; examination of the various aspects of pertarbation on aquatic systems; effects of energy related development on water and aquatic biota. *Mailing Add:* 9598 Anitoch Church Rd W Lenoir City TN 37772. *Fax:* 423-574-8543; *E-Mail:* vrt@ornl.gov

**TOLDERLUND, DOUGLAS STANLEY,** MARINE ECOLOGY, GLACIAL GEOLOGY. *Current Pos:* assoc prof marine sci, USCG Acad, 70-77, chmn, Marine Sci Sect, 78-83, head dept sci, 83-91, PROF MARINE SCI, USCG ACAD, 77- *Personal Data:* b Newport, RI, Jan 14, 39; m 61; c 2. *Educ:* Brown Univ, BA, 60; Columbia Univ, PhD(marine geol), 69. *Prof Exp:* Sr ecologist, Raytheon Co, 69-70. *Mem:* Am Geophys Union; Am Fisheries Soc; New Eng Estuarine Res Soc; Sigma Xi. *Res:* Estuarine ecology, especially water quality and finfish studies. *Mailing Add:* 61 Sill Lane Old Lyme CT 06371-1135. *Fax:* 860-444-8627

**TOLEDO, DOMINGO,** DIFFERENTIAL GEOMETRY, COMPLEX MANIFOLDS. *Current Pos:* from asst prof to assoc prof, 78-86, PROF MATH, UNIV UTAH, 86- *Personal Data:* b Hato Rey, PR, Apr 5, 45; m 86, Paula Schnitzer; c Laura, Roberto, David & Ramon. *Educ:* Stanford Univ, BS, 67; Cornell Univ, PhD(math), 72. *Prof Exp:* Mem, Inst Adv Studies, 72-74; J F Ritt asst prof math, Columbia Univ, 74-78. *Concurrent Pos:* Vis fel, Univ Warwick, 76; visitor, Inst Higher Sci Studies, 77, 82-83, & 88-89 & 96-97; Alfred P Sloan fel, 82-84; vis prof, Univ Bonn, 83-84. *Mem:* Am Math Soc. *Res:* Characteristic classes and coherent sheaves on complex manifolds; application of harmonic mappings to the geometry of Kahler manifold and locally symmetric spaces; fundamental groups of algebraic varieties; monodromy groups. *Mailing Add:* Univ Utah Salt Lake City UT 84112. *Fax:* 801-581-4148; *E-Mail:* toledo@math.utah.edu

**TOLEDO, ROMEO TRANCE,** CHEMICAL ENGINEERING, FOOD SCIENCE. *Current Pos:* asst prof, 68-76, assoc prof, 76-79, PROF FOOD SCI, UNIV GA, 79- *Personal Data:* b Philippines, Apr 27, 41. *Educ:* St Augustine Univ, Philippines, BSChE, 60; Univ Ill, MS, 65, PhD(food sci), 67. *Prof Exp:* Chem engr, Calif Packing Corp, 60-62; instr chem eng, St Augustine Univ, Philippines, 62-63; res asst, Univ Ill, 63-65, teaching asst food sci, 65-67; res chem engr, Libby McNeill & Libby, 67-68. *Concurrent Pos:* Consult, Mead Packaging Corp, 70-76. *Mem:* Assoc mem Am Inst Chem Engrs; Inst Food Technol; Am Soc Agr Engrs. *Res:* Engineering food processing and handling systems, heat transfer in food processing systems; rheological properties of food fluids and kinetics of food degradation and microbiological inactivation. *Mailing Add:* Dept Food Sci Univ Ga Athens GA 30609-4066

**TOLEDO-CROW, RICARDO,** MICROSCOPY & IMAGE PROCESSING. *Current Pos:* CONFOCAL APPLN RES SCIENTIST, NORAN INSTRUMENTS, 95- *Personal Data:* b Mexico City, Mex, Feb 23, 62; m 92, Citlali Lopez-Ortiz. *Educ:* Univ Mex, BS, 86; Rochester Inst Technol, PhD(imaging sci), 95. *Prof Exp:* Res staff, Instrument Ctr, Univ Mex, 86-90. *Mem:* Int Soc Optical Eng. *Res:* Three-dimensional optical microscopy and low light level detection; super resolution in optical microscopy. *Mailing Add:* 2551 W Beltline Hwy Middleton WI 53562. *Fax:* 608-836-7224; *E-Mail:* vtoledo@novan.com

**TOLEDO-PEREYRA, LUIS HORACIO,** BIOLOGICAL SCIENCES, MEDICINE. *Current Pos:* dir surg res, 79-84, CHIEF TRANSPLANTATION, MT CARMEL MERCY HOSP, 79-, DIR RES, 84- *Personal Data:* b Nogales, Ariz, Oct 19, 43; m 74; c 2. *Educ:* Colegio Regis, BS, 60; Univ Mex, MD, 67, MS, 70; Univ Minn, PhD(surg), 76, PhD(hist med), 84. *Honors & Awards:* Resident Res Award, Asn Acad Surg, 74; Cecile Lehman Mayer Res Award, Am Col Chest Physicians, 75. *Prof Exp:* Dir surg res & co-dir transplantation, Henry Ford Hosp, 77-79. *Concurrent Pos:* Instr biochem, Univ Mex, 63, clin instr internal med, 68; adj prof, Sch Health Sci, Mercy Col Detroit, 83-; consult transplantation, Hutzel Hosp, 84- *Mem:* NAm Soc Dialysis & Transplantation (pres, 82-84); Asn Acad Surg; Am Soc Transplant Surgeons; Am Diabetes Asn; Am Asn Immunologists. *Res:* Organ preservation and perfusion; modification of immune response by cyclosporine and lectins; islet cell transplantation; pancreas transplantation; new techniques to improve islet cell transplantation for diabetics; new ways of organ preservation for transplantation. *Mailing Add:* Dept Transplantation Borgess Med Ctr 1521 Gull Rd Kalamazoo MI 49001-1626. *Fax:* 616-342-7985

**TOLER, J C,** ELECTRICAL ENGINEERING. *Current Pos:* PRIN RES ENGR, GA INST TECHNOL, 66-, DIR, BIOENG CTR, 84-, CTR REHAB TECHNOL, 87- *Personal Data:* b Carthage, Ark, Jan 31, 36; c 2. *Educ:* Univ Ark, BSEE, 57; Ga Inst Technol, MSEE, 70. *Mem:* Fel Inst Elec & Electronics Engrs; Bioelectromagnetics Soc. *Res:* Interaction of electromagnetic waves with biological systems. *Mailing Add:* Bioeng Ctr Ga Inst Technol 225 North Ave NW Centennial Bldg Rm 329 Atlanta GA 30332

**TOLER, ROBERT WILLIAM,** VIROLOGY, PLANT PATHOLOGY. *Current Pos:* RETIRED. *Personal Data:* b Norphlet, Ark, Dec 15, 28; m 50; c 4. *Educ:* Univ Ark, BS, 50, MS, 58; NC State Univ, PhD(plant virol), 62. *Prof Exp:* Res technician, Rice Br, Exp Sta, Univ Ark, 51-54, specialist & plant pathologist, Agr Mission, Panama, 55-57; res plant pathologist, Coastal Plain Exp Sta, Agr Res Serv, USDA, Univ Ga, 61-65; cereal virologist, Tex A&M Univ, 66-93, assoc prof, 69-74, prof plant path, 74-93. *Concurrent Pos:* Consult, Foy Pittman Rice Farms, Ark, 50-51, Campos Manola Arca, SA, Manziuillo, Cuba, 54 & Ford Found, Antonia Narro Col Agr, Coahuila, Mex, 66; dir, Plant Protection Lab, Remote Sensing Ctr, Tex A&M Univ, 71- *Mem:* Am Phytopath Soc; Sigma Xi. *Res:* Physiological effects and host response in plant pathology; cereal virology identification and transmission of viruses that cause cereal diseases. *Mailing Add:* Dept Plant Path Tex A&M Univ College Station TX 77843-2132

**TOLGYESI, EVA,** ORGANIC CHEMISTRY, POLYMER CHEMISTRY. *Current Pos:* sr chemist, Harris Res Labs, 65-69, proj supvr polymer chem, 69-74, res supvr, 74-77, GROUP LEADER, GILLETTE RES INST, 77- *Personal Data:* b Budapest, Hungary. *Educ:* Budapest Technol Univ, BSc, 53; Univ Leeds, PhD(textile chem), 59. *Prof Exp:* Asst prof chem, Budapest Technol Univ, 53-56. *Mem:* Am Chem Soc; Soc Cosmetic Chemists; AAAS. *Res:* Keratin chemistry; chemical modification of wool; moth-proofing; cationic surfactants; fluoropolymers; silicones; hair cosmetics; hair removal; controlled release polymer systems. *Mailing Add:* 803 Tulane Pl Rockville MD 20850-1142

**TOLIN, SUE ANN,** PLANT VIROLOGY, PHYTOPATHOLOGY. *Current Pos:* from asst prof to assoc prof, 66-83, PROF PLANT PATH, VA POLYTECH INST & STATE UNIV, 83- *Personal Data:* b Montezuma, Ind, Nov 29, 38. *Educ:* Purdue Univ, BS, 60; Univ Nebr, MS, 62, PhD(bot), 65. *Prof Exp:* Res asst plant path, Univ Nebr, 60-65; res assoc bot & plant path, Purdue Univ, 65-66. *Concurrent Pos:* USDA rep, NIH Recombinant DNA Adv Comt, 79; spec consult, Coop State Res Serv, US Dept Agr, 79. *Mem:* Am Phytopath Soc; Am Soc Microbiol; Am Soc Virol; AAAS. *Res:* Identification, purification and molecular characterization of plant pathogenic viruses; electron microscopy; molecular genetic mechanisms of resistance of plants to viruses; biotechnology science policy. *Mailing Add:* Dept Plant Physiol Va Polytech Inst Blacksburg VA 24061-0330

**TOLINE, FRANCIS RAYMOND,** AEROSPACE ENGINEERING, NUCLEAR ENGINEERING. *Current Pos:* RETIRED. *Personal Data:* b Alliance, Nebr, Nov 3, 18; m 45; c 5. *Educ:* US Naval Postgrad Sch, BS, 52; Mass Inst Technol, SM, 53. *Prof Exp:* Br head air launched missile propulsion, Bur Naval Weapons, 59-60; from assoc prof to emer prof aerospace & nuclear eng, Tenn Technol Univ, 60-88. *Concurrent Pos:* NSF sci fac fel, 64-67. *Res:* Altitude simulation for environmental testing of nuclear rocket engines; ejector-diffuser systems used in altitude simulation. *Mailing Add:* 1856 E Spring St Cookeville TN 38506

**TOLIVER, ADOLPHUS P,** DNA REPLICATION, REGULATION GENE EXPRESSION. *Current Pos:* EXEC SECY, BIOCHEM STUDY SECT, DIV RES GRANTS, NIH, 75- *Personal Data:* b St Louis, Mo, Apr 9, 31. *Educ:* Purdue Univ, PhD(molecular biol & biochem), 68. *Prof Exp:* Asst prof biochem, Univ Calif, Davis, 70-75. *Mem:* Sigma Xi; Am Soc Biol Chemists. *Mailing Add:* NIH 45 Center Dr Bethesda MD 20892. *Fax:* 301-594-7384

**TOLIVER, MICHAEL EDWARD,** ENTOMOLOGY. *Current Pos:* ASSOC PROF BIOL, EUREKA COL, 81- *Personal Data:* b Albuquerque, NMex, Oct 1, 49; m 80. *Educ:* Univ NMex, BS, 73; Univ Ill, MS, 77, PhD(entom), 79. *Prof Exp:* Entomologist, City Urbana, 76; res asst, Univ Ill, 79-80; asst prof entom, 80; field supvr, Macon Mosquito Abatement Dist, 81. *Concurrent Pos:* Mem, Lepidopter Res Found. *Mem:* Lepidopterists Soc; AAAS. *Res:* Evolution of mimetic color patterns; biogeography of southwestern lepidopter. *Mailing Add:* Div Sci & Math Eureka Col 300 E College Ave Eureka IL 61530-1562

**TOLK, NORMAN HENRY,** SPACE PHYSICS, SURFACE PHYSICS. *Current Pos:* PROF PHYSICS, DEPT PHYSICS & ASTRON, VANDERBILT UNIV, 84-, DIR, VANDERBILT CTR ATOMIC & MOLECULAR PHYSIC SURFACE, 87- *Personal Data:* b Idaho Falls, Idaho, Jan 9, 38; m 61; c Jeffrey, Bentley, David, Rebecca & Amy. *Educ:* Harvard Col, AB, 60; Columbia Univ, PhD(physics), 66. *Honors & Awards:* Alexander von Humboldt Sr Sci Award, 87. *Prof Exp:* Grad res asst, Radiation Lab, Dept Physics, Columbia Univ, 60-61, & 63-66, teaching asst, 61-63, res physicist, 66-67, lectr & staff mem, 67-68, adj asst prof physics, 68-69; mem tech staff, AT&T Bell Lab, 68-83, Bell Commun Res, 84. *Concurrent Pos:* Harvard Nat fel & Gen Motors fel, 56-60; Brattle fel, Harvard Univ, 57; vis univ fel, Australian Nat Univ, Canberra, 75; vis scientist, Max Planck Inst Plasmaphysics, WGer, 78; NAm ed, Int J, Radiation & Solids; mem, div electron & atomic physics prog comt, Am Phys Soc, 76-77, int comt, Int Workshops on Inelastic Ion Surface Collisions, 82, Int Workshops Desorption Induced Electronics Transitions, adv bd, Int J Radiation Effects, exec comt, Vanderbilt Free Electron Laser Proj, exect comt, dept physics & astron, Vanderbilt Univ, 85-, comt atomic & molecular sci, Nat Res Coun, 84-; chmn, Int Workshop Desorption Induced Electronics Transitions, Williamsburg, 82, Int Conf Atomic Collision Solids, Washington, DC, 85, development comt & dir search comt, Free Electron Laser, patent comt, Vanderbilt Univ, 87-; consult, S-cubed Corp, Acurex Corp & Chem Div, Los Alamos Nat Lab, 86-, Lockheed Corp, 87; Eaton Corp, 87- Inst Defense Anal, 88-; US rep int comt, Int Conf Atomic Collisions Solids; thesis supvr, Mass Inst Technol, Univ Wis, Columbia & Vanderbilt Univ; invited speaker, Symp Surface Modification Directed Deposition Energy, Am Vacuum Soc, Physic Colloquium, Free Univ Berlin, Tech Univ Vienna, physics seminar, Univ Osnabruck, WGer, London Univ, Am Phys Soc Plasma Physics Meeting, Boston & Am Optical Soc Conf Luminescence, Madison, 84, Phys Chem Colloquium, Rice Univ, Smithsonian Astrophys Seminar, Harvard Univ, Second Spacecraft Glow Workshop, Chem Seminar, Los Alamos Nat Lab, 86, Physics Colloquium, Univ Ark, 87, Inst Defense Anal, Washington, DC, Fourth Int Symp Resonance Ionization Spectors, Mass, 88 & other various seminars, symp & lect from different univ, inst & soc, 84-88. *Mem:* Fel Am Phys Soc; Am Vacuum Soc; Am Optical Soc. *Res:* Desorption induced by electronic transitions, processes associated with electron and photon bombardment on surfaces; interaction of neutral atoms, in particular, atomic oxygen with variety of surface; atomic and molecular collisions on surfaces; author of over 150 publications on atomic and surface physics. *Mailing Add:* Dept Physics & Astron Univ Vanderbilt Box 1807 Sta B Nashville TN 37235. *Fax:* 615-343-7263; *E-Mail:* tolk@macpost.vanderbilt.edu

**TOLL, JOHN SAMPSON,** THEORETICAL PHYSICS, ELEMENTARY PARTICLE PHYSICS. *Current Pos:* pres & prof physics, Univ Md, 78-88, chancellor, 88-89, pres, Univs Res Asn, 89-94, EMER CHANCELLOR & PROF PHYSICS, UNIV MD, 89-; PRES, WASH COL, CHESTERTOWN, MD, 95- *Personal Data:* b Denver, Colo, Oct 25, 23; m 70, Deborah Taintor; c Dacia M Sampson & Caroline T. *Educ:* Yale Univ, BS, 44; Princeton Univ, AM, 48, PhD(physics), 52. *Hon Degrees:* DSc, Univ Md, Eastern Shore, 73 & Univ Wroclaw, 75; LLD, Adelphi Univ, 78; Univ Md, 93; Doctorate, Fudan Univ, China, 87; DHL, State Univ NY Stony Brook, 90. *Honors & Awards:* Golden Plate Award, Am Acad Achievement, 68; Copernicus Award, Govt Poland, 73. *Prof Exp:* Managing ed & actg chmn, Yale Sci Mag, 43-44; asst proctor fel, Princeton Univ, 46-49; theoret physicist, Los Alamos Sci Lab, 50-51; staff mem & assoc dir, Proj Matterhorn, Forrestal Res Ctr, Princeton Univ, 51-53; prof physics & chmn dept physics & astron, Univ Md, 53-65; prof physics & pres, State Univ NY, Stony Brook, 65-78. *Concurrent Pos:* Guggenheim Mem Found fel, Inst Theoret Physics, Univ Copenhagen & Univ Lund, 58-59; US deleg & head sci secretariat, Int Conf High Energy Physics, 60; mem-at-large US nat comn, Int Union Pure & Appl Physics, 61-63; nat chair, Fedn Am Scientists, 61-62; mem, Gov Adv Comt Atomic Energy, State of NY, 66-70; Nordita vis prof, Niels Bohr Inst Theoret Physics, Univ Copenhagen, 75-76; mem univ progs panel energy res bd, Dept Energy, 82-83, SBHE Adv Com, 83-89; bd dirs, Am Coun Educ, 86-89, bd trustees Aspen Inst Humanities, 87 & 89; chmn adv panel, tech risks & opportunities for US energy supply & demand, US Off Tech Assessment, 87, chmn adv panel, Int Collab in Defense Tech, US Off Tech Assessment, 89-91; mem, Grant Rev Panel, US Dept Com, 92- *Mem:* AAAS; fel Am Phys Soc; Am Asn Physics Teachers; Fedn Am Scientists; Sigma Xi; fel NY Acad Sci. *Res:* Elementary particle theory; scattering; theoretical physics, especially quantum field theory and elementary particles, including dispersion theory foundations, scattering, analyticity domains and integral representations from axiomatic theory, and applications, especially in quantum electrodynamics. *Mailing Add:* 4124 Dept Physics Univ Md College Park MD 20742-4111. *Fax:* 301-314-9525, 410-778-7850; *E-Mail:* john__toll@umail.umd.edu

**TOLLE, JON WRIGHT,** MATHEMATICS, OPERATIONS RESEARCH. *Current Pos:* asst prof, Univ NC, Chapel Hill, 67-73, assoc prof math & opers res, 73-78, chmn curric opers res, 74-79, PROF MATH & OPERS RES, UNIV NC, CHAPEL HILL, 78- *Personal Data:* b Mattoon, Ill, June 26, 39; m 95, Mary Blevins; c Cecily & Michael. *Educ:* DePauw Univ, BA, 61; Univ Minn, PhD(math), 66. *Prof Exp:* Res assoc, Argonne Nat Lab, 63; instr math, Univ Minn, 66-67. *Concurrent Pos:* Vis prof, Grad Sch Bus, Univ Chicago, 75 & 81-82; chmn, Math Sci Curric, Univ NC, Chapel Hill, 84-91 & 96-; fac assoc, Nat Inst Stand & Technol, 91- *Mem:* Opers Res Soc Am; Soc Indust & Appl Math; Math Asn Am. *Res:* Mathematical programming; optimization theory; numerical analysis. *Mailing Add:* Dept Math CB No 3250 Univ NC Chapel Hill NC 27599-3250. *E-Mail:* tolle@ior.unc.edu

**TOLLEFSON, CHARLES IVAR,** biochemistry, for more information see previous edition

**TOLLEFSON, ERIC LARS,** PHYSICAL CHEMISTRY, CHEMICAL ENGINEERING. *Current Pos:* assoc prof chem eng, 67-70, actg head dept, 71, head dept, 72-81, PROF CHEM ENG, UNIV CALGARY, 70-, ALTA GIL SANDS TECHNOL & RES PROF, 82- *Personal Data:* b Moose Jaw, Sask, Oct 15, 21; m 47; c 3. *Educ:* Univ Sask, BA, 43, MA, 45; Univ Toronto, PhD(phys chem), 48. *Prof Exp:* Demonstr chem, Univ Sask, 45, asst, Directorate Chem Warfare, 43-44; jr res officer, Nat Res Coun Can, 45; lab asst, Univ Toronto, 45-47, lectr, 47-48; jr res officer, Nat Res Coun Can, 48-49, asst res officer, 50-51; chemist, Process Res Div, Stanolind Oil & Gas Co, Okla, 51-52, sr chemist, 53-56; head phys chem sect, Res Dept, Can Chem Co, Ltd, 56-66, supt chem develop dept, 65-66, tech mgr, Can Chem Co Div, Chem-Cell Ltd, Alta, 66-67. *Mem:* Am Chem Soc; fel Chem Inst Can; Air Pollution Control Asn; Asn Prof Engrs. *Res:* Preparation of activated carbon from Alberta coals; recovery of hydrocarbons from aqueous wastes from oil sands; bitumen recovery operations; kinetics; atomic hydrogen with acetylene; oxidation of ethylene; Fischer-Tropsch synthesis; alcohol dehydrogenation; reduction of nitrogen oxides in stack gases; oxidation of low concentrations of hydrogen sulfide over activated carbon; biological oxidation, difficiency of waste gas flares. *Mailing Add:* Chem & Petrol Eng Dept Univ Calgary Calgary AB T2N 1N4 Can

**TOLLEFSON, JEFFREY L,** MATHEMATICS. *Current Pos:* assoc prof, 74-77, PROF MATH, UNIV CONN, 77-, DEPT HEAD, 85- *Personal Data:* b Hampa, Idaho, July 30, 42; m 65; c 2. *Educ:* Univ Idaho, BS, 65; Mich State Univ, MS, 66, PhD(math), 68. *Prof Exp:* NASA trainee, Mich State Univ, 65-68; asst prof math, Tulane Univ, 68-71 & Tex A&M Univ, 71-74. *Mem:* Am Math Soc. *Res:* Topology of manifolds. *Mailing Add:* Dept Math Univ Conn Storrs CT 06269-0001

**TOLLER, GARY NEIL,** GALACTIC RADIATION FIELD. *Current Pos:* CONSULT, INT ASTRON UNION, 82-; PROJ MGR, GEN SCI CORP, 89- *Personal Data:* b 1950; m 87, Ilene Gallner; c David & Jennifer. *Educ:* Dickinson Col, BS, 72; State Univ NY, Stony Brook, PhD(astron), 81. *Honors & Awards:* Group Achievement Award, NASA. *Prof Exp:* Astronr, Space Astron Lab, Univ Fla, 81-85. *Concurrent Pos:* Res assoc, Appl Res Corp, 85-89. *Mem:* Am Astron Soc; Int Astron Union. *Res:* Measurement of zodiacal light, integrated starlight, diffuse galactic light and extragalactic light at optical and infrared wavelengths for study of interplanetary dust and galactic structure; space-based experimentation. *Mailing Add:* 9364 Dewlit Way Columbia MD 21045

**TOLLES, WILLIAM MARSHALL,** PHYSICAL CHEMISTRY. *Current Pos:* supt chem, 84-88, ASSOC DIR RES, NAVAL RES LAB, WASHINGTON DC, 88- *Personal Data:* b New Britain, Conn, June 30, 37; m 59; c 2. *Educ:* Univ Conn, BA, 58; Univ Calif, Berkeley, PhD(phys chem), 62. *Prof Exp:* Fel, Rice Univ, 61-62; from asst prof to prof sci & eng, Naval Postgrad Sch, 62-78, dean res & dean sci & eng, 78-84. *Concurrent Pos:* Consult, Naval Weapons Ctr, China Lake, summers, 66-77. *Mem:* Optical Soc Am; Am Phys Soc; Am Chem Soc; Sigma Xi. *Res:* Microwave spectroscopy; rotational spectra of molecules; electron spin resonance; microwave properties of materials; non-linear molecular spectroscopy. *Mailing Add:* Assoc Dir Res 8801 Edward Gibbs Pl Alexandria VA 22309-2214

**TOLLESTRUP, ALVIN V,** SUPERCONDUCTING MAGNET DESIGN. *Current Pos:* MEM STAFF, FERMI NAT ACCELERATOR LAB, 77- *Personal Data:* b Los Angeles, Calif, Mar 22, 24; m 44; c 4. *Educ:* Univ Utah, BS, 44; Calif Inst Technol, PhD(physics), 50. *Honors & Awards:* Nat Medal Technol, 89; Wilson Prize, Am Phys Soc, 89. *Prof Exp:* Res fel physics, Calif Inst Technol, 50-53, from asst prof to prof physics, 53-77. *Concurrent Pos:* NSF fel, Europe Nuclear Res, 57-58. *Mem:* Nat Acad Sci; AAAS; Fel Am Phys Soc. *Res:* Design and operation of colliding beam detector; design and construction of superconducting magnets. *Mailing Add:* Fermilab MS 318 PO Box 500 Batavia IL 60510. *Fax:* 630-840-2968; *E-Mail:* alvin@fnal.gov

**TOLLETT, JAMES TERRELL,** ANIMAL WASTE MANAGEMENT, CURRICULUM WRITING. *Current Pos:* CHAIR & PROF AGR, SOUTHERN ARK UNIV, 90- *Personal Data:* b Nashville, Ark, June 14, 35; m 56, Joann Latimer; c Cheryl D. *Educ:* Univ Ark, BSA, 57, MSA, 58; Univ Ill, PhD(nutrit), 61. *Prof Exp:* Asst prof & farm mgr agr, Southern State Col, 60-61; tech field res, Dow Chem Co, Midland, Mich, 62-68, mgr animal res, Midland Mich, 73-74, group leader & sci res specialist, Freeport, Tex, 74-79, res mgr & group mgr toxicol, Midland, Mich, 79-85; dir, Occup-Tech Dept, NE Tex Community Col, 85-90. *Mem:* Am Soc Animal Sci; Poultry Sci Asn; Sigma Xi; Am Asn Lab Sci; Am Registry Prof Animal Scientists; Coun Agr Sci & Technol. *Res:* Developing innovative equipment and methods of utilizing animal waste in sustainable agriculture programs. *Mailing Add:* Southern Ark Univ PO Box 1343 Magnolia AR 71753

**TOLLIN, GORDON,** BIOPHYSICAL CHEMISTRY. *Current Pos:* from asst prof to assoc prof, 59-67, PROF CHEM, UNIV ARIZ, 67-, PROF BIOCHEM, 78- *Personal Data:* b New York, NY, Dec 26, 30; m 55, 78, Linda Meade; c Allen, Steven, Deborah & Amina. *Educ:* Brooklyn Col, BS, 52; Iowa State Univ, PhD, 56. *Prof Exp:* Res assoc chem, Fla State Univ, 56; chemist, Lawrence Radiation Lab, Univ Calif, 56-59, NSF fel, 56-57. *Concurrent Pos:* Sloan fel, 62-66. *Mem:* Am Soc Photobiol; Biophys Soc; Am Soc Biol Chemists. *Res:* Mechanism of redox protein action; photosynthesis; mechanisms of biological energy conversion; biological oxidation-reduction. *Mailing Add:* Dept Biochem Univ Ariz 1501 N Campbell Tucson AZ 85724

**TOLLMAN, JAMES PERRY,** pathology; deceased, see previous edition for last biography

**TOLMACH, L(EONARD) J(OSEPH),** cell biology, radiobiology, for more information see previous edition

**TOLMAN, CHADWICK ALMA,** INORGANIC & ORGANIC CHEMISTRY, SCIENCE EDUCATION. *Current Pos:* chemist, 65-90, RES FEL, EXP STA, E I DU PONT DE NEMOURS & CO, INC, 90- *Personal Data:* b Oct 11, 38; US citizen; m 62, Ann McCarthy; c Alison, Susan & Kenneth. *Educ:* Mass Inst Technol, BS, 60; Univ Calif, Berkeley, PhD(phys chem), 64. *Prof Exp:* Fel & res assoc chem, Mass Inst Technol, 64-65. *Concurrent Pos:* Vis prof, Ctr Nat Res Scientist, France, 81; exec on leave, Precol Educ, Sci Alliance, 90-91. *Mem:* Am Chem Soc; AAAS. *Res:* Mechanisms of homogeneous catalysis by transition metal complexes; hydrocarbon oxidations; kinetics and equilibria of organic and organometallic reactions; chemistry in zeolites, enzyme catalysis. *Mailing Add:* 2503 Raven Rd Wilmington DE 19810. *Fax:* 302-695-2504; *E-Mail:* tolman@esvax.dnet.dupont.com

**TOLMAN, EDWARD LAURIE,** PHARMACOLOGY, RESEARCH ADMINISTRATION. *Current Pos:* dir, Preclin Develop Coord Worldwide, 88-91, dir, Res & Develop Planning & Adminr, 91-94, SR DIR, DRUG DISCOVERY, R W JOHNSON PHARMACEUT RES INST, 94- *Personal Data:* b Chelsea, Mass, Oct 9, 42; m 67, Anita; c Jennifer. *Educ:* Univ Mass, BA, 64, MA, 65; State Univ NY Upstate Med Ctr, PhD(pharmacol), 70. *Prof Exp:* NIH fel physiol, Milton S Hershey Med Ctr, Pa State Univ, 69-71, res assoc, 71-72; sr res biologist, Lederle Labs, Am Cyanamid Co, 72-77, group leader, 77-80; sect head biochem res, Ortho Pharmacol Corp, 80-84, asst dir, biochem pharmacol/microbiol, 84-87, dir, drug metab, 87-89. *Mem:* Am Soc Pharmacol & Exp Therapeut; Am Diabetes Asn; AAAS; Am Soc Microbiol. *Res:* Disorders of carbohydrate and lipid metabolism; prostaglandins and inflammation. *Mailing Add:* R W Johnson Pharmaceut Res Inst Rte 202 Raritan NJ 08869. *Fax:* 908-722-6760

**TOLMAN, RICHARD LEE,** HETEROCYCLIC CHEMISTRY, CARBOHYDRATE SYNTHESIS. *Current Pos:* res fel synthetic org chem, Merck Res Labs, 73-79, asst dir, 79-82, dir, 82-93, SR DIR, MERCK RES LABS, 93- *Personal Data:* b Ames, Iowa, Nov 6, 41; m 64, Maralyn Daynes; c Joel R, J Samuel & Matthew A. *Educ:* Brigham Young Univ, BA, 65; Univ Utah, PhD(bioorg chem), 69. *Prof Exp:* Group leader, ICN Nucleic Acid Res Inst, 69-73. *Concurrent Pos:* Lectr, Merck Res Labs, 80- *Mem:* Am Chem Soc; Am Peptide Soc; Int Soc Antiviral Res; Am Soc Microbiol; Int Soc Heterocyclic Chem. *Res:* Chemistry of antiviral agents, nucleosides, heterocydes, and peptides; synthetic conjugate vaccines; AIDS-derived peptides and bacterial polysaccharides; chemotherapy of metabolic diseases, diabetes and benign prostatic hypertrophy. *Mailing Add:* 29 Upper Warren Way Warren NJ 07059-5326. *Fax:* 732-594-6449; *E-Mail:* rlt@merck.com

**TOLMAN, ROBERT ALEXANDER,** PHYSIOLOGY, ENDOCRINOLOGY. *Current Pos:* RETIRED. *Personal Data:* b Springfield, Mass, Feb 28, 24; m 49; c 3. *Educ:* Univ Mass, BS, 49; Ind Univ, MA, 50, PhD(zool), 54. *Honors & Awards:* Distinguished Serv Award, Endocrine Soc, 90. *Prof Exp:* Asst zool, Ind Univ, 50-53, asst chem embryol, 53-54; instr physiol & pharmacol, Col Osteop Med & Surg, 54-58; cardiovasc res trainee, Dept Physiol, Med Col Ga, 58-59; from instr to asst prof physiol & biophys, Sch Med, Univ Louisville, 59-67; grants assoc, NIH, 67-68, assoc, Myocardial Infarction Br, Nat Heart & Lung Inst, 68-69, dir Endocrinol Res Prog, Diabetes, Endocrinol & Metab Dis Progs, Nat Inst Diabetes & Digestive & Kidney Dis, 69-89. *Mem:* AAAS; Endocrinol Soc. *Res:* Thyroid, thyrotropic hormone interaction and thyroid-stimulating hormone assay; time of appearance of cardiac actin in chick embryo; ventricular pressure curves. *Mailing Add:* 14309 Briarwood Terr Rockville MD 20853-2218

**TOLNAI, SUSAN,** CELL BIOLOGY, HISTOLOGY. *Current Pos:* lectr, 62-63, from asst prof to prof, 63-97, EMER PROF HISTOL & EMBRYOL, FAC MED, UNIV OTTAWA, 97- *Personal Data:* b Budapest, Hungary, Nov 29, 28; Can citizen; m 50; c 2. *Educ:* Semmelweiss Med Univ, Budapest, MD, 53. *Prof Exp:* Bacteriologist, Lab Hyg, Dept Nat Health & Welfare, Can, 57-58, biologist, 58-62. *Concurrent Pos:* Nat Acad Sci Hungary fel, 53-56. *Res:* Myocardial enzymes, proteinases; medical education. *Mailing Add:* Dept Cellular & Molecular Med Fac Med Univ Ottawa 451 Smyth Rd Ottawa ON K1H 8M5 Can. *E-Mail:* stolnai@istar.ca

**TOLSMA, JACOB,** CHEMICAL ENGINEERING, POLYMER CHEMISTRY. *Current Pos:* RETIRED. *Personal Data:* b Passaic, NJ, Mar 4, 23; m 48; c 5. *Educ:* Newark Col Eng, BSChE, 56, MSChE, 65. *Prof Exp:* Chem engr, Res Ctr, Uniroyal, Inc, 56-65, res engr, 65-71; res engr, Weavenit Surg Corp, 71-80; Meadox Medicals Inc, 80-87. *Mem:* Am Chem Soc. *Res:* Chemical engineering development; polymers scale up; water pollution control. *Mailing Add:* 132 Ballentine Dr Haledon NJ 07508

**TOLSON, ROBERT HEATH,** ATMOSPHERIC SCIENCE & PLANETARY SCIENCES, SPACECRAFT DYNAMICS & CONTROL. *Current Pos:* Aerospace scientist lunar & planetary studies, Langley Res Ctr, NASA, 58-72, head, Planetary Physics Br, 72-75, head, Atmospheric Sci Br, 75-82, chief scientist, 82-84, head, Interdisciplinary Res Off, 84-90, PROF JIAFS, LANGLEY RES CTR, NASA, GEORGE WASHINGTON UNIV, 91- *Personal Data:* b Portsmouth, Va, July 23, 35; m 78, Carol; c Mark & Kim. *Educ:* Va Polytech Inst & State Univ, BS, 58, MS, 63; Old Dom Univ, PhD, 90. *Honors & Awards:* H J E Reid, Langley Res Ctr, NASA, 78. *Mem:* Am Geophys Union; Am Inst Aeronaut & Astronaut; Am Astronaut Soc; AAAS. *Res:* Stratospheric minor constituent distributions and transport; spacecraft dynamics and control; planetary atmospheres and gravity fields; vibrational modul identification. *Mailing Add:* Langley Res Ctr NASA George Washington Univ 6 E Taylor St Bldg 1244 Rm 227G Mail Stop 269 Hampton VA 23681-0001. *Fax:* 757-864-5394

**TOLSTEAD, WILLIAM LAWRENCE,** BOTANY. *Current Pos:* from assoc prof to prof, 57-76, EMER PROF BIOL, DAVIS & ELKINS COL, 76- *Personal Data:* b Howard Co, Iowa, Nov 25, 09. *Educ:* Luther Col, Iowa, BS, 33; Iowa State Univ, MS, 36; Univ Nebr, PhD(plant ecol), 42. *Prof Exp:* Biologist, Conserv & Surv Div, Univ Nebr, 35-42. *Concurrent Pos:* Chmn dept, Davis & Elkins Col, 72-84. *Mem:* Am Rhododendron Soc; Am Hort Soc; Royal Hort Soc. *Res:* Plant breeding rhododendron. *Mailing Add:* c/o Davis & Elkins Col 100 Campus Dr Elkins WV 26241

**TOLSTOY, ALEXANDRA,** ACOUSTICAL OCEANOGRAPHY, WAVE PROPAGATION. *Current Pos:* SR SCIENTIST, INTEGRATED PERFORMANCE DECISIONS, 94- *Personal Data:* b New York, NY, Aug 18, 47; m 74, Ron Colbroth. *Educ:* George Washington Univ, BA, 68, MA, 72; Univ Md, PhD(appl math), 83. *Prof Exp:* Sect leader, US Naval Res Lab, 80-94. *Concurrent Pos:* Mem, Acoust Oceanog Comt, Acoust Soc Am, 90-93; Underwater Acoust Tech Comt, 92-95; chair, Hawaii Chap, Ocean Eng Soc, Inst Elec & Electronics Engrs, 95- *Mem:* Sr mem Inst Elec & Electronics Engrs; Soc Indust & Appl Math; fel Acoust Soc Am; Am Geophys Union; Am Phys Soc; Sigma Xi; Asn Women Geoscientists; Asn Women Math; Asn Women Sci; Women Sci & Eng. *Res:* Acoustic and electromagnetic wave propagation; signal processing; applied mathematics; acoustic tomography; granted two patents. *Mailing Add:* Integrated Performance Decisions 4224 Waialae Ave Suite 5-260 Honolulu HI 96816. *Fax:* 808-735-8086; *E-Mail:* tolstoy@ipdinc.com

**TOLSTOY, IVAN,** UNDERWATER SOUND, WAVE THEORY. *Current Pos:* RETIRED. *Personal Data:* b Baden-Baden, Ger, Mar 30, 23; nat US; m 47, 64; c Alexandra, Elisabeth & Maya. *Educ:* Univ Sorbonne, Lic es sc, 45; Columbia Univ, MA, 47, PhD(geophys), 50. *Honors & Awards:* Pioneers of Underwater Acoust Medal, Acoust Soc Am, 90, hon mem, Sci Res Ctr, Far E Br, USSR Acad Nauk, 89. *Prof Exp:* Mem sci staff, Lamont Geol Observ, Columbia Univ, 48-51; sr res engr, Stanolind Oil & Gas Co, 51-53; res scientist, Hudson Lab, Columbia Univ, 53-60, sr res assoc 62-67, assoc dir, 64-67, prof ocean eng, 67-68; prof geol & fluid dynamics, Geophys Fluid Dynamics Inst, Fla State Univ, 68-74; prof math, Univ Leeds, 73-76, distinguished vis prof acoust, Naval Postgrad Sch, 77-78; consult, 79-90. *Concurrent Pos:* Chief scientist, Mid Atlantic Ridge Exped, Columbia Univ, 50; consult, Gen Elec Co & Carter Oil Co, 60-62 & Schlumberger Tech Co, 62; sr vis fel, Dept Appl Math Studies, Leeds Univ, 71-72, vis prof, 73-76; guest lectr, Int Sch Physics, 84. *Mem:* AAAS; Am Phys Soc; fel Acoust Soc Am; Am Geophys Union; Sigma Xi; NY Acad Sci. *Res:* Theory of acoustic and elastic wave propagation; hydrodynamics; theoretical mechanics; seismology; submarine topography and geology; applied mathematics; history science; author of approximately 100 publications. *Mailing Add:* Knockvennie DG7-3PA Castle Douglas SW Scotland

**TOM, BALDWIN HENG,** IMMUNOLOGY. *Current Pos:* PRES & CHIEF EXEC OFFICER, BALDWIN GROUP INC, 86- *Personal Data:* b San Francisco, Calif, Sept 19, 40. *Educ:* Univ Calif, Berkeley, BA, 63; Univ Ariz, MS, 67, PhD(microbiol), 70. *Prof Exp:* Fel, Stanford Univ Sch Med, 70-72, res assoc immunol, 72-73; instr, Sch Med, Northwestern Univ, 73-74, assoc, 74-75, asst prof surg & physiol, 75-77; asst prof, Univ Tex, Houston, 77-84, assoc prof biochem molecular biol & surg, Med Sch, 84-86, assoc dir, Bioprocessing Res Ctr Houston, Health Sci Ctr, 85-86. *Concurrent Pos:* Res career develop award, Nat Cancer Inst, 79-84; vis scientist, Prairie View A&M Univ, 81; Int Cancer Res exchange fel, Nottingham, Eng, 81. *Mem:* NY Acad Sci; Soc Exp Biol & Med; Tissue Cult Asn; Am Asn Immunol; Am Asn Cancer Res. *Res:* Dissection of the cellular and molecular bases for immune reactivities in tumor cell-lymphocyte interactions with liposomes and monoclonal antibodies; space bioprocessing. *Mailing Add:* PO Box 1127 Stafford TX 77497

**TOM, GLENN MCPHERSON,** INORGANIC CHEMISTRY, ANALYTICAL CHEMISTRY. *Current Pos:* VPRES RES, ADV TECHNOL MAT, 86- *Personal Data:* b Honolulu, Hawaii, Sept 1, 49; m 76; c 3. *Educ:* Univ Hawaii, BS, 71; Stanford Univ, PhD(inorg chem), 75. *Prof Exp:* Fel chem, Univ Chicago, 75-77; res chemist, Hercules Res Ctr, Hercules Inc, 77-86. *Mem:* Am Chem Soc. *Res:* Electroanalytic chemistry; inorganic and organometallic chemistry; Zeigler-Natta polymerizations; gas purification. *Mailing Add:* ATM Inc 7 Commerce Dr Danbury CT 06810-4131

**TOMA, RAMSES BARSOUM,** PROTEIN METABOLISM, FOOD FORMULATION & PRODUCT DEVELOPMENT. *Current Pos:* DISTINGUISHED PROF, CALIF STATE UNIV, LONG BEACH, 91- *Personal Data:* b Cairo, Egypt, Nov 9, 38; US citizen; m 69, Rosette Roushdy; c Normer & Kamy. *Educ:* Ain Shams Univ, Cairo, BSc, 59, MSc, 65; La State Univ, PhD(food sci & nutrit), 71, Univ Minn, MPH, 80. *Prof Exp:* Chemist, Ministry Food Supplies, Cairo, 60-68; res assoc food sci & grad asst, La State Univ, 69-71; asst prof, Univ NDak, 72-74, assoc prof & chmn, 74-79, prof food sci & nutrit, 79-84. *Concurrent Pos:* Dir food inspection, Cairo, Egypt, 60-68; dir qual & assurance, Crystal Foods, New Orleans, La, 69; dir res & develop, Food Prod Div, Evangeline Foods, La, 72; prin investr, Red River Proj, Nat Potato Coun, 75-78; mem, NDak Trade Mission to Mid East, 75-78; Egyptian-Am Scholars for Year 2000, 76-; vis assoc prof, Mansoura Univ, Egypt, 79-80, Univ Mexico, 89, Am Shams Univ, Cairo, Egypt, 94. *Mem:* Am Chem Soc; Inst Food Technologists; Am Dietetic Asn; Am Pub Health Asn; Am Asn Cereal Chemists; fel Am Inst Chemists; NY Acad Sci. *Res:* Food analyses; protein composition; naturally occurring toxicants in foods; protein metabolism; dietary patterns of selected ethnic groups; irradiated foods. *Mailing Add:* Foods & Nutrit Dept Calif State Univ-Long Beach 1250 Bellflower Blvd Long Beach CA 90840. *Fax:* 562-985-4414

**TOMAJA, DAVID LOUIS,** MINI-COMPUTER SYSTEMS SUPPORT. *Current Pos:* res chemist, 74-87, TECH COMPUT SYSTS SPECIALIST, PHILLIPS PETROL RES & DEVELOP CTR, 87- *Personal Data:* b Bridgeport, Conn, July 15, 46. *Educ:* Univ Conn, BA, 68; State Univ NY, Albany, PhD(chem), 74. *Prof Exp:* Chemist, Gen Elec Res & Develop Ctr, 68-70. *Res:* Development and support of personal computer work stations; development and maintenance of software applications for technical needs. *Mailing Add:* 46 Woodhaven Wood Dr The Woodlands TX 77380

**TOMALIA, DONALD ANDREW,** PHYSICAL ORGANIC CHEMISTRY & SYNTHETIC POLYMERCHEMISTRY, NANOSCOPIC CHEMISTRY & ARCHITECTURE. *Current Pos:* RES PROF, SR RES SCIENTIST & DIR NANOSCOPIC CHEM & ARCHIT, MICH MOLECULAR INST, 90- *Personal Data:* b Owosso, Mich, Sept 5, 38; m 59, 86, Janet Buchtenkirch; c 5. *Educ:* Univ Mich, BA, 61; Bucknell Univ, MS, 62; Mich State Univ, PhD(phys org chem), 68. *Honors & Awards:* Global Proj Prize, Ministry Int Trade & Indust, Japan, 88. *Prof Exp:* Proj leader, Dow Chem Co, 66-68, group leader, 68-71, res mgr, 71-76, assoc scientist, 76-79, sr assoc scientist, 79-84, res scientist, Functional Polymers & Process Div, 84-90. *Concurrent Pos:* Distinguished lectr, Japan Soc Polymer Sci, Kyoto, 84; adj prof, Mich Tech. *Mem:* Am Chem Soc; Sigma Xi. *Res:* Functional monomers and polymers usually incorporating heterocyclic moieties; unusual cross linking devices; betaine surfactants and chelating agents; onium type chemistry; water soluble polymer systems; polyamines; cationic polymerization; starburst dendrimers; polymer topology; molecular morphogenesis; precise macromolecular structure. *Mailing Add:* Mich Molecular Inst 1910 W St Andrews Rd Midland MI 48640-2696

**TOMAN, FRANK R,** PLANT BIOCHEMISTRY, PLANT METAL TOXICITY. *Current Pos:* from asst prof to assoc prof, 69-79, PROF BIOL, WESTERN KY UNIV, 79- *Personal Data:* b Ellsworth, Kans, June 6, 39; m 62, Judy Stephen; c Troy W & Tammara S. *Educ:* Kans State Univ, BS, 61, MS, 63, PhD(biochem), 67. *Prof Exp:* Instr, Kans State Univ, 64-66. *Concurrent Pos:* Res assoc, Plant Res Lab, Mich State Univ-AEC, 73-74; vis prof, Dept Plant Physiol, Univ Ky, 82; vis scientist, Dept Biochem, Kans State Univ, 84; Ogden Found fel instrnl improv, 84. *Mem:* Am Chem Soc; Sigma Xi. *Res:* Plant proteins and enzymes; metal toxicity in plants, particularly manganese, selenium, lead and copper effects on RUBP and actate dehydrogenase of wheat and tobacco. *Mailing Add:* Dept Biol Western Ky Univ Bowling Green KY 42101

**TOMAN, KAREL,** crystallography, for more information see previous edition

**TOMAN, KURT,** IONOSPHERIC PHYSICS. *Current Pos:* PHYSICIST, IONOSPHERIC PROPAGATION, ROME AIR DEVELOP CTR, 76- *Personal Data:* b Vienna, Austria, Aug 11, 21; US citizen; m 50, 58, Ludmilo V Malyshevsky; c Kathy, Nicholas & Marina. *Educ:* Vienna Tech Univ, MS, 49; Univ Ill, Urbana, PhD(elec eng), 52. *Prof Exp:* Lab engr, Lecher Inst, Reichenau, Austria, 43-44 & Ctr Tube Res, Tanvald, Czech, 44-45; asst electronics, Univ Ill, Urbana, 49-52, res assoc, 52; res fel, Harvard Univ, 52-55; physicist, Air Force Cambridge Res Lab, 55-63, supvry res physicist & br chief ionospheric radio physics, 63-73, sr scientist, 73-76. *Concurrent Pos:* Mem nat comn G, Int Union Radio Sci, 61-; chmn, Inst Elec & Electronics Engrs Wave Propagation Stands Comt, 72-83; US mem working group, Int Electrotech Comn, 79- *Mem:* Inst Elec & Electronics Engrs; Am Geophys Union; Sigma Xi; Antenna & Propagation Soc. *Res:* Dynamics of the ionosphere; radio wave propagation; spectral analysis of internal ionospheric gravity waves; high-frequency ionospheric ducting; group and phase path studies; ionospheric Doppler analysis; method of determining ionospheric reflection height; theoretical and experimental studies of high frequency ducted propagation; propagation study for a tropospheric transhorizon radar RADC-TR-81-166; experimental radar system auroral clutter statistics RADC-TR-84-157; Christian Doppler and the Doppler effect. *Mailing Add:* 85 Tobey Rd Belmont MA 02178

**TOMANA, MILAN,** CLINICAL IMMUNOLOGY. *Current Pos:* ASSOC PROF BIOCHEM, DEPT CLIN IMMUNOL & RHEUMATOLOGY, UNIV ALA, 68- *Personal Data:* b June 7, 32; c 2. *Educ:* Charles Univ Prague, PhD(biochem), 68. *Mem:* Am Asn Immunologists; Soc Complex Carbohydrates. *Res:* Immunoglobulin receptors on cells; glycosylation of immunoglobulins in various diseases; biological role of glycosyltransferases. *Mailing Add:* Dept Med Univ Ala Birmingham CH 19 Birmingham AL 35294-2041. *Fax:* 205-934-3894

**TOMANEK, GERALD WAYNE,** BOTANY. *Current Pos:* RETIRED. *Personal Data:* b Collyer, Kans, Sept 16, 21; m 45; c 3. *Educ:* Ft Hays State Univ, AB, 42, MS, 47; Univ Nebr, PhD, 51. *Prof Exp:* From asst prof to prof biol, Ft Hays State Univ, 47-87, chmn, Div Natural Sci & Math, 56-87, actg pres univ, 75-76, pres univ, 76-87. *Concurrent Pos:* Consult, Int Coop Admin Arg, 61. *Res:* Grassland ecology. *Mailing Add:* 1136 E Butterfield Pl Olathe KS 66062

**TOMANEK, ROBERT J,** CORONARY VESSELS, GROWTH FACTORS. *Current Pos:* postdoctoral fel, Univ Iowa, 69-71, asst prof, 72-76, assoc prof, 76-82, PROF, DEPT ANAT & CELL BIOL, UNIV IOWA, 82- *Personal Data:* b Omaha, Nebr, Apr 5, 37; m 61, Rita Svoboda; c Lisa R. (Kathe), Paul J., & Ann (Chalkley). *Educ:* Univ Omaha, BS, 59; Univ Iowa, PhD(anat), 67. *Prof Exp:* Asst prof, Simon Fraser Univ, 67-69. *Concurrent Pos:* Prin investr, NIH, 76-; mem, Prog Comt, Am Asn Anatomists, 97- *Mem:* Am Asn Anatomists; Am Soc Cell Biol; fel Am Physiol Soc; fel Am Heart Asn; Microcirculatory Soc. *Res:* Coronary vessels and circulation: vessel formation and regulation by growth factors and remodeling during development and during pathological states. *Mailing Add:* Dept Anat & Cell Biol Univ Iowa Iowa City IA 52242. *Fax:* 319-335-7198; *E-Mail:* robert-tomanek@uiowa.edu

**TOMAR, RUSSELL H,** IMMUNOLOGY, LABORATORY MEDICINE. *Current Pos:* assoc prof path, 76-79, ASST PROF MED, HEALTH SCI CTR, STATE UNIV NY, SYRACUSE, 71-, DIR, IMMUNOPATH LAB, 74-, PROF PATH, 79-; PROF PATH & LAB MED, UNIV WIS-MADISON, 88- *Personal Data:* b Philadelphia, Pa, Oct 19, 37; m 65, Karen Kent; c Elizabeth & David. *Educ:* George Washington Univ, BS, 59, MD, 63. *Prof Exp:* Resident, Barnes Hosp, Wash Univ, 63-65; surgeon, NIH, USPHS, 65-67; fel clin immunol, Univ Pa, 67-70, assoc, 70-71. *Concurrent Pos:* Mem immunopath test comt, Am Bd Path, 79-83; dir, AIDS Taskforce of Cent NY, 86-88; vis prof, Cleveland Clin, 88. *Mem:* Am Asn Immunol; Am Acad Allergy; Am Soc Clin Path; Clin Immunol Soc; Col Am Path. *Res:* Cellular immunity; immunopathogenesis of human immunodeficiency virus infection; immunodeficiency diseases. *Mailing Add:* Div Lab Med Univ Wis Hosp & Clin B4-251 CSC 600 Highland Ave Madison WI 53792-2472. *Fax:* 608-263-1568

**TOMARELLI, RUDOLPH MICHAEL,** biochemistry, nutrition, for more information see previous edition

**TOMAS, FRANCISCO,** SCIENTIFIC SYSTEMS ANALYST. *Current Pos:* RETIRED. *Personal Data:* b Montreal, Que, Dec 21, 30; m 81, Ida Parent; c Joanne & Eleanora. *Educ:* Sir George Williams Univ, BSc, 56. *Prof Exp:* Cur, Physics Lab, Sir George Williams Univ, 56-65, dir, 65-73; planning officer, Concordia Univ, 73-86, sci syst analyst, 86-95, dir, Physics Lab, 90-95. *Concurrent Pos:* Consult, Int Youth Sci Week, Expo 67, 66-67. *Mem:* Can Asn Physicists; Can Info Processing Soc. *Res:* Laboratory instruction and administration; programming; computerization of physics laboratory student testing; physics laboratory student testing; analytical chemistry database; instrumentation calculation aids; budget control; typesetting and telidon; laboratory reservation. *Mailing Add:* 4210 Chambli Apt 204 Montreal PQ H1S 3J7 Can. *Fax:* 514-848-2828; *E-Mail:* tomas.@alcor.concordia.ca

**TOMASCH, WALTER J,** EXPERIMENTAL SOLID STATE PHYSICS. *Current Pos:* PROF PHYSICS, UNIV NOTRE DAME, 68- *Personal Data:* b Cleveland, Ohio, July 26, 30; m 55; c 2. *Educ:* Case Western Res Univ, BS, 52, PhD(physics), 58; Rensselaer Polytech Inst, MS, 55. *Prof Exp:* Sr physicist, Atomics Int Div, Rockwell Corp, 58-68. *Mem:* Fel Am Phys Soc. *Res:* High-temperature superconductivity; physics of metals and alloys. *Mailing Add:* Dept Physics Univ Notre Dame Notre Dame IN 46556. *Fax:* 219-631-5952

**TOMASCHKE, HARRY E,** OPTICS. *Current Pos:* ASSOC PROF PHYSICS, GREENVILLE COL, 64- *Personal Data:* b Kendall, NY, Apr 25, 29; m 53; c 4. *Educ:* Mich State Univ, BS, 56; Univ Ill, MS, 58, PhD(physics), 64. *Prof Exp:* Res assoc, Coord Sci Lab, Univ Ill, Urbana, 58-64. *Mem:* Am Asn Physics Teachers; Optical Soc Am; Sigma Xi. *Res:* Electrical breakdown in vacuum; absorption of gases under ultrahigh vacuum conditions; thin film optics. *Mailing Add:* 2329 Lake Rd Ransomville NY 14131

**TOMASEK, JAMES J,** ANATOMY. *Current Pos:* ASSOC PROF ANAT, UNIV OKLA HEALTH SCI CTR, 88- *Personal Data:* b Peoria, Ill, Nov 15, 53. *Educ:* Univ Ill, BS, 80; State Univ NY, PhD(biol), 85. *Prof Exp:* Asst prof anat, New York Med Col, 85-88. *Mem:* Am Develop Biol Soc; Am Soc Cell Biol; Am Asn Anatomists. *Res:* Anatomy. *Mailing Add:* Dept Anat Sci Univ Okla Health Sci Ctr PO Box 26901 Oklahoma City OK 73190-0001

**TOMASETTA, LOUIS RALPH,** ELECTRICAL ENGINEERING, SEMICONDUCTORS. *Current Pos:* PRES & CHIEF EXEC OFFICER, VITESSE-SEMICONDUCTOR CORP, 84- *Personal Data:* b New York, NY, Nov 1, 48; m 73. *Educ:* Mass Inst Technol, BS & MS, 71, ScD(elec eng), 74. *Prof Exp:* Mem tech staff laser syst, Lincoln Lab, Mass Inst Technol, 74-77; group leader optical electronics, Rockwell Int, 77-84. *Mem:* Inst Elec & Electronics Engrs; Sigma Xi. *Res:* Semiconductor devices; fiber optics; optical communication laser; laser systems; optics. *Mailing Add:* Vitesse-Semiconductor Corp 741 Calle Plano Camarillo CA 93010

**TOMASHEFSKI, JOSEPH FRANCIS,** PHYSIOLOGY. *Current Pos:* INTERIM CHAIRPERSON, CLEVELAND METROHEALTH MED CTR. *Personal Data:* b Plymouth, Pa, Dec 30, 22; m 49; c 3. *Educ:* Hahnemann Med Col, MD, 47; Am Bd Prev Med, dipl & cert aerospace med. *Prof Exp:* Asst biol, Temple Univ, 41-43; intern, Wilkes-Barre Gen Hosp, Pa, 47-48, resident med, 48-49; resident pulmonary dis, Jefferson Med Col & Hosp, 49-51; asst prof med & physiol, Col Med, Ohio State Univ, 53-66, assoc prof prev med & physiol, 66-72; dir, Pulmonary Function Lab & staff physician, Dept Pulmonary Dis, Cleveland Clin, 71-, head dept, 73- *Concurrent Pos:* Dir res, Ohio Tuberc Hosp, 53-67; med res consult, Battelle Mem Inst, 59-67, med dir & med res adv, 67-77; dir, Pulmonary Function Labs, Univ Hosps, Ohio State Univ, 67; consult, USAF & Vet Admin; clin prof prev med, Col Med, Ohio State Univ, 72- *Mem:* Am Physiol Soc; Am Thoracic Soc; fel Am Col Chest Physicians; AMA; Aerospace Med Asn. *Res:* Pulmonary diseases; respiratory physiology; aviation medicine; pulmonary function testing; environmental medicine. *Mailing Add:* Dept Path Cleveland Metrohealth Med Ctr Cleveland OH 44109

**TOMASHEFSKY, PHILIP,** EXPERIMENTAL PATHOLOGY. *Current Pos:* RETIRED. *Personal Data:* b Brooklyn, NY, May 4, 24; m 48, Rhoda Tanenbaum; c Steven & Michael. *Educ:* City Col New York, BS, 46, MS, 51; NY Univ, MS, 63, PhD(biol), 69. *Prof Exp:* Chemist, Funk Found, 48-65 & US Vitamin Corp, 65; biochemist, Dept Urol, Col Physicians & Surgeons, Columbia Univ, 65-69, assoc, 69-71, asst prof path, 71-76, asst prof clin path, 76-89. *Mem:* Fel AAAS; NY Acad Sci; Sigma Xi; Am Inst Ultrasound Med. *Res:* Neoplastic and hyperplastic growth of the kidney and prostate and other urological tissues; chemotherapy and thermotherapy; metastasis. *Mailing Add:* 330 S Middletown Rd Pearl River NY 10965

**TOMASI, GORDON ERNEST,** BIOCHEMISTRY, ORGANIC CHEMISTRY. *Current Pos:* From asst prof to assoc prof, 62-70, PROF CHEM, UNIV NORTHERN COLO, 70-, CHMN, DEPT CHEM, 81- *Personal Data:* b Denver, Colo, Dec 16, 30; m 54; c 3. *Educ:* Colo State Col, BA, 57, MA, 58; Univ Louisville, PhD(biochem), 63. *Mem:* Sigma Xi. *Res:* Bioenergetics; nutritional biochemistry; mechanisms of organic reaction and enzyme catalyzed reactions. *Mailing Add:* Dept Biochem Univ Northern Colo Greeley CO 80639-0001

**TOMASI, THOMAS B, JR,** IMMUNOLOGY, MOLECULAR BIOLOGY. *Current Pos:* INST DIR, ROSWELL PARK CANCER INST, 85- *Personal Data:* b Barre, Vt, May 24, 27; m 48; c 3. *Educ:* Dartmouth Col, AB, 50; Univ Vt, MD, 54; Rockefeller Univ, PhD, 65. *Honors & Awards:* Woodbury Prize, Univ Vt, 54. *Prof Exp:* Intern & resident internal med, Columbia Presby Hosp, 54-57, chief resident, 57-58; assoc prof med & chmn, Div Exp Med, Col Med, Univ Vt, Burlington, 60-65; Buswell prof, div immunol & rheumatic dis & res prof microbiol, State Univ NY, Buffalo, 65-73; prof med & chmn, Dept Immunol, Mayo Med Sch, Rochester, Minn, 73-81, William H Donner prof immunol, 75-81; distinguished univ prof cell biol, chmn dept & dir, Cancer Ctr & Special Diag Lab, Univ NMex, 81-85. *Concurrent Pos:* Sr investr, Arthritis & Rheumatism Found, 60-65; dir, NIH training grant arthritis & metab dis; chief med, DeGoesbriand Hosp, 61-65; mem, Gen Med Study Sect, NIH; consult, Los Alamos Nat Lab, 82-; James Melville Cramer fel award, Dartmouth Col. *Mem:* Arthritis & Rheumatism Asn; Asn Am Physicians; Am Asn Immunologists; Am Fedn Clin Res; Am Soc Clin Invest; Am Asn Cancer Res; Am Soc Cell Biol. *Res:* Internal medicine; immunological diseases; immunochemistry. *Mailing Add:* Roswell Park Cancer Inst Elm & Carlton Sts Buffalo NY 14263-0001

**TOMASI, THOMAS EDWARD,** PHYSIOLOGICAL ECOLOGY, ANIMAL ENERGETICS. *Current Pos:* asst prof, 86-92, ASSOC PROF ANIMAL PHYSIOL, DEPT BIOL, SOUTHWEST MO STATE UNIV, 92- *Personal Data:* b San Diego, Calif, Aug 10, 55; m 78, Susan J Pelletier; c Danielle & Nathan. *Educ:* Univ RI, BS, 76, MS, 78; Univ Utah, PhD(biol), 84. *Prof Exp:* Vis lectr animal physiol, Univ Calif, Davis, 84-86. *Concurrent Pos:* Prin investr, NIH, 88-90 & 91-94; chair, Educ & Grad Student Comt, Am Soc Mammalogists, 88-90, Pub Educ Comt, 92- *Mem:* Am Soc Mammalogists; Soc Integrative & Comp Biol; Sigma Xi; Int Soc Cryptozool. *Res:* Interspecific and intraspecific comparative energetics; comparative thyroid function of mammals and its relationship to metabolic rate. *Mailing Add:* Dept Biol Southwest Mo State Univ Springfield MO 65804-0095. *Fax:* 417-836-6934

**TOMASOVIC, STEPHEN PETER,** RADIATION BIOLOGY, CELL BIOLOGY. *Current Pos:* from asst prof to assoc prof, MD Anderson Cancer Ctr, 80-92, chief, Sect Biol, 88-95, dep chair, 95, PROF, DEPT TUMOR BIOL, M D ANDERSON CANCER CTR, 92-, CHMN AD INTERIM, 95- *Personal Data:* b Bend, Ore, Jan 5, 47; m 70, Barbara J Davis. *Educ:* Ore State Univ, BS, 69, MS, 73; Colo State Univ, PhD(radiation biol), 77. *Prof Exp:* Fel, Dept Radiation Biol, Colo State Univ, 77; fel radiation biol, Dept Radiol, Med Ctr, Univ Utah, 78-79, asst prof, 78-80. *Concurrent Pos:* Mem grad fac, Univ Tex Health Sci Ctr, Houston, 81-; mem, NAm Hyperthermia Group, 86-, Coun Biol & Chem, 90-92; dir, Interdisciplinary Studies Cancer Biol, 87-90; assoc ed, Int J Radiation Oncol Biol Phys, 89-; ed, Cancer Bull, 91-95. *Mem:* AAAS; Radiation Res Soc; Am Asn Cancer Res; Am Soc Cell Biol; Am Soc Therapeut Radiol & Oncol; NAm Hyperthermia Soc. *Res:* Molecular biology; experimental combined modality therapy; biology of the cell cycle; tumor biology; experimental tumor metastasis; hyperthermic biology; heat shock proteins. *Mailing Add:* Dept Tumor Biol Box 108 M D Anderson Ctr 1515 Holcombe Blvd Houston TX 77030. *Fax:* 713-794-0209; *E-Mail:* stomas@tumorb01.mda.uth.tmc.edu

**TOMASZ, ALEXANDER,** BIOCHEMISTRY, CELL BIOLOGY. *Current Pos:* Am Cancer Soc fel & guest investr genetics, 61-63, from asst prof to assoc prof genetics & biochem, 63-77, PROF MICROBIOL & CHMN DEPT, ROCKEFELLER UNIV, 77- *Personal Data:* b Budapest, Hungary, Dec 23, 30; US citizen; m 56; c 1. *Educ:* Pazmany Peter Univ, Budapest, dipl, 53; Columbia Univ, PhD(biochem), 61. *Prof Exp:* Res assoc cytochem, Inst Genetics, Hungarian Nat Acad, 53-56. *Mem:* AAAS; Am Soc Microbiol; Am Soc Cell Biol; Harvey Soc. *Res:* Biosynthesis and functioning of cell surface structures; cell to cell interactions; control of cell division; molecular genetics. *Mailing Add:* Lab Microbiol Rockefeller Univ 1230 York Ave New York NY 10021

**TOMASZ, MARIA,** MEDICINAL CHEMISTRY, MOLECULAR PHARMACOLOGY. *Current Pos:* from asst prof to assoc prof, 66-78, PROF CHEM, HUNTER COL, CITY UNIV NY, 79- *Personal Data:* b Szeged, Hungary, Oct 18, 32; US citizen; m 88, Richard Marshall; c Martin A & Julia S. *Educ:* Univ Eotvos Lorand, Budapest, dipl chem, 56; Columbia Univ, MA, 59, PhD(chem), 62. *Honors & Awards:* Merit Award, Nat Cancer Inst, 88. *Prof Exp:* Res assoc, Rockefeller Inst, 61-62; res assoc biochem, NY Univ, 62-64, instr, 64-66. *Concurrent Pos:* Prin investr, NIH grants, 69-; mem, NIH Study Sect, 90-94. *Mem:* NY Acad Sci; Fedn Am Soc Exp Biol; Am Chem Soc; Am Asn Cancer Res; Biophys Soc; AAAS. *Res:* Chemistry of nucleic acids; chemical basis of action of antitumor agents and antibiotics; mode of action of cancer chemotherapeutic agents. *Mailing Add:* Dept Chem Hunter Col New York NY 10021-5024

**TOMAZIC, VESNA J,** IMMUNOLOGY. *Current Pos:* RES IMMUNOLOGIST, FOOD & DRUG ADMIN, 90- *Personal Data:* b Zagrdeb, India, Apr 18, 41. *Educ:* Univ Zagreb Sch Med, India, BA, 64, MS, 67, PhD, 70. *Prof Exp:* Asst prof immunol, Univ Md, 80-90. *Mem:* Am Asn Immunol. *Mailing Add:* Div Life Sci Food & Drug Admin 12709 Twinbrook Pkwy HFZ Rockville MD 20857-0001

**TOMBACK, DIANA FRANCINE,** EVOLUTIONARY ECOLOGY, PLANT-ANIMAL MUTUALISMS. *Current Pos:* asst prof biol, 81-86, actg dir, Environ Sci Grad Prog, 90- 91, ASSOC PROF, DEPT BIOL, UNIV COLO, DENVER, 86- *Personal Data:* b Los Angeles, Calif, June 9, 49; m 86. *Educ:* Univ Calif, Los Angeles, BA, 70, MA, 72; Univ Calif, Santa Barbara, PhD(biol sci), 77. *Prof Exp:* Teaching asst biol sci, Univ Calif, Santa Barbara, 72-73, teaching assoc, 73-76; instr biol, Dept Zool, Brigham Young Univ, 77; vis assoc prof zool, Pomona Col, 77-78; lectr biol, Univ Calif, Riverside, 78-79; postdoc fel zool, Colo State Univ, 79-81. *Mem:* Ecol Soc Am; Am Ornith Union; Soc Study Evolution; Am Soc Naturalists; AAAS. *Res:* Ecological relationship between Nucifraga columbiana and pines; avian foraging behavior. *Mailing Add:* Univ Colo PO Box 173364 Univ Colo PO Box 173364 Denver CO 80217-3364

**TOMBALAKIAN, ARTIN S,** CHEMICAL ENGINEERING, CHEMISTRY. *Current Pos:* Prof chem & chmn, Dept Chem & Eng, Laurentian Univ, 58-70, prof, 66-95, dir, 68-79, EMER PROF CHEM & CHEM ENG, LAURENTIAN UNIV, 95- *Personal Data:* b Jerusalem, Palestine, Nov 4, 29; Can citizen; m 59, Mary K Pandjacdjian; c Lisa M, Nora J & Celia M. *Educ:* Am Univ Beirut, BA, 52; Univ Toronto, MASc, 54, PhD(chem eng), 58. *Mem:* Fel Chem Inst Can. *Res:* Ion-exchange; diffusion; mass transfer; electrochemistry; sorption of crude oil derivatives on Arctic terrain; treatment of industrial waste waters; recovery of metals by hydrometallurgical techniques. *Mailing Add:* Sch Eng Laurentian Univ Sudbury ON P3E 2C6 Can

**TOMBAUGH, CLYDE W(ILLIAM),** ASTRONOMY. *Current Pos:* RETIRED. *Personal Data:* b Streator, Ill, Feb 4, 06; wid; c Annette & Alden. *Educ:* Kans Univ, AB, 36, MA, 39. *Hon Degrees:* DSc, Ariz State Col, 60. *Honors & Awards:* Jackson-Gwilt Medal, Royal Astron Soc, 31; Distinguished Serv Citation, Univ Kans, 66; Rittenhouse Award, 90. *Prof Exp:* Asst observer, Lowell Observ, 29-38, asst astronr, 38-43; instr physics & navigation, Ariz State Col, 43-45; vis asst prof astron, Univ Calif, Los

Angeles, 45-46; astronr, Ballistics Res Lab, White Sands Missile Range, 46-55, chief optical measurements sect, 47-51; astronr, Phys Sci Lab, NMex State Univ, 55-59, res ctr, 59-70, from assoc prof to emer prof earth sci & astron, 61-97. *Concurrent Pos:* Consult, Off Ord Res Proj, Small Earth Satellites, 53-59; mem, planetary atmospheres study group, Space Sci Bd, Nat Acad Sci, 60-61; prin investr, NASA grant; mem comn planets & satellites, Int Astron Union; lectr, discovery of Pluto, 86-90. *Mem:* Am Astron Soc; Meteoritical Soc; fel Am Inst Aeronaut & Astronaut; Asn Lunar & Planetary Observers; Astron Soc Pac; Int Astron Union. *Res:* Trans-Neptunian planet search; discovered ninth planet, Pluto; planetary observations; optics applied to rocket ballistics; hypothetical geology of Mars; interpretation of Martian features. *Mailing Add:* PO Box 306 Mesilla Park NM 88047

**TOMBAUGH, LARRY WILLIAM,** FOREST ECONOMICS. *Current Pos:* DEAN & PROF, COL FOREST RESOURCES, NC STATE UNIV, 89- *Personal Data:* b Erie, Pa, Jan 28, 39; m 60, Nancy J Graeber; c Loren D & Mark A. *Educ:* Pa State Univ, BS, 60; Colo State Univ, MS, 63; Univ Mich, PhD(resource econ), 68. *Prof Exp:* Economist, NCent Forest Exp Sta, 66-69; prin economist, Southeastern Forest Exp Sta, 69-71; prog mgr, NSF, 71-75, dir div advan environ res & technol, 75-76, dep asst dir anal & planning, 76-78; prof & chmn, Dept Forestry, Mich State Univ, 78-89. *Concurrent Pos:* Lectr resource econ, Univ Mich, 66-69. *Mem:* Fel AAAS; Sigma Xi; fel Soc Am Foresters. *Res:* Economics of the forest products industry; relationship between research & development and technological change. *Mailing Add:* Col Forest Resources 2028 Biltmore Hall PO Box 80001 Raleigh NC 27695-8001

**TOMBER, MARVIN L,** ALGEBRA. *Current Pos:* from asst prof to assoc prof, 55-65, PROF MATH, MICH STATE UNIV, 65- *Personal Data:* b South Bend, Ind, Aug 4, 25; m 48; c 2. *Educ:* Univ Notre Dame, BS, 46; Univ Pa, PhD(math), 52. *Prof Exp:* Instr math, Amherst Col, 52-55. *Mem:* Am Math Soc; Math Asn Am. *Res:* Non-associative algebras. *Mailing Add:* 2370 Huron Hill Dr Okemos MI 48864-2082

**TOMBES, AVERETT S,** INVERTEBRATE PHYSIOLOGY. *Current Pos:* VPRES RES & ECON DEVELOP, NMEX STATE UNIV, 88- *Personal Data:* b Easton, Md, Sept 13, 32; m 57, Jane Gill; c Thomas, Robert, Jonathan & Susan. *Educ:* Univ Richmond, BA, 54; Va Polytech Inst, MS, 56; Rutgers Univ, PhD, 61. *Prof Exp:* From asst prof to prof biol, Clemson Univ, 61-77, chmn zool, 68-71; prof biol, George Mason Univ, 77-81, dean, Grad Sch & Univ Res, 81-86; vpres res & grad studies, Wichita State Univ, 86-88. *Concurrent Pos:* Prin investr, NSF, NIH, USDA, Dept Defense, Environ Protection Agency & Water Resources Res Inst, 61-83; post doctoral fel, NIH, 65-66; NSF consult, Indian Coun Educ, 68-69; res fel, Nat Ctr Resource Recovery, 71-72; lectr, Univ de Lille, France, 71-72; Am Coun Educ fel, 80-81; mem, Pub Affairs Comt, Am Soc Cell Biol, 83-86; fel, AAAS, 85. *Mem:* Am Soc Cell Biol; Soc Res Adminr; Am Soc Zoologists; Sigma Xi; Am Physiol Soc; Entom Soc Am; fel AAAS. *Res:* Invertebrate physiology principally hormonal influences on growth, reproduction and reduced metabolism. *Mailing Add:* NMex State Univ Box 30001 Dept 3RED Las Cruces NM 88003-0001. *Fax:* 505-646-6530; *E-Mail:* atombes@nmsu.edu

**TOMBOULIAN, PAUL,** TOXIC SUBSTANCE MANAGEMENT. *Current Pos:* from asst prof to assoc prof, 59-67, PROF CHEM, OAKLAND UNIV, 67-, CHMN DEPT, 62-, COORDR ENVIRON STUDIES, 70-, DIR ENVIRON HEALTH, 75- *Personal Data:* b Rochester, NY, Oct 19, 34; m 57; c 3. *Educ:* Cornell Univ, AB, 53; Univ Ill, PhD(org chem), 56. *Prof Exp:* Res fel chem, Univ Minn, 56-59, instr, 57-58. *Mem:* Am Chem Soc. *Res:* Water resources; instrumental analysis; water quality studies. *Mailing Add:* Dept Chem Oakland Univ Rochester MI 48309

**TOMBRELLO, THOMAS ANTHONY, JR,** SURFACE SCIENCE, PLANETARY SCIENCE. *Current Pos:* res fel, 64-65, from asst prof to assoc prof, 65-71, PROF PHYSICS, CALIF INST TECHNOL, 71-, WILLIAM R KENAN JR PROF, 97- *Personal Data:* b Austin, Tex, Sept 20, 36; m 77, Stephanie Merton. *Educ:* Rice Univ, BA, 58, MA, 60, PhD(physics), 61. *Prof Exp:* Res fel physics, Calif Inst Technol, 61-63; from instr to asst prof, Yale Univ, 63-64. *Concurrent Pos:* NSF fel, 61-62; Alfred P Sloan Found fel, 71-73; consult, Schlumberger; assoc ed, Nuclear Physics, 72-89; Nuclear Sci Appl, 79- & Radiation Effect, 85-88; distinguished vis prof, Univ Calif, Davis, 84; Alexander von Humboldt Award, 84-85; vpres & dir res, Schlumberger-Doll Res, 87-89. *Mem:* Fel Am Phys Soc; Mats Res Soc; AAAS. *Res:* Surface physics; applications of nuclear physics; space physics. *Mailing Add:* Calif Inst Technol 200-36 Pasadena CA 91125. *Fax:* 626-683-9060; *E-Mail:* tat@cco.caltech.edu

**TOMCUFCIK, ANDREW STEPHEN,** ORGANIC CHEMISTRY. *Current Pos:* res chemist, Am Cyanamid Co, 50-53, res chemist, Lederle Labs, 53-55, dept head, 74-76, GROUP LEADER, LEDERLE LABS, AM CYANAMID CO, 55- *Personal Data:* b Czech, Oct 26, 21; nat US; m 54; c 5. *Educ:* Fenn Col, BS, 43; Western Res Univ, MS, 48; Yale Univ, PhD(org chem), 51. *Prof Exp:* Res chemist uranium refining, Mallinckrodt Chem Works, 46; instr chem, Fenn Col, 46-47; res chemist uranium refining, Mallinckrodt Chem Works, 49. *Mem:* AAAS; Am Chem Soc; NY Acad Sci; Royal Soc Chem; Sigma Xi. *Res:* Chemotherapy of cancer; parasitic infections; heterocyclic chemistry; cardiovascular-renal diseases. *Mailing Add:* 48 Dearborn Dr Old Tappan NJ 07675-7321

**TOMEI, L DAVID,** CELLULAR PHYSIOLOGY, CELL CYCLE REGULATION. *Current Pos:* VPRES, LXR BIOTECHNOL, RICHMOND, CALIF, 92- *Personal Data:* b Williamsport, Pa, Apr 27, 45; m 77; c 5. *Educ:* Canisius Col, BS, 68, MS, 70; State Univ NY, Buffalo, PhD(biochem & pharmacol), 74. *Prof Exp:* Chemist, Plum Island Animal Dis Ctr, USDA, 73-75; res scientist, Roswell Park Mem Inst, 75-81; res scientist, Ohio State Univ, 81-92, dir, Biomed Instrumentation Develop Prog, 84-92, dir, Chemosensitivity Testing Lab Comprehensive Cancer Ctr, 84-92. *Concurrent Pos:* Pres, Optical Anal Inc, Scanning Laser Imaging Develop. *Mem:* Am Asn Cancer Res; Cell Kinetics Soc. *Res:* In vitro cell growth and function: cell cycle regulation during G1, and the perturbation of regulation by drugs believed to be tumor promoters; the role of plant derived tumor promoting agents in malignant transformation of human cells in vitro by viruses; the function of tumor promoters in modulation of cellular gene directed death related to trauma, irradiation and psychological stress in humans; design and construct new instrumentation based on computer assisted scanning laser imaging technology of which Dr Tomei is primary inventor. *Mailing Add:* 4385 Hayden Falls Dr Columbus OH 43221

**TOMEK, WILLIAM GOODRICH,** AGRICULTURAL ECONOMICS. *Current Pos:* From asst prof to assoc prof, Cornell Univ, 61-70, NSF fel, 65, chmn, Dept Agr Econs, 88-93, PROF AGR ECONS, CORNELL UNIV, 70- *Personal Data:* b Table Rock, Nebr, Sept 20, 32. *Educ:* Univ Nebr, BS, 56, MA, 57; Univ Minn, PhD, 61. *Concurrent Pos:* Vis fel, Stanford Univ, 68-69, Univ New Eng, Australia, 88; ed, Am J Agr Econs, 75-77; vis economist, USDA, 78-79; co-ed, Rev Futures Markets, 93- *Mem:* Fel Am Agr Econs Asn (pres, 85-86); Am Econ Asn; Econometric Soc. *Res:* Agricultural economics; agricultural product markets and prices, including markets for futures and options contracts. *Mailing Add:* Cornell Univ Warren Hall Ithaca NY 14853-7801. *Fax:* 607-255-9984

**TOMEO-DYMKOWSKI, ALINE CLAIRE,** CARDIOVASCULAR PHYSIOLOGY. *Current Pos:* CLIN RES SCIENTIST, KENNETH L JORDAN RES CTR, 91- *Personal Data:* b Montclair, NJ, Sept 25, 65; m 93, Joseph F. *Educ:* Montclair State Col, BS, 87; Univ Med & Dent NJ, PhD(physiol), 91. *Honors & Awards:* Proctor & Gamble Prof Opportunity Award, Am Physiol Soc, 91. *Mem:* Am Heart Asn; Am Physiol Soc; Microcirculatory Soc. *Res:* Cardiovascular disease prevention via the use of antioxidants; evaluating the efficacy of vitamin E as a treatment modality for causing carotid artery disease regression in stroke patients. *Mailing Add:* Kenneth L Jordan Cardiac Res Ctr 48 Plymouth St Montclair NJ 07042

**TOMER, KENNETH BEAMER,** MASS SPECTROMETRY, ORGANIC CHEMISTRY. *Current Pos:* RES SCIENTIST, NAT INST ENVIRON HEALTH SCI, 86- *Personal Data:* b New Kensington, Pa, Mar 13, 44; m 82, Carol Moats; c 3. *Educ:* Ohio State Univ, BS, 66; Univ Colo, PhD(chem), 70. *Prof Exp:* Fel photochem, H C Orsted Inst, Univ Copenhagen, 70-71; fel mass spectrometry, Dept Chem, Stanford Univ, 71-73; asst prof chem, Brooklyn Col, 73-75; asst prof pediat, Med Sch, Univ Pa, 75-77; mem staff, Chem & Life Sci Div, Res Triangle Inst, 77-81; asst dir, Midwest Ctr Mass Spectrometry, Univ Nebr, Lincoln, 81-84, assoc dir & assoc res prof, 84-86. *Mem:* Am Chem Soc; Am Soc Mass Spectrometry. *Res:* Development and application of mass spectrometric techniques to structural studies of biomolecules, including epitope mapping of HIV-related proteins and structures of proetin radical adducts and to quantification by mass spectrometry. *Mailing Add:* Nat Inst Environ Health Sci PO Box 12233 Research Triangle Park NC 27709. *Fax:* 919-541-7880; *E-Mail:* tomer@niehs.nih.gov

**TOMERA, JOHN F,** SIGNAL TRANSDUCTION, SHOCK & TRAUMA. *Current Pos:* PRIN EXEC, INT CONSULT & PHARMACOLOGIST, SHRINERS BURNS INST, 93- *Personal Data:* b Johnstown, Pa, May 7, 52; m 77, Mona J Elensky. *Educ:* Univ Pittsburgh, BS, 74; Temple Univ Sch Med, PhD(pharmacol), 78. *Prof Exp:* Postdoc fel, Dept Nutrit, Harvard Sch Pub Health, 78-80; postdoc assoc, Dept Nutrit & Food Sci, Mass Inst Technol, 80-83; asst neurophysiol neurosurg, Neurosurg Serv Mass Gen Hosp, 83-85; from instr to asst prof anesthesiol, Harvard Med Sch, Boston, Mass, 85-93. *Concurrent Pos:* Instr anesthesiol, Harvard Med Sch, 85-87; asst pharmacologist anesthesia, Anesthesia Serv, Mass Gen Hosp & Shriners Burns Inst, 85-93; independent consult, Fisons Corp, 86-87; Upjohn young investr travel award, 88; Am Heart travel award, 90; res award, Shriners Hosp, 91-; invited lectr, Temple Univ Sch Med, 76-78, Northeastern Univ, 78-80, Mass Inst Technol, 80-82, Soc Toxicol, 85, Beth Israel Hosp, 86, Mass Gen Hosp, Shriners Burns Inst, 86-89 & 91-93. *Mem:* Am Burn Asn; Am Physiol Soc; Shock Soc; Shriners Burns Inst. *Res:* The effects of burn trauma on signal transduction, secondary messengers and end-organ effects; author of 85 publications. *Mailing Add:* 354 South St Medfield MA 02052

**TOMES, DWIGHT TRAVIS,** PLANT GENETICS, PLANT TISSUE CULTURE. *Current Pos:* PIONEER HI-BRED INT, INC, JOHNSTON, IOWA, 82- *Personal Data:* b Bowling Green, Ky, Sept 21, 46; m 66, 86, Nancy J; c 4. *Educ:* Western Ky Univ, BS, 68; Univ Ky, PhD(crop sci), 75. *Prof Exp:* Asst prof crop sci, Univ Guelph, 75-80, assoc prof, 80-82. *Mem:* Am Soc Agron; Sigma Xi; Tissue Cult Asn. *Res:* Use of cell and molecular biology for plant improvement, particularly genetic transformation and DNA fingerprinting in vegetable crops; in vitro selection and selection of genetic transformants in maize and other crop species. *Mailing Add:* Biotechnol Res PO Box 1004 Johnston IA 50131-1004. *Fax:* 515-270-3444

**TOMETSKO, ANDREW M,** biochemistry, organic chemistry; deceased, see previous edition for last biography

**TOMEZSKO, EDWARD STEPHEN JOHN,** PHYSICAL CHEMISTRY. *Current Pos:* asst prof chem, Pa State Univ, 71-78, assoc dir, 81-82, dir, 81-84, assoc dean Acad Affairs, Common Wealth Educ Syst, 84-85, asst vpres & dir, Div Technol, 85-86, ASSOC PROF CHEM, PA STATE UNIV, DEL COUNTY CAMPUS, 78-, CAMPUS EXEC OFFICER, 86- *Personal Data:* b Philadelphia, Pa, Apr 9, 35; m 62, Jean L; c 4. *Educ:* Villanova Univ, BS, 57; Pa State Univ, MS, 61, PhD(phys chem), 62. *Prof Exp:* Resident res assoc phys chem, Nat Bur Stand, 62-64; sr res chemist, Arco Chem Co Div, Atlantic Richfield Co, 64-71. *Concurrent Pos:* Vis lectr, Johnson Res Found, Col Med Univ Pa, 79-80. *Mem:* Am Chem Soc; Catalysis Soc; Sigma Xi. *Res:* Thermodynamics; homogeneous and heterogeneous catalysis; inorganic and organic synthesis. *Mailing Add:* 4 Prince Eugene Lane Media PA 19063. *Fax:* 610-892-1357; *E-Mail:* esti@oas.psu.edu

**TOMIC, ERNST ALOIS,** SYNTHETIC INORGANIC CHEMISTRY, CERAMICS BY SOL-GEL. *Current Pos:* PRES, CHEM & CERAMICS CONSULT, INC, 90- *Personal Data:* b Vienna, Austria, Feb 1, 26; m 52; c 2. *Educ:* Univ Vienna, PhD, 56. *Prof Exp:* Asst inorg, geochem & anal chem, Univ Vienna, 55-57; res chemist, Explosives Dept, E I DuPont de Nemours & Co Inc, 58-70, sr res chemist, Polymer Intermediates Dept, 70-74, staff res chemist, Polymer Intermediates Dept, 74-78, res assoc, Petrochem Dept, Exp Sta, 78-85, sr pres assoc, Du Pont Chem, 85-90. *Mem:* Sigma Xi; Am Chem Soc; Am Ceramic Soc; Mat Res Soc; Am Electrochem Soc. *Res:* Ion exchange; coordination chemistry; radiochemistry; inorganic synthesis; inorganic cements; molten salts; electrochemistry; hydrometallurgy; solution-derived ceramics. *Mailing Add:* 1430 Emory Rd Wilmington DE 19803

**TOMICH, CHARLES EDWARD,** DENTISTRY, ORAL PATHOLOGY. *Current Pos:* Assoc prof, 69-78, PROF ORAL PATH, SCH DENT, IND UNIV, INDIANAPOLIS, 78-, DEPT CHMN, 85- *Personal Data:* b Gallup, NMex, Oct 23, 37; m 59; c 3. *Educ:* Loyola Univ, La, DDS, 61; Ind Univ, Indianapolis, MSD, 68; Am Bd Oral Path, dipl. *Concurrent Pos:* USPHS training grant, Sch Dent, Ind Univ, Indianapolis, 66-69; ed, Oral Surg, Oral Med & Oral Path, Oral Path Sect, 72-76. *Mem:* Fel Am Acad Oral Path; Sigma Xi. *Res:* In vivo hard tissue marking agents; salivary gland histochemistry; oral neoplasms. *Mailing Add:* 9202 N Meridian St Indianapolis IN 46260

**TOMICH, PROSPER QUENTIN,** VERTEBRATE ZOOLOGY, ANIMAL ECOLOGY. *Current Pos:* PVT CONSULT, 86- *Personal Data:* b Orange Vale, Calif, Oct 11, 20; m 46; c 5. *Educ:* Univ Calif, Berkeley, AB, 43, PhD(zool), 59. *Prof Exp:* Lab asst plague res, Hooper Found, Univ Calif, 43-44, res zoologist, Hastings Natural Hist Reservation, 47-52; assoc zool, Univ Calif, Davis, 56-59; animal ecologist, State Dept Health, Hawaii, 59-85. *Concurrent Pos:* Adv, Naval Med Res Unit, Egyptian Govt, 46-47; arbovirus res training grant, Pa State Univ, 66-67; mem, Island Ecosysts Proj, Int Biol Prog, Univ Hawaii, 69-75; chmn, Hawaii Natural Area Reserves Syst Comn, 76-84; pvt consult, 86- *Mem:* Fel AAAS; Ecol Soc Am; Am Soc Mammalogists; Wildlife Soc; Am Ornithologists Union; Marine Mammal Soc. *Res:* Rodents, fleas, and plague; field ecology of mule deer, ground squirrel, mongoose, and of Arctic birds and mammals; leptospirosis in populations of small mammals; history and adaptation of mammals in Hawaiian Islands; rehabilitation of depleted subtropical rain-forest ecosystems. *Mailing Add:* PO Box 675 Honokaa HI 96727-0675

**TOMIKEL, JOHN,** EARTH SCIENCE. *Current Pos:* ASST PROF, EDINBORO UNIV, 90- *Personal Data:* b Cuddy, Pa, Apr 30, 28; m 49, 68, Bonnie Henderson; c April & Matthew. *Educ:* Clarion State Col, BS, 51; Univ Pittsburgh, MLitt, 56, PhD(higher educ), 70; Syracuse Univ, MS, 62. *Prof Exp:* Sci teacher, Fairview High Sch, 51-63; asst prof earth sci, Edinboro State Col, 63-65; prof, Calif State Col, Pa, 65-82, emer prof geog & earth sci, 82- *Mem:* Nat Asn Geol Teachers; Nat Wildlife Fedn; Sierra Club-Wilderness Soc. *Res:* Earth science education; author of 22 books. *Mailing Add:* 19323 Elgin Rd Corry PA 16407

**TOMITA, JOSEPH TSUNEKI,** CANCER DIAGNOSTICS, TUMOR MARKERS RESEARCH. *Current Pos:* res immunologist tumor marker, Dept Exp Biol, Abbott Labs, 71-76, head, Cancer Res Lab, Diag Div, 77-81, mgr cancer/cell biol, 81-84, dir cancer/immunol, 84-93, DIR MOLECULAR ONCOL, DIAG DIV, ABBOTT LABS, 93- *Personal Data:* b Los Angeles, Calif, Mar 23, 38; m 63; c 2. *Educ:* Stanford Univ, BA, 59, PhD(physiol), 66. *Prof Exp:* Res asst biochem res, Dept Pediat, Stanford Med Ctr, 60-62, teaching asst immunophysiol, 62-66, actg instr, 66-67; Nat Mult Sclerosis Soc fel, Dept Biol, Univ Calif, San Diego, 68-69; Nat Cystic Fibrosis Found fel, 69-70, asst res biologist neuroimmunol, 70-71. *Concurrent Pos:* Guest lectr, Dept Biol, Northwestern Univ, 72-73; assoc mem, Northwestern Univ Cancer Ctr, 91- *Mem:* Am Asn Immunol; Sigma Xi; AAAS. *Res:* Molecular biology approaches to diagnosis and prognosis of cancers; oncogenes, growth factor receptors; tumor antigen isolation and characterization, serum-based/immunocytochemical tumor marker assays. *Mailing Add:* Specialty Labs 2211 Michigan Ave Santa Monica CA 90404-3900. *Fax:* 847-938-5934

**TOMITA, TATSUO,** ENDOCRINOLOGY. *Current Pos:* fel, 74-75, from asst prof to assoc prof, 75-85, PROF PATH, UNIV KANS MED CTR, 85- *Personal Data:* b Tokyo, Japan, Apr 20, 39. *Educ:* Tokyo Med & Dent Univ, Japan, BS, 61, MD, 65. *Prof Exp:* Intern rotating, US Naval Hosp, Yokosuka, Japan, 65-66; resident path, Wash Univ Sch Med, 70-74. *Mem:* Fel Am Diabetes Asn; fel AAAS; fel Sigma Xi; fel Am Asn Pathologists; fel Can Acad Path; fel Am Acad Path. *Res:* Experimental diabetes in regards to secretion of pancreatic hormones; radioimmunoassay of peptide hormones; immunohistochemistry of endocrine tumors; anatomic pathology. *Mailing Add:* Dept Path Univ Kans Med Ctr 3901 Rainbow Blvd Kansas City KS 66160. *Fax:* 913-588-7073

**TOMIYASU, KIYO,** MICROWAVE ENGINEERING, ELECTRONICS ENGINEERING. *Current Pos:* consult, Martin Marietta, 93-95, M&DS FEL, LOCKHEED MARTIN CORP, 93- *Personal Data:* b Las Vegas, Nev, Sept 25, 19; m 47, Eiko Nakamizo. *Educ:* Calif Inst Technol, BS, 40; Columbia Univ, MS, 41; Harvard Univ, MES, 47, PhD(eng sci, appl physics), 48. *Honors & Awards:* C P Steinmetz Award, Gen Elec, 77; Microwave Career Award, Inst Elec & Electronics Engrs, 80, Centennial Medal, 84. *Prof Exp:* Instr, Lyman Lab, Harvard Univ, 48-49; proj engr, Sperry Gyroscope Co, 49-52, head, Eng Sect, 52-55; consult engr, Microwave Lab, Calif, Gen Elec Co, 55-60, & Res & Develop Ctr, NY, 60-69, consult engr, Space Div, 69-93. *Concurrent Pos:* Bd dirs, Inst Elec & Electronics Engrs, 85-86; mem, Admin Comt Microwave Theory & Tech Soc, 57, Geosci & Remot Sensing Soc, 82. *Mem:* Am Phys Soc; fel Inst Elec & Electronics Engrs. *Res:* Microwave radiometry; communications; atmospheric propagation; radar; tropospheric propagation; ionospheric propagation; synthetic aperture radar; satellites. *Mailing Add:* Lockheed Martin Corp PO Box 8048 Philadelphia PA 19101

**TOMIZAWA, JUN-ICHI,** GENETICS. *Current Pos:* dir gen, 89-97, HON PROF NAT INST GENETICS, MISHIMA, JAPAN, 97- *Personal Data:* b Tokyo, Japan, June 24, 24; m 50, Keiko Tomizawa. *Educ:* Tokyo Univ, BS, 47, PhD, 57. *Prof Exp:* Mem res staff, NIH, Japan, 47-61, head, Dept Chem, 61-66, sect chief molecular biol, Bethesda, Md, 71-89; prof biol, Osaka Univ, Japan, 66-71. *Mem:* Hon mem Nat Acad Sci; hon mem Am Acad Arts & Sci; Japan Acad. *Res:* Molecular genetics; discovered antisense regulation. *Mailing Add:* Nat Inst Genetics 1 111 Yata Mishima Shuzuoka 411 Japan

**TOMIZUKA, CARL TATSUO,** SOLID STATE PHYSICS. *Current Pos:* head dept, Univ Ariz, 70-77, assoc dean, 77-79, prof, 60-93, EMER PROF PHYSICS, UNIV ARIZ, 93- *Personal Data:* b Tokyo, Japan, May 24, 23; nat US; m 56, 87, Sheila Tobias; c Mari, Frank, David & John. *Educ:* Univ Tokyo, BS, 45; Univ Ill, MS, 51, PhD(physics), 54. *Prof Exp:* Asst physics, Univ Ill, 51-54, res assoc, 54-55, res asst prof physics & elec eng, 55-56; asst prof physics, Inst Study Metals, Univ Chicago, 56-60. *Concurrent Pos:* Consult, Res Corp Technol. *Mem:* Fel Am Phys Soc. *Res:* Solid state diffusion; anelasticity; high pressure; magnetism; computer-based instruction. *Mailing Add:* Dept Physics Univ Ariz Tucson AZ 85721

**TOMKIEWICZ, MICHA,** PHYSICAL CHEMISTRY. *Current Pos:* MEM FAC, DEPT PHYSICS, BROOKLYN COL, 80- *Personal Data:* b Warsaw, Poland, May 25, 39; Israeli citizen; c 1. *Educ:* Hebrew Univ, MS, 63, PhD(chem), 69. *Prof Exp:* Instr phys chem, Hebrew Univ, 67-69; fel, Univ Guelph, 69-71; Nat Inst Gen Med Sci fel biophys, Univ Calif, Berkeley, 71-72, Nat Inst Gen Med Sci spec fel, 72-73; fel biophys, Thomas J Watson Res Ctr, IBM Corp, 73-76; res scientist, Union Carbide Corp, Tarrytown Tech Ctr, 76-80. *Mem:* Am Phys Soc. *Res:* Using biophysical and electrochemical approaches to photolyse water with visible radiation for the purpose of converting solar energy to useful chemical energy. *Mailing Add:* Dept Physics City Univ NY Brooklyn Col 2901 Bedford Ave Brooklyn NY 11210-2813

**TOMKINS, BRUCE,** ANALYTICAL CHEMISTRY. *Current Pos:* RES STAFF LEVEL 1, OAK RIDGE NAT LAB, 78- *Personal Data:* b Providence, RI, Oct, 2, 51. *Educ:* Univ Conn, BS, 73; Univ Ill, MS, 75, PhD(chem), 78. *Mem:* Am Chem Soc; Sigma Xi; Am Inst Chemists. *Mailing Add:* 113-A Arcadian Lane Oak Ridge TN 37830-5842

**TOMKINS, FRANK SARGENT,** ATOMIC SPECTROSCOPY. *Current Pos:* RETIRED. *Personal Data:* b Petoskey, Mich, June 24, 15; m 42, 63, Mary Ann Lynch; c Frank. *Educ:* Kalamazoo Col, BS, 37; Mich State Col, PhD(phys chem), 42. *Honors & Awards:* William F Meggars Award, Optical Soc Am, 77. *Prof Exp:* Physicist, Buick Motor Div, Gen Motors Corp, Ill, 41-43; physicist, Argonne Nat Lab, 43-46, sr scientist & group leader, 46-85. *Concurrent Pos:* Guggenheim fel, Nat Ctr Sci Res, France, 60-61; consult, Bendix Corp, 63-75; Argonne Nat Lab-Argonne Univs Asn distinguished appt, 75; fel Sci Res Coun (England), 75; assoc, Harvard Col Observ, 77- *Mem:* AAAS; fel Optical Soc Am; fel Am Phys Soc; assoc French Phys Soc. *Res:* Physical chemistry; optical spectroscopy; laser spectroscopy. *Mailing Add:* 11714 83rd Ave Palos Park IL 60464

**TOMKINS, MARION LOUISE,** X-RAY FLUORESCENT SPECTROSCOPY. *Current Pos:* RETIRED. *Personal Data:* b Pembroke, NH, Mar 28, 26. *Educ:* Univ Tampa, BS, 52; Roosevelt Univ, MS, 62. *Prof Exp:* Jr res chemist, Int Minerals & Chem Corp, 52-58; chief spectrographer, Martin Marietta Corp, 58-71; dir labs, H Kramer & Co, 71-89. *Mem:* Am Chem Soc; Soc Appl Spectros; Am Soc Testing & Mat. *Res:* Methods of analyses for high temperature alloys, geological materials and pollution control. *Mailing Add:* 9045 N Menard Morton Grove IL 60053

**TOMKINS, ROBERT JAMES,** STRONG LIMIT THEOREMS, MARTINGALE THEORY. *Current Pos:* From asst prof to assoc prof math, 69-76, PROF MATH, UNIV REGINA, 76-, DEPT HEAD MATH & STATIST, 85- *Personal Data:* b Ottawa, Ont, Aug 14, 45; m 67, Sharon L Henderson; c 2. *Educ:* Univ Saskatchewan, BA, 65 & 66; Purdue Univ, MS, 67, PhD(statist), 70. *Honors & Awards:* Statist Soc Can Distinguished Serv Plaque, 90. *Concurrent Pos:* Mem scholar comt, 80-83, statist grant, Natural Sci & Eng Res Coun Can, 88-91. *Mem:* Statist Soc Can (secy, 82-85, prog secy, 86-91, pres elect, 93-94, pres, 94-95); Inst Math Statist; Math Asn Am; Bernoulli Soc Probability & Statist; Can Math Soc; Am Statist Asn. *Res:* Probability limit theory especially stability theorems, laws of iterated logarithm and laws of large numbers for independent random variables; sample maxima and martingales. *Mailing Add:* Dept Math & Statist Univ Regina Regina SK S4S 0A2 Can

**TOMLIN, ALAN DAVID,** entomology, zoology, for more information see previous edition

**TOMLIN, DON C,** ANIMAL NUTRITION. *Current Pos:* NATURAL RESOURCES SPECIALIST, BUR INDIAN AFFAIRS, US DEPT INTERIOR, 88- *Personal Data:* b Meridian, Idaho, Aug 29, 32; m 58; c 1. *Educ:* Calif State Polytech Col, BSc, 55; Univ Fla, MSc, 56, PhD(animal nutri), 60. *Prof Exp:* Res asst, Univ Fla, 55-60; animal nutrit, Madera Milling Co, Calif, 60; fel forage eval, Ohio Agr Exp Sta, 61-62; res officer, Exp Farm, Can Dept Agr, BC, 62-65; res assoc range livestock nutrit, Utah Agr Exp Sta, 65-67; animal scientist, US Sheep Exp Sta, USDA, Idaho, 67-70; asst prof animal sci, Univ Alaska, Fairbanks, 70-75; consult, Agro-North Assoc, 75-88. *Mem:* Sigma Xi; Am Soc Animal Sci; Soc Range Mgt. *Res:* Ruminant nutrition; evaluation and utilization of native and domestic forages. *Mailing Add:* HC-01 Box 6190A Palmer AK 99645

**TOMLINSON, BRUCE LLOYD,** DEVELOPMENTAL BIOLOGY, AMPHIBIAN LIMB REGENERATION. *Current Pos:* asst prof, 88-93, ASSOC PROF & CHAIR BIOL, STATE UNIV NY, FREDONIA, 93- *Personal Data:* b Toronto, Ont, Dec 15, 50; m 77. *Educ:* Univ Waterloo, BS, 75, MSc, 77, PhD(biol), 83. *Prof Exp:* Postdoctoral fel, Ohio State Univ, 83-88. *Mem:* AAAS; Sigma Xi; Soc Develop Biol. *Res:* Molecular biology of amphibian limb regeneration and differentiation at the onset of regeneration processes. *Mailing Add:* Dept Biol State Univ NY Fredonia NY 14003. *E-Mail:* tomlinson@fredonia.edu

**TOMLINSON, GEORGE HERBERT,** CHEMISTRY. *Current Pos:* res dir, 61-70, vpres res & environ technol, 70-77, SR SCI ADV, DOMTAR LTD, 77- *Personal Data:* b Fullerton, La, May 2, 12; m 37; c 3. *Educ:* Bishop's Univ, Can, BA, 31; McGill Univ, PhD(chem), 35. *Hon Degrees:* DCL, Bishop's Univ, 86. *Honors & Awards:* Medal, Tech Asn Pulp & Paper Indust, 69; Gold Medal, Can Pulp & Paper Asn, 91. *Prof Exp:* Res assoc cellulose & indust chem, McGill Univ, 35-36; chief chemist, Howard Smith Chem Ltd, 36-40; res dir, Howard Smith Paper Mills Ltd, 41-60. *Concurrent Pos:* Res adv bd, Int Joint Comn; mem, US/Can/Mex Tri-Acad Comt Acid Deposition. *Mem:* AAAS; hon mem Can Pulp & Paper Asn; hon mem Tech Asn Pulp & Paper Indust; Am Chem Soc; fel Chem Inst Can; fel Royal Soc Can. *Mailing Add:* 920 Perrot Blvd N Ile Perrot PQ J7V 3K1 Can

**TOMLINSON, GERALDINE ANN,** MICROBIOLOGY, BIOCHEMISTRY. *Current Pos:* asst prof, Univ Santa Clara, 67-72, assoc prof, 72-82, actg chmn dept, 78-79, PROF BIOL, UNIV SANTA CLARA, 82- *Personal Data:* b Vancouver, BC, Feb 5, 31; m 57, Raymond V. *Educ:* Univ BC, BSA, 57, PhD(agr microbiol), 64; Univ Calif, Berkeley, MA, 60. *Prof Exp:* Res assoc comp biol, Kaiser Res Ctr Comp Biol, 60-61; develop pharmacol, Dept Pediat, State Univ NY Buffalo, 64-65; asst prof biol, Rosary Hill Col, 65-66; res assoc agr biochem, Stauffer Agr Ctr, Calif, 66-67. *Concurrent Pos:* Ames Res Ctr, NASA-Univ Santa Clara res grants, Ames Res Ctr, 68-; assoc dir summer prog planetary biol-microbiol ecol, NASA, 80 & 82. *Mem:* AAAS; Sigma Xi; Am Soc Microbiol. *Res:* Microbial physiology and biochemistry; extremely halophilic bacteria. *Mailing Add:* Biol Alum Sci Bldg Santa Clara Univ 500 El Camino Real Santa Clara CA 95053-0001

**TOMLINSON, HARLEY,** PLANT PATHOLOGY. *Current Pos:* mem staff, 73-84, MGR ENVIRON CONTROL, CHEM RES & DEVELOP, HUMPHREY CHEM CO, 84- *Personal Data:* b Tunbridge, Vt, July 20, 32; m 58, Joyce E Thompson; c James A & David J. *Educ:* Univ Vt, BS, 59, MS, 61, PhD(bot), 65. *Prof Exp:* Asst plant pathologist, Conn Agr Exp Sta, 65-73. *Mem:* Am Chem Soc; Sigma Xi. *Res:* Chemical applications and plant sciences. *Mailing Add:* 191 Knob Hill Dr Hamden CT 06518

**TOMLINSON, JACK TRISH,** INVERTEBRATE ZOOLOGY. *Current Pos:* from instr to prof, 57-88, chmn dept, 75-76, EMER PROF BIOL, SAN FRANCISCO STATE UNIV, 88- *Personal Data:* b Bakersfield, Calif, Aug 22, 29; m 63, Regina E Hoefler; c Susan (Mitchell), James & Linda (Lawson). *Educ:* Univ Calif, AB, 50, MA, 52, PhD(zool), 56. *Prof Exp:* Instr biol, Oakland City Col, 54-57. *Concurrent Pos:* Teacher, Univ Mie, Japan, 63, Moss Landing Marine Lab, 68-71; grantee, NIH, 63-68. *Mem:* AAAS; Animal Behav Soc; Soc Syst Zool; Crustacean Soc; Ecol Soc; Am Soc Zoologists; Sigma Xi. *Res:* Invertebrate physiology; animal behavior; order Acrothoracica. *Mailing Add:* 1918 Blue Spruce Dr Oakdale CA 95361

**TOMLINSON, JAMES EVERETT,** RUMINANT NUTRITION, DAIRY MANAGEMENT. *Current Pos:* from asst prof to assoc prof res & teaching, 75-86, PROF RES TEACHING & EXTEN, MISS STATE UNIV, 87- *Personal Data:* b Petersburg, Va, July 8, 42; m 65; c 3. *Educ:* Va Polytech Inst & State Univ, BS, 64, MS, 68; Univ Ky, PhD(animal nutrit), 72. *Prof Exp:* Ruminant res assoc antibiotic res, Hoechst Pharmaceut Co, 72-73; dairy nutritionist, Ralston Purina Co, 73-75. *Concurrent Pos:* Nutrit consult. *Mem:* Am Soc Animal Sci; Am Dairy Sci Asn; Sigma Xi; Am Registry Prof Animal Scientists; Am Forage & Grassland Coun. *Res:* Energy sources for lactating dairy cows; supplemental concentrate feeding systems; ensiled forage utilization by dairy cows; dairy heifer feeding and management; forage systems for lactating dairy cows and heifers; protein sources for lactating dairy cows. *Mailing Add:* Dept Animal Sci Miss State Univ Box 5228 Mississippi State MS 39762-5228

**TOMLINSON, JOHN LASHIER,** PHYSICAL METALLURGY. *Current Pos:* from asst prof to assoc prof, 69-76, PROF CHEM & MAT ENG, CALIF STATE POLYTECH UNIV, POMONA, 76- *Personal Data:* b Salem, Ore, Sept 15, 35; m 58; c 2. *Educ:* Loma Linda Univ, BA, 58; Univ Ore, MA, 61; Univ Wash, PhD(metall), 67. *Honors & Awards:* Charles Babbage Award, Inst Electronic & Radio Engrs, London, 76. *Prof Exp:* Physicist, Naval Ord Lab, Calif, 60-63; res engr, Boeing Co, Wash, 63-64; res assoc metall eng, Univ Wash, 64-67; res physicist, Naval Weapons Ctr, Calif, 67-69. *Concurrent Pos:* Eve instr, Chaffey Col, 61-63; from asst prof to assoc prof, Sch Dent, Loma Linda Univ, 70-78, prof, 78-; consult, Naval Ocean Systs Ctr, San Diego, 71-78 & RSI Assocs, La Verne, Calif, 79- *Mem:* Metall Soc; Am Phys Soc; Sigma Xi. *Res:* Failure analysis and product liability; physical metallurgy of electronic materials; electrical properties of liquid metals and semiconductors; properties and structure of thin films; dental materials. *Mailing Add:* Dept Chem & Mat Eng Calif State Polytech Univ Pomona CA 91768-4069

**TOMLINSON, MICHAEL,** PHYSICAL CHEMISTRY. *Current Pos:* RETIRED. *Personal Data:* b Leeds, Eng, Mar 30, 29; m 59, Helen M; c 3. *Educ:* Univ Leeds, BSc, 49. *Prof Exp:* Asst exp officer radiation chem, Atomic Energy Res Estab, Harwell, Eng, 49-54; exp officer, Chalk River Nuclear Labs, Atomic Energy Can Ltd, 54-57; sr sci officer, Atomic Energy Res Estab, Harwell, Eng, 57-62; assoc res officer, Chalk River Nuclear Labs, Atomic Energy Can Ltd, 62-63, assoc res officer, Whiteshell Nuclear Res Estab, 63-71, head, Res Chem Br, 71-76, dir, Chem & Mat Sci Div, 76-86, mgr bus develop, 86-90, savant gen, 90-91. *Mem:* Fel Chem Inst Can. *Res:* Chemistry for nuclear power. *Mailing Add:* PO Box 93 Pinawa MB R0E 1L0 Can

**TOMLINSON, PHILIP BARRY,** BOTANY. *Current Pos:* PROF BOT, HARVARD UNIV, 71-, E C JEFFREY PROF BIOL, 86- *Personal Data:* b Leeds, Eng, Jan 17, 32; m 65; c 2. *Educ:* Univ Leeds, BSc, 53, PhD(bot), 55; Harvard Univ, AM, 71. *Prof Exp:* Fel bot, Univ Malaya, 55-56; lectr, Univ Col Ghana, 56-59 & Univ Leeds, 59-60; res scientist, Fairchild Trop Garden, Fla, 60-71. *Concurrent Pos:* Forest anatomist, Cabot Found, Harvard Univ, 65-71. *Res:* Morphology and anatomy of monocotyledons, especially palms; tropical botany. *Mailing Add:* Harvard Univ 26 Oxford St Cambridge MA 02138-2902

**TOMLINSON, RAYMOND VALENTINE,** biochemistry; deceased, see previous edition for last biography

**TOMLINSON, RICHARD HOWDEN,** PHYSICAL CHEMISTRY, INORGANIC CHEMISTRY. *Current Pos:* asst prof phys & inorg chem, 52-58, chmn dept, 67-74, PROF PHYS CHEM, MCMASTER UNIV, 58- *Personal Data:* b Montreal, Que, Aug 2, 23; m 49. *Educ:* Bishop's Univ, Can, BSc, 43; McGill Univ, PhD(chem), 48. *Prof Exp:* Nat Res Coun Can fel, Cambridge Univ, 49. *Mem:* The Chem Soc; Sigma Xi. *Res:* Diffusion; mass spectrometry; polymerization; radiochemistry. *Mailing Add:* Dept Chem McMaster Univ 1280 Main St W Hamilton ON L8S 4L8 Can. *Fax:* 905-522-2509

**TOMLINSON, ROGER W,** GEOGRAPHY. *Current Pos:* STAFF, TOMLINSON ASSOC LTD. *Honors & Awards:* Serv Award, Can Asn Geogr, 91. *Mailing Add:* Tomlinson Assocs Ltd 17 Kippewa Dr Ottawa ON K1S 3G3 Can

**TOMLINSON, WALTER JOHN, III,** MULTIWAVELENGTH OPTICAL NETWORKING, NONLINEAR OPTICS IN FIBERS. *Current Pos:* mem tech staff, Bell Labs, 65-81, supvr, optical disk recording group, 81-83, DIR, PHOTONIC COMPONENT RES, BELL COMMUN RES, 83- *Personal Data:* b Philadelphia, Pa, Apr 3, 38; m 61, Barbara Kellog; c Robin. *Educ:* Mass Inst Technol, BS, 60, PhD(physics), 63. *Prof Exp:* Consult, Edgerton, Germeshausen & Grier, Inc, 60-63; sr scientist, 63. *Mem:* Am Phys Soc; fel Optical Soc Am. *Res:* Optical fiber components, integrated optics and, nonlinear optics; photochemistry; gaseous optical masers, atomic and molecular; magnetic field effects in optical masers; optical disk memories; multiwavelength optical networking. *Mailing Add:* 22 Indian Creek Rd Holmdel NJ 07733. *E-Mail:* wjt@bellcore.com

**TOMLJANOVICH, NICHOLAS MATTHEW,** THEORETICAL PHYSICS, IONOSPHERIC PHYSICS. *Current Pos:* MEM TECH STAFF, MITRE CORP, 66- *Personal Data:* b Susak, Yugoslavia, Mar 5, 39; US citizen; m 66; c 1. *Educ:* City Col New York, BS, 61; Mass Inst Technol, PhD(physics), 66. *Prof Exp:* Physicist, US Weather Bur, 62; teaching asst physics, Mass Inst Technol, 62-64; res asst elem particle physics, Lab Nuclear Sci, 64-66. *Concurrent Pos:* Woodrow Wilson fel, 62; physicist, Nat Bur Stand, 63. *Mem:* Am Phys Soc; Sigma Xi. *Res:* Radar detection theory and electromagnetic wave propagation; holography; modern optics; scattering theory; plasma physics. *Mailing Add:* Third 131 Newell Farm Rd Carlisle MA 01741

**TOMMERDAHL, JAMES B,** electrical engineering, for more information see previous edition

**TOMOMATSU, HIDEO,** ORGANIC CHEMISTRY, FOOD CHEMISTRY. *Current Pos:* supvr, 71-80, sr staff, 80-82, PRIN SCIENTIST, RES LABS, QUAKER OATS CO, 82- *Personal Data:* b Tokyo, Japan, June 8, 29; m 68, Tadao; c Yuko Ito. *Educ:* Waseda Univ, Japan, BEn, 53; Univ of the Pac, MSc, 60; Ohio State Univ, PhD(org chem), 65. *Prof Exp:* Res chemist, Hodogaya Chem Co Ltd, Japan, 53-59 & Texaco Chem Co, Inc, Tex, 65-71. *Mem:* Am Chem Soc; Inst Food Technologists; Am Asn Cereal Chemists. *Res:* Synthesis of new elastomers and new polymers; synthesis of high power sweeters and heat stable food dyes; physiologically functional food components; published 9 articles and granted 21 US and foreign patents. *Mailing Add:* 987 Darlington Lane Crystal Lake IL 60010. *Fax:* 847-304-2166

**TOMONTO, JAMES R,** NUCLEAR PHYSICS. *Current Pos:* VPRES, HTH INC, 86- *Personal Data:* b White Plains, NY, Apr 14, 32; m 56, Irene T Terenzio; c Robert J, Charles V, Patrice I, Kristin E & Melissa E. *Educ:* Villanova Univ, BS, 54; Rensselaer Polytech Inst, MS, 59. *Prof Exp:* Engr, Airborne Instruments Lab, 57; anal physicist, Nuclear Power Eng Div, Alco Prod Inc, 58-59; exp physicist, Knolls Atomic Power Lab, 59-64; mgr nuclear eng dept, Gulf United Nuclear Fuels Corp, NY, 64-74; mgr, Nuclear Anal Dept, Fla Power & Light Co, 74-81, sr consult, 81-88. *Concurrent Pos:* Dir, Qualtec Inc, 88-91; exec consult, YFF, Inc, 89-93. *Mem:* Fel Am Nuclear Soc. *Res:* Design and analysis of water moderated power and research reactors; development of analysis methods relating to use of uranium and plutonium as a fuel in thermal power and fast breeder reactors; economic analysis of energy systems; development of computer analysis systems; economic and technical analysis of high level nuclear waste treatment and disposal. *Mailing Add:* 14311 SW 74 Ct Miami FL 33158-1655

**TOMOZAWA, YUKIO,** THEORETICAL HIGH ENERGY PHYSICS, GENERAL RELATIVITY & ASTROPHYSICS. *Current Pos:* from asst prof to assoc prof, 66-72, PROF PHYSICS, UNIV MICH, ANN ARBOR, 72- *Personal Data:* b Iyo-City, Japan, Sept 3, 29; nat US; m 57, Hideko Kira; c Peter K & Ken T. *Educ:* Univ Tokyo, BSc, 52, DSc(physics), 61. *Prof Exp:* Asst physics, Univ Tokyo, 56-57, Tokyo Univ Educ, 57-59, Cambridge Univ, 59-60 & Univ Col, Univ London, 60-61; res assoc, Inst Physics, Univ Pisa, 61-64; mem, Inst Advan Study, 64-66. *Mem:* Am Phys Soc. *Res:* Symmetries in elementary particle physics; high energy astrophysics; axiomatic field theory; black hole physics. *Mailing Add:* Dept Physics Univ Mich Ann Arbor MI 48109. *Fax:* 313-763-2213; *E-Mail:* tomozawa@mich.physics.lsa.umich.edu

**TOMPA, ALBERT S,** ANALYTICAL CHEMISTRY, PHYSICAL CHEMISTRY. *Current Pos:* res chemist, 60-74, RES CHEMIST, NAVAL SURFACE WARFARE CTR, NAVAL ORD STA, 74- *Personal Data:* b Trenton, NJ, Aug 26, 31; m 57; c 5. *Educ:* St Joseph Univ, BS, 54; Fordham Univ, MS, 57, PhD(analytical chem), 60. *Prof Exp:* Lab instr analytical chem, Fordham Univ, 54-59. *Mem:* AAAS; Am Chem Soc. *Res:* Infrared and thermal analysis study of polymers and energetic materials; toxicity and demil of propellants and explosives. *Mailing Add:* 3720 Laurel Dr Indian Head MD 20640-9624

**TOMPA, FRANK WILLIAM,** DATA STRUCTURES, DATABASES. *Current Pos:* from asst prof to assoc prof, 74-89, PROF COMPUT SCI, UNIV WATERLOO, 89- *Personal Data:* b New York, NY, Nov 5, 48; m 72, Helen Lomas; c David, Karen & Andrea. *Educ:* Brown Univ, ScB, 70, ScM, 70; Univ Toronto, PhD(comput sci), 74. *Prof Exp:* Lectr comput sci, Univ Toronto, 74. *Mem:* Asn Comput Mach. *Res:* Text-dominated databases; data structures design and specification; systems design for hypertexts; machine-readable dictionary systems. *Mailing Add:* Dept Comput Sci Univ Waterloo Waterloo ON N2L 3G1 Can. *Fax:* 519-885-1208; *E-Mail:* fwtompa@uwaterloo.ca

**TOMPKIN, GERVAISE WILLIAM,** physical chemistry, for more information see previous edition

**TOMPKIN, ROBERT BRUCE,** FOOD MICROBIOLOGY. *Current Pos:* Res microbiologist, Armour Swift-Eckrich, 64-65, head, Microbiol Res Div, 65-66, chief microbiologist, Swift & Co, 66-93, chief microbiologist & dir, Analytical Serv, 85-93, VPRES PROD SAFETY, ARMOUR SWIFT-ECKRICH, 93- *Personal Data:* b Akron, Ohio, Apr 2, 37; m 61, Elizabeth Hope; c Amy, Fred & Anne. *Educ:* Ohio Univ, BSc, 59; Ohio State Univ, MSc, 61, PhD(microbiol), 63. *Concurrent Pos:* Chmn, Food Microbiol Sect, Am Soc Microbiol, 72, Food Microbiol Div, Inst Food Technologists, 77, Comt Microbiol Food, Nat Acad Sci-Nat Res Coun Comt, Nitrite & Alternative Curing Agents in Foods, 80-82; mem, Int Comn Microbiol Specif Foods, 81-, Nat Adv Comt Microbiol Criteria Foods, 88-93, Sci Affairs Comt, Am Meat Inst, 80- *Mem:* Am Soc Microbiol; Am Meat Sci Asn; fel Inst Food Technologists; Int Asn Milk, Food & Environ Sanit; fel Am Acad Microbiol. *Res:* Prevention of food-borne diseases and food spoilage. *Mailing Add:* Armour Swift-Eckrich 3131 Woodcreek Dr Downers Grove IL 60515-5429

**TOMPKINS, CURTIS JOHNSTON,** ENGINEERING MANAGEMENT, STATISTICAL ANALYSIS. *Current Pos:* UNIV PROF & PRES, MICH TECHNOL UNIV, 91- *Personal Data:* b Roanoke, Va, July 14, 42; m 64, Mary K Hasle; c Robert, Joseph & Rebecca. *Educ:* Va Polytech Inst & State Univ, BS, 65, MS, 67; Ga Inst Technol, PhD(indust & systs eng), 71. *Honors & Awards:* Centennial Medallion, Am Soc Eng Educ, 93. *Prof Exp:* Indust eng, E I du Pont de Nemours Co Inc, 65-67 & SFulton Hosp, Atlanta, 68; res eng, Health Systs Res Ctr, Ga Tech, 68-70, instr indust eng, Sch Indust & Syst Eng, 69-71; from asst prof to assoc prof quant methods, Grad Sch Bus Admin, Univ Va, 71-77; prof & chmn indust eng, Dept Indust Eng, WVa Univ, 77-80, dean, Col Eng, 80-91. *Concurrent Pos:* Vis lectr, Indust Col Armed Forces, 74-77; consult, Western Electric, 75-81; lectr, Nat Acad Voluntarism, 76-; mem, Comn Eng Educ, Nat Asn State Univ & Land Grant Col, 85-89; chair, Plans & Planning, Eng Adv Comt, NSF, 89-91. *Mem:* Fel Inst Indust Engrs (pres, 88-89); fel Am Soc Eng Educ (pres, 90-91); Sigma Xi; Nat Soc Prof Engrs. *Res:* Investigation of group theoretic structures in the fixed charge transportation problem; integer programming methods for the cutting-stock problem; science education; research administration. *Mailing Add:* 2 Woodland Rd Houghton MI 49931. *Fax:* 906-487-2935; *E-Mail:* curt@mtu.edu

**TOMPKINS, DANIEL REUBEN,** HORTICULTURE, PLANT PHYSIOLOGY. *Current Pos:* PRIN HORTICULTURIST, COOP STATE RES SERV, USDA, 75- *Personal Data:* b New York, NY, Oct 2, 31; m 64, Linda Goff; c Laura & Carol. *Educ:* Univ Md, BS, 59, MS, 62, PhD, 63. *Prof Exp:* Asst horticulturist, Western Wash Res & Exten Ctr, Wash State Univ, 62-68; from assoc prof to prof hort food sci, Univ Ark, Fayetteville, 69-75. *Mem:* AAAS; fel Am Soc Hort Sci (vpres, 87-88); Sigma Xi; Plant Growth Regulator Soc Am. *Res:* Growth substances; physiology of horticultural plants and plant science research administration. *Mailing Add:* 509 N Yakima Ave Apt 304 Tacoma WA 98403

**TOMPKINS, DONALD ROY, JR,** PHYSICS. *Current Pos:* PRES, TERRENE CORP, 76- *Personal Data:* b Calif, 32; m 61; c 5. *Educ:* Univ NDak, BS, 55; Univ Colo, MS, 58; Univ Ariz, PhD(physics), 64. *Prof Exp:* Asst prof physics, La State Univ, 64-67 & Univ Ga, 67-70; assoc prof, Univ Wyo, 70-76. *Mem:* Am Phys Soc. *Res:* Geophysics; mathematical physics; elementary particles. *Mailing Add:* Terrene Corp 606 Travis St Refugio TX 78377

**TOMPKINS, HOWARD E(DWARD),** APPLIED COMPUTER SCIENCE, LIBRARY APPLICATIONS. *Current Pos:* RETIRED. *Personal Data:* b Brooklyn, NY, Apr 19, 22; m 43, Elizabeth C Cross; c Sandra, Deyne, Wendy & Linden. *Educ:* Swarthmore Col, BA, 42; Univ Pa, MS, 47, PhD(elec eng), 57. *Prof Exp:* Engr, Philco Corp, 42-47; instr & res asst, Moore Sch Elec Eng, Pa, 47-51, res assoc, 56-57, asst prof elec eng, 57-60; proj supvr, Burroughs Corp, 51-54, ed serv mgr, 55-56; prof elec eng, Univ NMex, 60-61; chief, Sect Tech Develop, Nat Inst Neurol Dis & Blindness-NIMH, 61-63; prof elec eng & head dept, Univ Md, 63-67; dir info serv, Inst Elec & Electronics Engrs, NY, 67-71; chmn dept, Ind Univ Pa, 71-77, prof comput sci, 71-87. *Mem:* Inst Elec & Electronics Engrs; Inst Elec & Electronics Engrs Comput Soc. *Mailing Add:* 865 Cent Ave Apt J-302 Needham MA 02192-1342

**TOMPKINS, JAY ALLEN,** PROTEIN SEQUENCING, PEPTIDE SYNTHESIS. *Current Pos:* SR RES SPECIALIST, UNIV MO, COLUMBIA, 91- *Personal Data:* b Vancouver, BC, Dec 12, 47. *Educ:* Univ Lethbridge, BA, 71; Okla State Univ, MS, 86, PhD(org chem), 88. *Prof Exp:* Postdoctoral res fel, Univ Mo, Kansas City, 88-91. *Mem:* Am Chem Soc; Am Inst Chemists. *Res:* Protein sequencing and peptide synthesis. *Mailing Add:* Univ Mo 117 Schweitzer Hall Columbia MO 65212

**TOMPKINS, LAURIE,** REPRODUCTIVE BEHAVIOR IN DROSOPHILA. *Current Pos:* from asst prof to assoc prof, 81-92, PROF BIOL, TEMPLE UNIV, 92- *Personal Data:* b New York, NY, Mar 29, 50; m 90, Lawrence N Yager. *Educ:* Swarthmore Col, BA, 72; Princeton Univ, PhD(biol), 77. *Prof Exp:* Fel, Brandeis Univ, 77-80. *Concurrent Pos:* Fac mem neural systs & behav, Woods Hole Marine Biol Labs, 85-88; vis prof, Univ Hawaii, 88, Yale Univ, 96. *Mem:* Sigma Xi; Genetics Soc Am; Behav Genetics Asn; Animal Behav Soc; Soc Study Evol; fel AAAS. *Res:* Reproductive behavior of Drosophila melanogaster and related Drosophila species, genetics of larval vision. *Mailing Add:* Dept Biol Temple Univ Philadelphia PA 19122. *E-Mail:* 72123.1662acompuserve.com

**TOMPKINS, ROBERT CHARLES,** ELECTROMAGNETIC THEORY. *Current Pos:* RETIRED. *Personal Data:* b Bucyrus, Ohio, Aug 23, 24; wid; c Michael, Stephen E Joan. *Educ:* Ohio State Univ, BSc, 44. *Prof Exp:* Res engr chem, Battelle Mem Inst, 44-45; asst, Univ Chicago, 46-47; phys scientist, US Army Nuclear Defense Lab, 49071; res chemist, US Army Ballistic Res Lab, 71-86. *Concurrent Pos:* Mem adv comt civil defense, Nat Acad Sci-Nat Res Coun, 70-73; lectr, St Mary's Univ, Md, 75. *Mem:* Am Chem Soc; Sigma Xi; Am Phys Soc; NY Acad Sci. *Res:* Fallout from nuclear weapons; chemistry of propellants and explosives; high-pressure effects on electronic spectra; electromagnetic signatures. *Mailing Add:* 541 Valley View Rd Towson MD 21286-1337

**TOMPKINS, RONALD K,** SURGERY. *Current Pos:* from asst prof to assoc prof, 69-79, assoc dean, 88-91, PROF SURG, SCH MED, UNIV CALIF, LOS ANGELES, 79- *Personal Data:* b Malta, Ohio, Oct 14, 34; m 56; c 3. *Educ:* Ohio Univ, BA, 56; Johns Hopkins Univ, MD, 60; Ohio State Univ, MS, 68. *Hon Degrees:* Dr, Univ Bordeaux, France, 96. *Prof Exp:* Instr surg, Ohio State Univ, 68-69. *Concurrent Pos:* NIH res grants, Inst Arthritis & Metab Dis, HEW, 68-71; res grants, John A Hartford Found, Inc, 70-78; consult, Sepulveda Vet Admin Hosp, 71-94, Rand Corp Study Cholecystectomy, 76; hosp rep, Am Col Surgeons Southern Calif Chap, 72-76, pres, 87-88; mem, Long Range Planning Comt, Soc Surg Alimentary Tract, 74-76, pres, 86-87; mem, Prog Comt, Soc Univ Surgeons, 74-77 & Asn Acad Surg, 75-77; pres, Int Biliary Asn, 79-81. *Mem:* Soc Clin Surg; Am Surg Asn; Soc Univ Surgeons; Soc Surg Alimentary Tract (secy, 82-86, pres, 86-87); Am Gastroenterol Asn. *Res:* Biochemical and nutritional research related to diseases of the gastrointestinal tract, especially hepatobiliary and pancreatic diseases. *Mailing Add:* Dept Surg Sch Med Ctr Health Sci Univ Calif Los Angeles Rm 74-121 CHS Los Angeles CA 90024

**TOMPKINS, STEPHEN STERN,** MATERIALS INTERACTION WITH SERVICE ENVIRONMENT, ENGINEER MECHANICS SCIENCE. *Current Pos:* PROF, VA STATE UNIV, 94- *Personal Data:* b Portsmouth, Va, Nov 1, 38; m 61, Linda; c Patricia & Karen. *Educ:* Va Polytech Inst & State Univ, BS, 62; Univ Va, MAE, 68; Old Dominion Univ, PhD(mech eng), 78. *Prof Exp:* Res engr heat & mass transfer, Langley Res Ctr, NASA, 62-72, res scientist, 72-78, sr res scientist mat, 78-94. *Mem:* Am Soc Composites; Soc Advan Mat & Process. *Res:* Analysis of the thermal and mechanical response of complex metallic and non-metallic composite materials over a wide range of space environments; composites for dimensionally critical application; dimensional stability of composites. *Mailing Add:* 117 Woodland Rd Williamsburg VA 23188

**TOMPKINS, VICTOR NORMAN,** PATHOLOGY. *Current Pos:* PROF PATH, ALBANY MED COL, 60- *Personal Data:* b Milbrook, NY, May 30, 13; m 38; c 4. *Educ:* Cornell Univ, AB, 34; Union Univ, NY, MD, 38; Am Bd Path, dipl, 46. *Prof Exp:* Resident path, New Eng Deaconess Hosp, 39-40, Albany Hosp, 40-41 & Pondville Hosp, 41-42; sr pathologist, Div Labs & Res, State Dept Health, NY, 47-49, asst dir in charge diag labs, 49-56, assoc dir, 56-58, dir, 58-68. *Concurrent Pos:* Assoc prof path, Albany Med Col, 53-60. *Mem:* AAAS; Am Soc Human Genetics; Am Soc Clin Path; Am Soc Exp Path; AMA; Sigma Xi. *Res:* Immunology. *Mailing Add:* 508 Windrush Bay Dr Tarpon Springs FL 34689

**TOMPKINS, WILLIS JUDSON,** BIOMEDICAL ENGINEERING, ELECTRICAL ENGINEERING. *Current Pos:* PROF RES & TEACHING, UNIV WIS, 74- *Personal Data:* b Presque Isle, Maine, July 20, 41; m 67; c 2. *Educ:* Univ Maine, BS, 63, MS, 65; Univ Pa, PhD(biomed eng), 73. *Prof Exp:* Elec engr res & develop, Sanders Assoc Inc, 65-68; assoc biomed comput, Univ Pa, 73-74. *Mem:* Sr mem Inst Elec & Electronics Engrs (pres); Biomed Eng Soc; Asn Adv Med Instrumentation; Am Soc Eng Educ. *Res:* Computers in medicine; microcomputer-based medical instruments; electrocardiography. *Mailing Add:* Dept Elec & Comput Eng Univ Wis 1415 Engineering Dr Madison WI 53706

**TOMPSETT, MICHAEL F,** COMMAND CONTROL & DETECTION SYSTEMS, ELECTRONICS DEVICES. *Current Pos:* DIR, ELECTRONIC DEVICES RES DIV, ARMY RES LAB, 91- *Personal Data:* b Eng, May 4, 39; m 67, Margaret; c Karen, Adrian, Kevin & Ellen. *Educ:* Cambridge Univ, BA, 62, MA & PhD(elec eng), 66. *Prof Exp:* Res asst mat sci, Cambridge Univ, 65-66; proj leader camera tubes, Eng Elec Valve Co, 66-69; supvr, Data Conversion Design Group, AT&T Bell Labs, 69-89. *Mem:* Fel Inst Elec & Electronics Engrs. *Res:* Opto electronic devices; electronic materials; IR imaging devices; micro electro mechanical systems; analog design. *Mailing Add:* 67 Oak Ridge Ave Summit NJ 07901

**TOMPSETT, RALPH RAYMOND,** internal medicine; deceased, see previous edition for last biography

**TOMPSON, CLIFFORD WARE,** PHYSICS. *Current Pos:* assoc prof, 59-72, PROF PHYSICS, UNIV MO-COLUMBIA, 72- *Personal Data:* b Mexico, Mo, Dec 12, 29; m 51; c 3. *Educ:* Univ Mo, BS, 51, AM, 56, PhD(physics), 59. *Prof Exp:* Physicist, US Navy Electronics Lab, San Diego, 51-55. *Mem:* Am Phys Soc; Am Asn Physics Teachers. *Res:* X-ray diffraction; neutron diffraction; structure of liquids; lattice vibrations. *Mailing Add:* 209 W Parkway Dr Columbia MO 65203

**TOMPSON, ROBERT NORMAN,** MEASURE AND INTEGRATION THEORY, TOPOLOGY. *Current Pos:* from assoc prof to prof, 56-91, chmn dept, 78-91, EMER PROF MATH & EMER CHMN MATH, UNIV NEB, RENO, 91- *Personal Data:* b Adrian, Mich, Jan 7, 20; m 47; c 1. *Educ:* Adrian Col, ScB, 41; Univ Nev, MS, 49; Brown Univ, PhD(math), 53. *Prof Exp:* Res inspector ord mat, US War Dept, 42-43; from asst to instr math, Univ Nev, 46-49; asst prof, Fla State Univ, 53-54; mem tech staff, Bell Tel Labs, Inc, 54-55; asst prof, Fla State Univ, 55-56; mathematician & programmer, Int Bus Mach Corp, 56. *Concurrent Pos:* Consult, NSF/AID Sci Asst to India Prog, 67-68. *Mem:* AAAS; Am Math Soc; Am Phys Soc. *Res:* Transform methods in applied mathematics; ordinary differential equations in a weakly-differentiable function setting; constructive caratheodory-measure characterization of radon measures. *Mailing Add:* 997 Meadow St Reno NV 89509

**TOMS, M ELAINE,** PHYSICS, PHOTONUCLEAR REACTIONS. *Current Pos:* RETIRED. *Personal Data:* b Seoul, Korea, 1917. *Educ:* Wilson Col, AB, 39; Univ Pa, MS, 49. *Prof Exp:* Res physicist, Naval Res Lab, Washington, 54-73. *Mem:* Fel Am Phys Soc; Sigma Xi. *Res:* Compiled a bibliography of photo and electro nuclear reactions; designed, conducted and analyzed experiments with photonuclear reactions and published results; compiled data from neutron nuclear reactions. *Mailing Add:* Covenant Village Cromwell Missionary Rd Apt 219 Cromwell CT 06416

**TOMSON, MASON BUTLER,** PHYSICAL CHEMISTRY, ENVIRONMENTAL SCIENCES. *Current Pos:* asst prof, 77-81, ASSOC PROF ENVIRON SCI & ENG, RICE UNIV, 81- *Personal Data:* b Syracuse, Kans, Nov 18, 46; m 68. *Educ:* Southwestern State Univ, BS, 67; Okla State Univ, PhD(chem), 72. *Prof Exp:* Teaching asst, Okla State Univ, 67-72; instr, Dept Chem, State Univ NY, Buffalo, 72-76, res asst prof, 76-77. *Concurrent Pos:* Compiler, IUPAC Solubility Data Proj, 78-79. *Mem:* Am Chem Soc. *Res:* Kinetics and thermodynamics of precipitation and dissolution of sparingly soluble salts; solution equilibria of electrolytes; trace level organics, analysis and fate in water. *Mailing Add:* Dept Environ Sci & Eng MS 317 Rice Univ PO Box 1892 Houston TX 77251-1892

**TOMUSIAK, EDWARD LAWRENCE,** THEORETICAL NUCLEAR PHYSICS. *Current Pos:* from asst prof to assoc prof, 66-76, PROF PHYSICS, UNIV SASK, 76- *Personal Data:* b Edmonton, Alta, Mar 3, 38; m 61; c 1. *Educ:* Univ Alta, BSc, 60, MSc, 61; McGill Univ, PhD(theoret physics), 64. *Prof Exp:* NATO overseas fel, Oxford Univ, 64-66. *Mem:* Can Asn Physicists. *Res:* Nuclear structure calculations using realistic two-nucleon potentials; nuclear models and electromagnetic interactions with nuclei. *Mailing Add:* Physics Bldg Univ Sask 116 Science Pl Saskatoon SK S7N 5E2 Can

**TONASCIA, JAMES A,** BIOSTATISTICS. *Current Pos:* Asst prof, 70-77, ASSOC PROF BIOSTATIST, JOHNS HOPKINS UNIV, 77- *Personal Data:* b Los Banos, Calif, Mar 2, 44; m 65. *Educ:* Univ San Francisco, BS, 65; Johns Hopkins Univ, PhD(biostatist), 70. *Mem:* Am Statist Asn; Biomet Soc; Inst Math Statist; Math Asn Am; Royal Statist Soc; Sigma Xi. *Res:* Biostatistical methods; epidemiology; statistical computing. *Mailing Add:* 5703 Downing Pl Baltimore MD 21212-2450

**TONDEUR, PHILIPPE,** MATHEMATICS. *Current Pos:* prof math, 68-90, assoc mem, Ctr Adv Study, 77-78 & 91-92, CHAIR, DEPT MATH, UNIV ILL, URBANA, 96- *Personal Data:* b Zurich, Switz, Dec 7, 32; m 65. *Educ:* Univ Zurich, PhD(math), 61. *Prof Exp:* Res fel math, Univ Paris, 61-63; lectr, Univ Zurich, 63-64; res fel, Harvard Univ, 64-65; lectr, Univ Calif, Berkeley, 65-66; assoc prof, Wesleyan Univ, 66-68. *Mem:* Am Math Soc; Math Soc France; Swiss Math Soc. *Res:* Geometry and topology; foliation theory. *Mailing Add:* Dept Math Univ Ill Urbana IL 61801. *E-Mail:* tondeur@math. uivc.edu

**TONDRA, RICHARD JOHN,** MATHEMATICS. *Current Pos:* Assoc prof, 68-80, PROF MATH, IOWA STATE UNIV, 80- *Personal Data:* b Canton, Ohio, Jan 23, 43; m 66; c 2. *Educ:* Univ Notre Dame, BS, 65; Mich State Univ, MS, 66, PhD(topology, manifold theory), 68. *Mem:* Am Math Soc. *Res:* Topological and piecewise linear manifold theory. *Mailing Add:* 122 S Riverside Dr Ames IA 50010

**TONE, JAMES N,** ANIMAL PHYSIOLOGY. *Current Pos:* RETIRED. *Personal Data:* b Grinnell, Iowa, Feb 9, 33; m 54; c 2. *Educ:* Coe Col, BA, 54; Drake Univ, MA, 61; Iowa State Univ, PhD(animal physiol), 63. *Prof Exp:* Prof physiol, Ill State Univ, 63- *Mem:* AAAS. *Res:* Physiological effects of gossypol on mammals. *Mailing Add:* RR 2 Box 6 Lexington IL 61753

**TONEGAWA, SUSUMU,** IMMUNOLOGY, IMMUNOBIOLOGY. *Current Pos:* PROF BIOL, CTR CANCER RES & DEPT BIOL, MASS INST TECHNOL, 81-, DIR, CTR LEARNING & MEMORY, 94- *Personal Data:* b Nagoya, Japan, Sept 5, 39; m; c 2. *Educ:* Kyoto Univ, Japan, BS, 63; Univ Calif, San Diego, PhD(biol), 68. *Hon Degrees:* PhD, Northwestern Univ, 87. *Honors & Awards:* Nobel Prize in Physiol & Med, 87; Avery Landsteiner Prize, WGer Soc Immunol, 81; Genetics Grand Prize, Genetics Found Japan, 81; V D Mattia Award, Roche Inst Molecular Biol, 83; Robert Koch Prize, Robert Koch Found, WGer, 86; Kihara Prize, Japanese Soc Genetics, Kyoto, Japan, 88; Rabbi Shai Shacknai Mem Prize Immunol & Cancer Res, Israel, 89; Order of Southern Cross, Pres of Brazil, 91; Medicus Magnus Golden Medal, Polish Acad Sci, 94. *Prof Exp:* Res asst, Dept Biol, Univ Calif, San Diego, 63-64, teaching asst, 64-68; staff mem immunol, Basel Inst Immunol, Switz, 71-81. *Concurrent Pos:* Investr, Howard Hughes Med Inst, 88- *Mem:* Foreign assoc Nat Acad Sci; hon mem Scand Soc Immunol; hon mem Am Asn Immunologists; hon mem Scand Soc Immunol; Am Acad Arts & Sci; hon mem Japanese Biochem Soc; hon mem Polish Acad Med. *Res:* Molecular biology. *Mailing Add:* Ctr Cancer Res Bldg E17 Rm 353 Mass Inst Technol 77 Massachusetts Ave Cambridge MA 02139-4307

**TONELLATO, PETER J,** BIOMATHEMATICS. *Current Pos:* ASSOC PROF MATH, MARQUETTE UNIV, 86-; ADJ ASSOC PROF, MED COL WIS, 86- *Personal Data:* b Casablanca, Morocco, July 19, 56. *Educ:* Univ Puget Sound, BS, 78; Univ Ariz, MS, 80, PhD(appl math), 85. *Mem:* Am Math Soc; Soc Indust & Appl Math; Soc Math Biol. *Mailing Add:* Dept Math Statist & Comput Sci Marquette Univ PO Box 1881 Milwaukee WI 53201-1881

**TONELLI, ALAN EDWARD,** POLYMER PHYSICS. *Current Pos:* PROF, COL TEXTILES, NC STATE UNIV, 91- *Personal Data:* b Chicago, Ill, Apr 14, 42; m 74; c 2. *Educ:* Univ Kans, BS, 64; Stanford Univ, PhD(polymer chem), 68. *Prof Exp:* Mem tech staff, Polymer Physics, Bell Labs, 68-91. *Mem:* Am Chem Soc; Am Phys Soc. *Res:* Study of the conformations and physical properties of synthetic and biological macromolecules. *Mailing Add:* Col Textiles NC State Univ Box 8301 Raleigh NC 27695-8301

**TONELLI, GEORGE,** VETERINARY MEDICINE. *Current Pos:* RETIRED. *Personal Data:* b Tenafly, NJ, Feb 20, 21; m 55; c 4. *Educ:* Parma Univ, DVM, 48. *Prof Exp:* Biologist, Peters Serum Co, Kans, 50; res vet, Animal Indust Sect, Am Cyanamid Co, 51-55; group leader & pharmacologist, Exp Therapeut Sect, 55-60, group leader endocrinol, Endocrine Res Dept, 60-68, group leader, Toxicol Dept, 68-73, mgr toxicol/pharmacol eval, Int Div, 73-77, mgr overseas toxicol, Med Res Div, Lederle Labs, 77-88. *Mem:* Am Soc Pharmacol & Exp Therapeut; Endocrine Soc. *Mailing Add:* 83 Little Tor Rd Nd New City NY 10956

**TONELLI, JOHN P, JR,** REMOTE SENSING FOR FORESTRY, MATERIALS RESEARCH. *Current Pos:* Res chemist, Int Paper Corp Res, 68-69, sr res chemist, 69-79, res technologist, 79-83, res & develop assoc, 83-87, sr res & develop assoc, 88-91, RES SCIENTIST, INT PAPER CORP RES, 91- *Personal Data:* b Grove City, Pa, Nov 27, 46; c 1. *Educ:* Slippery Rock State Univ, BA, 68; State Univ NY, MA, 81. *Concurrent Pos:* Res & develop assoc, Com Uses Space, NASA, 85-89; mem, Efforts to Prevent Solid Waste from Landfills, Am Forest & Paper Assn & Composting Coun, 92- *Mem:* Inst Packaging Prof; Tech Asn Pulp & Paper Indust. *Res:* Use of remote sensing technologies to obtain information on land resources; impact of companies products on environment; determine wood property-pulp, paper and solid wood product property relationships; evaluate new technologies applicable to paper industry; evaluate solid waste management techniques. *Mailing Add:* Int Paper Co 6283 Tri-Ridge Blvd Cincinatti OH 45140. *Fax:* 914-695-5236

**TONELLI, ROBERT J,** PHARMACY REGULATION. *Current Pos:* COMPLIANCE OFFICER, OFF COMPLIANCE, FOOD & DRUG ADMIN, 96- *Personal Data:* b Worcester, Mass, July 22, 45. *Educ:* Mass Col Pharm, BS, 67; Univ Iowa, MB, 67, MS. *Mem:* Am Soc Hosp Pharmacists; Asn Fed Pharmacists. *Mailing Add:* Off Compliance Food & Drug Admin HFD-330 Rm 200 MPN-1 Rockville MD 20857. *Fax:* 301-594-5998; *E-Mail:* tonelli@fda.gov

**TONER, JOHN JOSEPH,** condensed matter physics, for more information see previous edition

**TONER, MEHMET,** BIOARTIFICIAL ORGANS, CELL & TISSUE INJURY. *Current Pos:* fel, 89-90, ASST PROF SURG BIOENG, HARVARD MED SCH, 90-; ASST BIOENGR, MASS GEN HOSP, 90-; SCI STAFF, SHRINERS BURNS INST, 90-; LECTR MECH ENG, MASS INST TECHNOL, 90- *Personal Data:* b Istanbul, Turkey, July 28, 58; m, Irem Aktay; c Ali. *Educ:* Istanbul Tech Univ, BS, 82; Mass Inst Technol, MS, 85, PhD(med eng), 89; Harvard Univ, PhD(med eng), 89. *Concurrent Pos:* Consult, Organogenesis, 92-; mem, Comt Res, Mass Gen Hosp, 92- & K17 Comt Heat & Mass Transfer in Biotechnol, Am Soc Mech Engrs, 93- *Mem:* Soc Cryobiol; Am Inst Chem Engrs; Cell Transplantion Soc; Biophys Soc; Biomed Eng Soc; Am Soc Mech Engrs. *Res:* Artificial organs and tissue engineering with major emphasis on isolation, culture, preservation and reconstruction of functional tissues. *Mailing Add:* Shriners Res Ctr 1 Kendall Sq Bldg 1400 W Cambridge MA 02139. *Fax:* 617-374-5665

**TONEY, JOE DAVID,** INORGANIC CHEMISTRY. *Current Pos:* Teacher, 69-77, ASSOC PROF CHEM, CALIF STATE UNIV, FRESNO, 77- *Personal Data:* b Rosston, Ark, Aug 12, 42; m 64; c 2. *Educ:* Univ Ark, Pine Bluff, BS, 64; Univ Ill, Urbana, PhD(chem), 69. *Concurrent Pos:* Vis res assoc chem, Argonne Nat Lab, 72; lectr health manpower prog, Pac Col, 73. *Mem:* Am Chem Soc. *Res:* Syntheses and structural characterization of transition metal chelate compounds involving amino acid ligands; visible, infrared and Raman studies of bonding in chelate complexes. *Mailing Add:* Dept Chem Calif State Univ 2555 E San Ramon Fresno CA 93740-8034

**TONEY, MARCELLUS E, JR,** clinical microbiology; deceased, see previous edition for last biography

**TONEY, THOMAS WESLEY,** SEXUAL DIFFERENCES IN THE REGULATION OF THE HYPOTHALAMIC-PITUITARY-GONADAL AXIS, REPRODUCTIVE PHYSIOLOGY. *Current Pos:* Asst prof, 91-96, ASSOC PROF BIOL, DEPT BIOL & ENVIRON SCI, GA COL, 96- *Personal Data:* b Richmond, Va, Apr 20, 56; m 81, Eleanor Vidt. *Educ:* Va Polytech Inst & State Univ, BS, 78; Va Commonwealth Univ, MS, 80; Univ Ill, PhD(physiol), 86. *Prof Exp:* Fel, Dept Obstet & Gynec, Vanderbilt Univ, 86-88; fel, Dept Pharmacol & Toxicol, Mich State Univ, 88-89, res assoc, 89-91. *Concurrent Pos:* Prin investr, Ga Col, 94. *Mem:* Endocrine Soc; Soc Neurosci. *Res:* Sexual differences in the regulation of the hypothalamic-pituitary-gonadal axis, using rats as models; emphasizing tuberoinfundibular dopaminergic regulation of prolactin secretion and how it is influenced by the sex steroid hormonal mileu and or various punative neuropeptides. *Mailing Add:* Dept Biol Ga Col Milledgeville GA 31061

**TONG, ALEX W,** TUMOR IMMUNOLOGY, MONOCLONAL ANTIBODIES. *Current Pos:* res assoc cancer immunol, 82-86, ASSOC DIR, IMMUNOL LAB, BAYLOR-SAMMONS CANCER CTR, 86-; ASST PROF BIOMED SCI, INST BIOMED STUDIES, BAYLOR UNIV, WACO, 88- *Personal Data:* b Hong Kong, Apr 8, 52; US citizen; c 1. *Educ:* Univ Ore, BA, 73; Ore Health Sci Univ, PhD(microbiol & immunol), 80. *Prof Exp:* Fel immunother, Surg Res Lab, Portland Vet Admin Med Ctr, 80-82; res assoc immunol, Dept Microbiol & Immunol, Sch Med, Ore Health Sci Univ, 81-82. *Concurrent Pos:* Adj fac, Immunol Grad Study Prog, Southwestern Med Ctr, Univ Tex, Dallas, 82-; prin investr, Monoclonal Antibody Res, Baylor Res Inst, 86-, NIH, 93. *Mem:* Am Asn Immunologists; Am Asn Cancer Res; Am Soc Hemat; Clin Immunol Soc. *Res:* Development of murine monoclonal antibodies and gene therapy agents for treatment of human cancers, study of tumor antigen expression in human lung, liver cancers and hematologic malignancies; characterization of pathogenetic mechanisms of human plasma cell dyscrasia including oncogene expression, cytokine modulation and regulation of apoptotic activity; ribozymes, viral vectors. *Mailing Add:* Cancer Immunol Res Lab Baylor-Sammons Cancer Ctr Dallas TX 75246. *Fax:* 214-820-2780

**TONG, BOK YIN,** SOLID STATE PHYSICS, BIOPHYSICS. *Current Pos:* from asst prof to assoc prof, 67-76, PROF PHYSICS, UNIV WESTERN ONT, 76- *Personal Data:* b Shanghai, China, Mar 5, 34; m 69; c 1. *Educ:* Univ Hong Kong, BSc, 57; Univ Calif, Berkeley, MA & MS, 59; Univ Calif, San Diego, PhD(solid state physics), 67. *Prof Exp:* Asst librn, Oriental Collection, Univ Hong Kong, 59-61; asst lectr math, 61-65; lectr math, 65-67. *Mem:* Am Phys Soc. *Res:* Theory of metals, surface physics and amorphous material; DNA molecules, muscle contraction and membrane activity; amorphous silicon; solar cells and devices; recrystallization of amorphous silicon. *Mailing Add:* Dept Physics & Astron Univ Western Ont London ON N6A 3K7 Can

**TONG, EDMUND Y,** PHYSIOLOGY. *Current Pos:* Fel, 71-73, PROF BIOL, WHEATON COL, 74- *Personal Data:* b China, Mar 20, 43. *Educ:* Concord Col, BS, 65; Univ Wis, PhD(physiol), 70. *Mem:* Am Chem Soc; Am Phys Soc. *Mailing Add:* Biol Dept Wheaton Col Norton MA 02766

**TONG, JAMES YING-PEH,** PHYSICAL CHEMISTRY, FORENSIC CHEMISTRY. *Current Pos:* from asst prof to assoc prof, 57-68, PROF CHEM, OHIO UNIV, 68-; DIR FORENSIC CHEM, 76-; DIR VIS SCHOLARS, 79- *Personal Data:* b Shanghai, China, Dec 8, 26; US citizen; m 51; c 3. *Educ:* Univ Calif, Berkeley, BS, 50, MS, 51; Univ Wis, PhD(chem), 54. *Prof Exp:* Res chemist, Le Roy Res Lab, Durex Plastics & Chem, Inc, 53-54; res assoc phys inorg chem, Univ Ill, 54-57. *Concurrent Pos:* Chmn, policy adv comt, Hocking River Basin, 80- *Mem:* Am Chem Soc; fel Am Inst Chemists. *Res:* Environmental water chemistry; forensic chemistry; chemistry and history of photography; equilibrium and kinetics studies. *Mailing Add:* 21 Rocking St Athens OH 45701-2617

**TONG, LONG SUN,** HEAT TRANSFER. *Current Pos:* RETIRED. *Personal Data:* b China, Aug 20, 15; US citizen; m 39. *Educ:* Chinese Nat Inst Technol, BS, 40; Univ Fla, MS, 53; Stanford Univ, PhD(mech eng), 56. *Honors & Awards:* Mem Award, Am Soc Mech Engrs, 73; Don Q Kern Award, Am Inst Chem Engrs, 81. *Prof Exp:* Asst prof mech eng, Ord Eng Col, Taiwan, 47-52; sr engr, Atomic Power Dept, Westinghouse Elec Corp, 56-59, supvr thermal & hydraul design, Atomic Power Dept, 59-62, adv engr, 63-65, mgr thermal & hydraul design & develop, 65-66, mgr thermal & hydraul eng, 66-70, consult engr, PWR Syst Div, 70-72, sr consult, 72-73; asst dir, Div Reactor Safety Res, Nuclear Regulatory Comn, 73-81, chief scientist, 81-83. *Concurrent Pos:* Lectr, Univ Pittsburgh, 57-60, adj prof, 65-72; lectr, Carnegie Inst Technol, 61-67. *Mem:* Fel Am Soc Mech Engrs; fel Am Nuclear Soc. *Res:* Fluid flow; thermal and hydraulic design; analysis and development of pressurized water reactors; research in water reactor safety. *Mailing Add:* 9733 Lookout Pl Gaithersburg MD 20879

**TONG, MARY POWDERLY,** MATHEMATICS. *Current Pos:* RETIRED. *Personal Data:* b New York, NY, May 24, 24; m 56, Hing; c Christopher, Mary E, William, Jane F & James. *Educ:* St Joseph's Col, NY, BA, 50; Columbia Univ, MA, 51, PhD, 69. *Prof Exp:* Instr math, St Joseph's Col, NY, 51-54, City Col New York, 54 & Columbia Univ, 54-59; asst prof, Univ Conn, 60-66; from asst prof to assoc prof, Fairfield Univ, 66-70; prof math, William Paterson Col NJ, 70-84. *Concurrent Pos:* NSF fac fel, 59-60; Delta Epsilon Sigma res fel, 68. *Mem:* Am Math Soc; Math Asn Am; NY Acad Sci. *Res:* Topology; foundations of mathematics; applications of mathematics. *Mailing Add:* 725 Cooper Ave Oradell NJ 07649-2334

**TONG, PIN,** structural mechanics, for more information see previous edition

**TONG, STEPHEN S C,** ANALYTICAL CHEMISTRY, PHYSICAL CHEMISTRY. *Current Pos:* SR RES CHEMIST, CORNING INC, 68-; RES ASSOC CHEMIST, RES & DEVELOP LAB, 80- *Personal Data:* b Shanghai, China, May 3, 36; US citizen; m 67, Kathy; c 2. *Educ:* Univ Ottawa, BSc, 59; Mass Inst Technol, MS, 61; Cornell Univ, PhD(analytical chem), 66. *Honors & Awards:* Sullivan Award, 92. *Prof Exp:* Res chemist, Rohm & Hass Co, 61-62; fel, Argonne Nat Lab, 66-68. *Mem:* Am Chem Soc; Am Soc Mass Spectrometry; Sigma Xi; Soc App Spectros. *Res:* Trace analysis; spark source mass spectrometry; gas chromatography; neutron activation analysis; electron microprobe; secondary ion mass spectrometry; thermal analysis; gas chromatography-mass spectrometry; hot glass simulation. *Mailing Add:* Corning Inc HP-ME-02-038-H7 Corning NY 14831-0001

**TONG, THEODORE G,** PHARMACOLOGY, TOXICOLOGY. *Current Pos:* PROF PHARM, CLIN PHARMACOL & TOXICOL, COL PHARM, UNIV ARIZ, 82-; ASSOC DEAN ACAD AFFAIRS, COL PHARM, 87-; DIR, ARIZ POISON CONTROL SYST, 82- *Personal Data:* b La Jolla, Calif, Oct 8, 42. *Educ:* Univ Southern Calif, BS, 64; Ore State Univ, BS, 65; Univ Calif, PharmD, 69. *Prof Exp:* Instr nursing, Contra Costa Col, 72-74; clin instr pharm, Sch Pharm, Univ Calif, San Francisco, 69-73, asst clin prof, 73-78, assoc clin prof, 78-82; dir, San Francisco Bay Area Poison Control Ctr, 79-82. *Concurrent Pos:* Assoc, Div Clin Pharm & Toxicol, San Francisco Gen Med Ctr, 73-82; co-investr, Drug Dependence Clin Res Prog, Univ Calif, 79-82; ed, Poison Line, Am Asn Poison Control Ctrs, 82-85; sec, Am Asn Poison Control Ctrs, 86-; dir, Am Bd Appl Toxicol, 88-; mem, US Pharmacopeia Comn Rev, 90-95. *Mem:* Sigma Xi; fel Am Acad Clin Toxicol; Am Col Clin Pharm; Am Soc Clin Pharmacol & Therapeut; Am Asn Poison Control Ctrs; Am Pharm Asn. *Res:* Pharmacologic interactions of drugs and drugs of abuse, misuse and in overdose; toxicokinetics; poison control systems. *Mailing Add:* Col Pharm Univ Ariz Tucson AZ 85721

**TONG, WINTON,** PHYSIOLOGY, BIOCHEMISTRY. *Current Pos:* from asst prof to assoc prof, 62-71, dir, Grad Studies, 70-72, PROF PHYSIOL, SCH MED, UNIV PITTSBURGH, 71-, CHMN DEPT, 81- *Personal Data:* b Los Angeles, Calif, May 3, 27; m 51; c 3. *Educ:* Univ Calif, Berkeley, BS, 47, PhD(thyroid function), 53. *Honors & Awards:* Van Meter Prize, Am Thyroid Asn, 64. *Prof Exp:* Res physiologist, Univ Calif, Berkeley, 47-62. *Concurrent Pos:* USPHS res career develop award, 62-72; assoc ed, Am J Physiol, 77- *Mem:* AAAS; Am Soc Biol Chemists; Am Physiol Soc; Endocrine Soc; Am Thyroid Asn. *Res:* Mechanisms in the biosynthesis of thyroid hormones and thyroglobulin; mechanism of action of thyrotropin; physiology of thyroid function; cultivation of thyroid cells in vitro. *Mailing Add:* Dept Cell Biol & Physiol 6363 Christie Ave Emeryville CA 94608

**TONG, YOUDONG,** HETEROGENEOUS CATALYSIS, SURFACE CHEMISTRY. *Current Pos:* sr chemist, 90-93, SR RES CHEMIST, NALCO CHEM CO, 93- *Personal Data:* b China, Dec 25, 56; m, Jing Liu; c 2. *Educ:* Tsinghua Univ, China, BS, 82, MS, 84; Tex A&M Univ, PhD(chem), 91. *Prof Exp:* Asst prof, Petrol Univ, China, 84-86. *Mem:* Am Inst Chem Engrs; Nat Asn Corrosion Engrs. *Res:* Surface-gas phase (vapor also) interaction; heterogeneous catalysis; petrochemical industrial subjects. *Mailing Add:* 9903 S Dairy Ashford St Houston TX 77099

**TONG, YULAN CHANG,** ORGANIC CHEMISTRY. *Current Pos:* org res chemist, Edgar C Britton Res Lab, Mich, 62-65, res chemist, Res Lab, Western Div, 66-70, sr res chemist, 70-72, res specialist, 72-78, sr research specialist, 78-80, RES ASSOC, RES LAB, WESTERN DIV, DOW CHEM CO, 80- *Personal Data:* b Nanking, China, Oct 21, 35. *Educ:* Cheng Kung Univ, Taiwan, BS, 56; Univ Ill, MS, 58, PhD(org chem), 61. *Prof Exp:* Res assoc, Univ Mich, 61-62. *Mem:* Am Chem Soc; Int Soc Heterocyclic Chem; NY Acad Sci. *Res:* Heterocyclic chemistry. *Mailing Add:* 567 Monarch Ridge Dr Walnut Creek CA 94596-2950

**TONG, YUNG LIANG,** STATISTICS, MATHEMATICS. *Current Pos:* from asst prof to assoc prof, 70-76, PROF STATIST, UNIV NEBR-LINCOLN, 76-; MATH DEPT, GA TECH RES CORP. *Personal Data:* b Shantung, China, July 15, 35; m 65; c 3. *Educ:* Nat Taiwan Univ, BS, 58; Univ Minn, Minneapolis, MA, 63, PhD(statist), 67. *Prof Exp:* Asst prof statist, Univ Nebr, Lincoln, 67-69; vis asst prof, Univ Minn, 69-70. *Concurrent Pos:* Vis prof, Univ Calif, Santa Barbara, 78-79. *Mem:* Am Statist Asn; Inst Math Statist. *Res:* Mathematical and applied statistics; multivariate analysis; sequential analysis; probability inequalities. *Mailing Add:* Sch Math Ga Inst Technol Atlanta GA 30332

**TONIK, ELLIS J,** MEDICAL MICROBIOLOGY. *Current Pos:* RETIRED. *Personal Data:* b Philadelphia, Pa, Jan 9, 21; m 48, Patricia Ann Wallace; c Leigh, David & Valissa. *Educ:* Roanoke Col, BS, 50. *Prof Exp:* Med bacteriologist diag bact, Dept Pub Welfare, Ill, Chicago State Hosp, 50-51, supvry bacteriologist, East Moline State Hosp, 51-52 & Kankakee State Hosp, 52; med bacteriologist, Process Res & Pilot Plants Div, Chem Corps Res & Develop Labs, US Dept Army, 52-60, supvry bacteriologist, Tech Eval Div, 60, actg chief animal path sect, 60-61, chief exp animal sect, Appl Aerobiol Div, 61-71, sr investr, Microbiol Res Div, 71-72; chief microbiol, Ft Howard Vet Admin Hosp, 72-79. *Mem:* Am Soc Microbiol; Sigma Xi. *Res:* Experimental respiratory diseases of laboratory animals; aerobiological research and technology; experimental and clinical pathology; immunology; chemotherapeutic agents; virulence of airborne particulates; laboratory diagnosis and assay methods; management of laboratory animals. *Mailing Add:* 526 Mary St Frederick MD 21701

**TONKING, WILLIAM HARRY,** MINING GEOLOGY. *Current Pos:* INT GEOL CONSULT, 94- *Personal Data:* b Newton, NJ, Apr 22, 27; m 64, Edith Zirkel; c Lisbeth & Randy. *Educ:* Princeton Univ, AB, 49, PhD(geol), 53. *Honors & Awards:* Silver Medallist, Royal Soc Arts, 66. *Prof Exp:* Asst geol, Princeton Univ, 49-50 & 51-53; asst instr, Northwestern Univ, 50-51; geologist, Bear Creek Mining Co, 53-55 & Stand Oil Co, Tex, 55-62; dep mgr, Mohole Proj, Brown & Root Inc, 62-67, mgr spec projs, 67-75, sr mgr mining & geol & chief geologist, 75-79; exec vpres, Keplinger & Assocs, 79-81; exec vpres & dir, GCO Minerals Co, 81-85; int geol consult, 86-90; pres & chief exec officer, Tex Star Resources Corp, 90-93. *Mem:* Geol Soc Am; Royal Soc Arts. *Res:* Petrology; volcanic rocks and ore deposits in the Southwest; petroleum geology; deep ocean engineering, geology and geophysics; diamond exploration; development and production. *Mailing Add:* 12319 Rip Van Winkle 12319 Rip Van Winkle Dr Houston TX 77024. Fax: 713-688-3620

**TONKS, DAVID BAYARD,** BIOCHEMISTRY, CLINICAL CHEMISTRY. *Current Pos:* from asst prof to assoc prof, 62-75, PROF MED, MCGILL UNIV, 75-; CLIN CHEM CONSULT, DOUGLAS HOSP, 65- *Personal Data:* b Edmonton, Alta, Aug 31, 19; m 46, Emma Gibson; c David R & Laurie S. *Educ:* Univ BC, BA, 41; McGill Univ, PhD(org chem), 49. *Honors & Awards:* Warner-Chilcott Award, Can Soc Lab Technologists, 67; Ames Award, Can Soc Clin Chem, 68; Ann Award, Que Corp Hosp Biochemists, 72; Queen's Jubilee Medal, 77. *Prof Exp:* Sr chemist, Clin Labs, Lab Hyg, Dept Nat Health & Welfare, Can, 48-57; asst biochemist, Biochem Dept & Res Inst, Hosp Sick Children, Toronto, 57-62; dir, Div Clin Chem, Dept Med, Montreal Gen Hosp, 62-87. *Concurrent Pos:* Tech dir, Seaforth Clin Labs, Montreal, 64-77; mem bd dirs, Bio Res Labs, Point Claire, 65-72; lab consult, Reddy Men Hosp, Motreal, 66-, Cybernedix Ltd, Toronto, 69-91 & Gen Diag Div, Warner-Lanbert, Toronto, 70-78; Can nat rep, Int Comn Clin Chem, 66-70; secy, Sect Clin Chem, Int Union Pure & Appl Chem, 67-71, pres sect, 71-75, bur mem, 71-75, past-pres, 75-77, mem comn toxicol, 73-77, mem Can nat comt, 74-92; mem exec bd, Int Fedn Clin Chem, 67-75. *Mem:* Am Asn Clin Chemists; Can Biochem Soc; fel Chem Inst Can; Can Soc Clin Chem (from secy to pres, 57-66, treas, 74-76); NY Acad Sci; fel Can Acad; Int Union Pure & Appl Chem. *Res:* Development of synthetic antigens for serodiagnosis of syphilis; quality control and evaluation of laboratory precision in clinical chemistry laboratories; analytical methods in clinical chemistry; development of allowable limits of err or for clinical chemistry tests, based on reference values; trace metal analysis in biological specimens. *Mailing Add:* 1295 Carson Ave Dorval PQ H9S 1M5 Can

**TONKS, DAVIS LOEL,** PLASTIC FLOW IN METALS, FRACTURE. *Current Pos:* researcher, 81-82, code developer, 83-85, RESEARCHER PLASTICITY & FRACTURE, LOS ALAMOS NAT LAB, 86- *Personal Data:* b Pocatello, Idaho, May 6, 47; m 71; c 5. *Educ:* Brigham Young Univ, BSc, 72; Univ Utah, PhD(physics), 78. *Prof Exp:* Researcher, Dept Physics, Ariz State Univ, 78-81. *Concurrent Pos:* Res assoc, Ariz State Univ, 78-80. *Mem:* Am Phys Soc. *Res:* Modeling and theory of high-strain-rate plasticity and fracture in metals. *Mailing Add:* X4 MSF664 Los Alamos Nat Lab Los Alamos NM 87545

**TONKS, ROBERT STANLEY,** PHARMACOLOGY, GERIATRIC PHARMACOTHERAPY. *Current Pos:* prof & dir, Col Pharm, Dalhousie Univ, 73-77, dean, Fac Health Professions, 77-88, actg head, Div Geriat Med, 91-94, PROF, DIV GERIAT MED, DALHOUSIE UNIV & CAMP HILL MED CTR, 88- *Personal Data:* b Aberystwyth, Wales; Can citizen; m 53, Diana M Cownie; c Pamela M, Julia R, Robert M & Sara K. *Educ:* Univ Wales, BS, 51, Med Sch, PhD(pharmacol), 54; Inst Biol, Eng, fel, 73. *Prof Exp:* Organon fel, Welsh Nat Sch Med, Cardiff, 53-54, Nat Health Serv fel, Nevill Hall Hosp, 54-56, sr fel, 56-58, univ lectr, Dept Mat Media & Pharmacol & Therapeut, 58-72, sr lectr, 72-73. *Concurrent Pos:* Chmn, Pharmaceut Sci Grant Comt, Med Res Coun Can, 76-77, co-chmn Northeast Can-Am Health Coun, 80-91; mem, Personel Rev Comt, Nat Health & Welfare Can, 79-81, 82-84 & 90-93, Med Res Coun & Health-Welfare Can, Joint Comt on Nursing Res, 88-91, Nat Panel on Risk-Benefit of Pharmaceut, 89-92; consult, NB Dept Health, 74-, Health & Welfare Can, 77-, Rector Riyadh Univ & Ministers Health & Educ, Saudi Arabia, 80, Pew Charitable Trusts, 86; working group, sr's prescription drug plan, Med Soc NS, 93-94. *Mem:* Brit Pharmacol Soc; Can Asn Gerontol; Int Soc Thrombosis & Haemostasis; Can Soc Clin Invest; Gerontol Soc Am; Am Soc Clin Pharmacol & Therapeut. *Res:* Platelet micro-emboli in circulating human blood: their role in the production of primary pulmonary thrombosis and myocardial infarction in man and during the immune response, explaining tissue and organ transplant rejection; introduced aspirin for the treatment of recurrent myocardial infarction in the early sixties; prescription and non-prescription medicines use by the elderly patient; new methods of delivering health care to the rural frail elderly; pharmacoepidemiology. *Mailing Add:* Dalhousie Univ & Camp Hill Med Ctr Div Geriat Med 1763 Robie St Halifax NS B3H 3E2 Can

**TONKYN, RICHARD GEORGE,** ORGANIC CHEMISTRY, POLYMER CHEMISTRY. *Current Pos:* CONSULT, 92- *Personal Data:* b Portland, Ore, Mar 26, 27; c Michael Stephen, Paula Ruth, David William, Russell George, John Campbell & James Lewis. *Educ:* Reed Col, BA, 48; Univ Ore, MA, 51; Univ Wash, PhD(org chem), 60. *Prof Exp:* Instr org chem, Univ Ore, 52; supvr res, Analysis Labs, Titanium Metals Corp Am, Nev, 52-54; sr res anal chemist, Allegheny Ludlum Steel Corp, Pa, 54-55; res engr, Boeing Airplane Co, Wash, 55-59; NSF fel, Univ Col, Univ London, 60-61; chemist, Union Carbide Corp, NJ, 61-67; proj scientist, 67-69; sr res chemist, Betz Labs, Inc, 69-70, group leader, 70-72, mgr org res & process develop, 72-76; dir res & develop, Mogul Corp, 76-77, vpres res & develop, Mogul Div, Dexter Corp, 77-85; vpres res & develop, Petrolite Corp, 85-92. *Mem:* Am Chem Soc; Sigma Xi; Cooling Tower Inst; Asn Water Technol. *Res:* Monomer and polymer synthesis; oil and gas production chemicals for demulsification, corrosion, oilfield water treatment; polyelectrolyte synthesis; chemicals and processes for water treatment and water pollution control; corrosion and deposit control research; industrial cooling and boiler. *Mailing Add:* 27 Country Fair Lane St Louis MO 63141

**TONN, ROBERT JAMES,** RESEARCH ADMINISTRATION. *Current Pos:* ADJ PROF, UNIV TEX, EL PASO, 87- *Personal Data:* b Watertown, Wis, June 23, 27; m 61, Noemi C Torres; c Sigrid & Monica. *Educ:* Colo State Univ, BS, 49, MS, 50; Okla State Univ, PhD(entom), 59, MPH, 63. *Prof Exp:* Res assoc, Sch Med, La State Univ, 61-63; dir, Encephalitis Field Sta, Mass, 63-65; proj leader, WHO, 65-78; chief planning mgt, 83-87; regional adv entom, Pan Am Health Orgn, 78-83. *Concurrent Pos:* Consult, Vector Biol & Control, USAID, 87- *Mem:* Am Soc Trop Med & Hyg; Soc Vector Ecol (pres, 84); Am Mosquito Control Asn; US-Mex Pub Health Border Asn. *Res:* Vector borne disease prevention and control. *Mailing Add:* RR 3 Box 505 Park Rapids MN 56470-9363

**TONNA, EDGAR ANTHONY,** CELL PHYSIOLOGY, CELL CHEMISTRY. *Current Pos:* emer prof histol, Grad Sch Basic Med Sci, NY Univ, 67-, dir, Lab Cellular Res, 67-, dir, Inst Dent Res, Col Dent, 71-, chmn, Dept Histol & Cell Biol, 81-, EMER PROF CELLULAR PHYSIOL, NY UNIV, 91- *Personal Data:* b Malta, May 10, 28; nat US; m 51; c 4. *Educ:* St John's Univ, NY, BS, 51; NY Univ, MS, 53, PhD(biol), 56. *Prof Exp:* Res collabr, Div Exp Path, Med Res Ctr, Brookhaven Nat Lab, 56-59, head, Histochem & Cytochem Res Lab, 59-67. *Concurrent Pos:* Res biochemist, Hosp Spec Surg, New York, 53-56, head, Histochem & Cytochem Res Lab, 56-59; adj assoc prof, Grad Sch, Long Island Univ, 56-62; consult radiobiol, Inst Dent Res, NY Univ, 64-67; ed chief, Gerodontology, 81- *Mem:* Fel Geront Soc; fel NY Acad Sci; Histochem Soc; fel Royal Micros Soc; Sigma Xi. *Res:* Cellular contribution to skeletal and dental development, growth, repair and disease during aging; autoradiographic, cytochemical and cytological studies using optical analytical and electron microscopic techniques to determine biochemical and cell morphological changes in skeletal and dental cell parameters; cell gerontology. *Mailing Add:* Inst Dent Res NY Univ Col Dent 345 E 24th St New York NY 10010

**TONNE, PHILIP CHARLES,** MATHEMATICS. *Current Pos:* asst prof, 66-71, ASSOC PROF MATH, EMORY UNIV, 71- *Personal Data:* b Chicago, Ill, Apr 2, 38; m 63; c 2. *Educ:* Marquette Univ, BS, 60; Univ NC, MA, 63, PhD(math), 65. *Prof Exp:* Instr math, Univ NC, 65-66. *Mem:* Am Math Soc. *Res:* Classical analysis. *Mailing Add:* Dept Math Emory Univ 1784 N Decatur Rd Suite 100 Atlanta GA 30322

**TONNER, BRIAN P,** SURFACE SCIENCE. *Current Pos:* asst prof, 83-88, ASSOC PROF PHYSICS, UNIV WIS-MILWAUKEE, 88- *Personal Data:* b Jersey City, Sept 27, 53; m 84. *Educ:* Brown Univ, BSc, 76; Univ Pa, MSc, 78, PhD(physics), 82. *Prof Exp:* Fel physics, Univ Pa, 78-81; res assoc physics, Cornell Univ, 82-83. *Mem:* Am Phys Soc; Am Vacuum Soc. *Res:* Applications of synchrotron radiation to condensed matter physics; photoemission, photo absorption and x-ray scattering. *Mailing Add:* 3519 N Frederick Ave Milwaukee WI 53211

**TONNIS, JOHN A,** ORGANIC CHEMISTRY. *Current Pos:* asst prof, 68-70, assoc prof, 70-75, PROF CHEM, UNIV WIS-LA CROSSE, 75- *Personal Data:* b Scottsburg, Ind, Apr 18, 39; m 72. *Educ:* Hanover Col, BA, 61; Ind Univ, MS, 64, PhD(org chem), 68. *Prof Exp:* Res chemist, Reilly Tar & Chem Co, 64-65; fel org chem, Ind Univ, 68. *Mem:* AAAS; Am Chem Soc. *Res:* Preparation and use of sulfonamides as organic chelating reagents; new synthetic methods in organic chemistry. *Mailing Add:* Chem Dept Univ Wis La Crosse WI 54601

**TONRY, JOHN LANDIS,** EXTRAGALACTIC DYNAMICS, COSMOLOGY. *Current Pos:* PROF, INST ASTRON, HONOLULU, HAWAII, 90. *Personal Data:* US citizen. *Educ:* Princeton Univ, AB, 75; Harvard Univ, MA, 76, PhD(physics), 80. *Prof Exp:* Mem, Inst Advan Study, 80-82; Bantrell fel, Calif Inst Technol, 82-85; asst prof, Mass Inst Technol, 85-90, assoc prof, Physics Dept, 90- *Concurrent Pos:* Sloan Found fel, 86; NSF presidential young investr, 89. *Mem:* Am Astron Soc; Int Astron Union. *Res:* Observations of extragalactic objects intended to uncover the nature of dark matter; structure and evolution of the universe. *Mailing Add:* Inst Astron 2680 Woodlawn Dr Honolulu HI 96822

**TON-THAT, TUONG,** REPRESENTATIONS OF LIE GROUPS, MATHEMATICAL PHYSICS. *Current Pos:* from asst prof to assoc prof, 75-83, PROF MATH, UNIV IOWA, 83- *Personal Data:* b Hue, Vietnam, Feb 1, 43; m 75; Thai-Binh; c Thaian & Thaisan. *Educ:* Univ de Grenoble, France, Licence es Sci, Maitrise es Sci, 69; Univ Calif, MA, 71, PhD(math), 74. *Prof Exp:* Postdoctoral res fel math, Harvard Univ, 74-75. *Concurrent Pos:* Vis assoc prof, Univ Calif, Irvine, 81-82, Univ Southern Calif, 82-83. *Mem:* Am Math Soc; Math Asn Am. *Res:* Theory of representations of lie groups; harmonic analysis and the applications to quantum physics. *Mailing Add:* Dept Math Univ Iowa Iowa City IA 52242-0001. *Fax:* 319-335-0627; *E-Mail:* tonthat@math.uiowa.edu

**TONZETICH, JOHN,** GENETICS. *Current Pos:* Asst prof, 70-77, ASSOC PROF BIOL, BUCKNELL UNIV, 77- *Personal Data:* b Nanaimo, BC, Oct 28, 41; m 78, Susan R; c 2. *Educ:* Univ BC, BSc, 63; Duke Univ, MA, 67, PhD(zool), 72. *Concurrent Pos:* Vis prof, Univ Hawaii, 76-77, Univ BC, 85, Universidad Autonoma, Madrid, 92. *Mem:* Genetics Soc Am. *Res:* Chromosomal inversions in Drosophila species; heterochromatin in Drosophila. *Mailing Add:* Dept Biol Bucknell Univ Lewisburg PA 17837-2005. *Fax:* 717-524-3760; *E-Mail:* tonzetch@bucknell.edu

**TOOHEY, RICHARD EDWARD,** HEALTH PHYSICS. *Current Pos:* PROF HEALTH PHYSICS, COL PHARM, WASH STATE UNIV, 93-, ADJ PROF ENVIRON SCI, 93- *Personal Data:* b Cincinnati, Ohio, Sept 2, 45; m 68. *Educ:* Xavier Univ, AB, 68; Univ Cincinnati, MS, 70, PhD(physics), 73. *Prof Exp:* Asst physicist, Argonne Nat Lab, US Dept Energy, 73-79, biophysicist, 80-87, group leader, 83-87, health physics mgr, 87-90, dosimetry & analytical serv mgr, 91-93. *Concurrent Pos:* Assoc dir, US Transuranium & Uranium Registries; dir, Health Physics Soc, 90-93. *Mem:* Health Physics Soc; Am Phys Soc; Sigma Xi; Am Acad Health Physics. *Res:* Human radiobiology; whole-body counting; metabolism of radionuclides; radon measurements. *Mailing Add:* 114 Emory Lane Oak Ridge TN 37830-7734. *Fax:* 509-375-1817

**TOOHIG, TIMOTHY E,** EXPERIMENTAL HIGH ENERGY PHYSICS. *Current Pos:* DIR, JESUIT COMMUNITY, FAIRFIELD UNIV, 94- *Personal Data:* b Lawrence, Mass, Feb 17, 28. *Educ:* Boston Col, BS, 51; Univ Rochester, MS, 53; Johns Hopkins Univ, PhD(physics), 62; Woodstock Col, STB, 64, STL, 65. *Prof Exp:* Asst dir admin res, Inst Natural Sci, Woodstock Col, 63-66; assoc physicist, Brookhaven Nat Lab, 67-70; assoc head neutrino lab sect, Nat Accelerator Lab, 70-74; asst to head res div, Fermi Nat Accelerator Lab, 74-76, head, Meson Dept, 77-78, group leader construct & scheduling, Accelerator Div, 79-86, staff physicist, 86-89, dept head, Conventional Fac Div, URA Superconducting Supercollider, Cent Design Group, 85-89, dep assoc dir, Conventional Construct Div, Superconducting Supercollider Lab, 89-94. *Concurrent Pos:* Res physicist, Joint Inst Nuclear Res, Dubna, USSR, 78-79. *Mem:* Am Phys Soc; AAAS. *Res:* Elementary particle physics; investigation of the properties and interactions of elementary particles; high energy particle accelerators. *Mailing Add:* Jesuit Community Fairfield Univ Fairfield CT 06430

**TOOKE, WILLIAM RAYMOND, JR,** CHEMICAL ENGINEERING. *Current Pos:* head indust prod br, 66-72, PRES, TOOKE ENG ASSOCS, 72- *Personal Data:* b Atlanta, Ga, June 18, 25; m 48; c 3. *Educ:* Ga Inst Technol, BChE, 49, MSChE, 55. *Prof Exp:* Res asst, Ga Technol Exp Sta, 49-55; process engr, Am Viscose Corp, 55-58; tech dir paint res, Oliver B Cannon & Sons, 58-60; sr res engr, Eng Exp Sta, Ga Inst Technol, 60-66. *Concurrent Pos:* Consult, Am Viscose Corp, 60-61, Southern Mills, Inc, 62-64 & Thomas Mfg Co, 64-; NIH grant, 63-67; mem comt A2GO2, Hwy Res Bd. *Mem:* Am Chem Soc; Am Inst Chem Engrs; Am Soc Testing & Mat; Nat Asn Corrosion Engrs; Sigma Xi. *Res:* Protective coatings and plastics technology; thermoplastic films, corrosion engineering; instrumentation and testing methods for coatings and plastics. *Mailing Add:* PO Box 13804 Atlanta GA 30324-0804

**TOOKER, EDWIN WILSON,** ECONOMIC GEOLOGY. *Current Pos:* geologist, Base & Ferrous Metals Br & Pac Mineral Resources Br, 53-71, chief, Pac Mineral Resources Br, 71-72, chief, Off Mineral Resources, 72-76, RES GEOLOGIST MINERAL RESOURCES, WESTERN MINERAL RESOURCE BR, US GEOL SURV, 76- *Personal Data:* b Concord, Mass, May 9, 23; m 46; c 3. *Educ:* Bates Col, BS, 47; Lehigh Univ, MS, 49; Univ Ill, PhD(geol), 52. *Prof Exp:* NSF fel, Univ Ill, 52-53. *Mem:* Soc Econ Geologists; Geol Soc Am; Sigma Xi. *Res:* Geology of base and precious metals ore deposits of Utah; metalogenesis and environment of ore deposition; wall rock alteration; base metal commodity resources; industrial rock & mineral resources. *Mailing Add:* 1 W Edith Ave Apt B-209 Los Altos CA 94022

**TOOKER, GARY LAMARR,** TECHNICAL MANAGEMENT. *Current Pos:* Staff mem, Motorola Inc, 62-80, vpres & gen mgr, Int Semiconductor Div, 80-81, sr vpres & gen mgr, Semiconductor Prods Sector, 82-83, exec vpres & gen mgr, 83-86, sr exec vpres, 86-90, chief corp staff officer, 86-88, chief operating officer, 88-93, pres, 90-93, chief exec officer, 93-96, CHMN BD, MOTOROLA INC, 97- *Personal Data:* b Shelby, Ohio, May 25, 39. *Educ:* Ariz State Univ, BSEE, 62. *Mem:* Nat Acad Eng; Inst Elec & Electronics Engrs; Am Mgt Asn; Semiconductor Indust Asn; Am Electronics Asn. *Mailing Add:* Motorola Inc 1303 E Algonquin Rd Schaumburg IL 60196

**TOOKEY, HARVEY LLEWELLYN,** BIOCHEMISTRY. *Current Pos:* RETIRED. *Personal Data:* b Hooper, Nebr, Dec 2, 22; m 50; c 4. *Educ:* Univ Nebr, AB, 44, MS, 50; Purdue Univ, PhD(biochem), 55. *Prof Exp:* Sr control chemist, Norden Lab, Nebr, 46-48; res chemist, USDA, 55-77, res leader natural toxicants res, Northern Regional Res Ctr, 77-83. *Mem:* Sigma Xi. *Res:* Enzymes of lipid metabolism; proteinases, enzymes acting on glucosinolates; chemistry of natural products; alkaloids; non-infectious diseases of cattle. *Mailing Add:* 5330 N Isabel Ave Peoria IL 61614

**TOOLE, BRYAN PATRICK,** DEVELOPMENTAL & CELL BIOLOGY, CANCER. *Current Pos:* chair anat & cell biol, 85-92, PROF ANAT & CELLULAR BIOL, SCH MED, TUFTS UNIV, 80- *Personal Data:* b Clunes, Australia, Nov 6, 40; div; c 2. *Educ:* Univ Melbourne, BSc, 62; Monash Univ, Australia, MSc, 65, PhD(biochem), 68. *Prof Exp:* Instr med, Harvard Med Sch, 70-72, asst prof biochem, 72-75; asst biochemist med, Mass Gen Hosp, 72-78, assoc biochemist, 78-80; assoc prof anat, Med Sch, Harvard Univ, 75-80. *Concurrent Pos:* Estab investr, Am Heart Asn, 73-78, mem, basic sci coun, 76-78; prin investr, Nat Inst Dent Res, 75-, Nat Inst Childhealth, 88- *Mem:* Am Asn Cancer Res; Soc Develop Biol; Am Soc Cell Biol; AAAS. *Res:* Role of extracellular macromolecules in embryonic development and adult tissue remodelling and their influence on normal and aberrant cell behavior. *Mailing Add:* Dept Anat & Cell Biol Sch Med Tufts Univ 136 Harrison Ave Boston MA 02111-1800. *Fax:* 617-636-0380; *E-Mail:* btoole@infonet.tufts.edu

**TOOLE, JAMES FRANCIS,** STROKE, NEUROLOGY. *Current Pos:* chmn, Dept Neurol, 62-83, WALTER C TEAGLE PROF NEUROL & STROKE CTR DIR, BOWMAN GRAY SCH MED, 83- *Personal Data:* b Atlanta, Ga, Mar 22, 25; m 52; c 4. *Educ:* Princeton Univ, BA, 47; Cornell Univ, MD, 49; LaSalle Exten Univ, LLB, 63. *Prof Exp:* Intern, Univ Pa, 49-50, resident internal med, 53-55, resident neurol, 56-58, instr, 59-60, assoc, 60-61; flight surgeon, USN, 53-55. *Concurrent Pos:* Fulbright fel, Nat Hosp, London, 55-56; mem res comt, Am Heart Asn, 65, chmn, Med Ethics Comt, 66-70, ed, Current Concepts Cerebrovasc Dis-Stroke, 68-72; chmn, Sixth & Seventh Princeton Conf Cerebrovasc Dis, 68 & 70; vis prof, Univ Calif, San Diego, 69-70; mem exam bd, Nat Bd Med Examr & Am Bd Psychol & Neurol; consult, WHO, Japan, 72, Moscow, 68, Abidjean, Ivory Coast, 77 & Switz, 74; FDA adv comt, 76-80; mem, Stroke Long Range Planning Comt, Nat Inst Neurol & Commun Disorders & Stroke, 81, adv comt, 80-83; adv bd, Am Soc NeuroImaging, 83, vpres, 90; counr, Am Neurol Asn; ed-in-chief, J Neurol Sci, 90-97. *Mem:* Am Neurol Asn (secy-treas, 78-82, pres-elect, 84-85, pres, 85-86); Am Clin & Climat Asn; World Fedn Neurol (secy-treas gen, 82-89); Am Osler Soc; Ger Soc Neurol. *Res:* Cerebral circulation and cerebrovascular diseases; physiology and pathology of the brain. *Mailing Add:* Bowman Gray Sch Med Neurol Medical Center Blvd Winston Salem NC 27157-1068

**TOOLES, CALVIN W(ARREN),** CIVIL ENGINEERING. *Current Pos:* RETIRED. *Personal Data:* b Burlington, Vt, June 3, 21; m 43; c 1. *Educ:* Univ Vt, BS, 43; Iowa State Col, MS, 50. *Prof Exp:* Instr eng drawing, Univ Vt, 46-47; instr civil eng, Iowa State Col, 48-50; from asst prof to assoc prof, Va Polytech Inst, 51-60; assoc prof civil eng, Ga Inst Technol, 60-86. *Mem:* Am Soc Civil Engrs; Am Soc Eng Educ; Am Soc Photogram; Am Cong Surv & Mapping. *Res:* Geodetic and photogrammetric engineering. *Mailing Add:* 3632 Eaglerock Dr Atlanta GA 30340

**TOOLEY, RICHARD DOUGLAS,** GEOPHYSICS, SYSTEMS ENGINEERING. *Current Pos:* chief scientist mission & systs analysis unit, Northrop Systs Labs, Hawthorne, 64-69, Palos Verdes, 69-72, prin systs engr, Electro-Mech Div, 72-88, SR RES ENGR, ELECTRONIC SYST DIV, NORTHROP CORP, 88- *Personal Data:* b Baltimore, Md, Apr 11, 32; m 84; c 3. *Educ:* Mass Inst Technol, SB, 54, PhD(geophys), 58. *Prof Exp:* Res physicist, Calif Res Corp, 58-64. *Mem:* Sigma Xi; Am Defense Preparedness Asn; Asn Old Crows. *Res:* Space science; solid body geophysics; rock physics; ultrasonic wave propagation; data processing; electrooptical systems; infrared systems; military systems analysis. *Mailing Add:* 918 Brent Circle Placentia CA 92870-3603

**TOOLEY, WILLIAM HENRY,** pediatrics; deceased, see previous edition for last biography

**TOOM, PAUL MARVIN,** BIOCHEMISTRY. *Current Pos:* assoc vpres, Grad Studies & Res, 86-89, exec dir planning & policy, 89-92, PROF CHEM, SOUTHWEST MO STATE UNIV, 86- *Personal Data:* b Pella, Iowa, Apr 1, 42; m 65, Diane Schwartz; c 2. *Educ:* Cent Col, Iowa, BA, 64; Colo State

Univ, PhD(biochem), 69. *Prof Exp:* Res asst biochem, Colo State Univ, 67-68, asst prof, 69-70; from asst prof to prof biochem, Univ Southern Miss, 70-86, dir res & sponsored prog, 84-86. *Mem:* AAAS; Am Chem Soc; Sigma Xi. *Res:* Analytical biochemistry. *Mailing Add:* Dept Chem Southwest Mo State Univ Springfield MO 64804

**TOOME, VOLDEMAR,** PHYSICAL CHEMISTRY. *Current Pos:* sr phys res chemist, Hoffmann-La Roche, Inc, 57-66, res fel, 67-70, group chief, 70-77, sr group chief, 78-85, RES LEADER, HOFFMANN-LA ROCHE, INC, 85- *Personal Data:* b Estonia, Sept 10, 24; m 52, Heowig Lager; c Birgit K. *Educ:* Univ Bonn, dipl, 48 & 52, Dr rer nat, 54. *Prof Exp:* Sci asst, Inst Phys Chem, Univ Bonn, 54; dept head control div, Merck & Co, Ger, 54-57. *Concurrent Pos:* Ed, Analytical Sect, J Amino Acids, 89. *Mem:* Am Chem Soc; NY Acad Sci. *Res:* Ultraviolet and infrared spectroscopy; optical rotatory dispersion and circular dichroism; instrumental analysis; polarography; electrochemistry; dissociation constants of organic acids and bases; physical organic chemistry; microanalysis; gas chromatography, fourier transform infrared spectroscopy; mass spectroscopy; nuclear magnetic resonance spectroscopy. *Mailing Add:* 90 Versailles Blvd Cherry Hill NJ 08003

**TOOMEY, JAMES MICHAEL,** otorhinolaryngology, for more information see previous edition

**TOOMEY, JOSEPH EDWARD,** SYNTHETIC ORGANIC CHEMISTRY, STRUCTURAL CHEMISTRY. *Current Pos:* SECT HEAD, REILLY LAB, REILLY TAR & CHEM CO, 75- *Personal Data:* b Somerville, NJ, Aug 8, 43; m 67; c 4. *Educ:* Rider Col, BS, 70; Purdue Univ, PhD(org chem), 76. *Mem:* Am Chem Soc; AAAS. *Res:* Synthesis, isolation and structural determination of pyridine chemicals; electrochemistry of heterocyclic compounds; prediction of optical rotatory power, its relation to molecular structure and absolute configuration; unusual Diels-Adler condensation reactions; electroorganic synthesis; electroorganic synthesis. *Mailing Add:* 4840 Sunpoint Circle No 609 Indianapolis IN 46237

**TOOMRE, ALAR,** ASTRONOMY, APPLIED MATHEMATICS. *Current Pos:* C L E Moore instr math, 60-62, from asst prof to assoc prof, 63-70, PROF APPL MATH, MASS INST TECHNOL, 70- *Personal Data:* b Rakvere, Estonia, Feb 5, 37; US citizen; m 58, Joyce Stetson; c Lars, Erik & Anya. *Educ:* Mass Inst Technol, BS(aeronaut eng) & BS(physics), 57; Univ Manchester, PhD(fluid mech), 60. *Honors & Awards:* Brouwer Award, Am Astron Soc, 93. *Prof Exp:* Fel astrophys, Inst Advan Study, 62-63. *Concurrent Pos:* Guggenheim fel astrophys, Calif Inst Technol, 69-70; Fairchild fel, 75; MacArthur fel, 84-89. *Mem:* Nat Acad Sci; AAAS; Am Acad Arts & Sci; Am Astron Soc; Int Astron Union. *Res:* Dynamical studies of galaxies; aerodynamics; rotating fluids. *Mailing Add:* Dept Math Rm 2-371 Mass Inst Technol Cambridge MA 02139. *E-Mail:* toomre@math.mit.edu

**TOON, OWEN BRIAN,** ASTRONOMY, CLIMATOLOGY. *Current Pos:* PROF, DEPT ATMOSPHERIC & OCEANOG SCI, UNIV COLO, 97- *Personal Data:* b Bethesda, Md, May 26, 47; m 68; c 1. *Educ:* Univ Calif, Berkeley, AB, 69; Cornell Univ, PhD(physics), 75. *Honors & Awards:* Medal Except Sci Achievement, NASA, 83 & 89; Int Peace Garden Award, Univ NDak, 84; Leo Sziland Award, Am Physics Soc, 85. *Prof Exp:* Res assoc, Nat Res Coun, 75-77 & Cornell Univ, 77-78; res scientist, Ames Res Ctr, NASA, 78-97. *Mem:* Fel Am Meterol Soc; Am Astron Soc; fel Am Geophys Soc. *Res:* Physics of terrestrial and planetary climates with emphasis on clouds, aerosols and radiative transfer; volcanos and climate, troposheric aerosols and climate change on Mars; clouds of Mars, Venus and Titan; nuclear winter; ozone hole physics and chemistry. *Mailing Add:* Univ Colo Campus Box 392 Boulder CO 80309-0392. *Fax:* 650-604-3625

**TOONEY, NANCY MARION,** BIOCHEMISTRY, BIOPHYSICS. *Current Pos:* asst prof, Polytech Inst NY, 73-77, assoc dean Arts & Sci, 88-90, assoc provost acad affairs, 90-93, asst vpres acad affairs, 93-95, ASSOC PROF BIOCHEM, POLYTECH INST NY, 77-, ASST VPROVOST ACAD AFFAIRS, 96- *Personal Data:* b Ilion, NY, Feb 19, 39. *Educ:* State Univ NY, Albany, BS, 60, MS, 61; Brandeis Univ, PhD(biochem), 66. *Prof Exp:* Teaching intern biochem, Dept Chem & Biol, Hope Col, 66-67; fel biophys, Childrens Cancer Res Found & Sch Med, Harvard Univ, 67-73. *Concurrent Pos:* NIH fel, 67-70, res career develop award, Nat Heart, Lung & Blood Inst, 75-80; environ consult, 88- *Mem:* AAAS; Am Chem Soc; Sigma Xi; Asn Women Sci. *Res:* Protein chemistry, electron microscopy and optical methods of analysis; structure and function of fibronectin; the blood clotting protein, fibrinogen; biological macromolecules; environmental chemistry. *Mailing Add:* Polytech Univ 6 Metrotech Ctr Brooklyn NY 11201. *E-Mail:* ntooney@duke.poly.edu

**TOONG, TAU-YI,** mechanical engineering, for more information see previous edition

**TOOP, EDGAR WESLEY,** ORNAMENTAL HORTICULTURE. *Current Pos:* RETIRED. *Personal Data:* b Chilliwack, BC, Feb 26, 32; m 59, Muriel McPherson; c Laurie, Elizabeth, Amy & Lyle. *Educ:* Univ BC, BSA, 55; Ohio State Univ, MSc, 57, PhD(plant path). 60. *Prof Exp:* Res officer, Can Dept Agr, 55-56; instr bot, Ohio State Univ, 61-62; from asst prof to prof hort, Univ Alta, 62-87. *Mem:* Agr Inst Can; Can Soc Hort Sci (secy-treas, 78-81); Int Soc Hort Sci; Sigma Xi. *Res:* Greenhouse flower crops; herbaceous ornamentals; controlled environment studies. *Mailing Add:* 42 Lafonde Crescent St Albert AB T8N 2N6 Can

**TOOR, ARTHUR,** RADIATION TRANSPORT, ASTROPHYSICS. *Current Pos:* Staff physicist, High Altitude Physics Group, Lawrence Livermore Nat Lab, 63-76, leader, Laser Appln Prog, 76-78, Space Appln Proj, 78-81, Exp Non-Equilibrium Radiation Physics, 81-86, sci adv, Nuclear Testing Prog, 86-91, dep assoc dir nuclear testing & exp sci, 91-95, CHIEF SCIENTIST, LAWRENCE LIVERMORE NAT LAB, 95- *Personal Data:* b Altadena, Calif, Aug 17, 38; m 62, Djohariah Applewhite; c Abraham, Herbert, Mariam & Sarah. *Educ:* Univ Calif, Berkeley, BA, 62. *Hon Degrees:* PhD, Univ Leister, Eng, 77. *Honors & Awards:* Sci Excellence Award, Dept Energy, 85, Indus Res & Develop, 87. *Concurrent Pos:* Consult, NASA, 78-; pvt consult, Remote Sensing, 91- *Mem:* Am Astron Soc; Am Phys Soc; Soc Optical Engrs; AAAS. *Res:* High-energy astrophysics; dense plasma physics; space physics; x-ray laser kinetics; magneto-hydrodynamics; remote sensing instruments; buried object detection. *Mailing Add:* Physics Space Tech Lawrence Livermore Nat Lab PO Box 808 Livermore CA 94550. *Fax:* 510-423-6633; *E-Mail:* toor1@llnl.gov

**TOOR, H(ERBERT) L(AWRENCE),** CHEMICAL ENGINEERING. *Current Pos:* from asst prof to assoc prof chem eng, Carnegie Mellon Univ, 53-61, head dept, 67-70, dean eng, 70-79, prof, 61-80, MOBAY PROF CHEM ENG, CARNEGIE MELLON UNIV, 80- *Personal Data:* b Philadelphia, Pa, June 22, 27; m 50; c 3. *Educ:* Drexel Inst Technol, BS, 48; Northwestern Univ, MS, 50, PhD(chem eng), 52. *Honors & Awards:* Colburn Award, Am Inst Chem Engrs, 64, McAfee Award Chem Eng Excellence, 86; Award Excellence Mixing Res, NAm Mixing Forum, 93. *Prof Exp:* Res chemist, Monsanto Chem Ltd, 52-53. *Concurrent Pos:* UNESCO prof, AC Col, Madras, India. *Mem:* Nat Acad Eng; fel AAAS; fel Am Inst Chem Engrs; Am Chem Soc; Sigma Xi. *Res:* Transport phenomena; heat and mass transfer; chemical reactions with mixing. *Mailing Add:* Carnegie Mellon Univ Dept Chem Eng Pittsburgh PA 15213. *Fax:* 412-268-2183; *E-Mail:* ht16@andrew.cmu.edu

**TOOTHILL, RICHARD B,** ORGANIC CHEMISTRY. *Current Pos:* res chemist, 64-67, group leader, Bound Brook Labs, 67-73, dyes res group leader, 73-78, elastomers res group leader, 78-80, TECH DIR COLOR TEXTILE, CHEM INTERMEDIATES DEPT & TEXTILE CHEM & PLASTICS ADDITIVES DEPT, AM CYANAMID CO, 81- *Personal Data:* b Philadelphia, Pa, July 28, 36; m 59; c 2. *Educ:* Lehigh Univ, BS, 58; Mass Inst Technol, MS, 60; Univ Del, PhD(org chem), 64. *Prof Exp:* Tech serv rep paper chem, Hercules Powder Co, 60-61, chemist, 61-62. *Mem:* Am Chem Soc. *Res:* Thiosemicarbazones; s-triazines; benzothiazoles; anthraquinone derivatives; polyurethanes; millable gum; synthetic rubber; wrinkle recovery agents; light absorbers; antioxidants; lead stabilizers; pigments. *Mailing Add:* 16 Sunrise Dr Warren NJ 07059

**TOP, FRANKLIN HENRY, JR,** microbiology, virology; deceased, see previous edition for last biography

**TOPAZIAN, RICHARD G,** ORAL & MAXILLOFACIAL SURGERY. *Current Pos:* PROF ORAL & MAXILLOFACIAL SURG & HEAD DEPT, SCH DENT MED & PROF SURG, SCH MED, UNIV CONN, FARMINGTON, 75- *Personal Data:* b Greenwich, Conn, Feb 2, 30; m 58; c 4. *Educ:* Houghton Col, BA, 51; McGill Univ, DDS, 55; Univ Pa, cert oral surg, 57; Am Bd Oral Surg, dipl, 64. *Prof Exp:* Lectr dent & oral surg, Christian Med Col, Vellore, India, 59-61, reader, 61-63; from asst prof to assoc prof oral surg, Col Dent, Univ Ky, 63-67; prof & chmn dept, Sch Dent & Sch Med, Med Col Ga, 67-75. *Concurrent Pos:* Mem, Coun Dent Educ, Am Dent Asn; mem, Adv Comt, Am Bd Oral Surg, 67-75; sect ed, J Oral & Maxillofacial Surg, 82-93; dir, Dent Serv, Med Group Missions Int. *Mem:* AAAS; Am Dent Asn; Am Asn Oral & Maxillofacial Surgeons; Int Asn Dent Res; fel Am Col Dentists; fel Int Col Dentists. *Res:* Dental education; research in oral surgery; bone pathology; diseases of the temporomandibular joint; jaw infections. *Mailing Add:* 96 Tunxis Village Farmington CT 06032

**TOPCIK, BARRY,** CHEMICAL ENGINEERING. *Current Pos:* CONSULT, 87- *Personal Data:* b Passaic, NJ, Apr 7, 24; m 50, Marilyn Rothman. *Educ:* Cooper Union, BChE, 52; Newark Col Eng, MS, 60. *Prof Exp:* Sr develop engr, Uniroyal, Inc, 44-56; chief chemist, Eberhard Faber, Inc, 56-62; proj leader butyl lab, Columbian Div, Cities Serv Co, 62-64, asst mgr butyl lab, 64-67, mgr new appln lab, Cranbury, 67-77; tech mat mgr, Rhein Chemie, Trenton, 77-83; consult, Union Carbide Corp, Bound Brook, NJ, 84-87. *Mem:* Am Chem Soc; Am Inst Chem Engrs; Am Mgt Asn. *Res:* Rubber technology, including formulation, engineering, and product development associated with laboratory research and application to production; plastics compounding, moisture cure, adhesives, TPE's, polymer alloying, wire and cable formulation. *Mailing Add:* 7902 NW 86th Terr Tamarac FL 33321

**TOPEL, DAVID GLEN,** AGRICULTURAL RESEARCH. *Current Pos:* DEAN & DIR COL AGR, IOWA STATE UNIV, 88- *Personal Data:* b Lake Mills, Wis, Oct 24, 37; m 64, Jackie Richardson. *Educ:* Univ Wis-Madison, BS, 60; Kans State Univ, MS, 62; Mich State Univ, PhD(food sci), 65. *Honors & Awards:* Res Award, Am Asn Animal Sci, 79. *Prof Exp:* Prof animal sci, Iowa State Univ, 73-79; prof & head animal sci, Auburn Univ, 79-88. *Concurrent Pos:* Fulbright fel, Royal Vet & Agr Univ, Copenhagen, Denmark, 71-72; mem Gov's sci adv coun, State Iowa, 89-93. *Mem:* Am Meat Sci Asn; Am Soc Animal Sci. *Res:* Stress adaption with special emphasis on muscle physiology and metabolic functions with the pig. *Mailing Add:* 2630 Meadow Glen Rd Ames IA 50010

**TOPHAM, RICHARD WALTON,** BIOCHEMISTRY. *Current Pos:* from asst prof to assoc prof, 71-82, PROF & CHMN, DEPT CHEM, UNIV RICHMOND, 82- *Personal Data:* b Montgomery, WVa, May 22, 43; m 67; c 1. *Educ:* Hampden-Sydney Col, BS, 65; Cornell Univ, PhD(biochem), 70. *Prof Exp:* NIH fel, Fla State Univ, 69-71. *Concurrent Pos:* Res scientist, Res Corp grant, 75-77; NIH grant, 77- *Mem:* Am Chem Soc Res. *Res:* Role of copper-containing enzymes of blood serum in iron metabolism; mechanism and regulation of intestinal absorption; iron metabolism in marine organisms. *Mailing Add:* Rte 1 11821 Young Manor Dr Midlothian VA 23113-2026

**TOPICH, JOSEPH,** INORGANIC CHEMISTRY. *Current Pos:* ASST PROF CHEM, VA COMMONWEALTH UNIV, 76- *Personal Data:* b Steubenville, Ohio, Apr 25, 48; m 71; c 2. *Educ:* Columbia Univ, BA, 70; Case Western Res Univ, PhD(chem), 74. *Prof Exp:* Res assoc, Univ Chicago, 74-76. *Mem:* Am Chem Soc; Sigma Xi. *Res:* Synthesis and characterization of new molybdenum coordination complexes; chemical properties are correlated with ligand structure and molybdenum oxidation state. *Mailing Add:* Dept Chem Va Commonwealth Univ Richmond VA 23284-2006

**TOPLISS, JOHN G,** MEDICINAL CHEMISTRY. *Current Pos:* adj prof, 83-91, PROF MED CHEM, UNIV MICH, 92- *Personal Data:* b Mansfield, Eng, June 3, 30; nat US; m 58, Geraldine Brabazon; c Eric & Martin. *Educ:* Univ Nottingham, BSc, 51, PhD(chem), 54. *Prof Exp:* Res fel chem, Royal Inst Technol, Stockholm, Sweden, 54-56 & Columbia Univ, 56-57; from res chemist to sr res chemist, Schering-Plough Corp, 57-66, sect leader, 66-68, from asst dir to assoc dir chem res, 68-73, dir chem res, 73-75, sr dir chem res, 75-79; dir, 79-83, Warner Lambert/Parke Davis, vpres chem, 83-91. *Mem:* Am Chem Soc; Royal Soc Chem; fel AAAS. *Res:* Design, synthesis, and structure-activity relationships of drugs. *Mailing Add:* 364 Ausable Pl Ann Arbor MI 48104-1810

**TOPOFF, HOWARD RONALD,** BIOLOGY, ANIMAL BEHAVIOR. *Current Pos:* asst prof, 70-76, assoc prof, 76-79, PROF PSYCHOL, HUNTER COL, 80-; RES ASSOC ANIMAL BEHAV, AM MUS NATURAL HIST, 70- *Personal Data:* b New York, NY, May 7, 41. *Educ:* City Col NY, BS, 64, PhD(biol), 68. *Prof Exp:* Lectr biol, City Col NY, 67-68; res fel animal behav, Am Mus Natural Hist, 68-70. *Mem:* AAAS; Animal Behav Soc; NY Acad Sci. *Res:* Behavioral development in social insects; insect communication, behavior and physiology. *Mailing Add:* Dept Psychol Hunter Col New York NY 10021. *E-Mail:* htopoff@aol.com

**TOPOLESKI, LEONARD DANIEL,** PLANT BREEDING, VEGETABLE CROPS. *Current Pos:* From asst prof to assoc prof, 62-78, PROF VEG CROPS, PEST IDENTIFICATION & GEN HORT, NY STATE COL AGR & LIFE SCI, CORNELL UNIV, 78- *Personal Data:* b Wilkes-Barre, Pa, Apr 11, 35; m 58, Janice I Makaravitz; c Leonard D, Tamara A & Daniel T. *Educ:* Pa State Univ, BS, 57, MS, 59; Purdue Univ, PhD(genetics, plant breeding), 62. *Mem:* Am Soc Hort Sci. *Res:* Genetics; vegetative hybridization; physiology of interspecific incompatibility; greenhouse vegetable production. *Mailing Add:* Dept Fruit & Veg Sci Cornell Univ 151 Plant Sci Bldg Ithaca NY 14853-0001. *Fax:* 607-255-0599

**TOPOREK, MILTON,** BIOCHEMISTRY, LIVER METABOLISM. *Current Pos:* RETIRED. *Personal Data:* b New York, NY, Apr 18, 20; m 42, Pauline Schwartz; c 3. *Educ:* Brooklyn Col, BA, 40; George Washington Univ, MA, 48; Univ Rochester, PhD(biochem), 52. *Prof Exp:* Res assoc org chem, George Washington Univ, 48; res assoc biochem, Univ Rochester, 48-52; res chemist, Univ Mich, 52-57; from asst prof to assoc prof biochem, Jefferson Med Col, Thomas Jefferson Univ, 58-72, prof, 72-83. *Mem:* AAAS; Am Chem Soc; Am Inst Nutrit; Am Soc Biochem & Molecular Biol; NY Acad Sci; Sigma Xi. *Res:* Control of plasma protein synthesis by liver, relationship to disease states; vitamin B-12, intrinsic factor relationships. *Mailing Add:* 4667 Oak Forest Dr E Sarasota FL 34231-6416

**TOPP, EDWARD,** BIODEGRADATION OF ORGANIC POLLUTANTS, SOIL BIOGEOCHEMICAL CYCLING. *Current Pos:* RES SCIENTIST, PEST MGT RES CTR, AGR CAN RES BR, 88- *Personal Data:* b Montreal, Que, Apr 25, 58. *Educ:* McGill Univ, BSc, 81, MSc, 83; Univ Minn, PhD(microbiol), 88. *Concurrent Pos:* Adj prof microbiol, Dept Natural Resources Sci, McGill Univ, 92- *Res:* Physiology, biochemistry and genetics of pesticide degrading bacteria; bioremediation of soil contaminated with organic pollutions; effects of agrochemicals on soil microorganisms; methane oxidation by bacterial isolation and in soils. *Mailing Add:* Pest Mgt Res Ctr 1391 Sandford St London ON N5V 4T3 Can

**TOPP, G CLARKE,** SOIL SCIENCE, PHYSICS. *Current Pos:* res scientist soil physics, 65-87, Head Res Prog Land Resources, 87-91, RES SCIENTIST, CROP PROD, AGR CAN, 91- *Personal Data:* b Canfield, Can, Nov 12, 37; m 62, Eleanor Bruce; c Karen, Bruce & Brenda. *Educ:* Univ Toronto, BSA, 59; Univ Wis, MSc, 62, PhD(soils), 64. *Prof Exp:* Res asst soil physics, Univ Wis-Madison, 59-64; res assoc, Univ Ill, 64-65. *Concurrent Pos:* Adj prof, Dept Geog, Carleton Univ, 73-81; vis lectr, Dept Soil Sci, Univ Sask, 80; vis scientist, CSIRO, Australia, 92-93. *Mem:* Fel Can Soc Soil Sci (secy, 69-72, pres, 77-78); Sigma Xi; fel Soil Sci Soc Am; Am Geophys Union. *Res:* Development of instrument to measure soil water content; soil water properties; microhydrology of soils; soil structure; soil and crop management. *Mailing Add:* Eastern Cereal & Oilseed Res Ctr Agr Can Ottawa ON K1A 0C6 Can

**TOPP, WILLIAM CARL,** CELL BIOLOGY. *Current Pos:* GEN MGR, BIOTECHNOL ASSOCS, 86- *Personal Data:* b Cleveland, Ohio, Feb 3, 48; m 84, Marlene J Dermody; c Carl, Andrew & Bryan. *Educ:* Oberlin Col, BA, 69; Princeton Univ, MA, 71, PhD(chem), 73. *Prof Exp:* Res assoc physics, Princeton Univ, 73, instr chem, 73-74, res assoc, 74; res assoc biol, Cold Spring Harbor Lab Quant Biol, 74-76, staff scientist, 76-78, sr staff scientist, 78-83; pres & chief operating officer, Otisville Bio Technol, 83-84; dir molecular biol, Agr Res Div, Am Cyanamid, 85-86. *Concurrent Pos:* Gen mgr, Biotechnol Assoc, 86- *Mem:* Sigma Xi; Am Phys Soc. *Res:* Virus/cell interactions; cell growth control. *Mailing Add:* 351 Shoddy Hollow Rd Otisville NY 10963-2821

**TOPP, WILLIAM ROBERT,** MATHEMATICS. *Current Pos:* from asst prof to assoc prof, 70-79, PROF MATH, UNIV PAC, 80- *Personal Data:* b Milwaukee, Wis, May 27, 39. *Educ:* St Louis Univ, BA, 63, MA, 64; Univ Washington, MS, 67, PhD(math), 68. *Prof Exp:* Instr math, Univ Seattle, 67-68; asst prof, Marquette Univ, 69-70. *Mem:* Math Asn Am; Asn Comput Mach; Opers Res Soc Am. *Res:* Rings; algebras. *Mailing Add:* 456 S Regent St Stockton CA 95204

**TOPPEL, BERT JACK,** REACTOR PHYSICS. *Current Pos:* assoc physicist, 56-66, SR PHYSICIST, REACTOR ANALYSIS DIV, ARGONNE NAT LAB, 66- *Personal Data:* b Chicago, Ill, July 2, 26; m 50, Leona Weiss; c Alison B, Leslie J & Debra L. *Educ:* Ill Inst Technol, BS, 48, MS, 50, PhD(physics), 52. *Prof Exp:* Instr physics, Ill Inst Technol, 49-51; assoc physicist, Brookhaven Nat Lab, 52-56. *Mem:* Am Phys Soc; Am Nuclear Soc. *Res:* Nuclear reactions initiated by charged particles and neutrons; scintillation detector studies of gamma ray events; reactor critical facility experimentation; theoretical reactor physics calculations; reactor physics computer code development. *Mailing Add:* Reactor Analysis Div Argonne Nat Lab Argonne IL 60439

**TOPPER, LEONARD,** CHEMICAL ENGINEERING, SCIENCE POLICY. *Current Pos:* CONSULT, 79- *Personal Data:* b New York, NY, Jan 11, 29. *Educ:* City Col New York, BChE, 48; NY Univ, MChE, 49; Cornell Univ, PhD(chem eng), 51. *Prof Exp:* Asst prof chem eng, Johns Hopkins Univ, 53-55; prog mgr, US AEC, 57-73; sr policy analyst, Off Energy Res & Develop Policy, NSF, 73-75; dir, Div Technol Evaluation, Energy Res & Develop Admin, 75-76; sr policy analyst, Off Sci & Technol Policy, Exec Off President, 76-77; dir, Div Res Assessment, Off Energy Res, US Dept Energy, 77-79. *Mem:* Sigma Xi. *Res:* Energy technology; chemical engineering science; energy research policy. *Mailing Add:* 2126 Connecticut Ave NW Washington DC 20003

**TOPPER, ROBERT QUINN,** CLASSICAL & PATH-INTEGRAL MONTE CARLO COMPUTATIONAL METHODS, REACTION-RATE THEORY. *Current Pos:* ASST PROF CHEM, COOPER UNION ADVAN SCI & ART, 93- *Personal Data:* b Greeley, Colo, July 1, 63. *Educ:* Fla State Univ, BS, 86; Yale Univ, MS & MPhil, 89, PhD(theoret phys chem), 90. *Prof Exp:* Postdoctoral res fel, Minn Supercomput Inst, 90-91; postdoctoral res assoc, Univ Minn, 91-92, Univ RI, 92-93. *Mem:* Am Chem Soc; Am Phys Soc. *Res:* Applications of theoretical chemistry and computational molecular modeling to clusters, materials, superheated gases, DNA carcinogen complexes and airborne pollutants; chemical engineering education. *Mailing Add:* Dept Chem Cooper Union 51 Astor Pl New York NY 10003. *E-Mail:* topper@cooper.edu

**TOPPER, T(IMOTHY) H(AMILTON),** CIVIL ENGINEERING. *Current Pos:* Lectr, Univ Waterloo 62-63, from asst prof to assoc prof, 63-69, assoc chmn dept, 66-72, chmn dept, 72-78, PROF CIVIL ENG, UNIV WATERLOO, 69- *Personal Data:* b Kleinburg, Ont, May 20, 36; m 58; c 3. *Educ:* Univ Toronto, BASc, 59; Cambridge Univ, PhD(fatigue), 62. *Concurrent Pos:* Vis asst res prof, Univ Ill, 66, vis assoc prof, 68; vis res prof, Univ Paraiba, Brazil, 75- *Mem:* Am Soc Metals; Am Soc Testing & Mat; Soc Automotive Engrs. *Res:* Mechanical behavior and fatigue of metals including applications to structures. *Mailing Add:* Dept Civil Eng Univ Waterloo Waterloo ON N2L 3G1 Can. *Fax:* 519-888-6197; *E-Mail:* topper@konee. uwaterloo.ca

**TOPPER, YALE JEROME,** BIOCHEMISTRY. *Current Pos:* mem staff, 54-62, chief sect intermediary metab, 62-87, EMER SCIENTIST, NAT INST ARTHRITIS & METAB DIS, 87- *Personal Data:* b Chicago, Ill, Aug 11, 16; m 56; c 4. *Educ:* Northwestern Univ, BS, 42; Harvard Univ, MA, 43, PhD(chem), 47. *Prof Exp:* Assoc nutrit & physiol, Pub Health Res Inst, City of NY, Inc, 48-53; Am Heart Asn res fel, Biochem Res Lab, Mass Gen Hosp, 53-54. *Mem:* Endocrine Soc; Am Soc Biol Chem. *Res:* Biochemistry of development and differentiation. *Mailing Add:* Develop Biol Nat Inst Diabetes & Digestive & Kidney NIH Bldg 10 Rm 9B18 Bethesda MD 20892-1800. *Fax:* 301-496-0839

**TOPPETO, ALPHONSE A,** ELECTRICAL ENGINEERING. *Current Pos:* RETIRED. *Personal Data:* b Wheeling, WVa, Jan 7, 25; wid; c 3. *Educ:* Carnegie Inst Technol, BS, 48, MS, 49; Univ Mich, PhD(elec eng), 63. *Prof Exp:* From instr to asst prof elec eng, Univ Detroit, 50-60, assoc prof & vchmn dept, 60-63; res physicist, Aladdin Electronics Div, Aladdin Indust, Inc, 63-68, dir res, 66-68, dir res & eng, 68-76; res prof elec eng, Vanderbilt Univ, 76-77; mgr res & develop, Corcom Inc, 77-80 & appln eng, 80-89. *Concurrent Pos:* US deleg, Int Electrotech Comn, 74-89 & Int Comt Radio Interference, 81-89. *Mem:* Inst Elec & Electronics Engrs. *Res:* Characterization and application of ferrites; theoretical and practical design of filters and delay lines; computer aided design methods; development and design of RFI filters. *Mailing Add:* 2025 Roderick Circle Franklin TN 37064

**TOPPING, JOSEPH JOHN,** CHROMATOGRAPHY, SPECTROSCOPY. *Current Pos:* from asst prof to assoc prof, 70-82, PROF CHEM, TOWNSON STATE UNIV, 82- *Personal Data:* b Amsterdam, NY, Oct 9, 42; m 65, Lucille A Masciulli; c Jennifer, Jeffrey & David. *Educ:* Le Moyne Col, NY, BS, 64; Univ NH, MS, 67, PhD(anal chem), 69. *Prof Exp:* Res fel chem, Ames Lab, Iowa State Univ, 69-70. *Concurrent Pos:* Adj prof chem, Univ Md, Baltimore County, 79-86; chmn-elect, Md sect, Am Chem Soc, 88, chmn, 89. *Mem:* AAAS; Am Inst Chemists; Sigma Xi; NY Acad Sci; Am Chem Soc. *Res:* Determination of trace metals and organics in environmental systems; the study of sample/substrate interactions in chromatography; chromatography. *Mailing Add:* Dept Chem Towson State Univ Towson MD 21204. *Fax:* 410-830-2604; *E-Mail:* toppingudsj@toe.towson.edu

**TOPPING, NORMAN HAWKINS,** infectious diseases; deceased, see previous edition for last biography

**TOPPING, RICHARD FRANCIS,** PRODUCT DEVELOPMENT, GAS APPLIANCE ENGINEERING. *Current Pos:* res engr, 78-86, unit mgr, 86-88, DIR TECHNOL & PROD DEVELOP, ARTHUR D LITTLE, INC, 88- *Personal Data:* b Boston, Mass, Dec 19, 49; c 5. *Educ:* Tufts Univ, BS, 71; Mass Inst Technol, MS, 72. *Prof Exp:* Propulsion engr, USAF Aeropropulsion Lab, 72-75; res staff, Mass Inst Technol Energy Lab, 75-78. *Concurrent Pos:* Chmn, Tech Comt 7-1, Am Soc Heating, Refrig & Air Conditioning Engrs, 90-92. *Mem:* Am Soc Mech Engrs; Am Soc Heating, Refrig & Air Conditioning Engrs. *Res:* Product design and commercialization of consumer products, major appliances and natural gas fired equipment; technology-based consulting to global manufacturers of appliances and housewares. *Mailing Add:* Arthur D Little Inc 25 Acorn Park Cambridge MA 02140

**TOPUZ, ERTUGRUL S,** MINING ENGINEERING, MINERAL ECONOMICS & MINE VENTILATION. *Current Pos:* PROF MINING ENG, VA POLYTECH INST & STATE UNIV, 77- *Personal Data:* b Sumnu, Bulgaria, Dec 11, 35; US citizen; m 72; c 1. *Educ:* Istanbul Tech Univ, dipl eng, 59; Univ Calif, Berkeley, MEng, 72; Columbia Univ, DEngSc, 77. *Prof Exp:* Mining engr, Mineral Res & Explor Inst, 59-65, chief planning div, 65-67, asst gen dir, 67-69, mem sci bd, 69-70; asst prof, SDak Sch Mines & Technol, 76-77. *Mem:* Am Inst Mining, Metall & Petrol Engrs; Am Inst Indust Engrs; Chamber Turkish Mining Engrs. *Res:* Mining evaluation and analysis; mineral economics; application of mathematical optimization techniques to problems of mining industry; mine ventilation. *Mailing Add:* Dept Mining & Minerals Eng Va Polytech Inst & State Univ Blacksburg VA 24061-0239

**TORAASON, MARK,** CARDIOVASCULAR TOXICOLOGY. *Current Pos:* Staff mem toxicol, 77-89, CHIEF CELLULAR TOXICOL, CTRS DIS CONTROL, NAT INST OCCUP SAFETY & HEALTH, 89- *Personal Data:* b Spring Valley, Ill, Aug 20, 50. *Educ:* Loyola Univ, BA, 73; Southern Ill Univ, MS, 76; Univ Cincinnati, PhD(toxicol), 83. *Mem:* Am Soc Toxicol; Am Physiol Soc. *Mailing Add:* Ctrs Dis Control Nat Inst Occup Safety & Health 4676 Columbia Pkwy Cincinnati OH 45226-1922

**TORACK, RICHARD M,** PATHOLOGY. *Current Pos:* assoc prof, 68-70, PROF PATH & ANAT, WASHINGTON UNIV, 70- *Personal Data:* b Passaic, NJ, July 23, 27; wid; c 4. *Educ:* Seton Hall Univ, BS, 48; Georgetown Univ, MD, 52. *Prof Exp:* Asst pathologist, Montefiore Hosp, 58-59, asst neuropathologist, 59-61; asst prof path, NY Hosp-Cornell Med Ctr, 62-65, assoc attend pathologist, 62-68, assoc prof, 65-68. *Concurrent Pos:* Nat Cancer Inst fel path, Montefiore Hosp, 58-59; NIH res fel, Yale Med Sch, 61-62; consult, Mem Hosp, 64-68; assoc attend, Barnes Hosp, 68- *Mem:* AAAS; Am Asn Neuropath; Am Asn Path & Bact; Histochem Soc; Am Neurol Asn. *Res:* Electron histochemistry of disease of the nervous system; experimental induction of Alzheimer changes in rat brain. *Mailing Add:* Dept Path Washington Univ Sch Med 660 S Euclid Ave St Louis MO 63110-1010

**TORANZOS, GARY ANTONIO,** ENVIRONMENTAL MICROBIOLOGY & BIOTECHNOLOGY, EDUCATION. *Current Pos:* assoc, 86-88, asst prof, 88-92, ASSOC PROF, DEPT BIOL, UNIV PR, 92- *Personal Data:* b Cochabamba, Bolivia, Apr 5, 58. *Educ:* Univ Ariz, BS, 81, MS, 83, PhD(microbiol), 85. *Prof Exp:* Lab technician, Dept Microbiol, Univ Ariz, 80-82, res assoc, 82-85; assoc, Dept Cell Sci, Univ Fla, 85-86. *Concurrent Pos:* Assoc investr, Dept Path, Univ PR, 87-91, lectr, Dept Biol, 87-88; consult, UN Environ Prog, 91-93, UN Food & Agr Orgn, 93; vpres, Latin-Am Comt Environ Microbiol, 92- *Mem:* Am Soc Microbiol; Am Soc Testing & Mat; Am Water Works Asn. *Res:* Environmental microbiology; environmental biotechnology, bioremediation and the development of new indicators of fecal contamination in tropical waters; detection of pathogens in water, soil and air. *Mailing Add:* Dept Biol GPO Box 23360 San Juan PR 00931-3360. *Fax:* 787-764-3875

**TORBERT, ROY BANKS,** SPARE PLASMA PHYSICS MAGNETOSPHERIC & IONOSPHERIC PHYSICS. *Current Pos:* PROF PHYSICS, UNIV NH, 89- *Personal Data:* b Columbus, Ga, July 5, 49; m 75; c 3. *Educ:* Princeton Univ, BA, 71; Univ Calif, Berkeley, PhD(physics), 79. *Prof Exp:* Assoc res physicist, Univ Calif, San Diego, 81-85; assoc prof physics, Univ Ala, Huntsville, 85-89. *Mem:* Am Geophys Union. *Res:* Investigations into the interacting of the sun with planets and planetary magnetospheres and ionospheres; physics in aurora and in particular filamentary structures; early solar system physics and plasma physics. *Mailing Add:* Physics Dept Univ NH 227 Kingsbury Hall Durham NH 03824. *Fax:* 603-862-1915; *E-Mail:* torbert@unhesp.unh.educ

**TORBETT, EMERSON ARLIN,** OPERATIONS RESEARCH, MATHEMATICS. *Current Pos:* VPRES MKT, MULTIPOINT NETWORK, BELMONT, CALIF, 93- *Personal Data:* b Athens, Tenn, July 20, 39; m 61; c 3. *Educ:* Ga Inst Technol, BS, 61; Univ Md, College Park, MA, 66; Stanford Univ, PhD(opers res), 72. *Prof Exp:* Instr, Ga Inst Technol, 60-61; mathematician, Nat Security Agency, 61-63; res engr, Adaptronics, Inc 63-64 & SRI Int, 64-73; prog mgr, Systs Control, Inc, 73-78; dept mgr, Western Develop Labs Div, Ford Aerospace & Commun Corp, 78-80; dir eng, Icot Corp, 80-83; pres, Cascade Tech, 83-93. *Concurrent Pos:* Lectr, Univ Calif, Berkeley, 69-70; lectr, Stanford Univ, 69-70, res asst, 70-72; adj prof, San Jose State Univ, 73- *Mem:* Opers Res Soc Am; Inst Elec & Electronics Engrs. *Res:* System effectiveness analysis; system simulation; digital filtering and prediction; queueing theory; decision analysis under uncertainty; optimal control of stochastic systems; mathematical system reliability; design/analysis of communication networks/systems. *Mailing Add:* 190 Davis Dr Belmont CA 94002

**TORCH, REUBEN,** PROTOZOOLOGY. *Current Pos:* RETIRED. *Personal Data:* b Chicago, Ill, Dec 20, 26; m 49, Bernice Laffer; c Deborah, Ellen & Amy. *Educ:* Univ Ill, BS, 47, MS, 48, PhD(zool), 53. *Prof Exp:* From instr to assoc prof, Univ Vt, 53-65; from asst dean to actg dean, Col Arts & Sci, Oakland Univ, 66-73, prof biol, 65-80, dean, Col Arts & Sci, 73-80; vpres acad affairs & prof zool, Calif State Univ, Stanislaus, 80-88. *Mem:* Soc Protozoologists; Sigma Xi; Am Soc Cell Biol. *Res:* Taxonomy of marine psammophilic ciliates; nucleic acid synthesis and regeneration in ciliates. *Mailing Add:* 7370 Orangewood Lane Boca Raton FL 33433-7459

**TORCHIA, DENNIS ANTHONY,** BIOPHYSICS. *Current Pos:* BIOPHYSICIST, NAT INST DENT RES, 74- *Personal Data:* b Reading, Pa, June 15, 39; m 67; c 3. *Educ:* Univ Calif, Riverside, BA, 61; Yale Univ, MS, 64, PhD(physics), 67. *Prof Exp:* NIH fel, Med Sch, Harvard Univ, 67-69; mem tech staff polymer chem, Bell Labs, 69-71; physicist, Polymers Div, Nat Bur Stand, 71-74. *Mem:* Am Chem Soc; Am Phys Soc; Biophys Soc. *Res:* Solution state magnetic resonance studies of the molecular conformaton and motion of proteins. *Mailing Add:* NIH Bldg 30 Rm 132 Bethesda MD 20892. *Fax:* 301-402-1512

**TORCHILIN, VLADIMIR PETROVICH,** CONTROLLED DRUG DELIVERY, ARTIFICIAL MEMBRANES. *Current Pos:* DIR CHEM PROG, CTR IMAGING & PHARMACEUT RES, MASS GEN HOSP-HARVARD MED SCH, 93- *Personal Data:* b Moscow, USSR, Sept 13, 46; m 70, Vera Korovkin; c Ekaterina. *Educ:* Moscow State Univ, MS, 68, PhD(polymer chem), 72, DrSci, 81; Acad Mcd Sci, Prof, 85. *Honors & Awards:* Lenin Prize Sci & Technol, USSR, 82. *Prof Exp:* Asst chem, Moscow State Univ, 71-73; sr researcher, USSR Cardiol Res Ctr, 74-80, head lab enzyme eng, 81-91; assoc chemist, Mass Gen Hosp, 91-93. *Concurrent Pos:* Vis prof, Dept Org Chem, Univ Mainz, Ger, 86, Dept Biochem, Univ Tenn, 91; mem, Int Comn Pharmaceut Enzymes, 86-91; lectr drug delivery, Ministry Med Indust, USSR, 88-91; prof biotechnol, Lomonosov Inst Fine Chem Technol, Moscow, 89-91. *Mem:* Soc Nuclear Med; Soc Controlled Release; Am Chem Soc; Russian Acad Biotechnol. *Res:* Targeting and controlled delivery of therapeutic and diagnostic agents; surface-modified liposomes, including immunoliposomes, long-circulating and pH-sensitive liposomes; protein stabilization and immobilization; antibody modification with heavy metals; immunoimaging and immunotherapy; intratumor drug delivery; physiologically-active polymers. *Mailing Add:* CIDR-MGH-East 13th St Bldg 149 Charlestown MA 02129-2020. *Fax:* 617-726-7830

**TORCHINSKY, ALBERTO,** MATHEMATICAL ANALYSIS. *Current Pos:* asst prof, 75-77, assoc prof, 77-80, PROF MATH, IND UNIV, BLOOMINGTON, 80-, DEAN LATINO AFFAIRS, 81- *Personal Data:* b Buenos Aires, Arg, Mar 9, 44; m 69; c 2. *Educ:* Univ Buenos Aires, Licenciado, 66; Univ Wis-Milwaukee, MS, 67; Univ Chicago, PhD(math), 71. *Prof Exp:* Asst prof, Cornell Univ, 71-75. *Concurrent Pos:* Mem, Inst Adv Studies, 77-78; fel, Ctr Math Analysis, Australia Nat Univ, 84. *Mem:* Am Math Soc. *Res:* Problems related to singular integrals; Hp spaces and applications to differential equations. *Mailing Add:* Dept Math Ind Univ Rawles Hall Rm 5701 Bloomington IN 47405-5701

**TORDA, CLARA,** brain physiology, psychiatry, for more information see previous edition

**TORDOFF, HARRISON BRUCE,** ZOOLOGY. *Current Pos:* dir, Bell Mus Natural Hist, 70-82, prof, 70-92, EMER PROF ECOL & BEHAV BIOL, UNIV MINN, MINNEAPOLIS, 92- *Personal Data:* b Mechanicville, NY, Feb 8, 23; m 46; c 2. *Educ:* Cornell Univ, BS, 46; Univ Mich, MA, 49, PhD(zool), 52. *Prof Exp:* Cur birds, Sci Mus, Inst Jamaica, BWI, 46-47; asst prof zool, Univ & asst cur birds, Mus, Univ Kans, 50-57, assoc prof zool & assoc cur birds, 57; from asst prof to prof, Univ & cur birds, Mus Zool, Univ Mich, Ann Arbor, 57-70. *Concurrent Pos:* Ed, Wilson Bull, 52-54. *Mem:* Am Ornithologists' Union (pres, 78-80); Cooper Ornith Soc; Wilson Ornith Soc; fel Am Ornithologists Union. *Res:* Ornithology; systematics; paleontology; morphology; behavior; breeding biology. *Mailing Add:* Bell Mus Natural Hist Univ Minn Minneapolis MN 55455

**TORDOFF, WALTER, III,** POPULATION BIOLOGY. *Current Pos:* From asst prof to assoc prof, 70-81, PROF ZOOL SCI & CHMN, DEPT BIOL SCI, CALIF STATE UNIV, STANISLAUS, 81- *Personal Data:* b Newton, Mass, Jan 2, 43; m 65; c 3. *Educ:* Univ Mass, BA, 65; Colo State Univ, MS, 67, PhD(zool), 71. *Concurrent Pos:* Res consult Bur Land Mgt, Calif Dept Fish

& Game. *Mem:* Am Soc Ichthyologists & Herpetologists; Soc Study Evolution; Soc Study Amphibians & Reptiles; Sigma Xi. *Res:* Ecology and genetics of chapparal and montane populations of reptiles and amphibians, particularly Hydromantes brunus; Gambelia silus. *Mailing Add:* Dept Biol Sci Calif State Univ Stanislaus 801 W Monte Vista Ave Turlock CA 95382. *Fax:* 209-667-3694; *E-Mail:* wally@chem.csustan.edu

**TORELL, DONALD THEODORE,** ANIMAL SCIENCE. *Current Pos:* RETIRED. *Personal Data:* b Mont, Oct 19, 26; m 50; c 2. *Educ:* Mont State Col, BS, 49; Univ Calif, MS, 50. *Prof Exp:* Assoc animal husb, Univ Calif, 49-50, res asst beef cattle invest, 50-51; instr, Ariz State Col, 51; livestock specialist & lectr, Hopland Field Sta, Univ Calif, 51-81. *Concurrent Pos:* Fulbright res sr scholar, Uganda, 61-62; specialist, Univ Chile-Univ Calif Coop Prog, 69-70; livestock specialist & consult, 82- *Mem:* Am Soc Animal Sci. *Res:* Sheep nutrition, genetics, physiology and general sheep improvement. *Mailing Add:* 7950 S Highway 101 Ukiah CA 95482

**TOREN, GEORGE ANTHONY,** ORGANIC CHEMISTRY. *Current Pos:* RETIRED. *Personal Data:* b Chicago, Ill, June 12, 24; m 49. *Educ:* Hope Col, AB, 48; Purdue Univ, MS, 51, PhD(chem). 53. *Prof Exp:* Prod control specialtist, Minn Mining & Mfg Co, St Paul, 53-82. *Mem:* Am Chem Soc. *Res:* Boron and graphite advanced composites; pressure sensitive tapes; urethane foams and films. *Mailing Add:* 678 E Eldridge Ave E St Paul MN 55117-2210

**TOREN, PAUL EDWARD,** ANALYTICAL CHEMISTRY. *Current Pos:* sr chemist, 59-67, res specialist, 67-80, SR RES SPECIALIST, CENT RES LABS, 3M CO, 80- *Personal Data:* b Lincoln, Nebr, July 18, 23; wid; c 3. *Educ:* Univ Nebr, AB, 47, MS, 48; Univ Minn, PhD(chem), 54. *Prof Exp:* Chemist, Phillips Petrol Co, 53-59. *Mem:* Am Chem Soc; Electrochem Soc. *Res:* Electroanalytical chemistry; analytical instrumentation. *Mailing Add:* 805 Park Ave St Paul MN 55115

**TORESON, WILFRED EARL,** PATHOLOGY. *Current Pos:* RETIRED. *Personal Data:* b Calif, Dec 25, 16; m 45; c 1. *Educ:* McGill Univ, MD, 42, MSc, 48, PhD(path), 50; Am Bd Path, dipl & cert clin path, 53. *Prof Exp:* Lectr asst prof, McGill Univ, 46-50, asst prof, 50; from instr to prof, Univ Calif, San Francisco & pathologist, Univ Hosp, 50-66; prof path, State Univ NY Downstate Med Ctr & dir labs, Univ Hosp, 66-70; prof path, Sch Med, Univ Calif, Davis, 70-83. *Concurrent Pos:* Dir labs, South Pac Hosp, Calif, 52-58, consult, Letterman Army Hosp, 58-66; consult, Letterman Army Hosp, 58-66; attend, Ft Miley Vet Admin Hosp, 60-66. *Mem:* Am Asn Pathologists & Bacteriologists; AMA; Col Am Pathologists; Am Soc Clin Path; Int Acad Path. *Res:* Experimental diabetes; automation and computers in clinical pathology. *Mailing Add:* 2836 Lieno Lane Sacramento CA 95821

**TORFS, CLAUDINE PIERETTE,** EPIDEMIOLOGY OF BIRTH DEFECTS, GENETICS OF BIRTH DEFECTS. *Current Pos:* Child Health & Develop Ctr consult, 84-86, EPIDEMIOLOGIST & PRIN INVESTR, CALIF BIRTH DEFECTS MONITORING PROG, 86- *Personal Data:* b Brasschaet, Belg, Sept 21, 29; US citizen; wid; c Marc J Desoer, Michele M Desoer & Craig M Desoer. *Educ:* Liege Univ, Belg, Pre-med; Univ Calif, Berkeley, MS, 78, PhD (epidemiol), 83. *Honors & Awards:* Margaret Beattie Award, Univ Calif, Berkeley, 83. *Prof Exp:* Res fel, Children's Med Ctr, Harvard, 52-53; res reader, Univ Calif, Berkeley, 77, teaching asst, 77-78, res asst, Child Health & Develop Ctr, 78, teaching asst epidemol, Sch Pub Health, 78-79, assoc, 80, jr specialist, 82-83. *Concurrent Pos:* Vis lectr, Univ Calif, Sch Pub Health, 83. *Mem:* AAAS; Am Soc Human Genetics; Europ Teratology Soc; Soc Epidemiol Res; Teratology Soc; Int Genetic Epidemiologists Soc. *Res:* The causes and distribution of birth defects in populations; genetic environmental interactions in the etiology of birth defects. *Mailing Add:* Calif Birth Defects Monitoring Prog 1900 Powell St Suite 1050 Emeryville CA 94608-1811. *Fax:* 510-653-1678

**TORGERSEN, PAUL E,** MINING RESEARCH. *Current Pos:* prof & head, Dept Indust Eng & Opers Res, Va Polytech Inst & State Univ, 67-70, dean, Col Eng 70-90, John Grado prof indust eng & opers res, 87-89, interim pres, 88, John W Hancock, Jr, chair eng, 89-94, pres, Corp Res Ctr, 90-94, PRES, VA POLYTECH INST & STATE UNIV, 94- *Personal Data:* b New York, NY, Oct 13, 31; c 3. *Educ:* Lehigh Univ, BS, 53; Ohio State Univ, MS, 56 & PhD(indust eng), 59. *Prof Exp:* Instr, Ohio State Univ, 56-59; from asst prof to assoc prof, Okla State Univ, 59-66. *Concurrent Pos:* Res assoc, Opers Res Group, Ohio State Univ, 56-59; consult, var co & univs, 61-; dir, Queuing Systs Simulation Res Proj, NSF, 64-65; mem, Coun Tech Div & Comts, Am Soc Eng Educ, 66-68, Dean's Inst Comt, 71-81, bd dirs, 79-81 & Lamme Medal Comt, 90-; mem, Task Force Ethical Pract, Am Inst Indust Engrs, 70-77, chmn, 72-77; inspector, Accreditation Bd Eng & Technol, 70-, mem, Eng Accreditation Comn, 80-85; chmn, Eng Deans Coun, 79-81, Eng Comn, Nat Asn State Univ & Land-Grant Col, 79-83, mem, Comt Construct, Eng Grad Record Exam, 84-86; vpres, Educ & Prof Develop, Int Indust Engrs; dir, Va Mining & Mineral Resources & Res Inst, 79-87; dir, Roanoke Elec Stell, 86- *Mem:* Nat Acad Eng; sr mem Am Inst Indust Engrs; Am Soc Eng Educ (vpres, 80-81); Soc Logistics Engrs; Int Asn Qual Circles; Am Arbitration Asn; Nat Soc Prof Engrs. *Res:* Author of 5 books on industrial engineering; published numerous technical papers. *Mailing Add:* Dept Indust & Systs Eng Va Polytech Inst & State Univ 210 Burroughs Blacksburg VA 24061-0118. *Fax:* 540-231-4265; *E-Mail:* tennis@vt.edu

**TORGERSON, DAVID FRANKLYN,** WASTE MANAGEMENT. *Current Pos:* res chemist, Atomic Energy Can Ltd, 76-78, sect head, 78-79, head chem, 79-84, dir, Appl Sci Div, 84-86, Reactor Safety Div, 86-89, VPRES ENVIRON SCI & WASTE MGT, ATOMIC ENERGY CAN LTD, PINAWA, MAN, 89- *Personal Data:* b Winnipeg, Man, July 11, 42; m 66; c 3. *Educ:* Univ Man, BSc, 65, MSc, 66; McMaster Univ, PhD(chem), 69. *Prof Exp:* Asst prof chem, Dept Chem, 69-70, res scientist, 70-74, sr scientist chem, Cyclotron Inst, Tex A&M Univ, 74-76. *Mem:* Can Nuclear Soc; fel Chem Inst Can. *Res:* Waste management. *Mailing Add:* Atomic Energy Can Ltd Chaulk River Lab Chaulk River ON K0J 1J0 Can

**TORGERSON, RONALD THOMAS,** HIGH ENERGY PHYSICS, THEORETICAL PHYSICS. *Current Pos:* RETIRED. *Personal Data:* b Minneapolis, Minn, Sept 20, 36; m 63; c 2. *Educ:* Col St Thomas, BS, 58; Univ Chicago, MS, 62, PhD(physics), 65. *Prof Exp:* Instr physics, Univ Notre Dame, 65-68; asst prof, Ohio State Univ, 68-73; res assoc physics, Univ Alta, 73-77, programmer analyst, 77-96. *Mem:* Am Phys Soc. *Res:* Quantum field theory; high energy collisions; pi pi scattering; weak and electromagnetic interactions; hadron spectroscopy. *Mailing Add:* 3305-110 A St Edmonton AB T6G 3J3 Can

**TORGESON, DEWAYNE CLINTON,** PLANT PATHOLOGY. *Current Pos:* RETIRED. *Personal Data:* b Ambrose, NDak, Oct 1, 25; m 59; c 3. *Educ:* Iowa State Univ, BS, 49; Ore State Univ, PhD(plant path), 53. *Prof Exp:* Plant pathologist, Boyce Thompson Inst Plant Res, Inc, 52-85, prog dir bioregulant chem, 63-85, secy, 73-90, emer plant pathologist, 91- *Concurrent Pos:* Mem & chmn, Fed Insecticide, Fungicide & Rodenticide Act Sci Adv Panel, Environ Protection Agency, 76-81. *Mem:* Am Phytopath Soc. *Res:* Fungicides; discovery and development of pesticides. *Mailing Add:* 106 Berkshire Rd Ithaca NY 14850

**TORGOW, EUGENE N,** MICROWAVES, ENGINEERING MANAGEMENT. *Current Pos:* RETIRED. *Personal Data:* b Bronx, NY, Nov 26, 25; m 50, Cynthia Silver; c Joan, Martha & Ellen. *Educ:* Cooper Union, BSEE, 46; Polytech Inst Bklyn, MSEE, 49. *Prof Exp:* Mgr microwave lab, Allen B Dumont Labs, 51-53; res assoc, Microwave Res Inst, Polytech Inst Brooklyn, 53-59; mgr microwave prod, Dorne & Margolin Inc, 60-64; dir res, Rantec Div, Emerson Elec Co, 64-68; sr scientist, Missile Systs Group, Hughes Aircraft Co, 68-74, prog mgr, 74-81, assoc labs mgr, 81-85. *Concurrent Pos:* Teacher, Calif State Univ, Northridge, 85-91; consult eng mgt & training, 85- *Mem:* Sigma Xi; fel Inst Elec & Electronics Engrs; fel Inst Advan Eng. *Res:* Microwave filters and equalizers; management of major aerospace electronic system development programs; published over a dozen papers. *Mailing Add:* 9531 Donna Ave Northridge CA 91324. *E-Mail:* e.n. torgow@ieee.org

**TORIBARA, TAFT YUTAKA,** BIOPHYSICS, CHEMISTRY. *Current Pos:* scientist chem, Atomic Energy Proj, Univ Rochester, 48, from asst prof to assoc prof, 50-63, prof radiobiol & biophys, 63-87, prof, 87-89, emer prof toxicol biophys, 89-93, EMER PROF ENVIRON MED, MED SCH, UNIV ROCHESTER, 93- *Personal Data:* b Seattle, Wash, Apr 10, 17; m 48, Masako Ono; c Lynne S & Neil W. *Educ:* Univ Wash, BS, 38, MS, 39; Univ Mich, PhD(chem), 42. *Prof Exp:* Res chemist, Dept Eng Res, Univ Mich, 42-48. *Concurrent Pos:* Nat Gen Med Sci spec res fel, Univ Tokyo, 60-61. *Mem:* AAAS; Am Chem Soc. *Res:* Binding of ions and small molecules to serum proteins; analytical chemistry of trace materials in biological systems; trace element analysis along a single strand of hair by X-ray fluorescence; measurement of environmental pollutants; environmental sciences; toxicology. *Mailing Add:* Dept Environ Med Univ Rochester Med Ctr PO Box EHSC Rochester NY 14642

**TORIDIS, THEODORE GEORGE,** STRUCTURAL DYNAMICS, APPLIED MECHANICS. *Current Pos:* assoc prof eng mech, 64-77, PROF ENG & APPL SCI, GEORGE WASHINGTON UNIV, 77-, ASSOC DEAN ACAD AFFAIRS. *Personal Data:* b Istanbul, Turkey, Sept 7, 32; US citizen; m 61; c 2. *Educ:* Robert Col, Istanbul, BS, 54; Mich State Univ, MS, 61, PhD(civil eng), 64. *Prof Exp:* Design engr, EMC-RAR Contractors, 54-56; asst div engr, Raymond Concrete Pile Co, 56-57; rcs asst, Mich State Univ, 59-64. *Concurrent Pos:* NSF res grants, 65-67, prin investr, 70-; co-investr, David Taylor Model Basin Res contract & prin investr, Naval Ship Res & Develop Ctr contract, 66-69; sr res scientist, Nat Biomed Res Found, 66-70. *Mem:* AAAS; Am Soc Civil Engrs. *Res:* Elastoinelastic response of beams to moving loads; improved vibration analysis of beams and plates; biomechanics, stress analysis of a bone; seismic analysis of structures; nonlinear deformations of framed structures. *Mailing Add:* Off Assoc Dean Acad Affairs George Washington Univ 725 23rd St NW Washington DC 20052

**TORIELLO, HELGA VALDMANIS,** GENETICS. *Current Pos:* adj instr, 83-86, asst prof, 86-90, ASSOC PROF, DEPT PEDIAT & HUMAN DEVELOP, MICH STATE UNIV, 90-; DIR, GENETIC SERVS, BUTTERWORTH HOSP, 87- *Personal Data:* b May 20, 52; m 77, Dean; c Krista M & Allison L. *Educ:* Cornell Univ, BS, 73; Rutgers Univ, MS, 75; Mich State Univ, East Lansing, PhD genetics), 81. *Prof Exp:* Genetics clin coordr, Blodgett Mem Med Ctr, 78-82, med geneticist, 82-87, admin dir genetics, 85-87, asst dir, Oral Cleft Clin, 83-87. *Concurrent Pos:* Prof consult, Grand Rapids Area Spina Bifida & Hydrocephalus Asn, 79-83; co-dir, Oral Cleft Clin, Butterworth Hosp, 82-90, prof staff, 83-, med geneticist, 87-; prof staff, Blodgett Mem Med Ctr & St Mary's Hosp, 87- *Mem:* Fel Am Col Med Genetics; Europ Soc Human Genetics; Am Spina Bifida Asn; Am Soc Human Genetics; Am Cleft Palate Asn; Teratology Soc. *Res:* Dysmorphology, specifically syndrome identification and delineation. *Mailing Add:* 21 Michigan St Suite 465 Grand Rapids MI 49503. *Fax:* 616-732-8670

**TORIO, JOYCE CLARKE,** SCIENCE ADMINISTRATION, INFORMATION SCIENCE. *Current Pos:* HEAD INFO SERV, INT RICE RES INST, 74- *Personal Data:* b Biddeford, Maine, Oct 1, 34; m 55. *Educ:* Rutgers Univ, BS, 56, MS, 61, PhD(hort, soils), 65. *Prof Exp:* Ed biochem, hort & soils, Chem Abstr Serv, Am Chem Soc, 65-69; staff officer, Bd Agr & Renewable Resources, Nat Acad Sci, 69-74. *Concurrent Pos:* Consult, World Bank. *Mem:* Am Soc Hort Sci; Am Chem Soc; Am Inst Biol Sci; Sigma Xi. *Res:* Pomology, mineral nutrition and plants; soil fertility and analysis; plant physiology and pathology; rice culture and associated multiple cropping systems research-information management. *Mailing Add:* 10723 West Dr Apt 202 Fairfax VA 22030-4273

**TORKELSON, ARNOLD,** ORGANOMETALLIC CHEMISTRY. *Current Pos:* RETIRED. *Personal Data:* b Thompson, NDak, Oct 28, 22; m 44; c 4. *Educ:* Univ NDak, BSc, 46; Purdue Univ, MS, 48, PhD, 50. *Prof Exp:* Asst, Purdue Univ, 46-48; prod develop chemist, Silicone Prod Dept, Gen Elec Co, 50-58, mgr anal chem, 58-65, fluid prod develop, 65-72, specialities develop, 72-76, & fluids resins & specialities prod develop, 76-88. *Mem:* AAAS; Am Chem Soc; fel Am Inst Chem. *Res:* Synthesis of organosilicon compounds; rate studies on the cleavage of silicon-carbon bond; product development and research on silicone fluids, resins and specialty products. *Mailing Add:* River Rd West Lebanon NH 03784

**TORLEY, ROBERT EDWARD,** chemistry; deceased, see previous edition for last biography

**TORMANEN, CALVIN DOUGLAS,** ENZYMOLOGY. *Current Pos:* from asst prof to assoc prof, 81-91, PROF BIOCHEM, CENT MICH UNIV, 91- *Personal Data:* b Litchfield, Minn, Nov 24, 46; m 71, Susan Wood; c Elizabeth & Abigail. *Educ:* Univ Minn, BA, 68, PhD(biochem), 74. *Prof Exp:* Res fel, Univ NMex, 74-75; asst prof chem, Ambassador Col, 75-78; res asst prof, Univ NMex, 78-81. *Mem:* Am Chem Soc; Sigma Xi. *Res:* Effect of metal ions on zebra mussel arginase activity. *Mailing Add:* Dept Chem Cent Mich Univ Mt Pleasant MI 48859

**TORMEY, JOHN MCDIVIT,** PHYSIOLOGY, CELL BIOLOGY. *Current Pos:* asst prof, 68-70, assoc prof, 70-78, PROF PHYSIOL, UNIV CALIF, LOS ANGELES, 78- *Personal Data:* b Baltimore, Md, Oct 7, 34; div; c 2. *Educ:* Loyola Col, Md, BS, 56; Johns Hopkins Univ, MD, 61. *Prof Exp:* Fel ophthal, Johns Hopkins Univ, 61-62, instr, 62-63; res fel biol, Harvard Univ, 63-64; asst prof anat & ophthal, Johns Hopkins Univ, 64-66; staff assoc phys biol, Nat Inst Arthritis & Metab Dis, 66-68. *Concurrent Pos:* Nat Inst Neurol Dis & Blindness fel, 61-63, spec fel, 63-66, res grants, 65-66 & 68- *Mem:* Microbeam Analytical Soc; Am Physiol Soc; Am Soc Cell Biol; Am Asn Anat. *Res:* Relationship between structure and function of body tissues, especially epithelia and muscle; development of methods for localizing transport functions; electron microprobe analysis. *Mailing Add:* Dept Physiol Univ Calif-Los Angeles Ctr Health Sci 405 Hilgard Ave Los Angeles CA 90024-1751. *Fax:* 310-206-5661

**TORNABENE, THOMAS GUY,** MICROBIOLOGY. *Current Pos:* dir, Dept Appl Biol, 81-90, ASSOC DEAN, COL SCI, GA INST TECHNOL, 90- *Personal Data:* b Cecil, Pa, May 6, 37; m 62, 77, Kristi Broadwater; c Elene, Demitra, Joanna, Kari, Miki & Talia. *Educ:* St Edward's Univ, BS, 59; Univ Houston, MS, 62, PhD(biol chem), 67. *Prof Exp:* Instr biol, Univ Houston, 62-65; fel biochem, Nat Res Coun, Ottawa, Can, 67-68; from asst prof to assoc prof microbiol, Colo State Univ, 68-78, prof, 78-80, group mgr, solar Energy Res Inst, 80. *Mem:* Am Soc Microbiol; Am Oil Chem Soc. *Res:* Biogenesis and distribution of microbial hydrocarbons; microbial lipids and carbohydrates; metabolic pathways and mechanisms of synthesis of biochemical compounds; cell immobilization; fermentation processes. *Mailing Add:* Sch Biol Ga Inst Technol 225 N Ave NW Atlanta GA 30332. *Fax:* 404-894-7466; *E-Mail:* thomas_tornabene@cos.gatech.edu

**TORNESE, ANN C,** MEDICAL DEVICES, BIOMETRICS. *Current Pos:* DEP DIR DIV SURVEILLANCE SYST, H F Z, 96- *Personal Data:* b Terre Haule, Ind, May 22, 46. *Educ:* St Mary Woods Col, BS, 76. *Mailing Add:* Div Surv Syst USDHHS HFZ-530 1390 Piccard Dr Rockville MD 20850

**TORNG, HWA-CHUNG,** COMPUTER & ELECTRICAL ENGINEERING. *Current Pos:* From asst prof to assoc prof, 60-71, PROF ELEC ENG, CORNELL UNIV, 71- *Personal Data:* b Yangchow, China, Aug 12, 32; US citizen; m 60; c 2. *Educ:* Nat Taiwan Univ, BS, 55; Cornell Univ, MS, 58, PhD(elec eng), 60. *Concurrent Pos:* Mem tech staff, Switching Div, Bell Tel Labs, 66-67 & 80-81. *Mem:* Inst Elec & Electronics Engrs; Asn Comput Mach. *Res:* Very-large-scale intergration systems; computer structures and design; microprocessor systems; digital systems; telecommunications. *Mailing Add:* Sch Elec Eng Phillips Hall Cornell Univ 333 Eng & Theory Ctr Bldg Ithaca NY 14853-5401

**TORNHEIM, PATRICIA ANNE,** ANATOMY. *Current Pos:* asst prof, 73-80, ASSOC PROF ANAT, UNIV CINCINNATI, 80- *Personal Data:* b Chicago, Ill, June 12, 39. *Educ:* Rosary Col, BA, 61; Univ Ill, MS, 64; Univ Kans, PhD(anat), 73. *Prof Exp:* Instr anat, Univ Kans, 68-69; instr, Kansas City Col Osteop Med, 69-73. *Mem:* Fel AAAS; Am Asn Anatomists; Cajal Club. *Res:* Traumatic cerebral edema; metabolic cerebral edema; cerebrospinal fluid pathways. *Mailing Add:* Dept Anat Univ Cincinnati Col Med 231 Bethesda Ave Cincinnati OH 45267

**TORNQVIST, ERIK GUSTAV MARKUS,** POLYMER CHEMISTRY & BIOCHEMISTRY, SYNTHETIC INORGANIC & ORGANOMETALLIC CHEMISTRY. *Current Pos:* PRES, POLYMERIK, INC, 90- *Personal Data:* b Lund, Sweden, Jan 13, 24; m 69, Linnea Dagmar Lindborg; c Gunvor, Karin & Carl-Erik. *Educ:* Royal Inst Technol, Sweden, MSc, 48; Univ Wis, MS, 53, PhD(biochem), 55. *Honors & Awards:* John Ericsson Gold Medal, Am Soc Swed Engrs, 84. *Prof Exp:* First res asst, Div Food Chem, Royal Inst Technol, Sweden, 49-51; res asst, Dept Biochem, Univ Wis, 51-55; res chemist, Chem Res Div, Esso Res & Eng Co, 55-58, res assoc, 58-65; res assoc, Enjay Polymer Labs, 65-66; sr res assoc, 66-73; sr res assoc, Elastomers Technol Div, Exxon Chem Co, 86-90. *Concurrent Pos:* Vis prof, Dept Polymer Technol, Royal Inst Technol, Swed, 87. *Mem:* Am Chem Soc; NY Acad Sci; Sigma Xi; Swed Soc Chem Engrs; Swed Asn Grad Engrs; Am Soc Swed Engrs. *Res:* Organometallic chemistry and catalysis especially catalysts for stereospecific polymerition of olefins and dienes; polymer chemistry, especially synthesis and mechanisms of polymerization; biotechnical production of protein, fat, vitamins and antibiotics. *Mailing Add:* 38 Mareu Dr Watchung NJ 07060-5025. *Fax:* 908-322-6274

**TORO, RICHARD FRANK,** environmental engineering, chemical engineering, for more information see previous edition

**TOROK, ANDREW, JR,** CHEMISTRY. *Current Pos:* DIR RES & DEVELOP, FABER-CASTELL CORP, 74- *Personal Data:* b Hopewell, Va, Oct 30, 25; m 51; c 2. *Educ:* Pa State Univ, BS, 49; Stevens Inst Technol, MS, 56. *Prof Exp:* Analytical chemist, William P Warner, Inc, 49-51; res chemist, Venus Pen & Pencil Co, 51-53, chief chemist, 53-57, tech dir, 57-61; prod develop mgr, Ga Kaolin Co, 61-74. *Mem:* Am Chem Soc; Am Ceramic Soc; fel Am Inst Chemists; NY Acad Sci; Fine Particle Soc (treas, 70-73). *Res:* Clays and clay products, especially application in new fields. *Mailing Add:* 44 Long Ridge Rd RD 3 Randolph NJ 07869-4571

**TOROK, NICHOLAS,** otolaryngology; deceased, see previous edition for last biography

**TOROP, WILLIAM,** INORGANIC CHEMISTRY, SCIENCE EDUCATION. *Current Pos:* PROF CHEM, WEST CHESTER STATE UNIV, 71- *Personal Data:* b New York, NY, Jan 12, 38; m 90, Lisa Schwartz Kramer; c Elizabeth, Michael, Jesse & Josh. *Educ:* Univ Pa, AB, 59, MS, 61, EdD(sci educ), 68. *Prof Exp:* Prof employee chem, Upper Darby Sr High Sch, Pa, 60-68; asst prof chem & sci educ, St Joseph's Col, Pa, 68-71. *Concurrent Pos:* Elem sci consult, Interboro Sch Dist, Pa, 69-70; elem sci consult, Marple Newtown Sch Dist, 70-72; dir, Del Valley Inst Sci Educ, 71-; Commonwealth distinguished teaching chair. *Mem:* Am Chem Soc; Nat Sci Teachers Asn; Asn Educ Teachers Sci; Nat Asn Res in Sci Teaching. *Res:* Use of written laboratory reports in high school chemistry; trivalent basic polyphosphates; evaluation of elementary science programs; computer managed and computer assisted instruction. *Mailing Add:* Dept Chem West Chester State Univ West Chester PA 19383. *Fax:* 610-436-2890; *E-Mail:* wtorop@wcupa.edo

**TOROSIAN, GEORGE,** PHARMACY, PHARMACEUTICS. *Current Pos:* mgr mfg technol & res supvr, DuPont-Merck, 81-90, mgr mfg technol, DuPont Merck Pharm Co, 90-93, ASSOC DIR DEVELOP, DUPONT MERCK-PHARM CO, 93- *Personal Data:* b Racine, Wis, Jan 1, 36; div; c Michael J & Gregory A. *Educ:* Univ Wis, Madison, BS, 62, MS, 64, PhD(pharm), 66. *Prof Exp:* Sr pharm chemist, Menley & James Labs Div, Smith Kline & French Labs, Inc, 66-69; assoc prof pharm, Col Pharm, Univ Fla, 69-81. *Mem:* Am Pharmaceut Asn; Am Asn Cols Pharm; Acad Pharmaceut Sci; Am Asn Pharmaceut Sci. *Res:* Product development and design; biopharmaceutics; solution kinetics. *Mailing Add:* 123 Beach Rd Massapequa NY 11758

**TORP, BRUCE ALAN,** INORGANIC CHEMISTRY, COMPUTER SCIENCE. *Current Pos:* RETIRED. *Personal Data:* b Duluth, Minn, Sept 5, 37; m 60; c 3. *Educ:* Univ Minn, BA, 59; Iowa State Univ, MS, 62, PhD(inorg chem), 64. *Prof Exp:* Sr chemist, 3M Co, 64-68, supvr, Inorg Chem Res Group, 68-71, lab mgr, Physics & Mat Res Lab, 71-74, dir, Mat & Electronics Res Lab, Cent Res Labs, 75-77, dir, Data Rec Prod Div Labs, 77-86, tech dir tel comm prod, 86-96. *Mem:* Am Chem Soc. *Res:* Coordination, transition metal and solid state chemistry; semiconductor research; magnetic materials research; magnetic media development. *Mailing Add:* PO Box 957 Burnet TX 78611

**TORPHY, THEODORE JOHN,** MOLECULAR & PULMONARY PHARMACOLOGY. *Current Pos:* assoc dir, 88-90, dir, Dept I & R Pharmacol, 90-95, GROUP DIR, DEPT IMMUNOPHARMACOL & PULMONARY PHARMACOL, SMITH KLINE BEECHAM PHARMACEUT, 95- *Personal Data:* b Beloit, Wis, May 27, 52; m 88, Blanche Levitt; c Brenden & Patrick. *Educ:* Univ Wis, BS, 76; WVa Univ, PhD(pharmacol & toxicol), 80. *Prof Exp:* Fel med, Univ Calif, San Diego, 80-83, lectr, 82-83; assoc sr investr, Smith Kline & Fr Labs, 83-84, sr investr, 84-86, asst dir, 86-88. *Concurrent Pos:* Fel, NIH, 80-81, consult 87-92; Nat Res Serv Award, 81-83; assoc sr investr, Smith Kline & Fr Labs, Philadelphia, 83-84, sr investr, 84-86, asst dir, Dept Pharmacol, 86-88, assoc dir, 88-90; lectr, WVa Univ, 83-; adj asst prof, Dept pharmacol, Univ Nev, Reno, 84-, Dept Pharmacol & Toxicol, WVa Univ, 85- *Mem:* Am Soc Pharmacol & Exp Therapeut; Am Thoracic Soc; Am Physiol Soc. *Res:* Defining the molecular mechanisms by which the activities of inflammatory cells and airway smooth muscle are regulated by drugs, cytokines, neurotransmitters and hormones. *Mailing Add:* Dept Immunopharmacol & Pulmonary Pharmacol Smith Kline Beecham Pharmaceut 709 Swedeland Rd King of Prussia PA 19406-0939. *Fax:* 610-270-5381

**TORQUATO, SALVATORE,** STATISTICAL PHYSICS. *Current Pos:* PROF, CIVIL ENG MAT SCI, PRINCETON UNIV. *Personal Data:* b Falerna, Italy, Feb 10, 54; US citizen; m 75; c 1. *Educ:* Syracuse Univ, BS, 75; State Univ NY, Stony Brook, MS, 77, PhD(mech eng), 80. *Prof Exp:* Asst prof mech eng, Gen Motors Inst, 81-82; from asst prof to assoc prof, NC State Univ, 82-91, prof mech & aerospace eng, 91- *Concurrent Pos:* Prin investr, NSF, 82-88 & US Dept Energy, 86-; vis prof, Courant Insti Math Sci, NY Univ, 90-91. *Mem:* Am Soc Mech Engrs; Am Inst Chem Engrs; Soc Eng Sci; Am Inst Physics; Soc Appl & Indust Math. *Res:* The relationship of mechanical, electrical, thermal and chemical properties of composite and other heterogenous materials to their microstructures; author of 80 publications. *Mailing Add:* Dept Civil Eng Princeton Univ E307 Eng Quad Princeton NJ 08544

**TORRANCE, DANIEL J,** RADIOLOGY. *Current Pos:* ADJ PROF RADIOL, UNIV CALIF, LOS ANGELES, 76-; RADIOLOGIST, BAY SHORE MED CLIN, 85- *Personal Data:* b Peking, China, Nov 14, 21; US citizen; m 51, Elizabeth Emmons; c David & James. *Educ:* Univ Wash, BSc, 44; Johns Hopkins Univ, MD, 49. *Prof Exp:* Intern med, Johns Hopkins Hosp, 49-50, fel path, 50-51, asst resident radiol, 51-53, from instr to assoc prof, Sch Med, Johns Hopkins Univ, 53-63; head div, Scripps Clin & Res Found, La Jolla, Calif, 63-66; assoc prof, Sch Med, Wash Univ, 66-68; prof, Univ Calif, Los Angeles, 68-72; chief radiologist, Bay Harbor Hosp, Calif, 72-76; radiologist & chief, Chest & Gen Radiol Sect, Harbor Gen Hosp, 76-85. *Concurrent Pos:* Consult, USPHS Hosp, Baltimore, Md, 54-; radiologist, Johns Hopkins Hosp, 55-63; assoc radiologist, Mallinckrodt Inst Radiol, Barnes Hosp, St Louis, 66-; chief dept radiol, Harbor Gen Hosp, Torrance, Calif; clin prof radiol, Univ Calif, Los Angeles, 72-; consult, Vet Admin Hosp, Long Beach, Calif, 80- *Mem:* Am Col Radiol. *Res:* Chest radiograph in connection with the pulmonary circulation; problems in the radiography of pulmonary atelectasis; radiographic manifestations of pulmonary edema. *Mailing Add:* Habor Univ Calif Los Angeles Med Ctr Dept Res & Develop 1000 W Carson St Torrance CA 90509

**TORRANCE, JERRY BADGLEY, JR,** SYNTHETIC INORGANIC & ORGANOMETALLIC CHEMISTRY. *Current Pos:* Res physicist, Thomas J Watson Res Ctr, IBM, 69-76, mgr phys properties org solids group, 74-76, mgr, Almaden Res Ctr, 76-93, mgr magnetics, 81-93, TECH CONSULT MAT APPLN, IBM CORP, 93- *Personal Data:* b San Diego, Calif, July 20, 41; div; c 2. *Educ:* Stanford Univ, BS, 63; Univ Calif, Berkeley, MA, 66; Harvard Univ, PhD(appl physics), 69. *Mem:* Am Chem Soc; fel Am Phys Soc; Mat Res Soc. *Res:* High temperature superconductivity; synthesis of new materials; organic furomagnets; organic solids. *Mailing Add:* 1176 Lone Pine Lane San Jose CA 95120. *Fax:* 408-268-2377; *E-Mail:* jbtorrance@aol.com

**TORRANCE, KENNETH E(RIC),** PHOTOREALISTIC IMAGES, REMOTE SENSING. *Current Pos:* from asst prof to assoc prof, 69-81, assoc dean, Col Eng, 83-86, PROF MECH & AEROSPACE ENG, CORNELL UNIV, 81- *Personal Data:* b Minneapolis, Minn, Aug 23, 40; m 62, Marcia Greenfield; c Charles E, Deborah T (Kaufman) & Catherine T (McGrath). *Educ:* Univ Minn, Minneapolis, BS, 61, MSME, 64, PhD(mech eng), 66. *Honors & Awards:* Comput Graphics Achievement Award, Asn Comput Mach, 94. *Prof Exp:* Factory Mutual Eng Co res assoc, Nat Bur Stand, 66-68. *Concurrent Pos:* Sr fel, Nat Ctr Atmospheric Res, 74-75. *Mem:* AAAS; fel Am Soc Mech Engrs; Am Phys Soc; Asn Comput Mach. *Res:* Heat transfer; fluid mechanics; numerical computations; computer graphics; thermal radiation; electronics cooling. *Mailing Add:* 37 Deerhaven Dr Ithaca NY 14850. *Fax:* 607-255-1222; *E-Mail:* ket1@cornell.edu

**TORRE, DOUGLAS PAUL,** cryosurgery, dermatologic surgery; deceased, see previous edition for last biography

**TORRE, FRANK JOHN,** PHYSICAL CHEMISTRY. *Current Pos:* asst prof, 73-80, ASSOC PROF CHEM, SPRINGFIELD COL, 80- *Personal Data:* b Newark, NJ, Oct 6, 44; m 68; c 1. *Educ:* Monmouth Col NJ, BS, 67; Rutgers Univ, PhD(phys chem), 71. *Prof Exp:* Res chem, Bell Tel Labs, 67-68; fel, Univ Rochester, 71-73. *Mem:* Am Chem Soc. *Mailing Add:* Dept Chem Springfield Col Springfield MA 01109-3797

**TORRE-BUENO, JOSE ROLLIN,** PHYSIOLOGY. *Current Pos:* Res assoc physiol, 75-78, med res asst prof, Dept Physiol, Med Ctr, 78-84, PRES, AM INNOVISION, DUKE UNIV, 84- *Personal Data:* b Tucson, Ariz, Nov 20, 48; m 69; c 1. *Educ:* State Univ NY, Stony Brook, BS, 70; Rockefeller Univ, PhD(physiol), 75. *Mem:* Sigma Xi. *Res:* Respiratory physiology and energetics particularly during hypoxia. *Mailing Add:* 2909 Wishbone Way Encinitas CA 92020

**TORREGROSSA, ROBERT EMILE,** MICROBIAL PHYSIOLOGY, FERMENTATION TECHNOLOGY. *Current Pos:* MGR, BIOTECHNOL DIV, LOCKWOOD GREEN ENGRS, 92- *Personal Data:* b Bogalusa, La, Oct 24, 51; m 75; c 2. *Educ:* La Tech Univ, BS, 73; Univ Ga, PhD(microbiol), 77. *Prof Exp:* Res microbiologist fermentations, CPC Int Inc, 78-80; mem staff, Chem Div, Tethyl Corp, 80-82, Enzyme Technol Corp, 82-84, Phillips Petrol Co, 84-89; mgr process eng, Triad Technol Inc, 89-92. *Concurrent Pos:* NSF fel, Mass Inst Technol, 77-78. *Mem:* Am Soc Microbiol; Am Chem Soc; Parenteral Drug Asn; Int Soc Pharmaceut Eng. *Res:* Biochemistry; enzyme processes; immobilized cells and enzymes; biotransformations; hydrocarbon oxidation; rDNA fermentation scale-up; biopharmaceuticals. *Mailing Add:* 91 Green Meadow Dr Elkton MD 21921

**TORRELLAS, JOSEP,** COMPUTER ARCHITECTURE, PARALLEL PROCESSING. *Current Pos:* ASST PROF COMPUT SCI, UNIV ILL, URBANA, 92-; SR COMPUT SYST ENGR, CTR SUPERCOMPUT RES & DEVELOP, 92- *Personal Data:* b Catalonia, Spain, Mar 17, 63. *Educ:* Univ Politeonica Catalunya, BS, 86, Univ Wis, MS, 87; Stanford Univ, PhD(elec eng), 92- *Honors & Awards:* Res Initiation Award, US NSF, 93; Young Investr Award, 94. *Concurrent Pos:* Mem, Spec Interest Group, Asn Comput Mach; mem, Tech Comt Comput Archit, Inst Elec & Electronics Engrs. *Mem:* Asn Comput Mech; Inst Elec & Electronics Engrs. *Res:* Computer architecture, compilers and operating systems for uniprocensors and multiprocessors. *Mailing Add:* Univ Ill Urbana-Champaign Comput Sci 1304 W Springfield Ave Urbana IL 61801-2910. *Fax:* 217-333-3501; *E-Mail:* torrella@cs.uiuc.edu

**TORRENCE, PAUL FREDERICK,** INTERFERON, NUCLEIC ACIDS. *Current Pos:* Staff fel, Nat Inst Arthritis & Metab Dis, 69-71, sr staff fel, Nat Inst Arthritis, Metab & Digestive Dis, 71-74, RES CHEMIST, NAT INST ARTHRITIS, DIABETES & DIGESTIVE & KIDNEY DIS, NIH, 74- *Personal Data:* b New Brighton, Pa, April 22, 43; m 67; c 2. *Educ:* Geneva Col, Pa, BS, 65; State Univ NY, PhD(chem), 69. *Concurrent Pos:* Ad Hoc consult, Spec Proj Adv Comt, Nat Cancer Inst, 80 & Nat Inst Allergy Infectious Dis, 79- *Mem:* Am Chem Soc; Soc Exp Biol & Med; Am Soc Microbiol; AAAS. *Res:* Mechanisms of induction and action of interons; the role played by double-standard RNA and 2,5-oligoadenlates in these mechanisms and how this information may be used to design antiviral or antitumor agents. *Mailing Add:* US NIH Bldg 8 Rm B2A02 Bethesda MD 20892

**TORRENCE, ROBERT JAMES,** THEORETICAL PHYSICS. *Current Pos:* asst prof, 68-70, chmn div appl math, 75-77, ASSOC PROF MATH, UNIV CALGARY, 70- *Personal Data:* b Pittsburgh, Pa, June 7, 37; m 59. *Educ:* Carnegie-Mellon Univ, BS, 59; Univ Pittsburgh, PhD(physics), 65. *Prof Exp:* Res assoc physics, Syracuse Univ, 65-67; adj prof, Ctr Advan Studies, Nat Polytech Insti, Mex, 67-68. *Mem:* Am Phys Soc. *Res:* General relativity with emphasis on gravitational radiation. *Mailing Add:* Dept Math & Statist Univ Calgary Calgary AB T2N 1N4 Can

**TORRES, ADOLFO M,** DOMESTIC & INDUSTRIAL WASTEWATER TREATMENT, ENVIRONMENTAL LAB-QA & QC PROCEDURES. *Current Pos:* Adv chemist, Union Carbide Corp, 76-83, sr lab technician, 83-84, sect leader advan chem, 84-85, sr chemist, 85-88, STAFF CHEMIST, UNION CARBIDE CORP, 88- *Personal Data:* b Ponce, PR, Dec 24, 49; m, Lizzette Tarrats; c Adolfo R, Carlos E, Ana C & Mariana L. *Educ:* Cath Univ PR, BS, 74; WVa Univ, MSE, 92. *Mem:* Water Environ Fedn. *Res:* Waste treatment; chemical product, quality control procedures and environmental issues. *Mailing Add:* 2312 Walnut St Hurricane WV 25526. *Fax:* 304-744-3400

**TORRES, ANDREW M,** BOTANY. *Current Pos:* assoc prof, 64-70, assoc dean grad sch, 69-72, chmn dept, 79-81, PROF BOT & GENETICS, UNIV KANS, 70- *Personal Data:* b Albuquerque, NMex, Jan 20, 31; m 55; c 4. *Educ:* Univ Albuquerque, BS, 52; Univ NMex, MS, 58; Ind Univ, PhD(bot), 61. *Prof Exp:* Instr biol, Wis State Univ, Oshkosh, 60-61; asst prof bot & genetics, Univ Wis, Milwaukee, 61-64. *Concurrent Pos:* Ford Found sr adv, Univ Oriente, Venezuela, 66-67; chief party, Aid to higher educ, Dominican Republic, 68; Calif Avocado Adv Bd, 78; vis prof, Univ Calif, Riverside, 78, Univ Nat Del Sur, 81; consult, Agr Res Orgn, Bet Dagan, Israel, 81 & 85; sum vis scientist, Div Hort, Commonwealth Sci Indust Res Orgn, Adelaide, Australia, 84 & 85; sum vis prof, Univ Colo, 86-87. *Mem:* AAAS; Bot Soc Am; Soc Study Evolution; Genetics Soc Am; Sigma Xi. *Res:* Cytogenetics; alcohol dehydrogenase isozymes of sunflowers; genetics; paleozoic algae. *Mailing Add:* Dept Bot Univ Kans Lawrence KS 66045-0001

**TORRES, ANTHONY R,** BIOCHEMISTRY, MOLECULAR BIOLOGY. *Current Pos:* DIR, ZYMEQUEST, 93- *Personal Data:* b Trinidad, Colo, Apr 1, 43; m 75, Joyce M Marcroft; c 7. *Educ:* Univ Utah, BS, 70, MD, 74. *Prof Exp:* Res assoc, Nat Cancer Inst, 75-78, expert consult, 78-81; resident, Yale Univ, 81-83, asst prof lab med, 83-86; mem staff, Hyclone Lab Inc, 86-93. *Concurrent Pos:* Adj fac mem, Dept Med, Univ Utah, 90-94. *Mem:* NY Acad Sci. *Res:* Separation of biologically active proteins from complex mixtures using capacity and high resolution displacement chromatography; development of lymphocyte cell culture methods for use in adaptive immunotherapy and gene therapy. *Mailing Add:* 79 E 2050 N Centerville UT 84014

**TORRES, FERNANDO,** NEUROLOGY, NEUROPHYSIOLOGY. *Current Pos:* from instr to assoc prof, 56-64, PROF NEUROL, UNIV MINN, MINNEAPOLIS, 64- *Personal Data:* b Paris, France, Nov 29, 24; m 55; c 1. *Educ:* Ger Col, Colombia, BA, 41; Nat Univ Colombia, MD, 48; Am Bd EEG, dipl, 51; Am Bd Psychiat & Neurol, dipl, 61. *Prof Exp:* Asst neurosurg, Inst Cancer, Buenos Aires, Arg, 49-50; resident neurol, Montefiore Hosp, NY, 53-55. *Concurrent Pos:* Fel, Johns Hopkins Hosp, 50-52, NIH res fel, 52-53; asst, Columbia Univ, 54-55; consult prof, Univ PR, 61-64; NIH spec fel, LaSalpetriere Hosp, Paris, 63-64. *Mem:* AAAS; fel Am Acad Neurol; Am Neurol Asn; Soc Neurosci; Am Electroencephalog Soc. *Res:* Electroencephalography; clinical neurophysiology; epilepsy; cerebrovascular physiology; developmental cerebral physiology. *Mailing Add:* Dept Neurol Univ Minn Hosp PO Box 28 Minneapolis MN 55455-0028

**TORRES, JOSEPH CHARLES,** RADIOLOGY. *Current Pos:* PROF CARDIOVASC PHYSIOL & VCHMN, DEPT PHYSIOL & BIOPHYS, HAHNEMANN UNIV, 69- *Educ:* Boston Univ, PhD(physiol), 61. *Mailing Add:* Alleghany Univ Hahnemann Div Broad & Vine Philadelphia PA 19102

**TORRES, LOURDES MARIA,** bioinorganic chemistry & toxicology; deceased, see previous edition for last biography

**TORRES, MARTINE,** PHARMACOLOGY, CELL BIOLOGY. *Current Pos:* ASST PROF PEDIAT, CHILDRENS HOSP, LOS ANGELES, 86- *Personal Data:* b Paris, France. *Res:* Pharmacology; cell biology. *Mailing Add:* Dept Pediat Box 54 Childrens Hosp Los Angeles 4650 Sunset Blvd MS 57 Los Angeles CA 90027-6088

**TORRES-ANJEL, MANUEL JOSE,** CLINICAL EPIDEMIOLOGY & CLINICAL TRIALS, INTERNATIONAL SCIENTIFIC MASS MEDIA OF COMMUNICATIONS-PRINTED & BROADCASTING. *Current Pos:* health sci admin clin epidemiol, Nat Inst Allergy Infectious Dis, 88-90, Molecular Biol, Nat Cancer Inst, 90, HEALTH SCI ADMIN CLIN TRIALS, CANCER SPEC RES COMT, NAT CANCER INST, NIH, 90- *Personal Data:* b Bogota, Colombia, Apr 15, 42; US citizen; m 64, Amparo; c Pilar, Juanita, Manuel III & Roberto. *Educ:* Nat Univ Colombia, DVM, 64; Tulane Univ & Mich State Univ, MSc, 68; Univ Calif, Davis, MPVM, 72, PhD(comp path), 74. *Honors & Awards:* Res Award, Col Vet Med Asn Meeting, 77, Col Vet Med Asn, 78, Angel Escobar Found, 79. *Prof Exp:* Instr to prof microbiol, Nat Univ Colombia, 63-78; int scientist pub health, World (Pan Am) Health Orgn, 79-83; assoc scientist virol, Wistar Inst, Univ Pa, 83-84; assoc prof epidemiol, Univ Mo Columbia, 84-88. *Concurrent Pos:* Lectr & vis prof epidemiol, Univ Calif Davis, 71-78, fel res, 71-74; consult, Nestle Res Co, Vevey, Switz, 77-78; Food & Agr Orgn, UN, & WHO, 87-90; adj prof int health, Dept Prev Med, Cornell Univ, 79-83; clin prof epidemiol, Col Vet Med, Univ Pa, 83-84. *Mem:* Am Vet Med Asn; Am Asn Path; fel Am Col Epidemiol. *Res:* Virus induced cachexy/wasting syndrome; AIDS; hypothalamic-hypophyseal-thymic axis; diarrheal disease; coined the expressions macro- and micro-epidemiology and HAIDS for HIV-AIDS. *Mailing Add:* 212 New Mark Esplanade Rockville MD 20850. *Fax:* 301-496-6497; *E-Mail:* torresm@dea.nci.nih.gov

**TORRES-BLASINI, GLADYS,** MICROBIOLOGY. *Current Pos:* RETIRED. *Personal Data:* b Ponce, PR; c 2. *Educ:* Univ PR, BS, 48; Univ Mich, Ann Arbor, MS, 52, PhD(bact), 53; Duke Univ, cert mycol, 54. *Prof Exp:* Teaching asst bact, Univ, 52; from assoc prof to asst prof bact, Univ PR, 53-62, from assoc prof to prof mycol, 62-77, prof & head, Dept Microbiol & Med Zool, 77-84, dir, Dept Microbiol & Med Zool, Sch Med, 84-90. *Concurrent Pos:* USPHS fel mycol, 54; Hoffmann-La Roche grant fungistatic drugs, 54, Trichophyton species, 56; Vet Admin Hosp grant, 56 & 57; Univ PR Sch Med & NIH grant, 58; NIH grant, 58, 60, 64 & 68-70; lectr, Hahnemann Med Sch, 62; Univ PR Med Sch Gen Res Funds grant, 64; mem, Study Sect Res, Vet Admin Hosp, San Juan, PR, 70; mem, Acad Senate, Univ PR Sch Med, 77-84; mem, Int Activ Comt, Am Soc Microbiol, 78-81. *Mem:* Soc Am Bacteriologists; Sigma Xi; Tissue Cult Asn. *Res:* Bacteriology; comparison of phagocytosis of various candida species; medical education; medical mycology. *Mailing Add:* Dept Microbiol Univ PR Med Sci Box 5067 San Juan PR 00936

**TORRES-PINEDO, RAMON,** PEDIATRICS, GASTROENTEROLOGY. *Current Pos:* PROF PEDIAT & CHIEF PEDIAT GASTROENTEROL, 75- DIR, CLIN RES CTR, OKLA CHILDREN'S MEM HOSP, OKLAHOMA CITY, 78- *Personal Data:* b Burgos, Spain, Apr 3, 29; US citizen; m 57; c 4. *Educ:* Univ Granada, BS, 48; Univ Madrid, MD, 56. *Prof Exp:* Intern, San Juan City Hosp, PR, 58-59; resident pediat, San Juan City Hosp & Univ Hosp, 59-61; assoc, Univ Hosp, Univ PR, 63-65, from asst prof to prof, 65-75, asst dir pediat res, Clin Res Ctr, Sch Med, 63-75, prof physiol & head dept, 66-75. *Concurrent Pos:* Fels pediat res, Michael Reese Hosp & Med Ctr, Univ Ill, 61-63; consult physician, San Juan City Hosp, 64-75. *Mem:* Am Fedn Clin Res; Am Inst Nutrit; Am Pediat Soc; Soc Pediat Res; Sigma Xi. *Res:* Pediatric research; electrolyte transport; intermediary metabolism; nutrition. *Mailing Add:* Baptist Med Ctr 3366 NW Expressway Suite 350 Oklahoma City OK 73112. *Fax:* 405-271-3967

**TORREY, HENRY CUTLER,** NUCLEAR MAGNETIC RESONANCE, RELAXATION PHENOMENA. *Current Pos:* RETIRED. *Personal Data:* b Yonkers, NY, Apr 4, 11; m 37, Helen Hubert; c John C & Meriel (Borremans). *Educ:* Univ Vt, BSc, 32; Columbia Univ, MA, 33 & PhD(physics), 37. *Hon Degrees:* DSc, Univ Vt, 65. *Prof Exp:* From instr to asst prof, Penn State Univ, 37-42; from assoc prof to prof physics, Rutgers Univ, 46-76, dean, grad sch, 65-74, dir res arts & sci, 65-74. *Concurrent Pos:* Consult, Calif Res Corp, 52-65; prin investr, NSF & Off Naval Res, 48-65. *Mem:* Sigma Xi; AAAS; fel Am Phys Soc; Am Asn Physic Teachers. *Res:* Radio frequency spectra; spin diffusion and relaxation. *Mailing Add:* 7413 Monroe St Bridgewater NJ 08807

**TORREY, RUBYE PRIGMORE,** RADIATION CHEMISTRY, ANALYTICAL CHEMISTRY. *Current Pos:* Res assoc & instr chem, 48-57, from asst prof to assoc prof, 57-72, PROF CHEM, TENN STATE UNIV, 72- *Personal Data:* b Sweetwater, Tenn, Feb 18, 26; m 57; c 2. *Educ:* Tenn State Univ, BS, 46, MS, 48; Syracuse Univ, PhD(chem), 68. *Concurrent Pos:* Asst lectr, Syracuse Univ, 63-68; US AEC res grant & res collabr, Brookhaven Nat Lab, 70- *Mem:* AAAS; Am Chem Soc. *Res:* Electro-analytical chemistry; gas phase reaction mechanisms using alpha radiolysis and high-pressure impact mass spectrometry; effects of various factors on polarographic diffusion coefficients using chronopotentiometric technique. *Mailing Add:* PO Box 49084 Cookeville TN 38506-0084

**TORRIANI GORINI, ANNAMARIA,** BACTERIAL PHYSIOLOGY. *Current Pos:* from res assoc to prof, 59-91, EMER PROF MICROBIOL, MASS INST TECHNOL, 91- *Personal Data:* b Milan, Italy, Dec 19, 18; nat US; m 60, Luigi Gorini; c Daniel. *Educ:* Univ Milan, PhD(natural sci), 42. *Prof Exp:* Res asst physiol & bact, Pasteur Inst, Paris, 48-55; Fulbright fel microbiol, NY Univ, 55-58; res assoc, Biol Labs, Harvard Univ, 58-59. *Concurrent Pos:* NIH res career award, 63-73. *Mem:* Am Soc Biol Chemists; Am Soc Microbiol; AAAS; Genetics Soc Am. *Res:* Control of protein synthesis; bacterial genetics; bacterial spores germination; phosphate metabolism in microorganisms. *Mailing Add:* Dept Biol Rm 68-371 Mass Inst Technol 77 Massachusetts Ave Cambridge MA 02139-4325

**TORTONESE, MARCO,** INTEGRATED CIRCUIT MANUFACTURING, MICROFABRICATION. *Current Pos:* RES ASST APPL PHYSICS, GINZTON LAB, STANFORD UNIV, 89- *Personal Data:* b Rome, Italy, Dec 14, 62. *Educ:* Univ Genova, Italy, Laurea, 86; Stanford Univ, MSEE, 90. *Res:* Microfabrication of probes for scanning probe microscopy; atomic force microscopy; scanning ion conductance microscopy; near field scanning optical microscopy. *Mailing Add:* 12 Santa Maria Ave Portola Valley CA 94028

**TORTORA, ROBERT D,** PROBABILITY & STATISTICS. *Current Pos:* chief statist res div, 90-92, ASSOC DIR STATIST DESIGN, METHODOLOGY & STAND, CENSUS BUR, 92- *Personal Data:* b Youngstown, Ohio, Aug 20, 46. *Educ:* Youngstown State Univ, BS, 68; Cath Univ Am, MS, 72; Bowling Green State Univ, PhD(probability & statist), 75. *Prof Exp:* Mathematician, Nat Security Agency, 68-69; dir res & applns, Nat Agr Statist Servs, USDA, 75-90. *Concurrent Pos:* Chair, Subcomt Role of Telephone Data Collection in Fed Survs, Fed Comn Statist Methodology, 80-; co-chair, Comt Disclosure Risk Anal, Off Mgt & Budget; prog chair, Surv Methods Res, Am Statist Asn, 92. *Mem:* Am Statist Asn; Int Asn Surv Statisticians. *Res:* Mathematical statistics. *Mailing Add:* Gallup Orgn 3681 Meandering Way Suite 102 Woodbridge VA 22192

**TORTORELLO, ANTHONY JOSEPH,** ORGANIC NATURAL PRODUCT SYNTHESIS, POLYMER SYNTHESIS. *Current Pos:* SR RES ASSOC, DSM DESOTECH, ELGIN, ILL, 92- *Personal Data:* b Chicago, Ill, Sept 26, 45; m 71, Theresa M Tassone; c Maria, Antoinette & Mark. *Educ:* St Joseph's Col, BS, 67; Loyola Univ, Chicago, MS, 70, PhD(chem), 75. *Prof Exp:* Res scientist chem, Am Can Co, Barrington, 74-77; sr res chemist, DeSoto, Inc, Des Plaines, Ill, 77-87, mgr, Polymer Develop Dept, 87-91; dir supplies develop, Videojet Systs Int, Wooddale, Ill, 91-92. *Concurrent Pos:* Adj fac, Elmhurst Col, Loyola Univ; lectr, Gordon Res Conf, DePaul Univ. *Mem:* Am Chem Soc; Fed Soc Coatings Technol. *Res:* Polymer synthesis; organic coatings; polymer structure property relationships; radiation cure coatings; polymer synthesis and organic synthesis applied to understanding of structure; property relationships in organic coatings including radiation cured coating; technical management. *Mailing Add:* 449 East Ct Elmhurst IL 60126

**TORUN, BENJAMIN,** CLINICAL NUTRITION, HUMAN METABOLISM. *Current Pos:* med officer clin & exp nutrit, Inst Nutrit Cent Am & Panama, 65-67, med officer human nutrit, 72-80, div chief nutrit & health, 80-85, PROF BASIC & HUMAN NUTRIT, INST NUTRIT CENT AM & PANAMA, SAN CARLOS UNIV, 73-, PROG HEAD METAB & CLIN NUTRIT, 85- *Personal Data:* b Guatemala City, Guatemala, Dec 8, 39; m 67; c 3. *Educ:* San Carlos Univ, Guatemala, MD, 65; Harvard Univ, MA, 69; Mass Inst Technol, PhD(nutrit biochem & metab), 72. *Honors & Awards:* Nestlé Award, Guatemalan Pediat Asn, 89. *Prof Exp:* Fel physiol, Kellogg Found, Harvard Univ, 67-69; res assoc nutrit, Mass Inst Technol, 69-72. *Concurrent Pos:* Dir, Clin Res Ctr, Inst Nutrit Cent Am & Panama, 72-83; prin investr, various res projs, 73-; lectr numerous hosps, univs & insts in more than 20 countries, 73-; ed, J Guatemalan Med Col, 75-76 & 86-87; vis prof, Dept Nutrit & Food Sci, Mass Inst Technol, 77-79; consult-adv, WHO, UN Food & Agr Orgn, UN Univ, Int Dietary Energy Consultancy Group, Pan Am Health Orgn, 81-; vis scientist, Dept Appl Biol Sci, Mass Inst Technol, 84-85. *Mem:* Am Soc Clin Res; Am Inst Nutrit; Am Col Nutrit. *Res:* Protein-energy malnutrition; energy, protein and amino acid requirements; protein-energy interactions; nutrition and work capacity; physical activity and growth; nutrient absorption; nutritional status evaluation; diarrheal diseases. *Mailing Add:* Clinic Nutrit & Metab Div Nutrit & Health I NCAP Apartado Postal 1188 Guatemala City Guatemala

**TORVIK, PETER J,** AERONAUTICAL & ASTRONAUTICAL ENGINEERING. *Current Pos:* from asst prof to prof, 64-95, head, Dept Aeronaut & Astronaut, 80-90, EMER PROF AEROSPACE ENG & ENG MECH, AIR FORCE INST TECHNOL, 96- *Personal Data:* b Fergus Falls, Minn, Dec 6, 38; m 58, Patricia Nyhus; c Peter John Jr & Carl Fredric. *Educ:* Univ Minn, BS, 60, MS, 62, PhD(eng mech), 65; Wright State Univ, BA, 80. *Prof Exp:* Asst mech & mat, Univ Minn, 60-62, res fel & instr, 62-64. *Concurrent Pos:* Vis prof, Ohio State Univ, 79. *Mem:* Am Acad Mech; fel Am Soc Mech Engrs; fel Am Inst Aeronaut & Astronaut; Sigma Xi; fel Am Soc Mech Engrs. *Res:* Elasticity and wave propagation; material behavior; effects of high power lasers; vibrations. *Mailing Add:* 1866 Winchester Rd Xenia OH 45385. *E-Mail:* torvik@asme.org

**TORY, ELMER MELVIN,** APPLIED MATHEMATICS, CHEMICAL ENGINEERING. *Current Pos:* assoc prof, 65-73, PROF MATH, MT ALLISON UNIV, 73- *Personal Data:* b Vermilion, Alta, Dec 10, 28; m 56, Audrey Upton; c Heather & Kevin. *Educ:* Univ Alta, BSc, 52; Purdue Univ, PhD(chem eng), 61. *Prof Exp:* Res chemist, Aluminium Labs Ltd, 54-58; asst prof chem eng, McMaster Univ, 60-63; assoc chem engr, Brookhaven Nat

Lab, 63-65. *Concurrent Pos:* Adj prof appl math, Tech Univ NS, 93-; hon res assoc, Univ NB, 93- *Mem:* Can Appl Math Soc; Can Soc Chem Eng; AAAS; Can Math Soc. *Res:* Stochastic modelling of the slow sedimentation of small particles in a viscous fluid; stability of sedimenting clusters of identical spheres; computer simulation of random packing of spheres. *Mailing Add:* Dept Math & Comput Sci Mt Allison Univ Sackville NB E0A 3C0 Can. *Fax:* 506-364-2617; *E-Mail:* etory@mta.ca

**TOSATO, GIOVANNA,** IMMUNITY OF EPSTEIN-BARR VIRUS IN MEN. *Current Pos:* SR STAFF FEL, FOOD & DRUG ADMIN-NIH, 84- *Educ:* State Univ Rome, Italy, MD, 73. *Res:* Suppression in the defense against Epstein-Barr virus; B-cell activation by the Epstein-Barr virus. *Mailing Add:* Hemat Prod CBER Food & Drug Admin 8800 Rockville Pike Bldg 29A Rm 2D06 Bethesda MD 20817. *Fax:* 301-480-3256

**TOSCANO, WILLIAM AGOSTINO, JR,** BIOCHEMISTRY, CELL BIOLOGY. *Current Pos:* PROF TOXICOL & CHMN DEPT, TULANE UNIV, 93- *Personal Data:* b Santa Monica, Calif, June 26, 45; m 69, Diane Gallagher; c Mariana Patrizia. *Educ:* Ind Univ, Pa, BSc, 68, MSc, 72; Univ Ill, Urbana, PhD(biochem), 78. *Honors & Awards:* Pincus Award, Fedn Am Soc Exp Biol, 77. *Prof Exp:* Chemist, Gulf Res & Develop Co, Pittsburgh, Pa, 68-71; res assoc biochem, Univ Ill, Urbana, 78; res fel pharmacol, Univ Wash, Seattle, 78-80; from asst prof to assoc prof toxicol, Harvard Univ, 80-90; assoc prof toxicol, Univ Minn, 90-93. *Mem:* Am Chem Soc; Am Soc Biol Chemists; Am Soc Microbiol; Am Soc Cell Biol; Am Asn Cancer Res; Sigma Xi. *Res:* Regulation of cellular function by intracellular receptors; regulation of differentiation and proliferation of human cells; receptor-modulated carcinogenesis; role of cytokines in carcinogenesis. *Mailing Add:* Dept Environ Health Sci Tulane Univ Sch Pub Health Trop Med SL-29 1430 Tulane Ave New Orleans LA 70112-2699. *Fax:* 504-585-6939; *E-Mail:* wtoscan@tmc.tulane.edu

**TOSCANO, WILLIAM MICHAEL,** THERMODYNAMICS, HEAT TRANSFER. *Current Pos:* VPRES, MGA SOFTWARE, INC, 91- *Personal Data:* b Santa Barbara, Calif, June 22, 45; m 82, Karen V King; c Aaron Michael, Anissa Marie & Jason Ian. *Educ:* Univ Calif, Berkeley, BS, 67; Mass Inst Technol, SM, 69, ME,71, PhD(eng), 73; Boston Univ, MBA, 80. *Prof Exp:* Res engr thermodyn, Western Elec Eng Res Ctr, 69; res assoc cryog, Mass Inst Technol, 73-74; res & develop mgr cryogenic eng, Helix Technol Corp, 74-77; div mgr mech eng & consult, Foster-Miller, Inc, 77-82; div mgr thermal systs, ORFMA, 82-84; mkt dir software systs, Intermetrics, Inc, 84-87; pres, Systs Designers Software, Inc, 87-91. *Concurrent Pos:* Consult, 73-; co-founder & treas, Aspen Systs, Inc, 84-91; chmn, Cryog Comt, Am Soc Mech Engrs, 79-82 & paper review chmn, Proces Industs Div, 77-79. *Mem:* Sigma Xi; Am Soc Mech Engrs; AAAS; Asn Comput Mach; Soc Indust Appl Maths. *Res:* Cryogenic engineering research; heat pumps and heat engines; compressors and expanders; energy conservation; energy conversion and generation; appliances; burner technology; thermal systems; thermodynamics and heat transfer; refrigeration systems. *Mailing Add:* 82 Old Garrison Rd Sudbury MA 01776

**TOSCH, WILLIAM CONRAD,** OIL PRODUCTION. *Current Pos:* PROF, DEPT CHEM, COLO STATE UNIV, 92- *Personal Data:* b Lee's Summit, Mo, Jan 19, 34; m 57; c 3. *Educ:* Univ SDak, AB, 57; Purdue Univ, MS, 60, PhD(phys chem), 62. *Prof Exp:* Teaching asst chem, Purdue Univ, 57-61, res asst, 58-62; res scientist, Marathon Oil Co-Denver Res Ctr, 62-68, mgr, Res Dept, 68-86; prof petrol eng, Pa State Univ, 87-92; prof, Dept Chem, Univ Colo, Denver, 90-92. *Concurrent Pos:* Asst prof, Arapahoe Community Col, 66-67; lectr, Casper Col. *Mem:* Soc Petrol Engrs. *Res:* Recovery of petroleum products from water-depleted reservoirs, including interfacial phenomena, rock and fluid interactions, rheology, surfactancy, polymer chemistry, carbon dioxide flooding and thermal oil recovery. *Mailing Add:* 5000 Boardwalk Dr Apt 29 Ft Collins CO 80525

**TOSH, FRED EUGENE,** MEDICINE, EPIDEMIOLOGY. *Current Pos:* DIR, WICHITA-SEDGWICK CO DEPT COMMUNITY HEALTH, 80- *Personal Data:* b Bemis, Tenn, Feb 13, 30; m 55; c 3. *Educ:* Univ Tenn, MD, 54; Univ Calif, MPH, 63. *Prof Exp:* Intern, Baptist Hosp, Memphis, Tenn, 54-55; med epidemiologist, Commun Dis Ctr, USPHS, 55-57; pvt pract, Tenn, 57-58; med epidemiologist, Kansas City Field Sta, Ctr Dis Control, USPHS, 58-64, chief, Pulmonary Mycoses Unit, 64-66, dep dir, Ecol Invests Prog, 67-73, dir, Div Qual & Stand, 73-78, dir off regional health planning, USPHS Regional Off, Colo, 78-80. *Concurrent Pos:* Resident, Mo State Sanitorium, 60-61; instr med, Univ Kans, 64-70, asst clin prof, 70-73. *Mem:* AMA; Am Epidemiol Soc. *Res:* Public health. *Mailing Add:* Wichita-Sedgwick Co Community Health 1900 E Ninth St Wichita KS 67214-3115

**TOSI, JOSEPH ANDREW, JR,** ecology, for more information see previous edition

**TOSI, OSCAR I,** audiology, acoustics; deceased, see previous edition for last biography

**TOSKEY, BURNETT ROLAND,** mathematics, for more information see previous edition

**TOSNEY, KATHRYN W,** AXONAL GUIDANCE, MORPHOGENESIS. *Current Pos:* asst prof develop, 84-89, assoc chair, Dept Biol, 91-95, ASSOC PROF DEVELOP & PROF WRITING, UNIV MICH, 89-, COL EXEC COMT, 96- *Personal Data:* b Sept 3, 46. *Educ:* Univ Ore, BS, 75; Stanford Univ, PhD(biol), 80. *Prof Exp:* Postdoctoral fel, Yale Univ, 80-82, Univ Conn, 83-84. *Concurrent Pos:* Assoc ed, J Morphol, 85-90; mem, Neurol B2 Study Sect, NIH, 88-; assoc dir, Develop Neurosci Prog, Univ Mich, 91-; bd trustees, Soc Devel Biol, 96- *Mem:* Soc Neurosci; AAAS; Soc Develop Biol. *Res:* Ellucidate the mechanisms that control the guidance of axons; specific migration of neural crest cells; morphogenesis of muscle during development. *Mailing Add:* Dept Biol 1121 Nat Sci Bldg Univ Mich Main Campus 830 N University Ave Ann Arbor MI 48109-1048

**TOSTESON, DANIEL CHARLES,** PHYSIOLOGY, BIOPHYSICS. *Current Pos:* DEAN FAC MED, CAROLINE SHIELDS WALKER PROF CELL BIOL & PRES, MED CTR, HARVARD UNIV, 77- *Personal Data:* b Milwaukee, Wis, Feb 5, 25; m 49, 69; c 6. *Educ:* Harvard Univ, MD, 49. *Hon Degrees:* DSc, Univ Copenhagen, 79, Univ Liege, 83, Med Col Wis, 84, NY Univ, 92, Duke Univ, 96, Emory Univ, 96; LHD, Johns Hopkins Univ, 93-; Dr, Cath Univ Louvain, 96. *Honors & Awards:* Abraham Flexner Award, Asn Am Med Col, 91. *Prof Exp:* From intern to asst resident med, Presby Hosp, 49-51; res fel, Dept Med, Brookhaven Nat Lab, 51-53, Lab Kidney & Electrolyte Metab, Nat Heart Inst, 53-55 & 57-58, Biol Isotope Res Lab, Univ Copenhagen, 55-56 & Physiol Lab Cambridge, Eng, 56-57; assoc prof physiol, Sch Med, Washington Univ, 58-61; prof physiol & pharmacol & chmn dept, Sch Med, Duke Univ, 61-75, James B Duke distinguished prof, 71-75; dean, Div Biol Sci & Pritzker Sch Med, vpres, Med Ctr & Lowell T Coggeshall prof med sci, Univ Chicago, 75-77. *Concurrent Pos:* Mem, Molecular Biol Panel, NSF, Sci Rev Comt, NIH, 64-67, Off Technol Assessment, 76, Ethics Adv Bd, HEW, 77-80, Nat Adv Coun, Nat Inst Gen Med Sci, 82-86 & Panel Gen Prof Educ Physician, Asn Am Med Cols, 82-84; chmn, Coun Acad Socs, Asn Am Med Cols, 73-74, Flexner Award Comt, 78 & Task Force Physician Supply, 87-90. *Mem:* Inst Med-Nat Acad Sci; Nat Inst Med; Am Physiol Soc; Soc Gen Physiologists (pres, 68-69); Biophys Soc; fel AAAS; Am Acad Arts & Sci; Am Physiol Soc (pres, 73-74). *Res:* Membrane physiology. *Mailing Add:* Med Sch Harvard Univ 25 Shattuck St Boston MA 02115. *Fax:* 617-432-3907

**TOSTEVIN, JAMES EARLE,** PAPER CHEMISTRY. *Current Pos:* RES CHEMIST & GROUP LEADER ANALYSIS, ITT RAYONIER INC, 69- *Personal Data:* b Mandan, NDak, June 28, 38; m 65, Patricia Burke; c Carl & Lee A. *Educ:* Carleton Col, BA, 60; Inst Paper Chem, MS, 62, PhD(paper chem), 66. *Prof Exp:* Group leader anal, Columbia Cellulose Co, Ltd, 66-69. *Mem:* Am Soc Testing & Mat; Tech Asn Pulp & Paper Indust. *Res:* Research into application and properties of natural cellulose fibers. *Mailing Add:* 1043 Connection St Shelton WA 98584. *Fax:* 360-426-7537; *E-Mail:* j.tostevin@genie.geis.com

**TOTH, BELA,** PATHOLOGY, ONCOLOGY. *Current Pos:* assoc prof path, 68-72, PROF PATH, EPPLEY INST RES CANCER, COL MED, UNIV NEBR, OMAHA, 72- *Personal Data:* b Pecs, Hungary, Oct 26, 31; US citizen; m 63; c 4. *Educ:* Univ Vet Sci, Budapest, DVM, 56. *Prof Exp:* From res asst to res assoc oncol, Chicago Med Sch, 59-63, asst prof, 63-66; fel exp biol, Weizmann Inst, 66-67. *Concurrent Pos:* USPHS trainee path, 61-63, res career develop award, 69; Eleanor Roosevelt int cancer res fel, 67-68. *Mem:* AAAS; Am Asn Cancer Res; Am Soc Exp Path; NY Acad Sci; Am Asn Path & Bact. *Res:* Experimental oncology; chemical carcinogenesis; leukemogenesis. *Mailing Add:* Epply Inst Res Cancer Univ Nebr Med Ctr 600 S 42nd St Omaha NE 68198-6805. *Fax:* 402-559-4651

**TOTH, CAROL ANN,** immunology, for more information see previous edition

**TOTH, EUGENE J,** NEUROCHEMISTRY. *Current Pos:* RETIRED. *Personal Data:* b Csikvand, Hungary, Jan 27, 32; US citizen; m 55; c 2. *Educ:* State Col Peis Hungary, BS, 54; NY Med Sch, MS, 72, PhD(biochem), 78. *Prof Exp:* Chemist, NY State Res Inst, 61-66, res scientist, 66-77; sr res scientist, Ctr Neurochem, Rockland Res Inst, 77-95. *Mem:* Am Neurochem Soc; Int Neurochem Soc. *Res:* Transport and metabolism of amino acids in the central nervous system and their functional roles in health and in various neurological and mental disorders; synthesis and tumors of brain proteins; influences on protein metabolisms. *Mailing Add:* 12 Crossbar Rd Hastings on Hudson NY 10706

**TOTH, JOZSEF,** HYDROGEOLOGY. *Current Pos:* PROF, DEPT GEOL, UNIV ALTA, 80- *Personal Data:* b Bekes, Hungary, June 22, 33; Can & Hungarian citizen; c 2. *Educ:* Univ Utrecht, BSc, 58, MSc, 60, PhD(hydrogeol), 65. *Honors & Awards:* O E Meinzer Award, Geol Soc Am, 65. *Prof Exp:* From jr res officer to sr res officer hydrogeol, Res Coun Alta, 60-68, head ground water, Div Hydrogeol, 68-80. *Concurrent Pos:* Mem subcomt hydrol, assoc comt geod & geophys, Nat Res Coun Can, 63-68; lectr, Univ Alta, 66-71; vis prof, Univ Calgary, 78-79, Univ Neuchatel, Switz, 81; mem, tech adv comt, Atomic Energy Can, Ltd. *Mem:* Am Geophys Union; fel Geol Soc Am; Int Asn Hydrogeol; Geol Asn Can; Am Asn Petrol Geologists; Can Soc Petrol Geologists. *Res:* Hydrogeology; theoretical and practical investigations of the interaction between groundwater and the geologic environment and hydrogeological applications in water resources, soil mechanics, agriculture and mineral exploration; petroleum hydrogeology. *Mailing Add:* Dept Earth & Atmospheric Scis Univ Alberta Edmonton AB T6G 2E3 Can

**TOTH, KENNETH STEPHEN,** NUCLEAR PHYSICS. *Current Pos:* NUCLEAR PHYSICIST, OAK RIDGE NAT LAB, 59- *Personal Data:* b Shanghai, China, Mar 17, 34; m 56, Roberta J Kelly; c Deborah A & Kenneth S Jr. *Educ:* San Diego State Univ, AB, 54; Univ Calif, PhD(chem), 58. *Prof Exp:* Asst chem, Univ Calif, 54-55, asst, Lawrence Radiation Lab, 55-58; Fulbright fel, Inst Theoret Physics, Denmark, 58-59. *Concurrent Pos:* Guggenheim fel, Niels Bohr Inst, Copenhagen, Denmark, 65-66; exchange physicist, Joint Inst Nuclear Res, Dubna, USSR, Nat Acad Sci, 75. *Mem:* Am Chem Soc; Am Phys Soc. *Res:* Nuclear properties of radioactive isotopes in rare earth region; low energy; heavy-ion nuclear reactions; nuclei far from stability. *Mailing Add:* Physics Div Oak Ridge Nat Lab MS-6371 Oak Ridge TN 37831-6371. *Fax:* 423-574-1268; *E-Mail:* toth@orph01

**TOTH, LOUIS MCKENNA,** PHYSICAL CHEMISTRY. *Current Pos:* Chemist, 67-80, SR CHEMIST, OAK RIDGE NAT LAB, 80-, GROUP LEADER, 82- *Personal Data:* b Lexington, Ky, Aug 27, 41; m 62; c 3. *Educ:* La State Univ, Baton Rouge, BS, 63; Univ Calif, Berkeley, PhD(chem), 67. *Concurrent Pos:* Adj prof, Univ Tenn, Knoxville, 96- *Mem:* Am Chem Soc. *Res:* High temperature molten salt chemistry; infrared, Raman and Ligand-Field spectroscopy of molten salt systems; gas phase kinetics; aqueous actinide photochemistry; nuclear fuel reprocessing. *Mailing Add:* 170 Bayview Dr Ten Mile TN 37880

**TOTH, PAUL EUGENE,** INDUSTRIAL HYGIENE. *Current Pos:* PRES, PAUL E TOTH & ASSOC, 82- *Personal Data:* b Welland, Ont, July 11, 20; US citizen; wid; c 3. *Educ:* Lawrence Inst Technol, BSChE, 49. *Prof Exp:* Supvr chem, Qual Control Lab, Briggs Mfg Co, 42-49, indust hygienist, 49-54; indust hygienist, Chrysler Corp, 54-60; occup health engr indust hyg, Dept Health Mich, 60-61; mgr indust hyg & toxicol, Ford Motor Co, 61-82. *Concurrent Pos:* Chmn, Am Bd Indust Hyg, 75-76. *Mem:* Am Indust Hyg Asn (treas, 67-70, pres, 78-79); Acoust Soc Am; Am Soc Safety Engrs; Am Indust Hyg Found (pres, 81-82); Am Acad Indust Hyg. *Mailing Add:* Paul E Toth & Assoc 9611 Manor Ave Allen Park MI 48101

**TOTH, ROBERT ALLEN,** PHYSICS. *Current Pos:* RES SCIENTIST, INFRARED SPECTROS & REMOTE SENSING, JET PROPULSION LAB, 70- *Personal Data:* b Richmond, Ind, Aug 10, 39; div; c Amy, Alexis, Lydia & Nicole. *Educ:* Earlham Col, AB, 62; Fla State Univ, MS, 66, PhD(physics), 69. *Prof Exp:* Physicist, Infrared Spectros, Nat Bur Stand, 62-66; instr Earlham Col, 66-67; assoc, Fla State Univ, 69-70. *Mem:* Fel Optical Soc Am. *Res:* Infrared spectroscopy; high resolution, its application to laboratory and theoretical data and to remote sensing of the atmosphere. *Mailing Add:* 3075 Foothills Blvd No 117 La Crescenta CA 91214

**TOTH, ROBERT S,** SOLID STATE PHYSICS. *Current Pos:* PRES, DEXTER RES CTR, INC, 78- *Personal Data:* b Detroit, Mich, Sept 4, 31; m 53; c 3. *Educ:* Wayne State Univ, AB, 54, MS, 55, PhD(physics), 60. *Prof Exp:* Res assoc physics, Wayne State Univ, 55-60; sr scientist, sci lab, Ford Motor Co, 60-69; vpres, Sensors, Inc, 69-76. *Mem:* Am Phys Soc. *Res:* Metal oxide semi-conductors; crystal structure theory of alloy phases; magnetic structure of metals and alloys; thin film physics; epitaxy; thermoelectricity; infrared physics. *Mailing Add:* 8495 Mast Rd Dexter MI 48130

**TOTH, STEPHEN JOHN,** SOIL CHEMISTRY. *Current Pos:* Specialist forest soils, 37-39, instr agr chem, 39-42, asst soil chemist, NJ Agr Exp Sta, 39-81, from asst prof to prof soils, 46-81, assoc res specialist, 47-81, EMER PROF SOIL COLLOIDS, RUTGERS UNIV, NEW BRUNSWICK, 81- *Personal Data:* b Elizabeth, NJ, Feb 19, 12; m 46; c 1. *Educ:* Rutgers Univ, BS, 33, MS, 35, PhD(soil chem), 37. *Mem:* Fel AAAS; Am Chem Soc; Soil Sci Soc Am; fel Am Inst Chem; fel Am Geog Soc; Sigma Xi. *Res:* Soil chemistry; colloids; nutrition; radioisotopes; fertilizers; water quality; bottom sediments; wildlife crops; composts. *Mailing Add:* 187 Echo Ave Edison NJ 08837-2632

**TOTH, WILLIAM JAMES,** polymer chemistry, for more information see previous edition

**TOTO, PATRICK D,** ORAL PATHOLOGY. *Current Pos:* RETIRED. *Personal Data:* b Niles, Ohio, Jan 6, 21; m 45; c 3. *Educ:* Kent State Univ, BS, 48; Ohio State Univ, DDS, 48, MS, 50; Am Bd Oral Path, dipl, 48. *Prof Exp:* Asst prof, Loyola Univ Chicago, 50-53 & 55-57, clin dir, 55-57, assoc prof, dir res & coordr grad studies, 57-76, prof oral path & chmn dept, Sch Dent, 71-91. *Concurrent Pos:* Consult, Vet Admin Hosps, Hines, Ill, 53 & Chicago, 61- *Mem:* Int Asn Dent Res; Am Soc Clin Path; Am Acad Oral Path; NY Acad Sci; Am Dent Asn. *Res:* Lectin binding to premalignant and malignant oral neoplasms; induction of oral cancer; histiocyte modulation; immunopathology oral mucosa; pathogenesis of periodontitis. *Mailing Add:* 433 Gillett Ave Waukegan IL 60085

**TOTON, EDWARD THOMAS,** ASTROPHYSICS. *Current Pos:* AT LOGICON RDA, 93- *Personal Data:* b Philadelphia, Pa, Dec 6, 42; m 70. *Educ:* St Joseph's Col, Pa, BS, 64; Univ Md, College Park, PhD(physics), 69. *Prof Exp:* Air Force Off Sci Res fel, Inst Advan Study, 69-70; NSF fel, Inst Theoret Physics, Univ Vienna, 70-71; res assoc & assoc instr astrophys, Univ Utah, 71-72; res assoc physics, Univ Pa, 72-74; res physicist, Naval Surface Weapons Ctr, 74-82. *Concurrent Pos:* Vis asst prof physics, St Joseph's Col, Pa, 74-75; consult, Naval Res Lab, Washington, DC, 75- *Mem:* Am Phys Soc; AAAS. *Res:* Astrophysical studies related to structure of neutron stars, nature of radiation from galaxies, nature of universe at moment of creation; research in combustion physics, including flame propagation, ignition, quenching and noise generation; detonation physics. *Mailing Add:* 11417 Hollow Timber Ct Reston VA 22094

**TOTTA, PAUL ANTHONY,** MATERIALS SCIENCE, METALLURGY. *Current Pos:* RETIRED. *Personal Data:* b Middletown, NY, May 17, 30; m 54, Mary Ann Cashman; c Mark P & Michael J. *Educ:* Rensselaer Polytech Inst, BMetE, 52. *Honors & Awards:* Tech Achievement Award, Int Soc Hybrid Microelectronics, 84. *Prof Exp:* Metallurgist, Gen Elec Co, 54-58; staff metallurgist, Handy & Harman, 58-59; sr engr, IBM Corp, 59-72, mgr metal & insulator technol, 72-81, sr mem tech staff, 81-87. *Concurrent Pos:* IBM fel, 87- *Mem:* Am Vacuum Soc; fel Am Soc Metals; Sigma Xi; Int Soc Hybrid Microelectronics. *Res:* Thin film metallurgy deposited by vacuum evaporation or sputtering for use as conductors in monolithic integrated semiconductor devices; metal and insulator technology for integrated circuit semiconductors and electronic packaging. *Mailing Add:* 29 Sandi Dr Poughkeepsie NY 12603

**TOTTEN, GEORGE EDWARD,** QUENCHING OF FERROUS & NONFERROUS METALS. *Current Pos:* RES SCIENTIST, UNION CARBIDE CORP, 70- *Personal Data:* b Toledo, Ohio, June 26, 45; m, Alice M Quan; c Stephanie & Stephen. *Educ:* Fairleigh Dickinson Univ, BS, 74, MS, 78; NY Univ, PhD(phys org chem), 89. *Concurrent Pos:* Chmn several confs & comts, Am Soc Metals, 88- *Mem:* Am Soc Metals; Am Soc Testing & Mat; Am Soc Mech Engrs; Am Chem Soc; Nat Fire Protection Asn. *Res:* Quenching of ferrous and nonferrous metals and general aspects of hydraulic fluid technology; fire resistance using suchine oils and hydraulic fluids; chemistry testing in conjunction with hydraulics. *Mailing Add:* 9 Gilmore Dr Stony Point NY 10980-1399. *Fax:* 914-789-2123

**TOTTEN, JAMES EDWARD,** GEOMETRY. *Current Pos:* INSTR MATH & COMPUT, CARIBOO COL, KAMLOOPS, BC, 79- *Personal Data:* b Saskatoon, Sask, Aug 9, 47; m 68, Lynne Ladell; c Dean. *Educ:* Univ Sask, BA, 67; Univ Waterloo, MM 69, PhD(geom), 74. *Prof Exp:* Nat Res Coun Can fel geom, Univ Math Inst, Tubingen, WGer, 74-76; asst prof math, St Mary's Univ, NS, 76-78; vis asst prof math, Univ Sask, 78-79. *Mem:* Math Asn Am; Can Math Soc. *Res:* Linear spaces, a set of elements called points and distinguished subsets of points called lines, such that two points determine a unique line and all lines have at least two points. *Mailing Add:* Dept Math & Statist Univ Col Cariboo Kamloops BC V2C 5N3 Can. *Fax:* 250-371-5582

**TOTTEN, STANLEY MARTIN,** GEOLOGY. *Current Pos:* From asst prof to assoc prof, 62-71, PROF GEOL, HANOVER COL, 71- *Personal Data:* b Lodi, Ohio, July 15, 36; m 58; c 5. *Educ:* Col Wooster, BA, 58; Univ Ill, MS, 60, PhD(geol), 62. *Concurrent Pos:* NSF fel, Univ Birmingham, 68-69. *Mem:* Fel Geol Soc Am; Soc Econ Paleont & Mineral; Nat Asn Geol Teachers; Am Quaternary Asn. *Res:* Glacial geology; Pleistocene and Paleozoic stratigraphy; sedimentary petrology; history of geology. *Mailing Add:* Dept Geol Hanover Col Hanover IN 47243. *Fax:* 812-866-7114; *E-Mail:* totten@hanover.edu

**TOTTER, JOHN RANDOLPH,** BIOCHEMISTRY. *Current Pos:* RETIRED. *Personal Data:* b Saragosa, Tex, Jan 7, 14; m 38, Elizabeth Van Sant; c Lorena, Anita & John. *Educ:* Univ Wyo, AB, 34, AM, 35; Univ Iowa, PhD(biochem), 38. *Prof Exp:* Instr chem, Univ Wyo, 35-36; asst biochem, Univ Iowa, 36-38; instr, Univ WVa, 38-39; instr, Sch Med, Univ Ark, 39-42, from asst prof to assoc prof, 42-52; biochemist, Oak Ridge Nat Lab, 52-56; biochemist, USAEC, 56-58; biochemist, Univ of the Repub, Uruguay, 58-60; prof chem & chmn div biol sci, Univ Ga, 60-62; assoc dir res, Div Biol & Med, USAEC, 63-67, dir, 67-72; assoc dir biomed & environ sci, Oak Ridge Nat Lab, 72-74, biochemist, 74-78; scientist, Oak Ridge Assoc Univ, 78-85. *Concurrent Pos:* Nutrit biochemist, Univ Alaska, 47; prof biochem, Univ Tenn, 75-79. *Mem:* Am Chem Soc; Am Soc Exp Biol & Med; Am Soc Biol Chemists; Am Soc Photobiol. *Res:* Radiation effects; amino acid and formate metabolism; synthesis and metabolism of pterins; luminescence; cancer epidemiology. *Mailing Add:* 360 Laboratory Rd Oak Ridge TN 37830

**TOTUSEK, ROBERT,** ANIMAL NUTRITION. *Current Pos:* from asst prof to assoc prof, 52-60, PROF ANIMAL HUSB, OKLA STATE UNIV, 60- & HEAD, DEPT ANIMAL SCI, 77- *Personal Data:* b Garber, Okla, Nov 3, 26; m 47; c 3. *Educ:* Okla Agr & Mech Col, BS, 49; Purdue Univ, MS, 50, PhD(animal nutrit), 52. *Prof Exp:* Asst, Purdue Univ, 49-50, instr, 50-52. *Mem:* Am Soc Animal Sci. *Res:* Range cow nutrition and management. *Mailing Add:* 2201 Countryside St Stillwater OK 74074

**TOU, JAMES CHIEH,** ANALYTICAL CHEMISTRY, PHYSICAL CHEMISTRY. *Current Pos:* from res chemist to sr res chemist, Chem Physics Res Lab, 65-71, sr analytical specialist chem, 75-78, assoc scientist, 78-81, sr assoc scientist, 81-84, RES SCIENTIST, ANALYTICAL LAB, DOW CHEM CO, 84- *Personal Data:* b Su-yang, China, Apr 25, 36; US citizen; m 64; c 3. *Educ:* Taiwan Norm Univ, BSc, 61; Univ Utah, PhD(chem), 66. *Honors & Awards:* V A Stenger Analytical Sci Award, Dow Chem Co, 75. *Prof Exp:* Teaching asst chem, Taiwan Norm Univ, 60-61; res asst, Univ Utah, 62-65. *Mem:* NAm Thermal Analytical Soc; Am Chem Soc; Am Soc Testing & Mat; Am Soc Mass Spectrometry. *Res:* Organic mass spectrometry; chemical ionization; electron impact and field ionization; gas-chromatography-mass spectrometry; chemical property and analysis of bis-chloromethyl ether and chloromethyl methyl ether; thermal analysis; thermokinetics and high temperature chemistry; mass spectrometry; membrane permeation. *Mailing Add:* 1306 Foxwood Dr Midland MI 48642-7174

**TOU, JEN-SIE HSU,** LIPID BIOCHEMISTRY, METABOLISM OF PHOSPHOLIPIDS. *Current Pos:* trainee, 65-68, res fel, 68-71, from instr to res asst prof, 71-88, ASSOC PROF BIOCHEM, MED SCH, TULANE UNIV, 88- *Personal Data:* b Shantung, China, Sept 17, 36; US citizen; m 65, Patrick P. *Educ:* Nat Taiwan Univ, BS, 59; Baylor Univ, MS, 64; Tulane Univ, PhD(biochem), 68. *Prof Exp:* Teaching asst biochem, Med Col, Baylor Univ, 62-64; res asst, Med Sch, Harvard Univ, 64-65. *Concurrent Pos:* Spec res fel award, NIH, 72-74; res carrer develop award, 75-80; Albert L Hyman Res grant, Am Heart Asn, La, 85. *Mem:* Am Soc Biochem & Molecular Biol. *Res:* Regulation of the metabolism of phospholipids in human leukocytes; endocrinology. *Mailing Add:* Dept Biochem Tulane Univ Med Sch 1430 Tulane Ave New Orleans LA 70112-2699. *Fax:* 504-584-2739

**TOU, JULIUS T(SU) L(IEH),** ELECTRICAL ENGINEERING, COMPUTER & INFORMATION SCIENCE. *Current Pos:* GRAD RES PROF ELEC ENG, UNIV FLA, 67-, DIR, CTR RES INFO, 77- *Personal Data:* b Shanghai, China, Aug 15, 26; m 56; c 4. *Educ:* Chiao Tung Univ, BS, 47; Harvard Univ, MS, 50; Yale Univ, DEng, 52. *Honors & Awards:* Achievement Award, Comput & Automated Systs Asn. *Prof Exp:* Proj engr, Philco Corp, 52-55; asst prof elec eng, Univ Pa, 55-57; assoc prof, Purdue Univ, 57-61, vis prof, 61-62; prof & dir, Comput Sci Lab, Northwestern Univ, 61-64; dir info sci res, Battelle Mem Inst, 64-67. *Concurrent Pos:* Consult, Philco Corp, 55-57, Barber Colman Co, 56, Int Bus Mach Corp, 60, Gen Elec Co, 61, McDonnell Douglas, 69 & Martin Marietta, 81; adj prof, Ohio State Univ, 64-67; adv, Nat Inst Health, 83-87. *Mem:* Am Soc Eng Educ; fel Inst Elec & Electronics Engrs; Am Inst Mgt; Int Soc Cybernet Med; Comput & Automated Systs Asn; Academia Sinica. *Res:* Control and information systems; computer vision; digital control; artificial intelligence; pattern recognition; computer-based automation; knowledge engineering. *Mailing Add:* Univ Fla 339 Larsen Hall Gainesville FL 32611

**TOUBA, ALI R,** FOOD TECHNOLOGY. *Current Pos:* res assoc explor food res, 65-76. head explor food res, 76-81, DEPT HEAD, BETTY CROCKERS DIV, GEN MILLS, INC, 81- *Personal Data:* b Tabriz, Iran, Apr 25, 25; m 57; c 4. *Educ:* Rutgers Univ, BSc, 51, MSc, 52; Univ Ill, PhD(food technol), 56. *Prof Exp:* Asst food microbiol, Univ Ill, 53-56; assoc technologist food res, Res Ctr, Gen Foods Corp, 56-63; proj mgr food res, Tronchemics Res, Inc, 63-65. *Concurrent Pos:* Tech consult, Teheran, Iran, 60-63. *Mem:* Am Chem Soc; Inst Food Technologists; Am Asn Cereal Chemists; Am Soc Microbiol; Sigma Xi. *Res:* Food texture; fabricated foods; gums; space foods; freeze drying beverages; flavors; cereals and snacks; desserts; dehydrated products; fruit products; technical management. *Mailing Add:* 4609 Island View Dr Mound MN 55364

**TOUBASSI, ELIAS HANNA,** MATHEMATICS. *Current Pos:* res assoc, 70-71, from asst prof to assoc prof, 70-84, assoc head, Dept Math, 77-90, PROF MATH, UNIV ARIZ, 85- *Personal Data:* b Jaffa, Israel, May 28, 43; US citizen; m 67; c 2. *Educ:* Bethel Col (Kans), AB, 66; Lehigh Univ, MS, 69, PhD(math), 70. *Prof Exp:* Sr tech aide prog design, Bell Tel Labs, 66-67. *Mem:* Math Asn Am; Nat Coun Teachers Math. *Res:* Algebra, specifically infinite abelian groups; math education. *Mailing Add:* Dept Math Univ Ariz Tucson AZ 85721

**TOUCH, RALPH J,** HEALTH EDUCATION. *Current Pos:* dir prog planning eval, 88-94, asst dir, 94-96, CHIEF SANITARIAN, AGENCY TOXIC SUBSTANCE & DIS REGISTRY, USPHS, 94- *Personal Data:* b Carpendale, Pa, Aug 2, 35. *Educ:* St Mary's Col, BS, 57; Calif Coast Univ, MBA, 86, PhD(mgt), 88. *Mailing Add:* Agency Toxic Substances & Dis Registry 1600 Clifton Rd E28 Atlanta GA 30333. *Fax:* 404-639-0744; *E-Mail:* rjt1@atsoaa1.em.cdc.gov

**TOUCHBERRY, ROBERT WALTON,** ANIMAL BREEDING. *Current Pos:* RETIRED. *Personal Data:* b Manning, SC, Oct 27, 21; m 48; c 4. *Educ:* Clemson Col, BS, 45; Iowa State Col, MS, 47, PhD(animal breeding, genetics), 48. *Honors & Awards:* Animal Breeding & Genetics Award, Am Soc Animal Sci, 71. *Prof Exp:* Asst dairy sci, Univ Ill, Urbana, 48-49, asst prof dairy cattle genetics, 49-55, assoc prof genetics in dairy sci, 55-59, prof, 59-70; prof animal sci & head dept, Univ Minn, St Paul, 70-82; prof & chair, Dept Animal Sci, Univ Calif, Davis, 82-92. *Concurrent Pos:* Fulbright res fel, Denmark, 56-57; geneticist, Div Biol & Med, US AEC, 67-68. *Mem:* Fel AAAS; fel Am Soc Animal Sci; Genetics Soc Am; Am Diary Sci Asn; Am Genetic Asn. *Res:* Population genetics; quantitative genetics; effects of crossbreeding on the growth and milk production of dairy cattle; effects of x-irradiation on quantitative traits of mice and fruit flies; statistical studies of animal records; quantitative genetics of levels of hormones in the blood of dairy cattle. *Mailing Add:* 35 Ely Rd Ely IA 52227

**TOUCHSTONE, JOSEPH CARY,** CLINICAL CHEMISTRY & BIOCHEMISTRY, CHROMATOGRAPHY. *Current Pos:* res assoc med, Univ Pa, 52-56, assoc, Pepper Lab Clin Chem, Univ Hosp, 52-56, asst res prof obstet & gynec & res assoc, Harrison Dept Surg Res, 56-63, res assoc prof, 63-67, assoc prof res surg, 63-68, RES PROF OBSTET & GYNEC, SCH MED, UNIV PA, 67-, DIR, STEROID LAB & PROF RES SURG, 68-, EMER PROF, 92- *Personal Data:* b Soochow, China, Nov 27, 21; US citizen; m 55, Phyllis Kistler; c Michael C, David G & Andrew K. *Educ:* Stephen F Austin State Univ BS, 43; Purdue Univ, MS, 46; St Louis Univ, PhD(biochem), 53. *Honors & Awards:* Chromatography Forum Del Valley Award, 82. *Prof Exp:* Asst, Purdue Univ, 43-45; res assoc, Univ Tex, Southwestern Med Sch, 46-49. *Concurrent Pos:* NIH res career award, 61-71; pres & co-founder, Chromatog Forum, 66-67, pres, 71-72, exec comt, 66- *Mem:* Am Chem Soc; Endocrine Soc; Am Soc Biol Chemists; Am Asn Clin Chemists; Am Acad Forensic Sci. *Res:* Steroid chemistry; organic synthesis;

isolation and metabolism of steroid hormones; chromatography; adrenal physiology; chromatography of lipids; forensic and environmental methodology; phospolipids; thin layer chromatography, gas and liquid chromatography; published 300 articles in various journals and 15 books. *Mailing Add:* Univ Pa Hosp 3400 Spruce St Philadelphia PA 19104. *Fax:* 215-349-5118

**TOUGER, JEROLD STEVEN,** PHYSICS EDUCATION RESEARCH. *Current Pos:* From asst prof to assoc prof, 74-85, PROF PHYSICS, CURRY COL, 85- *Personal Data:* b Brooklyn, NY, Aug 6, 45; m 69; c 2. *Educ:* Cornell Univ, BA, 66; City Univ New York, PhD(physics), 74. *Concurrent Pos:* Proj dir, NSF grant, 80-82; adj prof physics, Univ Mass, Amherst, 87, vis res prof, 94-95. *Mem:* Am Asn Physics Teachers (pres New Eng Sect, 86-87). *Res:* Thermoelectric power; transport properties in magnetic alloys; cognitive science and structural linguistics applied to scientific and mathematical discourses and to research in physics and mathematics education; curriculum development in physics, calculus and integrated science. *Mailing Add:* Dept Nat Sci & Math Curry Col 1071 Blue Hill Ave Milton MA 02186

**TOUGH, JAMES THOMAS,** LOW TEMPERATURE PHYSICS. *Current Pos:* res assoc, Ohio State Univ, 64-65, from asst prof to prof, 65-96, vchmn, Grad Studies, 85-94, EMER PROF PHYSICS, OHIO STATE UNIV, 96- *Personal Data:* b Chicago, Ill, May 4, 38; m 60, Judith Willetts; c Jacquelyn & Jennifer. *Educ:* Univ Ill, BS, 60; Univ Wash, PhD(liquid helium), 64. *Concurrent Pos:* Hon vis prof, Univ St Andrews, Scotland, 73-74; prin investr, NSF, 75-96. *Mem:* fel Am Phys Soc. *Res:* Hydrodynamics and turbulence in liquid helium II. *Mailing Add:* 424 Colman Dr Port Townsend WA 98368

**TOUHILL, CHARLES JOSEPH,** ENVIRONMENTAL ENGINEERING. *Current Pos:* EXEC VPRES, EG&G ENVIRON, 94- *Personal Data:* b Newark, NJ, Aug 27, 38; m 60, Helen O'Malley; c Gregory, Stephen, Christopher & Kathleen. *Educ:* Rensselaer Polytech Inst, BCE, 60, PhD(environ eng), 64; Mass Inst Technol, SM, 61; Am Acad Environ Engrs, dipl, 70. *Honors & Awards:* Kappe Lectr, Am Acad Environ Engrs, 92. *Prof Exp:* Staff mem, Gen Elec Co, 64-65 & Battelle Pac NW Labs, 65-71; officer in consult firms, 71-77; pres, Baker/TSA, Inc, 77-90; group sr vpres, ICF Kaiser Engrs, Inc, 90-94. *Concurrent Pos:* US deleg, Int Asn Water Pollution Res, 70-71 & 79-83; mem bd trustees, Am Acad Environ Engrs, 71-78 & 83-86; fel, Rensselaer Alumni Asn, 94- *Mem:* Am Inst Chem Engrs; Am Chem Soc; Am Water Works Asn; Water Environ Fedn; Am Soc Civil Engrs. *Res:* Commercialization of new environmental technologies. *Mailing Add:* 2206 Almanack Ct Pittsburgh PA 15237

**TOULMIN, PRIESTLEY,** GEOLOGY. *Current Pos:* RETIRED. *Personal Data:* b Birmingham, Ala, June 5, 30; m 52, Martha J Slason; c Catharine B (Gibson) & Priestley C. *Educ:* Harvard Univ, AB, 51, PhD(geol), 59; Univ Colo, MS, 53. *Prof Exp:* Geologist, US Geol Surv, 53-56, chief br exp geochem & mineral, 66-72, geologist, 58-86. *Concurrent Pos:* Lectr vis geol scientist prog, Am Geol Inst, 64; adj assoc prof, Columbia Univ, 66; scientist, Proj Viking, NASA, 68-81; team leader inorg chem invest, 72-81; ed, J Translations, Geochem Soc, 65-68; assoc ed, Am Mineralogist, J Mineral Soc Am, 74-76; res assoc geochem, Calif Inst Technol, 76-77; dir, Petrogenesis & Mineral Resources Prog, NSF, 85. *Mem:* fel Mineral Soc Am; fel Geol Soc Am; Am Geophys Union; Mineral Asn Can; fel Soc Econ Geologists; Sigma Xi. *Res:* Igneous and sulfide petrology; phase equilibria and thermochemistry of ore minerals; mineralogy and geochemistry of Mars. *Mailing Add:* PO Box 183 Alexandria VA 22313-0183. *E-Mail:* 72405.577@compuserve.com

**TOULOUSE, JEAN,** COLLECTIVE STRUCTURAL DYNAMICS IN DISORDERED SOLIDS, RELAXATION PHENOMENA. *Current Pos:* asst prof, 84-89, ASSOC PROF PHYSICS, LEHIGH UNIV, 89- *Personal Data:* b Paris, France, Mar 18, 48; US citizen; m 73, Mary Teuchtler; c 4. *Educ:* Univ Paris France, MS, 71; Columbia Univ NY, MS, 77, PhD(solid state sci), 82. *Prof Exp:* Staff econ statist, Nat Inst Statist & Econ Studies, 71-73 & Usinor Steel Corp, NY, 73-75; res asst, Columbia Univ NY, 75-82, res assoc, 82-84. *Concurrent Pos:* Prin investr, Dept Energy Grant, 86- & Off Naval Res grant, 90-; guest ed, Ferroelectrics, 91; prin organizer, Conf Fundamental Exp in Ferroelectrics, 91. *Mem:* Am Phys Soc; Mat Res Soc. *Res:* Dielectric, ultrasonic, raman and neutron studies of structural phase transitions in disordered crystals and amorphous systems; relaxation phenomena solids; ferroelectricity. *Mailing Add:* Physics Dept Lehigh Univ Bethlehem PA 18015. *Fax:* 610-758-4561; *E-Mail:* jt02@lehigh.edu

**TOUMADJE, ARAZDORDI,** CIRCULAR DICHROISM STUDY OF PROTEIN STRUCTURE, POSTHARVEST PHYSIOLOGY OF FRUITS. *Current Pos:* Res asst, 84-86, fel, 86-92, SR RES ASST PROF, ORE STATE UNIV, 92- *Personal Data:* b Gorgan, Mazandaran, Mar 29, 51; m 75, Zolaikha Iri; c Kourosh & Aresh. *Educ:* Shiraz Univ, BS, 73; Univ Calif, Davis, MS, 80; Ore State Univ, PhD(hort), 84. *Mem:* AAAS. *Res:* Protein secondary structure in solution using circular dichroism spectroscopy; protein folding using short peptides; telomerase actitity in cell culture. *Mailing Add:* Dept Biochem-Biophys Ore State Univ ALS 2011 Corvallis OR 97331-7305. *Fax:* 541-737-0481; *E-Mail:* toumadja@ucs.orst.edu

**TOUPIN, RICHARD A,** RELATIVITY, ELECTROMAGNETISM. *Current Pos:* RETIRED. *Personal Data:* b Miami, Fla, Aug 20, 26; m 50; c Christine, Cecile & John. *Educ:* Univ SC, BS, 46; Univ Hawaii, MS, 49; Syracuse Univ, PhD(physics), 61. *Honors & Awards:* NY Acad Sci Ann Lectr, 65; First Int Agostinelli Prize, Acad Nat Lincei, 92. *Prof Exp:* Instr physics, Univ Hawaii, 49-50; res asst theoret mech, US Naval Res Lab, 50-62; res asst appl math, Res Ctr, IBM Sci Ctr, 62-74, dir math sci, 74-81, mem staff sci/eng comput,

Heidelberg, 83-86, mem, Almaden Lab, 87-90. *Concurrent Pos:* Vis scholar & consult prof, Stanford Univ, 87-90. *Mem:* Sr mem Soc Natural Philos (secy, 65-67). *Res:* Elasticity, dielectrics and electromagnetic theories; relativity; dielectrics; differential geometry; numerical analysis; wave mechanics. *Mailing Add:* 4551 Gulf Shore Blvd N Esplanade No 1800 Naples FL 33940. *E-Mail:* rtoupin@ibmnet.com

**TOUR, JAMES MITCHELL,** CONDUCTING POLYMERS, HETEROGENEOUS CATALYSIS. *Current Pos:* asst prof, 88-92, ASSOC PROF ORG/POLYMER, UNIV SC, COLUMBIA, 92- *Personal Data:* b New York, NY, Aug 18, 59; m 82; c 3. *Educ:* Syracuse Univ, BS, 81; Purdue Univ, PhD(chem), 86. *Honors & Awards:* George Wiley Award, Org Chem, 79; Am Inst Chemists Award, 81. *Prof Exp:* Fel org chem, Univ Wis-Madison, 86-87 & Stanford Univ, Calif, 87-88. *Concurrent Pos:* Fel, NIH, 87-88; vis lectr, IBM,, Almaden Res Ctr, San Jose, 88; young investr award polymer chem, Off Naval Res, 89-92; consult, Ethyl Corp, Baton Rouge, La, 90-; presidential young investr award polymer chem, NSF, 91- *Mem:* Am Chem Soc; Mat Res Soc. *Res:* Synthesis of conducting polymers; polymers for nonlinear optical applications; heterogeneous catalysis; metal deposition in sol-gel materials; follerene chemistry. *Mailing Add:* Chem Dept Univ SC Columbia SC 29208-0001. *Fax:* 803-777-9521; *E-Mail:* tour@chem.chem.scarolina.edu

**TOURGEE, RONALD ALAN,** MATHEMATICAL STATISTICS, COMPUTER SCIENCE. *Current Pos:* teacher math & comput sci, 68-, PROF COMPUT SCI, KEENE STATE COL. *Personal Data:* b Wakefield, RI, May 2, 38; c 3. *Educ:* Univ RI, BS, 60, MS, 62; Univ SFla, PhD(math), 75. *Prof Exp:* Teacher math, Keene State Col, 64-66 & Mt Holyoke Col, 66-68. *Mem:* Am Math Soc; Am Statist Asn. *Res:* Stochastic systems; mathematical statistics; applied probability. *Mailing Add:* Dept Math Sci Ctr Keene State Col 229 Main St MS 2001 Keene NH 03431-2001

**TOURIAN, ARA YERVANT,** BIOCHEMICAL GENETICS. *Current Pos:* ASSOC PROF MED, MED CTR, DUKE UNIV, 69- *Personal Data:* b Jerusalem, May 19, 33; US citizen; m 59; c 3. *Educ:* Am Univ Beirut, BS, 55; Iowa State Univ, MD, 58. *Prof Exp:* Intern med, Washington Hosp Ctr, DC, 58-59; resident neurol, NY Univ Med Ctr, 62-63, chief resident, 64-65; instr & fel biophys & neurol, Med Ctr, Univ Colo, 65-69. *Concurrent Pos:* NIH res career develop award, Med Ctr, Duke Univ; vis scientist cell biol, Dept Zool, Cambridge Univ, 75-76. *Mem:* AAAS; Am Soc Neurochem; Am Acad Neurol; Cambridge Philos Soc; NY Acad Sci; Int Soc Neurochem. *Res:* Biochemical genetics of Huntington's chorea, tissue culture/protein glycosylation and the control of hexosawine metabolism; metabolic and genetic control mechanisms of phenylalanine hydroxlase; the treatment of human pain in nervous system damaged patients. *Mailing Add:* Duke Univ Med Ctr Durham NC 27706

**TOURIN, RICHARD HAROLD,** ENERGY CONVERSION, ENERGY CONSERVATION. *Current Pos:* CONSULT, 87- *Personal Data:* b New York, NY, Dec 4, 22; m 48, Barbara Cotins; c Deirdre & Emily. *Educ:* City Col New York, BS, 47; NY Univ, MS, 48. *Prof Exp:* Res physicist, Warner & Swasey Co, 48-51, chief physicist, 51-59, mgr res lab, 59-63, div mgr, Control Instrument Div, 63-71; dir mkt, Klinger Sci Apparatus Corp, 71-73; dir new prog develop, NY State Energy Res & Develop Authority, 73-78; mgr indust mktg, Stone & Webster Eng Corp, 78-81; dir develop, Syska & Hennessy, Inc, 81-83; proj mgr, New York City Energy Off, 84-87. *Concurrent Pos:* Adj instr, Cooper Union, 55-60; US mem joint comt, Int Flame Res Found, 66-68; vchmn, eng sect, NY Acad Sci, 84-86 & 89-91, chmn, 87-88 & 92-94; mem, Energy Comt, Inst Elec & Electronics Engrs, 85-89. *Mem:* Fel Optical Soc Am; Combustion Inst; NY Acad Sci. *Res:* Energy conversion, spectroscopic gas temperature measurement; optical physics; remote sensing of environment; combined heat and power generation; rapid-scan spectroscopy; infrared spectra of hot gases; fuel utilization and the environment. *Mailing Add:* 195-10A 67th Ave Flushing NY 11365

**TOURLENTES, THOMAS THEODORE,** PSYCHIATRY, HOSPITAL ADMINISTRATION. *Current Pos:* CONSULT, 89- *Personal Data:* b Chicago, Ill, Dec 7, 22; m 56, Mona B Land; c Ted, Steve & Elizabeth. *Educ:* Univ Chicago, BS, 45, MD, 47, Am Bd Psychiat & Neurol, dipl, 53. *Prof Exp:* Resident psychiat, Northwestern Univ-Vet Admin Prog, 48-51; captain, US Army, Ft Carson, Colo, 52-54; supt psychiat, Galesburg State Res Hosp, 54-71; exec dir psychiat, Franciscan Ment Health Ctr, 71-85; chief psychiat serv, Vet Admin Outpatient Clin, Peoria, Ill, 85-88. *Concurrent Pos:* Clin prof, Dept Psychiat, Col Med, Univ Ill, 55-97; examnr, Am Bd Psychiat & Neurol, 60-93; regional adj psychiat, Ill Dept Ment Health, 62-71; trustee, Ill Hosp Asn, 65-67. *Mem:* Fel AAAS; fel NY Acad Sci; fel Am Psychiat Asn; fel Am Asn Psychiat Adminrs (pres, 79-80); fel Am Col Psychiatrists; fel Am Col Ment Health Adminrs; fel Cent Neuropsychiat Asn (pres, 86). *Res:* Brain-behavior interface and psychopharmacology; design and implementation of comprehensive systems of mental health care. *Mailing Add:* RR 2 Valley View Rd PO Box 251 Galesburg IL 61401-9544

**TOURNEY, GARFIELD,** PSYCHIATRY, HISTORY OF SCIENCE & MEDICINE. *Current Pos:* SCH MED, UNIV MISS, 92- *Personal Data:* b Quincy, Ill, Feb 6, 27; m 50, Helen W Wohler; c Carolyn (Florek), Patrick A & Catherine (Hughes). *Educ:* Univ Ill, BS, 46, MD, 48; State Univ Iowa, MS, 52. *Hon Degrees:* DLitt & LHD, Quincy Univ, Ill, 92. *Prof Exp:* Asst prof psychiat, Sch Med, Univ Miami, 54-55; from asst prof to prof, Sch Med, Wayne State Univ, 55-67; co-chmn dept, Sch Med, Wayne State Univ, 71-73, prof psychiat, 71-78, chmn dept, 73-78. *Concurrent Pos:* Assoc examnr, Am Bd Psychiat & Neurol, 67- *Mem:* Fel Am Psychiat

Asn; Am Osler Soc; Am Asn Hist Med; Am Med Asn. *Res:* Biochemical and clinical studies of schizophrenia and depressive illnesses; history of psychiatry; history of science, technology and medicine; philosophy of medicine; medical ethics. *Mailing Add:* 106 Cherry Hills Dr Jackson MS 39211-2507

**TOURTELLOTTE, CHARLES DEE,** BIOCHEMISTRY. *Current Pos:* instr med & biochem, Temple Univ, 63-65, from asst prof to assoc prof, 65-72, res asst prof biochem, 65-71, actg chief sect rheumatol, 66-67, PROF MED, SCH MED, TEMPLE UNIV, 72-, CHIEF SECT RHEUMATOL, SCH MED & UNIV HOSP, 67- *Personal Data:* b Kalamazoo, Mich, Aug 28, 31; m 55, Barbara Richwine; c 4. *Educ:* Johns Hopkins Univ, AB, 53; Temple Univ, MS & MD, 57; Am Bd Internal Med, dipl. *Prof Exp:* Intern med, Univ Mich, 57-58, resident & jr clin instr, 58-60; fel, Temple Univ, 60-61; guest investr, Rockefeller Univ, 61-63. *Concurrent Pos:* USPHS trainee rheumatol, Temple Univ, 60-61; Helen Hay Whitney Found fel biochem, Rockefeller Univ, 61-63; Arthritis Found fel, 63-66; mem, Gov Bd, Arthritis Found; consult, St Christopher's Childrens Hosp, Philadelphia. *Mem:* Fel Am Col Physicians; Am Fedn Clin Res; fel Am Col Rheumatology. *Res:* Biochemistry and physiology of connective tissue; endochondral ossification; amino acid metabolism; histidine; heritable disorders of bone and connective tissues; rheumatic diseases; medical education. *Mailing Add:* 6 Lane of Acres Haddonfield NJ 08033. *Fax:* 215-707-1694; *E-Mail:* etourtel@nimbus.ocis.temple.edu

**TOURTELLOTTE, MARK ETON,** BIOCHEMISTRY. *Current Pos:* RETIRED. *Personal Data:* b Worcester, Mass, Oct 25, 28; m 53; c 3. *Educ:* Dartmouth Col, BA, 50; Univ Conn, MS, 53, PhD(microbiol), 60. *Prof Exp:* From asst instr to instr bact, Univ Conn, 53-60; res assoc biophys, Yale Univ, 60-62; from assoc prof to prof animal path, Univ Conn, 63-90. *Mem:* AAAS; Am Soc Microbiol; Am Asn Avian Path; fel Am Inst Chem; NY Acad Sci. *Res:* Immunology; diagnostic bacteriology; lipids; chemistry and biosynthesis in mycoplasma; structure and function of biomembranes; mycoplasma toxins; mechanisms of pathogenesis. *Mailing Add:* 76 Aspen Rd Wakefield RI 02879

**TOURTELLOTTE, WALLACE WILLIAM,** NEUROLOGY. *Current Pos:* from asst prof to prof, 57-71, PROF NEUROL & VCHMN DEPT, UNIV CALIF, LOS ANGELES, 71-; CHIEF NEUROL SERV & DIR, NEUROL TRAINING PROG, VET ADMIN WADSWORTH MED CTR, LOS ANGELES, 71- *Personal Data:* b Great Falls, Mont, Sept 13, 24; m 53; c 4. *Educ:* Univ Chicago, PhB & BS, 45, PhD(biochem neuropharmacol), 48, MD, 51; Am Bd Psychiat & Neurol, dipl, 60. *Honors & Awards:* Mitchell Award, Am Acad Neurol, 59. *Prof Exp:* Res assoc & instr pharmacol, Univ Chicago, 48-51; intern med, Sch Med, Univ Rochester, 51-52; resident neurol, Med Sch, Univ Mich, 54-57. *Concurrent Pos:* Consult, Vet Admin Hosp, Ann Arbor, Mich, 58-71; chief neurol serv, Wayne County Gen Hosp, Detroit, 59-71; mem, Multiple Sclerosis Res Comt, Int Comn Correlation Neurol & Neurochem, World Fedn Neurol, 59-; vis assoc prof, Washington Univ, 63-64; asst examr, Am Bd Psychiat & Neurol, 64-; mem, Med Adv Bd, Nat Multiple Sclerosis Soc, 68-; exchange biomed investr, Vet Admin-Fr NIH & Med Res, Paris, 72; mem, Cerebrospinal Fluid & Immunol Comns, World Fedn Neurol; dir, Nat Neurol Res Bank, 71- *Mem:* AAAS; Am Neurol Asn; Am Soc Pharmacol & Exp Therapeut; Asn Res Nerv & Ment Dis; Am Acad Neurol. *Mailing Add:* 1140 Tellem Dr Pacific Palisades CA 90272

**TOURTELOT, HARRY ALLISON,** GEOLOGY. *Current Pos:* RETIRED. *Personal Data:* b Lincoln, Nebr, June 15, 18; m 40, 65, 77; c 6. *Educ:* Univ Nebr, AB, 40. *Prof Exp:* Proj technician, State Geol Surv, Ala, 40-42; geologist, US Geol Surv, 42-94. *Mem:* Fel Geol Soc Am; Geochem Soc; Soc Econ Paleont & Mineral; Clay Minerals Soc; Am Asn Petrol Geol. *Res:* Stratigraphy of continental tertiary rocks; geologic structure of Central Wyoming; geochemistry of sedimentary rocks; petrology of shale; environmental geochemistry; geochemistry and health. *Mailing Add:* 12140 Oak Ridge Dr Rolla MO 65401

**TOURYAN, KENELL JAMES,** SOLAR ENERGY TECHNOLOGIES. *Current Pos:* TECH TRANSFER SPEC, NAT RENEWABLE ENERGY LAB, 92-, CHIEF TECHNOL ANALYST. *Personal Data:* b Beirut, Lebanon, Dec 2, 36; US citizen; m 63; c 3. *Educ:* Univ Southern Calif, BS, 58, MS, 59; Princeton Univ, MA, 60, PhD(aerospace), 62. *Honors & Awards:* Energy Systs Award, Am Inst Aeronaut & Astronaut, 82. *Prof Exp:* Supvr reentry studies, Sandia Labs, 65-68, mgr, Aerothermodynamics Res, 68-75, mgr, Fluid & Plasmadynamics, 75-77, mgr, Fluid & Thermal Sci, 77-78; assoc dir res, Solar Energy Res Inst, 78-80, dep dir, 80-81; sr vpres res & technol, Flow Indust, 81-82; vpres res, Moriah Res, 82-87; dir energy tech, Tetra Corp, 87-92. *Concurrent Pos:* Adj prof, Dept Nuclear Eng, Univ NMex, 66-72; assoc ed, Am Inst Aeronaut & Astronaut J, 75-78, J Energy, 78-; high level expert, Panel UN & World Bank Renewable Energy Utilizaiton, 82-; Fulbright scholar USSR, 86. *Mem:* Am Inst Aeronaut & Astronaut; Am Phys Soc; AAAS; fel Am Sci Affil; Sigma Xi. *Res:* Fluid dynamics; plasmadynamics; solar and renewable energy; pulsed power technology. *Mailing Add:* Nat Renewable Energy Lab 1617 Cool Blvd Golden CO 80410-3393

**TOUSEY, RICHARD,** PHYSICS. *Current Pos:* head, Instrument Sect, US Naval Res Lab, 42-45, head, Micron Waves Br, 45-48, head, Rocket Spectros Br, 58-78, PHYSICIST, US NAVAL RES LAB, 41- *Personal Data:* b Somerville, Mass, May 18, 08; m 32, Ruth Lowe; c Joanna. *Educ:* Tufts Univ, AB, 28; Harvard Univ, AM, 29, PhD(physics), 33. *Hon Degrees:* ScD, Tufts Univ, 62. *Honors & Awards:* Hulburt Award, 48; Photog Soc Am Medal, 59; Ives Medal, Optical Soc Am, 60; Darwin Lectr, Royal Astron Soc, 63; Eddington Medal, 64; Russell Lectr, Am Astron Soc, 66, George Ellery Hale,

90; Except Sci Achievement Medal, NASA, 74. *Prof Exp:* Instr physics, Harvard Univ, 33-36, tutor, 34-36, Cutting fel, 35-36; res instr, Tufts Univ, 36-41. *Concurrent Pos:* Mem comt vision, Armed Forces-Nat Res Coun. *Mem:* Nat Acad Sci; fel Am Phys Soc; fel Optical Soc Am; Am Astron Soc (vpres, 64-66); fel Am Acad Arts & Sci. *Res:* Optical properties of the atmospheres; spectroscopy from rockets; physiological optics; photographic photometry; vacuum ultraviolet. *Mailing Add:* 10450 Lottsford Rd Apt 231 Mitchellville MD 20716

**TOUSIGNANT, MICHEL,** CULTURAL PSYCHOLOGY. *Current Pos:* PROF PSYCHOL, UNIV QUE, MONTREAL, 75- *Personal Data:* b Montreal, Que, May 4, 45; m 77, Sherry Simon; c Noemi & Tobie. *Educ:* Univ Montreal, MA, 68; Univ Chicago, PhD(human develop), 74. *Prof Exp:* Res assoc epidemiol, Univ Sherbrooke, 72-74. *Concurrent Pos:* Chmn, Lab Social & Human Ecol, 85-88. *Mem:* Am Psychol Asn; Am Anthrop Asn; Can Psychol Asn. *Res:* Epidemiology of suicide; adaptation of refugees. *Mailing Add:* Lab Social & Human Ecol Univ Que CP 8888 Montreal PQ H3C 3P8 Can. *E-Mail:* tousignant.michel@uqam.ca

**TOUSIGNAUT, DWIGHT R,** PHARMACY, COMPUTERIZED HEALTH INFORMATION DATABASES. *Current Pos:* dir, Dept Prof Pract, 66-72, assoc dir, Bur Communs & Publs, 72-81, VPRES, AM SOC HOSP PHARMACISTS, 82-, DIR, DIV DATA BASE SERV, 82- *Personal Data:* b Ironwood, Mich, Dec 4, 33; m 64; c 3. *Educ:* Univ Mich, BS, 59; Univ Calif, Pharm D, 61. *Honors & Awards:* Bristol Award, 59. *Prof Exp:* Residency hosp pharm, San Francisco Med Ctr, Univ Calif, 59-61; pharmacist, Queen Elizabeth Hosp & Royal Perth Hosp, Australia, 62-63; pharmacist, Stanford Med Ctr, 63-64; Fulbright prof hosp pharm, Cairo, 64-66. *Concurrent Pos:* Past mem, Nomenclature Adv Comt, Nat Libr Med; ed, Int Pharmaceut Abstracts, 66-; mem bd dir, Nat Fedn Abstracting & Info Serv, 87. *Mem:* Am Pharmaceut Asn; Am Soc Hosp Pharmacists; Drug Info Asn (vpres, 73-74, pres, 77-80); Fedn Int Pharm. *Res:* Drug information processing and searching; pharmacy education and practice standards; drug absorption from implanted or injected routes of administration; griseofulvin solubility studies; plastic drug sorption studies. *Mailing Add:* Am Soc Hosp Pharmacists 7272 Wisconsin Ave Bethesda MD 20814

**TOUSSIENG, POVL WINNING,** PSYCHIATRY. *Current Pos:* assoc prof child psychiat & pediat, 65-69, PROF CHILD PSYCHIAT, HEALTH SCI CTR, COL MED, UNIV OKLA, 69- *Personal Data:* b Nysted, Denmark, Sept 5, 18; US citizen. *Educ:* Copenhagen Univ, MD, 45. *Prof Exp:* Resident gen psychiat, Menninger Sch Psychiat, 50-53, John Harper Seeley fel child psychiat, Children's Div, Menninger Clin, 53-55, staff psychiatrist, 55-65. *Concurrent Pos:* Consult, Kans Indust Sch Boys, 53-61; mem fac, Menninger Sch Psychiat, 53-65; consult, Kans Neurol Inst, 64-65, Minn Dept Ment Health, Minneapolis, 65-66 & Spec Subcomt Indian Educ, US Senate Comt Labor & Pub Welfare, 69; mem, Nat Drafting Comt Juv Studies Proj, 73-; mem bd, Psychiat Outpatients Ctr Am, 73- *Mem:* Fel Am Psychiat Asn; fel Am Orthopsychiat Asn; Soc Res Child Develop. *Res:* Childhood autism; coping devices of normal and disturbed children; various modalities of psychotherapy; adolescent experience in changing times; delinquency; adoption; delivery systems of help. *Mailing Add:* Prof Corp Psychiat 6525 N Meridan Ave Suite 300 Oklahoma City OK 73116-1410

**TOUSTER, OSCAR,** MOLECULAR BIOLOGY, BIOCHEMISTRY. *Current Pos:* from instr to prof biochem, Vanderbilt Univ, 47-92, chmn Dept Molecular Biol, 63-91, prof, 73-92, EMER PROF MOLECULAR BIOL, VANDERBILT UNIV, 92- *Personal Data:* b New York, NY, July 3, 21; m 44, Eva Katherine B; c Alison (Touster-Reed). *Educ:* City Col New York, BS, 41; Oberlin Col, MA, 42; Univ Ill, Urbana, PhD(biochem), 47. *Honors & Awards:* Theobald Smith Award Med Sci, AAAS, 56. *Prof Exp:* Chemist, Atlas Powder Co, 42-43; res biochemist, Abbott Labs, 44-45. *Concurrent Pos:* Guggenheim fel, Oxford Univ, 57-58; H Hughes investr, Vanderbilt Univ & Oxford Univ, 57-60; consult, NIH, 61-70; mem, Subcomt Metab Intermediates, Nat Res Coun, 66-76; mem, Bd Dirs, Oak Ridge Assoc Univs, 73-, vpres, 74-76, pres, 76-88, chmn, 88-91; mem, Sci Adv Bd, Eunice Kennedy Shriver Ctr Ment Retardation, Waltham, Mass, 74-91; mem, Sci Adv Bd, St Jude Children's Res Hosp, 84-87. *Mem:* Fel AAAS; Am Soc Biol Chemists; Am Chem Soc; Sigma Xi. *Res:* Lysosome biochemistry; golgi enzymes; carbohydrate metabolism; glycoproteins; glycosidases. *Mailing Add:* Dept Molecular Biol Vanderbilt Univ Nashville TN 37235. *Fax:* 615-343-6707

**TOUTANJI, HOUSSAM A,** CHARACTERIZATION OF SMART MATERIALS, NON-DESTRUCTIVE EVALUATION OF CIVIL INFRASTRUCTURE. *Current Pos:* ASSOC PROF, DEPT CIVIL & ENVIRON ENG, UNIV ALA, HUNTSVILLE, 97- *Personal Data:* b Damascus, Syria, Jan 2, 63; US citizen; m 97, Petra. *Educ:* Northeastern Univ, BCE, 85, MS, 87, PhD(civil eng), 92. *Honors & Awards:* Exp Prog Stimulates Competitive Res Productivity Award, NSF, 95 & 96. *Prof Exp:* Concrete design, Worcester Polytech Inst, 91, postdoctoral fel, 92-93; asst prof, Univ PR, 93-96, assoc prof, 96-97. *Concurrent Pos:* Consult, Concrete 200, 93-94, MAZ Admixtures, 94-; concrete technol, Univ PR, 94, struct anal, 94, lectr, 95; Early Fac Career Award, NSF, 95-, FRP deleg, 96, Swiss deleg, 96 & 97, Japan deleg, 97; lectr, Transp Technol, 96 & 97; ed, Repair & Rehab J, 96-97. *Mem:* Am Civil Engrs; Mat Res Soc; Transp Res Bd; Am Soc Educ. *Res:* Durability characteristics of structural elements repaired with fiber reinforced plastic; non-destructive evaluation of concrete bridge decks; new tensile testing of cementitious composites. *Mailing Add:* Dept Civil & Environ Eng Univ Ala Huntsville AL 35899. *Fax:* 787-265-3390

**TOUTANT, JEAN-PIERRE,** NEUROSCIENCES, BIOCHEMISTRY. *Current Pos:* res assoc, 85-87, DIR RES NEUROBIOL, NAT INST AGRON RES, MONTPELLIER, FRANCE, 89-; PROF BIOCHEM, UNIV MONTPELLIER II, 90- *Personal Data:* b Paris, France, Nov 13, 44; m 71. *Educ:* Univ Paris, MSc, 68, Agregation, 69; Univ Nantes, France, PhD(biol), 79; Univ Paris VII, France, PhD(biochem), 85. *Prof Exp:* Asst prof animal physiol, Univ Nantes, 78-81; assoc prof neurobiol, Paris, 81-85; fel, Case Western Res Univ, Cleveland, Ohio, 87-89. *Mem:* Am Soc Biochem & Molecular Biol; Am Soc Cell Biol. *Res:* Structure, expression and regulation of cholinesterases in vertebrates and in the nematode Caenorhabditis elegans with the methods of biochemistry and molecular biology. *Mailing Add:* Animal Physiol INRA Pl Viala Montpellier 34060 France. *Fax:* 33467-54-56-94; *E-Mail:* toutant@ensam.inca.fz

**TOVE, SAMUEL B,** biochemistry, nutrition; deceased, see previous edition for last biography

**TOVE, SHIRLEY RUTH,** BACTERIOLOGY, BIOCHEMISTRY. *Current Pos:* assoc chief, 76-82, CHIEF, BIOL SCI PROG, CHEM & BIOL SCI DIV, US ARMY RES OFF, 82- *Personal Data:* b New York, NY, Jan 31, 25; m 45, Samuel B; c Michael, Nancy & Deborah. *Educ:* Cornell Univ, BS, 45; Univ Wis, MS, 48, PhD(bact, biochem), 50. *Prof Exp:* Instr chem, NC State Univ, 50-51, bact, 51-52; vis teacher biol, NC Col Durham, 64-65; assoc prof, Shaw Univ, 65-72, chmn dept, 65-75, consult planning, 65, prof biol, Div Natural Sci & Math, 72-77. *Concurrent Pos:* Adj prof, NC State Univ, 91- *Mem:* Am Soc Microbiol; Sigma Xi. *Res:* Biochemistry of nitrogen fixation. *Mailing Add:* US Army Res Off PO Box 12211 Research Triangle Park NC 27709. *E-Mail:* tove@aro.ncren.net

**TOVELL, WALTER MASSEY,** GEOLOGY. *Current Pos:* RETIRED. *Personal Data:* b Toronto, Ont, June 25, 16; m 72. *Educ:* Univ Toronto, BA, 40, PhD, 54; Calif Inst Technol, MS, 42. *Prof Exp:* Geologist, Calif Standard Co, 42-46; lectr geol, Univ Toronto, 49-50, assoc prof, Univ & Col Educ, 59-64; from asst prof to assoc prof geol, Univ Toronto, 62-81. *Concurrent Pos:* Mus asst, Royal Ont Mus, 46-48, cur geol dept, 48-72, assoc dir, 71-73, dir pro tem, 72-73, dir, 73-77; mem & vchmn info & educ comt, Met Toronto & Region Conserv Authority, 68-74, chmn, 75- *Mem:* Fel Geol Asn Can (secy-treas, 60-62); Mus Dirs Asn Can. *Res:* Stratigraphy and Pleistocene geology; research on geology history of Great Lakes with special emphasis on Georgian Bay. *Mailing Add:* Box 14 Violet Hill RR 4 Shelburne ON L0N 1S8 Can

**TOVERUD, SVEIN UTHEIM,** PHARMACOLOGY, ENDOCRINOLOGY. *Current Pos:* assoc prof pharmacol, Sch Med, & assoc prof oral biol, Sch Dent, 69-76, PROF PHARMACOL, SCH MED, UNIV NC, CHAPEL HILL, 76-, PROF ORAL BIOL, SCH DENT, 76- *Personal Data:* b Oslo, Norway, Dec 14, 29; m 54, Constance Ford; c Kirsten, Kari & Jon. *Educ:* Harvard Univ, DMD, 54; Norweg State Dent Sch, DDS, 56; Univ Oslo, PhD, 64. *Prof Exp:* Instr physiol, Univ Oslo, 62-63, res assoc, 63-64, from asst prof to assoc prof, 65-70. *Concurrent Pos:* Res fel physiol & biochem, Univ Oslo, 56-62; USPHS int fel, Sch Dent Med, Harvard Univ, 64-66; prin investr res grants, NIH, 79-97. *Mem:* Fel AAAS; US Endocrine Soc; Am Soc Pharmacol & Exp Therapeut; Am Soc Bone Mineral Res. *Res:* Hormonal regulation of calcium and bone metabolism, especially during lactation and the neonatal period; developmental aspects of vitamin D toxicity; purification, characterization and function of acid phosphatases. *Mailing Add:* Dent Res Ctr CB No 7455 Univ NC Chapel Hill NC 27599. *Fax:* 919-966-4599; *E-Mail:* stoverud@email.unc.edu

**TOW, JAMES,** ELECTRICAL ENGINEERING. *Current Pos:* MEM TECH STAFF, AT&T BELL LABS, 66- *Personal Data:* b Canton, China, June 25, 36; US citizen; m 68; c 1. *Educ:* Univ Calif, Berkeley, BS, 60, MS, 62, PhD(elec eng), 66. *Mem:* Inst Elec & Electronics Engrs. *Res:* Computer aided network and circuit analysis and design; active filter realization; digital signal processing; microprocessor applications. *Mailing Add:* AT&T Bell Labs Rm Mt 2E222 200 Laurel Ave Middletown NJ 07748

**TOWARNICKY, J,** ENVIRONMENTAL CHEMISTRY. *Current Pos:* ENVIRON CONSULT, SHARP ASSOCS, 91- *Personal Data:* b Cleveland, Ohio, Oct 26, 50. *Educ:* Northwestern Univ, BS, 72; Ohio State Univ, MS, 74, PhD(chem), 79, MBA, 87. *Prof Exp:* Consult, Metcalf & Eddy, 86-91. *Mem:* Am Mil Engrs Soc; Am Coal Found Soc. *Mailing Add:* 982 Brupper Ave Columbus OH 43231

**TOWBIN, EUGENE JONAS,** INTERNAL MEDICINE, PHYSIOLOGY. *Current Pos:* CHIEF OF STAFF, VET ADMIN HOSP, 68- *Personal Data:* b New York, NY, Sept 18, 18; m 49; c 4. *Educ:* NY Univ, BA, 41; Univ Colo, MS, 42; Univ Rochester, MD & PhD(physiol), 49. *Prof Exp:* Asst psychologist, Univ Rochester, 42-44; asst physiologist, Duke Univ, 44-47, intern med, 49-50, resident, 50-52; clin asst prof med, Univ Ark, Little Rock, 55-56, from asst prof to assoc prof, 56-69, assoc dean, 68-, prof med & physiol, Sch Med, 69- *Concurrent Pos:* Fel cardiol, Duke Univ, 52; ward physician, Vet Admin Hosp, 55-58, exec secy & mem res comt, 56-58, asst dir prof serv for res & educ, 58-61, assoc chief of staff for res & educ, 61-72. *Mem:* Am Fedn Clin Res; Geront Soc Am; Am Col Physicians; Am Physiol Soc; Soc Exp Biol & Med; Am Asn Med Syst & Informatics. *Res:* Water and electrolyte metabolism; physiological regulation of thirst and hunger. *Mailing Add:* 4300 W Seventh St Little Rock AR 72205-5411. *Fax:* 501-660-2041

**TOWE, ARNOLD LESTER,** PHYSIOLOGY, BIOPHYSICS. *Current Pos:* Res assoc, Sch Med, Univ Wash, 53-54, from instr to asst prof anat & physiol, 54-58, from asst prof to assoc prof physiol & biophys, 58-65, PROF PHYSIOL & BIOPHYS, SCH MED, UNIV WASH, 65- *Personal Data:* b Patterson, Calif, July 25, 27; wid. *Educ:* Pac Lutheran Col, BA, 48; Univ Wash, PhD(psychol, physiol), 53. *Concurrent Pos:* Mem, NIH Study Sect, 66-70, 78-82, 90-94. *Res:* Neurophysiology, particularly analysis of sensory and motor systems, including gross potentials and single unit activity; cortical physiology, brain evolution. *Mailing Add:* Dept Physiol & Biophys SJ-40 Univ Wash Sch Med Box 357290 Seattle WA 98195-7290. *Fax:* 206-685-0619

**TOWE, GEORGE COFFIN,** PHYSICS, SCIENCE EDUCATION. *Current Pos:* assoc prof physics, Alfred Univ, 62-65, chmn dept, 65-72, chmn, Div Spec Progs, 74-77, prof physics, 65-84, EMER PROF PHYSICS, ALFRED UNIV, 84- *Personal Data:* b Passaic, NJ, Nov 28, 21; m 47, Dorothy Etris; c Robert D. *Educ:* Hamilton Col (NY), BS, 43; Univ Mich, MS, 47, PhD(chem), 54. *Prof Exp:* Physicist, US Naval Ord Lab, 43-45; res assoc, Eng Res Inst, Univ Mich, 46-53; res engr, Sci Lab, Ford Motor Co, 53-55; from asst prof to assoc prof physics, Mont State Col, 55-61; prof physics, head dept & chmn, Div Natural Sci, Findlay Col, 61-62. *Concurrent Pos:* Lectr, Univ Wyo, 59; vis scientist, Atomic Energy Res Estab, Eng, 67-68; consult, Oak Ridge Inst Nuclear Studies, 66-72 & consult educ, Australian Univs, 77-78. *Mem:* Am Asn Physics Teachers. *Res:* Radioactivity; radiation; solid state diffusion; nuclear activation analysis. *Mailing Add:* 1506 Lorane Hwy Eugene OR 97405-1907

**TOWE, KENNETH MCCARN,** GEOLOGY, PALEOBIOLOGY. *Current Pos:* sr res geologist, 64-96, EMER RES ASSOC, DEPT PALEOBIOL, SMITHSONIAN INST, 96- *Personal Data:* b Jacksonville, Fla, Jan 31, 35; m 96, Harriet Lawson. *Educ:* Duke Univ, AB, 56; Brown Univ, MSc, 59; Univ Ill, PhD(geol), 61. *Prof Exp:* Res assoc electron micros, Univ Ill, 61-62; Ford Found res fel geol, Calif Inst Technol, 62-64. *Concurrent Pos:* Vis prof, Geol-Paleont Inst, Univ Tubingen, 73; assoc ed, Am Mineralogist, 76-81; judge, AAAS-Westinghouse Sci Jour Awards, 77-86; ed, J Foraminiferal Res, 81-85, Clays & Clay Minerals, 90-95. *Mem:* Fel AAAS; fel Geol Soc Am; Clay Minerals Soc (treas, 81-95, pres, 95-96); fel Mineral Soc Am; Int Asn Study Clays; fel Cushman Found Foraminiferal Res (pres, 89-90); Geol Soc Wash (pres, 84-85). *Res:* Biomineralogy; clay mineralogy; application of electron microscopy to geology and paleontology; Precambrian paleobiology. *Mailing Add:* Smithsonian Inst Nat Mus Washington DC 20560. *Fax:* 202-786-2832; *E-Mail:* towe@accucomm.net

**TOWELL, DAVID GARRETT,** GEOCHEMISTRY. *Current Pos:* asst prof, 64-68, ASSOC PROF GEOCHEM, IND UNIV BLOOMINGTON, 68-, ASSOC DIR, GEOL FIELD STA, 82- *Personal Data:* b Fillmore, NY, May 30, 37; m 60, Lindsay Burleson; c Garrett & Brian. *Educ:* Pa State Univ, BS, 59; Mass Inst Technol, PhD(geochem), 63. *Prof Exp:* Res fel geochem, Calif Inst Technol, 63-64. *Concurrent Pos:* Assoc chair, dept geol, 87-90. *Mem:* Geochem Soc; Geol Soc Am; Sigma Xi. *Res:* General inorganic, rare-earth, trace element and isotope geochemistry; igneous and metamorphic geology of the Northern Rocky Mountains. *Mailing Add:* Dept Geol Sci Ind Univ Bloomington IN 47405. *E-Mail:* towell@indiana.edu

**TOWELL, WILLIAM EARNEST,** FOREST POLICY, CONSERVATION. *Current Pos:* RETIRED. *Personal Data:* b St James, Mo, June 11, 16; m 40; c Jane (Darrough) & Linda (Pinney). *Educ:* Univ Michigan, BSF, 38, MF, 38. *Hon Degrees:* DSc, Univ Mo, 82. *Honors & Awards:* Schlich Medal, Soc Am Foresters, 75; Wander Medal, Am Forestry Assoc, 80. *Prof Exp:* Dir, Conservation, Mo Dept Conservation, 57-67; exec vpres, conservation, Am Forestry Assoc, 67-79. *Concurrent Pos:* Pres, Internat Assoc Fish & Wildlife Agencies, 65-66; ad, prof, NC State Univ, 79-; dir, Nat Wildlife Fedn, 79-87; dir, Forest Hist Soc, 80-88; pres, Soc Am Foresters, 85-86. *Mem:* Soc Am Foresters (pres, 85). *Mailing Add:* 4 Village Green Southern Pines NC 28387-6603

**TOWER, DONALD BAYLEY,** HISTORY OF NEUROCHEMISTRY. *Current Pos:* RETIRED. *Personal Data:* b Orange, NJ, Dec 11, 19; m 47, Arline B Croft; c Deborah A (Fretwell). *Educ:* Harvard Univ, AB, 41, MD, 44; McGill Univ, MSc, 48, PhD(exp neurol), 51. *Hon Degrees:* DSc, McGill Univ, 84. *Honors & Awards:* Hist Prize, Justus-Liebig-Univ, Giessen, WGer, 84. *Prof Exp:* Intern surg, Univ Minn Hosps, 44-45; asst resident neurosurg, Montreal Neurol Inst, McGill Univ, 48-49, assoc neurochemist, 51-53, lectr exp neurol, Fac Med, Univ, 51-52, asst prof, 52-53; chief, Sect Clin Neurochem, 53-60, chief, Lab Neurochem, 61-73, dir, 73-81, emer dir, Nat Inst Neurol & Commun Dis & Stroke, 81-; asst surgeon gen, USPHS, 75-81. *Concurrent Pos:* Res fel neurochem, Montreal Neurol Inst, McGill Univ, 47-51; Markle scholar med sci, 51-53; clin clerk, Nat Hosp, London, Eng, 51; assoc prof, Sch Med & consult, Georgetown Univ, 53-81; mem, Neurol Study Sect, Div Res Grants, NIH, 54-61; mem, US Bd Civil Serv Exam, 61-67; chmn, Neurochem Deleg to USSR, US-USSR Exchange Prog Health & Med Sci, 69; mem, Basic Res Task Force, Adv Comt Epilepsies, USPHS, 69-73; chief ed, J Neurochem, 69-73; mem, Neurochem Panel, Int Brain Res Orgn, mem, Cent Coun, 74-91; temp adv neurosci, World Health Orgn, 76-84; historian, Am Soc Neurochem, 84- *Mem:* Am Acad Neurol; Am Neurol Asn; Am Soc Biol Chemists; Int Soc Neurochem; Am Soc Neurochem (treas, 70-75); Am Neurol Asn; Peruvian Soc Psychiat, Neurol & Neurosurg; AAAS; Can Neurol Soc; Can Physiol Soc. *Res:* Neurochemistry of epilepsy; cerebral amino acids and electrolytes; history of neurochemistry. *Mailing Add:* NINCDS NIH 524 Russell Ave Gaithersburg MD 20877

**TOWERS, BARRY,** FOREST PATHOLOGY, MYCOLOGY. *Current Pos:* forest pathologist, 68-87, CHIEF, DIV FOREST PEST MGT, PA DEPT ENVIRON RESOURCES, 87- *Personal Data:* b Toledo, Ohio, July 20, 38; m 63, Jane Ford. *Educ:* Thiel Col, BA, 61; Duke Univ, MF, 61, DF(forest path), 65. *Prof Exp:* Res asst forest path, Duke Univ & Southern Forest Dis & Insect Res Coun, 62; fel phytotoxic air pollutants, Sch Pub Health, Univ NC, Chapel Hill, 65-68. *Res:* Diseases of forest trees and coniferous plantations, particularly root rot diseases; phytotoxicity of air pollutants. *Mailing Add:* Div Forest Pest Mgt 34 Airport Dr HIA Middletown PA 17057. *Fax:* 717-948-3957; *E-Mail:* towers.barry@al.dcnr.state .us

**TOWERS, BERNARD,** PSYCHIATRY, ANATOMY. *Current Pos:* prof pediat, Univ Calif, Los Angeles, 71-84, prof anat, Sch Med, 71-91, co-dir, Prog Med, Law & Human Values, 77-84, prof psychiat, 83-91, EMER PROF ANAT & PSYCHIAT, UNIV CALIF, LOS ANGELES, 91-; PVT PRACT, INTEGRATIVE MED, 91- *Personal Data:* b Preston, Eng, Aug 20, 22; c 4. *Educ:* Univ Liverpool, MB, ChB, 47; Cambridge Univ, MA, 54; Royal Col Physicians, Licentiate, 47. *Prof Exp:* House surgeon, Royal Infirmary, Liverpool, 47; asst lectr anat, Bristol Univ, 49-50; lectr anat & histol, Univ Wales, 50-54; lectr anat, Cambridge Univ, 54-70, dir med studies, 64-70. *Concurrent Pos:* Fel med, Jesus Col, Cambridge Univ, 57-70; ed, Brit Abstr Med Sci, 54-56; chmn, Teilhard Ctr Future Man, London, 66-69; consult, Inst Human Values Med, 71-; dir, Med Soc Forum, 74- *Mem:* Anat Soc Gt Brit & Ireland; Soc Health & Human Values (pres, 77-78); Am Asn Anatomists; fel Royal Soc Med; Brit Soc Hist Med; Am Asn Study Metall; Inst Asn Study Pain. *Res:* Fetal and neonatal lung; development of the heart and congenital anomalies; early detection of myocardial ischemia; primate evolution, especially human; medical humanities; medical history; medical ethics; somato psycho therapy. *Mailing Add:* 436 N Bedford Dr Suite 302 Beverly Hills CA 90210

**TOWERS, GEORGE HUGH NEIL,** PHYTOCHEMISTRY & PHOTOBIOLOGY, ETHNOPHARMACOLOGY. *Current Pos:* head dept, 64-70, PROF BOT, UNIV BC, 70- *Personal Data:* b Bombay, India, Sept 28, 23; div; c Christopher, Cedric, Charles, Kathleen, Jane, Neil, Thomas & Lilyelena. *Educ:* McGill Univ, BSc, 50, MSc, 51; Cornell Univ, PhD, 54. *Honors & Awards:* Lalor Found Award, 55; Flavelle Medal, Royal Soc Can; Gold Medal, Can Soc Plant Physiol. *Prof Exp:* From asst prof to assoc prof bot, McGill Univ, 53-62; sr res officer, Nat Res Coun Can, 62-64. *Mem:* Fel Royal Soc Can; Can Soc Plant Physiol (pres, 65-66); Phytochem Soc NAm. *Res:* Ethnopharmacology; phytochemistry; photobiology. *Mailing Add:* Dept Bot Univ BC 3529-6270 University Blvd Vancouver BC V6T 1Z4 Can. *Fax:* 604-822-6089; *E-Mail:* towers@unixo.ubc.ca

**TOWILL, LESLIE RUTH,** PLANT PHYSIOLOGY, PHOTOBIOLOGY. *Current Pos:* ASST PROF BOT, ARIZ STATE UNIV, 75- *Personal Data:* b Milwaukee, Wis, Nov 19, 44. *Educ:* Univ Wis-Milwaukee, BS, 66, MS, 68; Univ Mich, Ann Arbor, PhD(bot), 73. *Prof Exp:* Sr fel biochem, Univ Wash, 73-75. *Concurrent Pos:* Prin investr, NSF grant, 77-79. *Mem:* Am Soc Plant Physiologists; Am Soc Photobiol; Bot Soc Am. *Res:* Mechanism of light action on initial biochemical events in plant development. *Mailing Add:* Dept Bot & Microbiol Ariz State Univ Tempe AZ 85287-0001

**TOWLE, ALBERT,** invertebrate physiology, science education, for more information see previous edition

**TOWLE, DAVID WALTER,** MARINE PHYSIOLOGY, MEMBRANE MOLECULAR BIOLOGY. *Current Pos:* chairperson biol, 88-92, PROF BIOL, LAKE FOREST COL, 88-, CHAIR, 95- *Personal Data:* b Concord, NH, May 26, 41; m 74, Betty Massie; c 3. *Educ:* Univ NH, BS, 65, MS, 67; Dartmouth Col, PhD(biol sci), 70. *Prof Exp:* From asst prof to prof biol, Univ Richmond, 70-88. *Concurrent Pos:* Prin investr, Mt Desert Island Biol Lab, 83-88 & 90- *Mem:* Am Physiol Soc; Sigma Xi; Soc Integrative Comp Biol; fel AAAS. *Res:* Biochemistry and physiology of osmoregulation in marine and estuarine organisms; ion transport by membrane vesicles; molecular biology of transport proteins. *Mailing Add:* Dept Biol Lake Forest Col Lake Forest IL 60045. *E-Mail:* towle@lfc.edu

**TOWLE, HOWARD COLGATE,** MOLECULAR ENDOCRINOLOGY. *Current Pos:* asst prof med, 77-79, asst prof biochem, 79-83, ASSOC PROF BIOCHEM, UNIV MINN, 84- *Personal Data:* b Philadelphia, Pa, June 15, 47; m 76; c 3. *Educ:* Mich State Univ, BA, 69, PhD(biochem), 74. *Prof Exp:* Fel cell biol, Baylor Col Med, 74-76. *Mem:* Endocrine Soc; Am Soc Biol Chemists; Sigma Xi. *Res:* Intracellular mechanism of action of thyroid hormones; regulation of messenger RNA production by hormonal and dietary factors. *Mailing Add:* Dept Biochem Univ Minn 4-225 Millard Hall Minneapolis MN 55455-0347. *Fax:* 612-625-2163

**TOWLE, LOUIS WALLACE,** ANALYTICAL CHEMISTRY. *Current Pos:* res chemist, Apache Powder Co, 37-44, tech serv supvr, 44-51, tech dir, 51-54, gen supt, 54-65, vpres, 69-71, gen mgr, 65-79, pres, 71-80, CHMN BD, APACHE POWDER CO, 80- *Personal Data:* b Frog Mountain, Ala, Nov 21, 08; m 31; c 2. *Educ:* Univ Ariz, BS, 30, MS, 32. *Prof Exp:* Instr chem, Ariz State Col, 33; teacher high sch, Ariz, 33-36. *Mem:* Am Chem Soc; fel Am Inst Chem; Am Inst Mining Metall & Petrol Engrs. *Res:* Preparation and uses of acetylene di-carboxylic acid; analysis of albumen and globulin blood proteins; nitroglycerin blasting explosives; manufacturing heavy chemicals; nitric and sulphuric acids; ammonium nitrate; anhydrous ammonia; ammonium nitrate blasting agents. *Mailing Add:* PO Box 1300 Benson AZ 85602-1300

**TOWLER, MARTIN LEE,** NEUROLOGY, PSYCHIATRY. *Current Pos:* PROF NEUROL & PSYCHIAT, UNIV TEX MED BR, GALVESTON, 46- *Personal Data:* b Hockley, Tex, Sept 18, 10; m 40; c 5. *Educ:* Univ Tex, MD, 35; Am Bd Psychiat & Neurol, dipl, 42. *Prof Exp:* Intern, Med Br, Univ Tex, 36, resident neurol & psychiat, 39, instr, 39-41. *Concurrent Pos:* Rockefeller Found fel, Sch Med, Univ Colo, 41-42; pvt pract; consult, Surg Gen, US Army, 49; consult, Lackland AFB Hosp, 54- *Mem:* Am EEG Soc; fel Am Psychiat Asn; AMA; Asn Am Med Cols; fel Am Acad Neurol. *Res:* Effect of drugs on the electroencephalograph pattern; clinical value and limitation of antidepressant drugs. *Mailing Add:* 5115 Ave T Galveston TX 77551

**TOWNE, DUDLEY HERBERT,** THEORETICAL PHYSICS. *Current Pos:* From instr to assoc prof, 52-63, PROF PHYSICS, AMHERST COL, 63- *Personal Data:* b Schenectady, NY, Nov 7, 24. *Educ:* Yale Univ, BS, 47; Harvard Univ, MA, 49, PhD(physics), 54. *Concurrent Pos:* Staff mem, Rockefeller Found, 63-64. *Mem:* Am Asn Physics Teachers; Am Phys Soc. *Res:* Scattering of electromagnetic radiation; broadening of spectral lines; wave propagation in inhomogeneous media. *Mailing Add:* 30 Dana Pl Amherst MA 01002

**TOWNE, JACK C,** BIOCHEMISTRY, RADIOCHEMISTRY. *Current Pos:* PROF CHEM, UNIV DALLAS, 70-, CHMN DEPT, 72- *Personal Data:* b New York, NY, Apr 23, 27; m 51, Elizabeth F Pipkin; c Michael, Philip, Tamera, Stephen, Carol & Elizabeth K. *Educ:* Univ Calif, Los Angeles, BS, 50; Univ Wis, MS, 52, PhD(biochem), 55. *Prof Exp:* USPHS fel, 54-56; dir biochem lab, Inst Psychosom & Psychiat Res & Training, 56-58; prin scientist biochem, Vet Admin Hosp, Tucson, Ariz, 58-70. *Concurrent Pos:* Asst prof, Med Sch, Northwestern Univ, 58-65; holder & co-investr, NIH grants, 59-65; lectr, Univ of the Andes, Venezuela, 64; res assoc, Col Med, Univ Ariz, 65-70. *Mem:* AAAS; Am Chem Soc; NY Acad Sci; Sigma Xi. *Res:* Enzymology; intermediary and amine metabolism; radiometric syntheses and analyses. *Mailing Add:* Dept Chem Univ Dallas 1845 E Northgate Irving TX 75062-4799. *Fax:* 972-721-5393

**TOWNE, WILLIAM F,** BIOACOUSTICS, SOCIAL INSECT BEHAVIOR. *Current Pos:* ASSOC PROF BIOL, KUTZTOWN UNIV, 85- *Personal Data:* b Bethlehem, Pa, Jan 29, 56; m 90, Ann Priester; c W Samuel & Rachel M. *Educ:* Moravian Col, BS, 78; Princeton Univ, MA, 81, PhD(biol), 85. *Concurrent Pos:* Res assoc, Princeton Univ, 85-88. *Res:* Dance language of honey bees; sounds used by honey bees in communication. *Mailing Add:* Dept Biol Kutztown Univ Kutztown PA 19530. *Fax:* 610-683-1352; *E-Mail:* towne@acad.csv.Kutztown.edu

**TOWNER, HARRY H,** PHYSICS, NUCLEAR ENGINEERING. *Current Pos:* MEM PROF TECH STAFF, CONTROLLED NUCLEAR FUSION, PLASMA PHYSICS LAB, PRINCETON UNIV, 75- *Personal Data:* b Albany, NY, Sept 4, 49; m 72; c 1. *Educ:* State Univ NY, Albany, BS, 72; Univ Ill, Urbana, MS, 75. *Mem:* Am Phys Soc; Am Nuclear Soc. *Res:* Controlled nuclear fusion and in particular the plasma physics aspects. *Mailing Add:* Princeton Plasma Physics Lab Princeton Univ PO Box 451 Princeton NJ 08543

**TOWNER, HOWARD FROST,** BIOLOGY, ECOLOGY. *Current Pos:* Biol Dept chair, 87-91, PROF BIOL, LOYOLA MARYMOUNT UNIV, 84- *Personal Data:* b Los Angeles, Calif, Aug 10, 43; m 78, Linda L Pardee; c Mary & Elizabeth. *Educ:* Univ Calif, Riverside, AB, 65; Stanford Univ, PhD(biol), 70. *Prof Exp:* NIH fel, Univ Calif, Los Angeles, 70-71, asst res neurologist, Ctr Health Sci, 71-72. *Concurrent Pos:* Consult, Wadsworth Hosp, US Vet Admin, 72-89. *Mem:* Ecol Soc Am; Sigma Xi. *Res:* Ecology of desert organisms; cytogenetics and plant evolution. *Mailing Add:* Loyola Marymount Univ 7900 Loyola Rd Los Angeles CA 90045. *Fax:* 310-338-7339; *E-Mail:* htowner@lmumail.lmu.edu

**TOWNER, IAN STUART,** THEORETICAL NUCLEAR PHYSICS. *Current Pos:* ADJ PROF, QUEEN'S UNIV, KINGSTON, ON, CAN, 90- *Personal Data:* b Hastings, Eng, May 24, 40; m 66, Sandy; c Joanne, Kirsty & Nicola. *Educ:* Univ London, BSc, 62, PhD(nuclear physics), 66. *Prof Exp:* Res assoc, Nuclear Physics Lab, Oxford Univ, 65-70; res officer nuclear physics, Chalk River Nuclear Labs, Atomic Energy Can Ltd, 70-97. *Mem:* Can Asn Physicists. *Res:* Nuclear structure; models. *Mailing Add:* Box 1403 Deep River ON K0J 1P0 Can

**TOWNER, O W,** RADIO COMMUNICATIONS. *Current Pos:* RETIRED. *Personal Data:* b Peterson, Iowa, Mar 29, 03; m 33, Anne Roeder. *Educ:* Univ Kans, BS, 27, EE, 33. *Prof Exp:* Chief, Broadcasting Sta Opers, WREN, Lawrence, Kans, 26-27; mem staff, Broadcasting Transmitter Develop Dept, Bell Tel Labs, NY, 27-38; dir eng, Expansion Opers Personnel, AM/FM & FAX, WHAS Inc, Louisville, Ky, 38-42, dir broadcasting, 45-68; asst dir broadcast, War Res Proj, Airborne Instr Lab, Columbia Univ, NY, 42-45; engr consult, AM/FM & TV & shortwave, Anchorage, Ky, 68-80. *Mem:* Fel Inst Elec & Electronics Engrs. *Res:* Construction of broadcasting; facsimile and installation of technical equipment for data, AM/FM and television; field intensity measurements and performance. *Mailing Add:* 4260 Village Dr Apt 202 Kissimmee FL 34741

**TOWNER, R(AYMOND) J(AY),** METALLURGICAL ENGINEERING. *Current Pos:* fel scientist, Aerospace Elec Div, Westinghouse Elec Corp, Ohio, 63-69, FEL ENGR, BETTIS ATOMIC POWER LAB, WESTINGHOUSE ELEC CORP, 69- *Personal Data:* b Norwich, NY, Dec 23, 25; m 57; c 3. *Educ:* Rensselaer Polytech Inst, BMetE, 50, MMetE, 51;

Univ Pittsburgh, PhD(metall eng), 58. *Prof Exp:* Student aide trainee metall eng, Phys Metall Div, US Naval Res Lab, 49; res asst, Rensselaer Polytech Inst, 50-51; res engr, Alcoa Res Labs, Aluminum Co Am, 51-63. *Mem:* Am Soc Metals; Am Inst Mining, Metall & Petrol Engrs; Brit Inst Metals; Sigma Xi. *Res:* Physical metallurgy; development of aluminum powder metallurgy products; high strength aluminum alloys; high temperature ceramic to metal seals; dispersion strengthened magnetic materials; development and application of materials for nuclear power plants. *Mailing Add:* 85 Sandish Blvd Pittsburgh PA 15228

**TOWNER, RICHARD HENRY,** ANIMAL GENETICS. *Current Pos:* DIR GENETICS RES, H&N INT, 86- *Personal Data:* b Gunnison, Colo, Oct 7, 48; m 83, Sue Lindberg. *Educ:* Colo State Univ, BS, 70; Univ Wis-Madison, MS, 73, PhD(genetics, meat & animal sci), 75. *Prof Exp:* Geneticist, H&N Inc, 75-82; dir res, Tatum Farms, 82-86. *Concurrent Pos:* Affil asst prof, Col Ocean & Fisheries Sci, Univ Wash, 78- *Mem:* Am Soc Animal Sci; Am Poultry Sci Asn; Worlds Poultry Sci Asn. *Res:* Develop and improve the H & N white and brown egg layers utilizing the existing genetic differences between birds. *Mailing Add:* H & N Int 3825 154th Ave NE Redmond WA 98052. *Fax:* 425-885-3305; *E-Mail:* richard-towner@worldnet.att.net

**TOWNES, ALEXANDER SLOAN,** INTERNAL MEDICINE, RHEUMATOLOGY. *Current Pos:* CHIEF OF STAFF, VET ADMIN HOSP NASHVILLE, TENN, 87- *Personal Data:* b Birmingham, Ala, June 19, 29; m 51; c 5. *Educ:* Vanderbilt Univ, BA, 50, MD, 53. *Prof Exp:* From instr to assoc prof, Johns Hopkins Univ, 61-72; chief sect rheumatol, Univ Tenn, Memphis, 72-75, prof med, Col Med, 72- *Concurrent Pos:* Fel med, Sch Med, Johns Hopkins Univ, 59-61; asst physician in chief, Baltimore City Hosps, 63-70; chief med serv, Memphis Vet Admin Hosp, 75-85, chief of staff, 85-87. *Mem:* AAAS; fel Am Rheumatism Asn; Am Fedn Clin Res; fel Am Col Physicians; Am Asn Immunologists. *Res:* Clinical medicine and rheumatology; role immune reactions in pathogenesis of rheumatic diseases; correlation of clinical findings with immunologic changes and effects of therapy; auto immune arthritis in experimental animals. *Mailing Add:* Vet Admin Med Ctr 1310 24th Ave S Nashville TN 37212-2637. *Fax:* 615-321-6397

**TOWNES, CHARLES HARD,** PHYSICS. *Current Pos:* univ prof physics, 67-86, emer univ prof, 86-94, PROF, GRAD SCH, UNIV CALIF, BERKELEY, 94- *Personal Data:* b Greenville, SC, July 28, 15; m 41, Frances Brown; c Linda (Lewis), Ellen (Screven), Carla (Keith) & Holly (Robinson). *Educ:* Furman Univ, BA & BS, 35; Duke Univ, MA, 37; Calif Inst Technol, PhD(physics), 39. *Hon Degrees:* Numerous from US & foreign univs & cols, 60-97. *Honors & Awards:* Nobel Prize in Physics, 64; Res Corp Award, 58; Morris Liebmann Mem Prize, Inst Radio Engrs, 58; Comstock Prize, Nat Acad Sci, 59, John J Carty Medal, 62; Stuart Ballantine Medal, Franklin Inst, 59 & 62; Rumford Premium Award, Am Acad Arts & Sci, 61; Arnold O Beckman Award, Instrument Soc Am, 61; David Sarnoff Award in Electronics, Am Inst Elec Engrs, 61 & Medal Honor, 66; Thomas Young Medal & Prize, Brit Inst Physics & Phys Soc, 63; C E K Mees Medal, Optical Soc Am, 68, Frederic Ives/Jarus W Quinn Medal, 96; Golden Plate Award, Am Acad Achievement, 69; Michelson-Morley Award, 70; Wilhem-Exner Award, 70; Earle K Plyer Prize, Am Phys Soc, 77; Nat Medal Sci, 82. *Prof Exp:* Asst physics, Calif Inst Technol, 37-39; mem tech staff, Bell Tel Labs, 39-47; from assoc prof to prof, Columbia Univ, 48-61, exec dir, Radiation Lab, 50-52, chmn dept, 52-55; vpres & dir res, Inst Defense Anal, 59-61; prof physics & provost, Mass Inst Technol, 61-66, inst prof physics, 66-67. *Concurrent Pos:* Adams fel, 50; nat lectr, Sigma Xi, 50-51, Fulbright lectr, Univ Paris, 55-56 & Univ Tokyo, 56, Fulbright fel lectr, Col France & Ecole Normale Superieure, 87; Guggenheim fel, 55-56; lectr, Enrico Fermi Int Sch Physics, 55 & 60, dir, 63; mem, Coun Am Phys Soc, 59-62, College Park, Md, 65-71 & pres, 67; mem, President's Sci Adv Comt, Panel on Strategic Weapons, 60-63 & 66-70, chmn, Dept Defense, 61-62; trustee, Salk Inst Biol Studies, 63-68, Carnegie Inst, 65-, Rand Corp, 65-70 & Calif Inst Technol, 79-84 & Ctr Theol & Natural Sci, 89-; mem bd dirs, Perkin-Elmer Corp, 66-85, Gen Motors Corp, 73-78, Astron Soc Pac, 87-90; mem corp, Woods Hole Oceanog Inst, 69-, trustee, 71-88, hon trustee, 86-; mem sci adv bd, USAF, 58-61; chmn, Sci & Tech Adv Comt Manned Space Flight, NASA, 64-79, mem, Space Prog Adv Coun, 71-77; chmn, President-Elect's Task Force on Space, 68, mem, President's Task Force Policy, 69; coun mem, Nat Acad Sci, 69-72 & 78-81, chmn, Space Sci Bd, 70-73, Comt Int Security & Arms Control, 80-89; mem corp, Woods Hole Oceanog Inst, 69-, trustee, 71-74; chmn, Sci Adv Comt, Gen Motors Corp, 71-73; mem, President's Comt Sci & Technol, 76-77; mem bd trustees, Gen Motors Cancer Res Found, 78-86; chmn, Comt Scholarly Exchanges, Peoples' Repub China, 80-83; chmn, Comt MX Basing, 81; mem, Pontifical Acad Sci, Rome, 81-; mem, Defense Sci Bd, Dept Defense, 82-86; fac res lectr, Univ Calif, Berkeley, 85-86; trustee, Calif Acad Sci, San Francisco, 87-; trustee, Ctr Theol & Nat Sci, 89- *Mem:* Nat Acad Sci; fel Am Phys Soc (pres, 67); hon mem Optical Soc Am; Am Astron Soc; Am Acad Arts & Sci; Am Philos Soc; foreign fel Nat Acad Sci India; foreign fel Indian Nat Sci Acad; Inst Elec & Electronics Engrs; hon mem NY Acad Sci; hon fel Rozhdestrensky Optical Soc Russ. *Res:* Molecular and nuclear structure; masers; lasers; radio and infrared astronomy; microwave spectroscopy; optics; quantum electronics; molecular diversity; molecular recognition; self replicating and self assembling systems. *Mailing Add:* Dept Physics Univ Calif MC 7300 Berkeley CA 94720-7300. *Fax:* 510-643-8497; *E-Mail:* cht@sunspot.ssl.berkeley.edu

**TOWNES, GEORGE ANDERSON,** NUCLEAR FUEL REPROCESSING, NUCLEAR WASTE. *Current Pos:* VPRES & OWNER, BE, INC, 83- *Personal Data:* b Augusta, Ga, Oct 30, 43; m 68; c 2. *Educ:* Ga Inst Technol, BME, 65, MSME, 67. *Prof Exp:* Engr, USPHS, 68-70; sr engr & proj mgr, Allied-Gen Nuclear Serv, 71-83. *Concurrent Pos:* Chmn, Nuclear Lifting Devices, Am Nat Stand Inst, 75- *Res:* Investigations in the reprocessing and waste aspects of the nuclear fuel cycle including remote processing and handling of spent fuel; consolidation of spent fuel to enhance existing storage and transportation capacities. *Mailing Add:* Sweetwater Estates Barnwell SC 29812

**TOWNES, HARRY W(ARREN),** MECHANICAL ENGINEERING. *Current Pos:* Asst prof mech eng, Mont State Univ, 65-71, assoc prof aerospace & mech eng, 71-77, prof aerospace, 77-80, PROF MECH ENG, MONT STATE UNIV, 77- *Personal Data:* b Machias, Maine, Oct 12, 37. *Educ:* Brown Univ, BS, 59; Calif Inst Technol, MS, 60, PhD(mech eng), 65. *Mem:* Am Soc Mech Engrs. *Res:* Heat transfer; fluid mechanics; robotics. *Mailing Add:* 514 N Tenth Ave Bozeman MT 59715

**TOWNES, MARY MCLEAN,** CELL PHYSIOLOGY. *Current Pos:* From instr to assoc prof, 50-68, dean, grad sch arts & sci, 79-86, PROF BIOL, NC CENT UNIV, 68-, DEAN, SCH GRAD STUDIES, 86- *Personal Data:* b Southern Pines, NC, July 12, 28; m 54; c 2. *Educ:* NC Univ Durham, BS, 49, MSPH, 50; Univ Mich, MS, 53, PhD(cell physiol), 62. *Concurrent Pos:* Consult biol improv prog, NSF & NC Acad Sci Prog High Sch Teachers Biol, 65-66; consult minority access to res careers, Nat Inst Gen Med Sci, NIH, 75-79. *Mem:* AAAS; Soc Gen Physiologists; NY Acad Sci; Sigma Xi; Am Soc Zoologists. *Res:* pH relations of contractility of glycerinated stalks of Vorticella convallaria; contractile properties of glycerinated stalks of Vorticella. *Mailing Add:* 101 W Alton St Durham NC 27707-3006

**TOWNES, PHILIP LEONARD,** GENETICS. *Current Pos:* prof obstet & gynec & dir div genetics, 79-95, PROF PEDIAT, SCH MED, UNIV MASS, 79-, EMER PROF, 95- *Personal Data:* b Salem, Mass, Feb 18, 27; m 56. *Educ:* Harvard Univ, AB, 48; Univ Rochester, PhD(zool), 53, MD, 59; Am Bd Pediat, dipl, 80; Am Bd Genetics, dipl, 82. *Prof Exp:* Asst biol, Sch Med & Dent, Univ Rochester, 48-51, from instr to prof anat, 52-79, from asst prof to prof pediat, 65-79, prof genetics, 66-79. *Concurrent Pos:* Dir, Cytogenetics & Prenatal Diag Lab, Med Ctr, Univ Mass, 79-95. *Mem:* Soc Pediat Res; Am Pediat Soc; Am Soc Human Genetics. *Res:* Experimental embryology; cell movements; biochemical aspects of development; enzymes; proteins; metabolic inhibitors; physiology of development; human genetics and embryology. *Mailing Add:* Univ Mass Med Ctr Dept Pediat Lake Ave N Worcester MA 01605

**TOWNLEY, CHARLES WILLIAM,** PHYSICAL CHEMISTRY, RESEARCH ADMINISTRATION. *Current Pos:* RETIRED. *Personal Data:* b East Liverpool, Ohio, Oct 27, 34; m 57, Nancy Bailey; c 2. *Educ:* Ohio State Univ, BSc, 56, PhD(nuclear chem), 59. *Prof Exp:* Sr chemist, Battelle Mem Inst, 59-62, fel, 62-65, chief chem physics res, 65-67, chief struct physics res, 67-70, mgr mat sci, 70-73, mgr info & commun systs, 73-74, mgr, William F Clapp Labs, 74-77, sr prog mgr, Toxic Substance Res, 77-80, prog mgr, toxic & hazardous mat res, Columbus Labs, 80-91. *Mem:* Fel Am Inst Chem. *Res:* Environmental monitoring; research management. *Mailing Add:* 5441 Rockport St Columbus OH 43235

**TOWNLEY, JUDY ANN,** INFORMATION SCIENCE. *Current Pos:* PRES & SR SCIENTIST, SOFTWARE OPTIONS INC, 81- *Personal Data:* b San Antonio, Tex, Sept 19, 46. *Educ:* Univ Tex, Austin, BA, 68; Harvard Univ, SM, 69, PhD(appl math), 73. *Prof Exp:* Res fel appl math, Harvard Univ, 73-, dir Info Sci Prog, 75-79. *Mem:* Asn Comput Mach; Inst Elec & Electronics Engrs. *Res:* Programming languages; environments (software systems). *Mailing Add:* Software Options Inc 8 Shady Hill Sq Cambridge MA 02138-2036

**TOWNLEY, ROBERT WILLIAM,** CHEMISTRY. *Current Pos:* RETIRED. *Personal Data:* b Lampasas, Tex, Apr 28, 07; m 29; c 2. *Educ:* Austin Col, BA, 29; Univ Tex, MA, 35, PhD(phys chem), 38. *Prof Exp:* Analytical chemist, First Tex Chem Mfg Co, 31-33; from asst to instr chem, Univ Tex, 35-37; bacteriologist, State Dept Health, Tex, 37-38, from chemist to chief chemist, 38-41; res chemist, Humble Oil & Ref Co, 41-42; indust hyg engr, USPHS, Md, 42-44; res chemist, Ciba Pharmaceut Prod, Inc, NJ, 44-50; assoc prof chem, Drew Univ, 50-54; head res dept, Personal Prod Corp, 54-57; dir Townley Res & Consult, 57-73; assoc prof Fairleigh Dickinson Univ, 58-59. *Concurrent Pos:* Consult, 73-85. *Mem:* Am Chem Soc. *Res:* Foods; drugs; water; corrosion; air and water pollution; industrial hygiene; microbiology. *Mailing Add:* 1 Westchester Terrace Annandale NJ 08801

**TOWNLEY-SMITH, THOMAS FREDERICK,** PLANT BREEDING. *Current Pos:* RES SCIENTIST, WINNIPEG RES STA, 88- *Personal Data:* b Scott, Sask, Aug 27, 42; m 63; c 3. *Educ:* Univ Sask, BSA, 64, MSc, 65; Univ Guelph, PhD(plant breeding), 69. *Prof Exp:* Res asst plant breeding, Univ Guelph, 66-69; res scientist wheat breeding, Res Sta, Can Dept Agr, 68-85; dir, Res Sta, Regina, 85-88. *Concurrent Pos:* Sr wheat breeder, Plant Breeding Sta, Can Int Develop Agency, Njoro, Kenya, EAfrica, 72-74. *Mem:* Genetics Soc Can; Can Soc Agron. *Res:* Breeding durum wheat; genetics and cytogenetics of wheat; breeding triticale; physiology of drought resistance. *Mailing Add:* 195 Dafoe Rd Winnipeg MB R3T 2M9 Can

**TOWNS, CLARENCE, JR,** PATHOLOGY, HISTOLOGY. *Current Pos:* Instr histol, 68-69, asst instr basic sci, 70-72, ASST PROF HISTOL, COL DENT, UNIV ILL, 74- *Personal Data:* b Little Rock, Ark, July 22, 16; m 44; c 3. *Educ:* Cent YMCA Col, BS, 42; Univ Ill, DDS, 45, MS, 74; Am Bd Endodontic, dipl, 57. *Mem:* Sigma Xi; Am Acad Forensic Dent; Am Soc Oral Med; Am Asn Endodontics; Am Dent Asn. *Res:* Exfoliative cytology of the oral mucosa in the male Negro nonsmoker and smoker; ultra structures study of oral mucosa; comparison of normal and hyperkerototic human oral mucosa. *Mailing Add:* Col Dent 200 E 75th St Chicago IL 60619-2299

**TOWNS, DONALD LIONEL,** PHYSICAL ORGANIC CHEMISTRY, CHEMICAL ENGINEERING. *Current Pos:* FACILITY ENGRS INC, 94- *Personal Data:* b Sioux City, Iowa, Mar 8, 35; m 60, Joyce Harper; c Jean L & Erik D. *Educ:* Ga Inst Technol, BCheE, 57; Univ Wis, PhD(chem), 63. *Prof Exp:* Process res chemist, Agr Chem FMC Corp, 62-72, sr process res chemist, Niagara Chem Div, 72-73, process eng group leader, Indust Chem Div, 73-74, tech mgr, 74-75, Furadan prod mgr, 75-76, gen operating supt, 76-77, mgr pesticide formulation & delivery res, 77-80; proj mgr, Herzog-Hart Corp, 80-84, Carlson Assoc, 84-88 & Facil Group, 88-90 & Herzog-Hart Corp, 90-93; prog mgr, Advan Process Eng Prof Corp, 93-94. *Mem:* Am Chem Soc; Royal Chem Soc; Am Inst Chem Engrs; Prof Chem Consults; Int Soc Pharmaceut Engrs. *Res:* Technical improvement, environmental protection and production of the insecticide Furadan. *Mailing Add:* 1000 L'Ambiance Circle Unit 102 Naples FL 34108. *Fax:* 770-437-7554; *E-Mail:* don.towns@facilitygroup.com

**TOWNS, ROBERT LEE ROY,** CHEMISTRY. *Current Pos:* assoc prof, 73-77, PROF CHEM, CLEVELAND STATE UNIV, 78-, CHMN DEPT CHEM, 87- *Personal Data:* b Bartlesville, Okla, Oct 27, 40; m 60; c 2. *Educ:* Univ New Orleans, BS, 65; Univ Tex, Austin, PhD(phys chem), 69. *Prof Exp:* Vis asst prof chem, Univ New Orleans, 68-70; asst prof, Tex A&M Univ, 70-73. *Concurrent Pos:* NATO Advan Study Inst, Univ York, Eng, 71. *Mem:* Am Chem Soc; Am Crystallog Asn; Am Inst Physics. *Res:* X-ray fluorescence; trace and ultratrace metal analysis in human tissues and body fluids; instrument design, development and automation; x-ray crystallography; molecular structure determination. *Mailing Add:* Col Arts & Sci Cleveland State Univ Cleveland OH 44115

**TOWNSEND, ALDEN MILLER,** PLANT GENETICS, TREE PHYSIOLOGY. *Current Pos:* Res leader, 84-93, RES GENETICIST, US NAT ARBORETUM, 93- *Personal Data:* b Tulsa, Okla, Mar 4, 42; m 68, Anne Bushfield; c Jeffrey & David. *Educ:* Pa State Univ, University Park, BS, 64; Yale Univ, MF, 66; Mich State Univ, PhD(plant genetics & physiol), 69. *Honors & Awards:* Arboricultural Res Award, Int Soc Arboriculture, 82. *Concurrent Pos:* Res Geneticist, Nursery Crops Res Lab, USDA, 70-84; exec dir, Metrop Tree Improv Alliance, 82-85. *Mem:* Soc Am Foresters; Am Phytopath Soc; Int Soc Arboricult. *Res:* Genetic improvement of urban trees with emphasis on disease and insect resistance of maples; physiological genetics of Acer rubrum and elm hybrids. *Mailing Add:* US Nat Arboretum 11601 Old Pond Dr Glenn Dale MD 20769. *Fax:* 202-245-4579

**TOWNSEND, CHARLEY E,** PLANT BREEDING, GENETICS. *Current Pos:* RETIRED. *Personal Data:* b Decatur Co, Kans, July 2, 29; m 59; c 1. *Educ:* Kans State Univ, BS, 50, MS, 51; Univ Wis, PhD(agron, plant path), 56. *Prof Exp:* Res geneticist, Agr Res Serv, USDA & Colo State Univ, 56-94. *Mem:* Fel Am Soc Agron; fel Crop Sci Soc Am. *Res:* Breeding legumes for western ranges and pastures. *Mailing Add:* 638 Gregory Rd Ft Collins CO 80524

**TOWNSEND, CRAIG ARTHUR,** BIOORGANIC CHEMISTRY, ORGANIC CHEMISTRY. *Current Pos:* from asst prof to assoc prof, 76-85, chmn, dept, 90-94, PROF CHEM, JOHNS HOPKINS UNIV, 85- *Personal Data:* b Chicago, Ill, Aug 19, 47; m 71, S Darlene Dance; c Reed L & Andrew V. *Educ:* Williams Col, BA, 69; Yale Univ, PhD(org chem), 74. *Honors & Awards:* Stuart Pharmaceut Award in Chem, 86; Robert A Welch Found lectr, 89; H Martin Friedman lectr, Rutgers Univ, 90; Boehringer-Ingelheim lectr, Yale Univ, 92. *Prof Exp:* Int exchange fel bio-org chem, Swiss Fed Inst Technol, 74-76. *Concurrent Pos:* Mem, Spec Study Sect, NIH, 80-; res fel, Alfred P Sloan Found, 82-86; Camille & Henry Dreyfus teacher-scholar, 83-88; vis prof chem, Harvard Univ, 87. *Mem:* Am Chem Soc; Royal Soc Chem; AAAS. *Res:* Biosynthesis of natural products; stereochemical and mechanistic studies of enzyme action; application of spectroscopic techniques to the solution of biological problems; molecular biology of secondary metabolism; activation and mechanism of DNA cleavage by calicheamicin. *Mailing Add:* Dept Chem Johns Hopkins Univ Baltimore MD 21218-2680

**TOWNSEND, DAVID WARREN,** PLANKTON ECOLOGY, MARINE FISHES. *Current Pos:* RES ASSOC PROF OCEANOG, UNIV MAINE, 93- *Personal Data:* b Westbrook, Maine, Jan 14, 52; m 75, Roberta Campbell; c Karen & Kristy. *Educ:* Univ Maine, BA, 74, PhD(oceanog), 81; Long Island Univ, MS, 77. *Prof Exp:* Res scientist, Bigelow Lab Ocean Sci, 81-93. *Concurrent Pos:* Exec dir, Regional Marine Res Prog Gulf Maine, 93- *Mem:* Am Soc Limnol & Oceanog; Estuarine Res Fedn; Sigma Xi; AAAS. *Res:* Biological oceanography of estuarine, coastal and shelf seas. *Mailing Add:* 1 Page Pl Orono ME 04473-1300

**TOWNSEND, DOUGLAS WAYNE,** MATHEMATICS, STATISTICS. *Current Pos:* ASST PROF MATH, IND-PURDUE UNIV, 76- *Personal Data:* b Covington, Ky, Aug 7, 48; m 72. *Educ:* Ohio State Univ, BS, 70; Univ Ill, MSc, 75, PhD(math), 76. *Mem:* Am Math Soc; Math Asn Am; Sigma Xi. *Res:* Complex analysis, primarily Nevanlinna theory for complex valued functions of a single complex variable. *Mailing Add:* Dept Math Sci Ind Univ-Purdue Univ 2101 Coliseum Blvd E Ft Wayne IN 46805

**TOWNSEND, EDWIN C,** BIOMETRY. *Current Pos:* Staff asst comput, 61-62, res assoc, 62-63, assoc prof statist, 68-74, ASSOC DIR, WVA AGR & FORESTRY EXP STA, WVA UNIV, 75- *Personal Data:* b Vienna, WVa, July 7, 36; m 58; c 3. *Educ:* Univ WVa, BS, 58, MS, 64; Cornell Univ, PhD(biomet), 68. *Mem:* Biomet Soc; Am Statist Asn. *Mailing Add:* Dept Statist Knapp Hall WVa Univ Morgantown WV 26506-0002

**TOWNSEND, FRANK MARION**, PATHOLOGY. *Current Pos:* clin prof path, 69-72, prof & chmn dept, 72-87, EMER PROF & CHMN, UNIV TEX HEALTH SCI CTR, SAN ANTONIO, 87- *Personal Data:* b Stamford, Tex, Oct 29, 14; m 51; c 2. *Educ:* Tulane Univ, MD, 38. *Honors & Awards:* Moseley Award, Aerospace Med Asn, 62; Founders Medal, Asn Mil Surgeons US, 62; Ward Burdick Award, Am Soc Clin Pathologists, 83. *Prof Exp:* USAF, 40-65, pathologist, Sch Med, Washington Univ, 45-47, instr clin path, Col Med, Univ Nebr, 47-48, assoc pathologist, Scott & White Clin, Temple Tex, 49, regional consult path, Vet Admin Hosp, Tex & La, 50, chief, Lab Serv, Lackland AFB, 50-54, dep dir, Armed Forces Inst Path, 55-59, dir, 59-63, vcomdr, Aerospace Med Div, Air Force Systs Command, Brooks AFB, Tex, 63-65; pathologist, Tex State Dept Health, 65-69. *Concurrent Pos:* Assoc prof, Med Br, Univ Tex, 49-58, lectr, 58-63, assoc prof, Postgrad Sch, 53-54; consult, Surgeon Gen, 54-63, Bd Gov, Armed Forces Inst Path, 84-, NASA, 67-74, Armed Forces Epidemiol Bd, 83-; mem, Joint Comt Aviation Path, 56-63, chmn, 60-62; mem, Armed Forces Comt Bioastronaut, Nat Res Coun, 59-60, Nat Adv Cancer Coun, 59-63, Exp Adv Panel Cancer, WHO, 58-81 & Proj Mercury Recovery Team, NASA, 60-63; regional comnr lab accreditation, SCent Region, Col Am Pathologists, 70-84, adv, Coun Educ, 85-; chair path, Univ Tex, San Antonio, 89. *Mem:* Am Asn Pathol; fel Am Soc Clin Path; fel AMA; fel Am Col Physicians; fel Am Col Path; Int Acad Aviation & Space Med. *Res:* Aerospace and respiratory disease pathology. *Mailing Add:* 7703 Floyd Curl Dr San Antonio TX 78284-7750

**TOWNSEND, HERBERT EARL, JR**, CORROSION, METALLURGICAL ENGINEERING. *Current Pos:* Res engr, Bethlehem Steel Corp, 67-72, res supvr, 72-84, res mgr, 84-85, SR RES FEL, HOMER RES LABS, BETHLEHEM STEEL CORP, 85- *Personal Data:* b Bristol, Pa, July 1, 38; m 63, Carol Costanzo; c Anita, Lisa & Claressa. *Educ:* Drexel Univ, BS, 63; Univ Pa, PhD(metall eng), 67. *Honors & Awards:* D J Blickwede Award Res Excellence, 83. *Concurrent Pos:* Chmn, Corrosion Task Force, Am Iron & Steel Inst, 92-; adj prof, Old Dom Univ, 94. *Mem:* Am Soc Testing & Mats; Mat Asn Corrosion Engrs Int. *Res:* Corrosion-resistant low-alloy steels; metallic and organic coatings for protection of steel; corrosion testing. *Mailing Add:* Homer Res Labs Bethlehem Steel Corp Bethlehem PA 18016

**TOWNSEND, HOWARD GARFIELD, JR**, INSECT PEST MANAGEMENT. *Current Pos:* RES ENTOMOLOGIST & RES PROF ENTOM, STATE FRUIT EXP STA, SW MO STATE UNIV, 70- *Personal Data:* b Rochester, NY, Sept 10, 38; m 64, Janet Slate; c Lori (Dropik) & David G. *Educ:* Cornell Univ, BS, 60; Va Polytech Inst, MS, 63; Pa State Univ, PhD(entom), 70. *Prof Exp:* Res asst entom, Va Polytech Inst, 60-62; experimentalist II, NY Agr Exp Sta, Geneva, 63-65; instr, Pa State Univ, 65-69. *Mem:* Entom Soc Am; Am Registry Prof Entomologists. *Res:* Insect and mite pests of pome and stone fruits, grapes and small fruits; pest management. *Mailing Add:* Dept Fruit Sci Res Campus SW Mo State Univ Mountain Grove MO 65711-9201. *Fax:* 417-926-6646

**TOWNSEND, J(OEL) IVES**, genetics, for more information see previous edition

**TOWNSEND, JAMES COURTLAND**, MULTIDISCIPLINARY OPTIMIZATION RESEARCH, COMPUTER AIDED DESIGN. *Current Pos:* Aerospace engr, 63-88, asst br head, 88-92, SR RES SCIENTIST, LANGLEY RES CTR, NASA, 92- *Personal Data:* b Daytona Beach, Fla, July 7, 38; m 62, Judith Robinson; c David & Andrew. *Educ:* Brown Univ, ScB, 60; Princeton Univ, MSE, 64; Univ Va, PhD(aerospace eng), 75; Col William & Mary, MS, 89. *Mem:* Assoc Aerospace Indust Asn Am; Soc Indust & Appl Math. *Res:* Experimental, theoretical and numerical research in subsonic, supersonic and hypersonic flows; geometry and grid generation for high speed civil transport, preliminary design optimization frameworks. *Mailing Add:* MDO Branch MS 159 Hampton VA 23681-0001. *E-Mail:* j.c. townsend@larc.nasa.gov

**TOWNSEND, JAMES SKEOCH**, AGRICULTURAL ENGINEERING. *Current Pos:* PROF AGR ENG, UNIV MAN, 68- *Personal Data:* b Belwood, Ont, Apr 12, 34; m 60, Yvonne M Dawson; c Philip, Robert, Alan & Neil. *Educ:* Ont Agr Col, BSA, 56; Univ Toronto, BASc, 57; Cornell Univ, MS, 65, PhD(agr eng), 69. *Hon Degrees:* Dr, Khon Kaen Univ, Thailand, 88. *Prof Exp:* Teacher, St Catharines Col Inst, 60-62; instr agr eng, Cornell Univ, 64-66. *Concurrent Pos:* Nat Res Coun & Can Dept Agr grants, Univ Man, 69-72; prof, Khon Kaen Univ, Thailand, 72-74; team leader, Int Rice Res Inst, Rangoon, Burma, 79-82; consult, Can Int Develop Agency, Ottawa, 82-, Int Ctr Maize & Wheat Res, Mex, 85-86, CUSO, Ottawa, 87, Int Rice Res Inst, 89-90; postharvest res activ, Arequipa, Peru, Int Develop Res Ctr, Ottawa, 88-92. *Mem:* Am Soc Agr Engrs; Can Soc Agr Eng; Am Soc Eng Educ; Can Soc Mech Eng; Sigma Xi. *Res:* Mechanics of machine milking; agricultural mechanization; heat transfer problems in greenhouse operations; crop and animal modeling; conservation tillage; small-scale mechanization; food engineering. *Mailing Add:* 446 Kingston Crescent Winnipeg MB R2M 0T9 Can. *Fax:* 204-275-0233; *E-Mail:* james_townsend@umanitoba.ca

**TOWNSEND, JAMES WILLIS**, ultrastructural pathology, toxicology, for more information see previous edition

**TOWNSEND, JOHN FORD**, PATHOLOGY. *Current Pos:* resident, 62-66, from asst to assoc prof, 68-75, vchmn dept, 75-77, interim chmn dept, 77-78, PROF PATH, SCH MED, UNIV MO-COLUMBIA, 75-, CHMN DEPT, 78- *Personal Data:* b Kansas City, Mo, Jan 14, 36; m 59; c 3. *Educ:* Univ Mo-Columbia, AB, 58, MD, 61; Am Bd Path, dipl, 67. *Prof Exp:* Intern, Med Br, Univ Tex, 61-62. *Concurrent Pos:* Chief path serv, Vet Admin Hosp, Columbia, Mo, 72-75. *Res:* Electrical energy transport through tissue; uterine peroxidase; diabetes using animal model Mystromys albicandatus. *Mailing Add:* 807 Stadium Rd Columbia MO 65201-5276

**TOWNSEND, JOHN MARSHALL**, MEDICAL ANTHROPOLOGY. *Current Pos:* asst prof, 73-76, ASSOC PROF ANTHROP, SYRACUSE UNIV, 76- *Personal Data:* b Amarillo, Tex, Sept 1, 41; m 84; c 3. *Educ:* Univ Calif, Berkeley, BA, 63; Univ Calif, Santa Barbara, MA, 67, PhD(anthrop), 72. *Prof Exp:* Asst prof anthrop, Univ Mont, 72-73. *Mem:* Am Anthrop Asn; fel Soc Appl Anthrop; Soc Med Anthrop. *Res:* Cross-cultural mental health; labeling theory; health care delivery and human fertility; human sexuality and mate selection. *Mailing Add:* Dept Anthrop Syracuse Univ 100 University Pl Syracuse NY 13244-0001

**TOWNSEND, JOHN ROBERT**, PHYSICS. *Current Pos:* RETIRED. *Personal Data:* b Brooten, Minn, Oct 26, 30; m 48; c 2. *Educ:* Cornell Univ, BS, 45, PhD(physics), 51. *Prof Exp:* Physicist, Hanford Atomic Prod Opers, Gen Elec Co, Wash, 51-54; from instr to prof physics, Univ Pittsburgh, 54-88. *Mem:* Am Phys Soc; Am Asn Physics Teachers. *Res:* Radiation effects in solids; defects in metals. *Mailing Add:* 203 Carnegie Pl Pittsburgh PA 15208-2705

**TOWNSEND, JOHN WILLIAM, JR**, PHYSICS. *Current Pos:* RETIRED. *Personal Data:* b Washington, DC, Mar 19, 24; m 48; c 4. *Educ:* Williams Col, BA, 47, MA, 49. *Hon Degrees:* DSc, Williams Col, 61. *Honors & Awards:* Outstanding Leadership Medal, NASA, 62 & 90; Arthur S Fleming Award, 63. *Prof Exp:* Asst physics, Williams Col, 47-49; physicist, US Naval Res Lab, DC, 49-50, unit head, 50-52, sect head, 52-53, asst br head, 53-55, head rocket sonde br, 55-58; chief space sci div, NASA, 58-59, asst dir, Goddard Space Flight Ctr, 59-65, dep dir, 65-68; dep adminstr, Environ Sci Serv Admin, Nat Oceanic & Atmospheric Admin, 68-70, assoc adminr, 70-77; pres, Fairchild Space Co, Fairchild Industs, 77-85, corp vpres, 79-85, dir, Spacecom, Inc, 84-85, chmn bd, Am Satellite Co, 85, sr vpres & group exec, Aerospace, 86, exec vpres, 87; chief, Space Sci Div, NASA, 58-59, asst div, Space Sci & Satellite Appln, Goddard Space Flight Ctr, 59-65, dep dir, 65-68, dir, 87-90. *Concurrent Pos:* Mem comt aeronomy, Int Union Geod & Geophys; mem tech panel on rocketry, US Nat Comt, Int Geophys Year; exec secy, US Rocket & Satellite Res Panel, 58-; mem, Int Acad Astronaut & Int Astronaut Fedn; trustee, Int Acad Aeronaut; mem, Nat Res Coun, Prog Rev Comt, NASA, 81-87; dir & trustee, Telos Corp, Santa Monica, Calif, 90-92; mem adv bd, Loral Corp, 91-93. *Mem:* Nat Acad Eng; Am Phys Soc; fel Am Meteorol Soc; Sigma Xi; Am Geophys Union; fel AAAS; fel Am Inst Aeronaut & Astronaut. *Res:* Space science and space applications; aeronomy; upper atmosphere physics; composition of the upper atmosphere; mass spectrometry; scientific, meteorological and communications satellites; design and development of sounding rockets; author of various publications. *Mailing Add:* 15810 Comus Rd Clarksburg MD 20871

**TOWNSEND, JONATHAN**, ELECTRONICS ENGINEERING. *Current Pos:* from asst prof to assoc prof, 51-87, EMER PROF PHYSICS, WASH UNIV, 87- *Personal Data:* b Colo, July 17, 22; m 55; c 1. *Educ:* Univ Denver, BS, 43; Washington Univ, MA, 48, PhD(physics), 51. *Prof Exp:* Engr, Gen Elec Co, 43-44; physicist, Carbide & Carbon Chem Co, 45-46. *Mem:* AAAS; Am Phys Soc; Am Asn Physics Teachers. *Res:* Nuclear and paramagnetic resonance; electronics. *Mailing Add:* 6814 Waterman Ave St Louis MO 63130

**TOWNSEND, LAWRENCE WILLARD**, THEORETICAL NUCLEAR & MOLECULAR PHYSICS, SPACE RADIATION TRANSPORT. *Current Pos:* res scientist, 81-88, SR RES SCIENTIST, NASA LANGLEY RES CTR, 88- *Personal Data:* b Jacksonville, Fla, May 13, 47; m 69, Linda S Summerlin; c 3. *Educ:* US Naval Acad, BS, 69; US Naval Postgrad Sch, MS, 70; Univ Idaho, PhD(physics), 80. *Prof Exp:* Res asst prof, Old Dom Univ, 80. *Concurrent Pos:* Adj fac prof physics, Old Dominion Univ, 81-; adj fac math, Christopher Newport Col, 88-; mem, sci subcomn F 2, Comt Space Res & Sci Comt, 75, Nat Coun Radiation Protection & Measurements, 90-; prin investr, NASA Space Radiation Protection Prog, Langley Res Ctr, 82-91. *Mem:* Am Phys Soc; Radiation Res Soc; Comt Space Res. *Res:* Nuclear and particle physics (heavy ion collisions, nuclear theory, pion production mechanisms and interactions, relativistic nucleon-nucleus interactions); space radiation interactions; atomic and molecular collision theory. *Mailing Add:* 1612 Breezy Ridge Trail Knoxville TN 37922. *Fax:* 757-864-7730; *E-Mail:* lwt@hessb1.larc.nasa.gov

**TOWNSEND, LEROY B**, MEDICINAL CHEMISTRY. *Current Pos:* prof chem & med chem, 79-86, ALBERT B PRESCOTT PROF MED CHEM, UNIV MICH, ANN ARBOR, 79- *Personal Data:* b Lubbock, Tex, Dec 20, 33; m 53; c 2. *Educ:* NMex Highlands Univ, BA, 55, MS, 57; Ariz State Univ, PhD(chem), 65. *Prof Exp:* Res assoc chem, Ariz State Univ, 60-65; res assoc, Univ Utah, 65-67, asst res prof, 67-69; asst prof chem, 67-79, from assoc prof med chem to prof, 71-79. *Concurrent Pos:* Consult, Heterocyclic Chem Corp, 69-74, Warner Lambert-Parke Davis, 80- & Baxter Travenol, 81-83. *Mem:* Am Chem Soc; Royal Soc Chem; Int Soc Heterocyclic Chem (treas, 73-77, pres-elect, 78-79, pres, 80-81). *Res:* Nitrogen heterocycles, for example pyrrole, pyrimidine, imidazo(4,5-c)pyridine, pyrazole, pyrazolo(3,4-d)pyrimidine, purine, pyrrolo(2,3-d)pyrimidine, pyrazolo(4,3-d)pyrimidine imidazole and the nucleosides arabinofuranosides, ribopyranosides, 2'-deoxyribofuranosides and ribofuranosides of these systems with biological and chemotherapeutic interest as well as structure elucidation and chemical synthesis of certain antibiotics. *Mailing Add:* 3317 E Dobson Pl Ann Arbor MI 48105-2583

**TOWNSEND, MARJORIE RHODES**, AEROSPACE ENGINEERING, ELECTRONICS ENGINEERING. *Current Pos:* RETIRED. *Personal Data:* b Washington, DC, Mar 12, 30; m 48, Charles E; c Charles Jr, Lewis, John & Richard. *Educ:* George Washington Univ, BEE, 51. *Honors & Awards:*

Except Serv Medal, NASA, 71, Outstanding Leadership Medal, 80, Eye-of-the-Needle Award, 91; Knight, Italian Repub Order, 72; Fed Women's Award, 73. *Prof Exp:* Electronics engr basic & appl sonar res, Naval Res Lab, 51-59; sect head design & develop elec instruments, Goddard Space Flight Ctr, NASA, 59-65, tech asst to chief syst div, 65-66, proj mgr small astron satellites, 66-75, proj mgr appl explorer mission, 75-76, mgr preliminary syst design group advan syst design, 76-80; consult, 80-90; dir, Space Systs Eng, BDM Int, 90-93; consult, 93-96. *Mem:* Fel Inst Elec & Electronics Engrs; fel Am Inst Aeronaut & Astronaut; fel AAAS; Am Geophys Union; Soc Women Engrs; Int Acad Astronaut. *Res:* Advanced space and ground systems design for a large variety of missions in space and terrestrial applications and in space sciences; new applications for use of the space shuttle; improvements in space station data system design. *Mailing Add:* 3529 Tilden St NW Washington DC 20008-3194. *E-Mail:* mrtownsend@aol.com

**TOWNSEND, MILES AVERILL,** MECHANICAL ENGINEERING, BIOMECHANICS. *Current Pos:* chmn, 81-91, WILSON PROF MECH, AERO & NUCLEAR ENG, UNIV VA, 81- *Personal Data:* b Buffalo, NY, Apr 16, 35; m 57; c 5. *Educ:* Univ Mich, BS, 58; Univ Ill, Urbana, advan cert, 63, MS, 67; Univ Wis-Madison, PhD(mech eng), 71. *Honors & Awards:* Am Soc Eng Educ Outstanding Award, 78. *Prof Exp:* Res engr, Sundstrand Corp, Ill, 59-63; design engr, Twin Disc, Inc, 63-64; sr engr, Westinghouse Elec Corp, Calif, 64-66; proj engr, Twin Disc, Inc, Ill, 66-68; lectr mech eng, Univ Wis-Madison, 68-69; assoc prof, Univ Toronto, 71-74; prof mech eng, Vanderbilt Univ, 74-81. *Concurrent Pos:* US rep educ, Int Fedn Theory of Mach & Mech, 77-83; mem, Comt Productivity, Coun Engrs, Am Soc Mech Eng. *Mem:* Am Soc Mech Engrs; AAAS; Sigma Xi; NY Acad Sci. *Res:* Optimal design, optimal and adaptive control; biomechanics; modeling, dynamics. *Mailing Add:* Dept Mech Aero & Nuclear Eng Univ Va Charlottesville VA 22903. *E-Mail:* mat@virginia.edu

**TOWNSEND, PALMER W,** CHEMICAL ENGINEERING, FLUOROCHEMICALS. *Current Pos:* CONSULT, 72- *Personal Data:* b New York, NY, Aug 1, 26; m 49, Helen A Lydecker; c Janet, Martha, Andrew, Amy & Rebecca. *Educ:* Dartmouth Col, AB, 47; Columbia Univ, BS, 47, MS, 48, PhD(chem eng), 56. *Prof Exp:* Instr chem eng, Columbia Univ, 48-53; sr engr, Pilot Plant Div, Cent Res Labs, Air Reduction Co, Inc, 53-56, sect head, Chem Eng Div, 57-61, asst dir, 61-64, mgr exp eng, Cent Eng Dept, 64-66, asst to group vpres, 66-67, dir commercial develop, Airco Chem & Plastics Div, 67-70; dir commercial develop, Plastics Div, Allied Chem Corp, 70-72. *Mem:* Am Chem Soc; Am Inst Chem Engrs; Soc Plastics Engrs; Soc Plastics Indust; Sigma Xi; Asn Consult Chemists & Chem Engrs (pres, 90-91). *Res:* Plastics research and development in products and processes; chemicals and monomers; applications and market research; materials selection; energy development; fluorochemical specialty chemicals. *Mailing Add:* 93 Continental Rd Morris Plains NJ 07950-1291. *Fax:* 908-464-9070; *E-Mail:* pwtown@aol.com

**TOWNSEND, R REID,** PLASMA GLYCOPROTEINS. *Current Pos:* Teaching fel hemat, 78-82, ASSOC RES SCIENTIST, JOHNS HOPKINS UNIV, 82- *Personal Data:* b Atlanta, Ga, Dec 8, 51. *Educ:* Tulane Univ, MD, 76, PhD(biochem), 82. *Mem:* Am Soc Cell Biol; Soc Complex Carbohydrates; Math Asn Am; Am Chem Soc. *Mailing Add:* Pharm Chem Dept Univ Calif San Francisco 513 Parnassus San Francisco CA 94143-0446. *Fax:* 415-476-0688

**TOWNSEND, RALPH N,** MATHEMATICS. *Current Pos:* from asst prof to assoc prof, 60-71, asst dean, Col Arts & Sci, 69-75, PROF MATH, BOWLING GREEN STATE UNIV, 71-, ASSOC DEAN, COL ARTS & SCI, 75- *Personal Data:* b Normal, Ill, May 20, 31; m 58; c 2. *Educ:* Ill Wesleyan Univ, BS, 53; Univ Ill, MS, 55, PhD(math), 58. *Prof Exp:* Asst math, Univ Ill, 54-58; asst prof math, San Jose State Col, 58-60. *Mem:* Am Math Soc; Math Asn Am; Sigma Xi. *Res:* Analysis, including Schwartz distributions; complex analysis. *Mailing Add:* 1029 Carol Rd Bowling Green OH 43402-3643

**TOWNSEND, SAMUEL FRANKLIN,** BIOLOGY, ANATOMY. *Current Pos:* PROF BIOL & CHMN, DIV NATURAL SCI & MATH, HILLSDALE COL, MICH, 81- *Personal Data:* b Montague, Mich, Mar 22, 35; m 58; c 2. *Educ:* Kalamazoo Col, AB, 57; Univ Mich, MS, 59, PhD(anat), 61. *Prof Exp:* From asst prof to assoc prof biol, Kalamazoo Col, 61-69, chmn dept, 66-69; assoc prof anat, Col Med, Univ Cincinnati, 69-81. *Concurrent Pos:* Partic, NSF Res Participation Prog Col Teachers, 64-66. *Mem:* Am Asn Anatomists; AAAS. *Res:* Cellular differentiation in the adult rat; healing and control of experimental ulcers; diabetes. *Mailing Add:* Dept Biol Hillsdale Col Hillsdale MI 49242

**TOWNSEND, WILLIAM F,** EARTH SCIENCE. *Current Pos:* Staff, Wallops Flight Ctr, NASA, 63-77, exp mgr, Seasat Altimeter, 78, prog mgr, Poseidon prog, 80-88, chief, Flight Prog Br, Earth Sci & Appln Div, 88-91, dep dir, 91-93, dep assoc adminr, 93-96, ACTG ASSOC ADMINR, OFF MISSION PLANET EARTH, NASA, 96- *Personal Data:* b Nassawadox, Va, 1946; m, Carolyn; c Jason & Tiffany. *Educ:* Va Polytech Inst, BS, 70. *Honors & Awards:* Bronze Medal, French Space Agency, 94. *Mem:* Inst Elec & Electronics Engrs. *Res:* Scientific understanding of the entire Earth system by developing a deeper comprehension of the components of this system and the interactions among them. *Mailing Add:* NASA 300 E St SW Rm 5450 Washington DC 20546

**TOWNSHEND, JOHN LINDEN,** PLANT PATHOLOGY. *Current Pos:* RETIRED. *Personal Data:* b Hamilton, Ont, Feb 6, 26; m 53; c 2. *Educ:* Univ Western Ont, BSc, 51, MSc, 52; Imp Col, Univ London, dipl, 63. *Honors & Awards:* Hoechst Award, Can Soc Hort Sci, 85. *Prof Exp:* Tech officer, Forest Path Unit, Forest Prod Lab, Dept Northern Affairs & Nat Resources, Can, 52; res scientist, Res Br, Can Dept Agr, 52-89. *Mem:* Soc Nematol; Can Phytopath Soc; Europ Soc Nematol. *Res:* Ecology of plant parasitic nematodes; forage nematodes; host-parasite relationships-ultrastructures. *Mailing Add:* 10 Alan Circle Fonthill ON L0S 1E0 Can

**TOWNSLEY, JOHN D,** dental research, for more information see previous edition

**TOWNSLEY, PHILIP MCNAIR,** INDUSTRIAL MICROBIOLOGY. *Current Pos:* RETIRED. *Personal Data:* b Vancouver, BC, Nov 21, 25; m 52; c 3. *Educ:* Univ BC, BSA, 49; Univ Calif, Berkeley, MS, 50, PhD(comp biochem), 56. *Prof Exp:* Biochemist, Dept Agr, Govt Can, 56-61, group leader, Process & Prod Group, Fishery Res Bd, 61-63; group leader biochem, BC Res Coun, 63-67; prof, Univ BC, 67-91, emer prof indust microbiol, 91- *Concurrent Pos:* Mem bd dirs, John Dunn Agencies Ltd & Pac Micro-Bio Cult Ltd. *Mem:* Inst Food Technol; Can Inst Food Sci & Technol; Int Asn Plant Tissue Cult; Can Soc Microbiol. *Res:* Practical application of basic research. *Mailing Add:* 877 166th St South Ferry BC V4A 9C4 Can

**TOWNSLEY, SIDNEY JOSEPH,** RADIOBIOLOGY. *Current Pos:* RETIRED. *Personal Data:* b Colorado Springs, Colo, Aug 6, 24; m 50; c 5. *Educ:* Univ Calif, AB, 47; Univ Hawaii, MS, 50; Yale Univ, PhD(zool), 54. *Prof Exp:* Asst prof marine zool & asst, Marine Lab, Univ Hawaii, 54-60, assoc prof marine biol, 60-66, prof, 66-70, prof marine zool, 70- *Mem:* Am Soc Zoologists; Am Soc Limnol & Oceanog; Ecol Soc Am. *Res:* Ecology of radioisotopes in marine organisms; systematics; stomatopod Crustacea and cephalopod mollusks; histochemistry and physiology of heavy metals. *Mailing Add:* 327A Pauma Pl Honolulu HI 96822

**TOWSE, DONALD FREDERICK,** GEOLOGY. *Current Pos:* CONSULT, 90- *Personal Data:* b Somerville, Mass, Dec 5, 24; m 45; c 6. *Educ:* Mass Inst Technol, BS, 48, PhD(geol), 51. *Honors & Awards:* Pres Award, Am Asn Petrol Geologists, 52. *Prof Exp:* Geologist, Amerada Petrol Corp, 48-49, 50-51; asst prof geol, Univ NDak, 51-54; geologist, State Geol Surv, NDak, 51-54; consult geologist, 54-56; vis assoc prof, Univ Calif, Los Angeles, 56-57; proj geologist, Kaiser Aluminum & Chem Corp, 57-60, sr proj geologist, Kaiser Cement & Gypsum Corp, 60-71, sr geologist, Kaiser Explor & Mining Co, 71-73; geologist, Lawrence Livermore Nat Lab, Univ Calif, 74-80, sect leader, 80-82, sr scientist, 83-90. *Concurrent Pos:* Managing dir, Delta Res Inst, 79- *Mem:* Am Asn Petrol Geologists; Am Inst Mining, Metall & Petrol Engrs. *Res:* Stratigraphy and petroleum resources; carbonate oil reservoirs; cement raw materials; laterites; uranium ores; geothermal resources; geology and economics of geothermal energy deposits; geologic disposal of nuclear and hazardous waste; environmental and groundwater geology. *Mailing Add:* 2420 Ruby Ave San Jose CA 95148-1749. *Fax:* 408-238-2446; *E-Mail:* dtowse@delphi.com

**TOY, ARTHUR DOCK FON,** INDUSTRIAL CHEMISTRY, PHOSPHORUS CHEMISTRY. *Current Pos:* CONSULT, STAMFORD, CONN, 80- *Personal Data:* b Canton, China, Sept 13, 15; nat US; m 42, Hui-i Liang; c Larry, Alan & Howard. *Educ:* Univ Ill, BS, 39, MS, 40, PhD(chem), 42. *Honors & Awards:* Eli Whitney Award, Conn Patent Law Asn, 88. *Prof Exp:* Res chemist, Victor Chem Works Div, Stauffer Chem Co, 42-53, dir org res, 53-59, from assoc dir res to dir res, 59-65; vis scientist, Cambridge Univ, 65-66; sr scientist, Stauffer Chem Co, Westport, Conn, 66-68, sr scientist & actg mgr, Chem Res Dept, 68-70, sr scientist & actg mgr, Specialties Dept, 70-72, chief scientist, 72-74, dir, Eastern Res Ctr, 75-78, dir res, 79-80. *Mem:* Am Chem Soc; Royal Soc Chem; fel AAAS; Sigma Xi. *Res:* Organic phosphorus compounds for plastic applications and insecticides; allyl aryl-phosphonate flame resistant plastic; economic process for synthesis of phosphorus insecticides and insecticide intermediates; aquo ammono phosphoric acids; organic reaction mechanisms; new reactions leading to the formation of carbon to phosphorus bonds. *Mailing Add:* 14 Katydid Lane Stamford CT 06903

**TOY, ARTHUR JOHN, JR,** RADIATION BIOPHYSICS, HEALTH PHYSICS. *Current Pos:* RES & DEVELOP SCIENTIST ENVIRON SCI & HEALTH PHYSICIST, LAWRENCE LIVERMORE LAB, 69- *Personal Data:* b Pasadena, Calif. *Educ:* Calif State Univ, Hayward, BS, 69; Univ Kans, MS, 71, PhD(radiation biophys), 73. *Mem:* Sigma Xi; Health Physics Soc. *Res:* Radiation accidents. *Mailing Add:* 6800 Telsa Rd Livermore CA 94550

**TOY, MADELINE SHEN,** FLUORINE & POLYMER CHEMISTRY, PHOTOSONOCHEMISTRY. *Current Pos:* CONSULT, 93- *Personal Data:* b Shanghai, China, Nov 6, 28; US citizen; m 51, Stephen M; c Stephanie M. *Educ:* Col St Teresa, Minn, BS, 49; Univ Wis, MS, 51; Ohio State Univ, MS, 57; Univ Pa, PhD(org chem), 59. *Prof Exp:* Mgr org lab, Freelander Res & Develop Div, Dayco Corp, Calif, 59-60; asst prof, Calif State Univ, Northridge, 60-61; staff mem, Int Tel & Tel Corp, Fed Labs, 61-63; res scientist & sect chief, Astropower Lab, McDonnell Douglas Corp, 64-69, head polymer sci, Douglas Adv Res Labs, 69-70; sr polymer chemist, Stanford Res Inst, Menlo Park, 71-75; sr scientist, Sci Appln Int Corp, 75-88, head chem lab, 88; sr scientist, Anal Lab Inc, 88-93. *Concurrent Pos:* Mem exec comt, Div Fluorine Chem, Am Chem Soc; reviewer of polymer progs, NSF, Adv Chem Series, J Org Chem & J Phys Chem; prin investr, NASA, Jet Propulsion Lab, 69-70, Lewis, 72, Wright Patterson AFB, 72-73, Air Force

Off Sci Res, 73-79, NASA, Joint Strategic Comt, 75-77, Aerospace Corp, 77-78, Edwards AFB, 79, Navy 79 & 82, Elec Power Res Inst, 81-86, 87-90 & 93, Naval Weapons Ctr, 83-86, NASA Marshall Flight Ctr, 91, Boeing Corp, Huntsville, Ala, 92. *Mem:* Am Chem Soc; fel Royal Soc Chem. *Res:* Optically active polymers; fire retardant polyurethanes; high temperature plastics; thermoplastic films; high energy perfluorinated salts; surface polymerizations on metal substrates; fluoroelastomers; multifunctional fluoropolymers; perfluoropolymer-forming reactions; flame resistant surface treatments; organic chemistry; fuel cell electrolytes; photooxidative degradation studies of aromatic polyamide; photosonolysis for synthetic and degradation studies; aqueous chemistry. *Mailing Add:* 4190 Manuela Ave Palo Alto CA 94306

**TOY, TERRENCE J,** DISTURBED LAND RECLAMATION, EROSION. *Current Pos:* From asst prof to assoc prof, 75-86, dept chair, 87-93, PROF GEOG, UNIV DENVER, 86- *Personal Data:* b Sidney, Ohio, Aug 10, 46; m 68. *Educ:* State Univ NY, Buffalo, BA, 69, MA, 70; Univ Denver, PhD(geog), 73. *Concurrent Pos:* Prin investr, US Geol Surv, 75-79 & Northern Energy Resource Co, 80-85; vis res scientist, Agr Res Serv, 92-93; consult disturbed land reclamation. *Mem:* Soil Conserv Soc Am; Am Soc Surface Mining & Reclamation; Asn Am Geographers. *Res:* Geomorphology of disturbed lands; author of numerous publications and one book. *Mailing Add:* 2657 S Linden Ct Denver CO 80222. *Fax:* 303-871-2201; *E-Mail:* ttoy@ou.edu

**TOY, WILLIAM W,** stochastic processes, for more information see previous edition

**TOYODA, SHOICHIRO,** AUTOMOTIVE ENGINEERING. *Current Pos:* CHMN, TOYOTA MOTOR CORP, 92- *Honors & Awards:* Deming Prize, 80; Medal Blue Ribbon, Govt Japan, 84, Cordon Order Sacred Treas, 95; named Knight Comdr, Brit Empire, Govt UK. *Mem:* Nat Acad Eng. *Mailing Add:* Off Chmn Toyota Motor Corp 1 Toyota-cho Aichi Pref 471 Japan

**TOZER, E T,** GEOLOGY. *Current Pos:* RES SCIENTIST, GEOL SURV CAN, 52- *Personal Data:* b Kirkland, Ont, Mar 2, 24. *Educ:* Univ Toronto, BA, 47, MA, 49, PhD, 55. *Mem:* Geol Soc Am; Geol Asn Can; Paleont Soc Can. *Mailing Add:* Cordilleran Div Geol Surv Can 100 W Pender St Vancouver BC V6B 1R8 Can. *Fax:* 604-666-1124

**TOZER, THOMAS NELSON,** PHARMACEUTICAL CHEMISTRY, PHARMACY. *Current Pos:* from asst prof to assoc prof, 65-81, PROF PHARM & PHARMACEUT CHEM, UNIV CALIF, SAN FRANCISCO, 81- *Personal Data:* b San Diego, Calif, July 4, 36; m; c 4. *Educ:* Univ Calif, San Francisco, BS & PharmD, 59, PhD(pharmaceut chem), 63. *Prof Exp:* Lectr chem & pharmaceut chem, Univ Calif, San Francisco, 63; NIMH fel, 63-65. *Concurrent Pos:* Pharmacist, 59-; fel, Lab Chem Pharmacol, Nat Heart Inst, 63-65. *Mem:* AAAS; Am Pharmaceut Asn; Am Asn Pharmaceut Sci; Am Chem Soc; NY Acad Sci; Sigma Xi. *Res:* Toxicokinetics; colon specific drug delivery; pharmacokinetics and metabolic fate of contrast agents for magnetic resonance imaging; saturable first-pass metabolism; effect of disease states on drug pharmacokinetics. *Mailing Add:* Dept Pharm Univ Calif Med Sch 513 Parnassus Ave San Francisco CA 94122-2722

**TOZEREN, AYDIN,** BIOMEDICAL ENGINEERING, CELL ENGINEERING. *Current Pos:* PROF, BIOMED ENG DEPT, CATH UNIV AM, 85-, DIR DEPT, 89- *Personal Data:* b Ankara, Turkey, Sept 24, 48. *Educ:* Middle East Tech Univ, BS, 71; Columbia Univ, MS, 73, PhD(biomed eng), 74. *Prof Exp:* Res scientist, Biomed Br, NIH, 82-85. *Mem:* Am Soc Mech Engrs; Biophys Soc; NY Acad Sci; Biomed Eng Soc. *Mailing Add:* Biomed Eng Prog Mech Eng Dept Cath Univ Am Cardinall Station Washington DC 20064

**TOZIER, JOHN E,** EXPERIMENTAL DATA ANALYSIS WITH MACINTOSH-HP COMPUTERS, EXPERIMENTAL PREDICTIONS BASED ON MATH ANALYSIS. *Current Pos:* SR SCIENTIST, BACHARACH INC, 81- *Personal Data:* b DuBois, Pa, Nov 3, 42; m 65; c 1. *Educ:* Bucknell Univ, BS, 64. *Prof Exp:* Engr, Clevite Corp, 65-69, Bailey Controls, 69-71; sr engr, GTE Sylvania, 75-81. *Res:* Industrial research; catalytic combustion sensors; solid state hydrogen-sulphide sensors. *Mailing Add:* 286 Courtney Pl Wexford PA 15090

**TOZZI, JOHN T,** TECHNICAL MANAGEMENT. *Current Pos:* DIR, INFO & TECHNOL, USCG, 96- *Personal Data:* m, Mary; c Gregory. *Educ:* Mass Inst Tech, MS; Cath Univ Am, PhD(fluid mech). *Mailing Add:* USCG 2100 Second St SW Washington DC 20593-0001

**TOZZI, SALVATORE,** allergic disorders, for more information see previous edition

**TRABANT, EDWARD ARTHUR,** APPLIED MATHEMATICS. *Current Pos:* PRES, UNIV DEL & PROF ENG SCI, COL ENG, 68-, EMER PRES, COL ENG, 90- *Personal Data:* b Los Angeles, Calif, Feb 28, 20; m 43; c 3. *Educ:* Occidental Col, AB, 41; Calif Inst Technol, PhD(appl math), 47. *Prof Exp:* From instr to prof math & eng sci, Purdue Univ, 47-60; dean sch eng, State Univ NY Buffalo, 60-66; vpres acad affairs, Ga Inst Technol, 66-68. *Concurrent Pos:* Consult, Allison Div, Gen Motors, Ind, 50-55, Argonne Nat Lab, Ill, 55-61; Carborundum Corp, NY, 64-68 & Army Sci Adv Panel, 66-71. *Mem:* Am Soc Eng Educ; Am Soc Mech Eng; Am Math Soc; Am Nuclear Soc; Sigma Xi. *Mailing Add:* 102 Bellant Circle Wilmington DE 19807

**TRABER, DANIEL LEE,** PHYSIOLOGY, PHARMACOLOGY. *Current Pos:* asst prof physiol & res asst prof anesthesiol, Univ Tex Med Br, 66-70, dir, Interdisciplinary Labs, 70-72, assoc prof, 70-74, PROF ANESTHESIOL & PHYSIOL, UNIV TEX MED BR GALVESTON, 74-, DIR, INTEGRATED FUNCTIONAL LAB, 72- *Personal Data:* b Victoria, Tex, Apr 28, 38; m 59, Lillian Knight; c Daniel S & Kurt A. *Educ:* St Mary's Univ, Tex, BA, 59; Univ Tex, MA, 62, PhD(physiol), 65. *Prof Exp:* Asst physiol, Med Br, Univ Tex, 60-65; fel pharmacol, Col Med, Ohio State Univ, 65-66. *Concurrent Pos:* Chief, Div Anesthesia Res, Shriners Burn Inst, Galveston, 71-78. *Mem:* Am Thoracic Soc; Am Physiol Soc; Am Burn Asn; Soc Critical Care Med; Am Soc Pharmacol & Exp Therapeut. *Res:* Shock, endotoxemia and sepsis; investigations into cardiopulmonary function during sepsis and acute lung injury; studies in intact animals. *Mailing Add:* Dept Anesthesiol J91 Univ Tex Med Br Galveston TX 77551-1091. *Fax:* 409-772-6409; *E-Mail:* traber@marlin.utmb.edu

**TRABER, MARET G,** LIPOPROTEIN METABOLISM, VITAMIN E. *Current Pos:* asst res scientist, NY Univ Sch Med, 77-80, assoc res scientist, 80-82, res scientist, 82-86, res asst prof, 86-89, RES ASSOC PROF, DEPT MED, NY UNIV SCH MED, 89- *Personal Data:* b Stockton, Calif, Nov 4, 50; m 71; c 1. *Educ:* Univ Calif, Berkeley, BS, 72, PhD(nutrit), 76. *Prof Exp:* Instr, dept nutrit, Rutgers Univ, 76-77. *Mem:* Am Heart Asn; Am Inst Nutrit; Am Soc Clin Nutrit; Am Soc Biol Chemists. *Res:* Lipids and lipoprotein metabolism; vitamin E deficiency in humans. *Mailing Add:* Dept Molecular & Cell Biol Univ Calif 251 Life Sci Addn Berkeley CA 94720. *Fax:* 212-263-7190

**TRACE, ROBERT DENNY,** GEOLOGY. *Current Pos:* RETIRED. *Personal Data:* b Zanesville, Ohio, Oct 27, 17; m 50, Elsie Brooks; c Robert Brooks & Donald E. *Educ:* Southern Methodist Univ, BS, 40; Univ Calif, Los Angeles, MA, 47. *Prof Exp:* Geologist, US Geol Surv, 42-77; sr geologist, Ky Geol Surv, 77-81. *Concurrent Pos:* Instr, Hopkinsville Community Col, Ky, 66-70. *Mem:* Fel Geol Soc Am; Soc Econ Geol. *Res:* Stratigraphic and structural geology of fluorspar-zinc-lead deposits. *Mailing Add:* 4901 E State Hwy 107 No A-9 Edinburg TX 78539

**TRACEY, DANIEL EDWARD,** IMMUNOLOGY, INFLAMMATION RESEARCH. *Current Pos:* Sr res scientist, 83-87, ASSOC DIR, DEPT HYPERSENSITIVITY DIS RES, UPJOHN CO, 87- *Personal Data:* b Boston, Mass, Mar 31, 31; div; c 2. *Educ:* Johns Hopkins Univ, PhD(biochem), 73. *Mem:* Am Asn Immunol; NY Acad Sci. *Res:* Arthritis. *Mailing Add:* Dept Immunol BASF BioRes Corp 100 Research Dr Worcester MA 01605. *Fax:* 617-868-9266

**TRACEY, JOSHUA IRVING, JR,** MARINE GEOLOGY. *Current Pos:* Geologist, 42-86, EMER SCIENTIST, US GEOL SURV, 86-; RES ASSOC, DEPT PALEOBIOL, NAT MUS NATURAL HIST, 86- *Personal Data:* b New Haven, Conn, May 2, 15; m 46, Frances M Jones; c Dan B Jones & Douglas I. *Educ:* Yale Univ, BA, 37, MS, 43, PhD(geol), 50. *Concurrent Pos:* Chmn, Geol Names Comt, US Geol Surv, 81-86. *Mem:* Fel AAAS; fel Geol Soc Am; Am Asn Petrol Geol; Am Geophys Union; Sigma Xi. *Res:* Bauxite; geology and ecology of coral reefs; geology and resources of the Pacific Islands; Tertiary stratigraphy of the Fossil Basin in southwestern Wyoming. *Mailing Add:* NMR137 Nat Mus Natural Hist Smithsonian Inst Washington DC 20560

**TRACEY, MARTIN LOUIS, JR,** GENETICS, DNA FINGERPRINTING. *Current Pos:* from asst prof to assoc prof, 77-85, chmn dept, 79-85, PROF BIOL, FLA INT UNIV, 85- *Personal Data:* b Boston, Mass, Mar 3, 43; div; c Martin L & Marnie L. *Educ:* Providence Col, AB, 65; Brown Univ, PhD(biol), 71. *Prof Exp:* Fel genetics, Univ Calif, Davis, 71-73; dir genetics, Bodega Marine Lab, Calif, 73-74; asst prof biol, Brock Univ, 74-77. *Concurrent Pos:* Assoc ed, J Heredity & Biosci; chief exec officer, DNA Counrs. *Mem:* Fel AAAS; Genetics Soc Am; Can Genetics Soc; Am Genetics Asn (secy); Am Soc Human Genetics. *Res:* Speciation and genetic differentiation; recombination; polymorphism; DNA fingerprinting; sexual differentiation. *Mailing Add:* Dept Biol Sci Fla Int Univ Miami FL 33199

**TRACHMAN, EDWARD G,** COMPUTER SIMULATION, TRIBOLOGY. *Current Pos:* VPRES PROD ENG, HARMAN-MOTIVE, INC, 90- *Personal Data:* b New York, NY, Apr 10, 46; m 68, Harriet; c 2. *Educ:* Cooper Union, BE, 66; Calif Inst Technol, MS, 67; Northwestern Univ, Evanston, PhD(mech eng), 71; Mich State Univ, MBA, 83. *Honors & Awards:* Ralph R Teeter Indust lectr, Soc Automotive Engrs, 89. *Prof Exp:* Assoc sr res engr, Res Labs, Gen Motors Corp, 71-75; mem tech staff, RCA Labs, 75-77; head, Eng Anal Dept, Vadetec Corp, 77-81; chief engr appl res, Rockwell Int Corp, 81-85, dir, res & develop, 85-89, dir prod eng, automotive opers, 89-90. *Concurrent Pos:* Fac asst math, Lawrence Inst Technol, 71-75. *Mem:* Am Soc Mech Engrs; Audio Eng Soc; Soc Automotive Engrs. *Res:* Computer simulation of mechanical systems; tribology; traction drives; mechanical design; automotive audiophile systems. *Mailing Add:* 1719 Greenbriar Lane Bloomington IN 47401

**TRACHTE, GEORGE J,** NEUROSCIENCE, SIGNAL-TRANSDUCTION. *Current Pos:* from asst prof to assoc prof, 82-94, PROF PHARMACOL, UNIV MINN, DULUTH, 94- *Personal Data:* b Pottsville, Pa, Oct 29, 53; m 79, Patricia A; c Gregory A & Samantha A. *Educ:* Pa State Univ, BS, 75; Thomas Jefferson Univ, PhD(physiol), 79. *Honors & Awards:* A N Richards Award, Phila Physiol Soc, 82. *Prof Exp:* Fel pharmacol, Univ Va Med Sch, 79-82. *Concurrent Pos:* Vis scientist, Pharmakologisches Inst Univ Koln, 82; vis lectr, Thomas Jefferson Univ, 85; hon res fel, Univ Col London, 91-92.

*Mem:* Am Physiol Soc; Am Soc Pharmacol & Exp Therapeut; Sigma Xi. *Res:* Attempts to identify intracellular pathways controlling neurotransmitter release from adrenergic neurons; neuronal signal-transduction pathways for autacoids such as angiotensin II, atrial natriuretic peptides and thromboxane A2. *Mailing Add:* Dept Pharmacol Univ Minn Med Sch Duluth MN 55812. *Fax:* 218-726-6235; *E-Mail:* gtracht1@ua.umn.edu

**TRACHTENBERG, EDWARD NORMAN,** ORGANIC CHEMISTRY. *Current Pos:* from asst prof to assoc prof, 58-70, PROF CHEM, CLARK UNIV, 70- *Personal Data:* b New York, NY, Dec 8, 27; m 54, Victoria Gotsky; c Ellen, Judith & Richard. *Educ:* NY Univ, AB, 49; Harvard Univ, AM, 51, PhD(org chem), 53. *Prof Exp:* Instr chem, Columbia Univ, 53-58. *Concurrent Pos:* NSF fel, Univ London, 67-68. *Mem:* Am Chem Soc. *Res:* Mechanism of organic reactions; organic synthesis; selenium dioxide oxidation of organic compounds; 1,3-dipolar cycloadditions. *Mailing Add:* Dept Chem Clark Univ Worcester MA 01610. *Fax:* 508-793-8861; *E-Mail:* etrachtenber@clarku.edu

**TRACHTENBERG, ISAAC,** ELECTROCHEMISTRY. *Current Pos:* from adj prof to prof, 84-90, PAUL D & BETTY ROBERTSON MEEK CENTENNIAL PROF CHEM ENG, CHEM ENG DEPT, UNIV TEX, AUSTIN, 90- *Personal Data:* b New Orleans, La, Aug 20, 29; m 86, Helaine Crohn; c Joseph & Michael. *Educ:* Rice Inst, BA, 50; La State Univ, MS, 52, PhD(chem), 57. *Prof Exp:* From assoc chemist to chemist, Am Oil Co, Tex, 57-60, sr chemist & group leader, 60; mem tech staff, Tex Inst, 60-63, br head basic electrochem, 63-66, chem kinetics, 66-68, systs anal process control, 69-70, br head environ monitoring, 71-72, br head sensors res & develop, 72-74, mgr process control, Semiconductor Group, 74-75, mgr qual & reliability assurance, Semiconductor Group, 74-80, solar energy proj, 80-84. *Concurrent Pos:* VChmn & chmn, Gordon Res Con Electrochem, 68-69; ed, J Battery Div, Electrochem Soc, 69-72. *Mem:* Am Chem Soc; Electrochem Soc; Am Inst Chem Engrs. *Res:* Semiconductors; semiconductor device quality and reliability; energy conversion; electrochemistry; semiconductor device processing, plasma etching, aerosol etching; microelectronics packaging, electrochemistry and energy conversion; chemical vapor deposition; lithography. *Mailing Add:* 4711 Spicewood Springs Rd No 278 Austin TX 78759-8402. *Fax:* 512-471-7060

**TRACHTMAN, MENDEL,** RADIATION CHEMISTRY, PHOTOCHEMISTRY. *Current Pos:* PROF CHEM, PHILADELPHIA COL TEXTILES & SCI, 67- *Personal Data:* b May 6, 29; US citizen; m 50; c 3. *Educ:* Temple Univ, AB, 51; Drexel Inst Technol, MS, 56; Univ Pa, PhD(chem), 61. *Prof Exp:* Res chemist, Frankford Arsenal, Philadelphia, Pa, 51-67. *Concurrent Pos:* Res Corp res grant, Philadelphia Col Textiles & Sci, 72-74. *Mem:* Am Chem Soc. *Res:* Determination of quenching cross sections of aromatic molecules; fading properties of various dye molecules. *Mailing Add:* 1705 Tustin St Philadelphia PA 19152-1807

**TRACTON, MARTIN STEVEN,** METEOROLOGY. *Current Pos:* RES METEOROLOGIST, NAT METEOROL CTR, NAT OCEANIC & ATMOSPHERIC ADMIN, 75- *Personal Data:* b Brockton, Mass, Feb 9, 45; m 66; c 1. *Educ:* Univ Mass, Amherst, BS, 66; Mass Inst Technol, MS, 69, PhD(meteorol), 72. *Prof Exp:* Asst prof meteorol, Naval Postgrad Sch, 72-75. *Mem:* Am Meteorol Soc; Sigma Xi. *Res:* Synoptic-dynamic aspects of the role of cumulus convection in the development of extratropical cyclones; test and evaluation of numerical prediction models. *Mailing Add:* 13011 Rhame Dr Ft Washington MD 20744

**TRACY, C RICHARD,** ECOLOGY. *Current Pos:* from asst prof to assoc prof, 74-83, PROF ZOOL, COLO STATE UNIV, 83- *Personal Data:* b Glendale, Calif, May 24, 43; div; c 1. *Educ:* Calif State Univ, Northridge, BA, 66, MS, 68; Univ Wis, PhD(zool), 72. *Prof Exp:* Res assoc environ studies, Univ Wis, 72-73, lectr, 73-74, asst scientist, 73-74. *Concurrent Pos:* Prof biol, Univ Mich Biol Sta, 74-79; nat adv comt person, Univ Wis, Biotron, 74-; ed, Ecol & Ecological Monogr, 78-; Guggenheim fel, 80-81; vis distinguished prof, Pepperdine Univ, 86. *Mem:* AAAS; Am Soc Naturalists; Ecol Soc Am; Sigma Xi; Am Soc Ichthyologists & Herpetologists; Herpetologist League; Am Soc Zoologists. *Res:* Biophysical ecological method to study evolutionary ecological questions of adaptations to physical environments; dispersal; dispersion; habitat selection and space utilization in animals. *Mailing Add:* Biol Dept Univ Nev Reno NV 89557

**TRACY, CRAIG ARNOLD,** STATISTICAL MECHANICS. *Current Pos:* PROF MATH, UNIV CALIF, DAVIS, 84- *Personal Data:* b London, Eng, Sept 9, 45; US citizen; m 70; c 2. *Educ:* Univ Mo, BS, 67; State Univ NY, Stony Brook, PhD(physics), 73. *Prof Exp:* Woodrow Wilson fel, 67; res assoc physics, Univ Rochester, 73-75 & Inst Theoret Physics, State Univ NY, Stony Brook, 75-78; from asst prof to assoc prof math, Dartmouth Col, 78-84. *Mem:* Am Math Soc; Soc Indust & Appl Math. *Res:* Exactly solvable lattice models in statistical mechanics; theory of phase transitions; theory of completely integrable systems. *Mailing Add:* Dept Math Univ Calif Davis CA 95616-8633

**TRACY, DAVID J,** ORGANIC CHEMISTRY, SURFACTANT CHEMISTRY. *Current Pos:* Res specialist, GAF Corp, 64-69, tech assoc, 69-84, group leader, 84-87, sect mgr surfactants, 87-90, DIR SYNTHESIS RES, RHONE POULENC, 90- *Personal Data:* b Covington, Ky, Jan 22, 37. *Educ:* Villa Madonna Col, AB, 59; Univ Ill, MS, 61, PhD(chem), 64. *Mem:* Am Chem Soc; Am Oil Chem Soc. *Res:* Acetylenics; photographic couplers; surfactants. *Mailing Add:* 37-03 Ravens Crest Rd Plainsboro NJ 08536

**TRACY, DERRICK SHANNON,** MATHEMATICAL STATISTICS, MULTIVARIATE STATISTICAL ANALYSIS. *Current Pos:* assoc prof, 65-70, PROF MATH & STATIST, UNIV WINDSOR, 70- *Personal Data:* b Mirzapur, India, July 1, 33; Can citizen; m 69, Sheila Simon. *Educ:* Univ Lucknow, BSc, 51, MSc, 53; Univ Mich, MS, 60, ScD(math), 63. *Prof Exp:* Lectr math, Ewing Col, Allahabad, 53-55; sr lectr math statist, Govt Col Bhopal, 56-59; res asst math, Univ Mich, 61-63; asst prof statist, Univ Conn, 63-65. *Concurrent Pos:* Nat Res Coun Can res grants, 66-; Defence Res Bd Can res grants, 68-74; consult, Bell Tel Co Can & Ont Inst Studies Educ, 67-; consult, Walter Reed Army Res Inst, 68; vis prof, Univ Calif, Riverside, 72-73, Univ Waterloo, 74; assoc ed, Can J Statist, 73-77; Can Coun travel grant to Poland, 75 & India, 77; vis prof, Univ Fed do Rio de Janeiro, 76 & 78; Ministry External Affairs travel grant, Brazil & India, 76; Nat Res Coun exchange scientist, Brazil, 78; vis prof, Univ Amsterdam, 79, Indian Statist Inst, 80; consult, UN Food & Agr Orgn, Indian Agr Statist Inst, 87; vis prof, Tex A&M Univ, 89. *Mem:* Am Statist Asn; Sigma Xi; Int Statist Inst. *Res:* Products of generalized k-statistics; finite moment formulae; symmetric functions; finite sampling; matrix derivatives in multivariate analysis, multiresponse permutation procedures; randomized response techniques. *Mailing Add:* Dept Math & Statist Univ Windsor Windsor ON N9B 3P4 Can. *Fax:* 519-973-7050

**TRACY, JAMES FRUEH,** NUCLEAR PHYSICS. *Current Pos:* RETIRED. *Personal Data:* b Isle of Pines, July 29, 16; US citizen; m 57, Margaret L Jory; c Stephen R & Douglas G. *Educ:* Univ Ill, BSEE, 40; Univ Calif, MSEE, 49, PhD(physics), 53. *Prof Exp:* Elec engr, Gen Elec Co, NY, 40-46; opers analyst, Broadview Res & Develop, Calif, 53; physicist, Lawrence Livermore Lab, Univ Calif, 53-83. *Mem:* Am Phys Soc; AAAS. *Res:* Physics design of nuclear weapons; application of nuclear explosives to industry and science. *Mailing Add:* 1262 Madison Ave Livermore CA 94550-5020

**TRACY, JOSEPH CHARLES,** SOLID STATE PHYSICS, SURFACE PHYSICS. *Current Pos:* PRES, CARRIER COMPONENTS, 94- *Personal Data:* b Wilkes Barre, Pa, Jan 15, 43; m 66; c 3. *Educ:* Rensselaer Polytech Inst, BEE, 64; Cornell Univ, PhD(appl physics), 68. *Prof Exp:* Fel surface physics, NAm Rockwell Sci Ctr, Calif, 68-69, mem tech staff, 69-70; mem tech staff, Bell Tel Labs, Murray Hill, 70-73; group leader, Gen Motors Res Lab, 73-75, asst dept head, Dept Physics, 75-82; chief engr, Intergrated Circuits, Delco Electronics, 85-87, dept head, Electronics Dept & chief engr audio systs, 87-92; vpres, Carrier Electronics, 92-94. *Concurrent Pos:* Chmn, Nat Acad Sci Eval Panel Nat Bur Standards Ctr Thermodyn & Molecular Sci, 79-80, Eval Panel Ctr Chem Physics, Nat Bur Standards, 80-82; panel mem, Nat Acad Sci Eval Panel, Nat Bur Standards Nat Measurement Lab, 79-82. *Mem:* Fel Am Phys Soc; Inst Elec & Electronics Engrs. *Res:* Surface physics; electron spectroscopy; semiconductor physics; management of research. *Mailing Add:* 1 Carrier Pl Farmington CT 06034-4015

**TRACY, JOSEPH WALTER,** INORGANIC CHEMISTRY, MEAT SCIENCE. *Current Pos:* RETIRED. *Personal Data:* b Seattle, Wash, June 22, 24; m 50, Mary L Sumner; c Laurel (Falk), Daphne, Walter, Garland (Bradburn) & Heather (Wright). *Educ:* Univ Wash, BS, 51, MS, 54, PhD(chem), 60. *Prof Exp:* Assoc res engr, Boeing Airplane Co, 54-58; prof chem, Northwest Nazarene Col, 60-70; chemist-in-charge, Meat Inspection Lab, Idaho State Dept Agr, 70-81. *Res:* Meat analysis; x-ray crystallography; crystal structures of simple inorganic compounds. *Mailing Add:* 823 Ninth Ave S Nampa ID 83651

**TRACY, RICHARD E,** PATHOLOGY. *Current Pos:* asst prof, 67-73, assoc prof, 73-81, PROF PATH, SCH MED, LA STATE UNIV, NEW ORLEANS, 81- *Personal Data:* b Klamath Falls, Ore, Apr 30, 34; m 62; c 2. *Educ:* Univ Chicago, BA, 55, MD & PhD(path), 61. *Honors & Awards:* Bausch & Lomb Medal, 61; Joseph A Capps Prize, 65. *Prof Exp:* Intern, Presby Hosp, Denver, Colo, 61-62; res assoc path, Univ Chicago, 62-64, instr, 64-65; asst prof, Med Sch, Univ Ore, 65-67. *Concurrent Pos:* USPHS trainee, 62-65. *Mem:* AAAS; Am Heart Asn; Am Soc Exp Path. *Res:* Arteriosclerotic and hypertensive cardiovascular and renal disease; biostatistics. *Mailing Add:* Dept Path La State Univ Sch Med 1901 Perdido St New Orleans LA 70112-1328

**TRACY, WILLIAM E,** PEDODONTICS. *Current Pos:* RETIRED. *Personal Data:* b Memphis, Tenn, Aug 16, 34; m 56; c 3. *Educ:* Univ Tenn, DDS, 61; Am Bd Pedodont, dipl, 71. *Prof Exp:* Res asst dent mat, Dent Sch, Univ Ore, 60-61, instr pediat, Med Sch & instr dent, Dent Sch, 61-62, asst prof dent, 62-68, assoc prof dent, Dent Sch, 68-86, instr pediat & dent med, Med Sch, 67-68, mem staff, Child Study Clin, Univ Ore, 71-86. *Concurrent Pos:* Nat Inst Dent Res fel growth & develop, Dent Sch, Univ Ore, 61-62, spec fel, 65-; Nat Inst Child Health & Human Develop career develop award, 66-67, res grant, 66-71. *Mem:* AAAS; Am Acad Pedodont; Am Soc Dent Children; Am Dent Asn; Int Asn Dent Res. *Res:* Growth and development of children; dentofacial growth. *Mailing Add:* 12909 SW Timera Tigard OR 97224

**TRACY, WILLIAM FRANCIS,** PLANT BREEDING. *Current Pos:* from asst prof to assoc prof, 84-96, PROF AGRON, DEPT AGRON, UNIV WIS-MADISON, 96- *Personal Data:* b Cambridge, Mass, Oct 11, 54; m 77; c 1. *Educ:* Univ Mass, Amherst, BS, 76, MS, 79; Cornell Univ, PhD(plant breeding), 82. *Prof Exp:* Res scientist, Int Plant Res Inst, 82-83; plant breeder, Cargill Inc, 83-84. *Mem:* Crop Sci Soc; AAAS; Am Genetics Asn; Nat Sweet Corn Breeders Asn; Am Soc Hort Sci. *Res:* Sweet corn breeding and genetics; use of non-sweet corn germplasm in the improvement of quality, pest resistance and agronomic character. *Mailing Add:* 373 Moore Hall Univ Wis 1575 Linden Dr Madison WI 53706-1597. *E-Mail:* wftracy@facstaff.wisc.edu

**TRACZ, WILL,** COMPUTER SCIENCE, SOFTWARE REUSE. *Current Pos:* SR PROGRAMMER, 74- *Personal Data:* b Salamanca, NY, Sept 8, 50; m 72, Sharon A Mitchell; c Matthew, Nicholas & Megan. *Educ:* State Univ NY, BA, 72; Pa State Univ, MS, 74; Syracuse Univ, MS, 79; Stanford Univ, PhD, 97. *Concurrent Pos:* Vis prof, Rochester Inst Technol, 81; adj prof, Syracuse Univ, 83; chmn, Int Tech Liaison Micorprocessors, IBM Corp, 83-85 & Microprog Comt, Asn Comput Mach, 87-; chmn, Workshop Institutionalizing Reuse, 91-93. *Mem:* Asn Comput Mach; Inst Elec & Electronics Engrs. *Res:* Software engineering and software reuse; module composition languages and application generators; domain-specific software architectures. *Mailing Add:* Lockheed Martin Fed Systs MD 0210 Owego NY 13827. *Fax:* 607-751-6025; *E-Mail:* will.tracz@acm.org

**TRAEXLER, JOHN F,** MECHANICAL ENGINEERING, ELECTRICAL ENGINEERING. *Current Pos:* RETIRED. *Personal Data:* b Brooklyn, NY, Feb 21, 30; m 55; c 4. *Educ:* Pratt Inst Technol, BME, 51; Univ Pa, MSME, 54, PhD(eng mech), 65. *Prof Exp:* Design engr, Westinghouse Elec Corp, 51-57, sr engr, 57-62, fel engr, 62-67, mgr mech develop, 67-70, mgr technol develop, 70-77, adv engr, 77-78, mgr turbine develop, 78-80, mgr steam turbine generator eng, 80-88. *Concurrent Pos:* Mem, Pressure Vessel Res Comt, 59-79. *Mem:* Am Soc Mech Engrs. *Res:* Application of plasticity and creep to turbomachinery mechanical design; dynamics and vibrations problems in turbomachinery. *Mailing Add:* 319 Santiago Dr Winter Park FL 32789

**TRAFTON, LAURENCE MUNRO,** PLANETARY ATMOSPHERES. *Current Pos:* spec res assoc, 69-72, res scientist, 72-93, SR RES SCIENTIST, UNIV TEX, AUSTIN , 93- *Personal Data:* b Boston, Mass, July 31, 38. *Educ:* Calif Inst Technol, BS, 60, MS, 61, PhD(astron & physics), 65. *Honors & Awards:* NASA Award, Contrib Hubble Space Telescope Prog. *Prof Exp:* Proj officer, Weapons Lab, USAF, 65-68, proj scientist, 68-69. *Concurrent Pos:* Team mem, Instrument Develop Team High Resolution Spectrog Space Telescope, 77; assoc ed, Icarus, 79- *Mem:* Int Astron Union; Am Astron Soc; fel AAAS. *Res:* State, structure, composition, dynamics and energy balance in the atmospheres of the major planets and satellites; spectroscopic observations from infrared to ultraviolet; theoretica investigations; investigations from spacecraft. *Mailing Add:* McDonald Observ Univ Tex Austin TX 78712

**TRAFTON, WILBUR C,** OPERATIONS RESEARCH. *Current Pos:* DIR, SPACE STA PROG, 94-, ASSOC ADMINR, NASA OFF SPACE FLIGHT, WASHINGTON, DC, 96- *Personal Data:* m, Mary Grace Schwab. *Educ:* US Naval Postgrad Sch, Monterey, Calif, MS. *Prof Exp:* Exec Off USS Forrestal, commanding off, USS Seattle; exec asst to Comdr, Naval Air Systs Command; team chief, Contingency Planning & Crises Action, Pentagon; asst chief staff, Plans & Policy for Comdr US Pacific Fleet, 66-92; chief oper off & pres, Micro Res Ind, 92-93. *Mailing Add:* NASA Off Space Flight 300 E St SW Washington DC 20546

**TRAGER, WILLIAM,** PARASITOLOGY. *Current Pos:* fel, Rockefeller Inst, 34-35, asst, 35-40, assoc, 40-50, assoc mem, 50-59, from assoc prof to prof, 59-80, EMER PROF PARASITOL, ROCKEFELLER UNIV, 80- *Personal Data:* b Newark, NJ, Mar 20, 10; m 35; c 3. *Educ:* Rutgers Univ, BS, 30; Harvard Univ, AM, 31; PhD(biol), 33. *Hon Degrees:* ScD, Rutgers Univ, 65, Rockefeller Univ, 87. *Honors & Awards:* S T Darling Medal & Prize, World Health Orgn, 80; Leuckart Medal, Ger Soc Parasitol, 82; Manson Medal, Royal Soc Trop Med & Hyg, 86; Rameshwardas Birla International Award in Tropical Medicine, 82; Augustine Le Prince Medal, Am Soc Trop Med & Hyg, 91; Prince Mahidol Award Med Sci, 94. *Prof Exp:* Nat Res Coun fel med, 33-34. *Concurrent Pos:* Ed J, Soc Protozool, 53-65; mem study sect parasitol & trop med, Nat Inst Allergy & Infectious Dis, 54-58 & 66-70, microbiol & infectious dis adv comt, 78-80; mem training grant comt, 61-64; mem malaria comn, Armed Forces Epidemiol Bd, 65-70; guest investr, W African Inst Trypanosomiasis Res, 58-59; vis prof, Fla State Univ, 62, Med Sch, PR, 63 & Med Sch, Nat Univ Mex, 65; Guggenheim found fel, 73; mem malaria immunol steering comt, WHO; Avivah Zuckerman fel, Kuvin Ctr Infectious & Tropical Dis, Hebrew Univ, Jerusalem, 82; hon pres, Asia & Pac Conf Malaria, 85. *Mem:* Nat Acad Sci; Am Soc Parasitol (pres, 74); Soc Protozool (pres, 60-61); Am Soc Trop Med & Hyg (vpres, 64-65, pres, 78-79); NY Acad Sci. *Res:* Insect physiology; physiology of parasitisms; cultivation of intracellular parasites; malaria; culture of malaria parasites; extracellular cultivation of intracellular protozoa. *Mailing Add:* Rockefeller Univ York Ave & 66th St New York NY 10021

**TRAGER, WILLIAM FRANK,** PHARMACEUTICAL CHEMISTRY, ORGANIC CHEMISTRY. *Current Pos:* assoc prof, 72-77, PROF PHARMACEUT CHEM, SCH PHARM, UNIV WASH, 77- *Personal Data:* b Winnipeg, Man, Oct 17, 37; m 60; c 3. *Educ:* Univ San Francisco, BSc, 60; Univ Wash, PhD(pharmaceut chem), 65. *Prof Exp:* NIH fel pharm, Chelsea Col Sci & Technol, London, 65-67; fel, Univ Wash, 67; asst prof chem & pharmaceut chem, Sch Pharm, Univ San Francisco, 67-72. *Mem:* Am Chem Soc. *Res:* Drug metabolism studies and mass spectroscopy. *Mailing Add:* Sch Pharm BG20 Univ Wash Seattle WA 98195-0001

**TRAHAN, DONALD HERBERT,** MATHEMATICS. *Current Pos:* ASSOC PROF MATH, NAVAL POSTGRAD SCH, 66- *Personal Data:* b North Adams, Mass, Mar 14, 30; m 61, 76; c 1. *Educ:* Univ Vt, BS, 52; Univ Nebr, MA, 54; Univ Pittsburgh, PhD, 61. *Prof Exp:* Instr math, Univ Mass, 56-59; asst prof, Univ Pittsburgh, 61-65; asst prof & chmn dept, Chatham Col, 65-66. *Concurrent Pos:* Hays-Fulbright lectr, Nat Univ Ireland, 63-64. *Mem:* Am Math Soc; Math Asn Am. *Res:* Complex variables; univalent function theory; real analysis. *Mailing Add:* 19514 Creekside Ct Salinas CA 93908

**TRAHAN, RUSSELL EDWARD, JR,** CONTROL SYSTEMS, OPTIMIZATION. *Current Pos:* PROF ELEC ENG, UNIV NEW ORLEANS, 77- *Personal Data:* b New Orleans, La, Jan 30, 49; m 70, Lynette C; c Yvette & Russell III. *Educ:* Univ New Orleans, BS, 70, MS, 73; Univ Calif, Berkeley, PhD(elec eng), 77. *Honors & Awards:* Outstanding Eng Educr Award, Inst Elec & Electronics Engrs, 91- *Prof Exp:* Design engr, Tano Corp, 71-73. *Concurrent Pos:* Vis prof, Univ Calif, Berkeley, 80; consult, Litton Data Systs, 80-86, Naval Res Lab Stennis Space Ctr, 86-92. *Mem:* Inst Elec & Electronics Engrs; Inst Elec & Electronics Engrs Control Systs Soc; Am Soc Eng Educ; Instrument Soc Am. *Res:* Optimization applied to speech processing; optimal identification of control systems; optimization applied to ocean data acquisition systems. *Mailing Add:* 20501 Alba E New Orleans LA 70129. *Fax:* 504-280-3950; *E-Mail:* retee@uno.edu

**TRAHANOVSKY, WALTER SAMUEL,** ORGANIC CHEMISTRY. *Current Pos:* from instr to assoc prof, 64-74, PROF CHEM, IOWA STATE UNIV, 74- *Personal Data:* b Conemaugh, Pa, June 15, 38; m 67; c 3. *Educ:* Franklin & Marshall Col, BS, 60; Mass Inst Technol, PhD(chem), 63. *Prof Exp:* NSF fel chem, Harvard Univ, 63-64. *Concurrent Pos:* A P Sloan fel, 70-72. *Mem:* AAAS; Am Chem Soc; Royal Soc Chem. *Res:* Physical-organic chemistry, including the study of oxidations and reductions of organic compounds; oxidative cleavages; cyclization reactions; free radicals; carbocations; arene tricarbonylchromium complexes; flash vacuum pyrolysis; methylenecyclobutenones; tropolone derivatives. *Mailing Add:* Dept Chem Iowa State Univ Ames IA 50011-3111

**TRAIL, CARROLL C,** NUCLEAR PHYSICS. *Current Pos:* assoc prof, 64-68, chmn dept, 69-76, PROF PHYSICS, BROOKLYN COL, 68- *Personal Data:* b Forney, Tex, Dec 25, 27; m 51; c 3. *Educ:* Agr & Mech Col Tex, BS, 49, MS, 51, PhD, 56. *Prof Exp:* Asst physics, Argonne Nat Lab, 56-60, assoc physicist, 60-64. *Concurrent Pos:* Vis prof, Linear Accelerator Lab, Orsay, France, 70-71; vis scientist, Mass Inst Technol, 77-78; fel, Sci Fac Imp Prog, NSF, 77-78. *Mem:* Fel Am Phys Soc. *Res:* Low energy; nuclear experimentation. *Mailing Add:* 2304 N Lake Trail Denton TX 76201. *Fax:* 817-565-2227

**TRAIN, CARL T,** PARASITOLOGY, INVERTEBRATE ZOOLOGY. *Current Pos:* from asst prof to assoc prof, 67-79, PROF BIOL, SOUTHEAST MO STATE UNIV, 79-, CHMN DEPT, 84- *Personal Data:* b Lindsborg, Kans, Jan 19, 39; div; c 3. *Educ:* Bethany Col, Kans, BS, 61; Kans State Univ, MS, 63, PhD(parasitol), 67. *Prof Exp:* Asst zool, Kans State Univ, 61-64, instr, 66-67. *Mem:* Am Soc Parasitol; Am Micros Soc; Sigma Xi. *Res:* General parasitology, biology and reproduction of nematodes; life cycles of parasites; parasites of aquatic birds. *Mailing Add:* Dept Biol Southeast Mo State Univ Cape Girardeau MO 63701

**TRAINA, PAUL J(OSEPH),** CIVIL ENGINEERING. *Current Pos:* ENVIRON CONSULT, 85- *Personal Data:* b New York, NY, Mar 8, 34; m 55; c 5. *Educ:* Manhattan Col, BCE, 55; Univ Mich, MS, 60. *Prof Exp:* Chief water resources, Southeast Region, USPHS, 60-64; asst dir comprehensive planning, Fed Water Pollution Control Admin, 64-67, dir tech progs, Southeast Region, 67-71, dir off water progs, 71-73, dir enforcement, 73-79, dir, water div, Region IV, Environ Protection Agency, 79-85. *Mem:* Am Soc Civil Engrs; Water Pollution Control Fedn; NY Acad Sci; Am Acad Environ Engrs. *Res:* Water supply and water quality control; regional water programs; hazardous waste management. *Mailing Add:* 2366 Wood Creek Ct Tucker GA 30084

**TRAINA, VINCENT MICHAEL,** TOXICOLOGY. *Current Pos:* mgr toxicol, CIBA, 74-79, assoc dir toxicol & path, 79-82, dir toxicol, 82-84, exec dir toxicol & path, 84-88, vpres toxicol & path, 88-92, VPRES PRECLIN SAFETY INT, NOVARTIS, 92- *Personal Data:* b Oceanside, NY, May 8, 43; m 78, Lynn Miko; c Allison, Kimberly & Brent. *Educ:* Rutgers Univ, BA, 65, MS, 70, PhD(physiol), 73; Am Bd Toxicol, dipl, 81. *Honors & Awards:* Prinomide Award. *Prof Exp:* Res investr toxicol, Squibb Inst Med Res, 66-74. *Concurrent Pos:* Ind Relations Comt, Ciba, 89; mem fac, Residential Sch Med Chem, Drew Univ, Madison NJ, 89- *Mem:* Sigma Xi; Environ Mutagen Soc; Am Inst Biol Sci; Am Col Toxicol; Soc Toxicol; Soc Comp Ophthal. *Res:* Body fluid volumes and concentrations and electrolyte changes during periods of prolonged starvation; all phases of toxicology. *Mailing Add:* Novartis Morris Ave Summit NJ 07901. *Fax:* 908-277-5818

**TRAINER, DANIEL OLNEY,** WILDLIFE DISEASES, ECOLOGY OF DISEASES. *Current Pos:* dean, Col Natural Resources, 71-80, VCHANCELLOR, UNIV WIS-STEVENS POINT, 80-, EMER DEAN, 93- *Personal Data:* b Chicago, Ill, July 13, 26; m 55, Elizabeth; c Patrica & Daniel. *Educ:* Ripon Col, BS, 50; Univ Wis-Madison, MS, 55, PhD(bact), 61. *Honors & Awards:* Distinguished Serv Award, Wildlife Dis Asn. *Prof Exp:* Res virologist, Fromm Labs, 55-56; pathologist, Wis Conserv Dept, 56-62; from asst prof to prof vet sci, Univ Wis-Madison, 62-71. *Concurrent Pos:* Ed, Wild Dis J, 80-84. *Mem:* AAAS; Wildlife Dis Asn (vpres, 66-68, pres, 68-70); Wildlife Soc; Nature Conservancy; Soc Am Foresters. *Res:* Ecology of disease, especially diseases of wild or natural populations; environmental policy and law education. *Mailing Add:* Col Natural Resources Univ Wis 2100 Main St Stevens Point WI 54481-3871. *Fax:* 715-346-3624

**TRAINER, DAVID GIBSON,** PHYSIOLOGY. *Current Pos:* From asst prof to assoc prof, 75-82, PROF BIOL, ESTROUDSBURG UNIV, 78-, DEPT CHAIRPERSON, 90- *Personal Data:* b Allentown, Pa, Mar 11, 45; m 74, Robin Strong; c David & Karen. *Educ:* Washington & Jefferson Col, AB, 67; Univ Maine, MSc, 69; Univ NH, PhD(zool), 75. *Mem:* AAAS; Am Soc Zoologists; Sigma Xi. *Res:* Physiology of invertebrates. *Mailing Add:* Dept Biol East Stroudsburg Univ East Stroudsburg PA 18301

**TRAINER, FRANK W,** GEOLOGY. *Current Pos:* RETIRED. *Personal Data:* b Manchester, Eng, Dec 2, 21; c 2. *Educ:* Univ Va, BA, 43; Harvard Univ, PhD(geol), 54. *Prof Exp:* Geologist, US Geol Soc, 48-81. *Mem:* Asn Groundwater Scientists & Engrs; fel Geol Soc Am. *Mailing Add:* PO Box 1735 Corrales NM 87048

**TRAINER, JOHN EZRA, JR,** HELMINTHOLOGY, BIOLOGICAL CHEMISTRY. *Current Pos:* PRES, GA FOUND INDEPENDENT COLS, 96- *Personal Data:* b Allentown, Pa, Aug 31, 43; m 67; c 3. *Educ:* Muhlenburg Col, BS, 65; Wake Forest Univ, MA, 67; Univ Okla, PhD(zool), 71. *Prof Exp:* Teaching asst, Wake Forest Univ, 65-67; teaching asst, Univ Okla, 67-69; asst prof, Jacksonville Univ, 71-78, assoc prof biol, 78-, vpres & dean fac, 81- *Concurrent Pos:* Teaching asst, Biol Sta, Mich State Univ, 66 & Univ Okla, 67; consult, Environ Ctr. *Mem:* Am Soc Parasitol; Am Soc Zool; Am Inst Biol Sci; AAAS. *Res:* Ecology, biochemistry and ultrastructure of the Pentastomida and other parasitic helminths. *Mailing Add:* Ga Found Independent Cols 945 E Paces Ferry Rd Suite 1730 Resurg Plaza Atlanta GA 30326

**TRAINER, JOHN EZRA, SR,** ornithology, for more information see previous edition

**TRAINER, MICHAEL NORMAN,** LIGHT SCATTERING, FIBER OPTICS. *Current Pos:* PRIN SCIENTIST, LEEDS & NORTHRUP CO, 76- *Personal Data:* b Lehighton, Pa, Jan 26, 52; m 72. *Educ:* Lehigh Univ, BS, 73, MS, 91; Univ Rochester, MS, 76. *Prof Exp:* Physicist, NJ Zinc Co, 73-75. *Mem:* Optical Soc Am; Soc Photo-Optical Instrumentation Engrs. *Res:* Fiber optic sensors; optical data storage; optical instrumentation for size analysis of small particles; interferometry; signal processing; optical and electrical engineering. *Mailing Add:* 186 Fretz Rd Telford PA 18969

**TRAINHAM, JAMES A, III,** CHEMICAL ENGINEERING. *Current Pos:* TECH DIR RES & DEVELOP, EI DUPONT DE NEMOURS & CO, 92- *Personal Data:* b Oakland, Calif, May 22, 50. *Educ:* Univ Calif, Berkeley, BA, 73, PhD(chem eng), 79; Univ Wis, MA, 77. *Mem:* Nat Acad Eng; Electro Chem Soc. *Mailing Add:* Barley Mill Plaza Bldg 22 PO Box 80022 Wilmington DE 19880-0022. *Fax:* 303-992-2035; *E-Mail:* trainham@ a1esvac.umc.dupont.com

**TRAINOR, FRANCIS RICE,** PHYCOLOGY. *Current Pos:* From instr to assoc prof, 57-67, PROF BOT, UNIV CONN, 67- *Personal Data:* b Pawtucket, RI, Feb 11, 29; m 56. *Educ:* Providence Col, BS, 50; Vanderbilt Univ, MA, 53, PhD(biol), 57. *Honors & Awards:* Distinguished Fac Award, Univ Conn, 62; Darbaker Award, Bot Soc Am, 65. *Concurrent Pos:* Consult, Elec Boat Div, Gen Dynamics Corp, Conn, 58-61; Fulbright res scholar, Stockholm, 70; Fulbright lectr, Greece & Yugoslavia, 71. *Mem:* AAAS; Phycol Soc Am (vpres, 68, pres, 69); Brit Phycol Soc; Int Phycol Soc; Am Inst Biol Sci; Sigma Xi. *Res:* Sexual reproduction in unicellular algae; algal nutrition and morphogenesis; eutrophication. *Mailing Add:* Biol Sci U-42 Univ Conn 75 N Eagleville Storrs Mansfield CT 06269

**TRAINOR, GEORGE L,** BIO-ORGANIC CHEMISTRY. *Current Pos:* chemist org chem, 81-85, proj leader, 85-87, RES LEADER, CENT RES & DEVELOP, E I DU PONT DE NEMOURS & CO, INC, 87- *Personal Data:* b Staten Island, NY, Aug 19, 52; m 75; c 1. *Educ:* Stevens Inst Technol, BS, 74; Harvard Univ, MA & PhD(chem), 79. *Prof Exp:* Res asst org chem, Stevens Inst Technol, 71-74 & Harvard Univ, 75-79; res assoc, Columbia Univ, 79-81. *Concurrent Pos:* Teaching asst org chem, Stevens Inst Technol, 73-74, Harvard Univ, 74-77. *Mem:* Sigma Xi; Am Chem Soc. *Res:* Organic chemistry of biologically relevant processes. *Mailing Add:* 9 Carillon Ct Wilmington DE 19803-2900

**TRAINOR, JAMES H,** NUCLEAR RADIATION DAMAGE, COMPUTER SYSTEMS. *Current Pos:* Sr physicist & div chief cosmic ray physics, 64-83, dep dir sci, 83-86, DIR SPACE & EARTH SCI, GODDARD SPACE FLIGHT CTR, NASA, 86- *Personal Data:* b Lancaster, NH, Aug 22, 35. *Educ:* Univ NH, BC, 58, MS, 59, PhD(physics), 64. *Mem:* Am Geophys Union; fel Inst Elec & Electronics Engrs. *Mailing Add:* 935 Driftwood Ave Seal Beach CA 90740

**TRAINOR, LYNNE E H,** THEORETICAL PHYSICS. *Current Pos:* PROF PHYSICS, UNIV TORONTO, 63- *Personal Data:* b Chamberlain, Sask, Dec 4, 21; div; c 3. *Educ:* Univ Sask, BA, 46, MA, 47; Univ Minn, PhD(physics), 51. *Prof Exp:* Fel, Nat Res Coun Can, 51-52; asst prof physics, Queen's Univ, Ont, 52-55; vis prof, Univ BC, 55-56; from asst prof to prof, Univ Alta, 56-63. *Mem:* Am Phys Soc; Can Asn Physicists (secy, 66-68); Biophys Soc; Can Soc Clin Ecol. *Res:* Statistical mechanics of Bose-Einstein systems; properties of thin helium films; field approach to structuralism in theoretical biology; theoretical biology and biophysics; pattern formation and morphology of developmental systems; structure and function of DNA; transmembrane transport; neurophysics; brain theory. *Mailing Add:* Dept Physics Univ Toronto Toronto ON M5S 1A7 Can

**TRAINOR, ROBERT JAMES,** PHYSICS. *Current Pos:* group leader, High-Energy-Density Physics Group, 83-93, dep dir, Physics Div, 93-96, CHIEF SCIENTIST, ATLAS PROS, LOS ALAMOS NAT LAB, 97- *Personal Data:* b Bell, Calif, June 15, 44; m, Mary Stoddard. *Educ:* Calif State Polytech Univ, BS, 66; Univ Calif, Riverside, MS, 69, PhD(physics), 74. *Prof Exp:* Res assoc physics, Argonne Nat Lab, 74-76; physicist, Lawrence

Livermore Nat Lab, 76-82. *Mem:* Am Phys Soc. *Res:* Experimental condensed matter physics; properties of matter at extreme high pressures and temperatures; laser-matter interactions; properties of hot, dense plasmas. *Mailing Add:* MS D410 Los Alamos Nat Lab Los Alamos NM 87544

**TRAISMAN, HOWARD SEVIN,** PEDIATRICS, INSULIN DEPENDENT DIABETES MELLITUS. *Current Pos:* from instr to assoc, 52-57, from asst prof to assoc prof, 62-73, PROF PEDIAT, MED SCH, NORTHWESTERN UNIV, CHICAGO, 73- *Personal Data:* b Chicago, Ill, Mar 18, 23; m 56; c 3. *Educ:* Northwestern Univ, BS, 43, BM, 46, MD, 47. *Prof Exp:* Intern, Cook County Hosp, Chicago, 46-47; resident, Children's Mem Hosp, 49-51. *Concurrent Pos:* Attend pediatrician, Children's Mem Hosp, 52-, Evanston Hosp, 52-, Northwestern Mem Hosp, 67- *Mem:* Am Acad Pediat; Am Pediat Soc; Endocrine Soc; Lawson Wilkins Pediat Endocrine Soc; Am Diabetes Asn. *Res:* Juvenile diabetes mellitus. *Mailing Add:* 1325 W Howard St Evanston IL 60202-3766

**TRAITOR, CHARLES EUGENE,** PHARMACOLOGY, TOXICOLOGY. *Current Pos:* CONSULT, 93- *Personal Data:* b West Frankfort, Ill, Jan 28, 34; m 57, Edwyna Baker; c Ann & Charles J. *Educ:* St Louis Col Pharm, BS, 60; Purdue Univ, MS, 63, PhD(pharmacol), 65. *Prof Exp:* Res toxicologist, Med Res Div, Am Cyanamid Co, 65-93. *Mem:* Am Col Toxicol; NY Acad Sci; Sigma Xi. *Res:* Toxicology of drugs on various organ systems. *Mailing Add:* 187 S Highview Ave Pearl River NY 10965

**TRAJMAR, SANDOR,** ATOMIC & MOLECULAR PHYSICS. *Current Pos:* mem technol staff, Calif Inst Tech, 61-80, head, Electron Col Physics Group, 70-89, mgr planetary atmospheric sect, 83-85, SR RES SCIENTIST, JET PROPULSION LAB, CALIF INST TECHNOL, 80- *Personal Data:* b Bogacs, Hungary, Sept 7, 31; US citizen; m 57; c 1. *Educ:* Debrecen Univ, dipl, 55; Univ Calif, Berkeley, PhD(phys chem), 61. *Honors & Awards:* NASA Medal Except Sci Achievement, 73. *Prof Exp:* Chemist, N Hungarian Chem Works, 55-57; chemist, Stauffer Chem Co, 57-58. *Concurrent Pos:* Teaching asst, Dept Chem, Univ Calif, 58-59, res asst, Lawrance Radiation Lab, 59-61; res fel, Div Chem & Chem Eng, Calif Inst Technol, 64-66, sr res fel, 69-72; adj prof physics, Univ Southern Calif, 82-84; adj prof physics, Univ Calif, Riverside, 86- *Mem:* Am Chem Soc; fel Am Phys Soc. *Res:* High temperature chemistry; molecular spectroscopy; low-energy electron scattering; atomic physics. *Mailing Add:* Jet Propulsion Lab 183/601 Calif Tech 4800 Oak Grove Dr Pasadena CA 91109. *Fax:* 818-393-4605

**TRAMA, FRANCESCO BIAGIO,** LIMNOLOGY. *Current Pos:* asst prof, 60-63, ASSOC PROF ZOOL, RUTGERS COL, RUTGERS UNIV, NEW BRUNSWICK, 63-, ASSOC DEAN, 73- *Personal Data:* b Philadelphia, Pa, Dec 13, 27; m 54. *Educ:* Temple Univ, AB, 48, MA, 50; Univ Mich, PhD(zool), 57. *Prof Exp:* Asst limnol, Acad Natural Sci Philadelphia, 50-53; asst prof zool, Chicago Teachers Col, 57-60. *Concurrent Pos:* Res assoc, Great Lakes Res Inst, Univ Mich, 57-61. *Mem:* Fel AAAS; Am Soc Limnol & Oceanog; Ecol Soc Am; Sigma Xi. *Res:* Trophic dynamics and energy transfer in aquatic ecosystem; primary productivity in fresh water. *Mailing Add:* 4490 Plumosa St Spring Hill FL 34607-2429

**TRAMBARULO, RALPH,** PHYSICS, PHYSICAL CHEMISTRY. *Current Pos:* RETIRED. *Personal Data:* b East Longmeadow, Mass, Jan 24, 25; m 55; c 4. *Educ:* Yale Univ, BS, 44, PhD(phys chem), 49. *Prof Exp:* Res assoc, Duke Univ, 49-52; asst prof physics, Pa State Col, 52-53 & Univ Del, 53-56; mem tech staff, Bell Tel Labs, 56-90. *Mem:* Inst Elec & Electronics Engrs; Sigma Xi. *Res:* Microwave physics and spectroscopy; microwave integrated circuits. *Mailing Add:* 20 Irving Pl Red Bank NJ 07701-1710

**TRAMMEL, KENNETH,** ENTOMOLOGY. *Current Pos:* OWNER & PRES, AGR CHEM DEVELOP SERV, INC, 75- *Personal Data:* b Skipperville, Ala, Oct 30, 37; m 58; c 4. *Educ:* Univ Fla, BS, 60, PhD(entom), 65. *Prof Exp:* Res assoc citrus pest control, Citrus Exp Sta, Univ Fla, 64-65, asst entomologist, 65-67; entomologist, Ciba Agrochem Co, Fla, 67-69; assoc prof entom, NY State Agr Exp Sta, Cornell Univ, 69-75. *Mem:* Entom Soc Am; Weed Sci Soc Am. *Res:* Apple and pear pest management; field application of sex pheromones for monitoring and control of pests; pesticides on fruit, vegetables and field crops. *Mailing Add:* 1649 Lester Rd Phelps NY 14532

**TRAMMELL, GEORGE THOMAS,** THEORETICAL PHYSICS. *Current Pos:* PROF PHYSICS, RICE UNIV, 61- *Personal Data:* b Marshall, Tex, Feb 5, 23; m 45; c 4. *Educ:* Rice Inst, BA, 44; Cornell Univ, PhD, 50. *Prof Exp:* Physicist, Oak Ridge Nat Lab, 50-61. *Mem:* Fel Am Phys Soc. *Res:* Solid state theory. *Mailing Add:* Dept Physics Rice Univ 6100 Main St Houston TX 77005. *Fax:* 713-527-9033

**TRAMMELL, GROVER J(ACKSON), JR,** MECHANICAL ENGINEERING. *Current Pos:* RETIRED. *Personal Data:* b Attalla, Ala, July 17, 19; m 45; c 5. *Educ:* Tulane Univ, BS, 49, MS, 50. *Prof Exp:* Instr math, La State Univ, 50-52, asst prof eng mech, 52-57; prof mech eng, La Tech Univ, 57-84, dir continuing educ, 67-84. *Mem:* Am Soc Eng Educ; Am Soc Mech Engrs; Nat Soc Prof Engrs. *Res:* Vibrations; solid mechanics; thermodynamics. *Mailing Add:* 911 James St Ruston LA 71270

**TRAMMELL, REX COSTO,** NUCLEAR SCIENCE, SEMICONDUCTOR MATERIALS. *Current Pos:* b Sevier Co, Tenn, Nov 9, 38. *Educ:* Univ Tenn, BS, 65, MS, 69. *Honors & Awards:* EG&G Germeshausen Award, 78. *Prof Exp:* Staff physicist radiation detectors,

EG&G Ortec Inc, 65-71, staff physicist semiconductor mat, 71-78, sr scientist, 78-92, dir eng, 92-96. *Mem:* Sr mem Inst Elec & Electronics Engrs. *Res:* Germanium crystal growth technology as applied to germanium gamma-ray spectrometers. *Mailing Add:* EG&G Ortec Inc 100 Midland Rd Oak Ridge TN 37830

**TRAMONDOZZI, JOHN EDMUND,** ORGANIC CHEMISTRY, ANALYTICAL CHEMISTRY. *Current Pos:* From asst prof to assoc prof, 69-83, chmn, 87-93, PROF CHEM, CURRY COL, 83- *Personal Data:* b Malden, Mass, Aug 28, 42. *Educ:* Boston Col, BS, 64, PhD(chem), 72. *Mem:* Am Chem Soc; Sigma Xi. *Res:* Reactions and syntheses of organic sulfur compounds, especially sufinates and sulfones; organic reactions in fused salt media; chemical conservation of artistic objects. *Mailing Add:* Dept Chem Curry Col Milton MA 02186

**TRAMPUS, ANTHONY,** MATHEMATICS. *Current Pos:* mathematical statistician, 77-80, OPER RES ANALYST, FED ENERGY REGULATORY COMN, DEPT ENERGY, 80- *Personal Data:* b Cleveland, Ohio, July 22, 27. *Educ:* Case Inst Technol, BS, 51, PhD(math), 57; George Washington Univ, MS, 53. *Prof Exp:* Mathematician, Nat Bur Stand, DC, 51-53, Firestone Tire & Rubber Co, 53-56 & Gen Elec Co, 57-63; staff mathematician, Interstate Electronics Corp, Calif, 63-70; res mathematician, Univ Dayton Res Inst, 70-72; mathematician consult, Nat Space Technol Labs, Sperry Corp, 72-77. *Mem:* Math Asn Am. *Res:* Function theory in linear algebra; mathematical analysis in science and engineering. *Mailing Add:* 2001 Columbia Pike Apt 214 Arlington VA 22204

**TRAN, LOC BINH,** NUMERICAL CALCULATIONS OF PHYSICAL PROPERTIES OF DIATOMIC MOLECULES, SPECTROPHOTOMETRIC DETERMINATION OF CHEMICAL EQUILIBRIUM CONSTANTS UNDER HIGH PRESSURE. *Current Pos:* asst prof, 84-88, ASSOC PROF PHYSICS, KANS WESLEYAN UNIV, 88- *Personal Data:* b Hanoi, Vietnam, May 1, 46; US citizen; m 76, Ai H Nguyen; c Eric, Jana, Austin & Ethan. *Educ:* Univ Saigon, BS, 68, MS, 72; Univ Okla, MS, 78, PhD(physics), 81. *Prof Exp:* Res assoc, Univ Okla, 81-84. *Res:* Precision internuclear potential functions in solving the Schroedinger equation for a diatomic molecule, from which its physical properties can be calculated; computer modeling of chemical equilibrium. *Mailing Add:* Dept Physics Kans Wesleyan Univ Salina KS 67401. *E-Mail:* tran@diamond.kwu.edu

**TRAN, LONG TRIEU,** AUTOMATION, COMPUTER-INTEGRATED MANUFACTURING. *Current Pos:* prod engr, Gen Elec, Cleveland, 80-81, adv mfg engr, Louisville, 81-82, qual systs engr, 82-84, qual control engr, 84-86, sr qual info equip engr, 86-89, sr qual indust engr, 90-94, sr supplier tech assist engr, 94-96, SR ADVAN SUPPLIER QUAL ENGR, GEN ELEC, LOUISVILLE, 96- *Personal Data:* b Saigon, Vietnam, Oct 10, 56; US citizen; m 88, Khanh T Phan; c Chau M & Ngoc B. *Educ:* Univ Kansas, BS, 76; Mass Inst Technol, MS, 80; Univ Louisville, MBA, 93. *Prof Exp:* Libr staff, Harvard Med Sch Libr, 78-79; hosp staff, New England Deaconess Hosp, 78-80. *Concurrent Pos:* Teaching asst, Univ Calif, Berkeley & res asst, Lawrence Berkeley Labs, 77; pvt consult, 88- *Mem:* NY Acad Sci; Sigma Xi; Am Soc Qual Control; Am Soc Mech Engrs; sr mem Soc Mfg Engrs; AAAS. *Res:* Grinding processes and surface analysis; computer-integrated testing in manufacturing process control; real-time data collection and feedback systems in monitoring plant production and quality; manufacturing planning and management. *Mailing Add:* 3423 Brookhollow Dr Louisville KY 40220. *Fax:* 502-452-0533

**TRAN, NANG TRI,** THIN FILM TECHNOLOGY, SOLID STATE DEVICES. *Current Pos:* SR RES SPECIALIST & GROUP LEADER, 3M, 85- *Personal Data:* b Binh Dinh, Viet Nam, Jan 2, 48; m 82, Thu-Huong; c Helen, Florence, Irene & Kenneth. *Educ:* Kyushu Inst Technol, BEE, 73, MEE, 75; Univ Osaka, PhD(elec eng), 78. *Prof Exp:* Res scientist, Sharp Electronic Inc, 79-80; sr res scientist, Arco Solar Indust, 80-84. *Concurrent Pos:* Instr, Japaneses Cult Indust. *Mem:* Japan Soc Appl Physics; Inst Elec & Electronics Engrs. *Res:* Zinc sulfide thin film; electroluminescent displays, amorphous silicon semiconductors and devices based on these materials; solid state imaging devices; phosphor materials. *Mailing Add:* Graphic Res Lab 3M Co 201 3E-02 St Paul MN 55144

**TRANEL, DANIEL T,** neuropsychology, behavioral neurology, for more information see previous edition

**TRANIELLO, JAMES FRANCIS ANTHONY,** BEHAVIORAL ECOLOGY, SOCIOBIOLOGY. *Current Pos:* Lectr biol & ethol, 80-81, RES ASSOC ENTOM, HARVARD UNIV, 81-; ASSOC PROF BIOL, BOSTON UNIV, 81- *Personal Data:* b Somerville, Mass, Aug 24, 52; m 78, Dina A Brown; c Alexander & Ian. *Educ:* Boston Univ, AB, 74; Univ Mass, MS, 76; Harvard Univ, PhD(biol), 80. *Concurrent Pos:* NSF grant recipient, 82-85 & 86-90, Whitehall Found grant recipient, 86-91, A P Sloan Found, 92-93; pres, Entom Assoc, Inc. *Mem:* Int Union Study Social Insects; AAAS; Animal Behav Soc; Entom Soc Am; Behav Ecol Soc. *Res:* Behavioral ecology and sociobiology of insects, including communication, foraging behavior, defensive behavior and caste evolution. *Mailing Add:* Dept Biol Boston Univ 5 Cummington St Boston MA 02215

**TRANK, JOHN W,** CARDIOVASCULAR PHYSIOLOGY, MUSCLE PHYSIOLOGY. *Current Pos:* from asst prof to assoc prof, Med Ctr, 64-82, PROF PHYSIOL, UNIV KANS MED SCH, 82- *Personal Data:* b Minneapolis, Minn, July 24, 28; m 52, Lois M Heaney; c Steven, Timothy & Janet. *Educ:* Univ Minn, BEE, 51, MS, 56, PhD(physiol), 61. *Prof Exp:* From instr biophys to instr physiol, Univ Minn, 54-61; lectr, McGill Univ, 61-63, asst prof, 63-64. *Concurrent Pos:* Dep dir univ surg clin, Montreal Gen Hosp, 61-64. *Mem:* Am Physiol Soc; Inst Elec & Electronics Engrs; Biophys Soc. *Res:* Engineering analysis of cardiovascular control and instrumentation for biological research; bioengineering; mechanics of muscle contraction. *Mailing Add:* Dept Physiol Univ Kans Med Ctr 39th & Rainbow Kansas City KS 66160-7401. *Fax:* 913-588-7430; *E-Mail:* jtrank@kumc.edu

**TRANNER, FRANK,** COSMETICS & OTC PHARMACEUTICALS DEVELOPMENT. *Current Pos:* CONSULT, COSMETICS & TOILETRIES, 84- *Personal Data:* b Chelsea, Mass, May 22, 22; m 49, Patricia Eason; c 4. *Educ:* Mass Col Pharm, BS, 43. *Prof Exp:* Develop & control chemist, Hat Corp Am, 44-46; develop chemist, Remington Rand Inc, 47-54 & Rilling-Dermetics Inc, 54-56; asst chief chemist, Germaine Monteil Cosmetiques, 57-59; develop chemist & sect head, Chesebrough-Pond's Inc, 60-69, res mgr, 69-72, dir tech serv, 72-76, dir appl technol, 76-84. *Mem:* Fel Am Inst Chemists; Am Chem Soc; Am Pharmaceut Asn; fel Soc Cosmetic Chem; NY Acad Sci. *Res:* Cosmetic, toiletry and pharmaceutical products creation; formula development and claim support. *Mailing Add:* 23 Beech Tree Circle Trumbull CT 06611. *Fax:* 203-375-8744

**TRANQUADA, ROBERT ERNEST,** INTERNAL MEDICINE. *Current Pos:* dean & prof, 86-92, NORMAN TOPPING/NAT MED ENTERPRISES PROF MED & PUB POLICY, UNIV SOUTHERN CALIF SCH MED, 92-, DIR, HEALTH ADMIN PROG, SCI & PUB ADMIN, 94- *Personal Data:* b Los Angeles, Calif, Aug 27, 30; m 51, Margaret Janet Martin; c John, James & Katherine. *Educ:* Pomona Col, BA, 51; Stanford Univ, MD, 55; Am Bd Internal Med, cert, 63. *Hon Degrees:* DSc, Worcester Polytech Inst, 85. *Prof Exp:* Intern in med, Univ Calif Los Angeles, 55-57, asst resident, 56-57; intermediate resident, Los Angeles Vet Admin Hosp, 57-58; from instr to assoc prof, Univ Southern Calif Sch Med, Dept Med, 59-68, chmn, Dept Community Med & Pub Health, 66-69, prof community med & pub health, 68-75, assoc dean, 69-75; assoc dean regional & postgrad, Med Educ, Univ Calif, Los Angeles, Sch Med, 76-79, prof med, 76-79, prof pub health, 76-79, vchmn, Dept Med, 77-79; chancellor & dean, Med Ctr, Univ Mass, 79-86, prof med, 79-86. *Concurrent Pos:* Fel, Univ Calif Los Angeles Med Ctr, USPHS, 58-59; Univ Southern Calif, 59-60; attend physician med, Huntington Mem Hosp, Pasadena, Calif, 65-77; consult med, White Mem Hosp, Los Angeles, Calif, 65-77; assoc proj dir, SCent Multipurpose Health Serv Ctr, 66-68; mem bd dirs, Charles R Drew Univ Med & Sci, 66-75 & 86-; from attend physician to hon sr attend physician, Los Angeles Co-Univ Southern Calif Med Ctr, 69-76; mem, Prev Med & Dent Rev Comt, Bur Health Manpower Educ, Div Allied Health Manpower, Prog Asst Br, NIH, Bethesda, Md, 70-74; fac med teacher's training course, Paradeniya, Sri Lanka, 70; mem bd dir, Nat Med Fel, Inc, 71-, chmn, 80-86; consult, Fourth World Conf Med Educ, World Med Asn, Inc, 72; nat adv, Pub Health Training Coun, 75-77, Comt Vet Med, Univ Minn, 75; consult, Robert Wood Johnson Found, 75-78; attend internist, Harbor Gen Hosp, Torrance, Calif, 76-79, Univ Calif Los Angeles Hosp & Clin, 76-79; treas bd gov, Health Systs Agency, Los Angeles Co, Inc, 77-79; hon staff, Huntington Mem Hosp, Pasadena, Calif, 77-79; attend physician, Olive View Med Ctr, 77-79; mem rev panel, Div Med, Family Med, Bur Health Prof, 80-83; rev med educ, Inst Med-Nat Acad Sci, 82-83; mem, Mass Statewide Health Coord Coun, 82-83; corporator, Greater Worcester Community Found, Inc, 82-86; chmn admin bd, Coun Deans, Asn Am Med Cols, 90-91; vis prof, Ovenburg Med Inst, Russia, 94. *Mem:* Inst Med-Nat Acad Sci; NY Acad Sci; Am Diabetes Asn; Am Pub Health Asn; NY Acad Sci; fel AAAS; fel Am Antiquarian Soc; Asn Teachers Prev Med; Sigma Xi; AMA; fel Nat Health Found. *Res:* Fibrosis in scleroderma; phenethylbiquamide on human hepatic metabolism as measured; effect of insulin on lactic acid production by rat adipose tissue; spontaneous hypoglycemia; medical care research; author of 40 publications. *Mailing Add:* Univ Southern Calif VKC 368A Los Angeles CA 90089-0041

**TRANSUE, LAURENCE FREDERICK,** PHYSICAL CHEMISTRY. *Current Pos:* RETIRED. *Personal Data:* b Summerfield, Kans, Apr 2, 14; m 58. *Educ:* Tarkio Col, AB, 36; Univ Nebr, AM, 39, PhD(phys chem), 41. *Prof Exp:* Asst, Univ Nebr, 37-41; res chemist, E I du Pont de Nemours & Co, Inc, 41-50, supvr, 50-52, supt & res mgr, Photo-prod Dept, 52-79. *Mem:* Am Chem Soc; Soc Photog Sci & Eng. *Res:* Surface films; chemistry and physics of photography. *Mailing Add:* 110 Wendover Rd Rochester NY 14610-2349

**TRANSUE, WILLIAM REAGLE,** MATHEMATICAL ANALYSIS. *Current Pos:* RETIRED. *Personal Data:* b Pen Argyl, Pa, Nov 30, 14; m 36, Monique Serpette; c William R, Jacques H & John R. *Educ:* Lafayette Col, BS, 35; Lehigh Univ, MA, 39, PhD(math), 41. *Hon Degrees:* ScD, Kenyon Col, 82. *Prof Exp:* Asst, Inst Advan Study, 42-43; assoc physicist, Ord Dept, US Dept Army, 43-44, physicist, 44-45; assoc prof math, Kenyon Col, 45-48; asst, Inst Advan Study, 48-49; prof, Kenyon Col, 49-66; prof math, State Univ NY, Binghamton, 66-81. *Concurrent Pos:* Fulbright scholar, Italy, 51-52; NSF fac fel, Paris, 60-61. *Mem:* Am Math Soc; Math Asn Am. *Res:* Functional analysis; theory of measure and integration. *Mailing Add:* 1855 S Delaware Dr Mt Bethel PA 18343

**TRANT, TROY EDWARD,** HEAT TRANSFER & COMBUSTION RESEARCH, COMPUTATIONAL FLUID DYNAMICS. *Current Pos:* DESIGN ENGR, RHEEM MFG CO, 96- *Personal Data:* b Bossier City, La, Aug 18, 69. *Educ:* Univ Ala, Birmingham, BS, 93, MS, 96. *Mem:* Am Inst Aeronaut & Astronaut; Am Soc Mech Engrs; Am Soc Heating, Refrig & Air

Conditioning Engrs. *Res:* Computational fluid dynamics analysis of atmospheric flows, flow measurement, heat exchanger design and combustion research. *Mailing Add:* 3580 McGehee Pl Dr S Apt 703 Montgomery AL 36111

**TRAPANI, IGNATIUS LOUIS,** PHYSIOLOGY, IMMUNOLOGY. *Current Pos:* prof chem, Colo Mountain Col, 69-85, chmn, Dept Sci & Math, 75-82, instrnl supvr arts & sci, 82-85, EMER PROF CHEM, COLO MOUNTAIN COL, 85- *Personal Data:* b San Francisco, Calif, Nov 19, 25; m 52, Mariel Olson; c Teresa & Paul. *Educ:* Univ San Francisco, BS, 48, MS, 50; Stanford Univ, PhD(physiol), 56. *Prof Exp:* Asst physiol, Stanford Univ, 51-54, jr res assoc, 54-56; USPHS fel, Calif Inst Technol, 56-58, res fel immunochem, 56-60; asst chief dept exp immunol, Nat Jewish Hosp, 60-69, actg chief 63-69; asst prof microbiol, Univ Colo Med Ctr, Denver, 65-69. *Mem:* AAAS; Am Physiol Soc; Am Asn Immunol; Soc Exp Biol & Med; NY Acad Sci. *Res:* Physiological and physico-chemical properties of plasma substitutes; physiology and immunology of animals at high altitude and low temperatures; antigen-antibody complexes, immunophysiological parameters of antibody formation; appropriate technology; science and man; energy and its societal implications. *Mailing Add:* 0060 Ptarmigan Lane Glenwood Springs CO 81601. *E-Mail:* loumar@rof.net

**TRAPANI, ROBERT VINCENT,** BIOGEOCHEMISTRY, ENVIRONMENTAL PHOTOCHEMISTRY. *Current Pos:* ENVIRON HEALTH & SAFETY CONSULT, MILLER/THOMPSON CONSTRUCTORS INC, 95- *Personal Data:* b Johnston City, Ill, Apr 30, 55. *Educ:* Ariz State Univ, BA, 77; Univ Calif, Los Angeles, PhD(chem eng), 82. *Prof Exp:* Res assoc, Calif Inst Technol, 83-84; environ chemist, Environ Eng Lab, USN, 84-86; res chemist, Dynamic Disk, Inc, 86-88; chief sci consult, Anthro-Geo Res, Inc, 88-91; mgr & res scientist, H & H Environ Servs, 91-95. *Concurrent Pos:* Sci consult, Anthro-Geo Res Inc, 88-; environ consult, Pan Pac Environ Servs, 94- *Mem:* Fel Am Inst Chemists; Am Chem Soc; Am Indust Hyg Soc; Am Soc Safety Engrs; Nat Environ Training Asn; Nat Safety Mgt Soc. *Res:* New hazardous waste treatment using novel oxidants and ultrasound; global-scale environmental photochemical reactions and reaction networks in the atmosphere, biosphere, geosphere and hydrosphere with emphasis on biogeochemical cycles; pollutant and particle transport in alluvial stream and groundwater and buoyant discharge in coastal water. *Mailing Add:* 625 Burnett Ave No 1 San Francisco CA 94131

**TRAPANI, ROBERT-JOHN,** IMMUNOLOGY. *Current Pos:* RETIRED. *Personal Data:* b New York, NY, Sept 8, 29; m 54; c 2. *Educ:* NY Univ, AB, 49; Cath Univ Am, PhD, 60. *Prof Exp:* Med bacteriologist, Walter Reed Army Inst Res, 53-55 & Nat Cancer Inst, 55-61; dir, Dept Immunol, Microbiol Assocs, Inc, 61-84 & Immunol Serv, Electro-Nucleonic Inc, Pharm Diag, 84-93. *Res:* Natural resistance, immunity and influencing factors; gram-negative endotoxins; human histocompatability; transplantation immunity. *Mailing Add:* 1410 Stratton Dr Rockville MD 20854

**TRAPP, ALLAN LAVERNE,** VETERINARY PATHOLOGY. *Current Pos:* RETIRED. *Personal Data:* b Stockbridge, Mich, July 20, 32; m 55; c 4. *Educ:* Mich State Univ, BS, 54, DVM, 56; Iowa State Univ, PhD(vet path), 60. *Prof Exp:* Vet livestock investr, Animal Dis Eradication Br, USDA, 56-57; res assoc animal dis res, Iowa State Univ, 57-60; asst prof, Ohio Agr Exp Sta, Ohio State Univ, 60-65, assoc prof, Ohio Agr Res & Develop Ctr, 65-66; assoc prof, Mich State Univ, 66-70, prof animal dis diag work & teaching, 70-94. *Concurrent Pos:* Mem, Med Adv Coun, Detroit Zoo, 69- *Mem:* Wildlife Dis Asn; Am Vet Med Asn; Am Asn Vet Lab Diag. *Res:* Respiratory diseases of cattle; gastrointestinal diseases of cattle and swine; naturally occuring diseases in fishes; diseases of wild and pet birds. *Mailing Add:* 3106 Manley Dr PO Box 30076 Lansing MI 48910

**TRAPP, CHARLES ANTHONY,** PHYSICAL CHEMISTRY. *Current Pos:* assoc prof, 69-74, PROF CHEM, UNIV LOUISVILLE, 74- *Personal Data:* b Chicago, Ill, July 9, 36; m 58; c 2. *Educ:* Loyola Univ, Ill, BS, 58; Univ Chicago, MS, 60, PhD(chem), 63. *Prof Exp:* NSF fel physics, Oxford Univ, 62-63; asst prof chem, Ill Inst Technol, 63-69. *Concurrent Pos:* Petrol Res Fund starter grant, 63-64, type A res grant, 65-68; NSF res grant, 64-67; consult, Argonne Nat Lab, 69-72; Res Corp grant, 70-72. *Mem:* Am Phys Soc. *Res:* Magnetic properties of matter; electron spin resonance in transition metal compounds, organic free radicals and biologically important compounds; electrical conductivity studies of nonmetals. *Mailing Add:* Dept Chem Univ Louisville Louisville KY 40292

**TRAPP, GENE ROBERT,** MAMMALOGY & ETHOLOGY. *Current Pos:* from asst prof to assoc prof, 70-77, PROF BIOL, CALIF STATE UNIV, SACRAMENTO, 77- *Personal Data:* b Hammond, Wis, June 16, 38. *Educ:* Wash State Univ, BS, 60; Univ Alaska, MS, 62; Univ Wis, PhD(zool), 72. *Prof Exp:* Res asst, Coop Wildlife Res Unit, Univ Alaska, 60-62; teaching asst, Dept Biol, Univ NMex, 62-63; wildlife biologist, US Soil Conserv, Honesdale, Pa, 63-64 & Br River Basin Studies, US Fish & Wildlife Serv, Tex, 64-65; teaching asst, Dept Zool, Univ Wis-Madison, 65-70; collabr carnivore res, US Nat Park Serv, Zion Nat Park, 67-69. *Mem:* Am Soc Mammalogists; Animal Behav Soc; Wildlife Soc; Soc Northwestern Vertebrate Biol. *Res:* The behavioral ecology of mammals, especially carnivores. *Mailing Add:* Dept Biol Sci Calif State Univ 600 J St Sacramento CA 95819-2605. *Fax:* 916-278-5787; *E-Mail:* trappgr@csus.edu

**TRAPP, GEORGE E, JR,** APPLIED MATHEMATICS. *Current Pos:* Assoc prof, 70-76, PROF COMPUT SCI, WVA UNIV, 76-; CONSULT, WESTINGHOUSE ELEC CORP, 70- *Personal Data:* b Pittsburgh, Pa, June 30, 44; m 68; c 2. *Educ:* Carnegie-Mellon Univ, BS, 66, MS, 67, PhD(math), 70. *Concurrent Pos:* Consult, Brookhaven Nat Lab, 83. *Mem:* Soc Indust & Appl Math; Sigma Xi; Am Math Soc; Math Asn Am. *Res:* Algebraic analysis of electrical networks and numerical analysis, and product data modeling. *Mailing Add:* 1377 Braewick Dr Morgantown WV 26505-2723

**TRAPPE, JAMES MARTIN,** MYCOLOGY, MYCORRHIZAE. *Current Pos:* PROF BOT & FOREST SCI, ORE STATE UNIV, 76- *Personal Data:* b Spokane, Wash, Aug 16, 31; m 63, Beverly J Reller; c Matthew, Erica, John & Angela. *Educ:* Univ Wash, BS, 53, PhD(forest bot), 62; State Univ NY, MS, 55. *Honors & Awards:* Milestone Res Award, Univ Hannover, Ger, 85. *Prof Exp:* Forester, Colville Nat Forest, 53-56, res forester, Pac NW Forest & Range Exp Sta, US Forest Serv, 56-65, proj leader & prin mycologist, 65-86. *Concurrent Pos:* Assoc prof bot, Ore State Univ, 65-76, NSF grants, 66-71, 74, 76 & 78-94; Am Philos Soc grants for mycol res, Univ Torino, Italy, 67-68, Nat Polytech Inst, Mex, 72; Japan Soc Prom Sci res fel, 75; mem, Joint Comn on Rural Reconstruct, Repub China, 77, Kuwait Inst Sci Res, 79; Commonwealth Sci & Ind Res Orgn, Perth, Australia, 82 & 87-93; Indo-US Sci & Technol Initiative, New Delhi & Bangalore, 84-91; Australian Coun Int Arg Res; Sweden spec prof, Uppsala, 90-92. *Mem:* Fel AAAS; Brit Mycol Soc; Mex Soc Mycol; Mycol Soc Am (pres, 86-87); Sigma Xi; NAm Truffling Soc (pres, 70). *Res:* Taxonomy and ecology of fungi, especially hypogeous species, Mycorrhizae; soil microbial ecology of plant establishment in subalpine/alpine habitats; plant community oriented carbon allocation big root endophytic fungi. *Mailing Add:* Dept Forest Sci Ore State Univ Corvallis OR 97331-7501. *Fax:* 541-737-1393; *E-Mail:* trappej@fsl.orst.edu

**TRAQUAIR, JAMES ALVIN,** MYCOLOGY, PLANT PATHOLOGY. *Current Pos:* RETIRED. *Personal Data:* b London, Ont, Aug 1, 47; m 92, Diane A Cuppels. *Educ:* Univ Western Ont, BSc, 70; Univ Alta, PhD(mycol), 74. *Prof Exp:* Nat Res Coun Can fel plant path, Univ Western Ont, London, 74-77; res assoc mycol, Erindale Col, Univ Toronto, 77-78; plant pathologist forage path, Res Sta, Agr Can, Lethbridge, Alta, 78-81; tree fruit pathologist, Harrow, Ont, 81-92, fungal ecologist biol control, Res Ctr, London, Ont, 92. *Concurrent Pos:* Adj prof, Dept Plant Sci, Univ Western Ont. *Mem:* Can Phytopath Soc; Can Bot Asn; Brit Mycol Soc; Mycol Soc Am. *Res:* Biosystematics of polyporaceous basidiomycetes; microbial ecology; hyperparasitism of fungi; ultrastructure of fungi; host-parasite relations and epidemiology of snowmold diseases of winter cereals, forage legumes and grasses; biocontrol of cytospora canker, root rots and plant disorders; tree fruit mycorrhizae; biocontrol of rhizoctonia; fungal ecology. *Mailing Add:* Res Ctr Agr Can 1391 Sanford St London ON N5U 4T3 Can. *Fax:* 519-457-3997; *E-Mail:* traquairj@em.agr.ca

**TRASHER, DONALD WATSON,** MATHEMATICS. *Current Pos:* asst prof, 64-68 & 70-78, CHMN DEPT MATH, STATE UNIV, NY, GENESEO, 78-, ASSOC PROF, 87- *Personal Data:* b Malverne, NY, Nov 1, 37; m 59, Virginia Snow; c Dennis K, Laura (Bernhofen), Diane (Broberg), Steven & James. *Educ:* Houghton Col, BA, 59; Univ Buffalo, MA, 62. *Prof Exp:* Instr math, Univ Buffalo, 61-64; vis instr, Univ Ind, 69-70. *Concurrent Pos:* Dir, Math Enrichment Prog, Cheektowaga Central Sch, NY, 62-64; consult, GEM Prog for mathematically gifted, York Central Sch, NY, 79-80. *Mem:* Math Asn Am. *Res:* Geometry and the history of mathematics. *Mailing Add:* Dept Math State Univ NY Col Geneseo Geneseo NY 14454. *E-Mail:* trasherd@geneseo. bitnet

**TRASK, CHARLES BRIAN,** SEDIMENTOLOGY, SEDIMENTARY PETROLOGY. *Current Pos:* assoc geologist coal, Ill State Geol Surv, 81-87, assoc geologist environ studies & assessment, 87-93, staff geologist I, Lakes, Streams & Wetlands, 93-96, STAFF GEOLOGIST II, COASTAL & WETLANDS GEOL, ILL STATE GEOL SURV, 96- *Personal Data:* b Bar Harbor, Maine, June 13, 44; m 69; c 2. *Educ:* Amherst Col, AB, 66; Univ Tex, Austin, MA, 72; Syracuse Univ, PhD(geol), 76. *Prof Exp:* Res geologist, Gulf Sci & Technol Co, Gulf Oil Corp, 76-77. *Mem:* Geol Soc Am; Int Asn Sedimentologists; Soc Econ Paleontologists & Mineralogists; Sigma Xi; Soc Sedimentary Geol. *Res:* Sedimentology, engineering geology environmental geology & geology for planning. *Mailing Add:* 1409 W Healey Champaign IL 61821-3813. *E-Mail:* trask@geoserv.isgs.uiuc.edu

**TRASKOS, RICHARD THOMAS,** POLYMER SCIENCE, CHEMICAL ENGINEERING. *Current Pos:* RES ENGR, ROGERS CORP, 69- *Personal Data:* b New Britain, Conn, Jan 3, 40; m 64; c 2. *Educ:* Univ Notre Dame, BS, 61; Mass Inst Technol, DSc(chem eng), 66. *Mem:* Am Chem Soc; Soc Photog Sci & Eng. *Res:* Development of polymer-based printing plates; study of lithography. *Mailing Add:* 43 Herrick Rd Brooklyn CT 06234-1413

**TRASLER, DAPHNE GAY,** GENETICS. *Current Pos:* RETIRED. *Personal Data:* b Iquique, Chile, July 2, 26; Can citizen; m 51; c 2. *Educ:* McGill Univ, BSc, 48, MSc, 54, PhD, 58. *Prof Exp:* Demonstr genetics, McGill Univ, 47; chief asst plant genetics, Inst Cotton Genetics, Peru, 49-51; demonstr genetics, McGill Univ, 52-53, res assoc develop genetics & teratol, 58-70, assoc prof biol, 70-95, assoc prof, Ctr Human Genetics, 79-95. *Concurrent Pos:* Grants, NSF, 59-62, Asn Aid Crippled Children, 65-66, NIH, 66-69 & Nat Res Coun Can, 70-76 & Med Res Coun, 76; mem study sect, Div Res Grants, NIH, 80-82 & 84-88; vis fel, Physiol Dept, Fitzwilliam Col, Cambridge Univ, Eng, 81-82 & Human Anat Dept, Oxford Univ, Eng, 90. *Mem:* Genetics Soc Can; Teratology Soc (pres, 72-73). *Res:* Gene-teratogen interaction and embryonic mechanisms in mouse neural tube defects; mouse teratology. *Mailing Add:* Dept Biol McGill Univ 1205 Ave Docteur Penfield Montreal PQ H3A 1B1 Can

**TRASS, O(LEV)**, CHEMICAL ENGINEERING. *Current Pos:* From asst prof to assoc prof, 58-68, PROF CHEM ENG & APPL CHEM, UNIV TORONTO, 68- *Personal Data:* b Estonia, Oct 9, 31; m 61; c 2. *Educ:* Princeton Univ, BSE, 55; Mass Inst Technol, ScD(chem eng), 58. *Concurrent Pos:* Vis prof, Swiss Fed Inst Technol, 68-69; dir & consult, Chem Eng Res Consults, Ltd Can; mem, Grants Comt on Chem & Metall Eng, Nat Res Coun Can, 72-73, co-chmn, 73-74, chmn, 74-75; assoc chmn, Div Eng Sci, Univ Toronto, 74-77; vpres, Gen Comminution, Inc, 75-86, dir & chmn, 86-; vis prof, Ecole Nat Superieur Indust Chimiques, Nancy, France, 78; speaker, fac coun, Fac Appl Sci & Eng, Univ Toronto, 78-82. *Mem:* Am Chem Soc; Am Inst Chem Engrs; fel Chem Inst Can; Can Soc Chem Eng; Asn Advan Baltic Studies; Fine Particle Soc. *Res:* Fluid flow and mass transfer; solid-fluid interface phenomena, particularly rough surface phenomena; high temperature chemical reactions in shock tubes; comminution and particle dynamics; coal slurry fuels technology; coal beneficiation technology. *Mailing Add:* Dept Chem Eng Univ Toronto Toronto ON M5S 1A4 Can

**TRAUB, ALAN CUTLER**, ELECTRO-OPTICS. *Current Pos:* RETIRED. *Personal Data:* b Hartford, Conn, Jan 20, 23; m 51; c 3. *Educ:* Trinity Col, Conn, BS, 47; Univ Cincinnati, MS, 49, PhD(physics), 52. *Honors & Awards:* Soc Tech Writers & Publ Award of Excellence, 70. *Prof Exp:* Res physicist, Am Optical Co, 52-56; res physicist, Fenwal, Inc, 56-61, chief res engr, 61-63; mem tech staff, Mitre Corp, Mass, 63-70; chief scientist, Foto-Mem, Inc, 70-71; consult, 71-73; prod develop engr, Identicon Corp, 73-74; advan develop mgr, Vanzetti Infrared & Comput Systs, Inc, 74-80, advan develop mgr, Vanzetti Systs, Inc, 80-89. *Concurrent Pos:* Res fel, Tufts Univ, 72-73. *Res:* Spectrophotometry; colorimetry; thin optical films; optical and thermal sensors; visual perception; three-dimensional displays; fiber optics; aerospace electro-optical instrumentation; atmospheric optical propagation; optical communications systems; laser applications; optical memories. *Mailing Add:* 56 Donna Rd Framingham MA 01701

**TRAUB, JOSEPH FREDERICK**, THEORY. *Current Pos:* prof math & chmn, Dept Comput Sci, 79-89, EDWIN HOWARD ARMSTRONG PROF COMPUT SCI & MATH, COLUMBIA UNIV, 89- *Personal Data:* b Ger, June 24, 32; nat US; m 69, Pamela McCorduck; c Claudia R & Hillary A. *Educ:* City Col New York, BS, 54; Columbia Univ, PhD(appl math), 59. *Honors & Awards:* Emanuel R Piore Award, Inst Elec & Electronics Engrs, 91; Distinguished Serv Res Award, Comput Res Asn, 92. *Prof Exp:* Mem tech staff, Bell Tel Labs, Inc, NJ, 59-70; prof comput sci & math & head, Dept Comput Sci, Carnegie-Mellon Univ, 71-79; prof comput sci, Princeton Univ, 86-87, pres, John Von Neumann Nat Supercomputer Ctr, Consortium Sci Compt, 86-87. *Concurrent Pos:* Chmn, Award Comt, Asn Comput Mach, 72-76; mem adv comt fed judicial ctr; mem sci coun, Inst de Res d'Info et d'Automatique, Paris, 76-80, cent steering comt, Comput Sci & Eng Res Study, NSF & liaison to panel on theoret comput sci & panel on numerical anal, 74-80; mem adv comt, Carnegie-Mellon Inst Res, 78-79, Inst Defense Anal, 76-79 & mem adv comt, Math & Comput Sci, NSF, 78-; mem, Conf Bd Math Sci, Math Sci Res Inst, Berkeley, Calif, 85-86; dir, NY State Ctr Comput & Info Systs, 82-88; ed, J Complexity, Acad Press & Ann Rev Comput Sci, Ann Rev, Inc, 85-89; chmn, Comput Sci Technol Bd, Nat Acad Sci, 86-90, Comput Sci Telecommun Bd, 90-92; Sherman Fairchild distinguished scholar, Calif Inst Technol, 91-92; distinguished sr scientist award, Alexander von Humboldt Found, 92-; pres, Search Comt, Nat Acad Eng, 93-94. *Mem:* Nat Acad Eng; Soc Indust & Appl Math; fel Asn Comput Mach; Am Math Soc; Inst Elec & Electronics Engrs; fel AAAS; NY Acad Sci. *Res:* Computational complexity; financial mathematics; limits to scientific knowledge; numerical mathematics. *Mailing Add:* Columbia Univ Comput Sci Dept 456 Comput Sci Bldg New York NY 10027. *Fax:* 212-666-0140; *E-Mail:* traub@cs.columbia.edu

**TRAUB, RICHARD KIMBERLEY**, medical research, for more information see previous edition

**TRAUB, ROBERT**, MEDICAL ENTOMOLOGY. *Current Pos:* prof, 62-90, EMER PROF MICROBIOL, SCH MED, UNIV MD, 90- *Personal Data:* b New York, NY, Oct 26, 16; m 39; c 2. *Educ:* City Col New York, BS, 38; Cornell Univ, MS, 39; Univ Ill, PhD(med entom), 47. *Prof Exp:* Asst entom, Univ Ill, 39-41; chief dept parasitol, Med Ctr, US Army, 47-55, commanding officer, Med Res Unit, Malaya, 55-59, chief, Prev Med & Entom Res Br, Med Res & Develop Command, 59-62. *Concurrent Pos:* Parasitologist, 4th Hoogstraal Exped, Mex, 41; field dir, Army Med Res Units, Malaya, NBorneo & Labrador, 47-55; Comn Hemorrhagic Fever, Korea, 52 & 53; Univ Md Sch Med Res Units, Pakistan, Ethiopia, Burma, Australia, Thailand & New Guinea; hon assoc, Field Mus, Ill, Smithsonian Inst, DC, Carnegie Mus Natural Hist, Pittsburgh & Bishop Mus, Honululu; consult ectoparasite-borne dis, WHO, US Army & USN; mem, Comn Immunization, 48-53, Comn Riskettsial Dis, 64-73 & Armed Forces Epidemiol Bd. *Mem:* AAAS; Entom Soc Am; fel Am Soc Parasitol; fel Am Soc Trop Med & Hyg; Soc Syst Zool; Sigma Xi. *Res:* Ecology and control of vectors and reservoirs of disease; systematics of Siphonaptera and trombiculid mites. *Mailing Add:* 5702 Bradley Blvd Bethesda MD 20814-1026

**TRAUB, WESLEY ARTHUR**, HIGH ANGULAR RESOLUTION ASTROPHYSIC, STRATOSPHERIC COMPOSITION. *Current Pos:* PHYSICIST, CTR ASTROPHYS, SMITHSONIAN & HARVARD COL OBSERVS, 68-; LECTR ASTRON, HARVARD UNIV, 76- *Personal Data:* b Milwaukee, Wis, Sept 25, 40; m 63, Esther; c Jeremy. *Educ:* Univ Wis-Milwaukee, BS, 62; Univ Wis-Madison, MS, 64, PhD(physics), 68. *Concurrent Pos:* Res assoc eng & appl physics, Harvard Univ, 68-74. *Mem:* AAAS; Am Astron Soc; Int Astron Union; Optical Soc Am; Sigma Xi; Am Geophys Union. *Res:* Far-infrared spectroscopy of the terrestrial atmosphere to determine molecular abudances; ground-based Michelson spatial interferometry; Fourier-transform infrared spectrometers; astrophysical high angular resolution imaging. *Mailing Add:* Smithsonian Astrophys Observ 60 Garden St Cambridge MA 02138. *Fax:* 617-495-7467; *E-Mail:* traub@cfa.harvard.edu

**TRAUGER, DAVID LEE**, FISH & WILDLIFE SCIENCES, ECOLOGY. *Current Pos:* STAFF MEM, RESOURCES DIV, US GEOL SURV. *Personal Data:* b Ft Dodge, Iowa, June 16, 42; m, Alice L Faith; c Brent & Amy. *Educ:* Iowa State Univ, BS, 64, MS, 67, PhD(animal ecol), 71. *Prof Exp:* Instr zool & entom, Iowa State Univ, 67-70, asst prof zool & entom & exec secy environ coun, 70-72; wildlife res biologist, Northern Prairie Wildlife Res Ctr, Jamestown, NDak, 72-75, asst dir, 75-79, chief, Div Wildlife Ecol Res, 79-83, dir, Patuxent Wildlife Res Ctr, Fish & Wildlife Serv, US Dept Interior, 83-96, Dep Dir, Nat Biol Surv, 93-96. *Concurrent Pos:* Wildlife technician, Northern Prairie Wildlife Res Ctr, 66-70. *Mem:* Wildlife Soc; Soc Conserv Biol; Wildlife Mgt Inst; Int Asn Fish & Wildlife Agencies; Nat Wildlife Fed; Nature Conservancy. *Res:* Breeding biology, population dynamics, habitat requirements of waterfowl, particularly diving ducks in prairie parklands and subarctic taiga. *Mailing Add:* US Geol Surv Biol Resources Div MS300 12201 Sunrise Valley Dr Reston VA 20192. *Fax:* 703-648-4039; *E-Mail:* david_trauger@usgs.gov

**TRAUGER, DONALD BYRON**, PHYSICS. *Current Pos:* CONSULT, ENERGY TECHNOL, 93- *Personal Data:* b Exeter, Nebr, June 29, 20; m 45, Elaine Causey; c Bryon R & Thomas C. *Educ:* Nebr Wesleyan Univ, AB, 42. *Hon Degrees:* DSc, Wesleyan Univ, Nebr, 74 & Wesleyan Col, Tenn, 77. *Prof Exp:* Physicist, Manhattan Proj, Columbia Univ, 42-44; engr, Union Carbide Corp, 44-54; head, Irradiation Eng Dept, Oak Ridge Nat Lab, 54-64, dir, Gas-cooled Reactor Prog, 64-70, assoc dir, Nuclear & Eng Technol, 70-84, from sr tech asst to dir, 84-93. *Mem:* AAAS; fel Am Nuclear Soc; Am Phys Soc; Sigma Xi. *Res:* Reactor technology; gas cooled reactor fuels; nuclear irradiation tests of fuels and materials; liquid metals; behavior of gases; isotope separation. *Mailing Add:* 20 Palisades Pkwy Oak Ridge TN 37830-7200

**TRAUGER, FREDERICK DALE**, GEOLOGY. *Current Pos:* RETIRED. *Personal Data:* b Lindsay, Calif, Apr 21, 16; m 51, Jeanne M Morrow. *Educ:* Fresno State Col, BA, 39. *Prof Exp:* Geologist, US Bur Reclamation, 46; hydrologist, US Geol Surv, 47-73; geohydrologist, Geohydrology Consults Inc, 73-97. *Mem:* Fel Geol Soc Am; Am Geol Union; AAAS; Am Water Well Asn. *Res:* Quantitative and qualitative evaluation of ground-water resources for industrial and public supplies for municipal, county, state governments and rural subdivisions; groundwater recharge; movement of ground-water contaminants. *Mailing Add:* 1206 Field Dr NE Albuquerque NM 87112-5008. *Fax:* 505-884-0581

**TRAUGH, JOLINDA ANN**, BIOCHEMISTRY, MOLECULAR BIOLOGY. *Current Pos:* from asst prof to assoc prof, 73-82, chmn dept, 81-86, PROF BIOCHEM, UNIV CALIF, RIVERSIDE, 82- *Personal Data:* b Detroit, Mich; c 1. *Educ:* Univ Calif, Davis, BS, 60; Univ Calif, Los Angeles, PhD(microbiol), 70. *Prof Exp:* Res asst, Gerber Baby Foods, 60-62 & Univ Calif, Berkeley, 62-64; USPHS res fel molecular biol, Univ Calif, Davis, 71-73. *Concurrent Pos:* Resident scholar, Study & Conf Ctr, Rockefeller Found, Belliago, Italy, 79; biochem study sect, NIH, 76-80; bd sci coun, Nat Inst Environ Health Sci; sci adv comt biochem & endocrinol, Am Cancer Soc, 91- *Mem:* AAAS; Fedn Am Soc Exp Biol; Biophys Soc. *Res:* Regulation of protein synthesis; protein kinases. *Mailing Add:* Dept Biochem Univ Calif-Riverside Riverside CA 92521-0001. *Fax:* 909-787-3800

**TRAUGOTT, STEPHEN C(HARLES)**, FLUID DYNAMICS, HEAT TRANSFER. *Current Pos:* RETIRED. *Personal Data:* b Frankfurt, Ger, Dec 10, 27; nat US; m 55; c 2. *Educ:* Johns Hopkins Univ, BES, 49, MSE, 51, DEng, 56. *Prof Exp:* Sr scientist, Res Dept, Martin Co, 57-66, chief aerophys res staff, 60-62, prin res scientist & mgr mech, Martin Marietta Labs, 66-85; prog dir fluid dynamics & hydraul, NSF, 85-86, Eng Res Ctr, 86-87, prog dir fluid & particulate systs, 87-94. *Concurrent Pos:* Adj prof, Drexel Inst Technol, 59; vis lectr, Johns Hopkins Univ, 62-66; adj prof, Univ Md, 66-67; vis assoc prof, Cornell Univ, 67-68. *Mem:* Am Inst Aeronaut & Astronaut; Am Phys Soc; Soc Natural Philos; Sigma Xi. *Res:* High speed flow; radiation gas dynamics; dynamics of atmospheres; aluminum smelting; hydrodynamics. *Mailing Add:* 11219 Old Calliage Rd Glen Arm MD 21057

**TRAUMANN, KLAUS FRIEDRICH**, ORGANIC CHEMISTRY. *Current Pos:* RETIRED. *Personal Data:* b Schweinfurt, Ger, Mar 23, 24; nat US; m 58. *Educ:* Univ Heidelberg, PhD(org chem), 54. *Prof Exp:* Res chemist, Carothers Lab, E I Du Pont de Nemours & Co, Inc, 54-66, sr res chemist, Textile Res Lab, 67-73, develop assoc, Textile Res Lab, 73-86. *Mem:* Am Chem Soc. *Res:* Synthetic organic fibers. *Mailing Add:* 502 Whitby Dr Wilmington DE 19803

**TRAURIG, HAROLD H**, NEUROBIOLOGY, REPRODUCTIVE ENDOCRINOLOGY. *Current Pos:* From instr to assoc prof anat, 63-75, interim chair dept anat & neurobiol, 92-93, PROF ANAT, NEUROBIOL & NEUROL, MED CTR, UNIV KY, 75- *Personal Data:* b Chicago, Ill, July 28, 36; m 94, Gloria A Casale; c Lisa, Daniel, Gregory, Raymond, Roberta, Thomas & Bryon. *Educ:* Minn State Univ, Mankato, BS, 58; Univ Minn, PhD(anat), 63. *Honors & Awards:* Pro Meritus Medaille, Univ Gray, Austria, 83. *Concurrent Pos:* Res fel neurochem, Ohio State Univ, 70-71; vis res fel, Univ Graz, Austria, 83, Univ Ulm, Ger, 91 & Univ Innsbruck, Austria, 94. *Mem:* Neurosci Soc. *Res:* Cytology; neurobiology; reproductive biology; cell proliferation. *Mailing Add:* Dept Anat & Neurobiol Univ Ky Med Ctr Lexington KY 40536. *Fax:* 606-325-5946; *E-Mail:* traurig@pop.uky.edu

**TRAURING, MITCHELL,** OPERATIONS RESEARCH. *Current Pos:* CONSULT, OPERS ANALYSIS & FINANCE, 87- *Personal Data:* b Brooklyn, NY, Mar 8, 22; m 43; c 2. *Educ:* Brooklyn Col, BA, 41; Johns Hopkins Univ, MA, 47; Univ Calif, Los Angeles, MS, 76. *Prof Exp:* Physicist, Nat Adv Comt Aeronaut, 41-46; optical engr, Bur Ships, USN, 49; ballistician & sect head, Ballistics Res Labs, Ord Corps, US Dept Army, 49-53; sect head, Guided Missiles Div, Repub Aviation Corp, 53-57; asst sect head, Ground Systs Group, Hughes Aircraft Co, 57-59, sr staff physicist, Res Labs, 59-63, sr staff engr, Aerospace Corp, Calif, 63-68; sr mem tech staff, Data Systs Div, Litton Industs, Inc, 68-72; consult opers anal, 72-78; sr scientist, Hughes Aircraft Co, 78-87. *Mem:* Sigma Xi; Opers Res Soc Am. *Res:* Weapon, electronic and space systems; automatic recognition; business and international economics. *Mailing Add:* 1645 Comstock Ave Los Angeles CA 90024

**TRAUT, ROBERT RUSH,** BIOCHEMISTRY, MOLECULAR BIOLOGY. *Current Pos:* assoc prof, 70-76, PROF BIOL CHEM, SCH MED, UNIV CALIF, DAVIS, 76- *Personal Data:* b Utica, NY, Oct 21, 34; m 62; c 1. *Educ:* Haverford Col, AB, 56; Rockefeller Univ, PhD(biochem), 62. *Prof Exp:* Res asst, Inst Molecular Biol, Univ Geneva, 64-68, Am Heart Asn estab investr, 68-70. *Concurrent Pos:* Jane Coffin Childs Mem Fund fel molecular biol, Med Res Coun Lab Molecular Biol, Cambridge Univ, 62-64; Am Heart Asn estab investr, Univ Calif, Davis, 70-73. *Mem:* AAAS; Am Soc Microbiol; NY Acad Sci; Am Soc Biol Chem; Sigma Xi. *Res:* Mechanism and regulation of protein synthesis; structure and function of ribosomes. *Mailing Add:* Dept Med Biochem Sch Med Univ Calif-Davis Davis CA 95616-5224. *Fax:* 530-752-3516

**TRAUT, THOMAS WOLFGANG,** ENZYME REGULATION, PROTEIN STRUCTURE. *Current Pos:* ASSOC PROF BIOCHEM, SCH MED, UNIV NC, 78- *Personal Data:* b Mar 17, 43. *Educ:* Univ Southern Calif, PhD(molecular biol), 74. *Mem:* Am Soc Biochem & Molecular Biol; Protein Soc; AAAS. *Res:* Working with allosteric enzymes in nucleotide metabolism; the importance of enzyme polymer dissociation to change in specific activity; the relation of subunit size to enzyme function; we are exploring the hypothesis that enzymes are composed of modules that specifically bind some ligand. *Mailing Add:* Dept Biochem Sch Med Univ NC CB No 7260 Chapel Hill NC 27599-7260. *Fax:* 919-966-2852

**TRAUTMAN, DEFOREST L WOODY,** ELECTRICAL ENGINEERING. *Current Pos:* CONSULT, WOODY TRAUTMAN ASSOCS INC, 79- *Personal Data:* b 1920. *Educ:* Carnegie Univ, BS, 42, MS, 43; Stanford Univ, PhD(elec eng), 49. *Mem:* Fel Inst Elec & Electronics Engrs. *Mailing Add:* Woody Trautman Assocs Inc 2625 Middlesex Dr Toledo OH 43606

**TRAUTMAN, JACK CARL,** DAIRY SCIENCE, BIOCHEMISTRY. *Current Pos:* PRES, INT BIOCHEM TECHNOL, INC, 83- *Personal Data:* b Cushing, Okla, Dec 7, 29; m 57; c 1. *Educ:* Univ Idaho, BS, 51; Univ Calif, MS, 53; Univ Wis, PhD(dairy tech), 58. *Prof Exp:* Asst dairy indust, Univ Calif, 51-53; asst dairy & food indust, Univ Wis, 56-58, from instr to asst prof dairy indust, 58-59; asst prof dairy technol, Ohio State Univ, 59-60; supvr indust prod & processes, 60-72, mgr biol res, Oscar Mayer & Co, 72-83. *Concurrent Pos:* Mem sci adv comt, Fats & Protein Res Found; Mfg Enzymolgists. *Mem:* Am Chem Soc; Am Meat Sci Asn; Inst Food Technol. *Res:* Process development of animal biologicals; biologicals needed in human disease states; engineering scale-ups; enzymes, anti-coagulants and blood fractions. *Mailing Add:* 3017 Dianne Dr Middleton WI 53562

**TRAVELLI, ARMANDO,** NUCLEAR ENGINEERING & SCIENCE, TECHNICAL MANAGEMENT. *Current Pos:* asst nuclear engr, Argonne Nat Lab, 65-68, nuclear engr, 68-69, head, Fast Flux Test Facil Sect, 69-74, head, Physics Reactor Safety Sect, 74-76, assoc dir, Safety Test Facil Proj, 76-78, mgr, Arms Control Prog, 89-92, SR NUCLEAR ENGR, PHYSICS DIV, ARGONNE NAT LAB, 87-, MGR, ARMS CONTROL & NONPROLIFERATION PROG, TECH DEVELOP DIV, 92- *Personal Data:* b Rome, Italy, Feb 6, 34; m 70, Margaret Huntley; c Alexander, Cameron & Andrew. *Educ:* Univ Rome, Dr Ing, 58; Rensselaer Polytech Inst, PhD(nuclear eng, sci), 63; Univ Chicago, MBA, 84. *Honors & Awards:* IR-100 Award, 85; Lab Consortium Award for Excellence, 86. *Prof Exp:* Res asst nuclear eng & sci, Rensselaer Polytech Inst, 61-63; asst prof nuclear eng, Mass Inst Technol, 63-65. *Concurrent Pos:* Ford Found res fel eng, 63-65; mgr, RERTR Prog, Eng Physics Div, Argonne Nat Lab, 78- *Mem:* Am Nuclear Soc; AAAS; Sigma Xi. *Res:* Arms control verification technology; neutron transport and high-order perturbation theories; analysis of neutron waves and pulses; analyses and design of research reactors, safety test facilities, critical experiments and fast breeder reactors; patent on research reactor fuel. *Mailing Add:* Technol Develop Div Argonne Nat Lab 9700 S Cass Ave Argonne IL 60439. *E-Mail:* travelli@anl.gov

**TRAVER, ALFRED ELLIS,** MECHANICAL ENGINEERING, SYSTEMS ENGINEERING. *Current Pos:* DEPT MECH ENG, UNIV TEX, AUSTIN, 78- *Personal Data:* b New York, NY, Dec 17, 39; m 66, Carol Barnes; c Margaret & Alfred E. *Educ:* Mass Inst Technol, BS, 61; Iowa State, MS, Univ Tex, Austin, PhD(mech eng), 68, JD, 80. *Prof Exp:* Researcher, Mass Inst Technol-Harvard Joint Ctr Urban Studies, 60-61; aerosysts engr, Gen Dynamics Corp, 63-64; engr-scientist, Tracor, Inc, 66-70; prof mech eng & actg chmn, Dept Systs Eng, Tenn Technol Univ, 70-78. *Concurrent Pos:* consult engr; consult atty. *Mem:* Am Soc Mech Engrs; Opers Res Soc Am; Inst Elec & Electronics Engrs; Am Soc Eng Educ; Nat Soc Prof Engrs; Soc Mfg Engrs. *Res:* Simulation and modeling of dynamic systems; control systems; design studies; interface of technology and the law. *Mailing Add:* 3209 Pickwick Lane Austin TX 78746. *Fax:* 512-471-8727; *E-Mail:* aetraver@mcl.cc.utexas.edu

**TRAVERS, WILLIAM BRAILSFORD,** GEOLOGY. *Current Pos:* asst prof, 72-78, assoc prof, 78-84, PROF GEOL SCI, CORNELL UNIV, 84- *Personal Data:* b Long Beach, Calif, June 13, 34; m 58; c 3. *Educ:* Stanford Univ, BS, 56, MS, 59; Princeton Univ, PhD(geol), 72. *Prof Exp:* Geologist, Stand Oil Co, Calif, 59-61; geologist, Santa Fe Drilling Co, 61-63; chief geologist, Santa Fe Int, Inc, 63-67; asst instr geol, Princeton Univ, 67-71. *Concurrent Pos:* Consult petrol geologist; vpres, Anacapa Oil Co, 67-; vis prof, Stanford Univ, 79; res vis, Oxford Univ, 80. *Mem:* AAAS; fel Geol Soc Am; Am Asn Petrol Geol; Am Geophys Union; fel Geol Asn Can; Sigma Xi. *Res:* Problems of mountain building; deformation of continental margins; structural geology and sedimentology; continental rifting; tectonism in Italy, western United States and western Canada. *Mailing Add:* 421 Highland Rd Ithaca NY 14850

**TRAVERSE, ALFRED,** PALYNOLOGY, PALEOBOTANY. *Current Pos:* from assoc prof to prof, 66-95, EMER PROF PALYNOLOGY, PA STATE UNIV, UNIV PARK, 95- *Personal Data:* b Port Hill, Prince Edward Island, Sept 7, 25; nat US; m 51, Elizabeth Insley; c Paul, Martha, John & Celia. *Educ:* Harvard Univ, SB, 46, AM, 48, PhD(paleobot), 51; Episcopal Theol Sem Southwest, MDiv, 65. *Honors & Awards:* Int Prize Outstanding Achievement, Paleobot Soc India, 91 & 92. *Prof Exp:* Coal technologist, Lignite Res Lab, US Bur Mines, NDak, 51-55; head fuels micros lab, Colo, 55; geologist, Shell Develop Co, 55-62; palynological consult, Tex, 62-65; asst prof geol, Univ Tex, 65-66. *Concurrent Pos:* Mem, Int Comn Palynology, 73-76, pres, 77-80, archivist, 84-; vis prof, Swiss Fed Tech Inst, Zurich, 80-81; adj prof geobiol, Juniata Col, Huntingdon, Pa, 77-85; secy, Comm Fossil Plants, Int Asn Plant Taxon, 69-93; Fulbright res prof, Seuckenberg Mus, Frankfurt, Ger, 92. *Mem:* Am Asn Stratig Palynologists (secy-treas, 67-70, pres, 70-71); AAAS; fel Geol Soc Am; Bot Soc Am; Int Asn Plant Taxon; Soc Econ Paleontologists & Mineralogists. *Res:* Palynology of Cenozoic and older rocks; theory of palynology; plant evolution. *Mailing Add:* Dept Geosci Pa State Univ Deike University Park PA 16802. *Fax:* 814-863-7823; *E-Mail:* traverse@ems.psu.edu

**TRAVIS, DAVID M,** INTERNAL MEDICINE, PHARMACOLOGY. *Current Pos:* RETIRED. *Personal Data:* b Nashville, Tenn, June 6, 26; m 53; c 3. *Educ:* Vanderbilt Univ, BA, 47, MD, 51; Am Bd Internal Med, dipl, 60, recert, 77. *Honors & Awards:* Borden Res Award, 51. *Prof Exp:* Intern & resident med, Boston City Hosp, Harvard Univ, 51-54; from asst prof to prof pharmacol & med, Col Med, Univ Fla, 58-80; prof med & pharmacol, Univ NDak, 80-94. *Concurrent Pos:* Teaching fel, Harvard Med Sch, 52-54; Nat Heart Inst res fel, Peter Bent Brigham Hosp, Boston, 56-58; Nat Heart & Lung Inst sr res fel, Harvard Univ, 71-72; mem corp, Marine Biol Lab, Woods Hole, 62-94. *Mem:* Am Fedn Clin Res; Am Col Physicians; Am Physiol Soc; Soc Gen Physiol; Am Soc Pharmacol & Exp Therapeut. *Res:* Respiratory physiology and pharmacology; biological role of respiratory gases in health and disease. *Mailing Add:* 19 High St Woods Hole MA 02543-1221

**TRAVIS, IRVEN,** ELECTRICAL ENGINEERING, MATHEMATICS. *Current Pos:* RETIRED. *Personal Data:* b McConnelsville, Ohio, Mar 30, 04; m 35; c 3. *Educ:* Drexel Inst Technol, BS, 26; Univ Pa, MS, 28. *Hon Degrees:* DEng, Drexel Inst Technol, 62; DSc, 38. *Prof Exp:* Prof elec eng, Univ Pa, 28-49, supvr res, Moore Sch Elec Eng, 46-48; dir res, Burroughs Corp, 49-52, vpres, 52-69, mem bd dirs, 50-71. *Concurrent Pos:* Consult, Gen Elec Co, 38-40, Reeves Instrument Corp, 46-48 & Burroughs Corp, 48-49; chmn bd eng educ & vpres, IPAC, Pa State Univ; trustee, Detroit Inst Technol; mgt consult, 69- *Mem:* Fel AAAS; Am Soc Eng Educ; Am Soc Naval Engrs; Am Ord Asn; fel Inst Elec & Electronics Engrs. *Res:* Applied mathematics; weapons systems, especially antiaircraft fire control and missiles; information processing systems; communications. *Mailing Add:* 121 S Valley Rd Paoli PA 19301

**TRAVIS, J(OHN) C(HARLES),** electrical engineering, for more information see previous edition

**TRAVIS, JAMES,** BIOCHEMISTRY. *Current Pos:* from asst prof to prof, 67-87, RES PROF BIOCHEM, UNIV GA, 87- *Personal Data:* b Winnipeg, Can, Nov 11, 35; m 60, 89; c 4. *Educ:* Univ Man, BSc, 58, MSc, 60; Univ Minn, PhD(biochem), 64. *Honors & Awards:* Merit Award, NIH. *Prof Exp:* Fel biochem, Johns Hopkins Univ, 64-66; asst prof, Univ Md, 66-67. *Mem:* Am Soc Biol Chem. *Res:* Protein structure and function. *Mailing Add:* Dept Biochem FPO 3965083 Univ Ga Life Sci Rm A320A Athens GA 30602. *Fax:* 706-542-3719

**TRAVIS, JAMES ROLAND,** physics, explosives, for more information see previous edition

**TRAVIS, JOHN RICHARD,** COMPUTATIONAL FLUID DYNAMICS. *Current Pos:* SR SCIENTIST, SCI APPLICATIONS INT CORP, 90- *Personal Data:* b Billings, Mont, Sept 3, 42; div; c 2. *Educ:* Univ Wyo, BS, 65; Purdue Univ, MS, 69, PhD(nuclear eng), 71. *Prof Exp:* Asst scientist reactor anal & safety, Argonne Nat Lab, 71-73; staff mem numerical fluid dynamics, Los Alamos Nat Lab, 73-90. *Mem:* Am Soc Mech Soc; Am Nuclear Soc; Sigma Xi. *Res:* Develop computational fluid dynamics and transport phenomena models for analyzing safety issues involving nuclear reactors. *Mailing Add:* 3101 Old Pecos Trail Santa Fe NM 87505

**TRAVIS, JOSEPH,** ECOLOGICAL GENETICS, POPULATION BIOLOGY. *Current Pos:* From asst prof to assoc prof, 80-90, PROF BIOL, FLA STATE UNIV, 90- *Personal Data:* b Philadelphia, Pa, Dec 22, 53; m 83; c 2. *Educ:* Univ Pa, BA, 75; Duke Univ, PhD(zool), 80. *Concurrent Pos:* Fel,

Univ Va, 80-81, vis fac, 82-90; vis fac, Orgn Trop Studies, 86, Kellogg Biol Sta, 87; adv panel mem, Prog Pop Biol, NSF, 86-89; coun mem, Ecol Soc Am, 85-91 & Soc Study Evolution, 90-92. *Mem:* Soc Study Evol; Europ Soc Evol Biol; Ecol Soc Am; Am Soc Zoologists; AAAS; Am Soc Naturalists; Society for Study of Evol. *Res:* Factors that influence the dynamics of numbers of individuals and genetic variation in natural populations; ecological determinants of selection and genetic determinants of response to selection. *Mailing Add:* Dept Biol Sci Fla State Univ 600 W College Ave Tallahassee FL 32306-1096

**TRAVIS, LARRY DEAN,** SPACE PHYSICS. *Current Pos:* MEM STAFF, INST SPACE STUDIES, 73- *Personal Data:* b Burlington, Iowa, July 29, 43. *Educ:* Univ Iowa, BA, 65, MS, 67; Pa State Univ, University Park, PhD(astron), 71. *Honors & Awards:* Except Sci Achievement Medal, NASA, 80. *Prof Exp:* Asst prof physics, Pa State Univ, Worthington Scranton Campus, 71-73. *Mem:* AAAS; Am Astron Soc; Am Geophys Union. *Res:* Planetary atmospheres. *Mailing Add:* 214 Riverside Dr Apt 610 New York NY 10025-6807. *Fax:* 212-678-5622

**TRAVIS, LUTHER BRISENDINE,** PEDIATRIC NEPHROLOGY, PEDIATRIC DIABETES. *Current Pos:* from asst prof to assoc prof pediat, 62-73, co-dir pediat nephrology, 64-71, PROF PEDIAT, UNIV TEX MED BR, GALVESTON, 73-, DIR PEDIAT NEPHROLOGY & DIABETES, 71- *Personal Data:* b Atlanta, Ga, May 25, 31; m 80; c 6. *Educ:* NGa Col, BS, 51; Med Col Ga, MD, 55. *Honors & Awards:* Diabetes in Youth Award, Am Diabetes Asn, 82. *Prof Exp:* Intern, Med Col Va, 55-56; resident pediat, Wyeth Labs, Col Med, Baylor Univ, 58-60. *Concurrent Pos:* Nat Inst Arthritis & Metab Dis fel pediat nephrology, Univ Tex Med Br, Galveston, 60-62; vis prof, William Beaumont Army Hosp, El Paso, Tex, 66-85; consult, NIH, 78-85, Food & Drug Asn, 80-82, Tex Diabetes Coun, 82-86. *Mem:* Am Soc Nephrology; Am Soc Pediat Nephrology; Am Acad Pediat; Am Fedn Clin Res; Soc Pediat Res; Am Diabetes Asn. *Res:* Medical diseases of the kidney in children, particularly glomerulonephritis, nephrosis and pyelonephritis; juvenile Diabetes Mellitus; author or coauthor of over 150 publications. *Mailing Add:* Dept Pediat Univ Tex Med Br Galveston TX 77550

**TRAVIS, RANDALL HOWARD,** PHYSIOLOGY. *Current Pos:* RETIRED. *Personal Data:* b Curdsville, Ky, July 11, 24; div; c 2. *Educ:* Univ Chicago, BS, 47; Case Western Res Univ, MD, 52. *Prof Exp:* Intern, Univ Hosps, Cleveland, 52-53; jr asst resident, 53-54, asst resident, 54-55; sr instr physiol & med, Case Western Res Univ, 59-63, asst prof physiol, 63-68, prof med, 63-97, assoc prof physiol, 68-97, asst dir endocrinol, Cleveland Metrop Gen Hosp, 74-97. *Concurrent Pos:* Nat Heart Inst res fel, 55-57; Am Heart Asn res fel, 57-59; estab investr, Am Heart Asn, 59-64; asst physician, Univ Hosps, Cleveland, 59-, assoc dir employees clin & consult endocrinol, 67-; attend physician, Wade Park Vet Admin Hosp, 59-; asst phys, Cuyahoga Co Hosp, 73-75, assoc, 75- *Mem:* Endocrine Soc. *Res:* Experimental endocrinology, adrenal and renal hormones relating to cardiovascular system and to nervous system. *Mailing Add:* PO Box 553 Waterbury VT 05676

**TRAVIS, ROBERT LEROY,** PLANT PHYSIOLOGY, AGRONOMY. *Current Pos:* asst prof, 76-79, ASSOC PROF AGRON, UNIV CALIF, DAVIS, 79- *Personal Data:* b Oakland, Calif, Oct 7, 40; m 63; c 2. *Educ:* Univ Calif, Davis, BS, 64, MS, 66, PhD(plant physiol), 69. *Prof Exp:* Fel plant physiol, Univ Ga, 69-73, asst prof bot, 73-74; res agronomist herbicides, US Borax Res Corp, 74-76. *Mem:* Am Soc Plant Physiologists. *Res:* Development of plasma membrane in higher plants; protein synthesis; photosynthetic efficiency. *Mailing Add:* Dept Agron Univ Calif Davis CA 95616-5200

**TRAVIS, ROBERT VICTOR,** ENTOMOLOGY, ENVIRONMENTAL SCIENCES. *Current Pos:* PROF BIOL, WESTMINSTER COL, PA, 66- *Personal Data:* b Ames, Iowa, Aug 6, 33; m 55; c 5. *Educ:* Cornell Univ, BS, 55; Univ Md, MS, 57, PhD(entom), 61. *Prof Exp:* Horticulturist, Agr Res Serv, USDA, 55-60; teacher sci & chmn dept, Gwynn Park High Sch, Md, 60-63; assoc prof biol, Mansfield State Col, 63-66. *Concurrent Pos:* Owner, Garden Pest Control Co, 58-61. *Mem:* Nat Asn Biol Teachers; Entom Soc Am; Sigma Xi. *Res:* Computer modeling; use of insects and microorganisms in teaching; biological clocks; insect diapause. *Mailing Add:* 620 S Market St New Wilmington PA 16142-1309

**TRAVIS, RUSSELL BURTON,** EXPLORATION & PRODUCTION SYSTEMS DESIGN. *Current Pos:* RETIRED. *Personal Data:* b San Francisco, Calif, June 18, 18; m 40, 60, Dalia Figueroa; c 6. *Educ:* Colo Sch Mines, GeolE, 43; Univ Calif, PhD(geol), 51. *Prof Exp:* Geologist, Standard Oil Co Calif, 46; asst prof geol, Univ Idaho, 51; sr geologist, Int Petrol Co, Ltd, 51-53; asst prof geol, Colo Sch Mines, 53-56; sr geologist, Int Petrol Co, Ltd, Peru, 56-62, 67-68, Fla, 62-63 & Colombia, 63-67 & 69-73; consult petrol geol, 77-80; tech adv geol/comput appl, Petroleos Del Peru, 73-77 & 80-86; consult, Systs Design, 86-89. *Mem:* Am Inst Prof Geologists; fel Geol Soc Am; Am Asn Petrol Geologists. *Res:* Computer science in exloration/production in petroleum and minerals. *Mailing Add:* 5043 Shoshone Dr Pensacola FL 32507

**TRAVNICEK, EDWARD ADOLPH,** ORGANIC CHEMISTRY, CHEMICAL ENGINEERING. *Current Pos:* VISION-EASE CORP, FT LAUDERDALE, FLA, 86- *Personal Data:* b Morse Bluff, Nebr, Mar 19, 36; m 66; c 2. *Educ:* Univ Nebr, Lincoln, BS, 58, MS, 60; Kans State Univ, PhD(chem eng), 68. *Prof Exp:* Testing engr chem eng, Atomic Energy Div, Phillips Petrol Co, 59-61; mgr chem lab, TRW Capacitor, Nebr, 61-63, consult, 63-68; sr res chem engr, Monsanto Co, Mo, 68-70 & Mass, 70-72; sr res engr, Am Optical Corp, Southbridge, Ma, 72-86. *Concurrent Pos:* Lab asst, Kans State Univ, 66. *Mem:* Am Inst Chem Engrs; Am Chem Soc; Sigma Xi. *Res:* Polymer processing and formulation; dye and monomer synthesis, purification and analysis; gas chrom analytical techniques; mechanical, electrical and thermoelectric devices; liquid diffusion. *Mailing Add:* 9920 NW 39th Ct Coral Springs FL 33065-1527

**TRAWICK, WILLIAM GEORGE,** CLINICAL CHEMISTRY, PHYSICAL CHEMISTRY. *Current Pos:* prof chem, 61-85, chmn dept, 62-74, EMER PROF CHEM, GA STATE UNIV, 87- *Personal Data:* b Sandersville, Ga, Aug 16, 24; m 48, Margaret Gheesling; c Robert J & Charles D. *Educ:* Ga Inst Technol, BS, 48; PhD(phys chem), 55; Am Bd Clin Chem, dipl, 76. *Prof Exp:* Chemist, Union Carbide Nuclear Co, Tenn, 54-58; assoc prof phys chem, La Polytech Inst, 58-61. *Concurrent Pos:* Bd dirs, Nat Registry Clin Chem, 80-89; consult, 85- *Mem:* Am Chem Soc; Sigma Xi; Am Asn Clin Chemists. *Res:* Spectroscopy. *Mailing Add:* 2479 Burnt Leaf Lane Decatur GA 30033-2806. *E-Mail:* wtrawick@gsu.edu

**TRAWINSKI, BENON JOHN,** MATHEMATICAL STATISTICS. *Current Pos:* RETIRED. *Personal Data:* b Poland, Oct 20, 24; c 1. *Educ:* McMaster Univ, BSc, 58; Va Polytech Inst & State Univ, PhD(math statist), 61. *Prof Exp:* Asst prof statist, Va Polytech Inst & State Univ, 60-61; from asst prof to assoc prof biostatist, Tulane Univ, 61-65; assoc prof statist, Univ Ky, 65-66; assoc prof biostatist, Med Ctr, Univ Ala, Birmingham, 66-, dir grad prog, 69- *Concurrent Pos:* NIH fel, 62; Nat Res Coun Can grant, 63; vis lectr, NSF, 71-; univ statist & math sci curric consult. *Mem:* AAAS; Inst Math Statist; Am Statist Asn; Am Math Soc; NY Acad Sci. *Res:* Theoretical and applied research in statistics, especially order and nonparametric statistics and decision theory. *Mailing Add:* Dept Biostatist 232 Ryles Bldg Univ Ala, 1665 University Blvd Birmingham AL 35294-0022

**TRAWINSKI, IRENE PATRICIA MONAHAN,** MATHEMATICAL STATISTICS. *Current Pos:* ASSOC PROF BIOSTATIST, UNIV ALA, BIRMINGHAM, 66- *Personal Data:* b Bayonne, NJ, Mar 17, 29; m 63; c 1. *Educ:* Rutgers Univ, BSc, 50; Univ Ill, MS, 51; Va Polytech Inst, PhD(math statist), 61. *Prof Exp:* From instr to prof math, Keuka Col, 51-63, head dept, 57-63; assoc prof, La State Univ, New Orleans, 64-66. *Mem:* Math Asn Am; Inst Math Statist; Biomet Soc; Sigma Xi. *Res:* Multivariate analysis. *Mailing Add:* Dept Biostatist Univ Ala 232 Ryles Bldg 1665 Univesity Blvd Birmingham AL 35294-0022

**TRAXLER, JAMES THEODORE,** SYNTHETIC ORGANIC CHEMISTRY, PESTICIDE CHEMISTRY. *Current Pos:* RETIRED. *Personal Data:* b Le Center, Minn, Oct 17, 29; m 56, Gabrielle I Martens; c LisAnne, Peter, Martine, Karem & Madeleine. *Educ:* St John's Univ, Minn, BA, 51; Univ Notre Dame, PhD(org chem, biochem), 56. *Prof Exp:* Res chemist, Cent Res Labs, Armour & Co, Ill, 55-60 & Am Cyanamid Co, Conn, 60-62; head org lab, Durkee Foods Div, Glidden Co, Ill, 62-66; sr res chemist, Peter Hand Found, Ill, 66-69; org res specialist, Growth Sci Ctr, Int Minerals & Chem Corp, Libertyville, 69-74; sr scientist, Sandoz Crop Protection Corp, 74-92. *Concurrent Pos:* Free-lance scientific translator. *Mem:* Am Chem Soc; emer mem Sigma Xi. *Res:* Amino acids and alcohols; pesticides; heterocycles; natural products; polycyclic aromatics; antimalarials; 14 research publications, 12 US & foreign patents. *Mailing Add:* 917 Forest Ave Evanston IL 60202. *E-Mail:* traxjt@aol.com

**TRAXLER, RICHARD WARWICK,** BACTERIAL PHYSIOLOGY. *Current Pos:* prof plant path, entom & microbiol & chmn dept, 71-83, prof microbiol, 83-85, PROF FOOD SCI & MICROBIOL, UNIV RI, 85- *Personal Data:* b New Orleans, La, July 25, 28; m 52; c 3. *Educ:* Univ Tex, BA, 51, MA, 55, PhD(bact), 58. *Prof Exp:* Asst serologist, Port Arthur Health Dept, 49-52; asst, Univ Tex, 54-58; asst prof bact, Univ Southwestern La, 58-62, from assoc prof to prof microbiol, 62-71. *Mem:* Am Soc Microbiol; Soc Indust Microbiol. *Res:* Microbial physiology, especially degradation; aliphatic hydrocarbons and related molecules; aerobic and anaerobic fermentation, bacterial resistance to lead and other metals. *Mailing Add:* Dept Food Sci & Nutrit Univ RI Kingston RI 02881

**TRAYLOR, DONALD REGINALD,** MATHEMATICS. *Current Pos:* interim vpres acad affairs, 93-95, actg dean, Div Math, Nursing & Sci, 95-96, PROF MATH, UNIV INCARNATE WORD, 90-, DEAN, SCH GRAD STUDIES & RES, 96- *Personal Data:* b Shreveport, La, Apr 14, 37; m 59, Jacqueline R Pearson; c Chapman Parker, Kirby Russell & Pearson Hunt (deceased). *Educ:* Univ Tex, Austin, BA, 59; Auburn Univ, MS, 60, PhD(math), 62. *Prof Exp:* Asst prof math, Auburn Univ, 62-63; from asst prof to prof, Univ Houston, 63-77; pres, Traylor Prod & Servs, 77-90. *Concurrent Pos:* Prin investr, NSF, 66, NASA, 67, NIH, 89-90, Eisenhower Math, 93-95, NSF, 96-97. *Mem:* Am Math Soc; Math Asn Am; Am Asn Higher Educ. *Res:* Topology; patentee in field. *Mailing Add:* 4301 Broadway San Antonio TX 78209. *Fax:* 210-805-3559; *E-Mail:* traylor@universe.uiwtx.edu

**TRAYLOR, MELVIN ALVAH, JR,** ORNITHOLOGY. *Current Pos:* Assoc, Div Birds, 40-48, res assoc, 48-55, assoc cur, 55-62, cur birds, 72-77, chmn, Dept Zool, 77-80, EMER CUR, FIELD MUS NATURAL HIST, 81- *Personal Data:* b Chicago, Ill, Dec 16, 15; m 41, 70; c 2. *Educ:* Harvard Univ, AB, 37. *Concurrent Pos:* Mem expeds, Yucatan, Mex, 39-40, Galapagos Island, 41, US, 41, Mex, 48 & Africa, 61-62; pelagic fishing surv, Oper Crossroads, Bikini Atoll, 46. *Mem:* Wilson Ornith Soc; fel Am Ornith Union; hon mem Soc Orinthol France; Brit Ornith Union. *Res:* Taxonomy of Neotropical and African birds; biogeography of South America. *Mailing Add:* Field Mus Natural Hist Roosevelt Rd & Lake Shore Dr Chicago IL 60605

**TRAYLOR, PATRICIA SHIZUKO,** CHEMISTRY, BIOCHEMISTRY. *Current Pos:* from asst prof to prof chem, 66-87, CHMN DEPT, UNIV SAN DIEGO, 87- *Personal Data:* b San Francisco, Calif, Jan 21, 30; m 59; c 2. *Educ:* Univ Calif, Berkeley, AB, 51; Univ Wis, MS, 53; Harvard Univ, PhD(chem), 63. *Prof Exp:* Res biochemist, Univ Calif, Berkeley, 53-55; chemist, Dow Chem Co, 55-59; NIH res fel, 63-66. *Mem:* AAAS; Am Chem Soc; NY Acad Sci. *Res:* Mechanisms of reactions. *Mailing Add:* Pharmaceut Chem Univ Calif Sch Pharm San Francisco CA 92110-2429

**TRAYNHAM, JAMES GIBSON,** ORGANIC CHEMISTRY, HISTORY OF CHEMISTRY. *Current Pos:* from asst prof to prof, La State Univ, Baton Rouge, 53-63, chmn dept, 68-73, vchancellor advan studies & res & dean, Grad Sch, 73-81, prof chem, 63-88, EMER PROF CHEM, LA STATE UNIV, BATON ROUGE, 88- *Personal Data:* b Broxton, Ga, Aug 5, 25; m 48, 80, Gresdna A Doty; c David F & Peter C. *Educ:* Univ NC, BS, 46; Northwestern Univ, PhD(chem), 50. *Prof Exp:* Instr chem, Northwestern, 49-50; asst prof, Denison Univ, 50-53. *Concurrent Pos:* Res assoc, Ohio State Univ, 51-53; Am Chem Soc Petrol Res Fund int award, Swiss Fed Inst Technol, 59-60; NATO sr fel sci, Univ Saarland, 72; chmn, div hist chem, Am Chem Soc, 88. *Mem:* Am Chem Soc; Sigma Xi. *Res:* Mechanisms of reactions; halogenations; ipso aromatic substitutions; history of organic chemistry. *Mailing Add:* Dept Chem La State Univ Baton Rouge LA 70803-1804. *Fax:* 504-388-3458

**TRAYNOR, LEE,** ORGANIC CHEMISTRY, POLYMER CHEMISTRY. *Current Pos:* Res chemist, 64-67, sr res chemist, 67-72, RES ASSOC, B F GOODRICH CO, 72- *Personal Data:* b Flint, Mich, July 9, 38; m 60; c 2. *Educ:* Mich State Univ, BS, 60; Univ Mich, PhD(org chem), 64. *Mem:* Am Chem Soc. *Res:* Organic reaction mechanisms; heterogeneous catalysis; new methods in vinyl polymerization. *Mailing Add:* 2824 Yellowcreek Rd Akron OH 44333-2208

**TRAYNOR, SEAN G,** CHEMISTRY OF TURPENTINE, FLAVOR & FRAGRANCE CHEMISTRY. *Current Pos:* CHMN & CHIEF EXEC OFFICER, GARDEN STATE TANNING, 92- *Personal Data:* m 74, Geraldine; c Tara, Patrick & Kevin. *Educ:* Trinity Col, Dublin, BA, 71, PhD(org chem), 74. *Prof Exp:* Fel, Ohio State Univ, 74-75; res chemist, SCM Glidco Organics, 75-82, dir develop, 82-87, vpres sales & mkt, 87-92. *Concurrent Pos:* Chief exec officer, Garden State Tanning. *Mem:* Am Chem Soc; Am Leather Chemists Asn; Leather Inust Am. *Res:* Author or co-author of 30 scientific papers including 12 patents in terpene chemistry, chiral compounds, electrochemistry and mass spectrometry. *Mailing Add:* 504 Patriots Way Newtown Square PA 19073. *E-Mail:* scan—traynor@prodigy. com

**TRAYNOR-KAPLAN, ALEXIS,** CELL BIOLOGY. *Current Pos:* ASSOC PROF MED, UNIV CALF, MED CTR, SAN DIEGO, 88- *Personal Data:* b Chicago, Ill, Aug 22, 52; m, Richard. *Educ:* Univ Mich, BS, 74; Univ Calif, San Diego, PhD(neurosci), 79. *Honors & Awards:* Fiterman Award, Am Gastonology Asn. *Prof Exp:* Fel cell biol, Salk Inst, 79-83; res assoc, Scripps Clin Res Found, 84-88. *Concurrent Pos:* Founder, Inologic, 96. *Mem:* Int Neuro Chemist Soc; Am Soc Cell Biol; Am Gastonology Group Asn. *Res:* Cell biology; signal transduction; role of inositol-based compounds in signaling. *Mailing Add:* Dept Med H811D-2 Med Ctr Univ Calif San Diego CA 92103. *E-Mail:* atraynor@ucsd.edu

**TRAYSTMAN, RICHARD J,** CARDIOVASCULAR & PULMONARY PHYSIOLOGY. *Current Pos:* from asst prof to assoc prof environ physiol, 73-85, assoc prof anesthesiol, 80-85, PROF ENVIRON PHYSIOL, SCH HYG, JOHNS HOPKINS UNIV, 85-, PROF ANESTHESIOL & CRITICAL CARE MED, SCH MED, 85-, DIR RES LABS, ANESTHESIOL & CRITICAL CARE MED, 80- *Personal Data:* b Brooklyn, NY, April 5, 42; m 71. *Educ:* Long Island Univ, BS, 63, MA, 66; Johns Hopkins Univ, PhD(cardiopulmonary physiol), 71. *Prof Exp:* Teaching & res fel physiol, Brooklyn Col Med, 63-66; instr, Bowman Gray Sch Med, 71-72. *Concurrent Pos:* Fel, Bowman Gray Sch Med, 71-72. *Mem:* Am Physiol Soc; Microcirculatory Soc; Am Soc Anesthesiol; Am Thoracic Soc. *Res:* Control of cerebral circulation in fetal, neonatal and adult animals; physiological interrelationships between the circulatory system. *Mailing Add:* Dept Anesthesiol & Critical Care Med Johns Hopkins Sch Med 600 N Wolfe St Blalock Bldg 1408 Baltimore MD 21287-4961

**TREADWAY, WILLIAM JACK, JR,** IMMUNOLOGY, MEDICINE. *Current Pos:* instr, 81-92, PROF BIOCHEM & CHEM, PARKLAND COL, 92- *Personal Data:* b Johnson City, Tenn, Feb 22, 49; m 71. *Educ:* Univ Ill, Urbana-Champaign, BS, 72; Loyola Univ Chicago, PhD(biochem), 76. *Honors & Awards:* Bausch & Lomb Sci Award, 67. *Prof Exp:* Teaching asst biochem, Loyola Univ Chicago Med Ctr, 71-73, res asst, 73-75; res assoc immunochem, Jefferson Med Col, 75-77; res assoc immunol, Sch Med, Temple Univ, 77-78; res instr, Bowman Gray Sch Med, 78-80, res asst prof med, 80-81. *Concurrent Pos:* Chmn, Prof Develop Comt, Parkland Col, 85 & 88. *Mem:* Am Chem Soc; AAAS; Nat Inst Staff & Orgn Develop; Am Rheumatism Asn. *Res:* Immunology; immunochemistry; biochemistry; computer-assisted teaching strategies: using new innovative technology in the teaching of biochemistry and chemistry; three dimensional visualization and interactive videodisc lessons in the understanding of laboratory concepts and molecular topics. *Mailing Add:* Parkland Col 2400 W Bradley Ave Champaign IL 61821-1899

**TREADWELL, ELLIOTT ALLEN,** COMPUTER SCIENCE, PHYSICAL CHEMISTRY. *Current Pos:* res assoc, 78-81, ASSOC SCIENTIST ACCELERATOR & HIGH ENERGY PHYSICS, FERMI NAT ACCELERATOR LAB, 81-; PROF PHYSICS, CHICAGO STATE UNIV, 90- *Personal Data:* b Rockford, Ill, May 14, 47; m 80. *Educ:* Cent State Univ Ohio, BS, 69; State Univ NY Stony Brook, MA, 71; Cornell Univ, MS, 73, PhD(exp high energy physics), 78. *Prof Exp:* Res asst high energy physics, Wilson Synchrotron, Cornell Univ, 73-78. *Concurrent Pos:* Ford Found Panel Postdoctoral Fel Minorities, NSF grantee. *Mem:* Am Phys Soc; Nat Soc Black Physicists. *Res:* Neutrino-nucleon scattering at 400 billion electron volts, utilizing a 15 foot neon-hydrogen bubble chamber. *Mailing Add:* 1306 S Naperville Rd Wheaton IL 60187

**TREADWELL, GEORGE EDWARD, JR,** BOTANY, BIOCHEMISTRY. *Current Pos:* From asst prof to assoc prof, 70-85, PROF BIOL, EMORY & HENRY COL, 85- *Personal Data:* b Selma, Ala, Dec 22, 41. *Educ:* King Col, BA, 64; Iowa State Univ, MS, 67, PhD(biochem, plant physiol), 70. *Mem:* Am Chem Soc; Bot Soc Am. *Res:* Vitamin B-2; chromatography. *Mailing Add:* Emory & Henry Col Emory VA 24327

**TREADWELL, KENNETH MYRON,** MECHANICAL ENGINEERING, NUCLEAR ENGINEERING. *Current Pos:* PRES, TREADWELL CONSULT, 82- *Personal Data:* b Cleveland, Ohio, May 5, 23; m 51, Sally A Skeel; c Karen. *Educ:* US Naval Acad, BS, 48; US Naval Postgrad Sch, BS, 54; Mass Inst Technol, SM, 55. *Prof Exp:* Engr thermal design, Westinghouse Elec Corp, 55-59, supvr, 59-64, mgr thermal & fuel design, 64-68, mgr reactor anal, 68-70, mgr reactor eng, 70-72, mgr naval fuel element develop, 72-77, mgr fuel element develop & statist, Bettis Atomic Power Lab, 77-82. *Concurrent Pos:* Sr consult, Westinghouse Elec, 82-87, O'Donnell & Assocs, 87-92. *Mem:* Am Soc Mech Engrs; Am Soc Naval Engrs; Sigma Xi; Am Nuclear Soc. *Res:* Analysis, engineering design and operation of naval and power nuclear reactors; engineering and materials science. *Mailing Add:* 4983 Parkvue Dr Pittsburgh PA 15236

**TREAGAN, LUCY,** MICROBIOLOGY. *Current Pos:* RETIRED. *Personal Data:* b Novosibirsk, Russia, July 20, 24; US citizen; m 42; c 2. *Educ:* Univ Calif, Berkeley, AB, 45, PhD(bact), 61. *Prof Exp:* Lectr, Col Holy Names, Calif, 61-66; from asst prof to prof biol, Univ San Francisco, 66-87. *Concurrent Pos:* Lectr, Univ San Francisco, 62-66. *Mem:* Am Soc Microbiol; AAAS. *Res:* Viral inhibitors; immunological study of interferons; effect of metals on the immune response. *Mailing Add:* 906 Hilldale Ave Berkeley CA 94708

**TREANOR, CHARLES EDWARD,** PHYSICS, AERODYNAMICS. *Current Pos:* physicist, Cornell Aeronaut Lab, Inc, 54-68, head aerodyn res dept, 68-78, vpres phys sci group, 78-82, VPRES & CHIEF SCIENTIST, CALSPAN CORP, 82- *Personal Data:* b Buffalo, NY, Oct 22, 24; m 50; c 5. *Educ:* Univ Minn, BA, 47; Univ Buffalo, PhD(physics), 55. *Prof Exp:* Instr physics, Univ Buffalo, 53. *Mem:* Fel Am Phys Soc; fel Am Inst Aeronaut & Astronaut; Combustion Inst. *Res:* High temperature gases; spectroscopy; hypersonic flows; molecular interactions. *Mailing Add:* 140 Segsbury Dr Williamsville NY 14221-3425

**TREAT, CHARLES HERBERT,** numerical analysis, heat transfer, for more information see previous edition

**TREAT, DONALD FACKLER,** MEDICAL EDUCATION. *Current Pos:* RETIRED. *Personal Data:* b Hartford, Conn, Feb 14, 25; m 49; c 4. *Educ:* Univ Mich, Ann Arbor, BA, 46, MD, 49; Am Bd Family Pract, dipl. *Prof Exp:* Intern gen pract, Univ Hosp, Ann Arbor, Mich, 49-50, resident, 50-52; pvt pract, Springfield, Vt, 54-69; actg dir, Family Med Prog & dir Grad Educ Family Med, Univ Rochester, 78-81, assoc prof family med, Sch Med & Dent, 69-89, chmn dept, 81-89. *Concurrent Pos:* Vis prof, Univ Vt, 78, Univ Colo, 80 & Case Western Univ, 83. *Mem:* Soc Teachers Family Med; Am Acad Family Practioners. *Res:* Family medicine; medical audit and peer review; measurement of attitudinal change in residents; defining patterns of medical care. *Mailing Add:* 11 Surry Hill Dr Keene NH 03431

**TREAT, JAY EMERY, JR,** PHYSICS. *Current Pos:* asst prof nuclear physics, 51-58, ASSOC PROF PHYSICS, UNIV ARIZ, 58- *Personal Data:* b Trinidad, Colo, Nov 16, 20; m 45; c 4. *Educ:* Univ Ariz, BS, 42; Cornell Univ, PhD, 54. *Prof Exp:* Mem staff magnetrons, Radiation Lab, Mass Inst Technol, 42-45; asst gen physics, Cornell Univ, 45-48, cosmic rays & nuclear physics, 48-51. *Mem:* Am Phys Soc; Am Asn Physics Teachers; Sigma Xi. *Res:* Cosmic rays; electromagnetic theory; elementary particles. *Mailing Add:* 1910 E Hawthorne St Tucson AZ 85719

**TREAT-CLEMONS, LYNDA GEORGE,** GENETICS, BIOLOGY. *Current Pos:* sr chemist, 92-96, STAFF CHEMIST, ALZA CORP, PALO ALTO, CALIF, 97- *Personal Data:* b Wooster, Ohio, May 23, 46; m 79, Karl V; c Robert C. *Educ:* Ohio State Univ, BS, 73, MS, 74, PhD(genetics), 78. *Prof Exp:* Assoc genetics, Ohio State Univ, 73-78; sr chemist, Biotrack, Inc, Mountain View, Calif, 84-86; fel, Stanford Univ, 86-89; chromatography commun & appln chemist, Interaction Chem Inc, Mountain View, Calif, 89-91. *Mem:* AAAS; Sigma Xi. *Res:* Biochemistry. *Mailing Add:* PO Box 10950 Palo Alto CA 94303-0802

**TREBLE, DONALD HAROLD,** BIOCHEMISTRY. *Current Pos:* From asst prof to assoc prof, 63-75, PROF BIOCHEM, ALBANY MED COL, 75- *Personal Data:* b Liverpool, Eng, Apr 14, 34; m 59; c 2. *Educ:* Bristol Univ, BSc, 55; Univ Liverpool, PhD(biochem), 59. *Concurrent Pos:* Res fel biochem, Inst Animal Physiol, Babraham, Eng, 58-59, Cambridge Univ, 59-61 & Harvard Med Sch, 61-63. *Mem:* Am Soc Biol Chemists. *Res:* Lipid metabolism. *Mailing Add:* Dept Biochem A-10 Albany Med Col 47 New Scotland Ave Albany NY 12208-3412. *Fax:* 518-262-5689

**TREDICCE, JORGE RAUL,** optics, for more information see previous edition

**TREE, DAVID R,** ENERGY USAGE. *Current Pos:* Assoc prof, 66-74, PROF MECH ENG, PURDUE UNIV, 74- *Personal Data:* b Wanship, Utah, July 18, 36; m 58; c 5. *Educ:* Brigham Young Univ, BES, 62, MS, 63; Purdue Univ, PhD(mech eng), 66. *Concurrent Pos:* US Dept Health, Educ & Welfare fel, Univ Southampton, 70-71. *Mem:* Am Soc Heating, Refrig & Air-Conditioning; Am Soc Eng Educ. *Res:* Two-phase flow; air-conditioners and heat pumps; energy usage in residential buildings; thermal systems modeling; numerical methods applied to thermal systems. *Mailing Add:* 5121 N 225 W West Lafayette IN 47906

**TREECE, JACK MILAN,** clinical biochemistry, for more information see previous edition

**TREECE, ROBERT EUGENE,** ECONOMIC ENTOMOLOGY. *Current Pos:* RETIRED. *Personal Data:* b Bluffton, Ohio, Oct 1, 27; m 55; c 2. *Educ:* Ohio State Univ, BS, 51, MS, 53; Cornell Univ, PhD(econ entom), 57. *Prof Exp:* Asst exten specialist entom, Rutgers Univ, 56-58; asst prof & asst entomologist, Agr Exp Sta, Ohio State Univ, 58-64, from assoc prof to prof, Ohio Agr Res & Develop Ctr, 64-73, assoc chmn, Entom Dept, 73-91. *Mem:* Entom Soc Am; AAAS; Coun Agr Sci & Technol. *Res:* Bionomics and control of insect pests of livestock and forage crops. *Mailing Add:* 624 Meadow Lane Wooster OH 44691-1520

**TREFETHEN, JOSEPH MUZZY,** geology; deceased, see previous edition for last biography

**TREFETHEN, LLOYD MACGREGOR,** FLUID MECHANICS. *Current Pos:* RETIRED. *Personal Data:* b Boston, Mass, Mar 5, 19; m 44; c 2. *Educ:* Webb Inst Naval Archit, BS, 40; Mass Inst Technol, MS, 42; Cambridge Univ, PhD, 50. *Honors & Awards:* Golden Eagle Award, Comn Int Nontheatrical Events, 67; Prix de Physique, Inst Sci Film Festival, 68. *Prof Exp:* Appln engr, Gen Elec Co, 40-44; sci consult, US Off Naval Res, Eng, 47-50; physicist, tech aide to chief scientist & exec secy, US Naval Res Adv Comt, Washington, DC, 50-51; exec secy, Nat Sci Bd & tech aide to dir, NSF, 51-54; asst prof mech eng, Harvard Univ, 54-58; chmn dept, Tufts Univ, 58-69, 81, prof mech eng, 58-89. *Concurrent Pos:* NSF fel, Cambridge Univ, 56; vis prof, Univ Sydney, 65, 72 & 79, Stanford Univ, 79; vis fel, Seattle Res Ctr, Battelle Mem Inst, 71; hon res assoc, Harvard Univ, 78; Russell Springer prof mech eng, Univ Calif, Berkeley, 86. *Mem:* Am Soc Mech Engrs; fel AAAS. *Res:* Fluid mechanics; collection and dissemination of unanswered questions in fluid mechanics. *Mailing Add:* Tufts Univ Anderson Hall Medford MA 02155

**TREFETHEN, LLOYD NICHOLAS,** NUMERICAL ANALYSIS. *Current Pos:* PROF, CORNELL UNIV, 91- *Personal Data:* b Boston, Mass, Aug 30, 55. *Educ:* Harvard Col, BA, 77; Stanford Univ, MS, 80, PhD(comput sci), 82. *Honors & Awards:* Fox Prize, Inst Math & Appln, 85. *Prof Exp:* Adj asst prof comput sci, Courant Inst, New York Univ, 82-84; asst prof math, Mass Inst Technol, 84-91. *Mem:* Soc Indust & Appl Math; Am Math Soc; Inst Elec & Electronics Engrs. *Res:* Numerical analysis; solution of differential equations; numerical conformal mapping; approximation theory. *Mailing Add:* Dept Comput Sci Cornell Univ Upson Hall Ithaca NY 14853

**TREFFERS, HENRY PETER,** MICROBIOLOGY. *Current Pos:* RETIRED. *Personal Data:* b New York, NY, Aug 21, 12; wid; c 2. *Educ:* Columbia Univ, AB, 33, PhD(chem), 37. *Hon Degrees:* Yale Univ, MA, 50. *Prof Exp:* Asst chem, Univ Exten, Columbia Univ, 33-36, instr biochem, 36-42; asst prof comp path & biochem, Harvard Med Sch, 42-44; asst prof immunol, Sch Med, Yale Univ, 44-46, assoc prof immunochem, 46-49, prof microbiol & Davenport Col fel, 49-69, chmn dept microbiol, 50-61, prof path, 69-83. *Concurrent Pos:* Fulbright res scholar, Univ Otago, NZ, 54; USPHS spec fel, Wright-Fleming Inst, St Mary's Hosp, London, Eng, 61-62; consult, USPHS, 48-50, 58-61 & 66-69; asst, Presby Hosp, 36-42; assoc mem, Comn Immunization, US Army Epidemiol Bd, 47-55; vchmn, Sect Microbiol, Chem & Biol Coord Ctr, Nat Res Coun, 48-53; mem, Microbiol Panel, US Off Naval Res, 51-54; ed, J Am Asn Immunol, 52-57; vis instr, Univ Calif, San Diego, 69-70. *Mem:* Am Asn Immunologists. *Res:* Chemistry of non-aqueous solutions; quantitative chemistry of immune reactions; antibiotic resistance; bacterial genetics. *Mailing Add:* 550 Amith Rd Bethany CT 06524

**TREFFERS, RICHARD ROWE,** ASTRONOMY. *Current Pos:* ASST RES ASTRON, UNIV CALIF, 76- *Personal Data:* b Bethany, Conn, Nov 7, 47; m 72; c 2. *Educ:* Yale Univ, BA, 69; Univ Calif, Berkeley, PhD(astron), 73. *Prof Exp:* Asst res astron, Univ Ariz, 74-76; asst res astron, Ames Res Ctr, NASA, 76. *Mem:* Am Astron Soc. *Res:* Infrared astronomy and spectroscopy as applied to planets and interstellar matter. *Mailing Add:* 10 Vista Lane Walnut Creek CA 94595

**TREFFERT, DAROLD ALLEN,** MEDICINE, PSYCHIATRY. *Current Pos:* PVT PRACT GEN & FORENSIC PSYCHIAT, BROOKSIDE MED CTR, 91- *Personal Data:* b Fond du Lac, Wis, Mar 12, 33; m 55, Dorothy Songatz; c Jon, Joni, Jill & Jay. *Educ:* Univ Wis, BA, 55, MD, 58. *Hon Degrees:* DH, Marion Col, 87. *Prof Exp:* Intern, Sacred Heart Gen Hosp, Eugene, Ore, 58-59; resident psychiat, Univ Wis Hosp, Madison, 59-62; dir, Child-Adolescent Unit, Winnebago Ment Health Inst, 62-64, dir, 64-79; exec dir, Fond du Lac County Health Care Ctr, 79-91. *Concurrent Pos:* Assoc clin prof, Dept Psychiat, Univ Wis Med Sch, Madison, 65-78; chmn, Controlled Substances Bd Wis, 70-84; mem, Adv Coun Health Probs Educ, Dept Pub Instr Wis, 73- & Tech Adv Comt, Joint Comn Accreditation Hosps; mem, Wis Med Examr Bd, 96- *Mem:* Am Asn Psychiat Adminr (pres, 83-85); Am Psychiat Asn; Am Col Psychiat; AMA. *Res:* Infantile autism; alcoholism and drug abuse; rights of the mentally ill; the Savant Syndrome (idiot savant), islands of genius in severely handicapped persons; implications for understanding normal brain function, especially memory. *Mailing Add:* Brookside Med Ctr 481 E Division St Fond du Lac WI 54935. *Fax:* 920-921-6118

**TREFIL, JAMES S,** PARTICLE PHYSICS. *Current Pos:* CLARENCE J ROBINSON PROF PHYSICS, GEORGE MASON UNIV. *Personal Data:* b Chicago, Ill, Sept 10, 38; m 72; c 5. *Educ:* Univ Ill, BS, 60; Oxford Univ, BA & MA, 62; Stanford Univ, MS & PhD(physics), 66. *Prof Exp:* Res assoc physics, Stanford Linear Accelerator Ctr, 66; Air Force Off Sci Res fel, Europ Ctr Nuclear Res, 66-67; res assoc, Mass Inst Technol, 67-68; asst prof, Univ Ill, Urbana, 68-70; assoc prof physics & fel, Ctr Advan Studies, Univ Va, 70-75, prof, 75- *Concurrent Pos:* John Simon Guggeheim fel. *Mem:* Fel Am Phys Soc. *Res:* Theoretical studies of mass extinctions. *Mailing Add:* 207 East Bldg 1DE George Mason Univ 4400 University Dr Fairfax VA 22030-4444. *Fax:* 703-993-2175

**TREFNY, JOHN ULRIC,** PHYSICS. *Current Pos:* from asst prof to assoc prof, 77-84, head dept, 90-95, PROF PHYSICS, COLO SCH MINES, 84-, INTERIM VPRES ACAD AFFAIRS & DEAN FAC, 95- *Personal Data:* b Greenwich, Conn, Jan 28, 42; m 92, Sharon Livingston; c Benjamin. *Educ:* Fordham Univ, BS, 63; Rutgers Univ, New Brunswick, PhD(physics), 68. *Prof Exp:* Res assoc physics, Cornell Univ, 67-69; asst prof physics, Wesleyan Univ, 69-77. *Concurrent Pos:* Consult, Inst for Future, 70, Solar Energy Res Inst, 78-81, 86- *Mem:* Am Phys Soc; Sigma Xi; Am Asn Physics Teachers; AAAS; Nat Sci Supvr Asn. *Res:* Experimental studies of crystalline solids; superconductivity; general topics in low temperature physics; thermoelectric materials; photovoltaic materials; ferroelectrics. *Mailing Add:* Acad Affairs Colo Sch Mines Golden CO 80401. *Fax:* 303-273-3040; *E-Mail:* jtrefny@mines.edu

**TREFONAS, LOUIS MARCO,** STRUCTURAL CHEMISTRY, PHYSICAL BIOCHEMISTRY. *Current Pos:* assoc vpres res, 81-86, assoc vpres acad affairs & grad dean, 86-91, PROF CHEM, UNIV CENT FLA, 92- *Personal Data:* b Chicago, Ill, June 21, 31; m 57, Gail Thames; c Peter, Stephanie, Mark, Jennifer, Paul & Jason. *Educ:* Univ Chicago, BA, 51, MS, 54; Univ Minn, PhD, 59. *Prof Exp:* From asst prof to prof chem, Univ New Orleans, 59-81, chmn dept, 64-80. *Concurrent Pos:* NIH spec fel, 72-73; hon res assoc, Harvard Univ, 72-73. *Mem:* Am Chem Soc; Am Phys Soc; Am Crystallog Soc; Sigma Xi; AAAS. *Res:* Molecular structure studies by x-ray diffraction; small ring nitrogen compounds; structures of biologically interesting compounds by x-ray diffraction techniques. *Mailing Add:* Chem Dept Univ Cent Fla Orlando FL 32816. *Fax:* 407-823-2252

**TREHAN, RAJENDER,** SOLID STATE SURFACE SCIENCE. *Current Pos:* RES ASSOC CHEM, CTR SUPERCONDUCTIVITY, UNIV HOUSTON, 88- *Personal Data:* b Bihar, India. *Educ:* Panjab Univ, BSc, 73, MSc, 74; Univ Utah, PhD(chem), 85. *Prof Exp:* Sci officer radiochemistry, Bhabha Atomic Res Ctr, 75-78; fel phys chem, Pa State Univ, 85-87; lectr, Rutgers Univ, 87-88. *Mem:* Am Phys Soc; Am Chem Soc. *Res:* Electron and ion beam spectroscopy; high temperature superconductivity. *Mailing Add:* Dept Chem Tougaloo Col 500 Country Line Rd Tougaloo MS 39174

**TREHU, ANNE MARTINE,** SEISMOLOGY, MARINE GEOPHYSICS. *Current Pos:* GEOPHYSICIST, US GEOL SURV, 82-; ASSOC PROF, COL OCEANOG, ORE STATE UNIV. *Personal Data:* b Princeton, NJ, Jan 7, 55; m 86, John Nabelek; c Marc & Patrik. *Educ:* Princeton Univ, BA, 75; Mass Inst Technol, PhD(marine seismol), 82. *Mem:* Am Geophys Union; Geol Soc Am; Soc Explor Geophys; AAAS. *Res:* Imaging crustal architecture using active and passive seismic techniques to obtain constraints of geologic history and seismic hazards. *Mailing Add:* Col Oceanog & Atmospheric Sci Ore State Univ Corvallis OR 97331. *Fax:* 541-737-2655

**TREHUB, ARNOLD,** NEURONAL MODELS OF COGNITION. *Current Pos:* MEM GRAD FAC, UNIV MASS, AMHERST, 70-, ADJ PROF, 71- *Personal Data:* b Malden, Mass, Oct 19, 23; m 50; c 3. *Educ:* Northeastern Univ, AB, 49; Boston Univ, MA, 51, PhD(clin psychol), 54. *Prof Exp:* Clin psychologist, Northampton Vet Admin Med Ctr, 54-59, dir, Psychol Res Lab, 59-82. *Concurrent Pos:* Vis lectr, Univ Mass, 59-66; lectr, Clark Univ, 60-62. *Mem:* AAAS; NY Acad Sci; Soc Neurosci; Cognitive Sci Soc. *Res:* Electrophysiology of brain; biomathematics; artificial intelligence; neurophysiology; cognition. *Mailing Add:* 145 Farview Way Amherst MA 01002

**TREI, JOHN EARL,** RUMINANT NUTRITION, PHYSIOLOGY. *Current Pos:* assoc prof, 74-80, PROF ANIMAL SCI, CALIF STATE POLYTECH UNIV, 80-, SUPVR, BEEF UNIT & FEEDMILL, 75- *Personal Data:* b Freeport, Ill, Sept 19, 39; m 66; c 2. *Educ:* Univ Ill, BS, 61; Univ Ariz, MS, 63, PhD(agr biochem, nutrit), 66. *Prof Exp:* Res & teaching assoc animal sci, Univ Ariz, 63-66; sr scientist animal nutrit, Smith Kline & French Labs, 66-71, sr investr, Smith Kline Corp, 71-73, asst mgr develop animal health prod, 73-74. *Concurrent Pos:* Actg chair, Animal Sci Dept; chmn, steering comt, Calif Animal Nutrit Conf, 86-87. *Mem:* Am Soc Animal Soc; Am Inst Biol Sci; NY Acad Sci; Am Dairy Sci Asn; Sigma Xi; Am Registry Prof Animal Scientists. *Res:* Energy metabolism; feed additive evaluations. *Mailing Add:* 2117 Villa Maria Claremont CA 91711-1657

**TREICHEL, PAUL MORGAN, JR,** INORGANIC CHEMISTRY. *Current Pos:* from asst prof to assoc prof, 63-72, PROF CHEM, UNIV WIS-MADISON, 72-, CHMN, CHEM, 86- *Personal Data:* b Madison, Wis, Dec 4, 36; m 61, Isabel Walk; c Janet & David. *Educ:* Univ Wis, BS, 58; Harvard Univ, AM, 60, PhD(chem), 62. *Prof Exp:* Teaching asst chem, Harvard Univ, 61-62; NSF fel, Queen Mary Col, London, 62-63. *Mem:* Am Chem Soc; Royal Soc Chem. *Res:* Organometallic chemistry, including metal carbonyls, cyclopentadienyls, alkyls and related compounds; organophosphorus and organoboron chemistry. *Mailing Add:* Dept Chem Univ Wis 1101 University Ave Madison WI 53706-1322. *Fax:* 608-262-0381; *E-Mail:* treichel@macc.wisc.edu

**TREICHEL, ROBIN STONG,** TUMOR IMMUNOLOGY, IMMUNOTHERAPY. *Current Pos:* asst prof, 87-93, ASSOC PROF BIOL, OBERLIN COL, OHIO, 93- *Personal Data:* b Billings, Mont, Feb 13, 50; m 85. *Educ:* Macalester Col, BA, 72; Univ Wis-Madison, MS, 78, PhD(genetics), 81. *Prof Exp:* Postdoctoral tumor immunol, Univ Minn Med Sch, 81-84; postdoctoral molecular immunol, Southwest Found Biomed Res, San Antonio, Tex, 85-86; res scientist oncol, Childrens Hosp Orange Co, Calif, 86-87. *Concurrent Pos:* Instr, Trinity Univ, San Antonio, Tex, 85-86; adj asst prof, Univ Tex Health Sci Ctr, San Antonio, Tex, 85-86. *Mem:* Sigma Xi; Transplantation Soc; AAAS; Am Asn Immunologists. *Res:* Immunotherapy for the treatment of human leukemia; investigation of the susceptibility of multidrug-resistant leukemic cells to lysis mediated by natural cytotoxic cells and by antibody and complement; development of immunotoxins for purging autologous bone marrow grafts for subsequent transplantation into patients following high dose chemoradiotherapy. *Mailing Add:* Dept Biol Oberlin Col Oberlin OH 44074. *Fax:* 440-775-8960; *E-Mail:* robin.treichel@oberlin.edu

**TREICHLER, RAY,** AGRICULTURAL CHEMISTRY, BIOLOGICAL CHEMISTRY. *Current Pos:* TECH SERV MGR, H D HUDSON MFG CO, 68- *Personal Data:* b Rock Island, Ill, Sept 10, 07; m 42, Kathryn. *Educ:* Pa State Col, BS & MS, 29; Univ Ill, PhD, 39. *Prof Exp:* Chemist, Exp Sta, Agr & Mech Col, Tex, 29-37, 39-40; spec asst animal nutrit, Univ Ill, 37-38; vis scientist, Univ Ill, 40-41; chemist, US Fish & Wildlife Serv, 41-42, technologist, 42-43, chemist, 43-44; res & develop div & head biol activities sect, Off Qm Gen, US Dept Army, 45-52, head chem & biol br, 53; chief agts br, Res & Eng Command, US Army Chem Corps, 53-55, asst to dir med res, 55-58; scientist, USAF, 58-68. *Mem:* NY Acad Sci; Am Soc Trop Med & Hyg; Entom Soc Am; Am Mosquito Control Asn; Am Soc Agr Engrs; Am Chem Soc; Soc Vector Ecol; Am Soc Testing & Mat; Sigma Xi. *Res:* Biology of natural products; environmental pollution; research and development of pesticides; application equipment for pesticides; pesticide dissemination systems. *Mailing Add:* Essex Apt 402 4740 Conn Ave NW Washington DC 20008. *Fax:* 202-457-1277

**TREICK, RONALD WALTER,** MICROBIAL PHYSIOLOGY. *Current Pos:* from asst prof to assoc prof, 65-77, PROF MICROBIOL, MIAMI UNIV, 77- *Personal Data:* b Scotland, SDak, June 8, 34; m 55; c 2. *Educ:* Univ SDak, BA, 56, MA, 57; Ind Univ, PhD(bact), 65. *Prof Exp:* Med technician, Univ SDak, 57-58; res asst infectious dis, Upjohn Co, 58-62. *Concurrent Pos:* Res grants, Miami Univ, 65-66, 68-69, 70-71 & 72- *Mem:* AAAS; Am Soc Microbiol; Sigma Xi. *Res:* Antimicrobial agents; effect of metabolic inhibitors on bacterial macromolecular synthesis; inhibition of bacterial luminescence; bacteria lipid metabolism. *Mailing Add:* 724 Melissa Dr Oxford OH 45056-9005

**TREIMAN, SAM BARD,** THEORETICAL PHYSICS, ELEMENTARY PARTICLES. *Current Pos:* from instr to assoc prof, 52-63, PROF PHYSICS, PRINCETON UNIV, 63- *Personal Data:* b Chicago, Ill, May 27, 25; m 52, Joan Little; c Rebecca, Katherine & Thomas. *Educ:* Univ Chicago, PhD(physics), 52. *Honors & Awards:* Oersted Medal, Am Asn Physics Teachers. *Prof Exp:* Res assoc physics, Univ Chicago, 52. *Concurrent Pos:* Chmn, Physics Dept, Princeton Univ, 81-87; Univ Res Bd, 88-95. *Mem:* Nat Acad Sci; Am Phys Soc; Am Acad Arts & Sci. *Res:* Cosmic ray physics; fundamental particles; field theory; elementary particle theory, especially weak interactions, unified field theories and connections with cosmology. *Mailing Add:* Dept Physics Princeton Univ Princeton NJ 08540. *Fax:* 609-258-1549; *E-Mail:* treinan@pupgg.princeton.edu

**TREISMAN, PHILIP URI,** MATHEMATICS EDUCATION. *Current Pos:* DIR, CHARLES A DANA CTR, UNIV TEX, AUSTIN, 88-, PROF, DEPT MATH, 91- *Educ:* Univ Calif, BA, 69, MA, 83, PhD(sci & math), 85. *Hon Degrees:* LHD, Marymount Manhattan Col, 92; DSc, Washington Col, Md, 94. *Honors & Awards:* MacArthur Found Fel, 92-97. *Prof Exp:* Landscape designer, R F Bush Landscaping, 65-69; assoc dir, Undergrad Prog, Univ Calif, 78-87, dir, 87-89; E M Lang vis prof, Dept Math, Swarthmore Col, 90-91. *Concurrent Pos:* Dir, Summer Inst Univ Calif, 88-; mem, Math Sci Educ Bd, Nat Acad Sci, 90-93, chair, Task Force Teaching Growth & Effectiveness, 93; mem bd dirs, Am Asn Higher Educ, 91-95. *Res:* Mathematics; developed programs that have helped minority students to excel in mathematics. *Mailing Add:* Dept Math Univ Tex RLM 8-100 Austin TX 78712

**TREISTMAN, STEVEN NEAL,** NEUROBIOLOGY. *Current Pos:* staff scientist exp biol, 80-84, SR SCIENTIST, WORCESTER FOUND EXP BIOL, 84- *Personal Data:* b New York, NY, May 3, 45; m 67; c 2. *Educ:* State Univ NY, Binghamton, BA, 67; Univ NC, Chapel Hill, PhD(neurobiol), 72. *Prof Exp:* Teacher biol, Heuvelton Cent Sch, 67-69; neurobiol trainee, Sch Med, Univ NC, 69-72; fel, Sch Med, NY Univ, 72-75; res assoc, Friedrich Miescher Inst, Basel, 75-76; asst prof biol, Bryn Mawr Col, 76-80. *Concurrent Pos:* Scottish Rite Found Schizophrenia res grant, 73-75; NSF grant, 77-80; NIH res grant, 79-82, NSF res grant, 81-; corp mem, Marine Biol Lab, Woods Hole, Mass, 80-; adj assoc prof pharmacol, Univ Mass Med Ctr, 82- *Mem:* Soc Neurosci; AAAS; Biophys Soc. *Res:* Neurobiology of simple systems; biochemical correlates of long-term changes in electrical membrane characteristics. *Mailing Add:* Dept Pharmacol Univ Mass Med Ctr 55 Lake Ave N Worcester MA 01655. *Fax:* 508-856-5080

**TREITEL, SVEN,** GEOPHYSICS. *Current Pos:* RETIRED. *Personal Data:* b Freiburg, Ger, Mar 5, 29; US citizen; m 58, Renata; c Nadine, Corinna, Geoffrey & Michael. *Educ:* Mass Inst Technol, BS, 53, MS, 55, PhD(geophys), 58. *Honors & Awards:* Fessenden Medal, Soc Explor Geophys, 69, Ewing Medal, 89. *Prof Exp:* Geophysicist, Stand Oil Co, Calif, 58-60; res assoc commun theory, Pan Am Petrol Corp, 60-65, group supvr, 66-71, mgr res sect, 71-74, sr res assoc, 74-77, res consult, 77-93. *Mem:* Fel Inst Elec & Electronics Engrs; hon mem Soc Explor Geophys; Sigma Xi; Europ Asn Explor Geophys; Royal Astron Soc; Soc Indust Appl Math. *Res:* Application of statistical communication theory to seismic analysis. *Mailing Add:* 1503 E 27th St Tulsa OK 74114-4101. *Fax:* 918-660-4163; *E-Mail:* streitel@amoco.com

**TREITERER, JOSEPH,** TRANSPORTATION ENGINEERING. *Current Pos:* from asst prof to assoc prof, 63-72, PROF CIVIL ENG, OHIO STATE UNIV, 72- *Personal Data:* b Grafrath, Ger, Dec 7, 18; m 53; c 2. *Educ:* Munich Tech Univ, Dipl Ing, 49. *Hon Degrees:* DSc, Munich Tech Univ, 58. *Prof Exp:* Sci asst civil engr & lectr munic eng & city traffic, Munich Tech Univ, 48-55; chief res officer, Nat Inst Rd Res Coun Sci & Indust Res, SAfrica, 56-63. *Concurrent Pos:* Consult, Water Supply, Sewage & Traffic, Munich, 50-55; mem, Ger Res Coun Hwy Pract, 55; lectr, Pretoria Univ, 60-63; mem tech comt, Inter-Provincial Adv Bd Rd Traffic Legis, Repub SAfrica, 60-63; chmn steering comt transp planning, Natural Resources Develop Coun, 61-63; mem, Hwy Res Bd, Nat Acad Sci-Nat Res Coun, 64. *Res:* Automatic control and guidance of motor vehicles; theory of traffic flow; aerial photogrammetry techniques for traffic surveys; transportation systems. *Mailing Add:* 171 Medick Way Worthington OH 43085

**TRELA, WALTER JOSEPH,** LOW TEMPERATURE PHYSICS. *Current Pos:* staff mem, Los Alamos Nat Lab, 73-80, asst div leader, 80-83, prog mgr, 83-88, STAFF MEM, LOS ALAMOS NAT LAB, 88- *Personal Data:* b Pawtucket, RI, May 31, 36; m 62; c 2. *Educ:* Brown Univ, BS, 58; Stanford Univ, PhD(physics), 67. *Prof Exp:* Asst prof physics, Haverford Col, 67-72. *Mem:* Am Phys Soc; AAAS. *Res:* Low temperature physics with primary emphasis on liquid helium and superconductivity; quantum fluids and solids; atomic, molecular and solid state physics; x-ray optics; synchrotron radiation. *Mailing Add:* 137 San Juan St Los Alamos NM 87544

**TRELAWNY, GILBERT STERLING,** MICROBIAL PHYSIOLOGY. *Current Pos:* prof biol, 66-94, head dept, 71-93, EMER FAC, JAMES MADISON UNIV, 94- *Personal Data:* b Cincinnati, Ohio, Nov 12, 29; m 50; c 3. *Educ:* Delaware Valley Col, BS, 57; Lehigh Univ, MS, 60, PhD(biol), 66. *Prof Exp:* From instr to asst prof microbiol, Delaware Valley Col, 57-66. *Concurrent Pos:* NSF res grant, 67-69. *Res:* Microbial metabolism and nutrition. *Mailing Add:* Dept Biol James Madison Univ Harrisonburg VA 22807

**TRELEASE, RICHARD DAVIS,** FOOD CHEMISTRY. *Current Pos:* RETIRED. *Personal Data:* b Chicago, Ill, Sept 23, 17; m 91; c 11. *Educ:* Univ Ill, BS, 40. *Prof Exp:* Chemist, Swift & Co, 40-42, res chemist poultry, 43-44; food technician, Qm Food & Container Inst, 44-45; asst to vpres res, Swift & Co, 48-50, head frozen food res, 50-63, mgr processed meats res, 63-71, mgr meat res, 71-72, gen mgr, processed meats res, 72-73, mgr contract res, 73-80, mgr processed meats res, 80-83; consult, 83-97. *Mem:* Am Chem Soc; Inst Food Technol. *Res:* Food processing and preservation; poultry products; frozen foods; cured meats. *Mailing Add:* 6321 Auburn Ave Bradenton FL 34207-5063. *Fax:* 941-753-8771

**TRELEASE, RICHARD NORMAN,** PLANT CELL BIOLOGY, PLANT PHYSIOLOGY. *Current Pos:* from asst prof to assoc prof, 71-81, PROF BIOL, ARIZ STATE UNIV, 81- *Personal Data:* b Las Vegas, Nev, Nov 6, 41; m 65; c 2. *Educ:* Univ Nev, Reno, BS, 63, MS, 65; Univ Tex, Austin, PhD(cell biol), 69. *Prof Exp:* NIH fel, Univ Wis-Madison, 69-71. *Concurrent Pos:* Adv panel mem, NSF Cell Biol Prog, 78-80, Cellular Biochem Prog, 88-90. *Mem:* AAAS; Am Soc Cell Biol; Am Soc Plant Physiol; Sigma Xi. *Res:* Oilseed metabolism, especially cottonseeds, aspects of maturation and germination; protein and membrane intracellular trafficking; enzymology; cell fractionation. *Mailing Add:* Dept Bot Ariz State Univ Box 871601 Tempe AZ 85287-1601. *Fax:* 602-965-6899

**TRELFORD, JOHN D,** OBSTETRICS & GYNECOLOGY, ONCOLOGY. *Current Pos:* assoc prof, 70-75, PROF OBSTET & GYNEC, SCH MED, UNIV CALIF, DAVIS, 75- *Personal Data:* b Toronto, Ont, Feb 7, 31; US citizen; c 3. *Educ:* Univ Toronto, MD, 56; FRCS(C), 64; FRCOG. *Prof Exp:* Asst prof obstet & gynec, Med Sch, Ohio State Univ, 65-70. *Concurrent Pos:* Grants, Univ Calif, Davis, 71-72; dir, Oncol Serv, Sacramento Med Ctr, 72-; consult, Vet Admin Hosp, Martinez, Calif, 72-; dir, Am Cancer Soc, Yolo Co. *Mem:* Fel Am Col Surgeons; Soc Obstet & Gynec Can; fel Am Col Obstet & Gynec. *Res:* Antigenicity of the trophoblastic cell and its relationship to cancer. *Mailing Add:* 44218 Lakeview Dr El Macero CA 95618

**TRELKA, DENNIS GEORGE,** EXERCISE PHYSIOLOGY. *Current Pos:* from asst prof to assoc prof, 77-78, PROF BIOL, WASH & JEFFERSON COL, 88- *Personal Data:* b Lorain, Ohio, June 11, 40; m 66; c 2. *Educ:* Kent State Univ, BA, 67, MA, 68; Cornell Univ, PhD(animal physiol), 72. *Prof Exp:* Res asst invert zool, Kent State Univ, 67-68; res asst animal physiol, Cornell Univ, 68-72. *Mem:* Zool Soc Am; AAAS; Sigma Xi; Nat Strength & Conditioning Asn. *Res:* Research in areas of strength training; histological and pharmacological studies on the central nervous system of common garden slugs. *Mailing Add:* Dept Biol Wash & Jefferson Col 60 S Lincoln St Washington PA 15301-4812

**TRELOAR, ALAN EDWARD,** MEDICAL ANTHROPOLOGY, BIOMETRICS. *Current Pos:* RETIRED. *Personal Data:* b Melbourne, Australia, Sept 27, 02; nat US; m 29, 49; c 3. *Educ:* Univ Sydney, BSc, 26; Univ Minn, MS, 29, PhD(agr biochem), 30. *Prof Exp:* Demonstr geol, Univ Sydney, 24-25; from instr to assoc prof biomet, Univ Minn, 29-47, prof biostatist, Sch Pub Health, 47-56; asst dir res, Am Hosp Asn, 56-59; chief statist & anal br, Div Res Grants, NIH, 59-61, spec asst to dir for biomet, Nat Inst Neurol Dis & Blindness, 61-66, chief reproduction anthropometry sect, Nat Inst Child Health & Human Develop, 66-74; dir menstruation & reproduction hist res prog, Ruth E Boynton Health Serv, Univ Minn, Minneapolis, 74-77; from assoc dir to dir consult, menstrual & reproductive health res prog, Dept Obstet & Gynec, Univ NC, 77-81; vpres, Ctr Advan Reproductive Health, Chapel Hill, NC, 82-85. *Concurrent Pos:* Consult, USPHS, 53-58; dir, Hosp Res & Educ Trust, 57-59; assoc res prof, Col Nursing, Univ Utah, 81- *Mem:* Human Biol Coun; fel AAAS; fel Am Statist Asn; Pop Asn Am; Am Fertil Soc. *Res:* Biometry of the menstrual cycle and gestation period; relationship of menstrual history to illness; effects of oral contraceptives. *Mailing Add:* 4064 Army St San Francisco CA 94131-1919

**TRELSTAD, ROBERT LAURENCE,** EMBRYOLOGY, PATHOLOGY. *Current Pos:* ASST PATHOLOGIST, MASS GEN HOSP, SHRINERS BURN INST, 72-, CHIEF PATH, 75-, CHMN & PROF, PATH DEPT, ROBERT WOOD JOHNSON MED SCH. *Personal Data:* b Redding, Calif, June 16, 40; m 61; c Derek, Graham, Brian & Jeremy. *Educ:* Columbia Univ, BA, 61; Harvard Univ, MD, 66. *Prof Exp:* Intern path, Mass Gen Hosp, 66-67; NIH res assoc embryol, 67-69. *Concurrent Pos:* Helen Hay Whitney Found res fel path, Mass Gen Hosp, 69-72; Am Cancer Soc fac res award, 72-77; asst prof, Harvard Med Sch, 72-77, assoc prof path, Harvard Med Sch, 77-; mem cell biol study sect, NIH, 77-; assoc ed, Develop Biol, 78-; mem adv coun, Nat Inst Child Health & Human Develop, NIH, 93- *Mem:* Soc Develop Biol; Am Soc Cell Biol; Am Soc Invest Pathologists; Int Soc Develop Biol; Am Med Info Asn. *Res:* Biological function of connective tissues in normal growth and development and in disease; development of computer based teaching tools for biology and medicine. *Mailing Add:* Pathol Dept Robert Wood Johnson Med Sch New Brunswick NJ 08903-0019. *Fax:* 732-235-8124; *E-Mail:* trelstad@umdnj.edu

**TREMAINE, JACK H,** PLANT VIROLOGY. *Current Pos:* RETIRED. *Personal Data:* b Galt, Ont, June 15, 28; m 56; c 3. *Educ:* McMaster Univ, BSc, 51, MSc, 53; Univ Pittsburgh, PhD(virol), 57. *Prof Exp:* Plant pathologist, Can Dept Agr, 52-64, plant virologist, 64-91. *Mem:* Am Phytopath Soc; Can Phytopath Soc. *Res:* Structure of plant viruses; in vitro reassembly stabilizing interactions using monoclonal antibodies as structural probes of plant viruses; studies of plant viruses in pseudorecombinant studies. *Mailing Add:* 3936 W 22nd Vancouver BC V6S 1K1 Can

**TREMAINE, PETER RICHARD,** PHYSICAL CHEMISTRY, AQUEOUS SOLUTION CHEMISTRY. *Current Pos:* head, Dept Chem, 91-96, PROF CHEM, MEM UNIV, NFLD, 91-, PROF, CTR EARTH RESOURCES RES, 91- *Personal Data:* b Toronto, Ont, Dec 20, 47; m 72; c 2. *Educ:* Univ Waterloo, Ont, BSc, 69; Univ Alta, PhD(phys chem), 74. *Honors & Awards:* Gold Key Award, Soc Chem Indust, 69; Sunner Award, 87. *Prof Exp:* Nat Res Coun Can fel surface chem, McGill Univ & Pulp & Paper Res Inst Can, Montreal, 74-75; res scientist, Whiteshell Nuclear Res Estab, Atomic Energy Can, 75-80; assoc res officer, Alta Res Coun, 80-85, sr res officer phys chem & mgr fund res, Oil Sands Res Dept, 85-90. *Concurrent Pos:* Vis assoc prof, Geol Dept, Univ Alta, 84; mgr, AHa Oil Sands Technol & Res Auth, Univ Res Prog, 87, Indust Joint Res Prog Advan Thermal Recovery, 88-90; adj prof geol, Univ Alta, 87-91, chem eng, 89-92; chmn, Can Coun Univ Chem Chairs, 94-96; bd dirs, Chem Soc Can, 95-97. *Mem:* Chem Inst Can; Am Chem Soc; Geochem Soc. *Res:* Chemical thermodynamics of aqueous systems at elevated temperature and pressure by flow calorimetry, densimetry, solubility, and Raman spectroscopy; applications to thermal and nuclear heat-transport systems, geochemistry and hydrometallurgy. *Mailing Add:* Dept Chem Mem Univ Nfld St John's NF A1B 3X7 Can. *Fax:* 709-737-3702; *E-Mail:* tremaine@morgan.ucs.mun.ca

**TREMAINE, SCOTT DUNCAN,** STELLAR DYNAMICS, CELESTIAL MECHANICS. *Current Pos:* PROF, UNIV TORONTO, 85-, DIR CIAR PROG COSMOLOGY & GRAVITY, 96- *Personal Data:* b Toronto, Ont, May 25, 50; m 94. *Educ:* McMaster Univ, BSc, 71; Princeton Univ, MA, 73, PhD(physics), 75. *Hon Degrees:* DSc, McMaster Univ, 96. *Honors & Awards:* Helen B Warner Prize; Steacie Prize; Rutherford Medal in Physics; Carlyle S Beals Award; Dannie Heinemann Prize Astrophys. *Prof Exp:* Res fel, Calif Inst Technol, 75-77, Cambridge Univ, 77-78 & Inst Advan Studt, 78-81; assoc prof, Mass Inst Technol, 81-85; dir, Can Inst Theoret Astrophys, 85-96. *Concurrent Pos:* E W R Steacie Mem fel. *Mem:* Am Astron Soc; Int Astron Union; Can Astron Soc; Am Acad Arts & Sci; Royal Soc Can. *Res:* Theoretical studies in dynamics; galactic structure; comets; planet formation. *Mailing Add:* Univ Toronto-CITA McLennan Lab 60 St George St Toronto ON M5S 1A7 Can. *Fax:* 416-978-3921

**TREMBLAY, ANDRE-MARIE,** STRONGLY CORRELATED ELECTRONS. *Current Pos:* PROF RES TRAINING, UNIV SHERBROOKE, 80-, DIR, SOLID STATE PHYSICS RES CTR, CRPS, 91- *Personal Data:* b Montreal, Que, Jan 2, 53; m 75, Guylaine Seguin; c Noemie & Rachel. *Educ:* Univ Montreal, BSc, 74; Mass Inst Technol, PhD(physics), 78. *Honors & Awards:* Herzberg Medal, Can Asn Physicists, 86. *Prof Exp:* Fel res, Cornell Univ, 78-80. *Concurrent Pos:* Assoc prof, Univ Provence, France, 82; vis scientist, Cornell Univ, 86-87; Steacie fel, Natural Sci & Eng Res Coun, 87; vis scientist, Inst Theoret Physics, Univ Calif, Santa Barbara, 89 & 96; Killam fel, 92. *Mem:* Am Phys Soc; Can Asn Physicists. *Res:* Properties of stongly correlated electronic systems; high-temperature superconductivity; quantum Monte Carlo simulations. *Mailing Add:* Physics Dept Univ Sherbrooke Sherbrooke PQ J1K 2R1 Can. *Fax:* 819-821-8046; *E-Mail:* tremblay@physique.usherb.ca

**TREMBLAY, ANGELO,** NUTRITION, PHYSIOLOGY. *Current Pos:* PROF NUTRIT & PHYSIOL, LAVAL UNIV, 87- *Personal Data:* b Quebec City, Can, Jan 20, 52. *Educ:* Laval Univ, BA, MS & PhD physiol). *Prof Exp:* Assoc prof nutrit, McGill Univ, 83-87. *Mem:* Am Inst Nutrit; Am Col Sports Med; Can Asn Appl Physiol; Asn Can Sports Sci. *Res:* Nutrition; physiology. *Mailing Add:* Phys Activ Sci Lab-PEPS Laval Univ Ste Foy PQ G1K 7P4 Can

**TREMBLAY, GEORGE CHARLES,** BIOCHEMISTRY. *Current Pos:* from asst prof to assoc prof, 66-75, PROF BIOCHEM, UNIV RI, 75-, CHMN DEPT BIOCHEM & BIOPHYS, 84- *Personal Data:* b Pittsfield, Mass, Oct 13, 38; c 4. *Educ:* Mass Col Pharm, BS, 60; St Louis Univ, PhD(biochem), 65. *Prof Exp:* Am Cancer Soc fel biol chem, Harvard Univ, 65-66. *Concurrent Pos:* Res grants, Nat Inst Child Health & Human Develop, Nat Inst Arthritis & Metab Dis, Nat Cancer Inst, NSF, & Nat Inst Arthritis Metab & Diag Dis. *Mem:* AAAS; Am Soc Biol Chemists; Soc Study Inborn Errors Metab. *Res:* Regulatory mechanisms in metabolism. *Mailing Add:* Dept Biochem Univ RI 117 Morrill Hall Kingston RI 02881

**TREMBLAY, GILLES,** PATHOLOGY. *Current Pos:* PROF PATH, McGILL UNIV, 70-, SR PATHOLOGIST, ROYAL VICTORIA HOSP, 77- *Personal Data:* b Montreal, Que, Apr 18, 28; m 75; c 3. *Educ:* Univ Montreal, BA, 48, MD, 53. *Prof Exp:* Resident path, Hotel-Dieu Hosp, 54-55; resident path, New Eng Deaconess Hosp, Boston, Mass, 55-57; pathologist, Hotel-Dieu Hosp, Montreal, 59-61; pathologist, Notre-Dame Hosp, 61-64; prof path & chmn dept, Fac Med, Univ Montreal, 64-70. *Concurrent Pos:* Nat Res Coun Can med res fel, Hotel-Dieu Hosp, Montreal, 53-54; Can Cancer Soc Allan Blair Mem res fel histochem, Postgrad Med Sch, Univ London, 57-59. *Mem:* Am Asn Cancer Res; Am Asn Pathologists; Can Asn Path; Int Acad Path. *Res:* Experimental studies on tumor cell-host cell interaction; ultrastructural and cytochemical studies on breast carcinoma. *Mailing Add:* Dept Path McGill Univ 3775 University St Montreal PQ H3A 2B4 Can. *Fax:* 514-398-7446

**TREMBLAY, MICHAEL JOHN,** POPULATION ECOLOGY OF EXPLOITED MARINE SPECIES, LARVAL ECOLOGY. *Current Pos:* Res biologist, 83-91, RES SCIENTIST, DEPT FISHERIES & OCEANS, 92- *Personal Data:* b Oakville, Ont, Dec 24, 55; m 79, Linda I Van Kessel; c 3. *Educ:* Univ Guelph, BSc, 79, MSc, 82; Dalhousie Univ, PhD(marine biol), 91. *Mem:* Am Fisheries Soc; Nat Shellfisheries Asn. *Res:* Ecology of marine plankton; factors underlying variation in the population size of marine species. *Mailing Add:* B10 1 Challenger Dr PO Box 1006 Dartmouth NS B3J 2S7 Can. *E-Mail:* m_tremblay@bionet.dfo.ca

**TREMMEL, CARL GEORGE,** PHOTOGRAPHIC ANALYTICAL CHEMISTRY, BREATH & BLOOD ALCOHOL TESTING, FORENSIC CHEMISTRY. *Current Pos:* RETIRED. *Personal Data:* b Lakewood, Ohio, June 25, 33; m 54, Mary Palmer; c David, Melody & Dawn. *Educ:* Kent State Univ, BS, 55; Iowa State Univ, MS, 58. *Prof Exp:* Res chemist, Eastman Kodak Co, 58-75, photog anal chemist, 75-86,; tech consult, Brick Assoc, 86-96; forensic chemist, 89-96. *Concurrent Pos:* Tech consult, PRC, 86-; expert witness, Vt Ct Syst, 89-; NY Ct Syst, 92-; self-employed, 96-; alcohol prog coordr, Vt Dept Health, 90-96, sr chemist, 94-96; self-employed tech consult, forensic chem, 96- *Mem:* Am Chem Soc; Int Asn Chem Testing. *Res:* Photographic chemistry; physical chemistry of color photography; electrochemistry; photographic analytical chemistry; forensic chemistry; effects of alcohol on human body. *Mailing Add:* 130 Northshore Dr Burlington VT 05401-1272. *Fax:* 802-660-8350

**TREMOR, JOHN W,** COMPARATIVE PHYSIOLOGY, ENVIRONMENTAL BIOLOGY. *Current Pos:* RETIRED. *Personal Data:* b East Aurora, NY, Jan 24, 32; m 59; c 2. *Educ:* Univ Buffalo, BA, 53, MA, 57; Univ Ariz, PhD(zool), 62. *Prof Exp:* Res asst biochem, Vet Admin Hosp, Buffalo, NY, 58; teaching asst radiation biol, NSF Inst Biol Sta, Mont State Univ, 59; instr biol & bot, Phoenix Col, 62; asst prof physiol & embryol, Humboldt State Col, 62-63; group leader gen biol, Biosatellite Proj, 63-72, dep chief earth sci applns off, Ames Res Ctr, NASA, 72-74; proj scientist, biomed exp sci satellite & joint USSR/US biol satellite prog, 74-76; mgr space shuttle plant exp & dep proj scientist, Ames Life Sci Payload Spacelab III & prin investr, Spacelab IV, Ames Res Ctr, NASA, 77-94. *Mem:* AAAS. *Res:* Development and implementation of biological experiments for space flight; developmental biology of amphibians. *Mailing Add:* 13525 Surrey Lane Saratoga CA 95070

**TRENARY, ROBERT GLENN,** COMPUTER SCIENCE. *Current Pos:* ASSOC PROF COMPUT SCI, WESTERN MICH UNIV. *Concurrent Pos:* Fulbright grantee comput sci, Univ Botswana, 95-96. *Res:* Curriculum development in computer science. *Mailing Add:* Dept Comput Sci Western Mich Univ Kalamazoo MI 49008

**TRENBERTH, KEVIN EDWARD,** METEOROLOGY, CLIMATE DYNAMICS. *Current Pos:* scientist, Nat Ctr Atmospheric Res, 84-86, leader, Trop Oceans & Global Atmospheric Proj, 86-87 & empirical studies group, 87, dep dir, Climate & Global Dynamics Div, 91-95, SR SCIENTIST, NAT CTR ATMOSPHERIC RES, 86-, HEAD CLIMATE ANALYSIS SECT, 87- *Personal Data:* b Christchurch, NZ, Nov 8, 44; m 70, Gail Thompson; c Annika & Angela. *Educ:* Univ Canterbury, BSc(hons), 66; Mass Inst Technol, ScD, 72. *Honors & Awards:* Am Meteorol Soc Editors Award, 89. *Prof Exp:* Meteorologist res, NZ Meteorol Serv, 66-77, supt dynamic meteorol, 77; from assoc prof to prof meteorol, Univ Ill, 77-84. *Concurrent Pos:* Mem, NZ Working Group Global Data Processing Syst, Comn Basic Syst, World Meteorol Orgn, 75-77; NSF res grant, 78-88 & Nat Oceanic & Atmospheric Admin res grant, 86-; consult, Nat Oceanic & Atmospheric Admin, 80-, NASA, 81-; ed, Monthly Weather Rev, Am Meteorol Soc, 81-87, assoc ed, 87-88 & J Climate, 87-95; NZ res fel, 68-72; NASA res grant, 89-; mem, Comt Earth Scis, Space Sci Bd, 82-85, Polar Res Bd, Nat Acad Sci, 86-90, Climate Res Comt, Bd Atmospheric Scis & Climate, 87-90, Nat Oceanic & Atmospheric Admin Panel Climate & Global Change, 87-; mem, US Trop Oceans Global Atmosphere Adv Panel, 84-87; adj prof, Univ Ill, 84-89; Polar Res Bd, 86-90; mem, Int Sci Steering Group, Trop Oceans Global Atmospheric Programme, 89-94; coun deleg, Sect Atmospheric & Hydrospheric Sci, AAAS, 93-96; mem, Global Ocean Atmposhere Land Syst Panel, Nat Acad Sci, 94-; mem, Atmospheric Observ Panel Global Climate Observ Syst, 94-; ed, Earth Interactions, 96- *Mem:* Fel Am Meteorol Soc; fel AAAS; hon fel Royal Soc NZ; Meteorol Soc NZ. *Res:* Dynamics of climate and climate change; meteorology of the southern hemisphere; numerical weather prediction; dynamics of the stratosphere; global warming; El Niño-Southern Oscillation; climate system modeling; 1988 North American drought. *Mailing Add:* Nat Ctr Atmospheric Res PO Box 3000 Boulder CO 80307-3000. *Fax:* 303-497-1333; *E-Mail:* trenbert@ncar.ucar.edu

**TRENCH, ROBERT KENT,** MARINE BIOLOGY, BIOCHEMISTRY. *Current Pos:* assoc prof biol, 76-80, PROF BIOL & GEOL, UNIV CALIF, SANTA BARBARA, 80- *Personal Data:* b Belize City, Brit Honduras, Aug 3, 40; nat US; m 68. *Educ:* Univ West Indies, BSc, 65; Univ Calif, Los Angeles, MA, 67, PhD(invert zool), 69. *Prof Exp:* UK Sci Res Coun fel, Oxford Univ, 69-71; instr, Yale Univ, 71-72, asst prof, 72-76. *Mem:* AAAS; Am Soc Limnol & Oceanog; Am Soc Cell Biol; Soc Exp Biol UK; Sigma Xi. *Res:* Coral reef biology and ecology; biochemical integration of plasmids in autotroph-heterotroph endosymbioses; intercellular recognition phenomena. *Mailing Add:* Dept Biol Sci Univ Calif 552 University Ave Santa Barbara CA 93106-0002

**TRENCH, WILLIAM FREDERICK,** DIFFERENTIAL EQUATIONS, NUMERICAL LINEAR ALGEBRA. *Current Pos:* ANDREW G COWLES DISTINGUISHED PROF MATH, TRINITY UNIV, SAN ANTONIO, TEX, 86- *Personal Data:* b Trenton, NJ, July 31, 31; m 54, 81, Beverly; c Joseph W, Randolph C, John F & Gina M (Holub). *Educ:* Lehigh Univ, BA, 53; Univ Pa, MA, 55, PhD(math), 58. *Prof Exp:* Instr res, Moore Sch Elec Eng, Univ Pa, 53-56; appl mathematician, Missile & Space Vehicle Div, Gen Elec, 56-57; eng specialist, Philco Corp, Philadelphia, 57-59; class AA engr, Radio Corp Am, Moorestown, NJ, 59-64; from assoc prof to prof math, Drexel Univ, 64-86. *Mem:* Am Math Soc; Soc Indust & Appl Math; Math Asn Am; Int Linear Algebra Soc. *Res:* Asymptotic theory of solutions of differential equations and in numerical linear algebra; published papers in special functions, smoothing and prediction and elementary number theory. *Mailing Add:* Math Dept Trinity Univ San Antonio TX 78212. *Fax:* 210-736-8264; *E-Mail:* wtrench@trinity.edu

**TRENHOLM, ANDREW RUTLEDGE,** CHEMICAL CHEMISTRY. *Current Pos:* SECT HEAD, MIDWEST RES INST, 79- *Personal Data:* b Charleston, SC, May 1, 42; m 66; c 2. *Educ:* Clemson Univ, BS, 64; Ga Inst Technol, MS, 68. *Prof Exp:* Sanitary engr, Health Dept, Dade Couty, Fla, 64-67; chem engr, Union Carbide Corp, 68-70; environ engr, US Environ Protection Agency, 70-79. *Res:* Multimedia environmental research in air pollution, water pollution, solid waste and hazardous waste. *Mailing Add:* Midwest Res Inst 401 Harrison Oaks Blvd Cary NC 27513-2413. *Fax:* 919-870-0140

**TRENHOLM, HAROLD LOCKSLEY,** AGRICULTURE. *Current Pos:* SR SCIENTIST ADV, FEED & FOOD SAFETY & QUAL, ANIMAL RES CTR, CAN, 88- *Personal Data:* b Amherst, NS, July 24, 41; m 68; c 2. *Educ:* McGill Univ, BSc, 63; NY State Vet Col, Cornell Univ, PhD(biochem), 68. *Prof Exp:* Asst physiol, State Univ NY, Vet Col, Cornell, 63-67; res scientist, Toxicol Dept, Health Protection Br, Can Dept Health & Welfare, 67-73, dir res bur, Nonmed Use Drugs Directorate, 73-77; prog chmn, Animal Feed Safety & Nutrit, 77-88. *Concurrent Pos:* Computer processing. *Mem:* Am Chem Soc; Can Soc Res Toxicol; Can Soc Animal Sci; Sigma Xi. *Res:* Mycotoxins; toxicology; food safety. *Mailing Add:* 135 Pine Ridge Rd Carp ON K0A 1L0 Can

**TRENHOLME, JOHN BURGESS,** LASER ENGINEERING, NUMERICAL ANALYSIS. *Current Pos:* physicist laser fusion, 72-78, sr scientist, Solid State Laser Prog, 78-91, ASSOC PROG LEADER, LASER THEORY & DESIGN, LAWRENCE LIVERMORE LAB, 91- *Personal Data:* b Portland, Ore, Feb 4, 39; m 85, Keren Levy; c 1. *Educ:* Calif Inst Technol, BS, 61, MS, 62, PhD(mat sci), 69. *Prof Exp:* Scientist lasers & light sources, Naval Res Lab, Washington, DC, 69-72. *Mem:* AAAS. *Res:* Laser fusion; laser design and engineering; numerical simulation of laser pumping and propagation; nonlinear optics; optical design. *Mailing Add:* 1212 Upper Happy Valley Rd Lafayette CA 94549-2725. *Fax:* 510-423-6506; *E-Mail:* jbt@llnl.gov

**TRENKLE, ALLEN H,** NUTRITION, ENDOCRINOLOGY. *Current Pos:* from asst prof to prof, 62-83, DISTINGUISHED PROF ANIMAL SCI, IOWA STATE UNIV, 83- *Personal Data:* b Alliance, Nebr, July 23, 34; m 56, Donna Wendorff; c Ann, Laura & Janet. *Educ:* Univ Nebr, BSc, 56; Iowa State Univ, MSc, 58, PhD(nutrit), 60. *Prof Exp:* NIH res fel, Univ Calif, Berkeley, 61-62. *Mem:* Am Soc Animal Sci; Am Chem Soc; Soc Exp Biol & Med; Endocrine Soc; Am Inst Nutrit. *Res:* Physiology of growth hormone and insulin secretion; endocrinology studies with ruminants; influence of hormones on growth and development of mammals; molecular biology of growth; protein metabolism in ruminants. *Mailing Add:* 301 Kildee Hall Iowa State Univ Ames IA 50011. *Fax:* 515-294-2401; *E-Mail:* atrenkle@iastate.edu

**TRENT, DENNIS W,** IMMUNOLOGY, BIOCHEMISTRY. *Current Pos:* DIR SCI SERVS, FRANKLIN QUEST CONSULT GROUP, 97- *Personal Data:* b Bend, Ore, Oct 17, 35; m 55, Joyce Taylor; c 7. *Educ:* Brigham Young Univ, BS, 59, MS, 61; Univ Okla, PhD(med sci), 64. *Prof Exp:* From asst prof to assoc prof bact, Brigham Young Univ, 67-69; from asst prof to assoc prof microbiol, Univ Tex Med Sch, San Antonio, 69-74; chief molecular virol, Borne Dis Div, Ctr Dis Control, USPHS, 74-89, chief molecular biol, Div Vector-Borne Infectious Dis; asst dir lab sci & chief, Molecular Biol Br, 89-93, dir, Div Viral Prod Ctr Biol Eval & Res Fed Drug Admin, 93-97, Bethesda, Md. *Concurrent Pos:* NIH res grants, 66-72 & US Army contracts, 80-90; WHO res grants, 90-92. *Mem:* Am Soc Microbiol; Am Soc Virol; Am Soc Trop Med Hyg. *Res:* Biochemistry of togavirus and flavivirus replication; virus immunology; viral nucleic acids; vaccines; rapid diagnostics; molecular epidemiology. *Mailing Add:* Franklin Quest Consult Group 2200 W Parkway Blvd Salt Lake City UT 84119. *Fax:* 801-956-1597; *E-Mail:* dwtren@franklinquest.com

**TRENT, DONALD STEPHEN,** MECHANICAL ENGINEERING, APPLIED MATHEMATICS. *Current Pos:* sr res engr, Pac Northwest Lab, Battelle Mem Inst, 70-73, res assoc, 73-75, res & develop mgr, 76-87, CHIEF SCIENTIST, PAC NORTHWEST LABS, BATTELLE MEM INST, 87- *Personal Data:* b Cloverdale, Ore, Mar 29, 35; m 58; c Steve, Lynn & Greg. *Educ:* Ore State Univ, BS, 62, MS, 64, PhD(mech eng), 72. *Honors & Awards:* Fed Lab Consortium Award, 92. *Prof Exp:* Develop engr, Battelle Mem Inst, 64-67; lectr, Ore State Univ, 67-68, res asst, 68-70. *Concurrent Pos:* Mech engr, Environ Protection Agency, Ore, 68-70; instr, Columbia Basin Col, 70-72; stand chmn, Am Nat Stand Inst, 75-; consult, Am Soc Reactor Safety, 82-85; courtesy prof, Ore State Univ, 87-; res affil, Mass Inst Technol, 89- *Mem:* Am Soc Mech Engrs; Sigma Xi; NY Acad Sci. *Res:* Computational heat transfer and fluid flow in natural convecting systems; numerical modeling of free turbulence, thermal plumes and air-sea interactions; reactor heat transfer; thermal hydraulics of advanced energy systems; granted copyright for Tempess CFD code. *Mailing Add:* 721 Lynnwood Loop Richland WA 99352-1827. *E-Mail:* ds_trent@pnl.gov

**TRENT, JOHN ELLSWORTH,** ANALYTICAL CHEMISTRY. *Current Pos:* RES CHEMIST, AMOCO CORP, IND, 71- *Personal Data:* b Wabash, Ind, Sept 22, 42; m 68; c 2. *Educ:* Manchester Col, BA, 64; Ohio State Univ, PhD(org chem), 70. *Mem:* Am Chem Soc. *Res:* Analytical instrumentation. *Mailing Add:* PO Box 3011 Naperville IL 60566-7011

**TRENTELMAN, GEORGE FREDERICK,** PHYSICS. *Current Pos:* asst prof, 71-76, assoc prof, 76-82, PROF PHYSICS, NORTHERN MICH UNIV, 82- *Personal Data:* b Amsterdam, NY, Apr 27, 44. *Educ:* Clarkson Col Technol, BS, 66; Mich State Univ, MS, 68, PhD(physics), 70. *Prof Exp:* Res assoc nuclear physics, Mich State Univ, 70-71. *Concurrent Pos:* Vis physicist, Inst Nuclear Sci, Univ Tokyo, 72-73; res fel, Jet Propulsion Lab, 81, 82. *Mem:* Soc Photo Optical Instrument Eng. *Res:* Nuclear physics; optics. *Mailing Add:* Dept Physics Northern Mich Univ Marquette MI 49855

**TRENTHAM, DAVID R,** ENZYMOLOGY, MUSCLE PHYSIOLOGY. *Current Pos:* HEAD, DIV PHYS BIOCHEM & PHYSIOL & NEURAL MECHANISMS GROUP, NAT INST MED RES, LONDON, 84- *Personal Data:* b Solihull, Eng, Sept 22, 38. *Educ:* Cambridge Univ, BA, 61,

PhD(chem), 64. *Honors & Awards:* Colworth Medal, Biochem Soc UK, 75; Wilhelm Feldberg Prize, 91. *Prof Exp:* Lectr biochem, Biochem Dept, Univ Bristol, 66-77; chmn biochem & biophysics & Edwin M Chance prof biophysics, Univ Pa, 77-84. *Mem:* Fel Royal Soc; Biophys Soc; Biophys Soc UK; Am Soc Biochem & Molecular Biol; Physiol Soc UK; Biochem Soc UK; Am Chem Soc. *Res:* Mechanism of muscular contraction and its regulation studied through a variety of transient kinetic techniques including laser pulse photolysis of caged compounds to introduce biochemical metabolites rapidly into organized cellular preparations. *Mailing Add:* Div Phys Biochem Nat Inst Med Res The Ridgeway Mill Hill London NW7 1AA England. *Fax:* 44-81-959-4419

**TRENTHAM, JIMMY N,** MICROBIOLOGY. *Current Pos:* From asst prof to assoc prof microbiol, Univ Tenn, Martin, 65-73, chmn dept biol, 69-73, provost, 73-79, vchancellor, 76-79, PROF, UNIV TENN, MARTIN, 73-, ALUMNI DISTINGUISHED PROF, 90- *Personal Data:* b Dresden, Tenn, Jan 7, 36; m 65; c 2. *Educ:* Univ Tenn, Martin, BS, 58; Vanderbilt Univ, PhD(microbiol), 65. *Concurrent Pos:* NSF res fel, 67-69. *Mem:* AAAS; Am Soc Microbiologists; Am Inst Biol Sci; Sigma Xi. *Res:* Microbial ecology, including qualitative and quantitative fluctuations of bacterial populations in freshwater and effects of temperature and nutritional factors on the structure of bacterial communities in freshwater. *Mailing Add:* 429 Raven St Martin TN 38237-4001

**TRENTIN, JOHN JOSEPH,** experimental biology & hematology, for more information see previous edition

**TRENTO, ALFREDO,** SURGERY. *Current Pos:* DIR, HEART TRANSPLANT PROG, DEPT THORACIC & CARDIOVASC SURG, CEDARS-SINAI MED CTR, 88- *Personal Data:* b Cittadella, Italy, July 3, 50. *Educ:* Univ Padua, Italy, MD, 75. *Prof Exp:* Asst prof surg, Univ Pittsburgh Sch Med, 85-88, dir, Ecmo Prog, Children's Hosp, 87-88. *Concurrent Pos:* Lectr, Inst Giannina Gaslini, Italy, 87. *Res:* Cardiac and lung transplantation. *Mailing Add:* Cedars-Sinai Med Scr TCS 8700 Beverly Blvd 6215 Los Angeles CA 90048-1865

**TREPANIER, PIERRE,** VIROLOGY. *Current Pos:* assoc prof virol, Ctr Virol, 84-86, res & develop mgr, Div Viral Vaccines, 87-96, DIR VIRAL VACCINES, ARMAND FRAPPIER INST, 96-, DIR REGULATORY AFFAIRS, IAF BIOVAC. *Personal Data:* b Montreal, Que, Oct 29, 53. *Educ:* Univ Ottawa, BSc, 75; Univ Montreal, BSc, 77; Armand Frappier Inst, MSc, 79, PhD(virol), 82. *Prof Exp:* Res fel, Nat Sci & Eng Res Coun, Univ Melbourne, Australia, 82-84. *Res:* High density cell culture for the production of biologicals virus production, monoclonals; characterization of proteins antigenic determinants. *Mailing Add:* 525 Blvd Des Prairies Laval PQ H7N 4Z2 Can. *Fax:* 514-686-8288

**TREPKA, ROBERT DALE,** PHYSICAL ORGANIC CHEMISTRY. *Current Pos:* SR RES SPECIALIST, DIV PRINTING & PUBL SYSTS, 3M CO, 66- *Personal Data:* b Crete, Nebr, Dec 16, 38; m 61; c 3. *Educ:* Grinnell Col, BA, 61; Univ Calif, Los Angeles, PhD(org chem), 65. *Prof Exp:* NATO fel org chem, Munich, 65-66. *Mem:* Am Chem Soc; Soc Photog Sci & Eng. *Res:* Physical organic chemistry; organic stereochemistry; photographic chemistry; synthetic organic chemistry. *Mailing Add:* 1487 Jewel Dr St Paul MN 55125

**TREPKA, WILLIAM JAMES,** POLYMER CHEMISTRY, RUBBER CHEMISTRY. *Current Pos:* RETIRED. *Personal Data:* b Crete, Nebr, Apr 17, 33; m 55, Verna Slepicka; c William, Janet & John. *Educ:* Doane Col, BA, 55; Iowa State Univ, PhD(chem), 60. *Prof Exp:* Res chemist, Phillips Petrol Co, 60-93. *Mem:* Am Chem Soc. *Res:* Polymer and synthesis. *Mailing Add:* Rte 1 Box 362-B1 Bartlesville OK 74003

**TREPTOW, RICHARD S,** SCIENCE EDUCATION. *Current Pos:* from asst prof to assoc prof, 72-75, PROF CHEM, CHICAGO STATE UNIV, 78- *Personal Data:* b Chicago, Ill, Feb 8, 41; c 2. *Educ:* Blackburn Col, BA, 62; Univ Ill, Urbana, MS, 64, PhD(inorg chem), 66. *Prof Exp:* Staff chemist, Procter & Gamble Co, 66-72. *Mem:* Am Chem Soc. *Res:* Application of chemical thermodynamics to inorganic and industrial processes; calculation of species present in equilibrium systems; audiovisual programs for science education. *Mailing Add:* Dept Chem & Physics Chicago State Univ Chicago IL 60628. *E-Mail:* r-treptow@csu.edu

**TRESER, GERHARD,** nephrology; deceased, see previous edition for last biography

**TRESHOW, MICHAEL,** PLANT PATHOLOGY, AIR POLLUTION BIOLOGY. *Current Pos:* from asst prof to assoc prof bot, 61-67, assoc prof biol, 67-70, prof, 70-, EMER PROF BIOL, UNIV UTAH. *Personal Data:* b Copenhagen, Denmark, July 14, 26; nat US; m 51, 82; c 2. *Educ:* Univ Calif, Los Angeles, BS, 50; Univ Calif, Davis, PhD(plant path), 54. *Prof Exp:* Sr lab technician, Univ Calif, 52-53; plant pathologist, Columbia-Geneva Steel Div, US Steel Corp, 53-61. *Mem:* Air Pollution Control Asn; Am Phytopath Soc. *Res:* Environmental pathology, particularly diseases caused by air pollutants; environmental stress; impact of air pollution on forest species; study of growth trends based on dendrochronological methods. *Mailing Add:* 206 Bldg 44 Univ Utah Salt Lake City UT 84112

**TRESSLER, RICHARD ERNEST,** CERAMICS, MATERIALS SCIENCE. *Current Pos:* from asst prof to assoc prof, Pa State Univ, University Park, 72-81, prof & head ceramic sci & eng, 81-86, dir, Ctr Adv Mat, 86-91, HEAD DEPT MAT SCI & ENG, PA STATE UNIV, 91- *Personal Data:* b Bellefonte, Pa, June 14, 42; m 65; Sue Alexander; c Laura, Kristin & Jennifer. *Educ:* Pa State Univ, BS, 63, PhD(ceramic sci), 67; Mass Inst Technol, SM, 64. *Honors & Awards:* Sci Achievement Medal, Systs Command, USAF, 70; Pace-Schwartzwalder Award, Am Ceramic Soc; IR-100 Award. *Prof Exp:* Sr scientist mat res, Tem Pres Res, Inc, Pa, 67; nuclear res officer, US Air Force, McClellan AFB, 67-68, mat scientist, Mat Lab, Wright-Patterson AFB, 68-70, tech area mgr, 70-71; NSF fel, Univ Essex, 71-72. *Concurrent Pos:* Adj asst prof, Univ Cincinnati, 69-71; adv, US Arm Off Res, Mat Div, 79-80. *Mem:* Fel Am Ceramic Soc; Metall Soc; Nat Inst Ceramic Engrs; Electrochem Soc. *Res:* Fabrication and mechanical behavior of structural ceramic and composite materials; fracture and strengthening mechanisms; IC processing and properties. *Mailing Add:* Dept Mat Sci & Eng Pa State Univ 101 Steidle Bldg University Park PA 16802. *Fax:* 814-865-2917; *E-Mail:* ret1@oas.psu.edu

**TRETIAK, OLEH JOHN,** ELECTRICAL ENGINEERING, BIOMEDICAL ENGINEERING. *Current Pos:* assoc prof elec eng, 73-84, PROF ELEC ENG, DREXEL UNIV, 84-, MEM, BIOMED ENG & SCI INST, 73-, DIR, IMAGING & COMP VISION CTR, 81- *Personal Data:* b Podkamen, Ukraine, Jan 18, 39; US citizen; m 65; c 1. *Educ:* Cooper Union, BS, 58; Mass Inst Technol, SM, 60, ScD, 63. *Prof Exp:* Asst prof elec eng, Mass Inst Technol, 63-66, res assoc biomed, 66-73; proj engr storage tubes, Image Instruments, 66. *Concurrent Pos:* Consult, Raytheon Corp, 64-65; Cognos Corp, 70-71, E G & G Inc, 71-72, Kulicke & Soffa, 74-80 & RCA, 81-82, FAA, 86, SAIC, 87; Soviet Union exchange scholar, Nat Acad Sci, 72; adj prof, radiol dept, Sch Med, Univ Pa, 81- *Mem:* Inst Elec & Electronics Engrs; Asn Comput Mach; Soc Mfg Engrs; AAAS. *Res:* Medical imaging systems; ultrasonography, image processing & machine vision; pictorial pattern recognition; mathematical modeling of images; systems for image analysis of autoradiograms; image pattern recognition; quantitative ultrasonic imaging. *Mailing Add:* 2227 Green St Philadelphia PA 19130-3112

**TRETTER, JAMES RAY,** PHARMACEUTICAL CHEMISTRY. *Current Pos:* PRES & CHIEF EXEC OFFICER, IXSYS INC, 92- *Personal Data:* b Boone, Iowa, June 7, 33; m, Neltje Van Loon; c Elsa. *Educ:* Loras Col, BS, 56; Univ Calif, Berkeley, PhD(chem), 60. *Prof Exp:* Chemist, Pfizer Inc, 60-72, dir med chem, 72-74, dir chem process res, 75-77, exec dir develop res, 77-80; vpres res & develop, William H Rorer, Inc, 80-90; pres, Cent Res Div, Rhone-Poulenc Rorer, Paris, 90-92. *Res:* Pharmaceuticals. *Mailing Add:* 1839 Washington St Port Townsend WA 98368

**TRETTER, STEVEN ALAN,** ELECTRICAL ENGINEERING. *Current Pos:* ASSOC PROF ELEC ENG, UNIV MD, COL PARK, 66- *Personal Data:* b Greenbelt, Md, May 28, 40; m 68; c 1. *Educ:* Univ Md, Col Park, BSEE, 62; Princeton Univ, MA, 64, PhD(elec eng), 66. *Prof Exp:* Mem tech staff elec eng, Hughes Aircraft Co, 65-66. *Concurrent Pos:* Suppl engr, Ctr Explor Studies, IBM Corp, 68; consult, Vitro Corp Am, 69-70, Case Commun Inc, 70-, US Naval Res Lab, 74-86, Penril Data Comm, 86- *Mem:* Inst Elec & Electronics Engrs. *Res:* Statistical communication theory; error correcting codes; digital filtering and communications. *Mailing Add:* 601 Hawkesbury Terr Silver Spring MD 20904

**TREU, JESSE ISAIAH,** BIOPHYSICS, OPTICS. *Current Pos:* prog mgr adv develop, automated equip for hemat & histol, Technicon Corp, 77-; AT CW GROUP INC. *Personal Data:* b New York, NY, Apr 10, 47; m 70; c 1. *Educ:* Rensselaer Polytech Inst, BS, 68; Princeton Univ, MA, 71, PhD(physics), 73. *Prof Exp:* Physicist optics & immunol, 73-75, liaison scientist components & mat group, Gen Elec Res & Develop Ctr, 75-77. *Mem:* Am Phys Soc; Am Asn Physicists Med; Biophys Soc. *Mailing Add:* 140 Brookstone Dr Princeton NJ 08540

**TREU, SIEGFRIED,** HUMAN-COMPUTER INTERACTION, INTERFACE STRUCTURES. *Current Pos:* asst dir, Comput Ctr, Univ Pittsburgh, 67-70, from asst prof to assoc prof, 71-89, chmn, Dept Comput Sci, 84-86, PROF COMPUT SCI, UNIV PITTSBURGH, 89-, CO-DIR, CTR PARALLEL, DISTRIBUTED & INTEL SYSTS, 90-, ACTG DEAN, COL ARTS & SCI, 94- *Personal Data:* b Hohenwalde, Prussia, Ger, Jan 25, 40; US citizen; m 62, Erika T Knebel; c Kevin, Ramona, Marvin & Steven. *Educ:* Univ Wis-Madison, BS, 62, MS, 63, Univ Pittsburgh, Pa, PhD(info processing), 70. *Prof Exp:* Info systs specialist, Goodyear Aerospace Corp, 65-67; res assoc, Nat Res Coun, Nat Bur Stand, Washington, DC, 70-71. *Concurrent Pos:* Comput scientist & consult, Inst Comput Sci & Technol, Nat Bur Stand, Washington, DC, 71-81; chair, Spec Interest Group Off Info Systs, Asn Comput Mach, 83-87, area dir, Spec Interest Group Bd, 86- *Mem:* Asn Comput Mach. *Res:* Methodologies for structure-based design, measurement, and evaluation of adaptive, network-oriented human-computer interface systems. *Mailing Add:* Dept Comput Sci Univ Pittsburgh 322 Alumni Hall Pittsburgh PA 15260. *E-Mail:* treu@cs.pitt.edu

**TREUMANN, WILLIAM BORGEN,** PHYSICAL CHEMISTRY. *Current Pos:* from assoc prof to prof, Moorhead State Univ, 60-81, assoc dean acad affairs, 68-70, dean, 70-81, EMER PROF PHYS CHEM & DEAN FAC MATH & SCI, MOORHEAD STATE UNIV, 81- *Personal Data:* b Grafton, NDak, Feb 26, 16; m 45, 48, Mildred Jenkins; c Richard, Robert & Beverly. *Educ:* Univ NDak, BS, 42; Univ Ill, MS, 44, PhD(phys chem), 47. *Prof Exp:* Asst chem, Univ Ill, 42-46, asst math, 46; from asst prof to prof phys chem, NDak State Univ, 46-55. *Mem:* AAAS; Am Chem Soc; Am Inst Chemists. *Res:* Complex ion formation. *Mailing Add:* 1 South Second St Fargo ND 58103-2827

**TREVATHAN, LARRY EUGENE,** PLANT PATHOLOGY, PLANT PHYSIOLOGY. *Current Pos:* ASST PROF & ASST PLANT PATHOLOGIST, MISS STATE UNIV, 78- *Personal Data:* b Phoenix, Ariz, Apr 13, 47; m 70; c 2. *Educ:* Univ Tenn, BS, 69; Va Polytech Inst & State Univ, PhD(plant path), 78. *Mem:* Sigma Xi. *Res:* Physiology of pathogenesis of diseases of forage crops; genetic basis and inheritance of resistance in forage grasses. *Mailing Add:* Dept Entom & Plant Path Miss State Univ PO Box 9655 Mississippi State MS 39762

**TREVELYAN, BENJAMIN JOHN,** PULP & PAPER TECHNOLOGY. *Current Pos:* RETIRED. *Personal Data:* b Beamsville, Ont, Nov 8, 22; m 53, Elizabeth L Hurst; c Michael, David, Ian & Alexandra. *Educ:* McMaster Univ, BA, 44; McGill Univ, PhD(chem), 51. *Prof Exp:* Chemist, Aluminum Co Can, Ltd, Que, 44-47; asst res dir, Fraser Co, Ltd, NB, 51-53, res dir, 53-60; res scientist, WVa Pulp & Paper Co, 60-62; dir res, Celfibe Div, Johnson & Johnson, 62-65; mgr pulp res & eng, Kimberly-Clark Corp, 65-69, dir pulp & wood prep, Res & Eng, 69-73; indust liaison officer, Pulp & Paper Res Inst Can, 73-77; consult, Sync-Rust Ltd, Montreal, 77-78; assoc dir develop, ITT Rayonier, 78-80 & Rust Int, 80-85. *Mem:* Tech Asn Pulp & Paper Indust; Am Chem Soc; Can Pulp & Paper Asn. *Res:* Pulp and paper technology; all phases of the production of pulp from northern wood species; pulping of southern pines; pulping of vegetable fibers such as bagasse, flax and hemp; the application of fibers to the production of paper, dry-formed fiber products and cellulose products; application of research to the development and use of new processes on an industrial scale; financial analyses of industrial processes; mill evaluations and the evaluation of new equipment developments. *Mailing Add:* 200 Rockgreen Pl Santa Rosa CA 95409

**TREVES, DAVID,** MAGNETIC MATERIALS & MAGNETIZATION PROCESSES. *Current Pos:* DIR, KOMAG INC, MILIPITAS, CALIF, 87- *Personal Data:* b Milan, Italy, June 28, 30; Israeli citizen; m 54; c 3. *Educ:* Technion, Haifa, Israel, BSc, 53, MSc, 56, DSc(elec eng), 58. *Prof Exp:* Mem staff, Bell Tel Labs, Murray Hill, NJ, 60-62, Res Lab, Ampex Corp, Redwood City, Calif, 65-67, Xerox Palo Alto Res Ctr, 81-82, Optimem, Mountain View, 86-87. *Concurrent Pos:* Mem staff, Appl Physics, Weizmann Inst Sci, Rehovot, Israel, 57-86, chmn, Dept Electronics, 77-86. *Mem:* Am Optical Soc; Am Phys Soc; Soc Photo-Optical Instrumentation Engrs; fel Inst Elec & Electronics Engrs. *Res:* Basic studies of magnetic materials and magnetization processes; high resolution magnetooptics for research and memory applications; extensive work on lasers, holography, coherent optics and microwave printed-array antennae. *Mailing Add:* Komag 275 S Hillview Dr Milpitas CA 95035

**TREVES, JEAN FRANCOIS,** PURE MATHEMATICS. *Current Pos:* PROF MATH, RUTGERS UNIV, NEW BRUNSWICK, 71- *Personal Data:* b Brussels, Belg, Apr 23, 30; m 62; c 2. *Educ:* Univ Sorbonne, Lic, 53, Dr(math), 58. *Honors & Awards:* Chauvenet Prize, Am Math Soc, 71. *Prof Exp:* Asst prof math, Univ Calif, Berkeley, 58-60; assoc prof, Yeshiva Univ, 61-64; prof, Purdue Univ, 64-71. *Concurrent Pos:* Sloan fel, 60-64; mem, Mission Orgn Am States In Brazil, 61; vis prof, Univ Sorbonne, 65-67, Univ Paris, 74-75; Guggenheim fel, 77-78. *Mem:* Am Math Soc; Math Soc France. *Res:* Partial differential equations; functional analysis. *Mailing Add:* Dept Math Rutgers Univ New Brunswick NJ 08903-2101

**TREVES, S T,** NUCLEAR MEDICINE. *Current Pos:* PROF RADIOL, HARVARD MED SCH, 70-, CHIEF, DIV NUCLEAR MED, CHILDREN'S HOSP. *Personal Data:* b Ramallo, Arg, Aug 3, 40; US citizen; c 2. *Educ:* Nat Col III, Buenos Aires, BA, 59; Univ Buenos Aires, MD, 66; Harvard, MA, 92. *Prof Exp:* Asst physician, Ctr Nuclear Med, Hosp Clin, Univ Buenos Aires, 66; res fel, Inst Med & Exp Surg, Univ Montreal, 67; resident nuclear med, Royal Victoria Hosp, McGill Univ, 67-68; clin fel & res assoc nuclear med & clin fel med, Yale-New Haven Hosp, Sch Med, Yale Univ, 68-70. *Mem:* Soc Nuclear Med; Sigma Xi; Am Heart Asn; Soc Pediat Radiol; AMA. *Res:* Development of ultrashort lived radionuclide generators for angiocardiography in children; development of computer software for nuclear medicine functional studies; medical information systems. *Mailing Add:* Div Nuclear Med Children's Hosp 300 Longwood Ave Boston MA 02115

**TREVES, SAMUEL BLAIN,** IGNEOUS PETROLOGY. *Current Pos:* chmn dept, 64-70 & 75-89, assoc dean, Col Arts & Sci, 89-96, PROF GEOL, UNIV NEBR, LINCOLN, 66- *Personal Data:* b Detroit, Mich, Sept 11, 25; m 60, Jane P Mitoray; c John Samuel & David Samuel. *Educ:* Mich Col Mining & Technol, BS, 51; Univ Idaho, MS, 53; Ohio State Univ, PhD(geol), 59. *Prof Exp:* Geologist, Ford Motor Co, 51, State Bur Mines & Geol, Idaho, 52 & Otago Catchment Bd, NZ, 53-54; from instr to assoc prof geol, 59-65. *Concurrent Pos:* Fulbright scholar, Univ Otago, NZ, 53-54; chief scientist, Antartica Expeds, 60-75 & Greenland Exped, 62-64. *Mem:* Fel AAAS; fel Geol Soc Am; Am Mineral Soc; Sigma Xi. *Res:* Precambrian geology; antarctic geology; alkaline igneous rocks. *Mailing Add:* 1710 B St Lincoln NE 68502. *Fax:* 402-472-5281; *E-Mail:* streves@unlinfo.unl.edu

**TREVILLYAN, ALVIN EARL,** organic chemistry, for more information see previous edition

**TREVINO, DANIEL LOUIS,** NEUROPHYSIOLOGY. *Current Pos:* ASSOC PROF APPLIED PHYSIOL & ASST DEAN, MINORITY PROGS, PA STATE UNIV, 87- *Personal Data:* b Edinburg, Tex, May 15, 43; m 83, Linda Klebe; c 2. *Educ:* Univ Tex, Austin, BA, 65, PhD(physiol), 70. *Prof Exp:* Instr physiol, Sch Med Univ NC, Chapel Hill, 72-73; asst prof, 73-79; assoc dir student affairs & res asst prof anat, Sch Med, Univ NMex,

Albuquerque, 79-81; res assoc prof anat & asst dean student affairs, Sch Med, Univ Tex Med Br, Galveston, 81-87. *Concurrent Pos:* USPHS fel, Univ Tex Southwest Med Sch Dallas, 70 & Marine Biomed Inst, Galveston, 70-72; fel neurobiol, Sch Med, Univ NC, Chapel Hill, 72- *Mem:* AAAS; Sigma Xi; Soc Neurosci. *Res:* Sensory neurophysiology; pain. *Mailing Add:* Pa State Univ 113 Henderson University Park PA 16802. *Fax:* 814-865-3282

**TREVINO, SAMUEL FRANCISCO,** SPECTROSCOPY & SPECTROMETRY. *Current Pos:* RES PHYSICIST, ARDEC, PICATINNY ARSENAL, NJ, 64- *Personal Data:* b San Antonio, Tex, Apr 2, 36; m 58, Juliette Gonzales; c Samuel A, Leticia L, Jumge J, Felicitas & Magdalena. *Educ:* St Mary's Univ, Tex, BS, 58; Univ Notre Dame, PhD(physics), 63. *Honors & Awards:* Paul A Siple Award, Dept Army, 70. *Concurrent Pos:* Guest physicist, Reactor Radiation Div, Nat Bur Stand, 71- *Mem:* AAAS; Am Physics Soc. *Res:* Spectroscopy using inelastic scattering of low energy neutrons, particularly vibrational properties of molecular crystals; computer molecular dynamics simulation of condensed matter chemistry in both equilibrium and non-equilibrium environments via shock and detonation waves. *Mailing Add:* 14720 Waterway Dr Rockville MD 20853

**TREVITHICK, JOHN RICHARD,** BIOCHEMISTRY. *Current Pos:* asst prof, 67-72, assoc prof, 73-80, PROF BIOCHEM, UNIV WESTERN ONT, 80- *Personal Data:* b St Thomas, Ont, Nov 30, 38; m 29, Donna; c Caroline, Scott & Colleen. *Educ:* Queen's Univ, Ont, BSc, 61; Univ Wis-Madison, PhD(physiol chem), 65. *Prof Exp:* Nat Res Coun fel, Univ BC, 65-67; sabbatical, Inst Microbiol, Univ Berne, Switz, 72-73. *Concurrent Pos:* Ed, J Can Fedn Biol Socs, 71-72 & 77-80; assoc res vision ophthalmol, Int Soc Eye Res. *Mem:* Can Biochem Soc; Can Fedn Biol Socs. *Res:* Biochemistry of development and differentiation, mechanism and risk reduction agents for cortical cataract formation, especially diabetic, astronaut, aircrew and nuclear accident and microwave cataracts; extracellular enzymes of microorganisms; histones and nuclear proteins; the lens. *Mailing Add:* Dept Biochem Med Sch Univ Western Ont London ON N6A 5C1 Can. *Fax:* 519-661-3175; *E-Mail:* trevjohn@julian.uwo.ca

**TREVOR, ANTHONY JOHN,** BIOCHEMICAL PHARMACOLOGY, NEUROCHEMISTRY. *Current Pos:* Lectr, 64-65, from asst prof to assoc prof, 65-77, PROF PHARMACOL, SCH MED, UNIV CALIF, SAN FRANCISCO, 77-, ACTG CHMN, 78- *Personal Data:* b London, Eng, Dec 27, 34; m 63; c 4. *Educ:* Univ Southampton, BSc, 60; Univ London, PhD(biochem), 63. *Concurrent Pos:* NSF res grants, 72-74 & 75-; USPHS fel neuropharmacol, Sch Med, Univ Calif, San Francisco, 63-64, NIH res grants, 66-75. *Mem:* AAAS; Am Soc Pharmacol & Exp Therapeut; Am Soc Neurochem; Int Soc Neurochem; Soc Toxicol. *Res:* Brain enzymes purification, acetylcholinesterase, mechanisms of action and biodisposition of anesthetics. *Mailing Add:* Dept Pharmacol Therapeut Univ Calif San Francisco Sch Med 513 Parnassus Ave San Francisco CA 94122-2722

**TREVORROW, LAVERNE EVERETT,** INORGANIC CHEMISTRY, PHYSICAL CHEMISTRY. *Current Pos:* asst chemist, 55-59, ASSOC CHEMIST, ARGONNE NAT LAB, 59- *Personal Data:* b Moline, Ill, Nov 1, 28; m 50; c 2. *Educ:* Augustana Col, Ill, AB, 50; Okla State Univ, MS, 52; Univ Wis, PhD(chem), 55. *Prof Exp:* Asst, Okla State Univ, 50-52; asst, Univ Wis, 52-55. *Mem:* Am Chem Soc. *Res:* Chemistry of fluorine and metal fluorides; uranium, neptunium, plutonium and fission elements; molten salt batteries; analysis of radioactive waste disposal systems and nuclear fuel cycle systems; disposal of low-level radioactive waste and nuclear byproduct wastes; environmental impact assessment. *Mailing Add:* 406 Dorset Pl Glen Ellyn IL 60137

**TREVORS, JACK THOMAS,** PLASMID BIOLOGY, MICROBIOLOGY. *Current Pos:* From asst prof to assoc prof, 82-93, PROF MICROBIOL, UNIV GUELPH, 93- *Personal Data:* b Berwick, NS, Feb 24, 53; m 79, Karen E Saunders; c 1. *Educ:* Acadia Univ, BSc, 78, MSc, 79; Univ Waterloo, PhD(microbiol), 82. *Concurrent Pos:* Consult, Health & Welfare Can, 87, Agriculture Can, 88 & Environ Can; ed, Microbiol Ecol Sect, Can J Microbiol; ed, Antonie van Leeuwenhock Int J Gen & Molecular Microbiol. *Mem:* Can Soc Microbiol. *Res:* Physiology and genetics of metal-resistance mechanisms in bacteria; gene transfer between bacteria in soil and aquatic environments; methods for isolating DNA; development of electroporation protocols for transforming gram-negative and gram-positive bacteria; environmental microbiology; biotechnology; bioremediation; molecular evolution in bacteria; nucleic acids in the environment. *Mailing Add:* Dept Environ Biol Univ Guelph Guelph ON N1G 2W1 Can

**TREVOY, DONALD JAMES,** SOLID STATE CHEMISTRY, ENERGY CONVERSION. *Current Pos:* SR LAB HEAD, EASTMAN KODAK CO, 49- *Personal Data:* b Saskatoon, Sask, Jan 27, 22; m 46; c 4. *Educ:* Univ Sask, BE, 44, MSc, 46; Univ Ill, PhD(chem eng), 49. *Prof Exp:* Chem engr, Nat Res Coun Can, 44-46. *Mem:* Am Chem Soc; AAAS; NY Acad Sci; Electrochem Soc; Sigma Xi. *Res:* Liquid-liquid extraction; thermal diffusion; high vacuum evaporation of liquids; physical chemistry of lithography; antistatic agents; photochemistry; organic semiconductors; conducting coatings; batteries; solar energy conversion. *Mailing Add:* 13 Countryside Rd Fairport NY 14450-2807

**TREWELLA, JEFFREY CHARLES,** NUCLEAR MAGNETIC RESONANCE SPECTROSCOPY, MASS SPECTROMETRY. *Current Pos:* Res chemist, 79-81, SR RES CHEMIST, MOBIL RES DEVELOP CORP, 81- *Educ:* Lock Haven State Col, Pa, BS, 75; Pa State Univ, PhD(chem), 79. *Mem:* Am Chem Soc; Soc Appl Spectrosc. *Res:* Hydrogen bonding in liquids by nuclear magnetic resonance techniques; developed liquid chromatographic and high resolution mass spectrometric methods for the characterization of shale oils; developed inductively coupled plasma methods for multielemental analysis of both agreous and organic samples. *Mailing Add:* Mobil Res & Develop Corp PO Box 480 Paulsboro NJ 08066-0480

**TREWHELLA, JILL,** NEUTRON SCATTERING & ISOTOPE LABELING, BIOMOLECULAR COMPLEXES IN REGULATION OF BIOCHEMICAL PROCESSES. *Current Pos:* staff mem, Los Alamos Nat Lab, 84-88, sect leader, 88-90, dep group leader, 90-91, sci adv & staff mem, 91-92, group leader biosci & biotechnol, 92-95, LAB FEL, CHEM SCI & TECHNOL DIV, LOS ALAMOS NAT LAB, 95- *Personal Data:* b Sydney, Australia, Jan 24, 53; US citizen; m 91, Don Merrill Parkin; c Graham Andrew, Paul & Valerie. *Educ:* Univ NSW, BSc, 75, MSc, 78; Univ Sydney, PhD(inorg chem), 81. *Prof Exp:* Postdoctoral assoc, Yale Univ, 80-83, assoc res scientist, 83-84. *Concurrent Pos:* Adj assoc prof cell biol, Univ NMex, 89-; mem, Study Sect Molecular & Cellular Biophys, NIH, 96- *Mem:* Biophys Soc; Neutron Scattering Soc Am; Am Crystallog Soc; Protein Soc. *Res:* Molecular basis for biological function using biophysical structural biology tools; understanding the structural mechanisms for regulation of biochemical processes. *Mailing Add:* Chem Sci & Technol Div Los Alamos Nat Lab MS G758 Los Alamos NM 87545. *Fax:* 505-667-0110; *E-Mail:* jtrewhella@lanl.gov

**TREWILER, CARL EDWARD,** POLYMER CHEMISTRY. *Current Pos:* RETIRED. *Personal Data:* b Sheridan, NY, Sept 17, 34; m 54; c 4. *Educ:* Alfred Univ, BA, 56; Univ Akron, PhD(polymer sci), 66. *Prof Exp:* Resin chemist, Durez Plastics Div, Hooker Chem Co, 56-58; develop engr, Laminated Prod Bus Dept, Gen Elec Co, Ohio, 58-64; staff chemist polymerization, Akron Univ, 64-66; polymer chemist, 66-78, mgr paper & composite prod develop, laminated prod bus dept, Gen Elec Co, 78-92. *Mem:* Am Chem Soc. *Res:* Thermosetting resins and polymers in laminate applications. *Mailing Add:* 1979 Walnut Coshocton OH 43812

**TREWYN, RONALD WILLIAM,** CARCINOGENESIS, CELL BIOLOGY. *Current Pos:* asst prof, 78-83, ASSOC PROF PHYSIOL CHEM, OHIO STATE UNIV, 83- *Personal Data:* b Edgerton, Wis, Aug 24, 43; m 70; c 1. *Educ:* Wis State Univ, BS, 70; Ore State Univ, PhD(microbiol), 74. *Prof Exp:* Res assoc biochem, Univ Colo Health Sci Ctr, 74-77, instr, 77-78. *Concurrent Pos:* Res scientist, Comp Cancer Ctr, Ohio State Univ, 78-, dir, Tumor Procurement Serv, 81- *Mem:* Am Asn Cancer Res; Am Soc Biol Chem. *Res:* Cellular changes in the transfer RNA metabolism associated with carcinogenesis in an effort to elucidate the role of these changes in the neoplastic process and differentiation. *Mailing Add:* Comprehensive Cancer Ctr Ohio State Univ 410 W 12th Ave Columbus OH 43210-1214. *Fax:* 614-292-4767

**TREXLER, DENNIS THOMAS,** REMOTE SENSING, GEOTHERMAL. *Current Pos:* RETIRED. *Personal Data:* b Compton, Calif, Aug 6, 40; m 66. *Educ:* Univ Southern Calif, BS, 65, MS, 68. *Prof Exp:* Eng geologist, State Calif Dept Water Resources, 66-67; Geolabs, Inc, 67-68; staff geologist, Space Div, Aerojet-Gen Corp, 68-70; mgr, Microwave Sensor Systs Div, Spectran Inc, 70-71; res assoc, Mackay Sch Mines, Univ Nev, 71-74 & Nev Bur Mines & Geol, 74-81; dir & prin investr, Div Earth Sci, Environ Res Ctr, Univ Nev, Las Vegas, 81- *Concurrent Pos:* Consult, Am Mus Natural Hist, 74- *Mem:* Am Asn Petrol Geologists; Geothermal Resources Coun; Sigma Xi. *Res:* Assessment and application of geothermal resources; interpretation and application of remote sensing techniques; earthquake hazards assessment; geoarcheology to determine holocene climatic conditions. *Mailing Add:* 115 Blair Pl Reno NV 89509

**TREXLER, FREDERICK DAVID,** GEOLOGY, MICROCOMPUTER INTERFACING. *Current Pos:* From asst prof to assoc prof physics, 69-78, dept head, 78-82, PROF PHYSICS, HOUGHTON COL, 78-, DEPT HEAD, 88- *Personal Data:* b Rahway, NJ, Feb 24, 42; m 64, Valerie Bock; c Laurel & Michael. *Educ:* Houghton Col, BS, 64; Pa State Univ, University Park, PhD(solid state sci), 71. *Concurrent Pos:* Radio eng, 75-; secy, Houghton Col Radio Corp; secy & treas, NY State Sect, Am Phys Soc. *Mem:* Am Asn Physics Teachers; Sigma Xi; Am Phys Soc. *Res:* Micro-electronics. *Mailing Add:* Dept Physics & Earth Sci Houghton NY 14744. *E-Mail:* ftrexler@houghton.edu

**TREXLER, JOHN PETER,** GEOLOGY, STRATIGRAPHY. *Current Pos:* RETIRED. *Personal Data:* b Allentown, Pa, Nov 8, 26; m 50; c 2. *Educ:* Lehigh Univ, BA, 50, MS, 53; Univ Mich, PhD(geol), 64. *Prof Exp:* Asst geologist, Lehigh Portland Cement Co, 50-52; geologist, Fuels Br, US Geol Surv, 53-59; assoc prof geol, Juanita Col, 62-69, chmn dept, 62-69, chmn sci div, 67-70, prof geol, 69-89, chmn dept, 74-89. *Concurrent Pos:* NSF fel, Princeton Univ, 70-71; vis prof, Univ Edinburgh, 84. *Mem:* Fel Geol Soc Am; Am Asn Petrol Geologists; Sigma Xi. *Res:* Field geology; stratigraphy and structural geology of sedimentary rocks of central and eastern Pennsylvania, particularly in the anthracite region. *Mailing Add:* Box 294 RD 2 Huntingdon PA 16652

**TREYBIG, LEON BRUCE,** MATHEMATICS. *Current Pos:* PROF MATH, TEX A&M UNIV, 70- *Personal Data:* b Yoakum, Tex, Aug 29, 31; m 52; c 3. *Educ:* Univ Tex, BA, 53, PhD(math), 58. *Prof Exp:* Spec instr math, Univ Tex, 54-58; instr, Tulane Univ, 58-59, res assoc, 59-60, from asst prof to prof, 60-70. *Mem:* Am Math Soc. *Res:* Integer programming; separability in metric spaces; continuous images of ordered compacta; knot theory. *Mailing Add:* Dept Math Tex A&M Univ College Station TX 77843-1246

**TREZEK, GEORGE J,** MECHANICAL ENGINEERING. *Current Pos:* from asst prof to assoc prof, 66-74, PROF MECH ENG, UNIV CALIF, BERKELEY, 74- *Personal Data:* b Chicago, Ill, July 10, 37; m 62; c 3. *Educ:* Gen Motors Inst, BME, 61; Univ Ill, MS, 62, PhD(mech eng), 65. *Prof Exp:* Asst prof mech eng, Northwestern Univ, 65-66. *Concurrent Pos:* Consult engr. *Mem:* Am Soc Mech Engrs; Am Soc Testing & Mat. *Res:* Solid and hazardous waste management; size reduction, material and energy recovery from wastes; development of toxic waste treatment technology; power plant waste-heat dispersal and utilization problems; spray cooling system design. *Mailing Add:* 2210 Canyon Oak Lane Danville CA 94506

**TRIA, JOHN JOSEPH, JR,** PHYSICAL CHEMISTRY, THERMOCHEMISTRY. *Current Pos:* sr res chemist, Monsanto Co, 79-82, res specialist, 83-87, sr res specialist, 87-93, TECHNOL CONSULT, MONSANTO CO, 93- *Personal Data:* b Shelby, NC, May 26, 46; m 76, Barbara Hoffman. *Educ:* Duke Univ, BS, 68; Fla State Univ, PhD(phys chem), 77. *Prof Exp:* Res fel phys chem, dept chem, Fla State Univ, 77-78 & Ohio State Univ, 78-79. *Mem:* Am Chem Soc; Sigma Xi; Am Soc Testing & Mat; NAm Thermal Anal Sci. *Res:* Thermochemistry; physico-chemical property measurements; chemical instrumentation. *Mailing Add:* 800 N Linbergh Monsanto-S4B St Louis MO 63167-0001. *Fax:* 314-694-6727

**TRIANDAFILIDIS, GEORGE EMMANUEL,** CIVIL ENGINEERING, SOIL MECHANICS. *Current Pos:* assoc prof, 64-68, prof, 64-85, EMER PROF CIVIL ENG, UNIV NMEX, 85- *Personal Data:* b Istanbul, Turkey, Nov 6, 22; US citizen; m 56, Eugenia Terziogl; c Stephen & John. *Educ:* Robert Col, Istanbul, BS, 45; Univ Ill, Urbana, MS, 47, PhD, 60. *Prof Exp:* From instr to asst prof civil eng, Univ Ill, Urbana, 57-61; asst prof, Rice Univ, 61-64. *Concurrent Pos:* Consult, 57- & Eric H Wang Civil Eng Res Facility, 61-64; mem, Hwy Res Bd, Nat Acad Sci-Nat Res Coun. *Mem:* Am Soc Civil Engrs; Int Soc Soil Mech & Found Engrs; Sigma Xi. *Res:* Soil mechanics and foundations, especially dynamic properties of earth materials and soil-structure interaction phenomena; soil and rock mechanics; foundations and pavements. *Mailing Add:* 4611 Glenwood Hills Dr NE Albuquerque NM 87111. *Fax:* 505-884-4186

**TRIANDIS, HARRY CHARALAMBOS,** PSYCHOLOGY. *Current Pos:* From asst prof to assoc prof, 58-66, PROF PSYCHOL, UNIV ILL, 66- *Personal Data:* b Patras, Greece, Oct 16, 26; m 66, Pola Fotitch; c Louisa. *Educ:* McGill Univ, BE, 51; Univ Toronto Ont, MCom, 54; Cornell Univ, PhD, 58. *Hon Degrees:* Dr, Univ Athens, Greece, 87. *Honors & Awards:* Award, Interam Soc Psychol, 81. *Concurrent Pos:* Grantee, USPHS, 56-60 & 62, Social & Rehab Serv, HEW, 68-73, Ford Found, 73-75; ed consult, J Personality & Social Psychol, 63-71, J Applied Psychol, 70-79, J Cross-Cultural Psychol, 74-; sr fel, Ford Found, 64-65; consult, NSF, 68-75 & US Info Agency, 70-75; Guggenheim fel, 72-73. *Mem:* Soc Psychol Study Social Issues (pres, 75-76); Int Asn Cross-Cultural Psychol (pres, 74-76); Interam Soc Psychol (pres, 85-87); Soc Exp Social Psychol; Soc Personality & Social Psychol (pres, 76-77); Int Asn Appl Psychol (pres, 90-94). *Res:* Published author. *Mailing Add:* 1 Lake Park Rd Champaign IL 61821-7101

**TRIANO, JOHN JOSEPH,** neurophysiology, applied mechanics, for more information see previous edition

**TRIANTAFYLLOU, GEORGE S,** HYDRODYNAMIC STABILITY & TURBULENCE, DYNAMICS. *Current Pos:* assoc prof, 90-95, PROF MECH ENG, CITY COL NY, 95- *Personal Data:* b Istanbul, Turkey, 54. *Educ:* Nat Tech Univ Athens, dipl, 77; Calif Tech Inst, MS, 78; Mass Inst Technol, MS, 80, PhD(ocean eng), 83. *Prof Exp:* Res engr, Greek Navy, 83-85; res scientist, Mass Inst Technol, 85-89, prin res scientist, 89-90. *Mem:* Am Phys Soc. *Res:* Theoretical instability and pattern formation in physical systems; theoretical and computational turbulence in Newtonian fluids. *Mailing Add:* Levich Inst T-1M-9 New York NY 10031. *Fax:* 212-650-6835; *E-Mail:* gtrian@lid4a0.engr.ccny.cuny.edu

**TRIANTAFYLLOU, MICHAEL S,** VORTICITY CONTROL OF FLOWS, BIOMIMESIS. *Current Pos:* Res Assoc, Mass Inst Technol, 78-79, asst prof, 79-83, assoc prof, 83-90, Doherty prof, 83-85, PROF OCEAN ENG, MASS INST TECHNOL, 90- *Personal Data:* b Athens, Greece, Oct 27, 51; US citizen; m 85, Joan Kimball; c Stefanos & Kimon. *Educ:* Nat Tech Univ Athens, Bs, 74; Mass Inst Technol, SM(ocean eng) & SM(mech eng), 77, ScD(ocean eng), 79. *Concurrent Pos:* Dir testing tank, Mass Inst Technol, 90-; vis scientist, Woods Hole Oceanog Inst, 91-; assoc ed, J Fluids Eng, 96- *Mem:* Am Phys Soc; Soc Naval Architects & Marine Engrs; Am Soc Mech Engrs; Int Soc Offshore & Polar Engrs. *Res:* Control of steady and unsteady flows; fish hydrodynamics; biomimesis and marine robotics. *Mailing Add:* Mass Inst Technol Rm 5-323 77 Massachusetts Ave Cambridge MA 02139. *E-Mail:* mistetri@mit.edu

**TRIANTAPHYLLOPOULOS, EUGENIE,** clinical trials evaluation; deceased, see previous edition for last biography

**TRIANTAPHYLLOU, ANASTASIOS CHRISTOS,** CYTOGENETICS, NEMATODES. *Current Pos:* asst geneticist, 60-62, from asst prof to prof, 62-91, EMER PROF GENETICS, NC STATE UNIV, 91- *Personal Data:* b Amaliapolis-Volou, Greece, Nov 30, 26; m 60; c Christos. *Educ:* Athens Superior Sch Agr, Greece, BS, 49, MS, 50; NC State Univ, PhD(plant path, bot), 59. *Honors & Awards:* Ruth Allen Award, Am Phytopath Soc. *Prof Exp:* Nematologist, Benaki Phytopath Inst, Greece, 50-60. *Concurrent Pos:* Ed, J Nematol, 83-87, Revue de Nematologie, 84-90. *Mem:* AAAS; Genetics Soc Am; fel Soc Nematologists; Am Inst Biol Sci. *Res:* Cytogenetics, evolution, mode of reproduction and sexuality of nematodes; genetics and cytology of plant parasitic nematodes. *Mailing Add:* 106 Merwin Rd Raleigh NC 27606

**TRIANTAPHYLLOU, HEDWIG HIRSCHMANN,** PLANT NEMATOLOGY. *Current Pos:* RETIRED. *Personal Data:* b Fuerth, Bavaria, Ger, Jan 16, 27; nat US; m 60, Anastasios C; c Christos F. *Educ:* Univ Erlangen, PhD(zool), 51. *Honors & Awards:* Res Award, Sigma Xi, 62; Ruth Allen Award, Am Phytopath Soc, 93. *Prof Exp:* Tech asst, NC State Univ, 54-55, res instr, 55-57, from asst prof to assoc prof, 57-67, prof plant path, 67-92. *Concurrent Pos:* Ed, J , Soc Nematol, 69-73; ed, Nematologica Soc Europ Nematologists, 75-90. *Mem:* Soc Europ Nematologists; fel Soc Nematologists; Sigma Xi; Am Phytopath Soc. *Res:* Taxonomy and biology of free-living and plant-parasitic nematodes; ultrastructure of plant parasitic nematodes. *Mailing Add:* 106 Merwin Rd Raleigh NC 27606. *Fax:* 919-515-7716

**TRIBBEY, BERT ALLEN,** FRESHWATER ECOLOGY, RESERVOIR FISHERIES. *Current Pos:* From asst prof to assoc prof, 65-73, chmn dept, 72-78, PROF BIOL, CALIF STATE UNIV, FRESNO, 73- *Personal Data:* b Moorpark, Calif, Aug 8, 38; m 61, Edith Elliott; c Lee & Diane. *Educ:* Univ Calif, Santa Barbara, AB, 61; Univ Tex, PhD(zool), 65. *Concurrent Pos:* Vis prof, Mich State Univ, 78-79 & Univ Wis, 78. *Res:* Structure and succession of aquatic communities; ecology of temporary ponds; physiological ecology of freshwater invertebrates; Ecology of freshwater communities; ecological modelling; reservoir fisheries; physiological ecology of freshwater invertebrates. *Mailing Add:* Dept Biol Calif State Univ 2555 E San Ramon Fresno CA 93740-8034. *Fax:* 209-278-7139; *E-Mail:* bert@csofresno.edu

**TRIBBLE, LELAND FLOYD,** ANIMAL SCIENCE. *Current Pos:* prof, 67-89, EMER PROF ANIMAL SCI, TEX TECH UNIV, 89- *Personal Data:* b Oxnard, Calif, July 12, 23; wid; c Kent, Alan, Karen & Greg. *Educ:* Univ Mo, BS, 49, MS, 50, PhD(agr), 56. *Prof Exp:* Instr animal husb, Univ Mo, 49-56, assoc prof, 56-67. *Concurrent Pos:* Vis prof, Kans State Univ, 65-66; nonruminant nutritionist, USDA, Washington, DC, 74-75. *Mem:* Fel Am Soc Animal Sci. *Res:* Animal nutrition; swine production and management. *Mailing Add:* Tex Tech Univ 6613 Norfolk Lubbock TX 79413

**TRIBBLE, ROBERT EDMOND,** NUCLEAR PHYSICS. *Current Pos:* from asst prof to assoc prof, 75-82, head dept, 79-87, PROF PHYSICS, TEX A&M UNIV, 82- *Personal Data:* b Mexico, Mo, Jan 7, 47; m 86; c 1. *Educ:* Univ Mo, Columbia, BS, 69; Princeton Univ, PhD(nuclear physics), 73. *Prof Exp:* Instr physics, Princeton Univ, 73-75. *Concurrent Pos:* A P Sloan fel, 76-80; vis scientist, Max Planck Inst, Heidelburg, 77-78; assoc fac fel, Western Univ, 87-88. *Mem:* fel Am Phys Soc. *Res:* Experimental research to determine reaction rates, masses and radioactive decays pertinent to nuclear astrophysics; weak interaction experiments that will test the standard model of electro-weak interactions. *Mailing Add:* Cyclotron Inst Tex A&M Univ College Station TX 77843. *Fax:* 409-845-1899

**TRIBUS, MYRON,** ENGINEERING, QUALITY MANAGEMENT. *Current Pos:* DIR, EXERGY INC, HAYWARD, CALIF, 86- *Personal Data:* b San Francisco, Calif, Oct 30, 21; m 45, Sue Davis; c Lou & Kamala. *Educ:* Univ Calif, Berkeley, BS, 42, Los Angeles, PhD(eng), 49. *Honors & Awards:* Wright Bros Medal, Soc Automotive Engrs, 45; Bane Award, Inst Aerospace Sci, Am Inst Aeronaut & Astronaut, 46; Alfred Noble Prize, 52. *Prof Exp:* From lectr to assoc prof eng, Univ Calif, Los Angeles, 46-58, prof, 58-61; dean, Thayer Sch Eng, Dartmouth Col, 61-69; asst secy commerce for sci & technol, 69-71; sr vpres res & eng, Info Technol Group, Xerox Corp, 71-75; dir, Ctr Advan Eng Study, Mass Inst Technol, 75-86. *Concurrent Pos:* Consult, Gen Elec Co, 50- & NATO, 53; dir icing res, Univ Mich, 51-54; Presidential appointee, Nat Adv Comn Oceans & Atmosphere, 72- *Mem:* Nat Acad Eng; Am Soc Mech Engrs; Am Inst Aeronaut & Astronaut; Soc Automotive Engrs. *Res:* Heat transfer; thermodynamics; decision theory. *Mailing Add:* Exergy Inc 22320 Foothill Blvd Hayward CA 94538

**TRICE, VIRGIL GARNETT, JR,** nuclear waste management, for more information see previous edition

**TRICE, WILLIAM HENRY,** RESEARCH ADMINISTRATION. *Current Pos:* RETIRED. *Personal Data:* b Geneva, NY, Apr 4, 33; m 55; c 2. *Educ:* State Univ NY Col Forestry, BS, 55; Inst Paper Chem, MS, 60, PhD(phys chem), 63. *Prof Exp:* Res scientist, Union Camp Corp 63-66, group leader res & develop, 66-68, sect leader, 68-72, tech dir bleached div, 72-74, vpres res & develop, 74-79, sr vpres, 79-85, exec vpres res & develop, 85-96. *Concurrent Pos:* Pres, Paper Technol Found, Western Mich Univ, 79-81; chmn, Res Adv Comt, Inst Paper Chem, 82-83. *Mem:* Fel Tech Asn Pulp & Paper Indust; AAAS. *Res:* Fatty acid and terpene chemistry; pulp and paper chemistry; engineering in fields related to pulp and paper. *Mailing Add:* 6 Hanover Rd Mt Lakes Wayne NJ 07046

**TRICHE, TIMOTHY J,** CANCER DIAGNOSIS & TREATMENT, CHILDHOOD CANCER. *Current Pos:* CHMN & PATHOLOGIST-IN-CHIEF, DEPT PATH & MED LAB, CHILDRENS HOSP, LOS ANGELES, 88- *Personal Data:* b San Angolo, Tex, June 4, 44; c 3. *Educ:* Cornell Univ, AB, 66; Tulane Univ, PhD(med), 71. *Prof Exp:* Sect chief cell biol & histol, Lab Path, Nat Cancer Inst, NIH, 75-88. *Concurrent Pos:* Vchmn & prof, Dept Path, Univ Southern Calif, 88-; chmn, Path Discipline Comt, Childrens Cancer Study Group, 90- *Mem:* Am Soc Cell Biol; Int Acad Path; Soc Pediat Pathologists; Am Asn Pathologists; Am Soc Clin Pathologists; Am Asn Cancer Res. *Res:* Biologic behavior and genetic basis of childhood cancer using tumor cell lines and tumor tissue from childhood cancer patients. *Mailing Add:* Dept Path & Lab Med Childrens Hosp Los Angeles 4650 Sunset Blvd Box 43 Los Angeles CA 90027-6088. *Fax:* 213-667-1123

**TRICHOPOULOS, DIMITRIOS V,** BREAST CANCER EPIDEMIOLOGY & ETIOLOGY, PASSIVE SMOKING & HEALTH. *Current Pos:* lectr epidemiol, 69-70, PROF EPIDEMIOL & CANCER PREV, DEPT EPIDEMIOL, HARVARD SCH PUB HEALTH, 89-, DIR, CTR CANCER PREV, 92- *Personal Data:* b Volos, Greece, Dec 9, 38. *Educ:* Univ Athens, Med dipl, 63, Doctorate, 65, PhD(epidemiol), 71; Harvard Univ, MS, 68. *Hon Degrees:* Dr, Uppsala Univ, Sweden, 94. *Honors & Awards:* Officer Order Palmes Acad, Fr Govt, 83. *Prof Exp:* Res asst epidemiol, Univ Athens Med Sch, 63-65, lectr hyg & epidemiol, 65-67, assoc prof, 71-72, prof & dir, Dept Hyg & Epidemiol, 72-89. *Concurrent Pos:* Clin asst therapeut, Alexandra Teaching Hosp, Athens, 63-65; chmn, Health & AIDS Group, Europ Community Coun, 88. *Mem:* Am Epidemiol Soc; Am Col Epidemiol; Soc Epidemiol; foreign corresp mem Royal Acad Med Belg; foreign corresp mem Nat Acad Med France; Greek Soc Hyg & Epidemiol (pres, 78-80); Greek Soc Social Med (pres, 80-82). *Res:* Development and evaluation of hypothesis linking prenatal exposures to breast cancer risk in humans; study health effect of passive smoking; etiology of primary liver cancer. *Mailing Add:* Harvard Sch Pub Health 677 Huntington Ave Boston MA 02115. *Fax:* 617-566-7805

**TRICK, CHARLES GORDON,** MICROBIAL BIOCHEMISTRY, BIOGEOCHEMISTRY. *Current Pos:* PROF PLANT SCI, UNIV WESTERN ONT, 86- *Personal Data:* b Medicine Hat, Alta, Jan 29, 54; m 79; c 1. *Educ:* Univ Man, BSc, 75; Acadia Univ, MSc, 77; Univ BC, PhD(oceanog), 82. *Prof Exp:* Teaching fel biochem, Univ Calif, Berkeley, 82-84; asst prof environ studies, Inst Environ Studies, Univ Toronto, 84-86. *Mem:* Am Soc Limnol & Oceanog; Am Soc Microbiol; Phys Soc Am; Int Asn Great Lakes Res. *Res:* Mechanisms of microbial adaptation; use of molecular genetic techniques in environmental studies; plant and microbial biotechnology. *Mailing Add:* Dept Plant Sci Univ Western Ont 1151 Richmond St London ON N6A 3K7 Can. *Fax:* 519-661-3935; *E-Mail:* 11007_1120@uwovax.uwo.ca

**TRICK, GORDON STAPLES,** TECHNOLOGY COMMERCIALIZATION. *Current Pos:* SCI & TECHNOL CONSULT, 85- *Personal Data:* b Winnipeg, Man, May 6, 27; m 52, Ella Kenning; c Charles, David, Michael & Janice. *Educ:* McGill Univ, BS, 49, PhD(chem), 52; Univ Western Ont, MS, 50. *Prof Exp:* Ramsay Mem fel, London, 53; sci serv officer, Defence Res Bd Can, 53-56; sr res chemist & res scientist, Goodyear Tire & Rubber Co, 56-71; exec dir, Man Res Coun & Technol Div, Govt Man, 71-85. *Concurrent Pos:* Adj prof, Univ Man, 72-80; mem adv bd sci & tech info, Nat Res Coun Can, 72-78, Stand Coun Can, 78-85 & Strategic Res, 84-86. *Mem:* Sigma Xi; fel Chem Inst Can; Can Res Mgt Asn. *Res:* Gas and liquid phase kinetics; phase transitions in polymers; stress-strain properties; technology transfer; innovation development; science policy; economic analysis; manufacturing productivity. *Mailing Add:* Box 101 St Germain MB R0G 2A0 Can

**TRICK, TIMOTHY NOEL,** ELECTRICAL ENGINEERING. *Current Pos:* From asst prof to assoc prof elec eng, Univ Ill, Urbana, 65-75, dir, Coord Sci Lab, 83-85, dept head elec & comput eng, 85-95, PROF ELEC ENG, UNIV ILL, URBANA, 75-, DIR, SLOAN CTR ASYNCHRONOUS LEARNING ENVIRON, 95- *Personal Data:* b Dayton, Ohio, July 14, 39; m 58, Dorthe L Jacobs; c Paticia, Michael, Thomas, William, Gregory & Andrew. *Educ:* Univ Dayton, BEE, 61; Purdue Univ, MSEE, 62, PhD(elec eng), 66. *Honors & Awards:* Guillemin-Cauer Award, Inst Elec & Electronics Engrs, 76; Centennial Medal, 84, Meritorious Serv Award, 88; ME VanValkenburg Award, Circuit & Syst Soc, 94. *Concurrent Pos:* Summer fac fel, Am Soc Eng Educ-NASA, 70 & 71; consult, Rome Air Develop Ctr, 75-79, IBM, 82-83 & Cadence, 89-; vis assoc prof, Univ Calif, Berkeley, 73-74; vis lectr, Nat Inst Astrophys, Optics & Electronics, Mex, 75; vpres publ, Inst Elec & Electronics Engrs, 88-90, mem bd dirs, 86-90; pres, Nat Elec Eng Dept Heads Asn, 94-95. *Mem:* Fel Inst Elec & Electronics Engrs; Am Soc Eng Educators; fel AAAS. *Res:* Numerical methods and computer algorithms for the analysis and design of electrical circuits. *Mailing Add:* Dept Elec & Comput Eng Univ Ill 1406 W Green St Urbana IL 61801. *Fax:* 217-333-7427

**TRICKEY, SAMUEL BALDWIN,** THEORETICAL PHYSICS, SOLID STATE PHYSICS. *Current Pos:* vis asst prof, Univ Fla, 68-70, from asst prof to assoc prof, 70-77, dir comput & commun res, Col Lib Arts & Sci, 86-90, exec dir info technol & servs, 91-96, PROF PHYSICS & CHEM, UNIV FLA, 79- *Personal Data:* b Detroit, Mich, Nov 28, 40; m, Cynthia R Karle; c 2. *Educ:* Rice Univ, BA, 62; Tex A&M Univ, MS, 66, PhD(physics), 68. *Prof Exp:* Physicist, Mason & Hanger, Silas Mason Corp, Tex, 62-64; prof & chmn dept physics, Tex Tech Univ, 77-79. *Concurrent Pos:* Vis staff mem, Los Alamos Sci Lab, 71 & 91; consult, Quantum Physics Group, Redstone Arsenal, Ala, 72-76; consult phys sci, IBM Res Labs, San Jose, Calif, 75-76, Theoretical Div, Los Alamos Nat Lab, 84-; dir comput quantum theory proj, Univ Fla, 82-92, Inst Cond Matter Studies, Mich Tech Univ, 85-87; vis scientist, Max Planck Inst, Munich, 85-94; vis scholar, Tech Univ, Munich, 95- *Mem:* Fel Am Phys Soc; Am Asn Physics Teachers; Sigma Xi. *Res:* Theory of structure and energetics of crystals and thin films, computational physics, density functional theory; quantum chemistry; high performance computing and networking. *Mailing Add:* Dept Phys & Chem Univ Fla Williamson Hall Gainesville FL 32611. *Fax:* 352-392-8722; *E-Mail:* trickey@optp.ufl.edu

**TRICOLES, GUS PETER,** MICROWAVE IMAGING, OPTICAL COMPUTING. *Current Pos:* eng specialist, Gen Dynamics Electronics Div, 61-89, sr eng staff specialist, 89-94, SR ENG STAFF SPECIALIST, GDE SYSTS, INC, 94- *Personal Data:* b San Francisco, Calif, Oct 18, 31; wid; c Rosanne & Robin. *Educ:* Univ Calif, Los Angeles, BA, 55; San Diego State Univ, MS, 58; Univ Calif, San Diego, MS, 62, PhD(appl physics),71. *Prof*

*Exp:* Asst res engr, Gen Dynamics/Convair, 55, res engr, 55-59, sr res engr, 59; physicist, Smyth Res Assocs, 59-61 & Univ Calif, 62. *Concurrent Pos:* Consult, Belvoir Res & Develop Ctr, US Army, 87-89. *Mem:* Fel Inst Elec & Electronics Engrs; fel Optical Soc Am; Int Sci Radio Union; NY Acad Sci; Am Geophys Union. *Res:* optical computing; physical optics; subterranean imaging. *Mailing Add:* 4633 Euclid Ave San Diego CA 92115

**TRICOMI, VINCENT,** OBSTETRICS & GYNECOLOGY. *Current Pos:* PROF OBSTET & GYNEC, NY UNIV, 94- *Personal Data:* b New York, NY, Sept 16, 21; m 49; c 6. *Educ:* Syracuse Univ, AB, 42; State Univ NY Downstate Med Ctr, MD, 50. *Prof Exp:* From instr to assoc prof, State Univ NY-HSCB, 55-69, clin prof, 69-74, asst dean, 70-74, assoc dean, 70-93, prof obstet & gynec, 74-94, vpres med affairs, Brooklyn Hosp Ctr, 74-93. *Concurrent Pos:* Brooks scholar, 54-55; consult, Lutheran Med Ctr, 69- & Kings County Med Ctr, 71-; chmn, Dept Obstet/Gynec, Brooklyn Hosp Ctr, 65-95, dir, Grad Med Educ, 95-, emer chmn, 95- *Mem:* Soc Gynec Invest; Sigma Xi. *Res:* Human cytogenetics. *Mailing Add:* Brooklyn Hosp Ctr 121 DeKalb Ave Brooklyn NY 11201. *Fax:* 718-250-6605

**TRIEBWASSER, JOHN,** INTERNAL MEDICINE, CARDIOLOGY. *Current Pos:* physician-in-chg, Cent Med Serv, 85-87, DIR, OCCUP HEALTH & SAFETY, FORD MOTOR CO, 87- *Personal Data:* b Emery, SDak, Feb 16, 36; m 57; c 2. *Educ:* Univ Mo, MD, 61; Am Bd Internal Med, dipl, 68. *Honors & Awards:* Paul Dudley White Award, Asn Mil Surgeons US, 78. *Prof Exp:* Residency internal med, Wilferd Hall, USAF Med Ctr, Lackland AFB, Tex, 65; chief internal med sect, Wright Patterson USAF Med Ctr, 65-67; chief metab sect, Clin Sci Div, Sch Aerospace Med, Brooks AFB, Tex, 67-71, chmn dept med cardiovasc res, 73-78; fel cardiol, Univ Tex Southwestern Med Ctr, Dallas, 71-73; chmn dept med, Wright Patterson USAF Med Ctr, 78-80; dir Med Surveillance, Health & Environ Sci, Dow Chem USA, 80-83, med dir, Mich Div, 83-85. *Concurrent Pos:* Clin asst prof med, Univ Tex Med Sch, San Antonio, 69-71; clin assoc prof, Wright State Univ, Dayton, Ohio, 78- *Mem:* Am Col Physicians; fel Am Col Preventive Med; fel Aerospace Med Asn; Soc Physicians (pres, 77); AMA; fel Am Col Occup Med. *Res:* Exercise stress testing and the use of radionuclide imaging techniques for the detection of subclinical coronary artery disease; automated electrocardiogram analysis using mathematical approaches to signal analysis. *Mailing Add:* Ford Motor Co Occup Health Safety Human Resources The American Rd 471 Dearborn MI 48121

**TRIEBWASSER, SOL,** PHYSICS. *Current Pos:* RETIRED. *Personal Data:* b New York, NY, Aug 16, 21; m 41; c 2. *Educ:* Brooklyn Col, AB, 41; Columbia Univ, MA, 48, PhD, 52. *Prof Exp:* Instr physics, Brooklyn Col, 47-50; asst, Radiation Lab, Columbia, 51; mem tech staff, IBM Corp, 52-69, asst dir appl res, 69-81, prog mgr, Res Ctr, 81-89, dir tech J & prof relations, 89-96. *Mem:* Fel Am Phys Soc; Sigma Xi; fel Inst Elec & Electronics Engrs; fel AAAS. *Res:* Atomic structure; microwave spectroscopy; solid state physics; ferroelectricity; photoconductivity; semiconductors; microelectronics. *Mailing Add:* 56 Lakeview Ave W Cortlandt Manor NY 10566. *Fax:* 914-742-6033

**TRIEFF, NORMAN MARTIN,** ENVIRONMENTAL CHEMISTRY, TOXICOLOGY. *Current Pos:* asst prof toxicol & phys chem, 68-70, from asst prof to assoc prof, 70-72, PROF PREV MED & COMMUNITY HEALTH, UNIV TEX MED BR GALVESTON, 77- *Personal Data:* b Brooklyn, NY, May 11, 29; div; c 4. *Educ:* Polytech Inst Brooklyn, BS, 50; Univ Iowa, MS, 55; NY Univ, PhD(chem), 63. *Prof Exp:* Res asst biochem, Atran Labs, Mt Sinai Hosp, NY, 54-55; instr chem, Cooper Union, 55-58; res assoc biochem, Isaac Albert Res Ctr, Jewish Chronic Dis Hosp, Brooklyn, NY, 61-62; supvr blood res, Blood Derivatives Sect, Mich Dept Pub Health, 63-65; asst prof chem, Drexel Inst, 65-68. *Concurrent Pos:* Nat Ctr for Air Pollution Control grant, 66-68; consult, US Army Corps Engr, 67-68 & US Coast Guard, 70-71; Robert A Welch Found res grant, 70-; consult, La Conroe, Tex Pac Co, & Heat Systs Ultrasonics, Inc, Plainview, NY, 75- *Mem:* Fel Am Inst Chemists; Am Chem Soc; Air Pollution Control Asn; Am Indust Hyg Asn; Am Acad Indust Hyg; NY Acad Sci. *Res:* Environmental chemistry; development of analytic methods of drugs, toxins and environmental pollutants; odor analysis and olfaction; structure-activity relations. *Mailing Add:* Dept Prev Med Pub Health Univ Tex Med Sch 301 Univ Blvd Galveston TX 77550-2708

**TRIEMER, LINDA R,** CANCER EPIDEMIOLOGY, AIR POLLUTION. *Current Pos:* SR SCI ANALYST, JACOB, MEDINGER & FINNEGAN, LLP, 95- *Personal Data:* b Chicago, Ill, June 21, 47; m 89, Richard; c Donna Berrafato, James Berrafato, Daniel Berrafato & Marv Berrafato. *Educ:* Univ Ill, Chicago, BS, 75, George Williams Col, MS, 79; Univ Ill, Chicago, PhD(environ healthscci, epidemiol, biostatist), 85. *Prof Exp:* Postdoctoral res fel, Chem Indust Inst Toxicol, 85-86; asst prof environ & community med, Univ Med & Dent NJ, 86-89; sr staff toxicologist, Exxon Biomed Sci Inc, 89-95. *Concurrent Pos:* Indust hyg consult, Carnow Conibear & Assoc, 83-85; grad fac environ sci, Rutgers Univ, 86-89; mem, Environ & Occup Health Sci Inst, NJ, 86-89. *Mem:* Int Soc Exposure Anal; Am Pub Health Asn; Int Soc Environ Epidemiol. *Res:* Environmental epidemiology of inhaled chemicals and aerosols; environmental fate of chemicals such as atmospheric pollutants; pharmacokinetics and neurochemistry of substances. *Mailing Add:* 82 McGuffey Ave Somerset NJ 08873-2718. *E-Mail:* lrtriemer@aol.com

**TRIEMER, RICHARD ERNEST,** PHYLOGENY, PHYCOLOGY. *Current Pos:* PROF BIOL SCI, RUTGERS UNIV, 75- *Educ:* Univ NC, Chapel Hill, PhD(bot), 75. *Mem:* Phycological Soc Am; Soc Protozoologists; Int Soc Evolutionary Protistology. *Res:* Ultrastructure and molecular biology of protists; systematics. *Mailing Add:* Dept Biol Sci Rutgers Univ New Brunswick NJ 08903

**TRIER, JERRY STEVEN,** INTERNAL MEDICINE, GASTROENTEROLOGY. *Current Pos:* assoc prof, 73-76, PROF MED, HARVARD MED SCH, 76- *Personal Data:* b Frankfurt, Ger, Apr 12, 33; US citizen; m 57, Laurel Bryan; c Stanley Bruce, Stephen Bryan & Jeryl Joan. *Educ:* Univ Wash, MD, 57. *Hon Degrees:* AM, Harvard Univ, 73. *Prof Exp:* Intern med, Univ Rochester, 57-58, asst resident, 58-59; clin assoc, Nat Cancer Inst, 59-61; trainee gastroenterol, Univ Wash, 61-63; asst prof med, Univ Wis, 63-67; assoc prof, Univ NMex, 67-69; assoc prof med & anat, Sch Med, Boston Univ, 69-73. *Concurrent Pos:* USPHS grant, 64-67, Univ NMex, 67-69, Sch Med, Boston Univ, 69-; assoc physician, Univ Hosp, Boston & Boston City Hosp, 69-73; consult, Vet Admin Hosp, Boston, 69-, Chelsea Naval Hosp, 71-74 & US Vet Admin Cent Off, Washington, DC, 71-; sr physician, Brigham & Women's Hosp, Boston, 73-, dir, Div Gastroenterol, 73-89; NIH gen med & study sect, 74-78. *Mem:* Asn Am Physicians; Am Soc Clin Invest; Am Gastroenterol Asn (pres, 85-86); Am Fedn Clin Res; Am Soc Cell Biol. *Res:* Functional morphology of the gastrointestinal tract of humans in health and disease; developmental morphology of the intestine; cell renewal in the alimentary tract. *Mailing Add:* Div Gastroenterol Brigham & Women's Hosp 75 Francis St Boston MA 02115-6195. *Fax:* 617-730-5807

**TRIEZENBERG, STEVEN J,** REGULATION OF EUKARYOTIC GENE EXPRESSION, TRANSCRIPTIONAL ACTIVATION. *Current Pos:* asst prof, 87-92, ASSOC PROF BIOCHEM, MICH STATE UNIV, 92- *Personal Data:* b Oak Park, Ill, Apr 8, 57. *Educ:* Calvin Col, BS, 79; Univ Mich, PhD(cell & molecular biol), 84. *Prof Exp:* Helen Hay Whitney fel, Dept Embryol, Carnegie Inst Wash, 84-87. *Mem:* AAAS; Am Soc Microbiol; Am Soc Biochem & Molecular Biol. *Res:* Mechanisms of regulating gene expression, mechanisms of transcriptional activation; molecular biology; projects ranging from yeast genetics to crystallography; principal models come from herpes viruses, common human and agricultural pathogens. *Mailing Add:* Dept Biochem Mich State Univ East Lansing MI 48824-1319

**TRIFAN, DANIEL SIEGFRIED,** POLYMER CHEMISTRY, PHYSICAL ORGANIC CHEMISTRY. *Current Pos:* prof, 64-89, ADJ PROF CHEM, FAIRLEIGH DICKINSON UNIV, 90- *Personal Data:* b Cleveland, Ohio, Dec 23, 18; div; c Mariora, Daniel D & Richard D. *Educ:* Baldwin-Wallace Col, BS, 40; Western Res Univ, ms, 41; Harvard Univ, MA, 46, PhD(chem), 48. *Prof Exp:* Res fel phys & org chem, Univ Calif, Los Angeles, 48-49, instr org chem, 49-50; asst prof, Bowling Green State Univ, 50-51; from asst prof to assoc prof phys, org & polymer chem & head chem sect, Plastics Lab, Princeton Univ, 51-64. *Mem:* Am Chem Soc. *Res:* Organic reaction mechanisms; polymer chemistry. *Mailing Add:* 466 Liberty St Little Ferry NJ 07643

**TRIFARO, JOSE MARGA,** PHARMACOLOGY. *Current Pos:* CHMN PHARMACOL, UNIV OTTAWA, 86- *Personal Data:* b Mercedes, Arg, Nov 29, 36; m 64; c 2. *Educ:* Liceo Militar Gen San Martín, BA, 54; Univ Buenos Aires, MD, 61. *Honors & Awards:* Upjohn Award in Pharmacology, 89. *Prof Exp:* Demonstr anat, Univ Buenos Aires, 57-58, instr pharmacol, 61-62, lectr physiol, 62-64; lectr, 67-68, from asst prof to assoc prof, 72-78, prof pharmacol, McGill Univ, 78-86. *Concurrent Pos:* A Thyssen Found res fel, Arg, 62-63; res fel, Nat Res Coun, Arg, 63-64; Rockefeller Found res fel, US, 64-66; NIH res fel, 66-67; Med Res Coun Can scholar, 68. *Mem:* Am Soc Pharmacol & Exp Therapeut; Pharmacol Soc Can; Int Soc Neurochem. *Res:* Cellular and molecular mechanism of hormone and neurotransmitter release; role of contractile proteins in secretory cell functions. *Mailing Add:* Dept Pharmacol Univ Ottawa 451 Smyth Rd Ottawa ON K1H 8M5 Can

**TRIFFET, TERRY,** MATHEMATICAL MODELING & MECHANICS. *Current Pos:* EMER PROF MAT SCI, 93-; CONSULT, 94- *Personal Data:* b Enid, Okla, June 10, 22; m 46, Millicent McMaster; c Patricia A, Melanie K & Terrence P. *Educ:* Univ Okla, BA, 45; Univ Colo, BS, 48, MS, 50; Stanford Univ, PhD(struct mech), 57. *Honors & Awards:* Maxwell Prize, Fifth Int Math Model Conf. *Prof Exp:* Instr eng, Univ Colo, 47-50; gen engr rocket & guided missile res, US Naval Ord Test Sta, 50-55; gen engr radiol res & head radiol effects br, US Naval Radiol Defense Lab, 55-59; assoc prof appl mech, Mich State Univ, 59-63, prof mech & mat sci, 63-76; assoc dean res, Col Eng, Univ Ariz, 76-87, actg dean, 87, prof mat sci, 88-; dir, VA/NASA Space Eng Res Ctr, 88-93. *Concurrent Pos:* Mem apex comt, US Naval Res Labs, 59-65; consult, US Dept Defense, 59-65, Battelle Mem Inst, 65-68, Lear-Siegler, Inc, 65-, US Dept Energy, 78-, NASA, 82-, NSF, 83-; Australian Res Grants Comt res fel math physics, Univ Adelaide, 66-67 & 72-73, distinguished vis scientist, 85-86. *Mem:* Am Phys Soc; Am Math Soc; Soc Eng Sci; Soc Indust & Appl Math; Inst Elec & Electronics Engrs; Am Inst Aeronaut & Astronaut; Sigma Xi. *Res:* Mathematical modeling of neural systems; experimental development of neural systems; utilization of space resources. *Mailing Add:* 5871 N Pontatoc Rd Tucson AZ 85718

**TRIFUNAC, ALEXANDER DIMITRIJE,** PHYSICAL CHEMISTRY, MAGNETIC RESONANCE. *Current Pos:* asst scientist, 74-77, scientist, 77-86, SR SCIENTIST & GROUP LEADER RADIATION & PHOTOCHEM, CHEM DIV, ARGONNE NAT LAB, 82- *Personal Data:* b Yugoslavia, July 29, 44; US citizen; m 67. *Educ:* Columbia Univ, BA, 66; Univ Chicago, PhD(chem), 71. *Prof Exp:* Res asst chem, Univ Chicago, 66-71; res assoc chem, Univ Notre Dame, 71-72 & Univ Chicago, 72. *Concurrent Pos:* Presidential intern, Argonne Nat Lab, 72-73. *Mem:* Am Chem Soc; Sigma Xi; Radiation Res Soc. *Res:* Chemistry and physics of transient reactive intermediates in radiation and photochemistry; development of novel time resolved magnetic resonance methods for study of transient radicals and radical ions in liquids. *Mailing Add:* Chem Div Argonne Nat Lab 9700 S Cass Argonne IL 60439

**TRIFUNAC, NATALIA PISKER,** BIOCHEMISTRY. *Current Pos:* instr biochem, 72-75, asst prof, Dept Obstet & Gynec, Sect Reproductive Biol, 75-78, ASST PROF, RES BIOCHEM DEPT PATH, SCH MED, UNIV SOUTHERN CALIF, 78- *Personal Data:* b Budapest, Hungary, June 26, 42; US citizen; div; c Trena & Alexander. *Educ:* Univ Belgrade, BS, 65; Calif Inst Technol, PhD(chem), 69. *Prof Exp:* Res assoc, Dept Chem, Calif Inst Technol, 69-70; res assoc, Columbia Univ, 70-71, res assoc, Dept Biochem, Col Physicians & Surgeons, 71-72. *Concurrent Pos:* Consult, Jet Propulsion Lab, Calif Inst Technol, 78-, dir, Undergrad Labs, Dept Biol, Calif Inst Technol, 84- *Res:* Cell surface changes during lymphocyte transformation; reproductive biology; human spermatozoa metabolism and survival. *Mailing Add:* 1488 Old House Rd Pasadena CA 91107

**TRIGG, GEORGE L(OCKWOOD),** THEORETICAL PHYSICS. *Current Pos:* from asst ed to ed, 62-85, pub ed, Phys Rev Lett, 85-88, AM PHYS SOC, 88- *Personal Data:* b Washington, DC, Sept 30, 25; wid; c William & James. *Educ:* Washington Univ, AB, 47, AM, 50, PhD(physics), 51. *Prof Exp:* Asst physics, Washington Univ, 47-50; asst prof, Knox Col, 51-54, actg chmn dept, 51-52; from asst prof to assoc prof, Ore State Univ, 54-62. *Concurrent Pos:* NSF fel, 57-58; asst ed, Phys Rev & Phys Rev Letters, 58; consult, Funk & Wagnall's Dictionary, 66-71 & Am Heritage Dictionary, 67-70; mem comt symbols, units & terminology, Nat Res Coun, 71-; consult, Wiley Int Dictionary Med & Biol, 81-; freelance ed. *Mem:* Fel AAAS; fel Am Phys Soc; Fedn Am Sci; Soc Scholarly Publ. *Res:* Elementary particle theory; fundamentals of quantum theory; history of physics. *Mailing Add:* 275 Beaver Dam Rd Brookhaven NY 11719. *Fax:* 516-286-3635; *E-Mail:* gtrigg@hoflink.com

**TRIGG, WILLIAM WALKER,** INORGANIC CHEMISTRY. *Current Pos:* from instr to assoc prof, 59-75, PROF CHEM, ARK POLYTECH COL, 75-, HEAD DEPT, 66- *Personal Data:* b Little Rock, Ark, Dec 4, 31; m 57; c 2. *Educ:* Univ Ark, BSChE, 56, MS, 60; La State Univ, PhD(inorg chem), 66. *Prof Exp:* Control chemist, Niagara Chem Div, Food Mach & Chem Corp, 56-57. *Mem:* Am Chem Soc; Am Inst Chem Engrs. *Res:* Precipitation from homogeneous solution and studies of ion solvent effects in solvents of low dielectric constant. *Mailing Add:* Phys Sci Ark Tech Univ 215 W O St Russellville AR 72801-2230

**TRIGGER, KENNETH JAMES,** INDUSTRIAL & MANUFACTURING ENGINEERING. *Current Pos:* assoc, 39-40, from asst prof to prof, 40-77, EMER PROF MECH ENG, UNIV ILL, URBANA, 77- *Personal Data:* b Carsonville, Mich, Sept 6, 10; m 39, Florence Rothfuss; c James K, Kenneth T & Jeffrey C. *Educ:* Mich State Univ, BS, 33, MS, 35, ME, 43. *Honors & Awards:* Blackall Award, Am Soc Mech Engrs, 57; Frederick W Taylor Res Medal, Soc Mfg Eng, 59; William Tennor Mfg Technol Award, Am Soc Mech Engrs, 92. *Prof Exp:* Asst, Mich State Col, 33-34, instr mech eng, 35-36; instr mech eng, Swarthmore Col, 37-38 & Lehigh Univ, 38-39. *Concurrent Pos:* Consult, Nuclear Div, Union Carbide Corp, Continental Can Co, Aeroprojects Inc & Atlantic Richfield Co, Clifford-Jacobs Forging Co, Kennametal Inc. *Mem:* Fel Am Soc Mech Engrs; fel Am Soc Metals; Am Soc Eng Educ; fel Soc Mfg Engrs; Sigma Xi. *Res:* Metal cutting and machinability; physical metallurgy; cutting temperatures and temperature distribution in cutting of metals; mechanism of tool wear; manufacturing engineering. *Mailing Add:* 705 W Columbia Ave Champaign IL 61820

**TRIGGER, KENNETH ROY,** COMPUTER SIMULATIONS, SHOCK HYDRODYNAMICS. *Current Pos:* STAFF SCIENTIST, LAWRENCE LIVERMORE NAT LAB, 68- *Personal Data:* b Chicago, Ill, Mar 7, 24; m 46; c 4. *Educ:* Stanford Univ, BS, 49, MS, 50, PhD(physics). *Prof Exp:* Staff scientist, Los Alamos Sci Lab, 55-56, Hughes Res & Develop Labs, 56-58, Lawrence Livermore Lab, 58-62 & 64-65, Stanford Linear Accelerator Ctr, 62-64 & Appl Theory, Inc, 65-67. *Mem:* Am Phys Soc. *Res:* Chemical and nuclear explosive devices. *Mailing Add:* 1440 Via Loma Walnut Creek CA 94596

**TRIGGIANI, ROBERTO,** APPLIED MATHEMATICS, CONTROL THEORY. *Current Pos:* PROF MATH, UNIV VA, CHARLOTTESVILLE, 87- *Personal Data:* b Bolzano, Italy, Mar 28, 42. *Educ:* Univ Padova, Dr, 67; Univ Minn, PhD(math control theory), 73. *Prof Exp:* From asst prof to assoc prof math, Iowa State Univ Ames, 75-80; from assoc prof to prof math, Univ Fla, Gainesville, 80-87. *Concurrent Pos:* Vis prof, Univ Calif, Los Angeles, 79-80; prin co-investr, NSF, 81, Air Force Off Sci Res, 76-; assoc ed, Appl Math & Optimization, 85. *Res:* Mathematical control theory with emphasis on boundary control theory for partial differential equations. *Mailing Add:* 715 Tanglewood Rd Charlottesville VA 22901

**TRIGGLE, DAVID J,** PHARMACOLOGY, MEDICINAL CHEMISTRY. *Current Pos:* asst prof biochem pharmacol, State Univ NY, Buffalo, 62-65, assoc prof biochem pharmacol & theoret biol, 65-69, chmn dept biochem pharmacol, 71-88, dean, 88-96, PROF BIOCHEM PHARMACOL & THEORET BIOL, SCH PHARM, STATE UNIV NY, BUFFALO, 69-, VPROVOST GRAD EDUC, 96- *Personal Data:* b London, Eng, May 4, 35; m 59, Ann; c Andrew & Jocelyn. *Educ:* Univ Southampton, BSc, 56; Univ Hull, PhD(org chem), 59. *Hon Degrees:* DSc & Dr, Univ Camerino Ital. *Honors & Awards:* Volwiler Award, Am Asn Col Pharm; Otto Krayer Award, Am Soc Pharmacol Therapeuts. *Prof Exp:* Fel org chem, Univ Ottawa, 59-61; res fel, Bedford Col, London, 61-62. *Concurrent Pos:* NIH res grants, 64-; *Mem:* Am Chem Soc; Am Soc Pharmacol & Exp Therapeut; Brit Pharmacol Soc; fel AAAS. *Res:* Molecular pharmacology of adrenergic and cholinergic systems; organic reaction mechanisms; synthesis of organic heterocyclic systems; ion translocation and cell membranes; molecular basis of neurotransmitter action. *Mailing Add:* Grad Sch State Univ 410 Capen Buffalo NY 14260. *Fax:* 716-645-2941; *E-Mail:* triggle@acsu.buffalo.edu

**TRIGIANO, ROBERT NICHOLAS,** MICROPROPAGATION, FUNGAL PHYSIOLOGY. *Current Pos:* postdoctorial res assoc tissue cult, 84-86, asst prof, 87-91, ASSOC PROF ORNAMENTAL BIOTECHNOL, UNIV TENN, 91- *Personal Data:* b Johnstown, Pa, Nov 30, 53; m 83, Margaret K Treadwell; c Andrew N. *Educ:* Juniata Col, BS, 75; Pa State Univ, MS, 77; NC State Univ, PhD(bot & plant path), 83. *Honors & Awards:* Distinguished Young Scientist Award, Inst Agr, Univ Tenn, 91. *Prof Exp:* Assoc agronomist, Green Giant Co, 77-79; mushroom grower, Rol-Land Farms Ltd, 79-80. *Mem:* Mycol Soc Am; Am Soc Hort Sci; Int Soc Plant Morphologists; Int Soc Hort Sci; Sigma Xi. *Res:* Cell biology; development plant biology; somatic embryogenesis; plant pathology-diseases of woody ornamentals; transformation; molecular biology. *Mailing Add:* 10629 Eagles View Dr Knoxville TN 37922

**TRIGLIA, EMIL J,** ANALYTICAL CHEMISTRY. *Current Pos:* SR RES ASSOC, ESSEX CHEM CORP, 83- *Personal Data:* b Lucca, Italy, Aug 26, 21; US citizen; m 48; c 5. *Educ:* City Col New York, BS, 43. *Prof Exp:* Chemist, Ledoux & Co, Inc, 46-51; group leader anal chem, Chem Construct Corp & Am Cyanamid Co, 51-56; sr res chemist, Minerals & Chem, Philipp Corp, 56-61, res group supvr, 61-68; group leader anal & phys testing, Engelhard Minerals & Chem Corp, Menlo Park, 68-74, mgr anal & phys measurements, 74-81; res assoc, Ledoux & Co, 82-83. *Mem:* Am Chem Soc; Tech Asn Pulp & Paper Indust; Am Soc Testing & Mat; Acids Indust Chem. *Res:* Analyses of minerals, ores and rocks by chemical and instrumental methods; development of methods for the analysis of elements and metals in industrial chemicals by instrumental methods primarily spectrophotometric and atomic absorption by flame and flameless techniques. *Mailing Add:* 12 Sharon Ct Metuchen NJ 08840-1730

**TRILLING, CHARLES A(LEXANDER),** CHEMICAL ENGINEERING, NUCLEAR ENGINEERING. *Current Pos:* CONSULT, ENERGY-RELATED FIELDS, 83- *Personal Data:* b Wiesbaden, Ger, Apr 13, 23; nat US; m 49; c 3. *Educ:* Calif Inst Technol, BS, 44; Mass Inst Technol, ScD(chem eng), 49. *Prof Exp:* Res assoc, Chem Warfare Serv Develop Lab, Mass Inst Technol, 44-45, res assoc chem eng, 47-49; chem engr, Dennison Mfg Co, 49-50; sr res engr, Atomic Energy Res Dept, N Am Aviation, Inc, 50-52; process engr, United Engrs & Constructors, Inc, 52-54; sr res engr, Atomics Int Div, NAm Aviation, Inc, Rockwell Int, Canoga Park, 54-55, proj engr, 55-59, group leader org reactors develop, 56-59, chief proj engr, 59-61, assoc dir, Org Reactors Dept, 61-62, proj mgr org cooled reactors, 62-65, mgr heavy water org cooled reactors prog off, 65-67, mem tech staff, Fast Breeder Prog Off, Atomics Int Div, NAm Rockwell Corp, 67-69, pollution control technol, 69-72, proj mgr coal gasification, Rockwell Int, 73-78, prog mgr, Advan Technol Process Design, Environ & Energy Systs Div, 78-83. *Mem:* AAAS; Am Chem Soc; Am Nuclear Soc; Am Inst Chem Engrs. *Res:* Nuclear power reactor development and engineering; organic cooled reactor concept for economic generation of electric power; air pollution control; coal gasification and liquefaction. *Mailing Add:* 5254 Melvin Ave Tarzana CA 91356-2940

**TRILLING, DONALD R,** TRANSPORTATION POLICY. *Current Pos:* DIR, OFF ENVIRON, ENERGY & SAFETY, OFF SECY TRANSP, US DEPT TRANS, 87- *Personal Data:* b Philadelphia, Pa, Jan 23, 28; m 74, Shirley; c Jeff, James, Terry, Randy & Greg. *Educ:* Univ Pa, BA, 56, MA, 59, PhD, 69. *Prof Exp:* Dir, Pub Mgt Serv, Westinghouse Elec Co, 68-73; actg asst secy policy, US Dept Transp, 78-79, exec asst, 81-92. *Mem:* Nat Economists Club; Am Inst Aeronaut & Astronaut. *Mailing Add:* Off Secy Transp 400 Seventh St SW Washington DC 20590

**TRILLING, GEORGE HENRY,** ELEMENTARY PARTICLE PHYSICS. *Current Pos:* assoc prof, 60-64, prof physics, 64-94, chmn dept, 68-72, EMER PROF, UNIV CALIF, BERKELEY, 94- *Personal Data:* b Bialystok, Poland, Sept 18, 30; nat US; m 55, Madeleine; c Stephen, Yvonne & David. *Educ:* Calif Inst Technol, BS, 51, PhD(physics), 55. *Prof Exp:* Res fel physics, Calif Inst Technol, 55-56; Fulbright res fel, Polytech Sch, Paris, 56-57; from asst prof to assoc prof, Univ Mich, 57-60. *Concurrent Pos:* NSF sr fel, Europ Orgn Nuclear Res, 66-67, Guggenheim fel, 73-74. *Mem:* Nat Acad Sci; fel Am Phys Soc; fel Am Acad Arts & Sci. *Res:* Properties of elementary particles produced by high energy accelerators and colliders. *Mailing Add:* Dept Physics Univ Calif Berkeley CA 94720. *Fax:* 510-486-5101; *E-Mail:* ght@lbl.gov

**TRILLING, LEON,** AERONAUTICS & ASTRONAUTICS, SCIENCE TECHNOLOGY & SOCIETY. *Current Pos:* res assoc, 51-54, from asst prof to assoc prof, 54-62, PROF AERONAUT ENG, MASS INST TECHNOL, 62-, MEM FAC, COL SCI, TECHNOL & SOC, 78- *Personal Data:* b Poland, July 15, 24; nat US; m 46, Edna Yuval; c Alex & Roger. *Educ:* Calif Inst Technol, BS, 44, MS, 46, AeroEng, 47, PhD, 48. *Prof Exp:* Physicist, US Naval Ord Test Sta, 44-46; asst, Calif Inst Technol, 46-48, res fel, 48-49, instr, 49-50; Fulbright scholar, Univ Paris, 50-51. *Concurrent Pos:* Guggenheim fel & vis prof, Sorbonne Univ, 63-64; vis prof, Aeronaut Dept, Delft Tech Univ, Neth, 74-75, Carleton Col, 87; consult. *Mem:* Fel AAAS. *Res:* Aerodynamics; gas dynamics; kinetic theory of gases; gas surface interactions. *Mailing Add:* 180 Beacon St Boston MA 02116

**TRIM, CYNTHIA MARY,** ANIMAL PHYSIOLOGY, PHARMACOLOGY. *Current Pos:* assoc prof, 81-85, PROF ANESTHESIOL, UNIV GA, ATHENS, 85- *Personal Data:* b England, Apr 12, 47; m 78, James N Moore; c 2. *Educ:* Univ Liverpool, BVSc, 70. *Prof Exp:* Res asst vet anesthesiol, Univ Cambridge, Eng, 70-72; pvt practitioner vet med, Nixon & Partners, Suffolk, Eng, 72-74; asst prof anesthesiol, Univ Guelph, Can, 74-76 & Univ Ill, Urbana, 76-77; assoc prof, Univ Mo,

Columbia, 77-80. *Mem:* Royal Col Vet Surgeons; Am Vet Med Asn; Asn Vet Anaesthetists; Am Col Vet Anesthesiologists (pres, 85); Brit Vet Asn. *Res:* Cardiopulmonary physiology and pharmacology relating to anesthesiology of all species; physiology and treatment of equine endotoxemia. *Mailing Add:* Dept Large Animal Med Col Vet Med Univ Ga Athens GA 30602

**TRIMBERGER, GEORGE WILLIAM,** DAIRY SCIENCE. *Current Pos:* from asst prof to prof, 44-75, EMER PROF DAIRY HUSB, CORNELL UNIV, 75- *Personal Data:* b Neilsville, Wis, Dec 8, 09; m 38; c 3. *Educ:* Univ Wis, BS, 33; Univ Nebr, MS, 42, PhD(zool), 48. *Prof Exp:* Herd supt, Univ Nebr, 34-40, instr dairy prod, 40-44. *Concurrent Pos:* Vis prof & proj leader, Univ Philippines, 55-57 & 66-67 & Ahmadu Bello Univ, Nigeria, 75-77. *Mem:* AAAS; Am Soc Animal Sci; Am Diary Sci Asn; Am Genetic Asn. *Res:* Artificial insemination; reproduction and nutrition in dairy cattle. *Mailing Add:* 115 S Quarry St Apt C-304 Ithaca NY 14850

**TRIMBLE, DONALD E,** FIELD MAPPING GEOLOGY. *Current Pos:* RETIRED. *Personal Data:* b Westhope, NDak, Mar 6,16; m 48, Isabelle Brinig; c Stephen Alan. *Educ:* Wash State Univ, BS, 38. *Prof Exp:* US Army, 41-45; field mapping geologists, US Geol Surv, 46-80. *Concurrent Pos:* Pres, Colo Sci Soc, 78. *Mem:* Sr fel Geol Soc Am. *Res:* Strategy of structure. *Mailing Add:* 2640 Lamar Denver CO 80214

**TRIMBLE, MARY ELLEN,** PHYSIOLOGY, BIOLOGY. *Current Pos:* asst prof, 71-84, ASSOC PROF, HEALTH SCI CTR, SYRACUSE, STATE UNIV NY, 84- *Personal Data:* b Englewood, NJ, Nov 1, 36. *Educ:* Wellesley Col, AB, 58; Syracuse Univ, MA, 59; Case Western Reserve Univ, PhD(biol), 69. *Prof Exp:* Res assoc develop biol, Brown Univ, 68-70; res physiologist, Vet Admin Hosp, Syracuse, 71-86. *Mem:* AAAS; Am Soc Nephrology; Am Physiol Soc; Int Soc Nephrology; Am Soc Renal Biochem & Metab. *Res:* Renal physiology, particularly metabolic aspects of ion transport, lipid metabolism and fatty acid binding proteins. *Mailing Add:* Dept Physiol State Univ NY Health Sci Ctr-Syracuse 750 E Adams St Syracuse NY 13210. *Fax:* 315-464-7712

**TRIMBLE, ROBERT BOGUE,** CELL BIOLOGY, GLYCOPROTEIN BIOSYNTHESIS & PROCESSING. *Current Pos:* Health Res fel, Wadsworth Ctr Labs & Res, NY State Dept Health, 69-70, res scientist, 70-72, sr res scientist, 73-80, res scientist V, 81-93, RES SCIENTIST VI, WADSWORTH CTR LABS & RES, NY STATE DEPT HEALTH ALBANY, 94; PROF BIOMED SCI, SCH PUB HEALTH, STATE UNIV NY, ALBANY, 88- *Personal Data:* b Baltimore, Md, July 2, 43; m 69, 94, Elizabeth A Gould; c Alison. *Educ:* Rensselaer Polytech Inst, BS, 65, MS, 67, PhD(microbiol), 69. *Concurrent Pos:* Mem, US Pub Health Serv-NIH Sci Rev Group, 85-89, Reviewers Res, 89-93, Am Cancer Soc Personnel Rev Comt, 91-96. *Mem:* AAAS; Am Soc Microbiol; Am Soc Biochem & Molecular Biol; Sigma Xi; Soc Glycobiol. *Res:* Cell biology and biochemistry of glycoprotein biosynthesis and secretion in yeast and mammalian cells; N-linked glycan structure and function; oligosaccharide processing pathways; glycohydrolases and glycosyl transferases; oligosaccharide and protein structure; mass spectrometry and nuclear magnetic resonance spectroscopy. *Mailing Add:* NY State Dept Health Wadsworth Ctr Labs & Res C535 PO Box 509 Albany NY 12201-0509. *Fax:* 518-473-2900; *E-Mail:* robert.trimble@wadsworth.org

**TRIMBLE, RUSSELL FAY,** COORDINATION COMPOUNDS, CHEMICAL LITERATURE. *Current Pos:* from asst prof to prof, 54-92, EMER PROF CHEM, SOUTHERN ILL UNIV, CARBONDALE, 92- *Personal Data:* b Montclair, NJ, Feb 23, 27; m 50, Natalie Benda; c Kirsten, Carol & Margaret. *Educ:* Mass Inst Technol, BS, 48, PhD(chem), 51. *Prof Exp:* Instr chem, Univ Rochester, 51-54. *Concurrent Pos:* Abstractor, Chem Abstr, 54-88, Metals Abstr, 84-89, tech translator, 59-; vis lectr, Univ Ill, 63-64. *Mem:* AAAS; Am Chem Soc; fel Am Inst Chemists; Am Translators Asn; Sigma Xi; Hist Sci Soc. *Res:* History of chemistry; pseudosciences. *Mailing Add:* 1008 Walkup St Carbondale IL 62901

**TRIMBLE, VIRGINIA LOUISE,** ASTRONOMY, ASTROPHYSICS. *Current Pos:* from asst prof to vis assoc prof physics, 71-80, PROF PHYSICS, UNIV CALIF, IRVINE, 80- *Personal Data:* b Los Angeles, Calif, Nov 15, 43; m 72, Joseph Weber. *Educ:* Univ Calif, Los Angeles, BA, 64; Calif Inst Technol, MS, 65, PhD(astron), 68; Cambridge Univ, MA, 69. *Honors & Awards:* Sci Reviewing Award, Nat Acad Sci, 86. *Prof Exp:* Res fel astrophys, Inst Theoret Astron, Cambridge Univ, 68; asst prof astron, Smith Col & Four Cols Observ, 68-69; NATO sr fel, Inst Theoret Astron, Cambridge Univ, 69-70, vis fel, 70-71. *Concurrent Pos:* From vis asst prof to vis assoc prof astron, Univ Md, College Park, 72-80, vis prof, 80-; Sloan fel, 72-74; nat lectr, Sigma Xi, 74-77; ed, Comments Astrophys, 87-; assoc ed, Astrophys J, 89-; Tinsley vis prof astron, Univ Tex, Austin, 92. *Mem:* Am Astron Soc; Royal Astron Soc; Europ Phys Soc; Int Astron Union; Int Soc Gen Relativity & Gravitation; Am Phys Soc. *Res:* Late phases of stellar evolution; supernovae; white dwarfs; neutron stars; galactic evolution; binary stars; history and sociology of physics and astronomy. *Mailing Add:* Dept Physics Univ Calif Irvine CA 92697. *E-Mail:* vtrimble@uci.edu

**TRIMITSIS, GEORGE B,** ORGANIC CHEMISTRY. *Current Pos:* MEM FAC, DIV NAT SCI, UNIV PITTSBURGH, 76- *Personal Data:* b Assiut, Egypt, Nov 28, 39; m 64; c 1. *Educ:* Am Univ Cairo, BSc, 64; Va Polytech Inst & State Univ, PhD(org chem), 68. *Prof Exp:* Res assoc org res, Ohio State Univ, 68-69; asst prof org chem, Western Mich Univ, 69-76. *Mem:* Am Chem Soc. *Res:* Formation, study and synthetic applications of carbanions. *Mailing Add:* Div Nat Sci Univ Pittsburgh Johnstown PA 15904-2990

**TRIMMER, BARRY ANDREW,** CELL SIGNALLING. *Current Pos:* ASST PROF, TUFTS UNIV, 90- *Personal Data:* b Lutterworth, Eng, Jan 28, 58. *Educ:* Cambridge Univ Eng, BA (Hons), 79, PhD(zool & neurobiol), 83. *Prof Exp:* Res assoc, Dept Neurobiol, Harvard Univ, 83-86, Univ Calif, Berkeley, 87-88; res fel, Inst Neurosci, Univ Ore, Eugene, 88-90. *Mem:* Soc Neurosci; Int Brain Res Orgn. *Res:* Role of intracellular signals in modulating neural function. *Mailing Add:* Dept Biol Tufts Univ Medford MA 02155. *E-Mail:* btrimmer@pearl.tufts.edu

**TRIMMER, ROBERT WHITFIELD,** INDUSTRIAL ORGANIC CHEMISTRY. *Current Pos:* supvr lab prof develop & org chemist, Sumner Div, 73-77 & Corp Div, 77-80, SUPVR LAB PROD DEVELOP & ORG CHEMIST, AMES DIV DIAG GROUP, MILES LABS, INC, 80- *Personal Data:* b Binghamton, NY, Dec 13, 37; m 65; c 2. *Educ:* Hope Col, Mich, AB, 60; Rensselaer Polytech Inst, PhD(org chem), 73. *Prof Exp:* Asst res polymer chem, Schenectady Chem Co, 60; asst res med chemist, Sterling Winthrop Res Inst, Sterling Drug, Inc, 64-69. *Mem:* Am Chem Soc; AAAS; Org Reactions Catalysis Soc. *Res:* Hydrogenation technology; specialty products; pharmaceuticals; aryl and alkyl amines as intermediates and polymer catalysts; quaternary ammonium compounds, citric acid derivatives; heterocycles; organic photochemistry; development of new synthetic methods; peptide chemistry. *Mailing Add:* 20410 Bargene Way Germantown MD 20874-1160

**TRIMMER, WILLIAM S(TUART),** MICROMECHANICS & MICROELECTROMECHANICAL SYSTEMS. *Current Pos:* OWNER & PRES, BELL MEAD RES, 90- *Personal Data:* b Long Beach, Calif, Apr 12, 43; m 76; c 2. *Educ:* Occidental Col, BA, 62; Wesleyan Univ, PhD(physics), 72. *Prof Exp:* Asst prof, Montclair State Col, NJ, 71-72; asst prof & chmn, Physics Dept, Col Wooster, Ohio, 72-77; staff physicist, Singer Corp Res, 77-79; sr scientist, Johnson & Johnson, 79-82; res micromech & robotic syst develop, AT&T Bell Labs, 82-90. *Concurrent Pos:* Vis fel, Princeton Univ, 90-93; ed, J Mems, Inst Elec & Electronics Engrs & Am Soc Mech Engrs. *Mem:* Am Phys Soc; Inst Elec & Electronics Engrs; Am Soc Mech Engrs. *Res:* Help start the micro electr mechanical systems (or micromechanics, microdynamics) field; co-invented harmonic motor; co-developed sacrificial method for making micro gears, etc; developed genetic engineering probe; nine US patents; author of one book. *Mailing Add:* Belle Mead Res Inc 58 Riverview Terr Belle Mead NJ 08502

**TRINDLE, CARL OTIS,** THEORETICAL CHEMISTRY. *Current Pos:* dir, Curr One Prog, 81-86, DIR STUDIES, MONROE HILL COL, 86- ; ASSOC PROF THEORET CHEM, UNIV VA, 73- *Personal Data:* b Des Moines, Iowa, Aug 26, 41; m 62, 92, Barbara A Body; c John M. *Educ:* Grinnell Col, BA, 63; Tufts Univ, PhD(phys chem), 67. *Prof Exp:* NSF fel theoret chem, Yale Univ, 67-68; res assoc, Argonne Nat Lab, 68-69; asst prof, Univ Va, 69-73. *Concurrent Pos:* Consult, Argonne Nat Lab, 69-; vis asst prof, Mideast Tech Univ, 71; Sloan Found fel, 71-73; vis assoc prof, Mideast Tech Univ, 73; vis scientist, Israel Tech Technol, 76; Nat Acad Sci exchange fel, Yugoslavia, 79, Univ Ga, 81, Amherst Col, 86, Am Chem Soc Tour Lectr, 82, 87, 88, 89, 90; Fulbright fel, 93. *Mem:* AAAS; Am Chem Soc; Sigma Xi. *Res:* Impact of orbital topology on organic stereo-chemistry; localized description of charge distributions; group theory of easily rearranged systems; computer algebra systems; artificial intelligence applications in chemistry. *Mailing Add:* Chem Bldg Univ Va Charlottesville VA 22901. *E-Mail:* cot@virginia.edu

**TRINER, LUBOS,** ANESTHESIOLOGY, PHARMACOLOGY. *Current Pos:* residency anesthesiol, 70-73, from asst prof to assoc prof, 70-88, PROF ANESTHESIOL, COLUMBIA PRESBY MED CTR, NY, 88- *Personal Data:* b Czech Republic, Mar 29, 30; US citizen; m 58, Stania; c Lucas & Dana. *Educ:* Charles Univ, Prague, MD, 55, PhD(pharmacol), 62. *Prof Exp:* Asst prof pharmacol, Charles Univ, Prague, 55-64; res asst, Anesthesiol Col Physicians & Pharmacol, 65-85. *Mem:* Am Soc Anesthesiol; Int Anesthesia Res Soc; Am Soc Pharmacol & Exp Therapeut; Am Physiol Soc. *Res:* Pathophysiology. *Mailing Add:* 19 Avondale Ct Briarcliff Manor NY 10510

**TRINGIDES, MICHAEL C,** SURFACE PHYSICS, NANOSTRUCTURES. *Current Pos:* Asst prof, 87-92, ASSOC PROF PHYSICS, IOWA STATE UNIV, 92-, PHYSICIST, AMES LAB, 92- *Personal Data:* m 90, Maria Kyriacou; c Christina. *Educ:* Yale Univ, BA, 77; Univ Chicago, MSc, 84, PhD(physics), 84. *Mem:* Am Phys Soc; Am Vacuum Soc. *Res:* Experimental study with electron diffraction and scanning tunnelling microscopy of atomic scale processes (diffusion, nucleation, growth, desorption) that are critical for the growth of ultrathin films and nonstructures. *Mailing Add:* 805 Vermont Circle Ames IA 50014. *Fax:* 515-294-0689; *E-Mail:* tringides@ameslab.gov

**TRINKAUS, ERIK,** PHYSICAL ANTHROPOLOGY. *Current Pos:* PROF ANTHROP, DEPT ANTHROP, WASHINGTON UNIV, 97- *Personal Data:* b New Haven, Conn, Dec 24, 48. *Educ:* Univ Wis, BA, 70; Univ Pa, MA, 73, PhD(anthrop), 75. *Prof Exp:* From asst prof to assoc prof anthrop, Harvard Univ, 75-83; from asst prof to prof, Univ NMex, 83-97. *Mem:* Nat Acad Sci; Am Asn Phys Anthropologists. *Res:* Paleontological study of Middle and Upper Pleistocene hominids emphasizing the behavioral interpretation of fossil remains; reconstructing human evolutionary history using complex evolutionary models as well as comparative anatomy. *Mailing Add:* Dept Anthrop Wash Univ Campus Box 1114 1 Brookings Dr St Louis MO 63130

**TRINKAUS, JOHN PHILIP,** CELL BIOLOGY, DEVELOPMENTAL BIOLOGY. *Current Pos:* From instr to prof, 48-64, EMER PROF BIOL, YALE UNIV, 88- *Personal Data:* b Rockville Ctr, NY, May 23, 18; m 63, Madeleine F M Bazin; c Gregor, Tanya & Erik. *Educ:* Wesleyan Univ, BA, 40; Columbia Univ, MA, 41; Johns Hopkins Univ, PhD(embryol), 48. *Honors & Awards:* Edwin grant Conklin Medal, Soc Develop Biol, 95; Streisinger Lect, Calif State Univ, Hayward, 96. *Concurrent Pos:* Mem staff embryol, Marine Biol Lab, Woods Hole, 53-57, 70 & 78, trustee, 92-; master, Branford Col, Yale Univ, 66-73, dir grad studies biol, 65-66; Guggenheim fel, Lab Exp Embryol, Col France, 59-60; chmn, Gordon Conf Cell Contact & Movement, 79; merit award, NIH, 87- *Mem:* Soc Develop Biol; Am Soc Zoologists; Am Soc Cell Biol; Int Inst Embryol. *Res:* Cytodifferentiation; mechanism of morphogenetic cell movements; teleost development; contact behavior and locomotion of normal and transformed cells; gastrulation. *Mailing Add:* Dept Biol Yale Univ New Haven CT 06520. *Fax:* 203-432-3854

**TRINKAUS-RANDALL, VICKERY E,** OPHTHALMOLOGY. *Current Pos:* ASSOC PROF, DEPT BIOCHEM, BOSTON UNIV SCH MED, 94- *Personal Data:* b Albuquerque, NMex, Jan 11, 53; m, Greger; c Jennifer & Christopher. *Educ:* Kenyon Col, AB, 74; Univ Wis-Madison, PhD(zool), 81. *Prof Exp:* Fel, Marine Biol Lab, 81; res fel, Eye Res Inst Retina-Prior Found, 81-84. *Concurrent Pos:* Secy-treas fac coun, Boston Univ, 95-97. *Mem:* Sigma Xi; Asn Res Vision & Ophthal; Am Soc Biochem & Molecular Biol. *Res:* Role of signal transduction in adhesion, design of synthetic cornea, injury and repair mechanisms. *Mailing Add:* Dept Biochem K225 Boston Univ Sch Med 80 E Concord St Boston MA 02118-2394. *Fax:* 617-638-5337; *E-Mail:* vickery@med-biochm.bu.edu

**TRINKLEIN, DAVID HERBERT,** FLORICULTURE, PLANT GENETICS. *Current Pos:* ASST PROF HORT, UNIV MO, 77- *Personal Data:* b Jefferson City, Mo, July 3, 47. *Educ:* Lincoln Univ, BS, 69; Univ Mo, Ms, 71, PhD(hort), 74. *Prof Exp:* Res asst hort, Univ Mo, 70-75; res scientist plant sci, Farmland Industs, 75-76; exten horticulturist, Lincoln Univ, 76-77. *Mem:* Sigma Xi. *Res:* Physiology and genetics of flower crops with allied interest in energy conservation in the greenhouse. *Mailing Add:* Agron Univ Mo 210 Waters Hall Columbia MO 65211-0001

**TRINKO, JOSEPH RICHARD, JR,** NUCLEAR ENGINEERING, ELECTRICAL ENGINEERING. *Current Pos:* CONSULT, ENG COM & DEPT ENERGY FACIL, 79- *Personal Data:* b Washington DC, Dec 20, 39; m 65; c 2. *Educ:* Univ Tenn, BS, 63, MS, 65, PhD(nuclear eng), 67. *Prof Exp:* Asst nuclear engr, Exp Breeder Reactor, Argonne Nat Lab, 67-70; sr res scientist, Ebasco Serv, 70-73; sr nuclear engr reactor anal, Middle South Serv, 73-79. *Mem:* Elec Power Res Inst. *Res:* Advanced methods of reactor core analysis; stress corrosion mechanisms in nuclear systems. *Mailing Add:* 4300 Sandlewood Trail Rio Rancho NM 87124

**TRINLER, WILLIAM A,** ORGANIC CHEMISTRY. *Current Pos:* from asst prof to assoc prof, 60-74, PROF ORG CHEM, IND STATE UNIV, TERRE HAUTE, 74- *Personal Data:* b Louisville, Ky, Dec 24, 29; m 62; c 1. *Educ:* Univ Louisville, BS, 55, PhD(org chem), 59. *Prof Exp:* Chemist, E I du Pont de Nemours & Co, 59-60. *Mem:* Am Chem Soc; Am Inst Chemists; Sigma Xi. *Res:* Synthesis and polymerization of vinyl monomers; liquid chromatography. *Mailing Add:* RR 51 Terre Haute IN 47805

**TRIOLO, ANTHONY J,** PHARMACOLOGY. *Current Pos:* From instr to asst prof, 67-72, assoc prof, 72-81, PROF PHARMACOL, JEFFERSON MED COL, 81- *Personal Data:* b Philadelphia, Pa, Aug 8, 32; m 59; c 3. *Educ:* Philadelphia Col Pharm, BS, 59; Jefferson Med Col, MS, 62, PhD(pharmacol), 64. *Res:* Neuropharmacological effects of tremorine on motor reflex activity; toxicological interactions between organochlorine or organophosphate insecticides and Benzo-(a)-pyrene carcinogenesis. *Mailing Add:* Dept Pharmacol Jefferson Med Col 1020 Locust St Philadelphia PA 19107-6731

**TRIONE, EDWARD JOHN,** biochemistry, for more information see previous edition

**TRIPARD, GERALD EDWARD,** NUCLEAR PHYSICS. *Current Pos:* asst prof, 69-76, ASSOC PROF PHYSICS, WASH STATE UNIV, 76-, DIR, NUCLEAR RADIATION CTR, 91- *Personal Data:* b Saskatoon, Sask, Apr 18, 40; m 63; c 2. *Educ:* Univ BC, BSc, 62, MSc, 64, PhD(physics), 67. *Prof Exp:* Nat Res Coun Can fel, Swiss Fed Inst Technol, 67-69. *Concurrent Pos:* Mem, Los Alamos Meson Physics Facil. *Mem:* Nat Orgn Test, Res & Training Reactors; Am Phys Soc; Neutron Scattering Soc Am. *Res:* Neutron scattering; final state interactions; stopped pions. *Mailing Add:* 222 N Prospect Blvd Lewiston ID 83501. *Fax:* 509-335-4433; *E-Mail:* gtropard@wsuvms1.csc.wsu.edu

**TRIPATHI, BRENDA JENNIFER,** VISUAL SCIENCE, CELL BIOLOGY. *Current Pos:* PROF, DEPT MICROBIOL & IMMUNOL & ADJ PROF, DEPT PATH, SCH MED, UNIV SC, 93- *Personal Data:* b Rochford, Eng, July 5, 46; m 69, Ramesh; c Anita & Paul. *Educ:* Univ London, BSc, 67, PhD(med), 71. *Honors & Awards:* Cert Honor, Murgoci Award, Bedford Col, London, 65; Int Prize, Alcon Res Inst, 87; Spec Invited Lectr, Col Univ Chicago, 85; Serv Award, Am Acad Ophthal, 87, Honor Award, 88; Ida Mann Medal, Univ Oxford, 89. *Prof Exp:* Res asst path, Univ Col Hosp, London, 67-69; res asst, Inst Ophthal, Univ London, 69-72, lectr, 72-77; res assoc & assoc prof opthal, Univ Chicago, 77-93, assoc prof lectr, 79-84, assoc prof lectr, Biol Sci Col Div, 84-93. *Concurrent Pos:* Ocular microbiologist, Eye Path Lab, Univ Chicago, 77-93; sr lectr, Organismal Biol & Anat, Univ Chicago, 90-93; vis prof, over 20 insts US & abroad, 73-89; exec ed, Exp Eye Res, 91- *Mem:* Royal Soc Med, London; Asn Res Vision & Ophthal; Sigma Xi; AAAS; Am Acad Ophthal; Int Soc Eye Res; NY Acad Sci; Tissue Cult Asn; Soc Exp Biol & Med; Int Soc Ocular Toxicol; Am Soc Cell Biol; Fedn Am Socs Exp Biol. *Res:* Visual science; anatomy; physiology; experimental pathology; cell biology; electron microscopy; tissue culture; biochemistry; immunology; microbiology; cerebrospinal fluid physiology and pathology; molecular biology; over 280 articles to scientific publications. *Mailing Add:* Dept Path Univ SC Columbia SC 29208. *Fax:* 803-733-3192; *E-Mail:* brenda@dcsmserver.med.scarolina.edu

**TRIPATHI, GORAKH NATH RAM,** CHEMICAL PHYSICS, SOLID STATE PHYSICS. *Current Pos:* SR SCIENTIST RADIATION RES, RADIATION LAB, UNIV NOTRE DAME, 78- *Personal Data:* b Gorakhpur, India, Jan 1, 44; m 62, Poonam Tewari; c Pratibha, Pradeep & Amit. *Educ:* Univ Gorakhpur, India, BSc, 60, MSc, 62, PhD(physics), 68. *Prof Exp:* Fel physics, Univ Gorakhpur, India, 62-65; sr lectr, 65-76; vis sr lectr & sr acad staff fel, Dept Physics, Univ Manchester & Manchester Inst Sci & Technol, 76-77. *Res:* Time resolved resonance raman studies of structure and reactions of transient free radicals and excited states; physical and chemical properties of excited radical species; early chemical steps in radical reactions. *Mailing Add:* Radiation Lab Univ Notre Dame Notre Dame IN 46556. *Fax:* 219-631-8068; *E-Mail:* tripathi@marconi.nd.rad.edu

**TRIPATHI, RAMESH CHANDRA,** CLINICAL OPHTHALMOLOGY, GLAUCOMA. *Current Pos:* PROF & CHMN, DEPT OPHTHAL, UNIV SC SCH MED, 93-; DIR OPHTHAL EDUC, RICHLAND MEM HOSP, COLUMBIA, SC, 93- *Personal Data:* b Jamira, India, July 1, 36; US citizen; m 69; c 2. *Educ:* Lucknow Christian Col, India, ISc, 54; Univ Agra, MBBS(MD), 59; Univ Lucknow, MS, 63; DORCS&P, 65; Univ London, PhD(med), 70; Royal Col Pathologists, FRCPath, 74; Col Ophthalmologists, London, FCOphth, 88. *Hon Degrees:* FACS, Am Col Surgeons; FICS, Int Col Surgeons; FNASc, Nat Acad Sci, India. *Honors & Awards:* Ophthalmologic Prize, Royal Soc Med, 71; Royal Eye Hosp Prize, Ophthal Soc, UK, 76; Honor Award, Am Acad Ophthal, 84; Honor Award, Asn Indians Am, 84; Litchfield lectr, Univ Oxford, 86, Ida Mann Medal, 89; Honor Award, Nat Fedn Asian Indians, 86; Int Prize, Alcon Res Inst, 87. *Prof Exp:* Resident ophthal, Med Col Kanpur, Lucknow Univ, 59-64; res fel, Univ Ghent, 64-65; registrar, S W Middlesex Hosp, London, 65-67; lectr, Inst Ophthal, London Univ, 67-70, sr lectr, 70-77; prof ophthal & visual sci, Univ Chicago, 77-93, prof, The Col, 79-93. *Concurrent Pos:* Attend opthalmologist & asst surgeon, Div Railway Hosp, Govt India, 63-64; hon registrar, Charing Cross Hosp, 65-67; Hayward res fel, Inst Ophthal, Univ London, 67-68; sr registrar, Moorfields Eye Hosp, London, 67-68, chief clin asst, 68-72, consult ophthal & pathologist, 72-77; attend physician & electron microscopist, Univ Chicago Med Ctr, 77-93; ocular pathologist & dir, Eye Path Lab & NIH grant, 77-93, attend ophthalmologist, Oak Forest Hosp, 86-93; sect ed & exec ed, Exp Eye Res; life fel, Nat Acad Sci, India, 87; vis prof to many nat & int acad insts; adj prof, Dept Microbiol & Immunol, Sch Med, Univ SC, 93-; chmn opthal serv, attend ophthalmologist, eye pathologist & mem med staff, Vet Admin Hosp, Columbia, SC, 93-; attend opthalmologist, consult opthal pathologist & mem med staff, Richland Mem Hosp, Columbia, SC, 93- *Mem:* Asn Res Vision & Ophthal; Am Acad Ophthal; Royal Soc Med; Royal Col Pathologists; Sigma Xi; Physiol Soc London; AMA; Contact Lens Asn Ophthalmologists; Fedn Am Socs Exp Biol; Am Asn Pathologists; fel Int Col Surgeons; fel Nat Acad Sci India; fel Am Col Surgeons. *Res:* Ophthalmology; visual science; anatomy; physiology; surgical pathology; experimental pathology; clinical research; cell biology; electron microscopy; tissue culture; biochemistry; immunology; microbiology; micrography; ophthalmic microsurgery; laser surgery; physiology and pathology of cerebrospinal fluid; author of more than 440 publications and 30 monographs and chapters in scientific journals and books. *Mailing Add:* SC Eye Inst 4 Richland Med Park Suite 100 Columbia SC 29203

**TRIPATHI, SANJAY,** LIQUID CRYSTALS MATERIALS & DISPLAYS, OPTICAL COMMUNICATION & INTERCONNECTS. *Current Pos:* MEM RES STAFF, REVEO, INC, 95-; PRIN INVESTR, OPTICAL INTERCONNECTS, 97- *Personal Data:* b Kanpur, India, July 21, 67. *Educ:* Indian Inst Technol, MS, 90; Case Western Res Univ, PhD(liquid crystals), 95. *Prof Exp:* Res asst, Radio Astron Ctr, India, 88; teaching asst, Mich Technol Univ, 90. *Mem:* Int Liquid Crystal Soc. *Res:* Liquid crystals: materials, electro-optical properties and surface interactions of liquid crystals with glass, plastics and mica; optical interconnects: freespace, nonblocking, crossbar switches and routing logics. *Mailing Add:* Reveo Inc 8 Skyline Dr Hawthorne NY 10532. *E-Mail:* sxt8@po.cwru.edu

**TRIPATHI, SATISH CHANDRA,** cell cycle control, oncogene expression, for more information see previous edition

**TRIPATHI, SATISH K,** COMPUTER NETWORKING, MULTIMEDIA. *Current Pos:* Prof eng, 78-97, chmn dept, 89-95, DEAN & JOHNSON PROF ENG, UNIV MD, COLLEGE PARK, 95- *Personal Data:* b Patna, Faizabad, India, Jan 20, 51; m 70; c 2. *Educ:* Banaras Hindu Univ, BSc, 68; Univ Alta, MS, 74; Univ Toronto, MS, 76, PhD(computer sci), 79. *Concurrent Pos:* Vis prof, Univ Paris, Sud, 84-85, Univ Erlangen, Nunenburg, 85. *Mem:* Fel Inst Elec & Electronics Engrs; Asn Computer Mach. *Res:* Mobile computing; protocal evaluation; ATM networking; multimedia. *Mailing Add:* Bourns Col Eng Univ Calif Riverside CA 92521. *Fax:* 909-787-3188; *E-Mail:* tripathi@engr.ucr.edu

**TRIPATHI, UMA PRASAD,** INORGANIC & COSMETIC CHEMISTRY, INSECTICIDE CHEMISTRY. *Current Pos:* VPRES, RES & DEVELOP, PLAYTEX PROD INC, 89- *Personal Data:* b Lumbini, Nepal, Apr 29, 45; m 89, Margaret Aleles; c Ashok & Daniel. *Educ:* Univ Gorakhpur, India, BSc, 63; Univ Allahabad, India, MSc, 65; Mont State Univ, PhD(inorg chem), 72. *Prof Exp:* Anal chemist, Nepal Bur Mines, Kathmandu, 65; asst prof chem, Trichandra Col, Kathmandu, 65-67; sr res chemist, Cosmetics, Chesebrough-Pond's Inc, 72-75; sr chemist, Gillette Co, 75-76; group leader, Am Cyanamid Co, 76-78, sect mgr, 78-86; dir, Spectrum Group, 86-88; dir, Personal Prod, Unilever USA, 88-89. *Mem:* Soc Cosmetic Chemists; Am Chem Soc. *Res:* Elucidation of molecular and crystal structures of organometallics; inorganic synthesis; inorganic reaction mechanisms; emulsion technology; surface active agents; hair science; insecticides; household products; skin care; oral care; antiperspirants; suncare. *Mailing Add:* Playtex Inc 215 College Rd PO Box 728 Paramus NJ 07653-0728

**TRIPATHI, VIJAI KUMAR,** ELECTRICAL ENGINEERING. *Current Pos:* from asst prof to assoc prof, 74-85, PROF ELEC ENG, ORE STATE UNIV, 85- *Personal Data:* b Kanpur, India, Dec 23, 42; US citizen; m 68, Emma Terrazas; c Sanjai & Ajai. *Educ:* Agra Univ, BSc, 58; Univ Allahabad, MScTech, 61; Univ Mich, Ann Arbor, MS, 64, PhD(elec eng), 68. *Prof Exp:* Sr res asst elec eng, Indian Inst Technol, Bombay, 61-63; res asst, Electron Physics Lab, Univ Mich, Ann Arbor, 63-65, res assoc, 65-67; asst prof elec eng, Univ Okla, 68-74. *Concurrent Pos:* Guest prof, Chalmers Tech Univ, Gothenburg, Sweden, 81-82, Duisburg Univ, WGer, 82 & Univ Cent Fla, 90; consult, EESOF, 84- & Tektronix, 93- *Mem:* Fel Inst Elec & Electronics Engrs; Int Soc Hybrid Microelectronics. *Res:* Microwave circuits and devices; electromagnetic fields; electronic packaging. *Mailing Add:* Dept Elec & Comput Eng Ore State Univ Corvallis OR 97331. *Fax:* 541-737-1300; *E-Mail:* ukt@ece.ovst.edu

**TRIPATHY, DEOKI NANDAN,** VETERINARY MICROBIOLOGY, MOLECULAR BIOLOGY. *Current Pos:* Fel, Univ Ill, 64-65, res asst, 65-70, res assoc, 70-73, asst prof, 73-77, assoc prof, PROF VET MICROBIOL, UNIV ILL, URBANA, 83- *Personal Data:* b Dwarahat, India, July 1, 33; m 69, Vidya Pant; c Sandeep & Neena. *Educ:* Utter Pradesh Agr Univ, India, BVSc & AH, 64; Univ Ill, Urbana, MS, 67, PhD(vet microbiol), 70; Am Col Vet Microbiologists, dipl, 72. *Concurrent Pos:* World Bank consult, Univ Godjah Mada, Indonesia-Vet Biotechnol, l91; Food & Agr Orgn/UN consult, Indian Vet Res Inst, Izatnagar, 92; Fulbright res fel, 95. *Mem:* Am Vet Med Asn; Am Asn Avian Pathologists; Am Col Poultry Vet; Am Col Vet Microbiologists; US Animal Health Asn; Conf Res Workers Animal Dis. *Res:* Diseases of food producing animals; poxviruses of veterinary importance; leptospirosis in domestic animals; infection laryngotracheitis virus, poxvirus based recombinant vaccines; development of fowlpox, swine pox and infectious laryngotracheitis viruses as eucaryotic cloning and expression vectors for genes from poultry and swine pathogens. *Mailing Add:* 104 W McHenry St Urbana IL 61801. *Fax:* 217-244-7421; *E-Mail:* tripathy@uxl.cso.uiuc.edu

**TRIPATHY, SUKANT K,** STRUCTURE PROPERTY, POLYMER THEORY. *Current Pos:* prof, Univ Mass 86-91, univ prof chem, 91-94, provost & vchancellar acad affairs, 94-96, DIR, CTR ADVAN MAT, UNIV MASS, LOWELL, 92-, PROF, 96- *Personal Data:* b Chakradharpur, India, Aug 4, 52; m 81, Susan Thomson; c Sheila & Aneil. *Educ:* Indian Inst Technol, India, BSc, 72, MSc, 74; Case Western Res Univ, PhD(macromolecular sci), 81. *Honors & Awards:* Carl S Marvel Creative Polymer Chem Award, Am Chem Soc, 93. *Prof Exp:* Mem tech staff, 81-83, res mgr, GTE Labs Inc, 83-86. *Concurrent Pos:* Vis prof, Tokyo Univ, 89. *Mem:* Am Phys Soc; Am Chem Soc; AAAS; Sigma Xi; Soc Prof Educ; Mat Res Soc; Int Soc Optical Engrs. *Res:* Characterization and understanding of polymer microstructure using physical methods and theoretical modelling, establishing structure property relationships; novel polymeric applications; polymers with interesting electronic and optical properties; such as conducting polymers and nonlinear optical polymers. *Mailing Add:* Dept Chem Univ Mass Lowell MA 01854. *Fax:* 978-458-9571; *E-Mail:* tripathys@woods.uml.edu

**TRIPLEHORN, CHARLES A,** ENTOMOLOGY. *Current Pos:* from asst prof to prof, 62-92, EMER PROF ENTOM, OHIO STATE UNIV, 92- *Personal Data:* b Bluffton, Ohio, Oct 27, 27; m 49, 87, Linda S Shelton; c Bradley A & Bruce W. *Educ:* Ohio State Univ, BS, 49, MS, 52; Cornell Univ, PhD(entom), 57. *Prof Exp:* Asst prof entom, Univ Del, 52-54 Ohio Agr Exp Sta, 57-62; entomologist, US AID, Brazil, 64-66. *Mem:* Entom Soc Am (pres, 85); Coleopterists Soc (pres, 76); Royal Entom Soc London; Sigma Xi. *Res:* Taxonomy of Coleoptera; animal ecology; herpetology. *Mailing Add:* Dept Entom Ohio State Univ 1735 Neil Ave Columbus OH 43210

**TRIPLEHORN, DON MURRAY,** GEOLOGY. *Current Pos:* US GEOL SURV, DENVER, COLO, 79- *Personal Data:* b Bluffton, Ohio, July 24, 34; m 57, Julia; c Clay, Carl, Joel & Stella. *Educ:* Ohio Wesleyan Univ, BA, 56; Ind Univ, MA, 57; Univ Ill, PhD(geol), 61. *Prof Exp:* Instr geol, Col Wooster, 60-61; res geologist, Tulsa Res Ctr, Sinclair Oil & Gas Co, 61-69; from assoc prof to prof geol, Univ Alaska, 69-76. *Mem:* Geol Soc Am; Int Asn Sedimentologists; Am Asn Petrol Geologists; Soc Econ Paleontologists & Mineralogists; Am Asn Geol Teachers; Clay Mineral Soc. *Res:* Glauconite; coal geology; clay mineralogy; shale petrology; diagenesis; Cretaceous-Tertiary boundary; volcanic ash layers associated with coal. *Mailing Add:* Dept Geol & Geophys Univ Alaska Fairbanks AK 99775

**TRIPLETT, BARBARA ANN,** PLANT MOLECULAR BIOLOGY, CELL & DEVELOPMENTAL BIOLOGY. *Current Pos:* PLANT PHYSIOLOGIST/LEAD SCIENTIST, SOUTHERN REGIONAL CTR, AGR RES SERV, USDA, 83- *Personal Data:* b Seattle, Wash, June 19, 51; m 78, William H Busch. *Educ:* Reed Col, BA, 73; Univ Wis-Madison, MS, 75; Ore State Univ, PhD(plant develop), 79. *Prof Exp:* NIH fel biol, Johns Hopkins Univ, 79-80; NIH fel bot, Univ Minn, 80-81, asst prof plant physiol, 81-82, res assoc genetics & cell biol, 82-83. *Concurrent Pos:* Adj prof, Tex Tech Univ, 90-92, La Tech Univ & Univ Southwestern La, 94- *Mem:* Int Soc Plant Molecular Biologists; Am Soc Plant Physiol; Am Chem Soc; Sigma Xi; AAAS. *Res:* Physiology, chemistry and molecular biology of cotton fiber cell growth and development; cell wall biochemistry of higher plants; cotton fiber qualtiy improvement. *Mailing Add:* USDA SRRC 1100 Robert E Lee Blvd New Orleans LA 70124-4305. *Fax:* 504-286-4419; *E-Mail:* btriplett@nola.srrc.usda.gov

**TRIPLETT, EDWARD LEE,** ZOOLOGY. *Current Pos:* from instr to assoc prof, 55-73, PROF BIOL, UNIV CALIF, SANTA BARBARA, 73- *Personal Data:* b Denver, Colo, July 14, 30; m 51; c 3. *Educ:* Stanford Univ, BS, 51, PhD, 56. *Prof Exp:* Actg instr biol, Stanford Univ, 54-55. *Mem:* AAAS; Soc Develop Biol. *Res:* Development of the nervous system; cell differentiation of neural plate cells; control of protein synthesis in developing systems. *Mailing Add:* Dept Biol Sci Univ Calif 552 University Ave Santa Barbara CA 93106-0001

**TRIPLETT, GLOVER BROWN, JR,** AGRONOMY. *Current Pos:* PROF AGRON, MISS STATE UNIV, 83- *Personal Data:* b Miss, June 2, 30; m 51; c 1. *Educ:* Miss State Univ, BS, 51, MS, 55; Mich State Univ, PhD(farm crops), 59. *Prof Exp:* From asst prof to assoc prof, 59-67, prof agron, Ohio Agr Res & Develop Ctr, 67-83. *Concurrent Pos:* Agronomist, 59- *Mem:* Am Soc Agron; Weed Sci Soc Am; Sigma Xi. *Res:* Crop production and management; no-tillage cropping systems. *Mailing Add:* 1102 Nottingham Rd Starkville MS 39759. *Fax:* 601-325-8742

**TRIPLETT, KELLY B,** CERAMICS FROM CHEMICALS, ZIEGLER-NATTA PROCESSES. *Current Pos:* prog mgr & bus mgr, 87-90, DIR RES, AKZO CHEM INC, 90- *Personal Data:* b Cincinnati, Ohio; c 2. *Educ:* Northwestern Univ, BA, 68; Univ Mich, PhD(chem), 74. *Prof Exp:* Res assoc, Mich State Univ, 74-76; res chemist, Stauffer Chem Co, 76-78, supvr, 78-82, tech mgr, 82-84, bus mgr, 84-87. *Mem:* Am Ceramic Soc; Indust Res Inst. *Res:* Investigation of chemical routes to advanced ceramics; new polymerization products and process; organometallics and transition metal chemistries; research and development administration; development of new research and development methodologies. *Mailing Add:* Akzo Chem Inc 1 Livingstone Ave Dobbs Ferry NY 10522

**TRIPODI, DANIEL,** IMMUNOCHEMISTRY, MICROBIOLOGY. *Current Pos:* PRES, TRICON, 90- *Personal Data:* b Cliffside Park, NJ, May 13, 39; m 63. *Educ:* Univ Del, BS, 61, MS, 63; Temple Univ, PhD(microbiol, immunol), 66. *Prof Exp:* Asst microbiol, Univ Del, 63; sr scientist, Ortho Res Found, 66-69, dir div immunol & diag res, 69-74; from res asst prof to res assoc prof microbiol, Sch Med, Temple Univ, 69-77; gen mgr, biomed div, New Eng Nuclear Corp, 74-77; dir, tech planning group, Becton, Dickinson & Co, 77-80; dir tech serv, Ortho Diagnostics, 80-83; corp dir biotechnol, Johnson & Johnson, 83-87; vpres res, Therakos, Inc, 87-90. *Concurrent Pos:* Adj prof, Univ Del, Univ Pa & Temple Univ. *Mem:* Am Soc Microbiol; Am Asn Immunol; Sigma Xi. *Res:* Physical and chemical aspects of structures which display serological reactivity. *Mailing Add:* Tricon Consult 1 Burlinghoff Lane Lebanon NJ 08833

**TRIPP, JOHN RATHBONE,** INVERTEBRATE ZOOLOGY, EMBRYOLOGY. *Current Pos:* from asst prof to assoc prof, 71-84, PROF, DEPT BIOL, FLA SOUTHERN COL, 84-, CHMN, 96- *Personal Data:* b Barberton, Ohio, Oct 18, 39; m 71; c 3. *Educ:* Ore State Univ, BSc, 62; Ohio State Univ, MSc, 65, PhD(zool), 70. *Prof Exp:* Res specialist, Introductory Biol Prog, Ohio State Univ 69-70. *Concurrent Pos:* Prin investr, Cottrell Found Col Sci grant, 75. *Mem:* Am Inst Biol Sci; AAAS; Am Arachnological Soc; Soc Integrative & Comp Biol. *Res:* Spider embryology and marine invertebrate zoology. *Mailing Add:* Dept Biol Fla Southern Col 111 Lake Hollingworth Lakeland FL 33801-5698

**TRIPP, JOHN STEPHEN,** ELECTRONICS ENGINEERING, COMPUTER SCIENCE. *Current Pos:* AEROSPACE TECHNOLOGIST, LANGLEY RES CTR-NASA, 62- *Personal Data:* b Salina, Kans, Aug 3, 38. *Educ:* Kans State Univ, BS, 61, MS, 62; Univ Mich, Ann Arbor, MS, 67, PhD(comput sci), 71. *Concurrent Pos:* Lectr, George Washington Univ, 81- *Mem:* Inst Elec & Electronics Engrs. *Res:* Analysis and simulation of physical systems; synthesis of control techniques for automation of aerospace test facilities; application of digital computers to automatic control. *Mailing Add:* NASA Langley Res Ctr Mail Stop 238 Hampton VA 23665

**TRIPP, LEONARD L,** SOFTWARE DESIGN, SOFTWARE ENGINEERING STANDARDS. *Current Pos:* Appl programmer, Boeing Co, 67-71, Boeing Comput Serv, 71-73, software technol specialist, 73-79,sr comput scientist, 79-89, Boeing Com Airplane, 89-91, ASSOC TECH FEL, BOEING COM AIRPLANE, 91- *Personal Data:* b Los Angeles, Calif, Oct 21, 41; m 63, Celia Frank; c Valerie, Monica, Allyson, Justin, Mary E & Lee. *Educ:* Brigham Young Univ, BS, 65, MS, 67. *Honors & Awards:* Outstanding Contribution Award, Inst Elec & Electronics Engrs Comput Soc. *Concurrent Pos:* Chmn, working group for Inst Elec & Electronics Engrs Stand 1002, 83-87, chmn, Comput Sci Coord Comt, 90-91, Software Eng Stand Comt, 93-

& US Tech Adv Group ISO/IEC JTC1/SC7, Software Eng, 93-; vpres stand, Inst Elec & Electronics Engrs Comput Soc, 94. *Mem:* Asn Comput Mach; Math Asn Am; Inst Elec & Electronics Engrs; Am Soc Testing & Mat. *Res:* Development and implementation of techniques, methodologies, standards and tools for systems engineering, software requirements definition, software design, software verification, validation and testing and software project management. *Mailing Add:* 28632 Eighth Pl S Federal Way WA 98003

**TRIPP, MARENES ROBERT,** INVERTEBRATE PATHOLOGY. *Current Pos:* from asst prof to prof, 60-95, from interim dir to dir, Sch Life & Health Sci, 81-87, EMER PROF BIOL SCI, UNIV DEL, 95- *Personal Data:* b Poughkeepsie, NY, Aug 20, 31; m 55, Jane Martin; c Daniel L, Kenneth M, Andrew H & Steven P. *Educ:* Colgate Univ, AB, 53; Univ Rochester, MS, 56; Rutgers Univ, PhD(zool), 58. *Prof Exp:* Res fel trop pub health, Harvard Univ, 58-60. *Mem:* AAAS; Am Soc Parasitol; Soc Invert Path; Am Soc Zoologists; Int Soc Develop Comp Immunol. *Res:* Invertebrate defense mechanisms. *Mailing Add:* 43 Woodhill Dr Newark DE 19711

**TRIPP, R(USSELL) MAURICE,** RADIOLOGY, GEOPHYSICS. *Current Pos:* PRES, TRIPP RES CORP, 55-, SKIA CORP, 72-, AKTINA CORP, 84- *Personal Data:* b Holton, Kans, July 12, 16; m 37; c 7. *Educ:* Colo Sch Mines, GeolE, 39, MGeophysEng, 43; Mass Inst Technol, ScD(geol), 48. *Prof Exp:* Geophysicist, Geotech Corp, Tex, 36-41, asst to pres-in-chg res, 43-46; instr geol & geophys, Colo Sch Mines, 41-43; sr scientist, Bur Ships, US Dept Navy, 46; consult geologist & geophysicist, 47-49; vpres & dir res, Res Inc, 49-53; pres, Explor, Inc, 52-58. *Concurrent Pos:* Managing partner, Tripp Lead & Zinc Co, 52-, pres, Tripp Prod, Inc, 62-; dir, Sonic Res Corp, 56-; consult, Bostwick Propecting Co, 56- & Archilithic Corp, 58-; managing partner, Saratoga Develop Co; dir, Torginol Am. *Mem:* Soc Info Display; Soc Photog Scientists & Engrs; Soc Photo Optical Instrumentation Engrs; AAAS; Sigma Xi. *Res:* Geophysical and geochemical exploration for minerals; relation between clay minerals, organic matter and radioelements in sediments; genesis of uranium ore bodies; mineral benefication; free viewing depth-perception radiography; nuclear medicine instrumentation; animal genetics; ophthalmic surgical instrumentation. *Mailing Add:* 2405 Iowa Ave Alamogordo NM 88310

**TRIPP, ROBERT D,** PHYSICS. *Current Pos:* From asst prof to assoc prof, 60-66, PHYSICIST, LAWRENCE BERKELEY LAB, UNIV CALIF, BERKELEY, 55-, PROF PHYSICS, 66- *Personal Data:* b Oakland, Calif, Jan 9, 27; m 64; c 3. *Educ:* Mass Inst Technol, BS, 49; Univ Calif, PhD, 55. *Concurrent Pos:* Physicist, AEC, France, 59-60; NSF sr fel, Europ Orgn Nuclear Res, Switz, 64-65, vis scientist, 71-72. *Mem:* Am Phys Soc. *Res:* Elementary particle physics. *Mailing Add:* 50B-5230 Lawrence Berkeley Lab Berkeley CA 94720. *Fax:* 510-486-5401

**TRIPPE, ANTHONY PHILIP,** NUCLEAR ENGINEERING, TECHNICAL MANAGEMENT. *Current Pos:* Vpres survivability prods & EM products mgr, 88-91, ADVAN PROD DEVELOP, MAXWELL LABS, INC, 91- *Personal Data:* b Buffalo, NY, Aug 30, 43; m 65, Dorothy A Fazzina; c Anthony J, Michael A & Madonna M. *Educ:* Rochester Inst Technol, BS, 66; Fairleigh Dickinson Univ, MS, 72; US Int Univ, DBA, 82. *Prof Exp:* Chemist polymers, Smith Kline & French Labs, 66-67; reliability engr quality assurance, US Army Picatinny Arsenal, 67-72; prin engr, Calspan Corp, 72-76; mgr prog develop, IRT Corp, 77-84, mkt mgr, 84-88. *Concurrent Pos:* Fire protection engr, Allstate Insurance Co, 74-75; adv, Jr Achievement, 84-86. *Mem:* Am Defense Preparedness Asn; Asn Old Crows; Am Mgt Asn; Armed Forces Commun & Electronics Asn; Inst Elec & Electronics Engrs; Am Chem Soc. *Res:* Nondestructive testing using nuclear techniques; study of systems using computerized analytical models; application of pattern recognition to automated control; nuclear weapons effects on military systems; proton therapy cancer treatment; radiation oncology. *Mailing Add:* 5590 Antigua Blvd San Diego CA 92124-1305. *Fax:* 619-277-6754

**TRIPPE, THOMAS GORDON,** EXPERIMENTAL HIGH ENERGY PHYSICS. *Current Pos:* PHYSICIST, LAWRENCE BERKELEY LAB, 71- *Personal Data:* b Los Angeles, Calif, Nov 17, 39; m, Kirsten M Berg; c Tori (Boziki), Bradford & Eric. *Educ:* Univ Calif, Los Angeles, PhD(physics), 68. *Prof Exp:* Physicist, Univ Calif, Los Angeles, 68-69; physicist, Europ Orgn Nuclear Res, 69-70 & 73. *Concurrent Pos:* NSF fel, 69-70. *Mem:* Am Phys Soc. *Res:* Experimental weak interactions; particle properties. *Mailing Add:* Lawrence Berkeley Lab Particle Data Group Berkeley CA 94720. *Fax:* 510-486-4799

**TRIPPENSEE, GARY ALAN,** MECHANICAL ENGINEERING. *Current Pos:* proj mgr F14, Dryden Flight Res Ctr, NASA, Calif, 83-84, proj mgr F15, 84-85, Proj mgr X-29, 85-91, proj mgr X31, 91-92, dir, Int Test Orgn X31, 93-95, PROJ MGR, DRYDEN FLIGHT RES CTR, NASA, EDWARDS, CALIF, 79- *Personal Data:* b Jefferson City, Mo, May 23, 40; m 81, Concha Elvira Perez; c Jena & Darin. *Educ:* Univ Mo, Rolla, BSME, 62. *Prof Exp:* Aircraft flight test engr, McDonnell Douglas St Louis, 65-79. *Mem:* Am Inst Aeronaut & Astronaut. *Mailing Add:* 3773 Knox Ave Rosamond CA 93560-6413

**TRIPPODO, NICK CHARLES,** CARDIOVASCULAR PHYSIOLOGY, HYPERTENSION. *Current Pos:* head sect peptide pharmacol, Squibb Inst Med Res, 88-91, prin scientist, Pharmacol Dept, 91-94, SR PRIN SCIENTIST, CARDIOVASC DRUG DISCOVERY, BRISTOL-MYERS SQUIBB PHARMACEUT RES INST, 94- *Personal Data:* b Galveston, Tex, Sept 27, 45; m 67, Linda S Evers; c Joseph B & Julie R. *Educ:* Stephen F Austin State Univ, BS, 68, MS, 69; Univ Tex, Galveston, PhD(physiol), 74.

*Prof Exp:* Fel cardiovasc physiol, Univ Miss Med Ctr, 74-76; sci staff hypertension, Div Res, Alton Ochsner Med Found, 76-79, res coordr, 79-88, head vascular physiol, 88. *Concurrent Pos:* Assoc prof physiol, La State Univ Sch Med, 76-88; prin investr grant awards, Pub Health Serv, 79-88; estab investr, Am Heart Asn, 85-88; adj assoc prof physiol, Tulane Univ Sch Med, 88. *Mem:* Fel Am Physiol Soc; fel Am Heart Asn; fel High Blood Pressure Res Coun; Am Soc Hypertension. *Res:* Fluid and electrolyte homeostasis; arterial blood pressure regulation; cardiovascular actions of the hormone; atrial natriuretic factor; drug discovery for treatment of hypertension and heart failure in animal models. *Mailing Add:* 5 Water Lilly Way Newtown PA 18940. *Fax:* 609-252-6609; *E-Mail:* trippodo_nick_c.prilvms3@msmail.bms.com

**TRISCARI, JOSEPH,** OBESITY, LIPID METABOLISM. *Current Pos:* ASSOC DIR, BRISTOL-MYERS SQUIBB, 89- *Personal Data:* b Italy, Apr 17, 45; US citizen; m 66, Maria Difabio; c Joseph M, Craig A & Erica. *Educ:* Cornell Univ, BS, 71; Fairleigh Dickinson Univ, MS, 75; Columbia Univ, PhD(nutrit), 80. *Honors & Awards:* Gold Bond Award, Am Chem Soc. *Prof Exp:* Lab asst, Dept Biochem, Cornell Univ, 68-71; res investr, neurobiol & obesity, anti-infactives, Hoffman La Roche, 71-89. *Concurrent Pos:* Guest lectr, Columbia Univ, Iowa State Univ & New York Univ, 82, Univ Ga, 86. *Mem:* Am Inst Nutrit; Am Health Asn; AAAS; NY Acad Sci; Soc Study Ingestive Behav; Am Diabetes Asn. *Res:* Regulation of lipid and carbohydrate metabolism; endocrinology and pharmacology of insulin and CCK; pharmacologic treatment of obesity and hyperlipidemia; atherosclerosis; clinical pharmacokinetics; arrhythmia. *Mailing Add:* Dept Atherosclerosis Clin Res Bristol Myers-Squibb PO Box 4000 Princeton NJ 08543-4000. *Fax:* 609-252-6701; *E-Mail:* triscari@bms.com

**TRISCHAN, GLENN M,** ATOMIC SPECTROSCOPY, MOLECULAR SPECTROSCOPY. *Current Pos:* sr anal chemist, 80-86, mgr, Mat Test Lab, 86-88, MGR ANALYTICAL SERV, JOHNSON CONTROLS INC, 88- *Personal Data:* Milwaukee, Wis. *Educ:* Marquette Univ, BS, 72; Univ Iowa, MS, 74 & PhD(analytical chem), 77. *Prof Exp:* Res asst, dept chem, Univ Iowa, 73-76; assoc analytical chemist, Midwest Rest Inst, 76-80. *Mem:* Am Chem Soc; Sigma Xi; Am Indust Hygiene Asn; Soc Appl Spectroscopy; Am Lab Mgrs Asn. *Res:* Polymer stabilization and degradation at elevated temperatures; metallic corrosion mechanisms; trace element analysis in metal materials; analysis of aerosols and vapors in compressed gas systems; surface, reaction layer characterization; environmental analysis of process effluents from waste to energy processes; priority pollutant analysis of potw effluent; surface reactions in low temperate flames; granted one US patent. *Mailing Add:* 8322 N 51st St Brown Deer WI 53223-3515. *Fax:* 414-228-2008

**TRISCHKA, JOHN WILSON,** physics; deceased, see previous edition for last biography

**TRISCHLER, FLOYD D,** ORGANIC CHEMISTRY, POLYMER CHEMISTRY. *Current Pos:* PRES, IROQUOIS REALTY, INC, 78- *Personal Data:* b Pittsburgh, Pa, Aug 31, 29; m 51; c 6. *Educ:* Univ Pittsburgh, BS, 51. *Prof Exp:* Res chemist, Pa Indust Chem Corp, 53-55, asst lab mgr, 55-56; develop & tech chemist, Tar Prod Div, Koppers Co, 56-58, asst group leader, Res Dept, 58-63; sr res chemist, Narmco Res & Develop, Whittaker Corp, Calif, 63-65, prog mgr, 65-69; mgr mkt & admin asst to pres, Mat Systs Corp, Calif, 69-72; exec vpres, Taylor Bldg Corp, Ind, 72-73; pres, Guadalupe Builders, Ind, 73-78. *Mem:* Am Chem Soc; Int Asn Radiopharmacol. *Res:* Polymer applications and research; pulp and paper; organic coatings; fluorine compounds; elastomers; adhesives; high performance polymers. *Mailing Add:* 8249 Filly Lane Plainfield IN 46168

**TRISLER, JOHN CHARLES,** ORGANIC CHEMISTRY. *Current Pos:* From asst prof to assoc prof, 59-66, PROF CHEM, LA TECH UNIV, 66-, HEAD DEPT, 78- *Personal Data:* b Eva, La, Dec 24, 33; m 53; c 2. *Educ:* La Polytech Inst, BS, 56; Tex Tech Univ, PhD(org chem), 59. *Mem:* Am Chem Soc. *Res:* Organic reaction mechanisms. *Mailing Add:* PO Box 3044 Ruston LA 71272-0047

**TRISTAN, THEODORE A,** RADIOLOGY. *Current Pos:* RETIRED. *Personal Data:* b Mexico City, Mex, Oct 5, 24; US citizen; m 48; c 4. *Educ:* Univ Nebr, BS, 47, MD & MSc, 50; Univ Pa, MS, 58; Am Bd Radiol, dipl, 57. *Honors & Awards:* Gold Medal, Radiol Soc NAm. *Prof Exp:* Intern, Hosp, Univ Pa, 50-51; instr radiol, Med Ctr, Univ Rochester, 56-59, sr instr, 59; from asst prof to assoc prof, Univ Pa, 59-65, lectr, 65-70; prof radiol & anat, Hershey Med Ctr, Pa State Univ, 70-86, prof radiol & clin prof anat, 86-89. *Concurrent Pos:* Fel radiol, Univ Pa Hosp, 53-56; Am Cancer Soc fel, 53-54; NIH grants, Univ Rochester, 58-59 & Univ Pa, 59-63; Nat Res Coun Picker Found grant, Univ Pa, 58-65; mem & task group chmn, Int Comn Radiation Units & Measurements, 64-67; assoc prof radiol, Hahnemann Med Col, 70-73; consult, Pa Blue Shield, 70- *Mem:* Radiol Soc NAm (secy, 75-79, pres elect, 81 & pres, 82); Am Roentgen Ray Soc; AMA; fel Am Col Radiol; Sigma Xi; Asn Univ Radiol. *Res:* Image intensification, image quality and information development, storage and retrieval; analysis of the function of motion in cinefluorography with regard to its value in development of diagnostic criteria in clinical radiology. *Mailing Add:* 353 N 28th St Camp Hill PA 17011-2837

**TRISTRAM-NAGLE, STEPHANIE ANN,** MEMBRANE THERMODYNAMICS, MEMBRANE STRUCTURE. *Current Pos:* fel res membrane thermodyn, 82-86, RES BIOLOGIST STRUCT MEMBRANES, CARNEGIE-MELLON UNIV, PITTSBURGH, 86- *Personal Data:* b New York, NY, Nov 21, 48; m 80, John F Nagle; c Julia & Lara. *Educ:* Douglass

Col, BA, 70; Univ Calif, Berkeley, PhD(comp biochem), 81. *Prof Exp:* Clin & res lab technician, Clin Assays, Cambridge, Mass 72-75; teaching asst & reader, Membrane Bioenergetics Course, Univ Calif Berkeley, 76-78. *Concurrent Pos:* Reviewer, Biochimica Biophysica Acta (Elsevier), NHolland Biomed Press, 85- & Biochem, Univ Wash, Seattle, 87-; Samuel & Emma Winters grant, Winters Found, Pittsburgh, Pa, 85 & 89. *Mem:* Biophys Soc; Sigma Xi; Asn Women Sci; Sigma Xi (secy, 89-93, vpres, 93-94, pres, 94-95). *Res:* Structure and thermodynamic properties primarily of biomimetic membranes composed of purified lipids; x-ray diffraction of both oriented and dispersed lipids; differential dilatometry; differential scanning calorimetry; neutral buoyancy centrifugation. *Mailing Add:* Dept Biol Sci 4400 Fifth Ave Pittsburgh PA 15213-3890. *Fax:* 412-641-0648; *E-Mail:* stn+@andrew.cmu.edu

**TRITCHLER, DAVID LYNN,** BIOMETRICS, BIOSTATISTICS. *Current Pos:* AT PRINCESS MARGARET CANCER CTR, TORONTO. *Personal Data:* b Portage, Wis, Dec 17, 44; m 75. *Educ:* Univ Nebr, BA, 70, MS, 75; Harvard Sch Pub Health, ScD, 80. *Prof Exp:* Asst prof, Cornell Univ, 81; asst prof biostatist, Harvard Sch Pub Health, 81. *Concurrent Pos:* Assoc, Mem Sloan Kettering Cancer Ctr, 80-81; asst prof, Sidney Farber Cancer Inst, 81- *Mem:* Am Statist Asn; Biometric Soc; Soc Indust & Appl Math. *Res:* Computational algorithms for nonparametric statistics; survival analysis; discrete data analysis. *Mailing Add:* 21 Deerborn Ave Toronto ON M4K 1M6 Can

**TRITES, RONALD WILMOT,** physical oceanography; deceased, see previous edition for last biography

**TRITSCHLER, LOUIS GEORGE,** VETERINARY MEDICINE, VETERINARY SURGERY. *Current Pos:* RETIRED. *Personal Data:* b St Louis, Mo, Jan 24, 27; m 47; c 2. *Educ:* Univ Mo, BSAgr, 49, DVM, 60, MS, 62. *Prof Exp:* From instr to prof vet med & surg, Univ Mo, Columbia, 60-89, dir, Equine Ctr, 79-89. *Mem:* Am Vet Med Asn; Am Asn Equine Practrs; Am Asn Vet Clinicians. *Res:* Use of estrone in the treatment of anestrus in cattle; evaluation of bulls for breeding soundness; wound treatment and fracture repair in equine. *Mailing Add:* 7402 E Lost Woods Lane Centralia MO 65240

**TRITTON, THOMAS RICHARD,** BIOPHYSICAL CHEMISTRY, MOLECULAR PHARMACOLOGY. *Current Pos:* PRES, HAVERFORD COL, 97- *Personal Data:* b Lakewood, Ohio, Dec 20, 47; m 77; c Lara & Christiana. *Educ:* Ohio Wesleyan Univ, BA, 69; Boston Univ, PhD(chem), 73. *Prof Exp:* Fel biophys chem, Sch Med, Yale Univ, 73-75, asst prof, 75-80, assoc prof pharmacol, 80-85; prof pharmacol & dept dir, Vt Regional Cancer Ctr, Univ Vt, 85-97. *Concurrent Pos:* NIH fel, Yale Univ, 74-75, res career develop award, 80-85, exp ther study sect, 88-92, Am Cancer Soc Study Sect, 97- *Mem:* Am Chem Soc; Am Soc Biol Chemists; Am Asn Cancer Res. *Res:* Membrane mediated cytotoxicity; drug resistance; membrane dynamics and the cell surface as a target for antineoplastic agents; biophysical approaches to pharmacology. *Mailing Add:* Pres Off Haverford Col 370 Lancaster Ave Haverford PA 19041. *E-Mail:* ttriton@haverford.edu

**TRITZ, GERALD JOSEPH,** MICROBIOLOGY, GENETICS. *Current Pos:* assoc prof & chmn dept, 76-81, PROF & CHMN MICROBIOL & IMMUNOL, KIRKSVILLE COL OSTEOP MED, 81- *Personal Data:* b Sioux City, Iowa, Apr 12, 37; m 66; c 2. *Educ:* Utah State Univ, BS, 62; Colo State Univ, MS, 65; Univ Tex Med Sch Houston, PhD(biomed res), 70. *Honors & Awards:* M G Michael Award. *Prof Exp:* Res microbiologist, USPHS, 65-67; NIH fel microbiol, Univ Tex M D Anderson Hosp & Tumor Inst, Houston, 70; asst prof microbiol, Univ Ga, 70-76. *Concurrent Pos:* NSF grant, 71-78; Am Osteop Asn res grant, 79-85; citizen ambassador & vis scientist, Peoples Repub China, 83; Fermature Found grant, 85-89, Commerce Found grant, 87; vis scientist, minority student sci careers support prog, Am Soc Microbiol, 87-; ed, cellular & molecular biol. *Mem:* Am Soc Microbiol; Am Acad Microbiol. *Res:* Pyridine nucleotide metabolism and its control. *Mailing Add:* Dept Microbiol Kirksville Col Osteop Med 800 W Jefferson St Kirksville MO 63501

**TRIVEDI, BHANUMATI MULSHANKER,** PHARMACOLOGY, PHARMACEUTICAL TECHNOLOGY. *Current Pos:* SR VPRES & CHIEF EXEC OFFICER, CCA & NIRAMAYA INT, 88- *Educ:* Guj Univ, India, BPharm, 51, MPharm, 56; Charles Univ, PhD, 64. *Prof Exp:* Head, Dept Pharmacol Technol, Guj Univ, 51-88. *Concurrent Pos:* Consult nat & int pharmacy, food & cosmetic indust. *Mailing Add:* 6 Rock Glen Rd Medford MA 02155

**TRIVEDI, KISHOR SHRIDHARBHAI,** COMPUTER ENGINEERING. *Current Pos:* from asst prof to assoc prof, 75-83, PROF COMPUT SCI & ELEC ENG, DUKE UNIV, 83- *Personal Data:* b Bhavnagar, India, Aug 20, 46; m 73; c 2. *Educ:* Indian Inst Technol, Bombay, BTech, 68; Univ Ill, Urbana-Champaign, MS, 72, PhD(comput sci), 74. *Prof Exp:* Assoc customer engr, Int Bus Mach World Trade Corp, Bombay, 68-70; res asst comput sci, Univ Ill, Urbana-Champaign, 70-74, res assoc, 74-75. *Concurrent Pos:* Consult various res inst & indust labs, 79-; nat lectr, Asn Comput Mach, 81-82; ed, Inst Elec & Electronics Engrs Transactions Comput, 83-87. *Mem:* Comput Soc India; fel Inst Elec & Electronics Engrs; Inst Elec & Electronics Engrs Comput Soc. *Res:* Reliability and performance analysis of computer networks; reliability and performance analysis of fault-tolerant multiple processor systems. *Mailing Add:* Dept Elec Eng Duke Univ Durham NC 27708-0291. *Fax:* 919-660-5293; *E-Mail:* kst@ee.duke.edu

**TRIVEDI, MOHAN MANUBHAI,** SENSOR DRIVEN ROBOTICS. *Current Pos:* assoc prof, 86-90, PROF ELEC & COMPUT ENG, UNIV TENN, 90- *Personal Data:* b Wardha, India, Oct 4, 53; m 82. *Educ:* Birla Inst Tech & Sci, Pilani, India, BE, 74; Utah State Univ, ME, 76, PhD(elec eng), 79. *Honors & Awards:* Pioneer Award, Inst Elec & Electronics Engrs, 89, Meritorious Serv Award, 89. *Prof Exp:* Teaching asst, Utah State Univ, 75-76, res asst, Space Dynamics Lab, 76-79; assoc prof comput eng, La State Univ, 79-86. *Concurrent Pos:* Prin investr, var govt & indust res orgn, 79- consult, 83-; chmn, Pattern Recognition, Image Processing & Comput Vision Comt, Inst Elec & Electronics Engrs, 86- & Robotics Comt, 87 & assoc ed, Transa of Systs, Man & Cybernetics, Machine Vision & Appln J, Int J Approx Reasoning, 88-; lectr, Int Soc Optical Engrs, 87- *Mem:* Comput Soc; sr mem Inst Elec & Electronics Engrs; fel Int Soc Optical Engrs; Sigma Xi. *Res:* Design and engineering of computer vision systems including image processing, pattern recognition, knowledge representation, control, parallel architecture issues; development of sensor-driven intelligent robots including, sensor design, information processing, sensor fusion, image tactile, thermal infrared information acquisition and processing path planning. *Mailing Add:* Comput Vision & Robotics Res Lab Elec & Comput Eng Dept Univ Tenn Ferris Hall Knoxville TN 37996

**TRIVEDI, NAYAN B,** TECHNOLOGY MANAGEMENT, NEW FOOD PRODUCTS. *Current Pos:* DIR, RES & DEVELOP, UNIVERSAL FOODS CORP, 81- *Personal Data:* b Kapadwanj, India, Feb 13, 47; US citizen; m 70; c 2. *Educ:* Gujarat Univ, India, Sc, 67; Univ Baroda, India, MSc, 69; Univ Southwest La, PhD(microbiol), 73. *Prof Exp:* Dir labs, Arroyo Pharmaceut Corp, Chase Chem Co, 73-76; sr scientist, Schering Corp, 76; mgr, genetics-biochem, Standard Brands & Nabisco Brands, Inc, 76-81. *Concurrent Pos:* Asst prof biochem, Univ Conn, Danbury, 75. *Mem:* Am Soc Microbiol; Am Chem Soc; Soc Indust Microbiol; Am Asn Cereal Chemists; Am Soc Bakery Engrs; Inst Food Technologists. *Res:* Fermentation research including isolation, selection, mutation and genetic manipulation of microorganisms; recovery processes for fermentation products; yeast, mold actinomycetes and bacterial fermentations covering from cell mass and alcohol production to emulsifiers, antibiotics, vitamins and special enzymes using r-DNA technology. *Mailing Add:* 33 Parkview Rd Cranbury NJ 08512-2732

**TRIVEDI, ROHIT K,** METALLURGY, MATERIALS SCIENCE. *Current Pos:* SR METALLURGIST, AMES LAB, US DEPT ENERGY, 75- *Personal Data:* b Bhavnagar, India, Mar 8, 39; c 3. *Educ:* Indian Inst Technol, Kharagpur, BS, 60; Carnegie Inst Technol, MS, 64, PhD(metall, mat sci), 66. *Honors & Awards:* Sr Alexander von Humboldt Award, 77; Sr Fulbright Res Award, 77. *Prof Exp:* Res scientist, Sci Lab, Ford Motor Co, 63-64; res assoc metall, Inst Atomic Res, 65-66, asst prof, 66-70; assoc prof metall, Iowa State Univ, 70-75, prof mat sci & eng, 75- *Concurrent Pos:* Vis assoc prof, Stanford Univ, 69-70; guest prof, Tech Univ Braunschwieg, WGer, 77-78; invited prof, Fed Polytech Sch Lausanne, Switz, 84-85; invited prof, Université Aix-Marseille Ill, Marseille, France, 88, 89. *Mem:* Fel Am Soc Metals; Am Inst Mining, Metall & Petrol Engrs. *Res:* Solidification; stability of interphase boundaries. *Mailing Add:* 2143 Friley Rd Ames IA 50014

**TRIVELPIECE, ALVIN WILLIAM,** MICROWAVE DEVICES, PARTICLE ACCELERATOR. *Current Pos:* DIR, OAK RIDGE NAT LAB, 89-; PRES, LOCKHEED MARTIN ENERGY RES CORP, 96- *Personal Data:* b Stockton, Calif, Mar 15, 31; m 53, Shirley A Ross; c Craig E, Steve E & Keith E. *Educ:* Calif Polytech State Univ, BS, 53; Calif Inst Technol, MS, 55, PhD(elec eng & physics), 58. *Honors & Awards:* Secretarial Gold Medal, US Dept Energy, 87. *Prof Exp:* Fulbright scholar, Tech Hogesch, 58-59; from asst prof to assoc prof elec eng, Univ Calif, 59-66; prof physics, Univ Md, 66-76; vpres eng & res, Maxwell Labs, Inc, 76-78; corp vpres, Sci Appln, Inc, 78-81; dir, Off Energy Res, US Dept Energy, 81-87; exec dir, AAAS, 87-88; vpres, Martin Marietta Energy Systs, Inc, 89-95. *Concurrent Pos:* Guggenheim Found fel, 66; asst dir res, Div Controlled Thermonuclear Res, US AEC, 73-75; chmn, Div Plasma Physics, Am Phys Soc, 75; mem bd dirs, Bausch & Lomb, 90; chmn, Math Sci Educ Bd, 90-92 & Coord Coun Educ, Nat Res Coun, 91-92, State Tenn Sci & Technol Adv Coun, 96-, Physics Planning Comt, Am Phys Soc, 96- *Mem:* Nat Acad Eng; Am Nuclear Soc; fel Inst Elec & Electronics Engrs; Nuclear & Plasma Sci Soc; fel AAAS; Am Asn Physics Teachers; Am Asn Univ Prof; fel Am Phys Soc. *Res:* Plasma physics; controlled thermonuclear research; particle accelerators; granted several patents; author of various publications. *Mailing Add:* 8 Rivers Run Way Oak Ridge TN 37830. *Fax:* 423-576-2900; *E-Mail:* avt@ornl.gov

**TRIVETT, TERRENCE LYNN,** BACTERIOLOGY. *Current Pos:* From asst prof to assoc prof, 69-77, PROF BIOL, PAC UNION COL, 77- *Personal Data:* b Madison, Tenn, Oct 3, 40; m 65; c Michael & Mark. *Educ:* Southern Missionary Col, BS, 64; Univ Ore, PhD(microbiol), 69. *Mem:* Am Soc Microbiol; AAAS. *Res:* Carbohydrate metabolism of Listeria monocytogenes; pathogenesis of Neisseria meningitidis. *Mailing Add:* Dept Biol Pac Union Col Angwin CA 94508-9797. *Fax:* 707-965-7577; *E-Mail:* ttrivett@puc.edu

**TRIVISONNO, CHARLES F(RANCIS),** ANALYTICAL CHEMISTRY, ORGANIC CHEMISTRY. *Current Pos:* RETIRED. *Personal Data:* b Cleveland, Ohio, Dec 30, 24; m 58, Mary Kathryn Griffin; c Patricia, Michael & Mary. *Educ:* Case Inst Technol, BS, 45, MS, 49. *Prof Exp:* Squad trainee, Goodyear Tire & Rubber Co, 48, res chemist, 48-53, group leader uranium chem, Goodyear Atomic Corp, 53-65, supvr chem analysis, 65-70, supvr, Chem Dept, 70-73, supvr, Chem Analysis Dept, 73-82, supt, Analysis Serv Subdiv, 82-85. *Mem:* Am Chem Soc; Sigma Xi. *Res:* Preparation characterization and study of physical properties of condensation polymers; chemical development and chemical analyses, uranium, trace constituents, environmental, and industrial hygiene, related to operation of uranium isotope enrichment plant. *Mailing Add:* 2226 Micklethwaite Portsmouth OH 45662

**TRIVISONNO, JOSEPH, JR,** SOLID STATE PHYSICS. *Current Pos:* from asst prof to prof, 61-87, chmn dept, 79-89, CHAIR, JOHN CARROLL UNIV, 87- *Personal Data:* b Cleveland, Ohio, Feb 28, 33; m 57; c 4. *Educ:* John Carroll Univ, BS, 55, MS, 56; Case Western Res Univ, PhD( physics), 61. *Prof Exp:* Instr physics & math, John Carroll Univ, 55-58 & physics, Case Western Res Univ, 58-61. *Concurrent Pos:* Vis prof, Univ Ariz, 74; prog dir solid state physics, NSF, 86-87. *Mem:* Inst Elec & Electron Engrs Sonics & Ultrasonics; Am Phys Soc; Mat Res Soc; Coun Undergrad Res. *Res:* Elastic constants of metals; magnetoacoustic studies; ultrasonics; low temperature physics; superconductivity. *Mailing Add:* Dept Physics John Carroll Univ Cleveland OH 44118. *Fax:* 216-397-4256; *E-Mail:* trivisonno@jcvxa

**TRIZNA, DENNIS BENEDICT,** RADAR, PHYSICS. *Current Pos:* RES PHYSICIST RADAR, NAVAL RES LAB, 70-, PROG MGR, REMOTE SENSING, OFF NAVAL RES, 92- *Personal Data:* b Joilet, Ill, Oct 25, 41; m 63, Delia Slack; c Chris, Kevin & Jason. *Educ:* Ill Benedictine Col, BS, 63; Iowa State Univ, MS, 66, PhD(physics), 70. *Honors & Awards:* Res Publ Award, Naval Res Lab, 72, 77 & 83. *Mem:* Am Phys Soc; Inst Elec & Electronics Engrs; Am Geophys Union; Int Union Radio Scientists. *Res:* Remote sensing of geophysical phenomena with radar; remote sensing of ocean waves using high frequency radar; air-sea interaction and the marine boundary layer; general wave propagation. *Mailing Add:* 6130 Virgo Ct Burke VA 22015. *Fax:* 703-696-2170; *E-Mail:* triznad@onr.navy.mil

**TRKULA, DAVID,** VIROLOGY. *Current Pos:* ADJ INSTR BIOL, HOUSTON COMMUNITY COL SYST, 85- *Personal Data:* b Patton Twp, Pa, Aug 19, 27; m 54, Eleanor J Uhrrecht; c David A, Todd M & Carol L. *Educ:* Univ Pittsburgh, BS, 49, MS, 55, PhD(biophys), 59. *Prof Exp:* Instr physics, Johnstown Col, Univ Pittsburgh, 57-59; asst biophysicist, M D Anderson Hosp & Tumor Inst, 59-61; physicist, US Army Biol Labs, Ft Detrick, 61-68; asst prof biophys, Baylor Col Med, 68-85. *Mem:* Sigma Xi. *Res:* Biophysics of viruses including mammalian tumor viruses and herpes viruses; biophysics of bacterial toxin proteins. *Mailing Add:* 10603 Del Monte Dr Houston TX 77042

**TROEH, FREDERICK ROY,** SOIL SCIENCE. *Current Pos:* from asst prof to prof, 63-95, EMER PROF AGRON, IOWA STATE UNIV, 95- *Personal Data:* b Grangeville, Idaho, Jan 23, 30; m 51, 87, Zahra Ifnou; c Mildred, Stanley & Bruce. *Educ:* Univ Idaho, BSAgr, 51, MSAgr, 52; Cornell Univ, PhD(soil sci), 63. *Prof Exp:* Soil scientist, Soil Conserv Serv, 52-59. *Mem:* Am Soc Agron; Soil Sci Soc Am; Soil Conserv Soc Am. *Res:* Soil formation and classification; measuring the rate of soil creep; soil permeability relationships with microbial activity. *Mailing Add:* 4117 Quebec St Ames IA 50014

**TROELSTRA, ARNE,** PHYSICS, BIOENGINEERING. *Current Pos:* PROF PHYSICS, OKLA SCH SCI & MATH, 89- *Personal Data:* b Zelhem, Neth, Mar 30, 35; m 59; c 1. *Educ:* State Univ Utrecht, BS, 55, MS, 58, PhD(med physics), 64. *Prof Exp:* Res assoc vision res, Inst Perception, Nat Defense Res Orgn, Neth, 60-65; assoc prof bioeng, Univ Ill, Chicago, 65-69; from assoc prof to prof elec eng, Rice Univ, 69-80; consult, 80-89. *Concurrent Pos:* Assoc biomed eng, Presby-St Luke's Hosp, Chicago, 66-69; consult, Biosysts Div, Whittaker Corp, 66-69; lectr ophthal, Univ Tex Med Sch, Houston, 74-80. *Res:* Vision research; biological control systems; systems analysis of biological systems; electroretinography; biomedical instrumentation. *Mailing Add:* 501 NE 15th St Oklahoma City OK 73104. *Fax:* 405-521-6442; *E-Mail:* atroels@sciencei.ossm.edu

**TROEN, PHILIP,** ENDOCRINOLOGY, ANDROLOGY. *Current Pos:* physician-in-chief, 64-90, EMER PHYSICIAN-IN-CHIEF, MONTEFIORE UNIV HOSP, 90-; PROF MED, SCH MED, UNIV PITTSBURGH, 64-, INTERIM CHIEF, DIV ENDOCRINOL & METAB, 95- *Personal Data:* b Portland, Maine, Nov 24, 25; wid; c 3. *Educ:* Harvard Univ, AB, 44, MD, 48; Am Bd Internal Med, dipl. *Honors & Awards:* Distinguished Andrologist, Am Soc Andrology, 91, Distinguished Serv Award, 96. *Prof Exp:* Intern, Boston City Hosp, 48-49, asst resident med, 49-50; asst resident, Beth Israel Hosp, 50 & 52-53, resident, 53-54; asst, Harvard Univ, 53-54, instr, 56-59, assoc, 59-60, asst prof, 60-64. *Concurrent Pos:* Chief med serv, US Army Hosp, Japan, 50-52; Teaching fel, Harvard Univ, 52-53, res fel, 55-56; Ziskind teaching fel, Beth Israel Hosp, 55-60; fel endocrinol & metab, Mayo Clin, 54-55, Kendall-Hench res fel, 55; Guggenheim fel, Stockholm, Sweden, 60-61; from asst to assoc, Beth Israel Hosp, 55-64, asst vis physician, 59-64; chmn, Contract Rev Comt, Contraceptive Develop Br, Nat Inst Child Health & Human Develop; assoc chmn dept, Univ Pittsburgh, 69-79, vchmn dept, 79-90; mem, Nat Med Serv, Res Merit Rev Bd Endocrinol, Vet Admin, 79-82; mem, 84-87, chmn, Endocrinol & Metab Drugs Adv Comt, Food & Drugs Admin, 87-88; mem publ comt, Endocrine Soc, 84-87, chmn, 87-90; mem, prog organizing comts, Third & Fourth Int Cong Andrology, 85 & 89 & Seventh Int Cong Hormonal Steroids, 86; chmn publ comt, Am Soc Andrology, 90-93. *Mem:* Am Soc Clin Invest; Asn Am Physicians; Endocrine Soc; Am Soc Biochem & Molecular Biol; Am Soc Andrology (vpres & pres, 79-81); Int Soc Andrology (secy, 80-89, pres, 89-93); Cent Soc Clin Res; Am Fedn Clin Res. *Res:* Endocrinology; internal medicine; andrology. *Mailing Add:* Univ Pittsburgh Med Ctr 200 Lothrop St Pittsburgh PA 15213

**TROENDLE, GLORIA J,** ENDOCRINOLOGY. *Current Pos:* DEP DIR, DIV METAB & ENDOCRINE DRUG PROD, 86- *Personal Data:* b Yakima, Wash, July 30, 25; m, Francis J; c George E, Frederick J, August J, Lina J, Hazel F, Linda L & James F. *Educ:* Washington Univ, St Louis, MD, 50. *Res:* Bone metabolism; obesity drugs. *Mailing Add:* HFD-510 5600 Fishers Lane Rockville MD 20852. *E-Mail:* troendle@cder.fda.gov

**TROESCH, BEAT ANDREAS,** APPLIED MATHEMATICS. *Current Pos:* prof, 66-90, EMER PROF AEROSPACE ENG & MATH, UNIV SOUTHERN CALIF, 90- *Personal Data:* b Bern, Switz, Mar 2, 20; nat US; m 48, Margrit Ott; c Johann R, Claudia D, Peter G & Thomas M. *Educ:* Swiss Fed Inst Technol, Zurich, dipl, 47, PhD(math), 52. *Prof Exp:* Asst mech & physics, Swiss Fed Inst Technol, Zurich, 47-52; res assoc appl math, Inst Math, NY Univ, 52-56; head appl math sect, Comput Ctr, Ramo-Wooldridge Corp, 56-58 & Space Tech Labs, 58-61; mgr comput sci dept, Aerospace Corp, 61-66. *Concurrent Pos:* Consult, Aerospace Corp, 66- *Mem:* Math Asn Am; Am Math Soc. *Res:* Applied mathematics and numerical analysis in hydrodynamics and gas dynamics; elliptic and hyperbolic partial differential equations. *Mailing Add:* 523 N Elm Dr Beverly Hills CA 90210-3418

**TROFIMENKOFF, FREDERICK N(ICHOLAS),** ELECTRICAL ENGINEERING, PHYSICS. *Current Pos:* assoc prof, 66-68, head dept, 67-77, PROF ELEC ENG, UNIV CALGARY, 68- *Personal Data:* b Veregin, Sask, Aug 10, 34; m 57, Gayle L Ashworth; c Margo B (Doherty), Gregory W & Carmen G. *Educ:* Univ Sask, BSc, 57, MSc, 59; Univ London, PhD(elec eng); Imp Col, DIC, 62. *Honors & Awards:* Publ Award, Brit Inst Elec Engrs, 66. *Prof Exp:* Jr res off, Div Bldg Res, Nat Res Coun Can, 57-59; asst prof elec eng, Univ Sask, 62-66. *Concurrent Pos:* Consult to indust. *Mem:* Inst Elec & Electronics Engrs; Can Asn Physicists; Am Soc Eng Educ; Eng Inst Can. *Res:* Electronics and instrumentation related to oil and gas industry. *Mailing Add:* Univ Calgary 2500 University Dr NW Calgary AB T2N 1N4 Can. *Fax:* 403-282-6855; *E-Mail:* trof@enel.ucalgary.ca

**TROGDON, WILLIAM OREN,** SOILS. *Current Pos:* RETIRED. *Personal Data:* b Anadarko, Okla, Nov 1, 20; m 42, Florene Tucker; c Stephen. *Educ:* Okla State Univ, BS, 42; Ohio State Univ, PhD(soil fertility), 49. *Prof Exp:* Asst agronomist, Agr Exp Sta, Univ Tex, 48; soil scientist, Res Div, Soil Conserv Serv, USDA, 49; chmn dept agr & dir soils lab, Midwestern Univ, 49-53; agronomist, Olin Mathieson Chem Corp, 53-58; prof agron & head dept, Tex A&M Univ, 58-63; exec vpres, Best Fertilizers Co, Tex, 63-65; dir agron & mkt develop, Occidental Agr Chem Corp, 65-66; pres, Tarleton State Univ, 66-82, emer pres & prof agr, 82-91. *Mem:* Am Soc Agron; Crop Sci Soc Am; Soil Sci Soc Am; Sigma Xi. *Res:* Soil fertility and management, especially fertilizer usage; fertilizer technology; salinity control and water quality; polyphosphate fertilizers; academic administration. *Mailing Add:* 105 Sandra Palmer Stephenville TX 76401

**TROGLER, WILLIAM C,** INORGANIC ENVIRONMENTAL & CHEMISTRY. *Current Pos:* FAC MEM, UNIV CALIF, SAN DIEGO, 83- *Personal Data:* m 80, Judith Verbanets; c Jessica & Dorothy. *Educ:* Johns Hopkins Univ, BA & MA, 74; Calif Inst Technol, PhD, 78. *Prof Exp:* Fac mem, Northwestern Univ, 77-83. *Concurrent Pos:* Counr, Inorg Div, Am Chem Soc, 94- *Mem:* Am Chem Soc; fel AAAS. *Res:* Inorganic reaction mechanisms in environmental and atmospheric chemistry; metal-ligand complexes for DNA cleavage and antitumor applications. *Mailing Add:* Dept Chem 0358 Univ Calif San Diego La Jolla CA 92093-0358. *Fax:* 619-534-5383; *E-Mail:* wtrogler@ucsd.edu

**TROIANO, A(LEXANDER) R(OBERT),** PHYSICAL METALLURGY. *Current Pos:* assoc prof, Case Western Res Univ, 49-53, prof & head dept, 53-67, repub steel distinguished prof phys metall, 67-78, sr res scientist, 78-86, EMER PROF PHYS METALL, CASE WESTERN RES UNIV, 86- *Personal Data:* b Boston, Mass, Sept 5, 08; m 38; c 2. *Educ:* Harvard Univ, AB, 31, ScD(metall), 39; Mass Inst Technol, MS, 37. *Honors & Awards:* Hunt Award, Am Inst Mining, Metall & Petrol Engrs, 40; Howe Medal, Am Soc Metals, 57, Sauveur Achievement Medal, 68; Le Chatlier Gold Medal, 80; Nat Acad Engrs, 86. *Prof Exp:* Instr physics, Middlesex Col, 31-35; asst instr phys metall, Harvard Univ, 37-39; from assoc prof to prof, Univ Notre Dame, 39-49. *Concurrent Pos:* Keynote lectr, Brit Iron & Steel Res Inst, Harrogate, Eng, 62 & Int Conf Heat Treatment, Bremen, Ger, 66; distinguished vis prof, NY Univ, 65-66; keynote lectr, Int Conf Hydrogen in Metals, Paris, France, 72. *Mem:* Nat Acad Eng; Am Soc Testing & Mat; Am Foundrymen's Soc; Am Inst Mining, Metall & Petrol Engrs; Am Soc Metals. *Res:* Heat treatment of steels; phase transformations in solid state; gases in metals; stress corrosion; materials for geothermal energy. *Mailing Add:* Dept Metall Case Western Res Univ Cleveland OH 44106

**TROITSKY, MICHAEL S(ERGE),** civil engineering, for more information see previous edition

**TROJAN, PAUL K,** MATERIALS ENGINEERING. *Current Pos:* instr metall eng, Univ Mich, 58-61, from asst prof to assoc prof, 61-70, chmn, Div Eng, 62-64, actg dean, Sch Eng, 80-82 & 88-90, PROF MAT & METALL ENG, UNIV MICH-DEARBORN, 70- *Personal Data:* b Chicago, Ill, Sept 8, 31; m 53, Barbara Gardner; c Mark, Craig & Lynn (Lesko). *Educ:* Univ Mich, BS, 55, MS, 56, PhD(metall eng), 61. *Honors & Awards:* Howe Medal, Am Soc Metals, 63; Thomas Pangborn Gold Medal, Am Foundrymen's Soc, 78. *Prof Exp:* Engr-trainee, Engine & Foundry Div, Ford Motor Co, 52-53. *Concurrent Pos:* Mich Mem Phoenix res grant, 64-67; sr eng mfg & develop, Ford Motor Co, 64. *Mem:* Am Foundrymen's Soc; Am Soc Metals; Am Soc Eng Educ. *Res:* Cast metals; liquid metal processing solidification; relationship of processing and service performance; structure of engineering materials. *Mailing Add:* Mat & Metall Eng Univ Mich 4901 Evergreen Dearborn MI 48128-1491. *E-Mail:* trojan@umich.edu

**TROLINGER, JAMES DAVIS,** LASER APPLICATIONS, HOLOGRAPHY. *Current Pos:* PARTNER, METROLASER, 88- *Personal Data:* b Shelbyville, Tenn, Mar 2, 40. *Educ:* Univ Tenn, BS, 63, PhD(physics), 67; La State Univ, 64. *Prof Exp:* Scientist, Serdrup Technol, 58-63; assoc prof optics, Univ Tenn, 67-75; vpres, Spectron Inc, 75-88. *Concurrent Pos:* Scientist, Sci Appl Inc, 73-75; consult, NATO, 85-88; prin invest, Int Microgravity Space Lab, 87- *Res:* Coherent optics and holography; applications in flow diagnostics and non destructive evaluation. *Mailing Add:* 3417 Wimbledon Way Costa Mesa CA 92626

**TROLL, JOSEPH,** SOIL SCIENCE, AGROSTOLOGY. *Current Pos:* asst prof agron, 57-65, assoc prof plant & soil sci, 65-71, PROF PLANT & SOIL SCI, UNIV MASS, AMHERST, 71- *Personal Data:* b Paterson, NJ, May 5, 20; m 43; c 2. *Educ:* Univ RI, BS, 54, MS, 57; Univ Mass, PhD(nematol), 65. *Prof Exp:* Asst, Univ RI, 54-57. *Res:* Turf management; plant pathology and nematology. *Mailing Add:* 34 Comins Rd Hadley MA 01035

**TROLL, RALPH,** DEVELOPMENTAL BIOLOGY, VERTEBRATE ZOOLOGY. *Current Pos:* From inst to assoc prof, Augustana Col, 59-72, chmn dept, 68-77, chmn, Div Natural Sci, 83-86, PROF BIOL, AUGUSTANA COL, ILL, 72- *Personal Data:* b Reinheim, Ger, Oct 8, 32; US citizen; m 58, Loretta Glaser; c Michael, Karen & Krista. *Educ:* Univ Ill, BS, 57, MS, 58; Univ Minn, PhD(parasitol), 65. *Mem:* Am Fern Soc; Int Soc Hist Philos & Social Studies Biol; Nat Asn Biol Teachers. *Res:* Biology of ferns; Johann Wolfgang Von Goethe's contribution to science; plant-animal interactions; history of biology. *Mailing Add:* Dept Biol Augustana Col Rock Island IL 61201. *E-Mail:* bitroll@augustana.edu

**TROLL, WALTER,** BIOCHEMISTRY, ORGANIC CHEMISTRY. *Current Pos:* from asst prof to prof indust med, 56-76, prof environ med, 76-93, EMER PROF, SCH MED, NY UNIV, 93- *Personal Data:* b Vienna, Austria, Oct 25, 22; nat US; m 44; c 2. *Educ:* Univ Ill, BS, 44; Pa State Univ, MS, 46; NY Univ, PhD(biochem), 51. *Prof Exp:* Instr biochem, Univ Cincinnati, 51-52, asst prof, 52-54; assoc, Cancer Res Inst, New Eng Deaconess Hosp, 54-56. *Concurrent Pos:* Invited partic, Int Symp, Princess Takamatsu Cancer Res Fund, Japan, 73, 75 & 83, Coloquium der Gesellschaft Biologische Chemie, Mosbach, Ger, 79; invited chmn & partic, Third Int Conf Environ Mutagens, Japan, 81. *Mem:* Am Soc Biol Chem; Am Chem Soc; NY Acad Sci; AAAS; Harvey Soc; Am Asn Cancer Res. *Res:* Assay of amino acids; synthetic substrates for enzymes involved in blood clotting; metabolism of aromatic amines and its relation to carcinogenesis; role of free oxygen radicals in tumor promotion; chemopreventive agents, protease inhibitors and vitamin A suppress oncogene expression. *Mailing Add:* NY Univ Sch Med 550 First Ave New York NY 10016-6497

**TROLLER, JOHN ARTHUR,** MICROBIOLOGY. *Current Pos:* GROUP LEADER MICROBIOL, WINTON HILL TECH CTR, PROCTER & GAMBLE CO, 62-, SR RES SCIENTIST, 78- *Personal Data:* b Hartford, Wis, Apr 17, 33; m 56; c 4. *Educ:* Univ Wis, BS, 55, MS, 56, PhD(bact), 62. *Mem:* AAAS; Am Soc Microbiol; Inst Food Technologists; Soc Indust Microbiol; Brit Soc Appl Bact. *Res:* Food technology and microbiology; water relations of microorganisms; mechanism of action of food preservatives; staphylococcal food poisoning and other food-borne diseases; food hygiene and sanitation. *Mailing Add:* 314 Ritchie Ave Cincinnati OH 45215

**TROMANS, D(ESMOND),** PHYSICAL METALLURGY, CORROSION. *Current Pos:* Res assoc, 63-66, from asst prof to assoc prof, 66-81, PROF METALL ENG, UNIV BC, 81- *Personal Data:* b Birmingham, Eng, Mar 7, 38; Can citizen; m 61; c 2. *Educ:* Leeds Univ, BSc, 60, PhD(metall), 63. *Honors & Awards:* Campbell Award, Nat Asn Corrosion Engrs, 65. *Concurrent Pos:* Sr indust fel, Nat Res Coun, MacMillan Bloedel Res Ltd, Vancouver, 76; bd dirs, Can Comt Res Strength & Fracture Mat, 81-; fac assoc, Pulp & Paper Res Inst Can, 86- *Mcm:* Am Soc Metals; Nat Asn Corrosion Engrs; Brit Inst Metals; Electrochem Soc. *Res:* Stress corrosion; fracture of metals; electron diffraction and microscopy; corrosion; surface chemistry and electrochemistry; fatigue of metals. *Mailing Add:* Metals Mat & Eng Univ BC 309-6350 Stores Rd Vancouver BC V6T 1Z4 Can

**TROMBA, ANTHONY JOSEPH,** PURE MATHEMATICS. *Current Pos:* assoc prof, 70-77, PROF MATH, UNIV CALIF, SANTA CRUZ, 77- *Personal Data:* b Brooklyn, NY, Aug 10, 43; m 86. *Educ:* Cornell Univ, BA, 65; Princeton Univ, MA, 67, PhD(math), 68. *Prof Exp:* Asst prof math, Stanford Univ, 68-69; vis prof, Univ Pisa, Italy, 70. *Concurrent Pos:* Woodrow Wilson & NSF fels; vis prof, Univ Calif, Stony Brook, 74 & Bonn Univ; mem, Inst Advan Study, 75. *Mem:* Am Math Soc. *Res:* Topological methods in non-linear analysis; minimal surfaces Teichmuller theory. *Mailing Add:* 1400 Geary San Francisco CA 94109

**TROMBETTA, LOUIS DAVID,** CELL BIOLOGY, PATHOLOGY. *Current Pos:* PROF, ST JOHN'S UNIV, 80- *Personal Data:* b New York, NY, Sept 8, 46; m 73; c 2. *Educ:* Fordham Univ, BS, 68, MS, 69, PhD(biol), 74. *Prof Exp:* Res assoc path, Issac Albert Res Inst, 73-80. *Concurrent Pos:* Adj res assoc path, Kingsbrook Jewish Med Ctr. *Mem:* Soc Toxicol; Electron Micros Soc Am; Sigma Xi. *Res:* The effects of heavy metal toxicity on the central nervous system; the toxicity of the dithiocarbomates. *Mailing Add:* Dept Pharmacol St Johns Univ 8150 Utopia Pkwy Jamaica NY 11439-0001. *Fax:* 718-969-0753; *E-Mail:* zhltphs@sjumusic.stjohns.edu

**TROMBKA, JACOB ISRAEL,** RADIATION PHYSICS, SPACE PHYSICS. *Current Pos:* prog scientist, Hq, 64-65, STAFF SCIENTIST, GODDARD SPACE FLIGHT CTR, NASA, 65- *Personal Data:* b Detroit, Mich, Jan 7, 30; m 52; c 3. *Educ:* Wayne State Univ, BS, 52, MS, 54; Univ Mich, PhD(nuclear sci), 62. *Honors & Awards:* John Lindsay Mem Award, Goddard Space Flight Ctr, NASA, 72, Except Sci Achievement Medal, 73 & 93. *Prof Exp:* Res physicist, Oak Ridge Inst Nuclear Studies, 54-56; res assoc nuclear eng & fel gamma ray spectros, Univ Mich, 56-62; sr scientist, Jet Propulsion Lab, Calif Inst Technol, 62-64. *Concurrent Pos:* Mem panel in-flight exp, NASA, 63-66, mem working group, Manned Space Flight Exp Bd, 64-66, secy & mem, Geochem Working Group Planetology Subcomt, 65, mem, Terrestrial Bodies Sci Working Group, 77-; adj prof, Law Sch, Georgetown Univ, 67-; co-invstr, Apollo 15 & 16 x-ray, gamma ray & alpha particle spectrometer exp, 68-; mem Apollo sci working panel, 71-; prin investr, Apollo 17 & Apollo-Soyuz Crystal Activation Exp, 71 & 75-; vis prof, dept chem, physics & geol, Univ Md, 76-; mem, Coop Planetary Explor Prog, Nat Acad Sci, 83; mem, Instr Design Sci Team, Planetary Explor Prog, NASA, 83, team mem, Mars Observer Gamma Ray Spectrometer, 87 & proj scientist, Gamma Ray Spectrometer Mars Observer, 87, team leader, near Earth Asteroid Rendezvous Mission; Sr Goddard fel Prog Award, 94. *Mem:* Am Phys Soc; Am Nuclear Soc; Sigma Xi; NY Acad Sci. *Res:* Gamma ray spectroscopy; techniques in activation analysis, dosimetry and tracer techniques; planetary physics; gamma ray astrophysics; gamma-ray, x-ray and neutron-gamma ray in situ and remote sensing methods; gamma and x-ray imaging. *Mailing Add:* 11703 Farmland Dr Rockville MD 20852. *Fax:* 301-286-1648; *E-Mail:* uljit@lepvax,gsfc.nasa.gov

**TROMBULAK, STEPHEN CHRISTOPHER,** RODENT ECOLOGY, ANNUAL CYCLES OF RODENTS. *Current Pos:* ASST PROF BIOL, MIDDLEBURY COL, 85- *Personal Data:* US citizen; m 83; c 1. *Educ:* Univ Calif, Los Angeles, BA, 77; Univ Wash, PhD(zool), 83. *Prof Exp:* Instr biol, zool & environ studies, Univ Wash, 83-85. *Mem:* Am Soc Mammalogists; AAAS; Ecol Soc Am; Am Soc Zoologists; fel Sigma Xi. *Res:* Annual cycles of small mammals; environmental effects on reproductive effort and hibernation. *Mailing Add:* Dept Biol Middlebury Col Middlebury VT 05753

**TROMP, GERARDUS C,** BIOCHEMISTRY, DNA LINKAGE. *Current Pos:* ASST PROF, WAYNE STATE UNIV, DETROIT, 95- *Personal Data:* b Johannesburg, Transvaal, SAfrica, Aug 19, 58; Neth citizen; m 87, S Helena Kuivaniemi. *Educ:* Potchefstroom Univ, SAfrica, BS, 81, BSc, 82; Rutgers Univ, PhD(biochem), 89. *Prof Exp:* Fel, Thomas Jefferson Univ, 89-90, instr, 90-91, res asst prof biochem, 91-95. *Mem:* AAAS; Am Soc Human Genetics; NY Acad Sci; Am Genetic Asn. *Res:* Definition of the genes that harbor mutations including mutations in the genes that cause rare and common heritable disorders; define the genes that cause aortic as well as intracranial aneurysms. *Mailing Add:* Wayne State Univ Sch Med Scott Hall Basic Med Sci 540 Canfield Ave Rm 3116 Detroit MI 48201. *Fax:* 215-955-5393; *E-Mail:* tromp@sanger.bcm.tju.edu

**TROMP, JEROEN,** EARTH SCIENCE. *Current Pos:* ASST PROF, DEPT EARTH SCI, HARVARD UNIV. *Concurrent Pos:* Fel, David & Lucile Packard Found, 94. *Mailing Add:* Dept Earth Sci Harvard Univ Cambridge MA 02138-6502

**TROPF, CHERYL GRIFFITHS,** APPLIED MATHEMATICS. *Current Pos:* SELF EMPLOYED CPA, 84- *Personal Data:* b Newark, NJ, Oct 15, 46; m 68, William J; c Zachary. *Educ:* Col William & Mary, BS, 68; Univ Va, MAM, 72, PhD(appl math), 73, Georgetown Univ, MS, 83. *Prof Exp:* Sr mathematician, Appl Physics Lab, Johns Hopkins Univ, 73-80; cong sci fel, US Senate Subcomt Sci, Technol & Space, 80-81; proj mgr operating reactors, US Nuclear Regulatory Comn, 81-82; asst prof, Univ Baltimore, 83-85. *Concurrent Pos:* Instr, Johns Hopkins Evening Col, 74-76. *Mem:* Sigma Xi; Soc Indust & Appl Math; Am Inst Cert Publ Accts. *Res:* Application of analytical mathematical techniques to the modelling of physical systems; scientific/technological management and policy; finance. *Mailing Add:* 13060 St Patricks Ct Highland MD 20777. *E-Mail:* tropf@erols.com

**TROPF, WILLIAM JACOB,** OPTICS, MILITARY SYSTEMS. *Current Pos:* PRIN PHYSICIST, SUPVR, MISSILE ENG, APPL PHYSICS LAB, JOHNS HOPKINS UNIV, LAUREL, 77- *Personal Data:* b Chicago, Ill, Jan 14, 47; m 68, Cheryl Griffiths; c Zachary. *Educ:* Col William & Mary, BS, 68; Univ Va, PhD(physics), 73. *Prof Exp:* Proj dir, B-K Dynamics, Inc, Rockville, 73-76. *Mem:* Am Phys Soc; Optical Soc Am; Sigma Xi. *Res:* Analysis and modelling of missile guidance and control systems; optical properties of materials. *Mailing Add:* 13060 St Patricks Ct Highland MD 20777. *Fax:* 301-953-1093; *E-Mail:* bill.cropf@jhuapl.edu

**TROPP, BURTON E,** BIOCHEMISTRY. *Current Pos:* from asst prof to assoc prof, 70-76, PROF BIOCHEM, QUEEN'S COL, CITY UNIV NEW YORK, 76- *Personal Data:* b New York, NY, Aug 8, 40; m 65, Roslyn Goldman; c Jonathan, Matthew & Paul. *Educ:* Brooklyn Col, BS, 61; Harvard Univ, PhD(biochem), 66. *Prof Exp:* NIH fel bacteriol, Harvard Med Sch, 65-67; asst prof biochem, Richmond Col, NY, 67-70. *Concurrent Pos:* Vis scientist, Weizmann Inst, 78-79. *Mem:* AAAS; Am Chem Soc; Am Soc Microbiol; Am Soc Biochem & Molecular Biol. *Res:* Regulation of lipid metabolism. *Mailing Add:* Dept Chem & Biochem Queen's Col Flushing NY 11367. *E-Mail:* btr$chem@gcl.gc.edu

**TROPP, HENRY S,** MATHEMATICS, HISTORY OF MATHEMATICS. *Current Pos:* prof, 74-94, EMER PROF MATH, HUMBOLDT STATE UNIV, 94- *Personal Data:* b Chicago, Ill, July 15, 27; wid; c Stephen, Paula & Robin. *Educ:* Purdue Univ, BS, 49; Ind Univ, MS, 53. *Prof Exp:* Instr math, Mont Sch Mines, 55-57; from asst prof to assoc prof, Humboldt State Col, 57-72; prin investr, Comput Hist Proj, Smithsonian Inst, 71-74; sr hist comp, Mass Inst Technol Press. *Concurrent Pos:* Vis lectr, Asn Comput Mach, 73-87; vis fel, Clare Hall, Cambridge Univ, 87-88; life mem, 89-; mem, Prog Comt, Int Res Conf Hist Comput; vis prof, Comput Lab, Cambridge Univ, 89-94 & Dept Pure Math, 95- *Mem:* Math Asn Am; Hist Sci Soc; Asn Comput Mach; Brit Soc Hist Math. *Res:* History of mathematics; history of computers. *Mailing Add:* Humboldt State Univ Arcata CA 95521-5999. *E-Mail:* hst1@axe.humboldt.edu, hst@pmms.cam.ac.uk

**TROREY, A(LAN) W(ILSON),** ENGINEERING, PHYSICS. *Current Pos:* RETIRED. *Personal Data:* b London, Eng, May 8, 26; m 50; c 2. *Educ:* Univ BC, BASc, 49; Stanford Univ, MS, 51, PhD(electronic eng), 54. *Prof Exp:* Sr res assoc, Chevron Oil Field Res Co, Stand Oil Co Calif, 54-86. *Concurrent Pos:* Founding ed, Trans Geosci Electronics, Inst Elec & Electronics Engrs, 65-67; designed & installed seismic data process syst, Stand Oil Co, Calif, 67. *Mem:* Soc Explor Geophys. *Res:* Exploration seismology; elastic wave propagation; classical physics; mathematics of linear systems; digital computer systems. *Mailing Add:* 25295 Carmel Knoll Dr Carmel CA 93923-8827

**TROSCINSKI, EDWIN S,** CHEMICAL ENGINEERING. *Current Pos:* RETIRED. *Personal Data:* b Chicago, Ill, May 8, 28; m 52; c 7. *Educ:* Univ Ill, BS, 51. *Prof Exp:* Chem engr, Gen Labs, US Rubber Co, 51-53; process engr, Corn Prods Refining Co, 53-56; res engr, Standard Oil Co, Inc, -57, proj engr, 57-59, proj supvr, Stand Oil Co, Inc, 59-62; sr res chemist, Nalco Chem Co, 62-67, group leader, 67-69, tech dir, 69-72, mgr mkt & res, 72-74, mgr corp mkt servs, 74-76, mgr admin & planning servs, 76-81, proj mgr synfuels, 81-82, mgr mkt, 82-84, mgr admin, Nalco Chem Co, 84-92. *Mem:* Am Inst Chem Engrs; Nat Asn Corrosion Engrs; Soc Petrol Engrs. *Res:* Corrosion phenomena with respect to metal and alloys and of special environments; water technology, particularly stabilization and corrosion phenomena; oil field emulsion breaking. *Mailing Add:* 18 W 206 71st St Darien IL 60561

**TROSKO, JAMES EDWARD,** GENETICS, ONCOLOGY. *Current Pos:* asst prof sci & philos, Dept Natural Sci, 66-70, assoc prof, 70-77, PROF CARCINOGENESIS & MED ETHICS, DEPT HUMAN DEVELOP, MICH STATE UNIV, 77- *Personal Data:* b Muskegon, Mich, Apr 2, 38; m 60, Beverly K Dowell; c Philip R. *Educ:* Cent Mich Univ, BA, 60; Mich State Univ, MS, 62, PhD(radiation genetics), 63. *Honors & Awards:* Searle Award, UK Environ Mutagen Soc Award, 79; Sigma Xi Sr Scientist Award, Mich State Univ, 85. *Prof Exp:* Fel, Oak Ridge Nat Lab, 63-64 & Am Cancer Soc, 64-65; res scientist radiation biophys, Biol Div, Oak Ridge Nat Lab, 65-66. *Concurrent Pos:* Consult, Oak Ridge Nat Lab, 70-72; career develop award, Nat Cancer Inst, 72; vis prof oncol, McArdle Lab Cancer Res, Univ Wis-Madison, 72-73; consult, Wis Res & Develop Ctr Cognitive Learning, 73-74; mem, Biol Comt, Argonne Nat Lab, 76-79; Pancreas Cancer Working Group, Nat Cancer Inst; chief res, Radiation Effects Res Found, Hiroshima, Japan, 90-92. *Mem:* AAAS; Genetics Soc Am; Am Asn Cancer Res; Tissue Cult Asn; Soc Toxicol; Acad Toxicol Sci; Sigma Xi. *Res:* Molecular basis for genetic and environmental influences on carcinogenesis and aging; integration of science and human values; chemical modulation of intercellular communication & its consequences in teratogenesis/carcinogenesis/neurotocology & reproductive dysfunction. *Mailing Add:* Dept Human Develop Col Human Med Mich State Univ East Lansing MI 48824. *Fax:* 517-353-8464

**TROSMAN, HARRY,** PSYCHIATRY, PSYCHOANALYSIS. *Current Pos:* from asst prof to assoc prof, 54-74, PROF PSYCHIAT, PRITZKER SCH MED, UNIV CHICAGO, 75- *Personal Data:* b Toronto, Ont, Dec 9, 24; nat US; m 52, Marjorie G; c 3. *Educ:* Univ Toronto, MD, 48. *Honors & Awards:* Franz Alexander Prize, Chicago Inst Psychoanal, 65. *Prof Exp:* Intern, Grace Hosp, Detroit, Mich, 48-49; resident, Psychopath Hosp, Iowa City, Iowa, 49-51; resident, Cincinnati Gen Hosp, Ohio, 51-52. *Concurrent Pos:* Psychoanal training, Chicago Inst Psychoanal, 54-62; fac mem, 65-, training & supv analyst, 74- *Mem:* Am Psychiat Asn; Int Psychoanal Asn; fel Am Col Psychoanalysts; Am Psychoanal Asn. *Res:* Psychoanalysis and the arts; applied psychoanalysis; creativity. *Mailing Add:* Univ Chicago Sch Med 5841 S Maryland Ave Chicago IL 60637-1463

**TROSPER, JAMES HAMILTON,** MEDICAL ENTOMOLOGY. *Current Pos:* RETIRED. *Personal Data:* b Indianapolis, Ind, May 26, 44; m 68. *Educ:* Ind Univ, AB, 67; Univ Ga, MS, 71, PhD(entom), 74. *Prof Exp:* Entomologist, Dis Vector Ecol Control Ctr, USN, 74-76; entomologist, US Naval Med Res Unit 2, 76-79; mem staff, Malaria Br, Infectious Dis Prog Ctr, Naval Med Res Inst, 83-87; mem staff, Defensive Post Mgt Info Anal Ctr, 87-91; head, Entom Dept, Navy Environ & Prev Med Unit 6, Pearl Harbor, 91-94. *Mem:* Entom Soc Am; Sigma Xi. *Res:* Factors which control susceptibility of mosquitoes to malaria parasites; isolation of arboviruses and determination of their primary vectors; control of medically important insects. *Mailing Add:* c/o Dorothy Trosper 220 Delbrick Lane Indianapolis IN 46229

**TROSS, RALPH G,** MATHEMATICAL PHYSICS. *Current Pos:* asst prof, Univ Ottawa, 68-69, actg chmn, Dept Math, 70-71, chmn, Comput Comt, 71-75, dir continuing educ, 78-82, ASSOC PROF MATH, UNIV OTTAWA, 69- *Personal Data:* b Bad Kreuznach, Ger, Jan 17, 23; US citizen; m 47, Alison Squire; c Michael & Anthony. *Educ:* Sophia Univ, Japan, BS, 52; Mo Sch Mines, BS, 59; Univ Mo, Rolla, MS, 66, PhD(physics), 68. *Prof Exp:* Officer, US Army CEngrs, 43-64; NASA fel physics, Univ Mo, Rolla, 64-67, instr math, 67-68, res assoc physics, 68. *Concurrent Pos:* Nat Res Coun grant, 68-; mem adv comt, Algonquin Col, Ottawa, 71-75 & Univ Ottawa, St Lawrence, 78-81; educ develop grant, Comt Ont Univs, 74; sci secy, Pure & Appl Math Grant Selection Comt, Nat Sci & Engr Res Coun, 90-93. *Mem:* Am Phys Soc; Can Asn Physicists; Am Math Soc; Soc Indust & Appl Math; Sigma Xi; Can Math Soc; NY Acad Sci. *Res:* Statistical mechanics; Ising model; cooperative phenomena. *Mailing Add:* Dept Math Univ Ottawa Ottawa ON K1N 6N5 Can. *Fax:* 613-562-5776

**TROST, BARRY M,** ORGANIC CHEMISTRY. *Current Pos:* prof chem, 87-90, TAMAKI PROF, HUMANITIES & SCI, STANFORD UNIV, 90- *Personal Data:* b Philadelphia, Pa, June 13, 41; m, Susan Shapiro; c Aaron D & Carey D. *Educ:* Univ Pa, BA, 62; Mass Inst Technol, PhD(org chem), 65. *Hon Degrees:* Dr, Univ Claude Bernard, 94; DSc, Technion, Haifa, Israel, 97. *Honors & Awards:* Award, Am Chem Soc, 77, 81, 89 & 90, Rogers Adams Award, 94; Baekland Medal, 81; Merit Award, NIH, 88; Janssen Prize, 90; Pfizer Sr Fac Award, Pfizer, 92. *Prof Exp:* From asst prof to prof, Univ Wis-Madison, 65-76, Helfaer prof, 76-82, chmn, Dept Chem, 80-82, Vilas Res Prof, 82-87. *Concurrent Pos:* Assoc ed, J Am Chem Soc & adv, NSF Chem Sect, 73-; Sloan fel; Dreyfuss Found teacher-scholar grant; Am-Swiss Found fel; consult, Merck Co & E I Du Pont de Nemours & Co; mem, Comt Chem Sci, Nat Acad Sci, 80-; centenary lectr, Chem Soc London, 82; chmn, Med Chem Study Sect, NIH, 82-86. *Mem:* Nat Acad Sci; Royal Soc Chem; Am Chem Soc; fel AAAS; Am Acad Arts & Sci. *Res:* Development of new synthetic methods; synthesis of natural products and theoretically important systems; investigations of model biogenetic systems. *Mailing Add:* Dept Chem Stanford Univ Stanford CA 94305

**TROST, CHARLES HENRY,** VERTEBRATE ZOOLOGY, PHYSIOLOGICAL ECOLOGY. *Current Pos:* Grad fac grant, 69-70, asst prof biol, 68-81, ASSOC PROF BIOL, IDAHO STATE UNIV, 81- *Personal Data:* b Erie, Pa, Apr 4, 34; m 60; c 1. *Educ:* Pa State Univ, BS, 60; Univ Fla, MS, 64; Univ Calif, Los Angeles, PhD(zool), 68. *Mem:* Am Ornithologists Union; Cooper Ornith Soc; Wilson Ornith Soc; Am Soc Zoologists; Am Soc Mammalogists. *Res:* Water balance and energetics of birds and mammals; relation of behavior to the adaptations of animals to their environment. *Mailing Add:* Box 8007 Pocatello ID 83209

**TROST, HANS-JOCHEN,** PARTICLE DETECTOR DEVELOPMENT, ACCELERATOR TECHNOLOGY. *Current Pos:* ASSOC RES SCIENTIST, DEPT PHYSICS, TEX A&M UNIV, 92- *Personal Data:* b Neumunster, Schleswig-Holstein, Ger, June 4, 54; m 85, Ingeborg Eggers. *Educ:* Univ Hamburg, Ger, dipl, 77, PhD(exp nuclear physics), 81. *Prof Exp:* Sci employee, Inst Exp Physics, Univ Hamburg, Ger, 77-80, Deutches Elektronensynchroton, Ger, 81-84, Max-Planck Inst, Ger, 86-88; proj assoc physics, Univ Wis-Madison, 85-86; asst physicist, Argonne Nat Lab, 89-92. *Mem:* Am Phys Soc; Ger Phys Soc. *Res:* Development of detectors for experiments in elementary particle physics, including simulations and applications in biological research and medicine; planning of experiments in elementary particle physics; development of technologies for particle accelerators. *Mailing Add:* Dept Physics Tex A&M Univ College Station TX 77843. *E-Mail:* trost@phyacc.tamu.edu

**TROST, HENRY BIGGS,** ORGANIC CHEMISTRY. *Current Pos:* RETIRED. *Personal Data:* b Lancaster, Pa, Aug 18, 20; m 43; c 3. *Educ:* Franklin & Marshall Col, BS, 42. *Prof Exp:* Analytical chemist, Org Anal Group, Hercules Inc, 42-44. shift supvr, Acid Lab, Badger Ord Works, 44-45, Org Analysis Lab, 45-46, Size & Solvents Analysis Lab, Naval Stores Res Div, 55-61, mem staff, Indust Labs Div, 61-82. *Mem:* Am Chem Soc. *Res:* Product application, development, formulation and sales service type work on water soluble polymers and surface active agents. *Mailing Add:* 2603 Orchard Ave Wilmington DE 19805-2274

**TROSTEL, LOUIS J(ACOB), JR,** CERAMICS ENGINEERING. *Current Pos:* CONSULT, 90- *Personal Data:* b Baltimore, Md, May 21, 27; m 53, Mary Mitchell; c Louis, John & Thomas. *Educ:* Ohio State Univ, BCerE & MS, 51, PhD(ceramic eng), 55. *Prof Exp:* Res assoc ceramic eng, Res Found, Ohio State Univ, 50-51 & 52-55; ceramic res engr, Advan Ceramics, Norton Co, Worcester, 55-65, sr res engr, 65-69, res assoc, 68-78, res mgr, res & develop dept, 78-90. *Mem:* Fel Am Ceramic Soc; Nat Inst Ceramic Engrs; fel Am Soc Testing & Mat; Sigma Xi. *Res:* Ceramic applications and development of cermets; refractory coatings; special refractories. *Mailing Add:* PO Box 199 Princeton MA 01541. *Fax:* 978-464-2755; *E-Mail:* ljt@worldnet.att.net

**TROTT, GENE F,** RUBBER CHEMISTRY. *Current Pos:* TECH DIR, AM SYNTHETIC RUBBER CORP, LOUISVILLE, 77- *Personal Data:* b Louisville, Ky, May 27, 29; m 55; c 4. *Educ:* Univ Louisville, BA, 54, MS, 68, PhD, 71. *Prof Exp:* Chemist, Pillsbury Co, 54-56; res chemist & group leader, Am Synthetic Rubber Corp, 56-66; chemist, Gen Elec Co, Louisville, Ky, 66-73; mgr res & develop, Burton Rubber Processing Co, 73-77. *Mem:* Am Chem Soc; Soc Automotive Engrs. *Res:* Polymer chemistry; polymer characterization; biopolymeric interactions; polymerization kinetics. *Mailing Add:* 2301 St Andrews Rd Jeffersonville IN 47130-6763

**TROTT, KEITH DENNIS,** ELECTROMAGNETICS & SCATTERING, RADAR CROSS SECTION PREDICTION & MODELING. *Current Pos:* SR E MAG RES ENGR, MISSION RES CORP, 97- *Personal Data:* b Boston, Mass, Nov 17, 52; m 83, Natalie J Durbin; c Kerri, Jennifer,

Christopher & Kyle. *Educ:* State Univ NY, Plattsburgh, BS, 77; Syracuse Univ, MSEE, 81; Ohio State Univ, PhD(elec eng), 86. *Prof Exp:* Test & instrumentation engr, Rome Lab, USAF, 79-81, actg chief, Target Characterization Br, 90-91, Environ Effects Br, 91, radar cross sect res engr, 86-91, sr seeker technol res engr, Wright Lab, Armament Directorate, 91-92, br mgr radar sensors, 92-94, sr scientist, Munition Sensor Tech Br, 94-95, chief, Munition Sensor Technol Br, 95-97. *Concurrent Pos:* Continuing educ fac math, Daniel Webster Col, 88-91; invited lectr, Air Force Inst Technol, 88-93, adj asst prof, 90-93. *Mem:* Sr mem Inst Elec & Electronics Engrs; Sigma Xi. *Res:* Radar cross section phenomenology and electromagnetic scattering as it applies to exploitation and modeling of target physics of sensor and target interaction; active and passive millimeter wave phenomenology to determine parameters that may be exploitable to improve seeker guidance techniques. *Mailing Add:* 1804 Huntington Rd Niceville FL 32578. *E-Mail:* kntro@gnt.net

**TROTTA, PAUL P,** BIOCHEMISTRY. *Current Pos:* from instr to asst prof, 70-82, ASSOC PROF BIOCHEM, MED COL, CORNELL UNIV, 82- *Personal Data:* b Brooklyn, NY, Sept 10, 42. *Educ:* Columbia Col, BA, 64, Downstate Med Ctr, State Univ NY, PhD(biochem), 68. *Prof Exp:* Res fel, Sloan-Kettering Inst, 68-70, assoc cancer res, 74- 81. *Concurrent Pos:* Fac res award, Am Cancer Soc, 79; sect chief, protein chem, Schering Corp, 84, res fel, 87, dir, biotechnol-biochem. *Mem:* Am Soc Biol Chemists; Am Chem Soc; NY Acad Sci; Am Asn Cancer Res; AAAS; Interferon Soc; Protein Soc. *Res:* Structure-function relations and regulatory properties of proteins and polypeptides, especially cytokines; physico-chemical characterization of macromolecules; pre-clinical biology of cytokines. *Mailing Add:* Biol Health Div Appl Clin Commun 1160 Parsippany Blvd Parsippany NJ 07054. *Fax:* 908-298-7305

**TROTTER, GORDON TRUMBULL,** COMPUTER SCIENCES. *Current Pos:* COMPUT SCIENTIST & SUPVR APPLN DEVELOP, APPL PHYSICS LAB, JOHNS HOPKINS UNIV, 67- *Personal Data:* b Washington, DC, Aug 27, 34; m 65; c 2. *Educ:* Univ Md, BS, 56; Johns Hopkins Univ, MS, 72. *Prof Exp:* Mathematician, Nat Bur Stand, 56-58; from assoc mathematician to mathematician appl physics lab, Johns Hopkins Univ, 58-66; res mathematician & supvr comput opers, IIT Res Inst, 66-67. *Concurrent Pos:* Asst, Grad Sch, Univ Md, 56-58. *Mem:* Asn Comput Mach. *Res:* Information storage and retrieval systems; text processing; software management; programming theory. *Mailing Add:* 10626 Fable Row Columbia MD 21044

**TROTTER, HALE FREEMAN,** MATHEMATICS. *Current Pos:* vis assoc prof, 60-62, assoc prof, 63-69, PROF MATH, PRINCETON UNIV, 69-, ASSOC DIR COMPUT CTR, 62- *Personal Data:* b Kingston, Ont, May 30, 31. *Educ:* Queen's Univ, Ont, BA, 52, MA, 53; Princeton Univ, PhD(math), 56. *Prof Exp:* Fine instr math, Princeton Univ, 56-58; asst prof, Queen's Univ, Ont, 58-60. *Mem:* Am Math Soc; Can Math Cong; Math Asn Am; Asn Comput Mach. *Res:* Knot theory; computing. *Mailing Add:* Dept Math Princeton Univ Fine Hall Washigton Rd Princeton NJ 08544-1000

**TROTTER, JAMES,** PHYSICAL CHEMISTRY. *Current Pos:* from asst prof to assoc prof, 60-65, PROF CHEM, UNIV BC, 65- *Personal Data:* b Dumfries, Scotland, July 15, 33; m 57; c 2. *Educ:* Univ Glasgow, BSc, 54, PhD(chem), 57. *Hon Degrees:* DSc Univ Glasgow, 63. *Prof Exp:* Asst lectr chem, Univ Glasgow, 54-57, Nat Res Coun Can fel physics, 57-59, Imp Chem Indust fel chem, 59-60. *Mem:* AAAS; Am Crystallog Asn; Chem Inst Can; Royal Soc Chem; Royal Inst Chemists; Royal Soc Can. *Res:* Chemistry; crystallography. *Mailing Add:* Dept Chem Univ BC 2075 Wesbrook Mall Vancouver BC V6T 1W5 Can. *Fax:* 604-822-2847

**TROTTER, JOHN ALLEN,** ULTRASTRUCTURE, CYTOCHEMISTRY. *Current Pos:* asst prof, 78-89, PROF ANAT, MED SCH, UNIV NMEX, 89- *Personal Data:* b Robstown, Tex, May 26, 45; m 78; c 1. *Educ:* Johns Hopkins Univ, BA, 69; Univ Wash, PhD(biol structure), 76. *Prof Exp:* Guest worker, NIH, 77-78. *Concurrent Pos:* Assoc ed, Anatomical Record. *Mem:* Am Soc Cell Biol; Am Asn Anatomists; Biophys Soc; Orthop Res Soc; AAAS; Sigma Xi. *Res:* Functional morphology of muscle; structure, function, development and pathology of the muscle-tenden junction; molecular organization of collagenous tissues; morphometry. *Mailing Add:* Dept Anat Univ NMex Sch Med Basic Med Sci Bldg Albuquerque NM 87131-5211. *Fax:* 505-277-1754

**TROTTER, NANCY LOUISA,** CYTOLOGY, ELECTRON MICROSCOPY. *Current Pos:* RETIRED. *Personal Data:* b Monaca, Pa, July 26, 34. *Educ:* Oberlin Col, AB, 56; Brown Univ, ScM, 58, PhD(cytol), 60. *Prof Exp:* From instr to asst prof histol, Col Physicians & Surgeons, Columbia Univ, 61-68; assoc prof, Jefferson Col Med, Thomas Jefferson Univ, 68-90, emer assoc prof anat, 90. *Concurrent Pos:* USPHS trainee, 60, fel, 61, res grant, 62-68. *Mem:* Am Asn Anatomists. *Res:* Hepatomas; liver cytology; partial hepatectomy. *Mailing Add:* 1617 Huron Ave New Castle PA 16101

**TROTTER, PHILIP JAMES,** PHYSICAL CHEMISTRY. *Current Pos:* AT COHERENT INC. *Personal Data:* b Jackson, Mich, Jan 31, 41. *Educ:* Ill Inst Technol, BS, 64; Univ Colo, PhD(phys chem), 67. *Prof Exp:* Fel molecular complexes, New Eng Inst & Univ Conn, 67-69; res chemist Raman spectra & surface studies, Shell Res, Holland, 69-72; sr res chemist Raman & infrared spectra, Eastman Kodak Co, 73- *Mem:* Am Chem Soc; Soc Appl Spectros. *Res:* Reaction systems and dye structures; laser-Raman and infrared spectroscopic applications; surface reactions; instrument development. *Mailing Add:* 332 Canyon Dr Portola Valley CA 94028-7811

**TROTTER, ROBERT RUSSELL,** OPHTHALMOLOGY. *Current Pos:* RETIRED. *Personal Data:* b Morgantown, WVa, Apr 23, 15; wid. *Educ:* WVa Univ, AB & BS, 40; Temple Univ, MD, 42. *Prof Exp:* Asst ophthal res, Howe Lab, Harvard Med Sch, 47, instr, 52-55; instr ophthal, 56-60; clin assoc prof surg, Med Ctr, WVa Univ, 61-63, chmn div ophthal, 61-80, from assoc prof to prof surg, 63-88, emer prof ophthal, 80-88. *Concurrent Pos:* Fel, Harvard Med Sch, 48-49; resident ophthal, Mass Eye & Ear Infirmary, 49-51, dir glaucoma consult serv & asst to chief ophthal, 55-60. *Mem:* AMA; Am Acad Ophthal & Otolaryngol; Am Col Surgeons; Asn Res Vision & Ophthal. *Res:* Glaucoma; testing vision of pre-school children. *Mailing Add:* RR 1 Box 159 Aurora WV 26705

**TROTZ, SAMUEL ISAAC,** CHEMISTRY, ENVIRONMENTAL SCIENCE. *Current Pos:* CONSULT, 88- *Personal Data:* b Chattanooga, Tenn, Nov 6, 27; m 55, Vivian Garfinkel; c Susan & Marc. *Educ:* Univ Chattanooga, BS, 48; Univ Tenn, MS, 51; St Louis Univ, PhD, 56. *Prof Exp:* Asst chem, Univ Tenn, 48-50 & Univ St Louis, 52-55; res chemist, Olin Mathieson Chem Corp, 55, sr res chemist & group leader, 55-59, proj supvr org div, 59-66, sect mgr, 66-70, tech mgr chem group, 70-74, mgr res & develop, 74-82, consult scientist, Olin Corp, 83-88. *Mem:* AAAS; Am Chem Soc; Sigma Xi. *Res:* Synthesis; product development; custom chemicals process chemistry; oxyhalogens; water chemistry; antimicrobial agents; organic chemistry; organometallics; boranes; light metal hydrides; heterocyclics; polymers; microbiology. *Mailing Add:* 17 Gunning Point Falmouth MA 02540-1864

**TROUBETZKOY, EUGENE SERGE,** THEORETICAL PHYSICS. *Current Pos:* DIR RES & DEVELOP, CGI, 88- *Personal Data:* b Clamart, Seine, France, Apr 7, 31; US citizen; m 58; c 3. *Educ:* Univ Paris, B es Sc, 49, lic es Sc, 53; Columbia Univ, PhD(physics), 58. *Prof Exp:* Res asst physics, Columbia Univ, 53-58; sr scientist, United Nuclear Corp, NY, 58-64, adv scientist, 64-69; sr res assoc, Div Nuclear Sci & Eng, Columbia Univ, 69-70; consult, Magi Corp, 70-87. *Concurrent Pos:* Consult, 87- *Mem:* Am Phys Soc; Asn Comput Mach. *Res:* Software systems; computer graphics; neutrons; radiation transport theory and calculations applied to shielding and reactor calculations. *Mailing Add:* 42 Summit Dr Hastings-on-Hudson NY 10706

**TROUP, STANLEY BURTON,** INTERNAL MEDICINE, HEMATOLOGY. *Current Pos:* prof med, dir med ctr & vpres, 74-82, PROF MED, HEALTH CARE & HUMAN VALUES, UNIV CINCINNATI, 82- *Personal Data:* b Minneapolis, Minn, Feb 9, 25; m 49; c 2. *Educ:* Univ Minn, Minneapolis, BS, 48, BM, 49, MD, 50; Mass Inst Technol, MS, 72; Am Bd Internal Med, dipl, 57. *Prof Exp:* Intern med, Strong Mem Hosp, Univ Rochester, 49-50, intern path, 50-51, asst resident med, 51-52; resident, Beth Israel Hosp, Harvard Univ, 52-53; from instr to prof med, Strong Mem Hosp, Univ Rochester, 58-74. *Concurrent Pos:* Fel path, Strong Mem Hosp, Univ Rochester, 50-51, fel hemat, 55-58; NIH spec fel, Kocher Inst, Univ Bern, 61-62; Alfred P Sloan fel mgt, Mass Inst Technol, 71-72; chief med, Rochester Gen Hosp, 65-74; consult, Genesee, St Mary's & Highland Hosps, Rochester & Vet Admin Hosp, Bath, NY, 65-; consult spec ctrs res, NIH, 71-72; vis prof health mgt, Mass Inst Technol, 80. *Mem:* Fel Am Col Physicians; Am Fedn Clin Res; Am Soc Hemat. *Res:* Bleeding disorders; hemolytic anemia; medical education and management. *Mailing Add:* Univ Cincinnati 321 Bethesda Ave Cincinnati OH 45267-0562

**TROUSDALE, WILLIAM LATIMER,** PHYSICS. *Current Pos:* RETIRED. *Personal Data:* b Littleton, NH, Nov 10, 28; m 55; c 4. *Educ:* Trinity Col, Conn, BS, 50; Rutgers Univ, PhD, 56. *Prof Exp:* Asst prof physics, Trinity Col, Conn, 55-61; res assoc, Univ Pa, 61-62; assoc prof physics, Wesleyan Univ, 66-89. *Concurrent Pos:* Consult, United Aircraft Corp, 56-61; vis scientist, Brookhaven Nat Lab, 66-67. *Mem:* Am Phys Soc. *Res:* Mossbauer effect; magnetism; low temperature physics; physical electronics; holography. *Mailing Add:* 534 Pine St Middletown CT 06457

**TROUSE, ALBERT CHARLES,** AGRONOMY. *Current Pos:* soil scientist, 64-83, COLLABR, NAT TILLAGE MACII LAB, AGR RES SERV, SOUTHERN REGION, USDA, 83- *Personal Data:* b Hanford, Calif, May 19, 21; m 47; c 4. *Educ:* Univ Calif, BS, 43, MS, 48; Univ Hawaii, PhD(soil physics), 64. *Prof Exp:* Soil scientist, USDA, Nev, Calif & Hawaii, 46-51; assoc agronomist, Exp Sta, Hawaiian Sugar Planters Asn, 51-57, sr agronomist, 58-63. *Concurrent Pos:* Pres, Tilth Int, 83- *Mem:* Int Soil Tillage Res Orgn. *Res:* Soil physical properties; requirements for plant root bed and seed bed with respect to various crops and climatic situations, soil strength and aeration; interactions of roots of various species to each other. *Mailing Add:* 275 Oak St Auburn AL 36830

**TROUT, DENNIS ALAN,** AIR POLLUTION METEOROLOGY, ENVIRONMENTAL ENGINEERING. *Current Pos:* regional meteorologist & nat expert air pollution dispersion modeling, Region V, 78-84, RES PROG MGR, ACID DEPOSITION & GLOBAL CHANGE RES PROGS, OFF RES & DEVELOP, US ENVIRON PROTECTION AGENCY, WASHINGTON, DC, 84- *Personal Data:* b Washington, DC, July 26, 47; m 75. *Educ:* Pa State Univ, BS, 68, MS, 69, PhD(meteorol, air pollution), 73. *Prof Exp:* Res asst, Dept Meteorol, Pa State Univ, 68-70, res asst, Ctr Air Environ Studies, 70-71; environ/syst analyst, Environ Tech Appl Ctr, US Air Force, 71-73; scientist, Battelle Mem Inst, Columbus, Ohio, 73-76; sr scientist & mgr, Environ Studies Div, Environ Res & Technol, Inc, 76-78. *Concurrent Pos:* Lectr air pollution & meteorol, Ohio State Univ, 75. *Mem:* Am Meteorol Soc; Am Geophys Union; AAAS; Sigma Xi. *Res:* Ambient air quality measurements and analysis; computer modeling of atmospheric dispersion of air pollutants; development of emission control strategies; assessment of trace contaminant emissions and resulting ambient concentrations; assessment of emissions, transport, chemical transformation, and deposition of acidic substances and radiatively important trace gasses and their precursors; research program management: development, evaluation and application of regional and global atmospheric models for use in assessing ecological and other environmental effects. *Mailing Add:* 6121 18th St N Arlington VA 22205-2117

**TROUT, JEROME JOSEPH,** membrane transport, lysosomal system, for more information see previous edition

**TROUT, THOMAS JAMES,** IRRIGATION WATER MANAGEMENT, SOIL PHYSICS. *Current Pos:* AGR ENGR, USDA-AGR RES SERV, KIMBERLY, IDAHO, 82- *Personal Data:* b Bluffton, Ohio, Mar 30, 49; m 76; c 2. *Educ:* Case Western Res Univ, BS, 72; Colo State Univ, MS, 75, PhD(agr), 79. *Prof Exp:* Res assoc, Colo State Univ, 77-79, res asst prof, 79-82. *Concurrent Pos:* Consult, Univ Wis, 79 & World Bank & US AID, 80. *Mem:* Am Soc Agr Engrs; Am Soc Civil Engrs; Sigma Xi. *Res:* Methods of managing surface irrigation water at the farm level including both soil management and methods of water application. *Mailing Add:* US Dept Agr Agr Res Service Water Mgt Res Lab 2021 S Peach Ave Fresno CA 93727

**TROUT, WILLIAM EDGAR, III,** GENETICS. *Current Pos:* PRES, AM CANAL SOC, 85- *Personal Data:* b Staunton, Va, Apr 21, 37. *Educ:* Univ Richmond, BS, 59; Ind Univ, AM, 64, PhD(genetics), 65. *Prof Exp:* USPHS res fel radiation genetics, Biol Div, Oak Ridge Nat Lab, 65-66; res scientist, biol dept, City of Hope Med Ctr, 66-82. *Concurrent Pos:* Canal archaeol consult. *Mem:* Behav Genetics Asn; Sigma Xi. *Res:* Behavior genetics of Drosophila melanogaster. *Mailing Add:* 35 Towana Rd Richmond VA 23226-3124

**TROUTMAN, JAMES SCOTT,** ENGINEERING, OPERATIONS RESEARCH. *Current Pos:* weapon system analyst, Anser, Arlington, Va, 58-60, corp secy, 60-76, vpres, 76-83, sr vpres, 84-88; BD MEM & TRUSTEE, ANSER, 88- *Personal Data:* b Hannibal, Mo, Mar 7, 30; m 52; c 2. *Educ:* US Naval Acad, BS, 52. *Prof Exp:* Sr engr, Corvey Div, Melpar, Inc, 56-58. *Concurrent Pos:* Consult, 76-93. *Mem:* Fel Am Astronaut Soc; Nat Mil Intel Asn; Sigma Xi; Asn Former Intel Officers. *Res:* Electronics and communications systems; seismology; electronic parts for extreme environments; weapon systems analysis and operations research; intelligence systems; research and development management. *Mailing Add:* 5624 Newington Ct Bethesda MD 20816-3315

**TROUTMAN, RICHARD CHARLES,** OPHTHALMOLOGY. *Current Pos:* prof & chmn div, 55-83, EMER PROF OPHTHAL, STATE UNIV NY DOWNSTATE MED CTR, 83- *Personal Data:* b Columbus, Ohio, May 16, 22; c 3. *Educ:* Ohio State Univ, BA, 42, MD, 45; Am Bd Ophthal, dipl, 51. *Prof Exp:* Intern ophthal, NY Hosp, 45-46; resident, Cornell Med Ctr, 48-50, from instr to asst prof, Med Col, Cornell Univ, 52-55. *Concurrent Pos:* Instr, Manhattan Eye, Ear & Throat Hosp, 51-55, mem courtesy staff, 55-, surgeon dir, 61-; consult hosps, 54-; vis surgeon, Kings Co Hosp, 55-; mem courtesy staff, Cornell Med Ctr, New York Hosp, 55-, attend surgeon, 71-; mem courtesy staff, New York Eye & Ear Infirmary, 55-; mem ophthal postgrad training comt, Nat Inst Neurol Dis & Blindness, 59-63; consult neurol & blindness div, Bur State Serv, Dept Health, Educ & Welfare, 63-67; mem, Bd Dirs, Baraquer Inst, 63-73. *Mem:* Am Asn Res Vision & Ophthal; fel Am Col Surgeons; fel Am Acad Ophthal & Otolaryngol; fel NY Acad Med; Am Ophthal Soc; hon mem Asn Advan Ophthal Oper Techniques. *Res:* Orbital surgery and surgery of the anterior segment of the eye; microsurgery and refractive surgery. *Mailing Add:* 860 UN Plaza Apt 30A New York NY 10017-1817

**TROUTMAN, RONALD R,** ELECTRICAL ENGINEERING. *Current Pos:* staff engr, Gen Technol Div, IBM, 69-73, adv engr, 73-81, sr engr, 81-87, sr engr, T J Watson Res Ctr, 87-91, ENG STAFF MEM, T J WATSON RES CTR, IBM, 91- *Personal Data:* US citizen; m 66, Gail; c Kelby S & Ramsay O. *Educ:* Mass Inst Technol, BS, 62; NY Univ, MS, 63, PhD(elec eng), 66. *Prof Exp:* Proj officer, Off Naval Res, 66-68. *Concurrent Pos:* Fel, Ctr Advan Eng Studies, Mass Inst Technol, 83-84. *Mem:* Fel Inst Elec & Electronics Engrs; Soc Info Display; NY Acad Sci. *Res:* Research contract administration; random access memory design; semiconductor technology development; analysis and characterization of short channel effects; subthreshold behavior; hot electron phenomena in field-effect transistors; author of over 60 technical publications and 1 book; granted 14 patents; research on flat panel displays; development and commercialization of array tester for tft/lcds. *Mailing Add:* 38 Deer Hill Dr Ridgefield CT 06877

**TROUTNER, DAVID ELLIOTT,** nuclear chemistry; deceased, see previous edition for last biography

**TROUTT, LOUISE LEOTTA,** microtubule-based cell motility, electron microscopy, for more information see previous edition

**TROW, JAMES,** GEOLOGY. *Current Pos:* From asst prof to assoc prof geol, 47-59, PROF GEOL, MICH STATE UNIV, 59- *Personal Data:* b Chicago, Ill, Apr 21, 22; m 47; c 1. *Educ:* Univ Chicago, SB, 43, SM, 45, PhD(geol), 48. *Concurrent Pos:* Consult, US Geol Surv, 48-52, Cleveland Cliffs Iron Co, 58-60, Anaconda, 61-68, Elcor Corp, 69-70, Chevron Resources, 71-76, Mich Geol Surv, 77-79, Falconbridge Ltd, 81, & Exmin Corp, 86-88. *Mem:* Soc Mining Engrs; Can Inst Mining & Metall; Geol Soc Am; Am Geophys Union;

Prospectors & Developers Asn Can; Sigma Xi. *Res:* Inductive electrostatic gradiometry; chemical thermodynamics, structural geology and Pleistocene sedimentology applied to mining exploration for uranuim, gold, diamonds, copper and iron. *Mailing Add:* Dept Geol Sci Mich State Univ East Lansing MI 48824

**TROWBRIDGE, DALE BRIAN,** ORGANIC CHEMISTRY, ORGANOPHOSPHORUS CHEMISTRY. *Current Pos:* from asst prof to assoc prof, 69-77, PROF CHEM, CALIF STATE COL, SONOMA, 77- *Personal Data:* b Glendale, Calif, May 17, 40; m 66, Helen E Turner; c Katelin E & David B. *Educ:* Whittier Col, AB, 61; Univ Calif, Berkeley, MS, 64, PhD(org chem), 70. *Prof Exp:* Chemist, Aerojet Gen Corp, 61-62; teacher chem high sch, Calif, 64-66. *Concurrent Pos:* Vis prof, Univ Calif, Berkeley, 71, 72, 74 & 88; vis res assoc, Cambridge Univ, 78. *Mem:* Sigma Xi; Am Chem Soc; AAAS. *Res:* Preparation and study of organo-phosphorus compounds of biological interest. *Mailing Add:* Dept Chem Sonoma State Univ 1801 E Cotati Ave Rohnert Park CA 94928

**TROWBRIDGE, FREDERICK LINDSLEY,** NUTRITION, EPIDEMIOLOGY. *Current Pos:* DIR, NUTR DIV, CTR HEALTH PROM, CTR DIS CONTROL. *Personal Data:* b Newark, NJ, June 8, 42; m 70; c 2. *Educ:* Princeton Univ, BA, 64; Harvard Univ, MD, 68; London Sch Hyg & Trop Med, MSc, 74. *Prof Exp:* Med epidemiologist nutrit epidemiol, Ctr Dis Control, USPHS, 71-77; asst prof int health epidemiol, Sch Hyg & Pub Health, Johns Hopkins Univ, 77- *Mem:* Int Health Soc; Am Pub Health Asn. *Res:* Field assessment of nutrition status; epidemiologic studies in nutrition; methods of nutrional surveillance. *Mailing Add:* Nutrit Div 2254 Fair Oaks Rd NE Decatur GA 30033-1200. *Fax:* 770-488-4479

**TROWBRIDGE, GEORGE CECIL,** COMPUTER SCIENCE, MATHEMATICS. *Current Pos:* res mathematician electro-magnetic pulse, Hancock/Dikewood Serv Inc, 67-68, sr res mathematician & proj leader, 68-71, dep prog mgr, Dikewood Industs Inc, 71-79, DIR COMPUT SERV, HANCOCK/DIKEWOOD SERV INC, 79- *Personal Data:* b Delta, Colo, May 6, 38; m 58; c 2. *Educ:* Western State Col, Colo, BA, 60; Univ Ill, MS, 64. *Prof Exp:* Teacher math, Lamar High Sch, 60-61; teacher, Delta Co Jct Sch Dist number 50, 61-63 & 64-65; teacher, Western State Col, Colo, 65-67. *Res:* Application of computers to health care information; computer and mathematical applications in the physical sciences. *Mailing Add:* 7412 Gila Rd Albuquerque NM 87109

**TROWBRIDGE, IAN STUART,** MONOCLONAL ANTIBODIES, CELL SURFACE RECEPTORS. *Current Pos:* DIR CANCER BIOL, SALK INST, 72- *Personal Data:* b Apr 13, 47; m 70; c 2. *Educ:* Oxford Univ, Eng, BA, 69, PhD(immunol), 72. *Mem:* Asn Am Immunologists; Asn Am Cell Biologists. *Res:* Analysis of the structure-function relationships of cell surface receptors involved in cell growth or in the regulation of the immune response. *Mailing Add:* Dept Cancer Biol Salk Inst PO Box 85800 San Diego CA 92186-5800. *Fax:* 619-552-8285

**TROWBRIDGE, LEE DOUGLAS,** PHYSICAL CHEMISTRY. *Current Pos:* SECT HEAD, ENRICHMENT TECH ORGN, 87- *Personal Data:* b Akron, Ohio, Oct 25, 49; m 70; c 3. *Educ:* Mich State Univ, BS, 70; Harvard Univ, MA, 71, PhD(chem physics), 78. *Prof Exp:* Develop assoc, Oak Ridge Gaseous Diffusion Plant, Union Carbide, 78-81, develop staff member, Nuclear Div, 81-85; staff mem, Oak Ridge Nat Lab, 85-87. *Concurrent Pos:* Mem staff, fossil energy progs, Dept Energy, 85-87. *Mem:* Am Phys Soc; Am Vacuum Soc; Am Chem Soc. *Res:* Gas phase and surface reactions of uranium hexaflouride; materials and chemistry studies for the uranium enrichment program. *Mailing Add:* 131 Newell Lane Oak Ridge TN 37830

**TROWBRIDGE, LESLIE WALTER,** SCIENCE EDUCATION. *Current Pos:* from asst prof to prof, 62-70, chmn dept sci educ, 66-72 & 81-83, PROF SCI EDUC, EMER PROF, UNIV NORTHERN COLO, 70- *Personal Data:* b Curtiss, Wis, May 21, 20; m 46; c 4. *Educ:* Wis State Univ, Stevens Point, BS, 40; Univ Chicago, MS, 48; Univ Wis, MS, 53; Univ Mich, PhD(sci educ), 61. *Prof Exp:* Teacher jr high sch, Wis, 41 & 46, instr high sch, 46-54; univ scholar, Univ Mich, 54-62. *Concurrent Pos:* Fel, NY Univ, 69-70. *Mem:* Nat Sci Teachers Asn (pres, 73-74); Nat Asn Res Sci Teaching. *Mailing Add:* 2001 21st St Greeley CO 80639

**TROWBRIDGE, RICHARD STUART,** mammalian cell culture, mammalian virology, for more information see previous edition

**TROWER, W(ILLIAM) PETER,** EXPERIMENTAL PHYSICS. *Current Pos:* CHIEF SCIENTIST, WORLD PHYSICS TECHNOLOGIES INC, 90- *Personal Data:* b Rapid City, SDak, May 25, 35; m 57, 63; c Elizabeth A, Alexandra C & Andrea C. *Educ:* Univ Calif, Berkeley, AB, 57; Univ Ill, Urbana, MS, 63, PhD(physics), 66. *Honors & Awards:* Bronze Medal, Int Film & TV Festival NY, 73; Horsley Res Prize, Va Acad Sci, 93. *Prof Exp:* Physicist, Lawrence Radiation Lab, Univ Calif, Berkeley, 60-62; res asst, Digital Comput Lab & Dept Physics, Univ Ill, Urbana, 62-66; prof physics, Va Polytech Inst & State Univ, 66-98. *Concurrent Pos:* Chmn, Gordon Res Conf Multiparticle Prod Processes, 73; co-chmn, Physics in Collision Res Conf, 80, Magnetic Monopole Res Conf, 82. *Mem:* Fel Am Phys Soc; fel AAAS; Inst Elec & Electronics Engrs. *Res:* Nuclear and particle physics; scientific computing applications; instrumentation and software. *Mailing Add:* 1105 Highland Circle Blacksburg VA 24060. *Fax:* 540-552-2140; *E-Mail:* trower@bcv.net

**TROXEL, BENNIE WYATT,** GEOLOGY. *Current Pos:* RETIRED. *Personal Data:* b Osawatomie, Kans, Aug 9, 20; m 46, Betty L Patriquin; c Mona K (Winter) & Wyatt L. *Educ:* Univ Calif, Los Angeles, BA, 51, MA, 58. *Prof Exp:* Geologist, Calif Div Mines & Geol, 52-71; sci ed, Geol Soc Am, 71-75; mem fac, Calif State Univ, Sacramento, 75-77, Univ Calif, Davis, 77-89. *Concurrent Pos:* Mem staff, Calif Div Mines, 75-77; consult geologist, 77- *Mem:* Geol Soc Am. *Res:* Geology of Death Valley region; geologic factors that influence slope stability in urban areas of California; mineral resources; Precambrian stratigraphy and faults in Death Valley, California. *Mailing Add:* 2961 Redwood Rd Napa CA 94558

**TROXEL, DONALD EUGENE,** ELECTRICAL ENGINEERING. *Current Pos:* From instr to assoc prof, 61-85, PROF ELEC ENG, MASS INST TECHNOL, 85- *Personal Data:* b Trenton, NJ, Mar 11, 34; m 63; c 3. *Educ:* Rutgers Univ, BS, 56; Mass Inst Technol, SM, 60, PhD(elec eng), 62. *Concurrent Pos:* Ford Found fel, 62-64. *Mem:* Inst Elec & Electronics Engrs. *Res:* Digital systems applications; communications; electronics; computers; distributed design and fabrication of integrated circuits. *Mailing Add:* Dept Elec Eng Rm 36-287 Mass Inst Technol 77 Massachusetts Ave Cambridge MA 02139-4307

**TROXELL, TERRY CHARLES,** PHYSICAL CHEMISTRY. *Current Pos:* SCI ADMINR, FOOD & DRUG ADMIN, 77- *Personal Data:* b Allentown, Pa, Jan 1, 44; m 64; c 2. *Educ:* Muhlenberg Col, BS, 65; Cornell Univ, PhD(biophys chem), 71. *Prof Exp:* Res assoc phys chem, Univ Ore, 71-74; sr phys chemist, Eli Lilly & Co, 74-77. *Mem:* Am Chem Soc; AAAS. *Res:* Scientific policy and administration; food safety, especially regulation of food additives and food packaging. *Mailing Add:* 1522 Powells Tavern Pl Herndon VA 22070-2831

**TROXELL, WADE OAKES,** BEHAVIOR-BASED ROBOTICS, ENGINEERING DESIGN SUPPORT SYSTEMS. *Current Pos:* res asst & teaching asst, 80-82, instr, 85-88, ASST PROF MECH ENG, COLO STATE UNIV, 88- *Personal Data:* b Ft Collins, Colo, Nov 15, 56; m 81, Jean; c Graeme & Ellie. *Educ:* Colo State Univ, BS, 80, MS, 82, PhD(mech eng), 87. *Honors & Awards:* Haliburton Award of Excellence, 92. *Prof Exp:* Proj engr, Eastman Kodak Co, 71-83; Colo Div, 82-85. *Concurrent Pos:* Colo Inst Artificial Intel, 85-91; dir, Mfg & Robotic Systs Lab, 86-; NATO fel artificial intel, Univ Edinburgh, 87-88; dir, Mfg Excellence Ctr, Colo State Univ, 88-; examr, Coun Nat Acad Awards, UK, 90-; exec dir, Mid Am Mfg Technol Ctr, Colo Regional Off, 93- *Mem:* Am Soc Mech Engrs; Nat Soc Prof Engrs; Inst Elec & Electronics Engrs; Soc Mfg Engrs. *Res:* Engineering of robust task-achieving robots; formulation of robot control methodologies; engineering design support systems; robot programming and high level robot programming languages. *Mailing Add:* Mech Eng Colo State Univ Ft Collins CO 80523. *Fax:* 970-491-1055; *E-Mail:* wade@longs.lance.colostate.edu

**TROXLER, RAYMOND GEORGE,** PATHOLOGY, PUBLIC HEALTH. *Current Pos:* CONSULT CARDIOVASC DIS, SOUTHWEST RES INST, 85-; DIR, BRADY GREEN COMMUNITY HEALTH CTR, LIPID CLIN, 93- *Personal Data:* b New Orleans, La, Sept 21, 39; m 63, Barbara Keefe; c Karen & Pamela. *Educ:* Univ Southwestern La, BS, 64; La State Univ, MD, 64; Univ Tex, MPH, 87. *Honors & Awards:* Edward Rhodes Stitt Award, Best Res Lab Med, 78. *Prof Exp:* chief clin path, Clin Sci Div, USAF Sch Aerospace Med, 71-83; coordr patient care, Med Ctr Hosp, San Antonio, Texas, 83-85. *Concurrent Pos:* Clin assoc prof, Health Sci Ctr, Univ Tex, San Antonio, 72; staff physician, Acute Care Clinic, Dept Emergency Med,Brooke Army Med Ctr Hosp, Ft Sam, Houston. *Mem:* Am Heart Asn. *Res:* Early detection of latent coronary artery disease by laboratory screening of blood and serum. *Mailing Add:* 10318 Willowick San Antonio TX 78217. *Fax:* 210-656-4475; *E-Mail:* troxler@wthscsa.edu

**TROXLER, ROBERT FULTON,** BIOCHEMISTRY. *Current Pos:* res assoc med, 66-68, from asst prof to assoc prof, 68-80, PROF BIOCHEM, SCH MED, BOSTON UNIV, 80- *Personal Data:* b Santa Monica, Calif, July 11, 38; m 64. *Educ:* Grinnell Col, BS, 60; Pa State Univ, MS, 62; Univ Chicago, PhD(bot), 65. *Prof Exp:* Res assoc bot, Univ Chicago, 65-66. *Mem:* Am Soc Biol Chemists; AAAS; Am Soc Plant Physiologists; Int Asn Dent Res. *Res:* Porphyrin and bile pigment chemistry and biochemistry; structure and function of proteins; molecular biology. *Mailing Add:* Dept Biochem Boston Univ Sch Med 80 E Concord St Boston MA 02118-2394. *Fax:* 617-638-5339

**TROY, DANIEL JOSEPH,** MATHEMATICS. *Current Pos:* assoc prof, 67-94, PROF MATH, PURDUE UNIV, 94- *Personal Data:* b St Louis Co, Mo, Feb 2, 32; m 55, Mary A Murray; c Leonard, Kathleen (Smyser), Joseph, Stephen, Patrick & Jean (Swenson). *Educ:* St Louis Univ, BS, 53, MS, 58, PhD(math), 61; Univ Ill, MS. *Prof Exp:* Asst prof, Ohio State Univ, 61-67. *Mem:* Asn Comput Mach; Math Asn Am. *Res:* Complex variable; logical databases. *Mailing Add:* 17042 Evans Dr South Holland IL 60473. *Fax:* 219-989-2709; *E-Mail:* troydj@calumet.purdue.edu

**TROY, FREDERIC ARTHUR,** BIOCHEMISTRY, ONCOLOGY. *Current Pos:* from asst prof to assoc prof, 68-79, PROF BIOL CHEM, SCH MED, UNIV CALIF, DAVIS, 80-, CHMN, 91- *Personal Data:* b Evanston, Ill, Feb 16, 37; m 59; c 2. *Educ:* Washington Univ, BS, 61; Purdue Univ, West Lafayette, PhD(biochem), 66. *Prof Exp:* Am Cancer Soc res fel physiol chem, Sch Med, Johns Hopkins Univ, 66-68. *Concurrent Pos:* USPHS res grant, Sch Med, Univ Calif, Davis, Nat Cancer Inst res grant, 71-83; Nat Cancer Inst career res develop award, 75-80; co-dir tumor biol training grant, Nat Cancer Inst, 72-; Am Cancer Soc-Eleanor Roosevelt-Int Cancer fel, Int Union Against Cancer, Stockholm, 76-77; consult, NIH, NSF & Basic Sci Rev bd,

Vet Admin; ed, J Biol Chem, 88-; pres-elect & vpres, Bd Dirs, Soc Complex Carbohydrates, 91- *Mem:* Am Soc Microbiol; Am Inst Chemists; Am Soc Biol Chemists; Am Chem Soc; Brit Biochem Soc; Am Soc Cancer Res; Am Soc Enologists. *Res:* Membrane chemistry, biosynthesis of glycoconjugates; chemistry and biosynthesis of bacterial capsular polysaccharides; nuclear magnetic resonance studies of the conformation and dynamics of glycosyl carrier polyisoprenoids; membranes biogenesis of multi-enzyme complexes; role of polysialic acid in neural development and tumor metastasis. *Mailing Add:* Dept Biol Chem Univ Calif Sch Med Davis CA 95616

**TROY, WILLIAM CHRISTOPHER,** APPLIED MATHEMATICS. *Current Pos:* From asst prof to assoc prof, 74-86, PROF MATH, UNIV PITTSBURGH, 87- *Personal Data:* b Rochester, NY, July 7, 47. *Educ:* St John Fisher Col, BS, 69; State Univ NY, Buffalo, MA, 70, PhD(math), 74. *Mem:* Am Math Soc. *Res:* Application of the theory of differential equations to mathematical problems arising in biology, chemistry and engineering (fluid mechanics). *Mailing Add:* Dept Math Univ Pittsburgh 503 Thackeray St Pittsburgh PA 15260

**TROYER, ALVAH FORREST,** PLANT BREEDING, CORN BREEDING. *Current Pos:* CONSULT, CARGILL HYBRID SEEDS, AURORA, ILL, 93- *Personal Data:* b LaFontaine, Ind, May 30, 29; m 50; c 4. *Educ:* Purdue Univ, BS, 54; Univ Ill, MS, 56; Univ Minn, PhD(plant breeding & genetics), 64. *Honors & Awards:* Plant Breding Award, Agron Soc Am & Crop Sci Soc Am. *Prof Exp:* Res assoc, Univ Ill, Urbana, 55-56; res fel, Univ Minn, St Paul, 56-58; sta mgr, Pioneer Corn Co, Mankato, 58-65; res coordr, Northern Res, Pioneer Hi-Bred Int Inc, 65-77, Eastern Res, 71-77; dir, Res & Develop, Pfizer Genetics, Inc, St Louis, 77-81, vpres, 81-82; dir res & develop, De Kalb-Pfizer Genetics Inc, De Kalb, Ill, 82-93. *Concurrent Pos:* Pres, Agr Res Inst, Washington DC, 91; vpres, Nat Coun Com Plant Breeders. *Mem:* Sigma Xi; fel AAAS; fel Am Soc Agron; NY Acad Sci; fel Crop Sci Soc Am; Am Genetics Soc; Genetic Soc Am; Am Crop Sci Soc; Am Agron Soc. *Res:* Increasing the effectiveness and efficiency of corn breeding in all possible ways so that superior products for agriculture will be developed. *Mailing Add:* 611 Joanne Lane De Kalb IL 60115

**TROYER, JAMES RICHARD,** HISTORY OF BOTANY, PLANT PHYSIOLOGY. *Current Pos:* from asst prof bot to prof, 57-95, EMER PROF BOT, NC STATE UNIV, 95- *Personal Data:* b Goshen, Ind, Feb 26, 29; m 51, 85, Patricia Broomhall; c Margaret, Katherine & Rebecca. *Educ:* DePauw Univ, BA, 50; Ohio State Univ, MS, 51; Columbia Univ, PhD(bot), 54. *Prof Exp:* Vis asst prof biol, Univ Ala, 54-55; instr plant physiol, Sch Forestry, Yale Univ, 55-57. *Concurrent Pos:* Lalor Found fel, 55; fel, Biomath Training Prog, NC State Univ, 64-66. *Mem:* AAAS; Am Soc Plant Physiol; Bot Soc Am; Sigma Xi; Soc Hist Natural Hist; Hist Sci Soc. *Res:* Mathematical plant physiology; flavonoid substances of plants; history of botany. *Mailing Add:* Dept Bot Box 7612 NC State Univ Raleigh NC 27695-7612. *E-Mail:* jr_troyer@ncsu.edu

**TROYER, JOHN ROBERT,** anatomy; deceased, see previous edition for last biography

**TROYER, ROBERT JAMES,** MATHEMATICS. *Current Pos:* RETIRED. *Personal Data:* b Sturgis, Mich, Sept 21, 28; m 54, Mary L Stuckman; c Bradley J, Gregory C, Todd W & Curtis R. *Educ:* Ball State Univ, BS, 50; Ind Univ, MAT, 56, PhD(math), 60. *Prof Exp:* Instr math, Ind Univ, 60-62, asst prof, 62-65; vis fel, Dartmouth Col, 65-66; from asst prof to assoc prof, Univ NC, Chapel Hill, 66-68; vis assoc prof, Lake Forest Col, 68-69, assoc prof, 69-70, prof math, 70-92, actg dean fac, 93-94. *Concurrent Pos:* Vis scholar, Northwestern Univ, 74-75, Univ Toronto, 86-87. *Mem:* Math Asn Am. *Res:* Geometry; history of mathematics. *Mailing Add:* 555 N Sheridan Rd Lake Forest Col Lake Forest IL 60045

**TROZZOLO, ANTHONY MARION,** ORGANIC CHEMISTRY, PHOTOCHEMISTRY. *Current Pos:* Huisking prof chem, 75-92, HUISKING EMER PROF CHEM, UNIV NOTRE DAME, IND, 92-, ASST DEAN, COL SCI, 93- *Personal Data:* b Chicago, Ill, Jan 11, 30; m 55, Doris Stoffregen; c Thomas, Susan, Patricia, Michael, Lisa & Laura. *Educ:* Ill Inst Technol, SB, 50; Univ Chicago, SM, 57, PhD(chem), 60. *Honors & Awards:* Am Inst Chemists Award, 50; Halpern Photochem Award, NY Acad Sci, 80; Phillips lectr, Univ Okla, 71; Reilly lectr, Univ Notre Dame, 72; Brown lectr, Rutgers Univ, 75; Faraday lectr, Northern Ill Univ, 76; Butler lectr, SDak State Univ, 78; Chevron lectr, Univ Nev, Reno, 83; Hesburgh lectr, Univ Notre Dame, 86. *Prof Exp:* Asst chemist, Chicago Midway Labs, 52-53; assoc chemist, Armour Res Found, 53-56; mem tech staff, Bell Tel Labs, 59-75. *Concurrent Pos:* Adj prof, Columbia Univ, 71; assoc ed, J Am Chem Soc, 75-77; ed, Chem Rev, 77-84; mem bd trustees, Gordon Res Conf; vis prof, Univ Colo, 81; fac sci lectr, Leuven, Belg, 83; vis lectr, Acad Sinica, 84 & 85; vis prof, Max Planck Inst Radiation Chem, Mulheim, Ruhr, Ger, 90. *Mem:* Fel AAAS; Am Chem Soc; fel Am Inst Chemists; fel NY Acad Sci; Sigma Xi. *Res:* Free radicals; carbenes; charge transfer complexes; electron spin resonance; organic solid state; singlet molecular oxygen; polymer stabilization; chemically-induced dynamic nuclear polarization; laser spectroscopy. *Mailing Add:* 1329 E Washington St South Bend IN 46617-3340. *Fax:* 219-631-6652; *E-Mail:* anthony.m.trozzolo.4@nd.edu

**TRPIS, MILAN,** MEDICAL ENTOMOLOGY, VECTOR-BORNE DISEASES. *Current Pos:* from assoc prof to prof, Dept Immunol & Infectious Dis, 74-94, PROF MED ENTOM, DEPT MOLECULAR MICROBIOL & IMMUNOL, JOHNS HOPKINS UNIV, 95- *Personal Data:* b Mojsova Lucka, Slovakia, Dec 20, 30; US citizen; m 56, Ludmila Tonkovic; c Martin,

Peter & Katarina. *Educ:* Comenius Univ, Bratislava, Prom Biol, 56; Charles Univ, Prague, Dr Rer Nat(zool, med entom), 60, PhD(med entom). *Honors & Awards:* First Prize Award, Slovak Acad Sci, Bratislava, 61. *Prof Exp:* Res asst entom, Faunistic Lab, Slovak Acad Sci, 53-56, sci asst, Dept Biol, 56-60, scientist, 60-62, independent scientist & head, Dept Ecol Physiol Insects, Inst Landscape Biol, 62-65; res assoc med entom, Univ Ill, Urbana, 66-67; res assoc, Can Dept Agr, Alta, 67-68; independent scientist & head, Dept Ecol Physiol Insects, Slovak Acad Sci, 68-69; entomologist-ecologist, EAfrica Aedes Res Unit, WHO, UN, Tanzania, 69-71; from asst res fac fel to assoc fac fel, Vector Biol Labs, Dept Biol, Univ Notre Dame, Ind, 71-74. *Concurrent Pos:* Dir, Biol Res Inst Am, 72-77; proj dir epidemiol river blindness (onchocerciasis), Liberia & Sierra Leone, 81-84; onchocerciasis proj, Johns Hopkins Univ, Pieere Richet/Orstom, Ivory Coast, 93-96. *Mem:* AAAS; Am Soc Trop Med & Hyg; Am Soc Parasitologists; Entom Soc Am; Am Mosquito Control Asn; Sigma Xi. *Res:* Parasitic insects, particularly their population dynamics, ecological genetics of populations, behavior and behavioral genetics; embryonic development of insects; biological and genetic control of vectors; ecology of vector-borne diseases; invertebrate immunology. *Mailing Add:* 1504 Ivy Hill Rd Cockeysville MD 21030. *E-Mail:* mtrpis@phnet.sph.jhu.edu

**TRUAX, DONALD R,** MATHEMATICAL STATISTICS. *Current Pos:* from asst prof to prof, 59-93, EMER PROF MATH, UNIV ORE, 93- *Personal Data:* b Minneapolis, Minn, Aug 29, 27; m 50, Barbara Eckton; c Marg, Catherine, Patricia & Gayle. *Educ:* Univ Wash, BS, 51, MS, 53; Stanford Univ, PhD(statist), 55. *Prof Exp:* Res fel math, Calif Inst Technol, 55-56; asst prof, Univ Kans, 56-59. *Concurrent Pos:* Managing ed, Inst Math Statist, 75-81. *Mem:* Am Statist Asn; fel Inst Math Statist. *Res:* Testing statistical hypotheses; multiple decision problems. *Mailing Add:* Dept Math Univ Ore Eugene OR 97403

**TRUAX, ROBERT LLOYD,** MATHEMATICS. *Current Pos:* RETIRED. *Personal Data:* b Gillett, Ark, May 8, 28; m 52; c 2. *Educ:* Ark State Teachers Col, BSE, 50; Univ Miss, MA, 58; Okla State Univ, EdD(math educ), 64. *Prof Exp:* Coordr math, Pub Schs, Ark, 50-62; assoc prof math, Southern State Col, 63-65; assoc prof, Northeast La State Col, 65-67; assoc prof math, Univ Miss, 67- *Mem:* Math Asn Am. *Res:* Multivariable function approximations; statistical analysis of research related to paper industry. *Mailing Add:* 2336 Lee Loop Oxford MS 38655

**TRUBATCH, JANETT,** TECHNICAL MANAGEMENT, NEUROSCIENCE. *Personal Data:* b New York, NY, Oct 13, 45; c 4. *Educ:* Polytech Inst Brooklyn, BSc, 62; Brandeis Univ, MA, 64, PhD(physics), 68; Univ Miami, MBA, 91. *Prof Exp:* Asst prof physics, Calif State Univ, Los Angeles, 67-68; res fel biol, Calif Inst Technol, 68-74; asst prof physiol, NY Med Col, 74-77; prog dir neurobiol, NSF, 77-79; health sci admin, Neurol Dis Prog, NIH, 79-85; assoc vpres res, Univ Chicago, 85-89; vpres, Univ Indust & Govt Alliances, Oak Ridge Assocs, 91-93. *Mem:* Soc Neurosci; Am Physiol Soc; AAAS; Asn Univ Technol Mgrs. *Res:* Mechanisms of synaptic transmission; neural basis of memory and learning; synapse formation; mathematical modeling of biological systems. *Mailing Add:* 2100 Shore Dr Anchorage AK 99515

**TRUBATCH, SHELDON L,** THEORETICAL PHYSICS, BIOPHYSICS. *Current Pos:* ATTY, SIDLEY & AUSTIN, 89- *Personal Data:* b Brooklyn, NY, Mar 12, 42; m 62; c 4. *Educ:* Polytech Inst Brooklyn, BS, 62; Brandeis Univ, MA, 64, PhD(physics), 68. *Hon Degrees:* JD, Columbia Univ, 77. *Prof Exp:* Assoc prof physics, Calif State Univ, Long Beach, 67-77; mem staff, Off Gen Coun, US Nuclear Regulatory Comn, 77-80, spec asst technol affairs, 80-85; atty off staff coun, Commonwealth Edison, 85-89. *Mem:* Am Nuclear Soc. *Res:* Non-relativistic field theory; sensory physiology. *Mailing Add:* Winston & Strawn 1400 L St NW Washington DC 20005

**TRUBEK, MAX,** medicine, for more information see previous edition

**TRUBERT, MARC,** APPLIED MECHANICS, ELECTRONICS. *Current Pos:* RETIRED. *Personal Data:* b Soissons, France, Feb 7, 27; US citizen; m 89; c 2. *Educ:* Univ Paris, BS, 50; Spec Sch Pub Works, Paris, BS, 51; Univ Fla, MS, 60, PhD(eng mech), 62. *Honors & Awards:* Except Eng Achievement Medal, NASA. *Prof Exp:* Res engr, Nat Off Aeronaut Study & Res, Paris, 53-57; develop engr, Compagnie Generale de TSF, Paris, 57-58; asst in res eng mech, Univ Fla, 58-62, asst prof, 62-63; asst prof, Univ Calif, Berkeley, 63-65; res engr, Jet Propulsion Lab, 65-66, mem tech staff, 66-70, group supvr, 70-80, sr mem tech staff, 80-92. *Concurrent Pos:* Instr, Exten Sch, Univ Calif, Los Angeles, 65-70. *Mem:* Acoust Soc Am; Am Inst Aeronaut & Astronaut; Sigma Xi. *Res:* Structural dynamics; vibration, random vibration, frequency domain method and analog methods; attitude control of spacecraft; furlable antennas; load analysis and structural testing. *Mailing Add:* PO Box 2132 Corona CA 91718

**TRUBEY, DAVID KEITH,** RADIATION PHYSICS, RADIATION PROTECTION. *Current Pos:* CONSULT, 91- *Personal Data:* b Coldwater, Mich, Apr 23, 28; m 50, Jean Mains; c Robert & Richard. *Educ:* Mich State Univ, BS, 53; Univ Tenn, MS, 88. *Honors & Awards:* Tech Achievement Award, Radiation Protection & Shielding Div, Am Nuclear Soc, 83, Rockwell Lifetime Achievement Award, 92. *Prof Exp:* Physicist, Oak Ridge Nat Lab, 53-54 & 55-56, mgr radiation shielding info ctr, 66-70, mem staff, 53-91. *Concurrent Pos:* Lectr, Oak Ridge Sch Reactor Technol, 60-62; chmn, Stand Subcomt ANS-6, Am Nuclear Soc, 72-91 & Radiation Protection & Shielding Div, 74; mem, Comt N13 Radiation Protection, Am Nat Stand Inst, 82-85 & N17 Res Reactors, Reactor Physics & Shielding, 85- *Mem:* Fel Am Nuclear Soc; Health Physics Soc. *Res:* Radiation shielding, transport and dosimetry. *Mailing Add:* 10800 N Airway Loop Dunnellon FL 34434. *E-Mail:* davetrubey@aol.com

**TRUCE, WILLIAM EVERETT,** CHEMISTRY, ORGANIC SULFUR CHEMISTRY. *Current Pos:* from asst prof to prof, 46-88, EMER PROF CHEM, PURDUE UNIV, WEST LAFAYETTE, 88- *Personal Data:* b Chicago, Ill, Sept 30, 17; m 40, Eloise J McBrown; c Nancy J (Moore) & Roger W. *Educ:* Univ Ill, BS, 39; Northwestern Univ, PhD(chem), 43. *Prof Exp:* Instr chem, Wabash Col, 43-44; res chemist, Swift & Co, Ill, 44-46. *Concurrent Pos:* Guggenheim fel, Oxford Univ, 57; exec officer, Nat Org Symp, 61; pres, Purdue chap, Sigma Xi; chmn, Gordon Res Conf Org; asst dean, Purdue Grad Sch; consult, indust chem. *Mem:* Am Chem Soc. *Res:* Organic sulfur chemistry; acetylenes; vinylic halides; organic theory and its relationship to synthetic organic chemistry. *Mailing Add:* 220 Hopi Pl Boulder CO 80303

**TRUCHARD, JAMES JOSEPH,** ACOUSTICS, ELECTRONICS ENGINEERING. *Current Pos:* WITH NAT INSTRUMENTS, 80- *Personal Data:* b Sealy, Tex, June 25, 43; m 66; c 4. *Educ:* Univ Tex, BS, 64, MA, 67, PhD(elec eng), 74. *Prof Exp:* Lab res asst, Appl Res Labs, Univ Tex, Austin, 63-65, res scientist acoust electronics, 65-80. *Mem:* Acoust Soc Am. *Res:* Transducer measurement systems; digital signal processing of acoustic signals; nonlinear acoustics; parametric receiving arrays for acoustic signals. *Mailing Add:* 4406 Aqua Verde Austin TX 78746

**TRUDEL, MICHEL D,** VIROLOGY. *Current Pos:* asst prof, 74-78, dir, Ctr Virol, 90-93, PROF VIROL, INST ARMAND-FRAPPIER, 78-, SCI DIR, 93- *Personal Data:* b Montreal, Que, Feb 5, 44; m 67, 83, Fracine Nadon; c 3. *Educ:* Univ Montreal, BA, 65, BSc, 68, MSc, 70; Univ Sherbrooke, PhD(cell biol), 73. *Prof Exp:* Fel cell membranes, Nat Cancer Inst, 73-74. *Concurrent Pos:* Grants, Formation Researcher, Ministry of Educ, Que, 76-78 & 88-91, Health & Welfare, Can, 76-78, Nat Res Coun Can, 78-81 & 84-93 & Can Med Res Coun, 79-91, conseil de recherches en peche et agroalimentaire, Que, 85-89. *Mem:* Am Soc Virologists; Int Soc Antiviral Res; Can Asn Clin Microbiol Infectious Dis; Can Soc Microbiologists. *Res:* Viral subunit vaccines and the implication of the physical form of the viral proteins that induce the immune response; neutralization epitopes rubella, respiratory syncytial virus, bovine herpes virus 1; synthetic peptides; recombinant vaccines. *Mailing Add:* Inst Armand-Frappier 531 Boul des Prairies Ville De Laval PQ H7V 1B7 Can. *Fax:* 514-686-5501, 686-5626; *E-Mail:* michel__trudel@laf.nquebec.ca

**TRUDEN, JUDITH LUCILLE,** VIROLOGY. *Current Pos:* RETIRED. *Personal Data:* b Duluth, Minn, Sept 29, 31. *Educ:* Wayne State Univ, BA, 53, MS, 55; Univ Miami, PhD(microbiol), 67. *Prof Exp:* Technician virol, Henry Ford Hosp, Detroit, Mich, 55-59; USPHS res fel, Pub Health Res Inst, New York, 68-71; res instr, Med Col Wis, 71-74, res assoc, 74; scholar molecular biol, Univ Mich, Ann Arbor, 75-78; res assoc, Wayne State Univ, Detroit, 78-87. *Res:* Interferon and interferon antagonists; biochemistry and molecular biology of virus-inflected cells; autoimmune thyroiditis; liver fibrosis in schistosomiasis. *Mailing Add:* 12700 Greiner Detroit MI 48205

**TRUE, NANCY S,** PHYSICAL CHEMISTRY. *Current Pos:* from asst prof to assoc prof, 80-89, PROF CHEM, UNIV CALIF, DAVIS, 89- *Personal Data:* b Waterbury, Conn, Sept 30, 51. *Educ:* Univ Conn, PhD(phys chem), 77. *Honors & Awards:* Presidental Young Invest, 85. *Prof Exp:* Assoc chem, Univ Conn, 77-78, Univ Col London, 78-79 & Cornell Univ, 79-80. *Concurrent Pos:* Alfred P Sloan fel, 86-88. *Mem:* Am Phys Soc; Am Chem Soc; Sigma Xi. *Res:* Gas phase nuclear magnetic resonance spectroscopy and microwave spectroscopy. *Mailing Add:* Dept Chem Univ Calif Davis CA 95616. *E-Mail:* nstrue@ucdavis.edu

**TRUE, WILLIAM WADSWORTH,** PHYSICS, NUCLEAR STRUCTURE. *Current Pos:* from asst prof to assoc prof, 60-69, PROF PHYSICS, UNIV CALIF, DAVIS, 69- *Personal Data:* b Rockland, Maine, Dec 27, 25; m 54, Sarah E Goodwin; c William G, Kenneth W, Anne E & Katherine M. *Educ:* Univ Maine, BS, 50; Univ RI, MS, 52; Ind Univ, PhD(physics), 57. *Prof Exp:* Instr physics, Princeton Univ, 57-60. *Mem:* Am Phys Soc. *Res:* Theoretical nuclear physics. *Mailing Add:* 772 Elmwood Dr Univ Calif Davis CA 95616. *Fax:* 530-752-4717; *E-Mail:* true@physics.ucdavis.edu

**TRUEBLOOD, KENNETH NYITRAY,** CHEMISTRY, CHEMICAL CRYSTALLOGRAPHY. *Current Pos:* from instr to assoc prof, Univ Calif, Los Angeles, 49-60, prof chem, 60-89, chmn dept chem, 65-70 & 90-91, dean, Col Lett & Sci, 71-74, EMER PROF CHEM, UNIV CALIF, LOS ANGELES, 60- *Personal Data:* b Dobbs Ferry, NY, Apr 24, 20; m 70, Jean Turner. *Educ:* Harvard Univ, AB, 41; Calif Inst Technol, PhD(chem), 47. *Honors & Awards:* Tankuchen Award, Am Crystallog Asn, 95. *Prof Exp:* Asst chem, Calif Inst Technol, 43-46, res fel, 47-49. *Concurrent Pos:* Fulbright award, 56-57; mem, US Nat Comt Crystallog, 60-65; vis prof, Ibadan, 64-65; vis scientist, Inst Elemento-Org Compounds, Moscow, 65; Guggenheim fel, 76. *Mem:* Am Chem Soc; Am Crystallog Asn (pres, 61). *Res:* X-ray studies of molecular and crystal structure; molecular motion. *Mailing Add:* Dept Chem & Biochem Univ Calif Los Angeles CA 90024-1569. *Fax:* 310-206-4038; *E-Mail:* trueblood@uclach

**TRUELOVE, BRYAN,** weed science, herbicide resistance, for more information see previous edition

**TRUEMAN, THOMAS LAURENCE,** MANAGEMENT OF HIGH ENERGY, NUCLEAR PHYSICS RESEARCH. *Current Pos:* Res assoc physics, Brookhaven Nat Lab, 62-64, from asst physicist to physicist, 65-74, dep chmn physics dept, 80-86, assoc dir, 88-91, SR PHYSICIST & GROUP

LEADER, BROOKHAVEN NAT LAB, 74- *Personal Data:* b Media, Pa, Sept 24, 35; m 61; c 2. *Educ:* Dartmouth Col, AB, 57; Univ Chicago, MS, 58, PhD(physics), 62. *Concurrent Pos:* Guggenheim fel, Oxford Univ, 72-73; vis prof, Univ D'Aix-Marseille, 78-79, 86-87. *Mem:* Fel Am Phys Soc. *Res:* High energy theory; finite temperature field theory. *Mailing Add:* Brookhaven Nat Lab Upton NY 11973

**TRUESDELL, ALFRED HEMINGWAY,** GEOLOGY, CHEMISTRY. *Current Pos:* CONSULT, 91- *Personal Data:* b Washington, DC, Sept 10, 33; m 64. *Educ:* Oberlin Col, AB, 57; Harvard Univ, AM, 61, PhD(geol), 62. *Prof Exp:* Geochemist, US Geol Surv, 55-91. *Concurrent Pos:* Res assoc, Stanford Univ, 64- *Mem:* AAAS; Am Mineral Soc; Geochem Soc. *Res:* Application of physical chemistry to the study of geologic processes; electrochemistry of membranes; ion exchange equilibria and energetics; solution geochemistry; chemistry and physics of geothermal systems. *Mailing Add:* 700 Hermosa Way Menlo Park CA 94025

**TRUESDELL, CLIFFORD AMBROSE, III,** MECHANICS. *Current Pos:* prof, 61-89, EMER PROF RATIONAL MECH, JOHNS HOPKINS UNIV, 89- *Personal Data:* b Los Angeles, Calif, Feb 18, 19; m 39, 51; c 1. *Educ:* Calif Inst Technol, BS, 41, MS, 42, Princeton Univ, PhD(math), 43. *Hon Degrees:* Dr Eng, Milan Polytech Inst, 64; DSc, Tulane Univ, 76; Fil Dr, Uppsala Univ, 79; Dr Phil, Basel Univ, 79; Dr, Univ Ferrara, 92. *Honors & Awards:* Bingham Medal, Soc Rheol, 63; Panetti Int Medal & Prize, Acad Sci Turin, 67; Birkhoff Prize, Am Math Soc & Soc Indust & Appl Math, 78; Ritt lectr, Dept Math, Columbia Univ, 82; Page-Barbour lectr, Univ Va, 85; Humbolt Prize, US Sr Scientist Award, 85. *Prof Exp:* Asst math & hist, Calif Inst Technol, 41-42; asst mech, Brown Univ, 42; instr math, Princeton Univ, 42-43 & Univ Mich, 43-44; mem staff, Radiation Lab, Mass Inst Technol, 44-46; chief theoret mech subdiv, Naval Ord Lab, 46-48, head theoret mech sect, Naval Res Lab, 48-51; prof math, Ind Univ, 50-61. *Concurrent Pos:* From lectr to assoc prof, Univ Md, 46-50; consult, Naval Res Lab, 51-55, Nat Bur Stand, 59-62, Sandia Corp, 66, Ga Inst Technol, 73-74 & US Nuclear Regulatory Comn, 75-83; ed, J Rational Mech & Anal, 52-56 & Arch Hist Exact Sci, 60-; Guggenheim fel, 57; ed, Arch Rational Mech & Anal, 57-66, 85-90, co-ed, 67-85; co-ed, Results Appl Math, 57-62; NSF sr res fel, Univ Bologna & Univ Basel, 60-61; ed, Springer Tracts Natural Philos, 62-66 & 79-, co-ed, 67-78; Walker-Ames prof, Univ Wash, 64; distinguished vis prof, Syracuse Univ, 65; 75th Anniversary lectr, Drexel Inst Technol, 66-67; chmn, Soc Natural Philos, 67-68 & 83-84; Lincean prof, Ital Acad Lincei, Rome, 70, 73 & 74; lectr, Fed Univ Rio de Janeiro, 72; vis res scholar, Japan Soc Prom Sci, Kyoto, 80. *Mem:* Soc Natural Philos (secy, 63-65, 70-71 & 80-81); Int Acad Hist Sci; hon mem Polish Soc Theoret & Appl Mech; Int Acad Philos Sci; foreign mem Lincean Acad Sci; corresp mem Acad Brasileira Ciencias. *Res:* Rational mechanics. *Mailing Add:* Rational Mech Johns Hopkins Univ Baltimore MD 21218

**TRUESDELL, SUSAN JANE,** MOLECULAR BIOLOGY. *Current Pos:* MICROBIOLOGIST, PFIZER, INC, 73- *Personal Data:* b Oak Park, Ill, Mar 22, 45; m 78. *Educ:* Mich State Univ, BS, 67; Univ Calif, Los Angeles, PhD(molecular biol), 71. *Prof Exp:* Am Cancer Soc fel, Univ Mich, 71-73. *Concurrent Pos:* Instr introductory microbiol, Conn Col, 77 & 78. *Mem:* Am Soc Microbiol; Soc Indust Microbiol. *Res:* Genetics and physiology of penicillin production; viruses that infect penicillium chrysogenum; microbiol enzyme production; biotransformations; antibiotic and vitamin fermentations. *Mailing Add:* Central Res Pfizer Groton CT 06340

**TRUEX, RAYMOND CARL,** anatomy, for more information see previous edition

**TRUEX, TIMOTHY JAY,** INORGANIC CHEMISTRY. *Personal Data:* b Goshen, Ind, June 11, 45. *Educ:* Hanover Col, BS, 67; Mass Inst Technol, PhD(inorg chem), 72. *Prof Exp:* Res scientist inorg chem, Ford Motor Co, 72-80. *Mem:* Am Chem Soc. *Res:* Atmospheric environmental chemistry; catalysis chemistry; chemistry of surface coatings. *Mailing Add:* 1241 Coronet Dr Riverside CA 92506

**TRUFANT, SAMUEL ADAMS,** MEDICINE, NEUROLOGY. *Current Pos:* from asst prof to prof, 50-78, from asst dean to assoc dean, Col Med, 51-62, EMER PROF NEUROL, COL MED, UNIV CINCINNATI, 78-; PROF NEUROL, TULANE UNIV, 79-; STAFF NEUROLOGIST, VET ADMIN MED CTR, LA, 79- *Personal Data:* b New Orleans, La, May 24, 19; m 45; c 4. *Educ:* Tulane Univ, BS, 40, MD, 43; Am Bd Psychiat & Neurol, dipl, 51. *Prof Exp:* Asst gross anat, Tulane Univ, 40-41; Rockefeller fel neurol, Washington Univ, 47-49, USPHS res fel, 49-50. *Concurrent Pos:* Consult, Wright-Patterson AFB, Ohio, 52-; dir child neurol, Children's Hosp, 59-71; dir, Am Bd Psychiat & Neurol, 66-73, vpres, 71, pres, 72-; proj officer, India Neurol & Sensory Dis Serv Prog, USPHS, 66-; mem, Residency Rev Comt Psychiat & Neurol, 66-72, chmn, 70-72; ed, Trans, Am Neurol Asn, 68-73. *Mem:* Am Neurol Asn (vpres, 65, secy-treas, 68-73, pres, 75); Asn Res Nerv & Ment Dis; Asn Am Med Cols (asst secy, 59-64); Am Acad Neurol. *Res:* Clinical neurology; electroencephalography. *Mailing Add:* Tulane Med Ctr Hosp & Clin 1415 Tulane Ave New Orleans LA 70112-2605

**TRUHLAR, DONALD GENE,** CHEMICAL DYNAMICS, SCIENTIFIC COMPUTATION. *Current Pos:* from asst prof to assoc prof chem, 69-76, prof chem & chem physics, 76-93, DIR, MINN SUPERCOMPUT INST, UNIV MINN, MINNEAPOLIS, 88-, PROF, INST TECHNOL, 93- *Personal Data:* b Chicago, Ill, Feb 27, 44; m 65, Jane T Gust; c Sara E & Stephanie M. *Educ:* St Mary's Col, Minn, BA, 65; Calif Inst Technol, PhD(chem), 70. *Prof Exp:* Student aide chem, Argonne Nat Lab, 65. *Concurrent Pos:* Sr vis fel, Battelle Mem Inst, Columbus, 73 & Sloan res fel,

73-77; vis fel, Joint Inst Lab Astrophysics, Boulder, Colo, 75-76. *Mem:* Fel Am Phys Soc; Am Chem Soc; Soc Indust & Appl Math; World Asn Theoret Org Chemists; AAAS. *Res:* Theory and computations for collision processes involving atoms, molecules and electrons; potential energy surfaces for reactive and inelastic collisions; theory of molecular spectroscopy. *Mailing Add:* Chem Dept Univ Minn 207 Pleasant St SE Minneapolis MN 55455. *Fax:* 612-626-9390; *E-Mail:* truhlar@tl.chem.umn.edu

**TRUITT, EDWARD BYRD, JR,** PHARMACOLOGY. *Current Pos:* prog chief & prof, 76-84, res prof, 84-92, EMER RES PROF PHARMACOL, NORTHEASTERN OHIO UNIV, 92- *Personal Data:* b Norfolk, Va, Aug 23, 22; m 85, Jessie L Carter; c 2. *Educ:* Med Col Va, BS, 43; Univ Md, PhD(pharmacol), 50. *Prof Exp:* Asst prof pharmacol, Bowman Gray Sch Med, Wake Forest Col, 50-55; from assoc prof to prof, Sch Med, Univ Md, Baltimore City, 55-67; sr res fel, Columbus Labs, Battelle Mem Inst & prof, Col Med, Ohio State Univ, 67-72; res prof, Sch Med, George Washington Univ, 73-76. *Concurrent Pos:* Robins Co fel, Bowman Gray Sch Med, Wake Forest Col, 50-55. *Mem:* Res Soc Alcoholism; Am Soc Pharmacol & Exp Therapeut; Soc Exp Biol & Med; Sigma Xi; Int Soc Biol Res Alcoholism. *Res:* Neuropharmacology; psychopharmacology; drug metabolism; alcoholism; marijuana and drug abuse research; study of alcohol-acetaldehyde metabolism as a possible genetic and/or chemical risk marker for alcoholism. *Mailing Add:* Dept Pharmacol North Eastern Ohio Univ Col Med 7567 Birkner Dr Kent OH 44240-6303. *Fax:* 330-374-5053

**TRUITT, MARCUS M(CCAFFERTY),** CIVIL ENGINEERING. *Current Pos:* RETIRED. *Personal Data:* b Enid, Okla, Oct 10, 21; m 42; c 2. *Educ:* Okla State Univ, BS, 47; Harvard Univ, MS, 48; Stanford Univ, Engr, 51; Johns Hopkins Univ, PhD, 68. *Prof Exp:* Soil mech, United Fruit Co, Cent Am, 48-49; asst prof civil eng, Univ Ala, 49-50; from asst prof to prof eng, Tex A&I Univ, 51-77, chmn, Dept Civil & Mech Eng, 68-77, prof civil & mech eng, 77-84. *Concurrent Pos:* Consult, 53-; city engr, Kingsville, Tex, 53-; res assoc, Johns Hopkins Univ, 66- *Mem:* Am Soc Civil Engrs; Am Soc Eng Educ. *Res:* Municipal engineering; environmental engineering; application of computer simulation techniques to hurricane track predictions. *Mailing Add:* 504 E Ailsie Ave Kingsville TX 78363

**TRUITT, ROBERT LINDELL,** TUMOR IMMUNOLOGY, TRANSPLANTATION BIOLOGY. *Current Pos:* res assoc prof, 84-88, res prof, Dept Pediat, 88-91, PROF WITH TENURE, MED COL WIS, MILWAUKEE, 91- *Personal Data:* b Carbondale, Ill, July 26, 46; m 67, Dawn Kowalkiewicz; c Cabrina M, Valerie L, Tiffany D, Andrea L & Lyndell M. *Educ:* Southern Ill Univ, Carbondale, BA, 68, PhD(microbiol), 73. *Prof Exp:* Fel germfree syst, Lobund Lab, Univ Notre Dame, 72-74; res assoc, Winter Res Lab, Mt Sinai Med Ctr, 74-77, sr scientist, 77-83, assoc dir, 83-84. *Concurrent Pos:* Fel, United Cancer Coun, 72-73 & Damon Runyon Mem Fund Cancer Res, 73-75; NIH/Nat Cancer Inst res grants, 75-76, 77, 79, 81, 86, 92 & 97; spec fel, Leukemia Soc Am, 76-78, scholar, 78-83; assoc scientist, Univ Wis Med Sch, Milwaukee, 83-84; NIH/Nat Inst Allergy & Infectious Dis res grant, 84; mem, Cancer Res Manpower Review Comt, NIH/Nat Cancer Inst; doctorate staff, Children's Hosp Wis, 85- *Mem:* Am Asn Immunologists; Fedn Am Soc Exp Biol; AAAS; Am Soc Microbiol; Int Soc Exp Hemat; Asn Gnotobiotics; Int Asn Gnotobiol; Soc Biol Ther; Pediat Oncol Group; Am Soc Blood & Marrow Transplantation. *Res:* Germfree animal systems; tumor immunology; bone marrow transplantation; transplantation biology. *Mailing Add:* Med Col Wis Dept Pediat Milwaukee WI 53226. *Fax:* 414-266-8642; *E-Mail:* rtruitt@post.its.mcw.edu

**TRUJILLO, EDUARDO E,** PLANT PATHOLOGY. *Current Pos:* asst plant pathologist, Univ Hawaii, 62-65, asst prof plant path & asst specialist, 65-67, assoc prof, 67-74, prof plant path, 74-80, PROF BOT SCI, UNIV HAWAII, 80-, ASSOC PLANT PATHOLOGIST, 67- *Personal Data:* b Horconcitos, Panama, Apr 22, 30. *Educ:* Univ Ark, BSA, 56, MS, 57; Univ Calif, PhD(plant path), 62. *Prof Exp:* Res asst plant path, Univ Calif, 57-62. *Concurrent Pos:* Consult, Pac Southwest Forest & Range Exp Sta, US Forest Serv, 63- *Mem:* AAAS; Am Phys Soc; Am Soc Hort Sci. *Res:* Aspects of research dealing with soil borne pathogens, mainly ecology and epidemiology of Pythium and Phytophthoras in tropical environments; biology of Fusarium species. *Mailing Add:* Dept Plant Path Univ Hawaii Manoa Honolulu HI 96822-2270

**TRUJILLO, EDWARD MICHAEL,** CHEMICAL ENGINEERING. *Current Pos:* ASSOC PROF CHEM ENG, UNIV UTAH, 84- *Personal Data:* b Los Angeles, Calif, Apr 14, 47; m 88, Rose Alvarado; c Miguel. *Educ:* Univ Ariz, BS, 69; Calif Inst Technol, MS, 70; Univ Utah, PhD(chem eng), 75. *Prof Exp:* Prod engr, Kimberly-Clark Corp, 70-71; instr chem eng, Univ Utah, 71-75; res eng prod, Marathon Oil Co, 75-84. *Mem:* Am Inst Chem Engrs; Soc Petrol Engrs; Am Inst Mining, Metall & Petrol Engrs; Am Chem Soc. *Res:* Biochemical engineering; polymer rheology; flow through porous media; ultrafiltration of protein solutions; immobilized enzyme reactor systems; rheology of nanoparticle suspensions; acid mine drainage, environmental engineering. *Mailing Add:* 3290 Merrill Eng Bldg Salt Lake City UT 84112. *Fax:* 801-581-8692; *E-Mail:* etrujill@cc.utah.edu

**TRUJILLO, PATRICIO EDUARDO,** ANALYTICAL CHEMISTRY, GEOCHEMISTRY. *Current Pos:* RETIRED. *Personal Data:* b Santa Fe, NMex, Jan 21, 37; m 62; c 4. *Educ:* Univ NMex, BS, 60. *Prof Exp:* Chemist, NMex Bur Revenue, 59-60; lieutenant missile tech, USAF, 61-64; chief chemist, Eberline Instrument Corp, 64-67; staff mem chem, Los Alamos Nat Lab, 67-94. *Res:* Analytical chemistry related to geothermal energy. *Mailing Add:* 1069 Calle Largo Santa Fe NM 87501

**TRUJILLO, RALPH EUSEBIO,** BIOCHEMISTRY. *Current Pos:* MEM TECH STAFF, SANDIA LABS, 69- *Personal Data:* b Embudo, NMex, Sept 22, 40; m 70. *Educ:* Univ NMex, BS, 62; Ind Univ, PhD(biochem), 67. *Prof Exp:* Mem Peace Corps, Ecuador, 62-64; USPHS fel biochem, Univ Tex M D Anderson Hosp & Tumor Inst, 67-69. *Res:* Response of macromolecular systems to thermal, chemical and radiation environments. *Mailing Add:* 2701 Aliso Dr NE Albuquerque NM 87110

**TRUJILLO, STEPHEN MICHAEL,** ATOMIC PHYSICS, ELECTRICAL ENGINEERING. *Current Pos:* CONSULT, 92- *Personal Data:* b Culver City, Calif, Mar 5, 32; m 59, Josefina Caravaca. *Educ:* Univ Kans, BSc, 58; Univ London, DPhil(physics), 75. *Prof Exp:* Staff scientist physics, Convair Div, Gulf Oil Corp, 69-72; prin physicist, IRT Corp, 72-80 & 90-91; sr scientist, Inesco Inc, 80-83; staff scientist, S-Cubed Div, Maxwell Labs, Inc, 83-89. *Concurrent Pos:* Vis res fel physics, Univ London, 70-75. *Mem:* Am Phys Soc; Inst Physics, Eng; Inst Elec & Electronics Engrs; NY Acad Sci. *Res:* Molecular physics; scientific instrumentation; electro optics; x-ray technology. *Mailing Add:* 5931 Bellevue Ave La Jolla CA 92037

**TRULSON, MICHAEL E,** MICROANATOMY, DRUG ABUSE. *Current Pos:* PROF ANAT, TEX A&M UNIV, 84- *Educ:* Univ Iowa, PhD(biopsychol), 74. *Concurrent Pos:* Adj fac prof human behavior & develop, Amber Univ, 90- *Mailing Add:* Amber Univ 1700 EGate Dr Garland TX 75041-5510

**TRULY, RICHARD H,** AERONAUTICS & ASTRONAUTICS. *Current Pos:* VPRES & DIR, GA TECH RES INST, 92- *Personal Data:* b Fayette, Miss, Nov 12, 37; m, Colleen Hanner; c Richard, Michael, Daniel, Bennett & Lee M. *Educ:* Ga Inst Technol, BA, 59. *Honors & Awards:* Robert H Goddard Award, Am Inst Aeronaut & Astronaut, 90. *Prof Exp:* Astronaut, Manned Orbiting Lab, USAF, 65-69; astronaut, NASA, 69-92, comdr, Columbia Flight 2, 81, cmdr, Challenger Flight 3, 83, dir, Space Shuttle Prog, 86-89, adminr, 89-92. *Mailing Add:* Nat Renewable Energy Lab 1617 Cole Blvd Golden CO 80401

**TRUMAN, JAMES WILLIAM,** INVERTEBRATE NEURODEVELOPMENT. *Current Pos:* from asst prof to assoc prof, 73-78, PROF ZOOL, UNIV WASH, 78- *Personal Data:* b Akron, Ohio, Feb 5, 45; m 70. *Educ:* Univ Notre Dame, BS, 67; Harvard Univ, MA, 69, PhD(biol), 70. *Honors & Awards:* Newcomb Cleveland Prize, AAAS, 70. *Prof Exp:* Harvard Soc Fels jr fel, Harvard Univ, 70-73. *Concurrent Pos:* John Simon Guggenheim Fel, 86; NIH res career develop award, 76-81; McKnight Neurosci develop award, 82-84. *Mem:* Entom Soc Am; Soc Neurosci; Am Soc Zoologists. *Res:* Physiological aspects of circadian rhythms; interaction of hormones with the nervous system; nervous system development. *Mailing Add:* Dept Zool NJ-15 Univ Wash 3900 Seventh Ave NE Seattle WA 98195-0001

**TRUMBLE, ANN C,** GENETICS. *Current Pos:* COMPUT SPECIALIST, DIV EPIDEMIOL STATIST & PREV RES, NAT INST CHILD HEALTH & HUMAN DEVELOP, NIH, 92- *Personal Data:* b Cleveland, Ohio, Aug 4, 45. *Educ:* Ohio State Univ, BS, 67, MS, 70, PhD(genetics), 74. *Prof Exp:* Prog dir, ORI, 78-89. *Mem:* Soc Epidemiol Res; Am Pub Health Asn. *Mailing Add:* NICHHD-NIH Div Epidemiol Statist & Prev Res Rm 7B07 6100 Executive Blvd Bethesda MD 20892. *Fax:* 301-402-2084

**TRUMBLE, JOHN THOMAS,** INTEGRATED PEST MANAGEMENT, PLANT-INSECT INTERACTIONS. *Current Pos:* From asst prof to assoc prof, 80-90, PROF, DEPT ENTOM, UNIV CALIF, RIVERSIDE, 90- *Personal Data:* b Annapolis, Md, May 24, 52; m 75; c 3. *Educ:* Univ Del, BS, 74; Va Polytech Inst & State Univ, MS, 77, PhD(entom), 80. *Honors & Awards:* Bussart Award, Entom Soc Am, 93. *Mem:* AAAS; Entom Soc Am; Soc Invert Pathologists; Entom Soc Can; Soc Pop Ecol; Am Chem Soc. *Res:* Plant-insect interactions; plant secondary chemistry; effects of air pollutants on plants and insects; economics of low input pest management programs in vegetables grown in the United States and other countries. *Mailing Add:* Dept Entom Univ Calif Riverside CA 92521. *E-Mail:* john@ucraci.ucr.edu

**TRUMBO, BRUCE EDWARD,** STATISTICAL APPLICATIONS, EDUCATIONAL METHODS IN STATISTICS. *Current Pos:* from asst prof to assoc prof, 65-72, chmn dept, 70-75, PROF STATIST, CALIF STATE UNIV, HAYWARD, 72- *Personal Data:* b Springfield, Ill, Dec 12, 37. *Educ:* Knox Col, Ill, AB, 59; Univ Chicago, SM, 61, PhD(statist), 65. *Prof Exp:* Asst prof math, San Jose State Col, 63-64. *Concurrent Pos:* Consult, 64-70; vis assoc prof, Stanford Univ, 67-69, 71 & 81; coun fel, Acad Admin Internship Prog, Am Coun Educ, 68-69; prog dir statist res, NSF, 74-75, 78-79 & 85-86; ed, Am Statist Asn Electronic Pub & Serv. *Mem:* Fel Am Statist Asn; fel Inst Math Statist. *Res:* Application of statistical methods to social, behavioral and biological sciences; probability; statistical graphics; electronic publications. *Mailing Add:* Dept Statist Calif State Univ Hayward CA 94542. *Fax:* 510-885-4714; *E-Mail:* btrumbo@csuhayward.edu

**TRUMBORE, CONRAD NOBLE,** PHYSICAL CHEMISTRY. *Current Pos:* asst prof, 60-66, assoc prof chem, 66-, DIR GRAD STUDIES & ASST CHAIR, UNIV DEL, 89- *Personal Data:* b Denver, Colo, Feb 17, 31; m 92, Virginia Pihrens; c 2. *Educ:* Dickinson Col, BS, 52; Pa State Univ, PhD(chem), 55. *Prof Exp:* Fulbright grant, Inst Nuclear Res, Neth, 55-56; asst scientist, Argonne Nat Lab, 56-57; instr chem, Univ Rochester, 57-60. *Concurrent Pos:* USPHS spec fel, Inst Cancer Res, Sutton, Eng, 67-68. *Mem:* AAAS; Radiation Res Soc; Am Chem Soc. *Res:* Primary chemical processes in radiation chemistry of aqueous solutions; correlations between photochemistry and radiation chemistry; biological radiation chemistry; pulse radiolysis and flash photolysis; behavior of diffusing molecules in shear fields; characterization of mixtures by flow properties in capillaries. *Mailing Add:* 104 Cheltenham Rd Newark DE 19711-3616. *E-Mail:* conradt@udel.edu

**TRUMBORE, FORREST ALLEN,** PHYSICAL CHEMISTRY. *Current Pos:* CONSULT, 89-; ADJ ASSOC PROF, ROBERT WOOD JOHNSON MED SCH, UNIV MED & DENT NJ, 92- *Personal Data:* b Denver, Colo, Dec 28, 27; m 51; c 2. *Educ:* Dickinson Col, BS, 46; Univ Pittsburgh, PhD(chem), 50. *Honors & Awards:* Electronics Div Award, Electrochem Soc. *Prof Exp:* Aeronaut res scientist thermodyn alloys, Lewis Flight Propulsion Lab, Nat Adv Comt Aeronaut, 50-52; mem tech staff, Bell Labs, AT&T Inc, 52-89. *Mem:* AAAS; hon mem Electrochem Soc; Mat Res Soc; Am Asn Crystal Growth. *Res:* Solubilities and electrical properties of impurities in semiconductors; crystal growth; photoluminescence and electroluminescence in semiconductors; battery materials; lithium rechargeable batteries. *Mailing Add:* 30 Glen Oaks Ave Summit NJ 07901

**TRUMBORE, MARK W,** BIOPHYSICS. *Current Pos:* RES FEL BIOPHYS, UNIV CONN HEALTH CTR, 91- *Personal Data:* b Ft Lauderdale, Fla, Jan 22, 63. *Educ:* Lehigh Univ, BS, 85; Univ Conn, PhD(biomed sci), 91. *Mem:* Am Chem Soc; Biophys Soc. *Res:* Biophysics. *Mailing Add:* NCI NIH Bldg 37 Rm B109 Bethesda MD 20893

**TRUMBULL, ELMER ROY, JR,** ORGANIC CHEMISTRY. *Current Pos:* RETIRED. *Personal Data:* b Lawrence, Mass, Apr 5, 24; m 54, Patricia Starke; c Carolyn, Robert & Edward. *Educ:* Dartmouth Col, AB, 44; Univ Ill, PhD(org chem), 47. *Prof Exp:* Asst chem, Univ Ill, 44-46; res assoc, Mass Inst Technol, 47-48, Du Pont fel, 51-52; instr, Tufts Col, 48-51; asst prof chem, Brown Univ, 52-58; from asst prof to assoc prof, Colgate Univ 58-63, dir div natural sci & math, 64-70, prof chem, 63-87, chmn dept, 70-87. *Concurrent Pos:* NSF fac fel, Univ Ariz, 66-67; res assoc, Eidgenoessische Technische Hochschule, Zurich, 71-72; vis prof, Ore State Univ, 78-79, Univ Ga, 86-87. *Mem:* Am Chem Soc; Royal Soc Chem. *Res:* Elimination reactions; natural products. *Mailing Add:* Rte 1 Box 200 B Arnoldsville GA 30619

**TRUMMEL, J(OHN) MERLE,** MECHANICAL ENGINEERING. *Current Pos:* Instr mech eng, Univ Iowa, 41-44, from asst prof to prof, 44-86, actg chmn dept, 65-66, EMER PROF, UNIV IOWA, 86- *Personal Data:* b Maroa, Ill, Dec 28, 16; m 42; c 4. *Educ:* Univ Ill, BS, 39; Iowa State Univ, MS, 40; Univ Iowa, PhD(mech eng), 60. *Concurrent Pos:* Consult, Oak Ridge Nat Lab, 54-58, Hawkeye Prod Corp, Iowa, 60-61 & Pioneer-Cent Div Bendix Corp, 61-63. *Mem:* Am Soc Mech Engrs, Am Soc Eng Educ. *Res:* Heat transport by unsteady flows; design and analysis of mechanical systems; mechanical engineering measurement and instrumentation. *Mailing Add:* 2725 Hickory Trail Iowa City IA 52245

**TRUMMER, MAX JOSEPH,** THORACIC SURGERY. *Current Pos:* RETIRED. *Personal Data:* b Bogota, Colombia, Aug 12, 24; US citizen; m 45, Esther Carterette; c Max J Jr. *Educ:* Univ Ill, MD, 48; Univ Pa, MS, 65; Am Bd Surg, dipl, 58; Bd Thoracic Surg, dipl, 61. *Prof Exp:* Resident thoracic surg, US Naval Hosp, St Albans, NY, Med Corps, USN, 58-60, chief thoracic surgeon, US Naval Hosp, San Diego, 67-70; chief thoracic and cardiac surg, Los Angeles County-Olive View Med Ctr, 70-71; dir surg teaching prog, Mercy Hosp & Med Ctr, San Diego, 71-84; clin prof thoracic surg, Univ Southern Calif, 84-92. *Concurrent Pos:* Assoc clin prof thoracic surg, Univ Southern Calif, 69-84 & Univ Calif, San Diego, 70- *Mem:* Fel Am Col Surgeons; fel Am Col Chest Physicians; Soc Thoracic Surg; Am Asn Thoracic Surg; fel Am Col Cardiol. *Res:* Lung transplantation; open-heart surgery; cardiopulmonary physiology. *Mailing Add:* 711 Cornish Dr San Diego CA 92107-4225

**TRUMP, BENJAMIN FRANKLIN,** PATHOLOGY, CELL BIOLOGY. *Current Pos:* PROF & CHMN DEPT PATH, SCH MED, UNIV MD, BALTIMORE, 70- *Personal Data:* b Kansas City, Mo, July 23, 32; m 61; c 2. *Educ:* Univ Mo, Kansas City, BA, 53; Univ Kans, MD, 57. *Prof Exp:* Intern path, Med Ctr, Univ Kans, 57-58, resident, 58-59; resident anat, Sch Med, Univ Washington, 59-60, resident-trainee, 60-61, investr exp path, Armed Forces Inst Path, 61-63; asst prof, Sch Med, Univ Washington, 63-65; from assoc prof to prof, Med Ctr, Duke Univ, 65-70. *Concurrent Pos:* Fel, Med Ctr, Univ Kans, 58-59; US Food & Drug Admin fel, Univ Assoc for Res & Educ in Path; NIH fel & training grant, Univ Md; mem bd dirs, Univ Assoc for Res & Educ in Path, 70-; mem, Md Post Mortem Exam Comn, 70-; consult, US Food & Drug Admin, 71- & Vet Admin Hosp, Baltimore, Md, 72-; docent, Dept Cell Biol, Univ Jyvaskyla, Finland, 73-; Am Cancer Soc prof oncol, & dir, Md Cancer Prog, 77- *Mem:* AAAS; Am Asn Path & Bact; Am Soc Exp Path; Am Soc Cell Biol; Am Soc Microbiol. *Res:* Cellular and subcellular pathology; membrane structure and functions; lysosome structure and function; chemical carcinogenesis; kidney pathophysiology; fish physiology and pathology; environmental pathology. *Mailing Add:* Dept Path 7-34 MSTF Univ Md Sch Med 10 S Pine St Baltimore MD 21201-1192. *Fax:* 410-706-3743

**TRUMPOWER, BERNARD LEE,** BIOCHEMISTRY, YEAST MOLECULAR GENETICS. *Current Pos:* From asst prof to assoc prof, 72-82, PROF BIOCHEM, DARTMOUTH MED SCH, 82- *Personal Data:* b Chambersburg, Pa, July 20, 43; m 64. *Educ:* Univ Pittsburgh, BS, 65; St Louis Univ, PhD(biochem), 69. *Honors & Awards:* Humboldt Prize, Fed Rep Ger, 85. *Concurrent Pos:* NIH fel, Cornell Univ, 69-71; vis scientist, Whitehead Inst; chmn, Phys Biochem Study Sect, NIH, 81-84; estab investr,

Am Heart Asn. *Mem:* Fed Am Socs Exp Biol; NY Acad Sci; Am Soc Cell Biol; Genetic Soc Am. *Res:* Genetic aspects of organelle assembly with particular emphasis on genetic aspects of mammalian cell respiration and energy transduction. *Mailing Add:* Dept Biochem Dartmouth Med Sch 7200 Vail Bldg Hanover NH 03755-3844

**TRUMPY, D RUDOLF,** HISTORY OF SCIENCES. *Current Pos:* prof, Swiss Fed Inst Technol, 53-86, prof, Univ Zurich, 56-86, EMER PROF GEOL, UNIV ZURICH & SWISS FED INST TECHNOL, 86- *Personal Data:* b Glarus, Switz, Aug 16, 21; m 48; c 2. *Educ:* Swiss Fed Inst Technol, Dip (ing geol), 45, Dr, 47. *Hon Degrees:* DSc, Univ Pierre & Marie Curie, Paris, 77, Univ Lausanne, 87. *Honors & Awards:* Von Buch Medal, Deutsche Geol Gesellschaft; Penrose Medal, Geol Soc Am, 85; Suess Medal, Oesterreichische Geol Gesellschaft, 87. *Prof Exp:* Asst dept geol, Univ Lausanne, 47-53. *Concurrent Pos:* Treas, Int Union Geol Scis, 64-68, pres, 76-80; vis prof, Yale Univ, 81. *Mem:* Foreign assoc Nat Acad sci; hon mem geol Soc Am; Am Assoc Petroleum Geologist; foreign assoc Am Acad Arts & Sci; foreign assoc Acad Scis, Paris; Ger Acad Leopolidina. *Res:* Interrelation between sedimentary and structural evolution of Alps; other areas: Morocco, Spain, France, Greece; Traissic and Jurassic strutigraphy (Alps, Greenland); history of Geology. *Mailing Add:* Allmendboden 19 Kusnacht-8700 Switzerland

**TRUNEH, ALAN,** MOLECULAR BIOLOGY. *Current Pos:* ASSOC FEL IMMUNOL, SMITHKLINE BEECHAM LABS, 83- *Personal Data:* b Ethiopia, Nov 12, 51. *Educ:* Univ London, BS, 76, PhD(polymer chem), 81. *Mem:* Am Cell Biol Soc; Am Soc Immunol; Am Molecular Biol Soc; NY Acad Sci. *Mailing Add:* Immunol Dept L102 SmithKline Beecham Labs 709 Swedeland Rd King of Prussia PA 19406-0939

**TRUNK, GERARD VERNON,** ELECTRICAL ENGINEERING. *Current Pos:* head radar analysis staff, 75-79, HEAD, RADAR ANALYTICAL BR, NAVAL RES LAB, 79- *Personal Data:* b Baltimore, Md, May 9, 42. *Educ:* Johns Hopkins Univ, BES, 63, PhD(elec eng), 67. *Prof Exp:* Elec engr radar, Naval Res Lab, 67-74; vis fel elec eng, Johns Hopkins Univ, 74-75. *Concurrent Pos:* Sabatical lectr, Johns Hopkins Univ, 74- *Mem:* Sr mem Inst Elec & Electronics Engrs; Sci Res Soc Am. *Res:* Radar systems; detection and estimation theory; simulation; and pattern recognition. *Mailing Add:* Head Radar Analytical Br Naval Res Lab Radar Div Washington DC 20275

**TRUNZO, FLOYD F(RANK),** CHEMICAL ENGINEERING. *Current Pos:* RETIRED. *Personal Data:* b Apollo, Pa, Dec 3, 17; m 46; c 3. *Educ:* Univ Ala, BS, 41, MS, 47. *Prof Exp:* Observer, Process Control, Carnegie Ill Steel Corp, 41; jr engr pilot resin develop, Westinghouse Res Labs, 47-48, assoc engr wire insulation develop, 48-53, res engr, 53-62, sr res engr, 62-76, sr res scientist, 76-77, fel engr, 77-81. *Mem:* Am Chem Soc. *Res:* Wire insulation for motors, transformers and magnet wires; composite insulating materials for electrical power and generating equipment. *Mailing Add:* 106 Jamison Lane Monroeville PA 15146-2316

**TRUONG, XUAN THOAI,** PHYSICAL MEDICINE, PHYSIOLOGY. *Current Pos:* DIR RES & EDUC, INST PHYS MED & REHAB, 72- *Personal Data:* b French Cochin-China, Nov 17, 30; US citizen. *Educ:* West Liberty State Col, BS, 52; Columbia Univ, MD, 56; Univ Louisville, PhD(physiol), 64; Am Bd Phys Med & Rehab, dipl, 65; Am Bd Electrodiagnostic Med, 89. *Prof Exp:* Intern surg, Ind Univ Med Ctr, 56-57; resident phys med & rehab, Univ Louisville Hosps, 58-61, instr, Sch Med, Univ, 62-64; clin & res consult, Inst Phys Med & Rehab, 64-68; asst prof, Baylor Col Med, 68-71. *Concurrent Pos:* Clin investr, Vet Admin Hosp, Houston, 69-71; asst prof, Peoria Sch Med, Univ Ill, 72-; dir, Muscular Dystrophy Asn Clin, 78- *Mem:* Am Physiol Soc; Am Acad Phys Med & Rehab; Inst Elec & Electronics Engrs; Am Asn Electrodiag Med; Am Med Asn; Am Soc Clin Evoked Potentials. *Res:* Mechanical properties of muscle tissue; electrophysiology of neuro-muscular system; rehabilitation engineering. *Mailing Add:* 1406 W Hickory Trace Dunlap IL 61525

**TRUPIN, JOEL SUNRISE,** BIOCHEMISTRY, NUTRITION. *Current Pos:* ASSOC PROF BIOCHEM, MEHARRY MED COL, 71- *Personal Data:* b Brooklyn, NY, Mar 15, 34; m 57; c 1. *Educ:* Cornell Univ, BS, 54, MNS, 56; Univ Ill, PhD(biochem), 63. *Prof Exp:* Asst prof microbiol, Sch Med, St Louis Univ, 66-71. *Concurrent Pos:* Am Cancer Soc res fel biochem genetics, Nat Heart Inst, 63-66. *Mem:* AAAS; Am Chem Soc; Am Soc Microbiol; Am Soc Cell Biol. *Res:* Biochemistry and regulation of amino acid biosynthesis; transfer RNA; protein and amino acid nutrition; biochemistry and molecular biology of growth and metabolism of human dermal fibroblasts and of fibroblast functions relevant to normal and abnormal wound healing. *Mailing Add:* Dept Biomed Sci Meharry Med Col Nashville TN 37208-3599. *Fax:* 615-327-6084

**TRURAN, JAMES WELLINGTON, JR,** ASTROPHYSICS. *Current Pos:* PROF ASTRON ASTROPHYS, UNIV CHICAGO, 91- *Personal Data:* b Brewster, NY, July 12, 40; m 65, Carol Dellacy; c Elaina, Diana & Anastasia. *Educ:* Cornell Univ, BA, 61; Yale Univ, MS, 63, PhD(physics), 66. *Prof Exp:* Resident res assoc, Goddard Inst Space Studies, NASA, NY, 65-67; res fel physics, Calif Inst Technol, 68-69; from assoc prof to prof physics, Belfer Grad Sch Sci, 70-73; prof astron, Univ Ill, Urbana-Champaign, 73-91. *Concurrent Pos:* Mem bd contribr, Comments Astrophys & Space Physics, 73-74; ed, Contributions Nuclear & High-Energy Astrophys, Physics Lett B, 74-80; trustee, Aspen Ctr Physics, 79-85, vpres, 85-88; assoc, Ctr Advan Sci, Univ Ill; sr vis fel, Inst Astron, Univ Cambridge, Eng & Guggenheim Mem Found fel, 79-80; Alexander von Humboldt-Stiftung, Sr Scientist,

Max-Planck-Inst Astrophysics, Munich, Ger, 86-87. *Mem:* Fel Am Phys Soc; Am Astron Soc; Int Astron Union. *Res:* Nucleosynthesis; nuclear reactions in stars; mechanisms of nova and supernova explosions; stellar evolution; galactic evolution; origin of cosmic rays; white dwarfs; binary evolution. *Mailing Add:* Univ Chicago Dept Astron & Astrophys 933 E 56th St Chicago IL 60637. *E-Mail:* truran@nova.uchicago.edu

**TRUS, BENES L,** IMAGE PROCESSING. *Current Pos:* staff fel, Lab Biochem, Nat Inst Dent Res, NIH, 75-77, sr staff fel, 77-80, Res Chemist, Comput Syst Lab, Div Comput Res & Technol, NIH, 80-93, CHIEF, IMAGE PROCESSING RES SECT, COMPUT BIOSCI & ENG LAB, DIV COMPUT RES & TECHNOL, NIH, 93- *Personal Data:* b Tyler, Tex, May 9, 46; m 72, Susan Evans; c Aaron B & Anthony P. *Educ:* Tulane Univ, BS, 68; Calif Inst Technol, PhD(phys chem), 72. *Honors & Awards:* Dirs Award, NIH, 87 & 94. *Prof Exp:* Jane Coffin Childs fel, Calif Inst Technol, 72-75. *Concurrent Pos:* Researcher, Lab Struct Biol Res, Nat Inst Arthritis & Musculosketal & Skin Dis, NIH, 90- *Mem:* Sigma Xi; Micros Soc Am; NY Acad Sci. *Res:* Image processing of electron micrographs and other biomedical specimens; tree dimensional reconstructions of viruses and other macromolecular structures; structural biology; cataract detection, quantitation and classification. *Mailing Add:* Rm 2033 Bldg 12A NIH Bethesda MD 20892-5624. *E-Mail:* trus@helix.nih.gov

**TRUSAL, LYNN R,** CELLULAR PHYSIOLOGY, ELECTRON MICROSCOPY. *Current Pos:* res scientist, div path, 81-93, TECH STAFF OFFICER, US ARMY MED RES INST, 93- *Personal Data:* b Williamsport, Pa, Dec 4, 45. *Educ:* Pa State Univ, PhD(physiol), 75. *Mem:* Am Soc Cell Biol; Electron Micros Soc Am; Int Soc Toxinology. *Mailing Add:* 11212 Arrowleaf Ct Germantown MD 20876. *E-Mail:* lynntrusal@aol.com

**TRUSCOTT, FREDERICK HERBERT,** PLANT PHYSIOLOGY. *Current Pos:* from asst prof to prof, 58-88, chmn dept, 72-75, EMER PROF BIOL, STATE UNIV NY, ALBANY, 88- *Personal Data:* b Meredith, NY, Mar 16, 26; m 54; c 2. *Educ:* State Univ NY, Albany, AB, 50; Rutgers Univ, PhD(bot), 55. *Prof Exp:* Asst bot, Rutgers Univ, 52-55; res fel, Jackson Mem Lab, Bar Harbor, Maine, 55-56; instr, Univ RI, 56-58. *Mem:* Bot Soc Am; Am Soc Plant Physiologists; Am Inst Biol Sci. *Res:* Morphogenesis; photophysiology. *Mailing Add:* 18 Maynes Ave Albany NY 12203

**TRUSCOTT, ROBERT BRUCE,** VETERINARY MICROBIOLOGY. *Current Pos:* RETIRED. *Personal Data:* b Winnipeg, Man, July 9, 28; m 53; c 5. *Educ:* Univ Toronto, BSA, 50, MSA, 53, DVM, 62; Univ Waterloo, PhD(microbiol physiol), 66. *Prof Exp:* Supvr, Animal House, Univ Western Ont, 50; fermentation supvr, Merck & Co Ltd, Que, 50-51; res asst microbiol, Ont Agr Col, Guelph, 51-53; lectr poultry path, Ont Vet Col, Univ Guelph, 53-76, assoc prof vet microbiol, 69-76; res scientist, Health Animals Br, Can Dept Agr, Animal Path Lab, Sackville, NB, 77-85; res scientist, Animal Path Lab, Guelph, Ont, 85-89. *Mem:* Microbiol; Am Soc Microbiol; Am Asn Avian Pathologists; Can Vet Med Asn. *Res:* Avian salmonella; food microbiology. *Mailing Add:* 106 Dovercliffe Rd Guelph ON N1G 3A6 Can

**TRUSKEY, GEORGE A,** BIOMEDICAL ENGINEERING. *Current Pos:* ASST PROF BIOMED ENG, DUKE UNIV, 87- *Personal Data:* b Plainfield, NJ, Feb 14, 57. *Educ:* Univ Pa, BS, 79; Mass Inst Technol, PhD(chem eng), 85. *Prof Exp:* Asst prof chem eng, Tufts Univ, 85-87; vis res fel exp path, Brigham & Womens Hosp, 86-87. *Mem:* Am Inst Chem Engrs; NY Acad Sci; Am Chem Soc; AAAS; Biomed Eng Soc. *Mailing Add:* 908 W Markham Ave Durham NC 27701-1514

**TRUSSELL, HENRY JOEL,** COLOR MEASUREMENT & REPRODUCTION, DETECTION & ESTIMATION THEORY. *Current Pos:* assoc prof, 80-86, PROF ELEC ENG, NC STATE UNIV, 86- *Personal Data:* b Atlanta, Ga, Feb 3, 45; m 68; c 2. *Educ:* Ga Inst Technol, BS, 67; Fla State Univ, MS, 68; Univ NMex, PhD(elec eng & comput sci), 76. *Honors & Awards:* Sr Paper Award, Inst Elec & Electronics Engrs, 86. *Prof Exp:* Mem staff, Los Alamos Sci Lab, 69-80. *Concurrent Pos:* Adj prof, Univ NMex, 77; vis prof, Heriot-Watt Univ, Edinburgh, Scotland, 78-79. *Mem:* Inst Elec & Electronics Engrs; Optical Soc Am; Inter-Soc Color Coun. *Res:* Image processing; restoration, enhancement and pattern recognition; color image processing; scanning, restoration and reproduction. *Mailing Add:* ECE Dept NC State Univ PO Box 7911 Raleigh NC 27695-7911. *Fax:* 919-515-5523; *E-Mail:* hjt@ecehjt.ncsu.edu

**TRUSSELL, PAUL CHANDOS,** BACTERIOLOGY. *Current Pos:* CONSULT, 80- *Personal Data:* b Vancouver, BC, July 4, 16; m 43, Helen V Dreyer; c Devin B & Richard P. *Educ:* Univ BC, BSA, 38; Univ Wis, MS, 42, PhD(agr bact), 43. *Prof Exp:* Chief res microbiologist, Ayerst, McKenna & Harrison, Ltd, Montreal, Que, 44-47; head, Div Appl Biol, 47-61, dir, BC Res Coun, Vancouver, 61-80. *Mem:* Sigma Xi. *Res:* Agricultural bacteriology; industrial fermentations; marine borer control; industrial coatings; food spoilage; water pollution; bacteriological leaching of ores; forestry; research administration; pelleting forest and agricultural seeds. *Mailing Add:* 15270 17th Ave 202 White Rock BC V4A 1T9 Can

**TRUSSELL, R(OBERT) RHODES,** DRINKING WATER REUSE & DISINFECTION. *Current Pos:* staff, Montgomery Watson Inc, 72-76, vpres, 77-86, sr vpres, 86-88, dir appl technol, 88-92, SR VPRES & DIR CORP DEVELOP, MONTGOMERY WATSON INC, 92- *Personal Data:* b National City, Calif, Jan 8, 45; m 69, Elizabeth Shane; c Robert & Charles B. *Educ:* Univ Calif, Berkeley, BSCE, 66, MS, 67, PhD(civil eng), 72.

Concurrent Pos: Mem, Comt Water Treatment Chem, Nat Acad Sci, 80-82, US/Dutch Res Comt, Organics in Water, 82-83, US/Ger Res Comt, Corrosion Water Systs, 84-85 & Am Water Works Comn, 88-90; chmn, Comt Disinfection, Int Water Supply Asn, 94-, mem, Sci & Tech Coun, 94- Mem: Nat Acad Eng; Sigma Xi; Nat Asn Corrosion Engrs; Int Water Pollution Res Asn; Int Water Supply Asn; Am Chem Soc; Am Inst Chem Engrs; Water Works Asn; Water Pollution Control Fedn. Mailing Add: Montgomery Watson 300 N Lake Ave Suite 1200 Pasadena CA 91101-4106

**TRUST, RONALD I,** PROJECT MANAGEMENT, RESEARCH ADMINISTRATION. Current Pos: DIR PROJ MGT & ADMIN, ENZON INC, 93- Personal Data: b Philadelphia, Pa, May 23, 47; m 69, Arlene Sherman; c Phyllis & Paul. Educ: Drexel Univ, BS, 69; Calif Inst Technol, PhD(org chem), 74; Fairleigh Dickenson, MBA, 86. Prof Exp: Res & develop chemist, Ciba Geigy Corp, 73-74; res chemist, Am Cyanamid Co, 74-77, sr res chemist, 77-80, mgr overseas clin mat, 80-84, clin trials mat coordr, 84-86, clin trials coordr, 86-88, mgr, Clin Res Assocs, 88-90, asst dir, global coord oncol, 90-92, asst dir regulatory affairs, 92-93. Mem: Am Chem Soc; Assocs Clin Pharmacol; Drug Info Asn; AAAS; Int Photodynamic Asn; NY Acad Sci. Res: Taking chemical compounds from laboratory curiosity to medical reality; involved in laboratory testing, manufacturing and human testing of chemical compounds; photodynamic therapy; global coordination; oncology; regulatory affairs project management. Mailing Add: Pfizer Cent Res Regulatory Affairs Eastern Point Rd Groton CT 06340

**TRUST, TREVOR JOHN,** MICROBIOLOGY. Current Pos: from asst prof to assoc prof, 69-80, PROF MICROBIOL, UNIV VICTORIA, BC, 81- Personal Data: b Melbourne, Australia, June 24, 42. Educ: Univ Melbourne, BSc, 64, MSc, 66, PhD(microbiol), 69. Prof Exp: Lectr microbiol, Royal Melbourne Inst Technol, 69. Concurrent Pos: Vis res fel, Southampton Fac Med, 77-78. Mem: Can Soc Microbiol; Am Soc Microbiol; Brit Soc Gen Microbiol. Res: Fish diseases; molecular basis for bacterial virulence and immunogenicity; campylobacter, salmonella and enteric pathogens. Mailing Add: Astra Res Ctr Boston Inc 128 Sidney St Cambridge MA 02139

**TRUSZKOWSKA, KRYSTYNA,** SURFACE SCIENCE PHYSICS. Current Pos: SR ANALYSIS ENGR, GE MED SYST CORP, MILWAUKEE, 86- Personal Data: b Stare Rochowice, Poland. Educ: Univ Wroclaw, Poland, MS, 70; Tech Univ Wroclaw, PhD(solid state physics), 77. Prof Exp: Asst prof physics, Inst Physics, Tech Univ Wroclaw, Poland, 77-80 & Inst Physics, Univ Nat Autonoma, Mex, 81-83; res assoc, Dept Physics & Lab Surface Studies, Univ Wis-Milwaukee, 83-86. Concurrent Pos: Lectr, Dept Physics, Univ Wis-Milwaukee, 84-85. Mem: Am Phys Soc; Am Vacuum Soc. Res: New materials for optical interference coatings; structural characterization of thin metal films by electron microscopy; absorption and reactions of gases at solid surfaces; optics of thin solid films; mechanical engineering; physics engineering. Mailing Add: GE Med Systs PO Box 414 MC EA-36 Milwaukee WI 53201

**TRUXAL, FRED STONE,** SCIENCE ADMINISTRATION. Current Pos: cur entom, 52-61, chief cur, 61-82, EMER CHIEF CUR, LIFE SCI DIV, LOS ANGELES CO MUS NATURAL HIST, 82- Personal Data: b Great Bend, Kans, Feb 20, 22; m 43; c 2. Educ: Univ Kans, AB, 47, MA, 49, PhD(entom), 52. Prof Exp: Agent, Bur Entom & Plant Quarantine, USDA, 42; asst instr biol & entom, Univ Kans, 47-52. Concurrent Pos: Asst to state entomologist, Kans, 48-51; asst prof, Ottawa Univ, Kans, 51-52; adj prof, Univ Southern Calif, 57-82; biol consult, Pac Horizons; mem expeds, Mex, Cent Am, Brazil, Peru, Australia & Africa. Mem: Fel AAAS; Entom Soc Am; Soc Syst Zool; Sigma Xi. Res: Biology, ecology and taxonomy of aquatic Hemiptera. Mailing Add: Los Angeles Co Mus Natural Hist 900 Expos Blvd Los Angeles CA 90007-4057

**TRUXAL, JOHN G(ROFF),** ELECTRICAL ENGINEERING, COMMUNICATIONS. Current Pos: dean eng & appl sci, State Univ NY, Stony Brook, 72-76, prof, 76-77, distinguished teaching prof, 77-91, DISTINGUISHED TEACHING EMER PROF, STATE UNIV NY, STONY BROOK, 91- Personal Data: b Lancaster, Pa, Feb 19, 24; m 49; c 2. Educ: Dartmouth Col, AB, 44; Mass Inst Technol, BS, 47, DSc, 50. Hon Degrees: DE, Purdue Univ, 64 & Ind Inst Technol, 71. Honors & Awards: Lanchester Award, Opers Res Soc Am; Westinghouse Award, Am Soc Eng Educ. Prof Exp: Teaching & res asst, Mass Inst Technol, 46-50; from asst prof to assoc prof, Purdue Univ, 50-54; assoc prof, Polytech Inst Brooklyn, 54-57, prof & head dept, 57-61, vpres ed develop, 61-64, dean eng, 64-66, provost, 66-71. Concurrent Pos: Prin investr res grants, NSF, Alfred P Sloan Found & other govt & pvt agencies, 62-; co-dir, Eng Concepts Curric Proj, 65-74; mem, Pres Sci Adv Comt, 70-72; mem, Vis Comt, Nat Bur Stand, 72-76, var comts, Nat Acad Eng & Nat Res Coun & World Bk Phys Sci Comt, 83-90; dir, Nat Coord Ctr Curric Develop, State Univ NY, Stony Brook, 76-85 & Stony Brook Ctr New Lib Arts Prog & prin investr, State Univ Ny Res Found, 91-; chmn, Comt Pub Understanding Sci, AAAS, 79-82; mem, Coun Understanding Technol Human Affairs, chmn, 82-84. Mem: Nat Acad Eng; fel AAAS; Am Soc Eng Educ; fel Inst Elec & Electronics Engrs; fel Instrument Soc Am (pres, 65-66); Sigma Xi. Res: Network theory; feedback control systems; author of various publications. Mailing Add: Prog Technol & Soc State Univ NY Stony Brook NY 11794-2250

**TRUXILLO, STANTON GEORGE,** GEOPHYSICS. Current Pos: PETROL GEOPHYSICIST, AMOCO PROD CO, 81- Personal Data: b New Orleans, La, June 23, 41; m 65; c 2. Educ: Loyola Univ, La, BS, 63; La State Univ, Baton Rouge, PhD(physics), 69. Prof Exp: Fel, Coastal Studies Inst, La State Univ, Baton Rouge, 68-70; from ast prof to prof physics, Univ Tampa, 70-81. Concurrent Pos: Am Coun Educ Fel, 77-78. Mem: Am Phys Soc; Soc Explor Geophysicists; Southeastern Geophys Soc; Sigma Xi. Res: Time-dependent rotating fluid dynamics; fluid dynamics of circulatory system; acoustics. Mailing Add: 18219 Farnsfield Dr Houston TX 77084-2364

**TRYFIATES, GEORGE P,** BIOCHEMISTRY, CANCER. Current Pos: from asst prof to assoc prof, 67-83, PROF BIOCHEM, SCH MED, WVA UNIV, 83- Personal Data: b Mesolongi, Greece, Feb 26, 35; US citizen; m 59; c 4. Educ: Univ Toledo, BS, 58; Bowling Green State Univ, MA, 59; Rutgers Univ, PhD(biochem), 63. Prof Exp: Teaching & res asst biol, Bowling Green State Univ, 58-59; res asst biochem, Rutgers Univ, 59-62; res assoc, Grad Sch Med, Univ Pa & Sch Med, Temple Univ, 62-64; res biochemist, P Lorillard Co, NC, 64-66; instr pharmacol, Sch Med, Duke Univ, 66-67, assoc, 67. Concurrent Pos: USPHS trainee, Grad Sch Med, Univ Pa & Sch Med, Temple Univ, 62-64, USPHS grants, Nat Cancer Inst; ed, J Nutr Growth & Cancer. Mem: AAAS; Am Chem Soc; Soc Exp Biol & Med; Am Inst Nutrit; Am Soc Biochem & Molecular Biol; Am Asn Cancer Res. Res: Enzyme regulation in vivo and in vitro; novel tumor products and synthesis; nutritional oncology; tumor markers; cancer detection. Mailing Add: Dept Biochem WVa Univ Sch Med Health Sci Ctr-N PO Box 9142 Morgantown WV 26506-9142. Fax: 304-293-6946

**TRYON, EDWARD POLK,** HIGH ENERGY PHYSICS, COSMOLOGY. Current Pos: from asst prof to assoc prof, 71-79, PROF PHYSICS, HUNTER COL, CITY UNIV NY, 79- Personal Data: b Terre Haute, Ind, Sept 4, 40. Educ: Cornell Univ, AB, 62; Univ Calif, Berkeley, PhD(physics), 67. Prof Exp: Res assoc physics, Columbia Univ, 67-68, asst prof, 68-71. Concurrent Pos: Vis mem, Inst Advan Study, Princeton, 77-78; Sigma Xi Nat Lectr, 82-84. Mem: Am Phys Soc; NY Acad Sci; Sigma Xi. Res: Gravitational interactions; high energy theory; pion-pion interaction; origin of universe. Mailing Add: Dept Physics Hunter Col Hunter Col City Univ NY 695 Park Ave New York NY 10021

**TRYON, JOHN G(RIGGS),** ENGINEERING PHYSICS. Current Pos: chmn dept, 80-84, prof, 75-86, EMER PROF ELEC ENG, UNIV NEV, LAS VEGAS, 86- Personal Data: b Washington, DC, Dec 18, 20; m 48; c 2. Educ: Univ Minn, BS, 41; Cornell Univ, PhD(eng physics), 52. Prof Exp: Mem tech staff, Bell Tel Labs, Inc, 51-58; prof elec eng & head dept, Univ Alaska, 58-69; prof, Tuskegee Inst, 69-75. Mem: Am Phys Soc; Inst Elec & Electronics Engrs; Am Solar Energy Soc; Sigma Xi; Am Soc Eng Educ. Mailing Add: 631 Ave I Boulder City NV 89005-2729

**TRYON, ROLLA MILTON, JR,** BOTANY. Current Pos: CUR, HERBARIUM, UNIV SFLA, 89- Personal Data: b Chicago, Ill, Aug 26, 16; m 45. Educ: Univ Chicago, BS, 37; Univ Wis, PhM, 38; Harvard Univ, MS, 40, PhD(bot), 41. Prof Exp: Lab technician, Chem Warfare Serv, Mass Inst Technol, 42; instr bot, Dartmouth Col, 42, lab technician, 43-44; instr bot, Univ Wis, 44-45; asst prof plant taxon, Univ Minn, 45-48; assoc prof, Washington Univ, St Louis, 48-57; cur, herbarium & cur ferns, Gray Herbarium Harvard Univ, 58-89, prof biol, 72-89. Concurrent Pos: Cur, Herbarium, Minneapolis, Minn, 46-48; asst cur herbarium, Mo Bot Garden, 48-57. Mem: Am Soc Plant Taxon; Am Fern Soc; Bot Soc Am. Res: Taxonomy of pteridophytes; Doryopteris; Pteridium; ferns and fern allies of Wisconsin, Minnesota and Peru. Mailing Add: 11410 Robles Del Rio Temple Terrace FL 33617

**TRYON, WARREN W,** PSYCHOLOGY. Current Pos: From asst prof to assoc prof, 70-83, PROF PSYCHOL, FORDHAM UNIV, 83- Personal Data: b 1944; m 70, Georgiana Shick; c Elizabeth. Educ: Ohio Northern Univ, BA, 66; Kent State Univ, MA, 69, PhD, 70; Am Bd Prof Psychol, dipl. Mem: Am Psychol Asn; Asn Advan Behav Ther; NY State Psychol Asn. Res: Measurement of human activity under ambulatory conditions; therapy based on operant and respondent conditioning principles; tremor and other dyskinesias. Mailing Add: Dept Psychol Fordham Univ Bronx NY 10458-5198. Fax: 718-817-3785; E-Mail: wtryon@murray.fordham.edu

**TRYPHONAS, HELEN,** IMMUNOTOXICOLOGY, FOOD ALLERGY. Current Pos: supvr microbiol, 74-77, biologist II immunol, 77-82, SCIENTIST II IMMUNOTOXICOL, HEALTH & WELFARE CAN, 82- Personal Data: b Greece, June 21, 39; m 62; c 2. Educ: Univ Sask, BSc, 68, MSc, 72, PhD, 95. Prof Exp: Dept asst microbiol, West Col Vet Med, Univ Sask, 72-74. Res: Immunotoxicity studies of food additives and environmental contaminants in man and experimental animals; the casual relationship of food allergies to behavioral abnormalities in children. Mailing Add: Toxicol Res Div Bur Food Chem Health Protection Br Health & Welfare Tunney's Pasture PL2202D1 Ottawa ON K1A 0L2 Can

**TRYTTEN, GEORGE NORMAN,** MATHEMATICS. Current Pos: RETIRED. Personal Data: b Pittsburgh, Pa, Apr 21, 28; m 52; c 5. Educ: Luther Col, Iowa, AB, 51; Univ Wis, MS, 53; Univ Md, PhD(math), 62. Prof Exp: Asst math, Univ Wis, 51-53; asst, Inst Fluid Dynamics & Appl Math, Univ Md, 53-57; mathematician, US Naval Ord Lab, 57-62; res assoc math, Inst Fluid Dynamics & Appl Math, Univ Md, College Park, 62-63, from res asst prof to res assoc prof, 63-69, assoc dean sponsored res & fels, Grad Sch, 67-69; vpres, Math Sci Group, Inc, 69-70; free-lance filmstrip producer, 70-71; prof math & chmn dept, Hood Col, 71-72; from assoc prof to prof math, Luther Col, Iowa, 72-93. Mem: Am Math Soc; Math Asn Am. Res: Partial differential equations; fluid dynamics; numerical solution of partial differential equations; celestial mechanics. Mailing Add: 903 Fifth Ave Decorah IA 52101

**TRYTTEN, ROLAND AAKER,** CHEMISTRY. Current Pos: RETIRED. Personal Data: b Tower City, NDak, Oct 15, 13; m 42, Lorene A Thompson; c Katherine, Judith, Myrtle J, Christine, Nurl & Lorne. Educ: St Olaf Col, AB, 35; Univ Wis, PhD(chem), 41. Prof Exp: Control chemist, Kimberly-Clark Corp, 41-42; instr chem, Ripon Col, 42-45; instr, Cent State Teachers Col,

45-51, chmn dept, 49-51; chmn dept, Univ Wis-Stevens Point, 51-72, prof chem, 51-83. *Mem:* Am Chem Soc. *Res:* Foams; foaming tendency of aqueous aliphatic alcohol solutions; sulfur dioxide determination in polluted air. *Mailing Add:* 2809 Algoma St Stevens Point WI 54481-2835

**TRZASKOMA, PATRICIA POVILITIS,** ELECTROCHEMISTRY, SURFACE REACTIONS. *Current Pos:* RES CHEMIST, NAVAL RES LAB, WASHINGTON, DC, 79- *Personal Data:* b New York, NY, 1940; c Megan & Todd. *Educ:* Barnard Col, BA, 61; Am Univ, MS, 72, PhD(chem), 76. *Prof Exp:* Anal chemist, Gen Dynamics, 61-62; res chemist fuel cell res, Apollo Prog, Pratt & Whitney Aircraft Corp, 62-65; asst prof chem, George Mason Univ, 77-85. *Concurrent Pos:* Deleg, Pre-White House Conf Libr & Info Sci. *Mem:* Electrochem Soc; Am Chem Soc. *Res:* Electrochemistry with emphasis on kinetics of electrode surface reactions; fast reaction kinetics; corrosion behavior of aluminum; passivation and inhibition of metals and composites; coating development such as ion-implantation; chemical safety. *Mailing Add:* Code 6310-2 Naval Res Lab Washington DC 20375. *E-Mail:* treaskoma@anvm.navy.hil

**TRZCIENSKI, WALTER EDWARD, JR,** GEOLOGY, MATH. *Current Pos:* PROF GEOL, UNIV MONTREAL, 81- *Personal Data:* b Montague City, Mass, Sept 19, 42; m 65; c 1. *Educ:* Bowdoin Col, AB, 65; McGill Univ, PhD(geol), 71. *Prof Exp:* NASA fel, Princeton Univ, 71; asst prof geol, Brooklyn Col, 71-72; from asst prof to assoc prof, Ecole Polytech, Montreal, 72-81. *Mem:* Am Math Soc; Geol Soc Am; Mineral Soc Am; Mineral Asn Can; Mineral Soc; Am Geophys Union. *Res:* Metamorphic and igneous petrology and mineralogy-geochemistry, especially in the northern Appalachians. *Mailing Add:* 2001 Breezeway Ave Dorval PQ H9S 1C7 Can. *Fax:* 514-343-5782; *E-Mail:* trzwalt@ere.umontreal.ca

**TSAGARIS, THEOFILOS JOHN,** internal medicine, cardiology; deceased, see previous edition for last biography

**TSAI, ALAN CHUNG-HONG,** NUTRITION. *Current Pos:* asst prof, 73-76, ASSOC PROF NUTRIT, UNIV MICH, ANN ARBOR, 76- *Personal Data:* b Chang-hua Hsien, Taiwan, June 18, 43; m 69; c 2. *Educ:* Taiwan Prov Chung Hsing Univ, BS, 66; Wash State Univ, MS, 69, PhD(nutrit), 72. *Prof Exp:* Res assoc nutrit, Mich State Univ, 72-73. *Mem:* Am Inst Nutrit; NY Acad Sci. *Res:* Cholesterol feeding associated metabolic alterations including enzyme activities; microsomal activities; tissue lipid peroxidation and insulin metabolism; nutrition of dietary fiber, its effect on cholesterol metabolism and gastrointestinal functions; interaction of vitamin E and the function of thyroid hormones; metabolic effects of exercise training and detraining. *Mailing Add:* Human Nutrit Prog Univ Mich M5158 SPH II Ann Arbor MI 48109-0001. *Fax:* 313-764-5233

**TSAI, BILIN PAULA,** CHEMICAL PHYSICS. *Current Pos:* from asst prof to assoc prof, 76-92, assoc dean, Col Sci & Eng, 83-87, PROF CHEM, UNIV MINN, DULUTH, 92-, DEPT HEAD, 92- *Personal Data:* b Seattle, Wash, May 23, 49; m 77, Don Poe; c 2. *Educ:* Univ Chicago, BS, 71; Univ NC, Chapel Hill, PhD(chem physics), 75. *Prof Exp:* Res assoc chem physics, Univ Nebr, Lincoln, 75-76. *Mem:* Sigma Xi; Am Chem Soc. *Res:* Physical chemistry; gas phase ion fluorescence spectroscopy; photoionization; chemical dynamics. *Mailing Add:* Dept Chem Univ Minn Duluth MN 55812

**TSAI, BOH CHANG,** POLYMER SCIENCE, CHEMICAL ENGINEERING. *Current Pos:* SR SUPVR MATS SCI, AM CAN CO, 82- *Personal Data:* b Taiwan, China, Jan 2, 44; US citizen; m 69; c 2. *Educ:* Nat Taiwan Univ, BS, 67; Univ Akron, MS, 70, PhD(polymer sci), 73. *Prof Exp:* Staff mat engr polymer processing, Acushnet Co, 73-78. *Concurrent Pos:* Fel, Inst Polymer Sci, Univ Akron, 73-78; vis lectr polymer sci, Southeastern Mass Univ, 75-76. *Mem:* Am Chem Soc; Rheology Soc. *Res:* Interaction of structure-property-processing of polymeric materials. *Mailing Add:* 647 Thompson's Way Palatine IL 60067

**TSAI, CHESTER E,** ALGEBRA. *Current Pos:* from asst prof to assoc prof, 64-78, PROF MATH, MICH STATE UNIV, 78- *Personal Data:* b Amoy, China, Mar 7, 35; m 62; c 2. *Educ:* Nat Taiwan Univ, BA, 57; Marquette Univ, MS, 61; Ill Inst Technol, PhD(math), 64. *Prof Exp:* Instr math, Ill Inst Technol, 62-64. *Concurrent Pos:* Consult, World Bank Proj. *Mem:* Am Math Soc; Math Asn Am. *Res:* Non-associative algebra. *Mailing Add:* Dept Math 8212 Wells Hall Mich State Univ East Lansing MI 48824-0001

**TSAI, CHIA-YIN,** NITROGEN & CARBOHYDRATE METABOLISM. *Current Pos:* PROF GENETICS, NAT TAIWAN UNIV, 96- *Personal Data:* b Taichung, Taiwan, Dec 15, 37; m 67, Hsueh C Chen; c Henry & Susan. *Educ:* Nat Taiwan Univ, BS, 60; Purdue Univ, Lafayette, PhD(genetics), 67. *Prof Exp:* Res asst genetics, Purdue Univ, West Lafayette, 63-67, res assoc, 67-69, from asst prof to prof, 69-96. *Concurrent Pos:* Vis prof, Inst Bot, Acad Sinica, Taiwan, 76, Dept Bot, Nat Taiwan Univ, 92 & 94; mem, NIH panel, 81-85. *Mem:* Am Soc Plant Physiologists; Crop Sci Soc Am. *Res:* Carbohydrate metabolism and storage protein synthesis in maize; nutritional quality of protein and grain yield potential of maize; ammonium assimilation in maize roots; maize hybrid response to nitrogen fertility. *Mailing Add:* Dept Bot Nat Taiwan Univ Taipei 107 Taipei Taiwan

**TSAI, CHING-LONG,** SOLID STATE PHYSICS, MATERIALS SCIENCE ENGINEERING. *Current Pos:* res specialist, 84-92, SR RES SPECIALIST, 3M, 92- *Personal Data:* b Kaohsiung, Taiwan, May 25, 45; m 73, Yueh-Meei Peng; c Evan, Ethan & Andrew. *Educ:* La State Univ, PhD(physics), 76. *Prof Exp:* Res & teaching asst physics, La State Univ, 71-76; res assoc, Ill Inst Technol, 76-78; physicist, Nat Standards Co, 78-80; sr scientist, Northeastern Univ, 80-84. *Concurrent Pos:* Vis scientist, Mass Inst Technol, 82-84. *Mem:* Am Phys Soc; Am Inst Metall Engrs; Inst Elec & Electronics Engrs. *Res:* Low temperature solid state physics; material preparations and characterizations; rapid quenching technology; metallic glasses; magnetic materials. *Mailing Add:* 8010 Somerset Road Woodbury MN 55125. *Fax:* 612-736-5409; *E-Mail:* CTSAI@MMM.COM

**TSAI, CHISHIUN S,** BIOCHEMISTRY, ENZYMOLOGY. *Current Pos:* from asst prof to assoc prof, 65-76, PROF CHEM & BIOCHEM, CARLETON UNIV, 76- *Personal Data:* b Chia-yi, Taiwan, Dec 19, 33; m 65. *Educ:* Nat Taiwan Univ, BS, 56; Purdue Univ, MS, 61, PhD(biochem), 63. *Prof Exp:* Fel chem, Cornell Univ, 63; fel biosci, Nat Res Coun Can, 63-64, asst res officer, 64-65. *Concurrent Pos:* Res assoc, Univ Tex, 72; vis sci, Foxchase Cancer Res Inst, 73. *Mem:* Am Chem Soc; Can Biochem Soc; Am Soc Biol Chemists. *Res:* Function and reactivity of enzymes in relation with the structures of enzymes; substrates and inhibitors. *Mailing Add:* Dept Chem & Biochem Carleton Univ 1125 Colonel By Dr Ottawa ON K1S 5B6 Can

**TSAI, CHUANG-CHUANG,** SOLID STATE PHYSICS, SEMICONDUCTOR DEVICES. *Current Pos:* TECH PROG MGR, DPIX, A XEROX CO, 96- *Personal Data:* b Taipei, Taiwan; US citizen; c 2. *Educ:* Nat Taiwan Univ, BS, 72; Univ Chicago, MS, 73, PhD(physics), 79. *Prof Exp:* Mem res staff, Xerox Corp, Palo Alto Res Ctr, 78-96. *Mem:* Am Phys Soc; Mat Res Soc; Inst Elec & Electronics Engrs; Soc Info Display. *Res:* Active matrix liquid crystal display (AMLCD) and medical imaging technology; amorphous, microcrystalline and polycrystalline silicon materials and devices; plasma-enhanced chemical vapor deposition. *Mailing Add:* dpix a Xerox Co 3406 Hillview Ave Palo Alto CA 94304. *E-Mail:* tsai@dpix.com

**TSAI, CHUN-CHE,** PHYSICAL CHEMISTRY, BIOCHEMISTRY. *Current Pos:* asst prof chem, 76-80, ASSOC PROF CHEM, KENT STATE UNIV, 80- *Personal Data:* b Chiayi, Taiwan, China, Sept 17, 37; US citizen; m 63; c 3. *Educ:* Cheng-Kung Univ, Taiwan, BS, 60; Ind Univ, Bloomington, PhD(chem), 68. *Prof Exp:* Fel crystallog, Univ Pa, 68-69; fel bio-crystallog, Cornell Univ, 69-71; res chemist phys chem, Univ Colo, Boulder, 71-72; sr res assoc biophys chem & molecular biol, Univ Rochester, 72-76. *Concurrent Pos:* Res fac mem, Dept Microbiol & Immunol, Col Med, Northeastern Ohio Univ, 78- *Mem:* Am Chem Soc; Am Biophys Soc; Am Crystallog Asn; AAAS; Sigma Xi; Int Soc Antiviral Res. *Res:* Biological crystallography; drug-nucleic acid interactions; structure and function of nucleic acids; molecular associations and interactions in biological systems; quantitative structure-activity relationships. *Mailing Add:* Dept Chem Kent State Univ PO Box 5190 Kent OH 44242-0001. *Fax:* 330-672-3816

**TSAI, CHUNG-CHIEH,** RESIN TRANSFER MOLDING. *Current Pos:* prod develop specialist, 84-88, sr res chemist, 88-91, SR STAFF SCIENTIST, ASHLAND OIL CO, 91- *Personal Data:* b Taiwan, Oct 1, 48; c 3. *Educ:* Nat Cheng Kung Univ, Taiwan, BS, 71; Univ Mass, Lowell, MS, 77, PhD(chem), 80. *Prof Exp:* Lab instr chem, Nat Cheng Kung Univ, 73-74; res asst polymer, Univ Lowell, 75-79; res chemist polymer, Stauffer Chem Co, 79-84. *Mem:* Am Chem Soc; Soc Plastic Engrs. *Res:* Polyelectrolytes; unsaturated polyesters; vinyl esters; polyurethane; thermosets; polyester recycle; reactive polymers. *Mailing Add:* PO Box 45 Dublin OH 43017-0045

**TSAI, FRANK Y,** TECHNICAL MANAGEMENT, SCIENCE ADMINISTRATION. *Current Pos:* sr engr, HUD, 75-79, SR TECH ADVISOR, FED EMERGENCY MGT AGENCY, 79- *Personal Data:* b China; US citizen; m 64; c 2. *Educ:* Univ Minn, MS, 60, PhD(eng). *Prof Exp:* Res fel, St Anthony Falls Hydraul Lab, 60-68; asst prof, Iowa State Univ, 68-72; sect chief, Ebasco Serv Inc, 72-75. *Mem:* Sigma Xi; Am Soc Civil Engrs. *Res:* Flood insurance; hydromechanics; ocean and coastal engineering; risk assessment. *Mailing Add:* 522 S Larrimore St Arlington VA 22204

**TSAI, GOW-JEN,** FERMENTATION, PURIFICATION & PRODUCT RECOVERY. *Current Pos:* SR RES BIOCHEM ENGR, WYETH-AYERST RES, 96- *Personal Data:* b Tainan, Taiwan, Apr 20, 55; m 85, Chen-Yin Lai; c Victor & Stephanie. *Educ:* Nat Cheng Kung Univ, BS, 77; Nat Taiwan Univ, MS, 79; Purdue Univ, PhD(chem eng), 86. *Prof Exp:* Res assoc, Purdue Univ, 86-88, group leader, Lab Renewable Resources Engr, 88-91; sr res biochem engr, Am Cyanamid Co, 91-95. *Mem:* Am Inst Chem Engrs; Am Chem Soc. *Res:* Fermentation process development to produce antibiotics, therapeutic proteins and anticancer drugs; biochemical engineering and chemical reaction engineering. *Mailing Add:* 401 N Middletown Rd Pearl River NY 10965. *E-Mail:* tsaig@war.wyeth.com

**TSAI, JAMES HSI-CHO,** MYCOPLASMOLOGY, PLANT VIROLOGY. *Current Pos:* from asst prof to assoc prof, 73-84, PROF ENTOM, UNIV FLA, 84- *Personal Data:* b Fuzhou, Fujian, China, June 10, 34; US citizen; m 60, Sue C; c 2. *Educ:* Nat Chung Hsing Univ, Taiwan, BS; Mich State Univ, MS, PhD(entom). *Prof Exp:* Scientist entom, Int Inst Trop Agr, Nigeria, 69-70; res assoc entom, Mich State Univ, 70-72. *Concurrent Pos:* Vis prof, Shaanxi Acad Agr Sci, China, 81 & Chinese Acad, Beijing, 84. *Mem:* Entom Soc Am; Am Phytopath Soc; Int Orgn Citrus Virologists; Int Orgn Mycoplasmology; Ecol Soc China. *Res:* Plant prokaryotic diseases; vector-pathogen-host relationships; ecology and control of vector borne diseases. *Mailing Add:* Ft Lauderdale Res & Educ Ctr 3205 College Ave Ft Lauderdale FL 33314

**TSAI, JIR SHIONG,** INTERNAL MEDICINE, ENDOCRINOLOGY. *Current Pos:* ASSOC PROF CLIN MED, DEPT MED, NY UNIV MED CTR, 75- *Educ:* Nat Taiwan Univ, MD, 65. *Mailing Add:* 550 First Ave 4S New York NY 10016-6451

**TSAI, KUEI-WU,** SOILS, FOUNDATION ENGINEERING. *Current Pos:* From asst prof to assoc prof, 67-76, chmn dept, 81-89, PROF CIVIL ENG, SAN JOSE STATE UNIV, 76-, ASSOC DEAN ENG, 94- *Personal Data:* b Taiwan, Jan 22, 41; m 69, Leslie Wang; c Felix & Gordon. *Educ:* Nat Taiwan Univ, BSCE, 62; Princeton Univ, MSCE & MA, 65, PhD(soils eng), 67. *Concurrent Pos:* Proj engr, Dames & Moore, 69-74, sr engr, 74-75, consult, 75- *Mem:* Fel Am Soc Civil Engrs. *Res:* Shear strength of clays; slope stability; settlement; land reclamation and development; penetrometer method; difficult foundation problems; design of dams; soils investigation and foundation recommendation; site improvement; diaphragm wall construction. *Mailing Add:* Dept Civil Eng San Jose State Univ Washington Sq San Jose CA 95192. *Fax:* 650-941-8488

**TSAI, LIN,** ORGANIC CHEMISTRY. *Current Pos:* vis scientist, 59-62, ORG CHEMIST, NAT HEART, LUNG & BLOOD INST, 62- *Personal Data:* b Hong Kong, May 30, 22; US citizen. *Educ:* Chinese Nat Southwest Assoc Univ, BSc, 46; Univ Ore, MA, 49; Fla State Univ, PhD(org chem), 54. *Prof Exp:* Res assoc chem, Ohio State Univ, 54-57; res scientist, Worcester Found Exp Biol, 57-59. *Mem:* Am Chem Soc; Royal Soc Chem; Am Soc Biochem & Molecular Biol. *Res:* Syntheses, reactions and microbial degradations of heterocyclic compounds; stereochemistry of enzymic reactions. *Mailing Add:* Bldg 3 Rm 110 Nat Heart Lung & Blood Inst Bethesda MD 20892-0320. *Fax:* 301-496-0599

**TSAI, LUNG-WEN,** ROBOT MANIPULATORS & MACHINE DESIGN. *Current Pos:* assoc prof, 86-90, PROF MECH ENG, UNIV MD, 90- *Personal Data:* b Taipei, Taiwan, Feb 20, 45; US citizen; m 71; c 2. *Educ:* Nat Taiwan Univ, BS, 67; State Univ NY, MS, 70; Stanford Univ, PhD(mech eng), 73. *Honors & Awards:* Melville Medal, Am Soc Mech Engrs, 85, Mechanisms Comt Award, 84; Campbell Award, Gen Motors Res Labs, 86; A T Colwell Merit Award, Soc Automotive Engrs, 88; Award of Merit, Proctor & Gamble, 89 & 91. *Prof Exp:* Develop engr, Hewlett-Packard Corp, 73-78; sr staff res engr, Power Syst Res Dept, Gen Motors Corp, 78-86. *Mem:* Fel Am Soc Mech Engrs; Soc Automotive Engrs. *Res:* Design methodology; kinematics and dynamics of machinery; robotics; automotive engineering; electro-mechanical systems. *Mailing Add:* Mech Eng Dept Univ Md College Park MD 20742. *Fax:* 301-405-6707; *E-Mail:* lwtsai@src.umd.edu

**TSAI, MING-DAW,** BIOCHEMISTRY, ORGANIC CHEMISTRY. *Current Pos:* from asst prof to assoc prof, 86-90, PROF CHEM, OHIO STATE UNIV, 90- *Personal Data:* b Taiwan, Repub China, Sept 1, 50; US citizen; m 76; c 3. *Educ:* Nat Taiwan Univ, BS, 72; Purdue Univ, PhD(biochem), 78. *Prof Exp:* Postdoctoral assoc, Purdue Univ, 78-79, vis asst prof, 79-80; asst prof chem, Rutgers Univ, 80-81. *Concurrent Pos:* Alfred P Sloan fel, 83-85; Camille & Henry Dreyfus Teacher Scholar, Dreyfus Found, 85-90; mem, Phys Biochem Study Sect, NIH, 88-92. *Mem:* Am Chem Soc; Am Soc Biochem & Molecular Biol; AAAS; Sigma Xi. *Res:* Chemical basis of enzyme catalysis; structure-function relationship of proteins; mechanism of adenylate kinase and phospholipase A2; synthesis of phosphatidylinositides. *Mailing Add:* Dept Chem Ohio State Univ 120 W 18th Rm 100 Columbus OH 43210-1173

**TSAI, MING-JER,** BIOCHEMISTRY, MOLECULAR BIOLOGY. *Current Pos:* from instr to assoc prof, 73-87, PROF CELL BIOL, BAYLOR COL MED, 88- *Personal Data:* b Taichung, Taiwan, Nov 3, 43; m 71, Sophia Yang; c Linus T & Peter T. *Educ:* Nat Taiwan Univ, BS, 66; Univ Calif, Davis, PhD(biochem), 71. *Prof Exp:* Damon Runyon fel, Univ Tex M D Anderson Hosp & Tumor Inst Houston, 71-73. *Mem:* Am Soc Cell Biol; Sigma Xi; Am Soc Microbiol; Endocrinol Soc; Am Soc Biochem & Molecular Biol; Soc Chinese Bioscientists Am. *Res:* Hormonal regulation of gene expression; chromatin structure; precursors of mRNA and their processing; initiation of RNA synthesis by DNA-dependent RNA polymerases; development and differentiation. *Mailing Add:* Dept Cell Biol Baylor Col Med One Baylor Plaza Houston TX 77030-3498. *Fax:* 713-790-1275

**TSAI, MING-JONG,** OPTOELECTRONICS, SEMICONDUCTORS. *Current Pos:* VPRES, RES & DEVELOP DIV, LITE-ON INC, 88- *Personal Data:* b Taiwan, Aug 25, 50; US citizen; c 1. *Educ:* Nat Tsing Hwa Univ, Taiwan, BS, 72; Stanford Univ, MS, 77, PhD(mat sci & eng), 79. *Prof Exp:* Engr res & develop, Am Microsyst Inc, 79-80; engr & supvr res & develop, Hewlett-Packard, 80-84; dir eng, Compound Semiconductor, Inc, 84-86, vpres eng, 86-88. *Mem:* Inst Elec & Electronics Engrs. *Res:* Compound semiconductor materials and devices for the optoelectronics applications. *Mailing Add:* 37074 Penzance Common Fremont CA 94536

**TSAI, STEPHEN W,** MECHANICS. *Current Pos:* RES PROF, DEPT AERONAUT & ASTRONAUT, STANFORD UNIV, CALIF, 90- *Personal Data:* b Beijing, China, July 6, 29; US citizen; m 54; c 2. *Educ:* Yale Univ, BE, 52, DEng(mech), 61. *Prof Exp:* Proj engr, Foster Wheeler Corp, 52-58; dept mgr mat res, Aeronutronic Div, Philco Corp, 61-66; prof eng, Wash Univ, 66-68; chief scientist, Wright-Patterson AFB, 68-76, scientist, Air Force Mat Lab, 76-90. *Concurrent Pos:* Lectr, Univ Calif, Los Angeles, 65-66; ed-in-chief, J Composite Mat, 66-; ed, Int J Fibre Sci & Technol, 68-; affil prof, Wash Univ, 68-; Battelle vis prof, Ohio State Univ, 69. *Mem:* Nat Acad Eng; Sigma Xi; Am Phys Soc; Soc Rheol; Am Inst Aeronaut & Astronaut. *Res:* Mechanics of composite materials for structural applications. *Mailing Add:* 101 Alma St Apt 703 Palo Alto CA 94301

**TSAI, TSUI HSIEN,** pharmacology, for more information see previous edition

**TSAI, WEN-YING,** MECHANICAL ENGINEERING. *Current Pos:* RETIRED. *Personal Data:* b Xiamen, China, Oct 13, 28; nat US; m 68, Pei-De Chang; c Lun-yi & Ming Yi. *Educ:* Univ Mich, BSME, 53. *Prof Exp:* Consult engr, 53-63; proj mgr, Consentini Assoc, 62-63. *Concurrent Pos:* Proj engr, Guy B Panero Engrs, 56-60; John Hay Whitney fel, 63; Macdowell fel, 65; Ctr Advan Studies fel, Mass Inst Technol, 69-70. *Res:* Creator cybernetic sculpture based on principal harmonic motion, stroboscopic effects; creator spatial dynamic hydro-cybernetic systems; creator of first CD-ROM version of cybernetic sculpture; inventor upward falling fountain, computer mural, multiple light computer array, utilizing environment, feedback control systems. *Mailing Add:* 7 E 19th St New York NY 10003-9999

**TSAI, Y(U)-M(IN),** ENGINEERING MECHANICS. *Current Pos:* from asst prof to assoc prof eng mech, 67-77, PROF ENG MECH, IOWA STATE UNIV, 77- *Personal Data:* b Taiwan, Formosa, Mar 31, 37; m 63; c 1. *Educ:* Taipei Inst Technol, Taiwan, dipl civil eng, 57; Univ Tenn, ScM, 62; Brown Univ, ScM, 64, PhD(eng), 67. *Prof Exp:* Res assoc eng, Brown Univ, 66-67. *Concurrent Pos:* Nat Sci Found res initiation grants, 69-70. *Mem:* Sigma Xi. *Res:* Elasticity; stress waves; fracture mechanics. *Mailing Add:* Dept Eng Mech Iowa State Univ 2019 M E/E SM Bldg Ames IA 50011-2162

**TSAI, YUNG SU,** THEORETICAL PHYSICS, ELEMENTARY PARTICLE PHYSICS. *Current Pos:* Res assoc theoret physics, Stanford Univ, 59-61, asst prof, 61-63, SR STAFF MEM THEORET PHYSICS, STANFORD LINEAR ACCELERATOR CTR, STANFORD UNIV, 63- *Personal Data:* b Yuli, Taiwan, Feb 1, 30; US citizen; m 61; c 2. *Educ:* Nat Taiwan Univ, BS, 54; Univ Minn, MS, 56, PhD(physics), 58. *Mem:* Am Phys Soc; Sigma Xi. *Res:* Energy loss and straggling due to ionization; bremsstrahlung and pair productions; radiative corrections to scatterings; properties of tay leptons; physics of electron-positron collision; non linear effects in laser electron interaction. *Mailing Add:* 2508 Fairbrook Dr Mountain View CA 94040

**TSALIOVICH, ANATOLY,** ELECTROMAGNETIC COMPATIBILITY, ELECTRONIC CABLES. *Current Pos:* DISTINGUISHED MEM TECH STAFF, AT&T BELL LABS, 85- *Personal Data:* b USSR, 1936; US citizen. *Educ:* Odessa Elec Telecommun Inst, USSR, BSEE & MSEE, 60; Leningrad Elec Telecommun Inst, USSR, PhD(transmission lines & electromagnetic shielding), 66. *Honors & Awards:* Richard R Stoddard Award, Inst Elec & Electronics Engrs, Electromagnetic Compatibility Soc, 89. *Prof Exp:* Sr scientist & group mgr, Cent Res Telecommun Inst, USSR, 66-79; prod develop engr, Belden Corp, 80-84; fel engr, Thomas & Betts Corp, 84-85. *Concurrent Pos:* Assoc prof, Leningrad Elec Telecommun Inst, USSR, 63-79; tech translator, Scripta Technika, US & Kabelnaya Technika, USSR, 64-89; lectr & consult, Ctr Prof Advan, US-Neth, 85- *Mem:* Inst Elec & Electronics Engrs. *Res:* Electromagnetic compatibility; electromagnetic shielding; electronic and telephone cables; telecommunications lines and carrier systems; operations research application to telecommunications; radio frequency absorbers. *Mailing Add:* AT&T Bell Labs 101 Crawford Corners Rd PO Box 3030 Holmdel NJ 07733

**TSAN, MIN-FU,** HEMATOLOGY, NUCLEAR MEDICINE. *Current Pos:* ASSOC CHIEF STAFF RES & DEVELOP, ALBANY VET ADMIN MED CTR, 82-, PROF MED & PHYSIOL, ALBANY MED COL, 82- *Personal Data:* b Taiwan, Jan 27, 42; m 75, Linda Chen; c Gloria & Grace. *Educ:* Nat Taiwan Univ, MB, 67; Harvard Univ, PhD(physiol), 71; Am Bd Internal Med, dipl, 75, dipl hemat, 78; Am Bd Nuclear Med, dipl, 76. *Honors & Awards:* Sci Award, Chinese Am Med Soc, 90. *Prof Exp:* Intern med, Nat Taiwan Univ Hosp, 66-67; med officer, Chinese Navy, 67-68; med intern, Boston Vet Admin Hosp, 71-72; med resident, 72-73, fel hematol, Johns Hopkins Hosp, 73-75; asst prof med, radiol & radiol sci, Med Sch & asst prof environ health, Sch Pub Health & Hyg, Johns Hopkins Univ, 75-79, assoc prof med, radiol & radiol sci, Med Sch & assoc prof environ health, Sch Pub Health & Hyg, 79-82. *Concurrent Pos:* Pres, Albany Res Inst, Inc, 89- *Mem:* AAAS; Am Fedn Clin Res; Am Soc Hematol; Soc Exp Biol & Med; Am Physiol Soc. *Res:* Oxygen radical-induced tissue injury. *Mailing Add:* Res Serv Dept Vet Affairs Med Ctr 113 Holland Ave Albany NY 12208. *Fax:* 518-462-0626; *E-Mail:* tsan.min-fu@albany.va.gov

**TSANDOULAS, GERASIMOS NICHOLAS,** ELECTRICAL ENGINEERING. *Current Pos:* GROUP LEADER, SPACE RADAR TECHNOL GROUP, LINCOLN LAB, MASS INST TECHNOL, 82- *Personal Data:* b Preveza, Greece, Aug 14, 39; m 64, 74. *Educ:* Harvard Univ, BA, 61, BS, 63; Univ Pa, PhD(elec eng), 67. *Prof Exp:* Engr, Kel Corp, Mass, 63-64; staff mem antenna res, Mass Inst Technol, 67-74, staff scientist, EM Tech Group, 74-77, syst engr, Airborne Radar Group, Lincoln Lab, 77-79; asst leader & leader, ARPA Lincoln C-Band Observable Radar, US Army, Krems & Kwajalein, Marshall Islands, 79-81. *Mem:* AAAS; fel Inst Elec & Electronics Engrs; Sigma Xi. *Res:* Electromagnetic scattering and diffraction; antennas and arrays; wave propagation; radar systems; airborne moving target indicator radar; space based radar technology. *Mailing Add:* PO Box 510 APO AP San Francisco CA 96555

**TSANG, CHARLES PAK WAI,** ENDOCRINOLOGY, MOLECULAR BIOLOGY. *Current Pos:* RES SCIENTIST REPRODUCTIVE PHYSIOL, POULTRY ENDOCRINOL ANIMAL RES CTR, 71- *Personal Data:* Can citizen; c 3. *Educ:* McGill Univ, BSc, 61, MSc, 65, PhD(steroid biochem), 68. *Prof Exp:* Staff scientist, Worcester Found Exp Biol, 68-70; fel steroid & cyclic necleotide protein-binding assays, Queen Mary Hosp, Montreal, 70-71. *Concurrent Pos:* Res grant, Japan Soc Prom Sci, Nagoya Univ. *Mem:* Poultry Sci Asn; Can Soc Animal Sci; World's Poultry Sci; fel Japan Soc Prom Sci. *Res:* Hormonal control of egg production and shell quality in the hen; estrogens, vitamin D and calcium metabolism; gene expression for calcium binding protein synthesis. *Mailing Add:* Agr & Agr Food Can Ctr Food & Animal Res 930 Carling Ave Bldg 34 Rm 20 Ottawa ON K1A 0C5 Can. *Fax:* 613-943-2352

**TSANG, DEAN ZENSH,** OPTOELECTRONICS, OPTICAL INTERCONNECTIONS. *Current Pos:* STAFF MEM, LINCOLN LAB, MASS INST TECHNOL, 81- *Personal Data:* b Detroit, Mich, Aug 13, 52. *Educ:* Mass Inst Technol, SB, 74, ScD, 81; Univ Ill Urbana-Champaign, MS, 76. *Concurrent Pos:* Chmn, Cent New Eng, Inst Elec & Electronics Engrs Lasers & Electro-Optics Soc, 87-88, mem chapters comt, 88-92, eng comt, 89-93, chmn mem comt, 91-; bd electors, Sigma Xi. *Mem:* Sr mem Inst Elec & Electronics Engrs; Optical Soc Am. *Res:* Optical interconnections; semiconductor diode lasers, especially high speed dynamics; q-switched diode lasers; optoelectronic devices. *Mailing Add:* 34F Beacon St Burlington MA 01803-3814. *E-Mail:* tsang@ll.mit.edu

**TSANG, GEE,** FLUID MECHANICS, ICE ENGINEERING. *Current Pos:* RETIRED. *Personal Data:* b Macao, Mar 29, 38; Can citizen; m 70, M Potin lee; c Cindy & Cemaine. *Educ:* Univ New South Wales, BE, 63, MEngSc, 65; Univ Waterloo, PhD(fluid mech), 68. *Prof Exp:* Asst engr, New South Wales Water Conserv & Irrig Comn, 63-64; tech officer, Water Res Lab, Univ New South Wales, 64-65; instr fluid mech, Univ Guelph, 68-69; res assoc air pollution, Mass Inst Technol, 69-70; asst prof fluid mech & dynamics, Univ Guelph, 70-72; res scientist, Can Ctr Inland Waters, 72-90; res scientist, Nat Hydrol Res Inst, 90- *Concurrent Pos:* Vis scholar, Univ Cambridge, 86-87. *Mem:* Int Asn Hydraul Res; NY Acad Sci. *Res:* Air and water pollution; atmospheric diffusion; hydraulics of cold regions; ice mechanics; micrometeorology; oil spill containment and recovery technology; ice and hydraulics; cold weather hydraulic instrument development; lake rehabilitation. *Mailing Add:* Nat Hydrol Res Inst 11 Innovation Blvd Saskatoon SK S7N 3H5 Can. *Fax:* 306-975-5143

**TSANG, JAMES CHEN-HSIANG,** SOLID STATE PHYSICS. *Current Pos:* Res staff mem semiconductor physics, IBM Res Ctr, 73-83, IBM T J WATSON RES CTR, IBM CORP, 83- *Personal Data:* b New York, NY, June 1, 46. *Educ:* Mass Inst Technol, BS & MS, 68, PhD(elec eng), 73. *Mem:* Fel Am Phys Soc; fel Soc Photo-Optical Instrumentation Engrs. *Res:* Raman spectroscopy of solids and surfaces; optical spectroscopy of solids; time resolved spectroscopy. *Mailing Add:* IBM T J Watson Res Ctr PO Box 218 Rm 29-153 Ossining NY 10598

**TSANG, JOSEPH CHIAO-LIANG,** MICROBIAL BIOCHEMISTRY. *Current Pos:* from asst prof to assoc prof, 68-78, PROF CHEM & BIOCHEM, ILL STATE UNIV, 78-; HEAD DEPT APPL BIOL & CHEM TECHNOL, HONG KONG POLYTECH, KOWLOON, 87- *Personal Data:* b Hong Kong, Oct 11, 36; US citizen; m 69. *Educ:* Grantham Teachers Col, Hong Kong, dipl, 58; Univ Okla, BS, 62, MS, 65, PhD(biochem), 68. *Prof Exp:* Res asst, Okla Med Res Found, 64-68. *Concurrent Pos:* Adj prof, Peoria Sch Med, Univ Ill, 73-; prof biochem, Med Sch, Jinan Univ, China, 80-; vis prof biochem, Univ Hong Kong, 83-84 & 85-86. *Mem:* Am Chem Soc; Roayl Soc Chem; Am Soc Microbiol; fel Am Inst Chemists. *Res:* Biochemical and pharmacological studies of Serratia marcescens as a bacterium causing nosocomial diseases: role of the pigment, prodigiosin, in the stability of the cell envelope and transfer of R-plasmids; interactions of antibiotics and surfactants with the outer membrane components such as lipopolysaccharides and phospholipids. *Mailing Add:* 1317 E Washington St Bloomington IL 61701-4228

**TSANG, KANG TOO,** PLASMA PHYSICS. *Current Pos:* SR RES PHYSICIST, SCI APPLICATIONS, INC, 81- *Personal Data:* b Hong Kong. *Educ:* Chinese Univ Hong Kong, BSc, 70; State Univ NY, Stony Brook, MA, 71; Princeton Univ, PhD(plasma physics), 74. *Prof Exp:* Res staff plasma physics, Oak Ridge Nat Lab, 74-81. *Concurrent Pos:* Adj prof, Nuclear Eng Dept, NC State Univ, Raleigh, 78. *Mem:* Am Phys Soc. *Res:* Theoretical investigation of equilibrium, stability and transports in thermonuclear plasma. *Mailing Add:* 8820 Charles Hawkins Way Annandale VA 22003. *Fax:* 703-821-1134

**TSANG, LEUNG,** ELECTROMAGNETICS, OPTICAL PHYSICS. *Current Pos:* PROF ELEC ENG, UNIV WASH, 83- *Personal Data:* b Hong Kong, China, July 5, 50; US citizen; m 78, Wan; c Clarisse & Kaleb. *Educ:* Mass Inst Technol, BS, 71, MS, 73, PhD(elec eng), 76. *Prof Exp:* Res engr acoust, Schlumberger Doll Res Ctr, 76-78; res assoc elec eng, Mass Inst Technol, 78-80; prof elec eng, Tex A&M Univ, 80-83. *Concurrent Pos:* Assoc ed, Trans Geosci & Remote Sensing, Inst Elec & Electronics Engrs, 87-95 & Radio Sci, Am Geophys Union, 88-92; ed, Trans Geosci & Reomote Sensing, Inst Elec & Electronics Engrs, 96- *Mem:* Fel Inst Elec & Electronics Engrs; Am Geophys Union; fel Optical Soc Am; Am Phys Soc. *Res:* Developing theoretical models of wave propagation in random media and application to remote sensing; study of nonlinear optical properties of compound semiconductors; coauthor of one book; develop fast algorithm for solution of electromagnetics. *Mailing Add:* Elec Eng Dept Univ Wash FT-10 Seattle WA 98195. *Fax:* 206-543-3842

**TSANG, PETER H S,** CHEMICAL ENGINEERING, SPECIALTY MATERIALS. *Current Pos:* MGR ENG, ALLIED SIGNAL BRAKING SYSTS, 69- *Personal Data:* b Meishien, China, 1942. *Educ:* Hong Kong Baptist Col, BS, 63; Sul Ross Univ, MS, 64; Univ Houston, PhD(phys org chem), 69. *Mem:* Sigma Xi; Am Chem Soc. *Mailing Add:* Allied Signal 900 W Maple Rd Troy MI 48084

**TSANG, REGINALD C,** NEONATOLOGY, NUTRITION. *Current Pos:* from asst prof to assoc prof, 71-79, dir, Fels Div Pediat Res, 74-76, PROF PEDIAT & OBSTET & GYNEC, UNIV CINCINNATI, 79-, DAVID G & PRISCILLA R GAMBLE PROF NEONATOLOGY, 87- *Personal Data:* b Hong Kong, Sept 20, 40; US citizen; m 66; c 2. *Educ:* Univ Hong Kong, MBBS, 66. *Prof Exp:* Intern med & surg, Queen Mary Hosp, Hong Kong Univ, 64-65; resident pediat, 65-66; resident psychiat, Hong Kong Psychiat Hosp, 65; intern pediat & med, Michael Reese Hosp, Chicago, 66-67; resident pediat, 67-68, fel neonatology, 68-69; fel, Cincinnati Gen Hosp & Childrens Hosp, 69-71. *Concurrent Pos:* Attend pediatrician, Childrens Hosp, Cincinnati & NIH grant neonatal mineral metab, Nat Inst Child Health & Human Develop, 71-; attend pediat, Cincinnati Gen Hosp, 71-; dir, perinatal neonatology training, NIH, 78-, Diabetes prog PPG, 78-, Div Neonatology, 83-, Perinatal Res Inst, 86-, chief, Ctr Growth Retardation PERC, 85- *Mem:* Am Fedn Clin Res; Soc for Pediat Res; Am Soc Clin Nutrit; Am Pediat Soc; Perinatal Res Soc; Am Soc for Bone Mineral Res; NY Acad Sci; Nat Perinatal Asn; Endocrine Soc; fel Am Col Nutrit (secy-treas, 79-85, vpres, 85-86, pres, 89-91). *Res:* Pathophysiology of disturbances in calcium-phosphate-magnesium homeostasis in the neonate; examination of parathyroid hormone, vitamin D, glucagon and calcitonin; diabetic pregnancy; pediatric hyperlipoproteinemia; identification and prevention of premature atherosclerosis. *Mailing Add:* Dept Pediat/Neonatology Univ Cincinnati Univ Hosp Med Ctr Rm 6165 231 Bethesda Ave ML 541 Cincinnati OH 45267-0541. *Fax:* 513-558-0770

**TSANG, TUNG,** PHYSICAL CHEMISTRY, SOLID STATE PHYSICS. *Current Pos:* assoc prof, 69-75, PROF PHYSICS, HOWARD UNIV, 75- *Personal Data:* b Shanghai, China, Aug 17, 32; US citizen; m 57, Dolly; c Susan. *Educ:* Ta-Tung Univ, China, BS, 49; Univ Minn, MS, 52; Univ Chicago, PhD(chem), 60. *Prof Exp:* Chemist, Minneapolis-Honeywell Regulator Co, 52-56; asst chemist, Argonne Nat Lab, 60-64, assoc chemist, 64-67; phys chemist, Nat Bur Stand, 67-69. *Concurrent Pos:* Nat Acad Sci-Nat Res Coun sr res fel, NASA Goddard Space Flight Ctr, 75-76; consult, Naval Res Lab, 83- *Mem:* Am Phys Soc. *Res:* Magnetic resonance and susceptibility; statistical physics; photoelectron spectroscopy; superconductivity. *Mailing Add:* Dept Physics Howard Univ Washington DC 20059

**TSANG, VICTOR CHIU WAN,** PARASITE IMMUNOLOGY, DIAGNOSTIC ASSAYS. *Current Pos:* res chemist, 77-88, CHIEF IMMUNOL & MOLECULAR BIOL ACTIVITY, CTR DIS CONTROL, CTR INFECTIOUS DIS, DIV PARASITIC DIS, 88-, CHIEF, IMMUNOL BR, 92- *Personal Data:* b Hong Kong, June 20, 47; US citizen; m 72; c 1. *Educ:* ETex Baptist Col, BS, 67; Stephen F Austin State Univ, MS, 69; Notre Dame Univ, 72; Univ Ga, Athens, PhD(parasitic biochem immunol), 76. *Honors & Awards:* Distinguished Serv Award, US Dept Health & Human Serv, 89; Kimble Methodology Award, 92. *Prof Exp:* Postdoctoral parasitic biochem immunol, Univ Ga, Athens, 76-77. *Concurrent Pos:* Adj prof, Dept Biol, Natural Sci Col, Univ PR, 86-89; collab scientist, Div Pathobiol, Yerkes Regional Primate Res Ctr, Emory Univ, 86-; assoc, Dept Int Health, Sch Hyg & Pub Health, Johns Hopkins Univ, 89-; adj prof, Dept Chem, Ga State Univ, 89-, Dept Cell Biol & Dept Parasitol, Univ Ga, 92- *Mem:* Am Asn Immunol; Am Soc Parasitol; Am Soc Trop Med & Hyg. *Res:* Quantitative immunological assay systems; diagnostic assay invention for infectious diseases; human immunovirus; helminthis diseases; immunochemistry; schistosomiasis; cysticercosis; biologically active co-polymers; cryptosyzoridiosis. *Mailing Add:* Ctr Dis Control NCID DPD Immunol Br Mail Stop F13 Atlanta GA 30341-3724. *Fax:* 770-488-4109; *E-Mail:* vct1@cdc.gov

**TSANG, WAI LIN,** SATELLITE NAVIGATION, HIGH PERFORMANCE COMPUTING. *Current Pos:* SR ENGR NAVIG, SCI APPLN INT CORP, 88- *Personal Data:* b Toishan, Kwangtung, June 3, 51; US citizen; m 85; c 2. *Educ:* Northeastern Univ, BS, 74, MS, 75, PhD(elec eng), 81. *Prof Exp:* Asst prof, Northeastern Univ, 80-81; systs engr navig, Intermetrics Inc, 81-82; res engr commun, GTE Sylvania CSD, 82-86; mem tech staff C3I systs, Mitre Corp, 86-88. *Concurrent Pos:* Consult, Intermetrics Inc, 82-83; mem, Radio Tech Comn Aeronaut, 86-, Airlines Electronic Eng Comt, 89-, Air Traffic Tech Comt, 91- *Mem:* Sr mem Am Inst Aeronaut & Astronaut; sr mem Inst Elec & Electronics Engrs; Inst Navig. *Res:* Satellite navigation and communications; technology assessment studies on supercomputer; biotechnology; high dcfinition television; lithography; development of signal processing algorithms with applications to synthetic aperture radar, estimation/filtering, and electromagnetic interference. *Mailing Add:* 13414 Ellicott An Ct Herndon VA 20171

**TSANG, WON,** SEMICONDUCTOR LASER. *Current Pos:* Mem tech staff, 76-84, head, Electrophotonics Res Dept, 84-87, HEAD, SEMICONDUCTOR ELECTRONICS RES DEPT & FEL, AT&T BELL LABS, 87- *Personal Data:* b Oct 24, 50; m; c 3. *Educ:* Ga Inst Tech, BS, 71; Univ Calif, Berkeley, MS, 73, PhD(elec eng), 76. *Honors & Awards:* Adolph Lomb Medal, Optical Soc Am, 82; David Sarnoff Award, Inst Elec & Electronics Engrs, 94. *Concurrent Pos:* Mem, Nat Technol Develop Rep China, Taiwan, 85; mem, Comt Technol Eval Japanese Optoelectronics & Microelectronics, US Dept Com & NSF, 85; consult, Space Vacuum Epitaxy Ctr, Univ Houston & NASA, 87-91. *Mem:* Fel Inst Elec & Electronics Engrs; fel Am Phys Soc; fel Optical Soc Am; Electrochem Soc; Mat Res Soc; AAAS. *Res:* Management of semiconductor laser research and development; optoelectronic devices and material growth; author of 397 publications and granted 38 patents. *Mailing Add:* AT&T Bell Labs Rm 7B216 600 Mountain Ave Murray Hill NJ 07974

**TSANKOV, MINCHO A,** MICROWAVE PHYSICS & TECHNIQUE, MICROWAVE FERRITE DEVICES. *Current Pos:* sr staff scientist, 94-96, VPRES, FERRITE PROD, SIERRA MICROWAVE TECHNOL INC, 97- *Personal Data:* b Sofia, Bulgaria, Apr 25, 46; m 71, Rositsa Antonova; c Nadia & Alex. *Educ:* Tech Univ, Bulgaria, MS, 69, Bulgarian Acad Sci,

PhD(physics), 76; Sofia Univ, BS, 78. *Prof Exp:* Engr, Bulgarian Acad Sci, 69-72, res assoc, 72-89, sr res assoc & assoc prof, 89-91, head, Dept Microwave Magnetics, 89-91; vis prof, Colo State Univ, 91-94. *Concurrent Pos:* Consult, Elec Eng Dept, Colo State Univ, 91-94. *Mem:* Inst Elec & Electronics Engrs. *Res:* Theory and design of microwave ferrite devices; theoretical and experimental study of nonlinear waves in ferromagnetic films; microwave methods for measuring dielectric and ferromagnetic materials; nondestructive testing. *Mailing Add:* 1 Sierra Way Georgetown TX 78626. *E-Mail:* mincho@ix.netcom.com

**TSAO, BANG-HUNG,** CVD DIAMOND FILM-SILICON CARBON SEMICONDUCTOR MATERIAL & SILICON CARBON AS DIELECTRIC MATERIAL, THERMONIC ENERGY CONVERSION. *Current Pos:* SR SCIENTIST, K SYST, 95- *Personal Data:* b Taipei, Taiwan, Jan 10, 57; c Victor & Max. *Educ:* Nat Cheng Kung Univ, BS, 80; Ariz State Univ, MS, 86, PhD(mat sci), 89. *Prof Exp:* Mat specialist, Energy Resource Res, 82-83; scientist, UES, Inc, 89-95. *Concurrent Pos:* Consult, Forensic Eng, Inc, 86-89; prin investr, Ues, Inc, 89-90 & 92-94, co investr, 90-92. *Mem:* Minerals, Metals & Mat Soc; Am Soc Mat. *Res:* Principal investigator for CVD diamond film for insulator and electronic devices at the power semi-conductor technology section at the aero propulsion and power directorate; silicon carbon as dielectric material for advanced capacitor; electrical contact and diamond and silicon carbon film for electronic application. *Mailing Add:* 1522 Marsetta Dr Dayton OH 45432. *Fax:* 937-253-9386

**TSAO, CHEN-HSIANG,** ASTROPHYSICS. *Current Pos:* VIS SCHOLAR, ROANOKE COL, 95- *Personal Data:* b Shanghai, China, Jan 21, 29; US citizen; m 57, Florence Chiang; c Clinton & Daniel. *Educ:* Univ Wash, Seattle, BS, 53, MS, 56, PhD(physics), 61. *Prof Exp:* Res assoc particle physics, Univ Wash, Seattle, 56-60, res instr, 60-61; res assoc high energy physics, Enrico Fermi Inst Nuclear Studies, Univ Chicago, 61-65; Nat Acad Sci-Nat Res Coun resident res assoc fel, E O Hulbert Ctr Space Res, US Naval Res Lab, 65-67, res physicist, 67-95. *Concurrent Pos:* Chap pres, Naval Res Lab, 86-87. *Mem:* Am Phys Soc; Sigma Xi. *Res:* High energy particle interactions; cosmis-ray origin; radiation shielding; semiempirical proton-nucleus and nucleus-nucleus cross section. *Mailing Add:* Code 4154 US Naval Res Lab Washington DC 20375. *Fax:* 202-764-6473; *E-Mail:* tsao@osse.nrl.navy.mil

**TSAO, CHIA KUEI,** MATHEMATICAL STATISTICS. *Current Pos:* RETIRED. *Personal Data:* b China, Jan 14, 22; m 52, Ying Wang; c Anna, Marilyn, John & Josephine. *Educ:* Univ Ore, MA, 50, PhD(math statist), 52. *Prof Exp:* Asst math, Univ Ore, 48-52; from instr to assoc prof, Wayne State Univ, 52-63, prof math, 63-87. *Mem:* Am Math Soc; Math Asn Am; Inst Math Statist. *Res:* Nonparametric statistics. *Mailing Add:* 2254 Belmont Rd Ann Arbor MI 48104-2822

**TSAO, CHING H,** MECHANICAL ENGINEERING. *Current Pos:* RETIRED. *Personal Data:* b China, Nov 16, 20; US citizen; m 52; c 2. *Educ:* Chiao Tung Univ, BS, 41; Mich State Univ, MS, 48; Ill Inst Technol, PhD(eng mech), 52. *Prof Exp:* Asst prof civil eng, Univ Southern Calif, 53-55; res engr, Hughes Aircraft Co, 55-61; head, Stress Anal Sect, Aerospace Corp, 61-65; assoc prof to prof mech eng, Calif State Univ, Long Beach, 65-87. *Mem:* Am Soc Eng Educ; Soc Exp Stress Anal; Am Inst Aeronaut & Astronaut; Sigma Xi. *Res:* Theoretical and experimental stress. *Mailing Add:* Dept Mech Eng Calif State Univ Long Beach CA 90840

**TS'AO, CHUNG-HSIN,** PHYSIOLOGY, EXPERIMENTAL PATHOLOGY. *Current Pos:* asst prof, 73-75, assoc prof, 75-80, PROF PATH, MED SCH, NORTHWESTERN UNIV, CHICAGO, 80- *Personal Data:* b Nanking, China, 33; m 62; c 3. *Educ:* Tunghai Univ, Taiwan, BS, 60; Ind Univ, Bloomington, MA, 61; Yale Univ, PhD(physiol), 66. *Prof Exp:* Res assoc hemat, Montefiore Hosp & Med Ctr, 66-67; res assoc physiol, Sch Med, Univ Chicago, 67-72, asst prof path, 68-72. *Concurrent Pos:* Dir path, Coagulation Lab, Chicago Northwestern Mem Hosp, 73- *Mem:* AAAS; Am Soc Hemat; NY Acad Sci; Int Soc Thrombosis & Haemostasis; Am Soc Exp Path. *Res:* Experimental thrombosis; vascular morphology and function. *Mailing Add:* Dept Path Wesley Pavilion Northwestern Univ Mem Hosp 303 E Superior St Chicago IL 60611-3053. *Fax:* 312-908-6010

**TSAO, CONSTANCE S,** BIOCHEMISTRY. *Current Pos:* sr res scientist, 76-79, dir, Dept Physiochem, 79-82, DIR, NUTRIT BIOCHEM & CANCER RES, LINUS PAULING INST SCI & MED, 82- *Personal Data:* b Hong Kong, China, July 27, 34; US citizen; m 75. *Educ:* Tex Woman's Univ, BS, 62; Cornell Univ, PhD(chem), 67. *Prof Exp:* Res fel, Harvard Med Sch, 69-70; res sci, Tyco Lab, Inc, 70-73, Arthur D Little, Inc, 73-75. *Concurrent Pos:* Fel, Brandeis Univ, 67-69. *Mem:* NY Acad Sci; Am Chem Soc; Health Physics Soc. *Res:* Metabolism of vitamin C; biochemistry, nutrition, and cancer research; interaction of vitamins with mineral nutrients and neural chemicals; vitamins status and enzyme functions. *Mailing Add:* Linus Pauling Inst 440 Page Mill Rd Palo Alto CA 94306-2025

**TSAO, FRANCIS HSIANG-CHIAN,** BIOCHEMISTRY, ORGANIC CHEMISTRY. *Current Pos:* fel pulmonary dis, 74-76, asst scientist, 76-83, ASSOC SCIENTIST RES LUNG SURFACTANT, UNIV WIS, 83- *Personal Data:* b China, July 22, 36. *Educ:* Taiwan Chung Hsing Univ, BS, 61; Dalhousie Univ, MS, 66; Iowa State Univ, PhD(biochem), 72. *Prof Exp:* Anal chemist qual control, Biotech Indust, London, Ont, 67-68; fel lipolytic enzymes, Univ Chicago, 72-74. *Concurrent Pos:* Pediat award, Spec Ctr Res, NIH, 81-86. *Mem:* Sigma Xi; Am Chem Soc; Am Soc Biol Chemists. *Res:* Metabolism of lung surfactant phospholipids. *Mailing Add:* Dept Pediat Univ Wis Meriter Hosp 202 S Park St Madison WI 53715. *Fax:* 608-267-6377

**TSAO, GEORGE T,** CHEMICAL ENGINEERING, MICROBIOLOGY. *Current Pos:* PROF CHEM ENG, PURDUE UNIV, 77- *Personal Data:* b Nanking, China, Dec 4, 31; m 60; c 3. *Educ:* Nat Taiwan Univ, BSc, 53; Univ Fla, MSc, 56; Univ Mich, PhD(chem eng), 60. *Prof Exp:* Asst prof physics, Olivet Col, 59-60; chem engr, Merck & Co, Inc, 60-61; res chemist, Tenn Valley Authority, 61-62; sect leader hydrolysis & fermentation, Res Dept, Union Starch & Refining Co, Inc Div, Miles Labs, Inc, 62-65, asst res dir, 65-66; from assoc prof to prof chem eng, Iowa State Univ, 66-77. *Mem:* Am Chem Soc; Am Inst Chem Engrs; Am Soc Eng Educ. *Res:* Biological technology; fermentation; agricultural and natural products utilization; waste disposal; organic synthesis; industrial carbohydrates; process development; enzyme engineering. *Mailing Add:* Sch Eng Chem Purdue Univ West Lafayette IN 47907-9980

**TSAO, JEFFREY YEENIEN,** CRYSTAL GROWTH, THIN FILM MATERIALS. *Current Pos:* MEM TECH STAFF, 84-91, TECH MGR, SANDIA NAT LABS 91- *Personal Data:* b Santa Monica, Calif, May 27, 55; m 79, Sylvia; c Emil & Eugene. *Educ:* Stanford Univ, BS, 77, MS, 77; Harvard Univ, MS, 81, PhD(appl physics), 81. *Prof Exp:* Mem tech staff, Lincoln Lab, Mass Inst Technol, 81-84. *Mem:* Am Phys Soc; Mat Res Soc; Am Vacuum Soc. *Res:* Fundamental aspects of crystal growth; economics of scientific research. *Mailing Add:* Orgn 1126 Sandia Nat Labs PO Box 5800 Albuquerque NM 87185-0601

**TSAO, KEH CHENG,** mechanical engineering, for more information see previous edition

**TSAO, MAKEPEACE UHO,** CHEMISTRY. *Current Pos:* prof, 67-82, EMER PROF SURG, UNIV CALIF, DAVIS, 82- *Personal Data:* b Shanghai, China, Aug 28, 18; nat US; m 47; c 4. *Educ:* Univ Tatung, BS, 37; Univ Mich, MS, 41, PhD(pharmaceut chem), 44. *Prof Exp:* Wm S Merrill Co fel, Univ Mich, 44-45, sr biochemist, 46-48, head biochemist, 48-52, from asst prof to assoc prof biochem, 52-67. *Mem:* AAAS; Am Chem Soc; Am Soc Biol Chemists; Biomet Soc; NY Acad Sci. *Res:* Synthetic medicinals; physiological chemistry of premature and newborn infants; biochemical analytical methods; multiple molecular forms of enzymes; carbohydrate metabolism; experimental diabetes; Neurospora crassa. *Mailing Add:* 533 Antioch Dr Davis CA 95616-1839

**TSAO, MARK FU-PAO,** PHARMACEUTICAL CHEMISTRY. *Current Pos:* sr anal chemist, Ciba Vision Corp, 80-83, sr res scientist, 83-85, mgr solution develop, 85-91, res fel, 91-92, SR RES FEL, CIBA VISION OPHTHAL, 92- *Personal Data:* b Wusi, Kansu, China, May 21, 42; US citizen; m 75, H L Wu; c Philip. *Educ:* Tamkang Univ, BS, 67; Nat Taiwan Univ, MS, 69; Univ Ariz, MS, 75; Emory Univ, PhD(anal chem), 81. *Prof Exp:* Assoc prof anal chem, Nat Cent Univ, 69-78. *Mem:* Am Chem Soc; Asn Res Vision & Ophthal. *Res:* To develop new ophthalmic products. *Mailing Add:* 11460 Johns Creek Pkwy Duluth GA 30155

**TSAO, NAI-KUAN,** NUMERICAL ANALYSIS, ERROR ANALYSIS. *Current Pos:* asst prof, 74-80, ASSOC PROF COMPUT SCI, WAYNE STATE UNIV, 80- *Personal Data:* b Shanghai, China, June 25, 39; US citizen; m 65, Chung-Long Wong; c Eve D. *Educ:* Nat Taiwan Univ, BSEE, 61; Nat Chiao Tung Univ, MSEE, 64; Univ Hawaii, MS, 66, PhD(elec eng), 70. *Prof Exp:* Vis asst prof elec eng, Univ Hawaii, 71; res assoc, Aerospace Res Labs, 71-73, res analyst, 73-74. *Concurrent Pos:* Prin investr, Air Force Off Sci Res, 76-81. *Mem:* Asn Comput Mach; Math Asn Am; Soc Indust & Appl Math; Inst Elec & Electronics Engrs Comput Soc. *Res:* Numerical algorithms in linear algebra and fast Fourier transform using sequential or parallel machines. *Mailing Add:* Dept Comput Sci Wayne State Univ 422 State Hall Detroit MI 48202

**TSAO, PETER HSING-TSUEN,** MYCOLOGY. *Current Pos:* Jr plant pathologist, Univ Calif, Riverside, 56-58, asst plant pathologist, 58-64, assoc prof, 64-70, prof, 70-95, EMER PROF, PLANT PATH, UNIV CALIF, RIVERSIDE, 96- *Personal Data:* b Shanghai, China, Mar 22, 29; nat US; m 56, Pamela Wang; c Frederick B. *Educ:* Univ Wis, BA, 52, PhD(plant path), 56. *Concurrent Pos:* Guggenheim fel, 66-67; consult, UN Food & Agr Orgn, Thailand, 73-74 & 81, Malaysia, 82 & Indonesia, 83; res consult, Nat Sci Coun, Taiwan, 74-; lectr, Du Pont, 80; vis prof, Peking Agr Univ, 80, 84 & 86; GTZ consult, Philippines, 89-91. *Mem:* Fel Am Phytopath Soc; Mycol Soc Am; Brit Mycol Soc; Int Soc Citriculture; fel Am Phytopath Soc. *Res:* Phytophthora and other soil fungi; root diseases of citrus, avocado, black pepper, vanilla, and other subtropical and tropical crops. *Mailing Add:* Dept Plant Path Univ Calif Riverside CA 92521-0122

**TSAO, UTAH,** CHEMICAL ENGINEERING. *Current Pos:* process engr, 42-53, staff process engr, 53-64, mgr chem plant design, 64-78, CONSULT, LUMMUS CO, 78- *Personal Data:* b Shanghai, China, June 6, 13; nat US; m 40; c 2. *Educ:* Tatung Univ, China, BSc, 33; Univ Mich, MSc, 37, DSc(chem eng), 40. *Prof Exp:* Plant engr, Audubon Sugar Factory, La, 39-40; res engr, Eng Res Dept, Univ Mich, 40-41; petrol engr, Nat Resources Comn, China, 41-42. *Mem:* Fel Am Inst Chem Engrs; Chinese Inst Engrs (vpres, Am Sect, 48, pres, 67). *Res:* Design of ethylene oxide and glycol, vinyl acetate, polyvinyl alcohol, vinyl chloride, chloroform, carbon tetrachloride, urea, acetylene from hydrocarbons, polyvinyl pyrolidone, phenol and acetone plants, ethylene cracking heaters, caprolactum, chlorine-caustic, formaldehyde, styrene, aluminum chloride, aromatic nitriles; process improvements. *Mailing Add:* 1887 Kennedy Blvd Jersey City NJ 07305

**TSAO-WU, NELSON TSIN,** ELECTRONICS ENGINEERING. *Current Pos:* mem tech staff, 68-76, supvr, 76-84, gen mgr, AT&T Int, 84-86, dept head, Bell Tel Labs, 86-89, instr, AT&T Info Inst, 89-92, DEPT HEAD, BELL TEL LABS, 93- *Personal Data:* b Tientsin, China, Sept 9, 34; US citizen; m 59; c 3. *Educ:* Loughborough Col Technol, DLC, 57; Univ London, BSc, 57; Northeastern Univ, MSEE, 65, PhD(elec eng), 68. *Prof Exp:* Engr, Rediffusion Ltd, Hong Kong, 57-59; audio engr, Far East Broadcasting Co, Hong Kong, 59-60; asst educ officer, Hong Kong Govt, 61-63; biomed engr, Harvard Med Sch & Peter Bent Brigham Hosp, 65-67. *Mem:* Inst Elec & Electronics Engrs. *Res:* Switching networks; coding theory; mathematical modeling; signal theory; software engineering and development. *Mailing Add:* 18645 Klum Pl Rowland Heights CA 91748

**TSAROS, C(ONSTANTINE) L(OUIS),** CHEMICAL ENGINEERING, ENGINEERING ECONOMICS. *Current Pos:* RETIRED. *Personal Data:* b East Chicago, Ind, Sept 6, 21; m 50, Gladys Tall; c Jonell, Julia, Janet & Jennifer. *Educ:* Purdue Univ, BS, 43; Univ Mich, MS, 48. *Prof Exp:* Chem engr, Armour & Co, Ill, 43-46; assoc chem engr, Inst Gas Technol, Ill Inst Technol, 48-51; chem engr, Standard Oil Co, Ind, 51-57; chem engr, Inst Gas Technol, Ill Inst Technol, 57-64, supvr process econ, 64-70, mgr process econ, 70-83. *Mem:* Am Inst Chem Engrs; Am Asn Cost Engrs; Sigma Xi. *Res:* Chemical engineering design and process development; process economics in petroleum processing, hydrocarbon conversion, energy studies and synthetic fuels. *Mailing Add:* 5328 Lawn Ave Western Springs IL 60558

**TSAUR, BOR-YEU,** ELECTRONICS ENGINEERING. *Personal Data:* b Taiwan, June 8, 55. *Educ:* Nat Taiwan Univ, BS, 77; Calif Inst Technol, MS, 78, PhD(elec eng), 80. *Prof Exp:* Vis scientist, IBM Res Ctr, 79; res staff mem, Lincoln Labs, Mass Inst Technol, 80-85, group leader, 85-97. *Mem:* Am Phys Soc; Inst Elec & Electronics Engrs; Mat Res Soc; AmInst Metal Engrs Metall Soc. *Res:* Development of novel crystal growth technique for preparing large-area single-crystal semiconductor sheets on insulating substrates for integrated electronic devices; novel electronic devices or circuits; processing technologies; device physics based on the semiconductor on insulator structures; infrared detectors and focal plane arrays; active-matrix liquid-crystal flat panel displays. *Mailing Add:* Lincoln Lab Mass Inst Technol Lexington MA 02173. *E-Mail:* byt@11.mit.edu

**TSCHANG, PIN-SENG,** ELECTRICAL ENGINEERING. *Current Pos:* PRES, ACTIVE TEXT INC, 90- *Personal Data:* b Penang, Malaysia, May 14, 34; m 62; c 2. *Educ:* Ore State Univ, BS, 58, MS, 59; Newark Col Eng, DEngSci(elec eng), 67. *Prof Exp:* Instr elec eng, Newark Col Eng, 59-62; res engr, Electronics Res Labs, Columbia Univ, 62-65, sr res engr, 65-67; res assoc, Res Labs, Eastman Kodak Co, 67-90. *Mem:* Inst Elec & Electronics Engrs; Brit Inst Elec Engrs. *Res:* Electronics and scientific instrumentation; television; digital signal processing; electronic memories. *Mailing Add:* Active Text Inc 883 Winona Blvd Rochester NY 14617

**TSCHANTZ, BRUCE A,** CIVIL ENGINEERING, WATER RESOURCES. *Current Pos:* from asst prof to assoc prof, 69-76, PROF CIVIL ENG, UNIV TENN, KNOXVILLE, 76- *Personal Data:* b Akron, Ohio, Sept 15, 38; m 62; c 2. *Educ:* Ohio Northern Univ, BSCE, 60; NMex State Univ, MSCE, 62, ScD(civil eng), 65. *Honors & Awards:* Dow Chem Co Award, Am Soc Eng Educ, 69. *Prof Exp:* Civil engr, Facilities Div, White Sands Missile Range, 65. *Concurrent Pos:* Consult, Exec Off Pres, Off Sci & Technol Policy, Washington, DC, 77-79; chief, Fed Dam Safety, Fed Emergency Mgt Agency, Washington, DC, 80. *Mem:* Am Soc Eng Educ; Am Soc Civil Engrs. *Res:* Remote sensing of the environment, particularly water resources; analysis of the safety of dams; unsteady open channel flow; hydrologic impact of coal strip mining. *Mailing Add:* Dept Civil & Environ Eng Univ Tenn Knoxville 63 Perkins Hall Knoxville TN 37996-2010

**TSCHANZ, CHARLES MCFARLAND,** GEOLOGY. *Current Pos:* RETIRED. *Personal Data:* b Mackay, Idaho, July 9, 26; m 58; c 3. *Educ:* Univ Idaho, BS, 49; Stanford Univ, MS, 51. *Prof Exp:* Geologist, Colo, US Geol Surv, 49-50, Pioche, Nev, 51-53, chief uranium-copper proj, NMex, 53-55, geochem researcher, 55-56, chief mapping proj, Lincoln Co, Nev, 56-60, advisor, Bolivian Mineral Resources, US Opers Mission, USAID, 60-65, geol consult, Nat Mineral Inventory, Colombia, 65-69, proj chief, Boulder Mountains Mapping Proj, Idaho, 69-70, proj chief mineral eval, Sawtooth Nat Recreation Area, Idaho, 71-74, proj chief, Boulder Mountains, Idaho, 74-82. *Mem:* Geol Soc Am; Geochem Soc; Soc Econ Geol. *Res:* Regional mapping and economic evaluation as an integrated project; geochemistry, especially distribution of minor elements in igneous rocks; geology of eastern Nevada, Colorado Plateau, Bolivian Altiplano and Sierra Nevada of Santa Marta, Colombia. *Mailing Add:* 876 S Moore Lakewood CO 80226

**TSCHINKEL, WALTER RHEINHARDT,** BIOLOGY, INSECT BEHAVIOR. *Current Pos:* from asst prof to assoc prof, 70-80, assoc chmn, 85-87, PROF BIOL SCI, FLA STATE UNIV, 80- *Personal Data:* b Lobositz, Czech, Sept 15, 40; US citizen; m 68, Victoria Nierenberg; c Erika. *Educ:* Wesleyan Univ, BA, 62; Univ Calif, Berkeley, MA, 65, PhD(comp biochem), 68. *Prof Exp:* Fel biol, Dept Neurobiol & Behav, Cornell Univ, 68-70; lectr entom, Rhodes Univ, 70. *Concurrent Pos:* NSF grants, 71-; consult, Environ Protection Agency, 73-75; vis assoc prof, Entom Dept, Univ Calif, Berkeley, 77; mem, Panel Regulatory Biol, NSF, 77- & consult, Integrated Basic Res, 78-80; guest prof, Univ Pretoria, SAfrica, 82; Fla Pesticide Rev Coun, 84-90. *Mem:* AAAS; Entom Soc Am; Int Union Study Soc Insects. *Res:* Insect behavior and chemical communication; biology of ants; biology of tenebrionid beetles. *Mailing Add:* Dept Biol Sci Fla State Univ Tallahassee FL 32306-1096. *Fax:* 850-644-0481; *E-Mail:* tschinkel@bio.fsu.edu

**TSCHIRGI, ROBERT DONALD,** ACADEMIC ADMINISTRATION. *Current Pos:* vchancellor acad planning, 66-67, vchancellor acad affairs, 67-68, prof neurosci, 66-89, EMER PROF NEUROSCI, UNIV CALIF, SAN DIEGO, 89-, ASSOC DIR NSCORT/EXOBIOL, 92- *Personal Data:* b Sheridan, Wyo, Oct 9, 24; m 83, Elisabeth Baughman. *Educ:* Univ Chicago, BS, 45, MS, 47, PhD, 49, MD, 50. *Honors & Awards:* Distinguished Int Med Educ Award, Japan Soc Med Educ, 83. *Prof Exp:* Asst physiol, Univ Chicago, 45-48, from instr to asst prof, 48-53; from assoc prof to prof, Sch Med, Univ Calif, Los Angeles, 53-66, acad asst pres, 61-63, univ wide dean planning, 64-67. *Concurrent Pos:* Chmn, Symp Biol Neuroglia, NIH, 53-60; dir med sch planning, Univ Hawaii, 63-64; dir med sch curric, Brit Med Asn, 74; consult, NSF, NIH, Greek Govt, WHO, Brit Med Asn & var univs & med schs. *Mem:* Int Brain Res Orgn; fel AAAS; Am Physiol Soc; Biophys Soc; Sigma Xi. *Res:* Intracranial fluids and barriers; direct current potentials in central nervous system; evolution of perception. *Mailing Add:* NSCORT/Cal Space 0216 Univ Calif San Diego La Jolla CA 92093-0216. *Fax:* 619-534-2674; *E-Mail:* rtschirgi@ucsd.edu

**TSCHIRLEY, FRED HAROLD,** ECOLOGY. *Current Pos:* RETIRED. *Personal Data:* b Ethan, SDak, Dec 19, 25; m 48; c 5. *Educ:* Univ Colo, BA, 51, MA, 54; Univ Ariz, PhD, 63. *Prof Exp:* Res asst, Univ Ariz, 52-53, instr, 53-54; range scientist, Crops Res Div, Agr Res Serv, USDA, 54-68, asst br chief, Crops Protection Res Br, 68-71, asst coordr environ qual activ sci & educ, 71-73, coordr environ qual activ, Off Secy, 73-74; chmn dept, bot & plant path, Mich State Univ, 74-80, prof, 74-84; exec dir, Mich Agr/Bus Coun, 84-88. *Mem:* AAAS; Weed Sci Soc Am; Soc Range Mgt; Ecol Soc Am. *Res:* Woody plant control; pesticides. *Mailing Add:* 3401 Placita del Emblema Green Valley AZ 85614

**TSCHOEGL, NICHOLAS WILLIAM,** PHYSICAL CHEMISTRY. *Current Pos:* assoc prof mat sci, 65-67, prof, 67-85, EMER PROF CHEM ENG, CALIF INST TECHNOL, 85- *Personal Data:* b Zidlochovice, Czech, June 4, 18; m 46; c 2. *Educ:* New South Wales, BSc, 54, PhD(chem), 58. *Honors & Awards:* Alexander von Humboldt Found Award, 70. *Prof Exp:* Sr res officer, Bread Res Inst, Australia, 58-61; proj assoc dept chem, Univ Wis, 61-63; sr phys chemist, Stanford Res Inst, 63-65. *Concurrent Pos:* Consult, Phillips Petrol Co, 67-83. *Mem:* Am Phys Soc; Am Chem Soc; Soc Rheol; Brit Soc Rheol; Deutsche Rheologische Gesellschaft. *Res:* Polymer rheology; physical chemistry of macromolecules; mechanical properties of polymeric materials. *Mailing Add:* Calif Inst Technol 228 Spalding Pasadena CA 91125. *Fax:* 626-568-8743

**TSCHUDY, DONALD P,** INTERNAL MEDICINE, BIOCHEMISTRY. *Current Pos:* RETIRED. *Personal Data:* b Palmerton, Pa, Nov 8, 26; m 51; c 2. *Educ:* Princeton Univ, AB, 46; Columbia Univ, MD, 50; Am Bd Internal Med, dipl, 61. *Prof Exp:* Intern med, Presby Hosp, New York, 51-52, asst resident, 52-53; asst resident, Francis Delafield Hosp, 53-54; clin assoc, Clin Ctr, NIH, 54-55, sr investr, Metab Serv, Clin Ctr, Nat Cancer Inst, 55-85. *Mem:* Am Soc Clin Invest; Am Fedn Clin Res; Am Soc Biol Chemists; AMA. *Res:* Clinical and biochemical research on porphyrin metabolism and the porphyrias; research on tumor-host relationships. *Mailing Add:* 3905 Woodlawn Rd Chevy Chase MD 20815

**TSCHUIKOW-ROUX, EUGENE,** CHEMICAL KINETICS, THERMODYNAMICS. *Current Pos:* assoc prof, 61-71, head chmn dept, 73-77, PROF CHEM, UNIV CALGARY, 71- *Personal Data:* b Kharkov, USSR, Jan 16, 36; US citizen; m 59; c 1. *Educ:* Univ Calif, Berkeley, BS, 57, PhD(chem), 61; Univ Wash, Seattle, MS, 58. *Prof Exp:* Sr scientist, Jet Propulsion Lab, Calif Inst Technol, 60-65; Nat Acad Sci-Nat Res Coun res assoc chem, Nat Bur Stand, 65-66. *Concurrent Pos:* Vis scholar, Univ Calif, Santa Barbara, 72; consult, Jet Propulsion Lab, Calif Inst Technol, 73, 87; fel, Alexander von Humboldt Found, IRG, 80. *Mem:* Am Chem Soc; Am Phys Soc; Can Inst Chem. *Res:* Gas phase reaction kinetics; high temperature shock tube studies; kinetic isotope effects; photochemistry; reaction dynamics; unimolecular reactions; gas phase ion-molecule reactions; thermodynamics. *Mailing Add:* Dept Chem Univ Calgary Calgary AB T2N 1N4 Can

**TSCHUNKO, HUBERT F A,** PHYSICS, OPTICS. *Current Pos:* RETIRED. *Personal Data:* b Weidenau, Austria, Sept 9, 12; US citizen; m 46, Hildegard Salzborn; c Hagdis & Almuth. *Educ:* Darmstadt Tech Univ, Diplom-Ing, 35. *Honors & Awards:* Apollo Achievement Award, NASA, 69. *Prof Exp:* Develop engr aeronaut indust, Europe, 36-45; res assoc astron, Astron Observ, Heidelberg, 45-50; engr pvt indust, WGer, 51-57; physicist, USAF, Wright-Patterson AFB, 57-65; opticist Electronics Res Ctr, NASA, 65-70, Goddard Space Flight Ctr, 70-87. *Mem:* Optical Soc Am; Ger Soc Aeronaut & Astronaut. *Res:* Wave optics; performances of large and space optical systems, as space telescopes, space cameras, space energy collectors and space energy transmitters. *Mailing Add:* 12501 Raven Way Laurel MD 20708

**TSE, FRANCIS LAI-SING,** PHARMACOKINETICS, DRUG METABOLISM. *Current Pos:* DIR DRUG METAB, NOVARTIS PHARM CORP, 96- *Personal Data:* b Hong Kong, Jan 20, 52; US citizen; m 79, Irene Chow; c Clara. *Educ:* Univ Wis-Madison, BS, 74, MS, 75, PhD(pharmaceut), 78. *Prof Exp:* Asst prof pharmacokinetics, Rutgers Univ, 78-80; sr scientist & unit head, Sandoz Res Inst, 81-84, group leader, 85-90, asst dir, 91-92, dir drug metab, 93-96, assoc dir, 93-95. *Concurrent Pos:* Prin investr, Nat Inst Drug Abuse, 80-81; mem grad fac, Rutgers Univ, 80-81, vis asst prof pharmaceut, 81. *Mem:* Am Pharmaceut Asn; Int Soc Study Xenobiotics; fel Am Asn Pharmaceut Scientists; Am Soc Clin Pharmacol & Therapeut; fel Acad Pharmaceut Res & Sci; fel Am Col Clin Pharmacol. *Res:* Absorption, distribution, metabolism and excretion of therapeutic agents in laboratory animals and humans; influence of various environmental and physiological factors on drug pharmacokinetics. *Mailing Add:* Drug Metab Dept Novaris Pharm Corp East Hanover NJ 07936

**TSE, FRANCIS S,** MECHANICAL ENGINEERING. *Current Pos:* PROF MECH ENG, UNIV CINCINNATI, 63- *Personal Data:* b Canton, China, Dec 15, 19; US citizen; m 52; c 2. *Educ:* Univ Hong Kong, BSc, 41; Purdue Univ, Lafayette, MSME, 42; Univ Pa, MBA, 49; Ohio State Univ, PhD(mech eng), 57. *Prof Exp:* Jr engr, Baldwin Locomotive Works, Pa, 42-45; engr, Fairbanks Morse, Wis, 46-47; instr & res assoc mech eng, Ohio State Univ, 47-57; from asst prof to assoc prof, Mich State Univ, 57-62; NSF fel, Purdue Univ, Lafayette, 62-63. *Concurrent Pos:* NSF grants undergrad educ, Univ Cincinnati, 64-66. *Mem:* Am Soc Eng Educ; Am Soc Mech Engrs; Instrument Soc Am; Sigma Xi. *Res:* Vibrations; control theory; measurement and instrumentation; machine dynamics. *Mailing Add:* 10167 Lochcrest Dr Cincinnati OH 45231

**TSE, HARLEY Y,** NEUROIMMUNOLOGY, IMMUNOGENETICS. *Current Pos:* ASSOC PROF, SCH MED, WAYNE STATE UNIV, 86- *Personal Data:* b China, July 17, 47; US citizen; m 79, Kwai-Fong Chui; c Kevin, Alan & Leslie. *Educ:* Calif Inst Technol, BS, 72; Univ Calif, San Diego, PhD(immunol), 77; Rutgers Univ, MBA, 86. *Prof Exp:* Fel, NIH, 77-80; sr immunologist, Merck & Co, 80-86. *Concurrent Pos:* Adj assoc prof, Columbia Univ Col Surgeons & Physicians, 81-83; prin investr res grants, NIH, 88-, Nat Multiple Sclerosis Soc, 88-; coun mem, Immunol Autumn Conf, 90-; pres, Detroit Immunol Soc, 89-91; recipient, NIH Res Career Develop Award, 92- *Mem:* Am Asn Immunologists; Int Soc Neuroimmunol; Soc Chinese Bioscientists Am. *Res:* T cell functions in autoimmune diseases; molecular biology and genetics of T cell receptor genes; in vivo T cell trafficking; T cell activation signals. *Mailing Add:* Dept Immunol & Microbiol Wayne State Univ Sch Med 540 E Canfield Ave Detroit MI 48201-1908. *Fax:* 313-577-1155

**TSE, ROSE (LOU),** ORGANIC CHEMISTRY, MEDICINE. *Current Pos:* PVT PRACT, 83- *Personal Data:* b Shanghai, China, July 27, 27; US citizen; m 53. *Educ:* St John's Univ, China, BS, 49; Mt Holyoke Col, MA, 50; Yale Univ, PhD(org chem), 53; Med Col Pa, MD, 60; Am Bd Internal Med, dipl & cert rheumatology. *Prof Exp:* Instr, Ohio State Univ, 53-55; res assoc, Univ Pa, 55-56; intern, Philadelphia Gen Hosp, 60-61, resident internal med, 61-64; assoc med, Sch Med, Univ Pa, 68-71, asst prof clin med, 71-75, assoc prof med, 75-83. *Concurrent Pos:* Attend physician, Philadelphia Gen Hosp, 64-68, sr attend physician, 68-77, assoc chief spec ward cardiol, 68-71, chief rheumatology sect, 71-77; clin instr internal med, Med Col Pa, 64-68; assoc chief med, Philadelphia Gen Hosp, 75-77; chief rheumatology, West Park Hosp, 77-86; dir rheumatology, Jefferson Park Hosp, 87-94. *Mem:* Fel Am Col Physicians; fel Am Inst Chemists; fel Am Col Angiol; Am Heart Asn; Am Rheumatism Asn; fel Am Col Rheumatology. *Res:* Reaction mechanisms; organic synthesis; electrocardiology; inflammatory mediators; non-steroidal inflammatory agents; cardiology, rheumatology; catecholamines; cyclic adenosine monophosphate; prostaglandin; crystal-induced synovitis. *Mailing Add:* 2 Bala Plaza (IL-51) Bala-Cynwyd PA 19004

**TSE, WARREN W,** human physiology, for more information see previous edition

**TSENG, BEN Y,** MOLECULAR BIOLOGY, BIOCHEMISTRY. *Current Pos:* dir, Biochem Lab, 76-91, SCIENTIST BIOCHEM, GENTA, INC 91- *Personal Data:* b China, Feb 17, 44. *Educ:* Brandeis Univ, BS, 65; Yale Univ, PhD(med biol), 72. *Prof Exp:* Asst prof biochem, Univ Calif, San Diego, 72-76. *Mem:* Am Soc Cell Biol & Molecular Biol; Am Chem Soc. *Res:* Molecular biology; biochemistry. *Mailing Add:* 13255 Capstone Dr San Diego CA 92130

**TSENG, CHARLES C,** MOLECULAR BIOLOGY, CELL BIOLOGY. *Current Pos:* assoc prof, 75-80, PROF BIOL, PURDUE UNIV, CALUMET, 80- *Personal Data:* b Fuchow, Fukien, China, Dec 20, 32; m 65; c 2. *Educ:* Taiwan Norm Univ, BS, 55; Taiwan Univ, MS, 57; Univ Calif, Los Angeles, PhD(plant sci), 65. *Prof Exp:* From asst prof to assoc prof bot, Windham Col, 65-75. *Concurrent Pos:* Dir med genetics prog, Northwest Ctr Med Educ, Indiana Univ, Gary, Ind. *Mem:* AAAS; Bot Soc Am; Am Inst Biol Sci; Am Soc Plant Taxon. *Res:* Acid phosphatase isoenzymes of vertebrates and plants; plant molecular systematics; human karyology. *Mailing Add:* Dept Biol Purdue Univ Calumet 2233 171st St Hammond IN 46323-2051

**TSENG, CHIEN KUEI,** ORGANIC CHEMISTRY. *Current Pos:* RETIRED. *Personal Data:* b Tao Yuan, Taiwan, Feb 21, 34; m 66; c 2. *Educ:* Cheng Kung Univ, Taiwan, BS, 57; WVa Univ, MS, 64; Ill Inst Technol, PhD(chem), 68. *Prof Exp:* USPHS fels, Ill Inst Technol, 67-68; from res chemist to sr res chemist, Stauffer Chem Co, 68-71, supvr anal chem, 71-81; mgr spectros & phys chem, Zeneca Corp, 81-93. *Mem:* Am Chem Soc. *Res:* Nuclear magnetic resonance; structure determination; stereochemistry; phosphorus chemistry; infrared and mass spectroscopy; environmental fate studies. *Mailing Add:* 1228 Cabrillo St El Cerrito CA 94530

**TSENG, FUNG-I,** ELECTRICAL ENGINEERING, ELECTROMAGNETICS. *Current Pos:* from asst prof to assoc prof, 69-82, PROF ELEC ENG, ROCHESTER INST TECHNOL, 83- *Personal Data:* b Pingtung, Taiwan, Jan 12, 36; m 65; c 3. *Educ:* Nat Taiwan Univ, BS, 58; Chiao Tung Univ, MS, 60; Syracuse Univ, PhD(elec eng), 66. *Prof Exp:* Res engr antennas, Syracuse Univ, 66-69. *Mem:* Inst Elec & Electronics Engrs; Optical Soc Am. *Res:* Optimization of antenna arrays in noisy environments subject to random fluctuations. *Mailing Add:* Dept Elec Eng Rochester Inst Technol 1 Lomb Memorial Dr Rochester NY 14623-5603

**TSENG, LEON FU,** PAIN, OPIATES. *Current Pos:* from asst prof to assoc prof pharmacol, 78-89, PROF ANESTHESIOL, MED COL WIS, 89- *Personal Data:* b Tainan City, Taiwan, Nov 20, 37; US citizen; m 65, Grace; c Joshua, Danial, Joseph & Esther. *Educ:* Nat Taiwan Univ, Taipei, BS, 61, MS, 64; Univ Kans, PhD(pharmacol), 70. *Prof Exp:* Instr pharmacol, Nat Taiwan Univ, 66-67; asst res pharmacologist, Dept Pharmacol, Univ Calif, San Francisco, 72-75, asst prof, 75-78. *Mem:* Am Soc Pharmacol & Exp Therapeut; Soc Neurosci; Int Asn Study Pain; Am Pain Soc. *Res:* Neuronal mechanisms of analgesia induced by opioids and opioidpeptides; pain mechanism; mechanisms of opioid addiction. *Mailing Add:* Dept Anesthesiol MEB-462C Med Col Wis 8701 Watertown Plank Rd Milwaukee WI 53226. *Fax:* 414-266-8541; *E-Mail:* ltseng@post.its.mcw.edu

**TSENG, LINDA,** PHYSICAL CHEMISTRY, BIOCHEMISTRY. *Current Pos:* Assoc prof biochem, 76-80, ASSOC PROF OBSTET & GYNEC, HEALTH SCI CTR, STATE UNIV NY, STONY BROOK, 80- *Personal Data:* b China, Sept 29, 36; US citizen; m 63; c 1. *Educ:* Cheng Kung Univ, Taiwan, BS, 55; Univ NDak, PhD(chem), 68. *Honors & Awards:* Irma Hirsh Res Award, Irma Hirsh Inc, 76. *Mem:* AAAS; Endocrine Soc. *Res:* Steroid biochemistry; hormone action. *Mailing Add:* Dept Obstet & Gynec State Univ NY Health Sci Ctr Stony Brook NY 11794-0001

**TSENG, MICHAEL TSUNG,** EXPERIMENTAL PATHOLOGY, ONCOLOGY. *Current Pos:* ASSOC PROF ANAT & ONCOL ASSOC, CANCER CTR, HEALTH SCI CTR, UNIV LOUISVILLE, 78-, DIR, TUMOR EVAL LABS, 82-, PROF ANAT, 87- *Personal Data:* b Chungking, China, Jan 25, 44; US citizen; m 70, Shirley C Lu; c Sophia Y Tseng. *Educ:* Iowa State Univ, BS, 67; State Univ NY, Buffalo, PhD(exp path), 73. *Hon Degrees:* Dr, Henan Med Univ, China, 87. *Prof Exp:* Res assoc biochem, Ore Regional Primate Res Ctr, 73-74; asst prof anat, Upstate Med Ctr, State Univ NY, 74-78. *Concurrent Pos:* Instr anat, Sch Med, Univ Ore, 73-74; prin investr, Univ Award, State Univ NY, 73-76; prin investr, Am Cancer Soc, 78-82; actg dir, Anesthesia Critical Care Res Unit, Univ Louisville, 83-84; prin investr, NIOSH, 88-90; hon prof, Henan Med Univ, China. *Mem:* Am Asn Anatomists; Am Soc Cell Biol; Am Asn Cancer Res; NY Acad Sci; Endocrine Soc; Int Soc Prev Oncol; Sigma Xi; Soc Neurosci. *Res:* Photodynamic therapy; vitreoretinal research; environmental toxicology; neurobiology; cerebral ischemia and neuroprotectants. *Mailing Add:* Dept Anat/Neurobiol Univ Louisville Louisville KY 40292. *Fax:* 502-852-6228; *E-Mail:* mttsen01@ulkyvm.louisville.edu

**TSENG, SAMUEL CHIN-CHONG,** SOLID STATE ELECTRONICS. *Current Pos:* staff engr, 68-69, MEM RES STAFF, T J WATSON RES CTR, INT BUS MACH CORP, 69- *Personal Data:* b Tainan, Taiwan, Mar 6, 33; m 57. *Educ:* Ching-Kung Univ, Taiwan, BS, 56; Chiao Tung Univ, MS, 60; Yale Univ, ME, 61; Univ Calif, Berkeley, PhD(solid state electronics), 66. *Prof Exp:* Res engr, Electron Tube Div, Litton Indusiss, Inc, Calif, 66-68. *Mem:* Am Phys Soc; sr mem Inst Elec & Electronics Engrs. *Res:* Excitation, propagation and amplification of surface elastic waves in piezoelectric crystals and ceramics; application of surface waves to delay lines, matched filters, binary sequence recognitions and signal processing in general. *Mailing Add:* 7217 Silver Lode Lane San Jose CA 95120-6099

**TSENG, SHIN-SHYONG,** ORGANIC CHEMISTRY, COMPUTER APPLICATION IN CHEMISTRY. *Current Pos:* SR RES CHEMIST, AM CYANAMID CO, 77- *Personal Data:* b Tainan, Taiwan, Nov 24, 38; US citizen; m 67, Yea M Chang; c Eugene & Emily. *Educ:* Nat Taiwan Univ, BS, 61; Kent State Univ, MA, 64; Univ Chicago, PhD(org chem), 69. *Prof Exp:* Fel, Univ Chicago, 69-70, fel, Syva Res Inst, 70-72; res assoc, Ames Res Ctr, NASA, 72-73; assoc res scientist, Inst Environ Med, Med Ctr, NY Univ, 73-77. *Mem:* Am Chem Soc. *Res:* Chemiluminescence; photochemistry; chemical carcinogenesis; organic synthesis; heterocyclic chemistry; pharmaceuticals (central nervous system-geriatric agents), agrochemicals (herbidices); computer application in chemical database management. *Mailing Add:* 232 Windmill Ct Bridgewater NJ 08807. *Fax:* 609-275-3550; *E-Mail:* tsengs@pt.cyanamid.com

**TSERNOGLOU, DEMETRIUS,** biophysics, crystallography, for more information see previous edition

**TSIANG, EUGENE Y,** X-RAY OPTICS, ELECTRON BEAM OPTICS. *Current Pos:* ASTROPHYSICIST, HARVARD SMITHSONIAN CTR ASTROPHYS, 93- *Personal Data:* b Shanghai, China, Nov 11, 48; US citizen. *Educ:* Univ Calif, Santa Barbara, BA, 69; Columbia Univ, PhD(physics), 77. *Prof Exp:* Optical engr, Perkin-Elmer Corp, 79-81; sr scientist, Ion Beam Systs Inc, 84-87; mem tech staff, Hewlett-packard Corp, 88-89; mgr, Imatron Inc, 90-93. *Res:* Optical and electron optical engineering in astronomy, semiconductor and medical imaging equipment; calibration and control of opto-mechanical equipment; modeling of plasma and beam processing. *Mailing Add:* Smithsonian Inst 60 Garden St Cambridge MA 20138. *Fax:* 617-495-7040

**TSIATIS, ANASTASIOS A,** BIOMETRICS, BIOSTATISTICS. *Current Pos:* ASSOC PROF BIOSTATIST, SCH PUB HEALTH, HARVARD UNIV & SIDNEY FARBER CANCER INST, 81- *Personal Data:* b New York, NY, July 12, 48; m 70; c 1. *Educ:* Mass Inst Technol, BS, 70; Univ Calif, Berkeley, PhD(statist), 74. *Prof Exp:* Asst prof statist, Univ Wis-Madison, 74-79; assoc mem biostatist, St Jude Children's Res Hosp, 79-81. *Mem:* Am Statist Asn; Biometrics Soc; Inst Math Statist. *Res:* Application of survival analysis in clinical trials with specific emphasis on sequential rules for stopping a trial early if large treatment differences occur. *Mailing Add:* Dept Biostatist Harvard Sch Pub Health 677 Huntington Ave Boston MA 02115-6023

**TSIBRIS, JOHN-CONSTANTINE MICHAEL,** BIOCHEMISTRY, ENDOCRINOLOGY. *Current Pos:* ASSOC PROF, DEPT OBSTET/ GYNEC & PHYSIOL/BIOPHYSICS, MED CTR, UNIV ILL, CHICAGO, 79- *Personal Data:* b Jannina, Greece, Dec 22, 36; m 69; c 2. *Educ:* Nat Univ Athens, BSc, 59; Cornell Univ PhD(biochem), 65. *Prof Exp:* Vis scientist, Univ Fla, 69-71, asst prof biochem, 71-77, assoc prof, Dept Obstet & Gynec, 77-79. *Concurrent Pos:* NIH trainee biophys chem, 67-68, grant, 69-78, career develop award, 69-77; Am Diabetes Asn, 80-81. *Mem:* AAAS; NY Acad Sci; Am Chem Soc; Soc Gynecologic Invest; Sigma Xi. *Res:* Chemical carcinogenesis; steroid and peptide hormone receptors; diabetes; fertility control. *Mailing Add:* Obstet-Gynec Dept & Biochem-Molecular Biol Univ SFla 4 Columbia Dr Harbor Side Med Rm 524 Tampa FL 33606-3500. Fax: 813-254-0940

**TSIEN, HSIENCHYANG,** MICROBIOLOGY. *Current Pos:* res fel, 68-70, ASST PROF MICROBIOL, UNIV MINN, 75- *Personal Data:* b Nanking, China, July 26, 39; m 66; c 2. *Educ:* Nat Taiwan Univ, BS, 61; Cath Univ Louvain, Belg, DrS(microbiol & biochem), 67. *Prof Exp:* Asst, Cath Univ Louvain, 67-68 & 70-72; res instr microbiol, Temple Univ, 72-75. *Mem:* Am Soc Microbiol; AAAS. *Res:* Soil microbiology; microorganism-plant symbiotic nitrogen fixation; microbial ecology; microbial physiology; structure and function of bacterial cell membranes and cell walls. *Mailing Add:* 3462 Harriet Ct St Paul MN 55126

**TSIEN, RICHARD WINYU,** ION CHANNELS. *Current Pos:* GEORGE D SMITH PROF & CHMN DEPT MOLECULAR & CELLULAR PHYSIOL, STANFORD UNIV, 88- *Personal Data:* b Tating, China, Mar 3, 45; US citizen; m 71; c 3. *Educ:* Mass Inst Technol, SB, 65, SM, 66; Oxford Univ, DPhil, 70. *Honors & Awards:* Kenneth S Cole Award Contrib Membrane Biophys, 85; Otsuka Award Outstanding Res, Int Soc Heart Res, 85; Smith Kline Lectr, Univ Col London; Bass Lectr, Vanderbilt Univ; Sterling Lectr, Columbia Univ; Lewis Conner Lectr, Am Heart Asn, 89; Daniel A Nachshen Lectr, Univ Md, 89; Hoechst Lectr, Brain Res Asn, 90; Anton J Lectr, Univ Chicago, 93; Nahum Lectr, Yale Univ, 93; McDowell Lectr, Kings Col London, 93; Sherrington Lectr, Univ Liverpool, 94; Neil Graham Lectr, Univ Toronto, 96; C Ladd Prosser Lectr, UnivIll, 96; Walter B Cannon Mem Award, Am Physiol Soc, 96. *Prof Exp:* Lect fel, Balliol Col, Oxford, 69-70; from asst prof to prof, Dept Physiol, Yale Univ Sch Med, 70-88. *Concurrent Pos:* Weir jr res fel, Univ Col, Oxford, 66-70; estab investr, Am Heart Asn, 74-79, Javits investr, Nat Inst Neurol & Commun Dis & Stroke, 86-93; distinguished lectr, Stanford Univ; mem, US Nat Comt, Int Union Pure & Appl Biophys. *Mem:* Nat Acad Sci; Inst Med-Nat Acad Sci; Soc Gen Physiologists (pres, 87-88); Biophys Soc; Acad Sinica; fel AAAS. *Res:* Mechanisms of calcium delivery to neurons and muscle cells and their modulation by neurotransmitters, hormones and drugs; the function of heart, smooth muscle, neurons and their electrical activity and such functions as contraction and neurotransmitter release; author of numerous articles and papers. *Mailing Add:* Dept Physiol Stanford Univ Sch Med Stanford CA 94305-5070

**TSIEN, ROGER YONCHIEN,** CHEMISTRY, CELL BIOLOGY. *Current Pos:* from asst prof to prof, Dept Physiol-Anat, 81-89, PROF PHARMACOL & CHEM & INVESTR, HOWARD HUGHES MED INST, UNIV CALIF, SAN DIEGO, 89- *Personal Data:* b New York, NY, Feb 1, 52; m 82, Wendy M Globe. *Educ:* Harvard Univ, AB, 72; Univ Cambridge, PhD(physiol), 77. *Hon Degrees:* Dr, Katholieke Univ, Leuven, Belg, 95. *Honors & Awards:* Lamport Prize, NY Acad Sci, 86; W Alden Spencer Award Neurobiol, Columbia Univ, 91; Bowditch Lectr, Am Physiol Soc, 92; Hans L Falk Lectr, Nat Inst Environ Health Serv, 93; Pres Lectr, Am Thoracic Soc, 94; Int Award, Gairdner Found, 95; Basic Res Prize, Am Heart Asn, 95. *Prof Exp:* Res asst, Univ Cambridge, 75-78. *Concurrent Pos:* Comyns Berkeley res fel, Conville & Caius Col, Cambridge, 77-81; Searle scholar, 83-86; Javits neurosci investr, Nat Inst Neurol Dis & Stroke, 89-; T Y Shen vis prof med chem, Mass Inst Technol, 91. *Mem:* Inst Med-Nat Acad Sci; Soc Neurosci; Am Soc Cell Biol; Soc Gen Physiologists. *Res:* How living cells and neuronal networks process information; design, synthesize, and use new molecules to detect and manipulate intracellular biochemical signals, usually by optical means such as fluorescent readout or photochemical release of messenger substances. *Mailing Add:* Univ Calif Howard Hughes Med Inst M-047 Cellular & Molecular Med La Jolla CA 92093. Fax: 619-534-5270; E-Mail: rtsien@ucsd.edu

**TSIHRINTZIS, VASSILIOS ANDREW,** WETLAND & ECOLOGICAL ENGINEERING, WATER QUALITY & HYDRODYNAMIC MODELING. *Current Pos:* PROF WATER RESOURCES ENG, FLA INT UNIV, 92- *Personal Data:* b Athens, Greece, June 18, 59. *Educ:* Univ Patras, dipl, 82; Univ Ill, MS, 83, PhD(hydrosysts eng), 88. *Honors & Awards:* Award of Excellence, Am Soc Landscape Architects, 95. *Prof Exp:* Res asst, Univ Ill, Urbana, 82-87; engr, Simons, Li & Assocs, 87-88; sr engr, Psonas & Assocs, 89-92. *Concurrent Pos:* Res asst, Ill State Water Surv, 84-87; consult, 92- *Mem:* Am Soc Civil Engrs; Int Asn Hydraul Res; Int Water Resource Asn; Am Water Resource Asn; Am Inst Hydrol; Am Geophys Union. *Res:* Ecological engineering and wetlands, water resources engineering, hydrodynamic; water quality modeling, nonpoint source pollution, and sediment transport; published 25 journal papers, more than 50 conference papers and more than 90 technical reports. *Mailing Add:* 701 SW 25th Rd Miami FL 33129-2209. Fax: 305-348-2802; E-Mail: tsihrin@eng.fiu.edu

**TSILIBARY, EFFIE-CONSTANTINOS,** FUNCTIONAL BIOCHEMISTRY OF EXTRACELLULAR MATRIX, PATHOPHYSIOLOGY OF DIABETIC MICROVASCULAR COMPLICATIONS. *Current Pos:* ASSOC PROF, UNIV MINN, 92- *Personal Data:* b Athens, Greece, Mar 9, 48; US citizen; m, Aristidis S Charonis; c Spyros C & Yiorgos-Constantinos C. *Educ:* Athens Capodistrian Univ, MD, 74; Univ Calif, San Francisco, PhD(anat/cell biol), 80. *Prof Exp:* Fel, Cardiovasc Res Inst, Univ Calif, San Francisco, 80-82; res assoc, Childrens Hosp, Harvard Univ, 82, Yale Univ, 83-86. *Mem:* Am Soc Cell Biol; Fedn Am Soc Exp Biol; Am Diabetes Asn; NY Acad Sci. *Res:* To understand the molecular mechanisms which cause the microvascular complications of diabetes mellitus with emphasis on diabetic nephropathy and retinopathy. *Mailing Add:* 1812 Emerson Ave S Minneapolis MN 55405

**TSIN, ANDREW TSANG CHEUNG,** VISUAL BIOCHEMISTRY, NEUROBIOLOGY. *Current Pos:* From asst prof to assoc prof, Div Life Sci, Univ Tex, San Antonio, 81-90, from adj asst prof to adj assoc prof, Dept Ophthal, 84-90, PROF, DIV LIFE SCI, UNIV TEX, SAN ANTONIO, 90-, ADJ PROF, DEPT OPHTHAL, UNIV TEX HEALTH SCI CTR, 90- *Personal Data:* b Hong Kong, July 19, 50; Can citizen; m 79, Wendy; c Cathy. *Educ:* Dalhousie Univ, BSc, 73; Univ Alta, MSC, 76, PhD(zool), 79. *Concurrent Pos:* Ed consult vision res, Exp Eye Res, J Exp Biol, Arch Biochem & Biophys, Physiol & Behav & Brain Res Bull; reviewer and panelist, NIH & NSF; prin investr, NIH grant, NSF res grant; consult, Technol Inc, San Antonio, 85-86, Vision Res & Develop, Lubbock, 86-87 & Alcon Lab, Ft Worth, 89-90. *Mem:* Am Soc Zoologists; AAAS; Asn Researchers Vision & Opthal; Soc Neurosci; Am Soc Biochem & Molecular Biol; Am Physiol Soc. *Res:* Metabolism of vitamin A; rhodopsin biosynthesis; comparative physiology and biochemistry; disease mechanism of the eye. *Mailing Add:* Div Life Sci Univ Tex San Antonio TX 78249-0662. *Fax:* 210-458-4472; *E-Mail:* atsin@post3.utsa.edu

**TSINA, RICHARD VASIL,** PHYSICAL CHEMISTRY, SOLVATED ELECTRON-KINETICS & ELECTRON SPIN RESONANCE. *Current Pos:* continuing educ specialist, Univ Calif, Berkeley, 79-83, vchair eng, 83-95, asst dean, 90-95, CHMN CONTINUING EDUC ENG, UNIV CALIF, BERKELEY, 95- *Personal Data:* b Boston, Mass, Aug 31, 41; m 70, Irene Wang; c Lesley & Katherine. *Educ:* Boston Univ, BA, 63; Duke Univ, MA, 65; Tufts Univ, PhD(chem), 68. *Honors & Awards:* Creative Prog Award, Nat Univ Continuing Educ Asn, 90; Meritorious Achievement Award in Continuing Educ, Inst Elec & Electronics Engrs, 95. *Prof Exp:* Asst prof chem, Rutgers Univ, 70-73; vpres, Sultra Corp, 73-76; dean continuing educ, Cogswell Col, 76-79. *Concurrent Pos:* Chair, Prof Develop Comt, Inst Elec & Electronics Engrs, 97- *Mem:* Inst Elec & Electronics Engrs; Am Soc Eng Educ; Int Asn Continuing Eng Educ. *Res:* Kinetics of solvated electron weak acid reactions in nonaqueous media; structure of free radicals. *Mailing Add:* 1424 Dana Ave Palo Alto CA 94301. *Fax:* 510-642-6027; *E-Mail:* r.tsina@leee.org

**TSIPIS, KOSTA M,** NUCLEAR PHYSICS. *Current Pos:* Res assoc particle physics, Mass Inst Technol, 66-68, asst prof, 68-71, res fel biophys, 71-73, res fel, Ctr Int Studies, 73-78, res assoc Physics, 78-79, res sci physics 80-81, prin res sci physics, 81-83, DIR, PROG SCI & TECHNOL INT SECURITY, MASS INST TECHNOL, 78- & PRIN RES SCI TECHNOL & SOC, 83- *Personal Data:* b Athens, Greece, Feb, 12, 34; US citizen; m 70, Judith Ebel; c Mikael, Andreas & Yanni. *Educ:* Rutgers Univ, BSc, 58, MSc, 60; Columbia Univ, PhD(nuclear physics), 66. *Honors & Awards:* Szilard Award, Am Phys Soc, 84. *Concurrent Pos:* Sr consult, Stockholm Int Peace Res Inst, 73-77; adv, govt Greece, 77-; sci adv, World Coun Churches, 83-94. *Mem:* Fel Am Phys Soc; fel AAAS; fel NY Acad Sci. *Res:* Particle physics; technical and scientific aspects of national defense policy. *Mailing Add:* Prog Sci & Tech Int Security Mass Inst Technol 20A-011 Cambridge MA 02139. *E-Mail:* tsipis@mit.edu

**TSITLIK, JOSHUA E,** HEMODYNAMICS & THORACIC MECHANICS, MEDICAL INSTRUMENTATION. *Current Pos:* from res asst to res assoc med, Johns Hopkins Univ, 77-80, instr med & biomed eng, 80-84, asst prof, 84-92, ASSOC PROF MED & BIOMED ENG, JOHNS HOPKINS UNIV, 92- *Personal Data:* m 68, Victoria Plaks; c Anna. *Educ:* Leningrad Polytech Inst, MS, 64, PhD(elec eng), 72; Johns Hopkins Univ, MS, 80. *Prof Exp:* From engr to sr engr, Baku Electromech Inst, Azerbajan, 64- 67; sr engr, Design Co, Leningrad, Russia, 71-73; dir, Metrol & Automation Lab, Samoilova Curtain Factory, Leningrad, 73-76. *Concurrent Pos:* Mem, Stand Comt Blood Pressure Monitoring, Asn Advan Med Instrumentation, 88-; mem, Eng Med & Biol soc, Inst Elec & Electronics Engrs, 89-90. *Mem:* Inst Elec & Electronics Engrs; Asn Advan Med Instrumentation. *Res:* Study of the mechanisms of blood movement during cardiopulmonary resuscitation and related hemodynamic and biomechanical problems as well as development of MRI-compatible medical devices. *Mailing Add:* 720 Rutland Ave Rm 901 Traylor Bldg Baltimore MD 21205. *Fax:* 410-614-1980; *E-Mail:* jtsitlik@uereka.wbme.jhu.edu

**TSIVIDIS, YANNIS P,** ELECTRICAL ENGINEERING, ELECTRONICS. *Current Pos:* from asst prof to assoc prof, 76-84, PROF ELEC ENG, COLUMBIA UNIV, 84- *Personal Data:* b Piraeus, Greece, 46. *Educ:* Univ Minn, Minneapolis, BEE, 72; Univ Calif, Berkeley, MS, 73, PhD(eng), 76. *Honors & Awards:* Baker Prize, Inst Elec & Electronics Engrs; Darlington Prize, Circuit Systs Soc Inst Elec & Electronics Engrs. *Prof Exp:* Engr electronics, Motorola Semiconductor, Phoenix, Ariz, 74; lectr elec eng, Univ Calif, Berkeley, 76. *Concurrent Pos:* Mem tech staff, Bell Labs, Am Telephone & Telegraph Co, 77, resident vis, 77-87; vis assoc prof, Mass Inst Technol, 80. *Mem:* Fel Inst Elec & Electronics Engrs. *Res:* Design, analysis and simulation of integrated circuits; electronics; semiconductor device modelling; signal processing; circuit theory. *Mailing Add:* Dept Elec Eng Columbia Univ New York NY 10027

**TSO, MARK ON-MAN,** ophthalmology, pathology, for more information see previous edition

**TSO, PATRICK PO-WING,** INTESTINAL LIPID ABSORPTION, REGULATION OF FOOD INTAKE & OBESITY. *Current Pos:* assoc prof, 87-89, PROF PHYSIOL, LA STATE UNIV MED CTR, 90- *Personal Data:* b Hong Kong, Jan 4, 50; US citizen; m 91, Weiyi Li; c Wilfred. *Educ:* Univ Western Australia, BSc (Hons), 74; PhD(physiol), 78. *Prof Exp:* From asst prof to assoc prof physiol, Univ Tenn Med Ctr, 81-87. *Concurrent Pos:* Vis prof, Swedish Med Res Inst, 85; mem, Gen Med Study Sect, NIH, 87-91; Spec Rev Comt, Nat Inst Diabetes & Digestive & Kidney Dis, 91-; consult, Life Sci Res Orgn, Fedn Am Socs Exp Biol, 90-93. *Mem:* Am Physiol Soc; Am Gastroenterol Asn; NAm Asn Study Obesity. *Res:* Intestinal digestion, uptake and transport of lipids; regulation of food intake by apolipoprotein A-IV; obesity and fetal hypohalamic transplant. *Mailing Add:* Dept Physiol La State Univ Med Ctr 1501 Kings Hwy Shreveport LA 71130-3932. *Fax:* 318-674-6005

**TS'O, PAUL ON PONG,** BIOPHYSICAL CHEMISTRY. *Current Pos:* assoc prof biophys chem, 62-67, PROF BIOPHYS CHEM, JOHNS HOPKINS UNIV, 67-, DIR DIV BIOPHYSICS SCH HYG & PUB HEALTH, 73- *Personal Data:* b Hong Kong, July 17, 29; m 55; c 3. *Educ:* Lingnan Univ, China, BS, 49; Mich State Univ, MS, 51; Calif Inst Technol, PhD, 55. *Prof Exp:* Res fel biol, Calif Inst Technol, 55-61, sr res fel, 61-62. *Concurrent Pos:* Consult, Nat Cancer Inst; assoc ed, Molecular Pharmacol, 64-, Biochem, 66-74, Biophys J, 69-72, Biochem Biophys Acta, 71-81, Cancer Review, 73-, Cancer Res, 75-, J Environ Health Sci, 76-; mem, Biophys Study Sect, NIH, 76-80. *Mem:* Am Chem Soc; Am Soc Biol Chemists; Biophys Soc; Am Asn Cancer Res; Am Soc Microbiol; Am Soc Cell Biol. *Res:* Biophysics, chemistry and biology of nucleic acids; chemical carcinogenesis and mutagenesis; magnetic resonance; cell biology of differentiation and aging; interferon induction and function; DNA rearrangement and control of gene expression. *Mailing Add:* Dept Biochem Div Biophys Sch Hyg & Pub Health Johns Hopkins Univ 615 N Wolfe St Baltimore MD 21205-2103. *Fax:* 410-955-4392

**TSO, TIEN CHIOH,** PHYTOCHEMISTRY. *Current Pos:* res plant physiologist, Tobacco & Sugar Crops Res Br, USDA, 59-62, sr plant physiologist, 62-64, prin plant physiologist, 64-66, leader tobacco qual invests, Tobacco & Sugar Crops Res Br, 66-72, chief tobacco lab, 72-83, sr exec serv, 79-83, COLLABR TOBACCO & HEALTH, BELTSVILLE AGR RES CTR, AGR RES SERV, USDA, 84- *Personal Data:* b Hupeh, China, July 25, 17; nat US; m 49, Margaret Y Lu; c Elizabeth & Paul. *Educ:* Nanking Univ, China, BS, 41, MS, 44; Pa State Univ, PhD(agr biochem), 50. *Honors & Awards:* Coresta Prize, 78; US Presidential Rank Award, 84. *Prof Exp:* Supt exp farm, Ministry Social Affairs, China, 44-46; secy, Tobacco Improv Bur, 46-47; chemist res lab, Gen Cigar Co, 50-51; chemist div tobacco & spec crops, USDA, 52; asst prof & res assoc agron, Univ Md, 53-59. *Concurrent Pos:* Mem, Tobacco Chem Res Conf, Tobacco Workers Conf, World Conf Tobacco & Health, Tobacco Working Group, Lung Cancer Task Force & Int Tobacco Working Group; exec dir, Int Develop & Educ in Agr & Life Sci, 83-; sr consult, China Nat Tobacco Corp, 84-, US & foreign tobacco indust, 84- *Mem:* Fel AAAS; fel Am Agron Soc; Am Chem Soc; fel Am Inst Chem; Am Soc Plant Physiol; fel Chinese Acad Agr Sci; fel Phytochem Soc NAm. *Res:* Plant physiology; tobacco alkaloids; biochemistry; culture; radio elements; health related components; tobacco production research relating to smoking and health. *Mailing Add:* 4306 Yates Rd Beltsville MD 20705-2758

**TS'O, TIMOTHY ON-TO,** NEUROPHARMACOLOGY, BEHAVIORAL TOXICOLOGY. *Current Pos:* PSYCHIATRIST PVT PRACT, 81- *Personal Data:* b Hong Kong, Nov 9, 34; US citizen; m 63; c 2. *Educ:* Univ Hong Kong, MB & BS, 59; Stanford Univ, PhD(neuropharmacol & psychopharmacol), 68; Am Bd Psychiat & Neurol, dipl, 79. *Prof Exp:* Demonstr, Dept Path, Fac Med, Univ Hong Kong, 60-62; sr res specialist pharmacol, Dow Chem Co, Mich, 68-74; res prof human biol, Saginaw Valley State Col, Mich, 74-75; lab chief neuropharmacol, Long Island Res Inst, 75-79; psychiatrist, Vet Admin Med Ctr, Northport, NY, 77-79; assoc prof psychiat & behav sci, Univ Health Sci, Chicago Med Sch, 79-83; psychiatrist, Vet Admin Med Ctr, North Chicago, 79-81,. *Concurrent Pos:* House physician & surgeon, Govt Surg Unit & Univ Med Unit, Queen Mary Hosp, Hong Kong, 59-60; resident, Dept Psychiat, State Univ NY Stony Brook, 75-7, res asst prof, 77-79; psychiatrist, pvt pract, 81- *Mem:* NY Acad Sci; AAAS; Biophys Soc; Am Psychiat Asn; AMA; Am Pharm Asn; Am Med Soc Alcohol & Drug Dependancies. *Res:* Effects of central nervous system drugs and toxicants on performance, memory and learning; computer system applications in behavioral pharmacology and toxicology, psychiatry and in electroencephalogram analysis; biomathematics; broncho-genic carcinoma; congenital tumors. *Mailing Add:* St Therese Prof Off Bldg Suite 223 St Therese Med Ctr Waukegan IL 60085

**TSOKOS, CHRIS PETER,** APPLIED MATHEMATICS, STATISTICS. *Current Pos:* DIR GRAD PROG STATIST & STOCHASTIC SYSTS, UNIV SFLA, 72- & PROF MATH & STATIST, 72- *Personal Data:* b Greece, Mar 25, 37; US citizen; m 93, Deborah Bradney. *Educ:* Univ RI, BS & MS, 61; Univ Conn, PhD(math statist & probability), 67. *Prof Exp:* proj engr elec boat div, Gen Dynamics Corp, 61-63; asst prof math, Univ RI, 63-69; assoc prof statist, Va Polytech Inst, 69-71. *Concurrent Pos:* RI Res Coun res grants 65-66 & 67-68; NSF lectr, Univ RI, 65-68; consult, US Army Electronics Command Ctr, Ft Monmouth, NJ, USN Underwater Technol, AT&T, M&M Mars, Environ Protection Agency & Bur Land Mgt; dir contracts, AFSOR, 74-79, NASA, 75-79 & Bur Land Mgt, 74-77; vpres, Robert M Thrall & Assocs, Houston. *Mem:* AAAS; Am Math Soc; fel Am Statist Asn; Opers Res Soc Am; Int Fedn Nonlingar Analyst (vpres). *Res:* Statistical theory and applications; stochastic integral equations; stochastic systems theory; biomathematics; stochastic modeling; time series; stochastic differential games; Bayesian reliability theory simulation and reliability growth analysis. *Mailing Add:* Dept Math Univ SFla 4202 Fowler Ave Tampa FL 33620. *Fax:* 813-974-2700, 968-9464

**TSOLAS, ORESTES,** IMMUNOLOGY. *Current Pos:* PROF & HEAD LAB BIOL CHEM, SCH MED, UNIV IOANNINA, 78-, DIR, UNIV CLIN CHEM LAB, 83- *Personal Data:* b Istanbul, Turkey, Dec 5, 33; US citizen; m 86, Chariklia Bebou; c Amaryllis. *Educ:* Robert Col, Istanbul, BSc, 54; Cambridge Univ, BA, 57, MA, 61; Albert Einstein Col Med, PhD(molecular biol), 67. *Prof Exp:* Asst prof molecular biol, Albert Einstein Col Med, 70-72; asst mem, Roche Inst Molecular Biol, 72-78. *Concurrent Pos:* Prof, Univ Sao Paulo, 69-; vis lectr, Rotterdam Med Fac, Neth, 72; vis asst prof microbiol & immunol, Albert Einstein Col Med, 72-79; adj prof, Rutgers Univ, 74-78; dean Med Sch, Univ Ioannina, 80-83; sci coun, Hellenic Pasteur Inst, 83-85; Greek Nat Adv Coun Res, 85-91; vis scientist, Roche Inst Molecular Biol, 89; distinguished vis scientist, Roche Inst Molecular Biol, 94; dir, Gen Inst Pasteur Hellenique, Athens, 95. *Mem:* Am Soc Biochem & Molecular Biol; Am Chem Soc; Biochem Soc Gt Brit; Am Asn Clin Chem; Nat Acad Clin Biochem; Hellenic Biochem & Biophys Soc (vpres, 80-81, pres, 92-93). *Res:* Enzymes and immunopeptides, structure and function. *Mailing Add:* Lab Biol Chem Univ Ioannina Med Sch Ioannina GR-451 10 Greece. *Fax:* 30-651-33442

**TSONG, IGNATIUS SIU TUNG,** PHYSICS, MATERIALS SCIENCE. *Current Pos:* PHYSICS DEPT, ARIZ STATE UNIV, 81- *Personal Data:* b Hong Kong, Jan 4, 43; Australian citizen; m 70; c 1. *Educ:* Univ Leeds, BSc, 66, MSc, 67; Univ London, PhD(physics), 70. *Prof Exp:* Fel physics, Univ Essex, 70-73; sr tutor, Monash Univ, 73-76; res assoc, Pa State Univ, 76-78, asst prof mat res, 78-79, res assoc, 79-81. *Mem:* Am Phys Soc; Mineral Soc Am; Am Ceramic Soc; Am Vacuum Soc; AAAS; Electrochem Soc. *Res:* Sputter-induced optical emission; surface characterization using ion beam techniques; analysis of hydrogen in solids; physics of particle-solid interactions. *Mailing Add:* 1445 E Palomino Dr Tempe AZ 85284. *Fax:* 602-965-7954; *E-Mail:* tsong@phyast.1a.asu.edu

**TSONG, TIAN YOW,** BIOPHYSICAL CHEMISTRY, BIOCHEMISTRY. *Current Pos:* PROF BIOCHEM, UNIV MINN, 88- *Personal Data:* b Taiwan, Sept 6, 34; US citizen; m 71; c 2. *Educ:* Chung Hsing Univ, Taiwan, BS, 64; Yale Univ, MS, 67, MPh, 68, PhD(phys biochem), 69. *Prof Exp:* From asst prof to assoc prof, physiol chem, Sch Med Johns Hopkins Univ, 72-87. *Concurrent Pos:* Fel, Stanford Univ, 70-72; NSF res grant, Sch Med, Johns Hopkins Univ, 73-; NIH res grant, 75-; mem, NIH Study Sect, 80-84; Off Naval Res Contract, 87- *Mem:* Am Chem Soc; Biophys Soc; Am Soc Biol Chemists; AAAS. *Res:* Physical chemistry of proteins and membrane lipids, and its correlation to biological functions. *Mailing Add:* Dept Biochem CBS Univ Minn 1479 Gortner Ave St Paul MN 55108. *Fax:* 612-625-5780

**TSONG, TIEN TZOU,** SOLID STATE PHYSICS. *Current Pos:* Res assoc physics, 67-69, from asst prof to assoc prof, 69-74, PROF PHYSICS, PA STATE UNIV, 75- *Personal Data:* b Taiwan, China, Sept 6, 34; m 64; c 3. *Educ:* Taiwan Norm Univ, BSc, 59; Pa State Univ, MS, 64, PhD(physics), 66. *Concurrent Pos:* Fel, Japan Soc Prom Sci. *Mem:* Fel Am Phys Soc; Am Vacuum Soc; fel Japan Soc Promotion Sci; Mat Res Soc. *Res:* Surface physics; field effect on metal surface; field ionization; field desorption and field ion microscopy; atomic processes on solid surfaces. *Mailing Add:* Inst Physics Academia Sinica Nankang Taipei Taiwan. *Fax:* 886-2786-9601

**TSONG, YUN YEN,** BIOCHEMISTRY, ORGANIC CHEMISTRY. *Current Pos:* res assoc biochem, 70-72, SCIENTIST BIOCHEM, POP COUN, ROCKEFELLER UNIV, 74- *Personal Data:* b Taiwan, China, Jan 15, 37; m 67, Shin-Fang Lin; c Shirley & Jerry. *Educ:* Nat Taiwan Univ, BS, 60; Univ Wis-Madison, PhD(biochem), 68. *Prof Exp:* Sr med chemist, SmithKline & French Labs, 68-70. *Mem:* AAAS; Am Chem Soc; Endocrine Soc; Am Fertil Soc; NY Acad Sci. *Res:* Mechanism of action of steroid and peptide hormones; metabolism and microbial transformation of steroids; contraceptive developmemt; protein chemistry and pharmaceutical chemistry. *Mailing Add:* 33 Evergreen Dr North Caldwell NJ 07006. *Fax:* 212-327-7678; *E-Mail:* tsong@popcbr.rockefeller.edu

**TSONOPOULOS, CONSTANTINE,** CHEMICAL ENGINEERING, THERMODYNAMICS. *Current Pos:* Engr appl thermodyn, Exxon Res & Eng Co, 70-71, res engr, 71-74, sr res engr, 74-78, sr staff engr, 78-80, eng assoc, 80-82, sr eng assoc, 82-92, ENG ADV, EXXON RES & ENG CO, SUBSID EXXON CORP, 92- *Personal Data:* b Megalopolis, Greece, Sept 5, 41; US citizen; m 69; c Alexi & Oresti. *Educ:* Ga Inst Technol, BChemEng, 64, MS, 65; Univ Calif, Berkeley, PhD(chem eng), 70. *Concurrent Pos:* Tech Data Comt, Am Petrol Inst, 79-; Design Inst Phys Property Data, Am Inst Chem Engrs, 82; mem, working group, Int Union Pure & Appl Chem, 86-; mem, NSF adv cmt chem & process eng, 83-84, panel chem engrs, Nat Res Coun, 88-91, eng, 88-90. *Mem:* Am Inst Chem Engrs; Am Chem Soc; Am Petrol Inst; Sigma Xi; AAAS; Int Union Pure & Appl Chem. *Res:* Thermodynamics of fluid-phase equilibria; properties of polar systems and electrolyte solutions (hydrocarbon/water/weak electrolytes); heavy hydrocarbons and synthetic liquids (from coal, shale or gas). *Mailing Add:* Exxon Res & Eng Co PO Box 101 Florham Park NJ 07932-0101. *E-Mail:* costa.tsonopoulos@exxon.spring.com

**TSOTSIS, THOMAS KARL,** COMPOSITE MATERIALS, LONG TERM DURABILITY & AGING EFFECTS. *Current Pos:* PRIN ENGR & SCIENTIST, MCDONNELL DOUGLAS AEROSPACE, 96- *Personal Data:* b Sycamore, Ill, Oct 13, 61. *Educ:* Washington Univ, St Louis, BS, 83; Tex A&M Univ, MS, 86, PhD(mech eng), 89. *Prof Exp:* Sr res engr, Ciba Composites, 88-94, staff scientist, 94-96. *Mem:* Am Soc Testing & Mat; Soc Advan Mat & Process Engrs. *Res:* Long-term aging effects on composite materials focusing on high temperature and moisture effects; honeycomb sandwich structures and stitched resin film infusion processing. *Mailing Add:* 2401 Swardlow Rd MICCO71-0015 Long Beach CA 90807

**TSOU, CHEN-LU,** ENZYME MECHANISM, PROTEIN FOLDING. *Current Pos:* Res assoc, Inst Biochem, Academia Sinica, 51-56, res prof, 56-91, vdir, 77-83, DIR, NAT LAB BIOMACROMOLECULES, INST BIOPHYS, ACADEMIA SINICA, 88- *Personal Data:* b Wuxi, China, May 17, 23; m 49; c 1. *Educ:* Nat SW Univ, China, BSc, 45; Univ Cambridge, Eng, PhD(biochem), 51. *Concurrent Pos:* Ed, Fed Am Socs Exp Biol J, 88; vis prof, Harvard Univ Med Sch, 81-82; Fogarty scholar, NIH, 86-90. *Mem:* Hon mem Am Soc Biochem & Molecular Biol; NY Acad Sci. *Res:* Comparison of activity and conformational changes during enzyme folding and unfolding; mechanism and regulation of enzyme action; kinetics of irreversible inactivation of enzymes; effect of chemical modification on the activities of proteins. *Mailing Add:* Inst Biophys Academia Sinica 15 Datun Rd Chaoyang Dist Beijing 100101 People's Republic of China. *Fax:* 86-10-202-7837

**TSOU, F(U) K(ANG),** heat transfer, fluid mechanics, for more information see previous edition

**TSOULFANIDIS, NICHOLAS,** NUCLEAR ENGINEERING, PHYSICS. *Current Pos:* From instr to prof nuclear eng, Univ Mo, Rolla, 68-81, chmn dept, 81-85, interim vchancellor acad affairs, 85-86, PROF & ASST DEAN, UNIV MO, ROLLA, 87- *Personal Data:* b Ioannina, Greece, May 6, 38; m 64; c 2. *Educ:* Nat Univ Athens, BS, 60; Univ Ill, Urbana, MS, 65, PhD(nuclear eng), 68. *Concurrent Pos:* Sabbatical leave, Nuclear Res Ctr, Cadarache, France, 86-87; consult. *Mem:* Nat Soc Prof Engrs; Am Nuclear Soc; Health Physics Soc. *Res:* Neutron and gamma transport; health physics; nuclear fuel cycle; author of 2 books. *Mailing Add:* 10310 Line Ave Rolla MO 65401

**TSU, RAPHAEL,** CONDUCTIVITY IN SEMICONDUCTORS. *Current Pos:* PROF ELEC ENG, UNIV NC, CHARLOTTE, 79-, DIR, QUANTUM ELECTRONIC LAB. *Educ:* Univ Dayton, BS, 56; Ohio State Univ, MS, 57 PhD(elec eng), 60. *Honors & Awards:* Alexander von Humboldt Award, 75; Int New Mat Prize, Am Phys Soc, 85. *Prof Exp:* Res assoc, Bell Tel Labs, 61-65; IBM, T J Watson Res Ctr, 66-79. *Mem:* Fel Am Phys Soc. *Res:* Theory and experiment in solid state and semiconductor physics transport and optical properties; microwave and light scattering; thin film deposition; device physics; contributed numerous articles to publications. *Mailing Add:* Dept Elec Eng Univ NC Charlotte NC 28223

**TSU, T(SUNG) C(HI),** PROJECT PLANNING & EVALUATION. *Current Pos:* RETIRED. *Personal Data:* b Haining, China, Aug 27, 15; nat US; m 48; c 1. *Educ:* Chiao Tung Univ, BSc, 37; Univ Toronto, MASc, 41; Mass Inst Technol, ScD(aeronaut eng), 44. *Prof Exp:* Asst engr, Bur Aeronaut Res, China, 39-40; engr, Div Indust Coop, Mass Inst Technol, 44-45; consult engr, Gen Mach Corp, Ohio, 45-47; res assoc, Pa State Col, 47-49, assoc prof, 50-52; sr engr, Aviation Gas Turbine Div, Div Westinghouse Elec Corp, 52-55, res engr, Res Labs, 55-57, adv engr, 57-82. *Concurrent Pos:* Adj prof, Drexel Inst Technol, 53-54. *Mem:* AAAS; Am Soc Mech Engrs. *Res:* Space vehicles propulsion; magnetohydrodynamics; fluid mechanics; thermodynamics; energy conversion; design optimization. *Mailing Add:* 3540 Ridgewood Dr Pittsburgh PA 15235

**TSUANG, MING TSO,** PSYCHIATRY, PSYCHIATRIC EPIDEMIOLOGY. *Current Pos:* dir psychiat epidemiol, 85-, prof psychiat, Med Sch, 85-93, STANLEY COBB PROF PSYCHIAT, HARVARD UNIV, 93-, PROF & HEAD, DEPT PSYCHIAT, MASS MENT HEALTH CTR & SUPT, 93- *Personal Data:* b Tainan, Taiwan, Nov 16, 31; US citizen; m 58; c 3. *Educ:* Nat Taiwan Univ, MD, 57; Univ London, PhD(psychiat), 65, DSc, 81. *Hon Degrees:* MA, Brown Univ, 83; AM, Harvard Univ, 87. *Honors & Awards:* Clin Res Award, Am Acad Clin Psychiatrists, 83; Rema Lapouse Award, Am Pub Health Asn, 84; Stanley Dean Award for Res in Schizophrenia, Am Col Psychiatrists, 89; 67th Ann Maudsley Lectr, Royal Col Psych, 91; Lifetime Achievement Award, Int Soc Psychiat Genetics, 95. *Prof Exp:* Lectr psychiat & sr psychiatrist, Dept Neurol & Psychiat, Nat Taiwan Univ Hosp, 61-63; vis res worker, Med Res Coun Psychiat Genetics Res Unit, Maudsley Hosp & Inst Psychiat, Univ London, 63-65; lectr & sr psychiatrist, Dept Neurol & Psychiat, Nat Taiwan Univ Hosp, 65-68, assoc prof & sr psychiatrist, 68-71; vis assoc prof & staff psychiatrist, Barnes & Renard Hosp, Sch Med, Wash Univ, 71-72; assoc prof & staff psychiatrist, Iowa Psychiat Hosp, Col Med, Univ Iowa, 72-75, prof, 75-82; prof & vchmn, Dept Psychiat, Brown Univ, 82-85; chief, Psychiat Serv, Brocton-West Roxbury Vet Admin Ctr, 84-93; Fritz Redlich fel, Ctr Adv Study & Behav Sci, London, 91. *Concurrent Pos:* Res fel, Nat Coun Sci Develop, Repub China, 60-70; fel, Sino-Brit Fel Trust, UK, 63-65; collab investr, Int Pilot Study Schizophrenia, WHO, Geneva, Switz, 66-71; consult psychiatrist, Vet Admin Hosp, Iowa City, Iowa, 72-82; chief staff psychiatrist, E Ward, Psychiatr Hosp, Univ Iowa, 72-82; vis prof, Dept Psychiat, Univ Oxford, Eng, 79-80; Josiah Macy fac scholar award, 79-80; chief psychiat, Psychiat Serv, Brockton-West Roxbury Vet Admin Med Ctr, 85-; NIMH Merit Award on Psychopath & Heterogeneity of Schizophrenia, 88-93; mem, Med Res Serv Planning Coun, Vet Health Serv & Res Admin, Vet Admin Cent Off, 90- *Mem:* Inst Med-Nat Acad Sci; AAAS; Am Psychopath Asn; Behav Genetics Asn; Am Psychiat Asn; Sigma Xi; Psychiat Res Soc. *Res:* Long-term follow-up and family studies of schizophrenia, mania, depression and atypical psychoses; diagnostic classification of mental disorder; psychiatric genetics; clinical psychopharmacological research; heterogeneity of schizophrenia; genetic linkage studies of schizophrenia. *Mailing Add:* Supt Ment Health Ctr 74 Fenwood Rd Boston MA 02115

**TSUBOI, KENNETH KAZ,** BIOCHEMISTRY. *Current Pos:* assoc prof pediat, 60-66, sr res assoc, 66-73, adj prof, 73-82, PROF PEDIAT, SCH MED, STANFORD UNIV, 82- *Personal Data:* b Seno, Japan, Feb 7, 22; nat US; m 47; c 2. *Educ:* St Thomas Col, BS, 44; Univ Minn, MS, 46, PhD(biochem), 48. *Prof Exp:* Asst physiol chem, Univ Minn, 44-47; res assoc path, Wash Univ, 48; res assoc oncol, Univ Kans Med Ctr, Kansas City, 48-51; res assoc biochem, Columbia Univ, 51-55; asst prof, Med Col, Cornell Univ, 55-60. *Concurrent Pos:* Estab investr, Am Heart Asn, 59-64; vis prof, Univ Tokyo, 67. *Mem:* Am Soc Biol Chemists; Biophys Soc; Am Asn Cancer Res. *Res:* Cellular and muscle biochemistry; enzymology. *Mailing Add:* 844 Sonoma Terr Stanford CA 94305-1024

**TSUCHIYA, MIZUKI,** PHYSICAL OCEANOGRAPHY. *Current Pos:* from asst res oceanogr to assoc res oceanogr, 69-79, RES OCEANOGR, SCRIPPS INST OCEANOG, 79- *Personal Data:* b Matsuyama, Japan, May 2, 29; m 56, Kozuko Seki; c Akiko & Yoko. *Educ:* Univ Tokyo, BS, 53, DSc, 62. *Honors & Awards:* Okada Takematsu Prize, Oceanog Soc Japan, 67. *Prof Exp:* Res asst geophys, Univ Tokyo, 55-60; instr oceanog, Meteorol Col, Japan Meteorol Agency, 60-64; res assoc, Johns Hopkins Univ, 64-67; lectr, Univ Tokyo, 67-69. *Mem:* Am Geophys Union; Oceanog Soc. *Res:* Circulation and distributions of water characteristics in the ocean. *Mailing Add:* Scripps Inst Oceanog 0230 La Jolla CA 92093-0230

**TSUDA, ROY TOSHIO,** PHYCOLOGY. *Current Pos:* Instr biol, Univ Guam, 67-68, asst prof, Dept Biol & Marine Lab, 68-70, assoc prof marine biol, 70-74, dir, Marin Lab, 74-76, prof marine biol, 74-89, dean, Grad Sch & Res, 78-84, acad vpres, 84-89, EMER PROF MARINE BIOL, UNIV GUAM, 89-; CHIEF ENVIRON SERV, DUENAS & ASSOCS, INC, 90- *Personal Data:* b Honolulu, Hawaii, Dec 25, 39; m 59, Sally Y Kamiya; c Mark T, Craig H & Ryan Y. *Educ:* Univ Hawaii, BA, 63, MS, 66; Univ Wis-Milwaukee, PhD(bot), 70. *Concurrent Pos:* Gen ed, Micronesica, Univ Guam, 72-76, chmn, Coral Reef Comt, Pac Sci Asn, 75-81; chmn coral reef comt, Int Asn Biol Oceanog, 79-81; mem comt ecology, Int Union Conserv Nature & Natural Resources, 81-84, Survival Serv comt, 77-83. *Mem:* Phycol Soc Am; Int Soc Reef Studies; Int Phycol Soc; Jap Soc Phycol. *Res:* Taxonomy and ecology of tropical marine algae; primary productivity. *Mailing Add:* Univ Guam Sta PO Box 5316 Mangilao GU 96923. *Fax:* 671-646-6315

**TSUEI, YEONG GING,** APPLIED MECHANICS. *Current Pos:* from instr to prof, 61-91, EMER PROF MECH, UNIV CINCINNATI, 92-; PROF MECH ENG, NAT CHENG KUNG UNIV, 91- *Personal Data:* b China, Feb 25, 32; m 62, Judy; c Betty, Karen, Jennifer & Stephanie. *Educ:* Cheng Kung Univ, Taiwan, BSCE, 56; Colo State Univ, MCE, 60, PhD(fluid mech), 63. *Prof Exp:* Asst, Cheng Kung Univ, Taiwan, 56-58. *Mem:* Am Inst Aeronaut & Astronaut; Am Soc Civil Engrs; Am Soc Eng Educ. *Res:* Modal analysis and engineering mechanics; computer application. *Mailing Add:* 4802 Chapel Ridge Dr Cincinnati OH 45223-1275

**TSUI, BENJAMIN MING WAH,** MEDICAL IMAGING. *Current Pos:* assoc prof, 82-91, PROF BIOMED ENG & RADIOL, UNIV NC, CHAPEL HILL, 91- *Personal Data:* b Hong Kong, June 1, 48; m 75, Amy Ong; c Andrew S & Kevin S. *Educ:* Chung Chi Col, BSc, 70; Dartmouth Col, AM, 72; Univ Chicago, PhD(med physics), 77. *Honors & Awards:* Sci Res Award, Eastman Kodak Co, 77. *Prof Exp:* Res assoc med physics, Univ Chicago, 77-79, asst prof, Dept Radiol & Franklin McLean Res Inst, 79-82. *Mem:* Am Asn Physicists Med; Soc Nuclear Med; Soc Magnetic Resonance in Med; Inst Elec & Electronics Engrs; AAAS; Sigma Xi. *Res:* Theory and instrumentation in radiation detection; image formation and recording in nuclear medicine; emission computed tomography imaging; magnetic resonance imaging. *Mailing Add:* Dept Radiol & Biomed Eng CB 7575 Univ NC 152 MacNider Hall Chapel Hill NC 27599-7575. *Fax:* 919-966-2963; *E-Mail:* tsui@bme.unc.edu

**TSUI, DANIEL CHEE,** SOLID STATE PHYSICS. *Current Pos:* ARTHUR LEGRAND DOTY PROF ELEC ENG, PRINCETON UNIV, 82- *Personal Data:* b Henan, China, Feb 28, 39; US citizen; m 64; c 2. *Educ:* Augustana Col, BA, 61; Univ Chicago, MS & PhD(physics), 67. *Honors & Awards:* Oliver E Buckley Condensed Matter Physics Prize, Am Phys Soc, 84. *Prof Exp:* Res assoc, Univ Chicago, 67-68; mem tech staff, Bell Labs, Murray Hill, NJ, 68-82. *Mem:* Nat Acad Sci. *Res:* Electronic properties of metals, surface properties of semiconductors; low temperature physics. *Mailing Add:* Elec Eng Dept Princeton Univ Princeton NJ 08544. *Fax:* 609-258-6279

**TSUI, JAMES BAO-YEN,** ELECTRICAL ENGINEERING. *Current Pos:* ELECTRONICS ENGR, AVIONICS LAB, WRIGHT-PATTERSON AFB, 73- *Personal Data:* b Shantung, China; US citizen. *Educ:* Nat Taiwan Univ, BS, 57; Marquette Univ, MS, 61; Univ Ill, PhD(elec eng), 65. *Prof Exp:* From asst prof to assoc prof elec eng, Univ Dayton, 65-73. *Concurrent Pos:* Scientist, Labtron Corp Am, 68-69. *Mem:* Am Soc Eng Educ; Inst Elec & Electronics Engrs. *Res:* Rare earth cobalt permanent magnets and their applications; microwave receivers. *Mailing Add:* Air Force Wright Labs WI/Aawp-1 Wright-Patterson AFB OH 45433

**TSUI, LAP-CHEE,** BIOLOGICAL SCIENCE, GENETICS. *Current Pos:* fel, 81-83, scientist, 83-88, SR SCIENTIST, DEPT GENETICS, RES INST, HOSP SICK CHILDREN, 88-, SELLERS CHAIR, CYSTIC FIBROSIS RES, 89-; PROF, DEPT MOLECULAR & MED GENETICS, UNIV TORONTO, 90- *Personal Data:* b Shang-hai, China, Dec 21, 50; Can citizen; c 2. *Educ:* Chinese Univ Hong Kong, BSc, 72, MPhil, 74; Univ Pittsburgh, PhD(biol sci), 79. *Hon Degrees:* DSc, Univ NB, 91 & Chinese Univ Hong Kong, 92; Dr Civil Law, Univ King's Col, Halifax, 91; LLD, St Francis Xavier

Univ, Antigonish, NS, 94. *Honors & Awards:* Gold Medal Hon, Pharmaceut Mfr Asn Can, 89; Centennial Award, Royal Soc Can, 89; Gairdner Int Award, 90; Order Can, 91; Doris Tulcin Cystic Fibrosis Res Achievement Award, Cystic Fibrosis Found, 91. *Prof Exp:* Investr, Biol Div, Oak Ridge Nat Lab, 79-80. *Concurrent Pos:* From asst prof to assoc prof, Dept Med Genetics & Med Biophys, Univ Toronto, 83-90; assoc ed, Am J Human Genetics, 90-93 & Clin Genetics, 91-; Howard Hughes Int Scholar, 91- *Mem:* Am Soc Human Genetics; Asn Chinese Geneticists Am (past pres); Chinese Can Asn Biomed Prof (past pres); Human Genome Orgn; fel Royal Soc Can; Academia Sinica. *Res:* Molecular genetics of cystic fibrosis; characterization of human chromosome 7; regulation of gene expression in mammalian lens development; mapping of the responsible for the Tourette Syndrome. *Mailing Add:* Dept Genetics Hosp Sick Children 555 University Ave Toronto ON M5G 1X8 Can. *E-Mail:* cfdata@sickkids.on.ca

**TSUJI, FREDERICK ICHIRO,** BIOCHEMISTRY. *Current Pos:* assoc res biochemist, 79-82, RES BIOCHEMIST, SCRIPPS INST OCEANOG, UNIV CALIF, SAN DIEGO, 82- *Personal Data:* b Honolulu, Hawaii, Aug 23, 23; m, Masako Koga. *Educ:* Cornell Univ, AB, 46, MS, 48, PhD(biochem), 50. *Prof Exp:* Asst biochem & nutrit, Cornell Univ, 48-49; res biochemist, Children's Fund Mich, 49-50; asst prof biochem & pharmacol, Duquesne Univ, 50-52; res asst biol, Princeton Univ, 52-55; tech dir res lab, Vet Admin Hosp, Pittsburgh, Pa, 55-72; biochemist, Brentwood Vet Admin Hosp, Los Angeles, 72-76; prog dir biochem, NSF, 76-78. *Concurrent Pos:* Res assoc, Mercy Hosp, 51-52; Anathan fel inst res, Montefiore Hosp, 52; investr, Marine Biol Lab, Woods Hole, 53-54; lectr, Univ Pittsburgh, 56-65, from adj assoc prof to adj prof, 65-72; sr scientist, Te Vega Exped Pac Ocean, Hopkins Marine Sta, Stanford Univ, 66; mem Alpha Helix Biol Exped to New Guinea, Scripps Inst Oceanog, Univ Calif, San Diego, 69; Hancock fel, Univ Southern Calif, 72-76; vis prof dept med chem, Fac Med, Kyoto, Univ, Japan, 74; vis res prof, Univ Southern Calif, 78-82, res prof biol, 82-; biochemist, Brentwood Vet Admin Hosp, Los Angeles, 78-87; head, Dept Enzymes & Metab, Osaka Biosci Inst, 87-93; vis prof, Grad Sch Biol Sci, Nara Inst Sci & Technol, Japan, 96. *Mem:* Am Soc Biol Chem; Am Chem Soc; Biophys Soc; Am Asn Immunol; Soc Gen Physiol. *Res:* Bioluminescence; enzyme reactions. *Mailing Add:* Marine Biol Res Div 0202 Scripps Inst Oceanog Univ Calif San Diego La Jolla CA 92093. *E-Mail:* ftsuji@ucsd.edu

**TSUJI, GORDON YUKIO,** SOIL PHYSICS. *Current Pos:* Asst soil scientist, Dept Agron & Soil Sci, 71-74, proj mgr, Benchmark soils proj, 74-83, PROJ MGR, INT BENCHMARK SITES NETWORK FOR AGROTECH TRANSFER & US AID SUBGRANT ON TOPSOILS & SOIL MGT, UNIV HAWAII-US AID, 83- *Personal Data:* b Honolulu, Hawaii, July 31, 42; m 67, Sharon A; c Garvin, Stuart & Michael. *Educ:* Univ Hawaii, BS, 65, MS, 67; Purdue Univ, Lafayette, PhD(soil physics), 71. *Concurrent Pos:* AID fel, Univ Hawaii, 71- *Mem:* Am Soc Agron; Sigma Xi; Int Soc Soil Sci; Soil Sci Soc Am; NZ Soc Soil Sci. *Res:* Water movement in soils; infiltration of water into soils; water distribution under drip irrigation; tropical meteorology; United States soil taxonomy and agricultural development; agrotechnology transference; systems analysis; crop modeling; decision support systems. *Mailing Add:* 94381 Hokuili Pl Mililani HI 96789. *E-Mail:* gordont@uhunix.uhcc.hawaii.edu

**TSUJI, KIYOSHI,** ANALYTICAL MICROBIOLOGY, CHROMATOGRAPHY. *Current Pos:* res assoc analytical res & develop, Upjohn Co, 64-71, sr res scientist, Control Anal Res & Develop, 74-92, SR SCIENTIST V, UPJOHN CO, 92- *Personal Data:* b Kyoto, Japan, May 31, 31; m 58, Ruriko Ikenami; c Shoko, Hiroshi & Jun. *Educ:* Kyoto Univ, BS, 54; Univ Mass, MS, 56, PhD(food technol), 59. *Honors & Awards:* William E Upjohn Award, Upjohn Co, 71; Pioneer Lab Robotics Award, Lab Robotic Asn, 85; Nicholas Copernicus Award, Qual Control Acad, 86. *Prof Exp:* Fel food sci, Rutgers Univ, 59-60; staff microbiol, Nat Canners Asn, Calif, 60-63; res assoc food sci, Mass Inst Technol, 63-64. *Concurrent Pos:* Ed, J Lab Robotics & Automation & J Radiation Sterlization; vis scientist, Gray Freshwater Res Inst, Univ Minn, 88-89. *Mem:* Am Chem Soc; Am Soc Microbiol; Inst Food Technologists. *Res:* Analytical microbiology; microbioassay automation; analysis of antibiotics by gas-liquid chromatography and high-performance liquid chromatography; sterility test; bacterial endotoxin analysis of vitamins; endotoxin detection by Limulus amebocyte lysate; environmental microbiology; application of expert system; laboratory automation; vision systems; oligonucleotide probe; biotechnology; analysis of recombinant proteins by capillary electrophoresis. *Mailing Add:* 5616 Saddle Club Dr Kalamazoo MI 49009

**TSUK, ANDREW GEORGE,** PHYSICAL CHEMISTRY, POLYMER CHEMISTRY. *Current Pos:* RES ASST PROF, DEPT OPHTHAL, SCH MED, BOSTON UNIV, 92- *Personal Data:* b Budapest, Hungary, July 11, 32; US citizen; m 91, Susan H Frey; c Michael & Robert. *Educ:* Budapest Polytech Inst, dipl chem eng, 54; Polytech Inst Brooklyn, PhD(chem), 64. *Prof Exp:* Engr, Indust Fermentations, Hungary, 54-56; res chemist, Schwarz Biores, Inc, 58-62, tech asst to pres, 64-65, dir radiochem div, 65-66; sr res chemist, W R Grace & Co, Md, 66-72; group leader pharmaceut develop, Ayerst Labs Inc, 72-74, res assoc, 74-86; sr scientist, Biotek Inc, Woburn Mass, 86-92. *Concurrent Pos:* Lectr, Polmer Sci, Northeastern Univ, Boston, Mass, 86, 90-91. *Mem:* Am Chem Soc; Asn Res Vision Ophthalmol. *Res:* Polymers in pharmaceutical dosage forms; physical chemistry of polymers; polyelectrolytes; biomedical materials; biological macromolecules; ion-exchange and radioactive tracers. *Mailing Add:* 145 Robbins Rd Arlington MA 02174

**TSUKADA, MATSUO,** ECOLOGY, PALEOECOLOGY. *Current Pos:* assoc prof, 69-71, PROF BOT, UNIV WASH, 71-, DIR LAB PALEOECOL, 69-, ADJ PROF GEOL & QUATERNARY STUDIES, 76- *Personal Data:* b Nagano, Japan, Jan 4, 30; m 56; c 2. *Educ:* Shinshu Univ, Japan, BS, 53; Osaka City Univ, MA, 58, PhD(biol), 61. *Prof Exp:* Japan Acad Sci fel, Osaka City Univ, 61; Seessel fel, Yale Univ, 61-62, res assoc palynology, 62-66, lectr & res assoc biol, 66-68. *Concurrent Pos:* Sigma Xi res grant, Yale Univ, 63-64, Am Philos Soc res grant, 64-65; prin investr NSF res grants, Univ Wash, 70- *Mem:* Ecol Soc Am; Am Soc Limnol & Oceanog; Am Quaternary Asn; Am Asn Stratig Palynologists; Bot Soc Japan; Sigma Xi. *Res:* Present and past environmental changes on a global scale, mainly by means of modern and fossil plants, including pollen and also animals, chemicals and heavy metals, such as lead and cadmium. *Mailing Add:* 13809 SE 20th St Bellevue WA 98005-4007

**TSUNEWAKI, KOICHIRO,** BIOSCIENCE, GENETICS. *Current Pos:* PROF, DEPT BIOSCI, FUKUI PREFECTURAL UNIV, 93- *Personal Data:* b Nov 26, 30. *Educ:* Kans State Univ, PhD, 58. *Honors & Awards:* Japan Acad Award, 97. *Prof Exp:* Emer prof, Kyoto Univ, 93. *Mem:* Foreign assoc Nat Acad Sci; Genetics Soc Can; Genetics Soc Am; Genetics Soc Agron; Genetics Soc Japan. *Mailing Add:* Dept Biosci 42121 Kenjyojima Matsucka Yoshida-gu Fu Kai 910-11-411 Japan. *Fax:* 81-7-766-16015

**TSUNG, YEAN-KAI,** SOMATIC CELL GENETICS, TUMOR BIOLOGY. *Current Pos:* OWNER, CENIGIN, 93- *Personal Data:* b Taiwan, July 30, 43; US citizen; m 72; c 2. *Educ:* Nat Taiwan Univ, BS, 67; Univ Ill, MS, 71, PhD(plant path), 74. *Prof Exp:* Asst prof genetics, Univ Mich, 75-76; trainee immunol, Div Immunol, Duke Univ Med Ctr, 76-77; asst geneticist, E K Shriver Ctr Ment Retardation, 77-81; asst prof human genetics, Sch Med, Boston Univ, 82-93. *Concurrent Pos:* Consult, Brain Res, Inc, 80- *Mem:* AAAS. *Res:* Immunological identification of human cell membrane components by the development of cross membrane transport, defective mutants and monoclonal antibodies distinguishing the mutants from wild type population. *Mailing Add:* 4 Linnell Circle Billerica MA 01821

**TSURUTANI, BRUCE TADASHI,** SPACE PLASMA PHYSICS. *Current Pos:* RES SCIENTIST & MEM TECH STAFF PHYSICS, JET PROPULSION LAB, CALIF INST TECHNOL, 72- *Personal Data:* b Los Angeles, Calif, Jan 29, 41. *Educ:* Univ Calif, Berkeley, BA, 63, PhD(physics), 72. *Mem:* AAAS; Am Geophys Union; Int Union Radio Sci; Sigma Xi. *Res:* Plasma instabilities; wave-particle interactions; interplanetary and planetary magnetic fields; particle acceleration processes; magnetospheric and heliospheric physics; x-ray sources. *Mailing Add:* 3481 Stancrest Dr No 202 Glendale CA 91208

**TSUTAKAWA, ROBERT K,** STATISTICS. *Current Pos:* assoc prof, 68-78, chmn dept, 89-95, PROF STATIST, UNIV MO-COLUMBIA, 78- *Personal Data:* b Seattle, Wash, Mar 28, 30; m 61, Teruko Tsujihara; c 3. *Educ:* Univ Chicago, BS, 56, MS, 57, PhD(statist), 63. *Prof Exp:* Res specialist, Boeing Co, 58-60 & 63-65; res assoc statist, Univ Chicago, 65-68. *Concurrent Pos:* Ed, J Educ Statist, 89-91. *Mem:* Fel Am Statist Asn; Inst Math Statist. *Res:* Statistical inference. *Mailing Add:* Dept Statist 222 Math Sci Bldg Univ Mo Columbia MO 65211

**TSUTSUI, ETHEL ASHWORTH,** BIOCHEMISTRY. *Current Pos:* assoc prof biol, 69-71, assoc prof, 71-80, PROF BIOCHEM & BIOPHYS, TEX A&M UNIV, 80- *Personal Data:* b Geneva, NY, May 31, 27; m 56; c 1. *Educ:* Keuka Col, BA, 48; Univ Rochester, PhD(biochem), 54. *Prof Exp:* Res assoc med sch med & dent, Univ Rochester, 53-55; Nat Cancer Inst fel, Sloan-Kettering Inst Cancer Res, 55-56; lectr, Tokyo Med & Dent Univ, Japan, 56-57; asst prof biol & res biochemist, C F Kettering Found, Antioch Col, 57-60; res assoc Inst Cancer Res, Col Physicians & Surgeons, Columbia Univ, 60-63, res assoc dept biochem, 63-65; asst prof biol sci, Hunter Col, 65-69. *Mem:* AAAS; Am Asn Cancer Res; Am Chem Soc; fel NY Acad Sci; Harvey Soc. *Res:* Enzymatic methylation of nucleic acids; biochemistry of cancer cells; tRNA metabolism during insect development. *Mailing Add:* Dept Biochem & Biophys Tex A&M Univ College Station TX 77843-0100

**TSVANKIN, ILYA DANIEL,** SEISMIC WAVE PROPAGATION, SEISMIC EXPLORATION. *Current Pos:* assoc res prof geophys, 92-95, CO-LEADER CTR WAVE PHENOMENA, COLO SCH MINES, 92-, ASSOC PROF GEOPHYS, 95- *Personal Data:* b Moscow, Russia, Apr 6, 56; US citizen; c 2. *Educ:* Moscow State Univ, Russia, BSc & MSc, 78, PhD(geophys), 82. *Honors & Awards:* Gold Medal Young Scientists, Soviet Acad Sci, 88; Virgil Kauffman Gold Medal, Soc Explor Geophysicists, 96. *Prof Exp:* Res scientist, Inst Physics Earth, Moscow, Russia, 78-86, dep chief lab, 87-89; consult, Res Ctr, Amoco Prod Co, Tulsa, Okla, 90-92. *Concurrent Pos:* Mem transl comt, Soc Explor Geophysicists, 91- *Mem:* Soc Explor Geophysicists; Europ Asn Explor Geophysicists; Am Geophys Union; Sigma Xi. *Res:* Seismic modeling and inversion in anisotropic media, nongeometrical and surface waves, nonlinear seismic phenomena; author of more than 50 scientific papers and patents. *Mailing Add:* Dept Geophys Colo Sch Mines Golden CO 80401-1887. *Fax:* 303-273-3478; *E-Mail:* ilya@dix.mines.colorado.edu

**TTERLIKKIS, LAMBROS,** PHYSICS. *Current Pos:* from asst prof to assoc prof phys pharmaceut, 70-81, PROF PHARMACEUT, FLA A&M UNIV, 81- *Personal Data:* b Beirut, Lebanon, Oct 17, 34; US citizen; m 60; c 2. *Educ:* Walla Walla Col, BSc, 59; Univ Denver, MSc, 62; Univ Calif, Riverside, PhD(physics), 68. *Prof Exp:* Res asst solid state physics, Denver Res Inst, Univ Denver, 59-62; assoc physicist, IBM Corp, 62-63; NIH res assoc biophys, Inst Molecular Biophys, Fla State Univ, 68-70. *Mem:* AAAS; Soc Nuclear Med; Am Pharmaceut Asn. *Res:* Pharmacokinetics of drug metabolism; physicochemical properties of drugs; solid state physics; optical properties of biopolymers. *Mailing Add:* Col Pharm Fla A&M Univ Tallahassee FL 32307

**TU, ANTHONY T,** BIOCHEMISTRY. *Current Pos:* assoc prof, 67-70, PROF BIOCHEM, COLO STATE UNIV, 70- *Personal Data:* b Taipei, Formosa, Aug 12, 30; US citizen; m 57; c 5. *Educ:* Nat Taiwan Univ, BS, 53; Univ Notre Dame, MS, 56; Stanford Univ, PhD(biochem), 60. *Honors & Awards:* Merit Award, NIH, 87. *Prof Exp:* Res assoc biochem, Yale Univ, 61-62; asst prof, Utah State Univ, 62-67. *Concurrent Pos:* NIH career develop award, 69-73. *Mem:* Am Chem Soc; Am Soc Biol Chem & Molecular Biol. *Res:* Snake venom toxins and enzymes; metal-nucleotide interaction; raman spectroscopy; structure-function relationship of snake neurotoxins, hemorrhagic and myonecrotic toxins; application of raman spectroscopy to biological compounds. *Mailing Add:* Dept Biochem & Molecular Biol Colo State Univ Ft Collins CO 80523-1870. *Fax:* 970-491-6313

**TU, CHARLES WUCHING,** MOLECULAR BEAM EPITAXY, HIGH SPEED ELECTRONIC DEVICES. *Current Pos:* assoc prof, 88-91, PROF, UNIV CALIF, SAN DIEGO, 91- *Personal Data:* b 1951; m 76; c 2. *Educ:* McGill Univ, BSc, 71; Yale Univ, MPhil, 72, PhD(phys), 78. *Prof Exp:* Lectr physics, Yale Univ, 78-80; mem tech staff, AT&T Labs, 80-87, dist MTS, 87-88. *Mem:* Am Vacuum Soc; Mats Res Soc; Inst Elec & Electronics Engrs; Soc Minerals Metals & Mats. *Res:* Molecular beam epitaxy of compound semiconductor heterostructures; high speed and high frequency electronic devices based on semiconductor heterostructures; property of quantum wells & superlattices. *Mailing Add:* Elec & Comput Eng Mail Code 0407 Univ Calif San Diego 9500 Gilman Dr La Jolla CA 92093. *Fax:* 619-534-4687; *E-Mail:* ctu@ucsd.edu

**TU, CHEN CHUAN,** chemistry, for more information see previous edition

**TU, CHEN-PEI DAVID,** GENE EXPRESSION, TRANSPOSABLE ELEMENTS. *Current Pos:* from asst prof to assoc prof, 80-90, PROF BIOCHEM & MOLECULAR BIOL, PA STATE UNIV, 90- *Personal Data:* b Taipei, China, Nov 23, 48; US citizen; m, Yen-Sheng Liu; c Benjamin, Leslie & Kimberly. *Educ:* Nat Taiwan Univ, Taipei, BS, 70; Cornell Univ, PhD(biochem & molecular biol), 76. *Prof Exp:* Res fel biochem genetics, Med Sch, Stanford Univ, 76-80. *Concurrent Pos:* Fel, Am Cancer Soc, 76-78; res career develop award, USPHS, 85-90; mem, Environ Health Sci Rev Comt, Nat Inst Environ Health Sci, 89-93; mem, molecular biol study sect, 94- *Mem:* Am Soc Biochem & Molecular Biologists; AAAS; Sigma Xi; Soc Chinese Bioscientist Am. *Res:* Gene regulation, structure and function of glutathione S-transferases. *Mailing Add:* Dept Biochem & Molecular Biol Pa State Univ University Park PA 16802. *Fax:* 814-863-7024

**TU, CHIN MING,** SOIL MICROBIOLOGY, BIOCHEMISTRY. *Current Pos:* RES SCIENTIST, RES CTR, AGR & AGRIFOOD CAN, LONDON, ONT, 66- *Personal Data:* b Hsinchu, Taiwan, Dec 14, 32; Can citizen; m 61, Paiho Chen; c Geming, Kaymin, Eulla & Sasha. *Educ:* Chung Hsing Univ, Taiwan, BSc, 56; Univ Sask, MSc, 63; Ore State Univ, PhD(microbiol), 66. *Prof Exp:* Asst org chem & soil fertil, dept agr chem, Chung Hsing Univ, Taiwan, 57-60; asst soil sci, Univ Sask, 60-62; res fel microbiol, Ore State Univ, 63-66. *Concurrent Pos:* Supvr, Univ Western Ont, London, Can, 70-, Univ Guelph, Ont, Can, 75-; consult res grant, Nat Sci & Eng Res Coun Can, 78-87, USDA, 80-83. *Mem:* Am Soc Microbiol; Can Soc Microbiol; Soc Invert Path; Sigma Xi. *Res:* Interaction between pesticides and soil microorganisms; soil science; insect pathology; pesticide pollution; pesticide degradation; nitrogen fixation; rhizobia-leguminous plants symbiosis-pesticide interaction; microbial control of insect pests; soil fertility. *Mailing Add:* Res Ctr Agr & Agrifood Can 1391 Sandford St London ON N5V 4T3 Can. *Fax:* 519-457-3997; *E-Mail:* tuc@em.agr.ca

**TU, JUI-CHANG,** PHYTOPATHOLOGY. *Current Pos:* RES SCIENTIST, HARROW RES STA, AGR CAN, 78- *Personal Data:* b Tainan, Taiwan, Aug 14, 36; Can citizen; m 64; c 2. *Educ:* Nat Taiwan Univ, BSc, 59, MSc, 61; Wash State Univ, PhD(plant path), 66. *Honors & Awards:* Bailey Award, Can Phytopathol Soc, Outstanding Res Award. *Prof Exp:* Res assoc, Iowa State Univ, 67-69; res scientist, Univ Alta, 69-70, from asst prof to assoc prof & asst dir biol & electron micros, 70-78. *Concurrent Pos:* Adj prof, Dept Biol, Univ Windsor. *Mem:* Fel Am Phytopath Soc; Can Phytopath Soc; Sigma Xi; Can Seed Growers Asn. *Res:* Diseases of legume crops and their control. *Mailing Add:* Agr & Agr Food Can Greenhouse & Processing Crops Res Ctr 2585 Hwy 18 East Harrow ON N0R 1G0 Can

**TU, KING-NING,** MATERIALS SCIENCE. *Current Pos:* PROF MAT SCI, UNIV CALIF. *Personal Data:* b Canton, China, Dec 30, 37; m 65; c 2. *Educ:* Nat Taiwan Univ, BS, 60; Brown Univ, MS, 64; Harvard Univ, PhD(appl physics), 68. *Honors & Awards:* Appl to Pract Award, Metall Soc, 88. *Prof Exp:* Res asst mat sci, Brown Univ, 63-64; res asst appl physics, Harvard Univ, 66-68, res fel, 68; sr mgr thin film sci, IBM Watson Res Ctr, 78-84, mat sci, 84-86, res staff mem phys sci, 68- *Concurrent Pos:* Sci Res Coun sr vis fel, Cavendish Lab, Cambridge Univ, Eng, 75-76, Royal Soc guest res fel, 90-91. *Mem:* Fel Am Phys Soc; Mat Res Soc (pres, 81); fel Metall Soc. *Res:* Phase transformations in alloys; kinetics in thin solid films; electrical properties of metal-silicon interfaces and compounds; device metallurgy; lead-free solder. *Mailing Add:* Dept Mat Sci & Eng Univ Calif 6532 Boeiter Hall 405 Hilgard Ave Los Angeles CA 90095-1595. *Fax:* 301-206-7353

**TU, SHIAO-CHUN,** BIOCHEMISTRY, BIOPHYSICS. *Current Pos:* from asst prof to assoc prof, 77-85, chmn dept, 89-93, PROF BIOCHEM & BIOPHYSICS, UNIV HOUSTON, 85-, PROF CHEM, 93- *Personal Data:* b Henan, China, Dec 29, 43; US citizen; m 70; c 1. *Educ:* Nat Taiwan Univ, BS, 66; Cornell Univ, MNS, 69, PhD(biochem), 73. *Honors & Awards:* Sigma Xi Award, Univ Houston, 82; Tokten Award, UN, 87. *Prof Exp:* Res assoc biochem, Grad Sch Nutrit, Cornell Univ, 73; res fel biol, Biol Labs, Harvard Univ, 73-77. *Concurrent Pos:* Tutor biol, Harvard Univ, 74-75; NIH fel, 75-77, & mem study sect, phys biochem, 84-88, 93-97; assoc ed, Photochem & Photobiol, 85-92. *Mem:* Sigma Xi; AAAS; Am Soc Photobiol; Am Chem Soc; Am Soc Biochem & Molecular Biol; Soc Chinese Bioscientists in Am. *Res:* Mechanisms of biological oxidation; structure-function relationships of flavin-and pyridine nucleotide-dependent enzymes; enzyme biotechnology; bioluminescence. *Mailing Add:* Dept Biochem & Biophys Sci Univ Houston Houston TX 77204-5934. *Fax:* 713-743-8351; *E-Mail:* dtu@uh.edu

**TU, SHU-I,** BIOPHYSICAL CHEMISTRY. *Current Pos:* res chemist, 81-88, SUPVRY RES CHEMIST, EASTERN REGIONAL RES CTR, AGR RES SERV, USDA, PHILADELPHIA, 88- *Personal Data:* b Chungking, China, Jan 3, 43; m 69; c 1. *Educ:* Nat Taiwan Univ, BS, 65; Yale Univ, MPhil, 68, PhD(chem), 69. *Prof Exp:* Res assoc biochem, Yale Univ, 69-72; res asst prof, State Univ NY, Buffalo, 72-74; asst prof chem, State Univ NY, Stony Brook, 74-81. *Mem:* Am Chem Soc; Biophys Soc; Sigma Xi. *Res:* Bioenergetics of ion transport in plant root system,; H; interactions between soil and roots. *Mailing Add:* USDA Agr Res Serv E Reg Res Ctr 600 E Mermaid Lane Philadelphia PA 19118

**TU, YIH-O,** APPLIED MATHEMATICS. *Current Pos:* STAFF MATHEMATICIAN, IBM CORP, 59- *Personal Data:* b Jiangxi, China, Jan 8, 20; m 60; c 1. *Educ:* Col Ord Eng, Chungking, China, BS, 46; Carnegie Inst Technol, MS, 54; Rensselaer Polytech Inst, PhD(math), 59. *Prof Exp:* Designer mech eng, Rockwell Mfg Co, Pa, 53-55. *Mem:* Am Math Soc; Am Phys Soc; Am Soc Mech Eng; Soc Indust & Appl Math. *Res:* Fluid mechanics; elasticity; vibration and elastic stability; continuum mechanics. *Mailing Add:* 6716 Bret Harte Dr San Jose CA 95120-2015

**TUAN, DEBBIE FU-TAI,** PHYSICAL & QUANTUM CHEMISTRY, CHEMICAL PHYSICS. *Current Pos:* from asst prof to assoc prof, 65-73, summer res fel, 66, 68 & 71, PROF CHEM, KENT STATE UNIV, 73- *Personal Data:* b Kiangsu, China, Feb 2, 30; m 87, John W Reed. *Educ:* Nat Taiwan Univ, BS, 54, MS, 58; Yale Univ, MS, 60, PhD(chem), 61. *Honors & Awards:* Career Advan Award, NSF, 95. *Prof Exp:* Teaching asst chem, Nat Taiwan Univ, 54-55; NSF res fel, Yale Univ, 61-64; NASA res grant & proj assoc, Theoret Chem Inst, Univ Wis, 64-65. *Concurrent Pos:* Vis scientist, Belfer Grad Sch Sci, Yeshiva Univ, 66 & Stanford Res Inst Int, 81; vis prof, Academia Sinica China, Nat Taiwan Univ & Nat Tsing-Hwa Univ, 67, Ohio State Univ, 93 & 95; res fel, Harvard Univ, 70; res assoc, Cornell Univ, 83. *Mem:* Am Phys Soc; Am Chem Soc; Sigma Xi; Chinese Am Chem Soc. *Res:* Many electron theory of atoms and molecules; perturbation theory; applications of quantum mechanics to chemical problems; theoretical chemistry. *Mailing Add:* Dept Chem Kent State Univ Kent OH 44242-0001. *Fax:* 330-672-3816

**TUAN, HANG-SHENG,** ELECTRICAL ENGINEERING. *Current Pos:* asst prof elec sci, 65-69, assoc prof, 69-80, PROF ELEC ENG, STATE UNIV NY, STONY BROOK, 80- *Personal Data:* b Hankow, Hupei, China, Oct 23, 35; m 65. *Educ:* Nat Taiwan Univ, BS, 58; Univ Wash, MS, 61; Harvard Univ, PhD(appl physics), 65. *Prof Exp:* Res fel electronics, Harvard Univ, 65. *Mem:* Inst Elec & Electronics Engrs. *Res:* Electromagnetic theory; antenna and wave propagation; plasma physics, microwave acoustics. *Mailing Add:* Dept Elec Eng State Univ NY Nicolls Rd Stony Brook NY 11794

**TUAN, ROCKY SUNG-CHI,** CELL BIOLOGY, DEVELOPMENTAL BIOLOGY. *Current Pos:* PROF ORTHOPED SURG, BIOCHEM & MOLECULAR BIOL, DIR, ORTHO RES LAB, THOMAS JEFFERSON UNIV, 88- *Personal Data:* b Hong Kong, Mar 5, 51. *Educ:* Berea Col, BA, 72; Rockefeller Univ, PhD(life scis), 77; Univ PA, MA, 87. *Prof Exp:* Res fel, med & orthop surg, Harvard Med Sch, Mass Gen Hosp & Children's Hosp, 77-80; from asst prof to assoc prof biol, Univ Pa, 80-86. *Mem:* Soc Develop Biol; Am Soc Cell Biol. *Res:* Biochemistry and molecular biology of embryonic calcium metabolism; biology of cell formation; cell differentiation and extracellular matrix; cardiovascular functions during development. *Mailing Add:* Dept Orthopaedic Surg Thomas Jefferson Univ 501 Curtis Clin 1015 Walnut Philadelphia PA 19107

**TUAN, SAN FU,** THEORETICAL PHYSICS, APPLIED MATHEMATICS. *Current Pos:* PROF THEORET PHYSICS, UNIV HAWAII, 66- *Personal Data:* b Tientsin, China, May 14, 32; m 63; c 4. *Educ:* Oxford Univ, BA, 54, MA, 58; Univ Calif, PhD(appl math), 58. *Prof Exp:* Res assoc, Univ Chicago, 58-60; asst prof, Brown Univ, 60-62; assoc prof, Purdue Univ, 62-65; vis prof, Univ Hawaii, 65-66; mem inst adv study, Princeton Univ, 66-72. *Concurrent Pos:* Mackinnon scholar, Magdalen Col, Oxford Univ, 51-54; consult, Argonne Nat Lab, 63-70; John S Guggenheim fel, 65-66; dir & co-ed proc, Second, Third, Fifth, Sixth & Seventh Hawaii Topical Conf Particle Physics, 67, 69, 73, 75 & 77; vis lectr, Bariloche Atomic Ctr, Argentina & Univ Buenos Aires, 69-70; vis lectr, US-China Sci Coop Prog, 70-71; vis prof, Peking Univ & Inst Theoret Physics, 79-80. *Mem:* Am Math Soc; fel Am Phys Soc. *Res:* Mathematical physics; theory of elementary particles; superconductivity; political science. *Mailing Add:* 3634 Woodlawn Terr Pl Honolulu HI 96822. *Fax:* 808-956-2930

**TUAN, TAI-FU,** THEORETICAL PHYSICS, ATMOSPHERIC DYNAMICS. *Current Pos:* from asst prof to assoc prof, 65-71, PROF PHYSICS, UNIV CINCINNATI, 71- *Personal Data:* b Tientsin, China, Sept 7, 29; US citizen; m 68, Manlin Yu. *Educ:* Cambridge Univ, BA, 51; La State Univ, MS, 53; Univ Pittsburgh, PhD(physics), 59. *Prof Exp:* Instr physics, Northwestern Univ, 59-60; univ res fel, Univ Birmingham, 61-64, Dept Sci & Indust Res res fel, 64-65. *Concurrent Pos:* USAF res grant, 69-, NSF grant, 85-87. *Mem:* Am Phys Soc; Am Geophys Union; NY Acad Sci. *Res:* Scattering theory; atmospheric physics; research in airglow, gravity waves and magnetohydrodynamic models for magnetosphere; application of scattering theory for atmospheric dynamics; investigation of instability in gravity waves gravity-wave ducting through atmospheric structure; inhomogeneous dissipation; Brunt-Doppler mechanism; critical-layer effects on optical emissions; the use of optical model for gravity-wave scattering. *Mailing Add:* Dept Physics Univ Cincinnati Cincinnati OH 45221. *E-Mail:* taifu.tuan@uc.edu

**TUBA, I STEPHEN,** ELEVATED TEMPERATURE DESIGN, FAILURE ANALYSIS. *Current Pos:* PRES, BASIC TECHNOL INC, 70-; EXEC DIR, INT TECHNOL INST, 76- *Personal Data:* b Hungary, Jan 22, 32; US citizen; m 55; c 2. *Educ:* Tech Univ Budapest, BSME, 56; Carnegie-Mellon Univ, MSME, 60; Univ Pittsburgh, PhD(mech eng), 64. *Prof Exp:* Res engr & mgr, Anal Mech Res & Develop, Westinghouse, 57-70. *Concurrent Pos:* Sr lectr math & mech eng, Carnegie-Mellon Univ, 64-70; adj prof mech eng, Univ Pittsburgh, 64-70; lectr, univs, industs & tech socs, 70- *Mem:* Am Soc Mech Engrs; Sigma Xi; Int Technol Inst. *Res:* Solid mechanics: elasticity, plasticity, creep, fatigue; engineering analysis: finite element methods, non-linear, combustion; failure analysis: machinery, equipment, systems; technology transfer: international design, development. *Mailing Add:* Int Technol Inst 7125 Saltsburg Rd Pittsburgh PA 15235

**TUBB, RICHARD ARNOLD,** limnology, fisheries, for more information see previous edition

**TUBBS, ELDRED FRANK,** ATOMIC SPECTROSCOPY. *Current Pos:* MEM TECH STAFF, JET PROPULSION LAB, 79- *Personal Data:* b Buffalo, NY, Mar 31, 24; m 49, Virginia A Lefurgy; c Rebecca R, David H & William M. *Educ:* Carnegie Inst Technol, BS, 49; Johns Hopkins Univ, PhD(physics), 56. *Honors & Awards:* Prize, Am Asn Physics Teachers, 67. *Prof Exp:* Sr physicist res ctr, Am Optical Co, 55-58; res physicist, Microwave Physics Lab, Sylvania Elec Prod Inc, 58-60; res physicist, WCoast Br, Gen Tel & Electronics Labs, Inc, 60-63; from asst prof to assoc prof physics, Harvey Mudd Col, 63-72, prof, 72-79. *Concurrent Pos:* Consult, Mech Universe, 82-86. *Mem:* Optical Soc Am; Soc Photo-Optical Instrumentation Engrs; Sigma Xi. *Res:* Optical instruments and metrology; interferometry; absolute f-values; teaching apparatus and techniques. *Mailing Add:* 730 W 11th St Claremont CA 91711-3748. *E-Mail:* eldred.tubbs@jpl.nasa.gov

**TUBBS, RAYMOND R,** HEMATOPATHOLOGY, IMMUNOPATHOLOGY. *Current Pos:* Intern & resident med, 73-75, resident lab, 75-79, STAFF PATHOLOGIST, CLEVELAND CLIN FOUND, 79- *Personal Data:* b Ithaca, NY, Aug 23, 46; m 69; c 2. *Educ:* Bob Jones Univ, BS, 68; Kirksville Col Osteop Med, DO, 73; Am Bd Path, dipl, 79 & 83. *Concurrent Pos:* Clin assoc immunopath, Cleveland Clin Found, 79, fel, 79-80. *Mem:* Col Am Pathologists; Am Immunologists; Am Asn Pathologists; Am Asn Cancer Res; Int Acad Path; Am Soc Hemat. *Res:* Hematopathology; nephropathology; immunotyping support for biologic response modifiers research program. *Mailing Add:* Dir Immunotyping Lab Dept Path L2-25 Cleveland Clin Found 9500 Euclid Ave Cleveland OH 44195-0002

**TUBBS, ROBERT KENNETH,** COLLOID CHEMISTRY, SURFACE CHEMISTRY. *Current Pos:* RETIRED. *Personal Data:* b Gary, Ind, Nov 25, 36; m 56; c 3. *Educ:* Ohio State Univ, BS, 58, PhD(colloid chem), 62. *Prof Exp:* Res chemist, Electrochem Dept, E I du Pont de Nemours & Co, Inc, Del, 62-67, staff scientist, 67-68, res supvr, 68-70, gen tech supt, Indust Chem Dept, NY, 70-73, sr res supvr, Plastics Dept, 73-74, prod mgr, 74-75, develop mgr, Plastics Dept, 75-76, com develop mgr pharmaceut, 76-77, prod mgr, 78-85. *Concurrent Pos:* Consult chemist, 85-; vis prof, Bloomsburg Univ, 87, asst prof chem, 89-92. *Mem:* Am Chem Soc. *Res:* Structure and interactions of macromolecules; kinetics of polymerization; molecular biology; emulsion polymerization; coatings; adhesives. *Mailing Add:* RD 2 Box 140 A Gnoga Lakes Sweet Valley PA 17814

**TUBIS, ARNOLD,** PHYSIOLOGICAL ACOUSTICS. *Current Pos:* res assoc, Purdue Univ, 60-62, from asst prof to assoc prof, 62-69, asst head dept, 66-73, actg head dept, 88, PROF PHYSICS, PURDUE UNIV, 69-, HEAD DEPT, 89- *Personal Data:* b Pottstown, Pa, Mar 28, 32; m 59, Charlotte I Litman; c Cheryl (Brown) & Eliot J. *Educ:* Mass Inst Technol, BS, 54, PhD(theoret physics), 59. *Prof Exp:* Res asst, Mass Inst Technol, 54-57; asst prof physics, Worcester Polytech Inst, 58-60. *Concurrent Pos:* Asst physicist, Brookhaven Nat Lab, 59; res assoc, Argonne Nat Lab, 61; vis physicist, Lawrence Radiation Lab, 63, Stanford Linear Accelerator Ctr, 71, Los Alamos Sci Lab, 72, Naval Weapons Ctr, China Lake, 85-88. *Mem:* AAAS; Sigma Xi; Acoust Soc Am; fel Am Phys Soc; Am Asn Physics Teachers; Assoc Res Otolaryngol. *Res:* Physical, physiological and musical acoustics; theory of atomic structure; theory of interactions of nuclei and elementary particles. *Mailing Add:* 1396 Physics Bldg Purdue Univ West Lafayette IN 47907-1396. *Fax:* 765-494-0706; *E-Mail:* ata@physics.purdue.edu

**TUCCI, EDMOND RAYMOND,** catalysis consulting, for more information see previous edition

**TUCCI, JAMES VINCENT,** CHEMICAL PHYSICS. *Current Pos:* Instr physics, Univ Bridgeport, 66-67, from asst prof to assoc prof, 67-73, actg chmn dept, 67-71, chmn dept, 72-90, PROF PHYSICS, UNIV BRIDGEPORT, 73-, CHMN, DIV SCI & MATH, 90- *Personal Data:* b Hollis, NY, Feb 13, 39; m 62, Dorothy; c Angela. *Educ:* Hofstra Univ, BA, 62; Univ Mass, MS, 66, PhD(chem), 67. *Concurrent Pos:* NSF grant, 67-70; Conn Res Comn res grant, 68-70. *Mem:* Optical Soc Am; Am Phys Soc. *Res:* Laser Raman spectroscopy; vibrational spectroscopy. *Mailing Add:* Dept Physics Univ Bridgeport Bridgeport CT 06601. *E-Mail:* tucci@cse.bridgeport.edu, tucci@localnet.com

**TUCCIARONE, JOHN PETER,** MATHEMATICS. *Current Pos:* assoc prof, 74-80, PROF MATH, MERCY COL, 80-; DIR, PROB ANALYSIS CORP, 71- *Personal Data:* b New York, NY, Apr 9, 40; m 63; c 3. *Educ:* Fordham Univ, BS, 61; St John's Univ, NY, MA, 63, JD, 66; NY Univ, PhD(math), 69. *Prof Exp:* Asst prof math, St John's Univ, NY, 62-74. *Concurrent Pos:* Attorney pvt practice, NY, 70- *Mem:* Math Asn Am. *Res:* Numerical analysis; computer science; application of computers to instruction. *Mailing Add:* 390 Bedford Rd Pleasantville NY 10570

**TUCHINSKY, PHILIP MARTIN,** COMPUTER SCIENCE, APPLIED TO ENGINEERING ANALYSIS. *Current Pos:* res engr, Comput Sci Dept, Ford Res & Eng Ctr, 78-82, sr res engr, res staff, 82-85, prin res engr assoc, res staff, 85-93, prin eng specialist, 93-96, TECH SPECIALIST, FORD RES LAB, FORD MOTOR CO, 96- *Personal Data:* b Philadelphia, Pa, June 17, 45; m 92, Susan Titus. *Educ:* Queens Col, BA, 66; Courant Inst, NY Univ, MS, 68, PhD(math), 71. *Prof Exp:* Instr math, NY Univ, 69-70; adj instr, Cooper Union Advan Sci & Art, 70-71; asst prof, Kalamazoo Col, 71-72; asst prof math, Ohio Wesleyan Univ, 72-78. *Concurrent Pos:* Woodrow Wilson fel grad study, 66-67; NDEA Title IV fel, NY Univ, 67-69, res fel, 69-70; Great Lakes Col Asn teaching fel, Lilly Found Grant, 75; vis lectr, Math Asn Am, 76-; mem, Ford Aerospace Intelligent Systs Consortium, 86-90, Tech Training Adv Bd, Addison-Wesley Publ Co, 87-92; co-chair, Expert Systs Conf & Expository Planning Comt, 88-89, exec chair, 89-90. *Res:* Vehicle design and engineering software systems; advanced user interfaces. *Mailing Add:* 1528 Chateaufort Pl Detroit MI 48207

**TUCHMAN, AVRAHAM,** physics, thermal physics, for more information see previous edition

**TUCHOLKE, BRIAN EDWARD,** MARINE GEOLOGY, GEOPHYSICS. *Current Pos:* assoc scientist, 79-87, SR SCIENTIST, MARINE GEOL, WOODS HOLE OCEANOG INST, 87- *Personal Data:* b Hot Springs, SDak, Mar 19, 46; m 68, Anita K Smith; c Dacia & Rachelle. *Educ:* SDak Sch Mines & Technol, BS, 68; Mass Inst Technol & Woods Hole Oceanog Inst, PhD(oceanog), 73. *Honors & Awards:* Alan Berman Res Publ Award, Dept Navy, Naval Res Lab, 86; Silver Trout Award, Trout Unlimited, 88. *Prof Exp:* Fel, Lamont-Doherty Geol Observ, Columbia Univ, 73-74, from res assoc to sr res assoc, 74-79. *Concurrent Pos:* Corp mem, Woods Hole Oceanog Inst, 76-79; prin investr grants & contracts, NSF, Off Naval Res & US Dept Energy, 76-; vis sr res assoc, Columbia Univ, 79-82, adj sr res scientist, 82-91; Western NAtlantic proj co-leader, Decade NAm Geol, Geol Soc Am, 80-86; mem, Joint Oceanog Insts Deep Earth Sampling Passive Margin Panel, 81-83 & Atlantic Regional Panel, 84-87; mem, Interim US Sci Adv Comt, Advan Ocean Drilling Prog, 83; assoc ed, Geol Soc Am Bull, 85-88; Seward Johnson chair oceanog, Woods Hole Oceanog Inst, 86-88; mem, Am Geophys Union Comt Paleoceanog, 87-88, Joint Oceanog Insts Deep Earth Sampling Planning Comt, 87-92; mem, Comt Marine Geol, Am Asn Petrol Geologists, 87-90. *Mem:* Am Asn Petrol Geologists; Am Geophys Union; fel Geol Soc Am; fel Geol Asn Can; fel AAAS. *Res:* tectonic framework of Atlantic Ocean crust; structure/evolution of Atlantic passive margins; seismic stratigraphy; oceanic rock stratigraphy; paleo-oceanography; benthic boundary layer processes; physical properties of sediments; sedimentology. *Mailing Add:* Woods Hole Oceanog Inst Woods Hole MA 02543. *E-Mail:* btucholke@whoi.edu

**TUCK, DENNIS GEORGE,** INORGANIC CHEMISTRY, ORGANOMETALLIC CHEMISTRY. *Current Pos:* prof chem, 72-87, univ prof, 87-94, EMER UNIV PROF CHEM, UNIV WINDSOR, 94- *Personal Data:* b UK, Apr 8, 29; m 95, Rosemary Jull; c 3. *Educ:* Univ Durham, BSc, 49, PhD(chem), 56. *Hon Degrees:* DSc, Univ Durham, 71. *Honors & Awards:* Main Group Element Award, Royal Soc Chem, 86; Montreal Medal, Chem Inst Can, 87; Alcan Award, Can Soc Chem, 88. *Prof Exp:* Brit Coun fel, Inst du Radium, Paris, France, 52-53; sci officer chem, Windscale Works, UK Atomic Energy Auth, Eng, 53-56; lectr inorg chem, Univ Nottingham, 59-65; from assoc prof to prof chem, Simon Fraser Univ, 66-72. *Concurrent Pos:* Res fel chem, Univ Manchester, 56-59; res fel, Lab Nuclear Sci, Cornell Univ, 57-58; vis expert, Concepcion Univ, Chile, 64; mem, Chem Grant Selection Comt, Nat Res Coun Can, 72-74; dir, Can Patents & Develop Ltd, 81-86; mem bd, Can Soc Chem, 85-89. *Mem:* Royal Soc Chem; fel Chem Inst Can. *Res:* Coordination chemistry of non-transition metals, especially indium; complexes in solution; use of electrochemical methods in inorganic and organometallic chemistry; studies of eletron transfer reactions. *Mailing Add:* Dept Chem & Biochem Univ Windsor Windsor ON N9B 3P4 Can. *E-Mail:* dgtuck@uwindsor.ca

**TUCK, LEO DALLAS,** PHYSICAL CHEMISTRY. *Current Pos:* lectr & res asst chem, 48-50, instr, 50-51, from asst prof to assoc prof, 51-63, vchancellor acad affairs, 71-73, PROF CHEM & PHARMACEUT CHEM, SCH PHARM, UNIV CALIF, SAN FRANCISCO, 63-, ASSOC DEAN, 80- *Personal Data:* b San Francisco, Calif, Oct 12, 16; m 53; c 2. *Educ:* Univ Calif, AB, 39, PhD(chem), 48. *Prof Exp:* Res assoc radiation lab, Univ Calif, 42; res assoc chem dept, Univ Chicago, 42-43; res assoc radio res lab, Harvard Univ, 43-45. *Mem:* Fel AAAS; Am Chem Soc; Am Phys Soc; Am Pharmaceut Asn. *Res:* Thermodynamics and electrochemistry; thermodynamics of nonisothermal systems; chemistry of boron and uranium compounds; electrolytes in aqueous and nonaqueous solutions; microwave electronics; chemistry of free radicals; magnetic resonance spectroscopy. *Mailing Add:* Sch Pharm Univ Calif Med Ctr San Francisco CA 94143

**TUCKER, ALAN,** CARDIOPULMONARY PHYSIOLOGY. *Current Pos:* assoc prof, 79-86, PROF PHYSIOL, COLO STATE UNIV, 86- *Personal Data:* b Worthing, Eng, Sept 17, 47; US citizen; m 68; c 2. *Educ:* Univ Calif, Santa Barbara, BA, 68, PhD(biol), 72. *Honors & Awards:* Res Serv Award, Nat Heart & Lung Inst, 74. *Prof Exp:* Res assoc physiol, Cardiovasc Pulmonary Res Lab, Med Ctr, Univ Colo, 73-74, fel, 74-76; asst prof, Sch Med, Wright State Univ, 76-79. *Concurrent Pos:* Mem, Circulation Coun & Cardiopulmonary Coun, Am Heart Asn. *Mem:* Am Physiol Soc; Soc Exp Biol & Med; Am Heart Asn. *Res:* Control of the pulmonary circulation; hypoxia and high altitude physiology; pharmacology of pulmonary and systemic vasculature; respiratory physiology; environmental and exercise physiology. *Mailing Add:* Dept Physiol Colo State Univ Ft Collins CO 80523-0001. Fax: 970-491-7569

**TUCKER, ALAN CURTISS,** MATHEMATICS. *Current Pos:* from asst prof to prof, 70-89, chmn, 78-88, DISTINGUISHED TEACHING PROF APPL MATH & STATIST, STATE UNIV NY, STONY BROOK, 89- *Personal Data:* b Princeton, NJ, July 6, 43; m 68; c 2. *Educ:* Harvard Univ, BA, 65; Stanford Univ, MS, 67, PhD(math), 69. *Honors & Awards:* Trevor Evans Prize, Math Asn Am, 96. *Prof Exp:* Vis asst prof math, Math Res Ctr, Univ Wis-Madison, 69-70. *Concurrent Pos:* Res consult, Rand Corp, 64-71; vis assoc prof comput sci, Univ Calif, San Diego, 76-77; chmn panel gen math sci prog, 77-81, chmn publ comt, 82-87, chmn educ coun, 90-; mem, US Comn on Math Educ, 80-82; vis prof oper res, Stanford Univ, 83-84. *Mem:* Am Math Soc; Soc Indust & Appl Math; AAAS; Oper Res Soc Am; Math Asn Am (first vpres, 88-90); Sigma Xi. *Res:* Extremal characterization problems in graph theory; zero-one matrices; combinatorial algorithms. *Mailing Add:* 14 Scott Meadow Lane Stony Brook NY 11790. *E-Mail:* tucker@ams.sunysb.edu

**TUCKER, ALBERT WILLIAM,** linear & non-linear programming, game theory; deceased, see previous edition for last biography

**TUCKER, ALLEN B,** SOFTWARE ENGINEERING, PROGRAMMING LANGUAGES. *Current Pos:* chmn dept, 88-94, PROF COMPUT SCI, BOWDOIN COL, 88- *Personal Data:* b Worcester, Mass, Feb 19, 42; m 65; Maida Somerville; c Jennifer & Brian. *Educ:* Wesleyan Univ, BA, 63; Northwestern Univ, MS, 68, PhD(comput sci), 70. *Honors & Awards:* Outstanding Achievement Award, Asn Comput Mach, 91. *Prof Exp:* Systs analyst, Norton Co, 63-67; asst prof comput sci, Univ Mo, Rolla, 70-71; from asst prof to assoc prof comput sci, Georgetown Univ, 71-83, chmn dept & dir acad comput, 76-83; chmn dept, Colgate Univ, 83-86, Macarthur prof comput sci, 83-88, assoc dean fac, 86-88. *Concurrent Pos:* Prin investr, NSF grants, 71, 84 & 86, 91-94 & var found grants, 80-; consult, WHO, 73-80, var cols & univ, 82- & Smithsonian Inst, 84; assoc ed, J Comput Lang, 78-; vis assoc prof comput sci, Overseas Prog, Heidelberg, Ger, 82 & 84; vis prof comput sci, Brown Univ, 93. *Mem:* Fel Asn Comput Mach; Sigma Xi; Inst Elec & Electronics Engrs Comput Soc. *Res:* Automata theory; natural language analysis; programming languages; software engineering; computer science education. *Mailing Add:* Comput Sci Dept Bowdoin Col Brunswick ME 04011. *E-Mail:* allen@polar.bowdoin.edu

**TUCKER, ALLEN BRINK,** NUCLEAR PHYSICS. *Current Pos:* assoc prof, 70-77, PROF PHYSICS, SAN JOSE STATE UNIV, 77- *Personal Data:* b Highland, Ind, Oct 12, 36; m 63; c 2. *Educ:* Mass Inst Technol, BS, 58; Stanford Univ, PhD(physics), 65. *Prof Exp:* Asst prof physics, San Jose State Col, 63-65 & Iowa State Univ, 65-70. *Mem:* Am Phys Soc; Am Asn Physics Teachers. *Res:* Neutron scattering; nuclear spectroscopy; delayed neutrons. *Mailing Add:* Dept Physics San Jose State Univ Washington Sq San Jose CA 95192-0106. Fax: 408-924-4815

**TUCKER, BILLY BOB,** AGRONOMY. *Current Pos:* CONSULT, 89- *Personal Data:* b Cheyenne, Okla, Jan 13, 28; m 49; c 3. *Educ:* Okla State Univ, BS, 52, MS, 53; Univ Ill, PhD, 55. *Prof Exp:* Soil scientist, Agr Res Serv, USDA, 55-56; from asst prof to prof, Okla State Univ, 56-79, regents prof agron, 79- *Mem:* Am Soc Agron; Soil Sci Soc Am; Soil Conserv Soc Am. *Res:* Soil management, especially improvement and maintenance of soil productivity; soil chemistry, plant nutrition and fertilizer technology. *Mailing Add:* 1212 N Jardot Stillwater OK 74075

**TUCKER, CHARLES EUGENE,** BIOLOGY, ICHTHYOLOGY & HERPETOLOGY. *Current Pos:* RETIRED. *Personal Data:* b Montgomery, Ala, July 2, 33; m 58, Carol McManus; c Carles E Jr & Craig M. *Educ:* Huntingdon Col, BA, 59; Univ Ala, MS, 65, PhD(biol), 67. *Prof Exp:* Assoc prof biol, Livingston Univ, 67-80, chmn, Div Natural Sci & Math, 70-89, assoc dean, Gen Studies Health-Related Prog, 75-89, prof biol, 80-89. *Mem:* Am Soc Ichthyologists & Herpetologists; Sigma Xi. *Res:* Vertebrate field zoology; ichthyology; survey of fishes. *Mailing Add:* 1035 Meriwether Rd Pike Road AL 36064

**TUCKER, CHARLES L,** POLYMER PROCESSING, COMPOSITE MATERIALS. *Current Pos:* From asst prof to assoc prof 78-89, PROF MECH ENG, UNIV ILL, 89- *Personal Data:* b Durham, NC, July 29, 53; m 75; c 2. *Educ:* Mass Inst Technol, SB, 75, SM, 77, PhD(mech eng), 78. *Concurrent Pos:* Postdoctoral Award in Mfg Eng, TRW Found, 84; vis eng dept, Cambridge Univ, 84-85; vis fel commoner, Churchill Col, Cambridge, 84-85; mem adv comt, Mech & Struct Systs Div, NSF, 88-90. *Mem:* Am Soc Mech Engr; Soc Rheology; Polymer Processing Soc. *Res:* Processing of polymers and polymer-matrix composites; modeling and numerical simulation of flow, heat transfer, reaction, structure development; flow-induced fiber orientation; compression and injection molding; mechanical properties of composites. *Mailing Add:* Dept Mech Eng Univ Ill 1206 W Green St Urbana IL 61801-2906

**TUCKER, CHARLES LEROY, JR,** plant chemistry, for more information see previous edition

**TUCKER, CHARLES THOMAS,** MATHEMATICS. *Current Pos:* asst prof, 66-73, ASSOC PROF MATH, UNIV HOUSTON, 73- *Personal Data:* b Laredo, Tex, Aug 6, 36; m 64. *Educ:* Tex A&M Univ, BS & BA, 58; Univ Tex, MA, 62, PhD(math), 66. *Prof Exp:* Chem engr, Tracor, Inc, Tex, 60-62, engr & scientist, 63-66. *Mem:* Am Math Soc; Math Asn Am. *Res:* Sonar signal processing; pure mathematics. *Mailing Add:* Univ Houston Univ Park Houston TX 77204-3476

**TUCKER, DAVID PATRICK HISLOP,** HORTICULTURE. *Current Pos:* agronomist, Univ Fla, 66-74, assoc prof & assoc horticulturist, 74-80, prof fruit crops & horticulturist, Citrus Res & Educ Ctr, 80-90, PROF HORTICULTURE, EXTENSION SERV, UNIV FLA, 90- *Personal Data:* b Trinidad, West Indies, Oct 26, 34; m 66; c 1. *Educ:* Univ Birmingham, BSc, 58; Univ Calif, PhD(plant sci), 66. *Prof Exp:* Agronomist, Dept Agr, Brit Honduras, 60-63. *Mem:* Am Soc Hort Sci. *Res:* All aspects of citrus production. *Mailing Add:* Citrus Res Educ Ctr Univ Fla 700 Experiment Sta Rd Lake Alfred FL 33850

**TUCKER, DON HARRELL,** MATHEMATICS. *Current Pos:* from asst prof to assoc prof, 58-67, PROF MATH, UNIV UTAH, 67- *Personal Data:* b Brown Co, Tex, Jan 21, 30; m 51; c 5. *Educ:* WTex State Univ, BA, 51; Univ Tex, MA, 55, PhD(math), 58. *Prof Exp:* Res scientist mil physics res lab, Balcones Res Ctr, Univ Tex, 52-53, instr math, Univ, 53-58. *Concurrent Pos:* Vis prof, Cath Univ Am, 68-69; guest prof, Univ Marburg, 66 & 69, vis lectr, Math Asn Am, 71- *Mem:* Am Math Soc; Math Asn Am. *Res:* Functional analysis; abstract summability theory; differential equations. *Mailing Add:* Dept Math Univ Utah Salt Lake City UT 84112

**TUCKER, EDMUND BELFORD,** PHYSICS. *Current Pos:* RETIRED. *Personal Data:* b NS, Can, May 6, 22; m 46; c 3. *Educ:* Mt Allison Univ, BSc, 43; Oxford Univ, BA, 48; Yale Univ, MS, 49, PhD(physics), 51. *Prof Exp:* Res assoc physics, Univ Minn, 50-52, asst prof, 53, res assoc, 53-55; physicist res & develop ctr, Gen Elec Co, Conn, 55-66, mgr personnel & admin info sci lab, 66-69, consult educ rels, NY, 69-71, consult, Conn, 71-75, mgr sci & technol support prog, 75-84. *Mem:* AAAS; Am Soc Eng Educ; Sigma Xi; Am Phys Soc. *Res:* Linear accelerators; magnetic resonance; microwave ultrasonics; crystal fields; energy related problems. *Mailing Add:* 433 Prudden Lane Orange CT 06477-2325

**TUCKER, EDWARD B,** CELL TO CELL COMMUNICATION IN PLANTS. *Current Pos:* PROF BIOL, BARUCH COL, 86- *Personal Data:* b Edmonton, Alta, Aug 13, 44; US citizen; c Joseph & Arthur. *Educ:* Univ Alta, BSc, 69; MSc, 72; Univ Calgary, PhD(plant physiol), 75. *Prof Exp:* Asst prof biol, Vassar Col, 78-86. *Concurrent Pos:* Fel, Harvard Med Sch, 77-78; res assoc, Cornell Univ, 83; vis prof, Hebei Univ Peoples Repub China, 84; coordr bot cert prog, NY Bot Garden, 87-89; doctoral fac, City Univ NY, 87- *Mem:* Am Soc Plant Physiologists; Am Soc Cell Biol. *Res:* Plants response to their environment via signal perception; cell to cell communication; structure and function of plasmodesmator. *Mailing Add:* 8-237 Strawberry Hill Ave Stamford CT 06902

**TUCKER, GAIL SUSAN,** NEUROSCIENCES, SCIENCE EDUCATION. *Current Pos:* chairperson sci, 96-97, SCI TEACHER, NEW WORLD SCH ARTS, 87- *Personal Data:* b New York, NY, Aug 30, 45; m 87, Robert P Griffith; c Julie E. *Educ:* Mercy Col, BA, 67; Univ Kans, Lawrence, PhD(cell biol/develop biol), 73. *Prof Exp:* Res asst develop biol, 68-72, res asst mycology, Univ Kans, Lawrence, 72-73; instr, Mercy Col, 73-75; res assoc, Univ Miami, Bascom Palmer Eye Inst, Sch Med, 76-80, asst prof, 80-87. *Concurrent Pos:* Ida H Hyde grant in aid, Dept Physiol & Cell Biol, Univ Kans, 71; fel, Eye Inst, Col Physicians & Surgeons, Columbia Univ, 73-75; consult, Pub Sch Syst, Dade County, Fla, 77-86; vis fel, Biol Labs, Harvard Univ, 80; honoree, Am Soc Cell Biol, 84; adj prof, Miami Dade Community Col, 91-; fel, Access Excellence, 94, returning fel, 96, proj coordr, Sci Talk, 96-; fel, Tandy Technol, 96 & 97. *Mem:* Soc Neurosci; AAAS; Nat Sci Teacher Asn; Nat Asn Biol. *Res:* Light and electron microscopy of retinal development and cytoarchitecture of the normal and visually deprived amphibian, cat and rabbit retina; retinal aging in the human; corneal dystrophy in the cat; studies on retinal degeneration in retinitis pigmentosa in the human; development of science education strategies. *Mailing Add:* New World Sch Arts 300 NE Second Ave Miami FL 33132. *Fax:* 305-237-3794; *E-Mail:* gtucgrif@ix.netcom.com

**TUCKER, GARY EDWARD,** BOTANY, THREATENED & ENDANGERED SPECIES. *Current Pos:* ENVIRON CONSULT, 91- *Personal Data:* b Michigan Valley, Kans, Aug 17, 41; m 60, Sharon Thompson; c Carrie (Knight) & Melanie (Peters). *Educ:* Kans State Teachers Col, BA, 64; Univ NC, Chapel Hill, MA, 67; Univ Ark, PhD(bot), 76. *Prof Exp:* From asst prof to prof biol, Ark Tech Univ, 66-89, cur herbarium, 77-89; staff mem, US Forest Serv, 89-91. *Concurrent Pos:* Consult, var state & fed agencies; wetlands ecologist, FTN Assocs. *Mem:* Sigma Xi; Soc Wetland Scientists. *Res:* Endangered and threatened plant species of Southeastern states; endangered and threatened plant species of Arkansas; woody flora of Arkansas; wetland ecology of southeastern states. *Mailing Add:* 2606 W D St Russellville AR 72801. *Fax:* 501-225-6738

**TUCKER, GARY JAY,** PSYCHIATRY. *Current Pos:* PROF PSYCHIAT & CHMN DEPT, SCH MED, UNIV WASH, SEATTLE, 85- *Personal Data:* b Cleveland, Ohio, May 6, 34; m 56; c 2. *Educ:* Oberlin Col, AB, 56; Western Res Univ, MD, 60. *Prof Exp:* Asst med dir, Acute Psychiat Inpatient Div, Yale-New Haven Hosp, Yale Univ, 67-68, from asst prof to assoc prof psychiat, Sch Med, 67-71, med dir, Psychiat Inpatient Div, Med Ctr, 68-71, attend psychiatrist, 69-71, asst chief psychiat, 70-71; from assoc prof to prof psychiat, Sch Med, Dartmouth Univ, 71-85, dir residency training, 71-78, chmn dept, 78-85. *Concurrent Pos:* Fel psychiat, Sch Med, Yale Univ, 61-64; consult, Norwich State Hosp, Conn, 67-68, Univ Conn, 68-70, Off Aviation Med, Fed Aviation Admin, Dept Transp, 68-70, Vet Admin Hosp, West Haven, Conn, 70-71 & White River Junction, Vt, 71-85. *Mem:* Fel Am Psychiat Asn. *Res:* Behavioral implications of neurologic functions; psychopathology and hospital psychiatry. *Mailing Add:* Dept Psychiat Sch Med Univ Wash Seattle WA 98195

**TUCKER, HARVEY MICHAEL,** OTOLARYNGOLOGY, SURGERY. *Current Pos:* CHAIR, DEPT OTOLARYNGOL, COLUMBIA ST LUKES MED CTR, 93-; PROF OTOLARYNGOL, CASE WESTERN RES/UNIV HOSP CLEVELAND, 93- *Personal Data:* b New Brunswick, NJ, Nov 27, 38; m 81; c 3. *Educ:* Bucknell Univ, BS, 60; Jefferson Med Col, MD, 64. *Honors & Awards:* Benjamin Shuster Award, Am Acad Plastic & Reconstruct Surg, 70. *Prof Exp:* Resident, Jefferson Med Col, 69; asst otolaryngol, Barnes Hosp, Washington Univ, 69-70; assoc prof otolaryngol, State Univ NY Upstate Med Ctr, 70-75; chmn, Dept Otolaryngol & Commun Dis, Cleveland Clin Found, 75-93. *Concurrent Pos:* Fel head & neck surg, Barnes Hosp, Wash Univ, 69-70. *Mem:* Fel Am Col Surgeons; fel Am Acad Facial Plastic & Reconstruct Surg; Am Soc Surg; fel Am Acad Head & Neck Surg; fel Am Acad Ophthal & Otolaryngol. *Res:* Laryngeal reinnervation and transplantation; cancer surgery of the head and neck. *Mailing Add:* 3 Louis Dr Pepper Pike OH 44124

**TUCKER, HERBERT ALLEN,** ANIMAL PHYSIOLOGY, ENDOCRINOLOGY. *Current Pos:* From asst prof to assoc prof, 62-75, PROF MAMMARY PHYSIOL, MICH STATE UNIV, 75- *Personal Data:* b Milford, Mass, Oct 25, 36; m 59, Ann Merriam; c Glenn A, Wayne S & David A. *Educ:* Univ Mass, BS, 58; Rutgers Univ, MS, 60, PhD(animal physiol), 63. *Honors & Awards:* Borden Award, Am Dairy Sci Asn, 79; Upjohn Physiol Award, Am Dairy Sci Asn & Cyanamid Animal Physiol & Endocrinol Award, Am Soc Animal Sci, 83; L E Casida Award, Am Soc Animal Sci, 87. *Concurrent Pos:* NIH spec fel, Univ Ill, 69. *Mem:* Fel AAAS; Am Soc Animal Sci; Am Dairy Sci Asn; Soc Exp Biol & Med; Am Physiol Soc; Endocrine Soc. *Res:* Endocrinology of mammary development and lactation; environmental control hormones, growth, lactation; radioimmunoassay of hormones; hypothalamic regulation of hormone secretion; hormone binding to mammary cells. *Mailing Add:* Dept Animal Sci Mich State Univ East Lansing MI 48824. *E-Mail:* 22277hat@msu.edu

**TUCKER, HOWARD GREGORY,** MATHEMATICS. *Current Pos:* PROF MATH, UNIV CALIF, IRVINE, 68- *Personal Data:* b Lawrence, Kans, Oct 3, 22; m 46; c 4. *Educ:* Univ Calif, AB, 48, MA, 49, PhD(math), 55. *Prof Exp:* Instr math, Rutgers Univ, 52-53; asst prof, Univ Ore, 55-56; from asst prof to prof, Univ Calif, Riverside, 56-68. *Mem:* Am Math Soc; Math Asn Am; Inst Math Statist; Am Statist Asn; Biometric Soc. *Res:* Probability theory; mathematical statistics. *Mailing Add:* Dept Math Univ Calif Irvine CA 92697-3875

**TUCKER, IRWIN WILLIAM,** ORGANIC CHEMISTRY, ENVIRONMENTAL ENGINEERING. *Current Pos:* RETIRED. *Personal Data:* b New York, NY, Oct 30, 14; m 73; c 1. *Educ:* George Washington Univ, BS, 39; Univ Md, PhD(org chem), 48. *Prof Exp:* Chemist, USDA, Washington, DC, 36-45; asst, Univ Md, 45-48; res chemist, Ligget & Meyers Tobacco Co, NC, 48-51; indust specialist, Indust Eval Bd, US Dept Com, 51-53; dir res, Brown & Williamson Tobacco Corp, 53-59, mem, Bd Dirs, 56-59; prof eng res, Univ Louisville, 66-81, prof environ eng, 77-81, emer prof eng res & environ eng, 81-94. *Concurrent Pos:* Dir, Inst Indust Res, 66-72; pres, Coun Environ Balance, 73- *Mem:* Am Chem Soc; Air Pollution Control Asn; Inst Food Technologists. *Res:* Synthetic and determination of structure; fermentation chemistry; enzyme chemistry; chemistry of natural products; air pollution and solid wastes; energy resources, foods, agriculture, agricultural chemicals and product safety. *Mailing Add:* 2209 Newmarket Dr Louisville KY 40222-6315

**TUCKER, JOHN MAURICE,** botany, for more information see previous edition

**TUCKER, JOHN RICHARD,** ANALYSIS & FUNCTIONAL ANALYSIS, APPLIED STATISTICS. *Current Pos:* staff officer, 89-93, sr prog officer, 93-94, DIR, BD MATH SCI, NAT ACAD SCI, WASHINGTON, DC, 94- *Personal Data:* m 88, Robin Donaldson. *Educ:* Wash Col, Chestertown, Md, BA, 70; George Washington Univ, Wash, DC, MPh, 76, PhD(math), 80. *Prof Exp:* Math analyst & comput specialist, Chi Assocs, Inc, Arlington, Va, 76-80; asst prof appl math, Dept Math, Va Commonwealth Univ, Richmond, 80-83 & Mary Washington Col, Fredericksburg, 83-88. *Concurrent Pos:* Nat Res Coun prog officer, Nat Security Agency's Math Sci Prog, Nat Acad Sci, Washington, DC, 89-91 & Comt Appl & Theoret Statist, 90-94. *Mem:* Am Math Soc; Math Asn Am; Soc Indust & Appl Math. *Res:* Nonlinear dynamics; order and disorder; applied mathematics; mathematics applied to biological sciences; history of mathematics; applied statistics. *Mailing Add:* Bd Math Sci Rm NAS 315 Nat Acad Sci 2101 Constitution Ave NW Washington DC 20418. *Fax:* 202-334-1597; *E-Mail:* jtucker@nas.edu

**TUCKER, KATHERINE LOUISE,** NUTRITION, EPIDEMIOLOGY. *Current Pos:* asst prof, 89-96, ASSOC PROF NUTRIT, USDA HUMAN NUTRIT RES CTR, TUFTS UNIV, 96- *Personal Data:* b Baltimore, Md, Feb 2, 55; m 87, Luis M Falcon; c Alex T Falcon & Amanda K Falcon. *Educ:* Univ Conn, BS, 78; Cornell Univ, PhD(nutrit), 86. *Prof Exp:* Asst prof nutrit, Sch Dietetics & Human Nutrit, McGill Univ, 86-89. *Concurrent Pos:* Prin investr, Int Ctr Res Women, 88-89, Nat Inst Aging, 92- *Mem:* Am Inst Nutrit; Am Soc Clin Nutrit; Soc Int Nutrit Res; assoc mem Am Dietetics Asn. *Res:* Population studies of nutrition, diet and health; dietary methodology. *Mailing Add:* Epidemiol Prog USDA Human & Nutrit Res Ctr Tufts Univ 711 Washington St Boston MA 02111-1524. *Fax:* 617-556-3344; *E-Mail:* tucker@hnrc.tufts.edu

**TUCKER, KENNETH WILBURN,** APICULTURE. *Current Pos:* RETIRED. *Personal Data:* b Santa Barbara, Calif, Aug 8, 24; m 53. *Educ:* Univ Calif, BS, 50, PhD(entom), 57. *Prof Exp:* Res fel, Univ Minn, 54-60; instr biol, Lake Forest Col, 60-63; asst res apiculturist, Univ Calif, Davis, 63-66; res entomologist, USDA, 66-85. *Mem:* Entom Soc Am; Int Bee Res Asn; Genetics Soc Am; Am Genetic Asn. *Res:* Genetics of honey bees. *Mailing Add:* 39878 Primavera Rd Santa Barbara CA 93110

**TUCKER, PATRICIA ANNE,** MATHEMATICS, COMPUTER SCIENCE. *Current Pos:* assoc prof, 85-92, PROF MATH SCI, METROP STATE COL, DENVER, COLO, 92- *Personal Data:* b Emporia, Kans, Nov 4, 37; div; c William P & Brian T. *Educ:* Kans State Univ, BS, 57; Univ Wis-Madison, MS, 58, PhD(math), 61. *Prof Exp:* From instr to asst prof math, Univ Ill, Urbana, 61-67; assoc prof math, Univ Tenn, Knoxville, 67-75 & Univ Nebr, Omaha, 77-84. *Concurrent Pos:* Vis assoc prof comput sci, Univ Colo, Denver, 84-85; assoc prof comput sci, Western Ill Univ, 88-90. *Mem:* Am Math Soc; Math Asn Am; Asn Comput Mach; Asn Women Math. *Res:* Algebra; representations of finite groups; computer science education. *Mailing Add:* 20 E Maple Ave Denver CO 80209-1526. *E-Mail:* tuckerp@mscd.edu

**TUCKER, PAUL ARTHUR,** TEXTILES, MICROSCOPY. *Current Pos:* asst prof textiles, 75-80, ASSOC PROF TEXTILE MAT & MGT, SCH TEXTILES, NC STATE UNIV, 80- *Personal Data:* b Albemarle, NC, May 14, 41; m 65. *Educ:* NC State Univ, BS, 63, MS, 66, PhD(fiber & polymer sci), 73. *Prof Exp:* Instr textiles, NC State Univ, 64-71, asst prof, 73; NATO vis fel, Dept Textile Indust, Univ Leeds, 74. *Mem:* Royal Micros Soc. *Res:* Seeking the basic materials science underlying fibrous materials and relating applied technology to this science; polymer fine structure; microscopy; yarn processing; particulate analyses. *Mailing Add:* Dept Textile Mat NC State Univ Box 8301 Raleigh NC 27695-0001

**TUCKER, RAY EDWIN,** ANIMAL SCIENCE. *Current Pos:* RETIRED. *Personal Data:* b Somerset, Ky, Dec 31, 29; m 53; c 3. *Educ:* Univ Ky, BS, 51, MS, 66, PhD(animal nutrit), 68. *Prof Exp:* Asst prof animal sci, Va Polytech Inst & State Univ, 68-69; asst prof, Univ Ky, 69-80, assoc prof animal sci, 80. *Mem:* Am Soc Animal Sci. *Res:* Ruminant nutrition; starch utilization; urea utilization; magnesium deficiency; vitamin A antagonists; poultry litter as a feedstuff for ruminants. *Mailing Add:* 234 Tahoma Rd Lexington KY 40503

**TUCKER, RICHARD FRANK,** RESEARCH ADMINISTRATION. *Current Pos:* RETIRED. *Personal Data:* b New York, NY, Dec 25, 26. *Educ:* Cornell Univ, BChE, 50. *Prof Exp:* Esso Stand Oil Co, 50-55; Caltex Oil Co, 55-61; mem staff, Mobil Oil Corp, 61-91, pres, 86-91. *Mem:* Nat Acad Eng. *Mailing Add:* Mobil Corp PO Box 2072 New York NY 10163

**TUCKER, RICHARD LEE,** CIVIL ENGINEERING, CONSTRUCTION. *Current Pos:* C T WELLS PROF PROJ MGT, UNIV TEX, AUSTIN, 76-, DIR, CONSTRUCT INDUST INST, 83- *Personal Data:* b Wichita Falls, Tex, July 19, 35; m 56; c 2. *Educ:* Univ Tex, BS, 58, MS, 60, PhD(civil eng), 63. *Honors & Awards:* R L Peurifoy Res Award, Am Soc Civil Engrs, 86, Thomas F Rowland Prize, 87. *Prof Exp:* Proj engr, Eng-Sci Consult, 58-60; instr civil eng, Univ Tex, 60-62; from asst prof to prof, Univ Tex, Arlington, 62-74, assoc dean eng, 67-74; vpres, Luther Hill & Assoc, Inc, Dallas, 74-76. *Mem:* Nat Acad Eng; Am Soc Civil Engrs; Nat Soc Prof Engrs; Am Soc Testing & Mat; Soc Exp Stress Anal; Am Soc Eng Educ. *Res:* Construction engineering; project management. *Mailing Add:* Dept Civil Eng Univ Tex Austin TX 78712-1076

**TUCKER, ROBERT C, JR,** RESEARCH & DEVELOPMENT MANAGEMENT, FAILURE ANALYSIS. *Current Pos:* sr res metallurgist, Praxair Surface Technol, Inc, 67-72, mgr mat develop, 72-81, assoc dir technol, 81-91, corp fel & assoc dir technol, 91-93, CORP FEL & DIR, PRAXAIR SURFACE TECHNOL, INC, 93- *Personal Data:* b Kansas City, Mo. *Educ:* NDak State Univ, BS, 57; Iowa State Univ, MS, 64, PhD(metall), 67. *Prof Exp:* Chemist, Ames Lab, AEC, Iowa State Univ, 57-58 & 61-67. *Concurrent Pos:* Mem numerous adv comts, Am Soc Metals Int, Am Vacuum Soc, Nat Asn Corrosion Engrs & Am Soc Testing & Mat, 86-; adj prof, Univ Ill, Urbana, 89- *Mem:* Fel Am Soc Metals Int; Am Vacuum Soc; Nat Asn Corrosion Engrs; Am Soc Testing & Mat; Sigma Xi; Am Inst Mining Metall & Petrol Engrs; Thermal Spray Soc (pres, 96-98). *Res:* Metallic, ceramic and cermet coatings wear and corrosion resistance at low and high temperature; thermal barrier materials using thermal spray; chemical vapor deposition and physical vapor deposition. *Mailing Add:* 61 Ridgeway Dr Brownsburg IN 46112. *Fax:* 317-240-2464; *E-Mail:* rtucker@geof.psti.praxair.com

**TUCKER, ROBERT WILSON,** CELL BIOLOGY, MEDICAL ONCOLOGY. *Current Pos:* ASST PROF ONCOL & CELL BIOL, SCH MED, JOHNS HOPKINS UNIV, 79- *Educ:* Harvard Univ, MD, 70. *Mailing Add:* Comprehensive Cancer Ctr Bowman Gray Sch Med Wake Forest Univ Med Ctr Blvd Winston-Salem NC 27157. *Fax:* 410-955-1904

**TUCKER, ROGER A,** FORESTRY. *Current Pos:* WEATHER PROG MGR, NAT FOREST SYST, 86- *Personal Data:* b Ohio, June 9, 38. *Educ:* Aurora Univ, BS. *Mailing Add:* Nat Forest Syst PO Box 96090 Rm 35 Washington DC 20090-6090

**TUCKER, ROY WILBUR,** MATHEMATICS. *Current Pos:* from asst prof to assoc prof, Humboldt State Univ, 59-71, coordr comput ctr, 64-65 & consult, 65-66, PROF MATH, HUMBOLDT STATE UNIV, 71- *Personal Data:* b Exeter, Calif, Jan 25, 27; m 54; c 2. *Educ:* Stanford Univ, BS, 51, MA, 53, MS, 54. *Prof Exp:* Instr math, Colo Col, 54-55; instr, Modesto Jr Col, 55-59. *Mem:* Math Asn Am; Soc Indust & Appl Math; Asn Comput Mach. *Res:* Numerical analysis; linear algebra. *Mailing Add:* Humboldt State Univ 2234 Fickle Hill Rd Arcata CA 95521

**TUCKER, RUTH EMMA,** NUTRITION. *Current Pos:* prof & res prof food & nutrit, 44-72, EMER PROF FOOD & NUTRIT, UNIV RI, 72 - *Personal Data:* b Warrensburg, Ill, Feb 17, 01. *Educ:* Univ Ill, AB, 23, MS, 25; Univ Chicago, PhD(nutrit, food chem), 48. *Prof Exp:* Asst, Univ Ill, 23-25; instr food & nutrit, Kans State Col, 25-37; prof home econ, Univ Alaska, 37-42. *Mem:* AAAS; fel Am Pub Health Asn; Am Dietetic Asn; Am Home Econ Asn. *Res:* Food chemistry. *Mailing Add:* 160 Linden Dr Kingston RI 02881

**TUCKER, SHIRLEY COTTER,** BOTANY. *Current Pos:* from asst prof to prof, 68-95, EMER BOYD PROF, DEPT BOT, LA STATE UNIV, BATON ROUGE, 95-; ADJ PROF, UNIV CALIF, SANTA BARBARA. *Personal Data:* b St Paul, Minn, Apr 4, 27; m 53, Kenneth. *Educ:* Univ Minn, Minneapolis, BA, 49, MS, 51; Univ Calif, Davis, PhD, 56. *Honors & Awards:* Merit Award, Bot Soc Am; Cooley Award, Am Soc Plant Syst. *Prof Exp:* Instr bot, Univ Minn, 60; res fel biol, Northwestern Univ, 61-63; res fel bot, Univ Calif, 63-66. *Mem:* Bot Soc Am (pres-elect, 86-87, pres, 87-88); Am Bryol & Lichenological Soc; Brit Lichen Soc; Sigma Xi; fel Linnean Soc London; Am Soc Plant Taxonomists (pres, 95-96). *Res:* Developmental anatomy of flower and vegetative shoots; determinate growth; plant anatomy; morphology; lichenology. *Mailing Add:* Dept Biol (E E M B ) Univ Calif Santa Barbara CA 93106

**TUCKER, THOMAS CURTIS,** SOILS, PLANT NUTRITION. *Current Pos:* from assoc prof to prof agr chem & soils, Univ Ariz, 56-74, prof soils, water & eng & soil scientist, 74-82, prof soil & water sci, 82-89, EMER PROF SOIL & WATER SCI, AGR EXP STA, UNIV ARIZ, 89- *Personal Data:* b Hanson, Ky, Nov 1, 26; m 47, Inez Ashby; c 3. *Educ:* Univ Ky, BS, 49; Kans State Univ, MS, 51; Univ Ill, PhD, 55. *Prof Exp:* Asst soils, Kans State Univ, 49-51, instr, 51; asst soil fertility, Univ Ill, 51-55; asst prof soils, Miss State Univ, 55-56. *Concurrent Pos:* Vis prof, NC State Univ, 66-67; vis scientist, Univ Ariz, Tuscon, 77-78. *Mem:* Fel Soil Sci Soc Am; fel Am Soc Agron; Am Chem Soc. *Res:* Agronomy; soil fertility and chemistry; analytical chemistry; soil-plant relationships; soil nitrogen transformations, fixation, denitrification, fertilizer use efficiency using 15-nitrogen labelled materials. *Mailing Add:* Dept Soil & Water Sci Univ Ariz Tucson AZ 85721. *Fax:* 520-621-1647

**TUCKER, THOMAS WILLIAM,** TOPOLOGY, COMBINATORICS. *Current Pos:* from asst prof to assoc prof, Colgate Univ, 73-82, chmn, 82-86, actg dean, 91-92, dir, Div Natural Sci & Math, 93-96, PROF MATH, COLGATE UNIV, 83-, CHARLES G HETHERINGTON PROF MATH, 94- *Personal Data:* b Princeton, NJ, July 15, 45; m 68, Mollie Dalton; c Thomas J & Emily K. *Educ:* Harvard Univ, AB, 67; Dartmouth Univ, PhD(math), 71. *Prof Exp:* Instr math, Princeton Univ, 71-73. *Concurrent Pos:* Consult, Col Bds & Educ Testing Serv, 73-, Inst Defense Analysis, 74, 75, 78, 79, 84 & 85; prin investr, various NSF res grants; vis assoc prof, Darmouth Col, 78-79; chmn, AP Calculus Comt Col Bd, 83-87; Nat Adv Comt, NSF, 86, Westat Assessment, NSF/ILI Prog, 88-90, Nat Assessment Educ Prog, 88-; co-prin invester, Harvard Calculus Consortium, 89-, ed, NSF/MAA Surv Calculus Projs, 90; chmn & mem numerous comts, Math Asn Am, 88-; vpres, Math Asn Am, 90-92. *Mem:* Math Asn Am (first vpres, 90-); Am Math Soc. *Res:* Three-dimensional topology and combinatorics, especially topological graph theory. *Mailing Add:* Dept Math Colgate Univ Hamilton NY 13346. *Fax:* 315-824-7831; *E-Mail:* ttucker@center.colgate.edu

**TUCKER, VANCE ALAN,** COMPARATIVE PHYSIOLOGY. *Current Pos:* from asst prof to assoc prof zool, 64-73, PROF ZOOL, DUKE UNIV, 73- *Personal Data:* b Niagara Falls, NY, Apr 4, 36. *Educ:* Univ Calif, Los Angeles, BA, 58, PhD(zool), 63; Univ Wis, MS, 60. *Prof Exp:* NSF fel zool, Univ Mich, 63-64. *Concurrent Pos:* NSF res grants & Duke Univ Coun Res grants, 65-91. *Mem:* AAAS. *Res:* Vertebrate locomotion, respiration, circulation, energy metabolism; avian aerodynamics. *Mailing Add:* Box 90325 Durham NC 27708-0325

**TUCKER, W(ILLIAM) HENRY,** CHEMICAL & ENVIRONMENTAL ENGINEERING, ENERGY & MASS TRANSFER. *Current Pos:* prof chem eng & head dept, 69-84, dir, Energy Analysis & Diag Ctr, US Dept Energy, 84, EMER PROF CHEM, TRI-STATE UNIV, 84- *Personal Data:* b Seaford, Del, July 7, 20; m 85; c 2. *Educ:* Univ Va, BS, 42; Mass Inst Technol, MS, 46, ScD(chem eng), 47. *Prof Exp:* Res assoc, Manhattan Proj, 44-45; res engr & supvr eng res, Servel, Inc, 47-53; assoc prof chem eng, Purdue Univ, Lafayette, 53-69. *Concurrent Pos:* Adv, Cheng Kung Univ, Taiwan, 58-59; vis teacher, Swiss Fed Inst Technol, 59; consult, Whirlpool Res, 62-69; Am Inst Chem Eng traveling fel study co-op educ, Gt Brit, 69; mid-career fel, Lilly Endowment, Inc, 78-79; chmn, Theol Dialogue Sci & Technol, United Ministries Educ, 79-81, Chem Plant Safety Workshops, Taiwan, 85. *Mem:* Sigma Xi; Am Inst Chem Engrs. *Res:* Chemical heat pump; process design and economics; energy conservation; absorption refrigeration. *Mailing Add:* 4175 Stratus Ct S Salem OR 97302-2775

**TUCKER, WALLACE HAMPTON,** HIGH ENERGY ASTROPHYSICS, X-RAY ASTRONOMY. *Current Pos:* ASTROPHYSICIST, SMITHSONIAN ASTROPHYS OBSERV, 76- *Personal Data:* b McAlester, Okla, Nov 4, 39; m 57, Karen Slagle; c Kerry & Stuart. *Educ:* Univ Okla, BS, 61, MS, 62; Univ Calif, San Diego, PhD(physics), 66. *Prof Exp:* Res assoc, Cornell Univ, 66-67; asst prof space sci, Rice Univ, 67-69; sr staff scientist, Dept Am Sci & Eng, Harvard-Smithsonian Observ, 69-72, consult, 72-76. *Concurrent Pos:* Vis lectr physics, Univ Calif, Irvine, 80-86, vis prof, 86-89; res physicist, Univ Calif, San Diego, 92- *Mem:* Am Astron Soc; AAAS; Int Astron Union. *Res:* High energy astrophysics, particularly x-ray astronomy; writings in astronomy and cosmology for general audiences. *Mailing Add:* PO Box 266 Bonsall CA 92003

**TUCKER, WILLIAM PRESTON,** ORGANIC CHEMISTRY. *Current Pos:* from asst prof to assoc prof chem, 63-72, PROF CHEM, NC STATE UNIV, 72- *Personal Data:* b Louisville, Ky, Sept 23, 32; m 59; c 3. *Educ:* Wake Forest Col, BS, 57; Univ NC, MA, 60, PhD(chem), 62. *Prof Exp:* NIH fel, Univ Ill, 62-63. *Mem:* Am Chem Soc. *Res:* Chemistry of organic compounds of divalent sulfur; natural products. *Mailing Add:* Chem NC State Univ Box 8204 Raleigh NC 27695-0001

**TUCKER, WILLIE GEORGE,** ORGANIC CHEMISTRY. *Current Pos:* Prof, 62-89, head dept, 69-89, EMER PROF CHEM, SAVANNAH STATE COL, 90- *Personal Data:* b Tampa, Fla, Nov 26, 34. *Educ:* Tuskegee Inst, BS, 56, MS, 58; Univ Okla, PhD(org chem), 62. *Concurrent Pos:* Dir coop educ, Savannah State Col, 83-89. *Mem:* AAAS; Am Chem Soc; Sigma Xi. *Res:* Chlorination with cupric chloride; halogenation of pyridine; iodination of lactate dehydrogenase isoenzymes. *Mailing Add:* 1523 Cathy St Savannah GA 31401

**TUCKERMAN, MURRAY MOSES,** PHARMACEUTICAL QUALITY ASSURANCE, DRUG REGULATORY AFFAIRS. *Current Pos:* assoc prof chem, Temple Univ, 58-62, head dept, 61-72, prof chem, Sch Pharm, 62-90, dir radiol health specialist training prog, 63-69, dir progs for Pharmaceut Indus, 87-90, EMER PROF, TEMPLE UNIV, 90- *Personal Data:* b Boston, Mass, July 19, 28; m 48, Byrde Merican; c Hannah T (Rappolt), Susannah E (Blake), Seth M & Abigail M (Slayton). *Educ:* Yale Univ, BS, 48; Temple Univ, BS, 53; Rensselaer Polytech Inst, PhD(chem), 58. *Prof Exp:* Asst anal chem, Sterling-Winthrop Res Inst, 53-55, res assoc, 55-58. *Concurrent Pos:* Resident res assoc, Argonne Nat Lab, 59; mem bd revision, US Pharmacopeia, 60-70; consult clin ctr, NIH, 59-65; sci adv, Food & Drug Admin, 67-71; consult, Drug Regulatory Affairs, 71-; temp hon mem secretariat Europ pharmacopeia, Coun Europe, 74. *Mem:* Fel Am Inst Chem; fel Am Acad Pharmaceut Sci. *Res:* Drug standards; pharmaceutical quality assurance. *Mailing Add:* Gen Delivery Winchendon Springs MA 01477-9999

**TUCKETT, ROBERT P,** NEUROPHYSIOLOGY, SOMATOSENSORY PHYSIOLOGY. *Current Pos:* fel neurophysiol, Univ Utah, 72-77, res assoc, 77-79, res instr, 79-81, ASST RES PROF, UNIV UTAH, 81- *Personal Data:* b Salt Lake City, Utah, March 11, 43; m 69; c 2. *Educ:* Univ Utah, BS, 65, PhD(biophysics & bioeng), 72. *Prof Exp:* Biophysicist, Artificial Heart Test Ctr, 71-72. *Concurrent Pos:* Prin investr, NIH grant, 79- *Mem:* Am Physiol Soc; Soc Neurosci. *Res:* Study of cutaneous receptor behavior and transfer of information in somatosensory pathways; mechanism by which the sensation of itch is transmitted to central nervous system. *Mailing Add:* Dept Physiol Univ Utah 410 Chiptepa Salt Lake City UT 84108

**TUCKEY, STEWART LAWRENCE,** DAIRY TECHNOLOGY. *Current Pos:* Asst dairy mfg, 28-30, instr, 30-32, assoc, 32-37, from asst prof to assoc prof, 37-57, prof dairy technol, 57-72, EMER PROF DAIRY TECHNOL, UNIV ILL, URBANA, 72- *Personal Data:* b Browns Valley, Minn, Aug 24, 05; m 36, Frances Griswold; c Marcia. *Educ:* Univ Ill, Urbana, BS, 28, MS, 30, PhD(dairy tech), 37. *Honors & Awards:* Borden Award, 39; Charles E Pfizer Award, Am Dairy Sci Asn, 69. *Concurrent Pos:* Sabbatical, Neth Inst Dairy Res, Ede, 67. *Mem:* Am Chem Soc; Am Dairy Sci Asn; Sigma Xi. *Res:* Biochemical and microbiological changes in cheese; microbial clotting enzyme for cheese. *Mailing Add:* 919 W Charles St Champaign IL 61821-4527

**TUCKSON, REED V,** MEDICAL ADMINISTRATION. *Current Pos:* PRES, CHARLES R DREW UNIV MED & SCI, 91- *Personal Data:* b Washington DC. *Educ:* Howard Univ, BS; Georgetown Univ, MD. *Prof Exp:* Comnr pub health, DC; sr vpres progs, March Dimes Birth Defect Found. *Concurrent Pos:* Robert Wood Johnson Clin Scholar, Univ Pa. *Mem:* Inst Med-Nat Acad Sci; Asn Minority Health Professions Schs (pres). *Res:* Health reform; comprehensive universal health coverage. *Mailing Add:* Charles R Drew Univ Med & Sci 1621 E 120th St Los Angeles CA 90059

**TUDBURY, CHESTER A,** MECHANICAL ENGINEERING. *Current Pos:* RETIRED. *Personal Data:* b Warwick, RI, Jan 3, 13. *Educ:* Mass Inst Technol, BSEE & MSEE, 34. *Prof Exp:* Asst prof elec eng, Cleveland State Univ, 36-50; supvr develop lab, Ohio Crankshaft, Cleveland, 40-46, mgr eng, 48-57; supvr design, Budd Corp, Detroit, 46-48; self employed, consult, 79-83. *Concurrent Pos:* Tech adv to the pres, Thermatool, Stanford, Conn, 58-79. *Mem:* Fel Inst Elec & Electronics Engrs. *Res:* Author of a book. *Mailing Add:* Heartlands Apt 335 3004 N Ridge Rd Ellicott City MD 21043

**TUDDENHAM, W(ILLIAM) MARVIN,** ANALYTICAL PHYSICAL CHEMISTRY, FUEL TECHNOLOGY. *Current Pos:* INDEPENDENT CONSULT, 83-; PRES, MMA, 92- *Personal Data:* b Salt Lake City, Utah, July 8, 24; m 45, Dorothy Snelgrove; c William M Jr (deceased), Mary A (Milan), Laurie (Bagley) & Evelyn. *Educ:* Univ Utah, BA, 47, MS, 48, PhD(fuel technol), 54. *Prof Exp:* Res anal chemist, Eastman Kodak Co, 48-50; res lab technician, Kennecott Minerals Co, 53-55, sr scientist, 55-59, head chem, Phys Methods & Spec Studies Sect, 59-72, mgr, Anal Tech Dept, Metal Mining Div Res, 72-78, dir anal serv, Utah Copper Div, 78-80, mgr prod qual projs, 80-83. *Concurrent Pos:* Extractor, Copper Develop Asn, 84- *Mem:* Am Chem Soc; Am Inst Mining, Metall & Petrol Engrs; Sigma Xi. *Res:* Application of instrumentation in process control; application of solar energy for high temperature research; role of catalysis in the oxidation of carbon; electrowinning and electrorefining quality control in copper production. *Mailing Add:* 1828 Lincoln St Salt Lake City UT 84105-3308

**TUDOR, DAVID CYRUS,** POULTRY PATHOLOGY, PIGEON DISEASES. *Current Pos:* RETIRED. *Personal Data:* b Wildwood, NJ, May 10, 18; m 41, Emily Mitchell; c Diane (Louis). *Educ:* Rutgers Univ, BS, 40; Univ Pa, VMD, 51. *Honors & Awards:* Helyar House Award, 85. *Prof Exp:* Instr high sch, Voc Agr, NJ, 40-44; sr asst poultry path, Rutgers Univ, 51-59, assoc res specialist, 59-66, res prof poultry path, 66-78. *Concurrent Pos:* Instr, poultry path, animal path & gen biol, Cook Col, 51-78; assoc ed, Poultry Sci, Poultry Sci Asn, 73-75; small animal pract, 78-93. *Mem:* Am Vet Med Asn; Am Asn Avian Path; World Poultry Sci. *Res:* Poultry science; poultry diagnosis; Salmonella and chronic respiratory disease; mycoplasma; pox; pet bird diseases; pigeon diseases; pigeon health and disease. *Mailing Add:* 29 Station Rd Cranbury NJ 08512

**TUDOR, JAMES R,** ELECTRICAL ENGINEERING. *Current Pos:* from asst prof to assoc prof elec eng, 52-65, PROF ELEC ENG, UNIV MO-COLUMBIA, 65-, MO ELEC UTILITIES PROF POWER SYSTS ENG, 69- *Personal Data:* b Ft Smith, Ark, Mar 26, 22; m 72; c 1. *Educ:* Univ Mo, BS, 48, MS, 50; Ill Inst Technol, PhD(elec eng), 60. *Prof Exp:* Sr asst engr, Union Elec Co, 50-52. *Concurrent Pos:* Proj dir, Signal Corps, US Army, 56-57 & 58. *Mem:* Inst Elec & Electronics Engrs. *Res:* Transmission lines; energy conversion; electric circuits; power systems; computer control of electric power systems. *Mailing Add:* Dept Elec Eng 11 Jesse Hall Univ Mo 240 Elec Eng Bldg W Columbia MO 65211

**TUEL, WILLIAM GOLE, JR,** PARALLEL COMPUTING, COMPUTER GRAPHICS. *Current Pos:* SR SOFTWARE ENGR, IBM, 92- *Personal Data:* b Indianapolis, Ind, Apr 16, 41; m 63, Elizabeth Carpenter; c Beverly & Clifford. *Educ:* Rensselaer Polytech Inst, BEE, 62, MEE, 64, PhD(elec eng), 65. *Prof Exp:* Mem res staff, IBM Sci Ctr, 65-76, mgr power syst studies group, 70-72, mgr exp comput studies, 73-76, mem sci staff, 76-92, mgr explor graphic, 84-92. *Concurrent Pos:* Prog evaluator, Comput Sci Accreditation bd, 95- *Mem:* Inst Elec & Electronics Engrs; Asn Comput Mach. *Res:* Development of high performance message passing computer software. *Mailing Add:* 1326 Flatbush Rd Kingston NY 12401-7017. *E-Mail:* billtuel@vnet.ibm.com

**TUELLER, PAUL T,** PLANT ECOLOGY, RANGE MANAGEMENT. *Current Pos:* From asst prof to assoc prof range sci, 62-73, head, Div Renewable Natural Resources, 80, PROF RANGE SCI, UNIV NEV, RENO, 73- *Personal Data:* b Paris, Idaho, July 30, 34; m 63; c 4. *Educ:* Idaho State Univ, BS, 57; Univ Nev, MS, 59; Ore State Univ, PhD, 62. *Mem:* Soc Range Mgt; Soc Am Foresters; Am Soc Photogram. *Res:* Range ecology, especially vegetation-soil relationships; management of big game populations; remote sensing of renewable natural resources. *Mailing Add:* Dept Biol Univ Nev Reno NV 89557-0001

**TUERPE, DIETER ROLF,** CONVENTIONAL ORDNANCE, NUCLEAR PHYSICS. *Current Pos:* AT PHYSICS INT CO, 80- *Personal Data:* b Chemnitz, Ger, Dec 29, 40; US citizen; m 79; c 1. *Educ:* Polytech Inst Brooklyn, BS, 62; Univ Calif, Berkeley, MA, 66; Univ Calif, Davis, PhD(appl sci), 73. *Prof Exp:* Physicist, Lawrence Livermore Lab, 67-80. *Mem:* Am Phys Soc. *Res:* Nuclear Hartree-Fock calculation; atmospheric boundary layer models; equations of state; social and economic systems modelling; general ordnance research and development; shaped charge design. *Mailing Add:* Physics Int Co 2700 Merced St San Leandro CA 94577

**TUESDAY, CHARLES SHEFFIELD,** RESEARCH ADMINISTRATION. *Current Pos:* RETIRED. *Personal Data:* b Trenton, NJ, Sept 7, 27; m 52, Jean Quallis; c David S, Lora (Heathfield) & Verna J. *Educ:* Hamilton Col, NY, AB, 51; Princeton Univ, MA & PhD(phys chem), 55. *Honors & Awards:* Midglen Award, Am Chem Soc, 95. *Prof Exp:* Res chemist, Panelyte Div, St Regis Paper Corp, 50-51; res asst, Princeton Univ, 51-55; sr res chemist, Fuels & Lubricants Dept, Gen Motors Corp, 55-64, supvry res chemist, 64-67, from asst head to head, 67-72, head, Environ Sci Dept & actg head Phys Chem Dept, 72-74, tech dir, 74-88, exec dir, Res Labs, 88-92. *Concurrent Pos:* Consult vapor-phase org air pollutants panel, Nat Res Coun, 72-76; mem, Air Pollution Res Adv Comt, Coord Res Coun, 70-82, chmn, 78-80; mem comt mat substitution methodology, Nat Res Coun, 79-81; mem, Comt Corp Assocs, Am Chem Soc, 85-92; mem bd dir, Coord Res Coun, 87-92; chair, Indust Sci Sect, AAAS, 90-91. *Mem:* Fel AAAS; Am Chem Soc; Soc Automotive Engrs; Sigma Xi. *Res:* Physical chemistry; chemical energy exchange; environmental science; polymers; metallurgy; fuels and lubricants; biomedical science; analytical chemistry. *Mailing Add:* 2232 Sudbury Way Bloomfield Hills MI 48304

**TUFARIELLO, JOSEPH JAMES,** ORGANIC CHEMISTRY. *Current Pos:* assoc prof, 63-80, chmn, Dept Chem, 84-91, PROF ORG CHEM, STATE UNIV NY, BUFFALO, 80-, DEAN, FAC NATURAL SCI & MATH, 91- *Personal Data:* b Brooklyn, NY, Oct 3, 35; m 60, Agnes P Matze; c Catherine, Joann, Donna & Jennifer. *Educ:* Queens Col, NY, BS, 57; Univ Wis-Madison, PhD(chem), 61. *Prof Exp:* Assoc org chem, Purdue Univ, Lafayette, 62; NIH fel, Cornell Univ, 62-63. *Mem:* AAAS; Am Chem Soc; The Chem Soc. *Res:* Organic synthesis; synthesis and reactivity of strained or otherwise unique carbocyclic systems; synthesis of natural products; organometallic chemistry; chemistry of 1,3-dipolar compounds. *Mailing Add:* Dept Chem State Univ NY Buffalo NY 14214. *Fax:* 716-645-2534

**TUFF, DONALD WRAY,** PARASITOLOGY, TAXONOMY. *Current Pos:* From asst prof to assoc prof, 63-73, PROF BIOL, SOUTHWEST TEX STATE UNIV, 73- *Personal Data:* b San Francisco, Calif, May 4, 35; m 55; c 3. *Educ:* San Jose State Col, BA, 57; Wash State Univ, MS, 59; Tex A&M Univ, PhD(entomol), 63. *Mem:* Entom Soc Am; Soc Syst Zool; Wildlife Dis Asn. *Res:* Taxonomy of avian Mallophaga; parasites of wildlife. *Mailing Add:* Dept Biol Southwest Tex State Univ San Marcos TX 78666-4602

**TUFFEY, THOMAS J,** ENVIRONMENTAL SCIENCES. *Current Pos:* VPRES RESOURCES ENG, ROY F WESTON, INC, 76- *Personal Data:* US citizen. *Educ:* Rutgers Univ BS, 68, MS, 72, PhD(environ sci), 73. *Concurrent Pos:* Mem fac, Col Eng, Rutgers Univ, 76, vis asst prof, 77. *Res:* Surface water monitoring systems and water quality modeling simulations; nitrogen cycle-nitrication-dentrification; siting, restoration and environmental assessments of lakes and reservoirs; watershed management; land management of waste sludges. *Mailing Add:* 1213 Youngs Rd West Chester PA 19380

**TUFTE, MARILYN JEAN,** BIOTECHNOLOGY, CELL BIOLOGY. *Current Pos:* from asst prof to assoc prof, 68-76, PROF BIOL, UNIV WIS-PLATTEVILLE, 76- *Personal Data:* b Iron Mountain, Mich, Nov 20, 39; m 72, Fredric W. *Educ:* Northern Mich Univ, AB, 61; Univ Wis-Madison, MS, 65, PhD(bact), 68. *Prof Exp:* Trainee & fel, Univ Wis-Madison, 68. *Concurrent Pos:* Consult med prof, dairy indust & educ. *Mem:* Am Soc Microbiol; Sigma Xi. *Res:* Electron microscopic analysis of guinea pig peritoneal phagocytes infected with strains of Brucella abortus of different degrees of virulence; effects of vitamin A calcium and zinc gluconate on colon carcinoma in mice. *Mailing Add:* Dept Biol Univ Wis Platteville WI 53818

**TUFTE, OBERT NORMAN,** ELECTRON DEVICE PHYSICS, SILICON BASED SENSORS. *Current Pos:* RETIRED. *Personal Data:* b Northfield, Minn, May 30, 32; m 56, Doris H Wisbroecker; c Keith, Brian, Stephen & Jon. *Educ:* St Olaf Col, BA, 54; Northwestern Univ, PhD(physics), 60. *Prof Exp:* Asst physics, Northwestern Univ, 54-59; res scientist, Honeywell Inc, 60-70, dept mgr, Technol Ctr, 70-84, res fel, 84-87, chief scientist, 87-94. *Concurrent Pos:* Honeywell res fel, 84-87. *Mem:* Am Phys Soc; Inst Elec & Electronics Engrs. *Res:* Silicon based sensors; electrical and optical properties of semiconductors; solid state devices; silicon and gallium arsenic integrated circuit technology; research management. *Mailing Add:* 14937 Manitou Rd NE Prior Lake MN 55372

**TUFTS, DONALD WINSTON,** ELECTRICAL ENGINEERING. *Current Pos:* PROF ELEC ENG & COMPUT SCI, UNIV RI, 67- *Personal Data:* b Yonkers, NY, Mar 5, 33; m 56; c 3. *Educ:* Williams Col, BA, 55; Mass Inst Technol, BS & MS, 58, ScD(elec eng), 60. *Prof Exp:* Asst prof appl math, Harvard Univ, 62-67. *Mem:* AAAS; fel Inst Elec & Electronics Engrs. *Res:* Information theory; communication theory; computer science; signal processing; underwater sound; data transmission. *Mailing Add:* Dept Elec Eng Univ RI Kelley Hall Kingston RI 02881

**TUGAL, HALIL,** VACUUM SCIENCE IN SEMICONDUCTOR INDUSTRY, CHILLERS FOR SEMICONDUCTOR INDUSTRY. *Current Pos:* MGR ENG, EDWARDS HIGH VACUUM INT, 93- *Personal Data:* b Istanbul, Turkey, Nov 8, 49; US citizen; m 84, Lisa Schafert; c Erik & Kurt. *Educ:* Union Col, BS, 71; Univ NH, MS, 73, PhD(eng), 78. *Prof Exp:* Instr mech eng, Univ NH, 77-78; supvr eng anal, Ball Corp, Muncie, Indiana, 78-80; acoust & vibration engr, Gen Elec, Lynn, Mass, 80-84; sr engr & sr tech mktg engr, CTI-Cryogenics, Mansfield, Mass, 84-93. *Mem:* Am Vacuum Soc. *Res:* Vacuum sciences. *Mailing Add:* Edwards High Vacuum Int 301 Ballardvale St Wilmington MA 01887. *Fax:* 978-658-7969; *E-Mail:* hal.tugal@edwards.bac.com

**TUGWELL, PETER,** CLINICAL EPIDEMIOLOGY, INTERNAL MEDICINE. *Current Pos:* PROF & CHMN, DEPT MED, UNIV OTTAWA, 91- *Personal Data:* b Mar 30, 44; Can citizen; m 71; c 2. *Educ:* Univ London, MBBS, 69, MD, 76; FRCP(C), 76; McMaster Univ, MSc, 77. *Prof Exp:* House officer med, Royal Free & WMiddlesex Hosps, London, 69-70; sr house officer, Whittington Hosp, London, 70-71; res fel & registr, Ahmadu Bello Univ, Nigeria, 71-74; chief resident internal med, McMaster Univ, 75-76, clin epidemiologist & attend physician, 77-91, chmn, Dept Epidemiol & Biostatist, 79-89, prof med, 84-91. *Mem:* Royal Col Physicians & Surgeons Can; Am Asn of Rheumatology. *Res:* Rheumatology; effectiveness studies; educational evaluation; economic studies. *Mailing Add:* Ottawa Gen Hosp Dept Med 501 Smyth Rd Rm LM12 Ottawa ON K1H 8L6 Can

**TUITE, ROBERT JOSEPH,** RESEARCH MANAGEMENT, PHOTOGRAPHIC CHEMISTRY. *Current Pos:* MANAGING PARTNER, INNOVATION STRATEGY GROUP, INC, 92- *Personal Data:* b Rochester, NY, Aug 28, 34; m 58, Ruth Ann; c Robert J Jr, Michael J & Christopher P. *Educ:* St John Fisher Col, BS, 56; Univ Ill, PhD(org chem), 60. *Prof Exp:* Asst chem, Univ Ill, 56-57, asst pub health serv, 59; from res chemist to sr research chemist, Eastman Kodak Co, 59-67, res assoc res labs, 67-70, head color photo chem lab, 70-73, from head to sr head, Color Reversal Systs Lab, 73-74, asst dir, 74-76, dir Color Photog Div, 76-78, dir Color Instant Photog Div, 78-81, asst to the dir, Res Labs, 81-82, dir New Opportunity Develop, corp staff, 82-89; loaned exec, Hi Technol Rochester, 89-91; pres, RJ Tuite Assos, 91-92. *Concurrent Pos:* Mem, AMA coun res & develop mgt. *Mem:* Am Chem Soc; Soc Imaging Sci & Technol. *Res:* Color photographic imaging chemistry; color photographic systems design; parametrization of color photographic system response; technology based new business development, innovation management, technology business strategy. *Mailing Add:* 69 Heather Dr Rochester NY 14625-2509. *Fax:* 716-389-1751; *E-Mail:* rjtuite@aol.com

**TUITES, DONALD EDGAR,** POLYMER CHEMISTRY. *Current Pos:* RETIRED. *Personal Data:* b Saginaw, Mich, Dec 27, 25; m 50; c 4. *Educ:* Univ Rochester, BS, 49; Clarkson Tech Univ, MS, 52; Cornell Univ, PhD(org chem), 56. *Prof Exp:* Chemist, E I du Pont de Nemours & Co, Inc, Del & NY, 55-63, chemist Electrochem Dept, Del, 63-71, chemist, Plastics Prod & Resins Dept, 72-80. *Mailing Add:* 2515 Kittiwake Dr Wilmington DE 19805

**TUITES, RICHARD CLARENCE,** ORGANIC CHEMISTRY, POLYMER CHEMISTRY. *Current Pos:* RETIRED. *Personal Data:* b Rochester, NY, Oct 31, 33; m 54; c 4. *Educ:* Univ Rochester, BS, 55; Univ Ill, PhD(org chem), 59. *Prof Exp:* Res chemist, E I du Pont de Nemours & Co, Inc, 58-62; from chemist to sr chemist, Eastman Kodak Co, 62-72, res assoc, 72-91. *Mem:* Am Chem Soc; Soc Photog Scientists & Engrs. *Res:* Photographic chemistry. *Mailing Add:* 29 Little Brook Dr Pittsford NY 14534

**TUKEY, HAROLD BRADFORD, JR,** HORTICULTURE. *Current Pos:* dir, Ctr Urban Hort, 80-91, dir arboreta, 80-91, PROF URBAN HORT, UNIV WASH, 80- *Personal Data:* b Geneva, NY, May 29, 34; m 55, Helen Parker; c Ruth (Thurbun), Carol (Cameron) & Harold B III. *Educ:* Mich State Univ, BS, 55, MS, 56, PhD(hort), 58. *Hon Degrees:* Dr, Portuguese Asn Hort, 85. *Honors & Awards:* Citation Merit, Am Hort Soc, 81; B Y Morrison, Award, USDA, 87. *Prof Exp:* Res asst hort, S Haven Exp Sta, Mich State Univ, 55, AEC, 55-58; NSF fel, Calif Inst Technol, 58-59; from asst prof to prof hort, Cornell Univ, 59-80. *Concurrent Pos:* Consult, PR Nuclear Ctr, Rio Piedras, 56-66, Int Bonsai Mag, 80-, Elec Power Res Inst; NSF grant, 62 & 75, Bot Soc Am, 64; dir, eastern region Int Plant Propagators Soc, 69-71, Am Soc Hort Sci, 70-71, Am Hort Soc, 72-81, Bot Soc Am, Northwest Hort Soc & Arboretum Found, 80-, Ctr Urban Hort & Arboreta, Univ Wash, 80-; US deleg, Coun Int Soc Hort Sci, 71-90, chmn, Comm Amateur Hort, 74-83, chmn, Comm Urban Hort, 90-; regional vpres, Int Plant Propagators Soc, 72; vis prof, Univ Calif, Davis, 73, Univ Nebr, 84, Tex A&M Univ, 93 & Univ Nat Antonoma Mex, 93; mem var comts, Nat Acad Sci; mem adv comt, Seattle Univ Wash Arboretum & Bot Garden, 80-92, vchmn, 82, chmn, 86-87; bd dirs, Arbor Fund Bloedel Res, 80-92, pres, 83-84; mem, Nat Adv Comt, USDA, 90- *Mem:* Int Soc Hort Sci (vpres, 78-82, pres, 82-86, past pres, 86-90); Int Plant Propagators Soc (pres, 73, int pres, 76); Am Hort Soc (vpres, 78-80); fel Am Soc Hort Sci; Bot Soc Am Northwest Hort Soc; Sigma Xi. *Res:* Physiology of horticultural plants; urban horticulture; uptake and loss of substance through plant foliage; botanical garden administration. *Mailing Add:* Col Forestry Res A R-10 Univ Wash 3900 Seventh Ave NE Seattle WA 98195-0001. *Fax:* 206-685-2692

**TUKEY, JOHN WILDER,** STATISTICS, STATISTICAL ANALYSIS. *Current Pos:* prof statist, 65-85, Donner prof sci, 76-85, EMER PROF & SR RES STATISTICIAN & EMER DONNER PROF SCI, PRINCETON UNIV, 85- *Personal Data:* b New Bedford, Mass, June 16, 15; m 50. *Educ:* Brown Univ, ScB, 36, ScM, 37; Princeton Univ, MA, 38, PhD(math), 39. *Hon Degrees:* ScD, Case Inst Technol, 62, Brown Univ, 65, Yale Univ, 68, Univ Chicago, 69 & Temple Univ, 78. *Honors & Awards:* S S Wilks Medal, Am Statist Asn, 65; Nat Medal Sci, 73; Shewhart Medal, Am Soc Qual Control, 77, Deming Medal, 83; Medal Hon, Inst Elec & Electronics Engrs, 82; James Madison Medal, Princeton Univ, 84; Monei Ferst Award, Sigma Xi, 89. *Prof Exp:* Instr math, Princeton Univ, 39-41, res assoc, Fire Control Res Off, 41-45; mem tech staff, Bell Labs, 45-58, asst dir res commun prin, 58-61, assoc exec dir res commun, Princeton Div, 61-85. *Concurrent Pos:* From asst prof to prof math, Princeton Univ, 41-65, chmn, Dept Statist, 65-70; Guggenheim fel, 49-50; fel, Ctr Advan Study Behav Sci, 57-65; mem, Panel Environ Pollution, Off Sci & Technol, 64-65 & Panel Chem & Health, 71-72; mem, Sci Info Coun, NSF, 62-64; mem, Pres Air Qual Adv Bd, 68-71 & Pres Comn Fed Statist, 70-71; mem coun, Nat Acad Sci, 69-71 & 75-78, chmn class III,

69-72 & chmn climatic impact comt, 75-79; visitor, Commonwealth Sci & Indust Res Orgn, Canberra, Australia, 71-79 & Stanford Linear Accelerator Ctr, 72, 79; mem, US deleg, Tech Working Group 2 Conf Discontinuance Nuclear Weapon Tests, Geneva, Switz, 59 & UN Conf Human Environ, Stockholm, Sweden, 72; mem, Nat Ctr Atmospheric Res, Boulder, Colo, 78 & Dept Sci & Indust Res, Wellington, NZ, 79. *Mem:* Nat Acad Sci; Am Philos Soc; Am Acad Arts & Sci; Int Statist Inst; hon mem Royal Statist Soc. *Res:* Theoretical, applied and mathematical statistics; point set topology; fire control equipment; military analysis. *Mailing Add:* PO Box 2043 Princeton NJ 08543-2043. *Fax:* 609-924-5342

**TUKEY, LOREN DAVENPORT,** POMOLOGY, PLANT PHYSIOLOGY. *Current Pos:* from asst prof to prof, 50-91, EMER PROF POMOL, PA STATE UNIV, 91- *Personal Data:* b Geneva, NY, Dec 4, 21; m 52, Louise A Young; c David D & Barbara A (Shea). *Educ:* Mich State Univ, BS, 43, MS, 47; Ohio State Univ, PhD(hort), 52. *Honors & Awards:* Paul Howe Shepard Award, Am Pomol Soc, 64; Serv & Leadership Award, Am Dwarf Fruit Tree Asn, 88; Milo Gibson Award, NAm Fruit Explorers, 89. *Prof Exp:* Asst hort, Ohio State Univ, 47-50. *Concurrent Pos:* Mem, Coop Fruit Res Prog, Inst Nat Tech Agr, Arg, 65-70; assoc ed, J Hort Sci, Eng, 78-; ed, Pa State Hort Reviews, 62-; bus mgr, Am Pomol Soc, 68-90; res consult, Inst InterAm Coop Agr, Arg, 88; res consult cocoa, Malaysian Agr Res & Develop Inst, 93. *Mem:* Fel AAAS; fel Am Soc Hort Sci; Plant Growth Regulator Soc Am; Am Soc Plant Physiol; Int Soc Hort Sci; Am Pomol Soc (secy, 68-84, treas, 68-90); Brit Soc Plant Growth Regulation; corresp mem Acad Agr France. *Res:* Growth and development of tree fruits; growth regulating chemicals, environmental factors in fruit sizing, orchard productivity; intensive orchard systems and rootstocks; developer of Pennsylvania State low-trellis hedgerow system for apple culture. *Mailing Add:* Dept Hort Pa State Univ 102 Tyson Bldg University Park PA 16802. *Fax:* 814-863-6139

**TUKEY, ROBERT H,** PHARMACOLOGY. *Current Pos:* asst prof, 83-89, ASSOC PROF PHARMACOL, UNIV CALIF, SAN DIEGO, 89- *Personal Data:* m 71, Joan; c Jenna, Rachel, Valerie & Alexander. *Educ:* Univ Minn, BS, 71; Univ Iowa, PhD(pharmacol), 80. *Prof Exp:* Fel, NIH, 80-83. *Mem:* Am Soc Biochem & Molecular Biol; Am Soc Pharmacol & Exp Therapeut. *Res:* Underlying cellular and molecular events that control the regulation and expression of enzymes involved in drug metabolism. *Mailing Add:* Univ Calif San Diego Cancer Ctr 0063 La Jolla CA 92093-0063. *Fax:* 619-543-3943; *E-Mail:* rtukey@ucsd.edu

**TULAGIN, VSEVOLOD,** chemistry; deceased, see previous edition for last biography

**TULCHIN, NATALIE,** MEDICAL RESEARCH, PATHOLOGY. *Current Pos:* RES ASST & PROF PATH, MT SINAI MED CTR, 87- *Personal Data:* b Brooklyn, NY, June 4, 37. *Educ:* Barnard Univ, BA, 57; NY Univ, MS, 63, PhD(cell biol), 66. *Prof Exp:* Res instr path, Mt Sinai Sch Med, 80-87. *Mem:* Am Cell Biol Soc; AAAS; Women Sci Soc. *Res:* Medical Research; pathology. *Mailing Add:* Dept Path Mt Sinai Med Ctr Box 1194 Mt Sinai Sch Med 1 Gustavel Levy Pl New York NY 10029

**TULECKE, WALT,** BOTANY. *Current Pos:* RETIRED. *Personal Data:* b Detroit, Mich, Feb 10, 24; c Peg, Kari, Heidi & Kim. *Educ:* Univ Mich, BA, 46, MS, 50, PhD(bot), 53. *Prof Exp:* Asst prof bot, Ariz State Col, 53-55; res assoc, Brooklyn Bot Garden, 55-57; res botanist, Chas Pfizer & Co, 57-59; assoc plant physiologist, Boyce Thompson Inst, 59-67; prof biol, Antioch Col, 67-90. *Concurrent Pos:* Res plant physiologist, Univ Calif, Davis, 83-85 & 89. *Mem:* AAAS; Soc Econ Bot. *Res:* Plant tissue culture; Ginkgo; walnut. *Mailing Add:* Dept Biol Antioch Col Yellow Springs OH 45387

**TULEEN, DAVID L,** ORGANIC CHEMISTRY. *Current Pos:* asst prof, 63-68, assoc dean arts & sci, 74-92, ASSOC PROF ORG CHEM, VANDERBILT UNIV, 68-, ASSOC PROVOST, 92- *Personal Data:* b Oak Park, Ill, Sept 19, 36; m 60, Jean Brummer; c Elissa, Karin, Julia & Lucia. *Educ:* Wittenberg Univ, BS, 58; Univ Ill, PhD(org chem), 62. *Prof Exp:* Fel, Pa State Univ, 62-63. *Res:* Sulfur chemistry. *Mailing Add:* Off Provost Vanderbilt Univ 2305 West End Ave Nashville TN 37240

**TULENKO, JAMES STANLEY,** COMPUTER AIDED ENGINEERING. *Current Pos:* CHMN & PROF, NUCLEAR ENG SCI DEPT, UNIV FLA, 86- *Personal Data:* b Holyoke, Mass, June 1, 36; m 65, Lois Wagner; c Mark, Christina & Catherine. *Educ:* Harvard Univ, BA, 58, MA, 60; Mass Inst Technol, MS, 63; George Washington Univ, MBA, 80. *Honors & Awards:* Am Nuclear Soc Silver Award, 81. *Prof Exp:* Mgr nuclear develop, United Nuclear Corp, NY, 63-70; mgr physics, Nuclear Mat & Equip Corp, 70-71; mgr physics, Nuclear Power Generation Div, 71-74; mgr nuclear fuel eng, Babcock & Wilcox, 74-81; gen mgr, B & W Comput Serv, 81-83; mgr, Corp Eng Automation Serv, B & W/McDermott, 83-86; chmn, Fuel Cycle Div, Am Nuclear Soc, Nuclear Eng Div, Am soc Eng Educ, 91. *Concurrent Pos:* Adj prof systs anal, George Washington Univ; chmn, spec comt waste mgt, Am Nuclear Soc; emer chmn, Nuclear Dept Heads Orgn, 93; mem bd dirs, Am Soc Eng Educ. *Mem:* Fel Am Nuclear Soc; Am Soc Mfrg Engrs; Soc Mfrg Engrs; Inst Elec & Electronics Engrs Comput Soc; Am Soc Eng Educ. *Res:* Mechanical and material design nuclear fuel; radioactive waste management; reactor physics; fuel management of nuclear reactors; fuel cycle economics of nuclear power plants; robotics for nuclear maintenance; engineering information flow; storage and retrieval information. *Mailing Add:* Nuclear Engr Sci Dept Univ Fla 202 Nuclear Sci Ctr Gainesville FL 32611. *E-Mail:* tulenko@pine.circa.ufl.edu

**TULENKO, THOMAS NORMAN,** VASCULAR DISEASE, HYPERTENISON RESEARCH. *Current Pos:* ASST PROF OBSTET & GYNEC, MED COL PA, 81-, ASSOC PROF PHYSIOL, 82- *Personal Data:* b Pittsburgh, Pa, Dec 2, 42; m 73; c 1. *Educ:* Grove City Col, BS, 66; Duquesne Univ, MS, 68; Botson Univ, PhD, 72. *Prof Exp:* Lectr biol, Gwynedd Mercy Col, 74-76. *Concurrent Pos:* Dir, City-Wide Bd Rev, 81-; consult, McGraw-Hill Pub, 81-; appointee, Nat Bd Med Examrs, 84- *Mem:* Am Physiol Soc; AAAS; Am Heart Asn. *Res:* Regulation of arterial activity in human blood vessels and the nature of their involvement in various disease states; atherosclerosis, vasospasm, heart attack, certain forms of hypertension and intrauterine growth retardation. *Mailing Add:* Dept Physiol & Biochem Med Col Pa 2900 Queen Lane Philadelphia PA 19129-1033. *Fax:* 215-843-6516

**TULER, FLOYD ROBERT,** MATERIALS SCIENCE, MECHANICAL METALLURGY. *Personal Data:* b Chicago, Ill, May 24, 39; m 61; c 2. *Educ:* Univ Ill, Urbana, BS, 60, MS, 62; Cornell Univ, PhD(mat sci & eng), 67. *Prof Exp:* Tech staff mem, Sandia Labs, 66-69; vpres tech, Effects Technol Inc, 69-74; assoc prof mat sci, Hebrew Univ, Jerusalem, Israel, 74-80; prof mat eng, Worcester Polytechnic Inst, Mass, 81-91. *Concurrent Pos:* Panel mem, Nat Mat Adv Bd Ad Hoc Comt, Nat Acad Sci, 68-69; vis sci-assoc prof, Ctr for Policy Alternative & Dept of Mat Sci & Eng, Mass Inst Technol, 78-81; mgr process develop, ManLabs Div, Alcan Aluminum, 90-91. *Mem:* AAAS; Sigma Xi; Am Soc Metals Inst. *Res:* Mechanical properties of metals and reinforced composite materials, materials processing; fracture; fatigue initiation and propagation; impact and impulsive loading; mechanical testing and nondestructive testing techniques; failure prediction and analysis; risk analysis and management. *Mailing Add:* 241 Perkins St Apt F402 Jamaica Plain MA 02130

**TULEYA, ROBERT E,** GEOPHYSICAL FLUID DYNAMICS. *Current Pos:* meteorologist, Geophys Fluid Dynamics Lab, 71-72, RES METEOROLOGIST, GEOPHYS FLUID DYNAMICS LAB, NAT OCEANIC ATMOSPHERIC ADMIN, PRINCETON UNIV, 72- *Personal Data:* b York, Pa, Feb 22, 47; m 72. *Educ:* Pa State Univ, BS, 69, MS, 71. *Honors & Awards:* Banner Miller Award, Am Meteorol Soc, 84. *Prof Exp:* Res asst, Dept Meteorol, Pa State Univ, University Park, 69-71. *Mem:* Am Meteorol Soc. *Mailing Add:* 107 Ironmaster Rd Cherry Hill NJ 08034

**TULI, JAGDISH KUMAR,** NUCLEAR SPECTROSCOPY. *Current Pos:* PHYSICIST, BROOKHAVEN NAT LAB, 77- *Personal Data:* b India, Aug 7, 41; US citizen; m 75, Kiran Bahri; c Neal & Nevin. *Educ:* Delhi Univ, MS, 65; Ind Univ, MS, 69, PhD(physics), 71. *Prof Exp:* Res assoc, Nat Acad Sci, Ind Univ, 71-73; physicist, Dept Atomic Energy, India, 73-75, Lawrence Berkeley Lab, 76-77. *Concurrent Pos:* Ed, Nuclear Data Sheets, 81- *Mem:* Am Phys Soc. *Mailing Add:* Brookhaven Nat Lab 197D Upton NY 11973. *Fax:* 516-344-2806; *E-Mail:* tuli@bnl.gov

**TULIN, LEONARD GEORGE,** STRUCTURAL MECHANICS. *Current Pos:* From instr to assoc prof, 50-61, chmn dept, 72-77, prof, 61-90, EMER PROF CIVIL ENG, UNIV COLO, BOULDER, 90- *Personal Data:* b Mozyr, Russia, May 20, 20; US citizen; m 48; c 1. *Educ:* Univ Colo, BSCE, 50, MSCE, 52; Iowa State Univ, PhD(theoret & appl mech), 65. *Honors & Awards:* Wason Award, Am Concrete Inst, 64. *Mem:* Am Soc Civil Engrs; Am Concrete Inst; Am Soc Testing & Mat; Soc Exp Stress Anal; Masonry Soc. *Res:* Mechanics and materials; construction practices in reinforced masonry; design of timber structures; glass fiber reinforced concrete. *Mailing Add:* 1120 Fairway Club Lane Estes Park CO 80517-7455

**TULIN, MARSHALL P(ETER),** WAVES, CAVITATIONS & NAVAL HYDRODYNAMICS. *Current Pos:* prof, 82-94, EMER PROF MECH & ENVIRON ENG & DIR, OCEAN ENG LAB, UNIV CALIF, SANTA BARBARA, 94- *Personal Data:* b Hartford, Conn, Mar 14, 26; m 55; c 2. *Educ:* Mass Inst Technol, BS, 46, MS, 49. *Honors & Awards:* Wineblum Lectr, 84. *Prof Exp:* Aeronaut res scientist, Nat Adv Comt Aeronaut, 46-50; physicist & head, Turbulence & Frictional Sect, David W Taylor Model Basin, US Dept Navy, 50-54, aeronaut res engr, Mech Br, Off Naval Res, 54-57, sci liaison officer, London Br Off, 57-59; vpres & dir, Hydronautics, Inc, 59-71, chief exec officer & bd chmn, 71-82. *Concurrent Pos:* Bd chmn, Hydronautics-Israel, Ltd; pres chair, Univ Calif, 82-87. *Mem:* Nat Acad Eng. *Res:* Supercavitating, turbulent, stratified and polymer flows; hydrofoil and propeller theory; wakes. *Mailing Add:* Ocean Eng Lab Univ Calif Santa Barbara CA 93106. *Fax:* 805-893-4927; *E-Mail:* mpt@vortex.ucsb.edu

**TULINSKY, ALEXANDER,** BLOOD PROTEINS. *Current Pos:* assoc prof chem, 65-67, PROF CHEM, MICH STATE UNIV, 68- *Personal Data:* b Philadelphia, Pa, Sept 25, 28; m 55; c 4. *Educ:* Temple Univ, AB, 52; Princeton Univ, PhD(chem), 56. *Honors & Awards:* Alberta Heritage Found vis scientist award, Univ Calgary, 81. *Prof Exp:* Res assoc, Protein Struct Proj, Polytech Inst Brooklyn, 55-59; asst prof chem, Yale Univ, 59-65. *Concurrent Pos:* vis prof chem, Univ SC, Columbia, 82; chmn, Spec Interest Group Biol Macromolecules, Am Crystallog Asn, 77-78. *Mem:* Am Crystallog Asn; Am Chem Soc. *Res:* X-ray crystallographic structure determination of biological molecules; structure and function of enzymes; blood clotting proteins: thrombin, gla and tringle domains, protein inhibitor-enzyme complexes, other blood protein structural domains. *Mailing Add:* Dept Chem Mich State Univ East Lansing MI 48823

**TULIP, THOMAS HUNT,** ORGANOTRANSITION METAL CHEMISTRY. *Current Pos:* Res chemist, Cent Res & Develop, 78-85, chem supvr immunopharmaceut, Biomed Prod, 85-, SR DIR CUSTOMER RELS, E I DU PONT DE NEMOURS & CO INC, 96- *Personal Data:* b Anchorage, Alaska, Nov 16, 52; m 78. *Educ:* Univ Vt, BS, 74; Northwestern Univ, MS, 75, PhD(chem), 78. *Concurrent Pos:* Vis scientist, Osaka Univ, 74. *Mem:* Am Chem Soc; Soc Nuclear Med; AAAS. *Res:* Organometallic and bioorganic chemistry; metals in medicine; protein modification; attachment of binding agents to antibodies; radiochemistry; immunochemistry. *Mailing Add:* Du Pont Med Pharm Bldg 600-2 331 Treble Cove Rd North Billerica MA 01862-2897

**TULL, JACK PHILLIP,** MATHEMATICS, NUMBER THEORY. *Current Pos:* RETIRED. *Personal Data:* b Jackson, Mich, Dec 2, 30; m 52; c Laura, Andrew & Tara. *Educ:* Univ Ill, PhD(math), 57. *Prof Exp:* From instr to assoc prof math, Ohio State Univ, 56-87. *Concurrent Pos:* Vis sr lectr, Univ Adelaide, 63-64; prof & head dept, Univ Zambia, 70-71, dean humanities & social sci, 71; expert anal, World Bank Proj, Gadjah Mada Univ, Indonesia. *Mem:* Am Math Soc; Math Asn Am; London Math Soc. *Res:* Analytic theory of numbers. *Mailing Add:* 6323 21st Ave NE Seattle WA 98115-6915. *E-Mail:* jtul@scn.org

**TULL, JAMES FRANKLIN,** STRUCTURAL GEOLOGY, GEOTECTONICS. *Current Pos:* assoc prof geol, 81-84, dept chmn, 84-91, PROF GEOL, FLA STATE UNIV, 81- *Personal Data:* b New York, NY, May 26, 47; m 93, Elizabeth Doll; c 2. *Educ:* Univ NC, BS, 69; Rice Univ, PhD(geol), 73. *Prof Exp:* Asst prof geol, Univ Ala, 73-78, assoc prof, 78-81. *Concurrent Pos:* Consult, Geol Surv Ala, 75-76, E I du Pont de Nemours & Co, Inc, 78-, Amoco Petrol Co, 81-84, Champlin Petrol Co, 81 & J M Huber Co, 84, Hecla Mining Co, 87- *Mem:* Fel Geol Soc Am; Geol Soc Norway. *Res:* Structural evolution of mountain systems, particularly the development of metamorphic and igneous terraines; studying metamorphism associated with orogenesis and relationships between structural and metamorphic events. *Mailing Add:* Dept Geol Fla State Univ 600 W College Ave Tallahassee FL 32306-1096

**TULL, ROBERT GORDON,** ASTRONOMY, INSTRUMENTATION. *Current Pos:* Res assoc, Univ Tex, 61, from instr to asst prof, 62-70, res scientist astron, 70-83, SR RES SCIENTIST, MCDONALD OBSERV, UNIV TEX, AUSTIN, 83- *Personal Data:* b Jackson, Mich, May 1, 29; m 52, Catherine Ruble; c Patricia, Steven, Alan & Kendra. *Educ:* Univ Ill, BS, 52, MS, 57; Univ Mich, PhD(astron), 63. *Honors & Awards:* Maria & Eric Muhlmann Award, Astron Soc Pac, 96. *Concurrent Pos:* NSF grants, 63-66, 74-78, 78-82 & 88-91; mem high resolution spectrograph instrument definition team, NASA Large Space Telescope, 73-76; consult, Electronic Vision Co Div of Sci Appln Inc, 74-78; consult, Europ Southern Observ, 78-; consult, Asiago Observ, Italy & Wise Observ, Israel, 75-78; vis scientist, Chinese Acad Sci, 81; mem, Steering Comt, Nat New Technol Telescope, 81-83, High Resolution Spectrog Working Group, 85; proj scientist, 300-Inch Telescope, Univ Tex, 83-85, high resolution spectrograph, 2.7-m telescope, McDonald Observ, 88-; proj dir high res spectrog, Hobby-Eberly Telescope, 92-; NSF grant, 96- *Mem:* Int Soc Optical Eng; Am Astron Soc; Int Astron Union; Optical Soc Am. *Res:* Photoelectric spectrophotometry of astronomical sources; astronomical instrumentation; development and application of multi-channel image detectors for astronomical spectrophotometry; design of large telescopes and of high resolution spectrograph for astronomy. *Mailing Add:* Dept Astron Univ Tex Austin TX 78712. *E-Mail:* rgt@astro.as.utexas.edu

**TULL, WILLIAM J,** ELECTRICAL ENGINEERING. *Current Pos:* RETIRED. *Personal Data:* b Ontario, Can. *Educ:* Univ Mich, BSEE, 42. *Honors & Awards:* Thurlow Award, Inst Navig, 59. *Prof Exp:* Vpres & dir res & eng, Gen Porcelain Corp, NY, 64-69; pres, Tull Aviation, Armonk, NY, 69-78; vpres, Northrop Corp, Kansas City, MO, 78-82. *Mem:* Inst Navig; Fel Inst Elec & Electronics Engrs. *Res:* Inventor of the Doppler microwave navigation equipment. *Mailing Add:* 1 Sams Point Lane Hilton Head Island SC 29926

**TULLER, ANNITA,** mathematics, for more information see previous edition

**TULLER, HARRY LOUIS,** ELECTRONIC CERAMICS, SOLID STATE IONICS. *Current Pos:* PROF, MAT SCI & ENG, MASS INST TECHNOL, 75- & DIR, CRYSTAL PHYSICS & ELECTROCERAMICS LAB. *Personal Data:* b Apr 2, 45; c 2. *Educ:* Columbia Univ, New York, NY, BS, 66, MS, 67, EngScD, 73. *Honors & Awards:* Alexander von Humboldt Award, 96. *Prof Exp:* Res assoc physics, Technion-Israel Inst Technol, 74-75. *Concurrent Pos:* Mem, Nat Mat Adv Bd Comt Fuel Cell Mat Tech Vehicular Propulsion, 82-83 & Mass Inst Technol Comn Indust Productivity, 87-88; vis fel, Imp Col, London, 83; vis scientist, Raychem Corp, Menlo Park, Calif, 83; vis prof, Univ Pierre Marie Curie, Paris, 90; chair, Sumitomo Elec Industs, Ltd, 92; ed-in-chief, J Electroceramics. *Mem:* Fel Am Ceramic Soc; Electrochem Soc; Inst Elec & Electronics Engrs; Mat Res Soc. *Res:* Charge and mass transport in semiconducting and fast ion conducting ceramics and glasses; rectifying grain boundaries, and interfaces; defect theory; optical properties; sensors; semiconducting micromachining. *Mailing Add:* Dept Mat Sci & Eng Mass Inst Technol Rm 13-3126 Cambridge MA 02139

**TULLIO, VICTOR,** CHEMISTRY. *Current Pos:* res chemist, 51-61, supvr new dye eval, 64-69, tech asst textile dyes, 69-71, supvr new dye eval, 71-72, SR RES CHEMIST, E I DU PONT DE NEMOURS & CO, INC, 72- *Personal Data:* b Philadelphia, Pa, May 29, 27; m 51; c 2. *Educ:* Univ Pa, BS,

48; Univ Ill, PhD(org chem), 51. *Prof Exp:* Asst, Univ Ill, 48-49. *Mem:* Am Asn Textile Chemists & Colorists; Am Chem Soc. *Res:* Organic chemistry; dyes; dyeing of synthetic fibers. *Mailing Add:* 1304 Chadwick Rd Wilmington DE 19803-4116

**TULLIS, J PAUL,** CIVIL ENGINEERING. *Current Pos:* PROF CIVIL ENG, UTAH WATER RES LAB, UTAH STATE UNIV, 80- *Personal Data:* b Ogden, Utah, July 24, 38; m 58; c 4. *Educ:* Utah State Univ, BS, 61, PhD(civil eng), 66. *Prof Exp:* Gen contractor commercial construct, Paul & Milo Tullis Gen Contractors, 61-63; asst prof civil eng, Colo State Univ, 66-70, assoc prof, 70-80. *Res:* Cavitation research, viscous drag reduction and hydraulic modeling. *Mailing Add:* 815 Stewart Hill Dr Logan UT 84321

**TULLIS, JAMES EARL,** GENETICS. *Current Pos:* from asst prof to assoc prof, 65-85, PROF, IDAHO STATE UNIV, 85- *Personal Data:* b Cincinnati, Ohio. *Educ:* Miami Univ, BS, 51; Ohio State Univ, MS, 54, PhD(genetics), 61. *Prof Exp:* Instr zool, Ohio Univ, 56-59; asst prof, Wash State Univ, 61-65. *Mailing Add:* Dept Biol Sci Idaho State Univ 921 S Eighth St Pocatello ID 83209-0001

**TULLIS, JAMES LYMAN,** biochemistry; deceased, see previous edition for last biography

**TULLIS, JULIA ANN,** EXPERIMENTAL ROCK DEFORMATION. *Current Pos:* from asst res prof to assoc res prof, 71-79, assoc prof, 79- 87, PROF GEOL SCI, BROWN UNIV, 88- *Personal Data:* b Swedesboro, NJ, Feb 21, 43; div. *Educ:* Carleton Col, AB, 65; Univ Calif, Los Angeles, PhD(geol), 71. *Prof Exp:* Res asst geol, Inst Geophys, Univ Calif, Los Angeles, 69-70. *Mem:* Am Geophys Union; Mineral Soc Am; Sigma Xi; Geol Soc Am. *Res:* Experimental rock deformation; deformation mechanisms, microstructures, and rheology of crustal rocks and minerals. *Mailing Add:* Dept Geol Sci Brown Univ Providence RI 02912. *Fax:* 401-863-2058; *E-Mail:* yt@gech033.geo.brown.edu

**TULLIS, RICHARD EUGENE,** COMPARATIVE PHYSIOLOGY, COMPARATIVE ENDOCRINOLOGY. *Current Pos:* asst prof, 72-76, assoc prof, 76-81, PROF PHYSIOL, CALIF STATE UNIV, HAYWARD, 81- *Personal Data:* b Long Beach, Calif, Apr 26, 36; m 62; c 3. *Educ:* Univ Wash, BS, 63; Univ Hawaii, MS, 68, PhD(zool), 72. *Prof Exp:* Res asst, Univ Hawaii, 70-71. *Concurrent Pos:* Partic guest, Biomed Div, Lawrence Livermore Lab, 73-; NSF sci equip grant, 74. *Mem:* Sigma Xi; Am Soc Zoologists; AAAS. *Res:* Neuroendocrine control of hydromineral regulation in crustaceans including isolation of neuroendocrine substances, enzyme regulation mechanisms and target organ identification; basic physiological invertebrate functions affected by environmental and man-made substances. *Mailing Add:* Dept Biol Sci Calif State Univ Hayward CA 94542

**TULLIS, TERRY EDSON,** STRUCTURAL GEOLOGY, GEOPHYSICS. *Current Pos:* asst prof, 70-76, ASSOC PROF GEOL, BROWN UNIV, 76- *Personal Data:* b Rapid City, SDak, July 21, 42; m 65. *Educ:* Carleton Col, AB, 64; Univ Calif, Los Angeles, MS, 67, PhD(struct geol), 71. *Prof Exp:* Actg instr geol, Univ Calif, Los Angeles, 69-70. *Concurrent Pos:* Sloan res fel, Brown Univ, 73-75; vis fel res, Sch Earth Sci, Australian Nat Univ, 76; geologist, US Geol Surv, 77. *Mem:* Am Geophys Union; Geol Soc Am; AAAS. *Res:* Experimental rock deformation; tectonophysics; plate tectonics; origin of slaty cleavage and schistosity; thermodynamic systems under nonhydrostatic stress; rheology of rocks at high temperature and pressure; study of in situ stress; rock friction. *Mailing Add:* Dept Geol Sci Brown Univ Providence RI 02912-9127

**TULLIUS, THOMAS D,** CHEMISTRY. *Current Pos:* PROF CHEM, JOHNS HOPKINS UNIV, 82- *Personal Data:* b Fortuna, Calif, Mar 23, 52. *Educ:* Univ Calif, Los Angeles, BS, 73; Stanford Univ, PhD(chem), 79. *Prof Exp:* Fel, Columbia Univ, 79-82. *Mem:* Am Chem Soc; AAAS; Biophys Soc; Am Soc Biochem & Molecular Biol; Am Protein Soc. *Mailing Add:* Dept Chem Johns Hopkins Univ 34th & Charles Sts Baltimore MD 21218-2685

**TULLOCK, ROBERT JOHNS,** SOIL CHEMISTRY. *Current Pos:* ASST PROF SOIL SCI, CALIF STATE POLYTECH UNIV, POMONA, 76- *Personal Data:* b Atascadero, Calif, Oct 3, 40; m 62; c 3. *Educ:* Calif State Polytech Col, San Luis Obispo, BS, 67; Purdue Univ, West Lafayette, MS, 70, PhD(soil chem), 72. *Prof Exp:* Asst prof soil sci, Univ Calif, Riverside, 72-73; asst prof soil sci, Ore State Univ, 74-76. *Mem:* Am Soc Agron; Soil Sci Soc Am; Clay Minerals Soc. *Res:* Physicochemical properties of colloidal surfaces. *Mailing Add:* Dept Plant Sci Calif State Polytech Univ Pomona 3801 W Temple Ave Pomona CA 91768-2557

**TULLSON, PETER C,** MUSCULAR METABOLISM, PHYSIOLOGY. *Current Pos:* SR RES SCIENTIST PHYSIOL, STATE UNIV NY HEALTH SCI CTR, 88- *Personal Data:* b Providence, RI, Apr 17, 55. *Educ:* Boston Univ, BA, 77, PhD(physiol), 84. *Prof Exp:* Res fel physiol, Muscular Dystrophy Asn, 85-88. *Mem:* Am Physiol Soc; AAAS. *Res:* Muscular metabolism; physiology. *Mailing Add:* Dept Physiol State Univ NY Health Sci Ctr 750 E Adams St Syracuse NY 13210-2375

**TULLY, EDWARD JOSEPH, JR,** mathematics; deceased, see previous edition for last biography

**TULLY, FRANK PAUL,** PHYSICAL CHEMISTRY. *Current Pos:* mem tech staff, 80-93, MGR, COMBUSTION CHEM DEPT, SANDIA NAT LABS, LIVERMORE, CALIF, 93- *Personal Data:* b Hartford, Conn, Apr 27, 46; m 81; c 2. *Educ:* Clark Univ, BA, 68; Univ Chicago, MS, 69, PhD(chem), 73. *Prof Exp:* Res asst chem, Clark Univ, 65-68; res asst, Univ Chicago, 68-73; fel, Univ Toronto, 73-74; NSF fel chem, Mich State Univ, East Lansing, 74-76; mem fac eng exp sta, Appl Sci Div, Ga Inst Technol, 76-80. *Concurrent Pos:* NSF energy related fel, 75. *Mem:* Am Chem Soc. *Res:* Use of the crossed molecular beam method in studies of elastic, inelastic and reactive scattering; photoionization; gas-phase reaction kinetics; laser photochemistry. *Mailing Add:* Sandia Nat Labs MS 9055 PO Box 969 Livermore CA 94551-0969

**TULLY, JOHN CHARLES,** CHEMICAL PHYSICS, SOLID STATE PHYSICS. *Current Pos:* PROF CHEM, PHYSICS & APPL PHYSICS, YALE UNIV, 96- *Personal Data:* b New York, NY, May 17, 42; m 71, Mary Thomsen; c John T, Elizabeth A & Stephen T. *Educ:* Yale Univ, BS, 64; Univ Chicago, PhD(chem), 68. *Honors & Awards:* Peter Debye Award, Am Chem Soc, 95. *Prof Exp:* NSF fel chem, Univ Colo, 68-69 & Yale Univ, 69-70; mem tech staff, Bell Labs, 70-85, head, Mat Chem Res Dept, 85-96. *Concurrent Pos:* Vis prof chem, Princeton Univ, 81-82; mem, Nat Sci Found Adv Comt for Chem, 87- & Petrol Res Fund Adv Bd, 88-; distinguished vis lectr, Univ Tex, Austin, 87. *Mem:* Nat Acad Sci; fel Am Phys Soc; fel AAAS; Am Chem Soc. *Res:* Theory of chemical rate processes, molecular collisions and gas-surface interactions. *Mailing Add:* 260 Stonehedge Lane Guilford CT 06437

**TULLY, JOSEPH GEORGE,** MEDICAL MICROBIOLOGY. *Current Pos:* res microbiologist, 62-68, HEAD MYCOPLASMA SECT, NAT INST ALLERGY & INFECTIOUS DIS, 68- *Personal Data:* b Sterling, Colo, July 14, 25; m 57, Melba Weber; c 1. *Educ:* Portland Univ, BS, 49; Brigham Young Univ, MS, 51; Cincinnati Univ, PhD(microbiol), 55. *Hon Degrees:* Dr, Univ Bordeaux, France, 80. *Honors & Awards:* Klieneberger-Nobel Award, Int Orgn Mycoplasmology; J Roger Porter Award, Am Soc Microbiol, 82. *Prof Exp:* Asst prof microbiol, Col Med, Cincinnati Univ, 55-57; microbiologist, Walter Reed Army Inst Res, 57-61, chief, Dept Microbiol, 61-62. *Concurrent Pos:* China med bd fel, Cent Am, 56; attend microbiologist, Cincinnati Gen Hosp, Ohio, 56-57; mem bd, Food & Agr Orgn/WHO Prog on Comp Mycoplasmology, 69-78; chmn bd, 72-77; mem, Int Subcomt Taxon of Mollicutes, 70-; chmn, Int Org Mycoplasmology, 75-78; mem adv bd, Bergey's Manual Syst Bacteriol, 80-81; assoc ed, Int J Syst Bact, 83-90; trustee, Bergey's Manual Trust, 90-96. *Mem:* Fel AAAS; Am Asn Immunol; fel Am Acad Microbiol; Am Soc Microbiol; Soc Exp Biol & Med; Int Orgn Mycoplasmology. *Res:* Basic biology of the mycoplasmas; murine mycoplasmas; spiroplasmas; urogenital mycoplasmas; systematics of mollicutes. *Mailing Add:* Mycoplasma Sec Nat Inst Allergy & Infectious Dis Bldg 550 Frederick Cancer Res Ctr Frederick MD 21702-1201. *Fax:* 301-846-5165

**TULLY, PHILIP C(OCHRAN),** chemical & nuclear engineering, for more information see previous edition

**TULLY, RICHARD BRENT,** extragalactic astronomy, for more information see previous edition

**TULP, ORIEN LEE,** OBESITY DIABETES & METABOLISM, RESOURCE MANAGEMENT & MILITARY MEDICINE. *Current Pos:* PROF NUTRIT SCI, DREXEL UNIV, 83-, PROF, ENVIRON STUDIES INST, 85- *Personal Data:* b Newark, NJ, July 15, 36; c David, Bona & Susan. *Educ:* Univ Vt, BS, 68, MS, 70, PhD(pharmacol), 74. *Honors & Awards:* Order Mil Med Merit, Legion Merit. *Prof Exp:* Res asst, Univ Vt Col Med, 63-73, res assoc, 74-77 res assoc, Dept Med, 77-83. *Concurrent Pos:* Vis prof biochem, Colby Col, 81-83; adj fac, Univ Vt, Acad Health Sci & Drexel-US Army Grad Prog; consult & vis scientist, Auylin Pharmaceut. *Mem:* Am Inst Nutrit; Am Soc Clin Nutrit; Nutrit Soc; NAm Soc Study Obesity; fel Am Col Nutrit; Sigma Xi (pres, 90-91). *Res:* Mechanisms of energy metabolism and energy expenditure in obesity and diabetes; animal models of obesity; adipose tissue cellularity and metabolism; nutrient-endocrine interactions; nutritional biochemistry in obesity, diabetes and exercise; Brown adipose tissue; pharmacology and obesity and diabetes. *Mailing Add:* Drexel Univ 606 Nesbitt Hall 32nd & Chestnut Sts Philadelphia PA 19104. *Fax:* 215-895-2421

**TULS, JODY LYNN FOY,** PROTEIN SEPARATIONS, PROTEIN FOLDING. *Current Pos:* SR RES SCIENTIST, UPJOHN CO, 88- *Personal Data:* b Anniston, Ala, July 5, 60; m 83, James; c Brandon & Kelly. *Educ:* Hope Col, BA, 82; Univ Ark, PhD(biochem), 88. *Concurrent Pos:* Adj prof, Ferris State Univ, 93. *Mem:* AAAS; Fedn Am Soc Exp Biol; Am Soc Biochem & Molecular Biol; Fedn Am Soc Exp Biol. *Res:* Bioanalytical characterization of biotechnology candidates using HPLC (SEC, RP, ion exchange immunocolums), spectroscopy, sequencing and capillary electrophoresis; proteins of interest include hemoglobin and monoclonal antibodies. *Mailing Add:* 4861-259-277 7000 Portage Rd Kalamazoo MI 49001. *Fax:* 616-323-6743

**TULSKY, EMANUEL GOODEL,** RADIOLOGY. *Current Pos:* RADIOLOGIST & DIR DIV RADIATION THER & NUCLEAR MED, ABINGTON MEM HOSP, PA, 65- *Personal Data:* b Philadelphia, Pa, Dec 6, 23; m 50; c 2. *Educ:* Jefferson Med Col, MD, 48. *Prof Exp:* Attend radiologist, Delafield Hosp, New York, 52-53; assoc radiologist, Sch Med & Univ Hosp, Temple Univ, 53-55; assoc radiol, Div Grad Med & asst prof radiol, Univ Pa, 55-65. *Concurrent Pos:* Assoc radiologist & dir, Tumor Clin,

Hosp Univ Pa, 55-67; asst prof radiol, Med Col Pa, 62- *Mem:* Radiol Soc NAm; AMA; Am Col Radiol. *Res:* Intracavitary radiation dosimetry; isotopic studies of gastrointestinal absorption; cancer therapy; synergistic action of radiation and cytotoxics. *Mailing Add:* 24 W Butler Ave Chalfont PA 18914-3016

**TULUNAY-KEESEY, ULKER,** ophthalmology, psychophysics, for more information see previous edition

**TUMA, DEAN J,** BIOLOGICAL CHEMISTRY. *Current Pos:* Instr, 73-75, ASST PROF INTERNAL MED & BIOCHEM, COL MED, UNIV NEBR, 75-; RES CHEMIST BIOCHEM, VET ADMIN HOSP, OMAHA, 64- *Personal Data:* b Howells, Nebr, Oct 20, 41; m 64; c 3. *Educ:* Creighton Univ, BS, 64, MS, 68; Univ Nebr, PhD(biochem), 73. *Mem:* Am Asn Study Liver Dis; Am Fedn Clin Res. *Res:* Investigation of the role of ethanol, drugs and nutrition in liver metabolism and liver disease. *Mailing Add:* 2223 S 161st Circle Omaha NE 68130

**TUMA, GERALD,** ELECTRICAL ENGINEERING. *Current Pos:* From instr to prof, Univ Okla, 40-66, chmn dept, 58-62, dir sch, 66-77, DAVID ROSS BOYD PROF ELEC ENG, UNIV OKLA, 66- *Personal Data:* b Oklahoma City, Okla, July 19, 14; m 38; c 2. *Educ:* Univ Okla, BS, 39, MEE, 41. *Mem:* Am Soc Eng Educ; Inst Elec & Electronics Engrs; Sigma Xi. *Res:* Communications; feedback control systems; analog simulation; digital computers. *Mailing Add:* 1509 Ann Arbor Dr Norman OK 73069

**TUMA, RONALD F,** CEREBRAL PHYSIOLOGY, VASCULAR PHYSIOLOGY. *Current Pos:* PROF PHYSIOL & CHMN DEPT PHYSIOL, TEMPLE UNIV, SCH MED, 94- *Res:* Cerebral physiology; vascular physiology. *Mailing Add:* Dept Physiol Temple Univ Sch Med 3420 N Broad St Philadelphia PA 19140-5104

**TUMAN, VLADIMIR SHLIMON,** PHYSICS, GEOPHYSICS. *Current Pos:* RETIRED. *Personal Data:* b Kermanshah, Iran, May 21, 23; US citizen; m 51; c 3. *Educ:* Univ Birmingham, BSc, 48; Univ London, DIC, 49; Stanford Univ, PhD(geophys), 64. *Prof Exp:* Geophysicist, Anglo Iranian Oil Co, SW Iran, 50-52; actg chief petrol, Nat Iranian Oil Co, 52-55, engr trainee, Europe & USA, 55-56; sr petrol physicist, Nat Iranian Consortium, 56-57; res physicist, Atlantic Refining Oil Co, Dallas, Tex, 57-59; assoc prof petrol eng, Univ Ill, Urbana, 59-62; res assoc geophys, Stanford Univ, 62-65, res physicist, Res Inst, 65-66; assoc prof physics, Calif State Univ, Stanislaus, 66-67, chmn, Dept Phys Sci, 66-71, prof physics & astron, 67-93. *Concurrent Pos:* Calif Res Corp grant, 60-61; consult, Esso Res Lab, 61, Schlumberger Well Logging Co, 61 & Sinclair Oil Co, 61; Am Petrol Inst grants, 61-63; consult, Comput Symp, Stanford Univ, 63-64, res assoc, Physics Dept, 65-; lectr, Varian Assoc, Palo Alto, Calif, 66. *Mem:* fel Royal Astron Soc; Am Phys Soc; Am Asn Physics Teachers; Am Geophys Union; Soc Explor Geophys. *Res:* Development of cryogenic gravity meter to study earth eigen vibrations and detection gravitational radiation; evolution of Babylonian and Assyrian astronomy. *Mailing Add:* 1401 E Tuolumne Rd Turlock CA 95382

**TUMAY, MEHMET TANER,** GEOTECHNOLOGY. *Current Pos:* PROF CIVIL ENG & COORDR GEOTECH ENG, LA STATE UNIV, BATON ROUGE, 76- *Personal Data:* b Ankara, Turkey, Feb 2, 37; m 62, Karen Nutty Combe; c Peri & Suna. *Educ:* Robert Col, Turkey, BS, 59; Univ Va, MCE, 61; Tech Univ Istanbul, PhD, 71. *Prof Exp:* Instr civil eng, Univ Va, 61-62; asst prof, Univ Louisville, 62-63; teaching fel, Univ Calif, Los Angeles, 63-64; asst prof civil eng, Robert Col Sch Eng, Istanbul, 66-71; assoc prof, Bogazici Univ, Istanbul, 71-75; Fugro-Cesco res fel, Univ Fla, 75-76. *Concurrent Pos:* Geotech consult, Sauti, Spa, Consult Engrs, 69-72, Sofretu-RATP, Paris, 72-73, DEA consult Engrs, Istanbul, 74-75, Botek Ltd, Istanbul, 75-, Senler-Campbell Assocs, Louisville, 79- & Fugro Gulf-Geogulf, Houston, 80-; consult, UN Develop Prog, 82-84 & 87; Fr Ministry External Rels scholar, 82; dir, Geomech Prog, NSF, 90-; adv prof, Univ Viscosa, Brazil, 91- & Tongji Univ China, 91- *Mem:* Fel Am Soc Civil Engrs; Am Soc Eng Educ; Am Soc Testing & Mat; Int Soc Soil Mech & Found Eng; Sigma Xi. *Res:* Civil engineering. *Mailing Add:* 1915 W Magna Carta Pl Baton Rouge LA 70815-5521

**TUMBLESON, M(YRON) E(UGENE),** BIOCHEMISTRY, NUTRITION. *Current Pos:* PROF, COL VET MED, UNIV ILL, 86- *Personal Data:* b Mountain Lake, Minn, Mar 13, 37; m 83; c 3. *Educ:* Univ Minn, BS, 58, MS, 61, PhD(nutrit), 64. *Prof Exp:* From res assoc to asst prof animal sci, Univ Minn, 64-66; asst prof vet physiol & pharmacol, Univ Mo-Columbia & res assoc med biochem, Sinclair Comp Med Res, 66-69; assoc prof vet anat & physiol, Univ Mo, Columbia & Sinclair Comp Med res, 66-69, res assoc, 64-80, res prof, 80-86. *Mem:* Am Inst Nutrit; Soc Exp Biol & Med; Am Soc Neurochem; Am Soc Biol Chemists; Sigma Xi. *Res:* Protein-calorie malnutrition; alcoholism and aging, using miniature swine as biomedical research subjects. *Mailing Add:* Dept Vet Biosci Col Vet Med Univ Ill 2001 S Lincoln Urbana IL 61801-6178. *Fax:* 217-333-4628

**TUMELTY, PAUL FRANCIS,** MAGNETIC & OPTICAL PROPERTIES OF MATERIALS, TRANSPORT PROPERTIES. *Current Pos:* CONSULT, 88- *Personal Data:* b Boston, Mass, May 9, 41; m 85, Elisabeth Musso; c Kathleen E. *Educ:* Boston Col, BS, 62; Univ Iowa, MS, 64, PhD(physics), 70. *Prof Exp:* Prin res engr, Honeywell, Inc, 70-73; physicist, AlliedSignal Inc, 73-80, sr res physicist, 80-82, res assoc, 82-88. *Mem:* Am Phys Soc; Inst Elec & Electronics Engrs; Sigma Xi. *Res:* Superconductivity; magnetic and optical properties of epitaxially-grown oxide films; liquid-phase expitaxy of oxide films; transport properties of semiconductors; low-temperature physics. *Mailing Add:* 1 East Dr Convent Station NJ 07960

**TUMER, NIHAL,** PHARMACOLOGY. *Current Pos:* asst prof, 89-94, ASSOC PROF PHARMACOL, UNIV FLA, 94- *Personal Data:* m, Philip Scorpace; c Erin T. *Educ:* Hacettepe Univ, Turkey, MS, 72, PhD(biophysics), 80. *Prof Exp:* Biologist, Hacettepe Univ, Turkey, 73-76; fel pharmacol, Med Col Penn, 86-88, res asst prof, 88-89. *Concurrent Pos:* Prin investr, Am Fedn Aging Res, 87-88, Am Heart Asn, 88-89 & 91-93, Ciba-Geigy, 89, Vet Admin, 91-93, Univ Fla, 90 & 92; mem, Basic Sci Coun, Am Heart Asn. *Mem:* Soc Neurosci; Am Soc Pharmacol & Exp Therapeut; Geront Soc Am; Am Heart Asn. *Res:* Cardiovascular pharmacology and aging, basically biosynthesis of catecholamines with cold exposure, exercise and aging at molecular level. *Mailing Add:* VA Med Ctr Grecc 182 Gainesville FL 32602. *Fax:* 352-374-6142

**TUMLINSON, JAMES H, III,** ENTOMOLOGY. *Current Pos:* res chemist, Behav & Basic Biol Res Lab, Gainesville, Fla, 70-72, RES LEADER INSECT ATTRACTANTS, AGR RES SERV, USDA, 72- *Educ:* Va Mil Inst, BS, 60; Miss State Univ, MS, 66, PhD(organic chem), 69. *Honors & Awards:* Burdick & Jackson Int Award, Agrochem Div, Am Chem Soc, 86; J E Bussart Mem Award, Entom Soc Am 90; LeTourneau Mem Lectr, Univ Idaho, 94. *Prof Exp:* Postdoctoral pos, NY State Col Forestry, 69-70; chemist, Boll Weevil Res Lab, State Col, Miss, 64-69. *Concurrent Pos:* From adj asst prof to adj assoc prof, Dept Entom, Univ Fla, Gainesville, 70-82, adj prof & mem doctoral fac, Inst Food & Agr, Dept Entom & Nemat & Dept Chem, 82- *Mem:* Nat Acad Sci; fel Entom Soc Am; Int Soc Chem Ecol (vpres, 97, pres, 98). *Res:* Insect chemical communication and chemical ecology: defining chemical communications systems, including pheromones and other semiochemicals that mediate insect-insect and plant-insect interactions; biosynthesis of pheromones and plant chemical signals; insect behavior, including learning, mediated by semiochemicals; emphasis is on developing fundamental knowledge and principles that can be applied in environmentally safe pest management programs; over 220 publications and patents. *Mailing Add:* Ctr Med Agr & Agr Entom USDA PO Box 14565 Gainesville FL 32604. *Fax:* 352-374-5707; *E-Mail:* jtumlinson@gainesville.usda.ufl.edu

**TUMMALA, RAO RAMAMOHANA,** ELECTRON PACKAGING, MULTICHIP MODULE. *Current Pos:* JOSEPH M PETTIT CHAIR & PROF ELECTRONICS PACKAGING, GA INST TECHNOL, 93-, GA RES EMINENT SCHOLAR, 93- *Personal Data:* b Nandamuru, India, Feb 15, 42; US citizen; m 66, Ann E Mitran; c Dinesh, Vijay & Suneel. *Educ:* Loyola Col, BSc, 61; Indian Inst Sci, BE, 63; Queen's Univ, Can, MS, 65; Univ Ill, PhD(ceramics), 68. *Honors & Awards:* Gilpin Mem lectr, Clarkson Univ, 91; David Sarnoff Award, Inst Elec & Electronics Engrs, 91; Friedberg Award, Am Ceramic Soc, 92, John Jeppson Award, 97. *Prof Exp:* Process engr ceramics, Norton Co, 64-66; res asst, Univ Ill, 66-68; staff engr metall, IBM Corp, 68-70, adv engr ceramics, 70-76, sr engr glass-ceramics, 76-84, IBM fel comput packaging, 84-86, dir packaging, 86-88, IBM fel packaging, 88-93. *Concurrent Pos:* Mem adv bd, Univ Ill, 80-84; chmn adv bd, Univ Calif, Berkeley, 86-88, Mass Inst Technol, 90-91; vis prof, Polytech Inst NY, 87-88. *Mem:* Nat Acad Eng; fel Am Ceramic Soc; Fel Inst Elec & Electronics Engrs; Int Soc Hybrid Microelectronics (pres); Mat Res Soc. *Res:* Ceramics; glass; glass-ceramics; powder metallurgy; thin films; polymers; composites; interfaces; mechanical behavior of materials; ferroelectrics; electronic packaging. *Mailing Add:* Ga Inst Technol Sch Elec & Comput Eng Mfg Res Ctr 813 Ferst Dr NW Atlanta GA 30332-0560. *Fax:* 404-894-0957; *E-Mail:* res.tummadea@ee.gatech.edu

**TUMOSA, NINA JEAN,** ELECTROPHYSIOLOGY, IMMUNOCYTOCHEMISTRY. *Current Pos:* ASST PROF, UNIV MO, 89- *Personal Data:* b Dover-Foxcroft, Maine, Oct 12, 51. *Educ:* Rensselaer Polytech Inst, BS, 73, MS, 74; State Univ NY, Albany, PhD(neurosci), 82. *Prof Exp:* Fel anat, Med Sch, Univ Calgary, 82-84; fel neurosci, Univ Wis, 85-87 & AAAS, 88-89. *Concurrent Pos:* Res scientist, 87-88. *Mem:* Asn Res Vision & Opthal; AAAS; Am Women Sci; Nat Asn Female Execs; Women Neurosci; Soc Neurosci. *Res:* Integrated neuroscientific approach to the development of visual processing in vertebrates, with an emphasis on the effects of altered visual experience on the maintenance of binocularity. *Mailing Add:* Sch Optom Univ Mo St Louis MO 63121. *Fax:* 314-553-5150; *E-Mail:* sntumos@umslvma.umsl.edu

**TUN, ZIN,** MAGNETIC STRUCTURES & EXITATIONS, NEUTRON SCATTERING & SURFACE STRUCTURES. *Current Pos:* PHYSICIST, ATOMIC ENERGY CAN LTD, 89- *Personal Data:* b Rangoon, Burma, Nov 5, 57; m 85, Kay Win; c Kan Thit. *Educ:* Arts & Sci Unv, Rangoon, Burma, BS, 78; McMaster Univ, Hamilton, Ont, PhD(physics),85. *Prof Exp:* Res fel, Univ Edinburgh, UK, 85-87; res assoc, Univ Toronto, 87-89. *Concurrent Pos:* Assoc grad fac mem, Univ Guelph, 92-; adj prof, Univ Waterloo, 92- *Mem:* Can Asn Physicists; Am Phys Soc. *Res:* Magnetic structures in bulk materials and artificial layered superlattices; frustration due to antiferromagnetism and spin-glass behavior; magnetic excitations and spin waves; surface structures and changes due electrochemical reactions. *Mailing Add:* Atomic Energy Can Ltd Chalk River ON K0J 1J0 Can. *Fax:* 613-584-4040; *E-Mail:* tunz@aecl.ca

**TUNA, NAIP,** INTERNAL MEDICINE, CARDIOVASCULAR DISEASES. *Current Pos:* from instr to asst prof, 57-64, assoc prof, 64-80, PROF MED, MED SCH, UNIV MINN, MINNEAPOLIS, 80- *Personal Data:* b Constanta, Romania, Aug 18, 21; m 49; c 2. *Educ:* Istanbul Univ, MD, 47; Univ Minn, PhD(med), 58. *Prof Exp:* Asst med, Therapeut Clin, Istanbul Univ, 49-52; resident med, St Joseph's Hosp, Lexington, Ky, 52-53. *Concurrent Pos:* Am Heart Asn res fel, Univ Minn, Minneapolis, 58-59, advan res fel, 59-61. *Mem:* Fel Am Col Physicians; fel Am Col Cardiol; fel Am Heart Asn; Am Fedn Clin Res. *Res:* Electro and vector cardiography; cardiology. *Mailing Add:* Univ Hosp Box 481 Minneapolis MN 55455

**TUNC, DEGER CETIN,** PHYSICAL CHEMISTRY, BIOPOLYMERS. *Current Pos:* res scientist surg dressings, Johnson & Johnson, 66-74, sr res scientist bioeng & biochem, Cent Res, 74-81, res assoc Orthop Res, 81-85, prin scientist, 85-91, GROUP LEADER POLYMER RES, JOHNSON & JOHNSON ORTHOP, 91- *Personal Data:* b Izmir, Turkey, Apr 2, 36; m 63; c 2. *Educ:* Columbia Univ, BS, 63; Fairleigh Dickinson Univ, MA, 66; Rutgers Univ, PhD(phys chem), 72. *Prof Exp:* Res chemist cellulose, Eastern Res, ITT Rayonier, 63-66. *Concurrent Pos:* UN guest lectr, Dept Bioeng, Ege Univ, Izmir, Turkey, 79; Dept Chem, Tubitak, Izmit, Turkey, 81, Yale Univ Med Sch, 84, Cornell Univ, 88 & Clemson Univ, 90. *Mem:* Am Chem Soc; Soc Biomat; Soc Turkish Architects Engrs & Scientists Am (pres, 72-74); Orthop Res Soc. *Res:* Polyelectrolytes; body absorbable polymers; health care products in general; wound healing; orthopedics; gastrointestinal problems and drugs; controlled release membranes; biomedical devices; absorbable internal bone fixation devices; blood compatible polymers; 13 US patents and 69 international patents; 20 published articles. *Mailing Add:* 6 Springfield Rd East Brunswick NJ 08816-2640

**TUNE, BRUCE MALCOLM,** PEDIATRIC NEPHROLOGY, CLINICAL RENAL PHYSIOLOGY. *Current Pos:* chief resident pediat, Stanford Univ, 69-70, fel pediat renal dis, 70-71, from asst prof to assoc prof, 71-83, PROF PEDIAT, SCH MED, STANFORD UNIV, 83- *Personal Data:* b New York, NY, Aug 26, 39; m 69, Nancy C Doolittle; c Sara E & Steven M. *Educ:* Stanford Univ, AB, 63, MD, 65. *Prof Exp:* Intern med & pediat, Univ Rochester, 65-66; resident pediat, Stanford Univ, 66-67; res assoc renal physiol, Nat Heart Inst, NIH, 67-69, clin assoc renal dis, 68-69. *Concurrent Pos:* Dir pediat nephrol, Stanford Univ Hosp & Lucile Salter Packard Children's Hosp at Stanford, 71- *Mem:* Am Soc Nephrol; Int Soc Nephrol; Am Pediat Soc; Soc Pediat Res; Am Soc Pharmacol & Exp Therapeut; Am Soc Renal Biochem & Metab. *Res:* Investigation of molecular mechanisms of drug-induced injury to the kidney focused on the attack by Beta-Lactam antibiotics on renal tubular cell mitochondrial substrate transporters; identifying effective modes of therapy of the nephrotic syndrome caused by focal sclerosing glomerulonephritis. *Mailing Add:* Dept Pediat Stanford Univ Stanford CA 94305. *Fax:* 650-723-2137

**TUNG, AMAR S,** IMMUNOLOGY. *Current Pos:* DIR BIOCHEM, VERAX CORP, 84- *Personal Data:* b Fahabare, India, Mar 15, 48. *Educ:* Punjab Univ, India, BS, 67, MS, 69; Univ Ill, PhD(immunol), 75. *Prof Exp:* Res fel biochem, Univ Ill, 76-79; sr scientist, Merck Sharp & Dohme Res Labs, 79-84. *Mem:* Am Soc Immunol; Am Biochem Soc. *Res:* Immunology. *Mailing Add:* PK Tech 88 Etna Rd Lebanon NH 03766-7501

**TUNG, CHE-SE,** AUTONOMIC NERVOUS SYSTEM, NEURO-PSYCHOPHARMACOLOGY. *Current Pos:* asst instr physiol, Dept Biophys, Nat Defense Med Ctr, 75-78, from asst instr to prof, Dept Pharmacol, 78-90, chmn, Dept Physiol & Biophys, 91-96, PROF, DEPT PHYSIOL & BIOPHYS, NAT DEFENSE MED CTR, 91-, DEAN ACAD AFFAIRS, 96- *Personal Data:* b Nanking, China, Nov 19, 48; m 75, Chang-Chu Fu; c Chen-Wen & Chen-Li. *Educ:* Nat Defense Med Ctr, MD, 75; Vanderbilt Univ, PhD(pharmacol), 83. *Hon Degrees:* DSc, Vanderbilt Univ, 83. *Honors & Awards:* Res Scientist Develop Award, Nat Sci Coun; Twentieth Century Achievement Award, Am Biog Inst. *Prof Exp:* Jointed prof physiol, Dept Biomed Eng, Chung Yuan Christian Univ, Repub China, 90-92. *Concurrent Pos:* Mem, Coun Basic Sci, Am Heart Asn, 83-; res assoc, Dept Med & Pharmacol, Vanderbilt Univ, 83-84; bd trustee, Chinese Soc Pharmacol, 84-; basic res awards med sci, Dept Health, Repub China, 84-; consult, Bur Drug, Dept Health, Repub China, 85-88 & Dept Agr, 86-; student adv, Dr Med Sci, Grad Fac Coun, Nat Defense Med Ctr, 85-88, teaching comt mem, Educ Fac Coun, 85-, chief secy, S C Wang Found Neurosci Res, 90-; vis scientist, Dept Pharmacol, Karolinska Institutet, Sweden, 88-89; mem bd trustees, Chinese Soc Neruoscience, 91-; assoc ed, Chinese J Physiol. *Mem:* Am Fedn Clin Res; Am Soc Pharmacol & Exp Therapeut; NY Acad Sci; Am Heart Asn; Am Autonomic Soc; Planetary Soc; Asia Pac Soc Pharmacol. *Res:* Brain exerts control over the motivated behaviors and cardiovascular functions through the central monoaminergic neuronal pathways; physiological functions and pharmacological control of schedule-induced drinking, one of animal displacement behaviors using in vivo as well as in vitro techniques; using in vivo as well as in vitro techniques (eg microdialysis) to study physiological functions and pharmacological control of schedule-induced polydipsia, one of animal displacement behaviors. *Mailing Add:* Dept Physiol Nat Defense Med Ctr PO Box 90048-503 Taipei 107 Taiwan. *Fax:* 886-2-3689259

**TUNG, CHI CHAO,** STRUCTURAL MECHANICS. *Current Pos:* assoc prof, 69-76, PROF STRUCT ENG, NC STATE UNIV, 76- *Personal Data:* b Shanghai, China, Mar 24, 32; US citizen; m 64; c 2. *Educ:* Tung-Chi Univ, China, BS, 53; Univ Calif, Berkeley, MS, 61, PhD(struct eng & struct mech), 64. *Prof Exp:* Asst prof struct eng, Univ Ill, Urbana, 64-69. *Mem:* Am Soc Civil Engrs; Am Soc Eng Educ. *Res:* Application of probability and statistics to civil engineering problems; ocean engineering. *Mailing Add:* Dept Civil Eng NC State Univ 318 Mann Hall PO Box 7908 Raleigh NC 27695-7908. *E-Mail:* tung@eoc.ncsu.edu

**TUNG, FRED FU,** ENZYMOLOGY, PROTEIN CHEMISTRY. *Current Pos:* biochemist, 74-78, CLIN HEALTH SCIENTIST, MICH DEPT PUB HEALTH, 78- *Personal Data:* b Manchouli, Inner Mongolia, July 23, 34; m 71; c 2. *Educ:* Taiwan Prov Col Agr, BS, 56; Univ Vt, MS, 63; Univ Mich, MS, 66; Univ Mo, PhD(biochem), 70. *Prof Exp:* Res asst agr chem, Taiwan Prov Col Agr, 58-59; fel biochem, State Univ NY Albany, 70-73. *Mem:* Am Chem Soc; AAAS; NY Acad Sci. *Res:* Use of plasmin to modify immune serum globulin for intravenous administration; isolation and purification of anticancer drugs; research and development of bacterial vaccines (pertussis). *Mailing Add:* 1209 N Hayford Ave Lansing MI 48912

**TUNG, JOHN SHIH-HSIUNG,** MATHEMATICS. *Current Pos:* RETIRED. *Personal Data:* b Keelung, Taiwan, July 19, 28; m 54; c 4. *Educ:* Taiwan Norm Univ, BA, 50; Pa State Univ, MA, 60, PhD(math), 62. *Prof Exp:* Asst civil eng, Taihoku Imp Univ, Taiwan, 44-45; asst instr math, Taipei Inst Technol, 50-53; asst math & indust educ, Taiwan Norm Univ, 53-56, instr, 56-58; asst math, Pa State Univ, 58-60 & 61-62; from asst prof to prof, Miami Univ, Ohio, 62-92. *Mem:* Math Asn Am; Am Math Soc. *Res:* Theory of functions of a complex variable; infinite and orthogonal series. *Mailing Add:* 814 Melissa Dr Oxford OH 45056

**TUNG, KA-KIT,** DYNAMIC METEOROLOGY, FLUID MECHANICS. *Current Pos:* PROF APPL MATH, UNIV WASH, 89-; CHAIR DEPT, 93- *Personal Data:* b Canton, China, Dec 6, 48; US citizen; m 76, Patricia Mu; c 3. *Educ:* Calif Inst Technol, BSc & Msc, 72; Harvard Univ, PhD(appl math), 77. *Prof Exp:* Fel, Harvard Univ, 77-79; asst prof appl math, Mass Inst Technol, 79-84, assoc prof, 84-86; prof math & comput sci, Clakson Univ, 86-88. *Concurrent Pos:* assoc, Ctr Earth & Planetary Physics, Harvard Univ, 79-84; consult, Dynamics Technol Inc, 80-81; assoc, Ctr Meteorol & Phys Oceanog, Mass Inst Technol, 83-90, vis prof, 87-90; John Simon Guggenheim Found fel, 85-86. *Mem:* Am Meteorol Soc; Am Geophys Union; Meteorol Soc Japan; Royal Meteorol Soc. *Res:* Large scale wave motions in the earth's atmosphere; internal waves in the ocean; modeling of tracer transport in the stratosphere. *Mailing Add:* Dept Appl Math Box 352420 Univ Wash Seattle WA 98195. *Fax:* 206-685-1440; *E-Mail:* tung@amath.washington.edu

**TUNG, MARVIN ARTHUR,** FOOD PACKAGING, FOOD PROCESSING & FOOD MATERIAL SCIENCE. *Current Pos:* HEAD, DEPT FOOD SCI TECHNOL, UNIV NS, 87- *Personal Data:* b Sask, Can, Nov 9, 37; c 3. *Educ:* Univ BC, BSA, 60, teaching cert, 61, MSA, 67, PhD(food sci), 70. *Honors & Awards:* William J Eva Award, Can Inst Food Sci Technol, 85. *Prof Exp:* From asst prof to prof food sci, Univ BC, 70-87. *Mem:* Can Inst Food Sci & Technol; Inst Food Technologists; Brit Inst Food Sci & Technol; Can Soc Agr Eng; Micros Soc Can; Inst Thermal Processing Specialists; Soc Rheology. *Res:* Food rheology; microstructure of food systems; food processing and packaging. *Mailing Add:* Dept Food Sci Univ Guelth 50 Stone Rd Guelph ON N1G 2W1 Can

**TUNG, MING SUNG,** DENTAL CHEMISTRY. *Current Pos:* SR PROJ LEADER, DENT CHEM, AM DENT ASN HEALTH FOUND, PAFFENBARGER RES CTR, 74- *Personal Data:* b Taiwan, Feb 25, 42; US citizen; m 70; c 2. *Educ:* Cheng-Kung Univ, Taiwan, BS, 64; Brown Univ, PhD(chem), 73. *Honors & Awards:* E H Hatton Award, Int Asn Dent Res, 76. *Prof Exp:* Fel, Univ Md, 72-74, vis prof chem, 74. *Concurrent Pos:* Mem, Sci Adv Bd, Enamelon Inc, 92-96; expert, Food & Drug Admin, 91-93; adj clin prof, Dent Sch, Univ Wash, 94-96. *Mem:* Am Asn Dent Res; Int Asn Dent Res; Sigma Xi. *Res:* Calcium phosphate and fluoride chemistry as applied to dental and bone sciences; physical chemistry of biological systems; study of physical properties of biopolymers such as DNA, polypeptides, proteins and enzymes. *Mailing Add:* 15233 Falconbridge Terr Gaithersburg MD 20878. *Fax:* 301-963-9143

**TUNG, RAYMOND T,** PHYSICS. *Current Pos:* Mem tech staff, Bell Labs, 80-82, MEM TECH STAFF, AT&T BELL LABS, MURRAY HILL, 82- *Personal Data:* b Jan 1, 52; US citizen. *Educ:* Nat Taiwan Univ, Taipei, BS, 73; Univ Pa, Philadelphia, PhD(physics), 80. *Honors & Awards:* Peter Mark Mem Award, Am Vacuum Soc, 87. *Concurrent Pos:* Adj prof, Univ Pa, Philadelphia, 89-91. *Mem:* Bohmische Phys Soc; fel Am Phys Soc. *Res:* Physics. *Mailing Add:* AT&T Bell Labs 600 Mountain Ave Murray Hill NJ 07974

**TUNG, WU-KI,** THEORETICAL PHYSICS, ELEMENTARY PARTICLE PHYSICS. *Current Pos:* PROF, MICH STATE UNIV, 92- *Personal Data:* b Kunming, China, Oct 16, 39; m 63, Beatrice; c Lei H & Bruce Y. *Educ:* Univ Taiwan, BS, 60; Yale Univ, PhD(physics), 66. *Prof Exp:* Res assoc theoret physics, Inst Theoret Physics, State Univ NY Stony Brook, 66-68; mem staff, Inst Adv Study, Princeton, 68-70; asst prof physics & mem staff, Dept Physics, Enrico Fermi Inst, Univ Chicago, 70-75; from assoc prof to prof physics, Ill Inst Technol, 75-92, chmn dept, 81-84. *Mem:* Fel Am Phys Soc. *Res:* High energy theoretical physics. *Mailing Add:* Dept Physics Mich State Univ East Lansing MI 48824. *Fax:* 517-355-6661; *E-Mail:* tung@pa.msu.edu

**TUNG, YEOU-KOUNG,** RELIABILITY ANALYSIS, WATER RESOURCE SYSTEMS ANALYSIS. *Current Pos:* from asst prof to assoc prof, 85-93, PROF STATIST, UNIV wYO, 93- *Personal Data:* b Taiwan, Repub China, Mar 4, 54; US citizen; m 77, Be-Ling Lee; c 4. *Educ:* Tamkang Univ, BS, 76; Univ Tex, Austin, MS, 78, PhD(water resources), 80. *Honors & Awards:* Collingwood Prize, Am Soc Civil Engrs, 87; Ippen Award, Int Asn Hydraul Res, 93. *Prof Exp:* Res assoc water resources, Univ Tex, Austin, 80; asst prof civil eng, Univ Nev, Reno, 81-84. *Concurrent Pos:* Control mem, Task Comt Risk & Reliability Anal Water Distrib Systs, Am Soc Civil Engrs, 84-87 & Comt Probabilistic Approaches Hydraul, 84-90, chmn, 89; chmn, Subcomt Uncertainty & Reliability Anal Design Hydraul Struct, 89-91; sabbatical asst prof civil eng, Nat Chiao-Tung Univ, 91- *Mem:* Am Geophys Union; Am Soc Civil Engrs; Am Statist Asn; Int Asn Hydraul Res; Int Water Res Asn. *Res:* Water resource systems analysis; probabilistic analysis of hydrologic and hydraulic systems; decision making under uncertainty. *Mailing Add:* Statist Univ Wyo PO Box 3332 Laramie WY 82071-3332. *Fax:* 307-766-3785; *E-Mail:* tung@uwho.edu

**TUNHEIM, JERALD ARDEN,** SOLID STATE PHYSICS. *Current Pos:* PRES, SDAK STATE UNIV, 87- *Personal Data:* b Claremont, SDak, Sept 3, 40; m 63, Patricia A Weitham; c 3. *Educ:* SDak State Univ, BS, 62, MS, 64; Okla State Univ, PhD(physics), 68. *Prof Exp:* From asst prof to prof physics, SDak State Univ, 68-85, head dept, 80-85; dean sch math sci & technol, Eastern Wash Univ, 85-87. *Mem:* Am Phys Soc; Am Asn Physics Teachers; Nat Soc Prof Engrs. *Res:* Alpha particle model of sulphur nucleus; electron spin resonance measurements of transition metal ions in stannic oxide; surface effects on conductivity of stannic oxide; application and development of models for remote sensing application; electrolytic capacitors; science education. *Mailing Add:* Pres SDak State Univ Madison SD 57042-1799. *Fax:* 605-256-5316; *E-Mail:* tunheimj@columbia.dsu.edu

**TUNICK, MICHAEL HOWARD,** AGRICULTURAL & FOOD CHEMISTRY, ANALYTICAL CHEMISTRY. *Current Pos:* Chemist, USDA, 77-85, RES CHEMIST, USDA, 85- *Personal Data:* b Philadelphia, Pa, Dec 18, 54; m 85, Gail Seltzer; c Daniel & Susan. *Educ:* Drexel Univ, BS, 77; Temple Univ, PhD(phys-anal chem), 85. *Concurrent Pos:* Evening fac instr chem, St Joseph Univ, 86-88; chmn, Food & Nutrit Biochem Subdiv, Agr & Food Chem Div, Am Chem Soc, 96- *Mem:* Am Chem Soc; Am Dairy Sci Asn. *Res:* Investigates textural and functional properties of low fat cheeses and relates changes in these properties to changes in protein, fat and water during processing and aging. *Mailing Add:* USDA 600 E Mermaid Lane Wyndmoor PA 19038. *Fax:* 215-233-6795; *E-Mail:* mtunick@arserrc.gov

**TUNIK, BERNARD D,** PHYSIOLOGY. *Current Pos:* RETIRED. *Personal Data:* b New York, NY, Dec 22, 21; m 49; c 3. *Educ:* Univ Wis, BA, 42; Columbia Univ, MA, 51, PhD(zool), 59. *Prof Exp:* Asst cytol, Sloan-Kettering Inst, 50-52; asst zool, Columbia Univ, 52-55; instr anat, Sch Med, Univ Pa, 58-60; assoc prof biol sci, State Univ NY Stony Brook, 60-90, dep chmn dept, 62-63 & 64-65. *Concurrent Pos:* Nat Inst Arthritis & Metab Dis spec fel, Dept Polymer Sci, Weizmann Inst, 66-67; vis scholar, Dept Zool, Univ Calif, Berkeley, 75. *Res:* Cellular physiology; mechanochemical aspects of muscle contraction; triggers of muscle hypertrophy. *Mailing Add:* 6 University Dr East Setauket NY 11733

**TUNIS, C(YRIL) J(AMES),** ELECTRICAL ENGINEERING. *Current Pos:* DIR TECH EDUC, PAC BELL TECH EDUC, 88- *Personal Data:* b Montreal, Que, July 31, 32; m 51; c 3. *Educ:* McGill Univ, BEng, 54, MSc, 56; Univ Manchester, PhD(elec eng), 58. *Honors & Awards:* Babbage Award, Brit Inst Elec Engrs. *Prof Exp:* Dir tech educ, IBM Corp, Endicott, 58-88. *Concurrent Pos:* Lectr, Harpur Col, State Univ NY, 59-60 & Lehigh Univ, 61-62; vis prof, Stanford Univ, 66-67. *Mem:* Fel Inst Elec & Electronics Engrs. *Res:* Design of advanced digital computer systems. *Mailing Add:* 2600 Camino Ramon Rm 2N502 San Ramon CA 94583

**TUNIS, MARVIN,** BIOCHEMISTRY. *Current Pos:* assoc prof, 68-77, PROF CHEM, STATE UNIV NY COL BUFFALO, 77- *Personal Data:* b New York, NY, Apr 18, 25; m 52; c 4. *Educ:* Hunter Col, AB, 50; Univ Ill, MS, 51, PhD(biochem), 54. *Prof Exp:* Res assoc, Univ Ill, 54-55; USPHS fel, Col Physicians & Surgeons, Columbia Univ, 55-56; sr cancer res scientist, Roswell Park Mem Inst, 57-68. *Mem:* Am Chem Soc; Am Soc Biol Chemists; Am Asn Cancer Res. *Res:* Biochemistry and metabolism of nucleic acids, proteins, glycoproteins and mucopolysaccharides; enzymology. *Mailing Add:* 117 South Dr Buffalo NY 14226

**TUNKEL, ROMAN N,** BEHAVIOR OF MATERIALS UNDER ULTRA HIGH PRESSURE, STRESS ANALYSIS. *Current Pos:* SR RES ENGR, WATERJET SYST, INGERSOLL-RAND, 95- *Personal Data:* b St Petersburg, USSR, Dec 21, 53; m 80, Regina Krupitskaya; c Victoria. *Educ:* Univ Mining Mach & Systs, St Petersburg, Russia, BS, 74, MS, 76, PhD(mech eng), 86. *Prof Exp:* Sr res engr, Pneumatica Inc, 80-88; chief, Hydro-Pneumo Lab, Sci Complex Unitemp, 89-92, Res & Design Inst Robotics & Tech Cybernetics, 92-93; gen engr, US Indust Tools, 94-95. *Concurrent Pos:* Fac, Univ Mining Mach, St Petersburg, Russia, 87-89. *Res:* Pneumo-hydromechanical processes and devices; stress analysis for impact systems and ultra high pressurized components; methods of experimental research and mathematical simulation; fluid flow and heat transfer analyses. *Mailing Add:* 30084 Spring River Dr Southfield MI 48076-1045. *Fax:* 248-471-9113; *E-Mail:* tunkelr@juno.com

**TUNKEL, STEVEN JOSEPH,** CHEMICAL ENGINEERING, PHYSICAL CHEMISTRY. *Current Pos:* CHIEF CHEM ENGR FIRE & EXPLOSION, HAZARDS RES CORP, 72- *Personal Data:* b New York, NY, Jan 15, 29; m 52; c 3. *Educ:* Polytech Inst Brooklyn, BS, 51; Newark Col Eng, MS, 56. *Prof Exp:* Res engr pilot plants, Allied Chem Corp, 51-56; mgr res eng aerospace, Thiokol Chem Corp, 56-68; mgr mkt res jet engines, Austenal Div, Howmet Corp, 68-70; mgr process res new plant start-up, Celanese Chem Corp, 70-72. *Concurrent Pos:* Course lectr, Am Inst Chem Engrs & Nat Safety Coun. *Mem:* Am Chem Soc; Am Inst Chem Engrs; Combustion Inst; Nat Soc Prof Engrs. *Res:* Fire and explosion hazard evaluation of chemicals and chemical processes; vapor cloud explosions; metallic hydrode safety. *Mailing Add:* 37 Woodcrest Rd Whippany NJ 07981

**TUNNELL, WILLIAM C(LOTWORTHY),** MECHANICAL ENGINEERING. *Current Pos:* RETIRED. *Personal Data:* b Knoxville, Tenn, May 19, 15; m 42; c 2. *Educ:* Univ Tenn, BS, 40. *Prof Exp:* Engr, Blue Ridge Glass Corp, 40-43, Tenn Eastman Co, 43-47, Oak Ridge Nat Lab, 47-68 & Nuclear Div, Union Carbide Corp, 68-79. *Concurrent Pos:* Consult engr, 79- *Mem:* Nat Soc Prof Engrs. *Res:* Electromagnetic separation of isotopes; high temperature components of atomic power reactors; critical assemblies; nuclear reactions; liquid metals; pulse reactors; environmental statements for nuclear power plants. *Mailing Add:* 104 Ditman Lane Oak Ridge TN 37830

**TUNNICLIFF, DAVID GEORGE,** BITUMINOUS ENGINEERING. *Current Pos:* CONSULT ENGR, 79- *Personal Data:* b Ord, Nebr, Sept 18, 31; m 75, Joan Elizabeth Duchesneau; c Martha Allison (Loeb) & Vivian Jean. *Educ:* Univ Nebr, BSCE, 54; Cornell Univ, MS, 58; Univ Mich, PhD(civil eng), 72. *Honors & Awards:* Distinguished Serv Award, Transp Res Bd. *Prof Exp:* Sr engr, Nebr Dept Roads, 58-60; prof civil eng, Wayne State Univ, 60-67; chief engr, Warren Bros Co, 67-79. *Concurrent Pos:* Dir, Asn Asphalt Paving Technologists, 76-78. *Mem:* Hon mem Am Soc Testing & Mat; Asn Asphalt Paving Technologists; Transp Res Bd; Am Soc Civil Engrs; Nat Soc Prof Engrs. *Res:* Mixing asphalt concrete; mineral filler; moisture damage; antistripping additives; lime in asphalt concrete; quality control. *Mailing Add:* 9624 Larimore Ave Omaha NE 68134

**TUNNICLIFF, GODFREY,** NEUROCHEMISTRY. *Current Pos:* from asst prof to assoc prof, 78-86, PROF BIOCHEM, SCH MED, IND UNIV, 86- *Personal Data:* b Malvern, Eng, Jan 6, 41; m 71, Sally Stillinger; c Julie, Jennifer & Charles. *Educ:* Univ Col Wales, BSc, 64; Univ Southampton, MSc, 67, PhD(biochem), 69. *Prof Exp:* Res biochemist, Liebig's Extract Meat Co Ltd, London, 64-66; fel, City of Hope Nat Med Ctr, Duarte, Calif, 69-71; fel, Univ Sask, 71-72, asst prof biochem, 72-74; dir, Lab Neurochem, Clin Res Inst Montreal, Que, 74-77. *Mem:* Int Soc Neurochem. *Res:* Role of gamma-aminobutyric acid in the functioning of the central nervous system. *Mailing Add:* Ind Univ Sch Med 8600 Univ Blvd Evansville IN 47712. *Fax:* 812-465-1184; *E-Mail:* gtunnic@indyvax.iupui.edu

**TUNNICLIFFE, PHILIP ROBERT,** physics, for more information see previous edition

**TUNNICLIFFE, VERENA JULIA,** BIOGEOGRAPHY. *Current Pos:* Asst prof, 82-87, ASSOC PROF BIOL, UNIV VICTORIA, 88- *Personal Data:* b Deep River, Ont, June 6, 53; m 87; c 1. *Educ:* McMasters Univ, BSc, 75; Yale Univ, MPhil, 78, PhD(biol), 80. *Concurrent Pos:* Vis researcher, Ifremer, France, 88-89. *Mem:* Sigma Xi; Am Geophys Union; Can Meteorol & Oceanog Soc; Paleont Soc Am. *Res:* Ecology and evolution of marine communities with present emphasis on hydrothermal vent fauna and the development of biota on offshore seamounts. *Mailing Add:* PO Box 1700 Victoria BC V8W 2Y2 Can. *Fax:* 250-721-7120

**TUNSTALL, LUCILLE HAWKINS,** microbiology, immunology, for more information see previous edition

**TUOMI, DONALD,** THERMOELECTRIC ENERGY CONVERSION. *Current Pos:* RETIRED. *Personal Data:* b Willoughby, Ohio, Sept 12, 20; m 45, Ruth E Campbell; c Donna J (Beck) & Mary (Hammond). *Educ:* Ohio State Univ, BS, 43, PhD(phys chem), 52. *Honors & Awards:* Battery Div Award, Electrochem Soc, 68. *Prof Exp:* Res scientist, Columbia Univ, SAm Lab, 43-45 & Carbide & Carbon Chem Corp, 45-46; fel res assoc photoemissive surfaces, Res Found, Ohio State Univ, 50-53; mem staff semiconductor devices, Lincoln Lab, Mass Inst Technol, 53-54; res chemist, Baird Assocs, Inc, 54-55; res scientist, Thomas A Edison Res Lab, McGraw Edison, 55-61; staff scientist, RC Ingersoll Res Ctr, Borg Warner, 61-63; mgr solid state physics, 63-78, sr scientist, 78-83; pres, Donald Tuomi, PhD & Assoc Ltd, 83-96. *Mem:* Fel AAAS; Electrochem Soc; Am Phys Soc; Am Chem Soc; Am Crystal Soc; Sigma Xi; Am Inst Chem; Am Crystal Growth Soc. *Res:* Correlation of materials processing and composition variables to system performance and properties through solid state structural chemistry in polymer deformation-failure, thermoelectric energy conversion, and plated plastics. *Mailing Add:* 626 S Kaspar Ave Arlington Heights IL 60005

**TUOMINEN, FRANCIS WILLIAM,** BIOCHEMISTRY. *Current Pos:* VPRES CORP TECHNOL, ECOLAB, 85- *Personal Data:* b Floodwood, Minn, Mar 1, 43; m 64; c 4. *Educ:* Univ Minn, Duluth, BS, 65; Univ Minn, Minneapolis, MS, 68, PhD(biochem), 70. *Prof Exp:* NSF fel carcinogenesis, Oak Ridge Nat Lab, 70-71; sect leader, Gen Mills Chem Inc, 71-76, mgr res & develop, 76-78; dir res & develop chem, Henkel Corp, 78-85. *Concurrent Pos:* Consult, Sch Pub Health, Univ Minn, 65-66 & Oak Ridge Nat Lab, 71-72. *Mem:* Am Chem Soc; Am Soc Microbiol; Indust Res Inst; AAAS; Chem Specialities Mfrs Asn. *Res:* New products, processes and applications for specialty chemicals. *Mailing Add:* Ecolab Inc Ecolab Ctr St Paul MN 55102-1349

**TUOMINEN, MARK THOMAS,** PHYSICS EDUCATION, CONDENSED MATTER PHYSICS. *Current Pos:* ASST PROF ASTRON, UNIV MASS, 93- *Personal Data:* b Grand Rapids, Minn, Oct 27, 63. *Educ:* Univ Minn, BS, 86, PhD(physics), 90. *Honors & Awards:* Nat Young Investr Award, NSF, 94. *Mem:* Am Phys Soc. *Mailing Add:* Hasbrouck Lab Dept Physics & Astron Univ Mass Amherst MA 01003. *Fax:* 413-545-1691; *E-Mail:* tuominen@phast.umass.edu

**TUOVINEN, OLLI HEIKKI,** APPLIED & INDUSTRIAL MICROBIOLOGY. *Current Pos:* from asst prof to assoc prof, 80-85, PROF MICROBIOL, OHIO STATE UNIV, 85- *Personal Data:* b Helsinki, Finland, April 8, 44; m 72, Manel Yapa; c Henrikki, Katarina & Karolina. *Educ:* Univ Helsinki, Finland, MSc, 69, LicSc, 70; London, Eng, PhD(microbiol), 73. *Prof Exp:* Fel agr biochem, Waite Agr Res Inst, SAustralia, 73-76; assoc prof microbiol, Univ Helsinki, 76; res assoc biotechnol, Univ Minn, 78. *Concurrent Pos:* Chief investr, Int Atomic Energy Agency, Austria, 73-78; sr res fel, Acad Sci & Univ Helsinki, 76; prin investr, Ministry Trade & Indust, Finland, 78-79; vis assoc prof microbiol, Ohio State Univ, 78-80. *Mem:* Soc Int Limnol; Soc Gen Microbiol; Am Soc Microbiol; Soc Indust Microbiol.

*Res:* Biodegradation of pesticides; biohydrometallurgy; microbiological corrosion; drinking water microbiology. *Mailing Add:* Dept Microbiol Ohio State Univ 484 W 12th Ave Columbus OH 43210-1214. *E-Mail:* otuovine@magnus.acs.ohio—state.edu

**TUPIN, JOE PAUL,** PSYCHIATRY. *Current Pos:* assoc prof, Univ Calif, Davis, 69-71, vchmn dept, 70-76, chmn dept, 76-84, med dir, 84-93, PROF PSYCHIAT, SCH MED, UNIV CALIF, DAVIS, 71- *Personal Data:* b Comanche, Tex, Feb 17, 34; m 55, Betty Thompson; c Joe P Jr, Rebecca A & John D. *Educ:* Univ Tex, Austin, BS, 55; Univ Tex Med Br, Galveston, MD, 59. *Prof Exp:* Resident psychiatrist, Univ Tex Med Br, Galveston, 60-62; resident, NIMH, 63-64; NIMH career teaching award, Group Advan Psychiat, 64-66; assoc prof psychiat & assoc dean, Univ Tex Med Br, Galveston, 68-69. *Concurrent Pos:* Fel, Group Advan Psychiat, 60-62; dir, Psychiat Consult Serv, Sacramento Med Ctr, 69-; consult, Calif Med Facil, Vacaville, 69-; Twin & Sibling Study, NIMH, 69- & Dept Corrections, Calif, 71; chmn, Clin Psychopharmacol Rev Comt, NIMH, 75-77; mem, Comt Psychiat & Criminal Law, Am Bar Asn, 75-81 & Task Force Recertification, Am Psychiat Asn, 77-; consult & grant receiver, Orphan Drugs-Violence, FDA, 82-85. *Mem:* Fel Am Psychiat Asn; Soc Biol Psychiat; Am Col Psychiat; Soc Health & Human Values; Am Psychosomatic Soc. *Res:* Teaching of medical education; psychopharmacology; identification and treatment of violent behavior. *Mailing Add:* Davis Med Ctr Univ Calif 2315 Stockton Blvd Sacramento CA 95817

**TUPPER, CHARLES JOHN,** INTERNAL MEDICINE. *Current Pos:* RETIRED. *Personal Data:* b Miami, Ariz, Mar 7, 20; m 42; c Libby (Smith) & Chas Jr. *Educ:* San Diego State Col, BS, 43; Univ Nebr, MD, 48. *Hon Degrees:* DSc, Univ Nebr, 86. *Honors & Awards:* Billings Bronze Medal, AMA, 55. *Prof Exp:* Asst prof internal med, Med Sch, Univ Mich, 56-59, secy, Med Sch, 57, assoc prof & asst dean, 59-66; prof med & dean, Sch Med, Univ Calif, Davis, 66-80, prof internal med, Community Health & Family Practice, Sch Med, 80-90, actg chair, Dept Community Health, 90-91. *Concurrent Pos:* Consult, St Joseph Mercy Hosp, 56-; pres, Calif Med Asn, 79-80; trustee, AMA, 85-89. *Mem:* Am Soc Internal Med; AMA (pres, 90-91); Am Col Health Asn; Asn Am Med Cols; fel Am Col Physicians. *Res:* Medical education; application of principles of preventive medicine to care of the individual patient through periodic health examination; evaluation of diagnostic procedures for effectiveness and reliability; geriatrics. *Mailing Add:* Dept Community Health Univ Calif Sch Med Davis CA 95616

**TUPPER, KENNETH JOSEPH,** MOLECULAR DYNAMIC SIMULATIONS OF SURFACE PHENOMENA, REACTION THERMODYNAMICS MODELING. *Current Pos:* DIR COMPUTATIONAL CHEM, APPL RES CORP, 93- *Personal Data:* b Brooklyn, NY, Apr 15, 64; m, Donna A Hiestand. *Educ:* Adelphi Univ, BS, 86; Ind Univ, MS, 88, PhD(phys chem). *Prof Exp:* Fel, Naval Res Lab, 92-93. *Mem:* Am Chem Soc. *Res:* Monolayer films with an emphasis on modeling boundary layer lubricants using molecular dynamics; molecular mechanics and molecular orbital calculations. *Mailing Add:* 7122 Ducketts Lane No 301 Elkridge MD 21227. *Fax:* 301-731-0765; *E-Mail:* tupper@indy.arclch.com

**TUPPER, W R CARL,** OBSTETRICS & GYNECOLOGY. *Current Pos:* Head dept, Dalhousie Univ, 59-77, prof obstet & gynec, 59-81, mem fac, 81-88. EMER PROF OBSTET & GYNEC, DALHOUSIE UNIV, 88- *Personal Data:* b New Glasgow, NS, Feb 15, 15; m 43; c 3. *Educ:* Dalhousie Univ, BSc, 39, MD, CM, 43; FRCOG; FRCS(C). *Mem:* Am Col Surgeons; Am Col Obstet & Gynec; Can Soc Obstet & Gynec; Int Col Surgeons. *Mailing Add:* 5887 Rogers Dr Halifax NS B3H 1E9 Can

**TURBAK, ALBIN FRANK,** TEXTILES, NONWOVENS. *Current Pos:* PRES, FALCON CONSULTS, 93- *Personal Data:* b New Bedford, Mass, Sept 23, 29; m 52; c 2. *Educ:* Southeastern Mass Technol Inst, BS, 51; Inst Textile Tech, MS, 53; Ga Inst Technol, PhD, 57. *Honors & Awards:* Leadership & Serv Award, Tech Asn Pulp & Paper Indust, 95. *Prof Exp:* Res chemist, Esso Res Co, 57-63; corp res dir, Teepak Inc, 63-72; mgr basic res, ITT Rayonier Co, 72-82; prof & dir, Sch Textiles, Ga Inst Technol, 82-88; dir, S Tech Appl Res Ctr, 88-93. *Concurrent Pos:* Int consult mgt & res; mem bd dirs, IFT Inc. *Mem:* AAAS; Am Chem Soc; Am Asn Textile Chem & Colorists; NY Acad Sci; fel Royal Soc Dyers & Colorists; Sigma Xi; fel Am Inst Chemists; Tech Asn Pulp & Paper Indust. *Res:* Cellulose, natural and synthetic polymer research; polymer modification; new process and methods research; phosphorus chemistry; dyeing and finishing of textiles; food products research; paper products and wood research; nonwovens. *Mailing Add:* 7140 Brandon Mill Rd Sandy Springs GA 30328. *Fax:* 770-394-3128

**TURBYFILL, CHARLES LEWIS,** RESEARCH ADMINISTRATION. *Current Pos:* health sci adminr, Nat Heart, Lung & Blood Inst, NIH, 72-76, head instnl training, Nat Cancer Inst, 75-76, chief, Ctr & special proj sect, rev bd, Nat Heart, Lung & Blood Inst, NIH, 76-93, CONSULT, BIOREVIEW, INC, 93- *Personal Data:* b Newland, NC, Feb 27, 33; m 55; c 2. *Educ:* Univ Ore, BA, 55, MS, 57; Univ Ga, PhD(zool), 64. *Prof Exp:* Prin investr, Worcester Found Exp Biol, 64-66, Armed Forces Radiobiol Res Inst, 66-72. *Res:* Primate cardiovascular physiology, atherosclerosis. *Mailing Add:* 23000 Shiloh Church Rd Boyds MD 20841

**TURCHAN, OTTO CHARLES,** PHYSICS, ENGINEERING. *Current Pos:* PRIN SCIENTIST, NUCLEAR ENERGY SYSTS, 85- *Personal Data:* b Ostrava, Czech, Dec 30, 25; nat US; m 52; c 2. *Educ:* Tech Univ Brunn, Ger, Dipl Ing, 45; Charles Univ, Prague, RNDr(physics), 47; Detroit Univ, BS, 50, MS, 53. *Prof Exp:* Res engr, Junkers Airplane Works, Ger, 43; dir res &

develop, Turchan Follower Mach Co, Mich, 46-55; mem tech staff & group head inertial systs develop, Res & Develop Labs, Hughes Aircraft Co, Calif, 55-61; mem tech staff & sect head spec projs, Systs Res Labs, Space Technol Labs, Inc, 61-62; mem tech staff, Spec Studies Directorate, Satellite Systs Div, Aerospace Corp, 62-65; sr staff engr & tech consult spacecraft eng, Space Systs Div, Lockheed Missiles & Space Co, 65-66; sr tech specialist, Apollo Syst Develop Dept, Space Systs Div, NAm Aviation, Inc, 66-67; prog develop engr advan systs, Strategic Missile Systs Autonetics Div, NAm Rockwell Corp, 67-71; prin engr, Bedford Labs, Raytheon Co, 71-72; sr proj engr, Bechtel Power Corp, 72-85. *Mem:* AAAS; Am Phys Soc; Am Nuclear Soc; Am Geophys Union; Am Inst Aeronaut & Astronaut; NY Acad Sci. *Res:* Nuclear and plasma physics; astrophysics; celestial dynamics; space physics; space vehicle systems; aeronautical-astronautical navigation and guidance; astrionics systems; automatic control systems in nuclear power and propulsion; advanced nuclear and thermonuclear power systems; plasma systems; nuclear systems design; nuclear fusion power development; combustion technology and high energy fuels development. *Mailing Add:* 150 N Almont Dr Apt 102 Beverly Hills CA 90211

**TURCHI, JOSEPH J,** INTERNAL MEDICINE, ONCOLOGY. *Current Pos:* clin asst prof med, 69-80, CLIN ASSOC PROF MED, THOMAS JEFFERSON UNIV, 80- *Personal Data:* b Philadelphia, Pa, Feb 16, 33; m 59; c 4. *Educ:* Univ Pa, BA, 54; Jefferson Med Col, MD, 58. *Prof Exp:* Head clin hemat & cancer chemother, US Naval Hosp, Bethesda, Md, 62-64; sr investr med, Hahnemann Med Col, 64-69. *Concurrent Pos:* Nat Cancer Inst grant, Misericordia Hosp, 66-; assoc dept path, Hemat Sect & attend physician dept med, Misericordia Hosp, 64-, Nat Cancer Inst prin investr hemat res, 66- *Mem:* Am Col Physicians; Am Soc Clin Oncol. *Mailing Add:* Fitzgerald Mercy Hosp 1500 Lansdowne Ave Darby PA 19083

**TURCHI, PETER JOHN,** INDUCTIVE ENERGY SYSTEMS, ELECTRIC ROCKET PROPULSION. *Current Pos:* adj prof, 88-89, PROF, DEPT AERONAUT & ASTRONAUT ENG, OHIO STATE UNIV, 89- *Personal Data:* b New York, NY, Dec 30, 46; m 67, Judith Radogna; c Janita & Rebecca. *Educ:* Princeton Univ, BSE, 67, MA, 69, PhD(aero & mech sci), 70. *Prof Exp:* Res asst, Guggenheim Propulsion Labs, Princeton Univ, 63-70; plasma physicist, Air Force Weapons Lab, 70-72; res physicist, Naval Res Lab, 72-77, chief, Plasma Technol Br, 77-80; staff scientist, Res & Develop Assocs Inc, 80-81, dir, Wash Res Lab, 81-89; lectr, Dept Continuing Eng Educ, George Washington Univ, 86- *Concurrent Pos:* NSF Grad fel, 67-70; lectr, 4th Sch Plasma Physics, Novosibirsk, USSR, 74; Christophilos Mem Sch Plasma Physics, Greece, 77 & Air Force Pulsed Power Lectr Series, 80; chmn, 2nd Int Conf Megagauss Magnetic Field Generation, 79, Conf Prime-Power High Energy Space Systs, 82; tech chmn, Pulsed Power Conf, Inst Elec & Electronics Engrs, 85 & gen chmn, 87, int chmn, 18th, 19th, 21st, 22nd Int Elec Propulsion Conf, 85, 87, 90 & 91; ed, Megagauss Physics & Technol, Plenum Press, 80; mem, Tech Comt Plasmadynamics & Lasers, Am Inst Aeronaut & Astronaut, 84-87, Tech Comt Elecopropulsion, 87-93, chmn, 91-93; mem, Plasmasci & Applns Exec Comt, Inst Elec & Electronics Engrs, 85-89, Standing Comt Pulsed Power Sci & Technol, 96-; assoc ed, J Propulsion & Power, 89-94; lab consult, Los Alamos Nat Lab, 89-; sr res scientist, Phillips Lab, 89-, vis chief scientist advan weapons & survivability, 96-97. *Mem:* Am Phys Soc; Sigma Xi; Am Inst Aeronaut & Astronaut; sr mem Inst Elec & Electronics Engrs; Am Soc Engr Educ; Elec Rocket Propulsion Soc (pres, 96-). *Res:* Electromagnetic energy to create high energy density systems for rocket propulsion; controlled nuclear fusion; nuclear weapons simulation. *Mailing Add:* 6503 Masefield St Columbus OH 43085-3028. *Fax:* 614-292-8290; *E-Mail:* turchi.1@osu.edu

**TURCHINETZ, WILLIAM ERNEST,** PHYSICS. *Current Pos:* fel, Sloan Found, Mass Inst Technol, 59-69, mem res staff, 60-65, lectr, 65-68, head opers, Bates Linear Accelerator, 73-80, assoc dir, Bates Linear Accelerator, 80-91, SR RES SCIENTIST, MASS INST TECHNOL, 68- *Personal Data:* b Winnipeg, Man, Nov 18, 28; m 54; c 2. *Educ:* Univ Man, BSc, 52, MSc, 53, PhD(physics), 55. *Prof Exp:* Asst prof physics, Univ Man, 55-56; res fel, Australian Nat Univ, 56-59. *Concurrent Pos:* Chmn, Gordon Conf Photonuclear Reactions, 69-71. *Mem:* Fel Am Phys Soc; AAAS. *Res:* Nuclear physics; particle accelerators; science education. *Mailing Add:* Bates Linear Accelerator Mass Inst Technol PO Box 846 Middleton MA 01949

**TURCK, MARVIN,** INTERNAL MEDICINE, INFECTIOUS DISEASE. *Current Pos:* PROF MED, UNIV WASH, 72-, PHYSICIAN-IN-CHIEF DEPT MED, HARBORVIEW MED CTR, 72- *Personal Data:* b Chicago, Ill, June 13, 34; m 56; c 4. *Educ:* Univ Ill, BS, 57, MD, 59; Am Bd Internal Med, dipl. *Prof Exp:* Intern med, Res & Educ Hosp, Ill, 59-60; fel, Univ Wash, 60-62; resident & asst, Res & Educ Hosp, Ill, 62-63, chief resident, Cook Co Hosp Serv, 63-64; head, Div Infectious Dis & prog dir, Res Infectious Dis Lab, King Co Hosp, 64-68; chief med, USPHS Hosp, 68-72. *Concurrent Pos:* Instr, Univ Ill, 63-64; from asst prof to assoc prof, Univ Wash, 64-72; attend physician, King Co Hosp, Wash, 64-; attend physician & consult, Univ Wash Hosp, 66; attend physician, USPHS Hosp, 66. *Mem:* Am Fedn Clin Res; Infectious Dis Soc Am; fel Am Col Physicians. *Res:* Laboratory and clinical aspects of pyelonephritis; investigation of new antibiotics. *Mailing Add:* J Infectious Dis 1910 Fairview Ave E Suite 210 Seattle WA 98102-1699

**TURCO, CHARLES PAUL,** PARASITOLOGY, NEMATOLOGY. *Current Pos:* dir univ develop, 71-74, assoc prof, 65-81, dir develop, 74-81, PROF BIOL, LAMAR UNIV, 81-, DIR RES & PROGS, 81- *Personal Data:* b Brooklyn, NY, Sept 23, 34; m 55; c 4. *Educ:* St John's Univ, NY, BS, 56, MS, 58, MS, 60; Tex A&M Univ, PhD(biol), 69. *Honors & Awards:* Sigma Xi Res Award, 68. *Prof Exp:* Teacher, High Sch, NY, 56-64. *Mem:* Am Soc Parasitol; Am Inst Biol Sci; Am Soc Nematol; Sigma Xi. *Res:* Nematodes of rice and associated insect pests; nematode parasites associated with man's domestic animals. *Mailing Add:* 113 Briggs Beaumont TX 77707-2328

**TURCO, JENIFER,** RICKETTSIOLOGY & RICKETTSIAL DISEASES. *Current Pos:* fel, 78-82, from instr to asst prof, 83-90, ASSOC PROF DEPT MICROBIOL & IMMUNOL, COL MED, UNIV SALA, 90- *Personal Data:* b Morgantown, WVa, July 24, 50. *Educ:* Marywood Col, Scranton, Pa, BS, 72; WVa Univ, MS, 75, PhD(med microbiol), 78. *Concurrent Pos:* Nat Needs fel, NSF, 79-80; Nat Res Serv Award, Nat Inst Allergy & Infectious Dis, NIH, 80-82; co-prin investr, USPHS grant, 83-; counr-at-large, Am Soc Rickettsiology & Rickettsial Dis, 89-91. *Mem:* Am Soc Microbiol; Am Soc Rickettsiology & Rickettsial Dis; Am Asn Immunologists; Int Soc Interferon & Cytokine Res. *Res:* Interaction of obligate intracellular bacteria, particularly Rickettsia Prowazekii, with host cells; mechanisms of action of interferon-gamma and other cytokines in host defense against rickettsiae; role of antibody in host defense against rickettsiae. *Mailing Add:* Dept Biopl Valdosta State Univ Col Med Valdosta GA 31698-0015

**TURCO, RICHARD PETER,** AERONOMY, CLIMATOLOGY. *Current Pos:* chair, Dept Atmospheric Sci, 93-96, PROF, UNIV CALIF, LOS ANGELES, 88-; DIR, INST ENVIRON, 95- *Personal Data:* b New York, NY, Mar 9, 43; m 91, Linda Stevenson; c Richard C. *Educ:* Rutgers Univ, New Brunswick, BS, 65; Univ Ill, Urbana, MS, 67, PhD(elec eng), 71. *Honors & Awards:* H Julian Allen Award, NASA, 83, 88; Leo Szilard Award, Am Phys Soc, 85; MacArthur Found Award, 86. *Prof Exp:* NSF res grant, Space Sci Div, Ames Res Ctr, NASA, Moffett Field, Calif, 71; atmospheric scientist, R & D Assocs, 71-88. *Concurrent Pos:* Assoc ed, J Geophys Res, 81-92; mem, comt Causes & Effects of Ozone Change, Nat Acad Sci, 83-84, comt Atmospheric Effects Nuclear Explosions, 84-85, comt Environ Effects Nuclear War, Int Coun Sci Unions, 83-88; vis prof, Univ Calif, Los Angeles, 84-88; pres-elect, Atmospheric Sci Sect, Am Geophys Union, 90-92, pres, 92-94; distinguished fac fel, Univ Calif, Los Angeles, 93; mem, Climate Res Comt, Nat Res Coun, 93-95. *Mem:* Fel Am Geophys Union; Sigma Xi. *Res:* Ozone photochemistry and the ozone hole; global climate change; earth systems science; aerosol microphysics and chemistry; air pollution; nuclear winter; planetary atmospheres and clouds. *Mailing Add:* Dept Atmospheric Sci Univ Calif Los Angeles CA 90095-1565. *Fax:* 310-206-5219; *E-Mail:* turco@atmos.ucla.edu

**TURCO, SALVATORE J,** PHARMACY. *Current Pos:* from instr to asst prof, 67-73, assoc prof, 73-78, PROF PHARM, SCH PHARM, TEMPLE UNIV, 78- *Personal Data:* b Philadelphia, Pa, Mar 4, 32; m 57; c 2. *Educ:* Philadelphia Col Pharm & Sci, BSc, 59, MSc, 66, PharmD, 67. *Prof Exp:* Instr sterile prod, Philadelphia Col Pharm & Sci, 66-67. *Concurrent Pos:* Indust res grants, Temple Univ, 69, Roche award, 72, univ grant, 72-73. *Mem:* Am Pharmaceut Asn; Am Soc Hosp Pharmacists. *Res:* Parenteral products; particulate matter in parenterals; hospital pharmacy. *Mailing Add:* Dept Biochem MN 663 Univ Ky Col Med 800 Rose St Lexington KY 40536-0001. *Fax:* 606-258-1037

**TURCOTTE, DONALD LAWSON,** GEOPHYSICS, FLUIDS. *Current Pos:* from asst prof to prof aeronaut eng, 59-72, prof geol sci, 72-84, chmn geol sci, 80-84, MAXWELL UPSON PROF ENG, 84- *Personal Data:* b Bellingham, Wash, Apr 22, 32; m 57; c 2. *Educ:* Calif Inst Technol, BS, 54, DPh(aeronaut eng), 58; Cornell Univ, MAeroE, 55. *Honors & Awards:* Day Medal, Geol Soc Am, 81; Regents Medal, NY State, 84; Wegener Medal, Europ Union Geosci, 91; Whitten Medal, Am Geophys Union, 95. *Prof Exp:* Asst prof aeronaut eng, US Naval Postgrad Sch, 58-59. *Concurrent Pos:* NSF fel, Oxford Univ, 65-66, Guggenheim fel, 72-73. *Mem:* Nat Acad Sci; Geol Soc Am; Am Geophys Union; Seismol Soc Am; Am Phys Soc. *Res:* Mantle convection; fractals; behavior of faults; chaos; evolution of sedimentary basins; self-organized criticality. *Mailing Add:* Snee Hall Cornell Univ Ithaca NY 14853

**TURCOTTE, EDGAR LEWIS,** PLANT GENETICS. *Current Pos:* Plant geneticist, 58-92, BIOL SCI COLLARB, USDA, 92- *Personal Data:* b Duluth, Minn, June 7, 29. *Educ:* Univ Minn, BA, 51, MS, 57, PhD(genetics), 58. *Honors & Awards:* Cotton Genetics Res Award, USDA, 76. *Mem:* Am Genetic Asn; Am Soc Agron; Sigma Xi. *Res:* Breeding, genetics and speciation of Gossypium barbadense cotton. *Mailing Add:* Maricopa Agr Ctr 37860 W Smith Enke Rd Maricopa AZ 85239. *Fax:* 602-568-2556

**TURCOTTE, JEREMIAH G,** SURGERY. *Current Pos:* Resident, 58-63, from instr to assoc prof, 63-71, PROF SURG, MED SCH, UNIV MICH, ANN ARBOR, 71-, CHMN DEPT, 74- *Personal Data:* b Detroit, Mich, Jan 20, 33; m 58; c 4. *Educ:* Univ Mich, BS, 55, MD, 57; Am Bd Surg, dipl, 64. *Concurrent Pos:* Co-investr, USPHS Res Grant, 64-; consult, Ann Arbor Vet Admin Hosp & Wayne Co Gen Hosp. *Mem:* Fel Am Col Surg; Transplantation Soc; Soc Univ Surgeons; Soc Surg Alimentary Tract; Asn Acad Surg; Am Soc Transplant Surgeons; Cent Surg Asn (pres, 91). *Res:* Portal hypertension; organ transplantation. *Mailing Add:* Univ Mich Hosp Surg Box 0331 Rm 2924 TC 1500 E Medical Ctr Dr Ann Arbor MI 48106-0331

**TURCOTTE, JOSEPH GEORGE,** ORGANIC CHEMISTRY, MEDICINAL CHEMISTRY. *Current Pos:* from asst prof to assoc prof, 67-77, PROF MED CHEM, COL PHARM, UNIV RI, 77- *Personal Data:* b Boston, Mass, Dec 25, 36; m 62; c 5. *Educ:* Mass Col Pharm, BS, 58, MS, 60; Univ Minn, PhD(med chem), 67. *Prof Exp:* Sr biochemist, Spec Lab Cancer Res & Radioisotope Serv, Vet Admin Hosp, Minneapolis, 65-67. *Concurrent Pos:* Res comt grants, Univ RI, 67-69; res grants, Nat Cancer Inst, 67-70, RI Water Resources Ctr, 68-69, RI Heart Asn, 70-72 & Nat Heart & Lung Inst, 71- *Mem:* AAAS; NY Acad Sci; Am Chem Soc; Am Pharmaceut Asn. *Res:* Synthesis of potential medicinal agents, including phospholipids, anticancer agents, antihypertensives, molluscicides, parasympathomimetic and parasympatholytic agents. *Mailing Add:* 94 Greenwood Dr Peace Dale RI 02883

**TURCOTTE, WILLIAM ARTHUR,** IRON ORE FLOTATION & PROCESSING, MINERALS PROCESSING. *Current Pos:* Metall engr, Res Lab, Cleveland-Cliffs Iron Co, 68-71, metall engr, Res Pilot Plant, 71-74, plant metallurgist, Tilden Mine, 74-79, asst chief metallurgist, 79-83, chief metallurgist, Res & Develop, 83-87, dir, Res & Develop, 87-93, CHIEF METALLURGIST, CORP RES & DEVELOP, CLEVELAND-CLIFFS IRON CO, 93- *Personal Data:* b Stambaugh, Mich, May 6, 45; m 66, Betty Andreski; c Lori & Julie. *Educ:* Mich Technol Univ, BS, 68. *Concurrent Pos:* Plant Metallurgist, operating engr, concentrator, Tilden Mine. *Mem:* Soc Mining Engrs. *Res:* Research and development in iron ore and other mineral beneficiation, pelletizing and environmental related areas; iron ore plant operation. *Mailing Add:* Cleveland-Cliffs Iron Co Division St Ishpeming MI 49849

**TUREK, ANDREW,** GEOCHEMISTRY. *Current Pos:* assoc prof geol & chem, 71-77, PROF GEOL, UNIV WINDSOR, 77- *Personal Data:* b Lemberg, Poland, Nov 11, 35; Can citizen; m 58; c 2. *Educ:* Univ Edinburgh, BSc, 57; Univ Alta, MSc, 62; Australian Nat Univ, PhD(geophys), 66. *Prof Exp:* Chemist, Scottish Agr Industs, 57-58; mine geologist, Lake Cinch Mines Ltd, Can, 58-60 & Sherritt-Gordon Mines, 62-63; res coordr geol, Man Dept Mines & Natural Resources, 66-69; assoc prof, Northern Ill Univ, 69-71. *Concurrent Pos:* Vis scientist, US Geol Survey, Denver, 78-79; adj prof geophys, Univ Western Ont, 86- *Mem:* Geol Asn Can; Spectros Soc Can; Geochem Soc. *Res:* Economic geology; geochronology and isotope geology; analytical geochemistry, geostatistics. *Mailing Add:* Dept Earth Sci Univ Windsor Windsor ON N9B 3P4 Can

**TUREK, FRED WILLIAM,** REPRODUCTIVE ENDOCRINOLOGY, CIRCADIAN RHYTHMS. *Current Pos:* asst prof reproductive endocrinol, 75-80, assoc prof, 80-83, PROF NEUROBIOL & PHYSIOL, NORTHWESTERN UNIV, 83-, CHMN, 87-, ENDOWED CHARLES E & EMMA H MORISON PROF BIOL, 95- *Personal Data:* b Detroit, Mich, July 31, 47; c 3. *Educ:* Mich State Univ, BS, 69; Stanford Univ, PhD(biol sci), 73. *Honors & Awards:* Fogarty Sr Int Fel Award, 86 & 92; Curt Richter Psycheneuroendocrinology Award, 87. *Prof Exp:* Fel reproductive biol, Univ Tex, Austin, 73-75. *Concurrent Pos:* NIH fel, 73; res career develop award, 78-83; vis asst prof, Dept Anat, Univ Calif, Los Angeles, 79; vis scientist, Dept Zool, Univ Bristol, Eng, 81; Guggenheim mem fel, 82 & 91-92; vis prof, Free Univ Brussels, Belg; dir, Ctr Circadian Biol & Med. *Mem:* Soc Neurosci; Soc Study Reproduction; Am Physiol Soc; Endocrine Soc; AAAS; Soc Res Biol Rhythms. *Res:* Role of the photoperiod in regulating the hypothalamo-pituitary-gonadal axis in mammals; neural basis for the generation of circadian rhythms; importance of biological rhythm for human health and performance. *Mailing Add:* Dept Neurobiol & Physiol Northwestern Univ 633 Clark St Evanston IL 60208. *Fax:* 847-491-5211

**TUREK, WILLIAM NORBERT,** THREE-D COMPUTER GRAPHICS. *Current Pos:* From asst prof to assoc prof, 63-75, chmn dept, 77-84, PROF CHEM, ST BONAVENTURE UNIV, 75- *Personal Data:* b St Paul, Minn, June 30, 31; m 66. *Educ:* Univ St Thomas, BS, 53; Univ Md, PhD (org chem), 58. *Mem:* Am Chem Soc. *Res:* Tutorials using computer graphics; substituted furans. *Mailing Add:* Dept Chem St Bonaventure Univ St Bonaventure NY 14778-9999

**TUREKIAN, KARL KAREKIN,** GEOCHEMISTRY, ATMOSPHERIC SCIENCES. *Current Pos:* from asst prof to prof geol, Yale Univ, 56-72, Henry Barnard Davis prof geol & geophys, 72-85, chmn, Dept Geol, 82-88, BENJAMIN SILLIMAN PROF GEOL & GEOPHYS, YALE UNIV, 85-, DIR, CTR STUDY GLOBAL CHANGE, 89- *Personal Data:* b New York, NY, Oct 25, 27; m 62, Roxanne Hagopian; c Karla & Vaughan. *Educ:* Wheaton Col, Ill, AB, 49; Columbia Univ, MA, 51, PhD, 55. *Hon Degrees:* MAH, Yale Univ, 65; DSc, State Univ NY, Stony Brook, 89. *Honors & Awards:* V M Goldschmidt Medal, Geochem Soc, 89; Maurice Ewing Medal, Am Geophys Union, 97. *Prof Exp:* Lectr geol, Columbia Univ, 53-54, res assoc geochem, Lamont Doherty Earth Observ, 54-56. *Concurrent Pos:* Guggenheim fel, Cambridge Univ, 62-63; consult, Pres Comn Marine Sci Eng & Resources, 67-68 & Oceanog Panel, NSF, 68-71; ed, J Geophys Res, 69-75 & Earth & Planetary Sci Letters, 75-89, Global Biogeochem Cycles, 90-; mem, US Nat Comn Geochem, 70-73, Climate Res Bd, 77-80 & Ocean Sci Bd, 79-82; mem, Comn Phys Sci Mat Res, Nat Acad Sci, Nat Res Coun, 86-90, Comn Geosci Environ Res, 90-92; group experts Sci Aspects Marine Pollution, UN; Sherman Fairchild Distinguished Scholar, Caltech, 88. *Mem:* Nat Acad Sci; fel Geol Soc Am; Geochem Soc (pres, 75-76); fel Am Geophys Union; fel Meteoritical Soc; fel Am Acad Arts Sci. *Res:* Marine geochemistry; geochemistry of radionuclides and trace elements; planetary evolution; atmospheric chemistry; geochemical archeology; marine sciences. *Mailing Add:* Dept Geol & Geophys Yale Univ Box 208109 New Haven CT 06520-8109. *Fax:* 203-432-3134; *E-Mail:* kkt@hess.geology.yale.edu

**TURER, JACK,** ORGANIC CHEMISTRY, PHYSICAL CHEMISTRY. *Current Pos:* chem indust specialist toxic substances control act & fed regulations expert, Off Toxic Substances, 77-82, CONSULT, PESTICIDES ENVIRON PROTECTION AGENCY, 82- *Personal Data:* b New York, NY, Mar 18, 12; m 38; c 2. *Educ:* City Col New York, BS, 34; Fairleigh Dickinson Univ, MAS, 69. *Prof Exp:* Res chemist, US Pub Rds Admin, 36-39; res chemist, USDA, 39-41, Eastern Regional Res Labs, 41-45; chief chemist, Va-Carolina Chem Corp, 45-52; tech dir, Textile Chem, Witco Chem Corp, 52-66, tech mgr Automotive Lubricants & Petrol Prod, 66-72, corp dir Labeling Govt Regulations & Chem Adv, 72-77. *Concurrent Pos:* Abstr, Chem Abstracts, 53-; consult; co rep for Witco Corp at Chem Mfrs Asn, Chem Specialties Mfrs Asn & Petrol Packaging Asn. *Mem:* Am Chem Soc; Am Soc Test & Mat; Am Asn Textile Chem & Colorists; Am Inst Chem; Am Soc Lubrication Eng. *Res:* Soils; chemurgy; electrochemistry; oils and fats; proteins for synthetic textile fibers; textile chemicals and finishes; automotive lubricants and petrochemicals; pollution control; labeling; government regulations. *Mailing Add:* 2402 Antigua Circle Coconut Creek FL 33066

**TURESKY, SAMUEL SAUL,** DENTISTRY. *Current Pos:* Res assoc oral path & periodont, 47-55, from asst prof to assoc prof, 55-71, PROF PERIODONT, SCH DENT MED, TUFTS UNIV, 71- *Personal Data:* b Portland, Maine, Feb 22, 16; m 52, Barbara Proner; c Andrew, Jon, Robert, Philip & Lisa. *Educ:* Harvard Univ, AB, 37; Tufts Col, DMD, 41. *Mem:* Int Asn Dent Res; AAAS. *Res:* Histochemistry of gingiva; calculus and plaque formation and prevention; effect of supragingival plaque reduction on subgingival bacterial flora. *Mailing Add:* 84 Wallis Rd Chestnut Hill MA 02167

**TURGEON, JEAN,** MATHEMATICS. *Current Pos:* AT DEPT MATH & STATIST, UNIV MONTREAL. *Personal Data:* b Montreal, Que, May 8, 36. *Educ:* Univ Toronto, MA, 65, PhD, 68. *Prof Exp:* Asst prof math, Univ Montreal, 69-73; assoc prof math, Concordia Univ, 73- *Mem:* AAAS; Am Math Soc; Math Asn Am; Can Math Cong. *Res:* Geometry. *Mailing Add:* Univ Montreal C P 6128 Montreal PQ H3C 3J7 Can

**TURGEON, JUDITH LEE,** CELLULAR ENDOCRINOLOGY, NEUROENDOCRINOLOGY. *Current Pos:* from asst prof to assoc prof, 75-86, PROF HUMAN PHYSIOL, SCH MED, UNIV CALIF, DAVIS, 86- *Personal Data:* b Topeka, Kans, Mar 19, 42. *Educ:* Washburn Univ, BA, 65; Univ Kans, PhD(anat), 69. *Prof Exp:* Res assoc physiol, Sch Med, Univ Md, 69-71, asst prof, 71-75. *Concurrent Pos:* Mem ed bd, Am J Physiol, Endocrinol & Metab, 82-, Endocrinol, 83-87, Biol of Reproduction, 83-86; vis scientist, Inst Animal Physiol, Animal Res Ctr, Cambridge, Eng, 83; mem study sect, NIH, 85-89. *Mem:* Soc Study Reprod; Endocrine Soc; Am Physiol Soc. *Res:* Hypothalamic control of gonadotrophin secretion by the anterior pituitary; signal transduction mechanisms in hormone action; exocytosis. *Mailing Add:* Dept Human Physiol Sch Med Univ Calif Davis CA 95616. *Fax:* 530-752-5423

**TURI, PAUL GEORGE,** INDUSTRIAL PHARMACY, ANALYTICAL CHEMISTRY. *Current Pos:* sr scientist, 59-60, group leader anal res, 60-63, head anal labs, 63-70, mgr pharm res, 70-74, ASSOC SECT HEAD, SANDOZ PHARMACEUT, SANDOZ INC, 75- *Personal Data:* b Battonya, Hungary, Apr 16, 17; US citizen; m 41; c 1. *Educ:* Pazmany Peter Univ, Budapest, MS, 40, PhD(pharm), 46. *Prof Exp:* Mgr, Szanto Pharm Labs, Budapest, 46-48; res coord, Pharmaceut Indust Ctr, 48-49; dep dir, Pharm Res Inst, 50-53, head pharm res & develop, 55-56; dep mgr qual control dept, Chinoin Chem Works, 53-55; anal chemist, Chase Chem Co, NJ, 57-59. *Concurrent Pos:* Hon asst prof, Pazmany Peter Univ, Budapest, 46-48, hon adj prof, 48-56; lectr, Budapest Tech Univ, 52-55. *Mem:* Am Pharmaceut Asn; Acad Pharmaceut Sci; Int Pharmaceut Fedn; Am Chem Soc. *Res:* Pharmaceutical analysis; pharmacy research and development. *Mailing Add:* 5 Oxford Dr Livingston NJ 07039-1406

**TURI, RAYMOND A,** semi conductor physics, non volatile devices, for more information see previous edition

**TURIN, GEORGE L,** ELECTRICAL ENGINEERING. *Current Pos:* Prof elec eng, Univ Calif, Berkeley, 60-80, chmn, Dept Elec Eng & Comput Sci, 80-83, dean, Sch Eng, Los Angeles, 83-86, prof, Berkeley, 86-89, EMER PROF ELEC ENG & COMPUT SCI, UNIV CALIF, BERKELEY, 89-; VPRES, TEKUEKRON CORP, MENLO PARK, CALIF, 88- *Personal Data:* b New York, NY, Jan 27, 30. *Educ:* Mass Inst Technol, BS & MS, 52, ScD, 56. *Concurrent Pos:* Chmn, Info Theory Group, Inst Elec & Electronics Engrs, 61-62; Guggenheim fel, 66-67; sr fel, Brit Sci & Eng Coun, 83. *Mem:* Nat Acad Eng; fel Inst Elec & Electronics Engrs. *Res:* Communication theory and systems; communication networks urban radio communication. *Mailing Add:* Dept Elec Eng & Comput Sci Univ Calif 231 Cory Hall No 1770 Berkeley CA 94720-1770

**TURINO, GERARD MICHAEL,** MEDICINE. *Current Pos:* assoc, 56-60, from asst prof to prof, 60-83, JOHN H KEATING SR PROF MED, COL PHYSICIANS & SURGEONS, COLUMBIA UNIV, 83-; DIR, DEPT MED, ST LUKES-ROOSEVELT HOSP, NY, 83- *Personal Data:* b New York, NY, May 16, 24; m 51; c 3. *Educ:* Princeton Univ, AB, 45; Columbia Univ, MD, 48. *Honors & Awards:* Distinguished Achievement Award, Sci Coun, Am Heart Asn, 89, Dickinson Richards Lectr, 89. *Prof Exp:* Mem staff, Div Med Sci, Nat Res Coun, 51-53; resident med, Bellevue Hosp, NY, 53-54. *Concurrent Pos:* Nat Found Infantile Paralysis fel, Col Physicians & Surgeons, Columbia Univ, 54-56, NY Heart Asn sr fel, 56-60; asst physician, Presby Hosp, NY, 56-61, from asst attend physician to assoc attend physician, 61-72, dir, Cardiovasc Lab, 66-, attend physician, 72-; consult, Vet Admin Hosp, East Orange, NJ; mem, Career Invest Health Res Coun, NY, 61; vpres coun, Am Heart Asn, 78-81; chmn, Pulmonary Dis Adv Comt, Nat Heart, Lung & Blood Inst, NIH. *Mem:* AAAS; Harvey Soc; Asn Am Physicians; Am Soc Clin Invest; Am Physiol Soc; Am Thoracic Soc (pres, 86-87). *Res:* Internal medicine; cardio-pulmonary physiology. *Mailing Add:* Dept Med Columbia Univ St Luke's-Roosevelt Hosp Ctr Amsterdam Ave at 114th St New York NY 10025. *Fax:* 212-523-3416

**TURINSKY, JIRI,** PHYSIOLOGY, BIOCHEMISTRY. *Current Pos:* from asst prof to assoc prof, 70-79, PROF PHYSIOL, ALBANY MED COL, 79- *Personal Data:* b Prague, Czech, Apr 9, 35; m 64; c 2. *Educ:* Charles Univ, Prague, MD, 59, PhD(physiol), 62. *Prof Exp:* Instr & res assoc physiol, Med Sch, Charles Univ, Prague, 59-66, asst prof, 68-69. *Concurrent Pos:* Res fel surg, Med Sch, Univ Pa, 66-68. *Mem:* Am Physiol Soc; Am Diabetes Asn; Am Burn Asn. *Res:* Endocrine control of metabolism; control of metabolism after trauma. *Mailing Add:* Dept Physiol & Cell Biol Albany Med Col 47 New Scotland Ave Albany NY 12208

**TURINSKY, PAUL JOSEF,** COMPUTATIONAL ENGINEERING. *Current Pos:* dept head, 80-88, PROF NUCLEAR ENG, NC STATE UNIV, 88- *Personal Data:* b Hoboken, NJ, Oct 20, 44; m 66, Karen Am DeLuca; c Grant Dean & Beth Noel. *Educ:* Univ RI, BS, 66; Univ Mich, MSE, 67, PhD(nuclear eng), 70; Univ Pittsburgh, MBA, 79. *Honors & Awards:* Mark Mills Award, Am Nuclear Soc, 70; Glenn Murphy Award, Am Soc Eng Educ, 90. *Prof Exp:* Asst prof nuclear eng, Rensselaer Polytech Inst, 70-73; mgr core develop, Water Reactor Div, Westinghouse Elec Corp, 73-80. *Concurrent Pos:* Tech expert, Int Atomic Energy Agency, 78-; consult, Elec Power Res Inst, 80-90, Duke Power Co, 85-, Sci Appln Int, Corp, 90-92, Dept Energy, 93 & Nuclear Regulatory Comn, 96. *Mem:* Fel Am Nuclear Soc; Am Soc Eng Educ; Soc Indust & Appl Math; Comput Soc; AAAS. *Res:* Developing and applying numerical solution algorithms for reactor physics problems which take maximum advantage of computers with parallel architectures; applications include nuclear fuel management optimization, core physics benchmarks, and on-line digital control of nuclear power plants. *Mailing Add:* NC State Univ PO Box 7909 Raleigh NC 27695-7909. *Fax:* 919-515-5115; *E-Mail:* turinsky@eds.ncsu.edu

**TURITTO, VINCENT THOMAS,** BIOMATERIALS, HEMOSTASIS. *Current Pos:* PROF BIOMED ENG, MEMPHIS STATE UNIV, 90-, CHMN DEPT, 93- *Personal Data:* b New York, NY, June 4, 44; m 70, Rosemary Reicherter; c Christopher, Douglas, James & Caroline. *Educ:* Manhattan Col, BChemE, 65; Columbia Univ, DEngSc, 72. *Prof Exp:* Prof bioeng, Univ Rio de Janeiro, 72-73; res asst, F Hoffmann La Roche & Co, Ltd, 73-74; res assoc, St Lukes-Roosevelt Hosp & Columbia Univ, 74-84; from assoc prof to prof med, Mt Sinai Med Sch, 84-90. *Concurrent Pos:* Prin investr, Am Heart Asn, 77-80 & NIH, 82-; established investr, Am Heart Asn, 77-82; chmn, Int Comt Thrombosis & Hemostasis, Subcomt Rheology, 82-85; chmn, sect biomed eng, NY Acad Med, 88-89, prog comt, Biomed Eng Soc, 93- *Mem:* NY Acad Sci; AAAS; Sigma Xi; Biomed Eng Soc; Int Soc Thrombosis & Hemostasis; NY Acad Med; Am Heart Asn. *Res:* Application of engineering principles for understanding blood and surface interactions as they pertain in hemostasis and thrombosis. *Mailing Add:* Dept Biomed Eng Memphis State Univ Memphis TN 38152-0001

**TURK, AMOS,** ATMOSPHERIC CHEMISTRY & PHYSICS. *Current Pos:* from asst prof to assoc prof, 56-66, prof, 67-86, EMER PROF CHEM, CITY COL NEW YORK, 86-; CONSULT CHEMIST, 54- *Personal Data:* b New York, NY, Feb 28, 18; m 41, Pearl Mallove; c Janet, Jonathan & Daniel. *Educ:* City Col New York, BS, 37; Ohio State Univ, MA, 38, PhD(chem), 40. *Honors & Awards:* Activated Carbon Hall Fame Award, Int Activated Carbon Conf, 96. *Prof Exp:* Res assoc, Explosives Res Lab, Pa, 42-44 & Allegany Ballistics Lab, Md, 44-46; instr org chem, City Col New York, 46-49; dir res & develop, Connor Eng Corp, 49-54. *Mem:* Am Chem Soc; Am Soc Test & Mat; Am Soc Heating Refrigerating & Air-conditioning Engrs; Air Pollution Control Asn; NY Acad Sci. *Res:* Activated carbon; air analysis and purification; odors. *Mailing Add:* 7 Tarrywile Lake Rd Danbury CT 06810

**TURK, DENNIS CHARLES,** BEHAVIORAL SCIENCE. *Current Pos:* prof psychiat, Univ Pittsburgh, 85-96, mem, Pittsburgh Cancer Inst, 86-96, prof anesthesiol, 88-96, PROF BEHAV SCI, UNIV PITTSBURGH, 91-, JOHN & EMMA BONICA PROF ANESTHESIOL & PAIN RES, 96- *Personal Data:* b New York, NY, Mar 15, 46; m 69, Lorraine Meichenbuum; c Kenneth & Katharine. *Educ:* Univ Fla, BA, 67; Univ Waterloo, Can, MA, 75, PhD(clin psych), 78. *Honors & Awards:* Outstanding Sci Contrib Award, Am Psychol Asn, 93. *Prof Exp:* Asst prof psychol, Yale Univ, 77-82, assoc prof, 82-85. *Concurrent Pos:* Attend, W Haven Vet Admin Med Ctr, 79-85, Newington Vet Admin Med Ctr, 82-85; consult, Boehringer-Mannheim Diagnostics Inc, 83-88, SSA Comn Eval Pain, 87, Nat Ctr Health Statist, 87-; mem, Pittsburgh Cancer Inst, 86-96; vis prof, Univ Tubingen, WGer, 88 & Univ Otago, NZ, 90; mem, Guideline Panel Low Back Prob, Agency Health Care Policy, 92-94. *Mem:* Am Psychol Asn; Am Pain Soc; Int Asn Study Pain; Soc Behav Med; Acad Behav Med Res. *Res:* Multiaxial assessment and treatment of chronic pain with emphasis on the physiological mechanisms of cognitive variables; the integration of medical, psychosocial, and behavioral data, and the prescription of treatment based on the empirically-derived taxonomy of chronic pain patients. *Mailing Add:* Dept Anesthesiol Univ Wash Box 356540 Seattle WA 98195. *Fax:* 206-543-2958

**TURK, FATEH (FRANK) M,** AGRICULTURE, BIOLOGY. *Current Pos:* RETIRED. *Personal Data:* b June 11, 24; Can citizen; m 60; c 2. *Educ:* Univ Bombay, BSc, 47; Univ Sind Pakistan, MSc, 52; Univ Minn, PhD(plant path), 56. *Prof Exp:* Res scientist & lectr, Govt Res Sta & Sci Col, 47-52; res asst, Univ Minn, 53-55; tech adv, A M Lotia Chem Co, Pakistan, 56-57; microbiologist, Gallowhur Chem Can, Montreal, 60-78; sr eval officer pesticides, Agr Can, 61-88. *Concurrent Pos:* Adv, Western Comt Plant Dis Control, 77-81. *Mem:* Can Phytopath Soc; Can Pest Mgt Soc. *Res:* Fungicides and nematicides. *Mailing Add:* 3039 Highway 16 Nepean ON K2C 3H1 Can

**TURK, GREGORY CHESTER,** LASER SPECTROSCOPY, ATOMIC SPECTROMETRY. *Current Pos:* RES CHEMIST, NAT INST STAND & TECHNOL, 76- *Personal Data:* b Elizabeth, NJ, Nov 16, 51; m 74; c 3. *Educ:* Rutgers Col, BA, 73; Univ Md, PhD(anal chem), 78. *Mem:* Am Chem Soc; Soc Appl Spectros. *Res:* Application of lasers for spectroscopic chemical analysis, in particular the development of laser-enhanced ionization spectrometry in flames. *Mailing Add:* A223 Chem Nat Inst Stand & Technol Gaithersburg MD 20899

**TURK, LELAND JAN,** GEOLOGY, HYDROLOGY. *Current Pos:* PRIN HYDROGEOLOGIST & PRES, TURK ASSOCS, INC, ENVIRON CONSULTS, MENLO PARK, CALIF, 94- *Personal Data:* b Tulare, Calif, July 18, 38; m 84, Tina Stone; c 3. *Educ:* Fresno State Col, BA, 61; Stanford Univ, MS, 63 & 67, PhD(geol), 69. *Prof Exp:* Jr geologist, Mobil Oil Libya Ltd, Tripoli, Libya, 63-65, geologist, 65-66; from asst prof to prof geol, Univ Tex, Austin, 68-81, adj prof, 81-88; managing engr, Failure Anal Assoc Inc, Menlo Park, Calif, 89-90, sr managing engr, 90-93, prin engr, 93-94. *Concurrent Pos:* Prof engr, Tex; ed-in-chief, Environ Geol, 74-78; partner, Turk-Kehle & Assocs, Consult Geologists, 74-81; pres, Oiltex Int Ltd, 81-85, OSIRIS Petrol, Inc, 85-87; consult, Hall Southwest Water Consults, Inc, 86-89. *Mem:* Geol Soc Am; Nat Ground Water Asn; Am Inst Prof Geologists; Am Soc Civil Engrs. *Res:* Hydrogeology; environmental geology; petroleum geology; remediation of soil and ground water; reconstruction of pollution events. *Mailing Add:* 1924 W Cypress Point Austin TX 78746

**TURKANIS, STUART ALLEN,** ELECTROPHYSIOLOGY. *Current Pos:* From asst prof to assoc prof, 67-85, PROF PHARMACOL, SCH MED, UNIV UTAH, 85- *Personal Data:* b Everett, Mass, Dec 15, 36; m 64; c 2. *Educ:* Mass Col Pharm, BS, 58, MS, 60; Univ Utah, PhD(pharmacol), 67. *Concurrent Pos:* USPHS fel, Univ Col, Univ London, 67-69. *Mem:* Am Soc Pharmacol & Exp Therapeut; Soc Neurosci. *Res:* Pharmacology and physiology of synaptic transmission; mechanisms of action of antiepileptic drugs; pharmacology of marijuana and other drugs of abuse; studies of ion channels. *Mailing Add:* Dept Pharmacol Univ Utah 410 Chipeta Way 215 Salt Lake City UT 84108

**TURKDOGAN, ETHEM TUGRUL,** METALLURGY. *Current Pos:* CONSULT, PYROMETALL & THERMOCHEM, 86- *Personal Data:* b Istanbul, Sept 12, 23; m 50; c 2. *Educ:* Univ Sheffield, BMet, 47, MMet, 49, PhD, 51, DMet, 85. *Honors & Awards:* Brunton Medal, Univ Sheffield, 51; Andrew Carnegie Silver Medal, Brit Iron & Steel Inst, 53; Robert W Hunt Medal, Am Inst Mining, Metall & Petrol Engrs, 67; Mathewson Gold Medal, Metall Soc, 75; Chipman Award, Iron & Steel Soc, 78; Kroll Medal, Metals Soc, 78. *Prof Exp:* Res metallurgist, Res & Develop, Brit Oxygen Co, Eng, 50-51; head phys chem sect, Brit Iron & Steel Res Asn, 51-59; staff scientist, US Steel Tech Ctr, 59-64, mgr chem metall, 64-72, sr res consult, 72-86. *Mem:* Fel Am Inst Mining, Metall & Petrol Engrs; fel Inst Metals; fel Inst Mining & Metall. *Res:* Chemical metallurgy; physical chemistry of high temperature reactions of interest to metallurgical processes and related subjects. *Mailing Add:* 5820 Northumberland Pittsburgh PA 15217

**TURKEL, RICKEY M(ARTIN),** ORGANIC CHEMISTRY, ABSTRACTING. *Current Pos:* assoc abstractor, 70-71, assoc ed, 71-76, sr assoc ed, 77-82, sr ed, 82-87, SR ED, DOCUMENT ANALYSIS, CHEM ABSTR SERV, 87- *Personal Data:* b New York, NY, Apr 12, 43; wid; c 2. *Educ:* Hofstra Univ, BA, 63; Mass Inst Technol, PhD(org chem), 68; Ohio State Univ, MA, 76. *Honors & Awards:* Award, Am Chem Soc, 63. *Prof Exp:* Fel org chem, Hebrew Univ, Jerusalem, 68-69 & Tulane Univ, 69-70. *Concurrent Pos:* Consult, Transl Russian, Serbocroatian & Hebrew Tech Literature. *Mem:* Am Chem Soc; Sigma Xi. *Res:* Synthetic organic chemistry; organometallic chemistry; chemistry literature. *Mailing Add:* 150 S Cassingham Rd Columbus OH 43209-1845

**TURKELTAUB, PAUL CHARLES,** ALLERGY, CLINICAL IMMUNOLOGY. *Current Pos:* RES INVESTR ALLERGENIC PROD BR, BUR LOGICS, 77-; CHIEF, LAB ALLERGENIC PROD, FOOD & DRUG ADMIN, DEP DIR, DIV ALLERGENIC PROD & PARASITOL, 96- *Personal Data:* b Brooklyn, NY, Jan 10, 44; m 67; c 2. *Educ:* Brooklyn Col, BS, 65; Univ Pittsburgh, MD, 69. *Honors & Awards:* Commendation Medal, USPHS. *Concurrent Pos:* Consult, Nat Ctr Health Statist, 78-; instr, Johns Hopkins Univ Sch Med, 78-; vchmn, Comt Allergy Standardization, Am Acad Allergy, 97- *Mem:* Fel Am Acad Allergy; fel Am Col Chest Physicians; fel Am Col Physicians. *Res:* Investigating the potency, safety and efficacy of allergenic products used for the diagnosis and treatment of allergic diseases. *Mailing Add:* Berwyn Heights Med Bldg 8824 Cunningham Dr Suite C Berwyn Heights MD 20740. *Fax:* 301-496-4684; *E-Mail:* turkeltaub@al.cber.gov

**TURKEVICH, ANTHONY,** NUCLEAR CHEMISTRY, SPACE CHEMISTRY. *Current Pos:* from asst prof to prof, Univ Chicago, 46-86, James Franck prof, 65-71, James Franck distinguished serv prof, 71-86, EMER PROF CHEM, ENRICO FERMI INST & CHEM DEPT, UNIV CHICAGO, 86- *Personal Data:* b New York, NY, July 23, 16; m 48; c 2. *Educ:* Dartmouth Col, BA, 37; Princeton Univ, PhD(phys chem), 40. *Hon Degrees:* DSc, Dartmouth Col, 71. *Honors & Awards:* E O Lawrence Award, US AEC, 62; Atoms for Peace Award, 69; Nuclear Applns Award, Am Chem Soc, 72; Pregel Award, NY Acad Sci. *Prof Exp:* Res assoc molecular spectra, Dept Physics, Univ Chicago, 40-41, res chemist, Metall Lab, 43-45; res chemist, SAM Labs, Columbia Univ, 42-43; res physicist, Los Alamos Sci Lab, 45-46. *Concurrent Pos:* NSF fel, Europ Orgn Nuclear Res, Switz, 61-62; J W Kennedy Mem lectr, Univ Wash, St Louis, 64; NSF fel, Orsay, France, 70; consult, Labs, US AEC, Dept Energy. *Mem:* Nat Acad Sci; AAAS; Am Chem Soc; Am Acad Arts & Sci; Royal Soc Arts; NY Acad Sci. *Res:* Reactions of energetic particles with complex nuclei; radioactivity in meteorites; chemical composition of the moon and meteorites. *Mailing Add:* Univ Chicago Enrico Fermi Inst 5640 S Ellis Ave Chicago IL 60637

**TURKEVICH, JOHN,** PHYSICAL CHEMISTRY. *Current Pos:* from instr to prof, 36-55, Eugene Higgins prof, 55-75, EMER PROF CHEM, PRINCETON UNIV, 75-, MEM STAFF, FRICK CHEM LABS, 77- *Personal Data:* b Minneapolis, Minn, Jan 20, 07; m 34; c 2. *Educ:* Dartmouth

Col, BS, 28, MA, 30; Princeton Univ, AM, 32, PhD(chem), 34. *Hon Degrees:* DD, McMurry Col; DSc, Dartmouth Col. *Honors & Awards:* Mfg Chemists Asn Award, 56. *Prof Exp:* Instr, Dartmouth Col, 28-31. *Concurrent Pos:* Consult, M W Kellogg Co Div, Pullman, Inc, NY, 36-, Radio Corp Am Labs, 43-, Brookhaven Nat Lab, 47, US Energy Res & Develop Admin, 50- & US Dept State; chmn, US Deleg Educrs, USSR, 58; rep, US Sci Am Nat Exhib, Moscow, 59; actg sci attache, US Embassy, Moscow, 60, sci attache, 61; lectr, US Army War Col & US Air War Col; Phi Beta Kappa vis scholar, 61. *Mem:* Am Chem Soc; Am Phys Soc; Sigma Xi. *Res:* Catalysis; molecular structure; synthesis and characterization of monodisperse noble metals, sulica, alumina and zeolites for heterogeneous and homogeneous catalysis; synthesis of drugs for cancer and study of biochemistry of drug action and cancer. *Mailing Add:* 1 David Brainard Dr Munroe Village D109 Jamesburg NJ 08831-1913

**TURKINGTON, ROBERT (ROY) ALBERT,** PLANT ECOLOGY. *Current Pos:* from asst prof to assoc prof, 77-90, PROF BOT, UNIV BC, 90- *Personal Data:* b Portadown, Northern Ireland, Apr 8, 51; Brit & Can citizen; m 75, Evelyn Robinson; c Alistair & Andrea. *Educ:* New Univ Ulster, BSc, 72; Univ Col North Wales, dipl ecol, 74, PhD(plant ecol), 75. *Prof Exp:* Fel plant ecol, Univ Western Ont, 76-77. *Mem:* Brit Ecol Soc; Can Bot Asn; Ecol Soc Am. *Res:* Plant population biology, with special reference to neighbor relationships and to structure dynamics of herbaceous vegetation in the Boreal Forest and in the Neger Desert. *Mailing Add:* Dept Bot Univ BC Vancouver BC V6T 1Z4 Can. *Fax:* 604-822-6089; *E-Mail:* royt@unixg.ubc.ca

**TURKINGTON, ROGER W,** medicine, biochemistry, for more information see previous edition

**TURKKI, PIRKKO REETTA,** NUTRITION, FOOD SCIENCE. *Current Pos:* from asst prof to assoc prof, 68-78, asst dean, Col Human Develop, 75-79, PROF NUTRIT, SYRACUSE UNIV, 78- *Personal Data:* b Laitila, Finland, Aug 27, 34; m 57; c 2. *Educ:* Helsinki Home Econ Teacher's Col, dipl, 57; Univ Mass, Amherst, MS, 62; Univ Tenn, Knoxville, PhD(nutrit, food sci), 65. *Prof Exp:* Res assoc biochem, Univ Tenn, 65-66; NIH res fel, Albany Med Col, 66-68. *Mem:* Am Dietetic Asn; Am Inst Nutrit. *Res:* Phospholipid metabolism in choline deficiency; role of diet in hyperlipemia; riboflavin status in protein/energy deprivation; vitamin utilization during negative energy balance. *Mailing Add:* Dept Nutrit & Food Serv Mgt 034 Slocum Hall Col Human Develop Syracuse Univ Syracuse NY 13244-1250. *Fax:* 315-443-2562

**TURKOT, FRANK,** PHYSICS. *Current Pos:* PHYSICIST, FERMILAB, 74- *Personal Data:* b Woodlynne, NJ, Sept 29, 29; m 59; c 4. *Educ:* Univ Pa, BA, 51; Cornell Univ, PhD(physics), 59. *Prof Exp:* Res assoc particle physics, Lab Nuclear Studies, Cornell Univ, 59-60; from asst physicist to sr physicist, Brookhaven Nat Lab, NY, 60-74. *Mem:* Fel Am Phys Soc. *Res:* Experiments in elementary particle physics to study photoproduction processes and high energy collisions of strongly-interacting particles; particle accelerator research. *Mailing Add:* Fermilab PO Box 500 Batavia IL 60510. *Fax:* 312-840-3756

**TURKSTRA, CARL J,** CIVIL ENGINEERING, STRUCTURAL ENGINEERING. *Current Pos:* PRES TURKSTRA LUMBER CO, 91- *Personal Data:* b Hamilton, Ont, Oct 29, 36; m 64; c 2. *Educ:* Queen's Univ, Ont, BSc, 58; Univ Ill, MS, 60; Univ Waterloo, PhD(struct safety), 63, McGill Univ, dipl, 79; Univ Montreal, DEA, 80. *Honors & Awards:* State of the Art Award, Am Soc Civil Engrs, 72 & 88. *Prof Exp:* Engr, F R Harris, Consult Engrs, 62-63; lectr civil eng, Univ Col, Univ London, 63-65; from asst prof to prof civil eng, McGill Univ, 65-82; head dept, Polytech Univ, Brooklyn, 82-85, prof, 82-91. *Concurrent Pos:* Res grants, Nat Res Coun Can, 65-82, NSF, 83-87, City New York, 87-89, Nat Ctr Earthquake Eng Res, 87-, Nat Tran Res Ctr, City Univ NY, 88-; consult struct engr, 68-; mem, Int Joint Comt on Struct Safety, 76-; chmn, Comt Safety Bldg, Am Soc Civil Engrs, 87-90 & Nat Bldg Code Can, 77- *Mem:* Fel Am Soc Civil Engrs; Am Acad Mech; fel Can Soc Civil Eng; Int Asn Bridge & Struct Eng. *Res:* Choice of structural safety levels based on probabilistic and decision theory concepts; structural masonry; optimum structural design; earthquake risk analysis; bridge management systems. *Mailing Add:* 1050 Upper Wellington St Hamilton ON L9A 3S6 Can

**TURLAPATY, PRASAD,** HYPERTENSION, CLINICAL RESEARCH. *Current Pos:* ASSOC MED DIR, DEPT MED, DUPONT MERCK PHARMACEUT. *Personal Data:* b Vijayawada, India, June 1, 42; m 72, Snehalatha; c Neelima. *Educ:* Andhra Univ, India, BSc, 60, BPharm, 64, MPharm 65; Univ Hawaii, PhD(pharmacol), 71. *Prof Exp:* Fel pharmacol, Univ Tex Health Sci Ctr, San Antonio, 72-74; scientist pharmacol, Postgrad Med Inst, Pondicherry, India, 75-77; from instr to asst prof physiol, Downstate Med Ctr, State Univ NY, Brooklyn, 77-80; clin invest assoc, Ives Med Lab, New York, 80-81, sr clin invest assoc med, 82-; asst dir clin res, Med Dept, Am Critical Care. *Mem:* Am Physiol Soc; NY Acad Sci; AAAS; fel Am Col Clin Pharmacol; Am Soc Clin Pharmacol Ther; Am Soc Pharmacol & Ther; fel Am Col Cardiol. *Res:* Conduct of Phase I to Phase IV clinical trials towards new drugs development, design and development of clinical protocols in hypertension, stable & unstable angina, acute myocardial infraction, arrhythmias, preparation of medical summaries for USDA review towards new drug application; developing antitasombotic drugs including antiplatelets and antitasombins. *Mailing Add:* Dept CV/GI Clinic Res Solvay Pharmaceutical Inc 901 Sawyer Rd Marietta GA 30062-2224

**TURLEY, JUNE WILLIAMS,** X-RAY CRYSTALLOGRAPHY, TSCA REGULATORY COMPLIANCE. *Current Pos:* PROJ MGR, ALLIS INFO MGMT, 93-; INFO ANALYST. *Personal Data:* b Boston, Mass, Apr 12, 29; m 50, Sheldon G; c Sheldon G Jr, Cynthia (Kingsburg) & Linda (Barrow). *Educ:* Wilkes Col, BS, 50; Pa State Univ, MS, 51, PhD(biochem), 57. *Prof Exp:* Res asst, molecular struct via x-ray, Pa State Univ, 53-56, res assoc, 56-57; res specialist molecular struct & x-ray crystallog, Dow Chem Co, 57-71, res mgr, Anal Labs, 71-74, sr econ planner, Capital Projs, Bus Develop & Futures Studies, 74-84, sr res assoc regulatory compliance mgt, 84-93. *Concurrent Pos:* Media anal tech issues, Int Ctr Diffraction Data, desk top publ. *Mem:* Am Chem Soc; World Future Soc; fel AAAS; Am Women Sci; fel Sigma Xi. *Res:* Health and environmental regulatory issues, TSCA regulatory compliance; business analysis; computer applications; long range economic planning; single-crystal x-ray structure analysis; chemical identification using x-ray methods. *Mailing Add:* 1208 Wakefield Dr Midland MI 48640

**TURLEY, KEVIN,** CARDIAC SURGERY, PHYSIOLOGY. *Current Pos:* chief resident, 76-78, INSTR CARDIAC SURG, UNIV CALIF, SAN FRANCISCO, 78- *Personal Data:* b New York, NY, May 21, 46. *Educ:* Fordham Univ, BA, 68; Med Col Wis, MD, 72. *Prof Exp:* Intern surgery, Ohio State Univ, 72-73; gen surg resident, Univ SFla, 73-75, chief resident, 75-76. *Concurrent Pos:* Fel, Cardiovasc Res Inst, 78- *Res:* Cardiovascular research; right ventricular function pulmonary hypertension both chronic and acute; aortic insufficiency and deep hypothermia and total circulatory arrest. *Mailing Add:* Calif Pac Med Ctr 2100 Webster St Suite 332 San Francisco CA 94115

**TURLEY, RICHARD EYRING,** OPERATIONS RESEARCH, NUCLEAR & SYSTEMS ENGINEERING. *Current Pos:* RETIRED. *Personal Data:* b El Paso, Tex, Dec 29, 30; m 54, Jean Nickle; c Winifred, Richard, Stephanie, Teresa, William, Jeffrey & David. *Educ:* Univ Utah, BS, 55, MS, 58; Iowa State Univ, PhD(nuclear eng), 66. *Prof Exp:* Engr, Convair Div, Gen Dynamics Corp, Tex, 55-56 & El Paso Natural Gas Co, 56-57; asst prof mech & nuclear eng, Univ Utah, 57-62; asst prof eng sci & nuclear eng, Iowa State Univ, 63-67; sect mgr systs anal, Battelle-Northwest, 67-71, res assoc systs eng, 71-72; assoc prof, Univ Utah, 72-81, prof mech & indust eng, 81-89; pres, Utah Tech Finance Corp, 89-93. *Concurrent Pos:* alt state rep, Western Interstate Nuclear Bd, 72-78; exec dir, Utah Nuclear Energy Comn, 72-73; sci adv, State of Utah, 73-77; consult to indust; pres, Mex Hermosillo Mission, 83-85. *Mem:* Inst Indust Engrs. *Res:* Discrete-event simulation; operations research; technology assessment; energy conservation; engineering economics; energy; management and systems engineering; simulation and modeling; waste management. *Mailing Add:* 123 Second Ave No 513 Salt Lake City UT 84103. *Fax:* 801-532-2889

**TURLEY, SHELDON GAMAGE,** PHYSICS. *Current Pos:* res physicist, 57-62, SR RES PHYSICIST, DOW CHEM CO, 62- *Personal Data:* b Pa, June 13, 22; m 50; c 3. *Educ:* Pa State Univ, BS, 50, MS, 51, PhD(physics), 57. *Prof Exp:* Res assoc physics of aerosols, Pa State Univ, 52-53. *Mem:* Sigma Xi; Am Phys Soc. *Res:* High polymer physics, especially with dynamic mechanical and electrical properties of polymers and their relationship to molecular structure. *Mailing Add:* 1208 Wakefield Dr Midland MI 48640

**TURMAN, ELBERT JEROME,** ANIMAL SCIENCE. *Current Pos:* RETIRED. *Personal Data:* b Granite, Okla, Jan 26, 24; m 49; c 2. *Educ:* Okla State Univ, BS, 49; Purdue Univ, MS, 50, PhD(physiol), 53. *Prof Exp:* From instr to asst prof animal husb, Purdue Univ, 50-55; from asst prof to prof animal sci, Okla State Univ, 55-87. *Mem:* Soc Study Reproduction; Am Soc Animal Sci. *Res:* Physiology of reproduction of beef cattle, sheep and swine. *Mailing Add:* 3401 W 24th St Stillwater OK 74074

**TURNBLOM, ERNEST WAYNE,** ORGANIC CHEMISTRY. *Current Pos:* res chemist, Eastman Kodak Co, 74-77, res lab head, 77-83, mkt intelligence, 83-84, dir, planning & regulatory affairs, Bio-Prod Div, 85-88, dir, fine chem strategy, Lab & Res Prods Div, 88-89, mgr, technol develop, Graphics Imaging Systs Div, 89-92, PROD MGR, ENVIRON SYST PROF PRINTING & PUBL IMAGING, EASTMAN KODAK CO, 93- *Personal Data:* b Boston, Mass, Nov 1, 46; m 73; c 2. *Educ:* Worcester Polytech Inst, BS, 68; Columbia Univ, PhD(chem), 72. *Prof Exp:* Instr org chem, Princeton Univ, 72-74. *Concurrent Pos:* Adv coun, Mat Sci Prog, Roch Inst Tech. *Mem:* Am Chem Soc; Com Develop Asn. *Res:* Organophosphorus chemistry; pentaalkylphosphoranes and related compounds; chemistry of other main group elements; electrophotographic processes and materials; novel imaging systems. *Mailing Add:* 44 Morningside Dr Spencerport NY 14559

**TURNBULL, BRUCE FELTON,** PHYSICAL CHEMISTRY. *Current Pos:* RETIRED. *Personal Data:* b Cleveland, Ohio, Mar 2, 28; m 51; c 3. *Educ:* Case Inst Technol, BS, 50; Faith Theol Sem, BD, 54; Western Res Univ, MS, 55, PhD(phys chem), 63. *Prof Exp:* Chemist, Gen Motors Corp, Ohio, 50-51; asst prof chem, Cedarville Col, 55-63; from asst prof to prof, Cleveland State Univ, 63-85, ombudsman, 71-96. *Mem:* AAAS; Am Chem Soc; Am Asn Physics Teachers. *Res:* Thermodynamics; molecular structure studies with infrared spectroscopy. *Mailing Add:* 2503 Dover Center Rd Westlake OH 44145

**TURNBULL, BRUCE WILLIAM,** BIOMETRICS, BIOSTATISTICS. *Current Pos:* PROF OPER RES STATIST, CORNELL UNIV, 76- *Personal Data:* b Purley, Eng, Oct 8, 46; m 72; c 2. *Educ:* Cambridge Univ, BA, 67; Cornell Univ, MS, 70, PhD(statist), 71. *Honors & Awards:* Snedecor Award, Am Statist Asn, 79,. *Prof Exp:* Asst prof statist, Stanford Univ, 71-72; lectr math, Oxford Univ, 72-76. *Mem:* Biomet Soc; fel Am Statist Asn, 85; Oper Res Soc Am; Royal Statist Soc; Statist Soc Can. *Res:* Statistical design and analysis of long-term animal studies; general biomedical statistics; survival analysis; reliability and life testing; quality control. *Mailing Add:* Dept Indust Eng Cornell Univ 319 Upson Hall Ithaca NY 14853-7501

**TURNBULL, CRAIG DAVID,** BIOSTATISTICS, PUBLIC HEALTH. *Current Pos:* RETIRED. *Personal Data:* b Reading, Pa, Aug 28, 40; m 61; c 4. *Educ:* Albright Col, BA, 62; Univ NC, Chapel Hill, MPH, 65, PhD(biostatist), 71. *Prof Exp:* Statistician pub health, Pa State Health Dept, 62-64; biostatistician & clin instr, Res Found, State Univ NY, Buffalo, 65-68; from instr to assoc prof biostatist, Univ NC, Chapel Hill, 71-95. *Concurrent Pos:* Statist consult, Dept Pub Health, NC, 70-76, Am Col Obstet & Gynec, 71-74 & Sch Nursing, Univ NC, Chapel Hill, 72-75; statist consult & adv bd mem, Asn Schs Pub Health, 74-79; prin investr, Doctoral & Postdoctoral Res Training, 76-; prof dir, BSPH Biostatist, 76-; co-dir, Health Admin Postdoctoral Training, 78-80. *Mem:* Am Statist Asn; Am Pub Health Asn; Sigma Xi; Biomet Soc. *Res:* Public health statistics; perinatal mortality; mental health problems; complications of pregnancy; congenital malformations. *Mailing Add:* Dept Phys Educ Louisburg Col Louisburg NC 27549-2399

**TURNBULL, DAVID,** PHYSICAL CHEMISTRY, MATERIALS SCIENCES. *Current Pos:* Gordon McKay prof appl physics, EMER PROF PHYSICS, HARVARD UNIV, 85- *Personal Data:* b Kewanee, Ill, Feb 18, 15; m 46, Carol Cornell; c Lowell, Murray & Joyce. *Educ:* Monmouth Col, BS, 36; Univ Ill, PhD(phys chem), 39. *Hon Degrees:* ScD, Monmouth Col, 58, Case Western Res Univ, 90, Univ Claude Bernard, Lyon, France, 93. *Honors & Awards:* Acta Metallurgica Gold Medal, 79; Von Hipple Prize, Mat Res Soc, 79; Prize for New Mat, Am Physic Soc, 83; Hume-Rothery Award, 86; Japan Prize in Mat Sci & Technol, 86; Franklin Medal, 90; Bruce Chalmers Award, 90. *Prof Exp:* Instr phys chem, Case Inst Technol, 39-43, asst prof, 43-46, res proj leader, 45-46; res assoc, Res Lab, Gen Elec Co, 46-51, mgr, Chem Metall Sect, 51-58, phys chemist, 58-62. *Mem:* Nat Acad Sci; AAAS; fel Am Acad Arts & Sci; Am Chem Soc; fel Am Phys Soc; hon mem Am Ceramic Soc. *Res:* Thermionic emission; thermodynamic properties of gases at high pressures; corrosion in non-aqueous media; diffusion in metals; kinetics of nucleation in solid state transformation; solidification; theory of liquids; glass; crystal growth. *Mailing Add:* Div Appl Sci Pierce Hall Harvard Univ Cambridge MA 02138. *Fax:* 617-495-9837

**TURNBULL, G(ORDON) KEITH,** METALLURGY. *Current Pos:* res engr, Aluminum Co Am, 62-65, sr res engr, 65-69, group leader, 69-71, sect head, Pa, 71-77, div mgr, Alcoa Res Labs, 77-79, asst dir, 79-80, mgr, Corp Planning, 80-82, dir technol planning, 82-86, vpres technol planning, 86-91, EXEC VPRES, ALCOA BUS SYST, 96- *Personal Data:* b Cleveland, Ohio, Nov 10, 35; m 57, Sally Ewing; c Kenneth S, Stephen J, Lynn A (Bogolin), June P (Wakeley) & James R. *Educ:* Case Inst Technol, BS, 57, MS, 59, PhD, 62. *Mem:* Nat Acad Eng; Am Foundrymen's Soc; Am Inst Mining, Metall & Petrol Engrs; Sigma Xi; Am Soc Eng Educ; Soc Mfg Engrs; Am Soc Metals. *Res:* Solidification of metals; grain refinement of solidifying metals; aluminum alloy development; control of residual stresses in metals; aluminum and titanium forging research; ingot casting, melting, energy and fabricating; technology planning. *Mailing Add:* ALCOA 425 Sixth Ave 31st Floor Pittsburgh PA 15219. *Fax:* 412-553-4244; *E-Mail:* keith.turnball@alcoa.com

**TURNBULL, KENNETH,** MESOIONIC CHEMISTRY, ORGANOSULFUR CHEMISTRY. *Current Pos:* asst prof, 80-86, ASSOC PROF ORG CHEM, WRIGHT STATE UNIV, 86- *Personal Data:* b Edinburgh, Scotland, July 12, 51; m 85; c 2. *Educ:* Heriot Watt Univ, Scotland, BSc, 73, PhD(org chem), 76. *Prof Exp:* Res assoc, Erindale Col, Univ Toronto, 76-78; asst prof chem, Grinnell Col, 78-80. *Mem:* Am Chem Soc. *Res:* Preparation of novel, fused ring mesoionic compounds; photochromic sydnones; sulfur analogues of N-nitro samines; unusual compounds containing the S equal S linkage in stable configuration; polymer supported reagents. *Mailing Add:* Chem Dept Wright State Univ Dayton OH 45435-0002

**TURNBULL, ROBERT C,** AERONAUTICAL ENGINEERING. *Current Pos:* CHMN, T K ENG ASSOC, 95- *Personal Data:* b Kearney, NJ, Aug 26, 32. *Educ:* NJ Inst Technol, BS, 54. *Mem:* Nat Acad Eng; fel Am Inst Aeronaut & Astronaut. *Mailing Add:* 100 TriCounty Pkwy Cincinnati OH 45246. *Fax:* 813-865-9242

**TURNBULL, ROBERT JAMES,** ELECTROMECHANICS. *Current Pos:* From asst prof to assoc prof, 67-77, PROF ELEC ENG, UNIV ILL, URBANA, 77- *Personal Data:* b Washington, DC, July 26, 41; m 65, Patricia Barton; c Jeffrey & Douglas. *Educ:* Mass Inst Technol, BS & MS, 64, PhD(elec eng), 67. *Mem:* Inst Elec & Electronics Engrs. *Res:* Electromechanics; electrohydrodynamics; electric machines; power electronics. *Mailing Add:* Dept Elec & Comp Eng Univ Ill 1406 W Green St Urbana IL 61801. *Fax:* 217-333-1162; *E-Mail:* turnbull@uvuc.edu

**TURNBULL, WILLIAM DAVEY,** TERTIARY & MESOZOIC MAMMALS, TERTIARY & PLEISTOCENE-HOLOCENE AUSTRALIAN MAMMALS. *Current Pos:* preparator, Dept Geol, Field Mus, 46-56, from asst cur to assoc cur, 56-73, cur, 73-87, EMER CUR, FIELD MUS, 87- *Personal Data:* b Milwaukee, Wis, Jan 27, 22; m 48, 85, Hedy Mahler Brotman; c Jonathan. *Educ:* Univ Chicago, PhD(paleobiol), 67. *Prof Exp:* Temp res assoc, Nat Mus Victoria & Monash Univ, 63-64, 66-67, 76-77 & 84. *Concurrent Pos:* Lectr, Comn Evolutionary Biol, Univ Chicago, 75- *Mem:* Soc Vertebrate Paleont (vpres, 75, pres, 76 & 77); Paleont Soc;

Australian Mammal Soc; Australian Geol Soc; Am Soc Mammalogists; Soc Study Evolution. *Res:* Mammalian masticatory apparatus; forelimb anatomy of moles; eocine of Washakie-Basin; early Cretaceous of Trinity group; Australian Tertiary through Holocene. *Mailing Add:* Dept Geol Field Mus Chicago IL 60605-2496

**TURNEAURE, JOHN PAUL,** LOW TEMPERATURE PHYSICS. *Current Pos:* Res assoc, Stanford Univ, 66-69, res physicist, 69-75, actg asst prof, 70-73, sr res assoc, 75-88, PROF PHYSICS RES, STANFORD UNIV, 88- *Personal Data:* b Yakima, Wash, Jan 16, 39; m 68, Brigitte Mehrens; c Tanya & Stefan. *Educ:* Univ Wash, BS, 61; Stanford Univ, PhD(physics), 67. *Concurrent Pos:* Vis prof physics, Univ Wuppertal, Ger, 79. *Mem:* Am Phys Soc; Sigma Xi. *Res:* Study of radio frequency properties of superconductors, time variations of the fundamental physical constants and general relativistic effects; development of ultra-stable superconducting cavity oscillators; development of gyroscopes for measurement of general relativistic effects in earth orbit. *Mailing Add:* 845 Garland Dr Palo Alto CA 94303. *Fax:* 650-725-8312; *E-Mail:* john@relgyro.stanford.edu

**TURNER, ALBERT JOSEPH, JR,** SOFTWARE ENGINEERING, COMPUTER SCIENCE EDUCATION. *Current Pos:* asst prof math sci, Clemson Univ, 75-78, from asst prof to assoc prof, 78-84, head dept, 79-92, PROF COMPUT SCI, CLEMSON UNIV, 84- *Personal Data:* b Arcadia, Fla, June 21, 38. *Educ:* Ga Inst Technol, BS, 61; MS, 66; Univ Md, MS, 72, PhD(comput sci), 76. *Prof Exp:* Asst prof math, WGa Col, 64-70. *Concurrent Pos:* Chair, Educ Bd, Asn Comput Mach, 88-92; chmn, Comput Sci Accreditation Comn, 88-90 & 92-94. *Mem:* Asn Comput Mach (treas, 92); Inst Elec & Electronics Engrs Comput Soc; Am Asn Univ Prof. *Res:* Computer science education; software engineering. *Mailing Add:* Dept Comput Sci Clemson Univ Clemson SC 29631-1906. *Fax:* 864-656-0145; *E-Mail:* turner@cs.clemson.edu

**TURNER, ALMON GEORGE, JR,** ATMOSPHERIC CHEMISTRY, CHEMICAL DYNAMICS. *Current Pos:* assoc prof, 66-74, PROF CHEM, UNIV DETROIT, 74- *Personal Data:* b Detroit, Mich, June 9, 32; m 64; c 3. *Educ:* Univ Mich, BS, 55; Purdue Univ, MS, 56, PhD(inorg chem), 58. *Prof Exp:* Assoc prof inorg chem, NDak Agr Col, 58-59; instr & fel chem, Carnegie Inst Technol, 59-61; asst prof inorg chem, Polytech Inst, NY, 61-66. *Concurrent Pos:* Distinguished vis prof, USAF Acad, 81-82. *Mem:* Am Chem Soc; Am Phys Soc; Am Geophys Union. *Res:* Chemical bonding; electronic structure of molecules; nitrogen-sulfur chemistry; atmospheric chemistry. *Mailing Add:* 4013 Pinestead Dr Walled Lake MI 48390

**TURNER, ALVIS GREELY,** ENVIRONMENTAL HEALTH, ENVIRONMENTAL TOXICOLOGY. *Current Pos:* from asst prof to assoc prof environ sci, 66-84, prof, 84-96, EMER PROF ENVIRON TOXICOL, UNIV NC, CHAPEL HILL, 96- *Personal Data:* b Manheim, Pa, Feb 26, 29; m 56; c 2. *Educ:* Univ NC, BA, 52, MSPH, 58, PhD(environ sci), 70; Am Intersoc Acad Cert Sanit, dipl, 70. *Prof Exp:* Sr sanitarian, Caswell Co Health Dept, 54-58; supvr prev med, Arabian Am Oil Co, 58-66. *Mem:* Nat Environ Health Asn; Am Pub Health Asn; Sigma Xi. *Res:* Hazardous waste management; environmental risk assessment. *Mailing Add:* 802 Emory Dr Chapel Hill NC 27514

**TURNER, ANDREW,** CHEMICAL ENGINEERING. *Current Pos:* RETIRED. *Personal Data:* b Glasgow, Scotland, Dec 24, 22; nat US; m 50, Edna I Worley; c Donald B & Gail B. *Educ:* Univ Mich, BS, 49, MS, 50, PhD(chem eng), 58. *Prof Exp:* Chem engr, Union Carbide Corp, 53-71; sect chief, Ohio Environ Protection Agency, 72-78, asst off chief, 78-83, div chief, 83-91. *Mem:* Am Chem Soc; fel Am Inst Chem Engrs; Water Environ Fedn. *Res:* Synthetic resins and plastics. *Mailing Add:* 417 Montreal Pl Westerville OH 43081

**TURNER, ANDREW B,** ORGANIC CHEMISTRY. *Current Pos:* from asst prof to assoc prof chem, 80-91, chmn dept, 91-96, PROF CHEM, ST VINCENT COL, 91- *Personal Data:* b Lock Haven, Pa, Dec 23, 40. *Educ:* Franklin & Marshall Col, AB, 62; Bucknell Univ, MS, 65; Univ Va, PhD(chem), 68. *Prof Exp:* Interim asst prof chem; Univ Fla, 68-69; asst prof chem, Lycoming Col, 69-74 & St John Fisher Col, 74-80. *Concurrent Pos:* Coordr Natural Sci, 84- *Mem:* Am Chem Soc; Roy Soc Chem. *Res:* Aziridines; synthetic tropane alkaloid analogs; nuclear magnetic resonance spectroscopy. *Mailing Add:* Chem Dept St Vincent Col 300 Fraser Purchase Rd Latrobe PA 15650-2690

**TURNER, ANNE HALLIGAN,** MAGNETIC RESONANCE. *Current Pos:* res assoc, 79-85, asst prof, dept chem, 85-87, NMR LAB MGR, HOWARD UNIV, 87- *Personal Data:* b Columbus, Ohio, Feb 3, 41; m 66; c 2. *Educ:* Middlebury Col, AB, 63; Univ Rochester, PhD(chem), 69. *Prof Exp:* Lectr chem, Prince George's Commun Col, 69-79. *Concurrent Pos:* Instr chem, Grad Sch, USDA, 70-75. *Mem:* Am Chem Soc. *Res:* Application of nuclear magnetic resonance to problems of structure, kinetics and/or conformation in chemistry or biochemistry. *Mailing Add:* 7842 Godolphin Dr Springfield VA 22153-3309

**TURNER, ARTHUR FRANCIS,** optics, physics; deceased, see previous edition for last biography

**TURNER, BARBARA BUSH,** NEUROENDOCRINOLOGY, ENDOCRINOLOGY. *Current Pos:* assoc prof, Dept Physiol, Quillen Col Med, ETenn State Univ, 92, PROF, DEPT PHYSIOL, JAMES H QUILLEN COL MED. *Personal Data:* b Los Angeles, Calif; m 72; c 2. *Educ:* Immaculate Heart Col, BA, 67, MA, 70; Univ Calif, Los Angeles, PhD(neurosci), 74. *Prof Exp:* Fel B S McEwen Lab, Rockefeller Univ, 74-76; res assoc, Ment Health Res Inst, Univ Mich, 76-78; vis asst prof biol, Va Polytech Inst & State Univ, 79- *Concurrent Pos:* Res fel, NIH & Nat Inst Neurol & Commun Dis & Stroke, 74-76; NIMH fel res training biol sci, 76-77; vis asst prof psychol, Va Polytech Inst & State Univ, 78-81. *Mem:* Soc Neurosci; Endocrine Soc; Int Soc Psychoneuroendocrinol; NY Acad Sci; Int Soc Develop Neurosci. *Res:* Brain-hormone interactions; glucocorticoid binding in the brain; corticoid receptor regulation; endocrine immune interactions. *Mailing Add:* Dept Physiol ETenn State Univ Col Med PO Box 10001 Johnson City TN 37614-0002. *Fax:* 423-929-6249

**TURNER, BARBARA HOLMAN,** ECOLOGY. *Current Pos:* RETIRED. *Personal Data:* b Evergreen, Ala, Aug 31, 26; m 50; c 2. *Educ:* Miss State Col for Women, BS, 47; Univ Kans, MT, 48; Vanderbilt Univ, MA, 66, PhD(ecol), 72. *Prof Exp:* Asst prof biol, George Peabody Col, 66-72; from asst prof to prof micro-med technol, Miss State Univ, 73-90, asst dept head, 82-90. *Mem:* Am Inst Biol Sci; Am Soc Microbiology; Sigma Xi; Am Soc Med Technologists. *Res:* Interactions between microorganisms and higher plants. *Mailing Add:* 105 Spruce Lane Hanover IN 47243-7601

**TURNER, BARRY EARL,** RADIO ASTRONOMY. *Current Pos:* from res assoc radio astron to assoc scientist, 67-74, SCIENTIST, NAT RADIO ASTRON OBSERV, 74- *Personal Data:* b Victoria, BC, Sept 8, 36; m 62. *Educ:* Univ BC, BSc, 59, MSc, 62; Univ Calif, Berkeley, PhD(astron), 67. *Prof Exp:* Res off elec eng, Nat Res Coun Can, 62-64. *Concurrent Pos:* mem site rev team, Space Telescope, Assoc Univ, Inc, 80 & NSF, 81; titulaire & chmn vis comt, Observ Paris, 81. *Mem:* Int Astron Union; Am Astron Soc; Union Radio Sci Int. *Res:* Theoretical and observational studies of interstellar molecules, interstellar chemistry, physics of the interstellar medium. *Mailing Add:* Nat Radio Astron Observ 520 Edgemont Rd Charlottesville VA 22903. *Fax:* 804-296-0337

**TURNER, BILLIE LEE,** SYSTEMATIC BOTANY. *Current Pos:* From instr to assoc prof, 53-58, chmn dept, 67-74, PROF BOT & DIR PLANT RESOURCES CTR, UNIV TEX, AUSTIN, 59- *Personal Data:* b Yoakum, Tex, Feb 22, 25; div; c 4. *Educ:* Sul Ross State Col, BS, 49; Southern Methodist Univ, MS, 50; Wash State Univ, PhD(bot), 53. *Honors & Awards:* NY Bot Garden Award, 65; Merit Award, Bot Soc Am, 88. *Concurrent Pos:* Vis prof & NSF sr fel, Univ Liverpool, 65-66; assoc investr ecol study African veg, 56-57. *Mem:* AAAS; Bot Soc Am (secy, 58-59 & 60-64, vpres, 65); Am Soc Plant Taxon; Soc Study Evolution; Int Asn Plant Taxon; Sigma Xi. *Res:* Plant geography; chromosomal studies of higher plants; flora of Texas and Mexico; biochemical systematics. *Mailing Add:* Dept Bot Univ Tex Austin TX 78712-1104

**TURNER, BILLIE LEE, II,** GEOGRAPHY. *Current Pos:* from asst prof to assoc prof, 80-85, dir grad sch, 83-88 & 97-98, PROF GEOG, CLARK UNIV, WORCESTER, 85-, HIGGINS PROF ENVIRON & SOCIOL, 95- *Personal Data:* b Texas City, Tex, Dec 22, 45; m 68, Linda Lee-Van Zandt; c Billie L III & Victoria K. *Educ:* Univ Tex, BA, 68, MA, 69; Univ Wis-Madison, PhD, 74. *Prof Exp:* Asst prof geog, Univ Md, Catonsville, 74-76; asst prof, Univ Okla, Norman, 76-79; dir, George Perkins Marsh Inst, 91-97. *Concurrent Pos:* NSF res grant, 78-82, 84-85, 89-90 & 93-96; Guggenheim fel, 81-82; Green Ctr for Sci & Soc fel, 94; Ctr Advan Studies Behav Scis fel, 94-95. *Mem:* Nat Acad Sci; AAAS; Asn Am Geogrs; Soc Am Archaeol. *Res:* Examined nature of population, economy and environment relationships among the ancient Maya civilization and small borders throughout the tropics, and in terms of global environmental change; contributed articles to professional journals. *Mailing Add:* 19 Forum St Worcester MA 01602-2101. *E-Mail:* bturner@block.clark7.edu

**TURNER, BRUCE JAY,** ICHTHYOLOGY. *Current Pos:* asst prof, 78-83, ASSOC PROF BIOL, VA POLYTECH INST & STATE UNIV, 83- *Personal Data:* b Brooklyn, NY, Sept 19, 45; m 72; c 2. *Educ:* City Univ New York, Brooklyn, BS, 66; Univ Calif, Los Angeles, MA, 67, PhD(biol), 71. *Prof Exp:* Fel biochem genetics, Ment Health Res Unit, Neuropsychiat Inst, Univ Calif, 72-74; res assoc, Rockefeller Univ, 74-76; vis res scientist evolutionary biol, Mus Zool, Univ Mich, 76-78. *Mem:* Soc Study Evolution; Am Soc Naturalists; Am Soc Ichthyologists & Herpetologists; Soc Syst Zool; Am Fisheries Soc; Genetics Soc Am; Am Genetic Assoc. *Res:* Evolutionary and ecological genetics of fish populations (polymorphism and divergence interspecific hybridization, thelytoky); emphasis on biochemical genetic, molecular and chromosomal studies; general ichthyology and systematics. *Mailing Add:* Dept Biol 0406 Va Polytech Inst Blacksburg VA 24061-0406

**TURNER, CARLTON EDGAR,** chemistry, pharmacognosy, for more information see previous edition

**TURNER, CHARLES HALL,** CELLULAR MECHANOTRANSDUCTION, ENDOCRINOLOGICAL & BIO-MECHANICAL CAUSES OF OSTEOPOROSIS. *Current Pos:* DIR ORTHOP RES, MED SCH, IND UNIV, 91-, ASST PROF ORTHOP SURG, 91-; ASST PROF MECH ENG, PURDUE UNIV, 91- *Personal Data:* b Roswell, NMex, Nov 29, 61; m 93, Nancy J Wieczorek; c Charles J. *Educ:* Texas Tech Univ, BS, 83; Tulane Univ, PhD(biomed eng), 87. *Prof Exp:* Dir biomech & asst prof oral biol, med & anat, Creighton Univ, 87-91. *Concurrent*

*Pos:* Prin investr Whitaker Found, 89-93; prin investr, NIH, 91- *Mem:* Am Soc Mech Eng; Am Soc Biomech; AAAS; Am Soc Bone & Mineral Res; Orthop Res Soc. *Res:* Mechanotransduction mechanisms of bone cells-signal transduction in bone, fluoride effects on bone; improved methods for predicting hip fracture, stress analysis of hip replacement implants, biomechanical evaluation of osteoporosis treatments; published over 40 scientific papers. *Mailing Add:* Ind Univ 541 Clinical Dr Rm 600 Indianapolis IN 46202. *Fax:* 317-274-3702

**TURNER, CHARLIE DANIEL, JR,** AEROELASTICITY, STRUCTURAL DYNAMICS. *Current Pos:* SR STAFF ENGR, NICHOLS RES CORP, 89- *Personal Data:* b Birmingham, Ala, Feb 24, 46; m 67; c 2. *Educ:* Univ Ala, BS, 71; Va Polytech Inst & State Univ, MS, 76, PhD(aerospace eng), 80. *Prof Exp:* Aerospace engr structural dynamics, Air Force Armament Technol Lab, 71-78; group leader dynamics, Cessna Aircraft, 78-79; dynamics engr struct dynamics, Beech Aircraft, 79-81; asst prof aeroelasticity, NC State Univ, 81-83; sr res engr, NTI, 83-87; pres & consult, Aeroelastic Anal Inc, 87-89. *Concurrent Pos:* Adj prof, Wichita State Univ, 80-81; consult, Accident Reconstruct Anal Corp, 81 & Lewis, Wilson, Lewis & Jones, 81-82. *Mem:* Am Inst Aeronaut & Astronaut. *Res:* Analytical and experimental subcritical flutter analysis; feedback system approach for subcritical flight flutter testing; wing and control surface; tab aeroelastic analysis; wing and store aeroelastic analysis. *Mailing Add:* 29450 Elkwood Sect Rd Ardmore AL 35739

**TURNER, CHRISTY GENTRY, II,** DENTAL ANTHROPOLOGY. *Current Pos:* from asst prof to assoc prof, 66-75, asst dean, Grad Col, 72-76, PROF PHYS ANTHROP, ARIZ STATE UNIV, 75- *Personal Data:* b Columbia, Mo, Nov 28, 33; m 57; c 3. *Educ:* Univ Ariz, BA, 57, MA, 58; Univ Wis, Madison, PhD(phys anthrop), 67. *Prof Exp:* Actg asst prof phys anthrop, Univ Calif, Berkeley, 63-66. *Concurrent Pos:* Am Dent Asn & NIH dent epidemiol & biomet trainee; collabr phys anthrop, US Nat Park Serv, 69-; fel, Ctr Advan Study Behav Sci, Stanford Univ, 70-71; Nat Geog Soc grants, 72, 73 & 79-85, 88-90; Irex to USSR, 80-81, 84; NSF grants, 83-84 & 85; Nat Acad Scis to USSR, 87; Wenner-Gren Found grant, 91. *Mem:* Am Asn Phys Anthropologists; Sigma Xi; Soc Am Archaeol; AAAS; Am Quarternary Asn; Indo-Pac Prehist Asn. *Res:* Co-evolution of human biology and culture; dental morphology, genetics and related behavior; biology and culture of New World peoples, especially southwestern United States Indians and Alaskan Aleuts; origins of peoples of Pacific and New World; dental anthropology; origin of modern humans. *Mailing Add:* 2208 Campo Alegre Tempe AZ 85281

**TURNER, DANIEL SHELTON,** TRAFFIC ENGINEERING, ROADWAY TORT LIABILITY DEFENSE. *Current Pos:* assoc prof civil eng technol & actg dir, 76-84, PROF CIVIL ENG & DEPT HEAD, UNIV ALA, 84- *Personal Data:* b Montgomery, Ala, Dec 9, 45; m 78; c 4. *Educ:* Univ Ala, BS, 68, MS, 70; Tex A&M Univ, PhD(civil eng), 80. *Honors & Awards:* Hensley Award, 91. *Prof Exp:* Civil eng officer, USAF, 69-73; asst prof civil eng technol, Ga Southern Col, 73-76. *Concurrent Pos:* Mem staff, A C Parker & Son & Consult Engrs, 64-69; owner, Turner-Meadows Land Surv Co, 75-76; consult, 76-; asst res engr, Tex Transp Inst, Tex A&M, 79; univ res fel, 85; vchair, educators coun, Inst Transp Engrs, 90-91; chair, 91-92; comt chair, Transp Res Bd, 92-94; nat dir, Am Soc Civil Engrs. *Mem:* Transp Res Bd; fel Inst Transp Engrs; Am Soc Civil Engrs; Nat Safety Coun; Sigma Xi. *Res:* Highway research: 55 projects and over 200 publications; traffic engineering, traffic safety, and governmental defense of roadway tort liability. *Mailing Add:* Dept Civil Eng Univ Ala PO Box 870205 Tuscaloosa AL 35487-0205

**TURNER, DANIEL STOUGHTON,** PETROLEUM, GEOLOGY. *Current Pos:* prof, 65-85, EMER PROF GEOL, EASTERN MICH UNIV, 85-; CONSULT, COLO GEOL SURV, 88- *Personal Data:* b Madison, Wis, Feb 8, 17; m 44, Ruth Laatsch; c Diane, Sharon, Darlene & Paul. *Educ:* Univ Wis, PhB, 40, PhM, 42, PhD(geol), 48. *Prof Exp:* Field geologist, Buchans Mining Co, Nfld, 47; geologist, US AEC, Colo, 48; asst prof geol, Univ Wyo, 49-50; geologist, Carter Oil Co, Okla, 51 & Petrol Res Co, Colo, 52-53; div geologist, Wm R Whittaker Co, Ltd, 53; geol consult, 54-63; consult, Earth Sci Curric Proj, Boulder, 63-65. *Concurrent Pos:* Publ dir, Earth Sci Curric Proj; docent-lectr, 91- *Mem:* Am Inst Petrol Geologists; Am Asn Petrol Geol; Geol Soc Am. *Res:* Arctic geology and glaciation; permafrost; thermal activity of Yellowstone National Park; hydrodynamics of oil; Rocky Mountain petroleum exploration; earth science education; mineral deposits; Colorado geology and road logs. *Mailing Add:* 7175 S Poplar Way Englewood CO 80112

**TURNER, DANNY WILLIAM,** CLUSTER ANALYSIS, MULTIVARIATE GRAPHICS. *Current Pos:* asst prof, 76-79, ASSOC PROF MATH, BAYLOR UNIV, 79- *Personal Data:* b Shelby, NC, Oct 8, 47; m 70; c 1. *Educ:* Clemson Univ, BS, 69, PhD(math), 73. *Prof Exp:* Asst prof math, Baylor Univ, 73-76; software analyst, Tex Instruments, 76. *Mem:* Classification Soc; Math Asn Am; Am Statist Asn. *Res:* Cluster analysis and in particular multivariate graphics. *Mailing Add:* Dept Math Winthrop Univ Rock Hill SC 29733

**TURNER, DAVID GERALD,** OBSERVATIONAL ASTRONOMY, ASTROPHYSICS. *Current Pos:* assoc prof, 84-91, PROF ASTRON, ST MARY'S UNIV, HALIFAX, NS, 91- *Personal Data:* b Toronto, Ont, Dec 13, 45; m 70; c 1. *Educ:* Univ Waterloo, BSc, 68; Univ Western Ont, MSc, 70, PhD(astron), 74. *Prof Exp:* Postdoctorate fel astron, David-Dunlap Observ, 74-76; asst prof, Laurentian Univ, 76-78; asst prof astron, Univ Toronto, 78-80; from asst prof to assoc prof, Dept Physics & Astron, Laurentian Univ, 80-84. *Concurrent Pos:* Connaught fel, Univ Toronto, 75; Nat Sci & Eng Res Coun, Univ res fel, Laurentian Univ, 80-84, St Marys, 84-90. *Mem:* Can Astron Soc; Am Astron Soc; Royal Astron Soc Can; Int Astron Union; Int Planetarium Soc. *Res:* Interstellar extinction; star clusters and associations; variable stars and galactic structure; stellar spectroscopy. *Mailing Add:* Dept Astron St Mary's Univ Robie St Halifax NS B3H 3C3 Can

**TURNER, DAVID L(EE),** STATISTICAL ANALYSIS. *Current Pos:* MATH STATISTICIAN, USDA FOREST SERV, 89- *Personal Data:* b Afton, Wyo, Nov 20, 49; m 69, Lois Leffelbein; c Spring, Crystal, Forest & Louise. *Educ:* Colo State Univ, BS, 71, MS, 73, PhD(statist), 75. *Prof Exp:* From res asst to instr statist, Colo State Univ, 71-75; from asst prof to assoc prof statist, 75-81, Utah State Univ, 75-89. *Concurrent Pos:* Vis Ariz State Univ, 85. *Mem:* Sigma Xi; Am Statist Asn; Biomet Soc. *Res:* Analysis of unbalanced data, tolerance intervals and bands for regression; statistical computing, monitoring. *Mailing Add:* Forestry Sci Lab 860 N 1200 E Logan UT 84321. *Fax:* 435-755-3563; *E-Mail:* dturner@cc.usu.edu

**TURNER, DENNIS ROBERT,** ELECTROCHEMICAL PROCESSING. *Current Pos:* CONSULT, 85- *Personal Data:* b London, Eng, Jan 13, 20; US citizen; m 50, Phyllis Babcock; c Robert & Mark. *Educ:* Lake Forest, AB, 42; Univ Mich, MS, 47, PhD(chem), 50. *Honors & Awards:* Edward Goodrich Acheson Medal & Prize, Electrochem Soc, 92. *Prof Exp:* Res engr, Westinghouse Elec Corp, 42-52; mem tech staff/supvr, Bell Tel Labs, 52-85. *Mem:* Electrochem Soc (secy, 68-74, vpres, 75-78, pres, 78-79). *Res:* Electrochemical processes including lead acid and nickel cadmium batteries, electro deposition of various metals and semiconductor materials, industrial research on chemical processing electrodeposition and sensors. *Mailing Add:* 59 Susan Dr Chatham NJ 07928

**TURNER, DONALD LLOYD,** GEOLOGY, GEOCHRONOLOGY. *Current Pos:* assoc prof, 70-80, prof geol, geophys inst & dept geol, 80-88, EMER PROF GEOLOGY, UNIV ALASKA, FAIRBANKS, 88- *Personal Data:* b Richmond, Calif, Dec 21, 37; c 3. *Educ:* Univ Calif, Berkeley, AB, 60, PhD(geol), 68. *Prof Exp:* Nat Res Coun res assoc, Isotope Geol Br, US Geol Surv, Colo, 68-69, Calif, 69-70. *Res:* Geochronology, K-Ar and fission track dating applied to problems of regional tectonics; radiometric calibration of paleontological time scales and geothermal systems; geological and geophysical exploration for geothermal resources. *Mailing Add:* PO Box 85224 Fairbanks AK 99708

**TURNER, DONALD W,** inflammation, immune responses, for more information see previous edition

**TURNER, DOUGLAS HUGH,** BIOPHYSICAL CHEMISTRY. *Current Pos:* asst prof, 74-81, assoc prof, 81-86, PROF CHEM, UNIV ROCHESTER, 86- *Personal Data:* b Staten Island, NY, July 24, 46; m; c 1. *Educ:* Harvard Col, AB, 67; Columbia Univ, PhD(phys chem), 72. *Prof Exp:* Fel biophys chem, Univ Calif, Berkeley, 73-74. *Concurrent Pos:* Tech collabr, Brookhaven Nat Lab, 70-; Alfred P Sloan fel, 79-83; vis prof, Univ Colo, Boulder, 84-85; Guggenheim fel, 93-94. *Mem:* Am Chem Soc; AAAS. *Res:* Structure and function of nucleic acids; laser temperature jump kinetics. *Mailing Add:* Dept Chem Univ Rochester Rochester NY 14627

**TURNER, EDWARD C,** ALGEBRA & TOPOLOGY. *Current Pos:* from asst prof to assoc prof, 71-85, PROF MATH, STATE UNIV NY, ALBANY. *Personal Data:* b Princeton, NJ, Mar 16, 43. *Educ:* Univ Rochester, BA, 65; Univ Calif, Los Angeles, PhD(math), 68. *Prof Exp:* Instr math, Mass Inst Technol, 69-71. *Mem:* Am Math Soc; Math Asn Am. *Res:* Combinatorial group theory. *Mailing Add:* 25 Providence St Albany NY 12203-3609

**TURNER, EDWARD HARRISON,** magnetism; deceased, see previous edition for last biography

**TURNER, EDWARD V,** PEDIATRICS. *Current Pos:* From asst prof to assoc prof, 48-68, PROF PEDIAT, COL MED, OHIO STATE UNIV, 68- *Personal Data:* b Belmont, Ohio, May 19, 13; m 39; c 1. *Educ:* Ohio Univ, AB, 34; Harvard Med Sch, MD, 38. *Mem:* Fel Am Acad Pediat. *Res:* Clinical pediatrics; medical education. *Mailing Add:* 3341 E Livington Ave Columbus OH 43227-1949

**TURNER, EDWIN LEWIS,** EXTRAGALACTIC ASTRONOMY, COSMOLOGY. *Current Pos:* from asst prof to assoc prof, Princeton Univ Observ, 78-85, assoc dept chair, 88-95, actg dept chair, 95-96, PROF ASTROPHYS SCI, PRINCETON UNIV OBSERV, 85- *Personal Data:* b Knoxville, Tenn, May 3, 49; m 71, Joyce Beldon; c Alexander & Daniel. *Educ:* Mass Inst Technol, SB, 71; Calif Inst Technol, PhD(astron), 75. *Prof Exp:* Res fel physics & astron, Inst Advan Study, 75-77; asst prof astron, Harvard Col Observ, Harvard Univ, 77-78. *Concurrent Pos:* Alfred P Sloan res fel, 80; mem bd dir, Asn Univ Res Astron, 80-89; vis prof, Harvard Univ, 86, Mass Inst Technol, 86 & Nat Astron Observ, Japan, 90; dir, Apache Observ 3.5 Meter Telescope, 95- *Mem:* Am Astron Soc; Int Astron Union; Space Telescope Inst Coun. *Res:* Dynamics of galaxies and clusters of galaxies; quasars and active galactic nuclei; gravitational lenses, cosmology, cosmic structure formation. *Mailing Add:* 137 Peyton Hall Princeton Univ Observ Ivy Lane Princeton NJ 08544. *Fax:* 609-258-1020; *E-Mail:* elt@astro.princeton.edu

**TURNER, ELLA VICTORIA,** IMMUNOLOGY. *Current Pos:* DIR HISTOCOMPATIBILITY LAB, ST JUDE CHILDREN'S RES HOSP, MEMPHIS, TENN, 83- *Personal Data:* b Columbia, Mo, Jan 23, 46; m 66; c 2. *Educ:* Univ Ark, BA, 67; Univ Louisville, PhD(microbiol), 73. *Prof Exp:* Res asst, Univ Louisville, 73-74, res assoc, Dept Microbiol & Immunol, 74-78, adj asst prof, 78-80. *Concurrent Pos:* Consult, Tissue Typing Lab, Jewish Hosp, Louisville, 77-80. *Mem:* Am Asn Histocompatability & Immunogenetics; Am Soc Microbiol. *Res:* Immunologic parameters of tumor growth and rejection; effects of mediators of inflammation and of specific immunological responses on tumor growth; regulation of immune responses; biology of engraftment. *Mailing Add:* 6380 Candlewood Memphis TN 38119. *Fax:* 901-526-6261

**TURNER, ERNEST CRAIG, JR,** ENTOMOLOGY. *Current Pos:* RETIRED. *Personal Data:* b West Jefferson, NC, June 15, 27; m 53; c 3. *Educ:* Clemson Col, BS, 48; Cornell Univ, PhD(entom), 53. *Prof Exp:* Asst econ entom, Cornell Univ, 48-53; assoc prof entom, Va Polytech Inst & State Univ, 53 & 65, assoc entomologist, Agr Exp Sta, 53-92, prof entom, 65-92. *Mem:* Am Mosquito Control Asn; Entom Soc Am; Sigma Xi. *Res:* Medical and veterinary entomology. *Mailing Add:* 1413 Locust Ave Blacksburg VA 24060

**TURNER, EUGENE BONNER,** PHYSICS. *Current Pos:* RETIRED. *Personal Data:* b Wolf Point, Mont, Oct 6, 22; m 46; c 3. *Educ:* Mont State Col, BS, 44; Univ Mich, MS, 50, PhD(physics), 56. *Prof Exp:* Mem tech staff, Ramo-Wooldridge Corp, Calif, 56-58 & Space Tech Labs, Inc, 58-60; mem tech staff, Aerospace Corp, 60-68, head, Lasers & Optics Dept, Electronics Res Lab, 68-69, sr staff engr, Develop Planning Div, 69-73, staff engr, 73-75, staff scientist, Labs Div, 75-85. *Mem:* Am Phys Soc; Optical Soc Am; Soc Photo-Optical Instrument Eng (pres, 70); Sigma Xi; Am Inst Aeronaut & Astronaut. *Res:* Plasma physics; spectroscopy; optical and photographic instrumentation; lasers; optical systems; strategic space systems. *Mailing Add:* 23216 Juniper Ave Torrance CA 90505

**TURNER, FRED ALLEN,** ORGANIC CHEMISTRY. *Current Pos:* from instr to assoc prof, 62-74, PROF CHEM, ROOSEVELT UNIV, 74- *Personal Data:* b Chicago, Ill, Mar 16, 33; m 64, Brenda A Spiegel; c Arthur J & Sherilyn R. *Educ:* Univ Ill, BS, 55, MS, 58, PhD(pharmaceut chem), 63. *Prof Exp:* Instr, Univ Ill, Chicago, 58-59 & 61-62. *Concurrent Pos:* NSF fel, 59-61; chmn, Chicago Sect, Am Chem Soc, 96-97. *Mem:* Am Chem Soc; Sigma Xi. *Res:* Synthesis of medicinal compounds; study of organic halogenating agents; synthesis of heterocyclic systems. *Mailing Add:* Dept Chem Roosevelt Univ 430 S Michigan Ave Chicago IL 60605-1394. *Fax:* 312-341-3680

**TURNER, FREDERICK BROWN,** VERTEBRATE ZOOLOGY. *Current Pos:* RETIRED. *Personal Data:* b Carlinville, Ill, Feb 4, 27; div. *Educ:* Univ Calif, AB, 49, MA, 50, PhD(zool), 57. *Prof Exp:* Asst zool, Univ Calif, 50-52 & 55-56; instr, Ill Col, 52-53; seasonal park naturalist, Death Valley Nat Monument, Calif, 53-55; instr biol, Wayne State Univ, 56-60; univ res coun res fel, 60; vis asst prof zool, Univ Calif, Los Angeles, 60-61, mem staff, Lab Biomed & Environ Sci, 61-87. *Concurrent Pos:* NSF partic, Inst Desert Biol, Ariz State Univ, 59. *Res:* Population ecology of reptiles; ecosystem analysis; environmental effects of energy development in arid environments. *Mailing Add:* 711 Kingman Ave Santa Monica CA 90402

**TURNER, GEORGE CLEVELAND,** SCIENCE EDUCATION, RESEARCH ADMINISTRATION. *Current Pos:* RETIRED. *Personal Data:* b Spokane, Wash, Jan 26, 25; m 52; c 1. *Educ:* Stanford Univ, BA, 47; Utah State Univ, MS, 50; EWash State Col, MEd, 52; Ariz State Univ, EdD(sci ed), 64. *Prof Exp:* Teacher high schs, Wash, 52-53 & Calif, 53-60; from assoc prof to prof biol & sci educ, Calif State Univ, Fullerton, 60-83, chmn, Dept Sci Educ, 64-77, assoc vpres univ res, 77-82, dir & founder, Energy Consortium, 83-92. *Concurrent Pos:* Lectr, Claremont Grad Sch, 57-60; dir, NSF grants for adv topics inst for high sch biol teachers, 65-67, intern-master's degree prog for sci teachers, 67-, Human Ecol Inst, 69- & Urban Sci Intern Teaching Proj, 72-; dir, Off Educ grant for biol sci curric study test eval team, 66-67; pres, Calif Intersci Coun, 73-75; dir, Energy and the Environ Inst, 75- & Calif Statewide Energy Consortium, 73- *Mem:* Nat Sci Teachers Asn; Nat Asn Biol Teachers. *Res:* Ecology of rodents, Wasatch Mountains, Utah; scientific enquiry. *Mailing Add:* 1055 Harvard Ave Claremont CA 91711

**TURNER, HOWARD E,** FINE PARTICLE TECHNOLOGY. *Current Pos:* RETIRED. *Personal Data:* b Evanston, Ill, Apr 16, 16. *Educ:* Univ Minn, BS, 38, MS, 40. *Prof Exp:* Field engr, E I du Pont de Nemours, 40-51, group consult & sect mgr chem eng, DuPont Corp, 51-81. *Mem:* Fel Am Inst Chem Engrs. *Mailing Add:* 3425 Hillock Lane Wilmington DE 19808

**TURNER, HOWARD S(INCLAIR),** CHEMICAL ENGINEERING. *Current Pos:* RETIRED. *Personal Data:* b Jenkintown, Pa, Nov 27, 11; m 36, Katharine Swett; c Susan, Helen C & Barbara J. *Educ:* Swarthmore Col, AB, 33; Mass Inst Technol, PhD(org chem, chem eng), 36. *Hon Degrees:* LLD, Swardmore Col, 77. *Prof Exp:* Res chemist & supvr, E I du Pont de Nemours & Co, Del, 36-47; dir, Res & Develop Div, Pittsburgh Consol Coal Co, 47-54; vpres res & develop, Jones & Laughlin Steel Corp, 54-65; pres & dir, Turner Construct Co, 65-70, chmn, 71-78, chmn exec comt, 78-82, dir, 52-82. *Concurrent Pos:* Former dir, Ingersoll-Rand Co, Dime Savings Bank NY, GAF Corp, ASARCO Inc. *Mem:* Nat Acad Eng; Am Chem Soc; Sigma Xi. *Res:* Processes of iron ore beneficiation, reduction and steelmaking. *Mailing Add:* Dunwoody Village-Ch 125 3500 Westchester Pike Newtown Square PA 19073-4168

**TURNER, HUGH MICHAEL,** AQUATIC INVERTEBRATE ZOOLOGY. *Current Pos:* PROF ZOOL, PARASITOL HISTOL, DEPT BIOL & ENVIRON SCI, MCNEESE STATE UNIV, 77- *Personal Data:* b Marianna, Fla, Sept 20, 42; m 72, Patricia A Miller. *Educ:* Ga Southern Univ, BS, 65, MS, 72; La State Univ, PhD(zool), 77. *Concurrent Pos:* Jack V Doland Endowed prof zool, 92. *Mem:* Am Soc Parasitologists; Sigma Xi; Am Micros Soc; Soc Study Evol. *Res:* Host-parasite interactions including histopathology and immunity in the hosts of cestodes and digenetic trematodes; ecology, systematics and life histories of digenetic trematode parasites; use of animal parasites as indicators of water quality in both freshwater and marine habitats. *Mailing Add:* Dept Biol & Environ Soc McNeese State Univ Lake Charles LA 70609

**TURNER, J HOWARD,** human genetics; deceased, see previous edition for last biography

**TURNER, JACK ALLEN,** ECOLOGY. *Current Pos:* from asst prof to assoc prof biol, 74-84, PROF, UNIV SC, SPARTANBURG, 84- *Personal Data:* b Milner, Colo, Feb 2, 42; m 66; c 2. *Educ:* Colo State Univ, BS, 68; SDak State Univ, MS, 71; Univ Okla, PhD(ecol), 74. *Prof Exp:* Asst bact, SDak State Univ, 69-72. *Mem:* Am Soc Microbiol; Ecol Soc Am; Sigma Xi. *Res:* The antimicrobial activity of various types of textile finishes. *Mailing Add:* Dept Biol Univ SC 800 Univ Way Spartanburg SC 29303

**TURNER, JAMES A,** ORGANIC CHEMISTRY, PESTICIDE CHEMISTRY. *Current Pos:* Sr res chemist energy res, Hydrocarbons & Energy Lab, 76-78, SR RES CHEMIST AGR CHEM SYNTHESIS, AGR PROD RES, DOW CHEM CO, 78- *Personal Data:* b Anna, Ill, Jan 9, 48. *Educ:* Murray State Univ, BS, 71; Fla State Univ, PhD(org chem), 76. *Mem:* Am Chem Soc. *Res:* Synthesis of new agricultural chemicals. *Mailing Add:* Dowelanco PO Box 68955 Indianapolis IN 46268-1053

**TURNER, JAMES DAVID,** NUCLEAR PHYSICS. *Current Pos:* asst prof, 79-84, ASSOC PROF PHYSICS, FURMAN UNIV, 84- *Personal Data:* b Bristol, Va, Aug 23, 52. *Educ:* Wake Forest Univ, BS(physics) & BA(phil), 73; Duke Univ, PhD(physics), 78. *Prof Exp:* Asst prof physics, Eastern Ky Univ, 78-79. *Mem:* Am Phys Soc. *Res:* Studies of giant dipole resonances via polarized and unpolarized proton capture reactions. *Mailing Add:* Dept Physics Furman Univ 3300 Poinsett Hwy Greenville SC 29613

**TURNER, JAMES EDWARD,** RADIATION PHYSICS, HEALTH PHYSICS. *Current Pos:* PHYSICIST, OAK RIDGE NAT LAB, 62-, CORP FEL, 88-; ADJ PROF, UNIV TENN, 81- *Personal Data:* b Norfolk, Va, Feb 12, 30; m 55, Renate Gerike; c Thomas, Susan & William. *Educ:* Emory Univ, BA, 51; Harvard Univ, MS, 53; Vanderbilt Univ, PhD(physics), 56. *Honors & Awards:* Distinguished Sci Achievement Award, Health Physics Soc, 92. *Prof Exp:* Instr physics, Yale Univ, 56-58; physicist, US Atomic Energy Comn, 58-62. *Concurrent Pos:* Mem, Nat Coun Radiation Protection & Measurements, 77-83; ed, Health Physics, 74-79; assoc ed, Radiation Res, 80-83; mem bd dirs, Health Physics Soc, 80-83. *Mem:* Fel Health Physics Soc; fel Am Phys Soc; fel AAAS; Radiation Res Soc; Am Acad Health Physics (pres, 93). *Res:* Interaction of radiation with matter; early physical & chemical events; atomic & molecular interactions; interaction of metal ions with nucleic acids & proteins; chemical dosimetry. *Mailing Add:* Oak Ridge Nat Lab Bldg 4500-S MS-6123 PO Box 2008 Oak Ridge TN 37831-6123. *E-Mail:* turnerje@drnl.gov

**TURNER, JAMES ELDRIDGE,** NEUROBIOLOGY, ELECTRON MICROSCOPY. *Current Pos:* from asst prof to assoc prof, 74-83, PROF ANAT, BOWMAN GRAY SCH MED, 83-; VIS DISTINGUISHED PROF BIOL, VA MIL INST, 90- *Personal Data:* b Richmond, Va, Oct 1, 42; m 67; c 3. *Educ:* Va Mil Inst, BA, 65; Univ Richmond, MS, 67; Univ Tenn, PhD(zool), 70. *Honors & Awards:* Victory in Sight Award, Retinitis Pigmentosa Int, 88. *Prof Exp:* Teaching asst zool, Univ Tenn, 67-69; NIH res trainee neurobiol & electron micros, Dept Anat, Sch Med, Case Western Reserve Univ, 71, res fel, 72-74; asst prof biol, Va Mil Inst, 71-72. *Concurrent Pos:* Vis prof, Dept Neurochem, Max Planck Inst, Munich, WGermany, 80-81; Basil Oconnor Starter res fel, March Dimes, 75-78; Res Career Develop award, NIH, 78-83; assoc vis res opthal, Int Cong Eye Res. *Mem:* AAAS; Soc Neurosci; Am Soc Zool; Am Asn Anatomists; Sigma Xi. *Res:* Nerve injury, repair and regeneration; neurotrophic phenomenia; neuronal transplantation. *Mailing Add:* Dept Anat Bowman Gray Sch Med 300 S Hawthorne Winston-Salem NC 27157-0002

**TURNER, JAMES HENRY,** PARASITOLOGY. *Current Pos:* RETIRED. *Personal Data:* b Stuart, Va, June 13, 22. *Educ:* Univ Md, BS, 47, MS, 52, PhD(zool), 57. *Honors & Awards:* Ransom Mem Award, 60. *Prof Exp:* Entomologist, Div Insects, Dept Zool, US Nat Mus, 48; from jr parasitologist to sr res parasitologist, Animal Dis Parasite Res Div, Agr Res Serv, USDA, 48-62; prin res parasitologist, Beltsville Parasitol Lab & McMaster Health Lab, Commonwealth Sci & Indust Res Orgn, Australia, 62-64; health scientist adminstr, Immunobiol Study Sect, Div Res Grants, NIH, 64-80. *Concurrent Pos:* Tutorial lectr, Univ Md, 58-61; Fulbright res fel, Australia, 62-63. *Mem:* Am Soc Parasitol; Am Soc Trop Med & Hyg; Transplantation Soc; Am Phys Soc. *Res:* Pathogenesis and immunological aspects of parasitic infections. *Mailing Add:* 4927 Falcon Blvd Port St John FL 32927-3030

**TURNER, JAMES HOWARD,** ANALYTICAL CHEMISTRY. *Current Pos:* RETIRED. *Personal Data:* b Colorado Springs, Colo, July 18, 12. *Educ:* Colo Col, AB, 33; Univ Iowa, MS, 36. *Prof Exp:* Asst chem, Colo Col, 31-33 & Calif Inst Technol, 33-34; anal chemist, SW Shattuck Chem Corp, Colo, 41-44; asst chem, Univ Iowa, 45; chemist, Colo Fuel & Iron Corp, 47-48; res chemist, Holly Sugar Corp, 48-54; anal chemist, Holloman Air Force Base, NMex, 55-59 & US Bur Mines, 59-61; anal chemist, US Geol Surv, 61-78. *Mem:* Emer mem Am Chem Soc; assoc Cooper Ornith Soc; Am Ornith Union. *Res:* Spectrophotometric methods of analysis; sugar analysis; sugar beet by-products; rarer metal analysis; infrared analysis. *Mailing Add:* 807 N Wahsatch Ave Colorado Springs CO 80903

**TURNER, JAMES MARSHALL,** PLASMA PHYSICS. *Current Pos:* mem staff, 77-88, DIR WEAPONS PROG SAFETY, US DEPT ENERGY, 88- *Personal Data:* b Washington, DC, Aug 20, 44; m 67, 81; c 5. *Educ:* Johns Hopkins Univ, BA, 66; Mass Inst Technol, PhD(physics), 71. *Prof Exp:* Lectr physics, Lesley Col, 70-71; res staff mem, Mass Inst Technol, 66-71; asst prof, Southern Univ, 71-73; assoc prof physics, Morehouse Col, 73-77. *Mem:* Am Phys Soc; Am Geophys Union; Sigma Xi. *Res:* Instabilities in weakly ionized plasmas; MHD structures and plasma properties in the solar wind; structure of hemoglobin S. *Mailing Add:* 13845 Turnmore Rd Silver Spring MD 20906

**TURNER, JAMES N,** THREE DIMENSIONAL & QUANTITATIVE MICROSCOPY, BIOMEDICAL IMAGING & MICROSCOPY. *Current Pos:* RES SCIENTIST & PROF, WADSWORTH CTR, NY STATE DEPT HEALTH, 72-, DIR, 3-D LIGHT MICROS, 88- *Personal Data:* b Binghamton, NY, July 1944. *Educ:* State Univ NY, Buffalo, BS, 68, PhD(biophysics), 73. *Honors & Awards:* Diamond Cover Merit Award, Nat Soc Histotechnol, 90. *Prof Exp:* Postdoctoral fel, Electron Optics Lab, Roswell Park Mem Inst, 73-74, res scientist, 74-75; physicist & electron microscopist, Isaac Gordon Ctr Digestive Dis, Dept Path, Genessee Hosp, Rochester, NY, 75-77. *Concurrent Pos:* Res assoc, Dept Radiation & Biophysics, Unvi Rochester, NY, 76-77; prof, Sch Pub Health, State Univ NY, Albany, 85-; dir micros, NIH Biol Micros & Image Reconstruction Resources, 89-96; Nat Resources ed, Electron Micros Soc Am, 90-92, sci ed, 92-95; prof biomed eng, Rensselaer Polytech Inst, 91- *Mem:* Micros Soc Am; Electron Micros Soc Am; AAAS; NY Acad Sci; Int Soc Anal Cytol; Sigma Xi; Soc Neurosci. *Res:* Application of three-dimensional microscopic imaging; image analysis to problems in the biomedical sciences; clinical diagnosis; three-dimensional imaging of the central nervous system; development of neuroprosthetic devices for the central nervous system. *Mailing Add:* Wadsworth Ctr Box 509 Empire State Plaza Albany NY 12201-0509

**TURNER, JAN ROSS,** MICROBIOLOGY. *Current Pos:* RETIRED. *Personal Data:* b Okla, Sept 25, 37; m 62; c 2. *Educ:* Ore State Univ, BS, 61, MS, 63, PhD(microbial physiol), 65. *Prof Exp:* Res asst microbial physiol, Ore State Univ, 61-65; AEC fel microbiol, Biol Div, Pac Northwest Labs, Battelle Mem Inst, 65-67, sr res scientist, 67-73; microbiologist, Lilly Res Labs, 73-96. *Mem:* AAAS; Am Chem Soc; Am Soc Microbiol; Sigma Xi. *Res:* Microbial physiology; sterol biosynthesis; biochemical genetics; aromatic amino acid metabolism; medical mycology; clinical microbiology; antibiotic mechanisms; antibiotic biosynthesis. *Mailing Add:* 651 Ash Dr Carmel IN 46032

**TURNER, JANICE BUTLER,** MOLECULAR SPECTROSCOPY. *Current Pos:* From instr to assoc prof, 59-77, PROF CHEM, AUGUSTA COL, 77-, CHMN, 76- *Personal Data:* b Lincolnton, Ga, Dec 1, 36; m 58; c 1. *Educ:* Ga State Col for Women, AB, 58; Emory Univ, MS, 59; Univ SC, PhD(chem), 70. *Mem:* Sigma Xi; Coblentz Soc; Am Chem Soc. *Res:* Preparation and structure determination of organogermanes-microwave studies. *Mailing Add:* 3931 Belair Rd Augusta GA 30909-9685

**TURNER, JEFFERSON TAYLOR,** MARINE PLANKTON ECOLOGY, SCANNING ELECTRON MICROSCOPY. *Current Pos:* PROF BIOL, UNIV MASS, DARTMOUTH, 79- *Personal Data:* b Greensboro, NC, Apr 10, 47; m 71, Lynn Cormier; c Bethany L & Ashley J. *Educ:* Guilford Col, BS, 69; Univ S Fla, MA, 72; Tex A&M Univ, PhD(oceanog), 77. *Prof Exp:* Assoc res scientist, NY Ocean Sci Lab, 78-79. *Concurrent Pos:* Fishery biologist, Nat Marine Fisheries Serv, 81-84; sabbatical, Boston Univ, 89; consult, Battelle Ocean Scis, 92- *Mem:* Am Soc Limnol & Oceanog; Oceanog Soc; Soc Syst Biol. *Res:* Distributions, dynamics and trophic interactions of marine phytoplankton, zooplankton, ichthyoplankton and microbiol plankton. *Mailing Add:* Dept Biol Univ Mass Dartmouth 285 Old Westport Rd North Dartmouth MA 02747-2387. *Fax:* 508-999-8901

**TURNER, JOHN CHARLES,** statistics, for more information see previous edition

**TURNER, JOHN DEAN,** MEDICINE. *Current Pos:* MEM STAFF, COTTON, INC, NC. *Personal Data:* b Pasadena, Calif, Oct 2, 30. *Educ:* Univ Calif, Berkeley, BA, 52; McGill Univ, MD, CM, 56. *Prof Exp:* Intern med, Mass Gen Hosp, 56-57, asst resident, 57-58; attend physician, Nat Heart Inst, 61-65; asst prof med, Baylor Col Med, 65-71; assoc prof med, Sch Med, Univ Calif, San Diego, 71- *Concurrent Pos:* Paul Dudley White fel cardiol, Mass Gen Hosp, 59-60, teaching fels, 59-61; res fel med, Peter Bent Brigham Hosp, Harvard Univ, 58-59; staff assoc, President's Comn Heart Dis, Cancer & Stroke, 64; fel coun epidemiol, Am Heart Asn, 65-; mem staff, Vet Admin Hosp, La Jolla, 77- *Mem:* Am Heart Asn; fel Am Col Physicians; Am Oil Chem Soc; Am Pub Health Asn. *Res:* Cardiovascular hemodynamics and epidemiology; angiocardiography in the diagnosis of valvular and congenital heart disease; external scintillation counting in detection of intracardiac shunts; lipid composition in human erythrocytes and plasma; lipid and lipoprotein metabolism in human plasma. *Mailing Add:* 209 Westborne St La Jolla CA 92037-5344

**TURNER, JOHN E,** PHYSICS. *Current Pos:* MEM TECH STAFF, HEWLETT PACKARD LABS, 84- *Personal Data:* b June 29, 54. *Educ:* Univ Ill, Champaign-Urbana, BS, 76; Univ Calif, San Diego, MS, 77, PhD(physics), 82. *Prof Exp:* Res asst, Univ Calif, San Diego, 77-82; vis researcher, Lawrence Berkeley Labs, Univ Calif, Berkeley, 82-84. *Concurrent Pos:* Teaching asst physics, Univ Calif, San Diego, 77-78; phys sci instr, Univ, 78-80. *Mem:* Am Phys Soc; Am Vacuum Soc; Mat Res Soc. *Mailing Add:* Hewlett Packard Labs 3500 Deer Creek Rd 26L Palo Alto CA 94304

**TURNER, JOHN FREELAND,** ECOLOGY. *Current Pos:* PRES, CONSERV FUND, 93-; SR CONSULT, SCH ENVIRON & NAT RESOURCES, UNIV WYO, 93- *Personal Data:* b Jackson, Wyo, Mar 3, 42; m 69, Mary Kay Brady; c John F, Kathy M & Mark F. *Educ:* Univ Notre Dame, BS, 64; Univ Mich, MS, 68. *Honors & Awards:* Nat Conserv Achievement Award, Nat Wildlife Fedn, 84; Stewardship Award, Audobon Soc, 92; Nat Wetland Achievement Award, Duck Unlimited, 93; Nat Conserv Leadership Award, Chevron/Times-Mirror, 95. *Prof Exp:* Mem, House Reps, Wyo, 70-74; state sen, 74-89, Wyo, pres, 87-89; dir, Fish & Wildlife Serv, US Dept Interior, 89-93. *Concurrent Pos:* Nat Wetland Forum, 83 & 87; Chmn, Legis Mineral Bus & Econ Develop Comt, Teton County, Wyo, 87-89; adv, Hancock Timber Resource Group, 93-; bd dir, Land Trust Alliance, 94-; head, US Deleg Convention Int Trade Endangered Species. *Mailing Add:* Conservation Fund 1800 N Kent St Suite 1120 Arlington VA 22209-2109

**TURNER, JOHN K,** animal physiology; deceased, see previous edition for last biography

**TURNER, JOHN LINDSEY,** ENGINEERING MECHANICS. *Current Pos:* ENGR, BRIDGESTONE/FIRESTONE INC, 82- *Personal Data:* b Birmingham, Ala, Sept 9, 49; m 70; c 2. *Educ:* Auburn Univ, BSME, 71, MS, 72; Univ Ill, PhD(mech), 75. *Prof Exp:* Res scientist, Firestone Res Labs, 75-77; asst prof mech eng, Auburn Univ, 77-81, assoc prof agr eng, 81-82. *Mem:* Soc Exp Stress Analysis; Am Soc Agr Eng; Sigma Xi. *Res:* Experimental and numerical methods of stress analysis and structural mechanics; combined applications of experimental and computer based techniques for improved methods of analysis and design. *Mailing Add:* Bridgestone/Firestone Inc 1200 Firestone Pkwy Akron OH 44317

**TURNER, JOHN T,** RECEPTOR PHARMACOLOGY, RECEPTOR MOLECULAR BIOLOGY. *Current Pos:* Res assoc, pharmacol, Univ Mo, 81-84, instr, 84-85, asst prof, 85-92, ASSOC PROF PHARMACOL, UNIV MO, COLUMBIA, 92- *Personal Data:* b St Joseph, Mo, Nov 9, 45; m 77, Melinda K Elmore; c Denise & Andrew. *Educ:* Mo Western State Col, BA, 77; Univ Mo, PhD(biol sci), 81. *Concurrent Pos:* Prin invest res, Am Heart Asn, 82-84, NIH, 92- *Mem:* Am Soc Pharmmacol & Exp Therapeaut; Soc Neurosci; Am Peptide Soc; Sigma Xi; Int Asn Dent Res; Am Asn Dent Res. *Res:* Neurotransmitter receptors involved in the regulation of epithelial cell function, with emphasis on the receptors for peptides and nucleotides; author of 26 publications. *Mailing Add:* M517 HSC Univ Mo Columbia MO 65212-0001. *Fax:* 573-884-4558; *E-Mail:* pharmjt@mizzou1.missouri.edu

**TURNER, JOHN W, JR,** WILDLIFE CONTRACEPTION, PSYCHOPHYSIOLOGY. *Current Pos:* asst prof endocrinol & reproduction, 72-77, assoc prof physiol, 78-93, PROF PHYSIOL, MED COL OHIO, 93- *Personal Data:* div; c Melissa F & Delaney B. *Educ:* Franklin & Marshall Col, BA, 66; Cornell Univ, PhD(endocrinol), 70. *Prof Exp:* Fel neuroendocrinol, Univ Calif, Los Angeles, Sch Med & Brain Res Inst, 71. *Concurrent Pos:* Prin invest res, NIH, 75-84, Bur Land Mgt, Dept Interior, 92-; from adj asst prof to adj prof, Univ Toledo, 75-; co-prin investr, Dept Interior, Bur Land Mgt, 79-83; vis assoc prof, Univ Calif, Los Angeles Brain Res Inst, 83; mgt planning comt, Inyo Nat Forest, USDA, 87- *Res:* Development of a contraceptive vaccine with multi-year effectiveness when delivered remotely to free-roaming wildlife; psychophysiology of stress and the relaxation response associated with reduction of sensory stimulation in humans. *Mailing Add:* Dept Physiol Med Col Ohio PO Box 10008 Toledo OH 43699-0008

**TURNER, JONATHAN SHIELDS,** COMPUTER SCIENCE, ELECTRICAL ENGINEERING. *Current Pos:* from asst prof to assoc prof, 83-90, PROF COMPUT SCI, WASHINGTON UNIV, 90-, CHMN DEPT, 92-, HENRY EDWIN SEVER PROF ENG, 94- *Personal Data:* b Boston, Mass, Nov 13, 53; m, Helen Gaddy; c Gregory. *Educ:* Washington Univ, BSEE & BS(comput sci), 77; Northwestern Univ, MS, 79, PhD(comput sci), 82. *Honors & Awards:* Koji Kobayashi Comput & Commun Award, Inst Elec & Electronics Engrs, 94. *Prof Exp:* Mem tech staff, Bell Labs, 77-83. *Concurrent Pos:* Adv, NSF, 90- *Mem:* Fel Inst Elec & Electronics Engrs; Asn Comput Mach; Soc Indust & Appl Math. *Res:* Contributed numerous articles to professional journals; patentee in field. *Mailing Add:* Dept Comput Sci Washington Univ 1 Brookings Dr CB 1045 St Louis MO 63130

**TURNER, JUDITH ANN,** clinical psychology, chronic pain, for more information see previous edition

**TURNER, KENNETH CLYDE,** RADIO ASTRONOMY, RADIO INTERFEROMETRY. *Current Pos:* EXTERNAL RESOURCES COORDR, RES DEVELOP CTR, UNIV PR, MAYAGUEZ, 93- *Personal Data:* b Mt Vernon, Wash, Apr 6, 34; m 55, 95, Maureen J Wagley; c Catherine Elizabeth, Samuel Pereu, & Anne Marie. *Educ:* Portland Univ, BS, 57; Princeton Univ, PhD(physics), 62. *Prof Exp:* Instr physics, Princeton Univ, 62; Carnegie fel, 62-64; res staff assoc, Dept Terrestrial, Carnegie Inst Wash, 64-66, res staff mem, 66-78; sr res assoc, Nat Astron & Ionosphere Ctr, Arecibo, PR, 78-87, pres innovative systs, 86-93; prog dir extragalactic astron & cosmology, NSF, Washington, DC, 89-92. *Concurrent Pos:* Dir, Arg Inst Radio Astron, 70-73; vis prof, Nat Univ La Plata, 72-73; vis prof physics & comput sci, Inter Am Univ, San German, PR, 87-89. *Mem:* Am Astron Soc; Int Union Radio Sci; Int Astron Union. *Res:* Radio instrumentation; hydrogen line and galactic continuum radio astronomy; observational cosmology; experimental foundations of relativity; astrophysical jets. *Mailing Add:* External Resources Off Univ PR Mayaguez PR 00681-5000. *Fax:* 787-831-7944; *E-Mail:* ken@ore.upr.clu.edu

**TURNER, LEAF,** THEORETICAL PHYSICS. *Current Pos:* TECH STAFF MEM, LOS ALAMOS NAT LAB, UNIV CALIF, 74- *Personal Data:* b Brooklyn, NY, Mar 23, 43; m 66, Ruby A Sherman; c Alyssa W, Lara D, Ari M & Rima J. *Educ:* Cornell Univ, AB, 63; Univ Wis-Madison, MS, 64, PhD(theoret physics), 69. *Prof Exp:* Weizmann Inst Sci fel, Rehovot, Israel, 69; fel physics, Univ Toronto, 69-71; asst scientist, Space Sci & Eng Ctr, Univ Wis-Madison, 71-72, proj assoc, dept physics, 72-74. *Concurrent Pos:* Instr physics, Scarborough Col, Univ Toronto, 70-71; NSF fel, Inst Theoret Physics, Brandeis Univ, 70; vis prof, Dept Physics, Univ Wis-Madison, 84; coach, US Int Physics Olympiad Team, 97- *Mem:* Am Phys Soc; Sigma Xi. *Res:* Current algebra; phenomenological lagrangians; meson-baryon interactions; quantum field theory; symmetries in high energy physics; high energy phenomenology; scattering theory; plasma kinetic theory; magnetohydrodynamics; optics; plasma astrophysics; nonneutral plasma physics; fluid turbulence. *Mailing Add:* Los Alamos Nat Lab PO Box 1663 Mail Stop 216 T-3 Los Alamos NM 87545. *Fax:* 505-665-5926; *E-Mail:* tleaf@lanl.gov

**TURNER, LINCOLN HULLEY,** MATHEMATICS. *Current Pos:* RETIRED. *Personal Data:* b Chicago, Ill, June 30, 28. *Educ:* Univ Chicago, MS, 48; Purdue Univ, PhD(math), 57. *Prof Exp:* Mathematician, Space Tech Labs, Inc, 58-60; prof math, Univ Minn, 60-63; prof math, Univ Tenn, Knoxville, 63-78. *Mem:* Am Math Soc; Math Asn Am; Soc Indust & Appl Math. *Res:* Real variables; calculus of variations; applied mathematics. *Mailing Add:* 5709 Lyons View Pike No 2308 Knoxville TN 37919-6444

**TURNER, MALCOLM ELIJAH,** MATHEMATICAL BIOLOGY, STATISTICS. *Current Pos:* prof biostatist & biomath & assoc prof physiol & biophys, 70, prof biomath, 72-82, chmn dept, 75-82, PROF BIOSTATIST & BIOMATH, UNIV ALA, BIRMINGHAM, 82- *Personal Data:* b Atlanta, Ga, May 27, 29; m 48, 68, Rachel P Farmer; c Malcolm E IV, Allison A, Clay S, Margaret J, Aleta v, Leila S, Alexis S & Walter M. *Educ:* Duke Univ, BA, 52; NC State Univ, MES, 55, PhD(statist), 59. *Honors & Awards:* Smith Kline & French lectr, Med Ctr, Univ Kans, 65. *Prof Exp:* Asst biostatist, Univ NC, 53-54; sr res assoc biomet, Med Sch, Univ Cincinnati, 55, asst prof, 56-58; assoc prof & Williams res fel, Va Commonwealth Univ, 58-63, chmn div biomet, Dept Biophys & Biomet, 59-63; prof statist & biomet & chmn dept, Emory Univ, 63-69, prof math, 66-69. *Concurrent Pos:* Asst statistician, NC State Univ, 57-58; managing ed, Biometrics, 62-69; vis prof & chmn, Dept Biomet, Med Ctr, Univ Kans, 68-69; consult, Southern Res Inst, 74 - *Mem:* Fel AAAS; Soc Indust & Appl Math; hon fel Am Statist Asn; Biomet Soc; Sigma Xi. *Res:* Application of mathematics and statistics to biological research. *Mailing Add:* 1734 Tecumseh Trail Pelham AL 35124-1012

**TURNER, MANSON DON,** PHYSIOLOGY. *Current Pos:* assoc prof surg & physiol, 65-69, ASSOC PROF PHYSIOL & BIOPHYS & RES PROF SURG, SCH MED, UNIV MISS, 69- *Personal Data:* b Pleasanton, Tex, Nov 15, 28; m 53; c 3. *Educ:* Baylor Univ, BS, 50, MS, 51; Univ Tenn, PhD(physiol), 55. *Prof Exp:* Lab instr, Baylor Univ, 50-51; res asst, Univ Tenn, 51-54, instr clin physiol, 54-55; res asst prof surg, Sch Med, Univ Miss, 55-57, asst prof biochem, 58-61, assoc prof res surg & asst prof physiol & biophys, 61-65; supvry res physiologist, US Air Force Sch Aerospace Med, 65. *Concurrent Pos:* Attend in physiol, Vet Admin Hosp, Jackson, 58-; consult, Oak Ridge Inst Nuclear Studies, 62-65. *Mem:* Transplantation Soc; Cryobiol Soc; Am Heart Asn; Am Physiol Soc. *Res:* Organ preservation; cardiovascular physiology. *Mailing Add:* 5847 Pear Orchard Rd Jackson MS 39211

**TURNER, MATTHEW X,** cytology, immunology, for more information see previous edition

**TURNER, MICHAEL STANLEY,** COSMOLOGY, PARTICLE PHYSICS & COSMOLOGY. *Current Pos:* from asst prof to assoc prof astron & astrophys, 80-85, dept head, 89-93, PROF PHYSICS, ASTRON & ASTROPHYS, UNIV CHICAGO, 85-; SCIENTIST, FERMI NAT ACCELERATOR LAB, 83- *Personal Data:* b Los Angeles, Calif, July 29, 49; m 88, Barbara L Ahlberg; c Rachel & Joseph. *Educ:* Calif Inst Technol, BS, 71; Stanford Univ, MS, 73, PhD(physics), 78. *Honors & Awards:* Quantrell Prize, 83; Helen B Warner Prize, 84; Gravity Res Found First Prize, 91; Halley Lectr, 94; Julius Edgar Lilienfeld Prize, Am Phys Soc, 97. *Prof Exp:* Instr physics, Stanford Univ, 78; Enrico Fermi fel, Enrico Fermi Inst, 78-80. *Concurrent Pos:* Vis physicist, Inst Theoret Physics, Univ Calif, Santa Barbara, 81-82; Sloan fel, 83-88; pres, Aspen Ctr Physics, 89-93. *Mem:* Nat Acad Sci; fel Am Phys Soc; Am Astron Soc; Int Astron Union; fel Am Acad Arts & Sci; Sigma Xi. *Res:* Cosmology; study of earliest history of the universe; interplay of cosmology and particle physics. *Mailing Add:* Astron & Astrophys Ctr Univ Chicago 5640 S Ellis Ave Chicago IL 60637-1433. *Fax:* 773-702-8212; *E-Mail:* mturner@oddjob.uchicago.edu

**TURNER, MONTE EARL,** GENETIC OF HYPERTENSION. *Current Pos:* From asst prof to assoc prof, 82-92, PROF GENETICS, UNIV AKRON, 92- *Personal Data:* m 76, Melinda Baker; c Stephanie, Darbie, Whitney & Derrick. *Educ:* Brigham Young Univ, BS, 73, MS, 77; Univ Ga, PhD(genetics), 82. *Mem:* Fel Am Heart Asn. *Res:* Focus on genetics of hypertension using animal models of hypertension; analysis of mammalian Y chromosomes. *Mailing Add:* Dept Biol Univ Akron Akron OH 44325-3908. *Fax:* 330-972-8445; *E-Mail:* meturner@uakron.edu

**TURNER, MORTIMER DARLING,** ECONOMIC GEOLOGY, ENGINEERING GEOLOGY. *Current Pos:* lectr geol, 85-94, EMER RES ASSOC, INST ARCTIC & ALPINE RES, UNIV COLO. *Personal Data:* b Greeley, Colo, Oct 24, 20; m 45, 65, Joanna Church; c Satia, Ylla, Robert & Christopher. *Educ:* Univ Calif, Berkeley, BS, 43, MS, 54; Univ Kans, PhD, 72. *Prof Exp:* Mech & elec engr, Aberdeen Proving Grounds, US Dept Army, 46; asst geol sci, Univ Calif, Berkeley, 48; from jr mining geologist to asst mining geologist, Calif State Div Mines, 48-54; state geologist, Econ Develop Admin, PR, 54-58; phys sci administr & asst to dir, Antarctic Res Prog, NSF, 59-61; res assoc geol, Univ Kans, 62-65; prog dir, Antarctic Earth Sci, Off Antarctic Progs, NSF, 65-70, prog mgr, Polar Earth Sci, Div Polar Progs, 70-85; assoc prof lectr geol, George Washington Univ, 72-85. *Concurrent Pos:* Consult, 55-59; mem, Orgn Comt, 1st Conf Clays & Clay Technol, 52 & Caribbean Geol Conf, 59; mem, US Planning Comt, 2nd Int Conf Permafrost, Nat Acad Sci; mem, 19th, 20th (vpres), 21st, 22nd, 24th (US Govt deleg) and 25th Int Geol Congs; adj prof quaternary studies, Ctr Study Early Man, Inst Quaternary Studies, Univ Maine, Orono, 85-; chair, Sci Res Coun, Ctr Study First Americans, Ore State Univ; res assoc, Inst Arctic & Alpine Res. *Mem:* Geol Soc Am; Am Geog Soc; Antarctican Soc; Geol Asn PR; Am Polar Soc; Am Quaternary Asn. *Res:* Tectonics, economic geology and engineering geology of California, Puerto Rico, Caribbean area and Antarctica; geology of early man in North America and China; engineering geology of coastal zones. *Mailing Add:* Instaar Campus Box 450 Univ Colo Boulder CO 80309-0450. *Fax:* 303-492-6388; *E-Mail:* turnerm@colorodo.edu

**TURNER, NOEL HINTON,** PHYSICAL CHEMISTRY. *Current Pos:* RES CHEMIST, US NAVAL RES LAB, 68- *Personal Data:* b Redlands, Calif, Dec 24, 40; m 66; c 2. *Educ:* Univ Calif, Berkeley, BS, 62; Univ Rochester, PhD(phys chem), 68. *Mem:* AAAS; Am Chem Soc; Sigma Xi; Am Vacuum Soc. *Res:* Surface chemistry; analytical chemistry; electron spectroscopy for chemical analysis and auger electron spectroscopy; gas-solid and gas-liquid adsorption. *Mailing Add:* Naval Code 6170 Washington DC 20375-0001

**TURNER, R JAMES,** MEMBRANE TRANSPORT, MEMBRANE BIOLOGY. *Current Pos:* SECT CHIEF, EXOCRINE PHYSIOL, NIH, 85- *Personal Data:* b Chatham, Ont, Aug 26, 45. *Educ:* Univ Toronto, PhD(theoret physics), 71. *Prof Exp:* Vis assoc epithelial physiol, NIH, 79-83; assoc prof med, Univ Toronto, 83-85. *Mem:* Am Physiol Soc; Am Soc Nephrology; Biophys Soc. *Res:* Study of characteristics and regulation of transport related and intercellular events associated with fluid secretion in exocrine glands, especially salivary glands. *Mailing Add:* NIDR NIH Bldg 10 Rm 1A- 06 Bethesda MD 20892-0001. *Fax:* 301-402-1228

**TURNER, RALPH WALDO,** PHYSICAL CHEMISTRY, MATHEMATICS. *Current Pos:* prof sci educ, 67-68, prof chem & physics, 68-69, dir div basic studies, 69-77, PROF CHEM, FLA A&M UNIV, 69-, CHMN CHEM DEPT, 86- *Personal Data:* b Blakely, Ga, Nov 9, 38. *Educ:* J C Smith Univ, BS, 59; Univ Pittsburgh, PhD(phys chem), 65. *Prof Exp:* Res asst chem, Univ Pittsburgh, 60-64; res engr, Gen Tel & Electronics, 65-66, advan res engr, 66-67. *Concurrent Pos:* US Off Educ grant, Fla A&M Univ, 62-; dir 13 col prog, Fla A&M Univ, 68-69; consult, Inst Servs Educ, 68-72, Am Chem Soc, 80-; proposal reviewer, NIH & NSF, 87-; dir, Marc Prog, 86-, Fla Comprehensive State Ctr for Minorities, 89- *Mem:* AAAS; Am Chem Soc; Am Crystallog Asn; Sigma Xi. *Res:* Structure of metal ion aromatic complexes using x-ray crystallography; 113Cd NMR and structural studies of ceruloplasmin. *Mailing Add:* Dept Chem Fla A&M Univ Tallahassee FL 32307

**TURNER, RAYMOND MARRINER,** ECOLOGY. *Current Pos:* RETIRED. *Personal Data:* b Salt Lake City, Utah, Feb 25, 27; m 49; c 3. *Educ:* Univ Utah, BS, 48; State Col Wash, PhD(plant ecol), 54. *Prof Exp:* Instr range mgt, Univ Ariz, 54-56, asst prof, 56, instr bot, 56-57, asst prof, 57-62; res botanist, US Geol Surv, 62-92. *Concurrent Pos:* NSF res grant, 57-60. *Mem:* AAAS; Ecol Soc Am; Bot Soc Mex. *Res:* Ecology of arid and semi-arid regions. *Mailing Add:* 5132 E Ft Lowell Rd Tucson AZ 85712

**TURNER, REED JAMES,** ELECTRONIC MEASUREMENT, TRACTORS & TRACTION POWER SYSTEMS. *Current Pos:* PROJ ENGR, ALTA FARM MACH RES CTR, 88- *Personal Data:* b Ft Williams, Ont, Oct, 1948; US & Can citizen; m 73, Emma L Worthington; c Douglas J, Kristi A & Steven O. *Educ:* Brigham Young Univ, BSc & MEng, 74. *Honors & Awards:* Outstanding Eng Achievement Award, Am Soc Agr Engrs, 86; Glenn Downing Medal, Can Soc Agr Eng, 95. *Prof Exp:* Prod engr, John Deere Harvester Works, 74-83, engr advan res, 83-88. *Concurrent Pos:* Bd mem, Northern Tractor Resource Ctr, 90-; bd mem, NAm Farm & Environ Safety Ctr, 91-96, vchmn, 96-; mem, Can Expert Comt Mechanization, 95- *Mem:* Am Soc Agr Engrs; Can Soc Agr Eng; Sigma Xi. *Res:* Development and testing of agricultural machinery including tractors and traction and grain harvesting and grain cleaning; development of portable electronic measurement systems. *Mailing Add:* Box 180 Raymond AB T0K 2S0 Can. *Fax:* 403-328-5562

**TURNER, REX HOWELL,** CELLULOSE CHEMISTRY. *Current Pos:* sr res assoc, 74-87, MGR, TECH & PRODUCT DIV, INT PAPER CO, 87- *Personal Data:* b Birmingham, Ala, Aug 22, 41; m 60; c 2. *Educ:* Univ SAla, BS, 68; Univ Ga, PhD(chem), 73. *Prof Exp:* Res asst org chem, Univ Ga, 68-73; develop chemist, Millmaster Onyx Corp, 73-74. *Mem:* Am Chem Soc; Am Asn Textile Chemists & Colorists. *Res:* Isolation and enrichinhomogeneities; macrocyclic synthesis via thermochemical and photochemical decomposition of ketone peroxides; ozonolysis mechanism non-chlorine bleaching of wood pulp; acetylation of wood pulp. *Mailing Add:* 8885 Classic Dr Memphis TN 38125

**TURNER, ROBERT,** ELECTRICAL ENGINEERING. *Current Pos:* RETIRED. *Personal Data:* b Boston, Mass, Jan 23, 25; m 56; c 3. *Educ:* Mass Inst Technol, SB, 45; Harvard Univ, SM, 48. *Prof Exp:* Proj engr, Sperry Gyroscope Co, NY, 48-53; analyst, Opers Eval Group, Mass Inst Technol, Washington, DC, 53-55; sr engr, Johns Hopkins Univ, 55-80, prin staff engr, Appl Physics Lab, 80-89. *Mem:* Am Phys Soc. *Res:* Servomechanism design; systems analysis; plasma physics; gas lasers; light scattering. *Mailing Add:* 2639 N Lake Leelanau Dr Lake Leelanau MI 49653

**TURNER, ROBERT ALEXANDER,** RHEUMATOLOGY. *Current Pos:* DIR, ARTHRITIS CTR, HUMANA HOSP, 89- *Personal Data:* b Englewood, NJ, Oct 12, 37; m 60; c 3. *Educ:* Univ NC, BA, 59; Med Col Ala, Birmingham, MD, 66. *Prof Exp:* From asst prof to prof med, Bowman Gray Sch Med, Winston-Salem, NC, 71-89, chief, Rheumatology Sect, 79-89. *Concurrent Pos:* Clin prof med & rheum, Univ SFla. *Mem:* Fel Am Col Phys; Am Rheumatism Asn; Soc Exp Biol & Med. *Res:* Inflammatory components involved in pathogenesis of rheumatic diseases; evaluate newer agents for the treatment of these diseases as well as new lab and clinical methods for diagnosing specific entities; physical and occupational therapy and socio-economic factors affecting patients with rheumatic diseases. *Mailing Add:* Arthritis Ctr Gould Prof Bldg 201-203 2151 45th St West Palm Beach FL 33407-2026. *Fax:* 561-881-3088

**TURNER, ROBERT ATWOOD,** IMMUNOHISTOCHEMISTRY. *Current Pos:* RETIRED. *Educ:* Sam Houston Univ, MS, 52. *Prof Exp:* Dir, Electron Microscope Lab, Scott & White Hosp, Temple, 70- *Mem:* Microscope Soc Am. *Mailing Add:* 3914 Erie St Temple TX 76504

**TURNER, ROBERT DAVISON,** COMMAND & CONTROL SYSTEMS, SENSOR SYSTEMS. *Current Pos:* staff mem, Sci & Technol Div, 85-86, STAFF MEM, SYS EVAL DIV, INST DEFENSE ANALYSES, 86- *Personal Data:* b Goose Creek, Tex, Oct 16, 29; m 50, Nancy Reed; c Michael, Christie, Wendy & Elizabeth. *Educ:* St Lawrence Univ, SB, 49; Harvard Univ, AM, 51, PhD(appl math), 54. *Prof Exp:* Commun theory analyst & consult analysis & synthesis, Advan Electronics Ctr, Gen Elec Co, 54-63; staff mem, Inst Defense Analysis, 63-68, grp mem, 68-69, staff mem, Sci & Technol Div, 69-74; staff specialist, Net Tech Assessment, Off Dir Defense Res & Eng, Off Secy Defense, US Dept Defense, 74-77, spec asst tech plans & res, Off Asst Secy Defense, Commun, Command, Control & Intel, 77-81, dir strategic & theater nuclear forces command, control & commun, Off Secy Defense, 81-82, asst dep, Secy Defense, Syst Integration, 82-84. *Concurrent Pos:* Vis asst prof, Cornell Univ, 55; mem sci adv bd, USAF, 67-71, consult, 71-72; consult, Defense Sci Bd, Off Secy Defense, 71-78; mem, Naval Res Adv Comt, Lab Adv Bd Undersea Warfare, 71-74; mem, Chief Naval Opers Command Control Commun Adv Comt, 73-76; mem, Comt Counterforce Options Against Tactical Missile Systs, Comn on Eng & Tech Systs, Nat Res Coun, 92-93. *Res:* Synthesis and evaluation of communication networks and sensor information handling systems; analysis and planning of military command systems. *Mailing Add:* 109 Midtown Rd Gaithersburg MD 20878. *E-Mail:* rturner@ida.org

**TURNER, ROBERT E L,** MATHEMATICS. *Current Pos:* From asst prof to assoc prof, 63-71, PROF MATH, UNIV WIS-MADISON, 71- *Personal Data:* b Montclair, NJ, Nov 15, 36; m 60; c 3. *Educ:* Cornell Univ, BEngPhys, 59; NY Univ, PhD(math), 63. *Mem:* Am Math Soc. *Res:* Functional analysis; differential equations; hydrodynamics; neurophysiological modeling. *Mailing Add:* Dept Math Van Vleck Hall Univ Wis 480 Lincoln Dr Madison WI 53706-1388

**TURNER, ROBERT EUGENE,** WETLAND ECOLOGY, BIOLOGICAL OCEANOGRAPHY. *Current Pos:* Chair, Dept Marine Sci, 89-92, PROF, DEPT OCEANOG & COASTAL SCI, LA STATE UNIV, 83-, DIR, COASTAL ECOL INST, 96- *Personal Data:* b Niskayuna, NY, Apr 7, 45; m, Nancy N Rabalais; c Emily K H. *Educ:* Monmouth Col, Ill, BA, 67; Drake Univ, MS, 69; Univ Ga, PhD(zool), 74. *Concurrent Pos:* Chair, Intercol Wetland Working Group, 74-, Dept Marine Sci, La State Univ, 89-90, Dept Oceanog & Coastal Sci, 90-92; co-chair, Habitat Comt, Environ Protection Agency Gulf of Mex Prog, 90; panel mem, Marine Bd Comt, Nat Res Coun, 91-94; ed-in-chief, Wetlands Ecol & Mgt, 92-; managing ed, Am Geophys Union & Estuarine Coastal Sci, 93- *Mem:* AAAS; Soc Conserv Biol; Estuarine Res Soc; Am Geophys Union; Am Soc Limnol & Oceanog. *Res:* Wetland ecology and management, biological oceanography, ecosystem structure and function, natural resource science and management. *Mailing Add:* Dept Oceanog & Coastal Sci La State Univ Baton Rouge LA 70803. *Fax:* 504-388-6326

**TURNER, ROBERT HAROLD,** THERMAL SCIENCES & ENERGY CONSERVATION. *Current Pos:* assoc prof, 83-90, PROF THERMAL SCI, UNIV NEV, RENO, 90- *Personal Data:* b San Francisco, Calif, Sept 20, 41; m 69, Nancy Augdon; c Alexa G, Eric C & Tobias L. *Educ:* Univ Calif, Berkeley, BS, 64, MS, 65; Univ Calif, Los Angeles, PhD(heat transfer), 71. *Prof Exp:* Engr, Rohr Corp, 64, AiRes, 65-67; consult, Spectrolab Co, 67-71; head, Thermal Sect, Southern Res Inst, 71-72; engr & supvr, Nus Corp, 72-74 & Jet Propulsion Lab, 75-83. *Concurrent Pos:* Adj prof, Calif State Univ, 76-83; consult, 79- *Mem:* Am Soc Mech Engrs; Am Soc Heating Refrig & Air Conditioning Engrs; Sigma Xi. *Res:* Applied thermal sciences; ice formation conditions; mathematical modeling; solar energy; thermal systems; forensic engineering. *Mailing Add:* Dept Mech Eng Mail Stop 312 Univ Nev Reno NV 89557. *Fax:* 702-784-1701; *E-Mail:* turner@poginip.scs.edu

**TURNER, ROBERT JAMES,** organic chemistry, for more information see previous edition

**TURNER, ROBERT LAWRENCE,** ORGANIC POLYMER CHEMISTRY. *Current Pos:* res chemist, 72-74, staff chemist, 74-76, FROM RES SUPVR TO DIR, E I DU PONT DE NEMOURS & CO INC, 76- *Personal Data:* b Chicago, Ill, Nov 4, 45; m 66; c 2. *Educ:* Albion Col, BA, 67; Mich State Univ, PhD(org chem), 72. *Prof Exp:* Teaching asst org chem, Mich State Univ, 67-69, res asst, 71-72. *Res:* Development of new polymer-catalyst systems for use in low energy and nonpolluting protective organic coatings for industrial use. *Mailing Add:* DuPont Co 950 Stephenson Hwy Troy MI 48007-7013

**TURNER, ROBERT SPILMAN,** INTEGRATED ASSESSMENT, SCIENCE-POLICY INTERFACE. *Current Pos:* Wigner fel, Oak Ridge Nat Lab, 83-85, res assoc, 85-87, res staff mem, 87-90, biogeochem cycling group leader, Environ Sci Div, 90-95, SR RES STAFF MEM, OAK RIDGE NAT LAB, 96- *Personal Data:* m 82, Amy K Wolfe; c Julie & Mallory. *Educ:* Duke Univ, BS, 75; Univ Pa, MRP, 77, PhD(geol), 83. *Concurrent Pos:* Proj scientist, Distrib Active Archive Ctr, Oak Ridge Nat Lab, 92-96; dir, Nat Ctr Environ Decision-Making Res, 96- *Mem:* Am Geophys Union; Am Chem Soc; Ecol Soc Am; Soil Sci Soc Am. *Res:* Biogeochemical cycles and processes; air-plant-soil-rock-water-human interactions; regional analysis of ecosystem-landscape-human system characteristics and processes; science-policy interface and communications; integrated assessment. *Mailing Add:* Oak Ridge Nat Lab PO Box 2008 Oak Ridge TN 37831-6038

**TURNER, ROBERT STUART,** neuroanatomy; deceased, see previous edition for last biography

**TURNER, RUTH DIXON,** MALACOLOGY. *Current Pos:* res mollusks, Mus Comp Zool, 45-55, res assoc malacol & Agassiz fel oceanog & zool, 55-75, prof biol, 75-82, EMER PROF BIOL, HARVARD UNIV & CUR MALACOL, MUS COMP ZOOL, 82- *Personal Data:* b Melrose, Mass, Dec 7, 14. *Educ:* Bridgewater Teachers Col, BS, 36; Cornell Univ, MA, 43; Radcliffe Col, PhD, 54. *Hon Degrees:* DSC, New Eng Col, 79. *Prof Exp:* Teacher high sch, Vt, 36-37 & jr high sch, Mass, 37-40; asst ed, Boston Soc Natural Hist, 40-42, asst cur birds, 41-42; instr ornith, Vassar Col, 43-44; biologist, William F Clapp Labs, Mass, 44-45. *Concurrent Pos:* Res assoc, Inst Marine Biol, PR, 56-; consult, William F Clapp Labs, 57- *Mem:* AAAS; Soc Syst Zool; Am Malacol Union; Sigma Xi. *Res:* Marine boring and fouling mollusks; taxonomy and biology of mollusks, particularly Western Atlantic marine and North American freshwater. *Mailing Add:* 12 Saginaw Ave Cambridge MA 02140

**TURNER, S RICHARD,** SYNTHETIC POLYMER CHEMISTRY. *Current Pos:* res assoc, corp res, 82-93, SR RES ASSOC RES LABS, EASTMAN CHEM CO, 93- *Personal Data:* b Nashville, Tenn, Oct 17, 42; m 69, Pamela S Webb; c Lindsay & Lauren. *Educ:* Tenn Technol Univ, BS, 64, MS, 66; Univ Fla, PhD(org polymer chem), 71. *Prof Exp:* Fel polymer chem, Tech Univ, Darmstadt, WGer, 71-72; scientist, Webster Res, Xerox Corp, 72-79 & Corp Res, Exxon Corp, 80-82. *Concurrent Pos:* Vis adj prof polymer chem, Chem Dept, Univ Rochester, 82-; prog chmn, Div Polymer Mat, Am Chem Soc, 85-88, vchmn, 90, chmn elect, 91, chmn, 92, past-chair, 93. *Mem:* Am Chem Soc. *Res:* Synthetic polymer chemistry directed toward new polymer forming reactions; new routes to controlling polymer architecture; polyesters; ionomers and interacting polymers. *Mailing Add:* Eastman Chem Co PO Box 1972 Kingsport TN 37662

**TURNER, TERRY TOMO,** TESTIS FUNCTION & MALE INFERTILITY, EPIDIDYMAL FUNCTION. *Current Pos:* from asst prof to assoc prof, 76-91, PROF UROL, SCH MED, UNIV VA, 91- *Personal Data:* b Moultrie, Ga, 45; m 65, Susan Stegall; c Heather L & Patrick L. *Educ:* Univ Ga, BSA, 67, MS, 72, PhD(reprod biol), 74. *Prof Exp:* Rockefeller postdoctoral fel, Med Sch, Univ Tex, San Antonio, 75. *Concurrent Pos:* Prin investr NIH grants, 82- & Study Sect, 83 & 88; NSF reviewer, 96. *Mem:* Soc Study Reproduction; Am Soc Androl (pres, 97); Am Soc Cell Biol; Soc Basic Urol Res; NY Acad Sci; Am Fertil Soc. *Res:* Epithelial functions of the male reproductive tract, how those functions are regulated, how they are altered in pathophysiological conditions and the consequences of those functions on the development of fertile spermatozoa. *Mailing Add:* Dept Urol Sch Med Univ Va Box 422 Charlottesville VA 22908-0001. *E-Mail:* ttt@virginia.edu

**TURNER, THOMAS BOURNE,** MICROBIOLOGY, INTERNAL MEDICINE. *Current Pos:* lectr med & pub health admin, Sch Hyg & Pub Health, Johns Hopkins Univ, 36-39, prof microbiol, Sch Med, 39-57, dean, 57-68, EMER DEAN, SCH MED, JOHNS HOPKINS UNIV, 68- *Personal Data:* b Prince Frederick, Md, Jan 28, 02; wid; c Anna (Pope) & Pattie (Walker). *Educ:* St John's Col, Md, BS, 21; Univ Md, MD, 25. *Hon Degrees:* ScD, Univ Md, 66; LHD, Johns Hopkins Univ, 91. *Honors & Awards:* William F Snow Award, Am Soc Health Asn, 69. *Prof Exp:* Intern, Hosp Women Md, 25-26; resident, Mercy Hosp, 26-27; Loeb fel, Sch Med, Johns Hopkins Univ, 27-28, instr med, 28-31, assoc, 31-32; mem staff, Int Health Div, Rockefeller Found, 32-39, clin dir, Jamaica Yaws Comn, 32-34, labs, 34-36. *Concurrent Pos:* Consult, Surgeon Gen, US Army; vchmn comt virus & epidemiol, Nat Found, 49-67; coord, Regional Med Prog for Md, 67-68; physician, Out-Patient Dept, Johns Hopkins Hosp, 36-76; mem bd visitors, St John's Col, Md; pres, Alcoholic Beverage Med Res Found, 82-89; mem, Coun Health Res Facil, NIH. *Mem:* Emer mem Am Soc Clin Invest; emer mem Asn Am Physicians; Asn Am Med Cols (pres, 65-66); Am Med Soc Alcoholism; Am Epidemiol Soc; AMA; Am Venereal Dis Asn. *Res:* Spirochetal diseases; poliomyelitis; tetanus; internal medicine; author of numerous publications. *Mailing Add:* Johns Hopkins Univ Sch Med Suite 7100 1830 E Monument St Baltimore MD 21205

**TURNER, THOMAS JENKINS**, SOLID STATE PHYSICS. *Current Pos:* RETIRED. *Personal Data:* b Albany, Ga, Sept 11, 26; m 48; c 4. *Educ:* Univ NC, BS, 47; Clemson Col, MS, 49; Univ Va, PhD(physics), 51. *Prof Exp:* Instr physics, Clemson Col, 47-49; asst prof, Univ NH, 52; from asst prof to prof, Wake Forest Univ, 53-78, chmn dept, 56-74, vpres & dean, 78-81; provost, Stetson Univ, 81-82. *Mem:* Fel Am Phys Soc; Am Asn Physics Teachers. *Res:* Defects in crystalline materials; color centers; internal friction. *Mailing Add:* 101 Forest Ridge Dr Mars Hill NC 28754

**TURNER, WALTER W(EEKS)**, ELECTRICAL ENGINEERING. *Current Pos:* From instr to assoc prof, 47-65, PROF ELEC ENG, UNIV MAINE, ORONO, 65- *Personal Data:* b Augusta, Maine, Aug 3, 22; m 49; c 4. *Educ:* Mass Inst Technol, BS & MS, 47. *Mem:* Am Soc Eng Educ; sr mem Inst Elec & Electronics Engrs; Nat Soc Prof Engrs. *Res:* Instrumentation, communications and control. *Mailing Add:* College Ave Orono ME 04473

**TURNER, WAYNE CONNELLY**, ENERGY MANAGEMENT, ENVIRONMENTAL MANAGEMENT. *Current Pos:* REGENTS PROF, OKLA STATE UNIV, 86- *Personal Data:* b West Point, Va, May 7, 42; m 69, Kathleen McCawley; c 2. *Educ:* Va Polytech Inst & State Univ, BS, 64, MS, 69, PhD(indust eng). 71. *Prof Exp:* Mgr mfg engr, Modine Mfg Co, 64-67; grad asst indust eng, Va Polytech Inst & State Univ, 67-69, instr, 69-71, asst prof, 71-74; from assoc prof to prof, Okla State Univ, 74-85; prof & head indust eng, Mont State Univ, 85-86. *Concurrent Pos:* Consult, wide variety of govt & pvt firms, 70-; prin investr, US Dept Energy, 74-85; ed, Prentice Hall Ser on Energy, Prentice Hall Int, 80-85. *Mem:* Fel Inst Indust Engrs; Am Soc Eng Educr; Asn Energy Engrs; Am Inst Plant Engrs. *Res:* Energy, water and hazardous material management in industrial and other institutions. *Mailing Add:* Dept Indust Eng Okla State Univ Eng N Stillwater OK 74078

**TURNER, WILLIAM DANNY**, ENERGY CONSERVATION, MATERIALS SCIENCE. *Current Pos:* from assoc prof to prof thermodyn & energy systs, 81-89, interim dept head mech eng, 85-87, ASSOC DEAN, TEX A&M UNIV, COLLEGE STA, 89- *Personal Data:* b Moberly, Mo, Feb 14, 39; m 75; c 4. *Educ:* Univ Tex, Austin, BS, 61, MS, 62; Univ Okla, Norman, PhD(mech eng), 69. *Prof Exp:* Reliability engr, Ling-Temco-Vought Astronaut Div, 62-64; design engr, Gen Dynamics, Ft Worth, 64-66; from asst prof to assoc prof mat sci & heat transfer, Tex A&M Univ, 69-76; assoc prof, Univ Ark, Fayetteville, 76-81. *Concurrent Pos:* Consult, Argonne Nat Labs, 81-83 & Ministry Petrol Indust, People's Repub China, 86-87; dir, Dept Mech Eng, Energy Systs Lab, Tex A&M Univ, 84- *Mem:* Fel Am Soc Mech Engrs; Am Soc Eng Educ (vpres, 88-90); Asn Energy Engrs; Am Solar Energy Soc. *Res:* Energy conservation; cogeneration; residential radiant barrier testing; metallurgy. *Mailing Add:* Eng Acad Off Tex A&M Univ College Station TX 77843-3127

**TURNER, WILLIAM JOSEPH**, SOLID STATE PHYSICS. *Current Pos:* CONSULT, 89- *Personal Data:* b Canandaigua, NY, Mar 7, 27; m 51; c 4. *Educ:* Villanova Univ, BS, 49; Cath Univ, PhD(physics), 55. *Prof Exp:* Physicist, Naval Res Lab, Washington, DC, 51-52 & Nat Bur Standards, 52-56; assoc physicist, Phys Res Dept, IBM Corp, 56-57, staff physicist, Res Lab, 57-58, proj physicist, 58-59, develop physicist & res staff mem semiconductor physics, 59-61, res staff mem optical properties semiconductors, 61-64, mgr res staff opers, Thomas J Watson Res Ctr, 64-86, dir tech journ & prof rels, sci & tech staff, IBM Corp, 86-89. *Mem:* Fel Am Phys Soc. *Res:* Use of optical absorption, reflection and luminescence measurements to study the intrinsic, lattice and extrinsic properties of semiconductors. *Mailing Add:* 507 Croton Lake Rd RD 4 Mt Kisco NY 10549

**TURNER, WILLIAM JUNIOR**, ZOOLOGY, BOTANY-PHYTOPATHOLOGY. *Current Pos:* asst prof & asst entomologist, 70-76, ASSOC PROF ENTOM & ZOOL & ASSOC ENTOMOLOGIST, WASH STATE UNIV, 76- *Personal Data:* b Bell, Calif, June 27, 40; m 62; c 2. *Educ:* Univ Calif, Berkeley, AB, 63, MS, 66, PhD(entom), 71. *Prof Exp:* Lab technician entom, Univ Calif, Berkeley, 63-64, from asst to assoc entomologist, 64-67, NIH trainee, 67-70. *Concurrent Pos:* Dir, James Entomol Collection, Wash State Univ, 70-85. *Mem:* Entom Soc Am; Sigma Xi; Soc Syst Zool. *Res:* Insect biosystematics; systematic zoogeography, phylogeny and biology of Diptera; swarming behavior in insects; medical entomology, especially biting flies as vectors of pathogens. *Mailing Add:* Dept Entom Wash State Univ Pullman WA 99164-0001

**TURNER, WILLIAM RICHARD**, ANALYTICAL CHEMISTRY. *Current Pos:* RETIRED. *Personal Data:* b Drexel Hill, Pa, June 26, 36; m 60; c 3. *Educ:* Philadelphia Col Pharm, BS, 58; Univ Conn, MS, 61, PhD(anal chem), 63. *Prof Exp:* Chemist, Borden Chem Co, 58-59; fel, Univ Mich, 64; sr res chemist, ICI Am, 65-91. *Mem:* Am Chem Soc; Sigma Xi. *Res:* Liquid chromatography; electroanalytical chemistry, especially organic polarography, votammetry at solid electrodes, coulometric titrimetry and amperometric titrimetry. *Mailing Add:* Glen Willow Rd Avondale PA 19311

**TURNER, WILLIE**, VIROLOGY, IMMUNOLOGY. *Current Pos:* PROF MICROBIOL & CHMN DEPT, COL MED, HOWARD UNIV, 71- *Personal Data:* b Suffolk, Va, Feb 1, 35; m 64; c 2. *Educ:* Md State Col, BS, 57; Ohio State Univ, MS, 59, PhD(microbiol), 61. *Prof Exp:* NIH fel, Naval Med Res Inst, 61-62, Nat Inst Allergy & Infectious Dis grant, 62-64; asst prof microbiol, Meharry Med Col, 62-66; head microbiol sect, Viral Biol Br, Nat Cancer Inst, 70-71. *Concurrent Pos:* NIH staff fel oncol virol, Nat Cancer Inst, 66-69, sr fel, 69-70. *Mem:* AAAS; Am Soc Microbiol; Am Asn Immunologists; Am Asn Cancer Res; Soc Exp Biol & Med. *Res:* Oncogenic virology, especially interaction of oncogenic and nononcogenic viruses in vitro and in vivo; immunology of murine oncogenic virus as well as the immunology involved with tumors induced by these agents in vivo. *Mailing Add:* Dept Microbiol Howard Univ Col Med 520 West St NW Washington DC 20001-2337

**TURNEY, TULLY HUBERT**, ZOOLOGY. *Current Pos:* assoc prof biol, 65-74, chmn dept, 67-76, PROF BIOL, HAMPDEN-SYDNEY COL, 74- *Personal Data:* b Lakewood, Ohio, Sept 7, 36; m 62; c 1. *Educ:* Oberlin Col, AB, 58; Univ NC, PhD(zool), 63. *Prof Exp:* Fel, Oak Ridge Nat Labs, 63-64; instr zool, Univ NC, 64-65. *Mem:* AAAS; Am Inst Biol Sci. *Res:* Cell control mechanisms; molecular biochemistry; physiology; bioethics; computerized instruction. *Mailing Add:* Dept Biol Hampden-Sydney Col Hampden-Sydney VA 23943

**TURNIPSEED, GLYN D**, PLANT PHYSIOLOGY. *Current Pos:* asst prof, 73-80, ASSOC PROF BIOL, ARK POLYTECH COL, 80- *Personal Data:* b Hazlehurst, Miss, Dec 19, 42; m 67; c 1. *Educ:* Delta State Univ, BS, 66; Miss State Univ, PhD(bot), 73. *Prof Exp:* Sci teacher biol chem, Jackson Pub Schs at Wingfield High Sch, 66-70; asst bot, Miss State Univ, 70-73. *Concurrent Pos:* Ark Nat Heritage Comn. *Mem:* Soc Study Amphibians & Reptiles; Am Mus Nat Hist; Audubon Soc. *Res:* Nitrogen source preference of Oophila ambystomatis; feeding efficiency of larval anurans; population density of larval anurans; Arkansas amphibian and reptilian distributions. *Mailing Add:* Dept Biol Ark Tech Univ 215 W O St Russellville AR 72801-2230

**TURNIPSEED, MARVIN ROY**, REPRODUCTIVE PHYSIOLOGY, BIOCHEMISTRY. *Current Pos:* from asst prof to assoc prof, 78-84, PROF BIOL, QUINNIPIAC COL, HAMDEN, 84- *Personal Data:* b Carrollton, Miss, Nov 11, 34; m 57; c 2. *Educ:* Miss State Univ, BS, 56, MEd, 63; Univ Ga, PhD(zool), 69. *Prof Exp:* NIH fel steroid biochem, biochem dept, Med Sch, Univ Minn, Minneapolis, 69-71, res assoc steroid biochem, pediat dept, 71-77. *Concurrent Pos:* Res affil, dept obstet & gynec, Yale Univ, 80-85. *Mem:* Endocrine Soc; AAAS; Sigma Xi. *Res:* Placental aromatase action upon testosterone stearate and testosterone linolenate; anatomy and physiology and radiation biology; receptors involved in reproduction of female mammals; ovarian production of steroid hormones in response to trophic hormones; plasma and urinary estrogens and adrenal metabolism in newborn babies; endocrinology. *Mailing Add:* 71 St John St North Haven CT 06473-2332

**TURNLUND, JUDITH RAE**, NUTRITION, CHEMISTRY. *Current Pos:* RES NUTRIT SCIENTIST, USDA, 80- *Personal Data:* b St Paul, Minn, Sept 28, 36; m 57, Richard; c Michael, Mark & Todd. *Educ:* Gustavus Adolphus Col, BS, 58; Univ Calif, Berkeley, PhD(nutrit), 78. *Honors & Awards:* Cert of Merit, USDA, 84, 93; Am Inst Nutrit, Lederle Award, 96. *Prof Exp:* Fel human nutrit, Univ Calif, Berkeley, 78-80. *Concurrent Pos:* Lectr, Univ Calif, Berkeley, 81-82, 84-, adj assoc prof, 89-; vis prof, Am Univ Beirut, Lebanon, 79 & 80. *Mem:* Am Inst Nutrit; Am Soc Clin Nutrit; Am Dietetics Asn. *Res:* Enriched stable isotopes of minerals to study mineral metabolism and bioavailability in humans. *Mailing Add:* Western Human Nutrit Res Ctr PO Box 29997 San Francisco CA 94129. *E-Mail:* jturnlun@whnrc.usda.gov

**TURNOCK, A C**, GEOLOGIST. *Current Pos:* PROF GEOL, UNIV MANITOBA, 65- *Personal Data:* b Winnipeg, Can, Sept 11, 30. *Educ:* Univ Manitoba, BS, 53, MS, 56; Johns Hopkins Univ, PhD(geol), 60. *Mem:* Geol Soc Am; Sigma Xi; Minerol Soc Am; Minerol Soc Can; Geol Asn Can; Minerol Soc Gt Brit. *Mailing Add:* Geol Dept Univ Manitoba Winnipeg MB R3T 2N2 Can

**TURNOCK, WILLIAM JAMES**, POPULATION ECOLOGY, BIOLOGICAL CONTROL. *Current Pos:* sect head integrated pest control, 72-89, res scientist, 89-93, EMER RES SCIENTIST, RES BR, CAN DEPT AGR, 93- *Personal Data:* b Winnipeg, Man, May 17, 29; m 58, Elizabeth M Hart; c James L, David C & Robert W. *Educ:* Univ Man, BSA, 49; Univ Minn, MS, 51, PhD(entom), 58. *Prof Exp:* Res scientist, Div Forest Biol, Can Dept Agr, 49-61 & Forest Entom & Path Br, Can Dept Forestry, Man, 61-70; sci adv, Can Ministry State for Sci & Technol, 70-72. *Concurrent Pos:* Hon prof, Grad Sch, Univ Man, 65-70; vis scientist, Dept Zool, Agric Univ, Wageningen, Neth, 66-67, Dept Pure & Appl Biol, Imp Col, Silwood Park, Eng, 83-84; Can del, Int Coord Coun Man & Biosphere, UNESCO, 71. *Mem:* Sigma Xi; fel Entom Soc Can (pres, 79-80); Can Forum Biol Control. *Res:* Integrated and biological control of agriculture pests; effects of non-freezing low temperatures on the survival of insects. *Mailing Add:* Agr Res Sta 195 Dafoe Rd Winnipeg MB R3T 2M9 Can. *Fax:* 204-983-4604; *E-Mail:* lsturnock@mbrswi.agr.ca

**TURNQUIST, CARL RICHARD**, MEDICAL APPLICATIONS OF TEXTILE FIBERS. *Current Pos:* DIR, ADVAN WOUND CLOSURE TECHNOL, DEKNATEL INC, 92- *Personal Data:* b Midland, Mich, May 12, 44; m 69; c 3. *Educ:* Westminister Col, BA, 66; Univ Wis-Madison, PhD(chem), 72. *Prof Exp:* Res chemist textile fibers, E I Du Pont de Nemours, Co Inc, 72-75; sr chemist, C R Bard Inc, 75-78, res prog supvr, 78, chem & polymer supvr, Cardiol & Radiol Prod, 78-82, staff engr, USCI Cardiol & Radiol Div, 82, eng mgr, USCI Div, 82-84, Bard Crit Care Div, 84-86, technol develop mgr, Bard Vascular Systs Div, 86-92. *Concurrent Pos:* Secy, div-in-formation, Med Plastics Div, Soc Plastics Engrs, 77-80, secy, 80-83, mem div bd dirs, 83-86. *Mem:* Am Chem Soc; Soc Plastics Engrs. *Res:* Development of medical devices (implantable sutures and other wound closure devices); analysis; material and process development; biotesting; physician interactions; granted two US patents. *Mailing Add:* 106 Kenney Lane Concord MA 01742-2702. *Fax:* 508-677-6667; *E-Mail:* carltqst@ultranet.com

**TURNQUIST, MARK ALAN,** LOGISTICS, TRANSPORTATION ENGINEERING. *Current Pos:* assoc prof, Sch Civil/Environ Eng, 79-86, assoc dean comput, Col Eng, 84-86, PROF TRANSP ENG, SCH CIVIL/ ENVIRON ENG, CORNELL UNIV, 86- *Personal Data:* b July 26, 49; US citizen; m 71, Lynn Rutherford; c Alan & Matthew. *Educ:* Mich State Univ, BS, 71; Mass Inst Technol, SM, 72, PhD(transp systs anal), 75. *Prof Exp:* Asst prof transp eng, Dept Civil Eng & Transp Ctr, Northwestern Univ, 75-79. *Concurrent Pos:* Consult, Gen Motors, 84-, CSX Inc, 88-93, Union Pac Railroad, 90-93, IBM, 94- *Mem:* Prod & Oper Mgt Soc. *Res:* Logistics and production systems design, operations and control; vehicle routing and scheduling; hazardous materials transportation. *Mailing Add:* Sch Civil/ Environ Eng Cornell Univ Ithaca NY 14853

**TURNQUIST, PAUL KENNETH,** AGRICULTURAL ENGINEERING. *Current Pos:* PROF AGR ENG & HEAD DEPT, AUBURN UNIV, 77- *Personal Data:* b Lindsborg, Kans, Jan 3, 35; m 62; c 3. *Educ:* Kans State Univ, BS, 57; Okla State Univ, MS, 61, PhD(agr eng), 65. *Prof Exp:* Res engr, Caterpillar Tractor Co, 57; from instr to asst prof agr eng, Okla State Univ, 58-62; assoc prof, SDak State Univ, 64-70; engr in residence, Caterpillar Tractor Co, 70-71; prof agr eng, SDak State Univ, 71-76. *Concurrent Pos:* Vis prof, Purdue Univ, 85. *Mem:* Fel Am Soc Agr Engrs; Am Soc Eng Educ; Sigma Xi; Nat Soc Prof Engrs. *Res:* Agricultural power and machinery for tillage and harvesting; operator safety; environmental control. *Mailing Add:* 1216 Nixon Dr Auburn AL 36830-6302

**TURNQUIST, RALPH OTTO,** MECHANICAL ENGINEERING, INSTRUMENTATION. *Current Pos:* from asst prof to assoc prof, 65-77, PROF MECH ENG, KANS STATE UNIV, 77- *Personal Data:* b Lindsborg, Kans, Aug 10, 28; m 65; c 2. *Educ:* Kans State Univ, BS, 52, MS, 61; Case Inst Technol, PhD(fluid controls), 65. *Prof Exp:* Engr, Aircraft Gas Turbine Div, Westinghouse Elec Co, Mo, 54-59; instr mech eng, Kans State Univ, 59-62; res asst fluid control systs, Case Inst Technol, 62-65. *Mem:* Am Soc Mech Engrs; Am Soc Eng Educ; Instrument Soc Am; Fluid Power Soc. *Res:* Turbojet engine fuel distribution and atomization; automatic control theory; fluid control systems; fluidics; hydrostatic and power shift transmissions. *Mailing Add:* 1100 Pioneer Lane Manhattan KS 66502

**TURNQUIST, RICHARD LEE,** PHYSIOLOGY, BIOCHEMISTRY. *Current Pos:* ASST PROF BIOL, AUGUSTANA COL, 74- *Personal Data:* b Rugby, NDak, Aug 12, 44; m 66. *Educ:* Concordia Col, BA, 66; Utah State Univ, PhD(physiol), 71. *Prof Exp:* Fel biochem, Utah State Univ, 71-74. *Mem:* AAAS; Sigma Xi. *Res:* Ultrastructural changes and responses during detoxication of xenobiotics in mammals and insects. *Mailing Add:* Dept Biol Augustana Col 639 38th St Rock Island IL 61201-2210

**TURNQUIST, TRUMAN DALE,** ANALYTICAL CHEMISTRY. *Current Pos:* Assoc prof, 65-76, PROF CHEM, MT UNION COL, 76- *Personal Data:* b Kipling, Sask, Apr 8, 40; m 64; c 3. *Educ:* Bethel Col, Minn, BA, 61; Univ Minn, PhD(analytical chem), 65. *Mem:* Am Chem Soc. *Res:* Metal complex formation; solvent extraction of metal complexes; spectrophotometry. *Mailing Add:* 13905 Marlington NE Alliance OH 44601-4462

**TURNROSE, BARRY EDMUND,** SPACE ASTRONOMY, DIGITAL IMAGE PROCESSING. *Current Pos:* resident astronr image processing, Comput Sci Corp, 77-80, sect mgr, 80-82, asst dept mgr, 82-83, dept mgr, 83-86, OPER MGR, SCI PROG, COMPUT SCI CORP, 86- *Personal Data:* b New Britain, Conn, June 3, 47; m 70, Kathryn McQueen; c Heather I & Erik P. *Educ:* Wesleyan Univ, BA, 69; Calif Inst Technol, PhD(astron), 76. *Prof Exp:* Resident res assoc astron, NASA-Johnson Space Ctr, Houston, 75-77. *Mem:* Am Astron Soc; Sigma Xi. *Res:* Extragalactic astronomy; spectrophotometry of galaxies; stellar content of galaxies; surface photometry of extragalactic objects; astronomical image processing; ultraviolet astronomy. *Mailing Add:* 8294 Quill Point Dr Bowie MD 20720-4377

**TUROCZI, LESTER J,** GENETIC TOXICOLOGY, DEVELOPMENTAL BIOLOGY. *Current Pos:* From asst prof to assoc prof, 72-83, PROF BIOL, WILKES COL, WILKES-BARRE, PA, 84-, CHMN DEPT, 77- *Personal Data:* b Jersey City, NJ, Nov 13, 42. *Educ:* Rutgers Univ, BA, 65, MS, 67, PhD(zool), 72. *Concurrent Pos:* Vis prof, Pa State Univ, Lehman, 75-76. *Mem:* AAAS; Am Soc Zoologists; NY Acad Sci; Genetic Toxicol Asn; Biol Photogr Asn. *Res:* Utilization of the Ames Salmonella-microsomal mutagenicity assay and the Mouse Micronucleus Test as genetic toxicology methods for the study of various nutrients, food additives and natural products. *Mailing Add:* Dept Biol Wilkes Univ Wilkes-Barre PA 18766

**TUROFF, MURRAY,** COMPUTER SCIENCE. *Current Pos:* PROF COMPUT & INFO SCI, NJ INST TECHNOL, 73- *Personal Data:* b San Francisco, Calif, Feb 13, 36; m 61; c 2. *Educ:* Univ Calif, Berkeley, BA, 58; Brandeis Univ, PhD(physics), 65. *Prof Exp:* Syst engr, IBM Corp, 61-64; mem prof staff syst analysis, Inst Defense Analysis, 64-68; opers res & info systs, Off Emergency Preparedness, 68-73. *Concurrent Pos:* Lectr, Am Univ, 70-73. *Mem:* Inst Elec & Electronics Engrs; Inst Mgt Sci; Asn Comput Mach. *Res:* Delphi design; computerized conferencing systems; information systems design; technology assessment and forecasting; gaming, simulation and modeling; policy analyses; management of information systems. *Mailing Add:* NJ Inst Technol Dept Comput & Info Sci 323 Martin Luther King Blvd Newark NJ 07102. *E-Mail:* murray@eie32.njit.edu

**TURPEN, JAMES BAXTER,** DEVELOPMENTAL BIOLOGY, IMMUNOLOGY. *Current Pos:* asst prof, 86-88, ASSOC PROF, DEPT ANAT, COL MED, UNIV NEBR, 88-; ASST PROF BIOL, PA STATE UNIV, 76-, PROF, DEPT CELL BIOL & ANAT, 92- *Personal Data:* b Sheridan, Wyo, Sept 27, 45; m, Paula Smith; c J Matthew, John A, Ross M, Carrie E & Jessamine K. *Educ:* Univ Denver, BS, 67, MS, 69; Tulane Univ, PhD(biol), 73. *Honors & Awards:* Masua hon lectr, 87. *Prof Exp:* USPHS fel immunol, Med Ctr, Univ Rochester, 74-76. *Concurrent Pos:* Prin investr, USPHS-NIH grant, 77-85; USPHS res career develop award, 80-85; mem, Basel Inst Immunol, 85. *Mem:* Am Soc Zoologists; AAAS; Int Soc Study Differentiation; Am Asn Immunol; Int Soc Develop & Comp Immunol; Reticuloendothelial Soc. *Res:* Development of hematopoietic cells; comparative immunology. *Mailing Add:* Dept Cell Biol & Anat Univ Nebr Col Med 600 S 42nd St Omaha NE 68198-6395

**TURPIN, DAVID HOWARD,** BIOLOGY, BOTANY. *Current Pos:* from asst prof to assoc prof biol, Queen's Univ, 81-90, prof, 90-91, dean arts & sci, 93-95, VPRIN ACAD, QUEEN'S UNIV, 93- *Personal Data:* b Duncan, BC, July 14, 56; m 85, S Laurence Clark; c Chantal & Joshua. *Educ:* Univ BC, BSc, 77, PhD(bot & oceanog), 80. *Honors & Awards:* C D Nelson Award, Can Soc Plant Phycologists, 89; Darbaker Prize Phycol, Am Bot Asn, 91. *Prof Exp:* Res assoc, Simon Fraser Univ, 80; vpres, Sigma Res Consult, 80-81. *Concurrent Pos:* Postdoctoral res fel, Natural Sci & Eng Coun, 80-81; grantee, Nat Sci & Engr Res Coun, 82; E W R Stacie mem fel, Nat Sci & Eng Res Can, 89-90; prof & head bot, Univ BC, 91-93. *Mem:* Phycol Soc Am; Am Soc Limnol & Oceanog; Can Soc Plant Physiologists; Am Soc Plant Physiologists. *Mailing Add:* Off Vprin Acad Queen's Univ 239 Richardson Hall Kingston ON K7L 3N6 Can

**TURPIN, FRANK THOMAS,** ECONOMIC ENTOMOLOGY. *Current Pos:* From asst prof to assoc prof entom, 71-82, PROF ENTOM PURDUE UNIV, 82- *Personal Data:* b Troy, Kans, June 4, 43; m 70; c 2. *Educ:* Washburn Univ, BS, 65; Iowa State Univ, PhD(entom), 71. *Concurrent Pos:* Consult, US Environ Protection Agency, 73-, Pesticide Industs, 75- & USAID, Tanzania, 81. *Mem:* Entom Soc Am. *Res:* Biology; ecology; population dynamics and control of insects attacking corn. *Mailing Add:* 1158 Entom Hall Purdue Univ West Lafayette IN 47907-1158

**TURRELL, BRIAN GEORGE,** LOW TEMPERATURE PHYSICS, MAGNETISM. *Current Pos:* from asst prof to assoc prof, 64-70, head physics, 87-97, PROF PHYSICS, UNIV BC, 76-,. *Personal Data:* b Shoreham-by-Sea, Eng, May 6, 38; m 62, 70, Annie M Lindsay; c Simon F, Francescal & Susan J. *Educ:* Oxford Univ, BA, 59, MA & PhD(nuclear orientation), 63. *Prof Exp:* Asst lectr physics, Univ Sussex, 63-64. *Concurrent Pos:* Sr fel, Sci Res Coun, Oxford, 71-72; vis prof, Univ NSW, Duntroon, Australia, 78-79; vis scientist, Walther Meissner Inst & Tech Univ Munich, 85-86, Univ Bayreuth, 92. *Mem:* Can Asn Physicists; Am Asn Physic Teachers. *Res:* Nuclear orientation; nuclear magnetic resonance; use of these techniques to study hyperfine interactions in magnetic materials; cryogenic detectors. *Mailing Add:* Dept Physics Univ BC Vancouver BC V6T 1Z1 Can. *Fax:* 604-822-5324; *E-Mail:* turrell@physics.ubc.ca

**TURRELL, EUGENE SNOW,** PSYCHIATRY. *Current Pos:* STAFF PSYCHIATRIST, MIDTOWN COMMUNITY MENT HEALTH CTR, WISHARD MEM HOSP, 75-, MED DIR, 86-, MED DIR FORENSIC SERV, 87- *Personal Data:* b Hyattsville, Md, Feb 27, 19; m 88; c 1. *Educ:* Ind Univ, BS, 39, MD, 47; Am Bd Psychiat & Neurol, dipl, 53. *Prof Exp:* Asst physiol, Ind Univ, 39-42; res assoc, Fatigue Lab, Harvard Univ, 42-43; res assoc physiol, Ind Univ, 43-44, asst biochem, Sch Med, 45-47; med house officer, Peter Bent Brigham Hosp, Boston, 47-48; resident psychiat, Kankakee State Hosp, Ill, 48-49; clin asst, Sch Med, Univ Calif, 49-52; asst prof, Sch Med, Ind Univ, 52-53; assoc prof, Sch Med, Univ Colo, 53-58, asst dean sch, 57; prof & chmn dept, Sch Med, Marquette Univ, 58-63, clin prof, 63-69; sr psychiatrist, 69-72, dir, Ctr Spec Probs, Community Ment Health Serv, City & County of San Francisco, 72-75. *Concurrent Pos:* Resident, Langley Porter Clin, 49-50; chief psychiat consult serv, Robert W Long Hosp, Indianapolis, Ind, 52-53; med dir, Colo Psychopath Hosp, 53-54; assoc attend, Denver Gen Hosp, 53-57, dir psychiat serv, 57-58; attend, Vet Admin Hosp, Denver, 53-58; mem staff psychosom div, Colo Gen Hosp, 54-57; dir psychiat serv, Milwaukee Sanitarium Found, 58-65; consult, Hosp Ment Dis, Milwaukee, 58-69, Vet Admin Hosp, Wood, Wis, 58-69, Columbia Hosp, 59-69 & Milwaukee Children's Hosp, 60-69; assoc prof, dept psychiat, Ind Univ Sch Med, 75- *Mem:* AAAS; fel Am Psychiat Asn; AMA; Sigma Xi. *Res:* Psychosomatic medicine; psychotherapy. *Mailing Add:* 13322 Mango Dr Del Mar CA 92014-3535

**TURRELL, GEORGE CHARLES,** PHYSICAL CHEMISTRY, SPECTROSCOPY. *Current Pos:* PROF, INFRARED & RAMAN SPECTROS LAB, UNIV SCI TECH LILLE, FRANCE, 81- *Personal Data:* b Portland, Ore, June 19, 31; m 54, 70, Sylvia Jones; c Charles R, Jeanette L, Yvonne N & Marc D. *Educ:* Lewis & Clark Col, BA, 50; Ore State Univ, MS, 52, PhD(phys chem), 54. *Prof Exp:* Asst, Ore State Univ, 50-52; mem tech staff, Electron Device Dept, Bell Tel Labs, Inc, 54-56; res assoc, Metcalf Res Lab, Brown Univ, 56-57; instr chem, 57-58; Guggenheim fel, Bellevue Labs, Nat Ctr Sci Res, France, 58-59; asst prof chem, Howard Univ, 59-62, assoc prof, 62-67; exchange prof & Fulbright fel, Infrared Spectros Lab, Univ Bordeaux, 66-67, vis prof, 67-70; prof, Nat Univ Zaire, Kisangani, 70-71 & Kinshasa, 71-72; actg ed, Can Jour Spectroscopy, 72; vis prof chem, Univ Montreal, 72-74 & McGill Univ, 73-75; res prof chem, Univ Laval, Que, 75-79; engr, Bomem, Inc, 79-80; vis prof, Molecular Physics Lab, Univ Limoges, 80-81. *Concurrent Pos:* Vis scientist, IBM Almaden Res Lab, 89. *Mem:* Fel Am Phys Soc; Coblentz Soc; Can Spectros Soc; Sigma Xi; Fr Chem Soc. *Res:* Molecular spectroscopy; studies of molecular interactions in solids and liquids using infrared and Raman spectroscopy. *Mailing Add:* Univ Sci Tech Lille LASIR Bat C5 Villeneuve d'Ascq 59655 France. *Fax:* 33-20436755

**TURRO, NICHOLAS JOHN,** ORGANIC CHEMISTRY. *Current Pos:* Instr, 64-65, from asst prof to assoc prof, 65-69, PROF ORG CHEM, COLUMBIA UNIV, 69- *Personal Data:* b Middletown, Conn, May 18, 38; m 60, Sandra Misenti; c Cynthia & Claire. *Educ:* Wesleyan Univ, BA, 60; Calif Inst Technol, PhD(chem), 63. *Hon Degrees:* DSc, Wesleyan Univ, 84. *Honors & Awards:* Pure Chem Award, Am Chem Soc, 74; Halpern Award, NY Acad Sci, 77; Ernest Orlando Lawrence Award, Dept Energy, 83; Harrison Howe Award, Am Chem Soc, 86, Cope Scholar Award, 87; Norris Award, 88; Photochem Award, Inter-Am Photochem Soc, 91; Porter Medal, 94; Havinga Medal (Leiden), 94. *Concurrent Pos:* NSF fel, Harvard Univ, 63-64; consult, E I du Pont de Nemours & Co, 64-; vis prof, Pa State Univ, 66; Sloan Found fel, 66-68; W P Schweitzer prof chem, Columbia Univ, 81, chmn, chem dept, 81-84; Sherman Fairchild fel, Calif Inst Technol, 84-85; Guggenheim fel, Oxford Univ, 85. *Mem:* Nat Acad Sci; Am Chem Soc; fel NY Acad Sci. *Res:* Photochemistry; electronic energy transfer in fluid solution; cycloaddition reactions; thermal rearrangements; dioxetane chemistry; chemiluminescence; micellar chemistry; application of laser techniques to organic photochemistry; emulsion polymerization; magnetic field effects; polymer photochemistry and photo-physics; magnetic isotope and magnetic field effects on organic reactions; organic reactions on porous silica and zeolites. *Mailing Add:* 125 Downey Dr Tenafly NJ 07670. *Fax:* 212-932-1289; *E-Mail:* turro@chem.columbia.edu

**TURSE, RICHARD S,** ANALYTICAL CHEMISTRY, SPECTROCHEMISTRY. *Current Pos:* sr res chemist, 60-87, res assoc, 87-93, SR RES ASSOC, COLGATE-PALMOLIVE CO, 93- *Personal Data:* b Jersey City, NJ, Mar 24, 35; m 64, Dorothy Drew; c William, Nancy & Patricia. *Educ:* Rutgers Univ, BS, 56, MS, 58, PhD(analytical chem), 60. *Prof Exp:* Instr anal chem, Rutgers Univ, 56-58. *Mem:* Soc Appl Spectros; Am Pharm Asn. *Res:* Atomic absorption methods for determination of trace metals; x-ray diffraction and emission techniques for sample identification, secondary ion mass spectroscopy, electron spectroscopy chemical analysis and auger surface analysis; scanning electron microscopy; scanning probe microscopy, particle-size analysis, thermal analysis. *Mailing Add:* Colgate-Palmolive Co 909 River Rd Piscataway NJ 08855-1343. *Fax:* 732-878-6138

**TURZHITSKY, MICHAEL V,** ANALYSIS OF MULTIPHYSICS COUPLED PROCESSES IN WELDING, INDUCTION HEATING & METAL FORMING. *Current Pos:* PROCESS ENGR, THERMATOOL CORP, 93- *Personal Data:* b St Petersburg, Russia, Dec 3, 56; US citizen; m 79, Anna; c Yana & Vladimir. *Educ:* Marine Univ, St Petersburg, Russia, MS, 81; Polytech Univ, PhD(high frequency welding), 87. *Prof Exp:* Scientist, High Frequency Induction Res Inst, 81-89; proj engr, Transformer Technologies Corp, 90-93. *Res:* Analyzed heating and deformation process in induction welding; stress analysis in problems with high temperature gradient; application of finite element methods for nonlinear coupled problems of different physical nature. *Mailing Add:* 560 Summit Dr Orange CT 06477. *Fax:* 203-468-4284; *E-Mail:* miket@ttool.com

**TUSING, THOMAS WILLIAM,** PHARMACOLOGY. *Current Pos:* RETIRED. *Personal Data:* b New Market, Va, Feb 2, 20; m 49; c 5. *Educ:* George Washington Univ, BS, 42; Med Col Va, MD, 50. *Prof Exp:* Med dir, Hazleton Labs, Inc, 51-58, dir res & vpres, 58-69; med dir pharmaceut res & develop div, Mallindkrodt Inc, 69-85. *Mem:* AMA; Indust Med Asn; Soc Toxicol. *Mailing Add:* 1876 Lake Francis Dr Apopka FL 32712

**TUSTANOFF, EUGENE RENO,** BIOCHEMISTRY. *Current Pos:* assoc prof path chem, Univ Western Ont, 67-72, assoc prof clin biochem, 72-75, prof clin biochem & Dept Oncol, 75-94, EMER PROF, DEPT BIOCHEM UNIV WESTERN ONT, 95- *Personal Data:* b Windsor, Ont, Jan 30, 29; m 54; c 4. *Educ:* Assumption Col, BA, 52; Detroit Univ, MS, 54; Western Ont Univ, PhD(biochem), 59. *Prof Exp:* Res assoc biochem, Western Ont Univ, 55-59; fel, Western Res Univ, 59-61; Life Ins Med Res fel, Oxford Univ, 61-62; asst scientist, Hosp for Sick Children, Univ Toronto, 62-64; assoc biochem, Univ Toronto, 63-65, asst prof pharmacol, 64-65; assoc prof biochem, McMaster Univ, 65-67. *Mem:* Can Biochem Soc; Brit Biochem Soc; Am Soc Biol Chem; Am Asn Clin Chem; Can Soc Clin Chem; fel Can Acad Clin Biochem; Am Acad Clin Biochem; Can Soc Biochem, Molecular & Cellular Biol (Secy). *Res:* Biogenesis and control of mitochondria; biogenesis of membranes; biochemistry of tumour model systems; steroid receptors in breast cancer. *Mailing Add:* 839 Normandy Gate London ON N6H 4K5 Can. *Fax:* 519-661-3175; *E-Mail:* etustan@julian.uwo.ca

**TUSTING, ROBERT FREDERICK,** OCEAN ENGINEERING, INSTRUMENTATION. *Current Pos:* SR ENGR, HARBOR BR OCEANOG INST, 82- *Personal Data:* b Alameda, Calif, May 11, 33. *Educ:* Univ Calif, Berkeley, BS, 61, MS, 65. *Prof Exp:* Engr, Lawrence Radiation Lab, Berkeley, 61-64, design engr, 65-68; chief engr & design eng mgr, Delco Electronics, Gen Motors, Santa Barbara, 68-72; res prof marine sci, Rosenstiel Sch, Univ Miami, 72-81. *Concurrent Pos:* Adj prof, Indian River Community Col, 86-89; regist prof engr, State Fla, 92. *Mem:* Marine Technol Soc; Inst Elec & Electronics Engrs. *Res:* Ocean instrumentation; scientific sampling equipment design; optical and physical measurements; acoustic instrumentation; laser-based quantitative analysis; awarded seven US patents; author of 36 technical papers. *Mailing Add:* Harbor Br Oceanog Inst Inc 5600 US 1 N Ft Pierce FL 34946

**TUSTISON, RANDAL WAYNE,** THIN FILM TECHNOLOGY, OPTICAL MATERIALS. *Current Pos:* sr scientist, 78-81, prin scientist mat sci, Res Div, 82-93; MGR ADVAN MAT, RAYTHEON CO, 93-, CONSULT SCIENTIST, 97- *Personal Data:* b Ft Wayne, Ind, Dec 4, 47; m 75, Kathleen E Nelson; c Eric R & Anna E. *Educ:* Purdue Univ, BS, 70; Univ Ill, MS, 72, PhD(metall eng) 76,. *Prof Exp:* Res assoc physics, Mass Inst Technol, 76-78; thin film scientist mat sci, Res Div, 3M Co, 81-82. *Concurrent Pos:* Lectr, Northeastern Univ, 83-86; mem, Nat Prog Comt, Am Vacuum Soc, 86-91, chmn, Vacuum Tech Div, 90, critical mats working group-optical mats. *Mem:* Am Vacuum Soc; Am Phys Soc. *Res:* Thin film deposition processes; infrared optical materials and coatings; magnetic and ferroelectric materials and coatings; mechanical property characterization of thin films. *Mailing Add:* Raytheon Co 131 Spring St Lexington MA 02173. *Fax:* 781-860-3095; *E-Mail:* randal_w_tustison@raytheon.com

**TUSZEWSKI, MICHEL G,** PLASMA PROCESSING, NUCLEAR FUSION. *Current Pos:* tech staff mem, 80-96, LAB FEL, LOS ALAMOS NAT LAB, 97- *Personal Data:* b Lille, France, Oct 17, 48; US citizen; m, Krystyna Eichel; c Sophie & Liliane. *Educ:* Ecole Centrale, France, BS, 71; Univ Calif, Berkeley, MS, 73, PhD(nuclear eng), 76. *Prof Exp:* Res fel, Cornell Univ & Univ Calif, Berkeley, 77-79. *Concurrent Pos:* Fr govt grant, 72-73, Fulbright grant, 72-76; field-reversed config res, 80-85, 87-90; vis scientist, France, 85, Univ Calif, Berkeley, 92; vis scholar, Nagoya Univ, 90; consult, Procter & Gamble, 97. *Mem:* Fel Am Phys Soc; Am Vacuum Soc. *Res:* Magnetic fusion; applied plasmas; field reversed configurations and inductively coupled plasmas; contributed over 67 articles to journals. *Mailing Add:* 2186 47th St Los Alamos NM 87544. *Fax:* 505-665-3552; *E-Mail:* mgt7@lanl.gov

**TUSZYNSKI, ALFONS ALFRED,** electronics, microelectronics, for more information see previous edition

**TUSZYNSKI, GEORGE P,** PROTEIN CHEMISTRY, CELL BIOLOGY. *Current Pos:* ASSOC INVESTR PALETELET HEMAT, LANKENAU MED RES CTR, 84- *Educ:* Univ Pa, PhD(biochem), 73. *Res:* Paletes in coagulation in tumor cell metastasis. *Mailing Add:* Rm G81 Allegheny Univ Health Sci 2900 Queen Lane Philadelphia PA 19129-1121

**TUSZYNSKI, JACK A,** PHASE TRANSITIONS, BIOPHYSICS. *Current Pos:* asst prof physics, 88-93, PROF PHYSICS, UNIV ALTA, 93- *Personal Data:* b Poznan, Poland, July 24, 56; Can citizen; m 80; c 1. *Educ:* Univ Poznan, Poland, MSc, 80; Univ Calgary, PhD(solid state hysics), 83. *Prof Exp:* Fel chem, Univ Calgary, 83; asst prof physics, Mem Univ Nfld, 83-87. *Concurrent Pos:* Hon asst prof physics, Mem Univ Nfld, 88. *Mem:* Can Asn Physicists. *Res:* Applications of nonlinear differential equations to the linetics of phase transitions and other nonlinear phenomena; crystal lattice dynamics magnetic phase transitions. *Mailing Add:* Dept Physics Univ Alta Edmonton AB T6G 2J1 Can

**TUTHILL, ARTHUR F(REDERICK),** MECHANICAL ENGINEERING, THERMODYNAMICS. *Current Pos:* from instr to prof mech eng, 46-81, EMER PROF, UNIV VT, 81- *Personal Data:* b Cutchogue, NY, Dec 18, 16; m 41; c 5. *Educ:* Carnegie Inst Technol, BS, 38; Univ Wis, MS, 39. *Prof Exp:* Instr mech eng, Cooper Union, 39-42. *Mem:* Am Soc Mech Engrs; Am Soc Eng Educ. *Res:* Air distribution, environmental engineering. *Mailing Add:* 947 Williston Rd Williston VT 05495-9649

**TUTHILL, HARLAN LLOYD,** HEALTH & ENVIRONMENTAL SCIENCES. *Current Pos:* RETIRED. *Personal Data:* b Fillmore, NY, Nov 24, 17; m 41, 71, Barbara M Scott; c 2. *Educ:* Houghton Col, BS, 39; Cornell Univ, PhD(phys chem), 43. *Honors & Awards:* Ebert Award, Am Pharmaceut Asn. *Prof Exp:* Res chemist, Rohm & Haas Co, 43-46; head phys chem sect, Smith Kline & Fr Labs, 46-48, tech dir, 48-54, sci dir int div, 54-57, asst dir res & develop labs, 57-62, vpres, Smith Kline Instruments, Inc, 62-65; dir prod develop & assoc dir, Squibb Inst Med Res, Squibb Corp, 65-70; dir health & med res, Int Paper Co, 70-77, assoc dir Sci & Technol Lab, 77-84. *Concurrent Pos:* Consult univ/indust technol transfer, 85-90. *Mem:* Am Chem Soc; Sigma Xi. *Res:* Health and environmental sciences; analytical and materials sciences. *Mailing Add:* 1183 Candlewood Dr Pen Argyl PA 18072-9689

**TUTHILL, SAMUEL JAMES,** GEOLOGY, HYDROGEOLOGY. *Current Pos:* RETIRED. *Personal Data:* b San Diego, Calif, Sept 6, 25; m 52, Constance Howell; c Susan (Gimprich), James F & John H. *Educ:* Drew Univ, AB, 51; Syracuse Univ, MS, 60; Univ NDak, MA, 63, PhD(geol), 69. *Honors & Awards:* Arthur Gray Leonard Medal, Univ NDak, 96. *Prof Exp:* Geologist, NDak Geol Surv, 63-64; asst prof geol, Muskingum Col, 64-68; asst state geologist, Iowa Geol Surv, 68-69, dir & state geologist, 69-75; vpres energy resources/utilization, Environ & Res, Iowa Elec Light & Power Co, 77-78, sr vpres energy prod, 78-88; pres, Tuthill Inc, 88-91, sr sci assoc, 91-92. *Concurrent Pos:* NSF grants, Muskingum Col expeds Alaska, 65-66, 67-69; adj prof, Univ Iowa, 69-; adminr, Iowa Oil & Gas Admin, 69-; mem, Iowa Natural Resources Coun, 70-; mem, Iowa Land Rehab Coun, 70-; secy, Iowa State Map Adv Coun, 72; sci adv to US Secy Interior, 75-; spec asst energy policy to chmn Presidents Energy Resources Coun, 75-76; Off Indust Energy Conserv, US Dept Com, 75-76, Iowa Acad Sci, 87-90; adv, US Fed Energy Admin, 75-76, asst adminr conserv & environ, 76-77; comnr, Upper Miss River Basin Comn, Iowa, 80-82; chmn, Enerex Exec Comt; trustee, Herbert Hoover Presidential Libr Asn, Inc. *Mem:* Am Water Well Asn; fel Geol Soc Am; Asn Am State Geol; fel Explorers Club; Sigma Xi. *Res:* Research management; water; minerals; environmental protection; waste management; remote sensing; resources managemental development. *Mailing Add:* 177 S Shore Dr Grand Marais MN 55604. *E-Mail:* consamhi@boreal.org

**TUTHILL, SAMUEL MILLER**, ANALYTICAL CHEMISTRY. *Current Pos:* RETIRED. *Personal Data:* b Rocky Point, NY, Jan 7, 19; m 41, Frances M Hallock; c Arthur, Thomas & Anne. *Educ:* Wesleyan Univ, BA, 39, MA, 41; Ohio State Univ, PhD(chem), 48. *Honors & Awards:* Award Merit, Am Soc Testing & Mat, 89. *Prof Exp:* Lab asst chem, Wesleyan Univ, 39-41; anal chemist, Mallinckrodt Chem Works, 41-45; lab asst chem, Ohio State Univ, 45-46, from asst instr to instr, 47-48; anal lab supvr, Mallinckrodt Inc, 48-56, dir qual control, 56-70, corp dir qual control, 70-72, corp dir qual assurance, 72-76, dir corp anal serv, 76-81, tech comt & qual stand consult, 81-96. *Concurrent Pos:* Former mem, comt rev, US Pharmacopeia; consult, Comt Reagent Specif, Am Chem Soc; mem, E-15 comt, Am Soc Testing & Mat. *Mem:* Am Chem Soc; fel Am Soc Testing & Mat. *Res:* Methods of analysis of pharmaceutical, food, and reagent chemicals; separation by electrodeposition; instrumental methods of analysis; separation of rhodium from iridium by electrolysis with control of the cathode potential; determination of rare earths in steels; analysis of opium and narcotics; good manufacturing practice in manufacture of drugs. *Mailing Add:* 237 Olympia Dr Ferguson MO 63135-1559. *Fax:* 314-539-1198

**TUTIHASI, SIMPEI**, SOLID STATE PHYSICS. *Current Pos:* RETIRED. *Personal Data:* b Tokyo, Japan, Mar 2, 22; US citizen; m 47; c 2. *Educ:* Kyoto Univ, BSc, 46, DSc(physics), 56. *Prof Exp:* Res assoc solid state physics, Inst Optics, Univ Rochester, 56-59; sr engr, Sylvania Elec Prods, Inc, 59-64; scientist, Res Labs, Xerox Corp, 64-87. *Mem:* Am Phys Soc. *Res:* Solid state spectroscopy; spectroscopy of ordered crystals, photoconductivity, luminescence. *Mailing Add:* 274 Sudden Valley Bellingham WA 98226

**TUTSCHKA, PETER JOSEF**, BONE MARROW TRANSPLANTATION, ONCOLOGY. *Current Pos:* PROF MED & DIR BONE MARROW TRANSPLANT PROG, HEALTH CTR, UNIV CT, 92- *Personal Data:* b Prague, CSSR, Aug 19, 45; US citizen; m 69, Brigitte Ringer; c Cornelia Brigitte & Christian Peter. *Educ:* Univ Munich, Ger, MD, 70; Inst Hemat, Ger, PhD(hemat oncol), 70. *Prof Exp:* Asst prof oncol, Sch Med, Johns Hopkins Univ, 75-80, asst prof med, 76-80, asst prof oncol, 80-83, assoc prof med, 81-83; prof med, Ohio State Univ, 83-93, dir, Bone Marrow Transplant Prog, 83-93, prof path, 85-93, dir, Div BM Transplantation, 88-92, James Cancer Hosp & Res Inst, 90-93. *Concurrent Pos:* Chair Transfusion Med, Physician Health Servs, Am Red Cross, 94-; adv, Immunol Grad Prog, Univ Ct Health Ctr, 94- *Mem:* Int Soc Exp Hemat; Am Col Physicians; Am Soc Clin Oncol; Transplantation Soc; Am Asn Immunologist; Am Soc Hemat. *Res:* Immunobiology of bone marrow transplantation; graft versus host disease; immunodeficiency; drug development; preparative regimens; clinical complications. *Mailing Add:* 263 Farmington Ave Farmington CT 06030-1625. *Fax:* 860-679-4491

**TUTTE, WILLIAM THOMAS**, COMBINATORICS. *Current Pos:* prof math, 62-85, EMER PROF, DEPT COMBINATORICS & OPTIMIZATION, UNIV WATERLOO, 85- *Personal Data:* b Newmarket, Eng, May 14, 17; m 49. *Educ:* Cambridge Univ, PhD(math), 48. *Hon Degrees:* Doctor Math, Univ Waterloo, 87. *Honors & Awards:* Henry Marshall Tory Medal, Royal Soc Can, 75; Killam Prize, Can Coun, 82. *Prof Exp:* Lectr, Univ Toronto, 48-52, from asst prof to assoc prof, 52-62. *Mem:* Am Math Soc; Math Asn Am; fel Royal Soc Can; Can Math Soc; London Math Soc; fel Royal Soc London. *Res:* Graph theory; matroid theory. *Mailing Add:* c/o Mrs Jeanne Youlder 151 Maderston Rd New Market Suffolk England

**TUTTLE, DAVID B**, AERONAUTICAL & ASTRONAUTICAL ENGINEERING. *Current Pos:* gen engr, Syst Eng Br, Airway Facil Serv, Fed Aviation Admin, Washington, DC, 79-82, Req Identification & Anal Br, Syst Eng Serv, 82-83, actg mgr, 83-84, mgr, 84-88, asst mgr, Maintenance Automation Div, Prog Eng Serv, 88, mgr, Systs Technol Div, Res & Develop Serv, 89-92, Telecommun Mat & Opers Div, Syst Mgt Serv, 92-94, PROG DIR, NAT AIRSPACE SYST OPERS, AIRWAY FACIL SERV, AIR TRAFFIC SERVS, FED AVIATION ADMIN, WASHINGTON, DC, 94- *Educ:* Lowell Technol Inst, BS, 69; Univ Southern Calif, MS, 72; George Washington Univ, MPA, 89. *Prof Exp:* Electronics engr, Advan Technol Sect, asst comdr acquisition, Naval Air Systs Command, Washington, 69-75, Air Traffic Br, Aviation Progs Div, dep chief naval opers, Off Chief Naval Opers, Navy Dept, 75-78; gen engr, Off Automated Guideway Technol Appln, Off Technol Develop & Deployment, Urban Mass Transp Admin, Washington, 78-79. *Mailing Add:* Airway Facil Servs US Dept Transp 800 Independence Ave SW Washington DC 20591

**TUTTLE, DAVID F(EARS)**, ELECTRICAL ENGINEERING. *Current Pos:* prof, 48-79, EMER PROF ELEC ENG, STANFORD UNIV, 79- *Personal Data:* b Briarcliff Manor, NY, July 5, 14; m 44; c 2. *Educ:* Amherst Col, AB, 34; Mass Inst Technol, SB & SM, 38, ScD(elec eng), 48. *Prof Exp:* Mem tech staff, Bell Tel Labs, NY, 38-42. *Concurrent Pos:* Fulbright lectr, France, 54-55 & Spain, 61-62; assoc prof, Univ Aix-Marseille, 68-69; vis prof math, Ga Inst Tech, 81-82, Amherst Col, 83-84. *Mem:* Fel AAAS; fel Inst Elec & Electronics Engrs. *Res:* Network theory. *Mailing Add:* 713 Alvarado Row Palo Alto CA 94305-1010

**TUTTLE, DONALD MONROE**, ENTOMOLOGY, ACAROLOGY. *Current Pos:* prof & res entomologist, 52-83, EMER PROF, UNIV ARIZ, 83- *Personal Data:* b Bay City, Mich, Feb 1, 17; m 47, Dorothy Jayne Sheets; c Ronald James, Andrew Welsley & Timothy Daniell. *Educ:* Mich State Univ, BS, 40, MS, 47; Univ Ill, PhD(entom), 52. *Prof Exp:* Lab asst entom, Mich State Col, 40; instr, Univ Maine, 47-49; asst, Univ Ill, 49-52. *Concurrent Pos:* Consult & pest control adv. *Mem:* Entom Soc Am; Acarological Soc Am; Sigma Xi; hon mem Future Farmers Am; Native Plant Soc; Geneal Soc. *Res:* Citrus, alfalfa, melon and turf insects; systematics and biology of Tetranychoidea. *Mailing Add:* 308 22nd Ave Yuma AZ 85364-1718

**TUTTLE, ELBERT P, JR**, PHYSIOLOGY, INTERNAL MEDICINE. *Current Pos:* from asst prof to prof, 57-91, EMER PROF MED, SCH MED, EMORY UNIV, 91- *Personal Data:* b Ithaca, NY, Sept 1, 21; m 52; c 5. *Educ:* Princeton Univ, AB, 42; Harvard Univ, MD, 51. *Prof Exp:* Asst med, Harvard Med Sch & Mass Gen Hosp, 54-56. *Concurrent Pos:* Nat Heart Inst res fel, 53-56; Am Heart Asn res fel, 57; chair cardiovasc res, Ga Heart Asn, 58-72. *Mem:* Am Fedn Clin Res. *Res:* Inorganic metabolism; renal and circulatory physiology; hypertension; nephrology. *Mailing Add:* 120 Piedmont Ave Atlanta GA 30303-2418

**TUTTLE, ELIZABETH R**, MECHANISMS. *Current Pos:* From asst prof to prof physics, 64-86, PROF ENG, UNIV DENVER, 86- *Personal Data:* b Boston, Mass, Dec 5, 38. *Educ:* Univ NH, BS, 60; Univ Colo, MS, 61, MS, 87, PhD(physics), 64. *Mem:* Am Phys Soc; Am Asn Physics Teachers; Nat Soc Prof Engrs; Am Soc Mech Engrs; Am Soc Eng Educ; Soc Indust & Appl Math. *Res:* Type synthesis of planar mechanisms; laminar flow in curved pipes. *Mailing Add:* Dept Eng Univ Denver Denver CO 80208

**TUTTLE, JEREMY BALLOU**, TROPHIC & GROWTH FACTORS IN DISEASES, CELLULAR NEUROPHYSIOLOGY. *Current Pos:* asst prof, 84-93, ASSOC PROF UROL & NEUROSCI, SCH MED, UNIV VA, 93- *Personal Data:* b New York, NY, Oct 9, 47; m 70, Sara J Stasko. *Educ:* Univ Rochester, AB, 69, Johns Hopkins Univ, PhD(physiol & pharmacol), 77. *Prof Exp:* NIH fel, Univ Conn, 76-80, from vis asst prof to asst prof res, 80-84. *Mem:* Soc Neurosci; Biophys Soc; Sigma Xi; NY Acad Sci; Am Soc Cell Biol; Soc Basic Urol Res. *Res:* Control of neurotrophin production and consequences of disturbances in neurotrophin production in specific diseases and disease models, including interstitial cystitis, bladder obstruction, hypertension parkinson's disease and Alzheimer's disease. *Mailing Add:* 900 Stillwater Lane Earlysville VA 22936. *Fax:* 804-982-4159; *E-Mail:* tuttle@virginia.edu

**TUTTLE, KENNETH LEWIS**, FUELS COMBUSTION, GASIFICATION OF WOOD. *Current Pos:* PROF, NAVAL ACAD, 83- *Personal Data:* b Toledo, Ore, Apr 4, 44; m 67, Susanna Woodworth; c Stephanie, Meghan & Lewis. *Educ:* US Naval Acad, BS, 67; Ore State Univ, MS, 74, PhD(mech eng), 78. *Prof Exp:* Grad asst, Ore State Univ, 72-77; res engr, Weyerhaeuser Co, 77-81; prin, Solid Fuel Energy Assocs, 81-83. *Concurrent Pos:* Prin, Tuttle Energy Conversion & Exchange, 72-77 & Solid Fuel Res, 84-; dir, Marine Propulsion Labs, Naval Acad, 83-90; chmn, Ocean & Marine Eng Div, Am Soc Eng Educ, 89-91, Environ Panel, Soc Naval Archit & Marine Engrs. *Mem:* Nat Acad Sci; Nat Acad Eng; Am Soc Eng Educ; Soc Naval Archit & Marine Engrs; Combustion Inst. *Res:* Bio-mass energy; awarded one patent for a method of firing to reduce air pollution; internal combustion engines including gasohol, air pollution, and fuels; closed loop engines for deep submergence vehicles; reliability centered maintenance; computers in education; granted one patent. *Mailing Add:* 1098 Broadview Dr Annapolis MD 21401. *Fax:* 410-293-2591; *E-Mail:* tuttle@nadn.navy.mil

**TUTTLE, MERLIN DEVERE**, POPULATION ECOLOGY & BEHAVIOR, MAMMALOGY. *Current Pos:* FOUNDER & EXEC DIR, BAT CONSERVATION, INT, 82- *Personal Data:* b Honolulu, Hawaii, Aug 26, 41. *Educ:* Andrews Univ, BA, 65; Univ Kans, MA, 69, PhD(pop ecol), 74. *Prof Exp:* Co-dir, Smithsonian Venezuelan Res Proj, Smithsonian Inst, 65-67; res assoc pop ecol, Univ Minn, 72; cur mammals, Milwaukee Pub Mus, 75-85. *Concurrent Pos:* Consult endangered bats, Tenn Valley Authority, 76-; mem, Recovery Team Endangered Indiana & Gray Bats, US Fish & Wildlife Serv, 79-; pres, Bat Conserv Int, 82- *Mem:* Am Soc Mammalogists; Am Soc Naturalists; Ecol Soc Am; Soc Study Evolution; Nat Speleol Soc. *Res:* Predator/prey interaction, communication; foraging behavior in refuging species and the energetics of thermoregulation, hibernation and migration. *Mailing Add:* Bat Conservation Int PO Box 162603 Austin TX 78716-2603. *Fax:* 512-327-9724

**TUTTLE, RICHARD SUNESON**, PHYSIOLOGY, PHARMACOLOGY. *Current Pos:* Res fel, 60-64, RES ASSOC NEUROPHYSIOL, MASONIC MED RES FOUND, 64- *Personal Data:* b Pottsville, Pa, Aug 18, 30; m 60; c 1. *Educ:* State Univ NY, PhD(pharm), 60. *Concurrent Pos:* USPHS fel, 60-61; NIH grants, 63-; Fogarty fel, Sweden, 78; vis chair pharmacol, Div Astra, Hasssle Res Inst. *Mem:* Am Physiol Soc; Am Soc Pharmacol & Exp Therapeut. *Res:* Pharmacology of cardiac glycosides and electrolytes; neurophysiology of vasomotor regulation; centrally evoked histamine release; role of histamine in control of cardiovascular tone; cardiovascular effects of imidazoles and mesenteric Pacinian baroreceptors. *Mailing Add:* 5 Holemark Lane Savannah GA 31411

**TUTTLE, ROBERT LEWIS**, MICROBIOLOGY. *Current Pos:* RETIRED. *Personal Data:* b Boston, Mass, July 26, 22; m 42; c 2. *Educ:* Univ NH, BS, 43; Univ Rochester, MD, 47. *Prof Exp:* Asst trop med, Bowman Gray Sch Med, 48-50, from instr to assoc prof microbiol, 50-70, chmn dept, 55-62, assoc dean, 62-69, acad dean, 69-70; prof microbiol, Univ Tex Med Sch Houston, 70-80, assoc dean acad affairs, 70-75, dean, 75-81, Tex Tech Med Sch, Regional Dean, El Paso, 81-84. *Mailing Add:* 174 Wednesday Hill Rd Lee NH 03824

**TUTTLE, RONALD RALPH**, PHARMACOLOGY, PHYSIOLOGY. *Current Pos:* AT HOUGHTEN PHARMACEUT. *Personal Data:* b Colorado Springs, Colo, July 10, 36; m 63; c 1. *Educ:* Colo Col, BA, 60; Univ Man, MS, 64, PhD(pharmacol), 66. *Prof Exp:* Fel pharmacol, Emory Univ, 66-67; sr pharmacologist, Lilly Res Labs, 67-71, res scientist, 71-74, res assoc pharmacol, 74-78, res adv, 78-; vpres & dir, New Drug Develop, Key

Pharmaceut Inc. *Concurrent Pos:* Mem coun circulation fel, Am Heart Asn. *Mem:* Am Soc Pharmacol & Exp Therapeut. *Res:* Cardiovascular pharmacology. *Mailing Add:* Houghten Pharmaceut 3550 Gen Atomics Ct San Diego CA 92121

**TUTTLE, RUSSELL HOWARD,** PRIMATOLOGY, PALEOANTHROPOLOGY. *Current Pos:* PROF ANTHROP, UNIV CHICAGO, 64- *Personal Data:* b Marion, Ohio, Aug 18, 39; m 68, Marlene Benjamin; c Nicole Irene & Mathew. *Educ:* Ohio State Univ, BSc, 61, MA, 62; Univ Calif, Berkeley, PhD(anthrop), 65. *Honors & Awards:* Medal of Foundation, Singer-Polignac; Guggenheim Award. *Prof Exp:* Assoc scientist, Yerkes Primate Res Ctr. *Concurrent Pos:* Wenner-Gren res grants, Univ Chicago, 65, 66 & 69, NSF res grants, 66-77 & 85-89, USPHS res career develop award, 68-73; vis res prof, Japan Soc Prom Sci, 74 & 80; ed, Int J Primatology, 89- *Mem:* AAAS; Am Anthrop Asn; Am Asn Phys Anthropologists; Int Primatological Soc; Sigma Xi. *Res:* Behavior and comparative functional morphology of anthropoid primates and available fossils in order to elucidate the evolution of human bipedalism, tool use and other subsistence behaviors. *Mailing Add:* Dept Anthrop Univ Chicago 1126 E 59th St Chicago IL 60637. *Fax:* 773-702-4503; *E-Mail:* russt@cicero.spc.uchicago.edu

**TUTTLE, SHERWOOD DODGE,** GEOMORPHOLOGY. *Current Pos:* from asst prof to prof geol, Univ Iowa, 52-88, chmn dept geol, 63-68, assoc dean col lib arts, 70-84, EMER PROF GEOL, UNIV IOWA, 88- *Personal Data:* b Medford, Mass, June 8, 18; m 41, Esther Barrett; c Mark S, Beverly R (Storm) & Owen S. *Educ:* Univ NH, BS, 39; Wash State Univ, MS, 41; Harvard Univ, MA & PhD(geol), 53. *Prof Exp:* Instr geol, Wash State Univ, 41 & 46-48. *Concurrent Pos:* Res assoc, Woods Hole Oceanog Inst, 59-66; Fulbright lectr, Chinese Univ Hong Kong, 68-69. *Mem:* Col Fel Geol Soc Am; Nat Asn Geol Teachers; Am Inst Prof Geologists; Asn Earth Sci Eds. *Res:* Fluvial geomorphology; geology of national parks and national military parks. *Mailing Add:* 115 Wessex Pl Ft Thomas KY 41075

**TUTTLE, THOMAS R, JR,** PHYSICAL CHEMISTRY. *Current Pos:* from asst prof to assoc prof, 60-83, PROF CHEM, BRANDEIS UNIV, 83- *Personal Data:* b Somerville, Mass, Mar 28, 28; m 54; c 3. *Educ:* Northeastern Univ, BS, 53, MS, 55; Wash Univ, St Louis, PhD, 57. *Prof Exp:* Actg asst prof chem, Stanford Univ, 57-60. *Mem:* Am Chem Soc; Am Phys Soc; AAAS; Am Inst Chem; NY Acad Sci. *Res:* Determination of structures of chemical species in liquid solutions; thermodynamics of electrolytic solutions; properties of solvated electrons and metal solutions in polar solvents. *Mailing Add:* Dept Chem Brandeis Univ Waltham MA 02154

**TUTTLE, WARREN WILSON,** NEUROPHARMACOLOGY. *Current Pos:* actg chmn dept, 72-73, assoc prof & chmn dept, 72-83, PROF & CHMN DEPT PHARMACOL, COL OSTEOP MED, UNIV HEALTH SCI, 83- *Personal Data:* b Fulton, Mo, Aug 2, 30; m 52; c 4. *Educ:* Univ Mo, BA, 52; Univ Kans City, BS, 58, MS, 60; Univ Calif, San Francisco, PhD(pharmacol), 66. *Prof Exp:* Asst prof pharmacol, Univ Mo-Kans City, 65-68; asst prof med pharmacol & therapeut, Sch Med, Univ Calif, Irvine, 68-69; asst prof pharmacol, Univ Mo-Kans City, 69-72. *Mem:* Sigma Xi; Asn Med Sch Pharmacog; Am Soc Pharmacol & Exp Therapeut. *Res:* Drug metabolism; electroencephalographic investigation into the sites of action of various drugs in the central nervous system. *Mailing Add:* Dept Pharmacol Univ Health Sci 2105 Independence Blvd Kansas City MO 64124-2311

**TUTUPALLI, LOHIT VENKATESWARA,** PHARMACOGNOSY, PHYTOCHEMISTRY. *Current Pos:* RES SCIENTIST, CALIF CEDAR PROD RES LAB, 74- *Personal Data:* b Guntur, Andhra Pradesh, India, Aug 10, 45; m 74. *Educ:* Andhra Univ, BS, 63; Bombay Univ, BS, 66, MS, 68; Univ of the Pac, PhD(pharmacog), 74. *Prof Exp:* Res pharmacist product develop, M/S Pfizer (India), Ltd, Bombay, 68-69; from teaching asst to instr pharmacog, Univ of the Pac, 69-74. *Mem:* Am Pharmaceut Asn; Am Chem Soc; NY Acad Sci; Am Soc Pharmacog; Forest Prod Res Soc. *Res:* Investigating the economic uses of forest products. *Mailing Add:* 1131 Stanton Way Stockton CA 95207

**TUTWILER, GENE FLOYD,** BIOCHEMISTRY, ENDOCRINOLOGY. *Current Pos:* dir, Biol Res, 86-87, DIR, PROJ MGT, MCNEIL PHARMACEUT, 87- *Personal Data:* b Peoria, Ill, Sept 19, 45; m 68; c 2. *Educ:* Western Ill Univ, BS, 67; Univ Mich, Ann Arbor, PhD(biochem), 70. *Prof Exp:* Sr scientist, McNeil Pharmaceut, Inc, 70-74, group leader, 74-77, res fel, 77-80, sect head endocrinol & metab, Dept Biol Res, 80-84; dir biochem, Ayerst Res Labs, Inc, 84-86. *Concurrent Pos:* Teaching fel biochem, Univ Mich, Ann Arbor, 67-70; vis asst prof, Temple Univ, 73-74 & Bucks County Community Col, 74- & Univ Pa, 77-78; adj asst prof, Temple Univ, 79-83 & Univ Pa, 80-83; adj assoc prof, Temple Univ, 83- & Univ Pa, 83- *Mem:* Am Endocrine Soc; Am Diabetes Asn; Soc Exp Biol & Med; Am Soc Biochem Molecular Genetics; Am Soc Pharmacol & Exp Therapeut. *Res:* Diabetes; obesity; protein purification; isolation pituitary proteins; free fatty acid metabolism; carbohydrate metabolism; atherosclerosis. *Mailing Add:* Alpha Therapeut Corp 5555 Valley Blvd Los Angeles CA 90032. *Fax:* 909-399-1426

**TUUL, JOHANNES,** PHYSICS. *Current Pos:* from asst prof to prof, 65-91, chmn, Dept Physics & Earth Sci, 71-75, EMER PROF PHYSICS, CALIF STATE POLYTECH UNIV, 92- *Personal Data:* b Tarvastu, Estonia, May 23, 22; US citizen; div; c Melinda, Melissa & Johannes Jr. *Educ:* Stockholm Univ, BS, 55, MA, 56; Brown Univ, ScM, 57, PhD(physics), 60. *Prof Exp:* Res asst physics, Brown Univ, 55-57, 58-60, res assoc, 60; res physicist, Stamford Res

Labs, Am Cyanamid Co, Conn, 60-62; sr res physicist, Bell & Howell Res Ctr, Calif, 62-65. *Concurrent Pos:* Consult, Bell & Howell Res Ctr, 68 & Teledyne Inc, 68; vis assoc prof, Pahlavi Univ, Iran, 68-70; resident dir, Calif State Univ & Col Int Prog, Sweden & Denmark, 77-78. *Mem:* AAAS; Am Phys Soc; Am Asn Physics Teachers; NY Acad Sci. *Res:* Adsorption of gases on solids; low-energy electron diffraction studies of effects of adsorption and ion bombardment on initially clean surfaces; ultra-high vacuum technology; physics education; energy conservation and new energy technologies. *Mailing Add:* 1053 Airshire Lane Pomona CA 91766

**TUVE, RICHARD LARSEN,** PHYSICAL CHEMISTRY, INORGANIC CHEMISTRY. *Current Pos:* RETIRED. *Personal Data:* b Canton, SDak, Feb 1, 12; m 36, Maxine Duvel; c Richard L II & Christine. *Educ:* Am Univ, BA, 35. *Hon Degrees:* DSc, Carleton Col, 61. *Prof Exp:* Asst chemist, Res Assocs, Inc, 35-38; asst chemist, US Naval Res Lab, 38-40, assoc phys chemist, 40-41, head, Eng Res Br, 41-70; consult, Appl Physics Lab, Johns Hopkins Univ, Silver Spring, 70-80. *Concurrent Pos:* Mem comt fire res conf, Nat Acad Sci-Nat Res Coun, 55-68. *Mem:* Fel AAAS; Am Chem Soc; Am Inst Chem Eng; fel Am Inst Chem; Nat Fire Protect Asn. *Res:* Chemistry of fire extinguishment; foam extinguishment methods and materials; flame propagation; surface chemistry; special explosives; fire fighting equipment design; combustion inhibition; author of one textbook. *Mailing Add:* 9211 Crosby Rd Silver Spring MD 20910

**TUVESON, ROBERT WILLIAMS,** genetics, botany; deceased, see previous edition for last biography

**TUZAR, JAROSLAV,** MATHEMATICS. *Current Pos:* from assoc prof to prof, 70-84, EMER PROF MATH, NORTHWESTERN UNIV, 84- *Personal Data:* b Czech, Mar 25, 15; nat US; m 48; c 1. *Educ:* Charles Univ, Prague, MA, 39 & 45, ScD(math), 48. *Prof Exp:* Asst prof, State Tech Col, Prague, 45-48; Rockefeller Found fel, Univ Chicago, 48-50; dir control & res lab, Salerno-Megowen Biscuit Co, 50-70. *Concurrent Pos:* Lectr, Northwestern Univ, 60-70. *Mem:* Math Asn Am; Am Statist Asn. *Res:* Mathematical probability and statistics; pedagogy of mathematics. *Mailing Add:* 8929 Elmore St Niles IL 60648-1720

**TUZSON, JOHN J(ANOS),** FLUID MECHANICS, ROTATING MACHINERY. *Current Pos:* PRIN, JOHN TUZSON & ASSOCS, 94- *Personal Data:* b Budapest, Hungary, Apr 29, 29; US citizen; m 60, Ruth Post; c Emily, Martha & Ann. *Educ:* Conserv Nat Arts et Metiers, France, MMech Eng, 55; Mass Inst Technol, ScD(mech eng), 59. *Prof Exp:* Res asst mech eng, Mass Inst Technol, 56-58; res engr fluid dynamics, Whirlpool Corp, Mich, 58-61; assoc prof, Mich State Univ, 61; res engr fluid mech, IIT Res Inst, 62-63; asst dir, Res Ctr, Borg-Warner Corp, Des Plaines, 63-79; mgr fluid technol, Allis-Chalmers, Milwaukee, 79-83; prog mgr, Gas Res Inst, Chicago, 83-93. *Concurrent Pos:* Teaching asst, Ill Inst Technol, 62-72; ed, Proc Nat Conf Fluid Power, 62-72. *Mem:* Am Soc Mech Engrs. *Res:* Swirling flow; two phase flow; turbomachinery; hydraulic, pneumatic and fluidic controls; process equipment; slurry; industrial power generation; gas turbines; rotary engines. *Mailing Add:* 1220 Maple Ave Evanston IL 60202

**TUZZOLINO, ANTHONY J,** PHYSICS, SOLID STATE PHYSICS. *Current Pos:* PHYSICIST, UNIV CHICAGO, 58- *Personal Data:* b Chicago, Ill, July 1, 31; m 54; c 2. *Educ:* Univ Chicago, MS, 55, PhD(physics), 58. *Res:* Semiconductor nuclear particle and photon detectors. *Mailing Add:* 5640 S Ellis Ave Chicago IL 60637-1433

**TWARDOCK, ARTHUR ROBERT,** VETERINARY PHYSIOLOGY, NUCLEAR MEDICINE. *Current Pos:* from asst prof to assoc prof, Univ Ill, Urbana, 62-70, prof vet phys, 70-, assoc dean acad affairs, 73-86, actg head, Dept Vet Physiol & Pharm, 74-77, actg dean, Col Vet Med, 89- PROF VET BIOL SCI, UNIV ILL, URBANA. *Personal Data:* b Normal, Ill, July 20, 31; m 54; c 4. *Educ:* Univ Ill, BS, 54, DVM, 56; Cornell Univ, PhD(animal physiol), 61. *Prof Exp:* Vet practitioner, Hillcrest Animal Hosp, 56-57; res asst radiobiol, Cornell Univ, 57-60, res assoc phys biol, 60-62. *Mem:* AAAS; Am Physiol Soc; Am Soc Vet Physiol & Pharmacol; Am Vet Med Asn; Conf Res Workers Animal Diseases; Sigma Xi; Soc Nuclear Med. *Res:* Mineral metabolism; placental transfer of mineral elements; applications of radioisotope techniques in veterinary nuclear medicine. *Mailing Add:* Col Vet Med Univ Ill 220 Large Animal Clin 1102 Hazelwood Urbana IL 61801

**TWARDOWSKI, ZBYLUT JOZEF,** NEPHROLOGY, ARTIFICIAL INTERNAL ORGANS. *Current Pos:* PROF, DEPT MED, UNIV MO, 85- *Personal Data:* b Stanislawice, Poland, June 2, 34; US citizen; m 58, Halina Nowosielska; c Radomysl & Przemyslaw. *Educ:* Copernicus Med Acad, Krakow, Poland, MD, 59, PhD(med), 64; Silesian Med Acad, Katowice, Poland, 75. *Honors & Awards:* Torchbearer Award, Am Kidney Fund, 93. *Prof Exp:* Dir internal med, Hosp Miners, Bytom, Poland, 63-76; dir, Dept Nephrology, Med Acad, Lublin, Poland, 76-82. *Concurrent Pos:* Mem Transplantation & Dialysis Comt, Ministry of Health & Social Servs, 66-82; consult, Baxter-Travenol, 82-, prin investr, peritoneal dialysis, 83-; dir, Outpatient Peritoneal Dialysis Prog, Univ Mo, 85-; mem prog comt, Am Soc Artificial Internal Organs, 87- *Mem:* Europ Dialysis & Transplant Asn; Int Soc Nephrology; Am Col Physicians; Am Soc Artificial Internal Organs; Biomed Eng Soc; Int Peritoneal Dialysis Soc; hon mem Colombian Soc Nephrology. *Res:* Kinetics of peritoneal dialysis and modifications of peritoneal dialysis to achieve adequate treatment of renal failure; introduced two major modifications; access (catheter) for peritoneal dialysis and hemodialysis; developed new peritoneal dialysis catheters which when used are associated with markedly decreased complications; developed artificial kidney for daily home hemodialysis. *Mailing Add:* 304 Devine Ct Columbia MO 65203

**TWAROG, BETTY MACK,** PHYSIOLOGY, NEUROSCIENCES. *Current Pos:* RES SCIENTIST, BIGELOW LAB OCEAN SCI, 90- *Personal Data:* b New York, NY, Aug 28, 27; m 47; c Stanley. *Educ:* Swarthmore Col, AB, 48; Tufts Col, MS, 49; Radcliffe Col, PhD(biol), 52. *Prof Exp:* Asst, Harvard Univ, 52 & Res Div, Cleveland Clin, 52-53; res assoc & instr, Tufts Col, 53-55; res fel, Harvard Univ, 55-58; instr, 58-60; USPHS trainee, Oxford Univ, 60-61; asst prof physiol & biophys, Sch Med, NY Univ, 61-65; res fel, Harvard Univ, 65-66; prof biol, Tufts Univ, 66-75; prof physiol & anat sci, State Univ NY, Stony Brook, 75-81; prof & chmn biol, Bryn Mawr Col, 82-85; res scientist, Bockus Res Inst, 84-91. *Concurrent Pos:* John Simon Guggenheim Mem fel, Melbourne Univ, Australia, 72-73; prog dir, NSF, 77-78 & 90; adj prof physiol, Univ Pa, 84-91. *Mem:* Soc Gen Physiologists (pres, 78-79); Biophys Soc; Am Physiol Soc; fel AAAS; Am Soc Zoologists. *Res:* Physiology and pharmacology of smooth muscle; neurophysiology; neuropharmacology; control of contraction and relaxation in mollusc catch muscle; developmental and environmental regulation of pulmonary vascular smooth muscle phenotype; marine neurotoxins associated with algal blooms; effects on vector species. *Mailing Add:* Bigelow Lab Ocean Sci McKown Point West Boothbay Harbor ME 04575. *Fax:* 207-633-9641

**TWAROG, BRUCE ANTHONY,** PHOTOMETRY. *Current Pos:* from asst prof to assoc prof, 82-93, PROF ASTRON, UNIV KANS, 93- *Personal Data:* b Chester, Pa, Aug 10, 52; m 77; c 2. *Educ:* Case Western Res Univ, BS, 74; Yale Univ, MS, 78, PhD(astron), 80. *Honors & Awards:* Trumpler Prize, Astron Soc Pac, 82. *Prof Exp:* Vis instr astron, Univ Tex, Austin, 80-82. *Concurrent Pos:* Mem time allocation comt, Cerro Tololo InterAm Observ, 82-86; mem sci adv comt, NASA-Univ Ariz Astrometric Space Telescope, 85-86, HST PRE-TAC Panel, 92 & 96. *Mem:* Am Astron Soc; Int Astron Union; Sigma Xi; Astron Soc Pac. *Res:* Galactic evolution and stellar populations; stellar photometry. *Mailing Add:* Dept Physics & Astron Univ Kans Lawrence KS 66045

**TWAROG, ROBERT,** MICROBIAL BIOCHEMISTRY. *Current Pos:* asst prof, 65-74, ASSOC PROF BACT, SCH MED, UNIV NC, CHAPEL HILL, 74- *Personal Data:* b Lowell, Mass, Mar 17, 35; m 58; c 2. *Educ:* Univ Conn, BS, 56, MS, 58; Univ Ill, PhD(microbiol), 62. *Prof Exp:* Lab officer, USAF Epidemiol Lab, San Antonio, Tex, 62-65. *Mem:* AAAS; Am Soc Microbiol. *Res:* Control mechanisms of microbial processes; molecular biology; microbiology. *Mailing Add:* Dept Microbiol & Immunol Univ NC Chapel Hill Sch Med Chapel Hill NC 27599-7290

**TWAY, PATRICIA C,** CHROMATOGRAPHY, MASS SPECTROMETRY. *Current Pos:* Staff chemist anal res, Merck & Co, 69-70, res chemist, 70-73, sr res chemist, 73-78, res fel, 78-83, assoc dir, 84-86, dir, 86-88, sr dir, 88-90, exec dir, Merck Sharp & Dohme Res Lab, 90-, VPRES, MERCK & CO. *Personal Data:* b Worcester, Mass, Sept 29, 45; c 2. *Educ:* Mt Holyoke Col, BA, 67; Rutgers Univ, MS, 69; Seton Hall Univ, PhD(anal chem), 80. *Mem:* Am Chem Soc; Am Soc Mass Spectrometry. *Res:* Analytical methodology to support pharmaceutical development process research; test methods and specifications for raw materials, process intermediates and bulk drug. *Mailing Add:* Merck & Co Inc 1 Merck Dr PO Box 100 Whitehouse Station NJ 08889

**TWEDT, ROBERT MADSEN,** MICROBIOLOGY. *Current Pos:* RETIRED. *Personal Data:* b Rochester, Minn, July 4, 24; m 94, Patricia A Perkins; c David P. *Educ:* Univ Minn, BS, 45; Univ Colo, MS, 49, PhD(microbiol), 52. *Prof Exp:* Res fel microbiol, Western Res Univ, 52-54; asst scientist, Univ Minn, 54-56, res fel physiol chem, 56-59; from asst prof to assoc prof biol, Univ Detroit, 59-67; res microbiologist, Nat Ctr Urban & Indust Health, Food & Drug Admin, 67-69, from microbiologist to asst chief, Food Microbiol Br, 69-77, actg chief, 78-79, chief, Bacterial Physiol Br, 80-86, chief, Virulence Assess Br, 87-90. *Concurrent Pos:* Am Cancer Soc fel, 52-53; microbiologist, Fed Water Pollution Control Admin, 66; adj prof, Univ Detroit, 68-70; adj fac, Univ Ky, Jeff Comm Col, 93; consult, Ky Nat Res Environ Protection Lab, 94- *Mem:* Am Soc Microbiol; fel Am Acad Microbiol; Int Asn Milk, Food & Environ Sanitarians; Sigma Xi. *Res:* Research and field investigations to identify, evaluate and resolve microbiological problems of public health significance associated with foods. *Mailing Add:* 3525 Hwy 127 N Owenton KY 40359-9333

**TWEED, DAVID GEORGE,** SYSTEMS DESIGN. *Current Pos:* VPRES ENG, GEN SCANNING, 77- *Personal Data:* b Troy, NY. *Educ:* Mass Inst Technol, BS, 66. *Prof Exp:* Engr, Draper Labs, 66-67; sr engr, Electronic Image Systs, 67-72; prod mgr, Brattle Instruments, 72-77. *Res:* Research and development of advance laser based electro-photographic techniques. *Mailing Add:* 4077 Mallard Dr Melbourne FL 32934

**TWEED, JOHN,** APPLIED MATHEMATICS. *Current Pos:* assoc prof math, 74-77, PROF MATH & COMPUT SCI, OLD DOMINION UNIV, 77- *Personal Data:* b Greenock, Scotland, Mar 29, 42; m 66; c 2. *Educ:* Univ Strathclyde, MSc, 65; Univ Glasgow, PhD(appl math), 68, DSc, 81. *Prof Exp:* From asst lectr to lectr math, Univ Glasgow, 65-69; vis asst prof, NO State Univ, 69-70, Univ Glasgow, 70-73; vis prof, NC State Univ, 73-74. *Mem:* Soc Indust & Appl Math; fel Brit Inst Math & Appln; Am Acad Mech. *Res:* Applications of transform techniques and integral equations to the solution of mixed boundary value problems in fracture mechanics. *Mailing Add:* Dept Math Sci Norfolk VA 23508

**TWEEDDALE, MARTIN GEORGE,** CLINICAL PHARMACOLOGY. *Current Pos:* assoc physician internal med, 73-86, CHMN INTENSIVE CARE UNIT, VANCOUVER GEN HOSP, ST JOHNS NFLD, 86- *Personal Data:* b Bristol, Eng, Aug 22, 40. *Educ:* King's Col, Univ London, BSc, 62; PhD(pharmacol), 65; Westminister Med Sch, Univ London, MB, BS, 67; FRCPS(C), 72. *Prof Exp:* Asst prof med clin pharmacol, Mem Univ Nfld, 73-78, assoc prof, 78- *Concurrent Pos:* Develop grant, Can Found Advan Clin Pharmacol, 73-77. *Mem:* Can Soc Clin Invest; Can Crit Care Soc; Can Pharmacol Soc; Am Soc Clin Pharmacol & Therapeut; Soc Critical Care Med. *Res:* Plasma inhibitors of pulmonary surfactant and their role in human pulmonary disorders; isotopic investigation of physiological fluid volumes in the critically ill; the effects of and indications for high frequency jet ventilation. *Mailing Add:* Vancouver Gen Hosp ICU 855 W 12th Ave Vancouver BC V5Z 1M9 Can. *Fax:* 604-875-4816

**TWEEDELL, KENYON STANLEY,** DEVELOPMENTAL BIOLOGY, ONCOLOGY. *Current Pos:* from asst prof to prof, 58-94, EMER PROF BIOL, UNIV NOTRE DAME, 94- *Personal Data:* b Sterling, Ill, Mar 28, 24; m 56, Jean Ellen Werber; c Eric, Karen, Kristin, Lisa & Brigit. *Educ:* Univ Ill, BS, 47, MS, 49, PhD(zool,physiol), 53. *Prof Exp:* Res assoc biol, Control Systs Lab, Univ Ill, 51-54; from instr to asst prof zool, Univ Maine, 54-58. *Concurrent Pos:* Corp mem, Marine Biol Lab, Woods Hole. *Mem:* AAAS; Int Soc Develop Biol; Am Soc Zool; Sigma Xi; Soc Develop Biol. *Res:* Experimental pathology; transmissable tumors of Amphibia; developmental biology, especially oogenesis, ovulation, regeneration in invertebrates, cytodifferentiation in normal and malignant cells. *Mailing Add:* Dept Biol Sci Univ Notre Dame Notre Dame IN 46556. *E-Mail:* tweedell.1@nd.edu

**TWEEDIE, ADELBERT THOMAS,** POLYMER CHEMISTRY. *Current Pos:* RETIRED. *Personal Data:* b Saginaw, Mich, Jan 5, 31; m 53; c 3. *Educ:* Univ Mich, BSCh, 53; Univ Ill, PhD(org chem), 56. *Prof Exp:* Res chemist, Dow Chem Co, Mich, 56-58 & Aerojet-Gen Corp, Calif, 58-62; tech supvr rocket propellants, Union Carbide Corp, WVa, 62-64; mgr mat eng, Space Div, Gen Elec Co, King of Prussia, 64-89, chief scientist, 88-89. *Concurrent Pos:* Mem Mat Adv Comt, NASA. *Mem:* Am Inst Aeronaut & Astronaut; Am Chem Soc; AAAS. *Res:* Behavior of materials in the space environment; vibration damping; application of materials to spacecraft; polymers; solar energy; fracture mechanics of viscoelastic materials. *Mailing Add:* 218 Chester Rd Devon PA 19333-1627

**TWEEDIE, RICHARD LEWIS,** STOCHASTIC PROCESSES. *Current Pos:* PROF STATIST, COLO STATE UNIV, 91- *Personal Data:* b Weeton, New Australia, Aug 22, 47; m 71, Catherine Robertson; c Marianne L. *Educ:* Australian Nat Univ, BA(Hons), 68; MA, 69, DSc, 86; Cambridge Univ, PhD(probability), 72. *Prof Exp:* Fel, Australian Nat Univ, 73-74; res scientist, Commonwealth Sci & Indust Res Orgn, 74-81; assoc prof statist, Univ Western Australia, 79; managing dir, Siromath, 81-87; prof info sci & dean info & comput sci, Bond Univ, 87-91. *Mem:* Fel Inst Math Statist; Int Statist Inst; Am Statist Asn. *Res:* Development of structural results for stochastic models, especially stability and ergodicity of Markonian models; statistical methods of epidemiology. *Mailing Add:* 1609 E Lake St Ft Collins CO 80524

**TWEEDIE, VIRGIL LEE,** ORGANIC CHEMISTRY. *Current Pos:* RETIRED. *Personal Data:* b Norborne, Mo, Feb 18, 18; m 43, Helen Hultz; c Cheryl (Pearce), Kenneth & Martha (North). *Educ:* Univ Mo, AB, 41, MA, 43; Univ Tex, PhD(chem), 51. *Prof Exp:* Res chemist, Commercial Solvents Corp, 42-46; asst prof, Baylor Univ, 46-48, assoc prof, 50-53, prof chem, 53-88. *Mem:* Sigma Xi; Am Chem Soc; Nat Asn Adv Health Professions. *Res:* Allylic compounds; organometallics; complex metal hydrides and alkides; hydrogenolysis. *Mailing Add:* 7720 Tallahassee Rd Waco TX 76712-3817

**TWEEDLE, CHARLES DAVID,** neurobiology, for more information see previous edition

**TWEEDY, BILLY GENE,** PLANT PATHOLOGY. *Current Pos:* mgr residue invest, 73-78, DIR, BIOCHEM DEPT, CIBA-GEIGY CORP, 78- *Personal Data:* b Cobden, Ill, Dec 31, 34; m 57, Patsy A Glasco; c Lynn, Glenna & Carol. *Educ:* Univ Southern Ill, BS, 56; Univ Ill, MS, 59, PhD(plant path), 61. *Honors & Awards:* Medal, 8th Int Cong Plant Protection; Secy Agr Award, 9th Int Cong Plant Protection. *Prof Exp:* Asst plant pathologist, Boyce Thompson Inst Plant Res, 61-65; asst prof plant path, Univ Mo-Columbia, 65-69, from assoc prof to prof, 69-73. *Concurrent Pos:* USDA, 71-72. *Mem:* AAAS; Am Phytopath Soc; Am Chem Soc; Weed Sci Soc Am; Sigma Xi. *Res:* Degradation of pesticides; integrated pest control; fungus physiology; fruit pathology. *Mailing Add:* 111 Crest Hill Rd Jamestown NC 27282. *Fax:* 910-454-2799

**TWEEDY, JAMES ARTHUR,** HORTICULTURE. *Current Pos:* From asst prof to assoc prof, Southern Ill Univ, 66-74, asst dean, Sch of Agr, 74-75, asst vpres acad affairs & res, 76-78, dean, Col Agr, 86-88, PROF PLANT INDUST, PLANT & SOIL SCI DEPT, SOUTHERN ILL UNIV, 74- *Personal Data:* b Cobden, Ill, Nov 29, 39; m 64; c 2. *Educ:* Southern Ill Univ, BS, 62; Mich State Univ, MS, 64, PhD(hort), 66. *Mem:* Weed Sci Soc Am. *Res:* Influence of herbicides on plant physiological processes; evaluation of herbicides for weed control in agronomic and horticultural crops. *Mailing Add:* Admin Affairs Southern Ill Univ Carbondale IL 62901-4399

**TWEET, ARTHUR GLENN,** SOLID STATE PHYSICS. *Current Pos:* mgr Phys Imaging Br, Advan Imaging Technol Lab, Xerox Corp, 64-68, mgr, Imaging Res Lab, 68-72, mgr technol planning, Info Technol Group, 72-75, MGR, TECH STRATEGIC PLANNING, XEROX CORP, 75- *Personal Data:* b Aberdeen, SDak, Sept 20, 27; m 50; c 3. *Educ:* Harvard Univ, AB, 48; Univ Wis, MS, 49, PhD(physics), 53. *Prof Exp:* Physicist, Semiconductor Sect, Res Labs, Gen Elec Corp, 53-59, liaison scientist, 59-61, physicist, Biol

Studies Sect, 61-64. *Concurrent Pos:* Adj prof, Rensselaer Polytech Inst, 62. *Mem:* Fel Am Phys Soc. *Res:* Energy transfer in excited molecules; unconventional photographic systems; dye sensitized reactions; electrical and surface properties of polymers; surface chemistry of chromophores; optical properties of large molecules; imperfections in semiconductors and insulators; nonaqueous electrochemistry; decision analysis; technological forecasting; operations analysis and modelling. *Mailing Add:* 280 Weymouth Dr Rochester NY 14625

**TWELVES, ROBERT RALPH,** ORGANIC CHEMISTRY. *Current Pos:* RETIRED. *Personal Data:* b Chicago, Ill, Nov 4, 27; m 53; c 3. *Educ:* Univ Utah, BS, 50, MA, 52; Univ Minn, PhD(org chem), 57. *Prof Exp:* Asst, Univ Utah, 50-51; process develop chemist, Merck & Co, 52-53; asst, Univ Minn, 53-55; res chemist, E I du Pont de Nemours & Co, Inc, 57-88. *Mem:* Am Chem Soc; Sigma Xi. *Res:* Fluorochemicals; dyes and intermediates; synthetic organic chemistry; chemicals for elastomers; analytical chemistry of polymers. *Mailing Add:* 236 Duncan Ave McDaniel Cr Wilmington DE 19803

**TWENHOFEL, WILLIAM STEPHENS,** geology applied to disposal of radioactive waste; deceased, see previous edition for last biography

**TWENTE, JOHN W,** ZOOLOGY. *Current Pos:* assoc prof biol & investr, Dalton Res Ctr, 66-, EMER PROF, UNIV MO, COLUMBIA. *Personal Data:* b Lawrence, Kans, Dec 18, 26; m 53; c 1. *Educ:* Univ Kans, AB, 50; Univ Mich, MS, 52, PhD(zool), 54. *Prof Exp:* Interim instr biol, Univ Fla, 54-55; instr zool, Col Pharm, Univ Ill, 55-56; instr, Univ Utah, 57-58, asst prof, 58-62, res biologist, 62-66. *Mem:* Am Soc Zool; Ecol Soc Am; Am Soc Mammal; fel AAAS. *Res:* Physiological ecology and behavior; hibernation physiology. *Mailing Add:* Bio Sci 105 Lesevre Bldg Univ Mo Columbia MO 65211

**TWERSKY, VICTOR,** MATHEMATICAL PHYSICS, MULTIPLE SCATTERING THEORY. *Current Pos:* prof, 66-90, EMER PROF MATH, UNIV ILL, CHICAGO, 91- *Personal Data:* b Poland, Aug 10, 23; nat US; m 50, Shirley Fine; c Lori, Mark & Nina. *Educ:* City Col New York, BS, 47; Columbia Univ, AM, 48; NY Univ, PhD(physics), 50. *Prof Exp:* Assoc, Guid Device Proj, Biol Dept, City Col New York, 46-49; asst physics, NY Univ, 49, res assoc electromagnetic theory, Inst Math Sci, 50-53; assoc, Nuclear Develop Assocs, 51-53; specialist theoret physics, Electronic Defense Labs, Sylvania Electronic Systs-West, Sylvania Elec Prod, Inc Div, Gen Tel & Electronics Corp, 53-58, sr specialist & lab consult, 58-60, sr scientist, 60-66, head res, Electronics Defense Labs, 58-66 & Sylvania Electronic Systs-West, 64-66. *Concurrent Pos:* Mem tech res comt, Am Found Blind, 47-49; lectr math, Stanford Univ, 56-58; assoc ed, J Optical Soc, 61-68, subj ed, Scattering & Radiation, J Acoust Soc, 63-66, Electromagnetic Theory, I R E Trans Antennas & Propagation, 65-66, J Geophysical Res, 65-68, J Math Physics, 77-79, J Appl Math, 72-83; vis prof or vis scholar, Technion-Israel Inst Technol, 62-63, Courant Inst Math Sci, 63, Stanford Univ, 67-97, Hebrew Univ Jerusalem, 72 & Weizmann Inst Sci, Rehovoth & Ben-Gurion Univ Negev, Beer Sheva, 79; feature ed, Microwaves & Optics, J Appl Optics, 65; consult, Sylvania Elec Prod Inc Div, Gen Tel & Electronics Corp, 66; mem, Ctr Advan Study, Univ Ill, 69-70; Guggenehim fel, 72-73 & 79-80; mem at large, Conf Bd Math Sci, 75-77; mem US Comn B, Int Union Radio Sci. *Mem:* Fel AAAS; fel Am Phys Soc; fel Acoust Soc Am; fel Optical Soc Am; fel Inst Elec & Electronics Engrs; Am Math Soc; Soc Ind & Appl Math. *Res:* Multiple scattering of electromagnetic and acoustic waves; rough surfaces; gratings; scattering and propagation in random distributions; radiative diagnostics of biological cells; relativistic scattering; applied mathematics; obstacle perception by the blind. *Mailing Add:* 14848 Manuella Rd Los Altos Hills CA 94022

**TWETO, OGDEN,** ECONOMIC GEOLOGY. *Current Pos:* geologist, 40-61, chief, South Rockies Br, 61-65, asst chief geologist & chief off econ geol, 65-68, RES GEOLOGIST, US GEOL SURV, 68- *Personal Data:* b Abercrombie, NDak, June 10, 12; m 40; c 2. *Educ:* Univ Mont, AB, 34, MA, 37; Univ Mich, PhD(geol), 47. *Prof Exp:* Instr, Univ NC, 39-40. *Mem:* AAAS; Geol Soc Am; Soc Econ Geol; Mineral Soc Am; Am Inst Mining, Metall & Petrol Eng. *Res:* Geology and mineral deposits of Southern Rocky Mountains. *Mailing Add:* 1995 Taft Dr Lakewood CO 80215

**TWIDWELL, LARRY G,** EXTRACTIVE & CHEMICAL METALLURGY. *Current Pos:* assoc prof, 69-76, PROF METALL ENG & HEAD DEPT, MONT COL MINERAL SCI & TECHNOL, 76- *Personal Data:* b Jackson, Mo, July 5, 39; m 61; c 3. *Educ:* Mo Sch Mines, BS, 61, MS, 62; Colo Sch Mines, DSc, 66. *Prof Exp:* Develop engr, Rocky Flats Div, Dow Chem Co, 62-63; assoc metallurgist, Monsanto Res Corp, 65-67; staff mem nuclear reactors, Reactor Develop Div, Sandia Corp, 67-69; prof metall eng & pres, Monlanes Environ, 83- *Concurrent Pos:* Proj officer, Environ Protection Agency, 78-80. *Mem:* Am Inst Mining, Metall & Petrol Engrs; Am Soc Eng Educ; Am Inst Mining & Metall Engrs. *Res:* Containment of radioisotopes at elevated temperatures; reactor development; thermodynamics of metallic solutions; nonferrous and ferrous process metallurgy; environmental and thermodynamics of metallic solutions; self-paced instruction; treatment of wastes, hydromettalurgy. *Mailing Add:* 1600 Blacktail Loop Rd Butte MT 59701

**TWIEG, DONALD BAKER,** BIOMEDICAL NUCLEAR MAGNETIC RESONANCE IMAGING. *Current Pos:* AT PHILIPS MED CTR , SAN FRANCISCO VET ADMIN MED CTR, 88- *Personal Data:* b Port Arthur, Tex, Dec 8, 44; m 69; c 2. *Educ:* Rice Univ, BA, 68, MS, 71; Southern Methodist Univ, PhD(biomed eng), 77. *Prof Exp:* Engr, Boeing Co, 72-73; asst prof, Dept Radiol, Univ Tex Health Sci Ctr, Dallas, 77-87. *Concurrent Pos:* Fac mem, Biomed Eng Grad Prog, Univ Tex Health Sci Ctr, Dallas, 77-, Radiol Sci Grad Prog, 82- *Mem:* Inst Elec & Electronics Engrs; AAAS; Soc Magnetic Resonance Imaging. *Res:* Theoretical investigations of nuclear magnetic resonance imaging processes; modeling of nuclear magnetic resonance imaging performance in biomedical applications; applications of optimal estimation and sampling theory in nuclear magnetic resonance imaging. *Mailing Add:* Dept Biomed Eng Univ Ala UAB BEC 256 UAB Sta Birmingham AL 35294

**TWIEST, GILBERT LEE,** ORNITHOLOGY, MISCONCEPTIONS. *Current Pos:* Instr biol, Kellogg Community assoc prof, 68-76, prof, 76-97, EMER PROF SCI EDUC, CLARION UNIV, 97- *Personal Data:* b Grand Rapids, Mich, Apr 23, 37; m 58, Linda L Danez; c Mark G & Bradley J. *Educ:* Mich State Univ, BS, 61, MS, 63; Univ Toledo, PhD(sci educ), 68. *Honors & Awards:* Outstanding Leadership, Coun Elem Sci Int. *Concurrent Pos:* Ed, Newsletter, Coun Elem Sci Int; NDEA fel, 65-68. *Mem:* Nat Asn Res Sci Teaching; Nat Sci Teachers Asn; Coun Elem Sci Int (pres, 83-86); Wilson Ornith Soc. *Res:* Misconceptions and alternate frameworks. *Mailing Add:* RD 1 Box 136 Clarion PA 16214

**TWIGG, BERNARD ALVIN,** HORTICULTURE, FOOD SCIENCE. *Current Pos:* Asst hort, Univ Md, Col Park, 52-54, from instr to assoc prof, 54-69, chmn dept, 75-83, PROF HORT, UNIV MD, COL PARK, 69-, EMER PROF, 83- *Personal Data:* b Cumberland, Md, Oct 15, 28; m 51, Jean C Bryan; c Michael, Patricia, Stephen & Richard. *Educ:* Univ Md, BS, 52, MS, 54, PhD, 59. *Concurrent Pos:* Sci Adv Refrig Res & Educ Found, 82- *Mem:* Am Soc Hort Sci; fel Inst Food Technologists. *Res:* Objective evaluation of food products; statistical quality control; food chemistry and physics; horticultural food processing. *Mailing Add:* 3537 Duke College Park MD 20740. *Fax:* 301-935-5709

**TWIGG, HOMER LEE,** MEDICINE, RADIOLOGY. *Current Pos:* RETIRED. *Personal Data:* b Westminster, Md, Apr 10, 26; m 55, Bettyanne; c Homer, Theodore, Robert, John, Richard & Michael. *Educ:* Univ Md, MD, 51; Am Bd Radiol, dipl, 56. *Hon Degrees:* MD, Univ Md, 51. *Prof Exp:* Intern med, USPHS Hosp, Boston, 51-52, intern, Surg Serv Outpatient Clin, 52, resident radiol, New Orleans, 53-55, Baltimore, 55-56, chief radiol, Detroit, 56-57; actg chmn & dir dept, Georgetown Univ Hosp, 67-69, from asst prof to prof radiol, 57-96, chmn dept, 69-79. *Concurrent Pos:* Spec assignment, US Dept Interior, 52; consult, Vet Admin Hosp, DC, 60- *Mem:* AMA; fel Am Col Radiol; Am Roentgen Ray Soc; Radiol Soc NAm; Soc Thoracic Radiol. *Mailing Add:* 11700 Glenrose Lane SE Flintstone MD 21530

**TWILLEY, IAN CHARLES,** CHEMISTRY, CHEMICAL ENGINEERING. *Current Pos:* SR ASSOC, GEERDES INT, VA, 92- *Personal Data:* b London, Eng, Apr 4, 27; m 54, Margaret B Saull; c Howard, Caroline, Rosalind & Jonathan. *Educ:* Univ London, BSc, 53, FRSC, 62. *Prof Exp:* Sr chemist, Nelsons Silk Ltd, Eng, 53-56 & Micanite & Insulators, Ltd, 56-57; sr develop chemist, Textile Fibers Div, Du Pont of Can, 57-59; sect leader moulding polymers, Nat Aniline Div, Fibers & Plastics Co, Allied Corp, Petersburg, 59-60, group leader polymer res, 60-61, res supvr, 61-65, process develop supvr, 65-66, mgr systs eng, 66-68, mgr eng res, Fibers Div, 68-69, asst chief engr, 69, tech dir polyester, 69-72, tech dir home furnishings, 72-76, mgr govt & indust affairs & liaison, 76-77, mgr advan technol, Fibers Div, Allied Chem Corp, 77-81, dir advan technol, 81-87; dir, Textile Performance & Comfort Res Labs, Univ Md, 88-92. *Mem:* Am Chem Soc; Am Inst Chem Eng; Can Soc Chem Eng; fel Chem Inst Can; Royal Soc Chem; fel Inst Mat. *Res:* Polymeric and textile processes and products; production and design problems; polymer and textile chemistry; polyamide, polyolesine, and polyester technology. *Mailing Add:* 12625 Merry Dr Chester VA 23831. *Fax:* 540-972-1143

**TWIN, PETER JOHN,** PHYSICS. *Current Pos:* lectr, 64, SR LECTR & PROF EXP PHYSICS, UNIV LIVERPOOL, 88- *Personal Data:* b London, Eng, July 26, 37; m 63, Jean Leatherland; c 2. *Honors & Awards:* Tom W Bonner Prize Nucluear Physics, Am Phys Soc, 91. *Prof Exp:* Head, Nuclear Struct Facil, Daresbury Lab, 83-88. *Mailing Add:* Dept Physics Univ Liverpool POB 147 Liverpool L69 3BX England

**TWINING, LINDA CAROL,** IMMUNOPARASITOLOGY. *Current Pos:* ASSOC PROF IMMUNOL & PARASITOL, NE MO STATE UNIV, 81- *Personal Data:* b Paterson, NJ, July 8, 52; m 80, Charles F Gerdes; c Andrew & Emilie. *Educ:* William Paterson Col NJ, BA, 72; Rutgers Univ, MS, 75; Univ Ill Urbana-Champaign, PhD(zool), 82. *Prof Exp:* Teaching asst biol zool, Rutgers Univ, 72-74, immunol & parasitol, Univ Ill, 74-81. *Mem:* Am Soc Microbiol; AAAS; Asn Women Sci. *Res:* Immunoparasitology, particularly the immune response to Plasmodium and other protozoans, both the in vivo and in vitro response are of interest, especially the roles of the various immune cells; phenomenon of immunosuppression in protozoal and helminth infections. *Mailing Add:* Dept Sci NE Mo State Univ 100 E Normal St Kirksville MO 63501-4221

**TWINING, SALLY SHINEW,** PROTEASES, PROTEASE INHIBITORS. *Current Pos:* res assoc, Med Col Wis, 79-80, instr, 80-83, asst prof, 83- 89, ASSOC PROF BIOCHEM, MED COL WIS, 89- *Personal Data:* b Bowling Green, Ohio, July 28, 47; m 71, Carl; c JulLea. *Educ:* Bowling Green State Univ, BS, 69, MA, 71; Ohio State Univ, PhD(physiol chem), 76. *Prof Exp:* Instr chem, Bowling Green State Univ, 71-73; Mayo fel, immunol, Mayo Clin, 76-78. *Mem:* Sigma Xi; Am Chem Soc; AAAS; Am Soc Biol Chem; Asn Res

Vision & Ophthalmol. *Res:* Role of proteases and protease inhibitors in corneal degradation; role of the immune system in Pseudomonas keratitis; role of vitamin A in polymorphonuclear leukocyte function. *Mailing Add:* Dept Biochem Med Col Wis 8701 Watertown Plank Rd Milwaukee WI 53226. *Fax:* 414-266-8497

**TWISS, PAGE CHARLES,** GEOLOGY. *Current Pos:* from instr to prof, 53-95, head dept, 68-77, EMER PROF GEOL, KANS STATE UNIV, 95- *Personal Data:* b Columbus, Ohio, Jan 2, 29; m 54, Nancy Hubbard; c Stephen R, Catherine G & Thomas S. *Educ:* Kans State Univ, BS, 50, MS, 55; Univ Tex, PhD(geol), 59. *Prof Exp:* Photo-radar interpretation officer, USAF, 51-53. *Concurrent Pos:* Co-investr, NSF grants, 60-62, 66, 67-68; res scientist, Univ Tex, 66-67; fel, Pan Am Petrol Found, 57-58, Shell Found, 58-59; geologist, Agr Res Serv, USDA, 66-68. *Mem:* Fel Geol Soc Am; Am Asn Petrol Geol; Soc Econ Paleont & Mineral; Int Asn Sedimentologist; Int pour l'Etude des Argiles. *Res:* Sedimentary petrology; clay mineralogy; stratigraphy, tectonics, petrology and geochemistry of Mesozoic and Cenozoic rocks of Trans-Pecos Texas; grass phytoliths; petrology of recent dust deposits; stratigraphy of Permian rocks of Kansas. *Mailing Add:* 2327 Bailey Dr Manhattan KS 66502. *Fax:* 785-532-7004; *E-Mail:* pctwiss@ksu. ksu.edu

**TWISS, ROBERT JOHN,** ROCK DEFORMATION MECHANISMS & STRUCTURES. *Current Pos:* asst prof, 71-78, assoc prof, 78-92, PROF GEOL, UNIV CALIF, DAVIS, 92- *Personal Data:* b Baltimore, Md, May 12, 42; m 68; c 2. *Educ:* Yale Univ, BS, 64; Princeton Univ, MA, 68, PhD(geol), 70. *Prof Exp:* NATO fel geol, Australian Nat Univ, 70-71. *Mem:* Am Geophys Union; Geol Soc Am; Sigma Xi. *Res:* Continuum mechanics theory applied to understanding the behavior of geologic materials; deformation mechanisms in silicates; structural analysis of tectonites. *Mailing Add:* Dept Geol Univ Calif Davis CA 95616-8605. *Fax:* 530-752-0951

**TWITCHELL, PAUL F,** METEOROLOGY. *Current Pos:* CONSULT, ENVIRON SCIS, 88- *Personal Data:* b Somerville, Mass, Mar 7, 32; m 56; c 4. *Educ:* Boston Col, BS, 53, MS, 62; Pa State Univ, BS, 54; Univ Wis-Madison, PhD, 76. *Prof Exp:* Weather officer, US Air Force, 53-57; res engr, Res Dept, Melpar, Inc, Mass, 57-60; sr res engr, Appl Sci Div, 60-62; phys sci coordr, Boston Br, Off Naval Res, 62-72, phys sci adminr, 72-81; vis prof, US Naval Acad, 81-82; dir, Environ Progs, Hq Naval Air Systs Command, 82-86; mgr, Off Naval Res, Washington, 86-88. *Mem:* Am Meteorol Soc; Am Geophys Union. *Res:* Physical processes in the terrestrial atmosphere. *Mailing Add:* 509 Schley Rd Annapolis MD 21401-2274

**TWITCHELL, THOMAS EVANS,** NEUROLOGY. *Current Pos:* from instr to prof, 55-88, actg chmn dept, 83-85, EMER PROF NEUROL, SCH MED, TUFTS UNIV, 88- *Personal Data:* b Springfield, Ohio, Sept 4, 23; m 56; c 4. *Educ:* Univ Mich, MD, 46. *Prof Exp:* Res fel physiol, Med Sch, Yale Univ, 47; intern neurol, Boston City Hosp, 47-48, res fel, Harvard Med Sch & Boston City Hosp, 48-49; asst resident med, New Eng Ctr Hosp, 54, chief resident neurol, 54-55. *Concurrent Pos:* USPHS res fel, Yale Univ, 49-51; res assoc, Mass Inst Technol, 63-; neurologist, New Eng Med Ctr Hosps, 63-83, sr neurologist, 83-88. *Mem:* AAAS; Asn Res Nerv & Ment Dis; Am Neurol Asn; AMA; Am Fedn Clin Res; Sigma Xi; Am Acad Neurol. *Res:* Neurophysiology of primate motor function; physiologic nature of development of behavior in infants; sensory mechanisms in movement; clinical neurology; applied neurophysiology; neuropsychology. *Mailing Add:* 54 Longfellow Rd Wellesley Hills MA 02181

**TWOHY, DONALD WILFRED,** PARASITOLOGY. *Current Pos:* RETIRED. *Personal Data:* b Clackamas, Ore, Sept 9, 24; m 55; c 1. *Educ:* Ore State Col, BS, 48, MS, 51; Johns Hopkins Univ, ScD, 55. *Prof Exp:* Aquatic biologist, Ore State Game Comn, 49-51; res asst, Sch Hyg & Pub Health, Johns Hopkins Univ, 55-56; asst prof zool, Okla State Univ, 56-60; from instr to assoc prof microbiol, Mich State Univ, 60-94, prof pub health, 77-94. *Mem:* Am Soc Parasitologists; Am Soc Trop Med & Hyg; Soc Protozool; fel AAAS. *Res:* Parasitic protozoa; cellular immunity. *Mailing Add:* 22202 Haslett Rd East Lansing MI 48823

**TWOMBLY, JOHN C,** ELECTRICAL ENGINEERING. *Current Pos:* instr elec eng, Univ Colo, Boulder, 46-49, res assoc electronics, 51-58, assoc prof elec eng, 59-62, PROF ELEC ENG, UNIV COLO, BOULDER, 62- *Personal Data:* b Denver, Colo, Nov 26, 21. *Educ:* Univ Colo, BS, 44, PhD(elec eng), 59; Stanford Univ, MS, 50. *Prof Exp:* Engr, Manhattan Dist, Los Alamos Sci Labs, 45-46. *Concurrent Pos:* Fac study & res fel Univ Colo, Swiss Fed Inst Technol, 65-66. *Mem:* Inst Elec & Electronics Engrs. *Res:* Electron devices; space-charge dynamics; network theory. *Mailing Add:* 2500 Kohler Dr Boulder CO 80303

**TWOMEY, JEREMIAH JOHN,** CELLULAR IMMUNOLOGY. *Current Pos:* PVT PRACT. *Personal Data:* b Co Cork, Ireland, July 30, 34; m 77; c 3. *Educ:* Nat Univ Ireland, MB, BCh, BAO, 58. *Prof Exp:* From asst prof to prof med, Baylor Col Med, 67- *Mem:* Fel Am Col Physicians; Am Fedn Clin Res; fel Royal Irish Acad Med; Am Soc Hemat; Am Asn Immunologists. *Res:* Immune regulation-physiology and pathophysiology; lymphomas-immune responses; thymic hormone; immunobiology of aging. *Mailing Add:* 4151 Southwest Freeway Suite 610 Houston TX 77027

**TWOMEY, SEAN ANDREW,** ATMOSPHERIC CHEMISTRY & PHYSICS. *Current Pos:* CONSULT, 91- *Personal Data:* b Cork, Ireland; US citizen. *Educ:* Nat Univ Ireland, BSc, 48, MSc, 49, PhD(exp physics), 55. *Honors & Awards:* C G Rossby Medal, Am Meteorol Soc, 80. *Prof Exp:* Sr res officer, Radiophys Div, Commonwealth Sci & Indust Res Orgn, Australia, 50-59; atmospheric physicist, Nat Oceanic & Atmosphere Admin, Washington, DC, 59-63; consult physicist, Naval Res Lab, Washington, DC, 63-68; chief res scientist, Div Cloud Physics, 68-76; prof atmospheric physics, Inst Atmospheric Physics, Univ Ariz, 76-91. *Concurrent Pos:* Vis prof, Dept Atmospheric Sci, Univ Ariz, 73-74; vis res fel, Div Radiophys,. *Res:* Extension of mathematical inversion techniques to enable solution for large number of unknowns; influence of pollution on clouds as it relates to climate change. *Mailing Add:* 11250 E Outback Rd Tucson AZ 85730

**TYAGI, RAJESHWAR DAYAL,** MUNICIPAL SLUDGE, BIOLOGICAL WASTEWATER TREATMENT, REMOVAL OF TOXIC METALS FROM SEWAGE SLUDGE. *Current Pos:* from asst prof to assoc prof, 84-92, PROF ENVIRON ENG, UNIV QUE, 92- *Personal Data:* b New Delhi, June 5, 52; Can citizen; m 76, Nirmala; c Aditi & Nishant. *Educ:* Delhi Univ, BSc, 71; Kanpur Univ, BSc, 74; Indian Inst Technol, New Delhi, PhD(biochem eng), 78. *Honors & Awards:* Merit Award Outstanding Res, Nat Sci & Eng Res Coun Can, 87. *Prof Exp:* Lectr, Indian Inst Technol, New Delhi, 78-80 & 82-84; scientist, Univ Technol Compiegne, France, 80-82. *Concurrent Pos:* Consult, Ctr Que Valorisation Biomasse, 89-90, Tembec Inc, 92- *Res:* Removal of toxic metals from sewage sludge; biological treatment of municipal and industrial wastewaters; sludge digestion and sludge managements; production of biopesticides from wastes. *Mailing Add:* 2700 Rue Einstein Ste-Foy PQ G1V 4C7 Can. *Fax:* 418-654-2600; *E-Mail:* tyagi@ inrs-eau.uquebec.ca

**TYAGI, SURESH C,** REGULATION OF HIV & NEUTROPHIL PROTEASES, MECHANISM OF TRANSCRIPTION BY RNA POLYMERASE. *Current Pos:* res assoc pharmacol, 85-87, res assoc path, 87-89, INSTR BIOCHEM, STATE UNIV NY, 89- *Personal Data:* b Bankhandra, India, Jan 1, 55; Can citizen; m 80. *Educ:* Aligash Univ, PhD(chem), 80. *Honors & Awards:* Travel Award, Am Soc Biochem & Molecular Biol, 91. *Prof Exp:* Sr demonstr chem, Univ Cork, Ireland, 80-82; postdoctoral fel biochem, Univ BC, Can, 83-85. *Mem:* Am Soc Biochem & Molecular Biol; Can Biochem Soc. *Res:* Viral and human inflammatory cell proteases: biochemical and biophysical studies; prokaryote and eukaryotic RNA polymerases: mechanism of transcription. *Mailing Add:* Med Cardiol Univ Mo Med Sci Bldg Columbia MO 65212

**TYAN, MARVIN L,** INTERNAL MEDICINE, EXPERIMENTAL BIOLOGY. *Current Pos:* PROF MED, UNIV CALIF, LOS ANGELES, 77- *Personal Data:* b Los Angeles, Calif, Nov 29, 26; m 50; c 2. *Educ:* Univ Calif, Berkeley, BA, 49; Univ Calif, San Francisco, MD, 52. *Prof Exp:* Intern med, Boston City Hosp, Mass, 52-53; resident, Boston Vet Admin Hosp, 53-54; sr asst resident, San Francisco County Hosp, Calif, 54-55; fel hemat, Stanford Univ, 55-56; pvt pract, 56-61; sr investr exp path, US Naval Radiol Defense Lab, 61-68 & Stanford Res Inst, Calif, 68-71; prof bact, Immunol & Oral Biol, Dent Res Ctr, Univ NC, Chapel Hill, 71-77. *Concurrent Pos:* Fel, Tumor Biol Inst, Karolinska Inst, Sweden, 63-64. *Mem:* Am Asn Immunol. *Res:* Ontogeny of immune system of the mouse; processes involved in transplantation immunity. *Mailing Add:* Dept Med Vet Admin Wadsworth Hosp Ctr Univ Calif Wilshire & Sawtelle Blvds Los Angeles CA 90073. *Fax:* 310-268-4750; *E-Mail:* tyan@west-la.va.gov

**TYBERG, JOHN VICTOR,** CARDIOVASCULAR PHYSIOLOGY. *Current Pos:* PROF, DEPT MED & MED PHYSIOL & BIOPHYS, HEALTH SCI CTR, UNIV CALGARY, 81- *Personal Data:* b Grantsburg, Wis, May 4, 38; m 60, 79, Naomi M Anderson; c Anna V (de Tombe). *Educ:* Bethel Col, Minn, BA, 60; Univ Minn, PhD(physiol), 67, MD, 72. *Prof Exp:* Res assoc med, Harvard Med Sch, 69; res physiologist, Riverside Res Inst, 69-71; res scientist cardiol, Cedars-Sinai Med Ctr, 71-73; asst prof med & physiol & mem,, Cardiovasc Res Inst, Med Ctr Univ Calif, San Francisco, 74-81. *Concurrent Pos:* Lectr, Med Ctr, Univ Calif, San Francisco, 69-71; mem, Basic Sci Coun, Am Heart Asn, 74- *Mem:* Am Heart Asn; Am Physiol Soc; fel Am Col Cardiol. *Res:* Mechanics of ischemic myocardium; diastolic dynamics; pericardial physiology; venous hemodynamics. *Mailing Add:* Dept Med Physiol & Biophys Univ Calgary Health Sci Ctr 3330 Hosp Dr NW Calgary AB T2N 4N1 Can. *Fax:* 403-270-0313; *E-Mail:* jtyberg@cvr. ucalgary.ca

**TYBOR, PHILIP THOMAS,** FOOD SCIENCE. *Current Pos:* RETIRED. *Personal Data:* b Fredericksburg, Tex, Oct 3, 48; m 69; c 4. *Educ:* Tex A&M Univ, BS, 70, PhD(food sci), 73. *Prof Exp:* Dir protein res, Cent Soya Co Inc, 73-80, food prod develop dir, 80-86, head, Exten Food Sci Dept, 86-94. *Concurrent Pos:* Mem, Ga Agribus Coun. *Mem:* Inst Food Technologists; Am Asn Cereal Chemists; Am Chem Soc; Am Dairy Sci Asn. *Res:* Administration of research programs pertaining to the development of food products for food service, protein applications development and the exploration of new food technologies; technical service and instruction on food quality, safety, and sanitation. *Mailing Add:* 2011 Elder Rd Bishop GA 30621

**TYCE, FRANCIS ANTHONY,** PSYCHIATRY. *Current Pos:* from asst prof to assoc prof, 69-77, PROF PSYCHIAT, MAYO MED SCH, ROCHESTER, MINN, 77-; PVT PRACT PSYCHIAT, ROCHESTER, MINN; SUPT, ROCHESTER STATE HOSP, 71- *Personal Data:* b South Wales, Eng, Oct 31, 17; US citizen; m 52; c 1. *Educ:* Univ Durham, BS & MD, 52; Univ Minn, MS, 64; Am Bd Psychiat & Neurol, dipl, 64. *Prof Exp:* House surgeon, Teaching Hosp, Durham, Eng, 52-53; rotating intern, St Vincents Hosp, Erie,

Pa, 53-54; gen pract, Seaham Harbor, 54-56; actg supt, Rochester State Hosp, 60-61. *Concurrent Pos:* Fel psychiat, Mayo Clin, 56-60; lectr, Mayo Found, 65-; consult, WHO, 67-; vpres, Zumbro Valley Med Soc, Rochester, Minn, 71-72, pres, 72-73; task force comt, Psychiat Rehab in Correctional Systs, 73-; Field Rep Accreditation Coun for Psychiat Facil-Jt Comn on Accreditation of Hosps, 73-; mem, Juv Delinq-Nat Adv Comt on Criminal Justice Stand & Goals, 75-; chmn, Am Psychiat Asn. *Mem:* Fel Psychiat Soc; Asn Med Supt Ment Hosp (pres elect, 67-68, pres, 68-); Am Psychiat Asn. *Res:* Neurophysiology, especially electrical stimulation of the brain in rats; psychiatric program design in mental hospitals. *Mailing Add:* 929 11th St SW Rochester MN 55902-6324

**TYCE, GERTRUDE MARY,** BIOLOGY. *Current Pos:* res asst biochem, Mayo Clin, 58-63, res assoc, 63-71, assoc consult, 71-76, assoc prof, 76-81, PROF PHYSIOL, MAYO MED SCH, MAYO CLIN & FOUND, 81- *Personal Data:* b Wark, Eng, Mar 26, 27; m 52, Francis A; c John C. *Educ:* Univ Durham, BSc, 48, PhD(plant physiol & biochem), 52. *Prof Exp:* Instr chem, Villa Maria Col, Pa, 52-53; instr biol & chem, Nottingham & Dist Tech Col Eng, 54-56. *Concurrent Pos:* Asst ed, News in Physiol Sci, 88-; consult, reviewal of grants, NSF; asst ed, Soc Exp Biol & Med, 90- *Mem:* AAAS; Am Chem Soc; Am Soc Exp Path; Int Soc Neurochem; Soc Neurosci; Am Soc Neurochem; Sigma Xi; Soc Exp Biol & Med; NY Acad Sci. *Res:* Metabolism of glucose, amino acids and biogenic amines in brain and liver. *Mailing Add:* Dept Physiol Mayo Med Sch Rm 3-515 Rochester MN 55901-0001. *Fax:* 507-284-5075

**TYCE, ROBERT CHARLES,** MARINE PHYSICS, OCEAN ENGINEERING. *Current Pos:* RES ENGR, GRAD SCH OCEANOG, UNIV RI. *Personal Data:* b San Diego, Calif, July 9, 47. *Educ:* Univ Calif, San Diego, BA, 69, PhD(appl ocean sci), 77. *Prof Exp:* Asst programmer ocean instrumentation, Scripps Inst Oceanog, 69-70, res asst marine physics, Marine Phys Lab, 70-76; sr acoustics engr ocean vehicle instrumentation, Hydro Prod, 77-78; asst res engr marine physics, Marine Phys Lab, Scripps Inst Oceanog, 78- *Concurrent Pos:* Physicist, Scripps Inst Oceanog, 76-77, res fel, 77-78; consult, Hydro Prod, 78- *Mem:* Acoust Soc Am; assoc mem Soc Explor Geophysicists; Marine Technol Soc; Am Geophys Union; Inst Elec & Electronics Engrs. *Res:* Underwater acoustics and geophysics; deep ocean engineering and instrumentation; vehicle technology; computer science; digital signal processing. *Mailing Add:* Dept Ocean Eng Univ RI Narragansett RI 02882

**TYCKO, DANIEL H,** CYTOMETRY, LABORATORY INSTRUMENTATION. *Current Pos:* RETIRED. *Personal Data:* b Los Angeles, Calif, Nov 14, 27; m 52; c 3. *Educ:* Univ Calif, Los Angeles, BA, 50; Columbia Univ, PhD(physics), 57. *Prof Exp:* Sr res assoc, Nevis Labs, Columbia Univ, 57-66; assoc prof physics, Rutgers Univ, 66-67; assoc prof comput sci, State Univ NY, Stony Brook, 67-70, prof, 70-79, prof, State Univ NY, New Paltz, 79-80; consult, Technicon Instruments Corp, 70-80, prin scientist, 80-82. *Concurrent Pos:* Res collab, Saclay Nuclear Res Ctr, France, 61-62; consult, appl physics & comput sci, 82- *Mem:* Am Phys Soc; Asn Comput Mach; Inst Elec & Electronics Engrs; AAAS; Soc Anal Cytol. *Res:* Image processing by computers; pattern recognition; applications to cytology and hematology; flow cytometry instrumentation; application of light scattering to the measurement of the properties of cells. *Mailing Add:* 4 Hillsview Rd Stony Brook NY 11790

**TYCZKOWSKI, EDWARD ALBERT,** FLUORINE CHEMISTRY. *Current Pos:* vpres, 86-89, PRES, FLURA CORP, 89- *Personal Data:* b Providence, RI, May 15, 24; m 50, Ellen Murray. *Educ:* Brown Univ, ScB, 49; Duke Univ, PhD(chem), 53. *Prof Exp:* Res assoc, US Army Off Ord Res, Duke Univ, 52-53; res chemist, Gen Chem Div, Allied Chem & Dye Corp, 53-56 & Pennsalt Chem Corp, 56-62; process chemist, Air Prod & Chem Corp, 62-63; vpres, Hynes Chem Res Corp, 63-66; sr res chemist, Fibers Div, Beaunit Corp, 66-67, res assoc, 67-72; pres, Armageddon Chem Co, 72-86. *Mem:* AAAS; Am Chem Soc; Sigma Xi. *Res:* Organic fluorine chemistry; reactions of elementary fluorine with organic compounds; flame reactions; explosions; reactor design; organic synthesis; polymer chemistry; fiber structure. *Mailing Add:* 3216 Landmark Dr Morristown TN 37814. *Fax:* 423-623-8786

**TYE, BIK-KWOON,** MOLECULAR BIOLOGY, MOLECULAR GENETICS. *Current Pos:* asst prof, 77-84, assoc, prof biochem, 84-90, PROF, CORNELL UNIV, 91- *Personal Data:* b Hong Kong, Jan 7, 47; m 71; c 2. *Educ:* Wellesley Col, BA, 69; Univ Calif, San Francisco, MSc, 71; Mass Inst Technol, PhD(microbiol), 74. *Prof Exp:* Helen Hay Whitney Found fel biochem, Sch Med, Stanford Univ, 74-77. *Mem:* Genetics Soc Am. *Res:* DNA replication; transcription regulation; chromosome structure and function. *Mailing Add:* Dept Biochem Molecular & Cell Biol Biotechnol Bldg Cornell Univ Ithaca NY 14853-0001

**TYE, SZE-HOI HENRY,** THEORETICAL & ELEMENTARY PARTICLE PHYSICS. *Current Pos:* sr res assoc, 78-87, PROF PHYSICS, NEWMAN LAB NUCLEAR STUDIES, CORNELL UNIV, 87- *Personal Data:* b Shanghai, China, Jan 15, 47; m 71, Bik K Yeung; c 2. *Educ:* Calif Inst Technol, BS, 70; Mass Inst Technol, PhD(physics), 74. *Prof Exp:* Res assoc physics, Stanford Linear Accelerator Ctr, Stanford Univ, 74-77, Fermi Nat Accelerator Lab, 77-78. *Mem:* Am Phys Soc. *Res:* Elementary particle physics; quantum field theory, string theory cosmology. *Mailing Add:* Newman Lab Nuclear Studies Cornell Univ Ithaca NY 14853. *Fax:* 607-254-4552; *E-Mail:* tye@lnssun7.tn.cornell.edu

**TYERYAR, FRANKLIN JOSEPH,** MEDICAL MICROBIOLOGY. *Current Pos:* RETIRED. *Personal Data:* b Frederick, Md, Apr 29, 35; m 59; c 3. *Educ:* Univ Md, BS, 60, MS, 62, PhD(microbiol), 68. *Honors & Awards:* Leroy Fothergill Sci Award, Sci Res Soc Am, 70; Dirs Award, NIH, 79. *Prof Exp:* Microbiologist, US Bur Mines, US Dept Interior, 62-63, US Dept Army, Ft Detrick, 63-71 & Dept Microbiol, Naval Med Res Inst, 71-73; microbiologist, Nat Inst Allergy & Infectious Dis, 73-90, chief, Develop & Applns Br, 84-90. *Res:* Development and testing of bacterial and viral vaccines for clinical use; clinical evaluation of viral vaccines for efficacy; persistent viral infections; prevention and control of infectious diseases. *Mailing Add:* 7104 Autumn Leaf Lane Frederick MD 21702

**TYHACH, RICHARD JOSEPH,** IMMUNOCHEMISTRY, HEALTHCARE NEW PRODUCT DEVELOPMENT. *Current Pos:* res scientist biochem, Bayer Corp, 78-81 sr res scientist, 81-85, res & develop supvr, 85-87 res & develop mgr, 87-89, DIR NEW PROD DEVELOP, DIAG DIV, BAYER CORP, 89- *Personal Data:* b New York, NY, Aug 14, 49; m 73, Elaine Goral; c Jeffrey & Matthew. *Educ:* Queens Col, BA, 70, MA, 73; City Univ New York, PhD(biochem), 76. *Prof Exp:* Lectr chem, Queens Col, City Univ New York, 71-76; Damon Runyon-Walter Winchell Cancer Fund fel biol chem, Harvard Med Sch, 76-78. *Mem:* Am Chem Soc; Am Asn Clin Chem; Sigma Xi. *Res:* Dry reagent chemistry; clinical biochemistry and immunoassay technology; clinical instrumentation; system integration; product delivery team management. *Mailing Add:* 22986 Basswood Ct Elkhart IN 46515. *E-Mail:* ty22986@gte.net

**TYKOCINSKI, MARK L,** DEVELOPMENTAL BIOLOGY, HEMATOLOGY & ONCOLOGY. *Current Pos:* ASSOC PROF PATH, SCH MED, CASE WESTERN RES UNIV, 83-; STAFF PHYSICIAN, UNIV HOSPS CLEVELAND, 83- *Personal Data:* b Lakewood, NJ, Nov 26, 52; m 78; c 4. *Educ:* Yale Univ, BA, 74; NY Univ, MD, 78. *Prof Exp:* Resident internal med, Columbia-Presby Med Ctr, 78-79; resident anat path, NY Univ Med Ctr, 79-81; med staff fel immunogenetics, Nat Inst Allergy & Infectious Dis, NIH, 81-83. *Mem:* Am Asn Pathologists; Am Asn Cancer Res. *Res:* Study of human hematopoietic differentiation and leukemic cell induction using recombinant DNA technology; T cell biology; gene transfer technology. *Mailing Add:* Dept Path Case Western Reserve Univ BRB Rm 925 10900 Euclid Ave Cleveland OH 44106-4943. *Fax:* 216-368-1277

**TYKODI, RALPH JOHN,** PHYSICAL CHEMISTRY. *Current Pos:* assoc prof chem, Univ Mass, Dartmouth, 65-68, prof, 68-95, assoc dean, Col Arts & Sci, 69-72, EMER PROF, UNIV MASS, DARTMOUTH, 95- *Personal Data:* b Cleveland, Ohio, Apr 18, 25; m 55; c 3. *Educ:* Northwestern Univ, BS, 49; Pa State Univ, PhD, 54. *Prof Exp:* Instr, Ill Inst Technol, 55-57, from asst prof to assoc prof, 57-65. *Mem:* Am Chem Soc; Am Phys Soc. *Res:* Equliibrium and non-equilibrium thermodynamics. *Mailing Add:* Dept Chem Univ Mass Dartmouth North Dartmouth MA 02747

**TYLER, ALBERT VINCENT,** FISHERIES. *Current Pos:* ASSOC DEAN & PROF, SCH FISHERIES & OCEAN SCI, UNIV ALASKA, FAIRBANKS, 91- *Personal Data:* b Philadelphia, Pa, June 25, 38; m 60; c 3. *Educ:* Univ Pa, BA, 60; Univ Toronto, MA, 64, PhD(synecol), 68. *Prof Exp:* Scientist, Fisheries Res Bd Can, 64-74,; from assoc prof to prof fisheries, Ore State Univ, 74-82; res scientist, Groundfish Res Sect, Pac Biol Sta, Brit Col, 82-91. *Mem:* Am Fisheries Soc; Can Soc Zool; Sigma Xi. *Res:* Competitive and predatory relationships among fishes; population dynamics. *Mailing Add:* Sch Fisheries & Ocean Sci O'Neil Bldg Univ Alaska Fairbanks AK 99775-1090

**TYLER, AUSTIN LAMONT,** CHEMICAL ENGINEERING. *Current Pos:* PROF & CHMN CHEM ENG, UNIV UTAH, 70- *Personal Data:* b Provo, Utah, July 21, 36; m 60; c 5. *Educ:* Univ Utah, BS, 61, PhD(chem eng), 65. *Prof Exp:* Supvr & mem staff, Semiconductor Processing, Bell Tel Labs, 65-70. *Mem:* Am Inst Chem Engrs. *Res:* Particle behavior in acceleration gas streams; fabrication processes for silicon semiconductors; kinetics of oil shale retorting processes; fluid bed reactors. *Mailing Add:* 3810 Eastwood Lane Salt Lake City UT 84109

**TYLER, BONNIE MORELAND,** microbial physiology, molecular biology, for more information see previous edition

**TYLER, CARL WALTER, JR,** EPIDEMIOLOGY, PUBLIC HEALTH. *Current Pos:* epidemic intel serv officer, Bur Epidemiol Ctr Dis Control, 66-67, dir, Family Plan Eval Div, 67-80, asst dir sci, 80-82, actg dir, Ctr Health Prom & Educ, 82, dir Epidemiol Prog Off, 82-88, med epidemiologist off dir, 88-90, ASST DIR ACASD PROGS & PUB HEALTH PRACT PROG OFF, BUR EPIDEMIOL, CTR DIS CONTROL, 90- *Personal Data:* b Washington, DC, Aug 22, 33; wid; c Virginia L, Laureen, Jeffrey A & Cynthia T (Crenshaw). *Educ:* Oberlin Col, AB, 55; Case-Western Reserve Univ, MD, 59; Am Bd Ob-Gyn, dipl. *Honors & Awards:* Carl S Shultz Pop Award, Am Pub Health Asn, 76. *Prof Exp:* Rotating intern, Univ Hosps Cleveland, 59-60, resident ob-gyn, 60-64; med officer, USPHS, 64; ob-gyn, USPHS Indian Health Serv, 64-66. *Concurrent Pos:* NIH grantee, 61-64; clin asst prof ob-gyn, Emory Univ Sch Med, 66-80, clin assoc prof prev med & community health & adj prof sociol, Col Arts & Sci, 77-90, clin assoc prof ob-gyn, 80-, adj assoc prof pub health, Sch Pub Health, 90-; clin prof pub health & community med, Morehouse Sch Med, 90-; mem, Nat Sleep Dis Res Comn, 90- *Mem:* Fel Am Col Obstet & Gynec; fel Am Col Prev Med; fel Am Col Epidemiol; Am Epidemiol Soc; Int Epidemiol Asn; Asn Teachers Prev Med; Am Pub Health Asn; Asn Planned Parenthood Profs; Am Pop Asn. *Res:* Contributed articles to professional journals. *Mailing Add:* HHS Ctrs for Dis Control 1600 E Clifton Rd NE Mail Stop E-42 Atlanta GA 30333

**TYLER, CHRISTOPHER WILLIAM,** OPTOMETRY, PSYCHOLOGY. *Current Pos:* ASSOC DIR, SMITH-KETTLEWELL EYE RES INST, 90- *Personal Data:* b Leicester, UK, Dec 16, 43; m 85; c 1. *Educ:* Univ Leicester, UK, BA, 66; Univ Aston, UK, MSc, 67; Univ Keele, UK, PhD(communication), 70. *Prof Exp:* Asst prof, Northeastern Univ, Boston, 72-73; res fel, Dept Psychol, Univ Bristol, UK, 73-74 & Dept Sensory & Perception Progs, Bell Lab, 74-75, scientist, Smith-Kettlewell Inst Visual Sci, 75-80, sr scientist, William A Kettlewell Chair Res, 84-85. *Concurrent Pos:* Staff mem sch optom, Univ Calif, Berkeley, 86- *Mem:* Asn Res Vision Ophthal; Optical Soc Am. *Res:* Retinal diseases; how light is turned into electrical energy in the receptors of the retina; stereoscopic depth perception. *Mailing Add:* Smith-Kettlewell Eye Res Inst 2232 Webster St San Francisco CA 94115. *E-Mail:* cwt@skivs.ski.org

**TYLER, DAVID E,** VETERINARY PATHOLOGY. *Current Pos:* prof & head dept, 66-79, prof, 79-92, EMER PROF VET PATH, COL VET MED, UNIV GA, 92- *Personal Data:* b Carlisle, Iowa, July 12, 28; m 52; c 2. *Educ:* Iowa State Univ, BS, 53, DVM, 57, PhD(vet path), 63; Purdue Univ, MS, 60. *Honors & Awards:* Stange Award, 87. *Prof Exp:* Instr, Purdue Univ, 57-60; asst prof, Iowa State Univ, 60-64, assoc prof, 64-66. *Concurrent Pos:* Mem, Conf Res Workers Animal Dis. *Mem:* Am Vet Med Asn; Am Col Vet Path; Am Asn Vet Med Educr. *Res:* Epidemiology, pathology and immunology of the bovine mucosal disease-virus diarrhea complex; pathogenesis of equine colic; pathogenesis of porcine and equine salmonellosis. *Mailing Add:* 160 Sunnybrook Dr Athens GA 30605

**TYLER, DAVID RALPH,** PHOTOCHEMISTRY, REACTION MECHANISMS. *Current Pos:* assoc prof, 85-90, PROF CHEM, UNIV ORE, 90- *Personal Data:* b Willimantic, Conn, Apr 26, 53; m 73; c 2. *Educ:* Purdue Univ, BS, 75; Calif Inst Technol, PhD(chem), 79. *Prof Exp:* Asst prof chem, Columbia Univ, 79-85. *Concurrent Pos:* Sloan Found fel, 86. *Mem:* Am Chem Soc. *Res:* Mechanisms of inorganic and organometallic photochemical reactions; electron-transfer, hypervalent reaction intermediates and metal oxide complexes. *Mailing Add:* Dept Chem Univ Ore Eugene OR 97403

**TYLER, FRANK HILL,** MEDICINE. *Current Pos:* research instr, 47-54, from asst prof to assoc prof, 50-59, PROF MED, MED SCH, UNIV UTAH, 59- *Personal Data:* b Villisca, Iowa, Jan 5, 16; m 41; c 3. *Educ:* Willamette Univ, BA, 38; Johns Hopkins Univ, MD, 42. *Prof Exp:* Intern med, Johns Hopkins Hosp, 42-43; from asst resident to resident, Peter Bent Brigham Hosp, Boston, 43-47. *Mem:* Am Soc Clin Invest; Endocrine Soc; Am Fedn Clin Res; Asn Am Physicians; master Am Col Physicians. *Res:* Disease of the muscle; human inheritance; metabolism of steroids and metabolic disorders. *Mailing Add:* 50 N Medical Dr Univ Ut Sch Med Salt Lake City UT 84132-0001

**TYLER, GEORGE LEONARD,** PLANETARY EXPLORATION, RADAR ASTRONOMY. *Current Pos:* team leader, Voyager Radio Sci Team, 79-90, TEAM LEADER, MARS OBSERVER RADIO SCI TEAM, NASA, 86-; PROF ELEC ENG, STANFORD UNIV, 90-, DIR SPACE, TELECOMMUN & RADIOSCI LAB, 93- *Personal Data:* b Bartow, Fla, Oct 18, 40; m 77, Joanne L Phelps; c Virginia L & Matthew L. *Educ:* Ga Inst Technol, BS, 63; Stanford Univ, MS, 64, PhD(elec eng), 67. *Prof Exp:* Prof elec eng, Ctr Radar Astron, Stanford Univ, 67-79, res engr, 69-71, sr res assoc, 71-74, res prof, 74-89. *Concurrent Pos:* Consult, NASA & other res orgns; mem comt planetary explor; prin investr on numerous res projs; fel, NSF, 64-66. *Mem:* Fel Inst Elec & Electronics Engrs; Am Astron Soc; Am Geophys Union; Int Astron Union; Int Union Radio Sci. *Res:* Radio propagation experiments in space including theory and experiment; radio occultation measurements of planetary rings and atmospheres; radar astronomy including observation and interpretation of radiowave scatter from planetary surfaces using both spacecraft and ground based techniques; terrestrial applications of remote sensing. *Mailing Add:* Elec Eng Dept Stanford Univ Stanford CA 94305-9515. *Fax:* 650-723-9251; *E-Mail:* len@nova.stanford.edu

**TYLER, H RICHARD,** HISTORY NEUROLOGY. *Current Pos:* Teaching fel neurol, Harvard Med Sch, 53-54, asst instr, 56-59, instr, 59-61, assoc neurol, 61-64, from asst prof to assoc prof, 64-73, PROF NEUROL, HARVARD MED SCH, 74-; PROF HEALTH SCI, MASS INST TECHNOL, 87- *Personal Data:* b Kings County, NY, Oct 16, 27; m 51, Joyce Colby; c 4. *Educ:* Syracuse Univ, BA, 47; Wash Univ, BS, 51, MD, 51. *Hon Degrees:* Harvard Univ, MA, 88. *Concurrent Pos:* Head, sect neurol, Brigham & Womens Hosp, 56-88, sr physician neurol, 88-; sr neurologist, Beth Israel Hosp, 86- *Mem:* Am Acad Neurol; Am Neurol Assoc. *Res:* Neurological complications of medical diseases, especially renal disease; work on higher cortical visual disorder, Amyotrophic Laterel Sclerosis. *Mailing Add:* Brigham & Women Hosp 75 Francis St Boston MA 02115. *Fax:* 617-735-8722

**TYLER, JACK D,** ORNITHOLOGY, ECOLOGY. *Current Pos:* from instr to assoc prof biol, 67-78, PROF BIOL, CAMERON UNIV, 78- *Personal Data:* b Snyder, Okla, July 18, 40; m 69. *Educ:* Southwestern State Col, BS, 62; Okla State Univ, MS, 65; Univ Okla, PhD(zool), 68. *Prof Exp:* Teaching asst gen zool, Univ Okla, 64-66. *Concurrent Pos:* Ed, Bull Okla Orinth Soc, 72- *Mem:* Am Soc Mammal; Wilson Ornith Soc; Am Orinth Union. *Res:* Ecological relationships between certain birds in southwest Oklahoma and among vertebrates in prairie dog towns; mammals of Oklahoma. *Mailing Add:* Dept Biol Cameron Univ 2800 Gore Blvd Lawton OK 73505-6320

**TYLER, JAMES CHASE,** ICHTHYOLOGY. *Current Pos:* assoc dir, Nat Mus Natural Hist, 85-87, dep dir, 87-89, SR SCIENTIST, SMITHSONIAN INST, 90- *Personal Data:* b Shanghai, China, Mar 31, 35; US citizen; m 58; c 2. *Educ:* George Washington Univ, BS, 57; Stanford Univ, PhD(biol), 62.

*Honors & Awards:* Award for Outstanding Contrib to Syst Biol Community, Asn Syst Collections, 85. *Prof Exp:* Actg instr gen biol, Stanford Univ, 61; asst curichthyol, Acad Natural Sci Philadelphia, 62-66, assoc curr, 67-72; asst dir, Lerner Marine Lab, Am Mus Natural Hist, 72-73, dir, 73-75; prog mgr, Endangered Species, Nat Marine Fisheries Serv, 76-79; prog dir biol res resources, Div Environ Biol, NSF, Washington, DC, 80-84. *Concurrent Pos:* NSF grants, 63-72. *Mem:* Am Soc Ichthyol & Herpet. *Res:* Ichthyology, especially the anatomy and phylogeny of tetradontiform fishes and their classification; behavior and ecology of coral reef fishes. *Mailing Add:* Sr Scientist Smithsonian Inst Washington DC 20560

**TYLER, JOHN D,** IMMUNOLOGY. *Current Pos:* DIR, TRANSPLANT LAB, MED CTR, UNIV TENN, 83- *Personal Data:* b Cedar Rapids, Iowa, Oct 24, 47. *Educ:* Univ Mich, BA, 69; State Univ NY, PhD(immunol), 78. *Honors & Awards:* Walter Pinski Award, NIH. *Prof Exp:* Dir immunol, Univ Wash, 78-83. *Mem:* Am Soc Immunol; Am Transplant Soc. *Mailing Add:* Dept Surg Univ Tenn Med Ctr 1924 Alcoa Hwy Knoxville TN 37920-6999

**TYLER, JOHN HOWARD,** GEOLOGY. *Current Pos:* PROF GEOL, SAN FRANCISCO STATE UNIV, 66- *Personal Data:* b Madison, Wis, Aug 29, 35; m 75. *Educ:* Univ Wis, BS, 58; Va Polytech Inst, MS, 60; Univ Mich, PhD(geol), 63. *Prof Exp:* Res asst geol, Va Polytech Inst, 58-60; res asst geol & paleont, Univ Mich, 60-63; tech asst, US Geol Surv, Calif, 63-64; fel, Univ of Wales, Swansea, 64-65; air photo interpreter, Itek Corp, Calif, 65-66 & Mark Systs Inc, 66. *Mem:* Geol Soc Am; Soc Econ Paleont & Mineral. *Res:* Structural geology; remote sensing; stratigraphy. *Mailing Add:* Dept Geosci San Francisco State Univ 1600 Holloway Ave San Francisco CA 94132-1722

**TYLER, KENNETH LAURENCE,** NEUROVIROLOGY, CENTRAL NERVOUS SYSTEM INFECTIONS. *Current Pos:* assoc prof neurol med microbiol & immunol, 91-95, PROF NEUROL MED MICROBIOL & IMMUNOL, HEALTH SCI CTR, UNIV COLO, 95- *Personal Data:* b Boston, Mass, May 6, 53; m 79, Johnson; c Maxwell & Eric. *Educ:* Harvard Univ, AB, 74; Johns Hopkins Univ Sch Med, MD, 78. *Honors & Awards:* S Weir Mitchell Award, Am Acad Neurol, 83; Physician-Scientist Award, Nat Inst Allergy & Infectious Dis, 84. *Prof Exp:* Intern med, Peter Bent Brigham Hosp, 78-79, resident, 79-80; resident neurol, Mass Gen Hosp, 80-82, chief resident, 82-83, asst neurologist, 86-91; instr microbiol & molecular genetics, Harvard Med Sch, 84-86, asst prof neurol & neurosci, 86-91. *Concurrent Pos:* Alfred P Sloan res fel, 86-89, Milton fel, Harvard Univ, 86-88; co-prin investr, Nat Inst Neurol & Communicative Dis & Stroke Prog Proj Grant, 87-92; vis prof, Univ Ala Sch Med, 88, Med Univ SC, 90; assoc ed, J Neurol Sci, 90- *Mem:* Am Soc Neurol Invest (secy-treas, 83-84, pres, 84-85); fel Am Acad Neurol (pres hist sect, 89-91); Am Soc Virol; fel Am Col Physicians; Am Neurol Asn; Soc Exp Neuropath. *Res:* Study of how viruses produce diseases involving the central nervous system; identifying the role(s) played by specific viral genes at distinct stages in the pathogenesis of CNS infection; spread of virus to the central nervous system, tropism of virus for specific cell populations; mechanisms of virus-induced cell death. *Mailing Add:* Denver Vet Admin Med Ctr Neurol Serv 127 1055 Clermont St Denver CO 80220-3808. *Fax:* 303-393-4686; *E-Mail:* tylerk@essex.uchsc.edu

**TYLER, LESLIE J,** ORGANIC CHEMISTRY. *Current Pos:* RETIRED. *Personal Data:* b Salamanca, NY, Nov 2, 19; m 47; c 7. *Educ:* Univ Scranton, BS, 42; Pa State Univ, MS, 47, PhD(org chem), 48. *Prof Exp:* Res chemist silicon chem, Dow Corning Corp, 48-51, lab supvr resin res, 51-62, dir develop, 62-68, bus mgr fluids, 68-73, dir res, 73-75, vpres res & develop, 75-80. *Mem:* Am Chem Soc; Res Soc Am; Sigma Xi. *Res:* Silicon research; silica research; organosilicon research. *Mailing Add:* PO Box 177 Grawn MI 49637

**TYLER, MARY STOTT,** DEVELOPMENTAL BIOLOGY. *Current Pos:* from asst prof to assoc prof, 76-90, PROF ZOOL, UNIV MAINE, ORONO, 90- *Personal Data:* b Princeton, NJ, Apr 1, 49; m 70, Seth; c Anna & Matthew. *Educ:* Swarthmore Col, BA, 71; Univ NC, Chapel Hill, MS, 73, PhD(zool), 75. *Prof Exp:* NSF-NATO fel develop biol, Dalhousie Univ, 75-76. *Concurrent Pos:* Fac res grant, Univ Maine, 77-78; NIH res grant, 78-81. *Mem:* Soc Develop Biol; AAAS; Int Asn Dent Res; Sigma Xi. *Res:* Interacting systems in the developing vertebrate embryo; light-microscopic and ultrastructural aspects of tissue interactions; developmental capabilities of epithelial and mesenchymal tissues in experimental in vitro systems. *Mailing Add:* Dept Zool Univ Maine 5751 Murray Hall Orono ME 04469-5751. *Fax:* 207-581-2537

**TYLER, NOEL,** PETROLEUM GEOLOGY. *Current Pos:* DIR & STATE GEOLOGIST, TEX, 94- *Personal Data:* b Johannesburg, SAfrica, Dec 6, 50; US citizen; m, Erica Forster; c Kristin & Caroline. *Educ:* Univ Witwatersrand, BS, 75, Hons, 76, MS, 78; Colo State Univ, PhD(geol), 81. *Prof Exp:* Lectr geol, Dept Geol Sci, Tex, 88-90; res assoc, Bur Econ Geol, 81-85, res scientist, 85-87, prog coordr, 87-91, assoc dir, 91-94. *Concurrent Pos:* Lectr, Dept Energy, Texaco, Petrobras, Mobil, Chevron, Marathon, PdVSA, Tex Co, Columbia, Santos Australia & Southern Oil Explor Co, Soekor, SAfrica, 86-; mem, Comt Earth Resources, Nat Resource Coun, 94-; adj prof, Austin Univ, Technol, Perth, Australia. *Mem:* Am Asn Petrol Geologists; Soc Petrol Engrs; Soc Econ Paleontologists Mineralogists; Geol Soc Am. *Res:* Oil and gas resource evaluation and recovery optimization in complex reservoir systems worldwide. *Mailing Add:* University Sta Box X Austin TX 78713. *Fax:* 512-471-0140

**TYLER, R(ONALD) A(NTHONY),** THERMODYNAMICS, AERODYNAMICS. *Current Pos:* RETIRED. *Personal Data:* b Burnham, Eng, June 4, 20; nat Can; m 42; c 1. *Educ:* Univ London, BSc, 40. *Prof Exp:* Asst, Univ London, 40-42; engr, Bristol Aeroplane Co, Eng, 42-46; mathematician, Valve Res Labs, Stand Tel & Cables, Ltd, 46-47; asst res officer, Nat Res Coun Can, 47-51, assoc res officer, 51-55, sr res officer, 55-61, head, Gas Dynamics Lab, 77-85, prin res officer, Div Mech Eng, 61-85. *Mem:* Assoc fel Am Inst Aeronaut & Astronaut; assoc fel Can Aeronaut & Space Inst. *Res:* Turbomachinery, particularly aircraft turbines; locomotive gas turbine power plants; vertical take off and landing lift-propulsion systems. *Mailing Add:* 728 Lonsdale Rd Ottawa ON K1K 0K2 Can

**TYLER, SETH,** INVERTEBRATE ZOOLOGY, ELECTRON MICROSCOPY. *Current Pos:* from asst prof to assoc prof, 76-90, PROF ZOOL, UNIV MAINE, 90- *Personal Data:* b Chicago, Ill, Feb 26, 49; m 70; c 2. *Educ:* Swarthmore Col, BA, 70; Univ NC, Chapel Hill, PhD(zool), 75. *Prof Exp:* Killam fel anat, Dalhousie Univ, 75-76. *Concurrent Pos:* Prin investr, NSF grants, Univ Maine, 77-90; mem bd reviewers, Trans Am Micros Soc, 79-; assoc prof zool & dir, Electron Micros Ctr, Wash State Univ, 80; vis prof, Bermuda Biol Sta, 85. *Mem:* Am Soc Zoologists; Am Microscopical Soc; Sigma Xi; Electron Micros Soc Am; Int Asn Meiobenthologists; AAAS. *Res:* Comparative ultrastructure of lower metazoans; phylogeny of invertebrates; meiobenthology. *Mailing Add:* Dept Zool Univ Maine 5751 Murray Hall Orono ME 04469-5751

**TYLER, TIPTON RANSOM,** TOXICOLOGY, RISK ASSESSMENT. *Current Pos:* asst coord dir appl toxicol, 81-89, ASSOC DIR APPL TOXICOL, UNION CARBIDE CORP, 90- *Personal Data:* b Milwaukee, Wis, Jan 3, 41; m 62; c 3. *Educ:* Colo State Univ, BS, 63, PhD(nutrit), 68; NC State Univ, MS, 65; Am Bd Toxicol, dipl, 80. *Prof Exp:* Sr res chemist, Merck Sharp & Dohme Res Labs, 68-74; asst prof animal sci, Univ Ill, Urbana-Champaign, 74-75; sr scientist chem hyg fel, Carnegie-Mellon Univ, 76-81. *Concurrent Pos:* Adj assoc prof toxicol, Univ Pittsburgh, 79-82 & Col Grad Studies, WVa Univ, 82-85. *Mem:* AAAS; Am Chem Soc; Soc Toxicol; Am Soc Pharmacol & Exp Therapeut; Am Col Toxicol. *Res:* Toxicology; drug metabolism; residues in tissues; disposition and clearance from animals; toxicology; risk assessment. *Mailing Add:* P-2 592 Union Carbide Corp 39 Old Ridgebury Rd Danbury CT 06817-0001. *Fax:* 203-794-5275

**TYLER, VARRO EUGENE,** PHARMACOGNOSY. *Current Pos:* dean, Sch Pharm & Pharmacol Sci, Purdue Univ 66-86, Sch Pharm, Nursing & Health Sci, 79-86, exec vpres, Acad Affairs, 86-91, Lilly distinguished prof pharmacog, 91-96, DEAN & EMER DISTINGUISHED PROF, SCH PHARM & PHARMACAL SCI, PURDUE UNIV, 97- *Personal Data:* b Auburn, Nebr, Dec 19, 26; m 47, Virginia M Demel; c Jeanne L & David R. *Educ:* Univ Nebr, BS, 49; Univ Conn, MS, 51, PhD(pharmacog), 53. *Hon Degrees:* DSc, Univ Nebr, 87. *Honors & Awards:* Found Res Award, Am Pharmaceut Asn, 66. *Prof Exp:* Assoc prof pharmacog, Univ Nebr, 53-57; assoc prof pharmacog, Univ Wash, 57-61, chmn dept pharmacog & dir drug plant gardens, 57-66, prof, 61-66. *Concurrent Pos:* Vis prof, Inst Biochem Pflanzen, Ger, 63-64, Univ Gottingen, Ger, 84. *Mem:* Am Asn Cols Pharm (pres, 70-71); Am Soc Pharmacog (pres, 59-61); Am Pharmaceut Asn; Am Coun Pharmaceut Educ (pres, 74-78); fel Acad Pharmaceut Sci; fel Am Asn Pharmaceut Scientists. *Res:* Herbal medicine; drug plant cultivation; phytochemical analysis; medicinal and toxic constituents of higher fungi; alkaloid biosynthesis. *Mailing Add:* PO Box 2566 West Lafayette IN 47906. *Fax:* 765-463-7202

**TYLER, WALTER STEELE,** ANATOMY. *Current Pos:* Lectr vet sci, Univ Calif, Davis, 52-57, from asst prof to assoc prof vet med, 57-67, actg chmn dept, 65-67, chmn dept, 67-70, jr vet, Exp Sta, 52-56, asst vet, 56-62, prof vet med, 67-76, ANATOMIST, UNIV CALIF, DAVIS, 62-, PROF ANAT, 76- *Personal Data:* b Caspian, Mich, Nov 2, 25; m 49; c 2. *Educ:* Mich State Col, DVM, 51; Univ Calif, Davis, PhD(comp path), 56. *Concurrent Pos:* Fel, Postgrad Med Sch, Univ London, 63-64; dir, Calif Primate Res Ctr, 72- *Mem:* Am Asn Anatomists; Am Asn Vet Anat (secy-treas, 66-67); Am Physiol Soc; Am Soc Zool; Am Vet Med Asn; Sigma Xi. *Res:* Relationship of structure to function in health and disease; pulmonary anatomy; emphysema; air pollution; histochemistry; scanning and transmission; electron microscopy; comparative anatomy; primate morphology. *Mailing Add:* Dept Anat Sch Vet Med Univ Calif Davis CA 95616-8732. *Fax:* 530-752-7690

**TYLER, WILLARD PHILIP,** RUBBER & PLASTICS, CHEMISTRY & TECHNOLOGY. *Current Pos:* RETIRED. *Personal Data:* b Newton, Mass, Nov 8, 09; m 35, 55; c 3. *Educ:* Ore State Col, BS, 31, MS, 33; Univ Ill, PhD(analytical chem), 38. *Prof Exp:* Instr, Clark Jr Col, 34-36; res analyst, B F Goodrich Co, 38-45, sect leader, Res Ctr, 45-74. *Mem:* Am Chem Soc. *Res:* Classical and instrumental chemical analysis; absorption spectroscopy; x-ray diffraction; gas chromatography; electroanalytical methods; high polymers. *Mailing Add:* 8471 Whitewood Rd Brecksville OH 44141-1529

**TYLUTKI, EDMUND EUGENE,** MYCOLOGY. *Current Pos:* asst prof bot, 56-65, assoc prof, 65-91, EMER PROF BOT, UNIV IDAHO, 91- *Personal Data:* b Chicago, Ill, Nov 6, 26; m 56; c 6. *Educ:* Univ Ill, BS, 51, MS, 52; Mich State Univ, PhD(mycol), 55. *Prof Exp:* Asst bot, Univ Ill, 51-52; bot & plant path, Mich State Univ, 52-55; actg asst prof plant path & actg asst plant pathologist, Wash State Univ, 56. *Concurrent Pos:* Ed-in-chief, J Idaho Acad Sci, 65-, pres, 70-71; actg chmn, Dept Biol Sci, Univ Idaho, 75-76. *Mem:* Mycol Soc Am; Classification Soc; Int Asn Plant Taxonomists; Sigma Xi. *Res:* Computer applications to fungal taxonomy; taxonomy of fleshy fungi of the Pacific Northwest. *Mailing Add:* 116 N Cleveland St Moscow ID 83843

**TYMCHATYN, EDWARD DMYTRO,** GEOMETRIC TOPOLOGY, CONTINUUM THEORY & DYNAMICS. *Current Pos:* Asst prof, 68-71, assoc prof, 71-76, PROF MATH, UNIV SASK, 76- *Personal Data:* b Leoville, Sask, Nov 11, 42; m 42, Dixie Y Campbell. *Educ:* Univ Sask, BA, 63, Hons, 64; Univ Ore, MA, 65, PhD(math), 68. *Concurrent Pos:* Natural Sci & Eng Res Coun res grant, Univ Sask, 69-; vis assoc prof, Univ Ore, 75, vis prof, Ctr de Invest del Inst Politec Nac, Mexico City, 79 & Univ Ala, Birmingham, 81-82 & 88, Univ Houston, 89; mem fel comt, Natural Sci & Eng Res Coun, 79-82; vis prof, Univ Fla, 96, York Univ, 96, Univ Nipissing, 96. *Mem:* Am Math Soc; Can Math Soc. *Res:* Continuum theory, homeomorphism groups; homogeneity; menger spaces and universal spaces; mapping properties span; chainability; tree-like continua; ordered spaces; Bing partitioning; convexity; dynamics. *Mailing Add:* Dept Math & Statist Univ Sask 106 Wiggins Rd Saskatoon SK S7N 5E6 Can. *Fax:* 306-966-6086; *E-Mail:* tymchat@snoopy.usask.ca

**TYNDALL, JESSE PARKER,** BIOLOGY, SCIENCE EDUCATION. *Current Pos:* RETIRED. *Personal Data:* b Jones Co, NC, Jan 9, 25; m 65; c 1. *Educ:* Atlantic Christian Col, AB, 45; Univ NC, Chapel Hill, MA, 49; Univ Fla, EdD, 56. *Prof Exp:* Teacher, Jones County Bd Educ, NC, 45-47; from instr to assoc prof biol & sci educ, Atlantic Christian Col, 49-52, prof sci educ, 52-73, prof biol, 52-92, chmn, Dept Sci, 54-92. *Concurrent Pos:* Mem bd dirs, Joint Comn Nursing Educ, NC Bd Educ & Bd Gov, 69-72, chmn, 72-73. *Mem:* Fel AAAS. *Res:* Genetics; nursing education. *Mailing Add:* 314 Canterbury Rd Wilson NC 27896

**TYNDALL, JOHN RAYMOND,** PHYSICAL CHEMISTRY, STATISTICS. *Current Pos:* sr chemist, 80-82, SR SCIENTIST, GLYCO CHEMIST, 82-; CHEMTRONICS INC, 82- *Personal Data:* b Greensboro, NC, Feb 25, 42; m 84; c 2. *Educ:* Univ NC, Chapel Hill, BS, 63; Ill Inst Technol, Chicago, PhD(chem), 68; Univ Calif, San Diego, MA, 75. *Prof Exp:* Asst prof chem, Univ Pac, 70-74, sr chemist, Brin-Mont Chemicals, 75-78, Ethox Chemicals, 78-79. *Mem:* Am Chem Soc; Am Defense Preparedness Asn. *Res:* Specialty organics; electrically conducting polymers; ethoxylates and propoxylates; high temperature stable explosives; ultra-violet absorbers; flame retardants. *Mailing Add:* Pisgah Lab Box 567 Old Hwy 64 Pisgah Forest NC 28768-0567

**TYNER, C FRED,** neurophysiology, for more information see previous edition

**TYNER, DAVID ANSON,** ORGANIC CHEMISTRY. *Current Pos:* RETIRED. *Personal Data:* b Berrien Co, Mich, Feb 19, 22; m 49, Evelyn Pease; c Terry A (Tyner-Limorte), David A, Carol L (Tyner-Hanrahan) & Jennifer L (Tyner-Rapp). *Educ:* Univ Mich, BS, 44, MS, 49, PhD(org chem), 52. *Prof Exp:* Res chemist, G D Searle & Co, 52-86. *Concurrent Pos:* Civilian res chemist, Manhattan Proj, 44-45. *Mem:* Am Chem Soc. *Res:* Total and partial synthesis of steroids; peptides. *Mailing Add:* 909 Glendale Rd Glenview IL 60025

**TYNER, GEORGE S,** OPHTHALMOLOGY, LOW VISION. *Current Pos:* dean, 74-81, PROF OPHTHAL, SCH MED, TEX TECH UNIV, 71-, EMER DEAN, 81- *Personal Data:* b Omaha, Nebr, Oct 9, 16; c 2. *Educ:* Univ Nebr, BS, 40, MD, 42; Univ Pa, MS, 52; Am Bd Ophthal, dipl, 50. *Prof Exp:* Intern, Philadelphia Gen Hosp, 42-43, resident ophthal, 47-48; resident, Hosp Univ Pa, 48-51, asst instr ophthal, Sch Med, Univ Pa, 48-52; from asst instr to asst clin prof, Sch Med, Univ Colo, 52-61, assoc dean & asst to vpres med affairs, 63-71, chief glaucoma clin & assoc prof ophthal, 64-71. *Concurrent Pos:* Res fel, Univ Pa, 48-51; asst abstr ed, Am J Ophthal, 52-57; pvt pract, Colo, 52-61; mem, Colo State Bd Basic Sci Exam, 62-67; mem consult staff, Children's Hosp & Denver Gen Hosp; mem courtesy staff, St Luke's Hosp; mem hon staff, St Mary's Hosp, 73; active staff, Lubbock Gen Hosp. *Mem:* Fel Am Col Surg; Am Acad Ophthal & Otolaryngol; AMA. *Res:* Low vision rehabilitation. *Mailing Add:* 4006 Flint Ave Lubbock TX 79413-3114

**TYNER, MACK,** CHEMICAL ENGINEERING. *Current Pos:* RETIRED. *Personal Data:* b Laurel Hill, Fla, Feb 1, 16; m 46. *Educ:* Univ Fla, BSChE, 38; Univ Cincinnati, MS, 40, PhD(phys chem), 41. *Prof Exp:* Tech control engr, Kimberly Clark Corp, NY, 41-42; res engr, Univ Wis, 42-43; asst chem engr, Armour Res Found, Ill, 42-45; prof chem eng, Univ Fla, 45-82. *Mem:* Instrument Soc Am; Am Inst Chem Engrs. *Res:* Process dynamics and control; systems engineering; instrumentation; chemical reaction engineering. *Mailing Add:* 1421 SW 13th Ave Gainesville FL 32608-1117

**TYNER, WALLACE EDWARD,** NATURAL RESOURCE ECONOMICS, POLICY ANALYSIS. *Current Pos:* From asst prof to assoc prof, 77-84, PROF, DEPT AGR ECONS, PURDUE UNIV, 84-, DEPT HEAD, 89- *Personal Data:* b Orange, Tex, Mar 21, 45; m 70, Jean Margaret Young; c Davis & Jeffrey. *Educ:* Tex Christian Univ, BS, 66; Univ Md, 72, PhD(econs), 77. *Concurrent Pos:* Consult, Foreign Affairs Off, UN, 80, USAID, 83-95, USDA, 85-95, World Bank, 92-97, US Feed Grains Coun, 94. *Mem:* Am Agr Econ Asn; Am Econ Asn; Int Asn Agr Economists. *Res:* Development economics; natural resources economics; structural adjustment issues for economics undergoing major economics transformation towards a market economy. *Mailing Add:* 1145 Krannert Bldg West Lafayette IN 47907-1145. *Fax:* 765-494-9176; *E-Mail:* tyner@agecon.purdue.edu

**TYNES, ARTHUR RICHARD,** OPTICS. *Current Pos:* MEM TECH STAFF, AT&T BELL LABS, 61- *Personal Data:* b Great Falls, Mont, Oct 1, 26; m 46, Mary E Kittams; c Richard D, Cathlyn M (Dutzer), Julianne (Smith), Ronald E & Randal F. *Educ:* Mont State Univ, BS, 50; Ore State Univ, MS, 53, PhD(physics), 63. *Prof Exp:* Physicist, US Bur Mines, 51-54; instr physics,

Ore State Univ, 54-61. *Concurrent Pos:* Consult, 88- *Mem:* Optical Soc Am. *Res:* Spectroscopy; plasma diagnostics; physical optics; applications of lasers to optical measurements; light scattering and light transmission; fiber optics. *Mailing Add:* 2734 Fern Dr Great Falls MT 59404

**TYOR, MALCOLM PAUL,** MEDICINE. *Current Pos:* assoc, 55-57, from asst prof to assoc prof, 57-62, PROF MED, MED SCH, DUKE UNIV, 62-, CHIEF DIV GASTROENTEROL, MED CTR, 65- *Personal Data:* b New York, NY, Apr 20, 23; m 47; c 4. *Educ:* Univ Wis, AB, 44; Duke Univ, MD, 46; Am Bd Internal Med, dipl, 57. *Prof Exp:* Intern, Madison Gen Hosp, Univ Wis-Madison, 46-47; resident med, Bowman Gray Sch Med, Wake Forest Col, 49-51, fel gastroenterol, 51-52; clinician, Med Div, Oak Ridge Inst Nuclear Studies, 52-54; physician, pvt pract, 54-55. *Concurrent Pos:* Asst chief med serv & chief radioisotope serv & gastroenterol, Vet Admin Hosp, Durham, 55- *Mem:* AAAS; AMA; Am Gastroenterol Asn; Am Fedn Clin Res; Am Soc Clin Invest. *Res:* Gastroenterology. *Mailing Add:* 810 E Forest Hills Blvd Durham NC 27707

**TYREE, MELVIN THOMAS,** WHOLE PLANT PHYSIOLOGY, STRESS PHYSIOLOGY. *Current Pos:* res prof, 85-89, PROF PLANT BIOPHYS, BOT DEPT, UNIV VT, 90-; RES PLANT PHYSIOLOGIST, US FOREST SERV, 91- *Personal Data:* b Santa Ana, Calif, Nov 15, 46; Can & US citizen; m 70, E Loeta Smith; c Niki C. *Educ:* Pomona Col, BA, 68; Cambridge Univ, PhD(biophys), 72. *Honors & Awards:* CD Nelson Award, Can Soc Plant Physiologists, 79; Killam Award, 79. *Prof Exp:* Lectr, 71-72, from asst prof to prof plant physiol, Univ Toronto, 72-85. *Concurrent Pos:* Proj leader, N Eastern Forest Exp Sta, US Forest Serv, 88-90; adj staff scientist, Smithsonian Trop Res Inst, 90- *Mem:* Am Soc Plant Physiologists; Scand Soc Plant Physiologists. *Res:* Water stress physiol; multiple stress physiol; translocation in phloem & symplasm; mathematical models of transport in plants; membrane transport; cavitation and embolism in xylem. *Mailing Add:* One Northland Ct Colchester VT 05446. *Fax:* 802-899-5007

**TYRER, HARRY WAKELEY,** ELECTRICAL AND COMPUTER ENGINEERING, BIOLOGY. *Current Pos:* prof, Dept Comp Eng & Comp Sci, 85-95, INTERIM & FOUNDING CHAIR, 95-97, ASSOC CHAIR, UNIV MO, COLUMBIA, 97- *Personal Data:* b Palmira, Colombia, Sept 20, 42; US citizen; m 68; c 3. *Educ:* Univ Miami, BSEE, 65; Duke Univ, MS, 69, PhD(elec eng), 72. *Prof Exp:* Res & teaching assoc, Duke Univ, 67-72; asst prof elec eng, NC A&T Univ, 71-72; instrumentation engr, Becton Dickinson Res Ctr, 73-76, prin investr automated cytol, 76-79; dir, biomed eng & biophys, Cancer Res Ctr, 79-87. *Concurrent Pos:* Adj lectr, Sch Med, Johns Hopkins Univ, 78-90. *Mem:* Inst Elec & Electronics Engrs; Asn Comput Mach; Soc Anal Cytol. *Res:* Real-time operating systems, software engineering, computer design; high resolution image analysis and processing; acoustic imaging; computer networks, high speed computer networks, computer network performance and evaluation; computer aided electronic design; flow systems, applications and development. *Mailing Add:* Dept Elec & Computer Eng Univ Mo Columbia MO 64110

**TYREY, LEE,** NEUROENDOCRINOLOGY, REPRODUCTION. *Current Pos:* Assoc obstet, gynec & anat, Duke Univ Sch Med, 70-72, from asst prof to assoc prof obstet & gynec, 72-83, from asst prof to assoc prof anat, 76-88, PROF OBSTET & GYNEC, DUKE UNIV SCH MED, 83-, ASSOC PROF NEUROBIOL, 88- *Personal Data:* b Chicago, Ill, Oct 26, 37; m 61, Mary E James; c Scott J, Ann E & Marc R. *Educ:* Univ Ill, Urbana, BSc, 63, MSc, 64, PhD(physiol), 69. *Concurrent Pos:* NIH res fel, Med Ctr, Duke Univ, 69-70, Duke Endowment res grant, 71-73, Pop Coun res grant, 74-76; dir, Gynec Endocrinol Lab, Duke Univ Med Ctr, 70-, mem, Comprehensive Cancer Ctr, 78-; NC United Community Serv grant, 75-76; USPHS res grant, Nat Inst Drug Abuse, 78-89, mem, 83-87, chmn, Biomed Res Rev Comt, NIDA, 85-87; consult, NC Alcoholism Res Authority, 85-91; chmn, Instnl Animal Care & Use Comt, 89- *Mem:* Endocrine Soc; Soc Study Reproduction; Sigma Xi. *Res:* Neural control of gonadotropin secretion; effects of drugs of abuse on reproductive function; radioimmunoassay of protein hormones. *Mailing Add:* Dept Obstet-Gynec Duke Univ Med Ctr Box 3244 Durham NC 27710. *Fax:* 919-684-8560

**TYRL, RONALD JAY,** PLANT TAXONOMY. *Current Pos:* from asst prof to assoc prof, 77-88, PROF BOT & CUR HERBARIUM, OKLA STATE UNIV, 88- *Personal Data:* b Lawton, Okla, June 16, 43; m 65, Lynda Steele; c Ryan, Craig & Laura. *Educ:* Park Col, BA, 64; Ore State Univ, MS, 67, PhD(syst bot), 69. *Prof Exp:* Herbarium asst taxon, Ore State Univ, 65-69; asst prof biol, Park Col, 70-72. *Mem:* Am Soc Plant Taxon; Bot Soc Am. *Res:* Grass classification; plant biosystematics; evolutionary mechanisms. *Mailing Add:* Dept Bot Okla State Univ Stillwater OK 74078-0001

**TYROLER, HERMAN A,** MEDICINE. *Current Pos:* from assoc prof to prof, 60-79, alumni distinguished prof, 80-95, EMER PROF EPIDEMIOL, UNIV NC, CHAPEL HILL, 95- *Personal Data:* b New York, NY, Sept 5, 24. *Educ:* Ohio Univ, AB, 43; NY Univ, MD, 47. *Honors & Awards:* Wade Hampton Frost Lectr, Am Pub Health Asn, 85, John Snow Award, 88; Distinguished Achievement Award, Am Heart Asn, 94. *Prof Exp:* Resident physician internal med, Cornell Univ, 48-49; fel, NY Med Col & Metrop Hosp, 49-51; capt, Med Corps, USAF, Patrick AFB, 51-53; med consult & dir, Occup Health Serv, Asheville, NC, 53-58; res dir, Health Res Found, 58-60. *Concurrent Pos:* Consult occup & cancer epidemiol, Champion Paper Co, 55-68, NY Times, 55-72, NASA, 65-70, Upjohn Co, 72-73 & Reynolds Aluminum, 77-82; mem, Res Training Grants Comt, Commun Health Serv, USPHS, 65-67 & 67-69, Health Serv Res Study Sect, HEW, 70-73, Lipid Res Clin Prog, Nat Heart, Lung & Blood Inst, 72-, US Polish Steering Comt Collab Studies, 79-, US Fed Repub Ger Steering Comt Collab Training, 81; chmn,

Family Studies Comt, Nat Heart, Lung & Blood Inst, 72-81, Coun Epidemiol, Am Heart Asn, 83-85. *Mem:* Inst Med-Nat Acad Sci; Sigma Xi; Am Pub Health Asn; Soc Epidemiol Res; Int Epidemiol Asn; Am Epidemiol Soc; Am Heart Asn; Am Pub Health Asn. *Res:* Cardiovascular epidemiology; atherosclerosis risk in communities. *Mailing Add:* Dept Epidemiol Sch Pub Health Univ NC Chapel Hill NC 27514

**TYRRELL, DAVID JOHN,** BIOCHEMISTRY. *Current Pos:* RES SCIENTIST BIOCHEM, GLYCOMED INC, 89- *Personal Data:* b Hartford, Conn, Feb 11, 61. *Educ:* Hobart Col, BS, 83; Emeryville Sch Med, PhD(biochem), 88. *Prof Exp:* Fel chem, Univ Ill, 88-89. *Mem:* Am Cell Biol Soc; NY Acad Sci. *Mailing Add:* Dept Biochem Glycomed Inc 860 Atlantic Ave Alameda CA 94501-0001

**TYRRELL, ELIZABETH ANN,** MICROBIOLOGY. *Current Pos:* from instr to asst prof, 60-71, assoc prof microbiol, 71-79, PROF BIOL SCI, SMITH COL, 79- *Personal Data:* b Pittsfield, Mass, Oct 16, 31. *Educ:* Simmons Col, BS, 53; Univ Mich, MS, 56, PhD(bact), 62. *Prof Exp:* Res asst virol, Parke, Davis & Co, Mich, 53-55. *Mem:* AAAS; Am Soc Microbiol. *Res:* Concentrated culture of microorganisms; autolysis in bacteria. *Mailing Add:* Smith Col Biol Sci Burton Hall Northampton MA 01063

**TYRRELL, HENRY FLANSBURG,** NUTRITION, BIOMETRY. *Current Pos:* RES SCI, USDA CSRS, AEROSPACE CTR, 90-, STAFF SCI, USDA CSRS, 90- *Personal Data:* b Gloversville, NY, Aug 4, 37; m 69. *Educ:* Iowa State Univ, BS, 59; Cornell Univ, MS, 64, PhD(nutrit), 66. *Prof Exp:* Asst prof animal sci, Cornell Univ, 66-69; res dairy husbandman, Energy Metab Lab, Animal Husb Res Div, Agr Res Serv, USDA, 69-72, res animal scientist, Ruminant Nutrit Lab, Nutrit Inst, 72- *Mem:* Am Dairy Sci Asn; Am Soc Animal Sci. *Res:* Utilization of energy by domestic animals; nitrogen utilization by ruminant animals; energy requirements for growthl lactation in cattle. *Mailing Add:* USDA CSRS Aerospace Ctr Suite 330-B 901 D St SW Washington DC 20250-2200

**TYRRELL, JAMES,** THEORETICAL CHEMISTRY. *Current Pos:* from asst prof to assoc prof, Southern Ill Univ, 67-80, actg chmn chem, 80-81, chmn, 82-90, PROF CHEM, SOUTHERN ILL UNIV, 80-, DIR, CTR HEALTH & SAFETY, 92- *Personal Data:* b Kilsyth, Scotland, Apr 19, 38; m 92, Jie Zhang; c Dalton & Ran. *Educ:* Univ Glasgow, BS, 60, PhD(chem), 63. *Prof Exp:* Teaching fel chem, McMaster Univ, 63-65; fel, Div Pure Physics, Nat Res Coun, 65-67. *Mem:* Am Chem Soc; Sigma Xi; fel Am Inst Chem. *Res:* Theoretical calculations on atoms and molecules with particular application to transition metal systems and to the study of internal rotation. *Mailing Add:* 240 Midland Hills Rd Carbondale IL 62958. *Fax:* 618-453-7192; *E-Mail:* jim@ctrehs.c-cehs.siu.edu

**TYRRELL, WILLIS W, JR,** GEOLOGY. *Current Pos:* CONSULT GEOLOGIST, CHARLOTTE, NC, 89- *Personal Data:* b Mobile, Ala, Feb 12, 30; m 52, Loyce Harrell; c David W, Rebecca T (Freil), John E & Mark A. *Educ:* Fla State Univ, BS, 52; Yale Univ, MS, 54, PhD(geol), 57. *Prof Exp:* Asst, Fla State Univ, 52-53; field asst, Texaco, 54; geologist, Pan Am Petrol Corp, 55-64, res group supvr, 64-68; sr staff geologist, Amoco Prod Co, New Orleans, 68-77, sr geol assoc, Chicago, 77-81, sr consult geologist, Houston, Tex, 81-89. *Mem:* Geol Soc Am; Am Asn Petrol Geol. *Res:* Stratigraphy; petroleum exploration; seismic stratigraphy; carbonate geology. *Mailing Add:* 5718 Bentway Dr Charlotte NC 28226-8056

**TYSON, GRETA E,** ZOOLOGY. *Current Pos:* RETIRED. *Personal Data:* b Medford, Mass, Nov 2, 33; m 86. *Educ:* State Teachers Col Bridgewater, BS, 55; Univ NH, MS, 57; Univ Calif, Berkeley, PhD(zool), 67. *Prof Exp:* NIH fel biol struct, Univ Wash, 67-69, NIH fel path, 69-70, instr, 70-72; asst prof, Univ Md, Baltimore, 72-76; assoc prof, 76-80, prof, Miss State Univ, 80-90. *Concurrent Pos:* Head, Electron Microscope Ctr, 76- *Mem:* Am Soc Cell Biol; Am Soc Zool; Am Micros Soc; Electron Micros Soc Am; Crustacean Soc. *Res:* Comparative renal morphology; structure and function of microtubules and microfilaments; ultrastructure of crustacean organs. *Mailing Add:* PO Box 1593 Harwich MA 02645

**TYSON, J ANTHONY,** ASTROPHYSICS, IMAGING. *Current Pos:* MEM TECH STAFF, AT&T BELL LABS, LUCENT TECHNOL, 69- *Personal Data:* b Pasadena, Calif, Apr 5, 40; m 81; c 1. *Educ:* Stanford Univ, BS, 62; Univ Wis, MS, 64, PhD(physics), 67. *Honors & Awards:* IR 100 Award, 85. *Prof Exp:* Nat Res Coun-Air Force Off Sci Res fel, Univ Chicago, 67-68; vis lectr physics, Sussex Univ & Hebrew Univ, Jerusalem, 68-69. *Concurrent Pos:* Vis prof, Univ Calif, Berkeley, 75-76; chair, Adv Develop Prog, Nat Optical Astron Observ, 85-88, Dirs Adv Comt, 86-87; adj prof astrophys, Princeton Univ, 87-; adj staff mem, Lowell Observ, 87-; vchair, Astrophys Div, Int Union Pure & Appl Physics, 88-93; mem adv comts, NSF, 88-; mem vis comt, Nat Radio Astron Observ, 89-93, Nat Optical Astron Observ, 93-; adv, Bd NSF Ctr Particle Astrophys, 92- *Mem:* Nat Acad Sci; fel Am Phys Soc; Int Astron Union; Astron Soc Pac; Int Union Pure & Appl Physics; Am Astron Soc. *Res:* Optical astronomy; astrophysics; experimental gravitation and relativity; gravitational radiation; radio astronomy; CCD imaging systems and automated imaging processing software; image reconstruction; tensor tomography; dark matter mapping; applied physics; oceanography. *Mailing Add:* Lucent Tech 600 Mountain Ave Murray Hill NJ 07974

**TYSON, JOHN EDWARD ALFRED,** REPRODUCTIVE ENDOCRINOLOGY. *Current Pos:* PROF & CHMN, UNIV MAN, 78-, OBSTET & GYNEC CHIEF, 78-, PROF PHYSIOL, 79- *Personal Data:* b Hamilton, Ont, May 27, 35; c 3. *Educ:* Univ Western Ont, MD, 56 & 60; Am Bd Obstet & Gynec, dipl, 72 & 79. *Prof Exp:* Fel gynec & obstet, Sch Med, Johns Hopkins Univ, 66-68, instr, 68-69, asst prof, 69-71, assoc prof, 71-78. *Concurrent Pos:* Mem med adv bd, Planned Parenthood Md, 70-78; chmn, Comt Int Reference Prep Placental Lactogen 69; ed-in-chief, Current Topics Obstet & Gynec, 72-78; mem, Adv Bd Educ TV, Md State Bd Educ, 67-69, Am Asn Planned Parenthood Physicians, 69-71, Nat Primate Cent Comt, Ottawa, 78-, Fertil & Maternal Clin Trials, Med Res Coun, Can, 80-; consult, Planned Parenthood Md, 67-78, reprod, Nat Zoo, Smithsonian Inst, 74-78, res, Agency Int Develop, US Dept State, 74-78, Prog Pub Health Educ, Can Broadcasting Corp, 76-79, field consult, Inst Nutrit Cent Am & Panama, 77-78, Nat Heart, Lung & Blood Inst, NIH, 78- *Mem:* Fel Am Col Obstetricians & Gynecologists; Am Diabetes Asn; Soc Gynec Invest; Endocrin Soc; Perinatal Res Soc. *Res:* Reproductive endocrinology, principally in those areas having to do with gestational diabetes, infertility, endocrinology of breastfeeding and neuroendocrinology of reproduction and prolactin physiology. *Mailing Add:* 649 Queens Way W Mississauga ON L5B 1C2 Can

**TYSON, JOHN JEANES,** THEORETICAL BIOLOGY, CELL BIOLOGY & MOLECULAR BIOLOGY. *Current Pos:* prof biol, 78-96, UNIV DISTINGUSHED PROF, VA POLYTECH INST & STATE UNIV, 96- *Personal Data:* b Abington, Pa, Dec 12, 47; m 69; c 4. *Educ:* Wheaton Col, BS, 69; Univ Chicago, PhD(chem physics), 73. *Prof Exp:* NATO fel theoret biol, Max Planck Inst Biophys Chem, 73-74; asst prof math, State Univ NY, Buffalo, 74-75; Nat Cancer Inst fel cell biol, Inst Biochem & Cancer Res, Univ Innsbruck, 76-77. *Concurrent Pos:* Guest prof, Univ Utah, 85 & 96; sr vis res fel, Oxford Univ, 84, 86. *Mem:* AAAS; Soc Math Biol. *Res:* Control of cell cycle events; chemical oscillations and traveling waves. *Mailing Add:* Dept Biol Va Polytech Inst & State Univ Blacksburg VA 24061. *Fax:* 540-231-9307; *E-Mail:* tyson@vt.edu

**TYSON, JULIAN FELL,** ATOMIC SPECTROMETRY, FLOW INJECTION ANALYSIS. *Current Pos:* PROF CHEM, UNIV MASS AMHERST, 89- *Personal Data:* b Glasgow, Scotland, Aug 3, 49; c John A & Jennifer A. *Educ:* Aberdeen Univ, BSc, 71; Imp Col, DIC, 75; London Univ, PhD(anal chem), 75. *Honors & Awards:* SAC Silver Medal, Royal Soc Chem, 86, Distinguished Serv Award, 89. *Prof Exp:* Lectr analytical chem, Loughborough Univ Technol, 76-85, sr lectr, 85-89. *Mem:* Am Chem Soc; fel Royal Soc Chem; Soc Appl Spectros; Asn Sci Educ. *Res:* Improvement in methods of analysis for trace elements by atomic spectrometry techniques using continuous flow procedures for novel methods of sample pretreatment. *Mailing Add:* Dept Chem Univ Mass Amherst MA 01003-0035. *Fax:* 413-545-4846; *E-Mail:* tyson@chem.umass.edu

**TYSON, LAURA D'ANDREA,** ECONOMICS. *Current Pos:* PROF ECON & BUS ADMIN, UNIV CALIF, BERKELEY, 78-; NAT ECON ADV TO PRES US, NAT ECON COUN, WASHINGTON, 95- *Personal Data:* b Bayonne, NJ, June 28, 47; m, Eric Tarloff; c Elliot. *Educ:* Smith Col, BA, 69, Mass Inst Technol, PhD, 74. *Concurrent Pos:* Dir, Inst Int Studies & Res, Univ Calif, Berkeley; vis scholar, Inst Int Econ; mem, Subcomt Global Econ Strategy US; chmn, Pres's Coun Econ Advs, Washington, 93-95. *Mailing Add:* The White House Nat Econ Coun 2nd Floor West Wing Washington DC 20500

**TYSON, RALPH ROBERT,** surgery, for more information see previous edition

**TYSON, WILLIAM RUSSELL,** METALLURGY & PHYSICAL METALLURGICAL ENGINEERING. *Current Pos:* res scientist mat sci, 73-80, head, Eng Metal Phys Sect, 80-89, PROG COORDR, PMRL CANMET, 89- *Personal Data:* b Bourlamaque, Que, Sept 5, 39; m 73, Margaret Davies; c Rebecca, Miriam & Emily. *Educ:* Univ Toronto, BASc, 61; Cambridge Univ, PhD(metall), 65. *Honors & Awards:* Dofasco Award Mat Eng, Can Inst Mining, 91. *Prof Exp:* Fel metall, Univ Toronto, 66-67; fac mem physics, Trent Univ, 67-73. *Mem:* Am Soc Testing & Mat; fel Am Soc Metals; Can Inst Mining & Metall. *Res:* Hydrogen in metals; fracture mechanics. *Mailing Add:* 95 Kenora St Ottawa ON K1Y 3K9 Can. *Fax:* 613-992-8735

**TYSVER, JOSEPH BRYCE,** applied statistics, operations research, for more information see previous edition

**TYZBIR, ROBERT S,** NUTRITIONAL BIOCHEMISTRY. *Current Pos:* ASSOC PROF NUTRIT BIOCHEM & CHMN, DEPT NUTRIT SCI, COL AGR & LIFE SCI, UNIV VT, 73- *Personal Data:* m; c 2. *Educ:* Univ RI, PhD(biochem), 71. *Mem:* Sigma Xi; Am Inst Nutrit; Brit Nutrit Soc. *Res:* Energy metabolism; brown adipose tissue metabolism. *Mailing Add:* Dept Nutrit Sci Terrill Bldg Rm 315 Univ Vt Burlington VT 05405-0148. *Fax:* 802-656-0407

**TYZNIK, WILLIAM JOHN,** ANIMAL NUTRITION. *Current Pos:* RETIRED. *Personal Data:* b Milwaukee, Wis, Apr 26, 27; m 50; c 5. *Educ:* Univ Wis, BS, 48, MS, 49, PhD(nutrit), 51. *Prof Exp:* Asst nutrit, Univ Wis, 48-51; from asst prof to assoc prof animal nutrit, Ohio State Univ, 51-59, prof animal sci & vet prev med, 59-92. *Concurrent Pos:* Pres, Tizco Inc. *Mem:* Am Soc Animal Sci; Am Dairy Sci Asn; fel Soc Animal Sci. *Res:* Ruminant and monogastric nutrition; digestive physiology and mineral nutrition of equines and nutrition of zoological animals. *Mailing Add:* 1101 Urlin Ave Columbus OH 43212

**TZAFESTAS, SPYROS G,** ROBOTICS & CONTROL, EXPERT SYSTEMS. *Current Pos:* dir, Control Systs Lab, Nat Tech Univ, 74-84, Systs & Control Div, 82-84 & Comput Sci Div, 86-88, PROF ROBOTICS & CONTROL & DIR, INTEL ROBOTICS & AUTOMATIC LAB, NAT TECH UNIV, ATHENS, 85- *Personal Data:* b Corfu, Greece, Dec 3, 39; m 65; c 2. *Educ:* Athens Univ, BSc, 63; dipl electronics, 65; Univ London, MSc & DIC(elec eng), 67; Southampton Univ, PhD(control), 69. *Hon Degrees:* DSc, Southampton Univ, 97, Int Univ Found, 89; Dr-Ing, Munich Tech Univ, 97. *Prof Exp:* Dir comput control, Nat Res Ctr, Demokritos, Athens, 69-73; prof systs control, Patras Univ, Greece, 73-84. *Concurrent Pos:* Res fel, Nuclear Safety & Control, Nat Res Coun Demokritos, Athens, 75-84; vis prof fel, Southampton Univ, 75, Imp Col, Univ London, 81 & Denmark Techniske Hojskole, 83; vis prof adaptive control, Galabria Univ, Italy, 85, robotics, 87 & Tech Univ Delft, Neth, 91; external prof, Grande Ecole d'Ingenieurs Lille, France, 87- *Mem:* Fel Inst Elec & Electronics Engrs; Am Soc Mech Engrs; Int Asn Math & Comput Simulation; fel Inst Elec Engrs; Soc Intelligent Robotics & Expert Systs (hon pres); NY Acad Sci. *Res:* Control, robotics and sutomation; adaptive, robust, fuzzy and neural control; robot analysis, path/task planning and control; applications in process control/supervision, mobile robots and manufacturing systems; author, co-author or editor of 30 books and over 500 papers. *Mailing Add:* Comp Eng Div Robotics & Automation Lab Nat Tech Univ 15773 Zografou Athens Greece. *Fax:* 30-1-7722990; *E-Mail:* tzafesta@softlab.ece.ntua.gr

**TZAGOURNIS, MANUEL,** MEDICINE, ENDOCRINOLOGY. *Current Pos:* resident internal med, Univ Hosp, 61-62 & 64-65, chief resident internal med, 66-67, asst prof med, Col Med, 67-70, assoc prof med, 70-74, assoc dean, 75-76, PROF MED, COL MED, OHIO STATE UNIV, 74-, ASST DEAN RES & CONTINUING MED EDUC, 76- *Personal Data:* b Youngstown, Ohio, Oct 20, 34; m 58; c 5. *Educ:* Ohio State Univ, BS, 56, MD, 60, MMS, 65. *Prof Exp:* Intern med, Philadelphia Gen Hosp, Pa, 60-61. *Concurrent Pos:* USPHS fel endocrinol & metab, Ohio State Univ Hosp, 65-66. *Mem:* Am Fedn Clin Res; Am Diabetes Asn; AMA. *Res:* Diabetes, glucose metabolism and insulin secretion, especially as they relate to lipid disorders and coronary atherosclerosis. *Mailing Add:* Dean Med Admin Ohio State Univ Col Med 370 W Ninth Ave Columbus OH 43210-1238

**TZANAKOU, M EVANGELIA,** NEUROPHYSIOLOGY, NEURAL NETWORKS. *Current Pos:* from asst prof to assoc prof, 81-90, PROF BIOMED ENG & DEPT CHAIR, DEPT ELEC ENG, RUTGERS UNIV, 90- *Personal Data:* b Athens, Greece. *Educ:* Univ Athens, BS, 68; Syracuse Univ, MS, 74, PhD(physics), 77. *Honors & Awards:* Outstanding Adv Award, Inst Elec & Electronics Engrs, 85; Achievement Award, Soc Women Engrs, 92. *Prof Exp:* Fel biophys, Physics Dept, Syracuse Univ, 77-80. *Concurrent Pos:* Consult, Eye Defect & Vision Res Found, 78-80, biophysics, Syracuse Univ, 80-81; assoc ed, Inst Elec & Electronics Trans Neural Networking. *Mem:* Soc Neurosci; Asn Res Vision & Opthalmol; Biophys Soc; Sigma Xi; fel Inst Elec & Electronics Engrs; fel Int Asn Med & Biol Environ. *Res:* Information processing in the visual system is examined by computer controlled techniques; recordings are done both in animals and in humans with a response feedback method where the information flow is reversed and a feature extractor becomes a feature generator; pattern recognition; digital signal processing of biological signals; neural networks; data compression, image reconstruction; hearing aids; neural network modeling of the brain. *Mailing Add:* Dept Biomed Eng Rutgers Univ PO Box 909 Piscataway NJ 08855-0909. *Fax:* 732-932-3753; *E-Mail:* etzanako@gandalf.rutgers.edu

**TZENG, CHU,** FOOD SCIENCE & TECHNOLOGY. *Current Pos:* DAIRYLEA COOP, INC, 88- *Personal Data:* b Tainan, Taiwan, Sept 19, 40; US citizen; m 69; c 3. *Educ:* Nat Taiwan Univ, BS, 63, MS, 66. *Hon Degrees:* Scd, Mass Inst Technol, 72. *Honors & Awards:* Res Awards, Environ Protection Agency, NSF & NY State Res & Develop. *Prof Exp:* Res assoc biochem eng, Mass Inst Technol, 73-74; dir res & develop food indust, Milbrew Inc, 74-80; dir fermentation technol, Abcor Inc, 80-83; chmn, Hansen Lab, Inc, 83-87. *Mem:* Inst Food Technologists; Am Chem Soc; Am Soc Microbiol; Am Inst Chem Engrs; Soc Indust Microbiol. *Res:* Fermentation engineering in scale up; product recovery processing; utilization and development of food ingredients; product development and quality assurance, regulatory compliance. *Mailing Add:* 3732 Falkner Dr Naperville IL 60564

**TZENG, KENNETH KAI-MING,** ELECTRICAL ENGINEERING, COMPUTER SCIENCES. *Current Pos:* from asst prof to assoc prof elec eng, 69-77, interim chmn, 91-93, PROF ELEC ENG & COMPUT SCI, LEHIGH UNIV, 77- *Personal Data:* b Kaifeng, China, Aug 6, 37; m 61, Marjorie Kao; c Todd C & Ted C. *Educ:* Nat Taiwan Univ, BS, 59; Univ Ill, MS, 62, PhD(elec eng), 69. *Prof Exp:* Jr engr, IBM Corp, 62-63; elec res engr, Nat Cash Register Co, 63-65; res asst, Univ Ill, 65-69. *Concurrent Pos:* NSF res initiation grant, 70-71, res grants, 73-79 & 88-; mem tech staff, Bell Labs, 69, instr, In-Hour Continuing Educ Prog, 72-80, vis scientist, 81-82; vis asst prof, Univ Ill, 72; fac fel, NASA, 76; consult prof, Southwestern Jiaotung Univ, China, 87- *Mem:* Fel Inst Elec & Electronics Engrs. *Res:* Error control in computer and communication systems; computer networks; fault-tolerant computing. *Mailing Add:* Dept Elec Eng & Comput Sci Lehigh Univ Packard Lab 19 Memorial Dr W Bethlehem PA 18015-3084. *Fax:* 610-758-6279; *E-Mail:* kkt1@lehigh.edu

**TZENG, WEN-SHIAN VINCENT,** METALLURGICAL ENGINEERING. *Current Pos:* DIR MAT SCI, CHOMERICS, W R GRACE, 80- *Personal Data:* b Taipei, Taiwan, May 7, 43; m 72; c 2. *Educ:* Cheng Kung Univ, Taiwan, BSE, 66; Univ Conn, PhD(metall), 75. *Prof Exp:* Sr res scientist, Firestone Tire & Rubber Co, 75-80. *Mem:* Am Soc Metals; Am Vacuum Soc; Electron Micros Am; Am Powder Metall Inst; Microbeam Anal Soc. *Res:*

Metal powder surface chemistry and physics for electrical conductive behavior and their industrial application; electron microscopy; surface analysis; elastomer compounding and testing. *Mailing Add:* 54 Eastway Reading MA 01867

**TZIANABOS, THEODORE,** VIROLOGY. *Current Pos:* RES MICROBIOLOGIST VIROL, CTR DIS CONTROL, 71- *Personal Data:* b Manchester, NH, Feb 12, 33; m 62, Irene Davis; c Suzanne & Peter. *Educ:* Univ NH, BA, 55, MS, 59; Univ Mass, PhD(microbiol), 65; Am Bd Med Microbiol, dipl. *Prof Exp:* Res instr microbiol, Dept Poultry Dis, Univ NH, 55-57; microbiologist, Diagnostic Virol, State Mass, 59-60; res instr microbiol, Dept Vet Sci, Univ Mass, 60-65; resident, Ctr Dis Control, 65-67; res microbiologist, Med Sci Div, Ft Detrick, 67-70; microbiologist, Beckman Instruments, 70-71. *Concurrent Pos:* Mem bd trustees, Am Type Cult Collection, Rockville, Md, 78-82. *Mem:* Am Soc Microbiologists; Am Soc Trop Med & Hyg; Res Soc Am; Am Soc Rickettsiology; Am Acad Microbiol. *Res:* Development and research on rickettsial products involving serologic tests, including fluorescent microscopy; purification and protein composition of rickettsiae. *Mailing Add:* 6959 Lockridge Dr Doraville GA 30360

**TZOAR, N,** CONDENSED MATTER PHYSICS, PLASMA PHYSICS. *Current Pos:* assoc prof, 67-71, PROF PHYSICS, CITY COL NEW YORK, 71- *Personal Data:* b Tel Aviv, Israel, July 2, 30. *Educ:* Technion, Haifa, Israel, BS, 54, MS, 56; Univ Pa, PhD(physics), 60. *Prof Exp:* At Bell Labs, AT&T, 62-67. *Mem:* Am Phys Soc; Optical Soc Am. *Mailing Add:* Dept Physics City Col NY Convent Ave at 138th St New York NY 10031

**TZODIKOV, NATHAN ROBERT,** BIORGANIC CHEMISTRY, RADIOCHEMISTRY. *Current Pos:* EXEC DIR, MAGAININ PHARMACEUT INC, 95- *Personal Data:* b Brooklyn, NY, Feb 28, 52. *Educ:* State Univ NY, Stony Brook, BS, 73; Mass Inst Technol, PhD(org chem), 77. *Prof Exp:* Chemist radiochem res, NEN/Dupont Co, 78-80, group leader, 80-85. *Concurrent Pos:* Mkt mgr, Sadtler Div Bio Rad. *Mem:* AAAS; Am Chem Soc. *Res:* Pharmaceutical development; regulatory strategy. *Mailing Add:* 124 Avon Rd Haverford PA 19041-1611. *E-Mail:* ntzodikov@magainin.com

**TZOGANAKIS, COSTAS,** POLYMER PROCESSING & RHEOLOGY, COMPUTER-AIDED DESIGN IN POLYMER ENGINEERING. *Current Pos:* asst prof, 90-95, ASSOC PROF CHEM ENG, UNIV WATERLOO, 95- *Personal Data:* b Chania, Crete, Greece, May 14, 60; m 88. *Educ:* Univ Thessaloniki, Greece, dipl eng, 83; McMaster Univ, Can, PhD(chem eng), 89. *Prof Exp:* Res asst chem eng, McMaster Univ, 83-88; res scientist, Du Pont Can, Inc, 88-90. *Mem:* Sigma Xi; Can Soc Chem Eng; Am Inst Chem Eng; Soc Plastics Engrs; Polymer Processing Soc; Soc Rheol. *Res:* Reactive processing of polymers; melt phase polymer reaction kinetics; mathematical modeling and computer simulations of polymer processing; rheology of polymer melts; expert systems in polymer processing. *Mailing Add:* Dept Chem Eng Univ Waterloo Waterloo ON N2L 3G1 Can. *E-Mail:* ctzogan@cape.wwaterloo.ca

# U

**UBAN, STEPHEN A,** FILTRATION THEORY & PRACTICE, WATER TREATMENT. *Current Pos:* DIR & MGR RES & DEVELOP, JOHNSON FILTRATION & WHEELABRATOR CLEAN WATER SYSTS, 90- *Personal Data:* b Waterloo, Iowa, May 10, 50. *Educ:* Iowa State Univ, BS, 73. *Prof Exp:* Res & develop engr, Smith & Loveless Div Ecodyne, 74-77, sr res & develop engr, 77-78; spec projs engr, Microfloc Div Neptune, 78-80, proj cng mgr, 80-83, dir res & develop, 83-84; spec projs mgr, Johnson Filtration Systs, WTI Corp, 84-87, dir res & develop, 87-90. *Mem:* Am Water Works Asn; Prod Develop Mgt Asn; Am Filtration Soc; Am Mgt Asn. *Res:* Dept filtration; dissolved air flotation; underdrains and distributors; adsorption clarification; crossflow microfiltration; oil well screen design. *Mailing Add:* 13630 Paragon Ave N Stillwater MN 55082

**UBELAKER, DOUGLAS HENRY,** PHYSICAL ANTHROPOLOGY. *Current Pos:* chmn, Dept Anthrop, 80-85, CUR PHYS ANTHROP, SMITHSONIAN INST, 73- *Personal Data:* b Horton, Kans, Aug 23, 46; m 75; c 2. *Educ:* Univ Kans, Lawrence, BA, 68, PhD(anthrop), 73; Am Bd Forensic Anthrop, dipl. *Concurrent Pos:* Prof lectr, Dept Anat & Anthrop, George Washington Univ. *Mem:* AAAS; Am Asn Phys Anthrop; fel Am Acad Forensic Sci. *Res:* Physical anthropology of North America, Latin America; skeletal biology; prehistoric demography; forensic anthropology. *Mailing Add:* Nat Mus Natural Hist Smithsonian Inst Washington DC 20560

**UBELAKER, JOHN E,** PARASITOLOGY. *Current Pos:* asst prof biol, 68-71, assoc prof, 71-74, PROF BIOL, SOUTHERN METHODIST UNIV, 74- *Personal Data:* b Everest, Kans, Mar 21, 40. *Educ:* Univ Kans, BA, 62, MA, 65, PhD(zool), 67. *Prof Exp:* Fel parasitol, Emory Univ, 67-68. *Mem:* Am Soc Parasitol; Am Soc Zool; Am Micros Soc; Wildlife Dis Asn; Sigma Xi. *Res:* Helminthology; transmission, scanning electron microscopy; helminth reproduction; pathophysiology of lungworm infections. *Mailing Add:* 6580 Hwy 518 Ranchos de Taos NM 87557-9796

**UBELS, JOHN L,** OPHTHALMOLOGY. *Current Pos:* ASSOC PROF OPHTHAL, UNIV PITTSBURGH, 91- *Personal Data:* b Modesto, Calif, June 9, 52. *Educ:* Calvin Col, BS, 74; Mich State Univ, MS, 76, PhD(physiol), 79. *Prof Exp:* Assoc prof ophthal, Med Col Wis, 80-91. *Mem:* Am Physiol Soc; Sigma Xi; Int Sci Eye Res Asn; Asn Res Vision & Ophthal. *Res:* Ophthalmology. *Mailing Add:* Ophthal Eye & Ear Hosp 230 Lorthop St Pittsburgh PA 15213-2545

**UBERALL, HERBERT MICHAEL,** ACOUSTICS, RADAR. *Current Pos:* from assoc prof to prof, 64-94, EMER PROF PHYSICS, CATH UNIV AM, 94- *Personal Data:* b Neunkirchen, Austria, Oct 14, 31; US citizen; m 81; c 2. *Educ:* Univ Vienna, PhD(theoret physics), 53; Cornell Univ, PhD(theoret physics), 56. *Hon Degrees:* DSc, Univ LeHavre, France, 87. *Honors & Awards:* Achievement Award, Washington Acad Sci, 84; Foreign Med, Fr Acoust Soc, 96. *Prof Exp:* Res fel physics, Univ Liverpool, 56-57; Ford Found fel, Europ Org Nuclear Res, Geneva, Switz, 57-58; res physicist, Carnegie Inst Technol, 58-60; asst prof, Univ Mich, 60-64. *Concurrent Pos:* Sr res physicist, Conductron Corp, Mich, 61-64; consult, Naval Res Lab, Washington, DC, 66- & Naval Surface Weapons Ctr, White Oak, Md, 76-81; vis prof, Univ Paris, 84-85, Univ Le Havre, 90, 92, 94 & 96, Univ Bordeaux, 93 & 95. *Mem:* Fel Am Phys Soc; fel Acoust Soc Am; Am Asn Univ Prof; fel Inst Elec & Electronics Engrs; Int Union Radio Sci; Am Acad Mech. *Res:* Scattering and radiation theory; electromagnetic and acoustic waves; underwater acoustics; theoretical nuclear physics; wave mechanics; author, co-author and co-editor of 9 books and 350 articles in professional journals; nuclear physics. *Mailing Add:* Dept Physics Cath Univ Am Washington DC 20064. *Fax:* 202-319-4448, 301-656-6049

**UBEROI, M(AHINDER) S(INGH),** AERONAUTICAL ENGINEERING, ASTRONAUTICS. *Current Pos:* RETIRED. *Personal Data:* b Delhi, India, Mar 13, 24; nat US. *Educ:* Punjab Univ, India, BSc, 44; Calif Inst Technol, MS, 46; Johns Hopkins Univ, DEng, 52. *Prof Exp:* Res asst aeronaut eng, Johns Hopkins Univ, 52-53; res assoc aerospace eng, Univ Mich, 53-56, from assoc prof to prof, 56-63; chmn, Dept Aerospace Eng Sci, Univ Colo, Boulder, 63-77, prof aerospace eng sci & fel, Jt Inst Lab Astrophys, 63-74. *Concurrent Pos:* Guggenheim fel, 58-59; exchange scientist, US Nat Acad Soc, Bd Soviet Acad Sci, 66; vis prof Univ Que, Can 72-74; vis scientists, Max Planck Inst Astrophys, Munich, Ger, 74; Cosmical Gas Dynamics, 74; hon res fel, Harvard Univ, 75-76. *Mem:* Am Inst Aeronaut & Astronaut; Am Phys Soc; Am Soc Eng Educ. *Res:* Turbulent flows; statistical analysis of random functions; magnetohydrodynamics; aerothermodynamics; dynamics of ionized and neutral gases and liquids with and without chemical reaction, gravity and electromagnetic fields. *Mailing Add:* Dept Eng Univ Colo Campus Box 422 Boulder CO 80309

**UCCI, POMPELIO ANGELO,** PHYSICAL CHEMISTRY, MATHEMATICS. *Current Pos:* sr res chemist, Monsanto Co, 52-54, group leader synthetic fibers, 54-58, sect head, 58-69, site mgr, New Enterprise Div, 69-71, sr res specialist, 71-75, ENG FEL, TEXTILES DIV, MONSANTO CO, 75- *Personal Data:* b Warwick, RI, Jan 15, 22; m 49; c 4. *Educ:* Univ RI, BS, 43. *Prof Exp:* Res chemist, Celanese Corp Am, 43-44 & 46-52. *Mem:* AAAS; Am Chem Soc. *Res:* Solution and melt properties of natural and synthetic fiber forming polymers; fundamental mechanical and engineering properties; statistics and quality control; paper making from synthetic fibers; testing equipment and procedures. *Mailing Add:* 4070 Aiken Rd Pensacola FL 32503-3304

**UCHIDA, IRENE AYAKO,** CYTOGENETICS. *Current Pos:* prof, 69-85, dir, 69-91, EMER PROF PEDIAT & PATH REGIONAL CYTOGENETICS LAB, MED CTR, MCMASTER UNIV, 85- *Personal Data:* b Vancouver, BC, Apr 8, 17. *Educ:* Univ Toronto, PhD(human genetics), 51. *Hon Degrees:* DSc, Univ W Ont, 96. *Honors & Awards:* Officer Order Of Can, 93; Founder Award, Can Col Med Geneticists, 95. *Prof Exp:* Res assoc, Hosp Sick Children, Toronto, Ont, 51-59; proj assoc, Univ Wis, 59-60; lectr pediat, Univ Man, 60-62, from asst prof to assoc prof, 63-69, asst prof anat, 67-69. *Concurrent Pos:* Ramsay Wright scholar, Univ Toronto, 47; fel, Rockefeller Found, 59; vis prof, Univ Ala Med Sch, 68; vis scientist, Med Res Coun Can, 69, mem, Sci Coun Can & Grant Comt, 70-73 & vis prof, 73; Queen Elizabeth II speaker, Winnipeg, Man, 71; consult, Int Prog Radiation Genetics, Nuclear Energy Agency, Orgn Econ Coop & Develop, Paris, 73 & Am Bd Med Genetics, 80-82; mem, Adv Comt Genetic Serv, Ont Ministry Health, 79-85 & mem task force high technol diag procedures & equip, Ont Coun Health, 80-81; mem, Ment Retardation Comt, Nat Inst Child Health & Human Develop, 80-84; chmn, Genetic Cell Culture Comt, Ont Med Asn Lab Proficiency Testing Prog, 81-; Basic Sci Adv Comt, NY State Inst, 81-; dir cytogentics, Oshawa Gen Hosp, 91-95. *Mem:* AAAS; Am Soc Human Genetics (pres, 68); emer fel Can Col Med Geneticists; Genetics Soc Can; Genetics Soc Am; emer fel Am Col Med Genetics. *Res:* Human genetics; cytogenetics; etiology of abnormal chromosome division with emphasis on radiation as a cause of aneuploidy in mental retardation and spontaneous abortions. *Mailing Add:* Dept Pediat McMaster Univ Hamilton ON L8N 3Z5 Can. *Fax:* 905-521-1703

**UCHIDA, RICHARD NOBORU,** MARINE SCIENCES. *Current Pos:* RETIRED. *Personal Data:* b Honolulu, Hawaii, Sept 4, 29; m 93, Frances Kazusa; c Joann, Dean & Gail. *Educ:* Univ Wash, Seattle, BS, 51. *Prof Exp:* Fishery res biologist, US Dept Com, Nat Oceanic & Atmospheric Admin, Nat Marine Fisheries Serv, Southwest Fisheries Ctr, Honolulu Lab, 54-76, supvry biologist, 76-84, chief pelagic resources invest, 84. *Concurrent Pos:* Counr, Hawaiian Acad Sci, 75-76; consult, UN Food & Agr orgn, 77. *Mem:* Fel Am Inst Fishery Res Biol; Am Fisheries Soc. *Res:* Distribution, life history and relative abundance of demersal and pelgic fishes, mollusks, and crustaceans in waters surrounding central and western Pacific islands and overlying seamounts; life history studies on tunas, spiny lobsters, snappers, cichlids and deep-water shrimps. *Mailing Add:* 1586 Hoolehua St Pearl City HI 96782

**UCHRIN, CHRISTOPHER GEORGE,** MATHEMATICAL MODELING OF CONTAMINANTS IN ENVIRONMENTAL SYSTEMS. *Current Pos:* from asst prof to assoc prof, 80-90, PROF, DEPT ENVIRON SCI, RUTGERS UNIV, 90-, CHMN DEPT, 91- *Personal Data:* b South Amboy, NJ, Oct 27, 50; m 92, Janette Goleme. *Educ:* Manhattan Col, BE, 72, ME, 74; Univ Mich, PhD(environ & water resources), 80. *Prof Exp:* Environ engr, US Environ Protection Agency, 72-77; Rackham fel, Univ Mich, 77-78, res asst, 78-80. *Concurrent Pos:* Assoc ed. J Water Resources Planning & Mgt, Am Soc Civil engrs, 84-92; dir, Grad Prog Environ Sci, Rutgers Univ, 86-91. *Mem:* Am Soc Civil Engrs; Am Soc Testing & Mat; Soc Environ Toxicol & Chem; Water Environ Fedn; Am Water Resources Asn; Am Chem Soc. *Res:* Formulation and validation of mathematical models describing the transport and fate of organic and inorganic contaminants in ground and surface water systems. *Mailing Add:* Dept Environ Sci Rutgers Univ New Brunswick NJ 08903. *Fax:* 732-932-8644

**UCHUPI, ELAZAR,** GEOLOGY. *Current Pos:* res asst, Woods Hole Oceanog Inst, 62-64, assoc scientist, 64-79, sr scientist, 79-93, J Seward Johnson Chair Oceanog, 89-93, EMER SR SCIENTIST, WOODS HOLE OCEANOG INST, 93- *Personal Data:* b New York, NY, Oct 31, 28. *Educ:* City Col New York, BS, 52; Univ Southern Calif, MS, 54, PhD(geol), 62. *Honors & Awards:* Frances P Shepard Award, 91. *Prof Exp:* Res asst geol, Univ Southern Calif, 55-62. *Mem:* Am Geophys Union; Sociedad Geologica de España; Am Archeol Inst. *Res:* Sedimentation; submarine geomorphology; tectonics; geologic development of oceanic basins; author or co-author of approximately 191 publications in geology. *Mailing Add:* Dept Geol & Geophys Woods Hole Oceanog Inst Woods Hole MA 02543

**UCKO, DAVID A,** SCIENCE MUSEUM ADMINISTRATION. *Current Pos:* PRES, KANS CITY MUS, 90- *Personal Data:* b New York, NY, July 9, 48; m 72, Barbara Clark; c Aaron. *Educ:* Columbia Col, BA, 69; Mass Inst Technol, PhD(chem), 72. *Prof Exp:* Asst prof chem, Hostos Community Col, 72-76; from asst prof to assoc prof, Antioch Col, 76-79; res coordr, Mus Sci & Indust, Chicago, 79-80, sci dir, 81-87, prog div chmn, 85-86, vpres prog, 86-87; vpres, Calif Mus Found, 87-90. *Concurrent Pos:* NIH fel, Columbia Univ, 72; fac res fel, Res Found, State Univ NY, 75; adj staff scientist, C F Kettering Res Lab, 78; res assoc & assoc prof, Dept Educ, Univ Chicago, 82-87; host & producer, Sci Alive Radio Prog, 83-87; dep dir, Calif Mus Sci & Indust, 87-90; chair, Pub Comt, Asn Sci-Tech Centers, 88-94, Legis Comt, 96- *Mem:* Am Chem Soc; Sigma Xi; Am Asn Mus; fel AAAS (secy, 87-92). *Res:* Development of innovative ways to enhance public science literacy through informal education. *Mailing Add:* Kansas City Mus 3218 Gladstone Blvd Kansas City MO 64123-1199. *Fax:* 816-460-2220

**UDALL, JOHN ALFRED,** internal medicine, cardiology, for more information see previous edition

**UDALL, JOHN NICHOLAS, JR,** MEDICINE, NUTRITIONAL BIOCHEMISTRY. *Current Pos:* PROF & DR, CHILDREN'S HOSP, 92- *Personal Data:* b Washington, DC, Dec 30, 40; m 67; c 4. *Educ:* Brigham Young Univ, BSc, 65; Temple Univ, MD, 69; Mass Inst Technol, PhD(nutrit biochem), 80. *Prof Exp:* Intern med & pediat, Los Angeles Co/Univ Southern Calif Med Ctr, 69-70; general med officer, Indian Health Serv, USPHS, 70-72; resident pediat, Los Angeles County/Univ Southern Calif Med Ctr, 72-74; fel pediat nutrit & gastroenterol, Baylor Col Med, 74-76; fel clin nutrit, Mass Inst Technol, Mass Gen Hosp & Children's Hosp Med Ctr, 77-80; asst dir, Clin Res Ctr, Mass Inst Technol, 80-85; asst prof pediat, Harvard Med Sch, 81-92. *Concurrent Pos:* Nutrit consult eval acceptability & tolerance to purified single cell protein for adult human feeding, Dir, Nevin S Scrinshaw, 77-78; co-pirin investr, NIH grant, 78-80. *Mem:* Fel Am Acad Pediat; fel Am Bd Nutrit; NAm Soc Pediat Gastroenterol. *Res:* Effect of early nutrition on gastrointestinal development; obesity in infancy and childhood; pathophysiology of cholera. *Mailing Add:* Children's Hosp La State Univ Med Ctr 200 Henry Clay Ave New Orleans LA 70118

**UDANI, KANAKKUMAR HARILAL,** FOOD SCIENCE, CHEMICAL ENGINEERING. *Current Pos:* MGR PROG, DEPT ADVAN SOLUTIONS, BAXTER HEALTH CARE CORP, ROUNDLAKE, ILL, 90- *Personal Data:* b Rajkot, India, Dec 4, 36; US citizen; m 66; c 2. *Educ:* Gujarat Univ, India, BSc, 57; Univ Bombay, BSc, 59; Univ Ill, Urbana, MS, 61, PhD(food sci), 65. *Prof Exp:* Res fel chem eng, Univ Bombay, 59; supvr qual control, Accent Int, Div Int Minerals & Chem Corp, 61-62; sr food technologist, H J Heinz Co, 65-68; sr scientist oil prod, Res & Develop Div, Kraftco Corp, 68-79, res coordr, 79-87, sr res scientist, Kraft Inc, Glenview, 87-90. *Mem:* Inst Food Technologists. *Res:* Dehydration of foods; oils, fats and starch technology; aseptic systems; emulsifiers and stabilizers; processed food rheology; flavor science; product, process and market development. *Mailing Add:* Baxter Health Care Corp 1620 Waukegan Rd McGaw Park IL 60085

**UDANI, LALIT KUMAR HARILAL,** CHEMICAL ENGINEERING. *Current Pos:* CHEM ENGR CONSULT, 88- *Personal Data:* b Rajkot, India, Aug 19, 27; US citizen; m 70; c 1. *Educ:* Univ Bombay, BSc, 49; Univ Nagpur, BSc, 52; Univ Mich, Ann Arbor, MSE, 56, ScD(chem eng), 62. *Prof Exp:* Develop engr, Kordite Co, NY, 61-63; specialist process develop, Chem Div, Gen Elec Co, Mass, 63-67; res engr, Org Chem Div, FMC Corp, Md, 67-69; supvry process engr, Catalytic Inc, Philadelphia, 69-80, sr process specialist, 80-87. *Mem:* Am Chem Soc; Sigma Xi. *Res:* Organic chemicals and polymer process research; water pollution abatement for industrial systems; processes for clean fuels and electrode coke from coal, flue gas desulfurization; corporate planning and business development for synthetic fuels projects; coal-water slurry; composites. *Mailing Add:* 40 Masters Circle Marlton NJ 08053

**UDD, JOHN EAMAN,** ROCK MECHANICS, MINING ENGINEERING. *Current Pos:* DIR, MINING RES LABS, CAN CENTRE MINERAL & ENERGY TECHNOL NATURAL RESOURCES CAN, OTTAWA, 84- *Personal Data:* b Rochester, NY, June 18, 37; Can citizen; m 70, Mary T Barker; c John R & Thea L. *Educ:* McGill Univ, BEng, 59, MEng, 60, PhD(mining eng), 70. *Prof Exp:* Lectr, McGill Univ, 61-64, asst prof mining eng, 64-70, assoc prof, 70-82, dir mining prog, 78-82; sr stability engr, Falconbridge Ltd, Sudbury, Ont, 82-84. *Concurrent Pos:* Adj prof mining eng, McGill Univ & Univ BC; dir, Mining Res Lab, Canmet Gov Can, 84-96; distinguished lectr, Can Inst Mining, Metal & Petrol, 87-88. *Mem:* Fel Can Inst Mining & Metall; Can Rock Mech Asn; fel Can Acad Eng. *Res:* Applications of stress analysis to mining engineering; advanced technology needs of the mining industry; mining in arctic climates; ground control and mine stability; mine information; monitoring; control systems. *Mailing Add:* Canmet Gov Can Mining Res Labs 555 Booth St Ottawa ON K1A 0G1 Can. *Fax:* 613-996-2597; *E-Mail:* judd@cc2.smtp.nrcamiga.ca

**UDDIN, SHAHAB,** INTERFERON SIGNALING, DNA DRUG INTERACTION. *Current Pos:* RES INSTR, HEMAT-ONCOL, UNIV ILL, CHICAGO, 96- *Personal Data:* b Azamgarh, India, June 19, 63; m 76, Salma Sageer; c Aisha, Asma & Omar. *Educ:* Aligarh Muslim Univ, BSc, 82, MSc, 84, MPhil, 86, PhD(biochem), 88. *Prof Exp:* Jr & sr res fel, Dept Biochem, Aligarh Muslim Univ, India, 85-89; postdoctoral researcher, Dept Radiol, Ohio State Univ, 89-91; res assoc molecular & cellular biochem & hemat & oncol, Loyola Univ, Chicago, 91-96. *Mem:* AAAS; Soc Biol Chem. *Res:* Activation of the insulin receptor substrate signaling system by interferons; to study the IRS-1 and IRS-2 function as multisite SH-2-docking protein in type 1 interferon transduction; linking upstream tyrosine kinase to downstream signaling elements. *Mailing Add:* Hemat-Oncol Dept Med MBRB Rm 3268 Univ Ill 900 S Ashland Ave Chicago IL 60607-7173

**UDELL, JON GERALD, JR,** DIGITAL TEST ALGORITHMS & METHODOLOGIES, CAD SOFTWARE. *Current Pos:* Sr prin engr, NCR Microelectronics, 88-91, CONSULT ENGR, SYMBIOS LOGIC, 91- *Personal Data:* b Madison, Wis, May 16, 61. *Educ:* Univ Wis-Madison, BS(elec eng), BS(comput sci) & BS(math), 83; Stanford Univ, MS, 84, PhD(elec eng), 89. *Concurrent Pos:* Mem, Test Technol Tech Comt, Inst Elec & Electronics Engrs. *Mem:* Inst Elec & Electronics Engrs. *Res:* Various aspects of pseudo-exhaustive test; extended work with an improved segmentation algorithm; studies of automatic test program generation and simulation algorithms; conceived of and implemented a new partial scan technique that in some cases provides better fault coverage at a lower cost than automatic test program generation combined with full scan. *Mailing Add:* 4304 Whippeny Dr Ft Collins CO 80526. *E-Mail:* jon.udell@symbios.com

**UDELSON, DANIEL G(ERALD),** AEROSPACE & MECHANICAL ENGINEERING, URODYNAMICS & HEMODYNAMICS. *Current Pos:* Asst prof aero & mech eng, Col Indust Tech, Boston Univ, 60-64, assoc prof, Col Eng, 64-70, chmn aerospace mech eng, 81-92, PROF, COL ENG, BOSTON UNIV, 70-, PROF UROL, 93- *Personal Data:* b New York, NY, Mar 7, 29; m 67, Mary Ellen; c John & Christina. *Educ:* George Washington Univ, AB, 53; Harvard Univ, AM, 54, PhD, 61. *Concurrent Pos:* Consult, Avco Missile Systs Div, Ctr Nuclear Studies, Fr AEC & Cambridge Air Force Res Labs. *Res:* Fluid and applied mechanics. *Mailing Add:* 237 Marlborough St Boston MA 02116. *E-Mail:* dgu@buenga.bu.edu

**UDEM, STEPHEN ALEXANDER,** VIROLOGY, INFECTIOUS DISEASES. *Current Pos:* asst prof, 76-83, ASSOC PROF MED & DEPT MICROBIOL & IMMUNOL, ALBERT EINSTEIN COL MED, 83- *Personal Data:* b New York, NY, Apr 4, 44. *Educ:* City Col New York, BS, 64; Albert Einstein Col Med, PhD(genetics), 71, MD, 72. *Prof Exp:* Intern internal med, Bronx Munic Hosp Complex, 72-73, resident, 73-74; NIH fel infectious dis, Montefiore/Albert Einstein/Jacobi Hosps & Albert Einstein Col Med, 74-76. *Concurrent Pos:* Comt infectious dis, NY Acad Med. *Mem:* Am Soc Microbiol; Infectious Dis Soc. *Res:* Investigation of persistent viral infections and their relationship to the production of chronic disease, particularly chronic neurological and rheumatic diseases. *Mailing Add:* Bldg 211 Rm 353 Wyeth Lederle Vaccines/Ped 401 N Middletown Rd Pearl River NY 10965-1299

**UDEN, PETER CHRISTOPHER,** CHROMATOGRAPHY. *Current Pos:* from asst prof to assoc prof, 70-78, PROF ANALYTICAL CHEM, UNIV MASS, AMHERST, 78- *Personal Data:* b Southampton, Eng, May 19, 39; m 67, Janet Kopriva; c Michael, Andrew & David. *Educ:* Bristol Univ, BSc, 61, PhD(chem), 64. *Honors & Awards:* Benedetti-Pichler Award, Am Microchem Soc, 93; Cherynaev Medal, Russ Acad Sci, 93; Award, Royal Soc Chem. *Prof Exp:* Instr chem, Univ Ill, Urbana, 65-66; ICI fel, Univ Birmingham, 66-67; lectr, 67-70. *Concurrent Pos:* Mallinckrodt Chem Corp res assoc, Univ Ill, Urbana, 64-66; vis prof, State Univ Campinas, Brazil, 84; chmn, Comn Anal Separations & Chromatography, 89-93, Separations & Chromatopography, Am Chem Soc, 92-94. *Mem:* Am Chem Soc; Royal Soc Chem; UK Chromatographic Soc; Sigma Xi; Int Union Pure & Appl Chem. *Res:* Analytical and inorganic chemistry; separation and thermal methods; gas and liquid chromatography; mass spectrometry; metal complexes. *Mailing Add:* GRC Tower A Dept Chem Univ Mass Amherst MA 01003-4510. *E-Mail:* pcuden@chem.umass.edu

**UDENFRIEND, SIDNEY,** BIOCHEMISTRY. *Current Pos:* DIR, DANA RES INST, DREW UNIV, 96- *Personal Data:* b New York, NY, Apr 5, 18; m 43; c 2. *Educ:* City Col New York, BS, 39; NY Univ, MS, 42, PhD(biochem), 48. *Hon Degrees:* DSc, NY Med Col, 74, Col Med & Dent

NJ, 79 & Mt Sinai Sch Med City Univ NY, 81. *Honors & Awards:* Flemming Award, 58; Hillebrand Award, Am Chem Soc, 62; Van Slyke Award, 67; Gairdner Award, 67; Ames Award, Am Asn Clin Chem, 69; Torald Sollman Award, Am Soc Pharmacol & Exp Therapeut, 75; City of Hope Res Award, 75; Heinrich Waelsch Lectr Neurosci, 77; Rudolf Virchow Gold Medal Award, 79; Chauncey Leake Lectr, Univ Calif, San Francisco, 80; Wis Biol Div Hilldale Lect Award, Univ Wis, 85. *Prof Exp:* Lab asst bact, City Dept Health, NY, 40-42; asst chemist, Res Div, NY Univ, 42-45, asst biochem, Col Med, 45-48; instr, Sch Med, Wash Univ, 48-50; chief, Sect Cellular Pharmacol, Chem Pharmacol Lab, Nat Heart Inst, 50-56, chief, Lab Clin-Biochem, 56-58; dir, Roche Inst Molecular Biol, 68-83, head, Lab Molecular Neuro-Biol, emer dir, 83-96. *Concurrent Pos:* US Nat Comt Int Union Biochem; mem bd trustees, Wistar Inst, 68-71; adj prof, Dept Biochem, City Univ NY, 68-; adj prof, Dept Human Genetics & Develop, Columbia Univ Col Physicians & Surgeons, 69-; mem, Panel Narcotics, Off Sci & Technol, 72-73; mem, Sci Adv Bd, Scripps Clin & Res Found, 74-78 & Inst Cellular & Molecular Path, 74-; mem adv comt to dir, NIH, 76-78; mem adv bd, Weizmann Inst Sci, 78- *Mem:* Nat Acad Sci; AAAS; Am Chem Soc; Am Soc Biol Chemists; Am Soc Pharmacol & Exp Therapeut (secy, 62-64); Soc Exp Biol & Med; Asn Clin Chemist; NY Acad Sci; Harvey Soc; Int Union Biochem; Int Soc Neurochemistry; Am Col Neuropsychopharmacol; Am Acad Arts & Sci; hon mem Japanese Pharmacol Soc; hon mem Czech Pharmacol Soc. *Res:* Peptide and protein biochemistry; neurochemistry. *Mailing Add:* Dir Dana Res Inst Drew Univ Hall Sci Madison NJ 07940. *E-Mail:* sudenfri@drew.edu

**UDIN, SUSAN BOYMEL,** DEVELOPMENT NEUROBIOLOGY. *Current Pos:* from asst prof to assoc prof neurobiol, 79-92, PROF PHYSIOL, STATE UNIV NY, BUFFALO, 92- *Personal Data:* b Philadelphia, Pa, Aug 11, 47; m 67, David; c Rachel & Michael. *Educ:* Mass Inst Technol, BS, 69; PhD(life sci), 75. *Prof Exp:* Sr staff mem, Nat Inst Med Res, Mill Hill, 78-79. *Concurrent Pos:* Fel, Psychol Dept, Mass Inst Technol, 75-77, Nat Inst Med Res, Mill Hill, 77-78; prin investr, NY State Health Res Coun grant, 80-81; prin investr, Nat Eye Inst res grant, 80-, March of Dimes basic res grant, 83-85 & 89-93; mem, Visual Sci Study Sect, NIH, 86-90; grantee, Howard Hughes Med Inst, 93-94, NSF, 96-97. *Mem:* AAAS; Soc Neurosci; Sigma Xi; Asn Women Sci. *Res:* Effects of early visual experience on formation of connections in the brain and the role of glutamate receptors in control of plasticity. *Mailing Add:* State Univ NY Dept Physiol 313 Cary Hall Buffalo NY 14214. *Fax:* 716-829-3349; *E-Mail:* sudin@ubmedb.buffalo.edu

**UDIPI, KISHORE,** POLYMER CHEMISTRY. *Current Pos:* res specialist, 80-89, SR RES SPECIALIST & SCI FEL, MONSANTO PLASTICS & RESINS, 89- *Personal Data:* b Udipi, SIndia, May 19, 40; m 73; c 1. *Educ:* Univ Bombay, BSc Hons, 59, MSc, 63; Univ Akron, PhD(polymer chem), 72. *Prof Exp:* Works mgr paints & polymers, Bombay Paints, India, 63-68; fel, Princeton Univ, 72-73; res chemist polymer chem, Phillips Petrol Co, 73-80. *Mem:* Am Chem Soc. *Res:* Polymer synthesis; study of polymer microstructure and chemical modifications of polymers. *Mailing Add:* 66 Glenbrook Lane Longmeadow MA 01106-2810

**UDLER, DMITRY,** SOLID STATE PHYSICS, APPLIED MATHEMATICS. *Current Pos:* RES ASSOC, DEPT MAT SCI & ENG, NORTHWESTERN UNIV, 90- *Personal Data:* b Kharkov, USSR, Dec 15, 54. *Educ:* Inst Solid State Physics, Acad Sci Chernogslovka, USSR, Cand Sci Physics & Math, 88. *Prof Exp:* Res scientist, Inst Solid State Physics, Chernogslovka, USSR, 89. *Mem:* Mat Res Soc. *Res:* Computer simulations at internal interfaces in solids and related phenomena. *Mailing Add:* 8840 La Crosse Ave Skokie IL 60077

**UDO, TATSUO,** ELECTRIC POWER TRANSMISSION LINE INSULATION DESIGN, HIGH VOLTAGE TESTING FACILITIES. *Current Pos:* pres, 91-96, ADV, AMTECH CO LTD, 96- *Personal Data:* b Tokyo, Japan, Sept 15, 25; m 57, Yasuko Mano; c Tadaaki & Takako. *Educ:* Tokyo Univ, Bachelor, 49, Dr(eng), 60. *Honors & Awards:* Prizes of Tech Progress, Inst Elec Engrs Japan, 54, 62 & 83, Elec Power Eng Prize, 69. *Prof Exp:* Engr, Japan Generation & Transmission Co Inc, 49-52 & Bonneville Power Admin, 66-68; researcher high voltage, Cent Res Inst Elec Power Indust, 52-64, sect chief, Syst Insulation, 64-66, div mgr, 68-75, vpres, Elec Eng Lab, 75-83, vpres, Abiko Res Lab, 83-87, sr adv, 87-89; pres, Denryoku Comput Ctr Ltd, 88-93, chmn bd dir, 93-95. *Concurrent Pos:* Vis lectr, Fac Eng, Nagoya Univ, 74-79 & Tokyo Univ, 85-86; registered prof consult engr, Japanese Govt. *Mem:* Inst Elec & Electronics Engrs. *Res:* Insulation and electrical breakdown of extra high voltage and ultra high voltage power transmission systems. *Mailing Add:* Amtech Co Ltd 13-27 2-Chome Honkomagome Bunkyo-Ku Tokyo 113 Japan. *Fax:* 81-3-3430-3318

**UDOLF, ROY,** PSYCHOLOGY, ENGINEERING. *Current Pos:* assoc prof, 67-80, PROF PSYCHOL, HOFSTRA UNIV, 80- *Personal Data:* b New York, NY, Aug 7, 26; m 50, Marcelle Temkin; c Bruce Lee, Penny Jill, Brad Robert & David William. *Educ:* NY Univ, BEE, 50, Brooklyn Law Sch JD, 54; Hofstra Univ, MA, 63; Adelphi Univ, PhD(psychol), 71; Am Bd Forensic Psycol, dipl. *Prof Exp:* Test engr, Am Bosch Arma Corp, 56-63; asst dept head eng, Gyrodyne Co Am, 63-67. *Concurrent Pos:* Human factors consult, Litcom Div, Litton Industs, 71-73. *Mem:* Am Psychol Asn; Am Psychol-Law Soc. *Res:* Human engineering; hypnosis; forensic psychology. *Mailing Add:* New Col Hofstra Univ Hempstead NY 11550

**UDOVIC, DANIEL,** COMPUTERS IN EDUCATION, INTELLIGENT TUTORING SYSTEMS. *Current Pos:* Asst prof, 73-81, ASSOC PROF BIOL, UNIV ORE, 81-, DEPT HEAD, 89- *Personal Data:* b Cleveland, Ohio, July 9, 47; m 68; c 2. *Educ:* Univ Tex, Austin, BA, 70; Cornell Univ,

PhD(entom), 74; Univ Ore, MS. *Mem:* Asn Comput Mach. *Res:* Computers in biology education, with emphasis on development of intelligent tutoring systems for use in university level science courses. *Mailing Add:* 2401 Lincoln St Univ Ore Eugene OR 97405

**UDRY, JOE RICHARD,** DEMOGRAPHY. *Current Pos:* assoc prof, 65-69, dir, Carolina Pop Ctr, 77-92, PROF MATERNAL & CHILD HEALTH & SOCIOL, UNIV NC, CHAPEL HILL, 69-, KENAN PROF, 92- *Personal Data:* b Covington, Ky, Oct 12, 28; m 50; c 2. *Educ:* Northwestern Univ, BS, 50; Calif State Univ, Long Beach, MA, 56; Univ Southern Calif, PhD(sociol), 60. *Prof Exp:* Instr sociol, Chaffey Col, 60-62; asst prof, Calif State Polytech Col, 62-65. *Mem:* Am Pub Health Asn; Am Sociol Asn; Pop Asn Am (pres, 94); Nat Coun Family Rels. *Res:* Demography; family and sexual behavior; interaction of social and biological processes. *Mailing Add:* Dept Sociol Univ NC Chapel Hill NC 27599-3210

**UDVARDY, MIKLOS DEZSO FERENC,** ZOOLOGY, ORNITHOLOGY. *Current Pos:* prof, 66-90, EMER PROF BIOL SCI, CALIF STATE UNIV, 90- *Personal Data:* b Debrecen, Hungary, Mar 23, 19; nat US; m 51, Maud E Bjorkluni; c Beatrix, Andrew & Monica. *Educ:* Debrecen Univ, PhD, 42. *Hon Degrees:* Dr, Debrecen Univ, 90. *Prof Exp:* Asst biologist, Hungarian Inst Ornith, 42-45; res assoc, Biol Res Inst, Hungarian Acad Sci, 45-48; res fel zool, Univ Helsinki, 48-49 & Univ Uppsala, 49-50; asst cur, Swedish Mus Natural Hist, 51; vis lectr ecol, Univ Toronto, 51-52; lectr zool, Univ BC, 52-53, from asst prof to assoc prof, 53-66. *Concurrent Pos:* Asst scientist, Fisheries Res Bd Can, 52-55; vis prof, Univ Hawaii, 58-59; vis spec lectr, Univ Calif, Los Angeles, 63-64; vis prof, Univ Bonn, 70-71; Fulbright lectr, Honduras, 71-72; mem, Int Protecting Bd, Biol Sta Wilhelmiberg, Austria & Point Reyes Bird Observ; consult, Int Union Conserv Nature, 80- *Mem:* Fel AAAS; Cooper Ornith Soc; Nat Audubon Soc; Wilson Ornith Soc; Sigma Xi; corresp mem Finnish Ornithol Soc; corresp mem Argentinian Ornithol Soc. *Res:* Biogeography, especially distributional and ornithology. animal ecology and behavior; ornithology. *Mailing Add:* 6000 Jay St Sacramento CA 95819

**UDVARHELYI, GEORGE BELA,** neurosurgery, for more information see previous edition

**UEBBING, JOHN JULIAN,** ELECTRICAL ENGINEERING, ELECTRONICS. *Current Pos:* develop engr, Hewlett-Packard, 73-75, sect mgr optoelectronics, 75-80, proj mgr laser addressed crystal displays, 80-83, proj mgr obj oriented software for test measurements, 83-87, proj mgr LED printhead, displays, Optoelectronics Div, 88-93, PROJ LEADER REFLECTIVE SENSORS, OPTOCOUPLERS, IR MODULES, CSS DIV, HEWLETT-PACKARD, 93- *Personal Data:* b Chicago, Ill, July 7, 37; m 66, Roberta Flynn; c Mary F & Jack. *Educ:* Univ Notre Dame, BS, 60; Mass Inst Technol, MS, 62; Stanford Univ, PhD(elec eng), 67. *Prof Exp:* Staff engr, Gen Motors Defense Res Labs, 62-63; staff engr surface sci & electron spectros, Varian Assocs, 66-72; staff engr electronics, Electromagnetic Systs Lab, 72-73. *Concurrent Pos:* Consult, Stanford Univ, 74-77 & Radiologic Sci Inc, 75-77. *Mem:* Inst Elec & Electronics Engrs; Soc Info Display; Inst Elec & Electronics Engrs Comput Sci. *Res:* Light emitting diode products; plastic optics; electron spectroscopy; surface science. *Mailing Add:* Develop Engr Hewlett Packard 370 W Trimble Rd 91 ue San Jose CA 95131. *E-Mail:* john_vebbing@sj.hp.com

**UEBEL, JACOB JOHN,** ORGANIC CHEMISTRY. *Current Pos:* res scientist, 80-83, LAB HEAD, EASTMAN KODAK CO, ROCHESTER, NY, 83- *Personal Data:* b Chicago, Ill, Dec 25, 37; m 58; c 3. *Educ:* Carthage Col, BA, 59; Univ Ill, MA, 62, PhD(chem), 64. *Prof Exp:* Res assoc, Univ Mich, 64; from asst prof to assoc prof, Univ NH, 64-73, prof org chem, 73-80. *Concurrent Pos:* Vis prof, Univ Calif, Riverside, 71-72; vis scientist, Eastman Kodak Co, Rochester, NY & NSF sci fac fel, 78-79. *Mem:* Am Chem Soc; Sigma Xi; Int Fine Particle Res Inst. *Res:* Organic magnetic resonance and conformational analysis; particle characterization. *Mailing Add:* Five Landmark Lane Pittsford NY 14534

**UEBELE, CURTIS EUGENE,** POLYMER CHEMISTRY. *Current Pos:* Proj leader, 65-75, res assoc, 75, SUPVR POLYMER RES, B P AM, CLEVELAND, 78- *Personal Data:* b Kenosha Co, Wis, Dec 3, 35; m 58; c 6. *Educ:* Carroll Col, Wis, BS, 58; Univ Kans, PhD(chem), 65. *Mem:* Am Chem Soc. *Res:* Formulation and evaluation of polyvinyl and polyolefin resins. *Mailing Add:* 2655 Bethany Lane Hinckley OH 44233-9741

**UEBERSAX, MARK ALAN,** AGRICULTURE, FOOD SCIENCE. *Current Pos:* MEM FAC, DEPT FOOD SCI & HUMAN NUTRIT, MICH STATE UNIV, 77- *Personal Data:* b Baltimore, Md, Feb 13, 48; m 74. *Educ:* Delaware Valley Col, BS, 70; Mich State Univ, MS, 72, PhD(food sci), 77. *Prof Exp:* Food scientist prod develop, R T French Co, 73. *Mem:* Inst Food Technologists; Am Soc Hort Sci; Am Asn Cereal Chemists; Sigma Xi. *Res:* Chemical and physical evaluation of processed fruits and vegetables; evaluation of processing techniques on nutrient retention, yield and overall quality of processed foods. *Mailing Add:* Dept Food Sci & Human Nutrit Mich State Univ East Lansing MI 48824

**UECKER, FRANCIS AUGUST,** MYCOLOGY. *Current Pos:* RES MYCOLOGIST, BELTSVILLE AGR RES CTR, PLANT SCI INST, USDA, 65- *Personal Data:* b Ft Wayne, Ind, Dec 18, 30; m 61, Eileen Scheffer; c Gregory, George, Benjamin & Monica. *Educ:* Quincy Col, BS, 56; Univ Ill, Urbana, MS, 59, PhD(bot), 62. *Prof Exp:* Asst prof bot, Univ Ill, Urbana, 62-63, biologist, 63; asst prof, Winona State Col, 63-65. *Mem:*

AAAS; Sigma Xi; Mycol Soc Am; Am Inst Biol Scientists. *Res:* Development, cytology and taxonomy of fungi, especially pyrenomycetes and Fungi Imperfecti. *Mailing Add:* 4611 Barbara Dr Beltsville MD 20705. *Fax:* 301-504-5810

**UEDA, CLARENCE TAD,** PHARMACOKINETICS, BIOPHARMACEUTICS. *Current Pos:* From asst prof to assoc prof, Univ Nebr, 74-85, dir clin pharmacokinetics, Cardiovasc Ctr, 76-80, chmn dept, 76-87, PROF PHARMACEUT SCI, 85-, DEAN, UNIV NEBR, 87- *Personal Data:* b Kansas City, Mo, July 6, 42; m 71, Judith K Yokoyama; c Kimi (Rei) & Marc Ryan. *Educ:* Contra Costa Col, AA, 63; Univ Calif, San Francisco, PharmD, 67, PhD(bipharmaceut), 74. *Concurrent Pos:* Consult, Sandoz Ltd, 82-85, Comt Revisions, USP, 90-95, 96- *Mem:* Am Pharmaceut Asn; Acad Pharmaceut Sci & Res; Am Soc Clin Pharmacol & Therapeut; fel Am Col Clin Pharmacol; Am Asn Pharmaceut Sci; Am Asn Cols Pharm. *Res:* Intestinal lymphatic drug absorption; pharmacokinetics of cardiovascular drugs; placental drug transfer pharmacokinetics; renal pharmacokinetics. *Mailing Add:* Col Pharm Univ Nebr Med Ctr 600 S 42nd St Omaha NE 68198-6000. *Fax:* 402-559-5060

**UEDA, TETSUFUMI,** GLUTAMATE SYNAPTIC TRANSMISSION, PROTEIN PHOSPHORYLATION. *Current Pos:* from asst res scientist to assoc res scientist, Univ Mich, 78-88, from asst prof to assoc prof, 78-89, RES SCIENTIST, MENT HEALTH RES INST, UNIV MICH, 88-, PROF, 89- *Personal Data:* b Osaka, Japan, July 11, 40; m 70, Yasuko Amano; c Jane K & Judy Y. *Educ:* Kyoto Univ, BA, 66; Univ Mich, PhD(biochem), 71. *Prof Exp:* Assoc pharmacol, Yale Univ, 71-74, NIMH fel, 74-76, res assoc, 76-78. *Concurrent Pos:* Mem Neurol Sci Study Sect, NIH, 87-91; Javits Neurosci Investr Award, NIH, 88. *Mem:* NY Acad Sci; fel Am Soc Neurocehm; fel Int Soc Neurochem; fel Am Soc Biochem & Molecular Biol; fel AAAS. *Res:* Molecular mechanism and regulation of glutamate synaptic transmission and the role of phosphorylation in synaptic function. *Mailing Add:* Univ Mich Ment Health Res Inst 205 Zina Pitcher Pl Ann Arbor MI 48109-0720

**UEHARA, HIROSHI,** MATHEMATICS. *Current Pos:* RETIRED. *Personal Data:* b Kobe City, Japan, Mar 7, 23; m 47; c Yoko A & Henri U. *Educ:* Univ Tokyo, MS, 49; Osaka Univ, DSc, 54. *Prof Exp:* Instr math, Nagoya Univ, 49-51; asst prof, Math Inst, Kyushu Univ, 53-56 & Univ Southern Calif, 58-60; prof, Univ Andes & Nat Univ Colombia, 56-58; assoc prof, Univ Iowa, 60-64; prof, Okla State Univ, 64-88. *Concurrent Pos:* Vis Prof, Brown Univ, 53; lectr, Nat Univ Mex, 58. *Mem:* Am Math Soc; Math Soc France; Math Soc Japan. *Res:* Algebraic topology. *Mailing Add:* 614 N Grandview Stillwater OK 74075

**UELAND, KENT,** OBSTETRICS & GYNECOLOGY. *Current Pos:* prof, 77-89, EMER PROF OBSTET & GYNEC & CHIEF MATERNAL FETAL MED, STANFORD UNIV, 89- *Personal Data:* b Chicago, Ill, May 27, 31; m 54; c 4. *Educ:* Carleton Col, BA, 53; Univ Ill, BS & MD, 57; Am Bd Obstet & Gynec, dipl, 67; cert maternal-fetal med, 77. *Prof Exp:* Intern, Med Sch, Univ Ore, 57-58; asst resident obstet & gynec, King Co & Univ Hosps, 60-61; from asst instr to prof, Univ Wash, 61-77, dir obstet, Univ Hosp, 68-77. *Concurrent Pos:* Res fel cardiovasc res, Univ Wash, 63; res fel med, Univ Ore, 63-64; resident, King Co & Univ Hosps, 61-62, chief resident, 63; consult, Santa Clara Valley Med Ctr, San Jose, Calif, Naval Regional Med Ctr, Oakland, Calif, Childbirth Educ Asn & Nat Found March of Dimes. *Mem:* Perinatal Res Soc; Soc Obstet, Anesthesia & Perinatal; Am Col Obstet & Gynec; Soc Gynec Invest; Soc Perinatal Obstet. *Res:* Pregnancy and cardiovascular dynamics; toxemia of pregnancy; control of labor; pregnancy and heart disease. *Mailing Add:* 2750 Kalapu Dr Lahaina HI 96761-1937

**UEMURA, YASUTOMO J,** MAGNETISM, RANDOM SYSTEMS. *Current Pos:* ASSOC PHYSICIST, COLUMBIA UNIV, 90- *Personal Data:* b Tokyo, Japan, Nov 22, 53; m 83. *Educ:* Univ Tokyo, BSc, 77, MSc, 79, DSc(physics), 82. *Prof Exp:* Fel physics, Univ Tokyo, 82-83; Japan Soc Prom Sci spec res fel, Brookhaven Nat Lab, 83-85, assoc physicist, 85-90. *Res:* Condensed matter physics; muon spin relaxation methods; neutron scattering. *Mailing Add:* Dept Physics Columbia Univ 538 W 120th St Rm 1310 New York NY 10027

**UENG, CHARLES E(N) S(HIUH),** SOLID MECHANICS. *Current Pos:* from asst prof to assoc prof, 64-67, PROF ENG MECH, GA INST TECHNOL, 77-, DIR, COMPOSITES EDUC & RES CTR, 94- *Personal Data:* b Kiangtu, Kiangsu, China, Sept 8, 30; m 62, Shirley W Chen; c Vivian & Grace. *Educ:* Cheng Kung Univ, BS, 53; Kans State Univ, MS, 60, PhD(appl mech), 63. *Honors & Awards:* Serv Award, Am Soc Civil Engrs, 84. *Prof Exp:* Struct engr, Taiwan Power Co, China, 53-58; res assoc appl mech, Kans State Univ, 62-63, asst prof, 63-64. *Concurrent Pos:* Consult, Reliance Elec Co, Westinghouse Elec Corp, Combustion Eng, Inc, Electro-Mech Co, Victoreen Instruments & Wolfe & Mann Mfg Co; res grants, NASA & NSF. *Mem:* Am Soc Civil Engrs; Am Acad Mech; Soc Eng Sci; Am Soc Eng Educ; Sigma Xi. *Res:* Composite structures; vibration; elastic stability; variational principles; earthquake engineering. *Mailing Add:* Sch Civil Eng Ga Inst Technol Atlanta GA 30332-0355. *Fax:* 404-894-2278

**UENO, HIROSHI,** PROTEIN CHEMISTRY, ENZYMOLOGY. *Current Pos:* Res assoc, 82-83, Rockefeller Found fel, 84-85, ASST PROF BIOCHEM, ROCKEFELLER UNIV, 86-; ASSOC PROF AGR CHEM, KYOTO UNIV, 94- *Personal Data:* b Osaka, Japan, Dec 9, 50; m 78; c 1. *Educ:* Kyoto Univ, BE, 74; Brandeis Univ, MA, 76; Iowa State Univ, PhD(biochem), 82. *Concurrent Pos:* Summer investr, Woods Hole Marine Biol Lab, 84-; vis scientist, Pop Coun, 84-; ad hoc comt, Nat Heart, Lung &

Blood Inst, NIH, 87-; vis prof, Kumamoto Univ, Japan, 90; assoc prof biochem, Osaka Med Col, 91-94. *Mem:* Am Chem Soc; Am Soc Biol Chemists; Harvey Soc; NY Acad Sci. *Res:* Chemistry of gossypol, transaminases, hemoglobins. *Mailing Add:* Dept Agr Chem Kyoto Univ Fac Agr Sakyo Kyoto 606-01 Japan

**UETZ, GEORGE WILLIAM,** ECOLOGY, BEHAVIOR & ARACHNOLOGY. *Current Pos:* from asst prof to assoc prof, 76-87, PROF BIOL SCI, UNIV CINCINNATI, 87- *Personal Data:* b Philadelphia, Pa, Dec 8, 46. *Educ:* Albion Col, BA, 68; Univ Del, MS, 70; Univ Ill, PhD(ecol), 76. *Prof Exp:* Res asst entom, Univ Del, 68-70; teacher biol, Sanford Sch, 70-72; res asst zool, Univ Ill, 72-75, teaching asst ecol, 75-76. *Concurrent Pos:* Assoc cur, Cincinnati Mus Natural Hist, 76-84; Sigma Xi grant, 76-77; Nat Geog Soc grant, 78-79, 85-86 & 91-92; Elec Power Res Inst grant, 78-80; NSF grant, 87-89, 89-91, 90-92, 91-93. *Mem:* Am Arachnological Soc; Brit Arachnological Soc; Ecol Soc Am; Entom Soc Am; Animal Behavior Soc. *Res:* Ecology and behavior of spiders; behavioral reproductive isolation and sexual selection in wolf spiders; behavioral reproductive isolation in wolf spiders; spider community structure. *Mailing Add:* Dept Biol Sci Univ Cincinnati Cincinnati OH 45221-0001. *Fax:* 513-556-5299; *E-Mail:* uetzgw@ucbeh

**UFFEN, ROBERT JAMES,** GEOPHYSICS, SANTIARY & ENVIRONMENTAL ENGINEERING. *Current Pos:* dean fac appl sci, 71-80, prof geophys, 71-89, EMER PROF GEOPHYS, QUEEN'S UNIV, ONT, 89- *Personal Data:* b Toronto, Ont, Sept 21, 23; m 49; c 2. *Educ:* Univ Toronto, BASc, 49, MA, 50; Univ Western Ont, PhD(physics), 52. *Hon Degrees:* DSc, Univ Western Ont, 70, Queen's Univ, Ont, 67, Royal Mil Col Can, 78 & McMaster Univ, 83. *Honors & Awards:* Waddell Lectr, Royal Mil Col Can, 82; Centenial Medal Can, 67; Sigma Xi Medal, 80; Officer, Order of Can, 83; Pub Serv Medal, Asn Prof Engrs, Ont, 85. *Prof Exp:* Lectr physics & geol, Univ Western Ont, 51-53, from asst prof to assoc prof geophys, 53-58, prof & head dept, 58-61, actg head dept physics, 60-61, asst prin, Univ Col Arts & Sci, 60-61, prin, 61-65, dean col sci, 65-66; mem, Defence Res Bd Can, 63-66, vchmn, 66-67, chmn, 67-69; chief sci adv to cabinet, Can Govt, 69-71. *Concurrent Pos:* Consult, Kennco Explor Ltd, 52-59; res fel, Inst Geophys Univ Calif, Los Angeles, 53; Can deleg, Int Union Geod & Geophys, Rome, 54, Toronto, 57, Helsinki, 60, Tokyo, 62 & Int Union Geol Sci, New Delhi, 64; consult, Utah Construct Co, 55-58; mem Nat Adv Comt Res Geol Sci, 58-61; mem, Nat Res Coun Can, 63-66; mem, Nat Feasibility Comt Proj Oilsand, 59; chmn, Can Sci Comt, Int Upper Mantle Proj, 60-65; ed, Earth & Planetary Sci Lett, 65-69 & Tectonophysics, 67-70; mem, Coun Regents for Cols Appl Arts & Technol, Prov Ont, 66-69 & 72-75; mem Sci Coun Can, 67-71; chmn Can Eng Manpower Coun, 72-75; mem Ctr Resource Studies, 73-85; counr, Assoc Prof Engrs Ont, 75-79; mem Fisheries Res Bd Can, 75-78; vchmn bd, Ont Hydro, 74-79; comnr, Int Royal Comn Asbestos, 80-84 & Ont Comn Truck Safety, 81-83; chmn, Ont Explor Tech Develop Fund, 81-83; consult, Ministry State, Sci & Technol, 83-84, nuclear energy, Elec & Electronics Comn on Energy, 87-88; coordr, Summer Prog Sci Teachers, Queens Univ, 86-89. *Mem:* Fel AAAS; fel Royal Soc Can; Am Geophys Union; fel Geol Soc Am; Am Inst Mining, Metall & Petrol Eng; Can Geophys Union. *Res:* Geothermometry; internal constitution of the earth; paleomagnetism; science policy; radioactive waste management; occupational safety. *Mailing Add:* Dept Geol Queen's Univ Kingston ON K7L 3N6 Can. *Fax:* 613-545-6592

**UFFEN, ROBERT L,** MICROBIOLOGY. *Current Pos:* from asst prof to assoc prof, 70-84, PROF MICROBIOL, MICH STATE UNIV, 84-, PROF MICROBIOL, NSF, 92- *Personal Data:* b Oxnard, Calif, Dec 2, 37; m 78; c 2. *Educ:* Stanford Univ, BA, 62; Univ Mass, Amherst, MA, 64, PhD(microbiol), 68. *Prof Exp:* NIH fel, Univ Ill, Urbana, 68-70. *Concurrent Pos:* Guggenheim fel. *Mem:* AAAS; Am Soc Microbiol; Am Chem Soc. *Res:* General microbiology and microbial physiology; regulation during cell differentiation; hydrogen gas and carbon monoxide metabolism; ecology. *Mailing Add:* Mich State Univ Micro Biol East Lansing MI 48824

**UFIMTSEV, PYOTR YAKOVLEVICH,** DIFFRACTION OF ELECTROMAGNETIC & ACOUSTIC WAVES, WAVE PROPAGATION IN TRANSMISSION LINES. *Current Pos:* VIS PROF & ADJ PROF, UNIV CALIF, LOS ANGELES, 90- *Personal Data:* b Ust'-Chazyshskaya Pristan', Russia, July 8, 31; m 86; c Ivan & Vladimir. *Educ:* Odessa State Univ, Ukraine, MS, 54; Cent Res Inst Radio Indust, Moscow, PhD(radio eng), 59; Univ St Petersburg, Russia, DSc, 70. *Honors & Awards:* Leroy Randle Grumman Medal, 91. *Prof Exp:* Engr, sr engr & sr scientist, Cent Res Inst Radio Indust, Moscow, 54-73; sr scientist, Inst Radio Eng & Electronics Acad Sci, Moscow, 73-90. *Concurrent Pos:* Mem, Sci bd Radio Waves, Acad Sci, Moscow, 60-90. *Mem:* A S Popov Sci & Tech Soc Russia; Am Inst Aeronaut & Astronaut; Inst Elec & Electronics Engrs; Electromagnetics Acad. *Res:* Origination of physical theory of diffraction, used for design of American Stealth aircrafts and ships, for radar-cross-section calculation, and antenna design; contributed articles to professional journals. *Mailing Add:* Dept Elec Eng Univ Calif 1959 Barry Ave Los Angeles CA 90025

**UGARTE, EDUARDO,** BIOCHEMISTRY, MICROBIOLOGY. *Current Pos:* RES & DEVELOP DIR CONSULT, APROGEUEX, INC. *Personal Data:* b Santa Ana, El Salvador, Oct 22, 35; m 63; c 4. *Educ:* Nat Univ Mex, lic biochem, 62; Univ El Salvador, Dr(biochem), 65; Univ Rio de Janeiro, dipl oral microbiol, 66; Inter-Am Inst Agr Sci, El Salvador, dipl agr sci educ, 69. *Prof Exp:* Assoc prof biochem, Sch Dent, Univ El Salvador, 65-67, secy dept basic sci, 66, secy curriculum comn, 66-67, prof chem, Sch Agron Sci, 67-68, chief prof biochem, 68-70; researcher biochem, United Med Labs, 70-74; dir, Analytico Lab, 75; vpres, Page Biochem Labs, Inc, 75-76; tech dir, Nat Health

Labs, Ft Lauderdale, 76-77; mem staff res cancer tissue, Oncolnovairul, Life Sci Res Inc, St Petersburg Fla, 78-, Intersci Inc, Portland, Ore, ISOLAB, Inc, Akron, Ohio & Aprogeuex, Inc, Houston Tex. *Concurrent Pos:* Fel bact & virol, Life Labs, Ecuador, 63-64; fel oral microbiol, Pan-Am Health Orgn, Brazil, 66; lab clin supvr, Tampa Gen Hosp, Fla, 79-80; lab dir, St Petersburg Gen Hosp, Fla, 80-81; pres, Hemato Control Prod, Intersci Inc, Portland, Ore, 81-82. *Mem:* Am Chem Soc; Microbiol Soc El Salvador; Clin Chem Flowagtometry Asn. *Res:* Relation of the mechanism of different hormones between pituitary and thyroid glands; development of the radioimmunoassays for these hormones; radiolabeling materials for different fractions; stabilization matrices; hematology controls and immunohematology specialist. *Mailing Add:* 1321 Weathervane Lane Apt 213 Akron OH 44313. *Fax:* 330-864-1531; *E-Mail:* eugarte@msn.com

**UGENT, DONALD,** PLANT TAXONOMY, ECONOMIC BOTANY. *Current Pos:* From asst prof to assoc prof, 68-82, PROF BOT, SOUTHERN ILL UNIV, CARBONDALE, 82-, CUR, HERBARIUM, 68- *Personal Data:* b Chicago, Ill, Dec 20, 33; m 62; c 3. *Educ:* Univ Wis-Madison, BS, 56, MS, 61, PhD(bot), 66. *Concurrent Pos:* NSF Proj assoc, 66-67; mem trop studies comt, Assoc Univs Int Educ, 70-76; reviewer grants, NSF, 70- *Mem:* Soc Econ Bot; Sigma Xi. *Res:* Biosystematics of the wild and cultivated species of Solanum, section tuberarium, potatoes; ethnobotany; phytogeography and archaeo-botany. *Mailing Add:* 2004 W Norwood Dr Carbondale IL 62901-4399

**UGINCIUS, PETER,** GEODESY. *Current Pos:* RETIRED. *Personal Data:* b Geniai, Lithuania, Feb 23, 36; US citizen; m 62; c 4. *Educ:* Kalamazoo Col, BA, 58; Ind Univ, MS, 61; Cath Univ Am, PhD(physics), 68. *Prof Exp:* Res physicist, Naval Surface Warfare Ctr, 61-70, supvry geodist, 71-80, res assoc, 81-94. *Concurrent Pos:* Adj prof, Va Polytech Inst & State Univ, 72- *Mem:* Am Geophys Union. *Res:* Physical geodesy; earth gravitational field. *Mailing Add:* 111 Windsor Circle Fredericksburg VA 22405

**UGLEM, GARY LEE,** PARASITOLOGY, ZOOLOGY. *Current Pos:* asst prof, 74-78, ASSOC PROF BIOL SCI, UNIV KY, 78- *Personal Data:* b Grand Forks, NDak, Sept 19, 41; m 64; c 2. *Educ:* Univ NDak, BS, 66, MS, 68; Univ Idaho, PhD(zool), 72. *Prof Exp:* Instr parasitol, Univ Idaho, 71; NIH fel, Rice Univ, 72-74. *Mem:* Am Micros Soc; Am Soc Parasitologists; Am Inst Biol Sci. *Res:* Physiology of host-parasite relations; membrane transport in parasitic helminths; Acanthocephalan life histories. *Mailing Add:* Dept Biol Sci Univ Ky 500 S Limestone St Lexington KY 40506-0001

**UGOLINI, FIORENZO CESARE,** SOILS. *Current Pos:* PROF SOIL GENESIS, CLASSIFICATION & CARTOG, UNIV FLORENCE, ITALY, 90- *Personal Data:* b Florence, Italy, Jan 16, 29; m 63; c 2. *Educ:* Rutgers Univ, BS, 57, PhD(soils), 60. *Prof Exp:* Arctic Inst NAm fel, Rutgers Univ, 60-61, asst prof soils, 61-64; asst prof & res assoc, Ohio State Univ, 64-66; from assoc prof to prof soils, Univ Wash, 66-90. *Concurrent Pos:* NATO prof, Univ Milan. *Mem:* AAAS; Am Polar Soc; Am Soc Agron; Int Soc Soil Sci; fel Arctic Inst NAm; Int Union Quaternary Res; fel Soil Sci Soc Am. *Res:* Soil formation and weathering in the cold regions, including Arctic, Antarctica and Alpine environments; soil development and the impact of time on glacial deposits, chronologically different; forest soils; paleosoils. *Mailing Add:* Dept Soil Sci & Plant Nutrit Univ Florence Pizzale delle Cascine 15 Florence 50144 Italy

**UGURBIL, KAMIL,** NUCLEAR MAGNETIC RESONANCE SPECTROSCOPY. *Current Pos:* DIR, MAGNETIC RESONANCE RES CTR, UNIV MINN, 90- *Personal Data:* b Tire, Turkey, July 11, 49. *Educ:* Columbia Univ, NY, AB, 71, PhD(chem), 77. *Prof Exp:* Fel res biophysics, Bell Labs, 76-79; asst prof biochem, Columbia Univ, 79-85; mem staff, Gray Freshwater Bio Inst, 86-90. *Concurrent Pos:* Consult, Bell Labs, 80- *Mem:* Am Chem Soc; Biophys Soc; AAAS. *Res:* Applications of nuclear magnetic resonance spectroscopy to biological problems, primarily to studies of intact cells and organs. *Mailing Add:* Dept Biochem 140 Gortner Lab Millard Hall Univ Minn 385 E River Rd Minneapolis MN 55455

**UHART, MICHAEL SCOTT,** AGRICULTURAL METEOROLOGY, CLIMATOLOGY. *Current Pos:* Meteorologist, 76-79, forecaster, 79-82, METEOROLOGIST, PROG MGT, NAT WEATHER SERV, 83- *Personal Data:* b Sacramento, Calif, Nov 25, 48; m 76; c 2. *Educ:* Univ Calif, San Diego, BA, 70; Fla State Univ, MS, 76; Univ Okla, PhD(meteorol), 85. *Concurrent Pos:* Adj prof, Montgomery Col, Md, 89-; mem, Agr Meteorol Working Group. *Mem:* Agr Res Inst; World Meteorol Orgn. *Res:* Agricultural and fire weather, climatology and air pollution; economic impacts of climate change, drought and weather modification. *Mailing Add:* 14620 Gallant Fox Lane Gaithersburg MD 20878

**UHDE, THOMAS WHITLEY,** PSYCHOPHARMACOLOGY, BEHAVIORAL PHARMACOLOGY. *Current Pos:* assoc clin prof psychiat, 85-91, PROF CLIN PSYCHIAT, SCH MED, UNIFORMED SERV UNIV HEALTH SCI, 91-; PROF & CHMN, DEPT PSYCHIAT & BEHAV NEUROSCI, SCH MED, WAYNE STATE UNIV, 93-; PSYCHIATRIST-IN-CHIEF, DETROIT MED CTR, 93- *Personal Data:* b Louisville, Ky; m 77; c 2. *Educ:* Duke Univ, BS, 71; Univ Louisville, MD, 75. *Honors & Awards:* Nat Res Serv Award, NIMH, 79; A E Bennett Neuropsychiat Res Found Award, Soc Biol Psychiat, 84. *Prof Exp:* Resident, Dept Psychiat, Yale Univ, 75-79; chief resident, Clin Res Unit, 78; med staff fel, NIMH, 79-81, chief, Unit Anxiety & Affective Dis, 82-90, chief, Sect Anxiety & Afffective Dis, Biol Psychiat Br, 89-93; attend staff, NIH, 81-93. *Concurrent Pos:* Asst clin prof psychiat, Sch Med, Uniformed Serv Univ

Health Sci, Bethesda, Md, 82-85; consult, Develop Rev Comt, Dept Health & Human Serv, NIMH, 83-; mem, Nat Comn Sleep & Psychiat Dis, 90-91. *Mem:* Am Psychiat Asn; Soc Biol Psychiat; AAAS; Am Col Psychiatrists; Am Col Neuropsychopharmacol; Sleep Res Soc. *Res:* Phenomenology, longitudinal course, neurobiology, pharmacological treatment of mood and anxiety disorders; psychobiological relationship of panic disorder to major affective disorders using neurophysiological, pharmacologic, biochemical and receptor binding techniques; chemical models of human anxiety and the influence of diet and nutrition in animals. *Mailing Add:* Psychiat Children's Hosp Mich 3901 Beaubien Detroit MI 48201-2119. *Fax:* 313-577-5900

**UHER, RICHARD ANTHONY,** TRANSPORTATION RESEARCH, ENERGY RESEARCH. *Current Pos:* sr engr res, 75-80, DIR RES, RAIL SYSTS CTR, CARNEGIE-MELLON UNIV, 80- *Personal Data:* b McKeesport, Pa, June 8, 39; m 61, Janice Smith; c Christopher, Keith & Michaeleen. *Educ:* Carnegie-Mellon Univ, BS, 61, MS, 63, PhD(physics), 66. *Prof Exp:* Engr res, Westinghouse Elec Corp, 68-70, proj mgr, 70-75. *Concurrent Pos:* Sr lectr phyics & elec eng, Carnegie-Mellon Univ, 75-80; consult, 80- *Mem:* Sr mem Inst Elec & Electronics Engrs; Am Inst Physics; Am Railway Eng Asn; Transp Res Bd; Am Soc Civil Engrs; Am Soc Mech Engrs. *Res:* Modeling energy use in transportation systems; modeling railroad operations and safety in the area of tranportation. *Mailing Add:* 2013 Country Club Dr Mt Vernon PA 19131

**UHERKA, DAVID JEROME,** NUMERICAL ANALYSIS, CHAOTIC DYNAMICS. *Current Pos:* assoc prof, 68-76, chair, 93-96, PROF MATH, UNIV NDAK, 76- *Personal Data:* b Wagner, SDak, June 2, 38; m 65, Dorothy Malouf; c Kara & Michael. *Educ:* SDak Sch Mines & Technol, BS, 60; Univ Utah, MA, 63, PhD(math), 64. *Prof Exp:* Mathematician, US Naval Radiol Defense Lab, Calif, 62; mathematician & programmer, US Army Natick Labs, Mass, 64-66. *Concurrent Pos:* Consult, US Army Natick Labs, 66-68; sabbatical leave, scientist in residence, Agronne Nat Lab, 81-82; acad consult, Comput Ctr, Univ NDak, 82-84; sabbatical fel, Los Alamos Nat Lab, 91-92. *Mem:* Math Asn Am; Am Asn Univ Profs; Am Soc Eng Educ; Soc Indust & Appl Math; Nat Coun Teachers Math. *Res:* Functional and numerical analysis; computer applications; chaotic dynamics. *Mailing Add:* Math Dept Univ NDak Grand Forks ND 58202-8376

**UHERKA, KENNETH LEROY,** ADVANCED ENERGY SYSTEMS, THERMAL SCIENCES. *Current Pos:* PROJ MGR, ARGONNE NAT LAB, 73- *Personal Data:* b Wagner, SDak, May 30, 37; m 67; c 4. *Educ:* SDak Sch Mines & Technol, BS, 59; Univ Ariz, MS, 61; Purdue Univ, Lafayette, PhD(aeronaut & eng sci), 67. *Prof Exp:* Instr aerospace eng, Purdue Univ, Lafayette, 61-67; assoc scientist, Res Inst, Ill Inst Technol, 67-68; asst prof, Energy Eng Dept, Univ Ill, Chicago Circle, 68-73. *Mem:* Am Soc Mech Engrs; Sigma Xi. *Res:* Advanced nuclear reactor power systems; stirling engines and other energy conversion systems; energy conservation technologies; Maglev trains and other super conductor applications; fluid mechanics; heat transfer; atmospheric and plasma physics; environmental pollution control. *Mailing Add:* ET Div Bldg 335 9700 S Cass Ave Lemont IL 60439-4818

**UHL, ARTHUR E(DWARD),** ENERGY SYSTEMS ENGINEERING, RESOURCE DEVELOPMENT PROGRAM PLANNING & PROJECT MANAGEMENT. *Current Pos:* RETIRED. *Personal Data:* b Chicago, Ill, Nov 11, 29; m 57, Krista Wieneke; c Valery, Tanya & Andra. *Educ:* Southwestern La Inst, BS, 50; Univ Tulsa, BS, 52, MPE, 53. *Prof Exp:* Asst prof petrol eng, Univ Southwestern La, 58-60; res assoc prod-pipeline-reservoir eng, Inst Gas Technol, Ill Inst Technol, 60-65, asst prof, 60-65, asst chmn, Dept Gas Technol, 63-65; supvry engr, Bechtel Inc, 65-66, sr supvry engr, 66-68, asst chief engr, 68-69, chief engr, 69-71, prin engr, 71-72, asst mgr, Asia-Pac Opers, 72-74, mgr projs, 75-77, mgr resource develop progs, 78-79, eng mgr planning & develop, 79-80, mgr spec proj opers, 81-82; gen mgr, Conserv Comt Calif, 83; prin partner & pres, Proj Mgt Assocs, 84-96. *Concurrent Pos:* Consult, McGraw-Hill Publ Co, Inc, 58-60, Layne & Bowler, 59, Tenn Gas Transmission Co, 59, Oil Ctr Res, 60, Natural Gas Pipeline Co Am, Columbia Gas Syst, 63-65, S & Q Corp, 84-85, AMX Mgt Group, 86-88, Contractors Licensing Cols Calif, 88, Christenson Eng Corp, 88-89 & EPA SuperFund Oper, 89-95; mem, Gas Piping Stand Comn, Am Nat Stand Inst-Am Soc Mech Engrs, 70-74; mem, Liquified Natural Gas Task Force, Nat Energy Surv, Fed Power Comn, 71-72, mem tech adv subcomt, Comt Conserv Energy, 72-73; distinguished lectr, Am Inst Mining & Metall Engrs, 74-75. *Res:* Flow behavior in conduits; liquified natural gas systems; fuel energy production and delivery systems; energy resources development; regional and national energy planning. *Mailing Add:* 130 Harvard Ave Mill Valley CA 94941

**UHL, CHARLES HARRISON,** BOTANY. *Current Pos:* Asst, 41-42, 45-46, from instr to prof, 46-85, EMER PROF BOT, CORNELL UNIV, 85- *Personal Data:* b Schenectady, NY, May 28, 18; m 45, Natalie Whitford; c N Jean, Mary C, Charles H Jr & Elizabeth W. *Educ:* Emory Univ, BA, 39, MS, 41; Cornell Univ, PhD(bot), 47. *Mem:* AAAS; Bot Soc Am; fel Cactus & Succulent Soc Am; Int Asn Plant Taxon. *Res:* Chromosomes and evolution, especially of Crassulaceae. *Mailing Add:* 1504 Hanshaw Rd Ithaca NY 14850

**UHL, JOHN JERRY, JR,** MATHEMATICS. *Current Pos:* Asst prof, 68-72, assoc prof, 72-75, PROF MATH, UNIV ILL, URBANA-CHAMPAIGN, 75- *Personal Data:* b Pittsburgh, Pa, June 27, 40. *Educ:* Col William & Mary, BS, 62; Carnegie Inst Technol, MS, 64, PhD(math), 66. *Mem:* Am Math Soc; Math Asn Am; Soc Indust & Appl Math; Asn Comput Mach; AAAS; Inst Elec & Electronics Engrs. *Res:* Functional analysis and integration theory; calculus reform. *Mailing Add:* Dept Math Univ Ill 1409 N Green St Urbana IL 61801-2917

**UHL, ROBERT H,** transportation engineering; deceased, see previous edition for last biography

**UHL, V(INCENT) W(ILLIAM),** chemical engineering; deceased, see previous edition for last biography

**UHLENBECK, KAREN K,** MATHEMATICS. *Current Pos:* vis prof & Sid W Richardson Found Regents Chair Math, 87-88, Sid Richardson Centennial Chair, 88-92, SID RICHARDSON FOUND REGENTS CHAIR, UNIV TEX, 92- *Personal Data:* b Cleveland, Ohio, Aug 24, 42; div. *Educ:* Univ Mich, BA, 64; Brandeis Univ, PhD(math), 68. *Hon Degrees:* DSc, Knox Col, Ill, 88. *Honors & Awards:* Morse Lectr, Inst Advan Study, 82; MacArthur Fel, 83-88; Wittemore Lect, Yale Univ, 88; Noether Lect, Asn Women Math, 88; Ziwet Lects, Univ Mich, 88nn, 89; Barrett Mem Lects, Univ Tenn, 89; Harry E Valentine Lect, Kans State Univ, 91; Lewis Mem Lectrs, Rutgers Univ, 94; Leonardo da Vinci Lect, Univ Milan, 96. *Prof Exp:* Instr math, Mass Inst Technol, 68-69; lectr, Univ Calif, Berkeley, 69-71; asst prof, Univ Ill, Urbana, 71-76; from assoc prof to prof, Univ Ill, Chicago Circle, 76-83; prof, Univ Chicago, 83-88. *Concurrent Pos:* Sloan fel, 74-76; chancellors distinguished vis prof, Univ Calif, Berkeley, 79; vis mem, Math Sci Res Inst, Berkely, 82; vis prof, Harvard Univ, 83, Max Plank Inst Math, 85, Univ Calif, San Diego, 86; prog comt, Am Math Soc, 83-85; bd govs, Inst Math & Applns, 83-86. *Mem:* Nat Acad Sci; Asn Women Math; Am Math Soc (vpres, 87-90); Am Acad Arts Sci; Math Asn Am; Nat Asn Mathematicians; Soc Indust & Appl Math. *Res:* Calculus of variations; global analysis; gauge theories. *Mailing Add:* Dept Math Univ Tex Austin TX 78712. *Fax:* 512-471-9038; *E-Mail:* uhlen@math.utexas.edu

**UHLENBECK, OLKE CORNELIS,** RNA BIOCHEMISTRY. *Current Pos:* PROF CHEM & BIOCHEM & BIOCHEM DIV HEAD, UNIV COLO, 86- *Personal Data:* b Ann Arbor, Mich, Apr 20, 42; m 87, Lori Arp. *Educ:* Univ Mich, Ann Arbor, BS, 64; Harvard Univ, PhD(biophys), 69. *Honors & Awards:* Merit Award, NIH, 97. *Prof Exp:* Miller fel, Univ Calif, Berkeley, 69-71; from asst prof to prof biochem & chem, Univ Ill, Urbana, 71-86. *Concurrent Pos:* Guggenheim fel, Nat Acad Sci, 93-94. *Mem:* Nat Acad Sci; Am Chem Soc; Am Soc Biol Chemists; AAAS; Am Acad Arts & Sci; Sigma Xi; Am Soc Biochem & Molecular Biol; RNA Soc. *Res:* Nucleic acid interactions; structure and function of RNA; author of 147 publications. *Mailing Add:* Dept Biochem Box 215 Univ Colo Boulder CO 80309-0215. *Fax:* 303-492-3586

**UHLENBROCK, DIETRICH A,** APPLIED MATHEMATICS, MATHEMATICAL PHYSICS. *Current Pos:* from asst prof to assoc prof, 66-76, PROF MATH & PHYSICS, UNIV WIS-MADISON, 76- *Personal Data:* b Schweinfurt, Ger, Oct 13, 37. *Educ:* Univ Cologne, Vordiplom, 59; NY Univ, MS, 62, PhD(physics), 63. *Prof Exp:* Adj asst prof theoret physics, Univ & res assoc, Courant Inst, NY Univ, 63-64; vis mem, Inst Adv Study, NJ, 64-66. *Concurrent Pos:* Prof math, Free Univ Berlin, 73-78; vis prof math, Nat Autonomous Univ Mex, 81. *Res:* Classical and quantum statistical physics; quantum field theory; mathematical physics. *Mailing Add:* 2810 Warner Lane Madison WI 53713

**UHLENHOPP, ELLIOTT LEE,** BIOCHEMISTRY. *Current Pos:* asst prof, 78-80, ASSOC PROF CHEM, GRINNELL COL, 80-, CHMN DEPT, 85- *Personal Data:* b Hampton, Iowa, Dec 8, 42; m 67; c 2. *Educ:* Carleton Col, BA, 65; Columbia Univ, PhD(biochem), 71. *Prof Exp:* Res chemist, Univ Calif, San Diego, 73-74; asst prof chem, Whitman Col, 75-78. *Concurrent Pos:* Fel, Damon Runyon Mem Fund, Cancer Res Inc, 71-73; IPA fel, NIH, 82-84. *Mem:* Sigma Xi; Biophys Soc; Am Chem Soc; AAAS. *Res:* Viscoelastic characterization of high molecular weight native and denatured DNA from bacterial and eukaryotic cells; chromosome structure; DNA damage and repair. *Mailing Add:* Dept Chem Grinnell Col Grinnell IA 50112

**UHLENHUTH, EBERHARD HENRY,** PSYCHIATRY, PSYCHOPHARMACOLOGY. *Current Pos:* vchmn educ, 91-94, PROF PSYCHIAT, UNIV MEX, 85- *Personal Data:* b Baltimore, Md, Sept 15, 27; m 52, Helen Lyman; c Kim L, Karen J & Eric R. *Educ:* Yale Univ, BS, 47; Johns Hopkins Univ, MD, 51. *Honors & Awards:* Assoc Clin Psychiatrists' Award, 58; USPHS Res Sci Award, 76-81. *Prof Exp:* USPHS fel psychiat, Johns Hopkins Univ, 52-56, from instr to assoc prof, 56-68; chief, Adult Psychiat Clin, Univ Chicago, 68-76, from assoc prof to prof psychiat, 68-85, prof clin pharmacol, 75-85, actg chmn, Dept Psychiat, 83-85. *Concurrent Pos:* Consult, Patuxent Inst, 56-57; asst psychiatrist chg, Outpatient Dept, Johns Hopkins Hosp, 56-61, consult, Div Plastic Surg, 59-60, psychiatrist chg, Outpatient Dept, 61-62; USPHS career teacher trainee, Johns Hopkins Univ, 57-59, USPHS career res develop awards, 62-68; mem, Clin Psychopharmacol Res Rev Comt, Psychopharmacol Br, NIMH, 68-72, consult, Ment Health Task Force, Mid-Southside Planning Orgn, 70-75, Woodlawn Ment Health Ctr, 71-73 & US Food & Drug Admin, 71-74; consult, Ill State Psychiat Inst, 68-75. *Mem:* Fel Am Col Neuropsychopharmacol; fel Am Psychiat Asn; Col Int Neuro-Psychopharmacol; Psychiat Res Soc. *Res:* Clinical psychopharmacology; anxiety and depression; evaluation of treatments; consumption of psychotherapeutic drugs. *Mailing Add:* 1420 Ridgecrest Loop SE Albuquerque NM 87108. *Fax:* 505-272-5572; *E-Mail:* uhli@mail.unm.edu

**UHLER, MICHAEL DAVID,** SIGNAL TRANSDUCTION, REGULATION GENE EXPRESSION. *Current Pos:* asst prof, 88-93, ASSOC PROF BIOCHEM, UNIV MICH, 93-, ASSOC DIR, NEUROSCI PROG. *Personal Data:* b San Bernardino, Calif, Oct 3, 56; m 77; c 2. *Educ:* Seattle Univ, BS(chem), 77, BS(clin chem), 77; Univ Ore, PhD(biochem), 82. *Prof Exp:* Asst prof biochem, Ore Health Sci Univ, 86-88. *Mem:* AAAS; Am Soc Microbiol; Am Soc Biochem & Molecular Biol; Soc Neurosci. *Res:* Genes which code for signal transduction molecules of the nervous system and are required for intercellular coordination in proper nervous system function. *Mailing Add:* Dept Biol Chem Univ Mich 1103 E Huron Ann Arbor MI 48104-1687

**UHLHORN, KENNETH W,** SCIENCE EDUCATION. *Current Pos:* assoc prof, 63-68, dir, Sci Teaching Ctr, 66-93, PROF SCI EDUC, IND STATE UNIV, TERRE HAUTE, 68-, DIR, SCI EDUC DEPT, 93-, EMER CHMN, SCI TEACHING CTR. *Personal Data:* b Mankato, Minn, Sept 24, 33; m 54, Harriet; c Scott & Ann (Hoffman). *Educ:* Mankato State Col, BS, 54; Univ Minn, MA, 60; Univ Iowa, PhD(biol, sci educ), 63. *Prof Exp:* Teacher pub sch, Minn, 56-60; instr biol & physics, Univ Iowa, 60-63, asst prof biol, 63. *Mem:* Nat Asn Res Sci Teaching; Nat Sci Teachers Asn. *Res:* Preparation, use and application of science experience inventories and their role in teaching science; science for elementary education majors; children's concept of science and scientists based on their drawings of scientists; the physics and perception of photography to undergraduate and graduate students. *Mailing Add:* Dept Sci Educ Ind State Univ Terre Haute IN 47809. *Fax:* 812-237-8029

**UHLIR, ARTHUR, JR,** ELECTRICAL ENGINEERING, PHYSICS. *Current Pos:* chmn elec eng, 70-75, dean eng, 75-80, PROF ELEC ENG, COL ENG, TUFTS UNIV, 70- *Personal Data:* b Chicago, Ill, Feb 2, 26; m 54, Ingeborg Williams; c Steven, Donald & David. *Educ:* Ill Inst Technol, BS, 45, MS, 48; Univ Chicago, PhD(physics), 52. *Prof Exp:* Asst engr mech, Armour Res Found, 45-48; mem tech staff transistors, Bell Labs, 51-58; vpres & dir semiconductors, Microwave Assocs, Inc, 58-69; dir res, Comput Metrics Inc, 69-73. *Concurrent Pos:* Dir, Harvard Apparatus Corp, 75-79. *Mem:* Fel Inst Elec & Electronics Engrs; Am Phys Soc; Sigma Xi; fel AAAS. *Res:* Microwave devices and measurements. *Mailing Add:* Col Eng Tufts Univ 161 College Ave Medford MA 02155. *Fax:* 617-627-3220; *E-Mail:* auhlir@jade.tufts.edu

**UHLMANN, DONALD ROBERT,** GLASS TECHNOLOGY, POLYMER SCIENCE. *Current Pos:* PROF & DEPT HEAD, UNIV ARIZ, 86- *Personal Data:* b Chicago, Ill, Sept 22, 36; m 58, Eulalie T; c Donald R, Eugenie V, Angelique T, Melie C, Aurelie C & Elise V. *Educ:* Yale Univ, BS, 58; Harvard Univ, PhD(appl physics), 63. *Honors & Awards:* F H Norton Award, 79; George W Morey Award, Am Ceramic Soc, 81; Sosman lectr, 82. *Prof Exp:* Res fel appl physics, Harvard Univ, 63-65; from asst prof to assoc prof ceramics, Mass Inst Technol, 65-75, prof ceramics & polymers, 75-83, Cabot prof mat, 83-86. *Concurrent Pos:* Convenor, Sci Coun Mat Processing, Univ Space Res Asn, 77-78, mem, Sci Coun, 78-80; Guggenheim fel, 81-82. *Mem:* Nat Acad Eng; Am Inst Mining, Metall & Petrol Engrs; fel Am Ceramic Soc; fel Brit Soc Glass Technol; Ceramic Educ Coun; Soc Photogeog & Inst Engrs; Acad Ceramics; Am Phys Soc. *Res:* Structure and properties of glasses; crystallization phenomena; structure and properties of polymers; sol-gel produced materials. *Mailing Add:* 5309 E Mission Hill Dr Tucson AZ 85718. *Fax:* 520-322-2993

**UHR, JONATHAN WILLIAM,** MEDICINE, IMMUNOLOGY. *Current Pos:* PROF & CHMN, DEPT MICROBIOL, PROF INTERNAL MED & MARY NELL & RALPH ROGERS PROF IMMUNOL, UNIV TEX SOUTHWESTERN MED SCH, 72-, RAYMOND & ELLEN WILLIE DISTINGUISHED CHAIR CANCER RES, 90- *Personal Data:* b New York, NY, Sept 8, 27; m 54; c 2. *Educ:* Cornell Univ, AB, 48; NY Univ, MD, 52; Am Bd Internal Med, dipl, 60. *Honors & Awards:* Newcomb Cleveland Prize, AAAS, 63; Squibb Award, Infectious Dis Soc Am, 71. *Prof Exp:* Dazian fel, Dept Microbiol, Med Ctr NY Univ, 55-56, instr microbiol, Sch Med, 57-58, from asst prof to prof med, 58-72, dir, Irvington House Inst Rheumatic Fever & Allied Dis, 62-72. *Concurrent Pos:* Intern, Mt Sinai Hosp, 52-53, resident path, 53-54, asst resident med, 54-55, chief resident med, 56-57; assoc mem, Comn Immunization, Armed Forces Epidemiol Bd, 59-65, mem, 65-73, dep dir, 69-73; assoc vis physician, Bellevue Hosp, 59-72; Commonwealth fel, Walter & Eliza Hall Inst Med Res, 61-62; USPHS career develop award, 62; assoc attending physician, Univ Hosp, 63-72; consult internal med, Manhattan Vet Hosp, 64-74; assoc ed, J Immunol, 65-73, Advan Immunol, 84-; mem, Panel Regulatory Biol, NSF, 66-68; mem, Allergy & Immunol Study Sect, USPHS, 69-73; vis prof, Dept Microbiol, Yale Univ, 70-71; adv ed, Immunogenetics, 74-80; counr, Am Asn Immunologists, 78-85; US rep, Int Union Immunol Socs, 80-86; mem, US-Japan Panel Coop Sci Prog Immunol, 81-84, head, 84. *Mem:* Nat Acad Sci; Am Asn Immunologists (pres, 83-84); Am Soc Clin Invest; Am Asn Pathologists; Transplantation Soc; Asn Am Physicians; fel AAAS; fel Am Fedn Cancer Res. *Mailing Add:* Dept Microbiol Southwestern Med Sch Univ Tex 5323 Harry Hines Blvd Dallas TX 75235-8576. *Fax:* 214-648-1252; *E-Mail:* juhr@utsm.sw.edu

**UHR, LEONARD MERRICK,** COMPUTER SCIENCE, PSYCHOLOGY. *Current Pos:* PROF COMPUT SCI, UNIV WIS-MADISON, 65- *Personal Data:* b Philadelphia, Pa, June 26, 27; m 49; c 2. *Educ:* Princeton Univ, BA, 49; Johns Hopkins Univ, MA, 51; Univ Mich, PhD(psychol), 57. *Prof Exp:* Assoc prof psychol, Univ Mich & res psychologist & coordr psychol sci, Ment Health Res Inst, 57-65. *Mem:* Am Psychol Asn; Asn Comput Mach; Inst Elec & Electronics Engrs. *Res:* Dynamic computer models of perceptual and cognitive processes; perception; learning; computers and education; intelligent systems. *Mailing Add:* 211 Lathrop St Madison WI 53705

**UHRAN, JOHN JOSEPH, JR,** ELECTRICAL ENGINEERING, COMPUTER SCIENCES, ENGINEERING. *Current Pos:* from asst prof to assoc prof, 66-79, assoc chair elec eng, 86-90, PROF ELEC ENG, UNIV NOTRE DAME, 79-, PROF COMPUT SCI & ENG, 90-, ASSOC DEAN, COMPUT SCI & ENG, 95- *Educ:* Manhattan Col, BEE, 57; Purdue Univ, MSEE, 63, PhD(elec eng), 67. *Prof Exp:* Sr engr, Hazeltine Res Corp, 57-61; instr, Purdue Univ, 63-66. *Concurrent Pos:* Staff scientist, Lincoln Lab, Mass Inst Technol, 78-79, vis mem staff, 79-80; consult indust. *Mem:* Inst Elec & Electronics Engrs; Asn Comput Mach; Soc Comput Simulation; Sigma Xi. *Res:* Hardware/software development; microcomputer applications; modelling and simulation techniques; communication theory; digital signal processing; artificial intelligence and algorithms; path planning. *Mailing Add:* 257 Fitz Patrick Hall Univ Notre Dame Notre Dame IN 46556. *Fax:* 219-631-8007; *E-Mail:* jju@cse.nd.edu

**UHRICH, DAVID LEE,** PHYSICS. *Current Pos:* asst prof, 67-71, assoc prof, 71-77, PROF PHYSICS, KENT STATE UNIV, 77-, MEM LIQUID & CRYSTAL INST, 77- *Personal Data:* b Buffalo, NY, Jan 5, 39; m 61; c 3. *Educ:* Canisius Col, BS, 60; Univ Pittsburgh, PhD(physics), 65. *Prof Exp:* Fels, Univ Pittsburgh, 66 & Iowa State Univ, 66-67. *Mem:* Am Phys Soc. *Res:* Mossbauer effect studies of liquid crystals and solids. *Mailing Add:* 5754 Caranor Rd Kent OH 44240-4209

**UHRIG, JEROME LEE,** PERFORMANCE MODELING & ANALYSIS, SIGNAL PROCESSING. *Current Pos:* MEM TECH STAFF, AT&T BELL LABS, 66- *Personal Data:* b Pittsburgh, Pa. *Educ:* Ohio Univ, BS, 63; Carnegie Inst Technol, MS, 64, PhD(systs & commun sci), 66. *Mem:* Inst Elec & Electronics Engrs; Asn Comput Mach. *Res:* Systems engineering and partitioning methodologies; operational requirements analysis for real-time computer processing applications; performance modeling analysis; real-time computer architectures; optimization theory and application; signal processing applications. *Mailing Add:* Lucent Technol Bell Labs Whippany Rd Whippany NJ 07981

**UHRIG, ROBERT EUGENE,** NUCLEAR ENGINEERING, ARTIFICIAL INTELLIGENCE. *Current Pos:* DISTINGUISHED SCIENTIST, OAK RIDGE NAT LAB, 86-; DISTINGUISHED PROF ENG, UNIV TENN, 86- *Personal Data:* b Raymond, Ill, Aug 6, 28; m 54, Paula M Schnepf; c Robert J, Joseph C, Mary C (Floyd), Charles W, Jean M (Rieder), Thomas P & Fredrick J. *Educ:* Univ Ill, BS, 48; Iowa State Univ, MS, 50, PhD(eng mech), 54. *Honors & Awards:* Richards Mem Award, Am Soc Mech Engrs, 69; Res Award, Am Soc Eng Educ, 62, Glenn Murphy Award, 92. *Prof Exp:* Instr eng mech, Iowa State Univ, 48-51, res engr, Ames Lab, 51-54; instr, West Pt Mil Acad, NY, 54-56; assoc prof nuclear eng, Iowa State Univ, 56-60; dept chmn, Col Eng, Univ Fla, 60-68, dean, 68-73; vpres, Fla Power & Light Co, 73-86. *Concurrent Pos:* Asst dir res, US Dept Defense, 67-68; chmn, NSF Eng Adv Comt, 72-73; Nuclear Div, Am Soc Eng Educ, 73-88; mem, Nat Acad Sci/NRC Shuttle Criticality Rev & Hazards Anal Audit, 86-88; bd dir, Am Nuclear Soc, 65-68, Eng Coun Prof Develop, 68-72; mem, Nuclear Safety Res Comt, Nuclear Regulatory Comn, 89- *Mem:* Fel Am Nuclear Soc; fel Am Soc Mech Engrs; fel AAAS; Am Soc Eng Educ; Int Neural Network Soc; Inst Elec & Electronics Engrs. *Res:* Application of artificial intelligence (expert systems neural networks fuzzy systems and genetic algorithms) to improve the operation & safety of nuclear power plants and other complex systems; application of random noise techniques to nuclear reactor systems; neutron wave propagation in nuclear systems; approximately 200 publications in scientific or technical journals and author of one book and co-author of a second book. *Mailing Add:* 113 Connors Dr Oak Ridge TN 37830-7662. *Fax:* 423-974-0668; *E-Mail:* ruhrig@utn.edu

**UICKER, JOHN JOSEPH, JR,** MECHANICAL ENGINEERING, COMPUTER-AIDED ENGINEERING. *Current Pos:* From asst prof to assoc prof, Univ Wis-Madison, 67-75, dir, Comput-Aided Eng Ctr, 81-88, chair, Gen Eng Dept, 88-90, PROF MECH ENG, UNIV WIS-MADISON, 75- *Personal Data:* b Derry, NH, July 11, 38; div; c Theresa A, John J III, Joseph M, Dorothy J, Barbara A & Joan E. *Educ:* Univ Detroit, BME, 61; Northwestern Univ, Evanston, MS, 63, PhD(mech eng), 65. *Honors & Awards:* Ralph R Teeter Award, Soc Automotive Engrs, 68. *Concurrent Pos:* Mem, US Coun Int Fedn for Theory of Mach & Mechanisms, 69-, ed-in-chief, Mechanism & Mach Theory, 73-78; prin res engr assoc & Am Soc Eng Educ resident fel, Advan Anal Technol Dept, Ford Motor Co, Mich, 72-73; Sr Fulbright lectr, Cranfield, England, 78-79. *Mem:* Am Soc Mech Engrs; Am Soc Eng Educ; Asn Comput Mach. *Res:* Kinematic and dynamic analysis of mechanical systems; spatial linkage analysis; computer-aided design; computational geometry; simulation of solidification in metal castings. *Mailing Add:* Dept Mech Eng 1513 Univ Ave Madison WI 53706. *E-Mail:* uicker@engr.wisc.edu

**UITTO, JOUNI JORMA,** DERMATOLOGY, BIOCHEMISTRY. *Current Pos:* PROF DERMAT, BIOCHEM & MOLECULAR BIOL & CHMN DEPT DERMAT, JEFFERSON MED COL, THOMAS JEFFERSON UNIV, PHILADELPHIA, PA, 86- *Personal Data:* b Helsinki, Finland, Sept 15, 43; m 65, 82; c 3. *Educ:* Univ Helsinki, MB, 65, MD & PhD(med biochem), 70. *Honors & Awards:* William Montagna lectr, Soc Invest Dermat, 87; Hermann Pinkens Mem lectr, Am Soc Dermat Physicians, 88. *Prof Exp:* Intern med, surg & med biochem, Univ Helsinki Cent Hosp, 69; instr med biochem, Univ Helsinki, 70-71; clin asst dermat, Univ Cent Hosp, Univ Copenhagen, 71; from instr to asst prof biochem, Rutgers Med Sch, Col Med & Dent NJ, 73-75; instr med & resident fel dermat, Sch Med, Washington Univ, 75-78, asst prof med & biochem, 78-80; from assoc prof to prof med & assoc chief & dir res, Div Dermat, Harbor Med Ctr, Univ Calif, Los Angeles, 80-86. *Concurrent Pos:* Fel, Gen Clin Res Ctr, Philadelphia Gen Hosp & Dept Dermat, Univ Pa, 71-72. *Mem:* Soc Invest Dermat; Am Soc Clin Invest; Am Soc Biol Chem; Am Acad Dermat; Am Chem Soc; Am Dermat Asn; Asn Am Physicians. *Res:* Biochemistry and molecular biology of connective tissues; collagen metabolism; investigative dermatology. *Mailing Add:* Dermat Jefferson Med Col 233 S Tenth St Rm 450 Philadelphia PA 19107

**UKELES, RAVENNA,** microbiology; deceased, see previous edition for last biography

**UKLEJA, PAUL LEONARD MATTHEW,** PHYSICS, LIQUID CRYSTAL PHYSICS. *Current Pos:* from asst prof to assoc prof, 78-91, PROF PHYSICS, UNIV MASS-DARTMOUTH, 91- *Personal Data:* b Chicago, Ill, Nov 22, 46; m 67; c 1. *Educ:* New Col, Fla, BA, 67; Univ Chicago, MS, 69; Kent State Univ, PhD(physics), 76. *Honors & Awards:* Arthur K Doolittle Award, Am Chem Soc, 89. *Prof Exp:* Peace Corps vol sci & math, Govt Malta, 70-73; res assoc & fel, Kent State Univ, 76-78. *Concurrent Pos:* Assoc mem, Liquid Crystal Inst, 88; vis scientist, Kent State Univ, 87-88. *Mem:* Sigma Xi; Am Phys Soc; Am Asn Physics Teachers. *Res:* Liquid crystal physics, orientational ordering, and self diffusion in partially ordered systems. *Mailing Add:* 204 Maple St New Bedford MA 02740. *E-Mail:* puklesa@umassd.edu

**UKRAINETZ, PAUL RUVIM,** FLUID POWER. *Current Pos:* from asst prof to assoc prof, 62-71, dept head, 74-82, PROF MECH ENG, UNIV SASK, 71- *Personal Data:* b Erwood, Sask, Dec 28, 35; wid; c Grant, Garth & Owen. *Educ:* Univ Sask, BS, 57; Univ BC, MASc, 60; Purdue Univ, PhD(mech eng), 62. *Honors & Awards:* Ralph R Teetor Award, Soc Automotive Engrs, 74. *Prof Exp:* Eng trainee, Bristol Aeroplane Co Ltd, 57-59. *Concurrent Pos:* Vis prof, Monash Univ, Melbourne, Australia, 82-83 & Univ Bath, Eng, 89. *Mem:* Soc Automotive Engrs; Am Soc Eng Educ; Can Soc Mech Engrs; Eng Inst Can. *Res:* Investigations into problems associated with fluid power control systems; study of the dynamics of cables with particular reference to power transmission line vibration. *Mailing Add:* Dept Mech Eng Univ Sask 57 Campus Dr Saskatoon SK S7N 5A9 Can. *Fax:* 306-966-5427; *E-Mail:* paul__r__ukrainetz@engr.usask.ca

**ULABY, FAWWAZ TAYSSIR,** REMOTE SENSING. *Current Pos:* PROF ELEC ENG & COMPUT SCI, UNIV MICH, 84-, DIR, CTR SPACE TERAHERTZ TECHNOL, NASA, 88- *Personal Data:* b Damascus, Syria, Feb 4, 43; US citizen; m 68, Mary A Hammond; c Neda, Aziza & Laith. *Educ:* Am Univ Beirut, BS, 64; Univ Tex, Austin, MSEE, 66, PhD(elec eng), 68. *Honors & Awards:* Distinguished Achievement, Inst Elec & Electronics Engrs, 83, Centennial Medal, 84; Kuwait Prize Appl Sci, 87. *Prof Exp:* From asst prof to prof elec eng, 68-80, dir remote sensing lab, Ctr Res, Univ Kans, 76-84, J L Constant distinguished prof, 80-84. *Concurrent Pos:* Res grants, US Army, Univ Kans, 68-, NSF, 72- & 76-, Sandia Labs & Eglin AFB, 78- & NASA, 70-; assoc dir remote sensing lab, Ctr Res, Inc, Kans, 69-71; consult, govt & univ. *Mem:* Nat Acad Eng; Int Soc Photogram; Int Union Radio Sci; fel Inst Elec & Electronics Engrs. *Res:* Millimeter wave propagation; remote sensing; microwave radiometry; radar systems. *Mailing Add:* Dept Elec & Comput Eng 3228 Elec Eng Comput Sci Ann Arbor MI 48109

**ULAGARAJ, MUNIVANDY SEYDUNGANALLUR,** DIGITAL SIGNAL PROCESSING, SPEECH PROCESSING. *Current Pos:* PRES, INFO-TEK, EDMONTON, 93- *Personal Data:* b Tuticorin, India, Mar 4, 44; Can citizen; m 70, Santhi; c Monika & Vasli. *Educ:* Madras Univ, India, BSc, 64; Indian Agr Res Inst, New Delhi, MSc, 70; Univ Fla, Gainesville, PhD, 74. *Prof Exp:* Res asst, Tamil Nadu Govt, Coimbatore, India, 64-68; res & teaching asst, Univ Fla, Gainesville, 71-74, assoc, 74-75; res assoc, McGill Univ, MacDonald Campus, Montreal, 75-80; lectr, Comput Sci Dept, Concordia Univ, Montreal, 80-81; prog/systs anal, AGT Ltd, Edmonton, 81-89; researcher, Res & Develop, Corp Planning & Mgt Dept, 89-93. *Concurrent Pos:* Res assoc, Univ Fla, Gainesville, 74 & Purdue Univ, WLafayette, Ind, 75; lectr, Comput Sci Dept, Univ Alta, Edmonton, 84- *Mem:* AAAS; Acoust Soc Am; Inst Elec & Electronics Engrs Signal Processing Soc; Inst Elec & Electronics Engrs Commun Soc. *Res:* Speech recognition, speech synthesis, speech processing, spoken language systems; acoustics, software engineering, subscriber loop in telecommunication; electronic data processing teaching; personal computers; client/server computing; business process re-engineering. *Mailing Add:* Info-Tek Technol Consult & Training Inc 259 Burton Rd Edmonton AB T6R 1P7 Can. *Fax:* 403-988-8960; *E-Mail:* 76221.1003@compuserve.com

**ULANOWICZ, ROBERT EDWARD,** THEORETICAL ECOLOGY, NETWORK THEORY. *Current Pos:* res asst prof, Natural Resources Inst, 70-75, assoc prof, 75-80, PROF, CTR ENVIRON & ESTUARINE STUDIES, UNIV MD, 80- *Personal Data:* b Baltimore, Md, Sept 17, 43; m 67, Marie Chmilewsky; c Anastasia, Peter & Vera. *Educ:* Johns Hopkins Univ, BES, 64, PhD(chem eng), 68. *Prof Exp:* Res asst phys chem, Univ Gottingen, 64; res asst chem eng, Johns Hopkins Univ, 64-68; asst prof, Cath Univ Am, 68-70. *Concurrent Pos:* Mem Sci Comt Oceanic Res, Int Coun Sci Unions, Working Group No 59, Biol Models in Oceanog & Working Group No 73, Ecosystems Theory in Relation to Biol & Oceanog; Marine Sci Panel, working group monitoring Chesapeake Bay, Nat Res Coun; orgn comn, Venice Summer Sch. *Mem:* Int Soc Ecol Modelling; Estuarine Res Fedn. *Res:* Mass and energy transfer in ecosystems; ecosystem network analysis; thermodynamics of ecosystems; information theory in ecology. *Mailing Add:* Ctr Environ & Estuarine Studies Univ Md PO Box 38 Solomons MD 20688-0038. *Fax:* 410-326-7378; *E-Mail:* ulan@cbl.cees.edu

**ULBERG, LESTER CURTISS,** REPRODUCTIVE PHYSIOLOGY. *Current Pos:* assoc prof, 57-60, PROF ANIMAL HUSB, NC STATE UNIV, 60- *Personal Data:* b Wis, Dec 2, 17; m 45; c 1. *Educ:* Univ Wis, BS, 48, MS, 49, PhD(reprod physiol), 52. *Prof Exp:* Asst reprod physiol, Univ Wis, 47-50, instr, 50-52; instr animal husb, Miss State Col, 52-55, assoc prof, 55-57. *Concurrent Pos:* Agent, USDA, 50-52. *Mem:* AAAS; Am Soc Animal Sci; Am Dairy Sci Asn; Brit Soc Study Fertil. *Res:* Early embryonic development; hormone control of ovarian activity. *Mailing Add:* 812 Ravenwood Dr Raleigh NC 27606

**ULBRECHT, JAROMIR JOSEF,** ENGINEERING RHEOLOGY. *Current Pos:* chief 84-88, dept dir, Off Technol Eval & Assessment, 88-91, DIR, TECH PROGS, NAT INST STAND & TECHNOL, 91- *Personal Data:* b Ostrava, Czech, Dec 16, 28; US citizen; m 52; c 2. *Educ:* Czech Inst Technol, Prague, Ing, 52; Inst Chem Technol, Prague, PhD(chem eng), 58. *Honors & Awards:* Purkynie Medal, 93. *Prof Exp:* Assoc dir chem eng, Rubber Res Inst, 57-62; head eng rheology lab, Czech Acad Sci, 62-68; prof chem eng, Univ Salford, 68-78; prof & chmn, Dept Chem Eng, State Univ NY, Buffalo, 78-84.

Concurrent Pos: Res prof, Inst Chem Technol, Prague, 66-68; vis prof, Univ Technol, Aachen, Ger, 67-68; Alexander von Humboldt fel, 67; ed-in-chief, Chem Eng Commun, 77-84 & Chem Eng-Concepts & Rev, 84-; adj prof, Univ Md, 85- Mem: Fel Am Inst Chem Eng; Brit Inst Chem Eng; Soc Rheology; Brit Soc Rheology; Sigma Xi; Am Chem Soc. Res: Momentum and mass transfer in rheologically complex and multiphase systems; mixing and gas-liquid and liquid-liquid contacting; stirred chemical; biochemical reactors. Mailing Add: Nat Inst Stand & Technol Bldg 212 Rm A347 Gaithersburg MD 20899. Fax: 301-279-8973; E-Mail: 74434.377@compuserve.com

**ULBRICH, CARLTON WILBUR,** ATMOSPHERIC PHYSICS. Current Pos: asst prof, Clemson Univ, 66-74, assoc prof, 74-79, prof, 79-93, RES PROF PHYSICS, CLEMSON UNIV, 93- Personal Data: b Meriden, Conn, Oct 1, 32; m 62, Holley R Hewitt; c Christine, Carla & Katrina. Educ: Univ Conn, BSME, 60, MS, 62, PhD(physics), 65. Prof Exp: Res asst physics, Univ Conn, 61-65; asst prof, Wittenberg Univ, 65-66. Mem: Am Meteorol Soc; Am Geophys Union. Res: Radar meteorology; atmospheric physics. Mailing Add: 106 Highland Dr Clemson SC 29631-1922

**ULDRICK, JOHN PAUL,** mechanical engineering, theoretical mechanics, for more information see previous edition

**ULERY, DANA LYNN,** COMPUTER SCIENCE, SOFTWARE SYSTEMS. Current Pos: sr res scientist, 94-95, br chief, 95-96, DIV CHIEF, US ARMY RES LAB, 96-; SR RES SCIENTIST, GA INST TECHNOL, 94- Personal Data: b East St Louis, Mo, Jan 2, 38; m 59, 80, William H Fellner; c Bradford T & Terrie L. Educ: Grinnell Col, BA, 59; Univ Del, MS, 72, PhD(comput sci), 75. Prof Exp: Res engr, Jet Propulsion Lab, NASA, 60-63; programmer, Getty Oil Co, 63-64; lectr comput sci, Dept Comput Sci, Univ Del, 70-75, fel, 75-76, hons prog, 76-77; sr software engr, Du Pont Co, 77-82, prog mgr, 82-87, consult 87-90, sr consult, Du Pont Co, 90-93. Concurrent Pos: Consult, Am Univ Cairo, 76; vis lectr, Inst Statist & Comput Sci, Cairo Univ, 76; rep, Chem Indust Data Exchange, 86-92; chair work group, ANSI Accredited Stand Comt X12 Electronic Data Interchange, 86-95; X12 liaison to US Tech Adv Group to ISO Tech Comt 176 Qual Mgt & Qual Assurance 87-93; Pan Am deleg, Prod Data Chair UN EDIFACT Bd, 88-97; adj prof, Dept Math Sci, Univ Del, 89-95; US deleg to Pan Am EDIFACT Bd, 94-97. Mem: Sigma Xi; Inst Elec & Electronics Engrs Comput Soc; Asn Comput Mach; AAAS. Res: Software research and development; computing architecture and systems. Mailing Add: 18 Squirrel Lane Newark DE 19711

**ULEVITCH, RICHARD JOEL,** BIOCHEMISTRY, IMMUNOPATHOLOGY. Current Pos: Fel, Univ Minn, 71-72, 72-75, MEM STAFF, SCRIPPS CLIN & RES FOUND, 75- Personal Data: b Cleveland, Ohio, Apr 4, 44; m 74; c 1. Educ: Washington & Jefferson Col, BA, 66; Univ Pa, PhD(biochem), 71. Concurrent Pos: NIH fel, 78-81, 75-77. Mem: Am Asn Immunologists; Am Asn Path. Res: Biochemical mechanisms of inflammatory disease processes. Mailing Add: Dept Immunol Scripps Clin 10666 N Torrey Pines Rd La Jolla CA 92037-1092

**ULICH, BOBBY LEE,** LARGE TELESCOPE TECHNOLOGY, RADIO ASTRONOMY. Current Pos: KAMAN AEROSPACE. Personal Data: b Bryan, Tex, Aug 13, 47; m 65; c 1. Educ: Tex A&M Univ, BS, 69; Calif Inst Technol, MS, 70; Univ Tex, Austin, PhD(elec eng), 73. Prof Exp: Head telescope oper, Tucson Div, Nat Radio Astron Observ, Assoc Univs Inc, 73-79; asst dir, Multiple Mirror Telescope Observ, Univ Ariz, 79- Concurrent Pos: Mem, US Nat Comt Int Union Radio Sci, Comn J. Mem: Inst Elec & Electronics Engrs; Am Astron Soc; Int Astron Union. Res: Millimeter wavelength instrumentation and calibration techniques; solar system astronomy; interstellar molecules. Mailing Add: 5982 E Edison Pl Tucson AZ 85712

**ULICH, WILLIE LEE,** AGRICULTURAL ENGINEERING. Current Pos: RETIRED. Personal Data: b Somerville, Tex, Nov 10, 20; m 39; c 2. Educ: Tex A&M Univ, BS, 43, MS, 47; Harvard Univ, PhD(pub admin), 51. Honors & Awards: James F Lincoln Found Award, 49-50. Prof Exp: Res asst, Tex A&M Univ, 46-47, exten engr, 48-61; farm labor supvr, Fed Exten Serv, 47-48; prof agr eng & chmn dept, Tex Tech Univ, 61-84. Concurrent Pos: Mem, Tex Air Control Bd, 69, 71- Mem: Am Soc Agr Engrs; Am Soc Eng Educ. Res: Covance systems and particulate control in cotton gins; efficiency studies of irrigation well pumping plants; confined animal odor and waste disposal systems; soil surface modification for soil and water conservation; farm machinery design; brush harvesting. Mailing Add: Church Somerville TX 77879

**ULINSKI, PHILIP STEVEN,** NEUROANATOMY. Current Pos: from asst prof to assoc prof, 75-86, PROF CHMN ANAT, UNIV CHICAGO, 86- Personal Data: b Detroit, Mich, Feb 17, 43. Educ: Mich State Univ, BS, 64, MS, 67, PhD(zool), 69. Prof Exp: Asst prof biol, Oberlin Col, 69-70; asst prof anat, Sch Dent, Loyola Univ Chicago, 70-74. Concurrent Pos: NIH fel, Univ Chicago, 75-81. Mem: Am Soc Zool; Soc Neurosci; Am Asn Anat. Res: Comparative anatomy of reptilian nervous systems. Mailing Add: Dept Organismal Biol & Anat Univ Chicago 1025 E 57th St Chicago IL 60637

**ULLAH, ABUL JAFFOR,** CELL BIOLOGY, PLANT PHYSIOLOGY. Current Pos: RES BIOCHEMIST, SOUTHERN REGIONAL RES CTR, AGR RES SERV, USDA, 85- Personal Data: b Sylhet, Bangladesh, Jan 1, 48; US citizen; m 76, Monowara B Azwad; c Rashad J, Riaz Z & Rima F. Educ: Bangladesh Agr Univ, BS, 68, MS, 70; Univ Cincinnati, PhD(cell & molecular biol), 75. Prof Exp: Fel, Dept Biochem, State Univ NY, Stony Brook, 74-77;

res assoc, Dept Biochem, Univ Ill, Urbana-Champaign, 77-85. Mem: Sigma Xi. Res: Structure-function relationship in proteins; active-site mapping of phosphomonoesterases; protein purification and co-valent structure elucidation; protein structure refinement through site-directed mutagenesis and computer modeling. Mailing Add: USDA Agr Res Serv S Regional Res Ctr 1100 Robert E Lee Blvd New Orleans LA 70124. Fax: 504-286-4367; E-Mail: aullah@nola.srrc.usda.gov

**ULLIMAN, JOSEPH JAMES,** REMOTE SENSING, AERIAL PHOTO INTERPRETATION. Current Pos: assoc dean, 88-89, dept head forest resources, 89-96, PROF REMOTE SENSING, COL FORESTRY, WILDLIFE & RANGE SCI, UNIV IDAHO, 74- Personal Data: b Springfield, Ohio, July 7, 35; m 61, Barbara Gish; c Kathryn N, Anne & Mark J. Educ: Univ Dayton, BA, 58; Univ Minn, MF, 68, PhD(forestry remote sensing),71. Prof Exp: Instr aerial photog interpretation, Col Forestry, Univ Minn, 68-71, asst prof, 71-74. Concurrent Pos: Consult, USAID, 78-84; chmn, Int Soc Photogram & Remote Sensing, 80-84; dir, Forestry & Wildlife Remote Sensing Ctr, 81-; co-dir, remote sensing res unit, Univ Idaho, 81- Mem: Int Soc Photogram; Am Soc Photogram & Remote Sensing; Soc Am Foresters. Res: Small format camera system acquisition; Manual and digital analysis of aerial and satellite data for mapping, inventory, and geographic information systems. Mailing Add: Forest Resources Forestry Wildlife & Range Sci Univ Idaho Moscow ID 83844-1133. Fax: 208-885-6226; E-Mail: julliman@novell.uidaho.edu

**ULLMAN, ALAN HOWARD,** PROCESS ANALYTICAL CHEMISTRY, NEAR INFRARED SPECTROSCOPY. Current Pos: anal chemist, 78-85, TECHNOL LEADER, ENG DIV, PROCTER & GAMBLE CO, 85- Personal Data: b New York, NY, May 27, 52; m 74, Susan J Feldman; c Ian M & Joni M. Educ: Brooklyn Col, City Univ NY, BS, 72; Univ Del, PhD(chem), 77. Prof Exp: Res assoc, Univ Fla, 76-78. Concurrent Pos: Steering comt mem, Ctr Process Anal Chem, 92-; mem, Anal Div, Am Chem Soc & Coun Near Infrared Spectros. Mem: Am Chem Soc; Soc Appl Spectros; Instrument Soc Am; Macintosh Sci & Tech Users Asn. Res: Applications of near infrared spectroscopy to process measurements; research in various areas of analytical chemistry have led to more than 24 publications. Mailing Add: Procter & Gamble Co 6300 Center Hill Rd Cincinnati OH 45224-1795. E-Mail: ullman.ah@pg.com

**ULLMAN, EDWIN FISHER,** CLINICAL CHEMISTRY, IMMUNOCHEMISTRY. Current Pos: sci dir, Synvar Assocs, 66-70, VPRES & DIR RES, SYVA CO, 70- Personal Data: b Chicago, Ill, July 19, 30; m 54, Elizabeth Finlay; c Becky U & Linda J. Educ: Reed Col, AB, 52; Harvard Univ, AM, 54, PhD(org chem), 56. Honors & Awards: Mallinckrodt Award, Clin Ligand Assay Soc, 81; Van Slyke Award, NY Sect, Am Asn Clin Chem, 84. Prof Exp: Res chemist, Lederle Labs, Am Cyanamid Co, 55-60, group leader, Cent Res Div, 60-66. Concurrent Pos: Adv bd, J Org Chem, 70-75, J Immunoassay, 80- & J Clin Lab Anal, 85-87. Mem: Fel AAAS; Am Chem Soc; Royal Soc Chem; Am Asn Clin Chemists; Clin Ligand Assay Soc; Am Soc Biochem & Molecular Biol. Res: Organic photochemistry; immunochemical assay methods; effects of ligand-receptor binding on chemical reactivity; methods for detection of specific nucleic acid sequences. Mailing Add: 135 Selby Lane Atherton CA 94027. Fax: 650-493-8870

**ULLMAN, FRANK GORDON,** SOLID STATE PHYSICS. Current Pos: prof elec eng, Univ Nebr, Lincoln, 66-96, assoc chmn, 87-91, co-dir, Ctr Laser-Anal Studies Trace Gas Dynamics, 89-96, EMER PROF ELEC ENG, UNIV NEBR, LINCOLN, 96-, CO-DIR, CTR LASER-ANALYTICAL STUDIES TRACE GAS DYNAMICS, 89- Personal Data: b New York, NY, Dec 14, 26; m 51, Deborah Halpern; c Diane (Leininger), Marian (Ullman) & Eileen (Rendahl). Educ: NY Univ, BA, 49; Polytech Inst Brooklyn, PhD(physics), 58. Prof Exp: Res asst physics, Polytech Inst Brooklyn, 54-57, res assoc, 57-58; sr physicist, Nat Cash Regist Co, 58-66. Mem: Am Phys Soc; sr mem Inst Elec & Electronics Engrs; Sigma Xi. Res: Light scattering; ferroelectricity; photoconduction; luminescence; trace gas spectroscopy. Mailing Add: 209 N Walter Scott Engr Ctr Univ Nebr Lincoln NE 68588-0511

**ULLMAN, JACK DONALD,** SOLAR NEUTRINOS, SCIENCE EDUCATION. Current Pos: from assoc prof to prof, 70-96, EMER PROF PHYSICS, LEHMAN COL, 96- Personal Data: b Chicago, Ill, Sept 5, 29; m 72, Carol Richstone; c Esther & Anne. Educ: Univ Ill, BS, 51, MS, 56, PhD(physics), 60. Prof Exp: Physicist, Bur Ships, Dept Navy, 51-53 & US Bur Stand, 60-61; res assoc, Dept Nuclear Physics, Univ Strasbourg, 61-62; res assoc physics, Columbia Univ, 62-70. Mem: Am Phys Soc; NY Acad Sci. Res: Solar neutrino detection; science education. Mailing Add: Dept Physics & Astron Lehman Col Bedford Park Blvd Bronx NY 10468

**ULLMAN, JEFFREY D(AVID),** COMPUTER SCIENCE. Current Pos: chmn, 90-94, PROF COMPUT SCI, STANFORD UNIV, 79-, SW ASCHERMAN PROF ENG, 94- Personal Data: b New York, NY, Nov 22, 42. Educ: Columbia Univ, BS, 63; Princeton Univ, PhD(elec eng), 66. Hon Degrees: Dr, Free Univ Brussels, 75, Univ Paris, Dauphine, 92. Prof Exp: Mem tech staff, Bell Tel Labs, NJ, 66-69; assoc prof elec eng, Princeton Univ, 69-74, prof elec eng & comput sci, 74-79. Concurrent Pos: Vis lectr, Columbia Univ, NY, 66-68; Princeton Univ, 68, vis prof, Univ Calif, Berkeley, 73; mem, Adv Panel Comput Sci, NSF, 74-77, chmn, Coord Exp Res Prog Rev Panel, 83, mem, Adv Panel Parallel Software Res, 85, Adv Panel Info, Robotics & Intel Systs, 86-89; ed, J Comput & Systs Sci, 74-, Theoret Comput Sci, 74-, J Comput, Soc Indust Appl Math, 75-90, J Asn Comput Mach, 77-84, J Comput Lang, 74-81, J Parallel & Distributing Comput, 84-90, J Logic Programming, 86-; mem vis comt, Dept Comput Sci, State Univ NY, Albany,

78, Dept Elec Eng & Comput Sci, Univ Calif, San Diego, 84, Dept Comput Info Systs, Univ Calif, Santa Cruz, 85, Dept Comput Sci, Univ Southern Calif, 89; Einstein fel, Israeli Acad Sci, 84; mem tech adv bd, Atherton Technol, 87-89, Nucleus Int Corp, 89-91; Guggenheim fel, 88-89; bd mem, Comput Res Asn, 94-; bd dir, Junglee Corp, 96- *Mem:* Nat Acad Eng; fel Asn Comput Mach; Asn Logic Programming; Sigma Xi; Europ Asn Theoret Comput Sci. *Res:* Compilers; data bases; theory of algorithms; author of several technical publications. *Mailing Add:* Dept Comput Sci 411 Gates Hall 4A Wing Stanford Univ Stanford CA 94305-9040

**ULLMAN, JOSEPH LEONARD,** mathematics; deceased, see previous edition for last biography

**ULLMAN, NELLY SZABO,** APPLIED MATHEMATICS, BIOSTATISTICS. *Current Pos:* instr, Eastern Mich Univ, 63-64, asst prof, 64-66 & 68-71, assoc prof, 71-78, PROF MATH, EASTERN MICH UNIV, 78- *Personal Data:* b Vienna, Austria, Aug 11, 25; US citizen; wid; c 4. *Educ:* Hunter Col, BA, 45; Columbia Univ, MA, 48; Univ Mich, Ann Arbor, PhD(biostatist), 69. *Prof Exp:* Res assoc, Radiation Lab, Mass Inst Technol, 45; res assoc, Microwave Res Inst, Polytech Inst Brooklyn, 45-46, instr math, 45-63. *Mem:* Am Asn Univ Prof (treas, 71-); Am Math Asn; Am Statist Soc; Biomet Soc. *Res:* Integral equations; mathematical models in biological data; mathematical statistics. *Mailing Add:* 2360 St Francis Dr Ann Arbor MI 48104-4807

**ULLMANN, JOHN E,** MILITARY-INDUSTRIAL RELATIONSHIPS, TECHNICAL INNOVATION. *Current Pos:* prof, 61-94, EMER PROF MGT, HOFSTRA UNIV, 94- *Personal Data:* b Vienna, Austria, Dec 25, 23; US citizen; m 53, Eva Gruenwald; c James E & Catherine J (Newmark). *Educ:* Univ London, BSc, 48; Columbia Univ, MS, 51, PhD(indust eng), 59. *Prof Exp:* Asst proj engr, Bechtel Corp, 50-54; proj engr, Bulova Res & Develop Labs, 54-58; asst prof indust eng, Stevens Inst, 58-61. *Concurrent Pos:* Consult engr & mgt consult, 55- *Res:* Author of 30 books and monographs and over 100 publications on industrial development and innovation, statistics and quantitative methods; political, economic and technical aspects of military production; environmental issues; industrial history; quantitative analysis. *Mailing Add:* 2518 Norwood Ave North Bellmore NY 11710-1705. *Fax:* 516-463-4834

**ULLOM, STEPHEN VIRGIL,** MATHEMATICS. *Current Pos:* From asst prof to assoc prof, 70-78, PROF MATH, UNIV ILL, URBANA, 78- *Personal Data:* b Washington, DC, Nov 9, 38. *Educ:* Am Univ, BA, 62; Harvard Univ, MA, 64; Univ Md, PhD(math), 68. *Prof Exp:* NSF fel, Math Inst, Karlsruhe, Ger & King's Col, Univ London, 68-69. *Concurrent Pos:* mem, Inst Advan Study, 69-70. *Mem:* Am Math Soc. *Res:* Algebraic number theory; galois groups; galois module structure. *Mailing Add:* Dept Math Univ Ill Altgeld 1409 W Green St Urbana IL 61801

**ULLREY, DUANE EARL,** FISH & WILDLIFE SCIENCES. *Current Pos:* from asst prof to prof animal sci, 56-93, prof fish & wildlife, 73-93, EMER PROF ANIMAL SCI, FISH & WILDLIFE, MICH UNIV, 93- *Personal Data:* b Niles, Mich, May 27, 28; m 61, 76; c 3. *Educ:* Mich State Univ, BS, 50, MS, 51; Univ Ill, PhD(animal nutrit), 54. *Honors & Awards:* Am Feed Mfrs Asn Nutrit Res Award, 67; G Bohstedt Mineral Res Award, 69; Sr Res Award, Sigma Xi, 80. *Prof Exp:* Asst animal sci, Univ Ill, 51-54; instr physiol & pharmacol, Okla State Univ, 54-55. *Concurrent Pos:* Moorman fel nutrit res, 70; mem, Comt Animal Nutrit, Nat Res Coun; adv comt life sci, Coun Int Exchange Scholars Nat Acad Sci-Nat Res Coun, 74-77; dir, Mich State Univ Inst Nutrit, 74-76; res assoc, San Diego Zoo, 78-; consult, Int Study Vitamin E, WHO. *Mem:* Am Am Soc Animal Sci; Am Inst Nutrit; Am Asn Zoo Veterinarians; Sigma Xi; Equine Nutrit Physiol Soc. *Res:* Nutrient requirements of swine; normal development of the swine fetus; hematology of domestic animals; nutrition of wild animals; mineral and vitamin metabolism. *Mailing Add:* Dept Animal Sci Mich State Univ East Lansing MI 48823-0001

**ULLRICH, DAVID FREDERICK,** MATHEMATICS. *Current Pos:* RETIRED. *Personal Data:* b Waterbury, Conn, Sept 10, 37. *Educ:* Rensselaer Polytech Inst, BS, 59; Case Western Res Univ, MS, 62; Carnegie-Mellon Univ, PhD(differential equations), 67. *Prof Exp:* Asst prof math, NC State Univ, 66-96. *Mem:* Am Math Soc; Math Asn Am. *Res:* Non-linear ordinary differential equations. *Mailing Add:* 1617 Glenwood Ave Raleigh NC 27608

**ULLRICH, FELIX THOMAS,** PHYSICS, ELECTRICAL ENGINEERING. *Current Pos:* sr engr, 90-92, SR SCIENTIST, DCS, GRIM CORP, 92- *Personal Data:* b Elizabeth, NJ, June 1, 39; m 68; c 1. *Educ:* Rutgers Col, BA, 61; Univ Pittsburgh, PhD(physics), 70. *Prof Exp:* Mem tech staff physics, Riverside Res Inst, 70 & GTE Labs, 70-72; advan res & develop engr, GTE Sylvania, 72-75; prof tech staff mem elec eng, Plasma Physics Lab, Princeton Univ, 75-85; staff, Dowty RFL Industs, 85-90. *Mem:* Am Phys Soc. *Mailing Add:* 1328 Lower Ferry Rd Ewing NJ 08618

**ULLRICH, ROBERT CARL,** FUNGAL GENETICS. *Current Pos:* From asst prof to assoc prof, 74-86, PROF BOT, UNIV VT, 86- *Personal Data:* b Dumont, NJ, Aug 4, 40; m 64; c 2. *Educ:* Univ Minn, BSc, 68; Harvard Univ, AM, 69, PhD(biol), 73. *Mem:* Genetics Soc Am; Mycological Soc Am. *Res:* Fungal genetics of Basidiomycetes; molecular genetics of fungi including transformation and ribosomal RNA genes; molecular, classical and population genetic studies of sexuality and mating types in Basidiomycetes. *Mailing Add:* Dept Bot Marsh Life Sci Univ Vt Burlington VT 05405-0086

**ULLRICH, ROBERT LEO,** PATHOLOGY, RADIATION CARCINOGENESIS. *Current Pos:* Res assoc, 74-76, head radiation carcinogenesis unit, Biol Div, 76-87, PROF, HUMAN BIOL CHEM GENETICS, OAK RIDGE NAT LAB, 88-, VCHMN, DEPT RADIATION THER, 88- *Personal Data:* b Ottumwa, Iowa, Sept 8, 47. *Educ:* Creighton Univ, BS, 69, MS, 71; Univ Rochester, PhD(radiation biol), 75. *Concurrent Pos:* Mem, biol basis radiation protection criteria, Nat Coun Radiat Protection & Measurements Sci Comt, 77-; consult, Comt Fed Res Biol & Health Effects Ionizing Radiation, Nat Acad Sci, 80-81. *Mem:* Am Asn Cancer Res; Radiation Res Soc; AAAS; NAm Late Effects Group. *Res:* Mechanisms of radiation carcinogenesis and cocarcinogenesis. *Mailing Add:* Dept Radiation Ther 310 Gail Borden F-56 Galveston TX 77555-0656

**ULLRICK, WILLIAM CHARLES,** BIOPHYSICS, HISTORY & PHILOSOPHY OF SCIENCE. *Current Pos:* from instr to prof, 65-87, EMER PROF PHYSIOL, SCH MED, BOSTON UNIV, 87- *Personal Data:* b Evanston, Ill, June 6, 24; m 48, Doris R Burkholder; c John C, Christina L & Elizabeth L. *Educ:* Northwestern Univ, BS, 49; Univ Ill, MS, 51, PhD(physiol), 55. *Prof Exp:* Lab asst zool, comp anat & embryol, Northwestern Univ, 48-49; asst physiol, Col Med, Univ Ill, 50-54. *Concurrent Pos:* USPHS career res develop awards, 59-; mem bd dirs, Harvard Apparatus Co, Mass, 58-61. *Mem:* AAAS; Biophys Soc; Am Physiol Soc; NY Acad Sci. *Res:* Muscle physiology and biophysics; history of muscle physiology. *Mailing Add:* Dept Physiol Boston Univ Sch Med 80 E Concord St Boston MA 02118

**ULLYOT, GLENN EDGAR,** ORGANIC CHEMISTRY, MEDICINAL CHEMISTRY. *Current Pos:* CONSULT, 75- *Personal Data:* b Clark Co, SDak, Mar 11, 10; m 35. *Educ:* Univ Minn, BChem, 33; Univ Ill, MS, 35, PhD(org chem), 38. *Prof Exp:* Res chemist, Smith Kline & French Labs, 37-45, head, Org Chem Sect, 45-50, dir, Chem Labs, 50-57, assoc dir res, 57-67, dir, Sci Liaison Res & Develop Div, 67-75. *Concurrent Pos:* Mem ad hoc comt anticonvulsants, Nat Inst Neurol & Commun Dis & Stroke, 69-72, epilepsy adv comt, 72-76 & 81-84; consult, Epilepsy Br, Neurol Dis Progs, 75, Franklin Inst Res Lab, Sci Liaison, 76-80 & Biosearch Inc, 81-82. *Mem:* AAAS; Am Chem Soc; fel Am Inst Chem; Am Soc Pharmacol & Exp Therapeut. *Res:* Research and development administration; synthetic medicinal agents; central nervous system active agents; diuretics; structure-biological activity relation. *Mailing Add:* 2207 River Crescent Dr Annapolis MD 21407-7718. *E-Mail:* gullyot@aol.com

**ULM, EDGAR H,** BIOCHEMISTRY. *Current Pos:* SR DIR, DRUG SAFETY & DISPOSITION, LIGAND PHARM, INC, 90- *Personal Data:* b McKeesport, Pa, July 23, 42; m 65; c 1. *Educ:* Ind Univ Pa, BA, 65; Ohio Univ, MS, 67; Purdue Univ, PhD(biochem), 72. *Prof Exp:* Res assoc biochem, Med Sch, St Louis Univ, 71-73; sr res biochemist, Merck Inst, 73-76, res fel, 76-90. *Concurrent Pos:* NIH res fel, 72-73. *Mem:* Am Chem Soc; AAAS. *Res:* Biochemistry renin angiotensin; biochemistry of hypertension; rational drug design based on specific alterations of enzymatic activities; metabolism and disposition of enalaprilmaleate. *Mailing Add:* Ligand Pharm Inc 10255 Science Center Dr San Diego CA 92121

**ULM, LESTER, JR,** ELECTRICAL ENGINEERING. *Current Pos:* RETIRED. *Personal Data:* b Palm Harbor, Fla, Aug 5, 22; m 45; c 2. *Educ:* Ga Inst Technol, BEE, 49. *Prof Exp:* Test engr, Gen Elec Co, 49-50; student engr, Tampa Elec Co, 50, sr inspector, 50-51, from jr engr to sr engr, 51-57, from assoc engr to engr, 57-58, gen engr, 58-62, dir eng, 62-74, dir methods & procedures, 74-80, vpres serv, 80- *Mem:* Am Soc Eng Educ; Inst Elec & Electronics Engrs. *Res:* Electrical utility engineering. *Mailing Add:* 3006 Schiller St Tampa FL 33629

**ULMER, GENE CARLETON,** THERMODYNAMICS, ORE DEPOSITS. *Current Pos:* assoc prof, 69-74, chmn dept, 74-77, PROF GEOL, TEMPLE UNIV, 74- *Personal Data:* b Cincinnati, Ohio, Jan 28, 37; m 60, Dagmar Schroter; c Alexander, Susan C, Ekika D & Kirk B. *Educ:* Univ Cincinnati, BS, 58; Pa State Univ, PhD(geochem), 64. *Prof Exp:* Asst geochem, Pa State Univ, 59-62, staff res asst, Col Mineral Industs, 62-64; engr, Homer Res Labs, Bethlehem Steel Corp, Pa, 64-69. *Concurrent Pos:* Geol fieldwork, Italy, Ger, SAfrica, Iceland & Mont; Eberman Res Award, Temple Univ, 92; Fulbright Res Award, 92-94; Humboldt fel, 93-94. *Mem:* AAAS; Mineral Soc Am; Am Ceramic Soc; Am Geophys Union; Sigma Xi; Europ Union Geoscientists; fel Am Mineral Asn. *Res:* High temperature phase equilibria; oxide systems; oxidation reduction reactions, equilibria and kinetics; experimental petrology; materials research, especially spinels, diamonds and silicates, ultramafics in Africa and basalts in Idaho-Oregon; high pressure-high temperature research; nuclear waste management; platinum petrogenesis; mantle petrology. *Mailing Add:* Buery Hall Rm 307 Temple Univ Dept Geol Philadelphia PA 19122. *E-Mail:* ulmer@vm.temple.edu

**ULMER, JEFFREY BLAINE,** VACCINE RESEARCH, ANTIGEN PRESENTATION. *Current Pos:* sr res biochemist, 90-93, res fel, 93-96, SR RES FEL, MERCK RES LABS, 96- *Personal Data:* b Regina, Sask, Can, May 5, 56. *Educ:* Univ Regina, BSc, 78; McGill Univ, PhD(biochem), 85. *Prof Exp:* Fel, Dept Cell Biol, Yale Univ, 85-90. *Mem:* Am Soc Cell Biol; Int Soc Vaccines. *Res:* Research and development of polynucleotide vaccines including mechanisms of antigen presentation and generation of immune responses. *Mailing Add:* Dept Virus & Cell Biol 16-3 Merck & Co West Point PA 19486. *E-Mail:* jeff_ulmer@merck.com

**ULMER, MELVILLE PAUL,** X-RAY ASTRONOMY, GAMMA RAY ASTRONOMY. *Current Pos:* from asst prof to assoc prof, 76-87, PROF PHYSICS & ASTRON, NORTHWESTEREN UNIV, 87- *Personal Data:* b Washington, DC, Mar 12, 43; m 68; c 3. *Educ:* Johns Hopkins Univ, BA, 65; Univ Wis, PhD(physics), 70. *Prof Exp:* Res assoc physics, Univ Calif, San Diego, 70-74; astrophysicist, Smithsonian Astrophys Observ, 74-76. *Concurrent Pos:* Co-investr, NASA X-ray Astron Working Group, Compton Gamma Ray Observ Oriented Scintillation Spectrometer Exp. *Mem:* Am Astron Soc; Int Astron Union; fel Am Phys Soc; Royal Astron Soc. *Res:* Gamma ray astrophysics, x-ray astronomy instrumentation measurement of spectra and positions of galactic and extragalactic x-ray sources; application of x-ray and gamma ray astronomy to studies in cosmology, galactic structure, pulsars and the interstellar medium. *Mailing Add:* Dept Physics & Astron Northwestern Univ Evanston IL 60208. *Fax:* 847-491-3135; *E-Mail:* m-ulmer2@nwu.edu

**ULMER, MILLARD B,** MATHEMATICS. *Current Pos:* From asst prof to assoc prof, 72-83, PROF MATH, UNIV SC, 83- *Personal Data:* b Demopolis, Ala, June 9, 46; div; c 2. *Educ:* Univ Ala, PhD(math), 72. *Mem:* Math Asn Am; Nat Coun Teachers Math. *Res:* Queneing models; several papers. *Mailing Add:* Univ SC-Spartanburg 800 University Way Spartanburg SC 29303-9395

**ULMER, RAYMOND ARTHUR,** PATIENT COMPLIANCE RESEARCH EDUCATION, PATIENT COMPLIANCE CONTINUING. *Current Pos:* DIR PATIENT COMPLIANCE PROBS, NONCOMPLIANCE INST LOS ANGELES, 76- *Personal Data:* b Chicago, Ill, Nov 15, 23; div; c George H. *Educ:* Univ Chicago, MS, 49; La State Univ, PhD(psychol), 65. *Prof Exp:* Asst prof speech path, Univ Calif, Los Angeles, 64-65; asst prof psychol, Calif State Univ, 65-68; asst proj dir psychother, Univ Southern Calif, 68-69; asst proj dir res, Camarillo State Ment Health Ctr, 69-72; assoc prof patient compliance, Drew Med Sch, 73-81; proj dir cancer patient compliance, Univ Calif-Los Angeles Jonsson Comprehensive Cancer Ctr, 82-85. *Concurrent Pos:* Ed, J Compliance Health Care, 85-; consult, Boehringer Ingelheim Pharmaceut, 86-, Univ Calif-Los Angeles Hispanics, Cocaine & Health, Nat Inst Drug Abuse grant, 88-, Am Lung Asn, Los Angeles, 81-86, Univ Calif Los Angeles, Dept Pulmonary Med, 85-86. *Mem:* Am Psychol Asn; Am Col Legal Med. *Res:* Patient compliance issues; compliance problems of tuberculars, cancer patients and cocaine abusers; author of 27 publications; consultation in tobacco litigation and medical malpractice lawsuits. *Mailing Add:* 6411 W Fifth St Los Angeles CA 90048. *E-Mail:* rulmer@aol.com

**ULMER, RICHARD CLYDE,** PHYSICAL CHEMISTRY. *Current Pos:* RETIRED. *Personal Data:* b Lancaster, Ohio, July 4, 09; m 36; c 1. *Educ:* Ohio State Univ, AB, 30, PhD(chem), 36. *Prof Exp:* Chief chemist, Columbus & Southern Ohio Elec Co, 30-33; asst head, Chem Div, Res Dept, Detroit Edison Co, 36-45; tech dir, E F Drew & Co, Inc, 45-53; mgr res, Combustion Eng, Inc, Windsor, 53-66, exec engr, 66-74. *Mem:* Am Chem Soc; Am Soc Mech Eng. *Res:* Water treatment and corrosion in the power boiler and electric utility fields. *Mailing Add:* 6000 Riverside Dr Apt A334 Dublin OH 43017-2056

**ULOTH, ROBERT HENRY,** ORGANIC CHEMISTRY. *Current Pos:* RETIRED. *Personal Data:* b Valley City, NDak, Mar 17, 27; m 50; c 2. *Educ:* Valley City State Col, BS, 49; Univ NDak, MSc, 54. *Prof Exp:* Assoc chemist, Mead Johnson & Co, 54-58, chemist, 59-60, sr scientist, 60-68, res assoc, 68-69, patent coordr, 69-70, patent agt, 70-91. *Mem:* Am Chem Soc; Sigma Xi. *Res:* Synthetic pharmaceutical drugs. *Mailing Add:* 411 Westmore Dr Apt C Evansville IN 47712

**ULPIAN, CARLA,** NEUROLEPTIC DRUGS, DOPAMINE RECEPTORS. *Current Pos:* RES ASST PHARMACOL, UNIV TORONTO, 77- *Personal Data:* b Bacau, Romania, May 10, 47; Can citizen; m 69, Andrew; c Naomi & Sharon. *Educ:* Babes-Bolyai-Cluj, Romania, MS, 69, McGill Univ, Montreal, MS, 77. *Prof Exp:* Chemist, Res Inst, Bucharest, Romania, 69-73; res asst pharmacol, McGill Univ, 73-77. *Res:* Action of neuroleptic drugs in preventing delusions and hallucinations in paranoid schizophrenia; blockade of dopamine receptors by neuroleptics; measuring density of dopamine receptors in post-mortem brain tissue from schizophrenics; characterizing the dopamine receptors by polymerate chain reaction cloning, sequencing; identifying of mutations in the sequences of the dopamine receptors. *Mailing Add:* Dept Pharmacol Med Sci Bldg Rm 4344 Univ Toronto Toronto ON M5S 1A8 Can. *E-Mail:* carla.ulpian@utoronto.ca

**ULREY, STEPHEN SCOTT,** INDUSTRIAL ORGANIC CHEMISTRY, MANUFACTURE OF BULK DRUGS. *Current Pos:* DEVELOP CHEMIST, AM CYANAMID CO, 74; RES INVESTR, ABBOTT LABS. *Personal Data:* b Wilmington, Del, July 29, 46; m 69, Sue Buehler; c 2. *Educ:* WVa Univ, BS, 68; Ohio State Univ, PhD(org chem), 73. *Mem:* Am Chem Soc; Sigma Xi. *Res:* Chemical process development; process scale-up and operation. *Mailing Add:* D-54Q Abbott Labs 1401 Sheridan Rd North Chicago IL 60064

**ULRICH, AARON JACK,** NUCLEAR REACTOR PHYSICS. *Current Pos:* asst physicist, Argonne Nat Lab, 50-51, assoc physicist, 51-72, physicist, 72-85, SCIENTIST APPOINTEE, ARGONNE NAT LAB, 86- *Personal Data:* b Benton, Ill, Feb 27, 21; m 54; c 2. *Educ:* Univ Chicago, BS, 43, MS, 50. *Prof Exp:* Instr physics, Univ Chicago, 43-44; jr physicist, Oak Ridge Nat Lab, 44-46. *Mem:* Am Phys Soc; Am Nuclear Soc; Sigma Xi. *Res:* Nuclear fission power reactors, safety test reactor design, planning and analysis of critical experiments and reactor safety tests; energy conversion; plasma physics and thermonuclear power reactors. *Mailing Add:* 1677 Linstead Dr Lexington KY 40504-2008

**ULRICH, BENJAMIN H(ARRISON), JR,** AERONAUTICAL ENGINEERING. *Current Pos:* RETIRED. *Personal Data:* b Olean, NY, Nov 5, 22; m 45; c 3. *Educ:* Pa State Univ, BS, 44, MS, 49. *Prof Exp:* Aeronaut res scientist, Nat Adv Comt Aeronaut, 44 & 46-47; asst prof mech, Pa State Univ, 49-50; educ specialist, US Marine Corps Inst, 50-51; asst prof aeronaut eng, Univ WVa, 51-55, assoc prof aerospace eng, 56-66; prof aerospace eng & eng sci & chmn dept, Parks Col Aeronaut Technol, St Louis Univ, 66-87. *Concurrent Pos:* Stress analyst, NAm Aviation, Inc, 53; flight test engr, Boeing Aircraft Co, 55; ed, Aero Div J, Am Soc Eng Educ, 59-62. *Mem:* Am Soc Eng Educ; Soc Exp Stress Anal; Am Inst Aeronaut & Astronaut. *Res:* Theories of failure and structural loading. *Mailing Add:* 4846 Chapel Hill Rd St Louis MO 63128

**ULRICH, DALE V,** PHYSICS. *Current Pos:* Instr, 58-61, from asst prof to assoc prof, 64-67, PROF PHYSICS & DEAN COL, BRIDGEWATER COL, 85- *Personal Data:* b Wenatchee, Wash, Mar 1, 32; m 53; c 3. *Educ:* La Verne Col, BA, 54; Univ Ore, MS, 56; Univ Va, PhD(physics), 64. *Concurrent Pos:* NSF res grant, 64-68. *Mem:* Am Asn Physics Teachers; Am Phys Soc. *Res:* Partial specific volume studies on biological macromolecules; density studies in the critical region of single component systems. *Mailing Add:* Bridgewater Col Bridgewater VA 22812

**ULRICH, FRANK,** IMMUNOLOGY. *Current Pos:* RETIRED. *Personal Data:* b Frankfurt-am-Main, Ger, Aug 30, 26; nat US; m 57; c 3. *Educ:* Univ Calif, BA, 48, PhD, 52. *Prof Exp:* Jr res endocrinologist, Univ Calif, 52-53; estab investr, Am Heart Asn, 57-62; asst prof, Yale Univ, 62-67; sr res assoc, Grad Sch Nutrit, Cornell Univ, 67-69; assoc prof physiol, Dept Surg, Sch Med, Tufts Univ, 69- *Concurrent Pos:* Brown Mem fel physiol, Sch Med, Yale Univ, 53-54; Nat Cancer Inst fel, 54-56; Arthritis & Rheumatism Found fel, 56-57. *Mem:* Am Soc Cell Biol; Am Physiol Soc; Brit Biochem Soc; Soc Exp Biol Med. *Res:* Ion transport in mitochondria, ions and cell respiration; enzyme kinetics; macrophage physiology. *Mailing Add:* 294 South St Medfield MA 02052

**ULRICH, GAEL DENNIS,** CHEMICAL ENGINEERING. *Current Pos:* from asst prof to assoc prof, 70-81, PROF CHEM ENG, UNIV NH, 82- *Personal Data:* b Devils Slide, Utah, Oct 29, 35; m 58; c 5. *Educ:* Univ Utah, BS, 59, MS, 62; Mass Inst Technol, DSc(chem eng), 64. *Prof Exp:* Sr researcher chem eng, Atomics Int Div, NAm Aviation, 64-65; res engr, Billerica Res Ctr, Cabot Corp, 65-70. *Mem:* Combustion Inst. *Res:* Particle formation in flames; furnace combustion and · incineration; chemical engineering process design. *Mailing Add:* Dept Chem Eng Kingsbury Hall Univ NH Durham NH 03824

**ULRICH, HENRI,** ORGANIC POLYMER CHEMISTRY. *Current Pos:* CONSULT, 88- *Personal Data:* b Rheinsberg, Germany, May 4, 25; nat US; m 54, Franziska Schimitzek; c Stefan, Tomas, Barbara & Bertram. *Educ:* Univ Berlin, dipl, 52, Dr rer nat, 54. *Prof Exp:* Instr org chem, Univ Berlin, 53-54; res assoc, Res Found, Ohio State Univ, 55-59; group leader org res, Carwin Co, 59-62, head org res, Donald S Gilmore Res Lab, 62-65, mgr chem res & develop, 65-76, dir, 76-81, vpres, Donald S Gilmore Res Labs, Upjohn Co, 82-85; dir, NHaven Labs, Dow Chem, USDA, 85-88. *Mem:* AAAS; Am Chem Soc; Soc Ger Chem. *Res:* Isocyanates; polyurethanes; agricultural chemicals; light sensitive chemicals. *Mailing Add:* 180 Durham Rd Guilford CT 06437

**ULRICH, JOHN AUGUST,** MICROBIOLOGY, BACTERIOLOGY. *Current Pos:* RETIRED. *Personal Data:* b St Paul, Minn, May 15, 15; m 40, 86, Mary P Matchovich; c 6. *Educ:* St Thomas Col, BS, 38; Univ Minn, PhD(bact), 47; Am Bd Microbiol, dipl, 63. *Honors & Awards:* Silver Beaver; Bishops Medal. *Prof Exp:* Teacher, High Sch, Minn, 38-41; asst bact, 41-45 & Hormel Inst, 45-46; first asst, Mayo Clin, 49-50, consult, 50-65, assoc prof bact, Mayo Grad Sch Med, Univ Minn, 65-69, assoc prof microbiol, Univ, 66-69; prof microbiol, Med Sch, Univ NMex, 69-84. *Concurrent Pos:* Res fel, Hormel Inst, Univ Minn, 46-49; consult, Econ Labs, Mo, 45, Hormel Packing Plant, Minn, 47-, NIH, 56-, Nat Commun Dis Ctr, 63-, NASA, 65-, Vet Admin, 69-, Sandia Labs, 70- & Midwest Res Inst, 71-, Int Chem Inc, 79, 3M, 80 - *Mem:* AAAS; Am Soc Microbiol; Mycol Soc Am; Am Chem Soc; Am Acad Microbiol; Am Acad Dermat. *Res:* Skin bacteriology; hospital epidemiology; surgery air recirculation; infected wounds; chemotherapy; food preservation; low temperature; bacterial metabolism; medical mycology and bacteriology. *Mailing Add:* 3807 Columbia Dr Longmont CO 80503-2117

**ULRICH, MERWYN GENE,** ZOOLOGY. *Current Pos:* FINANCIAL ADV, AM EXPRESS, 84- *Personal Data:* b Norfolk, Nebr, July 14, 36; m 58. *Educ:* Westmar Col, BA, 58; Univ SDak, MA, 62; Univ Southern Ill, PhD(zool), 66. *Prof Exp:* From asst prof to assoc prof, Westmar Col, 66-74, adj prof biol, 74-76; teacher, North High Sch, Sioux City, Iowa, 76-84. *Concurrent Pos:* Vis prof biol, Silliman Univ, Phillippines, 72-73; aquacult specialist, World Bank Bangkok, Thailand, 74-75. *Mem:* Am Fisheries Soc; Sigma Xi. *Res:* Fisheries management and culture. *Mailing Add:* 816 E Saint Andrews Dakota Dunes SD 57049-5102

**ULRICH, ROGER STEFFEN,** ENVIRONMENTAL PSYCHOLOGY & PSYCHOPHYSIOLOGY, RESEARCH ADMINISTRATION IN ENVIRONMENTAL DESIGN PLANNING & CONSTRUCTION. *Current Pos:* PROF ARCHIT & LANDSCAPE ARCHIT, TEX A&M UNIV, 88-, ASSOC DEAN RES, COL ARCHIT, 88-, CO-DIR, CTR HEALTH SYST & DESIGN, 96- *Personal Data:* b Birmingham, Mich, Feb 20, 46; m 70, Ann-Margret Nilsson; c Kenneth & Michael. *Educ:* Univ Mich, BA, 68, MA, 71, PhD(geog), 73. *Honors & Awards:* Nat Award for

Exemplary Team Leadership in Higher Educ, Am Asn Univ Adminr, 90. *Prof Exp:* From asst prof to assoc prof geog, Univ Del, 74-88. *Concurrent Pos:* Vis prof, Sch Archit, Lund Inst Technol, Sweden, 77-78; vis researcher, Dept Clin Psychol, Uppsala Univ, Sweden, 84-85; bd dirs, Ctr Health Design, 96- *Mem:* Asn Am Geographers; Landscape Res Group; Environ Design Res Asn. *Res:* Effects of viewing natural and built environments on human physiological systems, behavior, stress and health; scientific research on effects of hospital design on patient stress and health outcomes. *Mailing Add:* Col Archit Dean's Off Tex A&M Univ College Station TX 77843-3137. *Fax:* 409-845-4491

**ULRICH, STEPHEN E,** IMMUNOLOGY. *Current Pos:* res assoc, M D Anderson Cancer Ctr, Univ Tex, 83-85, asst immunologist, 85-87, asst prof, 87-93, ASSOC PROF, M D ANDERSON CANCER CTR, UNIV TEX, 93- *Personal Data:* b Mineola, NY, Dec 25, 52; m 82, Ann Turnbach; c Elizabeth B & Kaitlyn A. *Educ:* Georgetown Univ, PhD(microbiol), 79. *Prof Exp:* Staff scientist, Frederick Cancer Res Ctr, 82-83. *Concurrent Pos:* Prin investr, NIH, 86-89 & 91-94, Am Heart Asn, 89-91 & NIH, 95. *Mem:* Am Asn Immunologists; Soc Invest Dermat; Transplantation Soc; Soc Leukocyte Biol; Am Asn Photobiol. *Res:* Examination of the mechanisms involved in modulation of immunity by ultraviolet radiation. *Mailing Add:* Dept Immunol 178 1515 Holcombe Blvd Houston TX 77030. *E-Mail:* sullrich@notes.wdace.tmc.edu

**ULRICH, WERNER,** PATENT LAW, ELECTRICAL ENGINEERING. *Current Pos:* Mem tech staff, AT&T Bell Labs, 53-58, supvr, Switching Syst Develop, 58-64, dept head, 64-68, dir advan switching technol, 68-77, head, Systs Reliability Design Dept, 77-81, mem legal & patent staff, 81-85, PATENT ATTORNEY, AT&T BELL LABS, 85- *Personal Data:* b Munich, Ger, Mar 12, 31; US citizen; m 59, Ursula Wolff; c Greta & Kenneth. *Educ:* Columbia Univ, BS, 52, MS, 53, EngScD(elec eng), 57; Univ Chicago, Grad Sch Bus, MBA, 75; Loyola Univ Sch Law, Chicago, JD, 85. *Concurrent Pos:* Vis lectr, Univ Calif, Berkeley, 66-67. *Mem:* Fel Inst Elec & Electronics Engrs. *Res:* System design and development of program controlled electronic telephone switching systems. *Mailing Add:* AT&T Bell Labs IH2A-407 2000 N Naperville Rd Naperville IL 60566. *Fax:* 630-979-2246

**ULRICH, WILLIAM FREDERICK,** INORGANIC CHEMISTRY, ANALYTICAL CHEMISTRY. *Current Pos:* DIR PROD DEVELOP, SMITHKLINE DIAGS, INC, 86- *Personal Data:* b Pinckneyville, Ill, Nov 4, 26; m 51; c 3. *Educ:* Southern Ill Univ, BS, 49; Univ Ill, PhD, 52. *Prof Exp:* Supvr spectrochem group, Shell Develop Co, 52-56; supvr appln eng, Beckman Instruments, Inc, 55-66, mgr appl res, Sci Instruments Dir, 66-74, mgr clin mkt develop, 74-86. *Mem:* Am Chem Soc; Soc Appl Spectros (treas, 67-69); Spectros Soc Can; Am Asn Clin Chemists. *Res:* Analytical instrumentation, ultraviolet and infrared spectrophotometry; atomic absorption; gas chromatography; electrochemistry; radioimmunoassay; enzyme immunoassay. *Mailing Add:* PO Box 4165 Incline Village NV 89450-4165

**ULRICHSON, DEAN LEROY,** CHEMICAL ENGINEERING. *Current Pos:* res asst chem eng, 69-70, from asst prof to assoc prof, 70-81, PROF CHEM ENG, IOWA STATE UNIV, 81- *Personal Data:* b Alma, Nebr, Mar 6, 37; m 61; c 3. *Educ:* Univ Nebr, Lincoln, BSc, 62; Univ Ill, Urbana, MSc, 63; Iowa State Univ, PhD(chem eng), 70. *Honors & Awards:* Fulbright lectr, 87-88. *Prof Exp:* Res engr, E I du Pont de Nemours & Co, Inc, 63-68. *Mem:* Am Inst Chem Engrs; Am Soc Eng Educ; Nat Soc Prof Engrs. *Res:* Modeling and simulation of chemical processes. *Mailing Add:* 2527 Park Vista Circle Ames IA 50014

**ULRYCH, TADEUSZ JAN,** GEOPHYSICS. *Current Pos:* assoc prof, 68-74, PROF GEOPHYS, UNIV BC, 74- *Personal Data:* b Warsaw, Poland, Aug 9, 35; Can citizen; m 58; c 2. *Educ:* Univ London, BSc, 57; Univ BC, MSc, 61, PhD(geophys), 63. *Prof Exp:* Asst prof geophys, Univ Western Ont, 61-64; Nat Res Coun fel, Oxford Univ, 64-65 & Bernard Price Inst Geophys, 65; asst prof, Univ BC, 65-67; vis prof, Petrobras, Salvador, Brazil, 67-68. *Concurrent Pos:* Consult var cos; lectr var insts & univs. *Mem:* Soc Explor Geophys. *Res:* Applications of communication theory to geophysics and astronomy; inverse theory. *Mailing Add:* Dept Earth & Ocean Sci Univ BC 2219 Main Mall Vancouver BC V6T 1Z4 Can

**ULSAMER, ANDREW GEORGE, JR,** BIOCHEMISTRY, TOXICOLOGY. *Current Pos:* res biochemist, Consumer Prod Safety Comn, 73-75, chief, Biochem Br, 75-80, dir, Div Health Effects, 80-87, ASSOC EXEC DIR HEALTH SCI, CONSUMER PROF SAFETY COMN, 87- *Personal Data:* b Yonkers, NY, Nov 13, 41; m 65; c 3. *Educ:* Siena Col, BS, 63; Albany Med Col, PhD(biochem), 67. *Prof Exp:* USPHS fel, Nat Heart Inst, Md, 67-68, staff fel, 68-70; res biochemist, Div Toxicol, US Food & Drug Admin, 70-73. *Concurrent Pos:* Proj adv group, Food & Drug Admin, Dept Housing & Urban Develop & Nat Inst Drug Abuse. *Mem:* Soc Toxicol; Asn Govt Toxicologist; Sigma Xi. *Res:* Evaluation of the hazards posed by toxic substances found in consumer products, with particular emphasis on indoor air pollutants. *Mailing Add:* 17 S Duke St Rockville MD 20850-1015

**ULSTROM, ROBERT A,** PEDIATRICS, ENDOCRINOLOGY & METABOLISM. *Current Pos:* assoc dean, Med Sch, 76-77, prof, 67-90, EMER PROF PEDIAT, MED SCH, UNIV MINN, MINNEAPOLIS, 90- *Personal Data:* b Minneapolis, Minn, Feb 23, 23; m 46, Mary J McGrath; c Jane (Brissett), Susan (Nierengarten) & Cynthia (Ulstrom). *Educ:* Univ Minn, BS, 44, MD, 46. *Prof Exp:* Intern & resident, Strong Mem Hosp, Rochester, NY, 46-48; from instr to asst prof pediat, Univ Minn, 50-53; asst prof, Univ Calif, Los Angeles, 53-56; from assoc prof to prof, Sch Med, Univ Minn,

56-64; prof & chmn dept, Sch Med, Univ Calif, Los Angeles, 64-67. *Concurrent Pos:* Markle scholar, 54-59; consult, Hennepin Co Gen Hosp, 56-; mem study sect, NIH, 64-68; examr, Am Bd Pediat, 71-, mem bd, 80-86; Pugh fel, Rand Corp, 85-86. *Mem:* AAAS; Soc Pediat Res; Endocrine Soc; Lawson Wilkins Pediat Endocrine Soc; Am Pediat Soc. *Res:* Metabolism of children, particularly the endocrine aspects of the neo-natal period; developmental endocrinology. *Mailing Add:* 4616 Sunset Ridge Minneapolis MN 55416

**ULTEE, CASPER JAN,** MOLECULAR SPECTROSCOPY, PHYSICAL CHEMISTRY. *Current Pos:* RETIRED. *Personal Data:* b Noordwyk, Neth, Apr 5, 28; nat US; m 50, Lorraine M Brower; c John A, Carol A, Linda M & Gary M. *Educ:* Hope Col, BA, 50; Purdue Univ, PhD(chem), 54. *Prof Exp:* Res chemist, Linde Co Div, Union Carbide Corp, 54-60; chemist, Res & Adv Develop Div, Avco Corp, 60-61; sr res scientist, United Aircraft Corp, 61-67, prin scientist, Res Lab, 67-76, mgr chem physics, 76-81, mgr chem physics & combustion sci, United Technol Res Ctr, 81-90. *Concurrent Pos:* Lectr chem, St Joseph Col, West Hartford, Conn. *Mem:* Am Chem Soc. *Res:* Infrared, Raman and electron spin resonance spectroscopy; molecular structure; chemical kinetics; spectroscopy of high temperature arcs; gas phase and chemical lasers. *Mailing Add:* 55 Harvest Lane Glastonbury CT 06033. *E-Mail:* casperu@aol.com

**ULTMAN, JAMES STUART,** CHEMICAL ENGINEERING, BIOMEDICAL ENGINEERING. *Current Pos:* From asst prof to assoc prof, 70-91, PROF CHEM ENG, PA STATE UNIV, UNIVERSITY PARK, 91- *Personal Data:* b Chicago, Ill, Oct 24, 43; m 67, Deena Shur; c Shari, Suzanne & Joanna. *Educ:* Ill Inst Technol, BS, 65; Univ Del, MChE, 67, PhD(chem eng), 69. *Honors & Awards:* Fulbright-Hays lectr, Technion-Israel Inst Technol, 77-78. *Concurrent Pos:* Instr, Univ Del, 69, NIH fel, 69-70; vis res prof, Duke Univ Med Ctr, 89-90. *Mem:* Am Inst Chem Engrs; Biomed Eng Soc. *Res:* Biotransport and phenomena; physiological modelling; respiration physiology; inhalation toxicology; air pollution and human health. *Mailing Add:* Dept Chem Eng 106 Fenske Lab Pa State Univ University Park PA 16802-4400. *Fax:* 814-865-7846; *E-Mail:* jsu@psu.edu

**ULTMANN, JOHN ERNEST,** HEMATOLOGY, ONCOLOGY. *Current Pos:* assoc prof, Cancer Res Ctr, Univ Chicago, 68-70, dean res & develop, 78-88, dir, 73-91, PROF MED, SCH MED, UNIV CHICAGO, 70-, ASSOC DIR, CANCER RES CTR, 91- *Personal Data:* b Vienna, Austria, Jan 6, 25; US citizen; m 52, Ruth Layton; c Monica, Michelle & Barry. *Educ:* Columbia Univ, MD, 52; Am Bd Internal Med, dipl, 60. *Hon Degrees:* MD, Heidelberg Univ, 87, Vienna Univ, 91. *Honors & Awards:* Seventeenth Kretschmer Mem Lectr, 71. *Prof Exp:* Intern, NY Hosp-Cornell Med Ctr, 52-53, asst resident med, 53-54, asst med & resident hemat, 54-55; instr med, Col Physicians & Surgeons, Columbia Univ, 56-61, assoc, 61-62, asst prof, 62-68. *Concurrent Pos:* Nat Cancer Inst trainee, NY Hosp-Cornell Med Ctr, 53-55; Am Cancer Inst Soc fel hemat, Col Physicians & Surgeons, Columbia Univ, 55-56; from asst vis physician to vis physician, Francis Delafield Hosp, 56-68; career scientist, Health Res Coun City New York, 59-68; asst physician, Presby Hosp, 59-65; asst attend physician, 65-68; clin asst vis physician, 1st Med Div, Bellevue Hosp, 61-62, asst vis physician, 63-68; consult, Harlem Hosp, 66-68; hon prof, Cancer Inst Chinese Acad Med Sci, Peoples Repub China, 88; mem, numerous comts & bds, 57- *Mem:* Fel Am Col Physicians; Am Asn Cancer Res; Am Soc Hemat; Am Soc Clin Oncol; Int Soc Hemat; NY Acad Sci; Am Fedn Clin Res; Am Asn Univ Prof; Am Soc Hemat; AAAS; Harvey Soc; Am Soc Clin Oncol; Cent Soc Clin Res. *Res:* Chemotherapy cancer, Hodgkin's disease, lymphoma and leukemia; pathophysiology of anemia of cancer; cancer of unknown primary site. *Mailing Add:* Dept Med & Hematol Univ Chicago Med Ctr 5841 Maryland Ave Chicago IL 60637-1463. *Fax:* 773-702-3163, 9311

**ULUG, ESIN M,** NEURAL NETWORKS & FUZZY LOGIC. *Current Pos:* PRES, INTELLIGENT NEURONS INC, 89- *Personal Data:* US citizen. *Educ:* Univ Durham, BSc, 53, MSc, 64; Carleton Univ, PhD(elec eng), 73. *Prof Exp:* Engr switching equip, Bell Can, 54-56; mgr eng, Can Gen Elec, 56-70; mgr tech develop, subsyst technol, Microsyst Int, 70-72; staff engr spec proj, Bell Can, 72-74; prof syst eng & comput sci, Carleton Univ, 74-78; mgr commun syst, Tex Instruments, 78-80; prog mgr & elec engr, Gen Elec Corp Res & Develop Ctr, 80-89. *Concurrent Pos:* Consult, Bell Can, Telesat Can & Govt Can, 74-78, Tex Instruments, 77-78. *Mem:* Inst Elec & Electronics Engrs. *Res:* Relational databases; local area networks; communication protocols; packet switched networks; artificial intelligence; neural network; fuzzy logic; intelligent decision systems. *Mailing Add:* 1537 E Hillsboro Blvd No 342 Deerfield Beach FL 33441

**ULVEDAL, FRODE,** PHYSIOLOGY, ENDOCRINOLOGY. *Personal Data:* b Oslo, Norway, Nov 20, 32; US citizen; m 57; c 1. *Educ:* St Svithun's Col, Norway, BS, 51; Drew Univ, BA, 55; Emory Univ, PhD(physiol), 59. *Prof Exp:* Chief, Physiol Support Div, Laughlin AFB, Tex, 59-60, aviation physiologist, USAF Scj Aerospace Med, 60-62, chief adv res unit, SMBE, 62-65, chief chem sect, 65-66, chief sealed environ sect & task scientist, 66-68, chief sealed environ br, 68-72; chief pulmonary dis br, Nat Heart & Lung Inst, 72-74; actg dir, Environ Protection Agency, 74-77, 82-84, supvry toxicologist & sr health scientist, Health Effects Div, 77-89. *Concurrent Pos:* Fel, Emory Univ, 66. *Mem:* Am Physiol Soc; Endocrine Soc; Am Col Toxicol. *Res:* Effects of altered atmospheric conditions like altitude and gaseous composition on man and other animals during prolonged exposures in space cabin environments; oxygen toxicity at decreased pressure, especially in regard to endocrinology, hematology and biochemistry; toxicology of environmental pollutants. *Mailing Add:* 17485 Sierra Way Monument CO 80132

**UMAN, MARTIN A(LLAN),** ELECTRICAL ENGINEERING. *Current Pos:* PROF ELEC & COMPUT ENG, UNIV FLA, 71-, CHMN, 91- *Personal Data:* b Tampa, Fla, July 3, 36; m 62, Dorit B Kalbas; c Jon D, Mara A & Derek J. *Educ:* Princeton Univ, BSE, 57, MA, 59, PhD(elec eng), 61. *Honors & Awards:* Group Achievement Award, Project Galileo, NASA, 92 & 96; Heinrich Hertz Metal, Inst Elec & Electronics Engrs, 96. *Prof Exp:* Assoc prof elec eng, Univ Ariz, 61-65; fel scientist, Westinghouse Res Labs, Pa, 65-71. *Mem:* Fel Inst Elec & Electronics Engrs; fel Am Geophys Union; fel Am Meteorol Soc; Int Union Geophys & Geod. *Res:* Lightning physics; lightning protection; electromagnetic field theory. *Mailing Add:* Dept Elec Comput Eng Univ Fla Gainesville FL 32611. *Fax:* 352-392-8671; *E-Mail:* muman@admin.ee.ufl.edu

**UMAN, MYRON F,** ELECTRICAL ENGINEERING, PLASMA PHYSICS. *Current Pos:* staff dir, Environ Studies Bd, 81-86, dir redesign, Space Shuttle Booster Rocket, 86-88, SR STAFF OFFICER, NAT ACAD SCI, 75-; ASST EXEC OFFICER, NAT RES COUN, 90- *Personal Data:* b Tampa, Fla, Oct 13, 39; m 63, Sandra Bloomberg; c Jennifer. *Educ:* Princeton Univ, BSEE, 61, MA, 66, PhD(elec eng), 68; Univ Ill, Urbana, MS, 62. *Honors & Awards:* Pub Serv Award, NASA, 88, Corps of Astronauts Personal Achievement Award, 89. *Prof Exp:* Res asst, Plasma Physics Lab, Princeton Univ, 64-68; asst prof elec eng, Univ Calif, Davis, 68-74; prog mgr, NSF, 74-75. *Concurrent Pos:* Chmn fac, Col Eng, Univ Calif, Davis, 70-71; Am Soc Eng Educ-Ford Found resident fel, E Fishkill Facil, IBM Systs Prods Div, NY, 72-73; Sloan resident fel, Nat Acad Sci, 73-74; spec asst to dir, US Geol Surv, 78; assoc dir, comt on sci, eng & pub policy, Nat Acad Sci, 87-88, dir, comm phys sci, math & resources, 88-90; lectr, George Mason Univ, 89-95; vis fel, Johns Hopkins Univ, 92-94. *Mem:* AAAS; Am Phys Soc; NY Acad Sci; Sigma Xi. *Res:* Applications of science and technology to public policy decision making; environmental, energy and mineral resource policy; acid deposition; engineering and management of aerospace systems; urban infrastructure. *Mailing Add:* 2101 Constitution Ave NW Washington DC 20418

**UMANS, ROBERT SCOTT,** BIOPHYSICAL CHEMISTRY, CELLULAR PHYSIOLOGY. *Current Pos:* ADJ ASSOC PROF CHEM & ASST DIR, UNDERGRAD LABS, BOSTON COL, 93- *Personal Data:* b New York, NY, Dec 17, 41. *Educ:* Columbia Univ, AB, 62; Yale Univ, MS, 63, PhD(chem), 66. *Prof Exp:* Res assoc biophys chem, Johns Hopkins Univ, 66-68, NIH fel, 67-68; res assoc, Inst Biophys & Biochem, Paris, 68-69; Mass Div, Am Cancer Soc res grant, Boston Univ, 71-72, asst prof chem, 69-75; asst prof chem, Boston Col, 76-77; asst prof chem, Wellesley Col, 77-80; res fel cancer biol, 80-83, res assoc, Sch Pub Health, Harvard Univ, 83-86; asst prof chem, Wellesley Col, 86-90; fac in residence, Dept Biochem, Univ NH, 91-93. *Mem:* Am Chem Soc. *Res:* Biochemical studies of the role in cancer causation and treatment of steroid hormones and chemicals. *Mailing Add:* Dept Chem Boston Col Chestnut Hill MA 02167

**UMANZIO, CARL BEEMAN,** MICROBIOLOGY. *Current Pos:* prof bact & parasitol & chmn, Dept Microbiol, 47-74, emer prof, 74-93, DISTINGUISHED EMER PROF MICROBIOL, KIRKSVILLE COL OSTEOP MED, 93- *Personal Data:* b Thompsonville, Conn, Apr 9, 07; m 29; c 1. *Educ:* Univ Boston, AM, 35; Wash Univ, St Louis, PhD, 50. *Prof Exp:* Asst med mycol, Sch Med, Univ Boston, 34-35; educ adv, Civilian Conserv Corps, 35-37; teacher, high sch, Mass, 37-39; mem staff pharm, Franklin Tech Inst, 39-47. *Concurrent Pos:* Mem staff pharm, Cambridge Jr Col, 42-47; consult, Microbiol & Allergic Dis, 47- *Mem:* Sigma Xi; Am Soc Microbiol; Mycol Soc Am; Am Soc Trop Med & Hyg; Nat Asn Biol Teachers. *Res:* Various publications, principally on parasitology, medical mycology, allergy and antibiotic hypersensitivity; parasitology; hypersensitivity; antibiotics. *Mailing Add:* 6647 El Colegio Rd Goleta CA 93117-4200

**UMBARGER, H EDWIN,** BIOCHEMISTRY. *Current Pos:* prof biol, 64-70, Wright distinguished prof, 70-92, WRIGHT DISTINGUISHED EMER PROF BIOL SCI, PURDUE UNIV, 92- *Personal Data:* b Shelby, Ohio, July 17, 21. *Educ:* Ohio Univ, BS, 43, MS, 44; Harvard Univ, PhD(bact), 50. *Prof Exp:* Instr bact & immunol, Harvard Med Sch, 50-53, from assoc to Silas Arnold Houghten asst prof, 53-60; staff investr, Biol Lab, Long Island Biol Asn, 60-64. *Concurrent Pos:* Guggenheim mem fel, Dept Biochem, Univ Leicester, Eng, 63-64; chmn, Div Microbiol Physiol, Am Soc Microbiol, 67-68; ed, J Bacteriol, 71-76. *Mem:* Nat Acad Sci; Am Chem Soc; Soc Am Bacteriologists; Am Soc Biol Chemists; Sigma Xi; Am Acad Arts & Sci. *Res:* Author of numerous publications. *Mailing Add:* Biol Sci Dept Purdue Univ West Lafayette IN 47907

**UMBERGER, ERNEST JOY,** PHARMACOLOGY, ENDOCRINOLOGY. *Current Pos:* RETIRED. *Personal Data:* b Burke, SDak, Aug 5, 09; m 32; c 3. *Educ:* George Washington Univ, BS, 37, MA, 41; Georgetown Univ, PhD(biochem), 48. *Prof Exp:* Asst sci aide fermentation sect, Bur Agr Chem & Eng, USDA, 37-39; jr chemist, Div Allergen Invests, 39-42, asst chemist, Naval Stores Res Div, 42-43; asst chemist, Div Pharmacol, US Food & Drug Admin, 43-44, pharmacologist, 44-47, chief endocrine sect, Drug Pharmacol Br, 57-67, chief, Drug Analysis Br, Div Pharmaceut Sci, Bur Sci Consumer Protection & Environ Health Serv, 67-70, dir, Div Drug Biol, Off Pharmaceut Res & Testing, Bur Drugs, 70-71. *Concurrent Pos:* Consult endocrinol & pharmacol, 71-75. *Mem:* Emer mem Am Chem Soc; Soc Exp Biol & Med; emer mem Endocrine Soc. *Res:* Fermentation; chemistry of allergenic proteins; rosin esters; absorption of calomel from ointments; bioassay of estrogens; androgens, gonadotropins and adrenocorticotropic hormone; metabolism of steroid hormones; central nervous systems endocrine relationships. *Mailing Add:* 9527 Veirs Dr Apt 3 Rockville MD 20850

**UMBREIT, GERALD ROSS,** ORGANIC CHEMICAL ANALYSIS, GAS CHROMATOGRAPHY. *Current Pos:* PRES, GREENWOOD LABS, 66- *Personal Data:* b Minneapolis, Minn, June 17, 30; m 53, Patricia R Dahl; c Kaytee L, Timothy D & Steven T. *Educ:* Augustana Col, SDak, BA, 54; Iowa State Univ, PhD(analytical chem), 57. *Honors & Awards:* Del Valley Chromatography Forum Award, 85. *Prof Exp:* Res asst, Ames Lab, AEC, Iowa, 54-57; res assoc, Upjohn Co, Mich, 58-63; res scientist, Lockheed Missiles & Space Co, Calif, 63-64; appln lab mgr, F&M Sci Div, Hewlett-Packard Co, Pa, 64-66. *Mem:* Am Chem Soc. *Res:* Chromatography; ion exchange; analytical method development; consulting; infrared spectrophotometry. *Mailing Add:* Greenwood Labs 903 E Baltimore Pike Kennett Square PA 19348. *Fax:* 610-388-7295

**UMBREIT, THOMAS HAYDEN,** ENVIRONMENTAL HEALTH-RISK ASSESSMENT, MEDICAL DEVICES. *Current Pos:* TOXICOLOGIST, CTR DEVICES, US FOOD & DRUG ADMIN, 94- *Personal Data:* b Rochester, NY, Feb 15, 47. *Educ:* Duke Univ, AB, 69; Univ Del, MS, 74; Univ Wis-Madison, PhD(bact), 77. *Prof Exp:* Fel, Waksman Inst Microbiol, Rutgers Univ, 77-79 & Sch Pharm, 81-83; res assoc, Dept Biol, Univ NMex, 80; vis assoc prof microbiol, Bowling Green State Univ, 80; sr res assoc toxicol, Univ Med Dent NJ, Robert W Johnson Med Sch, 83-85, asst prof, 85-90; sr toxicologist, Agency Toxic Substances, 91-94. *Mem:* Soc Toxicol; Am Soc Pharm & Exp Therapeut; Sigma Xi. *Res:* Mechanism of action, testing and research of dioxins; evaluation of toxic contamination sites; physiological effects and models of medical devices; risk assessment; estrogenic effects and endocrine disruptors. *Mailing Add:* CDRH-FDA-HFZ-112 12709 Twinbrook Pkwy Rockville MD 20857

**UMBREIT, WAYNE WILLIAM,** BACTERIOLOGY, BIOCHEMISTRY. *Current Pos:* RETIRED. *Personal Data:* b Marksan, Wis, May 1, 13; m 37; c 3. *Educ:* Univ Wis, BA, 34, MS, 36, PhD(bact, biochem), 39. *Honors & Awards:* Lilly Award, 47; Waksman Award, 57; Carski Award, 68. *Prof Exp:* Asst bact & biochem, Univ Wis, 34-37, instr bact & chem, 38-41, asst prof bact, 41-44; instr soil microbiol, Rutgers Univ, 37-38; assoc prof bact, Cornell Univ, 44-46, prof, 46-47; head, Enzyme Chem Dept, Merck Inst Therapeut Res, 47-56, assoc dir, 56-58; prof bact & head dept, Rutgers Univ, 58-75; S Br Watershed Asn, 75-90. *Mem:* AAAS; Am Soc Microbiol; Am Chem Soc; Am Soc Biol Chem; fel Am Acad Microbiol (vpres, 60). *Res:* Mode of action of antibiotics; nature of autotrophic bacteria; transformations of morphine by microorganisms. *Mailing Add:* 826 Covered Bridge Holland PA 18966

**UMEDA, PATRICK KAICHI,** MUSCLE DEVELOPMENT CARDIAC HYPERTROPHY. *Current Pos:* ASST PROF MED, UNIV CHICAGO, 82- *Educ:* Univ Chicago, PhD(biochem), 80. *Mailing Add:* Dept Med/Cardiol Univ Ala 703 S 19th St Ziegler Rm 302 Birmingham AL 35294-0007

**UMEN, MICHAEL JAY,** GENERAL MEDICAL SCIENCES, IMMUNOLOGY. *Current Pos:* INDEPENDENT CONSULT, MICHAEL UMEN & CO INC, 81- *Personal Data:* b Jamaica, NY, Feb 10, 48; m 69; c 3. *Educ:* Queens Col, BA, 69; Mass Inst Technol, PhD(org chem), 73. *Prof Exp:* Res scientist, sr scientist org med chem, Johnson & Johnson, 74-77, mgr, Res Info Serv Dept, McNeil Pharmaceut, 77-80, dir, 80-81. *Mem:* Am Chem Soc; Proprietary Asn; Am Med Writers Asn; Drug Info Asn. *Res:* Pharmaceutical and medical device development; preparation of regulatory documents, literature reviews, publication manuscripts and technology assessments; evaluation of new product and licensing opportunities; coordination of preclinical and clinical scientists; management consulting; regulatory affairs. *Mailing Add:* PO Box 885 Glenside PA 19038-2012

**UMEZAWA, HIROOMI,** theoretical physics, solid state physics; deceased, see previous edition for last biography

**UMHOLTZ, CLYDE ALLAN,** ARTIFICIAL INTELLIGENCE, INDUSTRIAL ENGINEERING. *Current Pos:* DEP ADMIN, DATA PROCESSING SYSTS, SHELBY CO GOVT, 84-, SPEC ASST, CO EXEC TECHNOL ASSESSMENT, 92- *Personal Data:* b Du Quoin, Ill, Dec 20, 47. *Educ:* Univ Ill, BS, 69; MBA, 71; Univ Melbourne, DSc, 75. *Hon Degrees:* Dr, Univ Memphis, 95. *Honors & Awards:* Pioneer Info Syst Award, Am Inst Elec Engrs, 96; Cotton Medal, Am Chem Soc, 96. *Prof Exp:* Eng planning analyst, Chem Mfg Group, W R Grace & Co & Subsidiaries, 75-78; mgr, Res Serv, Ctr Indust Consult, Memphis State Univ, 78-84. *Concurrent Pos:* Consult var comput energy, chem & nuclear industs, 77-; vis lectr, Eng Sch, var univs, 79-; adj prof, Memphis State Univ, 80-; partner, Custom Data Systs Inc, Memphis, Tenn, 87- & Western Technol Inc, 88-; adj prof, Univ Tenn, Memphis, 85-; bd dirs, Am Tech Inst, Memphis, 89- *Mem:* Nat Acad Sci; Am Chem Soc; Data Processing Mgt Asn; Am Inst Mfg Engrs; Am Inst Chem Engrs; NY Acad Sci; fel Southern Acad Sci. *Res:* Angle trisector; energy considerations of Haber cycle; comprehensive engineering and economic studies of the sulfur, sulfuric acid and phosphate manufacturing industries; cost and materials science studies for the nuclear industry; structured methodology in the development of artificial intelligence systems; distillation with vapor recompression; prototyping in development of computerized financial systems; context analysis in system design; computer aided software systems for engineering analysis and design methodologies; computerized strategic planning models for business and technology assessment. *Mailing Add:* 3580 Hanna Dr Memphis TN 38128

**UMIEL, TEHILA,** CANCER RESEARCH, HEMATOLOGY. *Current Pos:* RES SCIENTIST, CEDARS-SINAI MED CTR, 92-; ASSOC RESEARCHER, UNIV CALIF, LOS ANGELES, 92- *Personal Data:* b Budapest, Hungary, Sept 4, 42. *Educ:* Univ Wis, MSc, 68, PhD(zool), 71. *Prof*

*Exp:* Fel, Univ Wis, 71-72; res scientist, Weizmann Inst Sci, 72-78, sr scientist, 78-81; head, Res Lab, Beilinson Med Ctr, 83-91. *Concurrent Pos:* Vis scientist, Dana-Farber Cancer Inst, 81-82, Ger Cancer Res Ctr, 88-89 & Children's Hosp Los Angeles, 90-92; prin investr, Israel Cancer Asn, 84-87, Israel Cancer Res Fund, 88-89, Children Cancer Res Fund, 91-92 & Concern II Found, 92-93; sr lectr, Tel-Aviv Univ, 86-92. *Mem:* Am Asn Immunologists; Am Soc Hemat; AAAS. *Res:* Functional analysis of T cell antogeny; used program cell death to kill cancer cells; developed therapeutic models for leukemia in scid mice; regulation of genes involved in T and B Cell differentiation and in apoptosis. *Mailing Add:* Dept Pediat R4310 Cedars-Sinai Med Ctr 8700 Beverly Blvd Los Angeles CA 90048-0750. *Fax:* 310-659-0491

**UMLAND, SHELBY PRICE,** ALLERGY. *Current Pos:* SECT LEADER, SCHERING PLOUGH RES INST, KENILWORTH, NJ, 92- *Personal Data:* b Orange, NJ, Dec 24, 50. *Educ:* Gettysburg Col, BA, 72; Seton Hall Univ, MS, 79; Rutgers Univ, PhD(immunol), 86. *Prof Exp:* Fel, DNAX Res Inst, 86-88. *Mem:* Am Soc Microbiologists; Soc Leukocyte Biol; AAAS. *Res:* Allergy research. *Mailing Add:* Dept Immunol M5 K15 1700 Schering-Plough Res Inst 205 Galloping Hill Rd Kenilworth NJ 07033-0539. *Fax:* 908-298-7175

**UMLAUF, MARY GRACE,** OLDER ADULT POPULATIONS, NURSING. *Current Pos:* ASSOC PROF, GRAD PROG, SCH NURSING, UNIV ALA, 94- *Educ:* Univ Tex, Ba, 70, BSN, 79, PhD(nursing), 88; Tex Woman's Univ, MS, 83. *Prof Exp:* staff nurse nephrology & orthop, Brackenridge Hosp, Tex, 79-80; hemodialysis charge nurse, Austin Diag Clin & Renal Out-Patient Clin, 80-81; staff nurse, Gen Med & Pulmonary Serv, Vet Admin Med Ctr, 81-85, assoc chief, Nursing Serv Educ, 85-88; Pub Health Serv prog coordr, Sch Nursing, Tex Tech Univ Health Sci Ctr, 88-91, from asst prof to assoc prof, 88-93, dir res & develop, 90-93. *Concurrent Pos:* Scientist, Ctr Aging, Univ Ala, Birmingham, 94-; Fulbright scholar, Sch Nursing, Jordan Univ Sci & Technol, 95-97; grantee, Nat Inst Diabetes Digestive & Kidney Dis & Nat Inst Aging, 95- *Mem:* Geront Soc Am; Am Asn Univ Women; Soc Urol Nurses & Assocs. *Res:* Older adult populations; urinary incontinence; nocturnal bladder control; obstructive sleep apnea and falls; author of several publications. *Mailing Add:* Univ Ala University Sta Birmingham AL 35294

**UMMINGER, BRUCE LYNN,** INTEGRATIVE BIOLOGY, COMPARATIVE PHYSIOLOGY. *Current Pos:* dir, Regulatory Biol Prog, NSF, 79-84, dep dir, Div Cellular Biosci, 84-89, dir, 89-91, DIR, DIV INTEGRATIVE BIOL & NEUROSCI, NSF, 91- *Personal Data:* b Dayton, Ohio, Apr 10, 41; m 66, Judith Bryant; c Alison & April. *Educ:* Yale Univ, BS, 63, MS, 66, MPhil, 68, PhD(biol), 69. *Honors & Awards:* Sigma Xi Distinguished Res Award, 73. *Prof Exp:* From asst prof to prof biol sci, Univ Cincinnati, 69-81, actg head dept, 73-75, admin intern, Off Develop, 74-75, fel, Grad Sch, 77-81, dir grad affairs biol sci, 78-79. *Concurrent Pos:* Trainee, NASA, 64-67 & NSF, 67-69; NSF fel, 64 & NSF grant, Univ Cincinnati, 71-79; assoc ed, J Exp Zool, 77-79; mem, NSF rev panels, US-India Exchange Scholars Prog, 79-81, US-India Coop Res Prog, 81-82; chmn, Cong Sci Fel Prog Comt, Am Soc Zoologists, 86-89, mem, 91; exec secy, Nat Sci Bd Comt Ctr & Individual Investr, 86-88; chairperson, Sect G-Biol Sci, AAAS, 88-89, steering group, Sect Comt G, 87-90; mem, Group, Nat Experts on Safety in Biotechnol, Organ Econ Coop & Develop, 88-89, panel Study Biol Diversity, Bd Sci & Technol in Int Develop, Nat Res Coun, 89, planning comt NIH Develop Conf Modeling Biomed Res, 88-89, working group, Int Biotechnol, 88-94; sr adv health policy, Off Int Health Policy, Dept State, 88; chmn, Cell & Develop Biol Discipline Working Group, Space Biol Prog, NASA, 90-91, Gravitational Biol Panel, NASA Specialized Ctrs Res & Training, 90-; sr adv biodiversity, Smithsonian Inst, 93-94. *Mem:* Fel AAAS; Am Physiol Soc; Am Soc Zoologists (secy, 79-81); fel NY Acad Sci; Am Inst Biol Sci; Sigma Xi. *Res:* Research administration of programs in integrative biology and neuroscience; comparative physiology, biochemistry and endocrinology of fish; low temperature biology. *Mailing Add:* Div Integrative Biol & Neuosci 4201 Wilson Blvd Arlington VA 22230-0001. *Fax:* 703-306-0349; *E-Mail:* bumminge@nsf.gov

**UN, CHONG KWAN,** DIGITAL COMMUNICATIONS, DIGITAL SIGNAL PROCESSING. *Current Pos:* dean eng, 81-82, PROF ELEC ENG, KOREA ADVAN INST SCI & TECHNOL, 77-; DIR, CTR SPEECH INFO RES, 90- *Personal Data:* b Seoul, Korea, Aug 25, 40; US citizen; m 66, Sung J Kim; c Jean, Sue & Jung. *Educ:* Univ Del, BSEE, 64, MSEE, 66, PhD(elec eng), 69. *Honors & Awards:* Nat Hon Merit, Govt Korea, 82. *Prof Exp:* Asst prof elec eng, Univ Maine, 69-73; mem tech staff, SRI Int, 73-77. *Concurrent Pos:* Consult, Gold Star Elec Co, 77-87 & Digicom Inst Telematics, 87-; adv, Ministry Commun, Korea, 82-90 & Korea Inst Defense Analysis, 85- *Mem:* Fel Inst Elec & Electronics Engrs; NY Acad Sci; Korea Inst Telematics & Electronics; Korea Inst Commun Sci; Acoust Soc Korea. *Res:* Speech coding and processing; speech recognition and synthesis; adaptive filtering and signal processing; packet switching; voice-data integration; broadband integrated ser digital network. *Mailing Add:* Dept Elec Eng Korea Adv Inst Sci & Technol 73-1 Kusong-Dong Yusong-Ku Taejon 305-701 South Korea. *Fax:* 82-42-869-8520; *E-Mail:* chun@eehaist.kajst.ac.kr

**UN, HOWARD HO-WEI,** ORGANIC POLYMER CHEMISTRY. *Current Pos:* develop mgr, Fluoropolymers, 82-84, develop mgr, 84-86, BUS DEVELOP MGR, ASIA-PAC WIRE & CABLE, 86- *Personal Data:* b Hong Kong, June 8, 38; m 67; c 2. *Educ:* Beloit Col, BS, 60; Univ Mich, MSCh, 63, PhD(org chem), 65. *Prof Exp:* Res chemist, Exp Sta Lab, E I du Pont de Nemours & Co, Inc, 65-69, tech rep, Chestnut Run Lab, 69-71, tech rep, Fluorocarbons Mkt, 71-74, mkt rep, fluorocarbons sales, 74-76, sr mkt rep, 76-77, supvr & prod coord, Bus Servs Div, Plastic Prods & Resins Dept, 77-79, export mkt mgr, Int Mkt, Polymer Prod Dept, 79-82. *Mem:* Am Chem Soc. *Res:* Fluorocarbon chemistry and polymers; thermally stable polymers; wire and cable materials. *Mailing Add:* 3314 S Rockfield Dr Devon Wilmington DE 19810-3234

**UNAKAR, NALIN J,** CELL BIOLOGY. *Current Pos:* from asst prof to assoc prof, Oakland Univ, 69-74, prof & chmn dept, 74-87, PROF, DEPT BIOL SCI, OAKLAND UNIV, 74-, ADJ PROF BIOMED SCI, 83- *Personal Data:* b Karachi, Pakistan, Mar 26, 35; m 62, Nita; c Rita & Rupa. *Educ:* Gujarat Univ, India, BSc, 55; Univ Bombay, MSc, 61; Brown Univ, PhD(biol), 65. *Prof Exp:* Res asst biol, Indian Cancer Res Ctr, 55-61; res assoc path, Univ Toronto, 65-66. *Concurrent Pos:* Nat Cancer Inst Can fel, 65-66; NIH res grant, 71-; mem visual sci A study sect, NIH, 82-86; adj prof biol sci, Wayne State Univ Sch Med, 83- *Mem:* AAAS; Am Soc Cell Biol; Asn Res Vision & Opthal; Int Soc Eye Res. *Res:* Cell ultrastructure and function; control of cell division; human and experimental cataracts; wound healing. *Mailing Add:* Dept Biol Sci Oakland Univ Rochester MI 48309

**UNAL, AYNUR,** nonlinear acoustics, nonlinear dynamical systems, for more information see previous edition

**UNANGST, PAUL CHARLES,** MEDICINAL CHEMISTRY. *Current Pos:* SR RES ASSOC, WARNER-LAMBERT CO, 73- *Personal Data:* b Fountain Hill, Pa, Apr 19, 44; m 69, Fredda L Simon; c Marc J & Daniel S. *Educ:* Lehigh Univ, BS, 65; Carnegie-Mellon Univ, MS, 68, PhD(org chem), 70. *Prof Exp:* Res chemist, Ozone Systs Div, Welsbach Corp, 70-72; assoc chem, Lehigh Univ, 72-73. *Mem:* Am Chem Soc. *Res:* Medicinal chemistry; heterocycles; antiallergy and antiinflammatory agents. *Mailing Add:* Warner-Lambert/Parke-Davis 2800 Plymouth Rd Ann Arbor MI 48105. *Fax:* 313-996-5229

**UNANUE, EMIL R,** IMMUNOLOGY. *Current Pos:* MALLINCKRODT PROF & CHMN, DEPT PATH, SCH MED, WASHINGTON UNIV, ST LOUIS, MO, 85- *Personal Data:* b Havana, Cuba, Sept 13, 34; m 65; c 3. *Educ:* Inst Sec Educ, BSc, 52; Univ Havana, MD, 60. *Hon Degrees:* MA, Harvard Univ, 74. *Honors & Awards:* T Duckett Jones Award, Helen Hay Whitney Found, 68; Parke-Davis Award, Am Soc Exp Path, 73; Ecker Lectr, Western Res Univ, 79; D Allan Harmon Lectr, Okla Med Res Found, 85; Henry Kunkel Lectr, Johns Hopkins Univ, 85; Gerald Rodnan Lectr, Am Rheumatism Asn, 86; Albert H Coons Lectr, Harvard Med Sch, 88; William B Coley Award, Cancer Res Inst, 89; Gustave Dammin Lectr, Brigham & Women's Hosp, 91; Sidney Leskowitz Mem Lect, Tufts Univ & Swerling Lect, Dana-Farber Cancer Ctr, 92; Swerling Lect, Dana-Farber Cancer Ctr, 92; Baruy Benacenaf Lectr, Harvard Med Sch, 94; J S & H R Blumenthal Mem Lectr, Univ Minn, 95. *Prof Exp:* Intern path, Presby Univ Hosp, Pittsburgh, Pa, 61-62; res fel exp path, Scripps Clin & Res Found, 62-66, assoc, 68-70; res fel, Immunol Div, Nat Inst Med Res, London, Eng, 66-68; from asst prof to assoc prof path, Harvard Med Sch, 70-74, Mallinckrodt prof immunopath, 74-84. *Concurrent Pos:* Prof path, Harvard Med Sch; mem, Path A Study Sect, NIH, 73-77, Allergy & Immunol Res Comt, 80-85; consult path, Brigham & Women's Hosp, Boston, Mass, 77-84; Guggenheim fel, Biol Labs, Harvard Univ, 80-81; vis prof, Sch Med, Kuwait Univ, 82 & Royal Postgrad Med Sch, London Eng, 83; mem, Nat Sci Adv Coun, Nat Jewish Ctr Immunol & Respiratory Med, Denver, Colo, 85-86; counr, Am Asn Pathologist, Inc, 85-88, pres, 88-89; pathologist-in-chief, Barnes & Allied Hosps & St Louis Children's Hosp, 85-; sci adv bd, Harold C Simmons Arthritis Res Ctr, 87-; bd dirs, Barnes Hosp, 89-91; assoc ed, Immunity, 94-, ed, 96- *Mem:* Nat Acad Sci; Inst Med-Nat Acad Sci; Am Asn Immunologists; Brit Soc Immunol; Reticuloendothelial Soc; Am Soc Cell Biol; fel Am Cancer Soc; fel Am Acad Arts & Sci; hon mem Venezuelan Soc Allergy & Immunol; Am Asn Path. *Res:* Cellular basis of the immune response; regulatory mechanisms in immunity. *Mailing Add:* Dept Path Sch Med Washington Univ 660 S Euclid PO Box 8188 St Louis MO 63110

**UNBEHAUN, LARAINE MARIE,** PLANT PATHOLOGY. *Current Pos:* asst prof, 69-71, assoc prof, 71-80, PROF BIOL, UNIV WIS-LA CROSSE, 80- *Personal Data:* b Kearney, Nebr, May 4, 40; m 65. *Educ:* Kearney State Col, BAEd, 61; Univ Northern Colo, MA, 64; Va Polytech Inst & State Univ, PhD(plant path), 69. *Prof Exp:* Teaching assoc biol, Univ Colo, Boulder, 64-65. *Concurrent Pos:* Dir, Gen Honors Prog, Univ Wis, La Crosse, 86- *Mem:* Am Phytopath Soc; Sigma Xi. *Res:* Pectic enzyme production by Thielaviopsis basicola grown on synthetic and natural media; enzyme purification; characterization of pectic enzymes produced in black root rot diseased tobacco. *Mailing Add:* Dept Biol Cowley Hall Univ Wis-La Crosse La Crosse WI 54601

**UNDEEN, ALBERT HAROLD,** BIOLOGICAL CONTROL OF BITING FLIES, TRIGGERING MECHANISMS FOR FAST BIOLOGICAL REACTIONS. *Current Pos:* RES ENTOMOLOGIST, USDA AGR RES SERV, 80- *Personal Data:* b San Francisco, Calif, Oct 8, 37; m 85, Veda M Leap; c Gregory A, Sharon M, Mark A, Donald H & Ryan D. *Educ:* Western Wash State Col, BA, 66; Univ Ill, Urbana, MS, 69, PhD(zool), 73. *Prof Exp:* Res assoc parasitol, Univ Ill, Urbana, 73-75; dep dir, Res Unit Vector Path, Mem Univ Nfld, St Johns, Can, 76-80. *Concurrent Pos:* Adj assoc prof, Univ Fla, Gainesville, 81- *Mem:* Soc Invert Path; Sigma Xi; Soc Protozool; Am Mosquito Control Asn. *Res:* Mechanism of germination of microsporidian spores; practical goal oriented studies on the potential of insect pathogens for biological control of mosquitoes. *Mailing Add:* 2635 SW 35th Pl Apt 1206 Gainesville FL 32608-3257. *Fax:* 352-374-5922; *E-Mail:* auh@gnv.ifas.ufl.edu

**UNDEM, BRADLEY J,** PHARMACOLOGY. *Current Pos:* Asst prof, 87-91, ASSOC PROF MED, ASTHMA & ALLERGY CTR, JOHNS HOPKINS UNIV, 91- *Personal Data:* b Sock Center, Minn, Oct 19, 56. *Educ:* NDak State Univ, BS, 79; Univ Wis, MS, 82, PhD(pharmacol), 87. *Mem:* Am Phys Soc; Am Soc Pharmacol & Exp Therapeut. *Mailing Add:* Asthma & Allergy Ctr Johns Hopkins Univ 301 Bayview Blvd Unit Ofc 3 Baltimore MD 21224-6801

**UNDERDAHL, NORMAN RUSSELL,** BACTERIOLOGY, VIROLOGY. *Current Pos:* RETIRED. *Personal Data:* b Minn, June 5, 18; m 48; c 1. *Educ:* St Olaf Col, BA, 41; Univ Minn, MS, 48. *Prof Exp:* Asst scientist, Hormel Inst, Univ Minn, 46-55; from asst prof to prof vet sci, Univ Nebr, Lincoln, 55-85. *Concurrent Pos:* Mem, Conf Res Workers Animal Dis. *Mem:* Assoc Am Vet Med Asn; Asn Gnotobiotics; Am Soc Microbiol. *Res:* Elimination of swine diseases by repopulation with disease-free pigs; isolation of causative agents of swine diseases using antibody-devoid, disease-free pig, obtained by surgery, as the host animal. *Mailing Add:* 935 N 67th St Lincoln NE 68505

**UNDERDOWN, BRIAN JAMES,** IMMUNOLOGY. *Current Pos:* ASSOC DEAN RES, FAC HEALTH SCI, MCMASTER UNIV. *Personal Data:* b Montreal, Que, Mar 23, 41; m 65; c 5. *Educ:* McGill Univ, BSc, 64, PhD(immunol), 68. *Prof Exp:* Med Res Coun Can fel, Sch Med, Washington Univ, 68-70; prof med & grad secy, Inst Immunol, Univ Toronto, 70- *Mem:* Can Soc Immunol. *Res:* Studies of the IgA immune response; studies of the structure of antibody molecules. *Mailing Add:* 1755 Steeles Ave W North York ON M2R 3T4 Can

**UNDERHILL, ANNE BARBARA,** ASTROPHYSICS, HOT MASSIVE STARS. *Current Pos:* HON PROF, DEPT PHYSICS & ASTRON, UNIV BC, 85- *Personal Data:* b Vancouver, BC, June 12, 20. *Educ:* Univ BC, BA, 42, MA, 44; Univ Chicago, PhD(astrophys), 48. *Hon Degrees:* DSc, York Univ, 69, Univ BC, 92. *Prof Exp:* Nat Res Coun Can fel, Copenhagen Observ, 48-49; astrophysicist, Dom Astrophys Observ, 49-62; prof astrophys, State Univ Utrecht, 62-70; chief, Lab Optical Astron, Goddard Space Flight Ctr, NASA, 70-77; sr scientist, Astron & Solar Physics Lab, 77-85. *Concurrent Pos:* Vis lectr, Harvard Univ, 55-56; vis prof, Univ Colo, 67; Inst Astrophys, Paris, 78-79. *Mem:* Am Astron Soc; Astron Soc Pac; Royal Astron Soc Can; Royal Astron Union; Int Astron Union; fel Royal Soc Can, Acad III; Can Astron Soc. *Res:* Atmospheres of hot stars; Wolf-Rayet stars; model atmospheres; ultraviolet spectra of stars. *Mailing Add:* 4696 W Tenth Ave No 301 Vancouver BC V6R 2J5 Can. *Fax:* 604-822-6047

**UNDERHILL, EDWARD WESLEY,** PLANT BIOCHEMISTRY. *Current Pos:* RETIRED. *Personal Data:* b Regina, Sask, Jan 28, 31; m 54; c 3. *Educ:* Univ Sask, BScP, 54, MSc, 56; Univ RI, PhD(pharmacog), 60. *Prof Exp:* Lectr pharm, Univ Sask, 54-55, asst prof, 60-61; from asst res off to assoc res off, Nat Res Coun Can, 61-74, sr res off, 74-91. *Mem:* Am Entomicer Soc; Can Entomicer Soc. *Res:* Isolation and characterization of insect sex pheromones and attractants, paricularly of Lepidoptera; application of sex pheromones for monitoring and controlling insect populations; studies on plant-insect interaction, particularly plant derived semiochemical affecting insect behavior. *Mailing Add:* 1000 Park Blvd Apt 102 Victoria BC V8V 2T4 Can

**UNDERHILL, GLENN,** THEORETICAL PHYSICS, ASTRONOMY. *Current Pos:* assoc prof, 63-68, PROF PHYSICS, KEARNEY STATE COL, 68-, HEAD DEPT PHYSICS & PHYS SCI, 71- *Personal Data:* b Trenton, Nebr, Oct 30, 25; m 58; c 5. *Educ:* Nebr State Col, BS, 55; Univ Nebr, MA, 57, PhD(physics), 63. *Prof Exp:* Instr physics, Univ Nebr, 59-61. *Mem:* Am Phys Soc; Am Asn Physics Teachers; Am Sci Affiliation; Sigma Xi. *Res:* Structure of beryllium-9 nucleus; interaction of radiation with matter. *Mailing Add:* PO Box 70 Riverdale NE 68870-0070

**UNDERHILL, JAMES CAMPBELL,** ZOOLOGY. *Current Pos:* from asst prof to assoc prof, 59-69, coordr gen zool prog, 70-77, PROF ZOOL & BEHAV BIOL, UNIV MINN, MINNEAPOLIS, 69- *Personal Data:* b Duluth, Minn, June 8, 23; m 43; c 3. *Educ:* Univ Minn, BA, 49, MA, 52, PhD(zool), 55. *Prof Exp:* From asst prof to assoc prof zool, Univ SDak, 55-59. *Mem:* Am Soc Ichthyol & Herpet; Ecol Soc Am; Soc Study Evolution; Am Fisheries Soc; Am Soc Limnol & Oceanog; Sigma Xi. *Res:* Ecology of minnows and darters; variation in fishes; aquatic ecology. *Mailing Add:* 1262 Raymond Ave St Paul MN 55108

**UNDERKOFLER, WILLIAM LELAND,** ANALYTICAL CHEMISTRY. *Current Pos:* Staff chemist, 63-71, ADV CHEMIST, IBM CORP, 71- *Personal Data:* b Ames, Iowa, Nov 10, 36; m 61; c 3. *Educ:* Iowa State Univ, BS, 58; Univ Wis, PhD(analytical chem), 64. *Mem:* Am Chem Soc. *Res:* Electrochemistry; electrochemical analysis; electroplating; general chemical analysis. *Mailing Add:* 340 Raylene Dr Vestal NY 13850

**UNDERWOOD, ARTHUR LOUIS, JR,** biochemistry; deceased, see previous edition for last biography

**UNDERWOOD, BARBARA ANN,** NUTRITION, BIOCHEMISTRY. *Current Pos:* spec asst, Nutrit Res & Int Progs, 82-89, ASST DIR INT PROGS, NAT EYE INST, NIH, 89- *Personal Data:* b Santa Ana, Calif, Aug 24, 34. *Educ:* Univ Calif, Santa Barbara, BA, 56; Cornell Univ, MS, 58; Columbia Univ, PhD(nutrit biochem), 62. *Prof Exp:* Res asst nutrit, Cornell Univ, 58-59; res asst nutrit biochem, Columbia Univ & St Luke's Hosp, 59-61; res assoc, Inst Int Med, Univ Md, 62-64, asst prof, 64-66; res assoc, Columbia Univ, 66-68, asst prof nutrit sci, 68-72; assoc prof nutrit, Pa State Univ, 72-77, dir, Div Biol Health, 74-76; assoc prof nutrit, Mass Inst Technol, 78-82. *Concurrent Pos:* Nutrit Found future leaders grant, 67-69; adv comt mem, Am Found Overseas Blind, 73-; mem malnutrit panel, US-Japan Med Res Comt, 74-85; mem Nat Acad Sci-Int Nutrit Progs Comt, 74-79; Int Vitamin A consult group, 75-; US deleg, World Health Assembly, 75-; mem adv comt, Off Sci & Technol Policy, 78-79; assoc ed, Am J Clin Nutrit, 84-; mem, bd trustees, Helen Keller Int, 85-90 & bd dirs, Int Eye Found. *Mem:* Am Inst Nutrit; Am Pub Health Asn; NY Acad Sci; Am Soc Clin Nutrit. *Res:*

Malnutrition children; lipid metabolism; absorption and metabolism fat soluble vitamins in cystic fibrosis; vitamin A; breast feeding and child development; nutrition and nation development in developing countries. *Mailing Add:* Nat Eye Inst Off Dir Bldg 31 Rm 6A08 NIH 9000 Rockville Pike Bethesda MD 20892

**UNDERWOOD, DONALD LEE,** COSMETIC CHEMISTRY. *Current Pos:* Res chemist, Personal Care Div, Gillete Co, 54-55, from res supvr to sr res supvr, 55-73, prin engr, 73-80, asst dir res, Advan Technol Lab, 80-85, CONSULT & PAT SEARCH, GILLETE CO, 85- *Personal Data:* b Grand Rapids, Mich, Apr 20, 28; m 56, Genive E Smith; c Wesley K & Harold R. *Educ:* Wheaton Col, BS, 50; Princeton Univ, MA, 53. *Mem:* Sigma Xi. *Res:* Sorption and diffusion of salt, acid and water in human hair; hair cosmetics; physics; appliance engineering and development. *Mailing Add:* 125 Marilyn St Holliston MA 01746-2035

**UNDERWOOD, DOUGLAS HAINES,** MATHEMATICS. *Current Pos:* Assoc prof, 58-74, PROF MATH, WHITMAN COL, 74- *Personal Data:* b Ravenna, Ohio, Nov 29, 34; m 58; c 2. *Educ:* Case Inst Technol, BS, 56; Univ Calif, Berkeley, MA, 58; Univ Wis-Madison, PhD, 68. *Mem:* Am Math Soc; Math Asn Am. *Res:* Commutative rings. *Mailing Add:* Dept Math Whitman Col Walla Walla WA 99362

**UNDERWOOD, HERBERT ARTHUR, JR,** BIOLOGICAL RHYTHMS. *Current Pos:* from asst prof to assoc prof, 80-85, PROF ZOOL, NC STATE UNIV, 85- *Personal Data:* b Austin, Tex, Sept 4, 45; m 81, Melissa G Jones. *Educ:* Univ Tex, Austin, BA, 67, MA, 68, PhD(zool), 72. *Prof Exp:* Fel zool, Max-Planck Inst, 72-73; fel, Univ Tex, Austin, 73-75. *Concurrent Pos:* Res Carreer Develop Award, NIH, 79-84. *Mem:* Soc Integrative Comp Biol; AAAS; Sigma Xi; Soc Res Biol Rhythms. *Res:* Role of the eyes and extraretinal photoreceptors in the control of the biological clock of lizards and birds; vertebrate photoperiodism; behavioral thermoregulation in poikilotherms; involvement of the pineal system in vertebrate circadian rhythms. *Mailing Add:* Dept Zool NC State Univ Raleigh NC 27695-7617. *E-Mail:* herbert__underwood@ncsu.edu

**UNDERWOOD, JAMES HENRY,** SOLAR PHYSICS, OPTICS. *Current Pos:* LAWRENCE LIVERMORE NAT LAB, UNIV CALIF. *Personal Data:* b Minster, Eng, Apr 18, 38; m 81. *Educ:* Univ Leicester, BSc, 59, PhD(physics), 63. *Prof Exp:* Res assoc space res, Nat Acad Sci, NSF, 63-66; aerospace scientist, Goddard Space Flight Ctr, NASA, 66-72; staff scientist space res, Aerospace Corp, 72-77; mem staff, Inst Plasma Res, Stanford Univ, 77-80; res scientist, Jet Propulsion Lab, 80-83. *Mem:* Int Astron Union; Am Astron Soc; Optical Soc Am. *Res:* Application of x-ray techniques, in particular x-ray optics and crystal spectroscopy, to the study of hot plasmas, in particular the solar corona and other celestial x-ray sources. *Mailing Add:* Lawrence Livermore Berkeley Nat Lab Univ Calif One Cyclotron Rd Berkeley CA 94720

**UNDERWOOD, JAMES ROSS, JR,** PLANETARY GEOLOGY, GEOLOGICAL EDUCATION. *Current Pos:* head dept, 77-85, PROF GEOL, KANS STATE UNIV, 77- *Personal Data:* b Austin, Tex, May 15, 27; m 61, Margaret A Sanderford; c Marion, Ann & Elizabeth. *Educ:* Univ Tex, Austin, BS, 48, BS, 49, MA, 56, PhD(geol), 62. *Prof Exp:* Petrol eng trainee, Sohio Petrol Co, 49-50, jr petrol engr, 50-51, petrol engr, 53-54; instr geol, Univ Tex, 56-57, Univ Tex-Agency Int Develop Prog, asst prof, Univ Baghdad, 62-65; temp asst prof, Univ Fla, 65-67; from assoc prof to prof geol, WTex State Univ, 67-77. *Concurrent Pos:* Exxon-sponsored prof, Univ Libya, 69-71; discipline scientist, NASA Planetary Geol & Geophysics Prog, Washington, DC, 87-89. *Mem:* Fel Geol Soc Am; Am Asn Petrol Geol; Soc Econ Paleontologists & Mineralogists; Am Geophys Union; Soc Petrol Engrs; fel AAAS. *Res:* Structural geology; geomorphology; planetary geology, especially Mercury, Mars and moons of Jupiter; terrestrial impact structures; geology of Trans-Pecos Texas, northern Chihuahua and the Middle East; petroleum engineering, especially drilling and production. *Mailing Add:* Dept Geol Kans State Univ Thompson Hall Rm 108 Manhattan KS 66506-3201. *Fax:* 785-532-7004; *E-Mail:* jrujr@ksuvm.ksu.edu

**UNDERWOOD, LLOYD B,** HYDROLOGY, RECLAMATION. *Current Pos:* RETIRED. *Personal Data:* b Jackson, Mich, May 9, 19. *Educ:* Mich State Univ, BS, 42. *Honors & Awards:* Burwell Award, Geol Soc Am, 69; Clare Holdred Award, Asn Econ Geologists, 68. *Prof Exp:* Chief eng geologist, 42-80; consult, BC Hydrol Corp & US Bur Reclamation, 80- *Mem:* Geol Soc Am; Am Asn Petrol Geologists; Sigma Xi. *Mailing Add:* 15682 Leavenworth St Omaha NE 68118

**UNDERWOOD, LOUIS EDWIN,** PEDIATRICS, ENDOCRINOLOGY. *Current Pos:* from instr to assoc prof, 69-80, PROF PEDIAT, SCH MED, UNIV NC, CHAPEL HILL, 80- *Personal Data:* b Danville, Ky, Feb 20, 37; m 93; c 3. *Educ:* Univ Ky, AB, 58; Vanderbilt Univ, MD, 61. *Hon Degrees:* MD, Univ Rostock, Ger. *Honors & Awards:* Nutrit Award, Am Acad Pediat, 93. *Prof Exp:* From intern to asst resident pediat, Vanderbilt Univ, 61-63; asst resident, Univ NC, 63-64; instr, Vanderbilt Univ, 64-65; attend pediat, US Naval Hosp, Chelsea, Mass, 65-67. *Concurrent Pos:* USPHS fel endocrinol, 67-70. *Mem:* AAAS; Am Fedn Clin Res; Endocrine Soc; Soc Pediat Res; Lawson Wilkins Pediat Endocrine Soc; Am Pediat Soc. *Res:* Pediatric endocrine diseases; growth problems and hormonal control of growth. *Mailing Add:* Dept Pediat CB 7220 Univ NC Sch Med 509 Burnett-Womack Chapel Hill NC 27599. *Fax:* 919-966-2423

**UNDERWOOD, REX J,** medicine, for more information see previous edition

**UNDERWOOD, ROBERT GORDON,** APPLIED MATHEMATICS, OPERATIONS RESEARCH. *Current Pos:* ASST PROF MATH, COLO SCH MINES, 78- *Personal Data:* b Nashville, Tenn, Feb 3, 45; m 68; c 2. *Educ:* Univ NC, Chapel Hill, BS, 67; Univ Va, PhD(appl math), 74. *Prof Exp:* Health Serv Officer, USPHS, 68-70; asst prof, Univ SC, 74-78. *Mem:* Soc Indust & Appl Math; Am Math Asn; Sigma Xi. *Res:* Applied mathematics; optimization, game theory and control theory. *Mailing Add:* Dept Math Colo Sch Mines 1500 Illinois St Golden CO 80401-1887

**UNDEUTSCH, WILLIAM CHARLES,** ORGANIC CHEMISTRY, CHEMICAL LITERATURE. *Current Pos:* RETIRED. *Personal Data:* b Hamilton, Ohio, Oct 6, 25; m 54, Josepha K Fischer; c William A, Barbara E (Arnold), Susanna M (Thibault) & Mary A (Downs). *Educ:* Univ Cincinnati, BS, 48, MS, 50; Univ Del, PhD(chem), 53. *Prof Exp:* Lab technician, Children's Hosp Res Found, 48, 50; res chemist, Photo Prods Dept, E I du Pont de Nemours & Co, Inc, 53-58; sr ed chem abstr serv, Am Chem Soc, 58-89. *Res:* hydroxamic acids. *Mailing Add:* 4611 Coach Rd Columbus OH 43220-2901

**UNERTL, WILLIAM NELSON,** PHYSICS. *Current Pos:* PROF PHYSICS, UNIV MAINE, 86- *Educ:* Univ Wis-Madison, PhD(solid state physics), 73. *Prof Exp:* Res fel, Dept Mat Sci & Eng, Cornell Univ, 73-77. *Concurrent Pos:* Vis scientist, Chalk River Nuclear Lab, Can, Fritz Haber Inst, Berlin, Surface Sci Res Ctr, Univ Liverpool, Ohio, Univ Western Ont; dir, Lab Surface Sci & Technol, Univ Maine, 87-90. *Res:* Contributed more than 60 publications. *Mailing Add:* Sawyer Res Ctr Univ Maine Orono ME 04469-5764. *Fax:* 207-581-2255

**UNG, MAN T,** COMPUTER SCIENCE, MATHEMATICS. *Current Pos:* asst prof, 72-76, adj asst prof, 76-79, ADJ ASSOC PROF ELEC ENG, UNIV SOUTHERN CALIF, 79- *Personal Data:* b South Vietnam, Apr 1, 38; US citizen; m 60; c 2. *Educ:* Univ Wis, BS, 59; Ill Inst Technol, MS, 62; Univ Southern Calif, PhD(elec eng), 70. *Prof Exp:* Asst res engr, IIT Res Inst, 61-63; mgr educ & training, Electronic Assocs, Inc, 63-70; mgr comput & math serv, Dillingham Environ Co, 70-71. *Concurrent Pos:* Ed, Analog/Hybrid Comput Educ Soc, 65-68. *Mem:* Simulation Coun; Marine Technol Soc; Sr mem Soc Comput Simulation. *Res:* Modeling of ecological systems; hybrid computer applications in engineering. *Mailing Add:* Dept Elec Eng Systs Univ Southern Calif University Park Los Angeles CA 90089-0002

**UNGAR, EDWARD WILLIAM,** TECHNICAL MANAGEMENT, RESEARCH ADMINISTRATION. *Current Pos:* PRES, TARATEC CORP, 86- *Personal Data:* b New York, NY, Feb 6, 36; m 78; c 3. *Educ:* City Col New York, BME, 57; Ohio State Univ, MSc, 59, PhD(mech eng), 66. *Prof Exp:* Res engr, Battelle Mem Inst, 57-63, prog dir, Fluid & Thermal Mech Div, 63-66, assoc div chief, 66, chief fluid & gas dynamics div, 66-70, mgr eng physics sect, 70-71, mgr, Eng Physics Dept, 71-74, mgr, Energy & Environ Processes Res Dept, 74-76, assoc dir, 76-78, dir, Columbus Div, 78-85, vpres, 78-86. *Mem:* Am Soc Mech Engrs; AAAS; Sigma Xi. *Res:* Physical, life and social sciences. *Mailing Add:* 929 Harrison Ave Columbus OH 43215

**UNGAR, ERIC E(DWARD),** STRUCTURAL DYNAMICS, VIBRATION AND NOISE CONTROL. *Current Pos:* CHIEF ENG SCIENTIST, ACENTECH INC, 92- *Personal Data:* b Vienna, Austria, Nov 12, 26; nat US; m 51, Goldie Becker; c Judith (Fishman), Susan (Green), Ellen (Borgenicht) & Sharon (Lane). *Educ:* Wash Univ, BSME, 51; Univ NMex, MS, 54; NY Univ, DEngSc(mech eng), 57. *Honors & Awards:* Centennial Medallion, Am Soc Mech Engrs, 81; Trent-Crede Medal of Acoust, Soc Am, 95. *Prof Exp:* Aero-ord engr, Sandia Corp, 51-53; from instr to asst prof mech eng, NY Univ, 53-58, res scientist, 58; sr eng scientist & mgr appl physics dept, Bolt, Beranek & Newman, 58-68, assoc div dir, 68-76, prin engr, 76-84, chief consult engr, 85-96. *Mem:* Fel Am Soc Mech Engrs; assoc fel Am Inst Aeronaut & Astronaut; fel Acoust Soc Am; Inst Noise Control Eng. *Res:* Structural and machinery dynamics; vibrations and noise; stress analysis; machine design. *Mailing Add:* Acentech, Inc 33 Moulton St Cambridge MA 02138. *Fax:* 617-499-8074; *E-Mail:* eungar@acentech.com

**UNGAR, FRANK,** BIOCHEMISTRY, ENDOCRINOLOGY. *Current Pos:* from assoc prof to prof, 58-90, EMER PROF BIOCHEM, MED SCH, UNIV MINN, MINNEAPOLIS, 90- *Personal Data:* b Cleveland, Ohio, Apr 30, 22; m 48, Shirley K; c Leanne, William, Barbara & Joanne. *Educ:* Ohio State Univ, BA, 43; Western Res Univ, MSc, 48; Tufts Univ, PhD(biochem, physiol), 52. *Prof Exp:* Res staff mem, Cleveland Clin, 47-48; res staff mem, Worcester Found Exp Biol, 51-58. *Concurrent Pos:* Fulbright sr scholar, Univ Col, Cork, 74-75; asst vis prof chem, Clark Univ, 56-58; consult cancer chemother group, NIH, 65-72; Fogarty Int Sr fel, Weizmann Inst, Rehovot, Israel, 82-83. *Mem:* AAAS; Am Chem Soc; Endocrine Soc; Am Soc Biol Chem. *Res:* Regulation of hormone action; metabolism of steroid hormones. *Mailing Add:* Dept Biochem 4-217 OWRE Univ Minn Med Sch Minneapolis MN 55455

**UNGAR, GERALD S,** MATHEMATICS. *Current Pos:* PROF MATH, UNIV CINCINNATI, 70- *Personal Data:* b Wilkes-Barre, Pa, Jan 27, 41; m 59; c 3. *Educ:* Franklin & Marshall Col, BA, 61; Rutgers Univ, MS, 63, PhD(topol), 66. *Prof Exp:* Asst prof math, La State Univ, Baton Rouge, 66-68 & Case Western Res Univ, 68-70. *Mem:* Am Math Soc; Math Asn Am. *Res:* Fiber maps; local homogeneity. *Mailing Add:* 6271 Cortelyou Cincinnati OH 45213

**UNGAR, IRWIN A,** PLANT ECOLOGY. *Current Pos:* from asst prof to assoc prof, Ohio Univ, 66-73, chmn dept, 83-88, dir, MS Prog Environ Studies, 91-95, PROF BOT, OHIO UNIV, 74- *Personal Data:* b New York, NY, Jan 21, 34; m 59, Ana; c Steven, Sandra & Sharon. *Educ:* City Col New York, BS, 55; Univ Kans, MA, 57, PhD(bot), 61. *Prof Exp:* Instr bot, Univ RI, 61-62; asst prof, Quincy Col, 62-66. *Concurrent Pos:* Sigma Xi res awards, 59 & 66; NSF grants, 63-65, 67-69, 74-75, 76-78 & 80-83, panelist, 66; res grant, Ohio Univ, 66-68, 74-75, 78-79, 83-85, 88-89 & 94-95; John C Baker res grant, 72-73; res grant, Ohio Biol Surv, 70-71 & 74-75, John C Baker, 90-91; res assoc, Ctr Nat Res Sci grant, France, 72-73; Res Inst fel, Ohio Univ, 74; vis fel, Wolfson Col & vis prof, Dept Plant Sci, Oxford Univ, 90-91; petrol environ res. *Mem:* AAAS; Ecol Soc Am; Bot Soc Am; Sigma Xi; Int Asn Veg Sci. *Res:* Vegetation-soil relations on saline soils; ecology of halophytes; studies in salt tolerance and demography of species under field conditions; physiological ecology of halophytes. *Mailing Add:* Dept Environ & Plant Sci Ohio Univ Athens OH 45701. *E-Mail:* ungar@ohiou.edu

**UNGER, ELIZABETH ANN,** DATABASE SYSTEMS, SECURITY OF DATA SYSTEMS. *Current Pos:* assoc dir, Comput Ctr, Kans State Univ, 66-74, actg dir, 70, assoc dean, Grad Sch, 90-93, PROF COMPUT SCI, KANS STATE UNIV, 72-, VPROVOST, 95- *Personal Data:* b Saginaw, Mich, May 23, 39; m 63, Samuel G; c Mark, Michele & Kirsten. *Educ:* Mich State Univ, BS, 61, MS, 63; Kans State Univ, PhD(comput sci), 78. *Prof Exp:* Appl sci rep, IBM Corp, 58-62; user sci dir, Comput Lab, Mich State Univ, 63-66. *Concurrent Pos:* Vchair, Spec Interest Group Small Comput Systs & Applns, Asn Comput Mach, 80-93. *Mem:* Asn Comput Mach; Inst Elec & Electronics Engrs; Sigma Xi. *Res:* Integrity and secrecy (security) of data in data systems with a particular interest in inferential security in database systems; integrity of data through the capture of semantics in object oriented database management systems. *Mailing Add:* Vprovost Acad Serv & Technol 108 Anderson Hall Kans State Univ Manhattan KS 66506. *E-Mail:* beth@ksu.edu

**UNGER, HANS-GEORG,** OPTICAL COMMUNICATION, MICROWAVES. *Current Pos:* prof, 60-93, EMER PROF ELEC ENG & DIR, INST HIGH FREQUENCY TECHNOL, TECH UNIV BRAUNSCHWEIG, 93- *Personal Data:* b Braunschweig, Ger, Sept 14, 26; m 55, Gunda Schneider; c Barbara & Klaus. *Educ:* Tech Univ Braunschweig, Dipl Ing, 51, Dr-Ing, 54. *Hon Degrees:* Dr-Ing Eh, Tech Univ Munich, 85, Univ Ulm, 92; Dr rer nat hc Tech Univ Hamburg-Harburg, 93. *Honors & Awards:* Heinrich Hertz Medal, Inst Elec & Electronics Engrs, 88. *Prof Exp:* Develop engr, Siemens Ag, Munich, 51-54, dept head, 54-55; mem staff, US Spec Proj 63, 55-56; mem tech staff, Bell Labs, Holmdel, 56-59, dept head res commun technol, 59-60 & guided wave res, 61. *Concurrent Pos:* Dean elec eng, Tech Univ Braunschweig, 61-64; vis prof, Univ Wis, 64-65, Univ Ghent, 68, Univ Rennes & Tech Univ Delft, 73 & Univ Tokyo, 75; int chmn, Comn B, Int Union Radio Sci, 81-84. *Mem:* Inst Elec & Electronics Engrs; Polish Acad Sci. *Res:* Optical fiber guides and planar optical wave guides; waveguides components and circuits for optical communication, integrated optics and integrated optoelectronics; microwave electronics; microwave antennas. *Mailing Add:* Inst High Frequency Technol Tech Univ Braunschweig 38023 Braunschweig Germany. *Fax:* 49-531-391-5841

**UNGER, ISRAEL,** CHEMISTRY. *Current Pos:* from asst prof to assoc prof, 65-74, PROF CHEM, UNIV NB, FREDERICTON, 74-, DEAN SCI, 86- *Personal Data:* b Tarnow, Poland, Mar 30, 38; Can citizen; m 64, Marlene Parker; c Sharon L & Sheila L. *Educ:* Sir George Williams Univ, BSc, 58; Univ NB, MSc, 60, PhD(chem), 63. *Prof Exp:* Fel, Univ Tex, 63-65. *Concurrent Pos:* Adv bd, Can Inst Sci & Technol Info; mem, Prime Ministers Comt Excellence Educ, 92. *Mem:* Chem Inst Can; Inst Res Pub Policy. *Res:* Kinetics and photochemistry of small organic molecules; photochemistry of pesticides. *Mailing Add:* Dept Chem Univ NB Fredericton NB E3B 5E2 Can

**UNGER, JAMES WILLIAM,** PLANT MORPHOLOGY. *Current Pos:* prof bot & chmn dept, 53-67, PROF BIOL, UNIV WIS-OSHKOSH, 67- *Personal Data:* b Marshfield, Wis, Apr 1, 21; m 47; c 1. *Educ:* Wis State Col, Stevens Point, BS, 42; Univ Wis, MS, 47, PhD(bot), 53. *Prof Exp:* Asst prof bot, Hope Col, 47-51. *Mem:* Am Inst Biol Sci; Bot Soc Am; Sigma Xi. *Res:* Anatomical considerations of gymnosperm tissue cultures; anatomical studies of stem apices and stem to root vascular transitions; membrane permeability studies; tissue culture of orange. *Mailing Add:* 1212 E New York Ave Oshkosh WI 54901-4032

**UNGER, JOHN DUEY,** GEOPHYSICS, SEISMOLOGY. *Current Pos:* Geophysicist, Hawaiian Volcano Observ, US Geol Surv, Hawaii Nat Park, 69-74, geophysicist, Nat Ctr for Earthquake Res, 74-76, GEOPHYSICIST, BR ENG GEOL & TECTONICS, US GEOL SURV NAT CTR, RESTON, VA, 76- *Personal Data:* b Harrisburg, Pa, Mar 2, 43; m 66; c 3. *Educ:* Mass Inst Technol, BS & MS, 67; Dartmouth Col, PhD(geol), 69. *Mem:* AAAS; Geol Soc Am; Am Geophys Union; Seismol Soc Am. *Res:* Reflection seismology; deep crustal studies and tectonics; general microearthquake seismology; volcano geophysics. *Mailing Add:* US Geol Surv Nat Ctr MS-905 12201 Sunrise Valley Dr Reston VA 20192

**UNGER, KLAUS K,** CHEMISTRY. *Current Pos:* PROF INORG CHEM, JOHANNES GUTENBERG UNIV. *Honors & Awards:* Chromotog Award, Am Chem Soc, 95. *Mailing Add:* Dept Inorg Chem Johannes Gutenberg Univ 55099 Mainz Germany

**UNGER, LLOYD GEORGE,** PHYSICAL CHEMISTRY. *Current Pos:* assoc prof, 68-80 PROF PHYS SCI & CHEM, WRIGHT COL, 80- *Personal Data:* b Stickney, SDak, Feb 24, 18; m 47; c 4. *Educ:* Yankton Col, BA, 39; Pa State Univ, MS, 41, PhD(phys chem), 45. *Prof Exp:* Lab asst, Pa State Univ, 39-44; res chemist, CPC Int Inc, Ill, 44-68. *Mem:* Fel AAAS; Am Chem Soc; Sigma Xi. *Res:* Cereal proteins; textile chemicals. *Mailing Add:* 99 Lawton Rd Riverside IL 60546-2330

**UNGER, PAUL WALTER,** SOIL SCIENCE, AGRONOMY. *Current Pos:* SOIL SCIENTIST, AGR RES SERV, USDA, 65- *Personal Data:* b Winchester, Tex, Sept 10, 31; m 60, Barbara Dutton; c Jimmy, Donny, Carla, Karen, Gary & Paula. *Educ:* Tex A&M Univ, BS, 61; Colo State Univ, MS, 63, PhD(soil sci), 66. *Honors & Awards:* Res Award, Soil Sci Soc Am 91; Scientist of Year, Southern Plains Area, Agr Res Serv, US Dept Agr, 87. *Concurrent Pos:* Assoc ed, Soil Sci Soc Am J, 77-82, Iowa State J Res, 80-86; consult, Food Agr Orgn UN, 86; co-ed, proceedings, Int Conf Dry Land Farming, 88; div chmn, Am Soc Soil Sci, 86. *Mem:* Fel Am Soc Agron; fel Soc Soil Sci Am; fel Soil & Water Conserv Soc; Coun Agr Sci & Technol; Int Soil Sci Soc; Int Soil Tillage Res Orgn; World Asn Soil & Water Conserv. *Res:* Soil management and moisture conservation, especially tillage and crop residue management as they relate to soil structure, water movement and water storage in the soil. *Mailing Add:* Conserv & Prod Res Lab USDA Agr Res Serv PO Drawer 10 Bushland TX 79012. *E-Mail:* pwunger@ag.gov

**UNGER, ROGER HAROLD,** INTERNAL MEDICINE. *Current Pos:* clin instr, 52-59, from asst prof to assoc prof, 59-70, PROF MED, HEALTH SCI CTR, UNIV TEX, DALLAS, 71-, DIR, CTR DIABETES RES, SOUTHWESTERN MED SCH, 85-, TOCHSTONE-WEST DISTINGUISHED CHAIR DIABETES RES, 88- *Personal Data:* b New York, NY, Mar 7, 24; m 46, Marlise Mantel; c Christine, Craig, James & Romy-Michelle. *Educ:* Yale Univ, BS, 44; Columbia Univ, MD, 47; Am Bd Internal Med, dipl, 56. *Hon Degrees:* Dr, Univ Geneva, 76, Univ Liege, 78. *Honors & Awards:* Lilly Award, Am Diabetes Asn, 64; Tinsley Harrison Award, 67; Middleton Award, Vet Admin, 69; Solomon A Bernson Mem Lectr, NIH, 75; Int Diabetes Fedn & Am Diabetes Asn, 82; Banting Medal & Mem Lectr, Am Diabetes Asn, 75; David Rumbough Award, Juvenile Diabetes Found, 75; Francis D W Lukens Hon Lectr, Univ Pa, 75; Sandoz Award & Lectr, Can Soc Endocrinol & Metab, 76; Woodyatt Mem Lectr, Chicago, Ill, 77; Joslin Mem Lectr, Harvard Univ, 79; Claude Bernard Mem Medal & Lectr, Europ Asn Study Diabetes, 80; Arthur R Colwell Mem Lectr, Northwestern Univ, 81; Fred Conrad Koch Award, Endocrine Soc, 83; Mosenthal Lectr, NY Diabetes Asn, 88. *Prof Exp:* From intern to resident med, Bellevue Hosp, NY, 47-51; dir, Dallas Diabetes Unit, Tex, 51-52. *Concurrent Pos:* Clin instr, Postgrad Med Sch, NY Univ, 51-56; chief, Gastroenterol Sect, Vet Admin Hosp, Dallas, 58-64, chief, Metab Sect, 64-74, dir res, 65-75; mem, Res & Educ Comt, Vet Admin Cent Off, 71-; vis prof, Univ Geneva, 72-73; vpres, Solomon A Berson Fund Med Res, Inc, 73 & pres, 74-76; sr med investr, Vet Admin Med Ctr, Dallas, 75-; consult, Nat Comn Diabetes, 75-77; mem, Subcomt to Nat Comt Diabetes, Vet Admin, 75-77 & Comt Sci Progs, Am Diabetes Asn, 76-77; prin investr, NIH contract, 76-82; assoc ed, Diabetes, 79-83. *Mem:* Nat Acad Sci; Am Fedn Clin Res; emer mem Am Soc Clin Invest; Endocrine Soc; Am Asn Physicians; Am Diabetes Asn; Int Diabetes Found; AMA; Cent Soc Clin Res; fel Am Col Physicians. *Res:* Diabetes. *Mailing Add:* Gifford Labs Ctr Diabetes Res Southwestern Med Sch Univ Tex Dallas TX 75235

**UNGER, S(TEPHEN) H(ERBERT),** ELECTRICAL ENGINEERING, COMPUTER SCIENCE. *Current Pos:* from assoc prof to prof elec eng, 61-79, PROF COMPUT SCI, COLUMBIA UNIV, 79- *Personal Data:* b New York, NY, July 7, 31; m c 2. *Educ:* Polytech Inst Brooklyn, BEE, 52; Mass Inst Technol, SM, 53, ScD, 57. *Prof Exp:* Asst elec eng, Res Lab Electronics, Mass Inst Technol, 54-57; mem tech staff, Bell Tel Labs, Inc, 57-61. *Concurrent Pos:* Adj asst prof, Columbia Univ, 60-61; consult, Res Labs, RCA Corp, 64-69; Guggenheim fel, 67; consult, Western Elec Eng Res Ctr, 71 & IBM, 82-85; vis prof comput sci, Danish Tech Univ, 74-75. *Mem:* Fel AAAS; Am Asn Univ Professors; fel Inst Elec & Electronics Engrs; Asn Comput Mach. *Res:* Switching circuit theory; digital computer systems; programming theory; pattern recognition; technological aids to the democratic process; programming languages; computer conferencing; engineering ethics. *Mailing Add:* Dept Comput Sci Columbia Univ Broadway & N 116th St New York NY 10027

**UNGER, VERNON EDWIN, JR,** INDUSTRIAL ENGINEERING, OPERATIONS RESEARCH. *Current Pos:* PROF INDUST ENG & HEAD DEPT, AUBURN UNIV, 79- *Personal Data:* b Easton, Md, Dec 14, 35; m 58; c 2. *Educ:* Johns Hopkins Univ, BES, 57, MS, 64, PhD(opers res), 68. *Prof Exp:* Staff asst, AAI, Inc, 57-65; prof indust eng, Ga Inst Technol, 68-79, assoc dir res, 74-79. *Mem:* Opers Res Soc Am; Am Inst Indust Eng. *Res:* Operations research and engineering economics. *Mailing Add:* 526 Hamilton Hills Ct Auburn AL 36830

**UNGERBOECK, GOTTFRIED,** SATELLITE TRANSMISSION. *Current Pos:* syst engr, 65-67, res staff mem, 67-84, FEL, IBM ZURICH RES LAB, 84- *Personal Data:* b New York, NY, July 7, 31. *Educ:* Tech Univ, Austria, Dipl Ing, 64; Swiss Fed Inst Technol, PhD(elec eng), 70. *Hon Degrees:* Dr, Tech Univ, Vienna, 93. *Honors & Awards:* Edwin Howard Armstrong Mem Award, Inst Elec & electronic Engrs, 86, Koji Kobayashi Comput & Commun Award, 93; Eduard Rhein Prize, 94; Richard W Hamming Medal, 94. *Prof Exp:* Wiener Schwachstromwerke, 64; mil serv, Austrian Army, 64-65. *Concurrent Pos:* Assoc ed, Commun Theory, Inst Elec & Electronics Engrs, 78-84, Signal Processing Magnetic Rec, 88-89, Modulation, 89-92; mem bd govs, Info Theory Group, 87-89; ed, Inst Elec & Electronics Engrs Transactions Commun, 89-93; fel, IBM, 94; Marconi Int fel Award, 96. *Mem:*

Foreign assoc Nat Acad Eng; fel Inst Elec & Electronics Engrs; Swiss Electrotech Soc; Swiss Acad Tech Sci. *Res:* Pioneered several new signal processing techniques for digital data transmission and storage; most well known is his invention of trellis coded modulation. *Mailing Add:* IBM Res Lab Saumerstrasse 4 Rueschlikon CH-8803 Switzerland. *Fax:* 41-1-710-3781, 41-1-724-2795

**UNGLAUBE, JAMES M,** ORGANIC CHEMISTRY. *Current Pos:* DIR, COL & UNIV, DIV EDUC, EVANGEL LUTHERAN CHURCH, 87- *Personal Data:* b Milwaukee, Wis, Apr 13, 42; m 64; c 1. *Educ:* Carthage Col, BA, 63; Univ Iowa, MS, 66, PhD(org chem), 68. *Prof Exp:* Teaching asst org chem, Univ Iowa, 63-64; asst prof chem, Lenoir Rhyne Col, 67-70, assoc prof chem & acad dean, 70-77; asst dir, Dept Higher Educ, Lutheran Church Am, 77-82, dir, 82-87. *Mem:* Am Asn Higher Educ; Am Chem Soc; Sigma Xi. *Res:* Chemical education; organic chemistry syntheses, including heterocyclic nitrogen compounds. *Mailing Add:* Evangelical Luthern Church 8765 W Higgens Rd Chicago IL 60631-4177

**UNGURIS, JOHN,** SURFACE & THIN FILM PHYSICS, MICROSCOPY OF MAGNETIC MICROSTRUCTURES. *Current Pos:* Postdoctoral res assoc, 80-82, PHYSICIST, NAT INST STAND & TECHNOL, 82- *Personal Data:* b Dietz, WGer, Nov 25, 50; US citizen; m 73, Pamela Hudson; c Alexandra. *Educ:* Carnegie Mellon Univ, BS, 73; Univ Wis, PhD(physics), 80. *Mem:* Fel Am Phys Soc; Am Vacuum Soc; Electron Micros Soc. *Res:* Magnetic thin films and surfaces using various spin polarized electron microscopies and spectroscopies; thin film and multilayer growth; surface chemistry; electron and scanned probe microscopies. *Mailing Add:* Nat Inst Stand & Technol Bldg 220 B206 Gaithersburg MD 20899. *Fax:* 301-926-2746; *E-Mail:* unguris@epg.nist.gov

**UNGVICHIAN, VICHATE,** ANTENNA DESIGNS, COMPUTER MODELLING. *Current Pos:* RES ENGR, DEPT ELEC ENG, FLA ATLANTIC UNIV. *Personal Data:* b Bangkok, Thailand. *Educ:* Khon-Kaen Univ, Thailand, BSEE, 67; Ohio State Univ, MS, 74; Ohio Univ, PhD(elec eng), 81. *Prof Exp:* Fel electromagnetics, Elec Eng Dept, Ohio Univ, 81- *Mem:* Inst Elec & Electronics Engrs; Sigma Xi. *Res:* Electromagnetic fields as applied to instrument landing systems; electromagnetic interference; computer modeling. *Mailing Add:* Dept Elec Eng Fla Atlantic Univ Boca Raton FL 33431

**UNIK, JOHN PETER,** NUCLEAR CHEMISTRY. *Current Pos:* From asst chemist to assoc chemist, Argonne Nat Lab, 60-74, sect head, 72-74, assoc dir, Chem Div, 74-82, dir sci support, 83-84, assoc dir support serv, 84-93, SR CHEMIST, ARGONNE NAT LAB, 74-, DIR ELEC & COMPUT TECHNOL, 93- *Personal Data:* b Chicago, Ill, May 18, 34; m 57, Ruth A Cohenaur; c Carol & John. *Educ:* Ill Inst Technol, BS, 56; Univ Calif, Berkeley, PhD(chem), 60. *Concurrent Pos:* Consult, Oak Ridge Nat Lab, 74-81, US Nuclear Data Comt, 78-82, Lawrence Berkeley Lab, 79-82, Dept Energy, 94-96. *Mem:* Am Phys Soc; Am Chem Soc. *Res:* Nuclear fission and heavy ion reactions. *Mailing Add:* 208 Tanglewood Lane Naperville IL 60563

**UNKLESBAY, ATHEL GLYDE,** GEOLOGIC EDUCATION, EDUCATION ADMINISTRATION. *Current Pos:* RETIRED. *Personal Data:* b Byesville, Ohio, Feb 11, 14; m 40, Wanda Stravch; c Kenneth, Marjorie, Carolyn & Allen. *Educ:* Marietta Col, AB, 38; State Univ Iowa, MA, 40 & PhD(paleont), 42. *Hon Degrees:* SDc, Marietta Col, 77. *Prof Exp:* Geologist, US Geol Surv, 42-45, Iowa Geol Surv, 45-46; asst prof geol, Colgate Univ, 46-47; from asst prof to prof geol, Univ Mo, 47-67, vpres admin, 67-79; exec dir, Am Geol Inst, 79-85. *Mem:* Geol Soc Am; Am Asn Petrol Geologists; Paleontol Soc; Nat Asn Geol Teachers. *Res:* General geology for the layman and of Missouri. *Mailing Add:* 37 G Broadway Village Columbia MO 65201-8662

**UNKLESBAY, NAN F,** FOOD SCIENCE, NUTRITION. *Current Pos:* asst prof food systs mgt, 73-76, from asst prof to assoc prof, 76-85, PROF FOOD SCI & NUTRIT, UNIV MO, COLUMBIA, 85- *Personal Data:* b North Vancouver, BC, May 28, 44; m 74. *Educ:* Univ BC, BHE, 66; Univ Wis, Madison, MS, 71, PhD(food sci), 73. *Prof Exp:* Dietary consult, Dept Health, Govt Nfld & Labrador, 67-70. *Concurrent Pos:* Consult, NSF, 75-76. *Mem:* Inst Food Technologists; Am Dietetic Asn; Can Dietetic Asn. *Res:* Major amounts of energy utilization within the food industry; optimization of resource utilization in food services while maintaining microbial safety, quality and nutritional value. *Mailing Add:* Dept Food Sci-Nutrit Univ Mo-Columbia Columbia MO 65211

**UNLAND, MARK LEROY,** PHYSICAL CHEMISTRY. *Current Pos:* RES CHEMIST, MONSANTO CO, 66- *Personal Data:* b Jacksonville, Ill, Mar 17, 40; m 62; c 2. *Educ:* MacMurray Col, AB, 62; Univ Ill, Urbana, MS, 64, PhD(chem), 66. *Mem:* Am Chem Soc; Sigma Xi; Sci Res Soc NAm. *Res:* Molecular structure; catalyst development; fundamental studies of heterogeneous catalysts and catalysis mechanisms. *Mailing Add:* 12903 Mayerling Dr St Louis MO 63146-3601

**UNLU, M SELIM,** HIGH SPEED ELECTRONIC DEVICES, OPTOELECTRONIC DEVICES. *Current Pos:* ASST PROF ELEC ENGR, BOSTON UNIV, 92- *Personal Data:* b Sinop, Turkey, June 12, 64; m 93, Hale P Zengingonul. *Educ:* Middle East Tech Univ, Ankara, BS, 86; Univ Ill-Urbana, Champaign, MS, 88, PhD, 92. *Prof Exp:* Res engr, Aselsan, Mil Electronics Inc, Ankara, Turkey, 84-86; res asst, Coord Sci Lab, Univ ILL, 86-92. *Mem:* Inst Elec & Electronics Engrs; Lasers & Electrooptics Soc. *Res:*

Design and characterization of high speed electronic devices; optoelectronic devices for optical communication systems; analysis and modeling of heterojunction semiconductor devices; basic semiconductor phenomena. *Mailing Add:* Boston Univ Elec Compt & Syst Eng 44 Cummington St Boston MA 02215. *Fax:* 617-353-6440; *E-Mail:* selimstatsphoton.bu.edu

**UNNAM, JALAIAH,** MATERIALS SCIENCE. *Current Pos:* PRES, ANALYTICAL SERV & MAT, INC, 83- *Personal Data:* b Tangutur, India, Dec 1, 47; m 73; c 2. *Educ:* Indian Inst Technol, BTech, 70; Va Polytech Inst & State Univ, MS, 72, PhD(mat sci), 75. *Prof Exp:* Instr metall, Va Polytech Inst & State Univ, 74 & 75, res assoc mat sci, 75-77; res fel, George Washington Univ, 77-78; sr scientist, Vira Inc, 82-83. *Concurrent Pos:* Vis prof mat sci, Va Polytech Inst & State Univ, 78-82. *Mem:* Am Soc Metals; AIME; Sigma Xi. *Res:* Solid state diffusion; x-ray diffraction; composite materials; numerical analysis and computer programming; electron microprobe; scanning electron microscope; quantitative metallography; mechanical testing; electroplating; oxidation. *Mailing Add:* Analytical Serv & Mat 107 Research Dr Hampton VA 23666

**UNO, HIDEO,** COMPARATIVE PATHOLOGY, PHARMACO-MORPHOLOGY. *Current Pos:* SR SCIENTIST, WIS REGIONAL PRIMATE RES CTR, UNIV WIS-MADISON, 70- *Personal Data:* b Tokyo, Japan, Nov 28, 29; m 56; c 2. *Educ:* Yokohama Med Col, MD, 55, PhD(path), 60. *Prof Exp:* Intern gen med, Tokyo Munic Hiroo Hosp, 55-56; resident path, Yokohama Med Col, 56-60; asst prof path, Sch Med, Yokohama City Univ, 60-64; instr path, Jefferson Med Col, Philadelphia, Pa, 64-66; vis scientist cutaneous biol, Ore Primate Res Ctr, Beaverton, 66-68; assoc prof path, Sch Med, Yokohama City Univ, 68-70. *Concurrent Pos:* Scientist path, Ore Primate Res Ctr, 70-79; adj assoc prof, Dept Path & Lab Med, Sch Med, Univ Wis- Madison, 72-, adj prof, 89- *Mem:* Fedn Am Soc Exp Biol; Int Acad Path; Soc Invest Dermat; Japanese Soc Pathologists. *Res:* Comparative pathology of aging, spontaneous cancer, diabetes, cardiovascular disorders and aging brain disorders of rhesus monkeys; pharmaco-pathological study of dexamethasone to monkey fetal brain; effect of minoxidil and antiandrogen on macaque and human baldness; stress and brain damage. *Mailing Add:* Regional Primate Res Ctr Univ Wis 1223 Capitol Ct Madison WI 53715-1261

**UNOWSKY, JOEL,** INDUSTRIAL MICROBIOLOGY, MICROBIAL GENETICS. *Current Pos:* sr microbiologist, Hoffmann-La Roche Inc, 66-79, asst res group, 79, res group chief, 79-84, RES LEADER, HOFFMANN-LA ROCHE INC, 87- *Personal Data:* b St Paul, Minn, Dec 11, 38; m 75; c 4. *Educ:* Univ Minn, Minneapolis, BA, 61; Northwestern Univ, Evanston, PhD(bact), 66. *Prof Exp:* Res fel, E I du Pont de Nemours & Co, Inc, 65-66. *Concurrent Pos:* Adj assoc prof, Seton Hall Univ, 76. *Mem:* AAAS; Am Soc Microbiol; Sigma Xi; NY Acad Sci. *Res:* Resistance transfer factor; antibiotic strain development; antibiotic screening; mutation and genetics; chemotherapy; immunology; cytokines; immunmodulators; absorption of pharmaceuticals; study director, toxicology. *Mailing Add:* 503 Millgrove Dr Norristown PA 19403. *Fax:* 973-235-7636

**UNRATH, CLAUDE RICHARD,** HORTICULTURE. *Current Pos:* From asst prof to assoc prof, 68-84, PROF HORT/RES POMOLOGIST, NC STATE UNIV, 84- *Personal Data:* b Benton Harbor, Mich, Nov 29, 41; m 76; c 2. *Educ:* Mich State Univ, BS, 63, MS, 66, PhD(hort), 68. *Honors & Awards:* Raw Prod Res Award, Nat Canners Asn, 70. *Mem:* Am Soc Hort Sci; Am Pomol Soc. *Res:* Applied tree fruit physiology, apple research, growth regulator physiology, environmental control and modification and cultural improvement and efficiency. *Mailing Add:* Dept Hort Box 7609 NC State Univ Raleigh NC 27695-0001

**UNRAU, DAVID GEORGE,** BIOCHEMISTRY. *Current Pos:* PROG MGR, WEYERHAUSER CORP, 90- *Personal Data:* b Leamington, Ont, July 21, 38; m 62; c 4. *Educ:* Univ Toronto, BSA, 62; Purdue Univ, MS, 65, PhD(biochem), 67. *Prof Exp:* Res scientist, Union Camp Corp, NJ, 67-71; res chemist, ITT Rayonier Inc, Whippany, 71-90, res group leader, 74-90. *Mem:* Am Chem Soc. *Res:* Carbohydrate modification for industrial uses; flame retardants for cellulosics; viscose; new rayon fiber development. *Mailing Add:* 505 SW 335th St Federal Way WA 98023

**UNRUG, RAPHAEL,** BASIN ANALYSIS, REGIONAL TECTONICS. *Current Pos:* chair dept, 84-89, PROF GEOL, DEPT GEOL SCI, WRIGHT STATE UNIV, 84- *Personal Data:* b Cracow, Poland; US citizen. *Educ:* Tech Univ Mining & Metall, Cracow, MSc, 57; Jagiellonian Univ, Cracow, PhD(geol), 62, DSc (geodynamics), 68. *Prof Exp:* From asst prof to assoc prof geol, Dept Geol, Jagiellonian Univ, 62-74, from assoc prof to prof geol & chair dept, Inst Geol Sci, 74-79; prof, Dept Geol, Univ Zambia, 80-83. *Concurrent Pos:* Sr geologist, Cekop Consults Accra, Ghana, 62-63; vis res scientist, Univ Reading, UK & Univ Paris, 66; consult geologist, Polservice Consult Engrs, Tripoli, Libya, 74-76, Consol Oil Industs, Warsaw, 76-79 & Geoexplorers Int Inc, Denver, 82-84; vis prof, Univ Granada, Spain & Univ Bologna, Italy, 76; proj leader, Int Geol Correlation Prog Proj. *Mem:* Geol Soc Am; Am Asn Petrol Geologists. *Res:* Sedimentology, stratigraphy and basin analysis; regional tectonics; economic geology base and precious metals; oil geology. *Mailing Add:* Dept Geol Sci Wright State Univ 3640 Colonial Glenn Dayton OH 45435-0001

**UNRUH, HENRY, JR,** PHYSICS. *Current Pos:* assoc prof, 61-72, PROF PHYSICS, WICHITA STATE UNIV, 72- *Personal Data:* b Greensburg, Kans, Dec 31, 26; wid; c 2. *Educ:* Wichita State Univ, AB, 50; Kans State Univ, MS, 52; Case Inst Technol, PhD(physics), 60. *Prof Exp:* Instr physics, Fenn Col, 54-57; asst prof, Colo State Univ, 59-61. *Mem:* Am Phys Soc; Sigma Xi. *Res:* Magnetic properties of solids; simple liquids; many body problems. *Mailing Add:* 227 Oleander Ave Bakersfield CA 93304

**UNRUH, JAMES ARLEN,** BUSINESS, COMMUNICATIONS. *Current Pos:* vpres fin, Burroughs Corp, 82-84, sr vpres, 84-86, exec vpres, 86, exec vpres, 86-89, pres & chief oper officer, 89-91, CHMN BD DIRS & CHIEF EXEC OFFICER, UNISYS CORP, 91- *Personal Data:* b Goodrich, NDak, Mar 22, 41; m 84, Candace Leigh Voight. *Educ:* Jamestown Col, BSBA, 63; Univ Denver, MBA, 64. *Prof Exp:* Dir corp planning & analysis, Fairchild Camera & Instrument, 74-76, vpres treas & corp develop, 76-79, vpres fin, 79-80; vpres fin, Memorex Corp, 80-82. *Mailing Add:* Unisys Corp Township Line & Union Mtg Blue Bell PA 19424

**UNRUH, JERRY DEAN,** INDUSTRIAL ORGANIC CHEMISTRY, HOMOGENEOUS CATALYSIS. *Current Pos:* Res chemist, Corpus Christi Tech Ctr, Celanese Chem Co, 70-73, sr res chemist, 73-78, staff chemist, 78-81, res assoc, 81-82, sect leader, 82-86, res assoc, 86-91, SR RES ASSOC, HOECHST-CELANESE CHEM GROUP, 92- *Personal Data:* b Colorado Springs, Colo, Nov 4, 44; m 88, Diana P Peterson; c Karl, Ana, Amy & Ralph. *Educ:* Colo State Univ, BS, 66; Ore State Univ, PhD(org chem), 70. *Mem:* Sigma Xi; AAAS; Am Chem Soc. *Res:* Organic free radicals; linear free energy relationships; molecular orbital theory; organometallic chemistry; homogeneous catalysis. *Mailing Add:* 622 Bradshaw Corpus Christi TX 78412-3002. *Fax:* 512-242-4109; *E-Mail:* corhcc1@hcc.com

**UNRUH, WILLIAM GEORGE,** COSMOLOGY, QUANTUM NOISE & MEASUREMENT. *Current Pos:* from asst prof to assoc prof, 76-82, PROF PHYSICS, UNIV BC, 82-; DIR COSMOLOGY PROG, CAN INST ADVAN RES, 86- *Personal Data:* b Winnipeg, Man, Aug 28, 45; m 74; c 1. *Educ:* Univ Man, BSc, 67; Princeton Univ, MA, 69, PhD(physics), 71. *Honors & Awards:* Rutherford Medal, Royal Soc Can, 82 & Rutherford Lectr, Royal Soc London, 85; Hertzberg Medal, Can Asn Physics, 83; Steacie Medal, 84; Gold Medal, BC Sci Coun, 90. *Prof Exp:* Nat Res Coun Can fel physics, Birkbeck Col, Univ London, 71-72; Miller fel physics, Miller Inst Basic Res & Univ Calif, Berkeley, 73-74; asst prof appl math, McMaster Univ, 74-76. *Concurrent Pos:* Fel, Rutherford Mem, Royal Soc Can, 71, Nat Res Coun Teaching, 71-72, Miller Res, Univ Calif, Berkeley, 73-74, Alfred P Sloan Res, Univ BC, 78-80, Steacie, Nat Sci & Eng Res Coun, 84-86; chmn, Theoret Physics Div, Can Asn Physicists, 85-86. *Mem:* Fel Royal Soc Can. *Res:* Relation between quantum mechanics and gravitation; quantum gravity wave detectors; the early universe. *Mailing Add:* Dept Physics Univ BC 6224 Agr Rd Rm 325 Vancouver BC V6T 1Z1 Can. *E-Mail:* unruh@physics.ubc.ca

**UNSWORTH, BRIAN RUSSELL,** BIOCHEMISTRY. *Current Pos:* asst prof, 69-76, ASSOC PROF BIOL, MARQUETTE UNIV, 76- *Personal Data:* b London, Eng, July 30, 37; m 66; c 2. *Educ:* Univ London, BSc, 61, PhD(biochem), 65. *Prof Exp:* Proj assoc biochem, Univ Wis-Madison, 65-67; USPHS fel biol, Univ Calif, San Diego, 67-69. *Mem:* Am Col Sports Med. *Res:* Biochemical alterations in muscle with use and disuse; myogenesis in the rat; structural analysis of myosin light and heavy chains in various animal model systems; changes in sarcoplasmic reticulum structure and function during development. *Mailing Add:* Dept Biol Marquette Univ PO Box 1881 1515 W Wisconsin Ave Milwaukee WI 53201-1881

**UNT, HILLAR,** MECHANICAL ENGINEERING. *Current Pos:* asst prof, 60-65, assoc prof & chmn dept, 65-67, PROF MECH ENG, CALIF STATE UNIV, LONG BEACH, 70-, CHMN DEPT, 74- *Personal Data:* b Tallinn, Estonia, Mar 17, 35; US citizen; m 61. *Educ:* Univ Southern Calif, BS, 58, MS, 60, PhD, 69. *Prof Exp:* Lectr mech eng, Univ Southern Calif, 58-60. *Mem:* Am Soc Mech Engrs; Am Soc Metals; Am Inst Aeronaut & Astronaut; Acoust Soc Am; Soc Exp Stress Anal. *Res:* Mechanical vibration; bio-engineering; engineering education. *Mailing Add:* Dept Mech Eng Calif State Univ 8305 Csulb Long Beach CA 90840-0004

**UNTCH, KARL G(EORGE),** ORGANIC CHEMISTRY. *Current Pos:* CONSULT, 90- *Personal Data:* b Cleveland, Ohio, Apr 24, 31; m 53, Constance Ford; c Peter M & Katharine A. *Educ:* Oberlin Col, BA, 53; Univ NDak, MS, 55; Columbia Univ, MA, 57, PhD(org chem), 59. *Honors & Awards:* Alfred P Sloan fel, 67-69. *Prof Exp:* Du Pont teaching fel, Columbia Univ, 57-58; fel org chem, Univ Wis, 58-60; Fundamental Res staff fel, Mellon Inst, 60-66; assoc prof chem, Belfer Grad Sch Sci, Yeshiva Univ, 66-68; dept head, Syntex Res, 68-80, prin scientist, 80-81; instr, Evergreen Valley Col, 82-84, consult chem, 81-88; dir, Ctr Chem Res, Dept Chem, Columbia Univ, 88-90. *Mem:* Am Chem Soc. *Res:* Aromaticity; chemistry of unsaturated medium sized ring compounds; synthesis and structure of natural products; synthesis of heterocyclic systems; total synthesis of prostaglandins; synthesis of anti-infammatory and cardiovascular agents; enzyme immunodiagnostics; diagnostic tests. *Mailing Add:* 7203 Via Carrizo San Jose CA 95135

**UNTERBERGER, ROBERT RUPPE,** PHYSICS. *Current Pos:* PROF GEOPHYS, TEX A&M UNIV, 68- *Personal Data:* b New York, NY, Apr 27, 21; m 44, Betty Miller; c Glen, Gregg & Gail. *Educ:* State Univ NY Col Forestry, Syracuse, BS, 43; Syracuse Univ, BS, 43; Duke Univ, PhD(physics), 50. *Prof Exp:* Lab instr physics, Syracuse Univ, 43; electronics engr, Watson Labs, NJ, 46; res physicist, Chevron Res Co, Stand Oil Co, Calif, 50-52, sr res physicist, 52-54, tech asst mgr, 54-56, res assoc, 56-59, supvr res physicist, 59-65, sr res assoc, 65-68. *Concurrent Pos:* Electronic engr, White Sands Proving Ground, 46; consult to many salt and potash companies in US, Can, Europe & SAm. *Mem:* Am Phys Soc; Inst Elec & Electronics Engrs; Soc Explor Geophysists; Europ Asn Explor Geophysists. *Res:* Geophysics; acoustics; electronic instrumentation; microwave spectroscopy; structure of molecules; secondary frequency standards for K-band and higher frequencies; electron spin resonance; optical pumping; high sensitivity magnetometry; electromagnetic wave and acoustic wave propagation in rocks; ground probing radar studies; nonlinear acoustics in rocks. *Mailing Add:* 5004 Enchanted Oaks Dr College Station TX 77845. *E-Mail:* rru9300@aol.com

**UNTERSTEINER, NORBERT,** GLACIOLOGY, RESEARCH ADMINISTRATION. *Current Pos:* res assoc prof, 63-67, PROF ATMOSPHERIC SCI & GEOPHYS, UNIV WASH, 67- *Personal Data:* b Merano, Italy, Feb 24, 26. *Educ:* Innsbruck Univ, PhD(geophys), 50. *Honors & Awards:* Austrian Hon Cross Arts & Sci, 60. *Prof Exp:* Asst prof meteorol, Univ Vienna, 51-56, res meteorologist, Cent Estab Meteorol & Geodyn, Vienna, Austria, 57-62. *Concurrent Pos:* Docent, Univ Vienna, 61; consult, Rand Corp, Calif, 65-72; mem, Int Comn Polar Meteorol, World Meteorol Orgn, 66-74; mem comt polar res, Nat Acad Sci, 70-77; vpres, Int Comn Snow & Ice, Asn Sci Hydrol, Int Union Geod & Geophys, 61-76; proj dir, Div Marine Resources, 70-78; sci adv polar affairs, Off Naval Res, Washington, DC, 78-80; dir res & develop, Off Ocean Prog, Nat Oceanic & Atmospheric Admin, Washington, DC, 80-81; chmn dept atmospheric sci, Univ Wash, 88- *Mem:* Am Geophys Union; Ger Polar Soc; Norweg Polar Soc; Int Glaciol Soc. *Res:* Heat and mass budget of glaciers; physical properties of sea ice; sea-air interactions in polar regions; polar climatology. *Mailing Add:* Dept Atmospheric Sci Univ Wash 3900 Seventh Ave NE Seattle WA 98195-0001

**UNTI, THEODORE WAYNE JOSEPH,** optics, plasma physics, for more information see previous edition

**UNTRAUER, RAYMOND E(RNEST),** STRUCTURAL ENGINEERING. *Current Pos:* RETIRED. *Personal Data:* b Nevada, Iowa, Feb 9, 26; m 49, 89, Mary V Lengyel; c Steven, Julianne (Hagen), Lisa (Ford), Christopher, Jeanne (McCormack), Susan (Fenlin), Rachel (Koll), Mathew, Michael, Chrissy (McCoullough), Mark, Jeffrey & Scott. *Educ:* Iowa State Col, BS, 48; Univ Colo, MS, 51; Univ Ill, PhD(civil eng), 61. *Prof Exp:* Surveyor, Eng Dept, Mo Pac RR, Co, 48-49; instr civil eng, Univ Colo, 49-51; struct designer, C F Braun & Co, Calif, 51-52; from asst prof to assoc prof civil eng, Univ Ark, 52-57; res assoc, Univ Ill, 57-61; assoc prof, Iowa State Univ, 61-65; prof civil eng & dir struct res lab, Eng Res Inst, 65-72; head, Dept Civil Eng, Pa State Univ, 72-79, prof, 72-88, emer prof, 89. *Mem:* Am Soc Civil Engrs; Am Soc Eng Educ; Am Concrete Inst. *Res:* Reinforced and prestressed concrete; structural dynamics; analysis by numerical methods. *Mailing Add:* 218 Val Verda Dr Pennsylvania Furnace PA 16865-9544

**UNVER, ERCAN,** MICROBIOLOGY, MOLECULAR BIOLOGY. *Current Pos:* DIR BIOCHEM, DIAGNOSTIC PRODS CORP, 88- *Personal Data:* b Odemis, Turkey, Aug 6, 50; US citizen; m 78, Zehra Cagarli; c Beril & Peri. *Educ:* Mid East Tech Univ, Turkey, BS, 73; Calif State Univ, Long Beach, MS, 76; Aegean Univ, Turkey, PhD(biochem), 82. *Prof Exp:* Teaching asst, Calif State Univ, Long Beach, 74-76; lectr, Aegean Univ, Turkey, 76-82; asst prof res, Univ Southern Calif, 83-86. *Mem:* Am Chem Soc; AAAS; Am In-Vitro Allergy/Immunol Soc. *Res:* Purification of native and recombinant proteins; chemical characterization and modification of these proteins for the immunology systems. *Mailing Add:* Biochem Dept Diag Prod Corp 5700 W 96th St Los Angeles CA 90045-5544

**UNWIN, STEPHEN CHARLES,** RADIO ASTRONOMY. *Current Pos:* MEM TECH STAFF, JET PROPULSION LAB, 96- *Personal Data:* b Bromley, Eng, Sept 8, 53; m 88, Joan C Horvath. *Educ:* Univ Cambridge, BA, 76, PhD(radio astron), 79. *Hon Degrees:* MA, Univ Cambridge, 80. *Honors & Awards:* Group Achievement Award, NASA, 93. *Prof Exp:* Researcher, Dept Physics, Univ Cambridge, 76-79; res fel radio astron, Owens Valley Radio Observ, Calif Inst Technol, 79-82, mem prof staff, 82-96. *Mem:* Fel Royal Astron Soc; Am Astron Soc; Int Astron Union; Int Radio Sci Union. *Res:* Radio astronomy using interferometric techniques; dynamics of compact radio sources using very long baseline interferometric methods; galactic astrophysics using optical interferometry. *Mailing Add:* 2115 Brigden Rd Pasadena CA 91104. *E-Mail:* unwin@huey.jpl.nasa.gov

**UNZ, HILLEL,** WAVE PROPAGATION, QUANTUM WAVE MECHANICS. *Current Pos:* CONSULT, 58- *Personal Data:* b Darmstadt, Ger, Aug 15, 29; nat US; m 75; c 3. *Educ:* Israel Inst Technol, BS, 53, dipl, 61; Univ Calif, Berkeley, MS, 54, PhD(elec eng), 57. *Prof Exp:* Res asst, Microwave Res Lab, Univ Calif, Berkeley, 53-57; prof, Kans Univ, 57-96. *Concurrent Pos:* NSF fel, Cavendish Lab, Univ Cambridge, 63-64; vis prof, Israel Inst Technol, 64, UNESCO, 64. *Res:* Electromagnetic theory; antenna arrays; propagation in the ionosphere; plasma dynamics; moving plasmas; acoustic waves; theory of plates; quantum wave mechanics. *Mailing Add:* 1107 W 27th Terr Lawrence KS 66046-4513

**UNZ, RICHARD F(REDERICK),** ENVIRONMENTAL MICROBIOLOGY. *Current Pos:* from asst prof to assoc prof sanit microbiol, 66-81, PROF ENVIRON MICROBIOL, PA STATE UNIV, 81- *Personal Data:* b Syracuse, NY, Sept 15, 35; m 65; c 1. *Educ:* Syracuse Univ, BS, 57, MS, 60; Rutgers Univ, PhD(environ sci), 65. *Prof Exp:* Res chemist, Metrop Sanit Dist Greater Chicago, 65-66. *Concurrent Pos:* Ed, Appl & Environ Microbiol, 91- *Mem:* Am Soc Microbiol; Water Pollution Control Fedn; Am Acad Microbiol; Int Asn Water Quality. *Res:* Microbiological flocculation and zoogloeal bacteria; microbiology of acid mine drainage; ecology and physiology of filamentous microorganisms in waste waters; disinfection of water and wastewater; wetland microbiology and geochemistry. *Mailing Add:* Dept Civil Eng Pa State Univ 212 Sackett Bldg University Park PA 16802-1408. *Fax:* 814-863-7304; *E-Mail:* rfu1@psu.edu

**UNZICKER, JOHN DUANE,** entomology, for more information see previous edition

**UOTILA, URHO A(NTTI KALEVI),** GEODESY. *Current Pos:* res asst, Ohio State Univ, 52-53, res assoc, 53-58, lectr geod, 55-57, from asst prof to prof, 59-88, res supvr, 59-88, chmn, Dept Geod Sci, 64-84, EMER PROF GEOD & CHMN, OHIO STATE UNIV, 89- *Personal Data:* b Poytya, Finland, Feb 22, 23; nat US; m 49, Helena Vinhakartano; c Heidi, Kirsi, Elizabeth, Julie, Trina & Caroline. *Educ:* Finland Inst Tech, BS, 46, MS, 49; Ohio State Univ, PhD(geod), 59. *Honors & Awards:* Kaarina & W A Heiskanen Award, 62; Apollo Achievement Award, NASA, 69; Award for Except Serv, Am Cong Surv & Mapping, 80; Distinguished Serv Award, Survr Inst Sri Lanka; Fennell Award, Am Cong Surv & Mapping, 89. *Prof Exp:* Surveyor & geodesist, Finnish Govt, 44-46 & 46-51. *Concurrent Pos:* Geodesist, Swedish Govt, 46; mem, Solar Eclipse Exped Greenland, 54; mem geod adv panel, Nat Acad Sci to US Coast & Geod Surv, 64-66; mem geod & cartog working group, Space Sci Steering Comt, NASA, 65-67, geod & cartog adv subcomt, 67-72; mem bd trustees, Univ Space Res Asn, 73-75; mem bd dirs, Int Gravity Bur, France, 75-83; mem comt geod, Nat Acad Sci, 75-78. *Mem:* Fel Am Geophys Union (vpres geod sect, 64-68, pres, 68-70); fel Am Cong Surv & Mapping (vpres, 77-78, pres-elect, 78-79, pres, 79-80); Am Soc Photogram; Can Inst Surv; foreign mem Finnish Nat Acad Sci; Am Asn Geod Surv (pres, 84-86); fel Int Asn Geod. *Res:* Geometric and physical geodesy and statistical analysis of data. *Mailing Add:* Dept Civil Environ Eng & Geoetic Sci Ohio State Univ 470 Hitchcock Hall 2070 Neil Ave Columbus OH 43210-1275

**UPADHYAY, JAGDISH M,** MICROBIOLOGY, BIOCHEMISTRY. *Current Pos:* asst prof, 65-67, ASSOC PROF MICROBIOL, LOYOLA UNIV, LA, 68- *Personal Data:* b Jambusar, Gujerat, India, July 2, 31; m 63; c 1. *Educ:* Gujerat Univ, India, BPharm, 51; Univ Mich, MS, 57; Wash State Univ, PhD(bact), 63. *Prof Exp:* Chemist, Sarabhai Chem, India, 51-55; grant, Univ Tex, 63-65. *Concurrent Pos:* NIH grants, Schlieder Found, 70-72. *Mem:* Am Soc Microbiol; Brit Soc Gen Microbiol; Sigma Xi. *Res:* Growth and metabolism of psychrophilic microorganisms and soil amebas; lytic enzymes; cell-wall composition; thermophilic microorganisms; carotenoid pigments. *Mailing Add:* Dept Biol Loyola Univ 6363 St Charles Ave New Orleans LA 70118-6143

**UPADHYAYA, BELLE RAGHAVENDRA,** NEURAL NETWORKS APPLICATIONS, SIGNAL PROCESSING TECHNOLOGY. *Current Pos:* From asst prof to assoc prof, 78-89, PROF NUCLEAR ENG, UNIV TENN, KNOXVILLE, 89- *Personal Data:* b Mangalore, India; US citizen; m 79; c 1. *Educ:* Regional Eng Co, Suratkal, India, BE, 65; Univ Toronto, MASc, 68; Univ Calif, San Diego, PhD(syst sci), 75. *Concurrent Pos:* Adj res assoc, Oak Ridge Nat Lab. *Mem:* Inst Elec & Electronics Engrs; Am Nuclear Soc; Instrument Soc Am; Am Soc Eng Educ; Sigma Xi; Am Soc Nondestructive Testing. *Res:* Digital signal processing and system dynamic analysis with application to power plant monitoring and diagnostics; preventive maintenance technology and applied artificial intelligence. *Mailing Add:* 1223 Hamstead Ct Knoxville TN 37922

**UPATNIEKS, JURIS,** COHERENT OPTICS, HOLOGRAPHY. *Current Pos:* SR ENGR, APPL OPTICS, 93- *Personal Data:* b Riga, Latvia, May 7, 36; US citizen; m 68, Ilze Inouss; c Ivars & Ansis. *Educ:* Univ Akron, BS, 60; Univ Mich, MS, 65. *Honors & Awards:* Robert Gordown Mem Award, Soc Photog Instr Eng, 65; R W Wood Prize, Optical Soc Am, 75; Holley Medal Am Soc Mech Engrs, 76. *Prof Exp:* Instr microwaves, Ord Sch, US Army, 61-62; from asst to res engr, Willow Run Labs, Univ Mich, 60-72; res engr, Environ Res Inst Mich, 73-93. *Concurrent Pos:* Consult, var pvt & govt orgn, 66-; adj assoc prof, Dept Elec Eng & Comput Sci, Univ Mich, 74- *Mem:* Optical Soc Am; Soc Photo-Optical Instrumentation Engrs; Latvian Acad Sci. *Res:* Holography; optical data processing; holographic optical elements; coherent optics. *Mailing Add:* Appl Optics 2662 Valley Dr Ann Arbor MI 48103. *Fax:* 313-998-0425; *E-Mail:* upatnieks@applopt.com

**UPCHURCH, JONATHAN EVERETT,** TRANSPORTATION ENGINEERING. *Current Pos:* asst prof, 82-91, ASSOC PROF CIVIL ENG, COL ENG & APPL SCI, ARIZ STATE UNIV, 86- *Personal Data:* b Chicago, Ill, Jan 2, 51; m 71; c 1. *Educ:* Univ Ill, BS, 71, MS, 75; Univ Md, PhD(civil eng), 82. *Prof Exp:* Transp engr, Harland Bartholomew & Assocs, 72-76; dir tech affairs, Inst Transp Engrs, Washington, DC, 76-80; res engr, Off Res, Fed Hwy Admin, Washington, DC, 81-82. *Concurrent Pos:* Consult, Am Asn State Hwy & Transp Officials, 80-88; exec secy, Nat Comt Uniform Traffic Control Devices, 79-88. *Mem:* Transp Res Bd; Inst Transp Engrs (int pres, 91); Am Soc Civil Engrs. *Res:* Traffic engineering; traffic operations; development of standards for traffic control devices which result in the most economical operation for the motoring public. *Mailing Add:* Dept Civil Eng Ariz State Univ Tempe AZ 85287-0001

**UPCHURCH, ROBERT PHILLIP,** PLANT PHYSIOLOGY, WEED SCIENCE. *Current Pos:* head, Dept Plant Sci, Univ Ariz, 75-81, dir agr develop & assoc dir, Agr Exp Sta, 81-83, assoc dean, 83-88, dir agr alumni affairs, 88-90, DIR AGR DEVELOP, UNIV ARIZ, 90- *Personal Data:* b Raleigh, NC, Feb 9, 28; m 48; c 3. *Educ:* BS & MS, NC State Univ, 49; Univ Calif, PhD(plant physiol), 53. *Honors & Awards:* Sigma Xi Res Award, NC State Univ, 63. *Prof Exp:* Instr crop sci, NC State Univ, 49-51, from asst prof to prof, 53-65; sr res group leader, Monsanto Co, 65-70, res mgr, 70-73, mgr res, 73-75. *Concurrent Pos:* Consult, Shell Develop Co, 62-65 & Eli Lilly & Co, 79-88; mem, Weeds Subcomt, Nat Acad Sci, 64-68; ed, Southern Weed Conf, 66-69; adv, Am Coun & Health, 83-; dir, Boyce Thompson Southwest Arboretum, 85- *Mem:* Am Soc Plant Physiol; Am Soc Agron; Crop Sci Soc Am; fel Weed Sci Soc Am (pres, 72-); Plant Growth Regulator Soc (chmn, 72). *Res:* Response of plants to phytoactive chemicals and the influence of soil and climate factors on the expression of such responses. *Mailing Add:* 2637 W Crown King Dr Tucson AZ 85721

**UPCHURCH, SAM BAYLISS,** GROUND-WATER CHEMISTRY, SEDIMENTOLOGY. *Current Pos:* PRIN HYDROGEOLOGIST, ENVIRON RESOURCES MGT-SOUTH, 93- *Personal Data:* b Murfreesboro, Tenn, June 30, 41; m 64, Mary A Comer; c Samantha & William. *Educ:* Vanderbilt Univ, AB, 63; Northwestern Univ, Evanston, MS, 66, PhD(geol), 70. *Prof Exp:* Resident in res marine geol, Northwestern Univ, Evanston, 67-68; res phys scientist chem limnol, Lake Surv Ctr, Nat Oceanic & Atmospheric Admin, 68-71; asst prof geol, Mich State Univ, 71-74; from assoc prof to prof geol, Univ S Fla, 74-93, chmn dept, 81-93. *Concurrent Pos:* Mem limnol work group, Great Lakes Basin Comn, 68-75, mem bd tech adv, 69-75; consult hydrol & geoarcheol, 73-; mem, Fla Bd Prof Geologists, 88- *Mem:* Soc Econ Paleont & Mineral; fel Geol Soc Am; Am Water Resources Asn; Am Asn Petrol Geologists; Southeastern Geol Soc (vpres, 79-80, pres, 80-81); Nat Water Well Asn. *Res:* Trace element-sediment interaction; ground-water chemistry; carbonate sediment genesis and diagenesis; chert petrology; mathematical geology; geohydrology; land-use planning. *Mailing Add:* 3768 Parkway Blvd Land O Lakes FL 34639-4216. *Fax:* 813-621-8504

**UPDEGRAFF, DAVID MAULE,** MICROBIOLOGY. *Current Pos:* prof chem & geochem, 77-87, RES PROF, COLO SCH MINES, 88- *Personal Data:* b Woodstock, NY, Dec 19, 17; m 43; c 3. *Educ:* Univ Calif, Los Angeles, AB, 41; Univ Calif, PhD(microbiol), 47. *Prof Exp:* Res assoc & actg dir, Am Petrol Inst Res Proj, Scripps Inst, Univ Calif, 46; sr res chemist, Field Res Labs, Magnolia Petrol Co, 47-50; sr res technologist, 50-55; res microbiologist, Cent Res Dept, Minn Mining & Mfg Co, Minn, 55-68; head microbiol sect, Chem Div, Denver Res Inst, Univ Denver, 68-72; head, Basic Res Dept, Cawthron Inst, 72-75; vpres, Resource Industs Int, Ltd, 75-77. *Res:* Biochemistry of carotenoid pigments; bacterial physiology; marine and petroleum microbiology; applied microbiology; fermentations; ecology of water pollution and waste treatment; bioremediation. *Mailing Add:* Dept Chem & Geochem Colo Sch Mines Golden CO 80401

**UPDEGROVE, LOUIS B,** CHEMICAL ENGINEERING. *Current Pos:* PRES, TYLER SCOTT INC, TERRACE PARK, 77- *Personal Data:* b Kingsville, Tex, Sept 10, 28; m 52; c 2. *Educ:* Mass Inst Technol, SB, 53. *Prof Exp:* Chem engr, Chemstrand Corp, Fla, 53-56; res engr, Sci Labs, Ford Motor Co, 56-57; lab develop supvr, Kordite Corp, NY, 57-62; test dir, Standard Packaging Corp, 62-65; process develop mgr, Alcolac Chem Corp, 65; vpres & mgr res & develop, Vogt Mfg Corp, NY, 65-69; vpres eng, J H Day Co, Cincinnati, 69-77. *Mem:* Am Chem Soc; Soc Plastics Engrs. *Res:* Applied plastics research and development; packaging; coatings; emulsion polymers; polymer processing; solids drying; pigment dispersion; research management. *Mailing Add:* 313 Rugby Ave Terrace Park OH 45174

**UPDIKE, OTIS L(EE), JR,** BIOMEDICAL & CHEMICAL ENGINEERING. *Current Pos:* assoc prof chem eng, 46-60, res engr, Eng Exp Sta, 51-59, PROF CHEM ENG & MEM PARTIC FAC, RES LABS, ENG SCI, UNIV VA, 60-, PROF CHEM & BIOMED ENG, 67- *Personal Data:* b Roanoke, Va, Feb 12, 20; m 45; c 4. *Educ:* Univ Va, BChE, 41; Univ Ill, PhD(chem eng), 44. *Prof Exp:* Asst, Eng Exp Sta, Univ Ill, 41-44; chemist, Eng Res Dept, Westvaco Chlorine Prod Corp, 44-46. *Concurrent Pos:* Consult, Philip Morris & Co, 52-59; tech consult, US Naval Air Missile Test Ctr, 54-55; vpres, Jefferson Res Labs, 55-58; NSF sci fac fel & vis assoc, Calif Inst Technol, 59-60; chmn, Joint Automatic Control Conf, 69. *Mem:* AAAS; Am Inst Chem Engrs; Biomed Eng Soc; Inst Elec & Electronics Engrs; Instrument Soc Am. *Res:* Instrumentation and automatic control; computer applications in process and biomedical engineering; dynamics of process, physiological and instrumentation systems; data acquisition and interpretation. *Mailing Add:* Dept Biomed Eng Univ Va Med Ctr PO Box 377 Charlottesville VA 22908

**UPDIKE, RANDALL G,** EARTHQUAKE SEISMOLOGY. *Current Pos:* CHIEF SCIENTIST, GEOL HAZARDS TEAM, US GEOL SURV, 96- *Personal Data:* b Hondo, Tex, Nov 27, 43. *Educ:* Univ Mo, BS, 66; Ariz State Univ, MS, 68, PhD(geol), 72. *Mailing Add:* Denver Fed Ctr US Geol Surv Box 25046 MS 966 Denver CO 80225. *Fax:* 303-273-8583; *E-Mail:* updike@ usgs.gov

**UPESLACIS, JANIS,** PHARMACEUTICAL CHEMISTRY. *Current Pos:* res chemist, Lederle Labs, Am Cyanamid Co, 75-80, group leader, 81-86, proj mgr, biotechnol chem, 86-89, dept head, oncol & immunol res sect, 89-95, ASSOC DIR ONCOL, IMMUNOL CHEM, WYETH-AYERST RES, AM HOME PRODUCTS CO, 95- *Personal Data:* b Bad-Rothenfelde, Ger, Jan 12, 46; US citizen; m 68, Velta Neimanis; c Erik & Adam. *Educ:* Univ Nebr, Lincoln, BS, 67; Harvard Univ, MA, 69, PhD(org chem), 75. *Prof Exp:* Asst nuclear physics, Walter Reed Army Med Ctr, US Army, 69-71. *Mem:* Am Chem Soc. *Res:* Synthetic applications of carbohydrates; antiatherogenic agents; inhibitors of complement-mediated diseases; antineoplastic agents; synthetic vaccines; monoclonal antibodies as carriers of drugs. *Mailing Add:* Wyeth-Ayerst Res Pearl River NY 10965. *Fax:* 914-732-5561; *E-Mail:* upeslaj@war.wyeth.com

**UPGREN, ARTHUR REINHOLD, JR,** ASTRONOMY. *Current Pos:* from asst prof to assoc prof astron, Wesleyan Univ, 66-81, chmn dept, 68-86, adj prof, 66-73, dir, Van Vleck Observ, 73-, JOHN MONROE VAN VLECK PROF ASTRON, WESLEYAN UNIV, 81- *Personal Data:* b Minneapolis, Minn, Feb 21, 33; m 67; c 1. *Educ:* Univ Minn, BA, 55; Univ Mich, MS, 58; Case Inst Technol, PhD(astron), 61. *Prof Exp:* Res assoc astron, Swarthmore Col, 61-63; astronr, US Naval Observ, 63-66. *Concurrent Pos:* Vis lectr, Univ Md, 64-66, George Washington Univ, 65-66 & Yale Univ, 67-68; Am Philos Soc grant, 62, NSF grant, 67-; vpres & exec officer, Fund Astrophys Res Inc, 72-; adj prof, Univ Fla, 84-; pres, Comn 24, Int Astron Union, 85-88; chmn,

Sci Orgn Comt Symp, "Calibration Stellar Ages," 88. *Mem:* Am Astron Soc; Royal Astron Soc; Int Astron Union; Illuminating Eng Soc; Int Dark-Sky Asn; Astron Soc Pac. *Res:* Galactic structure; photographic astrometry. *Mailing Add:* Dept Astron Van Vleck Observ Wesleyan Univ 349 Sci Ctr Middletown CT 06459. *Fax:* 203-344-7981; *E-Mail:* aupgren@eagle. wesleyan.edu

**UPHAM, ROY WALTER,** VETERINARY MEDICINE, FOOD TECHNOLOGY. *Current Pos:* chief, Div Food, Drugs & Dairies, Regulatory Agency, Ill Dept Pub Health, Springfield, 66-83. *Personal Data:* b Ogden, Kans, Apr 11, 20; m 69. *Educ:* Kans State Univ, DVM, 43; Mass Inst Technol, MS, 60; Am Bd Vet Pub Health, dipl. *Prof Exp:* Instr food technol, US Army Med Serv Sch, 54-56, proj off radiation of foods prog, US Army, 56-58, mil adv, Food Prog for Vietnam, 62-63, chief lab br food testing, Defense Personnel Supply Command, 63-65, chief standardization br, Mil Specifications, Natick Army Lab, 65-66. *Mem:* Inst Food Technologists; Asn Food & Drug Officials (pres, 81-82). *Res:* Application of controlled food processing to safeguard and protect public health. *Mailing Add:* 1998 N Walnut Rd Rochester IL 62563

**UPHOLT, WILLIAM BOYCE,** MOLECULAR BIOLOGY, DEVELOPMENTAL BIOLOGY. *Current Pos:* assoc prof, 85-90, PROF, DEPT BIOSTRUCT & FUNCTION, HEALTH CTR, UNIV CONN, 90- *Personal Data:* b Orlando, Fla, Sept 14, 43; m 80, Mary L Morrison; c Gretchen & Boyce. *Educ:* Pomona Col, BA, 65; Calif Inst Technol, PhD(chem), 71. *Prof Exp:* Res fel molecular biol, Damon Runyon Mem Fund Cancer Res, Biochem Lab, Univ Amsterdam, 71-73; res fel, Dept Embryol, Carnegie Inst Wash, Baltimore, 73-75; res assoc molecular biol, Dept Pediat & Biochem, Univ Chicago, 75-85. *Mem:* Soc Develop Biol; Am Soc Chem Biol. *Res:* Physical chemistry of nucleic acids, organization of genetic material, developmental biology, control of gene expression during chick limb cartilage differentiation; type II collagen gene structure and regulation; skeletal pattern formation. *Mailing Add:* Dept Biostruct Function Univ Conn Health Ctr 263 Farmington Ave Farmington CT 06030-3705

**UPMEIER, HARALD,** FUNCTIONAL ANALYSIS, COMPLEX ANALYSIS. *Current Pos:* assoc prof, 84-86, PROF MATH, UNIV KANS, 86- *Personal Data:* b Mainz, Ger, Dec 29, 50. *Educ:* Univ Tubingen, PhD(math), 75. *Prof Exp:* Asst prof math, Univ Pa, 82-84. *Mailing Add:* Dept Math Univ Marburg Hans Meerwein St 35032 Marburg Lahnberge Germany

**UPPAL, PARVEZ N,** CONDENSED MATTER PHYSICS. *Current Pos:* scientist, 85-88, SR SCIENTIST, ULTRASTRUCT MAT DEPT, MARTIN MARIETTA LABS, BALTIMORE, 88- *Educ:* Punjab Univ, Pakistan, BSc, 71; Physics Univ, Pakistan, MSc, 73; Va Polytech Inst & State Univ, MS, 81, PhD(mat eng), 83. *Prof Exp:* Asst res engr, Univ Calif, Santa Barbara, 83-85. *Mem:* Am Phys Soc; Inst Elec & Electronics Engrs. *Res:* Growth and characterization of gallium arsenic materials and devices; growth of lattice-mismatched epitaxial layers; investigation of defect incorporation in molecular beam epitaxy growth of materials by studying novel crystal orientations. *Mailing Add:* Martin Marietta Labs 1450 S Rolling Rd Baltimore MD 21227

**UPPULURI, V R RAO,** MATHEMATICAL STATISTICS. *Current Pos:* mem staff, Nuclear Div, Union Carbide Corp, 74-77, SR RES STAFF MEM, UNION CARBIDE NUCLEAR DIV, 77- *Personal Data:* b Machilipattanam, India, Feb 22, 31; m 60; c 1. *Educ:* Andhra Univ, India, MA, 54; Ind Univ, Bloomington, PhD(math), 63. *Prof Exp:* Res asst math & statist, Tata Inst Fundamental Res, 54-57; res asst math, Ind Univ, Bloomington, 57-61; res assoc statist, Mich State Univ, 61-62, biophys & statist, 62-63; sr math statistician, Oak Ridge Nat Lab, 63-74. *Concurrent Pos:* Lectr, Oak Ridge Traveling Lect Prog, Oak Ridge Assoc Univs & Oak Ridge Nat Lab, 64-; sr engr & scientist, Douglas Aircraft Co, 66; vis lectr prog, Comt Statist Southern Regional Educ Bd, 67-; adj prof, Univ Tenn, 67-; consult, Syst Develop Corp, 67- & med div, Oak Ridge Assoc Univ, 67-; vis prof, Univ Sao Paulo, 70 & Univ Minn, 71. *Mem:* Fel AAAS; fel Am Statist Asn; Am Math Soc; Sigma Xi. *Res:* Probability; statistics; stochastic approach for a better understanding of the structure of physical and natural phenomena; limit theorems in random difference equations and applications of probability. *Mailing Add:* 130 Indian Lane Oak Ridge TN 37830-4957

**U'PRICHARD, DAVID C,** neuropharmacology, neurochemistry, for more information see previous edition

**UPSON, DAN W,** PHARMACOLOGY, PHYSIOLOGY. *Current Pos:* RETIRED. *Personal Data:* b Hutchinson, Kans, July 30, 29; m 59; c 3. *Educ:* Kans State Univ, DVM, 52, MS, 62, PhD(physiol), 69. *Prof Exp:* Vet, Pvt Pract, 52-59; instr pharmacol & physiol, Col Vet Med, Kans State Univ, 59-69, assoc prof pharmacol, 69-73, asst dean, 72-73, prof pharmacol, 73-, dir teaching resources, 75-94. *Concurrent Pos:* Consult, Tevcon Ind Inc, 70- *Mem:* Am Vet Med Asn; Am Acad Vet Pharmacol & Therapeut; Am Acad Vet Consult. *Res:* Veterinary pharmacology and clinical pharmacology. *Mailing Add:* 201 Cedar Dr Manhattan KS 66502

**UPTHEGROVE, W(ILLIAM) R(EID),** METALLURGICAL ENGINEERING, ENGINEERING EDUCATION. *Current Pos:* prof metall & mech eng & dean, Col Eng, 70-81, REGENTS PROF ENG, UNIV OKLA, 81- *Personal Data:* b Ann Arbor, Mich, Nov 10, 28; m 53; c 5. *Educ:* Univ Mich, BSE, 50, MSE, 54, PhD(metall eng), 57. *Prof Exp:* From asst prof to assoc prof metall eng, Univ Okla, 56-62, chmn sch, 56-62; sect leader powder metall res & develop, Res Labs, Int Nickel Co, Inc, NJ, 62-64; prof mech eng & chmn dept, Univ Tex, Austin, 64-70. *Concurrent Pos:* Indust consult, 64-; consult educ planning, US Overseas Inst, 70- & failure analysis & prod liability. *Mem:* Fel Am Soc Metals; Am Soc Mech Engrs; Nat Soc Prof Engrs; Am Soc Eng Educ; fel AAAS; Soc Antomotive Engrs. *Res:* Powder metallurgy; diffusion; design and materials properties. *Mailing Add:* 3941 Warwick Dr Norman OK 73072

**UPTON, ARTHUR CANFIELD,** EXPERIMENTAL PATHOLOGY, RADIOBIOLOGY. *Current Pos:* prof & dir, Inst Environ Med, 80-92, EMER PROF & DIR, NY UNIV, 92-; CLIN PROF RADIOL, SCH MED, UNIV NMEX, 93-; CLIN PROF ENVIRON & COMMUNITY MED, ROBERT WOOD JOHNSON MED SCH, UNIV MED & DENT NJ, 95- *Personal Data:* b Ann Arbor, Mich, Feb 27, 23; m 46, Elizabeth Bache Perry; c Rebecca, Melissa & Bradley. *Educ:* Univ Mich, BA, 44, MD, 46. *Honors & Awards:* Lawrence Award, 65; Comfort Crookshank Award for Cancer Res, 78; Claude M Fuess Award, 80; Sarah L Poilley Award, 83; CHUMS Physician of the Yr Award, 85; Basic Cell Res in Cytol Lectureship Award, 85; Fred W Stewart Award, 86; Ramazzini Award, 86; Lovelace Found Award, 93. *Prof Exp:* Intern & residency, Univ Hosp, Ann Arbor, Mich, 47-50; instr path, Med Sch, Univ Mich, 50-51; pathologist, Oakridge Nat Lab, 51-54, chief, Path-Physiol Sect, 54-69; prof, State Univ NY, Stony Brook, 69-77, dean, Sch Basic Health Sci, 70-75; dir, Nat Cancer Inst, 77-79. *Concurrent Pos:* Mem comt biol effectiveness of radiation & long term effects of radiation, Nat Acad Sci, Nat Res Coun, 57-; Ciba Found lectr, 59, Failla lectr, Radiation Res Soc, 77, IBM- Princess Takamatsu Cancer Res Found, 81, Failla Mem lectr, Health Physics Soc, 83, Fourth Ann Martin Schneider Mem Lectr, Univ Tex Med Br, 84; mem comt, Int Comn Radiol Protection, 64-, comnr, 73-80; mem, Nat Coun Radiation Protection & Measurements, 65-, adv comt, Ctr Human Radiobiol, Argonne Nat Lab, 72-76, sci adv group, US-Japan Coop Cancer Res Prog, 74-77, sci adv bd, Nat Ctr Toxological Res, 74-77, sci coun, Int Agency Res Cancer, WHO, 77; rep, USA Nat Comt Int Union Against Cancer, 72-; chmn, Health Res Coun, NY State, 81-92; Sigma Xi nat lectr, 90-91; pres, Ramazzini Inst, 92- *Mem:* Inst Med-Nat Acad Sci; AAAS; Sigma Xi; Radiation Res Soc (vpres, 64-65, pres, 65-66); Am Soc Exp Path (vpres, 66-67, pres, 67-68); Am Asn Cancer Res (vpres, 62-63, pres, 63-64); hon mem Peruvian Oncol Soc; hon mem Japan Cancer Asn; fel NY Acad Sci; Int Asn Radiation Res (vpres, 79-83, pres, 83-87); Soc Study Comparative Oncol. *Res:* Pathology of radiation injury and endocrine glands; cancer; carcinogenesis; experimental leukemia; aging; environmental toxicology. *Mailing Add:* Environ & Occup Health Sci Inst 681 Frelinghuysen Piscataway NJ 08855-1179. *Fax:* 505-984-2331

**UPTON, G VIRGINIA,** PHYSIOLOGY, BIOCHEMISTRY. *Current Pos:* assoc dir clin res, 74-78, dir, Wyeth Int Ltd, 84-86, ASSOC MED, WYETH INT LTD, 78-88, DIR CLIN DEVELOP, WYETH AYERST RES, 88- *Personal Data:* b New Haven, Conn, Oct 17, 29; wid; c 3. *Educ:* Albertus Magnus Col, BA, 51; Yale Univ, MS, 61, PhD(physiol), 64. *Prof Exp:* NIH fel peptide chem, Yale Univ, 63-66, chief endocrine & polypeptide lab, Vet Admin Hosp, Yale Univ, 66-74, sr res assoc med, Sch Med, 71-74. *Concurrent Pos:* Asst prof comp endocrinol, Eve Div, South Conn State Col, 66-67; assoc prof med, Med Col, PA, 82- *Mem:* Am Asn Cancer Res; Endocrine Soc; NY Acad Sci; Int Soc Neuroendocrinol; Am Physiol Soc; Am Fertil Soc. *Res:* Neuroendocrinology; hypothalamic-pituitary-adrenal relationships; isolation of pituitary peptides and tumor peptides with hormonal activity; relationship between endocrine disorders and hypothalamic dysfunction. *Mailing Add:* 208 Hermitage Dr Radnor PA 19087

**UPTON, RONALD P,** ANALYTICAL CHEMISTRY. *Current Pos:* DIR, QUAL ASSURANCE/QUAL CONTROL, NASKA PHARMACOL, 90- *Personal Data:* b Boston, Mass, May 6, 41; m 65, Mary A Fendersen; c Ellen, Matthew, David & Christopher. *Educ:* New Bedford Inst Tech, BS, 63; Univ Del, PhD(analytical chem), 68. *Prof Exp:* Staff chemist, Res Lab, Miles Labs, 67-70, mgr qual control, 70-84, dir qual asurance, 84-85; mgr analytical chem, Pennwalt Corp, 88-90. *Concurrent Pos:* Dir qual assurance/qual control, NASRA Pharmacol Co, Inc, Lincolnton, NC, 90-91. *Mem:* Am Chem Soc; Sigma Xi. *Res:* Quality control; instrumental analysis; infrared, ultraviolet, atomic absorption and nuclear magnetic spectroscopies; gas and high pressure liquid chromatography, in vitro diagnostics and pharmaceutical analysis. *Mailing Add:* 1587 Nottingham Dr Newton NC 28658-7408

**UPTON, STEVE JAY,** COCCIDIAL BIOLOGY, CRYPTOSPORIDIOSIS. *Current Pos:* asst prof to assoc prof biol, 86-96, PROF BIOL, KANS STATE UNIV, 96- *Personal Data:* b Portland, Ore, June 14, 53; m 91, Brenda Oppert; c Sierra H. *Educ:* Ore State Univ, BS, 75; Univ NMex, MS, 81; Auburn Univ, PhD(zool & entom), 83. *Honors & Awards:* H B Ward Medal, Am Soc Parasitol, 96. *Prof Exp:* Fel, Auburn Univ, 83-84; vis asst prof, Univ Tex, El Paso, 84-86. *Mem:* Am Soc Parasitologists; Soc Protozoologists; Wildlife Dis Asn. *Res:* Examining the molecular and cell biology of the acquired immunodeficiency syndrome related pathogen, Cryptosporidium parvum. *Mailing Add:* Div Biol Kans State Univ Manhattan KS 66506. *Fax:* 785-532-6653; *E-Mail:* coccidia@ksu.edu

**UPTON, THOMAS HALLWORTH,** CATALYSIS, SURFACE SCIENCE. *Current Pos:* Res chemist, 80-90, SECT HEAD, EXXON RES & ENG CORP, 90- *Personal Data:* b Dallas, Tex, Apr 14, 52; m 78; c 2. *Educ:* Stanford Univ, BS, 74; Calif Inst Technol, PhD(theoret), 80. *Mem:* Am Chem Soc. *Res:* Theoretical investigations of mechanisms in homogeneous, heterogeneous catalysis and surface science. *Mailing Add:* Corp Res Labs Exxon Res & Eng Annandale NJ 08801

**URALIL, FRANCIS STEPHEN,** POLYMER PHYSICS. *Current Pos:* SR RES PHYSICIST, SHELL OIL CO, 89- *Personal Data:* b Kerala, India, June 3, 50; m 80; c 1. *Educ:* Univ Kerala, BS, 69; Marquette Univ, MS, 72; Univ Del, PhD(physics), 76. *Prof Exp:* Res assoc polymer physics, Case Inst Technol, 76-78 & physics, Schlumberger, 78-79; scientist & group leader polymer physics, Battelle Inst, 79-89. *Mem:* Am Phys Soc; Am Chem Soc. *Res:* Structure-property relationships; dynamic mechanical behavior of materials; fracture and fatigue studies; dielectrics and composites. *Mailing Add:* 14815 Walbrook Dr Sugarland TX 77478

**URANO, MUNEYASU,** HYPERTHERMIA, RADIATION DOSE FRACTIONATION. *Current Pos:* PROF RADIATION BIOL, COL MED, UNIV KY, 89- *Personal Data:* b Osaka, Japan, Apr 21, 36; US citizen; m 63; c 2. *Educ:* Kyoto Prefectural Univ, MD, 61, PhD(radiation biol), 68. *Prof Exp:* Res fel radiation biol, M D Anderson Hosp, 66-68; asst prof radiol, Kyoto Prefectural Univ Med, 68-70; sr researcher radiol biol, Nat Inst Radiol Sci, 70-77; from asst prof to assoc prof radiation biol, Mass Gen Hosp, 77-89. *Mem:* Radiation Res Soc; Am Soc Therapeut Radiol & Oncol; NAm Hyperthermia Soc; AAAS; Am Asn Cancer Res. *Res:* Effect of hyperthermia given alone or in combination with radiation and/or chemotherapeutic agents in animal tumor and normal tissues and in cultured cell. *Mailing Add:* Radiation Med Univ Ky Med Sch 800 Rose St Lexington KY 40536-0001

**URBA, WALTER JOHN,** MEDICINE, ONCOLOGY. *Current Pos:* DIR CANCER RES IMMUNOL/ONCOL, EARLE CHILDS RES INST, PROVIDENCE MED CTR, 93- *Personal Data:* b Swinden, Eng, May 14, 52. *Educ:* Rutgers Univ, BS, 74; Univ Calif, Los Angeles, 79, PhD(immunol), 81; Univ Miami, MD, 84. *Prof Exp:* Dir clin sci res, Frederick Cancer Res & Develop Ctr, Nat Cancer Inst, 84-93. *Mem:* Am Soc Oncol; Am Soc Cancer Res; Am Immunol Soc. *Mailing Add:* Earle Childs Res Inst Providence Med Ctr 4805 NE Glisan St Portland OR 97213-2967

**URBACH, FREDERICK,** DERMATOLOGY. *Current Pos:* med dir, Skin & Cancer Hosp, 67-89, EMER PROF DERMAT, PHILADELPHIA, 89- *Personal Data:* b Vienna, Austria, Sept 6, 22; nat US; wid; c 3. *Educ:* Univ Pa, BS, 43; Jefferson Med Col, MD, 46; Am Bd Dermat, dipl, 53. *Hon Degrees:* Dr Med(hon), Univ Gottingen, WGer, 87. *Honors & Awards:* Hellerstrom Medal, Swed Derm Soc, 78; Ritter Medal, Polish Derm Soc, 79, Germ Derm Soc, 80, Austrian Dermat Soc, 84; Finsen Medal, 92. *Prof Exp:* Asst instr dermat, Med Sch, Univ Pa, 49-50, instr, 50-52, assoc, 52-54; chief dermat serv, Roswell Park Mem Inst, 54-58; assoc prof, Temple Univ, 58-60, prof res, 60-67, prof dermat & chmn dept, Sch Med, 67-89. *Concurrent Pos:* Fel, Hosp Univ Pa, 49-52; Damon Runyon res fel clin cancer, Univ Pa, 51-53; asst vis physician, Philadelphia Gen Hosp, 51-54; mem, Int Cong Dermat, London, 52; from asst med dir to assoc med dir, Skin & Cancer Hosp, Temple Univ, 58-67; mem, US Nat Comt Photobiol, Nat Res Coun, 73-80; dir, Ctr Photobiol, 77-89. *Mem:* Fel AAAS; Soc Invest Dermat; Soc Exp Biol & Med; Am Asn Cancer Res; Am Soc Photobiol (pres, 77); Asn Int Photobiol (pres, 80-84). *Res:* Blood supply of cancer; biologic effects of ultraviolet radiation; photobiology; epidemiology of cancer. *Mailing Add:* Temple Med Pract 220 Commerce Dr Ft Washington PA 19034. *Fax:* 215-643-6188

**URBACH, FREDERICK LEWIS,** INORGANIC CHEMISTRY. *Current Pos:* asst prof, 66-74, assoc prof, 74-80, PROF CHEM, CASE WESTERN RES UNIV, 80- *Personal Data:* b New Castle, Pa, Nov 21, 38; m 60, Carrie Grimm; c Deborah & Allison. *Educ:* Pa State Univ, University Park, BS, 60; Mich State Univ, PhD(chem), 64. *Prof Exp:* Res assoc & fel, Ohio State Univ, 64-66. *Mem:* Am Chem Soc. *Res:* Chemistry of metal chelates containing multidentate ligands; redox behavior of transition metal complexes; role of copper ions in biological processes; fuel cell electrocatalysis. *Mailing Add:* Dept Chem Case Western Res Univ 10900 Euclid Ave Cleveland OH 44106-7078. *Fax:* 216-368-3006; *E-Mail:* flu@po.cwru.edu

**URBACH, HERMAN B,** THERMODYNAMICS OF HEAT ENGINES, ELECTROCHEMISTRY. *Current Pos:* SCI STAFF ASST POWER & PROPULSION, POWER SYSTS DIV, USNR & DEVELOP CTR, ANNAPOLIS, 65- *Personal Data:* b New York, NY, Jan 19, 23; m 56, Joan Patterson; c Jacqueline & Jonathan. *Educ:* Univ Ind, AB, 48; Columbia Univ, MA, 50; Case Western Res Univ, PhD(phys chem), 54; George Washington Univ, MS, 76; Univ Md, MS, 76. *Prof Exp:* Group leader, Olin Mathieson Chem Corp, 53-59; res scientist, Res Lab, United Aircraft Corp, 59-65, consult electrochem, Pratt & Whitney Aircraft Div, 60-63. *Concurrent Pos:* Guest prof mech eng, US Naval Acad, 81-82. *Mem:* Am Inst Aeronaut & Astronaut; Am Soc Mech Engrs; NY Acad Sci; Sigma Xi; Am Chem Soc. *Res:* Kinetics of the oxygen electrode; fuel cells; theory of porous electrodes; ozone and plasma kinetics; atomic reactions; boranes; magnetohydrodynamics; biphase turbines; gas and steam turbines; thermodynamic cycle simulation. *Mailing Add:* Code 82T NSWC Annapolis MD 21402-5738. *Fax:* 410-293-3553; *E-Mail:* urbach@oasys.dt.navy.mil

**URBACH, JOHN C,** IMAGE SCIENCE, ELECTRONIC IMAGING & LASER SCANNING. *Current Pos:* VPRES, DEVELOP, STRATA SYSTS INC, 87-; CONSULT, OPTICAL ENG & TECH MGT, 87- *Personal Data:* b Vienna, Austria, Feb 18, 34; US citizen; m 56; c 3. *Educ:* Univ Rochester, BS, 55, PhD(optics), 62; Mass Inst Technol, MS, 57. *Prof Exp:* Assoc physicist, Int Bus Mach Corp, 57-58; NATO fel sci, Royal Inst Tech, Sweden, 61-62; scientist, Xerox Corp, NY, 63-66, sr scientist, 66-67, mgr, Optical & Imaging Analysis Br, 67-68, mgr, Optical Sci Br, 68-70, mgr, Optical Sci Area, 70-75, mgr, Optical Sci Lab, Palo Alto Res Ctr, 75-85, mgr, Color Systs Technol Res Group, 85-87. *Concurrent Pos:* Chmn tech group info processing & holography, Optical Soc Am, 76-77; mem, US Nat Comt, Int Comn Optics, 75-77. *Mem:* Fel Optical Soc Am; Soc Imaging Sci & Technol; Soc

Photo-Optical Instrumentation Engrs; Sigma Xi. *Res:* Optical techniques for information storage and retrieval; effects of recording materials upon holographic imaging; unconventional photography, especially electrophotography; evaluation of optical and photographic image quality; laser scanning; electo-optical printing and optical storage. *Mailing Add:* 142 Crescent Ave Portola Valley CA 94028

**URBACH, KARL FREDERIC,** HOSPITAL ADMINISTRATION. *Current Pos:* RETIRED. *Personal Data:* b Vienna, Austria, Nov 9, 17; nat US; m 52, Lilly Mendelsohn; c Katrina & Daniel. *Educ:* Reed Col, BA, 42; Northwestern Univ, PhD(chem), 46, MD, 51. *Prof Exp:* Asst, Eve Sch, Northwestern Univ, 42-46, asst chem, Dent Sch, 43-45, asst pharmacol, Med Sch, 45-47, lectr chem, Univ, 46-47, instr chem & pharmacol, Univ & Med Sch, 47-50; resident anesthesiol, USPHS Hosp, Staten Island, NY, 52-54; actg chief, USPHS Hosp, San Francisco, 54-55; chief anesthesiol, USPHS Hosp, Staten Island, 55-69; chief med educ & res, USPHS Hosp, San Francisco, 69-70, dir, 70-79. *Concurrent Pos:* NIH res fel, USPHS, 51-52. *Mem:* AAAS; Soc Exp Biol & Med; AMA; Am Soc Anesthesiol; Asn Mil Surg US. *Res:* Synthesis of vasopressors and testing, local anesthetics and testing; histamine methods for identification; actions; metabolism; pharmacology; evaluation of coronary dilators; anesthesia; hypnotics. *Mailing Add:* Two Atalaya Terr San Francisco CA 94117

**URBAIN, WALTER MATHIAS,** FOOD SCIENCE, FOOD IRRADIATION. *Current Pos:* prof, 65-75, EMER PROF FOOD SCI, MICH STATE UNIV, 75- *Personal Data:* b Chicago, Ill, Apr 8, 10; m 39, Ruth Lindahl; c Robert W & Elizabeth Balaze. *Educ:* Univ Chicago, SB, 31, PhD(chem), 34. *Honors & Awards:* Indust Achievement Award, Inst Food Technologists, 63; Food Eng Award, Dairy & Food Industs Supply Asn & Am Soc Agr Engrs, 76. *Prof Exp:* Phys chemist, Swift & Co, 33-50, assoc dir res, 50-59, dir, Eng Res & Develop Dept, 59-65. *Concurrent Pos:* Mem, Comn Radiation Preserv Foods, Nat Res Coun, 56-62, chmn, 59-62, mem, Adv Bd Mil Personnel Supplies, 58-75; mem, Adv Comt Isotopes & Radiation Develop, AEC, 64-66; sci ed, Food Technol & J Food Sci, Inst Food Technologists, 66-70; lectr, consult & writer, Int Atomic Energy Agency, 67-93; chmn, Adv Comt Radiation Pasteurization Foods, Am Inst Biol Sci, 71-; consult, US Food & Drug Admin, 74-80; vis prof food sci & technol, Univ Calif, Davis, 82 & 85; lectr, Miss State Univ, 88. *Mem:* Am Chem Soc; fel Inst Food Technologists; Optical Soc Am. *Res:* Activity coefficients; detergent action of soaps; meat pigments; color standards; egg processing; meat packaging and processing; spectrochemical analysis of foods; x-ray diffraction; instrumentation; microwave heating; treatment of foods with ionizing radiation; spun protein foods. *Mailing Add:* 13373 Plaza Del Rio Blvd Peoria AZ 85381

**URBAN, EDWARD ROBERT, JR,** BIVALVE FEEDING BEHAVIOR & PHYSIOLOGY. *Current Pos:* STAFF OFFICER, NAT RES COUN, 90- *Personal Data:* b San Diego, Calif, June 18, 57. *Educ:* Univ Calif, Los Angeles, BA, 79; Univ Del, MS, 82, MBA, 86, PhD(marine studies & appl ocean sci), 89. *Mem:* Am Soc Limnol & Oceanog; Am Geophys Union; Oceanog Soc; Estuarine Res Fedn; Nat Shellfisheries Asn. *Res:* Coastal oceanography, carbon chemistry in the ocean, biological diversity in the ocean and the use of science in policy-making. *Mailing Add:* Ocean Studies Bd HA 470 Nat Res Coun 2101 Constitution Ave NW Washington DC 20418. *Fax:* 202-334-2885; *E-Mail:* eurban@nas.edu

**URBAN, EMIL KARL,** ORNITHOLOGY, VERTEBRATE ZOOLOGY. *Current Pos:* PROF & CHMN BIOL, AUGUSTA COL, 76- *Personal Data:* b Milwaukee, Wis, May 27, 34; m 63; c 1. *Educ:* Univ Wis, BS, 56, PhD(zool), 64; Univ Kans, MA, 58. *Honors & Awards:* Louis K Bell Alumni Res Award, Augusta Col, 83. *Prof Exp:* From asst prof to assoc prof, Haile Sellassie I Univ, 64-75; assoc prof zool, Univ Ark, 75-76. *Concurrent Pos:* Vis prof, Univ Miami, 71. *Mem:* AAAS; fel Am Ornith Union; Brit Ornith Union; Cooper Ornith Soc; Wilson Ornith Soc. *Res:* Birds of Africa; biology of African pelicans, cormorants, ibises and cranes; monitoring of ciconiid colonies in Southeast United States. *Mailing Add:* Dept Biol Augusta State Univ Augusta GA 30904-2200

**URBAN, EUGENE WILLARD,** PHYSICS. *Current Pos:* physicist, 60-70, SUPVRY PHYSICIST SPACE RES, GEORGE C MARSHALL SPACE FLIGHT CTR, NASA, 70- *Personal Data:* b Omaha, Nebr, Apr 20, 35; m 60; c 8. *Educ:* Harvard Univ, BS, 57; Univ Ala, MS, 63, PhD(physics), 70. *Prof Exp:* Physicist space res, US Army Ballistic Missile Agency, 59-60. *Mem:* Am Phys Soc; Sigma Xi. *Res:* Low temperature physics; superconducting instruments for space experiments; properties and applications of superfluid liquid helium in space; superfluid helium systems for space experiment cooling. *Mailing Add:* 9 Grays Lane Fayetteville TN 37334

**URBAN, JAMES EDWARD,** MICROBIAL PHYSIOLOGY. *Current Pos:* NSF fel, 68-70, asst prof, 70-77, ASSOC PROF BIOL, KANS STATE UNIV, 77- *Personal Data:* b Dime Box, Tex, Jan 5, 42; m 63, Dianne Kieke; c Jill & Amy. *Educ:* Univ Tex, Austin, BA, 65, PhD(microbiol), 68. *Mem:* Am Soc Microbiol; Am Soc Gravitational & Space Biol. *Res:* Regulation of cell division; medium and growth rate influences on the bacterial cell cycle; bacteroid morphogenesis in the Rhizobium legume symbiosis. *Mailing Add:* Div Biol Ackert Hall Kans State Univ Manhattan KS 66506-4901. *Fax:* 785-532-6653; *E-Mail:* urban@ksu.edu

**URBAN, JOSEPH,** chemistry, metallurgy, for more information see previous edition

**URBAN, JOSEPH F,** IMMUNOLOGY. *Current Pos:* SUPVR MICROBIOL, USDA, 79- *Personal Data:* b Elizabeth, NJ, Dec 23, 48. *Educ:* Rutgers Univ, BS, 70; Syracuse Univ, PhD(microbiol), 75. *Prof Exp:* Fel, Johns Hopkins Univ, 75-79. *Mem:* Am Immunol Soc; Am Physiol Soc. *Mailing Add:* Helminthic Dis Lab USDA BARC-E Bldg 1040 Rm 2 Beltsville MD 20705-2350

**URBAN, SUSAN D,** COMPUTER SCIENCE. *Current Pos:* asst prof, 89-94, ASSOC PROF, COMPUT SCI & ENG DEPT, COL ENG & APPL SCI, ARIZ STATE UNIV, 94- *Educ:* Univ Southwestern La, BS, 76, MS, 80, PhD(comput sci), 87. *Prof Exp:* Asst prof, Elec & Comput Eng Dept, Col Eng, Univ Miami, 78-89. *Concurrent Pos:* Info analyst Div Systs & Comput Servs, Med Col Ga, 78-80; programmer analyst, Southern Flow Inc, La, 80-83; grantee, NSF, 89-, Defense Advan Res Proj Agency, 96- *Mem:* Fel Elec & Electronics Engrs Comput Soc; Asn Comput Mach. *Res:* Object oriented database systems; active database systems; constraint management; heterogeneous database systems; engineering databases. *Mailing Add:* Dept Comput Sci & Eng Col Eng Ariz State Univ Box 875406 Tempe AZ 85287

**URBAN, TIMOTHY L,** FACILITY LAYOUT ANALYSIS, INVENTORY THEORY. *Current Pos:* ASSOC PROF & CHMN QUANT METHODS & MGT INFO SYSTS, UNIV TULSA, 87- *Personal Data:* b Hays, Kans, Feb 11, 56; m 78, Marla Hopkins; c Alicia D & Gregory S. *Educ:* Kans State Univ, BSIE & BS, 77; Univ Tex, Arlington, MBA, 82, PhD(mgt sci), 87. *Prof Exp:* Indust engr, Gen Dynamics Corp, 78-81; sr indus engr, Johnson & Johnson, 81-83; opers analyst & proj leader, Fed Res Bank, Dallas, 83-87. *Concurrent Pos:* Asst mfg engr, Tex Instruments, Inc, 77; mem criminal justice task force, Dallas United, 85; Mayo excellence res award, Univ Tulsa, 93-94. *Mem:* Opers Res Soc Am; Inst Indust Engrs; Int Soc Inventory Res; Prod & Opers Mgt Soc; Decision Sci Inst; Inst Opers Res & Mgt Sci. *Res:* Facility layout analysis, particularly multiple criteria and dynamic models; inventory theory, particularly models in which the demand rate is not constant. *Mailing Add:* Dept Quant Methods & Info Systs Univ Tulsa 600 S College Tulsa OK 74104-3189. *E-Mail:* urban@utulsa.edu

**URBAN, WILLARD EDWARD, JR,** BIOMETRICS, ANIMAL BREEDING. *Current Pos:* from asst prof to assoc prof, Univ NH, 63-85, statistician, 63-72, from asst dir to assoc dir, 72-86, coordr info systs, Agr Exp Sta, 86-88, PROF BIOMET, UNIV NH, 85- *Personal Data:* b Chicago, Ill, Sept 16, 36; m 57, Sara R DeGroot; c 3. *Educ:* Va Polytech Inst & State Univ, BS, 58; Iowa State Univ, MS, 60, PhD(animal breeding), 63. *Prof Exp:* Animal husbandman, Animal Husb Res Div, Agr Res Serv, USDA, 58-63. *Concurrent Pos:* Adv, Int Crops Res Inst Semi-Arid Tropics, Hyderabad, India, 86-87 & 89. *Mem:* Biomet Soc; Am Soc Animal Sci. *Res:* Role of heredity and environment in economic traits of livestock; statistical methods for analyzing non-orthogonal data. *Mailing Add:* Off Biomet Pettee Hall Univ NH Durham NH 03824-3599. *E-Mail:* will@unh.edu

**URBANEK, VINCENT EDWARD,** PROSTHODONTICS, DENTISTRY. *Current Pos:* RETIRED. *Personal Data:* b Chicago, Ill, Jan 2, 27; m 49; c 2. *Educ:* Northwestern Univ, Evanston, BS, 51, MA, 52; Univ Ill, Chicago, DDS, 57. *Prof Exp:* Instr removable prosthodontics, Col Dent, Univ Ill Med Ctr, 57-63, asst prof, 63-67, assoc prof oral diag & oral med, 67-70; prof removable prosthodontics, Sch Dent, Med Col Ga, 70-89. *Concurrent Pos:* Mem attend staff, Eugene Talmadge Mem Hosp, 70- *Mem:* Fel Am Col Dent; Am Dent Asn; Am Prosthodont Soc; Am Acad Oral Med. *Res:* Removable prosthodontics; oral diagnosis; mandibular dysfunction as related to the temporomandibular joints, neuromuscular components and dental occlusion; effects of corticosteroids on vesiculobullous lesions of the oral mucosa. *Mailing Add:* 3231 Ramsgate Rd Augusta GA 30909

**URBANIK, ARTHUR RONALD,** PROCESS DEVELOPMENT. *Current Pos:* sr res chemist, 90-96, group leader res & develop, 96-97, TECH DIR RES & DEVELOP, HICKSON DANCHEM CORP, 97- *Personal Data:* b Union City, NJ, Apr 17, 39; m 66, Virginia McMullen; c Elizabeth & Geoffrey. *Educ:* St Vincent Col, BS, 61; WVa Univ, MS, 63, PhD(org chem), 67. *Prof Exp:* Sr res chemist, Bjorksten Res Labs, 67 & Dan River, Inc, 67-90. *Concurrent Pos:* Lectr chem, Stratford Col, 72-73. *Mem:* Am Chem Soc; Am Asn Textile Chem & Colorists. *Res:* Organic chemical process development. *Mailing Add:* 709 Brightwell Dr Danville VA 24540

**URBAS, BRANKO,** ORGANIC CHEMISTRY, BIOCHEMISTRY. *Current Pos:* RETIRED. *Personal Data:* b Zagreb, Yugoslavia, July 24, 29; m 56; c 1. *Educ:* Univ Zagreb, Dipl Chem, 53, DSc(org chem), 60. *Prof Exp:* Group leader, Synthetic Org Chem, Pliva Chem & Pharmaceut Works, Zagreb, Yugoslavia, 52-60; sect leader polymer chem, Org Chem Indust, 60-61; fel carbohydrates, Nat Res Coun Can, Ottawa Univ, Ont, 61-63; asst prof & NIH grant, Dept Biochem, Purdue Univ, Lafayette, 63-65; res scientist, Res Br, Can Dept Agr, 65-68; sr res chemist, Moffett Tech Ctr, CPC Int, Inc, ARGO, 68-87 & AKZO Chem Inc, 87-92. *Mem:* Am Chem Soc; Croatian Chem Soc. *Res:* Synthetic organic and carbohydrate chemistry. *Mailing Add:* 736 Island Way No 505 Clearwater FL 34630

**URBATSCH, LOWELL EDWARD,** SYSTEMATIC BOTANY. *Current Pos:* asst prof, 75-79, ASSOC PROF PLANT SYSTS, LA STATE UNIV, BATON ROUGE, 79- *Personal Data:* b Osage, Iowa, July 5, 42; div; c Amy & Erika. *Educ:* Univ Northern Iowa, BA, 64; Univ Ga, PhD(bot), 70. *Prof Exp:* Asst prof bot, Chadron State Col, 70-71; asst prof plant syst & biol, Univ Tex, Austin, 71-75. *Mem:* Bot Soc Am; Am Soc Plant Taxon; Int Asn Plant Taxon. *Res:* Cytological and biochemical systematics of genera in the Asteraceae; gene sequences and phylogenetic systematics in Asteraceae, Orchidaceae. *Mailing Add:* Dept Bot La State Univ Baton Rouge LA 70803-0001. *Fax:* 504-388-8459; *E-Mail:* Urbatsch@herb02.botany.lsu.edu

**URBSCHEIT, NANCY LEE,** RESPIRATORY PHYSIOLOGY, PHYSICAL MEDICINE. *Current Pos:* PROG DIR PHYS THER, UNIV LOUISVILLE. *Personal Data:* b Viroqua, Wis, Sept 7, 46. *Educ:* State Univ NY, Buffalo, BS, 68, MA, 70, PhD(physiol), 73. *Prof Exp:* From instr to asst prof physiol, State Univ NY, Buffalo, 73-76, asst to vpres health sci, 73-76; asst prof, Phys Ther Educ, Univ Iowa, Iowa City, 76-79; staff phys therapist, St Lawrence Hosp, Lansing, Mich, 79; chief phys therapist, Palo Alto Co Hosp, 80-81; assoc prof phys ther, ECarolina Univ, 81- *Res:* Motor unit discharge patterns in elderly man reciprocal inhibition in hemiparetic man; mapping the activity of intercostal muscles in anesthetized cats during mechanical loading, in particular, positive and negative pressure breathing, threshold loading and elastic loading and chemical loading of respiration. *Mailing Add:* Phys Ther Prog K Bldg Health & Sci Ctr Univ Louisville Louisville KY 40292

**URCH, UMBERT ANTHONY,** FERTILIZATION. *Current Pos:* ASST RES BIOCHEM, UNIV CALIF, DAVIS, 83- *Personal Data:* b San Francisco, Calif, Aug 15, 46. *Educ:* Univ Calif, Davis, PhD(biochem), 76. *Mailing Add:* 1309 Westwood Way Woodland CA 95695

**URDAL, DAVID L,** RECEPTOR BIOCHEMISTRY, LYMPHOKINE PURIFICATION. *Current Pos:* HEAD DEPT MEMBRANE BIOCHEM, IMMUNEX CORP, 83- *Educ:* Univ Wash, PhD(biochem-encol), 80. *Mailing Add:* 291 N Bernardo Ave Mountain View CA 94043

**URDANG, ARNOLD,** pharmaceutical chemistry, pharmacy, for more information see previous edition

**URDY, CHARLES EUGENE,** X-RAY CRYSTALLOGRAPHY, INORGANIC CHEMISTRY. *Current Pos:* MGR ENVIRON SCI & TECHNOL DEVELOP, LOWER COLO RIVER AUTHORITY, 93- *Personal Data:* b Georgetown, Tex, Dec 27, 33; m 62, Margaret Bright; c Steven & Christopher. *Educ:* Huston-Tillotson Col, BS, 54; Univ Tex, Austin, PhD(chem), 62. *Hon Degrees:* DSc, Huston-Tillotson Col, 94. *Prof Exp:* Prof chem, Huston-Tillotson Col, 61-62 & 72-93; assoc prof, NC Col, Durham, 62-63; prof, Prairie View Agr & Mech Col, 63-72. *Concurrent Pos:* Robert A Welch Found fel, Univ Tex, Austin, 62. *Mem:* Fel Am Inst Chem; Am Crystallog Asn; Am Chem Soc; Sigma Xi. *Res:* Determination of the crystal structures of coordination compounds of the transition metals by x-ray diffraction methods. *Mailing Add:* 7311 Hartnell Dr Austin TX 78723

**URELES, ALVIN L,** MEDICINE. *Current Pos:* from clin instr radiol & med to clin asst prof med, Univ Rochester, 51-64, assoc prof med, 64-67, clin assoc radiol, 61-67, PROF MED, SCH MED & DENT, UNIV ROCHESTER, 69-; ASSOC HEAD ENDOCRINOL & METAB DIV & CHIEF MED, GENESEE HOSP, 67- *Personal Data:* b Rochester, NY, Aug 8, 21; m 53; c 3. *Educ:* Univ Rochester, MD, 45; Am Bd Internal Med, dipl; Am Bd Nuclear Med, dipl. *Prof Exp:* Intern, Beth Israel Hosp, Boston, 45-46, from resident to chief resident med, 48-51. *Concurrent Pos:* Asst physician, Strong Mem Hosp, Rochester, NY, 51-58, sr assoc physician, 64- *Mem:* Fel Am Col Physicians; Int Soc Internal Med; Am Soc Internal Med; Endocrine Soc; AMA; Am Thyroid Asn. *Res:* Thyroid disease. *Mailing Add:* Med Dept Genesee Hosp 224 Alexander St Rochester NY 14607

**URENOVITCH, JOSEPH VICTOR,** EXPLOSIVES CHEMISTRY & ENGINEERING. *Current Pos:* VPRES RES & DEVELOP, ATLAS POWDER CO, 80- *Personal Data:* b Freeland, Pa, Nov 21, 37; m 59; c 4. *Educ:* Univ Pa, BA, 59, PhD(chem), 63. *Prof Exp:* Asst chem, Univ Wis, 62-63; res chemist, res & develop, Olin Mathieson Chem Corp, 64-65; section mgr corp res & develop, Air Prod & Chem Inc, 65-70, gen mgr specialty chem, 70-80. *Mem:* Am Chem Soc; Soc Explosives Engrs. *Res:* Development and commercialization of new commercial explosives products, new pharmaceutical intermediates, new pesticides and products for the aerospace industry. *Mailing Add:* RR 2 Box 136 Tamaqua PA 18252-0136

**URESK, DANIEL WILLIAM,** RANGE SCIENCE, WILDLIFE MANAGEMENT. *Current Pos:* pres intern, 72-73, RES BIOLOGIST RANGE-WILDLIFE, ROCKY MOUNTAIN FOREST & RANGE EXP STA, FOREST SERV, USDA, 77-, SUPVRY RES BIOLOGIST, 88- *Personal Data:* b Price, Utah, July 18, 43; m 71; c 2. *Educ:* Univ Utah, BS, 65, MS, 67; Colo State Univ, PhD(range sci), 72. *Prof Exp:* Res scientist, Battelle Pac Northwest Labs, 73-77. *Concurrent Pos:* Adj prof, SDak Sch Mines, SDak State Univ, fac affil & Colo State Univ, 78; referee, J Range Mgt, J Wildlife Mgt, Great Basin Naturalist, Prarie Naturalist, Northwest Sci, 78. *Mem:* Sigma Xi; Soc Range Mgt. *Res:* Basic range ecology; plant ecology; livestock grazing; dietary analysis; plant-animal wildlife relationships; nutrition studies, monitoring. *Mailing Add:* 4406 Ridgewood Rapid City SD 57702

**URETSKY, JACK LEON,** APPLIED MATH, MUON ASTRONOMY. *Current Pos:* assoc physicist, 61-72, GUEST PHYSICIST, ARGONNE NAT LAB, 73-; INSTR PHYSICS, COL DU PAGE, 87- *Personal Data:* b Great Falls, Mont, Mar 17, 24; div; c 2. *Educ:* Mass Inst Technol, SB, 45, SM, 52 & PhD(theoret physics), 56, JD, Univ Chicago, 75. *Prof Exp:* Physicist, Univ Calif Radiation Lab, Berkeley, 56-58; fel, Imp Col, London, 59; asst prof physics, Purdue Univ, 60-61. *Concurrent Pos:* Prof physics, Northern Ill Univ, 69-70; Nat Acad Sci exchange fel to Romania, 70; vis physicist, DESY, Hamburg, Ger, 70; practiced law, 75-85; assoc prof math, Elmhurst Col, Ill, 85-86; instr physics, Col DuPage, 87-94, Morton Col, 96. *Mem:* Fel Am Phys Soc; Am Bar Asn. *Res:* Elementary particle theory; high energy physics. *Mailing Add:* 206 N Grant Hinsdale IL 60521. *E-Mail:* jlu@hep.anl.gov

**URETSKY, MYRON,** COMPUTER SCIENCE, DATA PROCESSING. *Current Pos:* PROF INFO SYST, NY UNIV, 70- *Personal Data:* b New York, NY, May 28, 40; m 81; c 4. *Educ:* City Col NY, BBA, 61; Ohio State Univ, MBA, 62, PhD(acct), 62. *Prof Exp:* Asst prof acct, Univ Ill, 64-67; assoc prof bus, Columbia Univ, 67-70. *Concurrent Pos:* Fulbright scholar, 79; consult, 80- *Mem:* Inst Mgt Sci; Am Inst Cert Pub Acct; Asn Comput Mach. *Res:* Impact of computers on society; management fraud; simulation and gaming; East-West trade; technology assessment. *Mailing Add:* Dept Info Syst NY Univ Washington Sq Stern Sch Bus 44 W Fourth St Suite 9170 New York NY 10012-1126

**URETZ, ROBERT BENJAMIN,** BIOPHYSICS. *Current Pos:* asst cosmic rays, Univ Chicago, 48-50, from instr to assoc prof biophys, 54-64, prof, 64-73, chmn, Dept Biophys, 66-69, assoc dean, 69-70, dep dean basic sci, 70-76, assoc vpres, Med Ctr & dep dean acad affairs, 76, actg vpres, Med Ctr & actg dean, Div Biol Sci & Pritzker Sch Med, 76-77, vpres, Med Ctr & dean, Div Biol Sci & Pritzker Sch Med, 77-82, Ralph W Gerard Prof biophys & theoret biol, Div Biol Sci & Pritzker Sch Med, 73-94, EMER PROF BIOPHYS & THEORET BIOL, UNIV CHICAGO, 94- *Personal Data:* b Chicago, Ill, June 27, 24; m 55; c 2. *Educ:* Univ Chicago, BS, 47, PhD(biophys), 54. *Prof Exp:* Asst cosmic rays, 48-50, from instr to assoc prof biophys, 54-64, chmn, Dept Biophys, 66-69. *Mem:* Radiation Res Soc; Biophys Soc; Am Soc Cell Biol; Am Asn Med Cols; AMA. *Res:* Mechanism of biological effects of various radiations; optical analysis of biological structure. *Mailing Add:* Univ Chicago CLSC 920 E 58th St Chicago IL 60637

**URIBE, ERNEST GILBERT,** PLANT BIOCHEMISTRY, PLANT PHYSIOLOGY. *Current Pos:* assoc prof, 74-84, PROF BOT, WASH STATE UNIV, 85- *Personal Data:* b Sanger, Calif, Nov 25, 35; m 57; c 3. *Educ:* Fresno State Col, AB, 57; Univ Calif, Davis, MS, 62, PhD(plant physiol), 65. *Prof Exp:* Res asst bot & biochem, Univ Calif, Davis, 58-65; res assoc biochem, Johns Hopkins Univ, 65-66 & Cornell Univ, 66-67; asst prof biol, Yale Univ, 67-74. *Concurrent Pos:* Res fel, NSF, 65-66 & NIH, 66-67; prog dir, NSF, 92-93. *Mem:* AAAS; Am Soc Plant Physiologists; Biophys Soc; Am Soc Biol Chemists; Sigma Xi; Soc Chicanos & Native Am Sci. *Res:* Membrane transport in higher plants; energy conversion in photosynthesis mechanism of photosynthetic phosphorylation; bioenergetics. *Mailing Add:* Dept Bot Wash State Univ Pullman WA 99164. *Fax:* 509-335-3066

**URICCHIO, WILLIAM ANDREW,** BIOLOGY, MICROBIOLOGY. *Current Pos:* RETIRED. *Personal Data:* b Hartford, Conn, Apr 21, 24; m 50; c 5. *Educ:* Cath Univ, BA, 49, MS, 51, PhD(zool), 53. *Honors & Awards:* Bishop-Wright Award, 62; Knight of St Gregory the Great. *Prof Exp:* Asst prof biol, Carlow Col, 53, prof & chmn dept, 53-94. *Concurrent Pos:* Guest prof, Carnegie-Mellon Univ, 63-68 & NSF vis prof, 67-68; mem bd dirs, Duquesne Univ; pres, Int Fedn Family Life Prom. *Mem:* Fel AAAS; Sigma Xi; Nat Asn Sci Teachers. *Res:* Sexuality; science education; natural family planning. *Mailing Add:* 300 Fox Chapel Rd Pittsburgh PA 15238

**URICK, ROBERT JOSEPH,** underwater acoustics; deceased, see previous edition for last biography

**URIST, MARSHALL RAYMOND,** ORTHOPEDIC SURGERY. *Current Pos:* Adj assoc prof, 54-69, DIR, BONE RES LAB, UNIV CALIF, LOS ANGELES, MED CTR, 50-, PROF ORTHOP SURG, SCH MED, 69- *Personal Data:* b Chicago, Ill, June 11, 14; m 41, Alice Pfund; c Marshall (McLean), Nancy S (Miller) & John Baxter. *Educ:* Univ Mich, BA, 36; Univ Chicago, MS, 37; Johns Hopkins Univ, MD, 41; Am Bd Orthop Surg, dipl. *Hon Degrees:* MD, Univ Lund, Malmo, Sweden, 77. *Honors & Awards:* Sir Henry Wellcome Award, Asn Mil Surgeons US, 47; Dallas Phemister lectr, Univ Chicago, 78; Gold Medal Sci Achievement, Orthop Soc Spain, 88; Bristol Meyers Squibb Zimmer Award, 93. *Prof Exp:* Ed-in-Chief, Clin Orthop Rel Res, 66-93, emer, 94. *Concurrent Pos:* Pvt pract med spec orthop surg, Los Angeles, 48-; mem staff, US Vet Admin Hop, Wadsworth, Los Angeles, 48-69; consult to surgeon gen, US Army Comt Trauma, 63-71; Guggenheim Found fel, New York City, 72; honoree, Conf Bioactive Factors, Univ Tex, San Antonio, 88; hon intern, Conf Bone Morphogenetic Protein, Johns Hopkins Univ, 94. *Mem:* Fel Am Col Surgeons; fel Royal Col Surgeons; AAAS; Asn Bone & Joint Surgeons (pres, 67-68); Hip Soc (pres, 78-79); hon mem Am Orthop Asn. *Res:* Orthopedic surgery; bone and joint surgery; discovered bone morphogenetic protein in 1965. *Mailing Add:* Westwood Village 1033 Gayley Ave Los Angeles CA 90024-3417

**URITAM, REIN AARNE,** ELEMENTARY PARTICLE PHYSICS. *Current Pos:* asst prof, 68-74, ASSOC PROF PHYSICS, BOSTON COL, 74-, CHMN DEPT, 82- *Personal Data:* b Tartu, Estonia, Apr 11, 39; US citizen; m 70, Justine Kent; c Eliot & Jonathan. *Educ:* Concordia Col, Moorhead, Minn, BA, 61; Oxford Univ, BA, 63; Princeton Univ, MA, 65, PhD(physics), 68. *Prof Exp:* Res assoc physics, Princeton Univ, 67-68. *Mem:* Am Phys Soc; Philos Sci Asn; Hist Sci Soc. *Res:* Theory of elementary particles; weak interactions; current algebra; high-energy hadron collisions; history and philosophy of science. *Mailing Add:* Dept Physics Boston Col Higgins Hall Rm 561 Chestnut Hill MA 02167-3811

**URIU, KIYOTO,** POMOLOGY, PLANT PHYSIOLOGY. *Current Pos:* Prin lab technol, Univ Calif, Davis, 53-55, jr pomologist, 55-56, asst pomologist, 56-63, assoc specialist, 63-64, assoc pomologist, 64-70, POMOLOGIST, UNIV CALIF, DAVIS, 70-, LECTR, 62- *Personal Data:* b Berryessa, Calif, May 25, 17; m 49; c 4. *Educ:* Univ Calif, BS, 48, MS, 50, PhD(plant physiol), 53. *Mem:* Am Soc Hort Sci; Am Soc Plant Physiol; Sigma Xi. *Res:* Mineral nutrition, especially microelements of deciduous fruit trees; water relations of deciduous fruit trees. *Mailing Add:* 666 Elmwood Dr Davis CA 95616

**URKOWITZ, HARRY,** ELECTRICAL ENGINEERING. *Current Pos:* STAFF SCIENTIST, GOVT ELECTRONIC SYSTS DIV, GEN ELEC CO, 70- *Personal Data:* b Philadelphia, Pa, Oct 1, 21; m 46; c 2. *Educ:* Drexel Inst Technol, BS, 48; Univ Pa, MS, 54, PhD, 72. *Prof Exp:* From jr engr to sr engr, Res Div, Philco Corp, 48-53, proj engr, 53-56, sect engr, 56-58, sr res specialist, 58-64; sr eng specialist, Gen Atronics Corp, 64-70. *Concurrent Pos:* Adj prof, Drexel Univ, 52- *Mem:* Fel Inst Elec & Electronics Engrs. *Res:* Signal detection theory; signal processing; radar. *Mailing Add:* GE Aerospace Govt Elec Syst D Borton Landing Rd MS 108-102 Moorestown NJ 08057

**URNESS, PHILIP JOEL,** WILDLIFE. *Current Pos:* assoc prof, 73-88, PROF RANGE SCI, UTAH STATE UNIV, 88- *Personal Data:* b Wenatchee, Wash, Jan 18, 36; m 56; c 2. *Educ:* Wash State Univ, BS, 58, MS, 60; Ore State Univ, PhD(range sci), 66. *Prof Exp:* Res biologist wildlife sci, Utah Wildlife Resources, 60-62; res biologist, Ore Game Comn, 62-65; res scientist, Rocky Mountain Forest & Range Exp Sta, US Forest Serv, 65-73. *Concurrent Pos:* Proj leader res, Utah Div Wildlife Resources, 73-; vis assoc prof, Univ Calif, Davis, 80; consult, Chihuahua, Mex, 87; Fulbright res scholar, Nat Forest Corp, Chile, 88. *Mem:* Soc Range Mgt. *Res:* Wildlife interactions on wildlands of western North America including foraging behavior, nutritional ecology and competitive vs complemental relationships. *Mailing Add:* 1454 N 1600 E Logan UT 84322-5230. *Fax:* 435-750-3796

**URONE, PAUL,** CHEMISTRY, AIR POLLUTION CONTROL. *Current Pos:* prof atmospheric chem, 71-81, EMER PROF, CHEM & ENVIRON ENG SCI, UNIV FLA, 81- *Personal Data:* b Pueblo, Colo, Nov 29, 15; m 43, Florence Genova; c Paul P & Mayri A U. *Educ:* Western State Col Colo, AB, 38; Ohio State Univ, MS, 47, PhD, 54. *Prof Exp:* Teacher, High Sch, Colo, 38-42; chemist, Colo Fuel & Iron Corp, 42-45; chief chemist, Div Indust Hyg, State Dept Health, Ohio, 47-55; from asst prof to prof chem, Univ Colo, Boulder, 55-70. *Concurrent Pos:* Consult, Martin Co, 60-61; Univ Colo fac fel, Univ Calif, Los Angeles, 61-62; sci adv, Food & Drug Admin, 66-71; Dept HEW air pollution fel, Univ Fla, 67; mem, Air Pollution Nat Manpower Adv Comt; sulfur oxides subcomt, Intersoc Comt Methods Sampling & Anal; Inter Govt Personnel Act Fel, Denver Fed Ctr, 77-78 & Air Pollution Control, Repub Korea, 81. *Mem:* Am Chem Soc; Am Indust Hyg Asn; Am Conf Govt Indust Hygienists; Air Pollution Control Asn. *Res:* Polarography of hydrocarbon combustion products; chemical analysis of air contaminants in industrial hygiene and air pollution; theoretical and applied gas chromatography; thermal and photochemical reactions of sulfur dioxide in air; air pollution control; air flow measurements. *Mailing Add:* 3726 SW Sixth Pl Gainesville FL 32607

**URONE, PAUL PETER,** NUCLEAR PHYSICS, MEDICAL PHYSICS. *Current Pos:* from asst prof to assoc prof, 73-82, PROF PHYSICS, CALIF STATE UNIV & COL, 82- *Personal Data:* b Pueblo, Colo, Feb 11, 44; m 65; c 2. *Educ:* Univ Colo, BA, 65, PhD(physics), 70. *Prof Exp:* Teaching asst, Dept Physics, Univ Wash, 65-66; res asst nuclear physics, Univ Colo, 66-70; staff physicist, Kernfysisch Versneller Inst, Univ Groningen, Neth, 70-71; nuclear info res assoc, State Univ NY Stony Brook, 71-73. *Concurrent Pos:* Consult, Calif State Univ & Cols, 74-78, Crocker Nuclear Lab, Univ Calif, Davis, 74-80 & Univ Calif, Davis, Med Ctr, 85- *Mem:* Am Phys Soc; Sigma Xi; Am Asn Physics Teachers. *Res:* Optical model of nucleus, nuclear data compilations, basic and applied neutron physics, medical physics and radiology. *Mailing Add:* Dept Physics Calif State Univ 6000 J St Sacramento CA 95819

**URQUHART, ANDREW WILLARD,** CORPORATE MANAGEMENT, COMPOSITES. *Current Pos:* PRES, LANXIDE ELECTRONIC COMPONENTS, INC, 93- *Personal Data:* b Burlington, Vt, Aug 24, 39; m 63, Carolyn Powell; c Marion & Dorothy. *Educ:* Dartmouth Col, BA, 61, MS, 64, PhD(metall), 71. *Prof Exp:* Engr, Div Naval Reactors, USAEC, 62-67; Creare, Inc, 67-68; metallurgist, 71-75, Gen Elec Corp Res & Develop, br mgr inorg mat, 75-84; vpres res develop & engr, Lanxide Corp, 84-89, sr vpres technol, 89-93. *Mem:* Sigma Xi; Int Microelectronics & Packaging Soc. *Res:* Metal matrix composites used as thermal management and packaging components in electronics industry. *Mailing Add:* Lanxide Electronic Components Inc 1300 Marrows Rd PO Box 6077 Newark DE 19714-6077. *Fax:* 302-456-6223

**URQUHART, JOHN, III,** physiology, endocrinology, for more information see previous edition

**URQUHART, N SCOTT,** ENVIRONMENTAL STATISTICS. *Current Pos:* PROF, ENVIRON STATIST, ORE STATE UNIV, 91- *Personal Data:* b Columbia, SC, Mar 15, 40; m 59; c 7. *Educ:* Colo State Univ, BS, 61, MS, 63, PhD(statist), 65. *Prof Exp:* From asst prof to assoc prof biol statist, Cornell Univ, 65-70; from assoc prof to prof exp statist, NMex State Univ, 70-91. *Mem:* Am Statist Asn; Biomet Soc. *Res:* Development and dissemination of statistical methods used in biological research; teaching and development of teaching techniques for statistical methods. *Mailing Add:* 1320 NW Worden Circle Corvallis OR 97330

**URRY, DAN WESLEY,** NEW CLASS OF BIOMATERIALS, ELASTOMERIC POLYPEPTIDES. *Current Pos:* dir, Div Molecular Biophys, Lab Molecular Biol, 70-72, PROF BIOCHEM, UNIV ALA, BIRMINGHAM, 70-, DIR LAB MOLECULAR BIOPHYS, 72-, PROF PHYSIOL & BIOPHYS, 79- *Personal Data:* b Salt Lake City, Utah, Sept 14, 35; m 57, 74, Kathleen A Lake; c Weston, Douglas (deceased), David & Kelly. *Educ:* Univ Utah, BA, 60, PhD(phys chem), 64. *Honors & Awards:* Robert Rushmer Distinguished lectr, Univ Wash, Seattle, 93. *Prof Exp:* Fel, Univ Utah, 64; Harvard Corp fel, 64-65; vis investr, Chem Biodynamics Lab, Univ Calif, 65-66; prof lectr, Dept Biochem, Univ Chicago, 67-70. *Concurrent Pos:* Assoc mem, Inst Biomed Res, AMA, 65-69, mem, 69-70; vis invstr, Univ di Padova, Centro di Studi sui Biopolimeri, 77; vchmn, Southern Region Res Review & Cert Subcomt, Am Heart Asn, 79-80, chmn, 81-82; Alexander von Humboldt Found award, Ger, 79-80; mem, Biophys & Biophys Chem B Study Sect, Div Res Grants, NIH, 80-84. *Mem:* Biophys Soc; Am Inst Biol Chem. *Res:* Polypeptide and protein mechanisms as approached by repeating structural motifs with emphasis on ion channel mechanisms and on entropic elasticity and contractility addressed in terms of free energy transduction; new class of biomaterials with medical applications such as tissue reconstruction, a material to prevent post-surgical and post-trauma adhesions, burn cover, and drug delivery. *Mailing Add:* Univ Ala 1670 University Blvd VH300 Birmingham AL 35294-0019. *Fax:* 205-934-4256

**URRY, GRANT WAYNE,** INORGANIC CHEMISTRY, CHEMICAL BONDING. *Current Pos:* prof, Tufts Univ, 68-70, chmn dept, 68-73, Robinson prof chem, 70-92, EMER ROBINSON PROF CHEM, TUFTS UNIV, 92- *Personal Data:* b Salt Lake City, Utah, Mar 12, 26; m 46; c 4. *Educ:* Univ Chicago, SB, 47, PhD(chem), 53. *Prof Exp:* Asst bot, Univ Chicago, 46-47, res assoc, 47-48, asst chem, 49-52, res assoc, 53-55; asst prof, Washington Univ, 55-58; from assoc prof to prof, Purdue Univ, 58-68. *Concurrent Pos:* Sloan fel, 56-58; consult, E I du Pont de Nemours & Co, Inc. *Mem:* AAAS; Am Chem Soc; Fedn Am Scientists. *Res:* Chemistry of convalently bonded inorganic compounds and electron spin resonance; equilibrium chemistry of carbon. *Mailing Add:* 2 Black Horse Terr Winchester MA 01890-3046

**URRY, LISA ANDREA,** extracellular matrix & cell-cell adhesion, induction of cell types, for more information see previous edition

**URRY, RONALD LEE,** REPRODUCTIVE PHYSIOLOGY, UROLOGY. *Current Pos:* ASSOC PROF ZOOL, BRIGHAM YOUNG UNIV & RES ASSOC PROF SURG, DIV UROL, MED CTR, UNIV UTAH, 76-, PROF SURG, DIV UROL & DEPT OBSTET & GYNEC, SCH MED, SALT LAKE CITY, 84- *Personal Data:* b Ogden, Utah, June 5, 45; m 71, Pamela C; c 3. *Educ:* Weber State Col, BS, 70; Utah State Univ, MS, 72, PhD(physiol), 73. *Prof Exp:* Teaching & res asst physiol, Dept Biol, Utah State Univ, 70-72, NDEA fel, 72-73; dir urol res lab & asst prof urol surg, Sch Med & Dent, Univ Rochester, 73-76. *Concurrent Pos:* Dir IVF prog, Univ Utah Sch Med & Abbot Northwestern Hosp, Minneapolis. *Mem:* Soc Study Reproduction; AAAS; Am Fertil Soc; Endocrine Soc; Am Andrology Soc; Am Urol Asn. *Res:* Relationship of stress and biogenic amines to male reproduction; testicular tissue culture, testicular perfusion, male infertility studies, vasectomy and vasovasostomy, and testicular physiology and endocrinology; in vitro fertilization, gamese freezing, fertilization. *Mailing Add:* Dept Surg Urol Univ Utah Sch Med 50 N Medical Dr Salt Lake City UT 84132-0001. *Fax:* 801-581-6127

**URRY, WILBERT HERBERT,** chemistry; deceased, see previous edition for last biography

**URSCHEL, HAROLD C, JR,** CARDIOVASCULAR & THORACIC SURGERY. *Current Pos:* asst prof, 63-75, PROF CARDIOVASC & THORACIC SURG, SOUTHWESTERN MED SCH, 75- *Personal Data:* b Toledo, Ohio, Feb 17, 30; m 40, Elizabeth Bradley; c Harold C, Bradley V, Sterling L, Amanda (Goldstein) & Susanna M. *Educ:* Princeton Univ, AB, 51; Harvard Med Sch, MD, 55. *Hon Degrees:* DSc, Ohio State Univ, 80; LLD, Pikeville Col, 87. *Honors & Awards:* John H Gibbon lectr, Am Col Surgeons, 93. *Prof Exp:* Teaching fel surg, Harvard Med Sch, 62. *Concurrent Pos:* Chief consult, Surgeon Gen-USAF, 84-; Nat Advisory Bd, Humana Hosp Syst, 92-; Pres, Texas Surg Soc, 93; Pres, NTC-ACS, 93; John H Gibbon Lectr, Am Col Surgeons, 93. *Mem:* Am Col Surgeons; Am Col Chest Physicians (pres, 79); Soc Thoracic Surgeons (vpres, 82-83, pres, 83-84). *Res:* Cardiovascular and thoracic surgery. *Mailing Add:* Pro Med Health Serv Inc Suite 1055 15851 N Dallas Pkwy Dallas TX 75248. *Fax:* 214-824-2505

**URSELL, JOHN HENRY,** MATHEMATICS. *Current Pos:* ASST PROF MATH, QUEEN'S UNIV, ONT, 64- *Personal Data:* b Leeds, Eng, June 9, 38. *Educ:* Oxford Univ, BA, 59, MA & DPhil(math), 63. *Prof Exp:* Asst prof math, Pa State Univ, 62-63; assoc prof, Col Fredonia, State Univ NY, 63-64. *Mem:* Am Math Soc; Can Math Cong; Math Asn Am; fel Royal Asiatic Soc Gt Brit & Ireland. *Res:* Topological semigroups; algebra; graph theory; comparative religions; mathematical sociology; statistics; foundations of math; Fermat's last theorem and number theory. *Mailing Add:* PO Box 761 Kingston ON K7L 4X6 Can

**URSENBACH, WAYNE OCTAVE,** CHEMISTRY. *Current Pos:* CONSULT, 84- *Personal Data:* b Lethbridge, Alta, Dec 4, 23; m 44; c 7. *Educ:* Brigham Young Univ, BSc, 47, MSc, 48. *Prof Exp:* Asst chemist, Dept Agr Res, Am Smelting & Refining Co, 46-51; lab supvr health physics, Dow Chem Co, Colo, 51-52; asst, Explosives Res Group, Univ Utah, 52-55, res assoc, 55-59, asst res prof, Inst Metals & Explosives, 59-61; mgr prod & res develop, Inter-Mountain Res & Eng Co, 61-65, asst res dir, 65-66; prod mgr, Ireco Chem, 66-68, dir res, 68-69, mgr planning, 69-70; res assoc, Utah Eng Exp Sta, Univ Utah, 71-74, asst gen mgr, Res Inst, 74-75, vpres & dir, Appl Technol Div, 75-84. *Concurrent Pos:* Consult air pollution effects, fires, explosions & explosives, 71- *Mem:* Am Chem Soc; AAAS; Nat Fire Protection Asn. *Res:* Air pollution; agricultural chemistry; health physics; theory of detonation; explosion and long range blast effects; terminal ballistics; seismic effects of explosions; causes of fires and accidental explosions. *Mailing Add:* 4635 S 1175 E Salt Lake City UT 84117-4909

**URSIC, STANLEY JOHN,** WATERSHED MANAGEMENT, FOREST HYDROLOGY. *Current Pos:* RETIRED. *Personal Data:* b Milwaukee, Wis, Apr 2, 24; m 50; c Michael, Steven & Mark. *Educ:* Univ Minn, BS, 49; Yale Univ, MF, 50. *Prof Exp:* Res forester, Univ Ill, 50-51; proj leader, Southern Forest Exp Sta, USDA Forest Serv, 51-90. *Mem:* Soc Am Foresters. *Res:* Effects of forestry practices, including rehabilitation of eroding lands, on water quality, yields and distribution; flow processes on forested lands; effects of atmospheric deposition on forests and water quality. *Mailing Add:* 1031 Zilla Avent Dr Oxford MS 38655

**URSILLO, RICHARD CARMEN,** PHARMACOLOGY. *Current Pos:* RETIRED. *Personal Data:* b Lawrence, Mass, Oct 26, 26; m 66; c 2. *Educ:* Tufts Univ, BS, 49, PhD(pharmacol), 54; Univ Calif, MS, 52. *Prof Exp:* From instr to asst prof pharmacol, Univ Calif, Los Angeles, 54-62; sect head pharmacol, Lakeside Labs, 62-66, dir, Pharmacol Dept, 66-75; head, Dept Pharmacol, Merrell Res Ctr, 75-84; dir pharmacol sci, Merrel Dow Res Inst, 84-87, sr dir res sci, 87-89, dir res admin, 88-89, vpres res admin, 89-93. *Concurrent Pos:* USPHS spec fel, Inst Sanita, Italy, 60-61. *Mem:* Am Soc Pharmacol & Exp Therapeut. *Res:* Pharmacology of autonomic and central nervous systems. *Mailing Add:* 8153 Millview Dr Cincinnati OH 45249

**URSINO, DONALD JOSEPH,** PLANT BIOLOGY & SCIENCE EDUCATION. *Current Pos:* from asst prof to assoc prof biol, 69-92, CHMN, DEPT BIOL SCI, BROCK UNIV, 74-77 & 90-, PROF BIOL, 92- *Personal Data:* b Toronto, Ont, Nov 11, 35; m 60, Anne; c 4. *Educ:* Pomona Col, BA, 56; Queen's Univ, Ont, MSc, 64, PhD(biol), 67. *Prof Exp:* Teacher sci, High Sch, 57-63; Nat Res Coun Can fel, Milan, 67-69. *Mem:* AAAS; Am Inst Biol Sci; Am Col Sports Med. *Mailing Add:* Dept Biol Sci Brock Univ St Catharines ON L2S 3A1 Can. *Fax:* 905-688-1855; *E-Mail:* dursino@spartan.ac.brocku.ca

**URSINO, JOSEPH ANTHONY,** ORGANIC CHEMISTRY. *Current Pos:* From asst prof to assoc prof, 66-71, PROF CHEM, COL TECHNOL, STATE UNIV NY, FARMINGDALE, 71- *Personal Data:* b Brooklyn, NY, Feb 28, 39; m 73, Kathleen Combs. *Educ:* St John's Univ, NY, BS, 60, MS, 62, PhD(chem), 67. *Mem:* Am Chem Soc; NY Acad Sci; Am Soc Eng Educ. *Res:* Synthesis and properties of heterocyclic organotin compounds. *Mailing Add:* 2299 Narwood Ct Merrick NY 11566-3928

**URSO, PAUL,** immunology, immunotoxicology, for more information see previous edition

**URTASUN, RAUL C,** ONCOLOGY, EXPERIMENTAL RADIOBIOLOGY. *Current Pos:* PROF RADIATION ONCOL, UNIV ALTA, 70- *Personal Data:* Can citizen. *Educ:* Univ Buenos Aires, MD, 60; FRCP(C), 67; Am Bd Radiol, dipl radiother, 67. *Prof Exp:* Res fel oncol, Harvard Med Sch, 63-64; instr radiation oncol, Johns Hopkins Univ, 66-68; asst prof, McGill Univ, 68-70. *Mem:* Am Soc Therapeut Radiologists; Am Soc Clin Oncologists; Am Soc Cancer Res; Radiator Res Soc; Royal Col Physicians & Surgeons Can. *Res:* Clinical radiobiology; radiosensitizers; combined modalities in the treatment of cancer; high linear energy transfer particle radiation. *Mailing Add:* 26 Wellington Crescent Edmonton AB T5N 3V2 Can

**URTIEW, PAUL ANDREW,** THERMODYNAMICS, PHYSICS. *Current Pos:* Res assoc, Detonation Lab, Univ Calif, 59-64, asst res engr, Propulsion Dynamics Lab, 64-67, engr, Physics Dept, 67-73, ENGR, CHEM & MAT SCI DEPT, LAWRENCE LIVERMORE NAT LAB, UNIV CALIF, 73- *Personal Data:* b Nish, Yugoslavia, Feb 23, 31; US citizen; m 61, Svetlana Dombrovsky; c Andrei & Natasha. *Educ:* Univ Calif, Berkeley, BS, 55, MS, 59, PhD(mech eng), 64. *Concurrent Pos:* Consult, Hiller Aircraft Corp, Calif, 63-64 & MB Assocs, 66, Chevron, 90, Flour Daniel Inc, 91, NAO Inc, 92, John Zink Inc, 93-94. *Mem:* Combustion Inst; Am Inst Aeronaut & Astronaut; Am Phys Soc; Mat Res Soc. *Res:* High pressure physics of shocked solid materials; nonsteady wave dynamics; wave interaction processes in reactive and nonreactive media; graphical and experimental techniques applicable in research; diagnostic of high speed processes. *Mailing Add:* Lawrence Livermore Nat Lab L282 PO Box 808 Livermore CA 94550. *Fax:* 510-424-3281; *E-Mail:* urtiew1@llnl.gov

**URY, HANS KONRAD,** biostatistics, mathematical statistics, for more information see previous edition

**USBORNE, WILLIAM RONALD,** MEAT & FOOD SCIENCE. *Current Pos:* assoc prof meat sci, 69-79, PROF & CHMN FOOD SCI, UNIV GUELPH, 79- *Personal Data:* b Rochester, NY, Nov 22, 37; m 62; c 2. *Educ:* Cornell Univ, BS, 59; Univ Ill, Urbana, MS, 61; Univ Ky, PhD(meat & animal sci), 67. *Prof Exp:* Res asst meat sci, Univ Ill, 59-61; res assoc, Cornell Univ, 61-62; res asst, Univ Ky, 63-64 & 65-66, instr, 64-65; fel meat chem, Tex A&M Univ, 66-67; asst prof meat sci, Univ Minn, St Paul, 68-69. *Concurrent Pos:* Welch Found fel, 67-68; fel, Tex A&M Univ, 68. *Mem:* Am Soc Animal Sci; Am Meat Sci Asn; Am Inst Food Technologists; Can Inst Food Sci & Technol; Agr Inst Can. *Res:* Meat chemistry and technology; meat animal evaluation techniques; meat processing and quality. *Mailing Add:* Dept Food Sci Univ Guelph Guelph ON N1G 2W1 Can

**USCHEEK, DAVE PETROVICH,** ENVIRONMENTALLY COMPLIANT WATER-BASED & HIGH-SOLIDS COATINGS. *Current Pos:* CHEMIST, AKRON PAINT & VARNISH, 88- *Personal Data:* b University Heights, Ohio, July 9, 37. *Educ:* Case Western Res Univ, BS, 59. *Prof Exp:* Chemist, US Refining Co, 59-63, Glidden Co, 63-67, Mobil Chem Co, 67-71, Umbacker Coatings, 71-72; tech dir, Continetal Prods Inc, 71-78; group leader chem, Body Bros Inc, 79-82, Harrison Paint Corp, 82-86. *Concurrent Pos:* Owner-consult, Analyst, 90- *Mem:* Am Chem Soc; Int Union Pure & Appl Chem. *Res:* Formulation of coatings, inks, and adhesives that yield negligible amounts of hazardous volative organic compounds; extensive corrosion inhibition coupled with exceptional physical characteristics. *Mailing Add:* 8602 Auburn Rd Chardon OH 44024-8711. *Fax:* 440-773-1028

**USCHOLD, RICHARD L,** mathematics, for more information see previous edition

**USDIN, VERA RUDIN,** BIOCHEMISTRY. *Current Pos:* RETIRED. *Personal Data:* b Vienna, Austria, May 31, 25; nat US; m 49; c 4. *Educ:* Sterling Col, BS, 45; Duke Univ, MA, 47; Ohio State Univ, PhD(biochem), 51. *Prof Exp:* Res assoc physiol chem, Grad Sch Med, Univ Pa, 51-56; chemist, Res Labs, Rohm & Haas Co, 56-59; assoc res prof physiol chem, NMex Highlands Univ, 59-62; head, Physiol Chem Br, Melpar, Inc, Va, 62-67; proj supvr, Gillette Res Inst, Inc, 67-69, res supvr, 69-73, group leader, 73-79, prin scientist, 79-83, consult, 83-85; pres, Biotran Corp, 85-88. *Mem:* Am Chem Soc; Am Soc Cell Biol; Soc Invest Dermat. *Res:* Biochemistry of skin; enzyme inhibition; salivary proteins; dental plaque. *Mailing Add:* Six Stevens Ct Rockville MD 20850-1919

**USHER, DAVID ANTHONY,** BIO-ORGANIC CHEMISTRY. *Current Pos:* asst prof, 65-70, ASSOC PROF CHEM, CORNELL UNIV, 70- *Personal Data:* b Harrow, Eng, Nov 1, 36; m 74. *Educ:* Victoria Univ, NZ, BSc, 58, MSc, 60; Univ Cambridge, PhD(chem), 63. *Honors & Awards:* NZ Inst Chem Prize, 58. *Prof Exp:* Res fel chem, Harvard Univ, 63-65. *Concurrent Pos:* NIH career develop award, 68-73; vis prof, Oxford Univ, 71-72. *Mem:* Am Chem Soc; AAAS. *Res:* Chemical evolution; chemical reactions of nucleic acids; enzyme action. *Mailing Add:* Baker Lab Chem Cornell Univ Ithaca NY 14853-0001

**USHER, PETER DENIS,** ASTRONOMY. *Current Pos:* from asst prof to assoc prof, 68-85, PROF ASTRON, PA STATE UNIV, UNIVERSITY PARK, 86- *Personal Data:* b Bloemfontein, SAfrica, Oct 27, 35; US citizen; m 61; c 1. *Educ:* Univ Orange Free State, BS, 56, MS, 59; Harvard Univ, PhD(astron), 66. *Prof Exp:* Fel, Harvard Col Observ, 66-67; sr scientist, Am Sci & Eng, Inc, Mass, 67-68. *Mem:* Int Astron Union; Am Astron Soc; Royal Astron Soc. *Res:* Perturbation theory; stellar structure; faint blue objects; quasars. *Mailing Add:* 507 Davey Lab University Park PA 16802. *E-Mail:* usher@astro.psu.edu

**USHER, W(ILLIA)M MACK,** MATHEMATICAL STATISTICS, EDUCATIONAL ADMINISTRATION. *Current Pos:* dir instnl res, 67-69, DIR COMPUT & INFO SYST, OKLA STATE UNIV, 69- *Personal Data:* b Devol, Okla, Nov 10, 27; m 52. *Educ:* Okla State Univ, BS, 52, MS, 58. *Prof Exp:* Asst registr, Okla State Univ, 54-58; statistician, Tex Instruments, Inc, 58-59, opers res analyst, 59-61, mgr, 61-63, corp systs develop mgr, 63-67. *Mem:* Am Statist Asn; Asn Comput Mach; Asn Instnl Res. *Res:* Development of management information systems. *Mailing Add:* 1127 S Springdale St Stillwater OK 74074

**USHERWOOD, NOBLE RANSOM,** SOIL FERTILITY, PLANT NUTRITION. *Current Pos:* midwest agronomist, Potash & Phosphate Inst, Ill, 67-69, dir, Potash Res Asn Northern Latin Am, Guatemala, 69-71, dir Fla & Latin Am Potash Inst, 71-77, vpres, 77-, SE DIR, POTASH & PHOSPHATE INST. *Personal Data:* b Atlanta, Ill, Jan 13, 38; m 63; c 3. *Educ:* Southern Ill Univ, BS, 59, MS, 60; Univ Md, PhD(soils, plant physiol), 66. *Prof Exp:* Res asst soil fertil & test correlation, Univ Md, 60-66; asst prof soil fertil & plant nutrit, Univ Del, 66-67. *Concurrent Pos:* Assoc ed, J Agron Educ; chmn bd, Agron Sci Found. *Mem:* Fel Am Soc Agron; fel Soil Sci Soc Am; Brazilian Soc Sci; fel Crop Sci Soc Am. *Res:* Nitrogen, phosphorus, potassium, magnesium and manganese soil fertility and plant nutrition; sub-surface irrigation feasability studies. *Mailing Add:* Potash & Phosphate Inst 655 Engineering Dr Suite 110 Norcross GA 30092

**USHIODA, SUKEKATSU,** ELECTRONICS ENGINEERING. *Current Pos:* PROF, TOHOKU UNIV, 85-; PROF, JAPAN ADVAN INST SCI TECH, 93- *Personal Data:* b Tokyo, Japan, Sept 18, 41; m 85; c 3. *Educ:* Dartmouth Col, AB, 64; Univ Pa, MS, 65, PhD(physics), 69. *Prof Exp:* From asst prof to prof physics, Univ Calif, Irvine, 69-85. *Mem:* Optical Soc Am; Fel Am Phys Soc; Phys Soc Japan; Vacuum Soc; Japan Soc Appl Physics. *Res:* Solid state physics; Raman spectroscopy; surface physics; electron spectroscopy. *Mailing Add:* Res Inst Elec Comm Tohoku Univ 2-1-1 Katahira Aoba-ku Sendai 980-77 Japan. *Fax:* 81-22-217-5497; *E-Mail:* ushioda@riec.toholu.ac.jp

**USINGER, WILLIAM R,** IMMUNOLOGICAL ASPECTS OF BACTERIAL PRODUCTS. *Current Pos:* PRES, IMSUSIME, 90- *Personal Data:* b Chicago Ill, Mar 20, 51. *Educ:* Univ Wis-Madison, PhD(immunol), 80. *Prof Exp:* NIH fel & assoc res scientist, Dept Immunol, Univ Calif, Berkeley, 80-90. *Mem:* AAAS; Am Asn Immunologists; Reticuloendothelial Soc. *Mailing Add:* 25 Via Floreado Orinda CA 94563-1924. *Fax:* 510-254-9047

**USISKIN, ZALMAN P,** MATHEMATICS EDUCATION, CURRICULUM. *Current Pos:* From asst prof to assoc prof, 69-82, PROF EDUC, UNIV CHICAGO, 82- *Personal Data:* b Chicago, Ill, Jan 1, 43; m 79, Karen; c 2. *Educ:* Univ Ill, BS(educ) & BS(math), 63; Harvard Univ, MAT, 64; Univ Mich, PhD(educ), 69. *Concurrent Pos:* Dir, Sch Math Proj, Univ Chicago, 87-; mem, Nat Acad Math Sci Educ Bd, 88-91. *Mem:* Math Asn Am. *Res:* All aspects of math education with emphasis on matters related to curriculum & instruction; policy making; selection & organization of content. *Mailing Add:* 5835 S Kimbark Chicago IL 60637

**USLENGHI, PIERGIORGIO L,** ELECTROMAGNETICS, OPTICS. *Current Pos:* assoc prof info eng, 70-74, assoc dean eng, 82-87 PROF ELEC ENG, UNIV ILL, CHICAGO, 74- *Personal Data:* b Turin, Italy, Aug 31, 37; m 78, Shelly; c 3. *Educ:* Turin Polytech Inst, Laurea, 60; Univ Mich, MS, 64, PhD(physics), 67. *Prof Exp:* Asst prof elec eng, Turin Polytech Inst, 61; assoc res engr, Conductron Corp, 62-63; res physicist, Univ Mich, Ann Arbor, 63-70. *Concurrent Pos:* NASA, NSF & Dept Defense grants. *Mem:* Fel Inst Elec & Electronics Engrs; Int Union Radio Sci; Sigma Xi. *Res:* Antennas; radars; quantum electronics; nonlinear phenomena. *Mailing Add:* Univ Ill Chicago Dept Elec Eng & Comput Sci M/C 154 Box 4348 Chicago IL 60680. *Fax:* 312-413-0024

**USMANI, RIAZ AHMAD,** numerical analysis; deceased, see previous edition for last biography

**USSELMAN, MELVYN CHARLES,** BIOGRAPHY, CREATIVITY & ENTREPRENEURSHIP. *Current Pos:* Asst prof chem, Univ Western Ont, 75-81, asst prof, Dept Hist Med & Sci, 76-81, assoc chair, Dept Chem, 91-94, ASSOC PROF CHEM, UNIV WESTERN ONT, 81- *Personal Data:* b Ottawa, Ont, Jan 5, 46; m 79, Trixie Sennema; c Jasper, Charlotte, Richard & David. *Educ:* Univ Western Ont, BSc, 68, PhD(chem), 72, MA, 75. *Mem:* Hist Sci Soc; Am Chem Soc; Brit Soc Hist Alchemy & Chem; Can Soc Hist & Philos Sci; Can Sci & Technol Hist Asn. *Res:* History of chemistry, 18th-20th centuries; the work of W H Wollaston; platinum metallurgy, origin of chemical laws. *Mailing Add:* Dept Chem Univ Western Ont London ON N6A 5B7 Can. *Fax:* 519-661-3022; *E-Mail:* usselman@uwo.ca

**USSELMAN, THOMAS MICHAEL,** GEOPHYSICS, GEOCHEMISTRY. *Current Pos:* SR STAFF SCIENTIST & ASSOC DIR, NAT ACAD SCI, 78- *Personal Data:* b Bismarck, NDak, Aug 9, 47; m 73; c 1. *Educ:* Franklin & Marshall Col, BA, 69; Lehigh Univ, MS, 71, PhD(geol), 73. *Prof Exp:* Nat Res Coun res assoc geochem, Johnson Space Ctr, NASA, 73-75, fel, Lunar Sci Inst, 75-76; vis prof geol, State Univ NY, Buffalo, 76-78. *Concurrent Pos:* Co-ed, 7th Lunar Sci Conf Proc, 76. *Mem:* Am Geophys Union; fel Geol Soc Am; Urban & Regional Info Systs Asn. *Res:* Experimental geochemistry and geophysics including study of planetary interiors, crystallization of igneous melts, and effect of volatiles; applications of geographic information systems; spatial data policies. *Mailing Add:* Bd Earth Sci & Resources Nat Acad Sci 2101 Constitution Ave NW Washington DC 20418. *Fax:* 202-334-1377; *E-Mail:* usselman@nas.edu

**USTER, PAUL STEVEN,** DRUG DELIVERY SYSTEMS, LIPSOMES. *Current Pos:* from assoc res scientist to sr scientist, 86-91, ASSOC DIR FORMULATION DEVELOP, SEQUUS PHARMACEUTICALS, INC, 91- *Personal Data:* b Morristown, NJ, Jun 20, 54. *Educ:* Univ Calif, San Diego, BA, 76; Univ Calif, Davis, MA, 80, PhD(zool), 83. *Prof Exp:* Carnegie fel, Johns Hopkins Univ, 83-86. *Mem:* AAAS; Am Chem Soc; Parenteral Drug Asn. *Mailing Add:* 960 Hamilton Ct Menlo Park CA 94025-1430

**UTAGIKAR, AJIT PURUSHOTTAM,** engineering physics, for more information see previous edition

**UTECH, FREDERICK HERBERT,** SYSTEMATIC BOTANY, BOTANY. *Current Pos:* CUR BOT, CARNEGIE MUS NATURAL HIST, 76- *Personal Data:* b Merrill, Wis, Apr 19, 43; m; c 1. *Educ:* Univ Wis-Madison, BS, 66, MS, 68; Wash Univ, PhD(biol), 73. *Prof Exp:* Lectr bot, Univ Wis, Marshfield, 70; vis scientist, US-Jap Coop Sci Prog, 74-75; fel bot, Jap Soc Prom Sci, 75-76. *Concurrent Pos:* NSF fel, Wash Univ, 71-72 & 72-73; fel, Univ Wis-Madison & res assoc, Wash Univ, 74-76; adj res scientist, Hunt Inst Bot Doc, 77-; M Graham Netting Res Fund grant, Carnegie Mus, 77-87. *Mem:* Bot Soc Am; Int Asn Plant Taxon; AAAS; Am Soc Plant Taxonomists. *Res:* Biosystematic investigations of the living elements of the Arcto-Tertiary geoflora in the Northern hemisphere; floral vascular anatomy of the Liliaceae; cytotaxonomy and systematics of the Liliaceae. *Mailing Add:* Sect Bot Carnegie Mus Natural Hist 4400 Forbes Ave Pittsburgh PA 15213. *E-Mail:* utechf@clpgh.org

**UTERMOHLEN, VIRGINIA,** IMMUNOLOGY. *Current Pos:* asst prof, 77-80, ASSOC PROF, NY STATE COL VET MED, 80-; ASSOC PROF NUTRIT SCI, CORNELL UNIV, 81- *Personal Data:* b New York, NY, June 17, 43; div; c 2. *Educ:* Wash Univ, BS, 64; Columbia Univ, MD, 68; Am Bd Pediat, dipl. *Prof Exp:* Intern, resident & chief resident pediat, St Luke's Hosp, NY, 68-71; fel immunol, Rockefeller Univ, 71-74; asst prof biochem, Cornell Univ, 74-77, asst prof nutrit sci, 77-81. *Concurrent Pos:* NIH fel, 71-72; NY Heart Asn fel, 72-74; guest investr immunol, Rockefeller Univ, 74-76; asst dean, NY State Col Human Ecol, 86-87. *Mem:* Harvey Soc; Am Asn Immunologists; Am Med Women's Asn. *Res:* Nutrition and cell-mediated immunity. *Mailing Add:* Nutrit Sci Cornell Univ 124 Savage Hall Ithaca NY 14853-6301

**UTGAARD, JOHN EDWARD,** GEOLOGY, PALEOZOOLOGY. *Current Pos:* from asst prof to assoc prof geol, 65-73, PROF GEOL, SOUTHERN ILL UNIV, CARBONDALE, 73- *Personal Data:* b Anamoose, NDak, Jan 22, 36; m 61; c 4. *Educ:* Univ NDak, BS, 58; Ind Univ, AM, 61, PhD(geol). 63. *Prof Exp:* Res assoc paleont, US Nat Mus, Smithsonian Inst, 63-65. *Concurrent Pos:* Smithsonian fel evolutionary & syst biol, Smithsonian Inst, 72. *Mem:* Geol Soc Am; Am Asn Petrol Geologists; Paleont Soc; Brit Palaeont Asn; Soc Econ Paleont & Mineral; Sigma Xi. *Res:* Fossil bryozoans; carboniferous paleoecology and depositional environments; paleobiology of Paleozoic bryozoans; paleoecology of Late Paleozoic fossil communities. *Mailing Add:* Dept Geol Dept Geol Southern Ill Univ Carbondale IL 62901

**UTGARD, RUSSELL OLIVER,** GEOLOGY, SCIENCE EDUCATION. *Current Pos:* from asst prof to assoc prof geol, 69-92, EMER PROF, OHIO STATE UNIV, 92-; EISENHOWER PROG CONSULT, OHIO BD REGENTS. *Personal Data:* b Star Prairie, Wis, July 30, 33; m 56, Doris Schaffer; c Louise, Thomas & Jane. *Educ:* Wis State Col, River Falls, BS, 57; Univ Wis, MS, 58; Ind Univ, Bloomington, MAT, 66, EdD(sci), 69. *Prof Exp:* Instr geol, Joliet Jr Col, Ill, 58-67. *Concurrent Pos:* Teaching asst, Ind Univ, Bloomington, 65-66. *Mem:* Nat Asn Geol Teachers; Nat Sci Teachers Asn; Geol Soc Am. *Res:* Environmental geology. *Mailing Add:* Dept Geol Sci Ohio State Univ Columbus OH 43210

**UTGOFF, VADYM V,** AEROSPACE ENGINEERING. *Current Pos:* Assoc prof, 64-83, PROF EMER AEROSPACE ENG, US NAVAL ACAD, 84- *Personal Data:* b Sevastopol, Russia, Aug 3, 17; m 46; c 3. *Educ:* US Naval Acad, BS, 39; US Naval Postgrad Sch, BS, 48; Mass Inst Technol, MS, 49. *Mem:* Am Inst Aeronaut & Astronaut; Am Helicopter Soc. *Res:* Flight dynamics; rotary wing aerodynamics. *Mailing Add:* 2 Ridge Rd Annapolis MD 21401

**UTHE, JOHN FREDERICK,** FISHERIES. *Current Pos:* Res scientist, Fresh Water Inst, Fisheries Res Bd, 63-72, res mgr, Technol Br, 72-79, HEAD, INORGANIC CONTAMINANTS & STABLE ISOTOPES SECT, HALIFAX, FISHERIES & OCEANS CAN, 87- *Personal Data:* b Saskatoon, Sask, Feb 27, 38; m 63; c 3. *Educ:* Univ Sask, BA, 59, Hons, 60, MA, 61; Univ Western Ont, PhD(biochem), 68. *Res:* Analytical chemistry applied to toxic residues and the biochemical effects of such residues on fish. *Mailing Add:* 32 Simcoe Pl Halifax NS B3M 1H3 Can

**UTHUS, ERIC O,** NUTRITION, METABOLISM. *Current Pos:* chemist nutrit, 84-86, RES CHEMIST NUTRIT, USDA, 86- *Personal Data:* b Minot, NDak, Nov 29, 52. *Educ:* Univ NDak, BS, 74, MS, 76, PhD(biochem), 82. *Prof Exp:* Fel biochem, Univ NDak, 82-84. *Mem:* Sigma Xi; Soc Exp Biol & Med; Soc Exp Geochem Health; Am Inst Nutrit. *Mailing Add:* Grand Forks Human Nutrit Res Ctr USDA Agr Res Serv Univ Sta PO Box 9034 Grand Forks ND 58202-9034

**UTKE, ALLEN R,** INORGANIC CHEMISTRY. *Current Pos:* assoc prof, 64-78, PROF CHEM, UNIV WIS-OSHKOSH, 78- *Personal Data:* b Moline, Ill, Feb 5, 36; m 57; c 3. *Educ:* Augustana Col, Ill, BS, 58; Univ Iowa, MS, 61, PhD(inorg chem), 63. *Prof Exp:* Sr res chemist, Chem Div, Pittsburgh Plate Glass Co, Tex, 62-64. *Mem:* Am Chem Soc. *Res:* Chemistry of the alkali and alkaline earth metals and their reactions in liquid ammonia. *Mailing Add:* Dept Chem Univ Wis 800 Algoma Blvd Oshkosh WI 54901-3551

**UTKHEDE, RAJESHWAR SHAMRAO,** PLANT BREEDING, MICROBIOLOGY. *Current Pos:* PLANT PATHOLOGIST, RES STA, AGR CAN, 80- *Personal Data:* b Kalmeshwar, India, Apr 18, 39; c 2. *Educ:* Nagpur Univ, BSc, 61; Indian Agr Res Inst, PhD(genetics), 68. *Prof Exp:* Res assoc genetics, Rockefeller Found, 67-70; millet breeder, Haryana Agr Univ, 71-72; corn breeder, Ministry Agr, Tanzania, 72-75; fel plant path, Simon Fraser Univ, 75-77, res assoc, 77-80. *Concurrent Pos:* Res assoc, Can Ministry Manpower & Immigration, 75-76; consult, Food & Agr Orgn, UN, 84. *Mem:* Can Soc Phytopath; Am Phytopath Soc. *Res:* Breeding for disease resistance; control of soilborne and root diseases by integrated use of resistance, microbial antagonist and chemical treatment. *Mailing Add:* Res Sta Agr Can Agassiz BC V0M 1A0 Can. *Fax:* 604-796-0359; *E-Mail:* utkheder@em.agr.ca

**UTKU, BISULAY BEREKET,** ARCHITECTURAL ENGINEERING, ARCHITECTURAL DESIGN. *Current Pos:* res assoc energy conserv, 79-80, ADJ ASSOC PROF CIVIL ENG, DUKE UNIV, 87- *Personal Data:* b Bandirma, Turkey, Apr 28, 40; m 64; c 2. *Educ:* Istanbul Tech Univ, dipl arch ing, 62, PhD(archit eng), 78, docent arch, 82; NC State Univ, MArch, 73. *Prof Exp:* Teaching asst struct anal, Istanbul Tech Univ, 62-65, teaching asst arch struct, 74-78, from asst prof to assoc prof, 78-86. *Mem:* Nat Asn Arch Engrs. *Res:* Earthquake resistance of masonry structures; passive climate control; energy conservation in buildings. *Mailing Add:* Dept Civil & Environ Eng Duke Univ Durham NC 27706-7706. *Fax:* 919-660-5219; *E-Mail:* bu@egr.duke.edu

**UTKU, SENOL,** ENGINEERING & SIMULATIONS, ANALYSIS & CONTROL. *Current Pos:* assoc prof, Duke Univ, 70-72, dir, Undergrad Studies Civil Eng, 80-87, dir, Grad Studies Civil Eng, 87-89, DIR, COMPUT STRUCT ANALYSIS FUND, DUKE UNIV, 71-, PROF CIVIL ENG & COMPUT SCI, 72- *Personal Data:* b Suruc, Turkey, Nov 23, 31; US citizen; m 64, Bisulay Bereket; c Ayda & Sinan. *Educ:* Istanbul Tech Univ, Dipl Ing, 54; Mass Inst Technol, MS, 59, ScD(struct eng), 60. *Prof Exp:* Res engr, Math & Appln Dept, IBM Corp, 59-60; asst prof struct, Mass Inst Technol, 60-62; assoc prof, Mid East Tech Univ, Ankara, 62-63; exec chief, Comput Ctr,

Istanbul Tech Univ, 63-65; sr res engr, Jet Propulsion Lab, Calif Inst Technol, 65-68, mem tech staff, 68-70. *Concurrent Pos:* Consult, Math & Appln Dept, IBM Mach Corp & Lincoln Lab, Mass Inst Technol, 60-61, Mitre Corp, 61-62, Westinghouse Res & Develop Ctr, 70, Langley Res Ctr, NASA, 71 & Jet Propulsion Lab, Calif Inst Technol, 71-; lectr, Istanbul Tech Univ, 62-63, Univ Southern Calif, 66-70, Univ Wash, 68 & Duke Univ, 70-; mem, Study Group Comput Sci, NATO, Brussels, 68-70; consult, Tokten Prog, UN, 79, 80 & 81; prin investr, Parallel Processing Proj, Pres Fund Calif Inst Technol, 81-82 & State of Art Rev Adaptive Struct Japan Proj, NSF, 91-92. *Mem:* Fel Am Soc Civil Engrs, 94; Am Acad Mech; Am Soc Eng Educ; Sigma Xi. *Res:* Engineering and structural mechanics; applied mathematics; numerical analysis; concurrent processing; optimal control; adaptive structures; active vibration control in earthquake and wind engineering. *Mailing Add:* 134 Hudson Hall Duke Univ Durham NC 27708-0287. *Fax:* 919-660-5219; *E-Mail:* su@egr.duke.edu

**UTLAUT, WILLIAM FREDERICK,** TELECOMMUNICATIONS. *Current Pos:* DIR TELECOMMUN RES & ENG, INST TELECOMMUN SCI, NAT TELECOMMUN & INFO ADMIN, DEPT COM, 67- *Personal Data:* b Sterling, Colo, July 26, 22; m 46; c 3. *Educ:* Univ Colo, BSEE, 44, MSEE, 50, PhD(elec eng), 66. *Prof Exp:* Engr large motor design, Gen Elec Co, 46-48; instr elec eng, Univ Colo, 48-54; electronic engr radio propagation, Dept Commun, Nat Bur Stand, 54-64; dir, Ionospheric Telecommun Lab, Environ Sci & Serv Admin, Dept Com, 64-67. *Concurrent Pos:* Chmn, spectrum utilization & monitoring, US Study Group I, Radiocommun Sect, Int Telecommun Union, 72-; chmn, integrated serv digital networks tech subcomt of TI, 84-88; chair, serv archit & signaling tech subcomt of TI, 88-92, Joint Working Party on ISDN, 87-89, US Study Group B, Telecommun Stand Sect, Int Telecommun Union, 89- *Mem:* Int Union Radio Sci; fel Inst Elec & Electronics Engrs. *Res:* Radiowave propagation and ionospheric modification by high-powered ground-based radio frequency transmitters; radio spectrum utilization studies. *Mailing Add:* Inst Telecommun Sci Nat Telecommun & Info Admin US Dept Commerce 325 Broadway Boulder CO 80303-3328

**UTLEY, JOHN FOSTER, III,** PLANT SYSTEMATICS, BIOLOGY. *Current Pos:* from asst prof to assoc prof, 78-89, PROF BIOL, UNIV NEW ORLEANS, 90- *Personal Data:* b Detroit, Mich, June 23, 44; m 71, Kathleen Burt. *Educ:* Univ SFla, BA, 68; Duke Univ, PhD(bot), 77. *Prof Exp:* Cur bot, Div Natural Hist, Mus Nac de Costa Rica, 73-76; fel, US Nat Herbarium, Smithsonian Inst, 76-77. *Mem:* Sigma Xi; Soc Study Evolution; Int Asn Plant Taxonomists. *Res:* Systematics; evolution and ecology of epiphytic angiosperms. *Mailing Add:* Dept Biol Sci Univ New Orleans New Orleans LA 70148. *Fax:* 504-286-6121; *E-Mail:* jfubs@uno.edu

**UTLEY, PHILIP RAY,** ANIMAL SCIENCE. *Current Pos:* assoc prof, 70-78, PROF ANIMAL SCI, UNIV GA, COASTAL PLAINS EXP STA, TIFTON, 78- *Personal Data:* b Ill, Dec 18, 41; m 63; c 3. *Educ:* Southern Ill Univ, Carbondale, BS, 64; Univ Mo-Columbia, MS, 67; Univ Ky, PhD(animal sci), 69. *Prof Exp:* Asst instr animal sci, Southern Ill Univ, Carbondale, 63-65. *Mem:* Am Soc Animal Sci. *Res:* Beef cattle nutrition and management. *Mailing Add:* Interim Asst Dean CPES PO Box 748 Tifton GA 31793

**UTRACKI, LECHOSLAW ADAM,** POLYMER ENGINEERING, RHEOLOGY. *Current Pos:* SR RES OFFICER RHEOLOGY, NAT RES COUN CAN, 80- *Personal Data:* b Poland, Aug 1, 31; Can citizen; m 56; c 2. *Educ:* Polytech Lodz, Poland, BS, 53, MEng, 56. *Hon Degrees:* DSc, Polytechnic Lodz, Poland, 60; Habitation, 63. *Prof Exp:* Adj phys chem polymers, Polish Acad Sci, 56-65; vis scientist, Univ Southern Calif, 65-67; vis prof macromol sci, Case Western Res Univ, 67-68; researcher polymer eng, Gulf Oil Can Ltd, 68-71; vis scientist polymer rheology, McGill Univ, 71-73; group leader, CIL Inc, 73-80. *Concurrent Pos:* Fel, Univ Southern Calif, 60-62; dir, Plastic Eng, 82-; chmn, Versailles Proj Advan Mat & Sci, 85-; adj prof, Univ Que, 92- & McGill Univ, 96- *Mem:* Can Rheology Soc (pres, 84-86); Polymer Processing Soc (pres, 87-89); Am Chem Soc; Soc Plastic Eng; Chem Inst Can. *Res:* Preparation properties and performance of polymer alloys, blends and composites. *Mailing Add:* Indust Mat Inst Nat Res Coun Can 75 de Mortagne Boucherville PQ J4B 6Y4 Can. *Fax:* 514-641-5105; *E-Mail:* leszek.utracki@nrc.ca

**UTTER, FRED MADISON,** BIOCHEMICAL GENETICS. *Current Pos:* AFFIL PROF, UNIV WASH, 82- *Personal Data:* b Seattle, Wash, Nov 25, 31; m 58, Nancy Darrow; c Jennifer, Jeffrey & Judy. *Educ:* Univ Puget Sound, BSc, 54; Univ Wash, MSc, 64; Univ Calif, Davis, PhD(genetics), 69. *Hon Degrees:* Dr, Univ Dr Girona, 97. *Honors & Awards:* Award of Excellence, Am Fisheries Soc, 96. *Prof Exp:* Serologist, Biol Lab, US Bur Com Fisheries, 59-60, chemist, 60-80, geneticist, 80-83, supvry geneticist, 83-88. *Concurrent Pos:* Affil asst prof, Univ Wash, 71, affil assoc prof, 76; consult, appl pop genetics, 88-; vis prof, Autonomous Univ Barcelona, 88- & Univ Oviedo, 90- *Mem:* Am Fisheries Soc; fel Am Inst Fishery Res Biol; Am Genetical Asn; Soc Marine Molecular Biotechnol. *Res:* Use of biochemical methods for the detection of genetic variations in fish for use in studies of fish populations; induced gynogenesis and polyploidy in salmon. *Mailing Add:* 19424 Tenth NE Shoreline WA 98155. *Fax:* 206-685-7471; *E-Mail:* fmutter@u.washington.edu

**UTTERBACK, NYLE GENE,** EXPERIMENTAL PHYSICS. *Current Pos:* consult, TRW, Redondo Beach, Calif, 76-81, CONSULT, SANSUM MED RES FOUND, SANTA BARBARA, 81- *Personal Data:* b Oskaloosa, Iowa, Jan 19, 31; m 58; c 3. *Educ:* Iowa State Univ, BS, 53, PhD(physics), 57. *Prof Exp:* Res asst, Ames Lab, AEC, 51-57; Fulbright scholar, Ger, 57-58; sr physicist, Ord Res Lab, Univ Va, 58-59; asst prof & res physicist, Denver Res Inst, 59-63; staff scientist, Gen Motors Corp, Calif, 63-72; staff scientist, Mission Res Corp, Santa Barbara, 72-75. *Mem:* Am Phys Soc. *Res:* Laser technology; atomic and molecular reaction kinetics; diabetic microangiopathy. *Mailing Add:* 718 Willowglen Rd Santa Barbara CA 93105

**UTZ, JOHN PHILIP,** MEDICINE. *Current Pos:* dean fac, 73-78, PROF MED, GEORGETOWN UNIV, 73- *Personal Data:* b Rochester, Minn, June 9, 22; m 47; c 5. *Educ:* Northwestern Univ, BS, 43, MD, 47; Georgetown Univ, MS, 49. *Prof Exp:* Researcher, Lab for Infectious Dis, Nat Inst Allergy & Infectious Dis, 47-49, chief infectious dis serv, 52-65; prof med & chmn div immunol & infectious dis, Med Col Va, 65-73. *Concurrent Pos:* Fel, Mayo Found, 49-52; intern, Evans Mem Hosp, Boston, 46-47; consult, E I du Pont de Nemours & Co; pres, Nat Found Infectious Dis, 72-75. *Mem:* Am Fedn Clin Res; Am Col Physicians; Am Col Chest Physicians; Soc Exp Biol & Med; Am Thoracic Soc; Am Soc Clin Invest; Asn Am Phys. *Res:* Clinical investigations in infectious diseases. *Mailing Add:* 6551 Ridgewood Dr Pelican Bay Naples FL 33963-3433

**UTZ, WINFIELD ROY, JR,** MATHEMATICAL ANALYSIS. *Current Pos:* from asst prof to assoc prof, 49-69, PROF MATH, UNIV MO, COLUMBIA, 69-, CHMN DEPT, 70- *Personal Data:* b Boonville, Mo, Nov 17, 19; m 41, Jean Woolsey; c David, Charles & John. *Educ:* Cent Col, Mo, AB, 41; Univ Mo, MA, 42; Univ Va, PhD(math), 48. *Prof Exp:* Asst instr math, Univ Mo, 42; instr, Univ Notre Dame, 42-43 & Univ Va, 44-48; instr, Univ Mich, 48-49. *Concurrent Pos:* Mem, Inst Advan Study, Princeton Univ, 55-56; vis scholar, Univ Calif, Berkeley, 62-63; vis prof, Brown Univ, 69. *Mem:* Am Math Soc; Math Asn Am; London Math Soc. *Res:* Surface dynamics; topological dynamics; differential equations. *Mailing Add:* Dept Math Univ Mo Columbia MO 65211

**UWAYDAH, IBRAHIM MUSA,** ANTI-INFLAMMATORY, ANTIALLERGY. *Current Pos:* RES ASSOC, A H ROBINS CO, 77- *Personal Data:* b Qualqiliya, Jordan, Sept 18, 43; US citizen; m 68; c 4. *Educ:* Am Univ Beirut, BSc, 67; Univ Kans, Lawrence, PhD(med chem), 74. *Prof Exp:* Fel res assoc pharmacol, Med Col Va, 74-77. *Concurrent Pos:* Adj assoc prof pharmacol, Med Col Va, 78-; adj asst prof med chem, Med Col Va, 86- *Mem:* Am Chem Soc; NY Acad Sci; Sigma Xi; Int Soc Heterocyclic Chem. *Res:* Design and synthesis of potentially active bioactive agents; inflammation area; H2-antagonists (gastrointestinal); central nervous system area (analgesics); B-blockers. *Mailing Add:* Hoechst Celanese Corp, Clearlake Plant Pasadena TX 77507

**UY, WILLIAM CHENG,** ENGINEERING, CHEMICAL ENGINEERING. *Current Pos:* Res engr, 70-74, res assoc, 83-86, SR RES ENGR, E I DU PONT DE NEMOURS & CO, INC, 74-, SR RES ASSOC, 86- *Personal Data:* b Manila, Philippines, Feb 11, 40; US citizen; div; c 4. *Educ:* De La Salle Col, Philippines, BSChE, 65; Northwestern Univ, MS, 67, PhD(chem eng), 70. *Mem:* Soc Rheology; Am Chem Soc. *Res:* Polymer characterization; fiber fatigue resistance; fiber finishes; melt, wet and dry-jet fiber spinning; rheology; polymerization; biological fiber; process development; isotropic and anirotropic systems; granted eight patents. *Mailing Add:* DuPont Mats Sci & Eng PO Box 80302 Wilmington DE 19880-0302

**UYEDA, CARL KAORU,** ANATOMY, PATHOLOGY. *Current Pos:* RETIRED. *Personal Data:* b San Bernardino, Calif, July 11, 22; m 76; c 2. *Educ:* Syracuse Univ, BA, 47, MS, 49; Univ Md, PhD(anat path), 66. *Prof Exp:* Div head, Cancer Cytol Dept, Md State Dept Health, 50-58; instr cytopath, Sch Med, Univ Md, 58-64, instr anat, 62-67; asst prof path & anat, Sch Med, Univ Ark, Little Rock, 67-73, assoc dir, Sch Cytotechnol & dir, Cytopath Lab, 67-77, assoc prof path & anat, 73-77; cytopathologist, Path Lab, Los Gatos, Calif, 77-84 & Lab Serv, San Jose, Calif, 85-89. *Concurrent Pos:* Res assoc, Sch Med, Johns Hopkins Univ, 56-65, sr cytologist, 65-67; sr cytologist, Ark State Dept Health, 65-67; contractor, Nat Ctr Toxicol Res, Food & Drug Admin, Ark, 71-77; consult, Vet Admin Hosp, Little Rock, 72-77. *Mem:* Am Soc Cytol; Int Acad Cytopath Path; Pan-Am Cancer Cytol Soc; Am Asn Anat; NY Acad Sci; Sigma Xi. *Res:* Cytogenetics; abnormal cytogenetic changes; clinical carcinoma and congenital anomalies; spontaneous leukemic C3H and C57 mice; cytopathology, refinement of interpretation in structural change of cancer; neoplasm of mice bladder; circadian rhythmicity in bronchogenic carcinoma and mice tissue. *Mailing Add:* 9808 Catskill Rd Little Rock AR 72227-5525

**UYEDA, CHARLES TSUNEO,** MEDICAL MICROBIOLOGY. *Current Pos:* RETIRED. *Personal Data:* b Penryn, Calif, Feb 20, 29; m 56; c 2. *Educ:* San Jose State Col, BA, 51; Miami Univ, MA, 52; Stanford Univ, PhD(med microbiol), 56. *Prof Exp:* Officer-in-charge diag microbiol, 406th Med Gen Lab, US Army, Japan, 56-57; bacteriologist microbiol, 6th US Army Area Lab, Ft Baker, 57-58, lab serv, Vet Admin Hosp, Oakland, 58-63; microbiologist, Lab Serv, Vet Admin Med Ctr, Palo Alto, 63-96. *Concurrent Pos:* Clin lab officer, US Army Med Serv Corps, 58-; res assoc, Sch Med, Stanford Univ, 63-78, clin asst prof path, 78-; instr, San Francisco State Univ, 79- *Mem:* Am Soc Microbiol; Sigma Xi. *Res:* Rapid and automated methods in the diagnosis and treatment of infectious diseases as well as in the immunology of multiple sclerosis; serology and immunology. *Mailing Add:* 875 Norfolk Pine Ave Sunnyvale CA 94087

**UYEDA, KOSAKU,** BIOCHEMISTRY. *Current Pos:* From asst prof to prof, 67-81, PROF BIOCHEM, HEALTH SCI CTR, UNIV TEX, DALLAS, 82-; RES CHEMIST, VET ADMIN HOSP, 67-, CHIEF CELLULAR REGULATION, 71- *Personal Data:* b Kokawa Naga-gun, Japan, Mar 15, 32; US citizen; m 57; c 2. *Educ:* Ore State Univ, BS, 55, MS, 57; Univ Calif, Berkeley, PhD(biochem), 62. *Honors & Awards:* William S Middleton Award, 84. *Concurrent Pos:* Fel, Univ Calif, Berkeley, 62; NIH fel, Pub Health Res Inst NY, 62-64; scholar, Univ Calif, Berkeley, 64-67. *Mem:* Am Chem Soc; Am Soc Biol Chem. *Res:* Elucidation of the mechanism of action of enzymes and allosteric enzymes and their roles in regulation of carbohydrate metabolism. *Mailing Add:* Dept Biochem DVA Med Ctr 4500 S Lancaster Rd Dallas TX 75216-7167

**UYEHARA, OTTO A(RTHUR),** MECHANICAL ENGINEERING, COMBUSTION PROCESSES. *Current Pos:* Alumni Res Found fel, Univ Wis-Madison, 45-46, res assoc, 46-47, from asst prof to prof, 47-82, EMER PROF MECH ENG, UNIV WIS-MADISON, 82-; CONSULT, 82- *Personal Data:* b Hanford, Calif, Sept 9, 16; m 45; c 3. *Educ:* Univ Wis, BS, 42, MS, 43, PhD(chem eng), 45. *Honors & Awards:* Benjamin Smith Reynolds Award, 67; Horning Award, Soc Automotive Engrs, 67 & 69, Colwell Awards, Prize Sci Contrib, 87; Dugold Clerk Award, Brit Inst Mech Engrs, 71. *Concurrent Pos:* Invited lectr, India, 68, Japan, Internal Combustion Engines, 76 & Norway Technol Inst, 77; instr combustion, Nat Cheng Kung Univ, Taiwan, 85. *Mem:* Fel Soc Automotive Engrs; Am Soc Mech Engrs; hon mem Japan Soc Mech Engrs. *Res:* Emission and combustion in internal combustion engines; instantaneous flame temperature indicators; influence of operating variables; fuel droplet vaporization in transient state; compression temperature measurement in internal combustion engines; nitrous oxide reduction in internal combustion engines. *Mailing Add:* 544 S Bond St Anaheim CA 92805

**UYEKI, EDWIN M,** PHARMACOLOGY, RADIOBIOLOGY. *Current Pos:* assoc prof, 65-70, PROF PHARMACOL, MED CTR, UNIV KANS, 70- *Personal Data:* b Seattle, Wash, Mar 12, 28; m 51; c 3. *Educ:* Kenyon Col, AB, 49; Univ Chicago, PhD(pharmacol), 53. *Prof Exp:* Instr pharmacol, Univ Chicago, 53-54; instr, Sch Med, Western Res Univ, 54-60, sect assoc radiation biol, 54-60; sr scientist, Hanford Labs Gen Elec Co, 60-65. *Mem:* AAAS; Am Soc Pharmacol & Exp Therapuet; Am Soc Cell Biol; Radiation Res Soc. *Res:* Immunopharmacology; immunosuppressants on antibody formation; bone marrow transplantation in radiation chimeras; radiation effects; short term tissue culture. *Mailing Add:* Dept Pharmacol Univ Kans Med Ctr 3901 Rainbow Blvd Kansas City KS 66103-0001

**UYEMOTO, JERRY KAZUMITSU,** PLANT PATHOLOGY, PLANT VIROLOGY. *Current Pos:* PROF, USDA AGR RES SERV, UNIV CALIF, DAVIS, 86- *Personal Data:* b Fresno, Calif, May 27, 39; m 65; c 1. *Educ:* Univ Calif, Davis, BS, 62, MS, 64, PhD(plant path), 68. *Honors & Awards:* Lee M Hutchins Award, Am Phytopath Soc, 92. *Prof Exp:* Lab technician, Univ Calif, Davis, 63-67; from asst prof to assoc prof virol, Cornell Univ, 68-77; from assoc prof to prof, Kans State Univ, 77-83. *Mem:* Asn Appl Biologists; Am Phytopath Soc. *Res:* Epidemiology and control of plant virus diseases. *Mailing Add:* Dept Plant Path USDA Agr Res Serv Univ Calif Davis CA 95616. *Fax:* 530-752-5674

**UYENO, EDWARD TEISO,** BEHAVIORAL PSYCHOPHARMACOLOGY. *Current Pos:* RETIRED. *Personal Data:* b Vancouver, BC, Mar, 31, 21; m 69. *Educ:* Univ Toronto, BA, 47, MA, 52, PhD(psychol), 58. *Prof Exp:* Res asst, Univ Toronto, Can, 55-57; res assoc psychol, Stanford Univ, 58-61, res psychologist & pharmacologist, Stanford Res Inst, 61-94. *Concurrent Pos:* NIH grants, 63-66, 68-70, 71-73, 75-78 & 81-83. *Mem:* Am Soc Pharmacol & Exp Therapeut; Am Psychol Asn; Psychonomic Soc; Can Psychol Asn. *Res:* Behavioral psychopharmacology; effects of drugs on learning, retention, and reproduction of animals; interaction effects of drugs; self-administration of alcohol and narcotics by rats; analgesics and narcotic antagonists; behavioral toxicology; bioassay of peptides, anxiolytics, anti-convulsants, stimulants, depressants, and hallucinogens; author of over 90 scientific articles and of several chapters in books; tolerance and addiction to morphine and other narcotics; small animal surgery. *Mailing Add:* Life Sci Div Stanford Res Inst Menlo Park CA 94025

**UYS, JOHANNES MARTHINUS,** THERMODYNAMICS IRON & STEEL MAKING, METAL WORKING. *Current Pos:* PRES, J U CONSULTS INC, 93- *Personal Data:* b Heidelberg, Rep SAfrica, Oct 17, 25; m 52; c 3. *Educ:* Univ Pretoria, BSc, 46, MSc, 50; Mass Inst Technol, ScD(metall eng), 59. *Prof Exp:* Supvr, Ludlum Steel Corp, 59-61; asst dir res, Youngstown Sheet and Tube Co, 61-65, asst vpres opers, 65-70, dir res & develop, 70-71, dir tech servs, 71, vpres tech serv, Youngstown Sheet & Tube Co, 72-78; dir qual control, Jones & Laughlin Steel Corp, 79-83; dir, tech servs, McLouth Steel Prod Corp, 83-85; vpres technol, Sharon Steel Corp, 87-89 & 91-93; dir technol, Wheeling-Pittsburgh Steel Corp, 89-91. *Mem:* Fel Am Soc Mat; Asn Iron & Steel Eng; Am Soc Testing & Mat; Am Iron & Steel Inst. *Res:* Improvements of the processes used to produce iron and steel. *Mailing Add:* 2009 Guadalupe Ave Youngstown OH 44504

**UZ, MEHMET,** ATOMIC MASS TRANSPORT OF INTERSTITIAL SOLUTES IN METALS & ALLOYS, PROCESSING MICROSTRUCTURE & PROPERTIES OF NB-ZR-C ALLOYS. *Current Pos:* asst prof metall, Metall Eng Dept, 85-89, Chem Eng Dept, 89-91, ASSOC PROF METALL & MAT, CHEM ENG DEPT, LAFAYETTE COL, 91- *Personal Data:* b Senirkent, Isparta, Turkey, Feb 20, 53; m 80, Sultan Sinan; c Emel K & Bilge S. *Educ:* Iowa State Univ, BS, 78, MS, 80, PhD(metall), 85. *Prof Exp:* Res assoc, Ames Lab, US Dept Eng, 84-85, vis scientist, 86 & 89. *Concurrent Pos:* Fac fel, Lewis Res Ctr, NASA, 90, 91 & 93, vis scientist, 92-93; prin investr, Lafayette Col, 87, NASA, 92-93. *Mem:* Minerals Metals & Mat Soc; Am Soc Mat Int; Mat Res Soc; Sigma Xi. *Res:* Atomic mass transport of interstitial solutes in metals and alloy under chemical, temperature and electrical field gradients; processing, microstructure and properties of refactory metal alloys, especially Nb-Zr and Nb-C alloys. *Mailing Add:* 526 Mixsell St Easton PA 18042. *Fax:* 610-250-5059; *E-Mail:* um#0@lafayacs.bitnet

**UZAWA, HIROFUMI,** ENVIRONMENTAL ECONOMICS. *Current Pos:* PROF, FAC SCI, DEPT MATH, CHUO UNIV, 94- *Personal Data:* b Yonago, Japan, July 21, 28; m 58, Hiroko Aoyoshi; c Tohru, Satoru & Marie. *Educ:* Univ Tokyo, BS, 51; Tokoku Univ, PhD(econs), 63. *Honors & Awards:* Matsuna Prize, Matsunaga Mem Fund, 69; Yoshino Prize, Chuo-Koron Sha, 70. *Prof Exp:* Res assoc, Stanford Univ, 56-59, assoc prof econ & statist, 60-64; asst prof econ & math, Univ Calif, Berkeley, 59-60; prof econs, Univ Chicago, 64-69; prof, Univ Tokyo, 69-89, dean fac econ, 80-82. *Concurrent Pos:* Fel, Advan Ctr Behav Sci, Palo Alto, 60-61. *Mem:* Foreign assoc Nat Acad Sci; fel Economet Soc (pres, 76); foreign hon mem Am Econ Asn; Royal Econ Soc; Am Acad Arts & Sci; Japan Acad. *Res:* Public economics; public decision making. *Mailing Add:* 742-1 Higashinakano Hachioji-shi Tokyo 192-03 Japan

**UZER, AHMET TURGAY,** QUANTUM DYNAMICS OF ATOMS & MOLECULES, NONLINEAR DYNAMICS. *Current Pos:* asst prof, 85-90, assoc prof, 90-95, PROF, SCH PHYSICS, GA INST TECHNOL, 95- *Personal Data:* b Samsun, Turkey, Feb 1, 52. *Educ:* Mid East Tech Univ, Ankara, Turkey, BSc, 74; Harvard Univ, AM, 77, PhD(chem physics), 79. *Prof Exp:* Res asst, Dept Theoret Chem, Oxford Univ, UK, 79-81; res fel, Noyes Lab, Calif Tech, 82-83; res assoc, Joint Inst Lab Astrophys, Boulder, Colo, 83-85. *Concurrent Pos:* Res fel, Alexander Von Humboldt, 93, Max-Planck Inst Quantum Physics, Garching, Munich. *Mem:* Am Phys Soc; Am Chem Soc; Sigma Xi. *Res:* Dynamics of intramolecular energy transfer; quantization of nonlinear systems; quantum mechanics of chaotic systems; computational physics; semiclassical theories; Rydberg atoms and molecules. *Mailing Add:* Sch Physics Ga Inst Technol Atlanta GA 30332-0430. *Fax:* 404-894-9958; *E-Mail:* turgay.uzer@physics.gatech.edu

**UZES, CHARLES ALPHONSE,** THEORETICAL PHYSICS. *Current Pos:* from asst prof to prof physics, 67-97, EMER PROF MARINE SCI, UNIV GA, 97- *Personal Data:* b Downey, Calif, Dec 14, 39; m 67; c 1. *Educ:* Calif State Univ, Long Beach, BS, 62; Univ Calif, Riverside, MA, 64, PhD(physics), 67. *Mem:* Am Phys Soc. *Res:* The use of non-perturbative calculational methods in the nonlinear classical and quantum mechanical problems of field and many body theory, and in solid state physics. *Mailing Add:* Sch Marine Prog 220 Marine Sci Bldg Athens GA 30602

**UZGIRIS, EGIDIJUS E,** STRUCTURAL BIOLOGY, MAGNETIC RESONANCE IMAGING. *Current Pos:* PHYSICIST, GEN ELEC RES & DEVELOP CTR, 70- *Personal Data:* b Lithuania, Jan 11, 41; m 67, Irene Lendraitis; c 2. *Educ:* Univ Ill, BS, 62; Harvard Univ, MS, 64, PhD(physics), 68. *Prof Exp:* Res assoc, Harvard Univ, 68-69; res assoc, Joint Inst Lab Astrophys, Univ Colo, 69-70. *Concurrent Pos:* Vis scientist, INSERN, Nancy, France, 78 & Sch Med, Stanford Univ, 81-82. *Mem:* Am Phys Soc; Biophys Soc; NY Acad Sci; AAAS. *Res:* Structural biology, protein crystallization on membranes; light scattering and hydrodynamic measurements; cellular immunology and cell surface change measurements; frequency and wavelength standards; non linear laser spectroscopy; biophysics. *Mailing Add:* Gen Elec Corp PO Box 8 Schenectady NY 12301

**UZIEL, MAYO,** BIOLOGICAL & CLINICAL CHEMISTRY, CELL BIOLOGY. *Current Pos:* biochemist, Biol Div, 64-81, BIOCHEMIST, HEALTH & SAFETY RES DIV, OAK RIDGE NAT LAB, 81- *Personal Data:* b Seattle, Wash, May 3, 30; m 67; c 2. *Educ:* Univ Wash, BSc, 52, PhD(biochem), 55. *Prof Exp:* Nat Found Infantile Paralysis fel, Rockefeller Inst, 55-57; asst prof biochem, Sch Med, Tufts Univ, 57-62; biochemist, Mass Eye & Ear Infirmary, 62-64. *Concurrent Pos:* Mem subcomt specification & criteria nucleotides & related compounds, NSF-Nat Res Coun, 68-75; prof, Univ Tenn, 71- *Mem:* AAAS; Am Soc Biochem & Molecular Biol; Am Chem Soc. *Res:* Structure and function of biological macromolecules; risk assessment; bioindicators of injury and disease; human genonie. *Mailing Add:* 102 Newton Lane Oak Ridge TN 37830-8120

**UZODINMA, JOHN E,** preventive medicine, microbiology; deceased, see previous edition for last biography

**UZZELL, THOMAS,** SYSTEMATIC BIOLOGY, VERTEBRATE BIOLOGY. *Current Pos:* ASSOC PROF ECOL, ETHOLOGY & EVOLUTION, UNIV ILL, 85- *Personal Data:* b Charleston, SC, Apr 6, 32; m 75, Christina Spolsky; c Stephan T & Renata C. *Educ:* Univ Mich, BA, 53, MS, 58, PhD(zool), 62. *Prof Exp:* From instr to asst prof biol, Univ Chicago, 62-67; asst prof & asst cur herpet, Peabody Mus, Yale Univ, 67-72, fel, Berkeley Col, 70-72; assoc cur, Acad Natural Sci 72-77, cur herpet, 77-85; dir, Mus Natural Hist, 85-91. *Concurrent Pos:* Adj assoc prof, Univ Pa, 74-85. *Mem:* AAAS; Am Soc Ichthyol & Herpet; Soc Study Evolution; Soc Syst Zool. *Res:* Origin and evolution of hybrid species of vertebrates; determination of the generic and specific limits of South American lizards of the family Teiidae. *Mailing Add:* Ecol & Evolution Univ Ill Urbana 505 S Goodwin Ave Urbana IL 61801-3707. *Fax:* 217-244-1648; *E-Mail:* uzzell@uiuc.edu

# V

**VAAGE, JAN,** IMMUNOLOGY, EXPERIMENTAL PATHOLOGY. *Current Pos:* RES SCIENTIST IMMUNOL, ROSWELL PARK CANCER INST, 67- *Personal Data:* b Oslo, Norway, Aug 20, 28. *Educ:* Univ Calif, Berkeley, BS, 61; Univ Calif, Davis, PhD(immunol), 67. *Mem:* Am Cancer Soc; Am Soc Cell Biol; Am Soc Immunol. *Mailing Add:* 121 Meadow Stream Dr Buffalo NY 14226

**VAALER, JEFFREY DAVID,** ANALYTIC NUMBER THEORY, DIOPHANTINE APPROXIMATION. *Current Pos:* assoc prof, 83-87, PROF MATH, UNIV TEX, AUSTIN, 87- *Personal Data:* b Grand Forks, NDak, May 2, 48; m 70; c 1. *Educ:* Lawrence Univ, Appleton, Wis, BS, 70; Univ Ill, Urbana, MS, 71, PhD(math), 74. *Prof Exp:* Res instr math, Calif Inst Technol, 74-76; asst prof math, Univ Tex, Austin, 76-82; mem, Inst Advan Study, Princeton, 82-83. *Concurrent Pos:* Prin investr, NSF, 76- *Mem:* Am Math Soc. *Res:* Diophantine approximation; diophantine equations; fourier analysis; analytic number theory; applications of analysis to number theory. *Mailing Add:* Dept Math Univ Tex Austin TX 78712-1082

**VACHON, RAYMOND NORMAND,** ORGANIC & POLYMER CHEMISTRY, FIBER LUBRICANTS. *Current Pos:* from res chemist to sr res chemist, 72-86, SR TECH REP, MAT SAFETY PROG REGULATORY AFFAIRS, TENN EASTMAN CO, 86- *Personal Data:* b Lawrence, Mass, Jan 14, 40; m 70; c 5. *Educ:* Lowell Technol Inst, BS, 63; Princeton Univ, PhD(chem), 67. *Prof Exp:* Res grant, Inst Sci & Technol, Univ Manchester, 67-69; sr res chemist, Burlington Industs, Inc, 69-72. *Mem:* Am Chem Soc. *Mailing Add:* 2000 Lamont St Kingsport TN 37660

**VACHON, REGINALD IRENEE,** MECHANICAL ENGINEERING. *Current Pos:* pres, Vachon Nix & Assocs, 80-82, PRES, VNA SYSTS, INC, 82- *Personal Data:* b Norfolk, Va, Jan 29, 37; m 60, Mary E Grigg; c Reginald I Jr & Eleanor M. *Educ:* Auburn Univ, BME, 58, MSNS, 60; Okla State Univ, PhD(mech eng), 63; Jones Law Sch, LLB, 69. *Honors & Awards:* G Edwin Burks Award, Outstanding Mech Eng Educr in US, Am Soc Eng Educ. *Prof Exp:* Instr physics, Auburn Univ, 58-59, assoc researcher heat transfer, Res Found, 60-61, assoc prof mech eng, 63-67, alumni prof, 67-78, prof, 78-80. *Concurrent Pos:* Mem, Southern Interstate Nuclear Bd; chmn bd, Optimal Systs Int Inc, 69-; chmn, Global Risk Mgrs Inc; chief oper off, Thacker Orgn Inc, 81-91; pres, Compris Technologies, Inc, 91-92. *Mem:* Am Soc Mech Engrs; Am Inst Aeronaut & Astronaut; Am Soc Eng Educ; Nat Soc Prof Engrs; Am Bar Asn; Am Soc Eng Educ. *Res:* Thermoscience; conduction in solids; gas dynamics; boiling and convection heat transfer; power and energy systems; systems approach management; systems design of machine vision and artificial intelligence. *Mailing Add:* 1414 Epping Forest Dr NE PO Box 467069 Atlanta GA 30319-2539. *Fax:* 404-264-0160

**VACIK, JAMES P,** PHARMACEUTICAL CHEMISTRY, BIONUCLEONICS. *Current Pos:* ASSOC PROF PHARMACOL & DIR ENVIRON SAFETY, UNIV SALA, 76- *Personal Data:* b North Judson, Ind, Nov 30, 31; m 67, Dorothy; c Deborah A, Pamella S, James P II, Stephen M, Joshua D & Jonathan D. *Educ:* Purdue Univ, BS, 55, MS, 57, PhD(bionucleonics), 59. *Prof Exp:* Asst prof & res fel bionucleonics, Purdue Univ, 59-60; assoc prof pharmaceut chem & chmn dept, NDak State Univ, 60-63, prof pharmaceut chem & bionucleonics & chmn dept, 63-76. *Mem:* AAAS; Health Physics Soc; Am Pharmaceut Asn; Am Conf Gov & Ind Hyg; Am Chem Soc. *Res:* Bionucleonics including metabolism, uptake and distribution of radioisotope tracers and large animal biosynthesis; synthesis of benzodioxans; antiviral agents. *Mailing Add:* Univ SAla CC CB Fm 372 Mobile AL 36688-0001

**VACQUIER, VICTOR,** GEOPHYSICS. *Current Pos:* prof, Scripps Inst Oceanog, 57-74, EMER PROF GEOPHYS, UNIV CALIF, SAN DIEGO, 74- *Personal Data:* b Petersburg, Russia, Oct 13, 07; nat US; m 66, Mihoko Wada; c Victor D. *Educ:* Univ Wis, BS, 27, MA, 28. *Honors & Awards:* Witherill Medal, Franklin Inst; Fessenden Award, Soc Explor Geophys; J A Fleming Medal, Am Geophys Union. *Prof Exp:* Asst instr physics, Univ Wis, 27-30; geophysicist, Gulf Res & Develop Co, Pa, 30-42; mem staff airborne instruments lab, Columbia Univ, 42-44; marine instruments engr, Sperry Gyroscope Co, 44-53; prof geophys & prin geophysicist, NMex Inst Mining & Technol, 53-57. *Mem:* Geol Soc Am; Am Geophys Union; Franklin Inst. *Res:* Geomagnetism; airborne magnetometry; terrestrial heat flow. *Mailing Add:* 8338 La Jolla Shores Dr La Jolla CA 92037

**VACQUIER, VICTOR DIMITRI,** DEVELOPMENTAL & CELL BIOLOGY. *Current Pos:* assoc prof, 78-80, PROF MARINE BIOL, SCRIPPS INST OCEANOG, UNIV CALIF, SAN DIEGO, 80- *Personal Data:* b Pittsburgh, Pa, July 20, 40; m 73; c 2. *Educ:* San Diego State Univ, BA, 63; Univ Calif, Berkeley, PhD(zool), 68. *Prof Exp:* Researcher, Intern Lab, Genetics & Biophys, Naples, Italy, 68-69; mem staff, Hopkins Marine Sta, Stanford Univ, 70-71 & Scripps Inst Oceanog, Univ Calif, San Diego, 71-73; from asst prof to assoc prof zool, Univ Calif, Davis, 73-78. *Mem:* Fel AAAS; Am Soc Cell Biol; Soc Develop Biol; Int Soc Develop Biol. *Res:* Biochemistry of fertilization. *Mailing Add:* Marine Biol Res Div Univ Calif San Diego 9500 Gilman Dr La Jolla CA 92093-0202. *E-Mail:* vvacquier@ucsd.edu

**VADAS, PETER,** CLINICAL IMMUNOLOGY & ALLERGY, REGULATION OF INFLAMMATION. *Current Pos:* res assoc, Univ Toronto, 82-84, lectr, 87-89, ASST PROF, DIV IMMUNOL, DEPT MED, FAC MED, UNIV TORONTO, 90- *Personal Data:* b Can, Aug 5, 53. *Educ:* Univ Toronto, BSc, Hons, 76, PhD(exp path), 80, MD, 83; Am Bd Internal Med, dipl, 89; FRCP(C), 90. *Honors & Awards:* F M Hill Res Award, 87. *Prof Exp:* Med Res Coun fel, Dept Med, Div Immunol, Wellesley Hosp, Toronto, 84-86. *Concurrent Pos:* Ont-Que exchange fel, 80-81; med scientist award, Can Heart Found, 80-83; Samuel Castrilli award, 81-83; Walter F Watkins scholar, 82; lectr, Dept Path, Univ Toronto, 90-, dep dir, Inflammation Res Group; consult, Div Immunol & Gen Internal Med, Wellesley Hosp, Toronto, 90-, dir post grad med educ; Med Res Coun scholar, 91- *Mem:* NY Acad Sci; Am Rheumatism Asn; Can Soc Clin Invest; Royal Col Physicians & Surgeons; Inflammation Res Asn; Can Soc Immunol; Shock Soc. *Res:* Role of phospholipase A2 in the pathogenesis of local and systemic inflammation; awarded 2 patents. *Mailing Add:* Wellesley Hosp Rm 314 Jones Bldg 160 Wellesley St E Toronto ON M4Y 1J3 Can

**VADAS, ROBERT LOUIS,** MARINE ECOLOGY, PHYCOLOGY. *Current Pos:* Asst prof bot, Univ Maine, Orono, 67-72, asst prof zool, 68-72, assoc prof, 72-77, PROF BOT, OCEANOG & ZOOL, UNIV MAINE, ORONO, 77-, CHMN DEPT BOT & PLANT PATH, 83- *Personal Data:* b New Brunswick, NJ, Aug 5, 36; m 61; c 3. *Educ:* Utah State Univ, BS, 62; Univ Wash, PhD(bot), 68. *Concurrent Pos:* Maine Yankee Nuclear Atomic Power Co study grant, 69-74; Off Water Resources grants, 70-72 & 72-75. *Mem:* Ecol Soc Am; Am Soc Naturalists; Phycol Soc Am; Brit Phycol Soc; Int Phycol Soc. *Res:* Ecology of kelp communities; marine plant-herbivore interactions and biogeography; algal distributions; population genetics of marine organisms; ecological studies of Ascophyllum Nodosum. *Mailing Add:* Dept Bot & Oceanog Univ Maine Deering Hall Orono ME 04469

**VADER-LINDHOLM, CONNIE,** PHYSIOLOGY. *Current Pos:* LAB COORDR PHYSIOL, COLO STATE UNIV, 87- *Personal Data:* b Thornton, Colo, May 15, 49. *Educ:* Western State Col, BS, 71; Colo State Univ, MS, 79, PhD(physiol), 87. *Mem:* Am Physiol Soc; Sigma Xi. *Res:* Physiology. *Mailing Add:* Dept Physiol Colo State Univ Fort Collins CO 80523-0001

**VADHWA, OM PARKASH,** AGRONOMY. *Current Pos:* ASST PROF AGRON, ALCORN STATE UNIV, 72- *Personal Data:* b Mandi Maklot Ganj, India, May 10, 41; m 67; c 1. *Educ:* Rajasthan Univ, India, BS, 61; Punjab Agr Univ, MS, 63; Utah State Univ, PhD(agron), 71. *Prof Exp:* Lectr agron, Punjab Agr Univ, Hissar Campus, 63-65; fel agron & plant sci, Utah State Univ, 70-71; assoc prof natural resources, Ala A&M Univ, 71-72. *Mem:* Am Soc Agron; Am Asn Univ Prof. *Res:* Forage crops; crop production; soil fertility and plant nutrition; vegetable crops. *Mailing Add:* Dept Agr Alcorn State Univ 1000 ASU Dr Lorman MS 39096-9402

**VADLAMUDI, SRI KRISHNA,** MICROBIOLOGY, IMMUNOLOGY. *Current Pos:* EXEC SECY, PANELS IMMUNOL, CTR DEVICES & RADIOL HEALTH, FOOD & DRUG ADMIN, HHS, 75-, IMMUNOL BR CHIEF, 77-, SUPVR MICROBIOLOGIST, 91- *Personal Data:* b Moparru, Tenali, AP, India, Aug 15, 27; US citizen; m 54; c 4. *Educ:* Madras Univ, DVM, 52; Univ Wis-Madison, MS, 59, PhD(microbiol), 63. *Prof Exp:* Head cancer chemother res, Microbiol Asn, Inc, 66-74; sci expert cancer, Smithsonian Sci Info Exch, 75. *Concurrent Pos:* Vet surgeon, Animal Husbandry Dept, Govt AP, India, 52-55; res vet, Govt NVD Lab, Guntur, India, actg supt, Govt Livestock Res Sta, 57; proj asst, Dept Vet Sci, Univ Wis-Madison, 57-62; sr microbiologist, Dept Infectious Dis, Abbott Lab, 62-65; chief, Viral Chemother Div, Microbiol Asn, Inc, 65-66. *Mem:* Am Soc Microbiol; Am Asn Cancer Res; Am Asn Path; Am Vet Med Asn; Sigma Xi. *Res:* Cancer chemotherapy and immunotherapy; tumor biology and metastasis; immunotoxicology; epizootiology and epidemiology of viral diseases, particularly arbor viruses; infection and immunity; pharmacology. *Mailing Add:* Ctr Radiol Health & Med Devices Food & Drug Admin 2098 Gaithers Rd Rockville MD 20850

**VAFAI, KAMBIZ,** FLOW & HEAT TRANSFER, HEAT PIPE ANALYSIS. *Current Pos:* from asst prof to assoc prof, 81-91, PROF & CHMN GRAD STUDIES, OHIO STATE UNIV, 91- *Personal Data:* Kiumars & Keyian. *Educ:* Univ Minn, BS, 75; Univ Calif, Berkeley, MS, 77, PhD(mech eng), 80. *Prof Exp:* Res fel mech eng, Div Appl Sci, Harvard Univ, 80-81. *Concurrent Pos:* Consult, Performance Assessment Dept, Battelle, 82-86; vis prof, Tech Univ Munich, Ger, 89, Univ Bordeaux, France, 90; prin investr, AT&T Bell Labs, NSF, Dept Energy, Owens Corning Fiberglass Co, Battelle, BF Goodrich, Edison Welding Inst, Air Force, Aircraft Brake Syst Corp, Amoco & Argonne, State Admin Indust & Com; assoc ed, J Heat Transfer, Am Soc Chem Engrs. *Mem:* Fel Am Soc Mech Engrs; Am Inst Aeronaut & Astronaut. *Res:* Investigations in the areas of transport through porous media and multiphase transport, natural convection in complex configurations analysis; thermal design and modeling (computational and experimental), heat transfer augmentation investigations, feasibility, optimization and parametric studies for various engineering applications; conducting both basic and applied research in the areas of heat and mass transfer; author of over 80 publications. *Mailing Add:* Dept Mech Eng Ohio State Univ 206 W 18th Ave Columbus OH 43210-1107. *Fax:* 614-292-6560

**VAFAKOS, WILLIAM P(AUL),** STRESS ANALYSIS, VIBRATIONS. *Current Pos:* res assoc, 57-60, from asst prof to assoc prof, 60-68, PROF MECH ENG, POLYTECH UNIV, 68- *Personal Data:* b Brooklyn, NY, Oct 12, 27; m 62, Gloria Albantides; c Constance, Paul & George. *Educ:* Polytech Inst Brooklyn, BME, 51, MME, 55, PhD(appl mech), 60; Brooklyn Law Sch, JD, 76. *Prof Exp:* Engr, Westinghouse Elec Corp, 51-53; sr engr, Ford Instrument Co, 53-57. *Mem:* Am Soc Mech Engrs. *Res:* Thin-walled structures. *Mailing Add:* Polytech Univ 6 Metrotech Ctr Brooklyn NY 11201. *Fax:* 718-260-3532; *E-Mail:* woafakos@duke.poly.edu

**VAFOPOULO, XANTHE,** DEVELOPMENTAL BIOLOGY, INSECT ENDOCRINOLOGY. *Current Pos:* RES SCIENTIST, DEPT BIOL, YORK UNIV, 86- *Personal Data:* b Thessaloniki, Greece, Aug 22, 49; US citizen; m 92, Colin G Steel. *Educ:* Aristotelian Univ, BA, 72; Bridgewater State Col, MA, 78; Univ Conn, PhD(develop biol), 80. *Honors & Awards:* Young Investr Award, Soc Develop Biol, 80. *Prof Exp:* Teaching asst, Univ Conn, 76-80, asst prof residence biol & res assoc, Biol Dept, 81-86. *Concurrent Pos:* Lectr-instr, W Alton Jones Cell Sci Ctr & Tissue Cult Asn, Inc, 80-81. *Mem:* Can Soc Zoologists; Soc Develop Biol; Am Soc Zoologists; Can Fedn Biol Socs; Europ Soc Endocrinologists. *Res:* Circadian control of synthesis and release of developmentally significant hormones in insects; regulation of development by rhythmic release of hormones; comparative studies of growth regulators. *Mailing Add:* Dept Biol York Univ 4700 Keele St North York ON M3J 1P3 Can. *Fax:* 716-736-5698

**VAGELATOS, NICHOLAS,** PENETRATING RADIATION INSPECTION TECHNOLOGY. *Current Pos:* sr scientist, IRT Corp, 76-78, prin scientist, 78-83, mgr appl develop, 83-85, mgr tech support, 85-86, tech mkt mgr, Automation Systs Group, 86-87, MGR, PROG DEVELOP, NUCLEAR SYSTS DIV, IRT CORP, 87- *Personal Data:* b Kefallinia, Greece, Mar 8, 45; m 79; c 3. *Educ:* Univ Mich, BSE, 67, MSE, 69, PhD(nuclear eng), 73. *Prof Exp:* Res assoc neutron spectros, Nat Bur Stand, US Dept Com, 73-75. *Concurrent Pos:* Nat Res Coun fel, Nat Bur Stand, US Dept Com, 73-75. *Mem:* Am Soc Nondestructive Testing; Am Soc Testing & Mat. *Res:* Interaction of radiation with matter; radiation detection and measurement; nuclear technology applications in natural resources evaluation; penetrating radiation nondestructive inspection technology for quality and process control. *Mailing Add:* 13474 Black Hills Rd San Diego CA 92129

**VAGELOS, P ROY,** LIPID CHEMISTRY, ENZYME CHEMISTRY. *Current Pos:* CHMN BD, REGENERON PHARMACEUT, INC, 95- *Personal Data:* b Westfield, NJ, Oct 8, 29; m 55, Diana Touliatos; c 4. *Educ:* Univ Pa, AB, 50; Columbia Univ, MD, 54. *Hon Degrees:* DSc, Wash Univ, 80, Brown Univ, 82, Univ Med & Dent NJ, 84, NY Univ, 89 & Columbia Univ, 90; LLD, Princeton Univ, 90, NJ Inst Technol, 92, State Univ NY, Stony Brook, 94; DHL, Rutgers Univ, 91. *Honors & Awards:* Enzyme Chem Award, Am Chem Soc, 67. *Prof Exp:* Intern med, Mass Gen Hosp, Boston, 54-55, asst resident, 55-56; sr asst surgeon, Lab Cellular Physiol, Nat Heart Inst, 56-59, surgeon, 59-61, actg chief, Sect Enzymes, 59-60, sr surgeon, Lab Biochem, 61-62, sr surgeon & res chemist, 63-64, head, Sect Comp Biochem, 64-66; sr surgeon, Pasteur Inst, Paris, 62-63; chmn, Dept Biol Chem, Sch Med, Wash Univ, 66-75, dir, Div Biol & Biomed Sci, 73-75; sr vpres res, Merck Sharp & Dohme Res Labs Div, Merck & Co, Inc, 75-76, pres, 76-84, sr vpres, Merck & Co, Inc, 82-84, exec vpres, 84-85, bd dirs, 84-94, chief exec officer, 85-94, chmn bd dirs, 86-94. *Concurrent Pos:* NIH & NSF grants; Sloan vis prof chem, Harvard Col, 73, mem, Vis Comt Biochem & Molec Biol Dept, 81-; mem bd trustees, Rockefeller Univ, 76-, Danforth Found, 78-, Univ Pa, 88- & Partnership NJ, 89-; dir, TRW, Inc, 87-93, Prudential Ins Co Am, 89- & NJ Ctr Performing Arts, 89-, Inst Int Econs, Nat Found Biomed Res, 92-94, Pepsi Co Inc, 92-, McDonnell Douglas Corp, 95-, Am Sch Classical Studies, Athens, 95-, Estee Lauder Cos, 96-; mem, Conf Bd, Bus Coun, Policy Comt Bus Roundtable & Bd Managing Dirs, Metropolitan Opera Asn, Inc; vis comts & adv bds, Mass Inst Technol, Col Physicians & Surgeons, Columbia Univ, Cleveland Clin Found, NJ Ctr Advan Biotechnol & Med & Beckman Ctr Hist Chem; chmn bd trustees, Univ Pa, 94- *Mem:* Nat Acad Sci; Nat Inst Med; AAAS; Am Soc Biol Chem; Am Acad Arts & Sci; Am Philos Soc; Molecular Med Soc. *Res:* Mechanism of lipid biosynthesis; involvement of acyl carrier protein in fatty acid biosynthesis; author of over 100 scientific papers. *Mailing Add:* Merck & Co Inc PO Box 2000 Rahway NJ 07065

**VAGNINI, LIVIO L,** CHEMISTRY. *Current Pos:* RETIRED. *Personal Data:* b North Bergen, NJ, Apr 26, 17; m 49, Daniele S Hogge; c 3. *Educ:* Fordham Col, BS, 38. *Prof Exp:* Chemist, H A Wilson Co Div, Englehard Industs, Inc, NJ, 40-42; chief forensic chemist, US Army Criminal Invest Lab, France, 44-46, chief chemist, US Army Graves Regist Lab, Belg, 46-48, chief forensic chemist, Ger, 48-60; microanalyst, US Food & Drug Admin, Washington, DC, 60-63; sr chemist, Cent Intel Agency, 63-73; tech staff mem, Mitre Corp, Va, 73-75; consult criminalist, 75; tech staff, Planning Res Corp, Va, 75-77; prog dir, L Miranda & Assoc, 78-81. *Concurrent Pos:* Consult criminalist, 82-97. *Mem:* Fel Am Inst Chem; Am Chem Soc; Asn Off Anal Chem; fel Am Acad Forensic Sci; Int Soc Forensic Toxicol. *Res:* Forensic chemistry; microchemistry; serology of dried blood factors; analysis of narcotics; optical crystallography of drugs; microanalysis of foods and drugs; x-ray spectrometry. *Mailing Add:* 26069 Mesa Dr Carmel CA 93923

**VAGNUCCI, ANTHONY HILLARY,** MEDICINE, PHYSIOLOGY. *Current Pos:* from asst prof to assoc prof, 65-79, PROF MED, SCH MED, UNIV PITTSBURGH, 79-; HEAD ADRENAL UNIT, MONTEFIORE HOSP, 65-, HEAD ENDOCRINE UNIT, 77- *Personal Data:* b Terni, Italy, July 9, 28; US citizen; m 62; c 3. *Educ:* Univ Genoa, MD, 54. *Prof Exp:* Intern med, Wesson Mem Hosp, Springfield, Mass, 57-58; resident, NY Univ-Bellevue Med Ctr, 58-60; Am Heart Asn res fel renal physiol, Med Sch, NY Univ, 60-62; advan res fel, Hypertension Unit, Dept Med, Peter Bent Brigham Hosp, Boston, 62-63 & advan res fel endocrinol, 63-64; jr assoc med & assoc dir endocrinol metab unit, Peter Bent Brigham Hosp, 64-65. *Concurrent Pos:* Res assoc, Harvard Med Sch, 64-65; adj prof, elec eng, Univ Pittsburgh, 89. *Mem:* Am Fedn Clin Res; Endocrine Soc; NY Acad Sci; sr fel Inst Elec & Electronics Engrs. *Res:* Circadian physiopath pituitary-adrenal/receptors/pattern recognition. *Mailing Add:* 2187 Garrick Dr Pittsburgh PA 15235

**VAHALA, GEORGE MARTIN,** MAGNETOHYDRODYNAMICS, PLASMA PHYSICS. *Current Pos:* asst prof, 74-80, PROF PHYSICS, COL WILLIAM & MARY, 80- *Personal Data:* b Tabor, Czech, Mar 26, 46; Australian citizen; m 70. *Educ:* Univ Western Australia, BSc Hons, 67; Univ Iowa, MS, 69, PhD(physics), 72. *Prof Exp:* Res assoc plasma physics, Univ Tenn, Knoxville, 72; res scientist magnetohydrodynamics, Courant Inst Math Sci, NY Univ, 72-74. *Res:* Magnetohydrodynamics and guiding-center stability of containment devices; spectral theory and its interpretation in plasma physics as well as in magnetohydrodynamics; transport effects in plasmas; nonlinear dynamics. *Mailing Add:* 138 Nina Lane Williamsburg VA 23188

**VAHAVIOLOS, SOTIRIOS J,** PHYSICAL ACOUSTICS, CORPORATION, NONDESTRUCTIVE TESTING. *Current Pos:* PRES, CHIEF EXEC OFFICER & DIR, PHYS ACOUST CORP, 78- *Personal Data:* b Apr 16, 46; m 69, Aspasia F Nessas; c Athanasia, Athena & Kristy. *Educ:* Fairleigh Dickinson Univ, BS, 70; Columbia Univ, MS, 72, MPh, 75 PhD(elec eng), 76. *Honors & Awards:* Centennial Award, Inst Elec & Electronics Engrs, 84; Meritorious Award, Indust Electronics Soc, Inst Elec & Electronics Engrs, 79, Outstanding Young Engr, 84, Dr Ing Eugene Mittelmann Achievement Award, 93. *Prof Exp:* Mem res staff automation & comput aided testing & inspection, Bell Tel Lab, 70-72, proj leader & supvr, 72-77, dept head, 77-78. *Concurrent Pos:* Adv comt, Indust Elec Cent Instrumental Soc; assoc ed, Trans on Indust Electronics, 72-75, ed, 75-81; bd dirs, Am Soc Nondestructive Testing, 85. *Mem:* Fel Inst Elec & Electronics Engrs; Am Soc Testing & Mat; Sigma Xi; NY Acad Sci; fel Am Soc Nondestructive Testing (secy, 89, treas, 90, vpres, 91 & pres, 92); sr mem Indust Electronics Soc; sr mem Instrument Soc Am; Soc Exp Stress Anal; fel Acoust Emission Working Group. *Res:* Sensor fusion through advanced digital signal processing for computer aided testing and inspection of large mechanical structures including those related to the country's infrastructure; holds more than 10 patents; author of more than 50 publications. *Mailing Add:* 7 Ridgeview Rd Princeton NJ 08540-7601. *Fax:* 609-895-9726

**VAHEY, DAVID WILLIAM,** OPTICAL PHYSICS, ULTRASONICS. *Current Pos:* SR RES & DEVELOP SCIENTIST II, INT PAPER, 88- *Personal Data:* b Youngstown, Ohio, Nov 21, 44; m 77, Linda S Begley; c Brian & Michael. *Educ:* Mass Inst Technol, BS, 66; Calif Inst Technol, MS, 67, PhD(elec eng), 73. *Honors & Awards:* Indust R & D Top 100 Award, 81. *Prof Exp:* Fel physics, Battelle Mem Inst, 73-74, res scientist, 74-75, prin res scientist, 75-81; staff physicist, ABB Automation, 82-83, prin physicist, 83-88. *Mem:* Tech Asn Pulp & Paper Indust; Int Soc Optical Eng. *Res:* Optical inspection and measurement techniques; optical and ultrasonic measurements of paper properties related to structure and dimensional stability. *Mailing Add:* 89 Buena Vista Terr Central Valley NY 10917

**VAHLDIEK, FRED W(ILLIAM),** CHEMICAL ENGINEERING, CHEMISTRY. *Current Pos:* RES MAT ENGR & GROUP LEADER, AIR FORCE MAT LAB, WRIGHT-PATTERSON AFB, 59- *Personal Data:* b Eilsleben, Ger, Feb 5, 33; US citizen; m 59; c 1. *Educ:* Univ Halle, BSc, 53, MSc, 54. *Prof Exp:* Analytical chemist, Iron & Steel Co, Ger, 54-55 & E F Drew Co, NJ, 55-56. *Mem:* AAAS; Am Chem Soc; Sigma Xi; fel Am Inst Chemists. *Res:* High pressure-high temperature research on refractory, monmetallic materials; electron microscopy studies on metallic and nonmetallic high temperature materials; oxidation on metallic and refractory solids; high temperature x-ray of solids. *Mailing Add:* 5851 Barrett Dr Dayton OH 45431-2215

**VAICAITIS, RIMAS,** AERONAUTICAL ENGINEERING. *Current Pos:* from asst prof to prof, 70-80, DIR, INST FLIGHT STRUCT, COLUMBIA UNIV, 77- *Personal Data:* b Sakei, Lithuania, Apr 30, 41; US citizen; m 65, Jane A Paplenas; c Rima & Krista. *Educ:* Univ Ill, Urbana, BS, 67, MS, 68, PhD(aeronaut eng), 70. *Hon Degrees:* Dr, Kaunas Technol Univ, Lithuania, 93. *Prof Exp:* Res asst eng, Univ Ill, 67-70. *Concurrent Pos:* Consult, Modern Anal Inc, 74-, USAF, 75-, US Army, 76-, Rockwell Int, 78-; res engr, Langley Res Ctr, NASA, 76-77. *Mem:* Am Inst Aeronaut & Astronaut; Am Soc Civil Eng; Int Inst Acoustics & Vibration. *Res:* Fluid-solid interactions; random vibrations; structural acoustics. *Mailing Add:* Dept Civil Eng Columbia Univ New York NY 10027. *Fax:* 212-854-6267

**VAIDHYANATHAN, V S,** BIOPHYSICS, BIOMATHEMATICS. *Current Pos:* assoc prof theoret biol, State Univ NY, Buffalo, 66-70, assoc prof biophys, 67-72, assoc prof pharmaceut & biophys, 72-80, PROF BIOPHYS SCI, STATE UNIV NY, 80- *Personal Data:* b Madras, India, Dec 15, 33; m 65, Virginia; c 3. *Educ:* Annamalai Univ, Madras, BSC, 53, MA, 54; Ill Inst Technol, PhD(chem), 61. *Prof Exp:* Res assoc chem, Univ Kans, 60-62; chief math & statist sect, Southern Res Support Ctr, 62-63, chief theoret sci sect, 63-66. *Concurrent Pos:* Consult, Vet Admin Hosp, New Orleans; vis prof theoret biol, State Univ NY, Buffalo, 65; Europ Molecular Biol Orgn fel, 69. *Mem:* AAAS; Am Chem Soc; Biophys Soc. *Res:* Statistical mechanics; active transport; nerve potentials; biophysics of membranes; regulation X control. *Mailing Add:* Dept Biophys & Sci R 114B Cory Hall State Univ NY Health Sci Ctr 3435 Main St Buffalo NY 14214. *Fax:* 716-829-2415

**VAIDYA, AKHIL BABUBHAI,** MOLECULAR PARASITOLOGY, CELL BIOLOGY. *Current Pos:* from asst prof to assoc prof, 77-89, PROF MICROBIOL, HAHNEMANN UNIV, 89- *Personal Data:* b Gondal, India, Oct 24, 47; m 73; c 2. *Educ:* Univ Bombay, BSc, 67, PhD(appl biol), 72. *Prof Exp:* Res asst ultrastruct, Cancer Res Inst, Bombay, 70-72; res assoc molecular biol, Inst Med Res, 72-75, assoc, 75-77. *Concurrent Pos:* Mem, Spec Study Sect, NIH; expert reviewer, NSF. *Mem:* Am Soc Microbiol; AAAS. *Res:* Molecular biology of malarial parasites; organization and expression of organelle genomes; molecular evolution; Control of eukaryotic gene expression; Ribsomal functioning viruses. *Mailing Add:* 507 Moreno Rd Wynnewood PA 19096-1107

**VAIL, CHARLES R(OWE),** ELECTRICAL ENGINEERING, ACADEMIC ADMINISTRATION. *Current Pos:* assoc dean, Col Eng, Ga Inst Technol, 73-79, prof elec eng, 73-83, dir, Dept Continuing Educ, 79-83, EMER ASSOC DEAN ENG, COL ENG, GA INST TECHNOL, 83- *Personal Data:* b Glens Falls, NY, Oct 16, 15; m 39; c 3. *Educ:* Duke Univ, BSEE, 37; Univ Mich, MS, 46, PhD(elec eng), 56. *Prof Exp:* Engr, Gen Elec Co, 37-39; from instr to prof elec eng, Duke Univ, 39-67, exec officer, Dept Elec Eng, 53-56, chmn dept, 56-64, assoc dean grad study & res, Sch Eng, 64-67, actg dean, 65; prof elec eng & electronic sci, Southern Methodist Univ, 67-73, assoc dean eng, 67-70, vpres, Univ, 70-73. *Concurrent Pos:* Consult, Chem War Res Proj, Duke Univ, 45, Solid State Div, US Naval Res Lab, 52-58, Gen Elec Co, 56-58 & NC Res Triangle Inst, 60-63; mem, Gov's Sci Adv Comt,

NC, 61-64; mem, Tech Utilization Adv Bd, NC Bd Sci & Technol, 65-67; mem, Fac Coun, Univ Ctr, Ga, 73-83; agent & mem, Corp Sect, Asn Media-Based Continuing Educ for Engrs, Inc, 76-83. *Mem:* 111S; fel Inst Elec & Electronics Engrs; Nat Soc Prof Engrs; Sigma Xi. *Res:* High voltage phenomena; dielectric materials; superconducting circuitry; thin-film properties. *Mailing Add:* 2669 Peppermint Dr Tucker GA 30084

**VAIL, EDWIN GEORGE,** MEDICAL PHYSIOLOGY, BIOENGINEERING. *Current Pos:* RETIRED. *Personal Data:* b Toledo, Ohio, July 25, 21; m 46, Mary Janet McFarland; c Edwin Jay, Thomas Clair, Michael Andrew, Valerie Ann & Richard Austin. *Educ:* Univ Toledo, BSc, 47; Ohio State Univ, MSc, 48, PhD(aviation physiol), 53. *Prof Exp:* Proj engr, Aerospace Med Lab, Wright Air Develop Ctr, Ohio, 51-53, chief respiration sect, 53-54, proj scientist, 54-60, chief personnel protection equip & crew escape group X-20 syst prog officer, 60-62, asst chief, Bioastronaut Div, 63-64; chief human eng & space suit res & develop, Hamilton Standard, United Aircraft Corp, Conn, 64-69; mem staff physiol, Naval Coastal Systs Lab, Panama City, 70-78; pres, Vail Appl Res Co, Inc, 73-83. *Mem:* Aerospace Med Asn; Undersea Med Soc; Sigma Xi. *Res:* Aerospace and oceanographic physiology, including respiratory, cardiovascular, environmental stress tolerance; space-pressure suits, diving equipment and life support system research and development of medical devices. *Mailing Add:* 1374 Country Ridge Rd Hendersonville NC 28739

**VAIL, JOHN MONCRIEFF,** SOLID STATE PHYSICS. *Current Pos:* from asst prof math physics to assoc prof physics, 62-72, PROF PHYSICS, UNIV MAN, 72- *Personal Data:* b Winnipeg, Man, Oct 17, 31; m 54; c 1. *Educ:* Univ Man, BSc, 55, MSc, 56; Brandeis Univ, PhD(physics), 60. *Prof Exp:* IBM res asst, Brandeis Univ, 57-59; Nat Res Coun Can fel, McGill Univ, 60-61; Leverhulme fel, Univ Liverpool, 61-62. *Concurrent Pos:* Vis lectr, St Andrews Univ, 68-69; vis res assoc, Atomic Energy Res Estab Harwell, 75-76 & 82-83; hon res fel chem, Univ Col London, UK, 82-83; adj prof physics, Mich Technol Univ, 92- *Mem:* Can Asn Physicists; Am Phys Soc; Brit Inst Physics; Mat Res Soc. *Res:* Solid state theory and computer simulation applied to properties of localized defects in crystalline materials and computer simulation. *Mailing Add:* Dept Physics Univ Man Winnipeg MB R3T 2N2 Can. *E-Mail:* vail@cc.umanitoba.ca

**VAIL, PATRICK VIRGIL,** INSECT PATHOLOGY, MICROBIAL CONTROL. *Current Pos:* res entomologist, 78-82, LAB DIR, AGR RES SERV, USDA, 82- *Personal Data:* b Pasadena, Calif, Nov 16, 37; m 84; c 3. *Educ:* Calif State Univ, Fresno, BA, 60, MS, 62; Univ Calif, Riverside, PhD(entom), 67. *Prof Exp:* Res entomologist, Agr Res Serv, USDA, 62-69, res leader, 70-75; sect head, UN-Int Atomic Energy Agency, 75-78. *Concurrent Pos:* Adj prof entom, Univ Ariz, 70-75. *Mem:* Entom Soc Am; Soc Invert Path; AAAS. *Res:* Insect pathology, virology and microbial control; quarantine treatments; insect behavior, biology and ecology; microbial control of insects infesting dried fruits and nuts. *Mailing Add:* Hort Crops Res Lab Agr Res Serv USDA 2021 S Peach Ave Fresno CA 93727

**VAIL, PETER R,** SEISMIC STRATIGRAPHIC INTERPRETATION. *Current Pos:* W MAURICE EWING PROF OCEANOG, RICE UNIV, 86- *Personal Data:* b New York, NY, Jan 13, 30. *Educ:* Dartmouth Col, AB, 52; Northwestern Univ, MS & PhD, 56. *Honors & Awards:* Virgil Kauffman Gold Medal Award, 76; William Smith Lectr, London Geol Soc, 78, William Smith Medal, 86; Burwell Lectr, UK Geophys Soc, 83. *Prof Exp:* From res geologist to sr res scientist, Exxon Prod Res Co, 56-86. *Concurrent Pos:* Mem US Geodynamics Comt, Nat Acad Sci, 87-, US Dept Energy, 87-, Ocean Sci Bd, Nat Acad Sci, 79-82; Gallagher vis scientist, Univ Galgary, 80; vis scientist, Woods Hole Oceanog Inst, Mass, 76. *Mem:* Sigma Xi; fel Geol Soc Am; Am Asn Petrol Geologists; hon mem Soc Explor Geophysicists; Soc Econ Paleontologists & Mineralogists; fel AAAS; Europ Asn Explor Geophysicists. *Res:* Stratigraphic mapping; well log correlation; computer applications to geology; the stratigraphic and structural interpretation of seismic data the sequence stratigraphy of outcrops and well logs. *Mailing Add:* Dept Geol Rice Univ 6100 Main St Houston TX 77005-1827

**VAIL, SIDNEY LEE,** ORGANIC CHEMISTRY TEXTILES, SEED GERMINATION. *Current Pos:* RETIRED. *Personal Data:* b New Orleans, La, Aug 10, 28; m 53, Margaret Smith; c Kathy, Lee, Fay & Ann. *Educ:* Tulane Univ, BS, 49, PhD(org chem), 65; La State Univ, MS, 51. *Prof Exp:* Org chemist, Dow Chem Co, 51-53; sr chemist, Am Cyanamid Co, 55-59; proj leader, USDA, 59-72, res leader, Cotton Textile Chem Lab, 72-83, chief, 76-83, res leader, Crop Protection Chem, Southern Regional Res Ctr, 83-87, res chemist, Textile Finishing Chem, 87- 88. *Concurrent Pos:* Exchange scientist, Shirley Inst, Eng, 65-66; adj prof textile chem, Sch Textiles, NC State Univ, Raleigh, 79-83; consult, 88- *Mem:* Am Chem Soc; Sigma Xi. *Res:* Petrochemicals, synthesis and process chemistry; textile chemistry, organic synthesis and mechanisms; nuclear magnetic resonance; seed germination and parasitic weed chemistry; chemical modification of cotton. *Mailing Add:* 10137 Hyde Pl River Ridge LA 70123-1523

**VAILAS, ARTHUR C,** BIOMECHANICS. *Current Pos:* assoc prof, 88-91, DIR, BIODYNAMICS LAB, UNIV WIS-MADISON, 88-, PROF, 91- *Educ:* Univ NH, BS, 73; Univ Iowa, PhD(exercise physiol), 79. *Prof Exp:* From asst prof to assoc prof, Dept Kinesiol, Univ Calif, Los Angeles, 82-88. *Concurrent Pos:* Distinguished scientist, Calif State Univ. *Mem:* Nat Res Coun. *Res:* Biomechanics; exercise physiology; kinesiology; biodynamics. *Mailing Add:* Univ Wis 500 Lincoln Dr Madison WI 53706-1380

**VAILLANCOURT, REMI ETIENNE,** MATHEMATICS. *Current Pos:* chmn dept, 72-76, ASSOC PROF MATH, UNIV OTTAWA, 70- *Personal Data:* b Maniwaki, Que, June 16, 34. *Educ:* Univ Ottawa, BA, 57, BSc, 61, BTh, 63, MSc, 64, MTh, 65; NY Univ, PhD(math), 69. *Prof Exp:* Instr, NY Univ, 68-69; Off Naval Res res assoc, Univ Chicago, 69-70. *Mem:* Am Math Soc; Math Asn Am; Can Math Soc; French-Can Asn Advan Sci. *Res:* Partial differential equations; pseudo-differential operators; finite difference and finite element methods. *Mailing Add:* Dept Math Univ Ottawa Ottawa ON K1N 6N5 Can. *Fax:* 613-564-3822

**VAILLANT, GEORGE EMAN,** PSYCHIATRY. *Current Pos:* assoc prof, 71-76, PROF PSYCHIAT, HARVARD MED SCH, 76- *Personal Data:* b New York, NY, June 16, 34; m 71; c 5. *Educ:* Harvard Univ, AB, 55, MD, 59. *Prof Exp:* Resident, Mass Ment Health Ctr, 60-63; staff psychiatrist, USPHS, Lexington, Ky, 63-65; from asst prof to assoc prof psychiat, Sch Med, Tufts Univ, 66-71. *Concurrent Pos:* Dir study adult develop, Harvard Univ, 72-; consult, Div Manpower & Training, NIMH, 76-79; fel, Ctr Advan Study Behav Sci, 78-79; NIH res sci award, 81-; dir training, Dept Psychiat, Mass Ment Health Ctr, 81- *Mem:* Fel Am Psychiat Asn; Soc Life Hist Res Psychopath; Int Soc Study Behav Develop. *Res:* Long term follow up in adult development and in psychopathology. *Mailing Add:* Dartmouth Med Sch Hanover NH 03755-9999

**VAILLANT, HENRY WINCHESTER,** POPULATION BIOLOGY. *Current Pos:* res fel obstet & gynec, Harvard Med Sch, 67-68, ASST PROF POP STUDIES, SCH PUB HEALTH, HARVARD UNIV, 68- *Personal Data:* b New York, NY, Dec 17, 36; m 58; c 3. *Educ:* Harvard Univ, AB, 58, MD, 62, SMHyg, 69. *Prof Exp:* Intern med, Boston City Hosp, 62-63, resident, 63-64; res assoc, Nat Inst Child Health & Human Develop, 64-66; resident, Boston City Hosp, 66-67. *Concurrent Pos:* Consult, Cancer Control Prog, USPHS, 68; pres-elect, Emerson Hosp Med Staff, pres, 87- *Mem:* Am Pub Health Asn. *Res:* Clinical human reproductive physiology. *Mailing Add:* 321 Main Acton MA 01720-3718

**VAIRAVAMURTHY, MURTHY APPATHURAI,** SULFUR GEOCHEMISTRY, ORGANIC GEOCHEMISTRY. *Current Pos:* Alexander Hollaender distinguished fel, 89-91, asst scientist, 91-93, ASSOC SCIENTIST, BROOKHAVEN NAT LAB, 93- *Personal Data:* b Jaffna, Sri Lanka, Mar 28, 51; US citizen; m 80, Jamuna Rajaratnam; c Vidyasagar, Darshan & Jenanan. *Educ:* Univ Sri Lanka, BSc, 72; Univ Colombo, MSc, 82; Fla State Univ, MS, 84; Univ Miami, PhD(marine chem), 89. *Prof Exp:* Instr chem oceanog, Fla Inst Technol, 85-86. *Concurrent Pos:* Adj asst prof, Marine Sci Res Ctr, State Univ NY, Stony Brook, 93- *Mem:* Am Chem Soc; Am Geophys Union; Am Geochem Soc; Geol Soc Am. *Res:* Geochemistry of sulphur; organic geochemistry related to early diagenesis and preservation of organic matter in aquatic sediments; organic analytical chemistry concerned with applicants to environmental problems; applications of x-ray absorption spectroscopy in geochemistry and environmental chemistry. *Mailing Add:* Bldg 801 Brookhaven Nat Lab Upton NY 11973. *Fax:* 516-282-5526

**VAIRAVAN, KASIVISVANATHAN,** ELECTRICAL ENGINEERING, COMPUTER SCIENCE. *Current Pos:* asst prof elec eng, 68-71, assoc prof elec eng & comput sci, 71-77, PROF ELEC ENG & COMPUT SCI, UNIV WIS-MILWAUKEE, 77- *Personal Data:* b Madras, India, July 9, 39; m 67, Alamela; c Valli & Ashok. *Educ:* Univ Madras, BE, 62; George Washington Univ, MS, 65; Univ Notre Dame, PhD(elec eng), 68. *Prof Exp:* Jr elec engr, Madras State Elec Bd, 62-63. *Concurrent Pos:* Mem tech staff, Bell Tel Labs, 70; vis researcher, Hiroshima Univ, 80; vis lectr, var res ctrs in Japan. *Mem:* Inst Elec & Electronics Engrs. *Res:* Parallel computation; distributed processing; software science; computer organization. *Mailing Add:* Dept Elec Eng & Comput Sci Univ Wis PO Box 413 Milwaukee WI 53201. *E-Mail:* kv@cs.uwm.edu

**VAISEY-GENSER, FLORENCE MARION,** FOOD SCIENCE & TECHNOLOGY. *Current Pos:* from asst prof to assoc prof, Univ Man, 65-73, head dept, 78-80, assoc dean, Fac Grad Studies, 81-83, assoc vpres res, 83-91, PROF FOOD & NUTRIT, UNIV MAN, 73-, SR SCHOLAR, 93- *Personal Data:* b Winnipeg, Man, Apr 3, 29; m 53, 76; c 2. *Educ:* McGill Univ, BSc, 49; McGill Univ, MSc, 51. *Honors & Awards:* W J Eva Award. *Prof Exp:* Head food acceptance, Defense Res Med Labs, 51-53; metab dietitian, Victoria Gen Hosp, 53-54; lectr foods & nutrit, Ore State Col, Corvallis, 56-60; asst prof, Univ Guelph, 62-65. *Concurrent Pos:* Adv Bd, Can Food Prod Develop Ctr, 75-83; res grant, Agr Can, 75-77 & 80-, Alberta Agr, 79-82, Man Res Coun, 71-77, Canola Coun Can, 70-85 & Fisheries Res Bd, 66-69; guest prof, Swiss Fed Inst Technol, 71-72; chmn, Man Res Coun, 83-87; bd mem, assoc adv sci in Can, 84-86, Fisheries & Oceans Res Adv Coun, 86-89, Natural Sci & Engr Res Coun Scholar Comt, 88-, Nat Adv Bd Sci & Technol, 88-; mem, Can Res Mgr Asn, 88-90; mem, WPG 2000 Leaders Comn, 90-; pres, Can Found Dietetic Res. *Mem:* Can Inst Food Sci & Technol (vpres, 78-79, pres, 80-81); Can Dietetic Asn; Can Home Econ Asn; Am Asn Cereal Chem; Inst Food Technol. *Res:* Sensory evaluation of foods and their components; rapeseed oil; plant proteins; amino acids; functional properties of edible oils. *Mailing Add:* 408 Human Ecol Univ Man Winnipeg MB R3T 2N2 Can

**VAISHNAVA, PREM P,** SUPERCONDUCTIVITY, MOSSBAUER SPECTROSCOPY. *Current Pos:* assoc prof, 86-91, PROF PHYSICS, GMI ENG & MGT INST, FLINT, MICH, 91- *Personal Data:* b Jodhpur, India, Oct 10, 42; US citizen; m 72, Manju; c Sanjay, Ajay & Prashant. *Educ:* Jodhpur Univ, India, BSc, 63, MSc, 65, PhD(physics), 76. *Prof Exp:* Asst prof physics, Jodhpur Univ, 65-78; res assoc chem, Heriot-Watt Univ, Edinburgh, Scotland, 78-80; asst prof physics, WVa Univ, Morgantown, 80-83; res assoc mat sci, Argonne Nat Lab, 83-86; assoc prof physics, Northern Ill Univ, 83-86. *Concurrent Pos:* Sci res coun fel, Edinburgh, Scotland, 78-80; guest scientist, Brookhaven Nat Lab, 86-; acad affil fel, Mich State Univ, 88-91. *Mem:* Am Phys Soc; Mat Res Soc. *Res:* Investigate electronic, magnetic and lattice vibrational behavior of high temperature super conductors; Mossbauer spectroscopy; scanning transmission electron microscopy and SQUID magnetometer for these investigations. *Mailing Add:* Dept Sci & Math GMI Eng & Mgt Inst 1700 W Third Ave Flint MI 48504. *Fax:* 810-762-9796; *E-Mail:* pvaishna@nova.gmi.edu

**VAISNYS, JUOZAS RIMVYDAS,** PHYSICAL CHEMISTRY. *Current Pos:* ASSOC PROF APPL SCI, YALE UNIV, 67- *Personal Data:* b Kaunas, Lithuania, Mar 12, 37; US citizen. *Educ:* Yale Univ, BS, 56; Univ Calif, Berkeley, PhD(chem), 60. *Mem:* Am Phys Soc; Sigma Xi; Asn Advan Baltic Studies; Am Chem Soc. *Res:* Evolution; ecology; biological dynamics. *Mailing Add:* Dept Geol Yale Univ PO Box 208109 New Haven CT 06520-8109

**VAITKEVICIUS, VAINUTIS K,** ONCOLOGY. *Current Pos:* PRES & DIR, KARMANOS CANCER INST, 94- *Personal Data:* b Kaunas, Lithuania, Jan 12, 27; US citizen; m 51; c 6. *Educ:* Univ Frankfurt, MD, 51. *Prof Exp:* Intern med, Grace Hosp, Detroit, 51-52, resident, 55-56; resident internal med, Detroit Gen Hosp, 56-58; assoc physician, Henry Ford Hosp, Detroit, 59-62; clin dir oncol, Detroit Inst Cancer Res, 62-66; from assoc prof to prof med & dir, Sch Med, Wayne State Univ, 66-73, prof & chmn dept, 73-82, prof & chmn, Dept Internal Med, 82-89; pres, Mich Cancer Found, 91-94. *Concurrent Pos:* Fel cancer res, Detroit Inst Cancer Res, Mich, 58-59; consult, Beaumont Hosp, Harper Grace Hosps, Mt Carmel Mercy Hosp, Sinai Hosp & Vet Admin Hosp; clin dir, Comprehensive Cancer Ctr, Detroit, 78-82. *Mem:* AAAS; Am Col Physicians; Am Asn Cancer Res; Am Asn Cancer Educ; Am Soc Hemat. *Res:* Mechanism of metastases; pharmacology of cytostatic drugs. *Mailing Add:* 4100 John Rd Detroit MI 48201

**VAITUKAITIS, JUDITH L,** MEDICINE. *Current Pos:* dir, Gen Clin Res Ctr Prog, NIH, 86-91, actg dep dir, 90-91, dep dir, Extramural Res Resources, 91-93, DIR, NAT CTR RES RESOURCES, NIH, 93- *Personal Data:* b Hartford, Conn, Aug 29, 40. *Educ:* Tufts Univ, BS, 62; Boston Univ, MD, 66. *Honors & Awards:* Mallinckrodt Award Investigative Res, Clin Radioassay Soc, 80; 25th Ann Helen & Payne Whitney Lect Med, NShore Univ Hosp, 94; Pres Meritorious Exec Rank Award, 95. *Prof Exp:* Attend physician, Nat Inst Child Health & Human Develop, Clin Ctr, NIH, Bethesda, Md, 70-75; assoc prof med, Sch Med, Boston Univ, 74-77, co-prog dir, Gen Clin Res Ctr, 75-77, prog dir, 77-86, prof med, 77-86, prof physiol, 80-86. *Concurrent Pos:* Sr investr & med officer, Reprod Res Br, Nat Inst Child Health & Human Develop, NIH, 73-74, guest worker, 74-75, assoc dir clin res, Nat Ctr Res Resources, 86-91, actg dir, Biol Models & Mat Res Prog, Nat Ctr Res Resources, 90; head, Sect Endocrin & Metab, Boston City Hosp, Mass, 74-86; assoc prof physiol, Sch Med, Boston Univ, 75-80, assoc prof obstet & gynec, 77-80. *Mem:* Inst Med-Nat Acad Sci; Am Soc Clin Investigators; Asn Am Physicians; Am Fedn Clin Res; Am Soc Androl; Soc Exp Biol & Med; Endocrine Soc; Soc Study Reproduction. *Res:* Reproductive endocrinology; subcellular action of glycoprotein hormones; neuroendocrinology of reproduction and structure-function studies of gonadotropins; laboratory and clinical biomedical research, including complex biotechnologies, models of human disease science education and career development. *Mailing Add:* Nat Ctr Res Resources Bldg 12A Rm 4007 NIH Bethesda MD 20892-2128

**VAJK, J(OSEPH) PETER,** PHYSICS & MATH EDUCATION SPACE INDUSTRIALIZATION. *Current Pos:* TEACHER PHYSICS & MATH, ST JOSEPH NOTRE DAME HS, 95-, CHAIR, SCI DEPT, 97- *Personal Data:* b Budapest, Hungary, Aug 3, 42; US citizen; m 70, Helen T O'Keeffe; c Fiona C, Kevin M, Owen P & Stephen D. *Educ:* Cornell Univ, AB, 63; Princeton Univ, MA, 65, PhD(physics), 68. *Prof Exp:* Sr physicist, Lawrence Livermore Lab, Univ Calif, 68-76; consult, Sci Applns Inc, Calif, 76-79, sr scientist, 77-84; pvt consult, 84-92; proj mgr, Pac Knowledge, 92-94. *Concurrent Pos:* Math instr, Valley Col, Ca, 90-92; physics instr, Diablo Valley Col, Calif, 92-94. *Mem:* Am Phys Soc; Sigma Xi; Am Inst Aeronaut & Astronaut; Am Asn Physics Teachers. *Res:* Relativistic astrophysics and cosmology; general relativity theory; evolution of relativistic cosmological models; theory of electromagnetic pulses from nuclear explosions; world dynamics; socioeconomic implications of space industrialization and colonization; space technology assessment; atmospheric photochemistry and dynamics modeling; alternative futures research. *Mailing Add:* Suite 710 PO Box 8040 Walnut Creek CA 94596-8040. *E-Mail:* vajk@ix.netcom.com

**VAKILI, AHMAD D,** UNSTEADY FLOW, VORTEX DOMINATED FLOWS. *Current Pos:* assoc prof, 87-96, PROF MECH AEROSPACE ENG, SPACE INST, UNIV TENN, 96-, DEPT CHAIR, 97- *Personal Data:* b Birdjand, Iran, Sept, 1950; US citizen; m, Lisa K Branch; c Jennifer & Jessica. *Educ:* Univ Tenn, MS, 76, PhD(mech/aerospace), 78. *Concurrent Pos:* Consult. *Mem:* Fel Am Inst Aeronaut & Astronaut; Sigma Xi. *Res:* Various areas of aerodynamics and acoustics. *Mailing Add:* Univ Tenn MS 26 Tullahoma TN 37388-8897. *Fax:* 615-454-7721; *E-Mail:* avakili@utsi.edu

**VAKILI, NADER GHOLI,** PLANT PATHOLOGY, PLANT GENETICS. *Current Pos:* mem staff, 69-79, RES PLANT PATHOLOGIST, IOWA STATE UNIV, USDA, 79- *Personal Data:* b Bushir, Iran, Jan 14, 27; nat US; m 53; c 6. *Educ:* Northwestern Univ, BS, 52; Univ Chicago, MS, 53; Purdue Univ, PhD, 58. *Prof Exp:* Pathologist, United Fruit Co, 58-65; asst plant pathologist, Everglades Exp Sta, Univ Fla, 65-67; area agron adv, US Agency Int Develop, USDA, 67-69. *Mem:* Am Phytopath Soc; Am Soc Agron; Am Inst Biol Sci; Sigma Xi. *Res:* Genetics of pathogenicity; taxonomy and genetics of disease resistance in musa; vegetable diseases. *Mailing Add:* 1432 Crand Ames IA 50010

**VAKILZADEH, JAVAD,** PUBLIC HEALTH, EPIDEMIOLOGY. *Current Pos:* CONSULT EPIDEMIOLOGIST, HAITIAN-AM TUBERC INST, 63- *Personal Data:* b Esfahan, Iran, June 26, 27. *Educ:* Sharaf Col, Iran, BS, 48; Univ Teheran, DVM, 52; Univ Pittsburgh, CPH, 58; Univ NC, MPH, 59. *Prof Exp:* Epidemiologist, Int Coop Admin, Iran, 53-57; res scientist, NC Sanitorium Syst, 59-63, from asst to actg dir res respiratory dis, 63-68; mem fac, Med Ctr, Duke Univ, 68-72; epidemiologist, Int Fertil Res Prog, Pop Ctr, Univ NC, Chapel Hill, 72-80. *Mem:* Fel Am Pub Health Asn; Am Vet Med Asn; Am Vet Epidemiol Soc. *Res:* Research and teaching of epidemiology; environmental health; communicable disease control. *Mailing Add:* 634 Kensington Dr Chapel Hill NC 27514-5823

**VALA, MARTIN THORVALD, JR,** PHYSICAL CHEMISTRY, SPECTROCHEMISTRY. *Current Pos:* from asst prof to assoc prof, 68-78, PROF CHEM, UNIV FLA, 78- *Personal Data:* b Brooklyn, NY, Mar 28, 38; m 66, Vibeke Wilken-Jensen; c Lars, Carsten & Steffen. *Educ:* St Olaf Col, BA, 60; Univ Chicago, MS, 62, PhD(chem), 64. *Prof Exp:* NSF fel chem, Copenhagen Univ, 65-66; US-Japan Coop Sci Prog fel, Univ Nagoya, 66-67. *Concurrent Pos:* Merck Found fel, 70-71; vis prof, Advan Sch Physics & Chem, 73-74; NATO fel, 73-74; Fulbright sr fel, Franco-Am Scholar Exchange Comn, 73-74; vis scientist, US-India Exchange Scientists Prog, India, 77, Univ Poznan, Poland, 81, Sch Advan Physics & Chem, Paris,83 & 91. *Mem:* Am Phys Soc; Am Chem Soc; Am Inst Chem; InterAm Photochem Soc. *Res:* Optical and magnetic properties of organic molecules and transition metal atoms, dimers and complexes; cluster spectroscopy. *Mailing Add:* Dept Chem Univ Fla Gainesville FL 32611-2046. *Fax:* 904-392-0872; *E-Mail:* mvala@chem.ufl.edu

**VALACH, MIROSLAV,** INFORMATION & COMPUTER SCIENCE. *Current Pos:* Environ Studies, 83-92, VOLUNTEER, SAN JOSE STATE UNIV, 92- *Personal Data:* b Hnusta, Czech, Sept 12, 26; US citizen; m 52; c 1. *Educ:* Prague Tech Univ, ME, 51; Czech Acad Sci, PhD(math & physics), 58. *Prof Exp:* Mgr peripheral equip, Res Inst Mach, Czech, 51-64; consult engr, Gen Elec Co, Ariz, 65-69; prof into & comput sci, Ga Inst Technol, 69-74; res dir, Karsten Mfg Corp, 74-80; Friday Comput Inc, 80-83. *Mem:* Asn Comput Mach; Inst Elec & Electronics Engrs. *Res:* Switching theory; cybernetics; artifical intelligence; computer hardware; linguistics. *Mailing Add:* 763 Sweetbay Dr One Washington Square Sunnyvale CA 94086

**VALANIS, BARBARA MAYLEAS,** EPIDEMIOLOGY. *Current Pos:* assoc prof, 78-80, ASST PROF EPIDEMIOL, COL MED, UNIV CINCINNATI, 78-, PROF, COL NURSING & HEALTH, 80- *Personal Data:* b Harrisburg, Pa, Oct 4, 42; m 78; c 1. *Educ:* Cornell Univ, BS, 65; Columbia Univ, MEd, 71, DrPH(epidemiol), 75. *Prof Exp:* Dist nurse, Vis Nurse Serv NY, 65-69; instr pub health nursing, Columbia Univ Sch Nursing, 69-71; asst prof, Fairleigh Dickinson Univ, 72-73; res worker, Columbia Univ, 73-75, staff assoc, 75-77, res assoc epidemiol, 77-78. *Concurrent Pos:* Columbia Univ Cancer Res Ctr fel, 75-78; vpres & prog eval consult, Eval Assoc, Inc, 76-78. *Mem:* Am Pub Health Asn; Soc Epidemiol Res; Sigma Xi; Nat League Nursing. *Res:* Social epidemiology; cancer epidemiology; reproductive epidemiology; health services evaluation; stress; occupational exposures. *Mailing Add:* 8605 NW Lake Crest Ct Vancouver WA 98665

**VALASSI, KYRIAKE V,** HYPERALIMENTATION NUTRITION ASSESSMENT. *Current Pos:* PROF FOODS & NUTRIT, CATH UNIV AM, 56- *Personal Data:* b Salonika, Greece, May 15, 17; US citizen. *Educ:* Syracuse Univ, BS, 50; Cornell Univ, MS, 51; Ore State Univ, PhD(nutrit & biochem), 56. *Concurrent Pos:* Consult, Off Int Res, 61-67, Pan Am Health Orgn, 72-74, Food & Drug Admin, 78, Nat Coun Dis Control, 67-74, Nutrit Cancer NIH, 79; lectr, Corner Univ, 68, Ore State Univ, 69. *Mem:* Am Dietetic Asn; Soc Nutrit Educ; Am Inst Nutrit; Am Soc Parental & Enteral Nutrit. *Res:* Assessment of nutritional status of population groups; dietary survey methodology and training in foreign countries; nutritional management of cancer patients in a variety of therapeutic regiments; enteral hyperalimentation to patients undergoing treatment for burns. *Mailing Add:* 2700 Virginia Ave NW No 605 Washington DC 20037-1908

**VALBERG, LESLIE S,** MEDICINE. *Current Pos:* CONSULT, UNIV HOSP, LONDON, 75- *Personal Data:* b Churchbridge, Sask, June 3, 30; m 54; c 3. *Educ:* Queen's Univ, Ont, MD, 54, MSc, 58; FRCPS(C), 60. *Prof Exp:* Lectr med, Queen's Univ, Ont, 60-61; res assoc, Med Res Coun, Can, 61-65; from asst prof to prof med, Queen's Univ, Ont, 61-75; prof med & chmn dept, Univ Western Ont, 75-85, dean, fac med, 85-92. *Mem:* Am Gastroenterol Asn; Am Fedn Clin Res; fel Am Col Physicians; fel Royal Col Physicians & Surgeons Can; Can Soc Clin Invest. *Res:* Iron metabolism; absorption of metals; hemochromatosis. *Mailing Add:* 1496 Stoneybrook Crescent London ON N5X 1C5 Can

**VALDES, JAMES JOHN,** NEUROTOXICOLOGY. *Current Pos:* phys scientist, Toxicol Div, 82-85, pharmacologist, Biotechnol Div, 85-90, SCI ADV BIOTECHNOL, US ARMY CHEM RES & DEVELOP CTR, 90- *Personal Data:* b San Antonio, Tex, Apr 25, 51; m 92, Erica R Petersen; c Leah Ray. *Educ:* Loyola Univ, Chicago, BS, 73; Trinity Univ, MS, 76; Tex Christian Univ, PhD(neurosci), 79. *Prof Exp:* Res fel, Johns Hopkins Univ, 79-82, lectr, 80-86. *Concurrent Pos:* Instr, Hood Col, 82-83; ed, Neurobehav Toxicol & Teratol, 82-; chmn, Ann Conf Receptor Res, Johns Hopkins Appl Physics Lab, 85, 86 & 87; res assoc, Johns Hopkins Univ, 83-87, adj assoc prof, 87-90; adj prof, UTSA, 90-; adj prof, Univ Md Sch Med & Baylor Univ. *Mem:* Soc Neurosci; Soc Toxicol; Sigma Xi; Brit Brain Res Asn; Int Brain Res Asn; Europ Brain & Behav Soc; Soc Indust Microbiol. *Res:* Interaction of neurotoxins with receptor and ion channel proteins; synaptic mechanisms of neurotoxicity; biotechnology, including scale-up bioprocess engineering of recombinant proteins. *Mailing Add:* Sci Adv Biotechnol Attn: SCBRD-RT US Army Edgewood Res Develop & Eng Ctr Aberdeen Proving Ground MD 21010-5423. *E-Mail:* jjvaldes@cbdrom.apgea.army.mil

**VALDES, JOHN ANTHONY,** CHROMATOGRAPHY, INORGANIC CHEMISTRY. *Current Pos:* Lab tech analyst, Amoco Chem, 69-84, chemist, Amoco Refinery, 89-92, SR CHEMIST, AMOCO REFINERY, 92-; ADJ PROF CHEM, COL THE MAINLAND, 91- *Personal Data:* b Havana, Cuba, Feb 11, 43; US citizen; m 69, Zulima; c John A Jr & Anne M. *Educ:* Univ Houston, BS, 81, MS, 84. *Concurrent Pos:* Texas City rep, Tex Natural Resources Conserv Comn, 94- *Res:* Chromatography; setting up instrumentation and developing methods for refineries. *Mailing Add:* 2105 16th St N Texas City TX 77590

**VALDES-DAPENA, MARIE A,** PEDIATRICS. *Current Pos:* PROF PATH & PEDIAT, SCH MED, UNIV MIAMI, 76- *Personal Data:* b Pottsville, Pa, July 14, 21; div; c 11. *Educ:* Immaculate Col, Pa, BS, 41; Temple Univ, MD, 44. *Prof Exp:* St Christopher's Hosp Children grant, 59-76; instr, Grad Sch Med, Univ Pa, 48-55, vis lectr, 60-; consult pediat path, Div Med Exam, Dept Pub Health, Philadelphia, 67-70; mem, Perinatal Biol & Infant Mortality Res & Training Comt Nat Inst Child Health & Human Develop, 71-75; consult, Lankenau Hosp, Philadelphia, 71-76; consult & lectr, US Naval Hosp, Philadelphia, 72. *Mem:* Soc Pediat Path; Int Acad Path. *Res:* Causes of neonatal mortality; sudden infant death syndrome; gynecologic pathology in infancy and childhood; iatrogenic diseases in the perinatal period. *Mailing Add:* 179 Morningside Dr Miami FL 33166

**VALDEZ, ROBERT O,** CARE QUALITY, CHILD HEALTH. *Current Pos:* PROF HEALTH POLICY & MGT, UNIV CALIF, LOS ANGELES SCH PUB HEALTH, 85- *Personal Data:* b San Antonio, Tex. *Educ:* Univ Mich, MHSA, 80; Rand Grad Sch, PhD(policy anal), 85. *Prof Exp:* Dept asst seccy health & dir, Interagency Health Policy, US Dept Health & Human Servs, 93-96. *Concurrent Pos:* Sr health scientist, Rand, 80-; nat res dir, Inter-Univ Prog Latino Res, 97- *Mem:* Asn Health Servs Res; Am Pub Health Asn; Am Econ Asn; Am Population Asn; AAAS; Asn Pub Policy Anal & Mgt. *Mailing Add:* Dept Health Servs Sch Pub Health Univ Calif Los Angeles CA 90095-1772. *Fax:* 310-825-3317; *E-Mail:* rvaldez@ucla.edu

**VALDISERRI, RONALD O,** PUBLIC HEALTH. *Current Pos:* dir, Div Lab Systs, 89-91, dep dir, Div Sexually Transmitted Dis & HIV Prev, 91-93, AIDS, 93-94, DEP DIR, NAT CTR HIV, SEXUALLY TRANSMITTED DIS & TUBERCULOSIS PREV, CTR DIS CONTROL, 96- *Personal Data:* b Washington, Pa, Nov 11, 51. *Educ:* Washington & Jefferson Col, BA, 73; Univ WVa, MD, 77; Univ Pittsburgh, MPH, 88. *Prof Exp:* Dir, Falk Clin Labs, 81-88. *Mem:* Am Pub Health Asn; Int Soc AIDS Prev; Col Am Path. *Mailing Add:* NCHN Ctr Dis Control 1600 Clifton Rd MS-E07 Atlanta GA 30333

**VALDIVIA, ENRIQUE,** PATHOLOGY & ELECTROMICROSCOPY. *Current Pos:* PROF PATH & PREV MED, UNIV WIS-MADISON, 58- *Educ:* Univ Chile, MD, 49. *Res:* Enzymology. *Mailing Add:* Dept Path Univ Wis Med Sch 502 N Walnut Madison WI 53705-2368

**VALDSAAR, HERBERT,** HIGH TEMPERATURE CHEMISTRY, METAL CHLORIDES. *Current Pos:* RETIRED. *Personal Data:* b Tallinn, Estonia, Dec 6, 25; nat US; m 59, Ellen Parve; c Elo & Leelo. *Educ:* Aachen Tech Univ, Dipl, 50; Univ Maine, MS, 52; Univ Fla, PhD(chem), 56. *Prof Exp:* Res chemist, E I du Pont de Nemours & Co, Inc, 56-71, sr res chemist, 71-90, res assoc, 91-93. *Res:* High temperature inorganic reactions; preparation of high purity silicon; metal chlorides; environmental control of heavy metals; pigment coatings. *Mailing Add:* 316 Taft Ave Wilmington DE 19805

**VALEGA, THOMAS MICHAEL,** ORGANIC CHEMISTRY, DENTISTRY. *Current Pos:* health scientist adminr, Periodontal Dis Prog, 72-74, chief, Restorative Mat Prog, Extramural Progs, 74-83, SPEC ASST MANPOWER DEVELOP & TRAINING, NAT INST DENT RES, NIH, 84- *Personal Data:* b Linden, NJ, May 23, 37; m 58; c 4. *Educ:* Rutgers Univ, BS, 59, PhD(org chem), 63. *Honors & Awards:* Spec Award, Soc Biomat, 84. *Prof Exp:* Chemist, Pesticide Chem Res Br, Entom Res Div, Agr Res Serv, USDA, 63-67; grants assoc, NIH, 67-68, health scientist adminr, Nat Inst Environ Health Sci, 68-69, coordr, Contracts Artificial Kidney-Chronic Uremia Prog, Nat Inst Arthritis & Metab Dis, 69-72; prog analyst, Off Categorical Progs, Prog Planning & Eval, Environ Protection Agency, DC, 72. *Mem:* Int Asn Dent Res; AAAS; Am Chem Soc; Nat Audubon Soc; Soc Biomaterials. *Res:* Peroxide and carbamate chemistry; insecticide and insecticide synergist chemistry; insect attractant and insect pheromone chemistry; medicinal chemistry; dental materials bioengineering; biomaterials; health sciences administration; oral biology; dental chemistry. *Mailing Add:* PO Box 181725 Casselberry FL 32718-1725

**VALENCIA, MAURO EDUARDO,** nutritional evaluation of protein quality, chemical & biological methods, for more information see previous edition

**VALENCIA, VALORIE SHARRON,** ORGANIC ELECTROLUMINESCENCE, FEMTOSECOND SPECTROSCOPY. *Current Pos:* RES SCIENTIST ORG MAT, SANDIA NAT LABS, 94- *Personal Data:* b Hayre, Mont, Mar 31, 60. *Educ:* Univ Ariz, BS, 83, MS, 88, PhD(optical sci), 91. *Prof Exp:* Fel, Frontiers Res Prog, Lab Nonlinear Optics & Advan Mat, Japan, RIKEN, 91; res assoc, Dept Chem, Univ Ariz, 91-94. *Mem:* Optical Soc Am; Am Phys Soc. *Res:* Organic electroluminescent materials and light emitting diodes; research includes optical, electrical, opto-electronic, and ultrafast dynamics measurements on the above materials and devices. *Mailing Add:* Sandia Nat Labs PO Box 5800 MS 0815 Albuquerque NM 87185-0815. *Fax:* 505-844-8884; *E-Mail:* vswilli@sandia.gov

**VALENCIA-GO, GERALDINE NUCUM,** GERONTOLOGICAL NURSING, TRANSCULTURAL HEALTH CARE. *Current Pos:* chair, RN-BSN Prog, 93-94, ASSOC PROF, SCH NURSING, COL NEW ROCHELLE, 89-, CHAIR UNDERGRAD PROG, 94- *Personal Data:* b Pampanga, Philippines, Mar 19, 47; nat US; m 76, Richard J; c Kimberly. *Educ:* NY Univ, BSN, 76, MA, 77; Adelphi Univ, PhD(res & theory develop), 89. *Prof Exp:* Adj lectr, Dept Nursing, Long Island Univ, 75-76, from instr to asst prof, 76-83; substitute instr, Lehman Col, City Univ NY, 83-85; adj asst prof, City Col NY, 85-88. *Concurrent Pos:* Adj instr, Hunter-Bellevue, Sch Nursing, City Univ NY, 88-89, assoc prof, 89-; consult, Rutgers State Univ NJ, 89-95; postdoctoral fel, Kellogg Found, 90-91. *Mem:* Am Nurses Asn; Asn Geront Higher Educ; Geront Soc Am. *Res:* Transcultural perspectives nursing; psychological aspects of aging; health care service utilization by elderly immigrants. *Mailing Add:* 73-40 194th St Fresh Meadows NY 11366. *Fax:* 914-654-5994

**VALENCICH, TRINA J,** PHYSICAL CHEMISTRY. *Current Pos:* ASST PROF CHEM, CALIF STATE UNIV, LOS ANGELES, 77- *Personal Data:* b Long Beach, Calif, Feb 3, 43; c 1. *Educ:* Univ Calif, Irvine, BA, 68, PhD(chem), 74. *Prof Exp:* Adj asst prof chem, Univ Calif, Los Angeles, 73-76; asst prof, Tex A&M Univ, 76. *Mem:* Am Chem Soc; Am Physics Soc. *Res:* Classical trajectory simulation of microscopic physical and chemical processes. *Mailing Add:* Dept Chem Univ Mont Missoula MT 59812

**VALENSTEIN, ELLIOT SPIRO,** NEUROSCIENCES, PSYCHOLOGY. *Current Pos:* PROF PSYCHOL, NEUROSCI LAB, UNIV MICH, ANN ARBOR, 70- *Personal Data:* b New York, NY, Dec 9, 23; m 47; c 2. *Educ:* City Col New York, BS, 49; Univ Kans, MA, 53, PhD(psychol), 54. *Prof Exp:* Asst anat & psychol, Univ Kans, 51, asst, Endocrinol Lab, 53-54, USPHS res fel anat, 54-55; chief, Lab Neuropsychol, Walter Reed Army Inst Res, Walter Reed Army Med Ctr, 59-61; from assoc to prof psychol & sr res assoc, Fels Res Inst, Antioch Col, 61-70. *Concurrent Pos:* Mem, Exp Psychol Study Sect, Nat Sci Adv Bd, 64-66; vis prof, Univ Calif, Berkeley, 69-70; mem, Neurobiol Rev Panel, NSF, 71-72; mem, Exp Psychol Study Sect, NIH, 75-79; pres, Div Comp & Physiol Psychol, Am Psychol Asn, 75-76; mem, Maternal & Child Health Res Comn, Nat Inst Child Develop, 80-; Kenneth Craik res award, Cambridge Univ, 80-81. *Mem:* Fel AAAS; fel Am Psychol Asn; Int Brain Res Orgn; NY Acad Sci; Soc Exp Psychol. *Res:* Hormones and behavior; development of behavioral capacities; physiological and comparative psychology; nervous system and motivation. *Mailing Add:* 260 Indian River Pl Ann Arbor MI 48104

**VALENTA, ZDENEK,** ORGANIC CHEMISTRY. *Current Pos:* from asst prof to prof chem, 57-90, chmn dept, 63-72, RES PROF, UNIV NB, 90- *Personal Data:* b Havlickuv Brod, Czech, June 14, 27; Can citizen; m 57; c 3. *Educ:* Swiss Fed Inst Technol, Dipl Ing Chem, 50; Univ NB, MSc, 52, PhD(chem), 53. *Honors & Awards:* Merck, Sharp & Dohme Lect Award, Chem Inst Can, 67. *Prof Exp:* Spec lectr chem, Univ NB, 53-54, lectr, 54-56; Univ NB fel & res assoc, Harvard Univ, 56-57. *Mem:* Chem Inst Can; fel Royal Soc Can; Am Chem Soc. *Res:* Total synthesis of organic molecules of biological and pharmaceutical interest; study of organic reactions and stereochemistry. *Mailing Add:* Dept Chem Univ NB Bag Serv 45222 Fredericton NB E3B 2E9 Can. *Fax:* 506-453-4599; *E-Mail:* valenta@unb.ca

**VALENTEKOVICH, MARIJA NIKOLETIC,** CHEMISTRY. *Current Pos:* MEM TECH STAFF, DIAG PROD CORP, 89- *Personal Data:* b Dubrovnik, Croatia, Feb 5, 32; m 62; c 2. *Educ:* Univ Zagreb, MSChE, 57, PhD(chem), 63. *Prof Exp:* Res assoc, Rudjer Boskovic Inst, Zagreb, Yugoslavia, 57-65; fel & res assoc, Radiocarbon Lab, Univ Ill, Urbana, 65-67 & Univ Southern Calif, 67-68; sr chemist, Cyclo Chem Co, 68-69, dir qual control, 69-73; head, Dept Radioisotopes, Curtis Nuclear Co, 73-74; dir qual control, Nichols Inst, 74-76, dir radiochem, 76-79; prin develop chemist, Beckman Instrument Inc, 79-83; vpres immunochem, Innotron Diag, 83-86; oper mgr, Merel Inc, 87-88. *Mem:* Am Asn Clin Chem; Clin Ligand Assay Soc. *Res:* Clinical diagnostics, particularly immunoassays; radiolabelling of peptides and hormones; development and evaluation of new immunoassay techniques; production of non-radioisotopic tests. *Mailing Add:* 33 Silver Spring Dr Rolling Hills Estates CA 90274-2312. *Fax:* 213-776-0204

**VALENTICH, JOHN DAVID,** cell physiology, for more information see previous edition

**VALENTINE, BARRY DEAN,** SYSTEMATICS, WEEVIL BIOLOGY. *Current Pos:* from asst prof to assoc prof zool & entom, 60-74, prof zool, 74-88, EMER PROF ZOOL, OHIO STATE UNIV, 88- *Personal Data:* b New York, NY, June 6, 24; m 53, Susan & Nancy. *Educ:* Univ Ala, BS, 51, MS, 54; Cornell Univ, PhD(entom), 60. *Prof Exp:* Asst prof biol, Miss Southern Col, 55-57, actg head dept, 57. *Concurrent Pos:* Consult, Standard Fruit Co, 56, Lerner Marine Lab, Am Mus Natural Hist, 65, Dames & Moore Inc, 72 & US Army CEngr, 72, Rockefeller Brothers Fund, 78 & Nature Conserv, 93; entomologist zool expeds, Haiti & Jamaica, 56, Cent Am, 56, Mexico, 59, Bahama Islands, 65, 72, 82 & 83, Kenya & Tanzania, 71, 74, 75 & 86, Costa Rica, 87, Galapagos Islands, 87 & 88, SAfrica, 95, Virgin Islands, 96; Entom Soc Am travel grant, London, Eng, 64; Ohio State Univ develop fund travel grant, London, Copenhagen, Stockholm & Paris, 70; vis prof, Univ Okla Biol Sta, 65, 67-69; vis cur of Coleoptera, Am Mus Natural Hist, 77, B P Bishop Mus, 94; Nat Geog Soc res grant, Kenya & Seychelles Islands, 86; res assoc, Fla Dept Agr, 86- & Carnegie Mus, 90- *Mem:* Entom Soc Am; Coleopterists Soc; Am Soc Ichthyologists & Herpetologists; Soc Study Amphibians & Reptiles; Herpetologists League. *Res:* Theory and practice of systematics and zoogeography, especially the weevil family Anthribidae of the world and salamanders of Eastern United States; comparative grooming behavior of arthropods; invertebrate identification and classification. *Mailing Add:* 2359 E Cleft Dr Columbus OH 43221-1851. *Fax:* 614-292-7774

**VALENTINE, DANIEL T,** FLUID MECHANICS, HYDRODYNAMICS. *Current Pos:* ASSOC PROF MECH & AERONAUT ENG, CLARKSON UNIV, 83- *Personal Data:* b Brooklyn, NY, Dec 24, 46; m 67, Mary Ullrich; c Clara M. *Educ:* Rutgers Univ, BSME, 68, MS, 70; Cath Univ Am, PhD(fluid mech), 82. *Prof Exp:* Mech engr, David Taylor Res Ctr, 70-77; res engr, Davidson Lab, 77-80; prin scientist & vpres, Hydrodyn Res Assocs Inc, 80-83. *Concurrent Pos:* Dir, Clarkson Space Grant Prog, 89-; publ, Parallax, NY Space Grant Mag, 92- *Mem:* Am Soc Mech Engrs; Am Phys Soc; Soc Naval Architects & Marine Engrs; Sigma Xi. *Res:* Investigating rotating fluids, buoyancy driven flows, computational fluid dynamics, marine propeller design and marine hydrodynamics. *Mailing Add:* PO Box 426 Potsdam NY 13676

**VALENTINE, DONALD H, JR,** ORGANOMETALLIC CHEMISTRY, PHOTOCHEMISTRY. *Current Pos:* proj mgr, 84, tech dir, 85-86, DIR, AM CYANAMID, 87- *Personal Data:* b Orange, NJ, Nov 7, 40; m 66. *Educ:* Wesleyan Univ, BA, 62; Calif Inst Technol, PhD(photochem), 66. *Prof Exp:* NSF fel, Stanford Univ, 65-66; asst prof chem, Princeton Univ, 66-71; sr chemist, Hoffmann-La Roche Inc, 71-74, res fel, 74, group chief, 75-80; sr res assoc, Catalytica Asn 80, tech dir, 81-83. *Concurrent Pos:* Lectr, Bell Tel Labs, 70-71; lectr, Exten Div, Rutgers Univ, 72 & 76; ed, Molecular Photochem, 72-77; adj prof, Rutgers Univ, 79; fel, Hydrocarbon Res Inst, Univ Southern Calif, 80. *Mem:* Sigma Xi. *Res:* Redox reactions; spectroscopy; homogeneous catalysis; asymmetric synthesis; electronic chemicals; bioseparations. *Mailing Add:* 20 Blue Ridge Rd Ridgefield CT 06877-2307

**VALENTINE, FRED TOWNSEND,** IMMUNOLOGY, INFECTIOUS DISEASES. *Current Pos:* Asst prof, 69-75, ASSOC PROF MED, SCH MED, NY UNIV, 75- *Personal Data:* b Detroit, Mich, Sept 1, 34; m 64; c 2. *Educ:* Harvard Univ, AB, 56, MD, 60. *Concurrent Pos:* Attend med, Manhattan Vet Admin Hosp, 70-; assoc attend med, Univ Hosp & assoc attend physician, Bellevue Hosp, NY, 76- *Mem:* Am Asn Immunologists; Infectious Dis Soc Am; Transplant Soc; Harvey Soc. *Res:* Cellular immunology, immunological defenses against infectious agents and against neoplasia. *Mailing Add:* Dept Med NY Univ Sch Med 550 First Ave New York NY 10016-6402

**VALENTINE, FREDRICK ARTHUR,** FOREST GENETICS. *Current Pos:* RETIRED. *Personal Data:* b Detroit Lakes, Minn, June 26, 26; m 66; c 3. *Educ:* St Cloud State Teachers Col, BS, 49; Univ Wis, MS, 53, PhD(genetics), 57. *Prof Exp:* Instr genetics, Univ Wis, 54-56; from asst prof to assoc prof forest bot, Col Environ Sci & Forestry, State Univ NY, 56-69, prof environ & forest biol, 69-97. *Mem:* Genetics Soc Am; Am Genetic Asn. *Res:* Genetic control of growth and wood properties in Populus tremuloides, the genetics of Hypoxylon mammatum susceptibility to canker in Populus spp; genetics of resistance to verticillium wilt in urban maple trees. *Mailing Add:* Dept Environ & Forest Biol State Univ NY Col Environ Sci & Forestry Syracuse NY 13210-2778

**VALENTINE, JAMES K,** electronics design, systems intergration, for more information see previous edition

**VALENTINE, JAMES WILLIAM,** INVERTEBRATE PALEOBIOLOGY. *Current Pos:* prof, 90-93, EMER PROF INTEGRATIVE BIOL, UNIV CALIF, BERKELEY, 93- *Personal Data:* b Los Angeles, Calif, Nov 10, 26; m 57, 87, Diane Mondragon; c Anita, Ian & Geoffrey. *Educ:* Phillips Univ, BA, 51; Univ Calif, Los Angeles, MA, 54, PhD(geol), 58. *Prof Exp:* Asst geol, Univ Calif, Los Angeles, 52-55, asst geophys, 57-58; from asst prof to assoc prof geol, Univ Mo, 58-64; from assoc prof to prof, Univ Calif, Davis, 64-77; prof geol sci, Univ Calif, Santa Barbara, 77-90. *Concurrent Pos:* Fulbright res scholar, Australia, 62-63; Guggenheim fel. *Mem:* Nat Acad Sci; AAAS; Geol Soc Am; Paleont Soc (pres, 73-74); Am Acad Arts & Sci. *Res:* Evolutionary paleoecology; macroevolution. *Mailing Add:* Dept Int Biol Univ Calif Berkeley CA 94720

**VALENTINE, JIMMIE LLOYD,** PHARMACOLOGY. *Current Pos:* PROF PEDIAT, COL MED, UNIV ARK, 90- *Personal Data:* b Shreveport, La, Oct 18, 40; m 63, 84; c 3. *Educ:* Centenary Col La, BS, 62 & 64; Univ Miss, MS, 66, PhD(med chem), 68. *Prof Exp:* Sr scientist med chem, Mallinckrodt Pharmaceut, 68-73; asst prof, Univ Mo, Kansas City, 73-78; assoc prof pharmacol, Oral Roberts Univ, 78-84, prof & chmn, 84-90. *Concurrent Pos:* Consult, var pvt & pub orgn, 73-; adj prof, Univ Mo, 78-81. *Mem:* Am Chem Soc; Am Pharmaceut Asn; Am Soc Mass Spectrometry; AAAS; Am Soc Pharmacol & Exp Therapeut. *Res:* Analysis of physiological specimens; human breath analysis; drug effects on endocrine function; laser analysis of drugs and physiological fluids; gas liquid chromatography and high pressure liquid chromatography-mass spectrometry of physiological fluids; alcoholism. *Mailing Add:* Univ Ark Med Sci Ark Children's Hosp 800 Marshall St Little Rock AR 72202-3591

**VALENTINE, JOAN SELVERSTONE,** BIOINORGANIC CHEMISTRY, INORGANIC CHEMISTRY. *Current Pos:* assoc prof, 80-81, PROF CHEM, UNIV CALIF, LOS ANGELES, 81- *Personal Data:* b Auburn, Calif, Mar 15, 45. *Educ:* Smith Col, AB, 67; Princeton Univ, PhD(chem), 71. *Prof Exp:* Instr chem, Princeton Univ, 71-72; from asst prof to assoc prof, Douglass Col, Rutgers Univ, New Brunswick, 72-80. *Concurrent Pos:* Ed, Acc Chem Res, 94- *Mem:* Am Chem Soc; Biophys Soc; Protein Soc; AAAS; Am Soc Biochem & Molecular Biol. *Res:* Oxygen chemistry, biochemistry; biology copper-zinc superoxide dismutase. *Mailing Add:* Dept Chem & Biochem Univ Calif Los Angeles CA 90095-1569. *E-Mail:* jsv@chem.ucla.edu

**VALENTINE, JOSEPH EARL,** MATHEMATICS. *Current Pos:* RETIRED. *Personal Data:* b Kansas City, Kans, Apr 6, 33; m 55; c 2. *Educ:* Southwest Mo State Col, BSEd, 58; Univ Ill, Urbana, MS, 60; Univ Mo, Columbia, PhD(distance geom), 67. *Prof Exp:* Teacher high sch, Mo, 58-59; teacher & prin high sch, Mo, 60-61; from instr to asst prof math, Southwest Mo State Col, 61-68; from asst prof to assoc prof math, Utah State Univ, 68-77. *Concurrent Pos:* Fulbright fel, Univ Jordan, 71-72. *Mem:* Am Math Soc; Math Asn Am. *Res:* Distance geometry; non-euclidean geometry. *Mailing Add:* RR 2 Verona MO 65769

**VALENTINE, MARTIN DOUGLAS,** ALLERGY, CLINICAL IMMUNOLOGY. *Current Pos:* from asst prof to assoc prof, 70-85, PROF, SCH MED, JOHNS HOPKINS UNIV, 85- *Personal Data:* b Greenwich, Conn, Apr 13, 35; m 57; c 4. *Educ:* Union Col, BS, 56; Tufts Univ, MD, 60; Am Bd Internal Med, cert, 72; Am Bd Allergy & Immunol, cert, 74. *Honors & Awards:* Philip S Norman Lectr, Am Acad Allergy Immunol, 90. *Prof Exp:* Instr, Sch Med, Harvard Univ, 68-70. *Concurrent Pos:* Staff physician allergy, Lahey Clin Found, Boston, 68-70; physician allergy, Lahey Clin Found, Boston, 68-70; physician allergy, Johns Hopkins Hosp & Good Samaritan Hosp, Baltimore, 70-; chmn comt insects, Am Acad Allergy, 75-77, chmn res coun, 77-80, vpres, 89-90; chmn study group hymenotera venoms, Nat Inst Allergy & Infectious Dis, 77- *Mem:* Am Acad Allergy Immunol; Am Asn Immunologists; Am Thoracic Soc. *Res:* Mechanisms of immediate hypersensitivity reactions; allergy to hymenoptera venoms; allergic reaction to foods. *Mailing Add:* Dept Immunol John Hopkins Sch Med 1777 Reistertown Rd Suite 235 Baltimore MD 21208

**VALENTINE, NANCY M,** NURSING. *Current Pos:* asst chief med dir, Nursing Progs, 93-96, CHIEF CONSULT, NURSING STRATEGIC HEALTH CARE GROUP, DEPT VET AFFAIRS, 96- *Personal Data:* b Philadelphia, Pa. *Educ:* Rutgers Univ, BS; Univ Pa, MS; Harvard Univ, MPH; Brandeis Univ, PhD(econ & health policy). *Prof Exp:* Dir nursing, Boston City Hosp; adminr nursing, McLean Hosp. *Concurrent Pos:* Adj fac, Georgetown Univ Sch Nursing, Mass Gen Hosp Inst Health Prof, Harvard Med Sch. *Mem:* Fel Am Acad Nursing; Am Psychiat Nurses Asn (pres, 97). *Mailing Add:* Dept Vet Affairs Off Patient Care Serv 810 Vermont Ave NW Washington DC 20420. *Fax:* 202-273-9066

**VALENTINE, RAYMOND CARLYLE,** BIOCHEMISTRY. *Current Pos:* RETIRED. *Personal Data:* b Piatt Co, Ill, Sept 20, 36; m 58; c 1. *Educ:* Univ Ill, Urbana, BS, 58, MS, 60, PhD(microbiol), 62. *Prof Exp:* Asst microbiol, Univ Ill, Urbana, 58-62; fel, Rockefeller Inst, 62-64; asst prof biochem, Univ Calif, Berkeley, 64-70; asst prof in residence microbial biochem, Univ Calif, San Diego, 72-74; mem staff, Univ Calif, Davis, 74-77, assoc prof, Plant Growth Lab, 77-91. *Mem:* Am Soc Microbiol; fel Am Soc Biol Chemists. *Res:* Nitrogen fixation; ferredoxin; microbial biochemistry and genetics. *Mailing Add:* 338 Hidalgo Pl Davis CA 95616

**VALENTINE, WILLIAM NEWTON,** MEDICINE, HEMATOLOGY. *Current Pos:* asst clin prof, Sch Med, Univ Calif, Los Angeles, 49-50, from asst prof to prof, 50-88, chmn dept, 63-71, EMER PROF MED, SCH MED, UNIV CALIF, LOS ANGELES, 88- *Personal Data:* b Kansas City, Mo, Sept 29, 17; m 40; c 3. *Educ:* Tulane Univ, MD, 42; Am Bd Internal Med, dipl, 49. *Honors & Awards:* Mayo Soley Award, Excellence in Res, Western Soc Clin Res, 78; Henry Stratton Medalist, Am Soc Hemat, 78; John Phillips Mem Award Distinguished Achievements Internal Med, Am Col Physicians, 79. *Prof Exp:* Intern med, Strong Mem Hosp, Rochester, NY, 42-43, asst resident, 43, chief resident, 43-44; instr, Sch Med, Univ Rochester, 47-48, head, Sect Hemat, AEC Proj, 47-53. *Concurrent Pos:* Assoc, St John's Hosp, Santa Monica, Calif, 47, hon consult, 52; sr attend, Harbor Hosp, Torrance, 50; consult, AEC Proj, 53; consult, Hemat Study Sect, NIH, 55-58, mem coun, Inst Arthritis & Metab Dis, 66-70; mem, Am Bd Internal Med, 64-67; mem, Gov Adv Coun Southern Calif, Am Col Physicians, 64-74 & 81-85; mem adv coun, Am Soc Hemat, 69-74, counr, 76-77; outstanding fac res lectr, Dept Med, Univ Calif, Los Angeles, 74-75 & 53rd ann fac res lectr, 78. *Mem:* Nat Acad Sci; AAAS; Am Soc Clin Invest (vpres, 62); Asn Am Physicians; master Am Col Physicians; fel Am Acad Arts & Sci; AMA; fel Am Soc Hemat; fel Int Soc Hemat (vpres, 76-80); Western Soc Clin Res. *Mailing Add:* Div Hemat & Oncol 37-068-Ctr Health Sci Bldg Univ Calif Sch Med 10833 LeConte Ave Los Angeles CA 90024-1678

**VALENTINI, JAMES JOSEPH,** CHEMICAL DYNAMICS, SPECTROSCOPY. *Current Pos:* PROF, COLUMBIA UNIV, 90- *Personal Data:* b Martins Ferry, Ohio, Mar 20, 50; m 81; c Evan & Colin. *Educ:* Univ Pittsburgh, BS, 72; Univ Chicago, MS, 73; Univ Calif, Berkeley, PhD(chem), 76. *Prof Exp:* Chaim Weizmann fel, Harvard Univ, 77-78; J Robert Oppenheimer fel, Los Alamos Nat Lab, 78-80, staff mem, 80-84; prof, Univ Calif, Irvine, 84-90. *Mem:* Fel Am Phys Soc; Sigma Xi; Am Chem Soc; AAAS. *Res:* Chemical dynamics; experimental studies employing molecular beam and laser spectroscopic methods; molecular photochemistry. *Mailing Add:* Havemeyer Hall Box 766 Columbia Univ New York NY 10027. *Fax:* 212-932-1289; *E-Mail:* jjv1@columbia.edu

**VALENTY, STEVEN JEFFREY,** POLYMER SURFACE CHEMISTRY, PHOTOCHEMISTRY. *Current Pos:* PRES, ANALYZE INC. *Personal Data:* b Minneapolis, Minn, May 28, 44; m 69; c 2. *Educ:* Lewis Col, BA, 66; Pa State Univ, PhD(org chem), 71. *Prof Exp:* Fel, Royal Inst London, 71-72; staff scientist, Corp Rcs & Develop Ctr, Gen Elec Co, NY, 72- *Mem:* Am Chem Soc; AAAS. *Res:* Design and develop new materials and processes using the theory and tools of polymer surface science. *Mailing Add:* Analyze Inc 3185 S Bracken Lane Chandler AZ 85224

**VALENTY, VIVIAN BRIONES,** ORGANIC CHEMISTRY. *Current Pos:* VPRES, ANALYZE INC, 90-; PRES, VB COSMETICS INC, 93- *Personal Data:* b Tarlac, Philippines, Dec 15, 44; US citizen; m 69; c 2. *Educ:* Mapua Inst Technol, BS, 64; Pa State Univ, PhD(chem), 71. *Prof Exp:* Res asst cereal chem, Int Rice Res Inst, 64-66; asst prof chem, Skidmore Col, 75-77; res assoc, Div Labs & Res, NY State Dept Health, 77-81; res chemist, A E Staley Mfg Co, 81-83; prog leader, Gen Elec Co, 83-88, microsci, 88-90. *Mem:* Am Chem Soc. *Res:* Organic chemistry applied to biomolecules; chemicals from carbohydrates; polyimide siloxanes; coatings; cosmetics. *Mailing Add:* 7918 S Kenwood Lane Tempe AZ 85284-4706

**VALENZENO, DENNIS PAUL,** MEMBRANE BIOPHYSICS, PHOTOSENSITIZATION. *Current Pos:* asst prof, 80-86, ASSOC PROF PHYSIOL, MED CTR, UNIV KANS, 86- *Personal Data:* b Cleveland, Ohio, June 15, 49; m 72, 86, Marcia Yingst; c Jon, Dan, Laura & Matthew. *Educ:* Case Western Res Univ, BS, 71, MS, 75, PhD(physiol), 76. *Honors & Awards:* Porter vis lectr, Spelman Col, 78-79. *Prof Exp:* NIH fel, Emory Univ, 76-80. *Concurrent Pos:* Instr, Emory Univ, 79-80; prin investr, Am Heart Asn, 80, 83, Am Lung Asn, 84; vis prof, Univ L'Aquila, Italy, 85; mem, Am Soc Photobiol Educ Comt, 86-, Publ Comt, 87-, Pub Affairs Comt, 87-; ed, Am Soc Photobiol Newslett, 87- *Mem:* Am Soc Photobiol; Biophys Soc. *Res:* Membrane biophysics in nerve axons, cardiac cells, and red blood cells, particularly sensitization of membrane functions to visible light by photosensitizing dyes. *Mailing Add:* Dept Physiol Univ Kans Med Ctr 3901 Rainbow Blvd Kansas City KS 66160-7401. *Fax:* 913-588-7430; *E-Mail:* dvalenze@kumc.edu

**VALENZUELA, GASPAR RODOLFO,** AIR-SEA INTERACTION, NONLINEAR DYNAMICS. *Current Pos:* REMOTE SENSING CONSULT, COLUMBIA, MD, 93- *Personal Data:* b Coelemu, Chile, Jan 6, 33; US citizen; m 58, Martha C Payne; c Gregory N & Roderick T. *Educ:* Univ Fla, BSEE, 54, MSE, 55; Johns Hopkins Univ, DrEng, 65. *Prof Exp:* Assoc eng, Westinghouse Elec Corp, Md, 55-57; assoc sr res staff, Appl Physics Lab, Johns Hopkins Univ, 57-59, res staff asst, Carlyle Barton, 59-64, sr res staff, Appl Physics Lab, 64-68; supvry electronics eng, Naval Res Lab, 68-93. *Concurrent Pos:* Assoc ed, J Geophys Res Oceans, 82-85; rep, Sci Comt Oceanog Res, Int Union Radio Sci, 84-90; mem ad-hoc working group global change, Int Union Radio Sci, 87-90. *Mem:* Life mem Inst Elec & Electronics Engrs; Am Geophys Union; emer mem Int Union Radio Sci. *Res:* Electromagnetic theory; rough surface scattering theory; interaction of electromagnetic waves with ocean; oceanography; nonlinear interactions in geophysics; hydrodynamics; wave dynamics; radio-oceanography; remote sensing. *Mailing Add:* Remote Sensing Consult 10132 Spring Pools Lane Columbia MD 21044-1709

**VALENZUELA, PABLO,** GENETIC ENGINEERING, BIOCHEMISTRY. *Current Pos:* SR VPRES RES, CHIRON CORP, 81- *Educ:* Univ Chile, BS, 65; Northwestern Univ, PhD(biochem), 70. *Prof Exp:* Fel chem, Univ Calif, San Francisco, 70-74, prof med, 74-81. *Mem:* Am Chem Soc; Am Soc Cell Biol. *Res:* Genetic engineering; biochemistry. *Mailing Add:* Chiron Corp 4560 Horton Emeryville CA 94608-2916

**VALENZUELA, REINALDO A,** WIRELESS COMMUNICATIONS, SIGNAL PROCESSING. *Current Pos:* mem tech staff signal processing, Commun Methods Res Dept, 84-88, MEM TECH STAFF, COMMUN RES DEPT, AT&T BELL LABS, 90- *Personal Data:* b San Antonio, Chile, Aug 30, 52; m 75; c 2. *Educ:* Univ Chile, BSc, 75; Imp Col London, PhD(elec eng) & DIC, 81. *Prof Exp:* Sr engr data commun, Databit Ltd, 83-84; res asst signal processing, Imp Col, Univ London, 80-82; mgr voice res, CODEX Corp, 88-90. *Concurrent Pos:* Ed, Inst Elec & Electronics Engrs Trans on Commun, 90- *Mem:* Sr mem Inst Elec & Electronics Engrs. *Res:* Propagation modeling and system design for wireless communication systems and personal communication networks. *Mailing Add:* Mts Comm Sys Res Dept AT&T Bell Lab, Holmdel Keyprot Rd Rm Hoh-R225 Holmdel NJ 07733-0400

**VALEO, ERNEST JOHN,** PLASMA PHYSICS. *Current Pos:* RES PHYSICIST, PLASMA PHYSICS LAB, PRINCETON UNIV, 77- *Personal Data:* b New London, Conn, Aug 6, 45; m 70; c 3. *Educ:* Rensselaer Polytech Inst, BS, 67; Princeton Univ, MA, 69, PhD(astrophys sci), 71. *Prof Exp:* Res assoc, Plasma Physics Lab, Princeton Univ, 72-73; physicist, Lawrence Livermore Lab 73-76. *Concurrent Pos:* Consult, Lab Laser Energetics, Univ Rochester, 77- & Lawrence Livermore Lab, Univ Calif, 77- *Mem:* Am Phys Soc. *Res:* Theoretical plasma physics, especially as related to controlled thermonuclear fusion research. *Mailing Add:* 23 Monterey Dr Princeton Junction NJ 08550. *Fax:* 609-243-2662

**VALERIOTE, FREDERICK AUGUSTUS,** BIOPHYSICS. *Current Pos:* assoc prof, Edward Mallinckrodt Inst Radiol, 69-76, PROF RADIOL, MED SCH, WASHINGTON UNIV, 69-, ASSOC DIR, DEPT RADIATION ONCOL, 76-; STAFF MEM, MICH CANCER FOUND; AT HARPER HOSP. *Personal Data:* b Montreal, Que, May 19, 41; m 66; c 3. *Educ:* Univ Toronto, BSc, 62, MA, 64, PhD(med biophys), 66. *Prof Exp:* Can Cancer Soc fel, Ont Cancer Inst, 66-67; Med Res Coun Can fel, NIH, 67-68, USPHS vis fel, 68-69. *Concurrent Pos:* Mem ed bd, Cell & Tissue Kinetics. *Mem:* Am Asn Cancer Res; Cell Kinetics Soc (pres); Am Asn Cancer Educ. *Res:* Cancer research; experimental cancer chemotherapy; cell population kinetics. *Mailing Add:* 52623 Seven Oaks Dr Utica MI 48316

**VALI, GABOR,** ATMOSPHERIC PHYSICS. *Current Pos:* from asst prof to assoc prof, 69-76, PROF ATMOSPHERIC SCI, UNIV WYO, 76- *Personal Data:* b Budapest, Hungary, Oct 22, 36; US citizen; m 56; c 3. *Educ:* Sir George Williams Univ, BSc, 61; McGill Univ, MSc, 64, PhD(physics), 68. *Prof Exp:* Lectr agr physics, Macdonald Col, McGill Univ, 65-68, asst prof, 68-69. *Mem:* Am Meteorol Soc; Am Asn Aerosol Res; Sigma Xi; Royal Meteorol Soc; Int Asn Aerobiol. *Res:* Ice nucleation; development of ice elements in clouds; physics of precipitation; weather modification; atmospheric aerosols; human impact; biogenic ice nuclei. *Mailing Add:* Dept Atmospheric Sci Univ Wyo PO Box 3038 Laramie WY 82071-3038

**VALIA, HARDARSHAN S,** COAL CARBONIZATION, COAL COMBUSTION. *Current Pos:* SR STAFF RES ENGR, INLAND STEEL CO, 79- *Personal Data:* b Khurda Road, Orisa, India, June 15, 45; m 82, Bhunpinder K Soni; c Vikram S & Anu K. *Educ:* Nagpur Univ, BSc, 65, MSc, 68; Bryn Mawr Col, MA, 71; Boston Univ, PhD(geol), 76. *Honors & Awards:* Am Iron & Steel Inst Medal, 89. *Prof Exp:* Asst prof geol, Case Western Res Univ, 78, Oberlin Col, 78-79. *Concurrent Pos:* Mem, Tall Oven Task Group, Am Iron & Steel Inst (AISI), 88-90, Coal Selection for AISI Direct Steelmaking, 89-; mem, Subcomt Ind Coal Characterization, Ind Geol Surv, 91- *Mem:* Iron & Steel Soc; Soc Org Petrol. *Res:* Characterization of coals for carbonization; characterization of coals for pulverized coal injection into blast furnace; carbon additives in ironmaking and steelmaking; carbon material behavior and interactions during carbonization and combustion. *Mailing Add:* 2116 44th St Highland IN 46322. *Fax:* 219-399-6562; *E-Mail:* valia@inland. research.com

**VALIANT, LESLIE GABRIEL,** APPLIED MATHEMATICS, COMPUTER SCIENCE. *Current Pos:* vis prof, 82, GORDON MCKAY PROF COMPUTER SCI & APPL MATH, HARVARD UNIV, 82- *Personal Data:* b Mar 28, 49; m 77, Gayle L Dyckoff; c Paul A & Gregory J. *Educ:* Kings Col, MA, 70; Imperial Col, DIC, 73; Univ Warwick, UK, PhD, 74. *Honors & Awards:* Nevanlinna Prize, Int Math Union, 86. *Prof Exp:* Vis asst prof, Carnegie-Mellon Univ, 73-74; lectr, Univ Leeds, 74-76; lectr & reader, Univ Edinburgh, 77-82. *Concurrent Pos:* Guggenheim fel, 85-86. *Mem:* Fel Royal Soc; fel Am Asn Artificial Intel. *Mailing Add:* Harvard Univ 33 Oxford St Cambridge MA 02138-2901

**VALINSKY, JAY E,** EMBRYONIC CELL MIGRATION. *Current Pos:* ASST DIR RES & DEVELOP, NY BLOOD CTR, 83- *Educ:* Brandeis Univ, PhD(biochem), 74. *Res:* Cell-surface phenotypes. *Mailing Add:* Dept Spec Diag NY Blood Ctr 310 E 67th St New York NY 10021-6295. *Fax:* 212-794-0292

**VALK, HENRY SNOWDEN,** THEORETICAL NUCLEAR PHYSICS. *Current Pos:* dean, Col Sci & Liberal Studies, 70-82, actg dir physics, 91-96, PROF PHYSICS, GA INST TECHNOL, 70- *Personal Data:* b Washington, DC, Jan 26, 29; m 68, Gillian Wedderburn; c Alison, Diana, Robert & Richard. *Educ:* George Washington Univ, BS, 53, MS, 54; Wash Univ, PhD(physics), 57. *Honors & Awards:* Order of Brit Empire, 85. *Prof Exp:* Asst, Wash Univ, 54-56; asst prof physics, Univ Ore, 57-59; asst prog dir physics, NSF, 59-60; from asst prof to prof physics, Univ Nebr, Lincoln, 60-70, chmn dept, 66-70. *Concurrent Pos:* Prog dir theoret physics, NSF, 65-66; vis prof, Univ Frankfurt, 70, Rensselaer Polytech Inst, 82, 88, Cath Univ Am, 82-83, 88-89. *Mem:* Fel Am Phys Soc; Am Math Soc; Am Asn Physics Teachers; Math Asn Am. *Res:* Theoretical atomic and nuclear physics. *Mailing Add:* 3032 St Helena Dr Tucker GA 30084. *Fax:* 404-894-9958; *E-Mail:* henry.Valk@physics.gatech.edu

**VALK, WILLIAM LOWELL,** SURGERY. *Current Pos:* RETIRED. *Personal Data:* b Muskegon, Mich, Aug 23, 09; m 37; c 2. *Educ:* Univ Mich, AB, 34, MD, 37. *Prof Exp:* Instr surg, Med Sch, Univ Mich, 40-43; from assoc prof to prof surg, Univ Kans Med Ctr, 46-79. *Mem:* Soc Univ Surg; Clin Soc Genito-Urinary Surg; Am Surg Asn; Am Urol Asn; AMA. *Res:* Urological surgery; physiology of kidney. *Mailing Add:* 5401 W 81st St Shawnee Mission KS 66208

**VALLABHAN, C V GIRIJA,** CIVIL ENGINEERING, ENGINEERING MECHANICS. *Current Pos:* from asst prof to assoc prof, 66-80, PROF CIVIL ENG, TEX TECH UNIV, 80- *Personal Data:* b Trichur, India, May 24, 35; m 61; c 3. *Educ:* Univ Kerala, BSc, 57; Univ Mo-Rolla, MS, 60; Univ Tex, Austin, PhD(civil eng), 67. *Prof Exp:* Jr engr, Kerala Pub Works Dept, India, 57; lectr civil eng, Eng Col, Trichur, India, 58-59, asst prof, 60-64. *Mem:* Am Soc Civil Engrs. *Res:* Finite element technique for solving elasticity and plasticity problems in structural and soil mechanics; deterministic and probabilistic analysis of soil-structure interaction problems. *Mailing Add:* 1802 Albany Ave Lubbock TX 79416

**VALLBONA, CARLOS,** PEDIATRICS, COMMUNITY MEDICINE. *Current Pos:* from instr to assoc prof pediat & physiol, 56-67, from instr to assoc prof rehab, 57-67, PROF REHAB, BAYLOR COL MED, 67-, PROF & CHMN, DEPT COMMUNITY MED, 69-; CHIEF, COMMUN MED SERV, HARRIS COUNTY HOSP DIST, 69- *Personal Data:* b Barcelona, Spain, July 29, 27; m 56; c 4. *Educ:* Univ Barcelona, BA & BS, 44, MD, 50. *Prof Exp:* Physician, Sch Child Health, Spain, 51-52; intern & resident, Sch Med, Univ Louisville, 53-55. *Concurrent Pos:* Fel, Children's Int Ctr, Univ Paris, 52-53; consult, Nat Heart, Lung & Blood Inst, Nat Ctr Health Servs Res, Nat Ctr Health Care Technol, Nat Ctr Health Statist & Off Health Resources Opportunity. *Mem:* AAAS; Soc Pediat Res; Am Col Chest Physicians; Sigma Xi; AMA. *Res:* Pediatric rehabilitation; cardiorespiratory physiology in disabled persons and the newborn; application of electronic data processing techniques in health care; rehabilitation community medicine; community medicine; prevention of hypertension. *Mailing Add:* Dept Community Med Baylor Col Med One Baylor Plaza Houston TX 77030-3411

**VALLEAU, JOHN PHILIP,** STATISTICAL MECHANICS, CHEMICAL PHYSICS. *Current Pos:* from asst prof to prof, 61-96, EMER PROF CHEM, UNIV TORONTO, 96- *Personal Data:* b Toronto, Ont, Jan 17, 32; m 57, 86, Jean Smith; c Nicholas & Simon. *Educ:* Univ Toronto, BA, 54, MA, 55; Cambridge Univ, PhD(theoret chem), 58. *Prof Exp:* Nat Res Coun Can fel, 58-60. *Concurrent Pos:* Res visitor, Fac Sci, Orsay, France, 68-69, Norweg Inst Technol, Trondheim, 78-79, Dept Physics, Univ Roma, 85-86. *Mem:* Sci Peace Can. *Res:* Theory of liquids and phase changes and of solutions; Monte Carlo and molecular dynamic computations; theory of surface phenomena. *Mailing Add:* Lash Miller Lab Univ Toronto Toronto ON M5S 1A1 Can. *Fax:* 416-978-5325

**VALLEE, BERT L,** BIOCHEMISTRY, BIOPHYSICS. *Current Pos:* Res fel med, Harvard Med Sch, 45-49, from res assoc to assoc, 49-55, from asst prof to prof, 55-65, Paul C Cabot prof biol chem, 65-80, Paul C Cabot prof biochem sci, 80-89, head, Ctr Biochem & Biophys Sci & Med, 80-89, distinguished sr prof, 89-90, EDGAR M BRONFMAN DISTINGUISHED SR PROF, HARVARD MED SCH, 90- *Personal Data:* b Hemer, WGer, June 1, 19; nat US; m 47, Natalie Kugris. *Educ:* Univ Bern, BS, 38; NY Univ, MD, 43. *Hon Degrees:* MA, Harvard Univ, 60; Dr Med hon causa, Karolinska Inst, Sweden, 87; DSc, Univ Degli Studi di Napoli Federico II, Naples, Italy, 91, Ludwig Maximillian Univ, Munich, Ger, 95. *Honors & Awards:* Warner-Chilcott Award, Am Asn Clin Chem, 69; Arthur Kelley lectr, Purdue Univ, 63; DuPont lectr, Univ SC, 71; Venable lectr, Univ NC, 72; Bauchman lectr, Calif Inst Technol, 76; Linderstrom-Lang Medal & Award, 80; Willard Gibbs Medal & Award, Am Chem Soc, 81; William C Rose Award Biochem, 82; Messenger Lectr, Cornell Univ, 88; Order Andres Bello First Class, Repub Venezuela, 92. *Concurrent Pos:* Mem staff, Div Indust Coop, Mass Inst Technol, 45-48, res assoc biol, 48-, nat res coun sr fel, 48-51, vis prof med chem, 86; Hughes fel, Harvard Med Sch, 51-64; Merck Sharpe & Dohme prof, Univ Wash, 62; mem adv bd, La Trinidad Health Care Facil, Caracas, Venezuela, 70- & Metrop Univ, Caracas, 70-; mem bd gov, Tel Aviv Univ, 72-; chmn, US Nat Comt Int Union Biochem, 76, Sect Biochem, Nat Acad Sci, 81-84; Arthur K Watkins vis prof chem & life sci, Wichita State Univ, 78; vis prof, Univ Zurich & Fed Inst Technol, Zurich, 78; Tracy & Ruth Storer vis prof life sci, Univ Davis, Calif, 79, vis prof, Oberlin Col, Ohio, 79; head, Ctr Biochem & Biophys Sci & Med, Brigham & Women's Hosp, 80-89, biochemist-in-chief, Div Clin Chem, 80-89; vis prof biol chem, Emory Univ Sch Med, 87; vis lectr, Biochem Fundamental to Med, Weizmann Inst Sci, Rehovot, Israel, 87; hon prof, Tsinghua Univ, Beijing, China, 87. *Mem:* Nat Acad Sci; Biochem Soc; Am Soc Clin Invest; Am Chem Soc; Optical Soc Am; hon mem Japan Soc Anal Chem. *Res:* Composition, conformation, structure, function and mechanism of action of metalloenzymes; local conformation of enzymes; enzyme kinetics; physical chemistry; emission; atomic absorption; absorption spectroscopy; circular dichroism; magnetic circular dichroism; physics of spectrographic sources. *Mailing Add:* Ctr Biochem & Biophys Sci & Med Med Sch Harvard Univ Seeley G Mudd Bldg 1st Flr Boston MA 02115. *Fax:* 617-566-3137

**VALLEE, JACQUES P,** ASTROPHYSICS & RADIO ASTRONOMY, MAGNETIC FIELDS IN COSMOS. *Current Pos:* res asst, 75-76, RES OFFICER, HERZBERG INST, NAT RES COUN CAN, OTTAWA, 80- *Personal Data:* b Verdun, Que, Sept 5, 45. *Educ:* Univ Montreal, BA, 65, BSc, 68, MSc, 69; Univ Toronto, PhD(astron), 73. *Prof Exp:* Res fel astrophy, Sterrewacht te Leiden, Leiden Univ, Holland, 73-75; res assoc astrophys, Queen's Univ, Kingston, 76-80. *Concurrent Pos:* Mem, comt scientist observ astron, Mont Megantic, 79-80 & 84-86; vis lectr radio astron, Univ Montreal, 85; sabbat res, observatory, Univ Grenoble, France, 88; secondment astron, Royal Observ, Edinburgh, 89-91. *Mem:* Can Astron Soc; Am Astron Soc; Royal Astron Soc Can; Int Astron Union. *Res:* Molecular clouds, interstellar magnetic fields; nearby galaxies; computer modeling of astronomical processes; search for extraterrestial intelligence; submillimeter radio astronomy; polarization of dust emission; magnetic bending in dust clouds. *Mailing Add:* Herzberg Inst Nat Res Coun Can 5071 W Saanich Rd Victoria BC V8X 4M6 Can. *Fax:* 250-363-8483; *E-Mail:* jacques.vallee@hia.nrc.ca; Internet: http://www.hia.nrc.ca/staff/jpv

**VALLEE, RICHARD BERT,** CELL BIOLOGY, MOLECULAR BIOLOGY. *Current Pos:* STAFF SR & PRIN SCI, WORCESTER FOUND EXP BIOL, 78-, CO-DIR CANCER CTR, 87- *Personal Data:* b New York, NY. *Educ:* Swarthmore Col, BA, 67; Yale Univ MPh & PhD(biol), 74. *Prof Exp:* Fel molecular biol, Lab Molecular Biol, Univ Wis-Madison, 74-78. *Concurrent Pos:* Instr, Marine Biol Lab, Woods Hole, Ma, 84-88; ed, Methods Enzym; assoc ed, Cell Motility & Cytoskeleton. *Mem:* Biophys Soc; AAAS; Am Soc Cell Biol; Am Soc Biochem & Molecular Biol. *Res:* Motor proteins associated with cytoplasmic microtubles; Role of GT Pases in eudocytosis; enzymology; motility; post translational modification; molecular cloning; ultrastructure; immunological characterization. *Mailing Add:* Worcester Found Exp Biol 222 Maple Ave Shrewsbury MA 01545

**VALLEE, RICHARD EARL,** PHYSICAL CHEMISTRY, INORGANIC CHEMISTRY. *Current Pos:* chemist, Monsanto Chem Co, 52-59, group leader, 59-60, ASF fel, 61-62, group leader, Monsanto Res Corp, 62-63, sect mgr, 63-67, mgr, Nuclear Technol, 67-69, mgr, Non-Weapons Progs, 69-72, MGR TECHNOL APPLN & DEVELOP, MONSANTO RES CORP, 72- *Personal Data:* b Cincinnati, Ohio, June 21, 28; m 51. *Educ:* Univ Cincinnati, BS, 51, MS, 52, PhD(chem), 62. *Prof Exp:* Chemist, Procter & Gamble Co, 47-48; asst, Univ Cincinnati, 51. *Mem:* AAAS; Am Chem Soc. *Res:* Preparation, evaluation and handling of radioactive compounds; high temperature compounds; vacuum technology; isotope separation. *Mailing Add:* 619 S Bourbon St Blanchester OH 45107-1477

**VALLE-LEVINSON, ARNOLDO,** PHYSICS OF ESTUARIES & COASTAL OCEAN. *Current Pos:* Res asst prof, 93-96, ASST PROF PHYS OCEANOG, OLD DOMINION UNIV, 96- *Personal Data:* b Mexico City, Mex, Oct, 26, 62; m 90, Anne West; c Emiliano & Alvaro. *Educ:* Univ Baja Calif, Mex, BS, 85; State Univ NY, Stony Brook, MS, 88, PhD(phys oceanog), 93. *Mem:* Am Geophys Union. *Res:* Interaction between estuaries and coastal oceans; competition between buoyancy and mixing; dynamics of estuaries and bays. *Mailing Add:* Ctr Coastal Phys Oceanog Old Dominion Univ Norfolk VA 23529. *Fax:* 757-683-5550; *E-Mail:* arnoldo@ccpo.odu.edu

**VALLENTINE, JOHN FRANKLIN,** RANCH MANAGEMENT, GRAZING MANAGEMENT. *Current Pos:* prof, 68-93, EMER PROF RANGE SCI, BRIGHAM YOUNG UNIV, 93- *Personal Data:* b Ashland, Kans, Aug 1, 31; m 50; c 3. *Educ:* Kans State Univ, BS, 52; Utah State Univ, MS, 53; Tex A&M Univ, PhD(range mgt, animal nutrit), 59. *Prof Exp:* Res aide, Rocky Mountain Forest & Range Exp Sta, US Forest Serv, 52; range conservationist, US Bur Land Mgt, 55-56; res asst range mgt, Exp Sta, Tex A&M Univ, 56-58; exten range specialist, Utah State Univ, 58-62; assoc prof range exten & res, Univ Nebr, 62-68. *Mem:* Soc Range Mgt; Am Soc Animal Sci. *Res:* Range science and agricultural bibliography; range seeding; range improvements. *Mailing Add:* 1081 S 700 E Springville UT 84663

**VALLERA, DANIEL A,** IMMUNOTOXINS, BONE MARROW TRANSPLANTATION. *Current Pos:* Fel, Univ Minn, 78-79, res assoc, 79-80, from asst prof to assoc prof radiol & lab med, 81-87, assoc prof 87-89, DIR, SECT CANCER IMMUNOL, DEPT THERAPEUT RADIOL, UNIV MINN, 87-, PROF, SECT, CANCER IMMUNOL, 89- *Personal Data:* b E Liverpool, Ohio, Oct 31, 51; m; c 2. *Educ:* Ohio State Univ, Columbus, BS, 73, MS, 75, PhD(microbiol), 78. *Honors & Awards:* Am Cancer Soc Jr Fac Award, 83; Hubert H Humphrey Cancer Res Award, 81. *Concurrent Pos:* Leukemia Soc Am Scholar, 83; mem, Adv Comt, Am Cancer Soc, 90- *Mem:* Am Asn Immunologists; Transplantation Soc; AAAS; Am Soc Hemat; Am Asn Cancer Res. *Res:* Linkage of potent toxins and radionuclides to antibodies raised against human tumor cells to derive potent anti-tumor agents effective against a wide variety of human cancer cells; utilization of these agents in autologous and allogenic bone marrow transplantation for the treatment of leukemia; cellular and molecular biology of bone marrow transplantation. *Mailing Add:* Dept Therapy Radiol Univ Minn Box 367 Minneapolis MN 55455-0392. *Fax:* 612-626-6219

**VALLERAND, ANDRE L,** THERMAL PHYSIOLOGY. *Current Pos:* DEFENCE SCIENTIST, ENVIRON PHYSIOL SECT, DEFENCE & CIVIL INST ENVIRON MED, 86- *Personal Data:* b Sherbrooke, Que, Oct 21, 55; m 84, Lise Roy; c James & Isabelle. *Educ:* Univ Que, BSc, 77; Univ Sherbrooke, MSc, 81; Laval Univ, PhD(physiol), 86. *Concurrent Pos:* Adj prof, Univ Guelph, 87- & Univ Ottawa, 94-; vis fac, Med Res Inst Fr Army, Grenoble, France, 90-91. *Mem:* Aerospace Med Asn; Aerospace Physiol Soc; Am Physiol Soc; Physiol Asn Europe; Can Physiol Soc. *Res:* Influence of cold, heat, exercise and nutrition at the physiological and biochemical levels; thermogenesis; obesity; methods and techniques in research; research and development management. *Mailing Add:* DSAHP-3 Nat Defence Hq 190 Oconnor St Ottawa ON M3M 3B9 Can. *Fax:* 416-635-2104; *E-Mail:* alv@dciem.dnd.ca

**VALLERGA, BERNARD A,** ENGINEERING ADMINISTRATION. *Current Pos:* 0RES, B A VALLERGA, INC; CONSULT CIVIL ENG, OAKLAND, CALIF, 77- *Educ:* Univ Calif, Berkeley, BS, 43, MS, 48. *Honors & Awards:* Provost Hubbard Award, Am Soc Testing & Mat, 89; Recognition Award, Asn Asphalt Paving Technologists, 88. *Prof Exp:* Mat testing engr, Hershey Inspect Bur, Oakland, Calif, 46-48; asst prof civil eng, Univ Calif, Berkeley, 48-53; managing engr, Pac Coast Div, Asphalt Inst, San Francisco, Calif, 53-60; vpres prod develop & mkt, GBO Div, Witco Chem Co, Los Angeles, Calif, 60-64; pres & chief exec officer, Mat Res & Develop, Inc, Oakland, Calif, 64-72; vpres & managing prin, Woodward-Clyde Consults, San-Francisco-Oakland, Calif, 68-76. *Concurrent Pos:* Chmn, Triaxial Inst Struct Design Pavements, 50-52; mem bd dirs, Asn Asphalt Paving Technologists, 60-62 & 80-82 & bd dirs, Woodward-Clyde Consults; mem bd dirs & vpres, Asphalt Inst, 62-64; vpres, Design Div, Am Road Builders Asn, 68-70; chmn bd dirs, Woodward-Envicon, 69-72 & Subcomt Asphalt Durability, Transp Res Bd, 80-; mem, Airfield Pavement Comt, Am Soc Civil Engrs, 72-79, Air Transp Publ Comt, 72-79; gen consult, Off Energy Related Inventions, Bur Stand, Dept Com, 80- *Mem:* Nat Acad Eng; fel Am Soc Civil Engrs; Asn Asphalt Paving Technologists; Transp Res Bd; Am Soc Testing & Mat; Int Soc Asphalt Pavements; Sigma Xi. *Res:* Pavement design; construction; rehabilitation and maintenance of pavements; wind and water erosion and soil stabilization; hydraulic revetments; author of various publications. *Mailing Add:* B A Vallerga Inc 1330 Broadway Suite 720 Oakland CA 94612

**VALLE-RIESTRA, J(OSEPH) FRANK,** CHEMICAL ENGINEERING. *Current Pos:* RETIRED. *Personal Data:* b Oakland, Calif, Nov 12, 24; m 48; c 2. *Educ:* Univ Calif, BAS, 45; Calif Inst Technol, BS, 48, MS, 49. *Honors & Awards:* Chem Eng Pract Award, Am Inst Chem Engrs, 84. *Prof Exp:* Air pollution chemist, Los Angeles County Air Pollution Control Dist, Calif, 46-47; air pollution chemist, Truesdail Labs, 48; res asst chem eng, Calif Inst Technol, 48-49; res & develop engr, Dow Chem Co, 49-62, sr res engr, 62-75, res specialist, Western Div, 70-75, sr res specialist, 75-78, assoc scientist, 78-81, sr assoc scientist, Western Div, 81-83, res scientist, 83-86. *Concurrent Pos:* Lectr chem eng, Univ Calif, Berkeley, 74- *Mem:* Fel Am Inst Chem; fel Am Inst Chem Engrs; Am Soc Eng Educ. *Res:* Transport phenomena in electrochemical and high temperature gaseous systems; high temperature kinetics; physical chemistry of graphite; solvent extraction; secondary fiber technology; food process engineering; project evaluation methodology. *Mailing Add:* 140 Cora Ct Walnut Creek CA 94598

**VALLESE, FRANK M,** AGRICULTURAL & FOOD CHEMISTRY. *Current Pos:* sr res chemist analytical chem, M&M/Mars, 81-82, mgr, 82-85, dir res lab serv chem microbiol, sensory eval, 85-89, DIR FUNDAMENTAL RES CHEM, MICROBIOL, BIOTECHNOL, PROD EVAL SERV, BASIC RES, INFOSERV, QUAL ASSURANCE, M&M/MARS, 89- *Personal Data:* b New York, NY, July 12, 50; m 76; c 2. *Educ:* Wagner Col, Staten Island, NY, BS, 72; Rutgers Univ, NJ, MS, 76, PhD(food sci), 78. *Prof Exp:* Assoc chemist analytical chem, Lipton, Inc, 78-80, proj coordr flavor res, 80-81. *Mem:* Int Food Technologists; Am Oil Chemists Soc; Am Chem Soc; Asn Cereal Chemists. *Res:* Biotechnology; flavor research; analytical chemistry; corporate microbiology; microbiology research; sensory evaluation; marketing research; environmental research and progress; quality assurance, total quality management. *Mailing Add:* Res Lab Service 23 Nancy Terr M&M/Mars Res & Develop High St Hackettstown NJ 07840-5632

**VALLESE, LUCIO M(ARIO),** electrical engineering, physics; deceased, see previous edition for last biography

**VALLEY, JOHN WILLIAMS,** METAMORPHIC PETROLOGY, STABLE ISOTOPE GEOCHEMISTRY. *Current Pos:* from asst prof to assoc prof, 83-89, ROMNES PROF GEOL, UNIV WIS-MADISON, 89-, FULL PROF, 89-, CHAIR, DEPT GEOL & GEOPHYS, 96- *Personal Data:* b Feb 28, 48; m 72, Andree Taylor; c Matthew & David. *Educ:* Dartmouth Col, AB, 70; Univ Mich, MS, 77, PhD(geol), 80. *Prof Exp:* Asst prof, Rice Univ, 80-83. *Concurrent Pos:* Fulbright scholar, Univ Edinburgh, 89-90; counr, Mineral Soc Am, 93- *Mem:* Mineral Soc Am; Am Geophys Union. *Res:* Metamorphic evolution of the earth's crust during orogenesis with emphasis on thermal evolution, burial and uplift and the role of fluids. *Mailing Add:* Dept Geol & Geophys Univ Wis Madison WI 53706. *Fax:* 608-262-0693; *E-Mail:* valley@geology.wisc.edu

**VALLEY, LEONARD MAURICE,** HOLOGRAPHY, TEACHING. *Current Pos:* From asst prof to assoc prof, 60-72, chmn dept, 70-95, PROF PHYSICS, ST JOHN'S UNIV, MINN, 72- *Personal Data:* b Little Falls, Minn, July 3, 33; m 58, Mary Ann Ahart; c Michelle, Michael & Paul. *Educ:* St John's Univ, Minn, BA(physics) & BA(math), 55; Iowa State Univ, PhD(physics), 60. *Concurrent Pos:* Vis assoc prof, Univ Denver, 67-68, 83; prof, Ind Univ, Malaysia Coop prog, 87-89; vis prof, Univ Md, Europ Div. *Mem:* Am Asn Physics Teachers. *Res:* Vibrational, rotational and translational relaxation in gas molecules undergoing collisions; relaxation time; education. *Mailing Add:* Dept Physics St John's Univ PO Box 3000 Collegeville MN 56321-3000. *E-Mail:* lvalley@csbsju.edu

**VALLEY, SHARON LOUISE,** PHARMACOLOGY, INFORMATION SCIENCE. *Current Pos:* RETIRED. *Personal Data:* b Bay City, Mich, Oct 18, 41; m 75. *Educ:* Univ Mich, BS, 63, PhD(pharmacol), 67. *Honors & Awards:* Plaque and Gavel Award, Am Pharmaceut Asn, 62. *Prof Exp:* Intern pharm, Schulz Pharm, 60-62 & Health Serv Pharm, Univ Mich, 62-63; pharmacologist sci info, Nat Libr Med, NIH, 67- *Concurrent Pos:* Mem, Comt User Educ, Nat Fedn Abstracting & Indexing, 78-79; bd gov, Col Pharm Alumni Soc, Univ Mich, 78- *Mem:* Drug Info Asn; Am Pharmaceut Asn. *Res:* Cardiovascular pharmacology; toxicology. *Mailing Add:* 1140 Powder Horn Dr Potomac MD 20854-2539

**VALLIER, TRACY L,** MARINE GEOLOGY. *Current Pos:* MARINE GEOLOGIST, US GEOL SURV, 75- *Personal Data:* b Oakland, Iowa, Sept 19, 36; m 91, Sheila Canty; c Garry, Lane, Monte & Susan. *Educ:* Iowa State Univ, BS, 62; Ore State Univ, PhD(geol), 67. *Prof Exp:* Assoc prof geol, Ind State Univ, 66-72; geologist, Deep Sea Drilling Proj, Scripps Inst Oceanog, 72-75. *Concurrent Pos:* Affil Prof, Iowa State Univ. *Mem:* Geol Soc Am; Am Soc Petroleum Geol; Am Geophys Union. *Res:* Geology of the Aleutian Island Arcs; geology of Island Arc; igneous petrology; geology of Hells Canyon, Oregon and Idaho. *Mailing Add:* US Geol Surv MS 919 345 Middlefield Rd Menlo Park CA 94025. *Fax:* 650-354-3191; *E-Mail:* tracy@octopus.wy.usgs

**VALLOWE, HENRY HOWARD,** ENDOCRINOLOGY. *Personal Data:* b Pittsburgh, Pa, Nov 18, 24; m 48. *Educ:* Pa State Teachers Col, BS, 49; Univ Chicago, MS, 50, PhD(zool), 54. *Prof Exp:* Instr biol, Wright Jr Col, Ill, 52-56; assoc prof zool, Ohio Univ, 56-67; prof biol, Ind Univ, Pa, 67-87. *Mem:* AAAS; Am Soc Zoologists. *Res:* Endocrines of poikilotherms; sexual physiology; phylogeny of endocrines; circadian rhythms. *Mailing Add:* 12401 N 22nd St No A701 Tampa FL 33612

**VALLS, ORIOL TOMAS,** CONDENSED MATTER PHYSICS. *Current Pos:* from asst prof to assoc prof, 78-88, PROF PHYSICS, UNIV MINN, 88- *Personal Data:* b Barcelona, Spain, Oct 15, 47; US citizen; m 74, Maureen Doyle; c Andrew & Anthony. *Educ:* Univ Barcelona, BSc, 69; Brown Univ, MSc, 72, PhD(physics), 75. *Prof Exp:* Res assoc physics, James Franck Inst, Univ Chicago, 75-77; Miller fel, Univ Calif, Berkeley, 77-78. *Concurrent Pos:* Exchange prof, Univ Paris, 83; vis scientist, Argonne Nat Lab, 84-85; prof invite, Univ Paris, 88, 93; fel, Minn Supercomputer Inst, 89- *Mem:* Am Phys Soc; Sigma Xi. *Res:* Properties of quantum fluids; systems far from equilibrium; superconductivity. *Mailing Add:* Tate Lab Physics 116 Church St SE Minneapolis MN 55455. *Fax:* 612-624-0578; *E-Mail:* otvalls@maroon.tc.umn.edu

**VALOCCHI, ALBERT JOSEPH,** ENVIRONMENTAL ENGINEERING. *Current Pos:* From asst prof to assoc prof, 81-92, PROF CIVIL ENG, UNIV ILL, URBANA, CHAMPAIGN, 92- *Personal Data:* b Coatesville, Pa, Aug 20, 53. *Educ:* Cornell Univ, BS, 75; Stanford Univ, MS, 76, PhD(civil eng), 81. *Mem:* Am Soc Civil Engrs; Am Geophys Union; Asn Groundwater Scientist & Engrs; Sigma Xi; Asn Environ Eng Profs. *Res:* Study of the transport and fate of contaminants in groundwater and soils. *Mailing Add:* Dept Civil Eng Univ Ill 205 N Mathews Urbana IL 61801. *E-Mail:* avalocchi@civilgate.ce.uiuc.edu

**VALSAMAKIS, EMMANUEL,** SOLID STATE ELECTRONICS. *Current Pos:* adv physicist, IBM Corp, 67-76, mem res staff, 76-80, adv engr, 80-89, SR ENGR, IBM CORP, 90- *Personal Data:* b Istanbul, Turkey, May 11, 33; US citizen; m 60; c 2. *Educ:* Robert Col, Istanbul, BSEE, 55; Rensselaer Polytech Inst, MEE, 58, PhD(plasma physics), 63. *Prof Exp:* Instr elec eng, Rensselaer Polytech Inst, 56-61, res asst, 61-62; res scientist, Grumman Aircraft Eng Corp, 62-67. *Concurrent Pos:* Lectr, State Univ NY, New Paltz, 85- *Mem:* Inst Elec & Electronics Engrs; Am Phys Soc; NY Acad Sci. *Res:* Cryogenic tunneling device design and circuit analysis; experimental investigation of plasmas from pulsed plasma sources; bipolar, field effect transistor modeling, device design and circuit analysis for memory and logic applications. *Mailing Add:* 2685 Hilltop Dr Yorktown Heights NY 10598-3312

**VALSARAJ, KALLIAT THAZHATHUVEETIL,** FATE & TRANSPORT OF CHEMICALS IN ENVIRONMENT, MASS TRANSFER SEPARATION PROCESSES. *Current Pos:* Asst prof, 86-93, ASSOC PROF CHEM ENG DEPT, LA STATE UNIV, BATON ROUGE, 93- *Personal Data:* b Tellicherry, Kerala, India, Oct 2, 57; m 89, Nisha; c Viveca K & Vinay G. *Educ:* Univ Calicut, India, BS, 78; Indian Inst Technol, MS, 80; Vanderbilt Univ, PhD(chem), 83. *Prof Exp:* Fel & affil prof, Univ Ark, Fayetteville, 84-86. *Concurrent Pos:* Prin investr, NSF, Environ Protection Agency & La Bd Regents, 89- *Mem:* Am Chem Soc; Am Inst Chem Eng; AAAS. *Res:* Research in chemodynamics; development of innovative separation processes for waste treatment. *Mailing Add:* 1924 Hobbiton Rd Baton Rouge LA 70810. *Fax:* 504-388-1476; *E-Mail:* kvalsan@aol.com

**VALTIN, HEINZ,** RENAL PHYSIOLOGY, NEPHROLOGY. *Current Pos:* From instr to prof, Dartmouth Med Sch, 57-73, Andrew C Vail prof, 73-89, chmn dept, 77-89, CONSTANTINE & JOYCE HAMPERS PROF PHYSIOL, DARTMOUTH MED SCH, 89- *Personal Data:* b Hamburg, Ger, Sept 23, 26; nat US; m 53, Nancy Heffernan; c Thomas C & Alison E. *Educ:* Swarthmore Col, AB, 49; Cornell Univ, MD, 53. *Honors & Awards:* Purkinje Medal, Czechoslovak Physiol Soc, 89; I P Pavlov Medal, Soviet Physiol Soc, 91. *Concurrent Pos:* Consult, Dartmouth-Hitchcock Med Ctr, 61- *Mem:* Am Physiol Soc; Am Fedn Clin Res; Am Soc Clin Invest; Am Soc Nephrology; Int Soc Nephrology; Int Union Physiol Sci (treas, 84-90). *Res:* Kidney, electrolyte and water metabolism; neuroendocrinology. *Mailing Add:* Dept Physiol Dartmouth Med Sch Hanover NH 03755-3836. *Fax:* 603-650-1130; *E-Mail:* heinz__valtin@dartmouth.edu

**VALVANI, SHRI CHAND,** PHARMACEUTICAL CHEMISTRY, PHARMACEUTICS. *Current Pos:* From res scientist to sr res scientist, Upjohn Co, 70-83, res head, 83-85, assoc dir, 85-88, dir, drug delivery res & develop, 88-90, dir, Control Develop, 90-92, DIR, DRUG DELIVERY RES & DEVELOP, UPJOHN CO, 92- *Personal Data:* b Mar 20, 40; US citizen; c 3. *Educ:* Univ Saugar, BPharm, 65; Univ Mich, Ann Arbor, MS, 69, PhD(pharmaceut chem), 71. *Honors & Awards:* Prof Schroff Gold Medal, Indian Pharmaceut Asn, 65. *Mem:* Acad Pharmaceut Sci; Am Chem Soc; Am Pharmaceut Asn; Am Asn Pharmaceut Scientists. *Res:* Thermodynamics of solution process and its effect on drug design, physico-chemical and biochemical parameters influencing performance of various drug dosage forms and drug delivery systems, computer applications in stability testing in drug delivery research and development. *Mailing Add:* 5695 Blue Spruce Lane Kalamazoo MI 49009. *Fax:* 616-385-7325

**VALVASSORI, GALDINO E,** MEDICINE, RADIOLOGY. *Current Pos:* assoc prof, 65-67, PROF RADIOL, MED CTR, UNIV ILL, 67- *Personal Data:* b Milan, Italy, July 16, 26; US citizen; m 55, Divahe; c 4. *Educ:* Univ Milan, MD, 50; Am Bd Radiol, dipl, 59. *Prof Exp:* Resident radiol, Univ Milan, 51-53; resident, Mem Hosp, NY, 54-56; asst prof, Univ Chicago, 60-65. *Concurrent Pos:* Dir, Dept Radiol, Ill Eye & Ear Infirmary, Chicago, 65-; consult, Grant Hosp, Chicago, 66, 71; pres, Int Collegium Radiol in Otolaryngol, 79-82; consult, MacNeal Hosp, Berwyn, Ill; guest speaker, Royal Col Med, London. *Mem:* AMA; Am Col Radiol; Am Roentgen Ray Soc; Radiol Soc NAm; Am Acad Ophthal & Otolaryngol; hon mem Ger Otolaryngol Soc. *Res:* Radiology of the head and neck; development and refinement of new radiographic techniques for study of temporal bone in pathological conditions of the ear. *Mailing Add:* 697 Sheridan Rd Winnetka IL 60093

**VALVERDE, RODRIGO ALBERTO,** PLANT VIROLOGY. *Current Pos:* from asst prof to assoc prof, 88-97, PROF, DEPT PLANT PATH & CROP PHYSIOL, LA STATE UNIV, 97- *Personal Data:* b Pto Limon, Costa Rica, Mar 13, 52; US citizen. *Educ:* Univ Costa Rica, Ing Agr, 77; Univ Ark, MS, 81, PhD(plant path), 84. *Prof Exp:* Postdoctoral fel plant virol, Univ Calif, Riverside & Davis, 84-86; plant pathologist, Ball Pan Am Plant Co, 87-88. *Concurrent Pos:* Fulbright scholar, Inst Plant Molecular Biol, France, 95-96; assoc ed, Revista Mex de Fitopatologia, 96- *Mem:* Am Phytopath Soc; Am Soc Virol. *Res:* Plant viruses with emphasis in diagnosis and virus characterization; viral diseases of pepper and sweet potato. *Mailing Add:* Dept Plant Path La State Univ Baton Rouge LA 70803. *Fax:* 504-388-1415; *E-Mail:* rvalver@lsuvm.sncc.lsu.edu

**VALYASEVI, AREE,** COMMUNITY HEALTH & NUTRITION. *Current Pos:* founding dean, 68-77, founding dir, Inst Nutrit, 78-87, EMER PROF, MAHIDOL UNIV, 86-; PRES, NAT INST HEALTH RES, 96- *Personal Data:* b Bangkok, Thailand, Oct 20, 25; m 54, Som Savat; c Sukasith T, Apichart M & Rudd. *Educ:* Siriraj Hosp Med Col, Thailand, MD, 51; Univ Pa, MSc, 57, DSc, 59. *Hon Degrees:* DSc, Mahidol Univ, 89. *Honors & Awards:* Dushdi Mala Medal, Thailand, 83; Ramon Magsaysay Award, 87; E V McCollum Int Lectr, 89. *Prof Exp:* Prof pediat, Fac Med, Ramathibodi Hosp, 69-85. *Concurrent Pos:* Mem, Expert Comt, WHO, Geneva, 76-80, SE Asia, 90-; consult, UNICEF, Ministry Health, Saudi Arabia, 82, Thailand Health Sector, USAID, 83, UNICEF, Peoples Repub China, 85; coordr, Asiafoods, 83-; founding dean fac med, Thammasat Univ, 90-96; mem exec bd, Thai Res Fund, Bangkok, 91-96. *Mem:* Foreign assoc Nat Acad Sci; Int Union Nutrit Sci (vpres, 81-89, pres elect, 89-); Fedn Asian Nutrit Socs (pres, 83-87). *Res:* Investigate the etiologies of urinary bladder stone diseases in South and South-East Asia; improve protein quality and quantity of rice-based foods suitable for low socio-economic populations. *Mailing Add:* Nat Health Found Soi-Phaholydthin Rd 22 Bankok Thailand. *E-Mail:* phri@ infonewsco.ph

**VALYI, EMERY I,** APPLIED MECHANICS, MATERIAL SCIENCE. *Current Pos:* CONSULT, 71- *Personal Data:* b Murska Sobota, Slovenia, July 14, 11; nat US; m 39, Elizabeth Jenks; c Katherine & Thomas. *Educ:* Fed Inst Technol, Zurich, ME, 33, DSc(phys metall, appl mech), 37. *Prof Exp:* Res engr, Swiss Fed Inst Testing Mat, 34-37; metall engr, Injecta Ltd, 37-40; mgr, die casting mach div, Hydraul Press Mfg Co, 40-42; vpres, Sam Tour & Co, 43-45; pres, ARD Corp, 45-62; consult, Ford Motor Co, Int Harvester Co, Continental Can Co, Owens-Ill Inc, Olin Corp & Molins Mach Co, 62-71. *Concurrent Pos:* Consult, Nat Can Corp, 71-81; Husky Int Systs, Pepsi-Cola Co & E.I. DuPont de Neuiousis. *Mem:* Am Soc Metals; Am Inst Mining, Metall & Petrol Engrs; Soc Plastics Engrs; fel Am Inst Chemists; Soc Plastics Indust. *Res:* Materials technology; rheology; metal casting; plastic molding; container technology; polymeric barrier materials. *Mailing Add:* 102 Moseman Ave Katonah NY 10536. *Fax:* 914-962-1249

**VAMOS, TIBOR,** PATTERN RECOGNITION, EPISTEMOLOGY. *Current Pos:* dir res, 62-85, CHMN BD, COMPUT & AUTOMATION INST, HUNGARIAN ACAD SCI, 86- *Personal Data:* b Budapest, Hungary, June 1, 26; m 50, 73, Maria Fekete; c Peter. *Educ:* Budapest Tech Univ, MA, 50; Hungarian Acad Sci, PhD(power control), 58, Dr Sc(power systs), 64. *Hon Degrees:* Dr, Tallinn Tech Univ, 86. *Honors & Awards:* Krusper Award, 71; State Prize, 83; Neumann Award, 86; Outstanding Servs Award, Int Fedn Automatic Control, 90; Chorafas Prize, Swiss Academies, 94. *Prof Exp:* Dir construct, Power Plant Construct Co, 50-54; head dept, Power Syst Control, Power Res Inst, 57-62. *Concurrent Pos:* Prof, Budapest Tech Univ, 65-; hon pres, John V Neumann Soc Comput Sci, 86; adv, Int Fedn Automatic Control, 87; mem bd, Cent Europ Univ, 91-; distinguished affil prof, George Mason Univ, 93-; exec bd mem, Hungarian Acad Sci, 93- *Mem:* Int Fedn Automatic Control (pres, 80-84); fel Inst Elec & Electronics Engrs; Hungarian Acad Sci; hon mem Austrian Comput Soc; hon mem Austrian Soc Cybernetic Studies. *Res:* Process control; robot vision, pattern recognition; artificial intelligence, especially expert systems combining logic and pattern-like features of cognitive psychology related to those epistemic problems of computer science. *Mailing Add:* Comput & Automation Inst Hungarian Acad Sci Lagymanyosi u 11 Budapest 1111 Hungary. *Fax:* 36-1-2698275; *E-Mail:* h30vam@ella.hu

**VAMPOLA, ALFRED LUDVIK,** SPACE PHYSICS. *Current Pos:* CONSULT, SPACE ENVIRON, 90- *Personal Data:* b Dwight, Nebr, July 10, 34; m 56, Karen Kirkwood; c Joseph, John, Elaine, Mary, Mark, Robert, James & Donald. *Educ:* Creighton Univ, BS, 56; St Louis Univ, MS, 58, PhD(physics), 61. *Prof Exp:* Sr physicist, Convair Div, Gen Dynamics Corp, 61-62; staff scientist space physics, Aerospace Corp, 62-78, sr scientist, 78-90. *Concurrent Pos:* Assoc ed, J Spacecraft & Rockets, 84-87, 90-96; vis fel, Univ Otago, Dunedin, NZ, 86; res fel, Max Planck Inst Aeronaut, 91. *Mem:* Am Geophys Union; assoc fel Am Inst Aeronaut & Astronaut. *Res:* Magnetospheric physics; solar particles; spacecraft environment interactions. *Mailing Add:* Vampola PO Box 10225 Torrance CA 90505. *Fax:* 310-375-1012; *E-Mail:* vampola@envnet.gsfc.nasa.gov

**VANABLE, JOSEPH WILLIAM, JR,** DEVELOPMENTAL BIOLOGY. *Current Pos:* From asst prof to assoc prof, 62-82, PROF BIOL, PURDUE UNIV, WEST LAFAYETTE, 82- *Personal Data:* b Providence, RI, May 29, 36; m 62, Jane Wilson; c Mary E & Peter A. *Educ:* Brown Univ, AB, 58; Rockefeller Inst, PhD(biol), 62. *Honors & Awards:* Yasuda Award, Bioelec Repair & Growth Soc, 85. *Concurrent Pos:* NIH spec fels, Univ Ore, 69 & Yale Univ, 69-70. *Mem:* Soc Develop Biol. *Res:* Regeneration and wound healing; the role of endogenous electrical fields. *Mailing Add:* Dept Biol Sci Purdue Univ West Lafayette IN 47907-1392. *Fax:* 765-494-0876; *E-Mail:* jvanable@bilbo.bio.purdue.edu

**VANAKEN, TROY DEWAYNE,** AFFINE DIFFERENCE SETS, CODING THEORY. *Current Pos:* ASST PROF MATH, UNIV EVANSVILLE, 94-, ASST VPRES INSTRNL TECHNOL, 97- *Personal Data:* b Adrian, Mich, Dec 30, 67; m, Annette Marie; c Trey D. *Educ:* Hilsdale Col, BS, 89; Bowling Green State Univ, MA, 91, PhD(math), 94. *Mem:* Fel Math Asn Am; Nat Coun Teachers Math; Am Math Soc. *Res:* Exploring affine difference sets of even order and their associated codes in particular cyclic affine difference sets of order eight modulo sixteen. *Mailing Add:* 200 S Fairlawn Ave Evansville IN 47714. *Fax:* 812-479-2088; *E-Mail:* tv2@evansville.edu

**VAN ALFEN, NEAL K,** HOST-PATHOGEN RELATIONS. *Current Pos:* from asst prof to assoc prof, 75-82, PROF BIOL, UTAH STATE UNIV, 82- *Personal Data:* b Ogdan, Utah, July 17, 43; div; c 4. *Educ:* Brigham Young Univ, BS, 68; MS, 69; Univ Calif, Davis, PhD(plant path), 72. *Prof Exp:* Asst plant path, Conn Agr Exp Sta, New Haven, 72-75. *Concurrent Pos:* Consult, Kennecot Corp, 76-, USDA, 80-82 & 86; sr ed, Phytopath, 85- *Mem:* Am Phytopath Soc; Am Soc Microbiol; Am Soc Plant Physiologists; AAAS. *Res:* Mechanisms of virulence expression by plant pathogens; methods of reducing pathogen virulence for biological control of plant disease. *Mailing Add:* Dept Plant Path Tex A&M Univ College Station TX 77843-0100

**VAN ALLEN, JAMES ALFRED,** SPACE PHYSICS. *Current Pos:* prof physics, Univ Iowa, 51-72, head, Dept Physics & Astron, 51-85, Carver prof, 72-85, REGENT DISTINGUISHED PROF PHYSICS, UNIV IOWA, 85- *Personal Data:* b Mt Pleasant, Iowa, Sept 7, 14; m 45; c 5. *Educ:* Iowa Wesleyan Col, BS, 35; Univ Iowa, MS, 36, PhD(physics), 39. *Hon Degrees:* ScD, Iowa Wesleyan Col, 51, Grinnell Col, 57, Coe Col, 58, Cornell Col, 59, Univ Dubuque, 60, Univ Mich, 61, Northwestern Univ, 61, Ill Col, 63, Butler Col, 66, Boston Col, 66, Southampton Col, 67, Augustana Col, 69, St Ambrose Col, 82, Univ Bridgeport, 87. *Honors & Awards:* Hickman Medal, Rocket Soc, 49, First Annual Res Award, 61, Hill Award, Inst Aerospace Sci, 60; Space Flight Award, Am Astronaut Soc, 58, Kuyper Prize, 94; Space Flight Award, Int Acad Astronaut, 61; Elliot Cresson Medal, Franklin Inst, 61; Golden Omega Award, Elec Insulation Conf, 63; John A Fleming Awards, Am Geophys Union, 63; William Bowie Medal, 77; Gold Medal, Royal Astron Soc, London, 78; Space Sci Award, Am Inst Aeronaut & Astronaut, 82; Cospar Space Sci Award, 84; Nat Medal Sci, 87; Abelson Prize, AAAS, 86; Proctor Prize, Sigma Xi, 87; Crafoord Prize, Royal Swed Acad Sci, 89; Nansen Medal, Norweg Acad Sci & Lett, 90; Kuipeox Prize, Am Astron Soc, 94. *Prof Exp:* Carnegie res fel nuclear physics, Dept Terrestrial Magnetism, Carnegie Inst, 39-41, physicist, 41-42; physicist, Appl Physics Lab, Johns Hopkins Univ, 42 & 46-50. *Concurrent Pos:* Mem, Int Sci Radio Union; mem, Rocket & Satellite Res Panel, 46-, chmn, 47-48, mem exec comt, 58-; leader sci exped, Cent Pac, 49, Gulf Alaska, 50, Arctic, 52, Int Geophys Yr, Arctic, Atlantic, Cent Pac, SPac & Antarctic, 57; Guggenheim Mem Found fel, Brookhaven Nat Lab, 51; res assoc, Princeton Univ, 53-54; mem, Tech Panel Earth Satellite Prog, Int Geophys Yr, 55-58, chmn, Working Group Internal Instrumentation, 56-58, Tech Panel Rocketry, 55-58, Tech Panel Cosmic Rays, 56-68, Tech Panel Aurora & Airglow, 57-58; consult, Pres Sci Adv Comt, 57-60; mem, Space Sci Bd, Nat Acad Sci, 58-70 & 80-83, chmn, Ad Hoc Panel Small Planetary Probes, 66; mem, Panel Sci & Technol, Comt Sci & Astronaut, US House Rep, 59-72; consult, Particles & Fields Subcomt, NASA, 61-; chmn, Iowa's Int Coop Year Comt Sci & Advan Technol, 65; lectr, NATO Conf, Bergen, Norway, 65; mem, Planetary Missions Bd, 67-71. *Mem:* Nat Acad Sci; fel Am Phys Soc; fel Am Geophys Union (pres, 82-84); fel Inst Elec & Electronics Engrs; fel AAAS; Royal Astron Soc; foreign mem Royal Swed Acad Sci. *Res:* Planetary magnetosphere; cosmic rays; use of rockets in physical research; satellites and space probes in planetary and solar physics. *Mailing Add:* Dept Physics & Astron Univ Iowa Iowa City IA 52242-1410. *Fax:* 319-335-1753; *E-Mail:* ames_vanallen@uiowa.edu

**VAN ALLER, ROBERT THOMAS,** ORGANIC CHEMISTRY, BIOCHEMISTRY. *Current Pos:* chmn, Dept Chem, Univ Southern Miss, 68-70, dean, Col Sci, 70-71, interim dir, Gulf Coast Res Lab, 94-97, DEAN, GRAD SCH, UNIV SOUTHERN MISS, 71- *Personal Data:* b Mobile, Ala, June 18, 33; m 59; c 2. *Educ:* Univ Ala, BS, 60, MS, 62, PhD(sulfonyl halides), 65. *Prof Exp:* Res assoc chem, Univ Miss, 65-67; aerospace technologist, Marshall Space Flight Ctr, NASA, 67-68. *Mem:* Am Chem Soc. *Res:* Reactions of aliphatic sulfonyl halides; biosynthesis of phytosterols and monocyclic monoterpenes. *Mailing Add:* Univ Southern Miss Southern Sta PO Box 5024 Hattiesburg MS 39406-5024. *E-Mail:* rualler@whale.st.usm. edu

**VAN ALSTINE, JAMES BRUCE,** PALEOECOLOGY. *Current Pos:* From instr to asst prof, 74-84, ASSOC PROF GEOL, UNIV MINN, MORRIS, 85- *Personal Data:* b Whitefish Bay, Wis, July 30, 49; m 70; c 2. *Educ:* Winona State Univ, BA, 70; Univ NDak, MS, 74, PhD(geol), 80. *Mem:* Soc Econ Paleontologists & Mineralogists; Sigma Xi; Geol Soc Am. *Res:* Paleoecology of nonmarine and brackish water faunas of Cretaceous and Paleocene ages. *Mailing Add:* Dept Math & Sci Univ Minn Morris MN 56267-2134

**VAN ALSTYNE, JOHN PRUYN,** MATHEMATICS. *Current Pos:* assoc prof, 61-66, actg head dept, 68-71, PROF MATH, WORCESTER POLYTECH INST, 66-, DEAN ACAD ADVISING, 71- *Personal Data:* b Albany, NY, Sept 12, 21; m 44; c 3. *Educ:* Hamilton Col, BS, 44; Columbia Univ, MA, 52. *Prof Exp:* Vis instr math, Hamilton Col, 43-44, from instr to assoc prof, 48-61. *Mem:* Am Math Soc; Math Asn Am; Sigma Xi. *Res:* Functional equations; linear algebra. *Mailing Add:* 4 Lakeshore Lane Asheville NC 28804-2359

**VAN ALTEN, LLOYD,** INORGANIC CHEMISTRY. *Current Pos:* from asst prof to assoc prof, 55-68, PROF CHEM, SAN JOSE STATE UNIV, 68- *Personal Data:* b East Grand Rapids, Mich, Jan 2, 24; m 51, Grace Anena; c Ann (Hall) & Bonnie Wynne. *Educ:* Calvin Col, AB, 45; Purdue Univ, West Lafayette, MS, 48; Univ Wash, PhD(chem), 54. *Prof Exp:* Teacher, Lynden Christian High Sch, 48-50; Olin-Mathieson fel, Univ Wash-Boron Chem, 54-55. *Mem:* Am Chem Soc; Sigma Xi. *Res:* Boranes; carboranes; absolute intensities in infrared spectroscopy; environmental mercury. *Mailing Add:* 2991 Fireside Dr San Jose CA 95128-4003

**VAN ALTEN, PIERSON JAY,** IMMUNOLOGY, CELL BIOLOGY. *Current Pos:* From asst prof to prof, 60-93, EMER PROF ANAT, MED CTR, UNIV ILL, 93- *Personal Data:* b Grand Rapids, Mich, Feb 21, 28; m 53, Lucille Westendorp; c Faith & Daniel. *Educ:* Calvin Col, AB, 50; Mich State Univ, MS, 55, PhD(zool, physiol), 58. *Concurrent Pos:* NIH fel exp embryol & immunobiol, Univ Calif, Los Angeles, 58-60; vis assoc prof pediat, Univ Minn, 66-67; Am Cancer Soc scholar, Univ Bern, 73-74; guest prof immunobiol, Univ Bern, 73-74; mem, Res Comt, Ill Div Am Cancer Soc, 75-91; bd trustees, Calvin Col & Sem, 89-92. *Mem:* AAAS; Leukocyte Biol (treas, 78-80); Am Asn Immunol; Am Asn Anat; Soc Develop Biol; Transplantation Soc; Sigma Xi. *Res:* Immunological ability of gut-associated lymphoid tissue; experimental embryology and immunobiology; phagocytosis-promoting activity of plasma and cell surface fibronectins; graft-versus-host disease and immunological competence of chicken embryo; development of brain antigens in hamsters; culture of lymphocytes and human myeloma cells. *Mailing Add:* Dept Anat & Cell Biol MC 512 Univ Ill Col Med 803 S Wood St Chicago IL 60612-7308

**VAN ALTENA, WILLIAM F,** ASTRONOMY. *Current Pos:* chmn dept, 75-81, PROF ASTRON, YALE UNIV, 74-, PRES, YALE SOUTHERN OBSERV, INC, 75- *Personal Data:* b Hayward, Calif, Aug 15, 39; m 86, Alicia A Mora; c Paul D & Michael J. *Educ:* Univ Calif, Berkeley, BA, 62, PhD(astron), 66. *Hon Degrees:* MA, Yale Univ, 75. *Prof Exp:* From asst prof to assoc prof astron, Yerkes Observ, Univ Chicago, 66-74; dir observ, 72-74. *Concurrent Pos:* Mem, Comt Photographic Plates & Films, Am Nat Stand Inst, 74-86. *Mem:* Am Astron Soc; Int Astron Union; fel AAAS; Int Astron Union (vpres, 85-88, pres, 88-91); corresp mem Spain Acad Arts & Sci. *Res:* Trigonometric parallaxes and proper motions; space observations; precision measuring equipment; double stars. *Mailing Add:* Yale Univ Observ PO Box 208101 New Haven CT 06520-8101. *Fax:* 203-432-5048; *E-Mail:* vanalten@astro.yale.edu

**VANAMAN, SHERMAN BENTON,** MATHEMATICS. *Current Pos:* RETIRED. *Personal Data:* b Lexington, Ky, July 25, 28; m 55; c 2. *Educ:* Univ Louisville, BA, 49; Univ Ky, MS, 51; Univ Md, PhD(math educ), 67. *Prof Exp:* Instr math, Univ Ky, 51-55; assoc prof & actg head dept, Carson-Newman Col, 56-66; prof math & chmn dept, 66-95. *Mem:* Math Asn Am; Nat Coun Teachers Math. *Res:* Learning theory, especially mathematics-education. *Mailing Add:* Dept Math PO Box 1994 Carson-Newman Col Jefferson City TN 37760

**VANAMAN, THOMAS CLARK,** BIOCHEMISTRY, MICROBIOLOGY. *Current Pos:* chmn, 83-92, PROF, DEPT BIOCHEM, MED CTR, UNIV KY, 83- *Personal Data:* b Louisville, Ky, Aug 12, 41; m 62, 83 & 89, Julia Wardrap; c John, Thomas, Shannon & Jill. *Educ:* Univ Ky, BS, 64; Duke Univ, PhD(biochem), 68. *Prof Exp:* From asst prof to prof microbiol & immunol, Med Ctr, Duke Univ, 70-83, dir cancer ctr basic res, 81-83. *Concurrent Pos:* Am Can Soc fel, Med Ctr, Stanford Univ, 69-70, NSF, 71-73, 87-90 & NIH res grant, 71-; Josiah Macy, Jr Found fac scholar, 77-78; NIH study sect, 81-86 & 93-96; Am Heart Asn study sect, 83-86; assoc ed, J Biol & Chem, 96- *Mem:* NY Acad Sci; Am Soc Biochem & Molecular Biol; Am Chem Soc; Am Soc Neurobiol; Protein Soc. *Res:* Study of the structure, function and evolution of proteins; evolution, structure and function of calcium dependent regulatory proteins; mechanisms of stimulus-response coupling. *Mailing Add:* Dept Biochem Univ Ky Med Ctr 800 Rose St Lexington KY 40536

**VANAMBURG, GERALD LEROY,** PLANT ECOLOGY, BOTANY. *Current Pos:* From asst prof to assoc prof, 69-86, PROF BIOL, CONCORDIA COL, MOORHEAD, MINN, 76- *Personal Data:* b Hunter, Kans, Dec 17, 41; m 63, Janet Winford; c 2. *Educ:* Ft Hays Kans State Col, BS, 64, MS, 65; Tex A&M Univ, PhD(plant ecol), 69. *Concurrent Pos:* Expert, Int Atomic Energy Agency, 70-71. *Mem:* Ecol Soc Am; Am Inst Biol Sci; Sigma Xi. *Res:* Soil-vegetation relationships; biogeochemical cycling; prairie wetland ecosystems; watershed management. *Mailing Add:* Dept Biol Concordia Col Moorhead MN 56562. *Fax:* 218-299-3804; *E-Mail:* vanambur@cord.edu

**VANAMEE, PARKER,** nephrology; deceased, see previous edition for last biography

**VAN ANDEL, TJEERD HENDRIK,** MARINE GEOLOGY & GEOLOGICAL ARCHAEOLOGY. *Current Pos:* HON PROF EARTH SCI, CAMBRIDGE UNIV, ENG, 88- *Personal Data:* b Rotterdam, Neth, Feb 15, 23; US citizen; m 88, Katharine Pretty; c 6. *Educ:* State Univ Groningen, BSc, 46, MSc, 48, PhD(geol), 50. *Honors & Awards:* F P Shepard Medal, 78; N B Watkins Award, 80; Waterschoot Van der Gracht Medal, 84. *Prof Exp:* Asst prof geol, State Agr Univ, Wageningen, 48-50; sedimentologist, Royal Dutch Shell Res Lab, 50-53; sr sedimentologist, Cia Shell de Venezuela, 53-56; assoc res geologist, Scripps Inst Oceanog, Univ Calif, 57-64, lectr geol, 57-68, res geologist, 64-68; prof geol, Sch Oceanog, Ore State Univ, 68-76; Wayne Loel prof earth sci, Dept Geol, Stanford Univ, 76-88. *Concurrent Pos:* Vis prof, Univ Calif, Berkeley, 63; sr fel, Woods Hole Oceanog Inst, 63; sci adv, Deep Sea Drilling Proj, 64-68; res assoc geol, Scripps Inst Oceanog, Univ Calif, 68-72; mem geodynamics comt, Nat Acad Sci, 70-75; managing consult, Int Ocean Explor, NSF, 71-72; vis prof geophys, Stanford Univ, 74-75; group chmn, Sci Comt Ocean Res, UNESCO, 75-78; res fel, Archaeol Dept, Boston Univ, 89-; chair, Godwin Inst Quaternary Res, 95- *Mem:* Soc Field Archaeologists; Soc Econ Paleont & Mineral; Geol Soc Am; fel Am Geophys Union; fel Royal Neth Acad Sci; fel Soc Archaeol Sci. *Res:* Recent sediments of continents and oceans; origin and nature of the continental shelf; geology and geophysics of mid-ocean ridges; paleoceanography; deep-diving research submersibles; geo-archeology; neotectonics; paleoclimates; climate change and human prehistory. *Mailing Add:* Dept Earth Sci Cambridge Univ Downing St Cambridge CB2 3EQ England. *Fax:* 44-223-333450

**VANANTWERP, CRAIG LEWIS,** NUCLEAR MAGNETIC RESONANCE SPECTROSCOPY, MEDICAL EQUIPMENT CONTROL SOFTWARE. *Current Pos:* MGR, SOFTWARE ADVAN PROD DEVELOP, VARIAN ASSOC, 89- *Personal Data:* b Binghampton, NY, Feb 24, 50; m 91, Jane Van Wyk; c 2. *Educ:* Juniata Col, BS, 72; Stanford Univ, PhD(org chem), 77. *Prof Exp:* Asst prof chem, Rochester Inst Technol, 77-80; software develop engr, Nicolet Magnetics Corp, Div Nicolet Instruments, 80-89. *Res:* Develop and implement state of the art research capabilities into nuclear magnetic resonance spectrometer products. *Mailing Add:* 341 Laurel St Menlo Park CA 94025. *E-Mail:* clvana@aol.com

**VAN ANTWERP, WALTER ROBERT,** SOLID STATE PHYSICS, HEALTH PHYSICS. *Current Pos:* HEALTH PHYSICIST, MD DEPT ENVIRON, 86- *Personal Data:* b Franklin, Ind, Aug 16, 25; m 46; c 2. *Educ:* Ind Univ, AB, 49; Univ Md, MS, 58. *Prof Exp:* Res physicist, Chem Res & Develop Lab, US Dept Army, 50-58 & Nuclear Defense Lab, Edgewood Arsenal, 58-60, chief solid state physics br, 60-64, chief nuclear physics div, 64-69; chief, Exp Physics Br, Ballistics Res Labs, Aberdeen Proving Ground, 69-81; consult, 81-86. *Concurrent Pos:* Instr & researcher, Univ Del, 81-86, health physics, 86- *Mem:* AAAS; Am Phys Soc; Health Physics Soc. *Res:* Solid state and nuclear physics; radiation damage and detection; gamma-ray spectroscopy; thin films. *Mailing Add:* 110 Woodland Dr Bel Air MD 21014-5435

**VAN ARMAN, CLARENCE GORDON,** PHARMACOLOGY. *Current Pos:* RETIRED. *Personal Data:* b Detroit, Mich, Dec 29, 17; m 43, 69, Desiree A Armstrong; c Laura, John & Thomas. *Educ:* Univ Chicago, SB, 39; Northwestern Univ, MS, 48, PhD(pharmacol), 49. *Prof Exp:* Chemist, Price Extract Co, 39-40; chemist, G D Searle & Co, Ill, 40-41, pharmacologist, 50-60; res assoc pharmacol, Med Sch Northwestern Univ, 49-50; chief pharmacologist, Chem Therapeut Res Labs, Miles Labs, Inc, 60-61; dir, Pharmacol Res Dept, Chas Pfizer & Co, 63-65; sr res fel, 65-75; sr investr, Merck Inst Therapeut Res, 75-77; mgr, Pharmacol Eval Sect, Wyeth Labs, Inc, 61-63, dir biol res, 77-83. *Concurrent Pos:* Lectr, Med Sch, Northwestern Univ, 54-61. *Mem:* AAAS; Am Soc Pharmacol & Exp Therapeut; Soc Exp Biol & Med; Am Soc Clin Pharmacol & Therapeut; Am Rheumatism Asn. *Res:* Inflammation; polypeptides; analgesics; diuretics; cardiac drugs; glomerulonephritis. *Mailing Add:* 6020 Cannon Hill Rd Ft Washington PA 19034

**VAN ARSDEL, JOHN HEDDE,** ENGINEERING PSYCHOLOGY. *Current Pos:* writer med training manuals, Acad Health Sci, US Army, Ft Sam Houston, Tex, 81, OPERS RES ANALYST & ELECTRONIC ENGR, US ARMY, FT HUACHUCA, ARIZ, 81- *Personal Data:* b Chicago, Ill, Nov 22, 21; m 63; c 5. *Educ:* Purdue Univ, BS, 50; Commonwealth Univ, MA, 55, PhD(psychol), 56; Denver Univ, MA, 58. *Prof Exp:* Human factors engr, US Army Electronic Proving Ground, Ariz, 58-63; sr develop engr advan syst, Goodyear Aerospace Corp, Litchfield Park, Ariz, 63-66; sr human factors engr Minute Man III, Bell Aerosyst Corp, Niagara Falls, NY, 66-68; supvr comput lab, Col Bus Admin, Denver Univ, 68-73; human factors scientist syst eng, Syst Develop Corp, Colo Springs, Colo, 73-75; teacher & supvr acad & sci, Northrop, 76-80. *Concurrent Pos:* Consult, opers res anal & eng psychol. *Res:* Hypno-therapy in clinical treatment of demerol addiction; effectiveness and survival in hostile environments; launching system accessibility requirements; maintenance program human factors analysis. *Mailing Add:* 2364 Sonoita Dr Sierra Vista AZ 85635

**VAN ARSDEL, PAUL PARR, JR,** medicine; deceased, see previous edition for last biography

**VAN ARSDEL, WILLIAM CAMPBELL, III,** toxicology, animal ekg; deceased, see previous edition for last biography

**VAN ARTSDALEN, ERVIN ROBERT,** PHYSICAL CHEMISTRY, INORGANIC CHEMISTRY. *Current Pos:* head dept, 68-72, prof, 68-84, EMER PROF CHEM, UNIV ALA, 84- *Personal Data:* b Doylestown, Pa, Nov 13, 13; wid. *Educ:* Lafayette Col, BS, 35; Harvard Univ, AM, 39, PhD(phys chem), 41. *Prof Exp:* Asst chem, Harvard Univ, 36-40; from instr to asst prof, Lafayette Col, 41-45; res scientist, Los Alamos Sci Lab, 45-46; asst prof chem, Cornell Univ, 46-51; prin chemist, Oak Ridge Nat Lab, 51-56; asst dir res, Parma Res Ctr, Union Carbide Corp, 56-63; John W Mallet prof chem & chmn dept, Univ Va, 63-68. *Concurrent Pos:* Res assoc, Nat Defense Res Comt, Sch Med, Johns Hopkins Univ, 43-44; res assoc, Carnegie Inst Technol, 45; lectr, Western Res Univ, 59; mem coun, Oak Ridge Assoc Univs, 63-69, mem bd dir, 69-75, staff mem, Inst Energy Analysis, 75-76, Radiation Adv Bd Health, State Dept Health, Ala, 80. *Mem:* AAAS; Am Chem Soc; Am Phys Soc; fel Am Inst Chemists. *Res:* Energy analysis; adsorption indicators; photochemistry; bond strengths; reaction kinetics; thermodynamics and structure of inorganic systems; high temperature chemistry; fused salts; atomic energy; Moessbauer spectroscopy; radiochemistry; nuclear chemistry. *Mailing Add:* 1512 Bellingrath Dr PO Box 870336 Tuscaloosa AL 35406-2059

**VAN ASDALL, WILLARD,** PLANT ECOLOGY. *Current Pos:* RETIRED. *Personal Data:* b Knox, Ind, Apr 29, 34. *Educ:* Valparaiso Univ, AB, 56; Purdue Univ, SM, 58; Univ Chicago, PhD(bot), 61. *Prof Exp:* Instr biol, Knox Col, Ill, 61; asst prof, Duquesne Univ, 62-63; from asst prof to assoc prof bot, Univ Ariz, 62-76, assoc prof gen biol, 76-91. *Mem:* Ecol Soc Am; Bot Soc Am. *Res:* Physiological ecology of desert plant species, especially winter-spring desert ephemerals. *Mailing Add:* 4479 N Summer Set Loop Tucson AZ 85750

**VANASSE, GEORGE ALFRED,** OPTICS, SPECTROSCOPY. *Current Pos:* RETIRED. *Personal Data:* b Woonsocket, RI, Oct 8, 24; m 61; c 3. *Educ:* Univ RI, BS, 50; Boston Col, MS, 52; Johns Hopkins Univ, PhD(physics), 58. *Prof Exp:* Physicist spectros, Air Force Cambridge Res Lab, 52; teaching asst physics, Johns Hopkins Univ, 52-55, res asst, 55-58, res staff asst, 58-59; vis lectr, Goucher Col, 59; res physicist, Air Force Geophys Lab, Bedford, 59-89. *Concurrent Pos:* Vis lectr, Lowell Technol Inst, 64-65. *Mem:* Am Phys Soc; fel Optical Soc Am. *Res:* Spectrometric techniques. *Mailing Add:* 71 Old Stage Rd Chelmsford MA 01824

**VAN ASSENDELFT, ONNO WILLEM,** CLINICAL PATHOLOGY, CHEMICAL PHYSIOLOGY. *Current Pos:* chief gen hemat, Bur Labs, Ctr Dis Control, 76-80, Ctr Infectious Dis, 80-90, CHIEF, CLIN MED BR, DIV HOST FACTORS, DIV IMMUNOL, ONCOL, HEMAT DIS, CTR INFECTIOUS DIS, CTRS DIS CONTROL, 90-, ASST DIR, SCI RESOURCES PROG, DIR CLIA-REGULATED, DIAG LAB. *Personal Data:* b Brummen, Neth, Aug 23, 32; US citizen; m 60, Theodora H Teunissen; c Anne C, Frederik H, Albert H, Diederik A & Catharina E. *Educ:* Univ Groningen, Neth, MD, 59, PhD(med & physiol), 70. *Honors & Awards:* Russel J Eilers Award, Nat Comt Clin Lab Standards, 87; Spec Award, Nat Hemophilia Found, 92. *Prof Exp:* Med officer, Royal Dutch Army Med Corps, 59-61; sr res asst & asst prof physiol, Lab Chem Physiol, Univ Groningen, Neth, 61-76, secy & actg dean, Med Sch, 73-75. *Concurrent Pos:* Consult, Food & Drug Admin, 78- & Col Am Pathologists Hemat Resource Comt, 84-90; mem bd & secy, Int Coun Standardization Hemat, 79-; mem bd & pres, Nat Comt Clin Lab Stand, 83-94; chair US deleg, Clin Lab Testing & In Vitro Diag, 95- *Mem:* AAAS; Am Soc Hemat; NY Acad Sci; Int Soc Lab Hematol. *Res:* Reflection and transmission oximetry and spectrophotometry of hemoglobin derivatives, including standardization of hemoglobin determination; standards development of general hematology and clinical chemistry methods and quality control. *Mailing Add:* Ctr Dis Control & Prev Bldg I-2302 MS D17 1600 Clifton Rd Atlanta GA 30333. *Fax:* 404-639-3595; *E-Mail:* owv1@cidsrp1.em.cdc.gov

**VAN ATTA, CHARLES W,** FLUID MECHANICS. *Current Pos:* from asst prof to assoc prof, 65-75, PROF ENG SCI & OCEANOG, UNIV CALIF, SAN DIEGO, 75- *Personal Data:* b New London, Conn, Feb 24, 34; m 58; c Pamela. *Educ:* Univ Mich, BS, 58, MS, 59; Calif Inst Technol, PhD(aeronaut), 65. *Honors & Awards:* Fel Am Phys Soc. *Prof Exp:* Scientist, Jet Propulsion Lab, Calif Inst Technol, 64-65. *Concurrent Pos:* USSR Exchange fel, Nat Acad Sci, 72-73; Guggenheim fel, 72-73. *Mem:* Oceanog Soc; Am Phys Soc. *Res:* Transition and turbulence in fluid flow; geophysical fluid mechanics. *Mailing Add:* Ames 0411 Univ Calif San Diego CA 92093

**VANATTA, JOHN CROTHERS, III,** EPITHELIAL TRANSPORT, AMPHIBIAN ENDOCRINOLOGY. *Current Pos:* instr physiol & pharmacol, 49-50, from asst prof to assoc prof, 50-57, PROF PHYSIOL, UNIV TEX HEALTH SCI CTR DALLAS, 57- *Personal Data:* b Lafayette, Ind, Apr 22, 19; m 44; c 2. *Educ:* Ind Univ, AB, 41, MD, 44; Am Bd Internal Med, dipl, 53. *Prof Exp:* Intern, Wayne County Gen Hosp, 44-45, asst resident med, 46-47, fel physiol, Southwestern Med Col, 47-49. *Concurrent Pos:* Consult, Div Nuclear Educ & Training, USAEC, 64-67; adj prof physiol, Inst Technol, Southern Methodist Univ, 69-81; adj prof biomed sci & physiol, Baylor Col Dent, 91- *Mem:* Am Physiol Soc; Soc Exp Biol & Med; AMA. *Res:* Sodium metabolism; transport functions of urinary bladder of toad; epithelial transport, toad urinary bladder and frog skin. *Mailing Add:* Dept Physiol Southwest Med Sch Dallas TX 75235-9040. *Fax:* 214-648-8685

**VAN ATTA, LESTER CLARE,** physics, electrical engineering; deceased, see previous edition for last biography

**VAN AUKEN, OSCAR WILLIAM,** PHYSIOLOGICAL ECOLOGY, PLANT ECOLOGY. *Current Pos:* ASSOC PROF, DIV LIFE SCI, UNIV TEX, 76- *Personal Data:* b Morristown, NJ, Dec 7, 39; m 61; c 3. *Educ:* High Point Col, BS, 62; Univ Utah, MS, 65, PhD(biol), 69. *Prof Exp:* Asst prof biol, Southwest Tex State Univ, 69-71; sr res scientist, Southwest Res Inst, 71-73, mgr environ biol, 75-76; assoc found scientist, Southwest Found Res & Educ, 73-75. *Concurrent Pos:* Assoc ed, Plant Ecol, Southwestern Asn Naturalists, 84-86. *Mem:* Ecol Soc Am; AAAS; Bot Soc Am. *Res:* Plant, animal and environmental interaction; community ecology. *Mailing Add:* Div Life Sci Univ Tex 6900 N Loop 1604 W San Antonio TX 78249-1130

**VAN AUSDAL, RAY GARRISON,** MEDICAL & HEALTH PHYSICS, MUSICAL ACOUSTICS. *Current Pos:* CHIEF PHYSICIST RADIATION THER, YORK HOSP. *Personal Data:* b Cincinnati, Ohio, Sept 16, 43. *Educ:* Miami Univ, AB, 64, MA, 66; Univ Mich, Ann Arbor, PhD(physics), 72. *Prof Exp:* Asst prof physics, Northern Mich Univ, 72-73 & Kalamazoo Col, 73-74; assoc prof physics, Univ Pittsburgh, Johnstown, 74-89. *Res:* Development of effective teaching methods and materials in physics. *Mailing Add:* 3215 Lewisberry Rd York PA 17404

**VAN BAAK, DAVID ALAN,** MICROWAVE SPECTROSCOPY, ATOMIC BEAM SPECTROSCOPY. *Current Pos:* from asst prof to assoc prof, 80-87, PROF PHYSICS, CALVIN COL, 87- *Personal Data:* b Tokyo, Japan, July 13, 52; m 80; c 1. *Educ:* Calvin Col, BS, 73; Harvard Univ, MA, 75, PhD(physics), 79. *Prof Exp:* Nat Res Coun & Nat Bur Standards fel physics, Joint Inst Lab Astrophys, 79-80. *Concurrent Pos:* Vis assoc prof phys, Notre Dame Univ, 86-87. *Mem:* Am Phys Soc; Am Sci Affil. *Res:* Fine and hyperfine structure in simple atoms; quantum-electrodynamical effects; gavitation. *Mailing Add:* 1643 Hiawatha Dr SE Calvin Col Grand Rapids MI 49506. *Fax:* 616-957-8551

**VAN BEAUMONT, KAREL WILLIAM,** PHYSIOLOGY. *Current Pos:* asst prof, 68-73, ASSOC PROF PHYSIOL, SCH MED, ST LOUIS UNIV, 73- *Personal Data:* b Amsterdam, Neth, Sept 26, 30; US citizen; m 59; c 2. *Educ:* Acad Phys Educ, The Hague, BS, 55; Cath Univ Louvain, MS, 57; Univ Ill, MS, 62; Ind Univ, PhD(physiol), 65. *Prof Exp:* Instr physiol, Univ Ind, 64-66; res physiologist, Miami Valley Labs, Procter & Gamble Co, Ohio, 66-68. *Concurrent Pos:* Olympic coach, 80. *Res:* Temperature regulation; neural control systems; high altitude physiology; physiology of exercise; acceleration stress; biometeorology; body fluids and electrolytes; hematology. *Mailing Add:* Dept Physiol St Louis Univ Sch Med 1402 S Grand Blvd St Louis MO 63104-1004

**VAN BELLE, GERALD,** STATISTICS & BIOSTATISTICS, ENVIRONMENTAL RISK FACTORS FOR NEURODEGENERATIVE DISEASE. *Current Pos:* vis assoc prof, 74-75, assoc prof, 75-76, PROF BIOSTATIST, UNIV WASH, 76-, PROF & CHMN, DEPT ENVIRON HEALTH, 91- *Personal Data:* b Enschede, Neth, July 23, 36; Can citizen; m 63; c 5. *Educ:* Univ Toronto, BA, 62, MA, 64, PhD(math), 67. *Prof Exp:* Statistician, Connaught Med Res Labs, Univ Toronto, 57-62; from asst prof to assoc prof statist, Fla State Univ, 67-74, dir, Statist Consult Ctr, 71-74. *Mem:* Fel Am Statist Asn; Biomet Soc; Sigma Xi; Int Statist Inst; fel AAAS; Soc Risk Anal. *Res:* Application of statistics to biological and health-related problems. *Mailing Add:* Dept Environ Health Univ Wash Box 357234 Seattle WA 98195-7234

**VAN BERGEN, FREDERICK HALL,** ANESTHESIOLOGY. *Current Pos:* From instr to prof, Univ Minn, Minneapolis, 48-78, assoc dir, 53-54, actg dir, 54-55, head dept, 55-78, EMER PROF ANESTHESIOL, MED SCH, UNIV MINN, MINNEAPOLIS, 78- *Personal Data:* b Minneapolis, Minn, Sept 21, 14; c 4. *Educ:* Univ Minn, MB, 41, MD, 42, MS, 52. *Mem:* Am Soc Anesthesiol; Int Anesthesia Res Soc; AMA; Acad Anesthesiol. *Res:* Development and testing of respirators and respiratory assistors; evaluation of effects of respiratory patterns upon cardiovascular function; evaluation of pulmonary compliance under conditions of anesthesia; gas mass spectrometer. *Mailing Add:* 2005 Argonne Dr Minneapolis MN 55421-1315

**VAN BIBBER, KARL ALBERT,** HIGH ENERGY & NUCLEAR PHYSICS, ACCELERATOR PHYSICS. *Current Pos:* sr physicist, e-div physics, 85-91, GROUP LEADER N-DIV HIGH ENERGY PHYSICS & ACCELERATOR TECH, LAWRENCE LIVERMORE NAT LAB, 91- *Personal Data:* b New London, Conn, Dec 5, 50. *Educ:* Mass Inst Technol, BS & MS, 72, PhD(physics), 76. *Prof Exp:* Instr physics, Mass Inst Technol, 76-77; asst prof, Dept Physics, Stanford Univ, 80-85; res assoc, Lawrence Berkeley Lab, 77-79. *Concurrent Pos:* Lectr, Dept Nuclear Eng, Univ Calif, Berkeley, 77-78; A P Sloan Res fel, 82. *Mem:* Am Phys Soc. *Res:* High energy physics; manage design and construction of high energy physics, accelerators and detectors; dark matter of the universe. *Mailing Add:* L-028 Lawrence Livermore Nat Lab PO Box 808 Livermore CA 94551. *Fax:* 510-423-3371; *E-Mail:* vanbibber1@llnl.gov

**VANBLARICOM, GLENN R,** MARINE ECOLOGY, BIOLOGY OF MARINE MAMMALS. *Current Pos:* Wildlife res biologist, 77-93, ASST UNIT LEADER, FISH & WILDLIFE SERV, US DEPT INTERIOR, 93- *Personal Data:* b Shelton, Wash, Apr 16, 49. *Educ:* Univ Wash, Seattle, BS(zool) & BS(oceanog), 72; Univ Calif, San Diego, PhD(oceanog), 78. *Concurrent Pos:* Res assoc, Inst Marine Sci, Univ Calif, Santa Cruz, 84- *Mem:* Am Soc Naturalists; Ecol Soc Am; Soc Marine Mammal. *Res:* Studies of relationships of sea otters to nearshore marine benthic communities in California and Alaska; studies of impacts of offshore oil development and transport on sea otters in California. *Mailing Add:* Wash Coop Fish & Wildlife Res Unit Univ Wash Sch Fisheries PO Box 357980 Seattle WA 98195-7980

**VAN BLARICOM, RICHARD,** GEOPHYSICAL EXPLORATION, GEO-ELECTROCHEMICAL EXPLORATION. *Current Pos:* sr geophysicist, 76-82, CHIEF GEOPHYSICIST, COMINCO AM INC, 82- *Personal Data:* b Hood River, Ore, July 19, 37; m 65, Jeanne C Wiggans; c Heather (Gibson), Jennifer (Carlson), Todd & Richard II. *Educ:* Portland State Univ, BS, 65; Univ Ariz, MS, 71. *Prof Exp:* Field geophysicist, McPhar, 63-67; div geophysicist, Asarco, 67-74; chief geophysicist, Van Blaricom Geophys Serv, 74-76. *Concurrent Pos:* Course dir explor geophys, NW Mining Asn, 79 & 89; geophys ed, Soc Mining Engrs, 82. *Mem:* Soc Explor Geophysicists; Soc Mining Engrs; Am Geophys Union. *Res:* Geo-electrochemistry collection and analysis of low levels of trace cations in ground water. *Mailing Add:* Cominco Am Inc N 22710 Perry Rd Colbert WA 99005. *Fax:* 509-892-2591

**VANBLARIGAN, PETER,** KINEMATICS, ELECTROMECHANICS. *Current Pos:* SCIENTIST, SANDIA NAT LAB, 81- *Personal Data:* b Jersey City, NJ, Apr 17, 52; m 82; c 3. *Educ:* Va Polytech Inst & State Univ, BS, 74; Univ Calif, Berkeley, MS, 75, DEng(mech eng), 79. *Prof Exp:* Scientist, Lawrence Livermore Nat Lab, 76-81. *Res:* Development of novel simplifying solutions to complex engineering problems. *Mailing Add:* 11435 Thalin Dr Truckee CA 96161

**VAN BREEMAN, CORNELIS,** vascular & cellular physiology, for more information see previous edition

**VANBRUGGEN, ARIENA H C,** epidemiology, soil microbiology, for more information see previous edition

**VAN BRUGGEN, ARIENA H C**, EPIDEMIOLOGY, ECOLOGY. *Current Pos:* asst prof, 86-92, ASSOC PROF PLANT PATH, UNIV CALIF, 92- *Personal Data:* b Delfzije, Neth, Dec 7, 49. *Educ:* Agr Univ Wageningen, BS, 72 MSc, 76; Cornell Univ, PhD(plant path), 85. *Honors & Awards:* Ciba-Geigy Award, Am Phytopath Soc, 93; Jakob Eriksson Gold Medal, Swed Govt, 93. *Prof Exp:* Assoc expert plant path, Food Agr Orgn UN, 76-80; fel assoc, Boyce Thompson Inst, 84-86. *Concurrent Pos:* Prin investr, USDA-Ctr Int & Strategic Affairs, 88-92, USDA NRICGP, 93- *Mem:* Am Phytopath Soc; AAAS; Am Soc Microbiol. *Res:* Etiology and epidemiology of diseases of vegetable crops; integrated disease management using disease forecasting models; develop indicators for soil quality in relation to plant disease suppression. *Mailing Add:* 1703 Costa Verde St Univ Calif Davis CA 95616

**VAN BRUGGEN, THEODORE**, BOTANY. *Current Pos:* from asst prof to prof bot & chmn dept, 58-59, ASSOC DEAN COL ARTS & SCI, UNIV SDAK, VERMILLION, 69- *Personal Data:* b Hawarden, Iowa, Jan 26, 26; m 48; c 2. *Educ:* Buena Vista Col, BS, 48; Univ SDak, MA, 50; Univ Iowa, PhD(bot), 58. *Prof Exp:* Instr biol, Northwestern Col, 50-55. *Concurrent Pos:* Asst prog dir, NSF, 65-66. *Mem:* AAAS; Bot Soc Am; Mycol Soc Am; Am Soc Plant Taxon. *Res:* Plant systematics; flora of South Dakota, especially identification of vascular plants; flora of the Great Plains. *Mailing Add:* 1100 Valley View Dr Vermillion SD 57069

**VAN BRUNT, RICHARD JOSEPH**, ATOMIC PHYSICS, MOLECULAR PHYSICS. *Current Pos:* PHYSICIST GAS DISCHARGES, NAT INST STAND & TECHNOL, GAITHERSBURG, MD, 78- *Personal Data:* b Jersey City, NJ, May 11, 39; m 72; c 1. *Educ:* Univ Fla, BS, 61; MS, 64; Univ Colo, Boulder, PhD(physics), 69. *Honors & Awards:* Bronze Medal, US Dept Com, 84; R&D-100 Award, 90; Silver Medal, US Dept Com, 91; Whitehead Memorial Lectr, Inst Elec & Electronics Engrs, 94. *Prof Exp:* Res asst atomic & molecular physics, Univ Fla, 64 & Joint Inst Lab Astrophys, Univ Colo, Boulder, 64-69; res assoc, Univ Va, 69-71, asst prof atomic & molecular physics, 71-76; physicist & res assoc basic atomic physics, Joint Inst Lab Astrophys, Univ Colo, Boulder, 75-78. *Concurrent Pos:* Univ grant, Univ Va, 72-73; NASA fac fel, NASA/Goddard Space Flight Ctr, Greenbelt, Md, 74; vis mem, Joint Inst Lab Astrophys, Univ Colo, Boulder, 75-77; chmn, Int Swarm Sem, 89-90; secy, Gaseous Elec Conf, 93-94; assoc ed, Inst Elec & Electronics Engrs, Trans Dielectrics & Elec Insulation, 93. *Mem:* AAAS; Am Phys Soc; Inst Elec & Electronics Engrs; Am Asn Physics Teachers. *Res:* Experimental and theoretical studies of ionization and excitation by electron impact and photon absorption; measurement of electron-atom scattering and ion-molecule reaction rates; fundamental studies of high-voltage and rf gas discharge phenomena, corona and plasma chemistry. *Mailing Add:* 11517 Alcinda Lane Gaithersburg MD 20878. *E-Mail:* vanbrunt@eeel.nist.gov

**VAN BUIJTENEN, JOHANNES PETRUS**, FOREST GENETICS. *Current Pos:* RETIRED. *Personal Data:* b Neth, May 8, 28; nat US; m 63; c 3. *Educ:* State Agr Univ, Wageningen, BS, 52; Univ Calif, Berkeley, MS, 55; Tex A&M Univ, PhD(genetics), 56. *Prof Exp:* Forest geneticist, Inst Paper Chem, 56-60, Tex Forest Serv, 60-66 & Northeastern Forest Exp Sta, NH, 66-68; assoc prof, Tex Forest Serv, 68-71, prin geneticist, 68-85, head, Reforestation Dept, 85-93; prof forest genetics, Tex A&M Univ, 71-93, emer prof, 93. *Concurrent Pos:* NSF travel grant, 63; consult, Tex Forest Serv, 66-68. *Mem:* AAAS; Soc Am Foresters; fel Int Acad Wood Sci. *Res:* Genetic improvement of forest trees for growth rate, drought resistance, wood quality, disease resistance; physiology of forest trees as related to forest tree improvement. *Mailing Add:* Dept Forest Sci Tex A&M Univ College Station TX 77843-2135

**VAN BUREN, ARNIE LEE**, ACOUSTICS. *Current Pos:* HEAD, UNDERWATER SOUND REF DIV, NAVAL UNDERSEA WARFARE CTR, NEWPORT, RI, 96- *Personal Data:* b Reynoldsburg, Ohio, Nov 28, 39; m 90, Nan L Crawford; c David W, Rebecca L & Jessica L. *Educ:* Birmingham-Southern Col, BS, 61; Univ Tenn, PhD(physics), 67. *Prof Exp:* Res assoc acoust, Univ Tenn, 67-68; res physicist, Naval Res Lab, Washington, DC, 68-76; res physicist, Naval Res Lab, Orlando, Fla, 76-79, head methods sect, 79-82, Head Measurements Br, 82-96. *Concurrent Pos:* Chmn working group, Acoust Transducer Calibration, Am Nat Stand Inst, 83-88; mem, Comt Stand, Acoust Soc Am, 91-; chmn, Tech Prog, Third Int Workshop Power Transducers for Sonic & Ultrasonics, 92. *Mem:* Fel Acoust Soc Am. *Res:* Underwater acoustic measurements; acoustic radiation; nonlinear acoustics. *Mailing Add:* Code 216 Naval Undersea Warfare Ctr 1176 Howell St Newport RI 02841-1708. *Fax:* 401-841-2431; *E-Mail:* lvanburen@code2onl.nl.nuwg.navy.mil

**VAN BUREN, JEROME PAUL**, BIOCHEMISTRY. *Current Pos:* from asst prof to prof, 57-91, EMER PROF BIOCHEM, CORNELL UNIV, 91- *Personal Data:* b Brooklyn, NY, Oct 17, 26; m 53; c 3. *Educ:* Cornell Univ, BS, 50, MNS, 51, PhD, 54. *Prof Exp:* Proj leader cereal chem, Gen Mills, Inc, 54-57. *Concurrent Pos:* Consult food & agr, USPHS, 62-65; vis prof, Swiss Fed Inst Technol, 64-65; vis prof, Agr Univ, Holland, 71-72, Imp Col, London, 80, Inst Food Res, Norwich, 90. *Mem:* Am Chem Soc; Inst Food Technologists. *Res:* Protein interactions in food; anthocyanins and polyphenols; wine chemistry; effects of salts on vegetable texture; pectic substances; food color and pigments. *Mailing Add:* 106 Iroquois Pl Ithaca NY 14850

**VAN BURKALOW, ANASTASIA**, MEDICAL GEOGRAPHY. *Current Pos:* from instr to prof, 38-45 & 48-75, EMER PROF GEOL & GEOG, HUNTER COL, NY, 75- *Personal Data:* b Buchanan, NY, Mar 16, 11. *Educ:* Hunter Col, BA, 31; Columbia Univ, MA, 33, PhD(geomorphol), 44. *Hon Degrees:* DSc, Hunter Col, 96. *Prof Exp:* Res asst geomorphol, Columbia Univ, 34-37, Kemp fel geol, 37-38; res & ed asst geog, Am Geog Soc, 45-48. *Concurrent Pos:* Consult geologist, E I du Pont de Nemours & Co, Wilmington, Del, 45-59. *Mem:* Fel Geol Soc Am; fel AAAS; fel NY Acad Sci; Am Geophys Union; Asn Am Geographers; Sigma Xi. *Res:* Angle of repose of loose material; water resources; medical geography. *Mailing Add:* 160 E 95th St New York NY 10128-2511

**VAN CALSTEREN, MARIE-ROSE**, NUCLEAR MAGNETIC RESONANCE, STRUCTURE-ACTIVITY RELATIONSHIPS. *Current Pos:* Res asst, 87-88, chemist & nuclear magnetic resonance spectroscopist, 88-91, RES SCIENTIST, AGR CAN, 91- *Personal Data:* b Brussels, Belg, Mar 26, 58; Can citizen. *Educ:* Univ Sherbrooke, BSc, 80, MSc, 83; Univ Ottawa, PhD(chem), 91. *Concurrent Pos:* Demonstr, Univ Sherbrooke, 80-82 & Univ Ottawa, 82-87. *Mem:* Chem Inst Can; Can Soc Chem; Spectros Soc Can; Am Chem Soc; Int Soc Magnetic Resonance; Can-Fr Asn Advan Sci. *Res:* Application of nuclear magnetic resonance and other spectroscopic techniques to structure determination of natural products, to structure-activity relationships and to biomolecular interactions. *Mailing Add:* 3600 Casavant Blvd W St-Hyacinthe PQ J2S 8E3 Can. *Fax:* 514-773-8461; *E-Mail:* vancalsteren@qcrssh.agr.ca

**VAN CAMPEN, DARRELL R**, NUTRITION, BIOCHEMISTRY. *Current Pos:* ASSOC PROF ANIMAL NUTRIT, CORNELL UNIV, 80-; LAB DIR US PLANT, SOIL & NUTRIT LAB USDA, 80- *Personal Data:* b Two Buttes, Colo, July 15, 35; m 58; c 2. *Educ:* Colo State Univ, BS, 57; NC State Univ, MS, 60, PhD(nutrit), 62. *Prof Exp:* NIH fel biochem, Cornell Univ, 62-63; res chemist, US Plant, Soil & Nutrit Lab, USDA, 63-80; asst prof animal nutrit, Cornell Univ, 72-80. *Mem:* AAAS; Am Inst Nutrit; Soc Exp Biol & Med; NY Acad Sci. *Res:* Mineral metabolism; absorption and utilization of trace minerals. *Mailing Add:* Plant Soil & Nutrit Lab USDA Tower Rd Ithaca NY 14853-0001. *Fax:* 607-255-2459

**VANCE, BENJAMIN DWAIN**, PLANT PHYSIOLOGY. *Current Pos:* RETIRED. *Personal Data:* b Cave City, Ark, May 7, 32; m 52; c 4. *Educ:* Tex Tech Col, BS, 58; Univ Mo, AM, 59, PhD(bot), 62. *Prof Exp:* Asst prof biol, Tex Tech Col, 62-63; asst prof, NTex State Univ, 63-70, assoc prof, 70- *Concurrent Pos:* Res grants, NTex Fac Res-Tex Col & Coord Bd, 66-67, Nat Commun Dis Ctr, 66-68; Su Corps, Inc, 78-80 & Robert Welch Found. *Mem:* Aquatic Plant Mgt Soc. *Res:* Physiology of blue-green algae; phytohormones; aquatic angiosperm physiology. *Mailing Add:* 2124 Glen Gardens Denton TX 76207

**VANCE, DENNIS E**, PHOSPHOLIPID METABOLISM, LIPOPROTEIN METABOLISM. *Current Pos:* PROF BIOCHEM & DIR, LIPID & LIPOPROTEIN RES GROUP, UNIV ALTA, 86- *Personal Data:* b St Anthony, Idaho, July 14, 42; US & Can citizen; m 67, Jean Eaton; c Russell E & Fiona N. *Educ:* Dickinson Col, BS, 64; Univ Pittsburgh, PhD(biochem), 68. *Honors & Awards:* Bristol Lipoprotein Res Award, Can Lipoprotein Conf, 85; Boehringer-Mannheim Can Prize, Can Biochem Soc, 89, Heinrich Wipland Prize, 95. *Prof Exp:* From asst prof to prof biochem, Univ BC, 73-86, assoc dean med, 78-81, head, Dept Biochem, 82-86. *Concurrent Pos:* Adv bds, Biochem J, 84- & J Lipid Res, 89-; ed, Phosphatidylcholine Metab, 89; exec ed, Biochimila, Biophysica Alta, 95-; co-ed, Biochem Lipids, Lipoproteins & Membranes, 96 & Phospholipid Biosynthesis in Methods in Enzym, 92. *Mem:* Can Soc Biochem & Molecular Biol (vpres, 91-92, pres 92-93); Am Soc Biochem & Molecular Biol; Brit Biochem Soc; AAAS; fel Royal Soc Can. *Res:* Regulation of phosphatidycholine biosynthesis in animal cells; role of triacylglycerol hydrolase in the assembly and secretion of lipoproteins from hepatocytes; phospholipid synthesis. *Mailing Add:* Lipid Res Group Univ Alta Edmonton AB T6G 2S2 Can. *Fax:* 403-492-8286; *E-Mail:* dennis.vance@ualberta.ca

**VANCE, DENNIS WILLIAM**, ELECTROOPTICS. *Current Pos:* SCIENTIST, VERTEX VIDEO SYSTS, 79- *Personal Data:* b Quincy, Ill, Nov 20, 38; m 61; c 1. *Educ:* St Lawrence Univ, BS, 60; Univ Fla, MS, 62, PhD(physics), 65. *Prof Exp:* Scientist, Xerox Res Labs, 65-77, mgr display technol area, 75-77. *Mem:* Am Phys Soc. *Res:* Surface physics; display systems engineering and technology. *Mailing Add:* 7325 Linne Rd Paso Robles CA 93446

**VANCE, EDWARD F(LAVUS)**, ELECTRICAL ENGINEERING. *Current Pos:* res engr to sr res engr, Stanford Res Inst, 59-76, prog mgr, 76-80, staff scientist, 80-83, SR STAFF SCIENTIST, SRI INT, 83- *Personal Data:* b Mansfield, Tex, Sept 1, 29; m 56, Gladys L Linval; c Carolyn J, Cynthia L, Thomas E & Dana K. *Educ:* Univ Calif, Los Angeles, BS, 54; Univ Denver, MSEE, 58. *Prof Exp:* Design engr, NAm Aviation, Inc, 54-56; from instr to asst prof elec eng, Univ Denver, 56-59. *Concurrent Pos:* Several tech adv groups, DOD; Electromagnetic Pulse fel, 86. *Mem:* Fel Inst Elec & Electronics Engrs; Int Union Radio Sci. *Res:* Electromagnetic coupling; cable shields and transmission lines; high voltage phenomena; electrical discharges; aircraft and rocket electrification. *Mailing Add:* SRI Int 6885 Hwy 1187 Ft Worth TX 76140

**VANCE, ELBRIDGE PUTNAM**, MATHEMATICS. *Current Pos:* lectr, Oberlin Col, 43-46, from asst prof to prof, 46-83, chmn dept 48-77, actg dean fac, 65-66 & 70-71, EMER PROF MATH, OBERLIN COL, 83- *Personal Data:* b Cincinnati, Ohio, Feb 7, 15; m 75; c 4. *Educ:* Col Wooster, AB, 36; Univ Mich, MA, 37, PhD(math), 39. *Prof Exp:* Dir statist lab, Univ Mich, 38; from instr to asst prof math, Univ Nev, 39-43. *Concurrent Pos:* NSF fel, Stanford Univ, 60-61; Columbia Univ & US AID consult, Ranchi Univ, India, 65; math assoc, Univ Auckland, 67; instr, Glenville High Sch & Phillips Acad,

73; ed, Am Math Monthly, 49-57 & 64-67. *Mem:* AAAS; assoc Am Math Soc; assoc Math Asn Am; Nat Coun Tchrs Math; Sigma Xi. *Res:* Continuous transformations; foundations of mathematics; topology. *Mailing Add:* 315 Yorktown Pl D4 Vermilion OH 44089

**VANCE, GEORGE FLOYD,** ENVIRONMENTAL CHEMISTRY. *Current Pos:* head, Soil Sci Sect, 93-96, ASSOC PROF SOIL & ENVIRON CHEM, DEPT PLANT, SOIL & INSECT SCI, UNIV WYO, 89- *Personal Data:* b Royal Oak, Mich, May 8, 52; m 76, Maureen Quinn; c Christy A & Emily M. *Educ:* Mich State Univ, BS, 81, MS, 85; Univ Ill, PhD(soil chem), 89. *Prof Exp:* Res assoc, Dept Forestry, Univ Ill, 88-89. *Concurrent Pos:* Assoc ed, J Environ Qual, 94-; pres, Western Soc Soil Sci; western chair, Am Soc Surface Mining & Reclamation. *Mem:* Soil Sci Soc Am; Am Chem Soc Geochem Div; Am Soc Surface Mining & Reclamation. *Res:* Groundwater contamination, chemistry and bioavailability of waste constituents in soils, acid deposition, selenium chemistry in agriculture, mineland and military ecosystems, pesticide mobility and fate, and forest nutrient cyclying; sorption of hazardous organic compounds by organo-clays. *Mailing Add:* Dept Plant Soil & Insect Sci Univ Wyo Laramie WY 82071-3354. *Fax:* 307-766-5549; *E-Mail:* gfv@uwyo.edu

**VANCE, HUGH GORDON,** ANALYTICAL CHEMISTRY, BIOCHEMISTRY. *Current Pos:* RETIRED. *Personal Data:* b Forest, Ont, Sept 18, 24; m 53; c 1. *Educ:* Univ Western Ont, BSc, 50, PhD(path chem), 56. *Prof Exp:* Nat Res Coun Can fel, Dept Anat, McGill Univ, 55-57; res assoc biochem, Sinai Hosp of Baltimore, Ind, Md, 57-61, Nat Cancer Inst fel, Dept Med, 60-61; from asst prof to assoc prof chem, Morgan State Col, 65-86. *Mem:* Am Chem Soc. *Res:* Investigations of the nature and content of mucopolysaccharides in skin; structural determination of the carbohydrate moiety of glycoproteins. *Mailing Add:* 2908 Mayfield Ave Randallstown MD 21133

**VANCE, IRVIN ELMER,** MATHEMATICS EDUCATION. *Current Pos:* PROF MATH, MICH STATE UNIV, 89- *Personal Data:* b Mexico, Mo, Apr 8, 28; m 58, Ann Marlene; c Barbara, Katrina & Velesha. *Educ:* Wayne State Univ, BS, 57; Wash Univ, MA, 59; Univ Mich, Ann Arbor, DEduc(math), 67. *Prof Exp:* From asst prof to assoc prof math, Mich State Univ, 66-71; from assoc prof to prof math, NMex State Univ, 71-89. *Concurrent Pos:* Consult, Morel Lab Math Proj, 67; asst dir, Grand Rapids Math Lab Proj, 68-69; dir, Inner City Math Proj, Mich State Univ, 69-72, Sch-Community Outreach Proj One, 73-75 & Mich Minority Math Proj, 89-; dir, Elem Teachers Math Proj, NMex State Univ, 77-80. *Mem:* Nat Coun Teachers Math; Am Math Soc; Math Asn Am; Nat Asn Mathematicians. *Res:* Finite projective planes; inductive learning and teaching of mathematics; laboratory techniques at school level and individualized instruction at the college level; problem solving at middle grades. *Mailing Add:* Dept Math Mich State Univ East Lansing MI 48824

**VANCE, JEAN E,** LIPID TRANSPORT, LIPOPROTEIN ASSEMBLY. *Current Pos:* from asst prof to assoc prof med, 87-96, PROF MED, UNIV ALTA, 96- *Personal Data:* b Glasgow, Scotland, Feb 23, 43; Can citizen; m 67, Dennis; c Russell & Fiona. *Educ:* Univ London, BS, 64; Univ Pittsburgh, PhD(biochem), 69. *Prof Exp:* Instr biochem, Univ BC, 76-86. *Mem:* Amer Soc Cell Biol; Can Soc Biochem & Molecular Biol. *Res:* Mechanisms of intracellular lipid transport in eukaryotes; mechanisms of assembly of hepatic lipoproteins; regulation of neural synthesis of lipids. *Mailing Add:* Lipid & Lipoprotein Group Univ Alta 315 HMRC Edmonton AB T6G 2S2 Can. *Fax:* 403-492-3383; *E-Mail:* jvance@gpu.serv.ualberta.ca

**VANCE, JOHN MILTON,** MECHANICAL ENGINEERING, TURBOMACHINERY. *Current Pos:* PROF, TEX A&M UNIV, 78- *Personal Data:* b Houston, Tex, Oct 5, 37; m 58, 83; c 4. *Educ:* Univ Tex, Austin, BS, 60, MS, 63, PhD(mech eng), 67. *Honors & Awards:* Halliburton Award Execellence. *Prof Exp:* Mech engr, Houston Div, Armco Steel Corp, 60-62; res engr, Res & Tech Dept, Texaco Inc, 63-64; group leader missile decoy anal, Tracor, Inc, 67-69; asst prof mech eng, Univ Fla, 69-77. *Concurrent Pos:* Consult, Pratt & Whitney, 70-; sci adv, Air Mobility Res & Develop, US Army, 71-72; US Army res grant, Univ Fla, 72-73; Southwest Res Inst, 75-76; Dresser Industs assoc prof, Tex A&M Univ, 79-80, Shell, 81-82, Ctr Electromech, Univ Tex, 89 & 93. *Mem:* Am Soc Mech Engrs; Am Soc Eng Educ. *Res:* Dynamics of rotating machinery; dynamic stability of mechanical systems; bearings; mechanical design synthesis; turbomachinery; helicopters; vibration dampers for turbomachinery. *Mailing Add:* Dept Mech Eng Tex A&M Univ College Station TX 77843. *E-Mail:* jvance@mengr.tamu.edu

**VANCE, JOSEPH ALAN,** GEOLOGY. *Current Pos:* Asst prof geol, 57-68, assoc prof geol, 68-, EMER PROF GEOL, UNIV WASH, 68- *Personal Data:* b Aberdeen, Wash, Mar 15, 30; m 49; c 3. *Educ:* Univ Wash, BSc, 51, PhD, 57. *Mem:* Geol Soc Am; Mineral Soc Am. *Res:* Igneous and metamorphic petrology; structure and stratigraphy; geology of the Pacific Northwest. *Mailing Add:* Dept Geol 351310 Univ Wash Seattle WA 98195

**VANCE, JOSEPH FRANCIS,** MATHEMATICS, STATISTICS. *Current Pos:* from asst prof to assoc prof, 68-74, PROF MATH, ST MARY'S UNIV, TEX, 74- *Personal Data:* b Kansas City, Mo, July 24, 37. *Educ:* Southwest Tex State Col, BS, 59; Univ Tex, Austin, MA, 62, PhD(math), 67. *Prof Exp:* Teacher high sch, Tex, 60-61; spec instr math, Univ Tex, Austin, 66-67, asst prof, 67-68. *Mem:* Am Math Soc. *Res:* Analysis; specialty, integration theory. *Mailing Add:* Dept Math St Mary's Univ 1 Camino Santa Maria San Antonio TX 78228-5433

**VANCE, JUDY M,** INNER-ACTIVE ENGINEERING DESIGN. *Current Pos:* ASST PROF, MECH ENG, IOWA STATE UNIV, 84- *Personal Data:* b La Crosse, Wis, July 26, 55. *Educ:* Iowa State Univ, BS, 80, MA, 87, PhD(mech eng), 92. *Honors & Awards:* Dow Outstanding Young Fac Award, Am Soc Eng Educr, 89. *Prof Exp:* Mech engr, John Deer DesMoines Works, 79-84. *Concurrent Pos:* Tech fac fel, Iowa Ctr Emerging Mfg, 92. *Mem:* Am Soc Mech Engrs; Soc Mfg Engrs; Am Soc Eng Educr; Asn Comput Mach. *Mailing Add:* Dept Mech Iowa State Univ 2668 Black Eng Bldg Ames IA 50011

**VANCE, MILES ELLIOTT,** PHYSICAL & GEOMETRICAL OPTICS, OPTICAL COMMUNICATION. *Current Pos:* RETIRED. *Personal Data:* b Findlay, Ohio, Jan 2, 32; m 55, Bonnie Lou Osborn; c Barbara Sue, Karen Beth & Joseph Elliott. *Educ:* Bowling Green State Univ, BA, 53; Ohio State Univ, PhD(physics), 62. *Prof Exp:* Instr physics, Ohio State Univ, 61-62; res physicist, Res & Develop Lab, Corning Glass Works, NY, 62-68, sr res physicist, Electronics Res Lab, Raleigh NC, 68-73, sr res physicist, Biomed Tech Ctr, 73-76, sr res physicist, 75-90, res assoc, 90-95. *Mem:* Optical Soc Am; Inst Elec & Electronics Engrs; Sigma Xi. *Res:* Applied optics; interferometry; clinical instruments; microscopy; spectroscopy; optical communications. *Mailing Add:* 71 E Third St Corning NY 14830

**VANCE, OLLIE LAWRENCE,** ENGINEERING. *Current Pos:* ASSOC PROF ENG, UNIV ALA, BIRMINGHAM, 67-; CONSULT ENG, 70- *Personal Data:* b Birmingham, Ala, Feb 5, 37; m 56; c 2. *Educ:* Auburn Univ, BSME, 59, MSME, 61; Univ Tex, Austin, PhD(mech eng), 67. *Prof Exp:* Instr mech eng, Auburn Univ, 59-61; eng design analyst, Pratt & Whitney Inc, 61-62; asst prof mech eng, Auburn Univ, 62-64. *Mem:* Am Soc Mech Engr. *Res:* Vibrations; linear elasticity. *Mailing Add:* 3145 Wellington Pkwy Birmingham AL 35243

**VANCE, PAUL A(NDREW), JR,** ELECTRICAL ENGINEERING. *Current Pos:* RETIRED. *Personal Data:* b Ft Wayne, Ind, Feb 17, 30; m 53, Helen D Oakes; c Charles A, John M & Paul D. *Educ:* Univ Ill, BS, 51, MS, 52, PhD(elec eng), 54. *Prof Exp:* Res engr, Eng Res Lab, Exp Sta, E I DuPont de Nemours & Co, Inc, 54-58, res proj engr, 58-61, sr res engr, Mech Res, Eng Res & Develop Labs, 61-65, sr res engr, Orchem Dept, Jackson Lab, 65-77, sr engr, Photo Prod Dept, Instrument Prod Div, 77-79, sr engr, Photo Prod Dept, Clin Syst Div, 79-85. *Res:* Optics; electronics; electromechanics. *Mailing Add:* 201 Country Club Dr Newark DE 19711

**VANCE, ROBERT FLOYD,** INORGANIC CHEMISTRY. *Current Pos:* RETIRED. *Personal Data:* b Columbus, Ohio, May 12, 26; m 53; c 3. *Educ:* Otterbein Col, BS, 49; Univ Ill, MS, 50, PhD(chem), 52. *Prof Exp:* Res chemist, Battelle Mem Inst, 52-58; develop supvr, Girdler Catalysts Div, Chemetron Corp, 58-60; sr chemist, Gen Elec Co, 60-80; mgr, Environ Lab, State of Ky, 81- *Mem:* Am Chem Soc. *Res:* Gas chromatography; mass spectrometry; thermal analysis. *Mailing Add:* 7502 Tudor Ct Louisville KY 40222-4142

**VANCE, VELMA JOYCE,** VERTEBRATE ZOOLOGY. *Current Pos:* RETIRED. *Personal Data:* b Wilder, Idaho, May 13, 29. *Educ:* Col Idaho, BS, 51; Univ Ariz, MS, 53; Univ Calif, Los Angeles, PhD(zool), 59. *Prof Exp:* Asst, Crookham Co, 52-54 & Univ Calif, Los Angeles, 54-58; instr biol, Occidental Col, 59; from asst prof to prof zool, Calif State Univ, Los Angeles, 59-91. *Res:* Animal behavior; vertebrate biology. *Mailing Add:* 2398 E Gossamer Lane Boise ID 83706

**VANCE, WILLIAM HARRISON,** FLUID DYNAMICS, HEAT TRANSFER. *Current Pos:* sr engr, 64-76, FEL ENGR, BETTIS ATOMIC POWER LAB, WESTINGHOUSE ELEC CORP, 77- *Personal Data:* b Phoenix, Ariz, Nov 6, 34; m 73, Pamela Stapleton; c Karina (Gauthier) & Jeffery. *Educ:* Univ NMex, BS, 56; Univ Wash, PhD(chem eng), 62. *Prof Exp:* NSF fel, Swiss Fed Inst Technol, 62-63. *Mem:* Am Inst Chem Engrs. *Res:* Experimentation and analysis in fluid dynamics and heat transfer. *Mailing Add:* 205 Conover Rd Pittsburgh PA 15208

**VAN CITTERS, ROBERT L,** CARDIOVASCULAR PHYSIOLOGY, EDUCATIONAL ADMINISTRATION. *Current Pos:* from asst prof to assoc prof physiol & biophys, Sch Med, Univ Wash, 63-70, Robert L King chmn cardiovasc res, 63-68, mem staff, Regional Primate Res Ctr, 64-68, assoc dean, Sch Med, 68-70, dean, 70-81, PROF PHYSIOL, BIOPHYS & MED, SCH MED, UNIV WASH, 70- *Personal Data:* b Alton, Iowa, Jan 20, 26; m 49, Mary E Barker; c Robert, Mary, David & Sara. *Educ:* Univ Kans, AB, 49, MD, 53. *Hon Degrees:* DSc, Northwestern Col, Iowa, 78. *Honors & Awards:* Cummings Medal, 70. *Prof Exp:* Intern, Med Ctr, Univ Kans, 53-54, resident internal med, 55-58; res assoc, Scripps Clin Res Found, Univ Calif, 61-62. *Concurrent Pos:* Nat Heart Inst res fel, Univ Kans, 55-56 & trainee, 56-57, spec res fel, 58-59; res fel, Sch Med, Univ Wash, 59-62; NIH career res award, 62; exchange scientist, Joint US-USSR Sci Exchange, 62; res grants, Nat Heart Inst, 62-67, Am Heart Asn, 62-67 & USAF, 67; mem, Bd Trustees, Wash State Heart Asn; mem Admin Bd, Coun Deans, 72-, Exec Coun, Asn Am Med Col, 72-78; mem spec med adv group, Vet Admin, 74-78, chmn, 77-78; mem, Gen Res Support Prog Adv Comt, NIH, 75-78 & Nat Adv Res Resources Coun, 78-84; mem, Liaison Comt Med Educ, 81-84; chmn, Mech Circulatory Assistance Working Group, Nat Heart, Lung & Blood Inst, 83- & mem, Clin Applns & Prev Adv Comt, 85- *Mem:* Inst Med-Nat Acad Sci; Am Physiol Soc; Am Heart Asn; Am Fedn Clin Res; fel AAAS; Asn Am Med Col. *Res:* Cardiovascular physiology, left ventricular function and control, regional flow distribution, exercise and diving; development of instrumentation and techniques for studying cardiovascular dynamics in healthy subjects during spontaneous activity; prevention of cardiovascular disease. *Mailing Add:* Univ Wash Sch Med 356422 Seattle WA 98195. *Fax:* 206-543-3639

**VANCKO, ROBERT MICHAEL,** HISTORY OF MATHEMATICS, GENERAL ALGEBRAIC SYSTEMS. *Current Pos:* asst prof, 69-89, ASSOC PROF MATH, OHIO UNIV, 89- *Personal Data:* b Johnson City, NY, Sept 15, 42; m 66, Candace Shedd; c Robert Jr, Kathryn & Melissa. *Educ:* Pa State Univ, BA, 64, MA, 65, PhD(math), 69. *Prof Exp:* Lectr math, Univ Man, 67-69. *Mem:* Am Math Soc; Math Asn Am. *Res:* Universal algebra; general algebraic systems; history of mathematics. *Mailing Add:* Dept Math Ohio Univ Athens OH 45701

**VAN CLEAVE, HORACE WILLIAM,** ENTOMOLOGY. *Current Pos:* from asst prof to prof entom, 64-89, PROF & ASSOC HEAD ACAD PROGS, TEX A&M UNIV, 89- *Personal Data:* b Cherryvale, Kans, July 9, 31; m 56; c 2. *Educ:* Tex A&M Univ, BS, 52, MS, 58; Okla State Univ, PhD(entom), 69. *Prof Exp:* Teacher high sch, Tex, 54-56; surv entomologist, Okla State Univ, 58-61, instr, 62-64. *Mem:* Entom Soc Am; Am Registry Prof Entomologists (pres, 88). *Res:* Insect pests of pecans; taxonomy of aphids; economic entomology. *Mailing Add:* Dept Entom Tex A&M Univ College Station TX 77843-0100

**VAN CLEAVE, VICTOR HAROLD,** ANTIBODY GENERATION AND CHARACTERIZATION. *Current Pos:* PRIN SCIENTIST, GENETICS INST, ANDOVER, MASS, 90- *Personal Data:* b Jackson, Tenn, Apr 30, 55. *Educ:* Univ Tenn, Martin, BS, 77, MS, 78; Univ Tenn, Memphis, PhD(immunol), 87. *Prof Exp:* Fel, Univ Ala, Birmingham, 87-88; asst prof, Christian Bros Univ, Memphis, 88-90. *Mem:* Am Asn Immunologist; Sigma Xi. *Res:* Production and characterization of antibodies specific for various cytokines; design and implementation of pre-clinical studies to test the efficency of various cytokines. *Mailing Add:* Genetics Inst One Burtt Rd Andover MA 01810. *Fax:* 978-623-1389; *E-Mail:* vvancleave@genetics.com

**VAN CLEVE, JOHN WOODBRIDGE,** CARBOHYDRATE CHEMISTRY. *Current Pos:* RES CHEMIST, CEREAL CROPS LAB, NORTHERN REGIONAL RES LAB, USDA, 51- *Personal Data:* b Kansas City, Mo, Nov 22, 14; m 47; c 3. *Educ:* Antioch Col, BS, 37; Univ Minn, PhD(biochem), 51. *Prof Exp:* Jr res chemist, Aluminum Co Am, 43-45, assoc res chemist, 45-48. *Mem:* AAAS; Am Chem Soc; Sigma Xi; NY Acad Sci. *Res:* Carbohydrate chemistry; cooerelation of anomeric configuration of glycosides; methylation analysis of dextrans; synthesis of derivitives of erythrose and glucose. *Mailing Add:* 7 Northern Dr Decatur IL 62521

**VAN COTT, HAROLD PORTER,** ENGINEERING SCIENCE, ERGONOMICS. *Current Pos:* PRIN SCIENTIST, VAN COTT ASSOCS, 92- *Personal Data:* b Schenectady, NY, Nov 16, 25; m 53, Madeleine Bouvier; c Laurent, Jeanne & Anne. *Educ:* Univ Rochester, BA, 48; Univ NC, MA, 52, PhD(psychol), 53. *Prof Exp:* Prog dir, Am Inst Res, 55-58, dir, Inst Human Performance, 64-68; dir human ecol, 74-75; develop engr, IBM Corp, 58-64; dir, Off Commun, Am Psychol Asn, 68-74; chief human factors, Nat Bur Standards, 75-78, chief consumer sci, 78-81; chief scientist, Biotechnol, Inc, 81-82; vpres, Essex Corp, 82-87; prin staff officer, Nat Res Coun, 87-92. *Concurrent Pos:* Consult to various pvt & govt orgn, 64- *Mem:* Fel Am Psychol Asn; fel Human Factors Soc; fel AAAS; Sigma Xi. *Res:* Ergonomics as it is applied to the design and evaluation of products and systems. *Mailing Add:* 8300 Still Spring Ct Bethesda MD 20817. *Fax:* 301-365-1010

**VAN DAM, ANDRIES,** ELECTRICAL ENGINEERING. *Current Pos:* PROF COMPUT SCI & TECHNOL, BROWN UNIV, 65- *Personal Data:* b Dec 8, 38. *Educ:* Swarthmore Col, BS, 60; Univ Pa, MS, 63, PhD(elec eng), 66. *Mem:* Nat Acad Eng. *Mailing Add:* Brown Univ 115 Waterman St Providence RI 02912

**VAN DAM, JACQUES,** GASTROENTEROLOGY. *Current Pos:* instr, 89-93, ASST PROF MED, HARVARD MED SCH, 93- *Personal Data:* b Amersfoot, Neth, Mar 13, 53. *Educ:* Rutgers Univ, BA, 75; Hahnemann Med Col & Hosp, MS, 81; Georgetown Univ, MD, 84, PhD(physiol & biophys), 88. *Honors & Awards:* Res Award in Clin Gastroenterol, Am Col Gastroenterol, 91 & 94. *Prof Exp:* Instr, Dept Physiol & Biophys, Col Allied Health Professions, Hahnemann Med Col & Hosp, Philadelphia, 77-78; instr, Dept Hemat & Oncol, Children's Hosp Nat Med Ctr, Washington, DC, 80-81; clin fel med, New Eng Deaconess Hosp, Harvard Med Sch, 84-87, Beth Israel Hosp, 87-89 & Mass Gen Hosp, 88-89. *Concurrent Pos:* Asst med, Mass Gen Hosp, Harvard Med Sch, 88; staff physician, Brockton/West Roxbury Vet Admin Med Ctr, 89-90, attend physician, 89-90; assoc physician, Brigham & Women's Hosp, Harvard Med Sch, 91-, attend physician, 91-, assoc dir gastrointestinal endoscopy, 91-; mem, Res & Develop Comt, Am Soc Gastrointestinal Endoscopy, 91-93; consult, Laser Biomed Res Ctr, Mass Inst Technol, 92- *Mem:* AMA; Am Fedn Clin Res; Am Physiol Soc; Am Col Gastroenterol; Am Soc Gastrointestinal Endoscopy; Am Soc Laser Med & Surg; fel Am Col Physicians; fel Am Soc Laser Med & Surg. *Res:* Laser-induced fluoescence spectroscopy for in vivo detection of gastrointestinal disease; development and clinical application of diagnostic endoscopic ultrasonography; endoscopic variceal ligation for the primary prevention of variceal hemorrhage; laser application for treatment of gastrointestinal malignancies. *Mailing Add:* Dept Med & Gastroenterol Harvard Med Sch Brigham & Women's Hosp 75 Francis St Boston MA 02115

**VANDAM, LEROY DAVID,** ANESTHESIOLOGY. *Current Pos:* from assoc clin prof to clin prof, 54-67, prof, 67-79, EMER PROF ANESTHESIA, HARVARD MED SCH, 79- *Personal Data:* b New York, NY, Jan 19, 14; m 39, Regina Rutherford; c Albert R & Samuel W. *Educ:* Brown Univ, PhB, 34; NY Univ, MD, 38. *Hon Degrees:* MA, Harvard Univ, 68. *Honors & Awards:* Distinguished Serv Award, Am Soc Anesthesiol. *Prof Exp:* Fel surg,

Sch Med, Johns Hopkins Univ, 45-47; asst prof anesthesia, Sch Med, Univ Pa, 52-54. *Concurrent Pos:* Consult, Valley Forge Army Hosp & Philadelphia Naval Hosp, 52-54, Children's Boston Lying In, Chelsea Naval, West Roxbury Vet Admin, Winchester, Burbank & Nantucket Cottage Hosps, 54-; chmn adv panel anesthesiol, US Pharmacopoeia, 54-60; ed-in-chief, J Anesthesiol, 64; chmn comn anesthesia, Nat Acad Sci-Nat Res Coun, 65; pres, Boston Med Libr, 79-85. *Mem:* Am Soc Anesthesiol; AMA; Sigma Xi. *Res:* Pharmacology, physiology and biochemistry of surgery and anesthesia. *Mailing Add:* Ten Longwood Dr 268 Westwood MA 02090

**VANDE BERG, JERRY STANLEY,** ELECTRON MICROSCOPY, TISSUE CULTURE. *Current Pos:* asst prof, 87-92, ASSOC PROF, DEPT SURG, UNIV CALIF, SAN DIEGO, 92-; DIR CORE CLIN & RES EM FACIL, VET ADMIN MED CTR, 82- *Personal Data:* b Sheldon, Iowa, June 1, 40; m 94, Deborah Freitas; c Blaine, Joel & Christopher. *Educ:* Univ Nebr, BSc, 64, MSc, 65; Va Polytech Inst & State Univ, PhD(physiol), 69. *Prof Exp:* Instr entom, Va Polytech Inst & State Univ, 67-69; asst prof neurophysiol, Wayne State Univ, 69-74; res assoc, Univ Wis-Madison, 74-79; asst prof electron micros, Old Dominion Univ, 75-79; dir core res, Vet Admin Med Ctr, 79-82. *Concurrent Pos:* Prin investr, 75-; lectr, Univ Calif, San Diego Med Sch, 79-80, Eastern Va Med Sch, 78-79. *Mem:* Electron Micros Soc Am; AAAS; Wound Healing Soc. *Res:* Cellular mechanisms of contraction in wound healing; cellular mechanisms of wound repair in chronic wounds. *Mailing Add:* Vet Admin Med Ctr 151 3350 La Jolla Village Dr San Diego CA 92161. *Fax:* 619-552-2436; *E-Mail:* jvandeberg@vapop.ucsd.edu

**VANDEBERG, JOHN LEE,** MAMMALIAN GENETICS, DISEASE SUSCEPTIBILITY. *Current Pos:* assoc scientist genetics, 80-85, chmn genetics, 82-93, SCIENTIST GENETICS, SOUTHWEST FOUND BIOMED RES, 85-, SCI DIR, 93- *Personal Data:* b Appleton, Wis, June 14, 47; m 75, Jane F Barr; c Jason C & James R. *Educ:* Univ Wis-Madison, BS, 69; La Trobe Univ, Melbourne, BS, 70; Macquarie Univ, PhD(genetics), 75. *Prof Exp:* Tutor genetics, Macquarie Univ, Sydney, 73-75; res assoc genetics, Univ Wis-Madison, 75-79; asst scientist genetics, Wis Regional Res Ctr, Univ Wis- Madison, 79-80; from asst prof to assoc prof, Dept Cell & Struct Biol & Dept Path, Univ Tex Health Sci Ctr, San Antonio, 80-86. *Concurrent Pos:* Fulbright fel, 69-70; fel, Pop Coun, 76-77; NIH trainee, Univ Tex Health Sci Ctr, San Antonio, 77-78, prof, Dept Cell & Struct, 86- *Mem:* AAAS; Genetics Soc Am; Sigma Xi; Am Soc Human Genetics; Am Heart Asn; Am Soc Biochem & Molecular Biol. *Res:* Genetic aspects of heart disease and skin cancer and the genetic basis of susceptibility to infectious disease; sex chromosome evolution and dosage compensation; marsupial and primate models for biomedical research. *Mailing Add:* Southwest Found Biomed Res PO Box 760549 San Antonio TX 78245-0549. *Fax:* 210-670-3309; *E-Mail:* jlv@darwin.sfbr.org

**VANDEBERG, JOHN THOMAS,** SYNTHETIC INORGANIC & ORGANOMETALLIC CHEMISTRY. *Current Pos:* vpres technol, 90-95, VPRES TECHNOL GLOBAL, DSM DESOTECH INC, 95- *Personal Data:* b Great Falls, Mont, Aug 27, 39; c 2. *Educ:* Carroll Col, BA, 62; Loyola Univ, MS, 66, PhD(chem), 69; Northwestern Univ, MM, 88. *Honors & Awards:* Mat Mkt Asn Award, Fedn Socs Coatings Technol, 80; Res & Develop IR 100 Award, 86. *Prof Exp:* Sect leader, DeSoto Inc, 69-73, mgr, Res Serv, 73-78, mgr, Polymer Develop, 78-84, dir, 84-89, dir, Technol, 89-90. *Concurrent Pos:* Mem bd dirs, Fedn Socs Coatings Technol. *Mem:* Sigma Xi; Indust Res Inst; Am Chem Soc; Fedn Socs Coatings Technol. *Res:* Polymer chemistry; coatings for optical fibers; spectroscopy; analytical chemistry; tetraanglborates and additives for concrete; author of 20 publications and two books; holder of five patents. *Mailing Add:* DSM Desotech Inc 1122 St Charles St Elgin IL 60120

**VANDE BERG, WARREN JAMES,** PHYCOLOGY. *Current Pos:* From asst prof to assoc prof, 70-81, PROF BIOL, NORTHERN MICH UNIV, 81- *Personal Data:* b Orange City, Iowa, Sept 28, 43; m 62, Mary D Herder; c 3. *Educ:* Iowa State Univ, BS, 66; Ind Univ, Bloomington, PhD(phycol), 70. *Mem:* Phycol Soc Am. *Res:* Control of cellular development in Volvox. *Mailing Add:* Dept Biol Northern Mich Univ 1401 Presque Isle Ave Marquette MI 49855-5301

**VAN DE CASTLE, JOHN F,** ORGANIC, POLYMER & PETROLEUM CHEMISTRY. *Current Pos:* CONSULT, 92- *Personal Data:* b New York, NY, Sept 30, 33; m 57; c 4. *Educ:* St John's Col, BS, 55; Univ Md, PhD(org chem), 60. *Prof Exp:* Chemist, Hoffmann-La Roche, Inc, 55, Nat Bur Standards, 56 & Am Cyanamid Co, 57; group leader elastomers, Esso Res & Eng Co, NJ, 59-65, investment planning & mkt adv, Esso Chem Co, Inc, NY, 65-71; asst vpres, Englehard Minerals & Chem Co, 71-72, mgr com develop, 72-77; mgr technol acquisition, Arco Chem Co, 77-81, vpres, Arco Technol, 81-92. *Res:* Synthesis and characterization of ethylene propylene copolymers and terpolymers, polybutadienes; chemical modification of polymers; Ziegler and organometallic catalytic studies; technology licensing for chemical, petroleum and petrochemical industries; chemical petroleum and petrochemical processing; hydrogenation processes; hydrocarbon isomerization processes. *Mailing Add:* 20 Fox Chase Dr Watchung NJ 07060

**VANDEGAER, JAN EDMOND,** BIOMEDICAL CHEMISTRY, ENVIRON COAGULANTS. *Current Pos:* dir res, 74-77, vpres, 75-77, INDEPENDENT CONSULT, CHEM PROD DEVELOP, LEGAL EXPERT, 77- *Personal Data:* b Tienen, Belg, July 28, 27; nat US; m 51, Martha Strijckmans; c Koenraad, Machteld, Frieda & Ingrid. *Educ:* Cath Univ Louvain, BS, 48, MS, 50, PhD(phys chem), 52. *Prof Exp:* Asst res proteins, Cath Univ Louvain, 52-54; fel, Nat Res Coun Can, 54-55; res chemist, Dow Chem Co, 55-59; sr chemist & proj leader, J T Baker Chem Co,

59-60, sr chemist & group leader, 60-62; mgr polymer res, Wallace & Tiernan, Inc, 62-65, dir cent res, 65-70; dir lab res, Chem Group, Dart Industs Inc, 70-74. *Concurrent Pos:* Scholar, Biochem Inst, Finland, 53 & Cambridge, 54. *Mem:* Asn Res Dirs; Soc Plastics Engrs; Am Chem Soc. *Res:* Physical chemistry of proteins; polymer chemistry; correlation of physical properties of high polymers and molecular structure; biomedical applications; plastics engineering; microencapsulation; polyolefins, surfactants, cosmetics and emulsion polymerization; research administration; technical planning. *Mailing Add:* 427 Auds Lane Pasadena MD 21122

**VAN DE GRAAFF, KENT MARSHALL,** GROSS ANATOMY, MAMMALOGY. *Current Pos:* PROF HUMAN ANAT, WEBER STATE UNIV. *Personal Data:* b Ogden, Utah, May 21, 42; m 62; c 4. *Educ:* Weber State Col, BS, 65; Univ Utah, MS, 69; Northern Ariz Univ, PhD(zool), 73. *Honors & Awards:* A Brazier Howell Honoriarum, Am Soc Mammalogists, 72. *Prof Exp:* Asst prof vet sci, Univ Minn, St Paul, 73-75; asst prof human anat, Brigham Young Univ, 75- *Mem:* Am Soc Mammalogists; Am Soc Zoologists; Am Soc Vet Anatomists; Sigma Xi. *Res:* Functional morphological aspects of mammalian posture and locomotion. *Mailing Add:* 169 N 560 E Orem UT 84058

**VANDEGRIFT, ALFRED EUGENE,** research administration; deceased, see previous edition for last biography

**VANDEGRIFT, GUY GEORGE,** SCIENCE EDUCATION, PHYSICS OF VIOLIN. *Current Pos:* ASST PROF PHYSICS, UNIV TEX, EL PASO, 94- *Personal Data:* b Columbia, SC, Apr 3, 52; m 85, Valentina Akimova; c Bertha, Eve & Lena. *Educ:* Univ Calif, Berkeley, AB, 74, PhD(physics), 82. *Prof Exp:* Postdoctoral, Univ Calif, Irvine, 82-84; Columbia Univ, 86; vis scientist, Novosibirsk, Russia, 84; asst prof, Dickinson Col, 87-92; lectr, Univ NC, Greensboro, 92-94. *Mem:* Catgut Acoust Soc. *Res:* Science education and training of teachers; musical acoustics. *Mailing Add:* Physics Dept Univ Tex El Paso TX 79968-0515

**VANDEGRIFT, VAUGHN,** BIOCHEMISTRY. *Current Pos:* PROF & DEAN, SCH MATH & SCI, MONTCLAIR SATE COL, 88- *Personal Data:* b Jersey City, NJ, Dec 7, 46; m 69; c Beth, David & Mark. *Educ:* Montclair State Col, BA, 68, MA, 70; Ohio Univ, PhD(biochem), 74. *Prof Exp:* Teacher chem, River Dell Regional High Sch, Oradell, NJ, 68-70; asst prof chem & biol, Ill State Univ, 74-76; from asst prof to assoc prof chem, Murray State Univ, 76-84, prof & chmn, Dept Chem, 82-88. *Concurrent Pos:* Vis assoc prof biochem, Southern Ill Univ, Carbondale, 80-81; vis scientist, Sch Med, Ohio Univ, Athens, 82. *Mem:* Sigma Xi; Am Chem Soc; Am Asn Univ Adminrs; Am Asn Higher Educ. *Res:* Protein-nucleic ascid interactions; structure and function of genes. *Mailing Add:* Sch Math Sci Montclair State Col Upper Montclair NJ 07043. *Fax:* 973-655-4390; *E-Mail:* vandegrift@apollo.montclair.edu

**VANDEHEY, ROBERT C,** entomology, for more information see previous edition

**VAN DE KAMP, PETER CORNELIS,** GEOLOGY, GEOCHEMISTRY. *Current Pos:* INDEPENDENT CONSULT, 85- *Personal Data:* b Plainfield, NJ, Aug 25, 40; m 64; c 2. *Educ:* Lehigh Univ, BA, 62; McMaster Univ, MSc, 64; Univ Bristol, PhD(geochem), 67. *Prof Exp:* Geologist, Shell Develop Co, Tex & Calif, 67-71 & Shell Oil Co, Colo, 71-73; res prof, Univ Man, 73-74; vpres, Geo-Logic Inc, 74-77; independent petrol explor consult, 77-79; partner, Georesources assoc, 79-85. *Mem:* Soc Econ Paleont & Mineral; Geol Soc Am; Am Asn Petrol Geol. *Res:* Stratigraphy; sedimentary, metamorphic and igneous petrology and geochemistry. *Mailing Add:* 1750 Cabernet Lane St Helena CA 94574

**VAN DE KAR, LOUIS DAVID,** NEUROPHARMACOLOGY, NEUROENDOCRINOLOGY. *Current Pos:* from asst prof to assoc prof, 81-91, PROF PHARMACOL, STRITCH SCH MED, LOYOLA UNIV, 92- *Personal Data:* b Amsterdam, Neth, Apr 15, 47; m 78. *Educ:* Univ Amsterdam, BS, 71, MS, 74; Univ Iowa PhD(pharmacol), 78. *Prof Exp:* Res assoc pharmacol, Neth Cent Inst Brain Res, 74-75; fel physiol, Univ Calif, San Francisco, 79-81. *Concurrent Pos:* Fel, Fulbright-Hays Found, 75. *Mem:* Int Soc Neuroendocrinol; Am Soc Pharmacol Exp Ther; Am Physiol Soc; Soc Neurosci; Endocrine Soc. *Res:* Role of serotonergic neurons in the regulation of renin, adrenocorticotrophic hormone, oxytocin, vasopressin and prolactin secretion; neuroanatomy and physiology of brain serotonin; role of brain serotonin in cardiovascular homeostasis; stress and neuroendocrine function. *Mailing Add:* Dept Pharmacol Loyola Univ Stritch Sch Med 2160 S First Ave Maywood IL 60153. *Fax:* 708-216-6596

**VANDE KIEFT, LAWRENCE JOHN,** SOLID STATE PHYSICS, EXPLOSIVES. *Current Pos:* res physicist, Signature & Propagation Lab, US Army, Aberdeen Proving Ground, Md, 68-72, chief, Optical & Microwave Systs Br, Concepts Anal Lab, 72-75, dep prog mgr, 75-79, explosives formulation team leader, Terminal Ballistics Div, Ballistic Res Lab, 79-93, CONSULT, US ARMY RES LAB, ABERDEEN PROVING GROUND, MD, 93- *Personal Data:* b Grand Rapids, Mich, May 14, 32; m 62, Emlagene Lozon; c David M & Steven J. *Educ:* Calvin Col, BA, 53; Univ Conn, MS, 55, PhD(physics), 68. *Prof Exp:* Sr physicist, Bendix Res Labs, 58-62. *Mem:* Am Phys Soc. *Res:* Electron paramagnetic resonance investigations of radiation effects in single crystals; laser interactions with the atmosphere; laser semiactive terminal homing; computer simulation; development of safer energetic materials; patent on PEG/PMVT energetic binder for explosives; ultrasonics; patent on novel fire extinguishing system. *Mailing Add:* US Army Res Lab Attn AMSRL-WT-TB Aberdeen Proving Ground MD 21005-5066. *Fax:* 410-278-3337; *E-Mail:* ljv@arl.army.mil

**VAN DEMARK, DUANE R,** SPEECH PATHOLOGY. *Current Pos:* asst prof, 65-68, assoc prof speech path & otolaryngol, 68-75, PROF SPEECH PATH & OTOLARYNGOL & MAXILLOFACIAL SURG, UNIV IOWA, 75- *Personal Data:* b Elida, Ohio, Feb 26, 36; div; c 2. *Educ:* Hiram Col, BA, 58; Univ Iowa, MA & PhD(speech path, audiol), 62. *Prof Exp:* Instr speech path, Ind Univ, 62-65. *Concurrent Pos:* Ind Univ Found res grant, 65; Am-Scand Found George Marshall fel, 70; Nat Inst Dent Res spec fel, 70; partic, Int Cong Cleft Palate, 67-69 & 73, mem prog comt, 68, secy & asst to secy gen, 69; sect ed, Cleft Palate J. *Mem:* Am Cleft Palate Educ Found; Am Speech & Hearing Asn; Am Cleft Palate Asn (vpres, 80, pres, 82). *Res:* Cleft palate research. *Mailing Add:* Dept Otolaryngol Univ Iowa Col Med Iowa City IA 52242-1000

**VANDEMARK, NOLAND LEROY,** PHYSIOLOGY. *Current Pos:* dir, Agr Exp Sta, 74-81, prof, 74-83, EMER PROF ANIMAL SCI, CORNELL UNIV, 83- *Personal Data:* b Columbus Grove, Ohio, July 6, 19; m 40, Beda Basinger; c Gary, Judy & Linda. *Educ:* Ohio State Univ, BS, 41, MS, 42; Cornell Univ, PhD, 48. *Honors & Awards:* Borden Award, 59. *Prof Exp:* Asst animal husb, Ohio State Univ, 41-42; vitamin chemist, State Dept Agr, Ohio, 42; asst animal husb, Cornell Univ, 42-44, 48; livestock specialist, US Dept Army, Austria, 46-47; from asst prof to prof physiol, Univ Ill, Urbana, 48-64; prof dairy sci & chmn dept, Col Agr & Home Econ, Ohio State Univ & Ohio Agr Res & Develop Ctr, 64-73, mem fac, Coop Exten Serv, Univ, 64-73; dir res, NY State Col Agr & Life Sci, 74-81; distinguished bicentennial prof, Univ Ga, 85. *Mem:* AAAS; Am Soc Animal Sci; Am Dairy Sci Asn; Am Physiol Soc; Brit Soc Study Fertil. *Res:* Physiology and biochemistry of reproductive processes in cattle, especially semen production; sperm metabolism; female reproductive processes; artificial insemination and fertility-sterility problems; research management and creativity; author of two books. *Mailing Add:* 8801 Leesville Rd Raleigh NC 27613-1012

**VAN DE MERWE, WILLEM PIETER,** POLARIZED LIGHT SCATTERING, BIOMEDICAL LASER APPLICATIONS. *Current Pos:* DIR BIOMED INSTRUMENTATION CTR, UNIFORMED SERVS UNIV HEALTH SCIS, 86-, ASSOC PROF PREV MED, 87- *Personal Data:* b Rotterdam, Neth, Dec 26, 50; US citizen; m 81, Angela D Cole; c Rebekah, Daniel & Nathanael. *Educ:* Delft Univ Technol, BSc, 74, MSc, 75; Clemson Univ, PhD(physics), 80. *Prof Exp:* Vis asst prof physics, Clemson Univ, 80-81; fel, Univ Rochester, 81-83; nuclear med sci officer, US Army, 83-86. *Concurrent Pos:* Consult, Med Free Electron Laser Prog, Strategic Defense Orgn, 86-89. *Mem:* Optical Soc Am; Sigma Xi. *Res:* Rapid identification of microorganisms through means of polarized light scattering fluorescence and autocorrelation techniques; determination of physical parameters such as dimension and optical constants of bacteria and bacterial spores for purposes of medicine, environmental monitoring and national defense. *Mailing Add:* Dept Physics Ind Wesleyan Univ S Washington St Marion IN 46952. *Fax:* 301-295-3431; *E-Mail:* vandem@usuhssb.bitnet

**VAN DEN AKKER, JOHANNES ARCHIBALD,** OPTICS, THERMODYNAMICS. *Current Pos:* RETIRED. *Personal Data:* b Los Angeles, Calif, Dec 5, 04; m 30, 58, 90, Margaret Koller; c Valerie (Emmert). *Educ:* Calif Inst Technol, BS, 26, PhD(physics), 31. *Honors & Awards:* Res & Develop Award, Tech Asn Pulp & Paper Indust, 67, Gold Medal, 68. *Prof Exp:* Instr physics, Wash Univ, 30-35; res assoc & chmn dept, Inst Paper Chem, Lawrence Univ, 35-56, sr res assoc physics & chmn, Dept Physics & Math, 56-70, res counr, 65-70, emer prof physics, 70; consult, James River Corp, 70-80 & 82-85. *Concurrent Pos:* Sr Fulbright lectr, Univ Manchester Inst Sci & Technol, 61-62; consult res & develop, Am Can Co, Neenah, 71-82; gen consult, 85- *Mem:* Fel AAAS; fel Am Phys Soc; fel Optical Soc Am; Am Asn Physics Teachers; fel Tech Asn Pulp & Paper Indust. *Res:* Spatial distribution of x-ray photoelectrons; optical properties of paper; spectrophotometry and color measurement; instrumentation of all properties of paper; paper and fiber physics. *Mailing Add:* 1101 E Glendale Ave Appleton WI 54911

**VAN DEN AVYLE, JAMES ALBERT,** METALLURGY. *Current Pos:* STAFF MEM, SANDIA LABS, 68- *Personal Data:* b South Bend, Ind, Sept 13, 46; m 68. *Educ:* Purdue Univ, BS, 68; Mass Inst Technol, SM, 69, PhD(metall), 75. *Mem:* Am Soc Metals, Am Soc Testing & Mat. *Res:* Fracture of metals, mechanical properties of metals. *Mailing Add:* 4779 Corrales Rd PO Box 693 Corrales NM 87048

**VANDENBERG, EDWIN JAMES,** CHEMISTRY. *Current Pos:* adj prof, 83-91, RES PROF CHEM, ARIZ STATE UNIV, TEMPE, 92- *Personal Data:* b Hawthorne, NJ, Sept 13, 18; m 50, Mildred E Wright; c David J & Jean E. *Educ:* Stevens Inst Tech, ME, 39. *Hon Degrees:* Dr Eng, Stevens Inst Tech, 65. *Honors & Awards:* Polymer Chem Award, Am Chem Soc, 81, Appl Polymer Sci Award, 91, Charles Goodyear Medal, 91, Herman F Mark Award, 92, Solid Polymer Electrolyte Int Award, 94. *Prof Exp:* Res chemist Hercules Inc, Res Ctr, Wilmington, Del, 39-44 & 45-57, sr res chemist, 58-64, res assoc, 65-77, sr res assoc, 78-82; asst shift supvr, Sunflower Ord Works, Kans, 44-45. *Concurrent Pos:* Coun, Del Sect, Am Chem Soc, 74-81, chmn, 76, Div Polychem, 79, coordr indust sponsors, 82-; chmn, Gordon Res Conf Polymers, 78. *Mem:* Am Chem Soc. *Res:* Applied polymer science; polymer chemistry; biochemistry. *Mailing Add:* Ariz State Univ Dept Chem & Biochem Tempe AZ 85287-1604

**VANDENBERG, JOANNA MARIA,** HIGH RESOLUTION X-RAY DIFFRACTION,. *Current Pos:* fel, 68-69, MEM TECH STAFF, BELL LABS, MURRAY HILL, 72- *Personal Data:* b Heemstede, Neth, Jan 24, 38; m 93, James C Phillips; c Lucy Voorhoeve & Niels Voorhoeve. *Educ:* Leiden State Univ, BS, 59, MS, 62, PhD(struct chem), 64. *Prof Exp:* Teaching asst,

Lab Crystallog, Univ Amsterdam, 62-64; res chemist, Royal Dutch & Shell Lab, 64-68. *Concurrent Pos:* Mem tech staff, Bell Labs, 72. *Mem:* Am Phys Soc; Mat Res Soc. *Res:* High-resolution x-ray analysis of semiconductor multi-quantum well structures, and their related material and device properties; superconductivity of oxide materials; metalorganic chemical vapor deposition. *Mailing Add:* 204 Springfield Ave Summit NJ 07901-3909

**VANDENBERG, JOHN DONALD,** ENTOMOLOGY. *Current Pos:* res entomologist, Beltsville, Md, 83-87, res leader, Agr Res Serv, Logan, Utah, 87-93, AGR RES SERV, CORNELL UNIV, USDA, ITHACA, NY, 93- *Personal Data:* b Benton Harbor, Mich, Jan 24, 54; m 83, Alice C L Churchill. *Educ:* Univ Mich, BS, 75; Univ Maine, MS, 77; Ore State Univ, PhD, 82. *Prof Exp:* Assoc, Boyce Thompson Inst, Ithaca, NY, 82-83. *Concurrent Pos:* Actg asst dir, Midwest Area, Agr Res Serv, Peoria, Ill, 91. *Mem:* Soc Invertebrate Path; Entom Soc Am; Am Soc Microbiol; Sigma Xi (secy, 89-90, pres, 91). *Res:* Entomology; microbiology; invertebrate pathology; agriculture. *Mailing Add:* US Plant Soil & Nutrit Lab Cornell Univ USDA Agr Res Serv Tower Rd Ithaca NY 14853

**VAN DEN BERG, L,** BIOCHEMICAL ENGINEERING, FOOD SCIENCE. *Current Pos:* RETIRED. *Personal Data:* b Hattem, Neth, Mar 14, 29; Can citizen; m 53; c 4. *Educ:* State Agr Univ, Wageningen, MSc, 53; Univ Man, MSc, 55. *Prof Exp:* Sr res officer food technol, Nat Res Coun Can, 56-80, prin res officer, Biol Prod Fuels, Inst Bio Sci, 80-84, asst dir & head, Carbohydrate Lab, 84-90, dir, 90-92. *Mem:* Am Soc Microbiol; AAAS; Inst Food Technologists; Can Inst Food Sci & Technol. *Res:* Application of refrigeration to food preservation, including freezing and frozen storage of meat and vegetables and storage of fresh vegetables; anaerobic digestion of food plant waste; methanogenesis from biomass; fermenter design. *Mailing Add:* 2 Willeth Ave Nepean ON K2E 5C1 Can

**VANDENBERGH, DAVID JOHN,** MOLECULAR BIOLOGY, NEUROSCIENCES. *Current Pos:* SR RES FEL, MOLECULAR NEUROBIOL BR, ADDICTION RES CTR, NAT INST DRUG ABUSE, 90- *Personal Data:* b Athens, Ohio, May 7, 59; m 85; c 2. *Educ:* Univ NC, BS, 81; Pa State Univ, PhD(biochem), 87. *Prof Exp:* Grad res asst biochem, Pa State Univ, 81-87; res fel biol, Calif Inst Technol, 87-90. *Mem:* AAAS; Soc Neurosci. *Res:* Control of gene expression in neurons, particularly genes in drug abuse and the dopaminergic neurons. *Mailing Add:* Nat Inst Drug Abuse Addiction Res Ctr Molecular Neurobiol Br PO Box 5180 Baltimore MD 21224. *Fax:* 410-550-1535; *E-Mail:* vanden@ncifcrf.gov

**VANDENBERGH, JOHN GARRY,** ANIMAL BEHAVIOR, ENDOCRINOLOGY. *Current Pos:* head, Dept Zool, 76-90, PROF ZOOL, NC STATE UNIV, 76- *Personal Data:* b Paterson, NJ, May 5, 35; m 58, Barbara Doll; c David J & Michael P. *Educ:* Montclair State Col, AB, 57; Ohio Univ, MA, 59; Pa State Univ, PhD(zool), 62. *Prof Exp:* Res biologist, Nat Inst Neurol Dis & Blindness, 62-65; res scientist, NC Dept Ment Health, 65-76. *Concurrent Pos:* NIMH grant, 67-82 & 85-93, NSF grant, 82-85; mem, nat primate adv comt, NIH, rev comt basic behav processes, NIMH; mem psychobiol panel, NSF; mem, Comt Conserv Non-Human Primates, Nat Res Coun-Nat Acad Sci, Comt Rewrite Guide Care & Use Lab Animals; assoc ed, Am J Primatology; mem adv comt, Calif Primate Res Ctr, Caribbean Primate Ctr & Wis Regional Primate Res Ctr; mem, NASA Space Biol Rev Comt; dir, Triangle Consortium Reproductive Biol; mem, Scholarly Rev Comt, Smithsonian Inst; mem, Inst Animal Resources, NRS, NAS. *Mem:* Animal Behav Soc (pres, 82-83); Am Soc Mammal; Soc Study Reproduction; AAAS; Sigma Xi; Soc Behav Neuroendocrinol. *Res:* Environmental control of reproduction; endocrine basis of behavior; pheromones and reproduction; rodent and primate social behavior; prenatal endocrine effects. *Mailing Add:* Dept Zool NC State Univ PO Box 7617 Raleigh NC 27695-7617

**VAN DEN BERGH, SIDNEY,** ASTRONOMY. *Current Pos:* dir, 77-86, ASTRONR, DOMINION ASTROPHYS OBSERV, 86- *Personal Data:* b Wassenaar, Holland, May 20, 29; m 59, Paulette Serineau; c Peter, Mieke & Sabine. *Educ:* Princeton Univ, AB, 50; Ohio State Univ, MSc, 52; Univ Goettingen, Dr rer nat(astron), 56. *Honors & Awards:* Beals Award, Can Astron Soc, 88 & Isaac Killam Prize, 90; Russell Lectr, Am Astron Soc, 90; President's Medal, Nat Res Coun, 91. *Prof Exp:* Asst prof astron, Ohio State Univ, 56-58; from lectr to prof, Univ Toronto, 58-77. *Concurrent Pos:* Pres & chmn bd, Can, France & Hawaii Telescope Corp, 82; pres, Can Astron Soc, 90-92. *Mem:* Am Astron Soc; fel Royal Soc Can; Royal Astron Soc; Int Astron Union (vpres, 76-82); Royal Soc London. *Res:* Extragalactic nebulae; star clusters; variable stars; supernovae. *Mailing Add:* 418 Lands End Rd Sidney BC V8L 5L9 Can. *Fax:* 250-363-0045; *E-Mail:* vandenbergh@dao.nrc.ca

**VAN DEN BOLD, WILLEM AALDERT,** geology, paleontology, for more information see previous edition

**VANDEN BORN, WILLIAM HENRY,** WEED SCIENCE, PLANT PHYSIOLOGY. *Current Pos:* Fel, Dept Plant Sci, Univ Alta, 60-61, from asst prof to assoc prof, 61-72, chmn dept, 70-75, & 82-87, PROF WEED SCI & CROP ECOL, UNIV ALTA, 72- *Personal Data:* b Rhenen, Neth, Nov 17, 32; Can citizen; m 58; c 5. *Educ:* Univ Alta, BSc, 56, MSc, 58; Univ Toronto, PhD(plant physiol), 61. *Concurrent Pos:* Assoc ed, Weed Sci, 81-86 & Can J Plant Sci, 81-84. *Mem:* Fel Weed Sci Soc Am; Can Soc Plant Physiol; Can Soc Agron; Am Sci Affil; Am Soc Agron; Am Inst Biol Sci. *Res:* Herbicide physiology; physiology of herbicide action: absorption, translocation, mechanism of action, metabolism of systemic herbicides; weed biology and control, both annuals and perennials, chiefly in grain crops. *Mailing Add:* Dept Plant Sci Univ Alta Edmonton AB T6G 2M7 Can

**VANDENBOSCH, ROBERT,** NUCLEAR CHEMISTRY. *Current Pos:* PROF CHEM, UNIV WASH, 63- *Personal Data:* b Lexington, Ky, Dec 12, 32; m 56; c 2. *Educ:* Calvin Col, AB, 54; Univ Calif, PhD(chem), 57. *Prof Exp:* From asst chemist to assoc chemist, Argonne Nat Lab, 57-63. *Concurrent Pos:* Fulbright fel, Niels Bohr Inst, Copenhagen, 61-62. *Mem:* Fel Am Phys Soc; Am Chem Soc. *Res:* Heavy ion nuclear reactions and nuclear fission; atomic and molecular clusters. *Mailing Add:* Dept Chem Univ Wash PO Box 351700 Seattle WA 98195-1700

**VANDEN BOUT, PAUL ADRIAN,** INTERSTELLAR MEDIUM, RADIO ASTRONOMY. *Current Pos:* DIR, NAT RADIO ASTRON OBSERV, 85- *Personal Data:* b Grand Rapids, Mich, June 16, 39; m 61, Rachel A Eggebeen; c Thomas A & David A. *Educ:* Calvin Col, AB, 61; Univ Calif, Berkeley, PhD(physics), 66. *Prof Exp:* Teaching asst physics, Univ Calif, Berkeley, 61-66; teaching fel, Columbia Univ, 67-68, asst prof, 68-70; from asst prof to prof astron, Univ Tex, Austin, 70-84. *Mem:* Fel Am Phys Soc; Am Astron Soc; Int Astron Union; AAAS; Int Radio Sci Union. *Res:* Spectroscopic study of diffuse matter in space, particularly using radio techniques, interstellar matter, star formation, isotopic abundances, radio instrumentation and interferometry. *Mailing Add:* 2412 Pine Garth Run Charlottesville VA 22901. *E-Mail:* pvandenb@nrao.edu

**VANDENBURGH, HERMAN H,** PATHOLOGY. *Current Pos:* ASSOC PROF PATH, BROWN UNIV, MIRIAM HOSP, 87- *Personal Data:* b Albany, NY, Aug 10, 48. *Educ:* Boston Univ, BS, 70; Univ Pa, PhD(anat), 76. *Prof Exp:* Staff fel path, NIH, 82-87. *Mem:* AAAS; Am Cell Biol Soc; Am Phys Soc; Tissue Cult Asn. *Mailing Add:* Dept Path & Prog Med Brown Univ 164 Summit Ave Providence RI 02906

**VANDEN EYNDEN, CHARLES LAWRENCE,** NUMBER THEORY. *Current Pos:* assoc prof, 69-74, PROF MATH, ILL STATE UNIV, 74- *Personal Data:* b Cincinnati, Ohio, June 25, 36; m 67, Joan Brody; c Lisa & Jennifer. *Educ:* Univ Cincinnati, BS, 58; Univ Ore, MA, 60, PhD(math), 62. *Prof Exp:* NSF fel, Univ Mich, 62-63; asst prof math, Univ Ariz, 63-65 & Miami Univ, 65-67; asst prof math, Miami Univ, 65-67; vis asst prof, Pa State Univ, 67-68; asst prof, Ohio Univ, 68-69. *Concurrent Pos:* Vis prof, Portland State Univ, 77-78. *Mem:* Am Math Soc; Math Asn Am. *Res:* Diophantine approximation; elementary number theory; combinatorial theory; sequences of integers; covering congruences; graph decomposition. *Mailing Add:* Dept Math Ill State Univ 4520 Normal IL 61761-6901. *E-Mail:* cve@math.ilstu.edu

**VANDENHAZEL, BESSEL J,** INTEGRATED URBAN WASTE MANAGEMENT SYSTEMS. *Current Pos:* RETIRED. *Personal Data:* b Neth, 27; Can citizen; m 53, Mia; c 3. *Educ:* State Col Agr, Neth, I Ing, 53; Univ Western Ont, BA, 60; Northern Ill Univ, MSc, 69. *Honors & Awards:* Rolex Montres Award, Geneva, Switz, 87. *Prof Exp:* Instr physics, biol & environ studies, Ont Sec Schs, 55-75; prof sci & environ studies, Nipissing Univ Col, North Bay, 75-89. *Concurrent Pos:* Assoc ed, Crucible, Sci Teachers Asn Ont, 70-; prin investr, Lake Nipissing Underwater Archeol Proj, 80-89. *Mem:* Sci Teachers Asn. *Res:* Role of science in society; integrated urban waste management systems. *Mailing Add:* 20 Young St St Thomas ON N5R 4W5 Can

**VANDEN HEUVEL, WILLIAM JOHN ADRIAN, III,** DRUG METABOLISM, ENVIRONMENTAL IMPACT STUDIES. *Current Pos:* sr res biochemist, Merck Sharp & Dohme Res Labs, 64-67, res fel, Dept Biochem, 67-72, sr res fel, Dept Drug Metab, 72-76, sect dir, Animal Drug Metab & Radiochem, 76-79, SR INVESTR, MERCK SHARP & DOHME RES LABS, 79- *Personal Data:* b Brooklyn, NY, Mar 7, 35; m 60; c 3. *Educ:* Princeton Univ, AB, 56, AM, 58, PhD(org chem), 60. *Hon Degrees:* DSc, Bucknell Univ, 83. *Prof Exp:* Instr chem, Lipid Res Ctr, Col Med, Baylor Univ, 62, asst prof, Dept Biochem, 62-64. *Concurrent Pos:* Sr asst scientist, Nat Heart Inst, 60-62; vis scientist, Bucknell Univ, 79-88. *Mem:* AAAS; Am Chem Soc; Am Soc Mass Spectrometry; Am Soc Pharm Exp Therapeut; Soc Environ Toxicol & Chem; Int Soc Study Xenobiotics. *Res:* Identification and quantification of drugs, metabolites and natural products; environmental impact studies; drug residue studies; use of radioactive and stable isotopes in metabolism, residue and environmental studies. *Mailing Add:* 302 S Third St Lewisburg PA 17837-2102. *Fax:* 732-594-1449

**VAN DEN NOORT, STANLEY,** NEUROLOGY. *Personal Data:* b Lynn, Mass, Sept 8, 30; m 54, Jane Le Clere; c 5. *Educ:* Dartmouth Col, AB, 51; Harvard Univ, MD, 54. *Prof Exp:* Asst prof neurol, Sch Med, Case Western Res Univ, 65-71; prof med (neurol) & dean, Col Med, Univ Calif, Irvine, 73-85. *Mem:* AMA; Am Col Physicians; Am Acad Neurol; Am Neurol Asn. *Res:* Multiple Sclerosis, clinical immunology. *Mailing Add:* Med Plaza Dr Irvine CA 92715

**VANDE NOORD, EDWIN LEE,** SPACE PHYSICS. *Current Pos:* staff scientist, Ball Aerospace Systs Groups, 70-75, mgr advan progs, 75-78, asst dir, 78-80, dir, 80-84, vpres, Space Systs, 84-88, pres electro-optics & cryogenics div, 88-92, SR VPRES/GEN MGR, BALL AEROSPACE SYSTS DIV, 92- *Personal Data:* b Pella, Iowa, Sept 10, 38; m 62; c 2. *Educ:* Grinnell Col, BA, 60; Univ NMex, MS, 63, PhD(physics), 68. *Prof Exp:* Res asst physics, Grinnel Col, 60-61; asst, Univ NMex, 61-68, res assoc, 68-69; res scientist, Douglas Advan Res Labs, Calif, 69-70. *Mem:* Am Inst Aeronaut & Astronaut; Sigma Xi. *Res:* Photometry of zodiacal light; interplanetary dust; infrared Fourier transform spectroscopy; space instrumentation; remote sensing; earth radiation budget instrumentation. *Mailing Add:* 7128-4 Rivers Rd Boulder CO 80301

**VAN DEN SYPE, JAAK STEFAAN,** METALLURGICAL ENGINEERING. *Current Pos:* SR RES SCIENTIST, TARRYTOWN TECH CTR, PRAXAIR, INC, UNION CARBIDE CORP, 70- *Personal Data:* b Dendermonde, Belg, July 15, 35; m 75, Eni de Azambuja; c Jack. *Educ:* Univ Louvain, MetEng, 59; Univ Pa, MSc, 61, PhD(metall eng), 65. *Prof Exp:* Instr metall, Sch Metall Eng, Univ Pa, 66-67, asst prof, 67-70. *Mem:* Am Phys Soc; Am Ceramic Soc; Am Soc Metals; Metal Powder Indust Fed. *Res:* Surface physics; phase transformations; mechanical properties; materials science; catalysis; ceramics. *Mailing Add:* Praxair, Inc Tarrytown Tech Ctr Tarrytown NY 10591. *Fax:* 914-345-6405

**VANDEPOPULIERE, JOSEPH MARCEL,** NUTRITION, BIOCHEMISTRY. *Current Pos:* assoc prof, Dept Poultry Husb, 72-82, PROF ANIMAL SCI, UNIV MO, COLUMBIA, 82- *Personal Data:* b Parkville, Mo, June 21, 29; m 53; c 4. *Educ:* Cent Mo State Univ, AB, 51; Univ Mo, Columbia, MS, 54; Univ Fla, PhD(animal husb), 60. *Prof Exp:* Res asst agr chem, Univ Mo, Columbia, 51-54; asst mgr, Biol Lab, Ralston Purina, 54-57; res asst animal husb, Univ Fla, 57-60; asst mgr broiler res, Ralston Purina, 60-62, mgr broiler res, 62-69, mgr field res & tech serv US, Can & Mex, 69-72. *Concurrent Pos:* Travel grant, World Poultry Sci Asn, 78. *Mem:* Poultry Sci Asn (secy-treas, 77-); World Poultry Sci Asn; Can Feed Mfg Nutrit Coun; Sigma Xi. *Res:* Efficient conversion of agriculture and industrial residuals to human food through the use of a monogastric-polygastric biological team; insect and ectoparasite control in the avian species. *Mailing Add:* A104 Animal Sci Ctr Univ Mo Columbia MO 65211-0001

**VANDER, ARTHUR J,** PHYSIOLOGY. *Current Pos:* from instr to assoc prof, 60-69, PROF PHYSIOL, UNIV MICH, ANN ARBOR, 69- *Personal Data:* b Detroit, Mich, Dec 28, 33; m 55; c 3. *Educ:* Univ Mich, BA, 55, MD, 59. *Prof Exp:* Intern med, New York Hosp-Cornell Med Ctr, 59-60. *Mem:* AAAS; Am Physiol Soc; Am Soc Nephrol; Soc Exp Biol & Med. *Res:* Renal physiology. *Mailing Add:* 1678 Glenwood Rd Ann Arbor MI 48104

**VANDER BEEK, LEO CORNELIS,** plant physiology; deceased, see previous edition for last biography

**VANDERBERG, JEROME PHILIP,** PARASITOLOGY, CELL PHYSIOLOGY. *Current Pos:* from asst prof to assoc prof, 63-74, PROF PARASITOL, SCH MED, NY UNIV, 74- *Personal Data:* b New York, NY, Feb 5, 35; m 67, Thelma Lustig; c Charles & Hope. *Educ:* City Col New York, BS, 55; Pa State Univ, MS, 57; Cornell Univ, PhD(med entom), 61. *Prof Exp:* Fel biol, Johns Hopkins Univ, 62-63. *Concurrent Pos:* Pres, NY Soc Trop Med, chmn, Acad Affairs Comt. *Mem:* Am Soc Trop Med & Hyg; Am Soc Parasitol; Soc Protozool. *Res:* Cellular physiology of insects and of host-parasite complex; malariology; invasion of host cells by malaria parasite; immediate hypersensitivity to insect bites. *Mailing Add:* Dept Med & Molecular Parasitol Med Sch NY Univ 550 First Ave New York NY 10016. *Fax:* 212-263-8116; *E-Mail:* jerome.vanderberg@ccmail.med.nyu.edu

**VAN DER BIJL, WILLIAM,** METEOROLOGY. *Current Pos:* ASSOC PROF METEOROL, NAVAL POSTGRAD SCH, 61- *Personal Data:* b Alphen aan den Rijn, Neth, Aug 15, 20; nat US; wid; c Joan E & Baldwin J. *Educ:* Vrije Univ, Neth, BSc, 41, MSc, 43; Univ Utrecht, PhD(meteorol), 52. *Prof Exp:* Res assoc climat, Royal Neth Meteorol Inst, 46-56; assoc prof physics & meteorol, Kans State Univ, 56-61. *Concurrent Pos:* Fel statist & meteorol, Univ Chicago, 54-55. *Mem:* Am Meteorol Soc; Am Geophys Union; Sigma Xi. *Res:* Physics of the atmosphere; statistical treatment of data; statistical analysis of geophysical data. *Mailing Add:* Dept Meteorol Naval Postgrad Sch Monterey CA 93943-5000

**VANDERBILT, DAVID HAMILTON,** THEORY OF SURFACES AND INTERFACES OF SEMICONDUCTORS. *Current Pos:* AT DEPT PHYSICS & ASTRON, RUTGERS UNIV, 91- *Personal Data:* b Huntington, NY, Aug 20, 54; m 81; c 2. *Educ:* Swarthmore Col, BA, 76; Mass Inst Technol, PhD(physics), 81. *Prof Exp:* Fel, Univ Calif, Berkeley, 81-84; at Lyman Lab Physics, Harvard Univ, 84-90. *Mem:* Am Phys Soc; Sigma Xi. *Res:* Theoretical solid state physics; electronic structure of amorphous or other non-periodic systems, particularly semiconductors; chalcogenide glasses. *Mailing Add:* Dept Physics & Astron Rutgers Univ PO Box 849 Piscataway NJ 08855-0849. *Fax:* 732-932-4343

**VANDERBILT, JEFFREY JAMES,** ORGANIC CHEMISTRY. *Current Pos:* Res chemist, 78-80, SR CHEMIST ORG CHEM, TENN EASTMAN CO, 80- *Personal Data:* b Sheboygan, Wis, July 18, 51. *Educ:* Calvin Col, BS, 73; Univ Mich, MS, 76, PhD(org chem), 78. *Mem:* Am Chem Soc. *Res:* Process research and development. *Mailing Add:* 2403 Wood Hollow Ct Longview TX 75604-2150

**VANDERBILT, VERN C, JR,** ENGINEERING, ELECTRONIC INSTRUMENTATION. *Current Pos:* PRES, VANDERBILT ASSOCS, 74- *Personal Data:* b Indianapolis, Ind, Mar 29, 20; m 42, Gwen C Curry; c Vern C V III, Burton L V & Jeffry N V. *Educ:* Purdue Univ, BSME, 42, MSAeE, 47, PhD(elec eng), 54. *Prof Exp:* Asst prof aeronaut, Purdue Univ, 46-52; pvt pract, 52-54; res engr, Gen Elec Co, 54-55; chief res engr in charge, Gen Res & Road Testing Depts, Dynamometer Lab & Electronics Div, Perfect Circle Corp, 56-62, mgr, Electronics Div, 62-64; pres, Dynamic Precision Controls Corp, 64-74. *Concurrent Pos:* Adj prof, Purdue Prog, Ind Univ E, 75-; pres, Int Soc Prof Engrs, 78-79. *Mem:* Inst Elec & Electronics Engrs; Soc Automotive Engrs; Am Soc Metals; Inst Soc Am; Sigma Xi. *Res:* Electronic instrumentation and servo control as applied to internal combustion engines and automotive equipment and other mechanical devices. *Mailing Add:* Vanderbilt Assocs PO Box 31 Hagerstown IN 47346

**VANDERBORGH, NICHOLAS ERNEST,** ELECTROCHEMISTRY. *Current Pos:* staff mem, 75-77, ALT GROUP LEADER, LOS ALAMOS SCI LAB, 77- *Personal Data:* b Bay Shore, NY, June 24, 38; m; c 3. *Educ:* Hope Col, AB, 60; Southern Ill Univ, MS, 62, PhD(chem), 64. *Prof Exp:* Asst prof chem, Univ Minn, 64-66; from asst prof to assoc prof, Univ NMex, 66-75. *Concurrent Pos:* Staff mem, Sandia Labs, 66-69; guest staff mem, Univ New Castle Upon Tyne, 73; res fels, Mead John & Assoc Western Univs. *Mem:* Mat Res Soc; Electrochem Soc; Am Chem Soc; Am Inst Chem Engrs; Soc Petrol Eng. *Res:* Development of electrochemical power systems for transportation; ionic transport and electrocatalysis; hydrogen production from hydrocarbon fuels. *Mailing Add:* MS J576 Los Alamos Nat Lab Los Alamos NM 87545

**VANDERBURG, CHARLES R,** DEVELOPMENTAL BIOLOGY, CELLULAR BIOLOGY. *Current Pos:* RES ASSOC, HARVARD MED SCH, BOSTON, 89- *Personal Data:* b Langley, Va, Oct 14, 56; m 80; c 3. *Educ:* Univ Pittsburgh, BSc, 78; Seton Hall Univ, MSc, 84; Univ Med & Dent, NJ, PhD(cell biol), 89. *Honors & Awards:* Jan Langman Award, 87. *Prof Exp:* Res technician, Western Psychial Inst & Clin, Pittsburgh, 78-79; res & develop proj leader, Biotech Capital Corp, NY, 79-82; prod mgr, Clin Sci Inc, Whippany, NJ, 82-84. *Concurrent Pos:* Biomed consult, 83-86; instr anat, NJ Med Sch, 87-89; legis intern, NJ State Assembly Dist 24, 88-89. *Mem:* Am Asn Anatomists; Am Soc Cell Biologists; Electron Micros Soc Am; Sigma Xi; Microbeam Anal Soc. *Res:* Molecular biology of cells during development including cell motility and transformation, growth factors, electron microscopy; translational control, RNA processing and regulation; clinical diagnostic assay development. *Mailing Add:* Dept Cell Biol Harvard Med Sch 220 Longwood Ave Boston MA 02115. *Fax:* 617-432-0407; *E-Mail:* cvndrbrg@warren.med.harvard.edu

**VAN DER BURG, SJIRK,** RUBBER CHEMISTRY, TIRE TECHNOLOGY. *Current Pos:* TIRE CONSULT, 86- *Personal Data:* b Makkum, Neth, Mar 23, 26; nat US; m 54, Alida S Dalenoord; c Anna, Linso & Mimi. *Educ:* Univ Groningen, Drs, 55. *Prof Exp:* Asst, Univ Groningen, 52-55; res chemist, Rubber Found, Delft Univ Technol, 55-56 & Res Ctr, US Rubber Co, NJ, 56-61; mgr mat res, US Rubber Tire Co, 61-66, develop mgr, Uniroyal Europ Tire Develop Ctr, Ger, 66-67, dir, 67-80; dir, Tyre Tech Div, Dunlop Ltd, 80-86. *Mem:* Am Chem Soc; Royal Neth Chem Soc; Inst Mat. *Res:* Rubber chemistry and technology; plastics; technical management. *Mailing Add:* 39 Meadowview Rd PO Box 578 West Chatham MA 02669

**VANDERBURG, VANCE DILKS,** nuclear engineering, for more information see previous edition

**VANDERBY, RAY,** BIOMECHANICS. *Current Pos:* asst prof, 85-90, ASSOC PROF ORTHOP SURG & MECH ENG, UNIV WIS HOSPS & CLINS, 90- *Personal Data:* b Hammond, Ind, June 12, 46. *Educ:* Purdue Univ, BS, 68, MS, 72, PhD(biomech), 75. *Honors & Awards:* Volvo Award, Int Soc Study Lumbar Spine, 82; Cervical Spine Res Soc Award, 91. *Prof Exp:* Asst prof orthop surg & mech eng, Northwestern Univ, 83-85. *Mem:* Orthop Res Soc; Am Soc Mech Engrs; Am Soc Biomech. *Mailing Add:* Div Orthop Surg & Mech Eng Univ Wis Hosps & Clins Madison WI 53792

**VANDER FLEET, KATHLEEN MAE TIMMER,** SOFTWARE DEVELOPMENT. *Current Pos:* asst prof, 72-, PROF COMP INSTRNL SCI, JACKSONVILLE UNIV. *Personal Data:* b Ellsworth, Mich, July 21, 42. *Educ:* Calvin Col, BS, 64; Purdue Univ, MS, 66; Colo State Univ, PhD(math), 72. *Prof Exp:* Instr math, Calvin Col, 66-68. *Mem:* Am Math Soc. *Mailing Add:* Dept Math Jacksonville Univ Jacksonville FL 32211

**VANDERGRAAF, TJALLE T,** ANALYTICAL CHEMISTRY, RADIOCHEMISTRY. *Current Pos:* RES SCIENTIST, GEOCHEM RES BR, WHITESHELL LABS, AECL RES, 69-, HEAD, GEOCHEM SECT, 84- *Personal Data:* b 's Gravenmoer, Neth, Sept 3, 36; Can citizen; m 66, Evelyn I Cline; c 4. *Educ:* Calvin Col, BS, 63; Pa State Univ, PhD(analytical chem), 69. *Concurrent Pos:* Consult, OECD/NEA, 86- *Mem:* Fel Chem Inst Can; Can Nuclear Soc; Sigma Xi. *Res:* Radionuclide interaction with geological materials; redox reactions of multivalent radionuclides in geological environments; migration of radionuclides through crystalline rock formations; low temperature rock/water reactions; autoradiography of sorbed radionuclide distributions. *Mailing Add:* Geochem Res Br AECL Whiteshell Lab Pinawa MB R0E 1L0 Can. *Fax:* 204-753-2455; *E-Mail:* vandergraaft@aecl.ca

**VANDERGRAFT, JAMES SAUL,** NUMERICAL ANALYSIS, NUMERICAL SOFTWARE. *Current Pos:* SR ANALYST & PROJ MGR, COLEMAN RES CORP, COLUMBIA, MD, 90- *Personal Data:* b Gooding, Idaho, Apr 29, 37. *Educ:* Stanford Univ, BS, 59, MS, 63; Univ Md, PhD(math), 66. *Prof Exp:* Programmer, Lawrence Radiation Lab, 59-60; number analyst, Bellcomm Inc, Wash DC, 63-64; from asst prof to assoc prof comput sci, Univ Md, 66-79; asst dir, Automated Sci Group Inc, Silver Spring, Md, 79-84; staff analyst, Bus & Technol Systs, Inc, Greenbelt, Md, 84-88; Computational Eng Inc, Laurel, Md, 88-90. *Concurrent Pos:* Tech consult, Apollo Proj, Bellcomm Inc, 69-70; guest prof math, Swiss Fed Inst Zurich, 74. *Mem:* Soc Indust & Appl Math; Math Asn Am; Asn Comput Mach; Inst Elec & Electronics Engrs. *Res:* Numerical solution of linear and nonlinear systems of equations; numerical algorithms and numerical software; modeling and simulation. *Mailing Add:* 772 11th St SE Washington DC 20003

**VANDER HART, DAVID LLOYD,** PHYSICAL CHEMISTRY, POLYMER CHEMISTRY. *Current Pos:* RES CHEMIST, NAT INST STAND & TECHNOL, 69- *Personal Data:* b Rehoboth, NMex, May 20, 41; m 64, Mary Eldersveld; c Laura & Peter. *Educ:* Calvin Col, AB, 63; Univ Ill, Urbana, PhD(phys chem), 68. *Prof Exp:* Fel microwave spectros, Univ Ill, 68-69. *Mem:* Fel Am Phys Soc. *Res:* Nuclear magnetic resonance, particularly carbon-13, application to the characterization of polymer solids; solid state NMR of polymers. *Mailing Add:* VanderHart/David Lloyd Nat Inst Stand & Technol Gaithersburg MD 20899

**VANDERHEIDEN, GREGG,** REHABILITATION ENGINEERING TECHNOLOGY, UNIVERSAL DESIGN. *Current Pos:* ASSOC PROF TECHNOL & DISABILITY AGING, HUMAN FACTORS DIV, INDUST ENG, UNIV WIS, 86- *Personal Data:* b Norway, Mich, Oct 27, 49; m 85; c 1. *Educ:* Univ Wis-Madison, BS, 72, MS, 74, PhD(technol commun rehab), 84. *Honors & Awards:* Isabelle & Leonard Goldenson Award Outstanding Res Med & Technol, 78; Distinguished Serv Award, Rehab Eng Soc NAm, 78, 85 & 89; Clin Achievement Award, Am Social Health Asn, 85; 3rd Ann Award, Nat Coun Commun Dis, 85. *Concurrent Pos:* Dir, Trace Res & Develop Ctr, Univ Wis, 71-, mem staff, Commun Aids & Systs Clin, 80- *Mem:* Rehab Eng Soc NAm (secy, 88, pres-elect, 91); Int Soc Alternative & Augmentative Commun; Am Speech-Language-Hearing Asn; Asn Comput Mach; Inst Elec & Electronics Engrs; Inst Indust Engrs; Int Asn Med & Biol Environ. *Res:* Use of technology in a rehabilitation; access to standard computers, electronics devices and information systems, by persons with disabilities. *Mailing Add:* S-151 Waisman Ctr 1500 Highland Ave Madison WI 53705-2280

**VAN DER HEIJDE, PAUL KAREL MARIA,** GEOHYDROLOGY, WATER RESOURCES MODELLING. *Current Pos:* DIR, IGWMC, 91- *Personal Data:* b N Holland, Neth, May 29, 47; m 76; c 2. *Educ:* Tech Univ Delft, Neth, MSc, 77. *Prof Exp:* Geohydrologist, Orgn Appl Sci Res TNO, Inst Appl Geosci, Delft, Neth, 77-85; dir, Int Ground Water Modeling Ctr, Holcomb Res Inst, Butler Univ, Ind, 81-91, dir, water sci prog, 85-91, actg dean, 89-91. *Concurrent Pos:* Mem sci adv bd, Nat Ctr Ground Water Res, 86-; mem Groundwater Modeling Assessment Comt, Nat Res Coun; prin investr, various US Environ Protection Agency grants, 91- *Mem:* Am Geophys Union; Royal Inst Engrs Neth; Am Water Resources Asn; Nat Asn Groundwater Scientists & Engrs; Am Soc Civil Engrs. *Res:* Application of groundwater hydrology; advancing the use of quality assured modelling methodologies in the management of groundwater resources; development of the technology transfer methods in groundwater science. *Mailing Add:* 4040 Greenbriar Blvd Boulder CO 80303

**VAN DER HELM, DICK,** PHYSICAL CHEMISTRY. *Current Pos:* from asst prof to prof, 62-77, GEORGE LYNN CROSS RES PROF PHYS CHEM, UNIV OKLA, 77- *Personal Data:* b Velsen, Netherlands, Mar 16, 33; m 60; c 6. *Educ:* Univ Amsterdam, Drs, 56, DSc(x-ray diffraction), 60. *Prof Exp:* Res assoc x-ray diffraction, Ind Univ, 57-59 & Inst Cancer Res, Philadelphia, 59-62. *Concurrent Pos:* NIH Develop Award, 69-74. *Mem:* Am Chem Soc; Am Crystallog Asn; AAAS. *Res:* Molecular structure determination by means of x-ray diffraction of natural products, siderophores and peptides. *Mailing Add:* Dept Chem Univ Okla Norman OK 73069-0001

**VANDERHOEF, LARRY NEIL,** HORMONE PHYSIOLOGY, DEVELOPMENT. *Current Pos:* exec vchancellor, 84-91, exec vchancellor & provost, 91-93, ACTG CHANCELLOR, UNIV CALIF, DAVIS, 94- *Personal Data:* b Frazee, Minn, Mar 20, 41; m 63, Rosalie S Slifka; c Susan & Jonathan. *Educ:* Univ Wis-Milwaukee, BS, 64, MS, 65; Purdue Univ, Lafayette, PhD(plant physiol), 69. *Prof Exp:* Nat Res Coun fel, Univ Wis-Madison, 69-70; assoc prof, Univ Ill, Urbana, 70-76, head biol progs, 74-76, prof plant develop, 76-80, head, Bot Dept, 77-80; provost, Div Agr & Life Sci, Univ Md, College Park, 80-84. *Concurrent Pos:* Consult, Fed granting agencies; chair, Bd Trustees, Am Soc Plant Physiol; Eisenhower fel, 87. *Mem:* AAAS; Am Soc Plant Physiol. *Res:* Plant hormones and nucleic acid metabolism; nitrogen fixation. *Mailing Add:* 615 Francisco Pl Davis CA 95616-5224

**VANDERHOEK, JACK YEHUDI,** BIOCHEMISTRY, ORGANIC CHEMISTRY. *Current Pos:* from asst to assoc prof prof, 83-93, PROF BIOCHEM, GEORGE WASHINGTON SCH MED, WASHINGTON, DC, 94- *Personal Data:* b Hilversum, Neth, Jan 1, 41; US citizen; m 66; c 4. *Educ:* City Col New York, BS, 60; Mass Inst Technol, PhD(org chem), 66. *Prof Exp:* Sr res chemist, Gen Mills, Inc, 66-68; group leader vitamin E & sterol synthesis, 68-69; NIH spec fel, Princeton Univ, 69-70 & Univ Fla, 71; res assoc biochem, Univ Mich, Ann Arbor, 71-72, instr, 72-74; lectr, Hadassah Univ Hosp, Hebrew Univ Med Sch, Jerusalem, Israel, 74-76; res assoc med & pharmacol, Univ Conn Health Ctr, Farmington, 77-78. *Concurrent Pos:* Fulbright Scholar & Fogarty Sr fel, Cent Res Labs, Netherlands Red Cross, 89-90. *Mem:* Am Chem Soc; NY Acad Sci; AAAS; Fedn Am Socs Exp Biol. *Res:* Lipid metabolism including leukotrienes, prostaglandins and thromboxanes; lipid mediators in allergic and inflammatory disease. *Mailing Add:* Dept Biochem George Washington Univ Washington DC 20037. *Fax:* 202-994-8974; *E-Mail:* jyrdh@gwis2.circ.gwu.edu

**VANDERHOFF, JOHN W,** POLYMER CHEMISTRY, COLLOID CHEMISTRY. *Current Pos:* assoc prof, Lehigh Univ, 70-74, dir, Nat Printing Ink Res Inst, assoc dir coatings, 70-, PROF CHEM, LEHIGH UNIV, 74-, CO-DIR EMULSION POLYMERS INST, 75- *Personal Data:* b Niagara Falls, NY, Aug 2, 25; m 50; c 2. *Educ:* Niagara Univ, BS, 47; Univ Buffalo, PhD(phys chem), 51. *Hon Degrees:* DSc, Niagara Univ, 92. *Prof Exp:* Chemist, Phys Res Lab, Dow Chem Co, 50-56, proj leader, 56-58, assoc scientist, 58-70, Plastics Dept Res Lab, 63-70. *Concurrent Pos:* Partic, Dow Career Scientist Assignment Prog, Van't Hoff Lab, Utrecht, 65-66. *Mem:* AAAS; fel Am Inst Chem; Am Chem Soc; Sigma Xi; Am Inst Chem Engrs; Am Inst Aeronauts & Astronauts; Tech Asn Pulp & Paper Indust. *Res:* Polymerization kinetics; solution properties of polymers; mechanism of emulsion polymerization; latex properties; foamed plastics; mechanism of latex film formation; colloidal properties of latexes; monodisperse latexes; printing inks; deinking of wastepaper. *Mailing Add:* 345 Ninth Ave Bethlehem PA 18018

**VANDERHOLM, DALE HENRY,** AGRICULTURAL WATER QUALITY. *Current Pos:* ASSOC DEAN, AGR RES DIV, UNIV NEBR, LINCOLN, 83-, INTERIM VICE CHANCELLOR RES, 93- *Personal Data:* b Villisca, Iowa, Mar 28, 40; m 67, Margaret Trimmer; c Kimberly & Stephanie. *Educ:* Iowa State Univ, BS, 62, MS, 69; Colo State Univ, PhD(agr eng), 72. *Prof Exp:* Watershed planning engr, Iowa Soil Conserv Serv, USDA, 62-63; instr, Iowa State Univ, 67-68, asst prof agr eng water supply & waste treat, 72-73; from asst prof to prof agr eng water, water supply & waste treat, Univ Ill, Urbana-Champaign, 78-83, asst dir, Ill Agr Exp Sta, 81-83. *Concurrent Pos:* Res award, Great Plains Livestock Comt, 77; vis res fel, NZ Agr Inst, Lincoln Col, Cantebury, 79-80; vis res fel, Univ Caterbury, Christchurch, NZ, 92; pres-elect, Agr Res Inst, 97. *Mem:* Am Soc Agr Engrs; AAAS; Coun Agr Sci & Technol. *Res:* Treatment and handling of livestock wastes, particularly land application systems and feedlot runoff control systems; treatment of domestic sewage by recirculating sand filters and aerobic package systems. *Mailing Add:* Agr Res Div Univ Nebr 207 Agr Hall Lincoln NE 68583-0704. *Fax:* 402-472-9071; *E-Mail:* agr004@unlvm.unl.edu

**VAN DER HULST, JAN MATHIJS,** ASTROPHYSICS. *Current Pos:* ASSOC PROF ASTRON, UNIV GRONINGEN, 88- *Personal Data:* b 's-Gravenhage, Neth, Jan 26, 48; m 70, Brigit M van den Berg; c Marije, Rogier & Tjeerd. *Educ:* Univ Groningen, Drs, 73, PhD(astron), 77. *Prof Exp:* Res assoc astron, Nat Radio Astron Observ, 77-78; asst prof, Univ Minn, 79-82; res scientist, Neth Found Radio Astron, 82-88. *Mem:* Am Astron Soc; Nederlandse Astron Club; Int Astron Union. *Res:* Structure and evolution of galaxies, gas content of galaxies; dynamics of galaxies; nuclear activity in galaxies; star formation and interstellar medium in nearby galaxies. *Mailing Add:* Kapteyn Astron Inst Postbus 800 NL-9700 AV Groningen Netherlands. *Fax:* 31-50-3636100; *E-Mail:* vdhulst@astro.rug.nl

**VAN DE RIJN, IVO,** MICROBIOLOGY & IMMUNOLOGY. *Current Pos:* PROF MICROBIOL & IMMUNOL & ASSOC, DEPT MED, DIV INFECTIOUS DIS, BOWMAN GRAY SCH MED, 82- *Personal Data:* b Sept 30, 46; c 1. *Educ:* Univ Fla, PhD(microbiol), 72. *Mem:* Am Soc Microbiol; Am Soc Biochem & Molecular Biol. *Res:* Bacterial pathogenesis; bacterial endocarditis; hyaluronic acids synthesis. *Mailing Add:* Dept Microbiol & Immunol Bowman Gray Sch Med Med Ctr Blvd Winston-Salem NC 27157. *E-Mail:* ivr@bgsm.edu

**VAN DERIPE, DONALD R,** PHARMACOLOGY. *Current Pos:* RETIRED. *Personal Data:* b Lafayette, Ind, Feb 13, 34; m 64; c 1. *Educ:* Purdue Univ, BS, 56, MS, 58; Northwestern Univ, PhD(pharmacol), 63. *Prof Exp:* Fel cardiovasc pharmacol, Emory Univ, 63-65; res pharmacologist, Mallinckrodt Chem Works, Mallinckrodt, Inc, 65-75, dir tech eval, 75-95. *Res:* Radiopaque diagnostic agents; cardiovascular and radionuclide pharmacology. *Mailing Add:* 1534 Woodbury Dr St Charles MO 63304. *Fax:* 314-895-2344

**VANDER JAGT, DAVID LEE,** BIOCHEMISTRY. *Current Pos:* asst prof, 69-74, ASSOC PROF BIOCHEM, UNIV NMEX, 74- *Personal Data:* b Grand Rapids, Mich, Jan 13, 42; m 67. *Educ:* Calvin Col, AB, 63; Purdue Univ, Lafayette, PhD(chem), 67. *Prof Exp:* NIH fel biochem, Northwestern Univ, 67-69. *Concurrent Pos:* Res career develop award, Nat Cancer Inst, 74- *Mem:* AAAS; Am Chem Soc; Am Soc Biol Chemists. *Res:* Enzyme, coenzyme reaction mechanisms of glutathione requiring enzymes, especially glyoxalase; metabolic role of methylglyoxal; biomedical applications of 13-C; metabolism of chemical carcinogens. *Mailing Add:* Dept Biochem Univ NMex Sch Med Albuquerque NM 87131-0001

**VANDERJAGT, DONALD W,** COMBINATORICS. *Current Pos:* from asst prof to assoc prof, 64-75, PROF MATH, GRAND VALLEY STATE COLS, 75- *Personal Data:* b Muskegon, Mich, Feb 25, 38; m 58; c 4. *Educ:* Hope Col, AB, 59; Fla State Univ, MS, 61; Western Mich Univ, PhD(math), 73. *Prof Exp:* Instr math, Cent Univ Iowa, 62-64. *Mem:* Am Math Soc; Math Asn Am; Asn Comput Mach; Nat Coun Teachers Math. *Res:* Graph theory, local properties, degree sets, Hamiltonian properties, generalized Ramsey theory. *Mailing Add:* Dept Math & Comput Sci Grand Valley State Univ Allendale MI 49401

**VANDER KLOET, SAM PETER,** PLANT TAXONOMY, PLANT ECOLOGY. *Current Pos:* PROF BIOL & CUR E C SMITH HERBARIUM, ACADIA UNIV, 72- *Personal Data:* b Heidenschap, Frisia, Feb 18, 42; Can citizen; m 70; c 2. *Educ:* Queen's Univ, BA, 68, PhD(biol), 72. *Mem:* Bot Soc Am; Can Bot Asn; Int Asn Plant Taxon. *Res:* Biosystematics of Vaccinium. *Mailing Add:* Dept Biol Acadia Univ Wolfville NS B0P 1X0 Can

**VAN DER KLOOT, ALBERT PETER,** FOOD CHEMISTRY. *Current Pos:* chief chemist brewing & foods, 52-57, PRES, WAHL-HENIUS INST, INC, 57- *Personal Data:* b Chicago, Ill, Jan 22, 21; m 48, Shirley Archias; c 2. *Educ:* Mass Inst Technol, SB, 42. *Prof Exp:* Chemist flower preserv, Flower Foods,

Inc, 46-47; chemist biscuits & crackers, Independent Biscuit Mfg Tech Inst, 47-52. *Mem:* Am Soc Brewing Chem; Am Chem Soc; Inst Food Technol; AAAS. *Res:* Commercial application of plant tissue culture; soda cracker fermentation; freeze drying of microorganisms; vapor pressure-moisture relationships; statistical analysis of brewing process; gas chromatography; alcoholic beverages; trace components of food; traces of sea water on damaged materials. *Mailing Add:* 4206 N Broadway Chicago IL 60613-1610

**VAN DER KLOOT, WILLIAM GEORGE,** PHYSIOLOGY. *Current Pos:* chmn dept, 71-86, PROF PHYSIOL & BIOPHYS, STATE UNIV NY, STONY BROOK, 71- *Personal Data:* b Chicago, Ill, Feb 18, 27; m 84; c 2. *Educ:* Harvard Univ, SB, 48, PhD(biol), 52. *Hon Degrees:* Dr, Independent Univ Moldova, 96. *Prof Exp:* Nat Res Coun fel, Cambridge Univ, 52-53; instr biol, Harvard Univ, 53-56; from asst prof to assoc prof zool, Cornell Univ, 56-58; prof pharmacol & chmn dept, NY Univ, 58-61, prof physiol & chmn, Dept Physiol & Biophys, Sch Med, 67-71. *Concurrent Pos:* Consult, NSF, 59-65 & NIH, 68-; ed, Biosci, 81-84. *Mem:* AAAS; Sigma Xi; Am Physiol Soc; Physiol Soc UK; Soc Neurosci. *Res:* Neurophysiology and pharmacology. *Mailing Add:* Dept Physiol & Biophys Health Sci Ctr State Univ NY Stony Brook NY 11794-8661

**VANDERKOOI, GARRET,** STRUCTURE & PROPERTIES OF BIOLOGICAL MEMBRANES, LIPID BILAYERS. *Current Pos:* prof, 74-94, EMER PROF CHEM & BIOL SCI, NORTHERN ILL UNIV, 94- *Personal Data:* b Paterson, NJ, July 1, 39; m 62, Maryalice Rooze; c Mark & Ellen. *Educ:* Calvin Col, AB, 60; Univ Rochester, PhD(biochem), 66. *Prof Exp:* Fel, Chem Dept, Cornell Univ, 65-68; asst prof, Inst Enzyme Res, Univ Wis-Madison, 68-73, res assoc, Muscle Biol Lab, 73-74. *Mem:* Biophys Soc; Am Soc Biochem & Molecular Biol. *Res:* Effects of local anesthetics on membrane enzymes; computation of lipid bilayer structure by energy minimization. *Mailing Add:* Dept Chem Northern Ill Univ De Kalb IL 60115-2862

**VANDERKOOI, JANE M,** BIOCHEMISTRY, BIOPHYSICS. *Current Pos:* Fel biophys, Univ Pa, 71-73, res assoc, Johnson Found, 73-75, from asst prof to assoc prof, 75-87, PROF BIOCHEM, DEPT BIOCHEM & BIOPHYS, UNIV PA, 88- *Personal Data:* b Rochester, NY, Feb 28, 44. *Educ:* Cent Univ Iowa, BA, 67; St Louis Univ, PhD(biochem), 71. *Concurrent Pos:* NIH fel, 75. *Mem:* Biophys Soc; Am Soc Biol Chem; Am Chem Soc. *Res:* Membrane structure and function; excited state reactions. *Mailing Add:* Dept Biochem & Biophys Univ Pa Philadelphia PA 19104-6089. *Fax:* 215-573-2042; *E-Mail:* vanderkooi@mscf.med.upenn.edu

**VANDER KOOI, LAMBERT RAY,** ELECTRICAL ENGINEERING. *Current Pos:* assoc prof elec eng & technol, 70-, PROF, WESTERN MICH UNIV. *Personal Data:* b Lynden, Wash, Jan 8, 35; m 65; c 1. *Educ:* Univ Mich, BSE, 58, MSE, 61, PhD(elec eng), 68; Calvin Col, BS, 59. *Prof Exp:* Engr, Systs Div, Bendix Corp, 58-61; assoc res engr, Radar & Optics Lab, Inst Sci & Technol, Univ Mich, 61-68; engr, Res & Develop Div, Kelsh Instrument Co, 68; radar systs engr, Polhemus Assocs, Inc, Mich, 69-70. *Mem:* Inst Elec & Electronics Engrs. *Res:* Stochastic control systems; synthetic aperture radar systems; digital circuits and systems; active networks. *Mailing Add:* Dept Elec Eng Western Mich Univ Kalamazoo MI 49008

**VANDERKOOI, WILLIAM NICHOLAS,** INDUSTRIAL CHEMISTRY. *Current Pos:* RETIRED. *Personal Data:* b Paterson, NJ, Dec 19, 29; m 54, Lorna M Frieswyk; c Bruce, Paul & Joy. *Educ:* Calvin Col, AB, 51; Purdue Univ, MS, 53, PhD(phys chem), 55. *Prof Exp:* Lab asst chem & physics, Calvin Col, 48-51, asst, Off Naval Res, 50-51; chemist, Purdue Univ, 51-52, USAF contract, 52, instruments, 52-53; res chemist, C C Kennedy Res Lab, Dow Chem Co, 55-64, group leader, Polymer & Chem Res Lab, 64-69, assoc scientist, Hydrocarbon & Monomers Res Lab, 69-81, assoc scientist, Functional Polymers & Process Res Lab, 81-88, assoc scientist, Appl Org Lab, 88-91, mfg consult, acrylamide prod, dow chem co, 91- *Concurrent Pos:* Comput syst adminr, Midland Christian Sch, 96- *Mem:* Sigma Xi; Am Chem Soc. *Res:* Polymerization kinetics; radiation grafting; polymer synthesis and properties; metal chelation and purification; hydrocarbon analyses; high temperature reactions; hydrocarbon pyrolysis; acrylamide monomer process and acrylamide polymerization; processes; catalysis; data processing; plant simulation; miniplants; computer programming; artificial intelligence expert system development; computer network management. *Mailing Add:* 503 Crescent Dr Dow Chem Co Midland MI 48640

**VANDERKOOY, JOHN,** SOLID STATE PHYSICS, ELECTRO-ACOUSTICS. *Current Pos:* res assoc, 69-70, from asst prof to assoc prof, 70-89, PROF PHYSICS, UNIV WATERLOO, 89- *Personal Data:* b Neth, Jan 1, 41; Can citizen; m 65; c 1. *Educ:* McMaster Univ, BEng, 63, PhD(physics), 67. *Prof Exp:* Nat Res Coun Can fel physics, Cambridge Univ, 67-69. *Concurrent Pos:* Nat Res Coun Can grants, 69-81. *Mem:* Can Asn Physicists; Audio Eng Soc. *Res:* Low temperature solid state physics of metals; audio, transducer design and measurement. *Mailing Add:* Dept Physics Univ Waterloo 200 University Ave W Waterloo ON N2L 3G1 Can

**VANDERLAAN, WILLARD PARKER,** THYROID DISEASES. *Current Pos:* sci & exec dir, 82-92, EMER FOUNDING DIR, WHITTIER INST FOR DIABETES & ENDOCRINOL, LAJOLLA, 92-; HEAT LUTCHER BROWN CTR FOR DIABETES & ENDOCRINOL, SCRIPPS CLIN & RES FOUND, 56- *Personal Data:* b Muskegon, Mich, June 5, 17; m 44, Eileen Foster; c 3. *Educ:* Harvard Univ, MD, 42. *Honors & Awards:* Robert H Williams Distinguished Leadership Award, Endocrine Soc, 93. *Prof Exp:* Intern med, Boston City Hosp, 42-43, asst resident path; 43; instr

pharmacother, Harvard Med Sch, 44-45; fel endocrinol, J H Pratt Diag Hosp, Boston, 45-47; from asst prof to assoc prof med, Med Sch, Tufts Univ, 47-56; prof med, Univ Calif, San Diego, 68-82. *Concurrent Pos:* Fel med, Thorndike Mem Lab, Boston City Hosp, 44; consult, Boston Vet Admin Hosp, 54-56; mem endocrinol study sect, NIH, 71-75, chmn, 74-75. *Mem:* Am Thyroid Asn; Endocrine Soc; Am Soc Clin Invest. *Res:* Growth hormone; prolactin; thyroid physiology. *Mailing Add:* 8275 La Jolla Shores Dr La Jolla CA 92037

**VANDERLASKE, DENNIS P,** ELECTROOPTICS. *Current Pos:* Jr engr, US Army Electronics Res & Develop Command, 69-73, proj engr, 73-79, prog mgr, 79-82, chief, Target Signature Team, Visionics Div, 82-85, chief, Stand Advan Infrared Sensor Team, Night Vision & Electro-Optics Labs, 85-, DIR COUNTERMIND DIV, US ARMY ELECTRONICS RES & DEVELOP COMMAND. *Personal Data:* b Mineola, NY, Jan 15, 48; m 78; c 1. *Educ:* State Univ NY, Stony Brook, BE, 69; George Washington Univ, MS, 75; Cent Mich Univ, MA, 81. *Mem:* Inst Elec & Electronics Engrs. *Res:* Infrared imaging, primarily for military applications and relation with other electro-optical technologies and field evaluation of this technology; solid state electronics as applied to future generation thermal imaging system technology. *Mailing Add:* US Army Ctr Night Vision & Electronics Sensor Directorate AMSEL-RD-NV-CM Roseville CA 22060-5806

**VANDERLIND, MERWYN RAY,** PHYSICS, POLYMER CHEMISTRY. *Current Pos:* res physicist, Battelle Mem Inst, 66-73, mgr, Phys Sci Sect, 73-79, mgr, Venture Develop, 80-81, assoc dir, Corp Tech Develop, 82-83, dir, Indust Technol Ctr, Geneva, Switz, 83-84, vpres, Electronic & Defense Systs, 85-88, GROUP VPRES & GEN MGR, DEFENSE SYSTS & TECHNOL, BATTELLE MEM INST, 89-, SR VPRES & GEN MGR, NAT SECURITIES DIV, 89- *Personal Data:* b Grand Rapids, Mich. *Educ:* Hope Col, BA, 58; Ohio Univ, MS, 60, PhD(physics), 64. *Prof Exp:* Nuclear eng, Atomics Int, 60-61; res polymer physics, Rohm & Haas, 64-66. *Concurrent Pos:* Consult, Nat Acad Sci & Nat Acad Eng, 68-72; mem, Alumni Grad Coun Res, Ohio Univ, 76- *Mem:* Am Phys Soc; Sigma Xi. *Res:* Radiation transport; nuclear weapons effects; polymer physics; laser applications; reactor engineering. *Mailing Add:* Battelle Mem Inst 505 King Ave Columbus OH 43201-2693

**VANDERLINDE, RAYMOND E,** CLINICAL CHEMISTRY. *Current Pos:* prof & dir, Div Clin Chem, 77-90, EMER PROF, DEPT PATH & MED & DIV CLIN BIOCHEM, DEPT BIOL CHEM, HAHNEMANN MED COL, 91- *Personal Data:* b Newark, NY, Feb 28, 24; m 48, Ruth; c Susan, Jeanne & William. *Educ:* Syracuse Univ, AB, 44, MS, 45, MS, 47, PhD(biochem), 50; Am Bd Clin Chem, dipl, 60. *Honors & Awards:* Fisher Award, 85; Rheinhold Award, 92. *Prof Exp:* Teacher high sch, NY, 45-46; from asst prof to assoc prof biochem, Sch Med, Univ Md, 50-57; asst prof, Col Med, State Univ NY Upstate Med Ctr, 57-62; assoc lab dir & clin chemist, Mem Hosp Cumberland, Md, 62-65; dir labs clin chem, Div Labs & Res, NY State Dept Health, 65-77. *Concurrent Pos:* Lab admin dir & clin biochemist, Syracuse Mem Hosp, 57-62; consult, Madison Co Lab, NY, 59-62, Rome City Lab, 61-62 & Meyersdale Community Hosp Lab, Pa, 64-65; clin asst prof, Med Ctr, Univ WVa, 64-65; adj assoc prof, Albany Med Col, 70-; mem diag prods adv comt, Food & Drug Admin, 72-75; pres, Nat Comn Accreditation Clin Chem, 85-88; mem, NIH Lipid Standardization Panel, 86-88; chmn, Coun Nat Ref Systs Clin Lab, 88-90, mem, 78- *Mem:* Am Chem Soc; fel Am Asn Clin Chemists; Asn Clin Sci; assoc Am Soc Clin Path; Acad Clin Lab Physicians & Scientists; Sigma Xi. *Res:* Clinical chemistry; clinical enzymology and diabetes. *Mailing Add:* 719 Maiden Choice Lane Apt BR636 Catonsville MD 21228

**VAN DER LINDE, REINHOUD H,** mathematics; deceased, see previous edition for last biography

**VANDERLINDEN, CARL R,** MECHANICAL ENGINEERING. *Current Pos:* PRES, VANDERLINDEN & ASSOC CONSULT, 87- *Personal Data:* b Pella, Iowa, Sept 26, 23; m 45, Shirley Beatty; c Patricia & David. *Educ:* Univ Wash, BS, 44; Iowa State Univ, PhD(chem eng), 50. *Honors & Awards:* Lewis Lloyd Award, Perlite Inst, 83. *Prof Exp:* Instr chem eng, Iowa State Univ, 46-50; dir res & develop shelter prod, 69-73, dir res & develop govt contracts, 73-75, vpres dir, 75-79, vpres res & develop contracts & appl tech, Johns Mainville Sales Corp, 79-81, Manville Serv Corp , 81-86. *Concurrent Pos:* Chmn tech comt, Perlite Inst, 64-70, dir, 70-72, vpres, 72-74 & pres 74-76; mem, Bldg Futures Coun, Nat Inst Bldg Sci; mem bd dirs, Am Inst Chem Engrs, 79-81 & Bldg Thermal Envelope Coord Coun, 85-88; mem, Advan Indust Mat Guid Eval Bd, US Dept Energy, 86-, chmn, 89-90. *Mem:* Fel Am Inst Chem Engrs; Am Chem Soc; Nat Inst Bldg Sci; Soc Am Mil Engrs. *Res:* Minerals including diatomite and perlite; synthetic silicates; filtration; water treatment; building materials, construction systems and advanced industrial materials. *Mailing Add:* 5 Brassie Way Littleton CO 80123

**VANDERLIP, RICHARD L,** AGRONOMY. *Current Pos:* From asst prof to assoc prof, 64-76, PROF AGRON, KANS STATE UNIV, 76- *Personal Data:* b Woodston, Kans, May 6, 38; m 60; c 3. *Educ:* Kans State Univ, BS, 60; Iowa State Univ, MS, 62, PhD(agron), 65. *Mem:* Am Soc Agron; Soil Sci Soc Am; Crop Sci Soc Am; Sigma Xi. *Res:* Ecology of crop plants, especially climatic interrelationships. *Mailing Add:* Dept Agron Throckmorton Hall Rm 2004 Kans State Univ Manhattan KS 66506-5501

**VANDER LUGT, ANTHONY,** ELECTROOPTICS & ELECTRICAL ENGINEERING. *Current Pos:* prof, 88-94, EMER PROF, ELEC & COMPUT ENG, NC STATE UNIV, RALEIGH, NC, 94- *Personal Data:* b Dorr, Mich, Mar 7, 37; m 59, Marilyn J; c Elizabeth A & Robert A. *Educ:* Calvin Col, BS, 59; Univ Mich, BSEE, 59, MSEE, 62; Univ Reading, PhD, 69, DSc, 89. *Prof Exp:* Res asst, Radar & Optics Lab, Willow Run Labs, Inst Sci & Technol, Univ Mich, 59-63, res assoc, 63-64, assoc res engr, 64-65, res engr & asst head optics group, 65-69; mgr res & develop, Electro-Optics Ctr, Radiation Inc, 69-73; dir, Electro-Optics Dept, Harris Corp, 73-79, sr scientist, Advan Technol Dept, Govt Commun Systs Div, 79-86. *Concurrent Pos:* Consult, Gen Elec Co, 64-66, Tex Instruments, Inc, 65-66, Bendix Res Lab, Harris Corp, 86- & Syracuse Res Corp, 87-; Am ed, Optica Acta, 69-75; assoc ed, Wave Electronics, 81-84; topical ed, Appl Optics, 90- *Mem:* Fel Optical Soc Am; Inst Elec & Electronics Engrs; fel Photo Instrumentation Engrs. *Res:* Optical data-processing; complex spatial filtering and optical matched filtering; modulation transfer functions of recording media; holography; acousto-optic devices; optical storage and retrieval; optical signal processing. *Mailing Add:* 108 O'Kelly Lane Cary NC 27511-5530

**VANDER LUGT, KAREL L,** SOLID STATE PHYSICS. *Current Pos:* PROF PHYSICS, AUGUSTANA COL, SDAK, 69- *Personal Data:* b Pella, Iowa, Apr 25, 40; m 64, Joyce Dalebout; c Ellen & Bill. *Educ:* Hope Col, BA, 62; Wayne State Univ, PhD(exp solid state physics), 67. *Prof Exp:* Nat Res Coun assoc physics, Naval Res Lab, Washington, DC, 67-68. *Mem:* Am Asn Physics Teachers. *Res:* Radiation damage in crystals; experimental solid state physics. *Mailing Add:* 1904 Edgewood Rd Sioux Falls SD 57103. *E-Mail:* vanderlu@inst.augie.edu

**VAN DER MAATEN, MARTIN JUNIOR,** VETERINARY VIROLOGY. *Current Pos:* VET LAB OFFICER, NAT ANIMAL DIS CTR, US DEPT AGR, 67- *Personal Data:* b Alton, Iowa, Aug 6, 32; m 56, Muriel Jonker; c Mary & Patricia. *Educ:* Iowa State Univ, DVM, 56, PhD(vet bact), 64. *Prof Exp:* Vet practice, 58-60; res asst vet virol, Iowa State Univ, 60-61, Nat Inst Allergy & Infectious Dis fel, 61-64, asst prof, 64-67. *Mem:* Am Vet Med Asn; Am Soc Microbiol; Am Soc Virol. *Res:* Virological and serological studies of bovine lymphosarcoma and bovine leukemia virus; bovine viral reproductive disease; vesicular stomatitis virus; bovine lentivirus. *Mailing Add:* 2865 Torrey Pines Rd Ames IA 50014. *Fax:* 515-292-4241

**VANDERMEER, CANUTE,** IRRIGATION WATER MANAGEMENT. *Current Pos:* RETIRED. *Personal Data:* b Xiamen, Fujian, China, Apr 2, 30; US citizen; m 55, Joyce Green; c Kemrey & Tamsen. *Educ:* Hope Col, BA, 50; Univ Mich, MA, 56 & PhD(geog), 62. *Honors & Awards:* Fulbright-Hays lectr, Dept Agr Econ, Univ Philippines, 73. *Prof Exp:* Instr geog, Univ Mich, 60-61; instr, Univ Wis, Milwaukee, 61-62, from asst prof to assoc prof, 62-73, actg chmn dept, 70-71; chmn dept, Univ Vt, 73-85, prof geog, 73-95, 73-95. *Concurrent Pos:* Vis prof geog, Univ Hawaii, 72, Calif State Univ, Hayward, 74, Univ Tsukuba, Japan, 86-87. *Mem:* Asn Am Geographers; Asn Asian Studies; Am Asn Univ Professors. *Res:* Irrigation water distribution procedures and problems where hundreds or thousands of farmers receive water from a single irrigation system; farmers perceptions of irrigation problems. *Mailing Add:* 530 Sandlake Ct Mt Dora FL 32757-6081

**VANDERMEER, JOHN H,** POPULATION BIOLOGY. *Current Pos:* asst prof, 71-74, ASSOC PROF ZOOL, BIOL DEPT, UNIV MICH, ANN ARBOR, 74- *Personal Data:* b Chicago, Ill, July 21, 40; m 69; c 1. *Educ:* Univ Ill, Urbana, BS, 61; Univ Kans, MA, 64; Univ Mich, Ann Arbor, PhD(ecol), 69. *Prof Exp:* Sloan Found fel, Univ Chicago, 69-70; asst prof ecol, State Univ NY, Stony Brook, 70-71. *Mem:* Am Soc Ichthyologists & Herpetologists; Am Soc Naturalists; Ecol Soc Am. *Res:* Role of population processes as determiners of the structure of biological communities. *Mailing Add:* Dept Biol 1121 Nat Sci Bldg Univ Mich Main Campus 830 N University Ave Ann Arbor MI 48109-1048

**VAN DER MEER, JOHN PETER,** PHYCOLOGY, MOLECULAR GENETICS. *Current Pos:* RES OFFICER GENETICS, NAT RES COUN CAN, 74-, ASST DIR, 89-91, DIR MARINE BIOL, INST MARINE BIOSCI, 91- *Personal Data:* b Netherlands, June 25, 43; Can citizen; m 66, Nellie Slingerland; c Lawrence & Deborah. *Educ:* Univ Western Ont, BSc, 66; Cornell Univ, PhD(genetics), 71. *Prof Exp:* Fel biochem, Charles H Best Inst, Univ Toronto, 71-74. *Concurrent Pos:* Hon res assoc, Biol Dept, Dalhousie Univ, 81-93, hon adj prof, 93- *Mem:* Genetics Soc Can; Phycol Soc Am (vpres, 92-93, pres, 93-94); Int Phycol Soc (treas, 87-90); Can Soc Plant Molecular Biol. *Res:* Genetics of marine red algae. *Mailing Add:* Nat Res Coun Inst Marine Bio Sci 1411 Oxford St Halifax NS B3H 3Z1 Can. *Fax:* 902-426-9413; *E-Mail:* vandermeer@imb.lan.nrc.ca

**VANDERMEER, R(OY) A,** PHYSICAL METALLURGY. *Current Pos:* CONSULT, NAVAL RES LAB, 85- *Personal Data:* b Chicago, Ill, Sept 7, 34; m 56; c 2. *Educ:* Ill Inst Technol, BS, 56, PhD(phys metall), 61. *Prof Exp:* Res assoc metall, Ill Inst Technol, 58-60; metallurgist, Oak Ridge Nat Lab, 60-80; metallurgist, Nuclear Div, Y-12 Plant, Union Carbide Corp, 80; prof metall eng, Univ Tenn, 81-85. *Concurrent Pos:* Lectr, Univ Tenn, 63-66 & Ford Found grant prof, 66-80; vis prof mat sci, Univ Rochester, 74-75, vis prof metall eng, Ill Inst Tech, 80. *Mem:* Am Inst Mining, Metall & Petrol Engrs; Am Soc Metals. *Res:* Grain boundary migration in metals; recovery and recrystallization of metals and alloys; uranium alloy; phase transformations. *Mailing Add:* 7013 Dreams Way Ct Alexandria VA 22315

**VANDER MEER, ROBERT KENNETH,** CHEMICAL ECOLOGY, NATURAL PRODUCT CHEMISTRY. *Current Pos:* RES CHEMIST, AGR RES SERV, USDA, 77- *Personal Data:* b Chicago, Ill, Nov 29, 42; m 64, 86, Laurence Morel; c Jeffrey S, Elizabeth V, Nicolas A & Francois V. *Educ:* Blackburn Col, BA, 64; John Carroll Univ, MS, 66; Pa State Univ, PhD(org chem), 72. *Honors & Awards:* Patent Award, USDA, 85, Res Award, 86. *Prof Exp:* Lectr chem, Univ SPac, Fiji Islands, 72-76. *Concurrent Pos:* Am Cancer Soc fel, Cornell Univ, 76-77; adj asst prof, Zool Dept & Entom-Nematol Dept, Univ Fla, 83-; ed, Fire Ants & Leaf-Cutting Ants & Biol & Mgt, 86, Appl Myrmecology A World Perspective, 90; asst ed, Fla Entomologist, 93- *Mem:* Am Chem Soc; Int Soc Chem Ecol; Entom Soc Am; Sigma Xi; Int Union Study Social Insects. *Res:* Isolation and identification of insect pheromones and defensive secretions; analytical organic chemistry; insect biochemistry; the interaction of plants and insects; insect and animal behavior and physiology. *Mailing Add:* ARS-USDA PO Box 14565 Gainesville FL 32604. *E-Mail:* bobvm@nerum.nerdc.ufl.edu

**VAN DER MEER, SIMON,** ACCELERATORS. *Current Pos:* RETIRED. *Personal Data:* b The Hague, Neth, Nov 24, 25; m 66, Catharina Koopman; c Esther & Mathijs. *Honors & Awards:* Nobel Prize in Physics, 84. *Prof Exp:* Philips Phys Lab, Eindhoven, 52-56; sr engr, Europ Orgn Nuclear Res, 56-90. *Mem:* Am Acad Arts & Sci; Royal Neth Acad Sci. *Res:* Design and construction of particle accelerators. *Mailing Add:* 4 Chemin des Corbillettes 1218 GO-Saconnex Saconnex Switzerland

**VANDERMEULEN, JOHN HENRI,** OIL POLLUTION ECOTOXICOLOGY, ACQUATIC POLLUTION. *Current Pos:* RETIRED. *Personal Data:* b Ryswyk, Neth, Oct 2, 33; Can citizen; m 62, Eleanor G Reynolds; c Sean, Marianne, Patrick & Christina. *Educ:* Univ Alta, Can, BSc, 58, MSc, 67; Univ Calif, Los Angeles, PhD(biol), 72. *Prof Exp:* Res affil marine biol, Hawaii Inst Marine Biol, 69-71; teaching scholar, Dept Zool, Duke Univ, 72-73; res scientist environ oceanog, Marine Ecol Lab, Bedford Inst Oceanog, 73-96. *Concurrent Pos:* Mem, steering comt, Nat Acad Sci, 81-85; sr lectr, Int Ocean Inst, Malta, 81-; mem bd dirs, Int Ctr Ocean Develop, Halifax, 85-; hon res assoc, Dalhousie Univ, 85-, adj prof, Sch Resources & Environ Studies. *Res:* Physical and chemical fate of spilled petroleum hydrocarbons, and biological-ecological effects in marine and freshwater environments; pollution related physiological stress; ecotoxicology; biomineralization in marine invertebrate organisms; calcification in reef-corals, shell and ligament formation in bivalve molluscs; petroleum pollution in tropical ecosystems, mangroves and coral reefs; coastal zone management. *Mailing Add:* 153 Frenchman's Rd Oakfield NS B2T 1A9 Can. *Fax:* 902-426-2256

**VAN DER MEULEN, JOSEPH PIERRE,** NEUROLOGY, NEUROPHYSIOLOGY. *Current Pos:* prof neurol & chmn dept, 71-79, dir, Dept Neurol, 71-79, VPRES HEALTH AFFAIRS, UNIV SOUTHERN CALIF, 77- *Personal Data:* b Boston, Mass, Aug 22, 29; m 60, Ann Yadeno; c Elisabeth, Suzanne & Janet. *Educ:* Boston Col, AB, 50; Boston Univ, MD, 54. *Prof Exp:* Intern med, Cornell Med Div, Bellevue Hosp, New York, 54-55, asst resident, 55-56; asst resident neurol, Harvard Neurol Unit, Boston City Hosp, 58-59, resident, 59-60; Nat Inst Neurol Dis & Blindness fel, Nobel Inst Neurophysiol, Karolinska Inst, Sweden, 60-62; instr, Harvard Neurol Unit, Boston City Hosp, 62-66, assoc, 66-67; asst prof, Sch Med, Case Western Res Univ, 67-69, assoc prof neurol & biomed eng, 69-71. *Concurrent Pos:* Fel, Harvard Neurol Unit, Boston City Hosp, Mass, 62-66; ed, Arch of Neurol, 76-78. *Mem:* fel Am Acad Neurol; Am Neurol Asn. *Res:* Neurophysiology of abnormalities of posture and movement; computer assisted image analysis muscle biopsies; motor control systems in humans. *Mailing Add:* 39 Club View Lane Palos Verdes Peninsula CA 90274-4208

**VANDERPLAATS, GARRET NIEL,** automated design optimization, for more information see previous edition

**VANDERPLOEG, HENRY ALFRED,** AQUATIC ECOLOGY, NON-INDIGENOUS SPECIES. *Current Pos:* AQUATIC ECOLOGIST, GREAT LAKES ENVIRON RES LAB, NAT OCEANIC & ATMOSPHERIC ADMIN, 74- *Personal Data:* b Chicago, Ill, Aug 23, 44; m 68. *Educ:* Mich Technol Univ, BS, 66; Univ Wis-Madison, MS, 68; Ore State Univ, PhD(biol oceanog), 72. *Prof Exp:* Aquatic ecologist, Environ Sci Div, Oak Ridge Nat Lab, 72-74. *Mem:* AAAS; Am Soc Limnol & Oceanog; Sigma Xi; Int Soc Limnol; Oceanog Soc; World Asn Copepodologists. *Res:* Ecology of selective feeding of zooplankton; dynamics of seasonal succession of Great Lakes plankton; plankton life cycle strategies; non-indigenous species ecology; zebra mussel ecosystem effects. *Mailing Add:* Great Lakes Environ Res Lab Nat Oceanic & Atmospheric Admin 2205 Commonwealth Ann Arbor MI 48105

**VANDERRYN, JACK,** ENVIRONMENT & ENERGY TECHNICAL & GRANT ADMINISTRATION. *Current Pos:* PROG DIR ENVIRON, MORIAH FUND, 91- *Personal Data:* b Groningen, Neth, Apr 14, 30; nat US; m 56, Margrit Wolfes; c Amy, Danny & Judith. *Educ:* Lehigh Univ, BA, 51, MS, 52, PhD(chem), 55. *Prof Exp:* Asst, Lehigh Univ, 51-55; asst prof chem, Va Polytech Inst, 55-58; chemist, Res & Develop Div, US AEC, Tenn, 58-62, tech adv to asst gen mgr res & develop, Wash, DC, 62-67; US Dept State sr sci adv to US Mission, Int Atomic Energy Agency, 67-71; tech asst, Off Gen Mgr, US AEC, Wash, DC, 71-72, tech asst to dir, Div Appl Technol, 72-74, chief, Energy Technol Br, Div Appl Technol, 74-75, actg dir, Div Energy Storage, 75, dir, Off Int Res & Develop Progs, US Energy Res & Develop Admin, 75-77, dir, Off Int Res & Develop Progs, US Dept Energy, 77-82; agency dir, Energy & Natural Resources, US Agency Int Development, 82-91. *Mem:* AAAS. *Res:* Science policy development; Energy technology development; research and development administration; international cooperation in energy research and development; science policy; energy, environment and natural resource capacity strengthening in developing countries; foundation grant administration. *Mailing Add:* 8112 Whittier Blvd Bethesda MD 20817. *Fax:* 202-783-8499; *E-Mail:* jvanderr@moriahfund.org

**VANDERSALL, JOHN HENRY,** ANIMAL NUTRITION. *Current Pos:* from asst prof to prof, 59-92, EMER PROF ANIMAL SCI, UNIV MD, COLLEGE PARK, 92- *Personal Data:* b Helena, Ohio, July 20, 28; m 63; c 2. *Educ:* Ohio State Univ, BS, 50, MS, 54, PhD(dairy sci), 59. *Prof Exp:* Instr dairy sci, Agr Exp Sta, Ohio State Univ, 57-59. *Mem:* Fel AAAS; Am Soc Animal Sci; Am Dairy Sci Asn; Sigma Xi. *Res:* Effects of forages on milk production and growth and physiological bases for differences; effects of feeds upon the composition of milk. *Mailing Add:* 10906 Ashfield Rd Hyattsville MD 20783

**VANDER SANDE, JOHN BRUCE,** MATERIALS SCIENCE. *Current Pos:* from asst prof to assoc prof, 71-81, acting dean eng, 95-96, PROF MAT SCI, MASS INST TECHNOL, 81-, ASSOC DEAN ENG, 92- *Personal Data:* b Baltimore, Md, Mar 27, 44; m 72, Marie Melluzzo; c John F & Rosse M. *Educ:* Stevens Inst Technol, BE, 66; Northwestern Univ, Evanston, PhD(mat sci), 70. *Prof Exp:* Fulbright scholar metall, Oxford Univ, 70-71. *Concurrent Pos:* Cecil & Ida Green distinguished prof, 91- *Mem:* Am Inst Mining, Metall & Petrol Engrs; Electron Micros Soc Am; Am Ceramics Soc. *Res:* Physical and mechanical behavior of crystalline solids; electron microscopy and electron diffraction; superconductivity; characterization of respirable dust. *Mailing Add:* Dept Mat Sci & Eng Mass Inst Technol Rm 1-206 77 Massachusetts Ave Cambridge MA 02139. *Fax:* 617-253-8549; *E-Mail:* maj@mit.edu

**VANDERSLICE, JOSEPH THOMAS,** PHYSICAL CHEMISTRY. *Current Pos:* RES CHEMIST, BELTSVILLE HUMAN NUTRIT RES INST, USDA, BELTSVILLE, MD, 78- *Personal Data:* b Philadelphia, Pa, Dec 21, 27; m 54, Patricia M Horstman; c Sharon, Joseph, Peter, Julie, John, Polly, Jeffrey & Amy. *Educ:* Boston Col, BS, 49; Mass Inst Technol, PhD(phys chem), 53. *Honors & Awards:* Sigma Xi Award for Sci Achievement, 71. *Prof Exp:* From instr to asst prof chem, Cath Univ, 52-56; from asst prof to prof chem, Univ Md, College Park, 56-78, dir, Inst Molecular Physics, 67-68, prof molecular physics, 62-76, head, Dept Chem, 68-76. *Concurrent Pos:* Consult, US Naval Res Lab, 63-68. *Mem:* Inst Food Technol; Am Chem Soc; fel Am Phys Soc. *Res:* Intermolecular forces; thermodynamic temperature scale; interpretations of molecular beam experiments; transport properties of high temperature gases; franck-condon factors and interpretation of spectroscopic data on diatomic molecules; auroral spectroscopy; interpretation of rocket experiments on the ionosphere; vitamin B6; vitamin C, thiamine and folic acid composition in biological materials; theoretical foundations of flow injection analysis. *Mailing Add:* 14801 W Auburn Rd Accokeek MD 20607. *Fax:* 301-504-8314

**VANDERSLICE, THOMAS AQUINAS,** PHYSICAL CHEMISTRY. *Current Pos:* CHMN & CHIEF EXEC OFFICER, TAV ASSOCS, BOSTON, 95- *Personal Data:* b Philadelphia, Pa, Jan 8, 32; m 56, Margaret Hurley; c Thomas A Jr, John A, Paul A & Peter A. *Educ:* Boston Col, BS, 53; Cath Univ, PhD(phys chem), 56. *Prof Exp:* Asst, Cath Univ, 53-65, Fulbright fel, 56; res assoc, Res & Develop Ctr, Gen Elec Co, 56-62, mgr eng, Vacuum Prod Oper, 62-64, mgr, Vacuum Prod Bus Sect, 64-66, gen mgr, Info Devices Dept, Okla, 66-68, dep div gen mgr, Info Systs Progs Dep Div, Ariz, 68-70, vpres & div gen mgr, Electronic Components Bus Div, 70-72, vpres & group exec, Spec Systs & Prod Group, 72-77, vpres & sect exec, Power Systs Sect, 78-79; pres & chief oper officer, GTE Corp, 79-83; chief exec officer, Apollo Comput Inc, 84-89, chmn, 86-89; chmn & chief exec officer, M/A-Com Inc, 89-95. *Concurrent Pos:* Trustee, Comt Econ Develop; mem, Aspen Inst Humanistic Studies; chmn bd trustees, Boston Col; mem bd dirs, Texaco Inc. *Mem:* Nat Acad Eng; Nat Acad Sci; Am Chem Soc; Am Phys Soc; Am Vacuum Soc; Am Inst Physics; Sigma Xi. *Res:* Surface chemistry; mass spectrometry; high vacuum technology; gaseous discharges; granted over 12 patents and author of over 25 technical articles. *Mailing Add:* TAV ASSOCS 2 Int Pl Suite 3001 Boston MA 02110

**VANDER SLUIS, KENNETH LEROY,** PHYSICS. *Current Pos:* RETIRED. *Personal Data:* b Holland, Mich, Dec 19, 25; m 52, Joan C Harvie; c Lisa Joan, Stephen & David Kenneth. *Educ:* Baldwin-Wallace Col, BS, 47; Pa State Univ, MS, 50, PhD(physics), 52. *Prof Exp:* Physicist, Oak Ridge Nat Lab, 52-90. *Concurrent Pos:* Res guest, Spectros Lab, Mass Inst Technol, 60-61; mem comt line spectra of the elements, Nat Res Coun, 61-72. *Mem:* Am Phys Soc; Optical Soc Am; Sigma Xi. *Res:* Experimental atomic spectroscopy, echelle gratings, interferometry, gas laser systems. *Mailing Add:* 20 Raintree Pl Oak Ridge TN 37830-9002

**VAN DER SPIEGEL, JAN,** NEURAL NETWORK IMPLEMENTATIONS, INTEGRATED SENSOR TECHNOLOGY. *Current Pos:* Fel, 80-81, asst prof, 81-87, ASSOC PROF ELECTRONICS, DEPT ELEC ENG, UNIV PA, 87- *Personal Data:* b Aalst, Belg, Apr 12, 51. *Educ:* Kath Univ Leuven, Belg, BEE, 73, Masters, 74, PhD(elec eng), 79. *Hon Degrees:* MA, Univ Pa, 88. *Honors & Awards:* NSF Presidential Young Investr, 84. *Concurrent Pos:* Consult, I-Stat, Inc, Princeton, NJ, 83- & Corticon, Inc, Philadelphia, 90-; assoc prof, Dept Mat Sci & Eng, Univ Pa, 87-, dir, Ctr Sensor Technologies, 89-; vis prof, Scuola Superioe S Anna, Pisa, Italy, 89; mem adv bd, Ben Franklin Technol Ctr Mfg Processes & Sensor, 90- *Mem:* Sr mem Inst Elec & Electronics Engrs; Mat Res Soc; Int Neural Network Soc. *Res:* Integrated and smart sensors; hardware implementation of neural networks for sensory processing; sensor technologies and electronic materials for integrated circuits. *Mailing Add:* Dept Elec Eng Univ Pa 200 S 33rd St Philadelphia PA 19104-6390

**VANDERSPURT, THOMAS HENRY,** PHYSICAL INORGANIC CHEMISTRY. *Current Pos:* res chemist, 73-77, SR RES CHEMIST CATALYSIS CHEM, CELANESE RES CO, CELANESE INC, 77- *Personal Data:* b Lawrence, Mass, Apr 1, 46; m 71; c 2. *Educ:* Lowell Technol Inst, BS, 67; Princeton Univ, MA & PhD(chem), 72. *Prof Exp:* Fel catalysis chem, Princeton Univ, 72-73. *Mem:* NY Acad Sci; Sigma Xi; Am Chem Soc; NAm Catalysis Soc. *Res:* Supported metal alloy catalysts; metal/metal oxide selective oxidation catalysts; homogenous selective dimerization carbonylation catalysis; homogeneous selective aromatic acetoxylation; catalysis; supported hydroformylation catalysis. *Mailing Add:* 46 Upper Creek Rd Stockton NJ 08559-1205

**VANDER TUIG, JERRY G,** HUMAN NUTRITION. *Current Pos:* Asst prof human nutrit, 86-92, ASSOC PROF NUTRIT, LINCOLN UNIV, 92- *Personal Data:* b Sheldon, Iowa, May 8, 49. *Educ:* Calvin Col, BS, 71; Iowa State Univ, PhD(zool), 76. *Mem:* Am Inst Nutrit; NAm Soc Obesity; Soc Exp Biol & Med; Sigma Xi. *Res:* Human nutrition. *Mailing Add:* Human Nutrit Lab Schweich Hall Cooperative Res Dept Lincoln Univ 106A Foster Hall Jefferson City MO 65102-0029

**VAN DER VAART, HUBERTUS ROBERT,** BIOMATHEMATICS, STATISTICS. *Current Pos:* assoc prof, NC State Univ, 62-63, prof statist & math, 63-91, EMER PROF, NC STATE UNIV, 91- *Personal Data:* b Makassar, Celebes, Indonesia, Mar 2, 22; US citizen; m 50, Hennie Auwerda; c Marjo, Bert & Donald. *Educ:* Univ Leiden, Drs, 50, PhD(theoret biol), 53. *Prof Exp:* Sci officer, Univ Leiden, 50-57; vis assoc prof exp statist, NC State Col, 57-58 & statist, Univ Chicago, 58; extraordinary prof theoret biol, Univ Leiden, 58-60, prof, 60-62, dir, Inst Theoret Biol, 58-62, dir, Cent Comput Inst, 61-62. *Concurrent Pos:* Co-ed, Acta Biotheoretica, 53-75; Neth Orgn Pure Res fel, 57-58; co-ed, Statistica Neerlandica, 60-74; mem, Panel Life Sci, Comt Undergrad Prog Math, 67-70; mem, Panel Instrnl Mats Appl Math, Comt Undergrad Prog Math, Math Asn Am, 74-76. *Mem:* Biomet Soc; Am Math Soc; Math Asn Am; Inst Math Statist; Soc Indust & Appl Math; Soc Math Biol. *Res:* Mathematical statistics; probability; stochastic processes; theoretical biology; principles of scientific method; mathematical models for biosystems; chemical reaction kinetics; combustion theory; applied mathematics. *Mailing Add:* Dept Statist NC State Univ Campus Box 8203 Raleigh NC 27695-8203. *E-Mail:* vanderva@stat.ncsu.edu

**VANDERVEEN, JOHN EDWARD,** NUTRITION, CHEMISTRY. *Current Pos:* DIR DIV NUTRIT, CTR FOOD SAFETY & APPL NUTRIT, FOOD & DRUG ADMIN, DEPT HEALTH & HUMAN SERV, 75- *Personal Data:* b Prospect Park, NJ, May 13, 34; m 67; c 2. *Educ:* Rutgers Univ, BS, 56; Univ NH, PhD(chem, nutrit), 61. *Prof Exp:* Res chemist, USAF Sch Aerospace Med, 64-75. *Mem:* Am Inst Nutrit; Am Chem Soc; Am Soc Clin Nutrit; Inst Food Technologists; Am Dairy Sci Asn; Aerospace Med Asn. *Res:* Nutritional requirements of the American population; assessment of the nutritional quality of the national food supply; energy and mineral requirements and effects of excess nutrient intakes. *Mailing Add:* FDA (HFS-300) 200 C St SW Washington DC 20204-0001. *Fax:* 202-205-4594

**VANDERVEEN, JOHN WARREN,** CHEMICAL ENGINEERING. *Current Pos:* SUPVR CHEM PROCESSES SECT, PHILLIPS RES CTR, 65- *Personal Data:* b Mount Vernon, NY, Dec 2, 33; m 59; c 2. *Educ:* Univ Nebr, BS, 60, MS, 61; Univ Minn, PhD(chem eng), 65. *Mem:* Sigma Xi. *Res:* Reactor analysis; combustion; process simulation and optimization; chemical kinetics; fluid mechanics; process control; fermentation; economics; design. *Mailing Add:* 1410 Macklyn Lane Bartlesville OK 74006

**VANDER VELDE, GEORGE,** ANALYTICAL CHEMISTRY, MASS SPECTROMETRY. *Current Pos:* AT GOLZIER & ASSOC. *Personal Data:* b Chicago, Ill, June 24, 43; m 66; c 3. *Educ:* Hope Col, BA, 65; Univ Houston, PhD(biophysics), 71. *Prof Exp:* Res scientist assoc, natural prod, Dept Bot, Univ Tex, Austin, 70-73; instr biol, Exten Serv, 72-73; res chemist analytical chem, Nat Ctr Toxicol Res, Jefferson, 73-74; appl support chemist & prod mgr mass spectrometry, Finnigan Corp, Sunnyvale, Calif, 74-77; assoc dir, Finnigan Inst, 77-79; dir tech serv, O H Mat Co, Findlay, Ohio, 79-81; vpres develop, Environ Testing & Cert Corp, Edison, NJ, 82; vpres sci & technol, Chem Waste Mgt Corp, Oak Brook, Ill, 82- *Mem:* Am Chem Soc; Am Soc Mass Spectrometry; Am Soc Testing & Mat; Sigma Xi; NY Acad Sci. *Res:* Applications of analytical chemistry to environmental protection; development of new technology to environmental protection and cleanup; waste process technology; analytical chemistry methodology, development; hazardous materials characterization and analysis. *Mailing Add:* 7805 Landowne Dr 3105-C N Wilke Rd Arlington Heights IL 60004

**VANDER VELDE, JOHN CHRISTIAN,** PHYSICS. *Current Pos:* from instr to prof, 58-96, EMER PROF PHYSICS, UNIV MICH, ANN ARBOR, 96- *Personal Data:* b Mich, Sept 25, 30; m 53; c 3. *Educ:* Hope Col, AB, 52; Univ Mich, MA, 53, PhD(physics), 58. *Concurrent Pos:* Assoc in res, LePrince-Ringuet Lab, Polytech Sch, Paris, 66-67; mem, Prog Comt, Argonne Nat Lab, 71-74; mem, Users Exec Comt, Nat Accelerator Lab, 72-74; vis scientist, Saclay Nuclear Res Ctr, France, 74. *Mem:* Fel Am Phys Soc. *Res:* Elementary particle physics. *Mailing Add:* 400 Barton Shore Dr Ann Arbor MI 48105

**VANDER VELDE, W(ALLACE) E(ARL),** CONTROL SYSTEMS, NAVIGATION. *Current Pos:* asst prof aeronaut eng, 57-61, assoc prof aeronaut & astronaut, 61-65, PROF AERONAUT & ASTRONAUT, MASS INST TECHNOL, 65- *Personal Data:* b Jamestown, Mich, June 4, 29; m 54,

Winifred Bunai; c Susan J & Peter R. *Educ:* Purdue Univ, BSAE, 51; Mass Inst Technol; ScD(instrumentation), 56. *Honors & Awards:* Educ Award, Am Automatic Control Coun, 88. *Prof Exp:* Staff engr, Instrumentation Lab, Mass Inst, Technol, 53-56; dir applns eng, GPS Instrument Co, Inc, 56-57. *Concurrent Pos:* Consult, Control & Navig Systs. *Mem:* Fel Am Inst Aeronaut & Astronaut; Inst Elec & Electronics Engrs. *Res:* Automatic control systms; navigation and guidance of aerospace vehicles; instrumentation systems. *Mailing Add:* Dept Aeronaut & Astronaut Rm 9-467 Mass Inst Technol Cambridge MA 02139. *E-Mail:* wallyvv@mit.edu

**VANDERVEN, NED STUART,** PHYSICS. *Current Pos:* from instr to assoc prof, 61-79, PROF PHYSICS, CARNEGIE-MELLON UNIV, 79- *Personal Data:* b Ann Arbor, Mich, July 15, 32; m 61; c 2. *Educ:* Harvard Col, AB, 55; Princeton Univ, PhD(physics), 62. *Prof Exp:* Instr physics, Princeton Univ, 59-61. *Mem:* Am Phys Soc. *Res:* Magnetic resonance; solid state physics; biophysics. *Mailing Add:* Dept Physics 500 Forbes Ave Pittsburgh PA 15213

**VAN DER VINK, GREGORY E,** SCIENCE POLICY, ARMS CONTROL & ENVIRONMENT. *Current Pos:* DIR PLANNING, IRIS CONSORTIUM, 90- *Personal Data:* b New York, NY, Dec 14, 56; m 87; Jamie Broumas; c 2. *Educ:* Colgate Univ, BA, 79; Princeton Univ, MA, 81, PhD(geophys), 83. *Prof Exp:* Fel, Nat Res Coun, 83-85; cong fel, US Cong, Off Technol Assessment, 85-86, proj dir, 86-89. *Concurrent Pos:* Vis fac, Woodrow Wilson Sch Pub & Int Affairs, Princeton Univ, 92 & Dept Geol & Geophys Sci, 91-95; int affairs fel, Coun Foreign Rels, 92-93. *Mem:* Am Geophys Union; AAAS; NY Acad Sci. *Res:* Analysis of scientific and environmental policies. *Mailing Add:* Iris Consortium 1200 New York Ave NW Suite 400 Washington DC 22005. *Fax:* 703-527-7256; *E-Mail:* greg@iris.edu

**VAN DER VOO, ROB,** GEOLOGY, GEOPHYSICS. *Current Pos:* vis asst prof, Univ Mich, Ann Arbor, 70-72, from asst prof to assoc prof, 72-79, chmn Dept Geol Sci, 81-88 & 91-95, PROF GEOPHYS, UNIV MICH, ANN ARBOR, 79- *Personal Data:* b Zeist, Neth, Aug 4, 40; m 66, Tatiana M Graafland; c Serge N & Bjorn A. *Educ:* State Univ Utrecht, BSc, 61, Drs, 65 & 69, PhD(geol, geophys), 69. *Honors & Awards:* G P Woollard Award, Geol Soc Am, 92. *Prof Exp:* Res assoc paleomagnetism, State Univ Utrecht, 65-70. *Mem:* Am Geophys Union; Geol Soc Am; Ger Geol Asn; Royal Neth Geol & Mining Soc; Royal Acad Sci Neth. *Res:* Paleomagnetism, plate tectonics of the Atlantic Ocean and Mediterranean Sea; stratigraphy and tectonics of Appalachian, Hercynian, Laramide and Pyrenean-Alpine mountain belts. *Mailing Add:* Dept Geol Sci Univ Mich Ann Arbor MI 48109. *Fax:* 313-763-4690; *E-Mail:* voo@umich.edu

**VAN DER VOORN, PETER C,** ELECTROPHOTOGRAPHY. *Current Pos:* STAFF MEM, DANKA CORP, 90- *Personal Data:* b Haarlem, Netherlands, Feb 25, 40; US citizen; m 65. *Educ:* Wichita Univ, BS, 61; Univ Ill, PhD(inorg chem), 65. *Prof Exp:* Tech assoc, Eastman Kodak Co, 65-85, mgr qual assurance copy prods, 85-90. *Mem:* Am Chem Soc. *Res:* Electrophotographic developers; inorganic photoconductors; solid state chemistry. *Mailing Add:* 26 Tartarian Circle Rochester NY 14612

**VANDER VOORT, GEORGE FREDERIC,** QUANTITATIVE METALLOGRAPHY, STEREOLOGY & IMAGE ANALYSIS. *Current Pos:* DIR RES & TECHNOL, BUEHLER LTD, 96- *Personal Data:* b Philadelphia, Pa, Sept 1, 44; m 70, Brenda L Schlaner; c Robert T & Juliana. *Educ:* Drexel Univ, BS, 67; Lehigh Univ, MS, 74. *Honors & Awards:* Anthony DeBellis Mem Award, Am Soc Testing & Mat, 90; Jacquet-Lucas Gold Medal, Am Soc Metals Int-Metall Soc, 92; Bradley Stoughton Award, Lehigh Valley Chap, Am Soc Metals Int, 93; L L Wyman Mem Award, Am Soc Testing & Mat, 94. *Prof Exp:* Tech asst, Bethlehem Steel Corp, Bethlehem Plant, 67-68, investr, 68-69, exp engr, 69-72, asst metallogr, 72-73, res engr, Homer Res Lab, 73-83; supvr metal physics res, Carpenter Tech Corp, 83-92, supvr mat characterization, 92-96. *Concurrent Pos:* Chmn, Subcomt Quant Metallog, Am Soc Testing & Mat, 82-, Comt Metallog, 89-93; assoc ed, Mat Characterization, 91- *Mem:* Hon fel Am Soc Metals Int; Int Metallog Soc (secy, 77-79, vpres, 79-81, pres, 81-83); hon fel Am Soc Testing & Mat; Royal Micros Soc; Int Soc Stereol; Metall Soc; Micros Soc Am; Am Inst Mining, Metall & Petrol Engrs. *Res:* Use of light and electron microscopy to study the structure of metals; failure analysis; iron and nickel-based alloys; granted 4 US and 1 Canadian patent. *Mailing Add:* 2887 N Southern Hills Rd Wadsworth IL 60083-9293. *Fax:* 847-295-7942

**VANDERVOORT, PETER OLIVER,** ASTRONOMY. *Current Pos:* from asst prof to assoc prof astron, Univ Chicago, 61-80, master, Phys Sci Col Div, 91-97, assoc dean, Div Phys Sci, 91-97, PROF ASTRON & ASTROPHYS, UNIV CHICAGO, 80- *Personal Data:* b Detroit, Mich, Apr 25, 35; m 56, Frances Sheridan; c William F & Dirk S. *Educ:* Univ Chicago, AB, 54, SB, 55, SM, 56, PhD(physics), 60. *Prof Exp:* Vis res assoc, Nat Radio Astron Observ, Assoc Univs, Inc, WVa, 60; NSF fel, Princeton Univ Observ, 60-61. *Concurrent Pos:* NSF sr fel, Leiden Observ, Neth, 67-68. *Mem:* Int Astron Union; Am Astron Soc; Am Phys Soc; Royal Astron Soc; Sigma Xi. *Res:* Hydrodynamic stability; gas dynamics; interstellar matter; stellar dynamics; galactic structure. *Mailing Add:* Astron & Astrophys Ctr Univ Chicago 5640 S Ellis Ave Chicago IL 60637. *Fax:* 773-702-8212

**VANDER VORST, ANDRE,** MICROWAVE COMMUNICATIONS, BIOELECTROMAGNETICS. *Current Pos:* asst prof, Cath Univ Louvain, 62-68, head, Elec Eng Dept, 70-72, dean eng, 72-75, vpres, 73-75, pres, Open Fac, 73-87, PROF, CATH UNIV LOUVAIN, 68-, HEAD, MICROWAVES LAB, 90- *Personal Data:* b Schaerbeek, Belg, Oct 22, 35; wid; c Claire, Pierre,

Cecile, Catherine & Chantal. *Educ:* Cath Univ Louvain, Belg, Engr, 58, PhD(elec eng), 65; Mass Technol, MS, 65. *Honors & Awards:* Sitel Prize, Belg, 86. *Prof Exp:* Fel, Stanford Univ, 65-66. *Mem:* Fel Inst Elec & Electronics Engrs; Electromagnetics Acad; Inst Elec Engrs. *Res:* Microwaves; electrical engineering; design of circuits up to 100 gigahertz; atmospheric transmission up to 300 gigahertz; interaction of electromagnetic fields with the nervous system, using microwave acupuncture as a stimulus; author of several books and more than 100 publications. *Mailing Add:* Microwaves Univ Cath Louvain Batiment-Maxwell Louvain-la-Neuve B-1348 Belgium. *Fax:* 32-10-478705, 32-10-452272; *E-Mail:* vandervorst@emic.ucl.ac.be

**VANDER WALL, EUGENE,** PHYSICAL INORGANIC CHEMISTRY. *Current Pos:* mem sci staff, Aerojet-Gen Corp, Sacramento, 63-64, supvr liquid propellant res, 64-67, tech supvr res & develop, 67-71, supvr, Chem Res Lab, 71-74, mgr chem processes, 74-82, mgr, Eng & Mfg Labs, 83-89, SR MGR ENG LABS, AEROJET PROPULSION DIV, AEROJET LIQUID ROCKET CO, 90- *Personal Data:* b Munster, Ind, Feb 8, 31; m 53; c 4. *Educ:* Calvin Col, BS, 52; Univ Colo, PhD(chem), 57. *Prof Exp:* Res chemist, Atomic Energy Div, Phillips Petrol Corp, Idaho, 56-60, supvr chemist, 60-63. *Concurrent Pos:* Nat Reactor Testing Sta prof, Univ Idaho, 57-58 & 60-61; mem bd trustees, Bethesda Hosp, Denver, Colo. *Mem:* Fel Am Inst Chem; Am Chem Soc. *Res:* Gelation of liquids; characterization of hazardous chemicals; material-fluid compatibility evaluation; liquid propellant research; development of chemical processes for disposal of hazardous wastes. *Mailing Add:* 5552 Wildwood Way Citrus Heights CA 95610-6697

**VANDER WENDE, CHRISTINA,** BIOCHEMISTRY, PHARMACOLOGY. *Current Pos:* assoc prof pharmacol & biochem, 64-69, PROF PHARMACOL, RUTGERS UNIV, NEW BRUNSWICK, 69- *Personal Data:* b Paterson, NJ, June 12, 30. *Educ:* Upsala Col, BS, 52; Rutgers Univ, MS, 56, PhD(biochem), 59. *Prof Exp:* Jr pharmacologist, Wallace & Tiernan, Inc, 52-53 & Schering Corp, 53-55; pharmacologist, Maltbie Labs, 55-56; asst physiol & biochem, Rutgers Univ, 56-59; sr res scientist, E R Squibb & Sons, 59-60; sr res scientist, Vet Admin Hosp, 60-64. *Concurrent Pos:* Nat Cancer Inst res grant, 61-67; Eastern Leukemia Asn Inc res scholar, 67-69; Epilepsy Found grants, 69-70 & 72-73; Pharmaceut Mfrs Asn grant, 70-72; Nat Drug Abuse Inst grant, 73-76; lectr, Exten Serv, Rutgers Univ, 61-63; dir undergrad res, Upsala Col, 61-64; lectr, All Souls Hosp, Morristown, NJ, 62. *Mem:* AAAS; Am Soc Pharmacol & Exp Theraput; Soc Neurosci; Acad Pharmaceut Sci; NY Acad Sci; Sigma Xi. *Res:* Biochemical pharmacology of central nervous system metabolism and enzymology; toxicology. *Mailing Add:* 252 Carol Jean Way Somerville NJ 08876-3350

**VAN DER WERFF, TERRY JAY,** EDUCATIONAL ADMINISTRATION. *Current Pos:* PRES, VAN DER WERFF GLOBAL, LTD, INC, 91- *Personal Data:* b Hammond, Ind, May 16, 44; m 68; c 5. *Educ:* Mass Inst Technol, SB & SM, 68; Oxford Univ, DPhil(eng sci), 72. *Honors & Awards:* Teetor Award, Soc Automotive Engrs, 72. *Prof Exp:* Staff engr, ARO Inc, 67-68; asst prof mech eng, physiol & biophys & clin sci, Colo State Univ, 70-73; vis asst prof med, Univ Colo Med Ctr, 73-74; head, Dept Biomed Eng, Univ Cape Town & Groote Schuur Hosp, SAfrica, 74-80; dean sci & eng, Seattle Univ, 81-90; exec vpres acad affairs, St Joseph's Univ, 90-91. *Concurrent Pos:* Consult, Rand Corp, 67 & 69-70 & Los Alamos Sci Lab, 72. *Mem:* AAAS; Am Soc Mech Engrs; fel Biomed Eng Soc SAfrica; fel Royal Soc SAfrica. *Res:* Nonlinear oscillations; reaction-diffusion systems; cardiovascular fluid dynamics; similarity transformations; science and technology policy. *Mailing Add:* 2410 NE 123rd St Seattle WA 98125-5241. *Fax:* 206-364-1217; *E-Mail:* terryvdw@compuserve.com

**VANDERWERFF, WILLIAM D,** ORGANIC CHEMISTRY. *Personal Data:* b Philadelphia, Pa, Dec 31, 29; m 58, Betty; c Christina, Derek, Hilda & Nicholas. *Educ:* Univ Pa, BS, 51, PhD(org chem), 60. *Honors & Awards:* WH. *Prof Exp:* Prod supvr explosives, E I du Pont de Nemours & Co, 51-53; res chemist, Suntech, Inc, 59-70, chief new prods res, 70-77, staff scientist, 77-82, strategic planning specialist, 82, res sect chief, 82-83, res mgr, Sun Refining & Mkt Co, 83-88. *Res:* Auto-oxidation; hydrocarbon chemistry; petrochemicals; polymer technology. *Mailing Add:* 37 Green Tree Dr West Chester PA 19382-8408

**VANDERWIEL, CAROLE JEAN,** MICROSCOPIC ANATOMY, PHYSIOLOGY. *Current Pos:* EDUC CONSULT, MIDAS REX INST, FT WORTH, TEX, 91- *Personal Data:* b Cleveland, Ohio, May 6, 50; m 76, Felix R Schleenvoigt; c Kyle Andrew & Mindy Kathryn. *Educ:* Univ Tex, BS, 72; Baylor Univ Med Ctr, PhD(anat), 76. *Prof Exp:* Technician biochem, Univ Tex Health Sci Ctr, 68-70; technician serol, Harris Hosp, Ft Worth, 70-72; grad asst anat, Baylor Col Dent, Dallas, 73-76; res assoc endocrinol, Dent Res Ctr, Sch Med, Univ NC, 77-78, fel orthop, 78-80, asst prof, Dept Surg, 80-82; dir, Metab Bone Clin, Dallas, Tex, 82-86. *Concurrent Pos:* Grant, Baylor Col Dent, 74-76 & NSF, 80-83; nat res serv award, NIH, 78-80; Pfizer pharmaceut award, 81, young investr award, 82; res scientist award, Parathyroid Conf, 83. *Mem:* AAAS; Am Soc Bone & Mineral Res; Am Acad Orthop Res. *Res:* Role of hormones, especially parathyroid hormone and calcitonin, on calcium fluxes between bone fluid and blood utilizing histological and physiological techniques; diagnosis of metabolic bone disease by quantitative histomorphometric analysis of human bone biopsies. *Mailing Add:* 141 Vista Dr Weatherford TX 76087. *Fax:* 817-834-4835; *E-Mail:* carole.schleenvoigt@midasrex.com

**VANDERWIELE, JAMES MILTON,** DIGITAL TESTING, STATISTICAL PROCESS CONTROL. *Current Pos:* develop engr, AT&T Technol, Inc, 80-88, sr engr, 88-96, DISTINGUISHED MEM TECH STAFF, LUCENT TECHNOL, 96- *Personal Data:* b July 23, 58; US citizen. *Educ:* Okla State Univ, BS, 80; Univ Okla, MS, 87. *Mem:* Inst Elec & Electronics Engrs. *Res:* Data communications, specifically carrie sense multiple access protocols; digital circuitry testability. *Mailing Add:* 1712 Whispering Creek Ct Edmond OK 73013

**VANDERWIELEN, ADRIANUS JOHANNES,** ANALYTICAL CHEMISTRY, PHYSICAL CHEMISTRY. *Current Pos:* GROUP MGR, PHARM LAB, UPJOHN CO, 86- *Personal Data:* b Ger, Mar 28, 44; US citizen; m 68; c 2. *Educ:* San Diego State Univ, BSc, 70; Univ Calif, PhD(chem), 74. *Prof Exp:* Res fel phys chem, Univ Ala, 74-75; res scientist analytical chem, 75-80, mgr, Analytical Support, Control Div, 80-86. *Mem:* Am Chem Soc; Am Pharmaceut Asn. *Res:* Analytical research and development in particle sizing methods; physical characterization of pharmaceutical powders; thermal analyses; chromatography and methods validation. *Mailing Add:* 5503 Brockwood Dr Apt 3 Missoula MT 59802

**VANDERWOLF, CORNELIUS HENDRIK,** NEUROSCIENCE, BEHAVIOR-ETHOLOGY. *Current Pos:* assoc prof, 68-73, PROF PSYCHOL, UNIV WESTERN ONT, 73-, PROF, GRAD PROG NEUROSCI, 91- *Personal Data:* b Edmonton, Alta, Dec 13, 35; m 82, Judith A Sumner; c Charlotte, Karen & Sarah. *Educ:* Univ Alta, BSc, 58; McGill Univ, MSc, 59, PhD, 62. *Prof Exp:* Res fel biol, Calif Inst Technol, 62-63; Nat Res Coun fel, Brain Res Inst, Switz, 63-64; from asst prof to assoc prof psychol, McMaster Univ, 64-68. *Concurrent Pos:* Nat Res Coun res grants, 64- *Mem:* Sigma Xi; Soc Neurosci. *Res:* Role of forebrain structures in patterning and control of motor activity; role of cholinergic and serotonergic brain systems. *Mailing Add:* Dept Psychol Univ Western Ont London ON N6A 5C2 Can. *Fax:* 519-661-3961

**VANDERZANT, CARL,** FOOD MICROBIOLOGY. *Current Pos:* From asst prof to assoc prof dairy sci, 53-62, prof food microbiol, 62-91, EMER PROF FOOD MICROBIOL, TEX A&M UNIV, 91- *Personal Data:* b Nymegen, Neth, Sept 7, 25; nat US; m 52; c 2. *Educ:* State Agr Univ, Wageningen, BS, 47, MS, 49; Iowa State Univ, MS, 50, PhD(dairy bact), 53. *Mem:* Am Soc Microbiol; Inst Food Technologists. *Res:* Bacteriological problems of foods. *Mailing Add:* 5509 Columbine Lane San Angelo TX 76904

**VANDERZANT, ERMA SCHUMACHER,** BIOCHEMISTRY. *Current Pos:* BIOCHEMIST, COTTON INSECTS BR, ENTOM RES DIV, SCI & EDUC ADMIN-AGR RES, USDA, TEX A&M UNIV, 54- *Personal Data:* b Elwood, Ill, Jan 30, 20; m 52; c 2. *Educ:* Iowa State Univ, BS, 42, PhD(biochem), 53. *Honors & Awards:* J Everett Bussart Mem Award, Entom Soc Am, 71. *Mem:* Am Chem Soc; Entom Soc Am; Am Inst Nutrit; Sigma Xi. *Res:* Chemically defined diets for insects; nutrition and metabolism of growth factors, lipides and amino acids. *Mailing Add:* 5509 Columbine Lane San Angelo TX 76904

**VANDERZEE, CECIL EDWARD,** PHYSICAL CHEMISTRY. *Current Pos:* RETIRED. *Personal Data:* b Wetonka, SDak, Apr 26, 12; m 44. *Educ:* Jamestown Col, BS, 38; Univ Iowa, PhD(chem), 49. *Honors & Awards:* Huffman Mem Award, Calorimetry Conf, 75. *Prof Exp:* Instr, Jamestown Col, 39 & high sch, SDak, 39-42; from instr to assoc prof chem, Univ Nebr, Lincoln, 49-58, prof chem, 58-, vchmn dept, 65-70. *Concurrent Pos:* Mem bd dirs, Calorimetry Conf, 64-66, chmn elec, 67-68, chmn, 68-69, counsellor, 73-76; assoc mem, Comn Thermodyn, Int Union Pure & Appl Chem, 76-83. *Mem:* Am Chem Soc. *Res:* Thermodynamics; calorimetry. *Mailing Add:* 3320 Melrose Ave Lincoln NE 68506

**VAN DER ZIEL, JAN PETER,** SOLID STATE PHYSICS. *Current Pos:* PROF ELEC INST, UNIV TEX, 91- *Personal Data:* b Eindhoven, Neth, Aug 17, 37; US citizen; m 65; c 2. *Educ:* Univ Minn, BS, 59; Harvard Univ, MS, 61, PhD(appl physics), 64. *Prof Exp:* Res fel appl physics, Harvard Univ, 64-65; mem tech staff, Bell Labs, 65-91. *Mem:* Fel Inst Elec & Electronics Engrs; Am Phys Soc; Optical Soc Am. *Res:* Lasers and nonlinear optics; optical spectroscopy; integrated optics; semiconductor lasers. *Mailing Add:* EC-33 Univ Tex PO Box 830688 Richardson TX 75083. *Fax:* 972-883-6839; *E-Mail:* ziel@utdallas.edu

**VANDER ZWAAG, ROGER,** BIOSTATISTICS. *Current Pos:* ASSOC PROF BIOSTAT, UNIV TENN, 77- *Personal Data:* b Holland, Mich, Dec 27, 38; m 64; c 3. *Educ:* Hope Col, AB, 60; Purdue Univ, MS, 62; Johns Hopkins Univ, PhD(biostat), 68. *Prof Exp:* Asst prof biostat, Sch Med, Vanderbilt Univ, 68-77. *Mem:* Am Statist Asn. *Res:* Epidemiology. *Mailing Add:* 6157 Quince Rd Memphis TN 38119

**VAN DER ZWET, TOM,** PLANT PATHOLOGY. *Current Pos:* Plant pathologist, Tung Res Lab, Bogalusa, La, 59-65, Fruit Lab, Plant Genetics & Germplasm Inst, Agr Res Ctr, Beltsville, Md, 65-79, PLANT PATHOLOGIST, APPALACIAN FRUIT RES STA, KEARNEYSVILLE, WVA, USDA, 79- *Personal Data:* b Borneo, Indonesia, Apr 7, 32; nat US; m 55, 80; c 3. *Educ:* Col Trop Agr, Deventer, Netherlands, BS, 52; La State Univ, BS, 55, MS, 57, PhD(plant path), 59. *Honors & Awards:* Stark Award, Am Soc Hort Sci, 78. *Concurrent Pos:* Adj prof, WVa Univ, Morgantown, 79. *Mem:* Am Phytopath Soc; Int Soc Hort Sci; Int Soc Plant Path. *Res:* Diseases of tropical and subtropical crops; soil and leaf spot fungi; fire blight of pome fruit. *Mailing Add:* US Dept Agr 45 Wiltshire Rd Kearneysville WV 25430

**VAN DE SANDE, JOHAN HUBERT,** NUCLEIC ACIDS CONFORMATION. *Current Pos:* from asst prof to prof biochem, 72-88, head, Dept Med Biochem, 88-93, ASSOC DEAN, UNIV CALGARY, 93- *Personal Data:* b Bersen Op Zoom, Neth, Oct 28, 41; Can citizen; m 65; c 2. *Educ:* Univ Leiden, Neth, Candidaats, 63; Univ Alta, Can, PhD(org chem), 68. *Prof Exp:* Fel nucleic acids, Enzyme Inst, Madison, Wis, 68-70; res assoc biol & chem, Mass Inst Technol, 70-72. *Concurrent Pos:* Vis prof, Med Res Coun Can, 80-81. *Res:* Study of conformational polymorphism in topologically stressed DNA; proximal and distal effects of conformational transitions on gene expression; role of conformational parameters in DNA-protein interaction; enzymology of DNA repair. *Mailing Add:* Dept Med Biochem Fac Med Univ Calgary 3330 Hospital Dr Rm 382 Calgary AB T2N 4N1 Can

**VAN DE STEEG, GARET EDWARD,** RADIOCHEMISTRY, NUCLEAR CHEMISTRY. *Current Pos:* Sr res chemist, Kerr-McGee Corp, 68-75, proj res chemist, 75-78, sr proj analytical chemist, 78-83, mgr analytical chem, 83-89, SR PROJ MGR, KERR-MCGEE CORP, 89- *Personal Data:* b Minneapolis, Minn, Feb 8, 40; m 65, Dorothy; c 2. *Educ:* Marquette Univ, BS, 62; Univ NMex, PhD(chem), 68. *Concurrent Pos:* Adj prof, Univ Okla, 88- *Mem:* Sigma Xi; Am Chem Soc. *Res:* Environmental chemistry and process design; dilute solution chemistry of actinides, lanthanides, transition metals and fission products; solvent extraction of boron, actinides, lanthanides and transition metals; analytical methods development; radiochemical tracer studies; design, develop and install environmental control and remediation processes. *Mailing Add:* 2312 NW 113th Pl Oklahoma City OK 73120. *Fax:* 405-775-5632

**VAN DEUSEN, BRUCE DUDLEY,** ELECTROTHERMAL PROPULSION TECHNOLOGY, STATISTICAL ANALYSIS. *Current Pos:* PRES, EDUC SERV INC, 94- *Personal Data:* m 57, Ann Groves; c David Bruce, Elizabeth Ann & Janet Marie. *Educ:* Ohio Wesleyan Univ, BA, 52; Univ Mich, MS, 58, PhD(eng mech), 71. *Honors & Awards:* Arch T Colwell Award, Soc Automotive Engrs, 67. *Prof Exp:* Student engr, Chrysler Corp, 56-58, res scientist, 58-63, sr res scientist, 63-67, chief engr vehicle systs 67-82; dir advan progs, Gen Dynamics, 82-87, dir electrothermal progs, 87-93. *Res:* Developed analytical models for vehicle dynamics for both analog and digital computers; developed techniques for statistical analysis of experimental data; lead development of electrothermal launcher technology. *Mailing Add:* 1492 W Lincoln Birmingham MI 48009-1830

**VAN DEUSEN, PAUL COOK,** FOREST & WILDLIFE SAMPLING, DENDROCHRONOLOGY & REMOTE SENSING. *Current Pos:* QUANTITATIVE FOREST ECOLOGIST, NAT COUN PAPER INDUST AIR & STREAM IMPROV, 94- *Personal Data:* m 92, Shirley Tsaget; c Daryl. *Educ:* Univ Mass, Amherst, BS, 75; Miss State Univ, MS, 78; Univ Calif, Berkeley, PhD(forest biomet), 84. *Prof Exp:* Math statistician, USDA Forest Serv, 84-90, proj leader, Southern Forest Exp Sta, 91-94. *Mem:* Am Statist Asn; Soc Am Foresters. *Res:* Applying statistical theory to forest sampling, remote sensing; quantitative forest ecology. *Mailing Add:* NCASI Tufts Univ Anderson Hall Medford MA 02155. *Fax:* 617-627-3831; *E-Mail:* pvandeus@jade.tufts.edu

**VAN DEUSEN, RICHARD L,** polymer chemistry, for more information see previous edition

**VAN DE VAART, HERMAN,** SOLID STATE ELECTRONICS. *Current Pos:* RETIRED. *Personal Data:* b Arnhem, Neth, Apr 11, 34; m 60; c 2. *Educ:* Delft Univ Technol, Ing, 58, PhD(tech sci), 69. *Prof Exp:* Res asst elec eng, Delft Univ Technol, 56-58; res engr, Transitron Electronic Corp, Mass, 60-62; res asst, Sperry Rand Corp, 62-65, res staff mem, 65-73, mgr, Solid State Devices Dept, 73-80, mgr, Signal Processing Dept, 80-81, dir, Appl Physics Lab, Sperry Res Ctr, 81-95. *Mem:* Am Phys Soc; sr mem Inst Elec & Electronics Engrs. *Res:* Semiconductor technology; quadrupole and ferro magnetic resonance; microwave magnetics; solid state delay lines; ultrasonics; ferrites. *Mailing Add:* 14 Waldon Rd Califon NJ 07830

**VAN DE VEN, THEODORUS GERTRUDUS MARIA,** PHYSICAL CHEMISTRY. *Current Pos:* PRIN SCIENTIST, PULP & PAPER RES INST CAN, 78-; DIR, PULP & PAPER RES CTR, MCGILL UNIV, 80- *Personal Data:* b 's-Hertogenbosch, Holland, Feb 22, 46. *Educ:* State Univ Utrecht, BSc, 69, MSc, 71; McGill Univ, PhD(phys chem), 76. *Honors & Awards:* Colloid or Surface Chem Award, Am Chem Soc, 96. *Prof Exp:* Res fel rheology, Univ Sydney, 76-77. *Concurrent Pos:* C B Purves fel, 73-75; vis prof, Dept Chem, Univ Bristol, Eng, 87-88; Royal Soc Guest Res fel, 87-88; Paprican adj prof, Dept Chem, McGill Univ, 90; assoc, Can Inst Advan Res, 91- *Mem:* Can Pulp & Paper Asn; Soc Rheology; Int Asn Colloid & Interface Scientists; Polymer Colloid Group; Tech Asn Pulp & Paper Inst; Can Inst Chem; Can Rheology Group; Am Chem Soc. *Res:* Fundamental research in the areas of microrheology and wetting and spreading. *Mailing Add:* Pulp & Paper Res Ctr McGill Univ 3420 University St Montreal PQ H3A 2A7 Can. *Fax:* 514-398-6256

**VANDEVENDER, JOHN PACE,** INTENSE PARTICLE BEAMS, PULSED POWER. *Current Pos:* Mem tech staff res, Sandia Nat Lab, 74-79, div supvr, Pulsed Power Res, 79-82, dept mgr, Fusion Res, 82-84, prog mgr, Internal Fusion, 84-90, DIR PULSED POWER SCI, SANDIA NAT LAB, 84- *Personal Data:* b Jackson, Miss, Sept 12, 47; m 71; c 3. *Educ:* Vanderbilt Univ, BA, 69; Dartmouth Col, MA, 71; Imp Col Sci & Tech, Univ London, MPhil, 72, PhD(physics), 74. *Concurrent Pos:* Prog mgr, Inertial Fusion, Sandia Nat Lab, 84-90; comt mem, Strategic Defense Initiative Orgn & dir energy, 85-; res comt mem, Nat Acad Sci, Space Power, 87-88, Los Alamos Nat Lab, Chem & Lasers, 88- & Naval Studies Bd, 89- *Mem:* Fel Am Phys Soc; Inst Elec & Electronics Engrs. *Res:* Driving inertial confinement fusion with intense beams of lithium ions for military applications and economic power production is major initiative; exploring the feasibility of new concepts in directed and kinetic energy and understanding transient radiation effects on electronic systems. *Mailing Add:* Prosperity Inst 1155 University SE Albuquerque NM 87106

**VAN DE WALLE, CHRIS G,** COMPUTATIONAL PHYSICS, PHYSICS OF INTERFACES & DEFECTS. *Current Pos:* MEM RES STAFF, XEROX PALO ALTO RES CTR, 91- *Personal Data:* b Ghent, Belg, May 10, 59. *Educ:* Univ Ghent, Belg, Engr, 82; Stanford Univ, PhD(elec eng), 86. *Prof Exp:* Scientist, IBM, T J Watson Res Ctr, Yorktown Heights, NY, 86-88; sr mem res staff, Philips Labs, 88-91. *Concurrent Pos:* Adj prof mat sci, Columbia Univ, 91; chair, Conf Physics & Chem Semiconductor Interfaces, 96 & Gordon Conf Defects in Semiconductors, 98. *Mem:* Inst Elec & Electronics Engrs; Am Phys Soc; Mat Res Soc; fel Belg Am Educ Found. *Res:* Computational physics; semiconductor heterojunctions; defects and impurities in semiconductors; diffusion and reactions; hydrogen in semiconductors; wide-band-gap semiconductors. *Mailing Add:* Xerox PARC 3333 Coyote Hill Rd Palo Alto CA 94304. *E-Mail:* vandewalle@parc.xerox.com

**VAN DE WATER, JOSEPH M,** CARDIOVASCULAR & RESPIRATORY PHYSIOLOGY, TRAUMA SURGERY. *Current Pos:* PROF SURG, ALBERT EINSTEIN COL MED, 89-; DIR SURG EDUC, LONG ISLAND JEWISH MED CTR, 89- *Personal Data:* b Bonne Terre, Mo, Nov 26, 34. *Educ:* Stanford Univ, BS, 56, MD, 60. *Prof Exp:* Chief surg, Episcopal Hosp, 85-89. *Concurrent Pos:* Prof surg & physiol & co-dir trauma, Sch Med, Temple Univ, 85-89. *Mem:* Biomed Eng Soc; AMA; Am Col Surg; Soc Univ Surgeons; Am Asn Surg Trauma; Am Asn Thoracic Surg. *Mailing Add:* Dept Surg Carl Vinson VAMC Dublin GA 31021

**VAN DE WETERING, RICHARD LEE,** MATHEMATICS. *Current Pos:* From asst prof to assoc prof, 60-67, dept chair, 79-84, PROF MATH, SAN DIEGO STATE UNIV, 67- *Personal Data:* b Bellingham, Wash, Aug 2, 28; m 60; c 2. *Educ:* Univ Wash, Seattle, BS, 50; Western Wash State Col, EdM, 55; Stanford Univ, PhD(math), 60. *Concurrent Pos:* Res grant, Delft Univ Technol, 66-67; res assoc, Math Inst, Univ Groningen, 73-74. *Mem:* Am Math Soc; Math Asn Am. *Res:* Ordinary differential equations and integral transforms. *Mailing Add:* Dept Math San Diego State Univ San Diego CA 92182-7720

**VANDE WOUDE, GEORGE,** BIOCHEMISTRY, VIROLOGY. *Current Pos:* head, Human Tumor Studies Sect, Viral Biol Br, Nat Cancer Inst, Bethesda, 72-75, head, Virus Tumor Biochem Sect, 75-81, chief, Lab Molecular Biol, 81-83, DIR, BASIC RES PROG, ADVAN BIOSCI LAB, FREDERICK CANCER RES & DEVELOP CTR, NAT CANCER INST, 83- *Personal Data:* b Brooklyn, NY, Dec 25, 35; m 59; c 4. *Educ:* Hofstra Col, BA, 59; Rutgers Univ, MS, 62, PhD(biochem), 64. *Honors & Awards:* Merit Award, NIH, 82; Robert J & Claire Pasarow, Found Award Cancer Res, 89; Lifetime Achievement Award Technol Transfer, NASA, 92. *Prof Exp:* Res assoc fel, USDA, Plum Island, 64-65, res chemist, Plum Island Animal Dis Lab, 65-72. *Concurrent Pos:* Pres, Found Advan Cancer Studies, 85-; ed, J Virology; sci adv to dir basic sci, Nat Cancer Inst, 95- *Mem:* Nat Acad Sci; Am Chem Soc; Am Asn Cancer Res; Am Soc Microbiol; AAAS; Sigma Xi. *Res:* Molecular mechanisms of carcinogenesis; oncogenes; gene expression in eukaryotes; mammalian retrovirus vectors; author of over 200 scientific research articles and over 60 books or monographs. *Mailing Add:* ABL-Basic Res Prog Nat Cancer Inst Frederick Cancer Res & Develop Ctr Frederick MD 21702

**VAN DIJK, CHRISTIAAN PIETER,** physical organic chemistry, chemical engineering, for more information see previous edition

**VAN DILLA, MARVIN ALBERT,** MOLECULAR BIOLOGY. *Current Pos:* RETIRED. *Personal Data:* b New York, NY, June 18, 19; div; c 4. *Educ:* Mass Inst Technol, PhD(physics), 51. *Prof Exp:* Res asst, Mass Inst Technol, 46-51; asst res prof physics, Radiobiol Lab, Univ Utah, 51-57; mem staff, Biomed Res Group, Los Alamos Nat Lab, 57-72; cytophys sect leader, Lawrence Livermore Nat Lab, 72-82, sr scientist, Genetics Sect, Biomed Res Div, 83-92. *Mem:* AAAS; Soc Analytical Cytol; Am Soc Human Genetics. *Res:* Cell analysis and sorting by high speed flow methods; flow cytometry; cell cycle analysis; flow cytogenetics; sperm cell analysis; chromosome sorting; gene library construction. *Mailing Add:* 2601 College Ave Berkeley CA 94704

**VANDIVER, BRADFORD B,** GEOLOGY. *Current Pos:* prof, 65-, EMER PROF GEOL, STATE UNIV NY COL POTSDAM. *Personal Data:* b Orlando, Fla, Mar 7, 27; m 80; c 2. *Educ:* Univ Colo, BA, 57, MS, 58; Univ Wash, Seattle, PhD(geol), 64. *Prof Exp:* Explor geologist, Tenn Gas Transmission Co, Bolivia, 58-60; asst prof geol, Univ Idaho, 64 & Univ Ore, 64-65. *Concurrent Pos:* Vis prof, Univ Colo, 70 & 71; prof, Univ Munich, Ger, 72. *Mem:* Fel Geol Soc Am; Sigma Xi. *Res:* Metamorphic petrology and structural geology, Cascades, Rocky Mountains, Alps, Adirondacks, Odenwald, (Germany); environmental geology. *Mailing Add:* PO Box 324 Hannawa Falls NY 13647

**VANDIVIERE, H MAC,** preventive pediatrics, chest disease, for more information see previous edition

**VANDLEN, RICHARD LEE,** BIOCHEMISTRY, NEUROCHEMISTRY. *Current Pos:* sr scientist, 85-89, DIR, PROTEIN CHEM, GENENTECH INC, SOUTH SAN FRANCISCO, 89- *Personal Data:* b Battle Creek, Mich, Oct 22, 47; m 86; Mary A Napier; c Leanna. *Educ:* Mich State Univ, BS, 69, PhD(phys chem), 72. *Prof Exp:* Fel neurochem, Calif Inst Technol, 72-75, res fel, 75-76; sr res biochemist, Merck Sharp & Dohme Res Labs, 76-85. *Concurrent Pos:* NIH fel, Calif Inst Technol, 74-75. *Mem:* Sigma Xi; Am Crystallog Asn; NY Acad Sci; AAAS. *Res:* Regulation of hormone synthesis and release; hormone and neurotransmitter receptors; protein structure and function; protein sequence. *Mailing Add:* Genentech Inc 460 Pt San Bruno Blvd South San Francisco CA 94080-4990

**VAN DOEREN, RICHARD EDGERLY,** ACOUSTICS, ELECTRONICS. *Current Pos:* PRES, MIDWEST ACOUST & ELECTRONICS, INC, 74- *Personal Data:* b Tulsa, Okla, Mar 31, 37; m 60; c 3. *Educ:* Colo Sch Mines, BSc, 60; Ohio State Univ, MSc, 64, PhD(elec eng), 68. *Prof Exp:* Physicist, US Naval Air Develop Ctr, Pa, 60-64; res assoc electromagnetic theory, Electro Sci Lab, Ohio State Univ, 64-69; sr engr, N Star Res & Develop Inst, 69-74. *Mem:* Inst Elec & Electronics Engrs; Acoust Soc Am; Inst Noise Control Eng; Am Consult Engrs Coun; Audio Eng Soc; Am Soc Testing & Mat. *Res:* Acoustical noise reduction techniques, acoustical response of rooms; acoustic measurement techniques and systems; human response to sound; electroacoustic systems; computer methods in acoustics. *Mailing Add:* 6617 Limerick Lane Minneapolis MN 55439

**VAN DOLAH, ROBERT FREDERICK,** MARINE ECOLOGY, INVERTEBRATE ZOOLOGY. *Current Pos:* SR MARINE SCIENTIST MARINE ECOL & ASST DIR, SC MARINE RESOURCES RES INST, 88- *Personal Data:* b Portland, Ore, Nov 4, 49; c 2. *Educ:* Marietta Col, BS, 71; Univ Md, MS, 75, PhD(zool), 77. *Concurrent Pos:* Adj fac, Col Charleston. *Mem:* Ecol Soc Am; Estuarine Res Fedn. *Res:* Population and community ecology with particular emphasis on the regulatory processes operating in marine and estuarine systems; environmental research on effects of habitat perturbations and pollution. *Mailing Add:* 653 Wampler Dr Charleston SC 29412

**VAN DOLAH, ROBERT WAYNE,** CHEMISTRY. *Current Pos:* CONSULT, 78- *Personal Data:* b Cheyenne, Wyo, Feb 1, 19; m 42; c 3. *Educ:* Whitman Col, AB, 40; Ohio State Univ, PhD(org chem), 43. *Honors & Awards:* Distinguished Serv Medal, US Dept Interior, 65; Nitro Nobel Medal, 67; H H Storch Award, Am Chem Soc, 72. *Prof Exp:* Asst chem, Ohio State Univ, 40-42; asst to sci dir, William S Merrell Co, Ohio, 43-44, res chemist & group leader, 44-46; actg head, Org Chem Br, US Naval Ord Test Sta, Calif, 46-48, head, 48-53, head, Chem Div, 53-54; chief, Explosives Res Lab, Pittsburgh Mining & Safety Res Ctr, US Bur Mines, 54-71, res dir, 71-78. *Mem:* Fel AAAS; fel Am Inst Chem; Am Chem Soc; Sigma Xi; Nat Fire Protection Asn. *Res:* Propellants and explosives, combustion, mine safety, industrial safety. *Mailing Add:* 1150 Anchorage Lane No 310 San Diego CA 92106

**VAN DOMELEN, BRUCE HAROLD,** PHYSICS. *Current Pos:* RETIRED. *Personal Data:* b Shelby, Mich, May 27, 33; m 57; c 4. *Educ:* Kalamazoo Col, BA, 55; Univ Wis, MA, 57, PhD(physics), 60. *Prof Exp:* Staff mem, Sandia Nat Labs, 60-62; sect supvr phys metall, 62-65; div supvr anal physics, 65; tech adv syst res, 65-69, div supvr explor power sources, 69-78, Explosives Projs & Tests Div, 78-85, New Hire Projs, 85-88, div supvr technol transfer, 88-96. *Concurrent Pos:* Actg chmn, Governor's Sci Adv Comt, NMex, 66-70, Governor's sci adv, 66-75; NMex mem, Western Interstate Nuclear Bd, 67-77, chmn, 71-73; mem, Nat Governors' Coun Sci & Technol, 70-75. *Mem:* Am Phys Soc; Sigma Xi. *Res:* Explosives; physical chemistry. *Mailing Add:* 3204 La Sala Cuadra NE Albuquerque NM 87111

**VAN DONGEN, CORNELIS GODEFRIDUS,** ANIMAL HUSBANDRY, REPRODUCTIVE PHYSIOLOGY. *Current Pos:* PRES, BIO BREEDERS INC, 85- *Personal Data:* b Geertruidenberg, Neth, Mar 20, 34; m 69; c 2. *Educ:* Wageningen State Agr Univ, BS, 57, MS, 59; Univ Ill, Urbana, MS, 62, PhD(dairy sci), 64. *Prof Exp:* Res fel pharmacol, Harvard Univ, 64-65; res assoc physiol, Brown Univ, 66; asst prof pharmacol, NY Med Col, 66-67; res assoc, Bio-Res Inst, Inc, 67-76, vpres, 76-85. *Concurrent Pos:* Grants, NIH; investr, USDA Contract; consult, Bio Res Consults. *Mem:* Am Dairy Sci Asn; Am Soc Animal Sci; Brit Soc Study Fertil; Soc Study Reproduction; Am Asn Lab Animal Sci. *Res:* Management of breeding colony of inbred and hybrid Syrian hamsters; development of animal models of human disease; husbandry and nutritional factors; muscular dystrophy, carcinogenicity, aging, reproductive physiology and atherosclerosis. *Mailing Add:* Bio Breeders Inc 280 Sheldon Rd Fitchburg MA 01420

**VAN DOORNE, WILLIAM,** INORGANIC CHEMISTRY. *Current Pos:* From asst prof to assoc prof chem, 66-74, PROF CHEM, CALVIN COL, 74-, CHMN DEPT, 77- *Personal Data:* b Utrecht, Neth, Dec 12, 37; US citizen; m 61; c 3. *Educ:* Calvin Col, BS, 60; Univ Mich, MS, 62, PhD. *Concurrent Pos:* Vis assoc prof, Univ Hawaii, 72-73. *Mem:* Am Chem Soc. *Res:* Phophorus-nitrogen compounds; synthetic inorganic chemistry; crystallography. *Mailing Add:* 3201 Burton St SE Grand Rapids MI 49546-4349

**VAN DOP, CORNELIS,** PEDIATRIC ENDOCRINOLOGY. *Current Pos:* ASSOC PROF, UNIV CALIF, LOS ANGELES, 89- *Personal Data:* b Indonesia, June 12, 49; US citizen. *Educ:* Univ Wis-Madison, PhD(biochem), 77, MD, 78. *Honors & Awards:* Ann Lectr, Lawson Wilkins Pediat Endocrine Soc, 91. *Prof Exp:* Adj asst prof, Univ Calif, San Francisco, 83-84; asst prof, Johns Hopkins Univ, 84-87, Harvard Med Sch, 87-89. *Mem:* AAAS;

Endocrine Soc; Soc Pediat Res; Lawson Wilkins Pediat Endocrine Soc; Am Soc Biochem & Molecular Biol. *Res:* Determining the role of altered activity of quanine nucleotide-binding proteins in human diseases and growth abnormalities in endocrinologic diseases. *Mailing Add:* MDCC 22-315 CHS Univ Calif Los Angeles Med Ctr 10833 Le Conte Ave Los Angeles CA 90024. *Fax:* 310-206-5843; *E-Mail:* cvandop@ucla.edu

**VAN DOVER, ROBERT B,** HIGH TEMPERATURE SUPERCONDUCTIVITY. *Current Pos:* MEM TECH STAFF, SOLID STATE CHEM RES DEPT, AT&T BELL LABS, 80- *Personal Data:* b NJ, 1952. *Educ:* Princeton Univ, BS, 74; Stanford Univ, MA, 75, PhD(appl physics), 80. *Concurrent Pos:* Josephson Junet Develop Group, AT&T Bell Labs, 80-83, Metall Eng Res Dept, 83-87, Nonequilibrium Physics Res Dept, 87-88. *Mem:* Am Phys Soc; Mat Res Soc; Inst Elec & Electronics Engrs; Sigma Xi. *Res:* Published 3 patents and numerous articles to selected publications. *Mailing Add:* AT&T Bell Labs 600 Mountain Ave Murray Hill NJ 07974. *Fax:* 908-582-2521; *E-Mail:* brucc@allwise.att.com

**VAN DREAL, PAUL ARTHUR,** BIOCHEMISTRY, CYTOLOGY. *Current Pos:* ASSOC PROF, PATH DEPT, UNIV TEX SOUTHWESTERN MED SCH, 83-; TECH DIR, NAT HEALTH LABS, DALLAS, 90- *Personal Data:* b Chicago, Ill, Feb 15, 32; m 57; c 2. *Educ:* Calvin Col, BS, 57; Mich State Univ, PhD(bot, biochem, cytol), 61. *Prof Exp:* Clin biochemist, St Lawrence Hosp, 61-63; NIH fel, Biol Div, Oak Ridge Nat Lab, 63-64; asst prof biochem, Med Sch, Univ Ore, 64-66; from asst prof to assoc prof clin chem, Med Sch, Univ Wash, 66-71, dir, Lab Comput Div, 69-71; vpres & dir res, Hycel Inc, 71-72; tech mgr radioimmunoassay develop, Corning Glass Works, Inc, 72-73; assoc prof path & clin chem, Med Sch, Univ Ky, 73-74; lab dir & tech dir, Nat Health Labs, Inc, 74-75; vpres & lab dir, Herner Analytics, 75-77; lab dir, Clin Lab Med Serv, 77-80; mgr chem applicator, Diag Div, Abbot Labs, 80-83. *Concurrent Pos:* Lectr biochem, Mich State Univ, 62-63; Nat Cancer Inst fel carcinogenesis, Med Sch, Univ Ore, 64-66; consult, Ortec Div, EG&G, 67-71, Clin Instruments Div, Beckman Instruments, 67-, Pesticide Res Lab, Dept Health, State Wash, 68-69, Bausch & Lomb Inc, 69- & Corning Glass Inc, 74-; Bausch & Lomb Grant electrophoresis, Med Sch, Univ Wash, 69-70. *Mem:* AAAS; Am Chem Soc; fel Am Asn Clin Chemists; Am Soc Clin Path; Asn Clin Scientists; Sigma Xi. *Res:* New clinical laboratory diagnostic techniques; aging; patient normals as a function of age and disease onset; biochemistry of the cell cycle. *Mailing Add:* 25917 Sugar Leaf Trail Spring TX 77389

**VAN DRESER, MERTON LAWRENCE,** CERAMIC ENGINEERING, MATERIALS SCIENCE. *Current Pos:* CONSULT, 89- *Personal Data:* b Des Moines, Iowa, June 5, 29; m 52, Evelyn Manny; c Peter & Jennifer. *Educ:* Iowa State Univ, BS, 51. *Prof Exp:* Tech supvr fiberglass mfg, Owens-Corning Fiberglas Corp, 54-57; res engr, Kaiser Aluminum & Chem Corp, 57-60, res sect head basic refractory res, 60-63, lab mgr, 63-65, assoc dir res, 65-69, dir refractories res, 69-72, dir non-metall mat res, 72-83, vpres & dir res, indust chem & Harshaw/Filtrol partnership, 83-85, dir, Bus Div, 85-88, consult, Kaiser Aluminum & Chem Corp, 88-89. *Concurrent Pos:* Mem, Tech Adv Comn, Refractories Inst, 74-84, chmn, 80-84; mem adv bd, Dept Ceramic Eng, Univ Ill, 75-78; vol exec, Intl Exec Serv Corp, Pakistan, 90. *Mem:* Fel Am Ceramic Soc (vpres, 73-74); Brit Ceramic Soc; Nat Inst Ceramic Eng; Am Inst Mining, Metall & Petrol Eng; hon mem Am Soc Testing & Mat. *Res:* Refractories, sintering of refractory oxides and silicates; chemical and ceramic bonding of refractory powders; development of refractory products for application in iron, steel, glass, non-ferrous metal and petro-chemical industries. *Mailing Add:* 40 Castledown Rd Pleasanton CA 94566

**VAN DRIEL, HENRY MARTIN,** LASER PHYSICS, NONLINEAR OPTICS. *Current Pos:* PROF PHYSICS, UNIV TORONTO, 76- *Personal Data:* b Breda, Neth, Dec 27, 46; Can citizen; m 70; c 3. *Educ:* Univ Toronto, BSc, 70, MSc, 71 & PhD(physics), 75. *Prof Exp:* fel physics, Univ Ariz, 75-76. *Concurrent Pos:* Vis scientist, Harvard Univ, 83 & IBM, 83-85; John Simon Guggenheim Found fel, 86; Nat Res Coun fel, 75. *Mem:* Can Asn Physicists; Am Phys Soc; fel Optical Soc Am. *Res:* Usage of ultrafast laser pulses in investigating picosecond and femtosecond optoelectronic phenomena in semiconductor; nonlinear optical response of solids including metals and superlattice semiconductors. *Mailing Add:* Dept Physics Univ Toronto Huron & Russell Toronto ON M5S 1A7 Can. *Fax:* 416-978-3936

**VAN DRIESSCHE, WILLY,** GENERAL MEDICAL SCIENCES. *Current Pos:* PROF PHYSIOL, K U LEUVEN, 75- *Personal Data:* b Stekene, Belg, Feb 8, 40; m 65; c 2. *Educ:* K U Leuven, PhD(physics), 68. *Mem:* Am Physiol Soc; Ger Physiol Soc; Belg Physiol Soc. *Res:* Electrophysiology of epithelial cells; inlizo cellular ion concentration. *Mailing Add:* Dept Physiol K U Leuven Campus Gasthuisberg B-3000 Louvain Belgium. *Fax:* 32-16-345991; *E-Mail:* wvandriessche@cc3.kuleuven.ac.be

**VANDRUFF, LARRY WAYNE,** WILDLIFE BIOLOGY, URBAN ECOLOGY. *Current Pos:* asst prof vert biol, 70-77, assoc prof, 77-85, PROF WILDLIFE BIOL, STATE UNIV NY COL ENVIRON SCI & FORESTRY, 85- *Personal Data:* b Elmira, NY, Apr 28, 42; m 66, Mary A Douglass; c Brenda & Thomas. *Educ:* Mansfield State Col, BS, 64; Cornell Univ, MS, 66, PhD(wildlife ecol), 71. *Honors & Awards:* Daniel L Leedy Urban Wildlife Conserv Award, Nat Inst Urban Wildlife, 87. *Prof Exp:* Res asst vert ecol & genetics, Cornell Univ, 64-66, res asst wildlife ecol, NY Wildlife Res Unit, 66-70. *Mem:* Am Soc Mammal; Wildlife Soc; Ecol Soc Am. *Res:* Field studies in the ecology of urban wildlife species; wildlife management; dynamics of homeotherm populations and wildlife; habitat relationships. *Mailing Add:* State Univ NY Col Environ Sci & Forestry 320 Bray Hall Syracuse NY 13210. *Fax:* 315-470-6934

**VAN DUUREN, BENJAMIN LOUIS,** organic chemistry, for more information see previous edition

**VAN DUYNE, RICHARD PALMER,** ANALYTICAL CHEMISTRY, CHEMICAL PHYSICS. *Current Pos:* From asst prof to assoc prof anal chem, 71-79, prof anal & phys chem, 79-86, MORRISON PROF CHEM, NORTHWESTERN UNIV, EVANSTON, 86- *Personal Data:* b Orange, NJ, Oct 28, 45. *Educ:* Rensselaer Polytech Inst, BS, 67; Univ NC, PhD(anal chem), 71. *Honors & Awards:* Coblentz Mem Prize, 80; Fresenius Award, 81; Pittsburgh Spectros Award, 91; Excellence in Surface Sci Award, Surfaces in Biomats Found, 96. *Concurrent Pos:* Fel, Alfred P Sloan Found, 74-78. *Mem:* Am Chem Soc; fel AAAS; fel Am Phys Soc. *Res:* Radical ion chemistry; surface-enhanced Raman spectroscopy; chemical applications of lasers; time-resolved fluorescence spectroscopy; tunable dye laser resonance Raman spectroscopy; laboratory computer systems; microfabrication, scanning electron, tunneling and atomic force microscopy; theory of electron transfer. *Mailing Add:* Dept Chem Northwestern Univ Evanston IL 60208

**VAN DUZER, THEODORE,** CRYOELECTRONICS. *Current Pos:* asst engr, Univ Calif, Berkeley, 57-60, actg asst prof, 60, from asst prof to assoc prof, 61-91, PROF GRAD SCH, UNIV CALIF, BERKELEY, 92- *Personal Data:* b Dec 27, 27. *Educ:* Rutgers Univ, BS, 54; Univ Calif, Los Angeles, MS, 57; Univ Calif, Berkeley, PhD(elec eng), 60. *Prof Exp:* Mem tech staff, Hughes Aircraft Co, 54-57. *Concurrent Pos:* NSF postdoctoral fel, Tech Sch Vienna, 60-61; Ford Found vis prof, Cath Univ, Chile, 65-66; mem tech staff, Bell Telephone Lab, 70; co-founder, Conductus, 88, consult, 88-; tech coordr, Advan Technol Prog, Dept Com, 97; ed, Inst Elec & Electronics Engrs. *Mem:* Nat Acad Eng; fel Inst Elec & Electronics Engrs; Sigma Xi. *Res:* Cryoelectronics; high thermal conductivity superconductor films; Josephson junctions; signal processing; superconductive A/D converters and integrated circuits; superconductor-semiconductor hybrids. *Mailing Add:* Elec Eng & Comput Sci Dept 231 Cory Hall Univ Calif Berkeley CA 94720-1770

**VAN DYK, JOHN WILLIAM,** PHYSICAL CHEMISTRY, COMPUTER SOFTWARE. *Current Pos:* CONSULT, 85- *Personal Data:* b Paterson, NJ, May 2, 28; m 51, Audrey A DeVries; c Mark D, Drew E & Dirk M. *Educ:* Rutgers Univ, AB, 50; Columbia, AM, 51, PhD(chem), 54. *Prof Exp:* Asst chem, Columbia Univ, 50-52; E I DuPont de Nemours & Co, Inc, res chemist, Polychems Dept, 54-64, staff chemist, Fabrics & Finishes Dept, 64-82, res assoc, 82-85. *Mem:* Am Chem Soc; Sigma Xi. *Res:* Polymerization kinetics; surface chemistry; polymer chemistry; paint chemistry; color science; visual perception; computer science; solubility parameters, solvent selection; scientific computer program. *Mailing Add:* 106 Cambridge Dr Wilmington DE 19803-2606. *Fax:* 302-478-3147

**VAN DYKE, CECIL GERALD,** PLANT PATHOLOGY, FUNGUS-HOST ULTRASTRUCTURE. *Current Pos:* res assoc, 68-69, from instr to assoc prof, 69-89, PROF BOT, NC STATE UNIV, 89- *Personal Data:* b Effingham, Ill, Feb 4, 41; m 69; c 5. *Educ:* East Ill Univ, BSEd, 63; Univ Ill, Urbana, MS, 66, PhD(plant path), 68. *Prof Exp:* NIH res assoc, Univ Ill, Urbana, 68. *Mem:* Am Phytopath Soc; Mycol Soc Am; Sigma Xi; Creation Res Soc. *Res:* Ultrastructure of fungi and fungus-host pathological interactions and biological control. *Mailing Add:* Dept Bot PO Box 7612 NC State Univ Raleigh NC 27695-0001

**VAN DYKE, CHARLES H,** INORGANIC CHEMISTRY, ORGANOMETALLIC CHEMISTRY. *Current Pos:* Asst prof, 63-70, ASSOC PROF CHEM, CARNEGIE-MELLON UNIV, 70- *Personal Data:* b Rochester, Pa, Sept 19, 37; m 66; c 1. *Educ:* Geneva Col, BS, 59; Univ Pa, PhD(inorg chem), 64. *Mem:* Am Chem Soc; Royal Soc Chem. *Res:* Synthesis and study of volatile hydride derivatives of the Group IV elements. *Mailing Add:* Dept Chem Carnegie-Mellon Univ Doherty Hall 2114 Pittsburgh PA 15213

**VAN DYKE, CRAIG,** PSYCHIATRY, PSYCHOPHARMACOLOGY. *Current Pos:* PROF & CHMN, LANGLEY PORTER PSYCHIAT INST, 94- *Personal Data:* b Detroit, Mich, Oct 4, 41; m 69; c 2. *Educ:* Univ Wash, BS, 63, MD, 67. *Prof Exp:* Asst prof psychiat, Yale Univ, 74-78; from assoc prof to prof psychiat, Univ Calif, San Francisco, 79-86. *Mem:* Am Psychosom Soc; Int Col Psychosom Med; Soc Neurosci; Int Neuropsychol Soc. *Res:* Psychoimmunology; neuropsychiatry. *Mailing Add:* Langley Porter Psychol Inst Rm 346 401 Parnassus San Francisco CA 94143-0984

**VAN DYKE, HENRY,** MICROBIOLOGY. *Current Pos:* RETIRED. *Personal Data:* b Pittsburgh, Pa, Oct 1, 21; m 43; c 4. *Educ:* Western Reserve Univ, BS, 47; Univ Mich, MA, 49, PhD(zool), 55. *Prof Exp:* Malariologist, USPHS, 52; instr zool, Univ Mich, 52-53; asst prof biol, Carleton Col, 53-60 & Ore Col Educ, 60-63; prof biol, Ore State Univ, 63-86. *Mem:* AAAS; Soc Protozool; Am Soc Microbiol; Marine Biol Asn UK, Am Soc Limnol & Oceanog. *Res:* Ecology, physiology, culture and photobiology of marine communities. *Mailing Add:* 3300 NW Van Buren Ave Corvallis OR 97331

**VAN DYKE, JOHN WILLIAM, JR,** ORGANIC CHEMISTRY. *Current Pos:* sr res chemist, Therapeut Res Lab, Miles Labs, Inc, 62-82, staff scientist, Enzyme Res Dept, 82-88, Biotechnol Res & Develop, 88-90, STAFF SCIENTIST, DIAGNOSTICS DIV, MILES INC, 90- *Personal Data:* b Holland, Mich, Nov 15, 35; m 59, Patricia Brown; c Kathryn, Matthew & Peter. *Educ:* Hope Col, AB, 58; Univ Ill, PhD(org chem), 62. *Mem:* Am Chem Soc. *Res:* Organic synthesis of pharmacologically active compounds; immobilization of enzymes; food ingredients research; synthesis of chemicals for diagnostic testing. *Mailing Add:* 2917 E Jackson Blvd Elkhart IN 46516-5025

**VAN DYKE, KNOX,** PHARMACOLOGY, BIOCHEMISTRY. *Current Pos:* Res assoc pharmacol, WVa Univ, 66-68, sr res pharmacologist, 68-69, from asst prof to assoc prof pharmacol, 69-77, PROF PHARMACOL & TOXICOL, MED CTR, WVA UNIV, 77- *Personal Data:* b Chicago, Ill, June 23, 39; m 78; c 5. *Educ:* Knox Col, AB, 61; St Louis Univ, PhD(biochem), 66. *Concurrent Pos:* WHO grant, 70-, training grant malaria; WVa Heart Asn grant, 70-; NIH instnl cancer & gen res WVa rep, Oak Ridge Assoc Univs, 72-75, Merck, Sharp & Dohme, Sandoz, 86-88, Knoll, 88-, FDA US-Bur of Mines. *Mem:* AAAS; Am Chem Soc; Am Soc Pharmacol & Exp Therapeut; Int Soc Biochem Pharmacol; Am Soc Photobiol. *Res:* Malariology and mechanism of drug resistance; automated analysis of enzyme and nucleic acid systems; radioimmunoassay; mechanisms of antimalarial drugs; adrenergic transmitter-energy complexes; adenosine utilization and syntheses; measurement of bioluminescent and chemiluminescent reaction; inflammatory drugs and free radicals; multiple drug resistance. *Mailing Add:* Dept Pharmacol WVa Univ Med Ctr Morgantown WV 26506-0001

**VAN DYKE, MILTON D(ENMAN),** FLUID MECHANICS. *Current Pos:* prof aeronaut eng, 59-75, prof appl mech, 75-92, EMER PROF APPL MECH, STANFORD UNIV, 92- *Personal Data:* b Chicago, Ill, Aug 1, 22; m 46, 62, Sylvia Adams; c Russell, Eric, Nina, Brooke, Byron & Christopher. *Educ:* Harvard Univ, BS, 43; Calif Inst Technol, MS, 47, PhD(aeronaut), 49. *Prof Exp:* Aeronaut res scientist, Nat Adv Comt Aeronaut, 43-46 & 50-58; aeronaut engr, Douglas Aircraft Co, 48; consult aerodynamicist, Rand Corp, 49-50; vis prof, Univ Paris, 58-59. *Concurrent Pos:* Lectr, Stanford Univ, 50-58; Guggenheim fel, 54-55; Nat Acad Sci exchange vis, USSR, 65; pres, Parabolic Press. *Mem:* Nat Acad Eng; Am Phys Soc; Am Acad Arts & Sci. *Res:* Compressible flow theory; viscous flow theory. *Mailing Add:* Div Appl Mech Stanford Univ Stanford CA 94305-4040. *Fax:* 650-723-1778

**VAN DYKE, RUSSELL AUSTIN,** pharmacology, toxicology, for more information see previous edition

**VAN DYKE, WILLIAM ADOLPHUS, JR,** NUCLEAR ENERGY, COMBAT WEAPON SYSTEMS. *Current Pos:* PROG MGR TECHNOL, US DEPT ENERGY, 90- *Personal Data:* m 52, Patricia Ann Edwards; c William K, Jay P & Vicki L (Eddy). *Educ:* ETex State Univ, BS, 58; George Washington Univ, MS, 84, DSc(eng mgt), 90. *Prof Exp:* Tech supvr & proj engr aircraft systs, LTV, 58-65; prod engr high speed transp, United Aircraft Corp, 65-69; sect mgr eng design & radar systs, Sanders Assocs Inc, 69-72; assoc prin engr satellite commun, Harris Corp, 72-85; dir & chief engr ship & air systs & combat systs, Vitro Corp, 85-90. *Concurrent Pos:* Prof lectr, Univ Md, 91-93, George Washington Univ, 91- & Johns Hopkins Univ, 97-; sr vpres, Smart Int Co, 91- *Mem:* Int Coun Syst Eng; AAAS; Am Soc Eng Mgt; Soc Prof Engrs; Asn Unmanned Vehicle Systs; Am Defense Preparedness Asn. *Res:* Computer data communication and networks; systems engineering; engineering management; technology assessment; combat weapons; nuclear energy; separation and filtration; advanced computers and networks; superconducting materials; transportation/aerospace systems; electronic systems and antennas. *Mailing Add:* 19901 Germantown Rd Germantown MD 20874-1207. *E-Mail:* william.vandyke@hq.doc.gov

**VANE, ARTHUR B(AYARD),** PHYSICAL CHEMISTRY, ELECTRICAL ENGINEERING. *Current Pos:* RETIRED. *Personal Data:* b Portland, Maine, June 1, 15; m 42, Sylvia Brakke; c Ronald A, Linda B & Laura (Ames). *Educ:* Univ Wash, Seattle, BS, 37; Ore State Col, MS, 41; Stanford Univ, EE, 49. *Prof Exp:* Staff mem, Radiation Lab, Mass Inst Technol, 42-45; physicist, US Naval Ord Test Sta, 45-47; res assoc, Microwave Lab, Stanford Univ, 47-49; sr engr, Varian Assocs, 49-55, mgr systs develop, 55-58, mgr systs dept, Radiation Div, 58-62; mgr, Microwave Dept, Melabs, Inc, 62-65; sr scientist, Cent Res Labs, Varian Assocs, 65-71; vpres, Sonoma Eng & Res, Santa Rosa, 71-75; sr scientist, Addington Labs, Sunnyvale, 75-77; vpres, Westmont Labs, Palo Alto, 77-79. *Concurrent Pos:* Consult, Vane Microwave Consult Co, 78-; comptroller, Cult Systs Res, 79-; controller, Ballena Press, 82- *Mem:* AAAS; Sigma Xi; Am Chem Soc; Inst Elec & Electronics Engrs. *Res:* Microwave techniques; solid state microwave devices. *Mailing Add:* 823 Valparaiso Ave Menlo Park CA 94025. *Fax:* 650-321-2529

**VANE, FLOIE MARIE,** DRUG METABOLISM. *Current Pos:* Sr chemist, 64-72, Hoffmann-LaRoche, Inc, group chief, 73-78, sect head, 79-84, res investr, 85-91, RES LEADER, HOFFMANN-LA ROCHE, INC, 91- *Personal Data:* b Dawson, Minn, Nov 25, 37. *Educ:* Gustavus Adolphus Col, BS, 59; Mich State Univ, PhD(org chem), 63. *Concurrent Pos:* NIH fel, Mass Inst Technol, 63-64; vis asst prof, Baylor Col Med, 68-69. *Mem:* Am Chem Soc; Am Soc Pharmacol & Exp Therapeut; Sigma Xi. *Res:* Structure determination of organic compounds by spectroscopic methods such as nuclear magnetic resonance and mass spectroscopy; structure identification of drug metabolites. *Mailing Add:* 770 H Anderson Ave Apt 19A Cliffside Park NJ 07010

**VANE, JOHN ROBERT,** ENDOTHELIAL CELLS, PROSTAGLANDINS. *Current Pos:* PROF MED, NY MED COL, VALHALLA, 86-; DIR, WILLIAM HARVEY RES INST, ST BARTHOLOMEW'S HOSP MED COL, 86-, CHMN RES COMT, 87- *Personal Data:* b Worcestershire, UK, Mar 29, 27; m 48; c 2. *Educ:* Univ Birmingham, BSc, 46; Univ Oxford, BSc, 49, DPhil, 53, DSc, 70. *Hon Degrees:* DMed, Copernicus Acad Med, Carcow, 77; Dr, Rene Descartes Univ, Paris, 78; DSc, City Univ New York, 80, Aberdeen Univ, 83, NY Med Col, 84, Birmingham Univ, 84, Camerino Univ, Italy, 84, Cath Univ, Belg, 86, Univ Buenos Aires, Arg, 86. *Honors & Awards:* Nobel Prize Physiol, 82; Baly Medallist, Royal Col Physicians, 77; Albert Lasker Basic Med Res Award, Albert & Mary Lasker Found, 77; Joseph J Bunim Medal, Am Rheumatism Asn, 79; Peter Debye Prize, Univ Maastricht, Holland, 80; Nuffield Lectr & Gold Medal, Royal Soc Med, Eng, 80; Dale Medallist, Soc Endocrinol, 81; Galen Medallist, Worshipful Soc Apothecaries, 83; Louis Pasteur Found Prize, 84; Royal Medal, Royal Soc, 89; Hamburg Gold Medal, Royal Pharm Soc Gt Brit, 96. *Prof Exp:* Instr & asst prof pharmacol, Yale Univ, 53-55; sr lectr pharmacol, Inst Basic Med Sci, Royal Col Surgeons Eng, 55-61, reader, London Univ, 61-65, prof exp pharmacol, 66-73; group res & develop dir, Wellcome Found Ltd, 73-85. *Concurrent Pos:* Lectr numerous univs & soc, 68-88; Walter C MacKenzie vis prof, Univ Alta, 77, vis prof, Harvard Univ, 79, vis prof pharmacol, NY Med Col, 86-; mem coun, Imp Cancer Res Fund, 85-; chmn, Imp Cancer Res Technol Ltd, 87-; mem sci adv comt, Osaka Biosci Inst, Japan, 87-; mem, Sch Med Vis Comt, Case Western Reserve, Univ Cleveland, 88- *Mem:* Foreign assoc Nat Acad Sci; hon mem Brit Pharmacol Soc; hon mem Physiol Soc; fel Inst Biol; fel Royal Soc (vpres, 85-87); hon mem Am Physiol Soc; hon fel Am Col Physicians; foreign hon mem Am Acad Arts & Sci; foreign mem Nat Acad Med Buenos Aires; hon fel Royal Col Physicians. *Res:* Mode of action of aspirin and similar drugs; discovery prostacyclin and its relationship to other prostaglandins and thromboxanes; underlying mechanism which initiates atherosclerosis, especially in the involvement of endothelial cell. *Mailing Add:* William Harvey Res Inst St Bartholomew's Univ London Queen Mary Col London ECIM 6BQ England

**VAN ECHO, ANDREW,** ENGINEERING & MATERIALS SCIENCE. *Current Pos:* RETIRED. *Personal Data:* b Barton, Ohio, Jan 27, 18; m 45, Elizabeth J Lauer; c David A. *Educ:* Ohio State Univ, BS, 42. *Honors & Awards:* Award of Merit, Am Soc Testing & Mat, 73, Hon Award, 75. *Prof Exp:* Res asst, Battelle Mem Inst, Columbus, Ohio, 41-43, Manhattan Proj, Univ Chicago, 43-45; chief inspector, Joslyn Mfg & Supply Co, 45-47, asst works mgr, Wm E Pratt Mfg Co Div, Joslyn Stainless Steel Co, 47-49, asst supt wire mill, 49-54, supvr prod control, 54-56, chief metallurgist & mgr processing & qual control, 56-63; asst chief, Fuels & Mat Br, US AEC, 63-73; metall engr, US Energy Res & Develop Admin, 73-77; metall engr, US Dept Energy, 77-80, sr mat engr, 80-86, mgr metall absorbers & stand & mat eng, 86-90, mgr, Int Progs Div, sr mat engr, Off Nuclear Energy, 90-94. *Concurrent Pos:* Mem, World Metall Cong, 57; Govt liaison rep of Dept Energy, Nat Acad Sci adv bd, Comt on Fatigue Crack Initiation at Elevated Temperatures, 77-78; mem, Joint US-USSR Working Group Metall, Joint US-USSR Comn Sci & Tech Coop, 73-78 & 78- *Mem:* Am Soc Metals; fel Am Soc Testing & Mat. *Res:* Uranium processing and fabrication; stainless steel melting, processing and fabrication; refractory alloy consolidation, processing and fabrication; silicon vaporphase plating of steels; V-alloy development; engineering properties of structural materials for high temperature design; uranium dioxide, uranium-plutonium dioxide, uranium metal fuels for reactors; dispersion strengthened ferritic steels for advanced liquid metal reactors. *Mailing Add:* 8211 Jeb Stuart Rd Potomac MD 20854-6219

**VAN ECHO, DAVID ANDREW,** ANTICANCER DRUG DEVELOPMENT, MEDICAL ONCOLOGY. *Current Pos:* from asst prof to assoc prof med & oncol, 81-90, chief hemat & oncol, Dept Med, 93-96, PROF MED, ONCOL & PHARM, SCH MED & PHARM, UNIV MD, 90- *Personal Data:* b Ft Wayne, Ind, July 19, 47; m 71, Kathleen Berry; c David C, Matthew A & Kyra N. *Educ:* Xavier Univ, BS, 69; Univ Md, MD, 73; Am Bd Internal Med, cert internal med, 76, cert med oncol, 77. *Prof Exp:* Intern & resident internal med, Univ Hosp, Baltimore, Md, 73-75; clin assoc, Nat Cancer Inst, 75-77, sr investr, 77-81. *Concurrent Pos:* Prin investr antineoplastic drug develop, Nat Cancer Inst, 81- *Mem:* Am Soc Clin Oncol; Am Asn Cancer Res; Multinat Asn Supportive Care Cancer; Int Soc Hematother & Graft Eng. *Res:* Phase I and II studies in solid tumors and acute leukemia; whole-body hyperthermia. *Mailing Add:* Univ Hosp 22 S Greene St Baltimore MD 21201-1544. *Fax:* 410-328-6896

**VAN ECK, EDWARD ARTHUR,** microbiology; deceased, see previous edition for last biography

**VAN ECK, WILLEM ADOLPH,** SOIL SCIENCE, HYDROLOGY. *Current Pos:* PROF SOIL SCI & STATE EXTEN SPECIALIST, WVA UNIV, 72- *Personal Data:* b Wageningen, Netherlands, July 27, 28; nat US; m 56; c 3. *Educ:* Wageningen State Agr Univ, BSc, 51; Mich State Univ, MSc, 54, PhD(soil sci), 58. *Prof Exp:* Asst plant ecol, Wageningen State Agr Univ, 50, soil surv, 51; forester, Gold Coast Govt Surv Team, 52; asst soil fertil, Mich State Univ, 52-53, soil surv & forest soils, 52-56; from asst prof to assoc prof soil sci, WVa Univ, 57-66; sr lectr land planning, Univ EAfrica, 66-72. *Concurrent Pos:* Environ scientist, US Environ Protection Agency, Washington, DC, 76-77; pres, Acad Assocs, Econ-Environ Consults. *Mem:* AAAS; Soil Sci Soc Am; Ecol Soc Am; Sigma Xi; fel Soil Conserv Soc Am; Water Pollution Control Fedn. *Res:* Effect of environment on soil and vegetation development, especially as applied to forest and watershed management; relation of soil morphology and pedology to soil and water conservation and to physical land use planning; assessment of soil fertility in agronomy and forestry; water pollution control. *Mailing Add:* 1702 Kilarney Dr Cary NC 27511-5546

**VANEEDEN, CONSTANCE,** PROBABILITY. *Current Pos:* from assoc prof to prof, 65-89, EMER PROF MATH, UNIV MONTREAL, 89- *Personal Data:* b Delft, Neth, Apr 6, 27; wid, Charles H Kraft; c Kari. *Educ:* Univ Amsterdam, BSc, 49, MSc, 54, PhD(statist), 58. *Honors & Awards:* Gold Medal, Statist Soc Can, 90. *Prof Exp:* Res assoc, Math Ctr, Amsterdam, 54-60; vis assoc prof, Mich State Univ, 60-61; res assoc, Univ Minn, Minneapolis, 61-64, assoc prof & actg dir, Statist Ctr, 64-65. *Concurrent Pos:* Res mem, Math Res Ctr, Univ Wis-Madison, 69; assoc ed, Can J Statist, 80-; adj prof statist, Univ BC, 89-, adj prof math, Univ Que, Montreal, 89-; gen ed, Statist Theory & Method Abstr, 90- *Mem:* Can Statist Soc; Int Statist Inst;

fel Inst Math Statist; fel Am Statist Asn; Can Math Soc. *Res:* Mathematical statistics with special interest in problems of estimation in restricted parameter spaces, of nonparametrics and of subset selection; published 50 scientific papers. *Mailing Add:* Moerland 19 Broek-in-Waterland 1151 BH Netherlands. *E-Mail:* cve@xs4all.nl

**VANEFFEN, RICHARD MICHAEL,** ELECTROCHEMICAL METHODS. *Current Pos:* sr res chemist, 79-83, proj leader, 83-89, RES LEADER, DOW CHEM USA, 89- *Personal Data:* b Milwaukee, Wis, June 24, 53. *Educ:* Univ Notre Dame, BS, 75; Univ Wis-Madison, PhD(analytical chem), 79. *Mem:* Am Chem Soc; Sigma Xi; Soc Electroanal Chem. *Res:* Electrochemical analysis and fundamental electrochemical research; application of electrochemical techniques to the solution of industrial process problems. *Mailing Add:* 2587 S Five Mile Rd Midland MI 48640

**VANEGAS, HORACIO,** NEUROPHYSIOLOGY, PAIN & ANALGESIA. *Current Pos:* From asst prof to assoc prof, Inst Venezolano Invest Sci, 69-81, chair, Dept Biophysics & Biochem, 84-86, dep dir, 86-88, dir, 88-92, PROF, INST VENEZOLANO INVEST SCI, 81-; PROF, CENT UNIV VENEZUELA, 88- *Personal Data:* b Caracas, Venezuela, Sept 3, 39. *Educ:* Cent Univ, Venezuela, MD, 62; Yale Univ, PhD, 68. *Concurrent Pos:* Guest researcher, Max-Planck Inst, 75-76; vis prof, Univ Calif, 82-83; dir, Cent Latin-Am Biol Sci, UNESCO, 87-90; vpres, Univ Iberoamericana Postgrad, 89-93; founding pres, Quimbiotec Inc, 89-92; founding Venezuelan gov, Int Ctr Genetic Eng Biotech, Italy, 93-; guest scientist, Univ Wurzburg, 95-97. *Mem:* Int Asn Study Pain; Int Brain Res Orgn; Soc Neurosci; Europ Neurosci Asn; Venezuela Asn Study Pain (pres, 94-). *Res:* Supraspinal control of spinal transmission of pain signals; supraspinal analgesic effects of NSAIDS; spinal hyperexcitability due to peripheral inflammation. *Mailing Add:* Inst Venezolano Invest Sci Apt 21827 Caracas 1020A Venezuela. *Fax:* 582-504-1093; *E-Mail:* hvanegas@ivic.ivic.ve

**VAN EIKEREN, PAUL,** MEMBRANE SEPARATIONS, ENZYMOLOGY. *Current Pos:* VPRES DEVELOP, FEPRACOR INC. *Personal Data:* b Hilversum, Neth, July 6, 46; US citizen; m 70; c 2. *Educ:* Columbia Col, AB, 68; Mass Inst Technol, PhD(org chem), 71. *Prof Exp:* Dreyfus instr chem, Mass Inst Technol, 71-72; prof chem, Harvey Mudd Col Sci & Eng, 72-86; dir res, Bend Res, Inc, 86- *Concurrent Pos:* Vis prof, Inst Molecular Biol, Univ Ore, 79-81. *Mem:* Am Chem Soc. *Res:* Development of membrane-based systems for fermentation, enzymatic synthesis, natural product separation and controlled-release of pharmaceuticals; drug development; chemical and biochemical process research. *Mailing Add:* 3811 NW Summerfield Bend OR 97701

**VAN ELDIK, LINDA JO,** calcium binding proteins, for more information see previous edition

**VANELLI, RONALD EDWARD,** ORGANIC CHEMISTRY. *Current Pos:* RETIRED. *Personal Data:* b Quincy, Mass, July 5, 19; m 53; c 2. *Educ:* Harvard Univ, AB, 41, MA & PhD(chem), 50. *Prof Exp:* Sr res chemist, Photo Prods Dept, E I du Pont de Nemours & Co, 50-51; dir, Chem Labs & lectr chem, Harvard Univ, 51-89, dir sci ctr, 72-89. *Mem:* Am Chem Soc. *Res:* Isonorcamphor; color and constitution. *Mailing Add:* 89 Woodridge Rd Wayland MA 01778

**VAN EMDEN, MAARTEN HERMAN,** COMPUTER SCIENCE. *Current Pos:* PROF COMPUT SCI, UNIV VICTORIA, 87- *Personal Data:* b Rheden, Neth. *Educ:* Delft Univ Technol, MEng, 66; Univ Amsterdam, DSc(math & natural sci), 71. *Prof Exp:* Res assoc comput, Math Ctr, Amsterdam, 66-71; fel, IBM Thomas J Watson Res Ctr, 71-72; res fel artificial intel, Univ Edinburgh, 72-75; fac comput sci, Univ Waterloo, 75-87. *Mem:* Inst Elec & Electronics Engrs. *Res:* Constraint processing; verified engineering computations. *Mailing Add:* Dept Comput Sci Univ Victoria PO Box 3055 Victoria BC V8W 3P6 Can. *Fax:* 250-721-7292

**VAN ENKEVORT, RONALD LEE,** MATHEMATICS. *Current Pos:* asst prof, 71-77, ASSOC PROF MATH, UNIV PUGET SOUND, 77- *Personal Data:* b Escanaba, Mich, Dec 20, 39; m 62; c 1. *Educ:* Univ Wash, BS, 62; Ore State Univ, MS, 66, PhD(math), 72. *Prof Exp:* High sch teacher, 62-67. *Mem:* Am Math Soc. *Res:* Additive number theory. *Mailing Add:* Dept Math Univ Puget Sound Tacoma WA 98416-0001

**VAN EPPS, DENNIS EUGENE,** IMMUNOLOGY. *Current Pos:* DIR DEPT APPL CELLULAR BIOL, BAXTER HEALTH CARE INC, ILL, 88- *Personal Data:* b Rock Island, Ill, Nov 26, 46; m 73; c 2. *Educ:* Western Ill Univ, BS, 68; Univ Ill, PhD(microbiol), 72. *Honors & Awards:* Young Investr Pulmonary Res Award, Nat Heart & Lung Inst, 74; Sr Investr Award, Nat Arthritis Found. *Prof Exp:* NIH fel immunol, Univ NMex, 72-74, from asst prof to assoc prof med & microbiol, 72-85, prof med & path, 85-88. *Concurrent Pos:* Arthritis Found fel, 74-; sect ed, J Leukocyte Biol; mem, Neurol C Study Sect, NIH; prin investr grants, Nat Heart, Lung & Blood Inst, Nat Cancer Inst & Nat Inst Neurol & Commun Dis. *Mem:* Am Soc Microbiol; Am Asn Immunologists; Am Fedn Clin Res; Sigma Xi; Am Asn Pathologists; Reticuloendothelial Soc. *Res:* Normal and abnormal phagocytic cell function and humoral factors which may alter this function; basic mechanisms of leukocyte locomotion; neutrophyl activation; lymphokines; interaction of neuropeptides and the immune system; cell surface receptor modulation. *Mailing Add:* Baxter Health Care Corp Rte 120 & Wilson Rd Round Lake IL 60073-0490. *Fax:* 847-270-5406

**VAN ESELTINE, WILLIAM PARKER,** BACTERIOLOGY. *Current Pos:* asst prof vet hyg, Univ Ga, 52-59, assoc prof vet microbiol & prev med, 59-67, prof, med microbiol, 67-87, EMER PROF MED MICROBIOL, COL VET MED, UNIV GA, 87- *Personal Data:* b Syracuse, NY, Aug 21, 24; m 48, Marian Vanderburgh; c Kenneth & Karen. *Educ:* Oberlin Col, AB, 44; Cornell Univ, MS, 47, PhD(bact), 49. *Prof Exp:* Asst in bact, NY State Agr Exp Sta, 44-45 & Cornell Univ, 46-48; assoc prof, Clemson Col, 48-52. *Mem:* AAAS; Am Soc Microbiol; Am Inst Biol Sci; NY Acad Sci. *Res:* Microbiology of foods; bactericidal and bacteriostatic agents; physiology and taxonomy of bacteria, especially animal pathogens. *Mailing Add:* 237 Woodlawn Ave Athens GA 30606

**VAN ESSEN, DAVID CLINTON,** BIOLOGY, NEUROSCIENCE. *Current Pos:* PROF ANAT, SCH MED, WASH UNIV, ST LOUIS, 92- *Personal Data:* b Glendale, Calif, Sept 14, 45; m 69; c 2. *Educ:* Calif Inst Technol, BS, 67; Harvard Univ, PhD(neurobiol), 71. *Prof Exp:* Res fel neurobiol, Harvard Med Sch, 71-73, neurophysiol, Inst Physiol, Univ Oslo, 73-75 & anat, Univ Col London, 75-76; from asst prof to prof biol, Calif Inst Technol, 76-92. *Concurrent Pos:* Fel NIH, 71-73, Helen Hay Whitney Found, 73-76; mem adv panel, Sensory Physiol & Perception Prog, NSF, 78-81; Sloan res fel, 78-80. *Mem:* AAAS; Soc Neurosci; Asn Res Vision & Ophthal. *Res:* Visual cortex; functional organization of extrastriate areas in primates; neuromuscular development; control of synapse formation and elimination. *Mailing Add:* Dept Anat Wash Univ Sch Med 660 S Euclid Ave St Louis MO 63110-1010

**VAN ETTEN, HANS D,** PLANT PATHOLOGY. *Current Pos:* PROF PLANT PATH, UNIV ARIZ, 77- *Personal Data:* b Peoria, Ill, Sept 16, 41; m 63, 91, Martha Cander Hawes; c Erica Lynn & Laura Nadine. *Educ:* Wabash Col, BA, 63; Cornell Univ, MS, 66, PhD(plant path), 70. *Prof Exp:* From asst prof to assoc prof plant path, Cornell Univ, 70-77. *Concurrent Pos:* Vis prof, Univ Munster, WGer, 78-79; Alexander Von Humboldt fel, 78-79; Fulbright-Hays fel, 78-79; vis prof plant path, Univ Naples, Portici, Italy, 87. *Mem:* AAAS; fel Am Phytopath Soc; Int Soc Molecular Plant-Microbe Interactions; Am Soc Microbiol. *Res:* Physiology of disease; natural resistance mechanisms in plants and how fungal pathogens overcome these mechanisms. *Mailing Add:* Dept Plant Path Forbes Rm 104 Univ Ariz Tucson AZ 85721-0001

**VAN ETTEN, JAMES L,** MICROBIAL PHYSIOLOGY. *Current Pos:* from asst prof to assoc prof, 66-74, PROF PLANT PATH, UNIV NEBR, LINCOLN, 74- *Personal Data:* b Cherrydale, Va, Jan 7, 38; m 60; c 3. *Educ:* Carleton Col, BA, 60; Univ Ill, MS, 63, PhD(plant path), 65. *Prof Exp:* NSF fel microbiol, Univ Pavia, 65-66. *Mem:* AAAS; Am Phytopath Soc; Soc Gen Microbiol; Am Soc Microbiol; Am Soc Virol. *Res:* Biochemistry of fungal spore germination and bacteriophage and viruses of eukaryotic algae; biochemistry. *Mailing Add:* Dept Plant Path PS 406 Univ Nebr E Campus PO Box 830722 Lincoln NE 68583-0722

**VAN ETTEN, JAMES P(AUL),** ELECTRONICS ENGINEERING. *Current Pos:* RETIRED. *Personal Data:* b Perry, NY, Mar 27, 22; m 47, Mary Grace; c James Jr, William, Stephen, Mary G, John, Joan & Paul. *Educ:* US Coast Guard Acad, BS, 43; Mass Inst Technol, EE, 50. *Prof Exp:* Sr proj engr, ITT Corp, 58-59, exec engr, 59-60, assoc lab dir, 60-62, lab dir, 62-66, dir navig systs, 66-69, chief scientist avionics, 69-70, dir commun, navig & identification systs, labs, 70-73, tech adv to vpres & dir eng, 73-79, dir mkt, 80-84. *Concurrent Pos:* Mem, sci adv comt, US Coast Guard, 70-72; dir, Wild Goose Asn, 72-90; consult, 84-88. *Mem:* Am Inst Navig; fel Inst Elec & Electronics Engrs; Int Loran Asn (pres, 74-76). *Res:* Hyperbolic, rho-rho and rho-theta radio navigation systems and equipment; integrated airborne navigation systems and equipment; ground transmitting equipment for LORAN and TACAN; radio navigation systems. *Mailing Add:* 1706 Hemlock Farms Hawley PA 18428

**VAN ETTEN, ROBERT LEE,** ENZYMOLOGY, PROTEIN CHEMISTRY. *Personal Data:* b Evergreen Park, Ill, June 11, 37; c 3. *Educ:* Univ Chicago, BS, 59; Univ Calif, Davis, MS 64, PhD(chem), 65. *Honors & Awards:* Silver Medal, Polish Acad Sci, Krakow, 82. *Prof Exp:* Technician, Ben May Labs, Cancer Res, Univ Chicago, 57-59; teaching asst, Univ Calif, Davis, 60-63; NIH fel Northwestern Univ, 65-66; from asst prof to prof chem, Purdue Univ, West Lafayette, 66-83, head, Biochem Div, 83-87, assoc head, Chem Dept, 87-92, actg head, 92-93. *Concurrent Pos:* Res career develop award, NIH, 69-73; Alexander von Humboldt fel, Marburg, Ger, 75-76; Nat Acad Sci Exchange, Poland, 85. *Mem:* Am Chem Soc; Am Soc Biol Chemists; NY Acad Sci. *Res:* Mechanisms of enzymatic catalysis; phosphotyrosyl protein phosphatases; clinical chemistry of phosphatases and sulfatases; oxygen-18 isotope effects on carbon-13 and nitrogen-15 nuclear magnetic resonance spectra. *Mailing Add:* Dept Chem Purdue Univ West Lafayette IN 47907-1393

**VAN EYS, JAN,** BIOCHEMISTRY. *Current Pos:* prof pediat, Univ Tex, 73-79, Mosbacher chair pediat, M D Anderson Cancer Syst, 79-90, head dept pediat, 73-90, CHMN, DEPT PEDIAT, SCH MED, UNIV TEX, HOUSTON, 90- *Personal Data:* b Hilversum, Neth, Jan 25, 29; nat US; m 55; c 2. *Educ:* Vanderbilt Univ, PhD, 55; Univ Wash, MD, 66. *Prof Exp:* Fel biochem, McCollum-Pratt Inst, Johns Hopkins Univ, 55-57; from asst prof to prof biochem, Sch Med, Vanderbilt Univ, 57-73, from asst prof to prof pediat, 68-73. *Concurrent Pos:* Investr, Howard Hughes Med Inst, 57-66. *Mem:* Am Soc Biol Chemists; Am Inst Nutrit; NY Acad Sci. *Res:* Metabolism and enzymology in glycolysis; pediatric hematology, oncology and nutrition in cancer. *Mailing Add:* 3504 Rudland Pl Nashville TN 37215-1812. *Fax:* 713-794-4112

**VAN FAASEN, PAUL,** PLANT TAXONOMY. *Current Pos:* PROF BIOL, HOPE COL, 63- *Personal Data:* b Holland, Mich, June 6, 34; m 58; c 2. *Educ:* Hope Col, BA, 56; Mich State Univ, MS, 62, PhD(bot), 71. *Prof Exp:* Instr biol, Lake Forest Col, 62-63. *Mem:* Bot Soc Am; Am Soc Plant Taxonomists; Int Asn Plant Taxonomists. *Res:* Biosystematics of Aster, especially those of northeast United States; biology of weeds. *Mailing Add:* Dept Biol Hope Col 137 E 12th St Holland MI 49423-3607

**VAN FLANDERN, THOMAS C,** CELESTIAL MECHANICS. *Current Pos:* PRES, META RES, 90- *Personal Data:* b Cleveland, Ohio, June 26, 40; m 63, Barbara A Weber; c 4. *Educ:* Xavier Univ, Ohio, BS, 62; Yale Univ, PhD(astron), 69. *Prof Exp:* Astronr, US Naval Observ, Wash, 63-75, chief, Celestial Mech Br, 75-83. *Concurrent Pos:* Consult, Jet Propulsion Lab, 71; Phys Dept, Univ Md, 92- *Mem:* Am Astron Soc; Int Astron Union; AAAS; Am Geophys Union. *Res:* Lunar motion; asteroids; comets; occulations; cosmology; gravitation; solar system astronomy; relativity origins. *Mailing Add:* 6327 Western Ave NW Washington DC 20015. *Fax:* 202-362-8279; *E-Mail:* metares@well.sf.ca.us.

**VANFLEET, HOWARD BAY,** SOLID STATE PHYSICS. *Current Pos:* from asst prof to assoc prof physics, 60-69, chmn, Dept Physics, 79-88, PROF PHYSICS, BRIGHAM YOUNG UNIV, 69- *Personal Data:* b Salt Lake City, Utah, June 5, 31; m 54; c 7. *Educ:* Brigham Young Univ, BS, 55; Univ Utah, PhD(physics), 61. *Prof Exp:* Asst physics, Univ Utah, 56-60. *Concurrent Pos:* Res grants, USAF Off Sci Res, Brigham Young Univ, 62-66, NSF, 69-77; phys scientist, US Army Electronics Command, 66-67; vis prof physics, Am Univ, Cairo, 73-74; consult, Codevintec Pac, Inc, 75-76. *Mem:* Am Phys Soc; Am Asn Physics Teachers; Sigma Xi. *Res:* Ultra high pressure solid state physics; particular phenomena, such as solid state diffusion, Mossbauer effects, melting and high pressure calibration; high temperature superconductors. *Mailing Add:* Dept Physics Brigham Young Univ Provo UT 84602

**VAN FOSSAN, DONALD DUANE,** BIOCHEMISTRY. *Current Pos:* DIR CHEM, ST JOHN'S HOSP, 69-; CLIN PROF PATH, SOUTHERN ILL UNIV, 69-, ASST CHMN DEPT, 73- *Personal Data:* b El Paso, Tex, Jan 5, 29; m 49; c 3. *Educ:* Sul Ross State Col, BS, 49; Univ Tex, MA, 52, PhD(biochem), 54, MD, 61. *Prof Exp:* Asst, Univ Tex, 52-54; res biochemist, Air Force Sch Aviation Med, 54-57, head, Lab Sect, Dept Physiol-Biophys, 56-57; instr clin path & consult, Clin Labs, Hosp, Univ Tex Med Br, 57-61; intern, St Joseph Hosp, Ft Worth, Tex, 61-62, resident path, Univ Tex, 62-66; dir clin path, Med Ctr, Baylor Univ, 66-69. *Concurrent Pos:* Instr analytical chem, Trinity Univ, 56; dir clin path, St John's Hosp, 68-; med dir labs, St John's Hosp, 76- *Mem:* Col Am Pathologists; AMA; Am Soc Clin Pathologists. *Res:* Analytic biochemistry; pathology; endocrinology; toxicology. *Mailing Add:* 2011 Briarcliff Springfield IL 62704-4125

**VAN FOSSEN, DON B,** APPLIED MECHANICS, AEROSPACE ENGINEERING. *Current Pos:* PRES, FINITE ELEMENT TECHNOL CORP, 83- *Personal Data:* b Des Moines, Iowa, Apr 15, 42; m 62; c 1. *Educ:* Iowa State Univ, BS, 64; Univ Mo, Rolla, MS, 68. *Prof Exp:* Test engr struct, McDonnell Aircraft, 64-69; sr res engr, Babcock & Wilcox Co, 69-72, group supvr appl mech, 72-83. *Concurrent Pos:* mem subcomt shells, Pressure Vessel Res Comt, Welding Res Coun, 77-; tech adv, Struct Analysis Prog, User's Group, 77-83; past chmn, Cam Sect, Am Soc Mech Engrs & Pressure Vessel Piping Div, Am Soc Mech Engrs. *Mem:* Am Soc Mech Engrs. *Res:* Applied research in the application of the finite element method to structural analysis and heat transfer for general structures. *Mailing Add:* 10945 Hazelview Ave Alliance OH 44601

**VAN FRANK, RICHARD MARK,** CELL BIOLOGY, ANALYTICAL BIOCHEMISTRY. *Current Pos:* PUB POLICY ANALYST, IND ENVIRON INST, 91- *Personal Data:* b Lansing, Mich, Oct 11, 30; m 54; c 2. *Educ:* Mich State Univ, BS, 52, MS, 56. *Prof Exp:* Officer in-chg biol lab, US Naval Damage Control Training Ctr, Philadelphia, 52-54; sr scientist, Div Molecular & Cell Biol, Lilly Res Labs, Eli Lilly & Co, 57-90. *Mem:* AAAS; NY Acad Sci; Electrophoresis Soc. *Res:* Development of methodology for fractionation of cells and isolation and analysis of subcellular particles and substances; isolation and analysis of products produced using R-DNA technology; microsequencing of proteins; two dimensional gel electrophoresis image analysis. *Mailing Add:* 7620 Brookview Lane Indianapolis IN 46250

**VAN FURTH, RALPH,** IMMUNOLOGY, INFECTIOUS DISEASES. *Current Pos:* chief resident internal med & res fel, Dept Immuno-Hemat & Bloodbank, 61-63, chief clin, Dept Microbiol Dis, 64-72, HEAD LAB CELLULAR IMMUNOL, DEPT INFECTIOUS DIS, UNIV HOSP, LEIDEN, 67-, PROF INT MED & INFECTIOUS DIS, UNIV LEIDEN, 75- *Personal Data:* b The Hague, Neth, Apr 30, 29; m, Anne GH Vreede; c Eric F, Anne M & Wouter R. *Educ:* Univ Leiden, MD, 55, PhD(cum laude), 64; FRCP(E), 77. *Honors & Awards:* Macarthur Lect, Edinburg Univ Med Sch, 79; Alexandre Besredka Price, French Ger Found, Univ Berlin, 87; Friedrich Sasse Award, 88. *Prof Exp:* Asst psychiat, Univ Utrecht, 55; asst gen practr, 56; resident internal med, St Elisabeth's Hosp, Groote Gasthuis, Haarlem, 57-61. *Concurrent Pos:* Guest investr, Rockefeller Univ, 64-67 & 68; lectr, Internal Med & Immunol, Univ Leiden, 72-75; vis assoc prof, Rockefeller Univ, 72, vis prof, 74 & 85, Ruitinga Found, Acad Med Ctr, Amsterdam, 86; Lister fel, Royal Col Physicians, Edinburgh, 74, fel, 77; secy, Infectious Dis Soc, Neth & Flanders, 76-82; foreign corresp mem, Royal Acad Med, Belgium, 79; adv comt, Med Res, Neth Orgn, Adv Pure Res, 82-, Int Immunol-compromised Host Soc, 88-; chmn, Infectious Dis Soc, Neth & Flanders, 83-; Fulbright fel, 85; mem, Nat Comt AIDS Prev, 90-; Jury Found van Gysel, Med Res, 91-, Sci bd Nat AIDS Ther & Eval Ctr, 91-; mem, Sci Comt AIDS Res, Med Res Neth Orgn Advan Pure Res, 93. *Mem:* Brit Soc Immunol; Am Soc Microbiol; Europ Soc Clin Microbiol & Infectious Dis; Europ Soc Clin Invest; fel Infectious Dis Soc Am; NY Acad Sci; Brit Soc Study Infection; Dutch Soc Gen Path; Dutch Soc Hemat; Dutch Soc Immunol; Dutch Soc Internal Med; Dutch Soc Vet Med; Europ Network Study Exp Infectious. *Res:* Author of 300 publications and editor of 11 books. *Mailing Add:* Laan Van Oud Belgeest 44 Oegstgeest NL2341 Netherlands

**VAN GEET, ANTHONY LEENDERT,** PHYSICAL CHEMISTRY, ANALYTICAL CHEMISTRY. *Current Pos:* ASSOC PROF CHEM, STATE UNIV NY COL OSWEGO, 70- *Personal Data:* b Rotterdam, Neth, July 24, 29; US citizen; m 56, Johanna Everts; c Otto D, Corina J & Paul E. *Educ:* Delft Univ Technol, ChemEng, 55; Univ Southern Calif, PhD(phys chem), 61. *Prof Exp:* Res assoc chem, Mass Inst Technol, 61-63; asst prof, State Univ NY, Buffalo, 63-69; assoc prof, Oakland Univ, 69-70. *Mem:* AAAS; Am Chem Soc; Sigma Xi. *Res:* Nuclear magnetic resonance of protons, lithium, sodium and fluorine in solution; hydration, complexation and ion-pairing of monovalent ions; instrumentation. *Mailing Add:* Dept Chem State Univ Col Oswego NY 13126

**VANGEL, MARK GEOFFREY,** ENGINEERING STATISTICS, STATISTICAL INTERVALS. *Current Pos:* MATH STATISTICIAN, NAT INST STAND & TECHNOL, 93- *Personal Data:* b Boston, Mass, Feb 23, 58. *Educ:* Mass Inst Technol, SB, 80, SM, 81; Harvard Univ, MA, 89, PhD(statist), 92. *Prof Exp:* Math statistician, Army Res Lab, 84-93. *Concurrent Pos:* Nat Res Coun assoc, Nat Inst Stand & Technol, 93-95. *Mem:* Am Statist Asn; Math Asn Am; Inst Math Statist; Sigma Xi. *Res:* Statistical methods for random and mixed models, with an emphasis on tolerance limits and quality control. *Mailing Add:* Nat Inst Stand & Technol Bldg 101/A-337 Gaithersburg MD 20899-0001. *Fax:* 301-990-4127; *E-Mail:* vangel@cam. nist.gov

**VAN GELDER, ARTHUR,** ELECTRICAL ENGINEERING. *Current Pos:* DIR ELECTRONICS ENG, UNIV SCRANTON, 87- *Personal Data:* b Paterson, NJ, Jan 13, 38; m 60; c 2. *Educ:* Univ Pa, BSEE, 59; City Col New York, MEE, 64, PhD(elec eng), 68. *Prof Exp:* Asst proj engr, Kearfott Div, Gen Precision, Inc, 60-61; lectr elec eng, City Col New York, 61-68; asst prof, Univ Del, 68-75 & Miami Univ, 75-80; asst prof elec eng, Lafayette Col, 80-87. *Mem:* Inst Elec & Electronics Engrs; Am Soc Eng Educ. *Res:* Electronic circuits; control systems; digital systems. *Mailing Add:* 608 N Irving Ave Scranton PA 18510

**VAN GELDER, NICO MICHEL,** NEUROCHEMISTRY. *Current Pos:* assoc prof physiol, Univ Montreal, 67-77, bd adv, Neurochem Res, 75-88, exec, Neurol Sci Res Ctr, 76-82, prof, 77-97, asst vdean res, 89-90, EMER PROF PHYSIOL, UNIV MONTREAL, 97- *Personal Data:* b Sumatra, Indonesia, Dec 24, 33; Can citizen, m 59, Louise M Singer; c Terry, Steven & Gregory. *Educ:* McGill Univ, BSc, 55, PhD(biochem), 59. *Prof Exp:* Life Ins Med Res Fund fel, Cambridge Univ, Eng, 59-60; res fel neurophysiol & neuropharmacol, Harvard Med Sch, 60-62; asst prof pharmacol, Sch Med, Tufts Univ, 62-67. *Concurrent Pos:* Res grants, Nat Inst Neurol Dis & Blindness, 62-66, Nat Multiple Sclerosis Soc, 66- & Med Res Coun Can Neurol Sci Group, 67-79; UNESCO prof, grad studies, Latin Am, 73-; assoc ed, Can J Biochem, 76-78; med adv, Savoy Found Epilepsy, 80-87, pres med bd, 83-87; adj prof, Montreal Neurol Inst, 80-84; expert consult, Pan Am Health Orgn, 88-; mem bd, Spinal Cord Res Found, 89-97; vis prof, Queen's Univ, 96- *Mem:* Am Soc Neurochem; Int Soc Neurochem; NY Acad Sci; Int Brain Res Orgn; Europ Soc Neurochem; Venezuelan Soc Neurosci. *Res:* Biochemistry of epilepsy; brain damage and migrane; structure-activity relationships; malnutrition; genetic contribution to epilepsy; function of taurine. *Mailing Add:* Dept Chem Frost Bldg Queens Univ Kingston ON K7L 3N6 Can. *Fax:* 613-545-6669; *E-Mail:* uangelder@chem.queensu.ca

**VAN GELUWE, JOHN DAVID,** ENTOMOLOGY. *Current Pos:* RETIRED. *Personal Data:* b Rochester, NY, Sept 18, 16; m 53; c 3. *Educ:* State Univ NY, BS, 39. *Prof Exp:* Asst, Exten Serv, State Univ NY Col Agr, Cornell Univ, 39-44; dir res & develop, Soil Bldg Div, Coop GLF Exchange, Inc, 44-64; mgr prod develop, Agr Chem Div, Ciba-Geigy Corp, 64-67, tech dir, 67-70, asst dir field & farm res, 70-82. *Mem:* fel Am Soc Hort Sci; fel Entom Soc Am; fel Am Phytopath Soc; Weed Sci Soc Am. *Res:* Formulations, basic laboratory evaluation and field testing of insecticides, fungicides and herbicides. *Mailing Add:* 541 Seven Lakes N West End NC 27376

**VAN GEMERT, BARRY,** ORGANIC CHEMISTRY. *Current Pos:* Sr res chemist, PPG Industs, 76-88, res assoc, 89-93, sr res assoc, 94-95, SCIENTIST, PPG INDUSTS, 96- *Personal Data:* b Attleboro, Mass, Feb 17, 46; m 69, Janice McTammany; c Thomas, Wayne & Clinton. *Educ:* Univ Mass, BS, 68; Univ RI, MS, 72; Purdue Univ, PhD(org chem), 76. *Mem:* Am Chem Soc. *Res:* Organic synthesis; preparation of novel photochronic compounds for use in sunglass applications. *Mailing Add:* 2004 High Pointe Dr Murrysville PA 15668-8515. *E-Mail:* jangemert@ppg.com

**VAN GENUCHTEN, MARTINUS T,** SOIL PHYSICS, LAND DRAINAGE & IMPROVEMENT IN THE TROPICS. *Current Pos:* SUPV SOIL SCIENTIST & RES LEADER, AGR RES SERV, USDA, US SALINITY LAB, RIVERSIDE, CALIF, 86- *Personal Data:* b Vught, Neth, Feb 13, 45. *Educ:* Agr Univ, Neth, BS, 68, MS, 71; NMex State Univ, PhD(soil physics), 75. *Honors & Awards:* Soil Sci Res Award, Soil Sci Soc Am, 96. *Prof Exp:* Asst hydrol, State Ministry Agr, Madagascar, 68-69; res staff mem, Water Resources Prog, Dept Civil Eng, Princeton Univ, 75-78. *Concurrent Pos:* From asst to full res soil scientist, Dept Soil & Environ Sci, Univ Calif Irvine, 78-86, adj prof, soil physics, 87-; mem, Western Reg Tech Comt W155 &

W188, 78-; assoc ed, Water Resources Res, 84-90; mem, Task Comt Test Cases Eval Numerical Surface Water Contaminant Transp Models, Am Soc Civil Engrs, 84-, Grad Prog Admis & Rev Comt, 87-92, Kearney Found Tech Comt, Univ Calif, 90-, Int Assoc Hydrol Sci Comt Atmosphere Soil Veg Rel, 88-93; mem, Unsaturated Zone Comt, Am Geophys Union, 84-88, SSSA rep, 91-96, Water Resources Res Direction & Review Comt, 91-92, res ed search comt, 92, mem, hydrol Sect Fel Nomination Comt, 92-94, Robert E Horton Medal Nomination Comt, Am Geophys Union, 94-; vis scientist, Nat Inst Agron Res, Inra, Montfavet, France, 87-87; ed, US Nat Report, Hydrol Sect, Int Union Geod & Geophys, 87-90, 91; mem, A447 Environ Qual Res Award comt, Am Soc Agron, 90-91, chair, 91-92; chair, Soil Sci Soc Am Feasibility Comt new Vadose Zone Hydrol Jour, 92-96; consult ed, Soil Sci, 93-; guest prof, Swiss Fed Inst Technol, Zurich, Switz, 95-96; assoc ed, J Contaminant Hydrol, 96- *Mem:* AAAS; fel Am Geophys Union; fel Am Soc Agron; Int Soc Soil Sci; fel Soil Sci Soc Am; Int Asn Hydrol Sci; Sigma Xi. *Res:* Soil and water resources with special emphasis on studies that clarify and quantify fundamental mechanisms as well as practical aspects of water and solute movement in soil and ground water systems; author of numerous publications. *Mailing Add:* US Salinity Lab 450 W Big Springs Rd Riverside CA 92507-4617. *E-Mail:* rvang@usse.ars.usda.gov

**VAN GINNEKEN, ANDREAS J,** PHYSICS. *Current Pos:* PHYSICIST, FERMI NAT LAB, 70- *Personal Data:* b Wynegem, Belg, Jan 1, 35; m 72, Lydia Thompson; c Jonathan. *Educ:* Univ Chicago, MSc, 59, PhD(chem), 66. *Prof Exp:* Res assoc physics, McGill Univ, 66-70. *Mem:* Am Phys Soc. *Res:* Nuclear and particle physics; radiation physics. *Mailing Add:* Fermi Nat Lab Batavia IL 60510

**VAN GROENEWOUD, HERMAN,** FOREST ECOLOGY. *Current Pos:* RETIRED. *Personal Data:* b Breda, Netherlands, May 27, 26; Can citizen; m 50; c 2. *Educ:* Univ Sask, BA, 56, MA, 60; Swiss Fed Inst Technol, ScD(geobot), 65. *Prof Exp:* Res scientist forest path, Lab Saskatoon, Maritimes Forest Res Ctr, Govt Can, 54-65, res scientist forest ecol, 65-91. *Mem:* Can Bot Asn; Brit Ecol Soc; Ecol Soc Am; Can Inst Forestry. *Res:* Forest site studies; multivariate analysis; watershed studies. *Mailing Add:* RR 6 Fredericton NB E3B 4X7 Can

**VAN GUNDY, SEYMOUR DEAN,** PLANT PATHOLOGY, NEMATOLOGY. *Current Pos:* from asst nematologist to assoc nematologist, Univ Calif, Riverside, 57-68, assoc dean res, 68-71 & 85-88, asst vchancellor res, 71-72, chmn dept, 72-84, interim dean, 88-90, PROF NEMATOL, UNIV CALIF, RIVERSIDE, 68-, DEAN RES, 90- *Personal Data:* b Whitehouse, Ohio, Feb 24, 31; m 54; c 2. *Educ:* Bowling Green State Univ, BA, 53; Univ Wis, PhD, 57. *Prof Exp:* Res assoc, Univ Wis, 53-57. *Concurrent Pos:* NSF sr fel, Australia, 65-66; ed-in-chief, J Nematol, 67-71. *Mem:* Fel AAAS; fel Am Phytopath Soc; fel Soc Nematol (vpres, 72-73, pres, 73-74); Soc Europ Nematol; Am Inst Biol Sci. *Res:* Biology and control of nematodes. *Mailing Add:* 1188 Pastern Rd Riverside CA 92506

**VAN HALBIEK, HERMAN,** BIOCHEMISTRY. *Current Pos:* PROF BIOCHEM, UNIV GA, 85- *Personal Data:* b Sittard, Neth, Feb 23, 53. *Educ:* Univ Utrecht, BS, 78, PhD(biochem), 82. *Prof Exp:* Fel chem, Univ Utrecht, 82-85. *Mem:* Am Chem Soc; Am Soc Biochem & Molecular Biol. *Res:* Biochemistry. *Mailing Add:* Rega Inst Lab Med Chem Katholieke Universiteit Leuven Minderbroeders Straat 10 Leuven Belgium B-3000

**VAN HALL, CLAYTON EDWARD,** ANALYTICAL CHEMISTRY. *Current Pos:* RETIRED. *Personal Data:* b Grand Rapids, Mich, Apr 24, 24; m 51; c 2. *Educ:* Hope Col, AB, 49; Mich State Univ, MSc, 54, PhD(anal chem), 56. *Prof Exp:* Asst, Mich State Univ, 52-56; chemist, Dow Chem Co, 56-58, anal chemist, 58-61, anal specialist, 61-65, anal res specialist, 65-72, assoc scientist, 72-89. *Res:* Instrumental methods; trace gas methods; trace element methods; purity of inorganic compounds; primary standards; water analysis. *Mailing Add:* 3712 Wintergreen Dr Midland MI 48640

**VAN HANDEL, EMILE,** INSECT PHYSIOLOGY. *Current Pos:* biochemist, 58-83, PROF BIOCHEM, FLA MED ENTOM LAB, UNIV FLA, VERO BEACH, 83- *Personal Data:* b Rotterdam, Holland, Mar 29, 18; nat US; m 46; c 2. *Educ:* State Univ Leiden, BS, 38, MS, 41; State Inst Technol, Delft, MS, 41; Univ Amsterdam, PhD(biochem), 54. *Prof Exp:* Indust chemist, 45-54; res biochemist, St Anthon's Hosp, Voorburg, Holland, 54-55; asst prof physiol, Univ Tenn, 55-58. *Concurrent Pos:* Consult, study sect trop med & parasitol, NIH, 78-82. *Mem:* Am Soc Biol Chemists. *Res:* Lipid and carbohydrate chemistry and metabolism; insect biochemistry; atherosclerosis. *Mailing Add:* Fla Med Entom Lab Univ Fla 200 Ninth St SE Vero Beach FL 32962

**VAN HARN, GORDON L,** PHYSIOLOGY. *Current Pos:* PROF BIOL, CALVIN COL, 70- *Personal Data:* b Grand Rapids, Mich, Dec 30, 35; m 58; c 3. *Educ:* Calvin Col, AB, 57; Univ Ill, MS, 59, PhD(physiol), 61. *Prof Exp:* Assoc prof biol, Calvin Col, 61-68 & Oberlin Col, 68-70. *Concurrent Pos:* Res scientist, Blodgett Mem Hosp, 70-76. *Mem:* AAAS; Am Soc Affil. *Res:* Smooth muscle contractile and electrical activity; intestinal smooth muscle; cardiac muscle. *Mailing Add:* Provost Calvin Col 3201 Burton St SE Grand Rapids MI 49546-4349

**VAN HASSEL, HENRY JOHN,** DENTISTRY, PHYSIOLOGY. *Current Pos:* DEAN, SCH DENT, ORE HEALTH SCI UNIV, 84- *Personal Data:* b Paterson, NJ, May 2, 33; m 60. *Educ:* Maryville Col, BA, 54; Univ Md, DDS, 63; Univ Wash, MSD, 64, PhD(physiol), 69. *Honors & Awards:* Carl A

Schlack Award, Asn Mil Surgeons US, 71. *Prof Exp:* Asst prof endodont & physiol, Med Sch, Univ Wash, 69-71, res assoc physiol, Regional Primate Res Ctr, 69-76, assoc prof physiol, 71-, assoc prof endodont, Dent Sch, 71-, assoc prof biophys, 76-; dep chief dent serv & dir endodont residency, USPHS Hosp, Seattle, 71-; chmn, Dept Endodont, Univ Md. *Concurrent Pos:* Consult, US Army, Ft Lewis, Wash, 69-; chmn, Nat Workshop Pulp Biol, 71-; vchmn, Sect Physiol, Am Asn Dent Schs, 72- *Mem:* Am Dent Asn; Am Asn Endodont; Int Asn Dent Res. *Res:* Oral physiology; psychophysiology; neurophysiology of pain. *Mailing Add:* Sch Dent Ore Health Sci Univ 611 SW Campus Dr Portland OR 97201-3097

**VAN HAVERBEKE, DAVID F,** TAXONOMY, SILVICULTURE. *Current Pos:* RETIRED. *Personal Data:* b Eureka, Kans, July 15, 28; m 88, Nancy J Mattingly; c Georganna K, Gary S, David R, Denise M, Mark A & Karen S. *Educ:* Kans State Univ, BS, 50; Colo State Univ, MS, 59; Univ Nebr, PhD(bot), 67. *Prof Exp:* Res forester, Rocky Mountain Forest & Range Exp Sta, USDA, 58 & Southeastern Forest Exp Sta, 59-62, res forester, 62-89. *Concurrent Pos:* Adj prof forestry, Univ Nebr, Lincoln. *Res:* Forest botany and genetics; forest tree improvement; noise abatement; shelterbelt management. *Mailing Add:* 6919 W 101st St Shawnee Mission KS 66212

**VAN HECKE, GERALD RAYMOND,** PHYSICAL CHEMISTRY. *Current Pos:* from asst prof to assoc prof, 70-80, PROF CHEM, HARVEY MUDD COL, 80-, DEPT CHAIR, 89- *Personal Data:* b Evanston, Ill, Nov 1, 39. *Educ:* Harvey Mudd Col, BS, 61; Princeton Univ, AM, 63, PhD(phys chem), 66. *Prof Exp:* Chemist, Shell Develop Co, 66-70. *Concurrent Pos:* Vis res assoc fundamental physics, Univ Lille, France, 77; vis res assoc biophys, Boston Univ, 77; Nat Acad Sci exchange scientist, Inst Phys Chem, Polish Acad Sci, Warsaw, 80 & Cent Inst Electron Physics, Ger Dem Repub Acad Sci, EBerlin, 83; fac fel, Jet Propulsion Lab, NASA, 82, 83; univ guest researcher, Chem Thermodyn Lab, Osaka Univ, 84, 89; Camille & Henry Dreyfus scholar. *Mem:* AAAS; Am Chem Soc; Royal Soc Chem; Sigma Xi. *Res:* Light scattering of binary mixtures of simple liquids; thermodynamics and physical properties of liquid crystals; spectroscopy of metallomesogens. *Mailing Add:* Dept Chem Harvey Mudd Col Claremont CA 91711-5990. *Fax:* 909-607-7577

**VAN HEERDEN, PIETER JACOBUS,** PHYSICS. *Current Pos:* RETIRED. *Personal Data:* b Utrecht, Neth, Apr 14, 15; nat US; m 49; c 2. *Educ:* Univ Utrecht, PhD(physics), 45. *Prof Exp:* Res physicist, Bataafse Petrol Co, Neth, 44-45; vis lectr, Harvard Univ, 48-49, res fel nuclear physics, 49-53; res assoc, Gen Elec Res Lab, NY, 53-62; physicist, Polaroid Res Labs, 62-81; lectr & consult, Found Physics, Math Theory Intel & Artificial Intel, 82. *Mem:* Am Phys Soc; Neth Phys Soc; Am Philos Sci Asn; Inst Elec & Electronics Engrs; Cognitive Sci Soc. *Res:* Experimental nuclear and solid state physics; foundation of physics; foundation of scientific knowledge and intelligence. *Mailing Add:* 18217 145th Ct NE Woodinville WA 98072

**VAN HEUVELEN, ALAN,** PHYSICS. *Current Pos:* PROF PHYSICS, OHIO STATE UNIV, 93- *Personal Data:* b Buffalo, Wyo, Dec 15, 38; m 62; c 1. *Educ:* Rutgers Univ, BA, 60; Univ Colo, PhD(physics), 64. *Prof Exp:* From assoc prof to prof physics, NMex State Univ, 64-93. *Mem:* Am Phys Soc. *Res:* Biophysics using electron spin resonance to study enzymes. *Mailing Add:* Dept Physics Ohio State Univ 174 W 18th Ave Columbus OH 43210

**VAN HEYNINGEN, EARLE MARVIN,** ORGANIC CHEMISTRY. *Current Pos:* RETIRED. *Personal Data:* b Chicago, Ill, Oct 15, 21; m 51; c 4. *Educ:* Calvin Col, AB, 43; Univ Ill, PhD(org chem), 46. *Prof Exp:* Res chemist, Eli Lilly & Co, 46-65, res scientist, 65-66, res assoc, 66-69, dir agr chem, Greenfield Labs, 69-72, dir chem, 72-83, dir biochem & phys chem, Lilly Res Labs, 83-85. *Mem:* Am Chem Soc. *Res:* Synthesis of barbituric acids; antimalarials, anti-arthritics; cholesterol lowering agents; cephalosporin antibiotics. *Mailing Add:* 2919 S Post Rd Indianapolis IN 46239-9430

**VAN HEYNINGEN, ROGER,** solid state physics, for more information see previous edition

**VAN HISE, JAMES R,** PHYSICAL CHEMISTRY. *Current Pos:* PROF CHEM, PAC UNION COL, 72- *Personal Data:* b Tracy, Calif, Aug 11, 37; m 64, L Z Radomsky; c Milton L & Audrey M. *Educ:* Walla Walla Col, BS, 59; Univ Ill, PhD(phys chem), 63. *Prof Exp:* Res assoc nuclear chem, Oak Ridge Nat Lab, 63-65; from asst prof to assoc prof chem & physics, Andrews Univ, 65-69; prof physics & chmn dept, Tri-State Col, 69-72. *Concurrent Pos:* Consult radiol phys & nuclear chem. *Mem:* Am Chem Soc; Am Phys Soc; Sigma Xi; Am Asn Physicists Med. *Res:* nuclear photodisintegration; alpha, beta and gamma ray spectroscopy; positron annihilation in organic media. *Mailing Add:* PO Box 397 Angwin CA 94508. *Fax:* 707-965-6390; *E-Mail:* jvanhise@puc.edu

**VAN HOFF, JACK,** PEDIATRIC HEMATOLOGY, PEDIATRIC ONCOLOGY. *Current Pos:* fel pediat hemat-oncol, Sch Med, Yale Univ, 84-86, instr pediat, 86-87, asst prof, 87-93, ASSOC PROF PEDIAT, SCH MED, YALE UNIV, 93- *Personal Data:* b Paterson, NJ, June 21, 55; m 77, Barbara Kruis; c Jeremy, Ryan, Matthew, Peter & Daniel. *Educ:* Rensselaer Polytech Inst, BS, 77; Univ Med & Dent NJ, MD, 81. *Honors & Awards:* Career Develop Award Clin Oncol, Am Cancer Soc, 87. *Prof Exp:* Resident pediat, Yale-New Haven Hosp, 81-84. *Mem:* Am Soc Clin Oncol; Am Soc Pediat Hemat Oncol. *Res:* Clincial trials in pediatric oncology with a specific focus on supportive care. *Mailing Add:* Dept Pediat Yale Univ Sch Med 333 Cedar St New Haven CT 06520-8064. *Fax:* 203-785-7194

**VAN HOFTEN, JAMES DOUGAL ADRIANUS,** CIVIL ENGINEERING. *Current Pos:* SR VPRES & MGR NE ASIS, BECHTEL CIVIL CO, HONG KONG, 96- *Personal Data:* b Fresno, Calif, June 11, 44; m 75, Vallarie Davis; c Jennifer L, Jamie J & Victoria J. *Educ:* Univ Calif, Berkeley, BS, 66; Colo State Univ, MS, 68, PhD, 76. *Honors & Awards:* Aerospace Sci & Tech Appl Award, Am Soc Civil Engrs, 84. *Prof Exp:* Asst prof, Univ Houston, 76-78; astronaut, NASA, Houston, 78-86; sr vpres advan systs line, Bechtel Nat Inc, San Francisco, 86-93; proj mgr, Hong Kong New Airport Proj, 93-96. *Mem:* Assoc fel Am Inst Aeronaut & Astronaut; Am Soc Civil Engrs; Royal Geo Soc. *Mailing Add:* 10B The Harborview 11 Magazine Gap Rd Hong Kong China

**VAN HOLDE, KENSAL EDWARD,** PHYSICAL BIOCHEMISTRY. *Current Pos:* prof, 67-93, EMER PROF BIOPHYS, ORE STATE UNIV, 93- *Personal Data:* b Eau Claire, Wis, May 14, 28; m 50, Barbara Watson; c 4. *Educ:* Univ Wis, BS, 49, PhD(chem), 52. *Prof Exp:* Res chemist, Textile Fibers Dept, E I du Pont de Nemours & Co, 52-55; res assoc, Univ Wis, 55-56, asst prof chem, Univ Wis-Milwaukee, 56-57; from asst prof to prof, Univ Ill, Urbana, 57-67. *Concurrent Pos:* Guggenheim fel, 73-74; res prof, Am Cancer Soc, 76-93. *Mem:* Nat Acad Sci; Am Soc Biochem & Molecular Biol; Biophys Soc; Am Acad Arts & Sci. *Res:* Physical chemistry of biological macromolecules; biophysical chemistry. *Mailing Add:* Dept Biochem & Biophys Ore State Univ Corvallis OR 97331. *Fax:* 541-737-0481

**VAN HOOK, JAMES PAUL,** PHYSICAL CHEMISTRY, FUEL TECHNOLOGY. *Current Pos:* process technol mgr & lab coordr, Foster Wheeler Energy Corp, 77-81, technol mgr, Foster Wheeler Synfuels Corp, 81-86, SR RES ASSOC, FORSTER WHEELER DEVELOP CORP, 86- *Personal Data:* b Paterson, NJ, Oct 16, 31; m 57; c 5. *Educ:* Col of the Holy Cross, BS, 53; Princeton Univ, PhD(chem), 58. *Prof Exp:* Res chemist, M W Kellogg Co Div, Pullman, Inc, 57-62, supvr, 62-65, sect head process res, 65-74; process develop mgr, Corp Eng Dept, Allied Chem Corp, 74-76. *Mem:* AAAS; Am Chem Soc; Am Inst Chem Engrs. *Res:* Catalytic oxidation for chlorine production; steam-hydrocarbon reactions for production of synthesis gas, hydrogen or synthetic natural gas; coal gasification; air pollution control; delayed coking and solvent deasphalting; shale oil processing; petroleum engineering. *Mailing Add:* 102 Harrison Brook Dr Basking Ridge NJ 07920

**VAN HOOK, ROBERT IRVING, JR,** ENVIRONMENTAL SCIENCE, ECOLOGY. *Current Pos:* PRES, LOCKHEED MARTIN ENERGY SYSTS, 97- *Personal Data:* b Rome, Ga, Jan 21, 42; m 64, Nancy Hodges; c Mark & Sydney. *Educ:* Clemson Univ, BS, 66, PhD(entom), 69. *Prof Exp:* Assoc res ecologist radiation effects, Ecol Sci Div, Oak Ridge Nat Lab, 70-72, res ecologist animal ecol, Environ Sci Div, 73-76, tech asst life sci & dir staff, 76-77, prog mgr ecosyst studies, 77-80, sect head, Terrestrial Ecol Sect, Environ Sci Div, 80-88, assoc dir, Environ Sci Div, 88-90, dir, Environ Sci Div, 90-93, dep dir, 93-97. *Concurrent Pos:* Adj ecol prog fac, Univ Tenn, 77- *Mem:* Ecol Soc Am; Sigma Xi; fel AAAS; Asn Ecosyst Res Ctrs (pres, 94). *Res:* Management of fundamental and applied research; assessment and education in support of environmentally sound energy technology development; advanced materials; renewable/efficiency; resource utilization/reclamation; advanced energy systems; transportation; computational sciences. *Mailing Add:* Lockheed Martin Energy Syst PO Box 2009 Oak Ridge TN 37831-8001

**VAN HOOK, WILLIAM ALEXANDER,** PHYSICAL CHEMISTRY. *Current Pos:* from asst prof to assoc prof, 62-72, PROF CHEM, UNIV TENN, KNOXVILLE, 72- *Personal Data:* b Paterson, NJ, Jan 14, 36; m 62, Nancy Ashton; c 3. *Educ:* Col of the Holy Cross, BS, 57; Johns Hopkins Univ, MA, 59, PhD(chem), 61. *Prof Exp:* Res assoc phys chem, Brookhaven Nat Lab, 61-62. *Concurrent Pos:* Fulbright res fel, Belg, 67-68; Nat Acad Sci exchange fel, Yugoslavia, 71; vis prof, Univ Beijing, 85, Lunzhou, 87. *Mem:* AAAS; Am Chem Soc. *Res:* Isotope effects on chemical and physical properties of molecular systems; solutions; polymer solutions. *Mailing Add:* Univ Tenn 7114 Rotherwood Dr Knoxville TN 37919-7412

**VAN HOOSIER, GERALD L, JR,** LABORATORY ANIMAL SCIENCE, ANIMAL VIROLOGY. *Current Pos:* ED, LAB ANIMAL SCI, 95- *Personal Data:* b Weatherford, Tex, June 4, 34; m 59, Marlene Meyer; c Gunther & Paul. *Educ:* Agr & Mech Col Tex, DVM, 57. *Honors & Awards:* Charles A Griffin Award, 86. *Prof Exp:* Head, Animal Test Sect, Div Biol Stand, NIH, 57-59, in serv training, Viral & Rickettsial Dis Lab, Calif State Dept Health, 59-60, head, Appl Virol Sect, Div Biol Stand, 60-62; from instr to assoc prof exp biol, Baylor Col Med, 62-69; from asst prof to assoc prof vet path & dir, Lab Animal Resources, Wash State Univ, 69-75; dir, Div Animal Med & prof animal med & path, Univ Wash, 75-88, prof & chmn, Dept Comp Med, 89-95. *Concurrent Pos:* Resident path, Baylor Col Med, 69-70 & Wash State Univ, 70-71; mem, Animal Resources Adv Comt, Animal Res Bd, NIH, 74-78. *Mem:* AAAS; Am Asn Lab Animal Sci; Am Soc Exp Path; Am Vet Med Asn. *Res:* Laboratory animal disease and medicine; comparative pathology; animal virology. *Mailing Add:* Dept Comp Med Box 357190 Univ Wash Seattle WA 98195-7190

**VAN HORN, D(AVID) A(LAN),** CIVIL ENGINEERING. *Current Pos:* res assoc prof, 62-66, PROF CIVIL ENG, LEHIGH UNIV, 66-, CHMN DEPT, 67- *Personal Data:* b Des Moines, Iowa, Apr 4, 30; m 60; c 2. *Educ:* Iowa State Univ, BS, 51, MS, 56, PhD(struct eng), 59. *Prof Exp:* Hwy engr, Fed Hwy Admin, 51-54; asst, Iowa State Univ, 54-55, instr civil eng, 55 & 56-58, instr theoret & appl mech, 55-56, from asst prof to assoc prof civil eng, 58-62. *Mem:* Am Soc Civil Engrs; Am Concrete Inst; Am Soc Eng Educ; Sigma Xi. *Res:* Structural engineering; behavior of prestressed and reinforced concrete members and structures; behavior of structural materials; structural analysis. *Mailing Add:* 1440 Dartmouth Dr Lehigh Univ Fritz Lab 13 Bethlehem PA 18015-3044

**VAN HORN, DAVID DOWNING,** METAL PHYSICS, MATHEMATICS. *Current Pos:* RETIRED. *Personal Data:* b Rochester, NY, Apr 23, 21; m 45. *Educ:* Univ Rochester, BA, 42; Case Inst Technol, PhD(physics), 49. *Prof Exp:* Instr physics, Univ Rochester, 43-44; jr physicist, Clinton Eng Works, 44-46; instr physics, Case Inst Technol, 46-49; res assoc metall, Knolls Atomic Power Lab, Gen Elec Co, 49-57, group leader chem & metall eng, Incandescent Lamp Dept, 57-81, consult physicist, Incandescent & Specialty Lamp Eng Dept, 81-87. *Mem:* Am Phys Soc; Am Soc Metals; Am Asn Physics Teachers; Math Asn Am; Am Inst Mining, Metall & Petrol Engrs; Math Asn Am; Soc Indust Appl Math; Sigma Xi. *Res:* Solid state diffusion; mechanical properties; heat transfer; tungsten; incandescent lamps; radiation measurements. *Mailing Add:* 15959 Glynn Rd Cleveland OH 44112

**VAN HORN, DIANE LILLIAN,** physiology, electron microscopy, for more information see previous edition

**VAN HORN, DONALD H,** ECOLOGY. *Current Pos:* RETIRED. *Personal Data:* b Hinsdale, Ill, Oct 9, 28; m 59; c 2. *Educ:* Kalamazoo Col, BA, 50; Univ Ill, MS, 52; Univ Colo, PhD(zool), 61. *Prof Exp:* Asst prof biol, Lake Forest Col, 61-62 & Utica Col, 62-65; vis asst prof, Univ Colo, Colorado Springs Ctr, 65-71, assoc prof, 71-74, chmn dept, 74-77, prof biol, 74-89. *Mem:* AAAS; Am Ornith Union; Ecol Soc Am; Am Soc Zoologists. *Res:* Terrestrial ecology, especially community and population analysis of mountain animals. *Mailing Add:* 4118 Tumbleweed Dr Colorado Springs CO 80907

**VAN HORN, GENE STANLEY,** SYSTEMATIC BOTANY. *Current Pos:* from asst prof to assoc prof, 71-80, PROF BIOL, UNIV TENN, CHATTANOOGA, 80- *Personal Data:* b Oakland, Calif, June 26, 40; m 62, Ruth Turner; c Jody, Diane & David. *Educ:* Humboldt State Univ, AB, 63; Univ Calif, Berkeley, PhD(bot), 70. *Prof Exp:* Vis asst prof biol, Tex Tech Univ, 70-71. *Concurrent Pos:* Tex State Inst Funds grant, Tex Tech Univ, 71; Univ Chattanooga Found grant, Univ Tenn, Chattanooga, 72-73 & 86. *Mem:* Sigma Xi; Am Soc Plant Taxonomists. *Res:* Biosystematics and evolution of angiosperms, especially asteraceae; floristics; biogeography. *Mailing Add:* Dept Biol Univ Tenn 615 McCallie Ave Chattanooga TN 37403

**VAN HORN, HAROLD H, JR,** DAIRY SCIENCE. *Current Pos:* PROF DAIRY SCI & CHMN DEPT, UNIV FLA, 70-, ANIMAL NUTRITIONIST, 74- *Personal Data:* b Pomona, Kans, Jan 13, 37; m 58; c 3. *Educ:* Kans State Univ, BS, 58, MS, 59; Iowa State Univ, PhD(dairy nutrit), 62. *Prof Exp:* Assoc prof dairy nutrit & mgt & exten dairyman, Iowa State Univ, 61-70. *Mem:* Am Dairy Sci Asn; Am Soc Animal Sci. *Res:* Improved dairy feeding and management practices; nutrition research in the use of urea in dairy rations. *Mailing Add:* Dept Dairy & Sci Poultry Univ Fla PO Box 110920 Gainesville FL 32611

**VAN HORN, HUGH MOODY,** ASTROPHYSICS. *Current Pos:* DIR, DIV ASTRON SCI, NSF, 93- *Personal Data:* b Williamsport, Pa, Mar 5, 38; m 60, Mary S Boon; c Kathleen, Mary & Michael. *Educ:* Case Inst Technol, BS, 60; Cornell Univ, PhD(astrophys), 66. *Prof Exp:* Res assoc, Univ Rochester, 65-67, from asst prof to assoc prof astrophys, 67-77, prof physics & astron, 77-96, chmn, Dept Physics & Astron, 80-86, actg assoc dean, 87-89, actg chmn, Dept Physics & Astron, 92-93. *Concurrent Pos:* Vis fel, Joint Inst Lab Astrophys, Univ Colo, Boulder, 73-74; invited speaker, Am Astron Soc, 80; sr scientist, Lab Laser Energetics, Univ Rochester, 85-96; vis prof, Univ Tex, Austin, 87; chair sect astron, AAAS, 92-; chair publs bd, Am Astron Soc, 93-94; adj prof astron, Univ Rochester, 96- *Mem:* Int Astron Union; Am Astron Soc; fel AAAS. *Res:* Degenerate dwarfs, brown dwarfs, and neutron stars; structure, evolution, oscillations and atmospheres; nuclear reactions and equation of state in stars; accretion disk structure and oscillations. *Mailing Add:* NSF 4201 Wilson Blvd Arlington VA 22230. *Fax:* 703-306-0525; *E-Mail:* hvanhorn@nsf.gov

**VAN HORN, LLOYD DIXON,** CHEMICAL ENGINEERING. *Current Pos:* CONSULT ENGR, BILES & ASSOCS, HOUSTON, 72- *Personal Data:* b Bartlesville, Okla, Mar 25, 38; m 59; c 2. *Educ:* Rice Univ, BA, 59, PhD(chem eng), 66. *Prof Exp:* Res engr, Shell Oil Co, Tex, 66-68, supvr chem eng res & develop, 68-69, asst to mgr mfg res & develop, head off, NY, 69-70, sr engr, head off, Houston, 70-72. *Mem:* Am Chem Soc. *Res:* Chemical reactor analysis and simulation; multiphase fluid flow in packed beds; applications of advanced process computer control; thermodynamics of hydrocarbon-hydrogen systems. *Mailing Add:* 821 Hwy 159W Bellville TX 77418

**VAN HORN, RUTH WARNER,** ORGANIC CHEMISTRY. *Current Pos:* from asst prof to assoc prof, 49-64, PROF CHEM, FRANKLIN & MARSHALL COL, 64- *Personal Data:* b Waterloo, Iowa, Mar 24, 18; m 45. *Educ:* Univ Calif, Los Angeles, BA, 39, MA, 40; Pa State Univ, PhD(org chem), 44. *Prof Exp:* Org chemist, Am Cyanamid Co, 44-48; instr chem, Hunter Col, 48-49. *Mem:* AAAS; Am Chem Soc. *Res:* Synthesis. *Mailing Add:* 1726 Old Philadelphia Pike Lancaster PA 17602-2636

**VAN HORN, WENDELL EARL,** chemical engineering, for more information see previous edition

**VAN HORNE, ROBERT LOREN,** PHARMACOGNOSY, PHARMACY. *Current Pos:* RETIRED. *Personal Data:* b Malvern, Iowa, Dec 26, 15; m 41, 63; c 5. *Educ:* Univ Iowa, BS, 41, MS, 47, PhD, 49. *Prof Exp:* Instr pharm, Univ Iowa, 49-51, from asst prof to assoc prof pharmacog, 51-56; dean, Sch

Pharm, Univ Mont, 56-75, dir continuing educ, 75-80, prof pharm, 56-85. *Concurrent Pos:* Mem fac adv coun, Gov of Mont; secy-treas, Western States Pharm Conf, 66-83; dir, Western Area Alcohol Educ & Training Prog, Nev, 74-; chmn, Mont Adv Coun Alcohol & Drug Dependence, 76-85. *Mem:* Am Asn Cols Pharm; Am Pharmaceut Asn. *Res:* Water soluble embedding materials for microtechnique; polyethylene glycols as substitutes for glycerin and ethanol in pharmaceutical preparations; surfactants in the preparation of coal tar lotions; anionic exchange resins for alkaloid separation; phytochemistry of mistletoe species. *Mailing Add:* 91 Brookside Way Missoula MT 59802-3278

**VAN HOUTEN, FRANKLYN BOSWORTH,** GEOLOGY. *Current Pos:* from asst prof to prof, 47-85, EMER PROF GEOL, PRINCETON UNIV, 85- *Personal Data:* b New York, NY, July 14, 14; m 43; c 3. *Educ:* Rutgers Univ, BS, 36; Princeton Univ, PhD(geol), 41. *Honors & Awards:* Twenhofel Medal, Soc Econ Paleontologists & Mineralogists. *Prof Exp:* Instr geol, Williams Col, 39-42. *Concurrent Pos:* Consult, 41-; geologist, US Geol Surv, 48-55 & Geol Surv Can, 53; vis prof, Univ Calif, Los Angeles, 63, State Univ NY, Binghamton, 71 & Univ Basel, 71. *Mem:* Fel Geol Soc Am; hon mem Soc Econ Paleontologists & Mineralogists; Am Asn Petrol Geologists; Int Asn Sedimentol; hon mem Colombian Geol Soc. *Res:* Sedimentology; clay minerals; zeolites; iron oxides; red beds; Triassic rocks, eastern North America and northwestern Africa, continental drift reconstructions; Cenozoic nonmarine deposits, western United States and northern South America; modern marine sediments; molasse facies in orogenic belts; Phanerozoic oolitic ironstones and glauconitic greensands; Nubian sandstone of northern Africa. *Mailing Add:* 168 Fitzrandolph Rd Princeton NJ 08540

**VAN HOUTEN, ROBERT,** MATERIALS ENGINEERING, NUCLEAR ENGINEERING. *Current Pos:* SR ENGR, JUPITER CORP, 93- *Personal Data:* b Peoria, Ill, Oct 2, 23; m 47; c 4. *Educ:* Washington Univ, St Louis, BS, 47, PhD(chem eng), 50. *Prof Exp:* Res engr, Victor Div, Radio Corp Am, 50-52; sect head res eng, Metals & Ceramics Div, P R Mallory & Co, 52-56, assoc lab dir chem & metall res, 57-58; prin & lead engr, Aircraft Nuclear Propulsion Dept, Gen Elec Co, Ohio, 58-64, mgr reactor mat develop, Nuclear Mat & Propulsion Oper, 64-70; mem staff, Atomics Int, Canoga Park, 70-73; reactor safety engr, US Nuclear Regulatory Comn, 74-84, sr nuclear engr, 84-89, tech coordr, 90-92. *Concurrent Pos:* Consult, Oak Ridge Nat Lab, 56-59; lectr, Univ Cincinnati, 61-66, adj assoc prof, 66-70. *Mem:* Sigma Xi; Res Soc Am. *Res:* Chemical, metallurgical, electrochemical and nuclear materials and processes for high temperature extreme duty; metal hydrides fabrication; light water reactor nuclear fuels testing and evaluation under accident conditions. *Mailing Add:* 4968 Lamia Way Oceanside CA 92056

**VAN HOUTEN, RONALD G,** TRAFFIC SAFETY, BEHAVIOR MODIFICATION. *Current Pos:* PROF PSYCHOL, MT ST VINCENT UNIV, 71- *Personal Data:* b 1944; m 86; Joy Allyn; c Jason, Lisa, Jonathan, Courtney, Ashleigh, Andrew & Xanthe. *Educ:* State Univ NY, Stony Brook, BA, 68; Dalhousie Univ, MA, 69, PhD (psychol), 71. *Honors & Awards:* Can Crime Prev Award, 83. *Concurrent Pos:* Prin investr, 71-; assoc ed, Educ & Treat Children, 80-83, J Appl Behav Anal, 84-87; dir, Soc Exp Anal Behav, 84-91, vpres, 88; chair, Asn Behav Anal Right Effective Treat Task Force, 86-88. *Mem:* Asn Behav Anal; Can Psychol Asn; NY Acad Sci. *Res:* Treatment of severe behavioral problems in developmentally delayed children and adults; treatment of learning disabilities; treatment of bed wetting; variables influencing the effects of social antecedents and contingencies of human behavior; traffic safety, speed control, impaired driving, pedestrian safety. *Mailing Add:* Psychol Dept Mt St Vincent Univ Halifax NS B3M 2J6 Can. *Fax:* 902-434-7031; *E-Mail:* ron.vanhouten@msvu.ca

**VANHOUTTE, JEAN JACQUES,** PEDIATRIC RADIOLOGY. *Current Pos:* assoc prof, 71-74, PROF & VCHMN, DEPT RADIOL, UNIV OKLA, HEALTH SCI CTR, 74- *Personal Data:* b Courtrai, Belg, Aug 27, 32; US citizen; m 60; c 4. *Educ:* Cath Univ Louvain, MD, 59. *Prof Exp:* Instr radiol, Johns Hopkins Univ, 63-65; asst prof, Univ Colo, 65-71. *Concurrent Pos:* Chief radiologist, Okla Childrens Mem Hosp, 71- *Mem:* Fel Am Col Radiol; Am Roentgen Ray Soc; Radiol Soc NAm; Soc Pediat Radiol; Asn Univ Radiologists. *Res:* Application of radiological sciences and imaging sciences to pediatrics. *Mailing Add:* 3 Kinnard St Apt 2 Cambridge MA 02139

**VANHOUTTE, PAUL MICHEL,** PHARMACOLOGY, PHYSIOLOGY. *Current Pos:* PROF PHYS PHARMACOL, MAYO CLIN, 81- *Educ:* Univ Ghent, Belg, MD, 65; Univ Antwerp, Belg, PhD(pharmacol), 73. *Res:* Pharmacology and physiology of blood vessel walls; endothelium and autonomic nerves; hypertension and coronary vapospasm. *Mailing Add:* Inst Rech Int Serv 6 Pldes Pleiades Courbevoie 92415 France. *Fax:* 33-1-46417316

**VAN HOUWELING, CORNELIUS DONALD,** veterinary medicine, for more information see previous edition

**VAN HOVEN, GERARD,** PLASMA PHYSICS, SOLAR PHYSICS. *Current Pos:* from asst prof to assoc prof, 68-79, PROF PHYSICS, PRIN INVESTR, UNIV CALIF, IRVINE, 79- *Personal Data:* b Los Angeles, Calif, Nov 23, 32; m 56; c 2. *Educ:* Calif Inst Technol, BS, 54; Stanford Univ, PhD(physics), 63. *Prof Exp:* Mem tech staff, Bell Tel Labs, 54-56; electron physicist, Gen Elec Co, 56-63; res assoc, W W Hansen Labs Physics, Stanford Univ, 63-65, res physicist, Inst Plasma Res, 65-68. *Concurrent Pos:* Fulbright fel, Vienna Tech Univ, 63-64; consult, Gen Elec Co, 63-65, Varian Assocs, 65-68, Smithsonian Astrophys Observ, 75, Aerospace Corp, 75-77 & NASA, 79-81, 89; Langley-Abbot vis scientist, Ctr Astrophys, Harvard Univ, 75; vis

astrophysicist, Oss Astrofisico Arcetri, Univ Florence, 76, vis prof, 81-82, 88 & 94. *Mem:* Fel Am Phys Soc; Am Astron Soc; Int Astron Union; Am Geophys Union. *Res:* Solar-terrestrial activity magnetohydrodynamics, especially magnetic field evolution and reconnection, energy-transport instabilities and coronal structure. *Mailing Add:* Dept Physics Univ Calif Irvine CA 92697. *Fax:* 714-824-2174; *E-Mail:* vanhoven@uci.edu

**VANHOY, JEFFREY R,** NUCLEAR PHYSICS. *Current Pos:* Asst Prof, 89-94, ASSOC PROF PHYSICS, US NAVAL ACAD, 94- *Personal Data:* b Forsyth Co, NC, 59. *Educ:* Col Park Univ, BS, 80; Duke Univ, MA, 83, PhD(physics), 86. *Mem:* Am Phys Soc; Meteorol Asn. *Res:* Nuclear Physics. *Mailing Add:* Dept Physics US Naval Acad Annapolis MD 21402

**VAN HUYSTEE, ROBERT BERNARD,** BIOCHEMISTRY, BOTANY. *Current Pos:* asst prof radiobiol, 66-69, assoc prof plant sci, 69-79, PROF PLANT SCI, UNIV WESTERN ONT, 79- *Personal Data:* b Amsterdam, Holland, Sept 29, 31; Can citizen; m 58; c 1. *Educ:* Univ Sask, BA, 59, MA, 61; Univ Minn, St Paul, PhD(hort), 64. *Prof Exp:* Fel physiol, Purdue Univ, 64-66. *Concurrent Pos:* Exchange scientist Can-France, 70, 73; vis prof, Univ Paris, France, 87. *Mem:* Am Soc Plant Physiol; Can Soc Plant Physiol. *Res:* Process of cold acclimation in plants; metabolism in cultured plant cells; study of peroxidase, hemo-, glyco-, calcium protein. *Mailing Add:* Dept Plant Sci Univ Western Ont London ON N6A 5B9 Can

**VANICEK, C DAVID,** FISHERIES MANAGEMENT. *Current Pos:* from asst prof to assoc prof, 67-79, PROF BIOL, CALIF STATE UNIV, SACRAMENTO, 79- *Personal Data:* b Waterloo, Iowa, Oct 12, 39. *Educ:* Iowa State Univ, BS, 61, MS, 63; Utah State Univ, PhD(fishery biol), 67. *Prof Exp:* Fishery biologist, US Fish & Wildlife Serv, 63-67. *Mem:* Am Fisheries Soc; Am Inst Biol Sci; Am Inst Fishery Res Biol; Pac Fishery Biologists; Desert Fishes Coun. *Res:* Freshwater fishery biology and management. *Mailing Add:* 307 Sixth St Traer IA 50675

**VANICEK, PETR,** GEODESY, GEOPHYSICS. *Current Pos:* assoc prof, 71-76, dir grad studies, Dept Surv Eng, 83-85, PROF GEOD, UNIV NB, 76- *Personal Data:* b Susice, Czech, July 18, 35; m 91, Valeria Vasary; c Filip, Stepan & Naninka. *Educ:* Prague Tech Univ, Dipl Ing, 59; Czech Acad Sci, PhD(math physics), 68, DrSc, 93. *Hon Degrees:* DrSc, Czech Acad Sci, 93. *Honors & Awards:* Humboldt Distinguished Sr Scientist Award. *Prof Exp:* Div head land surv, Prague Inst Surv & Cartog, 59-63; consult numerical anal & comput prog, Fac Tech & Nuclear Physics, Prague Tech Univ, 63-67; sr res fel & sr sci officer, Inst Coastal Oceanog & Tides, Nat Environ Res Coun Gt Brit, 68-69; Nat Res Coun Can fel, Dept Energy, Mines & Resources, 69-71. *Concurrent Pos:* Can rep, Comn Recent Crustal Movements, Int Union Geod & Geophys, 77-91; secy, Subcomt Geod, Nat Res Coun Can, 72-74; mem, Can Subcomt Geodynamics, 75-80; vis prof, Nat Res Coun Can, Univ Parana, Brazil, 75, 76, 79, 84 & 87; vis prof, Univ Stuttgart, WGer, 82 & 83; mem, NAS Comt Geod, 82-85; prof surv sci, Univ Toronto, 81-83, adj prof, 83-90; pres spec study groups, Int Asn Geod, 83-87 & 89-92; vpres, Comn Recent Crustal Movement, In Asn Geod, chmn, Subcomn Geod Aspects Law of Sea. *Mem:* Fel Am Geophys Union; Can Inst Geomatics; fel Geol Asn Can; Can Geophys Union (pres, 87-89); Sigma-Xi. *Res:* Geodesy; earth tides, crustal movements and mean sea level; applied mathematics, especially spectral analysis and mechanics. *Mailing Add:* Dept Geod & Geomatics Eng Univ NB PO Box 4400 Fredericton NB E3B 5A3 Can. *Fax:* 506-453-4943; *E-Mail:* vanicek@und.ca

**VANIER, JACQUES,** QUANTUM ELECTRONICS, ATOMIC & MOLECULAR PHYSICS. *Current Pos:* RETIRED. *Personal Data:* b Dorion, Que, Jan 4, 34; m 61, Lucie Beauder; c Lyne & Pierre. *Educ:* Univ Montreal, BA, 55, BSc, 58; McGill Univ, MSc, 60, PhD(physics), 63. *Honors & Awards:* Centennial Medal, Inst Elec & Electronics Engrs. *Prof Exp:* Lectr physics, McGill Univ, 61-63; physicist, Quantum Electronics Div, Varian Assocs, Mass, 63-67 & Hewlett-Packard Co, 67; from assoc prof to prof elec eng, Laval Univ, 68-83; prin res, Nat Res Coun, 83-85, asst dir, Physics Div, 85-90, dir, Lab Basic Stand, 86-90, dir gen, Inst Nat Measurements Stand, 90-93. *Concurrent Pos:* Invited researcher, Univ Paris, 74 & 81-82, Instituto Eletrotecnico Nazionale, Italy, 75, Nat Bur Stand, US, 75 & 82; chmn, Study Group F, Comt Consult, Int des Radio Commun, 85-90; chmn, Comf Prec Electromagnetic Measurements, Ottawa, Can, 90; mem, Comt Int des Poids et Measures, Paris, 90. *Mem:* Can Asn Physicists; fel Inst Elec & Electronics Engrs; fel Am Phys Soc; fel Royal Soc Can. *Res:* Electron paramagnetic resonance; nuclear magnetic resonance; optical pumping; masers; frequency standards; atomic clocks; atomic and molecular physics; electromagnetism; solid state physics; thermal physics; writer on quantum physics and electronics. *Mailing Add:* Elec Dept Pouliot Campus LaVal Univ Quebec ON J1K 7P4 Can

**VANIER, PETER EUGENE,** MATERIALS SCIENCE, SOLID STATE PHYSICS. *Current Pos:* from asst scientist to assoc scientist, Mat Sci, Brookhaven Nat Lab, 78-83, scientist, 83-87, physicist, NPB Div, 87-90, PHYSICIST, ADV REACTOR DIV, BROOKHAVEN NAT LAB, 91-, APPL TECHNOL SSN DIV, 94- *Personal Data:* b St Kitts, Leeward Islands, Feb 26, 46; nat US; m 71; c 1. *Educ:* Cambridge Univ, BA, 67; Syracuse Univ, MS, 69, PhD(physics), 76. *Prof Exp:* Res assoc physics, Yeshiva Univ, 76-78. *Concurrent Pos:* Vis scientist, Electrotech Lab, Ibarak, Japan, 84. *Mem:* Am Phys Soc; Mat Res Soc. *Res:* High-temperature properties of carbon and carbides; electronic, magnetic, and optical properties of semiconductors; properties of amorphous semiconductors related to solar cell applications. *Mailing Add:* 3 Ben Pl Setauket NY 11733

**VAN INWEGEN, RICHARD GLEN,** biochemistry, physiology, for more information see previous edition

**VANITALLIE, THEODORE BERTUS,** MEDICINE, METABOLISM. *Current Pos:* instr, Columbia Univ, 52-55, from assoc clin prof to clin prof, 57-71, assoc dir, Inst Human Nutrit, 67-74, prof med, 71-88, EMER PROF MED, COL PHYSICIANS & SURGEONS, COLUMBIA UNIV, 88- *Personal Data:* b Hackensack, NJ, Nov 8, 19; m 48, 91, Sallie Newton; c Theodore B Jr, Lucy M (Borge), Christina M (Anderson), Elizabeth B (Morrow) & Katharine R. *Educ:* Harvard Univ, SB, 41; Columbia Univ, MD, 45; Am Bd Internal Med, dipl, 54. *Honors & Awards:* McCollum Award, Am Soc Clin Nutrit, 85; Goldberger Award, AMA, 85; Distinguished Scientist Award, Soc Study Ingestive Behav, 94. *Prof Exp:* Intern med, St Luke's Hosp, New York, 45-46, from asst resident to resident, 48-50; res fel nutrit, Sch Pub Health, Harvard Univ, 50-51, res assoc, 51-52, asst prof clin nutrit, Schs Med & Pub Health, 55-57. *Concurrent Pos:* From asst to assoc, Peter Bent Brigham Hosp, Boston, 50-57; dir lab nutrit res, St Luke's Hosp, 52-55, asst attend physician, 53-55, attend physician, 57-, dir med, 57-75; vis lectr, Sch Pub Health, Harvard Univ, 57-60; mem gastroenterol & nutrit training comt, NIH, 69-73; mem food & nutrit bd, Nat Acad Sci, 70-74; dir, Obesity Res Ctr, St Lukes-Roosevelt Hosp Ctr, 74-85, co-dir, 85-88; Nat Inst Arthritis, Metab & Digestive Dis Adv Coun, 78-81; ed-in-chief, Am J Clin Nutrit, 79-81; spec adv, Surgeon Gen Human Nutrit, 80-81. *Mem:* Soc Exp Biol & Med; Am Clin & Climat Asn; Am Fedn Clin Res; fel Am Col Physicians; Am Soc Clin Nutrit (pres, 75-76); fel Am Inst Nutrit; Am Soc Clin Invest; fel AAAS. *Res:* Carbohydrate and lipid physiology and biochemistry; clinical nutrition; metabolism; control of food intake and regulation of body fat; physiology of energy balance regulation; human body composition; causes and treatment of obesity; nutritional assessment and support. *Mailing Add:* PO Box 775 Boca Grande FL 33921-0775. *Fax:* 941-964-0747

**VAN KAMMEN, DANIEL PAUL,** PSYCHOPHARMACOLOGY. *Current Pos:* PROF PSYCHIAT, WESTERN PSYCHIAT INST & CLIN, 82-; CHIEF STAFF, VET AFFAIRS MED CTR, PITTSBURGH, 82- *Personal Data:* b Dordrecht, Neth, Aug 26, 43; US citizen; m 70, Welmoet Bok; c 1. *Educ:* Univ Utrecht Med Sch, MD, 66, PhD(pharmacol), 78. *Prof Exp:* Unit chief & staff psychiatrist, NIMH, 73-82. *Concurrent Pos:* Mem, Behav & Clin Res Rev Comt, 75-78; fac mem, Wash Sch Psychiat, 75-; vis prof, Dept Psychiat, Univ Ala, Birmingham, 78; consult, Vet Admin & Nat Inst Lung & Blood Inst, 79; mem, RAG Ment Health & Behav Sci, Va. *Mem:* Fel Am Col Neuropsychopharmacol; AAAS; Int Psychoneuroendocrinol; Soc Neurosci; Collegium Int Neuropsychopharmacol; Soc Biol Psychiat. *Res:* Biochemical and pharmacological exploration of schizophrenia; spinal fluid studies; endocrinology. *Mailing Add:* Dept Affairs Med Ctr Highland Dr Pittsburgh PA 15206-1297

**VANKIN, GEORGE LAWRENCE,** EVOLUTIONARY THEORY. *Current Pos:* from asst prof to assoc prof, 62-75, PROF BIOL, WILLIAMS COL, 75- *Personal Data:* b Baltimore, Md, Apr 22, 31; m 56; c 2. *Educ:* NY Univ, BS, 54, PhD(zool), 62; Wesleyan Univ, MA, 56. *Prof Exp:* Res asst genetics, Wesleyan Univ, 56; teaching fel biol, NY Univ, 56-59, res asst embryol, 59-62, lectr biol, 61-62. *Concurrent Pos:* Vis asst prof, Med Col, Cornell Univ, 68. *Mem:* Soc Syst Zool; Willi Hennig Soc. *Res:* Evolutionary theory; history and philosophy of evolutionism. *Mailing Add:* 88 Cole Ave Williamstown MA 01267

**VAN KLAVEREN, NICO,** KNOWLEDGE SYSTEMS, COMPUTER AIDED ENGINEERING. *Current Pos:* CONSULT, VANKAY CONSULT, 93- *Personal Data:* b Amersfoort, Neth, Feb 2, 34; m 59, Riet Terlouw; c 3. *Educ:* Delft Univ Technol, MSc, 59, DSc(chem eng), 66; Pepperdine Univ, MBA, 78. *Prof Exp:* Asst prof chem eng, Delft Univ Technol, 61-66; sr eng assoc, Chevron Res & Technol Co, 66-92. *Concurrent Pos:* Vis prof, Steven's Inst Technol, 64. *Mem:* Am Inst Chem Engrs; Neth Royal Inst Eng; Am Asn Artificial Intel. *Res:* Chemical engineering science; process design; user oriented software for process engineering and business and strategic planning; modeling of technical, economical and social processes; management of complex organizations; organizational development; application of artificial intelligence (knowledge systems); computer aided training/education. *Mailing Add:* 57 Rancho Del Sol Camino CA 95709. *E-Mail:* 72247.1355@compuserve.com

**VAN KLEY, HAROLD,** BIOCHEMISTRY, PROTEIN CHEMISTRY. *Current Pos:* PROF, DEPT CHEM, TRINITY CHRISTIAN COL, 82- *Personal Data:* b Chicago, Ill, Mar 7, 32; m 59, Helen P Hawks; c Cynthia & Michael. *Educ:* Calvin Col, AB, 53; Univ Wis, MS, 55, PhD(biochem), 58. *Prof Exp:* From instr to sr instr, Sch Med, St Louis Univ, 58-61, asst prof biochem, 61-82; dir biochem res, St Mary's Health Ctr, 67-82. *Concurrent Pos:* High Sch Student Res Apprenticeship Prog, Argonne Nat Lab, 83-88; chemist/consult, Chem Waste Mgt Tech Ctr, 89-91 & 93-94. *Mem:* AAAS; Am Chem Soc; Sigma Xi; Am Soc Biochem & Molecular Biol. *Res:* Protein structure, especially as related to biological function and regulatory mechanisms in metabolism; protein changes in neoplasia; pancreatic enzymes; metals analysis in hazardous waste. *Mailing Add:* Dept Chem Trinity Christian Col 6601 W College Dr Palos Heights IL 60463-0929. *E-Mail:* harold.vankley@truty.edu

**VAN KONYNENBURG, RICHARD ARIE,** NUCLEAR MATERIALS, RADIATION EFFECTS ON MATERIALS. *Current Pos:* student employee, Lawrence Livermore Nat Lab, 70-74, facil mgr, Nuclear Chem Div, 80-84, sect leader, Ceramics & Corrosion Sect, 94-95, ENGR, CHEM & MAT SCI DIRECTORATE, LAWRENCE LIVERMORE NAT LAB, 74-, GROUP LEADER, CORROSION TECHNOL GROUP, 95- *Personal Data:* b Modesto, Calif, Apr 24, 42; m, Diana G Pollard; c Christopher E & L Michael. *Educ:* Univ Calif, Davis, BS, 63, MS, 65, PhD(eng & appl sci), 74. *Prof Exp:* Res & develop coordr, US Army Mobility Equip Res & Develop Ctr, Ft Belvoir, 68-70. *Concurrent Pos:* Consult, Battelle Columbus Labs, 82, Argentine Atomic Energy Comn, 84; lectr, Int Atomic Energy Agency, 86,; lectr solid state physics, Dept Appl Sci, Univ Calif, Davis, 88-91. *Mem:* Mat Res Soc; Am Nuclear Soc. *Res:* Nuclear materials including metals and ceramics; radiation effects, radiation chemistry, radiation dosimetry, waste forms for nuclear waste, ceramics for immobilization of plutonium; biochemistry related to nutrition and disease and to radiation effects on biological systems. *Mailing Add:* 444 Ontario Dr Livermore CA 94550

**VAN KRANENDONK, JAN,** THEORETICAL PHYSICS. *Current Pos:* RETIRED. *Personal Data:* b Delft, Neth, Feb 8, 24; m 52; c 3. *Educ:* Univ Amsterdam, PhD(physics), 52. *Honors & Awards:* Steacie Prize, 64. *Prof Exp:* Res asst, Univ Amsterdam, 50-54; lectr, State Univ Leiden, 55-58; from assoc prof to prof physics, Univ Toronto, 58-90. *Concurrent Pos:* Neth Orgn Pure Res fel, Harvard Univ, 53-54. *Mem:* Am Phys Soc; fel Royal Soc Can; Can Asn Physicists; corresp mem Neth Acad Sci. *Res:* Molecular and solid-state physics. *Mailing Add:* 1129 Sunny Side Rd Kelowna BC V1Z 2N7 Can

**VAN KREY, HARRY P,** PHYSIOLOGY, AGRICULTURE. *Current Pos:* from assoc prof to prof, 65-91, EMER PROF AVIAN PHYSIOL, VA POLYTECH INST & STATE UNIV, 91- *Personal Data:* b Combined Locks, Wis, Oct 2, 31; m 52; c 2. *Educ:* Univ Calif, Davis, BS, 60, PhD(animal physiol), 64. *Prof Exp:* Fel, Univ Wis, 64-65. *Mem:* AAAS; Sigma Xi; Poultry Sci Asn; World Poultry Sci Asn; Soc Study Reproduction. *Res:* Avian reproductive physiology; poultry science. *Mailing Add:* 1837 St Andrews Circle Blacksburg VA 24060. *E-Mail:* hvankrey@vt.edu

**VAN KUYK, ROBERT WILLIAM,** gene therapy, immunotherapy, for more information see previous edition

**VAN LANCKER, JULIEN L,** PATHOLOGY. *Current Pos:* PROF PATH & CHMN DEPT, UNIV CALIF, LOS ANGELES, 70- *Personal Data:* b Auderghem, Belg, Aug 14, 24; m 49; c 3. *Educ:* Cath Univ Louvain, MD, 50. *Prof Exp:* Asst path, Cath Univ Louvain, 50-53; vis instr, Univ Kans, 53-54; Runyon fel oncol, Univ Wis, 54-55; asst path, Cath Univ Louvain, 55-56; asst prof, Univ Utah, 56-60; assoc prof & chief, Path Sect, Primate Res Ctr, Univ Wis, 60-66; prof med sci, Brown Univ, 66-70. *Mem:* Radiation Res Soc; Am Soc Exp Path; Am Soc Biol Chemists; NY Acad Sci; Int Acad Path. *Res:* Cell biology; chemical pathology; molecular mechanisms in disease. *Mailing Add:* Dept Path Univ Calif 10833 Le Conte Ave Los Angeles CA 90024-1732

**VAN LANDINGHAM, HUGH F(OCH),** ELECTRICAL ENGINEERING. *Current Pos:* from asst prof to assoc prof, 66-80, PROF ELEC ENG, VA POLYTECH INST & STATE UNIV, 80- *Personal Data:* b Greensboro, NC, Apr 12, 35; m 64; c 3. *Educ:* NC State Univ, BS, 57; NY Univ, MEE, 59; Cornell Univ, PhD(elec eng), 67. *Prof Exp:* Mem tech staff, Bell Tel Labs, NJ, 57-62. *Mem:* Inst Elec & Electronics Engrs. *Res:* Communication and control systems. *Mailing Add:* Dept Elec Eng Va Polytech Inst & State Univ Blacksburg VA 24061

**VAN LANEN, ROBERT JEROME,** PHYSICAL ORGANIC CHEMISTRY, CHEMICAL EDUCATION. *Current Pos:* asst prof, 73-77, chair, Sci Dept, 78-81 & 86-89, ASSOC PROF CHEM, ST XAVIER UNIV, 77- *Personal Data:* b Green Bay, Wis, July 30, 43; m 78, Jane Ulsafer; c Kathleen. *Educ:* St Norbert Col, BS, 65; Univ Colo, Boulder, PhD(org chem), 71. *Prof Exp:* NIH fel biochem, Univ Wis-Madison, 71-73. *Mem:* AAAS; Am Chem Soc. *Res:* Mechanisms of enzyme-catalyzed reactions; chemical education; chemistry of small ring compounds. *Mailing Add:* St Xavier Univ 3700 W 103rd St Chicago IL 60655-3198

**VAN LEAR, DAVID HYDE,** FORESTRY, SOILS. *Current Pos:* assoc prof, 71-77, PROF SILVICULT, CLEMSON UNIV, 77- *Personal Data:* b Clifton Forge, Va, Dec 1, 40. *Educ:* Va Polytech Inst, BS, 63, MS, 65; Univ Idaho, PhD(forest sci), 69. *Prof Exp:* Fel sch forestry, Univ Fla, 68-69; soil scientist, US Forest Serv, 69-71. *Mem:* Soc Am Foresters; Soil Sci Soc Am. *Res:* Hardwood silviculture; environmental forestry; forest fertilization; soil-site relationships; strip mining. *Mailing Add:* Dept Forestry Clemson Univ Clemson SC 29634-0001

**VAN LEER, JOHN CLOUD,** PHYSICAL OCEANOGRAPHY, OCEAN ENGINEERING. *Current Pos:* asst prof, 71-75, ASSOC PROF PHYS OCEANOG, ROSENSTIEL SCH MARINE & ATMOSPHERIC SCI, UNIV MIAMI, 76- *Personal Data:* b Washington, DC, Feb 14, 40; m 62; c 3. *Educ:* Case Inst Technol, BSME, 62; Mass Inst Technol, ScD(phys oceanog), 71. *Prof Exp:* Engr, Draper Lab, Mass Inst Technol, 62-65, from res asst to res assoc phys oceanog, 65-71. *Mem:* Sigma Xi; Am Geophys Union; Marine Technol Soc. *Res:* Physical oceanographic research on continental shelves and deep ocean; response to wind forcing, surface and bottom boundary layers; development of ocean instruments, notably the Cyclesonde, an automatic oceanographic radiosonde. *Mailing Add:* Univ Miami RSMAS Marine Biol & Fisheries Div 4600 Rickenbacker Causeway MSC Bldg Rm 364 Virginia Key Monterey FL 33149

**VAN LEEUWEN, GERARD,** PEDIATRICS. *Current Pos:* PROF PEDIAT, UNIV OSTEOP MED, DES MOINES, IA, 90- *Personal Data:* b Hull, Iowa, July 4, 29; m 52; c 2. *Educ:* Calvin Col, BA, 50; Univ Iowa, MD, 54. *Prof Exp:* Intern, Butterworth Hosp, Mich, 54-55; resident pediat, Univ Mo-Columbia, 57-59, from instr to asst prof, 62-69; prof pediat & chmn dept, Univ Nebr Med

Ctr, Omaha, 69-78; assoc med dir, Sect Med Care, Mo Div Health, 78-80; prof & chmn, pediat dept, Med Sch, Univ Kans, Wichita, 80-90. *Concurrent Pos:* NIH trainee, 62-64; Am Thoracic Soc fel, 64-66; Nat Found Birth Defects grant, 66; proj consult, Head Start, 65; dir, Nat Found Treatment Ctr, 66; dir, Emergency Med, Univ Nebr, 76-78. *Mem:* Am Acad Pediat; Am Pediat Soc. *Res:* Neonatal physiology and hypogylcemia; hyaline membrane syndrome; teratology. *Mailing Add:* 3200 Grand Ave Des Moines IA 50312

**VAN LENTE, KENNETH ANTHONY,** PHYSICAL CHEMISTRY. *Current Pos:* from asst prof to prof, 31-71, EMER PROF PHYS CHEM, SOUTHERN ILL UNIV, CARBONDALE, 71- *Personal Data:* b Holland, Mich, Mar 29, 03; m 29; c 4. *Educ:* Hope Col, AB, 25, MS, 26; Univ Mich, PhD, 31. *Prof Exp:* Asst, Univ Mich, 27-31. *Mem:* Am Chem Soc. *Res:* Liquid junction potentials; constant temperature baths; composition of plating baths; chemical education. *Mailing Add:* 1209 W Chautauqua Carbondale IL 62901-2454

**VAN LIER, JAN ANTONIUS,** PHYSICAL CHEMISTRY. *Current Pos:* TECHNOL ASSOC, WESTLAKE TECHNOL LAB, EVEREADY BATTERY CO, 86- *Personal Data:* b Ginneken, Neth, Nov 17, 24; m 54; c 4. *Educ:* Univ Utrecht, BS, 51, MS, 54, PhD(phys chem), 59. *Hon Degrees:* JD, Cleveland State Univ, 77. *Prof Exp:* Res assoc mineral eng, Mass Inst Technol, 55-58; instr colloid chem, Univ Utrecht, 58-59; res chemist, Philips Electronics, Holland, 59-60; sr res chemist, Parma Tech Ctr, Union Carbide Corp, 60-74, staff res chemist, 74-86. *Mem:* Am Chem Soc; Royal Neth Chem Soc; Sigma Xi. *Res:* Microbalance techniques; solubility of quartz; battery materials; differential and thermogravimetric analysis; solid electrolytes; basic electrochemistry; ternary phase diagrams; surface chemistry; wetting phenomena; plasma polymerization. *Mailing Add:* 9937 Little Mountain Rd Concord OH 44060-8037

**VAN LIER, JOHANNES ERNESTINUS,** BIOCHEMISTRY. *Current Pos:* from asst prof to assoc prof, 70-81, PROF NUCLEAR MED RADIOBIOL, MED CTR, UNIV SHERBROOKE, 81-, HEAD, 92- *Personal Data:* b Amsterdam, Neth, May 26, 42. *Educ:* Delft Univ Technol, Neth, 66; Univ Tex Med Br Galveston, PhD(biochem), 69. *Prof Exp:* Res assoc, Univ Tex Med Br Galveston, 66-69, instr, 69-70. *Concurrent Pos:* Med Res Coun Can res grant, 70- *Mem:* AAAS; Fedn Am Socs Exp Biol; Am Chem Soc; Can Fedn Biol Socs; Soc Nuclear Med. *Res:* Radiopharmaceuticals for nuclear med; photosensitizers and anticancer agents. *Mailing Add:* Dept Nuclear Med Univ Sherbrooke Med Ctr Sherbrooke PQ J1H 5N4 Can. *Fax:* 819-564-5442

**VAN LIEW, HUGH DAVENPORT,** MEDICAL PHYSIOLOGY. *Current Pos:* from asst prof to assoc prof, 63-74, PROF PHYSIOL, STATE UNIV NY, BUFFALO, 74- *Personal Data:* b Spokane, Wash, Jan 28, 30; m 59; c 3. *Educ:* State Col Wash, BS, 51; Univ Rochester, MS, 53, PhD(physiol), 56. *Honors & Awards:* Stover-Link Award, 86. *Prof Exp:* Res fel, Sch Pub Health, Harvard Univ, 59-61; asst prof physiol, Stanford Univ, 61-63. *Mem:* AAAS; Am Physiol Soc; Undersea & Hyperbaric Med Soc; Europ Undersea Biomed Soc. *Res:* Diffusion of gases through tissues; gas tensions in the tissues; subcutaneous gas pockets as models of decompression sickness bubbles; diffusion and convection in the lung; pulmonary function in hyperbaric environments; modeling of bubbles in the body. *Mailing Add:* Dept Physiol State Univ NY Buffalo NY 14214. *Fax:* 716-829-2344

**VAN LIEW, JUDITH BRADFORD,** PHYSIOLOGY, NEPHROLOGY. *Current Pos:* res assoc med, State Univ NY, Buffalo, 64-70, res asst prof, 70-74, from asst prof to assoc prof, 74-83, PROF PHYSIOL, SCH MED, STATE UNIV NY, BUFFALO, 83-; PROF PHYSIOL & RES PHYSIOLOGIST, VET ADMIN HOSP, BUFFALO, 73- *Personal Data:* b Boston, Mass, Jan 22, 30; m 59, Hugh D; c Gregory, Andrew & Joel. *Educ:* Bates Col, BS, 51; Univ Wash, MS, 54; Univ Rochester, PhD(physiol), 58. *Prof Exp:* Res assoc biochem, Woman's Med Col Pa, 58-60. *Mem:* Am Physiol Soc; Am Soc Nephrology. *Res:* Physiology of normal and abnormal proteinuria. *Mailing Add:* Dept Physiol State Univ NY Vet Admin Ctr 3495 Bailey Ave Buffalo NY 14215-1129. *Fax:* 716-862-3419

**VAN LIGTEN, RAOUL FREDRIK,** optical production, physical optics; deceased, see previous edition for last biography

**VAN LINT, VICTOR ANTON JACOBUS,** PHYSICS. *Current Pos:* CONSULT, 91- *Personal Data:* b Samarinda, Indonesia, May 10, 28; US citizen; m 50; c 4. *Educ:* Calif Inst Technol, BS & PhD(physics), 54. *Honors & Awards:* NASA Pub Serv Award, 81. *Prof Exp:* Instr physics, Princeton Univ, 54-55; physicist, Gen Atomic Div, Gen Dynamics Corp, 57-65, assoc dir, Spec Nuclear Effects Lab, 65-69, mgr, Defense Sci Dept, Gulf Radiation Technol, 69-70, vpres, Gulf Energy & Environ Systs & mgr, Gulf Radiation Technol Div, 70-73; pres, Intelcom Radiation Technol, 73-74, consult, 74-75; mgr, Elec Appln Div, Mission Res Corp, 75-82, spec asst to dep dir sci & technol, Defense Nuclear Agency, 82-83, mgr, Exp Physics Div, 83-91. *Mem:* Am Phys Soc; fel Inst Elec & Electronics Engrs. *Res:* Nuclear and high-power electromagnetic radiation effects, including solid state physics, atomic physics, and electronic systems analysis. *Mailing Add:* 1032 Skylark Dr La Jolla CA 92037-7733

**VAN LOON, EDWARD JOHN,** BIOCHEMISTRY. *Current Pos:* RETIRED. *Personal Data:* b Danville, Ill, Dec 3, 11; m 54; c 1. *Educ:* Univ Ill, AB, 36; Rensselaer Polytech Inst, MS, 37, PhD(chem), 39. *Prof Exp:* Res assoc & instr physiol & pharmacol, Albany Med Col, Union NY, 39-43; instr & asst prof

biochem, Mich State Univ, 46; asst & assoc prof, Sch Med, Univ Louisville, 46-49; chief, Med Res Lab, Vet Admin Hosp, 49-55; group leader & head biochem sect, Smith Kline & French Labs, 55-67; chief, Spec Pharmacol Animal Lab, Food & Drug Admin, 67-75. *Concurrent Pos:* Mem, Am Bd Clin Chemists. *Mem:* Am Soc Clin Invest; Am Inst Nutrit; Am Soc Pharmacol & Exp Therapeut; Am Chem Soc; Am Soc Biol Chem. *Res:* Clinical biochemistry; intermediary metabolism; biochemical pharmacology and drug metabolism; clinical biochemistry. *Mailing Add:* Carolina Meadows 3-303 Chapel Hill NC 27514-8505

**VAN LOON, JON CLEMENT,** GEOLOGY, CHEMISTRY. *Current Pos:* From asst prof to assoc prof analytical geochem, 64-77, PROF GEOL, UNIV TORONTO, 77- *Personal Data:* b Hamilton, Ont, Jan 9, 37; m 61; c 3. *Educ:* McMaster Univ, BSc, 59; Univ Toronto, PhD(analytical chem), 64. *Mem:* Sigma Xi. *Res:* Application of modern analytical methods, particularly ICP source mass spectrometry, to the analysis of natural products, with particular emphasis on environmental samples. *Mailing Add:* Dept Chem Univ Toronto St George Campus 170 College St Toronto ON M5S 1A1 Can

**VAN LOPIK, JACK RICHARD,** RESEARCH ADMINISTRATION, MARINE SCIENCES. *Current Pos:* chmn, Dept Marine sci, 68-74, dean, Ctr Wetland Resources, 70-91, PROF MARINE SCI & DIR SEA GRANT DEVELOP, LA STATE UNIV, BATON ROUGE, 68- *Personal Data:* b Holland, Mich, Feb 25, 29; m, Anna Hojdahl; c 1. *Educ:* Mich State Univ, BS, 50; La State Univ, MS, 53, PhD(geol), 55. *Prof Exp:* Field investr, Coastal Studies Inst, La State Univ, 51-54, instr geol, 54; geologist, Waterways Exp Sta, Corps Engrs, US Army, 54-57, asst chief & chief geol br, 57-61; res scientist, chief area eval sect & mgr space & environ sci prog, Geosci Opers, Tex Instruments Inc, 61-66, tech requirements dir, 66-68. *Concurrent Pos:* Mem, Nat Res Coun Earth Sci Div, Nat Acad Sci-Nat Res Coun, 67-72, chmn panel geog & human & cult resources, Comt Remote Sensing Progs for Earth Resources Surv, 69-77; mem, La Adv Comn Coastal & Marine Resources, 71-73; Nat Adv Comt on Oceans & Atmosphere, 78-84; mem bd dirs, Gulf South Res Inst, 74-84; chmn, Coastal Resources Directorate, US Nat Comt for Man & the Biosphere, US Nat Comn for UN Educ, Sci & Cult Orgn, 75-82; mem, Lower Miss River Waterways Safety Adv Comt, Eighth Coast Guard Dist, 83-93; mem adv coun, Nat Coastal Resources Res & Develop Inst, 85-; mem, Chief Engrs Environ Adv Bd, US Army CEngr, 88-92, bd dirs, La Partnership Technol & Innovation, 89-; pres, Sea Grant Asn, 88-89; mem, Marfin Steering Comt, 92-94. *Mem:* Fel Geol Soc Am; Am Mgt Asn; Soc Res Adminr; fel AAAS; sr mem Am Astronaut Soc; Am Geophys Union. *Res:* Photogeology and remote sensing; deltaic and arid zone geomorphology and sedimentation; military and engineering geology; terrain analysis and quantification; lunar and earth-orbiting-satellite exploration; coastal zone management. *Mailing Add:* La Sea Grant Program La State Univ Baton Rouge LA 70803-7500. *Fax:* 504-388-6331

**VAN LOVEREN, HENK,** IMMUNOTOXICOLOGY, IMMUNOPHARMACOLOGY. *Current Pos:* immunotoxicologist, 84-89, SECT HEAD IMMUNOTOXICOL, NAT INST PUB HEALTH & ENVIRON PROTECTION, 89- *Personal Data:* b Utrecht, Neth, Dec 1, 51; m 72; c 2. *Educ:* State Univ Utrecht, MSc, 75, PhD(immunol), 81. *Prof Exp:* Fel immunol, Yale Univ, New Haven, 82-83. *Concurrent Pos:* Prin investr, validation studies immunotoxicol, 87-; coordr, EC Res Prog Develop Immunotoxicol Test Batteries in collab UK, Ger & France, 90- *Mem:* Am Asn Immunologists; Soc Toxicol. *Res:* Test systems for assessing undesired effects of exposure to chemicals, environmental, natural or drugs, to the immune system. *Mailing Add:* Immunobiol & Hematol Nat Inst Pub Health & Environ PO Box 1 Bilthoven 3720 BA Netherlands. *Fax:* 31-30-285283

**VANMARCKE, ERIK HECTOR,** CIVIL ENGINEERING, OPERATIONS RESEARCH. *Current Pos:* PROF CIVIL ENG, PRINCETON UNIV, 85- *Personal Data:* b Menen, Belg, Aug 6, 41; m 65, Margaret Delesie; c Lieven, Anneke & Kristien. *Educ:* Cath Univ Louvain, Engr, 65; Univ Del, MS, 67; Mass Inst Technol, PhD(eng), 70. *Honors & Awards:* Raymond C Reese Res Prize, Am Soc Civil Engrs, 75, Walter Huber Res Prize, 84. *Prof Exp:* From instr to prof civil eng, Mass Inst Technol, 68-85. *Concurrent Pos:* Consult eng; NSF res grants, Mass Inst Technol, 70-; consult, Off Sci & Technol Policy, 78-80; ed, Struct Safety, 82-; vis scholar, Harvard Univ, 84-85; vis prof, Shimizu Corp, Stanford Univ, 91- *Mem:* Am Soc Civil Engrs; Earthquake Eng Res Inst; Am Geophys Union; Seismol Soc Am; Sigma Xi; AAAS. *Res:* Structural and geotechnical engineering; vibrations induced by wind, earthquakes and water waves; structural safety; random fields; risk assessment and risk management. *Mailing Add:* Dept Civil Eng & Opers Res E-QUAD E-223 Princeton Univ Princeton NJ 08544. *Fax:* 609-251-3791

**VAN METER, DAVID,** APPLIED PHYSICS, INFORMATION SCIENCES. *Current Pos:* RETIRED. *Personal Data:* b Southampton, NY, Mar 27, 19; m 50. *Educ:* Mass Inst Technol, BS & SM, 43; Harvard Univ, MA, 53, PhD, 55. *Prof Exp:* Mem tech staff, Bell Tel Labs, 43-46; asst prof elec eng, Pa State Univ, 46-52; lab mgr, Melpar, Inc, 55-60 & Litton Systs, Inc, 60-66; chief, Comput Res Lab, Electronics Res Ctr, NASA, 66-70; chief, Info Sci Div, US Dept Transp, 70-77, Systs Develop Div, 78-80, sr tech staff mem, Transp Systs Ctr, 80-84. *Concurrent Pos:* Lectr, Harvard Univ, 55 & 59; ed, Trans Info Theory, 64-67. *Res:* Computer science; information theory. *Mailing Add:* 105 Main St Rockport MA 01966

**VAN METER, DONALD EUGENE,** SOIL CONSERVATION. *Current Pos:* prof natural resources, 69-79, chmn dept, 79-87, ASSOC DEAN, COL SCI & HUMANITIES, BALL STATE UNIV, 87- *Personal Data:* b Ashtabula, Ohio, Aug 30, 42; m 64; c 1. *Educ:* Purdue Univ, Lafayette, BS, 64; Mich State Univ, MS, 65; Ind Univ, Bloomington, DEduc, 71. *Prof Exp:* County agt agr,

Coop Exten Serv, Purdue Univ, 65-68. *Mem:* Soil Conserv Soc Am; Am Soc Agron. *Res:* Natural resource management; agriculture extension education in developing nations. *Mailing Add:* Natural Resources Ball State Univ 2000 W University Muncie IN 47306-1022

**VAN METER, WAYNE PAUL,** INORGANIC CHEMISTRY. *Current Pos:* from asst prof to prof, 59-88, EMER PROF CHEM, UNIV MONT, 88- *Personal Data:* b Fresno, Calif, Feb 16, 26; m 48; c 4. *Educ:* Ore State Col, BS, 50, MS, 52; Univ Wash, PhD(inorg chem), 59. *Prof Exp:* Chemist, Hanford Atomic Prod Oper, Gen Elec Co, Wash, 51-56. *Mem:* Am Chem Soc. *Res:* Measurement of trace concentrations of metals in biological systems; development of sample processing techniques and instrumentation for atomic absorption spectrometry. *Mailing Add:* 2224 1/2 Rattlesnake Dr Missoula MT 59802

**VAN METRE, THOMAS EARLE, JR,** MEDICINE, ALLERGY. *Current Pos:* from instr to asst prof, 56-70, physician-in-chg, Adult Allergy Clin, 66-84, PHYSICIAN, JOHNS HOPKINS HOSP, 56-, ASSOC PROF MED, MED SCH, JOHNS HOPKINS UNIV, 70- *Personal Data:* b Newport, RI, Jan 11, 23; m 47; c 5. *Educ:* Harvard Univ, BS, 43, MD, 46; Am Bd Internal Med, dipl, 55. *Prof Exp:* Intern med, Johns Hopkins Hosp, 46-47, asst resident, 47-48, 50 & 51-52, Am Cancer Soc fel, 52-53; asst prof internal med, Sch Med, St Louis Univ, 53-54. *Concurrent Pos:* Pvt pract, 54-; mem attend staff, Baltimore City Hosp, 54- & Union Mem Hosp, 59- *Mem:* AMA; Am Fedn Clin Res; Am Col Physicians; Am Acad Allergy (pres, 78); Am Clin & Climat Asn. *Res:* Allergy; effect of corticosteroids on growth; uveitis; asthma. *Mailing Add:* 11 E Chase St Baltimore MD 21202-2516

**VANMIDDLESWORTH, FRANK L,** BIOORGANIC CHEMISTRY, MEDICINAL CHEMISTRY. *Current Pos:* natural prod chemist, 87-90, SYNTHETIC CHEMIST & RES FEL, MERCK & CO, 90- *Personal Data:* b Memphis, Tenn, Nov 26, 55; m 79. *Educ:* Vanderbilt Univ, BA, 77; Emory Univ, PhD(chem), 82. *Prof Exp:* Res assoc chem, Emory Univ, 77-82; res assoc, Dept Pharm, Univ Wis, 82-84; org chemist, Northern Regional Res Ctr, USDA, 84-87. *Concurrent Pos:* Adj prof, Plant Path Dept, Univ Ill, 86. *Mem:* Am Chem Soc; AAAS; Am Pharmacog Soc; Am Peptide Soc. *Res:* Medicinal, bioorganic, natural product, and immunochemistry; rational design and synthesis of biologically active compounds; chemico-enzymatic systhesis; isolation, structure determination, modification, and biosynthesis of natural products such as enzyme inhibitors, antibiotics and mycotoxins; peptidomimetic vaccines. *Mailing Add:* Glaxo Res Labs 5 Moore Dr Res Triangle Park NC 27701-4613

**VAN MIDDLESWORTH, LESTER,** PHYSIOLOGY, MEDICINE. *Current Pos:* from instr to assoc prof, 46-59, PROF PHYSIOL & BIOPHYS, CTR HEALTH SCI, UNIV TENN, MEMPHIS, 59-, PROF MED, 74- *Personal Data:* b Washington, DC, Jan 13, 19; m 48; c 4. *Educ:* Univ Va, BS, 40, MS, 42 & 44; Univ Calif, Berkeley, PhD(physiol), 47; Univ Tenn, MD, 51. *Prof Exp:* Chief chemist, Piedmont Apple Prod Corp, Va, 39-44; res assoc, Radiation Lab & teaching asst physiol, Univ Calif, 44-46. *Concurrent Pos:* Res asst physiol, Univ Va, 42-44; intern, John Gaston Hosp, 51-52; USPHS career res award, 61-89. *Mem:* Am Chem Soc; Am Physiol Soc; Endocrine Soc; Am Thyroid Asn; Health Physics Soc. *Res:* Vapor phase catalysis; hormone synthesis; carbohydrate metabolism; aviation medicine; anoxia; metabolism of plutonium, radium, iodide, thiocyanate and thyroxine; thyroid physiology; goiter; audiogenic seizures; radioactive fallout; mycotoxins. *Mailing Add:* Physiol Div Univ Tenn 894 Union Ave Memphis TN 38163

**VAN MIEROP, LODEWYK H S,** MEDICINE. *Current Pos:* assoc prof, 66-68, PROF PEDIAT & PATH, COL MED, UNIV FLA, 68-, GRAD RES PROF, 78- *Personal Data:* b Surabaya, Java, Mar 31, 27; US citizen; m 54; c 5. *Educ:* State Univ Leiden, MD, 52; Am Bd Pediat, cert pediat cardiol. *Prof Exp:* Lectr anat, McGill Univ, 61-62; from asst prof to assoc prof pediat, Albany Med Col, 62-66. *Concurrent Pos:* Res assoc, Mt Sinai Hosp, NY, 63-66; NIH res career develop award, 64-73; mem, Comt Nomenclature Heart, NIH, 67-68; mem, Southern Regional Res Rev Comt, Am Heart Asn, 68-72. *Mem:* Am Pediat Soc; Am Heart Asn; Am Asn Anat; fel Am Acad Pediat; fel Am Col Cardiol. *Res:* Pediatric cardiology; pathology and pathogenesis of congenital heart disease; cardiac embryology. *Mailing Add:* Dept Pediat Univ Fla Col Med Gainesville FL 32610

**VANN, DOUGLAS CARROLL,** IMMUNOBIOLOGY. *Current Pos:* from asst prof to assoc prof genetics, 70-95, DIR IMMUNOBIOL, NEUGENESIS, UNIV HAWAII, HONOLULU, 95- *Personal Data:* b Coronado, Calif, May 3, 39; m 61; c 1. *Educ:* Univ Calif, Berkeley, AB, 60; Univ Calif, Santa Barbara, PhD(biol), 66. *Prof Exp:* Jr scientist, Inter-Am Trop Tuna Comn, 60-62; res assoc immunol, Biol Div, Oak Ridge Nat Lab, 66-68; USPHS training grant, Scripps Clin & Res Found, 68-70. *Concurrent Pos:* Prin investr, USPHS res grant, 71-77. *Mem:* AAAS. *Res:* Cellular basis of immune responses. *Mailing Add:* 2060 Mott-Smith Dr Honolulu HI 96822-2510

**VANN, JOSEPH M,** RADIATION PROTECTION, EMERGENCY MANAGEMENT. *Current Pos:* SR ENGR, NUCLEAR ENG, WVALLEY NUCLEAR SERV, 90- *Personal Data:* b Clinton, NC, Dec 30, 37; m 61; c 1. *Educ:* NC State Univ, BS, 58; Univ NC, Chapel Hill, MEd, 61; ECarolina Univ, MPhysics, 72; Va Polytech Inst, MS, 73. *Prof Exp:* Prof math, Mt Olive Col, 61-71; safety & licensing engr, Nuclear Eng, Gen Pub Utilities, 73-76; nuclear engr, Nuclear Eng, NJ Radiation Protection, 76-81; sr engr, Nuclear Eng, Ebasco Serv, 81-89. *Mem:* Am Phys Soc; Sigma Xi. *Res:* Applications of Green's functions to reactor kinetics equations; transform and asymptotic

analysis of wave motion; integral transform theory; radiation protection and emergency planning concerns for nucleus facilities, including high-level radioactive waste facilities. *Mailing Add:* 23 Hillview Ave Madison NJ 07940-1738

**VANN, W(ILLIAM) PENNINGTON,** CIVIL ENGINEERING. *Current Pos:* ASSOC PROF CIVIL ENG, TEX TECH UNIV, 72- *Personal Data:* b Belton, Tex, Sept 9, 35; m 62; c 3. *Educ:* Columbia Univ, BA, 58, BS, 59, MS, 60; Rice Univ, PhD(civil eng), 66. *Prof Exp:* Struct designer civil eng, Walter P Moore, consult engr, Tex, 60; asst prof, Rice Univ, 66-72. *Concurrent Pos:* Mem, Earthquake Eng Res Inst, 67- *Mem:* Am Soc Civil Engrs; Am Concrete Inst; Seismol Soc Am; Sigma Xi. *Res:* Dynamic response of inelastic structural systems; static and dynamic behavior of inelastic structure, including buckling, energy absorption and failure; mobile homes; wind engineering. *Mailing Add:* Dept Civil Eng Tex Tech Univ Lubbock TX 79409

**VANN, WILLIAM L(ONNIE),** ELECTRICAL ENGINEERING. *Current Pos:* RETIRED. *Personal Data:* b McAlpin, Fla, Sept 21, 23; m 46, L V Grinstead; c George W. *Educ:* Univ Fla, BEE, 50. *Prof Exp:* Test engr, Gen Elec Co, 50; assoc engr, Johns Hopkins Univ, 50-55, sr engr, Appl Physics Lab, 55-88, proj supvr, 58-62, asst group supvr, 62-69, group supvr, 69-72. *Mem:* Inst Elec & Electronics Engrs. *Res:* Microwave and radar development; data acquisition and tracking radars; systems engineering; engineering management. *Mailing Add:* 5039 Cypress Lake Dr Lake Park GA 31636

**VAN NAME, FREDERICK W, III,** STRUCTURAL ENGINEERING, COMPOSITE MATERIALS. *Current Pos:* MGR ENG & QUAL ASSURANCE, COMPOSITES USA, 92- *Personal Data:* b Torrington, Conn, Apr 30, 46. *Educ:* Univ Del, BME, 82, MMAE, 85. *Prof Exp:* From eng analyst to mgr advan technol, Thiokol Corp, Md, 85-91; consult, Aerojet Corp/NASA, 91-92. *Concurrent Pos:* Consult composite mat, Condux, Cecon, Lern & Consult Bur, 91- *Mem:* Am Soc Mech Engrs; Am Inst Aeronaut & Astronaut; Am Soc Testing Mat; Astronaut Soc Can; Nat Asn Corrosion Engrs. *Res:* Computer software to perform laminate thermal-structural analyses; micromechanics; case cylinder design; dome contour analysis; winding pattern generation, braid pattern generation, polar boss design and orthotropic cylinder buckling; granted 10 patents. *Mailing Add:* 6 Francis Circle Newark DE 19711. *Fax:* 302-368-3087; *E-Mail:* rockerick@aol.com

**VAN NESS, HENDRICK C(HARLES),** VAPOR & LIQUID EQUILIBRIUM. *Current Pos:* from asst prof to prof chem eng, Rensselaer Polytech Inst, 56-83, chmn, Div Fluid, Chem & Thermal Processes, 69-74, inst prof, 83-89, EMER PROF CHEM ENG, RENSSELAER POLYTECH INST, 89- *Personal Data:* b New York, NY, Jan 18, 24; wid; c 1. *Educ:* Univ Rochester, BS, 44, MS, 46; Yale Univ, DEng, 53. *Honors & Awards:* Warren K Lewis Award, Am Inst Chem Engrs, 88. *Prof Exp:* Instr eng, Univ Rochester, 45-47; chem engr, M W Kellogg Co, Pullman, Inc, 47-49; asst prof chem eng, Purdue Univ, 52-56. *Concurrent Pos:* Fulbright lectr, King's Col, Univ Durham, 58-59; vis prof, Univ Calif, Berkeley, 66 & Inst for Chem Technol, Denmark Tech Sch, Lyngby, Denmark, 77. *Mem:* Am Chem Soc; fel Am Inst Chem Engrs. *Res:* Solution thermodynamics; phase equilibria. *Mailing Add:* Chem Eng Rensselaer Polytech Inst Ricketts Bldg Troy NY 12180-3590. *Fax:* 518-276-4030

**VAN NESS, JAMES E(DWARD),** ELECTRICAL ENGINEERING. *Current Pos:* Asst & res engr, Northwestern Univ, 49-51, lectr elec eng, 52-53, from asst prof to prof, 54-96, dir, Univ Comput Ctr, 62-65, chmn, Dept Elec Eng, 69-72, EMER PROF ELEC ENG & COMPUT SCI, NORTHWESTERN UNIV, EVANSTON, 96- *Personal Data:* b Omaha, Nebr, June 24, 26; m 48, Mary E Dolvin; c Rebecca, Barbara, Margaret & Julie. *Educ:* Iowa State Univ, BS, 49; Northwestern Univ, MS, 51, PhD(elec eng), 54. *Concurrent Pos:* Vis assoc prof, Univ Calif, 58-59; vis prof, Mass Inst Technol, 73-74. *Mem:* Fel Inst Elec & Electronics Engrs. *Res:* Use of digital computers in power system problems; numerical analysis; control systems. *Mailing Add:* Dept Elec Eng & Comput Sci Northwestern Univ Evanston IL 60208-3118. *Fax:* 847-491-4455; *E-Mail:* vanness@ecs.nwu.edu

**VAN NESS, JOHN WINSLOW,** REGRESSION, PATTERN RECOGNITION. *Current Pos:* assoc prof, Univ Tex, Dallas, 73-75, head, Prog Math Sci, 73-78, assoc dean, Sch Natural Sci & Math, 78-83, head, Prog Math Sci, 80-92, PROF, UNIV TEX, DALLAS, 75- *Personal Data:* b McLean Co, Ill, Aug 16, 36; m 64, Nancy Clark; c Karen & David. *Educ:* Northwestern Univ, BS, 59; Brown Univ, PhD(appl math), 64. *Prof Exp:* Vis asst prof statist, Stanford Univ, 64-65, actg asst prof, 65-66; asst prof math, Univ Wash, 66-71; assoc prof statist, Carnegie-Mellon Univ, 71-73. *Mem:* Fel Inst Math Statist; fel Am Statist Asn; Classification Soc; Sigma Xi; Pattern Recognition Soc. *Res:* Theoretical and applied statistics; biostatistics; multivariate and time series analysis; classification and discriminant analysis; nonstandard regression analysis; measurement error models. *Mailing Add:* Prog Math Sci Univ Tex-Dallas PO Box 830688 Richardson TX 75083-0688. *E-Mail:* ness@utdallas.edu

**VAN NESS, KENNETH E,** THERMODYNAMICS OF SURFACES. *Current Pos:* ASST PROF ENG, WASHINGTON & LEE UNIV, 86- *Educ:* Bucknell Univ, BS, 67; Rutgers Univ, PhD(mat sci), 86. *Mem:* Am Phys Soc. *Res:* Thermodynamics of surfaces; polymer liquids (evaluation of state, surface phenomena). *Mailing Add:* Dept Physics & Eng Washington & Lee Univ Lexington VA 24450-9904

**VAN NESTE, ANDRE,** MATERIALS SCIENCE, METALLURGY. *Current Pos:* assoc prof metall, 65-77, PROF METALL, DEPT METALL & VDEAN EDUC, FAC SCI & ENG, LAVAL UNIV, 77- *Personal Data:* b Brussels, Belg, July 15, 38; Can citizen; m 67; c 3. *Educ:* Laval Univ, BSc, 60, DSc(metall), 63. *Prof Exp:* Researcher electron micros, Chem Metall Div, Nat Ctr Sci Res, Paris, 63-65. *Concurrent Pos:* Asn Foreign Tech Trainees in France fel, 63-64; Nat Res Coun Can fel, 64-65. *Mem:* Am Soc Metals; Can Inst Mining & Metall; Am Soc Eng Educ. *Res:* Mechanical properties of materials, fatigue, fracture, wear; service failure analysis. *Mailing Add:* 1127 Beau-Pre Sainte-Foy PQ G1W 4B6 Can

**VAN NEVEL, J PAUL,** SCIENCE COMMUNICATIONS. *Current Pos:* dep assoc dir, 73-74, ASSOC DIR CANCER COMMUN, NAT CANCER INST, 74- *Educ:* Univ Wis-Madison, BS, 61. *Prof Exp:* Dir pub info, Univ Wis Med Ctr, 61-62 & 64-68; assoc dir pub rels, Johns Hopkins Med Inst, 68-69, dir, 69-73. *Concurrent Pos:* Liaison, Nat Commun Comt, Am Cancer Soc, 74-; mem, US Nat Comt, Int Union Against Cancer, 85-90; consult, Howard Hughes Med Inst, 87-; ed, News Sect, J Nat Cancer Inst, 88- *Mem:* Asn Am Med Col. *Res:* Author of published articles. *Mailing Add:* Off Cancer Commun Nat Cancer Inst 10A31 Pepper Bldg Bethesda MD 20892

**VANNICE, MERLIN ALBERT,** CHEMICAL ENGINEERING, CATALYSIS. *Current Pos:* assoc prof, 76-80, distinguished alumni prof eng, 85-91, distinguished prof eng, 91-95, PROF CHEM ENG, PA STATE UNIV, 80-, M R FENSKE PROF CHEM ENG, 96- *Personal Data:* b Broken Bow, Nebr, Jan 11, 43; m 71, Bette A Clark. *Educ:* Mich State Univ, BS, 64; Stanford Univ, MS, 66, PhD(chem eng), 70. *Honors & Awards:* Prof Progress Award, Am Inst Chem Engrs, 86; Emmett Award, NAm Catalysis Soc, 87; Schuit lectr, Univ Del, 89. *Prof Exp:* Engr, Dow Chem Co, 66; res engr, Corp Res Labs, Exxon Res & Eng Co, 71-75, sr res engr, 75-76. *Concurrent Pos:* Indust fel, Sun Oil Co, Pa, 69-71; Humboldt res award, 90; chmn, Gordon Conf on Catalysis, 82; consult, Eastman Kodak, 80-; assoc ed, J Catalysis, 94-; Fulbright award, 96- *Mem:* Am Chem Soc; Am Inst Chem Engrs; Catalysis Soc NAm; Sigma Xi; Mat Res Soc. *Res:* Adsorption and heterogeneous catalysis, including hydrogenation reactions of CO, aromatics and oxygenates, kinetics, catalyst preparation and characterization, metal-support interactions; nitrous oxide reduction. *Mailing Add:* Dept Chem Eng Pa State Univ University Park PA 16802. *Fax:* 814-865-7846; *E-Mail:* marche@engr.psu.edu

**VANNIER, WILTON EMILE,** IMMUNOCHEMISTRY, BIOCHEMISTRY. *Current Pos:* RETIRED. *Personal Data:* b Pasadena, Calif, June 6, 24; m 53; c 2. *Educ:* Univ Calif, San Francisco, MD, 48; Calif Inst Technol, PhD(immunochem), 58. *Prof Exp:* Instr exp med, Sch Pub Health, Univ NC, 51-54; immunochemist, Lab Immunol, Nat Inst Allergy & Infectious Dis, Md, 58-64, head, Immunochem Sect, 64-68; assoc prof biochem, Sch Med, Univ Southern Calif, 68-70; res med officer, Naval Med Res Inst, Nat Naval Med Ctr, 70-84. *Concurrent Pos:* Res fel, Calif Inst Technol, 57-60, vis assoc chem, 85-89. *Mem:* Fel AAAS; Am Chem Soc; Am Asn Immunol. *Res:* Parasite immunology; chemistry of antibodies and antigen-antibody reactions; liposome cell interactions. *Mailing Add:* 209 Oak Meadow Rd Sierra Madre CA 91024

**VAN NORMAN, GILDEN RAMON,** PHOTOGRAPHIC CHEMISTRY, POLYMER CHEMISTRY. *Current Pos:* RETIRED. *Personal Data:* b Jamestown, NY, Dec 11, 32; m 58; c 2. *Educ:* Univ Rochester, BS, 54; Mass Inst Technol, PhD(org chem), 57. *Prof Exp:* Tech assoc, Eastman Kodak Co, 57-91. *Mem:* AAAS; Am Chem Soc. *Mailing Add:* 317 Orchard Creek Lane Rochester NY 14612-3515

**VAN NORMAN, JOHN DONALD,** analytical chemistry; deceased, see previous edition for last biography

**VAN NOSTRAND, JOAN F,** PUBLIC ADMINISTRATION. *Current Pos:* chief longterm care statist, Nat Ctr Health Statist, Ctr Dis Control, 74-80, dep dir, Div Health Care Statist, 81-86, dir, 86-87, PROJ DIR INT COLLAB EFFORT ON AGING, NAT CTR HEALTH STATIST, CTR DIS CONTROL, 88- *Personal Data:* b Pittsburgh, Pa, Oct 1, 44; m 72, Lyman. *Educ:* Am Univ, BS, 66; Univ Southern Calif, MPA, 85, DPA, 94. *Honors & Awards:* Key Award, Am Pub Health Asn, 93; Award for Women of Achievement, Nordstrom Co, 94. *Concurrent Pos:* Mem, Comt Fed Pub Health Statist, Am Pub Health Asn, 82-85, chair, Geront Health Sect, 87-89, Inter-Sect Coun, 90 & mem, Work Group Principles Long Term Care, 92-94; chair, Task Force Data on Aging, Geront Soc Am, 84-89, liaison, Coun Prof Asns Fed Statist, 87-89. *Mem:* Fel Geront Soc Am; Am Pub Health Asn; Am Statist Asn; Can Asn Geront; Pop Asn Am. *Res:* Epidemiologic and policy-oriented research at the national level on the use of institutional long term care in the US and other developed nations; trends in the health of the elderly. *Mailing Add:* Nat Ctr Health Statist 6525 Belcrest Rd Hyattsville MD 20782. *Fax:* 301-436-4233; *E-Mail:* jfv2@cdc.gov

**VANNOTE, ROBIN L,** STREAM & RIVER ECOLOGY. *Current Pos:* DIR, STROUD WATER RES CTR, ACAD NATURAL SCI PHILADELPHIA, 66- *Personal Data:* b Summit, NJ, Aug 12, 34; m 59; c 4. *Educ:* Univ Maine, BS, 57; Mich State Univ, MS, 62, PhD(limnol), 63. *Prof Exp:* Biologist, Water Qual Br, Tenn Valley Authority, 63-65, chief biol sect, 65-66. *Concurrent Pos:* Mem pesticide monitoring subcomt, Fed Comt Pest Control, 64- 66; adj prof entom & appl ecol, Univ Del, 74- *Mem:* AAAS; Am Fisheries Soc; Am Soc Limnol & Oceanog; Ecol Soc Am; Sigma Xi; Am Entom Soc; NAm Benthological Soc. *Res:* Ecology of streams and rivers; interactions with terrestrial landscapes, production ecology; detrital systems, energy flow and nutrient budgets, geomorphology of streams; effects of channel modifications, drainage, and rural runoff on biotic productivity and system stability; ecology of regulated river systems. *Mailing Add:* 315 W Street Rd Kennett Square PA 19348

**VAN OERS, WILLEM THEODORUS HENDRICUS,** NUCLEAR & PARTICLE PHYSICS. *Current Pos:* assoc prof, 67-74, PROF PHYSICS, UNIV MAN, 74- *Personal Data:* b Amsterdam, Neth, Mar 17, 34; m 60, Margaretha Keuss; c Nicolai S C & Genevieve B O. *Educ:* Univ Amsterdam, BS, 55, MS, 59, PhD (math, physics), 63. *Prof Exp:* From res asst to res assoc, Inst Nuclear Physics Res, Amsterdam, Neth, 57-64; asst res physicist, Univ Calif, Los Angeles, 64-66. *Concurrent Pos:* Vis assoc prof, Univ Calif, Los Angeles, 71-72; vis scientist, CEN de Saclay, Gif-sur-Yvette, France, 75-76, Tri Univ Meson Facil, Vancouver, BC, 81-83, 87-89 & 91-95, Saturne Nat Lab, Gif-sur-Yvette, France, 89-90; vis staff mem, Los Alamos Sci Lab, NMex, 79-80; prog dir NSF, Washington, DC, 86-87; Killam fel, 87-89; guest prof, Univ Tokyo, 96. *Mem:* fel Am Phys Soc; Can Asn Physicists; Sigma Xi. *Res:* Nuclear reactions induced by various types of particle beams at low and intermediate energies; phenomenological and theoretical analyses of few-nucleon problems; nuclear optical model; fundamental symmetries; strangeness in nuclear matter; rare decays. *Mailing Add:* Dept Physics Univ Man Winnipeg MB R3T 2N2 Can. *Fax:* 604-222-1074, 204-269-8489

**VANONI, VITO A(UGUST),** HYDRAULICS. *Current Pos:* from proj supvr to hydraul engr & supvr lab, USDA, Calif Inst Technol, 35-47, assoc dir, Hydrodyn Lab, Nat Defense Res Comt, 41-46, from asst prof to prof hydraul, 42-74, EMER PROF HYDRAUL, CALIF INST TECHNOL, 74- *Personal Data:* b Camarillo, Calif, Aug 30, 04; m 34. *Educ:* Calif Inst Technol, BS, 26, MSc, 32, PhD(civil eng, hydraul), 40. *Prof Exp:* Jr struct engr, Bethlehem Steel Corp, 26-28 & 30-31; draftsman, Am Bridge Co, 28-30. *Mem:* Nat Acad Eng; hon mem Am Soc Civil Engrs. *Res:* Sediment transportation; hydraulics of open channels; harbor and coastal engineering. *Mailing Add:* Environ Eng Dept Calif Inst Technol Pasadena CA 91125. *Fax:* 626-395-2940

**VAN ORDEN, HARRIS O,** ORGANIC CHEMISTRY. *Current Pos:* from assoc prof to prof, 54-83, actg head dept, 58-59, EMER PROF CHEM, UTAH STATE UNIV, 83- *Personal Data:* b Smithfield, Utah, Oct 6, 17; m 48, Eleanor Young; c Pete L. *Educ:* Utah State Agr Col, BS, 38; Wash State Univ, MS, 42; Mass Inst Technol, PhD(org chem), 51. *Prof Exp:* From asst prof to assoc prof chem, Utah State Agr Col, 46-52; NIH spec fel, Univ Utah, 53. *Mem:* Fel AAAS; Am Chem Soc; Sigma Xi. *Res:* Synthetic organic and bio-organic chemistry; protein sequence studies; synthesis of peptides; enzyme specificity studies. *Mailing Add:* 281 E Eighth N Logan UT 84321-3329

**VAN ORDEN, LUCAS SCHUYLER, III,** CHEMICAL DEPENDENCY, PSYCHOPHARMACOLOGY. *Current Pos:* PVT PRACT PSYCHIAT, 95- *Personal Data:* b Chicago, Ill, Nov 3, 28; m 53; c 4. *Educ:* Northwestern Univ, BS, 50, MS, 52, MD, 56; Yale Univ, PhD(pharmacol), 66; Washington Univ, St Louis, 86, Bd Cert Psych, 88. *Prof Exp:* Intern, Harper Hosp, Detroit, 56-57; asst resident surg, Med Ctr, Yale Univ, 61-62; Nat Inst Neurol Dis & Blindness spec fel neuroanat, Dept Anat, Harvard Med Sch, 66-67; from asst prof to assoc prof, Univ Iowa, 67-73, prof pharmacol, Col Med, 73-77; attend psychiatrist, St Vincente Pinoy Hills Hosp, 86-95. *Concurrent Pos:* Resident psychiat, Univ of Iowa, 75-76; dir, Chem Dependency Unit, Ment Health Inst, Mt Pleasant & adj prof pharmacol & psychiat, Univ Iowa Col Med, 78-79. *Mem:* AMA; Am Med Soc Addictions; Am Psychiat Asn; Am Col Forensic Psychiat; Am Col Forensic Examrs. *Res:* Neuropharmacology; autonomic nervous system fine structure and histochemistry of adrenergic transmitter; quantitative cytochemistry, immunocytochemistry; alcohol and drug abuse. *Mailing Add:* 4 Moya Pl Sante Fe NM 87505

**VAN ORDER, ROBERT BRUCE,** ORGANIC CHEMISTRY. *Current Pos:* RETIRED. *Personal Data:* b Glenvale, Ont, Mar 19, 15; nat US; m 42; c 3. *Educ:* Queen's Univ, Can, BA, 38, MA, 39; NY Univ, PhD(org chem), 42. *Prof Exp:* Asst, NY Univ, 39-42; res org chemist, Stamford Res Labs, Am Cyanamid Co, 42-46, plant chemist, Calco Chem Div, 46-53, asst chief chemist, Org Chem Div, Bound Brook Lab, 53-55 & Mkt Develop Dept, 55-62; tech dir, Pearsall Chem Co, 62-63; mgr sales develop, Am Cyanamid Co, Bound Brook, 63-69, mgr org chem res & develop, Wayne, 69-77 & Bound Brook, 77-80. *Mem:* Fel Am Inst Chemists; Am Chem Soc. *Res:* Structure and synthesis of antibiotics; inorganic pigments and chemicals; dyestuffs and pigment dispersions; market development and sales development of new chemical products. *Mailing Add:* 58 Sycamore Ave Berkeley Heights NJ 07922-1615

**VAN OSS, CAREL J,** IMMUNOCHEMISTRY, PHYSICAL BIOCHEMISTRY. *Current Pos:* assoc prof, 68-72, HEAD, IMMUNOCHEM LAB, SCH MED, STATE UNIV NY, BUFFALO, 68-, PROF MICROBIOL, 72- *Personal Data:* b Amsterdam, Neth, Sept 7, 23; m 51; c 3. *Educ:* Univ Paris, PhD(phys biochem), 55. *Prof Exp:* Fel colloid chem, Van't Hoff Lab, Univ Utrecht, 55-56; fel phys chem, Ctr Electrophoresis, Sorbonne, 56-57; dir, Lab Phys Biochem, Nat Vet Col Alfort, 57-63; asst head, Dept Microbiol, Montefiore Hosp, NY, 63-65; assoc prof biol, Marquette Univ, 66-68. *Concurrent Pos:* French Ministry Agr res fel, 55-57; master res, French Nat Agron Inst, 62-63; consult, Amicon Corp, 64-67; dir, Serum & Plasma Depts, Milwaukee Blood Ctr, 65-68; prin investr, USPHS res grant, 66-75; consult, Gen Elec Co, 67; mem consult comt electrophoresis & other chem separation processes in outer space, NASA, 71-81; exec ed, Preparative Biochem, 71-, Separation & Purification Methods, 72-90, ed, Immunol Commun, 82-84 & Immunol Invest, 85-; consult mem, Immunol Panel Diag Prod Adv Comt, Food & Drug Admin, 75-83; adj prof chem eng,

State Univ NY, Buffalo, 79- *Mem:* Am Chem Soc; Am Asn Immunologists; Electrophoresis Soc. *Res:* Membrane separation methods; precipitation in immunochemical, organic and inorganic systems; diffusion; sedimentation; physical surface properties of cells; mechanism of phagocytic engulfment; cell separation methods; van der Waals and polar interactions between cells and/ or polymers in liquids; opsonins; hydrophobic interactions; colloid and surface science. *Mailing Add:* Dept Microbiol State Univ NY Sch Med Sherman Hall Buffalo NY 14214. *Fax:* 716-829-2158

**VAN OSTENBURG, DONALD ORA,** SOLID STATE PHYSICS. *Current Pos:* prof, 70-87, chmn, 87-93, PROF, PHYSICS DEPT, DE PAUL UNIV, 93- *Personal Data:* b East Grand Rapids, Mich, July 19, 29; m 51, Betty J Roskemp; c Suzanne L & Donald M. *Educ:* Calvin Col, BS, 51; Mich State Univ, MS, 53, PhD(physics), 56. *Prof Exp:* Assoc physicist, Armour Res Found, Ill Inst Technol, 56-59; from asst physicist to assoc physicist, Argonne Nat Lab, 59-70. *Concurrent Pos:* Pres, Cent States Univ Inc, 81-82. *Mem:* Fel Am Phys Soc; fel Am Sci Affiliation. *Res:* Static electrification; electron paramagnetic resonance; lattice dynamics; magnetism; nuclear magnetic resonance; electronic structure of metals and alloys; semiconductor devices; biophysics; catalysts. *Mailing Add:* Dept Physics De Paul Univ 2219 N Kenmore Chicago IL 60614-3504. *Fax:* 773-325-7334; *E-Mail:* dvanoste@ wppost.depaul.edu

**VAN OVERSTRAETEN, ROGER JOSEPH,** MICRO-ELECTRONICS, SOLAR CELLS. *Current Pos:* asst prof, 65-68, PROF SOLID STATE PHYSICS & ELECTRONICS, KATHOLIEKE UNIV, LEUVEN, BELG, 68-; PRES, IMEC, 84- *Personal Data:* b Vlezenbeek, Belg, Dec 7, 37; m 60; c 2. *Educ:* Katholieke Univ, Leuven, cert nuclear eng, 60; Univ Stanford, PhD(phys electronics), 63. *Hon Degrees:* Dr, INPG, France, 87. *Prof Exp:* Res asst, Univ Stanford, 62-65. *Concurrent Pos:* Lectr, Iria, France, 71 & Univ Newcaster Tyne, UK, 73; vis prof, Univ Fla, 74, Stanford Univ, 79 & Cent Electronic Res Inst, India, 80; mem, bd dirs, Imec, Cobrain, EDC, Janssen Pharmaceut & Soltech, 84- *Mem:* Fel Inst Elec & Electronics Engrs; Am Phys Soc. *Res:* Physics and electronics of semiconductor devices related to integrated circuits, sensors and solar cells. *Mailing Add:* Imec Kapeldreef 75 Leuven B 3001 Belgium

**VAN PATTER, DOUGLAS MACPHERSON,** NUCLEAR PHYSICS. *Current Pos:* BARTOL PROF PHYSICS & BARTOL RES FOUND, UNIV DEL, 76- *Personal Data:* b Montreal, Que, July 4, 23; m 50; c Scott, Kenneth, Bruce & Laurie. *Educ:* Queen's Univ, Can, BSc, 45; Mass Inst Technol, PhD(physics), 49. *Prof Exp:* Jr physicist, Nat Res Coun Can, 45-46; asst physics, Mass Inst Technol, 46-49, res assoc, 49-52; res assoc, Univ Minn, 52, asst prof, 52-54; physicist, Bartol Res Found, Franklin Inst, 54-76. *Concurrent Pos:* Chmn subcomt nuclear constants, Nat Acad Sci-Nat Res Coun, 59-64; vis prof, Inst Nuclear Physics, Univ Frankfurt, 72. *Mem:* Fel Am Phys Soc; AAAS; Meteoritical Soc. *Res:* Nuclear reactions using electrostatic accelerators; proton microprobe; elemental compositions using induced x-rays of tektites and meteorites. *Mailing Add:* 97 Sproul Rd Springfield PA 19064

**VANPEE, MARCEL,** PHYSICAL CHEMISTRY. *Current Pos:* RETIRED. *Personal Data:* b Hasselt, Belg, Dec 4, 16; US citizen; m 48; c 3. *Educ:* Cath Univ Louvain, BS, MS & PhD(phys chem), 40, Agrege de l'Enseignement Superieur, 56. *Honors & Awards:* Awards, Prix Jean Stass, 40, Prix Louis Empain, Belg Acad Sci, 43 & Prix Frederic Swartz, 54. *Prof Exp:* Nat Res fel radio & photochem, Nat Found Sci Res, Belg, 40-45; head lab sci res, Nat Inst Mines, Belg, 46-56; prof physics, Univ Leopoldville, Congo, 56-57; supvry chemist, US Bur Mines, Pa, 57-60; sr scientist, Reaction Motor Div, Thiokol Chem Corp, 60-68; prof chem eng, Univ Mass, Amherst, 68-80. *Concurrent Pos:* Lectr & researcher, Cath Univ Louvain, 40-45; mem, Nat Found Sci Res, Belg, 40-; res fel, Univ Minn, Minneapolis, 48; staff physicist, Edsel B Ford Inst, Mich, 50. *Mem:* Combustion Inst; Am Inst Aeronaut & Astronaut. *Res:* Radiochemistry; photochemistry; kinetics of combustion reactions; cool flames; ignition; flame spectroscopy and structure; high energy fuel and oxidizers; rocket exhaust radiation; hypergolic ignition; atomic and chemiluminescent reactions; reentry observables. *Mailing Add:* RR 2 Amherst MA 01002

**VAN PELT, ARNOLD FRANCIS, JR,** ECOLOGY OF ANTS, ANT COLONY BEHAVIOR. *Current Pos:* prof biol, Greensboro Col, 63-80, chmn, Dept Sci & Math, 64-71 & 81-83, dir, Allied Health Progs, 75-89, chmn, Div Natural Sci & Math, 81-83, Moore prof biol, 81-88, EMER DISTINGUISHED MOORE PROF BIOL, GREENSBORO COL, 83- *Personal Data:* b Orange, NJ, Sept 24, 24; m 47, Gladys Smith; c Stephen & Susan. *Educ:* Swarthmore Col, BA, 45; Univ Fla, MS, 47, PhD(biol), 50. *Prof Exp:* Assoc prof biol, Appalachian State Teachers Col, 50-54; prof, Tusculum Col, 54-57, prof biol & chem, 57-63. *Concurrent Pos:* Sewell grant, Highlands Biol Sta, 53-54; res grants, 53-78; NSF grants, 55-56 & 62; consult, Univ Ga ecol team, Savannah River Plant, AEC, 60, Oak Ridge Nat Lab, Biol Div, 69-70, 73; mem, conf plant biochem, Inst Paper Chem, 61, conf molecular genetics, SW Ctr Advan Studies, 68; Piedmont Univ Ctr grants, 64-67, 71 & 72; Res Corp Brown-Hazen Fund grant, 65-67; mem radiation biol conf, Oak Ridge Inst Nuclear Studies, 65; courtesy appointment, Sch Med Technol, Bowman Gray Sch Med, Winston-Salem, NC, 66-, physician asst prog, 71-, Sch Radiol Technol, Moses H Cone Mem Hosp, Greensboro, NC, 68-, Sch Med Technol, 85- & Sch Med Technol, Forsyth Mem Hosp, Winston-Salem, NC, 72-; Savannah River Ecol Lab, Ecol of Ants, 74, 76-78; adj prof, continuing educ, Univ NC-Greensboro, 74; vis lectr radiation biol, Moses H Cone Mem Hosp, Greensboro, NC, 75 & 77; Burroughs-Wellcome grant, 79, 86-88; Southern Regional Educ Bd grant, 82; Greensboro Col grants, 82-88; grants, Off Resource Mgt, Big Bend Nat Park, Tex, 82-95, Nat Park Syst grant-in-aid, Tex A&M Univ, 90, Nat Park Bibliog Proj, 94-97. *Mem:* AAAS;

Sigma Xi; Entom Soc Am. *Res:* Ecology of mountain ants; mouse genetics; guinea pig leukemia; nest relocation in harvester ants; insect inventories. *Mailing Add:* 203 Howell Pl Greensboro NC 27455-1712. *Fax:* 910-545-1702; *E-Mail:* avanpelt@aol.com

**VAN PELT, RICHARD H,** METALLURGICAL ENGINEERING. *Current Pos:* RETIRED. *Personal Data:* b St Louis, Mo, Apr 11, 22. *Educ:* Univ Ill, BS, 43. *Prof Exp:* Mgr, Res Metall Div, Caterpillar Inc, 46-85. *Mem:* Fel Am Soc Metals Int. *Mailing Add:* 915 Birchwood Dr Washington IL 61571

**VAN PELT, RICHARD W(ARREN),** NUMERICAL CONTROL, SERVO SYSTEMS. *Current Pos:* adv engr, Tape Div, 78-, SR ADV ENGR STORAGE-TECH, STORAGE TECHNOL CORP. *Personal Data:* b Chicago, Ill, Dec 22, 33; c 3. *Educ:* Stanford Univ, BS, 55; Univ Ill, MS, 60; Case Inst Technol, PhD(mech eng), 65. *Prof Exp:* Sr engr, Systs Develop Div, IBM Corp, 65-78. *Mem:* Instrument Soc Am; Inst Elec & Electronics Engrs. *Res:* Numerical control, development of special purpose computers for process control and for real time control of fluid and electric servo systems; simulation and analysis of dynamics of electromechanical systems. *Mailing Add:* 665 Meadowbrook Boulder CO 80303

**VAN PELT, ROLLO WINSLOW, JR,** PATHOLOGY. *Current Pos:* CHIEF OF STAFF & PATHOLOGIST, ALASKA VET MED CLIN, 78- *Personal Data:* b Chicago, Ill, Dec 14, 29; m 54; c 2. *Educ:* Wash State Univ, BA, 54, DVM, 56; Mich State Univ, MS, 61, PhD(path), 65; Am Col Vet Pathologists, dipl, 65. *Prof Exp:* Vet, Rose City Vet Hosp, Ore, 56-57, Tigard Vet Hosp, 57 & Willamette Vet Hosp, 57-59; res asst arthrology, Mich State Univ, 59-60, res assoc, 60-62, Nat Inst Arthritis & Metab Dis fel, 62-64, spec fel, 64-65, from asst prof to assoc prof path, 65-70; vis assoc prof zoophysiol & path, Inst Arctic Biol, Univ Alaska, Fairbanks, 70-71, assoc prof zoophysiol & path, 71-78. *Concurrent Pos:* Upjohn Co grant-in-aid, 62-64; All Univ res grant, Mich State Univ, 63-65; Paul Harris fel, Rotary Found, Rotary Int, 85. *Mem:* Am Vet Med Asn; Am Col Vet Pathologists; Am Vet Radiol Soc; Am Soc Vet Clin Path; Sigma Xi; US & Can Acad Path; NY Acad Sci. *Res:* Hereditary and congenital abnormalities of the respiratory tract in Alaskan husky dogs; exhaustrion pneumonia syndrome in racing sled dogs. *Mailing Add:* Alaska Vet Med Clin 104 Kutter Rd Fairbanks AK 99701-3120

**VAN PELT, WESLEY RICHARD,** HEALTH PHYSICS, INDUSTRIAL HYGIENE. *Current Pos:* PRES & CONSULT, WESLEY R VAN PELT ASSOC, INC, 85- *Personal Data:* b Passaic, NJ, Oct 17, 43; m 65, Barbara Savarese; c Meredith. *Educ:* Rutgers Univ, New Brunswick, BA, 65, MS, 66; NY Univ, PhD(nuclear eng), 71; Am Bd Health Physics, cert, 73, Am Bd Indust Hyg, 76. *Prof Exp:* Asst res scientist aerosol physics, Med Ctr, NY Univ, 67-71; environ scientist, Environ Analysts, Inc, NY, 71-72; indust hygienist, Radiation Safety Off, Hoffmann-La Roche, Inc, 72-77, asst mgr safety & indust hyg, 77-80, mgr safety & indust hygiene, 80-82, corp safety dir, 82-85. *Concurrent Pos:* Consult, NJ Comn Radiation Protection, 76-77 & mem, NJ X-ray Technol Bd Examnrs, 78- & NJ Panel Sci Adv, 81-85; adj asst prof, Univ Med & Dent, Robert Wood Johnson Med Sch, 86-; vis prof, Rutgers Univ, 91- *Mem:* Sigma Xi; Health Physics Soc; Am Indust Hyg Asn; NY Acad Sci; Am Chem Soc. *Res:* Applied health physics; radiation protection program development; non-ionizing radiation protection; measurement and study of the natural ionizing radiation background; indoor air pollution; laboratory and industrial health and safety. *Mailing Add:* 773 Paramus Rd Paramus NJ 07652-1710. *Fax:* 201-445-6488

**VAN PILSUM, JOHN FRANKLIN,** BIOCHEMISTRY. *Current Pos:* from asst prof to prof, 54-92, EMER PROF BIOCHEM, MED SCH, UNIV MINN, MINNEAPOLIS, 92- *Personal Data:* b Prairie City, Iowa, Jan 28, 22; m 58, Shirley E Newsom; c John R, Patricia M, Barbara J, Mary A, Elizabeth J & William F. *Educ:* Univ Iowa, BS, 43, PhD, 49. *Prof Exp:* Instr biochem, Long Island Col Med, 49-51; asst prof, Univ Utah, 51-54. *Mem:* Am Soc Biol Chemists; Am Inst Nutrit. *Res:* Guanidinium compound metabolism; dietary and hormonal control of biosynthetic enzymes. *Mailing Add:* Dept Biochem 4-225 Millard Hall Univ Minn Col Med Sci Minneapolis MN 55455

**VAN POOLEN, LAMBERT JOHN,** MECHANICAL ENGINEERING DESIGN, PHILOSOPHY OF TECHNOLOGY. *Current Pos:* PROF ENG, CALVIN COL, 69- *Personal Data:* b Detroit, Mich, Apr 20, 39; m 62; c 2. *Educ:* Calvin Col, BS, 64; Ill Inst Technol, BSME, 64, MSME, 65, PhD(mech & aerospace eng), 69. *Concurrent Pos:* Res scientist, Nat Inst Stand & Technol; consult, Prince Corp, Holland, Mich. *Mem:* Am Soc Eng Educ; Soc Philos & Technol; Am Soc Mech Engrs; Sigma Xi. *Res:* Thermodynamics; heat transfer; initiator and foremost authority on the use of liquid volume fractions to predict critical density and temperature of pure fluids and their mixtures; thermodynamic properties of coexistence data. *Mailing Add:* Dept Eng Calvin Col Grand Rapids MI 49546. *E-Mail:* vpol@calvin.edu

**VAN POZNAK, ALAN,** ANESTHESIOLOGY, PHARMACOLOGY. *Current Pos:* Asst instr surg, Cornell Univ Med Col, 55-56, asst resident & resident anesthesiol, 56-58, instr surg, 58-61, from asst prof to assoc prof, 61-72, PROF ANESTHESIOL, CORNELL UNIV, 72- *Personal Data:* b Newark, NJ, Dec 30, 27; m 50, D Beatrice Lehmann; c Christina, Theodore, John & Catherine. *Educ:* Cornell Univ, AB, 48, MD, 52. *Concurrent Pos:* Res fel pharmacol, Cornell Univ, 62-64, from clin asst prof to clin assoc prof, 67-73, assoc prof, 73-74, prof, 74- *Mem:* AMA; Am Soc Anesthesiol; Asn Univ Anesthesiologists. *Res:* New inhalation anesthetics; neuromuscular effects of inhalation anesthetics. *Mailing Add:* 525 E 68th St New York NY 10021

**VAN PRAAG, HERMAN M,** biological psychiatry, for more information see previous edition

**VANPRAAGH, RICHARD,** PEDIATRIC CARDIOLOGY, PEDIATRIC CARDIAC PATHOLOGY. *Current Pos:* clin assoc path, Harvard Med Sch, 65-67, asst clin prof, 67-70, assoc prof, 70-73, PROF PATH, HARVARD MED SCH, 74- *Personal Data:* b Ont, Can, Apr 11, 30; m 62, Stella Zacharioudakis; c Andrew, Helen & Alexander. *Educ:* Univ Toronto, MD, 54. *Hon Degrees:* AM, Harvard Univ, 89. *Honors & Awards:* Morgani lectr, Univ Padova, Italy, 73; Haile Selassie lectr, Nat Heart Hosp, London, 73; Hammersmith Cardiac Surg lectr, London, 76; Ann Taran Man lectr, Sch Med, NY Univ, 79; Beth Raby Lectr, Children's Hosp, Montreal, 88; Jerome Liebman Lectr, Rainbow Babies' & Children's Hosp, Cleveland, 90. *Prof Exp:* Asst prof pediat, Sch Med, Northwestern Univ, 65. *Concurrent Pos:* Asst dir, Congenital Heart Dis Res & Training Ctr, Hektoen Inst Med Res, Chicago, 63-65; dir cardiac path & embryol & res assoc, Children's Hosp, 65-; vis prof pediat & cardiol, Univ Ore, 78; Pfizer vis lectr, Children's Mem Hosp, Chicago, 86, 87; vis prof, Children's Nat Med Ctr, Washington, DC, 90. *Mem:* Fel Am Col Cardiol; corresp mem Brit Cardiac Soc. *Res:* correlation of clinical, pathologic, embryologic and etiologic findings concerning congenital heart disease, in order to improve diagnostic accuracy and surgical success; description of newly recognized forms of congenital heart disease; new surgical operations; causes of heart disease in infants and children. *Mailing Add:* Children's Hosp 300 Longwood Ave Boston MA 02115. *Fax:* 617-731-0954

**VAN PUTTEN, JAMES D, JR,** INDUSTRIAL PROCESS CONTROL. *Current Pos:* assoc prof, 67-70, PROF PHYSICS, HOPE COL, 70-, CHMN DEPT, 75-86 & 90-. *Personal Data:* b Grand Rapids, Mich, Apr 14, 34; m 59; c 2. *Educ:* Hope Col, AB, 55; Univ Mich, AM, 57, PhD(physics), 60. *Prof Exp:* Instr physics, Univ Mich, 60-61; NATO fel, Europ Orgn Nuclear Res, Geneva, 61-62; asst prof, Calif Inst Technol, 62-67. *Concurrent Pos:* Consult, Electro-Optical Systs, 63-67, Teledyne Corp, 67-70, Donnelly Inc, 67-, White Westing House, 82- & Gen Motors, 85- *Mem:* AAAS; Am Phys Soc. *Res:* Bubble chambers; counter and spark chamber techniques; satellite borne space physics experiments; nuclear charge structure; use of microcomputers in process control; real time statistical process control. *Mailing Add:* Dept Physics Hope Col 137 E 12th St Holland MI 49423-3698

**VAN RAALTE, JOHN A,** RESEARCH ADMINISTRATION, ENGINEERING MANAGEMENT. *Current Pos:* STAFF MEM, THOMSON CONSUMER ELECTRONICS, 88- *Personal Data:* b Copenhagen, Denmark, Apr 10, 38; US Citizen; m 63, Andree V Greene; c Kirsten A & James E. *Educ:* Mass Inst Technol, SB & SM, 60, EE, 62, PhD(solid state physics, elec eng), 64. *Prof Exp:* Res asst, Lab Insulation Res, Mass Inst Technol, 60-64; mem tech staff, RCA Res Labs, 64-70, head displays & device concepts, 70-79, head video disc rec & playback res, 79-83, dir video disc syst res, 83-84, dir syst mat & process res, 84-86; dir, Mat & Process Technol Lab, David Sarnoff Res Ctr, 86-88. *Concurrent Pos:* Mgr CRT eng, Lancaster, Pa, 90-92; gen mgr, Electronic Optics Lab, Genlis, France, 92. *Mem:* Fel Inst Elec & Electronics Engrs; fel Soc Info Display (secy, 81-82, treas, 81-, vpres, 83-84, pres, 84-86); Sigma Xi. *Res:* Materials; dielectrics; electro-optic materials; lasers; displays; video disc; consumer electronics; cathode-ray tubes. *Mailing Add:* Thomson Tubes & Displays Ave Du General De Gaulle Genlis 21110 France. *E-Mail:* 100565.603@compuserve.com

**VAN REEN, ROBERT,** BIOCHEMISTRY. *Current Pos:* prof, 70-85, chmn dept, 70-83, EMER PROF FOOD SCI & HUMAN NUTRIT, UNIV HAWAII, HONOLULU, 85- *Personal Data:* b Paterson, NJ, June 12, 21. *Educ:* NJ State Teachers Col, Montclair, AB, 43; Rutgers Univ, PhD(biochem), 49. *Honors & Awards:* McLester Award, Asn Mil Surgeons of US, 59. *Prof Exp:* Assoc biochemist, Brookhaven Nat Lab, 49-51; res assoc, McCollum-Pratt Inst, Johns Hopkins Univ, 51-53, asst prof biol, 53-56; supv chemist & assoc head, Dent Div, Naval Med Res Inst, 56-61, head, Nutrit Biochem Div, 61-70. *Mem:* Am Dietetic Asn; Soc Nutrit Educ; Am Soc Biochem & Molecular Biol; Inst Food Technologists; Am Soc Nutrit Sci. *Res:* Mammalian and avian nutrition; requirements and functions of vitamins and trace elements; interrelationships between trace elements and enzyme systems; experimental dental caries; metabolism in calcified tissues; nutrition and urolithiasis. *Mailing Add:* Dept Food Sci & Human Nutrit Univ Hawaii-Manoa 1800 E-W Rd Honolulu HI 96822-2318

**VAN RENSBURG, WILLEM CORNELIUS JANSE,** APPLIED GEOLOGY. *Current Pos:* assoc dir, Bur Econ Geol, 79-81, PROF GEOL & PETROL ENG, UNIV TEX, 81- *Personal Data:* b SAfrica, Nov 28, 38; m 62, Jennifer D Line; c Kathryn, Patricia & Jillian. *Educ:* Univ Pretoria, BSc, 61, MSc, 63; Univ Wis, PhD(geol), 65. *Prof Exp:* Sr geologist, SAfrica Geol Surv, 60-67; dep dir, SAfrica Nat Dept Planning, 67-73; head, Econ & Corting Div, Nat Inst Metall, 73-75; tech dir, SAfrica Minerals Bur, 79-81. *Concurrent Pos:* Comnr, Pres Comn Conserv SAfrica's Coal Resources, 70-75; B P prof, Rand Afrikaans Univ, 76-78; dir, Tex Mining & Mineral Resources Res Inst & Coal Res Consortium, Tex Univ, 79-81. *Mem:* Soc Econ Geologists; SAfrican Coal Processing Soc; Soc Petrol Engrs; Mineral Econs & Mgt Soc. *Res:* Strategic minerals; evaluation of coal resources; international coal trade; energy economics. *Mailing Add:* 6010 Sierra Arbor Ct Austin TX 78759. *Fax:* 512-918-0362

**VAN REUTH, EDWARD C,** CERAMICS ENGINEERING. *Current Pos:* PRES, TECHNOL STRATEGIES, INC, 84- *Educ:* Va Polytechnic Inst & State Univ, BS, MS; Univ Ill, PhD. *Honors & Awards:* George Kimball Burgess Award; Tech Achievement Award, Am Soc Mech Engrs; Distinguished Pioneer Award, Am Soc Mfg Engrs. *Prof Exp:* Asst prof mat eng, Va Polytechnic Inst & State Univ, 57-60; res asst, Univ Ill, 60-63; sr res scientist, David Taylor Res Lab, 63-66; res, Kammerlingh Onnes Lab, Univ Leiden, Neth, 66-67; head, Composites & Speciality Mat Br, David Taylor Res Lab, Annapolis, Md, 67-71, asst to dir, lab, & dir superconductivity, 71-72; staff specialist metall & ceramic sci, Defense Advan Res Proj Agency, 72-79, dir, Mat Sci Div, 79-83. *Concurrent Pos:* Partic adv group, Aeronaut Res & Develop, NATO; invited lectr, Switz, Ger, Gt Brit, France, Norway, Neth, Soviet Union & US; prof lectr, George Washington Univ. *Mem:* Fel Am Soc Metals Int. *Res:* Developing strategy for new or existing technologies, primarily in the areas of technology assessment; marketing strategies; system integration; advanced materials; superconductivity; advanced engines; chemical and metallurgical processing. *Mailing Add:* 204 Shipping Creek Stevensville MD 21666

**VAN RHEENEN, VERLAN H,** ORGANIC CHEMICAL PROCESS RESEARCH & DEVELOPMENT, MANAGEMENT. *Current Pos:* CONSULT, 84- *Personal Data:* b Oskaloosa, Iowa, Feb 15, 39; m 62; c 2. *Educ:* Cent Col, Iowa, BA, 61; Univ Wis, PhD(org chem), 66. *Prof Exp:* Distinguished scientist, Upjohn Co, 66-84. *Mem:* Am Chem Soc; Sigma Xi. *Res:* Total synthesis of natural products; new synthetic methods; steroid chemistry; prostaglandin synthesis. *Mailing Add:* 2112 Vanderbilt Rd Kalamazoo MI 49002-6065

**VAN RIJ, WILLEM IDANIEL,** COMPUTER SCIENCES, PLASMA PHYSICS. *Current Pos:* COMPUT PHYSICIST, OAK RIDGE NAT LAB, 74- *Personal Data:* b Brielle, Neth, Apr 19, 42; US citizen; m 68; c 2. *Educ:* Univ Auckland, BS, 64, MS, 66; Fla State Univ, PhD(physics), 70. *Prof Exp:* Res assoc theoret nuclear physics, Brookhaven Nat Lab, 70-72 & Univ Wash, 72-74. *Mem:* Am Phys Soc. *Res:* Computer simulations of plasmas for controlled thermonuclear research. *Mailing Add:* 7820 Castlecomb Rd Powell TN 37849

**VAN RIPER, CHARLES, III,** ORNITHOLOGY, EPIDEMIOLOGY, CONSERVATION BIOLOGY. *Current Pos:* unit leader, Coop Nat Park Resources Studies Unit, Davis, Calif, 79-87, asst adj prof, Dept Zool, 80-85, res scientist, Nat Park Serv, 87-90, UNIT LEADER, COOP NAT PARK RESOURCES STUDIES UNIT, 90-; PROF, NORTHERN ARIZ UNIV, FLAGSTAFF, 90- *Personal Data:* b Mahopac, NY, Sept 24, 43; m 77; c Charles IV, Jacqueline E, Kimberly A & Carenn J. *Educ:* Colo State Univ, BS, 66, MEd, 67; Univ Hawaii, PhD(zool), 78. *Honors & Awards:* Spec Merit Award, US Fish Wildlife Serv. *Prof Exp:* Instr, Mahopac High Sch, NY, 67-68, Hawaii Prep Acad, Kamuela, Hawaii, 68-72; teaching asst, Dept Zool, Univ Hawaii, Honolulu, 72-74, res asst, 74-75, asst researcher, 77-79. *Concurrent Pos:* Numerous res grants & fels, US Dept Interior, Nat Park Serv & Nat Park Res, 72-; Palila recovery team, US Fish & Wildlife Serv, 74, Peregrine Falcon recovery team Western US, 82, asst ed, J Wildlife Dis, 86, US Dept Interior Pub Task Force, 87, Wildlife biologist, Dept Interior, US Fish Wildlife Serv. *Mem:* Am Ornithologists Union; Ecol Soc Am; Soc Am Naturalists; Wildlife Dis Asn; hon mem Cooper Ornith Soc; Wilson Soc. *Res:* Seasonal change in bird communities of the chaparal and blue-oak woodlands in Central California and Colorado River drainage in Arizona; Mill and Deer Creek drainages; evaluation of wildlife habitat relationships database for predicting bird community composition in Central California; avian host/parasite interactions; over 80 publications of ornithological subjects. *Mailing Add:* PO Box 5614 Northern Ariz Univ Flagstaff AZ 86011-5614. *Fax:* 602-556-7500; *E-Mail:* cvr@nbs.nau.edu

**VAN RIPER, GORDON EVERETT,** AGRONOMY. *Current Pos:* RETIRED. *Personal Data:* b Flat Rock, Mich, Dec 7, 17; m 43, 75; c 1. *Educ:* Mich State Univ, BS, 55; Univ Wis, MS, 57, PhD(agron), 58. *Prof Exp:* From asst prof to assoc prof agron, Univ Nebr, 58-64; mgr, Dept Agron, Deere & Co, 64-69, mgr, Dept Res Coord, 69-73; pres, Jay Dee Equip Inc, 73-81; consult, 81-88. *Concurrent Pos:* Vpres, Agr Res Inst, 71-72; pres, Am Forage & Grassland Coun, 72. *Mem:* Am Soc Agron; Crop Sci Soc Am. *Res:* Crop physiology. *Mailing Add:* 28 Pine Tree Rd Kewanee IL 61443

**VANRIPER, KENNETH ALAN,** ASTROPHYSICS, PHYSICS. *Current Pos:* SCIENTIST, WHITE ROCK SCI, 96- *Personal Data:* b New Brunswick, NJ, Feb 7, 49. *Educ:* Cornell Univ, AB, 70; Univ Pa, PhD(physics), 76. *Prof Exp:* Res assoc, Enrico Fermi Inst, Univ Chicago, 76-78; res assoc astrophys, Dept Physics, Univ Ill, Urbana, 78-81; with Los Alamos Nat Lab, 81-95. *Mem:* Am Phys Soc; Am Astron Soc; Sigma Xi. *Res:* Stellar collapse and explosion; supernovae; neutrino astrophysics; neutron star formation and evolution; dense, hot matter. *Mailing Add:* PO Box 4729 Los Alamos NM 87544. *E-Mail:* kvr@rtgg.com

**VAN ROGGEN, AREND,** ELECTRODYNAMICS, COMPUTER SCIENCE. *Current Pos:* CONSULT, 82- *Personal Data:* b Nijmegen, Neth, Jan 2, 28; m 52; c 1. *Educ:* State Univ Leiden, Drs(phys chem), 53; Duke Univ, PhD(physics), 56. *Prof Exp:* Asst, Lab Phys Chem, State Univ Leiden, 48-54, sci asst, 56; asst physics, Duke Univ, 54-56; from res physicist to sr res physicist, E I du Pont de Nemours & Co, Inc, 56-72, sr res specialist, 72-75, res assoc, 75-81. *Concurrent Pos:* Ed, Inst Elec & Electronics Engrs Elec Insulation Soc Trans Elec Insulation, 77-; secy, Conf Elec Insulation & Dielec Phenomena, 80-81, vchmn-treas, 82-83 & chmn, 84-85; adj prof, molecular electronics, Cath Univ, 90- *Mem:* Am Phys Soc; Am Soc Testing & Mat; fel Inst Elec & Electronics Engrs; Inst Elec & Electronics Engrs Dielectrics & Elec Insulation Soc; NY Acad Sci. *Res:* Electronic and magnetic structure of matter; paramagnetic resonance; dielectrics; physics instrumentation; interaction of electric fields and materials; computational aspects of above. *Mailing Add:* Orchard Lane 501 Rd 2 Kennett Square PA 19348

**VAN ROOD, JOHANNES J,** INTERNAL MEDICINE. *Current Pos:* prof, 69-91, EMER PROF INTERNAL MED, LEIDEN UNIV, 91- *Personal Data:* b Hague, Neth, Apr 7, 26; m, Sacha B van Serooskerken; c Yanda, Peter & Tinka. *Educ:* PhD, 62. *Hon Degrees:* Dr, Univ Santiago, 68, Univ L'Aquila, 80, Univ Torino, 80, Univ Maastricht, 81, Univ Claude Bernard Lyon, 82, Cath Univ Louvain, 84 & 85 & Univ Essen, 88. *Honors & Awards:* John G Gibson Lectr, Columbia Univ, 67; Dutch Kidney Found Prize, 73; Karl Landsteiner Mem Award, 77; Robert Kock Medaille, 77; Wolf Prize, 78; Dutch Fedn Med Res Socs, 80; Franz-Oehlecker Medaille, Ger Soc Blood Transfusion & Immunohemat, 84; Amsterdam Prize Med, Royal Dutch Acad Sci, 90; Croonian Lectr, Royal Col Physicians, 90; Rose Payne Award, 91; Max Geldens Prize, 91. *Concurrent Pos:* Lectr internal med, 65-69; founder & pres, Eurotransplant Found, 67 & Europ Found Immunogenetics, 85-90; founder, Europdonor Found, 72; co-founder & chmn, Leiden Inst Immunol, 86-91; assoc ed, Bone Marrow Transplantation. *Mem:* Foreign assoc Nat Acad Sci; hon mem Am Asn Immunologists; hon mem Scand Soc Immunol; corresp mem Royal Acad Med Belg; Royal Dutch Acad Sci. *Res:* Genetics of histocompatibility antigens; organ and bone marrow transplantation; genetic factors in disease; blood banking; clinical hematology; clinical immunology; author of numerous articles. *Mailing Add:* Dept Immunohaemat & Blood Bank Bldg 1 E3-Q Univ Hosp Rijnsburgerweg 10 Leiden 2333 AA Netherlands. *Fax:* 31-71-5210457

**VAN ROOSBROECK, WILLY WERNER,** semiconductors; deceased, see previous edition for last biography

**VAN ROSSUM, GEORGE DONALD VICTOR,** CELL PHYSIOLOGY, BIOCHEMICAL PHARMACOLOGY. *Current Pos:* actg chmn dept, 73-75, PROF PHARMACOL, SCH MED, TEMPLE UNIV, 69- *Personal Data:* b London, Eng, Dec 13, 31; m 59; c 4. *Educ:* Oxford Univ, MA, 59, DPhil(biochem), 60. *Prof Exp:* NATO fel physiol chem, Univ Amsterdam, 60-62; NIH fel, Johnson Res Found, Univ Pa, 62-63, res assoc phys biochem, Sch Med, 63-64; reader biochem, Christian Med Col, Vellore, India, 65-67; vis asst prof phys biochem, Johnson Res Found, Sch Med, Univ Pa, 67-69. *Concurrent Pos:* NATO vis prof, Inst Gen Path, Cath Univ, Rome, 71; contract prof, Univ Rome, 85-86. *Mem:* Brit Biochem Soc; Am Soc Biol Chemists; Am Soc Pharmacol & Exp Therapeut; NY Acad Sci. *Res:* Ion and water transport; tissue electrolytes in cancer; control of energy metabolism; cell toxicity of lead. *Mailing Add:* 1085 Baus Rd East Greenville PA 18041

**VAN RYZIN, MARTINA,** HISTORY OF SCIENCE, MATHEMATICS. *Current Pos:* Head, Dept Math, 57-70, from instr to assoc prof, 60-69, PROF MATH, SILVER LAKE COL, 69-, ACAD DEAN, 70-, CHMN, DEPT MATH & COMPUT SCI. *Personal Data:* b Appleton, Wis, June 10, 23. *Educ:* Silver Lake Col, Wis, BA, 46; Marquette Univ, MS, 56; Univ Wis, PhD(hist of sci), 60. *Mem:* Math Asn Am; Hist Sci Soc. *Res:* History of mathematics, especially Medieval period; Arabic-Latin tradition of Euclid's elements in the 12th century. *Mailing Add:* Dept Introd Comput & Prog Silver Lake Col 2406 S Alverno Rd Manitowoc WI 54220-9319

**VAN SAMBEEK, JEROME WILLIAM,** MICROPROPAGATION & SAVANNA RESTORATION. *Current Pos:* RES PLANT PHYSIOLOGIST, NORTH CENTRAL FOREST EXP STA, MO, 97-. *Personal Data:* b Milbank, SDak, Aug 1, 47; m 72; c 5. *Educ:* SDak State Univ, BS, 69; Wash Univ, PhD(plant physiol), 75. *Honors & Awards:* Black Walnut Achievement Award, 88. *Prof Exp:* Fel plant path, Univ Mo, 75; res plant physiologist, Southern Forest Exp Sta, La, 75-79; res plant physiologist, North Cent Forest Exp Sta, ILL, 79-97, proj leader physiol, Genetics & Processing Cent Hardwoods, 89-96. *Concurrent Pos:* Adj asst prof, Southern Ill Univ, 80-; ed, Walnut Coun Bull, 84-88, Walnut Coun, 90-91. *Mem:* Walnut Coun; Am Soc Hort Sci; Northern Nat Growers Asn; Asn Temperate Agroforestry. *Res:* Physiological research on micropropagation, seedling establishment, ground cover management and fruiting of black walnut and the other fine hardwoods; role of legume plants in savanna restoration. *Mailing Add:* N Cent Forest Exp Sta, 1-26 Agr Bldg Univ Miss Columbia MO 65211-0001. *E-Mail:* jwrs@siu.edu

**VAN SANT, JAMES HURLEY, JR,** mechanical engineering, for more information see previous edition

**VAN SAUN, WILLIAM ARTHUR,** ORGANIC CHEMISTRY, PESTICIDE CHEMISTRY. *Current Pos:* res chemist, FMC Corp, 75-79, sr res chemist, 79-80, mgr org synthesis, 80-85, mgr biol eval, 85-87, dir, biol res, 87-91, DIR DISCOVERY RES, AGR PRODS GROUP, FMC CORP, 91- *Personal Data:* b Ashland, Pa, Dec 23, 46; m 69, Nancy L Kiefer; c Pieter, Robert & Alan. *Educ:* Ursinus Col, BS, 68; Villanova Univ, PhD(chem), 75. *Prof Exp:* Chemist med chem, Merck, Sharp & Dohme Res Labs, 68-72. *Concurrent Pos:* Adj asst prof, Mercer Co Community Col, 78-; vis lectr org chem, Rider Col, 79. *Mem:* Am Chem Soc; AAAS; Soc Chem Indust. *Res:* Organic synthesis, pesticides, quantitative structure-activity relationships; biological testing. *Mailing Add:* FMC Agr Prods Group PO Box 8 Princeton NJ 08543. *Fax:* 609-951-3330; *E-Mail:* william__vansalln@fmc.com

**VAN SCHILFGAARDE, JAN,** SOILS & SOIL SCIENCE. *Current Pos:* chief water mgt engr, Soil & Water Conserv Div, Agr Res Serv, 64-67, assoc dir, 67-71, dir, 71-72, dir, US Salinity Lab, USDA, 72-84, dir Mountain States Area, 84-87, assoc dir, Northern Plains Area, 87-91, assoc dep admin, natural resources, 91-96, DIR, PAC W AREA, AGR RES SERV, 96- *Personal Data:* b The Hague, Neth, Feb 7, 29; nat US; m 51, Roberta J Hansen; c Paul, Mark & Craig. *Educ:* Iowa State Col, BS, 49, MS, 50, PhD(agr eng, soil physics), 54. *Honors & Awards:* John Deere Medal, Am Soc Agr Engrs, 77; Royce J Tipton Award, Am Soc Civil Engr, 86. *Prof Exp:* Instr & assoc agr eng, Iowa State Col, 49-54; from asst prof to prof agr eng, NC State Col, 54-64. *Concurrent Pos:* Vis prof, Ohio State Univ, 62; adj prof soils, Univ Calif, Riverside, 74-84. *Mem:* Nat Acad Eng; hon mem Am Soc Civil Engrs; Soil Sci Soc Am; Soil Conserv Soc Am; Am Soc Agr Engrs. *Res:* Management of water for crop production, especially by agricultural drainage. *Mailing Add:* Agr & Res Serv Pre West Area 800 Buchanan St Albany CA 94710-1105

**VAN SCHMUS, WILLIAM RANDALL,** GEOCHRONOLOGY, PRECAMBRIAN GEOLOGY. *Current Pos:* From asst prof to assoc prof, 67-75, PROF GEOL, UNIV KANS, 75- *Personal Data:* b Aurora, Ill, Oct 4, 38; m 61; c 3. *Educ:* Calif Inst Technol, BS, 60; Univ Calif, Los Angeles, PhD(geol), 64. *Concurrent Pos:* Mem adv panels, NASA, NSF & Nat Acad Sci. *Mem:* Am Geophys Union; Geochem Soc; Meteoritical Soc; Geol Soc Am. *Res:* Geochronology and geochemistry of Precambrian continental crust. *Mailing Add:* Dept Geol Univ Kans Lawrence KS 66045

**VAN SCIVER, STEVEN W,** CRYOGENICS, HEAT TRANSFER. *Current Pos:* DISTINGUISHED RES PROF, MECHANICAL ENG, FLA STATE UNIV, 91- *Personal Data:* b Philadelphia, Pa, Mar 13, 48; m 69; c 2. *Educ:* Lehigh Univ, BS, 70; Univ Wash, MS, 72, PhD(physics), 76. *Prof Exp:* Proj assoc superconductivity, Univ Wis-Madison, 76-77, asst scientist, 77-79, from asst prof to assoc prof nuclear eng, 79-91. *Concurrent Pos:* Consult, Tex Accelerator Ctr, 80- *Mem:* Am Phys Soc; Inst Elec & Electronics Engrs. *Res:* Cryogenics; heat transfer and transport in superfluid helium; low temperature properties of materials; design of superconducting magnets for fusion and energy storage. *Mailing Add:* NHMFL Fla State Univ 1800 E Paul Dirac Dr Tallahassee FL 32306. *Fax:* 850-644-5038

**VAN SCOTT, EUGENE JOSEPH,** DERMATOLOGY. *Current Pos:* PROF DERMAT, HEALTH SCI CTR, TEMPLE UNIV, 68-; CLIN PROF, HAHNEMANN, 89- *Personal Data:* b Macedon, NY, May 27, 22; m 48; c 3. *Educ:* Univ Chicago, BS, 45, MD, 48. *Honors & Awards:* Taub Int Mem Award, 64; Clarke White Award, 65; Albert Lasker Award, 72; Stephen Rothman Award, Soc Invest Dermat, 75; Lila Gruber Cancer Res Award, Am Acad Dermat, 80; Howard Fox lectr, NY Acad Med, 81. *Prof Exp:* Intern, Millard Fillmore Hosp, Buffalo, NY, 48-49; resident physician dermat, Univ Chicago, 49-52; assoc, Univ Pa, 52-53; chief, Dermat Br, Nat Cancer Inst, 53-68, sci dir, Gen Labs & Clins, 66-68. *Concurrent Pos:* Assoc dir, Skin & Cancer Hosp, Philadelphia, 68-89. *Mem:* Hon mem Can Dermat Asn; Soc Invest Dermat; Am Dermat Asn; Am Asn Cancer Res; Am Soc Clin Invest; Am Acad Dermat. *Res:* Biology and physiology of epithelial growth; differentiation and neoplasia; pathogenesis of psoriasis; biology; immunologic aspects and clinical management of cutaneous lymphomas; dermatopharmacology. *Mailing Add:* Van Scott Assoc 3 Hidden Lane Abington PA 19001-4603

**VANSELOW, CLARENCE HUGO,** PHYSICAL CHEMISTRY. *Current Pos:* ASSOC PROF CHEM, UNIV NC, GREENSBORO, 64- *Personal Data:* b Syracuse, NY, Sept 30, 28; m 51; c 7. *Educ:* Syracuse Univ, BS, 50, MS, 51, PhD, 58. *Prof Exp:* Instr chem, Colgate Univ, 55-56; prof, Thiel Col, 56-64. *Mem:* Am Chem Soc. *Res:* Gas phase radiation chemistry; kinetic theory of precipitation processes. *Mailing Add:* 2416 Springwood Dr Greensboro NC 27403

**VANSELOW, NEAL A,** INTERNAL MEDICINE, ALLERGY & IMMUNOLOGY. *Current Pos:* chancellor, 89-94, PROF INTERNAL MED, MED CTR, TULANE UNIV, 89-, ADJ PROF HEALTH SYSTS MGT, 94- *Personal Data:* b Milwaukee, Wis, Mar 18, 32; m 58, Mary E McKenzie; c Julie & Richard. *Educ:* Univ Mich, AB, 54, MD, 58, MS, 63; Am Bd Internal Med, dipl, 65, cert, 68; Am Bd Allergy & Immunol, dipl, 72. *Prof Exp:* From instr to assoc prof internal med, Univ Mich Med Sch, Ann Arbor, 63-74, from assoc prof to prof postgrad med, 67-74, asst to chmn, Dept Postgrad Med, 68-71, actg chmn, 71-72, chmn, Dept Postgrad Med & Health Professions Educ, 72-74; prof internal med & dean, Col Med, Univ Ariz, 74-77; prof internal med & vpres, Univ Nebr, 77-82, chancellor, Med Ctr, 77-82; vpres health sci & prof internal med, Univ Minn, 82-89. *Concurrent Pos:* Staff physician, Univ Hosp, Ann Arbor, Mich, 63-74, Tucson, Ariz, 74-77, Univ Nebr Hosp, Omaha, 77-82, Univ Minn Hosp & Clin, 83-89, Tulane Univ Hosp & Clin, New Orleans, La, 90-; consult, Vet Admin Hosp, Ann Arbor, Mich, 65-74; surv team mem, Continuing Med Educ Accreditation Prog, AMA & Liaison Comt for Continuing Med Educ, 68-80; mem, Task Force Continuing Med Educ, Asn Am Med Cols, 75-76, Mgt Educ Network Adv Comt, 76-78, Task Force Minority Student Opportunities in Med, 76-78; mem, Adv Comt Governance Study, Consortium for Study of Univ Hosps, 81-82; mem, Nat Adv Panel, Essentials of Univ Educ for Nursing Proj, Am Asn Cols Nursing, 85-86; chairperson, Coun Grad Med Educ, US Dept Health & Human Serv, 86-91; chmn bd dirs, Asn Acad Health Ctrs, 87-88; mem, Comt to Study Strategies for Supporting Grad Med Educ in Primary Care, Inst Med-Nat Acad Sci, 89, mem, Comt Future Dent Educ, 92-94, chair, Comt Future Primary Care, 94-96, co-chair, Comt US Physician Supply, 95; mem, Mkt Mgt Gov Comt, Univ Hosp Consortium, 93-94. *Mem:* Inst Med-Nat Acad Sci; fel Am Col Physicians; Sigma Xi; fel Am Col Physician Execs; Soc Med Adminrs; AMA; fel Am Acad Allergy. *Res:* Internal medicine; health policy; author of numerous publications and several chapters in books; health manpower and workforce issues. *Mailing Add:* Tulane Univ Med Ctr 1430 Tulane Ave New Orleans LA 70112

**VANSELOW, RALF W,** PHYSICAL CHEMISTRY, SURFACE CHEMISTRY. *Current Pos:* from asst prof to assoc prof chem, Univ Wis-Milwaukee, 68-80, dir, Lab Surface Studies, 76-78, chmn dept, 78-81, & 93-96, PROF, UNIV WIS-MILWAUKEE, 80- *Personal Data:* b Berlin, Ger,

July 12, 31; m 61. *Educ:* Tech Univ Berlin, BS, 57, Dipl Ing, 62, Dr Ing, 66. *Prof Exp:* Res asst field emission micros, Fritz Haber Inst, Max Planck Soc, 52-66, res assoc, 66-68. *Mem:* Ger Chem Soc; Am Chem Soc; Am Vacuum Soc. *Res:* Studies of metal surfaces by means of field electron and field ion microscopy; adsorption; surface migration; epitaxial growth. *Mailing Add:* Dept Chem Univ Wis Milwaukee WI 53201. *Fax:* 414-229-5530; *E-Mail:* chemdept@alchemy.chem.uwm.edu

**VAN SICKLE, DALE ELBERT,** PHYSICAL ORGANIC CHEMISTRY. *Current Pos:* PRIN RES CHEMIST, EASTMAN CHEM CO, 69- *Personal Data:* b Ft Collins, Colo, Oct 8, 32; wid; c Craig E & Kent R. *Educ:* Colo State Univ, BS, 54; Univ Utah, MS, 56; Univ Calif, PhD, 59. *Prof Exp:* Asst chem, Univ Utah, 54-55 & Univ Calif, 56-59; org chemist, Stanford Res Inst, 59-69. *Mem:* AAAS; Am Chem Soc; Sigma Xi. *Res:* Mechanisms and kinetics of reactions; oxidation of hydrocarbons; free radical reactions; kinetics of esterification and ester hydrolysis. *Mailing Add:* 2113 Sheffield St Kingsport TN 37660. *Fax:* 423-229-4458

**VAN SICKLE, DAVID C,** HISTOLOGY, IMPLANT BIOCOMPATIBILITY. *Current Pos:* from instr to assoc prof, 61-75, head, Dept Anat, 82-94, PROF HISTOL & EMBRYOL, PURDUE UNIV, WEST LAFAYETTE, 75- *Personal Data:* b Des Moines, Iowa, Jan 9, 34; m 56, Aneta Smid. *Educ:* Iowa State Univ, DVM, 57; Purdue Univ, PhD(develop anat), 66. *Prof Exp:* Gen pract, Ill, 57-58 & 60-61. *Concurrent Pos:* Morris Animal Found fel, 64-66; adj prof anat, Sch Med, Ind Univ, 75-; pres, Confr Res Workers Animal Dis, 81; mem, Col USAFR, 77-82; adj prof grad studies, Wright State Univ, Ohio, 81- *Mem:* Sigma Xi; Am Asn Anat; Orthopedic Res Soc. *Res:* Osteogenesis and abnormalities associated with errors in osteogenesis; orthopedic pathobiology in arthritis, hip dysplasia and osteochondritis; fracture healing and effect of growth factors on bone and cartilage; biocompatibility of various types of implants; effects of quinvlones on articulations. *Mailing Add:* Dept Biomed Sci Purdue Univ West Lafayette IN 47907. *Fax:* 765-494-0733; *E-Mail:* sae@vet.vet.purdue.edu

**VAN SICLEN, CLINTON DEWITT,** CONDENSED MATTER PHYSICS, MATERIALS PHYSICS. *Current Pos:* LOCKHEED MARTIN IDAHO TECHNOL CO, 94-, CONSULT SCIENTIST, 96- *Personal Data:* b Houston, Tex, Nov 16, 53; m 78, Virginia Stout; c DeWitt & Arthur. *Educ:* Vanderbilt Univ, BA(physics) & BA(math), 75; Johns Hopkins Univ, MA, 79, PhD(physics), 82. *Prof Exp:* Postdoctoral fel, Dept Physics, Johns Hopkins Univ, 82-84; res physicist, Physics Group, EG&G Idaho, 84-94. *Concurrent Pos:* Vis scientist, Comput Mat Sci Prog, Sandia Nat Labs, 87-88. *Mem:* Sigma Xi; Am Phys Soc; Minerals, Metals & Mat Soc. *Res:* Dynamics of defects in materials; atom diffusion and clustering on metal surfaces; point defect interactions in solids; mechanisms for inclusion growth and diffusion in solids; interface dynamics during rapid solidification. *Mailing Add:* 3230 Tipperary Lane Idaho Falls ID 83404. *Fax:* 208-526-2814; *E-Mail:* cvs@inel.gov

**VAN SICLEN, DEWITT CLINTON,** TECTONICS. *Current Pos:* RETIRED. *Personal Data:* b Carlisle, Pa, Oct 25, 18; m 49; c Mary C, Clinton D, Sally J, & Henry K. *Educ:* Princeton Univ, AB, 40, MA, 47, PhD(geol), 51; Univ Ill, MS, 41. *Honors & Awards:* Cheney Sci Award, Am Asn Petrol Geologists, 88. *Prof Exp:* Jr geologist, Peoples Natural Gas Co, Pa, 41-42 & 46; field geologist, Drilling & Explor Co Inc, 47-50; exec officer, Off Sci Res, US Dept Air Force, 51-52; res geologist, Pan-Am Prod Co, 52-56; sr geologist, Pan-Am Petrol Corp, 56-59; from assoc prof to prof, Univ Houston, 59-82, chmn dept, 60-67, consult geologist, 66-82. *Concurrent Pos:* Consult geologist, 66- *Mem:* Am Asn Petrol Geologists; Nat Asn Geol Teachers; Am Inst Prof Geologists; Soc Petrol Engrs; Asn Eng Geologists; Geol Soc Am. *Res:* Behavior of subsurface fluids; petroleum migration and entrapment; surficial geology and active faults of Texas-Louisiana coastal plain; tectonics of Gulf of Mexico and surrounding regions. *Mailing Add:* 4909 Bellaire Blvd Bellaire TX 77401-4422

**VAN SLUYTERS, RICHARD CHARLES,** VISUAL NEUROBIOLOGY. *Current Pos:* PROF OPTOM VISION SCI, SCH OPTOM, UNIV CALIF, BERKELEY, 75-, PROF, OPTOM VISION SCI, 88- *Personal Data:* b Chicago, Ill, June 12, 45. *Educ:* Ill Col Optom, BS, 67, OD, 68; Ind Univ, Bloomington, PhD(physiol optics), 72. *Prof Exp:* Postdoctorial fel, Physiol Lab, Cambridge Univ, UK. *Concurrent Pos:* Chair, Animal Care & Use Comp, 86-; Nat Res Ctr, Inst Lab Animal Resources Coun, 92; optom fac chair, 92-94; fac asst vchancellor res, 94- *Mem:* Soc Neurosci; AAAS; Asn Res Vision & Ophthal; fel Am Acad Optom; Int Brain Res Org; World Fed Neuroscientists. *Res:* Neurobiology of developing mammalian visual systems. *Mailing Add:* Sch Optom Univ Calif Berkeley CA 94720-2020. *Fax:* 510-643-5109; *E-Mail:* rcvs@violet.berkeley.edu

**VAN SLYKE, RICHARD M,** OPERATIONS RESEARCH. *Current Pos:* dir, Telecommun Ctr, 83-88, PROF, POLYTECH UNIV, 88- *Personal Data:* b Manila, Philippines, Aug 17, 37; US citizen; m 69, Irene van Veen. *Educ:* Stanford Univ, BS, 59; Univ Calif, Berkeley, PhD(opers res), 65. *Prof Exp:* Asst prof elec & indust eng, Univ Calif, Berkeley, 65-69; vpres, Network Anal Corp, 69-80; prof elec eng & comput sci, Stevens Inst Technol, 80-83. *Concurrent Pos:* Consult. *Mem:* Soc Indust & Appl Math; Opers Res Soc Am; Asn Comput Math; Inst Elec & Electronics Engrs. *Res:* Mathematical techniques for optimization, especially for information network design and analysis. *Mailing Add:* Polytech Univ 6 Metrotech Ctr Brooklyn NY 11201. *E-Mail:* rvslyke@prism.poly.edu

**VANSOEST, PETER JOHN,** ANIMAL NUTRITION. *Current Pos:* assoc prof animal nutrit, 68-73, PROF ANIMAL NUTRIT, CORNELL UNIV, 73- *Personal Data:* b Seattle, Wash, June 30, 29; m 59; c 3. *Educ:* Wash State Univ, BS, 51, MS, 52; Univ Wis, PhD(nutrit), 55. *Honors & Awards:* Am Feed Mfrs Award, 67; Hoblitzelle Nat Award Agr, 68. *Prof Exp:* Biochemist, Agr Res Serv, USDA, 57-68. *Mem:* AAAS; Am Dairy Sci Asn; Am Soc Animal Sci; Asn Off Anal Chem. *Res:* Ruminant digestion and metabolism; chemistry of fibrous feedstuffs and methods of analysis; forage chemistry. *Mailing Add:* Dept Animal Sci Cornell Univ 149 Morrison Hall Ithaca NY 14853-4801. *Fax:* 607-255-9829

**VANSPEYBROECK, LEON PAUL,** X-RAY ASTRONOMY. *Current Pos:* STAFF SCIENTIST, CTR ASTROPHYS, 74- *Personal Data:* b Wichita, Kans, Aug 27, 35; m 59, Erin Harrington; c Elaine (Carmichael), David & Alexander. *Educ:* Mass Inst Technol, BS, 57, PhD, 65. *Honors & Awards:* Goddard Award, Int Soc Optical Eng, 85. *Prof Exp:* Res assoc high energy physics, Mass Inst Technol, 65-67; staff scientist x-ray astron, Am Sci & Eng, Inc, Mass, 67-74. *Concurrent Pos:* AXAF telescope scientist. *Mem:* Fel Am Phys Soc; Am Astron Soc; Int Astron Union. *Res:* X-ray optics; x-ray emission from normal galaxies and clusters of galaxies. *Mailing Add:* Ctr Astrophys 60 Garden St B423 Cambridge MA 02138. *E-Mail:* lvs@cfa.harvard.edu

**VAN STEE, ETHARD WENDEL,** PHARMACOLOGY, TOXICOLOGY. *Current Pos:* RETIRED. *Personal Data:* b Traverse City, Mich, July 17, 36; m 60; c 2. *Educ:* Mich State Univ, BS, 58, DVM, 60; Ohio State Univ, MS, 66, PhD(vet physiol, pharmacol), 70. *Prof Exp:* Res pharmacologist, Aerospace Med Res Lab, Wright-Patterson AFB, Ohio, 67-75; head, Inhalation Toxicol Sect, Nat Inst Environ Health Sci, 75-85. *Concurrent Pos:* Adj assoc prof pharmacol, Univ NC, 75- *Mem:* Soc Toxicol; Am Soc Pharmacol & Exp Therapeut; Am Vet Med Asn; AAAS; Am Soc Vet Physiologists & Pharmacologists. *Res:* Inhalation toxicology; halogenated alkanes, anesthetics; cardiovascular pharmacology. *Mailing Add:* 161 Distant Island Dr Beaufort SC 29902

**VAN STEENBERGEN, ARIE,** PHYSICS. *Current Pos:* head, Alternating Gradient Synchrotron Div, Brookhaven Nat Lab, 65-74, sr physicist, 75-77, head nat synchrotron light source, 77-96, EMER CONSULT, BROOKHAVEN NAT LAB, 96- *Personal Data:* b Vlaardingen, Neth, Feb 26, 28; m 53; c 4. *Educ:* Delft Univ Technol, MSc, 52; McGill Univ, PhD(physics, math), 57. *Prof Exp:* Res asst electron beam optics, Delft Univ Technol, 50-53; res physicist, Nat Defense Res Lab, The Hague, Neth, 53-54; res assoc nuclear magnetic resonance, McGill Univ, 54-57. *Concurrent Pos:* Consult, Radiation Dynamics, Inc, 60- *Mem:* Am Phys Soc; Europ Phys Soc. *Res:* High energy particle accelerators and storage rings; particle beam dynamics; synchrotron radiation sources. *Mailing Add:* Nat Synchrotron Light Source Div Bldg 715B Brookhaven Nat Lab Upton NY 11973

**VANSTONE, J R,** MATHEMATICS. *Current Pos:* RETIRED. *Personal Data:* b Owen Sound, Ont, Aug 12, 33; m 56; c 3. *Educ:* Univ Toronto, BA, 55, MA, 56; Univ Natal, PhD(math), 59. *Prof Exp:* Lectr math, Univ Toronto, 59-61, from asst prof to prof, 61-94. *Mem:* Can Math Cong; Math Asn Am; Am Math Soc; Soc Indust & Appl Math; Sigma Xi. *Res:* Differential geometry. *Mailing Add:* Dept Math Univ Toronto 100 St George St Sidney Smith Bldg Rm 4012 Toronto ON M5S 3G3 Can

**VANSTONE, SCOTT ALEXANDER,** MATHEMATICS. *Current Pos:* From asst prof to assoc prof, 74-85, PROF MATH, ST JEROME'S COL, 85- *Personal Data:* b Chatham, Ont, Sept 14, 47; m 70; c 1. *Educ:* Univ Waterloo, BMath, 70, MMath, 71, PhD(math), 74. *Concurrent Pos:* Ed-in-chief, Designs, Codes & Cryptography. *Res:* The existence and construction of balanced incomplete block designs and regular pairwise balanced designs which are closely related to finite linear spaces and balanced equidistant codes; coding theory; cryptography and finite fields. *Mailing Add:* Dept Combinatorics & Optimiz St Jerome's Col Westmount Rd N Waterloo ON N2L 3G3 Can

**VAN STRIEN, RICHARD EDWARD,** ORGANIC CHEMISTRY. *Current Pos:* RETIRED. *Personal Data:* b Battle Creek, Mich, Sept 17, 20; m 42; c 3. *Educ:* Hope Col, AB, 42; Univ Pa, MS, 44, PhD(org chem), 48. *Prof Exp:* Res chemist, Standard Oil Co, 47-60; sect leader, res & develop dept, Amoco Am Chem Corp, 60-61, sect leader in-chg prod appln new chem, 61-67, asst dir polymers & plastic div, 67-69, conensation polymer div, 69-76, div dir, explor res div, 76-82. *Mem:* Am Chem Soc; Sigma Xi. *Res:* Synthetic detergents; gelling agents; surface coatings; high-performance plastics; adhesives. *Mailing Add:* 9148 Southmoor Ave Highland IN 46322-2513

**VAN STRYLAND, ERIC WILLIAM,** LASER PHYSICS. *Current Pos:* PROF PHYSICS, ELEC & COMPUT ENG, UNIV CENT FLA, 87- *Personal Data:* b South Bend, Ind, June 3, 47; m 78. *Educ:* Humboldt State Univ, BS, 70; Univ Ariz, MS, 75, PhD(physics), 76. *Prof Exp:* Res assoc laser physics, Optical Sci Ctr, Univ Ariz, 72-76; res scientist, Ctr Laser Studies, Univ Southern Calif, 76-78; prof laser physics, dept physics, NTex State Univ, 78-87. *Mem:* Am Phys Soc; fel Optical Soc Am; Laser Inst Am; sr mem Inst Elec & Electronics Engrs; Mat Res Soc; Int Soc Optical Eng. *Res:* Ultrashort light pulses and their generation measurement and uses; optical coherent transient effects; lifetime measurements; nonlinear absorption; laser induced damage; laser material interactions. *Mailing Add:* Univ Cent Fla Creol Res Pavillion PO Box 162700 Orlando FL 32816-2700. *Fax:* 407-658-6880

**VAN SWAAY, MAARTEN,** COMPUTER SCIENCES. *Current Pos:* from asst prof to assoc prof anal chem, 63-81, assoc prof comput sci, 81-95, EMER ASSOC PROF COMPUT SCI, KANS STATE UNIV, 95- *Personal Data:* b The Hague, Neth, Aug 1, 30; m 54, Christina G Lantinga; c 4. *Educ:* State Univ Leiden, BS, 53, Princeton Univ, PhD(chem), 56, Drs, 56. *Prof Exp:* Sr res asst phys chem, State Univ Leiden, 56-59; res assoc instr analytical, Eindhoven Technol Univ, 59-63. *Concurrent Pos:* Consult, Am Inst Prof Educ. *Mem:* Asn Comput Mach; Sigma Xi; Inst Elec & Electronics Engrs Comput Soc. *Res:* Social and ethical issues. *Mailing Add:* Dept Comput & Info Sci Kans State Univ Nichols Hall Manhattan KS 66506. *E-Mail:* maarten@cis.ksu.edu

**VAN TAMELEN, EUGENE EARL,** CHEMISTRY. *Current Pos:* prof chem, 62-87, chmn dept, 74-78, EMER PROF CHEM, STANFORD UNIV, 87- *Personal Data:* b Zeeland, Mich, July 20, 25; m 51, Mary Houtman; c Jane, Carey & Peter. *Educ:* Hope Col, AB, 47; Harvard Univ, MA, 49, PhD(chem), 50. *Hon Degrees:* DSc, Hope Col & Bucknell Univ, 71. *Honors & Awards:* Award Pure Chem, Am Chem Soc, 61 & Award for Creative Work in Synthetic Org Chem, 70; Baekeland Award, 65. *Prof Exp:* From instr to prof org chem, Univ Wis, 50-61, Adkins prof chem, 61-62. *Concurrent Pos:* Guggenheim fels, 65 & 73; prof extraordinarius, Neth, 67-74; mem, Synthesis, 69- & Accounts Chem Res, 70-73; ed, Bioorg Chem, 71-82. *Mem:* Nat Acad Sci; Am Acad Arts & Sci; Am Chem Soc. *Res:* Chemistry of natural products including structure, synthesis and biosynthesis; new reactions. *Mailing Add:* 23570 Camino Hermoso Los Altos Hills CA 94024-6407

**VAN TASSEL, ROGER A,** AERONOMY, ATMOSPHERIC INFRARED RADIANCE & TRANSMISSION. *Current Pos:* Chemist, Lunar-Planetary Lab, 61-67, res chemist, Aeronomy Lab, 67-82, RES CHEMIST, INFRARED TECHNOL DIV, AIR FORCE GEOPHYS LAB, 83- *Personal Data:* b Orange, NJ, Oct 19, 36. *Educ:* Wesleyan Univ, AB, 58; Northeastern Univ, MS, 68, PhD, 72. *Mem:* AAAS; Sigma Xi; Am Geophys Union; Optical Soc Am. *Res:* Atomic spectra in the vacuum ultraviolet; oscillator strengths of atomic transitions; ultraviolet airglow originating in the upper atmosphere; Fourier infrared instrumentation. *Mailing Add:* Phillips Lab GPO 19 Greystone Ct 29 Randolph Rd Burlington MA 01803-3823. *Fax:* 617-377-8780; *E-Mail:* vantassel@plh.af.mil

**VAN TASSELL, JAY LEE,** STRATIGRAPHY, SEDIMENTATION. *Current Pos:* ASSOC PROF GEOL, EASTERN ORE STATE COL, 88- *Personal Data:* b Mt Kisco, NY, Oct 19, 52; m 91, April Evans. *Educ:* Bowdoin Col, BA, 74; Univ Wis-Madison, MS, 75; Duke Univ, PhD(marine geol), 79. *Prof Exp:* Vis instr geol, Guilford Col, 79-87. *Mem:* Geol Soc Am; Int Asn Sedimentologists; Soc Econ Paleontologists & Mineralogists; Nat Asn Geol Teachers; Sigma Xi. *Res:* Dynamics of turbidity current sedimentation; influence of orbitally-driven climate cycles on Devonian Catskill Delta sedimentationing; glaciatian and tectonic influence on sedimentation in the La Grande pull-apart basin. *Mailing Add:* Sci Dept Eastern Ore Univ La Grande OR 97850. *Fax:* 541-962-3873; *E-Mail:* vantasse@eosc.osshe.edu

**VAN TASSELL, MORGAN HOWARD,** microbiology, for more information see previous edition

**VAN THIEL, DAVID H,** HEPATOLOGY, GASTROENTEROLOGY. *Current Pos:* MED DIR, TRANSPLANT CTR, MED CTR, UNIV KY. *Personal Data:* b Cut Bank, Mont, Sept 5, 41. *Educ:* Univ Calif, Los Angeles, MD, 67. *Honors & Awards:* Res Award, Res Soc Alcoholism, 85. *Prof Exp:* From instr to prof med, surg & psychiat, Univ Pittsburgh Sch Med, 73-93; med dir transplantation, Okla Transplant Inst, Baptist Med Ctr Okla. *Concurrent Pos:* Res fel, Univ Calif Med Ctr, Los Angeles, 64; intern, NY Hosp, 67-68, asst resident, 68-69; clin assoc, Endocrinol Br, Nat Cancer Inst, 69-70 & Reprod Res Br, NIH, 70-71; sr asst resident, Univ Hosp, Boston, 71-72, res fel, 72-73; USPHS career develop award, NIH, 77. *Mem:* Am Fedn Clin Res; Am Asn Study Liver Dis. *Res:* Endocrine alterations associated with liver disease with special interest in alcoholic liver disease. *Mailing Add:* Gastroenterol Internal Med Dept Univ Ky A B Chandler Med Ctr Lexington KY 40536-0084

**VAN THIEL, MATHIAS,** PHYSICAL CHEMISTRY, PHYSICS. *Current Pos:* RES PHYSICIST HIGH PRESSURE EQUATION OF STATE, LAWRENCE LIVERMORE LAB, 59- *Personal Data:* b Sitobonda, Java, Sept 18, 30; US citizen; m 59; c 3. *Educ:* Cornell Univ, BA, 54, Univ Calif, Berkeley, PhD(phys chem), 58. *Prof Exp:* Fel phys chem & shock tube kinetics, Univ Minn, Minneapolis, 58-59. *Mem:* Am Chem Soc; AAAS; Sigma Xi; Am Physics Soc. *Res:* Infrared spectroscopy-matrix isolation; high temperature gas phase kinetics-shock tube; shock waves and high pressure equations of state; hydrodynamic code calculations; shaped charge design and penetration modeling; computation of explosive mixture properties; compilation of shock wave data. *Mailing Add:* 2519 Oakes Dr Hayward CA 94542

**VAN'T HOF, JACK,** CELL BIOLOGY, PLANT MOLECULAR BIOLOGY. *Current Pos:* cytologist, 66-80, SR CYTOLOGIST, BIOL DEPT, BROOKHAVEN NAT LAB, 80- *Personal Data:* b Grand Rapids, Mich, Apr 11, 32; m 52; c 2. *Educ:* Calvin Col, AB, 57; Mich State Univ, PhD(bot), 61. *Prof Exp:* Biologist, Hanford Labs, Gen Elec Corp, 61-62; res assoc radiobiol & fel, Biol Dept, Brookhaven Nat Lab, 62-64; asst cytologist, 64-65; asst prof cytol, Dept Bot, Univ Minn, 65-66. *Mem:* Am Soc Cell Biol; Bot Soc Am; Am Soc Plant Physiol; Genetics Soc Am. *Res:* Cellular and molecular biology of plant cell division and chromosomal DNA replication. *Mailing Add:* Biol Dept Brookhaven Nat Lab Gen Delivery Upton NY 11973-9999. *Fax:* 516-282-3407

**VANT HULL, LORIN LEE,** DEVELOPMENT OF ALTERNATIVE ENERGY TECHNOLOGY,. *Current Pos:* assoc prof, 69-77, PROF PHYSICS, UNIV HOUSTON, 77- *Personal Data:* b Sioux Co, Iowa, June 26, 32; m 55, Mary E Prunty; c Julia, Barry & Brian. *Educ:* Univ Minn, Minneapolis, BS, 54; Univ Calif, Los Angeles, MS, 56; Calif Inst Technol, PhD(physics), 67. *Prof Exp:* Res engr, Res Lab, Hughes Aircraft Co, 54-58; sr res scientist cryogenic devices, Sci Lab, Ford Motor Co, 66-69; AEC grant, Univ Calif, San Diego, 69. *Concurrent Pos:* Consult, Lawrence Berkeley Lab, Univ Calif, 70-71; Manned Spacecraft Ctr, NASA, 71-72; prin invest solar cent receiver anal & code develop, Univ Houston, 73-; div chief, Solar Thermal Div Energy Lab, Univ Houston, 75-92; prog mgr, Solar Thermal Adv Res Ctr, Univ Houston, 81-92; bd dirs, Am Solar Energy Soc, 95- *Mem:* Am Phys Soc; Sigma Xi; Int Solar Energy Soc. *Res:* Develop computer techniques for optimization and design of solar central receiver systems represented by Solar Two at Barstow, Calif; current efforts support commercialization of this new alternative energy technology. *Mailing Add:* Univ Houston Houston TX 77204-5506. *Fax:* 713-743-3589; *E-Mail:* vanthull@uh.edu

**VAN TIENHOVEN, ARI,** ANIMAL PHYSIOLOGY. *Current Pos:* from asst prof to assoc prof avian physiol, 55-69, prof, 69-87, EMER PROF ANIMAL PHYSIOL, COL AGR & LIFE SCI, CORNELL UNIV, 87- *Personal Data:* b The Hague, Neth, Apr 22, 22; nat US; m 50, Annie van Haselen; c Richard A, Arianne J & Andrew W. *Educ:* Univ Ill, MS & PhD(animal sci), 53. *Prof Exp:* Asst prof poultry husb, Miss State Col, 53-55. *Concurrent Pos:* NATO fel, 61-62; assoc ed, Biol Reproduction, 74- *Mem:* Fel AAAS; Am Soc Zoologists; fel Poultry Sci Asn; Am Asn Anat; Soc Study Reproduction. *Res:* Neuroendocrinology; reproductive physiology; temperature regulation of birds. *Mailing Add:* Dept Poultry & Avian Sci Cornell Univ 9 Hudson Pl Ithaca NY 14850-5755

**VAN TILBORG, ANDRE MARCEL,** REAL-TIME COMPUTING, PARALLEL COMPUTING. *Current Pos:* prog mgr comput systs, Off Naval Res, 87-89, dir, Comput Sci Div, 89-93, Eng Sci Dept, 91-93, DIR, MATH, COMPUT SCI & INFO SCI DIV, OFF NAVAL RES, 93- *Personal Data:* b Delft, Neth, Dec 6, 53; US citizen; m 90. *Educ:* State Univ NY, Buffalo, BA, 75, PhD(comput sci), 82. *Prof Exp:* Sr computer scientist, Calspan Corp, 80-83, prin comput scientist, 84; prin comput scientist, Honeywell Systs & Res Ctr, 83-84; sr scientist, Carnegie Mellon Univ, 84-86. *Concurrent Pos:* Lectr, State Univ NY, Buffalo, 77-80; chair, Tech Comt Real-Time Systs, Inst Elec & Electronics Engrs Comput Soc, 87-91. *Mem:* Inst Elec & Electronics Engrs Comput Soc; Asn Comput Mach; Sigma Xi. *Res:* Resource management in distributed computing systems; author of numerous technical publications. *Mailing Add:* 800 N Quincy St Arlington VA 22217. *Fax:* 703-696-0923; *E-Mail:* avantil@itd.nrl.navy.mil

**VAN TILL, HOWARD JAY,** ASTRONOMY. *Current Pos:* PROF PHYSICS, CALVIN COL, 67- *Personal Data:* b Ripon, Calif, Nov 28, 38; m 58; c 4. *Educ:* Calvin Col, BS, 60; Mich State Univ, PhD(physics), 65. *Prof Exp:* Res scientist physics, Univ Calif, Riverside, 65-66; asst prof, Univ Redlands, 66-67. *Concurrent Pos:* Res scientist, Dept Astron, Univ Tex, Austin, 74. *Mem:* Am Astron Soc; Am Phys Soc; Am Sci Affil. *Res:* Study of interstellar molecular clouds using millimeter-wave techniques. *Mailing Add:* 2210 Edgewood Ave SE Grand Rapids MI 49546-4388

**VAN'T RIET, BARTHOLOMEUS,** ANALYTICAL CHEMISTRY. *Current Pos:* assoc prof chem 64-85, EMER PROF CHEM, MED COL VA, 86- *Personal Data:* b Arnhem, Neth, June 25, 22; nat US; m 55, Judith Rottschaefer; c Rudolf D, Willem L & Margaret E. *Educ:* Vrye Univ, Neth, BSc, 50; Univ Minn, PhD(analytical chem), 57. *Honors & Awards:* Chem Pioneer Award, Am Inst Chemists, 73. *Prof Exp:* Asst analytical chem, Vrye Univ, Neth, 48-51; from asst to instr, Univ Minn, 51-57; instr chem, Univ Va, 58-64. *Mem:* Am Chem Soc; Am Inst Chemists; Sigma Xi. *Res:* Application of complexing agents in mammals; dispersion of calculi by surface reactions; drug analysis. *Mailing Add:* Dept Med Chem Med Col Va PO Box 540 Richmond VA 23298-0540. *Fax:* 804-828-8566

**VAN TRUMP, JAMES EDMOND,** ARAMID FIBERS, BALLISTICS PROTECTION. *Current Pos:* res chemist, Kingston Plant Fibers, 75-77 & Exp Sta Pigments, 77-79, RES ASSOC, DU PONT EXP STA FIBERS, 79- *Personal Data:* b Wood River, Nebr, Mar 1, 43; m 68; c 2. *Educ:* Univ Wyo, BS, 64; Univ Calif, San Diego, MS, 73, PhD(chem), 75. *Prof Exp:* Res chemist, Am Potash & Chem Corp, 68-70. *Mem:* Am Chem Soc. *Res:* Fiber science; manufacture, structure and use of high strength industrial fibers; aramid fibers, pulps and fibrids, carbon fibers, nylon and polyester fibers, papers, ballistic fibers. *Mailing Add:* 4A Wood Rd Wilmington DE 19806-2022

**VAN TUYL, ANDREW HEUER,** MATHEMATICS. *Current Pos:* RETIRED. *Personal Data:* b Fresno, Calif, July 6, 22; m 55, Mary R Dryden; c Andrew H, Mary C (Giorgis), Hugh L & Jean R (Bynum). *Educ:* Fresno State Col, AB, 43; Stanford Univ, MA, 46, PhD(math), 47. *Prof Exp:* Asst chem, Stanford Univ, 43-44, asst elec eng, 44-45, asst physics, 46, asst math, 46-47; mathematician, Naval Surface Warfare Ctr, 47-92. *Concurrent Pos:* Res assoc, Ind Univ, 53. *Mem:* Fel AAAS; Am Inst Aeronaut & Astronaut; Am Math Soc; Soc Indust & Appl Math; NY Acad Sci; Math Asn Am. *Res:* Potential theory; special functions; hydrodynamics; gas dynamics. *Mailing Add:* 1000 W Nolcrest Dr Silver Spring MD 20903-1040. *E-Mail:* avt@clark.net

**VAN TUYL, HAROLD HUTCHISON,** RADIOCHEMISTRY. *Current Pos:* res chemist, 65-70, mgr nuclear fuel cycle, 70-84, MGR, CRIT MASS LAB, PAC NORTHWEST LABS, BATTELLE MEM INST, 84- *Personal Data:* b Ft Worth, Tex, Oct 13, 27; m 52; c 4. *Educ:* Agr & Mech Col, Tex, BS, 48. *Prof Exp:* Res chemist, Gen Elec Co, 48-65. *Mem:* Am Nuclear Soc; Am Chem Soc. *Res:* Fission product recovery; dose rate and shielding calculations; fission product and transuranics generation calculations; transuranic element separations; nuclear chemistry. *Mailing Add:* 2158 Hudson Ave Richland WA 99352-2027

**VAN TUYLE, GLENN CHARLES,** BIOCHEMISTRY. *Current Pos:* ASSOC PROF BIOCHEM, MED COL VA, VA COMMONWEALTH UNIV, 74- *Personal Data:* b Wilkes-Barre, Pa, May 28, 43. *Educ:* Lafayette Col, AB, 65; Thomas Jefferson Univ, PhD(biochem), 71. *Prof Exp:* Chemist org chem, Rohm & Haas Chem Co, 66-68; teaching & res asst biochem, Thomas Jefferson Univ, 68-71; assoc, State Univ NY, Stony Brook, 71-74. *Concurrent Pos:* Assoc prof res grant, Nat Inst Gen Med Sci, 76-82. *Mem:* Am Soc Cell Biol; Am Soc Biol Chemists. *Res:* Mitochondrial biogenesis; DNA structure, packaging and replications. *Mailing Add:* Dept Biochem & Molecular Biophys Va Commonwealth Univ PO Box 980614 MCV Sta Richmond VA 23298-0614. *Fax:* 804-786-1473

**VAN TYLE, WILLIAM KENT,** PHARMACOLOGY. *Current Pos:* From asst prof to assoc prof, 72-83, PROF PHARMACOL, BUTLER UNIV, 83- *Personal Data:* b Frankfort, Ind, Feb 10, 44; m 82, Jeanne Hawkins; c Rachel & Emily. *Educ:* Butler Univ, BS, 67; Ohio State Univ, MSc, 69, PhD(pharmacol), 72. *Concurrent Pos:* Secy-treas, Dist 4, Am Asn Cols Pharm-Nat Asn Bds Pharm, 75-88. *Mem:* Am Asn Col Pharm; Am Pharm Asn. *Res:* Bioavailability of drugs to central nervous system and drug effects on central neurotransmitters. *Mailing Add:* Butler Univ 4600 Sunset Ave Indianapolis IN 46208

**VAN UITERT, LEGRAND G(ERARD),** MATERIALS SCIENCE, INORGANIC CHEMISTRY. *Current Pos:* RETIRED. *Personal Data:* b Salt Lake City, Utah, May 6, 22; m 45; c 3. *Educ:* George Washington Univ, BS, 49; Pa State Univ, MS, 51, PhD(chem), 52. *Honors & Awards:* W R G Baker Award, Inst Elec & Electronics Engrs, 71; H N Potts Award, Franklin Inst, 75; IRI Award, Indust Res Inst, 76; Creative Invention Award, Am Chem Soc, 78; Am Phys Soc Int Prize, 81. *Prof Exp:* Mem tech staff, Bell Tel Labs, Inc, 52-88. *Mem:* Nat Acad Eng; Am Chem Soc. *Res:* Magnetic oxides; luminesence; lasers, electro-optic and non-linear devices; magnetic bubble domain materials, fiber optics, passive displays and dielectric films. *Mailing Add:* 2 Terry Dr Morristown NJ 07960-4713

**VAN UMMERSEN, CLAIRE ANN,** DEVELOPMENTAL BIOLOGY, ANIMAL PHYSIOLOGY. *Current Pos:* PRES, CLEVELAND STATE UNIV, 93- *Personal Data:* b Chelsea, Mass, July 28, 35; m 58; c 2. *Educ:* Tufts Univ, BS, 57, MS, 60, PhD(biol), 63. *Prof Exp:* Res asst radiobiol, Tufts Univ, 57-60, res assoc, 60-67, lectr biol, 67-68; asst prof, Univ Mass, Boston, 68-74, assoc dean acad affairs, Liberal Arts Col, 75-76, assoc vchancellor acad affairs, 76-77, interim chancellor, 78-79, dir, Environ Sci Ctr & Biol Grad Prog, 79-81, assoc vchancellor acad affairs, Bd Regents, 81-85, assoc prof biol, 74-, vchancellor mgt systs & telecommun, Bd Regents, 85- *Concurrent Pos:* Fel, Tufts Univ, 63-67; mem teaching fac, Lancaster Courses in Ophthal, Colby Col, 62- *Mem:* AAAS; Am Soc Zoologists; Soc Develop Biol; Sigma Xi. *Res:* Biological effects of microwave radiation on the eye and the developing embryo. *Mailing Add:* Off Pres Cleveland State Univ 1983 E 24th Cleveland OH 44115-2403

**VAN VALEN, LEIGH MAIORANA,** PALEONTOLOGY. *Current Pos:* asst prof anat, Univ Chicago, 67-68, from asst prof to assoc prof evolutionary biol, 68-73, assoc prof to prof biol, 73-88, PROF ECOL & EVOLUTION & CONCEPTIONAL FOUND SCI, UNIV CHICAGO, 88- *Personal Data:* b Albany, NY, Aug 12, 35; m 74, Virginia Maiorana; c Tatina & Diana. *Educ:* Miami Univ, BA, 56; Columbia Univ, MA, 57, PhD(zool), 61. *Prof Exp:* Boese fel, Columbia Univ, 61-62; NATO fel, Univ Col, London, 62-63; res fel vert paleont, Am Mus Natural Hist, 63-66. *Concurrent Pos:* Res assoc geol, Field Mus Natural Hist, 71-; managing ed & ed, Evolutionary Theory, 73- & ed Evolutionary Monographs, 77- *Mem:* Soc Study Evolution (vpres, 73, 80); Soc Vert Paleont; Ecol Soc Am; Philos Sci Asn; Am Soc Naturalists (treas, 69-72, vpres, 74-75); Genetics Soc Am. *Res:* Energy in ecology and evolution; extinction; ecological control of large-scale evolutionary patterns; analytical paleoecology; mammalian evolution; the phenotype; competition; natural selection of plants and animals; evolutionary theory; biological variation; evolution of development; basal radiation of placental mammals; body size. *Mailing Add:* Dept Ecol & Evolution Univ Chicago 1101 E 57th St Chicago IL 60637

**VAN VALIN, CHARLES CARROLL,** ATMOSPHERIC CHEMISTRY, ATMOSPHERIC PHYSICS. *Current Pos:* RES CHEMIST ATMOSPHERIC RES, ENVIRON RES LABS, NAT OCEANIC & ATMOSPHERIC ADMIN, US DEPT COM, 66- *Personal Data:* b Wakefield, Nebr, Aug 10, 29; m 54. *Educ:* Nebr State Teachers Col, BA, 51; Univ Colo, Boulder, MS, 58. *Prof Exp:* Teacher sci, Ralston High Sch, Nebr, 53-54; chemist pesticide mfg, Shell Chem Co, Denver, 57-58; res chemist sugar chem, Great Western Sugar Co, Denver, 58-60; res chemist pesticide res, Fish-Pesticide Res Lab, Bur Sport Fisheries & Wildlife, Dept Interior, 61-66. *Concurrent Pos:* Abstractor, Chem Abstracts Serv, Am Chem Soc, 62-64. *Mem:* Am Chem Soc; Am Geophys Union; Sigma Xi. *Res:* Chemical and physical processes of acidic precipitation formation; reactions in polluted atmospheres; natural sources of acidic precursors; atmospheric transport of aerosols and trace gases. *Mailing Add:* 925 Gilbert Boulder CO 80302

**VAN VALKENBURG, JEPTHA WADE, JR,** physical chemistry, surface chemistry, for more information see previous edition

**VAN VALKENBURG, M(AC) E(LWYN),** ELECTRICAL ENGINEERING, SYSTEM THEORY. *Current Pos:* prof, Univ Ill, Urbana, 74-82, actg dean, 84-85, W W Grainger prof elec eng, 82-88, dean, 85-88, EMER DEAN, COL ENG, UNIV ILL, URBANA, 88- *Personal Data:* b Union, Utah, Oct 5, 21; m 43; c 6. *Educ:* Univ Utah, BS, 43; Mass Inst Technol, SM, 46; Stanford Univ, PhD(elec eng), 52. *Honors & Awards:* George Westinghouse Award, Am Soc Eng Educ, 63, Lamme Award, 78, Centennial Medallion, 93; Educ Medal, Inst Elec & Electronics Engrs, 72. *Prof Exp:* Mem staff, Radiation Lab, Mass Inst Technol, 43-45, asst, Electronics Lab, 45-46; from instr to assoc prof elec eng, Univ Utah, 46-55; actg instr, Stanford Univ, 49-51; from assoc prof to prof, Univ Ill, Urbana, 55-66, assoc dir, Coord Sci Lab, 59-66; prof & chmn dept, Princeton Univ, 66-74. *Concurrent Pos:* Ed, Trans Circuit Theory, Inst Elec & Electronics Engrs, 60-63, ed, Proc, 65-68, ed-in-chief, Press, 85-; vis prof, Univ Calif, Berkeley, 62-63 & Univ Hawaii, 78-79; Thompson vis prof, Univ Ill, 72-73 & Univ Ariz, 82-83. *Mem:* Nat Acad Eng; fel Inst Elec & Electronics Engrs (vpres, 69-71); fel Am Soc Eng Educ; Sigma Xi. *Res:* Circuit theory; analog filter theory; systems theory; energy systems. *Mailing Add:* 2609 SW 64th Pl Portland OR 97225

**VAN VECHTEN, DEBORAH,** LOW TEMPERATURE PHYSICS. *Current Pos:* prog officer, US off Naval Res, 96- *Personal Data:* b Washington, DC, Oct 24, 47; m 70, Joel F Liebman. *Educ:* Brown Univ, ScB, 69; Univ Md, College Park, MS, 75, PhD(physics), 79. *Prof Exp:* Vis asst prof physics, Ga Inst Technol, 78-79; asst prof physics, Howard Univ, 81-83; mat scientist, Sachs Freeman Assocs, 85-89; assoc, Nat Res Coun, US Naval Res Lab, 79-81, res assoc, 83-85, physicist, 89-96. *Concurrent Pos:* Guest scientist, Nat Bur Stand, 81. *Mem:* Am Phys Soc; Am Vacuum Soc; Mat Res Soc. *Res:* Non-equilibrium superconductivity; properties and applications of superconductors; high energy resolution x and gamma ray detectors; role of fluctuations in phase transitions; ion beam assisted thin film deposition; Josephson tunnel junctions; resistive phase transition in 2 dimensions; percolation theory; layered thin film structures including Rugates; quantum measurement theory; theoretical solid state physics; experiments which seek to define physical phenomena and on theoretical models of these phenomena, basic solid state physics. *Mailing Add:* 17512 Skyline Dr Ashton MD 20861. *Fax:* 703-696-2611; *E-Mail:* vanvecdeats.onr.navy.mil

**VAN VECHTEN, JAMES ALDEN,** THEORETICAL SOLID STATE PHYSICS. *Current Pos:* AT DEPT ELEC ENG, ORE STATE UNIV, 85- *Personal Data:* b Washington, DC, July 29, 42; m 83; c 2. *Educ:* Univ Calif, Berkeley, AB, 65; Univ Chicago, PhD(physics), 69. *Prof Exp:* Infrared res officer semiconductors, US Naval Res Lab, Wash, 69-71; mem tech staff electro optic res, Bell Tel Lab, Murray Hill, 71-74; res staff mem semiconductor physics, Thomas J Watson Res Ctr, IBM, 74-85. *Concurrent Pos:* Fannie & John Horte Found fel. *Mem:* Fel Am Phys Soc; Electrochem Soc; fel Inst Physics (London); sr mem Inst Elec & Electronics Engrs; Electrochem Soc Am; Mat Res Soc. *Res:* Theoretical study of covalently bonded solids, their electronic, optical, mechanical and thermochemical properties; co-developer of the dielectric scale of electronegativity; semiconductors. *Mailing Add:* Dept Elec & Comput Eng Ore State Univ Corvallis OR 97331. *Fax:* 541-737-1300

**VAN VELDHUIZEN, PHILIP ANDROCLES,** MATHEMATICS, STATISTICS. *Current Pos:* from assoc prof to prof, Fairbanks, 74-89, PROF MATH, UNIV ALASKA, ANCHORAGE, 89- *Personal Data:* b Hospers, Iowa, Nov 6, 30; m 84, Deborah S Judwin; c Robert, Jay, Varina & Heather. *Educ:* Cent Col, BA, 52; Univ Iowa, MS, 60. *Prof Exp:* Teacher jr high sch, 54; instr, Exten Ctr, Univ Ga, 54-56; instr math, Cent Col, 56-59; asst prof, Sacramento State Col, 60-63. *Concurrent Pos:* Spec lectr & resource personnel, Mod Math Prog, Fairbanks, Anchorage & Kodiak, Alaska, 64-67; mem adv bd, Pupil Eval Prog, Northwest Regional Lab, State Dept Educ, 75-81; clerk, Fairbanks NStar Borough Sch Bd, 78-80, mem, 78-81, treas, 80-81; mem, Nat Coun Teachers Math; Alaska state dir, Am Math Competition, 95- *Mem:* Math Asn Am; Am Statist Asn. *Res:* Social basis of mathematics teaching and learning; effect of the social setting has on the learning and teaching atmosphere in a secondary classroom. *Mailing Add:* PO Box 82593 Fairbanks AK 99708. *E-Mail:* ffpvv@aurora.alaska.edu

**VAN VERTH, JAMES EDWARD,** ORGANIC SYNTHESIS, ORGANIC MECHANISMS. *Current Pos:* from asst prof to assoc prof, 63-75, PROF CHEM, CANISIUS COL, 75- *Personal Data:* b Huntington, WVa, Jan 26, 28; m 65, Patricia Bylebyl; c James & Elizabeth. *Educ:* Xavier Univ, Ohio, BS, 50; Univ Detroit, MS, 52; Ind Univ, PhD(org chem), 57. *Prof Exp:* Sr res chemist, Monsanto Chem Co, 56-61; asst, Yale Univ, 61-63. *Concurrent Pos:* Prin investr, Petrol Res Fund grant, 68-69 & 81-83; vis scientist, State Univ NY, Buffalo, 80-81; vis prof, Univ Rochester, 93-94. *Mem:* Am Chem Soc. *Res:* Organic synthesis; computational studies of mechanisms. *Mailing Add:* Dept Chem Canisius Col Buffalo NY 14208-1098

**VAN VLACK, LAWRENCE H(ALL),** MATERIALS SCIENCE & ENGINEERING. *Current Pos:* from assoc prof to prof mat & metall eng, 53-88, chmn dept, 67-73, EMER PROF MAT & METALL ENG, UNIV MICH, ANN ARBOR, 88- *Personal Data:* b Atlantic, Iowa, July 21, 20; m 43, Frances Runnells; c 2. *Educ:* Iowa State Col, BS, 42; Univ Chicago, PhD(geol), 50. *Honors & Awards:* A Sauveur Award, Am Soc Metals, 79, Gold Medal, 84, White Award, 85; Pace Award, Iowa State Univ, 93. *Prof Exp:* Ceramist, US Steel Corp, 42-43, petrogr, 43-52, process metallurgist, 52-53. *Concurrent Pos:* Vis prof, Univ Calif, Berkeley, 61, Univ Melbourne, 67, Univ Kanpur, 69, Monash Univ, 73, & Zhejiang Univ, 84. *Mem:* Fel AAAS; fel Am Ceramic Soc; fel Am Soc Metals; Am Soc Eng Educ; Am Inst Mining, Metall & Petrol Engrs. *Res:* Refractories; slags; nonmetallic inclusions; ceramic materials; process metallurgy; materials science instruction; nickel oxide. *Mailing Add:* 1700 Bronson Way Apt 322 Kalamazoo MI 49009-1084

**VAN VLECK, FRED SCOTT,** CONTROL THEORY, MULTIPLE-VALUED FUNCTIONS. *Current Pos:* from asst prof to assoc prof, 62-68, PROF MATH, UNIV KANS, 68- *Personal Data:* b Clearwater, Nebr, Dec 12, 34; m 60; c 5. *Educ:* Univ Nebr, BSc, 56, MA, 57; Univ Minn, PhD(math), 60. *Prof Exp:* Instr math, Mass Inst Technol, 60-62. *Concurrent Pos:* Vis prof, Univ Colo, 71-72. *Mem:* Math Asn Am; Am Math Soc; Soc Indust & Appl Math. *Res:* Control theory; measurable multiplevalued functions; ordinary differential equations; optimization. *Mailing Add:* Dept Math Univ Kans Lawrence KS 66045-2142

**VAN VLECK, LLOYD DALE,** GENETICS, ANIMAL SCIENCE. *Current Pos:* PROF ANIMAL GENETICS, UNIV NEBR, LINCOLN, 88-; RES GENETICIST, USDA, 88- *Personal Data:* b Clearwater, Nebr, June 11, 33; m 58; c 2. *Educ:* Univ Nebr, BS, 54, MS, 55; Cornell Univ, PhD(animal breeding), 60. *Hon Degrees:* DSc, Univ Nebr, 86. *Honors & Awards:* Am Soc Animal Sci Award, 72; Nat Asn Animal Breeders Award, Am Dairy Sci Asn, 74 & 83. *Prof Exp:* Res assoc animal breeding, Cornell Univ, 59-60, res geneticist, 60-62, from asst prof to prof, 62-88. *Concurrent Pos:* Vis prof, Univ Nebr, Lincoln, 73; Scandinavian Grad Prog Animal Breeding, Uppsala, 75; Univ Calif, Davis, 85. *Mem:* Biomet Soc; Am Dairy Sci Asn; Am Soc Animal Sci; Am Genetic Asn. *Res:* Methods of improving genetic value of large animals using genetic theory, statistical technique for unbalanced data, and computer processing. *Mailing Add:* Animal Sci A218 Univ Nebr Lincoln NE 68583-0908

**VAN VLEET, JOHN F,** VETERINARY PATHOLOGY, CARDIAC PATHOLOGY. *Current Pos:* from asst prof to assoc prof, 67-76, PROF VET PATH, PURDUE UNIV, WEST LAFAYETTE, 76-, ASSOC DEAN ACAD AFFAIRS, 88- *Personal Data:* b Lodi, NY, Mar 23, 38; m 61, Nancy Coon; c Joanne & Teresa. *Educ:* Cornell Univ, DVM, 62; Univ Ill, MS, 65, PhD(vitamin E deficiency), 67. *Prof Exp:* Asst vet, 62-63; USPHS trainee vet path, Univ Ill, 63-66, instr, 66-67. *Mem:* Vet Med Asn; Int Acad Path; Am Col Vet Path; Am Asn Vet Med Col; Soc Toxicol Path; Am Asn Sci. *Res:* Ultrastructural and nutritional pathology; myocardial diseases; selenium-vitamin E deficiency; cardiomyopathy; cardiovascular and skeletal muscular pathology; cardiotoxicity; cardiac defibrillator damage. *Mailing Add:* 825 Ashland St West Lafayette IN 47906. *Fax:* 765-496-1261

**VAN VLIET, ANTONE CORNELIS,** WOOD SCIENCE, COMMUNICATIONS. *Current Pos:* asst prof wood prod, Extent, Ore State Univ, 63-71, from asst prof to assoc prof, 63-80, dir, Off Careers, Planning & Placement, 71-90, prof forest prod, 80-90, EMER PROF FOREST PROD, ORE STATE UNIV, 91- *Personal Data:* b San Francisco, Calif, Jan 11, 30; m 53; c 4. *Educ:* Ore State Univ, BS, 52, MS, 58; Mich State Univ, PhD, 70. *Prof Exp:* Instr forest prod, Ore State Univ, 55-59; asst to plant mgr plywood prod, Bohemia Lumber Co, 59-60. *Concurrent Pos:* State Rep, Dist 35, Ore Legis, 75, 77, 79, 81, 83, 85, 87, 89, 91 & 93; mem, Environ Qual Comn. *Mem:* Forest Prod Res Soc. *Res:* Plywood production; wood anatomy and utilization; company educational programs; behavioral aspect of communications; management science. *Mailing Add:* 1530 NW 13th Corvallis OR 97330. *Fax:* 541-754-8873

**VAN VLIET, CAROLYNE MARINA,** STATISTICAL MECHANICS. *Current Pos:* PROF ELEC & COMPUT ENG, FLA INT UNIV, 92- *Personal Data:* b Dordrecht, Neth, Dec 27, 29; US citizen; div; c 4. *Educ:* Free Univ, Amsterdam, BS, 49, MA, 53, PhD(physics), 56. *Prof Exp:* Fel elec eng, Univ Minn, Minneapolis, 56-57, asst prof, 57-58; asst dir, Physics Lab, Free Univ, Amsterdam; from assoc prof to prof elec eng, Univ Minn, Minneapolis, 60-66, prof elec eng & physics, 66-69; prof theoret physics, Ctr Math Res, Univ Montreal, 69-95. *Concurrent Pos:* Fulbright scholar, 56-58; vis prof, Univ Fla, 74 & 78-89, Fla Int Univ, 92- *Mem:* Am Phys Soc; fel Am Sci Affil; Europ Phys Soc; Can Asn Physicists; fel Inst Elec & Electronics Engrs; Can Res Inst Advan Women. *Res:* Non-equilibrium statistical mechanics; kinetic equations and electrical transport in solids; solid state electronics; noise and fluctuation phenomena. *Mailing Add:* Dept Elec & Comput Eng Fla Int Univ Univ Park Miami FL 33199. *Fax:* 305-348-3707; *E-Mail:* vanvliet@atseng.fin.edu

**VAN VOORHIES, WAYNE ALAN,** RESEARCHING CAUSES & MECHANISMS OF AGING RESEARCHING COSTS OF REPRODUCTION. *Current Pos:* RES ASSOC, UNIV ARIZ, 93- *Personal Data:* b Apr 4, 56; m 92, Laurie Abbott; c Skyler Scott. *Educ:* Prescott Col, BA, 78; Univ Ariz, MS, 88, PhD(ecol & evolutionary biol), 93. *Prof Exp:* Res specialist, Univ Ill, 78-82. *Concurrent Pos:* Instr, Outward Bound, 80-83; foreign fisheries observer, Nat Marine Fisheries, 89. *Mem:* AAAS; Soc Study Evolution. *Res:* Studying why organisms age and die contrary to standard assumptions on the costs of reproduction, found that increased sperm production dramatically reduces lifespan in male nematode worms; effects of temperature and organisms body size and the bioenergetic costs of growth. *Mailing Add:* 1125 N Olsen Ave Tucson AZ 85719. *Fax:* 520-621-3709; *E-Mail:* voorhies@ccit.arizona.edu

**VAN VORIS, PETER,** ECOLOGY, ECOSYSTEM ANALYSIS. *Current Pos:* res scientist ecol, Columbus Div, Battelle Mem Inst, 77-82, STAFF SCIENTIST, EARTH SCI DEPT, BATTELLE NORTHWEST, RICHLAND, WA, 83- *Personal Data:* b Bethlehem, Pa, Mar 10, 48; m 71; c 1. *Educ:* Kenyon Col, BA, 70; State Univ NY, Buffalo, MS, 73; Univ Tenn, PhD(ecol), 77. *Honors & Awards:* Outstanding Col & Univ Educator Award, Asn Am Cols & Univs, 74. *Prof Exp:* Instr biol & ecol, Trocaire Col, 72-74; res asst, Oak Ridge Nat Lab, 74-76. *Concurrent Pos:* Fed fel, State Univ NY, Buffalo, 71-72; consult, Chem-Trol Pollution Serv Inc, Model City, NY, 71-73; Dept Energy/Oak Ridge Assoc Univs fel, Oak Ridge Nat Lab, 76-77.

*Mem:* Ecol Soc Am; Am Inst Biol Sci; AAAS; Am Soc Naturalists; Audubon Soc; Am Soc Testing & Mat; Soc Environ Toxicol & Chem. *Res:* Phenomena of stability in ecosystems; the relationship of the measure of complexity with ecosystem stability; terrestrial microcosm development; environmental toxicology. *Mailing Add:* Pac NW Lab Batelle Mem Inst PO Box 999 Mail Stop K4-12 Richland WA 99352

**VAN VOROUS, TED,** ANALYTICAL CHEMISTRY. *Current Pos:* PRES, VAN VOROUS CONSULTS & E-LINE/USA, 81-; PRES, VACUUM INC, 82- *Personal Data:* b Billings, Mont, Jan 6, 29; m 51; c 5. *Educ:* Mont State Col, BS, 53, MS, 54. *Prof Exp:* Anal chemist, Dow Chem Co, 54-56, scientist-chemist, 56-59, sr chemist, 59-60, group supvr, 60-62, res group mgr, 62-69; pres, VTA Inc, 69-75; pres, Vac-Tac Systs, 76-81. *Mem:* Am Vacuum Soc; Geochem Soc; Sigma Xi. *Res:* High vacuum research; evaporation processes; ionphenomena; electron microsopy-metallurgy; electron microprobe analysis; instrumentation development; x-ray and emission spectroscopy; high temperature materials; epitaxial structures; planar magnetron sputtering. *Mailing Add:* Van Vorous Consults 5547 Central Ave Boulder CO 80302

**VAN VORST, WILLIAM D,** ALTERNATE FUELS & WASTE MINIMIZATION, HYDROGEN ENERGY SYSTEMS. *Current Pos:* from lectr to prof eng, 46-87, chmn, Eng Syst Dept, 75-78, PROF ENG, UNIV CALIF, LOS ANGELES, 73- *Personal Data:* b Cuthbert, Ga, Aug 20, 19; m 49; c 3. *Educ:* Rice Inst, BS, 41, ChE, 42; Mass Inst Technol, SM, 43; Univ Calif, Los Angeles, PhD, 53. *Honors & Awards:* Ralph Teetor Award, Soc Automotive Engrs. *Prof Exp:* Res engr, Northrop Aircraft, Inc, 43-46 & NAm Aviation, Inc, 46. *Concurrent Pos:* Consult, Aerospace Industs, Inc, 49-59; overseas exp & consult int develop, 59-; vpres acad affairs, Robert Col, Istanbul, 69-71, adv foreign fac, Bogazici Univ, 71-72. *Mem:* AAAS; Am Soc Eng Educ; fel Am Inst Chem Engrs; fel Inst Advan Eng; Int Asn Hydrogen Energy. *Res:* Engineering systems; industrial development and role of technology in developing countries; environmental engineering-pollution abatement; hydrogen and alcohols as alternative vehicular fuels; energy conversion-alternative sources. *Mailing Add:* 5531 Boelter Hall Univ Calif 405 Hilgard Ave Los Angeles CA 90095-1592

**VAN VUNAKIS, HELEN,** BIOCHEMISTRY. *Current Pos:* from asst prof to assoc prof, 58-74, PROF BIOCHEM, BRANDEIS UNIV, 74- *Personal Data:* b New York, NY, June 15, 24; m 58; c 2. *Educ:* Hunter Col, BA, 46; Columbia Univ, PhD(biochem), 51. *Prof Exp:* USPHS fel & res assoc, Johns Hopkins Univ, 51-54; sr res scientist, State Dept Health, NY, 54-58. *Concurrent Pos:* NIH career res award; mem, Soc Scholars, Johns Hopkins Univ. *Mem:* Am Soc Biol Chem. *Res:* Structure of proteins and nucleic acids; nicotine metabolism; assay and metabolism of other tobacco compounds. *Mailing Add:* Dept Biochem Brandeis Univ Waltham MA 02254-9110

**VAN WAGENEN, BRADFORD CARR,** MEDICINAL CHEMISTRY, SYNTHETIC ORGANIC & NATURAL PRODUCTS CHEMISTRY. *Current Pos:* RES SCIENTIST MED CHEM, NPS PHARMACEUT, INC, 89- *Personal Data:* b Price, Utah, Dec 18, 59; m 91, Ione Ravndal. *Educ:* Southern Utah State Univ, BS, 83; Mont State Univ, PhD(chem), 88. *Prof Exp:* Res assoc, Dept Chem, Mont State Univ, 88-89. *Mem:* Am Chem Soc. *Res:* Design, synthesis and structure-activity relationships of various types of medicinal agents, particularly calcium receptor modulators used for the treatment of stroke, pain, osteoporosis and primary hyperparathyroidism. *Mailing Add:* NPS Pharmaceut Inc 420 Chipeta Way Salt Lake City UT 84108. *Fax:* 801-583-4961

**VAN WAGNER, EDWARD M,** ELECTRICAL ENGINEERING. *Current Pos:* RETIRED. *Personal Data:* b Highland Falls, NY, Nov 3, 24; m 52; c 3. *Educ:* Univ Rochester, BS, 51. *Prof Exp:* Lab technician, Distillation Prod Div, Eastman Kodak Co, 51-53; elec engr, Consol Vacuum Corp, Xerox Corp, Rochester, 53-55, physicist, Haloid Co, 55-58 & Haloid Xerox Corp, 58-65, scientist, 65-67, mgt photoceptor process design 67-69, systs anal, Res Lab Div, 69-97. *Res:* Vacuum gauges; electrical instrumentation and control of vacuum production systems; graphic arts applications for xerography; design of chemical process equipment; vacuum equipment; welding and forming equipment and electrooptical test equipment. *Mailing Add:* 89 Anytrell Dr Webster NY 14580

**VAN WAGTENDONK, JAN WILLEM,** FOREST ECOLOGY. *Current Pos:* RES SCIENTIST FIRE ECOL, YOSEMITE NAT PARK, NAT PARK SERV, 72- *Personal Data:* b Palo Alto, Calif, Feb 21, 40; m 68; c 2. *Educ:* Ore State Univ, BS, 63; Univ Calif, Berkeley, MS, 68, PhD(wildland mgt sci), 72. *Mem:* Soc Am Foresters; Ecol Soc Am. *Res:* Ecological role of fire in the Sierra Nevada ecosystems; recreational carrying capacities for wilderness areas. *Mailing Add:* 9985 Incline Rd Yosemite Nat Park El Portal CA 95389

**VAN WART, HAROLD EDGAR,** BIOCHEMISTRY, PHYSICAL CHEMISTRY. *Current Pos:* from asst prof to assoc prof 78-86, PROF CHEM, FLA STATE UNIV, 86- *Personal Data:* b Bay Shore, NY, Oct 29, 47; m 74; c 3. *Educ:* State Univ NY, Binghamton, BA, 69; Cornell Univ, MS, 71, PhD(biophys chem), 74. *Prof Exp:* Temp asst prof chem, Cornell Univ, 74-75; NIH fel biochem & assoc staff med, Harvard Med Sch, 75-78. *Concurrent Pos:* NSF, undergrad res Participation grant, 67-68; res assoc, Univ Vienna, Austria, 69; teaching asst, Cornell Univ, 69-71; NIH trainee, Cornell Univ, 74-75; fel, Harvard Med Sch, 75-78; NIH Res Career Develop Award, 82-87; dir, Molecular Biophys, PhD Prog, 82-86; dir, Molecular Biophys Laser Spectros Lab, 80-; vis lectr, var schs, co & socs. *Mem:* Am Chem Soc; AAAS; Fedn Am Soc Biol Chemists; Am Soc Biochem &

Molecular Biol. *Res:* Structure-function relationships in enzymes, enzyme mechanism, Raman and resonance Raman studies of biomolecules; enzymology, proteolytic enzymes, role of proteolysis in biological control, metalloenzymes. *Mailing Add:* Inst Biochem & Cell Biol Syntex USA 3401 Hillview Ave Palo Alto CA 94304-1397. *Fax:* 650-354-7554

**VAN WAZER, JOHN ROBERT,** CHEMISTRY. *Current Pos:* prof, 68-88, EMER PROF CHEM, VANDERBILT UNIV, 88- *Personal Data:* b Chicago, Ill, Apr 11, 18; m 96, Elizabeth M Markley; c Mary E (Van Wazer). *Educ:* Northwestern Univ, BS, 40; Harvard Univ, AM, 41, PhD(phys chem), 42. *Prof Exp:* Phys chemist, Eastman Kodak Co, 42-44; res group leader, Clinton Eng Works, Tenn, 44-46; phys chemist, Rumford Chem Works, RI, 46-49; head physics res, Great Lakes Carbon Corp, 49-50; sr scientist, Monsanto Co, 50-68. *Concurrent Pos:* Asst res dir, Monsanto Co, 51-60, dir chem dynamics res, 64-67. *Mem:* AAAS; Am Chem Soc; Soc Rheol; NY Acad Sci; Royal Soc Chem London. *Res:* Applied quantum mechanics; chemistry of phosphorus compounds; substituent-exchange or redistribution reactions; inorganic chemistry; rheology; applied nuclear-magnetic resonance; photoelectron spectroscopy; nutrition. *Mailing Add:* 9650 S Ocean Dr No 806 Jensen Beach FL 34957

**VAN WEERT, GEZINUS,** EXTRACTIVE METALLURGY, CHLORIDE HYDROMETALLURGY. *Current Pos:* ADJ PROF, MCGILL UNIV, 95-; PRES, ORETOME LTD, 96- *Personal Data:* b Rotterdam, Neth, Aug 24, 33; Can citizen; m 58, Roel Lageveen; c C Calvin & Ingrid I. *Educ:* Technol Univ Delft, BEng, 56, MEng, 58, DTechnol, 89; Univ Toronto, MASc, 59. *Honors & Awards:* Technol Award, Metall Soc, Am Inst Mining, Metall & Petrol Engrs, 73; Sherritt Hydrometall Award, 79. *Prof Exp:* Test engr metall, Inco, Copper Cliff, Ont, 59-61; res & develop investr, NJ Zinc, Pa, 61-63; mgr process metall, Falconbridge Nickel Mines, Toronto, 63-78; dir, tech & econ serv, QIT-Fer Et Titane Inc, 78-85; mgr, Metall Technol, Prochem Ltd, 85-86; gen mgr, Hydrochem Developments Ltd, 86-89; prof mineral processing & extractive metall, Technol Univ Delft, 90-95. *Concurrent Pos:* Chmn, Hydrometall Sect, Can Inst Mining & Metall, 72-77; ed, CIM Bulletin, 78-85; dir, Que Metal Powders, 81-85. *Mem:* Fel Can Inst Mining & Metall; Am Inst Mining, Metall & Petrol Engrs; Am Inst Chem Engrs; Inst Mining & Metall UK; Royal Dutch Inst Engrs. *Res:* Non-ferrous extractive metallurgy, both hydro and pyro, and operational aspects of the ductile iron foundry industry; mineral dressing; fluid bed chloride pyrohydrolysis; transfer in agitated tanks. *Mailing Add:* Oretome Ltd 16668 Humberstation Rd RR 3 Caledon East ON L0N 1E0 Can. *Fax:* 905-880-3748

**VAN WIJNGAARDEN, ARIE,** PHYSICS. *Current Pos:* Teacher physics, 62-70, assoc prof, 70-73, PROF PHYSICS, UNIV WINDSOR, 73- *Personal Data:* b Holland, Apr 8, 33; Can citizen; m 57; c 3. *Educ:* McMaster Univ, PhD(physics), 62. *Concurrent Pos:* Nat Res Coun-Ont Res Found res grants, 62- *Res:* Radiative processes and lamb shift. *Mailing Add:* Dept Physics Univ Windsor Windsor ON N9B 3P4 Can

**VAN WINKLE, LON J,** BIOCHEMISTRY. *Current Pos:* Assoc prof, 76-86, PROF BIOCHEM, MIDWESTERN UNIV, 86- *Personal Data:* b Ann Arbor, Mich, Mar 21, 46. *Educ:* Eastern Mich Univ, BA, 68; Wayne State Univ, PhD(biochem & genetics), 75. *Mem:* Am Soc Study Reproduction; Am Soc Biochem & Molecular Biol; Sigma Xi; Am Physiol Soc. *Res:* Biochemistry. *Mailing Add:* 6033 N Sheridan Rd Apt 18E Chicago IL 60660-3030

**VAN WINKLE, MICHAEL GEORGE,** IMMUNOLOGY, IMMUNOCHEMISTRY. *Current Pos:* SR RES IMMUNOCHEMIST, CLIN IMMUNOASSAY RES & DEVELOP, BECKMAN INSTRUMENTS, INC, 78- *Personal Data:* b Newark, Ohio, July 25, 39; c 3. *Educ:* Ohio State Univ, BSc, 62, MSc, 64, PhD(immunol), 66. *Prof Exp:* Group leader res atopic allergy, Riker Lab, 3M Co, 66-71; head, Dept Immunol, Nucleic Acid Res Inst, Int Chem & Nuclear Corp, 71-73; mgr, Dept Hepatitis, Curtis Labs, Inc, 73-76; mgr hepatitis opers, Nuclear Med Labs, Inc, 76-78. *Mem:* Am Asn Immunol; Am Soc Microbiol; AAAS. *Res:* Research and development on clinical immunoassays. *Mailing Add:* Beckman Instruments Inc 200 S Kraemer Blvd Brea CA 92621-6228. *Fax:* 714-961-4817

**VAN WINKLE, QUENTIN,** CHEMISTRY. *Current Pos:* res assoc chem, 46-48, from asst prof to prof, 48-80, EMER PROF, OHIO STATE UNIV, 80- *Personal Data:* b Grand Forks, NDak, Mar 10, 19; m 41, Mildred Knutson; c Robert, Jean A, James & Gretchen. *Educ:* SDak Sch Mines & Technol, BS, 40; Ohio State Univ, PhD(chem), 47. *Prof Exp:* Asst chem, Ohio State Univ, 40-43, res assoc eng, Exp Sta, 44; asst chemist metall lab, Univ Chicago, 44-46. *Concurrent Pos:* Consult, E I du Pont de Nemours & Co, 57-75. *Mem:* AAAS; Am Chem Soc. *Res:* Physico-chemical properties of proteins, high polymers; nucleic acids; surface chemistry. *Mailing Add:* 271 S Main St West Mansfield OH 43358

**VAN WINKLE, WEBSTER, JR,** ENVIRONMENTAL SCIENCES. *Current Pos:* res assoc, 72-75, res staff mem, Environ Sci Div, 75-78, HEAD, AQUATIC ECOL SECT, OAK RIDGE NAT LAB, 79- *Personal Data:* b Plainfield, NJ, Nov 18, 38; m 61; c 3. *Educ:* Oberlin Col, BA, 61; Rutgers Univ, New Brunswick, PhD(zool), 67. *Prof Exp:* Res assoc, Shellfish Res Lab, Rutgers Univ, 66-67; asst prof biol, Col William Mary, 67-70; USPHS fels, NC State Univ, 70 & 72. *Concurrent Pos:* NSF fel, Marine Lab, Duke Univ, 69; NSF sci fac fel, NC State Univ, 71-72. *Mem:* AAAS; Ecol Soc Am; Am Fisheries Soc. *Res:* Assessment of environmental impacts on aquatic ecosystems; fish population modeling; spectral analysis of environmental time series; data analysis. *Mailing Add:* Environ Sci Div Bldg 1505 Oak Ridge Nat Lab Oak Ridge TN 37831-6038

**VAN WINTER, CLASINE,** MATHEMATICAL PHYSICS. *Current Pos:* PROF MATH & PHYSICS, UNIV KY, 68- *Personal Data:* b Amsterdam, Neth, Apr 8, 29. *Educ:* Univ Groningen, BSc, 50, MSc, 54, PhD(physics), 57. *Prof Exp:* Res asst physics, Univ Groningen, 51-58, sci officer, 58-68. *Concurrent Pos:* Fel physics, Univ Birmingham, 57 & Niels Bohr Inst Theoret Physics, Univ Copenhagen, 63; vis assoc prof physics, Ind Univ, Bloomington, 67-68; scientist-in-residence, Math & Comput Sci Div, Argonne Nat Lab, 85. *Mem:* Am Math Soc; Am Phys Soc; Int Asn Math Physics. *Res:* Three-and more-body problem in quantum mechanics; quantum scattering theory; functional analysis; complex variables. *Mailing Add:* Dept Math Univ Ky Chem-Physics Bldg Lexington KY 40506-0055

**VAN WOERT, MELVIN H,** INTERNAL MEDICINE. *Current Pos:* prof internal med & head, Sect Clin Pharmacol, 74-78, PROF PHARMACOL, MT SINAI SCH MED, 74-, PROF NEUROL, 78- *Personal Data:* b Brooklyn, NY, Nov 3, 29; m 55. *Educ:* Columbia Univ, BA, 51; NY Med Col, MD, 56. *Prof Exp:* From intern to resident internal med, Univ Chicago, 56-60, res asst gastroenterol, 62-63; from asst scientist to assoc scientist, Brookhaven Nat Lab, 63-67; from asst prof to assoc prof med & pharmacol, Sch Med, Yale Univ, 67-74. *Mem:* AAAS; fel Am Col Physicians; Soc Neurosci; Soc Neurochem; Am Soc Pharmacol & Exp Therapeut. *Res:* Neuropharmacological approaches to extrapyramidal disease; serotonin metabolism and myoclonus. *Mailing Add:* Mt Sinai Sch Med New York NY 10029

**VAN WORMER, KENNETH A(UGUSTUS), JR,** CHEMICAL ENGINEERING. *Current Pos:* from instr to assoc prof, 54-79, chmn dept, 71-81, PROF CHEM ENG, TUFTS UNIV, 79- *Personal Data:* b Mannsville, NY, Oct 4, 30; m 57; c 4. *Educ:* Clarkson Col Technol, BS, 52, MS, 54; Mass Inst Technol, ScD(chem eng), 61. *Prof Exp:* Engr chem eng, Gen Elec Co, 52-53. *Mem:* Am Soc Eng Educ; Am Inst Chem Engrs. *Res:* Solar engineering; energy conservation; waste water treatment; liquid-liquid extraction; heterogeneous catalysis in the direct reduction of iron ore; applied thermodynamics; applications of digital computers to chemical engineering; reaction kinetics; contribution of nucleation to phase transformations; applied mathematics; optimization; electronic materials processing. *Mailing Add:* Dept Chem Eng Tufts Univ Medford MA 02155-5555

**VAN WYK, CHRISTOPHER JOHN,** OBJECT-ORIENTED PROGRAMMING, COMPUTATIONAL GEOMETRY. *Current Pos:* assoc prof, 90-92, PROF COMPUT SCI, DREW UNIV, 92- *Personal Data:* b Fairborn, Ohio, Sept 5, 55; m 80; c 2. *Educ:* Swarthmore Col, BA, 77; Stanford Univ, PhD(comput sci), 80. *Prof Exp:* Mem tech staff, AT&T Bell Labs, 80-91. *Concurrent Pos:* Instr, NJ Gov Sch Sci, 84 & 89; vis asst prof, Stevens Inst Technol, 84-85; vis lectr, Princeton Univ, 87; assoc ed, J Comput & Syst Sci, 90-; consult, AT&T, 91- *Mem:* Math Asn Am; Asn Comput Mach; Inst Elec & Electronics Engrs; Sigma Xi; Soc Indust & Appl Math. *Res:* Application of techniques from data structures, algorithms and computational geometry to problems in graphics, circuit design and document preparation. *Mailing Add:* 111 N Passaic Ave Chatham NJ 07928-2609. *Fax:* 973-408-3572; *E-Mail:* cvanwyk@drew.edu

**VAN WYK, JUDSON JOHN,** PEDIATRICS, ENDOCRINOLOGY. *Current Pos:* from asst prof to prof, 55-75, KENAN PROF PEDIAT, SCH MED, UNIV NC, CHAPEL HILL, 75-, PROF BIOL, 88- *Personal Data:* b Maurice, Iowa, June 10, 21; m 44, Persis Parker; c Judith, Peresis A, Peter & Judson J Jr. *Educ:* Hope Col, AB, 43; Johns Hopkins Univ, MD, 48; Am Bd Pediat, dipl. *Hon Degrees:* ScD, Hope Col, 76; Laurea Hon Causa, Univ Genoa, Italy, 92. *Honors & Awards:* Fred Konrad Koch Award & Medal, Endocrine Soc, 88. *Prof Exp:* Fel biochem, St Louis Univ, 43-44; Henry Strong Dennison scholar physiol chem, Johns Hopkins Univ, 47, intern & asst resident pediat, Johns Hopkins Hosp, 48-50; investr metab, Nat Heart Inst, 51-53; fel pediat endocrinol, Johns Hopkins Univ, 53-55. *Concurrent Pos:* Attend physician, NC Mem Hosp, 55-; Markle scholar med sci, 56-61; USPHS res career award, 62-88; mem training grants comt in diabetes & metab, NIH, 67-71 & endocrine study sect, 71-75; vis scientist, Karolinska Inst, Sweden, 68-69; consult, Womack Army Hosp, Ft Bragg; assoc ed, J Clin Endocrinol & Metab, 84-89. *Mem:* Endocrine Soc; Soc Pediat Res; Fel Am Acad Pediat; Am Pediat Soc; Lawson Wilkins Pediat Endocrine Soc (pres, 76). *Res:* Human sex differentiation; pituitary function and hormonal control of growth and sexual maturation; isolation and physiologic role of somatomedin; growth factors in cellular proliferation. *Mailing Add:* Univ NC Chapel Hill Div Pediat Endocrinol CB No 7220 509 Burnett-Womack Chapel Hill NC 27599-7220. *Fax:* 919-966-2423; *E-Mail:* judvw@med.unc.edu

**VAN WYLEN, GORDON J(OHN),** MECHANICAL ENGINEERING. *Current Pos:* pres, 72-87, EMER PRES, HOPE COL, 87- *Personal Data:* b Grant, Mich, Feb 6, 20; m 51, Margaret DeWitt; c 5. *Educ:* Calvin Col, AB, 42; Univ Mich, BSE, 42, MSE, 47; Mass Inst Technol, ScD(mech eng), 51. *Hon Degrees:* DLitt, Hope Col, 72. *Prof Exp:* Indust engr, E I du Pont de Nemours & Co, 42-43; instr mech eng, Pa State Univ, 46-48; asst, Mass Inst Technol, 49-51; from asst prof to prof, Univ Mich, Ann Arbor, 51-72, chmn dept, 58-65, dean col eng, 65-72. *Mem:* Fel AAAS; fel Am Soc Mech Engrs. *Res:* Thermodynamics and cryogenics. *Mailing Add:* 817 Brook Village Dr Holland MI 49423

**VANYO, JAMES PATRICK,** ROTATING FLUIDS, HELIOTROPIC STROMATOLITES. *Current Pos:* from asst prof to assoc prof, 71-84, PROF ENG, UNIV CALIF, SANTA BARBARA, 84- *Personal Data:* b Wheeling, WVa, Jan 29, 28. *Educ:* WVa Univ, BSME, 52; Salmon P Chase Col, JD, 59; Univ Calif, Los Angeles, MA, 66, PhD(eng), 69. *Prof Exp:* Asst supvr commun, Am Tel & Tel Co, NY, 52-53; pres, Van Industs, Inc, Ohio, 54-59;

asst to pres, Remanco, Inc, Calif, 59-61; proposal specialist, Marquardt Corp, 61-63; planning analyst, Litton Industs, 69-70. *Concurrent Pos:* Lectr, Sinclair Col, Ohio, 56-57; consult rotating fluids; vis mem staff, Commonwealth Sci Indust Res Orgn, Div Atmos Physics, Melbourne, Australia, 80, Sch Phys, Univ Newcastle, Eng, 83, & Geophys Inst, Fairbanks, Alaska, 87, Dept Geol Sci, Univ Calif, Santa Barbara, 92. *Mem:* Am Phys Soc; Am Geophys Union. *Res:* Dynamics of rotating nonrigid bodies and fluids; Earth-Sun-Moon dynamics and heliotropic stromatolites; luni-solar precession and the geodynamo. *Mailing Add:* Dept Mech Eng Univ Calif Santa Barbara CA 93106. *Fax:* 805-893-8651; *E-Mail:* vanyo@engineering.ucsb.edu

**VANYSEK, PETR,** ELECTROCHEMISTRY, ELECTROANALYTICAL CHEMISTRY. *Current Pos:* ASSOC PROF ANALYTICAL CHEM, NORTHERN ILL UNIV, 85- *Personal Data:* b Ostrava, Czech, June 12, 52. *Educ:* Charles Univ Prague, MS, 76, RNDr, 77; Czech Acad Sci, PhD, 82. *Prof Exp:* Res fel, Univ NC, 82-84; fac in residence chem, Univ NH, 84-85. *Mem:* Electrochem Soc; Soc Electroanal Chem; Int Soc Electrochem. *Res:* Electrochemical properties of interfaces between immiscible solutions, impedance studies of electrochemical systems; electroanalytical chemistry and small domain electrochemistry; editing of electrochemical literature and data; computer interfacing in electrochemistry; physical electrochemistry; surface science. *Mailing Add:* Dept Chem Northern Ill Univ DeKalb IL 60115-2862. *Fax:* 815-753-4802; *E-Mail:* pvanysek@niu.edu

**VAN ZANDT, LONNIE L,** solid state physics; deceased, see previous edition for last biography

**VAN ZANDT, PAUL DOYLE,** PARASITOLOGY. *Current Pos:* RETIRED. *Personal Data:* b Vandalia, Ill, Dec 29, 27; m 54; c 1. *Educ:* Greenville Col, AB, 52; Univ Ill, MS, 53; Univ NC, MSPH, 55, PhD(parasitol), 60. *Prof Exp:* Asst pub health, Univ NC, 58-61; from asst prof to prof biol, Youngstown State Univ, 61-91. *Mem:* Fel AAAS; Am Soc Parasitol; Am Soc Trop Med & Hyg; Royal Soc Trop Med & Hyg. *Res:* Immunology of animal parasites; medical parasitology and microbiology. *Mailing Add:* 7222 Pittsburgh Rd Poland OH 44514

**VAN ZANDT, THOMAS EDWARD,** RADAR METEOROLOGY. *Current Pos:* PHYSICIST, AERONOMY LAB, NAT OCEANIC & ATMOSPHERIC ADMIN, 57- *Personal Data:* b Highland Park, Mich, July 10, 29; m 61; c Tineke & Saskia. *Educ:* Duke Univ, BS, 50; Yale Univ, PhD, 55. *Prof Exp:* Physicist, Sandia Corp, 54-57. *Concurrent Pos:* Vis lectr, Univ Colo, 61-70, adj prof, 70- *Mem:* Am Geophys Union; Am Meteorol Soc; Int Union Radio Sci. *Res:* Atmospheric internal gravity waves; interpretation of clear-air doppler radar observations. *Mailing Add:* 2025 Alpine Dr Boulder CO 80304

**VAN ZEE, RICHARD JERRY,** ELECTRON SPIN RESONANCE SPECTROSCOPY. *Current Pos:* FEL PHYS CHEM, UNIV FLA, 75- *Personal Data:* b Kalamazoo, Mich, Feb 15, 47; m 77, Margaret Madison; c Rena, Carl, Joseph, Theodore, Dora & Raymond. *Educ:* Western Ky Univ, BA, 69; Mich State Univ, PhD(phys chem), 76. *Prof Exp:* Grad asst chem, Mich State Univ, 69-75. *Res:* The electronic and magnetic characterization of high temperature, high spin molecules; high temperature vaporization techniques. *Mailing Add:* 18420 SW 75th Ave Archer FL 32618-9452. *E-Mail:* vanzee@pine.circa.efl.edu

**VAN ZWALENBERG, GEORGE,** MATHEMATICS. *Current Pos:* chmn dept, 74-77, PROF MATH, CALVIN COL, 68- *Personal Data:* b Neth, Sept 7, 30; US citizen; m 53, 76, 89; c 3. *Educ:* Calvin Col, BS, 53; Univ Fla, MA, 55; Univ Calif, Berkeley, PhD(math), 68. *Prof Exp:* Instr math, Bowling Green State Univ, 59-60; vis lectr, Calvin Col, 60-61, asst prof, 61-63; asst prof, Calif State Univ, Fresno, 63-67. *Concurrent Pos:* Math Asn Am vis lectr, High Schs, 65-66; head, Math Dept, Egyptian Air Force Acad, Bilbeis, Egypt, 86-88. *Mem:* Math Asn Am. *Res:* Complex variables. *Mailing Add:* Dept Math Calvin Col 3201 Burton St Grand Rapids MI 49546

**VAN ZWIETEN, MATTHEW JACOBUS,** VETERINARY PATHOLOGY. *Current Pos:* assoc dir, Merck Res Labs, 84-86, dir path, 86-89, sr dir, 89-92, EXEC DIR, DEPT SAFETY ASSESSMENT, MERCK RES LABS, 92- *Personal Data:* b Zeist, Neth, Apr 6, 45; US citizen; m 66; c 2. *Educ:* Univ Calif, Davis, BS, 67, DVM, 69; Am Col Vet Pathologists, dipl, 74; Univ Utrecht, PhD, 84. *Prof Exp:* Sci investr cell biol & path, Med Res Inst Infectious Dis, US Army, 69-71; res fel, New Eng Regional Primate Res Ctr & Animal Res Ctr, Harvard Med Sch, 71-75, assoc path, 75-76; mem staff, Inst Exp Gerontol, 76-84. *Concurrent Pos:* Res assoc path, Angell Mem Animal Hosp, 71-74, consult, 75-76; res assoc path, Children's Hosp Med Ctr, 73-75; head diag procedures, New Eng Regional Primate Res Ctr & Animal Res Ctr, Harvard Med Sch, 75-76. *Mem:* Am Col Vet Pathologists; Int Acad Path; Am Asn Lab Animal Sci; Am Vet Med Asn; Soc Toxicol Pathologists. *Res:* Pathology of aging in laboratory animals; mechanisms of radiation induced mammary carcinogenesis in rats; identification and development of spontaneous animal diseases as models for their human counterparts. *Mailing Add:* Dept Safety Assessment Merck Res Labs West Point PA 19486

**VAN ZYTVELD, JOHN BOS,** SOLID STATE PHYSICS. *Current Pos:* from asst prof to assoc prof, 68-76, dept chmn, 85-90, PROF PHYSICS, CALVIN COL, 76- *Personal Data:* b Hammond, Ind, Nov 12, 40; m 61; c 3. *Educ:* Calvin Col, AB, 62; Mich State Univ, MS, 64, PhD(physics), 67. *Prof Exp:* Fel physics, Univ Sheffield, 67-68. *Concurrent Pos:* Res physicist, Battelle Mem Inst, Ohio, 69; sr fel, Dept Physics, Univ Leicester, Eng, 74-75; Fulbright-Hays sr lectr physics, Yarmouk Univ, Irbid, Jordan, 80-81; assoc prog dir, Solid State Phys Prog, Div Mat Res, NSF, Washington, DC, 83-84, prog dir, 84-85; mem phys coun, Undergrad Res, 85-90, pres, 88-90; Fulbright res fel, Inst Electronic Struct & Laser, Found Res & Technol, Hellas, Heraklion, Crete, Greece, 90; guest prof, Kyoto Univ, Kyoto, Japan, 91; sr prog dir, Murdock Charitable Trust, Vancouver Wash, 96- *Mem:* AAAS; Am Phys Soc; Am Asn Physics Teachers; fel Am Sci Affil. *Res:* Electron transport properties of solid and liquid metals, alloys and semiconductors. *Mailing Add:* 1903 NE 107 Ave Vancouver WA 98664. *E-Mail:* jvanzytv@calvin.edu

**VARADAN, VASUNDARA VENKATRAMAN,** ENGINEERED SCIENCES. *Current Pos:* PROF, DEPT ENG SCI & MECH, PA STATE UNIV, 85- *Personal Data:* b Guntur, India, June 10, 48; m 73; c 3. *Educ:* Kerala Univ, India, BSc, 67, MSc, 69; Univ Ill, Chicago Circle, PhD(physics), 74. *Prof Exp:* Res assoc mech, Cornell Univ, 74-77; from asst prof to assoc prof mech, Ohio State Univ, 77-85. *Concurrent Pos:* Prin investr, Rockwell Int, 77-81; co-prin investr, Off Naval Res, 78-, & Res Ctr Eng Electronic & Acoust Mat; Nat Oceanic & Atmospheric Asn grant, 78-80, Naval Res Lab, 79 & Ames Lab, Army Res Off & Naval Coastal Systs Ctr, 81-; ed, J Wave-Mat Interaction; chmn bd, HVS Technols Inc, 88-; distinguished prof eng sci & mech & elec eng, Pa State Univ. *Mem:* Fel Acoust Soc Am; Soc Eng Sci; Inst Elec & Electronics Engrs. *Res:* Wave-material interaction; composite materials; radar materials, chiral materials, active control, saw sensors. *Mailing Add:* Dept Eng Sci & Mech Pa State Univ Hammond Bldg rm 149 University Park PA 16802

**VARADAN, VIJAY K,** ELECTROMAGNETIC ABSORBING, OPTICAL COATINGS & SENSORS. *Current Pos:* PROF ENG SCI, PA STATE UNIV, 83-, PROF ENG SCI & ELEC ENG, & DIR, CTR ENG ELECTRONIC & ACOUST MAT, 86-, ALUMNI DISTINGUISHED PROF ENG, 88- *Personal Data:* b Madurai, India, Feb 23, 43; US citizen; m 73, Vasundara Venkatraman; c Haima, Venkatesh & Sailesh. *Educ:* Univ Madras, BE, 64; Pa State Univ, MS, 69; Northwestern Univ, PhD(eng mech), 74. *Prof Exp:* Asst prof eng, Cornell Univ, 75-77; from asst prof to assoc prof eng, Ohio State Univ, 77-83, dir, Wave Propagation Lab, 79-83. *Concurrent Pos:* Mem adv bd mat, Serial Digit Input/Output Civil Appln, 86- *Mem:* Am Soc Mech Engrs; fel Acoust Soc Am; Inst Elec & Electronics Engrs; Am Defense Preparedness Asn; Am Ceramics Soc; Mat Res Soc. *Res:* All aspects of wave-material interaction, sonar, radar, microwave and optically absorbing composites and piezoelectric, chiral, ferrite and polymer composites and conducting polymers; involved in the design and development of various electronic, acoustic and structural composites and devices including sensors, transducers, acoustic and ultrasonic wave absorbers and filters; also interested in microwave and ultrasonic experiments to measure the dielectric, magnetic, mechanical and optical properties of composites; microwave welding of ceramics, polymers and composites, electromagnetic interference/radio frequency interference materials, coatings, gaskets, sealants; magnetic shileding for power lines, computers; electromagnetic interference conformal coatings for circuit boards. *Mailing Add:* Dept Eng Sci & Mech Pa State Univ 149 Hammond Bldg rm 149 University Park PA 16802

**VARADARAJAN, KALATHOOR,** MATHEMATICS, TOPOLOGY. *Current Pos:* assoc prof, 71-73, PROF MATH, UNIV CALGARY, 73- *Personal Data:* b Bezwada, India, Apr 13, 35; m 61, Pattu; c Suchitra & Srinivasan. *Educ:* Loyola Col, Madras, India, BA, 55; Columbia Univ, PhD(topology), 60. *Prof Exp:* Res fel math, Tata Inst Fundamental Res, India, 60-61, fel, 61-67; vis assoc prof, Univ Ill, Urbana, 67-69; reader, Tata Inst Fundamental Res, India, 69-71; vis prof, Ramanujan Inst, Madras, 71. *Mem:* Am Math Soc; Can Math Cong. *Res:* Algebraic and differential topology; homological algebra. *Mailing Add:* Dept Math Statist & Comput Sci Univ Calgary 2500 University Dr Calgary AB T3A 1L9 Can. *E-Mail:* varadara@math.ucalgary.ca

**VARADHAN, SRINIVASA S R,** MATH, STATISTICS. *Current Pos:* vis mem, Courant Inst Math Sci, 63-66, from asst prof to assoc prof math, 66-72, dir, 80-84, PROF MATH, COURANT INST MATH SCI, 72- *Personal Data:* b Madias, India, Jan 2, 40. *Educ:* Madias Univ, BSc, 59; Indian Statist Inst, PhD(statist), 63. *Honors & Awards:* George David Birkhoff Prize, Am Math Soc, 94, Steele Prize, 96. *Prof Exp:* Instr, Indian Statist Inst, 62-63. *Concurrent Pos:* Alfred P Sloan fel, 69-70; Guggenheim fel, 84-85. *Mem:* Nat Acad Sci; Am Acad Arts & Sci; Third World Acad Sci; Am Math Soc. *Mailing Add:* Courant Inst Math NY Univ 251 Mercer St New York NY 10012-1110. *Fax:* 212-995-4121; *E-Mail:* varadhan@cims.nyu.edu

**VARADY, JOHN CARL,** BIOSTATISTICS. *Current Pos:* CONSULT, 93- *Personal Data:* b Niagara Falls, NY, Feb 26, 35; m 66. *Educ:* Calif Inst Technol, BS, 56; Univ Wash, MA, 58; Univ Calif, Los Angeles, PhD(biostatist), 65. *Prof Exp:* Opers res analyst, Radioplane Div, Northrop Corp, 57-58; sr mathematician, Systs Develop Corp, 58-65; chief biostatist, Calif Dept Ment Hyg, 65-66; dir comput servs, Univ Cincinnati, 66-70; dir biostatist, Syntex Labs, 70-93. *Mem:* Am Statist Asn; Asn Comput Mach. *Mailing Add:* 47 Oak St Los Altos CA 94022

**VARAIYA, PRAVIN PRATAP,** ELECTRICAL ENGINEERING, ECONOMICS. *Current Pos:* from asst prof to assoc prof, 66-70, PROF ELEC ENG, UNIV CALIF, BERKELEY, 70-, PROF ECON, 77- *Personal Data:* b Bombay, India, Oct 29, 40; m 63. *Educ:* Univ Bombay, India, BS, 60; Univ Calif, Berkeley, MS, 62, PhD(elec eng), 66. *Prof Exp:* Mem tech staff commun, Bell Tel Labs, 62-63. *Concurrent Pos:* Fel Guggenheim Found, 71-72; vis prof elec eng, Mass Inst Technol, 74-75; res prof, Miller Found, 78-79. *Mem:* Inst Elec & Electronics Engrs. *Res:* System theory; urban economics; computer communications. *Mailing Add:* Dept Elec Eng & Comput Sci Univ Calif Berkeley CA 94720

**VARAN, CYRUS O,** CIVIL ENGINEERING. *Current Pos:* CONSULT, 90- *Personal Data:* b Hamadan, Iran, Mar 26, 34; m; c 1. *Educ:* SDak State Univ, BS, 58; Univ Kans, MS, 60; Univ Del, PhD(appl sci), 64. *Prof Exp:* Struct engr, Howard, Needles, Tammen & Bergendoff, Consult Engrs, 58-60; from asst prof to assoc prof civil eng, Univ NMex, 64-90. *Concurrent Pos:* Res assoc, Univ Del Res Found res grant, 63-64; prin investr, grants, Univ NMex, 65, NSF, 65-67 & Sandia Labs, 70-71 & 71-72; investr, US CEngr grant, 70. *Mem:* Am Soc Civil Engrs; Am Soc Eng Educ. *Res:* Dynamics of structures; discrete and macro mechanics; design of guyed towers and articulated lattice shell structures; dynamics of grid-stiffened and ribbed plates; seismic design of building structures. *Mailing Add:* 19 Siempre Verde Albuquerque NM 87123

**VARANASI, PRASAD,** PLANETARY ATMOSPHERES, SPECTROSCOPY. *Current Pos:* From asst prof to assoc prof eng physics, 67-81, PROF ATMOSPHERIC SCI, STATE UNIV NY, STONY BROOK, 81- *Personal Data:* b Vijayavada, India, Dec 20, 38; m 72. *Educ:* Andhra Univ, India, BSc Hons, 57; Indian Inst Sci, Bangalore, MSc, 61; Mass Inst Technol, SM, 62; Univ Calif, San Diego, PhD(eng physics), 67. *Concurrent Pos:* NASA grants; assoc ed, J Quant Spectros & Radiative Transfer, 73; mem, Atmospheric Spectras Applns Working Group, 88- *Mem:* Am Geophys Union; Optical Soc Am; Am Astron Soc. *Res:* Infrared spectroscopy as applied to planetary atmospheres; experimental work on collision broadening of spectral lines and molecular structure; global warming; remote sensing of atmosphere; atmospheric radiation measurements. *Mailing Add:* Inst Terrestrial & Planetary Atmospheres State Univ NY Stony Brook NY 11794-2300. *Fax:* 516-632-6251

**VARANASI, SURYANARAYANA RAO,** ENGINEERING MECHANICS. *Current Pos:* UNIT CHIEF, RENTON STRUCT ENGR, 93- *Personal Data:* b Narsapur, India, Oct 4, 39; US citizen; m 65. *Educ:* Andhra Univ, BE, 60; Calif Inst Technol, MS, 61; Univ Wash, PhD(aerospace eng), 68. *Prof Exp:* Res engr appl mech, Gas Turbine Div, Boeing Co, 65-66; res engr, Dept Comput, Boeing Com Airplane Co, 66-69, specialist engr fatigue & fracture res, struct technol, 69-93. *Concurrent Pos:* Consult, Math Sci Corp, 63. *Mem:* Am Soc Testing & Mat. *Res:* Fracture mechanics; fatigue; structural integrity; damage tolerance; stress analysis; finite element methods; plasticity; viscoelasticity; wave propagation; applied mathematics; computer applications; working with civilian military aircraft air worthiness. *Mailing Add:* Struct Eng Boeing Co Mail Stop 7061 Seattle WA 98124

**VARANASI, USHA,** environmental biochemistry, aquatic toxicology, for more information see previous edition

**VARANI, JAMES,** METASTASIS, CELL BIOLOGY. *Current Pos:* ASSOC PROF IMMUNOL, MED SCH, UNIV MICH, 80- *Educ:* Univ NDak, PhD(microbiol), 74. *Res:* Cancer. *Mailing Add:* Dept Path Univ Mich Med Sch 1301 Catherine Rd Box 0602 Ann Arbor MI 48109-0602. *Fax:* 313-936-0755

**VARBERG, DALE ELTHON,** MATHEMATICS. *Current Pos:* From asst prof to prof, 58-90, EMER PROF MATH, HAMLINE UNIV, 90- *Personal Data:* b Forest City, Iowa, Sept 9, 30; m 55, Idella Vall; c Joel, Karen & Thomas. *Educ:* Univ Minn, BA, 54, MA, 57, PhD(math), 59. *Concurrent Pos:* NSF fel, Inst Advan Study, 64-65; sci fac fel, Univ Wash, 71-72. *Mem:* Am Math Soc; Math Asn Am. *Res:* Stochastic and Gaussian processes; measure theory; convexity theory. *Mailing Add:* 1363 W Roselawn St Paul MN 55113-5823

**VARCO-SHEA, THERESA CAMILLE,** ELECTROCHEMICAL SENSOR DESIGN. *Current Pos:* electrochem design engr, Div High Voltage Eng, 87-88, TECH DIR, ANACON CORP, 88- *Personal Data:* b Buffalo, NY, Apr 23, 59; m 82; c 1. *Educ:* St John Fisher Col, BS, 81; Univ Tex, Austin, PhD(analytical chem), 87. *Prof Exp:* Consult, Hydrolab Corp, 86-87. *Mem:* Am Chem Soc. *Res:* Design of process control instrumentation for a wide range of industries; electrochemical sensor design. *Mailing Add:* 15 Cross St Westborough MA 01581-2025

**VARDANIS, ALEXANDER,** BIOCHEMISTRY. *Current Pos:* RES OFF BIOCHEM, RES INST, CAN DEPT AGR, UNIV WESTERN ONT, 61- *Personal Data:* b Athens, Greece, Mar 13, 33; Can citizen; m 59; c 3. *Educ:* Univ Leeds, BSc, 55; McGill Univ, MSc, 58, PhD(biochem), 60. *Concurrent Pos:* Nat Res Coun Can fel, 59-61. *Mem:* Chem Inst Can; Am Soc Biochem & Molecular Biol. *Res:* Intermediary metabolism of carbohydrates, particularly glycogen metabolism; chitin biosynthesis; protein kinases. *Mailing Add:* 147 Wychwood Pl London ON N6G 1S7 Can. *Fax:* 519-645-5476

**VARDARIS, RICHARD MILES,** NEUROENDOCRINOLOGY, NEUROPSYCHOPHARMACOLOGY. *Current Pos:* From asst prof to assoc prof, 67-77, PROF PSYCHOL, KENT STATE UNIV, 78- *Personal Data:* b Lakewood, Ohio, Nov 28, 34; m 70; c 2. *Educ:* Case Western Res Univ, BA, 62; Univ Ore, MS, 67, PhD(med psychol), 68. *Concurrent Pos:* NIH res grants, 72-82; chmn, Biopsychol Prog, Kent State Univ, 76-, dir, Div Biomed Sci, 76-79; res prof neurobiol, Northeastern Col Med, Ohio Univ, 77-; co-prin investr, NSF res grant, 78-80. *Mem:* Soc Neurosci; NY Acad Sci; AAAS; Sigma Xi. *Res:* Effects of steroid hormones and related compounds on excitability of brain tissue; behavioral effects of gonadal steroids and drugs of abuse; neurobiological analysis of linguistic phenomena. *Mailing Add:* Dept Psychol Kent State Univ Kent OH 44242-0001

**VARDEMAN, STEPHEN BRUCE,** ENGINEERING STATISTICS, STATISTICAL QUALITY CONTROL. *Current Pos:* from asst prof to assoc prof statist, 81-86, assoc prof indust eng, 83-86, PROF STATIST, IOWA STATE UNIV, AMES, 86-, PROF INDUST ENG, 86- *Personal Data:* b Louisville, Ky, Aug 27, 49; m 70, Jo E Nollsch; c Micah S & Andrew D. *Educ:* Iowa State Univ, BS, 71, MS, 73; Mich State Univ, PhD(statist), 75. *Prof Exp:* Asst prof, Purdue Univ, 75-81. *Concurrent Pos:* Assoc ed, Am Statistician, 84-87, Technometrics, 86-91, ed, 93-; chair, Sect Phys & Eng Sci, Am Statist Asn, 91. *Mem:* Fel Am Statist Asn; Am Soc Qual Control; Inst Math Statist; Int Statist Inst; Am Soc Eng Educ. *Res:* Statistical quality control; general engineering statistics; applied stochastic control; reliability. *Mailing Add:* 812 Northwestern Ave Ames IA 50010. *Fax:* 515-294-4040; *E-Mail:* vardeman@iastate.edu

**VARDI, JOSEPH,** CHEMICAL ENGINEERING. *Current Pos:* Engr, 64-67, SR RES ENGR, EXXON RES & ENG CO, 67- *Personal Data:* US citizen. *Educ:* Univ Cincinnati, PhD(chem eng), 64. *Mem:* Am Inst Chem Engrs; Am Chem Soc; Sigma Xi. *Res:* Air pollution and fuels research; impact of fuels and their combustion products on the environment; application of catalysis and adsorption to new processes to control automotive air pollution; conduction and radiation heat transfer. *Mailing Add:* Exxon Res & Eng Co PO Box 51 Linden NJ 07036-0051

**VARDI, MOSHEY,** LOGIC IN COMPUTER SCIENCE, DATABASE SYSTEMS. *Current Pos:* NOAH HARDING PROF COMPUT SCI, RICE UNIV, 93-, CHAIR DEPT, 94- *Personal Data:* b Haifa, Israel, July 4, 54. *Educ:* Bar Elan Univ, BS, 74; Weizmann Inst, MS, 80; Hebrew Univ, PhD(comput sci), 81. *Prof Exp:* Wiezmann postdoctoral fel, Stanford Univ, 81-85, res assoc, 84-85; res staff mem, IBM Res, 85-89, dept mgr, 89-93. *Concurrent Pos:* Fulbright award, US-Israel Educ Found, 81; vis scientist, IBM Res, 83-84; consult prof, Stanford Univ, 89-95. *Mem:* Asn Comput Mach. *Res:* Applied logic in computer science, including databases, complexity theory, multi-agent systems and design verification. *Mailing Add:* Rice Univ 6100 S Main St Houston TX 77005-1892. *Fax:* 713-285-5930; *E-Mail:* vardi@rice.edu

**VARDI, YEHUDA,** INFERENCE & ESTIMATION FROM BIASED & INCOMPLETE DATA, STATISTICAL METHODS IN TOMOGRAPHY & IMAGE ANALYSIS. *Current Pos:* PROF STATIST, RUTGERS UNIV, 87- *Personal Data:* US citizen. *Educ:* Hebrew Univ, BSc, 70; Technion Univ, MSc, 73; Cornell Univ, MSc, 75, PhD(opers res), 77. *Prof Exp:* Scientist math & statist, AT&T Bell Labs, 77-87. *Mem:* Am Statist Asn; Inst Math Statist; Int Statist Inst. *Res:* Developing statistical methods for real life application, including image reconstruction from projections, inference from sample-selection-biased data. *Mailing Add:* Statist Dept Rm 506 Rutgers Univ Hill Ctr Busch Campus Piscataway NJ 08854

**VARDIMAN, LARRY,** CLOUD PHYSICS, PALEOCLIMATOLOGY. *Current Pos:* chmn physics & atmospheric sci, Dept Astrogeophysics, 89-94, PROF ATMOSPHERIC SCI, INST FOR CREATION RES, 89- *Personal Data:* b Litchfield, Ill, Jan 13, 43; m 65, Jeanette; c Michelle, Daniel, Laura & Kelly. *Educ:* Univ Mo, BS, 65; St Louis Univ, BS, 67; Colo State Univ, MS, 72, PhD(atmospheric sci), 74. *Prof Exp:* Asst chief, Aerospace Modification Div, Air Weather Serv, USAF, 67-70; res meteorologist, Dept Interior, US Bur Reclamation, 74-82; chmn, Div Sci Physics & Math, Christian Heritage Col, 82-89, acad dean, 87-89. *Concurrent Pos:* Consult meteorologist, Western Sci Serv, Inc, 72-74; lectr meteorol, Sierra Col, Calif, 81-82; prin investr, Off Res, USAF, 85-86. *Mem:* Am Meteorol Soc; Sigma Xi. *Res:* Investigation of ice core and sea-floor sediment data with a catastrophic young earth climate model; simulation of paleoclimates using a global circulation model and standard radiation codes. *Mailing Add:* 8533 Carlton Oaks Dr Santee CA 92071

**VARDIMAN, RONALD G,** MATERIALS CHARACTERIZATION, MECHANICAL PROPERTIES. *Current Pos:* METALLURGIST, MAT SCI & TECH, US NAVAL RES LAB, WASHINGTON, DC, 61- *Personal Data:* b Louisville, Ky, Sept 17, 32; m 69; c 2. *Educ:* Univ Notre Dame, BS, 54, MS, 56, PhD(metall), 61. *Mem:* Sigma Xi; Minerals, Metals & Mat Soc; Am Soc Metals. *Res:* Materials characterization and effects of defect structure on properties, including work on ion implantation, superconducting materials, diffusion, dislocation observation, sintering and crystal growth. *Mailing Add:* 7230 Parsons Ct Alexandria VA 22306

**VARDY, ALEXANDER,** ERROR-CORRECTING CODES, INFORMATION THEORY & COMMUNICATIONS. *Current Pos:* ASSOC PROF ELEC & COMPUT ENG, UNIV ILL, 93-, ASSOC PROF MATH, 95- *Personal Data:* b Moscow, USSR, Nov 12, 63; m 88, Hagit M Itzkowitz. *Educ:* Technion-Israel Inst Technol, BSc, 85; Tel-Aviv Univ, PhD(elec eng), 91. *Honors & Awards:* Career Award, NSF, 95; Award Sci & Eng, Packard Found, 96. *Prof Exp:* Sr res & develop engr, Israeli Air Force Systs Div, 85-90; assoc, IBM Sci & Technol Ctr, Israel, 91-92, vis scientist, Res Div, Almaden Res Ctr, 92-93. *Concurrent Pos:* Sci consult, Telecommun Group, Tadiran Inc, Israel, 91-92; prin investr, NSF, 94-; fel, Ctr Advan Study, Univ Ill, 96-; sci consult, AT&T Res Labs, 96- *Mem:* Inst Elec & Electronics Engrs; Am Math Soc; AAAS. *Res:* Digital communications, in particular coding theory; error-correcting codes, signal constellations and sphere packings, modulation and error-control coding for storage devices and computational complexity in coding theory; granted four patents. *Mailing Add:* 1308 W Main St Urbana IL 61801-2918. *Fax:* 217-244-1642; *E-Mail:* vardy@shannon.cslu.uluc.edu

**VARGA, GABRIELLA ANNE,** ANIMAL NUTRITION, NUTRITION. *Current Pos:* DEPT DAIRY & ANIMAL SCI, PA STATE UNIV. *Personal Data:* b Budapest, Hungary, Aug 8, 51; US citizen; m 77. *Educ:* Duquesne Univ, BS, 73; Univ RI, MS, 75; Univ Md, PhD(animal sci), 78. *Prof Exp:* Res asst ruminant nutrit, Univ RI, 73-75; res asst, Univ Md, 75-78; fel, Ruminant Nutrit, WVa Univ, 79- *Concurrent Pos:* Res animal scientist, Ruminant Nutrit Lab USDA, Beltsville, MD, 82-85. *Mem:* Am Soc Animal Sci; AAAS; Appl Environ Micros; Am Soc Dairy Soc; Sigma Xi. *Res:* Specializing in utilization of non-protein nitrogen compounds by ruminants; feeding of animal waste to ruminants; utilization and microbiological aspects are also of interest; effect of feed intake in dairy cows in early lactation; utilization of dietary fiber by dairy cows; digesta kinetics; nutrient absorption; amino acid metabolism; forage and fiber utilization by ruminants. *Mailing Add:* Dept Animal Sci Pa State Univ 324 Henning Bldg University Park PA 16802-3503

**VARGA, GIDEON MICHAEL, JR,** INORGANIC CHEMISTRY. *Current Pos:* PROG MGR, US DEPT ENERGY, 91- *Personal Data:* b Brooklyn, NY, Feb 13, 41. *Educ:* Manhattan Col, BS, 62; Georgetown Univ, PhD(inorg chem), 67; New York Univ, MBA, 74. *Prof Exp:* Staff scientist, Exxon Res & Eng Co, 67-86; consult, VIC Int, 87-89; consult scientist, Ebasco Environ, 89-91. *Mem:* Am Chem Soc; Sigma Xi; Combustion Inst; Air & Waste Mgt Asn; Commercial Develop Asn. *Res:* Energy conservation; characterization of inorganic and organic compounds; nox emission control; pollution monitoring instrumentation; properties and production of aviation and distillate fuels; combustion control; electrochemistry; heteropoly electrolytes and blues; polarography; heterogeneous catalysis; fuel cells. *Mailing Add:* 1400 S Joyce St Apt 1209 Arlington VA 22202-1841

**VARGA, JANOS M,** RADIO-DERIVATIZATION OF POLYMERS, LIGAND-BINDING ASSAYS. *Current Pos:* PROF BIOCHEM, UNIV INNSBRUCK, AUSTRIA, 88- *Personal Data:* b Nagyoroszi, Hungary, June 19, 35; US citizen; c Daniel, Paul & Elisabet. *Educ:* Univ Technol, Budapest, Hungary, BS, 59; Eotvos L Univ, Budapest, Hungary, PhD(biochem), 65. *Prof Exp:* Fel biochem, Royal Inst Technol, Stockholm, 67-69; res assoc molecular biol, Dept Molecular Biol & Biochem, Yale Univ, 69-71, res assoc immunochem, Sch Med, 71-74, asst prof, 74-76, assoc prof melanoma, 76-81, prof & sr scientist, 81-84; prog dir molecular immunol, Nat Cancer Inst, NIH, 84-87. *Concurrent Pos:* Res career develop award, NIH, 86; consult, Epipharm Co, 88- *Mem:* Am Asn Immunologists; Austrian Biochem Soc. *Res:* Isolation of new antibiotics; in vitro diagnosis for allergies; hormone receptors on cancer cells; drug targeting; multispecificity of antibodies; multispecific allergic reactions; solid-phase assays; allergy diagnostics. *Mailing Add:* Dept Theoret Chem Univ Innsbruck Innrain 52 Innsbruch 6020 Austria. *Fax:* 43-512-504-2990

**VARGA, LOUIS P,** ANALYTICAL CHEMISTRY, RADIOCHEMISTRY. *Current Pos:* asst prof chem, 61-67, ASSOC PROF CHEM, OKLA STATE UNIV, 67- *Personal Data:* b Portland, Ore, Mar 25, 22; m 48; c 4. *Educ:* Reed Col, BA, 48; Univ Chicago, MS, 50; Ore State Univ, PhD(anal chem), 60. *Prof Exp:* Chemist, Hanford Labs, 50-53; instr & res assoc, Reed Col, 53-57; res assoc anal chem, Mass Inst Technol, 60-61. *Concurrent Pos:* Vis staff mem, Los Alamos Sci Lab, 68-78. *Mem:* Am Chem Soc; Sigma Xi. *Res:* Analytical instrumentation; water analysis; rare earth spectra. *Mailing Add:* Dept Chem Okla State Univ Stillwater OK 74078

**VARGA, RICHARD S,** NUMERICAL ANALYSIS, LINEAR ALGEBRA. *Current Pos:* UNIV PROF MATH, KENT STATE UNIV, 69- *Personal Data:* b US, Oct 9, 28; m 51, Esther Pfister; c Gretchen M. *Educ:* Case Inst Technol, BS, 50; Harvard Univ, AM, 51, PhD(math), 54. *Hon Degrees:* Dr, Univ Karlsruhe, Ger, 91 & Univ Lille, France, 93. *Prof Exp:* Adv mathematician, Bettis Atomic Power Lab, Westinghouse Elec Co, 54-60; prof math, Case Western Res Univ, 60-69. *Concurrent Pos:* Consult, Gulf Res & Develop Co, 60, Argonne Nat Lab, 61 & Los Alamos Sci Lab, 68-; Guggenheim fel, Harvard Univ & Calif Inst Technol, 63; Sherman Fairchild scholar, Calif Inst Technol, 74; Gast prof, Munich Tech Univ, 76; von Humboldt prize, 82. *Mem:* Am Math Soc; Soc Indust & Appl Math; Sigma Xi. *Res:* Numerical analysis; approximation theory; scientific computation, iterative methods for solving large systems of linear equations. *Mailing Add:* Dept Math & Comput Sci Kent State Univ Kent OH 44242. *Fax:* 330-672-7824; *E-Mail:* varga@mcs.kent.edu

**VARGAS, FERNANDO FIGUEROA,** MICROCIRCULATION, CELL BIOLOGY. *Current Pos:* SCIENTIST, CELL BIOL, FOOD & DRUG ADMIN, 88- *Personal Data:* b Puerto Montt, Chile, Aug 9, 26; US citizen; m 51; c 3. *Educ:* Univ Chile, BSc, 45, DDS(oral surg), 51; Univ Minn, PhD, 63. *Honors & Awards:* Winthrop Award, Chilean Biol Soc, 58. *Prof Exp:* Asst prof physiol, Inst Physiol, Univ Concepcion, 52-55; assoc prof, Inst Physiol, Univ Chile, 58-65, prof, Sch Sci, 65-70; lectr physiol, Univ Minn, 74-80; prof physiol, Univ PR, 80-88. *Concurrent Pos:* Vis prof, dept physiol, Univ Calif, Los Angeles, 67; mem bd, Univ Chile, 70-72; consult, Medtronic Inc, 79-80; chmn, dept biol, Sch Sci, Univ Chile, 67-70, Atomic Energy Comn, Chile, 72-73, Gordon Conf, Microcirculation, 85; prin investr & dir, Univ PR, Health Sci Campus, NIH, Mem Prog, 85-88. *Mem:* Am Physiol Soc; NY Acad Sci; Microcirculation Soc; AAAS. *Res:* Permeability of vascular endothelium to water and non electrolytes; endothelial cell electrophysiology and surface phenomena and their relationship with permeability of endothelium; mechanisms of plasma protein effects on hydraulic and electrical conductivity of large vessel endothelium. *Mailing Add:* FDA Dept Cardiorenal Drugs Bldg Rm 8 403 Lab Cell Biol & Genetics NIH Bethesda MD 20892-0001

**VARGAS, HUGO MARTIN,** ADRENERGIC RECEPTOR PHARMACOLOGY, ALZHEIMERS DISEASE THERAPEUTICS. *Current Pos:* sr res pharmacologist, 91-94, res assoc, 94-96, SCIENTIST, HOECHST-ROUSSEL PHARMACEUT, 96- *Personal Data:* b Weehawken, NJ, June 22, 61; m 85, Teresa Speranza; c Miranda, Martina & Cordelia. *Educ:* St Peter's Col, BS, 83; Univ Med & Dent NJ, PhD(pharmacol), 88. *Honors & Awards:* Young Investr Award, Am Heart Asn, 89; Young Scientist Travel Award, Am Soc Pharmacol & Exp Therapeut, 91. *Prof Exp:* NIH fel, Dept Pharmacol, Univ Calif, Los Angeles, 88-90; asst res pharmacologist, 90-91. *Concurrent Pos:* Lectr, Dept Pharmacol, Univ Calif, Los Angeles, 90-91. *Mem:* Am Soc Pharmacol & Exp Therapeut; Soc Neurosci. *Res:* Alpha-adrenergic receptor pharmacology; synthetic cholinergic drugs; Alzheimer's disease therapeutics; structure-activity relationships; receptor studies. *Mailing Add:* Hoechst Marion Roussel Rte 202-206 Bridgewater NJ 08807. *Fax:* 908-231-2413; *E-Mail:* vargas1@brwhcc3.hcc.com

**VARGAS, JOSEPH MARTIN, JR,** PLANT PATHOLOGY. *Current Pos:* from asst prof to assoc prof, 68-82, PROF BOT & PLANT PATH, MICH STATE UNIV, 82- *Personal Data:* b Fall River, Mass, Mar 11, 42; m 63; c 2. *Educ:* Univ RI, BS, 63; Okla State Univ, MS, 65; Univ Minn, Minneapolis, PhD(plant path), 68. *Mem:* Am Phytopath Soc; Am Soc Agron; Int Turfgrass Soc. *Res:* Turfgrass pathology; resistance to fungicides; biological control. *Mailing Add:* Dept Bot MSU 166 Plant Biol East Lansing MI 48823-1312

**VARGAS, ROGER I,** ENTOMOLOGY. *Current Pos:* RES SCIENTIST, TROP FRUIT & VEG RES LAB, HONOLULU, 80- *Personal Data:* b Long Beach, Calif. *Educ:* Univ Calif, Riverside, BA, 69; San Diego State Univ, MS, 74; Univ Hawaii, PhD(entom), 79. *Prof Exp:* Res assoc entom, Univ Hawaii, 79-80. *Concurrent Pos:* Affil fac, Univ Hawaii, 82-91. *Mem:* AAAS; Entom Soc Am. *Res:* Ecology; pest management, mass rearing and eradication of tropical fruit flies. *Mailing Add:* USDA-ARS Trop Fruit Veg & Ornamental Crop Res Lab PO Box 4459 Hilo HI 96720

**VARGHESE, SANKOORIKAL LONAPPAN,** EXPERIMENTAL ATOMIC PHYSICS. *Current Pos:* from asst prof to assoc prof, 80-85, PROF PHYSICS, UNIV SALA, 85-, CHAIR, 93- *Personal Data:* b Narakal, Kerala, Mar 13, 43; US citizen; m 71, Leela Philip; c Teena-Ann, Emma-Betty, Geena-Mary & Binu-John. *Educ:* Kerala Univ, BSc, 63, MSc, 65; Univ Louisville, MS, 67; Yale Univ, PhD(physics), 74. *Prof Exp:* Res asst physics, Yale Univ, 68-74; res staff physicist, 74; res assoc physics, Kans State Univ, 74-76; vis asst prof, Univ Okla, 76-77, E Carolina, 77-80. *Concurrent Pos:* Consult, Burroughs-Wellcome Co, 81-85; vis researcher, Oak Ridge Nat Lab, 81-; US patent, high-pressure chromatographic system. *Mem:* Am Phys Soc; Sigma Xi. *Res:* Positron and positronium research, first observation of the n-2 state of positronium; accelerator based atomic physics, first direct lifetime measurement of x-ray emitters in the pico-second range; Mo06ssbauer studies. *Mailing Add:* Dept Physics Univ S Ala Mobile AL 36688

**VARGO, STEVEN WILLIAM,** AUDIOLOGY. *Current Pos:* PVT PRACT AUDIOL, 79- *Personal Data:* b Whiting, Ind, Sept 9, 31; m 56; c 3. *Educ:* Ind State Univ, BS, 54; Purdue Univ, MS, 57; Ind Univ, PhD(audiol), 65. *Prof Exp:* Assoc prof audiol, Ill State Univ, 65-71; Nat Inst Neurol Dis & Stroke spec res fel, Auditory Res Lab, Northwestern Univ, Evanston, 71-73; assoc prof surg, Hershey Med Ctr, Pa State Univ, 73-79. *Concurrent Pos:* Mem, State Bd Examr Audiol & Speech Path Pa. *Mem:* Am Speech & Hearing Asn; Am Audiol Asn; Am Acad Dispensing Audiologists. *Res:* Scientific study of communication behavior with primary emphasis on the auditory mechanism of both normal and abnormal systems. *Mailing Add:* 431 E Chocolate Ave Hershey PA 17033

**VARIN, ROBERT ANDRZEJ,** MATERIALS SCIENCE & ENGINEERING. *Current Pos:* asst prof, 83-88, assoc prof, 88-92, PROF MAT SCI & ENG, UNIV WATERLOO, 92- *Personal Data:* b Piastow, Poland, May 1, 46; Can citizen; m 67; c 2. *Educ:* Warsaw Tech Univ, MASc, 72 & PhD(mats sci & eng), 76. *Prof Exp:* Asst prof, Warsaw Tech Univ, 76-78 & 80-82; fel, Univ Man, 78-80, res assoc, 82-83. *Mem:* Metall Soc; Am Soc Metals Int; NY Acad Sci; Mat Res Soc; Can Asn Composite Struct & Mat. *Res:* Mechanical properties of metallic polycrystalline materials and advanced composites with special emphasis on the role of grain boundaries and interfaces in their behavior; intermetallics and their composites. *Mailing Add:* Dept Mech Eng Univ Waterloo 200 University Ave W Waterloo ON N2L 3G1 Can. *Fax:* 519-888-6197; *E-Mail:* ravarin@mechoffice.watstar.uwaterloo.ca

**VARIN, ROGER ROBERT,** PHYSICAL CHEMISTRY, COMPOSITES. *Current Pos:* PRES, VARINIT CORP, 71- *Personal Data:* b Bern, Switz, Feb 15, 25; nat US; m 51; c 3. *Educ:* Univ Bern, PhD(chem), 51. *Prof Exp:* Fel phys chem, Harvard Univ, 51-52; res chemist, E I Du Pont de Nemours & Co, 52-57, res assoc, 57-62; dir res, Riegel Textile Corp, 62-71. *Concurrent Pos:* Pres, Technol Assocs, Greenville, SC, 71- & Varinit S A, Carouge, Switz, 74- *Mem:* AAAS; Am Chem Soc; Fiber Soc; Soc Advan Mat & Process Eng; Soc Mfg Engrs. *Res:* Fiber physics and chemistry; textile technology; polymer physics and chemistry; rheology; composites. *Mailing Add:* 4 Barksdale Rd Greenville SC 29607

**VARINEAU, VERNE JOHN,** MATHEMATICS. *Current Pos:* from instr to prof, 40-85, EMER PROF MATH, UNIV WYO, 85- *Personal Data:* b Escanaba, Mich, Mar 11, 15; m 45; c 4. *Educ:* Col St Thomas, BS, 36; Univ Wis, AM, 38, PhD(math), 40. *Prof Exp:* Asst, Univ Wis, 36-39. *Concurrent Pos:* NSF sci fac fel, Stanford Univ, 63-64. *Mem:* Am Math Soc; Math Asn Am. *Res:* Matrices with elements in a principal ideal ring. *Mailing Add:* 714 Tenth St Laramie WY 82070

**VARKEY, THANKAMMA EAPEN,** organic chemistry, for more information see previous edition

**VARKI, AJIT POTHAN,** CANCER BIOLOGY, GLYCOBIOLOGY. *Current Pos:* from asst prof to assoc prof, 82-91, co-head, Div Hemat-Oncol, 87-89, PROF MED, UNIV CALIF, SAN DIEGO, 91- *Personal Data:* b Jan 4, 52; US citizen; c 1. *Educ:* Christian Med Col, India, MB, BS, 75. *Prof Exp:* Resident med officer, Malankara Mission Hosp, 75; res asst biochem, Univ Nebr, 76, resident, 77-78; resident med, Episcopal Hosp, Temple Univ, 76-77; fel hemat & oncol, Sch Med, Wash Univ, 78-82, instr med, 80-82. *Concurrent Pos:* Prin investr, Nat Inst Gen Med Sci, 83- & Nat Cancer Inst, 85-; dir training prog cancer res, Nat Cancer Inst, 85-; prog leader, Glycobiol Prog, 90-; ed, J Clin Invest, 92- *Mem:* Am Soc Biol Chem & Molecular Biol; Am Fedn Clin Res; Am Col Physicians; Am Soc Clin Invest. *Res:* Glycobiology: exploring the structure, biosynthesis and biological roles of oliaosaccharides. *Mailing Add:* Med Hem/Oncol H-811K Univ Calif San Diego Med Sch La Jolla CA 92093-5003. *Fax:* 619-534-5792; *E-Mail:* avarki@ucsd.edu

**VARLASHKIN, PAUL,** SOLID STATE PHYSICS. *Current Pos:* RETIRED. *Personal Data:* b San Antonio, Tex, Aug 28, 31; m 54, Charlotte Duke; c 4. *Educ:* Univ Tex, BS, 52, MA, 54, PhD(physics), 63. *Prof Exp:* Asst, Defense Res Lab, Univ Tex, 51-52, physicist, 52-53; from res scientist to chief res & develop, Electro-Mech Co, 53-63; fel & res assoc, Univ NC, 64-66; asst prof physics, La State Univ, Baton Rouge, 66-72; assoc prof, ECarolina Univ, 72-96. *Concurrent Pos:* Res physicist, White Sands Proving Grounds, 52. *Mem:* Am Phys Soc; Sigma Xi. *Res:* Positron annihilation; liquid metals; positronium formation; solid state physics; chemical physics; metal-ammonia solutions. *Mailing Add:* 305 Prince Rd Greenville NC 27858

**VARMA, ANDRE A O,** MEDICINE, BIOSTATISTICS. *Current Pos:* assoc prof, 74-81, PROF COMMUNITY & PREV MED, STATE UNIV NY, STONY BROOK, 81- *Personal Data:* b Paramaribo, Surinam, June 10, 27; nat US; m 52; c 3. *Educ:* Sch Med Surinam, Med Doct, 50; Columbia Univ, MSc, 60. *Prof Exp:* Dist health officer med, Govt Surinam, 58-60, head biostatist pub health, 60-67; from asst prof to assoc prof biostatist, Pub Health, Columbia Univ, 67-74. *Concurrent Pos:* Fel, Surinam Govt, 62-64 $ US & Surinam Govts, 68-70; consult, Neth Govt, 65-66, Pan Am Health Orgn, 66 & WHO, 78; chmn, Dept Community Med, State Univ NY, Stony Brook, 78- *Mem:* Am Statist Asn; Biomet Soc; Am Pub Health Asn; NY Acad Sci; Asn Teachers Prev Med. *Res:* Design and analysis of clinical trials; epidemiology of cancer; emergency medical services; complications in post-abortion pregnancies; public health. *Mailing Add:* State Univ NY HSC L3-086 100 N Colls Rd Stony Brook NY 11794-8000

**VARMA, ARUN KUMAR,** mathematics, for more information see previous edition

**VARMA, ARVIND,** CHEMICAL REACTION ENGINEERING, SYNTHESIS OF ADVANCED MATERIALS. *Current Pos:* from asst prof to prof chem eng, 75-88, chmn dept, 83-88, ARTHUR J SCHMITT PROF CHEM ENG, UNIV NOTRE DAME, 88- *Personal Data:* b Ferozabad, India, Oct 13, 47; nat US; m 71, Karen K Guse; c Anita & Sophia. *Educ:* Panjab Univ, India, BS, 66; Univ NB, MS, 68; Univ Minn, PhD(chem eng), 72. *Honors & Awards:* R H Wilhelm Award, Am Inst Chem Engrs, 93. *Prof Exp:* Asst prof chem eng, Univ Minn, 72-73; sr res engr, Union Carbide Corp, 73-75. *Concurrent Pos:* Vis prof, Univ Wis-Madison, 81, Chevron vis prof, Calif Inst Technol, 82, vis prof, Indian Inst Technol, Kanpur, 89 & vis chair prof, Univ Caligari, Italy, 89 & 92; co-ed, Math Understanding Chem Eng Systs, 80 & Chem Reaction & Reactor Eng, 87; Fulbright scholar award, Indo-Am fel, 88-89; vis fel, Princeton Univ, 96- *Mem:* Am Inst Chem Engrs; Am Chem Soc; Sigma Xi; fel Am Inst Chemists; Am Ceramic Soc; Am Soc Eng Educ. *Res:* Fundamental research in chemical and catalytic reaction engineering and synthesis of advanced materials; co-author of one publication. *Mailing Add:* Dept Chem Eng Univ Notre Dame Notre Dame IN 46556-5637

**VARMA, ASHA,** ANALYTICAL CHEMISTRY. *Current Pos:* chemist, Naval Air Develop Ctr, 82-87, team leader, Analytical Group, 83-88, assoc tech base mgr, 88-90, asst dir, 90-92, actg dir, 92, PROG MGR, OFF SCI & TECHNOL, NAVAL AIR WARFARE CTR, 93-, PROG MGR, NAVAL AVIATION SCI & TECHNOL OFF, 96- *Personal Data:* b Bareilly, India, Mar 19, 42; US citizen; m 67, Vinod Agarwala; c Veena & Vinay. *Educ:* Agra Univ, India, BSc, 58, MSc, 60; Banaras Hindu Univ, India, PhD(chem), 63. *Prof Exp:* Sr res fel chem, Banaras Hindu Univ, India, 63-64, Nat Chem Lab, 64-66; asst dir res chem, Forensic Sci Lab, Sagar, India, 66-68; sci pool officer chem, H B Technol Inst, Kanpur, India, 69-70; res assoc anal chem, Inst Mat Sci, Univ Conn, Storrs, 73-75; res scientist, Lab Res Struct Matter, Univ Pa, 77-82. *Concurrent Pos:* Res fel, Banaras Hindu Univ, Varanasi, India, 60-63; fel chem, Univ Conn, Storrs, 66-67 & 73-75; asst dir, Forensic Sci Lab, Sagar, India, 67-69; prog mgr, Res & Univ Progs, 93- *Mem:* Am Chem Soc; fel Am Inst Chemists; Int Union Pure & Appl Chem; Coblentz. *Res:* Manage multimillion dollar research programs; provide technical direction and focus; lead research projects and interact with federal, state and local agencies, industry and academia; authored and published four handbooks (CRC) and over eighty technical publications. *Mailing Add:* Naval Aviation S&T Code 4-OT Bldg 2187 Unit 5 Naval Air Warfare Ctr Shaw Rd Lexington Park MD 20673-1906. *Fax:* 301-342-0235

**VARMA, BAIDYA NATH,** SOCIOLOGY. *Current Pos:* EMER PROF SOCIOL, CITY UNIV NEW YORK. *Personal Data:* m, Savitri Devi. *Educ:* Columbia Univ, PhD, 58. *Concurrent Pos:* Radio broadcaster, India, UN; Asian news moderator, Nat Educ Television Network; lectr numerous univs, US, Can, Eng & India; chair, Plenary Sessions World Cong Sociol, Int Cong Anthrop & Enthological Scis; consult, Nat Endowment Humanities, Ctr Migration Studies, Dept Energy, Wenner-Gren Found Anthrop Res US, Can

Coun & Indian Univs; vis prof, Columbia Univ & other US & Indian Univs Law Inst; sr fac fel, Am Inst Indian Studies, 64-65 & 84-85; guest fel, Oxford Univ, Sorbonne & Inst Advan Study. *Mem:* NY Acad Scis; Soc Indian Acads Am; Global Orgn. *Res:* Sociology; enthnology; anthropology. *Mailing Add:* 62 Belvedere Dr Yonkers NY 10705

**VARMA, CHANDRA M,** THEORETICAL PHYSICS. *Current Pos:* Fel, Dept Theoret Physics, AT&T Bell Labs, 68-70, mem tech staff, Dept Theoret Physics Res, 70-82, dept head, 82-85, DISTINGUISHED MEM TECH STAFF, AT&T BELL LABS, 85- *Personal Data:* b Akalgarh, India, June 15, 42; US citizen. *Educ:* Osmania Univ, Hyderabad, India, BS, 63; Univ Minn, MS, 66, PhD(physics), 68. *Concurrent Pos:* Vis assoc prof, Dept Physics & James Franck Inst, Univ Chicago, 71-72; sr vis fel, Cavendish Lab, Cambridge Univ, Eng, 77. *Res:* Theoretical physics research; author of over 150 publications. *Mailing Add:* AT&T Bell Labs Rm 1D-370 Lucent Tech Rm 1D-370 Murray Hill NJ 07974

**VARMA, DAYA RAM,** REPRODUCTIVE TOXICITY, ENVIRONMENTAL CHEMICALS. *Current Pos:* ASSOC PROF PHARMACOL, MCGILL UNIV, 61- *Educ:* McGill Univ, PhD(pharmacol), 61. *Mailing Add:* Dept Pharmacol & Therapeut Mc Gill Univ 3655 Drummond St Montreal PQ H3G 1Y6 Can. *Fax:* 514-398-7120

**VARMA, MAN MOHAN,** environmental engineering; deceased, see previous edition for last biography

**VARMA, MATESH NARAYAN,** PHYSICS, RADIATION PHYSICS. *Current Pos:* PROG MGR RADIOL & CHEM PHYSICS, DOSIMETRY RADON, OFF HEALTH ENVIRON RES, US DEPT ENERGY, 84- *Personal Data:* b Saugor, India, Sept 9, 43; m 67, Neelima; c Namita, Ramit & Samit. *Educ:* Univ Jabalpur, India, BSc, 61, MSc, 63; Case Western Res Univ, MS, 69; Case Inst Technol, PhD(physics), 71. *Prof Exp:* Sci officer reactor eng, Bhabha Atomic Res Ctr, India, 63-67; univ fel physics, Case Western Res Univ, 67-71, res assoc solid state physics, 71-72; sr scientist radiation physics, Safety & Environ Protection Div, Brookhaven Nat Lab, 72-87. *Concurrent Pos:* Mem, Comt Interagency Radiation Res & Policy Coord, Radiation Res Soc. *Mem:* Health Physics Soc; Bevalac Users Asn; Radiation Res Soc. *Res:* Microdosimetry; surface physics; thin films; Mossbauer spectroscopy; ultrahigh vacuum technology; reactor physics; health physics; radiological and chemical physics; biophysics and biophysical modeling. *Mailing Add:* 7220 Deer Lake Lane Derwood MD 20855. *Fax:* 301-903-0567; *E-Mail:* matesh.varma@oer.doe.gov

**VARMA, RAJ NARAYAN,** NUTRITION IN CANCER, ANTIOXIDENT VITAMINS IN CORONARY ARTERY DISEASE. *Current Pos:* Assoc prof, 83-94, PROF NUTRIT, YOUNGSTOWN STATE UNIV, 94- *Personal Data:* b Oct 11, 28; c 2. *Educ:* Univ Calif, Davis, PhD(biochem), 62. *Mem:* Am Dietetic Asn; Am Soc Parenteral & Enteral Nutrit. *Res:* Nutrition in sickle cell anemia; nutrition and the elderly; nutrition research; plasma antioxidant vitamins in coronary artery disease patients. *Mailing Add:* Dept Human Ecol Youngstown State Univ 410 Wick Ave Youngstown OH 44555

**VARMA, RAJENDER S,** ORGANIC CHEMISTRY. *Current Pos:* SR SCIENTIST, HOUSTON ADVAN RES CTR, 93-; RES PROF, DEPT CHEM & PROJ MGR, TEX REGIONAL INST ENVIRON STUDIES, SAM HOUSTON STATE UNIV, 95- *Personal Data:* b New Delhi, July 26, 51; m 77, Manju; c Abhishek & Prashant. *Educ:* Punjab Univ, India, BSc, 70; Kurukshetra Univ, MSc, 72; Univ Delhi, PhD(natural prod chem), 76; Norweg Inst Technol, dipl, 78. *Honors & Awards:* Majorie W Margolin Prize, Retina Res Found, 96. *Prof Exp:* Asst res, Inst Cellulose Technol, Norway, 77-79; res fel, Dept Org Chem, Univ Liverpool, Eng, 79-82; res assoc chem, Univ Tenn, Knoxville, 82-86; asst prof, Ctr Biotechnol, Baylor Col Med, 86-93. *Concurrent Pos:* Norweg Agency Int Develop fel, Norweg Inst Technol, Trondheim; group leader, Houston Biotechnol Inc, 86-90; grantee, Am Cancer Soc, 88-91. *Mem:* Am Chem Soc. *Res:* Reduction of nitroalkenes to useful synthetic precursors; chemiselective reductions; synthesis of novel heterocycles; development of environmentally benign new synthetic methods using microwaves; granted 4 US patents. *Mailing Add:* 8 Spurwood Ct The Woodlands TX 77381-2526. *Fax:* 409-204-1585; *E-Mail:* chm_rsv@shsu.edu, varma@herc.edu

**VARMA, RAVI KANNADIKOVILAKOM,** MEDICINAL CHEMISTRY. *Current Pos:* CHEMIST, NAT CNACER INST, 90- *Personal Data:* b Tripunithura, India, Dec 23, 37; wid; c Deep & Jay. *Educ:* Maharaja's Col, Ernakulam, India, BSc, 57, MSc, 59; Univ Poona, PhD(org chem), 65. *Prof Exp:* Sci asst chem, Nat Chem Labs, Poona, India, 59-65; res fel org chem, Purdue Univ, Lafayette, 65-66; staff scientist bio-org chem, Worcester Found, Mass, 66-69; res fel org chem, Harvard Univ, 70-72; res chemist & res fel, Bristol Myers Squibb Co, 72-90. *Mem:* Am Chem Soc; Sigma Xi. *Res:* Organic synthesis; chemistry of biologically active molecules; mechanism of action of drugs; organic process development. *Mailing Add:* 620 Northcliffe Dr Rockville MD 20850. *E-Mail:* varma@dtpvx2.fcrdc.gov

**VARMA, SHAMBHU D,** BIOCHEMISTRY. *Current Pos:* PROF & DIR RES EYE BIOCHEM, DEPT OPHTHAL, MED SCH, UNIV MD, 76- *Personal Data:* b Ghazipur, India; US citizen; m; c 3. *Educ:* Univ Allahabad, India, BSc, 55, MSc, 57; Univ Rajasthan, PhD(biochem), 64. *Honors & Awards:* William Friedkin Res Award, 77; Alexander Von Humboldt Prize, 87. *Prof Exp:* Chmn biochem, chem dept, Punjab Agrc Univ, India, 65-69; vis scientist, Nat Eye Inst, NIH, Bethesda, Md, 72-76. *Concurrent Pos:* Consult, Nat Eye Inst,

NIH. *Mem:* AAAS; Asn Res Vision & Ophthal. *Res:* Intermediary metabolism, diabetes; sorbitol pathway in lens; aldose reductase; mechanism of action of flavonoids and other drugs in lens; superoxide, its implications in ocular diseases, particularly cataracts; nutrients and ocular manifestations; transport mechanisms. *Mailing Add:* Ophthal Dept Sch Med Univ Md 10 S Pine St Baltimore MD 21201

**VARMA, SURENDRA K,** PEDIATRICS, ENDOCRINOLOGY. *Current Pos:* from asst prof to assoc prof pediat, Tex Tech Univ Health Sci Ctr, 74-83, actg assoc chmn, 77-79, assoc chmn, 79-87, interim chmn, 84-86, asst dean, Sch Med, 87-89, PROF PEDIAT, TEX TECH UNIV HEALTH SCI CTR, 83-, ASSOC CHMN PEDIAT, 91- *Personal Data:* b Lucknow, India, Dec 10, 39; m 67, Kamlesh; c Ritu & Rishi. *Educ:* King George Med Col, MBBS, 62, MD, 68; SN Med Col, Agra, DCH, 64; Am Bd Pediat, dipl, 76, dipl & cert endocrinol, 78. *Prof Exp:* Res assoc endocrinol, Dept Nutrit & Food Sci, Mass Inst Technol, 72-74; instr pediat, Harvard Med Sch, 73-74. *Concurrent Pos:* Res fel, K G Med Col, 65-66; res fel, Harvard Med Sch, Peter Bent Brigham Hosp, 68-69 & Children's Hosp Med Ctr, 69-71; clin res fel, Mass Gen Hosp, 72-73, clin assoc, 73-74; dir, Endocrine Div, Tex Tech Univ Sch Med, 78-; pres, Am Diabetes Asn, NTex Affil, Inc, 81-82, Tex Affil, 82. *Mem:* Endocrine Soc; Am Thyroid Asn; Lawson Wilkins Pediat Endocrine Soc; Am Diabetes Asn; Am Acad Pediat. *Res:* Perinatal thyroid pathophysiology; growth hormone and factors; carbohydrate metabolism. *Mailing Add:* Dept Pediat Tex Tech Univ Sch Med Lubbock TX 79430. *Fax:* 806-743-2314

**VARMUS, HAROLD ELLIOT,** MOLECULAR VIROLOGY, ONCOGENESIS. *Current Pos:* DIR, NIH, 93- *Personal Data:* b Oceanside, NY, Dec 18, 39; m 69, Constance Casey; c Jacob & Christopher. *Educ:* Amherst Col, BA, 61; Harvard Univ, MA, 62; Columbia Univ, MD, 66. *Honors & Awards:* Nobel Prize Physiol or Med, 89; Melanie Bronfman Award Breast Cancer. *Prof Exp:* Intern & residence, Int Med, Columbia-Presby Hosp, NY; clin assoc, Nat Inst Arthritis & Metabolic Dis; lectr, Univ Calif, San Francisco, 70-72, from asst prof to prof microbiol, 72-82, prof biochem & biophys, 82-94. *Concurrent Pos:* Assoc ed, Cell & Virol, 74-; hon prof molecular virol, Am Cancer Soc; chmn bd biol, Nat Res Coun; co-chmn, New Deleg Biomed Res. *Mem:* Nat Acad Sci; Inst Med-Nat Acad Sci; Am Soc Microbiol; Am Soc Virol; AAAS; Am Acad Arts & Sci. *Res:* Mechanisms of viral replication and oncogenesis, using retroviruses and hepatitis B viruses; biochemical properties HIV; mammory tumors in mice; author or editor of 4 books and over 300 scientific papers. *Mailing Add:* Off Dir NIH Bldg 1 Rm 126 900 Rockville Pike Bethesda MD 20892-0148

**VARNELL, THOMAS RAYMOND,** BIOCHEMISTRY, PHYSIOLOGY. *Current Pos:* RETIRED. *Personal Data:* b Whiteriver, Ariz, Jan 27, 31; m 57; c 3. *Educ:* Univ Ariz, BS, 57, MS, 58, PhD(agr biochem), 60. *Prof Exp:* Instr animal nutrit, Univ Wyo, 60-62; res biochemist, Dept HEW & Food & Drug Admin, 62-63; asst prof animal nutrit, Univ Wyo, 63-65, from asst prof to assoc prof animal physiol, 65-73, prof animal physiol, 73-84. *Concurrent Pos:* Stanford Res Inst grant, 61-64. *Mem:* Animal Nutrit Res Coun. *Res:* Metabolism of vitamin A and carotene; lipid metabolism; intestinal transport and metabolism of amino acids; potassium requirements and availability. *Mailing Add:* 914 Stratton Dr Safford AZ 85546

**VARNER, HUGH H,** BIOCHEMISTRY. *Current Pos:* SR SCIENTIST BIOCHEM, BIOTECH INC, 84- *Personal Data:* b Laurell, Miss, Oct 3, 50. *Educ:* Millsaps Col, BS, 72; Northeastern La Univ, MS, 74; SC Med Sch, PhD(biochem), 79. *Prof Exp:* Res fel biochem, SC Med Sch, 80-84. *Mem:* Am Soc Cell Biol; Sigma Xi; Asn Res Vision & Ophthal. *Res:* Biochemistry. *Mailing Add:* Chesapeak Biol Labs 6000 Metro Dr Baltimore MD 21215

**VARNER, JOSEPH ELMER,** plant physiology; deceased, see previous edition for last biography

**VARNER, LARRY WELDON,** ANIMAL NUTRITION, WILDLIFE RESEARCH. *Current Pos:* CONSULT NUTRITIONIST, PURINA MILLS INC, 89- *Personal Data:* b San Antonio, Tex, June 25, 44; m 67; c 1. *Educ:* Abilene Christian Col, BS, 66; Univ Nebr, Lincoln, MS, 68, PhD(nutrit), 70. *Prof Exp:* Asst animal sci, Univ Nebr, Lincoln, 66-69, res assoc animal nutrit, 69-70, asst prof, 70-71; res scientist, USDA, 71-74, assoc prof animal nutrit, Tex A&M Univ, 74-88; consult, natural res, 88-89. *Mem:* Wildlife Soc; Am Soc Animal Sci; Soc Range Mgt. *Res:* Ruminant nutrition; nitrogen and energy metabolism; wildlife nutrition. *Mailing Add:* 447 Lakeview Blvd New Braunfels TX 78130

**VARNERIN, LAWRENCE J(OHN),** SOLID STATE PHYSICS, MATERIALS SCIENCE. *Current Pos:* chmn, Elec Eng & Comput Sci Dept, 86-91, CHANDELR WEAVER EMER PROF ELEC ENG, LEHIGH UNIV, 91- *Personal Data:* b Boston, Mass, July 10, 23; m 52, Marie E Hynes; c 8. *Educ:* Mass Inst Technol, SB, 47, PhD(physics), 49. *Prof Exp:* Res engr, Electronics Div, Sylvania Elec Prod, Inc, 49-52; res physicist, Res Labs, Westinghouse Elec Corp, 52-57; mem tech staff solid state devices, AT&T Bell Labs, 57-66, head, Magnetic & Microwave Mat & Device Dept, 66-80, head, microwave device dept, 80-84, head, Heterojunction ICS & Mat Dept, 85-86. *Concurrent Pos:* Assoc ed, J Magnetism & Magnetic Mat, 73-94. *Mem:* Fel Am Phys Soc; Inst Elec & Electronics Engrs. *Res:* Gallium arsenide integrated circuits, microwave field effect transistors and associated materials. *Mailing Add:* PO Box 1107 Wolfeboro NH 03894

**VARNES, DAVID JOSEPH,** ENGINEERING GEOLOGY, SEISMOLOGY. *Current Pos:* recorder & jr geologist, US Geol Surv, 41, from asst geologist to assoc geologist, 43-48, chief br eng geol, 61-64, geologist, 48-95, EMER GEOLOGIST, US GEOL SURV, 95- *Personal Data:* b Howe, Ind, Apr 5, 19; m 43, 66, Katharine Lutz; c Richard V, Elizabeth (Brende), Laura (Tenbroeck), Charles B & Carol A. *Educ:* Calif Inst Technol, BS, 40. *Honors & Awards:* E B Burwell Jr Award, Geol Soc Am, 70 & 76, Distinguished Prof Pract, 87; Hans Cloos Medal, Int Asn Eng Geol, 89; Geologists Holdredge Award, Asn Eng, 96. *Prof Exp:* Lab instr geol, Northwestern Univ, 40-41. *Concurrent Pos:* Mem comts, Transp Res Bd, Nat Acad Sci-Nat Res Coun, 53-73; vis lectr, Chinese Univ Develop Proj, 87; Acad Sinica res on landslides, US Geol Surv, 84. *Mem:* Hon mem Asn Eng Geologists; fel Geol Soc Am; Int Asn Eng Geol (vpres, 82-86); fel Geol Soc London; Nat Soc Rock Mech; Am Geophys Union. *Res:* Geologic studies of Lake Bonneville; landslides; mechanics of soil and rock deformation; logic of mapping; nonlinear dynamics of earthquakes and prediction. *Mailing Add:* US Geol Surv MS 966 Box 25046 Denver Fed Ctr Denver CO 80225. *Fax:* 303-273-8600; *E-Mail:* varnes@gldvxa.cr.usgs.gov

**VARNES, MARIE ELIZABETH,** BIOCHEMISTRY, RADIATION BIOLOGY. *Current Pos:* Res asst, 76-77, res assoc, 77-79, instr, 79-81, ASST PROF, DEPT RADIOL, DIV RADIATION BIOL, CASE WESTERN RESERVE UNIV, 81- *Personal Data:* b Cleveland, Ohio, Dec 20, 42; m 68; c 2. *Educ:* Notre Dame Col, BS, 65; Ind Univ, PhD(biochem), 73. *Concurrent Pos:* Co-investr, Am Cancer Soc grant, 77-78 & Nat Cancer Inst grant, 78- *Mem:* Radiation Res Soc; Sigma Xi; Am Asn Cancer Res. *Res:* Metabolism of nitro drugs used as radiosensitizers; influence of hormones and thiols on radiation response; modification of repair of radiation damage in tumor cells. *Mailing Add:* 2549 Kingston Rd Cleveland OH 44118

**VARNEY, EUGENE HARVEY,** BOTANY, MYCOLOGY. *Current Pos:* asst res specialist, 56-59, from assoc prof plant path to prof plant path, 59-88, EMER PROF PLANT PATH, RUTGERS UNIV, NEW BRUNSWICK, 88- *Personal Data:* b South Egremont, Mass, Dec 25, 23; m 56, Ruth V Holland; c Ellen C, Caroline A & Stephen H. *Educ:* Univ Mass, BS, 49; Univ Wis, PhD, 53. *Prof Exp:* Plant pathologist, USDA, 53-56. *Mem:* Am Inst Biol Sci; Am Phytopath Soc; Mycol Soc Am; Sigma Xi. *Res:* Diseases of small fruits; plant virology; mycology. *Mailing Add:* 17 Hadler Dr Somerset NJ 08873. *E-Mail:* ervarney@aol.com

**VARNEY, ROBERT NATHAN,** MOLECULAR PHYSICS. *Current Pos:* CONSULT, 78- *Personal Data:* b San Francisco, Calif, Nov 7, 10; m 48; c 2. *Educ:* Univ Calif, AB, 31, MA, 32, PhD(physics), 35. *Hon Degrees:* DSc, Univ Innsbruck, Austria, 83. *Honors & Awards:* Austrian Cross Honor for Sci & Art, 81. *Prof Exp:* Instr physics, Univ Calif, 35-36 & NY Univ, 36-38; asst prof, Univ Wash, 38-41, from assoc prof to prof, 46-64; asst exp labs officer, USNR, 41-45; sr mem & sr consult scientist, Lockhead Palo Alto Res Lab, 64-75; NSF sr fel, US Army Ballistic Res Labs, 75-76. *Concurrent Pos:* Vis mem tech staff, Bell Tel Labs, NJ, 51-52; mem exec comt, Gaseous Electronics Conf, 51-53, 60-62 & 65-68, secy, 67; NSF sr fel, Royal Inst Technol, Sweden, 58-59; mem, Gov Sci Adv Comt, Mo, 61-64; Fulbright lectr, Inst Atomic Physics, Innsbruck Univ, 71-72, 76-77, guest prof atomic physics, 77-78. *Mem:* Fel AAAS; fel Am Phys Soc; Am Asn Physics Teachers. *Res:* Ion-molecule reactions; collisions of positive ions in gases; spark breakdown; secondary electron emission. *Mailing Add:* 4156 Maybell Way Palo Alto CA 94306

**VARNEY, WILLIAM YORK,** ANIMAL HUSBANDRY. *Current Pos:* RETIRED. *Personal Data:* b Forest Hills, Ky, Apr 1, 17; m 40; c 2. *Educ:* Univ Ky, BS, 51, MS, 52; Mich State Univ, PhD, 60. *Prof Exp:* Prin pub schs, Ky, 39-43; dist mgr, Southern States Coop, Va, 52-53; sales promoter, Swift & Co, Ill, 53-54; from instr to prof animal husb, Univ Ky, 54-77, exten prof animal sci, 77-82. *Mem:* Am Soc Animal Sci; Inst Food Technologists. *Res:* Carcass studies of beef, pork and lamb. *Mailing Add:* 317 Malabu Circle Lexington KY 40502

**VARNUM, WILLIAM SLOAN,** PHYSICS. *Current Pos:* STAFF MEM PHYSICS, LOS ALAMOS SCI LAB, 74- *Personal Data:* b St Louis, Mo, Jan 23, 41. *Educ:* Washington Univ, BS, 63; Fla State Univ, PhD(physics), 67. *Prof Exp:* Instr physics, Fla State Univ, 67-68; assoc scientist missile physics, Radiation Serv Co, 68-69; guest res scientist, Max-Planck-Institut Plasmaphysik, 69-70; res fel ionospheric physics, Max Planck Institut Ionosph-ren-Physik, 70-72; asst prof physics, New Col Sarasota, 72-73; NIH fel med physics, Univ Calif, Los Angeles, 73-74. *Concurrent Pos:* Consult, Rand Corp, 73-75. *Mem:* Am Phys Soc. *Res:* Plasma physics; laser fusion; nuclear weapons design. *Mailing Add:* Los Alamos Nat Lab PO Box 1663 MS B220 Los Alamos NM 87545. *Fax:* 301-903-4096

**VARON, MYRON IZAK,** radiobiology, medicine, for more information see previous edition

**VARON, SILVIO SALOMONE,** NEUROCHEMISTRY, NEUROBIOLOGY. *Current Pos:* assoc prof, 67-72, PROF NEUROBIOL, DEPT BIOL, MED SCH, UNIV CALIF, SAN DIEGO, 72- *Personal Data:* b Milan, Italy, July 25, 24; c 2. *Educ:* Univ Lausanne, EngD, 45; Univ Milan, MD, 59. *Prof Exp:* Resident asst prof neurochem, Inst Psychiat, Univ Milan, 60-63; res assoc, Dept Biochem, City of Hope Med Ctr, Duarte, Calif, 61-63; res assoc neurobiol, Dept Biol, Wash Univ, 63-64, assoc prof, 64-65; vis assoc prof, Dept Genetics, Sch Med, Stanford Univ, 65-67. *Concurrent Pos:* App mem, Pres Coun Spinal Cord Injury. *Mem:* Int Soc Neurochem; Am Soc Neurochem; Soc Neurosci; Am Soc Cell Biol; Int Soc Develop Neurosci. *Res:*

Structure and properties of the nerve growth factor protein; dissociation fractionation and culture of cells from nervous tissues; in vitro study of neuroglial cells; molecular mechanism of action of nerve growth factor; search for trophic factors directed to neurons and glial cells; in vivo models for neural regeneration. *Mailing Add:* Dept Biol M-001 Univ Calif San Diego Med Sch 9500 Gilman Dr La Jolla CA 92093-5003. *Fax:* 619-534-0128

**VARRESE, FRANCIS RAYMOND,** METALLURGICAL ENGINEERING, MATERIALS SCIENCE. *Current Pos:* SR PRIN MAT ENGR, HONEYWELL, 78- *Educ:* Lehigh Univ, BS, 61. *Prof Exp:* Mat engr, Pratt & Whitney Aircraft, 61-63; metallurgist, Cabot Stellits Div, 63-65; sr metallurgist, SPS Technologies, 65-68, mgr metall & chem eng, 68-70, staff metallurgist, Tool Div, 71-73, corp mgr mat res, 73-78; plant metallurgist, Robert Wooler Co, 70-71. *Concurrent Pos:* Mem, Adv & Tech Awareness Coun, Am Soc Metals Int, 76-79 & Handbk Comt, 77. *Mem:* Fel Am Soc Metals Int; Am Soc Testing & Mat. *Res:* Application of development of materials, processing, research, and engineering in the fastener and process control industry. *Mailing Add:* 258 W Mt Pleasant Ave Ambler PA 19002

**VARRICCHIO, FREDERICK,** BIOCHEMISTRY, DEVELOPMENTAL BIOLOGY. *Current Pos:* resident path, 86-91, CONSULT, COOK CO HOSP, CHICAGO, 89-; FOOD & DRUG ADMIN, MED OFFICER, 92- *Personal Data:* b Brooklyn, NY, May 18, 38; m 62; c 2. *Educ:* Univ Maine, Orono, BS, 60; Univ NDak, MS, 64; Univ Md, Baltimore, PhD(biochem), 66; Univ Autonoma de Ciudad Juarez, MD, 86. *Prof Exp:* Asst biochem, Univ Freiburg, WGer, 66-67; researcher molecular biol, Nat Ctr Sci Res, France, 67-69; fel internal med, Yale Univ, 69-72; asst prof, Mem Sloan-Kettering Inst Cancer Res, 72-77; prof exp oncol, Nova Univ, 77-79; prof chem & chmn dept, Nat Col, Lombard, Ill, 80-83; fac res assoc, Oak Ridge Nat Lab, 79-84. *Concurrent Pos:* Vis prof, Max Planck Inst Nutrit, Dortmund, Ger, 79; adj prof chem, Col DuPage, 80-84; res assoc, Argonne Nat Lab, 80- *Mem:* Am Soc Biol Chemists; Am Chem Soc; Am Soc Microbiol; Am Asn Pathologists; Ger Soc Biol Chemists; Sigma Xi. *Res:* Nuclear proteins; transfer ribonucleic in growth, differentiation and tumors. *Mailing Add:* 6130 Roseland Dr Rockville MD 20852

**VARSA, EDWARD CHARLES,** SOIL FERTILITY. *Current Pos:* asst prof, 70-84, ASSOC PROF SOILS, SOUTHERN ILL UNIV, CARBONDALE, 84- *Personal Data:* b Marissa, Ill, Oct 18, 38; m 65; c 2. *Educ:* Southern Ill Univ, Carbondale, BS, 61; Univ Ill, Urbana, MS, 65; Mich State Univ, PhD(soil sci), 70. *Honors & Awards:* Res of the Year Award, Fluid Fertilizer Found. *Prof Exp:* Asst agron, Univ Ill, 64-65; asst soil sci, Mich State Univ, 65-66, instr, 66-68, teaching asst, 68-70. *Mem:* Am Soc Agron; Soil Sci Soc Am; Sigma Xi. *Res:* Soil fertility research on, and the fate of, applied fertilizer nitrogen in soils. *Mailing Add:* Dept Plant & Soil Sci Southern Ill Univ Carbondale IL 62901. *Fax:* 618-453-7457

**VARSAMIS, IOANNIS,** PSYCHIATRY. *Current Pos:* ASSOC PROF PSYCHIAT, UNIV MAN, 67-; PSYCHIATRIST, GRACE GEN HOSP, 74-; PSYCHIATRIST, MAN ADOLESCENT TREAT CTR. *Personal Data:* b Alexandria, Egypt, July 24, 32, Can citizen; m 58. *Educ:* Univ Alexandria, MB, ChB, 57; Conjoint Bd, London, Eng, dipl psychol med, 61; Univ Man, dipl psychiat, 64; FRCP(C), 65. *Prof Exp:* Psychiatrist, Winnipeg Psychiat Inst, 64-68, med supt, 68-73. *Mem:* Can Med Asn; Can Psychiat Asn. *Res:* Phenomenology of schizophrenia; geriatric psychiatry. *Mailing Add:* Man Adolescent Treat Ctr 120 Tecumseh St Winnipeg MB R3E 2A9 Can

**VARSEL, CHARLES JOHN,** FOOD CHEMISTRY, FOOD BIOCHEMISTRY. *Current Pos:* RETIRED. *Personal Data:* b Fayette City, Pa, Jan 11, 30; m 50, Shirley A Muller; c Charles Jr, Deborah, Mark, Kevin, Kathleen & Karen. *Educ:* St Vincent Col, BA, 54; Univ Richmond, MS, 58; Med Col Va, PhD, 70. *Prof Exp:* Chemist, Linde Air Prod Co, Union Carbide & Carbon Corp, 54-55 & Res & Develop Dept, Philip Morris, Inc, 55-59; res assoc fuel technol, Pa State Univ, 59-60; from res chemist to sr res chemist, Res & Develop Dept, Philip Morris, Inc, Va, 60-69; prin chemist, Food Div, Citrus Res & Develop, Coca-Cola Foods, 69-70, mgr chem, 70-73, dir citrus res & develop, 73, dir res & develop, 73-92. *Concurrent Pos:* Counr, Tex Sect Inst Food Technol; bd gov, Food Update; consult, Coca-Cola Foods, 92- *Mem:* AAAS; Am Chem Soc; Inst Food Technol; NY Acad Sci. *Res:* Instrumental analysis; citrus chemistry; essential oils; mass spectroscopy; chemistry of natural products. *Mailing Add:* Minute Maid Co Dept Res & Develop PO Box 2079 Houston TX 77252-1900. *Fax:* 713-888-5792, 281-251-4292

**VARSHAVSKY, ALEXANDER JACOB,** MOLECULAR BIOLOGY. *Current Pos:* H SMITS PROF CELL BIOL, CALIF INST TECHNOL, PASADENA, 92- *Personal Data:* b Nov 8, 46; m 90, Vera Bingham; c Anna, Roman & Victoria. *Educ:* Moscow State Univ, BS, 70; Inst Molecular Biol, PhD(biochem), 73. *Prof Exp:* From asst prof to prof, Mass Inst Technol, 77-92. *Mem:* Nat Acad Sci; Am Acad Arts & Sci. *Res:* Discoveries in the fields of DNA replication; chromosome structure and intracellular protein turnover; granted 8 patents. *Mailing Add:* Div Biol Calif Inst Technol Pasadena CA 91125. *Fax:* 626-440-9821; *E-Mail:* varshavskya@starbase1.caltech.edu

**VARSHNEY, PRAMOD KUMAR,** COMMUNICATIONS, COMPUTER ENGINEERING. *Current Pos:* from asst prof to assoc prof, 76-86, assoc chair, 93-96, PROF ELEC & COMPUT ENG, SYRACUSE UNIV, 86- *Personal Data:* b Allahabad, India, July 1, 52; m 78, Anju; c 2. *Educ:* Univ Ill, Urbana-Champaign, BS, 72, MS, 74, PhD(elec eng), 76. *Honors & Awards:* Am Soc Eng Educ. *Prof Exp:* Teaching asst elec eng, Univ Ill,

Urbana-Champaign, 72-76. *Concurrent Pos:* Res assoc, Rome Air Develop Ctr, 79; vis prof, Ind Inst Technol, Delhi, India, 84-85. *Mem:* Fel Inst Elec & Electronics Engrs. *Res:* Communication theory; communication networks; distributed algorithms for signal processing; knowledge-based signal processing; sensor and data fusion; parallel processing. *Mailing Add:* 121 Link Hall Syracuse Univ Syracuse NY 13244-1240. *Fax:* 315-443-2583; *E-Mail:* varshney@cat.syr.edu

**VARSHNI, YATENDRA PAL,** ASTROPHYSICS, THEORETICAL PHYSICS. *Current Pos:* from asst prof to assoc prof, 62-69, PROF PHYSICS, UNIV OTTAWA, 69- *Personal Data:* b Allahabad, India, May 21, 32; Can citizen. *Educ:* Univ Allahabad, BSc, 50, MSc, 52, PhD(physics), 56. *Prof Exp:* Asst prof physics, Univ Allahabad, 55-60, fel, Nat Res Coun Can, 60-62. *Mem:* Am Phys Soc; Can Asn Physicists; Brit Inst Physics; Royal Astron Soc UK; Am Astron Soc; AAAS. *Res:* Molecular and atomic structure; quasi-stellar objects; quantum theory; energy levels of nuclei. *Mailing Add:* Dept Physics Univ Ottawa Ottawa ON K1N 6N5 Can. *Fax:* 613-562-5190; *E-Mail:* ypvsj@uottawa.ca

**VARTANIAN, LEO,** INTERNATIONAL TECHNICAL LIAISON, TECHNOLOGY LICENSING. *Current Pos:* Mem tech staff, Monsanto Chem Co, 54-66, supvr plant technol, 67-71, opers supt, 71-73, gen supt, 73-81, mgr plastics res & develop, 81-85, mgr int liaison, 85-90, MGR PLASTICS MKT DEVELOP, MONSANTO CHEM CO, 90- *Personal Data:* b Ludlow, Mass, Apr 22, 33; m 68, Elizabeth Manoogian. *Educ:* Rensselaer Polytech Inst, BChE, 54; Am Int Col, MBA, 59; Stanford Univ, MChE, 67. *Res:* Polymerization processes and products; coordination of technology exchange including worldwide conferences; technology in and out licensing and alliances. *Mailing Add:* 500 Innerness Lane Longmeadow MA 01106

**VARTANIAN, PERRY H(ATCH), JR,** electrical engineering, for more information see previous edition

**VARTY, ISAAC WILLIAM,** FOREST ENTOMOLOGY. *Current Pos:* RETIRED. *Personal Data:* b Consett, Eng, Feb 9, 24; m 52; c 3. *Educ:* Aberdeen Univ, BSc, 50, PhD(entom), 54. *Prof Exp:* Asst forest zool, Aberdeen Univ, 50-54; dist forest officer, Forestry Comn, Scotland, 54-58; forest res scientist, Maritimes Forest Res Ctr, Can Forestry Serv, 58-88. *Mem:* Fel Entom Soc Can; Can Inst Forestry. *Res:* Environmental impact of forest spraying; introduction of exotic parasites for control of forest pests; insecticide spray efficacy. *Mailing Add:* RR No 1 Ripples NB E0E 1M0 Can

**VARUGHESE, KURIAN,** WATER CHEMISTRY, WASTEWATER CHEMISTRY. *Current Pos:* CHIEF ANALYST, WATER QUAL LAB, CITY LAS CRUCES, NMEX, 94- *Personal Data:* b Kaviyoor, India, Aug, 37; m 64, Gracy K Thomas; c Asha M. *Educ:* Travancore Univ, India, BSc, 56; ViKram Univ, India, MSc, 58; Jabalpur Univ, India, PhD, 72; Portland State Univ, MST, 85, NMex State Univ, MS, 88. *Prof Exp:* Lectr chem, Holkar Col, 58-64; ViKram Univ, 65-66; Govt Eng Col, 67-72 & Nat Defense Acad, 73-76 & 80; prof, Ethopian Naval Col, 77-79; assoc prof, Asmara Univ, 81-83; dir, GMA Inc Environ Lab, 90-93. *Res:* Homogeneous precipitations in analytical chemistry; non voltammetric accumulation of metal compexes on dropping mercury electrode; modified enzyme electrodes. *Mailing Add:* 4775 Agave Dr Las Cruces NM 88001. *Fax:* 505-526-5007

**VARY, JAMES CORYDON,** SPORE GERMINATION, SPORULATION. *Current Pos:* PROF BIOCHEM, UNIV ILL, CHICAGO, 69- *Personal Data:* b Feb 24, 39; m, Patricia A Link; c Catherine & James C Jr. *Educ:* Univ Wis, MS, 64, PhD(bacteriol), 67. *Prof Exp:* Postdoctoral fel, Stanford Univ, 67-69. *Concurrent Pos:* Nat Bd Dent Examiners, 72-78. *Mem:* Am Soc Microbiol; AAAS; Am Soc Biochem & Molecular Biol. *Res:* Biochemical mechanisms for triggering germination and sporulation. *Mailing Add:* Sch Med Dept Biochem M/C 536 Univ Ill 1819 W Polk Chicago IL 60612-7334. *E-Mail:* jvary@uic.edu

**VARY, JAMES P,** THEORETICAL & APPLIED PHYSICS. *Current Pos:* PROF, IOWA STATE UNIV, 81- *Educ:* Boston Col, BS, 65; Yale Univ, MS, 67, MPh, 68, PhD, 70. *Prof Exp:* Res assoc, Ctr Theoret Physics, Mass Inst Technol, 70-72; from asst physicist to assoc physicist, Brookhaven Nat Lab, 72-75; from asst prof to assoc prof, Iowa State Univ, 75-79, prog dir, Theoret Nuclear Physics & prog coordr nuclear sci, Ames Lab, 77-79; Alexander von Humboldt fel, Univ Heidelberg, 79-81. *Concurrent Pos:* Vis prof, Univ Ariz, 83, Caltech, 86, Univ Wash, 92 & Univ Heidelberg, 93; univ distinguished vis prof, Ohio State Univ, 87-88; actg dir, Int Inst Theoret & Appl Physics, 93; Alexander von Humboldt sr fel, 93-95. *Mem:* Fel Am Phys Soc. *Res:* International aspects of science education and research especially for developing countries. *Mailing Add:* Dept Physics & Astron Iowa State Univ Ames IA 50011-3160. *Fax:* 515-294-9933

**VARY, PATRICIA SUSAN,** MICROBIAL GENETICS, GENE REGULATION. *Current Pos:* from asst prof to assoc prof, 73-78, presidential res prof, 91-96, DISTINGUISHED RES PROF, NORTHERN ILL UNIV, 96- *Personal Data:* b Wewoka, Okla, Nov 20, 41; div; c Catherine & James Jr. *Educ:* Tex Christian Univ, BS, 63, MS, 65; Univ Wis-Madison, MS, 67; Stanford Univ, PhD(microbiol genetics), 69. *Prof Exp:* Asst prof chem, NCent Col, 77. *Concurrent Pos:* Indust consult, 86-; mem, adv bd, Bacillus Stock Cult Colle & study group, Int Comn Taxon Viruses, 88-; vis researcher, Inst Pasteur, Paris, 89-90; sr fel, Fogarty Int Ctr, NIH, 89-90. *Mem:* Am Soc Microbiol; Genetics Soc Am; Sigma Xi; AAAS. *Res:* Genetic methods for Bacillus megaterium; isolation of the only transducing phages, plasmid analysis, transposition, mapping; cell reaction to stress such as sporulation, heat shock; cloning hosts for industrial applications. *Mailing Add:* Dept Biol Sci Northern Ill Univ Dekalb IL 60115-2861. *Fax:* 815-753-0461; *E-Mail:* pvary@niu.edu

**VAS, STEPHEN ISTVAN,** MEDICAL MICROBIOLOGY, IMMUNOLOGY. *Current Pos:* assoc prof med, 77-80, PROF MED MICROBIOL, UNIV TORONTO, 77-, PROF MED, 80- *Personal Data:* b Budapest, Hungary, June 4, 26; Can citizen; m 53. *Educ:* Pazmany Peter Univ, Budapest, MD, 50, PhD(microbiol), 56. *Prof Exp:* Lectr microbiol, Pazmany Peter Univ, 48-49, asst prof, 49-50; Rockefeller res fel microbiol, McGill Univ, 57-59, asst virologist, 59-60, from asst prof to prof immunol, 60-77, chmn dept, 72-77. *Concurrent Pos:* Microbiologist-in-chief & sr physician, Royal Victoria Hosp, 72-77; microbiologist-in-chief & physician, Toronto Western Hosp, 77- *Mem:* Am Soc Microbiol; Can Soc Microbiol; Can Soc Immunol; Can Med Asn; Can Asn Med Microbiol. *Res:* Antibody synthesis; synthesis of complement; effect of antibodies on bacteria and on tissue cells; peritoneal dialysis. *Mailing Add:* Dept Microbiol Toronto Western Hosp 399 Bathurst St Toronto ON M5T 2S8 Can

**VASARHELYI, DESI D,** CIVIL ENGINEERING. *Current Pos:* res engr, 50-52, from instr to prof, 52-80, EMER PROF CIVIL ENG, UNIV WASH, 80- *Personal Data:* b Hungary, Sept 27, 10; nat US; m 57. *Educ:* Univ Cluj, BA, 28; Budapest Tech Univ, Dipl, 33, DSc(eng), 44. *Prof Exp:* Asst bridge struct & concrete, Budapest Tech Univ, 32; design & field engr, Palatinus Co, 36; lectr, Inst Higher Tech Educ, Budapest, 44; engr, Brit Army, Austria, 46. *Mem:* Am Soc Civil Engrs; Am Welding Soc; Soc Exp Stress Anal; Int Asn Bridge & Struct Engrs. *Res:* Stress analysis; structural theory; engineering materials; steel structures. *Mailing Add:* 4055 NE 57th St Seattle WA 98125

**VASAVADA, KASHYAP V,** THEORETICAL PHYSICS. *Current Pos:* assoc prof, 70-74, PROF PHYSICS, IND UNIV, PURDUE UNIV, INDIANAPOLIS, 74- *Personal Data:* b Ahmedabad, India, July 25, 38; m 69; c 2. *Educ:* Univ Baroda, BS, 58; Univ Delhi, MS, 60; Univ Md, PhD(physics), 64. *Prof Exp:* Nat Acad Sci fel physics, Goddard Space Flight Ctr, NASA, 64-66; asst prof, Univ Conn, 66-70. *Concurrent Pos:* NIH sr fel, 85-86. *Mem:* Am Phys Soc. *Res:* High energy physics; scattering theory; magnetic resonance; theoretical physics. *Mailing Add:* 1316 Brookton Ct Indianapolis IN 46260-3368. *E-Mail:* vasavada@indyvax.iupui.edu

**VASCO, DONALD WYMAN,** SEISMOLOGY, GEOPHYSICAL INVERSE THEORY. *Current Pos:* Postdoctoral seismol, Geophys Lab, 87-89, Seismographic Sta, 89-91, STAFF SCIENTIST SEISMOL, EARTH SCI DIV, LAWRENCE BERKELEY LAB, UNIV CALIF, 91 *Personal Data:* b Oakland, Calif, Jan 22, 58. *Educ:* Univ Tex, Austin, BSc, 81; Univ Calif, Berkeley, PhD(seismol), 87. *Concurrent Pos:* Vis fel, Australian Nat Univ, 91. *Mem:* Am Geophys Union; Soc Explor Geophys; Soc Indust & Appl Math; Seismol Soc Am. *Res:* Development of a technique to determine fluid intrusion within the earth using observations of surface displacement; analysis of global seismic traveltime observations for the velocity structure of the earth's mantle; development of techniques for the inversion of geophysical data; author of numerous publications. *Mailing Add:* Ctr Computational Seismol Earth Sci Div Bldg 90 Lawrence Berkeley Lab One Cyclotron Rd Berkeley CA 94720. *Fax:* 510-486-5686; *E-Mail:* dwvasco@lbl.gov

**VASCONCELOS, AUREA C,** PLANT PHYSIOLOGY. *Current Pos:* vis asst prof plant physiol, 70-72, assoc prof bot, 72-90, PROF BOT, RUTGERS UNIV, 90- *Personal Data:* b Caguas, PR, Dec 25, 35; US citizen; m 68. *Educ:* Univ PR, BS, 57; George Washington Univ, MA, 61; Univ Chicago, PhD(biol), 69. *Prof Exp:* Asst prof biol, Univ PR, 61-65. *Concurrent Pos:* Mem, Int Cell Res Orgn, UNESCO. *Mem:* AAAS; Am Soc Plant Physiol; NY Acad Sci; Am Soc Cell Biol; Int Soc Plant Biol. *Res:* Chloroplast development; import of nuclear coded polypeptides into chloroplasts. *Mailing Add:* Dept Biol Sci Rutgers Univ New Brunswick NJ 08903

**VASCONCELOS, WOLNER V,** ALGEBRA, COMPUTER ALGEBRA. *Current Pos:* From asst prof to assoc prof, 67-75, PROF MATH, RUTGERS UNIV, 75- *Personal Data:* b Recife, Brazil, May 17, 37. *Educ:* Univ Chicago, PhD(math), 66. *Mailing Add:* Dept Math Rutgers Univ New Brunswick NJ 08903-2101

**VASEEN, V(ESPER) ALBERT,** ACCELERATED GROWTH OF CLONES OF PLANT TISSUE BY DUAL HYDROPHONIC MEANS, CONTINUOUS PROCESSING FERMENTER VEHICLE. *Current Pos:* PRES & CONSULT ENVIRON TECHNOL AVASCO, 79- *Personal Data:* b Denver, Colo, Sept 13, 17; m 41, June L Novak; c Gail (Moler) & Dale. *Hon Degrees:* Dr Sci, Univ Del Norte, Coquimbo, Chile, 81. *Honors & Awards:* Cert Accomplishment, Int Graphoanal Soc Inc, 62, Master Graphoanal, 64. *Prof Exp:* Asst state sanit engr, Colo State Health Dept, 41-43; sanit officer, US Army, 43-46; pres, Ripple & Howe Inc, 46-66; proj engr, Stearns Rogers Inc, 66-80. *Concurrent Pos:* Trustee, Water Pollution Control Fedn, 56-58; mem, US Dept Com, 55-78, Int Exec Serv Corps, 68-, adv bd, Chem Week Mgt, 74; consult coal gasification, In Situ Technol Inc, 79-80; pres & consult, Technometrics Inc, 80-87. *Mem:* Water Pollution Control Fedn; Inter Am Asn Sanit Engrs. *Res:* Inventor of over 300 disclosures relating to environment and power; 33 US patents; development of continuous processing formenter; author of numerous publications. *Mailing Add:* 9840 W 35th Ave Wheat Ridge CO 80033

**VASEK, FRANK CHARLES,** BOTANY. *Current Pos:* RETIRED. *Personal Data:* b Maple Heights, Ohio, May 9, 27; m 54; c 2. *Educ:* Ohio Univ, BS, 50; Univ Calif, Los Angeles, PhD(bot), 55. *Prof Exp:* Asst bot & teaching asst, Univ Calif, Los Angeles, 50-54; from instr to prof bot, Univ Calif, Riverside, 54-89. *Mem:* Bot Soc Am; Ecol Soc Am; Soc Study Evolution; Am Soc Plant Taxon. *Res:* Plant taxonomy; evolution; population dynamics. *Mailing Add:* 18756 Los Hermanus Ranch Rd Valley Center CA 92082

**VASERSTEIN, LEONID, IV,** ALGEBRAIC K-THEORY, ARITHMETIC GROUPS. *Current Pos:* PROF MATH, PA STATE UNIV, 79- *Personal Data:* b Kuibyshev, USSR, Sept 15, 44; m 68; c 2. *Educ:* Moscow State Univ, MS, 66, PhD(math), 69. *Prof Exp:* Sr researcher & head, Sect Oper Res & Prog, All-Union Inst Info & Tech Econ Res Elec Indust, 69-78. *Concurrent Pos:* Mem jury, All-Union Math Olympiads, USSR, 62-77; vis prof, Univ Bielefeld, Inst des Hautes Etudes Sci, France, 78, Univ Chicago, 79 & Cornell Univ, 79-80; Guggenheim fel, 84. *Mem:* Am Math Soc. *Res:* Operations research, dynamical systems. *Mailing Add:* Dept Math Rm 205 McAllister Bldg Pa State Univ University Park PA 16802-6401

**VASEY, CAREY EDWARD,** BIOLOGY OF BRACHYCEROUS DIPTERA, FAMILIES STRATIOMYIDA TABANIDAE & RHAGIONIDAE. *Current Pos:* asst prof, 64-74, assoc prof, 74-91, EMER PROF BIOL, COL ARTS & SCI, STATE UNIV NY, GENESEO, 91- *Personal Data:* b Bristol, Pa, Feb 12, 27; m 49, Alberta Wicks; c Brian & April. *Educ:* Lycoming Col, BA, 53; Syracuse Univ, MS, 59; State Univ NY Col Environ Sci & Forestry, PhD(forest entom), 75. *Prof Exp:* Indust microbiologist vitamin assay, Publicker Indust, Philadelphia, Pa, 51-53; lab technician histol technol, Med Ctr, Univ Kans, 53-55; teacher biol, James Buchanan Sch, Mercersburg, Pa, 55-58 & Coatesville Area Schs, Coatesville, Pa, 59-60; instr, Philadelphia Col Pharm & Sci, 60-64. *Mem:* Soc NAm Dipterists. *Res:* Systematics morphology and ultrastructure of selected families of diptera; tabanidae of western NY state. *Mailing Add:* 11 Wadsworth St Geneseo NY 14454

**VASEY, EDFRED H,** SOIL FERTILITY, SOIL CONSERVATION. *Current Pos:* From asst prof to assoc prof, 61-67, head Plant Sci Sect, NDak Coop Exten Serv, 71-82, EXTEN SOILS SPECIALIST, EXTEN SERV, NDAK STATE UNIV, 67-, PROF SOILS, 69- *Personal Data:* b Mott, NDak, Aug 29, 33; m 55; c 4. *Educ:* NDak State Univ, BS, 55, MS, 57; Purdue Univ, PhD(plant nutrit), 62. *Concurrent Pos:* Assoc ed, Appl Agr Res, Springer-Verleg, New York, NY. *Mem:* Soil Sci Soc Am; Coun Agr Sci & Technol; Sigma Xi; Soil & Water Conserv Soc. *Res:* Fertility needs of crops grown on North Dakota soils; computer software for crop production. *Mailing Add:* 2802 Maple St N Box 5575 Fargo ND 58102

**VASEY, FRANK BARNETT,** RHEUMATOLOGY, INTERNAL MEDICINE. *Current Pos:* ASST PROF MED, RHEUMATOLOGY, UNIV SFLA, 77- *Personal Data:* b Webster City, Iowa, Feb 6, 42; m 68; c 1. *Educ:* Cornell Col, BA, 64; Univ NDak, BS, 66; Univ Pa, MD, 68. *Prof Exp:* Asst prof internal mcd, McGill Univ & Royal Victoria Hosp, Montreal, 76-77. *Concurrent Pos:* Rheumatology fel, Royal Victoria Hosp, McGill Univ, 74; dir, Rheumatology & Immunol Clin Lab, Univ SFla, 77-78 & Rheumatology & Immunol Res Lab, Vet Admin Hosp, Tampa, 78- *Mem:* Fel Am Col Physicians. *Res:* Immunogenetics basis of psoriatic arthritis. *Mailing Add:* Univ SFla 12901 Bruce B Downs Blvd Tampa FL 33612-4742

**VASHISHTA, PRIYA DARSHAN,** SOLID STATE PHYSICS, MATERIALS SCIENCE. *Current Pos:* FLOATING POINT SYST CHAIRED PROF COMPUTATIONAL METHODS, DEPT PHYSICS, LA STATE UNIV, 90- *Personal Data:* b Aligarh, India, Aug 24, 44; m 70; c 1. *Educ:* Agra Univ, BS, 60; Aligarh Univ, MS, 62; Indian Inst Technol, PhD(physics), 67. *Prof Exp:* Fel, St Andrews Univ, UK, 66-68; res assoc, McMaster Univ, 68-70; asst prof physics, Northwestern Univ, 70-71; asst prof, Western Mich Univ, 71-72; res physicist, Argonne Nat Lab, 72-90, dir, Solid State Sci Div, 79-90. *Concurrent Pos:* Vis scientist, Theoret Physics Div, Atomic Energy Res Estab, UK, 68, Inst Theoret Physics, Sweden, 71; fel appl comput, Thomas J Watson Res Ctr, IBM, 72; mem tech staff, Bell Labs, 76; vis assoc prof, Univ Calif, San Diego, 76-77; co-ed, J Solid State Ionics, Amsterdam, 79-; mem, Solid State Sci Panel, NSF, 79-82. *Mem:* Am Phys Soc; AAAS; Sigma Xi. *Res:* Theoretical physics of condensed matter; electron-phonon interaction and superconductivity in metals and alloys; many-body interactions in metals and semiconductors; molecular dynamics studies of condensed matter; phase transitions on surfaces. *Mailing Add:* 1211 Applewood Rd Baton Rouge LA 70808. *Fax:* 504-388-5855

**VASICEK, DANIEL J,** PARALLEL PROGRAMMING, FUNCTIONAL LANGUAGES. *Current Pos:* sem leader math & res assoc math, physics, eng & statist, 73-89, SEM LEADER COMPUT SCI, AMOCO PROD CO, 85- *Personal Data:* b Cleveland, Ohio, Nov 6, 42; m 73; c 4. *Educ:* Purdue Univ, BS, 64, MS, 65; Univ Colo, PhD(aerospace eng sci), 73. *Prof Exp:* Dir pre-eng prog, Univ Colo, 72-75. *Concurrent Pos:* Instr calculus, Tulsa Jr Col, 76; sem leader kinetic theory, Tulsa Free Univ, 83; adj prof, Tulsa Univ, 79- *Mem:* Asn Comput Mach; Soc Indust & Appl Math. *Res:* Parallel extensions for programming languages; successful demonstration of a practical parallel program of large size, 100,000 lines; statistical analysis of seismic, well log and core data; numerical representations of the rotation group; interpolation and smoothing. *Mailing Add:* Amoco Prod Co PO Box 3385 Tulsa OK 74102. *Fax:* 918-660-4163; *E-Mail:* dvasicek@trc.amoco.com

**VASIL, INDRA KUMAR,** BOTANY. *Current Pos:* from assoc prof to prof, 67-79, GRAD RES PROF, UNIV FLA, 79- *Personal Data:* b Basti, India, Aug 31, 32; m 59, Vimla; c Kavita & Charu. *Educ:* Banaras Hindu Univ, BSc, 52; Univ Delhi, MSc, 54, PhD(bot). 58. *Honors & Awards:* Sr US Scientist Award for Res, Fed Repub Ger, 74. *Prof Exp:* Res asst bot, Univ Delhi, 54-58, asst prof, 59-63; res assoc, Univ Wis, 63-65; scientist, Indian Agr Res Inst, 65-67. *Concurrent Pos:* Res assoc, Univ Ill, 62-63. *Mem:* AAAS; Int Asn Plant Tissue Cult; Bot Soc Am; Int Soc Plant Morphol; Int Soc Plant Molecular Biol. *Res:* Developmental morphology; physiology of reproduction in flowering plants; morphogenesis and differentiation in higher plants; plant tissue and organ culture, especially of cereals and grasses. *Mailing Add:* 4901 NW 19th Pl Gainesville FL 32605. *Fax:* 352-392-9366; *E-Mail:* lkv@gm.jkas.ufl.edu

**VASIL, MICHAEL LAWRENCE,** PARASITOLOGY, BIOCHEMISTRY. *Current Pos:* from asst prof to assoc prof, 78-90, PROF MICROBIOL, MED SCH, UNIV COLO, 90- *Personal Data:* b San Diego, Calif, Sept 6, 45; m 71; c 1. *Educ:* Univ Tex, El Paso, BS, 71, Med Sch Dallas, PhD(microbiol), 75. *Prof Exp:* Chief bacteriologist, Providence Hosp, 67-71; res asst, Univ Tex, 71-75; instr, Univ Ore Med Sch, 75-77; asst prof, Univ Calif, Los Angeles Sch Med, 77-78. *Concurrent Pos:* Prin investr res grants, Procter & Gamble, 80-86, Cystic Fibrosis Found, 79-81 & NIH, 79-93. *Mem:* Am Soc Microbiol; Am Soc Clin Pathologists; Sigma Xi. *Res:* Mechanism of bacterial pathogenesis and the development of bacterial vaccines; clinical microbiology-DNA probes; microbial genetics as well as recombinant DNA technology in psendomenas aeruginosa escherichia coli, staphylococcus anreus; industrial microbiology-over expression of gene products by bacteria. *Mailing Add:* Dept Microbiol & Immunol Univ Colo Med Sch 4200 E Ninth Ave Denver CO 80220-3706

**VASIL, VIMLA,** CELL & PROTOPLAST CULTURE, TISSUE CULTURE. *Current Pos:* assoc bot, 67-69, assoc res scientist, 79-85, RES SCIENTIST, UNIV FLA, 85- *Personal Data:* b New Delhi, India, Dec 11, 32; US citizen; m 59, Indra K; c Kavita & Charu. *Educ:* Univ Delhi, BSc, 53, MSc, 55, PhD(bot), 59. *Prof Exp:* Res assoc bot, Univ Delhi, 59-62; res assoc agron, Univ Ill, 62-63; res assoc plant path, Univ Wis, 63-65; scientist, Coun Sci & Indust Res, New Delhi, 66. *Mem:* Bot Soc Am. *Res:* Developmental morphology and embryology of angiosperms and gymnosperms; cell and tissue culture of higher plants, particularly cereal and grass species. *Mailing Add:* 4901 NW 19th Pl Gainesville FL 32605

**VASILAKOS, NICHOLAS PETROU,** CHEMICAL ENGINEERING. *Current Pos:* ASST PROF CHEM ENG, UNIV TEX, AUSTIN, 81- *Personal Data:* b Athens, Greece, Jan 1, 54. *Educ:* Nat Tech Univ Athens, BS, 76; Calif Inst Technol, MS, 78, PhD(coal desulfurization), 81. *Mem:* Am Inst Chem Engrs; Am Chem Soc; Sigma Xi. *Res:* Coal desulfurization by chemical treatment; coal liquefaction by super critical solvent extraction; production of liquid hydrocarbon fuels from urban, industrial and agricultural wastes by catalytic hydrogenolysis. *Mailing Add:* 20 Armatolon St Ano Dafni Gr 17235 Athens Greece

**VASILATOS-YOUNKEN, REGINA,** GROWTH HORMONE, GROWTH HORMONE BINDING PROTEINS. *Current Pos:* res assoc molecular & cell biol, 83, asst prof poultry sci, 83-89, ASSOC PROF POULTRY SCI, PA STATE UNIV, 89- *Personal Data:* b New York, NY, Nov 30, 54; m 83. *Educ:* Univ Maine, Orono, BS, 76; Pa State Univ, PhD(animal nutrit), 82. *Prof Exp:* Res fel nutrit, Roman L Hruska US Meat Animal Res Ctr, 82-83. *Concurrent Pos:* Assoc ed, Physiol & Reproduction Sect, Poultry Sci, 88-; chair, Physiol Prog, Poultry Sci Asn, 89. *Mem:* AAAS; Am Inst Nutrit; Endocrine Soc; Am Soc Animal Sci; Poultry Sci Asn. *Res:* Endocrine regulation of growth and development with emphasis on factors influencing the biological action of growth hormone and growth hormone binding proteins. *Mailing Add:* Dept Poultry Sci Pa State Univ 203 William L Henning Bldg University Park PA 16802-0001

**VASILE, MICHAEL JOSEPH,** ION BEAM TECHNOLOGY, MICRO SYSTEMS TECHNOLOGY. *Current Pos:* TOLBERT PIPES PROF MECH ENG, LA TECH UNIV, 93- *Personal Data:* b Newton, NJ, May 11, 40; c 3. *Educ:* Rutgers Univ, BSc, 62; Princeton Univ, MS, 64, PhD(phys chem), 66. *Prof Exp:* Res fel chem, Nat Res Coun Can, 66-68; mem tech staff, Bell Labs, 68-93. *Mem:* Electrochem Soc; Am Vacuum Soc; Mat Res Soc; Precision Eng Soc. *Res:* Plasma chemistry; surface chemistry; electronic materials. *Mailing Add:* La Tech Univ 600 Mountain Ave Ruston LA 71272

**VASILIAUSKAS, EDMUND,** ORGANIC CHEMISTRY. *Current Pos:* from instr to assoc prof, 71-80, PROF CHEM, MORAINE VALLEY COMMUNITY COL, 80- *Personal Data:* b Lithuania, June 18, 38; US citizen; m 95, Maria Indriunas; c 4. *Educ:* Rochester Inst Technol, BS, 63; Loyola Univ Chicago, PhD(org chem), 70. *Prof Exp:* Chemist, Olin Corp, 63-65 & Witco Chem Corp, 70-71. *Mem:* Am Chem Soc. *Res:* Study of the derivatives of benzonorbornene. *Mailing Add:* Dept Chem Moraine Valley Community Col Palos Hills IL 60465

**VASILOS, THOMAS,** CERAMICS, CHEMISTRY. *Current Pos:* sect chief metals & ceramics, Res & Adv Develop Div, 57-66, mgr, Mat Sci Dept, Avco Systs Div, 66-77, mgr, Mat Develop Dept, Avco Corp, 77-79, prin scientist, Avco Systs Div, 79-87, PROF CHEM ENG, UNIV LOWELL, 87- *Personal Data:* b New York, NY, Oct 18, 29; m 54; c 2. *Educ:* Brooklyn Col, BS, 50; Mass Inst Technol, DSc(ceramics), 54. *Honors & Awards:* Ross Coffin Purdy Award, Am Ceramic Soc, 67. *Prof Exp:* Asst ceramics, Mass Inst Technol, 50-53; res engr, Ford Motor Co, 53; mgr, Ceramics Res Dept, Corning Glass Works, 55-57. *Concurrent Pos:* Consult, Mat Adv Bd, Nat Acad Sci, 61- *Mem:* Fel Am Ceramic Soc. *Res:* Thermal and mechanical properties of ceramics; crystal growing; ferroelectric ceramics and crystals; nuclear fuel ceramics; ceramic coatings; metal reinforced ceramics; diffusion in crystals; plastic-ceramic composites; composite formulation and properties; refractory metals. *Mailing Add:* 92 Bartlett Rd Winthrop MA 02152-2243

**VASINGTON, FRANK D,** BIOCHEMISTRY. *Current Pos:* RETIRED. *Personal Data:* b Norwich, Conn, Nov 3, 28; div; c 4. *Educ:* Univ Conn, AB, 50, MS, 52; Univ Md, PhD(biochem), 55. *Prof Exp:* Asst prof biochem, Sch Med, Univ Md, 55-57; Nat Found res fel, McCollum-Pratt Inst, Johns Hopkins Univ, 57-59, asst prof physiol chem, Sch Med, 59-64; from assoc prof to prof biochem, Univ Conn, 64-93, head biol sci group, 67-71, head biochem & biophys sect, 67-77, assoc dean, Col Lib Arts & Sci, 76-78, assoc vpres acad affairs, 78-82, interim dean, Col Lib Arts & Sci, 86-88, dean, 88-93; interim dean, Col Lib Arts & Sci, 86-93. *Res:* Biosynthesis and turnover of intracellular membranes; secretion; active transport processes in mitochondria and bacteria. *Mailing Add:* 172 Highland Mansfield CT 06268

**VASKA, LAURI,** INORGANIC CHEMISTRY, CATALYSIS. *Current Pos:* from assoc prof to prof, 64-90, EMER PROF INORG CHEM, CLARKSON UNIV, 90- *Personal Data:* b Rakvere, Estonia, May 7, 25; nat US; m 54, Mary E Tucker; c Andres, Marcus, Kristina, Matthias & Paul. *Educ:* Univ Gottingen, BS, 49; Univ Tex, PhD(chem), 56. *Honors & Awards:* Boris Pregel Award, NY Acad Sci, 71. *Prof Exp:* Fel magnetism & chemisorption, Northwestern Univ, 56-57; res fel inorg chem, Mellon Inst, 57-64. *Concurrent Pos:* Fulbright-Hays fel, Univ Helsinki, 72. *Mem:* Fel AAAS; Am Chem Soc; fel NY Acad Sci; fel Am Inst Chemists. *Res:* Coordination chemistry; catalysis; oxygen-carrying complexes; noble metal chemistry; bioinorganic chemistry; organometallic chemistry. *Mailing Add:* Clarkson Univ Box 5810 Potsdam NY 13699-5810. *Fax:* 315-268-6610

**VASKO, JOHN STEPHEN,** cardiovascular & thoracic surgery; deceased, see previous edition for last biography

**VASKO, MICHAEL RICHARD,** NEUROCHEMISTRY, NEUROPHARMACOLOGY. *Current Pos:* assoc prof pharmacol, 88-93, PROF PHARMACOL & ANESTHESIA, SCH MED, IND UNIV, 93- *Personal Data:* b Detroit, Mich, Mar 29, 48; m 80, Rebecca Anderson; c Catherine & Joshua. *Educ:* Univ Mich, Ann Arbor, BS, 70, PhD(pharmacol), 76. *Prof Exp:* Res fel, Dept Pharmacol, Med Sch, Univ Mich, Ann Arbor, 71-75; instr pharmacol & neurol, Univ Tex Health Sci Ctr Dallas, 75-77, asst prof, 77-80; vis res fel, Dept Pharmacol, Inst Animal Physiol, Eng, 80-81; asst prof, Dept Pharmacol & mem grad fac biomed sci, Univ Tex Health Sci Ctr, Dallas, 81-88. *Concurrent Pos:* Chief, Neuropharmacol Lab & staff pharmacologist, Vet Admin Med Ctr, Dallas, 75-80, Pharmacol Sect, 81-88; res fel, Nat Inst Drug Abuse, 80. *Mem:* Soc Neurosci; Int Soc Neurochem; Am Soc Pharmacol Exp Therapeut; Am Pain Soc. *Res:* Involvement of neurotransmitters in the antinociceptive effects of narcotic analgesics; regulation of neurotransmitter release from sensory neurons. *Mailing Add:* Dept Pharmacol & Toxicol Ind Univ Sch Med 635 Barnhill Dr Indianapolis IN 46202-5120. *Fax:* 317-274-1560

**VASLOW, DALE FRANKLIN,** PLASMA PHYSICS. *Current Pos:* RADIOLOGIST, MO MED IMAGING INC, 97- *Personal Data:* b Chicago, Ill, Aug 27, 45. *Educ:* Univ Wis, BS, 67, MS, 69, PhD(elec eng), 73. *Prof Exp:* Staff scientist plasma physics, Gen Atomic Co, 74-84; physician, USCD Med Ctr, 84-89; radiol resident, Univ Tenn, 92-96; fel, Univ Cincinnati, 96-97. *Mem:* Inst Elec & Electronics Engrs; Sigma Xi. *Res:* Solid state laser design; low light level image detection system; optical design; laser Thomson Scattering experiment; solid ablation in a plasma; fast neutron induced chemistry. *Mailing Add:* 403 Meier Dr Jefferson City MO 65109

**VASOFSKY, RICHARD WILLIAM,** PHYSICAL CHEMISTRY, SURFACE SCIENCE. *Current Pos:* PVT CONSULT, 84- *Personal Data:* b Waukegan, Ill, May 14, 46. *Educ:* Univ Denver, BS, 68; Ore State Univ, MS, 71, PhD(phys chem), 75. *Prof Exp:* Res asst phys chem, Ore State Univ, 69-74; res assoc physics, Clarkson Col Technol, 75-77, res asst prof, 78; consult surface sci, Rome Air Develop Ctr, 78-80. *Mem:* Am Chem Soc; Am Vacuum Soc; Clay Mineral Soc; Int Soc Hybrid Microelectron; AAAS; Sigma xi. *Res:* Adsorption by clays; gas-solid interactions; chemisorption; thin films; desorption; vacuum and ultramicrobalance techniques and applications. *Mailing Add:* RR 3 Box 846 Loudon TN 37774-9803

**VASQUEZ, ALPHONSE THOMAS,** MATHEMATICS AND COMPUTER SCIENCE, ALGORITHMS FOR ALGEBRAIC GEOMETRY. *Current Pos:* assoc prof, 67-77, PROF MATH & COMPUT SCI, GRAD DIV, CITY UNIV NEW YORK, 77- *Personal Data:* b Boston, Mass, Apr 19, 38; m 65. *Educ:* Mass Inst Technol, BS, 59; Univ Calif, Berkeley, PhD(math), 62. *Prof Exp:* Mem, Inst Advan Study, 62-64; res assoc math, Brandeis Univ, 64-65; asst prof, 65-67. *Concurrent Pos:* Vis prof, Univ Mich, Univ Calif, Berkeley. *Mem:* Am Math Soc. *Res:* Algebraic and differential topology; homological algebra; error-correcting codes; computational complexity of curves defined over finite fields. *Mailing Add:* Grad Div & Univ Ctr City Univ New York 33 W 42nd St Rm GS718 New York NY 10036-8099

**VASSALLE, MARIO,** CARDIOVASCULAR & ELECTROPHYSIOLOGY. *Current Pos:* from asst prof to assoc prof, 65-71, PROF PHYSIOL, HEALTH SCI CTR, STATE UNIV NY, 71- *Personal Data:* b Viareggio, Italy, May 26, 28; US citizen; m 59; c 5. *Educ:* Liceo-Ginnasio G Carducci, Viareggio, BA, 47; Univ Pisa, MD, 53. *Hon Degrees:* Dr, Univ Ferrara, 91. *Honors & Awards:* Sinsheimer Fund Award, 66-71. *Prof Exp:* Actg chief resident med, Fr Hosp, NY, 58-59; NIH trainee, Cardiovasc Res & Training Prog, Med Col Ga, 59-60; teaching fel, Dept Physiol, State Univ NY, Downstate Med Ctr, 60-61, NY Heart Asn fel, 61-62, instr, 62; NIH fel, Physiol Inst, Bern, Switz, 62-64. *Concurrent Pos:* Mem, Coun Basic Sci, Am Heart Asn, 69- & Nat Conf Cardiovasc Dis, 69; assoc ed, Am J Physiol, 76-80; consult, NIH; vis prof, Dept Gen Physiol, Univ Ferrara, Italy, 71, Dept Physiol & Biophys, Univ Vt, Burlington, 78 & Dept Med, Cath Univ A Gemelli, Rome, Italy, 84-85; mem, NY Health Res Coun, 72-75. *Mem:* AAAS; Am Physiol Soc; Harvey Soc; NY Acad Sci; Am Heart Asn; Cardiac Muscle Soc; Sigma Xi. *Res:* Cardiac electrophysiology, particularly cardiac automaticity and its control. *Mailing Add:* Dept Physiol Box 31 State Univ Ny Health Sci Ctr 450 Clarkson Ave Brooklyn NY 11203-2012. *Fax:* 718-270-3103

**VASSALLO, DONALD ARTHUR,** POLYMER CHEMISTRY. *Current Pos:* RETIRED. *Personal Data:* b Waterbury, Conn, June 7, 32; m 60; c 4. *Educ:* Univ Conn, BA, 54; Univ Ill, MS, 56, PhD(anal chem), 58. *Prof Exp:* res assoc, Plastics Dept, E I du Pont de Nemours & Co, Inc, 58-85, consult, 86-87. *Concurrent Pos:* Consult, Maldermid Chem Co, 55, Naugatuck Chem Co, 56-57. *Mem:* AAAS; Am Chem Soc; Soc Plastics Eng; Sigma Xi. *Res:* Automatic nonaqueous titrations; thermogravimetry; differential thermal analysis, especially polymers; polymer melt rheology; polymer structure-property correlations; polyolefins; polyvinyl alcohol; polymeric gas barriers. *Mailing Add:* 5 Aldham Ct Wilmington DE 19803-1701

**VASSALLO, FRANKLIN A(LLEN),** MECHANICAL ENGINEERING. *Current Pos:* RETIRED. *Personal Data:* b Waterbury, Conn, Feb 22, 34; m 66, Linda Sue McMahon; c Peter, Andrew & Melissa. *Educ:* Univ Conn, BS, 56; Univ Ill, MS, 57. *Prof Exp:* Asst mech engr, Cornell Aeronaut Lab, 57-59, assoc mech engr, 59-62, res engr, 62-67, prin res engr, 67-70, sect head, 70-78. *Concurrent Pos:* sect head, Calspan SRL Corp, 78-97, consult, 97- *Mem:* Nat Res Coun. *Res:* Heat transfer and erosion in rapid fire weapons; determination of gas enthalpy; heat transfer and flow processes in high heat flux environments; hazardous materials transport; assessment of use of non-metallic composite materials in conventional weapon systems; space refrigeration. *Mailing Add:* 1273 Ransom Rd Lancaster NY 14086

**VASSALLO, PAUL,** INFORMATION SCIENCE & SYSTEMS. *Current Pos:* DIR, OFF INFO SERVS, NAT INST STAND & TECHNOL, 93- *Personal Data:* b Aug 3, 37. *Educ:* Univ Mich, MA, 62. *Concurrent Pos:* Sr exec fel, Harvard Univ Kennedy Sch Govt, 94. *Mailing Add:* Nat Inst Stand & Technol Info Serv Off Rte 270 Bldg 101 Gaithersburg MD 20899. *E-Mail:* paul. vassallo@nist.gov

**VASSAMILLET, LAWRENCE FRANCOIS,** SOLID STATE ANALYSIS. *Current Pos:* RETIRED. *Personal Data:* b Elizabethville, Congo, Sept 14, 24; nat US; m 54, Edith Pennoyer; c Laura A & Martha L. *Educ:* Mass Inst Technol, BSc, 46, MS, 50; Univ Liege, DSc(phys sci), 52; Carnegie Inst Technol, PhD(physics), 57. *Prof Exp:* Jr physicist, Monsanto Chem Co, Ohio, 47-48; physicist, Nat Carbon Co Div, Union Carbide Corp, 53; fel, Carnegie-Mellon Univ, 57-63, sr fel, Inst Sci, 63-67, assoc prof metall & mat sci, 67-80; prin res scientist, Columbus Labs, Battelle Mem Inst, 80-83; mgr anal lab, Varian Spec Metals Div, 84-88 & Toson SMD, 88-90. *Res:* X-ray diffraction; imperfections in crystals; electron probe microanalysis; electron microscopy. *Mailing Add:* 113 Calais Ct Naples FL 34112

**VASSEL, BRUNO,** BIOCHEMISTRY. *Current Pos:* DIR RES, JOHNSON & JOHNSON BRAZIL, 55-, MEM EXEC COMT, 59- *Personal Data:* b Allahabath, Brit India, Oct 17, 08; nat US; m 36; c 3. *Educ:* Yale Univ, BS, 36; Univ Mich, MS, 37, PhD(biochem), 39. *Honors & Awards:* Robert W Johnson Medal Res & Develop, 64. *Prof Exp:* Lab asst biochem, Univ Mich, 37-39; res biochemist, Am Cyanamid Co, 39-43; assoc prof biochem & res agr chemist exp sta, NDak Col, 43-46; supvr org & biochem res, Int Minerals & Chem Corp, 46-55. *Mem:* AAAS; Am Chem Soc; Am Oil Chem Soc; Am Soc Sugar Beet Technol. *Res:* Protein isolations; monosodium glutamate processes; amino acid analyses and syntheses; pharmaceuticals; polarograph; flotation reagents; detergents; starch derivatives; surgical and pharmaceutical products. *Mailing Add:* 13 Northridge Way Sandy UT 84092

**VASSELL, GREGORY S,** ELECTRICAL ENGINEERING. *Current Pos:* CONSULT, 88- *Personal Data:* b Moscow, Russia, Dec 24, 21; m 57; c 2. *Educ:* Tech Univ, Berlin, Ger, Dipl Eng, 51; NY Univ, MBA, 54. *Prof Exp:* From asst engr to sr engr elec eng, Am Elec Power Serv Corp, 51-61, sect head high voltage planning, 62-66, assoc chief syst planning engr, 66-67, chief syst planning engr, 67-68, asst vpres bulk power supply planning, 68-73, vpres syst planning & dir, 73-76, sr vpres systs planning & dir, 76-88. *Concurrent Pos:* Chmn, Syst Reliability Adv Panel, East Cent Area Reliability Group, 67-69; mem, Tech Adv Comt Transmission, Fed Power Comn, 68-70, NCent Reg Task Force, Fed Energy Regulatory Comn, 79-81, US Nat Comt, World Energy Conf; mem comt rev, Nat Comm Syst Initiatives, Nat Res Coun, 82-84, Comt Elec Energy Systs, 85; mem, Atlantic Coun, USA World Energy Conf Study Group on Energy In Less Develop Countries, 84-86. *Mem:* Nat Acad Eng; Int Conf Large High Voltage Elec Systs; fel Inst Elec & Electronics Engrs. *Res:* Electric power supply planning; energy resource planning. *Mailing Add:* Consult 2247 Pinebrook Rd Columbus OH 43220. *Fax:* 614-459-2337

**VASSELL, MILTON O,** THEORETICAL SOLID STATE PHYSICS. *Current Pos:* SR RES SCIENTIST, GTE LABS, INC, 64- *Personal Data:* b Jamaica, West Indies, May 8, 31; m 58; c 2. *Educ:* NY Univ, BA, 58, PhD(physics), 64. *Mem:* Am Phys Soc; Sigma Xi; NY Acad Sci. *Res:* Many particle physics; transport theory in semiconductors and metals; nonlinear optics; physics of lasers; acoustic surface wave propagation; acousto-electric effects; electron optics; integrated optics; optical guided wave propagation; heterostructure device physics. *Mailing Add:* 33 Flint Rd Acton MA 01720

**VASSILIADES, ANTHONY E,** PHYSICAL CHEMISTRY, POLYMER CHEMISTRY. *Current Pos:* PRES, EPACOR, 80- *Personal Data:* b Chios, Greece, Nov 26, 33; US citizen; m 57; c 2. *Educ:* Wagner Col, BS, 56; Syracuse Univ, MS, 58; Polytech Inst Brooklyn, PhD(phys chem), 62. *Prof Exp:* From asst prof to assoc prof chem, Wagner Col, 61-66; assoc dir res, Champion Papers, Inc, 66-68, dir res, Champion Papers Group, US Plywood-Champion Papers, Inc, 68-70, vpres & dir res & develop, 70-76, vpres & dir sci, Champion Int Corp, 76-78. *Concurrent Pos:* Consult, Champion Papers, Inc, 64-66. *Mem:* Am Chem Soc; NY Acad Sci; Soc Plastics Eng. *Res:* Coacervation of charged colloidal systems; transport phenomena in liquids; physical chemistry of high polymers; surface phenomena; engineering plastics; carbonless papers. *Mailing Add:* 8738 Tanager Woods Dr Cincinnati OH 45249

**VASSILIADIS, DIMITRIS V,** PLASMA PHYSICS, ASTRONOMY. *Current Pos:* Resident res assoc, RES SCIENTIST, UNIV SPACE RES ASN, GODDARD SPACE FLIGHT CTR, NASA, 94- *Personal Data:* b Thessaloniki, Greece, Mar 22, 65. *Educ:* Univ Thessaloniki, Greece, BSc, 86; Univ Md, MSc, 89, PhD(physics), 92. *Prof Exp:* Res assoc, Nat Res Coun, 92-94. *Mem:* Am Geophys Union. *Res:* Nonlinear dynamical, data-based and electrodynamic modeling of solar wind-magnetosphere-ionosphere interactions, with direct applications to space weather prediction; theoretical implications for the self-organization observed in space plasmas. *Mailing Add:* Goddard Space Flight Ctr NASA Code 696 Greenbelt MD 20771. *Fax:* 301-286-1648; *E-Mail:* vassi@lepgst.gsfc.nasa.gov

**VASSILIOU, ANDREAS H,** mineralogy, for more information see previous edition

**VASSILIOU, EUSTATHIOS,** COATINGS CHEMISTRY & PHYSICS, INTELLECTUAL PROPERTY. *Current Pos:* RETIRED. *Personal Data:* b Athens, Greece, Aug 22, 34; m 60, Kleoniki Parri; c Theodore, Helen & Evelyn. *Educ:* Nat Tech Univ Athens, BScChE, 58; Univ Manchester, PhD(chem), 64. *Prof Exp:* Res chemist, Nuclear Res Ctr, Democritus, Greece, 64-66; res fel solid state physics, Harvard Univ, 66-67; res chemist, E I Du Pont de Nemours & Co, Inc, 67-73, staff chemist, 73-78, res assoc, Marshall Lab, 78-79, res supvr, 79-80, res assoc, 80-84, sr res assoc, Exp Sta, 84-91; pres, WTPA Inc, 91, *Concurrent Pos:* Fel, Intellectual Property, 91. *Mem:* Asn Harvard Chemists. *Res:* Inorganic physical chemistry; physics and chemistry of glasses; vanadium; thermistors; anodic films; luminescence; ozone physics; semiconductor surface phenomena; magnetic phenomena; lubrication; structural plastics; fluorocarbon and other high temperature resistant coatings; corrosion resistant coatings; electrodeposition of coatings; photoresists; electronic materials for hybrid circuits; food technology; lucineration. *Mailing Add:* 12 S Townview Lane Newark DE 19711. *Fax:* 302-292-0714

**VASSILIOU, MARIUS SIMON,** COMPUTATIONAL PHYSICS & ENGINEERING, PUBLISHING SYSTEMS. *Current Pos:* mem tech staff & proj mgr, 85-93, SR RES MGR, ROCKWELL INT SCI CTR, 93- *Personal Data:* b June 7, 57; US citizen; m 89, Cynthia Kohn. *Educ:* Harvard Univ, AB, 78; Calif Inst Technol, MS, 79, PhD(geophys & elec eng), 83; Univ Southern Calif, MS, 87; Univ Calif, Los Angeles, MBA, 91. *Prof Exp:* Grad res asst, Calif Inst Technol, 79-83, sr scientist, 83; sr res geophysicist, Arco Oil & Gas Co, 83-85. *Concurrent Pos:* Consult, Rockwell Int Sci Ctr, 81-82 & TRW, Inc, 82-83; vis prof, Univ Tex, Dallas, 84 & Moorpark Col, 86; Europ community vis fel, Technol Transfer, 92. *Mem:* Sr mem Inst Elec & Electronics Engrs; Soc Explor Geophysicists; Asn Comput Mach; Sigma Xi. *Res:* Technology management; technology transfer; technology policy; signal processing for multimedia applications. *Mailing Add:* Rockwell Int 1049 Camino Dos Rios PO Box 1085 Thousand Oaks CA 91360. *E-Mail:* msv@alumni.caltech.com

**VASSOS, BASIL HARILAOS,** ANALYTICAL CHEMISTRY, COMPUTERS & THE INTERNET. *Current Pos:* PROF ANALYTICAL CHEM, UNIV PR, 73-; SCI ADV, FOOD & DRUG ADMIN, 83- *Personal Data:* b Urzitzeni, Romania, Sept 3, 30; US citizen; m 66, Aurora I Rincon; c Patricia & Irene. *Educ:* Univ Bucharest, BSc, 52; Univ Mich, MSc, 62, PhD(chem), 65. *Prof Exp:* Lectr chem, Univ Bucharest, 52-60; res nuclear chem, Democritos Nuclear Res Ctr, Athens, 61-62; Alexander von Humboldt Found fel, Max Planck Inst Metall Res, 67-68; asst prof anal chem, Seton Hall Univ, 68-72; fel, Colo State Univ, 72-73. *Mem:* Am Chem Soc. *Res:* Computer-controlled experiments. *Mailing Add:* Box 21426 University Sta San Juan PR 00931. *E-Mail:* bvassos@caribe.net

**VASTANO, ANDREW CHARLES,** PHYSICAL OCEANOGRAPHY, NUMERICAL ANALYSIS. *Current Pos:* instr, 64, ASSOC PROF OCEANOG, TEX A&M UNIV, 69- *Personal Data:* b New York, NY, Feb 26, 36; m 58; c 4. *Educ:* NC State Univ, BS, 56; Univ NC, MS, 60; Tex A&M Univ, PhD(phys oceanog), 67. *Prof Exp:* Anal engr, Pratt & Whitney Aircraft Corp, 56-57; sonar engr, Western Elec Co, Bell Tel Co, 60-62; instr physics, Tex A&M Univ, 62-63, res scientist, 63-66; assoc prof phys oceanog, Univ Fla, 66-67; asst scientist, Woods Hole Oceanog Inst, 67-69. *Mem:* Am Geophys Union. *Res:* Numerical studies of tsunami and storm surges; theory of gravity waves; mesoscale ocean dynamics; topographic interaction of current systems. *Mailing Add:* 1020 Guadalupe Dr College Station TX 77840

**VASTOLA, FRANCIS J,** LABORATORY INSTRUMENTATION & CONTROL. *Current Pos:* asst & res assoc, 56-59, from asst prof to prof, 59-86, EMER PROF FUEL SCI, PA STATE UNIV, 86- *Personal Data:* b Buffalo, NY, Feb 22, 28; m 69. *Educ:* Univ Buffalo, BA, 50; Pa State Univ, PhD(fuel technol), 59. *Prof Exp:* Chemist, Nat Bur Stand, Washington, DC, 50-52. *Mem:* Am Chem Soc; Sigma Xi. *Res:* Mass spectrometry; solid and gaseous combustion; kinetics and instrumentation. *Mailing Add:* 406 Hillcrest Ave State College PA 16803-3418

**VASU, BANGALORE SESHACHALAM,** BIOLOGY. *Current Pos:* PROF BIOL, MENLO COL, 78- *Educ:* Univ Madras, BSc, 49, MSc, 62; Stanford Univ, PhD(biol), 65. *Prof Exp:* Asst prof zool, Pachaiyappa's Col, Madras Univ, 50-59, lectr, Zool Res Lab, 59-62; Fulbright res fel biol, Stanford Univ, 62-65; AEC fel, Univ Notre Dame, 65-67; asst prof zool, Ohio Wesleyan Univ, 67-68; UNESCO specialist biol, Univ Zambia, 68-73; asst prof biol, Calif State Univ, Chico, 74-77. *Concurrent Pos:* Fulbright grant, US Educ Found India, 62. *Mem:* Sigma Xi; Am Inst Biol Sci; AAAS; Radiation Res Soc; Marine Biol Asn UK. *Res:* Age-related changes at the cellular and molecular level; biotechnology management. *Mailing Add:* 36586 Nuttman Lane Fremont CA 94536-2546. *E-Mail:* bvasu@worldnet.att.net

**VATASSERY, GOVIND T,** BIOCHEMISTRY. *Current Pos:* Fel chem, 70-73, DIR NEUROCHEM LAB, VET ADMIN MED CTR, 74- *Personal Data:* b Karla, India, Feb 22, 39. *Educ:* Univ Karla, India, BS, 57, MS, 60; Univ Minn, PhD(org chem), 69. *Mem:* Am Neurochem Soc; Am Inst Nutrit; Am Soc Cell Biol; Sigma Xi. *Res:* Biochemistry. *Mailing Add:* Neurochem GRECC & Neurol Vet Admin Med Ctr One Veterans Dr Minneapolis MN 55417

**VATISTAS, GEORGIOS H,** VORTEX DYNAMICS, MICROGRAVITY FLUID MECHANICS. *Current Pos:* Res asst mech eng, Concordia Univ, 78-82, teacher & lab instr, 82-85, from asst prof to assoc prof, 85-94, PROF MECH ENG, CONCORDIA UNIV, 94-, ASSOC DEAN FAC ENG & COMPUT SCI, 95- *Personal Data:* b Neapolis, Laconias, Greece, Jan 25, 53; Can citizen; m 82; c 2. *Educ:* Concordia Univ, BEng, 78, MEng, 80, PhD(mech eng), 84. *Honors & Awards:* Ralph R Teetor Educ Award, Soc Automotive Engrs, 87. *Mem:* Am Inst Aeronaut & Astronaut. *Res:* Flow instabilities; dynamics of concentrated vortices; physics of fluids; microgravity fluid mechanics; dynamics of liquid sloshing; biofluid mechanics; computational fluid dynamics. *Mailing Add:* Dept Mech Eng Concordia Univ 1455 de Maisonneuve Blvd W Montreal PQ H3G 1M8 Can

**VATNE, ROBERT DAHLMEIER,** PARASITOLOGY. *Current Pos:* res specialist, 70-73, Dow Chem Co, USA, 70-73, regist specialist, 74-81, assoc scientist, 86-90, sr res scientist, Dow Elanco, 91-93, PROD REGIST MGR, DOW CHEM CO, USA, 81-; ADV, DOW ELANCO, 93- *Personal Data:* b Pipestone, Minn, Oct 21, 34; m 63, Marianne; c Stacy. *Educ:* Augustana Col, SDak, BA, 56; Kans State Univ, MS, 58, PhD(parasitol), 63. *Prof Exp:* Asst prof biol, St Cloud State Col, 63-64; Salsbury Labs, Iowa, 65-69. *Mem:* Am Soc Parasitol. *Res:* Etiology and chemotherapy of histomoniasis, coccidiosis and helminthiasis. *Mailing Add:* Dow Elanco 9330 Zionsville Rd Indianapolis IN 46268-1054. *Fax:* 317-337-4736; *E-Mail:* rdvatne@dowelanco.com

**VATSIS, KOSTAS PETROS,** ENZYMOLOGY. *Current Pos:* RES SCIENTIST, MED SCH, UNIV MICH, 87- *Personal Data:* b Patras, Greece, May 6, 45; m 89, Athina Kotsopoulou. *Educ:* Calif State Univ, Long Beach, BS, 67, MS, 69; Univ Ill Med Ctr, PhD(pharmacol), 75. *Prof Exp:* Res asst pharmacol, Col Med, Univ Ill, 69-75; scholar biol chem, Med Sch, Univ Mich, 75-76, lectr, 76-78; from asst prof to assoc prof pharmacol, Med Sch, Northwestern Univ, 78-87. *Concurrent Pos:* Consult, Dept Pharmacol, Col Med, Univ Ill, 77-; prin investr, starter grant, Pharmaceut Mfg Asn Fedn, Inc, 80-81, res grant NIH, 80-83. *Mem:* Am Soc Pharmacol & Exp Therapeut; Soc Toxicol; Am Soc Biochem Molecular Biol. *Res:* Physicochemical studies on the mechanism of interaction of components of the nicotinamide-adenine dinucleotide phosphate and nicotinamide dinucleotide linked electron transport chains in mammalian hepatic microsomes: modulation of the cytochrome P-450 containing monooxygenase system by cytochrome b5 and related membrane-bound proteins. *Mailing Add:* Dept Biol Chem Univ Mich Med Sch Med Sci 1 M5440-0606 Ann Arbor MI 48109-0606

**VAUCHER, JEAN G,** COMPUTER SCIENCE. *Current Pos:* from asst prof to assoc prof, 70-80, chmn, 81-83, PROF COMPUT SCI, UNIV MONTREAL, 80- *Personal Data:* b Can, 42; m; c 2. *Educ:* Univ Ottawa, BSc, 62; Univ Manchester, MSc, 64, PhD, 68. *Prof Exp:* Researcher, IBM, Can, 68-70. *Concurrent Pos:* Athlone fel, 62-64. *Mem:* Asn Comput Mach. *Res:* Simulation; intelligent systems; parallelism; structured programming. *Mailing Add:* Dept Informatique Sci & RO PO 6128 Sta A Montreal PQ H3C 3J7 Can. *E-Mail:* vaucher@iro.umontreal.ca

**VAUGHAN, BURTON EUGENE,** PHYSIOLOGY, SYSTEMS LEVEL EARTH & ENVIRONMENTAL SCIENCES. *Current Pos:* mgr univ progs, 89-91, ADJ FAC ENVIRON SCI, WASH STATE UNIV, TRICITIES, 91- *Personal Data:* b Santa Rosa, Calif, May 31, 26; m 49; c 2. *Educ:* Univ Calif, Berkeley, AB, 49, PhD, 55. *Prof Exp:* Vis scientist, White Mountain High Altitude Res Sta, Calif, 53-54; proj leader, Oper Deepfreeze I, US Exped to Antarctic, 55; staff scientist, Biophys Br, US Naval Radiol Defense Lab, 56-61, br head, 62-69; mgr, Environ Sci Dept, Pac NW Labs, Battelle Mem Inst, 69-88. *Concurrent Pos:* Actg instr, Sch Med, Stanford Univ, 57, lectr, 60-63, res assoc, 63-70; consult, Clin Invest Ctr, Oakland Naval Hosp, 60-61 & US Naval Med Res Unit 2, Taipei, Taiwan, 61, 64 & 65; trustee, Independent Sch Dist, 63, presiding off, 64-65; rep, Co Comt Sch Dist Orgn, 65; mem bd educ, Castro Valley Unified Sch Dist, 65, pres, 66-67; consult,

Govt Health Facil, Manila, Philippines; sci coun chmn, Pac Sci Ctr Found, Seattle, 75-78, mem exec comn & trustee, 78-79. *Mem:* Am Inst Biol Sci; Am Physiol Soc; Radiation Res Soc; Sigma Xi; AAAS. *Res:* Systems aspects of environmental science; technology impacts on resources and physical and chemical processes that affect life support systems at a holistic level. *Mailing Add:* 2456 Harris Ave Richland WA 99352. *Fax:* 509-375-5337

**VAUGHAN, CHRISTOPHER LEONARD,** BIOMECHANICS OF THE MUSCULOSKELETAL SYSTEM, SIMULATION OF NEUROMUSCULAR SYSTEM WITH ARTIFICIAL NEURAL NETS. *Current Pos:* DIR, MOTION ANALYSIS & ASSOC PROF ORTHOP & BIOMED ENG, UNIV VA, 89- *Personal Data:* b Blyvooruitzicht, SAfrica, Apr 21, 53, Brit citizen; m 77, Joan D Blair; c Bronwyn L & Gareth I. *Educ:* Rhodes Univ, BSc, 74, BSc, Hons, 75; Univ Iowa, PhD(biomech), 80. *Honors & Awards:* Presidential Young Investr Award, SAfrican Coun Sci & Indust Res, 85. *Prof Exp:* Res officer, Appl Physiol Lab, Chamber Mines, 76; res asst, Univ Iowa, 77-80; chief biomed engr, Groote Schuur Hosp, 80-86; assoc prof bioeng, Clemson Univ, 86-89. *Concurrent Pos:* Sr lectr biomed eng, Univ Cape Town, 80-86; fel, Oxford Univ, UK, 83-84; software consult, Micron Technol, 85-87; pres, Gastonia, 87-89; design consult, Becton Dickinson, 88-; Alta Heritage vis prof, Univ Calgary, Can, 91; Robert P Kelly vis prof, Emory Univ, 91; vis prof, Tokyo Med & Dent Univ, 92. *Mem:* Int Soc Biomech; Am Soc Biomech; Inst Elec & Electronics Engrs; Biomed Eng Soc. *Res:* Human gait; basic issues as well as applied clinical studies. *Mailing Add:* Anat Fac Med Univ Cape Town Private Bage Rodebosch 7700 Cape Town South Africa. *E-Mail:* kvaughan@anat.uct.ac.za

**VAUGHAN, DAVID ARTHUR,** NUTRITION. *Current Pos:* RETIRED. *Personal Data:* b Mattoon, Wis, Mar 5, 23; m 51; c 1. *Educ:* Univ Calif, BA, 49; Univ Ill, MA, 54, PhD(animal nutrit), 55. *Prof Exp:* Res physiologist, Arctic Aeromed Lab, USAF, 55-59, supvry chemist, 59-68, res biochemist, USAF Sch Aerospace Med, 68-69; res biochemist, Nutrit Inst, Sci & Educ Admin-Agr Res, USDA, 69-79. *Mem:* Am Physiol Soc; Am Inst Nutrit. *Res:* Survival nutrition in the Arctic; vitamin B requirements and intermediary metabolism during stress; biochemistry of hibernation; protein nutrition. *Mailing Add:* 8533 Pineway Dr Laurel MD 20723-1239

**VAUGHAN, DEBORAH WHITTAKER,** NEUROANATOMY. *Current Pos:* USPHS fel, 71-72, res asst prof, 72-78, ASST PROF NEUROANAT, SCH MED, BOSTON UNIV, 78- *Personal Data:* b Concord, NH, Nov 30, 43; m 66. *Educ:* Univ Vt, BA, 66; Boston Univ, PhD(biol), 71. *Res:* Electron microscopic analysis of neocortex, primarily of rat, in regards to the effects of aging on the brain. *Mailing Add:* Dept Anat & Neurobiol Boston Univ Sch Med 80 E Concord St Boston MA 02118-2394

**VAUGHAN, DOUGLAS STANWOOD,** POPULATION DYNAMICS, RISK ASSESSMENT. *Current Pos:* leader, Stock Dynamics Br, 82-85, leader, Menhaden Team, Lab, Southeastern Fisheries Ctr, 85-95, LEADER, POP DYNAMICS TEAM, BEAUFORT LAB, NAT MARINE FISHERIES, 96- *Personal Data:* b Biddeford, Maine, July 12, 46; m 76, Nancy Donovan. *Educ:* Univ NH, BS, 68; Pa State Univ, MA, 70; Univ RI, PhD(oceanog), 77. *Prof Exp:* Statistician, Environ Protection Agency, 71-73; res assoc, Oak Ridge Nat Lab, 77-82. *Mem:* Biomet Soc; Am Fisheries Soc; fel Am Inst Fish Res Biol; Sigma Xi. *Res:* Application of statistical methods and population and community modeling approaches to assessing the effects of one or more stresses on fish populations, and the development of approaches for environmental risk assessment; application of statistics to fish stock assessment; use of matrix models for describing population dynamics. *Mailing Add:* Nat Marine Fisheries Serv Beaufort Lab Beaufort NC 28516

**VAUGHAN, J RODNEY M,** microwave engineering, computer aided design; deceased, see previous edition for last biography

**VAUGHAN, JAMES ROLAND,** MICROBIOLOGY, BIOCHEMISTRY. *Current Pos:* From instr to assoc prof microbiol, Muhlenberg Col, 56-67, head dept, 65-90, PROF MICROBIOL, MUHLENBERG COL, 67-, SR PROF, 90- *Personal Data:* b Allentown, Pa, June 7, 28; m 50; c 3. *Educ:* Muhlenberg Col, BS, 52; Lehigh Univ, MS, 54, PhD(biol), 61. *Mem:* AAAS; Am Soc Microbiol; Am Chem Soc; Am Soc Cell Biol; Sigma Xi. *Res:* Microbial physiology. *Mailing Add:* 522 N Berks St Allentown PA 18104-4937

**VAUGHAN, JERRY EUGENE,** MATHEMATICS, TOPOLOGY. *Current Pos:* assoc prof, 73-76, PROF MATH, UNIV NC, GREENSBORO, 76- *Personal Data:* b Gastonia, NC, Oct 30, 39; m 69. *Educ:* Davidson Col, BS, 61; Duke Univ, PhD(math), 65. *Prof Exp:* Teaching asst math, Duke Univ, 62-63; assoc prof, Eve Div, Univ Md, 66-67; asst prof, Univ NC, Chapel Hill, 67-73. *Mem:* Am Math Soc; Math Asn Am. *Res:* General topology; generalized metric spaces; product spaces; cardinal invariant properties. *Mailing Add:* Dept Math Univ NC Greensboro NC 27412-0001

**VAUGHAN, JOHN DIXON,** PHYSICAL CHEMISTRY. *Current Pos:* assoc prof, 64-71, PROF PHYS CHEM, COLO STATE UNIV, 71- *Personal Data:* b Clarksville, Va, Mar 3, 25; m 62. *Educ:* Col William & Mary, BS, 50; Univ Ill, PhD(chem), 54. *Prof Exp:* Asst phys chem, Univ Ill, 50-51, AEC, 51-54; res chemist, Chem Dept, Exp Sta, E I du Pont de Nemours & Co, 54-58; asst prof phys chem, Va Polytech Inst, 59-62 & Univ Hawaii, 62-64. *Mem:* Am Chem Soc; Sigma Xi. *Res:* Computation chemistry, molecular modeling; reaction profile modeling. *Mailing Add:* 3600 Woodridge Rd Ft Collins CO 80524

**VAUGHAN, JOHN HEATH,** IMMUNOLOGY, MEDICINE. *Current Pos:* PROF MED RESIDENCE, UNIV CALIF, SAN DIEGO, 90- *Personal Data:* b Richmond, Va, Nov 7, 21; m 46, 83, Marjorie Seybold; c John Jr, Nancy T, David H & Margaret P. *Educ:* Harvard Univ, AB, 42, MD, 45. *Honors & Awards:* Gold Medal Award, Am Col Rheumatology, 90. *Prof Exp:* Intern med, Peter Bent Brigham Hosp, 45-56, resident, 48-51; Nat Res Coun fel med sci, Col Physicians & Surgeons, Columbia Univ, 51-53; asst prof, Med Col Va, 53-58; assoc prof med & asst prof bact, Sch Med & Dent, Univ Rochester, 58-63, prof med & head div immunol & infectious dis, 63-70; chmn clin div, Scripps Clin & Res Found, 70-74, chmn dept clin res, 74-77, head div clin immunol, 77-87. *Concurrent Pos:* Fel, Peter Bent Brigham Hosp, Boston, 48-51; consult, NIH, 56-63, mem bd sci counr, Nat Inst Allergy & Infectious Dis, 68-72; mem allergy clin immunol res comt, NIH, 80-84. *Mem:* Am Soc Clin Invest; Asn Am Physicians; Am Asn Immunol; Am Rheumatism Asn (pres, 70-71); Am Acad Allergy (pres, 66-67). *Res:* Immunological phenomena in internal medicine; the basis of poor anti-viral responses in autoimmune and acquired immunodeficiency diseases; immunity to Epstein-Barr virus; autoimmunity and rheumatoid arthritis. *Mailing Add:* Dept Med Univ Calif San Diego La Jolla CA 92093-0663. *Fax:* 619-534-5399; *E-Mail:* jvaughan@ucsd.edu

**VAUGHAN, JOHN THOMAS,** VETERINARY MEDICINE. *Current Pos:* chmn, Dept Large Animal Surg & Med, 74-77, dean, Col Vet Med, 77-93, EMER DEAN, AUBURN UNIV, 93-, CONSULT. *Personal Data:* b Tuskegee, Ala, Feb 6, 32; m 56, Ethel Sell; c J Thomas Jr, Faythe & Michael S. *Educ:* Auburn Univ, DVM, 55, MS, 63. *Prof Exp:* From instr to assoc prof large animal surg & med, Auburn Univ, 55-70; prof vet surg & dir, Large Animal Hosp, NY State Vet Col, Cornell Univ, 70-74. *Mem:* Am Vet Med Asn; Am Asn Equine Practitioners (pres, 81); Am Asn Vet Clinicians; Am Col Vet Surg (pres, 80); Asn Am Vet Med Cols; Nat Academies Pract. *Res:* Large animal and equine surgery and medicine; general surgery of the equine system with emphasis on urogenital and gastrointestinal surgery. *Mailing Add:* Col Vet Med Auburn Univ 104 Greene Hall Auburn AL 36849. *Fax:* 334-844-3697; *E-Mail:* vaughjt@auducadm.auburn.edu

**VAUGHAN, LINDA ANN,** HUMAN NUTRITION. *Current Pos:* ASST PROF, DEPT HOME ECON, ARIZ STATE UNIV, 79- *Personal Data:* b Brooklyn, NY, July 26, 50; m 74; c 1. *Educ:* Univ Calif, Davis, BS, 72; Cornell Univ, MNS, 74; Univ Ariz, PhD(agr biochem, nutrit), 77. *Prof Exp:* Nutritionist II pub health nutrit, Maricopa Co Health Dept, 74-75; nutrit consult cardiac rehab, Dr A E Smith, Tempe, Ariz, 77; asst prof, Dept Food & Nutrit, Univ Nebr, 77-79. *Mem:* Am Dietetic Asn; Inst Food Technologists; Soc Nutrit Educ; Am Inst Nutrit; Am Sch Health Asn. *Res:* Maternal and infant nutrition; composition of human milk. *Mailing Add:* Food & Nutrit Lab Ariz State Univ Cowden Bldg Rm 102 Tempe AZ 85287-2502. *Fax:* 602-965-6779

**VAUGHAN, LOY OTTIS, JR,** MATHEMATICS. *Current Pos:* Asst prof, 69-80, ASSOC PROF MATH, UNIV ALA, BIRMINGHAM, 80- *Personal Data:* b Birmingham, Ala, June 30, 45; m 66; c 1. *Educ:* Fla State Univ, BA, 66; Univ Ala, MA, 67, PhD(math), 70. *Mem:* Am Math Soc; Math Asn Am. *Res:* General topology, fixed and almost fixed point theory of continua. *Mailing Add:* Dept Math Univ Ala Birmingham AL 35294-0001

**VAUGHAN, MARTHA,** BIOCHEMISTRY. *Current Pos:* chief, Lab Cellular Metab, Nat Heart Lung & Blood Inst, 74-94, DEP CHIEF, PULMONARY-CRITICAL CARE MED BR, NAT HEART LUNG BLOOD INST, HIH, 94- *Personal Data:* b Dodgeville, Wis, Aug 4, 26; wid; c Jonathan M, David G & Gregory J Orloff. *Educ:* Univ Chicago, PhB, 44; Yale Univ, MD, 49. *Honors & Awards:* G Burroughs Mider Lectr, NIH, 79; Harvey Soc Lectr, 82. *Prof Exp:* Asst instr res med, Univ Pa, 51-52; Nat Res Coun fel, NIH, 52-54; sr asst surgeon to med dir, USPHS, 54-89. *Concurrent Pos:* Mem metab study sect, Div Res Grants, USPHS, 65-68, head sect metab, 68-74; int fel rev comt, Fogarty Int Ctr, 73-74, 77-78; actg chief, Molecular Dis Br, Nat Heart & Lung Inst, 74-76; bd dir, Found Adv Educ Sci, Inc, 79-; vchmn, Gordon Conf Cyclei Nucleotides, 81, chmn, 82; ed, Biochem Biophys Res Commun, 90-91; assoc ed, J Biol Chem. *Mem:* Nat Acad Sci; Am Soc Biochem & Molecular Biol; Am Soc Clin Invest; Asn Am Physicians; Harvey Soc; AAAS. *Res:* Mechanisms of biological signal transduction. *Mailing Add:* 11608 W Hill Dr Rockville MD 20852-3751

**VAUGHAN, MARTHA,** BIOCHEMISTRY. *Current Pos:* Chief, Lab Cellular Metab, 74-94, DEP CHIEF, PULMONARY CRITICAL CARE MED BR, NAT HEART, LUNG & BLOOD INST, NIH, 94- *Personal Data:* b Dodgeville, Wis, Aug 4, 26; wid; c Jonathan M, David G & Gregory J. *Educ:* Univ Chicago, PhB, 44; Yale Univ, MD, 49. *Concurrent Pos:* Assoc ed, J Biol Chem, 92. *Mem:* Nat Acad Sci; Am Acad Arts & Sci; Am Soc Biochem & Molecular Biol; Asn Am Physicians. *Res:* Mechanisms of action and regulatory functions of specific GTP-binding proteins in eukaryotic cells. *Mailing Add:* NIH Nat Heart Lung & Blood Inst Bldg 10 Rm 5N 307 Bethesda MD 20892. *Fax:* 301-402-1610

**VAUGHAN, MARY KATHLEEN,** PINEAL, NEUROENDOCRINOLOGY. *Current Pos:* fel, 73-75, asst prof, 75-80, ASSOC PROF CELL & STRUCT BIOL, HEALTH SCI CTR, UNIV TEX, 80- *Personal Data:* b Houston, Tex, Sept 7, 43; m 66; c Thomas, Charles & Christopher. *Educ:* Univ St Thomas, Houston, BA, 65; Univ Tex, Galveston, PhD(anat), 70. *Prof Exp:* Lectr human anat & fel, Univ Rochester, NY, 70-71; guest worker, NIH, Bethesda, Md, 71-73. *Mem:* Endocrine Soc; Soc Neurosci; Am Asn Anatomists; Int Soc Chronobiol; Am Soc Zoologists; Int Soc Psychoneuroendocrinol. *Res:* Interaction of the natural environment and pineal gland on the neuroendocrine-gonadal and neuroendocrine-thyroid axes. *Mailing Add:* Dept Cell & Struct Biol Univ Tex Health Sci Ctr 7703 Floyd Curl Dr San Antonio TX 78284-7762

**VAUGHAN, MICHAEL RAY,** POPULATION DYNAMICS, HABITAT ECOLOGY. *Current Pos:* WILDLIFE SCIENTIST, NAT BIOL SURV, 80- *Personal Data:* b Newport News, Va, Aug 11, 44; m 71; c 3. *Educ:* NC State Univ, BS, 71; Ore State Univ, MS, 74; Univ Wis-Madison, PhD(wildlife ecol), 79. *Prof Exp:* Res asst wildlife ecol, Ore State Univ, 71-74, Univ Wis-Madison, 74-79; actg asst leader, Wis Coop Wildlife Res Univ, Va Polytech Inst & State Univ, US Fish & Wildlife Serv, 79-80, asst leader, Va Coop Wildlife Res Unit Pop Dynamics, 80-82, leader, Va Coop Wildlife Res Unit, 82-85. *Mem:* Wildlife Soc; Int Bear Asn. *Res:* Population dynamics and cyclic phenomena especially snowshoe hares, mountain goats, black bears, wild turkeys and white-tailed deer. *Mailing Add:* Va Coop Fish & Wildlife Res Unit 148 Cheatham Hall Va Polytech Inst & State Univ Blacksburg VA 24061-0321

**VAUGHAN, MICHAEL THOMAS,** MINERALS ELASTICITY, MANTLE MINERALOGY. *Current Pos:* DEPT EARTH & SPACE SCI, STATE UNIV NY. *Personal Data:* b Washington, DC, Sept 29, 40; m 78; c 2. *Educ:* Shimer Col, BS, 60; Univ Cincinnati, MS, 65; State Univ, NY, MS, 76, PhD(geophysics), 79. *Prof Exp:* Instr physics, Thomas More Col, 68-70; asst prof, WVa State Col, 71-74; teaching asst geol, State Univ NY, 75-76, fel res asst geophys, 76-79; asst geophysicist, Hawaii Inst Geophys, 79-81; asst prof geol, Univ Ill, Chicago, 81- *Mem:* Am Geophys Union; Geol Soc Am; Mineral Soc Am. *Res:* Relations between crystal structure and elasticity, especially in high-pressure phases of oxides and silicates, by measuring the single-crystal elastic constants of suitable well-characterized crystals with known crystal structures. *Mailing Add:* Dept Earth & Space Sci State Univ NY Stonybrook NY 11794

**VAUGHAN, NICK HAMPTON,** MATHEMATICS. *Current Pos:* assoc prof, 68-78, PROF MATH, UNIV NTEX, 78- *Personal Data:* b Graham, Tex, Feb 11, 23; m 60, Grace Lee; c Steve & Linda. *Educ:* NTex State Univ, BS, 47, MS, 48; La State Univ, PhD(math), 68. *Prof Exp:* Mathematician, US Naval Ord Plant, Ind, 51-53; res assoc math, Statist Lab, Purdue Univ, Lafayette, 53-55; sr aerophysics engr, Gen Dynamics, Tex, 55; instr math, La State Univ, 55-58; asst prof, NTex State Univ, 58-65; instr, La State Univ, 65-68. *Mem:* Am Math Soc; Math Asn Am. *Res:* Commutative rings; ideal theory; algebraic number theory. *Mailing Add:* Dept Math NTex State Univ Denton TX 76203-6737

**VAUGHAN, TERRY ALFRED,** VERTEBRATE ZOOLOGY. *Current Pos:* PROF ZOOL, NORTHERN ARIZ UNIV, 70- *Personal Data:* b Los Angeles, Calif, May 5, 28; m 50; c 2. *Educ:* Pomona Col, BA, 50; Claremont Cols, MA, 52; Univ Kans, PhD, 58. *Prof Exp:* Asst zool, Univ Kans, 52-54 & 56-58; asst biologist, Colo State Univ, 58-64, assoc biologist, 64-70. *Mem:* Am Soc Mammalogists; Cooper Ornith Soc. *Res:* Chiropteran and rodent ecology; functional morphology. *Mailing Add:* 4720 Smoke Signal Way Rimrock AZ 86335

**VAUGHAN, THERESA PHILLIPS,** ALGEBRA. *Current Pos:* LECTR MATH, UNIV NC, GREENSBORO, 74- *Personal Data:* b Kearney, Nebr, Oct 13, 41; m 69. *Educ:* Antioch Col, BA, 64; Am Univ, MA, 68; Duke Univ, PhD(math), 72. *Prof Exp:* Math programmer, Naval Ship Res & Develop Ctr, 64-69; asst prof math, NC Wesleyan Col, Rocky Mt, 72-73. *Mem:* Am Math Soc; Sigma Xi. *Res:* Polynomials and linear structure of finite fields; enumeration of sequences of integers by patterns; 2x2 matrices with positive integer entries; computation of discriminants. *Mailing Add:* 4112 Dogwood Dr Greensboro NC 27410-5608

**VAUGHAN, VICTOR CLARENCE, III,** PEDIATRICS. *Current Pos:* CLIN PROF PEDIAT, STANFORD UNIV, 87- *Personal Data:* b Toledo, Ohio, July 19, 19; m 41, Iris Litt Figarsky; c Jonathan, Sarah & Joanna. *Educ:* Harvard Univ, AB, 39, MD, 43; Am Bd Pediat, dipl, 51, cert pediat allergy, 60, cert allergy/immunol, 72, cert pediat, 87, 90 & 95. *Prof Exp:* Instr pediat, Sch Med, Yale Univ, 45-47 & 49-50, asst prof, 50-52; assoc prof, Sch Med, Temple Univ, 52-57; prof & chmn dept, Med Col Ga, 57-64; chmn dept, Sch Med, Temple Univ, 64-76, prof pediat, 64-77; sr med eval officer, Nat Bd Med Examrs, 81-87. *Concurrent Pos:* Res fel, Harvard Med Sch, 47-49; mem bd, Am Bd Pediat, 60-65 & 68-73, secy, 63-65, pres, 73; med dir, St Christopher's Hosp Children, 64-76. *Mem:* Fel Am Acad Allergy; Soc Pediat Res (vpres, 64-65); Am Acad Pediat; Am Fedn Clin Res; Am Pediat Soc. *Res:* Hemolytic disease of newborn; human genetics; allergic disorders of children; human growth and development; medical education and evaluation. *Mailing Add:* 350 El Caminito Carmel Valley CA 93924-9635

**VAUGHAN, WILLIAM MACE,** ENVIRONMENTAL SCIENCE, MEASUREMENT SERVICES. *Current Pos:* PRES, ENVIRON SOLUTIONS INC, 87-; PRES, REMOTE SENSING AIR, INC, 92- *Personal Data:* b Mt Vernon, NY, Aug 26, 42; m 65; c Mace & Blake. *Educ:* Wittenberg Univ, BS, 64; Univ Ill, Urbana-Champaign, MS, 66, PhD(biophys), 69. *Prof Exp:* Res assoc radiation sensitivity environ & monitoring, Ctr Biol Natural Systs, Wash Univ, St Louis, 69-71, coordr nitrogen proj, fertilizers-environ impact, 71-74; pres software serv, Eng Mgt Info Corp, 81-84; vpres serv, Air Qual Measurements, Environ Measurements Inc, 74-88; mgr midwest opers, Aerovironment, Inc, 85-87. *Concurrent Pos:* Lectr dept technol & human affairs, Wash Univ, 73-77; chmn EM-6 comt, Remote & Moving Measurements Air & Waste Mgt Asn, 85- *Mem:* Air & Waste Mgt Asn; AAAS; Am Asn Radon Scientists & Technologists. *Res:* Air toxic investigations; document progress in environment cleanup; assessment of hazardous waste problems through audits and field measurements; indoor air quality surveys; field determination of important processes in the transport and transformation of air pollutants through ambient measurements. *Mailing Add:* Environ Solutions Inc 8147 Delmar St Louis MO 63130. *Fax:* 314-721-0759

**VAUGHAN, WILLIAM WALTON,** AEROSPACE ENVIRONMENT. *Current Pos:* dir res inst, 86-94, RES PROF, UNIV ALA, HUNTSVILLE, 86- *Personal Data:* b Clearwater, Fla, Sept 7, 30; m 51, Geraldine Stapleton; c Stephen, David, William & Robert. *Educ:* Univ Fla, BS, 51; Fla State Univ, cert meteorol, 52; Univ Tenn, PhD, 76. *Honors & Awards:* Exceptional Serv Medal, NASA, 69; Losey Atmospheric Sci Medal, Am Inst Aeronaut & Astronaut, 80. *Prof Exp:* Staff meteorologist, USAF, 52-55, res & develop meteorologist, Air Force Armament Ctr, 55-57, tech asst meteorol, Army Ballistic Missile Agency, 58-60; chief, Aerospace Environ Off, 60-65, chief, Aerospace Environ Div, 65-76, chief, Atmospheric Sci Div, Marshall Space Flight Ctr, NASA, 76-86. *Concurrent Pos:* Consult, Aerospace Environ Off. *Mem:* Am Meteorol Soc; Am Inst Aeronaut & Astronaut; Am Geophys Soc; AAAS; Sigma Xi. *Res:* Applied research in aerospace sciences and especially atmospheric science relative to space system design requirements, spacecraft experiment development and management of interdisciplinary research program. *Mailing Add:* 5606 Alta Dena Dr Huntsville AL 35802. *Fax:* 205-895-6848

**VAUGHAN, WORTH E,** PHYSICAL CHEMISTRY. *Current Pos:* from asst prof to assoc prof, 61-78, PROF CHEM, UNIV WIS-MADISON, 78- *Personal Data:* b New York, NY, Feb 1, 36; m 69; c 4. *Educ:* Oberlin Col, AB, 57; Princeton Univ, AM, 59, PhD(phys chem), 60. *Prof Exp:* Res assoc phys chem, Princeton Univ, 60-61. *Mem:* AAAS; Am Phys Soc; Am Chem Soc. *Res:* Dielectric and nuclear magnetic relaxation in liquids; irreversible statistical mechanics. *Mailing Add:* Dept Chem Univ Wis Madison WI 53706

**VAUGHEN, VICTOR C(ORNELIUS) A(DOLPH),** CHEMICAL ENGINEERING, CHEMISTRY. *Current Pos:* PRES, VAUGHEN ENT, 90- *Personal Data:* b Wilmington, Del, Oct 8, 33; m 91, Janet Wallace; c Robin, Jon, Leonard, Bruce, Eric & Rebecca. *Educ:* Stetson Univ, BS, 57; Mass Inst Technol, SB, 56, SM, 57, PhD(chem eng), 60. *Prof Exp:* Group leader, Martin Marietta Energy Systs, Inc, 63-76, mgr hot cell opers, 76-80, mgr fossil energy assessments, 80-81, prog mgr fossil energy eval, 81, sect head, Eng Coord & Anal Sect, Chem Technol Div, Oak Ridge Nat Lab, 81-90. *Concurrent Pos:* Exchange scientist, Fed Repub Ger, 72-74; Oak Ridge assoc univ travelling lectr, ethics of technol, 83; chmn session on ethics & technol (nuclear power, biotechnology, etc), Welding & Testing Technol Energy Conf. *Mem:* Am Inst Chem Engrs; Nat Soc Prof Engrs; AAAS; Sigma Xi. *Res:* Nuclear fuel reprocessing; safety and radiation control; professional and business ethics, conflict resolution by arbitration or mediation. *Mailing Add:* 1136 Harrogate Dr Knoxville TN 37923-1953. *E-Mail:* vic_vaughen@compuserve.com

**VAUGHN, CHARLES MELVIN,** parasitology, protozoology; deceased, see previous edition for last biography

**VAUGHN, CLARENCE BENJAMIN,** ONCOLOGY, PHYSIOLOGICAL CHEMISTRY. *Current Pos:* NIH res fel, 62-64, asst prof oncol, 67-81, CLIN ASSOC PROF INTERNAL MED, SCH MED, WAYNE STATE UNIV, 78-; DIR ONCOL, PROVIDENCE HOSP, 78- *Personal Data:* b Philadelphia, Pa, Dec 14, 28; m 53; c 4. *Educ:* Benedict Col, BS, 51; Howard Univ, MS, 55, MD, 57; Wayne State Univ, PhD(physiol chem), 65. *Concurrent Pos:* Lab instr, Wayne State Univ, 63-67, assoc dept biochem, 68-; res physician, Milton A Darling Mem Ctr, Mich Cancer Found, 64-70, clin dir, 70-72; mem consult staff, Depts Med, Oakwood Hosp, 68-, Detroit Mem Hosp, 70-, Harper Hosp, 73-, Hutzel Hosp, 75-, Southfield Rehab, 76-, Sinai Hosp, 77-, Detroit Macomb Hosp Corp, 88-, Oakland Gen Hosp, 89-; mem, HEW Pub Adv Comt, 76-, Nat Cancer Inst Educ Rev Comt, 83-, adv comt, Nat Cancer Inst, 85- & bd trustees, Providence Hosp Found, 87-89; med dir oncol, Samaritan Health Ctr, 86-; clin prof, Wayne State Univ, 88-, Oakland Univ, 89-; chmn, Minority Res Subcomt, SWOG, 90- *Mem:* AMA; Am Col Physicians; NY Acad Sci; Am Chem Soc; Am Cancer Soc; AAAS; fel Am Col Clin Pharmacol; Am Soc Clin Oncol; Am Soc Prev Oncol; fel Am Inst Chemists. *Res:* Organic acid metabolism; ferritin; monoclonal antibodies; estrogen; progesterone receptors. *Mailing Add:* Southfield Oncol Inst Inc 21751 West 11 Mile Southfield MI 48076. *Fax:* 313-356-8805

**VAUGHN, DANNY MACK,** REMOTE SENSING, GEOGRAPHIC INFORMATION SYSTEMS. *Current Pos:* PROF, GEOMORPHOL & AIR PHOTO MAP INTERPRETATION, UNIV MO, KANSAS CITY, 85-; PROF, DEPT GEOSCI & DIR REMOTE SENSING, GIS LAB, WEBER STATE UNIV, OGDEN, UTAH, 90- *Personal Data:* b Muskegon, Mich, Aug 19, 48; m 78, Mary K Frisz; c Benjamin P & Emity E. *Educ:* Ind State Univ, BS, 78, PhD(phys geog), 84. *Prof Exp:* Fel phys geog, Ind State Univ, 79-83; asst prof geog & geol, Lake Superior State Col, 84-85; asst prof geol & geog, Univ Mo, Kansas City, 85-87, Jacksonville State Univ, 87-90. *Concurrent Pos:* Hemingway scholar, 93 & 96; prin investr, NASA/Jove Grant, NSF grant. *Mem:* Asn Am Geographers; Geol Soc Am; Nat Speleol Soc; Sigma Xi; Am Soc Photogram & Remote Sensing. *Res:* Geologic and geomorphic interpretations from remote sensed imagery and topographic maps; paleohydrology; fluvial processing; geoarcheology; digital image processing; coastal processes; surface modeling and an integration of remote sensing; GIS and land surface processes through computer assisted techniques. *Mailing Add:* Dept Geosci Weber State Univ Ogden UT 84408-2507. *E-Mail:* dvaughn@weber.edu

**VAUGHN, JACK C,** CELL BIOLOGY. *Current Pos:* from asst prof to assoc prof, 66-75, PROF ZOOL, MIAMI UNIV, 75- *Personal Data:* b Burbank, Calif, July 4, 37; m 63; c 3. *Educ:* Univ Calif, Los Angeles, BA, 60; Univ Tex, PhD(bot), 64. *Prof Exp:* Asst zool, Univ Calif, Los Angeles, 60-61; USPHS fel, Univ Wis, 64-66. *Concurrent Pos:* NSF res grant, 67-69 & 70-71; investr, Marine Biol Lab, Woods Hole, 70 & 71. *Mem:* AAAS; Am Inst Biol Scientists; Am Soc Cell Biol; Int Fedn Cell Biol; Am Soc Zoologists; Am Phys Soc. *Res:* Cell biology; chromosome structure and function. *Mailing Add:* Dept Zool Miami Univ 500 E High St Oxford OH 45056-1618

**VAUGHN, JAMES E, JR,** MOLECULAR NEUROMORPHOLOGY, DEVELOPMENTAL NEUROBIOLOGY. *Current Pos:* assoc chmn, 83-86, HEAD SECT MOLECULAR NEUROMORPHOL, CITY OF HOPE, 70-, CHMN, DIV NEUROSCI, BECKMAN RES INST, 86- *Personal Data:* b Kansas City, Mo, Sept 17, 39; m 61; c 2. *Educ:* Westminster Col, BA, 61; Univ Calif, Los Angeles, PhD(anat), 65. *Prof Exp:* Fel brain res, Univ Edinburgh, 65-66; asst prof anat, Boston Univ, 66-70. *Concurrent Pos:* Prin investr, NIH & NSF grants, 69-; fel, Neurosci Res Prog, 69; prog dir NIH prog proj grant, 80-; assoc ed J Neurocytol, 78-86, ed Synapse, 86-; pres res staff, Orgn of City of Hope, 86. *Mem:* Soc Neurosci Am Asn Anat; Am Soc Cell Biol; Int Brain Res Orgn; NY Acad Sci; AAAS. *Res:* Fine structure, molecular morphology and immunocytochemistry of adult and developing central nervous system. *Mailing Add:* Div Neurosci Beckman Res Inst City Hope 1450 E Duarte Rd Duarte CA 91010-0269. *Fax:* 626-301-8470; *E-Mail:* jvaughn@smtplink.coh.org

**VAUGHN, JAMES L,** INSECT PATHOLOGY. *Current Pos:* supvry microbiologist, Insect Path Lab, USDA, 65-79, res leader, 79-90, res leader, Insect Biocontrol Lab, 90-95, RES MICROBIOLOGIST, USDA, 95- *Personal Data:* b Marshfield, Wis, Mar 2, 34; m 89, Carol S Schiller; c Susan, Katherine, Michael & David. *Educ:* Univ Wis, BS, 57, MS, 59, PhD(bact), 62. *Prof Exp:* Res officer tissue cult virol, Insect Path Res Inst, Can Dept Forestry, 61-65. *Concurrent Pos:* Invert ed, In Vitro. *Mem:* Am Soc Microbiol; Soc Invert Path; Soc Invitro Biol; AAAS. *Res:* Methods for growth of insect tissue in vitro; study of processes of viral infection and development in in vitro insect systems. *Mailing Add:* Insect Biocontrol Lab Rm 214 Bldg 011A Agr Res Ctr-W USDA Beltsville MD 20705. *Fax:* 301-504-5104; *E-Mail:* jvaughn@assr.arsusda.gov

**VAUGHN, JOE WARREN,** INORGANIC CHEMISTRY, PHYSICAL CHEMISTRY. *Current Pos:* from asst prof to assoc prof, 61-70, PROF CHEM, NORTHERN ILL UNIV, 70-, CHMN DEPT, 84- *Personal Data:* b Otterbein, Ind, Oct 8, 33; m 55, Jean C Risley; c Joe, John, Jennifer & Julia. *Educ:* DePauw Univ, BA, 55; Univ Ky, MS, 57, PhD(phys chem), 59. *Prof Exp:* Welch Found fel, Univ Tex, 59-61. *Mem:* Am Chem Soc. *Res:* Nonaqueous solvent; fluoro complexes of trivalent chromium; stereochemistry of coordination compounds; synthesis of cis-trans isomers. *Mailing Add:* Dept Chem Northern Ill Univ De Kalb IL 60115

**VAUGHN, JOHN B,** EPIDEMIOLOGY. *Current Pos:* From instr to asst prof, Tulane Univ, 57-60, assoc prof, 70-79, assoc dean, 77-79, PROF EPIDEMIOL & ACTG CHMN, DEPT APPL HEALTH SCI, SCH PUB HEALTH & TROP MED, TULANE UNIV, 79- *Personal Data:* b Birmingham, Ala, Mar 3, 24; m 45; c 6. *Educ:* Auburn Univ, DVM, 49; Tulane Univ, MPH, 56. *Concurrent Pos:* Consult, Epidemiol Sect, La State Dept Health, New Orleans, 57-; epidemic aid coordr & liaison person, Sch Pub Health & Trop Med with Asn Schs Pub Health & Ctr Dis Control, 80-; mem contrib fac, Prev Med Residency Training Prog, Sch Pub Health & Trop Med, 80- *Mem:* Am Pub Health Asn; Soc Epidemiol Res. *Res:* Zoonotic epidemiology; author of numerous publications. *Mailing Add:* Dept Pub Health Tulane Univ Sch Pub Health 1430 Tulane Ave New Orleans LA 70112-2699

**VAUGHN, MICHAEL THAYER,** UNIFIED GAUGE THEORIES. *Current Pos:* assoc prof, 64-73, PROF, NORTHEASTERN UNIV, 73- *Personal Data:* b Chicago, Ill, Aug 6, 36; m 88, Penelope E Reader. *Educ:* Columbia Univ, AB, 55; Purdue Univ, PhD(physics), 60. *Honors & Awards:* Karl Lark Horovitz Prize, Purdue, 59. *Prof Exp:* Res assoc physics, Univ Pa, 59-62; asst prof, Ind Univ, 62-64. *Concurrent Pos:* Vis scientist, Argonne Nat Lab, 67, Deutsches Elektronen Synchrotron, Hamburg, 70, Univ Vienna, 70 & Int Ctr Theoret Physics, Trieste, 71; vis prof, Tex A&M Univ, 75 & Southampton Univ, 79; sr vis fel, Sci Res Coun, UK, 79, 86; vis lectr, Vanderbilt Univ, 85. *Mem:* Am Phys Soc; AAAS. *Res:* Unified gauge theories; renormalization group analysis; group theory; mathematical methods. *Mailing Add:* Dept Physics Northeastern Univ Boston MA 02115. *Fax:* 617-373-2943; *E-Mail:* mtvaughn@neu.edu

**VAUGHN, MOSES WILLIAM,** food technology; deceased, see previous edition for last biography

**VAUGHN, RICHARD CLEMENTS,** INDUSTRIAL ENGINEERING. *Current Pos:* RETIRED. *Personal Data:* b Ionia, Mich, Jan 17, 25; m 47; c 5. *Educ:* Mich State Univ, BA, 48; Toledo Univ, MIE, 55. *Prof Exp:* Res & indust engr, various Ohio Co, 51-57; asst prof indust eng, Univ Fla, 57-62; from assoc prof to prof, Iowa State Univ, 62-86, emer prof indust eng, 87- *Concurrent Pos:* Consult, Liberty Bell Mfg Co, 59-61; instr math, Univ Toledo, 51-57; sabbatical, Univ Wales, Swansea, 80-81. *Mem:* Sigma Xi; Am Soc Eng Educ; Am Soc Qual Control; Inst Mgt Sci. *Res:* Quality control, product liability, operations research. *Mailing Add:* 1519 Harding Ave Ames IA 50010

**VAUGHN, THOMAS HUNT,** organic chemistry, for more information see previous edition

**VAUGHN, WILLIAM KING,** biostatistics, for more information see previous edition

**VAUGHT, JIMMIE BARTON,** EPIDEMIOLOGY OCCUPATIONAL CANCER. *Current Pos:* MEM STAFF, DEPT OCCUP STUDIES, WESTAT INC. *Educ:* Med Col Ga, PhD(biochem), 77. *Mailing Add:* Dept Biochem Epidemiol Microbiol Assoc 900 Black Well Rd Rockville MD 20805. *Fax:* 301-294-3928, 294-2030; *E-Mail:* Bitnet: dit@nihcu

**VAUGHT, ROBERT L,** MATHEMATICS. *Current Pos:* from asst prof to assoc prof, 58-63, PROF MATH, UNIV CALIF, BERKELEY, 63- *Personal Data:* b Alhambra, Calif, Apr 4, 26; m 55; c 2. *Educ:* Univ Calif, AB, 45, PhD(math), 54. *Honors & Awards:* Carol Karp Prize, Int Asn Symbolic Logic, 78. *Prof Exp:* From instr to asst prof math, Univ Wash, 54-58. *Concurrent Pos:* Fulbright scholar, Univ Amsterdam, 56-57; NSF fel, Univ Calif, Los Angeles, 63-64; Guggenheim fel, 67. *Mem:* Am Math Soc; Int Asn Symbolic Logic. *Res:* Foundations of mathematics. *Mailing Add:* Dept Math Univ Calif Berkeley CA 94720-0001

**VAUN, WILLIAM STRATIN,** medicine, for more information see previous edition

**VAUPEL, DONALD BRUCE,** PHARMACOLOGY. *Current Pos:* PHARMACOLOGIST, ADDICTION RES CTR, NAT INST DRUG ABUSE, 72- *Personal Data:* b Hackensack, NJ, Aug 30, 42; m 67; c 2. *Educ:* Wittenberg Univ, BA, 64; Univ Ky, MS, 70, PhD(pharmacol), 74. *Prof Exp:* Chemist qual control, Lederle Labs, Am Cyanamid Co, 64-66. *Concurrent Pos:* Asst adj prof pharmacol, Col Med, Univ Ky, 78- *Mem:* Sigma Xi; Am Soc Pharmacol & Exp Therapeut; Soc Neurosci. *Res:* Assess pharmacological equivalence and study mechanisms of action of abused drugs, particularly opioids and hallucinogens; animal physiology and behavior isolated tissue preparations subjective assessments in humans. *Mailing Add:* NIDA Addiction Res Ctr PO Box 5180 Baltimore MD 21224-0180. *Fax:* 410-550-1645

**VAUSE, EDWIN H(AMILTON),** CHEMISTRY, EARTHQUAKE PREPAREDNESS. *Current Pos:* RETIRED. *Personal Data:* b Chicago, Ill, Mar 30, 23; m 51, Harriet E Oestmann; c Karen, Russell, Kurt, Dirk & Luke. *Educ:* Univ Ill, BS, 47, MS, 48; Univ Chicago, MBA, 52. *Hon Degrees:* DSc, Univ Evansville, 77. *Prof Exp:* Chem engr, Stand Oil Co, 48-49, sr chem engr, 49-50, res projs engr, 50-51, asst gen foreman, Mfg Projs Div, 51-52, Light Oils Div, 52-53 & Hwy Oils Div, 53-57; dir lab admin, Mead Johnson & Co, 57-60; vpres, Charles F Kettering Found, 60-88. *Mem:* Am Inst Chem Engrs; NY Acad Sci; Agr Res Inst. *Res:* Management of research on science technology and public policy formulation; science and technology policy issues. *Mailing Add:* 11834 Calle Parral San Diego CA 92128

**VAUSE, RICHARD C,** AVIATION MEDICINE, PRIMARY CARE. *Current Pos:* CHIEF PHYSICIAN ASST, FED BUR PRISONS, 94- *Personal Data:* b Philadelphia, Pa, Mar 1, 51; c Rayna Angelina. *Educ:* St Josephs Univ, BS, 73; Allegheny Col, BSPA, 78. *Concurrent Pos:* Clin staff, D Lorenzo Health Clin, The Pentagon. *Mem:* Am Acad Physicians Assts; Asn Military Surgeons US. *Mailing Add:* PO Box 6122 Silver Spring MD 20916. *Fax.* 202-305-0862; *E-Mail:* richie@nmaa.org

**VAUX, HENRY JAMES,** ECONOMICS POLICY. *Current Pos:* from lectr to assoc prof forestry, Sch Forestry, 48-53, prof, 53-78, dean, Sch Forestry & assoc dir, Agr Exp Sta, 55-65, EMER PROF FORESTRY, SCH FORESTRY, UNIV CALIF, BERKELEY, 78- *Personal Data:* b Bryn Mawr, Pa, Nov 6, 12; m 37; c 2. *Educ:* Haverford Col, BS, 33; Univ Calif, MS, 35, PhD(agr econ), 48. *Hon Degrees:* DSc, Haverford Col, 85. *Honors & Awards:* Gifford Pinchot Medal, Soc Am Foresters, 83. *Prof Exp:* Instr forestry, Ore State Col, 37-42; asst economist, La Agr Exp Sta, 42-43; assoc economist, US Army, 43; assoc economist, US Forest Serv, 46-48. *Concurrent Pos:* Consult ed, McGraw-Hill Bk Co, 54-76; chmn, Calif Bd Forestry, 76-83. *Mem:* AAAS; fel Soc Am Foresters; Forest Hist Soc; hon mem Soc Foresters Finland. *Res:* Long term timber supply; price behavior and market structures for forest products. *Mailing Add:* 622 San Luis Rd Berkeley CA 94707

**VAUX, JAMES EDWARD, JR,** CHEMISTRY, STATISTICS. *Current Pos:* SR LECTR CHEM, UNIV PITTSBURGH, 65- *Personal Data:* b Pittsburgh, Pa, June 13, 32; div; c 3. *Educ:* Carnegie Inst, BS, 52, MS, 64, PhD(chem), 67. *Prof Exp:* Chemist, E I du Pont de Nemours & Co, Inc, 53-57; teacher, Shady Side Acad, 57-64. *Concurrent Pos:* asst dir, Found Study Cycles, 64-67, exec dir, 67-76; assoc prof & chmn, Carlow Col, 81-92. *Mem:* Am Chem Soc; Am Statist Asn. *Res:* Organic and analytical chemistry; statistics. *Mailing Add:* 503 Newport Dr Pittsburgh PA 15235-3228

**VAVICH, MITCHELL GEORGE,** NUTRITION. *Current Pos:* RETIRED. *Personal Data:* b Miami, Ariz, Aug 24, 16; m 37; c 1. *Educ:* Univ Ariz, BS, 38, MS, 40; Pa State Univ, PhD(biochem), 43. *Prof Exp:* Asst physiol chem, Pa State Univ, 40-42, instr biochem, 43-46; from assoc prof to prof agr biochem, Univ Ariz, 46-75, head dept, 69-75, prof food sci, 75-81, emer prof, 81. *Concurrent Pos:* Spec field staff mem, Rockefeller Found, 65-67; chmn, Comt Agr Biochem & Nutrit, 69- *Mem:* AAAS; Am Chem Soc; Am Inst Nutrit. *Res:* Fluorides, ascorbic acid; vitamins in canned foods; interrelationships of vitamins and other food components; carotenes and vitamin A; nutritional status; biochemistry of cyclopropenoid fatty acids; nutrient value of dietary proteins. *Mailing Add:* 6277 N Calle Del Halcon Tucson AZ 85718-2634

**VAVRA, JAMES JOSEPH,** INFECTIOUS DISEASES. *Current Pos:* CONSULT, 89- *Personal Data:* b Boulder, Colo, Aug 30, 29; m 51, Georgia A Woelbing; c 5. *Educ:* Univ Colo, BA, 51; Univ Wis, MS, 53, PhD, 55. *Prof Exp:* Res assoc, dept biochem, Upjohn Co, 55-57, res assoc & proj leader, dept microbiol, 57-62, sr res scientist, dept clin res, 62-64 & dept microbiol, 64-68, assoc dir infectious dis res, 68-89. *Mem:* AAAS; Am Soc Microbiol; NY Acad Sci; Sigma Xi. *Res:* Fermentation biochemistry, especially metabolism; antibiotic-pathogen relationships, especially resistance development. *Mailing Add:* 1505 Royal Oak Ave Portage MI 49024

**VAWTER, ALFRED THOMAS,** ECOLOGY. *Current Pos:* ASST PROF BIOL, WELLS COL, 78- *Personal Data:* b Los Angeles, Calif, Mar 30, 43. *Educ:* Univ Calif, Irvine, BS, 70; Cornell Univ, PhD(biol), 77. *Prof Exp:* Lectr ecol, Cornell Univ, 76-77; scholar evolution, Univ Calif, Los Angeles, 77-78. *Concurrent Pos:* Consult, Resource Planning Assocs, 78-80, Glacier Nat Park, 87. *Mem:* Am Soc Naturalists; Soc Study Evolution; Soc Conserv Biol; Lepidoptera Res Found. *Res:* Population biology, especially ecological genetics of Lepidoptera; molecular evolution; conserv biol. *Mailing Add:* Dept Biol Wells Col Aurora NY 13026

**VAWTER, SPENCER MAX,** PHYSICS. *Current Pos:* PRES, CAMILE PROD, LLC, 97- *Personal Data:* b Morgan Co, Ind, Feb 18, 37; m 72; c 3. *Educ:* Franklin Col, BA, 59; DePaul Univ, MS, 67; Univ Mich, Ann Arbor, cert physiol, 68; Univ Southern Calif, cert compt systs, 70. *Prof Exp:* Student, Defense Projs Div, Western Elec Co at Lincoln Lab, Mass Inst Technol, 59-60, systs planning & develop engr, 60-63; dir, Ionizing Radiation Sect, AMA, Chicago, 63-66 & Med Physics Sect, 66-70, assoc dir, Dept Med Instrumentation, 70-73; asst to pres, Bio-Dynamics, Inc, 73-76; pres, Bio-Sound, Inc, 76-85, chmn bd, 85-86; pres, Vascular Diag, Inc, 86-87; Labsonics, Inc, 87; Avalon Technol Corp, 88-92; pres, Mentor Urol, 93-95; consult, 95-97. *Mem:* Am Phys Soc; Instrument Soc Am; Asn Advan Med Instrumentation. *Res:* Interaction of electromagnetic energy with human tissue, especially the effect of laser energy on the human eye; application of physical principles to medical practice; application of physical sciences to health care. *Mailing Add:* 3330 Bay Rd South Dr Indianapolis IN 46240

**VAYO, HARRIS WESTCOTT,** APPLIED MATHEMATICS. *Current Pos:* from asst prof to assoc prof, 65-74, PROF MATH, UNIV TOLEDO, 74- *Personal Data:* b Chicago, Ill, Nov 15, 35; m 62, Susan Lyter; c Scott, Lynette & Isaac. *Educ:* Culver-Stockton Col, BA, 57; Univ Ill, MS, 59, PhD(math), 63. *Prof Exp:* Asst math, Univ Ill, 57-62; res fel biomath, Harvard Univ, 63-65. *Concurrent Pos:* Mem coun basic sci, Am Heart Asn, 67-; vis prof, McGill Univ, 76, Ill Col, 86-87; vis scientist, Cornell Univ, 89. *Mem:* Am Math Soc; Soc Math Biol; Soc Indust & Appl Math. *Res:* Applications of mathematics to biological and medical problems, particularly cardiovascular work and red cell biomechanics; acquired immune deficiency syndrome virus geometry. *Mailing Add:* Dept Math Univ Toledo Toledo OH 43606

**VAZ, NUNO A,** FLAT PANEL DISPLAYS & LIQUID CRYSTAL DEVICES, ELECTRO-OPTICS. *Current Pos:* sr res scientist, 84-86, STAFF RES SCIENTIST, GEN MOTORS RES LABS, 86- *Personal Data:* b Carmona, Portugal, Nov 23, 51; US citizen; m 77; c 3. *Educ:* Tech Univ Lisbon, Portugal, EE, 75; Kent State Univ, BS, 77, PhD(physics), 80. *Honors & Awards:* Campbell Award, 90. *Prof Exp:* Res asst, Inst Physics & Math, Lisbon, Portugal, 75-76; res fel, Dept Physics, Kent State Univ, 81-82, res assoc, 82-83. *Concurrent Pos:* Fel, Matsumae Int Found, 83. *Mem:* Sigma Xi; Am Phys Soc; Int Soc Magnetic Resonance; Soc Automotive Engrs. *Res:* Experimental and applied research on liquid crystals, in particular, phase behavior, phase transitions and microdispersions, using primarily optical techniques, nuclear magnetic resonance and other spectroscopic techniques. *Mailing Add:* Dept Physics Gen Motors Res Labs Warren MI 48090

**VAZQUEZ, ALFREDO JORGE,** NEUROPHARMACOLOGY, ELECTROPHYSIOLOGY. *Current Pos:* ASSOC PROF PHARMACOL, CHICAGO MED SCH, 71-, VCIIMN DEPT, 77- & ACTG CHMN DEPT, 85- *Personal Data:* b Buenos Aires, Arg, Jan 21, 37; m 62; c 1. *Educ:* Bernadino Rivadavia Col, Arg, BS, 54; Univ Buenos Aires, MD, 62. *Prof Exp:* From intern to resident med, Tigre Hosp, Arg, 59-61; instr pharmacol, Chicago Med Sch, 62-65, assoc, 65-67; asst prof, Fac Med, Univ Man, 67-71. *Concurrent Pos:* Res assoc, Lab Psychopharmacol, Nat Neuropsychiat Inst, Buenos Aires, 60-62. *Mem:* Am Soc Pharmacol & Exp Therapeut. *Res:* Physiology and pharmacology of the cerebral cortex; epilepsy; drug abuse and hallucinogenic drugs; cardiovascular. *Mailing Add:* Dept Pharmacol Finch Univ Chicago Med Sch 3333 N Greenbay Rd North Chicago IL 60064-3037. *Fax:* 847-578-3401

**VEACH, ALLEN MARSHALL,** ACCELERATOR PHYSICS. *Current Pos:* RETIRED. *Personal Data:* b Lancaster, SC, Sept 21, 33; m 73, Lynn Hawkins; c Allen M Jr, Olivia V (Broody), Alvis L & Sarah V (Shadburn). *Educ:* Univ Ala, BS, 56; Univ Akron, MS, 59. *Prof Exp:* Physicist phys testing, B F Goodrich Co, 56-57, microscopist chem micros, 57-59; develop specialist isotope separation, Oak Ridge Nat Lab, 59-60, physicist plasma physics, 60-70, res physicist ion sources & accelerators, 70-91. *Mem:* Am Phys Soc. *Res:* Plasma physics; accelerators; ion sources; high vacuum; isotope separation; electron and ion emission; electrical and gas discharges; ion and electron optics; ionization phenomena; mass spectroscopy; hold 10 patents. *Mailing Add:* 912 Turkey Oak Rd Crossville TN 38555

**VEAL, BOYD WILLIAM, JR,** SOLID STATE PHYSICS. *Current Pos:* asst physicist, 69-73, PHYSICIST, ARGONNE NAT LAB, 73- *Personal Data:* b Chance, SDak, May 21, 37; m 62; c 2. *Educ:* SDak State Univ, BS, 59; Univ Pittsburgh, MS, 62; Univ Wis, PhD(physics), 69. *Prof Exp:* Engr, Westinghouse Res Labs, 59-63. *Mem:* Am Phys Soc. *Res:* Electronic properties of solids. *Mailing Add:* Div Mat Univ Argonne Nat Lab 9700 Cass Ave Argonne IL 60439. *Fax:* 630-252-4798

**VEAL, DONALD L,** METEOROLOGY. *Current Pos:* PRES & CHIEF EXEC OFFICER, PARTICLE MEASURING SYSTS, INC, 87- *Personal Data:* b Chance, SDak, Apr 17, 31; m 53; c 2. *Educ:* SDak State Univ, BS, 53; Univ Wyo, MS, 60, PhD, 64. *Prof Exp:* Instr civil eng, SDak State Univ, 57-58; from instr to prof atmospheric sci, Univ Wyo, 58-87, asst dir, Natural

Resources Res Inst, 67-70, head dept, 70-77, vpres res, 77-81, pres res, 81-87. *Mem:* Am Meteorol Soc; Royal Meteorol Soc; Sigma Xi; Am Soc Eng Educ; Am Soc Civil Engrs; Nat Soc Prof Engrs; Am Geophys Union. *Res:* Cloud physics and weather modification. *Mailing Add:* 7018 Indian Peaks Trail Boulder CO 80301-3627

**VEALE, WARREN LORNE,** PHYSIOLOGY, NEUROPSYCHOLOGY. *Current Pos:* from asst prof to assoc prof, 70-76, PROF MED PHYSIOL, FAC MED, UNIV CALGARY, 76-, ASSOC DEAN RES & ADMINR GRAD STUDIES PROG, 74- *Personal Data:* b Antler, Sask, Mar 13, 43; m 66; c 1. *Educ:* Univ Man, BSc, 64; Purdue Univ, West Lafayette, MSc, 68, PhD(neuropsychol), 71. *Prof Exp:* Instr psychol, Brandon Univ, 64-66, lectr, 66-67. *Concurrent Pos:* Vis scientist, Nat Inst Med Res, London, Eng, 69; mem sci adv comt non-med use of drugs, Nat Health & Welfare-Med Res Coun, 73-74, chmn comt, 74-77; mem, Med Res Coun, 77-, mem, Studentship Comt, 77-, chmn, 78-, mem, Prog Grants Comt, 78-; consult, Health & Welfare, Health Prevention & Promotion Directorate, 78-; mem res comt, Alta Provincial Cancer Hosps Bd, 78-; regional ed, Pharmacol, Biochem & Behav. *Mem:* Can Psychol Soc; Soc Neurosci; Can Biochem Soc; NY Acad Sci; Am Physiol Soc. *Res:* Central nervous systems' involvement in temperature regulation, fever and action of antipyretics; neurohumoral changes in brain related to alcoholism. *Mailing Add:* Dept Med Physiol Fac Med Univ Calgary 3330 Hospital Dr NW Calgary AB T2N 1N4 Can. *Fax:* 403-282-7298

**VEATCH, ROBERT MARLIN,** MEDICAL ETHICS, PHILOSOPHY. *Current Pos:* dir, 89-96, PROF MED ETHICS, KENNEDY INST ETHICS, GEORGETOWN UNIV, 79-, PROF PHILOS, 81- *Personal Data:* b Utica, NY, Jan 22, 39; m 87, Ann Bender; c Paul M & Carlton E. *Educ:* Purdue Univ, BS, 61; Univ Calif, San Francisco, MS, 62; Harvard Univ, BD, 64, MA, 70, PhD, 71. *Prof Exp:* Assoc med ethics, Inst Soc, Ethics & Life Scis, Hastings-on-Hudson, NY, 70-75, sr assoc, 75-79; res assoc med, Col Physicians & Surgeons, Columbia Univ, 71-72. *Concurrent Pos:* Adj prof, Depts Community & Family Med & Obstet/Gynec, 84-; mem gov bd, Wash Regional Transplant Consortium, 88-; bd dirs, Hospice Care, DC, 89-96, pres, 93-96; sr ed, Kennedy Inst Ethics J, 91- *Mem:* Soc Christian Ethics. *Res:* Medical ethics; family medicine; obstetrics; gynecology; philosophy; death and dying; human subjects research; organ transplantation; philosophy of science. *Mailing Add:* Georgetown Univ Kennedy Inst Ethics Washington DC 20057. *E-Mail:* veatchr@gomet.georgetown.edu

**VEAZEY, SIDNEY EDWIN,** PHYSICS. *Current Pos:* PRES, S E VENTURES, INC, 89- *Personal Data:* b Wilmington, NC, Sept 18, 37; m 62, Joy Galantin; c Karen E, Edwin G, Virginia (Geertsema) & Warren T. *Educ:* US Naval Acad, BS, 59; Duke Univ, PhD(physics), 65. *Prof Exp:* Electronics mat officer & main propulsion asst, USS Pollack, 66-68, navigator-opers off, USS Ulysses S Grant, 68-71 & USS James Madison, 71-72, dep dir Trident submarine design develop proj, Naval Ship Eng Ctr, 72, chief Naval mat, Combat Systs Adv Group, Naval Mat Command, 72-73, exec asst to chief Naval develop, 73-74, design mgr nuclear attack submarines, Naval Ship Eng Ctr, 74-76, dep div head, Combat Systs Dept, Naval Surface Weapons Ctr, 76-77, dep dept head, Strategic Systs Dept, 77-78, dept comndr eval & officer-in-chg, Naval Surface Weapons Ctr, White Oak Lab, Silver Spring, Md, 78-80, chmn, Naval Syst Eng Dept, US Naval Acad, Annapolis, 80-82; exec scientist, ORI Inc, 82-84; div dir, ASG, Inc, 84-86; partner, Creative Eng & Construct, 86-89. *Concurrent Pos:* Prof mech eng, Va. *Mem:* Am Soc Naval Engrs. *Res:* Microwave spectroscopy of the alkali fluorides; application of lasers to communication from ships; SEAMOD weapons systems for advanced platforms; nuclear power; submarines. *Mailing Add:* 8267 Lighthouse Lane King George VA 22485

**VEAZEY, THOMAS MABRY,** ORGANIC CHEMISTRY. *Current Pos:* SECY-TREAS, WYOMING ANALYSIS LAB, 79- *Personal Data:* b Paris, Tenn, Jan 13, 20; m 38; c 3. *Educ:* Murray State Univ, BS, 40; Univ Ill, PhD(org chem), 53. *Prof Exp:* Chemist & job instr supvr, E I du Pont de Nemours & Co, Inc, 41-45; res chemist, Devoe & Raynolds Co, 45-50; res chemist, Chemstrand Corp, 53-55, develop group leader synthetic fibers, 55-58, supvr develop, 58-63; mgr patent liaison, Monsanto Textiles Div, Monsanto Textiles Co, 63-70, sr develop assoc, 71-82. *Mem:* Am Chem Soc; Sigma Xi. *Res:* Chemical and spinning process development of synthetic textile fibers. *Mailing Add:* 2026 Woodland St SE Decatur AL 35601

**VEBER, DANIEL FRANK,** MEDICINAL CHEMISTRY, PEPTIDE CHEMISTRY. *Current Pos:* sr fel, 93-94, DIR, SMITHKLINE BEECHAM PHARMACEUT, 94- *Personal Data:* b New Brunswick, NJ, Sept 9, 39; m 59, Marilyn Franck; c Paul D & David F. *Educ:* Yale Univ, BA, 61, MS, 62, PhD(org chem), 64. *Honors & Awards:* Alan E Pierce Award, Am Peptide Soc, 91; Philadelphia Sect Award, Am Chem Soc. *Prof Exp:* Sr chemist, Merck Sharp & Dohme Res Labs, 64-66, res fel, 66-72, sr res fel, 72-75, assoc dir med chem, 75-79, dir, 79-80, sr dir, 80-93. *Concurrent Pos:* Mem planning comt, Am Peptide Symp, 79-85; consult, NIH Contraceptive Develop Br, 81-82, 85; Biorg Study Sect, NIH & Pharmacol Sci Rev Comt, 81-85; vis prof chem, Wis Univ, 83; fac, Residential Sch Med Chem, Drew Univ, 87-91; invited expert analyst, Biochem & Molecular Biol, Chemtracts, 90-92; counr, Am Peptide Soc, 90-; co-chair, Gordon Res Conf, 94. *Mem:* NY Acad Sci; AAAS; Am Chem Soc; Am Soc Biol Chemists; Am Peptide Soc. *Res:* New methods and protecting groups in organic synthesis; chemical and biological properties of enzymes and peptide hormones; chemistry of heterocyclic compounds; conformational analysis; combinatorial chemistry; medicinal chemistry. *Mailing Add:* 290 Batleson Rd Ambler PA 19002. *Fax:* 610-270-6609

**VEBLEN, DAVID RODLI,** MINERALOGY, PETROLOGY. *Current Pos:* from asst prof to assoc prof, 81-84, PROF GEOL, JOHNS HOPKINS UNIV, 84- *Personal Data:* b Minneapolis, Minn, Apr 27, 47; div; c Annie, Krista & Bonnie. *Educ:* Harvard Univ, BA, 69, MA, 74, PhD(geol), 76. *Honors & Awards:* Mineral Soc Am Award, 83. *Prof Exp:* fac res assoc geol, Ariz State Univ, 76-79, asst prof geol, 79-81. *Mem:* Mineral Soc Am; Am Geophys Union; Mineral Asn Can; AAAS; Electron Micros Soc Am; Microbeam Analysis Soc. *Res:* Crystal chemistry and defect structures of silicate minerals, especially chain and sheet silicates; solid state reactions; x-ray diffraction and electron microscopy; applications of mineralogy to igneous and metamorphic petrology. *Mailing Add:* Dept Earth Sci Johns Hopkins Univ 3400 N Charles St Baltimore MD 21218-2608. *Fax:* 410-516-7933

**VEDAM, KUPPUSWAMY,** SOLID STATE PHYSICS, MATERIALS SCIENCE & OPTICS. *Current Pos:* sr res assoc, 62-64, assoc prof, 63-70, PROF PHYSICS, PA STATE UNIV, 70- *Personal Data:* b Vedharanyam, India, Jan 15, 26; m 56, Nalini Subramanyam; c Saraswathi & Subramanyam. *Educ:* Univ Nagpur, BSc, 46, MSc, 47; Univ Saugor, PhD(physics), 51. *Prof Exp:* Lectr physics, Indian Govt Educ Serv, 46-47; lectr, Univ Saugor, 47-48 & 51-53; sr res asst, Indian Inst Sci, 53-56; res assoc, Pa State Univ, 56-57, asst prof, 57-59; sr res officer, Atomic Energy Estab, Bombay, India, 60-62. *Concurrent Pos:* Mem panel piezoelec transducers, Indian Stand Inst, 61-62. *Mem:* Fel Am Phys Soc; fel Optical Soc Am; Phys Soc Japan; Sigma Xi. *Res:* Crystal physics; optics; ferroelectricity; x-ray and neutron diffraction; high pressure physics, physics of surfaces and materials characterization; spectroscopic ellipsometry. *Mailing Add:* Mat Res Lab Pa State Univ University Park PA 16802. *Fax:* 814-865-2326; *E-Mail:* k1n@email.psu.edu

**VEDAMUTHU, EBENEZER RAJKUMAR,** food science & technology, microbiology, for more information see previous edition

**VEDDER, JAMES FORREST,** POLAR OZONE DEPLETION, MICROPARTICLE ACCELERATORS. *Current Pos:* RETIRED. *Personal Data:* b Pomona, Calif, June 3, 28; m 70, Leslys S Garrow; c Nicholas & Robin. *Educ:* Pomona Col, BA, 49; Univ Calif, PhD(nuclear physics), 58. *Prof Exp:* Asst nuclear physics, Radiation Lab, Univ Calif, 51-58; res scientist, Missiles & Space Co, Lockheed Aircraft Corp, 58-63; res scientist, Ames Res Ctr, NASA, 63-89; res assoc, San Jose State Univ Found, 90-92. *Mem:* Am Phys Soc; Am Geophys Union; Sigma Xi; Archaeol Inst Am. *Res:* Nuclear physics; beta decay; space physics; meteoroids; microparticle accelerators; craters formed by hypervelocity microparticles; remote sensing of soil moisture; measurement of stratospheric halocarbons, methane, nitrous oxide, ozone, etc; polar ozone depletion. *Mailing Add:* 26355 Calle del Sol Los Altos Hills CA 94022-3301

**VEDECKIS, WAYNE V,** BIOCHEMISTRY, MOLECULAR BIOLOGY. *Current Pos:* PROF BIOCHEM & MOLECULAR BIOL, LA STATE UNIV, 79- *Personal Data:* b Chicago, Ill, Aug 25, 47. *Educ:* Loyola Univ, BS, 70, MS, 71; Northwestern Univ, PhD(biol), 74. *Prof Exp:* Res fel biol, Baylor Col Med, 74-79. *Mem:* Sigma Xi; Am Soc Biochem & Molecular Biol; AAAS; Am Endocrinol Soc. *Res:* Biochemistry; molecular biology. *Mailing Add:* Dept Biochem La State Univ Med Ctr 1901 Perdido St New Orleans LA 70112-1328

**VEDEJS, EDWIN,** ORGANIC CHEMISTRY. *Current Pos:* assoc prof, 67-77, PROF CHEM, UNIV WIS-MADISON, 77- *Personal Data:* b Riga, Latvia, Jan 31, 41; US citizen. *Educ:* Univ Mich, Ann Arbor, BS, 62; Univ Wis-Madison, PhD(chem), 66. *Prof Exp:* Nat Acad Sci-Air Force Off Sci Res fel chem, Harvard Univ, 66-67. *Concurrent Pos:* A P Sloan fel, 71-73. *Mem:* Am Chem Soc; Sigma Xi. *Res:* Synthetic organic and organophosphorus chemistry; thermal rearrangements. *Mailing Add:* Dept Chem 1101 Univ Ave Madison WI 53706-1322

**VEDERAS, JOHN CHRISTOPHER,** BIOORGANIC CHEMISTRY. *Current Pos:* from asst prof to assoc prof, 77-87 PROF CHEM, UNIV ALTA, 87- *Personal Data:* b Detmold, Ger, 47; US citizen; m 91, Andrea Oplenorth. *Educ:* Stanford Univ, BSc, 69; Mass Inst Technol, PhD(chem), 73. *Honors & Awards:* Merck, Sharp, Dohme Award, Chem Inst Can, 86, Labatt Award, 91. *Prof Exp:* Res assoc chem, Univ Basel, Switz, 73-76 & Purdue Univ, 76-77. *Concurrent Pos:* Chmn, Biol Chem Div, Chem Inst Can, 83-84, fel, 86; chmn, Org Chem Div, Univ Alta, 94- *Mem:* Am Chem Soc; Brit Chem Soc; Chem Inst Can; Sigma Xi. *Res:* Mechanism and stereochemistry of enzymes in amino acid metabolism; radiochemical synthesis; biosynthesis of secondary metabolites. *Mailing Add:* Dept Chem Univ Alta Edmonton AB T6G 2G2 Can. *Fax:* 403-492-8231

**VEDROS, NEYLAN ANTHONY,** MICROBIOLOGY, IMMUNOLOGY. *Current Pos:* res microbiologist, Biol Lab, 66-68, DIR NAVAL BIOMED RES LAB & PROF MED MICROBIOL & IMMUNOL, UNIV CALIF, BERKELEY, 68- *Personal Data:* b New Orleans, La, Oct 6, 29; m 55; c 2. *Educ:* La State Univ, BSc, 51, MSc, 57; Univ Colo, PhD(microbiol), 60. *Honors & Awards:* Lab Sect Award, Am Pub Health Asn, 66. *Prof Exp:* Nat Inst Allergy & Infectious Dis fel, Med Sch, Univ Ore, 60-62; Bact Div, Naval Med Res Inst, Bethesda, Md, 62-66. *Mem:* Int Asn Aquatic Animal Med; Am Soc Microbiol; Am Asn Immunol; Soc Exp Biol & Med; Asn Mil Surg US. *Res:* Immunochemistry of Neisseria Meningitidis; host-parasite studies in marine pinnipeds; ecology of terrestrial and marine fungi. *Mailing Add:* 2610 Evelyn Ct Alameda CA 94501

**VEDVICK, THOMAS SCOTT,** HEMOGLOBINOPATHIES, PROTEINS. *Current Pos:* Lectr, biol, 76-77, asst res biochemist, 72-87, RES SCIENTIST, AGOURON INST, 88-, STAFF SCIENTIST, 89- *Personal Data:* b Tacoma, Wash, June 23, 44; m 67; c 2. *Educ:* Univ Puget Sound, BS, 66; Western Wash State Col, MS, 68; Univ Ore, PhD(biochem), 72. *Concurrent Pos:* Prin investr, NIH, 78-80; lectr, chem dept, Univ Calif, San Diego, 81- *Mem:* Sigma Xi; Protein Soc; Asn Biomolecular Res Facil. *Res:* Thalassemia syndromes; primary structure of proteins, development of techniques, and equipment for microsequencing; determination of the microheterogeneity of human fetal hemoglobin gamma chains; protein sequencing. *Mailing Add:* 2708 Jacaranda Ave Carlsbad CA 92009

**VEECH, RICHARD L,** BIOCHEMISTRY, MEDICINE. *Current Pos:* CHIEF, LAB METAB, NAT INST ALCOHOL ABUSE & ALCOHOLISM, 78- *Personal Data:* b Decatur, Ill, Sept 19, 35; m 65; c 3. *Educ:* Harvard Univ, BA, 57, MD, 62; Oxford Univ, PhD(biochem), 69. *Mem:* Brit Biochem Soc; Am Soc Biol Chemists; Am Inst Nutrit; Neurochem Soc. *Res:* Control of metabolic processes. *Mailing Add:* Nat Inst Alcohol Abuse & Alcoholism NIH 12501 Washington Ave Rockville MD 20852. *Fax:* 301-443-5894

**VEECH, WILLIAM AUSTIN,** MATHEMATICS. *Current Pos:* assoc prof, 69-72, chmn dept, 82-86, PROF MATH, RICE UNIV, 72-, MILTON BROCKETT PORTER PROF, 88- *Personal Data:* b Detroit, Mich, Dec 24, 38; m 65, Kathryn Lunceford; c Kathryn Muriel & Maude Elizabeth. *Educ:* Dartmouth Col, AB, 60; Princeton Univ, PhD(math), 63. *Prof Exp:* H B Fine instr math, Princeton Univ, 63-64, Higgins lectr, 64-66; asst prof, Univ Calif, Berkeley, 66-69. *Concurrent Pos:* Mem math, Inst Advan Study, Princeton Univ, 68-69, 72, 76-77 & 83-84; NSF grant, Rice Univ, 69-, Alfred P Sloan fel, 71-73; adv comt math & comput sci, NSF, 79-82; ed bd, Ergodic Theory & Dynamical Systs, 81-91, Annals of Math, 85-90; at-large-mem & cour, Am Math Soc, 86-90. *Mem:* Am Math Soc. *Res:* Topological dynamics; ergodic theory; probability theory; functional analysis; almost periodic functions; number theory. *Mailing Add:* Dept Math Rice Univ PO Box 1892 Houston TX 77251-1892. *E-Mail:* veech@rice.edu

**VEEN-BAIGENT, MARGARET JOAN,** NUTRITION. *Current Pos:* RETIRED. *Personal Data:* b Toronto, Ont, Dec 23, 33; m 69; c 2. *Educ:* Univ Toronto, BA, 55, MA, 56, PhD(nutrit), 64. *Prof Exp:* From lectr to asst prof, Sch Hyg, Univ Toronto, 56-75, assoc prof nutrit, Fac Med, 75-93. *Mem:* Nutrit Soc Can; Brit Nutrit Soc; Am Inst Nutrit; NY Acad Sci. *Res:* Calcium requirements. *Mailing Add:* 11 Feldbar Ct Willowdale ON M2N 4P7 Can

**VEENEMA, RALPH J,** UROLOGY. *Current Pos:* asst resident & resident, Columbia-Presby Med Ctr, Columbia Univ, 50-52, from asst to assoc, 53-58, asst clin prof, 58-60, from asst prof to prof clin urol, 60-87, EMER PROF CLIN UROL, COL PHYSICIANS & SURGEONS, COLUMBIA UNIV, 87- *Personal Data:* b Prospect Park, NJ, Dec 13, 21; m 44; c 4. *Educ:* Calvin Col, AB, 42; Jefferson Med Col, MD, 45; Am Bd Urol, dipl, 57. *Honors & Awards:* 2nd Prize, Am Urol Asn, 62, 1st Prize, 64. *Prof Exp:* Asst resident, Vet Admin Hosps, Alexandria, La, 46 & Jackson, Miss, 47; asst resident path, Paterson Gen Hosp, 48; surg path, Col Physicians & Surgeons, Columbia Univ, 49, asst resident urol, Vet Admin Hosp, Bronx, 49. *Concurrent Pos:* Assoc urologist, St Joseph Hosp, Paterson, NJ, 53-56; chief, Urol Outpatient Clin, Columbia-Presby Med Ctr, 55-60, from asst attend urologist to assoc attend urologist, 55-68, attend urologist, 68-; attend urologist & chief urol serv, Valley Hosp, Ridgewood, NJ, 56-60, consult, 60-; chief urol, Francis Delafield Hosp, Cancer Res Inst, 60-75; consult, USPHS Hosp, Staten Island, NY, 61- & Harlem Hosp, NY, 62- *Mem:* Am Asn Genito-Urinary Surg; Am Urol Asn; fel Am Col Surgeons; fel AMA; NY Acad Med (secy, 60-61). *Res:* Pathophysiology of genitourinary neoplasms. *Mailing Add:* 40 Nelson Ave PO Box 882 Cooperstown NY 13326

**VEENHUIZEN, JEFFREY J,** ANIMAL PHYSIOLOGY, NUTRITION. *Current Pos:* Res specialist nutrit, 88-92, RES GROUP LEADER ENDOCRINOL, MONSANTO CO, 92- *Personal Data:* b Moscow, Idaho, July 14, 59. *Educ:* Purdue Univ, BS, 81; Iowa State Univ, MS, 83, PhD(physiol), 88. *Mem:* Am Soc Animal Sci; Sigma Xi. *Mailing Add:* Monsanto Co BB2K 700 Chesterfield Village Pkwy St Louis MO 63198-0001

**VEENING, HANS,** ANALYTICAL CHEMISTRY. *Current Pos:* From instr to assoc prof, 58-72, presidential prof, 90-93, PROF CHEM, BUCKNELL UNIV, 72-, DEPT CHMN, 86- *Personal Data:* b Neth, May 7, 31; nat US; m 57, Elizabeth I Timmerman. *Educ:* Hope Col, AB, 53; Purdue Univ, MS, 55, PhD, 59. *Concurrent Pos:* NSF fac fel with Dr J F K Huber, Univ Amsterdam, 66-67; NIH spec res fel, Biochem Separations Sect, Oak Ridge Nat Lab, 72-73; NSF grants, 68-72, 76-78 & 84-85; Petrol Res Fund grants, 68-86; prof in charge short course on automated anal, Am Chem Soc, 76-78; NIH grant, 78-81; mem, Anal Chem Deleg Sci Exchange Vis to People's Repub China, 85; NSF res grant, Univ Amsterdam, 84-85; vis prof, Inst Mass Spectrometry, Univ Amsterdam, 95. *Mem:* Sigma Xi; Am Chem Soc; Royal Dutch Chem Soc. *Res:* High performance liquid chromatography of biochemically active compounds; mass spectrometry of biochemically active compounds; gas chromatography; capillary electrophoresis. *Mailing Add:* Dept Chem Bucknell Univ Lewisburg PA 17837. *Fax:* 717-524-1739; *E-Mail:* hveening@bucknell.edu

**VEERAVALLI, MADHAVAN,** PROCESS DEVELOPMENT, SCALE UP. *Current Pos:* Scientist appl res, 88-91, scientist prod develop, 91-93, DEVELOP ENGR, SHERWIN WILLIAMS CO, 93- *Personal Data:* b India, Feb 1, 61; m 88, Vanitha; c Sutikshna. *Educ:* Osmania Univ, India, BS, 82; Univ Toledo, MS, 85, PhD(chem eng), 89. *Mem:* Am Chem Soc; Sigma Xi; Am Inst Chem Engrs. *Mailing Add:* 549 E 115th St Chicago IL 60628

**VEESER, LYNN RAYMOND,** NUCLEAR PHYSICS, FIBER OPTIC SENSORS. *Current Pos:* STAFF MEM PHYSICS, LOS ALAMOS SCI LAB, 67- *Personal Data:* b Sturgeon Bay, Wis, Sept 18, 42; m 76. *Educ:* Univ Wis-Madison, BS, 64, MS, 65, PhD(physics), 68. *Mem:* Am Phys Soc; Soc Photo-Optical Instrumentation Engrs. *Res:* Pulse power diagnostics. *Mailing Add:* Los Alamos Nat Lab PO Box 1663 Los Alamos NM 87545. *Fax:* 505-667-7684

**VEGA, ANTHONY JUDE,** SYNOPTIC CLIMATOLOGY, GLOBAL CHANGE & VARIABILITY. *Current Pos:* ASST PROF CLIMAT, CLARION UNIV, 94- *Personal Data:* b New Orleans, La, Apr 14, 64; m 91, Mary J Fluker. *Educ:* Univ New Orleans, BA, 87; Miss State Univ, MS, 90; La State Univ, PhD(phys geog), 94. *Prof Exp:* Instr earth sci/geog, Southeastern La Univ, 91; adj instr geog, Univ New Orleans, 91-92. *Concurrent Pos:* Prin investr, Clarion Univ, 94, State Syst Higher Educ, 96-97 & NASA-Jove, 96-; consult, 94-; lectr, Dept Geog, Pa State Univ, 95 & Kent State Univ, 97; NASA Jove res fel, Goddard Space Flight Ctr, NASA, 96. *Mem:* Ash Am Geogrs; Am Meteorol Soc; Nat Weather Asn. *Res:* Global and hemispheric climate change and variability; synoptic climatologies which relate primary modes of atmospheric variability to the surface climate; author of several publications. *Mailing Add:* AGES Dept Clarion Univ Clarion PA 16214. *Fax:* 814-226-2004; *E-Mail:* avega@vaxa.clarion.edu

**VEGH, EMANUEL,** MATHEMATICS. *Current Pos:* RETIRED. *Personal Data:* b New York, NY, Nov 20, 36; m 60, Marilyn Bass; c Esther, Mark & Sharon. *Educ:* Univ Del, BA, 58, MA, 60; Univ NC, PhD(math), 65. *Honors & Awards:* Res Publ Award, US Naval Res Lab, 69, 86 & 87. *Prof Exp:* Lectr math, Univ Del, 58-60 & Univ NC, 60-63; res mathematician, US Naval Res Lab, 63-96. *Concurrent Pos:* Assoc prof lectr, Univ Md, 67-89; assoc prof lectr, George Washington Univ, 65-67, prof lectr, 89- *Mem:* Math Asn Am; Am Math Soc; Reg Educ Serv Agency. *Res:* Number theory; applied mathematics. *Mailing Add:* Marilyn Vegh 2475 Virginia Ave NW Apt 330 Washington DC 20037

**VEGORS, STANLEY H, JR,** NUCLEAR PHYSICS. *Current Pos:* assoc prof, Idaho State Univ, 58-61, head dept, 58-65, prof, 61-92, EMER PROF PHYSICS, IDAHO STATE UNIV, 92- *Personal Data:* b Detroit, Mich, Jan 5, 29; m 51, Ann Hope Starr; c Eric, Susan & Heidi. *Educ:* Middlebury Col, BA, 51; Mass Inst Technol, BS, 51; Univ Ill, MS, 52, PhD(physics), 55. *Prof Exp:* Res assoc physics, Univ Ill, 55-56; physicist, Phillips Petrol Co, 56-58. *Concurrent Pos:* Prof physics, Univ Petrol & Minerals, Saudi Arabia, 82-84. *Mem:* Am Phys Soc; Int Solar Energy Soc. *Res:* Radioactivity, solar energy, nuclear safeguards; nuclear waste disposal. *Mailing Add:* Dept Physics Idaho State Univ Pocatello ID 83209-0009

**VEGOTSKY, ALLEN,** BIOLOGICAL CHEMISTRY. *Current Pos:* res adminr, 78-88, SCI PROG DIR, AM CANCER SOC, 88- *Personal Data:* b New York, NY, Mar 2, 31; m 67; c Sarah. *Educ:* City Col New York, BS, 52; Fla State Univ, MS, 57, PhD(chem), 61. *Prof Exp:* Asst biochem, NY Univ, 52, US Army Chem Corps Lab, 53-55 & Fla State Univ, 55-60; NIH fel, Purdue Univ, 60-63; asst prof biol & chem, Wheaton Col, Mass, 63-69; assoc prof, Wells Col, 69-74; biosci coordr, Biomed Interdisciplinary Curric Proj, 74-77; asst med dir, Cystic Fibrosis Found, 77-78. *Mem:* Am Asn Cancer Res; Am Inst Hist Pharm; Soc Hist Archeol. *Res:* Research administration; cancer research; history of pharmacy; historic archaeology. *Mailing Add:* 2215 Greencrest Dr Atlanta GA 30345

**VEHAR, GORDON ALLEN,** IDENTIFICATION & PRECLINICAL EVALUATION OF POTENTIAL THERAPEUTICS. *Current Pos:* sr scientist, 80-86, dir cardiovasc res, 86-90, STAFF SCIENTIST, GENENTECH INC, 90- *Personal Data:* b Cleveland, Ohio, Apr 26, 48; m 77, Janet Cox; c Kevin Cox & Julia Victoria. *Educ:* Bowling Green State Univ, BS, 70; Univ Cincinnati, PhD(biol chem), 76. *Honors & Awards:* Murray Thelin Award for Outstanding Res, Nat Hemophilia Found, 89. *Prof Exp:* Fel, Dept Biochem, Univ Wash, 75-80. *Mem:* Am Soc Biochem & Molecular Biol; Am Fedn Clin Res; Int Soc Thrombosis & Hemostasis. *Res:* Treatments for hemophilia and myocardial infarction; treatments for solid tumors; recombinant DNA technology. *Mailing Add:* 110 Leslie Dr San Carlos CA 94070. *E-Mail:* vehar.gordon@gene.com

**VEHLOW, RICHARD EDWARD,** INSTITUTIONAL BUILDING HEATING VENTILATION AIR CONDITIONING DESIGN. *Current Pos:* Jr mech struct engr, 94-96, jr heating vent & air conditioning engr, 96-97, ASST HEATING VENT & AIR CONDITIONING ENGR, OFF GEN SERV, NY STATE, 97- *Personal Data:* b Jamaica Estates, NY, July 1, 69. *Educ:* Rensselaer Polytechnic Inst, BS, 91, MS, 93. *Concurrent Pos:* Co-op engr, Elec Boat Div, Gen Dynamics, 92. *Mem:* Am Soc Mech Engrs; Am Soc Heating Refrig & Air Conditioning Engrs; Soc Automotive Engrs; Am Inst Aeronaut & Astronaut; Nat Space Soc. *Mailing Add:* 100 McChesney Ave Apt H8 Troy NY 12180. *Fax:* 518-474-8900; *E-Mail:* vehlor@rpi.edu

**VEHRENCAMP, SANDRA LEE,** ANIMAL BEHAVIOR, ORNITHOLOGY. *Current Pos:* Lectr, 76-79, asst prof, 79-85, ASSOC PROF BIOL, UNIV CALIF, SAN DIEGO, 85- *Personal Data:* b Glendale, Calif, Feb 11, 48; m 73; c 2. *Educ:* Univ Calif, Berkeley, BA, 70; Cornell Univ, PhD(animal behav), 76. *Concurrent Pos:* Exped leader, grant, Nat Geog Soc, 78-79; mem, NIMH panel, 81-85. *Mem:* Am Ornith Union. *Res:* Evolution of avian and mammalian social organization and communication; sociobiology, ecological energetics. *Mailing Add:* Dept Biol 0322 Univ Calif San Diego 9500 Gilman Dr La Jolla CA 92093-0322

**VEHSE, ROBERT CHASE,** SOLID STATE PHYSICS. *Current Pos:* PROCESS RE-ENG DIR, AT&T NETWORK, 93- *Personal Data:* b Morgantown, WVa, Sept 9, 36; m 61; c 2. *Educ:* WVa Univ, BA, 58; Univ Tenn, Knoxville, PhD(physics), 64. *Prof Exp:* Mem tech staff compound semiconductor mat, Bell Tel Labs, 68-72, supvr compound semiconductor mat group, Bell Labs, 73-93. *Mem:* Am Phys Soc; Electrochem Soc; Sigma Xi. *Res:* Development of processes useful for production of epitaxial layers of semiconductor materials. *Mailing Add:* 12 Lincoln Circle E Red Bank NJ 07701-5815

**VEHSE, WILLIAM E,** physics; deceased, see previous edition for last biography

**VEICSTEINAS, ARSENIO,** TEMPERATURE REGULATION, ELECTRICITY. *Current Pos:* PROF PHYSIOL, UNIV BRESCIA, 87- *Personal Data:* b Bellano, Italy, Oct 9, 44; m 70; c 3. *Educ:* Univ Milan, Italy, Med Dr. *Prof Exp:* From asst prof to assoc prof physiol, Univ Milan, 71-87. *Concurrent Pos:* Chmn, Sch Specialization Sport Med, 88- *Mem:* Am Physiol Soc; Ital Physiol Soc. *Res:* Cardiorespiratory and metabolic changes during muscular exercise in healthy and disabled persons; temperature regulation in water immersion in humans; physiology of muscle contraction; effects of electromagnetic fields on animals; sport medicine. *Mailing Add:* Inst Physiol Umana Sch Med Univ Brescia Via Valsabbina 19 Brescia 25124 Italy. *Fax:* 39-30-3701157

**VEIDIS, MIKELIS VALDIS,** chemistry, for more information see previous edition

**VEIGA, ROBERT V,** FAMILY PRACTICE, PUBLIC HEALTH. *Current Pos:* MED CONSULT, OFF BUR PRIMARY HEALTH CARE, 96- *Personal Data:* b Stoughton, Mass, Oct 4, 46. *Educ:* Northeastern Univ, BA, 69; Chicago Med Sch, MD, 73; Johns Hopkins Univ, MPH, 76. *Prof Exp:* Dep dir clin affairs, Fed Occup Health, 93-96. *Concurrent Pos:* Adj prof, Bowie State Univ, 92- *Mem:* AMA; Nat Med Asn. *Mailing Add:* Bur Primary Health Care 4350 EW Hwy Bethesda MD 20814. *Fax:* 301-594-4072; *E-Mail:* rveiga@hrsa.ssw.dhhs.gov

**VEIGEL, JON MICHAEL,** SCIENCE POLICY, ENERGY POLICY. *Current Pos:* CHIEF EXEC OFFICER, SUN RUNNER ASSOC LIC, CEDAR CITY, UTAH, 97- *Personal Data:* b Mankato, Minn, Nov 10, 38; m 62, Carol J Bradley. *Educ:* Univ Wash, BS, 60; Univ Calif, Los Angeles, PhD(phys inorg chem), 65. *Prof Exp:* Res chemist, Jackson Lab, E I du Pont de Nemours & Co, Inc, Del, 65; asst prof phys inorg chem & res chemist, F J Seiler Res Lab, USAF Acad, 65-68; asst prof, Joint Sci Dept, Claremont Cols, 68-73; assoc prof energy & environ, Calif State Col, Domingue Hills, Calif, 73-74; dir energy prog & cong sci fel, Off Technol Assessment, US Cong, 74-75; adminr, Alternatives Div, Energy Comn, Sacramento, Calif, 75-78; chief mkt develop, Solar Energy Res Inst, Golden, Colo, 78-79, asst dir technol commercialization, 79, div mgr planning appln & impacts, 79-81; pres, Alternative Energy Corp, Res Triangle Park, NC, 81-88; pres, Oak Ridge Assoc Univs, Oak Ridge, Tenn, 88-96. *Concurrent Pos:* Mem, Synthesis Panel, Nat Acad Study Nuclear Power & Alternative Systs, 75-76; mem, Sci & Pub Policies Comt, AAAS, 75-79; mem, NC Energy Develop Authority, 83-88, chmn, 87-88; chmn, Oak Ridge Community Found, 89-92; bd mem, Alliance Environ Educ, 89-91, Am Coun Energy Efficient Econ, 89-, energy & eng bd, Nat Acad Sci & Eng, 89-; mem, bd trustees, Mendeleyev Univ, Moscow, Russia, 93-; mem bd dirs, Pac Int High Technol Res Ctr. *Mem:* AAAS. *Res:* National science policy; energy policy; technology assessment. *Mailing Add:* PO Box 2005 Cedar City UT 84721

**VEIGELE, WILLIAM JOHN,** PHYSICS. *Current Pos:* LECTR & VIS ASSOC PROF PHYSICS, MECH ENG, ELEC & COMPUTER ENG, NUCLEAR & CHEM ENG, UNIV CALIF, SANTA BARBARA, CALIF, 78- *Personal Data:* b New York, NY, June 18, 25; m 56; c 4. *Educ:* Hofstra Col, Hempstead, NY, BA, 49, MA, 51; Univ Colo, Boulder, PhD(physics), 60. *Prof Exp:* Testing engr, NY Testing Labs, 49-50; instr physics, Williams Col, Mass, 51-52; instr eng & physics, Hofstra Col, NY, 52-57; instr physics, Univ Colo, Boulder, 57-58; thermodynamicist, Cryogenic Sect, Nat Bur Stand, 58-59; prof & head, Physics Dept, Parsons Col, Iowa, 60-61; sr scientist, Solid State Physics Lab, Martin Marietta Aerospace Corp, 61-64; sr scientist & proj mgr, Kaman Sci Corp, 64-74; founder & pres, Resource Sci Inc, 74-78. *Concurrent Pos:* Lectr physics, Univ Colo, Colorado Springs, 66-77; prog mgr, sr scientist & prod line mgr, Santa Barbara Res Ctr, 78-84; dept dir & prog mgr, GRC, 84-89; consult, GRC, Santa Barbara, Calif, Raytheon Electromagnetics Systs Div, Santa Barbara, Calif, Santa Barbara Res Ctr, Goleta, Calif & Co of Santa Barbara; consult, Med Care & Res Found, Denver, Colo, Colo Dept Hwys, Denver, Colo Fairchild Camera & Instrument Corp, Long Island, NY & Elec & Comput Eng Dept, Univ Calif, Santa Barbara; NSF sci fac fel. *Mem:* Sigma Xi; Am Phys Soc; Am Asn Physics Teachers. *Res:* Radiation effects; solid state and atomic physics; thermodynamics; electrooptics; infrared technology; Monte Carlo photon transport codes; photon cross sections; three-phase equations of state; author of 75 publications. *Mailing Add:* 333 Old Mill Rd No 324 Santa Barbara CA 93110

**VEILLEUX, RICHARD ERNEST,** CELL CULTURE APPLICATIONS TO PLANT BREEDING, POTATO GENETICS. *Current Pos:* From asst prof to assoc prof, 81-92, PROF HORT, VA POLYTECH INST & STATE UNIV, 92- *Personal Data:* b Claremont, NH, Nov 15, 48; m 72, Karen Ziegelman; c Zachary & Micah. *Educ:* Tufts Univ, BS, 70; Univ BC, MSc 76; Univ Minn, PhD(hort), 81. *Concurrent Pos:* Consult, Univ Minn Mohacco Proj, 85-90;

prin investr, USDA competitive grant, 85-87, Jeffress trust, 86-87, BARD grant, 88-90 & 92-94, USDA Agr Res Serv, 91 & 93-94; vis prof, Univ Thessaloniki, Greece, 94. *Mem:* Am Soc Hort Sci; Potato Asn Am; Can Genetics Soc; Europ Asn Potato Res; Plant Molecular Biol Asn. *Res:* Application of cell culture techniques to potato breeding and genetics, including derivation and utilization of androgenic haploids, protoplast isolation, culture and fusion; plant germplasm development and enhancement. *Mailing Add:* Dept Hort Va Polytech Inst & State Univ Blacksburg VA 24061. *E-Mail:* potato@vt.edu

**VEILLON, CLAUDE,** ANALYTICAL CHEMISTRY, SPECTROSCOPY. *Current Pos:* RES CHEMIST, HUMAN NUTRIT RES CTR, 76- *Personal Data:* b Church Point, La, Jan 11, 40; m; c 2. *Educ:* Univ Southwestern La, BS, 62; Univ Fla, MS, 63, PhD(anal chem), 65. *Prof Exp:* Res chemist, Nat Bur Stand, 65-67; from asst prof to assoc prof anal chem, Univ Houston, 67-74; vis scientist, Harvard Med Sch, 74-76. *Concurrent Pos:* Nat Acad Sci-Nat Res Coun res assoc, 65-67; res fel, NIH/Nat Cancer Inst, 74-76. *Mem:* Am Chem Soc; Soc Appl Spectros; Optical Soc Am; Am Inst Physics. *Res:* Isotopic analysis; trace metal analysis; analytical instrumentation; trace metal metabolism. *Mailing Add:* USDA Bldg 307 Rm 226A Beltsville MD 20705

**VEINOTT, ARTHUR FALES, JR,** OPERATIONS RESEARCH. *Current Pos:* From asst prof to assoc prof indust eng, 62-67, chmn dept, 75-85, PROF OPERS RES, STANFORD UNIV, 67- *Personal Data:* b Boston, Mass, Oct 12, 34; m 60, 88; c 2. *Educ:* Lehigh Univ, BS & BA, 56; Columbia Univ, EngScD(indust eng), 60. *Concurrent Pos:* Western Mgt Sci Inst grant, 64-65; Off Naval Res contract, 64-80; consult, Rand Corp, 65- & IBM Res Ctr, 68-69; grant, NSF, 67-, mem, Res Intitiation Grant Panel, 71; vis prof, Yale Univ, 72-73; ed, J Math Opers Res, 74-80; Guggenheim fel, 78-79. *Mem:* Nat Acad Eng; Inst Mgt Sci; Opers Res Soc Am; fel Inst Math Statist. *Res:* Development of lattice programming, a qualitative theory of optimization for predicting the direction of change of optimal decisions resulting from alteration of problem parameters; structure and computation of optimal policies for inventory systems and dynamic programs. *Mailing Add:* Dept Eng Economic Syst Oper Res Stanford Univ Stanford CA 94305-4022

**VEINOTT, CYRIL G,** ACOUSTIC MEASUREMENTS OF MACHINES. *Current Pos:* PVT INDUST CONSULT, 70- *Personal Data:* b Somerville, Mass, Feb 15, 05; m 36; c 1. *Educ:* Univ Vt, BS, 26. *Hon Degrees:* DEng, Univ Vt, 51. *Honors & Awards:* Tesla Medal, Inst Elec & Electronics Engrs, 77, Centennial Medal, 84. *Prof Exp:* Mgr, Indust Sect, Westinghouse Elec Corp, 26-52; chief, AC Eng, Reliance Elec Co, 53-70; invited prof elec machs, Univ Laval, Que, 70-72; vol exec, Int Exec Serv Corps, 72-79. *Mem:* Inst Elec & Electronics Engrs (vpres, 49-51). *Res:* Investigation and development of tools and methods for the design of electric machinery; the use of digital computers using thenavaoluble mainframes and personal computers; author of books; holds US patent. *Mailing Add:* 4197 Oakhurst Circle W Sarasota FL 34233

**VEIRS, VAL RHODES,** INTELLIGENT SYSTEMS. *Current Pos:* asst prof, 71-80, ASSOC PROF PHYSICS, COLO COL, 80- *Personal Data:* b Allegan, Mich, Sept 20, 42; m 64; c 1. *Educ:* Case Inst Technol, BS, 64; Ill Inst Technol, PhD(physics), 69. *Prof Exp:* Res physicist, Zenith Radio Corp, 64-65; asst prof physics, Ill Inst Technol, 69-71. *Mem:* AAAS; Am Asn Physics Teachers. *Res:* Intelligent tutoring. *Mailing Add:* 1823 Wood Ave Colorado Springs CO 80907

**VEIS, ARTHUR,** BIOCHEMISTRY, PHYSICAL CHEMISTRY. *Current Pos:* assoc prof biochem, Northwestern Univ, Chicago, 60-65, asst dean grad affairs, 68-70, assoc dean med & grad schs, 70-76, chmn, Dept Oral Biol, Sch Dent, 77-93, PROF BIOCHEM, SCH MED, NORTHWESTERN UNIV, CHICAGO, 65-, PROF MOLECULAR BIOL, 80-, CHMN, DEPT BASIC & BEHAV SCI, 93- *Personal Data:* b Pittsburgh, Pa, Dec 23, 25; m 51, Eve Zenner; c Judith H, Sharon L & Deborah J. *Educ:* Univ Okla, BS, 47; Northwestern Univ, PhD(phys chem), 51. *Honors & Awards:* Biol Mineralization Award, Int Asn Den Res, 81. *Prof Exp:* Instr phys chem, Univ Okla, 51-52; res chemist, Dept Phys Chem, Armour & Co, 52-60, head dept, 59-60. *Concurrent Pos:* Spec instr, Crane Jr Col, 55-56 & Loyola Univ, 57-58; Guggenheim fel, 67; fel NIH Fogarty Sr Int Scholar Award, European Molecular Biol Lab, Grenoble & Weizmann Inst Sci, Rehovot, Israel, 77; chmn & mem spec prog adv comt, Nat Inst Dent Res, Dent Res Inst, 74-78; centennial scholar, Case Inst Technol, 80; distinguished vis prof, Univ Adelaide, Australia, 81; mem pathobiochem study sect, NIH, 83-87; chmn, Gordon Conf Chem & Biol Bones & Teeth, 85 & Gordon Conf Struct Macromolecules-Collagen, 81; pres, Int Conf Chem & Biol Mineralized Tissues, 89-95; ed-in-chief, Connective Tissue Res, 82- *Mem:* Am Chem Soc; Am Soc Biochem & Molecular Biol; Biophys Soc; NY Acad Sci; Int Asn Dent Res; fel AAAS. *Res:* Physical chemistry and biology of the connective tissue systems; colloid chemistry; biological mineralization; study of the connective tissue macromolecules, particularly the collagens and the phosphorylated proteins of mineralized tissues; mechanism of biomineralization. *Mailing Add:* Dept Basic Sci Northwestern Univ Dent Sch Chicago IL 60611. *Fax:* 312-503-2544

**VEIT, BRUCE CLINTON,** MICROBIOLOGY, IMMUNOLOGY. *Current Pos:* CHIEF SECT IMMUNOL & MICROBIOL, DEPT CLIN INVEST, WILLIAM BEAUMONT ARMY MED CTR, 84-; ASSOC PROF BIOL, UNIV TEX, EL PASO, 85- *Personal Data:* b Cleveland, Ohio, Aug 22, 42; div; c Heather & Brian. *Educ:* Univ Cincinnati, PhD(microbiol), 72. *Prof Exp:* Asst mem, Dept Immunol, St Jude Childrens Res Hosp, Memphis, Tenn, 76-84. *Concurrent Pos:* Asst adj prof, Ctr Health Sci, Univ Tenn, 78-84. *Res:* Immuno-regulation in allergy; measles immunity; apoptosis and growth factor regulation in breast cancer; PCR detection of human papilloma virus in gynecologic tissues and mycobacteria in crown's disease. *Mailing Add:* Dept Clin Invest William Beaumont Army Med Ctr 5005 N Piedras St El Paso TX 79920-5001. *Fax:* 915-569-1500; *E-Mail:* veit@mail.utep.edu

**VEIT, JIRI JOSEPH,** optics, nuclear physics, for more information see previous edition

**VEITCH, FLETCHER PEARRE, JR,** ENZYME ISOLATION, ENZYME KINETICS. *Current Pos:* prof, 47-74, EMER PROF BIOCHEM, UNIV MD, 75- *Personal Data:* b College Park, Md, Dec 21, 08; m 39, Marian Morton; c Fletcher P III & Michael M. *Educ:* Univ Md, BS, 31, MS, 33, PhD(org chem), 35. *Prof Exp:* Res chemist, Nat Canners Asn, 35-37; asst prof biochem, Sch Med, Georgetown Univ, 37-47. *Mem:* Sigma Xi; Am Chem Soc; AAAS. *Res:* Hormones and enzymes. *Mailing Add:* Box 513 Lexington Park MD 20653-0513

**VEITH, DANIEL A,** SOLID STATE PHYSICS. *Current Pos:* PROF PHYSICS, NICHOLLS STATE UNIV, 67- *Personal Data:* b Metairie, La, Apr 18, 36; m 56; c 2. *Educ:* Tulane Univ, BS, 56, PhD(physics), 63; Univ Calif, Los Angeles, MS, 58. *Prof Exp:* Mem tech staff, Hughes Aircraft Co, 56-59; sci specialist, Space Div, Chrysler Corp, 63-67. *Res:* Nucleation and growth of thin crystalline films. *Mailing Add:* Dept Phys Sci Nicholls State Univ Thibodaux LA 70310-2003. *Fax:* 504-448-4927; *E-Mail:* phyc-dav@nich-nsunet.nich.edu

**VEITH, FRANK JAMES,** SURGERY, TRANSPLANTATION BIOLOGY. *Current Pos:* assoc prof, 67-71, PROF SURG, ALBERT EINSTEIN COL MED, 71-; ATTEND SURG & CHIEF VASCULAR SURG, MONTEFIORE HOSP, 72- *Personal Data:* b New York, NY, Aug 29, 31. *Educ:* Cornell Univ, AB, 52, MD, 55. *Prof Exp:* NIH fel, Harvard Med Sch, 63-64; asst prof surg, Cornell Univ, 64-67. *Concurrent Pos:* Markle scholar acad med, Cornell Univ, Albert Einstein Col Med & Montefiore Hosp, 64-69; career scientist award, Health Res Coun, New York & Montefiore Hosp, 65-72; assoc attend surgeon, Montefiore Hosp, 67-71; co-dir, Kidney Transplant Unit, Montefiore Hosp, 67-76, dir, 76-89, interim chmn, Dept Surg, 91-92; consult, Heart-Lung Proj Comt, 71- *Mem:* Soc Univ Surgeons; Soc Vascular Surg; Am Surg Asn; Eastern Vascular Soc; Soc Clin Vascular Surg; Southern Asn Vascular Surg. *Res:* Limb salvage and endovascular stented grafts repair for the treatment of arterial occlusive traumatic onysmal lesions. *Mailing Add:* Dept Surg Albert Einstein Col Med 111 E 210th St Bronx NY 10467. *Fax:* 718-231-9811

**VEIZER, JÁN,** EARTH SCIENCE, GEOCHEMISTRY. *Current Pos:* NORANDA/CIAR PROF GEOL, UNIV OTTAWA, CAN, 73-; PROF & CHAIR GEOL, RUHR UNIV, BOCHUM, GER, 88- *Personal Data:* b Pobedim, Slovakia, June 22, 41; Can citizen; m 66, Elena Ondrus; c Robert & Andrew. *Educ:* Comenius Univ, Slovakia, PG, 64, RNDr, 68; Slovak Acad Sci, Slovakia, CSc, 68; Australian Nat Univ, PhD(geochem), 71. *Honors & Awards:* Killam Res Prof, Can Res Coun, 86; Past-Pres Medal, Geol Asn Can, 87, Logan Medal, 95; Willet G Miller Medal, Royal Soc Can, 91; Gottfried W Leibniz Prize, Ger. *Prof Exp:* Lectr, Comenius Univ, Slovakia, 63-66; res sci geol, Slovak Acad Sci, Slovakia, 66-71; vis asst prof, Univ Calif, Los Angeles, 72; vis res scientist geochem, Univ Gottingen, WGer, 72-73; res scientist geol, Univ Tubingen, WGer, 73. *Concurrent Pos:* Vis prof, Univ Tubingen, WGer, 74, Northwestern Univ, 83; vis fel, Australian Nat Univ, 79; consult, NASA, 83-87; Lady Davis prof, Hebrew Univ, Israel, 87. *Mem:* Fel Royal Soc Can; fel Geol Asn Can; fel Geol Soc Am; Geochem Soc Am; Int Geochem Soc. *Res:* Evolution of sedimentation, atmosphere and life in geologic history; environmental geochemistry, aquatic systems. *Mailing Add:* Dept Geol Univ Ottawa Ottawa ON K1N 6N5 Can. *Fax:* 613-562-5192; *E-Mail:* veizer@geol.uottawa.ca

**VEJVODA, EDWARD,** INDUSTRIAL CHEMISTRY. *Current Pos:* PRIN ENGR, LOS ALAMOS TECH ASSOCS, 89- *Personal Data:* b New York, NY, Apr 18, 24; m 49, Mary E Smith; c Mary D (Astley), Karl S & Mary E (Smith). *Educ:* Univ Northern Colo, BA, 49, MA, 51. *Prof Exp:* Anal chemist, Anal Labs, Dow Chem Co, 52-56, res chemist, 56-60, sr res chemist, Res & Develop Labs, 60-62, anal supvr, 62-64, anal proj supvr, Dow Chem Int, Ger, 64-65, res staff asst, Chem-Physics Res & Develop Labs, 65-68, res mgr, Chem Res & Develop, 68-75, sr res mgr, 75-81; chem opers dir, Rockwell Int, 75-81, plutonium opers dir, 82-87; consult, Lamb Assoc & Actinide Process Chem & Plutonium Recovery & Nuclear Mat Mgt, 87-89. *Mem:* Am Chem Soc; Sigma Xi; Inst Nuclear Mat Mgt. *Res:* Actinide chemistry; development of analytical methods for the assay and impurity analysis of the actinide elements; process development for the separation and purification of plutonium compounds; radioactive waste management and nuclear materials storage and control. *Mailing Add:* 2625 Juilliard St Boulder CO 80303

**VELA, ADAN RICHARD,** PHYSIOLOGY. *Current Pos:* asst prof surg, 63-71, ASSOC PROF SURG, SCH MED, MED CTR, LA STATE UNIV, 71- *Personal Data:* b Laredo, Tex, Oct 28, 30; m 55; c 4. *Educ:* Baylor Univ, BS, 52; Univ Tenn, PhD(physiol) 62. *Prof Exp:* Res assoc data anal, Comput Ctr, Univ Tenn, 63. *Mem:* Sigma Xi; Am Physiol Soc; Gastrointestinal Res Group. *Res:* Gastrointestinal physiology; esophageal motility; small intestine motility; andrectal manometry endotoxin. *Mailing Add:* 5024 Tartan Dr Metairie LA 70003-2550

**VELA, GERARD ROLAND,** MICROBIOLOGY, ENVIRONMENTAL SCIENCE. *Current Pos:* RETIRED. *Personal Data:* b Eagle Pass, Tex, Sept 18, 27; m 53, Emma L Codina; c Jerry, Anna M, Yolanda & Jaime. *Educ:* Univ Tex, BA, 50, MA, 51, PhD(microbiol), 63. *Prof Exp:* Res asst, Univ Tex, 50-51; res asst biochem, Southwest Found Res, 52-54; res asst immunol, Sch Pub Health, Harvard Univ, 54-57; head clin chemist, Santa Rosa Hosp, San Antonio, Tex, 57-59; res microbiologist, USAF Sch Aerospace Med, 59-65; from asst prof to prof microbiol, NTex State Univ, 65-85, assoc dean, Sci-Tech A&S, 85-90. *Concurrent Pos:* Fulbright lectr, Bogota, Colombia, 72; ed, Tex J Sci, 75-83; adj prof microbiol, Univ Monterey, Nuevo Leon, Mex, Univ Granada, Spain, Univ Tex, Austin, Univ Chihuahua, Mex. *Mem:* Am Acad Microbiol; Am Soc Microbiol; Soc Gen Microbiol; Can Soc Microbiol; AAAS; Sigma Xi; Am Asn Univ Prof. *Res:* Nature of microorganisms in their natural habitat; biochemical interrelationships in mixed cultures of microorganisms; physiology and morphology of azotobacter; microbiology of industrial waste-waters; radiation effects on microorganisms; ATP-ADP-AMP kinetics. *Mailing Add:* Dept Biol Sci Univ NTex Denton TX 76203. *Fax:* 817-565-3821

**VELAPOLDI, R A,** SYNTHETIC, INORGANIC & ORGANOMETALLIC CHEMISTRY. *Current Pos:* DIV CHIEF, SURFACE & MICROANAL SCI DIV, NAT INST SCI & TECHNOL, 88- *Personal Data:* b White Plains, NY, Oct 24, 38. *Educ:* Univ Conn, BS, 60; Ohio Univ, PhD(chem), 65. *Mailing Add:* Nat Inst Sci & Technol Chem B364 Rte 270 Gaithersburg MD 20899

**VELARDO, JOSEPH THOMAS,** PHYSIOLOGY, MORPHOLOGICAL SCIENCES. *Current Pos:* CONSULT BIOSCIENTIST, 88- *Personal Data:* b Newark, NJ, Jan 27, 23; wid. *Educ:* Univ Northern Colo, AB, 48; Miami Univ, SM, 49; Harvard Univ, PhD(biol, physiol, endocrinol), 52. *Honors & Awards:* Rubin Award, Am Soc Study Steril, 55. *Prof Exp:* Res asst org & inorg chem, Univ Northern Colo, 47-48; asst & instr zool & human heredity, Miami Univ, 48-49; teaching & res fel, biol & endocrinol & histochem morphol, Harvard Univ, 49-52, res fel biol & endocrinol, 52-53, res assoc path, Sch Med, 53-54, res assoc surg, 54-55; asst prof anat, Sch Med, Yale Univ, 55-61, Lederle Med Fac Award, 55-58; prof & chmn dept anat, NY Med Col, 61-62; dir, Inst Study Human Reproduction & dir educ prog, 62-67; chmn dept, Stritch Sch Med, Loyola Univ, Chicago, 67-73, prof anat, 67-88. *Concurrent Pos:* Asst surg, Peter Bent Brigham & Women's Hosp, Boston, 54-55; Lederle med fac award, 55-58; prof biol, John Carroll Univ, 62-67; US deleg, Int Cong Reproduction, Vatican, 64; head, Dept Res, St Ann Hosp, Cleveland, 64-67; pres, Midwest Asn anat, 73-74; hon vpres, res, develop & educ, Univ Res Systs, 73-82; pres & dir res & develop, Univ Res Systs, Lombard, Ill, 79-; dir biomed, Curric Consult, 83-; mem adv coun, Int Biographical Centre, Cambridge, Eng, 90- *Mem:* Brit Soc Endocrinol; Endocrine Soc; fel Geront Soc; Am Physiol Soc; fel NY Acad Sci; fel AAAS; Am Asn Anat; Soc Zool; Pan Am Asn Anat; Midwest Asn Anatomists (pres, 73-74). *Res:* Endocrinology of reproduction; anatomy, physiology, biochemistry, molecular biology, histochemistry and cytochemistry of reproductive organs; molecular interactions and steroid-gonadotropic hormone interrelationships-induction in ovulation; zoology; research administration; science education; science policy, educational administration. *Mailing Add:* 607 E Wilson Rd Old Grove East Lombard IL 60148-4062

**VELECKIS, EWALD,** CHEMISTRY. *Current Pos:* RETIRED. *Personal Data:* b Kybartai, Lithuania, Aug 1, 26; US citizen; m 55, Cese Povilaitis; c Linda. *Educ:* Univ Ill, BS, 53; Ill Inst Technol, MS, 57, PhD(chem), 60. *Prof Exp:* Chemist, Argonne Nat Lab, 59-89. *Res:* Phase equilibria in inorganic systems; molecular beams; alloy thermodynamics; metallic solutions and liquid state; fusion reactors; metal hydrides; hydrogen storage. *Mailing Add:* 23 Ruggles Ct Orland Park IL 60462. *E-Mail:* eveleckis@msn.com

**VELENYI, LOUIS JOSEPH,** CATALYSIS, FUELS TECHNOLOGY. *Current Pos:* RES SCIENTIST, BP AM, 88- *Personal Data:* b Budapest, Hungary, June 17, 34; US citizen; m 57; c 3. *Educ:* Case Western Res Univ, BA, 70, PhD(chem), 75. *Prof Exp:* Res asst clin chemist, Case Western Res Univ, Highland View Hosp, 62-72; proj leader, chemist, Stand Oil Co, Ohio, 75-87. *Mem:* Am Chem Soc; Sigma Xi. *Res:* Synthesis and nuclear magnetic resonance study of porphyrins and phthalocyanines; catalysis of various reactions; carbon chemistry; fuels technology. *Mailing Add:* 1266 Roland Rd Cleveland OH 44124-1274

**VELETSOS, A(NESTIS),** CIVIL ENGINEERING, STRUCTURAL ENGINEERING & MECHANICS. *Current Pos:* prof & chmn, Dept Eng, 64-72, BROWN & ROOT PROF ENG, RICE UNIV, 66- *Personal Data:* b Istanbul, Turkey, Apr 28, 27; nat US; m 66, Katherine Economou; c Ann Marie & Melinda. *Educ:* Robert Col, Istanbul, BS, 48; Univ Ill, Urbana, MS, 50, PhD(civil eng), 53. *Honors & Awards:* Norman Medal, Am Soc Civil Engrs, 59 & 90, Res Prize, 61, Newmark Medal, 78, Howard Award, 90; Housner Medal, Earthquake Eng Res Inst, 97. *Prof Exp:* From asst prof to prof civil eng, Univ Ill, Urbana, 53-64, assoc mem, Ctr Advan Study, 61-62. *Concurrent Pos:* Struct designer, F L Ehasz, NY, 50 & Skidmore, Owings & Merrill, Ill, 53; consult, 53-; NSF consult, Indian Inst Technol, Bombay, 69; mem, Earthquake Eng Res Inst, vpres, 74-77; vis prof, Cath Univ Rio de Janeiro & Unif Calif, Berkeley, 77; chmn, US Joint Comt Earthquake Eng, 77-80; mem, Eng Mech Div, Am Soc Civil Engrs, 84-88. *Mem:* Nat Acad Eng; Am Soc Civil Engrs; Seismol Soc Am; Int Asn Bridge & Struct Engrs; Earthquake Eng Res Inst. *Res:* Structural engineering and mechanics, particularly dynamics of structures and earthquake engineering; offshore structures. *Mailing Add:* Dept Civil Eng Rice Univ PO Box 1892 Houston TX 77251-1892. *Fax:* 713-285-5268

**VELEZ, SAMUEL JOSE,** NEUROPHYSIOLOGY. *Current Pos:* asst prof, 76-82, ASSOC PROF BIOL SCI, DARTMOUTH COL, 82- *Personal Data:* b San Juan, PR, July 19, 45; m 67, Myrna Agostini; c Lisanne, Karin, Darik & Kevin. *Educ:* Univ PR, BS, 66, MS, 69; Yale Univ, PhD(neurophysiol), 74. *Prof Exp:* Instr biol, Univ PR, 66; biologist, US Naval Sta, San Juan, PR, 66 & 67-68; res asst pharmacol, Sch Med, Univ PR, 67-68; teaching asst neurophysiol, Yale Univ, 70 & 71; NIH fel zool, Univ Tex, Austin, 74-76. *Mem:* AAAS; Soc Neurosci; Sigma Xi. *Res:* Patterns of neuronal connections; nerve-muscle trophic interactions; facilitation at the neuromuscular junction; regeneration of neuromuscular connections; developmental neurobiology; synaptic plasticity. *Mailing Add:* Dept Biol Sci Dartmouth Col Hanover NH 03755. *Fax:* 603-646-1347

**VELEZ, WILLIAM YSLAS,** NUMBER THEORY, ALGEBRA. *Current Pos:* asst prof, 77-80, ASSOC PROF MATH, UNIV ARIZ, 81- *Personal Data:* b Tucson, Ariz, Jan 15, 47; m 68; c 2. *Educ:* Univ Ariz, BS, 68, MS, 72, PhD(math), 75. *Prof Exp:* Mem tech staff math, Sandia Labs, 75-77. *Concurrent Pos:* Prog dir, Algebra & Number Theory Prog, NSF, 92-93. *Mem:* Am Math Soc; Math Asn Am; Soc Advan Chicanos & Native Am Sci. *Res:* Elementary and algebraic number theory; field theory. *Mailing Add:* Dept Math Univ Ariz Tucson AZ 85721. *Fax:* 520-621-8322; *E-Mail:* velez@math.arizona.edu

**VELICK, SIDNEY FREDERICK,** BIOCHEMISTRY. *Current Pos:* prof & head dept, 64-79, EMER PROF BIOL CHEM, COL MED, UNIV UTAH, 88- *Personal Data:* b Detroit, Mich, May 3, 13; m 41; c 2. *Educ:* Wayne State Univ, BS, 35; Univ Mich, MS, 36, PhD(biol chem), 38. *Honors & Awards:* Sr Alexander von Humboldt Award, 73. *Prof Exp:* Rockefeller Found fel, Johns Hopkins Univ, 39-40; Int Cancer Res Found fel, Yale Univ, 41-45; from asst prof to prof biol chem, Sch Med, Wash Univ, 45-64. *Concurrent Pos:* Mem, Biochem Study Sect, NIH, 65-69; assoc ed, Archives Biochem. *Mem:* Nat Acad Sci; Am Soc Biol Chemists; Am Chem Soc; AAAS. *Res:* Bacterial lipids; protein chemistry and metabolism; mechanism of enzyme action. *Mailing Add:* 4183 Parkview Dr Salt Lake City UT 84124

**VELIKHOV, YENGENIY PAVLOVICH,** PHYSICS. *Current Pos:* PRES, RUSS ACAD SCI, MOSCOW. *Honors & Awards:* Leo Szilard Award, Am Phys Soc, 95. *Mailing Add:* Kurchatov Inst Atomic Energy Bolshaya Tulkskaya Ulitsa 62 Moscow 113191 Russia

**VELIKY, IVAN ALOIS,** BIOLOGICAL CHEMISTRY. *Current Pos:* PRES, TIVELCO INT INC, 90- *Personal Data:* b Zilina, Czech, Mar 23, 29; m 52; c 2. *Educ:* Slovak Tech Univ, Bratislava, EngC, 50, DiplEng, 52; Slovak Acad Sci, PhD, 60. *Prof Exp:* From asst prof to assoc prof biochem, Slovak Tech Univ, Bratislava, 52-65; fel, Prairie Regional Lab, Nat Res Coun Can, 65-67, assoc res officer, 67-75, sr res officer, Div Biol Sci, 75-90. *Concurrent Pos:* Sr sci adv & consult mem, Sci Adv Bd. *Mem:* Chem Inst Can; Can Biochem Soc; Int Asn Plant Tissue Cult; Can Soc Microbiologists. *Res:* Physiology and biochemistry of microorganisms; physiology of cell growth in suspension cultures (fermentors); biosynthesis of secondary metabolites and biotransformation of biologically active compounds by cell cultures; immobilized cells and proteins; synthesis of surfactants, fine chemicals; cosmetics; skin and hair care products; formulations. *Mailing Add:* Tivelco Int Inc 613 Fielding Dr Ottawa ON K1V 7G7 Can. *Fax:* 613-731-2189; *E-Mail:* iveliky@fox.nstn.ca

**VELLA, FRANCIS,** BIOCHEMISTRY, GENETICS. *Current Pos:* RETIRED. *Personal Data:* b Malta, July 24, 29; m 56, Lena Goss; c Celia, Rosalind, Mark, Pauline & Darwin. *Educ:* Royal Univ Malta, BSc, 49, MD, 52; Oxford Univ, BA, 54, MA, 58; Univ Singapore, PhD(biochem), 62. *Hon Degrees:* DSc, Univ Malta, 89. *Honors & Awards:* Chevalier, Order of St Sylvester, Vatican City, Italy, 65. *Prof Exp:* Asst lectr biochem, Univ Singapore, 56-57, lectr, 57-60; sr lectr, Univ Khartoum, 60-64, reader biochem genetics, 64-65; vis assoc prof biochem, Univ Sask, 65-66, from assoc prof to prof chem, 66-96. *Concurrent Pos:* Tutor, WHO Lab Course in Abnorm Hemoglobins, Ibadan, Nigeria, 63; lectr, NATO Advan Course in Pop Genetics, Rome, Italy, 64; vis prof biochem, Univ Cambridge, 73-74; mem, Comt Educ, Int Union Biochem, 79-, chmn, Comt on Educ, 83-; external examr & vis prof, El Fateh Univ, Libya, 80-, Kuwait Univ, 81-; chmn, Comt Educ, Int Union Biochem, 82-91; numerous workshops on biochem educ. *Res:* Molecular genetics; abnormal human hemoglobins; hereditary enzyme deficiencies in man; teaching methods in biochemistry. *Mailing Add:* Dept Biochem Univ Sask Saskatoon SK S7N 0W0 Can. *Fax:* 306-966-8718

**VELLACCIO, FRANK,** BIO-ORGANIC CHEMISTRY. *Current Pos:* asst prof chem, Col Holy Cross, 74-81, dean, 86-87, vpres acad affairs, 87-95, ASSOC PROF CHEM, COL HOLY CROSS, 81-, PROVOST, 96- *Personal Data:* b New Haven, Conn, Sept 24, 48; m 70, Cathy; c Jessica, Amanda, Jacob, Samantha & Adia. *Educ:* Fordham Univ, BS, 70; Mass Inst Technol, PhD(org chem), 74. *Mem:* Sigma Xi; Am Chem Soc. *Res:* Synthetic methods for peptide synthesis; intromolecular acyl transfers. *Mailing Add:* Provost's Off Col Holy Cross Worcester MA 01610. *Fax:* 508-793-3723; *E-Mail:* provost@holycross.edu

**VELLA-COLEIRO, GEORGE,** PHYSICS. *Current Pos:* Mem tech staff physics, 67-80, SUPVR, BELL LABS, 80- *Personal Data:* b Malta, Mar 15, 41. *Educ:* Royal Univ Malta, BSc, 61; Oxford Univ, MA, 63, DPhil(physics), 67. *Concurrent Pos:* Rhodes Scholar, 61-64. *Mem:* Am Phys Soc; Inst Elec & Electronics Engrs. *Res:* Magnetism; semiconductors; Josephson devices. *Mailing Add:* Lucent Tech 3F220 67 Whippany Rd Whippany NJ 07981

**VELLEKAMP, GARY JOHN,** PROTEINS. *Current Pos:* sr scientist, 87-90, PRIN SCIENTIST, SCHERING-PLOUGH RES, 91- *Personal Data:* b Englewood, NJ, May 29, 51. *Educ:* Hartwick Col, Oneonta, BA, 73; State Univ NY, Binghamton, MA, 78, PhD(biol sci), 82. *Prof Exp:* Postdoctoral, State Univ NY, Binghamton, 82-83 & Univ Conn Health Ctr, 83-87. *Mem:* Am Soc Biochem & Molecular Biol; Protein Soc; AAAS; Am Chem Soc. *Res:* Protein purification processes for potential human therapeutics. *Mailing Add:* Schering-Plough Corp U-13-117 1011 Morris Ave Union NJ 07083-7120. *Fax:* 908-820-6785

**VELLEMAN, DANIEL JON,** SET THEORY, PHILOSOPHY OF MATHEMATICS. *Current Pos:* PROF MATH, AMHERST COL, 83- *Personal Data:* b Manhasset, NY, Aug 10, 54; m 79, Shelley L Jeffery. *Educ:* Dartmouth Col, BA, 76; Univ Wis, PhD(math), 80. *Honors & Awards:* Lester R Ford Award, Math Asn Am, 94; Carl B Allendoerfer Award, 96. *Prof Exp:* Instr math, Univ Tex, Austin, 80-83. *Concurrent Pos:* Vis asst prof math, Univ Toronto, 82; prin investr, NSF, 82-87. *Mem:* Am Math Soc; Math Asn Am; Asn Symbolic Logic. *Res:* Set theory: morasses; constructivism and natural numbers; author of book on mathematical proofs and papers on problems in combinatorics, probability and topology. *Mailing Add:* Math & Comput Sci Amherst Col Amherst MA 01002. *E-Mail:* djvelleman@amherst.edu

**VELLETRI, PAUL A,** HEALTH SCIENCE ADMINISTRATION. *Current Pos:* sr staff fel, Nat Inst Gen Med Sci, NIH, 83-84, prog adminr pharmacol, 85-89, health sci adminr, Nat Heart Lung Blood Inst, 89-91, prog adminr, 91-93, dep chief, Hypertension & Kidney Dis Br, 93-94, chief, 94-95, HYPERTENSION RES GROUP LEADER, NAT HEART LUNG BLOOD INST, 95- *Personal Data:* b 1950; m 72, Ann Knox. *Educ:* George Washington Univ, PhD(pharmacol), 81. *Mem:* Am Soc Pharmacol & Exp Therapeut; AAAS; Am Heart Asn. *Res:* Angiotensin-converting enzyme; hypertension; molecular pharmacology; neurobiology. *Mailing Add:* Hypertension Res Group-Vascular Res Prog Div Heart & Vascular Dis 6701 Rockledge Dr Bethesda MD 20892-7456

**VELLTURO, ANTHONY FRANCIS,** APPLIED CHEMISTRY, ORGANIC CHEMISTRY. *Current Pos:* CONSULT, 91- *Personal Data:* b Ansonia, Conn, Dec 3, 36; m 76, Barbara Parisi. *Educ:* Yale Univ, BS, 58, MS, 59, PhD(org chem), 62. *Prof Exp:* NIH fel, Tulane Univ, La, 64-65; sr res chemist, Techni-Chem Co, Conn, 65-70; sr develop chemist, Ciba-Geigy Corp, 70-73, group leader, 73-77, mgr, Tech Dept, 77-85, prod mgr, 85-87, sr staff scientist, 87-91. *Mem:* Am Chem Soc. *Res:* Reaction mechanisms; synthetic organic chemistry; synthesis and reactions of small ring, strained systems. *Mailing Add:* RR 3 Box 1007A Bethel VT 05032

**VELTMAN, JAMES C,** PHARMACOLOGY. *Current Pos:* RES SCIENTIST CELL CULT, ALCON LABS INC, 88- *Personal Data:* b Chicago, Ill, Feb 16, 51. *Educ:* Loyola Univ, BS, 74, MS, 79; Univ Ill, PhD(pharmacol), 86. *Prof Exp:* Fel pharmacol, Univ Rochester, 86-88. *Mem:* Am Chem Soc; Am Soc Biochem & Molecular Biol; AAAS; NY Acad Sci. *Mailing Add:* Toxicol Res & Develop R3-22 Alcon Labs Inc 6201 S Freeway Fort Worth TX 76134

**VELTMAN, MARTINUS J,** PHYSICS. *Current Pos:* JOHN D MACARTHUR PROF PHYSICS, UNIV MICH, ANN ARBOR. *Honors & Awards:* High Energy & Particle Physics Prize, Europ Physics Soc, 93. *Mailing Add:* Dept Physics Univ Mich 500 E University Ave Ann Arbor MI 48108-1105

**VELTRI, ROBERT WILLIAM,** CANCER RESEARCH & IMMUNOPHARMACEUTICALS, UROLOGY ONCOLOGY & IMAGE ANALYSIS. *Current Pos:* vpres res & develop & chief sci officer, 90-94, VPRES & GEN MGR, CYTO DIAG, 94- *Personal Data:* b McKeesport, Pa, Dec 1, 41; m 62, Suzanne Jones; c Anthony J & Katherine M (deceased). *Educ:* Youngstown Univ, BA, 63; WVa Univ, MS, 65, PhD(microbiol), 68. *Prof Exp:* Asst prof microbiol, Med Ctr, WVa Univ, 68-72, dir otolaryngic res, Div Otolaryngol, 68-81, assoc prof, 72-75, prof microbiol & otolaryngol, 76-81; dir res & develop, Cooper Biomed Inc, 81-84; pres & co-founder, Am Biotechnol Co, 84-88; exec vpres & chief sci officer, Theracel, 88-90. *Concurrent Pos:* Immunol consult, Dent Sci Inst, Univ Tex, Houston, 72-74; regional dir, Cancer Res Lab, Nat Found Cancer Res, 79-86; vis prof microbiol, Univ Chile, Santiago, 81; adj prof path, Okla Univ Health Sci, 93-; Uvo Sci Group, Uvo Cov, Inc, Okla. *Mem:* AAAS; Sigma Xi; Am Soc Microbiol; Am Asn Cancer Res; Am Asn Immunol; Soc Basic Urol Res; Licensing Exec Soc; Asn Univ Technol Mgrs. *Res:* Role of tonsils in immunobiology; virology and immunology of herpesvirus infections; microbiology and immunology of otolaryngic infections; isolation and identification of human tumor-associated antigens; Epstein-Barr virus-host relationships; development of synthetic butyvolactone immunopharmaceuticals; patents issued and pending in field of immunopharmaceuticals, anti cancer therapy; immunodiagnostics; drug delivery immunodiagnostic assays for cancer; quantitative cell morphometry for cell identification; three-dimensional in vitro tumor modeling; gene discovery using RNA fingerprinting; molecular diagnostics. *Mailing Add:* 7301 NE 106th St Oklahoma City OK 73151. *E-Mail:* vveltri@ionet.net

**VELU, JOHN G,** NUTRITION. *Current Pos:* RES SPECIALIST, UNIV ILL, 66- *Personal Data:* b Bombay, India, Feb 7, 27. *Educ:* Univ India, BS, 50; Univ Ill, MS, 59, PhD(nutrit), 66. *Prof Exp:* Prof animal sci, Univ India, 59-66. *Mem:* Am Inst Nutrit; Fedn Am Socs Exp Biol. *Mailing Add:* Plant & Animal Biotech Lab Rm 228 PABL Univ Ill Col Agr 1201 W Gregory Dr Urbana IL 61801-4726

**VEMULA, SUBBARAO,** FRICTION, DESIGNS. *Current Pos:* RETIRED. *Personal Data:* b Andhra Pradesh, India, Dec 30, 24; m 56, Sarojini; c 2. *Educ:* Rensselaer Polytech Inst, MS, 68, PhD(mech), 74. *Prof Exp:* Jr civil engr design bridges, Struct Eng Resource & Syst Group, 77-79, asst civil engr, 79-81, civil engr II, 81-93. *Mem:* Am Soc Mech Engrs. *Res:* Friction. *Mailing Add:* 27 Pinehurst Ave Albany NY 12205

**VEMURI, SURYANARAYANA (SURI),** ELECTRIC POWER SYSTEM ANALYSIS. *Current Pos:* PRIN ENGR, HARRIS CONTROLS DIV, 79- *Personal Data:* b Dec 23, 43; m 68; c 2. *Educ:* Osmania Univ, BE, 65; Indian Inst Sci, ME, 68; Univ NB, MScE, 70, PhD(elec eng), 75. *Honors & Awards:* Elec Power Res Inst Award. *Prof Exp:* Res assoc, Univ NB, 73-75; asst prof, Univ Alaska, Fairbanks, 75-76; asst prof elec eng, Univ Nebr, 77-79. *Concurrent Pos:* Consult, Lincoln Elec Syst, 78; adj prof, Fla Inst Technol, 79-; NSF grant. *Mem:* Inst Elec & Electronics Engrs. *Res:* Computer modeling and analysis of electric power systems; optimum operation of power systems including network analysis, unit maintenance scheduling, thermal and hydro resource scheduling over long term, short term and daily problems; unit commitment and load forecasting. *Mailing Add:* Harris Controls Div Harris Corp PO Box 430 Melbourne FL 32901. *Fax:* 407-242-4379; *E-Mail:* suv@ccd.harris.com

**VEMURI, VENKATESWARARAO,** DISTRIBUTED PROCESSING, ARTIFICIAL NEURAL NETWORKS. *Current Pos:* PROF, DEPT APPL SCI, UNIV CALIF, DAVIS, 85-, VCHAIR, 95- *Personal Data:* b Chodavaram, India, Jan 17, 38; m 65; c 3. *Educ:* Andhra Univ, India, BE, 58; Univ Detroit, MS, 63; Univ Calif, PhD(eng), 68. *Prof Exp:* Tech asst elec testing, Bhilai Steel Works, India, 58-61; jr engr, RCA, 63-64; systs analyst, Environ Dynamics, Inc, 68-69; asst res engr, Univ Calif, Los Angeles, 69-70; asst prof aeronaut, astronaut & eng sci, Purdue Univ, 70-73; assoc prof comput sci, State Univ NY, Binghamton, 73-81; mem tech staff, TRW, Redondo Beach, Calif, 81-85. *Concurrent Pos:* Res engr, Univ Southern Calif, 68-69 & Lawrence Livermore Nat Lab, 85; lectr, Asn Comput Mach, 93-94. *Mem:* Asn Comput Mach; Inst Elec & Electronics Engrs. *Res:* Computational methods and computer architecture; distributed processing; modeling and simulation; artificial neural networks; genetic algorithms. *Mailing Add:* Univ Calif PO Box 808 L 794 Livermore CA 94550. *E-Mail:* vemuri1@llnl.gov

**VENABLE, D LAWRENCE,** ECOLOGY, BIOCHEMISTRY. *Current Pos:* From asst prof to assoc prof, 81-94, PROF, DEPT ECOL & EVOLUTIONARY BIOL, UNIV ARIZ, 94- *Personal Data:* b Cincinnati, Ohio, June 10, 51. *Educ:* Grinnell Col, BA, 73; Univ Tex, Austin, PhD(bot), 79. *Concurrent Pos:* Grantee, NSF, 86-90, 91-94 & 95- & Nat Geog Soc, 89-91 & 93-95; Lady Davis vis prof bot, Hewbrew Univ, Jerusalem, 89 & Univ Paris, 90; Fulbright fel, 95-96. *Mem:* Ecol Soc Am; Am Soc Naturalists; Brit Ecol Soc; Mex Bot Soc; Soc Study Evolution. *Mailing Add:* Dept Ecol Univ Ariz Biosci West Rm 310 Tucson AZ 85721. *E-Mail:* dlv@ccit.arizona.edu

**VENABLE, DOUGLAS,** PHYSICS. *Current Pos:* RETIRED. *Personal Data:* b Charleston, WVa, Aug 17, 20; m 88, Mary R Kerslake; c Gordon. *Educ:* Hampden-Sydney Col, BS, 42; Univ Va, MS, 47, PhD(physics), 50. *Prof Exp:* Design engr indust electronics div, Westinghouse Elec Corp, 42-46; mem staff, Los Alamos Nat Lab, Univ Calif, 50-57, alt group leader, 57-65, group leader, 65-72, alt div leader, 72-76, dep asst dir, 76-79, prog mgr, 79-80, dep assoc dir, 80-82. *Concurrent Pos:* Adj prof, Los Alamos Grad Ctr, Univ NMex, 57, 58 & 61. *Mem:* Fel AAAS; fel Am Phys Soc; Sigma Xi. *Res:* Crystal physics; electron beam dynamics; electron linear accelerators, gaseous discharges; flash radiography; detonation phenomena; hydrodynamics and shock wave phenomena. *Mailing Add:* 107 Piedra Loop Los Alamos NM 87544. *E-Mail:* dougven@aol.com

**VENABLE, EMERSON,** physical chemistry; deceased, see previous edition for last biography

**VENABLE, JOHN HEINZ, JR,** MOLECULAR BIOPHYSICS. *Current Pos:* asst prof molecular biol, 67-72, ASSOC PROF MOLECULAR BIOL, VANDERBILT UNIV, 72-, ASSOC DEAN, 81- *Personal Data:* b Atlanta, Ga, June 9, 38; m 62. *Educ:* Duke Univ, BS, 60; Yale Univ, MS, 63, PhD(biophys), 65. *Prof Exp:* Vis scientist, King's Col, Univ London, 65-67. *Concurrent Pos:* NSF fel, 65-66; USPHS fel, 66-67. *Mem:* AAAS; Biophys Soc; Sigma Xi. *Res:* Macromolecular structure; biophysical chemistry; transition-metal complexes; x-ray diffraction; electron paramagnetic resonance. *Mailing Add:* Vanderbilt Univ 101 Kirkland Hall Nashville TN 37240

**VENABLE, WALLACE STARR,** ENGINEERING EDUCATION, ENGINEERING MECHANICS. *Current Pos:* Instr, 66-72, lectr, 72-74, asst prof mech, 74-80, ASSOC PROF MECH & AEROSPACE ENG, WVA UNIV, 80- *Personal Data:* b Wilkensburg, Pa, Apr 19, 40; m 62. *Educ:* Cornell Univ, BA, 62; Univ Toledo, MSES, 64; WVa Univ, EdD(eng educ), 72. *Concurrent Pos:* Eng analyst, Hedenburg & Venable, 62- *Mem:* Fel Am Soc Eng Educ; Am Soc Mech Engrs. *Res:* Development and evaluation of educational methods and materials in engineering; accident analysis. *Mailing Add:* RR 1 Morgantown WV 26505

**VENABLES, JOHN ANTHONY,** ELECTRON MICROSCOPY MATERIALS, SURFACE PHYSICS. *Current Pos:* lectr, 64-71, reader, 71-88, PROF PHYSICS, UNIV SUSSEX, BRIGHTON, UK, 88-; PROF PHYSICS, ARIZ STATE UNIV, 85- *Personal Data:* b Leicester, UK, May 19, 36; m 61, Delia Poole; c 2. *Educ:* Cambridge Univ, UK, BA, 58, PhD(physics), 61. *Hon Degrees:* MA, Cambridge Univ, UK, 61. *Prof Exp:* Res assoc & asst prof physics, Univ Ill, Urbana, 61-64. *Concurrent Pos:* Vis scientist, Max Planck Inst Stuttgart, Ger, 69; fel, Inst Physics, Eng, 72; prof assoc, CRMC2-CNRS, Marseille, 73-82, France, 74-86; fel, Japan Soc Prom Sci, 76; sci adv bd, Fritz-Haber Inst, Berlin, 81-, Lab Maurice lectr, Nancy, France, 89-; vis prof, Ariz State Univ, 84-85; dean math & phys scis, Univ Sussex, 92-94. *Mem:* Inst Physics; Am Inst Physics; Electron Micros Soc Am; Europ Phys Soc; Brit Asn Crystal Growth; Mat Res Soc; Royal Micros Soc. *Res:* Electron microscopy and surface science; adsorption and crystal growth mechanisms; development of analytical techniques; auger electron and other spectroscopies; molecular solids and interatomic forces. *Mailing Add:* Dept Physics & Astron Ariz State Univ Tempe AZ 85287-1504

**VENABLES, JOHN DUXBURY,** MATERIALS SCIENCE, AEROSPACE MATERIALS. *Current Pos:* PRES, VENABLES & ASSOCS, 90- *Personal Data:* b Cleveland, Ohio, Feb 6, 27; m 48, Kathryn E Heinz; c Jess, David & Lee. *Educ:* Case Inst Technol, BS, 54; Univ Warwick, PhD, 71. *Honors & Awards:* Adhesion Soc Award for Excellance, 91. *Prof Exp:* Physicist, Parma Res Ctr, Union Carbide Corp, 54-64; assoc dir & corp scientist, Martin Marietta Labs, 64-90. *Concurrent Pos:* Lectr, Univ Calif, 87; Mem, Bd Army Sci & Technol-Div of Nat Res Coun; Bd Visitors Off Naval Res, 90-95. *Mem:* Mat Res Soc; Sigma Xi. *Res:* Defect structure of solids; radiation effects in solids; ordering effects in transition metal carbides; high temperature ceramics; adhesive bonding; electron microscopy. *Mailing Add:* Venables & Assocs 848 Bosley Ave Baltimore MD 21204

**VENARD, CARL ERNEST,** zoology; deceased, see previous edition for last biography

**VENCILL, WILLIAM KEITH,** WEED SCIENCE. *Current Pos:* ASST PROF AGRON, UNIV GA, 89-, ASSOC PROF CROP SCI, 96- *Personal Data:* b Richlands, Va, Jan 5, 62; m 91, Anne M Tisler; c Elizabeth A, Theresa M & Benjamin T. *Educ:* Univ Va, BS, 84; Va Polytech Inst & State Univ, MS, 86, PhD(plant physiol/weed sci), 88. *Mem:* Weed Sci Soc Am; Europ Weed Res Soc. *Res:* Herbicide action in plants, herbicide interaction with soil and weed management in conservation-tillage. *Mailing Add:* 3111 Miller Plant Sci Athens GA 30602-7272. *E-Mail:* wvencill@uga.cc.uga.edu

**VENDITTI, JOHN M,** PHARMACOLOGY, BIOCHEMISTRY. *Current Pos:* SR SCIENTIST, SAIC, 94- *Personal Data:* b Baltimore, Md, Feb 19, 27; m 51, Nancy Orth; c Nancy M, Mary R & J Michael. *Educ:* Univ Md, BS, 49, MS, 57; George Washington Univ, PhD(pharmacol), 65. *Prof Exp:* Biologist, Nat Cancer Inst, 51-58, pharmacologist, 58-66, chief drug eval br, 66-86; vpres & dir res, MicroBiotest, Inc, 87-91; sr scientist, Tech Resources Inc, 91-93. *Concurrent Pos:* Head, Screening Sect, Nat Cancer Inst, 63-73; dir, NCDDG Prog, 87-91. *Mem:* AAAS; Am Asn Cancer Res; Soc Exp Biol & Med; Am Soc Pharmacol & Exp Therapeut; NY Acad Sci; Am Soc Microbiol. *Res:* Experimental cancer chemotherapy, biochemical and pharmacological actions of potential antitumor agents; antimicrobiol efficacy. *Mailing Add:* 6222 Stoneham Ct Bethesda MD 20812

**VENEMA, GERARD ALAN,** TOPOLOGY. *Current Pos:* from asst prof to assoc prof, 79-83, PROF MATH, CALVIN COL, 83- *Personal Data:* b Grand Rapids, Mich, Jan 26, 49; m 69; c 3. *Educ:* Calvin Col, AB, 71; Univ Utah, PhD(math), 75. *Prof Exp:* Instr math, Univ Tex, Austin, 75-77; mem, Inst Advan Study, Princeton, NJ, 77-79. *Concurrent Pos:* Chmn, Dept Math & Comput Sci, Calvin Col. *Mem:* Am Math Soc; Math Asn Am; Coun Undergrad Res. *Res:* Geometric topology and the theory of topological embeddings. *Mailing Add:* Dept Math Calvin Col Grand Rapids MI 49546-4388

**VENEMA, HARRY J(AMES),** ELECTRICAL ENGINEERING. *Current Pos:* RETIRED. *Personal Data:* b Grand Rapids, Mich, July 28, 22; m 45; c 5. *Educ:* Univ Ill, BS, 44, MS, 47, PhD(elec eng), 50. *Prof Exp:* Asst, Elec Eng Lab, Univ Ill, 47-50; elec engr, Missile Guid Sect, Gen Elec Co, 50-53, elec engr, Magnetic Appln Sect, 53-56; mgr mil eng, Electronics Div, Stewart-Warner Corp, 56-59; electronic res, Roy C Ingersoll Res Ctr, Borg-Warner Corp, 59-86. *Mem:* Sigma Xi; Inst Elec & Electronics Engrs. *Mailing Add:* 1908 Driving Park Rd Wheaton IL 60187

**VENEMAN, PETER LOURENS MARINUS,** SOIL GENESIS, SOIL PHYSICS. *Current Pos:* From asst prof to assoc prof, 77-89, PROF SOILS, UNIV MASS, AMHERST, 89- *Personal Data:* b Oudenrijn, Neth, Nov 27, 47; m 73; c 2. *Educ:* State Agr Univ, Wageningen, BS, 72; Univ Wis-Madison, MS, 75, PhD(soils), 77. *Mem:* Am Soc Agron; Soil Sci Soc Am; Int Soil Sci Soc; Soil Conserv Soc Am. *Res:* Formation, morphology and classification of spodosol soils, suitability rating of soils for the disposal of liquid wastes; suitability of soil for fruit production; lead and arsenic pesticide residues in soils; hydric soils; wetland identification. *Mailing Add:* 32 Hulst Rd Amherst MA 01002-3523

**VENER, KIRT J,** CHRONOBIOLOGY. *Current Pos:* spec asst to assoc dir digestive dis & nutrit, Nat Inst Diabetes, Digestive & Kidney Dis, NIH, 79-81, prog dir, Gastric Esophageal & Colonic Dis, 81-87, exec secy, Nat Inst Arthritis, Muscoloskeletal & Skin Dis, 87-92, CHIEF, PREV, EPIDEMOL & CONTROL REV SECT, NAT CANCER INST, NIH, 92- *Personal Data:* b Highland Park, Mich, Feb 1, 43; m 67; c 2. *Educ:* Wayne State Univ, Bs, 64, PhD(biol), 74. *Prof Exp:* Prin investr, NSF, 73-74; asst prof, Dept Biol, Layola Univ Chicago, Ill, 74-75. *Concurrent Pos:* Asst vchancellor res affairs, Univ Tenn, Memphis, 87. *Mem:* Int Soc Chronobiol. *Res:* The time domain in experimental biology and medicine. *Mailing Add:* NCI NIH EPN Rm 622B Bethesda MD 20892-0001. *Fax:* 301-496-6497

**VENETSANOPOULOS, ANASTASIOS NICOLAOS,** ELECTRICAL ENGINEERING, COMMUNICATIONS. *Current Pos:* lectr elec eng, Univ Toronto, 68-70, from asst prof to assoc prof, 70-81, chmn commun group, 74-78, assoc chmn dept, 78-79, prof elec eng & chmn commun group, 81-86, PROF ELEC & COMPUT ENG, UNIV TORONTO, 86- *Personal Data:* b Athens, Greece, June 19, 41; m 87, Vasiliki Koronakis; c Elizabeth & Dominique. *Educ:* Nat Tech Univ, Athens, dipl elec & mech eng, 65; Yale Univ, MS, 66, MPh, 68, PhD(commun), 69. *Hon Degrees:* DEng, Nat Univ Athens, Greece, 94. *Prof Exp:* Res asst, N V Phillips, Neth, 64; asst in instr, Yale Univ, 66-68, res asst, 68-69. *Concurrent Pos:* Consult, Elec Eng Consociates Ltd, 69-; fel, Nat Sci & Eng Res Coun Can, Univ Toronto, 69-; Defense Res Bd Can fel, 72-75; lectr continuing educ, George Washington Univ, 80-, Northeastern Univ & Univ Southern Calif; vis prof, Fed Univ Rio de Janeiro, 79-80 & Swiss Fed Inst Technol, 86-87. *Mem:* Fel Inst Elec & Electronics Engrs; fel Eng Inst Can (vpres, 82-85); Sigma Xi; AAAS; Can Soc Elec Engrs (pres, 82-85); NY Acad Sci. *Res:* Digital signal processing; neural networks; neural networks; signal design; image processing, analysis and computer vision. *Mailing Add:* Dept Elec & Comput Eng Univ Toronto Toronto ON M5S 3G4 Can. *Fax:* 416-978-4425; *E-Mail:* anv@asp.toronto.edu

**VENEZIAN, GIULIO,** HYDRODYNAMICS, APPLIED MECHANICS. *Current Pos:* ASSOC PROF, SOUTHEAST MO STATE UNIV, 89- *Personal Data:* b Torino, Italy, Dec 9, 38; m 68, Jill Barber; c Sarah & Rachel. *Educ:* McGill Univ, BEng, 60; Calif Inst Technol, PhD(eng sci), 65. *Prof Exp:* Res fel eng sci, Calif Inst Technol, 65-68; from asst prof to assoc prof ocean eng, Univ Hawaii, 68-79; assoc prof civil & ocean eng, Tex A&M Univ, 80-86; assoc prof physics, Col Charleston, 87-89. *Mem:* Am Soc Eng Educ; Am Soc Civil Engrs. *Res:* Rotating fluid dynamics; magnetohydrodynamics; classical physics; water waves; geophysical fluid dynamics. *Mailing Add:* 2415 Saddle Ridge Lane Cape Girardeau MO 63701. *Fax:* 573-651-2223; *E-Mail:* c147scp@semovm.semo.edu

**VENEZKY, DAVID LESTER,** INORGANIC CHEMISTRY. *Current Pos:* res chemist, Naval Res Lab, 62-69, head reaction mechanism sect, Inorg Chem Div, 69-75, head, Solution Chem Sect, 75-81, head, Inorg & Electrochem Br & assoc supt, Chem Div, 81-84, liaison scientist chem, London Br Off, Off Naval Res, 84-85, sci dir, 85- 87, HEAD, SURFACE CHEM BR, CHEM DIV, NAVAL RES LAB, WASHINGTON, DC, 87- *Personal Data:* b Washington, DC, Sept 12, 24; m 50; c 2. *Educ:* George Washington Univ, BS, 48; Univ NC, PhD(chem), 62. *Prof Exp:* Phys sci aide, Trace Elements Unit, US Geol Surv, 48-49; chemist, US Naval Res Lab, 49-55; instr chem, Univ NC, 58-60; asst prof inorg chem, Auburn Univ, 60-62. *Mem:* Am Chem Soc; Sigma Xi; Royal Chem Soc. *Res:* Coordination compounds and aggregation of inorganic substances in solutions; studies to elucidate the methods of preparation, structure and properties of inorganic polymers; chemical microsensors. *Mailing Add:* 8707 Bradgate Rd Alexandria VA 22308-2312

**VENHAM, LARRY LEE,** PEDODONTICS, PSYCHOLOGY. *Current Pos:* PVT PRACT. *Personal Data:* b Akron, Ohio, June 24, 41; m 63; c 1. *Educ:* Ohio State Univ, DDS, 65, MS, 67, PhD(psychol), 72. *Prof Exp:* NIH fel, 67-69; asst prof, 70-78, assoc prof dent educ, Health Ctr Sch Dent Med, Univ Conn, 78-85. *Concurrent Pos:* Am Inst Res Creative Talent Award, 72; Nat Inst Dent Res Spec Dent Award, 75- *Mem:* Am Psychol Asn; Int Asn Dent Res; Soc Res Child Develop; Am Soc Dent Children. *Res:* Child development; situational stress, anxiety and coping behavior in response to dental stress; developmental factors in developing stress tolerance. *Mailing Add:* 390 Broad St Windsor CT 06095

**VENIER, CLIFFORD GEORGE,** ORGANIC SULFUR CHEMISTRY, LUBRICATION CHEMISTRY. *Current Pos:* sr res assoc, 84-97, VPRES ADVAN TECHNOL, PENNZOIL PROD CO, 97- *Personal Data:* b Trenton, Mich, June 17, 39; m 65, Lynn C Finell; c John J, Andrew D & Jennifer L. *Educ:* Univ Mich, BS, 62; Ore State Univ, PhD(org chem), 66. *Prof Exp:* Res assoc chem, Univ Tex, 66-67; asst prof chem, Tex Christian Univ, 67-74, assoc prof, 74-80; sr chemist, Ames Lab, Iowa State Univ, 80-84. *Concurrent Pos:* Vis assoc prof, Univ Nijmegen, Neth, 75. *Mem:* Am Chem Soc; Royal Soc Chem; Sigma Xi. *Res:* Organic sulfur chemistry; coal chemistry with chemistry of lubrication; quantum organic chemistry. *Mailing Add:* Pennzoil Prod Co PO Box 7569 The Woodlands TX 77387-7569. *E-Mail:* cliffordvenier@pennzoil.com

**VENIT, STEWART MARK,** MATHEMATICS. *Current Pos:* Asst prof, 71-77, assoc prof, 77-80, PROF MATH, CALIF STATE UNIV, LOS ANGELES, 80- *Personal Data:* b New York, NY, Apr 4, 46; m 72. *Educ:* Queens Col, NY, BA, 66; Univ Calif, Berkeley, MA, 69, PhD(math), 71. *Mem:* Am Math Soc. *Res:* Numerical solution of partial differential equations. *Mailing Add:* Dept Math Calif State Univ 5151 State University Dr Los Angeles CA 90032

**VENKATA, SUBRAHMANYAM SARASWATI,** ELECTRICAL ENGINEERING, ELECTRICAL POWER & ENERGY. *Current Pos:* PROF ELEC ENG, UNIV WASH, 79- *Personal Data:* b Nellore, India, June 28, 42; Indian & US citizen; m 71, Padma Mahadevan; c Sridevi & Harish. *Educ:* Andhra Univ, BSEE, 63; Indian Inst Technol, MSEE, 65; Univ SC, PhD(eng), 71. *Prof Exp:* Lectr elec eng, Coimbatore Inst Technol, 65-66; asst, Univ SC, 68-71; instr, Univ Lowell, 71-72; from asst prof elec eng to assoc prof, WVa Univ, 72-79. *Concurrent Pos:* Consult, SC Elec & Gas Co, 69-70; fel, Univ SC, 71; consult, Union Carbide Corp, 77-78, Puget Sound Power & Light, 79-, UIC, 84-, Scott & Scott Consults, 88- *Mem:* Fel Inst Elec & Electronics Engrs; Am Soc Eng Educ; Sigma Xi; Nat Soc Prof Engrs. *Res:*

Six-phase power transmission; mine power system safety; reliability, availability and optimum maintainability; energy conservation; digital and analog simulation of energy systems; electrical power distribution. *Mailing Add:* Dept Elec Eng Box 352500 Univ Wash Seattle WA 98195

**VENKATACHALAM, MANJERI A,** ANATOMIC PATHOLOGY. *Current Pos:* PROF PATH, HEALTH SCI CTR, UNIV TEX, SAN ANTONIO, 79- *Personal Data:* b Calcutta, India, May 24, 40. *Educ:* Calcutta Med Col, BS & MS, 62. *Mem:* Am Asn Pathologists; Am Soc Cell Biol; Am Soc Clin Invest; Int Acad Path; AAAS; Am Soc Nephrology. *Mailing Add:* Dept Path Univ Tex Health Sci Ctr 7703 Floyd Curl Dr San Antonio TX 78284-7750. *Fax:* 210-567-2367

**VENKATACHALAM, TARACAD KRISHNAN,** ORGANIC CHEMISTRY. *Current Pos:* Res chemist, 65-69, sr res chemist, 69-85, RES ASSOC, E I DU PONT DE NEMOURS & CO, INC, 85- *Personal Data:* b Cochin, India, Apr 28, 37. *Educ:* Univ Bombay, BSc, 58, MSc, 62; Univ Louisville, PhD(chem), 65. *Mem:* Am Chem Soc; Indian Chem Soc; Royal Inst Chem. *Res:* Polymer technology; natural and synthetic resins; rubber chemistry; textile fibers; tire cord adhesion and processing; ropes and cables; tires; seat belts. *Mailing Add:* Du Pont Co Fibers Dept Bldg 702 Chestnut Run Plaza Wilmington DE 19805

**VENKATARAGHAVAN, R,** BIO & STRUCTURAL INFORMATICS. *Current Pos:* mem staff, Res Data Processing, Lederle Labs, 77-80, dept head, 80-84, dir, Res Comput, 84-95, SR RES FEL, LEDERLE LABS, AM CYANAMID CO, 95- *Personal Data:* b Madras, India, June 29, 39; m, Usha Baratan. *Educ:* Univ Madras, BSc, 58, MSc, 60; Indian Inst Sci, Bangalore, PhD(chem), 63. *Prof Exp:* Fel spectros, Nat Res Coun Can, 63-65; NIH res assoc mass spectros, Purdue Univ, Lafayette, 65-69; sr res assoc chem, Cornell Univ, 69-77. *Concurrent Pos:* Consult, US Army Labs; mem bd sci adv, Nat Cancer Inst; adj fac, Princeton Univ. *Mem:* AAAS; Am Chem Soc. *Res:* Molecular and structural biology; bioinformatics; computer aided analytical techniques; structure-activity studies; artificial intelligence techniques; structural biology; structure-function studies. *Mailing Add:* Wyeth Lederle Labs Pearl River NY 10965. *Fax:* 914-732-4941; *E-Mail:* venkataraghaven@pr.cyanamid.com

**VENKATARAMAN, M,** T&B LYMPHOCYTES SUBSETS, HUMAN LUNG CANCER. *Current Pos:* ASST PROF IMMUNOL, MT SINAI HOSP MED CTR, 79- *Personal Data:* b June 10, 43; US citizen; m 75; c 2. *Educ:* Madras Vet Col, India, BVSc, 67; Inst Med Sci, New Delhi, India, MSc, 72, PhD(immunol), 75. *Mem:* Am Asn Immunologists; Soc Cryobiol. *Res:* Cellular immunology; tumor immunology; cell growth and differentiation factors; cryopreservation effects on immunocompetent cell functions; monoclonal antibodies; hybridomas; bone marrow transplantation; radiation effects. *Mailing Add:* Dept Med Mt Sinai Hosp Med Ctr Calif Ave & 15th St Chicago IL 60608. *Fax:* 773-257-6208

**VENKATARAMANAN, RAMAN,** BIOPHARMACEUTICS, PHARMACOKINETICS. *Current Pos:* from asst prof to assoc prof, 80-91, PROF PHARM, UNIV PITTSBURGH, 91-, DIR, CLIN PHARMACOKINETICS LAB. *Personal Data:* b Kallal, Madras, India, Aug 30, 51; m 84, Padma. *Educ:* Madras Med Col, BS, 72; Birla Inst Technol & Sci, MS, 74; Univ BC, PhD(pharmacokinetics & biopharmaceut), 79. *Prof Exp:* Fel pharm, Univ Wash, Seattle, 78-80. *Concurrent Pos:* Hosp training, Stanley Hosp, Madras, India, 71-72; mem, Task Force Bioequivalence, Dept Health; mem, Study Group Cyclosporine, Nat Asn Clin Biochemists; consult transplant teams, Univ Pittsburgh; consult, Magee Women's Hosp Pittsburgh; vis scientist, Alta Heritage Found, 85, Med Res Coun, 90; spec vis scientist, Med Res Coun Can, 90. *Mem:* Fel Am Col Clin Pharm; fel Am Asn Pharmaceut Sci; Am Asn Col Pharm; fel Am Asn Clin Pharmacol. *Res:* Pharmacokinetic and pharmacodynamic studies of drugs in organ transplant patients in order to optimize drug therapy in this patient population. *Mailing Add:* 718 Salk Hall Univ Pittsburgh Pittsburgh PA 15261. *Fax:* 412-648-7671; *E-Mail:* venkat@druginfonet.pharm__epid.pitt.edu

**VENKATESAN, DORASWAMY,** space physics, astrophysics; deceased, see previous edition for last biography

**VENKATESAN, MALABI M,** MICROBIOL PATHOGENESIS, CELL BIOLOGY. *Current Pos:* sr nat res coun fel, 85-87, res chemist bact immunol, 87-93, RES CHEMIST, DEPT ENTERIC INJECTIONS, WALTER REED ARMY INST RES, 93- *Personal Data:* b Ranchi, India, July 3, 50; US citizen; m 71, Sundararajan Venkatesan; c Aradhana & Siddhartha. *Educ:* Nagpur Univ, BSc, 67, MSc, 69; Univ Pittsburgh, PhD(biochem), 77. *Prof Exp:* Jr res fel, Dept Biochem, All India Inst Med Sci, 69-71; grad teaching asst, Dept Molecular Biol, State Univ NY, Stony Brook, 71-72; grad teaching asst, Dept Biochem, Univ Pittsburgh, Pa, 72-77; vis fel, Lab Biochem & Pharmacol, Nat Inst Arthritis, Diabetes & Digestive & Kidney Dis, NIH, 78-81, staff fel, Lab Cell & Develop Biol, 81-84, sr staff fel, 84-85. *Concurrent Pos:* Prin investr, Prog Appropriate Technol Health, USAID, Seattle, Wash, 89-91; found lectr, Am Soc Microbiol, 90-91; sponsor, Nat Res Coun, Washington, DC, 90- *Mem:* Am Soc Microbiol. *Res:* Characterization of bacterial and host-associated factors that determine pathogenesis of bacillary dysentery; construction of live vaccines for Shigella-induced dysentery; construction of DNA and immunoreactive reagents for diagnosis of Shigella. *Mailing Add:* Enteric Injections Walter Reed Army Inst Res Washington DC 20307-5100. *Fax:* 202-782-0748; *E-Mail:* dr__malabi__venkatesan@wrsmtp__ccmail.army.mil

**VENKATESAN, S,** MOLECULAR BIOLOGY, AIDS RETRO VIRUS. *Current Pos:* SR SCIENTIST, FREDRICK CANCER CTR, NIH, GOVT RES INST, 77- *Educ:* Guntur Med Col AP Guntur, India, MD, 67. *Mailing Add:* 10201 Fleming Ave Bethesda MD 20814-2133. *Fax:* 301-480-3010

**VENKATESAN, THIRUMALAI,** PHYSICS. *Current Pos:* PROF ELEC ENG & PHYSICS, CTR SUPERCONDUCTIVITY RES, DEPT PHYSICS, UNIV MD, COLLEGE PARK, 89- *Personal Data:* b Madras, India, June 19, 49; m 77. *Educ:* Indian Inst Technol, Kharagpur, BS, 69, Kanpur, MS, 71; City Univ New York, PhD(physics), 77. *Prof Exp:* Mem tech staff, Optical Commun Res, Bell Labs, 77-79, mem staff, Radiation Physics Res, 79-89. *Concurrent Pos:* Mgr, Mat Modifications Group, Bellcore Dir, Lab Surface Modification. *Mem:* Sigma Xi; Am Inst Physics; fel Am Phys Soc. *Res:* Ion solid interaction, ion beam lithography, germanium selenide resists, metal-insulatory transition; optical properties of semiconductors; optical nonlinear devices; optical communication systems and associated solid state and device physics; laser-solid interaction; epitaxial crystalline metal oxides and high temperature superconducting film; physics and applications. *Mailing Add:* Ctr Superconductivity Res Dept Physics Univ Md College Park MD 20742. *Fax:* 301-314-9541

**VENKATESH, YELDUR PADMANABHA,** PROTEINS & ENZYMOLOGY, ALLERGY. *Current Pos:* SCIENTIST FEL, CENT FOOD TECHNOL RES INST, MYSORE, 96- *Personal Data:* b Kalale, India, Dec 2, 53; m 81, Poornima; c Madhava. *Educ:* Bangalore Univ, BS, 70; Univ Mysore, MS, 74; Indian Inst Sci, PhD (biochem), 81. *Prof Exp:* Lectr biochem, Kasturaba Med Col, 74-75; fel, Sch Med, Wash Univ, 81-83, NIH trainee immunol, 84-85; res assoc, Smith, Kline & French Labs, 85-87; asst res scientist, Immunogen Inc, 87-88, from res scientist to sr res scientist, 88-95. *Concurrent Pos:* Prin investr, Proj Food Allergens, Cent Food Technol Res Inst, Mysore, 97- *Mem:* India Soc Biol Chemists; India Asn Food Scientists & Technol Logistics; Indian Immunol Soc. *Res:* Structure-function relationships of proteins (ribonuclease A, complement protein C3, monoclonal antibodies, ricin), protein folding, immunoconjugates for specific targeting, protein-carbohydrate interactions, process optimization of proprietary toxin (blocked ricin) production, preparation and characterization of immunotoxins, protein-protein interactions, limited proteolysis. *Mailing Add:* Dept Biochem & Nutrition CFTRI Mysore Karnataka 570 013 India. *Fax:* 91-821-517233; *E-Mail:* ban@cscftri.ren.nic.in

**VENKATESWARAN, UMA D,** SOLID STATE PHYSICS-EXPERIMENTAL, SEMICONDUCTORS. *Current Pos:* asst prof, 91-95, ASSOC PROF PHYSICS, OAKLAND UNIV, 95- *Personal Data:* b India, Aug 6, 53. *Educ:* Madurai Univ, India, BSc, 73, MSc, 75; Univ Mo, Columbia, PhD(physics), 85. *Prof Exp:* Scientist, Mat Sci Lab, Kalpakkam, India, 76-82; guest scientist, Max-Planck-Inst, Stuttgart, Ger, 86-88; postdoctoral res assoc, Dept Physics, State Univ NY, Buffalo, 88-90. *Concurrent Pos:* Lectr, Dept Physics, State Univ NY, Buffalo, 91. *Mem:* Am Phys Soc; Sigma Xi; Mat Res Soc. *Res:* Study of optical properties of electro-optic materials and fullerenes under high hydrostatic pressure (0-20GPa). *Mailing Add:* Dept Physics Oakland Univ Rochester MI 48309. *Fax:* 313-370-3408; *E-Mail:* venkat@oakland.edu

**VENKATU, DOULATABAD A,** METALLURGY, CERAMICS. *Current Pos:* SR ENG SPECIALIST, GOODYEAR AEROSPACE CORP, 73- *Personal Data:* b Bangalore, India, July 31, 36; m 67; c 2. *Educ:* Univ Mysore, BSc, 55; Indian Inst Sci, Bangalore, Dipl, 58; Univ Notre Dame, MS, 61, PhD(metall eng & mat sci), 65. *Prof Exp:* Sr res asst metall, Indian Inst Sci, Bangalore, 58-59; res asst metall eng, Univ Notre Dame, 59-64; asst prof, Clemson Univ, 64-67; res assoc, Rensselaer Polytech Inst, 67-68; asst prof, Clemson Univ, 68-69; sr mat scientist, Owens-Ill Inc, 69-73. *Mem:* Am Soc Metals; Am Inst Mining, Metall & Petrol Engrs; Am Ceramic Soc. *Res:* Fatigue of metals; fracture mechanics; light metals technology; powder metallurgy; high temperature and technical ceramics. *Mailing Add:* 1278 Goldfinch Trail Cuyahoga Falls OH 44224

**VENKAYYA, VIPPERLA,** STRUCTURAL ENGINEERING. *Current Pos:* AEROSPACE ENGR, AIR FORCE FLIGHT DYNAMICS LAB, WRIGHT-PATTERSON AFB, 67- *Personal Data:* b Raghudevapuram, Andhra, India, May 16, 31; m 65, Janaki Tumu; c Rajeev & Arvndhatj. *Educ:* Andhra Univ, BSc, 52; Indian Inst Technol, BTech, 56; Univ Mo, MS, 59; Univ Ill, Urbana, PhD(struct eng), 62. *Honors & Awards:* Gen Foulois Award, Air Force Flight Dynamics Lab; Scientists & Engrs Award, Affil Socs Coun, 78. *Prof Exp:* Asst engr, Damodar Valley Corp, India, 56-57; bridge engr, State Hwy Dept, Pa, 58-59; asst prof struct eng, State Univ NY, Buffalo, 62-67. *Concurrent Pos:* Assoc ed, Am Inst Aeronaut & Astronaut J, 78-80; adj prof, Air Force Inst Technol, 78-; adj prof, Wright State Univ, Ohio, fel, Wright Lab, 89. *Mem:* Am Soc Civil Engrs; fel Am Inst Aeronaut & Astronaut; Am Soc Mech Engrs; Am Acad Mech. *Res:* Response of discrete and continuous elastic systems to static and dynamic disturbances, particularly civil and aeronautical structures; stability of elastic systems; dynamics and control of space structures, multi-disciplinary design optimization. *Mailing Add:* 5464 Honeyleaf Way Dayton OH 45424. *Fax:* 937-255-3740; *E-Mail:* venkayya@fltvei.flight.wpafb.af.mil

**VENNART, GEORGE PIERCY,** PATHOLOGY. *Current Pos:* PROF PATH & CHMN DIV CLIN PATH, MED COL VA, 65-, CHMN DEPT PATH, 78- *Personal Data:* b Boston, Mass, Apr 1, 26; m 51; c 3. *Educ:* Wesleyan Univ, AB, 48; Univ Rochester, MD, 53. *Prof Exp:* Asst biol, Wesleyan Univ, 47-48; intern & resident path, NC Mem Hosp, 53-56; asst prof, Col Physicians & Surgeons, Columbia Univ, 56-60; assoc prof path, Univ NC, 60-65. *Concurrent Pos:* Instr, Univ NC, 54-56; asst attend pathologist, Preby Hosp, NY, 56-60. *Res:* Experimental liver disease; platelet agglutination; pulmonary morphology and physiology. *Mailing Add:* Box 662 MCV Station Richmond VA 23205-0662

**VENNERSTROM, JONATHAN LEE,** ANTIMALARIAL DRUG DESIGN. *Current Pos:* asst prof, 87-92, ASSOC PROF, MED CTR, UNIV NEBR, 87- *Personal Data:* b Chicago, Ill, Jan 27, 56. *Educ:* Univ Minn, BS, 79, PhD(med chem), 85. *Prof Exp:* Nat Res Coun fel, Walter Reed Army Inst Res, 85-87. *Mem:* Am Chem Soc; Am Soc Trop Med & Hyg; Am Soc Pharmacog. *Res:* Antimalarial drug design and synthesis; redox modulation of drug toxicity. *Mailing Add:* Univ Nebr Med Ctr 600 S 42nd St Omaha NE 68198-6025

**VENNES, JACK A,** GASTROENTEROLOGY, INTERNAL MEDICINE. *Current Pos:* STAFF MEM, MED SCH, UNIV MINN, 90- *Personal Data:* b Wheeler, Wis, June 12, 23. *Educ:* Univ Minn, BS, 47, MD, 51. *Prof Exp:* Intern med, Hennepin County Med Ctr, Minneapolis, 51-52; residency, Vet Admin Hosp, Minneapolis, 52-55; pvt pract, St Louis Park Med Ctr, Minneapolis, 57-63; staff physician gastroenterol, Vet Admin Hosp, Minneapolis, 64-67, 71-90, asst chief med, 67-71. *Concurrent Pos:* Instr med, Univ Minn, 55-57, from asst prof to assoc prof, 65-76, prof med, 76- *Mem:* Am Gastroenterol Asn; Am Soc Gastrointestinal Endoscopy; Am Asn Study Liver Dis; Am Soc Clin Invest; Am Fedn Clin Res. *Res:* Development and applications of fiberoptic endoscopy to improved diagnosis in upper gastrointestinal tract, pancreas and biliary tree; treatment of gastrointestinal hemorrhage; non-surgical endoscopic removal of common duct gallstones; improved teaching methods of fiberoptic endoscopy. *Mailing Add:* 8221 Amsden Rd Minneapolis MN 55438

**VENNES, JOHN WESLEY,** BACTERIOLOGY. *Current Pos:* from instr to assoc prof, 56-66, actg dean, sch med, 73-75, assoc dean acad affairs, 73-77, PROF BACT, UNIV NDAK, 66-, CHMN, DEPT MICROBIOL, 81- *Personal Data:* b Grenora, NDak, Aug 28, 24; m 48; c 3. *Educ:* Univ NDak, BS, 51, MS, 52; Univ Mich, PhD(bact), 57. *Prof Exp:* Instr bact, Univ NDak, 52-54; asst, Univ Mich, 54-56. *Mem:* Am Soc Microbiol. *Res:* Bacterial physiology and industrial microbiology. *Mailing Add:* 3214 Chestnut St Grand Forks ND 58201

**VENNESLAND, BIRGIT,** ENZYMOLOGY. *Current Pos:* ADJ PROF, BIOCHEM & BIOPHYSICS, UNIV HAWAII, 87- *Personal Data:* b Kristiansand, Norway, Nov 17, 13; US citizen. *Educ:* Univ Chicago, BS, 34, PhD(biochem), 38. *Hon Degrees:* DSc, Mt Holyoke Col, 60. *Honors & Awards:* Hales Award, Am Soc Plant Physiol, 50; Garvan Medal, Am Chem Soc, 64. *Prof Exp:* Asst biochem, Univ Chicago, 38-39; fel, Harvard Med Sch, 39-41; from instr to prof biochem, Univ Chicago, 41-68; dir, Max Planck Inst Cell Physiol, WBerlin, Ger, 68-70; leader, Vennesland Res Inst, WBerlin, Ger, 70-81, emer, 81- *Mem:* Am Chem Soc; Am Soc Biol Chemists; fel AAAS; fel NY Acad Sci; Am Soc Plant Physiologists. *Res:* Carboxylation reactions in animals and plants; mechanisms of hydrogen transfer in pyridine nucleotide dehydrogenases; enzymology and mechanism of photosynthesis; mechanism of nitrate reduction. *Mailing Add:* 1206 Mokapu Blvd Kailua HI 96734

**VENNOS, MARY SUSANNAH,** CHEMISTRY. *Current Pos:* assoc prof, 70-80, PROF CHEM, ESSEX COMMUNITY COL, BALTIMORE COUNTY, MD, 80- *Personal Data:* b Oct 14, 31; Can citizen; m 58; c 4. *Educ:* Univ London, BSc, 53; Univ NB, Fredericton, PhD(chem), 56. *Prof Exp:* Instr chem, Univ NB, 56-59; from asst prof to assoc prof, Russell Sage Col, 59-70. *Mem:* Am Chem Soc; Sigma Xi. *Res:* Analytical instrumentation; polarography and chemical kinetics. *Mailing Add:* 4003 Milldale Ct Phoenix MD 21131-2103

**VENNUM, WALTER ROBERT,** IGNEOUS & METAMORPHIC PETROLOGY, MINERALOGY & ECONOMIC GEOLOGY. *Current Pos:* From asst prof to assoc prof, 71-80, PROF GEOL, SONOMA STATE UNIV, CALIF, 80- *Personal Data:* b Seattle, Wash, May 10, 41; div. *Educ:* Univ Mont, BA, 64; Stanford Univ, PhD(geol), 71. *Honors & Awards:* Antarctic Serv Medal, US Cong, 78; Antarctic Geographic Feature Names in Honor, Mt Vennum, 80. *Prof Exp:* Geol instr, Stanford Univ, 70. *Concurrent Pos:* Geologist, US Geol Surv, 72-73, 74, 77-78, 81, 84-85 & 88-89; igneous petrologist, Joides Deep Sea Drilling Proj, 74, Int Prog Ocean Drilling, 76, Macalester Col, Minn, 79-80; vis prof petrol, Univ Mont, 78; geologist, Brit Antarctic Surv, Columbia Univ, 83-84; geol instr, Univ Wis-Oshkosh, 85 & Santa Rosa Jr Col, 87. *Mem:* Nat Speleogical Soc; Am Alpine Club. *Res:* Petrology, mineralogy and geochemistry of Northern California, Alaska, Saudi Arabia and West Antarctic igneous rocks; mineralogy of West Antarctica clay minerals and evaporite deposits; mineralogy of caves; authored 38 articles. *Mailing Add:* 3925 Kim Ct Sebastopol CA 95472. *Fax:* 707-664-3012; *E-Mail:* cheryl.moore@sonoma.edu

**VENT, ROBERT JOSEPH,** UNDERWATER ACOUSTICS. *Current Pos:* PROG STAFF ENGR, HUGHES AIRCRAFT. *Personal Data:* b Ford City, Pa, Feb 13, 40; m; c 2. *Educ:* San Diego State Univ, BS, 61, MS, 69. *Prof Exp:* Physicist underwater acoust, Navy Electronics Lab, 61-68; supv physicist, Naval Undersea Ctr, 68-77, res physicist acoust, Naval Ocean Systs Ctr, 77- *Concurrent Pos:* Work in musical acoust. *Res:* Underwater acoustics, especially attenuation, surface, bottom and volume scattering; applied ocean sciences. *Mailing Add:* PO Box 1684 Julian CA 92036

**VENTA, PATRICK JOHN,** RECOMBINANT DNA, HUMAN GENETICS. *Current Pos:* ASST PROF, MICH STATE UNIV, 90- *Personal Data:* b Rock Springs, Wyo, Nov 6, 51; m 79; c 1. *Educ:* Univ Calif, Irvine, BS, 74; Univ Mich, MS, 77, PhD(human genetics), 83. *Prof Exp:* Scholar, 83-84, res assoc human genetics, Univ Mich, 84-90. *Mem:* AAAS; Genetics Soc Am; Am Soc Human Genetics. *Res:* Structure and regulation of eukaryotic genes; molecular evolution; mapping mammalian genomes. *Mailing Add:* Small Animal Clin Mich State Univ VCC25A East Lansing MI 48824-1314

**VENTER, J CRAIG,** GENOMIC RESEARCH. *Current Pos:* PRES & DIR, INST GENOMIC RES. *Personal Data:* b Salt Lake City, Utah, Oct 14, 46; m 81. *Educ:* Univ Calif, San Diego, BA, 72, PhD(physiol & pharmacol), 75. *Prof Exp:* Res assoc cardiovasc pharmacol, Univ Calif, San Diego, 75-76; asst prof pharmacol, State Univ NY, Buffalo, 76-81, assoc prof biochem, 82- *Concurrent Pos:* Mem, Basic Sci Coun, Am Heart Asn. *Mem:* Am Soc Pharmacol & Exp Therapeut; AAAS. *Res:* Purification and molecular characterization of B-adrenergic and muscarinic acetylcholine receptors; production of monoclonal antibodies to each receptor. *Mailing Add:* Inst Genomic Res 9712 Medical Center Dr Rockville MD 20850

**VENTER, RONALD DANIEL,** MECHANICAL ENGINEERING. *Current Pos:* asst prof, Dept Mech Eng, Univ Toronto, 75-78, assoc chmn dept, 79-81, chmn, 81-91, PROF MECH ENG, UNIV TORONTO, 81-, VDEAN, FAC APPL SCI & ENG, 93-, WALLACE G CHALMERS PROF ENG DESIGN, 93- *Personal Data:* b East London, Repub SAfrica, Jan 3, 44; m 75, Beryl. *Educ:* Univ Witwatersrand, Johannesburg, BASc, 66; McMaster Univ, MEng, PhD, 71. *Prof Exp:* Head mech div, Indust Diamond Div, DeBeers, Johannesburg, 71-72, head high pressure systs, 72-74. *Concurrent Pos:* Dir, Ont Ctr Automotive Arts Tech, St Catherine's, 83-89, Ctr Hydrogen & Electrochem Studies, Toronto, 86-, Indust Res & Develop Inst, Midland, Ont, 92- *Mem:* Am Soc Mech Engrs; Soc Mfg Engrs. *Res:* Plane strain slip line fields. *Mailing Add:* Univ Toronto 35 St George St Rm 173 Toronto ON M5S 1A4 Can

**VENTERS, MICHAEL DYAR,** NONINVASIVE VASCULAR DIAGNOSTICS. *Current Pos:* DIR, CLIN PHYSIOL & CARDIOL SERV, ST JOSEPH HEALTHCARE CORP, 80- *Educ:* Univ NMex, PhD(physiol), 79. *Res:* Critical care physiological monitoring. *Mailing Add:* 10608 Prestwick NE Albuquerque NM 87111-6565

**VENTRE, FRANCIS THOMAS,** BUILDING SCIENCE, REGULATION OF TECHNOLOGY. *Current Pos:* RETIRED. *Personal Data:* b Old Forge, Pa, Sept 16, 37; m 64; c 2. *Educ:* Pa State Univ, BArch, 61; Univ Calif, Berkeley, MCP, 66; Mass Inst Technol, PhD(urban studies & planning), 73. *Prof Exp:* Asst prof urban design, Univ Calif, Los Angeles, 66-68; res assoc bldg technol, Mass Inst Technol, 70-73; asst chief, Off Bldg Stand & Codes, Ctr Bldg Technol, Nat Bur Stand, 73-75, asst to dir, Inst Appl Technol, Nat Eng Lab, 77-78, chief, Environ Design Res Div, Ctr Bldg Technol, 78-83; prof environ design & policy, Col Archit & Urban Studies, Va Polytech Inst & State Univ, 83-91. *Concurrent Pos:* Guest lectr, Sch Archit, Carnegie Mellon Univ, 80 & Pa State Col Eng, 81; vis prof, Sch Archit, Univ Md, 82-83; mem, Comt Technol Advan Bldgs, Bldg Res Bd, Nat Acad Sci-Nat Acad Eng, 85-87; prin investr, NSF grant, 85-87. *Mem:* Environ Design Res Asn; Am Econ Asn; Am Soc Testing & Mat; Am Inst Architects; Am Planning Asn. *Res:* Methods for measuring building performance; competitive conditions for international trade in design and construction services; size, structure, deployment and economic impact of the design and construction services industries; measurement theory; design theory. *Mailing Add:* 4007 Rickover Rd Silver Spring MD 20902

**VENTRES, CHARLES SAMUEL,** aeronautical engineering, for more information see previous edition

**VENTRESCA, CAROL,** PERFORMANCE IMPROVEMENT IN MANUFACTURING. *Current Pos:* VPRES, JAMES GREGORY ASSOCS, INC. *Personal Data:* b Columbus, Ohio; c 2. *Educ:* Ohio State Univ, BS, 78, MS, 81. *Prof Exp:* Tech staff, Metrek Div, Mitre Corp, 78; vpres & chief exec officer, SynGenetics Corp, 88-90; res scientist, Battelle Mem Inst, 79-85, mgr, 85-88, sr mgr mfg software systs, 90- *Mem:* Opers Res Soc Am; Mil Opers Res Soc; Am Defense Preparedness Asn; Soc Mfg Engrs. *Res:* Assists manufacturing companies in improving performance in 6 key areas: quality, cost, timeliness, product performance, legal/social impact and risk; solutions include product design engineering, process optimization, automation, computer integrated manufacturing, computer system maintenance and enhancement; applies operations research analysis techniques to a variety of problems for government and industry; chemical warfare defense; nuclear waste isolation; cost analysis and other types of optimization. *Mailing Add:* PO Box 826 Delaware OH 43015

**VENTRICE, CARL ALFRED,** PLASMA PHYSICS, NUCLEAR PHYSICS. *Current Pos:* PROF ELEC ENG, TENN TECHNOL UNIV, 68- *Personal Data:* b York, Pa, Aug 7, 30; m 60; c 3. *Educ:* Pa State Univ, BS, 56, MS, 58, PhD(physics), 62. *Prof Exp:* Sr analyst, Anal Serv Inc, 63-64; assoc prof physics, Tenn Technol Univ, 64-66; assoc prof elec eng, Auburn Univ, 66-68. *Mem:* AAAS; Inst Elec & Electronics Engrs; Am Phys Soc. *Res:* Interaction of electromagnetic waves in plasmas; plasma stability; lasers. *Mailing Add:* Eng Tenn Technol Univ Box 5005 TTU Cookeville TN 38505

**VENTRICE, MARIE BUSCK,** THERMAL & FLUID SCIENCES. *Current Pos:* Instr eng sci, 69-70, from asst prof to assoc prof, 74-86, PROF MECH ENG, TENN TECHNOL UNIV, 86- *Personal Data:* b Allentown, Pa, Oct 17, 40; m 60, Carl A; c Ruth E, Carl A Jr & James A. *Educ:* Tenn Technol Univ, BSES, 66, PhD(mech eng), 74; Auburn Univ, MS, 68. *Concurrent Pos:* Interim dir, Ctr Elec Power, Tenn Technol Univ, 85-88, assoc dean eng, 89- *Mem:* Am Soc Mech Engrs; Am Soc Eng Educ; Nat Soc Prof Engrs; Sigma Xi; Am Inst Aeronaut & Astronaut. *Res:* Experimental studies of liquid propellant rocket combustion instabilities using an analog technique; cogeneration. *Mailing Add:* Col Eng Tenn Technol Univ Cookeville TN 38505. *E-Mail:* mbv9994@tntech.edu

**VENTRIGLIA, ANTHONY E,** APPLIED MATHEMATICS. *Current Pos:* RETIRED. *Personal Data:* b New York, NY, June 20, 22; m 53, Lois Richter; c Patricia (Maguire) & Linda (Carella). *Educ:* Columbia Univ, AB, 42; Brown Univ, ScM, 43. *Prof Exp:* Instr math, Rutgers Univ, 47; from instr to asst prof math, Manhattan Col, 47-92. *Concurrent Pos:* Social Sci Res Fel, Stanford Univ, 57, instr, Hunter Col, 61-63; adj asst prof, City Col New York; NSF fel, Inst Math Teachers, Univ Wyo, 59. *Mem:* AAAS; Am Math Soc; Math Asn Am; Am Acad Polit & Soc Sci; Am Asn Univ Prof. *Res:* Linear algebra and analysis; partial differential equations. *Mailing Add:* One Georgia Ave Bronxville NY 10708

**VENTURA, JOAQUIN CALVO,** PATHOLOGY. *Current Pos:* SR LECTR PATH, UNIV MONTREAL, 58-; MEM STAFF, SANTA CABRINI HOSP, 71- *Personal Data:* b Cadiz, Spain, Mar 22, 29; Can citizen; m 61, Margo; c Philippe & Vincent. *Educ:* Univ Seville, MD, 52; Univ Montreal, PhD, 58; FRCP(C), 61. *Concurrent Pos:* Chief serv & dir res, St Joseph of Rosemont Hosp, Montreal, 62-69; consult pathologist, Louis H LaFontaine Hosp, Montreal, 69- & Maisonneuve Rosemont Hosp, Montreal, 70-; assoc dir labs, Santa Cabrini Hosp, 69-70. *Mem:* Can Asn Path; NY Acad Sci; Can Med Asn. *Res:* Chronic bronchitis, role of sensitization; pathogenesis of bronchiectasis; effects of pollution on chronic experimental bronchitis. *Mailing Add:* 1140 Jeantalum Montreal PQ H2R 1V9 Can

**VENTURA, JOSE ANTONIO,** MATHEMATICAL PROGRAMMING, PRODUCTION SCHEDULING. *Current Pos:* from asst prof to assoc prof, 89-95, PROF OPERS RES, PA STATE UNIV, 95- *Personal Data:* b Barcelona, Spain, Nov 3, 54; m 81, Marta Jaen; c Marta, Laura & Luis. *Educ:* Polytech Univ Barcelona, Spain, BSIE, 79; Univ Fla, ME, 84, PhD (indust eng), 86. *Honors & Awards:* Ralph R Teetor Award, Soc Automotive Engrs, 89. *Prof Exp:* Asst prof opers res, Univ Mo, Columbia, 86-89. *Concurrent Pos:* Panelist, NSF, 89-; NSF Presidential Young Investr, 90; assoc ed, Inst Indust Engrs Trans, 93-; J Mgf Systs, 93- *Mem:* Inst Opers Res & Mgt Sci; sr mem Inst Indust Engrs. *Res:* Applied optimization; production management; applied probability; machine vision. *Mailing Add:* 207 Hammond Bldg Pa State Univ University Park PA 16802. *Fax:* 814-863-4745; *E-Mail:* javie@engr.psu.edu

**VENTURA, LAWRENCE J,** VETERINARY MEDICINE. *Current Pos:* staff regulatory vet, Ctr Vet Med, Food & Drug Admin, 91-92, sr staff regulatory vet, 92-93, sr regulatory mgt officer, 93-95, PROG MGT OFFICER, CTR VET FMED, FOOD & DRUG ADMIN, 95- *Educ:* Utah State Univ, BS, 74; Colo State Univ, DVM, 80; Hood Col, MBA, 94. *Prof Exp:* Pvt pract vet, Denver, Colo, 80-89; supvry vet, NCent Region, Food Safety & Inspection Serv, USDA, 89-91. *Mem:* Am Vet Med Asn. *Mailing Add:* HFA-240 Off Facil Acquistion 7500 Standish Pl Rockville MD 20855

**VENTURA, WILLIAM PAUL,** ECOLOGY. *Current Pos:* CHMN, ENVIRON SCI, SOUNDVIEW PREP SCH, 89- *Personal Data:* b Braddock, Pa, Dec 1, 42; m 69, Marion R Simpson; c Alexander W & Christine A. *Educ:* Duquesne Univ, BS, 64, MS, 66; New York Med Col, PhD(pharmacol), 69, Pace Univ, MBA, 80. *Prof Exp:* Res assoc endocrinol, Duquesne Univ, 66; from instr to asst prof pharmacol, New York Med Col, 69-74; from assoc prof to prof pharmacol, Pace Univ, 74-85, chmn, Dept Biol Sci, 81-85. *Concurrent Pos:* Lalor Found grant, 70; NSF equip grant, 80, Dorr Found grant, 89; Dyson Col fel, 85. *Mem:* Am Physiol Soc; NY Acad Sci; Int Fertil Asn; Am Chem Soc; Am Col Clin Pharm. *Res:* Reproductive pharmacology, male and female reproductive studies. *Mailing Add:* 368 Elm Rd Briarcliff Manor NY 10510

**VENTURELLA, VINCENT STEVEN,** HIGH PRESSURE LIQUID CHROMATOGRAPHY. *Current Pos:* group leader, Anaquest Div, BOC Group, 85-88, SECT MGR, ANAQUEST INC, 88- *Personal Data:* b Pittsburgh, Pa, Aug 24, 30; m 54; c 3. *Educ:* Univ Pittsburgh, BS, 54, MS, 56, PhD(med chem), 61. *Prof Exp:* Asst prof pharm chem, Fordham Univ, 60-63; anal res chemist, Abbott Labs, 63-64; asst prof pharm & pharm chem, Temple Univ Philadelphia, Pa, 64-67; mgr anal res, Hoffman-LaRoche Inc, 67-71, group leader, 72-76, mgr anal develop, 76-79, sr tech fel, 79-85; chief res br, US Bur Customs Lab, New York, 71-72. *Concurrent Pos:* Adj asst prof, Dept Chem, Rutgers Univ, 69-70, vis prof, Sch Pharm, 81-; adj assoc prof, Fairleigh Dickinson Univ, Rutherford, NJ, 72-75; consult nuclear magnetic resonance, NF Rev Comt, 72-78. *Mem:* NY Acad Sci; Am Pharmaceut Asn; Am Chem Soc; NAm Thermal Anal Soc; Int Soc Magnetic Resonance; Soc Appl Spectros. *Res:* Method development for bulk pharmaceutical chemicals, drug products, metabolisms and degradation products; identification of impurities and intermediates by high resolution nuclear magnetic resonance and mass spectroscopy, particularly carbon 13 and phosphorous 31 resonance. *Mailing Add:* Ventura Assoc 9 Ring Pl Cedar Grove NJ 07009-1037

**VENUGOPALAN, CHANGARAM,** VETERINARY PHYSIOLOGY, PHARMACOLOGY. *Current Pos:* PROF, DEPT VET PHYSIOL, PHARMACOL & TOXICOL, SCH VET MED, LA STATE UNIV. *Personal Data:* b Oct 8, 42; m, Sheela Venugopal; c Rashmi & Jay. *Educ:* Kerala Univ, India, BVSc, 63; Calicut Univ, India, MSc, 71; Mass Col Pharm & Allied Health Sci, MS, 75, PhD, 80. *Prof Exp:* Fel, Harvard Univ, 80-81. *Concurrent Pos:* Consult pulmonary pharmacol, USDA, 84-86; new investr res award, NIH, 84. *Mem:* Fel Am Acad Vet Pharamcol & Therapeut; Sigma Xi; Am Soc Pharmacol & Exp Therapeut; Soc Neurosci; Asn Scientists Indian Origin in Am. *Res:* Non-adrenergic non-cholinergic inhibitory innervation in animals to unravel the mode of neutrotransmission and mediators involved; adrenoceptor interconversion in the respiratory system; characterization of chemical mediators of immediate hypersensitivity reactions (asthma) and their antagonists; in-vivo and in-vitro studies. *Mailing Add:* Dept Vet Physiol & Pharmacol & Toxicol Sch Vet Med La State Univ Baton Rouge LA 70803-0001

**VENUGOPALAN, SRINIVASA I,** LASER SPECTROSCOPY, CONDENSED MATTER PHYSICS. *Current Pos:* asst prof, 81-84, ASSOC PROF PHYSICS, STATE UNIV NY, BINGHAMTON, 84- *Personal Data:* b Madras, Tamilnadu, India, Dec 19, 44; Indian citizen; m 70; c 2. *Educ:* Univ Madras, BSc, 63; Purdue Univ, MS, 69, PhD(physics), 73. *Prof Exp:* Sci officer, Bhabha Atomic Res Ctr, India, 63-67; res/teaching asst physics, Purdue Univ, 67-73; scientist, Raman Res Inst, India, 73-79; res physicist, Purdue Univ, 79-81. *Concurrent Pos:* Vis scientist, US Naval Res Lab, 83; consult, IBM-Endicott, 83-87; vis assoc prof, Purdue Univ, 84 & Cornell Univ, 87-88. *Mem:* Sigma Xi. *Res:* Experimental solid state physics; raman, infrared and quasielastic light scattering investigations of excitations in semiconductors, liquid crystals, colloidal materials, and magnetically ordered systems. *Mailing Add:* Dept Physics State Univ NY Binghamton NY 13901

**VENUTI, WILLIAM J(OSEPH),** CIVIL ENGINEERING. *Current Pos:* assoc prof, 55-63, prof, 63-87, EMER PROF CIVIL ENG, SAN JOSE STATE UNIV, 87- *Personal Data:* b Philadelphia, Pa, Aug 16, 24; m 49, Twila Black; c David W, Thomas E, Paul E, Lisa L, Stephen R & Philip J. *Educ:* Univ Pa, AB, 47; Univ Colo, BS, 50, MS, 55; Stanford Univ, PhD(civil eng), 63. *Prof Exp:* Civil engr, US Bur Reclamation, Colo & Mont, 49-52; instr civil eng, Univ Colo, 52-55. *Concurrent Pos:* Sr design engr, Food Mach & Chem Corp, 56-63; assoc, Boeing Airplane Co, 59; prof struct eng, SEATO Grad Sch Eng, Bangkok, Thailand, 64-66; vis prof, Stanford Univ, 70-71, 78- & Univ Dundee, 72; NSF int travel grant, India, 72. *Mem:* Fel Am Soc Civil Engrs; fel Am Concrete Inst; Am Rwy Eng Asn; Prestressed & Precast Concrete Inst. *Res:* Lightweight prestressed concrete; framed structures; effects of impact loads on structures; fatigue of concrete; structural dynamics; blast loading and effects; prestressed concrete connectors; concrete railroad ties. *Mailing Add:* 16091 Greenwood Rd Monte Sereno CA 95030. *Fax:* 408-354-3800; *E-Mail:* hvrm97a@prodigy.com

**VENUTO, PAUL B,** PROCESS CATALYTIC CHEMISTRY, UNDERGROUND RECOVERY PROCESSES. *Current Pos:* CONSULT. *Personal Data:* b Flushing, NY, Feb 8, 33; m 58; c 3. *Educ:* Univ Pa, AB, 54, PhD(org chem), 62. *Honors & Awards:* Ipatieff Award, Am Chem Soc, 71. *Prof Exp:* Res & develop chemist, Columbian Carbon Co, 57-59; sr res chemist, Mobil Oil Corp, 62-66, group leader heterogeneous catalysis, 66-67, group leader appl res & develop div, 67-69, res assoc, Paulsboro Res Lab, 69-75, mgr anal & spec technol, Cent Res Lab, 75-77, mgr, heavy oils & energy minerals, Dallas Res Lab, 77-82, mgr, Enhanced Oil Recovery, Dallas Res Lab, 82-86, mgr catalysis, Ctr Res Lab, Mobil Res & Develop Corp, 86-93. *Mem:* Am Chem Soc; Am Inst Chem Engrs; Soc Petrol Engrs. *Res:* Organic heterogeneous catalysis; zeolite technology; process scoping and economics; catalysis in petroleum refining; uranium in-situ leaching; heavy oil and tar sands thermal recovery; enhanced oil recovery. *Mailing Add:* 1073 Princeton Dr Yardley PA 19067. *Fax:* 215-321-8938

**VENZKE, WALTER GEORGE,** VETERINARY ANATOMY. *Current Pos:* RETIRED. *Personal Data:* b White Lake, SDak, June 18, 12; m 39; c 1. *Educ:* Iowa State Col, DVM, 35, PhD(vet anat), 42; Univ Wis, MS, 37. *Prof Exp:* Asst genetics, Univ Wis, 35-37; instr vet anat, Iowa State Col, 37-41, asst prof, 41-42, vet physiol, 42; instr zool, Ohio State Univ, 46, asst prof vet prev med, 46-48, assoc prof vet med, 48-53, prof vet anat & head dept, 54-80, asst dean & secy, Col Vet Med, 60-80. *Mem:* Am Vet Med Asn; Am Asn Anat; Conf Res Workers Animal Dis. *Res:* Endocrinology of the thymus and pineal gland. *Mailing Add:* 2535 Andover Rd Columbus OH 43221

**VEOMETT, GEORGE ECTOR,** CELL BIOLOGY, ENDOCRINOLOGY. *Current Pos:* asst prof, 77-81, ASSOC PROF CELL BIOL, UNIV NEBR, 81-, VDIR, 91- *Personal Data:* b Rochester, NY, Aug 27, 44; m 70, Marilyn Jaeger; c Elizabeth, Yuri, Angela & Ellen. *Educ:* Univ Rochester, AB, 66; Univ Colo, PhD, 72. *Prof Exp:* Res assoc virol, Univ Colo, Boulder, 72-74, res assoc cell biol, 74-76. *Concurrent Pos:* Prin investr, USDA grant, 87- *Mem:* AAAS; Am Soc Cell Biol. *Res:* Role of insulin-like growth factors and their binding proteins in cancer cell biology. *Mailing Add:* Sch Life Sci Univ Nebr Lincoln NE 68588-0001

**VER, ISTVAN LASZLO,** NOISE & VIBRATION CONTROL, ACOUSTICS RESEARCH & CONSULTING. *Current Pos:* sr scientist noise & vibration control, Bolt Beranek & Newman Inc, 65-73, actg dir, Archit Tech Div, 71, lectr, Prog Advan Studies, 72-73, PRIN CONSULT, BOLT BERANEK & NEWMAN SYSTS & TECHNOLOGIES, 76- *Personal Data:* b Tapioszecso, Hungary, Dec 22, 34; US citizen; m 61, Elisabeth Waltering; c Kristina. *Educ:* Tech Univ, Budapest, BS, 56; Tech Univ, Aachen, Ger, MS, 59, Tech Univ, Munich, Ger, PhD(acoust), 63. *Honors & Awards:* Sr US Scientist Award, Alexander von Humboldt Found, 78. *Prof Exp:* Res & develop engr, Rhode & Schwarz, Ger, 60-65. *Concurrent Pos:* Lectr, Mass Inst Technol, 72; mem bd dirs, Inst Noise Control Eng, 76-77. *Mem:* Inst Noise Control Eng; fel Acoust Soc Am; Europ Acoust Asn. *Res:* Noise and vibration control of automobiles, aircrafts, spacecrafts and consumer products; use of reciprocity and statistical energy analyses in noise control diagnoses; acoustic design of wind tunnels, jet engine test cells, power plants, microelectronic manufacturing facilities, acoustic test facilities; active and passive silencers for high temperature contaminate flow environment. *Mailing Add:* BBN Systs & Technologies 10 Moulton St Cambridge MA 02138. *Fax:* 617-873-2918; *E-Mail:* iver@bbn.com

**VERBANAC, FRANK,** ORGANIC CHEMISTRY. *Current Pos:* RETIRED. *Personal Data:* b Yugoslavia, Jan 12, 20; nat US; m 45; c 2. *Educ:* Wayne State Univ, BS, 41; Univ Ill, PhD(chem), 49. *Prof Exp:* Chemist, Gelatin Prod Corp, 42-46 & Merck & Co, Inc, 49-57; sr res chemist, A E Staley Mfg Co, 57-60, group leader, 60-70, sr scientist, 70-85. *Mem:* AAAS; Am Chem Soc; Sigma Xi. *Res:* N-arylpyrazolines; antibiotics; natural products; carbohydrates; polymers; proteins. *Mailing Add:* 12 Dakota Dr Decatur IL 62526-2331

**VERBEEK, EARL RAYMOND,** MINERAL LUMINESCENCE. *Current Pos:* GEOLOGIST, PLANNING & ENVIRON COORDR, BUR LAND MGT, TONOPAH, NEV, 95- *Personal Data:* b Philadelphia, Pa, Mar 4, 48; div. *Educ:* Pa State Univ, BS, 69, PhD(struct geol), 75. *Prof Exp:* Geologist, Struct Geol, US Geol Surv, 74-95. *Mem:* Franklin-Ogdensburg Mineral Soc. *Res:* Minor structures of deformed rocks; mechanics of folding, origin of joints and quantitative characterization of three-dimensional joint networks in rock masses; luminescence spectroscopy of minerals. *Mailing Add:* Burland Mgt PO Box 911 Tonopah NV 89049

**VERBEKE, JUDITH ANN,** PLANT ANATOMY, DEVELOPMENTAL PLANT BIOLOGY. *Current Pos:* ASSOC PROF PLANT SCI, UNIV ARIZ, TUCSON, 90- *Personal Data:* b St Louis, Mo, Jan 27, 48; m 91, Rick C Heupel; c Richard & Christina. *Educ:* Rockhurst Col, BS, 80; Univ Calif, Los Angeles, PhD(biol), 85. *Prof Exp:* Asst prof plant biol, Univ Ill, Chicago, 85-90. *Concurrent Pos:* Prog dir develop biol, NSF, 93-94. *Mem:* AAAS; Bot Soc Am; Am Soc Plant Physiologists; Am Soc Cell Biol; Int Soc Plant Molecular Biologists; Soc Develop Biol. *Res:* Cell communication and differentiation in plants from a cellular and organismal point of view; redifferentiation response in the form of diffusible factors which move between cells. *Mailing Add:* Dept Plant Sci Univ Ariz Tucson AZ 85721. *Fax:* 520-621-2012; *E-Mail:* verbeke@ag.arizona.edu

**VERBER, CARL MICHAEL,** OPTICAL PHYSICS. *Current Pos:* PROF ELEC ENG, GA TECH, 86- *Personal Data:* b New York, NY, May 20, 35; m 57; c 2. *Educ:* Yale Univ, BS, 55; Univ Rochester, MA, 58; Univ Colo, PhD(physics), 61. *Prof Exp:* Sr physicist, Columbus Lab, Battelle Mem Inst, 61-86. *Mem:* AAAS; fel Optical Soc Am; Soc Photo-Optical Instrumentation Engrs; sr mem Inst Elec & Electronics Engrs. *Res:* Optical properties of solids; integrated optics; optical data processing; optical computing. *Mailing Add:* Ga Inst Technol Sch Elec Eng 777 Atlantic Dr Atlanta GA 30332-0250

**VERBINSKI, VICTOR V,** NUCLEAR PHYSICS. *Current Pos:* MEM STAFF, SCI APPLN, INC, 75- *Personal Data:* b Shickshinny, Pa, May 7, 22; m 58; c 5. *Educ:* Mass Inst Technol, SB, 48; Univ Pa, PhD(physics), 57. *Prof Exp:* Physicist, Gen Elec Co, 57-59, Oak Ridge Nat Lab, 59-67 & Gulf Gen Atomic, 67-74; mem staff, IRT Corp, 74-75. *Mem:* Am Phys Soc; Am Nuclear Soc. *Res:* Low energy nuclear physics; neutron spectroscopy; nuclear structure physics; photonuclear reactions and fission studies; radiation measurements in nondestructive testing. *Mailing Add:* 8871 Cliffridge Ave La Jolla CA 92037

**VERBISCAR, ANTHONY JAMES,** SYNTHETIC ORGANIC & NATURAL PRODUCTS CHEMISTRY. *Current Pos:* PRES, ANVER BIOSCI DESIGN, 65-; PRES NUTRIT, 96- *Personal Data:* b Chicago, Ill, Mar 22, 29; m 59, Sheila Walsh; c Stephen, Paul & Ann. *Educ:* DePaul Univ, BS, 51; Univ Notre Dame, PhD(org chem), 55. *Prof Exp:* Res chemist, Hercules, US Army Sci & Prof Personnel Prog, Edgewood Arsenal 54-56; fel, Univ Chicago, 56-57; vpres res, Regis Technol, Inc, 57-63; fel, Univ Calif, Los Angeles, 64-65. *Concurrent Pos:* Chmn subcomt biogenic amines, spcif & criteria biochem compounds, Nat Res Coun, NSF, 71-77; prin investr, Nat Cancer Inst, NIMH, Nat Lib Med, Nat Inst Diabetes, Digestive & Kidney Dis, NSF, Food & Drug Admin & US Army Res Develop Command. *Mem:* Am Chem Soc; Am Inst Chemists; Sigma Xi; Am Soc Pharmacog; Orient Healing Arts Inst; Asn Advan Indust Crops. *Res:* Organic synthesis; medicinal chemistry; natural products; biogenic amines, indole chemistry; drug metabolism; plant materials, jojoba, guayule and red squill, oleander, antiviral and anticancer plant derived polysaccharide immunomodulators, bioflavoniods. *Mailing Add:* Anver Biosci Design Inc 160 E Montecito Ave Sierra Madre CA 91024. *Fax:* 626-355-1568

**VERBRUGGE, CALVIN JAMES,** POLYMER CHEMISTRY. *Current Pos:* Sr chemist, S C Johnson & Son, Inc, 63-69, sr res chemist, 69-80, res assoc, 80-94, SR RES SCIENTIST, S C JOHNSON & SON, INC, 94- *Personal Data:* b Sioux Falls, SDak, July 26, 37; m 61, Pauline Koene; c Helen & Susan. *Educ:* Calvin Col, BA, 59; Purdue Univ, PhD(org chem), 63. *Mem:* Am Chem Soc. *Res:* Polymer emulsion and solution polymerization and coatings therefrom; Alpha olefin maleic anhydride polymers. *Mailing Add:* Technol Develop Dept S C Johnson Polymer 8310 16th St PO Box 902 Sturtevant WI 53177-0902. *Fax:* 414-631-4039

**VERBY, JOHN E,** FAMILY MEDICINE, COMMUNITY HEALTH. *Current Pos:* prof, 69-94, EMER PROF FAMILY PRACT & COMMUNITY HEALTH, MED SCH, UNIV MINN, MINNEAPOLIS, 94- *Personal Data:* b St Paul, Minn, May 24, 23; m 46; c 4. *Educ:* Carleton Col, BA, 44; Univ Minn, MB, BS, MD, 47. *Prof Exp:* Physician pvt family pract, Minn, 49-68. *Concurrent Pos:* Sci assoc, Mayo Clin, Rochester, Minn, 67-68. *Mem:* Int Soc Gen Med; Am Asn Family Pract; AMA. *Res:* Thyroid disease. *Mailing Add:* 9609 Washburn Ave S Minneapolis MN 55431

**VERCELLOTTI, JOHN R,** CARBOHYDRATE CHEMISTRY & BIOCHEMISTRY, AGRICULTURAL & FOOD CHEMISTRY. *Current Pos:* VPRES & SR CHEMIST, U-LABS, INC, COVINGTON, LA, 95- *Personal Data:* b Joliet, Ill, May 2, 33; m 66, Sharon Vergez; c Ellen T & Paul A. *Educ:* St Bonaventure Univ, BA, 55; Marquette Univ, MS, 60; Ohio State Univ, PhD(chem), 63. *Honors & Awards:* Crinos Fel, Univ Milan, 77-78; Melville L Wolfrom Award, Am Chem Soc, 94. *Prof Exp:* Asst chem, Marquette Univ, 58-60; fel Ohio State Univ, 60-63, lectr & vis res assoc, 63-64; asst prof, Marquette Univ, 64-67; assoc prof, Univ Tenn, Knoxville, 67-70; assoc prof, Va Polytech Inst & State Univ, 70-74, prof biochem & nutrit, 74-80; suprvy chemist & res leader, Southern Regional Res Ctr, Agr

Res Serv, USDA, New Orleans, 85-95. *Concurrent Pos:* Res chemist, Freeman Chem Corp, Wis, 59 & V-Labs, Inc, Covington, La, 80-85; consult, US Vet Hosp, Wood, Wis, 65-67 & Oak Ridge Nat Lab, 67-71; vis scientist, Ronzoni Inst, Milan Italy, 77-78; indust & res grants, NSF, NIH, USDA & NATO; chmn, Carbohydrate Div, Am Chem Soc, 88; sr res adv, Sugar Processing Res Inst, Inc, 95- *Mem:* Am Chem Soc; Royal Soc Chem; Am Soc Biol Chem & Molecular Biol; Inst Food Technologists; Sigma Xi; Am Inst Chem. *Res:* Biosynthesis and reactivity of glycoproteins and mucopolysaccharides; bacterial and fungal carbohydrate metabolism; food flavor quality and sensory evaluation; carbohydrate chemistry and enzymology. *Mailing Add:* 113 E 25th Ave Covington LA 70433-2819. *Fax:* 504-893-0517; *E-Mail:* v_labs@wild.net

**VERCH, RICHARD LEE,** AQUATIC BIOLOGY. *Current Pos:* asst prof, 71-75, ASSOC PROF BIOL & CHMN, DIV NATURAL SCI, NORTHLAND COL, 75- *Personal Data:* b Wakefield, Mich, Feb 15, 37; m 66; c 1. *Educ:* Northland Col, BS, 62; Northern Mich Univ, MA, 66; Univ NDak, DA(biol), 71. *Prof Exp:* Asst prof biol, Bay de Noc Col, 66-69. *Mem:* Am Inst Biol Scientists; Nat Asn Biol Teachers; Nat Asn Sci Teachers. *Res:* Biology teaching, self study units. *Mailing Add:* 906 Ellis Ave Ashland WI 54806

**VERDEAL, KATHEY MARIE,** MAMMALIAN & ENVIRONMENTAL TOXICOLOGY. *Current Pos:* DIR TOXICOL. *Personal Data:* b Denver, Colo, June 29, 49; div. *Educ:* Colo State Univ, BS, 76; Univ Wis-Madison, MS, 78, PhD(environ toxicol), 82. *Honors & Awards:* James Price Cancer Res Award. *Prof Exp:* Territorial mgr, Upjohn Pharmaceut Co, 85; toxicologist, Chematox Lab, Inc, 85-87. *Concurrent Pos:* Assoc scientist, Wis Clin Cancer Ctr. *Mem:* AAAS. *Res:* Alteration of pituitary hormones as a side effect of the use of antidepressant and antianxiety agents, their resultant carcinogenic potential; oncology. *Mailing Add:* 4481 Clay Boulder CO 80301

**VERDERBER, NADINE LUCILLE,** MATHEMATICS EDUCATION. *Current Pos:* from instr to assoc prof, 65-92, PROF MATH, SOUTHERN ILL UNIV, EDWARDSVILLE, 92- *Personal Data:* b St Louis, Mo, Jan 28, 40. *Educ:* Wash Univ, AB, 62; Univ Mo, MA, 65; Ohio State Univ, PhD(math educ), 74. *Prof Exp:* Teaching asst math, Univ Mo, 63-64. *Concurrent Pos:* Teaching asst, Ohio State Univ, 71-72. *Mem:* Nat Coun Teachers Math; Am Asn Univ Profs; Math Asn Am. *Res:* Mathematics education; readability of mathematics texts; teaching mathematics with a spread sheet; spatial visualization; graphics calculators. *Mailing Add:* Dept Math Statist PO Box 1653 Southern Ill Univ Edwardsville IL 62026-1653

**VERDEYEN, JOSEPH T,** ELECTRICAL ENGINEERING, PLASMA PHYSICS. *Current Pos:* from instr to assoc prof, 62-69, PROF ELEC & NUCLEAR ENG, UNIV ILL, URBANA, 69-, DIR, GASEOUS ELECTRONIC LAB, 72- *Personal Data:* b Terre Haute, Ind, Aug 15, 32; m 54; c 4. *Educ:* Rose Polytech Inst, BS, 54; Rutgers Univ, MS, 58; Univ Ill, Urbana, PhD(elec eng), 62. *Prof Exp:* Mem tech staff, Bell Tel Labs, 54-55 & 57; asst instr elec eng, Rutgers Univ, 57-58. *Concurrent Pos:* Mem tech staff, Stavid Eng, 57-58; mem awards comt, Nat Electronics Conf, 65; consult, Corps Engrs, 70-, Zenith Radio Corp, Chicago, 71-79, Gen Elec Lamp Div, 76- & Lucitron Inc, 79-81, Sandia Nat Labs, 74-; dir, Ctr Compound Semiconductor Microelectronics, 88-89; chmn, Gaseous Elec Conf, 84-85, sec, 90. *Mem:* Am Phys Soc; Inst Elec & Electronics Engrs; Sigma Xi. *Res:* Studies of laser discharges and plasmas used for semiconductor processing; semiconductor lasers; microwave. *Mailing Add:* Gaseous Elec Lab 607 E Healey Champaign IL 61820. *Fax:* 217-333-5422

**VERDI, JAMES L,** physiology, for more information see previous edition

**VERDIER, PETER HOWARD,** PHYSICAL CHEMISTRY, POLYMER PHYSICS. *Current Pos:* CHEMIST, NAT INST STANDARDS & TECHNOL, 75- *Personal Data:* b Pasadena, Calif, Feb 16, 31; m 53; c 1. *Educ:* Calif Inst Technol, BS, 52; Harvard Univ, PhD(phys chem), 57. *Prof Exp:* Res assoc chem, Mass Inst Technol, 57-58; res fel, Harvard Univ, 58-59; res chemist, Union Carbide Res Inst, 59-64, staff consult, 64-65; chemist, Nat Bur Standards, 65-70, chief molecular characterization sect, Polymers Div, 70-75. *Mem:* Am Phys Soc. *Res:* Chemical physics, especially molecular structure and dynamics; polymer solution properties; polymer chain dynamics; polymer molecular weight determination. *Mailing Add:* Polymer Div Nat Inst Stand & Technol Gaithersburg MD 20899

**VERDINE, GREGORY LAWRENCE,** CHEMISTRY. *Current Pos:* asst prof chem, Fac Arts & Sci, 88-92, Thomas D Cabot assoc prof, 92-94, PROF CHEM, HARVARD UNIV, 94- *Personal Data:* b Somers Pt, NJ, June 10, 59; m 87, Kasumi Koseki; c Vanessa Kaori, Lauren Arika & Erika Rose. *Educ:* St Joseph's Univ, BS, 82; Columbia Univ, MA, 83, PhD, 86. *Hon Degrees:* AB, Harvard Univ, 95. *Honors & Awards:* Presidential Young Investr Award, NSF, 91; Arthur C Cope Scholar Award, Am Chem Soc, 94. *Prof Exp:* Fel, Mass Inst Technol, 86-87; Harvard Med Sch, 87-88. *Concurrent Pos:* Young fac fel, 88; Searle scholar, 90; Eli Lilly grantee, 90; Alfred P Sloan fel, 91; consult, Hoffman-La Roche, Nutley, NJ, 91- *Mem:* AAAS; Am Chem Soc. *Res:* Chemical genetics: the propagation, preservation and expression of genetic information. *Mailing Add:* Harvard Univ 91 Outlook Dr Lexington MA 02175

**VERDON, CHARLES P,** PHYSICS. *Current Pos:* RES SCIENTIST, LAB LASER ENERGETICS, UNIV ROCHESTER. *Honors & Awards:* Excellence in Plasma Physics Award, Am Physics Soc, 95. *Mailing Add:* Lab Laser Energetics Univ Rochester 250 E River Rd Rochester NY 14603

**VERDON, JOSEPH MICHAEL,** THEORETICAL & COMPUTATIONAL FLUID DYNAMICS, MECHANICAL SYSTEMS. *Current Pos:* sr res engr, 72-81, prin scientist, 81-88, MGR, THEORET FLUID DYNAMICS, UNITED TECHNOL RES CTR, 88- *Personal Data:* b New York, NY, July 4, 41; m 63; c 3. *Educ:* Webb Inst Naval Archit, BS, 63; Univ Notre Dame, MS, 65, PhD(eng sci), 67. *Prof Exp:* Res engr, United Aircraft Res Labs, 67-68; asst prof mech eng, Univ Conn, 68-72. *Concurrent Pos:* Consult, Pratt & Whitney Aircraft, 70-71; prin investr, res contracts sponsored by NASA, USN & USAF, 77-; assoc ed, Am Inst Aeronaut & Astronaut J, 88 - *Mem:* Am Soc Mech Engrs; Soc Indust & Appl Math; Am Inst Aeronaut & Astronaut; Sigma Xi; Am Acad Mech. *Res:* Unsteady aerodynamics, viscous flows, random vibrations; applied mathematics; author of several survey articles on unsteady aerodynamics for turbomachinery. *Mailing Add:* 19 Briarwood Lane Vernon CT 06066-5905

**VERDU, SERGIO,** INFORMATION THEORY, COMMUNICATION THEORY. *Current Pos:* Asst prof elec eng & comput sci, 84-89, assoc prof, 89-92, PROF ELEC ENG, PRINCETON UNIV, 93- *Personal Data:* b Barcelona, Spain, Aug 15, 58; m 82, Mercedes Paratje; c Ariana. *Educ:* Polytech Univ Barcelona, Engr, 80; Univ Ill, Urbana, MS, 82, PhD(elec eng), 84. *Honors & Awards:* Presidential Young Investr Award, NSF, 89. *Concurrent Pos:* Fac develop award, Int Bus Mach, 86; NSF presidential young investr award, 87; prin investr, Off Naval Res & Army Res Off, 87-; assoc ed, Inst Elec & Electronics Engrs Trans Automatic Control, 87-90 & Trans Info Theory, 90-; vis fel, Inst Advan Study, Australian Nat Univ, 89; mem bd gov, Inst Elec & Electronics Engrs Info Theory Soc, 89-; consult, Bell Commun Res, 90-95. *Mem:* Fel Inst Elec & Electronics Engrs; Inst Elec & Electronics Engrs Info Theory Soc (pres, 97). *Res:* Communication and information theory of noisy channels; analysis and design of multiuser communication systems; statistical signal processing in decision and communication systems. *Mailing Add:* Dept Elec Eng Princeton Univ Princeton NJ 08544. *E-Mail:* verdu@princeton.edu

**VERDUIN, JACOB,** PLANT PHYSIOLOGY. *Current Pos:* prof bot, 64-84, EMER PROF, SOUTHERN ILL UNIV, CARBONDALE, 84- *Personal Data:* b Orange City, Iowa, Nov 19, 13; m 42; c 5. *Educ:* Iowa State Col, BS, 39, MS, 41, PhD(plant physiol), 47. *Prof Exp:* Instr bot, Iowa State Col, 41-42, instr plant physiol, 45-46; assoc prof bot & head dept, Univ SDak, 46-48; prof biol & dept chmn, Bowling Green State Univ, 55-64. *Concurrent Pos:* Consult, Commonwealth Edison, Chicago, 73- & Nat Environ Res Ctr, Environ Protection Agency, Nev, 75-77. *Mem:* AAAS; Ecol Soc Am; Am Soc Limnol & Oceanog; Am Fisheries Soc; Am Inst Biol Scientists. *Res:* Photosynthesis under natural conditions; respiration; diffusion problems; aquatic ecology; impact of electric power on aquatic systems. *Mailing Add:* 2999 Country Club Rd Carbondale IL 62901-7334

**VERDY, MAURICE,** OBESITY, DIABETES & THYROID. *Current Pos:* PROF MED, UNIV MONTREAL, 76- *Personal Data:* b Montreal, Que, Sept 14, 33; c 3. *Educ:* Univ Montreal, MD, 56. *Prof Exp:* ENDOCRINOLOGIST, HOTEL-DIEU HOSP, 63- *Mailing Add:* Hotel-Dieu Hosp Univ Montreal 3840 rue St Urbain Montreal PQ H2W 1T8 Can

**VEREBEY, KARL G,** CLINICAL PHARMACOLOGY, ANALYTICAL & FORENSIC TOXICOLOGY. *Current Pos:* ASSOC PROF PSYCHIAT, HEALTH SCI CTR, STATE UNIV NY, BROOKLYN, 81-; PRES & DIR, LEADTECH CORP, BERGEN, NJ, 92- *Personal Data:* b Budapest, Hungary, Mar 12, 38; US citizen; m 62, Debra Adler; c Todd, Marc & Rita. *Educ:* City Univ New York Hunter Col, BA, 65, MA, 68; Cornell Univ, Med Col, PhD(pharmacol), 72. *Prof Exp:* Res assoc neurol & postdoctoral fel, Cornell Univ Med Col, 72-73; dir, clin pharmacol, NY Med Col, 73-84, asst dir, NY State DSAS Testing & Res Labs, 84-88, res prof psychiat, Valhalla, 76-88; clin lab dir, Psychiat Diag Lab Am, 82-89; chief toxicologist, City NY, 89-92; dir toxicol, NY State Inst Basic Res, 92-95. *Concurrent Pos:* USPHS fel, 68-73; sr res assoc, Biobehav Res Found, Inc, 81-; clin lab dir, Am Bd Bioanal, 88; adv, Nat Comt Clin Lab Stand. *Mem:* Am Soc Pharmacol & Exp Therapeut; NY Acad Sci; fel Am Acad Forensic Sci; Soc Forensic Toxicologists; Int Asn Forensic Toxicologists. *Res:* Clinical pharmacology; analytical toxicology; psychopharmacology; drug biotransformation in animals and man; identification of new metabolites and toxic drug interactions; development of sensitive analytical methods for various drugs; contributed over 100 articles to professional journals; expert witness in drugs of abuse, alcohol pharmacology, toxicology and behavior. *Mailing Add:* Dir Toxicol 638 Debchar Ct Rivervale NJ 07675-6409. *Fax:* 201-868-3994

**VEREEN, LARRY EDWIN,** MICROBIOLOGY. *Current Pos:* ASSOC PROF BIOL, LANDER COL, 70- *Personal Data:* b Loris, SC, Mar 24, 40. *Educ:* Clemson Univ, BS, 63, MS, 64; Colo State Univ, PhD(microbiol), 68. *Prof Exp:* Asst prof food sci & biochem, Clemson Univ, 68-70. *Mem:* Am Soc Microbiol. *Res:* Behavior of Clostridium perfringens in vacuum-sealed foods. *Mailing Add:* 213 Alabama Ave Greenwood SC 29646

**VERELL, RUTH ANN,** ORGANIC CHEMISTRY, SCIENCE EDUCATION ADMINISTRATION. *Current Pos:* INDEPENDENT CONSULT, 92- *Personal Data:* b New York, NY, Mar 8, 35; m 66, T Jackson; c Thomas J Jr & Karl R. *Educ:* Allegheny Col, BS, 57; Univ Ill, MS, 58; Columbia Univ, PhD(chem), 62. *Prof Exp:* Res chemist, Nat Bur Stand, 62-64; prof asst, 64-65, asst prog dir, Instrnl Sci Equip Prog, 65-68, assoc prog dir, Col Sci Improv Progs, 68-69 & 71-73, proj mgr exp projs & develop progs, NSF, 73-76, prof assoc, Energy Res & Develop Admin, 76-77; employee develop specialist, Dept Air Force, 82-88; mem prof staff, US Dept Energy, 77-82, dep dir, Div Univ & Indust Progs, 88-90, dep assoc dir, Univ & Sci

Educ, 90-92. *Concurrent Pos:* Fel, Assoc Western Univ, 93- *Mem:* AAAS; Am Chem Soc; Sigma Xi. *Res:* Cyclopropenones; alkaline conversions of labeled sugars. *Mailing Add:* 6215 Thornwood Dr Alexandria VA 22310-2961. *E-Mail:* ravgolf@aol.com

**VERESS, SANDOR A,** PHOTOGRAMMETRY, GEODESY. *Current Pos:* RETIRED. *Personal Data:* b Jaszkiser, Hungary, Mar 13, 27; US citizen; m 51; c 2. *Educ:* Univ Forestry & Timber Indust, Hungary, BS, 51; Hungarian Tech Univ, Sopron, MS, 56; Laval Univ, DSc(photogram), 68. *Honors & Awards:* Pres Citation, Am Soc Photogram, 77 & 79, Am Cong Surv & Mapping, 80. *Prof Exp:* From instr to asst prof geod & photogram, Univ Forestry & Timber Indust, Hungary, 51-56; asst prof, Univ BC, 56-59; photogrammetrist, Ohio State Hwy Dept, 60-62; asst prof surv & mapping, Purdue Univ, 62-65; prof civil eng, Univ Wash, 65-96. *Concurrent Pos:* Consult to several pvt & fed photogram orgns, 61- *Mem:* Am Soc Civil Engrs; Am Cong Surv & Mapping; Am Soc Photogram; Sigma Xi. *Res:* Determination of structural deformations by photogrammetry; biomedical and x-ray photogrammetry. *Mailing Add:* 1934 Ridgewater Way Sutherlin OR 97479

**VERGARA, WILLIAM CHARLES,** ELECTRONICS ENGINEERING. *Current Pos:* RETIRED. *Personal Data:* b Far Rockaway, NY, July 6, 23; m 46. *Educ:* Rensselaer Polytech Inst, BEE, 45. *Prof Exp:* Engr, Cardwell Mfg Corp, 46-48; proj engr, Commun Div, 48-53; prin engr, 53-58, dir advan res, 58-72, dir phys electronics, commun div, 72-76, head microelectronics engr, Bendix Corp, Baltimore, 76-82. *Concurrent Pos:* Mem, Gov Sci Adv Bd, State of Md, 66- *Mem:* Inst Elec & Electronics Engrs. *Res:* Physics of thin films; microelectronics; radiowave propagation; radio receiver design. *Mailing Add:* 910 Dunellen Dr Baltimore MD 21286

**VERGENZ, ROBERT ALLAN,** CHEMISTRY, PHYSICS. *Current Pos:* ASST PROF CHEM & PHYSICS, UNIV NFLA, JACKSONVILLE, 87- *Personal Data:* b Milwaukee, Wis, Dec 26, 56; m 82. *Educ:* Rollins Col, Winter Park, Fla, BA, 78; Rutgers Univ, New Brunswick, NJ, MS, 85, PhD(chem), 89. *Prof Exp:* Anal chemist, Merck Chem Mfg, Albany, Ga, 78-80. *Mem:* Am Chem Soc. *Res:* Electronic state of matter from theory and experiment; chemical education; interrelations of science and technology. *Mailing Add:* Dept Natural Sci Bldg 3 Rm 2200 Univ NFla 4567 St Johns Bluff Rd S Jacksonville FL 32224

**VERGHESE, KURUVILLA,** NUCLEAR ENGINEERING. *Current Pos:* Asst prof, 63-84, grad adminr, 76-82, PROF NUCLEAR ENG, NC STATE UNIV, 84- *Personal Data:* b Kottayam, India, June 29, 36; m 64; c 3. *Educ:* Univ Kerala, BSc, 58, Univ Iowa, MS, 60, PhD(nuclear eng), 63. *Honors & Awards:* Glenn Murphy Award, Am Soc Eng Educ. *Concurrent Pos:* Consult, var indust corps. *Mem:* Am Nuclear Soc; Am Soc Eng Educ. *Res:* Reactor physics problems; radiation applications. *Mailing Add:* PO Box 7909 Raleigh NC 27695-7909

**VERGHESE, MARGRITH WEHRLI,** GENETICS, IMMUNOGENETICS. *Current Pos:* res assoc, Duke Univ, 75- *Personal Data:* b Davos, Switz, May 12, 39; m 64; c 3. *Educ:* Iowa State Univ, BS, 61, PhD(poultry breeding), 64. *Honors & Awards:* Nat Res Serv Award, NIH, 75. *Prof Exp:* Res asst poultry breeding, Iowa State Univ, 62-64; res assoc quant genetics, NC State Univ, 65-68; researcher biostatist, Univ NC, Chapel Hill, 68-69. *Mem:* AAAS; Am Asn Immunologists. *Res:* Quantitative genetics; selection theory for quantitative traits; interaction between artificial and natural selection in genetic populations; simulation of genetic populations; effects of murine anti-H-Z sera and human anti-DrW sera on the human mixed lymphocyte culture reaction; Con-A induced suppression in human cellular immune function. *Mailing Add:* 5709 Crutchfield Rd Raleigh NC 27606

**VERGONA, KATHLEEN ANNE DOBROSIELSKI,** CELLULAR AGING, GERIATRIC DENTAL. *Current Pos:* fel, Sch Dent Med, Univ Pittsburgh, 77-79, asst prof histol, 76-81, actg chmn, Dept Anat & Histol, 90-91, chmn, 91-92, RES ASST PROF, SCH MED, UNIV PITTSBURGH, 75-, ASSOC PROF HISTOL, SCH DENT MED, 81- *Personal Data:* b Pittsburgh, Pa, Dec 6, 48; m 73, Ronald J; c Raymond J. *Educ:* Univ Pittsburgh, BS, 70, PhD(cell biol), 76. *Prof Exp:* Fel res assoc, Cancer Res Unit, Allegheny Gen Hosp, 76. *Concurrent Pos:* Curric coordr, Geriat Educ Ctr Pa, gerondontology educ consult; chair, Anat Sci Sect, Am Asn Dent Schs. *Mem:* Am Soc Cell Biol; Tissue Cult Asn; Sigma Xi; Am Asn Dent Res; Am Asn Dent Schs; Am Asn Oral Biol (pres-elect, 93-94). *Res:* Regulation of salivary gland glucose-6-phosphatase, in vivo and in primary cell cultures; age-related changes in salivary gland; gamma glutamyl-transpeptidase function in salivary glands; needs assessment in geriatric dentistry. *Mailing Add:* 615-2 Salk Hall Sch Dent Med Univ Pittsburgh Pittsburgh PA 15261. *Fax:* 412-648-8219

**VERHAGE, HAROLD GLENN,** CELLULAR REPRODUCTIVE BIOLOGY, OVIDUCT PHYSIOLOGY. *Current Pos:* PROF, UNIV ILL, CHICAGO, 88- *Personal Data:* b May 18, 37; m; c 3. *Educ:* Colo State Univ, PhD(reproductive biol), 72. *Mem:* Soc Study Reprod; Soc Gynec Invest. *Res:* Mechanisms of hormone action; steroid induced proteins. *Mailing Add:* Dept Obstet & Gynec M/c 808 Univ Ill Col Med 820 S Wood St Chicago IL 60612-7313. *Fax:* 312-996-4238

**VERHALEN, LAVAL M(ATHIAS),** COTTON BREEDING & GENETICS, COTTON CULTURAL STUDIES. *Current Pos:* From instr to assoc prof, 67-77, PROF AGRON, OKLA STATE UNIV, 77- *Personal Data:* b Knox City, Tex, May 8, 41; m 64, 88, Janice Medford; c Lisa (Konemann), Amy (Case), Sheri (Rawlins) & Rhonda (Wilde). *Educ:* Tex Tech Col, BS, 63; Okla State Univ, PhD(plant breeding, genetics), 68. *Honors & Awards:* Cotton Genetics Res Award, Joint Cotton Breeding Policy Comt, Nat Cotton Coun Am, 88. *Concurrent Pos:* Prin investr, Cotton Breeding & Genetics, 67-93, Eval Cotton Varieties for Okla, 67-, Cotton Cult Studies, 93-; secy grad fac genetics, Okla State Univ, 70-72, group I-biol sci grad fac, 85-87, vchair, 87-89, chair, 89-91; chmn, 26th Cotton Improv Conf, 73-74, S-77 ann meeting, 80-81; assoc ed, Crop Sci, 81-85, mem, Subcomt Crop Regist Cotton, 92-; treas, Sigma Xi, Okla State Univ, 82-84, vpres, 92-93, pres, 93-94; mem, Planning Comm W Cotton Prod Conf, 84, 89, Tech Panel Determine Minimum Distance Cotton, Am Seed Trade Asn, 88-93; consult for several co, 85, 87-91; deleg, SW Reg Task Force, Nat Cotton Coun Am, 87. *Mem:* Sigma Xi; Am Soc Agron; Crop Sci Soc Am. *Res:* Cotton breeding; genetics, particularly quantitative genetics; variety testing, particularly genotype by evironment interaction; cultural practices, particularly weed and disease control, planting dates and rates, experimental methodology. *Mailing Add:* Dept Agron Okla State Univ Stillwater OK 74078-6028. *Fax:* 405-744-5269; *E-Mail:* imv@soilwater.agr.okstate.edu

**VERHANOVITZ, RICHARD FRANK,** SYSTEMS ENGINEERING. *Current Pos:* SR PROGRAMMER, SPACE DIV, GEN ELEC CO, 75-, MGR SYSTS ENG, 80-, PROG MGR, 85- *Personal Data:* b Walsenburg, Colo, Sept 20, 44; m 67; c 2. *Educ:* Wilkes Col, BS, 66; Lehigh Univ, MS, 69, PhD(physics), 74. *Prof Exp:* Mathematician, Defense Intel Agency, Dept Defense, 66; engr, Univac, Sperry-Rand Corp, 66-67. *Mem:* Am Phys Soc; AAAS; NY Acad Sci; Opers Res Soc. *Res:* Low energy nuclear physics; two and three body interactions; charge symmetry and nuclear coulomb interactions; computer simulation and numerical analysis. *Mailing Add:* 10 Wampenog Circle Royersford PA 19468

**VERHEY, ROGER FRANK,** MATHEMATICS & COMPUTER EDUCATION. *Current Pos:* Lectr, Univ Mich, Dearborn, 65-66, from asst prof to assoc prof, 66-72, chmn, Dept Math & Statist, 71-77, PROF MATH, UNIV MICH, DEARBORN, 72-, DIR, CIS PROG, 82- *Personal Data:* b Grand Rapids, Mich, Sept 12, 38; m 60; c 4. *Educ:* Calvin Col, AB, 60; Univ Mich, MA, 61, PhD(math), 66. *Concurrent Pos:* Fulbright lectr, Univ Ceylon, 69-70. *Mem:* Math Asn Am; Nat Coun Teachers Math; Int Coun Comput Educ. *Res:* Mathematics education; computers in the classroom. *Mailing Add:* 1454 Crawford Lane Ann Arbor MI 48105-2829

**VERHEYDEN, JULIEN P H,** ORGANIC CHEMISTRY, MOLECULAR BIOLOGY. *Current Pos:* fel, Syntex Inst Bio-Org Chem, 61-63, res chemist, 63-72, head bio-org dept, Syntex Inst Molecular Biol, 70-77, head dept, Syntex Int Org Chem, 77-81, ASST DIR, SYNTEX INST BIO-ORG CHEM, 85-, HEAD, DEPT CHEM, 81- *Personal Data:* b Brussels, Belg, May 22, 33; m 59, Danielle Isbecque; c Evelyne & Anne. *Educ:* Free Univ Brussels, Lic en sci, 55, PhD(chem), 58. *Honors & Awards:* Syntex Sci Award, 91 *Prof Exp:* Res assoc, Free Univ Brussels, 58-59; res assoc, Inst Sci Res Indust & Agr, Brussels, Belg, 60-61. *Mem:* Am Chem Soc; Chem Soc Belg; Royal Soc Chem. *Res:* Carbohydrates; nucleosides; nucleotides; genetic engineering. *Mailing Add:* PO Box 404 Sheridan OR 97378-0404. *Fax:* 650-354-2442; *E-Mail:* julien.verheyden@synmail.syntex.com

**VERHOEK, FRANK HENRY,** PHYSICAL CHEMISTRY, CHEMICAL KINETICS. *Current Pos:* from instr to assoc prof, 36-53, vchmn, Dept Chem, 60-64 & 66-68, PROF CHEM, OHIO STATE UNIV, 53- *Personal Data:* b Grand Rapids, Mich, Feb 12, 09; m 40, Cordula Thurow; c Susan, Helen & Louise. *Educ:* Harvard Univ, SB, 29; Univ Wis, MS, 30, PhD(phys chem), 33; Oxford Univ, DPhil(phys chem), 35. *Prof Exp:* Asst chem, Univ Wis, 29-33; Rhodes scholar, Oxford Univ, 33-35, Copenhagen Univ, 35-36. *Concurrent Pos:* Res chemist, Gen Elec Co, 38; res assoc, Stanford Univ, 40; consult, Liberty Mirror Div, Libby-Owens-Ford Glass Co, 43-52; prin chemist, Argonne Nat Lab, 47; counr, Am Chem Soc, 50-52; sr chemist, Olin Mathieson Chem Corp, 55; consult, US Naval Weapons Ctr, 57-62; vis prof chem, Univ Fla, 58-59; lectr, Chem Bond Approach Proj, NSF, 59-68. *Mem:* Am Chem Soc. *Res:* Solution kinetics; gas kinetics; complex ion equilibria; strength of acids in nonaqueous solvents; solubility of electrolytes in nonaqueous solvents; hydrocarbon oxidation; oxidation of boron alkanes. *Mailing Add:* 37 E Riverglen Dr Worthington OH 43085-3663

**VERHOEK, SUSAN ELIZABETH,** ECONOMIC BOTANY, BIOSYSTEMATICS & PLANT MATERIALS. *Current Pos:* from asst prof to assoc prof, 74-85, PROF BIOL, LEBANON VALLEY COL, 85-, DIR ARBORETUM, 96- *Personal Data:* b Columbus, Ohio, May 1, 42; m, Stephen E Williams; c 1. *Educ:* Ohio Wesleyan Univ, BA, 64; Ind Univ, MA, 66; Cornell Univ, PhD(bot), 75. *Prof Exp:* Herbarium supvr, Mo Bot Garden, 66-70. *Concurrent Pos:* Bot consult, Merrill Publ Co, 87-88; vis prof, Chicago Bot Gardens, 91; interpretive consult, ZooAm, Hershey, Pa, 91. *Mem:* Am Soc Plant Taxon; Bot Soc Am; Soc Econ Bot (vpres, 84-85, pres, 85-86); Am Asn Bot Gardens & Arboreta. *Res:* Biosystematics, economic botany, hybridization and pollination of tribe Poliantheae (Agavaceae); US eastern spring flora. *Mailing Add:* Dept Biol Lebanon Valley Col Annville PA 17003-0501. *Fax:* 717-867-6075

**VERHOEVEN, JOHN DANIEL,** PHYSICAL METALLURGY. *Current Pos:* From asst prof to assoc prof, 63-69, PROF METALL, IOWA STATE UNIV, 69- *Personal Data:* b Monroe, Mich, Aug 26, 34; m 62, Elizabeth Nutting; c Charles, Ann, Mary, Amy & Sarah. *Educ:* Univ Mich, BS, 57, MS, 59, PhD(metall eng), 63. *Mem:* Am Soc Metals; Am Inst Mining, Metall & Petrol Engrs. *Res:* Solidification in metals and metal alloys; physical metallurgy; superconducting alloys. *Mailing Add:* Dept Mat Sci Iowa State Univ 3053 Gilman Ames IA 50011-2221. *Fax:* 515-294-4291; *E-Mail:* jver@iastate.edu

**VERINK, ELLIS D(ANIEL), JR,** METALLURGICAL ENGINEERING. *Current Pos:* assoc prof metall, Univ Fla, 65-68, asst chmn, Dept Metall & Mat Eng, 70-73, chmn, Mat Sci & Eng Dept, 73-86, PROF METALL, UNIV FLA, 68-, DISTINGUISHED SERV PROF, 84- *Personal Data:* b Peking, China, Feb 9, 20; US citizen; m 42, Martha E Owens; c Barbara Ann & Wendy S. *Educ:* Purdue Univ, BS, 41; Ohio State Univ, MS, 63, PhD(metall eng), 65. *Honors & Awards:* Sam Tour Award, Am Soc Testing & Mat, 78; Willis Rodney Whitney Award, Nat Asn Corrosion Engrs, 82; Educator Award, Metall Soc, 88; Donald E Marlowe Award, Am Soc Eng Educ, 91. *Prof Exp:* Engr, Aluminum Co Am, 46-48, mgr, Chem Sect, Develop Div, 48-59, mgr chem & petrol indust sales, 59-62. *Concurrent Pos:* Consult, Aluminum Asn, 67-86, Copper Develop Asn, 84-; pres, Mat Consult, Inc. *Mem:* Am Inst Mining, Metall & Petrol Engrs (pres, Metall Soc, 84); fel Am Soc Metals; Am Welding Soc; fel Nat Asn Corrosion Engrs; Nat Soc Prof Engrs. *Res:* Corrosion; materials selection. *Mailing Add:* Dept Mat Sci & Eng Univ Fla Gainesville FL 32611. *Fax:* 352-392-6359; *E-Mail:* everi@mse.ufl.edu

**VERITY, MAURICE ANTHONY,** PATHOLOGY, NEUROPATHOLOGY. *Current Pos:* vis asst prof pharmacol, 59-60, assoc resident path, Sch Med, 60-61, assoc prof, 68-74, MEM, BRAIN RES INST, SCH MED, UNIV CALIF, LOS ANGELES, 67-, PROF PATH, 74- *Personal Data:* b Bradford, Eng, Apr 21, 31; c 3. *Educ:* Univ London, MB, BS, 56. *Prof Exp:* Intern surg, Paddington Gen Hosp, London, Eng & Portsmouth Group Hosps, 56; intern med, Royal Hosp, Wolverhampton, 57; clin pathologist, United Bristol Hosps, 58-59. *Concurrent Pos:* NIH travel award, Int Neuropath-Neurol Cong, Europe , 65 & 70; NIH fel biochem, Med Sch, Bristol Univ, 68-69; Milheim Found grant, Sch Med, Univ Calif, Los Angeles, 70-71, USPHS grant, 71-74. *Mem:* AAAS; Am Soc Exp Path; Am Asn Pathologists & Bacteriologists; foreign mem Royal Soc Med; Brit Biochem Soc. *Res:* Biochemical and histochemical studies of subcellular organelle function in pathologic states, including mercury intoxication, partial hepatectomy; investigations of neurogenic control of vascular smooth muscle; thyroid hormone modulation of brain development. *Mailing Add:* 9431 Texhoma Ave Northridge CA 91325

**VERKADE, JOHN GEORGE,** BIOINORGANIC CHEMISTRY, ORGANOMETALLIC CHEMISTRY. *Current Pos:* From instr to assoc prof, 60-70, PROF INORG CHEM, IOWA STATE UNIV, 70- *Personal Data:* b Chicago, Ill, Jan 15, 35; div; c 3. *Educ:* Univ Ill, BS, 56, PhD(inorg chem), 60; Harvard Univ, AM, 57. *Concurrent Pos:* Grants, NSF, 61-, Petrol Res Found, 63-66 & NIH, 72-78; Sloan fel, 66-68. *Mem:* Am Chem Soc; Sigma Xi. *Res:* Spectroscopic studies of coordination compounds containing phosphorus ligands; catalytic studies of transition metal compounds hypervalent non metallic compounds; stereospecific reactions of phosphorus compounds. *Mailing Add:* Dept Chem Iowa State Univ Sci Technol Ames IA 50011-0061

**VERLANGIERI, ANTHONY JOSEPH,** BIOCHEMISTRY, TOXICOLOGY. *Current Pos:* PROF PHARMACOL & TOXICOL, UNIV MISS, 80- *Personal Data:* b Newark, NJ, Aug 2, 45; m 67; c 3. *Educ:* Rutgers Univ, BS, 68; Pa State Univ, PhD(biochem), 73. *Prof Exp:* Asst biochem, Pa State Univ, 68-72; asst prof toxicol, Cook Col, Rutgers Univ, 72-80. *Concurrent Pos:* Consult toxicologist, independent labs & litigation. *Mem:* Am Col Vet Toxicol; Am Chem Soc; Am Inst Ultrasound Med; Tissue Cult Asn; AAAS; Am Col Toxicol; Soc Environ Toxicol & Chem. *Res:* Effects of sulfating agents on atherogenesis and the influence of lead intoxication on the central nervous system, behavior and learning; sulfated glycosaminoglycans, analytical methods, role in atherogenesis; endothelial cell culture model systems; animal models of atherogenesis and diabetes; ultrasound carotid analysis in primates; nutrition; pathology. *Mailing Add:* Dept Pharmacol Univ Miss Sch Pharm University MS 38677-9999. *Fax:* 601-232-5118

**VERLEUR, HANS WILLEM,** PHYSICS, MATERIAL SCIENCE. *Current Pos:* RETIRED. *Personal Data:* b Hillegom, Holland, July 1, 32; US citizen; m 56, 83, Sharon Boudman; c 4. *Educ:* Cooper Union, BS, 63; NY Univ, MS, 64, PhD(physics), 66. *Prof Exp:* Supvr, Display Develop Group, Bell Labs, 60-85, design, develop & mfg mgr, Plasma Display Prod, AT&T Technol, Inc, 85-88, mfg dir, Lightwave Commun Prod, AT&T Microelectronics, Inc, 88-92. *Mem:* Soc Info Display. *Res:* Optoelectronic device research. *Mailing Add:* 143 Woodhill Dr Fleetwood PA 19522

**VERLEY, FRANK A,** GENETICS. *Current Pos:* from asst prof to assoc prof, 67-74, PROF BIOL GENETICS, NORTHERN MICH UNIV, 74- *Personal Data:* b Kingston, Jamaica, Dec 18, 33; m 67. *Educ:* Univ Conn, BS, 59; Univ Ill, Urbana, MS, 60, PhD(genetics), 64. *Prof Exp:* Resident res assoc radiation genetics, Argonne Nat Lab, 64-67. *Mem:* Genetics Soc Am; Am Inst Biol Sci; Am Genetics Asn; Biomet Soc Am. *Res:* Genetic effects of a recessive sex-linked lethal gene on prenatal development in mice, copper metabolism in the mottled mice and biosynthesis of metallothionein in mice; restriction mapping of mouse X-chromosome and mitochondrial DNA; DNA sequence analysis of restriction fragment of X-chromosome and mitochondrial DNA. *Mailing Add:* Dept Biol Northern Mich Univ 1401 Presque Isle Ave Marquette MI 49855-5301

**VERLINDE, HERMAN L,** PHYSICS. *Current Pos:* ASST PROF, DEPT PHYSICS, PRINCETON UNIV. *Concurrent Pos:* Fel, David & Lucille Packard Found, 93. *Mailing Add:* Dept Physics Princeton Univ Jadwin Hall Princeton NJ 08544-1019

**VERMA, AJIT K,** POLYAMINES IN GROWTH CONTROL, VITAMIN A MECHANISM OF ACTION. *Current Pos:* Fel cancer res, McArdle Lab, Univ Wis-Madison, 76-79, proj assoc, 79-81, scientist, Human Oncol, Clin Cancer Ctr, 81-84, asst prof, 84-88, ASSOC PROF CANCER RES, HUMAN ONCOL, CLIN CANCER CTR, UNIV WIS-MADISON, 88- *Personal Data:* b India, Aug 9, 44; US citizen; m 69; c 4. *Educ:* Punjab Agr Univ, India, BSc, 66, MSc, 68; Flinders Univ SAustralia, PhD(biochem & cancer bone), 76. *Mem:* Am Asn Cancer Res; AAAS; Am Soc Biol Chemists. *Res:* Analyze the biochemical and molecular mechanisms of the induction of cancer as a rational approach for the choice of agents for cancer prevention. *Mailing Add:* Dept Human Oncol K4/532 CSC Univ Wis Comprehension Cancer Ctr 600 Highland Ave Madison WI 53792-0001. *Fax:* 601-232-5118

**VERMA, ANIL KUMAR,** PLASMA MEMBRANE CALCIUM TRANSPORT ATPASE. *Current Pos:* PROF ASSOC RES BIOCHEM & MOLECULAR BIOL, MAYO CLIN-FOUND, 79-, INSTR, 87- *Personal Data:* b Lucknow, India, Dec 15, 50; US citizen. *Educ:* Lucknow Univ, BSc, 69, MSc, 71; Kanpur Univ, PhD(biochem), 76. *Prof Exp:* Jr res fel biochem, Cent Drug Res Inst, Lucknow, India, 71-75; fel biochem, Univ Ala, 75-76; fel biochem, McGill Univ, 77-79. *Concurrent Pos:* Vis fel cell biol, NIH, 76-77; fel biochem, McGill Univ, 77-79. *Mem:* Am Soc Biochem & Molecular Biol. *Res:* Molecular biology of plasma membrane calcium transport atpase. *Mailing Add:* Mayo Clin-Found Guggenheim 16 Floor Rochester MN 55906. *Fax:* 507-284-9759; *E-Mail:* verma@mayo.edu

**VERMA, DEEPAK KUMAR,** DIGITAL MAGNETIC RECORDING, TRIBOLOGY & FAILURE ANALYSIS. *Current Pos:* PROCESS DEVELOP SCIENTIST, MONSANTO CORP, 96- *Personal Data:* b India; US citizen; m 73, Chitram Prasad; c Vicki, Archi & Neil. *Educ:* Bihar Inst Technol, India, BS, 67; Univ Mass, MSME, 70; Ga Inst Technol, PhD(mat sci), 79. *Prof Exp:* Trainee engr, Hindustan Motors Ltd, India, 67-68; res fel mech eng, Univ Mass, 68-71; tech asst, Tata Steel Ltd, India, 71-73; tech exec, Texmaco Ltd, India, 73-74; teaching fel mat eng, Ga Inst Technol, 74-78; res develop engr, Southwire Corp, Ga, 78-80; staff engr, IBM Corp, Minn, 80-90; freelance consult, 90-96. *Concurrent Pos:* Consult eng/scientist, 90- *Mem:* Am Soc Mech Engrs; Am Soc Metals. *Res:* Ultra-high data storage density in digital magnetic recording; science of surfaces and interfaces; metals processing; failure analysis. *Mailing Add:* 7919 Cross Creek Circle Breinigsville PA 18031

**VERMA, DEVI C,** agricultural biochemistry, for more information see previous edition

**VERMA, GHASI RAM,** APPLIED MATHEMATICS. *Current Pos:* assoc prof, 64-80, PROF MATH, UNIV RI, 80- *Personal Data:* b Sigari, India, Aug 1, 29; m 54, Rukmini Kaswan; c Om, Subhash & Anand. *Educ:* Birla Eng Col, India, BA, 50; Benaras Hindu Univ, MA, 54; Univ Rajasthan, India, PhD(math), 57. *Prof Exp:* Tutor math, Birla Eng Col, India, 54-57, lectr, 57-58; fel, Courant Inst Math Sci, NY Univ, 58-59; asst prof, Fordham Univ, 59-61; reader, Birla Inst Technol & Sci, India, 61-64. *Concurrent Pos:* Sr sci res fel, Coun Sci & Indust Res, New Delhi, India, 55-57. *Mem:* Am Math Soc; Math Asn Am; Soc Indust & Appl Math. *Res:* Elasticity; fluid mechanics. *Mailing Add:* Dept Math Univ RI Kingston RI 02881-0816. *Fax:* 401-874-4617; *E-Mail:* verma@math.uri.edu

**VERMA, INDER M,** GENETICS. *Current Pos:* From asst prof to assoc prof, Salk Inst, 74-83, sr mem, Molecular Biol & Viol Lab, 83-85, prof molecular biol, 85-95, PROF, LAB GENETICS, SALK INST, 95- *Personal Data:* b Sangrur, Punjab, India, Nov 28, 47; US citizen; c 1. *Educ:* Lucknow Univ, India, MSc, 66; Weizmann Inst Sci, Rehovot, Israel, PhD(biochem), 71. *Honors & Awards:* John E Whitemore Mem Lectr, Purdue Univ, 91; Melville Hare Mem Lectr, Univ Rochester, 94. *Concurrent Pos:* Reverend Soloman B Caulker Mem fel, 67-70; fel, Jane Coffin Childs Mem Fund, Med Res, 70-73; adj assoc prof, Univ Calif, San Diego, 79-83, adj prof, Dept Biol, 83-; mem, Virol Study Sect, 81-85; medal outstanding scientist, NAm Scientists Indian Origin, 85-86; merit award, NIH, 87, outstanding investr award, 88; mem bd trustees, Salk Inst, 89-91 & 94-, mem acad coun, 89-, vchmn, Fac & Acad Coun, 89-90 & 94-95, chmn, 91-92 & 96-97; prof, Molecular Biol, Am Cancer Soc, 90; lectr, Purdue Univ, 91; Sch Med, Vanderbilt Univ, 92, TATA Mem Hosp, Bombay, India, 92, Univ Health Scis-Chicago Med Sch, 92, Queenstown, NZ, 93, Med Ctr, NY Univ, 93, Bar-Ilan Univ, Ramat Gan, Israel, 94, XVI Int Cancer Cong & IUBMB, Delhi, India, 94, 22nd Int Cong, Mex City, 94, Third Symp, Max Delbruck Conf, Berlin, Ger, 95, Med Col Ohio, 95, NIH Asian/Pac Heritage Symp, Bethesda, 95, Tsumagoi Conf, Kakegawa, Japan, 95, Int Symp, Inuyama & Nagoya, Japan, 95, Vanderbilt Univ, 95; ann award, Thrombosis Res Inst, London, 93, lectr, 93; ed, J Virol, 93-, Gene, 95- *Mem:* Nat Acad Sci; Am Cancer Soc. *Mailing Add:* Salk Inst Biol Studies 10010 N Torrey Pines Rd La Jolla CA 92037. *Fax:* 619-588-7454

**VERMA, LALIT RAJ,** RESEARCH & EDUCATION ADMINISTRATION, POST HARVEST PROCESSING ENGINEERING. *Current Pos:* from asst prof to assoc prof, 79-85, PROF AGR ENG, AGR CTR, LA STATE UNIV, 85-, HEAD BIOL & AGR ENG DEPT, 92-, H ROUSE CAFFEY ENDOWED PROF, 96- *Personal Data:* b Nagpur, India, July 27, 51; US citizen; m 78, Aruna Khurana; c Amit & Pooja. *Educ:* JN Agr Univ India, BTech, 72; Mont State Univ, MS, 73; Univ Nebr, PhD(eng), 76. *Honors & Awards:* Young Researcher Award, Agri Eng, 91. *Prof Exp:* Grad res asst, Agr Eng Dept, Univ Nebr, 74-76, res assoc, 76-77; asst prof agr eng, SDak State Univ, 77-79. *Concurrent Pos:* Vis prof, Asian Inst Technol, Bangkok, Thailand, 87. *Mem:* Am Soc Agr Engrs; Am Soc Eng Educ; Inst Biol Eng. *Res:* Post harvest and value added processing engineering; by products utilization of rice and other agricultural products; granted 1 US patent. *Mailing Add:* Biol & Agr Eng La State Univ Baton Rouge LA 70803-4505

**VERMA, PRAMODE KUMAR,** ELECTRICAL ENGINEERING. *Current Pos:* dist mgr, AT&T, 80-84, SUPVR, AT&T BELL LABS, 84- *Personal Data:* b Barauli, India, Sept 1, 41; Can citizen; m 66; c 1. *Educ:* Patna Univ, BSc hons, 59; Indian Inst Sci, BEng, 62; Sir George Williams Univ, DEng(elec eng), 70, Univ Pa, Wharton Sch, MBA, 84. *Prof Exp:* Sr res asst elec commun eng, Indian Inst Sci, 62-64; asst div engr commun, Indian Posts & Tel, 64-67; asst prof elec eng & comput sci, Sir George Williams Univ, 71; supv engr comput commun, Bell Can, 72-78; mem tech staff comput commun, Bell Labs, 78-80. *Concurrent Pos:* Lectr, Univ Ottawa, 75-78; gov, Int Coun Comput Commun, Washington, DC. *Mem:* Sr mem Inst Elec & Electronics Engrs; Commun Soc. *Res:* Computer networks; communication networks. *Mailing Add:* AT&T 200 Laurel Ave Rm 4K129 Middletown NJ 07748

**VERMA, RAM D,** SPECTROSCOPY. *Current Pos:* RETIRED. *Personal Data:* b May 31, 29; Can citizen; m 62; c 3. *Educ:* Univ Agra, BSc, 52, MSc, 54, PhD(physics), 58. *Prof Exp:* Lectr physics, Dav Col, Aligarh, 54-55; res asst, Aligarh Muslim Univ, India, 55-57, sr res fel, 57-58; res assoc, Univ Chicago, 58-61; fel, Nat Res Coun Can, 61-63; from asst prof to prof physics, Univ Nebr, 63-94. *Concurrent Pos:* Can deleg, Int Conf Spectros, 67; vis prof, Univ Calif, Santa Barbara, Univ Stockholm & Bhabha Atomic Res Ctr, Bombay, India. *Mem:* Am Phys Soc; Can Asn Physicists. *Res:* Molecular structure and spectra of stable and free radicals; investigation covering region from near infrared to far ultraviolet; laser physics and laser spectroscopy. *Mailing Add:* 195 Colonial Heights Fredericton NB E3B 5M2 Can

**VERMA, RAM S,** CLINICAL CYTOGENETICS, HUMAN GENETICS. *Current Pos:* from instr to assoc prof, 76-85, PROF, DEPT ANAT & CELL BIOL, HEALTH SCI CTR, STATE UNIV NY, BROOKLYN, 85-; CHIEF, DIV GENETICS, LONG ISLAND COL HOSP, 86- *Personal Data:* b Barabanki, India, Mar 3, 46; nat US; m 62; c Harendra K & Narendra K. *Educ:* Agra Univ, India, BSc, 65, MSc, 67; Univ Western Can, PhD(cytogenetics), 72; Royal Col Pathologists, London, DCC, 84. *Prof Exp:* Res assoc, dept pediat, Med Ctr, Univ Colo, Denver, 73-74, fel, 74-76; chief, Div Cytogenetics, Interfaith Med Ctr, Brooklyn, NY, 80-88. *Concurrent Pos:* Consult, Phototake, 82-87; mem cytogenetic adv comt, Dept Health, New York, 78-; mem Genetic Task Force New York, 76-; consult, Nat Geog Socd, Washington, DC, 82; consult, WHO, Geneva, Switz, 82. *Mem:* Fel AAAS; Am Fedn Clin Res; Am Genetic Asn; Am Soc Cell Biol; Am Soc Human Genetics; Europ Soc Human Genetics; Royal Col Path; Inst Biol. *Res:* Structural organization of human chromosomes with respect to banding techniques; molecular roots of cancer including the role of oncogenes in pathogenesis of cancer; author of three books, over 350 original articles and 300 abstracts and presentations. *Mailing Add:* 45-38 Springfield Blvd Bayside NY 11361

**VERMA, SADANAND,** ALGEBRA, TOPOLOGY. *Current Pos:* chmn dept 68-90, PROF MATH, UNIV NEV, LAS VEGAS, 67- *Personal Data:* b Muzaffarpur, India, Jan 24, 30. *Educ:* Patna Univ, BSc, 50; Univ Bihar, MSc, 52; Wayne State Univ, MS & PhD(math), 58. *Prof Exp:* Hon lectr math, L S Col, Univ Bihar, 52-53, lectr univ, 53-55 & 58-60; asst prof, Univ Windsor, 60-65; assoc prof, Western Mich Univ, 65-67. *Mem:* Math Asn Am; Can Math Cong; Asn Comput Mach. *Res:* Algebraic topology; homotopy theory; elementary number theory; magnetohydrodynamics; general topology; elementary ordinary differential equations. *Mailing Add:* Dept Math Univ Nev Las Vegas 4505 S Maryland Pkwy Las Vegas NV 89154-0001

**VERMA, SHASHI BHUSHAN,** AGRICULTURAL SCIENCES, ATMOSPHERIC PHYSICS & SCIENCES. *Current Pos:* asst prof, Agr Meteorol Sect, Dept Agr Eng, 74-78, assoc prof, Ctr Agr Meteorol & Climat, 78-84, PROF, DEPT AGR METEOROL, UNIV NEBR, LINCOLN, 84-, CO-DIR, CTR LASER-ANALYSIS STUDIES TRACE GAS DYNAMICS, 88- *Personal Data:* b Buxar, Bihar, India, July 27, 44; US citizen; m 72; c Anita (Shefalika) & Amit. *Educ:* Ranchi Univ, India, BS, 65; Univ Colo, MS, 67; Colo State Univ, PhD(fluid dynamics), 71. *Prof Exp:* Res asst, Colo State Univ, 67-71, fel, Fluid Dynamics & Diffusion Lab, 71-72; res assoc, Agr Meteorol Sect, Dept Hort & Forestry, Univ Nebr, 72-74, staff meteorologist, Dames & Moore, San Francisco, 74. *Concurrent Pos:* Res grants, NSF, 75-, US Dept Agr, 79-83, Nebr Soybean Develop, 80 & 82-83, Nebr Grain Sorghum Develop, 82-84, Nat Aeronaut & Space Admin, 85-; lectr, NSF, US-India Exchange Scientists Prog, 81 & Univ Tuscia, Italy, 85; mem, Comt Agr & Forest Meteorol, Am Meteorol Soc, 83-86, Coun Agr Sci & Technol Task Force on Improving Irrig Efficiency, 86-87, Adv Panel, Nat Ctr Atmospheric Res Field Observing Facil, 86-89; mem, Field Lab Task Force, Univ Nebr, 83-84 & Oversight Comt, Agr Res & Develop Ctr, 84-; consult, World Meteorol Orgn-UN Develop Prog, Proj India, 89 & 90. *Mem:* Am Meteorol Soc; AAAS; Am Soc Agron; Sigma Xi. *Res:* Micrometeorology; atmosphere-biosphere interactions; surface exchange processes; trace gas fluxes; energy and matter exchanges; water use efficiency; micrometeorological/eddy correlation instrumentation. *Mailing Add:* Dept Agr Meteorol Univ Nebr Lincoln NE 68583. *Fax:* 402-472-6614

**VERMA, SURENDRA KUMAR,** MECHANICAL & CHEMICAL ENGINEERING. *Current Pos:* DEVELOP SCIENTIST TECH CTR, UNION CARBIDE CORP, 74- *Personal Data:* b India, Jan 1, 43; m 75. *Educ:* Agra Univ, India, BSc, 61; Indian Inst Technol, Kharagpur, BTech, 65; Univ Louisville, MS, 70, PhD(chem eng), 74. *Prof Exp:* Mech engr, Shriram Fertilizers & Chem, India, 65-68; res assoc mech eng, Univ Louisville, 70; res assoc, Universal Restoration, Washington, DC, 73-74. *Mem:* Am Inst Chem Engrs; Sigma Xi. *Res:* New separation techniques development for energy conservation and process improvement; hydrocarbons and amines technology. *Mailing Add:* Union Carbide Corp PO Box 8361 South Charleston WV 25303-0361

**VERMA, SURENDRA P,** CELL FUNCTIONS, LIPOSOMES. *Current Pos:* ASSOC PROF COMMUNITY HEALTH, TUFTS UNIV, SCH MED, BOSTON, 88- *Personal Data:* b Manglore, India, Jan 1, 41; US citizen; m; c 3. *Educ:* Agra Univ, India, BSc, 60; Aligarh Univ, India, MSc, 62; Roorkee Univ, India, PhD(chem), 66. *Prof Exp:* Res assoc biophys, Mich State Univ, East Lansing, 68-70 & Nat Res Coun Can, 70-72; from instr to assoc prof radiobiol, Tufts New Eng Med Ctr, Boston, 72-88. *Concurrent Pos:* Vis prof, INSERM, Unit 58, Montplier, France, 82-83; consult, Allied Instrumentation Lab, Lexington, Mass, 83-86; prin investr, NIH & Environ Protection Agency grants, 83- *Res:* Biophysics; membrane structure; raman spectroscopy; radiation effects on cell membrane structure; effect of pesticides on membrane structure. *Mailing Add:* 20 Adams Rd Sudbury MA 01776

**VERMAAS, WILLEM F J,** PHOTOSYNTHESIS, DIRECTED MUTAGENESIS. *Current Pos:* from asst prof to assoc prof, 86-94, dir, Ctr Study Early Events Photosynthesis, 94-97, PROF BOT, ARIZ STATE UNIV, 94- *Personal Data:* b Rhoon, Neth, June 3, 59; m 85, Meintje K Van der Heide; c Joshua V & Theodore W. *Educ:* Agr Univ, Wageningen, Neth, Ingenieurs, 82, Doctorate agr sci, 84. *Honors & Awards:* Unilever Chem Award, 80; Pres Young Invesr Award, 90. *Prof Exp:* Res assoc plant biol, Univ Ill, Urbana-Champaign, 80-81 & Mich State Univ, 81-82; res assoc biophys, Tech Univ, Berlin, Ger, 82-83; scientist, Agr Univ, Wageningen, Neth, 83-84; vis scientist, E I du Pont de Nemours & Co, Inc, 84-86. *Concurrent Pos:* Prin investr, NSF, 87-, NASA, 88-, Dept Energy,89-,NIH, 94-; vis prof, Stockholm Univ, Sweden, 92-93. *Mem:* AAAS; Int Soc Plant Molecular Biol. *Res:* Using molecular biological tools, specific cyanobacterial mutants are generated with alterations at targeted sites of photosynthesis related proteins, and analyzed in terms of structure and function of the photosynthetic machinery; structure/function relationships specific proteins and residues. *Mailing Add:* Dept Bot Ariz State Univ Box 871601 Tempe AZ 85287-1601. *Fax:* 602-965-6899; *E-Mail:* wim@asu.edu

**VERMEER, KEES,** CONSERVATION & ECOLOGY OF MARINE BIRDS, EVALUATION OF ENVIRONMENTAL DISTURBANCES ON MARINE BIRDS & THEIR FOOD CHAINS. *Current Pos:* Biologist III, Can Wildlife Serv, 66-70, res scientist II, 70-80, res scientist III, 80-90, RES SCIENTIST IV, CAN WILDLIFE SERV, 90- *Personal Data:* b Noordeloos, Neth, July 14, 30; Can citizen; M 68, Rebecca L Arrieta; c Lotus A. *Educ:* Univ BC, BS, 59, MS, 63; Univ Alta, PhD(ecol), 67. *Honors & Awards:* Cliff Shaw Mem Award, Sask Natural Hist Soc, 70. *Concurrent Pos:* mem, Stand Comt Seabird Res, Int Ornith Cong, 78-; chmn, Conserv Comt, Pac Seabird Group, 82-86; assoc ed, Northwest Bird & Mammal Soc Murrelet, 82-83. *Mem:* Soc Northwestern Vert Biol (vpres, 76-77 & 87-89); Pac Seabird Group (secy, 76-78). *Res:* Ecology of marine birds, investigate the effects of human disturbance (habitat destruction, predation by introduced predators, pollution by oil, chlorinated hydrocarbons and heavy metals, and promote their conservation. *Mailing Add:* Inst Ocean Sci PO Box 6000 Sidney BC V8L 4B2 Can. *Fax:* 250-363-6390

**VERMEIJ, GEERAT JACOBUS,** BIOGEOGRAPHY. *Current Pos:* PROF GEOL, UNIV CALIF, DAVIS, 89- *Personal Data:* b Sappemeer, Neth, Sept 28, 46; m 72; c 1. *Educ:* Princeton Univ, AB, 68; Yale Univ, MPhil, 70, PhD(biol), 71. *Honors & Awards:* MacArthur Fel, John D & Catherine T MacArthur Found, 92- *Prof Exp:* From instr to prof zool, Univ Md, College Park, 71-88. *Concurrent Pos:* J S Guggenheim Mem fel, 75-76; vis assoc prof, Friday Harbor Labs, Univ Wash, 76, Univ Guam Marine Lab, 79; res assoc, Smithsonian Inst, Nat Mus Nat Hist, 77-; scientist, Moro Exped, 79; vis prof, Friday Harbor Labs, Univ Wash, 89. *Mem:* Soc Study Evolution; Ecol Soc Am; Soc Am Naturalists (pres, 97); Paleont Soc; Neth Malacol Soc; fel AAAS; Inst Malacol. *Res:* Comparative ecology and history of shallow-water benthic marine communities; adaptive morphology, especially molluscs and decapods; temporal patterns of adaptation. *Mailing Add:* Dept Geol Univ Calif Davis CA 95616-8605

**VERMEIRE, BETTY ANNE,** HEMISPHERIC SPECIALIZATION OF THE BRAIN, SPLIT-BRAIN RESEARCH. *Current Pos:* vis asst prof, 91-94, ASST RES SCIENTIST, COL MED, HEALTH SCI CTR, TEXAS A&M UNIV, 94- *Personal Data:* b Sharon, Pa, Feb 5, 52. *Educ:* Allegheny Col, BS, 74; Calif Inst Technol, PhD(psychobiol), 80. *Prof Exp:* Sr fel psychol, Univ Wash, 80-81; asst scientist, Calif Inst Technol, 81-86, assoc scientist, 86-91. *Mem:* Soc Neurosci; Int Primatol Soc; AAAS. *Res:* Study of right and left hemispheric brain function of Rhesus monkeys; demonstrated complimentary specialization in a non-human primate, suggesting it is a basic principle of brain organization rather than being uniquely human. *Mailing Add:* Human Anat & Med Neurobiol Dept Col Med Tex A&M Univ College Station TX 77843-1114. *E-Mail:* chamilton@tamu.edu

**VERMEULEN, CARL WILLIAM,** MICROBIOLOGY, BIOCHEMISTRY. *Current Pos:* Asst prof microbiol & biochem, 66-71, ASSOC PROF MICROBIOL, COL WILLIAM & MARY, 71- *Personal Data:* b Chicago, Ill, July 23, 39; m 89, Sandra J Vernon; c Kevin & Susan. *Educ:* Hope Col, AB, 61; Univ Ill, Urbana, MS, 63, PhD(microbiol), 66. *Concurrent Pos:* Fulbright award, Denmark, 87; summer prof biol, Univ Calif, San Diego. *Mem:* Fel Am Inst Chemists; Royal Soc Chem. *Res:* Microbial genetics; quantification of bacterial capsular polysaccharides; LPS-based vaccine development; bacteriocidal mechanisms of fever. *Mailing Add:* Dept Biol Col William & Mary Williamsburg VA 23185. *Fax:* 757-221-6483

**VERMEULEN, MARY WOODALL,** BIOCHEMISTRY. *Current Pos:* instr med, 87-88, ASST PROF MED, HARVARD MED SCH, 88-; ASST BIOLOGIST, MASS GEN HOSP, 88-; STAFF SCIENTIST, SHRINERS HOSP BURN INST, 89- *Personal Data:* b Akron, Ohio, Oct 13, 55. *Educ:*

Col Wooster, BA, 77; Univ Minn, MS, 82, PhD(biochem), 83. *Prof Exp:* Louise T Dosdall fel sci, 82-83; res fel rheumatology & immunol, Brigham & Womens Hosp, 84-87, assoc immunochemist, 87-88. *Concurrent Pos:* Res fel med, Harvard Med Sch, 84-87; travel award, Am Asn Immunologists; prin investr, Mass Thoracic Soc, 89-91, Am Cancer Soc, 91-92. *Mem:* Int Soc Immunopharmacol; Soc Leukocyte Biol; Am Asn Immunologists; Int Endotoxin Soc; Am Thoracic Soc; Am Soc Microbiol. *Res:* Immunology of acute and chronic lung injuries; macrophage response to microorganisms; macrophage involvement in inflammation; macrophage immunoregulation; biology of cytokines. *Mailing Add:* Dept Med Pulmonary Res Lab Harvard Med Sch Mass Gen Hosp E 149 13th St Charlestown MA 02129-2060

**VERMEULEN, THEODORE (COLE),** CHEMICAL ENGINEERING, CATALYSIS WATER TECHNOLOGY. *Current Pos:* assoc prof chem eng, Univ Calif, Berkeley, 47-51, chmn div, 52-53, Miller res prof, 59-60, PROF CHEM ENG, UNIV CALIF, BERKELEY, 51-, DIR WATER TECHNOL CTR, 80- *Personal Data:* b Los Angeles, Calif, May 7, 16; m 39; c 2. *Educ:* Calif Inst Technol, BS, 36, MS, 37; Univ Calif, Los Angeles, PhD(chem), 42. *Honors & Awards:* W H Walker Award, Am Inst Chem Engrs, 71. *Prof Exp:* Jr chem engr, Union Oil Co, 37-39; asst chem, Univ Calif, Los Angeles, 39-41; chem engr, Shell Develop Co, 41-47. *Concurrent Pos:* Consult, Lawrence Berkeley Lab, 47-, Savannah River Lab, E I du Pont de Nemours & Co, 61-67, US Borax Res Corp, 63-67, Upjohn Co, 67-71, Teknekron, Inc, 71-76 & Exxon Res & Eng, 80-; Fulbright prof, Univ Liege & Ghent, 53; vis prof, French Petrol Inst, 54, Nat Univ Mex, 67 & South China Inst Technol, 81; consult & dir, Memorex Corp, 63-81; Guggenheim fel, Cambridge Univ, 64; res assoc, Scripps Inst Oceanog, 70-71. *Mem:* Am Nuclear Soc; fel Am Inst Chem Engrs; Am Chem Soc; Am Inst Aeronaut & Astronaut; Am Water Works Asn. *Res:* Water purification and recovery; magnetochemistry and coal liquefaction; multicomponent thermodynamics and diffusion; homogeneous and heterogeneous catalysis; chemical kinetics and reactor design; liquid extraction; agitation and fluidization; ion exchange; adsorption; interfacial phenomena; atmospheric modeling. *Mailing Add:* 725 Cragmont Ave Berkeley CA 94708

**VERMILLION, ROBERT EVERETT,** TEACHING PHYSICS. *Current Pos:* From asst prof to assoc prof 65-77, PROF PHYSICS, UNIV NC, CHARLOTTE, 77- *Personal Data:* b Kingsport, Tenn, Aug 17, 37; m 63, Sandra L Dodd; c L Arthur & Diane R. *Educ:* King Col, AB, 59; Vanderbilt Univ, MS, 61, PhD(physics), 65. *Mem:* Am Phys Soc; Am Asn Physics Teachers; Sigma Xi. *Res:* Electric shock-tube production of plasmas; techniques and apparatus for teaching undergraduate physics; experimental plasma physics. *Mailing Add:* Dept Physics Univ NC Charlotte NC 28223. *Fax:* 704-547-3160; *E-Mail:* revermil@uncc.edu

**VERMILYEA, BARRY LYNN,** FOOD SCIENCE, MICROBIOLOGY. *Current Pos:* DIR, QUAL CONTROL, LAND O'LAKES INC, MINNEAPOLIS, MINN, 82- *Personal Data:* b Dayton, Ohio, Dec 17, 41; m 65; c 2. *Educ:* Univ Wyo, BS, 64; Iowa State Univ, MS, 67, PhD(food sci), 69. *Prof Exp:* Sr scientist food sci, Gen Mills Inc, 69-70; develop mgr food sci, Cargill Inc, 70-71; tech mgr food sci, Int Multifoods Inc, 71-80; food consult, Kingdom Saudi Arabia, Riyadh, 80-82. *Mem:* Inst Food Technol. *Res:* New foods products, processes and packaging concepts for retail, industrial and institutional areas. *Mailing Add:* 7417 N Douglas Dr Minneapolis MN 55443

**VERMILYEA, D(AVID) A(UGUSTUS),** METALLURGY. *Current Pos:* RETIRED. *Personal Data:* b Troy, NY, Oct 11, 23; m 50; c 3. *Educ:* Rensselaer Polytech Inst, PhD(metall), 53. *Honors & Awards:* Whitney Award, Nat Asn Corrosion Engrs, 75; Acheson Award. *Prof Exp:* Instr, Rensselaer Polytech Inst, 48-51; chemist, Gen Elec Co, 51-58, mgr, Chem Metall Sect, Res Lab, 58-59, metallurgist, Phys Chem Lab, 59-74, energy analyst, Energy Sci & Eng Sector, 74-78, consult res & develop strategic anal, Gen Elec Res & Develop Ctr, 78-84. *Res:* Oxidation of metals; crystal growth; electrochemistry; corrosion. *Mailing Add:* 2505 Whamer Lane Niskayuna NY 12309

**VERMUND, HALVOR,** RADIOLOGY. *Current Pos:* prof radiol & dir radiother res & develop, 68-78, EMER PROF RADIOL, UNIV CALIF, IRVINE, 78- *Personal Data:* b Norway, Aug 8, 16; nat US; m 43; c 2. *Educ:* Univ Oslo, MD, 43; Univ Minn, PhD(radiol), 51. *Prof Exp:* Fel, Halden Munic & Vestfold Co Hosps, Norway, 44-48; Picker Found fel radiol, Univ Minn, 51-53, res assoc radiol, 53, from asst prof to assoc prof, 54-57; prof radiol & dir radiation ther, Univ Wis-Madison Hosps, 57-68. *Concurrent Pos:* Mem, Radiation Study Sect, NIH, 62-66, 65-69; mem, Comt Diag & Ther Cancer, Am Cancer Soc Adv Comt on Ther Cancer, 60-62, 72-76; mem staff, Norweg Radiumhosp, Oslo, Norway, 78-85; vis prof radiation oncol, Univ Wis-Madison, 85-87; consult, Wendt Regional Cancer Ctr, Dubuque, Iowa, 87-89; vis prof, ECarolina Sch Med, 89-95. *Mem:* Fel Am Col Radiol; Soc Exp Biol & Med; Am Radium Soc; Radiol Soc NAm; Am Roentgen Ray Soc; hon mem Soc Oncol & Therapeut Radiol Norway, 87. *Res:* Radiation therapy; medical radiology; radioactive isotopes. *Mailing Add:* 1210 Sand Point Way Corona Del Mar CA 92625

**VERMUND, STEN HALVOR,** infectious disease epidemiology, pediatrics, for more information see previous edition

**VERNADAKIS, ANTONIA,** DEVELOPMENTAL NEUROBIOLOGY. *Current Pos:* from asst prof to assoc prof, 67-78, PROF PSYCHIAT & PHARMACOL, SCH MED, UNIV COLO, 78- *Personal Data:* b Canea, Crete, Greece, May 11, 30; m 61, Harold L Ockerman. *Educ:* Univ Utah, BA,

55, MS, 57, PhD(anat, pharmacol), 61. *Prof Exp:* Interdisciplinary training prog fel pharmacol, Univ Calif Sch Med, San Francisco Med Ctr, 64-65; asst res physiologist, Univ Calif, Berkeley, 65-67. *Concurrent Pos:* Res scientist develop award, NIMH, 69-79; Fogarty fel, 77; vis prof, Univ Athens, Greece, 81 & Univ Zimbabwe Sch Med, Harare, 83; Raven scholar, Int Soc Neurochem. *Mem:* Am Soc Pharmacol & Exp Therapeut; Am Neurochem Soc; Int Soc Neurochem; Int Soc Develop Neurosci (pres, 83-85). *Res:* Regulatory mechanisms in brain maturation; drugs and hormones; neurotransmission maturation; neural cell growth and differentiation using neural cell culture; neuron-glia interactions during development and aging. *Mailing Add:* Depts Psychiat & Pharmacol Univ Colo Sch Med 4200 E Ninth Ave Denver CO 80220-3706. *Fax:* 303-315-7097

**VERNAZZA, JORGE ENRIQUE,** PLASMA PHYSICS. *Current Pos:* MEM STAFF, LAWRENCE LIVERMORE NAT LAB, 79- *Personal Data:* b Buenos Aires, Arg, Jan 16, 43; US citizen; m 73; c 2. *Educ:* Univ Buenos Aires, Licenciate, 67; Harvard Univ, PhD(astron), 72. *Prof Exp:* Res fel astron, Harvard Univ, 72-74, res assoc, 74-79. *Mem:* Am Astron Soc; Am Phys Soc. *Res:* Radiative transfer; plasma physics. *Mailing Add:* 225 Sheila Ct Moraga CA 94556. *Fax:* 510-423-0925; *E-Mail:* vernazzaj@llnl.gov.

**VERNBERG, FRANK JOHN,** MARINE BIOLOGY, PHYSIOLOGICAL ECOLOGY. *Current Pos:* Baruch prof marine biol & dir, Baruch Coastal Res Inst, Univ SC, 69-96, interim dean, Col Sci & Math, 93-94, dean, Sch Environ, 95-96, DISTINGUISHED EMER PROF, UNIV SC, 96- *Personal Data:* b Fenton, Mich, Nov 6, 25; m 45; c 3. *Educ:* DePauw Univ, AB, 49, MA, 50; Purdue Univ, PhD(zool), 51. *Honors & Awards:* Russell Award, 77; W S Proctor Award, Sigma Xi, 83; Wildlife Fed Conservationist of Yr, 83; Drug Sci Found Res Award, 87; Waddell Lifetime Achievement Award, 90. *Prof Exp:* From instr to prof zool, Duke Univ, 51-69, asst dir res, 58-63, asst dir, Marine Lab, 63-69. *Concurrent Pos:* Guggenheim fel, 57-58; Fulbright-Hayes res award, Brazil, 65 & Fulbright-Hayes fel, 65; lectr, Univs Kiel & Sao Paulo, Chulalongkorn Univ, Thailand; mem comt, Manned Orbital Res Lab, Am Inst Biol Sci, 66-; dir, Int Biol Prog-Prog Exp Anal, Biogeog of the Sea, Nat Acad Sci, 67-69; consult, Environ Protection Agency, 74-, Nat Sci Found, 80-; mem, Coun Ecol Soc, 69-91 & 76-78; chmn, Comn Physiol Ecol, Int Asn Ecol; managing ed, J Exp Marine Biol & Ecol, 78- *Mem:* AAAS; Estuarine Res Fedn (pres, 75-77); Am Soc Zoologists (pres, 82); Ecol Soc Am; Int Asn Ecol. *Res:* Physiological ecology of marine animals; distribution of decapod crustacea; tissue metabolism; mechanisms of temperature acclimation; physiological diversity of latitudinally separated populations; pollution of estuaries; long-term ecological research. *Mailing Add:* Baruch Coastal Res Inst Univ SC Columbia SC 29205

**VERNBERG, WINONA B,** ESTUARINE SYSTEMS, ENVIRONMENTAL PHYSIOLOGY. *Current Pos:* res prof biol, Univ SC, 69-75, prof pub health & prog dir, Environ Health Staff, 75-77, actg dean, Sch Pub Health, 77-78, dean, 78-79, dean, Sch Pub Health, 79-95, interim provost, 96, EMER DISTINGUISHED PROF & EMER DEAN, UNIV SC, 96- *Personal Data:* b Kans, Jan 9, 24; c 3. *Educ:* Kans State Col, BS, 44; DePauw Univ, MA, 47; Purdue Univ, PhD, 51. *Honors & Awards:* Proctor Prize, Sigma Xi, 83. *Prof Exp:* Instr DePauw Univ, 47-49; res assoc, Duke Univ, 51-73. *Concurrent Pos:* Mem, Nat Adv Comt Oceans & Atmosphere, 74-76, exec comt sci adv bd, Environ Protection Agency, 78-82, Nat Adv Coun, NASA, 79-80, educ comt, Asn Sch Pub Health, 81, peer rev panel, Off Explor Res, Environ Protection Agency, 87-90; chairperson, Sci Adv Comt Off Toxic Substances, Environmental Protection Agency, 78-82; pres, Coun Educ Pub Health, 85 & 86; bd dir, Univ SC Educ Found, 86 & 90. *Mem:* Am Pub Health Asn; Sigma Xi; Royal Soc Trop Med & Hyg; Am Soc Zoologists (treas, 73-76). *Res:* Effects of urbanization; various sources of pollution; other potential disturbances on the coastal estuarine system. *Mailing Add:* Sch Pub Health Univ SC Columbia SC 29208. *E-Mail:* wvernberg@sph.sc.edu

**VERNEKAR, ANANDU DEVARAO,** METEOROLOGY. *Current Pos:* from asst prof to assoc prof, 69-79, PROF METEOROL, UNIV MD, COLLEGE PARK, 79- *Personal Data:* b Hosali, India, July 5, 32; m 59; c 3. *Educ:* Univ Poona, BSc, 55, BSc, 56, MSc, 59; Univ Mich, MS, 63, PhD(meteorol), 66. *Prof Exp:* Sci asst meteorol, Upper Air Sect, India Meteorol Dept, 56-61; res scientist, Travelers Res Ctr, Inc, 67-69. *Mem:* Am Geophys Union; Am Meteorol Soc. *Res:* Dynamical meteorology; general circulation; theory of climate and statistical meteorology. *Mailing Add:* Dept Meteorol Univ Md College Park MD 20742

**VERNER, JAMES HAMILTON,** MATHEMATICS, NUMERICAL ANALYSIS. *Current Pos:* res assoc, 69-72, from asst prof to assoc prof, 72-93, PROF MATH, QUEENS UNIV, ONT, 93- *Personal Data:* b Hitchin, Eng, Feb 22, 40; Can citizen; m 64; c 3. *Educ:* Queen's Univ, Ont, BSc, 62, MSc, 65; Univ Edinburgh, PhD(comput sci), 69. *Prof Exp:* Lectr math, Royal Mil Col Can, 63-64; External Aids Off teaching adv, Umuahia, Eastern Nigeria, 64-66. *Concurrent Pos:* Hon lectr math, Univ Auckland, NZ, 75-76. *Mem:* Soc Indust & Appl Math. *Res:* Numerical analysis, especially numerical solution of initial value problems for ordinary differential equations. *Mailing Add:* Dept Math & Statist Queen's Univ Kingston ON K7L 3N6 Can. *Fax:* 613-545-2964; *E-Mail:* jim@jhv.mast.queensu.ca

**VERNER, JARED,** ANIMAL ECOLOGY. *Current Pos:* res wildlife biologist, 76-78, proj leader, 78-95, SR SCIENTIST, FORESTRY SCI LA, FRESNO, 95- *Personal Data:* b Baltimore, Md, Aug 16, 34; m 58, Marlene Bailor; c Mendilynn, Jonica & Matthew. *Educ:* Wash State Univ, BS, 57; La State Univ, MS, 59; Univ Wash, PhD(zool), 63. *Honors & Awards:* Chuck Yeager Award, Nat Fish & Wildlife Found, 91. *Prof Exp:* Res assoc zool, Univ Calif, Berkeley, 63-65; from asst prof to prof biol, Cent Wash State Col, 65-73; prof biol, Ill State Univ, 73-76, adj prof ecol, 77-80. *Concurrent Pos:* NSF fel, 63-65, res grant, 66-71. *Mem:* Fel Am Ornith Union; Cooper Ornith Soc (pres, 89-91); Wilson Ornith Soc; Ecol Soc Am; Wildlife Soc; Soc Conserv Biol. *Res:* Evolution and natural selection; avian social organization and communication systems; avian population ecology; wildlife habitat relations; conservation biology. *Mailing Add:* 8306 N Classics Ave Fresno CA 93720

**VERNIER, ROBERT L,** PEDIATRICS, NEPHROLOGY. *Current Pos:* PROF PEDIAT, MED SCH, UNIV MINN, 68- *Personal Data:* b El Paso, Tex, July 29, 24; m 45; c 5. *Educ:* Univ Dayton, BS, 48; Univ Cincinnati, MD, 52. *Honors & Awards:* Mead Johnson Award Pediat Res, 62; Kidney Award, Am Acad Pediat, 93. *Prof Exp:* Clin fel pediat, Univ Ark, 52-54; clin fel, Univ Minn, 54-55, USPHS res fel, 55-57, Am Heart asn res fel, 57-59; asst prof & Am Heart Asn estab investr, Med Sch, Univ Minn, 59-65; prof, Sch Med, Univ Calif, Los Angeles, 65-68. *Concurrent Pos:* Estab investr, Am Heart Asn, 59-60; Guggenheim fel, Dept Biophys, State Serum Inst, Copenhagen, Denmark, 60-61; sr fel, Fogarty Inst Ctr, Dept Path, Grotingen, Neth, 75-76. *Mem:* AAAS; Am Soc Clin Invest; Am Soc Exp Path; Soc Pediat Res; Am Soc Nephrology (pres, 79-80); Am Soc Pediat Nephrology (pres, 76-77). *Res:* Clinical pediatrics; renal disease in childhood; electron microscopy in the kidney. *Mailing Add:* Dept Pediat Univ Minn Mayo Box 491 Minneapolis MN 55455-0362

**VERNIER, VERNON GEORGE,** PHARMACOLOGY. *Current Pos:* CONSULT, PHARMACEUT INDUST, 85-; PROF PHYSIOL, UNIV DEL, 96- *Personal Data:* b Norwalk, Conn, Nov 14, 24; m 55; c 4. *Educ:* Univ Ill, BS, 47, MD, 49. *Prof Exp:* Intern, Res & Educ Hosp, Univ Ill, 49-50, res assoc pharmacol, Med Col, 50-51, instr, 51-52; res assoc, Sharpe & Dohme, Inc, 52-54; res assoc physiol, Merck Inst Therapeut Res, 56-63; mgr, Pharmacol Sect, Stine Lab, 63-74, dir pharmacol, 74-82, assoc dir prof serv, Med Res, E I du Pont de Nemours Co, 82-85. *Concurrent Pos:* Lectr, Sch Med, Temple Univ, 56-66, vis prof, 66-87. *Mem:* AAAS; Am Soc Pharmacol & Exp Therapeut; Am Col Neuropsychopharmacol; NY Acad Sci; Sigma Xi. *Res:* Neuropsychopharmacology; psychopharmacology; toxicology. *Mailing Add:* 303 Lark Dr Newark DE 19713-1215. *E-Mail:* vernier@vdel.edu

**VERNIKOS, JOAN,** ENDOCRINE PHARMACOLOGY, STRESS & COPING. *Current Pos:* Nat Acad Sci-Nat Res Coun res assoc, Ames Res Ctr, NASA, 64-66, res scientist, 66-93, chief human studies br, 72-76, actg dep dir life sci, 76, actg assoc dir space res, 86-93, actg chief, Life Sci Div, 88-93, DIR, LIFE SCI, NASA HQ, 93- *Personal Data:* b Alexandria, Egypt, May 9, 34; m 60, 78, Geoffrey C Hazzan; c Eftihia & George D. *Educ:* Univ Alexandria, BPharm, 55; Univ London, PhD(pharmacol), 60. *Honors & Awards:* NASA Medal for Except Sci Achievement, 73; Hubertus Strughold Award Space Med, 90; Jeffries Med Res Award, Am Inst Aeronaut & Astronaut, 94. *Prof Exp:* Muelhaupt scholar, Ohio State Univ, 60-61, asst prof pharmacol, 61-64. *Concurrent Pos:* HEW/NIH, Pharmacol Study Sect, 74-78; assoc ed, Pharmacol Rev, 77-81; hon clin prof pharmacol, Sch Med, Wright State Univ, Ohio, 75-81, ASPET subcomt, Women in Pharmacol, 79-83; Life Sci & Systs Tech Comt, Am Inst Aeronaut & Astronaut, 90-93; Const & By-laws comt, Aerospace Med Asn, 90-95. *Mem:* Endocrine Soc; fel Aerospace Med Asn; Int Neuroendocrine Soc; Am Soc Pharmacol & Exp Therapeut; Int Brain Res Orgn; Int Acad Astronaut. *Res:* Stress and the environmental, behavioral and physiological factors that affect the stress response including weightlessness and inactivity; mechanisms regulating pituitary-adrenal function, fluids, electrolytes; gravitational and space physiology. *Mailing Add:* Life Scis, NASA HQ Code UL 300 E St SW Washington DC 20546. *Fax:* 202-358-4781; *E-Mail:* jverniko@hq.nasa.gov

**VERNON, C(ARL) WAYNE,** ELEMENTARY PARTICLE PHYSICS. *Current Pos:* From asst prof to assoc prof, 66-80, PROF PHYSICS, UNIV CALIF, SAN DIEGO, 80- *Personal Data:* b Alamosa, Colo, Oct 29, 39; m 58; c 2. *Educ:* Univ Wash, BPhys, 61; Princeton Univ, PhD(physics), 66. *Res:* Cosmic ray and deep inelastic scattering muons; electron-positron colliding beam physics; x-ray detectors for crystallography; free-electron lasers and particle accelerators. *Mailing Add:* Dept Physics 0319 Univ Calif San Diego 9500 Gilman Dr La Jolla CA 92093-0319

**VERNON, FRANK LEE, JR,** LOW TEMPERATURE PHYSICS, QUANTUM PHYSICS. *Current Pos:* SR STAFF SCIENTIST LOW TEMPERATURE & QUANTUM PHYSICS, AEROSPACE CORP, 61- *Personal Data:* b Dallas, Tex, Sept 16, 27; m 50; c 3. *Educ:* Southern Methodist Univ, BS, 49; Univ Calif, Berkeley, MS, 52; Calif Inst Technol, PhD(elec eng, physics), 59. *Prof Exp:* Asst recorder geophys prospecting, Tex Co, 49-50; head, Sect Microwave Physics, Hughes Aircraft Co, 51-61. *Concurrent Pos:* Res fel physics, Calif Inst Technol, 59-60. *Mem:* Am Phys Soc; Inst Elec & Electronics Engrs; Sigma Xi; AAAS. *Res:* Experimental and theoretical investigations in the fields of low temperature, microwave and quantum physics including superconductors, lasers and the interaction of electron tunneling mechanisms with high frequency radiation. *Mailing Add:* 1560 Knollwood Terr Pasadena CA 91103

**VERNON, GREGORY ALLEN,** PHYSICAL CHEMISTRY. *Current Pos:* RES CHEMIST, NAVAL AIR WARFARE CTR, CHINA LAKE, 80- *Personal Data:* b Akron, Ohio, July 27, 47. *Educ:* Pa State Univ, BS, 69; Univ Ill, MS, 71, PhD(chem), 75. *Prof Exp:* Res anal chemist, Atomic Int Div, Rockwell Int, 75-80. *Mem:* Am Chem Soc; Sigma Xi. *Res:* Detonation physics; thermal hazards; decomposition kinetics. *Mailing Add:* 632 Sherwood Ct Ridgecrest CA 93555-3646

**VERNON, JACK ALLEN,** OTOLARYNGOLOGY. *Current Pos:* PROF OTOLARYNGOL, ORE HEALTH SCI, UNIV PORTLAND, 66-, DIR, ORE HEARING RES CTR, 66- *Personal Data:* b Kingsport, Tenn, Apr, 6, 22; m 73, Mary B Meikle; c Stephen M & Victoria L. *Educ:* Univ Va, BA, 48, MA, 50, PhD(psychol), 52. *Prof Exp:* Instr psychol, Princeton Univ, NJ, 52-54, from asst prof to prof, 54-66. *Mem:* Asn Res Otolaryngol (pres, 73-74); Am Acad Opthal & Otolaryngol. *Res:* Otolaryngology; psychology; opthalmology; health science; hearing research. *Mailing Add:* Ore Health Sci Univ Sch Med 3181 SW Sam Jackson Portland OR 97201-3011

**VERNON, JOHN ASHBRIDGE,** ORGANIC CHEMISTRY, TECHNICAL MANAGEMENT. *Current Pos:* mgr labs, Vick Mfg Div, Richardson-Vicks, Inc, 73-77, qual assurance mgr, 77-85, group dir tech serv/qual assurance, 85-90, group mgr tech serv, Vicks Health Care Div, 90-92, TECH SERV & QUAL ASSURANCE FOR CONTRACT, RICHARDSON VICKS, INC, 92- *Personal Data:* b Camden, NJ, Jan 19, 40; m 62, Carol A Naskins; c John, Douglas & Steven. *Educ:* Rutgers Univ, BS, 61; Univ Md, PhD(org chem), 65. *Prof Exp:* Asst chem, Univ Md, 61-63, Gillette Harris res fel org chem, 63-64; res chemist, E I du Pont de Nemours & Co, Inc, 65-70; plant mgr, Pioneer Labs, Chesebrough-Ponds, Inc, 71-73. *Mem:* Am Chem Soc. *Res:* Reactions of organic compounds over alumina; synthesis and reaction of azides; heterocyclic compounds; synthesis of liquid crystals. *Mailing Add:* 330 Warminster Rd Hatboro PA 19040. *Fax:* 215-956-1059

**VERNON, LEO PRESTON,** BIOCHEMISTRY, IMMUNOLOGY. *Current Pos:* PROF CHEM, BRIGHAM YOUNG UNIV. *Personal Data:* b Roosevelt, Utah, Oct 10, 25; m 46, Fern Trunkey; c Richard, Elise, Martin, Jillaine & Eric. *Educ:* Brigham Young Univ, BA, 48; Iowa State Col, PhD, 51. *Honors & Awards:* Utah Award, Am Chem Soc, 85. *Prof Exp:* Fel, Enzyme Inst, Univ Wis, 51-52; res assoc, Wash Univ, 52-54; assoc prof chem, Brigham Young Univ, 54-61; dir, C F Kettering Res Lab, Kettering Found, Ohio, 61-70; dir res, Brigham Young Univ, 70-74; asst acad vpres res, 74-81; vpres, Billings Energy Corp, 81- *Concurrent Pos:* Researcher, Nobel Inst, Stockholm, Sweden, 60-61. *Mem:* Am Soc Biol Chem; Am Soc Plant Physiol. *Res:* Photosynthesis; cytochrome chemistry; respiratory enzymes; peptide toxins; immunoregulation. *Mailing Add:* Dept Chem & Biochem Brigham Young Univ 675 WIDB Provo UT 84602-1001. *Fax:* 801-378-5474

**VERNON, LONNIE WILLIAM,** PHYSICAL CHEMISTRY, FUEL SCIENCE. *Current Pos:* SR RES ASSOC, EXXON RES & ENG CO, 52- *Personal Data:* b Dallas, Tex, Mar 16, 22; m 49; c 3. *Educ:* Rice Univ, BA, 48, MA, 50, PhD(chem), 52. *Mem:* Am Chem Soc; Sigma Xi. *Res:* Coal conversion processes; surface chemistry; catalysis. *Mailing Add:* 5017 Ashwood Dr Baytown TX 77521

**VERNON, MARY K,** COMPUTER MODELING. *Current Pos:* PROF, COL ENG, UNIV WIS-MADISON. *Educ:* Univ Calif, Los Angeles, BS, 75, MS, 79, PhD(comput sci), 83. *Mem:* Fel Asn Comput Mach. *Res:* Stochastic modeling techniques useful for understanding design trade-offs for parallel computer systems; computer system performance modeling and analysis; parallel architectures; models of parallel computation. *Mailing Add:* 6361 Comput Sci & Statist 1210 W Dayton St Madison WI 53706

**VERNON, RALPH JACKSON,** OCCUPATIONAL HEALTH, SAFETY ENGINEERING. *Current Pos:* prof eng technol & indust eng, 68-77, HEAD INDUST HYG & SAFETY ENG DIV, TEX A&M UNIV, 68-, PROF INDUST ENG, 77- *Personal Data:* b Greenville, SC, Apr 6, 20; m 47; c 3. *Educ:* Clemson Univ, BS, 50; Tex A&M Univ, MEd, 51; Univ Iowa, PhD(prev med, environ hyg), 68. *Prof Exp:* Instr safety, Tex A&M Univ, 51-53; safety engr, Liberty Mutual Ins Co, 53-60, loss prev mgr, 60-66. *Concurrent Pos:* Vpres, Hill, Stocker, Vernon & Assocs, 70-; mem, Bd Cert Safety Prof. *Mem:* Human Factors Soc; Am Inst Indust Engrs; Am Indust Hyg Asn; Am Conf Govt Indust Hyg; Am Pub Health Asn; Sigma Xi. *Res:* Occupational diseases; accident causation; noise; biodynamics and resulting effects on performance decrement. *Mailing Add:* 1003 Hereford St College Station TX 77840

**VERNON, ROBERT CAREY,** SOLID STATE PHYSICS. *Current Pos:* chmn dept physics, 61-72, prof, 61-85, EMER PROF PHYSICS, SIMMONS COL, 85- *Personal Data:* b Wilmington, Ohio, Feb 7, 23; m 49; c 2. *Educ:* Bates Col, BS, 47; Wesleyan Univ, MA, 49; Pa State Univ, PhD(physics), 52. *Prof Exp:* Asst physics, Pa State Univ, 49-52; instr, Williams Col, 52-54, lectr, 54-55, asst prof, 55-58; asst prof, Clarkson Col Technol, 58-60, assoc prof, 60-61. *Mem:* Am Phys Soc; Am Asn Physics Teachers; Geol Soc Am. *Res:* Imperfections in nearly perfect crystals; optical properties of semiconductors. *Mailing Add:* 55 Pingree Rd New London NH 03257-4809

**VERNON, RONALD J,** ELECTRICAL ENGINEERING. *Current Pos:* From asst prof to assoc prof, 65-77, PROF ELEC ENG, UNIV WIS-MADISON, 77- *Personal Data:* b Chicago, Ill, June 3, 36; m 71. *Educ:* Northwestern Univ, BS, 59, MS, 61, PhD(elec eng), 65. *Concurrent Pos:* NSF res grants, 66 & 68. *Mem:* Inst Elec & Electronics Engrs. *Res:* Electromagnetic field theory; microwave engineering; microwave interaction with solids; semiconductor physics. *Mailing Add:* Dept Elec Eng 3546a Eng Bldg Univ Wis 1415 Engineering Dr Madison WI 53706

**VERNON, WILLIAM WALLACE,** GEOLOGY, ARCHAEOLOGY. *Current Pos:* from asst prof to assoc prof geol, Dickinson Col, 57-71, chmn dept, 65-74 & 89-91, prof geol & anthrop, 71-91, EMER PROF GEOL & ANTHROP, DICKINSON COL, 91- *Personal Data:* b Concord, NH, Nov

1, 25; m 51, Joyce Thomas; c Thomas L. *Educ:* Univ NH, BA, 52; Lehigh Univ, MS, 55, PhD, 64; Univ Pa, MS, 84. *Prof Exp:* Civil engr, Dept Pub Rds & Hwys, NH, 52-53; geologist, US Geol Surv, 56-57. *Concurrent Pos:* Res assoc, Univ Mus, Univ Pa, Philadelphia. *Mem:* AAAS; Sigma Xi; Archaeol Inst Am; Geol Soc Am. *Res:* Mineralogy, petrology and structure of igneous and metamorphic rocks in south-central New Hampshire; archaeological investigations of Early Man in New York State; archaeoceramic and archaeometallurgical investigations of bronze age cultures in Thailand. *Mailing Add:* Dept Geol Dickinson Col Carlisle PA 17013. *E-Mail:* willver@mailhost.epix.net

**VERONA, ANDREI,** DIFFERENTIAL TOPOLOGY, NON LINEAR ANALYSIS. *Current Pos:* PROF MATH, CALIF STATE UNIV, LOS ANGELES, 84- *Personal Data:* b Bucharest, Romania, Aug 24, 43; US citizen. *Educ:* Univ Bucharest, Romania, MS, 65, PhD(math), 71. *Honors & Awards:* Titeica Prize, Romanian Acad Sci, 73. *Prof Exp:* Researcher, Inst Math, Bucharest, Romania, 66-75, Nat Inst Sci Creation, 75-81; vis prof math, Univ Bonn & Max-Planck Inst, Ger, 81-83, Ohio State Univ, 83-84. *Concurrent Pos:* Vis prof math, Univ Genoa, Italy, 78; vis researcher, IHES, France, 80 & 81, Inst Advan Study, Princeton, NJ, 83. *Mem:* Am Math Soc. *Res:* Lie group representations; stratified spaces and maps; maximal monotone operators. *Mailing Add:* Dept Math Calif State Univ Los Angeles CA 90032. *E-Mail:* averona@calstatela.edu

**VERONIS, GEORGE,** OCEANOGRAPHY. *Current Pos:* HENRY BERNARD DAVIS PROF GEOPHYS & APPL SCI, YALE UNIV, 66- *Personal Data:* b New Brunswick, NJ, June 3, 26; m 63, Anna M Olsson; c Melissa & Benjamin. *Educ:* Lafayette Col, AB, 50; Brown Univ, PhD(appl math), 54. *Hon Degrees:* MA, Yale Univ, 66; LLD, Lafayette Col, 97. *Honors & Awards:* Alexander von Humboldt Award, 86; Robert L & Bettie P Cody Award in Ocean Sci, 89; Henry Stommel Res Medal, Am Meteorol Soc, 97. *Prof Exp:* Staff meteorologist, Inst Advan Study, 53-56; staff mathematician, Woods Hole Oceanog Inst, 56-63; assoc prof oceanog, Mass Inst Technol, 61-63, res oceanogr, 64-66. *Concurrent Pos:* Dir geophys fluid dynamics, Woods Hole Oceanog Inst, 59-; Guggenheim fel, Stockholm, Sweden, 60-61 & 66-67; ed, J Marine Res, 73-; Sr Queen's fel, Australia, 81. *Mem:* Nat Acad Sci; fel Am Geophys Union; Am Acad Arts & Sci; Norweg Acad Arts & Lett; AAAS. *Res:* Ocean circulation; rotating and stratified fluids; double diffusion; fluid dynamics laboratory experiments. *Mailing Add:* Dept Geol & Geophys Yale Univ Box 208109 New Haven CT 06520-8109. *Fax:* 203-432-3134; *E-Mail:* george.veronis@yale.edu

**VEROSUB, KENNETH LEE,** PALEOMAGNETISM, TECTONICS. *Current Pos:* from asst prof to assoc prof, 75-84, PROF GEOPHYS, UNIV CALIF, DAVIS, 84- *Personal Data:* b New York, NY, July 10, 44; m 67; c 2. *Educ:* Univ Mich, BA, 66; Stanford Univ, MS, 71, PhD(physics), 73. *Prof Exp:* Asst prof geophys, Amherst Col, 72-75. *Concurrent Pos:* Vis researcher, Ctr Faibles Radioactivities, Gif-Sur-Yvette, France, 82-83; vis prof, Ctr Geol & Geophys, Univ Sci Tech Languedoc, Montpellier, France; Fulbright fel, France, 89-90. *Mem:* Am Geophys Union; Geol Soc Am; Sigma Xi; Earthquake Eng Res Inst; Nat Asn Geol Teachers. *Res:* Paleomagnetism of sediments; history of the earth's magnetic field; geomagnetic polarity transitions and excursions; tephrostratigraphy; California tectonics; gravity and magnetic modelling; geologic hazards; satellite remote sensing. *Mailing Add:* Dept Geol Univ Calif Davis CA 95616

**VERPOORTE, JACOB A,** BIOPHYSICAL CHEMISTRY. *Current Pos:* from asst prof to assoc prof, 67-84, PROF BIOCHEM, DALHOUSIE UNIV, 84- *Personal Data:* b Utrecht, Neth, Oct 17, 36; m 61; c 2. *Educ:* Univ Utrecht, MSc, 60; Univ Pretoria, PhD(biochem), 64. *Prof Exp:* Fel phys protein chem, Univ Alta, 64-65 & Harvard Univ, 65-67. *Concurrent Pos:* Muscular Dystrophy Asn Can fel, 64-66. *Res:* Isolation and characterization of biologically active proteins; physico-chemical studies, including studies on the structure of proteins. *Mailing Add:* Dept Biochem Dalhousie Univ Fac Med Sir Charles Tupper Bldg Halifax NS B3H 4H7 Can

**VERRALL, RONALD ERNEST,** PHYSICAL CHEMISTRY. *Current Pos:* from asst prof to assoc prof, 68-77, PROF CHEM, UNIV SASK, 77- *Personal Data:* b Ottawa, Ont, Feb 26, 37; m 61, Grace E Strong; c John R & Tanya C. *Educ:* Univ Ottawa, Ont, BSc, 62, PhD(phys chem), 66. *Prof Exp:* Nat Res Coun Can-NATO fel, Mellon Inst, Carnegie-Mellon Univ, 66-68. *Concurrent Pos:* Vis fel, Mellon Inst, Carnegie-Mellon Univ, 68. *Mem:* Sigma Xi; AAAS; Chem Inst Can. *Res:* Thermodynamic, spectroscopic and kinetic studies of self-aggregating systems in aqueous media. *Mailing Add:* Dept Chem Univ Sask Saskatoon SK S7N 0W0 Can. *Fax:* 306-966-4730; *E-Mail:* verrallr@sask.usask.ca

**VERRIER, RICHARD LEONARD,** BEHAVIORAL BIOLOGY, NERVOUS SYSTEM. *Current Pos:* ASSOC PROF CARDIOVASC DIS, SCH PUB HEALTH, HARVARD UNIV, 83- *Educ:* Univ Va, PhD(cardiovasc physiol), 69. *Res:* Neural factors and cardiac arrhythmias. *Mailing Add:* Inst Prev Cardiovasc Dis Harvard Med Sch 1 Autumn St Fifth Floor Boston MA 02215

**VERRILL, HARLAND LESTER,** CLINICAL BIOCHEMISTRY. *Current Pos:* CLIN BIOCHEMIST, HURLEY MED CTR, 76-; MCLAREN MED CTR, 90-; CLINICAL BIOCHEM INSTR, UNIV MICH, FLINT, 90- *Educ:* Otterbein Col, BS, 70; Ohio State Univ, PhD(clin biochem), 76. *Mem:* Am Asn Clin Chem; AAAS. *Res:* Clinical enzymology of human myopathies; development of clinical laboratory methodologies; use of monoclonal antibodies for the diagnosis and treatment of human colon cancer. *Mailing Add:* Dept Path Hurley Med Ctr Flint MI 48502

**VERRILL, STEVE PATRICK,** GOODNESS-OF-FIT TESTS, DESIGN OF EXPERIMENTS. *Current Pos:* MATH STATISTICIAN, FOREST PRODS LAB, USDA FOREST SERV, 88- *Personal Data:* b Peoria, Ill, Nov 23, 52. *Educ:* Univ Wis-Madison, BA, 76, MA, 79, PhD(statist), 81. *Prof Exp:* Mathematician, Lawrence Livermore Nat Lab, 81-88. *Mem:* Am Statist Asn; Soc Indust & Appl Math; Soc Wood Sci & Technol. *Res:* Goodness-of-fit tests; predictor sort sampling; duration of load; statistical computing; nonlinear random effects; underdetermined regressions. *Mailing Add:* 6337 Stonefield Rd Middleton WI 53562. *Fax:* 608-231-9592; *E-Mail:* steve@wslo.fpl.fs.fed.us

**VERRILLO, RONALD THOMAS,** PSYCHOPHYSICS, NEUROSCIENCES. *Current Pos:* asst prof spec educ, Syracuse Univ, 57-62, res assoc, Bioacoust Lab, 59-63, res fel, Lab Sensory Commun, 63-67, assoc prof sensory commun, 67-74, prof sensory sci, 74-83, assoc dir, Inst Sensory Res, 80-84, dir, Inst Sensory Res, 84-93, prof neurosci, 83-94, EMER PROF NEUROSCI, SYRACUSE UNIV, 94- *Personal Data:* b Hartford, Conn, July 31, 27; m 50, Violet Silverstein; c Erica, Dan & Thomas. *Educ:* Syracuse Univ, BA, 52; Univ Rochester, PhD(psychol), 58. *Honors & Awards:* Res Award, Am Personnel & Guid Asn, 62. *Concurrent Pos:* NATO sr fel, Oxford Univ, 70-71; vis prof, Karolinska Hosp, Stockholm, Sweden, 77; Sigma Xi fac res award, 82. *Mem:* Fel Acoust Soc Am; Psychonomic Soc; Int Asn Study Pain; Soc Neurosci; NY Acad Sci. *Res:* Cutaneous sensitivity; effects of the physical parameters of vibratory stimuli on threshold and suprathreshold responses in humans; sensory characteristics of pain. *Mailing Add:* Inst Sensory Res Syracuse Univ Merrill Lane Syracuse NY 13244-5290. *Fax:* 315-443-1184; *E-Mail:* ron__verrillo@isr.syr.edu

**VERSCHINGEL, ROGER H C,** chemical instrumentation; deceased, see previous edition for last biography

**VERSCHOOR, J(ACK) D(AHLSTROM),** HEAT TRANSFER, BUILDING CONSTRUCTION TECHNOLOGY. *Current Pos:* CONSULT, VERSCHOOR ASSOCS, 82- *Personal Data:* b Grand Rapids, Mich, Nov 11, 23; m 47, Frances Johnson; c Peter, John & Karen. *Educ:* Univ Mich, BS, 45; Calif Inst Technol, MS, 47. *Prof Exp:* Physicist heat transfer, Johns-Manville Res Ctr, 47-59, proj mgr, Johns-Manville Corp, 59-69, mgr corp planning, 69-72, mgr venture anal & develop, 72-75, res assoc testing & contracts, Johns-Manville Res & Develop Ctr, 75-82. *Concurrent Pos:* Teaching fel, Calif Inst Technol, 45-47; instr, Rutgers Univ, 47-58; adv comt mem, US Dept Energy, 79-81. *Mem:* Am Soc Testing & Mat; Sigma Xi. *Res:* Energy conservation for industrial and building applications; air leakage; moisture and sound control in building construction; physics of heat transfer in thermal insulations; development of heat transfer test apparatus. *Mailing Add:* 179 Gail Lane Bailey CO 80421-1820

**VERSCHUREN, JACOBUS PETRUS,** ENGINEERING, HYDROLOGY. *Current Pos:* EMER CONSULT, 88- *Personal Data:* b Delft, Neth, Apr 13, 30; nat Can; m 54; c 2. *Educ:* Delft Univ Technol, CE, 52; Univ Alta, MSc, 60; Colo State Univ, PhD, 68. *Prof Exp:* Asst civil eng, Lehigh Univ, 52-53; engr, Howard Needles Tammen & Bergendoff, NY, 53; soil mech, Soil Mech Labs, Delft Univ Technol, 53-54; resident bridge engr, Prov Dept of Hwy, Man, 54-55; lectr, Univ Alta, 55-57, from asst prof to assoc prof civil eng, 57-70, prof 70-88. *Concurrent Pos:* Dir, T Blench & Assocs, Ltd, 59-; spec consult, Northwest Hydraul Consult, Ltd. *Mem:* Can Water Resources Asn. *Res:* Engineering and environmental aspects of hydrology. *Mailing Add:* 15409 Rio Terrace Dr Edmonton AB T5R 3L1 Can

**VERSCHUUR, GERRIT L,** ASTRONOMY. *Current Pos:* ADJ PROF PHYSICS, UNIV MEMPHIS, 96- *Personal Data:* b Capetown, SAfrica, June 5, 37; m 86, Joan Schmelz; c 1. *Educ:* Rhodes Univ, SAfrica, BSc, 57, MSc, 60; Univ Manchester, PhD(radio astron), 65. *Prof Exp:* Jr lectr physics, Rhodes Univ, SAfrica, 60; lectr, Univ Manchester, 64-67; res assoc, Nat Radio Astron Observ, 67-69, asst scientist, 69-72, assoc scientist, 72-73; prof astrogeophys & dir, Fiske Planetarium, Univ Colo, Boulder, 73-80; vpres mkt & sales, AET, Boulder, 82-84; prof physics/astron, Rhodes Col, 92-96. *Concurrent Pos:* Vis scientist, Nat Radio Astron Observ, 84-85; lectr, Univ Md, 88-92. *Mem:* Am Astron Soc; Int Astron Union. *Res:* Interstellar neutral hydrogen studies; interstellar magnetic field measurements. *Mailing Add:* Physics Dept Univ Memphis Memphis TN 38152. *E-Mail:* gverschr@cc.memphis.edu

**VERSEPUT, HERMAN WARD,** PAPER TECHNOLOGY. *Current Pos:* RETIRED. *Personal Data:* b Grand Rapids, Mich, Sept 25, 21; m 51. *Educ:* Yale Univ, BE, 42; Lawrence Univ, MS, 48, PhD(pulp & paper technol), 51. *Prof Exp:* Res chemist, Robert Gair Co, Inc, 51-56, chief appl res sect, Gair Paper Prod Group, Continental Can Co, Inc, 56-61; dir res & develop, Folding Carton Div, Riegel Paper Corp, 61-66; sr develop engr, Beloit Corp, 67-71; res mgr paperboard, Boxboard Res & Develop Asn, 71-92. *Mem:* Tech Asn Pulp & Paper Indust; Am Chem Soc. *Res:* Product and process development in the manufacture of packaging materials from recycled fibers. *Mailing Add:* 1927 Winchell Ave Kalamazoo MI 49008-2207

**VERSES, CHRIST JAMES,** PHYSIOLOGY, MOLECULAR BIOLOGY. *Current Pos:* asst prof, Sacred Heart Univ, 73-75, dir honors prog, 78-81, dir allied health sci, 81-93, ASSOC PROF BIOL, SACRED HEART UNIV, 75- *Personal Data:* b Stamford, Conn, Apr 12, 39; div; c 1. *Educ:* Valparaiso Univ, BS, 61; Univ Conn, PhD(bact), 67. *Prof Exp:* Fel microbiol, Univ Colo, Med Ctr, 66-68; asst prof biol, Moorhead State Col, 68-69; res microbiologist, Pollution Control Industs Inc, 69-72; dir, Pub Health Lab, Water & Sewage Anal, State of Conn, 72-73. *Concurrent Pos:* Owner anal lab; Lilly vis fac fel,

Yale Univ. *Mem:* Fel Am Inst Chemists; Am Soc Microbiologists; assoc Sigma Xi. *Res:* Pollution survey of municipal harbor systems; mechanism of attachment of phage to a host cell; biochemical reactions; viral genetics; new sterilization device and indicators; heart metabolism; microbiology; monoamine oxidase inhibition. *Mailing Add:* Sacred Heart Univ 5151 Park Ave Fairfield CT 06432-1000

**VERSIC, RONALD JAMES,** PRODUCT DEVELOPMENT. *Current Pos:* vpres, 79-88, PRES, RONALD T DODGE CO, 88- *Personal Data:* b Dayton, Ohio, Oct 19, 42; m 66; c 2. *Educ:* Univ Dayton, BS, 64; Johns Hopkins Univ, MA, 68; Ohio State Univ, PhD(mat eng), 69. *Prof Exp:* Sr scientist, Stand Register Co, 71-76; dir res & develop, Monarch Marking Systs, Subsid Pitney Bowes, 76-79. *Concurrent Pos:* Adj asst prof, Univ Cincinnati, 89- *Mem:* Sigma Xi; AAAS; Am Chem Soc; Am Asn Physics Teachers; Soc Imaging Sci & Technol. *Res:* Engineering management related to commercial product development in the chemical and paper converting areas. *Mailing Add:* Ronald T Dodge Co PO Box 41630 Dayton OH 45441-0630

**VERSTEEGH, LARRY ROBERT,** DRUG REGULATORY AFFAIRS, QUALITY ASSURANCE. *Current Pos:* PROCTER & GAMBLE PHARMACEUT. *Personal Data:* b Minneapolis, Minn, Feb 13, 49; m 70; c 2. *Educ:* Cent Col, Iowa, BA, 71; Iowa State Univ, PhD(biochem), 75. *Prof Exp:* Staff scientist, Procter & Gamble Co, 75-79; assoc dir drug regulatory affairs, Mead Johnson Pharmaceut Co, 79-82; dir regulatory affairs, NAm, G D Searle, 82-87; sr vpres regulatory & sci affairs, Pharmacia Adria, 87- *Concurrent Pos:* Lectr biol sci, Univ Cincinnati, 76-77. *Mem:* AAAS; Regulatory Affairs Profs Soc; Fedn Am Scientists, Drug Info Asn. *Res:* Drug regulatory affairs; drug development; quality assurance; quality control. *Mailing Add:* Procter & Gamble Pharmaceut 11450 Grooms Rd Cincinnati OH 45242. *Fax:* 614-764-8272

**VERSTRAETE, MARY CLARE,** GAIT ANALYSIS, MOTION ANALYSIS. *Current Pos:* Asst prof, 88-93, ASSOC PROF BIOMED ENG & DIR, WOMEN ENG PROG, UNIV AKRON, 93- *Personal Data:* b Detroit, Mich, Jan 7, 60. *Educ:* Mich State Univ, BS, 82, MS, 84, PhD(eng mech & biomech), 88. *Mem:* Am Soc Mech Engrs; Am Soc Biomech; Sigma Xi; Soc Women Engrs; Biomed Eng Soc. *Res:* Dynamics of human movements; human locomotion, including joint forces, moments and motions; muscle activity during motion. *Mailing Add:* Dept Biomed Eng 301-H Olson Res Ctr Univ Akron Akron OH 44325

**VER STRATE, GARY WILLIAM,** POLYMER CHEMISTRY, POLYMER PHYSICS. *Current Pos:* SR RES ASSOC, EXXON CHEM CO, 82- *Personal Data:* b Metuchen, NJ, Jan 29, 40; m 92, Mary A Kennedy; c Andrew & Amy. *Educ:* Hope Col, BS, 63; Univ Del, PhD(chem), 67. *Prof Exp:* Sr res chemist, Exxon Chem Co, Linden, 66-75, res assoc, 75-82. *Mem:* Am Phys Soc; Am Chem Soc; Soc Rheology. *Res:* Crystallinity; rheological properties; characterization by physical methods; light scattering; kinetics and molecular weight distribution; branching; cationic polymerization; chemical modification of polymers; polymer networks; liquid rubbers; lube oil viscosity modification. *Mailing Add:* 162 Longwood Dr Manalapan NJ 07726. *Fax:* 908-474-2123; *E-Mail:* gverstrate@aol.com

**VERTER, HERBERT SIGMUND,** ORGANIC CHEMISTRY. *Current Pos:* CHMN, SCI DEPT, WOODMERE ACAD, 79- *Personal Data:* b New York, NY, Jan 30, 36; m 60, 81; c 1. *Educ:* City Col New York, BS, 56; Harvard Univ, MA, 57, PhD(chem), 60. *Prof Exp:* NATO fel, Imp Col, Univ London, 60-61; asst prof chem, Cent Mich Univ, 61-66; assoc prof, Inter-Am Univ, PR, 66-67, dean acad affairs, 73, prof chem, 67-77, chmn dept, 66-72 & 74-77; admin dir, Dept Chem, Brandeis Univ, 77-79. *Mem:* Am Chem Soc; Sigma Xi. *Res:* Chemistry of natural products; organic synthesis; mechanism; carbon oxides. *Mailing Add:* PO Box 758 Ramsey NJ 07446

**VERTER, JOEL I,** BIOSTATISTICS. *Current Pos:* sr statistician, 90-92, RES PROF, HENRY FORD HOSP, 92- *Personal Data:* b Brooklyn, NY, June 14, 42. *Educ:* City Col NY, BS, 65; Univ Mass, MS, 67; Univ NC, PhD(biostatist), 79. *Prof Exp:* Statistician, Biostatist Res Br, Nat Heart, Lung & Blood Inst, NIH, 67-90. *Mem:* Am Statist Asn; Biomet Soc; Soc Clin Trials. *Mailing Add:* Biostat Ctr George Washington Univ 6110 Executive Blvd Suite 750 Rockville MD 20852

**VERTES, AKOS,** MASS SPECTOMETRY, MATHEMATICAL MODELING. *Current Pos:* PROF CHEM, GEORGE WASHINGTON UNIV, 91- *Personal Data:* b Budapest, Hungary, Dec 19, 52; m 96. *Educ:* Eotvos Lorand Univ, Budapest, BS, 74, PhD(chem), 79. *Prof Exp:* Res assoc, Cent Res Inst Physics, Budapest, 79-87, dep head, Chem Dept, 86-89, sr res assoc, 87-90; asst prof chem, Univ Antwerp, Belg, 87-91. *Concurrent Pos:* Guest res, Naval Res Lab, 93- *Mem:* Am Chem Soc; Microbeam Anal Soc; Am Soc Mass Spectros; Europ Microbeam Anal Soc. *Res:* Biomedical and environmental analysis; mathematical modeling. *Mailing Add:* Dept Chem George Washington Univ Washington DC 20052. *Fax:* 202-994-5873; *E-Mail:* vertes@gwis2.circ.gwu.edu

**VERTES, VICTOR,** INTERNAL MEDICINE. *Current Pos:* demonstr & instr med, 58-62 & 64, from asst clin prof to assoc clin prof, 64-72, PROF MED, SCH MED, CASE WESTERN RES UNIV, 72-, DIR, DEPT MED, MT SINAI MED CTR, 64- *Personal Data:* b Cleveland, Ohio, Sept 10, 27. *Educ:* Western Res Univ, BS, 49, MD, 53; Am Bd Internal Med, dipl, 62. *Prof Exp:* Intern med, Univ Hosps, Cleveland, 53-54; resident, Mt Sinai Hosp, Cleveland, 54-56; fel metab & endocrinol, NY Hosp, Cornell Med Ctr, 56-57.

*Concurrent Pos:* Assoc vis physician, Mt Sinai Hosp, 58-64, dir, Metab & Endocrine Lab, 59-65, proj dir, Chronic Dialysis Ctr, 65-68; investr, USPHS, 65-; mem, Coun Hemoglobin-Blood Pressure Res. *Mem:* Fel Am Col Physicians; Am Soc Nephrology; fel Am Col Angiol; Pan-Am Med Asn; Europ Dialysis & Transplant Asn. *Res:* Treatment and mechanisms of uremia; role of the kidney in hypertension. *Mailing Add:* One Mt Sinai Dr Mt Sinai Med Ctr Cleveland OH 44106-4198

**VERTREES, ROBERT LAYMAN,** NATURAL RESOURCES POLICY. *Current Pos:* ASST PROF LAND & WATER RESOURCES PLANNING & POLICY, OHIO STATE UNIV, 76- *Personal Data:* b Louisville, Ky, Nov 1, 39; m 66; c 3. *Educ:* Purdue Univ, BS, 61; Mich State Univ, MS, 67, PhD(resource develop), 74. *Prof Exp:* Instr resource econ, Dept Agr & Food Econ, Univ Mass, 69-72; asst prof, Dept Econ, SDak State Univ, 73-76. *Mem:* Am Water Resources Asn; Soil Conserv Soc Am. *Res:* Economic and land-use impacts of alternative water and land resource programs and projects; formulation and implementation of public water and land resource projects, policies and programs; natural resources information systems. *Mailing Add:* Sch Natural Resources Ohio State Univ 2021 Coffey Rd Columbus OH 43210-1085

**VERVOORT, GERARDUS,** MATHEMATICS EDUCATION, COMMUNICATIONS SCIENCE. *Current Pos:* PROF MATH & EDUC, LAKEHEAD UNIV, 70- *Personal Data:* b Utrecht, Neth, July 17, 33; Can citizen; m 64; c 2. *Educ:* Loras Col, BA, 60; Univ Iowa, MSc, 64, PhD(math), 70. *Prof Exp:* Teacher sec sch, Dept Indian Affairs, Alta, 60-62. *Concurrent Pos:* IBM Corp grant, Lakehead Univ, 71-72; consult, Ont Educ Commun Authority, 74-75; dept commun res contract, 74-75 & 75-76. *Mem:* Math Asn Am; Can Asn Prof Educ. *Res:* Instructor effectiveness in the teaching of university and college level mathematics courses; satellite communication for delivery of higher education in remote areas. *Mailing Add:* Dept Math Sci Lakehead Univ 955 Oliver Rd Thunder Bay ON P7B 5E1 Can

**VERWOERDT, ADRIAN,** psychiatry, psychoanalysis; deceased, see previous edition for last biography

**VESELL, ELLIOT S,** PHARMACOGENETICS, BIOCHEMICAL PHARMACOLOGY. *Current Pos:* EVAN PUGH PROF PHARMACOL, GENETICS & MED & CHMN DEPT PHARMACOL, COL MED, HERSHEY MED CTR, PA STATE UNIV, 68-, ASST DEAN GRAD EDUC, 73- *Personal Data:* b New York, NY, Dec 24, 33. *Educ:* Harvard Univ, MD, 59. *Hon Degrees:* Dsc, Philadelphia Col Pharm & Sci, 88. *Honors & Awards:* Samuel James Meltzer Award, 67; Am Soc Pharmacol & Exp Therapeut Award, 71; Julius W Sturmer Mem Lectr; Allan D Bass Lectr, dept pharmacol, Sch Med, Vanderbilt Univ, Nashville, Tenn, 85. *Prof Exp:* Intern pediat, Mass Gen Hosp, 59-60; res assoc human genet & asst physician, Rockefeller Inst, 60-62; asst resident med, Peter Bent Brigham Hosp, 62-63; clin assoc, Nat Inst Arthritis & Metab Dis, 63-65, head sect pharmacogenet, Lab Chem Pharmacol, Nat Heart Inst, 65-68. *Concurrent Pos:* William N Creasy vis prof clin pharmacol, Sch Med, George Washington Univ, 75, Sch Med, Univ Conn, 79; Pfizer lectr clin pharmacol, Univ Iowa, Med Col Pa, 76, Univ Conn, 77, Med Col Wis, 78, Georgetown Univ, 79, State Univ NY, Buffalo, 81, Morehouse Sch Med, Atlanta, Ga & Col Med, Howard Univ, Washington, DC, 85; Wellcome vis prof basic med sci, Col Physicians & Surgeons, Columbia Univ, NY, 82. *Mem:* Harvey Soc; Am Soc Human Genetics; Soc Exp Biol & Med; Am Soc Clin Invest; Am Fedn Clin Res; Am Asn Physicians; Am Soc Clin Pharmacol & Therapeut; Asn Med Sch Pharmacol. *Res:* Multiple molecular forms of enzymes; effect of heredity and environmental factors on disposition of drugs; biochemical pharmacology. *Mailing Add:* Pharmacol Hershey Med Ctr Pa State Univ Hershey PA 17033

**VESELY, DAVID LYNN,** ENDOCRINOLOGY & METABOLISM. *Current Pos:* PROF MED, PHYSIOL, BIOPHYS, HEALTH SCI CTR, UNIV SFLA, 89-, CHIEF, ENDOCRINOL, JAMES A HALEY VET ADMIN HOSP, 93- *Personal Data:* b Omaha, Nebr, Mar 6, 43; m 74, Clo Farrell; c Susanna, Catherine, Matthew, Brian & Jonathan. *Educ:* Creighton Univ, BS, 67; Univ Ariz, MD & PhD(Physiol), 72. *Honors & Awards:* Lange Award, Lange Publ Co, 72; Mosby Award, Mosby Publ Co, 72. *Prof Exp:* Fel, NIH, Univ Ariz, 68-72; intern med, Univ Miami Affil Hosp, 72-73, resident internal med, 73-74, fel endocrinol, 74-76; asst prof med, Univ Miami Med Sch, 76-78; from asst prof to prof med, Univ Ark Med Sci, 83-89. *Concurrent Pos:* Fel, NIH, Univ Miami, 74-76; actg chief endocrinol, Univ Ark Med Sci, 78-85; sr int scholar, Fogarty Int Ctr, Nat Inst Health, Nice, France, 84-85; distinguished vis prof, Christchurch, NZ, 95. *Mem:* Endocrine Soc; NY Acad Sci; Am Fedn Clin Res; Southern Soc Clin Invest; fel Am Asn Clin Endocrinologists; fel Am Col Physicians. *Res:* Atriol natriuretic factor and prohormone; atrial natriuretic factor peptides in normal and pathophysiologic states with respect to their circulating concentrations, physiologic effects and cellular mechanism of action; author of 220 medical publications. *Mailing Add:* James A Haley Vet Admin Hosp 13000 Bruce B Downs Blvd Tampa FL 33612

**VESLEY, DONALD,** ENVIRONMENTAL HEALTH. *Current Pos:* From instr to assoc prof, 60-78, PROF PUB HEALTH, UNIV MINN, MINNEAPOLIS, 78-, DIR ENVIRON HEALTH & SAFETY, 80- *Personal Data:* b Astoria, NY, Nov 7, 32; m 62; c 1. *Educ:* Cornell Univ, BS, 55; Univ Minn, MS, 58, PhD(environ health), 68. *Mem:* Am Soc Microbiol; Am Pub Health Asn; Am Biol Safety Asn. *Res:* Environmental microbiology. *Mailing Add:* Univ Minn Med Sch 420 Delaware St SE Minneapolis MN 55455-0374

**VESSEL, EUGENE DAVID,** ORGANIC POLYMER CHEMISTRY. *Current Pos:* RES SPECIALIST NONMETALLIC MAT, COM AIRPLANE GROUP, BOEING CO, 67- *Personal Data:* b Mt Olive, Ill, Dec 1, 27; m 46; c 2. *Educ:* Univ Ill, BS, 57; Univ Iowa, MS, 59, PhD(org chem), 60. *Prof Exp:* Res chemist, Chevron Res Corp, Standard Oil Calif, 60-61; sr res chemist, United Tech Ctr, United Aircraft Corp, 61-67. *Mem:* Am Chem Soc; Sigma Xi. *Res:* Adhesives; elastomers; plastics; composite materials; materials research; fire research and technology. *Mailing Add:* 12521 Roosevelt Rd Snohomish WA 98290

**VESSELINOVITCH, STAN DUSHAN,** physiology, oncology; deceased, see previous edition for last biography

**VESSEY, ADELE RUTH,** IMMUNOLOGY, VIROLOGY. *Personal Data:* b South Charleston, WVa, 47. *Educ:* Ohio Univ, BS, 69, MS, 72; Case Western Res Univ, PhD(microbiol), 76. *Prof Exp:* Fel immunol, Cleveland Clin Found, 76-80. *Mem:* Am Soc Microbiol; Int Asn Comp Res Leukemia & Related Dis; Sigma Xi. *Res:* Interaction of leukemia viruses with the immunological system; autoaggressive and immunosuppressive properties of lymphomas. *Mailing Add:* RD 3 Box 194B Elverson PA 19520

**VESSEY, JOSEPH KEVIN,** N-TWO FIXATION IN LEGUMES, PLANT & MICROBE INTERACTIONS. *Current Pos:* ASST PROF PLANT PHYSIOL, UNIV MAN, 89- *Personal Data:* b Charlottetown, PEI, July 2, 58. *Educ:* Dalhousie Univ, BSc, 80, MSc, 83; Queens Univ, Kingston, PhD(biol), 87. *Honors & Awards:* RH Award, RH Inst, 92. *Prof Exp:* Res assoc, Dept Soil Sci, NC State Univ, 87-89. *Concurrent Pos:* Mem, Meeting Site Comt, Can Soc Plant Physiologist, 93- *Mem:* Can Soc Plant Physiologist; Am Soc Plant Physiol; Swed Soc Plant Physiol; Am Soc Agron; Can Soc Agron; Crop Sci Soc Am. *Res:* Factors affecting the rates of nodulation, nitrogenase activity and growth of legumes (soybeans, peas, common bean, lentils); the contribution of alfalfa to nitrogen budgets in crop rotations. *Mailing Add:* Dept Plant Sci Univ Man Winnipeg MB R3T 2N2 Can. *Fax:* 204-261-5732; *E-Mail:* vessey@bldgagric.lan1.umanitoba.ca

**VESSEY, STEPHEN H,** ANIMAL BEHAVIOR, ECOLOGY. *Current Pos:* from asst prof to assoc prof, 69-80, PROF BIOL SCI, BOWLING GREEN STATE UNIV, 80- *Personal Data:* b Stamford, Conn, Mar 7, 39; m 62; c 2. *Educ:* Swarthmore Col, BA, 61; Pa State Univ, MS, 63, PhD(zool), 65. *Prof Exp:* Biologist, NIH, 65-69. *Mem:* Am Soc Primatologists; fel Animal Behav Soc; Am Soc Mammal; AAAS; Int Primatol Soc; Sigma Xi. *Res:* Social behavior and population dynamics; field studies of non-human primates and small mammals. *Mailing Add:* Dept Biol Bowling Green State Univ Bowling Green OH 43403. *E-Mail:* svessey@bgnet.bfsu.edu

**VESSEY, THEODORE ALAN,** MATHEMATICAL ANALYSIS. *Current Pos:* from asst prof to assoc prof, 70-79, PROF MATH, ST OLAF COL, 79- *Personal Data:* b St Paul, Minn, June 16, 38; m 65, Marge Thorpe; c James & David. *Educ:* Univ Minn, BA, 60, PhD(math), 66. *Prof Exp:* Assoc res engr, Honeywell, Inc, 62-63; asst prof math, Univ Wis-Milwaukee, 66-70. *Concurrent Pos:* Adj prof, Naval Grad Sch, 77; vis scholar, Stanford Univ, 77-78 & Chiang Mai Univ, Thilane; vis prof, Univ Lund, Sweden, 86-87. *Mem:* Am Math Soc; Math Asn Am. *Res:* Cluster set theory in determination of boundary behavior of complex functions; analytic properties of strchastic processes. *Mailing Add:* Dept Math St Olaf Col Northfield MN 55057-1574. *E-Mail:* vessey@stolaf.edu

**VESSOT, ROBERT F C,** PHYSICS. *Current Pos:* physicist, 69-72, SR PHYSICIST, SMITHSONIAN ASTROPHYS OBSERV, CAMBRIDGE, 72- *Personal Data:* b Montreal, Que, Apr 16, 30; m 59, Norma Wight; c 3. *Educ:* McGill Univ, BA, 51, MSc, 54, PhD(physics), 57. *Honors & Awards:* Exceptional Sci Achievement Medal, NASA, 78; Rabi Award, Inst Elec & Electronics Engrs, 93. *Prof Exp:* Mem, Div Sponsored Res Staff, Mass Inst Technol, 56-60; mgr maser res & develop, Varian Assocs, 60-67 & Hewlett-Packard Co, 67-69. *Mem:* Fel Am Phys Soc; Sigma Xi. *Res:* Physical electronics; noise in electron beams; atomic beams; atomic resonance physics; atomic hydrogen maser frequency standard; tests of gravitation and relativity. *Mailing Add:* 334 Ocean Ave Marblehead MA 01945

**VEST, CHARLES MARSTILLER,** MECHANICAL ENGINEERING, OPTICS. *Current Pos:* PRES, MASS INST TECHNOL, CAMBRIDGE, 90- *Personal Data:* b Morgantown, WVa, Sept 9, 41; m 63, Rebecca McCue; c John & Kemper. *Educ:* Univ WVa, BSME, 63; Univ Mich, MSE, 64, PhD(mech eng), 67. *Hon Degrees:* Dr, Mich Tech Univ, 92, WVa Univ, 94. *Honors & Awards:* Centennial Medallion, Am Soc Eng Educ, 93. *Prof Exp:* From asst prof to assoc prof, Univ Mich, Ann Arbor, 68-72, assoc dean acad affairs, 81-86, prof mech eng & dean, Col Eng, 86-88, provost, 89-90. *Concurrent Pos:* Vis assoc prof aero & elec eng, Stanford Univ, 74-75; assoc ed, J Optical Soc Am, 82-83; trustee, Environ Res, Inst Mich, WGBH Educ Found & New Eng Aquarium; coop mem, Woods Hole Oceanog Inst. *Mem:* Nat Acad Eng; fel Optical Soc Am; fel Am Acad Arts & Sci; AAAS; Sigma Xi; Am Soc Mech Engrs. *Res:* Heat transfer and fluid mechanics; hydrodynamic stability; optical holography and coherent optical measurement techniques; computer tomography. *Mailing Add:* Mass Inst Technol 77 Massachusetts Ave Bldg 3 Rm 208 Cambridge MA 02139-4307. *Fax:* 617-253-3124

**VEST, FLOYD RUSSELL,** MATHEMATICS EDUCATION. *Current Pos:* asst prof, 61-74, ASSOC PROF MATH, NTEX STATE UNIV, 74- *Personal Data:* b Orland, Calif, Feb 12, 34; m 55; c 2. *Educ:* ECent State Col, BSEd, 56; Univ Okla, MA, 59; NTex State Univ, EdD(math), 68. *Prof Exp:* Instr math, ETex State Univ, 59-61. *Mem:* Math Asn Am. *Res:* Learning theory; curriculum. *Mailing Add:* 1103 Brighton Terr Denton TX 76201-1158

**VEST, HYRUM GRANT, JR,** PLANT PATHOLOGY, PLANT GENETICS. *Current Pos:* head, Plants, Soils & Biometerol Dept, 89-95, ASSOC DIR, AGR EXP STA, UTAH STATE UNIV, 95- *Personal Data:* b Salt Lake City, Utah, Sept 23, 35; m 58, Gayle Pixton; c Kelly, Lani, Kari, Kamille & Kyle. *Educ:* Utah State Univ, BS, 60, MS, 65; Univ Minn, PhD(plant path), 67. *Prof Exp:* Res plant pathologist, Crops Res Div, Agr Res Serv, USDA, Md, 67-70; assoc prof hort, Mich State Univ, 70-76; prof hort & head dept, Okla State Univ, 76-83; head hort sci, Tex A&M Univ, 83-89. *Concurrent Pos:* Mem, Nat Plant Genetic Resources Bd, USDA, 82-88. *Mem:* Fel Am Soc Hort Sci; Am Soc Agron. *Res:* Genetics of nodulation and nitrogen fixation in soybean; breeding and genetics of onions, lettuce and asparagus. *Mailing Add:* Plants Soils & Biometeorol Logan UT 84322-4820. *Fax:* 435-750-3376

**VEST, ROBERT W(ILSON),** PHYSICAL CHEMISTRY, MATERIALS ENGINEERING. *Current Pos:* prof, 66-72, Basil S Turner prof eng, 72-92, EMER PROF, PURDUE UNIV, WEST LAFAYETTE, 92- *Personal Data:* b Lawrenceburg, Ind, Oct 17, 30; m 52, 82; c 3. *Educ:* Purdue Univ, BS, 52; Iowa State Univ, PhD, 57. *Honors & Awards:* Ross Coffin Purdy Award, Am Ceramic Soc, 67; Tech Achievement Award, Int Soc Hybrid Microelectronics, 81. *Prof Exp:* Chemist, Nat Lead Co Ohio, 52-53; asst, Ames Lab & Inst Atomic Res, Iowa State Univ, 53-57; res chemist, Monsanto Chem Co, 57-61; sr scientist, Systs Res Labs, Inc, 61-66. *Concurrent Pos:* Consult, CTS Microelectronics, Inc, 66 & Gen Motors Corp, 72- *Mem:* Am Soc Metals; fel Am Ceramic Soc; Nat Inst Ceramic Engrs; Int Soc Hybrid Microelectronics. *Res:* Electrical properties of metal oxides; electroceramics; transport properties on non-metallic materials; hybrid microelectronics. *Mailing Add:* 1500 Marilyn Ave West Lafayette IN 47906

**VESTAL, BEDFORD MATHER,** ANIMAL BEHAVIOR, BEHAVIORAL ECOLOGY. *Current Pos:* asst prof, 73-80, ASSOC PROF ZOOL, UNIV OKLA, 80- *Personal Data:* b Gainesville, Tex, Mar 8, 43; m 65; c Warden, Wesley & Sarah. *Educ:* Austin Col, BA, 65; Mich State Univ, MS, 67, PhD(zool), 70. *Prof Exp:* Instr biol, Univ Mo, St Louis, 69-70, asst prof, 70-73. *Concurrent Pos:* Res assoc, Mich State Univ, 70-71; res cur, Oklahoma City Zoo, 73-76; vis scientist zool, Monash Univ, 83-84; fac admin fel, Col Lib Studies, Univ Okla, 89-94, interim dean, 94-95, assoc dean, 96- *Mem:* AAAS; Animal Behav Soc; Sigma Xi; Nat Asn Biol Teachers. *Res:* Comparative social behavior of mammals; behavioral ecology of rodents; teaching biology to non-major students. *Mailing Add:* Col Lib Studies Univ Okla 1700 Asp Ave Suite 226 Norman OK 73072-6400

**VESTAL, CHARLES RUSSELL,** CHEMICAL ENGINEERING. *Current Pos:* assoc engr, Marathon Oil Co, 65-69, engr, 69-72, advan engr, 72-74, res engr chem eng, 74-77, adv res engr, 77-80, res engr, 80-82, sr res engr, Denver Res Ctr, 82-84, ADVAN SR ENGR, PETROL TECHNOL CTR, MARATHON OIL CO, 84- *Personal Data:* b Moran, Kans, Feb 21, 40; m 62; c 2. *Educ:* Colo Sch Mines, BS, 62, MS, 69, PhD(chem eng), 73. *Prof Exp:* Process design engr, Continental Oil Co, 62-63. *Concurrent Pos:* Adj assoc prof, Colo Sch Mines, 75-78; lectr, Univ Colo, Boulder, 75-84. *Mem:* Am Inst Chem Engrs; Soc Petrol Engrs. *Res:* Geostatistics, supercomputing and petroleum reservoir simulation. *Mailing Add:* 2446 S Dover Ct Denver CO 80227

**VESTAL, CLAUDE KENDRICK,** METEOROLOGY, CLIMATOLOGY. *Current Pos:* PVT CONSULT, 71- *Personal Data:* b High Point, NC, Mar 11, 16; m 46. *Educ:* Guilford Col, AB, 46. *Prof Exp:* Observer, Weather Bur, NC, 37-39, observer & forecaster, DC, 39-42, proj head climat, NY, 42-43, sect head, DC, 43-50; foreign serv staff officer, Dept State, Monrovia, Liberia, 50-52; sect head, Weather Bur, DC, 52-56, regional climatologist, Tex, 57-71. *Res:* Application of modern statistical methods to climatological data analysis, for design purposes and evaluation of operational risks. *Mailing Add:* 1720 Gun Wood Pl Crofton MD 21114

**VESTAL, J ROBIE,** microbiology; deceased, see previous edition for last biography

**VESTAL, ROBERT ELDEN,** INTERNAL MEDICINE, CLINICAL PHARMACOLOGY. *Current Pos:* STAFF PHYSICIAN, DEPT VET AFFAIRS MED CTR, 77-, CHIEF CLIN PHARMACOL & GERONTOL RES UNIT, ASSOC CHIEF STAFF RES & DEVELOP, 85- *Personal Data:* b Auburn, Calif, Oct 25, 45; m 68, Bonita Klahn; c Zachary & Sarah. *Educ:* Stanford Univ, AB, 67; Univ Calif, San Francisco, MD, 71. *Honors & Awards:* Arthur S Flemming Award, 82. *Prof Exp:* Intern med, Univ Col Med Ctr, 71-72, resident, 72-73; clin assoc, Geront Res Ctr, Nat Inst Aging, NIH, 73-75; fel clin pharmacol, Vanderbilt Univ, 75-77. *Concurrent Pos:* Asst med, Johns Hopkins Univ, 73-75; vis physician, Baltimore City Hosp, 73-75; instr pharmacol & med, Vanderbilt Univ, 76-77; from asst prof to assoc prof, 77-88, prof med, Univ Wash, 88-; mem, Adv Panel Geriat, US Pharmacopeial Conv, 81-, chmn, 90-; mem, Res Adv Group, Vet Admin, 83-86, Merit Rev Bd, 86-89; mem, Comt Chem Toxicity & Aging, Nat Res Coun, Nat Acad Sci, 86-87; mem, Gen Comt Revision, US Pharmacopeial Conv, 90-; dir, Mountain States Med Res Inst, 94- *Mem:* Am Soc Pharmacol & Exp Therapeut; Am Soc Clin Pharmacol & Therapeut; fel Am Col Physicians; Brit Pharmacol Soc; fel Gerontol Soc Am; Am Fedn Med; hon fel Am Col Clin Pharmacol; fel AAAS. *Res:* Effects of aging on drug metabolism and drug response; the clinical pharmacology of methylxanthines and adenosine; drug interactions; research administration. *Mailing Add:* Res Serv 151 Dept Vet Affairs Med Ctr 500 W Fort St Boise ID 83702. *Fax:* 208-422-1155; *E-Mail:* rvestal@micron.net

**VESTER, JOHN WILLIAM,** BIOCHEMISTRY, INTERNAL MEDICINE. *Current Pos:* assoc prof biochem, Col Med, Univ Cincinnati, 67-74, assoc prof med, 67-71, asst dean, 81-85, PROF MED, COL MED, UNIV CINNCINNATI, 91-, PROF BIOCHEM, 74-, ASSOC DEAN, 85- *Personal Data:* b Cincinnati, Ohio, June 5, 24; c 5. *Educ:* Univ Cincinnati, MD, 47. *Prof Exp:* Porter fel res med, Hosp Univ Pa, 54-56; from asst prof to assoc prof biochem & nutrit, Grad Sch Pub Health, Univ Pittsburgh, 56-61, from asst prof to assoc prof med, Sch Med, 56-67, asst prof biochem, 61-67. *Concurrent Pos:* Asst ward chief, Hosp Univ Pa, 54-56; chief, Sect Isotopes & Metab, Vet Admin Hosp, Pittsburgh, Pa, 61-67 & assoc chief of staff, 62-67; dir res, Good Samaritan Hosp, 67- *Mem:* Endocrine Soc; Am Fedn Clin Res; Am Diabetes Asn; fel Am Col Physicians; fel Am Col Cardiol. *Res:* Diabetes and mechanism of insulin actions; alcoholism; obesity; muscle diseases. *Mailing Add:* 4 Waljo Trail Milford OH 45150-1439

**VESTLING, CARL SWENSSON,** BIOCHEMISTRY. *Current Pos:* VIS PROF BIOCHEM, UNIV ARIZ, 82- *Personal Data:* b Northfield, Minn, May 6, 13; m 38; c Martha M, Christina L & Anne S. *Educ:* Carleton Col, BA, 34; Johns Hopkins Univ, PhD(biochem), 38. *Prof Exp:* From instr to prof chem, Univ Ill, Urbana, 38-63; prof biochem, Univ Iowa, 63-81, head dept, 63-76. *Concurrent Pos:* Guggenheim fel, Nobel Inst, Sweden, 54. *Mem:* AAAS; Am Chem Soc; Am Soc Biol Chemists; Soc Exp Biol & Med; Brit Biochem Soc. *Res:* Isolation, structure, mechanism, lactate and malate dehydrogenases and certain other liver and hepatoma enzymes. *Mailing Add:* 7981 N Sendero Uno Tucson AZ 85704-2066

**VESTLING, MARTHA MEREDITH,** ORGANIC CHEMISTRY. *Current Pos:* DIR MASS SPECTROMETRY, DEPT CHEM, UNIV WIS-MADISON, 96- *Personal Data:* b Urbana, Ill, Sept 4, 41. *Educ:* Oberlin Col, AB, 62; Northwestern Univ, Evanston, PhD(chem), 67. *Prof Exp:* Fel, Univ Fla, 67-68; res assoc, Vanderbilt Univ, 68-69; from asst prof to assoc prof chem, State Univ NY, Brockport, 70-90; vis assoc prof, Dept Chem & Biochem, Univ Md, Baltimore Co, 90-95; res assoc, Dept Chem & Biochem, Univ Del, Newark, 95-96. *Mem:* Am Chem Soc; AAAS; Am Soc Mass Spectrometry; Asn Women Sci; Sigma Xi. *Res:* Mass spectrometry; separations of biomolecules. *Mailing Add:* Dept Chem Univ Wis Madison WI 53706

**VETELINO, JOHN FRANK,** ELECTRICAL ENGINEERING, PHYSICS. *Current Pos:* From asst prof to assoc prof, 69-79, PROF ELEC ENG, UNIV MAINE, ORONO, 79- *Personal Data:* b Westerly, RI, Oct 17, 42; m 67; c 2. *Educ:* Univ RI, BS, 64, MS, 66, PhD(elec eng), 69. *Concurrent Pos:* Consult, Navy Underwater Systs Ctr, Allied Chem Corp. *Mem:* Am Phys Soc; Acoust Soc Am; sr mem Inst Elec & Electronics Engrs. *Res:* Microwave acoustics; surface acoustic waves; solid state phenomena; lattice dynamics and related thermodynamic optical and electronic properties of solids; phase transitions and impurity studies; electromagnetic and acoustic wave propagation; switched capacitor filters, sonar signal processing. *Mailing Add:* Dept Elec Eng Univ Maine Barrows Hall Orono ME 04469

**VETHAMANY, VICTOR GLADSTONE,** BIOLOGY, ANATOMY. *Current Pos:* RETIRED. *Personal Data:* b Servaikaramadam, India, Feb 7, 35; Can citizen; m 62; c Ravi Anand. *Educ:* Univ Madras, BA, 54, MA, 57; Univ Toronto, PhD(zool), 65. *Honors & Awards:* Nat Sci Prize, 54; Bourne Prize, 57. *Prof Exp:* Asst lectr biol, Univ Madras, 57-59; high sch teacher, Ethiopia, 60-61; demonstr zool, Univ Toronto, 61-64; res assoc path, Isaac Albert Res Inst, Kingsbrook Med Ctr, 65-67; from asst prof to assoc prof anat, Med Sch, Dalhousie Univ, 67-95. *Concurrent Pos:* Student, Nat Res Coun Can, 62-65; vis scientist, Med Res Coun, Inst Cellular Path, Paris, 73-74. *Mem:* AAAS; Am Asn Anat; Can Asn Anat Neurobiol & Cell Biol; NY Acad Sci; Can Fed Biol Soc. *Res:* Ultrastructure and histochemistry of blood cells and blood forming organs; ultrastructural studies on Niemann-Pick disease; comparative ultrastructural studies of blood in vertebrates and invertebrates; chemotaxis and cell injury; literature research on enviornmentally friendly practices industrial and natural NOW. *Mailing Add:* 5510 Stoneham Ct Halifax NS B3K 4A5 Can. *Fax:* 902-454-4559

**VETTE, JAMES IRA,** PHYSICS. *Current Pos:* RETIRED. *Personal Data:* b Evanston, Ill, Mar 4, 27; m 51; c 4. *Educ:* Rice Univ, BS, 52; Calif Inst Technol, PhD(physics), 58. *Honors & Awards:* Except Achievement Award, NASA, 69 & Goddard Group Achievement Award, 79; Scostep Award, 84. *Prof Exp:* Jr geophysicist, Humble Oil Co, 52; asst physics, Calif Inst Technol, 52-54; staff scientist, Sci Res Lab, Convair Div, Gen Dynamics Corp, 58-62, sr staff scientist, Sci Res Lab, Astronaut Div, 62; mgr nuclear physics, Vela Satellite Prog, Aerospace Corp, 62-63, staff scientist, Space Physics Lab, 63-67; dir, Goddard Space Flight Ctr, 67-84, sr staff scientist, Nat Space Sci Data Ctr, 84-88. *Mem:* AAAS; Am Phys Soc; Am Geophys Union; Inst Elec & Electronics Engrs; Sigma Xi. *Res:* Synchrotron; meson physics; high altitude radiation with balloons; solar physics; high energy physics; cosmic rays; magnetospheric physics; satellite measurements; space physics. *Mailing Add:* 12502 White Dr Silver Spring MD 20904

**VETTER, ARTHUR FREDERICK,** CHEMICAL & NUCLEAR ENGINEERING. *Current Pos:* assoc prof, 62-87, EMER PROF CHEM ENG, UNIV IOWA, 87- *Personal Data:* b De Witt, Iowa, July 26, 18; m 41; c 4. *Educ:* Coe Col, BA, 39; NC State Col, MS, 56. *Prof Exp:* Meteorologist, USAF, 47-54, res administr, 56-57; asst prof physics & nuclear eng, Air Force Inst Technol, 57-61; mem staff, Hq, 61-62. *Concurrent Pos:* Mem fac, Dept Nuclear Eng, Univ Ill, Urbana, 69-71. *Mem:* Am Inst Chem Engrs; Am Nuclear Soc; Fine Particle Soc; Sigma Xi. *Res:* Radiation protection; particle morphology; abrasive wear. *Mailing Add:* 201 N First Ave Apt 109 Iowa City IA 52245-3610

**VETTER, BETTY M,** science & engineering manpower; deceased, see previous edition for last biography

**VETTER, JAMES LOUIS,** FOOD TECHNOLOGY. *Current Pos:* dir res, 77-80, VPRES TECH, AM INST BAKING, 81- *Personal Data:* b St Louis, Mo, Jan 26, 33; m 54, Rose M Gentille; c Douglas J & Debra D. *Educ:* Washington Univ, AB, 54; Univ Ill, MS, 55, PhD(food technol), 58. *Prof Exp:* Food technologist, Monsanto Chem Co, 58-63; mgr res & develop labs, Keebler Co, Ill, 63-67, dir res & develop, 67-72; corp dir res & develop, Confectionery, Nut & Snack Prod Lab, Planters/Curtiss Div, Standard Brands, Inc, 72-74, vpres & tech dir res & develop lab, 74-75; vpres food sci & technol, Triticale Industs, Inc, Amarillo, Tex, 75-77. *Mem:* Am Asn Cereal Chem (secy, 83-85, pres-elect, 85-86, pres, 86-87); Inst Food Technologists. *Res:* Basic, nutrition and applied research on cereal grains and their utilization in processed, grain-based foods. *Mailing Add:* Am Inst Baking 1213 Bakers Way Manhattan KS 66502. *Fax:* 785-537-1493; *E-Mail:* jlvetter@aol.com

**VETTER, RICHARD J,** HEALTH PHYSICS, RADIOBIOLOGY. *Current Pos:* from asst prof to prof bionucleonics, 70-80, PURDUE UNIV PROF BIOPHYSICS, MAYO CLIN, 80-, HEAD OCCUP SAFETY SECT, 90- *Personal Data:* b Castlewood, SDak, July 17, 43; m 65; c 2. *Educ:* SDak State Univ, BS, 65, MS, 67; Purdue Univ, PhD(bionucleonics), 69. *Prof Exp:* Asst prof biol, Point Park Col, Pittsburgh, 69-70. *Concurrent Pos:* Asst radiol control officer, Purdue Univ, 70-80; asst radiation safety officer, Mayo Clin, 80-83, radiation safety officer, 83-; ed-in-chief, Health Physics, 88- *Mem:* AAAS; Health Physics Soc; Int Radiation Protection Asn; Soc Nuclear Med; Sigma Xi; Am Asn Physicists Med. *Res:* Biological effects and dosimetry of ionizing and nonionizing radiation including radioecology. *Mailing Add:* Radiation Control Mayo Clin 200 1st St SW Rochester MN 55905. *Fax:* 507-284-0150; *E-Mail:* rvetter@mayo.edu

**VETTER, RICHARD L,** ANIMAL SCIENCE, ENVIRONMENTAL SCIENCES. *Current Pos:* DIR RES, A O SMITH HARVESTORE PROD, INC, 78- *Personal Data:* b Henry Co, Ill, Dec 28, 30; m 50; c 2. *Educ:* Univ Ill, BS, 53, MS, 57; Univ Wis, PhD(nutrit, biochem), 60. *Prof Exp:* Asst, Univ Ill, 55-57; asst biochem, Univ Wis, 57-60, fel, 60-61; res nutritionist, Hess & Clark Co Div, Richardson-Merrill, Inc, 61-62; from asst prof to prof animal sci, Iowa State Univ, 62-78. *Concurrent Pos:* Researcher, Inst Animal Physiol, Cambridge, Eng, 68-69; mem Coun Agr Sci & Technol. *Mem:* Am Soc Animal Sci; Am Soc Dairy Sci; Am Inst Nutrit; Fedn Am Soc Exp Biol; Am Regist Prof Animal Scientists. *Res:* Nutrition and metabolic disorders; animal production; chemistry, nutrition and utilization of plant, animal and by-product wastes; bioenergy production and nutrient conservation. *Mailing Add:* A O Smith Harvestore Prod Inc 345 Harvestore Dr De Kalb IL 60115-9607. *Fax:* 815-756-2821

**VETTER, WILLIAM J,** ELECTRICAL ENGINEERING. *Current Pos:* prof, 71-77, PROF ENG & APPL SCI, MEM UNIV NFLD, 77- *Personal Data:* b Gronfell, Sask. *Educ:* Univ Toronto, BASc, 59; Univ Waterloo, MASc, 61, PhD(elec eng), 65. *Prof Exp:* Lectr elec eng, Univ Waterloo, 61-65, from asst prof to assoc prof, 65-71. *Mem:* Inst Elec & Electronics Engrs. *Res:* Theoretical and practical aspects of dynamical systems, particularly modeling, analysis, control and simulation; instrumentation and computer control of industrial systems and processes. *Mailing Add:* Dept Eng Mem Univ Nfld St John's NF A1B 3X5 Can

**VETTERLING, JOHN MARTIN,** PROTOZOOLOGY, PARASITOLOGY. *Current Pos:* PVT CONSULT, PARASITOLOGIC SERV, FT COLLINS, 86- *Personal Data:* b Fitzsimons, Colo, July 21, 34; m 57; c 3. *Educ:* Colo State Univ, BS, 56, MS, 62; Univ Ill, PhD(vet med sci), 65, Univ Calif, Davis, MPVM, 85. *Prof Exp:* Sr res parasitologist, Beltsville Parasitol Lab, Sci & Educ Admin-Agr Res, 65-76, asstt area dir, Sci & Educ Admin-Agr Res, 76-81, dir, Rocky Mountain Area, Agr Red Serv, USDA, 81-86. *Mem:* Am Soc Parasitol; World Asn Advan Vet Parasitol; Sigma Xi; Am Asn Vet Parasitol. *Res:* Biology and taxonomy of coccidia; pathogenesis of intestinal parasites. *Mailing Add:* PO Box 475 Ft Collins CO 80522-0475

**VETTERLING, WILLIAM THOMAS,** SOLID STATE PHYSICS, NUMERICAL ALGORITHMS. *Current Pos:* sr scientist, 84-86, PRIN SCIENTIST, POLAROID CORP, 86- *Personal Data:* b Greenfield, Mass, July 16, 48; m 73, Mary Anne Lee. *Educ:* Amherst Col, BA, 70; Harvard Univ, MA, 71, PhD(physics), 76. *Prof Exp:* From asst prof to assoc prof physics, Harvard Univ, 76-84. *Concurrent Pos:* Vpres, Numerical Recipes Software. *Mem:* Am Phys Soc; Inst Elec & Electronics Engrs; Soc Photo-Optical Instrument Engrs. *Res:* Solid state physics; image processing; solid-state imagers and novel photographic systems. *Mailing Add:* 35 Turning Mill Rd Lexington MA 02173

**VEUM, TRYGVE LAURITZ,** ANIMAL SCIENCE & NUTRITION. *Current Pos:* From asst prof to assoc prof, 67-80, PROF ANIMAL NUTRIT, UNIV M0, COLUMBIA, 80. *Personal Data:* b Virogua, Wis, Mar 16, 40; m 67, Margie Sutch; c Eric L & Kristen S. *Educ:* Univ Wis, BS, 62; Cornell Univ, MS, 65, PhD(animal nutrit, vet physiol & path), 68. *Honors & Awards:* Young Researcher Award, Am Soc Animal Sci, 80; George C Marshall Mem Fun, Sabbatical Award, Copenhagen, Denmark, 76. *Concurrent Pos:* Vis Scientist Nat Agr Res Inst, Dept Pigs & Horses, Copenhagen, Denmark, 76. *Mem:* Am Soc Animal Sci; Am Inst Nutrit. *Res:* Swine nutrition; minerals; amino acids; bioavailability. *Mailing Add:* Animal Sci Res Ctr Univ Mo Columbia MO 65211. *Fax:* 573-882-6827; *E-Mail:* trygve_veum@muccmail.missouri.edu

**VEVERKA, JOSEPH F,** PLANETARY SCIENCE, ASTRONOMY. *Current Pos:* Res assoc, Cornell Univ, 70-72, sr res assoc space sci, 72-74, asst prof, 74-77, ASSOC PROF ASTRON, CORNELL UNIV, 77- *Personal Data:* b Pelrimov, Czech, June 8, 41; Can citizen; m 69; c 1. *Educ:* Queen's Univ,

Kingston, Ont, BSc, 64, MSc, 65; Harvard Univ, MA, PhD(astron), 70. *Mem:* Am Astron Soc; Am Geophys Union; Meteoritical Soc; Royal Astron Soc Can. *Res:* Spacecraft investigation of planetary and satellite surfaces; evolution of planets and satellites. *Mailing Add:* Dept Astron Cornell Univ 320 Space Sci Bldg Ithaca NY 14853-0001

**VEZERIDIS, MICHAEL PANAGIOTIS,** SURGICAL ONCOLOGY. *Current Pos:* CHIEF SURG ONCOL, VET ADMIN MED CTR, BROWN UNIV, RI, 84-, ASSOC CHIEF SURG, 86-, ASSOC DIR DIV SURG ON COL, 89-, PROF SURG, 94- *Personal Data:* b Thessaloniki, Greece, Dec 16, 43; m 78, Therese M Statz; c Peter S & Alexander M. *Educ:* Nat Univ Athens Med Sch, MD, 67. *Hon Degrees:* MA, Brown Univ, 89. *Prof Exp:* Attend surgeon, Roswell Park Mem Inst, 81-82, staff surgeon, Vet Admin Med Ctr, Providence, RI, 82-84, asst prof surg, Brown Univ, 82-88, assoc prof surg, 88-94. *Concurrent Pos:* Prin investr, Heterogeneity & Metastasis in Human Pancreatic Cancer, Vet Admin Merit Rev Grant, 83-89; consult, Roger Williams Gen Hosp, RI, 86-89, active staff 89-, RI Hosp, Providence, 87-; vis prof, Univ Patras Med Sch, Greece, 88. *Mem:* NY Acad Sci; Am Col Surgeons; Asn Acad Surg; Am Soc Clin Oncol; Soc Surg Oncol; Am Asn Cancer Res; Soc Surg Alimentary Tract. *Res:* Heterogeneity and metastasis of human pancreatic cancer and other solid human tumors; human tumor metastasis; clinical research in cancer treatment. *Mailing Add:* 50 Limerock Dr East Greenwich RI 02818-1643. *Fax:* 401-456-2035

**VEZINA, CLAUDE,** microbial genetics & biochemistry; deceased, see previous edition for last biography

**VEZIROGLU, T NEJAT,** HEAT TRANSFER, NUCLEAR ENGINEERING. *Current Pos:* assoc prof mech eng, 62-66, chmn dept, 71-75, assoc dean res, 75-79, PROF MECH ENG, UNIV MIAMI, 66-, DIR, CLEAN ENERGY RES INST, 74- *Personal Data:* b Istanbul, Turkey, Jan 24, 24; m 61, Bengi Isikli; c Emre & Oya. *Educ:* Univ London, BSc, 46, PhD(heat transfer), 51, Imp Col, dipl, 47. *Prof Exp:* Sci adv, Off Soil Prod, Ankara, Turkey, 53-55, assoc dir steel silos, 55-57; eng consult, 57-59; tech dir, M K Veziroglu Construct Co Ltd, Istanbul, 59-62. *Concurrent Pos:* Ed, Int J Hydrogen Energy. *Mem:* Fel AAAS; fel Am Soc Mech Engrs; Am Inst Aeronaut & Astronaut; fel Brit Inst Mech Engrs; Int Asn Hydrogen Energy (pres). *Res:* Thermal conductance of metal surfaces in contact; two-phase flow instabilities; solar and hydrogen energy. *Mailing Add:* Col Eng Univ Miami PO Box 248294 Coral Gables FL 33124. *Fax:* 305-284-4792; *E-Mail:* vezirogl@eng.mia.edu

**VIA, FRANCIS ANTHONY,** CHEMISTRY, SYNTHETIC INORGANIC & ORGANOMETTALLI CHEMISTRY. *Current Pos:* MGR CATALYSTS & MATS RES, AKZO CHEM, INC, 82- *Personal Data:* b Frostburg, Md; m 70; c 2. *Educ:* WVa Univ, BS, 65; Ohio State Univ, MS, 67, PhD(phys org chem), 70. *Prof Exp:* Teaching asst chem, Ohio State Univ, 65-66, res fel phys org chem, 66-70; from res chemist to sr res chemist, 70-75, supvr org res, 75-76, asst to res dir, 76-78, mgr inorg res, Stauffer Chem Co, 78-82. *Mem:* Am Chem Soc; Sigma Xi; AAAS; Am Ceramic Soc; Mats Res Soc. *Res:* Zeigler-Natta catalysis; materials research-electronic and structural; homogenous and heterogenous catalysis; main group inorganic chemical sulfur, phosphorus; sol-gel synthesis-oxide powders and films; specialty chemicals and agricultural chemicals. *Mailing Add:* AKZO Chem Dobbs Ferry Dobbs Ferry NY 10522-1697

**VIA, WILLIAM FREDRICK, JR,** PEDODONTICS. *Current Pos:* RETIRED. *Personal Data:* b Ironton, Ohio, Dec 27, 20; m 47; c 2. *Educ:* Ohio State Univ, DDS, 45; Univ Mich, MS, 53. *Prof Exp:* Instr oper dent, Col Dent, Ohio State Univ, 48-51; instr, Col Dent, Univ Calif, 51-52; mem staff, Henry Ford Hosp, Detroit, Mich, 53-68; chmn dept oral radiol, Sch Dent Med, Univ Conn, 68-69; prof oral diag & chmn dept, Sch Dent, Univ NC, Chapel Hill, 69-80. *Mem:* AAAS; fel Am Acad Dent Radiol; Am Acad Pedodontics; Int Asn Dent Res. *Res:* Prenatal, neonatal and post-natal influences upon dental enamel development; healing of dental pulp following bacterial, chemical or mechanical trauma; oral roentgenographic technique. *Mailing Add:* 810 Indian Spring Rd Chapel Hill NC 27514

**VIAL, JAMES LESLIE,** VERTEBRATE BIOLOGY, POPULATION ECOLOGY. *Current Pos:* CONSULT, APACHE ENVIRON, 94- *Personal Data:* b Taft, Calif, Dec 19, 24; div; c 1. *Educ:* Calif State Univ, Long Beach, BA, 52, MA, 54; Univ Southern Calif, PhD, 65. *Prof Exp:* From instr to assoc prof biol, Los Angeles Valley Col, 55-61; vis prof zool, Univ Costa Rica, 61-62, Ford Found Prof ecol, 62-64; vis assoc prof biol, Western Mich Univ, 64-66; from assoc prof to prof, Univ Mo-Kansas City, 66-75, assoc dean res & dir res admin, 66-68; chmn fac biol sci, Univ Tulsa, 75-82, prof biol, 75-91; int prog coordr, IUCN World Conserv, 91-93. *Concurrent Pos:* Assoc dir, Orgn Trop Studies, Inst Trop Ecol, Costa Rica, 63, dir, 64; herpet ed, Am Soc Ichthyologists & Herpetologists, 72-78; managing ed, J Herpetol, 83-90; cert sr ecol, Ecol Soc Am, 84; res assoc, Ariz-Sonora Desert Mus, 93- *Mem:* AAAS; Ecol Soc Am; Am Soc Mammal; Soc Study Amphibians & Reptiles (pres, 77); Am Soc Icthyologists & Herpetologists; Sigma Xi; Am Inst Biol Sci; Herpetologists League; Soc Conserv Biol. *Res:* Vertebrate ecology and population dynamics, especially amphibians and reptiles, conservation biology; environmental inventories and impact reports. *Mailing Add:* PO Box 35 Copper Queen Sta Bisbee AZ 85603. *E-Mail:* jlvial@primenet.com

**VIAL, LESTER JOSEPH, JR,** MEDICINE, PATHOLOGY. *Current Pos:* instr, 74-75, ASST PROF PATH, MED SCH, LA STATE UNIV, 75- *Personal Data:* b New Orleans, La, Mar 19, 44; m 71. *Educ:* La State Univ, New Orleans, BS, 66; Med Sch, La State Univ, MD, 70; Am Bd Path, dipl,

74. *Prof Exp:* Intern path, Charity Hosp, New Orleans, 70-71, resident, 71-74. *Concurrent Pos:* Vis staff, Charity Hosp, New Orleans, 74- *Mem:* AOA; Am Soc Clin Path; Am Soc Cytol. *Mailing Add:* LSU Med Sch Path 1901 Perdido St New Orleans LA 70112-1328

**VIAL, THEODORE MERRIAM,** RUBBER CHEMISTRY. *Current Pos:* RETIRED. *Personal Data:* b Ware, Iowa, Feb 27, 21; m 49; c 5. *Educ:* Univ Md, BS, 42; Univ Ill, PhD(chem), 49. *Prof Exp:* Res chemist, Chas Pfizer & Co, 48-50; res chemist, Am Cyanamid Co, 50-51, tech rep, 51-58, tech mgr, Rubber Chem Dept, 58-60, com develop rubber chemicals & elastomers, 60-66, group leader, Chem Res Div, 66-86. *Mem:* AAAS; Am Chem Soc; Sigma Xi. *Res:* Rubber and elastomer compounding; theory and application of vulcanization and protective agents; polyacrylate and other specialty elastomers. *Mailing Add:* 35 Woodside Lane Princeton NJ 08540-5417

**VIANNA, NICHOLAS JOSEPH,** epidemiology, for more information see previous edition

**VIANO, DAVID CHARLES,** INJURY BIOMECHANICS, AUTOMOTIVE SAFETY ENGINEERING. *Current Pos:* sr res engr, Biomed Sci Dept, Gen Motors Res Labs, 74-76, staff res engr, 76-78, asst dept head, 78-87, PRIN RES SCIENTIST, AUTOMOTIVE SAFETY & HEALTH DEPT, GEN MOTORS RES LABS, 87- *Personal Data:* b San Mateo, Calif, May 7, 46; m, Sharon L Henderson. *Educ:* Santa Clara Univ, BS, 68; Calif Inst Technol, MS, 69, PhD(appl mech), 72. *Honors & Awards:* R H Isbrandt Medal, Soc Automotive Engrs, 81, 85, 86 & 93, Colwell Award, 82, 88, 89, 90 & 92; Award for Safety Eng Excellence, Nat Hwy Traffic Safety Admin, 89. *Prof Exp:* Postdoctoral biomed sci, Univ & Swiss Fed Inst Technol, Zurich, Switz, 72-74. *Concurrent Pos:* Chmn, Passenger Protection Comt, Soc Automotive Engrs, 80-; from adj asst prof to adj assoc prof eng, Wayne State Univ, Detroit, 81-89, adj prof, 89-; mem, Comt Fed Trauma Res, Nat Acad Sci, Nat Res Coun, 84-85, Comt Sch Bus Safety, Transp Res Bd, 87-89, Comt Occupant Restraint Res Needs, 88-90, Adv Comt Injury Prev & Control, Ctr Dis Control, 89-92 & bd dirs, Nat Head Injury Found, 87-92; assoc ed, Accident Anal & Prev, 88- *Mem:* Fel Asn Advan Automotive Med (pres, 89); fel Am Soc Mech Engrs; fel Soc Automotive Engrs; fel Am Inst of Med & Biol Engrs; Am Trauma Soc; Am Soc Biomech. *Res:* Injury biomechanics, human tolerance, trauma mechanisms, injury disability; automotive safety, crash injury prevention, occupant protection by safety belts, airbags; public health programs for injury control; safety research and policy; author of numerous publications. *Mailing Add:* Gen Motors Res & Develop Ctr Warren MI 48090-9055. *E-Mail:* dviano@cmsa.gmr.com

**VICK, CHARLES BOOKER,** WOOD ADHESIVES SCIENCES & TECHNOLOGY. *Current Pos:* Forest prod technologist, 58-60, wood scientist, 60-74, prin wood scientist, 74-86, RES SCIENTIST, FOREST PROD LAB, SOUTHEASTERN FOREST EXP STA, 86- *Personal Data:* b Seaboard, NC, Sept 15, 32; m 63; c 2. *Educ:* Duke Univ, AB, 54, MF, 58. *Concurrent Pos:* Chmn, Subcomt Construct Adhesives, Am Soc Testing & Mat, 75. *Mem:* Am Soc Testing & Mat; Forest Prod Res Soc; Adhesion Soc. *Res:* Develop the technology to bond wood that has been chemically treated; with preservatives, and dimensional stabilizers. *Mailing Add:* Forest Prod Lab One Gifford Pinchot Dr Madison WI 53705-2798

**VICK, ERIK PAUL,** CHEMICAL VAPOR DEPOSITION OF THIN FILMS, SEMICONDUCTOR EQUIPMENT ENGINEERING. *Current Pos:* SR ASSOC ENGR, INT MICROCIRCUITS INC, 96- *Personal Data:* b Cincinnnati, Ohio, Aug 7, 69. *Educ:* NC State Univ, BS, 93, MS, 96. *Mem:* Inst Elec & Electronics Engrs; Nat Soc Prof Engrs. *Res:* Development for black-end-of-the-line integrated circuit processing; thin line deposition; etching; photolithography. *Mailing Add:* 3808 Oak Park Rd Raleigh NC 27612-5622

**VICK, GEORGE R,** ALGEBRA, GEOMETRY. *Current Pos:* RETIRED. *Personal Data:* b New Waverly, Tex, Dec 18, 20; m 43; c 2. *Educ:* Sam Houston State Teachers Col, BA, 41, MA, 42; Univ Tex, PhD(math), 64. *Prof Exp:* Teacher high sch, Tex, 41-42; from asst prof to assoc prof math, Sam Houston State Univ, 46-51, assoc prof, 55-56, actg dir dept, 56-64, dir dept, 64-67, prof, 64-91. *Mem:* Math Asn Am; Nat Coun Teachers Math. *Res:* Foundations of geometry; mathematical pedagogy at all levels, especially training and re-training teachers. *Mailing Add:* 2101 Ave Q Huntsville TX 77340

**VICK, GERALD KEITH,** TEACHING. *Current Pos:* ADJ INSTR, BUCKS CO COMMUNITY COL, 88- *Personal Data:* b Dixon, Ill, Mar 6, 30; m 50, Patricia Kenney; c Roger K, Kathryn A (Alexis) & Christopher A. *Educ:* Univ Ill, BS, 52; Univ Rochester, PhD(org chem), 56. *Prof Exp:* Res chemist, Esso Res & Eng Co, 55-58, proj leader engine oils, 58-62, sect head motor fuels & lubricants, 62-65, sr staff adv petrol fuels & lubricants, 65-67, dir lubricants & specialties lab, 67-75, sr planning adv, Corp Planning Dept, Exxon Corp, 75-76, sr staff adv, Petrol & Synthetic Fuels Res, Exxon Res & Eng Co, 76-86. *Mem:* AAAS; Am Chem Soc; Soc Automotive Eng; fel Am Inst Chemists. *Res:* Organic chemistry; fuel technology and petroleum engineering; chemistry education. *Mailing Add:* 3 Devon Dr New Hope PA 18938

**VICK, JAMES,** HERPETOLOGY, MARINE BIOLOGY. *Personal Data:* b Crookston, Minn, Sept 6, 31. *Educ:* Univ NDak, MS, 55, PhD(pharmacol), 58. *Honors & Awards:* Cert Recognition, Sigma Xi, 91; Sir Henry Wellcome Medal, 92. *Prof Exp:* Chief CU Labs, Walter Reed, Army, 69-73 & neurophysiol, Aberdeen Proving Grounds, 74-78; NATO prin deleg, Surgeon

Gen Off, Pentagon, 78-80; div dir (A), Food & Drug Admin, Washington, DC, 91-92. *Concurrent Pos:* Assoc prof pharmacol, Univ Md, 79-81; assoc prof pathophysiol, Walter Reed Army Inst Res, Washington, DC, 85-; prof pharmacol, Am Univ, 89-91; chmn, Inst Animal Care & Use Comt, Food & Drug Admin, 90- *Mem:* Underseas Med Soc; Sigma Xi; Soc Exp Biol Med; Am Col Clin Pharmacol. *Res:* Shock; venoms; toxins; treatment of cyanide poisoning; nerve agent toxicity; author of 275 publications. *Mailing Add:* Food & Drug Admin 200 C St SW Washington DC 20204. *Fax:* 301-594-3037

**VICK, JAMES WHITFIELD,** MATHEMATICS. *Current Pos:* from asst prof to assoc prof, 70-82, asst dean, 80-83, PROF MATH, UNIV TEX, AUSTIN, 82-, ASSOC DEAN, COL NATURAL SCI, 83- *Personal Data:* b Hope, Ark, Mar 8, 42; m 64; c 2. *Educ:* La State Univ, Baton Rouge, BS, 64; Univ Va, MA, 66, PhD(math), 68. *Prof Exp:* Instr math, Princeton Univ, 68-70. *Mem:* Math Asn Am; Am Math Soc; AAAS. *Res:* Algebraic and differential topology, K-theory and transformation groups. *Mailing Add:* Dept Math Univ Tex Austin TX 78712

**VICK, JOHN,** ELECTRICAL ENGINEERING. *Current Pos:* VPRES RES & ENG, LOCKHEED, FT WORTH, 91-; DIV VPRES RES & ENG, GEN DYNAMICS, FT WORTH, 91- *Personal Data:* b Feb 12, 33. *Educ:* Tex A&M Univ, BEE & MEE. *Prof Exp:* Mem aerophysics group res & eng, Gen Dynamics, Ft Worth, 59-61, from sr aerosyst engr to proj aerosyst engr, F-111 Radar Group, 61-67, group engr, F-111 Aerosyst Proj Off, 67-68, asst proj engr, 68-73, aerosyst group engr, Elec Fabrication Ctr, 73-75, chief, 75-77, mgr, 77-80, dir support req & syst dept, 80-88, div vpres mil electronics, 88-91. *Mailing Add:* Lockheed Corp Lockheed Blvd PO Box 748 Ft Worth TX 76101

**VICK, ROBERT LORE,** PHARMACOLOGY, PHYSIOLOGY. *Current Pos:* from asst prof to prof, 61-85, PROF MOLECULAR PHYSIOL & BIOPHYS, BAYLOR COL MED, 85- *Personal Data:* b Courtland, Miss, Sept 1, 29; m 53; c 1. *Educ:* Univ Miss, BS, 52, MS, 54; Univ Cincinnati, PhD(pharmacol), 57. *Prof Exp:* Actg asst prof pharm, Southwestern Okla State Col, 53; instr, Univ Miss, 53-54; res assoc pharmacol, Univ Cincinnati, 57-58; instr physiol, State Univ NY Upstate Med Ctr, 58-61. *Concurrent Pos:* USPHS Career Develop Award 66-71. *Mem:* AAAS; Am Physiol Soc; Am Soc Pharmacol & Exp Therapeut; Soc Exp Biol & Med. *Res:* Heart and circulation; ion movements; electrophysiology; autonomic nervous system. *Mailing Add:* 3512 Bellaire Blvd Houston TX 77025-1314. *Fax:* 713-798-3475

**VICKERS, DAVID HYLE,** ENTOMOLOGY, BIOCHEMISTRY. *Current Pos:* asst prof physiol, Fla Technol Univ, 69-72, actg chmn dept, 74-75, chmn, 75-81, ASSOC PROF PHYSIOL, UNIV CENT FLA, 72- *Personal Data:* b Sturgis, Miss, Jan 14, 40; m 70; c 2. *Educ:* Miss State Univ, BS, 61, MS, 64; La State Univ, PhD(entom), 69. *Prof Exp:* Instr entom, Southeastern La Col, 64-66. *Mem:* AAAS. *Res:* Genetics; molecular biology. *Mailing Add:* Dept Biol Univ Cent Fla PO Box 25000 Orlando FL 32816-0001

**VICKERS, FLORENCE FOSTER,** PHARMACOLOGY. *Current Pos:* ASSOC DIR CLIN RES, CIBA-GEIGY PHARMACEUT, 88- *Personal Data:* b Philadelphia, Pa; m 76. *Educ:* Pa State Univ, BS, 69, Hahnemann Med Col, PhD(cardiovasc physiol & pharmacol), 81. *Prof Exp:* Res biologist, Merck Sharp & Dohme Res Labs, 69-74, med writer, 74-78; res fel, Hahnemann Med Col, 78-81, instr, 79-80; clin res assoc, Cardiovasc Div, Merck Sharp & Dohme, 82-84; assoc dir clin res, Wyeth Int Ltd, 84-87. *Concurrent Pos:* Vis assoc prof, Col Med, Pa State Univ, 87- *Mem:* AAAS; Am Soc Clin Pharmacol & Therapeut; fel Am Col Clin Pharmacol; Drug Info Asn; Sigma Xi; Soc Exp Biol & Med; Am Asn Study Liver Dis; Am Soc Pharmacol & Exp Therapeut. *Res:* Cardiovascular physiology and pharmacology; renin-angiotension system; anti hypertensive drugs; beta adrenoceptor antagonists; catecholamines; drug metabolism. *Mailing Add:* Box 1031 Ctr Sch & Slotter Rds Bedminster PA 18910. *Fax:* 908-277-3840

**VICKERS, JAMES HUDSON,** VETERINARY MEDICINE, PATHOLOGY. *Current Pos:* dir Path & Primatol Br, Ctr Drugs & Biol, 73-92, DIR, DIV VET SERV, FOOD & DRUG ADMIN, 92- *Personal Data:* b Columbus, Ohio, Apr 21, 30; m 64; c Valerie J May; c Dana (Carleton). *Educ:* Ohio State Univ, BSc, 52, DVM, 58; Univ Conn, MS, 66; Am Col Vet Pathologists, dipl, 75. *Honors & Awards:* Presidential Citation, 79; Commissioner's Spec Citation, Food & Drug Admin, 88. *Prof Exp:* Vet, Columbus Zoo, Ohio, 58-60; vet, Lab Animal Colony, Lederle Labs, Am Cyanamid Co, NY, 60-64, pathologist, 64-66, head dept vet path, 66-68, head dept exp path, 68-70; vpres & dir res, Primelabs, Inc, 70-73. *Concurrent Pos:* Lectureship, State Univ NY Downstate Med Sch; Food & Drug Admin rep, Interagency Animal Res Comt, 74-, proj officer, Primate Breeding Colony Contracts. *Mem:* Am Vet Med Asn; Am Asn Lab Animal Sci; Am Col Vet Pathologists; Soc Toxicol; Int Acad Pathol. *Res:* Diseases and pathology of primates, laboratory animals and exotic zoological species; testing and quality control of vaccines, especially polio vaccine, toxicological testing and pathology of pharmaceuticals. *Mailing Add:* 2324 Oak Dr Ijamsville MD 21754. *Fax:* 301-402-2408

**VICKERS, ROGER SPENCER,** REMOTE SENSING, MEASUREMENT TECHNOLOGY. *Current Pos:* DIR, ULTRA-WIDEBAND RADAR PROG, SRI INT, 73- *Personal Data:* b Hitchin, Eng, Nov 13, 37; m 67; c 3. *Educ:* Univ Southampton, BSc, 59, PhD(physics), 63. *Honors & Awards:* IR-100 Award, 76. *Prof Exp:* Res physicist, IIT Res Inst, 63-66 & Stanford Univ, 66-68; res assoc remote sensing, Colo State Univ, 68-69; vpres, Environ Res Assocs, 69-70; assoc prof remote sensing, Colo State Univ, 70-73.

*Concurrent Pos:* Consult, commercial & indust, 71-81 & NSF, 74-79. *Mem:* Inst Elect & Electronics Engrs. *Res:* Remote sensing techniques; high resolution radars; subsurface profiling; radar sounding of ice; development of electromagnetic geophysical techniques; airborne ground-penetrating radar; folinge penetrating radar. *Mailing Add:* SRI Int Menlo Park CA 94025. *Fax:* 650-859-5149

**VICKERS, STANLEY,** DRUG METABOLISM. *Current Pos:* res fel, 69-80, SR RES FEL DRUG METAB, MERCK RES LABS, 80- *Personal Data:* b Blackpool, Eng, Sept 27, 39; US citizen. *Educ:* Univ London, BSc, 62; State Univ NY, Buffalo, PhD(biochem pharm), 67. *Prof Exp:* Fel, Univ Kans, 66-69. *Mem:* Am Soc Pharmacol & Exp Therapeut; Am Chem Soc; AAAS; NY Acad Sci. *Res:* Detoxification mechanisms and metabolic transformations which control the fate of foreign compounds. *Mailing Add:* Merck Res Labs Bldg 26A 2044 West Point PA 19486-0004

**VICKERS, THOMAS J,** ANALYTICAL CHEMISTRY. *Current Pos:* From asst prof to assoc prof, 66-76, PROF ANALYTICAL CHEM, FLA STATE UNIV, 76- *Personal Data:* b Miami, Fla, Mar 29, 39; m 63; c Thomos, Andrew, Patrick & Catherine. *Educ:* Spring Hill Col, BS, 61; Univ Fla, PhD(chem), 64. *Mem:* Am Chem Soc; Soc Appl Spectros. *Res:* Spectroscopic methods of analysis; Raman spectroscopy. *Mailing Add:* Dept Chem Fla State Univ Tallahassee FL 32306-3006. *E-Mail:* vickers@chem.fsu.edu

**VICKERS, WILLIAM W,** ATMOSPHERIC PHYSICS. *Current Pos:* RETIRED. *Personal Data:* b San Francisco, Calif, June 21, 23; m 54; c 3. *Educ:* Univ Calif, BA, 54, MA, 56; McGill Univ, PhD(hydrol, meteorol), 65. *Prof Exp:* Res assoc, Inst Polar Studies, Ohio State Univ, 57-61; head geophys res group, Tech Opers, Inc, 61-66; sr sci exec, EG&G, Inc & Environ Sensor Systs Div, Mitre Corp, Bedford, 66-85; consult, 85-87. *Concurrent Pos:* Dir, Explorers Club, 69-72. *Mem:* Am Geophys Union; Am Meteorol Soc; NY Acad Sci; Cosmos Club. *Res:* Studies of snow and ice in Antarctica during the geophysical year; Air Force investigations of weather modification; atmospheric transport of toxic materials; atmospheric effects on radio-radar propagation; analyses of electronic warfare scenarios. *Mailing Add:* Box 471 Bell Ave Fair Haven NY 13064

**VICKERS, ZATA MARIE,** FOOD SCIENCE. *Current Pos:* Asst prof, 75-80, ASSOC PROF FOOD SCI, UNIV MINN, ST PAUL, 80- *Personal Data:* b Salem, Ore, Oct 13, 50. *Educ:* Ore State Univ, BS, 72; Cornell Univ, PhD(food sci), 75. *Mem:* Inst Food Technol. *Res:* Relationships between the physical, acoustical and sensory properties of foods. *Mailing Add:* Dept Food Sci & Nutrit 225 Food Sci N Ctr Univ Minn 1334 Eckles Ave St Paul MN 55108-1040

**VICKERS-RICH, PATRICIA,** VERTEBRATE PALEONTOLOGY, BIOGEOGRAPHY. *Current Pos:* LECTR & READER, DEPT EARTH SCI & DEPT ECOL, EVOLUTIONARY BIOL, MONASH UNIV, 76-, PROF PALEONT, 95- *Personal Data:* b Exter, Calif, July 11, 44; m 66, Tom; c Leaellyn S & Tim. *Educ:* Univ Calif, Berkeley, AB, 66; Columbia Univ, MA, 69, PhD(geol), 73. *Prof Exp:* Asst geol, Columbia Univ, 67-68; asst prof geosci geol, Dept Geosci, Tex Tech Univ & assoc cur vert paleont, Mus, 73-76. *Concurrent Pos:* Fulbright fel, Australian Am Educ Found, Australia, 73-74; Sunshine Found, Utah Mining, Ingram Trust grants, 76-; hon res assoc, Mus Victoria, 78 & 80-; Nat Geog Soc grants, 78, 80-; Australian Res grants Comn grantee, 78-; Australian Acad Sci Chinese exchange scientist, 79; Australian China Coun grantee, 80-81; Australian Nat Parks Wildlife grantee, 81; dir, Monash Sci Ctr & Great Russ Dinosaurs Exhib, 93- *Mem:* Am Ornith Union; Geol Soc Australia; Royal Australian Ornith Union; Soc Vert Paleont; Orgn Trop Studies; Planetary Soc; Australian Asn Paleout; Australian Conserv Found; Sigma Xi. *Res:* Evaluation of cenozoic fossil birds from Australasia; mesozoic/paleogene birds from Asia and South America; Neogene avifaunas from SAfrica; development of bird bone key for archaeological use; investigation into phylogenetic value of avian quadrate; development of a machine translation system for Chinese scientific literature; avian systematics; polar dinosaurs and other biota from late mesozic polar environment in Gondwana; changing climate and geography of Australasia from mesozoic to present; paleoclimatology. *Mailing Add:* Dept Earth Sci Monash Univ Clayton Victoria 3168 Australia. *Fax:* 61-3-9905-4903; *E-Mail:* prich@artemis.earth.monash.edu.au

**VICKERY, LARRY EDWARD,** ENZYMOLOGY, STEROID CHEMISTRTY. *Current Pos:* asst prof biophys, 77-82, assoc prof, physiol, biophys & biol chem, 82-88, PROF PHYSIOL, BIOPHYS & BIOL CHEM, UNIV CALIF, IRVINE, 88- *Personal Data:* b Atlanta, Ga, Nov 26, 45; c 2. *Educ:* Univ Calif, Santa Barbara, BA, 67, PhD(biol), 71. *Prof Exp:* Res assoc biochem, Western Regional Res Lab, USDA, 71; res assoc biophys chem, Lawrence Berkeley Lab, 72; fel, Univ Calif, Berkeley, 73-74, res assoc, Dept Chem, 75-76. *Concurrent Pos:* Res assoc, Nat Res Coun, Nat Acad Sci, Nat Acad Engr, 71; fel, Nat Inst Gen Med Sci, USPHS, 73-74. *Mem:* Biophys Soc; AAAS; Am Soc Biochem & Molecular Biol; Protein Soc. *Res:* Investigations on the molecular mechanisms and regulation of steroid hormone biosynthesis; characterization of enzymes and reaction mechanisms involved; development of inhibitors of steroid synthesis; protein chemistry, engineering and mutagenesis. *Mailing Add:* Dept Physiol & Biophys Univ Calif Irvine CA 92717. *Fax:* 714-856-8540; *E-Mail:* lvickery@uci.edu

**VICKERY, ROBERT KINGSTON, JR,** PLANT EVOLUTION. *Current Pos:* from instr to assoc prof biol, 52-64, head dept genetics & cytol, 62-65, prof biol, 64-93, EMER PROF BIOL, UNIV UTAH, 93- *Personal Data:* b Saratoga, Calif, Sept 18, 22; m 51, Marcia Hoak; c David K & Peter H. *Educ:* Stanford Univ, AB, 44, AM, 48, PhD(biol, bot), 52. *Prof Exp:* Instr bot, Pomona Col, 50-51. *Concurrent Pos:* Researcher, Carnegie Inst Wash, 48-52; res fel, Calif Inst Technol, 55; vis assoc prof, Harvard Univ, 63; mem, Cellular Biol & Genetics Fel Panel, NIH, 65-69, 7th, 12th & 13th Int Bot Cong & 10th-13th Int Gen Cong; assoc ed, Evolution, Soc Study Evolution, 68-72; mem, Int Orgn Plant Biosysts Coun, 75-81. *Mem:* AAAS; Soc Study Evolution (vpres, 77-78); Am Soc Nat; Ecol Soc Am; Genetics Soc Am. *Res:* Cytogenetics, ecologic, numerical and classical taxonomic, and biochemical approaches to problems of the evolutionary mechanisms and patterns of the genus Mimulus, particularly sections Simiolus and Erythranthe. *Mailing Add:* Dept Biol Univ Utah Salt Lake City UT 84112

**VICKERY, WILLIAM LLOYD,** BEHAVIOURAL ECOLOGY, POPULATION DYNAMICS. *Current Pos:* PROF BIOL, UNIV QUE, MONTREAL, 80- *Personal Data:* b Wolfville, Nova Scotia, July 3, 50; m 76; c 3. *Educ:* McGill Univ, BS, 71; MS, 73, PhD(renewable resources), 76. *Prof Exp:* Fac lectr ecol, Univ Western Ont, 76-80; fel environ res, Atomic Energy Can Ltd, 80. *Mem:* Am Soc Mammologists. *Res:* Modelling of the evolution of animal behaviour, empirical studies of small mammal population and community dynamics and analysis of statisical tests in ecology. *Mailing Add:* UQAM Box 8888 Sta A Montreal PQ H3C 3P8 Can. *Fax:* 514-987-4648

**VICKREY, HERTA MILLER,** IMMUNOLOGY, MEDICAL MICROBIOLOGY. *Current Pos:* PUB HEALTH MICROBIOLOGIST, TULARE COUNTY PUB HEALTH LAB, 84- *Personal Data:* b San Gregorio, Calif; div; c 4. *Educ:* Jan Jose State Col, BA, 57; Univ Calif, Berkeley, MA, 63, PhD(bact & immunol), 70. *Prof Exp:* Microbiologist, Viral & Rickettsial Dis Lab, Calif State Dept Pub Health, 57-60, 61-62; res bacteriologist, Univ Calif, Berkeley, 63-64; asst prof immunol, virol & microbiol, Univ Victoria, BC, 70-72; res assoc cancer immunol, dept res & educ, Wayne County Gen Hosp, 72-83; lab supvr, dept med admin, Univ Mich, Ann Harbor, 77-83; lab dir pub health, Shasta County Pub Health Lab, 83-84. *Concurrent Pos:* Bacteriologist, Children's Hosp Med Ctr Northern Calif, Oakland, 58-70; res grants, Univ Victoria, BC, 70-72; med staff res & educ grants, 73-83; vis scientist, dept nutrit & food sci, Mass Inst Technol, Cambridge, 82; mycol trainer, Calif State Dept Health Serv, Berkeley, 85-86. *Mem:* Am Soc Microbiol; Clin Ligand Assay Soc; Am Soc Clin Path; NY Acad Sci. *Res:* Cellular immunological resistance: tuberculosis and oncogenesis; cell culture assays to autoallergies, oncogenesis and hypersensitivities; tissue culture studies: lymphatic leukemia immunotherapy; growth and metabolic responses of liver cells (canine, rabbit, murine-diabetic versus normal) to hormones, drugs, lectins, medium additives; hybridoma immunological technology; general medical sciences. *Mailing Add:* Tulare Co Pub Health Lab 1062 S K St Tulare CA 93274

**VICKROY, DAVID GILL,** ANALYTICAL CHEMISTRY. *Current Pos:* Res chemist, Celanese Fibers Co, 69-72, sr res chemist, 72-75, res assoc anal chem, 75-76, group leader, 76-82, MGR, HOECHST CELANESE RES DIV, 82- *Personal Data:* b San Antonio, Tex, July 5, 41; m 64; c 2. *Educ:* Vanderbilt Univ, BA, 63; Rice Univ, MA, 66; Univ Tenn, PhD(inorg chem), 69. *Mem:* Sigma Xi; Am Chem Soc; NY Acad Sci. *Res:* Analytical characterization of complex mixtures such as tobacco smoke and environmental samples; development of synthetic alternatives to natural products; analytical testing of advanced materials. *Mailing Add:* 30 Canterbury Lane Short Hills NJ 07078-3302

**VICK ROY, THOMAS ROGERS,** automatic control of chemical processes, computer control of industrial processes, for more information see previous edition

**VICKROY, VIRGIL VESTER, JR,** POLYMER CHEMISTRY, PHYSICAL CHEMISTRY. *Current Pos:* RES CHEMIST, ALLIED CORP, 75- *Personal Data:* b San Antonio, Tex, Aug 8, 31; m 55; c 2. *Educ:* Auburn Univ, BS, 52; Univ Akron, MS, 62, PhD(polymer sci), 65. *Prof Exp:* Jr chemist, B F Goodrich Co, 55-61; res chemist, Harrison-Morton Labs, Ohio, 61-63; res chemist, Univ Akron, 63-65; sr res chemist, Monsanto Co, 65-73; lab mgr, Marathon-Morco Co, 73-74; prin chemist, Dart Industs, 74-75. *Mem:* Am Chem Soc; Soc Rheology; NAm Thermal Anal Soc; Soc Plastics Engrs. *Res:* Effect of thermal and thermo-oxidative history on morphological, mechanical and molecular properties of polyolefins; physical chemistry of Ziegler and Phillips catalyst systems. *Mailing Add:* 15452 Altus Ave Baton Rouge LA 70817-2103

**VICORY, WILLIAM ANTHONY,** HIGH STRENGTH FIBER OPTIC SPLICING, MECHANICAL FIBER OPTIC SPLICING. *Current Pos:* Sr tech assoc, 82-90, MEM TECH STAFF, AT&T BELL LABS, 90- *Personal Data:* b Beaufort, SC, June 7, 58; m 82, Deborah Scarborough; c Andria, Joey & Tony. *Educ:* Southern Col Technol, BMET, 82; Brigham Young Univ, MS, 95. *Res:* Fiber optic splicing design and development; testing; customer interfacing; documentation; granted four patents. *Mailing Add:* 2000 Northeast Expressway Rm 1B01 Norcross GA 30071

**VICTERY, WINONA WHITWELL,** ENVIRONMENTAL RESEARCH. *Current Pos:* health scientist, Environ Criteria & Assessment Off, 86-92, SCIENTIST, US ENVIRON PROTECTION AGENCY, 92- *Personal Data:* b Abilene, Tex, Apr 15, 41; m 63. *Educ:* Rice Univ, BA, 63; Univ Wis-Madison, MS, 67; Univ Mich, Ann Arbor, PhD(physiol), 78; Am Bd Toxicol, dipl, 86. *Prof Exp:* Res biologist nuclear med, Univ Calif, Los Angeles, 67-74; scholar physiol, Univ Mich, 78-81; scholar pharm, Nat Inst Environ Health Sci, 81-83, expert, Biomet & Risk Assessment Prog, 83-86. *Mem:* Am Physiol Soc; Soc Risk Anal. *Res:* Physiological relationships between essential and toxic trace metals; risk assessment and risk communication. *Mailing Add:* US Environ Protection Agency Reg 1X P-2-1 75 Hawthorne St San Francisco CA 94105-3919. *Fax:* 415-744-2499

**VICTOR, ANDREW C,** ENGINEERING PHYSICS. *Current Pos:* CONSULT PHYSICIST, VICTOR TECHNOL, 90- *Personal Data:* b New York, NY, Nov 4, 34; m 55, Dorothy Tresselt; c Lisa A, Jean S & Joseph A. *Educ:* Swarthmore Col, BA, 56; Univ Md, MS, 61. *Prof Exp:* Physicist, Nat Bur Stand, 56-62; head, Stand Lab, US Naval Ord Test Sta, US Naval Weapons Ctr, 62-64, physicist systs analysis & rocket plume technol, 64-68, head, Analytical Br, 68-73, head Propulsion Analalytical Br, 73-76, head appl propulsion res, 76-79, coordr independent explor develop, 79-80, proj mgr explosives advan develop, 80-81, head, Thermal/Struct Br, 81-84, prog mgr, Navy Insensitive Munitions Advan Develop Propulsion Prog, 84-89. *Concurrent Pos:* Chmn, plume technology subcomt, JANNAF, 78-80, mem exhaust plume technol subcomt, 64-89, propulsion systs hazards subcomt, 84-89; TTcp lead focus officer, propulsion hazards, 85-89; mem, plume technol working group, 87-89; US focus officer plume technol, 67-78. *Mem:* Assoc fel Am Inst Aeronaut & Astronaut; Sigma Xi; Syst Safety Soc; Technol Transfer Soc; Int Pyrotechnic Soc. *Res:* Missile propulsion analysis; rocket exhaust plume; ramjet engine cost analysis; weapon energy utilization; energetic material hazards; insensitive munitions; detonation physics. *Mailing Add:* Victor Technol 1537 4th Suite 218 San Rafael CA 94901

**VICTOR, GEORGE A,** ATOMIC AND MOLECULAR PROCESSES AND APPLICATIONS. *Current Pos:* PHYSICIST PHYSICS, SMITHSONIAN ASTROPHYS OBSERV, 71- *Personal Data:* b Ridgway, Pa, Nov 15, 36; m 63; c 2. *Educ:* Rensselaer Polytech Inst, BS, 58; Queen's Univ, Belfast, PhD(appl math-physics), 66. *Prof Exp:* Staff scientist physics, GCA Corp, 61-71. *Concurrent Pos:* Sr res fel, Queen's Univ, Belfast, 66-67; lectr, dept astron, Harvard Univ, 71-; vis fel, Joint Inst Lab Astrophys, Univ Colo Nat Bur Standards, 78-79; prog comt, Am Phys Soc, 83-85. *Mem:* Am Asn Physics Teachers; Am Geophys Union; Sigma Xi; fel Am Phys Soc. *Res:* Quantum theory of atomic and molecular structure and scattering processes; interaction of radiation with matter; applications of cross section data to problems in atmospheric physics, astrophysics, lasers and plasmas. *Mailing Add:* 23 Peter Rd North Reading MA 01864. *Fax:* 617-495-5970

**VICTOR, JOE MAYER,** ELECTRONICS ENGINEERING, LASER SYSTEMS. *Current Pos:* ENG SPECIALIST III, HERNANDEZ ENGR, 96- *Personal Data:* b Houston, Tex, Sept 20, 39; m 81, Jean Zeisman; c Kayla, Jeffrey, Melissa, Joshua, Karen & Rebecca. *Educ:* Univ Tex, Austin, BS, 62, MS, 64, PhD(elec eng), 67. *Prof Exp:* Teaching asst elec eng, Univ Tex, Austin, 61-66; sr res engr, Southwest Res Inst, 66-75; eng mgr, Petrolite Instruments, 75-83; sys eng, Bio Quantum Technol, 83-88; advan syst eng specialist, Lockheed Eng & Sci Co, 88-95. *Res:* Design and development of laser systems. *Mailing Add:* 5754 Bankside Houston TX 77096

**VICTOR, JONATHAN DAVID,** VISUAL NEUROPHYSIOLOGY, MATHEMATICAL MODELLING. *Current Pos:* from asst prof to assoc prof, 86-91, PROF NEUROL & NEUROSCI, MED COL & GRAD SCH MED SCI, CORNELL UNIV, 91- *Personal Data:* b Yonkers, NY, Nov 21, 54; c 2, Rosemarie Gruss; c Stefanie & Alexander. *Educ:* Harvard Col, BA, 73; Rockefeller Univ, PhD(neurophysiol), 79; Cornell Univ, MD, 80. *Prof Exp:* Asst prof biophys, Rockefeller Univ, 84-86. *Concurrent Pos:* Consult, Bell Tel Labs, 83; adj prof, Rockefeller Univ, 86-; assoc attend, Rockefeller Univ Hosp, 86-, NY Hosp, 87- & Hosp Spec Surg, 90- *Mem:* Soc Neurosci; Asn Res Vision & Opthal; Sigma Xi; Am Neurol Asn; Asn Res Nerv & Ment Dis; Biomed Eng Soc. *Res:* Neural computations underlying the process of visual information by the mammalian brain at retinal, thalamic, and cortical levels; new techniques of nonlinear systems analysis and their application; evoked potentials. *Mailing Add:* 1300 York Ave New York NY 10021

**VICTOR, LEONARD BAKER,** CLINICAL PATHOLOGY, LEGAL MEDICINE. *Personal Data:* b Schenectady, NY, Aug 3, 34; m 66, Rona; c Brian & Sarah. *Educ:* NY Univ, AB, 53; Univ Brussels, MD, 60; Royal Col Trop Med, TMD, 60. *Prof Exp:* Intern & resident path, Strong Hosp, Univ Rochester, 61-65, sr instr, Univ Rochester, 65-67; assoc prof path & lab med, Meharry Med Col, 68-72, assoc prof path, Grad Sch & dir, Meharry Multiphasic Lab, 68-72; prof path, Univ Tenn, Memphis & dir clin labs, City of Memphis Hosps, 72-78; prof & chmn, Dept Path, Sch Med, Marshall Univ, 78-80; dean clin sci, Sch Med, Ross Univ, 84-85. *Concurrent Pos:* Dep med examr, Monroe Co, NY, 65-67; consult, State Hosp, Rochester, NY, 65-67; assoc prof biomed eng, Sch Eng, Vanderbilt Univ, 69-72; chmn, Comt Health Fitness Sci, Nashville, 70-71; chmn, Nat Adv Task Force for Regional Med Prog Eval of Automated Multiphasic Health Testing, 72; med dir & dir, Mid-South Comprehensive Home Health Serv Agency, 73-77; mem bd dirs, Mid-South Regional Blood Ctr, 73-77. *Mem:* Fel Col Am Path; fel Am Soc Clin Path; fel Soc Advan Med Systs; fel Royal Soc Health; AMA. *Res:* Administrative and legal medicine and pathology including curriculum development and interdisciplinary functions; lab medicine and prospective medicine, including automation, computerization and management techniques, continuous quality improvement. *Mailing Add:* 5480 Shawnee Circle No 9 Huntington WV 25705-3333

**VICTOR, WALTER K,** RADIO SYSTEMS FOR SPACE COMMUNICATION. *Current Pos:* RETIRED. *Personal Data:* b Bronx, NY, Dec 18, 22. *Mem:* Nat Acad Eng; fel Inst Elec & Electronics Engrs. *Mailing Add:* 1630 Pegfair Estates Dr Pasadena CA 91103-1934

**VICTORIA, EDWARD JESS, JR,** BIOCHEMISTRY, CELL BIOLOGY. *Current Pos:* ASSOC RES BIOCHEMIST, DEPT PATH, UNIV CALIF, SAN DIEGO, 73- *Personal Data:* b San Diego, Calif, Sept 11, 41. *Educ:* Univ Calif, Los Angeles, AB, 63, MA, 65, PhD(molecular & cell biol), 68. *Prof Exp:* Asst res biologist, Univ Calif, Los Angeles, 68-69; fel, Univ Utrecht, 70-71; spec res fel, Lab Biochem, NIH, 71-73. *Concurrent Pos:* Res fel, Am Cancer Soc, Biochem Lab, Utrecht, Neth, 70-71; USPHS, NIH fel, 71-73; prin investr, NIH res grant, 78- *Mem:* Am Chem Soc; Am Soc Cell Biol; AAAS; Biochem & Molecular Biol. *Res:* Membrane biochemistry. *Mailing Add:* 3503 Pershing Ave San Diego CA 92104-3413. *Fax:* 619-452-6893

**VICTORICA, BENJAMIN (EDUARDO),** PEDIATRICS. *Current Pos:* from resident pediat to chief resident, Col Med, Univ Fla, 64-66, instr & spec trainee pediat cardiol, 67-70, from asst prof, 70-74, assoc prof, 70-79, PROF PEDIAT CARDIOL, COL MED, UNIV FLA, 80- *Personal Data:* b Mendoza, Arg, June 9, 36; m 63; c 3. *Educ:* Nat Univ Cuyo, MD, 62; Educ Coun for Med Grad, cert, 63; Am Bd Pediat, dipl, 68, cert pediat cardiol, 71. *Prof Exp:* Intern, Med Sch, Nat Univ Cuyo, 63-63 & St Benedict's Hosp, Ogden, Utah, 63. *Mem:* Fel Am Acad Pediat; Am Col Cardiol. *Res:* Pediatric cardiology. *Mailing Add:* Dept Pediat & Cardiol Univ Fla Col Med Health Sci Ctr PO Box 100296 Gainesville FL 32610-0296

**VICTORIUS, CLAUS,** organic coatings, for more information see previous edition

**VIDA, JULIUS,** MEDICINAL CHEMISTRY. *Current Pos:* PRES, VIDA INT PHARMACEUT CONSULT. *Personal Data:* b Losonc, Czech, May 30, 28; US citizen; c 4. *Educ:* Pazmany Peter Univ, Budapest, Dipl, 50; Carnegie Inst Technol, MS, 59, PhD(org chem), 60; Columbia Univ, MBA, 81. *Prof Exp:* Chemist, EGIS Co, (Wander Co) Hungary, 50-56 & Merck & Co, Inc, NJ, 57-58; res fel, Harvard Univ, 61-62; chemist, Worcester Found Exp Biol, Mass, 62-67; group leader, T Clark Lab, Kendall Co, Lexington, Mass, 67-72, sect head, 72-75; asst dir res planning & licensing, Bristol Lab, 75-76; dir chem, Bristol-Myers Co, Int Div, 76-79, dir chem res, develop & licensing, 80-93, vpres bus develop licensing & strategic planning, 85-93. *Concurrent Pos:* Adj prof med chem, Grad Sch Pharmaceut Sci, Northeastern Univ, 73-75; lectr ophthal, Columbia Univ, 77-84; mem bd dir, Biotechnol Cos. *Mem:* Sigma Xi; Am Chem Soc; AAAS; NY Acad Sci. *Res:* Drugs acting on the central nervous systems; Cardiovascular agents; antibiotics; anticonvulsants; anabolic agents; antiosteoporotics. *Mailing Add:* 27 Sachem Rd Greenwich CT 06830

**VIDAL, JACQUES J,** COMPUTER SCIENCE, NEUROSCIENCES. *Current Pos:* from asst prof to assoc prof, 63-70, PROF ENG, UNIV CALIF, LOS ANGELES, 70- *Personal Data:* b Liege, Belg, Apr 18, 30; div; c 2. *Educ:* Univ Liege, MS, 54; Saclay Nuclear Res Ctr, France, nuclear engr, 58; Univ Paris, PhD(elec eng), 61. *Prof Exp:* Lectr, Univ Liege, 56-63. *Concurrent Pos:* Orgn Econ Coop & Develop & NATO res fels, 62-63; consult comput educ, USAID mission to Tunisia, 70-85; mem, Brain Res Inst; res fel, Inst Nat Sante & Rech Med, France, 78-81; prof, Univ Paris VII, France, 89. *Mem:* Inst Elec & Electronics Engrs; Soc Neurosci. *Res:* Early research: hybrid computing, sensitivity analysis, control and man-machine communication; current work: neural networks, fuzzy systems, genetic search, pattern recognition (speech and handwriting) and robot control. *Mailing Add:* Dept Comput Sci 3731 Boelter Univ Calif 405 Hilgard Ave Los Angeles CA 90024-1596. *Fax:* 310-206-5115; *E-Mail:* vidal@cs.ucla.edu

**VIDALE, JOHN EMILIO,** SEISMOLOGY, TECTONICS. *Current Pos:* GEOPHYSICIST, US GEOL SURV, 91- *Personal Data:* b Mar 15, 59; c Laura. *Educ:* Yale Univ, BS, 81; Calif Inst Technol, PhD(seismol), 86. *Honors & Awards:* Macelwane Medal, Am Geophys Union, 94. *Prof Exp:* Res scientist, Univ Calif, Santa Cruz, 87-90. *Mem:* Fel Am Geophys Union; Seismol Soc Am. *Res:* Investigate earthquake and earth structure. *Mailing Add:* 156 Archer Dr Santa Cruz CA 95060. *Fax:* 650-329-5163; *E-Mail:* vidale@vidale.wr.usgs.gov

**VIDALE, RICHARD F(RANCIS),** SYSTEMS ENGINEERING, SOFTWARE ENGINEERING. *Current Pos:* From asst prof to assoc prof, 64-70, prof syst eng & chmn dept, 70-81, PROF ELEC, COMPUT & SYST ENG, BOSTON UNIV, 84- *Personal Data:* b Rochester, NY, Apr 22, 36; m 65; c 2. *Educ:* Univ Rochester, BS, 58; Univ Wis, PhD(mech), 64. *Concurrent Pos:* Consult, Raytheon Co, Space & Info Systs Div, Sudbury, 66-67; Sanders Assocs, Inc, Bedford, 67-70; Chas T Main, Int, 77-, GTE, Needham Heights, 82, Mitre Corp, 84-, Data Gen Corp, Westboro, 85-, Charles Stark Draper Lab, Cambridge, 85-, Kollsman, Inc, Merrimack, NH, 87, Anal Scis Corp, Reading, 87-88. *Mem:* Inst Elec & Electronics Engrs; Asn Comput Mach. *Res:* Software engineering; real-time systems; theory and applications of Petrinets. *Mailing Add:* Dept Elec & Comput Eng Col Eng Boston Univ Boston MA 02215. *Fax:* 617-353-6440; *E-Mail:* rfv@enga.bu.edu

**VIDALI, GIAN FRANCO,** SURFACE PHYSICS, LOW TEMPERATURE PHYSICS. *Current Pos:* asst prof, 84-90, ASSOC PROF PHYSICS, SYRACUSE UNIV, 90- *Personal Data:* b Trieste, Italy. *Educ:* Univ Genoa, DSc, 77; Pa State Univ, PhD(physics), 82. *Prof Exp:* Res fel chem eng, Calif Inst Technol, 82-83, res fel low temperature physics, 83-84. *Concurrent Pos:* Alfred P Sloan fel, 86. *Mem:* Am Phys Soc; Am Asn Physics Teachers; Sigma Xi; Mat Res Soc. *Res:* Experimental surface and low temperature physics; interaction of atoms or molecules with surfaces using atom beam scattering and other probes; adsorption-desorption phenomena at low temperature; thin film growth. *Mailing Add:* Dept Physics Syracuse NY 13244-0001. *E-Mail:* gvidali@mailbox.syr.edu

**VIDAURRETA, LUIS E,** ANALYTICAL CHEMISTRY. *Current Pos:* RETIRED. *Personal Data:* b Havana, Cuba, Dec 15, 20; US citizen; m 43; c 2. *Educ:* Univ Havana, PhD(chem), 43. *Prof Exp:* Prof anal chem, Univ Havana, 43-65; assoc prof chem, La State Univ, Baton Route, 66- *Mem:* Am Chem Soc; Asn Off Analytical Chemists; Am Soc Sugar Cane Technologists. *Res:* Instrumental analysis; gas chromatography; sugar and sugar by-products analysis. *Mailing Add:* 1246 Seyburn Dr Baton Rouge LA 70808-5559

**VIDAURRI, FERNANDO C, JR,** CHEMICAL ENGINEERING. *Current Pos:* sr develop engr, Phillips Petrol Co, Okla, 68-78, tech mgr, Phillips Chem Co, Tex, 78-81, opers mgr, Petrochem Plant, 81-82, opers mgr engr, Plastics Plant, 82-85, mgr engr, Plastics Plant, 85-92, MGR, SEPARATIONS RES, PHILLIPS PETROL CO, OKLA, 92- *Personal Data:* b Laredo, Tex, Feb 23, 39; m 67; c 3. *Educ:* Tex Tech Univ, BSChE, 62, MSChE, 65, PhD, 68. *Prof Exp:* Develop engr, Phillips Petrol Co, 62-63; teaching asst, Tex Tech Univ, 64-68. *Mem:* Am Inst Chem Engrs. *Res:* Process development; kinetics; heat transfer; high temperature polymers; experimental and theoretical thermodynamics; acid gas treating; economic evaluation; mixing and reactor design. *Mailing Add:* 5925 Martin Lane Bartlesville OK 74006

**VIDAVER, ANNE MARIE KOPECKY,** BACTERIOLOGY, PLANT ASSOCIATED BACTERIA. *Current Pos:* Instr bact, 65-66, Univ Nebr, res assoc plant path, 66-72, from asst prof to assoc prof, 72-79, PROF, DEPT PLANT PATH, UNIV NEBR, LINCOLN, 79-, HEAD DEPT, 84- *Personal Data:* b Vienna, Austria, Mar 29, 38; US citizen; wid; c 2. *Educ:* Russell Sage Col, BA, 60; Ind Univ, Bloomington, MA, 62, PhD(bact), 65. *Honors & Awards:* Sci Award Agr Excellence Nat Agri-Mkt Asn, 91. *Concurrent Pos:* Interim dir, Ctr Biotechnol, 88-89 & 97-98. *Mem:* Am Soc Microbiol; fel Am Phytopath Soc (secy, 80-83, vpres, 84-85, pres elect, 85-86, pres, 86-88); fel AAAS. *Res:* Phytopathogenic and beneficial bacteria; bacteriophages; bacteriocins. *Mailing Add:* Dept Plant Path Univ Nebr Lincoln NE 68583-0722. *Fax:* 402-272-2853; *E-Mail:* path001@unlvm.unl.edu

**VIDAVER, WILLIAM ELLIOTT,** PLANT PHYSIOLOGY. *Current Pos:* assoc prof biol, 65-69, prof biol, 69-, EMER PROF BIOL, SIMON FRASER UNIV. *Personal Data:* b San Francisco, Calif, Feb 2, 21; m 51; c 3. *Educ:* San Francisco State Univ, AB, 58; Stanford Univ, PhD(biol), 64. *Prof Exp:* Fel plant biol, Carnegie Inst Dept Plant Biol, 63-65. *Concurrent Pos:* Nat Res Coun Can operating grants, 65- *Mem:* AAAS; Am Soc Plant Physiol; Can Soc Plant Physiol; Am Inst Biol Sci; Sigma Xi; Am Soc Photobiol. *Res:* Mechanisms of photosynthesis; physiological investigations related to vigor, survivorship phenotypic expression and general development of forest tree, horticultural and crop plants undergoing in vitro clonal micropropagation. *Mailing Add:* Dept Biol Sci Simon Fraser Univ Burnaby BC V5A 1S6 Can

**VIDEON, FRED F(RANCIS),** CIVIL ENGINEERING. *Current Pos:* From asst prof to prof, 65-88, EMER PROF CIVIL ENG & ENG MECH, MONT STATE UNIV, 90-; SR STRUCT ENGR, HKM ASSOC, 88- *Personal Data:* b Hayden, Colo, Oct 4, 34; m 57; c 3. *Educ:* Colo State Univ, BS, 58, MCE, 60; Univ Ill, PhD(civil eng), 65. *Honors & Awards:* Western Elec Award, Am Soc Eng Educ. *Mem:* Am Soc Civil Engrs. *Res:* Feasibility of using nuclear explosives for peaceful purposes; brittle fracture of mild steel; state of stress in solids containing cracks; structural mechanics and design; structural design and loading; plate girder behavior; post tensioned concrete systems; design of steel, concrete and segmental bridges. *Mailing Add:* 408 W Koch St Bozeman MT 59715

**VIDMAR, PAUL JOSEPH,** UNDERWATER ACOUSTICS. *Current Pos:* ST ACOUSTICIAN, SCI APPLNS INT CORP, MCLEAN, VA, 87- *Personal Data:* b Vallejo, Calif, May 22, 44; m 86, Joyce Elam. *Educ:* Univ Notre Dame, BS, 66; Univ Calif, San Diego, MS, 72, PhD(physics), 75. *Prof Exp:* Res assoc physics, Fusion Res Ctr, Univ Tex, Austin, spec res assoc, Appl Res Lab, 78-87. *Concurrent Pos:* Adj prof, Univ Miami. *Mem:* Acoust Soc Am; Am Phys Soc; Am Geophys Union. *Res:* Theoretical studies of long-range propagation and bottom interaction in underwater acoustics. *Mailing Add:* 920 Andres Ave Miami FL 33134

**VIDOLI, VIVIAN ANN,** PHYSIOLOGY, NEUROPHYSIOLOGY. *Current Pos:* From asst prof to assoc prof, 70-78, PROF BIOL, CALIF STATE UNIV, FRESNO, 78-, ASST DIR, DIV HEALTH PROFESSIONS, 78-, DEAN, DIV GRAD STUDIES & RES, 80- *Personal Data:* b Bridgeport, Conn, Nov 2, 41. *Educ:* Southern Conn State Col, BS, 63; Ariz State Univ, MS, 66, PhD(zool & physiol), 69. *Concurrent Pos:* Consult, Area Health Educ Consortium, San Joaquin Valley, Calif, 74- *Mem:* Am Physiol Soc; AAAS; Sigma Xi. *Res:* Anatomical and physiological correlates of sensory mechanisms. *Mailing Add:* Cal State Univ Fresno 5241 N Maple Ave Fresno CA 93740-0051. *Fax:* 209-278-4658; *E-Mail:* vivianv@zimmer.csufresno.edu

**VIDONE, ROMEO ALBERT,** PATHOLOGY. *Current Pos:* CHMN DEPT PATH, HOSP ST RAPHAEL, 77- *Personal Data:* b Greenwich, Conn, July 1, 30; m 55; c 3. *Educ:* Davis & Elkins Col, BS, 52; Yale Univ, MD, 57. *Prof Exp:* From instr to assoc prof, 59-68, ASSOC CLIN PROF PATH, YALE UNIV, 68- *Concurrent Pos:* Asst clin prof, Health Ctr, Univ Conn, 72-; pvt pract; dir lab, Charlotte Hungerford Hosp, 68-77. *Mem:* Am Soc Clin Path; Col Am Path; AMA; Int Acad Path; Am Cancer Soc. *Res:* Cardiopulmonary physiology and pathology; cancer, clinicopathologic correlation of tumors. *Mailing Add:* Hosp St Raphael 1450 Chapel St New Haven CT 06511-4440. *Fax:* 203-789-3068

**VIDOSIC, J(OSEPH) P(AUL),** ENGINEERING DESIGN. *Current Pos:* dean admin, 68-73, EMER DEAN, MID GA COL, 73-; EMER REGENTS PROF, GA INST TECHNOL, 73- *Personal Data:* b Lovran, Austria, June 10, 09; US citizen; m 35, Martha M Vanden; c Dorothy M (Smith), Bulck & Richard P. *Educ:* Stevens Inst Technol, ME, 32, MS, 34; Purdue Univ, PhD(mech), 51. *Honors & Awards:* Am Defense Medal, 45. *Prof Exp:* Instr elec, Stevens Inst Technol, 32-34; res engr, Keuffel & Esser Co, 35-36; plant engr, Whitlock Cordage Co, 36-37; from instr to assoc prof theoret mech, Ga Inst Technol, 38-49; instr mech eng, Purdue Univ, 49-51; prof, Ga Inst Technol, 51-59, regents' prof, 60-68. *Concurrent Pos:* Vis prof, Univ Baghdad, 64-65, Tuskegee Inst Technol, 67-68 & 74, Korea Advan Inst Sci & Eng, 79. *Mem:* Fel Am Soc Mech Engrs; Am Soc Eng Educ; Soc Exp Stress Anal; Sigma Xi. *Res:* Stress analysis; lubrication; bearings; vibration; photoelasticity; plastics; design; mechanics; mechanisms; materials science. *Mailing Add:* 38 Walnut St Cooperstown NY 13326

**VIDRINE, MALCOLM FRANCIS,** ARTHROPOD-VECTORS, AQUATIC MOLLUSKS. *Current Pos:* from instr to asst prof, 84-90, ASSOC PROF, LA STATE UNIV, EUNICE, 90- *Personal Data:* b Eunice, La, June 23, 49; m 83, Gail J Quillman; c Malcolm F II, Daniel J & Caroline E. *Educ:* La State Univ, BS, 70, MS, 74; Univ Southwestern La, PhD(biol), 80. *Prof Exp:* Biologist, Gulf S Res Inst, 73-76; instr zool & physiol, Univ Southwestern La, 77-80; asst dir, Jefferson Davis Parish Mosquito Abatement Dist, 80-84. *Concurrent Pos:* Jessup fel, Acad Nat Sci Philadelphia, 78. *Mem:* Sigma Xi; Am Malacol Union. *Res:* Aquatic ecology; invertebrates in aquatic ecosystems; parasitology; evolution and systematics of fresh-water mollusks and their parasites; evolution and systematics of unionicolid water-mites of the world; biodiversity. *Mailing Add:* Dept Sci La State Univ PO Box 1129 Eunice LA 70535-1129. *Fax:* 318-546-6620; *E-Mail:* malcolm@eunice.lsue. edu

**VIDT, EDWARD JAMES,** COAL CONVERSION, COST ENGINEERING. *Current Pos:* CHEM ENG CONSULT, 87- *Personal Data:* b Pittsburgh, Pa, June 16, 27; m 53, Jane H Throop; c 2. *Educ:* Carnegie Inst Technol, BSc, 48. *Prof Exp:* Sr develop engr chem eng, Air Reduction Co, 59-60; process proj engr, Chem Plants Div, Blaw-Knox Co, 60-65, asst mgr synthetic fuels, 65-72; sr res scientist, Westinghouse Elec Corp, 72-74, fel engr, 74-78, adv engr chem eng, Process Eng Dept, 78-87. *Concurrent Pos:* Mem, Ad Hoc Comt Data Coal Conversion, Nat Bur Standards, 72-74; mem, Tech Adv Comt, US Off Coal Res, 74-75. *Mem:* Am Inst Chem Engrs; Carnegie Inst. *Res:* Coal conversion to synthetic fuels for clean, efficient production of heat and power. *Mailing Add:* Consult Engr 2510 Hollywood Dr Pittsburgh PA 15235

**VIEBROCK, FREDERICK WILLIAM,** BIOCHEMISTRY. *Current Pos:* SR SCIENTIST BIOCHEM, JOHNSON & JOHNSON RES CTR, 72- *Personal Data:* b Staten Island, NY, Nov 23, 35; m 56; c 2. *Educ:* Wagner Col, BS, 57; Polytech Inst Brooklyn, MS, 68; Va Polytech Inst & State Univ, PhD(biochem), 74. *Prof Exp:* Res scientist enzymol, Wallerstein Lab, Div Travenol Lab, 58-69. *Mem:* AAAS; Am Chem Soc; Sigma Xi. *Res:* Purification and kinetic analysis of enzymes of the purine metabolic pathways; wound healing; eczematous skin diseases; local anesthetic; interactions of flouride with tooth enamel. *Mailing Add:* 558 Woodspring Rd Mt Pleasant SC 29464

**VIECHNICKI, DENNIS J,** CERAMICS, MATERIAL SCIENCE. *Current Pos:* br chief, Processing & Applications Br, 68-87, BR CHIEF, CERAMICS RES BR, US ARMY MAT TECHNOL LAB, 87-, DIV CHIEF CERAMICS METAL DIV, MAT DIRECTORATE, US ARMY RES LAB, WATERTOWN SITE. *Personal Data:* b Passaic, NJ, Dec 25, 40; m 65; c 4. *Educ:* Rutgers Univ, BS, 62; Pa State Univ, PhD(ceramics), 66. *Prof Exp:* Sr scientist, Westinghouse Res & Develop Labs, 66. *Concurrent Pos:* Nat Sci Res Ctr-NSF France-US exchange of scientists grant, Lab Appl Solid State Chem, Metall Chem Res Ctr, Vitry-sur-Seine, France, 72-73. *Mem:* Fel Am Ceramic Soc. *Res:* Reactions in oxides above 1000 C; eutectoid decomposition; high temperature growth using heat exchanger method of sapphire, spinel, Nd:YAG and eutectics; ceramic-metal seals; radome materials; high energy laser-ceramic interactions; ceramic processing; ceramic properties at high strain rates; armor materials. *Mailing Add:* 5 Poplar Rd Wellesley MA 02181

**VIEHLAND, LARRY ALAN,** CHEMICAL PHYSICS. *Current Pos:* from asst prof to assoc prof, 77-82, PROF CHEM, PARKS COL, 82-, DEPT CHAIRPERSON, 95- *Personal Data:* b St Louis, Mo, Apr 30, 47; m 69, Claudia K Winters; c Jeremy S & Brian D. *Educ:* Mass Inst Technol, BS, 69; Univ Wis-Madison, PhD(chem), 73. *Prof Exp:* Res assoc chem, Brown Univ, 73-76, asst prof (res) chem, 76-77. *Concurrent Pos:* Fulbright scholar, Australia, 88. *Mem:* Sigma Xi; Am Phys Soc. *Res:* Theoretical chemistry and atomic physics, specifically kinetic theory and nonequilibrium statistical mechanics as a tool for understanding intermolecular potentials and other microscopic properties. *Mailing Add:* Parks Col St Louis Univ Cahokia IL 62206. *Fax:* 618-332-6802; *E-Mail:* viehland@ions.slu.edu

**VIEIRA, DAVID JOHN,** NUCLEAR CHEMISTRY. *Current Pos:* dir fel, Los Alamos Nat Lab, 78-79, staff scientist, 79-85, sect leader, 85-89, TEAM LEADER NUCLEAR CHEM, LOS ALAMOS NAT LAB, 89- *Personal Data:* b Oakland, Calif, May 5, 50; m 72, Catherine Evans; c Mia, Carrie & Matthew. *Educ:* Ore State Univ, BS, 72; Univ Calif, Berkeley, PhD(nuclear chem), 78. *Prof Exp:* NSF fel, Ore State Univ, 71; res asst, Los Alamos Sci Lab, 72; res & teaching asst nuclear chem, Univ Calif, Berkeley & Lawrence Berkeley Lab, 72-78. *Concurrent Pos:* Adj prof, Physics Dept, Utah State Univ, 84-; Alexander von Humboldt fel, GSI, Darmstadt, Ger, 90-91. *Mem:* Am Chem Soc; Am Phys Soc. *Res:* High precision tests of electroweak theory

in radioactive nuclei, mass measurements and decay studies of exotic nuclei; radioactive beams research, recoil spectrometers; fast-timing detectors, beam optics; author of numerous papers. *Mailing Add:* CST-11 MS J514 Los Alamos Nat Lab Los Alamos NM 87545. *Fax:* 505-665-5886; *E-Mail:* vieira@lampf.lanl.gov

**VIEIRA, MARIO EDMUNDO CARNEIRO,** PHYSICAL OCEANOGRAPHY, ESTUARINE & COASTAL CIRCULATION & DYNAMICS. *Current Pos:* ASSOC PROF OCEANOG, US NAVAL ACAD, 90- *Personal Data:* b Lagos, Port, Aug 4, 41. *Educ:* Portuguese Naval Acad, BS, 62; US Naval Postgrad Sch, MS, 74; Johns Hopkins Univ, MA, 78, PhD(oceanog), 83; Univ Lisbon, PhD(geophys sci), 85. *Prof Exp:* Ensign to commander, Portuguese Navy, 62-82; postdoctoral & asst res prof oceanog, State Univ NY, Stony Brook, 83-90. *Concurrent Pos:* Vis prof, Southampton Col, Long Island Univ, 84-85. *Mem:* Sigma Xi; Am Geophys Union; Estuarine Res Fedn; Atlantic Estuarine Res Soc (treas, 94-96). *Res:* Wind driven circulation in estuaries; interdisciplinary studies of algal blooms; estuarine hydrodynamic modelling. *Mailing Add:* Oceanog Dept US Naval Acad Annapolis MD 21402-5026. *Fax:* 410-293-2137; *E-Mail:* vieira@nadn. navy.mil

**VIELE, GEORGE WASHINGTON,** GEOLOGY, TECTONICS. *Current Pos:* from asst prof to assoc prof, 59-72, chmn dept, 74-77, PROF GEOL, UNIV MO, COLUMBIA, 72- *Personal Data:* b Wausau, Wis; m 58; c 2. *Educ:* Yale Univ, BS, 51; Univ Utah, PhD(geol), 60. *Prof Exp:* Geologist, US Geol Surv, 51-56 & Stand Oil Co, Calif, 57-59. *Mem:* Geol Soc Am; Am Geophys Union. *Res:* Structural geology; regional tectonics; Northern Rocky and Ouachita Mountains. *Mailing Add:* Dept Geol Sci Univ Mo Columbia MO 65201

**VIEN, STEVE HUNG,** INORGANIC & ORGANIC ANALYSES. *Current Pos:* SR RES CHEMIST, DOW CHEM, 88- *Personal Data:* b Sept 13, 57; m; c 1. *Educ:* Iowa State Univ, BS, 81; Kans State Univ, MS, 86, PhD(anal chem), 88. *Prof Exp:* Anal chemist, Sterling Drug Inc, 81-83. *Mem:* Am Chem Soc; Appl Spectros Soc. *Res:* Developing methods for inorganic and organic analyses; solving problems related to chemical production. *Mailing Add:* 4415 Warwick Dr Sugar Land TX 77479

**VIER, DWAYNE TROWBRIDGE,** THERMODYNAMICS & MATERIAL PROPERTIES. *Current Pos:* RETIRED. *Personal Data:* b Washington, DC, Sept 17, 14; m 51; c David Corson & Alan Dwayne. *Educ:* Univ NH, BS, 37, MS, 39; Columbia Univ, PhD(chem phys), 43. *Prof Exp:* Asst, Univ NH, 37-39 & Columbia Univ, 39-40; asst chem, SAM Labs, 40-42, res chemist, 43-45; assoc scientist, Manhattan Dist, 45-46; group leader, Los Alamos Sci Lab, 46-70, staff mem, Los Alamos Nat Lab, Univ Calif, 70-82, consult, NMex, 82-92. *Mem:* Am Chem Soc; AAAS. *Res:* Fields in physical chemistry; inorganic chemistry of rare radioactive elements; high temperature chemistry. *Mailing Add:* 764 43rd St Los Alamos NM 87544-1808

**VIERCK, CHARLES JOHN, JR,** NEUROSCIENCE, SOMATOSENSATION. *Current Pos:* asst prof, 65-71, assoc prof, 71-76, PROF NEUROSCI, COL MED, UNIV FLA, 76- *Personal Data:* b Columbus, Ohio, July 6, 36; m 60; c 2. *Educ:* Univ Fla, BS, 59, MS, 61, PhD(psychol), 63. *Prof Exp:* Fel neurosci, Inst Neurol Sci, Univ Pa, 63-65. *Concurrent Pos:* Nat Inst Neurol Dis & Stroke res grant, 67-, mem neurol B study sect, 72-76; adj res prof physiol, Sch Med, Univ NC, 75-; assoc ed, J Neurosci, 80-83; mem, Animal Resources Rev Comt, 81-85; ed, Somatosensory Res, 83- *Mem:* Am Psychol Asn; Psychonomic Soc; Soc Neurosci; Int Neuropsychol Soc; Int Asn Study Pain. *Res:* Central nervous system mechanisms relating to somesthetic discrimination; discrimination and perception of pain; recovery of function after nervous system damage. *Mailing Add:* 9331 NW 15th Pl Gainesville FL 32606

**VIERCK, ROBERT K,** ENGINEERING MECHANICS. *Current Pos:* from asst prof to prof eng mech, 43-73, actg head dept, 65-67, EMER PROF ENG MECH, PA STATE UNIV, 73- *Personal Data:* b Avoca, Iowa, Jan 5, 08; m 33; c 3. *Educ:* Univ Iowa, BS, 32, MS, 33. *Prof Exp:* Engr, State of Iowa, 33-34; jr engr, US Bur Reclamation, 34-36; instr eng, Univ Ill, 36-39; from asst engr to assoc engr, Fed Power Comn, 39-43. *Concurrent Pos:* Consult, Boeing Co, Wash, 54 & NAm Aviation, Inc, Calif, 55. *Mem:* Am Soc Eng Educ; Am Acad Mech. *Res:* Mechanical vibrations; mechanical properties of materials. *Mailing Add:* 299 Nimitz Ave State College PA 16801

**VIERECK, CHRISTOPHER,** DENTISTRY. *Current Pos:* assoc dir, 90-93, DIR CLIN RES, HOECHST-ROUSSEL CAN, 93- *Personal Data:* b Ft William, Ont, Oct 27, 57; m 89, Sitta Cohen; c Jonathan D. *Educ:* McGill Univ, BSc, 82; Univ Western Ont, 85; Univ Basel, PhD(neurobiol), 89. *Prof Exp:* Clin res coordr, Merck Frosst Can, 89-90. *Mem:* Soc Neurosci (pres, 89-); Soc Cell Biol (pres, 88-). *Res:* Clinical research activities to achieve fastest development possible. *Mailing Add:* Hoechst Marion Roussel 10236 Marion Park Dr Kansas City MO 64137-1406. *Fax:* 514-333-2952

**VIERECK, LESLIE A,** PLANT ECOLOGY, PLANT TAXONOMY. *Current Pos:* PRIN PLANT ECOLOGIST, INST NORTHERN FORESTRY, 63- *Personal Data:* b New Bedford, Mass, Feb 20, 30; m 55, Eleanor G Norton; c 3. *Educ:* Dartmouth Col, BA, 51; Univ Colo, MA, 57, PhD(plant ecol), 62. *Hon Degrees:* DSc, Univ Alaska, Fairbanks, 93. *Prof Exp:* Asst bot, McGill Subarctic Res Sta, 54-55; asst, Herbarium, Univ Colo, 55-57, actg cur, 56-57, res assoc ecol, Inst Arctic & Alpine Res, 55-59; res assoc ecol, Univ Alaska, 59-60, asst prof bot, 60-61; res biologist, Alaska Dept

Fish & Game, 61-63. *Concurrent Pos:* Affil prof div life sci, Univ Alaska, 75-; co-prin investr, Bonanzo Creek Long Term Ecol Res Prog, 88- *Mem:* Fel AAAS; fel Arctic Inst NAm; Ecol Soc Am; Soc Am Foresters; Sigma Xi. *Res:* Plant ecology and plant taxonomy of arctic, subarctic and alpine regions. *Mailing Add:* 1707 Red Fox Dr Fairbanks AK 99709-6625. *E-Mail:* lviereck@lternet.edu

**VIERLING, RICHARD ANTHONY,** DEVELOPMENT OF VALUE-ADDED SOYBEAN VARIETIES, MAPPING OF AGRONOMICALLY IMPORTANT PLANT TRAITS. *Current Pos:* PROG DIR GENETICS LAB, IND CROP IMPROVEMENT ASN, 92- *Personal Data:* b St Louis, Mo, June 13, 60; m 87, Therese A Laychak; c Rachel, Angela & Richard. *Educ:* Univ Mo, Columbia, BS, 83, MS, 85; Tex Tech Univ, PhD(genetics), 92. *Concurrent Pos:* Vis scientist, Wash Univ, St Louis, 91; adj asst prof agron, Purdue Univ, 92-; several grants from state, gov & private cos, 93- *Mem:* Crop Sci Soc Am; Agron Soc Am; Int Soc Plant Molecular Biol. *Res:* Development of soybean varieties that produce high levels of enzymes with industrial applications; development of a gene expression system to produce pharmaceuticals and high value proteins in soybeans. *Mailing Add:* Ind Crop Improvement Asn 3510 US 52 S Lafayette IN 47905. *Fax:* 765-474-8959; *E-Mail:* vierling@omni.cc.purdue.edu

**VIERNSTEIN, LAWRENCE J,** ELECTRONICS ENGINEERING. *Current Pos:* RETIRED. *Personal Data:* b New York, NY, Feb 20, 19; m 69; c 2. *Educ:* Okla State Univ, BS, 50, MS, 51; Johns Hopkins Univ, PhD, 70. *Prof Exp:* Mem assoc staff, Appl Physics Lab, Johns Hopkins Univ, 52-57; sr physicist, 57-59, mem prof staff, Appl Physics Lab, 59-81, Dept Physiol, 61-66, Wilmer Inst, 66-76, mem prof staff, neurosurg, 76- *Mem:* Sigma Xi. *Res:* Theoretical biology and biomedical engineering; neurophysiology; artificial intelligence in medicine. *Mailing Add:* 12 W 96th St Apt 5D New York NY 10025

**VIERS, JIMMY WAYNE,** PHYSICAL CHEMISTRY. *Current Pos:* ASSOC PROF CHEM, VA POLYTECH INST & STATE UNIV, 71- *Personal Data:* b Grundy, Va, Feb 26, 43; m 65; c 2. *Educ:* Berea Col, AB, 65; Wake Forest Univ, MA, 67; Stanford Univ, PhD(chem), 71. *Mem:* Am Chem Soc. *Res:* Quantum chemistry. *Mailing Add:* Dept Chem Va Polytech Inst & State Univ PO Box 2212 Blacksburg VA 24063-0001

**VIERTL, JOHN RUEDIGER MADER,** ELECTROMAGNETISM, SOLID STATE PHYSICS. *Current Pos:* Res training prog,physics & geophys fission tracks & semiconductors, 67-69, RES PHYSICIST ULTRASONIC PHENOMENA & LASER INTERACTIONS, GEN ELEC TURBIN TECHNOL LAB, 73- *Personal Data:* b New York, NY, Sept 25, 41; m 69; c 2. *Educ:* Fordham Univ, BS, 63; Rutgers Univ, MS, 65; Cornell Univ, PhD(appl physics), 73. *Honors & Awards:* Managerial Award, Gen Elec Turbine, 85. *Mem:* Fel Am Phys Soc; Soc Photo-Optical Instrumentation Engrs; Am Soc Nondestructive Testing. *Res:* Optical properties of thin films; point defects in solids; ultrasonic imaging, scattering theory, phenomena, ultrasonic non destructive testing; laser target interactions; ultrasonic transducer design; electromagnetism, eddy currats, coatings metallic and non metallic automotive testing systems. *Mailing Add:* 1403 Clifton Park Rd Schenectady NY 12309. *Fax:* 518-385-9717

**VIESSMAN, WARREN, JR,** HYDROLOGY, WATER RESOURCES. *Current Pos:* chmn & prof environ eng sci, 83-90, assoc dean res & grad study, 90-91, ASSOC DEAN ACAD PROG, UNIV FLA, GAINESVILLE, 91- *Personal Data:* b Baltimore, Md, Nov 9, 30; m 53, Elizabeth G Rothe; c Wendy, Stephen, Michael, Suzanne, Thomas, Sandra, Sheila, Heather & Joshua. *Educ:* Johns Hopkins Univ, BE, 52, MSE, 58, DEng(water resources), 61. *Honors & Awards:* Icko Iben Award, Am Water Resources Asn, 83, Henry P Caulfield Jr Medal, 96; Julian Hinds Award, Am Soc Civil Engrs, 89; Warren A Hall Medal, Univ Coun Water Resources, 94. *Prof Exp:* Proj engr, Johns Hopkins Univ, 57-61; from asst prof to assoc prof civil eng, NMex State Univ, 61-66; prof civil eng & dir water resources ctr, Univ Maine, 66-68; prof civil eng & dir water resources res inst, Univ Nebr, Lincoln, 68-75; sr specialist eng & pub works, Cong Res Serv, Libr of Cong, 75-83. *Mem:* Am Soc Civil Engrs; Am Water Resources Asn; AAAS. *Res:* Water resources systems and policy; water management; environmental policy. *Mailing Add:* Col Eng Univ Fla Gainesville FL 32611. *Fax:* 352-392-9673; *E-Mail:* wvies@eng.ufl.edu

**VIEST, IVAN M,** STRUCTURAL ENGINEERING, ENGINEERING PROMOTION. *Current Pos:* CONSULT STRUCT ENGR, 83- *Personal Data:* b Slovakia, Oct 10, 22; nat US; m 53, Barbara K Stevenson. *Educ:* Slovak Tech Univ, Slovakia, CE, 46; Ga Inst Technol, MS, 48; Univ Ill, PhD(eng), 51. *Honors & Awards:* Wason Medal, Am Concrete Inst, 55; Res Prize, Am Soc Civil Engrs, 58, Ernest E Howard Award, 91; Construct Award, Eng News Rec, 62. *Prof Exp:* Asst, Univ Ill, 48-51, from res assoc to res assoc prof, 51-57; bridge res eng, Am Asn State Hwy Off Rd Test, Nat Acad Sci, 57-61; struct engr, Bethlehem, Steel Corp, 61-67, sr struct consult, 67-70, asst mgr sales eng, 70-82. *Concurrent Pos:* Consult, Nelson Student Welding, Ohio, 54-61; mem bd, Eng Found, 75-87, Am Soc Civil Engrs, 69-71 & 74-75. *Mem:* Nat Acad Eng; hon mem Am Soc Civil Engrs (vpres, 74-75); fel Am Concrete Inst; Int Asn Bridge & Struct Eng; Trans Res Bd. *Res:* Steel structures; composite construction; reinforced concrete structures. *Mailing Add:* IMV Consult PO Box 132 Hellertown PA 18055. *Fax:* 610-865-3300

**VIETH, JOACHIM,** PLANT MORPHOLOGY. *Current Pos:* RETIRED. *Personal Data:* b Hamburg, Ger, Oct 26, 25; m 53, Ruth V Goettel; c 2. *Educ:* Univ Saarbruecken, Lic natural sci, 53, Dr rer nat, 57; Univ Dijon, DSc(bot), 65. *Prof Exp:* Asst bot, Univ Saarbruecken, 53-57; res fel, Nat Ctr Sci Res,

Univ Dijon, 57-65; vis prof, Univ Montreal, 66-67, from assoc prof to prof bot, 67-92. *Mem:* Can Bot Asn. *Res:* Anatomy of flowers and inflorescences, both normal and anomalous; relationship between vegetative and inflorescential regions, between normal and anomalous forms experimentally induced; plant propagation by tissue culture. *Mailing Add:* Dept Biol Sci Univ Montreal CP 6128 Succursale A Montreal PQ H3C 3J1 Can

**VIETH, WOLF R(ANDOLPH),** CHEMICAL ENGINEERING. *Current Pos:* chmn Chem & Biochem Eng Dept, 68-78, PROF CHEM & BIOCHEM ENG, RUTGERS UNIV, NEW BRUNSWICK, 68- *Personal Data:* b St Louis, Mo, May 5, 34; m 57; c 4. *Educ:* Mass Inst Technol, SB, 56, ScD(chem eng), 61; Ohio State Univ, MSc, 58. *Prof Exp:* Res engr, NAm Aviation, Inc, 56-57; Ford fel eng, 61-62; dir practice sch sta, Mass Inst Technol Sta-Am Cyanamid Co, NJ, 62-64; from asst prof to assoc prof chem eng, Mass Inst Technol, 62-68, overall dir sch chem eng pract, 65-68. *Concurrent Pos:* Consult, Am Cyanamid Co, 63, Ashland Oil Co, 63-, Carter's Ink, 64- & US Army Natick Labs, 65- *Mem:* Am Chem Soc; Am Inst Chem Engrs. *Mailing Add:* 16 Partridge Run Belle Mead NJ 08502

**VIETMEYER, NOEL DUNCAN,** ECONOMIC BIOLOGY, SCIENCE WRITING. *Current Pos:* SR PROG OFFICER, NAT ACAD SCI, 70- *Personal Data:* b Wellington, NZ, Nov 9, 40; m 65; c 3. *Educ:* Univ Otago, NZ, BSc, 63; Univ Calif, Berkeley, PhD, 67. *Prof Exp:* Lectr org chem, Univ Calif, Berkeley, 67-68; NIH fel, Stanford Univ, 68-69, fel, 68-70. *Res:* Innovative technology for developing countries; development of neglected plants and animals with promising economic potential. *Mailing Add:* Nat Acad Sci 2101 Constitution Ave Washington DC 20418

**VIETOR, DONALD MELVIN,** CROP PHYSIOLOGY. *Current Pos:* from asst prof to assoc prof, 76-91, chmn, Fac Plant Physiol, 91-92, PROF AGRON, DEPT SOIL & CROP SCI, TEX A&M UNIV, 92- *Personal Data:* b Urbana, Ill, Sept 29, 45; m 71, Teddie Small; c Shawn & Michael. *Educ:* Univ Minn, BS, 67, MS, 69; Cornell Univ, PhD(crop sci), 75. *Prof Exp:* Biol sci asst soil sci, US Army Cold Regions Res & Engr Lab, 69-71; asst prof agron, Univ Mass, 74-76. *Concurrent Pos:* Chmn, Student Activ, Am Soc Agron, 84; res, Curric Proj, Nat Agr, 84-89, chmn, Crop Physiol & Metabolism Div, Crop Sci Soc Am, 96- *Mem:* Am Soc Agron; Crop Sci Soc Am; Am Soc Plant Physiol; Soc Risk Anal. *Res:* Physical and enzymatic regulation of carbon export from leaves, and of carbon partitioning within plant during growth and development; probabilistic risk assessment in agriculture; systems approach to research planning. *Mailing Add:* Dept Soil & Crop Sci Tex A&M Univ College Station TX 77843. *Fax:* 409-845-0456; *E-Mail:* c040ag@tamrm1.tamu.edu

**VIETS, FRANK GARFIELD, JR,** SOIL SCIENCE. *Current Pos:* RETIRED. *Personal Data:* b Stanberry, Mo, Apr 3, 16; wid; c John G, James N & Sandra K (Dunning). *Educ:* Colo Agr & Mech Col, BS, 37; Univ Calif, MS, 39, PhD(plant physiol), 42. *Prof Exp:* Agent div cereal crops, USDA, Calif, 37-39; asst div plant nutrit, Univ Calif, 39-42; supv chemist, Cutter Labs, Calif, 42-44; assoc agr chemist, Exp Sta, SDak State Col, 44-45; agronomist div soil mgt & irrig, USDA, 45-49, soil scientist, Agr Res Serv, 49-53, soil & water conserv res div, 53-74; consult agr, 80-92. *Concurrent Pos:* Vis prof, Univ Ill, 59 & Iowa State Univ, 64, Col State Univ, 74 & Univ Saskatchewan, 75; ed in chief, Soil Sci Soc Am, 63-65; agr consult, 74- *Mem:* Fel AAAS; hon mem Soil Sci Soc Am (vpres, 66, pres, 67); fcl Am Soc Agron. *Res:* Mineral nutrition of plants; zinc deficiency in soils and plants; water pollution by animal wastes, fertilizers and agriculture; soil fertility and productivity; tropical soils. *Mailing Add:* 201 Yale Way Ft Collins CO 80525-1718

**VIETS, HERMANN,** AEROSPACE ENGINEERING, MECHANICAL ENGINEERING. *Current Pos:* PRES, MILWAUKEE SCH ENG. *Personal Data:* b Quedlinburg, Ger, Jan 28, 43; US citizen; m 68; c 4. *Educ:* Polytech Inst Brooklyn, BS, 65, MS, 66, PhD(astronaut), 70. *Honors & Awards:* Gov Award for Sci & Technol, 87. *Prof Exp:* Res asst fluid mech res, Polytech Inst Brooklyn, 68-69; group leader, Aerospace Res Labs, US Air Force, 70-75; assoc prof mech eng, Wright State Univ, 76-80, prof, 80-81; prof mech eng & assoc dean, WVa Univ, 81-83; prof & dean, Univ RI, 83- *Concurrent Pos:* NATO res grant, 69-70, fel, von Karman Inst, Brussels, Belg, 69-70; USAF Off Aerospace res grant, 77-; consult, USAF Aero Propulsion Lab, 76-80; chmn bd, Precision Stampings Inc, Beaumont, Calif, 78-; mem & bd dir, Astro-Med Inc, West Warwick, RI, Promptus Commun, Portsmouth, RI. *Mem:* Assoc fel Am Inst Aeronaut & Astronaut; Am Helicopter Soc; Soc Mfg Engrs; Ger Soc Air & Space Travel. *Res:* Positive aspects of time dependent flows; fluidically and mechanically generated unsteadiness; advanced ramjet combustors; vortex dynamics; jets and wakes; computational methods; nozzles, diffusers and thrust augmentors. *Mailing Add:* 4216 N Lake Dr Milwaukee WI 53211

**VIETTE, MICHAEL ANTHONY,** PHYSICS. *Current Pos:* VPRES ENG, RAINWISE, 87- *Personal Data:* b Pittsburg, Kans, Mar 27, 41; m 63; c 1. *Educ:* Kans State Col Pittsburg, BA, 64, MS, 66; Univ Mo, Rolla, PhD(physics), 72. *Prof Exp:* Res asst cloud physics, Grad Ctr Cloud Physics Res, Univ Mo, Rolla, 66-70; asst prof, Univ Maine, Orono, 71-76, assoc prof physics, 80-87. *Concurrent Pos:* NSF res grant, 72- *Mem:* Am Phys Soc; Am Geophys Union; Am Meteorol Soc. *Res:* Condensation and growth of micron sized water droplets. *Mailing Add:* Box 443 25 Fed St Bar Harbor ME 04609

**VIETTI, TERESA JANE,** PEDIATRICS, HEMATOLOGY & ONCOLOGY. *Current Pos:* from asst prof to assoc prof, 61-72, PROF PEDIAT, SCH MED, WASH UNIV, 72-, PROF PEDIAT IN RADIOL, 80- *Personal Data:* b Ft Worth, Tex, Nov 5, 27. *Educ:* Rice Inst, AB, 49; Baylor

Univ, MD, 53; Am Bd Pediat, dipl, 59; Bd Pediat Hemat & Oncol, dipl, 74. *Honors & Awards:* John Krey II Mem Award, Am Cancer Soc, 92; Distinguished Career Award, Am Soc Pediat Hemat/Oncol, 94. *Prof Exp:* Instr pediat, Wayne State Univ, 58, Southwestern Med Sch, Univ Tex, 58-60; vis pediatrician, Hacettepe Children's Hosp, Ankara, Turkey, 60-61. *Concurrent Pos:* Dir hemat labs, attend pediatrician & consult, Tex Children's Hosp, Dallas, 58-60; attend pediatrician & consult, Parkland Mem Hosp, 58-60; Am Cancer Soc fel, 58-59; USPHS trainee, 59-60, grant, 61-; vchmn, Southwest Oncol Group, 61-; asst pediatrician, St Louis Children's Hosp, 61-65, assoc pediatrician, 65-72, dir div hemat & oncol, 70-86, pediatrician, 72-; from asst pediatrician to assoc pediatrician, Barnes & Allied Hosps, 61-65; consult, St Louis County Hosp; assoc in pediat, Mo Crippled Children's Serv, 66-; mem, Cancer Clin Invest Rev Comt, 74-78; pediat consult high risk maternity & child care prog, Mo Div Health, 75; consult hemat & oncol, Shriner's Hosp Crippled Children, St Louis, Mo, 76-; prin investr, NIH Pediat Oncol, Washington Univ, 78-96, Pediat Oncol Group, 92-96 & Lipincott-Raven Press, 93-; chmn, Pediat Oncol Group, 81-85; vchmn, Am Cancer Soc, 82-83; ed-in-chief, J Pediat Hemat/Oncol, 93- *Mem:* Am Hemat Soc; Int Soc Hemat; Am Asn Cancer Res; Am Pediat Soc; Am Soc Clin Oncol; Am Soc Pediat Hemat/Oncol; Int Soc Pediat Oncol; Am Soc Cancer Educ. *Res:* Oncology; cancer chemotherapy; sarcomas of children and phase I therapy; author of 9 publications. *Mailing Add:* St Louis Childrens Hosp One Childrens Pl St Louis MO 63110-1014

**VIG, BALDEV K,** CYTOGENETICS. *Current Pos:* from asst prof to assoc prof biol, 68-78, PROF GENETICS, UNIV NEV, RENO, 78-, FOUND PROF. *Personal Data:* b India, Oct 1, 35; c 2. *Educ:* Khalsa Col, India, BSAgr, 57; Panjab Univ, India, MS, 61; Ohio State Univ, PhD(genetics), 67; Am Bd Med Genetics, dipl. *Prof Exp:* Demonstr agr, Khalsa Col, India, 58-61; assoc prof bot, Rajasthan Col Agr, India, 61-64; res cytogeneticist, Dept Pediat, Children's Hosp, Ohio State Univ, 67-68. *Concurrent Pos:* Consult, Western Environ Res Ctr, Environ Protection Agency; human & med geneticist, Nev Ment Health Inst, 76-81; res grant, Environ Protection Agency, NIH & Univ Nev, 78-; Humboldt fel & Jones fel, Ger Cancer Res Ctr fel; dir, NATO-ARW. *Mem:* Am Genetics Asn; Genetic Soc Am; Genetics Soc Can; Environ Mutagen Soc; Sigma Xi; Am Soc Human Genetics; fel Am Col Med Genetics. *Res:* Action of antileukemic drugs on chromosomes; sequence of centromere separation; kinetochore/centromere function. *Mailing Add:* Dept Biol Univ Nev Reno NV 89557-0001. *Fax:* 702-784-6544; *E-Mail:* vig@unr. edu

**VIG, PARMINDER JIT SINGH,** NEURODEGENERATIVE DISEASES, NEUROCHEMISTRY. *Current Pos:* Instr neurol, 92-94, ASST PROF NEUROL, MED CTR, UNIV MISS, 94- *Personal Data:* b Amritsar, India, Aug 19, 60; m 86, Vibha Gupta; c Khushdeep S. *Educ:* Panjab Univ, India, BSc(hons), 81, MSc(hons), 82; Inst Med Educ & Res, India, PhD(biochem), 88. *Concurrent Pos:* Res consult & mentor, Tougaloo Col & Jackson State Univ, 94- *Mem:* Am Soc Pharmacol & Exp Therapeut; Soc Neurosci; NY Acad Sci; Sigma Xi. *Res:* Role of calcium binding proteins in the pathogenesis of human spinocerebellar ataxias and in transgenic mice; mechanism of epileptogenesis in an animal model in relation to nitric oxide synthase and growth factors. *Mailing Add:* 2500 N State St Jackson MS 39216. *Fax:* 601-984-6626; *E-Mail:* vig@fiona.umsmed.edu

**VIGDOR, STEVEN ELLIOT,** EXPERIMENTAL NUCLEAR PHYSICS. *Current Pos:* from asst prof to assoc prof, 76-82, PROF PHYSICS, IND UNIV, 82- *Personal Data:* b New York, NY, July 23, 47; m 87, Beata Winnicka; c Jacob, Alex & Pauline (Fatyga). *Educ:* City Col NY, BS, 67; Univ Wis-Madison, MS, 69, PhD(physics), 73. *Prof Exp:* Res assoc, Dept Physics, Univ Wis, 73-74; fel appointee, Argonne Nat Lat, 74-76, res assoc, 76. *Concurrent Pos:* Vis scientist, Saturn Nat Lab, Fr, 90-91. *Mem:* Am Phys Soc. *Res:* Nuclear structure and nuclear reactions at intermediate energies; broken symmetries of the strong interaction; polarization phenomena; hadron-hadron scattering; meson production. *Mailing Add:* Dept Physics Ind Univ Bloomington IN 47405. *Fax:* 812-855-6645; *E-Mail:* vigdor@iucf. indiana.edu

**VIGEE, GERALD S,** PHYSICAL INORGANIC CHEMISTRY. *Current Pos:* ASSOC PROF CHEM, UNIV ALA, BIRMINGHAM, 69- *Personal Data:* b Crowley, La, Mar 4, 31; c 3. *Educ:* US Mil Acad, BS, 54, La State Univ, Baton Rouge, BS, 60, PhD(chem), 68. *Prof Exp:* Prof engr, NASA, Ala, 60-61; propulsion design engr, Chrysler Corp, 61-64; asst prof chem, Univ Miss, 68-69. *Mem:* Sigma Xi. *Res:* Synthesis of coordination complexes, investigation of the magneto chemistry and spectroscopic energy levels of these complexes. *Mailing Add:* 2304 Pine Crest Dr Birmingham AL 35216-2112

**VIGERS, ALISON J,** BIOCHEMISTRY. *Personal Data:* b Eng, Jan 20, 58. *Educ:* Oxford Univ, BS, 80; Univ Colo, PhD(biochem), 92. *Prof Exp:* Fel biochem, Univ Colo, 89-94. *Mem:* Am Soc Cell Biol. *Res:* Biochemistry. *Mailing Add:* 510 Maxwell Ave Boulder CO 80304

**VIGFUSSON, NORMAN V,** GENETICS, MEDICAL GENETICS. *Current Pos:* Asst prof genetics, 69-72, from assoc prof to prof, 72-86, EMER PROF BIOL, EASTERN WASH UNIV, 86-; DIR CYTOGENETICS LAB, SACRED HEART MED CTR. *Personal Data:* b Ashern, Man, July 1, 30; m 54, Doris R; c Sandra D, Dean N, Sherri A, Trevor N & Tracey L. *Educ:* Univ Man, BSA, 51; Univ Alta, PhD(fungal genetics), 69; Am Bd Med Genetics, cert clin cytogentics. *Concurrent Pos:* Genetic consult, Sacred Heart Med Ctr, Spokane, Wash, 75- *Mem:* Genetics Soc Am; AAAS; Sigma Xi; Am Soc Human Genetics. *Res:* Sexuality in Neorospora crassa with respect to stages and control of the sexual cycle and attempts to arrive at elucidation of incompatibility control mechanism; human cytogenetics. *Mailing Add:* Sacred Heart Med Ctr Cyto-Genetic Lab 101 W Eighth PO Box 2555 Spokane WA 99220-2555

**VIGGERS, ROBERT F,** mechanical engineering; deceased, see previous edition for last biography

**VIGGIANO, ALBERT,** ATMOSPHERIC ION CHEMISTRY, STATE SELECTED REACTIVITY. *Current Pos:* RES CHEMIST, GEOPHYS DIRECTORATE, PHILLIPS LAB, 83- *Personal Data:* b Derby, Conn, Feb 28, 54. *Educ:* Univ Calif, Berkeley, BS, 76; Univ Colo, Boulder, PhD(chem physics), 80. *Prof Exp:* Res chemist, Max Planck Inst, 80-82. *Mem:* Am Chem Soc; Am Soc Mass Spectrometry; Am Geophys Union. *Res:* Kinetic energy, temperature, rotational and vibrational energy dependencies on the rate constants and branching ratios of ion molecule reactions in the gas phase. *Mailing Add:* 19 Stone Rd Arlington MA 02174-2030

**VIGIL, EUGENE LEON,** CELL BIOLOGY, PLANT PHYSIOLOGY. *Current Pos:* res assoc, 81-88, PLANT PHYSIOLOGIST, BELTSVILLE AGR RES CTR, USDA, 88- *Personal Data:* b Chicago, Ill, Mar 14, 41; div; c 3. *Educ:* Loyola Univ Chicago, BS, 63; Univ Iowa, MS, 65, PhD(bot), 67. *Prof Exp:* NIH fel, Univ Wis-Madison, 67-69; trainee cell biol, Univ Chicago, 69-71; asst prof cell biol, Marquette Univ, 71-79; plant cell biologist, Univ Md, 79-81. *Concurrent Pos:* Distinguished vis scientist, Dept Physiol & Biophys, Colo State Univ, 74-75; prog chmn, Histochem Soc, 76-79, counr, 79-82. *Mem:* NY Acad Sci; Am Soc Cell Biol; Am Soc Plant Physiol; Histochem Soc. *Res:* Biogenesis and turnover of microbodies in cotyledons of fatty seeds during germination; effects of drought stress on development and utilization of protein bodies in radicles of oil seeds; effects of drought stress on cotton fiber development and maturity. *Mailing Add:* MORE Div NIGMS NIH 45 Center Dr Bldg 45 Rm 2AS37 MSC 6200 Bethesda MD 20892-6200. *Fax:* 301-504-7521

**VIGIL, JOHN CARLOS,** NUCLEAR ENGINEERING. *Current Pos:* Staff mem reactor physics, Los Alamos Nat Lab, 63-77, group leader, Thermal Reactor Safety group, 77-80, asst div leader, Energy Div, 80-81, asst to assoc dir, 81-84, dep div leader, Personnel Admin, 84-86, dir staff, 86-89, div leader, Human Resources Develop, 89-93, ADMINR, DIR RES & DEVELOP PROG, LOS ALAMOS NAT LAB, 94- *Personal Data:* b Espanola, NMex, Mar 28, 39; m 58, Elizabeth Salazar; c Anna, Dennis, Charles & Valerie. *Educ:* NMex Inst Mining & Technol, BS, 61; Univ NMex, MS, 63, PhD(nuclear eng), 66. *Concurrent Pos:* Mem, Bd Regents, NMex State Univ, 89-95. *Mem:* Am Nuclear Soc; NY Acad Sci; Sigma Xi. *Res:* Reactor safety, physics, codes and computations; energy technology; basic research. *Mailing Add:* 215 Kimberly Los Alamos NM 87544. *Fax:* 505-665-6163; *E-Mail:* vigil_john_carlos@lanl.gov

**VIGLIERCHIO, DAVID RICHARD,** NEMATOLOGY. *Current Pos:* RETIRED. *Personal Data:* b Madera, Calif, Nov 25, 25; m 67; c 1. *Educ:* Calif Inst Technol, BS, 50, PhD(bio-org chem), 55. *Honors & Awards:* Minister Agr Invitation Lectr, PRC, 81. *Prof Exp:* Jr res nematologist, Univ Calif, Davis, 55-57, asst res nematologist, 57-63, assoc nematologist, 63-69, chmn nematol, 78-85, nematologist, 69-92. *Concurrent Pos:* Fulbright fel, 64-65, 76-77; J S Guggenheim fel, 65; partic, US Antarctic Prog, 69-70; Nat Acad Sci exchange USSR, 70-71; Minister Agr & Forestry fel, WGer, 84. *Mem:* Am Chem Soc; Soc Nematol; Soc Europ Nematol; AAAS. *Res:* Chemistry and physiology of plant parasitic and free-living nematodes; host-parasite relationships; physiological methods of nematode control; behavioral properties of nematodes. *Mailing Add:* 710 Miller Dr Davis CA 95616

**VIGLIONE, SAM S,** ELECTRICAL ENGINEERING. *Current Pos:* CONSULT. *Personal Data:* b Erie, Pa, July 12, 29; m 57; c 4. *Educ:* Carnegie Inst Technol, BS, 54; Univ Southern Calif, MS, 56. *Prof Exp:* Electronic engr, Hughes Aircraft Co, 54-58; sr design engr, Astronaut Div, Convair Corp, 58-59; sr res scientist, Aeronutronic Div, Ford Motor Co, 59-61; mgr, Pattern Recognition Systs Dept, McDonnell Douglas Corp, Huntington Beach, 61-76, dir, Res & Develop Directorate, 76-78; sr dir, S S Viglione & Assocs, 78-; pres, Interstate Voice Prods. *Mem:* Sr mem Inst Elec & Electronics Engrs. *Res:* Mathematical procedures for the simulation of pattern recognition systems; pattern recognition systems for classification of photographic and physiologic data; investigation of biological neural networks and their electronic replication; development of speech recognition systems. *Mailing Add:* 13301 Prospect Santa Ana CA 92705

**VIGNERY, AGNES M C,** BONE CELL BIOLOGY. *Current Pos:* ASST PROF ORTHOP SURG, SCH MED, YALE UNIV, 77- *Personal Data:* b Poitieres, France, Mar 2, 49. *Educ:* Paris Univ, DDS, 72, PhD, 75. *Mem:* Am Soc Cell Biol; Am Soc Bone & Mineral Res; Calcified Tissue Soc. *Mailing Add:* Dept Orthop Cell Biol Yale Univ Sch Med 333 Cedar St PO Box 208044 New Haven CT 06510-8044. *Fax:* 203-737-2701; *E-Mail:* Bitnet: vignery@ yalemed

**VIGNOS, JAMES HENRY,** MATHEMATICS. *Current Pos:* sr res scientist, 74-78, prin res scientist, 78-84, CONSULT SCIENTIST, CORP RES CTR, FOXBORO CO, 84- *Personal Data:* b Cleveland, Ohio, July 27, 33; m 62; c 2. *Educ:* Case Inst, BS, 55; Yale Univ, MS, 57, PhD(physics), 62. *Prof Exp:* Vis res scientist, Low Temperature Inst, Bavarian Acad Sci, Ger, 62-64; resident res assoc, Chem Div, Argonne Nat Lab, 64-66; asst prof physics, Dartmouth Col, 66-72. *Concurrent Pos:* Fulbright res scholar, 62-63; von Humboldt fel, 63-64; asst ed, Am J Physics, 70-73, ed, Am J Physics Ten-Year Cumulative Index, 63-72 & 72-73; mem exec comt, Am Phys Soc, New Eng, 75-77; subcomt, MFC-SC9, Ultrasonic Flowmeters, Coun Codes & Standards, Am Soc Mech Engrs, 76-, subcomt, MFC-SC15, Installation Effects on Primary Devices, 79-, chmn subcomt, MFC-SC5, electromagnetic flowmeters, 88-, mem main comt, MFC, 88- *Mem:* Am Phys Soc; Sigma Xi.

*Res:* Acoustic, electromagnetic, thermal and fluid mechanic investigations relating to advanced approaches to fluid flow measurement; liquid and solid helium; superconductivity; ultrasonics. *Mailing Add:* 129 Manning St Needham Heights MA 02194-1535. *Fax:* 508-549-4380

**VIGNOS, PAUL JOSEPH, JR,** MYOLOGY, RHEUMATOLOGY. *Current Pos:* Res fel med, Sch Med, 50-51, USPHS fel pharmacol, 51-52, from instr to prof, 52-85, EMER PROF MED, SCH MED, CASE WESTERN RES UNIV, 85- *Personal Data:* b Canton, Ohio, Nov 10, 19; m 46; c 3. *Educ:* Univ Notre Dame, BS, 41; Western Reserve Univ, MD, 44. *Honors & Awards:* Medal, Univ Marseille. *Prof Exp:* From intern to resident, Univ Hosps, Cleveland, 44-46; resident, Presby Hosp, New York, 48-49; Am Cancer Soc fel, Univ Hosps, Cleveland, 49-50. *Mem:* Am Rheumatism Asn; Am Cong Med Rehab; Cent Soc Clin Res; Royal Soc Health; AAAS. *Res:* Bioclinical effect of myopathic disease of the locomotor system on skeletal muscle and ambulation; biochemistry of normal and diseased muscle. *Mailing Add:* 2875 Chagrin River Rd Chagrin Falls OH 44022

**VIGO, TYRONE LAWRENCE,** POLYMER & TEXTILE CHEMISTRY, ORGANIC CHEMISTRY. *Current Pos:* Res chemist, Southern Regional Res Ctr, Agr Res Serv, USDA, 63-66, proj leader textile & polymer chem, 68-76, dir & res leader, Textiles & Clothing Lab, 76-85, LEAD SCIENTIST, SOUTHERN REGIONAL RES CTR, AGR RES SERV, USDA, 85- *Personal Data:* b New Orleans, La, Feb 1, 39; m 63, Eileen Castel; c Stephen & Craig. *Educ:* Loyola Univ, La, BS, 60; Tulane Univ La, MS, 63, PhD(org chem), 69. *Concurrent Pos:* Vis prof, Chem Dept, Tulane Univ, La, 70-75, 87-; adj prof, Textile Dept, Univ Ga, 90- *Mem:* Fiber Soc; Am Chem Soc; Am Asn Textile Chemists & Colorists; Textile Inst. *Res:* Chemical modification of polymers and textiles by application of new synthetic techniques; synthetic organic chemistry; polymer chemistry and physics of textiles and polymers; industrial microbiology of polymeric materials; thermal analysis. *Mailing Add:* Southern Regional Res Ctr USDA Agr Res Serv PO Box 19687 New Orleans LA 70179. *Fax:* 504-286-4419; *E-Mail:* tvigo@nola.sttc.usda.gov

**VIGRASS, LAURENCE WILLIAM,** GEOLOGY, ENGINEERING. *Current Pos:* head dept, 88-91, prof, 73-91, EMER PROF GEOL, UNIV REGINA, 91- *Personal Data:* b Melfort, Sask, May 9, 29; m 54, Glenna Graham; c Richard, Lauren & Mark. *Educ:* Univ Sask, BE, 51, MSc, 52; Stanford Univ, PhD(geol), 61. *Prof Exp:* Geologist, Calif Stand Co, 52-55; res geologist, Imp Oil Ltd, 58-65; consult geologist, Western Resources Consult Ltd, 65-68; assoc prof geol, Univ Sask, Regina, 68-73, actg chmn dept, 72-73, dir energy res, 76-87. *Concurrent Pos:* Consult, 91- *Mem:* Can Inst Mining & Metall; Am Asn Petrol Geol; Can Soc Petrol Geologists; Can Geothermal Energy Asn. *Res:* Sedimentary geology; occurence of petroleum and natural gas; geothermal energy in sedimentary basins; water movement and occurrence in the subsurface. *Mailing Add:* Dept Geol Univ Regina Regina SK S4S 0A2 Can. *Fax:* 306-757-4070

**VIJAY, HARI MOHAN,** MECHANISMS OF HYPERSENSITIVITY. *Current Pos:* RES SCIENTIST, NAT HEALTH & WELFARE CAN, 74- *Personal Data:* Can citizen; m 68; c 2. *Educ:* Univ Bombay India BSc, 56, MSc, 58; Univ Manchester Eng, MSc, 63; Univ Birmingham, PhD(org chem), 66. *Prof Exp:* Fel indole alkaloids, Univ Man, 68-70, res assoc immunol, 70-74. *Concurrent Pos:* Assoc prof, Univ Montreal; adj prof, Univ Ottawa. *Mem:* Can Soc Immunol; Int Asn Aerobiol; Am Asn Immunologists; NY Acad Sci; fel Am Acad Allergy & Immunol. *Res:* Standardization of allergens. *Mailing Add:* 24 Swans Way S Gloucester ON K1J 6H9 Can

**VIJAY, INDER KRISHAN,** BIOCHEMISTRY, FOOD SCIENCE. *Current Pos:* asst prof, 75-80, ASSOC PROF DAIRY SCI, UNIV MD, 80- *Personal Data:* b Lahore, India, Dec 25, 40. *Educ:* Panjab Univ, BS, 61; Univ Sask, MS, 66; Univ Calif, Davis, PhD(biochem), 71. *Prof Exp:* Prod supvr food prod, Nestle Int, 61-63; fel biochem, Sch Med, Univ Mich, 71-72; NIH trainee & fel, Sch Med, Univ Calif, Davis, 72-75. *Concurrent Pos:* Multiple grants, 75-; NIH res career develop award, 78-83. *Mem:* AAAS; Am Dairy Sci Asn; Inst Food Technologists; Sigma Xi. *Res:* Biochemistry of glycoproteins; enzyme activities in sterilized milk. *Mailing Add:* Dept Animal Sci Univ Md Animal Sci Ctr College Park MD 20742-2311. *Fax:* 301-314-9059; *E-Mail:* ivi@umail.umd.edu

**VIJAY, MOHAN MADAN,** HIGH PRESSURE WATER JET TECHNOLOGY. *Current Pos:* SR RES OFFICER, INST MECH ENG, NAT RES COUN CAN, 75- *Personal Data:* b Hospet, Karnataka, India, may 18, 37; Can citizen; m 68; c 2. *Educ:* Univ Bombay, India, BS, 59; Univ Manchester, UK, BS, 63; Univ Birmingham, UK, MS, 65; Univ Man, PhD(nuclear eng), 78. *Prof Exp:* Lectr mech eng, Univ Man, Winnipeg, Can, 66-74. *Concurrent Pos:* Ed, Int J Water Jet Technol, 90-; vis prof, Colo Sch Mines, Golden, 90- *Mem:* Sigma Xi; Water Jet Technol Asn (vpres, 89-); Int Soc Water Jet Technol (pres, 90-). *Res:* High speed water jets; field of water jet technology including manufacturing, mining, medical applications and worldwide transfer of technology. *Mailing Add:* 24 Swans Way Gloucester ON K1J 6H9 Can

**VIJAYAGOPAL, PARAKAT,** BIOCHEMISTRY. *Current Pos:* res assoc, La State Univ Med Ctr, 78-79, instr, 79-83, from asst prof to assoc prof, 83-92, PROF MED, MED CTR, LA STATE UNIV, 92- *Personal Data:* b June 7, 45; US citizen; m 71, Valsala Mannadiar; c Anupama & Pramod. *Educ:* Univ Kerala, India, BS, 66, PhD(biochem), 73; Banaras Hindu Univ, MS, 68. *Prof Exp:* Res asst biochem, Univ Kerala, India, 68-70, lectr, 73-75; teaching fel, Australian Nat Univ, 75-77. *Mem:* Am Soc Biol Chemists; Am Heart Asn; Sigma Xi. *Res:* Arterial wall proteoglycan metabolism in normal and atherosclerotic state; lipoprotein-proteoglycan interactions in cultured cells. *Mailing Add:* Dept Med La State Univ Med Ctr 1542 Tulane Ave New Orleans LA 70112. *Fax:* 504-568-2127; *E-Mail:* pvijay@lsumc.edu

**VIJAYAN, SIVARAMAN,** CHEMICAL ENGINEERING, SURFACE SCIENCE. *Current Pos:* ASST PROF CHEM ENG, MCMASTER UNIV, 78- *Personal Data:* b Thuckalay, Madras, June 14, 45. *Educ:* Madras Univ, BSc, 64; Indian Inst Technol, Madras, B Tech, 67, M Tech, 69; Univ NB, MSc, 71; Swiss Fed Inst Technol, Lausanne, DSc(chem eng), 74. *Prof Exp:* First res asst & lectr, Swiss Fed Inst Technol, Lausanne, 72-76. *Concurrent Pos:* Fel McMaster Univ, 76-77; adj asst eng, Univ Fla, 77-78; grant, Swiss Nat Found Advan Sci Res, 73-76; consult, Biazzi, SA, Vevey, Switz, 75-76; ed, J Chem Eng 73-76. *Mem:* Can Soc Chem Eng; Can Asn Physicists; Am Inst Chem Eng; Brit Inst Chem Eng; Indian Inst Chem Eng. *Res:* Interfacial phenomena in chemical engineering transport processes; stability of macroemulsions; surface chemistry; surfactants microstructure; dispersion phase separation. *Mailing Add:* Atomic Energy Can Ltd Chalk River Lab Chalk River ON K0J 1J0 Can

**VIJAYAN, VIJAYA KUMARI,** HUMAN ANATOMY, NEUROANATOMY. *Current Pos:* ASST PROF HUMAN ANAT, MED SCH, UNIV CALIF, DAVIS, 73- *Personal Data:* b Trivandrum, India, Feb 25, 42; m 66; c 2. *Educ:* Univ Kerala, MBBS, 65; Univ Calif, Davis, PhD(anat), 72. *Prof Exp:* Tutor human anat, Med Col, Trivandrum, India, 65-68. *Res:* Biochemistry and ultrastructure of developing and aging nervous system; neuroglial reaction to injury; neurotransmitters. *Mailing Add:* Dept Cell Biol & Human Anat Univ Calif Sch Med TB171 Davis CA 95616

**VIJAYARAGHAVAN, SRINIVASAN,** BIOCHEMISTRY. *Current Pos:* asst scientist, 84-90, ASSOC SCIENTIST BIOCHEM, ORE REGIONAL PRIMATE RES CTR, 90- *Personal Data:* b Madras, India, July 23, 50. *Educ:* Madras Col, India, BS, 71; Indian Inst Technol, MS, 73; Indian Inst Med Sci, PhD(biochem), 80. *Prof Exp:* Res fel, Indian Inst Med Sci, 81-84. *Mem:* Am Soc Molecular Biol. *Res:* Biochemistry. *Mailing Add:* Dept Reprod Sci Ore Regional Primate Res Ctr 505 NW 185th Ave Beaverton OR 97006-3449

**VIJAYASARADHI, SETALURI,** IMMUNOLOGY, CELL BIOLOGY. *Current Pos:* SR STAFF MEM IMMUNOL, ROCKEFELLER UNIV, 92- *Educ:* Vepvenkeutesuara Univ, India, BS, 76; G B Phantian Univ, India, MS, 80; Olfamina Univ, India, PhD(biochem), 85. *Prof Exp:* Staff mem immunol, Sloan Kettering Cancer Ctr, 87-92. *Mem:* Am Immunologist Soc; Am Chem Soc. *Res:* Immunology; cell biology. *Mailing Add:* Rockefeller Univ 1230 York Ave New York NY 10021-6341

**VIJAYENDRAN, BHIMA R,** COLLOID & SURFACE CHEMISTRY. *Current Pos:* CONSULT, BATTELLE, COLUMBUS, OHIO, 95- *Personal Data:* b Bangalore, India, 1941; m 70, Levi; c Ravi & Anil. *Educ:* Univ Madras, BTech, 63, MTech, 65; Univ Southern Calif, PhD(chem), 69; Univ New Haven, MBA, 77. *Honors & Awards:* Technol & Innovation Award, Air Prods & Chems Inc, 91. *Prof Exp:* Lectr, Cent Leather Res Inst, India, 65-66; indust fel surface chem, R J Reynolds Indust, NC, 69-70; chemist, Copier Prod Div, Pitney Bowes, Inc, 70-77, mgr res, 74-75; res assoc, Celanese Res Co, 76-78, proj mgr surface & colloid chem, Celanese Polymer Specialty Co, 78-83; venture mgr, Air Prod & Chem, New Polymer Technol, 83-91; assoc dir res & develop, PPG Indust Inc, Monroeville, PA, 91-95. *Concurrent Pos:* Teaching asst, Univ Southern Calif, 66-68; adj fac, Ind Univ, 81-83. *Mem:* Am Chem Soc; Soc Petrol Engrs; Sigma Xi; Soc Plastic Inst; Tech Asn Paper & Pulp; NY Acad Sci. *Res:* Physical chemistry of surfaces; colloidal systems; emulsions; biopolymers and synthetic polymers; interfacial phenomena and their application in graphic arts such as printing, photography, xerography and other reprographic techniques; emulsion and water borne polymers for coatings, adhesives and sealants; extrusion technology for food and industrial packaging; water soluble polymers in oil field chemicals, paper and water treatment; optical/ophthalmic applications. *Mailing Add:* 5924 Brigids Close Dr Dublin OH 43017. *Fax:* 614-424-7479; *E-Mail:* vijayenb@battelle.org

**VIJH, ASHOK KUMAR,** INTERFACIAL ELECTROCHEMISTRY. *Current Pos:* MASTER-IN-RES, RES INST, HYDRO-QUE, 69- *Personal Data:* b Multan, India, Mar 15, 38; Can citizen; div; c Aldous. *Educ:* Punjab Univ, India, BSc, 60, MSc, 61; Ottawa Univ, PhD(electrochem), 66. *Hon Degrees:* LLD, Concordia Univ, 88; DSc, Waterloo Univ, 93. *Honors & Awards:* Lash Miller Award, Can Sect, Electrochem Soc, 73; Noranda Award, Chem Inst Can, 79; Archambault Prize, French-Can Asn Advan Sci, 84; Killam Mem Prize Eng, Can Coun, 87; Knight of the Nat Order of Que, 87; Thomas Eadie Medal, Royal Soc Can, 89; Palladium Medal, Chem Inst Can, 90; Officer, Order of Can, 90; Knight of Malta, 92. *Prof Exp:* Staff mem, Res & Develop Labs, Sprague Electric Co, North Adams, Mass, 66-69. *Concurrent Pos:* Invited prof, INRS-Energy, Univ Que, 70- *Mem:* Fel Nat Acad Sci India; fel Royal Soc Can; fel Royal Soc Chem UK; fel Am Phys Soc; fel Inst Elec & Electronics Engrs; fel Inst Physics UK; fel Chem Inst Can; assoc fel Third World Acad Sci; Europ Acad Arts Sci & Humanities. *Res:* Mechanisms of electrochemical reactions; interfacial electrochemistry in relation to the principles of solid state physics; electrochemical physics. *Mailing Add:* IREQ CP 1000 Varennes PQ J0L 2P0 Can. *Fax:* 514-652-8424

**VIKIS, ANDREAS CHARALAMBOUS,** PHYSICAL CHEMISTRY. *Current Pos:* res officer, Atomic Energy Can Ltd Res, 79-85, head res chem, 85-90, dir chem div, 90-95, DIR CHEM & CHEM ENG DIV, ATOMIC ENERGY CAN LTD, 95- *Personal Data:* b Moni, Cyprus, July 8, 42; Can citizen; m 71, Ava; c Haris & Elena. *Educ:* Col Emporia, BSc, 64; Kans State Univ, PhD(phys chem), 69. *Prof Exp:* Fel, Univ Toronto, 69-70, lectr & res assoc, 70-74, asst prof & res assoc, 74-75; asst res officer chem, Nat Res Coun Can, 75-79. *Mem:* Am Chem Soc; fel Can Inst Chem; Can Nuclear Soc. *Res:* Gas phase kinetics; photochemistry; isotope enrichment; reactor safety; nuclear waste management; air pollution. *Mailing Add:* Chem & Chem Eng Div Whiteshell Labs Atomic Energy Can Ltd Pinawa MB R0E 1L0 Can. *Fax:* 204-753-2635; *E-Mail:* vikisa@wl.aecl.ca

**VIKRAM, CHANDRA SHEKHAR,** OPTICS. *Current Pos:* SR RES SCIENTIST, UNIV ALA, HUNTSVILLE, 89-, RES PROF, OPTICAL SCIS & ENG PROG, 93- *Personal Data:* b Payagpur, India, Oct 31, 50; m 75, Bina Singh; c Preeti & Tushar. *Educ:* Indian Inst Technol, Delhi, MTech, 70, PhD(optics), 73. *Prof Exp:* Sr res fel holography, Indian Inst Technol, Delhi, 70-75, sci pool officer, 75-77; res assoc holography, Pa State Univ, University Park, 77-82, sr res assoc optics, 82-89. *Mem:* fel Optical Soc Am; Soc Photo-Optical Instrumentation Engrs. *Res:* Holography; speckle metrology; particle analysis; ultra-low thermal expansion measurements; space optics. *Mailing Add:* Ctr Appl Optics Univ Ala Huntsville AL 35899. *Fax:* 205-890-6618; *E-Mail:* vikramc@email.uah.edu

**VIKSNE, ANDY,** GEOPHYSICS. *Current Pos:* CHIEF, GEOPHYS SECT, US BUR RECLAMATION, 72- *Personal Data:* b Jan 27, 34; m, Carol Sorensen. *Educ:* Harvard Univ, AB, 56; Univ Utah, MS, 58. *Prof Exp:* Geophysicist, Texaco, Inc, 59-65, Systs Sci Corp, 65-66; scientist, Raytheon Co, 67-68; geophysicist, US Bur Mines, 68-72. *Mem:* Soc Explor Geophys; Europ Asn Explor Geophysicists; Earthquake Eng Res Inst. *Res:* Application of geophysical exploration methods in solving geotechnical engineering problems; in situ determination of elastic moduli for earth dams and foundation sites; strong motion earthquake instrumentation and site characteristics. *Mailing Add:* 1440 St Andrews Dr Broomfield CO 80020-1547

**VILA, SAMUEL CAMPDERROS,** astrophysics, for more information see previous edition

**VILCEK, JAN TOMAS,** CYTOKINES, GROWTH FACTORS. *Current Pos:* from asst prof to assoc prof, Sch Med, NY Univ, 65-72, dir, microbiol grad training prog, 84-92, PROF MICROBIOL, SCH MED, NY UNIV, 72-, HEAD, CYTOKINE RES UNIT, 84- *Personal Data:* b Bratislava, Czech, June 17, 33; m 62, Marica Gerhath. *Educ:* Univ Bratislava, MD, 57; Czech Acad Sci, CSc(virol), 62. *Honors & Awards:* Recognition Award, Japanese Inflammation Soc, 89; Outstanding Investr Award, Nat Cancer Inst, NIH, 91; Elliott Osserman Award, 96. *Prof Exp:* Res assoc virol, Inst Virol Czech Acad Sci, Bratislava, 57-59, head lab, 62-64. *Concurrent Pos:* Am Cancer Soc grant, 65-66; USPHS grants, 65-, career develop award, 68-73 & contract, 70-81; Irwin Strasburger Mem Med Found grant, 69-73; ed, Arch Virol, 72-74, ed in chief, 75-84 & assoc ed, 84-; assoc ed, Virol, 77-79, Interferon Monographs, 79-88, J Interferon Res, 80-92, Appl Biochem Biotechnol, 81-86 & Infect Immunity, 83-85, J Cell Physiol, 88-, Cytokine, 89-, Biologicals, 89-95, Acta Virol, 91-, Int Arch Allergy Immunol, 92- & Cell Immunol, 92-96; chmn, adv comt microbiol & virol, Am Cancer Soc, 84; assoc ed, J Immunol Methods, 86- & J Immunol, 87-89, J Biol Chem, 88-90; adv ed, ISI Atlas Sci Immunol, 87-89; mem, Sci Adv Bd, Max-Planck-Inst Biochem, Munich, Ger, 87-95; Human Frontier Sci Prog grant, 92-95; Cytokine & Growth Factor Reviews, 95- *Mem:* AAAS; Am Asn Immunol; Am Soc Microbiol; Am Soc Virol; Int Soc Interferon Res; Czech Immunol Soc. *Res:* Cytokine actions; interferous; tumor necrosis factors. *Mailing Add:* Dept Microbiol NY Univ Sch Med 550 First Ave New York NY 10016. *Fax:* 212-263-7933; *E-Mail:* vilcej01@mcrcr.med.nyu.edu

**VILCHES, OSCAR EDGARDO,** LOW TEMPERATURE, SURFACE PHYSICS. *Current Pos:* asst prof, 68-73, assoc prof, 73-80, PROF PHYSICS, UNIV WASH, 80- *Personal Data:* b Mercedes, Arg, Feb 20, 36; US citizen. *Educ:* Nat Univ Cuyo, Lic physics, 59, Dr en Fisica, 66. *Prof Exp:* Investr physics, Cent Atomico Bariloche, Arg, 60-64; res asst, Univ Ill, Urbana, 64-65, res assoc, 65-67; res assoc, Univ Calif, San Diego, 67-68. *Concurrent Pos:* NSF res grant, 70-; vis prof, Unicamp, Brazil, 75, Univ Luminy, France, 81 & 95; vis scientist, Weizmann Inst, Israel, 86. *Mem:* Fel Am Phys Soc. *Res:* Properties of liquid and solid helium and helium films; experimental physical adsorption; measurement of thermodynamic properties of very thin films, with emphasis on quartum monolayers of helium and hydrogen. *Mailing Add:* Dept Physics Box 351560 Univ Wash Seattle WA 98195-1560. *Fax:* 206-685-0635; *E-Mail:* vilches@phys.washington.edu

**VILENKIN, ALEXANDER,** THEORETICAL PHYSICS. *Current Pos:* vis asst prof, 78-79, from asst prof to assoc prof, 79-87, PROF PHYSICS, TUFTS UNIV, 87-; DIR, INST COSMOLOGY, 89- *Personal Data:* b Kharkov, USSR, May 13, 49; m 73; c 1. *Educ:* Kharkov State Univ, USSR, MS, 71; State Univ NY, Buffalo, PhD(physics), 78. *Prof Exp:* Res assoc physics, Case Western Res Univ, 77-78. *Concurrent Pos:* Presidential young investr award, 84-; Sherman Fairchild Distinguished Scholar, Caltech, 92. *Mem:* Fel Am Phys Soc. *Res:* General relativity; quantum field theory; cosmology. *Mailing Add:* Dept Physics Tufts Univ Medford MA 02155. *Fax:* 617-627-3878; *E-Mail:* vilenkin@cosmos2.phy.tufts.edu

**VILGALYS, RYTAS,** BOTANY. *Current Pos:* PROF BOT, DUKE UNIV. *Honors & Awards:* Alexopoulos Prize, Mycol Soc Am, 95. *Mailing Add:* Dept Bot Duke Univ Durham NC 27706

**VILKER, VINCENT LEE,** COLLOID SCIENCE, BIOENGINEERING. *Current Pos:* from asst prof to assoc prof, 75-86, PROF CHEM ENG, UNIV CALIF, LOS ANGELES, 86- *Personal Data:* b Beaver Dam, Wis, Jan 17, 43; m 81; c 1. *Educ:* Univ Wis-Madison, BS, 67; Mass Inst Technol, PhD(chem eng), 76. *Prof Exp:* Res engr, Exxon Res & Eng, 67-70. *Concurrent Pos:* Prin investr, Nat Ctr Intermedia Transp Res, Univ Calif, Los Angeles, 80-; Fulbright Fel, 844-85; vchmn, Dept Chem Eng, Univ Calif, Los Angeles, 86- *Mem:* AAAS; Am Chem Soc; Am Inst Chem Engrs. *Res:* Physical chemistry of solutions of biological macromolecules; membrane transport phenomena; bioelectrochemistry of redox enzymes; movement and fate of toxic materials (viruses, volatile organics) in soils. *Mailing Add:* Biotechnol Div 222/A353 Gaithersburg MD 20899

**VILKITIS, JAMES RICHARD,** RESOURCE PLANNING & MANAGEMENT, POLLUTION CONTROL. *Current Pos:* PROF NATURAL RESOURCES MGT, CALIF POLYTECH STATE UNIV, 80-, DIR, COASTAL RESOURCES INST, 91- *Personal Data:* b Rush, Pa; m 91, Nancy L Raetz. *Educ:* Mich State Univ, BS, 65; Univ Idaho, MS, 68; Univ Mass, PhD(wildlife biol), 70. *Honors & Awards:* Cert Merit, USDA, 88. *Prof Exp:* Res asst, Water Resource Res Ctr, 68-70; spec big game wildlife leader, Dept Inland Fisheries & Game, 70-71; prin partner, Carlozzi, Sinton & Vilkitis Inc, 71-79; owner & mgr, TLC Leather, 76-81; statewide acad senator, Calif Polytech State Univ, 90-95. *Concurrent Pos:* Biostatistician, Regional Plannning & Design Assocs, 69-71; lectr, Univ Mass, 71-79; fel, Univ Mass, 72; res assoc ecol, Inst Man & Environ, 73-74; asst prof biol sci, Mt Holyoke Col, 79-80; assoc, R Stollars Assocs, 86-; staff officer, Land Mgt Planning, US Forest Serv, 87-88. *Mem:* Wildlife Soc; Am Forestry Asn; Asn Environ Prof. *Res:* Developing regional resource planning, management and environmental assessment strategies for terrestrial, aquatic, coastal and riparian systems; wastewater recycling and use; nonpoint source of pollution control using natural vegetation and artificial wetlands. *Mailing Add:* Dept Natural Resource Mgt Calif Polytech State Univ San Luis Obispo CA 93407. *Fax:* 805-756-1402; *E-Mail:* james__vilkiti@nrm.calpoly.edu

**VILKOMERSON, DAVID,** ULTRASOUND MEDICAL DEVICES. *Current Pos:* CO-FOUNDER & EXEC VPRES, ECHO CATH, INC, 90- *Personal Data:* b Boston, Mass, Feb 1, 41; m 69, Barbara Epstein; c Rebecca & Sara. *Educ:* Mass Inst Technol, BS, 62; Univ Pa, MS, 64; Columbia Univ, PhD(appl physics), 69. *Honors & Awards:* IR-100 Award, Indust Res & Develop, 68 & 69; Matzuk Award, Am Inst Ultrasound Med, 93 & 95. *Prof Exp:* Mem tech staff, David Sarnoff Res Ctr, RCA Labs, 62-77; dir res & develop, Johnson & Johnson, 77-80, managing dir, Spec Res Group, 80-82; founder, pres & chief exec officer, Ultramed Inc, 82-90. *Concurrent Pos:* Postdoctorial fel, Hebrew Univ, Jerusalem, 69-70. *Mem:* Am Inst Ultrasound Med; Sigma Xi; Nat Acad Advan Sci; Inst Elec & Electronics Engrs; NY Acad Sci. *Res:* Inventing, developing and bringing to market medical devices that utilize ultrasonic and electronic technology for improved medical treatment; granted over 30 US patents. *Mailing Add:* PO Box 7224 Princeton NJ 08543-7224. *Fax:* 609-987-1019; *E-Mail:* dvilk@aol.com

**VILKS, GUSTAVS,** MICROPALEONTOLOGY. *Current Pos:* Micropaleontologist, 62-93, EMER SCIENTIST, BEDFORD INST OCEANOG, 93- *Personal Data:* b Riga, Latvia, May 7, 29; Can citizen; wid; c 2. *Educ:* McMaster Univ, BSc, 61; Dalhousie Univ, MSc, 66, PhD, 73. *Mem:* Geol Asn Can. *Res:* Ecology and paleoecology of Recent Foraminifera in the Canadian Arctic and Labrador Shelf; ecology of planktonic Foraminifera in the North Atlantic; glacial limits off eastern Canada; sedimentary processes on Labrador shelf and Abyssal Plains. *Mailing Add:* Atlantic Geosci Ctr PO Box 1006 Bedford Inst Oceanog Dartmouth NS B2Y 4A2 Can

**VILKS, PETER,** COLLOIDS & ORGANIC COMPLEXES IN GROUNDWATER. *Current Pos:* RES SCIENTIST, ATOMIC ENERGY CAN LTD, 85- *Personal Data:* b Hamilton, Ont, Mar 30, 56; m 78, Florence Briggs; c Crystal, Tracy & Kirk. *Educ:* Dalhousie Univ, BSc, 78; McMaster Univ, MSc, 81, PhD(geol), 85. *Res:* Effect of colloids and organic complexes on contaminant transport in the subsurface; kinetic approach to the study of metal sorption mechanisms on clay. *Mailing Add:* 9 Dalhouise Dr Pinawa MB R0E 1L0 Can. *Fax:* 204-753-2455

**VILLA, JUAN FRANCISCO,** INORGANIC CHEMISTRY. *Current Pos:* from asst prof to assoc prof, 71-78, actg dean natural & soc sci, 80-81, PROF CHEM, LEHMAN COL, 78- *Personal Data:* b Matanzas, Cuba, Sept 23, 41; US citizen; m 67, Elena M Baez; c John F, Ellen M, Paul A & Irene L. *Educ:* Univ Miami, BS, 65, MS, 67, PhD(inorg chem), 69. *Prof Exp:* Teaching asst chem, Univ Miami, 65-69; res assoc inorg chem, Univ NC, Chapel Hill, 69-71. *Concurrent Pos:* George N Shuster fel, Lehman Col, 71-72 & 74-77; Petrol Res Fund fel, 71-73; Fulbright-Hays sr lectr, Colombia, SAm, 76; adj prof, Sarah Lawrence Col, 77 & 78. *Mem:* Am Chem Soc; The Chem Soc; Sigma Xi. *Res:* Study of transition metal coordination compounds of biological importance including synthesis, electron paramagnetic resonance spectroscopy, magnetic susceptibility measurements, electronic and infrared spectra; ligand field and molecular orbital calculations. *Mailing Add:* Dept Chem Herbert H Lehman Col Bronx NY 10468. *Fax:* 718-960-8750; *E-Mail:* villa@lcvax.lehman.cuny.edu

**VILLA, VICENTE DOMINGO,** MICROBIAL PHYSIOLOGY. *Current Pos:* PROF BIOL & DISHMAN CHMN SCI, SOUTHWESTERN UNIV, 85- *Personal Data:* b Laredo, Tex, Dec 1, 40; m 62; c 2. *Educ:* Univ Tex, Austin, BA, 64; Rice Univ, PhD(microbiol), 70. *Prof Exp:* Fel molecular biol, Molecular Biol Lab, Univ Wis, 69-71; res assoc, Rosenstiel Res Ctr, Brandeis Univ, 71-72; from asst prof to prof, NMex State Univ, 72-84. *Concurrent Pos:* NIH fel, 70-71; ad hoc consult, Minority Biomed Support Prog, NIH, 72-75, mem gen res support prog adv comt, Div Res Resources, 76-80; panelist, NSF Rev Panel-Res Initiation & Support Prog, 76. *Mem:* Am Soc Microbiol. *Res:* Cell wall polyuronides and morphogenesis in fungi; chracterizing the polyuronides found in the cell wall of Mvcor and relating their characteristics to the morphogenetic development of the organism. *Mailing Add:* Dept Biol Southwestern Univ Georgetown TX 78626. *Fax:* 512-863-5788; *E-Mail:* villav@ralph.txswu.edu

**VILLABLANCA, JAIME ROLANDO,** NEUROPHYSIOLOGY, EXPERIMENTAL NEUROLOGY. *Current Pos:* assoc res anat & psychiat, 71-72, PROF PSYCHIAT, UNIV CALIF, LOS ANGELES, 72-, PROF ANAT, 77- *Personal Data:* b Chillan, Chile, Feb 28, 29; US citizen; m 55,

Guillermins Nieto; c Ampara C, Jaime E, J Pablo, Francis X & Caludio L. *Educ:* Univ Chile, BA, 46, Lic Med, 53, Dr(med), 54; Univ Calif, Los Angeles, cert neurophysiol, 68. *Honors & Awards:* Decorated Order Franciso de Miranda, Caracas, Venezuela, 88; Queen Sophia Award, Madrid, Spain, 90. *Prof Exp:* From instr to prof pathophysiol, Sch Med, Univ Chile, 54-71. *Concurrent Pos:* Rockefeller Found fel physiol, Johns Hopkins Univ, 59-61; fel, Neurol Unit, Harvard Med Sch, 61; USAF Off Sci res grant, 62-65; NIH fogarta res fel anat, Univ Calif, Los Angeles, 66-68; Found Fund Res in Psychiat grant, 69-72; Nat Inst Child Health & Human Develop prog proj grant, 71-94; Nat Inst Drug Abuse Grant, 81-85; mem, Ment Retardation Res Ctr, Univ Calif, Los Angeles; chmn, Brain Res Inst, Univ Calif, Los Angeles; sci adv coun, Int Inst Res & Advice Ment Deficiency, Madrid, Spain; Nat Inst Neurol Commun Dis & Stroke grant, 88-92; Sci Coun Avepane, Caracas, Venezuela; chief ed, J Develop Brain Dysfunction. *Mem:* Am Asn Anatomists; Am Physiol Soc; Soc Neurosci; Sigma Xi; Int Brain Res Orgn. *Res:* Age defendant morphological and cerebral metabolic neuroplasticity and the long term behavioral outcome of brain damage using an animal model. *Mailing Add:* Dept Psychiat Univ Calif Los Angeles CA 90024. *Fax:* 310-206-5060; *E-Mail:* jvillablanca@npih.mednet.ucla.edu

**VILLACORTE, GUILLERMO VILAR,** ALLERGY, IMMUNOLOGY. *Current Pos:* CONSULT, 90- *Personal Data:* b Rizal NE, Philippines, Dec 25, 33; m 61; c 2. *Educ:* Univ St Tomas, Manila, AA, 52, MD, 57; Am Bd Allergy & Immunol, dipl, 74, recert, 80. *Prof Exp:* Asst prof pediat, Creighton Univ, Sch Med, 69-79; mem staff, allergy-immunol serv, Wilford Hall Med Ctr, Lackland AFB, Tex, 79-84; mem staff, Allergy Immunol Serv, USAFR, 84-90. *Concurrent Pos:* Res pediat, Good Samaritan Hosp, Cincinnati, Ohio, 62-65; fels pediat allergy & immunol, Univ Cincinnati, Med Ctr, 65-67; fel immunol, Univ Cincinnati, Med Ctr, 67-69. *Mem:* Fel Am Acad Allergy. *Res:* Etiopathogenesis of allergic and immunodeficiency diseases. *Mailing Add:* 8306 Brixton San Antonio TX 78250-2402

**VILLAFANA, THEODORE,** NUCLEAR MEDICAL PHYSICS, MEDICAL IMAGING PHYSICS. *Current Pos:* PROF RADIOL PHYSICS, MED CTR, TEMPLE UNIV, 75- *Personal Data:* b New York, NY, Sept 23, 36; m 61; c 4. *Educ:* Hunter Col, BA, 59; Univ Pittsburgh, MSc, 65; Johns Hopkins Univ, PhD(radiol physics), 69. *Prof Exp:* Physicist, Columbia-Presby Med Ctr, 59-63 & Montefiore Hosp, Pittsburgh, 63-65; asst prof radiol physics, PR Nuclear Ctr, Univ PR, 69-72; assoc prof, George Washington Univ Med Sch, 72-75. *Concurrent Pos:* Vis prof, Univ PR, Med Sch, 77-; consult, Hahnemann Univ, Med Sch, 80-; mem, radiographics panel, Radiol Soc NAm, 83-91, bd dirs, Am Asn Physicists Med, 86-89 & Task Force Educ, Am Col Radiol, 88-91. *Mem:* Am Asn Physicists Med; Health Physics Soc; Radiol Soc NAm; Am Col Radiol. *Res:* Mammographic medical imaging; magnetic resonance imaging; publications on radiological physics. *Mailing Add:* Radiol Dept Temple Univ Hosp 3400 N Broad Philadelphia PA 19140-5196

**VILLAFRANCA, JOSEPH JOHN,** BIOCHEMISTRY, BIO-ORGANIC CHEMISTRY. *Current Pos:* from asst prof to prof, 71-76, EVAN PUGH PROF CHEM, PA STATE UNIV, UNIVERSITY PARK, 86- *Personal Data:* b Silver Creek, NY, Mar 23, 44; m 90; c 2. *Educ:* State Univ NY Col Fredonia, BS, 65; Purdue Univ, Lafayette, PhD(biochem), 69. *Prof Exp:* USPHS fel, Inst Cancer Res, 69-71. *Concurrent Pos:* NSF grant, 72- & USPHS grant, 74-; estab investr, Am Heart Asn, 78-83, mem brant rev comt, 84- 86; mem, Biochem Study Sect, NIH, 82-86, chmn, 85-86; prog chmn, Am Chem Soc, 82-84; mem adv comt, Oak Ridge Nat Lab, 88-91; mem, Major Chem Instrument Rev Panel, NJF, 90-93. *Mem:* Am Chem Soc; Biophys Soc; Am Soc Biol Chemists. *Res:* Mechanism of enzyme action studied by magnetic resonance techniques; biophysics. *Mailing Add:* Bristol-Myers Squbb Pharm Res Inst PO Box 4000 Princeton NJ 08543-4000

**VILLA-KOMAROFF, LYDIA,** MOLECULAR BIOLOGY NEUROSCIENCE. *Current Pos:* SR RES ASSOC, DEPT NEUROL, DIV NEUROSCI, 85-, ASSOC DIR, MENT RETARDATION CTR, CHILDREN'S HOSP, BOSTON; ASSOC PROF, DEPT NEUROL, HARVARD MED SCH, 85- *Personal Data:* b Las Vegas, NMex, Aug 7, 47; m 70, Anthony L. *Educ:* Goucher Col, AB, 70; Mass Inst Technol, PhD(cell biol), 75. *Prof Exp:* Res fel biol, Harvard Univ, 75-78; from asst prof to assoc prof microbiol, Med Sch, Univ Mass, 78-85. *Concurrent Pos:* Vis fel, Cold Spring Harbor Lab, 76-77; fel, Helen Hay Whitney Found, 75-78; mem, Mammalian Genetics Study Sect, NIH, 82-84, Neurol Dis Prog Proj Rev Comt, 89-94; chair, Neurol Res Steering Comt, Children's Hosp, Boston, 88-94. *Mem:* Am Soc Microbiol; Am Soc Cell Biol; AAAS; Fedn Am Sci; Sigma Xi; Soc Neurosci. *Res:* Growth factors in brain development; structure & function of insulin-like growth factors; structure and function of genes expressed in central and peripheral nervous system. *Mailing Add:* 65 South St Boston MA 02111. *Fax:* 617-730-0636; *E-Mail:* komaroff@a1.tch.harvard.edu

**VILLANI, FRANK JOHN, SR,** MEDICINAL CHEMISTRY, SYNTHESIS. *Current Pos:* RETIRED. *Personal Data:* b Brooklyn, NY, May 9, 21; m 51, Florence J Brykowski; c Frank J Jr, Marianne (London), Thomas S & John R. *Educ:* Brooklyn Col, BA, 41; Fordham Univ, MS, 43, PhD(chem), 46. *Prof Exp:* Org chemist, Schering Corp, Bloomfield, 46-64, sr fel med chem, 64-83. *Mem:* Am Chem Soc. *Res:* Aldehyde condensations; synthetic medicinals; heterocyclic chemistry; antihistamines; non sedating antihistamine. *Mailing Add:* 22 Oakland Terr Fairfield NJ 07004-3827

**VILLANUEVA, ANTONIO R,** HISTOLOGY, HISTOMORPHOMETRY. *Current Pos:* SR RES SCIENTIST & HEAD HISTOL & HISTOMORPHOMETRY, HARRINGTON RES CTR, 88- *Personal Data:* b San Fernando, La Union, Philippines, Oct 17, 26; US Citizen; m 54, Carmen

E Perez; c Yvette & Suzanne. *Educ:* Detroit Inst Technol, BS, 61; Cent Mich Univ, MA, 78; Columbia Pac Univ, PhD(health sci), 83. *Honors & Awards:* Hektoen Gold Medal, AMA, 63. *Prof Exp:* Res coordr, Orthop Res Lab, Henry Ford Hosp, 59-68, tech dir, 68-76, dep dir, Bone & Mineral Res Lab, 76-88. *Concurrent Pos:* Ed-in-chief, J Histotechnol, 76-79; chmn histol sci assembly, Am Soc Med Technol, 77-80; consult, Biol Stain Comn, 81-; prin investr, Greening Found 89-91, Sandoz Found Geront Res, 90-91. *Mem:* NY Acad Sci; Histochem Soc; Soc Quant Morphol; Am Soc Clin Path; Int Soc Stereology; Am Soc Bone & Mineral Res. *Res:* Investigation of bone cells in patients with osteoporosis treated with sodium fluoride; osteoporosis in regard to mechanism of bone loss, statics and dynamics of bone remodeling; microcracks in avascular necrosis in the human femoral head. *Mailing Add:* 1344 E Sheena Dr Phoenix AZ 85022. *Fax:* 602-253-4817

**VILLANUEVA, GERMAN BAID,** antithrombin, thrombin-heparin reaction; deceased, see previous edition for last biography

**VILLANUEVA, JOSE,** MECHANICAL ENGINEERING. *Current Pos:* assoc prof, 68-77, actg chmn dept, 71-77, PROF MECH ENG, FLA ATLANTIC UNIV, 77- *Personal Data:* b Santiago de Cuba, Cuba, Mar 31, 37; US citizen; m 61; c 2. *Educ:* Ga Inst Technol, BS, 59, MS, 61, PhD(eng mech), 65. *Honors & Awards:* Ralph R Teetor Award, Soc Automotive Engrs, 67. *Prof Exp:* Prof docent mech eng, Univ Oriente, Cuba, 61; asst prof eng mech, Ga Inst Technol, 61-68. *Concurrent Pos:* Eng consult, Am Art Metals, Ga, 61 & Lockheed-Ga Co, 66- *Mem:* Am Soc Mech Engrs. *Res:* Continuum mechanics; dynamics and vibrations; sloshing of liquids and design of mechanical models to describe the phenomena; energy efficiency in buildings. *Mailing Add:* Dept Mech Eng Fla Atlantic Univ 777 Glades Rd Boca Raton FL 33431-0991

**VILLARD, OSWALD G(ARRISON), JR,** ELECTRONICS, DEFENSE RESEARCH. *Current Pos:* actg asst prof elec eng, Stanford Univ, 46-50, from asst prof to assoc prof, 50-55, dir, Radiosci Lab, 60-73, dir ionospheric dynamics lab, 70-72, PROF ELEC ENG, STANFORD UNIV, 55-; SR SCI ADV, SYST TECHNOL DIV, SRI INT, 72- *Personal Data:* b Dobbs Ferry, NY, Sept 17, 16; wid; c Thomas, Suzanne & John. *Educ:* Yale Univ, AB, 38; Stanford Univ, EE, 43, PhD(radio eng), 49. *Honors & Awards:* Morris Liebmann Mem Award, Inst Elec & Electronics Engrs, 57, Centennial Award, 85; SRI Int Presidential Fel Award for Excellence, 88. *Prof Exp:* Actg instr elec eng, Stanford Univ, 41-42; spec res assoc, Radio Res Lab, Harvard Univ, 42-43, mem sr staff, 43-46. *Concurrent Pos:* Emer mem, Air Force Studies Bd, Nat Res Coun, 62-; mem geophys panel, USAF Sci Adv Bd, 66-75; mem, Naval Res Adv Comt, 69-75, chmn, 72-75; mem adv bd, Nat Security Agency, 76-86. *Mem:* Nat Acad Sci; Nat Acad Eng; fel AAAS; fel Inst Elec & Electronics Engrs; Am Geophys Union; fel Am Acad Arts & Sci; Int Sci Radio Union. *Res:* Ionospheric radio propagation; upper atmosphere research; radar techniques; defense electronic systems. *Mailing Add:* SRI Int 333 Ravenswood Ave Menlo Park CA 94025

**VILLAREJO, MERNA,** BIOCHEMISTRY. *Current Pos:* asst prof, 75-82, assoc prof, 82-88, ASSOC DEAN BIOL SCI, UNIV CALIF, DAVIS, 87-, PROF BIOCHEM, 88- *Personal Data:* b New York, NY, June 19, 39; m 59; c 2. *Educ:* Univ Chicago, BS, 59, PhD(biochem), 63. *Prof Exp:* Res assoc & asst prof biochem, Univ Chicago, 63-68; res assoc biol chem, Sch Med, Univ Calif, Los Angeles, 68-75. *Concurrent Pos:* USPHS fel, Univ Chicago, 63-65; prin investr, NIH, 75-; Howard Hughes Med Inst Grants, 89-94. *Mem:* Am Soc Biochem & Molecular Biol; Am Soc Microbiol. *Res:* Regulation of gene expression in response to osmotic stress. *Mailing Add:* Sec Microbiol Univ Calif Davis CA 95616-5224

**VILLAREJOS, VICTOR MOISES,** epidemiology, tropical medicine, for more information see previous edition

**VILLAR-PALASI, CARLOS,** PHARMACOLOGY, BIOCHEMISTRY. *Current Pos:* assoc prof, 69-73, PROF PHARMACOL, UNIV VA, 73- *Personal Data:* b Valencia, Spain, Mar 3, 28; m 57, Amparo Bosalvez; c Victor, Carlos, Juan & Maria. *Educ:* Univ Valencia, MS, 51; Univ Madrid, PhD(biochem), 55; Univ Barcelona, MS, 62. *Honors & Awards:* AAAS Res Award, 60; Span Soc Biochem Res Award, 72. *Prof Exp:* NIH fel, Case Western Res Univ, 57-60, res assoc pharmacol, 63-64; res assoc enzymol, Univ Madrid, 60-63, asst prof, 62-63; res assoc biochem, Univ Minn, Minneapolis, 64-65, asst prof, 65-69. *Concurrent Pos:* Span Res Coun fel, Univ Hamburg, 53-54; NIH grant, Univ Va, 70- *Mem:* AAAS; Am Soc Biol Chemists; Am Soc Pharmacol & Exp Therapeut. *Res:* Control of metabolic and muscle function by phosphorylation of proteins; protein kinases and phosphatases; glycogen metabolism; mechanism of action of insulin, glucagon and adrenergic hormones; contractile protein structure and function; carbohydrate metabolism; hormonal effects on energy metabolism. *Mailing Add:* Dept Pharmacol Sch Med Univ Va Charlottesville VA 22903-2543. *Fax:* 804-924-1942

**VILLARREAL, JESSE JAMES,** speech pathology; deceased, see previous edition for last biography

**VILLARREAL, LUIS PEREZ,** MOLECULAR VIROLOGY. *Current Pos:* PROF MOLECULAR BIOL & BIOCHEM, UNIV CALIF, IRVINE. *Personal Data:* b Los Angeles, Calif, July 6, 49; m 82. *Educ:* Los Angeles State Univ, BS, 71; Univ Calif, San Diego, PhD(biol), 76. *Prof Exp:* Fel molecular biol, Biochem Dept, Stanford Univ, 76-78; asst prof microbiol & virol, Health Sci Ctr, Univ Colo, 78- *Concurrent Pos:* Res fel, Jane Coffin Childs Mem Res Fund, 76. *Mem:* Am Soc Microbiol. *Res:* Control of gene expression in animal viruses. *Mailing Add:* Dept Molecular Biol & Chem Univ Calif Irvine CA 92717-0001

**VILLARS, FELIX MARC HERMANN,** THEORETICAL PHYSICS, GENERAL PHYSIOLOGY. *Current Pos:* res assoc 50-52, from asst prof to prof, 52-91, EMER PROF PHYSICS, MASS INST TECHNOL, 91- *Personal Data:* b Biel, Switz, Jan 6, 21; nat US; m 49, Jacqueline Dubois; c J Frederick, Cecile, Monique & Philip. *Educ:* Swiss Fed Inst Technol, Dipl, 45, DSc, 46. *Prof Exp:* Res asst physics, Swiss Fed Inst Technol, 46-49; vis mem, Inst Adv Study, 49-50. *Concurrent Pos:* Consult, Lincoln Lab, 54-64, 68-70; Guggenheim fel, 56-57; lectr physics, Harvard Med Sch, 74- *Mem:* Am Phys Soc; Am Acad Arts & Sci; NY Acad Sci. *Res:* Nuclear physics, mainly nuclear models and reactions; quantum field theory; physics of upper atmosphere; turbulence; plasma probes; biophysics; biophysical chemistry; general physiology. *Mailing Add:* Dept Physics Rm 6-306 Mass Inst Technol Cambridge MA 02139

**VILLEE, CLAUDE ALVIN, JR,** BIOCHEMISTRY. *Current Pos:* from instr to assoc prof biol chem, 46-63, TUTOR PRECLIN SCI, MED SCH, HARVARD UNIV, 47-, PROF BIOL CHEM, 63-, ANDELOT PROF, 64- *Personal Data:* b Lancaster, Pa, Feb 9, 17; m 52; c 4. *Educ:* Franklin & Marshall Col, BS, 37; Univ Calif, PhD(physiol genetics), 41. *Hon Degrees:* AM, Harvard Univ, 57; ScD, Franklin & Marshall, 91. *Honors & Awards:* Ciba Award, Endocrine Soc, 56; Rubin Award, Am Soc Study Steril, 57. *Prof Exp:* Res assoc zool, Univ Calif, 41-42; from instr to asst prof, Univ NC, 42-45. *Concurrent Pos:* Asst prof, Armstrong Col, 41-42; tech aide, Comt Growth, Nat Res Coun, 46; Lalor fel, Marine Biol Lab, Woods Hole, 47 & 48; Guggenheim fel, Denmark, 49-50; res assoc, Boston Lying-in-Hosp, 50-; consult, Mass Gen Hosp, 50- & NSF, 59-; consult, NIH, 58-, mem, Nat Adv Child Health & Human Develop Coun, 63-65; dir, Lab Reproductive Biol, Boston Hosp Women, 66-; mem, Sci Adv Comt, Ore Regional Primate Ctr, 70-; distinguished vis prof, Univ Belgrade & Mahidol Univ, Bangkok, 74; consult, March Dimes Found, 78- *Mem:* Hon mem Soc Gynec Invest; hon fel Am Col Obstet & Gynec; hon fel Am Gynec Soc; Am Soc Biol Chemists; Genetic Soc Am. *Res:* Nucleic acid chemistry and metabolism; carbohydrate metabolism; effects of hormones on intermediary metabolism; function of the placenta; biochemical genetics; metabolism of fetal tissues. *Mailing Add:* Carrell 12 Coantway Libr Harvard Med Sch 10 Shattuck St Boston MA 02115

**VILLEE, DOROTHY BALZER,** pediatric endocrinology, aging, for more information see previous edition

**VILLEGAS, CESAREO,** BAYESIAN INFERENCE. *Current Pos:* from assoc prof to prof, 70-91, EMER PROF STATIST, SIMON FRASER UNIV, 91- *Personal Data:* b Montevideo, Uruguay, April 5, 21; Can citizen; m 50, Nellie C Norman; c George, Lewis, Nellie & Maria. *Educ:* Univ de La Repub, Uruguay, Ing Ind, 53. *Prof Exp:* Prof math, Univ de La Repub, Uruguay, 58-68; vis assoc prof, Univ Rochester, 68-70. *Mem:* Inst Math Statist. *Res:* Developing a new approach to statistics called geometric bayesian inference, and its applications, especially to linear functional models. *Mailing Add:* Dept Math & Statist Simon Fraser Univ 8888 University Dr Burnaby BC V5A 1S6 Can

**VILLEMEZ, CLARENCE LOUIS, JR,** BIOCHEMISTRY. *Current Pos:* assoc prof, 72-74, PROF BIOCHEM, UNIV WYO, 74- *Personal Data:* b Port Arthur, Tex, Sept 6, 38; m 64, Jane A Barker; c 4. *Educ:* Harvard Univ, AB, 58; Purdue Univ, MS, 61, PhD(biochem), 63. *Prof Exp:* Fel biochem, Purdue Univ, 63-65; asst res biochemist, Univ Calif, Berkeley, 65-66; res assoc biochem, Univ Colo, 66-67; from asst prof to assoc prof, Ohio Univ, 67-72. *Concurrent Pos:* Vis prof microbiol, Health Sci Ctr, Univ Tex, Dallas, 79-80. *Mem:* Am Soc Cell Biol; AAAS; Am Soc Biol Chemists; Am Soc Plant Physiologists; NY Acad Sci. *Res:* Polysaccharide biosynthesis; cell wall formation; protein glycosylation; hybridomas; specific cytotoxic reagents. *Mailing Add:* Dept Molecular Biol Univ Wyo Laramie WY 82071-3944. *Fax:* 307-766-5098; *E-Mail:* villemez@plains.uwyo.edu

**VILLEMURE, M PAUL JAMES,** MATHEMATICS. *Current Pos:* from instr math to asst prof math, 59-69, PROF MATH, BARRY COL, 69- *Personal Data:* b Newberry, Mich, Nov 28, 28. *Educ:* Siena Heights Col, BS, 50; Univ Notre Dame, PhD(math), 58. *Prof Exp:* Teacher high sch, 58-59; instr math & sci, Col San Antonio, 51-54. *Mem:* Math Asn Am. *Mailing Add:* Dept Math Barry Univ 11300 NE Second Ave Miami Shores FL 33161-6690

**VILLENEUVE, A(LFRED) T(HOMAS),** ANTENNAS, MICROWAVES. *Current Pos:* RETIRED. *Personal Data:* b Syracuse, NY, Mar 14, 30; m 56; c 5. *Educ:* Manhattan Col, BEE, 52; Syracuse Univ, MEE, 55, PhD(elec eng), 59. *Prof Exp:* Res assoc elec eng, Syracuse Univ, 52-56, instr, 56-59, asst prof, 59; mem tech staff, Hughes Aircraft Co, 59-60, staff engr, 60-63, sr staff engr, 63-72, sr scientist, 72-84; chief scientist, Antenna Systs Lab, 84-89. *Concurrent Pos:* Lectr, Univ Southern Calif, 59, Loyola Univ, Calif, 62 & Univ Calif, Los Angeles, 69; mem comn B, Int Union Radio Sci. *Mem:* Inst Elec & Electronics Engrs; Sigma Xi. *Res:* Ultra-high-frequency and microwave antennas; microwave filters; large aperture antennas; electromagnetic fields in anisotropic media; advanced antenna techniques; satellite antennas; space communications; phase scanned arrays. *Mailing Add:* 8123 Kenyon Ave Los Angeles CA 90045-2736

**VILLENEUVE, ANDRE,** NEUROPSYCHOPHARMACOLOGY, FORENSIC PSYCHIATRY. *Current Pos:* lectr, 68-70, assoc prof, 70-76, PROF, DEPT PSYCHIAT, LAVAL UNIV, QUE, 77- *Personal Data:* b Chicoutimi, Que, Sept 17, 32; m 58, Gisele; c Anik. *Educ:* Laval Univ, BA, 52, MD, 58; McGill Univ, MSc, 66; FRCPS(C); FRCPsychiat. *Honors & Awards:* Heinz Lehmann Award, 91. *Prof Exp:* Residency psychiat, Cent Islip

State Hosp & NY Sch Psychiat, 61-64; researcher psychiat, Fac Grad Studies, McGill Univ, Montreal & clin fel, Royal Victoria Hosp, 64-66, researcher psychopharmacol, Hosp St Anne & Fac Med, Paris, 66-67. *Concurrent Pos:* Res psychiatrist neuropsychopharmacol, Univ Ctr Hosp Robert Giffard, Beauport, Que, 67-86, chief, 67-74 & 79-86; dir res, Dept Psychiat, Hosp de l'Enfant-Jesus, Que, 73-82; pres, Examining Bd, French Sect, Psychiat Specialty, Royal Col Physicians & Surgeons, Can, 78-84; chief, Neuropsychopharmacol Sect, Clinique Roy-Rousseau, Beauport, Que, 82-, chief, Dept Psychiat, 83-; hon mem, Foreign Sci Adv Bd, Vinohrady Sch Med, Charles Univ, Prague, Czech, 90- *Mem:* Fel Am Psychiat Asn; fel Am Col Physicians; fel Am Col Forensic Psychiat; fel Col Int Neuropsychopharmacol; found fel & pres Can Col Neuropsychopharmacol (past pres, 92-94); fel Royal Col Psychiatrists (Eng). *Res:* Methodology; clinical trials; pharmacokinetics; drug interactions; extrapyramidal system (side effects, tardive dyskinesia, endorphins, estrogens); neuropsychoendocrinology; forensic psychiatry. *Mailing Add:* Centre Hosp Robert Gifford Pavillon Roy-Rousseau 2601 Dela Cavardier Beauporte Quebec PQ G1J 2G3 Can. *Fax:* 418-663-5727

**VILLET, RUXTON HERRER,** BIOCHEMISTRY, BIOCHEMICAL ENGINEERING. *Current Pos:* nat prog leader, 86-92, DEP ASST ADMINR, AGR RES SERV, USDA, WASHINGTON, DC, 92- *Personal Data:* b June 26, 33; US citizen; m 60; c 2. *Educ:* Univ Cape Town, BSc, 53; Princeton Univ, MS, 59; Univ Oxford, DPhil(biochem), 68. *Prof Exp:* Chem engr petrol, Mobil Oil Refinery, SAfrica, 53-57; chem engr res, Shell Develop Co, Calif, 59-60; assoc prof chem eng, Univ Witwatersrand, 61-65; res biochem, Inst Nat de la Sante et de la Rech Medicale, France, 73-75; reader, biochem eng, Massey Univ, NZ, 76-78; br chief, Biotechnol Br, Solar Energy Res Inst, Colo, 78-82. *Concurrent Pos:* Res fel, Calif Inst Technol, 68-70 & Max-Planck Inst, WGer, 71-73; dir res biotechnol, Elf Aquitaine, France, 82-83, consult, 83-85; dir biotechnol consortium, ARBS, France, 83-84; mgr, Dept Biotechnol, Stauffer Chem Co, Calif, 85-86. *Mem:* Am Inst Chem Engrs. *Res:* Biochemical, molecular genetic and chemical engineer research directed toward developing biotechnological processes. *Mailing Add:* USDA/OIRP Rm 102 Bldg 005 Barc-West Beltsville MD 20705-2350

**VILMS, JAAK,** MATHEMATICS. *Current Pos:* ASSOC PROF MATH, COLO STATE UNIV, 71- *Personal Data:* b Viljandi, Estonia, Jan 30, 37; US citizen; m 62; c 2. *Educ:* Dickinson Col, AB, 59; Columbia Univ, MS, 61, PhD(math), 67. *Prof Exp:* Instr math, Purdue Univ, 65-67, asst prof, 67-71. *Mem:* Am Math Soc; Math Asn Am. *Res:* Differential geometry. *Mailing Add:* Dept Math Colo State Univ Ft Collins CO 80523-0001

**VILNER, BERTOLD JACOB,** CELL DEVELOPMENT, RECEPTOR MECHANISMS. *Current Pos:* VIS SCIENTIST, NAT INST DIABETES & DIGESTIVE & KIDNEY DIS, NIH, 91- *Personal Data:* b Leningrad, USSR, Mar 14, 31; m 74, Lucy M Stepanova; c Galina (Zybco) & Alex. *Educ:* State Med Inst, Minsk, USSR, MD, 55; Inst Exp Med, Riga, USSR, PhD(neurosci), 61. *Prof Exp:* Assoc prof & chief of group, Physiol Inst Byeloruss Acad Sci, Minsk, USSR, 68-89; tech consult, Div Endocrinol, RI Hosp, 90-91; res asst, Sect Biochem, Div Biol Med, Brown Univ, 90-91. *Concurrent Pos:* Sci secy, Sect Neuron, In Vitro Soc Biophys, USSR, 70-89. *Mem:* Soc Neurosci. *Res:* Model demyelination in cultures of central nervous system and peripheral nervous system; environmental influence on the development of autonomic nervous system in vitro; sigma-receptor physiology and pharmacology. *Mailing Add:* 4904 Cushing Dr Kensington MD 20895. *Fax:* 301-402-0589; *E-Mail:* vilnerb@bdg8.niddk.nih.gov

**VILTER, RICHARD WILLIAM,** MEDICINE, HEMATOLOGY & ONCOLOGY. *Current Pos:* from asst prof to assoc prof med, Col Med, Univ Cincinnati, 42-56, asst to dean, Col Med, 43-45, asst dean, 45-48, dir, Lab Hemat & Nutrit, 45-56, asst dir dept, 52-56, Taylor prof med & dir, Dept Internal Med, 56-78, Taylor Prof Med, 78-81, TAYLOR EMER PROF MED, COL MED, UNIV CINCINNATI, 81- *Personal Data:* b Cincinnati, Ohio, Mar 21, 11; m 35, Kathryn S Potter; c Richard W Jr. *Educ:* Harvard Univ, BA, 33, MD, 37; Am Bd Internal Med, dipl; Am Bd Nutrit, dipl, MA, Am Col Physicians, 80. *Honors & Awards:* Goldberger Award, AMA, 60, Tehan Award, 78; Musscr lectr, Sch Med, Tulane Univ, 65; Daniel Drake Medal Award, 85. *Prof Exp:* Intern, Cincinnati Gen Hosp, Ohio, 37-38, jr resident, 38-39, sr asst resident, 40-41, chief resident, Med Serv, 41-42. *Concurrent Pos:* Fel nutrit, Hillman Hosp, Ala, 39-40; attend physician, Cincinnati Gen Hosp, 45-; consult, UN WHO, Egypt, 54, Pan Am Sanit Bur Anemias Kwashiorkor, Guatamala & Panama, 55; chmn, Comt Invest & Ther Cancer, Am Cancer Soc, 61-64 & 63-64, Hemat Study Sect, NIH, 65-69; chmn, Nat Adv Comt, Malnutrit Res Ctr, Chiengmai, Thailand, 65-75; vis lectr, Queens Hosp, Hawaii, 66. *Mem:* Am Soc Clin Invest; Am Clin & Climat Asn (vpres, 64-65, 83-84); Asn Am Physicians; Am Col Physicians (secy-gen, 74-77, pres-elect, 78-79, pres, 79-80, emer pres, 84); Am Soc Hemat; Am Soc Clin Nutrit (pres, 60-61). *Res:* Hematology; nutrition; refractory and aplastic anemias; megaloblastic anemias; nutritional anemias. *Mailing Add:* 6067 Col Med Bldg 231 Bethesda Ave Cincinnati OH 45267-0562

**VIMMERSTEDT, JOHN P,** SOIL SCIENCE, FORESTRY. *Current Pos:* from asst prof to assoc prof, 63-95, EMER ASSOC PROF FOREST SOILS, SCH NATURAL RESOURCES, OHIO STATE UNIV, 95- *Personal Data:* b Jamestown, NY, June 5, 31; m 53, Mary E Galt; c Carol, Margaret, William & Laura. *Educ:* State Univ NY, Syracuse, BS, 53; Yale Univ, MS, 58, DF, 65. *Prof Exp:* Res forester, Southeastern Forest Exp Sta, 55-58. *Mem:* Soil Sci Soc Am; fel Soc Am Foresters; AAAS; Sigma Xi. *Res:* Mineral nutrition of trees; reclamation of spoil banks from coal mining; soil fauna; tree ring chemistry as indicator of past chemical environment; soil forming factors and soil formation; ecosystem restoration. *Mailing Add:* Dept Forestry Ohio Agr Res & Develop Ctr Wooster OH 44691-4096. *Fax:* 216-263-3658; *E-Mail:* vimmerstedt1@osu.edu

**VINA, JUAN R,** BIOCHEMISTRY. *Current Pos:* titular prof, 89-90, PROF BIOCHEM, DEPT BIOCHEM, UNIV VALENCIA, 91- *Personal Data:* b Valencia, Spain, Feb 11, 56; m 87; c 1. *Educ:* Univ Valencia, MD, 79, PhD(biochem), 81. *Prof Exp:* Asst prof biochem, Fac Med, Valencia, Spain, 81-82; asst prof metab res, Dept Anesthesia, Hershey Med Ctr, 83 & 87-88. *Mem:* Am Physiol Soc; Biochem Soc; Nutrit Soc. *Res:* Role of the gamma-glutamyl cycle in mammalian cells. *Mailing Add:* Dept Biochem Fac Med Univ Valencia Ave Blasco Ibanez 17 Valencia 46010 Spain. *Fax:* 34-6-3864173

**VINAL, RICHARD S,** INORGANIC CHEMISTRY. *Current Pos:* RETIRED. *Personal Data:* b Worcester, Mass, May 5, 38; m 61; c 2. *Educ:* Bates Col, BS, 60; Cornell Univ, PhD(inorg chem), 65. *Prof Exp:* Sr res chemist, Eastman Kodak Co, 65-71, res assoc, 71-92. *Mem:* Am Chem Soc; Soc Photog Scientists & Engrs; Sigma Xi. *Res:* Transition metal; coordination chemistry; structural studies; photographic science; redox reactions; non-silver photographic systems development. *Mailing Add:* 350 Mt Airy Dr Rochester NY 14617-2126

**VINATIERI, JAMES EDWARD,** INTERACTIVE COMPUTER GRAPHICS. *Current Pos:* Sr res chemist, 73-81, syst specialist, 82-84, STAFF DIR, PHILLIPS PETROL CO, 84- *Personal Data:* b Yankton, SDak, June 27, 47; m 69; c 2. *Educ:* Univ SDak, BA, 69; Univ Nebr, PhD(chem), 74. *Mem:* Am Chem Soc. *Res:* Chemical and physical properties of surfactant systems for enhanced oil recovery, especially phase behavior and interfacial phenomena. *Mailing Add:* 4627 Rolling Meadows Dr Bartlesville OK 74006-5529

**VINAY, PATRICK,** RENAL PHYSIOLOGY, NEPHROLOGY. *Current Pos:* PROF MED NEPHROLOGY, UNIV MONTREAL, 75- *Personal Data:* m 68, Francine Tetrault; c Marie C, Dominique & Anne M. *Educ:* Univ Montreal, MD, 68, CSPQ, 75, PhD(renal metab), 79. *Prof Exp:* Nephrologist, res, Hotel-Dieu de Montreal, 75-85, Hosp Notre-Dame, 85; pres, Found Res, Que, 88-92. *Concurrent Pos:* Mem study sect, NIH, 85-87. *Mem:* Am Soc Nephrology; Can Soc Nephrology (pres, 89-90); Can Soc Clin Res (vpres, 94); Am Soc Renal Biochem Metab (pres, 93-); Int Soc Nephrology; Can Inst Acad Med. *Res:* Studies of the energetics of ion and solutes transport along the nephron with special emphasis on acid-base equilibrium. *Mailing Add:* 2950 Soissons Ave Montreal PQ H2S 1W2 Can. *Fax:* 514-876-5315

**VINCE, ROBERT,** MEDICINAL CHEMISTRY. *Current Pos:* from asst prof to assoc prof, 67-73, PROF MED CHEM, COL PHARM, UNIV MINN, 76- *Personal Data:* b Auburn, NY, Nov 20, 40; m 61, Maureen Ramsey; c Susan & Sharon. *Educ:* Univ Buffalo, BS, 62; State Univ NY, Buffalo, PhD(med chem), 66. *Honors & Awards:* Lunsford Richardson Grad Res Award, Richarson-Merrell Inc, 66. *Prof Exp:* Asst prof med chem, Col Pharm, Univ Miss, 66-67. *Concurrent Pos:* Res career develop award, Nat Cancer Inst, 72-76; vis scientist, Roche Inst Molecular Biol, 74-75. *Mem:* Am Chem Soc; Am Pharmaceut Asn; Am Soc Biol Chemists; Am Asn Cancer Res; Sigma Xi; Am Soc Microbiol; AAAS. *Res:* Design and synthesis of inhibitors of protein biosynthesis; nucleoside analogs as cancer chemotherapy agents; antiviral drug design. *Mailing Add:* Col Pharm Health Sci Unit F Univ Minn Minneapolis MN 55455. *Fax:* 612-624-2974; *E-Mail:* vince001@maroon.tc.umn.edu

**VINCENT, C,** INTEGRATED PEST MANAGEMENT, INSECT BEHAVIOR. *Current Pos:* RES SCIENTIST, AGR CAN, 83- *Personal Data:* b June 30, 53; m, France Labreche; c Philippe & Louis. *Educ:* Laval Univ, BSc, 78; McGill Univ, MSc, 80, PhD(entom), 83. *Honors & Awards:* Jean-Charles Magnan Prize, Order Agron Que, 89; Leon Provancher Prize, Entom Soc Que, 91. *Concurrent Pos:* Adj prof entom, McGill Univ, 86, Univ Que, Montreal, 90. *Mem:* Entom Soc Am; Entom Soc Can. *Res:* Rationalize the use of pesticides in agro-ecosystems by developing biological or physical control methods against insect pests. *Mailing Add:* Sta Res Agr Can 430 Blvd Gouin St Jean PQ J3B 3E6 Can. *Fax:* 514-346-7740; *E-Mail:* vincentc@ncccot2.agr.ca

**VINCENT, DAYTON GEORGE,** METEOROLOGY. *Current Pos:* from asst prof to assoc prof, 70-82, PROF ATMOSPHERIC SCI, DEPT GEOSCI, PURDUE UNIV, WEST LAFAYETTE, 82- *Personal Data:* b Hornell, NY, Apr 23, 36; m 59, 75, 86; c 4. *Educ:* Univ Rochester, AB, 58; St Louis Univ, dipl meteorol, 59; Univ Okla, MS, 64; Mass Inst Technol, PhD(meteorol), 70. *Prof Exp:* Weather officer meteorol, Air Weather Serv, USAF, 59-62; res asst, Univ Okla Res Inst, 64; res meteorologist, Naval Weapons Lab, Dahlgren, Va, 64-65; res assoc, Mass Inst Technol, 69-70. *Mem:* Fel Am Meteorol Soc; Sigma Xi; Royal Meterol Soc. *Res:* Impact of convection on large-scale circulations in the tropics and mid-latitudes. *Mailing Add:* Dept Earth & Atmospheric Sci Purdue Univ West Lafayette IN 47907

**VINCENT, DIETRICH H(ERMANN),** SURFACE STUDIES, GASES IN METALS & AMORPHOUS MATERIALS. *Current Pos:* from assoc prof to prof, 60-89, EMER PROF NUCLEAR ENG, UNIV MICH, ANN ARBOR, 89- *Personal Data:* b Leszno, Poland, May 11, 25; m 54, Elisabeth E Schmidt; c Martin J & Dorothea A. *Educ:* Univ Goettingen, dipl phys, 50, Dr rer nat, 56. *Prof Exp:* Sci asst, Isotope Lab, Max Planck Inst Med Res, 51-58; resident res assoc, Argonne Nat Lab, 58-60. *Concurrent Pos:* Int Atomic Energy Agency expert, Nat Tsing-Hua Univ, Hsinchu, Taiwan, Repub China, 68-69; vis prof, Taiwan Univ & Nat Taiwan Normal Univ, Taipei, Taiwan, Repub China, 69; Inter-Agency Personnel Agreement assignee, Ctr Anal Chem, Nat Bur Stand, Washington, DC, 82-83; guest researcher, Nat Inst Stand & Technol, Gaithersburg, Md, 91-92. *Mem:* Am Phys Soc; Sigma Xi. *Res:* Radiation effects in solids; Mossbauer spectroscopy; ion beam analysis; gases in metals; gases in amorphous semiconductors; cold-neutron prompt-gamma ray analysis. *Mailing Add:* 3024 Phoenix Lab Univ Mich Ann Arbor MI 48109-2100

**VINCENT, DONALD LESLIE,** ORGANIC CHEMISTRY. *Current Pos:* RETIRED. *Personal Data:* b St John, NB, Can, July 23, 21; m 49; c 3. *Educ:* Acadia Univ, BSc, 42; McGill Univ, PhD(chem), 53. *Prof Exp:* Instr chem, Acadia Univ, 46-49; asst res officer, Nat Res Coun Can, 53-60; org group leader res lab, Coal Tar Prod Div Dom Tar & Chem Co, Ltd, 60-63; group leader organic chem, Domtar Res Ctr, 63-79, sr res scientist, 79-85. *Mem:* Chem Inst Can. *Res:* Wood chemistry; lignin; carbohydrates; pulp and paper; natural products; organic synthesis. *Mailing Add:* 153 Douglas Shand Ave Pointe Claire PQ H9R 2E2 Can

**VINCENT, GERALD GLENN,** RESEARCH ADMINISTRATION, POLYMER CHEMISTRY. *Current Pos:* asst dir res, 73-74, DIR RES, CENT RES, CROWN ZELLERBACH, 74- *Personal Data:* b Winnipeg, Man, Apr 13, 34; m 56; c 4. *Educ:* Univ Man, BS, 58, MS, 60, PhD(phys chem), 63. *Prof Exp:* Res chemist adhesion, Dow Chem Co, 63-65, proj mgr adhesives, 65-67; sect leader resins, DeSoto Inc, Des Plaines, 67-69, tech mgr aerospace, 69-72, mgr resin res, 72-73. *Mem:* Am Chem Soc; Sigma Xi; Tech Asn Pulp & Paper Indust; Indust Res Inst. *Res:* Adhesion chemistry. *Mailing Add:* 35005 Classic Dr Memphis TN 38125

**VINCENT, HAROLD ARTHUR,** ANALYTICAL CHEMISTRY. *Current Pos:* CHEMIST, US ENVIRON PROTECTION AGENCY, LAS VEGAS, 87- *Personal Data:* b Lake City, Iowa, Jan 19, 30; m 57, Ida M Bingham; c Craig & Pamela. *Educ:* Univ Iowa, BS, 53; Univ Nev, MS, 60; Univ Ariz, PhD(chem), 64. *Prof Exp:* Chemist, Mining Anal Lab, Univ Nev, Reno, 56-68; chief chemist, Anaconda Co, 68-77, dir, Geol Labs, 77-81, mgr geol res, 81-84; consult, 85-86. *Mem:* Am Chem Soc; Soc Appl Spectros. *Res:* Electroanalytical chemistry; fast neutron activation analysis; flame emission and absorption spectroscopy; x-ray emission spectroscopy; thermal methods of analysis. *Mailing Add:* 9149 E Chirco Pl Tucson AZ 85710-3130. *Fax:* 702-798-2107

**VINCENT, JAMES SIDNEY,** PHYSICAL CHEMISTRY. *Current Pos:* ASSOC PROF CHEM, UNIV MD, BALTIMORE COUNTY, 71- *Personal Data:* b Redlands, Calif, Sept 19, 35; m 69; c 2. *Educ:* Univ Redlands, BS, 57; Harvard Univ, PhD(chem), 63. *Prof Exp:* Fel, Harvard Univ, 63-64 & Calif Inst Technol, 64-65; asst prof chem, Univ Calif, Davis, 65-71. *Mem:* Am Phys Soc; Soc Appl Spectroscopists. *Res:* Raman and infrared spectroscopic investigations of proteins and model membrane systems. *Mailing Add:* Dept Chem Univ Md Baltimore Co Catonsville MD 21228-5329

**VINCENT, JERRY WILLIAM,** PALEONTOLOGY, PALEOECOLOGY. *Current Pos:* CONSULT. *Personal Data:* b Chicago, Ill, June 24, 35; m 59; c 3. *Educ:* Univ Maine, Orono, BA, 58; Tex A&M Univ, MEd, 66, PhD(geol), 71. *Prof Exp:* Teacher geol & biol, N Yarmouth Acad, 58-61; teacher high sch, Maine, 61-67; assoc prof, Stephen F Austin State Univ, 69-80, prof geol, 80- *Concurrent Pos:* Consult. *Mem:* Soc Econ Paleont & Mineral; Nat Asn Geol Teachers. *Res:* Paleoecology of carbonate rocks, numerical taxonomy of various fossil taxa; biostratigraphy of lower Cretaceous rocks of Texas; invertebrate paleontology; earth science education in elementary and secondary schools. *Mailing Add:* RFD 2 Box 906D Bethel ME 04217

**VINCENT, LEONARD STUART,** ARANEOLOGY. *Current Pos:* PROF BIOL, FULLERTON COL, 87- *Personal Data:* b Cleveland, Ohio, July 27, 47; m, Beth Crawford. *Educ:* Calif State Univ, Northridge, BA, 70; Univ Calif, Davis, MS, 72; Univ Calif, Berkeley, PhD(entom), 80. *Prof Exp:* Lectr biol & arachnol, Univ Calif, Berkeley, 80-81; asst prof biol, Ga Southern Univ, 81-87. *Mem:* Sigma Xi; Am Arachnol Soc; Brit Arachnol Soc; Entom Soc Am. *Res:* Ecology and natural history of spiders. *Mailing Add:* Div Biol Sci Fullerton Col 321 E Chapman Ave Fullerton CA 92632-2011

**VINCENT, LLOYD DREXELL,** nuclear physics; deceased, see previous edition for last biography

**VINCENT, MONROE MORTIMER,** CELL BIOLOGY, IMMUNOBIOLOGY & VIROLOGY. *Current Pos:* CONSULT, 74-; SR RES ASSOC, DEPT PEDIAT, SCH MED, UNIFORMED SERV UNIV HEALTH SCI, BETHESDA, MD, 78- *Personal Data:* b Cleveland, Ohio, July 28, 12; m 41; c 1. *Educ:* Adelbert Col, Western Res Univ, BA, 34; Edinburgh Univ, BA, 35. *Prof Exp:* Res asst parasitol, Univ Chicago, 36-41; parasitologist, US Army, Maj, SNC, Cmndg Officer, 15th Malaria Surv Unit, 42-46, vpres, North-Strong Corp, 48-50; vpres, Microbiol Assocs, 50-74. *Concurrent Pos:* Assoc ed, In Vitro, 70-79; mem bd dir, Am Found Biol Res, 74-82; exec ed, Tissue Cult manual, 74-79; exec ed, Index Tissue Cult, 71-80. *Mem:* Tissue Cult Asn; Soc Cryobiol (treas, 73-74); Am Soc Cell Biol; Am Soc Trop Med; NY Acad Sci; Am Asn Tissue Banks. *Res:* Cell tissue and organ culture, virology, cell-mediated immunity, cryobiology. *Mailing Add:* 3905 Jones Bridge Rd Chevy Chase MD 20815-6721

**VINCENT, MURIEL C,** PHARMACY, PHARMACEUTICAL CHEMISTRY. *Current Pos:* from asst prof to assoc prof, NDak State Univ, 56-58, chmn dept, 58-74, asst dean, Col Pharm, 65-82, PROF PHARM PRACT, COL PHARM, NDAK STATE UNIV, 58- *Personal Data:* b Spokane, Wash, Sept 8, 22. *Educ:* Ore State Col, BS, 44; Univ Wash, MS, 51,

PhD, 55. *Prof Exp:* Instr pharm, Univ Wash, 53-54 & Ore State Col, 54-56. *Concurrent Pos:* Consult, Vet Admin Hosp, 60-74. *Mem:* AAAS; Am Chem Soc; Am Pharmaceut Asn; Acad Pharm Sci. *Res:* Application of ion exchange resins and chromatography to the analysis of pharmaceutical products; drug absorption. *Mailing Add:* 515 30th Ave N Apt 13 Fargo ND 58102-1546

**VINCENT, PHILLIP G,** BIOCHEMISTRY, MICROBIOLOGY. *Current Pos:* res phytopathologist, Agr Environ Inst, USDA, 67-68, res microbiologist, 68-78, res plant physiologist, 78-85, PROJ LEADER & SR SCIENTIST, AGR ENVIRON INST, USDA, 85- *Personal Data:* b East Machias, Maine, July 18, 41; m 72; c 4. *Educ:* Univ Md, BS, 64, PhD(fungus physiol), 67. *Prof Exp:* Res asst bot, Univ Md, 64, res fel fungus physiol & biochem, 65-67. *Concurrent Pos:* Consult, UN Div Narcotics, secy, working group on Papaver bracteatum, UN Secretariat; chmn, peer rev comt, Nat Inst Drug Abuse; peer reviewer, drug abuse biomed res rev comt, Alcohol, Drug Abuse, Ment Health & Human Serv, HEW; mem, plant derived narcotics comt, Weed Sci Soc Am. *Mem:* AAAS; Am Soc Microbiol; Am Phytopath Soc; Scand Soc Plant Physiol; Sigma Xi; NY Acad Sci; Am Inst Chemists; Am Chem Soc; Am Inst Biol Sci. *Res:* Fungus physiology and biochemistry; mechanism of action of toxicants; phytopathology; plant physiology; biochemical characteristics and mechanisms of quality deterioration of meat; narcotic plant research, including marijuana, opium, poppy and cocaine. *Mailing Add:* FDA 1451 Rockville Pike Rm 2040A Rockville MD 20852

**VINCENT, STEVEN ROBERT,** NEUROSCIENCES. *Current Pos:* fel physiol, 82-83, from asst prof to assoc prof psychiat, 83-93, PROF PSYCHIAT, UNIV BC, 93- *Personal Data:* b New Westminster, BC, Oct 12, 54; c 1. *Educ:* Carleton Univ, BSc, 76; Univ BC, PhD(interdisciplinary), 80. *Honors & Awards:* Killam Res Prize. *Prof Exp:* Asst histol, Karolinska Inst, 80-82. *Concurrent Pos:* Scholar, Med Res Coun Can, 83-88, scientist, 88-93, sr scientist, 95-; prof, Acad Sci, France, 96. *Mem:* Soc Neurosci; Can Asn Neurosci. *Res:* Biochemical and neuroanatomical organization of the mammalian brain; localization and function of neurotransmitters, their receptors and second messengers and involvement of these systems in human neuro-degenerative disease. *Mailing Add:* Dept Psychiat Div Neurol Sci Univ BC 2194 Health Sci Mall Vancouver BC V6T 1W5 Can

**VINCENT, THOMAS LANGE,** AEROSPACE ENGINEERING. *Current Pos:* from asst prof to assoc prof, 63-68, PROF AEROSPACE & MECH ENG, UNIV ARIZ, 68- *Personal Data:* b Portland, Ore, Sept 16, 35; c 2. *Educ:* Ore State Univ, BS, 58, MS, 60; Univ Ariz, PhD(aerospace eng), 63. *Prof Exp:* Res engr, Boeing Airplane Co, Wash, 59-60. *Concurrent Pos:* Guest prof, Tech Univ Munich, 67; NSF sci fac fel, Univ Calif, Berkeley, 69-70; guest lectr, Inst Mech & Appl Mach, Univ Genoa, 70; recipient, US-Australia Coop Sci Prog Award, NSF, 76-77, 83-84, 85 & 89; Hill vis prof, Univ Minn, 90. *Mem:* Am Inst Aeronaut & Astronaut. *Res:* Optimal control and game theory with applications in control design, management programs for dynamical systems and evolution and adaption of biological systems. *Mailing Add:* Dept Aerospace & Mech Eng Univ Ariz Tucson AZ 85721. *Fax:* 520-621-8191; *E-Mail:* vincent@u.arizona.edu

**VINCENT, WALTER SAMPSON,** bacterial adhesion, for more information see previous edition

**VINCENTI, WALTER G(UIDO),** HISTORY OF TECHNOLOGY, GAS DYNAMICS. *Current Pos:* prof, 57-83, EMER PROF AERONAUT ENG, STANFORD UNIV, 83- *Personal Data:* b Baltimore, Md, Apr 20, 17; m 47, Joyce Weaver; c Margaret A (Brown) & Marc G. *Educ:* Stanford Univ, AB, 38. *Honors & Awards:* Rockefeller Pub Serv Award, 56; Usher Prize, 84. *Prof Exp:* Aeronaut res scientist, Ames Aeronaut Lab, Nat Adv Comt Aeronaut, Calif, 40-57. *Concurrent Pos:* Lectr, Stanford Univ, 46-47 & 52-54; Guggenheim fel, 63; co-ed, Ann Rev Fluid Mech, 70-77. *Mem:* Nat Acad Eng; Newcomen Soc; Soc Hist Technol; corresp mem Int Acad Astronaut; Hist Sci Soc; fel Am Inst Aeronaut & Astronaut. *Res:* History and philosophy of technology, especially regarding nature and sources of engineering knowledge. *Mailing Add:* Dept Aeronaut & Astronaut Stanford Univ Stanford CA 94305-4035

**VINCENZ, STANISLAW ALEKSANDER,** EXPLORATION GEOPHYSICS, GEOMAGNETISM & PALEOMAGNETISM. *Current Pos:* assoc prof geophys & geophys eng, 61-67, prof, 67-85, EMER PROF GEOPHYS, ST LOUIS UNIV, 85- *Personal Data:* b Oskrzesince, Poland, Feb 4, 15; m 49; c 1. *Educ:* Univ London, ARCS & BSc, 37, DIC, 39, PhD(geophys), 52. *Prof Exp:* Demonstr geophys, Imp Col, London, 48-49, asst lectr, 49-51, res asst, 51-53; geophysicist & head geophys div, Jamaica Indust Develop, Corp, Jamaica, WI, 53-61. *Concurrent Pos:* NSF prin investr grants, St Louis Univ, 62-67, 67-68, 69-70, 71-73 & 74-85 & US Geol Surv, 73-76. *Mem:* Soc Explor Geophys; Am Geophys Union; fel Royal Astron Soc; Europ Asn Explor Geophys; Sigma Xi. *Res:* Exploration geophysics; rock magnetism and paleomagnetism; geomagnetism; paleomagnetic investigations of Paleozoic sediments of Spitsbergen and of Central North America; interpretation of aeromagnetic anomalies of Northern Mississippi Embayment, specifically New Madrid earthquake zone. *Mailing Add:* 805 Pinetree Lane St Louis MO 63119

**VINCENZI, FRANK FOSTER,** PHARMACOLOGY. *Current Pos:* from asst prof to assoc prof, 67-80, PROF PHARMACOL, SCH MED, UNIV WASH, 80-, VCHMN DEPT, 77- *Personal Data:* b Seattle, Wash, Mar 14, 38; m 60; c 3. *Educ:* Univ Wash, BS, 60, MS, 62, PhD(pharmacol), 65. *Prof Exp:* NSF fel, Berne, 65-67. *Mem:* AAAS; NY Acad Sci; Am Soc Pharmacol & Exp Therapeut; Biophys Soc; Cardiac Muscle Soc; Oxygen Soc. *Res:* Autonomic transmitters; mechanisms of cardioactive drugs; membrane transport; red blood cell physiology and pathology; calmodulin and anti-calmodulin drugs; microcomputers in research and teaching; free radicals and health and disease. *Mailing Add:* Dept Pharmacol Univ Wash Seattle WA 98195. *Fax:* 206-685-3822; *E-Mail:* vincenzi@u.washington.edu

**VINCETT, PAUL STAMFORD,** THIN FILM PHYSICS, PHOTOGRAPHIC SCIENCE. *Current Pos:* PRES, FAIR COPY SERV INC, XEROX CO, 91- *Personal Data:* b Southend, Eng, Jan 23, 44; m 65, Marion R Barrett; c Giselle, Matthew & Peter. *Educ:* Univ Cambridge, BA, 65, PhD(physics), 68. *Honors & Awards:* Kosar Mem Award, Soc Photog Scientists Engrs, 87- *Prof Exp:* Fel physics, Simon Fraser Univ, 68-70; scientist, Corp Lab, ICI Ltd, Runcorn, Eng, 70-74; scientist physics, Xerox Res Ctr Can, Xerox Can Inc, 74-80, mgr thin film sci & memory, 80-88, mgr, Advan Technol, 88-91. *Concurrent Pos:* Tutor, Open Univ, NW Region, Manchester, Eng, 71-74; mem ed bd, Thin Solid Films, 80-85; chmn, Div Appl Physics, Can Asn Physicists, 89-90; dir, Corp Members, 90-93; vpres, Natural Sci & Eng Res Coun Can, 93-95, pres, 95-96, group chair physics, 96- *Mem:* Can Asn Physicists (vpres, 93-95, pres, 95-96); Soc Photog Scientists & Engrs. *Res:* Solid state and chemical physics, particularly thin film physics and conduction processes in insulating solids and liquids; novel electrophotographic and photographic processes; high density information recording; business development of new technologies; general management. *Mailing Add:* RR 5 Georgetown ON L7G 4S8 Can. *Fax:* 905-873-2943; *E-Mail:* paul_vincett@torho.xc.xerox.com

**VINCIGUERRA, MICHAEL JOSEPH,** PHYSICAL CHEMISTRY. *Current Pos:* From asst prof to assoc prof chem, State Univ NY, 70-78, asst vpres acad affairs, 80-83, vpres, 83-87, PROF CHEM, AGR & TECH COL, STATE UNIV NY, FARMINGDALE, 78-, CHMN, DIV ARTS & SCI, 76-, PROVOST, 87- *Personal Data:* b New York, NY, Mar 19, 45; m 70; c 1. *Educ:* Iona Col, BS, 66; Adelphi Univ, MS, 69, PhD(phys chem), 71. *Concurrent Pos:* Res asst, Adelphi Univ, 71-72; adj asst prof, St John's Univ, NY, 72; res consult, Unichem Res Assoc, 75- *Mem:* Am Chem Soc; NY Acad Sci; Am Asn Higher Educ; AAAS. *Res:* Physical properties of bio-polymers; light scattering by biological gels; nuclear magnetic relaxation of polymer solutions. *Mailing Add:* 930 Park Ave Huntington NY 11743-4526. *Fax:* 516-420-2753; *E-Mail:* vincigmj

**VINCOW, GERSHON,** PHYSICAL CHEMISTRY. *Current Pos:* chmn, Dept Chem, Syracuse Univ, 71-77, vpres res & grad affairs, 77-78, actg dean, 79-80, dean, Col Arts & Sci, 80-85, VCHANCELLOR ACAD AFFAIRS, SYRACUSE UNIV, 85- *Personal Data:* b New York, NY, Feb 27, 35; m 64; c 2. *Educ:* Columbia Univ, AB, 56, MA, 57, PhD(chem), 59. *Prof Exp:* Fel, Hebrew Univ, Israel, 60; NSF fel, Calif Inst Technol, 60-61; from asst prof to prof chem, Univ Wash, 61-71. *Concurrent Pos:* Sloan Found res fel, 64-67; NSF fel, Harvard Univ, 70-71. *Mem:* Am Chem Soc; Am Phys Soc; fel AAAS. *Res:* Electron paramagnetic resonance spectroscopy. *Mailing Add:* Syracuse Univ 304 Admin Bldg Syracuse NY 13244

**VINE, JAMES DAVID,** GEOCHEMISTRY. *Current Pos:* RETIRED. *Personal Data:* b Detroit, Mich, Dec 14, 21; m 48, Blanche L Wise; c Nancy E (Kellogg) & Bruce E. *Educ:* Univ Mich, BS, 43. *Prof Exp:* Geologist, US Geol Surv, 46-80; consult, 80-86. *Concurrent Pos:* Mem, Nat Battery Adv Comt. *Res:* Exploration for lithium brines and clays. *Mailing Add:* 21736 Panorama Dr Golden CO 80401

**VINES, DARRELL LEE,** ELECTRICAL ENGINEERING. *Current Pos:* instr elec eng, Tex Tech Univ, 62-63, instr, 63-66, assoc prof, 66-76, assoc dean engr, 84-90, PROF ELEC ENG & COMPUT SCI, TEX TECH UNIV, 76- *Personal Data:* b Crane, Tex; c 3. *Educ:* McMurry Col, BA, 59; Tex Tech Univ, BS, 59, MS, 60; Tex A&M Univ, PhD(elec eng), 67. *Honors & Awards:* Meritorious Serv, Inst Elec & Electronics Engrs Educ Soc, 90. *Prof Exp:* Engr, Tex Instruments, 60-62. *Concurrent Pos:* Distinguished vis prof, USAF Acad, 81-82; instr skill dynamics, IBM, 92-93. *Mem:* Inst Elec & Electronics Engrs; Am Soc Eng Educ. *Res:* Computer applications and logic circuit design; instrumentation and measurement. *Mailing Add:* Dept Elec Eng & Comput Sci Tex Tech Univ Lubbock TX 79409-3102. *E-Mail:* vines@coe2.coe.ttu.edu

**VINES, HERBERT MAX,** PLANT PHYSIOLOGY. *Current Pos:* RETIRED. *Personal Data:* b Ala, Feb 4, 18; m 42; c 2. *Educ:* Ala Polytech Inst, BS, 40; Univ Calif, MS, 49; Univ Calif, Los Angeles, PhD, 59. *Prof Exp:* Specialist postharvest physiol, Univ Calif, 49-53; tech rep nutrit, Shell Chem Co, 53-56; technician plant biochem, Univ Calif, 57-59, fel, 59-60; assoc biochemist, Citrus Exp Sta, Univ Fla, 61-67; prof plant physiol, Univ Ga, 67-88. *Mem:* Am Soc Hort Sci; Am Soc Plant Physiol. *Res:* Post-harvest physiology; plant metabolism, especially metabolic blocks in electron transport system. *Mailing Add:* 494 W Cloverhurst Ave Athens GA 30606

**VINET, LUC,** PHYSICS. *Current Pos:* from asst prof to assoc prof, 82-92, PROF PHYSICS, UNIV MONTREAL, 92- *Personal Data:* b Montreal, Que, Apr 16, 53; m 89, Letitia Muresan; c Jean-Francois & Laurent. *Educ:* Univ Montreal, BSc, 73, MSc, 74, PhD, 80. *Hon Degrees:* Dr, Univ P&M Curie, Paris, 79. *Prof Exp:* Res assoc, Mass Inst Technol, 80-82. *Concurrent Pos:* Invited prof, Univ Cath de Louvain, 80-81; res fel, Natural Sci & Eng Res Coun Can, 82-92; vis prof, Univ Calif, Los Angeles, 89-90; dir, Ctr Res Math, Montreal, 93- *Mem:* Am Phys Soc; Am Math Soc; Soc Indust & Applied Math; Can Asn Physics; Can Math Soc. *Res:* Contributions in theoretical physics and mathematics; symmetry studies of difference equations; algebraic interpretation of q-special functions using quantum groups; applications of

Berry potentials in the nuclear collective model; identification of Lie superalgebras as dynamical algebras in quantum mechanics; development of dimensional reduction in Yang Mills theories. *Mailing Add:* Math Res Ctr Univ Montreal 4992 12345 Pl St-Germain Montreal PQ H4J 2A8 Can

**VINEYARD, BILLY DALE,** BIOORGANIC & PEPTIDE CHEMISTRY. *Current Pos:* sr res chemist, Org Div, Monsanto Co, 60-64, res specialist, 64-68, sci fel, 68-76, sr fel, 76-86, DISTINGUISHED FEL, MONSANTO CO, 86- *Personal Data:* b Clarkton, Mo, Sept 7, 31; m 56; c 1. *Educ:* Southeast Mo State Col, BS, 53; Univ Mo, PhD(org chem), 59. *Prof Exp:* Res chemist, Celanese Corp, 59-60. *Mem:* Am Chem Soc; AAAS. *Res:* Catalytic homogeneous asymmetric hydrogenation; food, fine and feed chemicals. *Mailing Add:* 754 Ambois Dr St Louis MO 63141-7302

**VINGIELLO, FRANK ANTHONY,** CHEMISTRY. *Current Pos:* PROF ORG CHEM, NORTHEAST LA UNIV, 68- *Personal Data:* b New York, NY, Aug 20, 21; m 42; c 3. *Educ:* Polytech Inst Brooklyn, BS, 42; Duke Univ, PhD(org chem), 47. *Honors & Awards:* J Shelton Horsley Award, Va Acad Sci, 66. *Prof Exp:* Lab instr org chem, Polytech Inst Brooklyn, 43-44; lab instr, Duke Univ, 44-47; instr, Univ Pittsburgh, 47; res assoc, Northwestern Univ, 47-48; from asst prof to assoc prof chem, Va Polytech Inst & State Univ, 48-57, prof org chem, 57-68. *Concurrent Pos:* Chemist, WVa Ord Works, 42-43; consult chem indust. *Mem:* Am Chem Soc; NY Acad Sci. *Res:* Organic synthesis in steroids and aromatic molecules; mechanisms of organic reactions; cyclization of o-benzylphenones; synthesis of aromatic hydrocarbons, research in air pollution. *Mailing Add:* 3712 Lafayette St Northeast La Univ 700 University Ave Monroe LA 71203

**VINH, NGUYEN XUAN,** ANALYSIS & FUNCTIONAL ANALYSIS. *Current Pos:* assoc prof, 68-72, PROF AEROSPACE ENG, UNIV MICH, ANN ARBOR, 72- *Personal Data:* b Yenbay, Viet Nam, Jan 3, 30; m 55, Joan Cung; c Alphonse, Phuong, Phoenix & John. *Educ:* Air Inst, France, BS, 53; Univ Marseille, MS, 54; Univ Colo, MS, 63, PhD(aerospace), 65; Univ Paris, DSc(math), 72. *Honors & Awards:* Mech & Control Flight Award, Am Inst Aeronaut & Astronaut, 94; Excellence 2000 Award, US Pan Asian Am Chamber Com, 96. *Prof Exp:* Asst prof aerospace eng, Univ Colo, 65-68. *Concurrent Pos:* Vis lectr, Univ Calif, Berkeley, 67; vis prof ecol nat sup aero, France, 74; assoc ed, Acta Astronautica, 79-; chair prof, Nat Tsing Hua Univ, Taiwan, 82. *Mem:* Math Asn Am; Int Acad Astronaut; Fr Nat Acad Air & Space. *Res:* Ordinary differential equations; astrodynamics and optimization of space flight trajectories; theory of non linear oscillations. *Mailing Add:* Dept Aerospace Eng Univ Mich Ann Arbor MI 48109-2118

**VINICK, FREDRIC JAMES,** SYNTHETIC ORGANIC CHEMISTRY. *Current Pos:* ASST DIR MED CHEM, CENT RES, PFIZER, INC, 78- *Personal Data:* b Amsterdam, NY, June 18, 47; m 70; c 3. *Educ:* Williams Col, BA, 69; Yale Univ, PhD(chem), 73. *Prof Exp:* NIH res fel, Columbia Univ, 73-75; sr scientist org chem, Pharmaceut Div, Ciba-Geigy Corp, 75-78. *Concurrent Pos:* NSF fel. *Mem:* Am Chem Soc; NY Acad Sci. *Res:* Synthesis of biologically and/or medicinally important compounds; discovery of new drug leads. *Mailing Add:* Genzyme Corp 1 Kendall Sq Cambridge MA 02139

**VINICOR, FRANK,** DIABETICS RESEARCH. *Current Pos:* DIR, DIV DIABETICS TRANSLATION, NAT CTR CHRONIC DIS PREV & HEALTH PROM, CTR DIS CONTROL & PREV, 89-; DIR, WHO COLLAB CTR DIABETES MELLITUS, 89- *Personal Data:* b Potsdam, NY, Mar 21, 41; c Rachel, Sarah & Kirsten. *Educ:* Yale Univ, BA, 63; Washington Univ, MD, 67; Univ NC, MPH, 93; Am Bd Internal Med, cert, 72, cert endocrinol/metab, 74. *Honors & Awards:* Charles H Best Award, Am Diabetes Asn, 91. *Prof Exp:* Chief, Dept Hosp Clins, Ireland Army Hosp, Ft Knox, Ky, 69-71; chief resident med, Ind Univ Med Ctr, 72-73, fel, Endocrinol Sect, 73-75, asst prof med, 74-78, co-dir, Diabetes Res & Training Ctr, 79-89. *Concurrent Pos:* Dir, Diabetes Clin, Wishard Mem Hosp, Indianapolis, 76-89; vis assoc prof, Dept Med, Univ NC Sch Med, 86-87; clin assoc, Ind Univ Med Ctr, 88-; clin assoc prof med, Emory Univ Sch Med, 90- *Mem:* AMA; fel Am Col Physicians; Am Fedn Clin Res; Am Diabetes Asn (vpres, 93-94, pres-elect, 94, pres, 95); Am Pub Health Asn; Endocrine Soc. *Mailing Add:* Ctr Dis Control 4770 Buford Hwy NE (K-10) Atlanta GA 30341-3724

**VINING, LEO CHARLES,** BIO-ORGANIC CHEMISTRY, MICROBIOLOGY. *Current Pos:* prof biol, 71-86, Killam Prof, 86-90, prof, 90-92, EMER PROF BIOL, DALHOUSIE UNIV, 92- *Personal Data:* b Whangarei, NZ, Mar 28, 25; m 53, 89; c 4. *Educ:* Univ NZ, BSc, 48, MSc, 49; Cambridge Univ, PhD, 51. *Honors & Awards:* Harrison Prize, Royal Soc Can, 72; Can Soc Microbiologists Award, 76; Merck, Sharpe & Dohme lectr, 65; John Labatt Award, 85; Charles Thom Award, Soc Indust Microbiol, 85. *Prof Exp:* Scholar, Univ Kiel, Ger, 51-53; fel, Rutgers Univ, 53-54, instr, Inst Microbiol, 54-55; asst res off, Prairie Regional Lab, Nat Res Coun Can, 55-58, assoc res off, 58-62, sr res off, Atlantic Regional Lab, 62-69, prin res off, 69-71. *Concurrent Pos:* Vis scientist, Mass Inst Technol, 77-78 & Univ Alta, 84-85. *Mem:* Fel Royal Soc Chem; fel Can Inst Chem; Can Soc Microbiol; Am Soc Microbiol; fel Royal Soc Can; Soc Gen Microbiol. *Res:* Chemistry of antibiotics; fungal metabolites; biosynthesis of natural products; control of secondary metabolism; evolution of secondary metabolism. *Mailing Add:* Dept Biol Dalhousie Univ Halifax NS B3H 4J1 Can. *Fax:* 902-494-3736

**VINOGRADE, BERNARD,** MATHEMATICS. *Current Pos:* RETIRED. *Personal Data:* b Chicago, Ill, May 7, 15; m 42; c 4. *Educ:* City Col, BS, 37; Univ Mich, MA, 40, PhD(math), 42. *Prof Exp:* Instr math, Univ Wis, 42-44 & Tulane Univ, 44-45; staff mem, Radiation Lab, Mass Inst Technol, 45; from

asst prof to assoc prof math, Iowa State Univ, 45-55, prof, 55-74, distinguished prof sci & humanities, 74-80, chmn dept, 61-64, actg head, 60. *Concurrent Pos:* Opers analyst, Standby Unit, USAF, 50-; vis prof, San Diego State Col, 59-60 & City Col New York, 64-65. *Mem:* Am Math Soc; Math Asn Am. *Res:* Abstract and linear algebra; field theory; forest resouce management. *Mailing Add:* PO Box 1089 Santa Clara UT 84765-1089

**VINOGRADOFF, ANNA PATRICIA,** PHARMACEUTICAL CHEMISTRY & AGRICULTURAL PRODUCTS CHEMISTRY. *Personal Data:* b Essex, Eng; div. *Educ:* Univ Calif, Los Angeles, BSc, 76, PhD(chem), 81. *Prof Exp:* Teaching asst org chem, Univ Calif, Los Angeles, 76-77, res assoc, 78-80; sr res chemist, Dow Chem USA, 80-84, proj leader, 84-92. *Mem:* Am Chem Soc. *Res:* Organic synthesis with emphasis on molecules of biological interest and natural products. *Mailing Add:* 478 Merritt Ave Apt 4 Oakland CA 94610-5157

**VINOGRADOV, SERGE,** BIOCHEMISTRY. *Current Pos:* asst prof biochem, 66-68, assoc prof, 68-71, PROF BIOCHEM & ADJ ASSOC PROF BIOL, WAYNE STATE UNIV, 71- *Personal Data:* b Beirut, Lebanon, Aug 27, 33; US citizen; c 2. *Educ:* Am Univ Beirut, BA, 52, MA, 54; Ill Inst Technol, PhD(phys chem), 59. *Prof Exp:* Fel, Univ Alta, 59-62; res assoc, Yale Univ, 62-66. *Mem:* Am Soc Biol Chem; The Chem Soc; Am Chem Soc; Biophys Soc. *Mailing Add:* Dept Biochem Wayne State Univ 540 E Canfield Ave Detroit MI 48201

**VINOKUR, MARCEL,** FLUID MECHANICS, NUMERICAL ANALYSIS. *Current Pos:* RETIRED. *Personal Data:* b Moravska-Ostrava, Czech, Feb 16, 29; US citizen; m 54, 63, Kathryn B Clark; c David J. *Educ:* Cornell Univ, BEngPhys, 51; Princeton Univ, PhD(aeronaut eng), 57. *Prof Exp:* Assoc res scientist, Lockheed Palo Alto Res Lab, 55-59, res scientist, Lockheed Missiles & Space Co, Calif, 59-61, staff scientist, 61-71; lectr mech, Univ Santa Clara, 65-75, res assoc mech eng, 75-84; res specialist, Sterling Software, 84-95. *Concurrent Pos:* Ames assoc, Ames Res Ctr, NASA, 95- *Mem:* Assoc fel Am Inst Aeronaut & Astronaut. *Res:* Inviscid flow; radiation gas dynamics; non-equilibrium flow; numerical methods; computational fluid dynamics; computational electromagnetics. *Mailing Add:* 919 Channing Ave Palo Alto CA 94301

**VINORES, STANLEY ANTHONY,** OPHTHALMOLOGY, DEVELOPMENTAL NEURO-ONCOLOGY. *Current Pos:* asst prof, 91-92, ASSOC PROF OPHTHAL, SCH MED, JOHNS HOPKINS UNIV, 92- *Personal Data:* b Pottsville, Pa, July 7, 50; m 77, Ann L Musgrove; c 4. *Educ:* Pa State Univ, BS, 72; Univ Tex, PhD(zool), 76. *Prof Exp:* Teaching asst biol & zool, Univ Tex, 72-74, trainee carcinogenesis & genetics, 74-76; fel, Ohio State Univ, 77-78; staff fel, NIH, 78-81; res assoc, Inst Cancer Res, 81-82; res asst prof, Med Sch, Univ Va, 82-91. *Mem:* Asn Res Vision & Ophthal; NY Acad Sci; Soc Neurosci; Am Soc Invest Path; Int Soc Eye Res; Am Diabetes Asn; Histochem Soc. *Res:* Immunocytochemistry and electron microscopy of diabetic retina and nervous system tumors; blood-retinal barrier; growth factors. *Mailing Add:* Dept Ophthal Maumenee 825 Johns Hopkins Hosp 600 N Wolfe St Baltimore MD 21287-9289. *Fax:* 410-550-5382

**VINSON, DAVID BERWICK,** PSYCHOPHYSIOLOGY. *Current Pos:* PRES, ASSESSMENT SYSTS INC, 67-, PRES, FACTOR, INC, 86- *Personal Data:* b Houston, Tex, Oct 7, 17; m 40, H Patricia Freiday; c David B III (deceased) & H Catharine. *Educ:* Univ Calif, Los Angeles, AB, 41; Univ London, PhD, 52. *Honors & Awards:* Lab named in honor, David B Vinson Lab, Psychol Res, Univ Tex, El Paso. *Prof Exp:* Dir, Tex Acad Advan Life Sci, 60-87, pres, Microset Inc, 78-87. *Concurrent Pos:* Consult, Life Sci, 54- *Mem:* Am Psychol Asn; Inst Elec & Electronics Engrs; Soc Biol Psychiat; Sigma Xi. *Res:* Man-machine systems; neuropsychology. *Mailing Add:* 161 Schattenbaum Fredericksburg TX 78624-9137. *Fax:* 210-997-8762

**VINSON, JAMES S,** PHYSICS. *Current Pos:* DEAN COL ARTS & SCI, UNIV HARTFORD, 78- *Personal Data:* b Chambersburg, Pa, May 17, 41; m 67. *Educ:* Gettysburg Col, BA, 63; Univ Va, MS, 65, PhD(physics), 67. *Prof Exp:* Res asst low temperature physics, Univ Va, 64-67; asst prof physics, MacMurray Col, 69-71; assoc prof, Univ NC, Asheville, 71-75, chmn dept, 71-78, dir comput ctr, 74-78, prof physics, 75-78. *Mem:* AAAS; Am Phys Soc; Am Asn Physics Teachers; Nat Sci Teachers Asn; World Future Soc; Sigma Xi. *Res:* Low temperature physics; scintillations in liquid helium; quantum mechanics; computer based instructions; future studies. *Mailing Add:* Univ Evansville 1800 Lincoln Ave Evansville IN 47722

**VINSON, JOE ALLEN,** ANALYTICAL CHEMISTRY, NUTRITION. *Current Pos:* assoc prof, 74-90, PROF CHEM, UNIV SCRANTON, 90- *Personal Data:* b Ft Smith, Ark, Nov 16, 41; m 66; c 2. *Educ:* Univ Calif, Berkeley, BS, 63; Iowa State Univ, MS, 66, PhD(org & analytical chem), 67. *Prof Exp:* Res asst, Analytical Chem Sect, Ames Lab, AEC, 66-67; asst prof chem, Shippensburg State Col, 67-68 & Washington & Jefferson Col, 68-72; mem staff, J T Baker Chem Co, 72, prod develop chemist, 72-74. *Concurrent Pos:* Res Corp Cottrell grant, 69-70; Law Enforcement Assistance Admin grant, 71-72; NSF Instruct Sci Equip grant, 75-77; Int Copper Res Asn grant, 79-82, Ben Franklin grant, 88-90; nat tour speaker, Am Chem Soc, 84-, seed grant, 88. *Mem:* Am Chem Soc; NY Acad Sci. *Res:* Clinical, drug and pollution analysis; thin layer chromatography; analysis of marijuana in biological fluids; vitamins and minerals in health and disease; antioxidants in health and disease. *Mailing Add:* Dept Chem Univ Scranton Scranton PA 18072. *Fax:* 717-941-7510; *E-Mail:* vinson@tiger.uofs.edu

**VINSON, RICHARD G,** MATHEMATICS. *Current Pos:* PROF MATH, UNIV S ALA, 69- *Personal Data:* b Prattville, Ala, Nov 18, 31; m 55; c 2. *Educ:* Huntingdon Col, BA, 54; Fla State Univ, MA, 56; Univ Ala, PhD(math), 62. *Prof Exp:* Instr math, Fla State Univ, 55-56, Univ Tenn, 56-58 & Univ Ala, 58-61; prof, Huntingdon Col, 61-69. *Concurrent Pos:* Instr state-wide educ TV network, 63-67; dir NSF two-yr col prog. *Mem:* AAAS; Am Math Soc; Math Asn Am; Am Asn Univ Professors; Nat Coun Teachers Math. *Res:* Non-Euclidean geometry; statistics; calculus. *Mailing Add:* Dept Math Univ SAla Mobile AL 36688-0002

**VINSON, S BRADLEIGH,** CHEMICAL ECOLOGY. *Current Pos:* assoc prof, 69-75, PROF ENTOM, TEX A&M UNIV, 75- *Personal Data:* b Mansfield, Ohio, Apr 8, 38; m 60, Patricia Kidner; c Stuart B & Shirleigh B. *Educ:* Ohio State Univ, BS, 61; Miss State Univ, MS, 63, PhD(entom), 65. *Honors & Awards:* Outstanding Res Award, Am Registry Prof Entomologists, 79, Ital Silvestry Award Biol Control, 86. *Prof Exp:* Res asst entom, Miss State Univ, 64-65, asst prof, 65-69. *Concurrent Pos:* Prog chmn, Entom Soc Am, 73, chmn physiol sect, 79; subj ed, Entom Sci, 84-; chmn, Imported Fire Ant Rev Comt, Environ Protection Agency, 80. *Mem:* AAAS; fel Entom Soc Am; Am Inst Biol Sci; Am Soc Zool; Am Chem Soc. *Res:* Vertebrate insecticide resistance; mechanisms of arthropod resistance; insect physiology; parasite-host and predator-host relationships; biology of social insects. *Mailing Add:* Dept Entom Tex A&M Univ College Station TX 77843. *Fax:* 409-847-8668; *E-Mail:* bvinson@acs.tamu.edu

**VINSON, WILLIAM ELLIS,** POPULATION GENETICS, DAIRY SCIENCE. *Current Pos:* asst prof dairy cattle genetics, 71-76, assoc prof, 76-82, PROF DAIRY SCI, VA POLYTECH INST & STATE UNIV, 82-, DEPT HEAD, 87- *Personal Data:* b Greensboro, NC, Apr 4, 43; m 63; c 2. *Educ:* NC State Univ, BS, 65, MS, 68; Iowa State Univ, PhD(pop genetics), 71. *Honors & Awards:* J L Lush Award, Am Dairy Sci Asn. *Mem:* Am Dairy Sci Asn; Am Genetic Asn; Am Soc Animal Sci; Biomet Soc; Sigma Xi. *Res:* Direct and correlated responses to selection; pedigree evaluation of genetic merit; inheritance of discontinuous characters; genetic evaluations from field data; computer simulation of genetic populations. *Mailing Add:* Dept Dairy Sci Va Polytech Inst & State Univ Blacksburg VA 24060

**VINSONHALER, CHARLES I,** MATHEMATICS. *Current Pos:* Asst prof, 68-76, ASSOC PROF MATH, UNIV CONN, 76- *Personal Data:* b Winfield, Kans, Mar 29, 42. *Educ:* Calif Inst Technol, BS, 64; Univ Wash, PhD(math), 68. *Mem:* Am Math Soc. *Res:* Ring theory and Abelian groups. *Mailing Add:* Dept Math Univ Conn 196 Auditorium Rd U-9 Storrs CT 06269-3009

**VINT, LARRY FRANCIS,** ANIMAL BREEDING, POULTRY BREEDING. *Current Pos:* asst dir, Res Poultry Breeding, De Kalb AgRes, 74-88, dir Vet & Tech Serv, 88-91, DIR RES POULTRY BREEDING, DE KALB POULTRY RES, 91- *Personal Data:* b Davenport, Iowa, May 12, 41; m 85; c 6. *Educ:* Iowa State Univ, BS, 63, MS, 69, PhD(animal breeding), 71. *Prof Exp:* Data processing mgr biomet, Pilch-De Kalb, De Kalb AgRes, 71-72, dir res poultry breeding, 72-73, res investr corp develop, 73-74; geneticist animal breeding, USDA, 74. *Mem:* Am Soc Animal Sci; Poultry Sci Asn; Coun Agr Sci & Technol; AAAS; World's Poultry Asn. *Res:* Genetic improvement in poultry populations; poultry management systems, growth and nutrition. *Mailing Add:* 6091 Pioneer Terr De Kalb IL 60115

**VINTERS, HARRY VALDIS,** NEUROPATHOLOGY, CLINICAL NEUROSCIENCES. *Current Pos:* ASST PROF PATH & MEM, BRAIN RES INST, MED CTR, UNIV CALIF, LOS ANGELES, 85- *Personal Data:* b Port Arthur, Ont, Can, Dec 8, 50. *Educ:* Univ Col, Univ Toronto, BSc, 72, MD, 76; FRCPS(C), 81. *Honors & Awards:* Desmond Magner Award, Nat Cancer Inst, Can, 80. *Prof Exp:* Fel neuropath, Med Ctr, Univ Calif, Los Angeles, 82-83; asst prof path & clin neurol sci, Univ Western Ont, 84-85. *Concurrent Pos:* Staff neuropathologist, Univ Hosp, London, Can, 84-85 & Med Ctr, Univ Calif, Los Angeles, 85-; prin investr, NIH First Award, Nat Inst Neurol Commun Dis & Stroke; Can Heart Found fel, 84-85; John D French Found & Wilson Found fel, 88-89. *Mem:* Can Asn Neuropathologists; Am Asn Neuropathologists; Am Soc Cell Biol; AAAS. *Res:* Micro-vascular changes in brain related to aging and Alzheimer's disease; neurologic and neuropathologic complications of AIDS; miscellaneous basic and clinical aspects of stroke and cerebro-vascular disease. *Mailing Add:* UCLA Med Ctr Path Rm 18-170 NPI Los Angeles CA 90095. *Fax:* 310-206-5178

**VINYARD, GARY LEE,** AQUATIC ECOLOGY, BEHAVIORAL ECOLOGY. *Current Pos:* asst prof, 78-84, ASSOC PROF DEPT BIOL, UNIV NEV, 84- *Personal Data:* b Harrisburg, Ill, Mar 13, 49. *Educ:* Univ Kans, BA, 71, PhD(biol), 77. *Prof Exp:* Vis asst prof, Sch Biol Sci, Okla State Univ, 76-77; asst prof, Dept Zool, Univ Mont, 77-78. *Mem:* Am Soc Limnol & Oceanog; AAAS; Ecol Soc Am; Sigma Xi; Am Fish Soc. *Res:* Predatory interactions of aquatic organisms, both fish and invertebrates; behavioral ecology of aquatic organisms. *Mailing Add:* Dept Biol 314 Univ Nev Reno NV 89557-0001

**VINYARD, WILLIAM CORWIN,** BOTANY. *Current Pos:* from asst prof to assoc prof, 58-72, PROF BOT, HUMBOLDT STATE UNIV, 72- *Personal Data:* b McArthur, Calif, Apr 30, 22; m 60. *Educ:* Chico State Col, BA, 42; Mich State Univ, MS, 51, PhD(bot), 58. *Prof Exp:* Instr bot, Univ Okla, 53-54; instr, Mich State Univ, 55-56; instr, Univ Mont, 56-57; asst prof, Univ Kans, 57-58. *Concurrent Pos:* Algological consult, Calif State Dept Water Resources, 62-64 & Klamath Basin Study, US Dept Interior, 67-68 & Nat Park Serv, 71-72, Phycol Soc Am; Int Asn Plant Taxon; Int Phycol Soc. *Mem:* Sigma Xi. *Res:* Taxonomy and ecology of freshwater algae; synopsis of the desmids of North America; algae of western North America; relation of algae to water pollution; algal food of herbivorous fishes; eipzoic algae. *Mailing Add:* Bot Biol Dept Humboldt State Univ Arcata CA 95521

**VIOLA, ALFRED,** PHYSICAL ORGANIC CHEMISTRY. *Current Pos:* from asst prof to assoc prof, 57-68, PROF CHEM, NORTHEASTERN UNIV, 68- *Personal Data:* b Vienna, Austria, July 8, 28; nat US; m 63, Joy D Winkie. *Educ:* Johns Hopkins Univ, BA, 49, MA, 50; Univ Md, PhD(chem), 55. *Prof Exp:* Asst instr chem, Johns Hopkins Univ, 49-50; teaching asst, Univ Md, 50-54; res assoc, Boston Univ, 55-57. *Concurrent Pos:* Vis prof, Univ Munich, Ger, 77, Monash Univ, Melbourne, Australia, 84 & Wellesley Col, 91-92. *Mem:* Am Chem Soc; Sigma Xi. *Res:* Preparation and properties of highly unsaturated organic compounds; thermal rearrangements; stereochemistry of transition states; pericyclic reactions of acetylenes and allenes. *Mailing Add:* Dept Chem Northeastern Univ Boston MA 02115. *Fax:* 617-373-8795

**VIOLA, JOHN THOMAS,** TECHNICAL MANAGEMENT. *Current Pos:* instr & asst prof chem, USAF Acad, 71-74, assoc prof & dir advan courses chem, 74-75, prog mgr chem, Directorate Chem Sci, Air Force Off Sci Res, 75-78, dir bus mgt, E-4 Prog Off, 78-80, prog dir, Jt Surveillance Systs, 80-82, dep space transp systs & testing, Air Force Space Div, El Segundo, Calif, 82-84, prog mgr space progs, Rockwell Int Sci Ctr, 84-92, prog mgr imaging, 92-95, SR PROG MGR ELECTRONIC DEVICES LAB, ROCKWELL INT SCI CTR, USAF, 96- *Personal Data:* b Haverhill, Mass, Mar 6, 38; m 60, Beverly M Gaunya; c Lisa M & Julie K. *Educ:* Univ NH, BS, 60; Pa State Univ, MS, 61; Mass Inst Technol, PhD(chem), 67. *Prof Exp:* USAF, 60-84, nuclear effects res officer, thermodyn, Air Force Weapons Lab, Albuquerque, NMex, 61-64, physicist, 67-71. *Res:* Infrared detectors materials and devices, development of infrared focal plane arrays, microgravity materials processing and crystal growth, mercury cadmium telluride crystal growth and characterization. *Mailing Add:* 1007 Brookview Ave Westlake Village CA 91361. *Fax:* 805-373-4719; *E-Mail:* jtviola@scimail.risc.rockwell.com

**VIOLA, RONALD EDWARD,** ENZYMOLOGY, MAGNETIC RESONANCE SPECTROSCOPY. *Current Pos:* assoc prof, 84-89, PROF BIOCHEM, UNIV AKRON, 89- *Personal Data:* b Brooklyn, NY, July 28, 46; m 71, Arleen Jung; c Kimberly & Jessica. *Educ:* Fordham Univ, BS, 67; Pa State Univ, MS, 73, PhD(biochem), 76. *Prof Exp:* Asst biochem, Univ Wis, 76-79; asst prof, Southern Ill Univ, 79-84. *Mem:* Am Chem Soc; Am Soc Biochem & Molecular Biol; Int Soc Magnetic Resonance, protein Soc. *Res:* Magnetic resonance studies of metal ion complexes; determination of enzyme mechanisms by kinetic analysis; chemical modification and site-directed mutagenesis. *Mailing Add:* Dept Chem Univ Akron 190 E Buchtel Commons Akron OH 44325-3601. *Fax:* 330-972-7370; *E-Mail:* rviola@uakron.edu

**VIOLA, VICTOR E, JR,** NUCLEAR CHEMISTRY. *Current Pos:* dir, Cyclotron Facil, 86-87, prof, 80-90, DISTINGUISHED PROF CHEM, IND UNIV, 90- *Personal Data:* b Abilene, Kans, Apr 8, 35; m 62, Nancy Weaver; c V Charles, Randall W & Gina M. *Educ:* Univ Kans, AB, 57; Univ Calif, Berkeley, PhD(nuclear chem), 61. *Honors & Awards:* Am Chem Soc Award in Nuclear Chem, 86. *Prof Exp:* Instr & res fel nuclear chem, Univ Calif, Berkeley, 61-62; NSF fel, Europ Orgn Nuclear Res, 63, Ford fel, 64; res assoc chem, Argonne Nat Lab, 64-66; from asst prof to assoc prof chem, Univ Md, College Park, 66-74, prof, 74-80. *Concurrent Pos:* Consult, Argonne Nat Lab, 66-73; vis prof, Univ Calif, Berkeley, 73-74; Guggenheim fel, 80-81; consult, Lawrence Berkeley Lab, 81-83; Lawrence Livermore Lab, 88-90, Brookhaven nat Lab, 96-; chair, Gordon Conf Nuclear Chem, 81; div assoc ed, Phys Dev Lett, 88-90. *Mem:* Fel AAAS; Am Chem Soc; fel Am Phys Soc; Sigma Xi. *Res:* Reaction mechanism studies in heavy ion and intermediate-energy collisions; nuclear equation of state and reaction dynamics; nuclear astrophysics. *Mailing Add:* Dept Chem Ind Univ Bloomington IN 47405. *Fax:* 812-855-6645; *E-Mail:* vicv@iucf.indi.ana.edu

**VIOLANTE, MICHAEL ROBERT,** COLLOID CHEMISTRY, PHYSICAL CHEMISTRY. *Current Pos:* asst prof, 74-82, ASSOC PROF RADIOL, SCH MED & DENT, UNIV ROCHESTER, 82-; VPRES RES & DEVELOP, STERILIZATION TECH SERV INC, 83- *Personal Data:* b Buffalo, NY, Mar 6, 44; div; c Monica A & Kara L. *Educ:* State Univ NY, Buffalo, BA, 66; Fla State Univ, PhD(inorg chem), 70. *Prof Exp:* Res scientist pulp & paper, Res & Develop Div, Union-Camp Corp, 70-74. *Mem:* Am Chem Soc; NY Acad Sci; AAAS. *Res:* Development and formulation of particulate drug delivery system; water insoluble drugs can be administered intravenously, orally or by any other route of administration; membrane transport phenomena; colloid and solution chemistry. *Mailing Add:* Dept Radiol Med Ctr Univ Rochester 601 Elmwood Ave Rochester NY 14642-0001. *Fax:* 716-273-1033

**VIOLET, CHARLES EARL,** SOLID STATE PHYSICS. *Current Pos:* Physicist, Lawrence Livermore Nat Lab, Univ Calif, 50-57, test group dir, Oper Plumbbob, 57-58, dep test mgr, Oper Hardtack, 58-59, test div leader, 59-61, physicist, 61-94, TECH DIR, RAINER PROJ, LAWRENCE LIVERMORE NAT LAB, UNIV CALIF, 94- *Personal Data:* b Des Moines, Iowa, May 1, 24; m 51, Eileen Lindquist; c Mark, David, Deborah, Jeffrey & Richard. *Educ:* Univ Chicago, SB, 48; Univ Calif, AB, 49, PhD(physics), 53. *Concurrent Pos:* Prof physics, Univ Calif, 54 & Howard Univ, 70. *Mem:* Am Phys Soc; fel Am Phys Soc. *Res:* Mossbauer spectroscopy; magnetism of metals and alloys; physical metallurgy; high Tc superconductors; short range ordering; metals. *Mailing Add:* 805 La Gonda Way Danville CA 94526. *Fax:* 510-837-4965

**VIOLETT, THEODORE DEAN,** PHYSICS. *Current Pos:* PROF PHYSICS, WESTERN STATE COL COLO, 59- *Personal Data:* b Great Bend, Kans, Apr, 27, 32; m 53; c 3. *Educ:* Univ Mo, BS, 53, MA, 54; Univ Colo, PhD(physics), 59. *Mem:* Am Phys Soc; Am Asn Physics Teachers. *Res:* Vacuum ultraviolet radiation and solar spectroscopy. *Mailing Add:* Dept Sci Western State Col Gunnison CO 81231. *Fax:* 970-943-7069

**VIOLETTE, JOSEPH LAWRENCE NORMAN,** ELECTRICAL ENGINEERING. *Current Pos:* PRES & FOUNDER, EMC & SYSTS ENG, JLN VIOLETTE & ASSOC. *Personal Data:* b Winslow, Maine, Aug 24, 32; m 57; c 7. *Educ:* Rensselaer Polytech Inst, BEE, 56; NC State Univ, PhD(elec eng), 71; Auburn Univ, Montgomery, MBA, 72. *Prof Exp:* USAF, 56-77, from instr to asst prof elec eng, USAF Acad, 62-67, proj mgr tactical air commun systs, Electronic Systs Div, L G Hanscom Field, Mass, 69-71, proj mgr, Advan Res Projs Agency, Washington, DC, 72-73; C3I proj engr, Washington Off, TRW, 77-79; prin engr, Don White Consults, EMC eng, 80-90. *Mem:* Inst Elec & Electronics Engrs. *Res:* Integral equation solution for nonplanar obstacles in coaxial waveguides obtained from dyadic Green's function formulation of boundary value problem; computer solution of singular integral equations so derived. *Mailing Add:* Violette Eng Corp 120 E Brad St PO Box 639 Falls Church VA 22040

**VIOLINI, GALILEO,** PHYSICS. *Current Pos:* ASSOC PROF, UNIV CALABRIA, ITALY, 87- *Personal Data:* b Rome, Italy, Aug 16, 42; c Paolo & Guido. *Educ:* Inst Massimo, Lic Liceale, 60; Univ Rome, Laurea(physics), 65. *Honors & Awards:* Wheatly Award, Am Phys Soc, 95. *Prof Exp:* Assoc prof, Univ Rome, 70-87. *Mem:* Am Phys Soc. *Mailing Add:* Avenida ZZ No 39-79 Bogota Colombia

**VIRARAGHAVAN, THIRUVENKATACHARI,** WATER TREATMENT, WASTEWATER TREATMENT. *Current Pos:* assoc prof, 82-83, PROF, FAC ENG, UNIV REGINA, 83- *Personal Data:* b Madras, India, July 15, 34; m 67, Saroja; c Roopa & Praveen. *Educ:* Univ Madras, India, BE, 55, MSc, 63; Univ Ottawa, PhD(civil eng), 75. *Honors & Awards:* Nawab Zain Yar Jung Bahadur Mem Gold Medal, Inst Engrs (India), 77-78. *Prof Exp:* Jr public health engr, Dept Pub Health Eng & Munic Works, Govt Madras, India, 55-61, asst pub health engr, 61-65; asst adv pub health eng, Ministry Health, Govt India, New Delhi, 65-70; res asst fluid mech, Dept Civil Eng, Univ Ottawa, 70-75; sr environ engr, ADI Ltd Consult Engrs, NB, Can, 75-82. *Concurrent Pos:* Hon res assoc, Univ NB, 78-86. *Mem:* Fel Inst Engrs; fel Am Soc Civil Engrs; fel Can Soc Civil Eng; Am Water Works Asn; Water Environ Fedn. *Res:* On-site wastewater treatment and disposal; biological treatment of wastewaters, especially anaerobic treatment of wastewaters; use of peat fly ash and bentonite in pollution control; groundwater pollution; water and sanitation in developing countries. *Mailing Add:* Fac Eng Univ Regina Regina SK S4S 0A2 Can. *Fax:* 306-585-4855; *E-Mail:* t.viraraghavan@uregina.ca

**VIRASORO, MIGUEL ANGEL,** PHYSICS. *Current Pos:* PROF, DEPT PHYSICS, UNIV ROME, 82-; DIR, INT CTR THEORET PHYSICS, UN EDUC SCI & CULTURAL ORGN, 95- *Personal Data:* b Buenos Aires, Arg, May 9, 40; m, Sylvia T Strusberg; c Diego Miguel. *Educ:* Univ Buenos Aires, Lic, 62, PhD(physics), 67. *Honors & Awards:* Richard Ganz, 89; Rammel Medal, 93. *Prof Exp:* Postdoctoral fel, Weizmann Inst Sci, 67-68, Dept Physics, Univ Wis, 68-70, Univ Calif, Berkeley, 70-71; asst prof, Dept Physics, Univ Buenos Aires, 71-74; sr researcher, Consejo Nat Invest Sci & Technol, 74-75, Inst Advan Studies, NJ, 75-76, Ecole Normale Superieure, Paris, 76-77, Nat Inst Nuclear Physics, 77-80, Europ Orgn Nuclear Res, 80-81; prof, Dept Physics, Univ Lecce, Italy, 81-82. *Concurrent Pos:* Guggenheim fel, 87; assoc ed, Int J neural Systs, 90-, Lett Modern Physics B, 90-, Int J Modern Physics B, 90-, Lett Modern Physics A, 90-93, Int J Modern Physics A, 90-93; mem, Comt Direzione, Syst Intel, 91-; guest scientist, Niels Bohr Inst, Ecole Normale Superieure, Univ Florence, Pontificia Univ, Univ Sao Paulo, Inst Theoret Physics, Kyoto Univ, Hebrew Univ. *Mem:* Fel Third World Acad Sci. *Mailing Add:* Int Ctr Theoret Physics Strada Costiera 11 PO Box 586 Trieste 34100 Italy

**VIRELLA, GABRIEL T,** CLINICAL & DIAGNOSTIC IMMUNOLOGY. *Current Pos:* from asst prof to assoc prof, 76-80, PROF IMMUNOL & MICROBIOL, MED UNIV SC, 80-, PROF PATH & LAB MED, 82- *Personal Data:* b Vilanova ila Geltiu, Barcelona, Spain, May 23, 43; US citizen; m 67; c 2. *Educ:* Med Sch Univ Lisbon, Portugal, MD, 67, PhD(microbiol), 74; Am Bd Med Lab Immunol, cert, 79. *Honors & Awards:* Pfizer Award, Pfizer Inc, 73. *Prof Exp:* Res immunol, Gulbenkian Inst Sci, Portugal, 74-75. *Concurrent Pos:* Consult, Dept Path Lab Med, Med Sch Univ SC, 76; prin investr, Kroc Found Grant, 82-84, Juvenile Diabetes Found Grant, 82-84. *Mem:* Brit Soc Immunol; Am Asn Immunologist; Am Acad Microbiol; Asn Med Lab Immunologist; Clin Immunol Soc. *Mailing Add:* Dept Immunol & Microbiol Med Univ SC 171 Ashley Ave Charleston SC 29425-2230. *Fax:* 803-792-2464; *E-Mail:* gabevirella@smtpgw.musc.edu

**VIRGILI, LUCIANO,** THERMAL ANALYSIS, MICROSCOPY. *Current Pos:* ASST MGR, E R SQUIBB & SONS, INC, 78- *Personal Data:* b Carassai, Italy, Mar 15, 48; m 72; c 2. *Educ:* Univ Firenze, Italy, Dr, 75. *Mem:* Am Chem Soc. *Res:* Methods development in pharmaceuticals and related raw materials; problem solving; non routine complaint analysis; materials characterization and properties particle analysis. *Mailing Add:* 426 Wheeler Rd North Brunswick NJ 08902-2710

**VIRGO, BRUCE BARTON,** TOXICOLOGY, DRUG & STEROID METABOLISM. *Current Pos:* PROF TOXICOL/PHARMACOL & DIR, CTR TOXICOL, MEMORIAL UNIV, 89-, CHAIR, INTERDISCIPLINARY GRAD PROG TOXICOL, 93- *Personal Data:* b Vancouver, BC, Mar 18, 43; Can citizen; m 69, N Sheila Ricardo; c Geoffrey & Catherine. *Educ:* Univ BC, BSc, 65, MSc, 70, PhD(pharmacol, toxicol), 74. *Prof Exp:* Res biologist econ ornith, Can Wildlife Serv, Govt Can, 65-66, contractee ecol, 67-68; Nat Res Coun fel toxicol, McGill Univ, 74-75; Nat Res Coun fel pharmacol, Univ Montreal, 75; asst prof, Univ Windsor, 75-81, assoc prof physiol & pharmacol, 81-88. *Concurrent Pos:* Consult, Indust Res Inst, Windsor, 79-87 & Govt New Brunswick, 80; assoc ed, Can J Physiol

Pharmacol, 84-; bd mem, Can Fed Biol Soc, 89-92; mem, Pharmacol Grant Panel, MRCC, 90-93. *Mem:* Soc Toxicol Can (secy, 89-95); Pharmacol Soc Can; Soc Toxicol. *Res:* Pharmacology of the hepatic drug and steroid metabolizing enzymes; physiology, pharmacology and toxicology of reproduction processes at all organizational levels; toxicology of environmental chemicals with emphasis on the effects of chronic, low-dose exposure. *Mailing Add:* Ctr Toxicol Fac Pharm Mem Univ St John's NF A1B 3V6 Can. *Fax:* 709-737-7044; *E-Mail:* bvirgo@morgan.ucs.mun.la

**VIRK, KASHMIR SINGH,** COMBUSTION CHAMBER DEPOSITS EFFECTS ON OCTANE REQUIREMENT. *Current Pos:* Sr proj engr, 83-88, TECHNOLOGIST, TEXACO RES CTR, 89- *Personal Data:* b India; US citizen; m 58; c 2. *Educ:* U P Agr Univ, India, BSc, 66; Univ Ill, MS, 68. *Mem:* Soc Automotive Engrs. *Res:* Diesel exhaust filters; diesel fuel composition effect on exhaust emissions; diesel fuel additives effect on exhaust emissions. *Mailing Add:* 12 La Due Hopewell Junction NY 12533

**VIRKAR, RAGHUNATH ATMARAM,** physiology, invertebrate zoology, for more information see previous edition

**VIRKKI, NIILO,** INSECT CYTOGENETICS. *Current Pos:* RETIRED. *Personal Data:* b Vuoksela, Finland, May 7, 24; m 49, Sylvi Impola; c Jaana L, Anu M (Zapfe) & Jyri J. *Educ:* Univ Helsinki, Lic phil, 51, PhD(genetics), 52. *Prof Exp:* Inspector pest animals, Vet Sect, Health Bd, Helsinki, Finland, 49-53; lab keeper, Univ Helsinki, 53-61, asst prof genetics, 55-61; from asst cytogeneticist to cytogeneticist, Agr Exp Sta, Univ PR, 61-95. *Concurrent Pos:* Fel, Fores Insect Lab, Can Dept Agr, Ont, 55-56; NSF grants, 65-68, Fundacao Amparo de Pesquisa de Sao Paulo grant, 80; vis prof, Univ Cuzco, Peru, 66, Univ Estadual Paulista, Brazil, 81. *Res:* Problems concerning evolution of karyotypes in the beetle sub-family Alticinae, especially formation of giant asynaptic sex chromosomes and their mode of orientation and segregation in meiosis; beetle cytogenetics. *Mailing Add:* PO Box 702500-158 San Juan PR 00936. *Fax:* 787-758-5158; *E-Mail:* m_santiago%rumad@upr.clu.edu

**VIRNIG, MICHAEL JOSEPH,** ORGANIC CHEMISTRY, SOLVENT EXTRACTION & METAL CHELATION. *Current Pos:* sr res chemist, Henkel Corp, 75-80, group leader, 80-84, res assoc, 84-88, tech mgr, 88-91, DIR TECH, HENKEL CORP. *Personal Data:* b Rochester, Minn, Mar 31, 46; m 68; c 3. *Educ:* St Mary's Col, BA, 68; Iowa State Univ, PhD(org chem), 74. *Prof Exp:* Tech mgr, Cognis Inc, 91- *Mem:* Am Chem Soc; Am Inst Mining Engrs; Sigma Xi. *Res:* Solvent extraction, process development organic synthesis, natural products. *Mailing Add:* Henkel Corp 2430 N Huachuca Dr Tucson AZ 85745

**VIRNSTEIN, ROBERT W,** MARINE ECOLOGY. *Current Pos:* ENVIRON SPECIALIST, ST JOHNS RIVER WATER MGT DIST, 87- *Personal Data:* b Washington, DC, Mar 19, 43; m 69, Elisabeth Lane; c Douglas & Julie. *Educ:* Johns Hopkins Univ, BA, 66; Univ SFla, MA, 72; Col William & Mary, PhD(marine sci), 76. *Prof Exp:* Marine scientist, Va Inst Marine Sci, 75-76; fel, Harbor Br Inst, 76-77, asst res scientist, Harbor Br Found, 77-85. *Concurrent Pos:* Consult, Seagrass Ecosysts Analysts, 85- *Mem:* Ecol Soc Am; Int Asn Meiobenthologists; Southeastern Estuarine Res Soc. *Res:* Estuarine benthic ecology; trophic relationships; experimental field ecology; role of predation; benthic invertebrate taxonomy; seagrass growth rates; seagrass communities. *Mailing Add:* 142 Elgin Rd East Palatka FL 32131. *Fax:* 904-329-4329

**VIRTUE, ROBERT,** anesthesiology; deceased, see previous edition for last biography

**VISCOMI, B(RUNO) VINCENT,** ENGINEERING MECHANICS. *Current Pos:* from asst prof to prof, Civil Eng Dept, Lafayette Col, 64-89, head, 72-89, prof civil & environ eng, 89-94, SIMON CAMERON LONG PROF, LAFAYETTE COL, 94- *Personal Data:* b Philadelphia, Pa, Sept 21, 33; m 58, Mary Hughes; c Vincent, Christopher & Roseann. *Educ:* Drexel Inst, BS, 56; Lehigh Univ, MS, 57; Univ Colo, PhD(civil eng), 69. *Prof Exp:* Engr, Westinghouse Elec Co, 57; res engr, Philadelphia Elec Co, 58-62, nuclear engr, 62-64. *Concurrent Pos:* NSF fel, Nat Ctr Resource Recovery, 74; consult, Resource Recovery Serv, Woodbridge, NJ & Naval Sea Systs Command, Washington, DC, 81; res engr & cluster group leader, Nat Found ATLSS Ctr, Lehigh Univ, 88, NSF Eng Res Ctr, ATLSS Ctr, 88-; prin investr, NSF, Regist Prof Engr, Pa, NJ. *Mem:* Am Soc Eng Educ; NY Acad Sci; Am Soc Civil Engrs; Sigma Xi; Am Soc Testing & Mat. *Res:* Dynamic response of elastic mechanisms; structural dynamics; structural analyses and design of integrated building systems; automated construction of building systems; dynamic response of building systems and dynamic response of elastic mechanisms. *Mailing Add:* Dept Civil & Environ Eng Lafayette Col Rm 301 AHE Easton PA 18042

**VISCONTI, JAMES ANDREW,** PHARMACY. *Current Pos:* asst prof pharm, 68-72, ASSOC PROF PHARM, COL PHARM, OHIO STATE UNIV, 72-, DIR, DRUG INFO CTR, UNIV HOSPS, 68- *Personal Data:* b St Louis, Mo, Apr 13, 39; m 63; c 2. *Educ:* St Louis Col Pharm, BS, 61, MS, 63; Univ Miss, PhD(pharm), 69. *Prof Exp:* Resident, John Cochran Vet Admin Hosp, St Louis, Mo, 63, staff pharmacist, 64-66; res pharmacist, Vet Admin Hosp, Long Beach, Calif, 63-64. *Concurrent Pos:* Lehn & Fink Pharm gold medal award, 61-62; Robert Lincoln McNeil citation fel award, 66-67. *Mem:* Am Soc Hosp Pharmacists; Am Pharmaceut Asn; assoc mem AMA; Drug Info Asn. *Res:* Epidemiology and econmics of adverse drug reactions;

pharmacology of drug-drug, drug-laboratory tests and drug-food interactions; computerized drug information services; health and disease economics. *Mailing Add:* Dept Pharmacol Ohio State Univ Col Med 500 W 12th Ave Columbus OH 43210-1214

**VISEK, WILLARD JAMES,** NUTRITION, MOLECULAR BIOLOGY. *Current Pos:* EMER PROF INTERNAL MED & NUTRIT SCI, COL MED, UNIV ILL, URBANA, 75-, PROF NUTRIT & METAB, DEPT NUTRIT SCI, 78-, PROF, DEPT INTERNAL MED, 84- *Personal Data:* b Sargent, Nebr, Sept 19, 22; m 49, Priscilla Flagg; c Dianna, Madeleine & Clayton P. *Educ:* Univ Nebr, BSc, 47; Cornell Univ, MSc, 49, PhD(nutrit biochem), 51; Univ Chicago, MD, 57. *Hon Degrees:* DSc, Univ Nebr, 80. *Honors & Awards:* Osborne Mendel Award, 85; Hogan Mem lectr, Univ Mo, 87. *Prof Exp:* Asst animal nutrit, Cornell Univ, 48-51; AEC fel, Univ-Atomic Energy Agr Res Prog, Tenn, 51-52, res assoc, 52-53; res asst pharmacol, Univ Chicago, 53-57, from asst prof to assoc prof, 57-64; prof nutrit & comp metab, Cornell Univ, 64-75. *Concurrent Pos:* Intern univ hosp & clins, Univ Chicago, 57-59; mem, Teratol Subcomt, Comn Drug Safety, 63 & Subcomt Animal Nutrit, Nat Res Coun-Nat Acad Sci, 65-72, adv coun, Inst Lab Animal Resources, 66-69, Subcomt Animal Care Facil surv, 68-70; consult, Sect Health Related Facil, USPHS, 67; assoc ed, Nutrit Rev, 68-71; Nat Cancer Inst-USPHS spec fel, Mass Inst Technol, 70-71; res fel, Mass Gen Hosp, 70-71; grad fac rep nutrit, Cornell Univ, 74-; mem adv comt, Diet, Nutrit & Cancer Prog, Nat Cancer Inst, 76-; mem inst rev bd, Univ Ill, 76-; mem exec comt, Sch Basic Med Sci & Clin Med, Univ Ill, Urbana-Champaign; consult & mem dean's comt, Danville Vet Admin Hosp, 77-; mem, Study Sect Nutrit, NIH, 80-84; Brittingham vis prof, Univ Wis-Madison, 82-83; comt technol options to improve health, 86-88; mem, Nutrit Res Sci Adv Comt, Nat Dairy Coun, 87-90; mem, Coun Sci Adv Human Nutrit, USDA, 88-; mem bd dirs, Am Bd Nutrit, 88; sr univ scholar, Univ Ill, 88-91; ed-in-chief, J Nutrit, 90-; Burroughs Wellcome vis prof, Ore State Univ, 92-93. *Mem:* Fel AAAS; Am Soc Pharmacol & Exp Therapeut; Soc Exp Biol & Med; fel Am Soc Animal Sci; Am Soc Clin Nutrit; fel Am Soc Nutrit Sci; Am Asn Cancer Res; Am Gastroenterol Asn; Cent Soc Clin Res. *Res:* Effects of ammonia on energy metabolism, urea cycle activity and nucleic acid synthesis; interactions of amino acids; enzyme immunity; influence of diet on cancer incidence and influence of dietary fat level on gene expression. *Mailing Add:* 190 Med Sci Bldg Univ Ill 506 S Mathews Urbana IL 61801

**VISHER, FRANK N,** HYDROLOGY, GEOLOGY. *Current Pos:* geologist, US Geol Surv, 48-56, engr, 56-66, hydrologist, Fla, 66-67, res hydrologist, 67-80, CONSULT HYDROLOGIST, US GEOL SURV, 80- *Personal Data:* b Twin Falls, Idaho, Mar 10, 23; m 48; c 4. *Educ:* Tex Tech Col, BS, 46 & 47. *Prof Exp:* Apprentice engr, Tex Hwy Dept, 47-48. *Mem:* AAAS. *Res:* Hydrologic studies, especially the principals of occurrence of ground water, water budget studies, fresh-salt water interrelationships, geochemistry of water and relation of geomorphology to ground water; environmental studies. *Mailing Add:* 3351 Vivian Ct Wheat Ridge CO 80033

**VISHER, GLENN S,** GEOLOGY, STRATIGRAPHY & SEDIMENTOLOGY, HISTORY SCIENCE EDUCATION. *Current Pos:* PRES, GEOL SERV & VENTURES INC, 80- *Personal Data:* b May 20, 30; US citizen; m 53, Bettye Gentry; c Christine A, Lynda (West) & Sara C. *Educ:* Univ Cincinnati, BS, 52; Northwestern Univ, MS, 56, PhD(geol), 60. *Prof Exp:* Explorationist, Shell Oil Co, 58-60; res geologist, Sinclair Res, Inc, 60-66; from adj asst prof to prof geol, Univ Tulsa, 64-80. *Concurrent Pos:* Lectr training courses, Domestic & Int Petrol Co Personnel; consult, Int Petrol Co; adj res prof, Wichita State Univ, 86-, Univ Okla, 88-; mem, grad fac, Okla State Univ, 96- *Mem:* Am Asn Petrol Geol; fel Geol Soc Am; Soc Econ Paleont & Mineral; Int Asn Sedimentol; fel AAAS; emer mem Am Asn Petrol Geologists. *Res:* Stratigraphic models; depositional processes; physical characteristics of sandstone units; system analysis of depositional systems; development of cultures; history and philosophy of science. *Mailing Add:* 7149 S Indianapolis Ave Tulsa OK 74136-5947

**VISHNIAC, ETHAN TECUMSEH,** COSMOLOGY, ASTRO PHYSICAL FLUID DYNAMICS. *Current Pos:* lectr astron, 82-84, from asst prof to assoc prof, 84-93, PROF ASTRON, UNIV TEX, 93- *Personal Data:* b New Haven, Conn, Sept 29, 55; m 76, Ilene J Busch; c Cady A & Miriam R. *Educ:* Univ Rochester, BS, 76, BA, 76; Harvard Univ, AM, 80, PhD(astron), 80. *Honors & Awards:* Pres Young Investr, NSF, 85; Alfred P Sloan fel, Sloan Found, 86; Helen B Warner Prize, Am Astron Soc, 90. *Prof Exp:* Res assoc, Princeton Univ, 80-82. *Mem:* Am Astron Soc; Am Phys Soc; Int Astron Union. *Res:* Expert on linear and nonlinear instabilities in strong shocks, this production of secondary irregularities in the cosmic microwave background, galaxy formation and the transport of angular momentum in astrophysical accretion disks. *Mailing Add:* 4012 Greenhill Pl Austin TX 78759. *Fax:* 512-471-6016; *E-Mail:* ethan@astro.as.utexas.edu

**VISHNIAC, HELEN SIMPSON,** MICROBIAL ECOLOGY, MYCOLOGY. *Current Pos:* from asst prof to assoc prof, Dept Cell, Molecular & Develop Biol, 78-89, prof microbiol, 89-94, EMER PROF MICROBIOL, OKLA STATE UNIV, 94- *Personal Data:* b New Haven, Conn, Dec 22, 23; wid; c Obadiah (deceased), Ethan & Ephraim. *Educ:* Univ Mich, BA, 45; Radcliffe Col, MA, 47; Columbia Univ, PhD(bot), 50. *Prof Exp:* Tutor biol, Queens Col, NY, 48-51, instr, 51-52; lectr microbiol, Sch Med, Yale Univ, 53-61; res assoc biol, Univ Rochester, 74-78. *Concurrent Pos:* Lectr, Nazareth Col Rochester, 75-76; fel, Am Asn Univ Women, 75-76; vis assoc prof, State Univ NY, Brockport, 76-78. *Mem:* AAAS; Mycol Soc Am; Am Soc Microbiol. *Res:* Antarctic yeasts, aquatic fungi; molecular systematics. *Mailing Add:* Dept Microbiol & Molecular Genetics Okla State Univ Stillwater OK 74078. *E-Mail:* hsvishi@osuunx.ucc.okstate.edu

**VISHNUBHOTLA, SARMA RAGHUNADHA,** COMPUTER SCIENCE. *Current Pos:* FAC, DEPT ENG, OAKLAND UNIV, ROCHESTER, MICH 78- *Personal Data:* b Masuli Patam, India, July 7, 46; m 74. *Educ:* Madras Inst Technol, India, DMIT, 68; Wash Univ, MS, 72, DSc(comput sci), 73. *Prof Exp:* Asst prof comput sci, Cent Mich Univ, 73-78, assoc prof, 78- *Mem:* Asn Comput Mach; Inst Elec & Electronics Engrs. *Res:* Computer science education; fault diagnosis in computer hardware and software systems; data structures and data bases. *Mailing Add:* Dept Comput Sci Oakland Univ 108 Dodge Hall Rochester MI 48309

**VISICH, MARIAN, JR,** AEROSPACE ENGINEERING. *Current Pos:* RETIRED. *Personal Data:* b Brooklyn, NY, Jan 8, 30; m 59; c 3. *Educ:* Polytech Inst Brooklyn, BAeE, 51, MAeE, 53, PhD, 56. *Prof Exp:* From asst to res assoc aeronaut eng, Polytech Inst Brooklyn, 51-56, from res asst prof to prof, 56-77; assoc dean, Col Eng & Appl Sci, State Univ NY, Stony Brook, 77-97. *Concurrent Pos:* Consult, Curtiss-Wright Corp, 55, Gen Elec Corp, 56, Gen Appl Sci Lab, 56-68, Advan Technol Labs, US Army Res Labs, 69-75. *Mem:* AAAS; Am Inst Aeronaut & Astronaut; Am Soc Eng Educ; Sigma Xi. *Res:* Physics of fluids; high-speed aerodynamics; aircraft and missile propulsion. *Mailing Add:* 8 Whitehall Dr Huntington NY 11743

**VISKANTA, RAYMOND,** HEAT TRANSFER. *Current Pos:* assoc prof, 62-66, prof mech eng, 66-86, GOSS DISTINGUISHED PROF ENG, PURDUE UNIV, 86- *Personal Data:* b Lithuania, July 16, 31; US citizen; m 56, B B Barpsys; c Renata, Vitas & Tada. *Educ:* Univ Ill, BS, 55; Purdue Univ, MS, 56, PhD(heat transfer), 60. *Honors & Awards:* US Sr Scientist Award, Alexander von Humboldt Found, 75; Heat Transfer Mem Award, Am Soc Mech Engrs, 76; Thermophys Award, Am Inst Aeronaut & Astronaut, 79; Sr Res Award, Am Soc Eng Educ, 84; Max Jakob Mem Award, Am Soc Mech Engrs-Am Inst Chem Engrs, 86; Melville Medal, Am Soc Mech Engrs, 88. *Prof Exp:* Asst mech engr heat transfer, Argonne Nat Lab, 56-58, assoc mech engr, 60-62. *Concurrent Pos:* Vis prof mech eng, Univ Calif, Berkeley, 68-69; consult to various pvt & govt orgn, 72-; Alexander von Humboldt Found award, 76-78; guest prof mech eng, Tech Univ Munich, 76-77; vis prof, Tokyo Inst Technol, 83. *Mem:* Nat Acad Eng; fel Am Inst Aeronaut & Astronaut; fel Am Soc Mech Engrs; Combustion Inst. *Res:* Radiation transfer in gases and solids; applied thermodynamics; heat transfer in combustion systems; solar energy utilization; solid/liquid phase change heat transfer; heat transfer in materials processing. *Mailing Add:* Sch Mech Eng Purdue Univ West Lafayette IN 47907. *Fax:* 765-494-5632

**VISNER, SIDNEY,** physics, nuclear reactor safety, for more information see previous edition

**VISOTSKY, HAROLD M,** MEDICINE, PSYCHIATRY. *Current Pos:* prof psychiat & chmn dept, Med Sch, 69-91, dir, Inst Psychiat, 75-91, DIR RES & EDUC DEVELOP, NORTHWESTERN & MEM HOSP, 93- *Personal Data:* b Chicago, Ill, May 25, 24; m 55, Glady Maurich; c Jeffrey & Robin. *Educ:* Univ Ill, BS, 48, MD, 51. *Honors & Awards:* Edward A Strecker Award, Inst Pa Hosp, 69; Bowis Award, Am Col Psychiat, 81, Distinguished Serv Award, 88; Simon Bolivar Award, Am Psychiat Asn, 82, Presidential Commendation Award, 88. *Prof Exp:* Coordr psychiat residency training, Med Sch, Univ Ill, Chicago, from asst prof to assoc prof psychiat, 59-69; dir, Ill Dept Ment Health, 62-70. *Concurrent Pos:* Nat Found Infantile Paralysis res fel, 55-56; chief of serv, Chicago State Psychiat Hosp, 57-59; dir ment health sect, City Bd Health, Chicago, 59-62; chmn task force, Joint Comn Ment Health of Children, 66-68; mem adv comt, Secy Dept HEW, 66-67; mem, Eval Ment Health Prog, First Mission, USSR, 67, NIMH Stud Mission, USSR, 89 & IOM Study Vet Admin Resources, 88-; mem task force, President's Comn Ment Health; sr consult Ctr Ment Health & Psychiat Serv, Am Hosp Asn, 79-; chmn, Int Comn Abuse Psychiat & Psychiatrists, Am Psychiat Asn, 80-84, Coun Int Affairs, 84-; mem, Mission to Japan Ment Health Syst, Int Comn Jurists, 85-87; sr consult, WHO. *Mem:* Am Asn Social Psychiat (vpres, 76-77, pres, 88-91); Am Hosp Asn; Am Psychiat Asn (secy, 71-73, vpres, 73-74); Am Col Psychoanalysts; Am Orthopsychiat Asn (pres, 76-77); Am Col Psychiatrists (pres, 83-84). *Res:* Social and milieu psychiatry; effects of hallucinogenic drugs in understanding mental illness; stress: coping and adaptation; stress research; set up the Asher Research Center for studies of depression. *Mailing Add:* Dept Psychiat & Behav Sci Northwestern Univ Med Sch 303 E Ohio St Chicago IL 60611. *E-Mail:* h-visotsky@mwu.edu

**VISSCHER, PIETER BERNARD,** NON-EQUILIBRIUM STATISTICAL MECHANICS, COLLOID RHEOLOGY. *Current Pos:* from asst prof to assoc prof, 78-84, PROF PHYSICS, UNIV ALA, 84- *Personal Data:* b Minneapolis, Minn, Dec 11, 45; m 72, Helga Bjornson; c Kristina M & Paul J. *Educ:* Harvard Univ, BA, 67; Univ Calif, Berkeley, MA, 68, PhD(solid state physics), 71. *Prof Exp:* Res assoc, Univ Ill, Urbana, 71-73; res physicist, Univ Calif, San Diego, 73-75; asst prof physics, Univ Ore, 75-78. *Concurrent Pos:* Prin investr, NSF res grant, 79-84 & 92-94; consult, Los Alamos Nat Lab, 85-86; res fel, Univ Surrey, UK, 92-93. *Mem:* Am Phys Soc; Am Asn Univ Profs; Am Asn Physics Teachers. *Res:* Developed exactly renormalizable theory of transport; applications to calculation of liquid viscosity, disordered systems and viscoelastic hydrodynamics; computer simulation of magnetic colloids. *Mailing Add:* Dept Physics & Astron Univ Ala Tuscaloosa AL 35487-0324. *Fax:* 205-348-5051; *E-Mail:* pvissche@ua1vm.ua.edu

**VISSCHER, SARALEE NEUMANN,** ENTOMOLOGY, INSECT DEVELOPMENT & PLANT PHYSIOLOGY. *Current Pos:* asst prof entom, 62-65, assoc prof, 67-71, PROF ENTOM, MONT STATE UNIV, 72- *Personal Data:* b Lewistown, Mont, Jan 9, 29; m 69, Paul H; c Constance V Currie, Amy R & Ernst W. *Educ:* Univ Mont, BA, 49; Mont State Univ, MS, 58, PhD(entom), 63. *Prof Exp:* NIH res fel insect develop, Univ Va, 65-66.

*Concurrent Pos:* Co-investr, NIH res grant, 65-69; US-Japan grant, 77-79; AID grant, 79-80, 85-87; Rockefeller grant, 80-81; Dow Chem grant, 80-81; NSF grant, 80-82; Agr & Resources Inventory Surv through Aerospace Remote Sensing grant, 80-82; hon guest, Arthropodan Embryol Soc Japan. *Mem:* AAAS; Int Soc Develop Biol; Int Soc Chem Ecol. *Res:* Maternal/embryonic interrelationships; physiology of embryonic diapause of insects; role of plant growth hormones in regulation of insect growth, reproduction and longevity; host plant effects on grasshopper population dynamics. *Mailing Add:* 18 Hitching Post Rd Bozeman MT 59715

**VISSCHER, WILLIAM M,** THEORETICAL PHYSICS, THERMODYNAMICS & MATERIAL PROPERTIES. *Current Pos:* staff mem theoret physics, 56-91, LAB ASSOC, LOS ALAMOS SCI LAB, 91- *Personal Data:* b Memphis, Tenn, May 16, 28; m 51, Jean Dininny; c Wendy, Judith, James & Jonathan. *Educ:* Univ Minn, BA, 49; Cornell Univ, PhD(theoret physics), 53. *Prof Exp:* Res assoc physics, Univ Md, 53-56. *Concurrent Pos:* Vis prof, Univ Wash, 67. *Mem:* Fel Am Phys Soc; Sigma Xi. *Res:* Meson theory; theory of nuclear structure and spectra; lattice dynamics and Mossbauer effect; particle accelerator physics; solid state physics; statistical mechanics; random packing; transport processes; scattering theory; materials science; acoustics. *Mailing Add:* 102 Loma Del Escolar Los Alamos NM 87544. *E-Mail:* wmv@rho.lanl.gov

**VISSERS, DONALD R,** ELECTROCHEMISTRY, ADVANCED BATTERY DEVELOPMENT. *Current Pos:* SECT MGR ADVAN BATTERY DEVELOP & ELECTROCHEM RES, ARGONNE NAT LAB, 65- *Personal Data:* b Bowler, Wis, Aug 8, 31; m 58, Mary A Lodzinski; c Kathleen, Linda & Daniel. *Educ:* Univ Wis-Stevens Point, BS, 53; Univ Wis-Madison, PhD(inorg chem), 60. *Prof Exp:* Res chemist, Morton Chem, Woodstock, Ill, 59-62, Oak Ridge Nat Lab, 62-65. *Mem:* Am Chem Soc; Electrochem Soc. *Res:* Development of advanced batteries for EV applications and the optimization thereof. *Mailing Add:* Argonne Nat Lab 9700 S Cass Ave Argonne IL 60439. *Fax:* 630-252-4176; *E-Mail:* vissers@cmt.anl.gov

**VISTE, ARLEN E,** INORGANIC CHEMISTRY. *Current Pos:* from asst prof to assoc prof, 64-73, PROF CHEM, AUGUSTANA COL, SDAK, 73- *Personal Data:* b Austin, Minn, Aug 13, 36; m 59, Elizabeth Lindbeck; c Solveig, David & Mark. *Educ:* St Olaf Col, BA, 58; Univ Chicago, PhD(inorg chem), 62. *Prof Exp:* Asst prof chem, St Olaf Col, 62-63; NSF fel, Columbia Univ, 63-64. *Concurrent Pos:* Partic fac res participation prog, Argonne Nat Lab, Ill, 70-71; vis scientist, Dept Phys Chem, Abo Akademi, Turku, Finland, 81-82. *Mem:* Am Chem Soc; Royal Soc Chem; Sigma Xi. *Res:* Reaction mechanisms; relativistic quantum chemistry; spectroscopy. *Mailing Add:* 1500 W 30th St Sioux Falls SD 57105. *Fax:* 605-336-5299; *E-Mail:* viste@inst.augie.edu

**VISTICA, DAVID T,** PHARMACOLOGY. *Current Pos:* RES PHARMACOLOGIST, CELL BIOL CANCER & AIDS RES, NIH, 76- *Personal Data:* b Portland, Ore, Nov 9, 46. *Educ:* Loyola Univ, BS, 68; Calif State Univ, MS, 70; Iowa State Univ, PhD(molecular biol), 75. *Mem:* Am Soc Cell Biol; Am Asn Cancer Res. *Res:* Pharmacology. *Mailing Add:* 3536 Runkles Rd Monrovia MD 21770

**VISVANATHAN, T R,** earth science, statistics, for more information see previous edition

**VISWANADHAM, RAMAMURTHY K,** CEMENTED CARBIDES & COMPOSITES, STRUCTURE PROPERTY RELATIONSHIPS. *Current Pos:* DIR RES & DEVELOP, MULTI-METALS/VT-AM, LOUISVILLE, KY, 88- *Personal Data:* b Tiruvur, India, July 16, 46; US citizen; m 70, Mantha Subhadra; c Madhuri & Srikant. *Educ:* Osmania Univ, Hyderabad, India, BE, 68; Univ Ill, Urbana-Champaign, MS, 70, PhD(metall eng), 73. *Honors & Awards:* Robert Glen Lye Mem Award, 77 & 81. *Prof Exp:* Sr scientist res & develop, Martin Marietta Labs, Baltimore, Md, 75-79, staff scientist, 86-88; mgr res & develop, Reed Tool Co/Baker Int, Houston, Tex, 79-86. *Concurrent Pos:* Chmn, First Int Conf Sci Hard Mat, 80-81; mem, ed bd, Metall Trans, Metall Soc, Am Inst Mining, Metall & Petrol Engrs, 80-86; int liaison, Second Int Conf Sci Hard Mat, 83-84. *Mem:* Am Soc Mat; Mat Res Soc; Am Powder Metall Inst; Am Inst Mining & Metall Engrs. *Res:* Injection molding of cemented carbide composites; process development and process optimization; structure-property relationships in a variety of different composites. *Mailing Add:* 5201 Olde Creek Way Prospect KY 40059. *Fax:* 502-587-5656

**VISWANATH, DABIR S,** THERMODYNAMICS, REACTION ENGINEERING. *Current Pos:* PROF CHEM ENG, UNIV MO, COLUMBIA, 80-, CHMN DEPT, 90-, JAMES C DOWELL PROF, 90- *Personal Data:* b Bangalore, India, Aug 5, 34; US citizen; m 67, Pramila Nadig; c Srikant (deceased) & Arvind. *Educ:* Mysore Univ, BS, 53; Indian Inst Sci, DII Sc, 56; Univ Rochester, MS, 60, PhD(chem eng), 62. *Prof Exp:* Chem engr res, Sarabhai-Merck, India, 56-57; asst prof chem eng, Bucknell Univ, 62-63; asst prof, assoc prof & chmn, Indian Inst Sci, 65-78; vis prof, Tex A&M Univ, 78-79. *Concurrent Pos:* Vis prof, Southern Ill, Carbondale, 86-89. *Mem:* Fel Am Inst Chemists; Sigma Xi; fel Am Inst Chem Engrs; Am Chem Soc. *Res:* Coal conversion; properties of liquid, gases and mixtures; water based treatment; vapor-liquid equilibrium; oxidation of methane to methanol, supercritical fluids; polymer degradation in ceramics, thermophysical properties of ceramics and composites, and ultrafine particles; materials. *Mailing Add:* Dept Chem Eng Univ Mo Columbia MO 65211. *Fax:* 573-884-4940

**VISWANATHA, THAMMAIAH,** BIOCHEMISTRY. *Current Pos:* PROF CHEM, UNIV WATERLOO, 64- *Personal Data:* b Channapatna, India, Sept 22, 26. *Educ:* Univ Mysore, PhD, 55. *Prof Exp:* Rask-Orsted fel, Carlsberg Lab, Denmark, 56-57; res assoc, Univ Minn, 57-58; vis scientist, Nat Inst Arthritis & Metab Dis, 58-62 & Inst Molecular Biol & Dept Chem, Univ Ore, 62-64. *Mem:* Sigma Xi. *Res:* Enzymes; proteins; nucleic acids. *Mailing Add:* Dept Chem Univ Waterloo Waterloo ON N2L 3G1 Can

**VISWANATHAN, CHAND R,** SOLID STATE PHYSICS, ELECTRONICS. *Current Pos:* asst prof eng, Univ Calif, Los Angeles, 62-68, assoc prof eng & appl sci, 68-74, asst dean, Sch Eng & Appl Sci, 74-77, chmn, Elec Eng Dept, 79-85, PROF ENG & APPL SCI, UNIV CALIF, LOS ANGELES, 74- *Personal Data:* b Madras, India, Oct 23, 29. *Educ:* Univ Madras, BSc, 48, MA, 49; Univ Calif, Los Angeles, MS, 59, PhD(solid state physics), 64. *Honors & Awards:* Centennial Medal, Inst Elec & Electronics Engrs. *Prof Exp:* Engr, Res Dept, All India Radio, 49-57. *Mem:* Fel Inst Elec & Electronics Engrs; Am Phys Soc. *Res:* Solid state electronics; magnetic properties of materials; electron energy levels in solids; electron emission from solids; semiconductor device physics; integrated electronics. *Mailing Add:* Elec Eng Dept Univ Calif 66-147-Eng IV 405 Hilgard Ave Los Angeles CA 90024

**VISWANATHAN, KADAYAM SANKARAN,** PHYSICS, FIELD THEORY. *Current Pos:* from asst prof to assoc prof, 65-81, PROF THEORET PHYSICS, SIMON FRASER UNIV, 81- *Personal Data:* b Madras, India, Apr 25, 37; m 67, Jacqueline J Delord; c Usha & Sophie. *Educ:* Univ Madras, BSc, 57; Univ Calif, Riverside, MA, 64, PhD(physics), 65. *Prof Exp:* Res officer crystallog, Atomic Energy Estab, India, 57-60. *Mem:* Am Phys Soc; Can Asn Physicists. *Res:* Theoretical high energy physics; string theories in flat and curved backgrounds; d-branes and blackholes. *Mailing Add:* Dept Physics Simon Fraser Univ Burnaby BC V5A 1S6 Can. *Fax:* 604-291-3592; *E-Mail:* kviswana@sfu.ca

**VISWANATHAN, R,** LOW TEMPERATURE PHYSICS, SURVIVABILITY. *Current Pos:* proj leader, Int Minerals & Chem Co, 81-88, asst proj mgr, 88-89, dept mgr, 90-93, SCIENTIST-4, INT MINERALS & CHEM CO, 93-; SR MEM TECH STAFF, HUGHES AIRCRAFT CO, 78- *Personal Data:* b Tenkasi, India, Dec 17, 38; US citizen; m 65; c 2. *Educ:* Univ Madras, India, MA, 60, MSc, 60; Indian Inst Sci, PhD(physics), 64. *Prof Exp:* Res assoc, Univ Ill, 65-66; res physicist, Battelle Mem Inst, 66-67; res assoc, Univ Cincinnati, 67-69; asst scientist, Univ Calif, San Diego, 69-74; assoc scientist, Brookhaven Nat Lab, 74-78. *Concurrent Pos:* Vis scientist, Inst Solid State Physics, Ger, 73; prin investr, Hughes Aircraft Co, 78-79. *Mem:* Am Phys Soc; AAAS. *Res:* Low temperature calorimetry; radiation damage in superconductors and devices; physical property measurements; electrostatic discharge; spacecraft hardening; author or coauthor of over 50 publications in international journals. *Mailing Add:* 30711 Casilina Dr Rancho Palos Verdes CA 90275. *E-Mail:* 0055707@ccmail.emis.hac.com

**VISWANATHAN, RAMA,** LASER-SURFACE INTERACTIONS, SPECTROELECTROCHEMISTRY. *Current Pos:* from asst prof to assoc prof, 83-96, PROF CHEM & COMPUT EDUC, BELOIT COL, WIS, 96- *Personal Data:* b Ranchi, India. *Educ:* Bombay Univ, BSc, 73; Indian Inst Technol, MSc, 75; Univ Ore, Eugene, PhD(phys chem), 80. *Prof Exp:* Fel dept chem, Northwestern Univ, 80-83. *Concurrent Pos:* Vis scientist, IBM Almaden Res Ctr, San Jose, 86-87; vis assoc prof, Dept Chem, Northwestern Univ, 89-90; dir, Acad Comput, Beloit Col, 90-93. *Mem:* Am Chem Soc. *Res:* Chemical physics and physical chemistry; molecular beams, laser-surface interactions and spectroelectrochemistry; parallel processing computer hardware; remote procedure calls (RPCs). *Mailing Add:* Dept Chem Beloit Col 700 College St Beloit WI 53511

**VITAGLIANO, VINCENT J,** COMPUTER AIDED DESIGN, INTERACTIVE COMPUTER GRAPHICS. *Current Pos:* CONSULT, 90- *Personal Data:* b New York, NY, Oct 29, 27; m 51, Audrey Fabini; c Rita (Gleason), Mary (Russell), Teresa (Golden), Aldo, Blaise (Vitale), Norma (Drummond), Laura, Grace (Roth) & Jay. *Educ:* Manhattan Col, BCE, 49; Va Polytech Inst, MS, 51; NY Univ, EngScD, 60. *Prof Exp:* Instr appl mech, Va Polytech Inst, 49-50; struct designer, Praeger-Maguire, Consult Engrs, 50-52 & M W Kellogg Co, Pullman, Inc, NY, 52-54; from instr to assoc prof civil eng, Manhattan Col, 54-63; univ consult, IBM Corp, 63-90. *Concurrent Pos:* Consult, 55-; Smith-Mundt vis lectr, AlHikma Univ Baghdad, 61-62. *Mem:* Am Soc Civil Engrs; Am Soc Eng Educ. *Res:* Structural engineering; electronic computers. *Mailing Add:* 20532 Sausalito Dr Boca Raton FL 33498

**VITALE, JOSEPH JOHN,** NUTRITION, BIOCHEMISTRY. *Current Pos:* AT MALLORY INST-PATH, BOSTON CITY HOSP. *Personal Data:* b Boston, Mass, Dec 14, 24; m 49; c Laura & Ruth. *Educ:* Northeastern Univ, BS, 47; NY Univ, MS, 49; Harvard Univ, DSc(nutrit biochem), 51; Antioquia Univ, Colombia, MD, 66. *Prof Exp:* Res assoc nutrit, Sch Pub Health, Harvard Univ, 51-54, assoc, 54-55, asst prof, 55-66; prof food, nutrit & med, Univ Wis, 66-67; dir nutrit progs, Sch Med, Tufts Univ, 67-72; prof path & community med, Sch Med, Boston Univ, 72- *Concurrent Pos:* Res assoc path, Sch Med, Boston Univ, 52-66; spec consult, Interdept Comt Nutrit for Nat Defense, 59-; Claude Bernard prof, Med Sch, Univ Montreal, 60; vis prof, Univ del Valle, Colombia, 60-62. *Mem:* Am Inst Nutrit; Am Soc Clin Nutrit; Brit Nutrit Soc; Sigma Xi. *Res:* Atherosclerosis, gastrointestinal metabolism, nutritional anemias and public health. *Mailing Add:* 160 Heritage Lane Weymouth MA 02189-1061. *Fax:* 617-534-5315

**VITALE, RICHARD ALBERT,** MATHEMATICS, STATISTICS. *Current Pos:* assoc prof, 77-84, prof math, Claremont Grad Sch, 84-87, PROF STATIST, UNIV CONN, 87. *Personal Data:* b New Haven, Conn, Sept 7, 44. *Educ:* Harvard Univ, AB, 66; Brown Univ, PhD(appl math), 70. *Prof Exp:* Asst prof appl math, Brown Univ, 70-76; asst scientist, Math Res Ctr, Madison, 76-77. *Mem:* Sigma Xi; Am Math Soc; Bernoulli Soc Math Statist & Probability; Soc Indust & Appl Math; Inst Math Statist; Math Asn Am. *Res:* Probability and statistics. *Mailing Add:* Univ Conn 11 Glen Hollow West Hartford CT 06117-3023. *Fax:* 860-486-4113

**VITALIANO, CHARLES JOSEPH,** GEOLOGY. *Current Pos:* assoc prof, 47-57, PROF GEOL, IND UNIV, BLOOMINGTON, 57- *Personal Data:* b New York, NY, Apr 2, 10; m 40; c Judith E & Peter W. *Educ:* City Col New York, BS, 36; Columbia Univ, AM, 38, PhD(mineral), 44. *Prof Exp:* Asst mineral, Columbia Univ, 37-39, lab instr gems & precious stones, Exten, 39-40; instr ceramic petrog, Rutgers Univ, 40-42; from asst geologist to assoc geologist, US Geol Surv, 42-46. *Concurrent Pos:* James Furmankemp fel, Columbia, 39-40; geologist, US Geol Surv, 46-59; Fulbright scholar, NZ Geol Surv, 54-55; NSF grant, 57-60 & 62-67; mem consortium crystalline basement rocks cent US, 80-82; mem sci comt, Ind Univ, 79-83; panelist, Archaeol Implications of Minoan Eruption of Santorini Volcano, Oxford Univ, Eng; chmn elect, Archaeol Geol Div, Geol Soc Am, 85-86. *Mem:* Fel Mineral Soc Am; Soc Econ Geologists; fel Geol Soc Am; fel AAAS. *Res:* Geology and ore deposits of the Paradise Peak Quadrangle, Nevada; igneous and metamorphic petrography of western Nevada, southern New Zealand and southwest Montana; volcanic rocks of western United States; archaeological geology of Mediterranean regions. *Mailing Add:* 1036 Sassafras Circle Bloomington IN 47408

**VITALIANO, DOROTHY BRAUNECK,** GEOLOGY. *Current Pos:* FREE-LANCE GEOL TRANSLR, 86- *Personal Data:* b New York, NY, Feb 10, 16; m 40; c Judith E & Peter W. *Educ:* Barnard Col, AB, 36; Columbia Univ, AM, 38, MPhil, 73. *Prof Exp:* Teaching asst geol, Barnard Col, 36-39; field asst, US Geol Surv, 42-43; geologist, 53-86. *Concurrent Pos:* Mem-at-large, Sect Comt E Geol & Geog, AAAS, 78-82; nat lectr, Sigma Xi, 81-83; adj prof geol, Ind Univ, 83-86. *Mem:* Fel Geol Soc Am; Geosci Info Soc; fel AAAS. *Res:* Bronze Age eruption of Santorini Volcano; scientific basis of Atlantis; geomythology; technical translation; tephrochronology; archeological geology. *Mailing Add:* 1001 Sassafrass Bloomington IN 47408

**VITELLO, PETER A,** THEORETICAL ASTROPHYSICS. *Current Pos:* MEM STAFF, LAWRENCE LIVERMORE NAT LABS, 89- *Personal Data:* b Glendale, Calif, Sept 15, 50; m 76. *Educ:* Univ Southern Calif, BS, 72; Cornell Univ, PhD(theoret phys), 77. *Prof Exp:* Fel theoret astrophys, Ctr Astrophys, Harvard Col Observ, 77-80; mem staff, Sci Applns, Inc. 80-89. *Mem:* Sigma Xi; Am Astron Soc. *Res:* Theoretical studies of radiation-driven stellar winds in binary x-ray source systems, and of accretion onto black holes. *Mailing Add:* Lawrence Livermore Nat Lab 7000 East Ave L-014 PO Box 808 Livermore CA 94550. *Fax:* 510-424-4320

**VITERBI, ANDREW J,** COMMUNICATIONS. *Current Pos:* prof, 85-97, EMER PROF ELEC & COMPUT ENG, UNIV CALIF, SAN DIEGO, 97- *Personal Data:* b Bergamo, Italy, Mar 9, 35; US citizen; m 58; c 3. *Educ:* Mass Inst Technol, BS & MS, 57; Univ Southern Calif, PhD(elec eng), 62. *Hon Degrees:* Dr, Univ Waterloo, 90. *Honors & Awards:* Inst Elec & Electronics Engrs Award, 62, Ann Award, 68, Alexander Graham Bell Medal, 84; Columbus Int Commun Award, Ital Nat Res Coun, 75; Eduard R Hein Award, 94. *Prof Exp:* Res engr, Commun Res Sect, Jet Propulsion Lab, Calif Inst Technol, 57-62, res group supvr, 62-63; from asst prof to prof eng, Univ Calif, Los Angeles, 63-73; exec vpres, Linkabit Corp, 73-82, pres, 82-84. *Concurrent Pos:* Chmn vis comt, Elec Eng Dept, Technion Israel Inst Technol; mem, Mass Inst Technol Corp vis comt elec eng & comput sci Army Sci Bd; chmn, US Comn Signal Processing, Int Radio Sci Union; distinguished lectr, Univ Ill Coord Sci Lab; vchmn & chief tech officer, Qualcomm, Inc, 85-; Marconi Int fel award, 90. *Mem:* Nat Acad Sci; Nat Acad Eng; fel Inst Elec & Electronics Engrs. *Res:* Communication and information theory; coding; detection; modulation; signal processing; new spread spectrum processing techniques for jam resistant communications and for digital cellular radio; author of various publications. *Mailing Add:* 6455 Lusk Blvd San Diego CA 92121

**VITETTA, ELLEN S,** MICROBIOLOGY, IMMUNOLOGY. *Current Pos:* PROF, MICROBIOL, SOUTHWESTERN MED SCH, UNIV TEX, DALLAS, DIR, CANCER IMMUNOL CTR & SHERYLE SIMMONS PATIGIAN DISTINGUISHED CHAIR CANCER IMMUNOBIOL. *Educ:* Conn Col, BA; NY Univ, MS, 66, PhD, 68. *Honors & Awards:* Taittinger Breast Cancer Res Award, Komen Found, 83; Pierce Immunotoxin Award, 88; Abbot Clin Immunol Award, Am Soc Microbiologists, 92. *Concurrent Pos:* Mem sci bd, Ludwig Inst, 83-; assoc ed, Cancer Res, 86-; merit award, NIH, 87-; mem, Task Force Immunol, Nat Inst Allergy & Infectious Dis, 89-90; mem sci adv bd, Howard Hughes Med Inst, 92-; mem bd sci coun, Nat Cancer Inst, Cancer Treat Bd, 93-; co-ed in chief, Therapeut Immunol, 92- *Mem:* Nat Acad Sci; Int Soc Immunopharmacol; Am Asn Immunologists (pres, 93-). *Res:* Co-discovery of IL-4; development of immunotoxins and identification of murine boron cells. *Mailing Add:* Southwestern Med Sch Univ Tex 5323 Harry Hines Blvd Dallas TX 75235-9048

**VITKAUSKAS, GRACE,** ANTI-TUMOR DRUGS, METABOLIC COOPERATION. *Educ:* Univ Conn, PhD(molecular biol), 79. *Prof Exp:* Assoc res scientist, Dept Pharmacol, Yale Univ, 80-88. *Res:* Cell-to-cell interactions. *Mailing Add:* 105 Cold Spring Circle Naugatuck CT 06770

**VITKOVITS, JOHN A(NDREW),** MECHANICAL ENGINEERING. *Current Pos:* RETIRED. *Personal Data:* b Cleveland, Ohio, Apr 7, 21; m 48; c 2. *Educ:* Southern Methodist Univ, BS, 48. *Prof Exp:* Proj engr, Lubrizol Corp, Ohio, 48-49; mech engr, Southwest Res Inst, 49-55, asst sect mgr, 55-56, mgr, Stand Tests Sect, 56-59, dir, Dept Engines, Fuels & Lubricants Eval, 57-72, vpres, Div Engines, Fuels & Lubricant Eval, 72-86. *Concurrent Pos:* Mem diesel rating panel & comt automatic transmission fluids, Coord Res Coun, Inc, 56-; mem automatic transmission fluid panel, Gen Motors Corp. *Mem:* Soc Automotive Engrs. *Res:* Automotive engines; torque converters; high speed and high torque hypoid gear lubricant evaluation; copper-lead, tin overlay and babbitt bearing endurance testing; design of engine research labs. *Mailing Add:* 131 Mountridge Dr San Antonio TX 78228-1717

**VITOLS, VISVALDIS ALBERTS,** ELECTRICAL ENGINEERING, INFORMATION SCIENCE. *Current Pos:* MGR, INFO SCI, 75- *Personal Data:* b Riga, Latvia, Aug 24, 36; US citizen; m 63; c 2. *Educ:* Iowa State Univ, BS, 58, MS, 59, PhD(elec eng), 62. *Prof Exp:* Asst prof elec eng, Iowa State Univ, 62-63; group scientist, NAm Aviation, Inc, 63-65; mem tech staff comput technol, IBM Corp, 65-68; mgr pattern recognition, Rockwell Int, 68-75. *Concurrent Pos:* Consult, Nat Acad Sci, 69-72. *Mem:* Inst Elec & Electronics Engrs; Sigma Xi; Int Asn Identification. *Res:* Pattern recognition and signal processing techniques utilizing general and special purpose digital processors; processor architectures for information classification and retrieval systems; machine recognition of unconstrained speech and image processing; imaged based scene and target recognition. *Mailing Add:* 505 S Aberdeen St Anaheim Hills CA 92807-4656

**VITOSH, MAURICE LEE,** AGRONOMY, SOIL SCIENCE. *Current Pos:* EXTEN SPECIALIST SOIL FERTIL PROF CROP & SOIL SCI, MICH STATE UNIV, 68- *Personal Data:* b Odell, Nebr, Jan 16, 39; m 63; c 1. *Educ:* Univ Nebr, BS, 62, MS, 64; NC State Univ, PhD(soils), 68. *Prof Exp:* Agronomist, NC Dept Agr, 65-68. *Mem:* Am Soc Agron; Soil Sci Soc Am; Potato Asn Am; Am Soybean Asn. *Res:* Soil fertility with potato, corn, soybeans and field beans. *Mailing Add:* Dept Crop & Soil Sci Mich State Univ East Lansing MI 48824-1325

**VITOUSEK, MARTIN J,** GEOPHYSICS. *Current Pos:* RETIRED. *Personal Data:* b Honolulu, Hawaii, July 30, 24; m 65; c 4. *Educ:* Stanford Univ, BS, 49, PhD(math), 54. *Prof Exp:* Radar lab worker, Pearl Harbor, 43-46; asst prof math, Univ Hawaii, 53-55; sr engr, Scripps Inst, Calif, 56-59; from assoc geophysicist to geophysicist, Hawaii Inst Geophys, Univ Hawaii, Manoa, 61-74, specialist oceanog instrument, 74-90. *Mem:* Marine Technol Soc; Solar Energy Soc. *Res:* Applied mathematics; solid earth geophysics and oceanography; long period ocean waves, instrumentation and analysis. *Mailing Add:* Jimar PO Box 150 Kealakekua HI 96750

**VITOUSEK, PETER MORRISON,** ECOLOGY. *Current Pos:* ASSOC PROF & PROF BIOL SCI, STANFORD UNIV, 84-, CLIFFORD G MORRISON PROF POP & RESOURCE STUDIES, 93- *Personal Data:* b Honolulu, Hawaii, Jan 24, 49. *Educ:* Amherst Col, BA, 71; Dartmouth Col, PhD(biol sci), 75. *Honors & Awards:* W S Cooper Award, Ecol Soc Am, 92, R H MacArthur Award, 93. *Prof Exp:* Asst prof biol & zool, Ind Univ, Bloomington, 75-79; assoc prof bot, Univ NC, Chapel Hill 80-83. *Mem:* Fel Nat Acad Sci; AAAS; Soil Sci Soc Am; Ecol Soc Am; Am Acad Arts & Sci. *Res:* Regulation of nutrient cycling in terrestrial ecosystems; land-water interactions. *Mailing Add:* Dept Biol Herrin Labs Rm 445 Stanford Univ Stanford CA 94305

**VITOVEC, FRANZ H,** PHYSICAL METALLURGY, FRACTURE MECHANICS. *Current Pos:* prof metall eng, Univ Alta, 65-81, chmn, Dept Mineral Eng, 71-80, prof mech eng, 81-87, EMER PROF MECH ENG, UNIV ALTA, 87- *Personal Data:* b Vienna, Austria, June 7, 21; nat Can; m 42, Elfriede Waldhausl; c 2. *Educ:* Vienna Tech Univ, dipl, 46, Dr tech sci, 47. *Prof Exp:* Docent, Vienna Tech Univ, 51; from asst prof to assoc prof mech & mat, Univ Minn, 52-58; from assoc prof to prof metall eng & nuclear eng, Univ Wis, 58-65. *Mem:* Am Soc Metals. *Res:* Relationship between the mechanical behavior of metals and alloys, their microstructure, and the environment. *Mailing Add:* 8942 Forest Park Dr Sydney BC V8L 5A7 Can

**VITRUK, PETER,** OPTOELECTRONICS. *Current Pos:* SR SCIENTIST, SYNRAD INC, 95- *Personal Data:* b Ternopol, Ukraine, Feb 2, 62. *Educ:* Moscow Physics & Technol Inst, MSc, 85, PhD(physics), 90. *Prof Exp:* Res scientist, Inst Probs Mech, USSR Acad Sci, 85-91; res assoc, Heriod-Wah Univ, Edinburgh, UK, 91-95. *Mem:* Inst Physics; Inst Elec & Electronics Engrs; Am Inst Physics. *Res:* High power sealed industrial gas lasers including carbon dioxide CO and Xe lasers. *Mailing Add:* Synrad 6500 Harbour Heights Pkwy Mukilteo WA 98275. *Fax:* 425-485-4882; *E-Mail:* pvitruk@ aol.com

**VITT, DALE HADLEY,** BOTANY, BRYOLOGY. *Current Pos:* From asst prof to prof, 70-88, MC CALLA PROF BOT, UNIV ALTA, 88- *Personal Data:* b Washington, Mo, Feb 9, 44; c 2. *Educ:* Southeast Mo State Col, BS, 67; Univ Mich, Ann Arbor, MS, 68, PhD(bot), 70. *Mem:* Int Asn Plant Taxon; Am Bryol & Lichenological Soc; Can Bot Soc; Danish Bryol Soc; Brit Bryol Soc; Japanese Bryol Soc. *Res:* Taxonomic, phylogenetic and ecological studies of bryophytes; monographic treatment of arctic, antarctic and tropical mosses; ecological analyses and productivity of bryophytes in arctic and alpine tundras and evolution and development of boreal peatlands; biogeochemistry of wetlands; peatland ecology. *Mailing Add:* Dept Biol Sci Univ Alta Rm CW405 Biol Sci Bldg Edmonton AB T6G 2E9 Can

**VITT, LAURIE JOSEPH,** ECOLOGY, HERPETOLOGY. *Current Pos:* asst prof, 81-85, ASSOC PROF BIOL, UNIV CALIF, LOS ANGELES, 85- *Personal Data:* b Bremerton, Wash, Aug 20, 45; m. *Educ:* Western Wash State Col, BA, 67, MS, 71; Ariz State Univ, PhD(zool), 76. *Prof Exp:* Res fel ecol, Academia Brasileira de Ciencas, Brazil, 77-78; scholar ecol, Mus Zool, Univ Mich, 78-79; res assoc fel, Mus Natural Hist, Univ Ga, 79-81, res assoc, 81. *Concurrent Pos:* Res ecologist, Ariz State Univ grant, 73-75, res assoc, 75-76; consult, Desert Plan Off, Bur Land Mgt, 78 & Athene Wildlife Found, 79; adj asst prof, Savannah River Ecol Lab & Univ Ga, 81- *Mem:* Am Soc Ichthyol & Herpet; Soc Study Evolution; Herpet League; Soc Study Amphibians & Reptiles; Ecol Soc Am; Sigma Xi. *Res:* Community structure, competition, predation, reproductive effort, parental investment, demographics, life histories and reproduction of vertebrates, tail autotomy of lizards. *Mailing Add:* Okla Mus Natural Hist 1335 Asp Ave Norman OK 73019-6070

**VITTER, JEFFREY SCOTT,** ANALYSIS OF ALGORITHMS, COMPUTATIONAL COMPLEXITY. *Current Pos:* PROF COMPUT SCI, BROWN UNIV, 88- *Personal Data:* b New Orleans, La, Nov 13, 55; m 82; c 2. *Educ:* Univ Notre Dame, BS, 77; Stanford Univ, PhD(comput sci), 80. *Hon Degrees:* AM, Brown Univ, 86. *Honors & Awards:* Fac Develop Award, IBM, 84; Presidential Young Investr Award, NSF, 85-91. *Prof Exp:* from asst prof to assoc prof, Comput Sci, Brown Univ, 80-88. *Concurrent Pos:* Grad fel, NSF, 77-80; Teaching fel, Stanford Univ, 79; consult, IBM, Xerox, Inst Defense Anal, Knowledge Eng, Univ Space Res Asn, 81-; prin investr, NSF & IBM, 81- & Defense Advan Res Proj Agency-Off Naval Res, 83-85; guest ed, Inst Elec & Electronics Engrs Trans on Comput, 85 & J Algorithmica, 88 & 92; vis scientist, Inst Nat Res Informatics & Automation, 86-87; mem, Math Sci Res Inst, 86; mem-at-large, Spec Interest Group Automata & Computability Theory, 87-91; ed, Inst Elec & Electronics Engrs Trans on Comput, 87-91, Commun Asn Comput Mach, 88-, Soc Indust & Appl Math J Comput, 89-; Guggenheim fel, 86- *Mem:* Asn Comput Mach; Inst Elec & Electronics Engrs; Sigma Xi. *Res:* Software design and optimization; order statistics; concept learning; parallel optimization; computational geometry; parallel processing; machine learning. *Mailing Add:* Dept Comput Sci Duke Univ D315 Levine Sci Res Ctr Durham NC 27708

**VITTETOE, MARIE CLARE,** CLINICAL LABORATORY SCIENCES. *Current Pos:* PROF MED TECHNOL, UNIV KY, LEXINGTON, 78- *Personal Data:* b Keota, Iowa, May 19, 27. *Educ:* Marycrest Col, BS, 50; WVa Univ, Morgantown, MS, 71, EdD(higher educ admin), 73. *Prof Exp:* Staff technician, St Joseph Hosp, Ottumwa, Iowa, 50-67, lab supvr, 67-70; asst prof health occup, Univ Ill, Urbana-Champaign, 73-78. *Concurrent Pos:* Instr microbiol & chem, Sch Nursing, St Joseph Hosp, 50-70; instr, didactic & clin, Ottumwa Sch Med Technol, 57-70. *Mem:* Am Soc Med Technol; Am Soc Allied Health Professions; affil mem Am Soc Clin Pathologists. *Res:* Administration in science education: program development, cost effectiveness and student learning patterns. *Mailing Add:* Med Technol Univ Ky 7500 S Limestone St Lexington KY 40536-0001. *Fax:* 606-258-1058

**VITTI, TRIESTE GUIDO,** BIOPHARMACEUTICS, PHARMACOKINETICS. *Current Pos:* PROF BIOPHARMACEUT, FAC PHARM, UNIV MAN, 72- *Personal Data:* b Detroit, Mich, May 22, 25; m 53; c 4. *Educ:* Univ Detroit, BS, 49, MS, 51; Wayne State Univ, PhD(biochem), 61. *Prof Exp:* Lectr pharmacol, Fac Med, Univ Man, 64-67; chief bioavailability, Upjohn Co, Mich, 67-71; dir clin res, Bur Drugs, Food & Drug Admin, 71-72. *Concurrent Pos:* USPHS fel, Univ Man, 64-67; consult, Biodecision Labs, Pittsburgh, Pa, 72-76; mem permanent adv expert comt bioavailability, Health & Welfare, Health Progs Bd, Can, 74-; mem bd, Alcohol & Drug Educ Serv, Man, 78-; mem adv res comt, Col Family Physicians, Family Med Ctr, Winnipeg, 78-80. *Mem:* Am Chem Soc; Pharmacol Soc Can; Can Pharmaceut Asn; Sigma Xi. *Res:* Biochemical pharmacology. *Mailing Add:* Fac Pharm Univ Man Winnipeg MB R3T 2N2 Can

**VITTITOE, CHARLES NORMAN,** ELECTROMAGNETIC PULSE, NUMERICAL MODELING. *Current Pos:* staff mem, Radiation Phenomena Div, Sandia Labs, 66-70, staff mem, 70-84, distinguished mem tech staff, Electromagnetic Applns Dir, 84-90, DISTINGUISHED MEM TECH STAFF, RADIATION & ELECTROMAGNETIC ANALYSIS DIV, SANDIA LABS, 90- *Personal Data:* b Louisville, Ky, Oct 3, 34; m 58, Mary A Aldridge; c Dorothy & Victoria. *Educ:* Univ Ky, BS, 56; Univ Ky, MS, 58; Univ Ky, PhD(physics), 63. *Prof Exp:* Instr physics, Univ Ky, 59-60, from res asst to res assoc, 62-63; asst prof, Univ Ohio, 63-66, univ res comt, grant, 66. *Concurrent Pos:* Guest ed, J Radiation Effects Res & Eng, 84. *Mem:* Am Phys Soc. *Res:* Nuclear Weapon effects; optical transport theory; central receiver solar energy collection; geological probing by electrical methods; time-domain finite-difference solutions; to boundary-valve problems of electrodynamics; non-linear effects; computerized tomography subject models. *Mailing Add:* 3304 Ocotillo Ct NE Albuquerque NM 87111. *Fax:* 505-845-3471

**VITTORIA, CARMINE,** MAGNETISM, MICROWAVE MATERIALS. *Current Pos:* PROF, NORTHEASTERN UNIV, 85- *Personal Data:* b Avella, Italy, May 15, 41; US citizen; m 67; c 3. *Educ:* Toledo Univ, BS, 62; Yale Univ, MS, 67, PhD(physics), 70. *Honors & Awards:* Outstanding Achievement Award, Naval Res Lab, 72 & 74. *Prof Exp:* Elec engr bionics, Naval Ord Lab, 62-63; teacher elec eng, Toledo Univ, 63-64; physicist, Naval Res Lab, 70-85. *Concurrent Pos:* Naval Res Coun adv, Naval Res Lab, 74, res award, 76; mem tech prog comt, Nat Magnetism Conf, 78; consult, Navy Electronic Syst Agencies. *Mem:* Fel Am Phys Soc; fel Inst Elec & Electronics Engrs; Sigma Xi. *Res:* Electromagnetic wave propagation in magnetic materials; microwave magnetic materials; superconducting devices. *Mailing Add:* 300 Commercial St Boston MA 02109. *Fax:* 617-373-4853; *E-Mail:* vittoria@northeastern.edu

**VITTUM, MORRILL THAYER,** HORTICULTURE, AGRONOMY. *Current Pos:* from asst prof to prof, 46-83, head dept, 60-69 & 71-83, EMER PROF VEG CROPS, NY STATE AGR EXP STA, CORNELL UNIV, 83- *Personal Data:* b Haverhill, Mass, May 4, 19; m 41; c 3. *Educ:* Univ Mass, BS, 39; Univ Conn, MS, 41; Purdue Univ, PhD(soil sci), 44. *Prof Exp:* Asst agron, Univ Conn, 39-41; asst agron, Purdue Univ, 41-42, tech asst soils, 42-45. *Concurrent Pos:* Actg asst olericulturist, Univ Calif, Davis, 56-57; vis prof hort, Ore State Univ, 64; proj leader, Univ Philippines-Cornell Grad Educ Prog, Col Agr, Univ Philippines, 69-71; actg horticulturist, Coop State Res Serv, USDA, 73-74 & 80-81. *Mem:* Am Soc Agron; Soil Sci Soc Am; fel Am Soc Hort Sci; Int Soc Hort Sci; Int Soc Soil Sci. *Res:* Effects of fertilizers, irrigation, rotation and cultural practices on the yield and quality of processing vegetables; evapotranspiration and soil-plant-water relationships. *Mailing Add:* 18 Main St Phelps NY 14532

**VITUS, CARISSIMA MARIE,** SCANNING PROBE MICROSCOPY, CORROSION. *Current Pos:* ASST SCIENTIST, BROOKHAVEN NAT LAB, 92- *Personal Data:* b Youngstown, Ohio, June 9, 64. *Educ:* Youngstown State Univ, BS, 86; Purdue Univ, PhD(analytical chem), 91. *Prof Exp:* Teaching asst gen chem, Purdue Univ, 86-90; fel, WVa Univ, 90-92. *Mem:* Electrochem Soc; Am Chem Soc. *Res:* Use of scanning probe techniques in conjunction with the electrochemical methods to further understand the processes which lead to aqueous localized corrosion. *Mailing Add:* 15 Spencer Path Dr St Peters MO 63376

**VIVIAN, J(OHNSON) EDWARD,** chemical engineering; deceased, see previous edition for last biography

**VIVIAN, VIRGINIA M,** NUTRITION. *Current Pos:* RETIRED. *Personal Data:* b Barneveld, Wis, July 1, 23. *Educ:* Univ Wis, BS, 45; Columbia Univ, MS, 47; Univ Wis, PhD(home econ, biochem), 59. *Prof Exp:* Instr foods, nutrit & dietetics, Sch Nursing, Presby Hosp, 48-49; instr foods, nutrit & dietetics, Sch Nursing, Univ Mich, 49-51, asst dir dietary dept, Univ Hosp, 51-55; from asst prof to prof home econ, Ohio State Univ & Ohio Agr Res & Develop Ctr, 59-77, chairperson dept human nutrit & food mgt, 77-82, Carol S Kennedy distinguished prof nutrit, 82-88. *Concurrent Pos:* Pvt consult, 88- *Mem:* AAAS; Am Home Econ Asn; Am Dietetic Asn; Am Inst Nutrit; NY Acad Sci; Sigma Xi. *Res:* Amino acid-lipid metabolism with humans, adolescent and elderly dietary adequacy and nutrition status studies; exercise, diet and metabolism. *Mailing Add:* 1298 La Rochelle Dr Columbus OH 43221-1532

**VIZY, KALMAN NICHOLAS,** APPLIED PHYSICS, IMAGING SCIENCES. *Current Pos:* IMAGING SCI CONSULT, 91- *Personal Data:* b Gyor, Hungary, July 7, 40; US citizen; m 68, M A Smith; c Anne & Edward. *Educ:* Cleveland State Univ, BEE, 63, BS, 64; John Carroll Univ, MS, 67; Walden Inst Advan Studies, PhD, 90. *Honors & Awards:* Autometric Award, Am Soc Photogram & Am Soc Mech Engrs, 75. *Prof Exp:* Dept head sci, Byzantine Educ Ctr, 64-67; sr physicist, Res Labs, Eastman Kodak Co, 67-80, corp consult, 80-91. *Concurrent Pos:* Adj lectr modern physics, Rochester Inst Technol, 67-; adj asst prof radiol, Univ Rochester, 90-; lectr modern technol. *Mem:* Am Soc Mech Engrs; Am Asn Physics Teachers; Am Asn Physicists Med; Am Phys Soc; Soc Photog Scientists & Engrs; Am Soc Prof Engrs; Am Col Radiol. *Res:* Research and development on the application of imaging for reconnaissance, micrographics, and medical applications; systems designer and analyst. *Mailing Add:* 16 Clearview Dr Spencerport NY 14559-1118

**VLACH, JIRI,** ELECTRICAL ENGINEERING. *Current Pos:* PROF ELEC ENG, UNIV WATERLOO, 69- *Personal Data:* b Praha, Czech, Oct 5, 22; m 49, Dagmar Gutova; c Martin. *Educ:* Prague Tech Univ, Dipl Eng, 47, PhD(elec eng), 57. *Prof Exp:* Mem res staff, Res Inst Radiocommun, Czech, 48-67; vis prof elec eng, Univ Ill, 67-69. *Mem:* Fel Inst Elec & Electronics Engrs. *Res:* Network theory; computer aided design; VLSI; witched networks. *Mailing Add:* Dept Elec Eng Univ Waterloo Waterloo ON N2L 3G1 Can. *Fax:* 519-746-5195; *E-Mail:* jvlach@vlsi.uwaterloo.ca

**VLACHOPOULOS, JOHN A(POSTOLOS),** CHEMICAL ENGINEERING. *Current Pos:* from asst prof to prof chem, 68-79, chmn, 85-88, DIR, CENTRE ADVAN POLYMER PROCESSING & DESIGN, CAPPA-D, MCMASTER UNIV, 94- *Personal Data:* b Volos, Greece, Aug 11, 42. *Educ:* Athens Tech Univ, dipl, 65; Wash Univ, St Louis, MS, 68, DSc, 69. *Concurrent Pos:* Sabbatical, Univ Stuttgart Ger, 75 & Ecole Des Mines, Paris, 81-82 & 88-89. *Mem:* Am Inst Chem Engrs; Soc Plastics Engrs; Soc Rheol; fel Chem Inst Can; Can Soc Chem Eng; Sigma Xi; Polymer Proc Soc. *Res:* Polymer processing and polymer rheology; finite difference and finite element methods for numerical simulations; fluid mechanics; polymer extrusion; calendering; injection molding; thermoforming; compression molding; rotational molding. *Mailing Add:* Dept Chem Eng 1280 Main St W Hamilton ON L8S 4L7 Can. *Fax:* 905-522-5004; *E-Mail:* vlachopj@mcmaster.ca

**VLADECK, BRUCE C,** HEALTH ADMINISTRATION. *Current Pos:* ADMINR, HEALTH CARE FINANCING ADMIN, 94- *Personal Data:* b New York, NY, Sept 13, 49; m 73, Fredda Wellin; c Elizabeth, Stephen & Abagail. *Educ:* Harvard Univ, BA, 70; Univ Mich, MA, 72, PhD, 73. *Hon Degrees:* DSc, State Univ NY, 94. *Prof Exp:* From asst prof to assoc prof pub health & health admin, Ctr Community Health Systs, Columbia Univ, 74-79; asst comnr, Div Health Planning & Resources Develop, NJ State Dept Health, 79-82; asst vpres, Robert Wood Johnson Found, 82-83; pres, United Hosp Fund NY, 83-94. *Concurrent Pos:* Consult, Off Secy, US Dept HEW,

78; mem, Comt Health Planning, Inst Med-Nat Acad Sci, 79-80; vis lectr, Princeton Univ, 81-83; adj prof pub admin, NY Univ, 88- *Mem:* Inst Med-Nat Acad Sci; fel NY Acad Med. *Mailing Add:* Health Care Financing Admin 200 Independence Ave SW Rm 314G Washington DC 20201. *Fax:* 202-690-6262

**VLADUTIU, ADRIAN O,** CLINICAL PATHOLOGY, IMMUNOPATHOLOGY. *Current Pos:* res asst prof microbiol, State Univ NY, Buffalo, 69-71, clin assoc prof path, 77-81, res assoc prof med, 79-86, PROF PATH, SCH MED, STATE UNIV NY, BUFFALO, 81-, PROF MICROBIOL, 82-, RES PROF MED, 86- *Personal Data:* b Bucharest, Romania, Aug 5, 40; US citizen; m 71, Georgirene Dietrich; c Christina L & Catherine J. *Educ:* Spiru Haret, Romania, BS, 56; Bucharest Univ, MD, 62; Jassy Univ, PhD(immunopath), 68. *Prof Exp:* Asst prof physiopath, Sch Med, Univ Bucharest, 68-71. *Concurrent Pos:* Intern, G Marinesco Hosp, Bucharest, 62-65, Millard Fillmore Hosp, Buffalo, 71-72; res fel, Med Res Coun, Can 68-69; resident, State Univ NY, Buffalo, E J Meyer & Buffalo Gen Hosp, 72-74; dir, Immunopath Lab, Buffalo Gen Hosp, 74-, assoc pathologist, 79-82, dir, Chem Lab, 81-, dir, Clin Lab, 82-, pathologist, 82-; consult, path, Niagara Falls Mem Hosp, 76-82, Tri-County Hosp, Gowanda, NY, 91-93; mem, E Witebsky Ctr Immunol, 81-; prin investr, NIH, 85-89. *Mem:* Am Asn Immunologists; Soc Exp Biol & Med; AAAS; NY Acad Sci; Am Soc Invest Pathol. *Res:* Autoimmunity in animals and man; diagnosis, pathogenesis and particularly its genetic control; laboratory medicine particularly isoenzymes, immune complexes, receptor assays and differential diagnosis of pleural effusions; tumor markers. *Mailing Add:* Dept Path State Univ NY Buffalo Gen Hosp 100 High St Buffalo NY 14203. *Fax:* 716-845-2893; *E-Mail:* vladutiu@acsu.buffalo.edu

**VLADUTIU, GEORGIRENE DIETRICH,** INBORN ERRORS OF METABOLISM, NEWBORN SCREENING. *Current Pos:* From res instr to res assoc prof, 76-84, actg dir, Div Human Genetics, 86-89, DIR, BIOCHEM GENETICS LAB, CHILDREN'S HOSP, BUFFALO, 84-; ASSOC PROF PEDIAT, STATE UNIV NY, BUFFALO, 84- *Personal Data:* b Bremerton, Wash, Dec 21, 44; m 71, Adrian; c Christina & Catherine. *Educ:* Syracuse Univ, BS, 66; State Univ NY, Buffalo, MA, 70, PhD(microbiol), 73; Am Bd Med Genetics, dipl clin biochem genetics, 93. *Concurrent Pos:* Prin investr, NSF, 77-79, NIH, 79-85 & Cystic Fibrosis Found, 81-82; Res Career Develop Award, Nat Inst Child Health & Human Develop, 80-85. *Mem:* Am Soc Biol Chemists; Am Soc Human Genetics; Soc Pediat Res; Soc Inherited Metal Dis; Am Soc Cell Biol; Soc Study Inborn Errors Metab. *Res:* Screening tests for inborn errors of metabolism; metabolic disease of muscle such as mitochondrial myopathics, glycogen store diseases and malignant hyperthermia. *Mailing Add:* Children's Hosp 936 Delaware Ave Buffalo NY 14209. *Fax:* 716-878-7980; *E-Mail:* gdv@acsu.buffalo.edu

**VLAHAKIS, GEORGE,** GENETICS. *Current Pos:* RETIRED. *Personal Data:* b New York, NY, Oct 12, 23; m 49, Wanda Ginter; c John & Anthony. *Educ:* Johns Hopkins Univ, AB, 51; Univ Tex, MA, 53. *Prof Exp:* Biologist, NIH, 52-53; chemist, US Testing Co, 54-55; biologist, Nat Cancer Inst, 55-86. *Mem:* AAAS. *Res:* Role of genes and their relationship to non-genetic factors in the development of tumors in mice. *Mailing Add:* 1720 Evelyn Dr Rockville MD 20852

**VLAHOS, CHRIS JOHN,** BIOCHEMISTRY. *Current Pos:* Sr scientist, 87-92, RES SCIENTIST BIOCHEM, ELI LILLY & CO, LILLY CORP CTR, 92- *Personal Data:* b San Francisco, Calif, June 15, 60. *Educ:* Santa Clara Univ, BS, 82; Univ Mich, MS, 84, PhD(biochem), 87. *Mem:* Am Chem Soc; AAAS; Am Soc Biochem & Molecular Biol. *Res:* Biochemistry. *Mailing Add:* Cardiovascular Res Eli Lilly & Co Lilly Corp Ctr Indianapolis IN 46285-0403

**VLAOVIC, MILAN STEPHEN,** TOXICOLOGICAL PATHOLOGY. *Current Pos:* PATHOLOGIST, EASTMAN KODAK CO, 78- *Personal Data:* b Novi Sad, Yugoslavia, Feb 1, 36; m 69, Sharon H Rabatich; c Steven A, Sofija A & Peter M. *Educ:* Univ Belgrade, DVM, 61; Univ Sask, MSc, 70; Univ Mo, Columbia, PhD(vet med), 74. *Prof Exp:* Gen practr, WGer, 65-67; tech officer, Can Dept Agr, 67-68; res asst vet microbiol, Univ Sask, 68-70; res asst, Wash State Univ, 70-71; res assoc, Univ Mo, 71-74; vet pathologist, Frederick Cancer Res Ctr, 74-77; toxicol pathologist, IBT, 77-78. *Mem:* Am Vet Med Asn; Am Asn Lab Animal Sci; Soc Toxicol Pathologists. *Res:* Immunopathology; toxicological pathology. *Mailing Add:* 7 Dixon Woods Honeoye Falls NY 14472

**VLASES, GEORGE CHARPENTIER,** PLASMA PHYSICS. *Current Pos:* SCI ASST TO DIR, JET JOINT UNDERTAKING, 89- *Personal Data:* b New York, NY, Oct 22, 36; m 58; c 4. *Educ:* Johns Hopkins Univ, BES, 58; Calif Inst Technol, MS, 59, PhD(aeronaut), 63. *Prof Exp:* Res fel aeronaut, Calif Inst Technol, 63; from asst prof to assoc prof aerospace eng sci, Univ Colo, Boulder, 63-69; res assoc prof, Aerospace Res Lab, Univ Wash, 69-73; prof nuclear eng, 73-89. *Concurrent Pos:* Consult, Aerospace Corp, Calif, 63 & Spectra Technol, Inc; vis scientist, Max Planck Inst Plasma Physics, Munich, 81 & 85. *Mem:* Am Phys Soc. *Res:* Plasma physics and controlled thermonuclear fusion. *Mailing Add:* Jet Joint Undertaking Bldg K-1 Abingdon Oxon OX143EA England. *Fax:* 44-235-464766

**VLASUK, GEORGE P,** PROTEOLYTIC ENZYMES, INHIBITION OF PROTEOLYTIC ENZYMES. *Current Pos:* sr res biochemist, 85-87, res fel biol chem, 87-90, ASSOC DIR PHARMACOL, MERCK SHARP & DOHME, 90- *Personal Data:* b Miami, Fla, Oct 9, 55; m 81; c 2. *Educ:* Miami Dade Community Col, AA, 75; Univ SFla, BS, 77; Kent State Univ, PhD(biochem), 81. *Prof Exp:* Postdoctoral molecular biol, State Univ NY,

Stony Brook, 82-83; staff scientist, Calif Biotechnol Inc, 83-85. *Concurrent Pos:* Mem Thrombosis Coun, Am Heart Asn. *Mem:* Am Soc Biochem & Molecular Biol; AAAS; Am Heart Asn. *Res:* Identification and utilization of specific inhibition of blood coagulation factors to understand the mechanism of vascular thrombosis in vivo and in vitro. *Mailing Add:* Molecular Pharmacol Corvas Int 3030 Sci Park Rd San Diego CA 92121-1102. *Fax:* 619-455-7895

**VLATTAS, ISIDOROS,** ORGANIC CHEMISTRY. *Current Pos:* res chemist, 68-80, sr staff scientist org chem, 80-90, SR RES FEL, CIBA GEIGY CORP, 90- *Personal Data:* b Chios, Greece, Apr 28, 35; US citizen; m 67, Argyro; c John, Angela & Christina. *Educ:* Nat Univ Athens, BS, 59; Univ BC, MsD, 63, PhD(chem), 66. *Prof Exp:* Fel, Harvard Univ, 67-68. *Mem:* Am Chem Soc. *Res:* Natural products; medicinal organic chemistry research; peptide synthesis. *Mailing Add:* Ciba Geigy Corp 556 Morris Ave Summit NJ 07901

**VLAY, GEORGE JOHN,** MATHEMATICS, SYSTEMS DESIGN & SYSTEMS SCIENCE. *Current Pos:* PRES, SYSTS MGT ASSOCS, 90- *Personal Data:* b Buffalo, NY, Dec 1, 27; m 49, Betty J Wayland; c Vanessa M, Susan V & George J Jr. *Educ:* Univ Buffalo, BS, 53. *Honors & Awards:* Eng Award of Excellence, Electronic Industs Asn, 90. *Prof Exp:* Mgr advan req satellite prog, Ford Aerospace Corp, W Develop Labs, 68-73, mgr advan space systs satellite design, 74-75, mgr commun systs satellite commun systs, 76-77, dir bus develop & planning, plans & mkt, 78-82, dir tech affairs IR&D, 82-85, dir prod assurance qual, reliability & metrol, Space Systs Div, 85-88, dir systs mgt, 88-90. *Concurrent Pos:* Mem, Coun Defense Space Indust Asn-Streamling Acquisition, 87- & USAF/AFSC Indust RFP Crit Process Team, 89-; distinguished lectr, Am Inst Aeronaut & Astronaut, 89-91. *Mem:* Assoc fel Am Inst Aeronaut & Astronaut; sr mem Inst Elec & Electronics Engrs; Am Soc Eng Mgt; Nat Coun Systs Eng. *Res:* Program management; systems engineering management; risk management. *Mailing Add:* 32 Yerba Buena Ave Los Altos CA 94022-2208. *Fax:* 650-941-1530; *E-Mail:* 07g21b49@supal.org

**VLCEK, DONALD HENRY,** electronics, research administration; deceased, see previous edition for last biography

**VLIET, DANIEL H(ENDRICKS),** ELECTRICAL ENGINEERING. *Current Pos:* Assoc prof, 58-65, prof, 65-86, EMER PROF ELEC ENG, TULANE UNIV LA, 86- *Personal Data:* b New Orleans, La, May 30, 21; m 43; c 3. *Educ:* Tulane Univ, BSEE, 49; Univ Mich, MSEE, 52; Univ Wis, PhD, 65. *Mem:* Am Soc Eng Educ; Inst Elec & Electronics Engrs. *Res:* Power system analysis; electrical machinery; automation and control. *Mailing Add:* 168 Cherry Creek Dr Madeville LA 70448

**VLIET, GARY CLARK,** HEAT TRANSFER, SOLAR ENERGY. *Current Pos:* assoc prof, 71-79, PROF MECH ENG, UNIV TEX, AUSTIN, 79-, W R WOOLRICH PROF, 85- *Personal Data:* b Bassano, Alta, June 3, 33; US citizen; m 62; c 3. *Educ:* Univ Alta, BSc, 55; Stanford Univ, MS, 57, PhD(mech eng), 62. *Prof Exp:* Res scientist, Lockheed Missiles & Space Co, 61-71. *Concurrent Pos:* Consult, Various Cos; Fluor fel, Stanford, 56. *Mem:* Assoc mem Am Soc Mech Engrs; Int Solar Energy Soc; Am Soc Heating, Refrig & Air-Conditioning Engrs. *Res:* Thermal energy systems; solar energy; energy conversion. *Mailing Add:* 6407 Shoal Creek Blvd Austin TX 78757

**VNENCAK-JONES, CINDY LENORE,** HUMAN MOLECULAR GENETICS. *Current Pos:* Fel, 85-88, res instr, 88-89, ASST PROF PATH & PEDIAT & DIR, MOLECULAR GENETICS LAB, VANDERBILT UNIV, MED SCH, 89- *Personal Data:* b Stuttgart, Ger, Dec 20, 58; US citizen; m 80, Donald S; c Cameron & Kelly. *Educ:* Univ SC, BS, 80; Med Col Va, PhD(human genetics), 85. *Mem:* Am Col Med Genetics; Am Soc Human Genetics. *Res:* Identification of DNA mutations associated with specific inherited and somatic diseases; development of DNA based diagnostic tests for the identification of DNA mutations and detection of infectious agents. *Mailing Add:* Med Ctr Vanderbilt Univ 21st Ave S & Garland Nashville TN 37232-0001. *Fax:* 615-343-8420

**VOBACH, ARNOLD R,** MATHEMATICS. *Current Pos:* ASSOC PROF MATH, UNIV HOUSTON, 68- *Personal Data:* b Chicago, Ill, Nov 20, 32; m 57, Carol Jones; c 2. *Educ:* Harvard Univ, AB, 54, SB, 56; Ill Inst Technol, MS, 59; La State Univ, PhD(math), 63. *Prof Exp:* From instr to asst prof, Univ Ga, 62-68. *Mem:* Am Math Soc; Math Asn Am. *Res:* Topology; logic; cryptology. *Mailing Add:* Dept Math Univ Houston Cullen Blvd Houston TX 77204-3476. *Fax:* 713-743-3505

**VOBECKY, JOSEF,** EPIDEMIOLOGY OF CHRONIC DISEASE, NUTRITION EPIDEMIOLOGY. *Current Pos:* from asst prof to prof epidemiol, 69-93, chmn, Dept Community Health Sci, 78-85, HON PROF, MED FAC, UNIV SHERBROOKE, 93- *Personal Data:* b Brno, Czech, Sept 29, 23; m 55; c 3. *Educ:* Masaryk Univ, Brno, MD, 50; Postgrad Med Sch, Prague, DPH, 56, dipl epidemiol, 60; CSPQ, 74. *Prof Exp:* Epidemiologist, Czech Pub Health Serv, Prague, 50-55, head dept epidemiol, Brno, 56-62; dir dept epidemiol, Inst Epidemiol & Microbiol, Prague, 63-68. *Concurrent Pos:* Vis prof, Fac Med, Charles Univ, Prague, 60-62; consult field proj, WHO, Mongolia, 63-65, Iraq, 66, lectr, 66-69; sr lectr, Postgrad Med Sch, Prague, 66-69. *Mem:* Int Epidemiol Asn; Soc Epidemiol Res; fel Am Col Epidemiol; NY Acad Sci. *Res:* Epidemiology of nutrition; epidemiological surveillance; chronic disease epidemiology; environmental factors; cancer epidemiology. *Mailing Add:* Dept Community Med Fac Med Univ Sherbrooke Sherbrooke PQ J1H 5N4 Can

**VOCCI, FRANK JOSEPH,** TOXICOLOGY. *Current Pos:* DEP DIR MEDICATION DEVELOP DIV, NAT INST DRUG ABUSE/NIH, 90- *Personal Data:* b Baltimore, Md, Aug 13, 24; wid. *Educ:* Loyola Col, Md, BS, 49. *Prof Exp:* Group leader & gen chemist, Aerosol Br, Food & Drug Admin, 49-61, chief, Basic Toxicol Br, Toxicol Div, Edgewood Arsenal, 61-76, chief, Whole Animal Toxicol Br, Toxicol Div, 76-80, consult, Toxicol, DOD, Ctr Dis Control, ENVRON, EPA(Dynamac), 80-90. *Mem:* Sigma Xi; Am Chem Soc; Am Indust Hyg Asn. *Mailing Add:* 2310 Cider Mill Rd Baltimore MD 21234-2506

**VOCKE, MERLYN C,** ELECTRICAL ENGINEERING. *Current Pos:* From instr to assoc prof, 55-76, PROF ELEC ENG, VALPARAISO UNIV, 76- *Personal Data:* b Milwaukee, Wis, Nov 17, 33; m 61; c 3. *Educ:* Valparaiso Univ, BS, 55; Univ Notre Dame, MS, 57; Univ Iowa, PhD, 71. *Honors & Awards:* Centennial Medal, Inst Elec & Electronics Engrs. *Concurrent Pos:* Consult, Naval Weapons Support Ctr. *Mem:* Inst Elec & Electronics Engrs; Am Soc Eng Educ. *Res:* Microprocessor applications; digital and analog system design. *Mailing Add:* 203 Mayfield Ave Valparaiso IN 46383-6493

**VODICNIK, MARY JO,** METABOLISM & PHARMACOKINETICS, REPRODUCTIVE TOXICOLOGY. *Current Pos:* Asst toxicol, 78-80, asst prof, 80-84, ASSOC PROF PHARMACOL & TOXICOL, MED COL WIS, 84- *Personal Data:* b Milwaukee, Wis, Dec 23, 51; m 75. *Educ:* Marquette Univ, BS, 74, PhD(biol & comp physiol), 78. *Concurrent Pos:* Mem, spec study sect, NIH, 83-85 & metab path study sect, 85-, chmn, physiol chem ad hoc study sect, 86; prin investr, Nat Inst Environ Health Sci, NIH, 81-90. *Mem:* Am Soc Pharmacol & Exp Therapeut; Int Soc Study Xenobiotics; Soc Toxicol. *Res:* Mechanisms responsible for transplacental and milk transfer of environmental chemicals; effects of pregnancy and lactation on pharmacokinetics; effects of pregancy on efficacy and toxicity of drugs and environmental chemicals. *Mailing Add:* Lilly Res Labs Eli Lilly & Co PO Box 708 Greenfield IN 46140-0708. *Fax:* 317-277-4436

**VO-DINH, TUAN,** ENVIRONMENTAL & BIOMEDICAL MONITORING, ADVANCED INSTRUMENTATION. *Current Pos:* staff scientist, 77-84, GROUP LEADER & CORP FEL, MONITORING DEVELOP GROUP, HEALTH & SAFETY RES DIV, OAK RIDGE NAT LAB, 84- *Personal Data:* b Nhatrang, Vietnam; US citizen. *Educ:* Swiss Fed Inst Tech, Lausanne, Switz, BS, 70; Swiss Fed Inst Technol, Zurich, Switz, PhD(phys chem), 75. *Honors & Awards:* RD-100 Award, Res & Develop Mag, 81 & 87 & 92; Tech Event Award, Martin Marietta Energy Systs, 86; Excellence Award, Fed Lab Consortium, 86; Gold Medal Award, Soc Appl Spectros, 88; Languedoc-Rousillon Medal, Univ Perpignan, France, 89. *Prof Exp:* Res assoc, Dept Chem, Univ Fla, 75-76. *Concurrent Pos:* Chmn, Dept Energy, Sci Panel Monitoring Instrumentation, Off Health & Environ Res, 84; co-chmn, Int Comt Polycyclic Aromatic Compounds, 86-; adj prof, Univ Tenn, 88-; tech ed, Polycyclic Aromatic Compounds J, 89-; chmn, Subcomt E13-09, Asn Stand & Testing Mat; chmn, Comn V-4, Int Union Pure & Appl Chem, 91- *Mem:* Fel Am Inst Chemists; Am Chem Soc; Int Union Pure & Appl Chem; Soc Appl Chem; Soc Advan Sci; Asn Stand & Testing Mat; Int Soc Polycyclic Aromatic Compounds (pres, 91-93). *Res:* Development of advanced methods and instrumentation for the detection of environmental pollutants and health effects associated with industrial processes and technology development. *Mailing Add:* Oak Ridge Nat Lab Bldg 4500 S PO Box 2008 MS-6101 Oak Ridge TN 37831-6101

**VODKIN, LILA OTT,** PLANT MOLECULAR BIOLOGY. *Current Pos:* assoc prof, 88-95, PROF AGRON, UNIV ILL, URBANA, 95- *Personal Data:* b Laurens, SC, Dec 21, 50; m 75, Michael. *Educ:* Univ SC, BS, 73, MS, 75; NC State Univ, PhD, 78. *Prof Exp:* Res geneticist, USDA, Beltsville, Md, 78-87. *Mem:* Genetics Soc Am; Am Soc Plant Physiologists; Crop Sci Soc Am. *Res:* Gene expression in soybeans. *Mailing Add:* Agron Dept Turner Hall Univ Ill Urbana IL 61801-4709

**VODKIN, MICHAEL HAROLD,** GENETICS, MOLECULAR BIOLOGY. *Current Pos:* SCIENTIST, ILL NATURAL HIST SURV, 92- *Personal Data:* b Boston, Mass, Dec 4, 42; m 75, Lila Ott. *Educ:* Boston Col, BS, 64, MS, 66; Univ Ariz, PhD(genetics), 71. *Prof Exp:* Fel genetics, Cornell Univ, 71-73; asst prof biol, Univ SC, 73-79; staff fel, NIH, 79-81; mem staff, Med Res Inst Infectious Dis, US Army, 81-88; res specialist, Path Dept, Univ Ill, 88-92. *Mem:* Sigma Xi; Genetics Soc Am; Am Soc Microbiol. *Res:* Genetics and biochemistry of hemoparasites; cloning of antigens for use as vaccines. *Mailing Add:* Div Path Col Vet Med Univ Ill Urbana IL 61801. *Fax:* 217-333-2359; *E-Mail:* vodkin@a.psc.edu

**VOEDISCH, ROBERT W,** ORGANIC CHEMISTRY, ENVIRONMENTAL SCIENCES. *Current Pos:* RETIRED. *Personal Data:* b Ft Eustis, Va, Nov 5, 24; m 52, 84, Karen Johnson; c 3. *Educ:* Beloit Col, BS, 48. *Prof Exp:* res & develop chemist, Lawter Int Inc, Chicago, 50-55, group leader, 55-56, chief chemist, 56-60, tech dir, 60-67, vpres res & develop, 67-85, consult, 85-96. *Mem:* AAAS; Am Chem Soc; Am Inst Chemists; Int Union Pure & Appl Physics. *Res:* Luminescent compounds; ink vehicles; synthetic resins; alkyds, phenolics, maleics, ketone and polyamide resins; environmental science. *Mailing Add:* 722 N Hadow St Arlington Heights IL 60004-5616

**VOEKS, ROBERT ALLEN,** TROPICAL RAIN FORESTS, BIOGEOGRAPHY. *Current Pos:* ASSOC PROF GEOG, CALIF STATE UNIV, FULLERTON, 87- *Personal Data:* b Seattle, Wash, Nov 10, 50; m 86; c 2. *Educ:* Portland State Univ, BS, 75, MS, 80; Univ Calif, Berkeley, PhD(geog), 87. *Concurrent Pos:* Prin investr, Siuslaw Nat Forest, US Forest Serv, 89; vis prof, Fed Univ Bahia, Brazil, 90-91. *Mem:* Asn Am Geographers. *Res:* Ecology, biogeography and human use of tropical forests; African ethnobotany in the New World; palm ecology; tropical folk medicine. *Mailing Add:* Geog Dept Calif State Univ Fullerton CA 92631-3599

**VOELCKER, HERBERT B(ERNHARD),** MECHANICAL ENGINEERING, INDUSTRIAL & MECHANICAL ENGINEERING. *Current Pos:* CHARLES LAKE PROF MECH ENGR, CORNELL UNIV, 86- *Personal Data:* b Tonawanda, NY, Jan 7, 30; m 54; c 2. *Educ:* Mass Inst Technol, BS, 51, MS, 54; Imp Col, Univ London, PhD(eng), 61. *Honors & Awards:* Inst Elec & Electronics Engrs Award, 67. *Prof Exp:* Lectr elec eng, Imp Col, Univ London, 60-61; from asst prof to prof elec eng, Univ Rochester, 71-85, dir, Prod Automation Proj, 72-85; dep dir, DMCE Div, NSF, 85-86. *Concurrent Pos:* US Army Signal Corps, 51-58; consult indust, 58-; NATO fel, 67-68; sr vis scientist, UK Sci Res Coun, 81-83; dir, Cornell Mfg Eng & Productivity Prog, 87-91. *Mem:* Fel Inst Elec & Electronics Engrs; Asn Comput Mach; Am Soc Mech Engrs; Soc Mfg Engrs. *Res:* Automation engineering for design and production in the mechanical industries; national science and technology policy. *Mailing Add:* Sibley Sch Mech Eng Cornell Univ Ithaca NY 14853-7501

**VOELKER, ALAN MORRIS,** SCIENCE EDUCATION. *Current Pos:* fac chair elem educ, Northern Ill Univ, 80-82 & 89-91, dept chair curric & inst, 89-92, asst to pres, 92-95, ASSOC PROF & PROF SCI EDUC, COL EDUC NORTHERN ILL UNIV, 73- *Personal Data:* b Eau Claire, Wis, Aug 12, 38; m 60; c 2. *Educ:* Wis State Univ, River Falls, BS, 59; Syracuse Univ, MS, 63; Univ Wis-Madison, PhD(sci educ), 67. *Prof Exp:* Teacher chem, physics, gen sci & math & chmn dept, High Schs, Wis, 59-64; asst prof sci educ, Ohio State Univ, 67-69; asst prof sci educ, Univ Wis-Madison & prin investr cognitive learning, Res & Develop Ctr, 69-73. *Concurrent Pos:* Mem, adv bd sci educ sect, Educ Resources Info Ctr, Info Anal Ctr Sci, Math & Environ Educ, 72-76; dist dir VIII, Nat Sci Teachers Asn, 84-86. *Mem:* Fel AAAS; Nat Sci Teachers Asn; Nat Asn Res Sci Teaching; Am Educ Res Asn; Asn Educ Teachers Sci; Sch Sci & Math Asn. *Res:* Science concept learning; science teacher education; attitudes toward science; scientific literacy; attentive publics for organized science; staff development, evaluation. *Mailing Add:* Curric & Instr Northern Ill Univ De Kalb IL 60115. *Fax:* 815-753-9040; *E-Mail:* avoelker@niu.edu

**VOELKER, C(LARENCE) E(LMER),** CHEMICAL ENGINEERING. *Current Pos:* process engr, Dow Chem Co, 52-56, group leader, Process Eng Dept, 56-57, proj leader polychems, Res Dept, 57-59, from res engr to sr res engr, Process Fundamentals Res Lab, 59-64, sr process engr, Comput Res Lab, 64-65, sr process engr, Process Eng Dept, 65-68, tech expert, 68-70, SR PROCESS SPECIALIST, PROCESS ENG DEPT, DOW CHEM CO, 70- *Personal Data:* b Two Rivers, Wis, July 6, 23; m 47; c 3. *Educ:* Univ Wis, BS, 49, MS, 50. *Prof Exp:* Process control engr, Food Mach & Chem Corp, 50-52. *Mem:* AAAS; Am Chem Soc; Sigma Xi; Am Inst Chem Engrs. *Res:* Heat transfer; fluid dynamics; mathematics; crystallization. *Mailing Add:* 300 Sinclair St Midland MI 48640-6014

**VOELKER, DENNIS R,** BIOCHEMISTRY. *Current Pos:* STAFF MEM BIOCHEM, NAT JEWISH CTR, 81- *Personal Data:* b Richmond Hall, NY, Aug 24, 50. *Educ:* Ind Univ, BS, 68; Univ Tenn, PhD(biochem), 78. *Prof Exp:* Fel biochem, Harvard Univ, 78-81. *Mem:* Am Soc Biochem & Molecular Biol; Am Cem Soc. *Res:* Biochemistry. *Mailing Add:* Nat Jewish Hosp Immunol/ Respiratory Med 1400 Jackson St G-606 Denver CO 80206-1900

**VOELKER, RICHARD WILLIAM,** VETERINARY PATHOLOGY. *Current Pos:* DIR PATH, HAZLETON LABS AM, 73- *Personal Data:* b Stanton, Nebr, July 16, 36; m 61; c 4. *Educ:* Kans State Univ, BS & DVM, 59; Purdue Univ, MS, 64, PhD(vet path), 69; Am Col Vet Pathologists, cert, 70. *Prof Exp:* Vet food inspector, US Army Vet Corps, 59-61; med lab officer, US Armed Forces, Europe, 61-64; instr vet path, Purdue Univ, West Lafayette, 64-68; staff pathologist, Hazleton Labs, 68-71; sect head toxicol, William S Merrell Co, 71-73. *Concurrent Pos:* Adj asst prof path, Med Sch, Univ Cincinnati, 71-73. *Mem:* Am Vet Med Asn; Int Acad Path; Am Col Vet Pathologists; Soc Pharmacol & Environ Pathologists; Indust Vet Asn. *Res:* Toxocologic pathology in the investigation and description of various tissue responses caused by a wide variety of chemical and pharmaceutical compounds; tumor induction in laboratory animals by a wide variety of environmental. *Mailing Add:* 10409 Huntrace Way Vienna VA 22182

**VOELKER, ROBERT HETH,** INTEGRATED CIRCUIT DESIGN, COMPUTATIONAL ELECTROMAGNETICS. *Current Pos:* ASST PROF ELEC ENG, UNIV NEBR, LINCOLN, 90- *Personal Data:* US citizen. *Educ:* Univ Mich, BSE, 82, MSE, 83, PhD(elec eng), 89. *Mem:* Inst Elec & Electronics Engrs; Am Soc Eng Educ. *Res:* Electromagnetic field analysis of signal propagation in high-speed digital and microwave integrated circuits; computer-aided design of integrated circuits; high-speed electro-optical measurements; supercomputing. *Mailing Add:* 243 N Walter Scott Eng Ctr Univ Nebr Lincoln NE 68588. *Fax:* 402-472-4732; *E-Mail:* bob@cray3.unl.edu

**VOELLMY, RICHARD WALTER,** RECOMBINANT DNA, GENETICS. *Current Pos:* PROF BIOCHEM, SCH MED, UNIV MIAMI, 82- *Educ:* Swiss Fed Inst Technol, Zurich, PhD(biochem), 75. *Mailing Add:* Sch Med Dept Biochem PO Box 016129 Univ Miami 1011 NW 15th St Miami FL 33101-6129

**VOELZ, DAVID GEORGE,** ELECTRONICS ENGINEERING. *Current Pos:* ELECTRONIC ENGR, PHILLIPS LAB, 86- *Personal Data:* b Idaho Falls, Idaho, Feb 24, 59; m 83, Judi Rae Gore. *Educ:* Univ Ill, MSEE, 83, PhD(elec eng), 87. *Honors & Awards:* Eng Excellence Award, Optical Soc Am, 95. *Mem:* Inst Elec & Electronics Engrs; Soc Photo-Optical Instrumentation Engrs; Optical Soc Am. *Res:* Contributed articles to professional journals. *Mailing Add:* 5232 Camino Sandia NE Albuquerque NM 87111-5769

**VOELZ, FREDERICK,** ENVIRONMENTAL ENGINEERING. *Current Pos:* proj chemist, Sinclair Res, Inc, 55-62, sr res physicist, 62-69, sr proj engr spec projs, 69-78, RES ASSOC NEW TECHNOL APPL, ATLANTIC RICHFIELD CO, 78- *Personal Data:* b Wheaton, Ill, May 22, 27; m 50; c 2. *Educ:* Ill Inst Technol, BS, 51, MS, 53, PhD(physics, math), 55. *Prof Exp:* Asst, Ill Inst Technol, 51-55. *Mem:* Soc Automotive Engrs; Air Pollution Control Asn; Sigma Xi. *Res:* Raman and infrared spectroscopy; molecular structure; automotive exhaust emissions instrumentation and testing; ambient air and environmental technology. *Mailing Add:* 1338 Macarthur Blvd Hammond IN 46321

**VOELZ, GEORGE LEO,** OCCUPATIONAL MEDICINE. *Current Pos:* RETIRED. *Personal Data:* b Wittenberg, Wis, Oct 13, 26; m 50, Mary Wesselman; c Valerie, David, Brian, Sharon, Eric & Julie. *Educ:* Univ Wis, BS, 48, MD, 50. *Prof Exp:* AEC fel indust med, 51-52; indust physician, Los Alamos Sci Lab, Univ Calif, 52-57; chief med br, Idaho Opers Off, AEC, 57-63, asst dir, Health Serv Lab, 63-67, dir, 67-70; health div leader, Los Alamos Sci Lab, 70-82, asst div leader, Health, Safety & Environ Div, 82-87, sect leader epidemiol, 87-91; staff mem, 91-95. *Concurrent Pos:* Mem, Nat Coun Radiation Protection & Measurements, 75-; ed adv, Occup Health & Safety J; mem, Int Comn Radiol Protection, 84-92. *Mem:* Am Col Occup & Environ Med; AAAS; Health Physics Soc. *Res:* Occupational health problems, especially in the atomic energy industries; radiological health problems; radiobiological research and radiation dosimetry; epidemiology. *Mailing Add:* 117 La Vista Dr Los Alamos NM 87544. *Fax:* 505-665-5643

**VOELZ, MICHAEL H,** INSTRUMENT DESIGN, PHYSIOLOGIC HUMAN & ANIMAL MONITORING. *Current Pos:* nurse technician, 91-93, STAFF NURSE, HOME HOSP, 93-, INTENSIVE CARE NURSE, 94- *Personal Data:* b Columbus, Ind, March 5, 56; m 81; c 2. *Educ:* Purdue Univ, BS, 79; St Elizabeth Hosp Sch Nursing, GN, 93, RN, 93. *Prof Exp:* Res assoc psychol, Purdue Univ Biomed Ctr, 79-81; design asst blood oxygenation, Bio-Tek Inc, Ohmeda, 81-82; develop engr blood pheresis, Cobe Labs Inc, 82-83, proj engr blood oxygenation, 83-85; mgr res & develop physiologic instrument, Lafayette Instruments, 85-91; dir res & develop, Bissell Health Care, 88-93. *Concurrent Pos:* Consult PC comput; owner, ERN Prod. *Mem:* Am Asn Critical Care Nurses. *Res:* Research and products development research in physiologic monitoring, especially non-invasive monitoring; blood pressure measurement, analog and digital circuit design and human physiology; patient care; medical surgical nursing; cardio-respiratory patient care; intensive care nursing; nursing aid products. *Mailing Add:* PO Box 326 Battle Ground IN 47920. *E-Mail:* voel2@dcwi.com

**VOET, DONALD HERMAN,** CRYSTALLOGRAPHY, BIOCHEMISTRY. *Current Pos:* asst prof, 69-74, ASSOC PROF CHEM, UNIV PA, 74- *Personal Data:* b Amsterdam, Neth, Nov 29, 38; US citizen; m 65, Judith Greenwald; c Wendy & Douglas. *Educ:* Calif Inst Technol, BS, 60; Harvard Univ, PhD(chem), 67. *Prof Exp:* Res assoc biol, Mass Inst Technol, 66-69. *Mem:* Am Chem Soc; Am Crystallog Asn; Sigma Xi. *Res:* X-ray structural determination of molecules of biological interest, particularly proteins, and nucleic acids; author of one textbook on biochemistry. *Mailing Add:* Dept Chem Univ Pa Philadelphia PA 19104-6382. *Fax:* 215-898-5747; *E-Mail:* voet@dv.chem.upenn.edu

**VOET, JUDITH GREENWALD,** BIOCHEMISTRY. *Current Pos:* asst prof, 78-85, ASSOC PROF CHEM, SWARTHMORE COL, 85-, CHEM DEPT CHAIR, 89- *Personal Data:* b New York, NY, Mar 10, 41; m 65; c 2. *Educ:* Antioch Col, BS, 63; Brandeis Univ, PhD(biochem), 69. *Prof Exp:* Res assoc, Haverford Col, 72-74 & Inst Cancer Res, 75; vis scientist, Univ Oxford, 76; lectr chem, Univ Pa, 76-77; vis asst prof, Univ Del, 77-78. *Concurrent Pos:* NIH fel, 70-72. *Mem:* Am Chem Soc; AAAS; Am Soc Plant Physiologists; Sigma Xi. *Res:* Mechanisms of enzyme action; chemical modification of enzymes; membrane transport mechanisms. *Mailing Add:* Dept Chem Swarthmore Col Swarthmore PA 19081

**VOGAN, DAVID A, JR,** GROUP REPRESENTATIONS. *Current Pos:* From asst prof to assoc prof math, 79-84, PROF MATH, MASS INST TECHNOL, 84- *Personal Data:* b Mercer, Pa, Sept 8, 54. *Educ:* Mass Inst Technol, PhD(math), 76. *Mailing Add:* Dept Math Mass Inst Technol Cambridge MA 02139-4307

**VOGAN, ERIC LLOYD,** PHYSICS. *Current Pos:* RETIRED. *Personal Data:* b London, Ont, Sept 3, 24; m 51; c 3. *Educ:* Univ Western Ont, BSc, 46, MSc, 47; McGill Univ, PhD(physics), 52. *Prof Exp:* Sci officer, Defense Res Telecommun Estab, Can, 52-57; Can liaison officer, Lincoln Lab, Mass Inst Technol & Air Force Cambridge Res Ctr, 57-60; sci officer, Defense Res Telecommun Estab, Can, 60-64; assoc prof physics, Univ Western Ont, 64-70, prof, 70- *Mem:* Am Asn Physics Teachers; Am Geophys Union; Can Asn Physicists. *Res:* Aeronomy; physics of the upper atmosphere. *Mailing Add:* Dept Physics Univ Western Ont London ON N6A 3K7 Can

**VOGEL, ALFRED MORRIS,** CHEMISTRY, INSTRUMENTATION. *Current Pos:* PROF CHEM, C W POST COL, LONG ISLAND UNIV, 67-, CHMN DEPT, 74- *Personal Data:* b New York, NY, Mar 11, 15; m 40; c 2. *Educ:* City Col New York, BS, 34; NY Univ, MS, 48, PhD(chem), 50. *Prof Exp:* Jr chemist, USN, 36-41; chemist, New York City Bd Transp, 41-47; asst, NY Univ, 47-49; instr, Sch Indust Technol, 49-51; from asst prof chem to prof chem, Adelphi Univ, 50-67, chmn dept, 53-67. *Mem:* Am Chem Soc; Sigma Xi. *Res:* Analytical and chemical instrumentation; methods of assay of pharmaceutical products; coordination compounds. *Mailing Add:* 20920 18th Ave 4E Bayside NY 11360-1409

**VOGEL, ARTHUR MARK,** TUMOR DIAGNOSIS, MELANOMA. *Current Pos:* Asst prof path, Univ Wash, 79-87. *Educ:* NY Univ, PhD(path) & MD, 75. *Res:* Cancer research. *Mailing Add:* Path Cyto Lab 5334 Tallman Ave NW Seattle WA 98107

**VOGEL, CARL-WILHELM E,** ANTIBODY CONJUGATES, COMPLEMENT SYSTEM. *Current Pos:* asst prof, 82-87, ASSOC PROF BIOCHEM & MED, GEORGETOWN UNIV SCH MED & DENT & GRAD SCH ARTS & SCI, WASHINGTON, DC, 87- *Personal Data:* b Hamburg, Ger, Mar 9, 51; m 89. *Educ:* Univ Hamburg, WGer, MD, 76, PhD(biochem), 85. *Honors & Awards:* Alan Beuman Award, 88. *Prof Exp:* Intern, Dept Med, Univ Hosp, Christian-Aalbrechts Univ, Kiel, WGer & Dept Surg, Gen Hosp, Geesthacht, WGer, 76-77; res fel, Dept Enzym, Inst Physiol Chem, Univ Hamburg, WGer, 78; res fel, Dept Molecular Immunol, Res Inst Scripps Clin, La Jolla, Calif, 79-82, res assoc, Depts Molecular Immunol & Immunol, 82. *Concurrent Pos:* Mem, Int Ctr Interdisciplinary Studies Immunol, Georgetown Univ Med Ctr, Washington, DC, 82-, sci dir, 87-; mem, Vincent T Lombardi Cancer Res Ctr, Georgetown Univ Med Ctr, 82-; mem spec rev comt, Nat Cancer Inst, 87, 89 & 90; mem ad hoc study sect exp immunol, NIH, 87. *Mem:* Ger Soc Biol Chem; Am Soc Microbiol; Am Asn Immunologists; Am Soc Biol Chemists; Int Soc Develop & Comp Immunol; AAAS; Am Asn Cancer Res; Am Soc Trop Med & Hyg; Am Fedn Clin Res; Ger Soc Immunol; AMA. *Res:* Molecular mechanisms of complement killing of tumor cells; biochemistry of complement protein. *Mailing Add:* Dept Biochem & Molecular Biol Univ Hamburg Martin Luther King Pl 6 20146 Hamburg Germany. *Fax:* 49-40-4123-2848

**VOGEL, FRANCIS STEPHEN,** PATHOLOGY. *Current Pos:* PROF PATH, MED CTR, DUKE UNIV, 61- *Personal Data:* b Middletown, Del, Sept 29, 19; m 49; c 5. *Educ:* Villanova Col, AB, 41; Western Res Univ, MD, 44; Am Bd Path, dipl, 51. *Prof Exp:* From asst prof to assoc prof path, Med Col, Cornell Univ, 50-61, asst prof path in surg, 50-61. *Concurrent Pos:* Consult, Vet Admin Hosp, NY. *Mem:* Am Soc Exp Path; Am Asn Pathologists & Bacteriologists. *Res:* Neuropathology; metabolic function of mitochondrial nucleic acids. *Mailing Add:* Dept Path US Can Acad Path 3643 Walton Way Ext Augusta GA 30909

**VOGEL, GEORGE,** ORGANIC CHEMISTRY. *Current Pos:* from asst prof to assoc prof, 56-69, PROF CHEM, BOSTON COL, 69- *Personal Data:* b Prague, Czech, May 28, 24; nat US; m 50; c 2. *Educ:* Prague Inst Technol, DSc(chem), 50. *Prof Exp:* Lectr chem, Univ Col, Ethiopia, 51-54; res chemist, Monsanto Chem, Ltd, Eng, 54-55; res fel, Ohio State Univ, 55-56. *Mem:* Am Chem Soc. *Res:* Heterocyclic chemistry; steric effects in conjugated systems; mass spectrometry. *Mailing Add:* Dept Chem Boston Col 2609 Beacon St Chestnut Hill Boston MA 02167-3800

**VOGEL, GERALD LEE,** MICRO-ANALYTICAL CHEMISTRY. *Current Pos:* PROJ LEADER, AM DENT ASN HEALTH FOUND, 74- *Personal Data:* b Janesville, Wis, Feb 6, 43; m 93, Mitsuko Tsuchiya. *Educ:* Univ Wis-Madison, BS, 65; Georgetown Univ, MS, 70, PhD(chem), 73. *Prof Exp:* Supvr, Washington Ref Lab, 71-73, Pharmacopathics Res Lab, 73-74. *Mem:* Int Asn Dent Res. *Res:* Dissolution and precipitation of biological calcium phosphates as it relates to dental caries-ultra microanalysis of oral fluids. *Mailing Add:* Am Dent Asn Health Found Passenbarger Res Ctr Nat Inst Stand & Technol Gaithersburg MD 20899. *Fax:* 301-963-9143; *E-Mail:* jerry.vogel@nist.gov

**VOGEL, GLENN CHARLES,** INORGANIC CHEMISTRY. *Current Pos:* Asst prof, 70-74, assoc prof, 74-82, PROF CHEM, ITHACA COL, 82- *Personal Data:* b Columbia, Pa, Mar 7, 43; m 69. *Educ:* Pa State Univ, University Park, BS, 65; Univ Ill, Urbana, MS, 67, PhD(inorg chem), 70. *Concurrent Pos:* Grants, Am Chem Soc-Petrol Res Fund, 73, NATO, 79 & Res Corp, 80, W R Grace, 89-91; fac res opportunity award, NSF, 83 & 85; Dana teaching fel. *Mem:* Sigma Xi; Am Chem Soc. *Res:* Complex formation of metalloporphyrins; transition metal complexes of oxocarbon ligands; ternary copper catechol complexes; zeolites. *Mailing Add:* S411D Dept Chem Ithaca Col Ithaca NY 14850-5801

**VOGEL, HENRY,** MICROBIOLOGY, SEROLOGY. *Current Pos:* RETIRED. *Personal Data:* b New York, NY, Sept 2, 16; m 47; c 1. *Educ:* La State Univ, BS, 40; NY Univ, MS, 49, PhD(biol), 56. *Prof Exp:* Bacteriologist, Jewish Mem Hosp, NY, 45-49; sr bacteriologist, Willard Parker Hosp, NY, 49-52; sr bacteriologist, Bur Labs, New York City Dept Health, 52-66, sr res scientist, 66-79. *Mem:* NY Acad Sci; Brit Soc Appl Bact; Brit Soc Gen Microbiol; Sigma Xi. *Res:* Enteric microbiology; metabolism of cold-blooded acid fast organisms; metabolism of Leptospira; serologic studies of genetic relationships and diagnosis. *Mailing Add:* Dept Path Col Physicians & Surgeons Columbia Univ New York NY 10032

**VOGEL, HENRY ELLIOTT,** SOLID STATE PHYSICS. *Current Pos:* From instr to assoc prof, Clemson Univ, 50-65, head Dept Physics, 67-71, dean, Col Sci, 71-87, prof physics, 65-90, EMER PROF PHYSICS, CLEMSON UNIV, 90- *Personal Data:* b Greenville, SC, Sept 16, 25; m 53, Barbara Gladden; c Alisabeth V (Pickens), Henry L II, Barbara V (Evers) & Susan V (Keck). *Educ:* Furman Univ, BS, 48; Univ NC, MS, 50, PhD(physics), 62. *Mem:* Am Phys Soc; Am Asn Physics Teachers. *Res:* Superconductivity; thin vacuum-deposited films; tunneling between films. *Mailing Add:* 222 Wyatt Ave Clemson SC 29631

**VOGEL, HOWARD H, JR,** ZOOLOGY. *Current Pos:* prof radiol, physiol & biophys & head radiation biol, Dept Radiation Oncol, 67-80, prof radiation oncol, 73-80, EMER PROF RADIOL, CTR HEALTH SCI, UNIV TENN, MEMPHIS, 80- *Personal Data:* b New York, NY, Nov 30, 14; m 40, 61, Barbara Russell; c Nancy E, Diana, Naomi R (deceased) & Tom H. *Educ:* Bowdoin Col, AB, 36; Harvard Univ, MA, 37, PhD(biol), 40. *Prof Exp:* From asst prof to assoc prof, Wabash Col, 41-47, actg head dept, 46; chmn col biol sci, Univ Chicago, 47-50; assoc biol & group leader neutron radiobiol, Argonne Nat Lab, 50-67. *Concurrent Pos:* Ornithologist, Bowdoin-MacMillan Arctic Exped, 34; assoc, Roscoe B Jackson Mem Lab; res, Frederic Joliet Cupres Nat Res Inst of Radiol, Am Acad Sci & Hungarian Acad Sci, 80-82; adj prof biol, Memphis State Univ, 83-94; mem nat lectr comt, Sigma Xi, 89-; Austin teaching fel, Harvard & Radcliffe Col; chmn, Environ Radiation Coun, Memphis. *Mem:* AAAS; Am Soc Zool; assoc Am Ornith Union; assoc Arctic Int NAm; Transplantation Soc; Sigma Xi; Radiation Res Soc. *Res:* History of arctic aviation; social behavior of birds and mammals; skin transplantation; radiobiology; biological effects of neutrons; radiation carcinogenesis; life history and ecology of the yellow-billed tropicbird. *Mailing Add:* 280 Ben Avon Way Memphis TN 38111

**VOGEL, JAMES ALAN,** occupational physiology, body composition, for more information see previous edition

**VOGEL, JAMES JOHN,** BIOCHEMISTRY, NUTRITION. *Current Pos:* asst mem, Dent Br, Univ Tex, 67-71, assoc prof, 71-86, interim chmn, Dept Basic Sci, 93-96, PROF, DENT BR, UNIV TEX, 86-, PROF, DEPT BASIC SCI, 96- *Personal Data:* b Longmont, Colo, June 16, 35; m 60, Jacqueline B Martin; c 2. *Educ:* William Jewell Col, AB, 57; Univ Wis, MS, 59, PhD(biochem), 61. *Prof Exp:* Res fel dent biochem, Forsyth Dent Ctr, Harvard Univ, 61-63; res assoc biochem, Med Sch, Univ Minn, 63-67. *Mem:* Int Asn Dent Res; Am Chem Soc; NY Acad Sci; Sigma Xi. *Res:* Dietary factors involved in dental caries; nutritional and metabolic aspects of magnesium, phosphorus and fluorine with respect to skeletal tissues; microbiologic calcification; phospholipid-protein interactions in calcification. *Mailing Add:* Univ Tex Dent Br PO Box 20068 Houston TX 77225. *Fax:* 713-500-4500; *E-Mail:* jvogel@bite.db.uth.tmc.edu

**VOGEL, KATHRYN GIEBLER,** EXTRACELLULAR MATRIX BIOCHEMISTRY, PROTEOGLYCANS. *Current Pos:* res assoc, Univ NMex, 75-77, from asst prof to assoc prof, 77-89, assoc dean, Col Arts & Sci, 93-96, PROF BIOL, UNIV NMEX, 89- *Personal Data:* b Los Angeles, Calif, May 19, 42; m 64, Albert; c 3. *Educ:* Pomona Col, BA, 63; Univ Calif, Los Angeles, MA, 66, PhD(zool & chem), 68. *Prof Exp:* Asst cell physiol, Boston Biomed Res Inst, 72-74; asst prof, Simmons Col, Boston, 74-75. *Concurrent Pos:* Vis res prof, Univ Lund, Sweden, 82-83; chmn, Women in Cell Biol; ann res lectr, Univ NMex, 96. *Mem:* Am Soc Cell Biol; Soc Complex Carbohydrates; Orthop Res Soc. *Res:* Structure, metabolism and role of proteoglycans in fibrous tissues; how the type and amount of proteoglycan content is regulated, how these interact with collagen in forming matrix and how that matrix suits the mechanical forces to which it is subjected. *Mailing Add:* Dept Biol Univ NMex Albuquerque NM 87131. *Fax:* 505-277-0304; *E-Mail:* kgvogel@unm.edu

**VOGEL, MARTIN,** ORGANIC CHEMISTRY, POLYMER CHEMISTRY. *Current Pos:* sr res chemist, 65-83, res fel, 83-87, SR RES FEL, ROHM & HAAS CO, 87- *Personal Data:* b Los Angeles, Calif, Mar 7, 35; m 63; c 2. *Educ:* Calif Inst Technol, BS, 55, PhD(org chem), 61. *Prof Exp:* Asst prof org chem, Rutgers Univ, 60-65. *Mem:* Am Chem Soc. *Res:* Organic coatings; emulsion polymerization; latex paints. *Mailing Add:* 550 Pine Tree Rd Jenkintown PA 19046-2228

**VOGEL, NORMAN WILLIAM,** ZOOLOGY. *Current Pos:* RETIRED. *Personal Data:* b Brooklyn, NY, May 17, 17; m 47; c 4. *Educ:* Univ Mich, AB, 40, MS, 43; Univ Ind, PhD(zool), 56. *Hon Degrees:* ScD, Col Washington & Jefferson, 86. *Prof Exp:* Asst zool, Univ Mich, 42-43; asst physiol, Vanderbilt Univ, 43-44; Lawrason Brown res fel, Saranac Lab, NY, 48-49; instr biol, Champlain Col, 49-52; asst zool, Univ Ind, 52-55; from asst prof to prof, Washinton & Jefferson Col, 56-85, emer prof biol, 85- *Concurrent Pos:* USPHS res grant, Nat Cancer Inst, 58-59; Fulbright-Hays lectr physiol, Fac Med, Univ Nangrahar, Afghanistan, 68-69. *Mem:* AAAS; Am Inst Biol Sci. *Res:* Role of the pituitary gland in chick growth and development prior to hatching by accomplishing hypophysectomy through ablation of the free-head region of the early embryo. *Mailing Add:* PO Box 468 Pleasant Hill TN 38578-0468

**VOGEL, PAUL WILLIAM,** PHYSICAL CHEMISTRY. *Current Pos:* RETIRED. *Personal Data:* b Swayzee, Ind, Oct 5, 19; m 48, Mary Hallawell; c Susan L & William A. *Educ:* DePauw Univ, AB, 41; Ind Univ, PhD(org chem), 46. *Prof Exp:* Asst, Ind Univ, 41-44; res chemist, Lubrizol Corp, 45-46, res supvr, 47-50, tech asst to dir res & develop, 50-53, supvr org & anal res, 53-59, dir testing, 59-62, dir chem res, 62-78. *Mem:* AAAS; Am Chem Soc; Sigma Xi. *Res:* Synthetic organic chemistry; pyroxonium and pyrylium salts; organic phosphorous compounds; lubricant additives. *Mailing Add:* 348 Thistle Trail Cleveland OH 44124-4182

**VOGEL, PETER,** NUCLEAR PHYSICS. *Current Pos:* sr res fel physics, 70-75, res assoc, 75-81, SR RES ASSOC PHYSICS, CALIF INST TECHNOL, 81- *Personal Data:* b Prague, Czech, Aug 12, 37. *Educ:* Czech Inst Technol, Prague, EngrTechPhysics, 60; Acad Sci USSR, CandSci(physics), 66. *Prof Exp:* Res fel, Joint Inst Nuclear Res, Dubna, USSR, 62-66, Nuclear Res Inst, Rez, Czech, 66-68 & Niels Bohr Inst, Copenhagen, Denmark, 68-69; res assoc, Nordic Inst Theoret Atomic Physics, Univ Bergen, 69-70. *Mem:* Am Phys Soc. *Res:* Nuclear structure theory; vibrations, rotations and deformations of nuclei; intermediate energy physics, mesonic atoms, neutrinos. *Mailing Add:* Dept Physics 161-33 Calif Tech 1200 E California Blvd Pasadena CA 91125

**VOGEL, PHILIP CHRISTIAN,** PHYSICAL ORGANIC CHEMISTRY. *Current Pos:* res staff scientist, BASF Corp, 75-76, deleg Dyestuffs Div, BASF Ag, 76-78, mgr tech develop, Colors & Auxiliaries Div, 78-82, mgr tech develop & qual control, Dyestuffs Div, 82-86, MGR PROD SERVS, RENSSELAER WORKS, BASF CHEMICALS, BASF CORP, 86- *Personal Data:* b Fargo, NDak, Nov 28, 41; m 66; c 2. *Educ:* Lawrence Univ, AB & BS, 63; Ind Univ, PhD(chem), 67. *Prof Exp:* From res assoc to sr res assoc chem, Yeshiva Univ, 67-70; asst prof chem, Col Pharmaceut Sci, Columbia Univ, 70-73; guest scientist, Max Planck Inst Chem, 73-75. *Mem:* Am Chem Soc. *Res:* Theory of isotope effects in organic reaction mechanisms; theory of structure of aqueous solutions. *Mailing Add:* 30 Woodmont Dr Delmar NY 12054

**VOGEL, RICHARD CLARK,** physical chemistry, for more information see previous edition

**VOGEL, RICHARD E,** COMPUTER SCIENCE. *Current Pos:* PRES, DATA MGT ASSOCS INC, 69- *Personal Data:* b Chicago, Ill, July 7, 30; m 53; c 2. *Educ:* Colo State Univ, BS, 53; Univ NMex, MS, 60. *Prof Exp:* Staff scientist, Los Alamos Sci Lab, 57-59; consult statist & comput, Corp Econ & Indust Res, 59-60; dir comput facil, Kaman Nuclear Div, Kaman Aircraft Corp, 60-69. *Concurrent Pos:* Lectr, Univ Colo, 61-; adj prof, Colo Col, 65- *Mem:* Am Meteorol Soc. *Res:* Statistics; meteorology; mathematics. *Mailing Add:* W-4927 Vogel Rd Jefferson WI 53549

**VOGEL, RICHARD M,** CIVIL ENGINEERING. *Current Pos:* ASSOC PROF, DEPT CIVIL ENG, TUFTS UNIV, 84- *Personal Data:* b New York, NY, Aug 16, 53; m, Frances Yuan; c Jarred, Noah & Eli. *Educ:* Univ Va, BS, 77, MS, 79; Cornell Univ, PhD, 84. *Honors & Awards:* Walter L Huber Civil Eng Res Prize, Am Soc Chem Engrs, 95. *Mem:* Am Geophys Union; Am Water Res Asn; Am Soc Eng Educ. *Mailing Add:* Dept Civil Eng Tufts Univ 113 Anderson Hall Medford MA 02155

**VOGEL, RICHARD W,** ADVANCED SYSTEMS IN MARKET DEVELOPMENT, RESEARCH & DEVELOPMENT. *Current Pos:* Adv syst mgr, 90-94, CHIEF ENGR ENVIRON SYST, PRW, 94- *Personal Data:* b Billings, Mont, 36. *Educ:* Gonzaga Univ, BS, 59; St Louis Univ, MS, 61; Fla State Univ, PhD(physics), 67. *Mem:* Am Phys Soc. *Res:* Advanced systems in market development; research and development. *Mailing Add:* 12500 Charles Stewart Ct Fairfax VA 22033

**VOGEL, ROGER FREDERICK,** CATALYSIS, SYNTHESIS. *Current Pos:* SR RES CHEMIST, CHEVRON CORP, 85- *Personal Data:* b Pittsburgh, Pa, Nov 1, 42; m 69, Corinne Seibel; c Geoffrey, Melissa, Cindy, Shelia, William, Gregory, Bradley, Lyndsey, Robyn, Britney & April. *Educ:* Valparaiso Univ, BS, 64. *Prof Exp:* Chemist, Sherwin Williams Co, 64-66; sr res chemist, Gulf Oil Corp, 66-85. *Res:* Synthesize new catalytic materials for process applications; hydrothermal synthesis of molecular sieves, precipitation, forming, metal addition, and characterization of catalysts. *Mailing Add:* 1814 Salisbury Dr Fairfield CA 94533. *Fax:* 510-242-2823

**VOGEL, STEFANIE N,** MACROPHAGES, ENDOTOXINS. *Current Pos:* ASSOC PROF MICROBIOL & IMMUNOL, UNIFORMED SERV UNIV HEALTH SCI, 80- *Educ:* Univ Md, PhD(microbiol), 77. *Mailing Add:* Dept Microbiol & Immunol Uniformed Serv Univ Health Sci 4301 Jones Bridge Rd B103 Bethesda MD 20814-4799. *Fax:* 301-295-1545

**VOGEL, STEVEN,** BIOLOGY, BIOFLUIDMECHANICS. *Current Pos:* From asst prof to prof, 66-93, JAMES B DUKE PROF ZOOL, DUKE UNIV, 93- *Personal Data:* b Beacon, NY, Apr 7, 40; m 63, 74, Jane Gregory; c Roger B. *Educ:* Tufts Univ, BS, 61; Harvard Univ, AM, 63, PhD(biol), 66. *Concurrent Pos:* Jr fel, Harvard Univ, 64-66; vis fac, Marine Biol Lab, 72, Marine Lab, Univ Wash, 79-83, Tjarno, Sweden Marine Lab, 89, Ben Gurion Univ, Israel, 95; Richard H Lufkin prof eng, Tufts Univ, 93. *Mem:* Fel AAAS; Sigma Xi; Soc Integrative & Comparative Biol. *Res:* Fluid flow through and around organisms of all phyla in both air and water; convective cooling; general writing in comparative biomechanics; organismal biology. *Mailing Add:* Dept Zool Duke Univ PO Box 90325 Durham NC 27708-0325. *Fax:* 919-684-6168; *E-Mail:* svogel@acpub.duke.edu

**VOGEL, THOMAS A,** PETROLOGY, VOLCANOLOGY. *Current Pos:* assoc prof, 68-74, PROF GEOL, MICH STATE UNIV, 74-, CHAIR, 91- *Personal Data:* b Janesville, Wis, July 5, 37; m 87; c 3. *Educ:* Univ Wis, BS, 59, MS, 61, PhD(geol), 63. *Prof Exp:* Asst prof geol, Rutgers Univ, New Brunswick, 63-68. *Concurrent Pos:* Vis prof, Univ SC, 74-75; vis scientist, Lawrence Livermore Nat Labs, 81-82 & 88-89, consult, 82-91. *Mem:* Geol Soc Am; Am Geophys Union. *Res:* Evolution of high-level silicic magma bodies; origin of batholiths; origin of studies of zoned ash-flow sheets; emplacement of magma bodies. *Mailing Add:* Dept Geol Mich State Univ East Lansing MI 48824. *Fax:* 517-353-8787; *E-Mail:* vogel@pilot.msu.edu

**VOGEL, THOMAS TIMOTHY,** HISTORY & PHILOSOPHY OF SCIENCE. *Current Pos:* Teaching asst physiol, 59-61, instr surg, 69-70, CLIN ASST PROF SURG, OHIO STATE UNIV, 73- *Personal Data:* b Columbus, Ohio, Feb 1, 34; m 65; c 4. *Educ:* Col Holy Cross, AB, 55; Ohio State Univ, MS, 60, PhD(physiol), 62; Georgetown Med Sch, MD, 65. *Concurrent Pos:* Consult, Bur Voc Rehab, Ohio, 70-; adv, Peer Rev Orgn, 85-91; Ethix Corp, HealthPro, 91- *Mem:* Am Physiol Soc; Fed Am Socs Exp Biol; Soc Acad Surg; Am Col Surgeons. *Res:* Metabolism in critically ill patients; tumors producing hormones; blood flow in activity; insulin relationships to muscle metabolism. *Mailing Add:* 621 S Cassingham Rd Columbus OH 43209-2403

**VOGEL, VERONICA LEE,** TOXICOLOGY, CLINICAL CHEMISTRY. *Current Pos:* CONSULT, 84- *Personal Data:* b New York, NY, Mar 9, 43; m 69. *Educ:* Univ Mich, BS, 64; NY Univ, MS, 67, PhD(phys chem), 72. *Prof Exp:* Res fel chem, NSF, Feltman Res Lab, 72-74; asst prof chem, County Col Morris, 74-75; lectr chem, Rutgers Univ, 75-79; anal chemist, Forensic Toxicol Lab, NJ State Med Examr's Off, 79-81; lab dir, Spec Chem, Toxicol & Environ Lab, MetPath Clin Labs, Teterboro, NJ, 81-83; dir, Lifechem Lab, Nat Med Care, 83-84. *Concurrent Pos:* Consult, Energetics Mat Lab, 74-81 & Batelle Res Labs; postdoctoral fel, NSF. *Mem:* Am Chem Soc; Am Asn Clin Chem. *Res:* Theoretical quantum chemistry, approximate molecular orbital calculations; drug analysis. *Mailing Add:* 3 Ihnen Ct Montvale NJ 07645-1113

**VOGEL, W MARK,** BRONCHOPULMONARY & CARDIOVASCULAR PHARMACOLOGY. *Current Pos:* RES INVESTR, HOFFMANN-LAROCHE INC, 91- *Personal Data:* b Delaware Co, Pa, Jan 16, 53; m, MaryLou Lynn; c Joshua D & Aaron J. *Educ:* Temple Univ, BA, 74; Univ Mich, PhD(pharmacol), 79. *Prof Exp:* From asst to assoc prof pharmacol, Sch Med, Boston Univ, 83-91, asst prof med, 83-91. *Concurrent Pos:* Adj assoc prof pharmacol, Boston Univ Sch Med, 92-; mem, Coun Basic Sci, Am Heart Asn. *Mem:* Am Heart Asn; Int Soc Heart Res; Am Soc Pharmacol Exp Therapeut; Am Thoracic Soc. *Res:* Pharmaceutical research and development of drugs for treatment of asthma and other respiratory diseases; evaluation of hemodynamic effects of drugs. *Mailing Add:* FDA Pulm Div HFD-570 5600 Fishers Lane Rockville MD 20857-0001. *Fax:* 973-235-8897

**VOGEL, WILLIS GENE,** SURFACE MINE REVEGETATION, RANGE SCIENCE. *Current Pos:* Range conservationist, Soil Conserv Serv, USDA, Idaho, 59-60, range conservationist, Forest Serv, Mo, 60-63, range scientist, Forest Serv, Northeastern Forest Exp Sta, 63-86. *Personal Data:* b Seward, Nebr, Nov 27, 30; m 54; c 4. *Educ:* Univ Nebr, BS, 52; Mont State Col, MS, 61. *Mem:* Sigma Xi. *Res:* Revegetation of coal strip mine spoils. *Mailing Add:* 116 Cumberland St Berea KY 40403

**VOGEL, WOLFGANG HELLMUT,** BIOCHEMISTRY, PHARMACOLOGY. *Current Pos:* assoc prof, 67-74, PROF PHARMACOL, THOMAS JEFFERSON UNIV, 74-, JEFFERSON MED COL, 74-, PROF PSYCHIAT & HUMAN BEHAV, 76-, VCHMN, DEPT PSYCHIAT, 84-, ACTG CHMN, 87- *Personal Data:* b Dresden, Ger, Aug 4, 30; m 61; c 2. *Educ:* Dresden Tech Univ, BS, 49; Stuttgart Tech Univ, MS, 56, PhD(chem), 58. *Honors & Awards:* Humboldt Prize; Lindback Award. *Prof Exp:* Postdoctoral fel, Upstate Med Ctr, State Univ NY, 58-59; chemist, Farbwerke Hoechst, Ger, 59-61; res assoc biochem pharmacol, Col Med, Univ Ill, 61-63, instr, 63-64; vis scientist, NIH, 64-65; asst prof pharmacol, Col Med, Univ Ill, 65-67. *Concurrent Pos:* Med res assoc, L B Mendel Res Lab, Elgin State Hosp, 65-67. *Res:* Biochemistry of mental disorders; biochemical pharmacology; stress research; development of drug assays; neurochemical correlates of behavior. *Mailing Add:* Dept Pharmacol Thomas Jefferson Univ 1020 Locust St Philadelphia PA 19107-6731

**VOGELBERGER, PETER JOHN, JR,** NUCLEAR ENGINEERING. *Current Pos:* RETIRED. *Personal Data:* b Youngstown, Ohio, Apr 14, 32; m 54; c 4. *Educ:* US Naval Acad, BS, 54. *Prof Exp:* Assoc nuclear engr, Argonne Nat Lab, 63-65; mgr tech liaison, Isotopes, Inc, 65-67, vpres & gen mgr, Energy Systs Div, Teledyne Isotopes, Inc, 68-76, pres, Teledyne Energy Systs, Timonium, 76-93. *Concurrent Pos:* Mem, Md Adv Comn Atomic Energy, 68-78. *Res:* Design, development and production of nuclear and fossil-fuel thermoelectric power systems for space and terrestrial use; electrochemical gas generators and fuel cell. *Mailing Add:* 2202 Dykman Circle Little River SC 29566

**VOGELFANGER, ELLIOT AARON,** POLYMER SCIENCE, ORGANIC CHEMISTRY. *Current Pos:* MGR RES & DEVELOP, SOLTEX POLYMER CORP, 74- *Personal Data:* b New York, NY, Apr 5, 37; m 58; c 2. *Educ:* Columbia Univ, BA, 58; Univ Calif, Los Angeles, PhD(phys org chem), 63. *Prof Exp:* Res chemist, Esso Res & Eng Co, 63-66; group leader polymer sci, Celanese Corp, 66-74. *Concurrent Pos:* Lectr, Hunter Col, 65-71. *Mem:* Am Chem Soc; Soc Plastics Engrs; Am Soc Testing & Mat; Sigma Xi. *Res:* Polymer rheology; high temperature polymers; physical organic chemistry; polyolefins research, application, development, and catalysis. *Mailing Add:* 7 Hampton Ct Houston TX 77024-5447

**VOGELI, BRUCE R,** MATHEMATICS. *Current Pos:* prof math, Teachers Col, 65-76, CLIFFORD BREWSTER UPTON PROF, COLUMBIA UNIV, 76- *Personal Data:* b Alliance, Ohio, Nov 25, 29; m 56; c 2. *Educ:* Mt Union Col, BS, 51; Kent State Univ, MA, 57; Univ Mich, PhD(math educ), 60. *Honors & Awards:* Harold Benjamin Prize. *Prof Exp:* Assoc prof math, Bowling Green State Univ, 59-65. *Concurrent Pos:* Vis prof, Lenin Inst, Moscow, USSR, 64 & Kurukshetra Univ, India, 65; consult, Ministry Educ, Chile, 66-67 & Silver Burdett Co, 60-; NSF fel; sr Fulbright lectr. *Mem:* Math Asn Am; Nat Coun Teachers Math. *Res:* Mathematics education; international mathematical activities. *Mailing Add:* Dept Math & Sci Educ Teachers Col Columbia Univ Box 195 New York NY 10027

**VOGELMAN, JOSEPH H(ERBERT),** ELECTRONICS, BIOMEDICAL ENGINEERING. *Current Pos:* PRES, VOGELMAN DEVELOPMENT CO, 73-; CHIEF SCIENTIST, ORENTREICH FOUND ADVAN SCI, 73- *Personal Data:* b New York, NY, Aug 18, 20; m 46, Norma Schneider; c Jeffrey A, Leslie S & Linda L (Bernstein). *Educ:* City Col New York, BS, 40; Polytech Inst Brooklyn, MEE, 48, DEE, 57. *Honors & Awards:* USAF Outstanding Performance Award, 58. *Prof Exp:* Res analyst, Signal Corps Radar Lab, US Dept Army, 42, proj engr, 42-43, proj engr, Signal Corps Eng Labs, 43-44; chief test equip sect, Watson Labs, USAF, 44-47, chief develop br, 47-51; chief scientist gen eng, Rome Air Develop Ctr, NY, 51-52, chief electronic warfare lab, 52-55, dir commun & electronics, 55-59; vpres res & develop, Capehart Corp, 59-64; dir electronics, Chromalloy Am Corp, 64-67, vpres, 67-73, gen mgr, Pocket Fone Div, 65-67, vpres, 67-73; vpres & dir, Cro-Med Bionics Corp, 68-73; vchmn bd & sr vpres, Laser Link Corp, 71-73. *Concurrent Pos:* Mem, Army-Navy Radio Frequency Cable Coord Comt, 44-48; mem test equip comt, Res & Develop Bd, 48-52, chmn waveguide comt, 48-52; chmn commun tech adv comt, Air Res & Develop Command, 58-59, award, 58, consult, 59-; consult, Dept of Defense, 59-67; vpres, ACR Electronics Corp, 66-68; dir & consult, Orentreich Found Advan Sci, 63-73. *Mem:* Fel AAAS; fel Inst Elec & Electronics Engrs; Sigma Xi. *Res:* Radio frequency instrumentation; microwave theory and techniques; bio-medical instrumentation; communications; computers for medicine; biochemistry; radio immune assays; chromatography; computer applications for medical laboratory technology; epidemiological studies of hormones and diseases. *Mailing Add:* 48 Green Dr Roslyn NY 11576-3221

**VOGELMANN, ANDREW MARK,** ATMOSPHERIC RADIATIVE TRANSFER, CLIMATE RESEARCH. *Current Pos:* FEL, INST ATMOSPHERIC PHYSICS, UNIV ARIZ, 94- *Personal Data:* b Burlington, Vt, June 19, 62. *Educ:* Univ Vt, BS, 84; Univ Md, MS, 86; Pa State Univ, PhD(meteorol), 94. *Prof Exp:* Grad res asst, Dept Meteorol, Univ Md, 84-86, Pa State Univ, 88-94; res scientist, Atmospheric & Environ Res Inc, 86-88. *Mem:* Am Geophys Union; Am Inst Physics. *Res:* Atmospheric radiative transfer, the scattering properties of aerosols and nonspherical particles, cloud radioactive forcing, and the atmospheric transmission of ultraviolet radiation and its biological impact. *Mailing Add:* Univ Calif San Diego Scripps Inst Oceanog 9500 Gilman Dr M/C 0239 La Jolla CA 92093. *Fax:* 520-621-6833

**VOGELMANN, HUBERT WALTER,** BOTANY. *Current Pos:* RETIRED. *Personal Data:* b Buffalo, NY, Nov 13, 28; m 51, Marie Folk; c Thomas, James & Andrew. *Educ:* Heidelberg Col, BS, 51; Univ Mich, MA, 52, PhD(bot), 55. *Prof Exp:* Asst prof taxon bot, Univ Vt, 59-62, assoc prof, 62-70, prof bot, 70-92. *Concurrent Pos:* Pres, Conserv & Res Found; bd, Conserv Fund. *Mem:* Ecol Soc Am. *Res:* Ecology of mountain forests; natural areas protection. *Mailing Add:* RR3 Box 485 Jericho VT 05465

**VOGELSTEIN, BERT,** ONCOLOGY. *Current Pos:* PROF, DEPT ONCOL, SCH MED, JOHNS HOPKINS UNIV, 78- *Educ:* Univ Pa, BS, 70; Johns Hopkins Univ, MD. *Honors & Awards:* Gairdner Found Int Award, 92; Medal of Honor, Am Cancer Soc, 92; Richard Lounsbery Award, Nat Acad Sci, 93. *Prof Exp:* Res assoc, Nat Cancer Inst, 76-78. *Concurrent Pos:* Adv, Sci Rev Groups, Nat Cancer Inst, NIH. *Mem:* Nat Acad Sci; Am Acad Arts & Sci. *Res:* Revolutionizing our understanding of complex genetic mutations that occur when a normal bowel epithelial cell is transformed into a malignant cell. *Mailing Add:* Sch Med Johns Hopkins Univ 424 N Bond St Baltimore MD 21231

**VOGH, BETTY POHL,** PHARMACOLOGY, PHYSIOLOGY. *Current Pos:* Res assoc physiol, Col Med, Univ Fla, 65-66, res assoc pharmacol, 66-67, asst prof, 68-74, ASSOC PROF PHARMACOL, COL MED, UNIV FLA, 74- *Personal Data:* b Georgetown, Ohio, Apr 19, 27; m 47; c 4. *Educ:* Tex Woman's Univ, BA, 46; Univ Fla, PhD(physiol), 64. *Mem:* Sigma Xi. *Res:* Physiology and pharmacology of body fluids; regulation of cerebrospinal fluid. *Mailing Add:* 1119 SW 11th Ave Gainesville FL 32601-7842

**VOGL, OTTO,** POLYMER SCIENCE & ENGINEERING. *Current Pos:* prof, 70-83, EMER PROF POLYMER SCI ENG, UNIV MASS, AMHERST, 83-; HERMAN F MARK PROF, POLYTECH UNIV, 83- *Personal Data:* b Traiskirchen, Austria, Nov 6, 27; nat US; m 55; c 2. *Educ:* Univ Vienna, PhD, 50. *Hon Degrees:* Dr, Univ Jena. *Honors & Awards:* Humboldt Award, Fed Repub Ger, 77; W H Rauscher Mem lectr, 84; Mobay lectr, Univ Pittsburgh, 85; Chem Pioneer Award, Am Inst Chemists, 85; Exner Medal, 87; Chem & Phys Medal, Austrian Res Inst, 89; Appl Polymer Chem Award, Am Chem Soc, 90. *Prof Exp:* Instr chem, Univ Vienna, 48-53; res assoc, Univ Mich, 53-55 & Princeton Univ, 55-56; chemist, E I du Pont de Nemours & Co, Del, 56-70. *Concurrent Pos:* Vis prof, Kyoto Univ & Osaka Univ, 68 & 80, Royal Inst Technol, Stockholm, 71 & 87, Univ Freiburg, 73, Univ Strasburg, 76, Univ Berlin, 77 & Tech Univ Dresden, 82; chmn, Div Polymer Chem & Conn Valley Sect, Am Chem Soc, 74; comt mem macromolecular chem, Nat Res Coun-Nat Acad Sci, 75-78, chmn, 78-80; pres, Pac Polymer Fedn, 87-90; Fulbright fel, 76; sr scientist fel, Japan Soc Promotion Sci, 80. *Mem:* AAAS; Am Chem Soc; Austrian Chem Soc; Japanese Soc Polymer Sci; NY Acad Sci; foreign mem Austrian Acad Sci; Sigma Xi. *Res:* Ionic and stereoselective polymerization; polyaldehydes; ring opening polymerization; regular copolyamides; reactions on polymers; functional polymers; biologically and ultraviolet active polymers; head to head polymers; optically active polymers. *Mailing Add:* Dept Polymer Sci & Eng Univ Mass Amherst MA 01003

**VOGL, RICHARD J**, BOTANY, ECOLOGY. *Current Pos:* PROF BOT, CALIF STATE UNIV, LOS ANGELES, 61- *Personal Data:* b Milwaukee, Wis, Jan 19, 32; m 61; c 3. *Educ:* Marquette Univ, BS, 53, MS, 55; Univ Wis, PhD(ecol), 61. *Prof Exp:* Instr bot, Marquette Univ, 55-56; res asst, Univ Wis, 58-61. *Concurrent Pos:* Ed, Ecol Soc Am, 72-75. *Mem:* Ecol Soc Am; Wildlife Soc. *Res:* Plant and fire ecology. *Mailing Add:* 9866 Joel Dr Cypress CA 90630

**VOGL, THOMAS PAUL**, COMPUTER MODELING OF BIOLOGICAL LEARNING, SCIENCE POLICY & ADMINISTRATION. *Current Pos:* SR RES SCIENTIST & MGR, ADVAN CONCEPTS DEPT, ENVIRON RES INST MICH, 86- *Personal Data:* b Vienna, Austria, July 10, 29; nat US; c 3. *Educ:* Columbia Univ, BA, 52; Univ Pittsburgh, MS, 57; Carnegie-Mellon Univ, PhD(syst sci), 69. *Prof Exp:* Sr res physicist, Res Lab, Westinghouse Elec Corp, 52-60; head infrared sect, Res Labs, Hughes Aircraft Co, 60-61; mgr optical physics, Res Labs, Westinghouse Elec Corp, 61-69, mgr optics, 69-74; prin staff officer, Assembly Life Sci, Nat Acad Sci, 74-77; exec secy, Nat Comn Digestive Dis, NIH, 77-79, nutrit coordr comt, off dir, 79-86. *Concurrent Pos:* Lectr, Univ Calif, Los Angeles, 59-74; mem comt phototherapy in newborn, Div Med, Nat Acad Sci-Nat Res Coun & chmn subcomt bioeng aspects; adj prof radiation biophys, Dept Radiol & Pediat, Col Physicians & Surgeons, Columbia Univ, 73-79, mem, Bioeng Inst, 75-79; prof, MBTI & CSI, George Mason Univ, 95- *Mem:* Optical Soc Am; AAAS; Am Soc Photobiol; Int Neural Network Soc; Pattern Recognition Soc; Soc Neurosci. *Res:* Computer models of cortical information processing and associative learning; non-linear optimization; phototherapy of hyperbilirubinemia; biological and artificial neural networks. *Mailing Add:* 29 Scotchman's Lane PO Box 3022 West Tisbury MA 02575. *Fax:* 301-986-5517; *E-Mail:* tvogl@gmu.edu

**VOGLER, LARRY B**, B LYMPHOCYTE GROWTH & DIFFERENTIATION. *Current Pos:* ASSOC PROF PEDIAT, EMORY UNIV, 92- *Personal Data:* b Houston, Tex, Feb 5, 47. *Educ:* Baylor Col Med, MD, 73. *Prof Exp:* Asst prof immunol, Sch Med, Vanderbilt Univ, 81- *Mem:* Soc Pediat Res; Am Asn Immunol. *Mailing Add:* Dept Pediat Sch Med Emory Univ 2040 Ridgewood Dr NE Atlanta GA 30322-1101

**VOGT, ALBERT R**, PLANT PHYSIOLOGY. *Current Pos:* DIR, SCH NATURAL RESOURCES, UNIV MO, COLUMBIA, 85- *Personal Data:* b St Louis, Mo, Apr 6, 38; c 2. *Educ:* Univ Mo, BS, 61, MS, 62, PhD(forestry), 66. *Prof Exp:* Instr forestry, Univ Mo, 65-66; from asst prof to prof tree physiol, Ohio Agr Res & Develop Ctr, Ohio State Univ, 66-85, from actg assoc chmn to chmn, Div Forestry, 69-85. *Mem:* Am Soc Plant Physiol; Soc Am Foresters. *Res:* Physiology of tree growth and development; bud dormancy in oak; flowering of trees. *Mailing Add:* Dept Forestry Univ Mo 1-30 Ag Bldg Columbia MO 65211-0001

**VOGT, ERICH WOLFGANG**, NUCLEAR REACTIONS, INTERMEDIATE ENERGY PHYSICS. *Current Pos:* prof, 65-95, EMER PROF PHYSICS, UNIV BC, 95- *Personal Data:* b Steinbach, Man, Nov 12, 29; m 52, Barbara M Greenfield; c Edith Susan, Elizabeth Mary, David Erie, Jonathan Michael & Robert Jeremy. *Educ:* Univ Man, BSc, 51, MSc, 52; Princeton Univ, PhD(physics), 55. *Hon Degrees:* DSc, Univ Man, 82, Queens Univ, 84, Carleton Univ, 88; LLD, Univ Regina, 86, Simon Fraser Univ, 96. *Honors & Awards:* Centennial Medal Can, 67; Medal Achievement Physics, Can Asn Physicists, 88. *Prof Exp:* Nat Res Coun Can fel, Univ Birmingham, 55-56; res officer physics, Atomic Energy Can Ltd, 56-65. *Concurrent Pos:* Vis assoc prof, Univ Rochester, 58-59; Nat Res Coun Can sr travelling fel, Oxford Univ, 71-72; vpres fac & student affairs, Univ BC, 75-81; chmn, Sci Coun BC, 78-80; dir, Triumpf Proj, Can Nat Meson Lab, 81-94. *Mem:* Am Phys Soc; fel Royal Soc Can; Can Asn Physicists (pres, 70-71). *Res:* Theory of nuclear reactions, nuclear structure and intermediate energy physics; physics of pion-nucleus interactions. *Mailing Add:* Triumf 4004 Wesbrook Mall Vancouver BC V6T 2A3 Can. *E-Mail:* vogt@triumf.ca

**VOGT, HERWART CURT**, POLYMER CHEMISTRY. *Current Pos:* sr res chemist, BASF Wyandotte Corp, 59-66, res assoc, 67-73, supvr, 73-77, corp toxicologist 77-79, MGR ADMIN, BASF WYANDOTTE CORP, 79- *Personal Data:* b Elizabeth, NJ, Sept 14, 29; m 58; c 2. *Educ:* Northwestern Univ, 52; Univ Del, MS, 54, PhD(chem), 57; Wayne State Univ, MS, 77. *Prof Exp:* Res chemist, Hercules Inc, 57-59. *Concurrent Pos:* Vis lectr, Oakland Univ, 66-69 & Wayne State Univ, 69-71; exchange chemist, BASF-AG, WGer, 71-73; adj prof, Upsala Col, 81- *Mem:* Am Chem Soc; AAAS; Sigma Xi. *Res:* Organic phosphorus compounds pertaining to polymers; novel halogen containing unsaturated polyesters; isocyanate and urethane chemistry; chlorine containing elastomers; noncellular urethane plastics. *Mailing Add:* 6 Meadowbrook Terr Sparta NJ 07871-1238

**VOGT, KRISTIINA ANN**, MICROBIAL ECOLOGY, FORESTRY. *Current Pos:* FAC, DEPT FORESTRY, YALE UNIV. *Personal Data:* b Turku, Finland, Mar 3, 49; US citizen; m 73. *Educ:* Univ Tex, El Paso, BS, 71; NMex State Univ, MS, 74, PhD(biol), 75. *Prof Exp:* Res assoc ecosyst, Col Forestry Resources, Univ Wash, 76-80, res asst prof, 80- *Mem:* Soc Industr Microbiol; AAAS; Sigma Xi. *Res:* Physiology; decomposition and nutrient cycling; mycorrhizae and below ground root dynamics. *Mailing Add:* Dept Forestry Yale Univ PO Box 208240 New Haven CT 06520

**VOGT, MOLLY THOMAS**, CLINICAL EPIDEMIOLOGY, OSTEOPOROSIS. *Current Pos:* res asst biochem path, Sch Med, Univ Pittsburgh, 62-63, from asst prof biochem to assoc prof, 70-78, chmn, Div Health Related Prof Interdisciplinary Progs, 72-74, assoc dean, 77-83, dir continuing med educ, 84-86, NIH fel cardiovasc epidemiol, 89-93, PROF BIOCHEM, SCH HEALTH RELATED PROF, UNIV PITTSBURGH, 78-, VIS ASSOC PROF, ORTHO SURG, 93- *Personal Data:* b Lyndhurst, Eng, Apr 15, 39; m 93, Edward N Peterson; c William & Keith. *Educ:* Bristol Univ, BSc, 60; Univ Pittsburgh, PhD(biochem), 67, MPH, 90, DrPH, 91. *Honors & Awards:* President's Award, Am Soc Allied Health Professions, 81. *Prof Exp:* Jr res officer, Toxicol Unit, Med Res Coun, Eng, 60-62; assoc dean, Med Col Ohio, 86-89. *Concurrent Pos:* NIH fel biochem, Sch Med, Univ Pittsburgh, 67-70, Health Res Serv Found grant, 70-71; Am Coun Educ Admin intern, 74-75; mem, Coun Epidemiol, Am Heart Asn. *Mem:* Soc Epidemiol Res; Am Geriat Soc; Sigma Xi; fel Am Soc Allied Health Professions. *Res:* Lower extremity arterial disease; women's health; gerontology; falls; osteoporosis. *Mailing Add:* 107 Crofton Dr Pittsburgh PA 15238. *Fax:* 412-687-3724

**VOGT, PETER KLAUS**, GENETICS, MOLECULAR BIOLOGY. *Current Pos:* MEM & HEAD ONCOUIROLOGY, SCRIPPS RES INST, 93- *Personal Data:* b Broumov, Czech, Mar 10, 32; US citizen. *Educ:* Univ Wurzburg, Ger, BS, 55; Univ Tubingen, Ger, PhD(biol), 59. *Hon Degrees:* Dr, Univ Wurzburg, 95. *Honors & Awards:* Vogeler Prize, Max-Planck-Soc, 76; Alexander von Humboldt Award, Fed Repub Ger, 84; Ernst Jung Prize Med, 85; Waterford Biomed Sci Award, 86; Robert J & Claire Pasarow Award, 87; Paul-Ehrlich & Ludwig-Darmstaedter Prize, 88; Bristol Myers Award, 89; ICN Int Prize Virol, 89; Charles S Mott Prize, GM Can Res Found, 91. *Prof Exp:* From asst prof to assoc prof path, Sch Med, Univ Colo, 62-67; from assoc prof to prof microbiol, Sch Med, Univ Wash, 67-71; Hastings prof, Univ Southern Calif, Los Angeles, 71-78, Hastings distinguished prof, 78-80, prof & chmn, Dept Microbiol, Sch Med, 80-93. *Concurrent Pos:* Damon Runyon cancer fel, Virus Lab, Univ Calif, Berkeley, 59-62; res grants, USPHS, 62- & Am Cancer Soc, 63-68; mem, Virol Study Sect, NIH, 67-71; mem, Cell Biol & Virol Adv Comt, Am Cancer Soc, 72-76; bd sci consults, Sloan Kettering Inst Cancer Res, 72-80, chmn, 80-81; mem, Coun Res & Clin Invest, Am Cancer Soc, 79-82. *Mem:* Nat Acad Sci; hon mem Japanese Cancer Asn; Am Soc Microbiol; AAAS; Genetics Soc Am; Am Soc Virol; Am Asn Cancer Res. *Res:* Mechanism of neoplastic cellular transformation induced by viruses; virology; genetics; cellular differentiation; neoplastic transformation; immunology development. *Mailing Add:* Scripps Res Inst 10550 N Torrey Pines Rd La Jolla CA 92037

**VOGT, PETER RICHARD**, MARINE GEOPHYSICS. *Current Pos:* Geophysicist, US Naval Oceanog Off, 67-75, GEOPHYSICIST, NAVAL RES LAB, 76-77 & 78- *Personal Data:* b Hamburg, Ger, June 8, 39; US citizen; m 67, Randi Stampen; c Anton E & Jason A. *Educ:* Calif Inst Technol, BS, 61; Univ Wis, MA, 65, PhD(oceanog), 68. *Honors & Awards:* Henry A Kaminski Award, Sci Res Soc Am. *Concurrent Pos:* Mem staff, Univ Oslo, Norway, 77-78; assoc ed, Geol Soc Am Bull. *Mem:* Am Geophys Union; fel Geol Soc Am. *Res:* Geophysical research on the constitution and history of the crust beneath the sea, especially the analysis of marine magnetic field, gravity, altimetry, acoustic backscatter, and topographic anomalies and mantle hot spot phenomena as related to ocean floor (plate) movement, sea-floor sediment dynamics. *Mailing Add:* Scientists Cliff St Leonard MD 20685. *Fax:* 202-767-0167

**VOGT, RICHARD LEE**, ALGEBRA, NUMBER THEORY. *Current Pos:* PROF MATH & COMPUT SCI, NEBR WESLEYAN UNIV, 83- *Personal Data:* b Lincoln, Nebr, Nov 11, 44; m 86, Cynthia Lee Didion; c Gary Lee. *Educ:* Univ Nebr, Lincoln, BS, 67, MS, 69; Univ Ill, Urbana, PhD(math), 74. *Prof Exp:* Prof math, comput sci & astron, Butler Univ, 74-83. *Concurrent Pos:* Dir, Holcomb Observ & Planetarium, Butler Univ, 78-83. *Mem:* Math Asn Am; Nat Coun Teachers Math. *Res:* Algebraic number theory. *Mailing Add:* 3054 N 60th St Lincoln NE 68507

**VOGT, ROCHUS E**, PHYSICS, GRAVITATION. *Current Pos:* from asst prof to assoc prof physics, Calif Inst Technol, 62-70, chmn fac, 75-77, chief scientist, Jet Propulsion Lab, 77-78, chmn, Div Physics, Math & Astron, 78-83, vpres & provost, 83-87, dir, Laser Interfeometer Gravitation Wave Observ Proj, 87-94, PROF PHYSICS, CALIF INST TECHNOL, 70-, R STANTON AVERY DISTINGUISHED SERV PROF, 82- *Personal Data:* b Neckarelz, Ger, Dec 21, 29; US citizen; m 58, Micheline A Y Bauduin; c Michele & Nicole. *Educ:* Univ Chicago, SM, 57, PhD(physics), 61. *Prof Exp:* Res assoc cosmic rays, Univ Chicago, 61-62. *Concurrent Pos:* Actg dir, Owens Valley Radio Observ, Calif, 80-81; vis prof, Mass Inst Technol, 88- *Mem:* Fel Am Phys Soc; fel AAAS. *Res:* Cosmic rays; astrophysics; experimental gravitation. *Mailing Add:* 51-33 Calif Inst Technol Pasadena CA 91125. *Fax:* 626-449-6460; *E-Mail:* vogt@ligo.caltech.edu

**VOGT, STEVEN SCOTT**, ASTRONOMICAL INSTRUMENTATION. *Current Pos:* Asst prof & asst astronr, 78-84, assoc prof & astronr, 84-87, PROF & ASTRONOMER, LICK OBSERV, UNIV CALIF, SANTA CRUZ, 87- *Personal Data:* b Rock Island, Ill, Dec 20, 49; m 80, Zarmina Dastagir; c Crystal, Alexander & Sophia. *Educ:* Univ Calif, Berkeley, AB(physics) & AB(astron), 72; Univ Tex, MA, 75, PhD(astron), 78. *Honors & Awards:* Muhlmann Award, 95. *Mem:* Am Astron Soc; Astron Soc Pac; Soc Photo-Optical Instrumentation Engrs; Int Astron Union; Sigma Xi. *Res:* Astronomical instrumentation; solid state imaging detectors, stellar spectroscopy; optical design. *Mailing Add:* Lick Observ Univ Calif Santa Cruz CA 95064. *Fax:* 408-426-3115; *E-Mail:* vogt@ucolick.org

**VOGT, THOMAS CLARENCE, JR**, PHYSICAL CHEMISTRY, PETROLEUM ENGINEERING. *Current Pos:* RETIRED. *Personal Data:* b San Antonio, Tex, Sept 21, 32; m 63; c 6. *Educ:* St Mary's Univ, BS, 54, Univ Notre Dame, PhD(phys chem), 61. *Prof Exp:* Res chemist, Mobil Oil Corp,

57; asst, Univ Notre Dame, 57-58, fel diffusion kinetics, Radiation Proj, 58-61; assoc chemist, Field Res Lab, Mobil Res & Develop Corp, 61-80, res assoc, 80-82; uranium field opers mgr, Mobil Alternative Energy, Inc, 82-84; eng supvr, Mobil Oil Corp, Denver-West, 85-87, compl eng adv, 88-89, acquisitions trades & sales, 90, completions adv, 91-92. *Concurrent Pos:* Chem instr, Metropolitan State Col, Denver, 92- *Mem:* Sigma Xi; Am Chem Soc; Soc Petrol Eng. *Res:* Diffusion and recombination of free radicals in liquid systems; effects of high pressure on reaction rates; chemical stimulation of petroleum production wells; in-situ uranium leaching; hydraulic fracturing of subsurface formations; economics of well treatments; in situ coal gasification. *Mailing Add:* 5158 W Lake Pl Littleton CO 80123

**VOGT, WILLIAM G(EORGE),** COMPUTER CONTROL, ACQUISITION & POINTING & TRACKING. *Current Pos:* res engr, Eng Res Div, 53-60, assoc prof, 62-68, PROF ELEC ENG, UNIV PITTSBURGH, 68- *Personal Data:* b McKeesport, Pa, June 1, 31; div; c 2. *Educ:* Univ Pittsburgh, BS, 53, MS, 57, PhD(elec eng), 62. *Prof Exp:* Engr, Adv Systs & Eng Div, Westinghouse Elec Corp, 61. *Concurrent Pos:* NASA res assoc, Univ Pittsburgh, 63-64; consult, Astrionics Labs, Marshall Space Flight Ctr, NASA, Ala, 64-67, Fecker Systs Div, Owens-Ill, Pa, 68-74, Contraves-Goerz, 78-, TASC, 78-, NASA Indust Appln Ctr, 82-, Compunetics, Inc, 82- & Tex Instruments, Inc, 83-; NSF fel, 61-62 & NSF sci fac fel, 75-76; mem bd dirs, Univ Res & Develop Assocs, Inc. *Mem:* Inst Elec & Electronics Engrs; Am Soc Mech Engrs; Instrument Soc Am; Sigma Xi; Soc Comput Simulation. *Res:* Computer control; robotics; high speed real time digital signal processing; acquisition, pointing and tracking systems; visual inspection systems; parallel processing; microcomputer and personal computer applications; modeling and simulation. *Mailing Add:* 2814 Waterman Ave Pittsburgh PA 15227

**VOHR, JOHN H,** MECHANICAL ENGINEERING. *Current Pos:* RETIRED. *Personal Data:* b Laconia, NH, Nov 27, 34; m 56, Sandy McBrian; c Mark, Neal, Eric & Jill. *Educ:* Harvard Univ, AB, 56; Columbia Univ, MS, 58, PhD(mech eng), 64. *Honors & Awards:* Best Paper of Yr Award, Lubrication Div, Am Soc Mech Engrs, 67. *Prof Exp:* Res engr, Mech Tech Inc, NY, 62-68, supvr anal mech, 68-69; from asst prof to assoc prof mech eng, Rensselaer Polytech Inst, 69-73, chmn mech eng curric, 70-73; prin engr, Gen Elec Co, 73-95. *Mem:* Am Soc Mech Engrs; Am Soc Lubrication Engrs. *Res:* Analytical studies of hydrodynamic and hydrostatic bearings; heat transfer analysis and two-phase flow studies; rotor dynamic analysis. *Mailing Add:* 1400 Dean St Schenectady NY 12309

**VOHRA, PRAN NATH,** NUTRITION, BIOCHEMISTRY. *Current Pos:* asst res nutritionist, Dept Poultry Husb, 62-70, from assoc prof to prof, 70-89, EMER PROF AVIAN SCI, UNIV CALIF, DAVIS, 89- *Personal Data:* b Gwaliar, India, June 11, 19. *Educ:* Univ Panjab, India, MSc, 42; Wash State Univ, MS, 54; Univ Calif, Davis, PhD(nutrit), 59. *Honors & Awards:* Am Feed Mfrs Asn Award. *Prof Exp:* Res asst chem, Sci & Indust Res Orgn, India, 42-49; int trainee fermentations, Joseph E Seagram & Sons, Ky, 49-50; specialist nutrit, Dept Poultry Husb, Univ Calif, Davis, 58-59; asst, BO&C Mills, Eng, 59-60; specialist poultry, US AID India, 61-62. *Concurrent Pos:* Consult. *Mem:* Poultry Sci Asn; Am Inst Nutrit; Brit Biochem Soc; Brit Nutrit Soc. *Res:* Trace elements in nutrition; improvement of nutrition in developing countries; comparative nutrition of avian species; nutrition evaluation of cereals and legumes; poultry husbandry. *Mailing Add:* Dept Avian Sci Univ Calif Davis CA 95616

**VOHRA, YOGESH K,** SOLID STATE & HIGH PRESSURE PHYSICS, DIAMOND SCIENCE & TECHNOLOGY. *Current Pos:* assoc prof, 92-96, PROF, DEPT PHYSICS, UNIV ALA, BIRMINGHAM, 96- *Personal Data:* b Delhi, India, Dec 15, 53; US citizen; m 80, Anju Khanna; c Shikhar & Vaibhav. *Educ:* Univ Delhi, India, BS, 72, MS, 74; Univ Bombay, India, PhD(physics), 80. *Prof Exp:* Sci officer, Bhabha Atomic Res Ctr, Bombay, 75-84; res assoc, Dept Mat Sci & Eng, Cornell Univ, 84-88, asst prof, 88-92. *Concurrent Pos:* Alexander Von Humboldt fel, Fed Repub Ger, 81-82. *Mem:* Am Phys Soc. *Res:* Study properties of materials at high pressures and high temperatures; synthesize new materials harder than diamond; new forms of metals and alloys under pressure; growth and properties of diamond. *Mailing Add:* Dept Physics 310 Campbell Hall Univ Ala 1300 University Blvd Birmingham AL 35294-1170. *Fax:* 205-934-8042; *E-Mail:* vohra@phy.uab.edu

**VOHS, JAMES A,** MEDICINE. *Current Pos:* RETIRED. *Personal Data:* b Idaho Falls, Idaho, Sept 26, 28; m 53, Janice Hughes; c Laura, Carole, Nancy & Sharla. *Educ:* Univ Calif, Berkeley, BA, 52. *Honors & Awards:* Justin Ford Kimball Award, Am Hosp Asn. *Prof Exp:* Chmn & chief exec officer, Kaiser Found Health Plan & Hosp, 80-93. *Mem:* Inst Med-Nat Acad Sci. *Mailing Add:* 17 Westminster Dr Oakland CA 94618

**VOHS, PAUL ANTHONY, JR,** ZOOLOGY. *Current Pos:* RETIRED. *Personal Data:* b Kansas City, Kans, Jan 19, 31; m 53; c 5. *Educ:* Kans State Univ, BS, 55; Southern Ill Univ, MA, 58; Iowa State Univ, PhD, 64. *Prof Exp:* Proj leader, Coop Proj, Ill Dept Conserv, Ill Natural Hist Surv & Southern Ill Univ, 55-58; res assoc, Coop Wildlife Res Proj, Southern Ill Univ, 59-61; res asst, Coop Wildlife Res Unit, Iowa State Univ, 61-62, instr zool & entom, 63-64, asst prof zool, 64-68, assoc prof wildlife biol, 68; assoc prof wildlife ecol, Ore State Univ, 68-73, prof & exten wildlife specialist, Coop Exten Serv & Dept Fisheries & Wildlife, 73-74; prof wildlife & fisheries sci & head dept, SDak State Univ, Brookings, 74-76; leader, Okla Coop, Wildlife Res Unit, Okla State Univ, Fish & Wildlife Serv, Stillwater, 76-79; supvr, Coopr Wildlife Res Units, US Dept Interior-Fish & Wildlife Serv, Washington, DC, 79-81; dir, Denver Wildlife Res Ctr, Denver, Colo, 82-87; leader, Iowa Coop Fish

& Wildlife Res Unit, Iowa State Univ Fish & Wildlife Serv, Ames, Iowa, 87-92; Nat Biol Surv, 92- *Mem:* Wilson Ornith Soc; Wildlife Soc; Am Soc Mammal; Ecol Soc Am; Am Ornith Union. *Res:* Vertebrate ecology; response of birds and mammals to manipulations of habitat; landscape ecology. *Mailing Add:* 2631 Dumire Ct Ft Collins CO 80526

**VOICHICK, MICHAEL,** MATHEMATICS. *Current Pos:* from asst prof to assoc prof, 64-73, PROF MATH, UNIV WIS-MADISON, 73- *Personal Data:* b Yonkers, NY, May 28, 34; m 60; c 3. *Educ:* Oberlin Col, BA, 57; Brown Univ, PhD(math), 62. *Prof Exp:* Res instr math, Dartmouth Col, 62-64. *Mem:* Am Math Soc; Math Asn Am. *Res:* Function theory. *Mailing Add:* Dept Math 405 Van Vieck Hall 480 Lincoln Dr Madison WI 53706-1388

**VOICULESCU, DAN-VIRGIL,** OPERATOR ALGEBRAS, NONCOMMUTATIVE PROBABILITY THEORY. *Current Pos:* vis prof, 86-87, PROF MATH, UNIV CALIF, BERKELEY, 87- *Personal Data:* b Bucharest, Romania, June 14, 49; m 79, Ioana M Petrescu. *Educ:* Univ Bucharest, Licensed Mathematician, 72, DrMath, 77. *Prof Exp:* Asst, Dept Math, Univ Bucharest, 72-73; researcher, Math Inst, Romanian Acad, Bucharest, 73-75, Math Dept, Increst, Bucharest, 75-86. *Mem:* Am Math Soc; Int Asn Math Physics. *Res:* Approximation of Hilbert space operators; K-theory of C-algebras; entropy in operator algebras; noncommutative probability approach to free product von Neumann algebras and random matrices. *Mailing Add:* Dept Math Univ Calif Berkeley CA 94720-0001

**VOIGE, WILLIAM HUNTLEY,** ENZYMOLOGY. *Current Pos:* from asst prof to assoc prof, 75-91, PROF CHEM, JAMES MADISON UNIV, 91- *Personal Data:* b Pittsburgh, Pa, Sept 15, 47. *Educ:* Mich State Univ, BS, 69; Case Western Res Univ, PhD(biochem), 75. *Prof Exp:* Instr chem, St Olaf Col, 74-75. *Concurrent Pos:* Vis fel biochem, Princeton Univ, 82-83, Sheffield Univ, 90-91. *Mem:* AAAS. *Res:* Enzyme purification. *Mailing Add:* Dept Chem James Madison Univ Harrisonburg VA 22807. *Fax:* 540-568-7938; *E-Mail:* voigewh@jmu.edu

**VOIGHT, BARRY,** GEOLOGY. *Current Pos:* Asst prof eng geol, 64-70, assoc prof, 70-78, PROF GEOL, PA STATE UNIV, 78- *Personal Data:* b Yonkers, NY, Dec 17, 37; m 59; c 2. *Educ:* Univ Notre Dame, BS, 59 & 60, MS, 61; Columbia Univ, PhD(struct geol), 65. *Honors & Awards:* Res award, Nat Res Coun, 84; George Stephenson Medal, Inst Civil Engrs London, 84. *Concurrent Pos:* Vis prof, Delft Technol Inst, 72, Univ Toronto, 73 & Univ Calif, Santa Barbara, 81; adj geologist, US Geol Survey, 80-; consult, US Geol Surv Rev Volcano Prog, 86 & Nat Res Coun Comt Ground Failure Hazard, 82- *Mem:* Geol Soc Am; Int Soc Rock Mech. *Res:* Stress measurements; residual stresses in rocks; fault mechanics; engineering geology; rock mechanics; mechanics of landslides; geology of Iceland; geology of Mt St Helens and Cascade volcanos; disaster prevention of landslides and volcano eruptions; failure predictions; methods to predict volcano eruptions; applied volcanology world wide. *Mailing Add:* Dept Geosci 334 Dieke Bldg Pa State Univ University Park PA 16802

**VOIGHT, JANET RUTH,** SYSTEMATICS. *Current Pos:* Asst cur, 90-96, ASSOC CURATOR INVERT ZOOL, FIELD MUS, 96- *Personal Data:* b Davenport, Iowa, July 13, 55. *Educ:* Iowa State Univ, BS, 77; Univ Ariz, PhD(ecol & evolutionary biol), 90. *Concurrent Pos:* Lectr comt evolutionary biol, Univ Chicago, 93- *Mem:* Soc Syst Biologists; Soc Study Evolution; Am Malacologists Union. *Res:* Using morphological criteria analyses, reconstructiing evolutionary relationships among the cephalopod molluscs, cosmopolitan marine predators to elucidate patterns of the origin of deep water taxa and historical biogeography of marine fauna. *Mailing Add:* Field Museum Roosevelt Rd & Lake Shore Dr Chicago IL 60605

**VOIGT, ADOLF F,** NUCLEAR CHEMISTRY. *Current Pos:* From asst prof to prof, 46-55, EMER PROF CHEM, IOWA STATE UNIV, 82- *Personal Data:* b Upland, Calif, Jan 31, 14; m 41; c 2. *Educ:* Pomona Col, BA, 35; Claremont Col, MA, 36; Univ Mich, PhD, 41. *Concurrent Pos:* Asst dir, Ames Lab, 65-80. *Mem:* Am Chem Soc; Am Phys Soc; Am Nuclear Soc; AAAS; Sigma Xi. *Mailing Add:* 2426 Hamilton Dr Ames IA 50014-8202

**VOIGT, CHARLES FREDERICK,** ORGANIC CHEMISTRY. *Current Pos:* Assoc indexer org chem, Chem Abstr Serv, 70-71, sr assoc ed macromolecular chem, 71-73, sr ed appl chem, 73-79, asst mgr chem technol, 79-85, Patent Serv, 85-87, doc anal mgr, patent serv, 87-90, dept mgr, chem technol, 90-93, SR SCI INFO ANALYST, CHEM ABSTR SERV, 93- *Personal Data:* b Woodside, NY, Dec 17, 42; m 62; c Charles Jr, Timothy & Terrence. *Educ:* Univ SFla, Tampa, BA, 65; Duke Univ, PhD(org chem), 70. *Mem:* Am Chem Soc. *Res:* Heterocyclic chemistry; polymers; applied chemistry. *Mailing Add:* Chem Abstr Serv Dept 59 PO Box 3012 Columbus OH 43210-0012

**VOIGT, EVA-MARIA,** PHYSICAL CHEMISTRY, MOLECULAR PHYSICS. *Current Pos:* RETIRED. *Personal Data:* b Dortmund, WGer, Feb 2, 28; Can citizen. *Educ:* McMaster Univ, BSc, 53, MSc, 54; Univ BC, PhD(phys chem), 63. *Prof Exp:* Head res sect, Aylmer Foods, Inc, 55-56; lectr chem, Mt Allison Univ, 56-57; fel phys chem, Univ Calif, Berkeley, 63-65; from asst prof to prof chem, Simon Fraser Univ, 66-95. *Mem:* AAAS; Am Chem Soc; Am Phys Soc; Chem Inst Can; Can Inst Phys. *Res:* Molecular spectroscopy; charge-transfer interactions; energy transfer. *Mailing Add:* Dept Chem Simon Fraser Univ Burnaby BC V5A 1S6 Can

**VOIGT, GARTH KENNETH,** SOILS, PLANT NUTRITION. *Current Pos:* from asst prof to prof, Yale Univ, 55-67, Margaret K Musser prof, 67-89, actg dean, Sch Forestry, 70-71, 75-76 & 86-87, dir admis, 70-75, dir grad studies, Dept Forestry, 71-75, EMER PROF FOREST SOILS, YALE UNIV, 89-; SCI COUN, GREATER YELLOWSTONE COALITION, 91- *Personal Data:* b Merrill, Wis, Jan 17, 23; m 46, Jane Wurster; c Timothy, Valerie (Olson) & Jeff. *Educ:* Univ Wis, BS, 48, MS, 49, PhD(soils), 51. *Prof Exp:* From instr to asst prof soils, Univ Wis, 51-55. *Concurrent Pos:* Collabr, Lake States Forest Exp Sta, US Forest Serv, 54-60. *Mem:* AAAS; Soil Sci Soc Am; Am Soc Agron; Am Soc Plant Physiol. *Res:* Relationships between soil and the growth of plants. *Mailing Add:* 3318 Sundance Dr Bozeman MT 59715-9265

**VOIGT, GERD-HANNES,** MAGNETO-HYDRODYNAMICS, SPACE PHYSICS. *Current Pos:* sr res scientist, 80-85, DISTINGUISHED FAC FEL, RICE UNIV, 85- *Personal Data:* b Ger; m 75. *Educ:* Brunswick Tech Univ, Dipl, 70, PhD(physics), 75. *Prof Exp:* Sci asst teach & res, Tech Univ Brunsick, 70-75, Univ Darmstadt, 75-80. *Concurrent Pos:* Mem magnetospheric working group, Int Asn Geomagnetism & Aeronomy, 78-; prof physics, Fachhochschule Aachem, Ger. *Mem:* Am Geophys Union; Ger Geophys Soc; Europ Geophys Soc. *Res:* Theory of planetary magnetospheres; development of computer codes for earth's magnetosphere; development of numerical methods for solving non linear equations in magneto-hydrodynamics; space plasma physics. *Mailing Add:* Space Phys & Astron Rice Univ PO Box 1892 Houston TX 77251. *E-Mail:* voigt@hwth_aachem.de

**VOIGT, HERBERT FREDERICK,** AUDITORY NEUROSCIENCE, NEUROPHYSIOLOGY. *Current Pos:* Fel, Neural Encoding Lab, 79-80, ASSOC PROF BIOMED ENG, COL ENG & ASSOC PROF OTOLARYNGOL, SCH MED, BOSTON UNIV, 81- *Personal Data:* b New York, NY, Oct 27, 52; m 75, Ronit Gunst; c Justin David & Emily Talia. *Educ:* City Col New York, BE, 74; Johns Hopkins Univ, PhD(biomed eng), 80. *Concurrent Pos:* Panelist, NSF fel prog, 85-87; chmn biomed eng, Col Eng, Boston Univ, 92-95. *Mem:* Acoust Soc Am; AAAS; Inst Elec & Electronics Engrs; Int Brain Res Orgn; Soc Neurosci; World Fedn Neuroscientists; Biomed Eng Soc. *Res:* Auditory neuroscience; physiology of the auditory nerve and cochlear nucleus; correlation of physiological responses with anatomical properties of neurons in cochlear nucleus; multi-unit recording and analysis; mathematical modeling of the neuronal circuitry of the cochlear nucleus. *Mailing Add:* Dept Biomed Eng Boston Univ 44 Cummington St Boston MA 02215. *Fax:* 617-353-6766; *E-Mail:* hfu@enga.bu.edu

**VOIGT, PAUL WARREN,** PLANT BREEDING. *Current Pos:* Res geneticist, Southern Great Plains Field Sta, USDA, 67-74, res geneticist, 74-80, supvr res geneticist & res leader, Grassland, Soil & Water Res Lab, 80-93, RES GENETICIST, APPALACHIAN SOIL & WATER CONSERV LAB, AGR RES SERV, USDA, 93- *Personal Data:* b Ann Arbor, Mich, Mar 20, 40; m 63, Josephine Bergeret; c Valorie C, Suzanna J & Peter C. *Educ:* Iowa State Univ, BS, 62; Univ Wis, MS, 64, PhD(agron), 67. *Concurrent Pos:* Assoc ed, Crop Sci, 80-82, tech ed, 85-87. *Mem:* Fel Am Soc Agron; fel Crop Sci Soc Am; Soc Range Mgt; Am Forage & Grassland Coun. *Res:* Forage, legume and grass breeding and genetics. *Mailing Add:* Appalachian Soil & Water Conserv Res Lab PO Box 400 Beaver WV 25813-0400

**VOIGT, ROBERT GARY,** NUMERICAL ANALYSIS. *Current Pos:* HPPC COODR, NSF, 93- *Personal Data:* b Olney, Ill, Dec 21, 39; m 62, Susan J Strand; c Christine S & Jennifer A. *Educ:* Wabash Col, BA, 61; Purdue Univ, West Lafayette, MS, 63; Univ Md, College Park, PhD(math), 69. *Prof Exp:* Res assoc, Comput Sci Dept, Univ Md, 69-70, vis asst prof, 70-71; mathematician, Naval Ship Res & Develop Ctr, Washington, DC, 71-73; asst dir, Inst Comput Applns Sci & Eng, 73-83, assoc dir, 83-93. *Mem:* Soc Indust & Appl Math; Asn Comput Mach; Am Math Soc; AAAS; Inst Elec & Electronics Engrs. *Res:* Numerical analysis for parallel and vector computers and the development of parallel computing systems. *Mailing Add:* NSF 4201 Wilson Blvd Arlington VA 22230. *E-Mail:* rvoigt@nsf.gov

**VOIGT, ROBERT LEE,** PLANT BREEDING. *Current Pos:* from asst prof & asst plant breeder to assoc prof & assoc plant breeder, 59-69, EMER PROF PLANT SCI & PLANT BREEDER, AGR EXP STA, UNIV ARIZ, 69- *Personal Data:* b Hebron, Nebr, Nov 23, 24; m 51; c 4. *Educ:* Univ Nebr, BS, 49, MS, 55; Iowa State Univ, PhD(crop breeding), 59. *Prof Exp:* Instr soybeans, Iowa State Univ, 55-59. *Concurrent Pos:* Ed, Sorghum Newslett, Sorghum Improvement Conf NAm, 72- *Mem:* Am Soc Agron; Crop Sci Soc Am; Nat Asn Cols & Teachers Agr; Coun Agr Sci & Technol. *Res:* Crop breeding; forage and grain sorghum; soybeans. *Mailing Add:* 2131 E La Madera Dr Tucson AZ 85719

**VOIGT, WALTER,** BIOCHEMISTRY, ENDOCRINOLOGY. *Current Pos:* Res assoc skin biochem, 69-70, asst prof dermat, 70-74, ASSOC PROF PATH & ONCOL, SCH MED, UNIV MIAMI, 74- *Personal Data:* b Havana, Cuba, Feb 26, 38; US citizen; m 61; c 3. *Educ:* Univ Villanueva, Cuba, MS, 60; Univ Miami, PhD(biochem), 68. *Concurrent Pos:* Fel bile acid metab, Sch Med, Univ Miami, 68-69, Am Cancer Soc grant, 70-71, Nat Cancer Inst grant, 72-75. *Mem:* AAAS; Brit Biochem Soc; Am Chem Soc; Endocrine Soc; Am Fedn Clin Res; Sigma Xi. *Res:* Mechanism of androgen action and prostatic neoplasia; enzymes of bile acids and steroid metabolism; biochemistry of the skin; membrane electron transport; cancer. *Mailing Add:* Dept Path Univ Miami Sch Med 1475 NW 12th Ave UMHC Bldg Miami FL 33136. *Fax:* 305-547-3813

**VOISARD, WALTER BRYAN,** AIRCRAFT ACCIDENT INVESTIGATION, PROPELLER SYSTEMS. *Current Pos:* RETIRED. *Personal Data:* b Dayton, Ohio, Dec 14, 25; m 46, Mildred Singleton; c Steven B, Terri (Weber), Richard K & Suzanne R. *Educ:* Univ Cincinnati, BSME, 50. *Prof Exp:* Proj engr, Haines Designed Prod Co, 50-53, proj engr & chief eng, McCauley Indust Corp, 53-60, chief engr, 60-82, gen mgr, McCauley Assessory Div, Cessna Aircraft Co, 82-90. *Concurrent Pos:* Consult, Aircraft Accident Invest, 68-; assoc teaching staff, Transp Safety Inst, Aircraft Accident Invest Prin & Procedures, 86- *Mem:* Soc Automotive Engrs; Am Inst Aeronaut & Astronaut; Soc Air Safety Invest. *Res:* Aircraft propellers, propeller deicing, governors, synchrophasers and aircraft wheels and brakes; aircraft accident investigation; propeller systems. *Mailing Add:* 1072 Grange Hall Rd Dayton OH 45430

**VOIT, EBERHARD OTTO,** MATHEMATICAL MODELLING, NONLINEAR SYSTEMS ANALYSIS. *Current Pos:* PROF BIOMET, MED UNIV SC, 86- *Personal Data:* b Dortmund, Ger, Feb 8, 53; m 80, Ann L; c Walter E, Richard A & Benedict F. *Prof Exp:* Res asst, Dept Ecol, Univ Koln; asst, Univ Mich, 81-82, sr res assoc, 85, asst res scientist, Dept Microbiol & Immunol, 85-86. *Mem:* NY Acad Sci; Soc Indust & Appl Math; Soc Math Biol; Sigma Xi; Environmetrics Soc; Soc Risk Anal. *Res:* Nonlinear formalism for description, analysis and understanding of organizationally complex systems; biomedical phenomena. *Mailing Add:* Dept Biomet Med Univ SC 909 Harborview Tower Charleston SC 29425-2501

**VOITLE, ROBERT ALLEN,** POULTRY PHYSIOLOGY. *Current Pos:* ASSOC DEAN, COL AGR, AUBURN UNIV, 81- *Personal Data:* b Parkersburg, WVa, May 12, 38; m 75, Linda E Loveday; c Vanessa V, Christian B, Robert A Jr & Elizabeth A. *Educ:* WVa Univ, BS, 62, MS, 64; Univ Tenn, PhD(physiol), 69. *Prof Exp:* From asst prof to assoc prof physiol, Univ Fla & from asst poultry to assoc physiologist, 69-79; prof physiol & head, Dept Poultry Indust, Calif Polytech State Univ, 79-81. *Concurrent Pos:* Dir, mgr & pres, Alachia County Fair Asn, 69-79; vpres, Ala Agr in the Classroom, 83- *Mem:* Poultry Sci Asn; Sigma Xi. *Res:* Environmental and reproductive physiology with special emphasis on the effect of nutrition and photoperiod; breeding and genetics, especially radiation effects. *Mailing Add:* 107 Comer Hall Col Agr Auburn Univ Auburn AL 36849. *Fax:* 334-844-4814; *E-Mail:* rvoitle@ag.auburn.edu

**VOJNOVICH, THEODORE,** CERAMIC ENGINEERING. *Current Pos:* SR ENGR, RES LABS, WESTINGHOUSE ELEC CO, 67- *Personal Data:* b Weirton, WVa, Oct 7, 32; m 58; c 2. *Educ:* Iowa State Univ, BS, 59, MS, 61, PhD(ceramic eng), 67. *Prof Exp:* Mgt trainee, Weirton Steel Co Div, Nat Steel Corp, 59-60; planning engr, Western Elec Co, 61-64. *Mem:* Am Ceramic Soc; Nat Inst Ceramic Engrs; Am Soc Metals. *Res:* Electronic and magnetic properties of materials; high temperature properties of oxides and alloys; materials processing including sintering, chemical vapor deposition and sputtering. *Mailing Add:* 500 Colony Ct NW Vienna VA 22180

**VOJTA, PAUL ALAN,** ARAKELOU THEORY, DIOPHANTINE APPROXIMATION. *Current Pos:* assoc prof, 89-92, PROF MATH, UNIV CALIF, BERKELEY, 92- *Personal Data:* b Minneapolis, Minn, Sept 30, 57. *Educ:* Univ Minn, BM, 78; Harvard Univ, MA, 80, PhD, 83. *Honors & Awards:* Frank Nelson Cole Number Theory Prize, Am Math Soc, 92. *Prof Exp:* Instr, Yale Univ, 83-86; fel, Math Sci Res Inst, Berkeley, 86-87 & Miller Inst Basic Res, Berkeley, 87-89. *Concurrent Pos:* Mem, Inst Advan Study, Princeton, 89-90 & 96-97. *Mem:* Am Math Soc; Math Asn Am. *Res:* Diophantine approximations and value distribution theory. *Mailing Add:* Dept Math Univ Calif Berkeley CA 94720-3840. *E-Mail:* vojta@math.berkeley.edu

**VOKES, EMILY HOSKINS,** INVERTEBRATE PALEONTOLOGY, MALACOLOGY. *Current Pos:* Cur paleont, Dept Geol, Tulane Univ, 57-74, assoc prof, 73-81, chmn dept, 74-82, PROF GEOL, TULANE UNIV, 81- *Personal Data:* b Monroe, La, May 21, 30; m 59. *Educ:* Tulane Univ, La, BS, 60, MS, 62, PhD(paleont), 67. *Concurrent Pos:* Lectr geog, Tulane Univ, 69-; assoc ed, Tulane Studies Geol & Paleont, 70-; vis prof, Univ Rio Grande do Sul, Brazil, 71; vis cur, Australian Mus, 80; actg dean, Newcomb Col, Tulane Univ, 87-88. *Mem:* Am Malacol Union; Paleont Soc; Paleont Res Inst; Sigma Xi. *Res:* Systematic paleontology and zoology of Cenozoic Gastropoda, including both fossil and recent members. *Mailing Add:* Dept Geol Tulane Univ New Orleans LA 70118

**VOKES, HAROLD ERNEST,** stratigraphy, invertebrate paleontology, for more information see previous edition

**VOLANTE, RALPH PAUL,** ORGANIC CHEMISTRY. *Current Pos:* SR DIR PROCESS RES, MERCK & CO, 77- *Personal Data:* b Nelson, Pa, Aug 10, 49; m 91, Denise Mole. *Educ:* Pa State Univ, BS, 71; Harvard Univ, MA, 73, PhD(org chem), 76. *Prof Exp:* Fel org chem, Cornell Univ, 76-77. *Mem:* Am Chem Soc; Sigma Xi. *Res:* Synthetic organic chemistry, reaction processes and mechanisms; new synthetic methods. *Mailing Add:* Merck & Co Bldg 801-201 PO Box 2000 Rahway NJ 07065-0900

**VOLAVKA, JAN,** PSYCHIATRY, ELECTROPHYSIOLOGY. *Current Pos:* PROF PSYCHIAT, NY UNIV, 79- *Personal Data:* b Prague, Czech, Dec 29, 34; m 86; c 1. *Educ:* Charles Univ, Prague, BA & MD, 59; Czech Acad Sci, PhD(med sci), 65. *Prof Exp:* Intern internal med, Psychiat Hosp, Horni Berkovice, Czech, 59-60, resident psychiat, 60-63; res psychiatrist, Psychiat Res Inst, Prague, 63-66; electroencephalographer, London Hosp, Eng, 66-67;

resident psychiatrist, Psychiat Res Inst, Prague, 67-68; fel neurophysiol, Max Planck Inst Psychiat, 68-69; asst prof, New York Med Col, 69-73, assoc prof psychiat, 73-76; prof psychiat, Inst Psychiat, Univ Mo, 76-79. *Concurrent Pos:* Prin investr, NIMH grant, 87- *Mem:* Soc Biol Psychiat; Am Psychiat Asn. *Res:* Psychopharmacology; EEG. *Mailing Add:* Nathan S Kline Inst Psych Res Orangeburg NY 10962

**VOLBERG, THOMAS M,** MOLECULAR BIOLOGY, CELL BIOLOGY. *Current Pos:* asst prof cell biol, 93-, PROF BIOMED SCI, CREIGHTON UNIV SCH MED. *Personal Data:* b Philadelphia, Pa, Dec 6, 54. *Educ:* LaSalle Col, BS, 76; Thomas Jefferson Univ, PhD(path), 84. *Prof Exp:* Researcher cell biol, Nat Inst Environ Health Sci, NIH, 87-93. *Mem:* AAAS; Am Soc Cell Biol; Am Asn Cancer Res. *Res:* Molecular biology; cell biology. *Mailing Add:* Dept Biomed Sci Med Sch Creighton Univ Omaha NE 68178

**VOLBORTH, ALEXIS,** MINERALOGY, GEOLOGICAL ENGINEERING. *Current Pos:* prof geochem, Mont Tech, Butte, 79-95, dir, Accelerator Lab, sr radiation safety officer, 83-86, prof geol eng, 87-90, EMER PROF GEOCHEM & CHEM, MONT TECH, BUTTE, 95- *Personal Data:* b Viipuri, Finland, July 11, 24; nat US; m 47, Nadia Hasso; c Tanya, Lana, Maria, Gregory, Anna, Nicholas & Elizabeth. *Educ:* Univ Helsinki, PhC, 50, PhLic & PhD(geol, mineral), 54. *Honors & Awards:* White Cross, Finnish Chem Soc, 55. *Prof Exp:* Res asst, Geol Surv, Finland, 50, field asst, 52; asst, Inst Technol, Finland, 50-51; field geologist, Finnish Mineral Co, 53; sr asst geol, Univ Helsinki, 53-54; traveling res fel, Outokumpu Found, Univ Vienna, Univ Heidelberg, 54-55; Calif Inst Technol, Hoover fel, 55-56; from asst mineralogist to mineralogist, Nev Mining Anal Lab, Univ Nev, Reno, 56-68; res assoc & consult, Desert Res Inst, 61-62, assoc prof, 63, prof, 64-68, mem, Radioactive Safety Bd, 64-66; Killam vis prof geol, Dalhousie Univ, 68-71, Killam res prof, 71-72; vis prof, Lunar Sci Inst, NASA, Univ Houston, 72-73; vis res chemist, Univ Calif, Irvine, 73-76; prof geol & chem, NDak State Univ, 75-78; prof geol & scientist, Nuclear Radiation Ctr, Wash State Univ, 78-79. *Concurrent Pos:* Consult, first seismic underground atomic test, US AEC, Proj SHOAL, 61-63, geochem King Abdul Aziz Univ, Jeddah, Saudi Arabia, 75; Australian Acad Sci sr fel, 65; J S Guggenheim Mem Found fel, 65; adj prof geol, MacKay Sch Mines, Univ Nev, Reno, 69-73; prin investr, Stoichiometry Study Lunar Rocks, NASA, 72-73; consult, US AEC, 61-63, NASA, 65-73, Anaconda Co, 68 & Johns Manville Corp, Chevron 80-83, Pegasus Gold Inc, 87-88; US Rep, Second Conf Natural Reactors, OKLO Phenomenon, Int Atomic Energy Agency, Paris, 77, rep, Int Geol Correlation Prog, Prog 315, 90-; consult & interpreter, Soviet Siberia & Kazakhstan, Major US & Can Mining Co, 90-; Placer Dome Inc, Echo Bay, Inc, 90. *Mem:* Fel Mineral Soc Am; fel Am Inst Chemists; Am Chem Soc; Am Nuclear Soc; Soc Econ Geologists; Int Precious Metals Inst. *Res:* Geochemistry and analytical chemistry of complex systems, mainly nondestructive instrumental neutron activation and x-ray fluorescence analysis of major and trace elements; oxygen stoichiometry in rocks, minerals, chemicals and industrial products; mineralogy of and deficiency of oxygen in lunar rocks and fines; nondestructive analysis of coal and lignite; mineralogy of platinum group elements; gold deposits; tin deposits; pegmatites. *Mailing Add:* PO Box 80 Dayton MT 59914. *Fax:* 406-849-5212

**VOLCANI, BENJAMIN ELAZARI,** MICROBIOLOGY, BIOCHEMISTRY. *Current Pos:* prof microbiol, Univ Calif, 59-85, EMER PROF, SCRIPPS INST OCEANOG, 85- *Personal Data:* b Ben-Shemen, Israel, Jan 4, 15; US citizen; m 48, Eleanor T Solomons; c Yanon. *Educ:* Hebrew Univ, MSc, 36, PhD, 41. *Prof Exp:* Vis scientist microbiol, Inst Tech, Delft Univ, 37-38 & chem, State Univ Utrecht, 38-39; mem staff, Sieff Res Inst, Weizmann Inst, 39-58. *Concurrent Pos:* Res fel, Univ Calif, Berkeley, 45-46, res assoc biochem, 56-59; res fel microbiol, Hopkins Marine Sta, Stanford Univ, 46-47 & Calif Inst Technol, 47; res fel biochem, Univ Wis, 48; res assoc, Pasteur Inst, Paris, 51; vis prof, Univ Col, Welsh Nat Sch Med, Cardiff, Wales, UK, 73-74 & Ctr Molecular Genetics, Univ Calif, San Diego, 87. *Mem:* Am Soc Cell Biol; Am Soc Microbiol; Soc Gen Microbiol; AAAS. *Res:* Microbial metabolism and ecology; antimetabolites; bacterial pigments; halophilic microorganisms; biochemistry and ultra-fine structure of the diatoms; siliceous organisms and dinoflagellates; silicon metabolism; mineralization in biological systems; role of silicon in life processes and pathogenicity; molecular biology of silicon; first discoverer of microorganisms in the Dead Sea. *Mailing Add:* Scripps Inst Oceanog Univ Calif 9500 Gilman Dr La Jolla CA 92093-0202. *Fax:* 619-534-7313

**VOLD, BARBARA SCHNEIDER,** BIOCHEMISTRY, MOLECULAR BIOLOGY. *Current Pos:* SR RES MGR, HUMAN DIS MARKERS, SYVA CO, 90- *Personal Data:* b Oakland, Calif, Jan 3, 42. *Educ:* Univ Calif, Berkeley, BA, 63; Univ Ill, MS, 64, PhD(cell biol), 67. *Prof Exp:* NIH fel biol, Mass Inst Technol, 67-69; assoc microbiol, Scripps Clin & Res Found, 69-76; mem staff, Biomed Res Dept, SRI Int, 77-85, mem, Molecular Biol Dept, 85-90. *Concurrent Pos:* Nat Inst Gen Med Sci career develop award, 71-76; consult, Physiol Chem Study Sect, NIH, 73-77 & NSF Study Sect, 88; mem ed bd, J Biol Chem, 86-90. *Mem:* Am Soc Microbiol; Am Soc Biochem & Molecular Biol; Am Diabetes Asn. *Res:* New diagnostic marker for human disease; structure and function of transfer ribonucleic acids; antibodies to modified nucleosides. *Mailing Add:* Behring Diag 3403 Yerba Buena Rd MSE1-352 San Jose CA 95135

**VOLD, CARL LEROY,** SOLID STATE PHYSICS, METALLURGY. *Current Pos:* RES PHYSICIST, US NAVAL RES LAB, 59- *Personal Data:* b McVille, NDak, Dec 9, 32; m 61; c 2. *Educ:* Concordia Col, Moorhead, Minn, BA, 54; Iowa State Univ, MS, 59. *Prof Exp:* Jr scientist, Ames Lab, Iowa State Univ, 54-56. *Mem:* Am Soc Metals; Am Crystallog Asn; Sigma Xi. *Res:* Application of x-ray diffraction techniques to the study of defects in metals; energetics of solid-liquid and solid-solid interfaces in pure metals; crystalline anisotrophy; dislocation energetics. *Mailing Add:* 9631 Burke View Ave Burke VA 22015

**VOLD, MARJORIE JEAN,** COLLOID CHEMISTRY. *Current Pos:* res assoc & lectr, 41-58, adj prof, 58-73, EMER PROF CHEM, UNIV SOUTHERN CALIF, 73- *Personal Data:* b Ottawa, Ont, Oct 25, 13; US citizen; wid; c 3. *Educ:* Univ Calif, BS, 34, PhD(chem), 36. *Honors & Awards:* Garvan Medal, Am Chem Soc, 67. *Prof Exp:* Jr res assoc chem, Stanford Univ, 37-41. *Concurrent Pos:* Res chemist, Union Oil Co Calif, 42-46; Guggenheim Mem fel, State Univ Utrecht, 53-54. *Mem:* Am Chem Soc; Royal Soc Chem; Int Asn Colloid-Interface Scientists; AAAS; Sigma Xi. *Res:* Association colloids; mesomorphic phases; gels and other colloidal solids; stability of emulsions, foams, films and suspensions; adsorption; rheology; computer simulation of colloidal processes. *Mailing Add:* 15632 Pomerado Rd Poway CA 92064-2456

**VOLD, REGITZE ROSENORN,** NUCLEAR MAGNETIC RESONANCE, MOLECULAR DYNAMICS. *Current Pos:* res chemist, 71-82, PROF, UNIV CALIF, SAN DIEGO, 82- *Personal Data:* b Copenhagen, Denmark, July 2, 37; US citizen; div. *Educ:* Tech Univ Denmark, MS, 60, PhD(org chem), 62. *Prof Exp:* Lectr org chem, Tech Univ Denmark, 62; fel chem, Univ NMex, 62-64; staff fel magnetic resonance, NIH, 65-71. *Concurrent Pos:* Fel, NIH, 68-69; guest worker, Nat Bur Stand, 69-71; lectr chem, Univ Calif, San Diego, 72-82; mem bd trustees, Exp Nuclear Magnetic Resonance Conf, 74-78 & 81-84, treas, 75-78, chairwoman, 83; assoc ed, J Am Chem Soc, 77-79. *Mem:* Am Chem Soc; fel AAAS; Protein Soc; Int Soc Magnetic Resonance (treas, 89-). *Res:* Nuclear magnetic resonance as used in study of molecular dynamics in solids, liquid crystals, proteins and paramagnetic materials. *Mailing Add:* Dept Chem & Biochem Univ Calif 9500 Gilman Dr La Jolla CA 92093-0359. *Fax:* 619-534-6174; *E-Mail:* rvold@ucsd.edu

**VOLD, ROBERT LAWRENCE,** CHEMICAL PHYSICS. *Current Pos:* FAC, DEPT APPL SCI, COL WILLIAM & MARY. *Personal Data:* b Los Angeles, Calif, Sept 20, 42; m 71. *Educ:* Univ Calif, Berkeley, BS, 63; Univ Ill, Urbana, MS, 65, PhD(chem), 66. *Prof Exp:* From asst prof to assoc prof chem, Univ Calif, San Diego, 68-80, prof, 80- *Concurrent Pos:* A P Sloan fel, 72-74. *Mem:* Am Inst Physics; Am Chem Soc. *Res:* Nuclear magnetic resonance; relaxation mechanisms; theory and applications of pulsed nuclear magnetic resonance techniques. *Mailing Add:* Dept Appl Sci Col William & Mary Williamsburg VA 23187-8795

**VOLESKY, BOHUMIL,** BIOCHEMICAL ENGINEERING, WATER POLLUTION CONTROL. *Current Pos:* ASSOC PROF BIOCHEM ENG, MCGILL UNIV, 73- *Personal Data:* b Prague, Czech, Oct 29, 39; m 67. *Educ:* Prague Tech Univ, MESc, 62; Univ Western Ont, PhD(biochem eng), 71. *Prof Exp:* Proj engr, Cent Res Inst Food Indust, 63-66; res assoc food eng, Prague Tech Univ, 66-67; res asst biochem eng, Univ Western Ont, 67-70, teaching & res fel, Fanshawe Col Arts & Technol, 70-72, lectr, 72-73. *Concurrent Pos:* Consult, var assignments, 70-; vis prof chem eng, Univ PR, Mayaquez, 81, Ecole Polytech Fed, ETH, Lausanne, Switz, 88-89; exchange scientist, Acad Sci, Prague, Czech, 81, 83 & 87, Nankai Univ, Tianjin, China, 88, Ecole Polytech, Lorraine, Nancy, France, 88, Swiss Nat Sci Found, 88-89; pres, BV Sorbex, Inc, 88- *Mem:* Am Chem Soc; Chem Inst Can; Can Soc Chem Engrs; Eng Inst Can. *Res:* Biotechnology; fermentation process engineering and optimization; microbial product/process development; biosorbent detoxification of industrial effluents; biosorbent recovery of nuclear fuel and metallic elements; development of new biosorbent materials; industrial water pollution control; environmental studies. *Mailing Add:* Dept Chem Eng McGill Univ 3610 University St Montreal PQ H3A 2B2 Can

**VOLGENAU, LEWIS,** PAPER CHEMISTRY. *Current Pos:* mgr res & develop, 72-82, ASST VPRES, BETZ DEARBORN, INC, 82- *Personal Data:* b Buffalo, NY, Nov 30, 40; m 69; c 2. *Educ:* Syracuse Univ, BE, 61; Inst Paper Chem, MS, 65, PhD(paper chem), 69. *Prof Exp:* Engr res & develop, Riegel Paper, 61-63; engr pulp & paper, Champion Int, 69-72. *Res:* Corrosion, scale and foam control in aqueous systems; development of biocides and specialty chemical formulations; development of computer controlled chemical feed systems. *Mailing Add:* 200 Precision Dr Horsham PA 19044-1227. *Fax:* 215-957-4604

**VOLICER, LADISLAV,** GERIATRICS, DEMENTIA. *Current Pos:* from asst prof to assoc prof, 69-77, ASST PROF MED, SCH MED & GRAD SCH, BOSTON UNIV, 77-, PROF PHARMACOL, 77- *Personal Data:* b Prague, Czech, May 21, 35; m 72, Beverly Beers; c Irena, Katerina, Zuzka, Marika & Nadine. *Educ:* Charles Univ, Prague, MD, 59; Czech Acad Sci, PhD(pharmacol), 64. *Prof Exp:* Resident med, Hosp Jindr Hradec, 59-61; instr pharmacol, Sch Pediat, Charles Univ, Prague, 61-65; vis assoc, Nat Heart Inst, Md, 65-66; res assoc & lectr, Inst Pharmacol, Czech Acad Sci, 66-68; res asst prof, Sch Med, Univ Munich, 68-69. *Concurrent Pos:* Asst vis physician, Boston City Hosp, 75-86; clin pharmacologist, Geriat Res Educ Clin Ctr, Vet Admin Hosp, Bedford, 80-86, dep dir, 86-91, actg dir, 91-92, clin dir, 92- *Mem:* Soc Neurosci; Am Soc Pharmacol & Exp Therapeut; fel Geront Soc; Am Geriat Soc. *Res:* Pharmacology of aging; Alzheimer's disease; neurochemical and clinical research. *Mailing Add:* GRECC 182B E N Rogers Mem Vet Hosp Bedford MA 01730. *Fax:* 781-687-3515; *E-Mail:* volicer.ladislav@bedford.va.gov

**VOLIN, RAYMOND BRADFORD,** horticulture, agronomy, for more information see previous edition

**VOLK, BOB G,** SOIL CHEMISTRY. *Current Pos:* FAC, WATER CTR, UNIV NEBR, 90- *Personal Data:* b Auburn, Ala, July 13, 43; m 66; c 4. *Educ:* Ohio State Univ, BS, 65, MS, 67; Mich State Univ, PhD(soil sci), 70. *Prof Exp:* Asst prof soil sci, Agr Res & Educ Ctr, Belle Glade, Fla, 70-73; from asst prof to assoc prof, Univ Fla, 73-84; Dept Agron, Univ Mo, Columbia, 85-90. *Concurrent Pos:* Vis prof, Environ Protection Agency, Ore State Univ, Corvallis, 76-77. *Mem:* Am Soc Agron; Soil Sci Soc Am; Int Soil Sci Soc; Int Humic Acid Soc. *Res:* Chemistry of soil organic matter and the movement of nutrients through the soil profile; effects of acid rain on soils. *Mailing Add:* 6711 Northfork Circle Lincoln NE 68516

**VOLK, BRUNO W,** diabetes, tay-sachs disease; deceased, see previous edition for last biography

**VOLK, MURRAY EDWARD,** ORGANIC CHEMISTRY, RADIOCHEMISTRY. *Current Pos:* PRES, ISOLAB INC, 69- *Personal Data:* b Cleveland, Ohio, Aug 23, 22; m 49; c 3. *Educ:* Oberlin Col, BA, 43; Univ Chicago, MS, 48; Temple Univ, PhD(chem), 53. *Prof Exp:* Assoc chemist, Nuclear Instrument & Chem Corp, 53-55; pres, Volk Radiochem Co, 55-65; mkt mgr res prod, Miles Labs, 66-69. *Mem:* AAAS; Am Chem Soc; Am Asn Clin Chem; Soc Nuclear Med; Sigma Xi. *Res:* Application of isotopes to biological and chemical research; preparation of radioactive pharmaceuticals; liquid chromatography applied to clinical diagnostic problems. *Mailing Add:* 160 Kendall Dr Oberlin OH 44074-7507

**VOLK, RICHARD JAMES,** PLANT NUTRITION. *Current Pos:* from asst prof to assoc prof, 56-66, PROF SOIL SCI, NC STATE UNIV, 66- *Personal Data:* b Tela, Honduras, Nov 5, 28; m 51, Barbara Boyd; c Cheri (Courtright), Judith (Hill) & Nancy (Wells). *Educ:* Purdue Univ, BS, 50, MS, 51; NC State Univ, PhD(soil chem), 54. *Honors & Awards:* Co-recipient Campbell Award, Am Inst Biol Sci, 65. *Prof Exp:* Res specialist, Crops Div, Biol Warfare Labs, Ft Detrick, Md, 54-56. *Concurrent Pos:* Grants, NSF, 62-64, 78-80 & 82-84, Am Potash Inst, 63-66, USDA-Off Int Coop & Develop, 91-94, USDA-NRI, 93-; res contract, USDA, 65-68, Westraco, 82-85 & Enichem Americas, Inc, 88-90; vis scientist, Australian Nat Univ, 81, Nat Inst Agr Res, France, 88. *Mem:* Am Soc Plant Physiol; Soil Sci Soc Am; Crop Sci Soc Am; fel Am Soc Agron. *Res:* Application of mass spectrometry and stable isotopes to plant nutrition and biochemistry; absorption and metabolism of ammonium and nitrate nitrogen by plants; regulatory role of mineral nutrition in photosynthesis and respiration. *Mailing Add:* Dept Soil Sci NC State Univ Box 7619 Raleigh NC 27695. *Fax:* 919-515-2167; *E-Mail:* richard__volk@ncsu.edu

**VOLK, THOMAS LEWIS,** HUMAN PATHOLOGY, ENDOCRINOLOGY. *Current Pos:* DIR LABS, MD CYTOLOGY, 87-, ALTA DIST HOSP, 96- *Personal Data:* b Dayton, Ohio, Nov 4, 33; m 61; c 4. *Educ:* Univ Dayton, BS, 55; Marquette Univ, MD, 59. *Prof Exp:* Instr path, Ohio State Univ, 65-66; asst prof, Univ Kans, 66-67; asst prof path, Univ Calif, Davis, 68-72. *Concurrent Pos:* NIH path training grant, 63-65; Am Cancer Soc adv clin fel, 65-66; consult, Vet Admin Hosp, Kansas City, Mo, 67-68 & Sacramento Co Hosp, Calif, 68-72. *Mem:* AMA; Int Acad Path; Am Asn Path & Bact; Can Asn Path; Am Soc Clin Path. *Res:* Ultrastructural-functional relationships of steroidogenesis in the adrenal cortex and placenta, ovary and testis; ultrastructural changes in the adrenal cortex and placenta, produced by drugs inhibiting steroidogenesis. *Mailing Add:* PO Box 749 215 S Willis St Visalia CA 93279-0749

**VOLK, VERIL VAN,** SOIL CHEMISTRY. *Current Pos:* from asst prof to assoc prof, 66-80, PROF SOILS, ORE STATE UNIV, 80-, ASSOC DIR, ORE AGR EXP STA. *Personal Data:* b Montgomery, Ala, Nov 18, 38; m 68; c 2. *Educ:* Ohio State Univ, BS, 60, MS, 61; Univ Wis, PhD(soils), 66. *Prof Exp:* Proj assoc soils, Univ Wis, 66. *Concurrent Pos:* Coop State Res Serv, Washington, DC, 84-85. *Mem:* Am Soc Agron; Soil Sci Soc; Coun Agr Sci & Technol. *Res:* Ion exchange and soil acidity interactions; waste utilization on soils. *Mailing Add:* 2280 NW Huntington Dr Corvallis OR 97330

**VOLK, WESLEY AARON,** MICROBIOLOGY. *Current Pos:* From asst prof to assoc prof, 51-64, PROF MICROBIOL, SCH MED, UNIV VA, 64- *Personal Data:* b Mankato, Minn, Nov 23, 24; m 45; c 2. *Educ:* Univ Wash, BS & BS(food technol), 48, MS, 49, PhD, 51. *Concurrent Pos:* NIH spec fel, 62-63; spec fel, Max-Planck Inst Immunobiol, 69-70; fel, Pasteur Inst, 83-84. *Mem:* Am Soc Microbiol; Am Soc Biol Chemists. *Res:* Carbohydrate metabolism; monoclonal antibodies; virus neutralization; tetanus toxin. *Mailing Add:* Dept Microbiol Box 441 Univ Va Sch Med Charlottesville VA 22908-0441. *Fax:* 804-982-1071; *E-Mail:* wav@virginia.edu

**VOLKAN, VAMIK,** PSYCHIATRY, PSYCHOANALYSIS. *Current Pos:* from instr to assoc prof, 63-72, PROF PSYCHIAT, SCH MED, UNIV VA, 72-, DIR, CTR STUDY MIND & HUMAN INTERACTION, 87- *Personal Data:* b Nicosia, Cyprus, Dec 13, 32; US citizen; m, Elizabeth Palonen; c Kevin, Susan, Alev & Kurt. *Educ:* Univ Ankara, MD, 56; Wash Psychoanal Inst, grad, 71; bd cert psychoanal, 73. *Honors & Awards:* Nevitt Sanford Award, Int Soc Polit Psychol, 94; Max Hayman Award, Am Orthopsychiat Asn, 95. *Prof Exp:* Staff physician, NC State Hosp, 61-63. *Concurrent Pos:* Vis prof psychiat, Univ Ankara, Turkey, 74-75; dir, Blue Ridge Hosp Div, Univ Va, 78-95 & Div Psychoanal Studies, 79-88. *Mem:* Am Psychoanal Asn; fel Am Psychiat Asn; Int Psychoanal Asn; Int Soc Polit Psychol (pres, 83-84). *Res:* Psychotherapy of schizophrenia; pathological grief reactions; psycho-history; psycho-politics. *Mailing Add:* Ctr Study Mind & Human Interaction Drawer A Blue Ridge Hosp Charlottesville VA 22901. *Fax:* 804-982-2524; *E-Mail:* mind@virginia.edu

**VOLKER, EUGENE JENO,** ORGANIC CHEMISTRY. *Current Pos:* From asst prof to assoc prof, 69-79, PROF CHEM, SHEPHERD COL, WVA, 79- *Personal Data:* b Sopron, Hungary, May 13, 42; US citizen; m 79, Katalin Almay; c Ilona & Gabor. *Educ:* Univ Md, BS, 64; Mass Inst Technol, MS, 67; Univ Del, PhD(chem), 70. *Concurrent Pos:* Vis sci, Frederick Cancer Res Facil, 86-90. *Mem:* Am Chem Soc. *Res:* Chemical education; coal chemistry; peptide chemistry. *Mailing Add:* Dept Chem Shepherd Col King St PO Box 3210 Shepherdstown WV 25443-3210

**VOLKERT, WYNN ARTHUR,** RADIOCHEMISTRY, RADIOBIOLOGY. *Current Pos:* NASA fel, 67-69, from asst prof to assoc prof, 69-80, PROF RADIOL SCI & BIOCHEM, UNIV MO, COLUMBIA, 80- *Personal Data:* b St Louis, Mo, Apr 6, 41; m 67; c 3. *Educ:* St Louis Univ, BS, 63; Univ Mo, Columbia, PhD(chem), 68. *Concurrent Pos:* NIH grant, Univ Mo, Columbia, 73-; consult, Vet Admin Hosp, Columbia, 73- *Mem:* Radiation Res Soc; Biophys Soc; Soc Exp Biol & Med; Am Chem Soc; Soc Nuclear Med; Radiophys Sci Coun (pres-elect, 87, pres, 88). *Res:* Radiopharmaceutical chemistry; chemistry of Tc-99m nitrogen ligands; radionuclidic therapy. *Mailing Add:* Dept Radiol E-204 Med Sci Univ Mo Columbia MO 65212-0001

**VOLKIN, ELLIOT,** BIOCHEMISTRY. *Current Pos:* CONSULT, 85- *Personal Data:* b Mt Pleasant, Pa, Apr 23, 19; m 47; c 2. *Educ:* Pa State Col, BS, 42; Duke Univ, MA, 45, PhD(biochem), 47. *Prof Exp:* Res assoc biochem, Duke Univ, 47-48; sci dir biochem, Oak Ridge Nat Lab, 48-65, sr res scientist, 65-84. *Concurrent Pos:* Prof, Univ Tenn, 77-84. *Mem:* Fel AAAS; Am Chem Soc; Am Soc Biol Chem; Am Soc Microbiol; Sigma Xi. *Res:* Biochemical and biophysical studies of nucleic acids and nucleoproteins. *Mailing Add:* 899 W Outer Dr Oak Ridge TN 37830. *E-Mail:* elvolkin@worldnet.att.net

**VOLKMAN, ALVIN,** PATHOLOGY, IMMUNOLOGY & RESEARCH ADMINISTRATION. *Current Pos:* actg chmn, 89-90, PROF PATH, SCH MED, ECAROLINA UNIV, 77-, ASSOC DEAN RES & GRAD STUDIES, 90- *Personal Data:* b Brooklyn, NY, June 10, 26; wid; c 7. *Educ:* Union Col, BS, 47; Univ Buffalo, MD, 51; Oxford Univ, DPhil, 63. *Prof Exp:* Asst prof path, Columbia Univ, 60-66; from asst mem to assoc mem, Trudeau Inst, 66-77. *Concurrent Pos:* Arthritis & Rheumatism Found fel, 52-54; resident to sr resident path, Peter Bent Brigham Hosp; Am Cancer Soc scholar, 61-62; adj assoc prof path, Sch Med, NY Univ, 69-79; mem, IMS study sect, NIH, 75-79, chmn, 77-79. *Mem:* Am Asn Immunol; AAAS; Am Soc Hemat; Am Soc Microbiology; NY Acad Sci; Reticuloendothelial Soc; Am Soc Invest Path; Sigma Xi; Soc Leukocyte Biol. *Res:* Origin and differentiation of mononuclear phagocytes, mononuclear phagocyte function. *Mailing Add:* 1324 Forest Acres Dr Greenville NC 27834-8824. *Fax:* 919-816-3260; *E-Mail:* adamvie@aol.com

**VOLKMAN, DAVID J,** INTERNAL MEDICINE, ALLERGY & IMMUNOLOGY. *Current Pos:* ASSOC PROF MED, STATE UNIV NY, STONY BROOK, 85-, DIR, FLOW CYTOMETRY LAB, HEALTH SCI CTR, 91- *Personal Data:* b Brooklyn, NY, Jan 11, 45; m 67, Pamela Bickerman; c Eric S & Aaron J. *Educ:* Union Col, BS, 66; Univ Rochester, PhD(biochem), 71, MD, 76; Am Bd Internal Med, cert, 79; Am Bd Allergy & Immunol, cert, 81. *Prof Exp:* Res assoc, Sloan-Kettering Inst, 71-72; med intern, Univ Pittsburgh, 76-77, med resident, 77-78; clin fel, Nat Inst Allergy & Infectious Dis, NIH, 78-80, med officer, 80-82, sr investr, 82-85. *Concurrent Pos:* Assoc ed, J Immunol, 87-91 & Clin Immunol & Immunopath, 91-; mem, Univ Hosp Res Comt, 88- *Mem:* Fel Am Col Physicians; fel Am Acad Allergy & Immunol; Am Fedn Clin Res; Am Asn Immunologists; Clin Immunol Soc; Sigma Xi. *Res:* Characterization of the cellular mechanisms involved in human T and B lymphocyte responses to natural infection; development of antigen-specific clonal populations; application of principles of immunobiology to the understanding and therapy of human infectious and autoimmune diseases including human immunovirus and lyme disease. *Mailing Add:* Health Sci Ctr T-1604 State Univ NY Stony Brook NY 11794-8161. *Fax:* 516-444-2475; *E-Mail:* dvolkman@epo.som.sunnys

**VOLKMANN, FRANCES COOPER,** EXPERIMENTAL PSYCHOLOGY, NEUROSCIENCE. *Current Pos:* lectr, Smith Col, 66-67, from asst prof to assoc prof, 67-78, dean fac, 83-88, PROF PSYCHOL, SMITH COL, 78- *Personal Data:* b Harlingen, Tex, May 4, 35; wid; c Stephen & Thomas. *Educ:* Mt Holyoke Col, AB, 57; Brown Univ, MA, 59, PhD(psychol), 61. *Hon Degrees:* DSc, Mt Holyoke Col, 87. *Prof Exp:* USPHS fel, Brown Univ, 61-62; res assoc psychol, Mt Holyoke Col, 64-65. *Concurrent Pos:* Lectr, Univ Mass, 64-65; vis assoc prof, Brown Univ, 74, vis prof, 78-82; NSF res grant, Smith Col & Brown Univ, 74-78; Nat Eye Inst res grant, Brown Univ, 78-82; actg pres, Smith Col, 91. *Mem:* Fel Am Psychol Asn; fel AAAS; fel Optical Soc Am; Soc Neurosci; Asn Res Vision & Ophthal; Psychonomic Soc. *Res:* Vision and visual perception; vision during eye movements; visual development. *Mailing Add:* Clark Sci Ctr Smith Col Northampton MA 01063

**VOLKMANN, KEITH ROBERT,** MICROBIOLOGY. *Current Pos:* ASST PROF ORAL BIOL, SCH DENT, MED COL GA, 76- *Personal Data:* b Milwaukee, Wis, May 30, 42; m 65; c 1. *Educ:* Univ Rochester, BA, 65, PhD(microbiol), 73; Ga Sch Dent, DMD, 76. *Prof Exp:* Res asst virol, Univ Rochester, Med Ctr, 68-73. *Mem:* Int Asn Dent Res. *Res:* Penetration of oral antigens into oral mucosa and connective tissue; effect of endotoxins on the human periodontium. *Mailing Add:* Med Col Ga 1120 15th St Augusta GA 30912-1126

**VOLKMANN, ROBERT ALFRED,** ORGANIC CHEMISTRY. *Current Pos:* RES SCIENTIST ORG CHEM, PFIZER INC, 74- *Personal Data:* b Pittsburgh, Pa, Aug 21, 45; m 79; c 1. *Educ:* Lafayette Col, AB, 67; Univ Pittsburgh, PhD(org chem), 72. *Prof Exp:* Res assoc, Stanford Univ, 72-74. *Concurrent Pos:* Instr, Conn Col, 76- *Mem:* Am Chem Soc. *Res:* Development of novel methodology for the design and or synthesis of biologically active molecules. *Mailing Add:* 135 Dogwood Lane Mystic CT 06355-1040

**VOLKOFF, GEORGE MICHAEL,** THEORETICAL PHYSICS. *Current Pos:* head, Dept Physics, Univ BC, 61-72, prof, 46-79, dean, 72-79, EMER DEAN, UNIV BC, 79- *Personal Data:* b Moscow, Russia, Feb 23, 14; Can citizen; m 40; c 3. *Educ:* Univ BC, BA, 34, MA, 36; Univ Calif, PhD(theoret physics), 40. *Hon Degrees:* DSc, Univ BC, 45. *Honors & Awards:* Centennial Medal Can, 67. *Prof Exp:* Asst prof physics, Univ BC, 40-43; assoc res physicist, Montreal Lab, Nat Res Coun, Can, 43-45, res physicist & head theoret physics br, Atomic Energy Proj, Que & Ont, 45-46. *Concurrent Pos:* Ed, Can J Physics, 50-56; mem, Nat Res Coun Can, 69-75; ed, Soviet Physics Usp, 79-; mem, Tech Adv Comt, Nuclear Fuel Waste Mgt Progr, Atomic Energy Can Ltd, 79-89. *Mem:* Fel AAAS; fel Am Phys Soc; Am Asn Physics Teachers; fel Royal Soc Can; Can Asn Physicists (vpres, 61-62, pres, 62-63). *Res:* Theoretical nuclear physics; neutron diffusion; nuclear magnetic and quadrupole resonance. *Mailing Add:* 1776 Western Parkway Vancouver BC V6T 1V3 Can

**VOLKOV, ANATOLE BORIS,** NUCLEAR PHYSICS. *Current Pos:* from asst prof to assoc prof, 64-68, PROF PHYSICS, MCMASTER UNIV, 68- *Personal Data:* b San Francisco, Calif, Oct 29, 24; m 50; c 2. *Educ:* Univ NC, BS, 48; Univ Wis, MS, 50, PhD(physics), 53. *Prof Exp:* Longwood fel, Univ Del, 53-55; asst prof physics, Univ Miami, 58-59; sr lectr, Israel Inst Technol, 59-62; res intermediate scientist, Weizmann Inst, 62-63; Ford Found fel, Niels Bohr Inst, Copenhagen, Denmark, 63-64. *Mem:* Fel Am Phys Soc; Can Asn Physicists. *Res:* Theoretical physics, especially low energy nuclear physics and nuclear deformations. *Mailing Add:* Dept Physics & Math McMaster Univ 1280 Main St W Hamilton ON L8S 4M1 Can

**VOLKSEN, WILLI,** POLYMER CHEMISTRY, MATERIALS SCIENCE. *Current Pos:* MEM RES STAFF POLYMER CHEM, IBM CORP, 77- *Personal Data:* b Gitter, Ger, Mar 9, 50; m 72; c 2. *Educ:* NMex Inst Mining & Technol, BS, 72; Univ Lowell, PhD(polymer chem), 75. *Prof Exp:* Fel polymer chem, Calif Inst Technol, 75-76; sr scientist, Jet Propulsion Lab, 76-77. *Mem:* Am Chem Soc. *Res:* Synthesis of new and novel polymeric materials including polyelectrolytes and polymers of high temperature stability. *Mailing Add:* 372 El Portal Way San Jose CA 95123-5115

**VOLL, MARY JANE,** bacterial genetics, for more information see previous edition

**VOLLE, ROBERT LEON,** PHARMACOLOGY. *Current Pos:* PRES, NAT BD MED EXAMR, NAT BD MED, 86- *Personal Data:* b Houston, Pa, June 2, 30; m 52; c 5. *Educ:* WVa Wesleyan Col, BS, 53; Univ Kans, PhD(pharmacol), 59. *Prof Exp:* From instr to assoc prof pharmacol, Sch Med, Univ Pa, 60-65; prof, Sch Med, Tulane Univ, 65-68; prof pharmacol, chmn & assoc dean, Sch Med, Univ Conn, 68-83; prof & assoc vpres, res & grad studies, WVa Univ, 83-84, vpres acad affairs & res, 84-85; prof & assoc dean of res & basic sci, Univ Ky, 85-86. *Concurrent Pos:* Marsh fel pharmacol, Sch Med, Univ Pa, 59-60, Pa Plan scholar, 60-63; USPHS career develop award, 63-65. *Mem:* Fel AAAS; Am Soc Pharmacol & Exp Therapeut; Soc Neurosci; Sigma Xi. *Res:* Neuropharmacology. *Mailing Add:* 442 Leopard Rd Berwyn PA 19312. *Fax:* 215-590-9555

**VOLLENWEIDER, RICHARD A,** LIMNOLOGY. *Current Pos:* RETIRED. *Personal Data:* b Zurich, Switz, June 27, 22; m 65. *Educ:* Univ Zurich, dipl biol, 46, PhD(biol), 51. *Hon Degrees:* DSc, McGill Univ, Montreal, 86. *Honors & Awards:* Int Award, Premio Cervia/Ambiente, 78; Int Tyler Prize Environ Achievement, 86; Naumann-T Lienemann Medal, 87. *Prof Exp:* Teacher undergrad schs, Lucern, Switz, 49-54; fel limnol, Ital Hydrobiol Inst, Palanza, Italy, 54-55 & Swiss Swed Res Coun, Uppsala, 55-56; field expert limnol & fisheries, UNESCO Dept Agr, Egypt, 57-59; res assoc limnol, Ital Hydrobiol Inst, Pallanza, 59-66; consult water pollution, Orgn Econ Coop Develop, Paris, France, 66-68; chief limnoligist & head, Fisheries Res Bd, Can Centre Inland Waters, 68-70, chief, Lakes Res Div, 70-73, sr scientist, 73-88. *Concurrent Pos:* Consult, Pan Am Health Orgn, Venezuela, 77-80, Italy, 77-, Arg, 80-, Ecuador, 82-, Brazil, 83, Mex, 83-, Int Lake Environ Comn, 85 & WHO, 85-; prof biol, McMaster Univ, Hamilton, Ont, 78. *Mem:* Ital Asn Ecol; Int Asn Theoret & Appl Limnol; Royal Soc Can. *Res:* Inland and marine water research; biological communities; water chemistry and physics; eutrophication; water pollution. *Mailing Add:* 262 Townsend Ave Burlington ON L7R 4A6 Can

**VOLLHARDT, K PETER C,** ORGANIC SYNTHESIS, MECHANISTIC CHEMISTRY. *Current Pos:* from asst prof to assoc prof, 74-82, PROF CHEM, UNIV CALIF, BERKELEY, 82- *Personal Data:* b Madrid, Spain, Mar 7, 46; US citizen; m 91, Sat; c Paloma C. *Educ:* Univ Munich, Ger, dipl, 67; Univ Col, London, Eng, PhD(chem), 72. *Honors & Awards:* Adolf Windaus Medal, Ger Chem Soc, 83; Organometallic Chem Award, Am Chem Soc, 87, Arthur C Cope Scholar Award, 91; Humboldt Sr Scientist Award, 85, 93; Otto Bayer Prize, 90. *Prof Exp:* Fel, Cal Inst Technol, 72-74. *Concurrent Pos:* Fel, Regents' Summer Fac, 75, Alfred P Sloan Found, 76-80; prin investr, Mat & Molecular Res Div, Lawrence Berkeley Lab, Calif, 75-; vis prof, Univ Paris-Orsay, 79, Univ Bordeaux, 85, Univ Lyon, 87, Univ Rennes, 91, Univ Paris VI, 92, Tech Univ, Munich, 93; ad hoc reviewer, Med Chem Study Sect, NIH, 84; assoc ed, Synthesis, 84-89; mem, Comt Org Chem, Int Union Pure & Appl Chem, 87-; ed, Synlett, 89- *Mem:* Am Chem Soc; Ger Chem Soc; Sigma Xi. *Res:* Transition metals in organic synthesis; organometallic clusters in catalysis; new synthetic methods; antiaromatics; strained systems; natural products; gas phase pyrolyses; pyrolyses. *Mailing Add:* Dept Chem Univ Calif Berkeley CA 94720. *Fax:* 510-643-5208

**VOLLMAR, ARNULF R,** ORGANIC CHEMISTRY. *Current Pos:* assoc prof, 65-74, PROF CHEM, CALIF STATE POLYTECH UNIV, POMONA, 74- *Personal Data:* b Pluderhausen, Ger, Apr 15, 28. *Educ:* Univ Heidelberg, dipl chem, 55, PhD(org chem), 57. *Prof Exp:* Res assoc, Univ Heidelberg, 57-58; fel, Univ Calif, Los Angeles, 58-60; res chemist, Chevron Res Corp, Calif, 60-64. *Concurrent Pos:* NSF res grant, 69. *Mem:* Am Chem Soc; Sigma Xi. *Res:* Chemistry of nitronium acetate adducts of alkylbenzenes and furan derivatives. *Mailing Add:* 2219 Brescia Ave Claremont CA 91711-1807

**VOLLMER, ERWIN PAUL,** PHYSIOLOGY, ENDOCRINOLOGY. *Current Pos:* RETIRED. *Personal Data:* b New York, NY, Jan 16, 06; m 34, Aline Fruhauf; c 2. *Educ:* Dartmouth Col, AB, 29; NY Univ, MS, 39, PhD(physiol), 41. *Prof Exp:* Bacteriologist, Calco Chem Co Div, Am Cyanamid Co, 37; asst instr biol, NY Univ, 41-42; tutor, Brooklyn Col, 42-43; physiologist, US Naval Med Inst, 47-56; chief endocrinol, Cancer Chemother Nat Serv Ctr, 56-66; chief endocrine eval br, Gen Labs & Clins & exec secy breast cancer task force, Nat Cancer Inst, Bethesda, 66-74; pres, DC Inst Ment Hyg, 85-87. *Mem:* Fel AAAS; Endocrine Soc; fel NY Acad Sci; Am Asn Cancer Res. *Res:* Physiology of resistance to infection; endocrine factors in hemopoiesis; endocrine etiology and chemotherapy in cancer; oncology. *Mailing Add:* 7202 44th St Chevy Chase MD 20815

**VOLLMER, FREDERICK WOLFER,** STRUCTURAL GEOLOGY. *Current Pos:* from instr to asst prof, 84-90, ASSOC PROF GEOL, STATE UNIV NY, NEW PALTZ, 90-, DEPT CHAIR, 91- *Personal Data:* b Corning, NY, Apr 18, 56; c 2. *Educ:* Univ Calif, Davis, BS, 78; State Univ NY, Albany, MS, 81; Univ Minn, PhD(geol), 85. *Prof Exp:* Teaching asst geol, State Univ NY, Albany, 78-80, res asst, 79-81; teaching asst, Univ Minn, Minneapolis, 81-84, res asst, 82-83. *Concurrent Pos:* Prin investr, Res Found State Univ NY, 90-92. *Mem:* Am Geophys Union; Geol Soc Am; Int Asn Struct Tectonic Geologists. *Res:* Structural geology; fold-nappes; analysis of complexly deformed regions; stress and strain theory; melange fabric. *Mailing Add:* Dept Geol Sci State Univ NY New Paltz NY 12561. *E-Mail:* vollmerf@npvm. newpaltz.edu

**VOLLMER, JAMES,** PHYSICS. *Current Pos:* RETIRED. *Personal Data:* b Philadelphia, Pa, Apr 19, 24; m 46; c 3. *Educ:* Union Col, BS, 45; Temple Univ, MA, 51, PhD(physics), 56; Harvard Univ, advan mgt prog, 71. *Honors & Awards:* Centennial Award, Inst Elec & Electronics Engrs, 84. *Prof Exp:* Instr physics, Temple Univ, 46-51; res engr, Indust Div, Honeywell Inc, 51-59; engr appl res, RCA Corp, 59, group leader appl plasma physics, 59-63, mgr appl physics, 63-66, mgr dir, Advan Technol Labs, 68-72, gen mgr, Palm Beach Div, 72-74; div vpres & gen mgr, 74-75, div vpres & gen mgr, Govt Commun Systs Div, 75-76 div vpres & gen mgr, Govt Systs Div, 76-79, group vpres, 79-83, sr vpres, 83-84; pres, James Vollmer Assoc, 84-95. *Concurrent Pos:* Lectr, Temple Univ, 57-59; adj prof, Drexel Inst Technol, 64-66; chmn session on low noise technol, Int Conf Commun, 66; chmn, Bd Dirs, Bartol Res Inst, Bd Gov, Franklin Inst. *Mem:* Fel AAAS; fel Inst Elec & Electronics Engrs; Am Phys Soc. *Res:* Infrared properties of materials; plasma physics; quantum electronics; microsonics; lasers; photosensors; radiometry. *Mailing Add:* 212 Turtle Creek Dr Tequesta FL 33469

**VOLLMER, REGIS ROBERT,** CARDIOVASCULAR PHARMACOLOGY. *Current Pos:* ASST PROF PHARMACOL, SCH PHARM, UNIV PITTSBURGH, 77- *Personal Data:* b Wilkinsburg, Pa, Aug 20, 46; m 67; c 2. *Educ:* St Vincent Col, Latrobe, Pa, BA, 68; Univ Houston, PhD(pharmacol), 75. *Prof Exp:* Res scientist, Squibb Inst Med Res, 75-77. *Concurrent Pos:* Prin investr, NIH grant, 81- *Mem:* Am Soc Pharmacol & Exp Therapeut; AAAS; Sigma Xi; Am Heart Asn. *Res:* Cardiovascular pharmacology with specific focus upon the role of dietary sodium and its influence on the sympathetic nervous system control of cardiovascular function relating to hypertensive disease; antihypertensive drugs. *Mailing Add:* Dept Pharmaceut Sci Univ Pittsburgh Sch Pharm Pittsburgh PA 15261-1905. *Fax:* 412-648-8219

**VOLMAN, DAVID H,** PHYSICAL CHEMISTRY. *Current Pos:* from asst prof & asst chemist to assoc prof & assoc chemist, Exp Sta, Univ Calif, Davis, 46-56, chmn dept, 74-80, prof, 56-87, EMER PROF CHEM, UNIV CALIF, DAVIS, 87- *Personal Data:* b Los Angeles, Calif, July 10, 16; m 44, Ruth Jackson; c Thomas, Susan & Daniel. *Educ:* Univ Calif, Los Angeles, AB, 37, AM, 38; Stanford Univ, PhD(chem), 40. *Prof Exp:* Asst chem, Univ Calif, Los Angeles, 37-38, res chemist, Nat Defense Res Comt Proj, 41-42; asst chem, Stanford Univ, 38-39; instr chem & jr chemist, Exp Sta, Univ Calif, 40-41; res chemist, Off Sci Res & Develop, Northwestern Univ, 41-45 & Univ Ill, 45-46. *Concurrent Pos:* Guggenheim fel, Harvard Univ, 49-50; Stand Oil Co Calif fel, Stanford Univ, 39-40; vis prof, Univ Wash, 58; ed bd, J Photochem, 72-; ed, Advan Photochem, 83- *Mem:* Am Chem Soc; Int-Am Photochem Soc. *Res:* Photochemistry; kinetics; chemistry of the atmosphere. *Mailing Add:* Dept Chem Univ Calif Davis CA 95616. *Fax:* 530-752-8995; *E-Mail:* volman@chem.ucdavis.edu

**VOLOSHIN, ARKADY S,** EXPERIMENTAL MECHANICS. *Current Pos:* assoc prof, 84-90, PROF MECH ENG & MECH, LEHIGH UNIV, 90- *Personal Data:* b Kishinev, USSR, Aug 7, 46; m 72, Ilana Gitelman; c Ron & Dan. *Educ:* Leningrad Polytech Inst, USSR, dipl, 69; Tel-Aviv Univ, Israel, PhD(mech), 78. *Prof Exp:* Sr res officer, Kishinev Inst Non-Destructive Testing, 69-70; asst exp stress anal, Tel-Aviv Univ, 73-78, fel biomech, 78-79; asst prof exp stress anal & biomech, Iowa State Univ, 79-84. *Mem:* Soc Exp Mech; Am Soc Biomech. *Res:* Biomechanics of gait and impulse wave propagation through human locomotor system; photoelasticity through digital image analysis-application to fracture mechanics and nondestructive evaluation; fractional fringe moire; composite materials; fiber optic sensors. *Mailing Add:* 354 Packard Lab Dept Mech Eng & Mech Lehigh Univ Bethlehem PA 18015. *E-Mail:* av01@lehigh.edu

**VOLP, ROBERT FRANCIS,** METABOLISM OF FOREIGN COMPOUNDS, BIOCHEMICAL TOXICOLOGY. *Current Pos:* asst prof, 83-88, ASSOC PROF CHEM, MURRAY STATE UNIV, 88- *Personal Data:* b Elkhorn, Wis, Oct 20, 52; m 77; c 4. *Educ:* Univ Wis-Stevens Pt, BS, 75; Univ Wis-Madison, MS, 77, PhD(pharmacol & toxicol), 79. *Prof Exp:* Res assoc, Inst Pharmacol & Toxicol, Univ Gottingen, Fed Repub Ger, 79-80, Univ Ariz, 80-82; res asst prof, Primate Res Inst, NMex State Univ, 82-83. *Concurrent Pos:* Prin investr, NIH, 85-87 & 90-92. *Mem:* Am Chem Soc; Soc Toxicol. *Res:* Metabolism of halogenated aliphatic compounds; biochemical mechanisms of toxicity of halogenated aliphatic compounds; regulation of cellular UDPGA metabolism. *Mailing Add:* Dept Chem Murray State Univ Murray KY 42071-3312. *E-Mail:* bobvolp@msumusik.mursuky.edu

**VOLPE, ANGELO ANTHONY,** ORGANIC CHEMISTRY, POLYMER CHEMISTRY. *Current Pos:* PRES & PROF CHEM, TENN TECHNOL UNIV, 87- *Personal Data:* b New York, NY, Nov 8, 38; m 65, Jennette Murray. *Educ:* Brooklyn Col, BS, 59; Univ Md, MS, 62, PhD(org chem), 66. *Hon Degrees:* ME, Stevens Inst Technol, 75. *Prof Exp:* Res chemist, US Naval Ord Lab, 61-66; from asst prof to prof chem, Stevens Inst Technol, 66-77, actg head dept chem & chem eng, 74-75; prof chem, ECarolina Univ, 77-87, chair, 77-80, dean, Col Arts & Scis, 80-83, vice chancellor acad affairs, 83-87. *Mem:* Am Chem Soc; Sigma Xi. *Res:* Correlation of polymer properties to molecular structure; synthesis and mechanisms of formation and degradation of thermally stable polymers; monomer synthesis; synthesis and study of biopolymers; educational administration. *Mailing Add:* Walton House Tenn Tech Univ PO Box 5007 Cookeville TN 38505. *Fax:* 615-372-3898

**VOLPE, ERMINIO PETER,** GENETICS & GENERAL MEDICAL SCIENCES. *Current Pos:* PROF BASIC MED SCI, SCH MED, MERCER UNIV, 81- *Personal Data:* b New York, NY, Apr 7, 27; m 91, Lesley D Smith; c Laura, Liza & John. *Educ:* City Col New York, BS, 48; Columbia Univ, MA, 49, PhD(zool), 52. *Prof Exp:* Asst zool, Columbia Univ, 48-51; instr biol, City Col New York, 51-52; from asst prof to prof zool, Newcomb Col, Tulane Univ, 52-81, chmn col dept, 54-64, chmn univ dept, 64-66, assoc dean, Grad Sch, 67-69, chmn dept, 69-79. *Concurrent Pos:* Mem steering comt, Biol Sci Curric Study, 66-69; consult, Comn Undergrad Educ Biol Sci, NSF, 67-70; US Nat comnr, UNESCO, 68-72; mem exam comt, Col Entrance Exam Bd, Princeton Univ, 69-72; Sigma Xi ann award outstanding fac res, Tulane Univ, 71; chmn advan placement test biol, Educ Testing Serv, 75-81; ed, Am Zoologist, Am Soc Zoologists, 76-81; mem grad record exam comt biol, Educ Testing Serv, 81-90. *Mem:* Fel AAAS; Genetics Soc Am; Soc Study Evolution; Am Soc Zoologists (pres, 81); Soc Syst Zool; Am Soc Naturalists; Am Soc Human Genetics. *Res:* Embryology, genetics and evolution of amphibians; transplantation immunity and tolerance in anurans; writer in medical genetics. *Mailing Add:* Sch Med Mercer Univ Macon GA 31207. *Fax:* 912-752-5489; *E-Mail:* volpe.p@gain.mercer.edu

**VOLPE, GERALD T,** ELECTRICAL ENGINEERING. *Current Pos:* STAFF ELEC ENG, SILICON VALLEY GROUP, WILTON, CONN, 90- *Personal Data:* b New York, NY, Feb 15, 35; m 57; c 2. *Educ:* City Col New York, BEE, 57, MEE, 61; NY Univ, EngScD, 64. *Prof Exp:* Jr engr, Bendix Res Labs, Mich, 57-59; design engr, Loral Electronics Div, Loral Corp, NY, 59-61; instr elec eng, NY Univ, 61-64; sr eng, CBS Labs, Columbia Broadcasting Syst, 64-66, Marchand Electronic Labs, 66-67 & Perkin-Elmer Corp, Conn, 67-68; assoc prof elec eng, Cooper Union, 68-80; prof elec eng, Univ Bridgeport, 80-90. *Concurrent Pos:* Consult, Perkin-Elmer Corp, 69-78 & Gen Instrument Corp, NY, 73-77. *Mem:* Inst Elec & Electronics Engrs; Optical Soc Am. *Res:* Feedback controls; communication theory; electro-optics and acoustics; circuit theory. *Mailing Add:* SVG Lithography 77 Danbury Rd Wilton CT 06897

**VOLPE, JOSEPH J,** PEDIATRICS, NEUROLOGY. *Current Pos:* Bronson Crothers prof neurol, Harvard Med Sch, NEUROLOGIST-IN-CHIEF, CHILDREN'S HOSP, BOSTON, MASS, 90- *Personal Data:* b Salem, Mass, Dec 17, 38. *Educ:* Harvard Univ, MD, 64. *Prof Exp:* Prof pediat neurol & biol chem, Washington Univ, St Louis, Mo, 80-90. *Mem:* Inst Med-Nat Acad Sci. *Mailing Add:* Neurologist-in-Chief Harvard Med Sch Childrens Hosp 300 Longwood Ave Boston MA 02115

**VOLPE, P(ETER) J, JR,** CHEMICAL ENGINEERING, ECONOMICS. *Current Pos:* VPRES, DEAN WITTER REYNOLDS, 85- *Personal Data:* b New York, NY, Mar 13, 34; m 57; c 4. *Educ:* Rice Inst, BA, 56, BS, 57. *Prof Exp:* Jr prod engr, Celanese Chem Co, 57-58, from jr engr to engr, 58-60, from res engr to sr res engr, 60-65, group leader chem eng econ & design, 65-66, sect head process develop, 66-71, mgr chem eng, 71-74, tech mgr, 74-76, opers mgr, Bishop Tex Plant, 76-80, mgr facil & admin, Tech Ctr, 80-81, dir fac, Corpus Christi Plant, 81-85. *Mem:* Am Inst Chem Engrs. *Res:* Laboratory and pilot plant process development for bulk organic chemicals, especially nylon salt; economics and process design for new bulk organic chemical products and processes. *Mailing Add:* 318 Cape Hatteras Dr Corpus Christi TX 78412

**VOLPE, RICHARD ALAN,** REAL TIME CONTROL SYSTEMS, SENSOR BASED ROBOTICS. *Current Pos:* MEM TECH STAFF, JET PROPULSION LAB, CALIF INST TECHNOL, 90- *Personal Data:* b Balitmore, Md, May 19, 63. *Educ:* Loyola Col, BS, 84; Carnegie Mellon Univ, MS, 86, PhD(appl physics), 91. *Prof Exp:* Teaching asst, Carnegie Mellon Univ, 84-86, res asst, 86-87, USAF res fel, 87-90. *Concurrent Pos:* Cognizant engr, NASA-Jet Propulsion Lab, Calif Inst Technol, 94-97. *Mem:* Inst Elec & Electronics Engrs. *Res:* Planetary mobile robots; real-time sensor based robotics; real-time software/system design; real-time obstacle avoidance; robot trajectory planning. *Mailing Add:* Jet Propulsion Lab Calif Inst Technol 4800 Oak Grove Dr Mail Stop 198-219 Pasadena CA 91109. *Fax:* 818-393-5007; *E-Mail:* volpe@telerobotics.jpl.nasa.gov

**VOLPE, ROBERT,** IMMUNOLOGY. *Current Pos:* from clin teacher to prof, 65-91, EMER PROF FAC MED, UNIV TORONTO, 91-; DIR, ENDOCRINE RES LAB, WELLESLEY HOSP, 67- *Personal Data:* b Toronto, Ont, Mar 6, 26; m 49, Ruth; c Catherine L, Elizabeth A, Peter G, Edward J & Rose E. *Educ:* Univ Toronto, MD, 50; FRCP(C), 56; FACP, 65; FRCP(Edinburgh), 92; London, 95. *Honors & Awards:* Jamieson Prize, Can Soc Nuclear Med, 80; Baxter Prize lectr, Toronto Soc Clin Res, 84; Sandoz Prize lectr, Can Soc Endocrinol Metab, 85; Novo-Nordisk Prize, Irish Endocrine Soc, 90; Hashimoto Mem lectr, Kyushu Univ, Fukuoka, Japan, 92. *Prof Exp:* Dept Vet Affairs med res fel, Clin Invest Unit, Sunnybrook Hosp, Toronto, 52-53; Med Res Coun Can fel, Toronto Gen Hosp, 55-57; sr res fel endocrinol, Fac Med, Univ Toronto, 57-65. *Concurrent Pos:* Physician-in-chief, Dept Med, Wellesley Hosp, Toronto, 74-87; gov, Am Col Physicians, 80-84; dir, Div Endocrinol, Metab, Univ Toronto, 87-92; mem coun, Royal Col Physicians, 88-96. *Mem:* Fel Am Col Physicians; Am Thyroid Asn (pres, 80-81); Am Fedn Clin Res; Endocrine Soc; Can Soc Endocrinol & Metab (pres, 72); Assoc Am Physicians; fel Royal Col Physicians Can (vpres, 94-96). *Res:* Immune mechanisms in thyroid diseases; autoimmunity in endocrine system; immunoregulatory abnormalities in autoimmune endocrine diseases; thyroid diseases. *Mailing Add:* 3 Daleberry Pl Don Mills ON M3B 2A5 Can. *Fax:* 416-966-5046

**VOLPE, ROSALIND ANN,** HEALTH EFFECTS OF LEAD & CADMIUM & ZINC, ENVIRONMENTAL & OCCUPATIONAL HEALTH. *Current Pos:* asst mgr, 80-86, MGR ENVIRON HEALTH, INT LEAD ZINC RES ORG, 86- *Personal Data:* b New Haven, Conn, May 1, 54; m 87. *Educ:* Barnard Col, BA, 75; Columbia Univ, MS, 80, PhD(environ sci), 88. *Prof Exp:* Res asst virol & oncol, Rockefeller Univ, 75-77; intern, NY Atty Gen Off Environ Proj Dir, 79. *Concurrent Pos:* Asst dir environ health, Lead Ind Assoc, 84-86; counr, Soc Geochem & Health, 88-; prin invest, Impart Eng Control, 88. *Mem:* Am Indust Hyg Asn; Soc Environ Geochem Health. *Res:* Managed program covering the heavy metals lead zinc and cadmium; most studies directed at human target organs and range from occupational, general population, epidemiology and toxicology projects, environment, conferences and information exchanges. *Mailing Add:* ILZRO 2525 Meridian Pkwy PO Box 12036 Research Triangle Park NC 27709-2036

**VOLPP, GERT PAUL JUSTUS,** AGRICULTURAL CHEMISTRY. *Current Pos:* interdisciplinary scientist, FMC Corp, 63-65, mgr explor org res, 65-72, mgr prod res, 72-73, tech dir alkali chem, 73-75, asst venture mgr pyrethroids, 75-76, asst dir res, 76-77, acquisition mgr, 77-79, DIR COM DEVELOP, FMC CORP, 80- *Personal Data:* b Loerrach, Ger, July 30, 30; nat US; m 62; c 4. *Educ:* Univ Basel, PhD(chem), 58. *Prof Exp:* Res fel org chem, Harvard Univ, 58-63. *Mem:* Am Chem Soc; NY Acad Sci. *Res:* Synthetic organic chemistry; intermediates for dyestuffs; additives for plastics; antioxidants; detergent chemistry; agricultural chemistry; manufacturing technology for soda ash, caustic, chlorine, glycerine, allyl alcohol, barium and strontium chemicals; commercial development of pesticides. *Mailing Add:* 116 Poe Rd Princeton NJ 08540-4122

**VOLTZ, STERLING ERNEST,** PHYSICAL CHEMISTRY, RESEARCH ADMINISTRATION. *Current Pos:* PVT CONSULT, 86- *Personal Data:* b Philadelphia, Pa, Apr 17, 21; m 43, Betty Morgan; c Sandra & Karen. *Educ:* Temple Univ, AB, 43, MA, 47, PhD(phys chem), 52. *Prof Exp:* Lab asst, Temple Univ, 46-47; res fel, Univ Pa, 47-48; instr, Temple Univ, 48-51; res chemist, Houdry Process Corp, 51-58; group leader, Sun Oil Co, 58-60; supv chemist, Missile & Space Div, Gen Elec Co, 60-62, consult liaison scientist, 62-68; res assoc, Mobil Res & Develop Corp, Paulsboro, NJ, 68-80, admin adv, 80-82, admin mgr, 82-86. *Mem:* AAAS; Am Chem Soc; Catalysis Soc; Sigma Xi. *Res:* Catalysis; surface and solid state chemistry; chemical kinetics; electrochemistry; fuel cells; petroleum and petrochemical processes; synthetic fuels; automotive emission control systems; program management; research administration and planning; research contracts. *Mailing Add:* 6 E Glen Circle Media PA 19063

**VOLTZOW, JANICE,** INVERTEBRATE ZOOLOGY, FUNCTIONAL MORPHOLOGY. *Current Pos:* ASST PROF BIOL, CTR BIOL, INVERT BIOL & EVOLUTION, UNIV SCRANTON, 96- *Personal Data:* b New Haven, Conn, May 7, 58; m 86, Ned Fetcher; c Clarissa & Timothy. *Educ:* Yale Univ, BS, 80; Duke Univ, PhD(zool), 85. *Prof Exp:* Teaching asst zool, Duke Univ, 80-82, trainee, Cocos Found, 82-85; fel, Friday Harbor Labs, Univ Wash, 85-86; from asst prof to assoc prof zool & marine biol, Univ PR, 87-96. *Concurrent Pos:* Chairperson, Pub Affairs Comt, Am Soc Zoologists, 87-89; counr-at-large, Am Malacol Union, 90-92. *Mem:* Soc Integrative

Comp Biol, Unitas Malacologica; Am Malacol Union; Sigma Xi; AAAS. *Res:* Development, organization, biomechanics and evolution of invertebrates, especially marine prosobranch gastropods. *Mailing Add:* Dept Biol Univ Scranton Scranton PA 18510-4625. *E-Mail:* voltzowj2@uofs.edu

**VOLWILER, WADE,** MEDICINE. *Current Pos:* from instr to prof, 49-82, head, Div Gastroenterol, 50-81, EMER PROF MED, SCH MED, UNIV WASH, 82- *Personal Data:* b Grand Forks, NDak, Sept 16, 17; m 43, Catherine Davies; c Craig, Susan & Timothy. *Educ:* Oberlin Col, AB, 39; Harvard Med Sch, MD, 43; Am Bd Internal Med, dipl, 50, recert, 77; Am Bd Gastroenterol, dipl, 54. *Honors & Awards:* Friedenwald Medal, Am Gastroenterol Asn, 81. *Prof Exp:* From intern to resident med, Mass Gen Hosp, Boston, 43-45, asst, 45-48; asst, Harvard Med Sch, 46-48. *Concurrent Pos:* Teaching fel med, Harvard Med Sch, 45-46; res fel gastroenterol, Mass Gen Hosp, Boston, 45-48; Am Gastroenterol Asn res fel, 47; Nat Res Coun fel, 48-49; Markle scholar, 50-55; res assoc, Mayo Found, Univ Minn, 48-49; attend physician, King County Hosp Syst, Seattle, 50-82 & Vet Admin Hosp, 51-82; consult, USPHS Hosp, 55-82 & Univ Wash Hosp, 60-82; mem subspecialty bd gastroenterol, Am Bd Internal Med, 70-76. *Mem:* Am Soc Clin Invest; Am Gastroenterol Asn (secy, 59-62, pres, 67); Asn Am Physicians; Am Asn Study Liver Dis (pres, 56). *Res:* Liver diseases; gastroenterology; plasma proteins. *Mailing Add:* Dept Med Div Gastroenterol Box 356424 Univ Wash Sch Med Seattle WA 98195

**VOLZ, FREDERIC ERNST,** ATMOSPHERIC PHYSICS. *Current Pos:* RETIRED. *Personal Data:* b Singen, Ger, Oct 29, 22; m 57; c 3. *Educ:* Univ Frankfurt, dipl, 50, PhD(meteorol), 54. *Prof Exp:* Res asst, Lichtklimat Observ Arosa, 50-52; res asst meteorol, Univ Mainz, 52-57; res fel atmospheric physics, Harvard Univ, 57-61 & Astron Inst, Univ Tubingen, 62-67; res physicist, Air Force Geophys Lab, 67- *Mem:* Am Meteorol Soc; Am Geophys Union; Optical Soc Am; Ger Meteorol Soc. *Res:* Atmospheric optics, optical constants of aerosol, twilight, stratospheric aerosol; infrared. *Mailing Add:* 24 Tyler Rd Lexington MA 02173

**VOLZ, JOHN EDWARD,** ADIPOSE TISSUE, TEMPOROMANDIBULAR JOINT. *Current Pos:* ASSOC PROF GROSS ANAT, MED SCH, TEMPLE UNIV, 73- *Personal Data:* b Baltimore, Md, March 23, 40; m 61; c 4. *Educ:* Towson State Univ, BS, 69; Univ Md, PhD(anat), 75. *Concurrent Pos:* Consult, Vet Admin Hosp, Dent Br, Del, 86. *Mem:* Am Asn Anatomists; Am Asn Dent Sch. *Res:* Adipose tissue, especially the effects of diet and exercise on the growth and development of fat stores in rats and mice; temporomandibular joint disfunction. *Mailing Add:* 265 W Morris Rd Coupeville WA 98239

**VOLZ, MICHAEL GEORGE,** ENVIRONMENTAL BIOCHEMISTRY & MICROBIOLOGY. *Current Pos:* assoc sanit microbiologist, Sanit & Radiation Lab, Calif State Dept Health, 77-82, pub health chemist, Hazardous Mat Lab, 82-84, environ biochemist, Sanit & Radiation Lab, 85-89, res scientist, 89, chief, Div Labs, 89-93, ASST DEP DIR LAB SCI, CALIF STATE DEPT HEALTH, 93- *Personal Data:* b Long Beach, Calif, Nov 30, 45; m 68, Adrienne J Machado; c Carla, Eric (deceased) & Raphael. *Educ:* Univ Calif, Berkeley, BS, 67, PhD(soil sci, plant physiol), 72. *Prof Exp:* Asst res biochemist, Univ Calif, Berkeley, 72-74, res biochemist, 74-75; asst plant physiologist, Conn Agr Exp Sta, 75-77. *Concurrent Pos:* Mem, Comt Environ Health, Asn State & Territorial Pub Health Labs Dirs, Comt Lab Stands & Pract, Am Pub Health Asn. *Mem:* Am Water Works Asn; AAAS; Am Pub Health Asn; Asn State & Territorial Pub Health Lab Dirs. *Res:* Assessing the significance of environmental microbiol/chemical contamination, attendant environmental data quality and subsequent influence on regulatory decisions and activities impacting upon the public health. *Mailing Add:* Lab Sci State Calif Dept Health Serv 2151 Berkeley Way Berkeley CA 94704-9980

**VOLZ, PAUL ALBERT,** MYCOLOGY, BOTANY. *Current Pos:* asst prof & mycologist, 69-72, assoc prof, 72-80, PROF BOT & MYCOL, EASTERN MICH UNIV, 80- *Personal Data:* b Ann Arbor, Mich, Mar 26, 36. *Educ:* Heidelberg Col, BA, 58; Mich State Univ, MS, 62, PhD(mycol), 66; Century Univ, PhD(bus admin), 91. *Honors & Awards:* Kholodny Medal, Inst Bot, Acad Sci, USSR. *Prof Exp:* Instr bot, Univ Wis-Milwaukee, 62-63; USPHS postdoctoral res grant, Med Ctr, Ind Univ, 67-68; assoc prof bot & mycol, Purdue Univ, 68-69. *Concurrent Pos:* Sr res assoc, Nat Res Coun, 71-73; res contractor, NASA Manned Spacecraft Ctr, 71-74; vis prof mycol, Nat Taiwan Univ, 74-75; Wayne State Univ, 80-81 & NATO Advan Study Inst, 82-; People to People Citizen Ambassador delg, Egypt, Turkey & Israel, 96. *Mem:* AAAS; Am Inst Biol Sci; NY Acad Sci; Asn Trop Biol; Am Soc Eng Educ. *Res:* Fern anatomy; marine and soil fungi of the Bahamas and The Republic of China; keratinophilic fungi; drug sensitivity and nutritional requirements of fungi; effects of space flight parameters on select fungal species; fungal cytogenetics and morphology; medical mycology; microbial ecology. *Mailing Add:* 1805 Jackson Ave Ann Arbor MI 48103

**VOLZ, RICHARD A,** ROBOTICS, REAL TIME COMPUTING. *Current Pos:* PROF & HEAD COMPUT SCI, TEX A&M UNIV, 88- *Personal Data:* b Woodstock, Ill, July 10, 37; m 61, Mary Jensen; c Keith, Richard & Cynthia. *Educ:* Northwestern Univ, BS, 60, MS, 61, PhD(elec eng), 64. *Prof Exp:* From asst prof to prof, Elec & Comput Eng Dept, Univ Mich, Ann Arbor, 64-88, assoc chmn, 78-79, dir, CIPRNET, 78-85, assoc dir, Comput Ctr, 79-82, dir, Robotics Lab, 81-88. *Concurrent Pos:* NSF grants, 65-68, 70-72, 85-87 & 92-95; Air Force Off Sci Res contract, 82-88; assoc ed, Robotics, Trans Aerospace & Electronics Systs, Inst Elec & Electronics Engrs, 82-95 & Trans Robotics & Automation, 89-94, ed, 94-; mcm, Automation & Robotics Conf, Inst Elec & Electronics Engrs, 90; grantee, NASA, 85-94; gen chair, Robotics Conf, Inst Elec & Electronics Engrs, 90; Royce E Wisenbaker prof eng, Tex

A&M Univ. *Mem:* Fel Inst Elec & Electronics Engrs; Asn Comput Mach. *Res:* Robotics; real-time computing techniques, particularly real-time software; distributing languages for embedded real-time systems. *Mailing Add:* Dept Comput Sci Tex A&M Univ College Station TX 77843. *Fax:* 409-862-4813; *E-Mail:* volz@cs.tamu.edu

**VOLZ, WILLIAM K(URT),** chemical engineering, for more information see previous edition

**VOMACHKA, ARCHIE JOEL,** REPRODUCTIVE BIOLOGY, ENDOCRINOLOGY. *Current Pos:* ASST PROF HUMAN PHYSIOL, MARQUETTE UNIV, 81- *Personal Data:* b Duluth, Minn, Sept 28, 46; m 73. *Educ:* Univ Minn, Duluth, BA, 68; Mich State Univ, PhD(zool), 76. *Prof Exp:* Fel reprod physiol, Univ Kans Med Ctr, 76-79; lectr exp vert biol, Princeton Univ, 79-81. *Concurrent Pos:* Res assoc, Princeton Univ, 79-81. *Mem:* Animal Behav Soc; AAAS; Sigma Xi. *Res:* Neural and hormonal regulation of sexual behavior in rodents, including the sexual differentiation of behavior and endocrine physiology in hamsters. *Mailing Add:* Dept Biol Beaver Col 450 S Easton Rd Glenside PA 19038-3215

**VOMHOF, DANIEL WILLIAM,** FORENSIC SCIENCE, CHEMISTRY. *Current Pos:* PRES, EXPERT WITNESS SERV, 74-; PRES, 4N6XPRT SYSTS, 91- *Personal Data:* b Grant, Nebr, Apr 19, 38; m 60, 78; c 3. *Educ:* Augsburg Col, BA, 62; Univ Ariz, MS, 66, PhD(plant physiol), 67; Nat Univ, MS & BS, 86. *Prof Exp:* Chemist, Ariz Agr Exp Sta, Univ Ariz, 63-67; res chemist, Corn Refiners Asn, 67-69; dir, Region IX Lab, US Bur Customs, Ill, 69-72, forensic scientist, Region VII, 72-74, dir, Lab Div, US Customs Serv, Region IX, Chicago, 74. *Concurrent Pos:* Res assoc, Nat Bur Stand, 67-69; adj prof occup safety, Nat Univ, 84-95; chmn gen educ, Coleman Col, La Mesa Ca, 86-90. *Mem:* AAAS; Am Chem Soc; fel Am Inst Chemists; Sigma Xi; Am Soc Testing & Mat; fel Am Col Forensic Examrs. *Res:* Accident dynamics; document identification; biomechanics; analytical chemistry; driver behavior; safety engineering, human factor; intelligent systems. *Mailing Add:* Expert Witness Serv 8387 University Ave La Mesa CA 92041. *Fax:* 619-464-2206

**VOMOCIL, JAMES ARTHUR,** SOIL SCIENCE, AGRONOMY. *Current Pos:* RETIRED. *Personal Data:* b Jacumba, Calif, Sept 12, 26; m 46; c 3. *Educ:* Univ Ariz, BS, 50; Mich State Univ, MS, 52; Rutgers Univ, PhD, 55. *Prof Exp:* Asst soil sci, Mich State Univ, 50-52, instr, 52; asst, Rutgers Univ, 52-55; instr soil physics, Univ Calif, Davis, 55, from asst prof to assoc prof & assoc exp sta, 55-67; exten soils specialist & prof soils, Ore State Univ, 67-92. *Mem:* Am Soc Agron; Soil Sci Soc Am; Int Soil Sci. *Res:* Soil physical condition and plant growth; soil strength and deformation. *Mailing Add:* 24617 Llewellyn Corvallis OR 97333

**VON, ISAIAH,** INDUSTRIAL ORGANIC CHEMISTRY. *Current Pos:* CONSULT, 81- *Personal Data:* b Philadelphia, Pa, Dec 28, 18; m 45; c 3. *Educ:* Univ Buffalo, BA, 40; Univ Pa, MS, 41, PhD(org chem), 43. *Prof Exp:* Res assoc, Nat Defense Res Comt Proj, Univ Pa, 43-45, mem, Comt Med Res Proj, 45-46; res chemist, Am Cyanamid Co, 46-53, develop chemist, 53-54, group leader, 54-56, sect chief chemist, 56-64, dep chief chemist, 65-81. *Mem:* Am Chem Soc; Am Asn Textile Chemists & Colorists. *Res:* Dyestuffs; pigments; organic intermediates. *Mailing Add:* Apt 16E 1050 George St New Brunswick NJ 08901

**VONA, JOSEPH ALBERT,** ORGANIC CHEMISTRY. *Current Pos:* mgr, Tech Serv Lab, 55-69, DIR, MTD LAB, CELANESE CHEM CO, 69- *Personal Data:* b Brooklyn, NY, Aug 15, 20; m 46; c 2. *Educ:* Brooklyn Col, BA, 41, MA, 44; Polytech Inst Brooklyn, PhD, 54. *Prof Exp:* Head lab sect plastics res, Barrett Chem Co, 45-46; res & develop chemist, Nat Lead Co, 46-50; asst to tech dir, Baker Castor Oil Co, 50-55. *Mem:* Am Chem Soc; Com Develop Asn; Chem Indust Asn; Asn Res Dirs; NY Acad Sci. *Res:* Research and development in radiation technology; new types of coatings; emulsion solution and bulk polymerization of monomers; new compounds which can produce durable coatings. *Mailing Add:* 108 Marlboro St Westfield NJ 07090-2216

**VON ADERKAS, PATRICK JURGEN CECIL,** CONIFER TISSUE CULTURE, EXPERIMENTAL EMBRYOGENESIS. *Current Pos:* asst prof, 89-93, ASSOC PROF BOT, CTR FOREST BIOL, DEPT BIOL, UNIV VICTORIA, 93- *Personal Data:* b London, Ont, Mar 29, 54; m, Elizabeth N Wells; c Eleanor, Edward & Max. *Educ:* Univ Guelph, BS, 77; Univ Manchester, PhD(bot), 81. *Prof Exp:* Fel, Nat Res Coun Can, 81-85, Can Forestry Serv, 85-89. *Mem:* Fel Linnean Soc London; AAAS; Bot Soc Am; Can Bot Asn; Int Asn Plant Tissue Cult. *Res:* Lab works on in vitro studies of embryo development in conifers; somatic embryogenesis haploid embrogenesis and in vitro fertilization are our present focus. *Mailing Add:* Dept Biol Univ Victoria Victoria BC V8W 2Y2 Can. *Fax:* 250-721-7120

**VON ALMEN, WILLIAM FREDERICK I,** PALYNOLOGY, GEOLOGY. *Current Pos:* geologist, Stand Oil Co Tex, 60-64, geologist-palynologist, 66-68, palynologist, Chevron Oil Field Res Co, 68-69, from lead palynologist to div paleontologist, 69-71, SR PALEONTOLOGIST, CHEVRON USA, INC, 71- *Personal Data:* b Olney, Ill, May 6, 28; m 50; c 4. *Educ:* Southern Ill Univ, Carbondale, BA, 57; Univ Mo, Columbia, MA, 59; Mich State Univ, PhD(geol), 70. *Prof Exp:* Geologist, Pure Oil Co, 59-60. *Mem:* Am Asn Stratig Palynol. *Res:* Palynology of Devonian-Mississippian Boundary; Mesozoic palynostratigraphy. *Mailing Add:* 110 Holly Dr Metairie LA 70005

**VON AULOCK, WILHELM HEINRICH,** ELECTRICAL & SYSTEMS ENGINEERING. *Current Pos:* RETIRED. *Personal Data:* b Pirna, Ger, Jan 24, 15; US citizen; m 56; c 4. *Educ:* Tech Univ, Berlin, Dipl Eng, 37; Stuttgart Tech Univ, DEng, 53. *Prof Exp:* Div head engr, Torpedoversuchsanstalt Eckernfoerde, Ger, 42-45; physicist, Bur Ships, Navy Dept, Washington, DC, 47-53; mem tech staff, Bell Labs, 54-62, dept head nuclear effects, 62-71, dir tech support, Am Bell Int, 77-79, dept head installation studies, 71-79, dept head develop, planning & analysis, 79-85. *Concurrent Pos:* Instr, Postgrad Sch, Univ Md, 51-52. *Mem:* Fel Inst Elec & Electronics Engrs. *Res:* Guided acoustic torpedoes; electromagnetic fields in sea water; microwave ferrite materials and devices; phased arrays for radar applications; systems engineering for communication facilities. *Mailing Add:* Hornstr 13 80797 Munich Germany

**VON BAEYER, HANS CHRISTIAN,** THEORETICAL PHYSICS, PHYSICS POPULARIZATION. *Current Pos:* from asst prof to assoc prof, 68-75, chmn dept, 72-78, PROF PHYSICS, COL WILLIAM & MARY, 75- *Personal Data:* b Berlin, Ger, Apr 6, 38; US citizen; m 83; c 4. *Educ:* Columbia Univ, AB, 58; Univ Miami, MSc, 61; Vanderbilt Univ, PhD(physics), 64. *Prof Exp:* Res assoc physics, McGill Univ, 64-65, asst prof, 65-68. *Concurrent Pos:* Vis prof, Tri-Univ Meson Facil & Simon Fraser Univ, 78-79; dir, Va Asn Res Campus, 79-84; secy, Southeastern Univ Res Asn, 80-85. *Mem:* Fel Am Phys Soc; Fedn Am Sci; Am Asn Univ Prof; Am Asn Physics Teachers. *Res:* Theory of elementary particles; public understanding of science. *Mailing Add:* Dept Physics Col William & Mary PO Box 8795 Williamsburg VA 23187. *Fax:* 757-221-3540

**VON BARGEN, KENNETH LOUIS,** TRACTOR & EQUIPMENT TESTING, APPLICATION TECHNOL. *Current Pos:* from instr to asst prof agr eng, 56-69, assoc prof systs eng, 69-77, PROF BIO SYSTS ENG, UNIV NEBR, LINCOLN, 77- *Personal Data:* b Alliance, Nebr, Apr 6, 31; m 82, Ernestine Rieger; c Lisa, Brian & Jill. *Educ:* Univ Nebr, Lincoln, BS, 52, MS, 62; Purdue Univ, Lafayette, PhD(agr eng), 70. *Prof Exp:* Design engr, Lockwood Grader Corp, Nebr, 55-56. *Concurrent Pos:* Mem bd dirs, Am Forge & Grasslands Coun, 77-80; mem, Nebr Bd Tractor Testing Engrs, 76-, chmn, 81-92. *Mem:* Sigma Xi; Am Soc Agr Engrs; Soc Automotive Engrs; Int Soc Optical Eng. *Res:* Planning and management of agricultural and processing equipment systems; tractor and machine performance evaluation; energy requirements; application technology, optical reflectance sensing for sprayer control and sub-surface insecticide placement. *Mailing Add:* 6110 Elkcrest Circle Lincoln NE 68516. *Fax:* 402-472-6338

**VON BERG, ROBERT L(EE),** PROCESS DESIGN, REACTOR DESIGN. *Current Pos:* from asst prof to prof, 46-88, EMER PROF CHEM ENG, CORNELL UNIV, 88- *Personal Data:* b Wheeling, WVa, June 14, 18; m 47, Kate L Hopkins; c Eric, Gretchen, Karl & Karin. *Educ:* WVa Univ, BSChE, 40, MS, 41; Mass Inst Technol, ScD(chem eng), 44. *Prof Exp:* Instr chem eng, WVa Univ, 39-40; indust engr, E I du Pont de Nemours & Co, Del, 44-46. *Concurrent Pos:* Consult, AEC, 50-60 & Dow Chem Co, Mich, 53-54; NATO res fel, Delft Univ Technol, 60-61; vis prof, Los Alamos Sci Lab, 67-68, Univ Newcastle, Australia, 74-75, Univ Canterbury, NZ, 82, 88, 92. *Mem:* Am Chem Soc; Am Inst Chem Engrs. *Res:* Chemical processes; liquid-liquid extraction; reaction kinetics and reactor design; nuclear processing; radiation chemistry. *Mailing Add:* 501 Hanshaw Rd Ithaca NY 14850

**VON BERNUTH, ROBERT DEAN,** AGRICULTURAL ENGINEERING. *Personal Data:* b Del Norte, Colo, Apr 14, 46; m 69, Judy M Wehrman; c Jeanie & Suzie. *Educ:* Colo State Univ, BSE, 68; Univ Idaho, MS, 70; Claremont Grad Sch, Calif, MBA, 80; Univ Nebr, PhD(eng), 82. *Honors & Awards:* Person of Yr, Irrigation Asn, 94. *Prof Exp:* Instr agr eng, Univ Nebr, Lincoln, 80-82; from assoc prof to prof, Univ Tenn, Knoxville, 82-90; prof & chmn, Mich State Univ, East Lansing, 90-97. *Concurrent Pos:* Vpres, Von-Sol Consults, Lincoln, 80-82; prin, Von Bernuth Agr; consult, Knoxville, E Lansing, 82-; regist prof engr, Calif & Nebr. *Mem:* Am Soc Civil Engrs; Am Soc Agr Engrs; Irrigation Asn. *Res:* Irrigation management; sprinkler irrigation design; effects of wind on sprinkler irrigation; microclimate modification by irrigation; nutrient management, nutrient balance. *Mailing Add:* Mich State Univ Agr Eng 215 Farrall Hall East Lansing MI 48824

**VON BODUNGEN, GEORGE ANTHONY,** PHYSICAL CHEMISTRY. *Current Pos:* Sr res chemist, 66-80, PROCESS DEVELOP GROUP LEADER, COPOLYMER RUBBER & CHEM CORP, 80- *Personal Data:* b New Orleans, La, Oct 12, 40; m 69; c 3. *Educ:* Loyola Univ, New Orleans, 62; Tulane Univ La, PhD(phys chem), 66. *Mem:* Soc Plastics Engrs. *Res:* Synthesis and rheology of impact resistant plastics and thermo plastic elastomers; computer simulations and mathematical models of process and products; applied mathematics; development and scale-up of emulsion products and processes. *Mailing Add:* 1157 Tara Blvd Baton Rouge LA 70806-7824

**VON BORSTEL, ROBERT CARSTEN,** GENETICS, BIOPHYSICS. *Current Pos:* chmn dept, Univ Alta, 71-81, prof, 71-92, McCalla res prof, 84-85, EMER PROF GENETICS, UNIV ALTA, 92- *Personal Data:* b Kent, Ore, Jan 24, 25; m 48, Patricia Crutcher; c Robert C II & Reid W. *Educ:* Ore State Col, BA, 47, MS, 49; Univ Pa, PhD(zool), 53. *Hon Degrees:* DSc, York Univ, 87. *Honors & Awards:* Award Excellence, Genetics Soc Can, 83. *Prof Exp:* Fel, Carnegie Inst, NY, 52-53; biologist, Oak Ridge Nat Lab, 53-71. *Concurrent Pos:* NSF fel, Univ Pavia, 59-60; prof biomed sci, Univ Tenn, 69-71; mem, Basel Inst Immunol, 81-82 & 87-89; vis prof, Univ Parma, 90 & Univ Saleburg, 96. *Mem:* Genetics Soc Am; AAAS; Genetic Soc Can (pres, 79-80); Int Asn Environ Mutagen Socs (secy, 73-78); Am Environ Mutagen Soc; Radiation Res Soc. *Res:* Dominant lethality and cell-killing by radiation; microorganism genetics; spontaneous mutation rates; mutator genes in yeast; antimutagenesis. *Mailing Add:* 12312 Grandview Dr Edmonton AB T6H 4K4 Can. *Fax:* 403-492-1903; *E-Mail:* rc.von_borstel@ualberta.ca

**VON BUN, FRIEDRICH OTTO,** PHYSICS, MATHEMATICS. *Current Pos:* RETIRED. *Personal Data:* b Vienna, Austria, June 22, 25; US citizen; m 52; c 2. *Educ:* Vienna Tech Univ, MS, 52; Graz Tech Univ, PhD(physics, math), 56. *Prof Exp:* Physicist, US Army Signal Corps, 53-57, chief, Molecular Beam Sect, Atomic Resonance Br, 57-59, sr scientist & dir, Frequency Control Div, 59-60; consult, Tracking & Data Systs Directorate, NASA, 60-61, head, Plans Off, 61-63, chief, Systs Anal Off, 63-65, Mission Anal Off, 65-67, Mission & Trajectory Anal Div, 67-71, Trajectory Anal & Geodyn Div, Mission & Data Opers Directorate, 71-72, Geodyn Prog Div, Goddard Space Flight Ctr, 72-82, asst dir appl sci, Appln Directorate, 74-79. *Concurrent Pos:* Mem, Panel Tracking & Data Anal, Nat Acad Sci, 63-65; spec adv, Range Tech Adv Group, 66-; mem, Steering Comt, Working Group 1, COSPAR, 72-; chmn, Working Group Earth & Ocean Dynamics, Int Astronaut Fedn, 75 & Working Group Global Data Collection, 76. *Mem:* Assoc fel Am Inst Aeronaut & Astronaut; Am Geophys Union; Int Astronaut Fedn. *Res:* Space systems analysis; navigation; geodynamics; ocean dynamics; gravity and magnetic field studies; active and passive microwave observations of the Earth's surface from space; application of space science and technology toward solutions of practical problems. *Mailing Add:* 12506 White Dr Silver Spring MD 20904-3532

**VONDERHAAR, BARBARA KAY,** ENDOCRINOLOGY. *Current Pos:* cancer expert, Nat Cancer Inst, 76-80, sr res chemist, Lab Pathophysiol, 80-85, sr res chemist, 85-93, SECT CHIEF, LAB TUMOR IMMUNOL BIOL, NAT CANCER INST, 93- *Personal Data:* b Des Moines, Iowa, July 4, 43; m 74, Brendan A McShane; c Justin & Kevin. *Educ:* Clarke Col, BA, 65; Univ Wis-Madison, PhD(oncol), 70. *Honors & Awards:* NIH Award of Merit, 95. *Prof Exp:* Fel, McArdle Lab Cancer Res, 70-71; staff fel, Nat Inst Arthritis, Metab & Digestive Dis, 71-73, sr staff fel, 73-76. *Concurrent Pos:* Assoc ed, Cancer Res, 85-89; mem coun, Gordon Res Conf, 85-88; mem comt, Mammary Gland Biol & Lactation, 85-97; Buroughs Wellcome vis prof, Clarke Col, Dubuque, Iowa, 84-85; bd gov, Int Asn Breast Cancer Res, 91-97; assoc ed, J Mammary Gland Biol & Neoplasma, 95- *Mem:* AAAS; Endocrine Soc; Am Soc Cell Biol; Am Soc Biochem & Molecular Biol; Int Asn Breast Cancer Res; Am Asn Cancer Res. *Res:* Multiple hormone interactions in mammary gland development and milk protein production; the effects of neonatal hormone treatment on development of mammary glands and tumor formation; thyroid hormone and prolactin interactions in breast development and tumorigenesis. *Mailing Add:* NIH Bldg 10 Rm 5B56 Bethesda MD 20892-1402. *Fax:* 301-402-0711; *E-Mail:* barbarav@helix.nih.gov

**VONDER HAAR, THOMAS HENRY,** METEOROLOGY, SPACE SCIENCE. *Current Pos:* assoc prof, 70-77, actg dean, Col Eng, 82, HEAD DEPT, COLO STATE UNIV, 74-, PROF ATMOSPHERIC SCI, 77-, DIR, COOP INST RES, 80-, PROF & DIR, CIRA. *Personal Data:* b Quincy, Ill, Dec 28, 42; m 80, Dee M Clark; c Kim, Kurt, Nicholas, Krista & Matthew. *Educ:* St Louis Univ, BS, 63; Univ Wis-Madison, MS, 64, PhD(meteorol), 68. *Honors & Awards:* Second Half Century Award, Am Meteorol Soc, 81. *Prof Exp:* Assoc scientist meteorol, Space Sci & Eng Ctr, Univ Wis, 68-70. *Concurrent Pos:* Consult, US Army, McDonnell-Douglas Corp, Ball Bros & Res Corp, 69-, NASA & Sci Tech Corp; mem int radiation comn, Int Union Geod & Geophys, 75; mem climate res comt, Nat Acad Sci, Bd Atmospheric Sci & Climate; Haltiner res chair, USN Postgrad Sch, 87. *Mem:* Am Meteorol Soc; Sigma Xi. *Res:* Application of measurements from meteorological satellites to problems of atmospheric and environmental science; radiation measurement; air pollution; weather forecasting. *Mailing Add:* Atmospheric Sci Colo State Univ Ft Collins CO 80523-0001. *E-Mail:* vonderhaar@phobos.cira.colostate.edu

**VONDRA, CARL FRANK,** GEOLOGY. *Current Pos:* from asst prof to assoc prof, 63-71, PROF GEOL, IOWA STATE UNIV, 71- *Personal Data:* b Seward, Nebr, June 3, 34; m 55; c 4. *Educ:* Univ Nebr, BS, 56, MS, 58, PhD(geol), 63. *Prof Exp:* Develop geologist, Calif Co, 61-62; geologist, Pan Am Petrol Corp, 62-63. *Mem:* Geol Soc Am; Am Asn Petrol Geol; Paleont Soc; Soc Vert Paleont; Soc Econ Paleont & Mineral. *Res:* Stratigraphy of the Eocene deposits of the Big Horn Basin, Wyoming; stratigraphy of the upper Eocene and Oligocene deposits of Egypt; stratigraphy of the Siwalik deposits in northern India; stratigraphy and sedimentation of the Plio-Pleistocene deposits in the East Rudolf Basin, Kenya. *Mailing Add:* Dept Geol Iowa State Univ Ames IA 50011-2010

**VONDRAK, EDWARD ANDREW,** MATHEMATICS. *Current Pos:* from asst prof to assoc prof, 67-72, PROF PHYSICS & MATH, UNIV INDIANAPOLIS, 72- *Personal Data:* b Chicago, Ill, Nov 12, 38; m 61; c 3. *Educ:* Knox Col, AB, 60; Vanderbilt Univ, MA, 63, PhD(physics), 65. *Prof Exp:* Teaching fel physics, Vanderbilt Univ, 61-64. *Mem:* Am Asn Physics Teachers; Math Asn Am. *Mailing Add:* 8219 Burn Ct Indianapolis IN 46217-4967

**VON DREELE, MARGARET M,** PHYSIOLOGY. *Current Pos:* ASSOC PROF NURSING, ORE HEALTH SCI UNIV, 88- *Personal Data:* b Pittsburgh, Pa, Apr 9, 37. *Educ:* Duke Univ, BS, 59; Univ Calif, San Francisco, MS, 63; Univ Cincinnati, PhD(physiol), 76. *Prof Exp:* Assoc prof nursing, Rush Presby Med Sch, 82-88. *Mem:* Am Physiol Soc; AAAS; Am Heart Asn; Am Soc Hypertension. *Res:* Physiology. *Mailing Add:* Community Health Care Syst Ore Health Sci Univ 3181 SW Sam Jackson Park Rd Portland OR 97201-2984

**VON DREELE, ROBERT BRUCE,** SOLID STATE CHEMISTRY, CRYSTALLOGRAPHY. *Current Pos:* STAFF MEM, LOS ALAMOS NAT LAB, 86- *Personal Data:* b Minneapolis, Minn, Dec 10, 43; m 78; c 1. *Educ:* Cornell Univ, BS, 66, PhD(chem), 71. *Prof Exp:* From asst prof to prof chem,

Ariz State Univ, 71-86. *Concurrent Pos:* NSF fel, Dept Inorg Chem, Oxford Univ, 72-73; Fulbright fel, Rutherford Lab, 86. *Mem:* Am Crystallog Asn; Sigma Xi. *Res:* Neutron scattering x-ray crystal structure analysis; solid state chemistry; powder diffraction. *Mailing Add:* 3841 Villa St Los Alamos NM 87544

**VONEIDA, THEODORE J,** NEUROBIOLOGY. *Current Pos:* PROF & CHMN, NEUROBIOL DEPT, COL MED, NORTHEASTERN OHIO UNIV, 76- *Personal Data:* b Auburn, NY, Aug 26, 30; m 56, Swanhild Bekkedahl; c Dorianne, James & Audrey. *Educ:* Ithaca Col, BS, 53; Cornell Univ, MEd, 54, PhD(zool), 60. *Honors & Awards:* Environ Qual Award, Environ Protection Agency, 74. *Prof Exp:* Res assoc neuroanat, Walter Reed Army Inst Res, 54-56; asst comp neurol, Cornell Univ, 56-59; USPHS res fel neurobiol, Calif Inst Technol, 60-62; from asst prof to prof, Sch Med, Case Western Res Univ, 62-76. *Concurrent Pos:* adj prof anat & biol, Case Western Res Univ, 76-; vis lectr, Hawaii Col Med, 82. *Mem:* Am Asn Anatomists; Soc Neurosci; Sigma Xi; Int Coun Human Duties. *Res:* Utilization of neuroanatomical and behavioral techniques to investigate the central nervous system. *Mailing Add:* Northeastern Ohio Univ Col Med PO Box 95 Rootstown OH 44272-0095. *Fax:* 440-325-2524

**VON ESCHEN, GARVIN L(EONARD),** aeronautical engineering, for more information see previous edition

**VON ESSEN, CARL FRANCOIS,** RADIOTHERAPY & ONCOLOGY. *Current Pos:* PROF, MED FAC, UNIV BASEL, SWITZ, 82-; ADJ PROF, RADIATION MED, BROWN UNIV, PROVIDENCE, RI, 85- *Personal Data:* b Tokyo, Japan, May 17, 26; nat US; m 79, Manisha Roy; c 3. *Educ:* Stanford Univ, AB, 48, MD, 52; Am Bd Radiol, dipl, 58. *Honors & Awards:* Swiss Cancer Prize, 81. *Prof Exp:* Res fel cancer, Stanford Univ, 57-59; from instr to assoc prof radiol, Yale Univ, 59-69; prof radiol & oncol & dir radiation ther, Univ Calif, San Diego, 69-77; res prof radiol, Univ NMex, 77-78; leader, Pion Ther Proj, Swiss Inst Nuclear Res, 78-84. *Concurrent Pos:* Vis prof, Christian Med Col, Vellore, India, 65-66; mem rev comt, Radiation Study Sect, NIH, 67-69 & Cancer Res Ctr, 70-74; mem staff, Ludwig Inst Cancer Res, 75-76; WHO consult, Sri Lanka, 84-85, Zimbabwe & Jordan, 88; clin assoc radiation med, Mass Gen Hosp, 85-; dir, Dept Radiation Oncol, Southwood Community Hosp, Norfolk, Mass, 85- *Mem:* Am Soc Ther Radiologists; Europ Soc Therapeut Radiol Oncol; emer fel Am Col Radiol. *Res:* Organization of postgraduate training programs in oncology and radiotherapy in developing countries. *Mailing Add:* 34 Register Rd Southwood Community Hosp Marion MA 02738. *Fax:* 508-748-6793; *E-Mail:* essenrog@pop.tiac.net

**VON EULER, LEO HANS,** PATHOLOGY. *Current Pos:* scientist, Sect Nutrit Biochem, Nat Inst Arthritis & Metab Dis, 66-67, prog adminr path res training progs, 67-72, spec asst to dir, 72-74, DEP DIR, NAT INST GEN MED SCI, 74-, ACTG DIR, PHYSIOL & BIOMED ENG PROG, 78- *Personal Data:* b Stockholm, Sweden, Jan 31, 31; US citizen; c 2. *Educ:* Williams Col, BA, 52; Yale Univ, MD, 59. *Prof Exp:* Trainee path, Sch Med, Yale Univ, 59-61, trainee pharmacol, 61-63; fel hemat, Dept Clin Path, NIH, 65-66. *Mem:* Am Asn Path. *Res:* Purine and pyrimidine metabolism; orotic acid induced fatty liver in the rat; biochemical and histological changes. *Mailing Add:* 5900 Ramsgate Rd Bethesda MD 20816

**VON GIERKE, HENNING EDGAR,** BIOACOUSTICS, BIOMECHANICS. *Current Pos:* consult, Wright-Patterson AFB, 47-54, chief, Bioacoust Br, 54-63, dir, Biodynamics & Bionics Div, 63-88, EMER DIR, BIODYNAMICS & BIOCOMMUN DIV, ARMSTRONG LAB, WRIGHT PATTERSON AFB, 88- *Personal Data:* b Karlsruhe, Ger, May 22, 17; US citizen; m 50, Hanlo Weil; c Karin J & Susanne M. *Educ:* Karlsruhe Tech, Dipl Ing, 43, DrEng, 44. *Honors & Awards:* Eric LiljenKrantz Award, Aerospace Med Asn, 66 & Arnold D Tuttle Award, 74; Hubertus Strughold Medal, 80; Silver Medal, Acoust Soc Am, 81; H R Lissner Award, Am Soc Mech Engrs, 83; Rayleigh Medal, UK Inst Acoust, 89. *Prof Exp:* Asst acoust, Inst Theoret Elec Eng & Commun Techniques, Karlsruhe Tech, 44-47, lectr, 46. *Concurrent Pos:* Mem comt hearing bioacoust & biomech, Nat Res Coun, 53-93; mem bioastronaut comt, 59-61; mem adv comt flight med & biol, NASA, 60-61; assoc prof, Ohio State Univ, 63-89; mem, White House Ad Hoc Panel Jet Aircraft Noise, 66; clin prof, Sch Med, Wright State Univ, 80- *Mem:* Nat Acad Eng; fel Aerospace Med Asn (vpres, 66-67); hon fel Inst Environ Sci; Int Acad Astronaut; fel Acoust Soc Am (pres, 78); Int Acad Aviation & Space Med; Inst Noise Control Eng; Biomed Eng Soc; fel Am Inst Med & Biol Eng. *Res:* Physical, physiological and psychological acoustics; biodynamics; effects of noise, vibration and impact on man; communication biophysics; bionics; bioengineering; author of over 160 technical publications, book chapters. *Mailing Add:* 1325 Meadow Lane Yellow Springs OH 45387. *Fax:* 937-767-2181

**VON GOELER, EBERHARD,** HIGH ENERGY PHYSICS INSTRUMENTATION. *Current Pos:* from asst prof to assoc prof, 63-73, PROF PHYSICS, NORTHEASTERN UNIV, 73- *Personal Data:* b Berlin, Ger, Feb 22, 30; m 60, Marleen D Poole; c Friedel, John & Katherine. *Educ:* Univ Ill, MS, 55, PhD(physics), 61. *Prof Exp:* Res assoc physics, Univ Ill, 60-61; res scientist, Deutsches Elektronen Synchrotron, Hamburg, Ger, 61-63. *Concurrent Pos:* Vis prof, Univ Hamburg, 67-68; vis scientist, Nat Accelerator Lab, Ill, 71-72 & Stanford Linear Accelerator, Calif, 78-79; exec officer, Physics Dept, Northeastern Univ, 80-81; vis prof, Univ Houston, 86-87. *Mem:* Am Phys Soc. *Res:* Surface physics; tests of quantum electrodynamics; photoproduction of vector mesons, antibaryons; meson spectroscopy; high mass bosons; colliding electron beam experiments; non-accelerator elementary particle physics; nucleon spin-structure functions; counter techniques in high energy physics; hadron collider physics. *Mailing Add:* 111 Dana Res Ctr Northeastern Univ Boston MA 02115. *Fax:* 617-373-2943; *E-Mail:* evg@neu.edu

**VON GOELER, SCHWEICKHARD E,** PLASMA PHYSICS. *Current Pos:* Res assoc, Princeton Plasma Physics Lab, Princeton Univ, 64-66, res staff, 66-69, res physicist, 69-77, PRIN RES PHYSICIST, PRINCETON PLASMA PHYSICS LAB, PRINCETON UNIV, 77- *Personal Data:* b Berlin, Ger, 1931; m 63, Adelheid Gradmann; c Hanna, Ruth & Dorothea. *Educ:* Marburg Univ, Ger, PhD(physics), 64. *Honors & Awards:* Excellence Plasma Res Award, Am Phys Soc, 84; Sr Scientist Award, Alexander von Humboldt Soc, 86. *Concurrent Pos:* Lectr, Princeton Univ, 77-92. *Mem:* Fel Am Phys Soc. *Res:* Plasma physics associated with magnetic nuclear fusion devices in particular the x-ray and neutron emission from high temperature plasmas. *Mailing Add:* Princeton Plasma Physics Lab Princeton Univ PO Box 451 Princeton NJ 08543. *Fax:* 609-243-2160; *E-Mail:* svongoeler@pppl.gov

**VON GUTFELD, ROBERT J,** SOLID STATE PHYSICS. *Current Pos:* RES STAFF MEM, T J WATSON RES CTR, IBM CORP, 60- *Personal Data:* b Berlin, Ger, Mar 5, 34; US citizen; m 77, Deanna Kropfl; c Andrew & Sonia. *Educ:* Queens Col, BS, 54; Columbia Univ, MA, 57; NY Univ, PhD(physics), 65. *Honors & Awards:* Res Award, Electrochem Soc, 84. *Prof Exp:* Substitute instr physics, Queens Col, 54-55; engr, Sperry Gyroscope Co, 57-60. *Mem:* Fel Am Phys Soc; Electrochem Soc; Optical Soc Am. *Res:* Thermal transport in solids using heat pulse techniques; amorphous semiconductor and dye laser research and applications to optical memories; transverse thermoelectric effects in metallic thin films; laser thermoelastic waves; laser enhanced plating and etching; electrochemical techniques for repair of microcircuits. *Mailing Add:* T J Watson Res Ctr IBM Corp Yorktown Heights NY 10598. *E-Mail:* vong@watson.ibm.com

**VON HAGEN, D STANLEY,** PHARMACOLOGY. *Current Pos:* instr, 67-69, ASST PROF PHARMACOL, NJ MED SCH, COL MED & DENT, NJ, 69- *Personal Data:* b Nashville, Tenn, Dec 21, 37; m 59; c 2. *Educ:* Carson-Newman Col, BS, 59; Vanderbilt Univ, PhD(pharmacol), 65. *Prof Exp:* Res assoc pharmacol, Vanderbilt Univ, 65-66, instr, 66. *Mem:* AAAS; NY Acad Sci; Sigma Xi. *Res:* Smooth muscle physiology and pharmacology; physiological role of calcium ion in smooth muscle function. *Mailing Add:* Dept Pharmacol NJ Col Med 185 S Orange Ave I Level South Orange NJ 07103-2714. *Fax:* 973-456-4554; *E-Mail:* vonhagen@njmsa.umdnj.edu

**VON HERZEN, RICHARD P,** MARINE GEOPHYSICS. *Current Pos:* assoc scientist, Woods Hole Oceanog Inst, 66-73, chmn, sr scientist, 73-96, Dept Geol & Geophys, 82-85, EMER SCIENTIST, WOODS HOLE OCEANOG INST, 96- *Personal Data:* b Los Angeles, Calif, May 21, 30; m 58, Janice Rutter; c Brian & Lane. *Educ:* Calif Inst Technol, BS, 52; Harvard Univ, AM, 56; Univ Calif, PhD(oceanog), 60. *Prof Exp:* Lab asst oceanog, Scripps Inst Oceanog, 52-53, geophysicist, 58-60, asst res geophysicist, 60-64; dep dir, Off Oceanog, UNESCO, 64-66. *Concurrent Pos:* Assoc ed, J Geophys Res, Am Geophys Union, 69-71; vis res geophysicist & lectr, Scripps Inst Oceanog, 74-75; vis prof & lectr, Mass Inst Technol, 82; pres, Tectonophysics Sect, Am Geophys Union, 86-88. *Mem:* Fel Am Geophys Union. *Res:* Structure and dynamics of the earth beneath the ocean floor especially as evidenced from geothermal studies. *Mailing Add:* Woods Hole Oceanog Inst Woods Hole MA 02543

**VON HIPPEL, ARTHUR R,** MOLECULAR ENGINEERING. *Current Pos:* RETIRED. *Personal Data:* b Rockstock MecKlenburg, EGer, Nov 19, 1898; wid; c 5. *Educ:* Univ Gottingen, PhD, 24. *Prof Exp:* Prof molecular sci, Gottingen Univ, 26-34; prof, Nils Bohr Lab, Copenhagen, 35-36; prof molecular sci, Lab Insulation Res, Mass Inst Technol, 36-85, emer prof, 85- *Mem:* Nat Acad Eng; Am Phys Soc; AAAS. *Mailing Add:* 265 Glen Rd Weston MA 02193

**VON HIPPEL, FRANK NIELS,** THEORETICAL PHYSICS, NUCLEAR NONPROLIFERATION. *Current Pos:* ASST DIR NAT SECURITY, OFF SCI & TECHNOL POLICY, EXEC OFF PRES, 93- *Personal Data:* b Cambridge, Mass, Dec 26, 37; m 87, Patricia Bardi; c Paul. *Educ:* Mass Inst Technol, SB, 59; Oxford Univ, DPhil(physics), 62. *Honors & Awards:* Am Phys Soc Award, 77; Pub Interest Award, Fedn Am Scientists, 90; Arms Control Prize, ΛΛΛS, 94. *Prof Exp:* Res assoc physics, Univ Chicago, 62-64; res assoc, Cornell Univ, 64-66; asst prof, Stanford Univ, 66-70; mem staff theory group, High Energy Physics Div, Argonne Nat Lab, 70-73; resident fel, Nat Acad Sci, 73-74; res scientist, Princeton Univ, 74-78, sr res physicist, Ctr Environ Studies, 78-83, prof pub & int affairs, 83-93. *Concurrent Pos:* Sloan Found fel, 67-70; consult nuclear energy policy, Off Technol Assessment, Gen Acct Off, House Interior Comt, US Cong, Nuclear Regulatory Comn, Dept Energy, 75; chmn, Fedn Am Scientists Fund, 86-93, 95- *Mem:* Am Phys Soc; AAAS; Fedn Am Scientists. *Res:* Nuclear energy policy; energy general policy; nuclear arms control, nonproliferation and disarmament. *Mailing Add:* Dept Pub Int Affairs Princeton Univ Princeton NJ 08544. *Fax:* 609-258-3661; *E-Mail:* fvhippel@princeton.edu

**VON HIPPEL, PETER HANS,** BIOPHYSICAL CHEMISTRY, MOLECULAR BIOLOGY. *Current Pos:* res assoc, Univ Ore, 67-69, dir, Inst Molecular Biol, 69-80, chmn dept, 80-86, PROF CHEM, UNIV ORE, 67- *Personal Data:* b Gottingen, Ger, Mar 13, 31; US citizen; m 54, Josephine; c David F, James A & Benjamin J. *Educ:* Mass Inst Technol, BS, 52, MS, 53, PhD(biophys), 55. *Honors & Awards:* Merit Res Award, NIH, 88. *Prof Exp:* Asst phys biochem, Mass Inst Technol, 53, NIH fel, 55-56; phys biochemist, US Naval Med Res Inst, Md, 56-59; from asst prof to assoc prof biochem, Dartmouth Med Sch, 59-67. *Concurrent Pos:* Sr fel, NIH, 59-67; chmn, Gordon Res Conf Physics & Phys Chem Biopolymers, 68; Guggenheim Found fel, 73-74; mem, Corp Vis Comt, Dept Biol, Mass Inst Technol, 73-77; mem bd sci counr, Nat Inst Arthritis, Metab & Digestive Dis, NIH, 74-78; mem coun, Inst Gen Med Sci, NIH, 81-86; ed, J Molecular Biol, 86-94; mem adv comt to dir, NIH, 87-92; res prof, Am Cancer Soc, 89-; bd dirs, Fedn Am Soc Exp Biol, 94-, Faconi Anemia Res Fund, 97- *Mem:* Nat Acad Sci; AAAS; Biophys Soc (pres, 73-74); Am Soc Biol Chem; Am Chem Soc; Soc Gen Physiol; fel Am Acad Arts & Sci; Sigma Xi; Am Asn Univ Profs; Am Soc Biochem & Molecular Biol; Fedn Am Scientists. *Res:* Physical biochemistry of macromolecules; structure, function and interactions of proteins and nucleic acids; molecular aspects of control of genetic expression. *Mailing Add:* Inst Molecular Biol & Dept Chem Univ Ore Eugene OR 97403

**VON HOERNER, SEBASTIAN,** ASTRONOMY, ENGINEERING. *Current Pos:* RETIRED. *Personal Data:* b Goerlitz, Ger, Apr 15, 19; m 42; c 3. *Educ:* Univ Gottingen, Ger, dipl, 49, PhD(physics), 51. *Honors & Awards:* Alexander von Humboldt Award, 84. *Prof Exp:* Scientist astrophys, Max Planck Inst Physics, Gottingen, 49-57; Fulbright fel, Mt Wilson & Palomar Observ, Pasadena, Calif, 55-56; scientist, Astron Rechen-Inst, Heidelberg, Ger, 57-62; scientist astrophys & eng, Nat Radio Astron Observ, Green Bank, 62-85. *Concurrent Pos:* Vis prof, Univ Switz, 62, Univ Calif, Los Angeles, 69, Nat Univ, Mexico City, 71, Max Planck Inst Radioastron, Bonn, 72 & 75, Cornell Univ, Ithaca, NY, 74 & Univ Okla, Norman, 77; eng consult, 85- *Mem:* Deut Astron Gesellschaft; Max-Planck-Gesellschaft; Ver Deut Wiss; Int Astron Union; Union Concerned Scientists. *Res:* Astrophysics, star formation, stellar dynamics; radio astronomy, cosmology; antenna design, structural optimization; life in space; interstellar communication. *Mailing Add:* Krummenacker-Str 186 73733 Esslingen Germany

**VON HUENE, ROLAND,** geology, for more information see previous edition

**VON HUNGEN, KERN,** NEUROCHEMISTRY, PSYCHOPHARMACOLOGY. *Current Pos:* res chemist, Neurochem Lab, 76-79, CHIEF, BRAIN BIOCHEM LAB, VET ADMIN MED CTR, SEPULVEDA, CALIF, 79- *Personal Data:* b Modesto, Calif, May 2, 40; m 67; c 2. *Educ:* Reed Col, BA, 62; Ind Univ, PhD(biol chem), 68. *Prof Exp:* Fel neurobiochem, Chem Biodynamics Lab, Univ Calif, Berkeley, 68-70; fel neurobiochem, Dept Biol Chem, Univ Calif, Los Angeles, 70-71. *Concurrent Pos:* Asst res biochemist, Dept Biol Chem, Univ Calif, Los Angeles, 71- *Mem:* Am Soc Neurochem. *Res:* Functional neurochemistry: regulatory mechanisms involving brain membranes, proteins, neurotransmitters and cyclic nucleotides and the effects of alcohol and age on these systems; biochemical aspects of behavior. *Mailing Add:* 897 Chattanooga Ave Pacific Palisades CA 90272

**VON KLITZING, KLAUS,** SOLID STATE PHYSICS. *Current Pos:* DIR, MAX-PLANCK INST SOLID RES, STUTTGARD, 85- *Personal Data:* b Schroda, Ger, June 28, 43. *Educ:* Technische Univ Braunschweig, 69; Univ Wurzburg, PhD, 72. *Hon Degrees:* Dr, chemnitz, Md, Antwerp, Monpellier, Bath, Tsukuba. *Honors & Awards:* Nobel Prize in Physics, 85; Schottky Prize, 81; Hewlett Packard Prize, 82. *Prof Exp:* Prof physics, Technische Univ, Munich, 80-85. *Mem:* Nat Acad Sci. *Res:* Semiconductor quantumstructures. *Mailing Add:* Max-Planck Inst fur Festkorperforschung Heisenbergstr 1 Postfach 800665 70569 Stuttgart Germany

**VON KORFF, RICHARD WALTER,** BIOCHEMISTRY, ENZYMOLOGY. *Current Pos:* RETIRED. *Personal Data:* b Davenport, Iowa, Jan 6, 16; wid; c Gerald W, Michael R & Lynn A. *Educ:* Univ Minn, BA, 47, PhD(physiol chem), 51; Am Bd Clin Chem, dipl, 74. *Prof Exp:* Anal chemist, Testing & Res Lab, Deere & Co, Moline, Ill, 37-41; asst & sr sci aide, Anal & Phys Chem Div, Northern Regional Res Lab, USDA, 41-43, jr chemist, Agr Residues Div, Peoria, Ill, 43-45; asst prof pediat & physiol chem, Univ Minn, 55-66; dir biochem res, Friends of Psychiat Res, Spring Grove State Hosp, Baltimore, Md, 66-68; dir biochem res, Md Psychiat Res Ctr, Baltimore, 68-77; res prof biochem, Mich Molecular Inst, Midland, Mich, 77-85. *Concurrent Pos:* Fel, Inst Enzyme Res, Univ Wis, 51-52; Whitney Found fel biochem, Dept Pediat, Heart Hosp, Univ Minn, 52-53, Am Heart Asn fel, 53-55, USPHS sr res fel biochem, 60-66; chmn subcomt enzymes, Comt Biol Chem, Nat Acad Sci-Nat Res Coun, 61-67 & 69-76, adj prof, Dept Med Chem, Sch Pharm, Univ Md, Baltimore, 71-73; adj assoc prof, Dept Macromolecular Sci, Case-Western Univ, 79-84; adj prof, Dept Biochem, Dent Sch, Univ Md, 75-77; adj prof dept chem, Cent Mich Univ, 80-85. *Mem:* Am Soc Biol Chemists; Am Chem Soc; Nat Acad Clin Biochem; Int Soc Neurochem; Am Soc Neurochem. *Res:* Monoamine oxidase, reaction mechanism, nature of action of reversible inhibitors; enzymic control mechanisms; monoamine oxidase. *Mailing Add:* 15 Rosemary Ct Midland MI 48640

**VON LEDEN, HANS VICTOR,** LARYNGOLOGY. *Current Pos:* prof biocommun, 66-86, EMER PROF BIOCOMMUN, UNIV SOUTHERN CALIF, 86-; PVT PRACT, 86- *Personal Data:* b Ger, Nov 20, 18; nat US; m 48, Mary Louise Shine; c Jon E & Lisa M (van Houten). *Educ:* Loyola Univ, Ill, MD, 42; Am Bd Otolaryngol, dipl, 45. *Honors & Awards:* Bucranio, Univ Padua, 58; Gold Medal, Ital Res Cross, 59; Hektoen Medal, AMA, 60; Sci Awards, Am Speech & Hearing Asn, 60, 62 & 65; Casselberry Award, Am Laryngol Asn, 62; Manuel Garcia Prize, Int Asn Logoped & Phoniatrics, 68; Gutzmann Medal, Ger Soc Otolaryngol, 80; Sci Achievement Award, AMA, 80; Golden Award, Int Fedn Oto-Rhino-Laryngol Socs, 89; Award for Monumental Contributions to Sci & Med, Voice Found, 94. *Prof Exp:* Intern, Mercy Hosp-Loyola Univ Clins, 41-42; resident, Presby Hosp, Chicago, 42-43; fel otolaryngol & plastic surg, Mayo Found, Univ Minn, 43-45, first asst, Mayo Clin, 45; clin assoc otolaryngol, Stritch Sch Med, Loyola Univ, Ill, 47-51; from asst prof to assoc prof, Sch Med, Northwestern Univ, 52-61; assoc prof surg, Sch Med, Univ Calif, Los Angeles, 61-66. *Concurrent Pos:* Consult, USN, 47-; assoc prof, Cook County Grad Sch Med, 49-58; med dir, William & Harriet Gould Found, 55-59; pres, Inst Laryngol & Voice Dis, 59-65, med dir, 65-; vis prof, US & 27 foreign countries. *Mem:* Fel AAAS; fel Am Acad

Otolaryngol; fel Am Col Surgeons; fel Int Col Surgeons (pres, 72); fel Am Speech & Hearing Asn; Sigma Xi. *Res:* Voice and speech; laryngology. *Mailing Add:* 8631 W Third St Suite 625-E Los Angeles CA 90048-5910. *Fax:* 310-471-9963

**VON LICHTENBERG, FRANZ,** PATHOLOGY OF INFECTIOUS DISEASES. *Current Pos:* instr, Harvard Med Sch, 58-59, assoc, 59-62, from asst prof to assoc prof, 62-74, PROF PATH, HARVARD MED SCH, 74- *Personal Data:* b Miskolc, Hungary, Nov 29, 19; nat US; m 49, Sandra; c 6. *Educ:* Nat Univ Mex, MD, 45; Am Bd Path, dipl, 51. *Hon Degrees:* Dr, Nat Univ Nicaragua, 59; MA, Harvard Univ, 68. *Prof Exp:* Pathologist, Hosp Exp Nutrit, Mex, 47; prof path, Nat Univ Mex, 48-52; from asst prof to assoc prof, Univ PR, 53-58. *Concurrent Pos:* Fel, Mex Dept Health, 46; fels, Kellogg Found, Am Col Physicians & Latin Am, 50-51; pathologist, Clin Hosp, Bahia, Brazil, 51-52; Gen Hosp, Mex, 52-53 & San Juan City Hosp, PR, 53-58; assoc pathologist, Peter Bent Brigham Hosp, 58-62; sr assoc, 62-68, pathologist, 68-81, sr pathologist, 82; assoc mem comn parasitol, Armed Forces Epidemiol Bd, 59, mem, 64-71; consult, Div Parasitic Dis, WHO, 65; mem study sect trop med & parasitol, NIH, 68-73; mem steering comn Schistosomiasis, WHO-TDR, 77- (chmn, 83); James W McLaughlin vis prof, Univ Tex Med Br, 80; Theobald Smith Lectr, NY Soc Trop Med, 80; Fogarty Scholar-in-Residence, NIHFIC, 83, 85; Wellcome lectr, London, 86; Costero lectr, Mexico City, 93. *Mem:* Am Soc Trop Med & Hyg (vpres, 76, pres, 85); Am Asn Path; Fedn Am Socs Exp Biol. *Res:* Tropical and parasitic diseases; schistosomiasis; filariasis; liver pathology; immunopathology. *Mailing Add:* Brigham & Women's Hosp 75 Francis St Boston MA 02115. *Fax:* 617-277-9015; *E-Mail:* fvlichtenberg@bics.bwh.harvard.edu

**VON-LIEBIG, WILLIAM JOHN,** NEW PRODUCT DEVELOPMENT, WORLDWIDE DISTRIBUTION. *Current Pos:* PRES & CHIEF EXEC OFFICER, MEADOX MEDICALS, INC, 61-, DIR, 82- *Personal Data:* b Huntingdon, Pa, Mar 24, 23; m 78; c 1. *Educ:* Juanita Col, BS, 43; Augustana Col, 43; Univ Pa, 47; Philadelphia Col Textiles & Sci, MS, 49; New York Univ, MBA, 51. *Honors & Awards:* Gold Hektoen Award, AMA, 76. *Prof Exp:* Vpres & gen mgr, Meadox Weaving Co, 54-55; pres, Dormeyer Sales Corp, 55-60. *Concurrent Pos:* Fel, Augustana Col, Rock Island, Ill, 43 & Univ Pa, 47; div mgr, Susquehanna Mills, Inc, 49-54; div sales mgr, Webcor, Inc & Camfield, Inc, 55-60; chmn, Liebig Found, 61-; vpres & dir, Huntingdon Throwing Mills, 67-; dir, Meadox Ltd, UK, 78-, Brazil, 81-, Surgimed A-S, 82-, France, 83-, Deutschland GMBH, 86- *Mem:* Asn Advan Med Instrumentation; Health Indust Mfr's Asn. *Res:* Cardiac and vascular prosthetics, biological and synthetic, for surgical implant purposes. *Mailing Add:* Drax Holding LP 281 Broad Ave S Naples FL 34102

**VON MALTZAHN, WOLF W,** BIOMEDICAL INSTRUMENTATION & CLINICAL ENGINEERING, MEDICAL DEVICES. *Current Pos:* PROG DIR, BIOMED ENG RES GRANTS, WHITAKER FOUND, 95- *Personal Data:* b Ger, Oct 3, 46; m 73, Jane; c Philip, Geoffrey & Julia. *Educ:* Ohio State Univ, MS, 71; Univ Stuttgart, Ger, dipl elec eng, 74; Univ Hannover, Ger, Dr(biomed eng), 79. *Prof Exp:* Res assoc med instrumentation, Inst Biomed Eng, Univ Stuttgart, 71-74; asst prof physiol, Inst Physiol, Univ Essen, Ger, 74-79; from asst prof to assoc prof biomed & elec eng, Univ Tex, Arlington, 79-92, prof biomed eng, 92-94; prof elec eng & dir, Inst Biomed Eng, Univ Karlsruhe, Ger, 94-95. *Concurrent Pos:* Consult investr, St Elizabeth Hosp, Beaumont, 87; mem, forensic testing staff, St Michael's Hosp, 88 & P Chamblin, Weber & Mahaffy, Attorneys, 90. *Mem:* Sr mem Inst Elec & Electronics Engrs; Am Soc Eng Educ; Biomed Eng Soc; fel Am Inst Med & Biol Eng. *Res:* Invasive and noninvasive measurement of physiological variables in the human body. *Mailing Add:* Whitaker Found 1700 N Moore St Suite 2200 Rosslyn VA 22209

**VON MAYRHAUSER, ANNELIESE,** SOFTWARE MAINTENANCE, SOFTWARE TESTING & EVOLUTION. *Current Pos:* assoc prof, 91-94, PROF COMPUT SCI, COLO STATE UNIV, 94-; DIR, COLO ADVAN SOFTWARE INST, 96- *Personal Data:* b Waging, Ger, Apr 17, 52. *Educ:* Duke Univ, MS, 78, PhD(comput sci), 79. *Prof Exp:* From asst prof to assoc prof, Ill Inst Technol, 80-91. *Concurrent Pos:* Consult, AT&T Bell Labs, 86-87, Motorola, 91; researcher, BGS Systs, 82; bd gov, Inst Elec & Electronics Engrs Comput Soc, 91-93. *Mem:* Inst Elec & Electronics Engrs Comput Soc (vpres, 93-95); Inst Elec & Electronics Engrs Reliability Soc. *Res:* Software maintenance and evolution; software testing to increase efficiency and effectiveness of testing. *Mailing Add:* Dept Comput Sci Colo State Univ Ft Collins CO 80523. *Fax:* 970-491-2466; *E-Mail:* avm@cs.colostate.edu

**VON MEERWALL, ERNST DIETER,** PHYSICS. *Current Pos:* asst prof, 71-74, assoc prof, 74-80, PROF PHYSICS, UNIV AKRON, 80- *Personal Data:* b Vienna, Austria, Dec 29, 40. *Educ:* Northern Ill Univ, BS, 63, MS, 65; Northwestern Univ, Evanston, PhD(physics), 69. *Prof Exp:* Res assoc, Dept Metall & Mat Res Lab, Univ Ill, Urbana, 69-71. *Mem:* Am Phys Soc; Sigma Xi. *Res:* Solid state experiment; nuclear magnetic resonance, Mossbauer effect and magnetic susceptibility; alloys; nuclear quadrupole effect; polymers; numerical methods. *Mailing Add:* 4810 Ranchwood Rd Akron OH 44333-1342

**VON MOLNR, STEPHAN,** SEMICONDUCTORS, MAGNETISM. *Current Pos:* DIR, CTR MAT RES & TECHNOL & PROF PHYSICS, FLA STATE UNIV, 94- *Personal Data:* b Leipzig, Ger, June 26, 35; US citizen; m 56, Jean A Sullivan; c Christopher & Marc. *Educ:* Trinity Col, Conn, BS, 57; Univ Maine, MS, 59; Univ Calif, Riverside, PhD(physics), 65. *Honors & Awards:* Alexander von Humboldt Sr US Scientist Award, 86. *Prof Exp:* Mem res staff physics, Polychem Div, Exp Sta, E I du Pont de Nemours & Co, 59-60; mgr,

Coop Phenomena Group, IBM Res, 68-89, mem res staff physics, Thomas J Watson Res Ctr, IBM Corp, 65-93, sr mgr novel struct physics, 89-93. *Concurrent Pos:* Vis scientist, Cavendish Lab, Cambridge, 69; sr res fel, Imp Col, Univ London, 73-74; vis scientist, Nat Ctr Sci Res, Grenoble, 82 & 83 & Max-Planck Inst Solid State Physics, Stuttgart, Ger, 87; mem, Prog Adv Comt, Meson Physics Facil, Los Alamos Nat Lab, 84-87; mem, Pane Lon Diluted Magnetism Semiconductors, Comn Phys Sci, Nat Res Coun, 89-92. *Mem:* Fel Am Phys Soc; Mat Res Soc. *Res:* Paramagnetic and ferromagnetic resonance; transport, optical and magneto-optical properties of magnetic semiconductors; tunneling spectroscopy of superconductors and semiconductors; low temperature specific heat; fabrication and characterization of nano-magnets. *Mailing Add:* Ctr Mat Res & Technol Fla State Univ 406 Keen Bldg Tallahassee FL 32306. *Fax:* 850-644-6504; *E-Mail:* molnar@magnet.fsu.edu

**VONNEGUT, BERNARD,** PHYSICAL CHEMISTRY. *Current Pos:* PROF ATMOSPHERIC SCI, STATE UNIV NY, ALBANY, 67-, SR RES SCIENTIST, ATMOSPHERIC SCI RES CTR, 67- *Personal Data:* b Indianapolis, Ind, Aug 29, 14; wid; c 5. *Educ:* Mass Inst Technol, BS, 36, PhD(phys chem), 39. *Prof Exp:* Res assoc, Preston Labs, Pa, 39-40 & Hartford Empire Co, Conn, 40-41; chem eng, Mass Inst Technol, 41-42, meteorol, 42-45; res labs, Gen Elec Co, 45-52; mem staff, Arthur D Little Inc, 52-67. *Mem:* AAAS; Am Meteorol Soc; Am Geophys Union; Meteorol Soc Japan; Royal Meteorol Soc. *Res:* Nucleation phenomena; cloud seeding; surface chemistry; aerosols; atmospheric electricity. *Mailing Add:* Atmospheric Sci State Univ NY 1400 Washington Ave Albany NY 12222-1000

**VON NEIDA, ALLYN ROBERT,** METALLURGY, MATERIALS SCIENCE. *Current Pos:* DIR, ELECTRON SOURCE TECHNOL, LEPTON INC, 90- *Personal Data:* b West Reading, Pa, May 7, 32; m 55, Caryl Hart; c Philip, William & Anne. *Educ:* Lehigh Univ, BS(elec eng) & BS(metall eng), 55; Yale Univ, PhD(metall), 60. *Prof Exp:* Res metallurgist, Olin Mathieson Chem Corp, 55-57; res asst metall, Yale Univ, 60-61; mem tech staff, Bell Tel Labs, Murray Hill, 61-89. *Res:* Magnetics; crystal growth; field emission. *Mailing Add:* 133 Ashland Rd Summit NJ 07901

**VON NOORDEN, GUNTER KONSTANTIN,** OPHTHALMOLOGY. *Current Pos:* PROF OPHTHAL, BAYLOR COL MED, 72- *Personal Data:* b Frankfurt, Ger, Mar 19, 28; US citizen; c 1. *Educ:* Univ Frankfurt, MD, 54; State Univ Iowa, MS, 60. *Honors & Awards:* Hectoen Gold Medal, AMA, 60; Honor Award, Am Acad Ophthal & Otolaryngol, 70. *Prof Exp:* Rotating intern, St Vincent Infirmary, Little Rock, Ark, 54-56; fel ophthal, Cleveland Clin, 56-57; resident, Med Ctr, State Univ Iowa, 57-60, asst prof, Sch Med, 61-63; from assoc prof to prof, Johns Hopkins Univ, 63-72. *Concurrent Pos:* Nat Inst Neurol Dis & Blindness spec trainee, Univ Tubingen, 60-61; Nat Inst Neurol Dis & Blindness spec fel, Univ Iowa, 61-62; mem, Armed Forces Nat Res Coun Vision, 64-68; Int Strabismological Asn Bielschowsky lectr, 70; adj prof neurol sci, Sch Biol Sci, Univ Tex, 72-; pres, Am Orthoptic Coun, 73-74. *Mem:* Am Ophthal Soc; fel Am Acad Ophthal & Otolaryngol; Asn Res Strabismus (secy, 72-73); Int Strabismological Asn (secy-treas, 68-74); Pan Am Ophthal Asn. *Res:* Investigation of clinical and laboratory aspects of neuromuscular anomalies of the eyes, especially amblyopia; improvement of our knowledge of strabismus and the basic morphological and neurophysiological aspects of different forms of amblyopia. *Mailing Add:* Tex Childrens Hosp 6621 Fannin St Houston TX 77030

**VON OHAIN, HANS JOACHIM P,** ENERGY CONVERSION, GAS TURBINE TECHNOLOGY. *Current Pos:* RETIRED. *Personal Data:* b Dessau, Ger, Dec 14, 11; US citizen; m 49, Hanny Lemke; c Stephen, Christopher, Catherine & Stephanie. *Educ:* Univ Gottingen, PhD(physics), 35. *Honors & Awards:* Goddard Award, Am Inst Aeronaut & Astronaut, 66, Daniel Guggenheim Medal Award. 91; Aachen & Munich Prize Technol & Appl Natural Sci, 85; Charles Stark Draper Prize, Nat Acad Eng, 91; R Tom Sawyer Award, Am Soc Mech Engrs, 90. *Prof Exp:* Inventor & developer, Heinkel A/C Co, Ger, 36-47; res scientist, Aero Res Labs, 47-63; chief scientist, Aero Space Res Lab, USAF, 63-75, Propulsion Lab, Wright-Patterson AFB, 75-79; prof mech eng, Univ Dayton, 84-91, sr res engr, Res Inst, 89-91. *Concurrent Pos:* Adj prof aero propulsion, Res Inst, Univ Dayton, 79-84; adj prof, Univ Fla; consult aero propulsion, 80-; Charles Lindbergh prof, Nat Air & Space Mus, Smithsonian Inst, 84-85. *Mem:* Nat Acad Eng; hon fel Am Inst Aeronaut & Astronaut; Jet Pioneer's Asn USA. *Res:* Advanced ejector application to aircraft; advanced methods for particle separation in multicomponent flows; feasibility of a vapor injection heat pipe; multicomponent flow compressor concept; ejector heat pump system concept. *Mailing Add:* 3305 Nan Pablo Dr Melbourne FL 32934

**VON OSTWALDEN, PETER WEBER,** ORGANIC CHEMISTRY. *Current Pos:* from asst prof to assoc prof, 63-77, PROF CHEM, YOUNGSTOWN STATE UNIV, 77- *Personal Data:* b Reichenberg, Czech, June 1, 23; m 46; c 1. *Educ:* Univ Graz, Doctorandum, 50; Columbia Univ, MA, 54, PhD(pyridine chem), 58. *Prof Exp:* Process develop chemist, Merck & Co, Inc, Cherokee Plant, Pa, 57-63. *Concurrent Pos:* Vis assoc, Calif Inst Technol, 70-71; vis fel, Princeton Univ, 79-80. *Mem:* Am Chem Soc; Sigma Xi. *Res:* Pyridine and steroid chemistry; heterocyclic nitrogen oxides; chemistry of heterocyclic compounds; spectroscopy; organic applications. *Mailing Add:* 228 Edna St Poland OH 44514-3703

**VON-RECKLINGHAUSEN, DANIEL R,** ACOUSTICS, ELECTRONICS ENGINEERING. *Current Pos:* CONSULT, D R VON-RECKLINGHAUSEN CONSULTS, 84- *Personal Data:* b New York, NY, Jan 22, 25; m 60; c 2. *Educ:* Mass Inst Technol, SB, 51. *Honors & Awards:* Gold Medal, Audio Eng Soc, 78. *Prof Exp:* Chief engr, HH Scott, 51-73; staff consult, Electro-Audio Dynamics, 73-84. *Mem:* Fel Inst Elec & Electronics Engrs; Audio Eng Soc; Acoust Soc Am. *Mailing Add:* D R Von-Recklinghausen Consults 17 Glen Dr Hudson NH 03051

**VON RECUM, ANDREAS F,** BIOMATERIALS, HISTOPATHOLOGY OF BIOCOMPATIBILITY. *Current Pos:* prof, 78-93, HUNTER PROF, DEPT BIOENG, COL ENG, CLEMSON UNIV, 93- *Personal Data:* b Dillingen, Bavaria, Ger, July 5, 39; US citizen; m 65, Gudrun Bredenbrocker; c Derik, Vera, Uta, Horst, Thomas & Elsa. *Educ:* Univ Giessen, Ger, BS, 64; Free Univ Berlin, DVM, 68, PhD(vet med), 69; Colo State Univ, PhD(vet surg), 74. *Honors & Awards:* Clemson Award, Soc Biomat, 91. *Prof Exp:* Clin staff, Small Animal Clin, Freie Univ Berlin, Ger, 69-71; dir surg res, Sinai Hosp, Detroit, 74-77. *Concurrent Pos:* Adj prof surg, Univ SC, 84-, Med Univ SC, 87-; Fulbright sr scientist award, Fulbright Found, 90-91; sr scientist award, Alexander von Humboldt Found, 90-91; adj prof dent, Univ Nijmegen, Neth, 93- *Mem:* Soc Biomat (pres, 93-94); Acad Surg Res (pres, 82-83). *Res:* Basic and applied investigations in the biocompatibility of implantable prosthetic devices and biomaterials; design of percutaneous devices for long term implants penetrating through the skin. *Mailing Add:* Clemson Univ 501 Rhodes Clemson SC 29634-0905. *Fax:* 864-656-4466; *E-Mail:* vandrea@ces. clemson.edu

**VON RIESEMANN, WALTER ARTHUR,** STRUCTURAL MECHANICS, SEISMIC ENGINEERING. *Current Pos:* RETIRED. *Personal Data:* b Brooklyn, NY, Feb 12, 30; c James & Paul. *Educ:* Polytech Inst Brooklyn, BCE, 58; Univ Ill, Urbana, MSCE, 59; Stanford Univ, PhD(civil eng), 68. *Honors & Awards:* Robert Ridgway Award, Am Soc Civil Engrs, 58. *Prof Exp:* Res engr, Alcoa Res Labs, 59-60; staff mem, Sandia Nat Labs, 60-77, supvr struct mech, 77-91, mgr, 91-95. *Concurrent Pos:* Adj prof, Univ NMex, 74-77; pres, NMex Sect, Am Soc Civil Engrs, 75-76; chmn, NMex Sect, Am Soc Mech Engrs, 80-81; mem, Sr Seismic Rev & Adv Panel, Nuclear Regulatory Comn, 84- *Mem:* Am Nuclear Soc; Am Soc Civil Engrs; Am Soc Mech Engrs. *Res:* Analytical (finite element method) and experimental investigations of mechanical components and nuclear power plant containments; high-speed aircraft impact tests. *Mailing Add:* 7928 Woodhaven Dr NE Albuquerque NM 87109-5261. *Fax:* 505-822-1975; *E-Mail:* waltvonr@aol.com

**VON RIESEN, DANIEL DEAN,** ORGANIC CHEMISTRY. *Current Pos:* PROF CHEM, ROGER WILLIAMS UNIV, 72- *Personal Data:* b Beatrice, Nebr, Nov 20, 43; m, Lois Puccio. *Educ:* Hastings Col, BA, 65; Univ Nebr, PhD(chem), 71. *Prof Exp:* Instr chem, Hastings Col, 70-71; asst prof, Hamilton Col, 71-72. *Concurrent Pos:* Vis prof, Univ Nebr, 84; high performance liquid chromatography specialist, Isco Inc, 85-86; consult, 91- *Mem:* Am Chem Soc. *Res:* Cycloaddition reactions of heterocumulenes; chemical education; biopolymer separations; high performance liquid chromatography; microcomputer applications. *Mailing Add:* 18 Poplar Ave Riverside RI 02915

**VON ROSENBERG, DALE URSINI,** KINETIC MODELS FOR GENERATION OF PETROLEUM FROM SOURCE ROCKS, PETROLEUM EXPLORATION & PRODUCTION. *Current Pos:* RETIRED. *Personal Data:* b Austin, Tex, Sept 5, 28; m 53, Marjorie Taylor; c Carol, Eugene, Byron & Clyde. *Educ:* Univ Tex, BS, 49; Mass Inst Technol, ScD(chem eng), 53. *Prof Exp:* Sr res engr, Humble Oil & Refining Co, 53-57; assoc prof chem eng, La State Univ, 57-63; prof, Tulane Univ, 63-76 & Univ Tulsa, 76-79; sr res assoc, Mobil Res & Develop Corp, 79-92. *Concurrent Pos:* Consult, Esso Res Labs, 55-62; prin investr, NASA, 65-70; vis prof, Univ Tex, 75-79. *Mem:* Soc Petrol Engrs. *Res:* Development of methods for numerical solution of partial differential equations which describe problems in engineering; new applications of mathematics to solve real world problems. *Mailing Add:* 104 High Trail Dr Georgetown TX 78628

**VON ROSENBERG, H(ERMANN) E(UGENE),** CHEMICAL ENGINEERING. *Current Pos:* Res chem engr, Exxon Res & Eng Co, 54-60, sr res chem engr, 60-65, res specialist, 65-72, res assoc, 72-77, HEAD M&C, EXXON RES & ENG CO, 77- *Personal Data:* b Austin, Tex, Mar 6, 26; m 57. *Educ:* Univ Tex, BS, 49, MS, 51; Univ Del, PhD(chem eng), 55. *Mem:* Am Chem Soc; Am Inst Chem Engrs; Sigma Xi. *Res:* Chemical reactor dynamics applied chiefly to the petroleum refining processes; feed, catalyst and process studies in fluid catalytic cracking; coal utilization and gasification. *Mailing Add:* 105 Crow Rd Baytown TX 77520-1809

**VON ROSENVINGE, TYCHO TOR,** SPACE PHYSICS. *Current Pos:* Nat Acad Sci fel, 69-71, ASTROPHYSICIST, HIGH ENERGY ASTROPHYS DIV, GODDARD SPACE FLIGHT CTR, NASA, 71-, PROJ SCIENTIST, INT COMETARY EXPLORER, 72- *Personal Data:* b Beverly, Mass, Apr 18, 42; m 66; c 3. *Educ:* Amherst Col, AB, 63; Univ Minn, PhD(physics), 70. *Mem:* Am Phys Soc; Am Geophys Union. *Res:* Charge composition of solar energetic particles; charge composition, origin and propagation of galactic cosmic rays. *Mailing Add:* Code 661 NASA Goddard Space Flight Ctr Greenbelt MD 20771

**VON RUMKER, ROSMARIE,** PESTICIDE EFFICACY. *Current Pos:* RETIRED. *Personal Data:* b Halberstadt, Ger, July 30, 26; nat US. *Educ:* Univ Bonn, dipl & DAgr(plant path, entom, agr econ), 50. *Prof Exp:* Farm adminr seed breeding, Ger, 50-51; agr res biologist, Farbenfabriken Bayer, Ag, 51-54; dir res, Chemagro Corp, NY, 54-58, vpres res & develop, Kansas City, Mo, 59-71; managing partner, RVR Consults, 71-89. *Concurrent Pos:* Mem state & nat sci & environ adv comt, Sci Adv Bd, US Environ Protection Agency & Nat Acad Sci. *Res:* Crop protection; benefits, costs and environmental effects of pesticides; pest management problems and opportunities; pesticide research, development, marketing and economics, market research and forecasting. *Mailing Add:* 6400 Hodges Dr Shawnee Mission KS 66208

**VON SCHONFELDT, HILMAR ARMIN,** PETROLEUM ENGINEERING, ROCK MECHANICS. *Current Pos:* HVS CONSULT, COAL BED METHANE, GEOMECH MINING SYST, 93- *Personal Data:* b Delitzsch, Ger, May 3, 37. *Educ:* Clausthal Tech Univ, Dipl Ing, 64; Univ Minn, Minneapolis, PhD(mineral resources), 70. *Prof Exp:* Res engr, Shell Develop Co, 66 & Continental Oil Co, 67; asst prof petrol eng, Univ Tex, Austin, 69-77; mgr mining res, Occidental Res Corp, 77-93. *Mem:* Soc Petrol Engrs. *Res:* In situ stress measurement; hydraulic fracturing; drilling; underground caverns; solution mining. *Mailing Add:* 4898 Hartland Pkwy Lexington KY 40515

**VON STRANDTMANN, MAXIMILLIAN,** CHEMICAL RESEARCH & DEVELOPMENT, CHEMICAL MANUFACTURING. *Current Pos:* PRES, MEDEA RES LABS, 85- *Personal Data:* b Grodno, Poland, April 17, 27; US citizen; m 49, 93, Agnieszka Badowska; c Marina, Vera, Maximilian, Sophia & Alexander. *Educ:* Univ Bamberg, BS, 52, MS, 53; Univ Erlagen, PhD(org chem), 55. *Honors & Awards:* Res Award, NIH, 89 & 92; Cystinosis Found Award, 91. *Prof Exp:* Scientist med chem res, Chem Factory, Bamberg, Ger, 55-57; scientist, Warner Lambert Res Inst, 57-60, sr scientist, 61-67, sr res scientist, 68-74, assoc dir org chem & med chem res, 75-76; prin chem, Imp Chem Indust, 77-79; vpres res & develop, Custom Chem Labs, 80-84. *Mem:* Am Chem Soc; NY Acad Sci. *Res:* Organic chemical research in reactive intermediates, heterocyclic chemistry, new synthetic pathways and building blocks; medicinal chemistry research in immune system diseases, antimicrobials and central nervous system; research and development in cystinosis. *Mailing Add:* 200 Wilson St Unit No D6 Port Jefferson Station NY 11776-1150. *Fax:* 516-331-0563

**VON STRYK, FREDERICK GEORGE,** organic chemistry, for more information see previous edition

**VON TERSCH, LAWRENCE W,** ELECTRICAL ENGINEERING. *Current Pos:* RETIRED. *Personal Data:* b Waverly, Iowa, Mar 17, 23; m 48. *Educ:* Iowa State Univ, BS, 43, MS, 48, PhD(elec eng), 53. *Prof Exp:* From asst prof to prof elec eng, Iowa State Univ, 46-56; chmn dept elec eng, Mich State Univ, 58-65, assoc dean eng, 65-67, actg dean, 67-68, prof elec eng & dir comput lab, 56-89, dean, Col Eng, 68-89. *Mem:* Inst Elec & Electronics Engrs. *Res:* Computer applications. *Mailing Add:* Mich State Univ East Lansing MI 48824

**VON TURKOVICH, BRANIMIR F(RANCIS),** MATERIALS SCIENCE, MECHANICAL ENGINEERING. *Current Pos:* PROF MECH ENG & CHMN DEPT, UNIV VT, 70-; DIV DIR, NSF, 88- *Personal Data:* b Zagreb, Croatia, Dec 23, 24; US citizen; m 51; c 5. *Educ:* Univ Naples, BSc, 47; Univ Madrid, MSc & DNav Eng, 51; Univ Ill, Urbana, PhD(mech eng, physics), 62. *Honors & Awards:* Res Medal, Soc Mfg Engrs, 76. *Prof Exp:* Naval architect, Forgas & Font SA, Madrid, 50-51; sr res engr, Kearney & Trecker Corp, Wis, 52-57; lectr mech eng, Univ Ill, Urbana, 57-62, assoc prof mech eng & physics, 62-69, prof mech & indust eng, 69-70. *Concurrent Pos:* Lectr, Marquette Univ, 55-57; vis prof, Torino Polytech, Italy, 67-68; consult, Vermont Am Corp, Louisville, Ky, 71-; NATO sr prof, Italy, 76, 84, 87. *Mem:* Fel Am Soc Mech Engrs; Am Phys Soc; Int Inst Prod Res; fel Soc Mfg Engrs; Sigma Xi; Metall Soc. *Res:* Mechanical and physical metallurgy; production engineering; theoretical and applied mechanics; metal cutting and forming. *Mailing Add:* Dept Mech Eng Univ Vt 201 Votey Bldg Burlington VT 05405-0156

**VONVOIGTLANDER, PHILIP FRIEDRICH,** NEUROPHARMACOLOGY. *Current Pos:* from res scientist to sr res scientist, 72-82, sr scientist, 82-89, DISTINGUISHED SCIENTIST & DIR, CENT NERV SYST RES, UPJOHN CO, 91- *Personal Data:* b Jackson, Mich, Feb 3, 46; m 68, Barbara Armstrong; c Erika A, Charlotte E & Karin C. *Educ:* Mich State Univ, BS, 68, DVM, 69, MS, 71, PhD(pharmacol), 72. *Prof Exp:* NIH trainee, Cent Nerv Syst Pharmacol, Mich State Univ, 69-72. *Concurrent Pos:* Adj prof pharmacol, La State Univ, 85- & Mich State Univ, 86- *Mem:* Soc Neurosci; Am Soc Pharmacol & Exp Therapeut; Can Int Neuro-Psycho-Pharmacol; Neurotrauma Soc; Can Col Neuropsychopharmacol. *Res:* Development of animal models of psychiatric and neurological diseases for the purpose of studying the mechanisms of action of centrally acting drugs and identification of new therapeutic agents. *Mailing Add:* Upjohn Co Kalamazoo MI 49001-0199. *Fax:* 616-385-4525

**VON WEIZSACKER, ERNEST ULRICH,** ENVIRONMENTAL SCIENCE. *Current Pos:* PRES, INST CLIMATE, ENVIRON & ENERGY, WUPPERTAL INST, 91- *Personal Data:* b Zurich, Switz, June 25, 39; m, Christine Radtke; c Jakob, Paula, Adam, Franz & Maria. *Educ:* Univ Hamburg, dipl, 65; Univ Freiburg, PhD(biol), 69. *Prof Exp:* Fel, Protestant Interdisc Res Inst, 69-72; prof biol, Univ Essen, 72-75; pres, Univ Kassel, 75-80; dir, UN Ctr Sci & Technol, 81-84, Inst Europ Environ Policy, 84-91. *Mem:* AAAS; Ger Zool Soc. *Mailing Add:* Wuppertal Inst Doeppersberg 19 42103 Wuppertal Germany

**VON WINBUSH, SAMUEL,** INORGANIC CHEMISTRY, PHYSICAL CHEMISTRY. *Current Pos:* prof, 71-80, DISTINGUISHED PROF CHEM, STATE UNIV NY COL OLD WESTBURY, 80- *Personal Data:* b Henderson, NC, Aug 2, 32; m 62; c 1. *Educ:* Tenn State Univ, AB, 53; Iowa State Univ, MS, 56; Univ Kans, PhD(inorg chem), 60. *Prof Exp:* Asst prof chem & chmn dept, Tenn State Univ, 60-62; prof, NC A&T State Univ, 62-65; prof, Fisk Univ, 65-71. *Concurrent Pos:* Consult metals & ceramics div, Oak Ridge Nat Lab, 66-; vis prof, Wesleyan Univ, 69-70; consult, State Univ NY Col Old Westbury, 70-71. *Mem:* AAAS; Am Chem Soc; Sigma Xi. *Res:*

Coordination chemistry; ligand field and charge transfer spectra; inorganic polymers; unfamiliar oxidation states of metals in molten salts and other nonaqueous solvents. *Mailing Add:* Dept Chem & Physics State Univ NY Box 210 Old Westbury NY 11568-0210

**VON WINKLE, WILLIAM A,** HYDRODYNAMICS, UNDERWATER ACOUSTICS. *Current Pos:* electronic engr, USN Underwater Sound Lab, 52-61, electronic engr, mgr & dir, Bur Ships Trident Lab, Bermuda, 61-63, head signal processing br, 63-66, assoc tech dir res, 66-70, ASSOC TECH DIR TECHNOL, NAVAL UNDERWATER SYSTS CTR, 70- *Personal Data:* b Bridgeport, Conn, Nov 29, 28; m 40; c 8. *Educ:* Yale Univ, BSEE, 50, MSEE, 52; Univ Calif, Berkeley, PhD(eng sci), 61. *Prof Exp:* Asst, Yale Univ, 50-52. *Concurrent Pos:* Instr, YMCA Jr Col, 51-52 & Mitchell Jr Col, 54-57; vis lectr, Univ Conn, 54-81 & lectr, 81-, distiguished lectr, Univ New Haven, 81-; assoc ed, Acoust Signal Processing, Acoust Soc Am, 69-81 & 85-; adj asst prof, Rensselaer Polytech Inst, 55-65; instr, Univ Md, 62; US Nat Rep to Sci Comn of Nat Rep, NATO, Saclant Res Ctr, 71- *Mem:* Fel Inst Elec & Electronics Engrs; fel Acoust Soc Am; Sigma Xi. *Res:* Acoustics, sonar systems, target characteristics, transducer array design, fire control, submarine weaponry, hydrodynamics, optical signal processing, transient detection and classification, adaptive filtering techniques and holography; boundary layer hydrodynamics with application to naval warfare problems. *Mailing Add:* 105 Gardner Ave New London CT 06320-4354

**VON ZELLEN, BRUCE WALFRED,** PARASITOLOGY, PROTOZOOLOGY. *Current Pos:* RETIRED. *Personal Data:* b Ann Arbor, Mich, Feb 14, 22; m 49; c 1. *Educ:* Northern Mich Col, AB, 47; Univ Mich, MS, 49; Duke Univ, PhD(zool), 59. *Prof Exp:* Lab asst physiol & zool, Univ Mich, 49-50; assoc prof biol sci, Ky Wesleyan Col, 50-57; instr zool, Duke Univ, 57-59; assoc prof biol sci, Northern Ill Univ, 59-89. *Concurrent Pos:* Consult, panels on equip grants, NSF, Washington, DC & Chicago. *Mem:* AAAS; Am Soc Trop Med & Hyg; Soc Protozool; Am Soc Parasitol. *Res:* Parasitic protozoa; life history of coccidiosis; blood parasite infection; cell culture. *Mailing Add:* 136 Ilehamwood Dr De Kalb IL 60115

**VOOGT, JAMES LEONARD,** PHYSIOLOGY, NEUROENDOCRINOLOGY. *Current Pos:* assoc prof, 77-82, PROF PHYSIOL, UNIV KANS, 82-, CHMN, DEPT PHYSIOL, 93- *Personal Data:* b Grand Rapids, Mich, Feb 8, 44; m 66, Mary Jane; c Eric, Rachel & Jason. *Educ:* Mich Technol Univ, BS, 66; Mich State Univ, MS, 68, PhD(physiol), 70. *Prof Exp:* NIH fel, Med Ctr, Univ Calif, San Francisco, 70-71; asst prof physiol, Univ Louisville, 71-77, NIH res grant, 72-81. *Mem:* Am Physiol Soc; Int Soc Neuroendocrinol; Endocrine Soc; Soc Neurosci; Sigma Xi. *Res:* Control of anterior pituitary function by hypothalamus; feedback systems; hormone analysis; reproduction control. *Mailing Add:* Dept Physiol Univ Kans Sch Med Kansas City KS 66160-7401. *Fax:* 913-588-7430; *E-Mail:* jvoogt@kume.edu

**VOOK, FREDERICK LUDWIG,** PHYSICS. *Current Pos:* CONSULT, 93- *Personal Data:* b Milwaukee, Wis, Jan 17, 31; m 58, Frederica J Sandin; c Eric R & Dietrich W. *Educ:* Univ Chicago, BA, 51, BS, 52; Univ Ill, MS, 54, PhD(physics), 58. *Prof Exp:* Mem staff, Sandia Labs, 58-62, div supvr, 62-71, dept mgr, 71-78, dir, 78-93. *Concurrent Pos:* Chmn, Oliver & Buckley Prize Selection Comt, Am Phys Soc, 87; mem policy bd, Nanofabrication Facil, Cornell Univ, Col Eng Adv Bd, Univ Ill. *Mem:* Fel Am Phys Soc; Mat Res Soc; Bohmishe Phys Soc; Sigma Xi; sr mem Inst Elec & Electronics Engrs. *Res:* Defects in solids, primarily semiconductors; defects investigated by means of radiation damage at low temperatures; infrared absorption; ion implantation in semiconductors; ion backscattering and channeling studies of solids. *Mailing Add:* 7416 Carriveau Ave NE Albuquerque NM 87110-1467. *Fax:* 505-844-6098; *E-Mail:* flvook@sandia.somnet.sandia.gov

**VOOK, RICHARD WERNER,** ENGINEERING PHYSICS. *Current Pos:* assoc prof metall, Syracuse Univ, 65-70, prof mat sci, 70-84, chmn, Solid State Sci & Technol Prog, 84-87 & 90-91, prof physics, 84-93, dir, Electron Micros Lab, 68-93, res prof, 93-97, EMER PROF PHYSICS, SYRACUSE UNIV, 93- *Personal Data:* b Milwaukee, Wis, Aug 2, 29; m 57, Julia Deskins; c Katherine, Elizabeth, Richard S & Frederick. *Educ:* Carleton Col, BA, 51; Univ Ill, MS, 52, PhD(physics), 57. *Honors & Awards:* L P Pfeil Medal & Prize, Metals Soc Gt Brit, 83. *Prof Exp:* Mem res staff, Res Ctr, IBM, NY, 57-61; res labs, Franklin Inst, Pa, 61-65. *Concurrent Pos:* Consult, Alcoa, 90, Amperex Corp, 72, Carrier Corp, 72-73, Revere Copper & Brass, 77 & 84-86, Inficon Leybold-Heraeus, 81 & 84-90, Litton Panelvision, 87, Forensic Sci, 67-94, US Dept Educ, 88-89, 91, 95, 97, Mobil Chem Co, 91-92, Niagara Mohawk Power Corp, 94; prin investr, AEC, 66-72, NSF, 66-77, 81, 87-90, & 89-92, Energy Res Develop Agency, 77-78, Dept Energy, 78-89, Off Naval Res, 79-82 & 86-90, IBM Corp, 82-84 & 88-89, Niagara Mohawk Power Corp, 83-86, Sandia Nat Lab, 84-86, Alcoa Found, 83-89, Rome Air Develop Command, USAF, 89-91. *Mem:* Am Vacuum Soc; Micros Soc Am; Mat Res Soc. *Res:* Electron microscopy and diffraction; x-ray diffraction; thin films; epitaxial growth; surface physics and chemistry; imperfections in solids; electrical contact phenomena; electromigration. *Mailing Add:* 201 Physics Bldg Syracuse Univ Syracuse NY 13244-1130. *Fax:* 315-443-9103; *E-Mail:* vook@suhep.phy.syr.edu

**VOORHEES, BURTON HAMILTON,** BIOMATHEMATICS. *Current Pos:* ASSOC PROF MATH, ATHABASCA UNIV, 82- *Personal Data:* b Tucson, Ariz, Dec 3, 42. *Educ:* Univ Calif, Berkeley, AB, 64; Univ Ariz, MS, 66; Univ Tex, Austin, PhD(physics), 71. *Prof Exp:* Asst prof math & physics, Pars Col, Iran, 71-73; res assoc math, Univ Alta, 73-82. *Res:* Stochastic geometry; quantization of gravitation; black hole physics; mathematical models of evolutive processes; general systems theory. *Mailing Add:* Dept Math Athabasca Univ Box 10000 Athabasca AB T9S 1A1 Can

**VOORHEES, FRANK RAY,** PHYSIOLOGY. *Current Pos:* PROF BIOL, CENT MO STATE UNIV, 75- *Personal Data:* b Pekin, Ill, Dec 8, 35; m 58; c 2. *Educ:* Univ Fla, BS, 58; Univ Ill, MS, 68, PhD(entom), 69. *Mem:* Entom Soc Am; Soc Develop Biol; Am Mosquito Control Asn. *Res:* Gender-determining mechanisms in mosquitos. *Mailing Add:* Dept Biol WCM 306 Cent Mo State Univ Warrensburg MO 64093-5053

**VOORHEES, HOWARD R(OBERT),** CHEMICAL ENGINEERING, MATERIALS SCIENCE. *Current Pos:* TECH DIR, MAT TECHNOL CORP, 64- *Personal Data:* b Eatontown, NJ, Feb 13, 21; m 46; c 3. *Educ:* Rutgers Univ, BS, 42; Mass Inst Technol, MS, 47; Univ Mich, PhD(chem & metall eng), 56. *Prof Exp:* Asst prof chem eng, Univ Toledo, 48-50; instr chem & metall eng, Univ Mich, 50-55, assoc res engr, 55-63. *Mem:* Am Soc Testing & Mat; Am Soc Metals. *Res:* Creep-rupture of alloys under variable and complex stresses. *Mailing Add:* 2646 Park Ridge Dr Ann Arbor MI 48103. *Fax:* 313-665-9370

**VOORHEES, JOHN E,** MACHINE DESIGN & VIBRATION CONTROL. *Current Pos:* ENG CONSULT, 86- *Personal Data:* b Lima, Ohio, Aug 20, 29; m 53; c 2. *Educ:* Univ Toledo, BSME, 51; Ohio State Univ, MSME, 52. *Prof Exp:* Prin mech engr, Battelle Mem Inst, 52-58, asst chief mech res, 58-60, group dir mech dynamics, 60-66, chief mech dynamics, 66-70; mgr res & develop, Minster Mach Co, 70-77; mgr res, Hobart Corp, 77-86. *Concurrent Pos:* Westinghouse fel, 52-53. *Mem:* Am Soc Mech Engrs. *Res:* Vibrations analysis; design of balancing equip; control system and machine design; development of high speed mechanisms and heavy machines; dynamic analysis of heavy machinery; design of machine foundations and mounts. *Mailing Add:* 1429 Fox Dale Pl Sidney OH 45365

**VOORHEES, JOHN JAMES,** DERMATOLOGY, MEDICAL RESEARCH. *Current Pos:* Intern internal med, Univ Hosp, Univ Mich, Ann Arbor, 63-64, trainee clin internal med, 66, NIH trainee biochem, 67-68, trainee clin dermat, 67-69, Carl Herzog scholar biochem, 68-70, from instr to assoc prof dermat, 69-74, PROF DERMAT, MED SCH, UNIV MICH, ANN ARBOR, 74-, CHMN DEPT, 75-, CHIEF DERMAT SERV, UNIV HOSP, 75- *Personal Data:* b Cleveland, Ohio, Dec 5, 38; m 61; c 4. *Educ:* Bowling Green State Univ, BS, 60; Univ Mich, Ann Arbor, MD, 63. *Honors & Awards:* Taub Int Mem Award Psoriasis Res, 73; Henry Russell Award Distinguished Res, Univ Mich, 73; Outstanding Serv Award, Nat Psoriasis Found, 73. *Concurrent Pos:* Consult dermat, Dept Med, Wayne County Gen Hosp, 69-84, Vet Admin Hosp, Ann Arbor, 71-, St Joseph Mercy Hosp, 78- & Chelsea Community Hosp, 80-; assoc ed, J Cutaneous Path, 72-; mem, Med & Sci Adv Bd, Nat Psoriasis Found, 71-; mem, Revision Panel, 1980 Ed, US Pharmacopeia, 75-80; contrib ed, Int Psoriasis Bull; chmn, Dermat Found. *Mem:* Am Soc Clin Invest; Am Soc Pharmacol & Exp Therapeut; Am Soc Exp Path; Am Soc Cell Biol; Soc Exp Biol & Med; AMA; Soc Investigative Dermat; Skin Pharmacol Soc; Am Asn Cancer Res; Endocrine Soc. *Res:* Role of cyclic nucleotides, glucocorticoids, the arachidonate, HETE, thromboxane, prostaglandin cascade and immunology in the molecular pathophysiology and pharmacology of skin diseases with inflammation, induced proliferation and reduced differentiation. *Mailing Add:* Dept Dermat Med Ctr Univ Mich 1910 Taubman Health Ctr Ann Arbor MI 48109-0314. *Fax:* 313-936-8927

**VOORHEES, KENT JAY,** MATERIAL SCIENCE, CHEMOMETRICS. *Current Pos:* assoc prof, 79-85, PROF CHEM, COLO SCH MINES, 85- *Personal Data:* b Provo, Utah, Sept 7, 43; m 66, Tamara Lasson; c 2. *Educ:* Utah State Univ, BS, 65, MS, 68, PhD(org chem), 70. *Prof Exp:* Res fel phys chem, Mich State Univ, 70-71; instr org chem, Univ Utah, 71-73, asst res prof anal polymer chem, 73-76, assoc res prof, 76-79. *Concurrent Pos:* Res fel, Nat Ctr Toxicol, 95. *Mem:* Am Chem Soc; Am Soc Mass Spectrometry. *Res:* Formulation of complex structures and/or degradation mechanisms by the application of gas chromatography and/or mass spectrometry in the analysis of thermal decomposition products of synthetic and natural polymers; flammability of materials. *Mailing Add:* Dept Chem Colo Sch Mines Golden CO 80401

**VOORHEES, LARRY DONALD,** ZOOLOGY & ECOLOGY, ENVIRONMENTAL DATA & INFORMATION MANAGEMENT. *Current Pos:* res assoc, 76-83, mem res staff, 83-90, RESEARCH & DEVELOP GROUP LEADER, OAK RIDGE NAT LAB-LOCKHEED MARTIN, 90- *Personal Data:* b Benson, Minn, Dec 23, 46; m 70, Carol Groneberg; c Luke & Kimberly. *Educ:* Univ Minn, Morris, BS, 70; NDak State Univ, MS, 72, PhD(zool), 76. *Prof Exp:* Instr zool, NDak State Univ, 74-75, res assoc ecol, 75-76. *Concurrent Pos:* Comt mem, Roadside Maint Transp Res Bd, Nat Res Coun, 78-85, Task Force, Wildlife & Fisheries Issues, 81. *Mem:* Wildlife Soc; AAAS; Sigma Xi; Ecol Soc Am. *Res:* Applied problems in terrestrial community ecology; management of habitat for wildlife; management and analysis of environmental monitoring data. *Mailing Add:* Environ Sci Div Oak Ridge Nat Lab MS-6407 Oak Ridge TN 37831-6407. *Fax:* 423-574-4665; *E-Mail:* ldv@ornl.gov

**VOORHEES, PETER WILLIS,** PHASE TRANSFORMATIONS, THERMODYNAMICS. *Current Pos:* ASSOC PROF, DEPT MAT SCI & ENG, NORTHWESTERN UNIV. *Personal Data:* b Staten Island, NY, Dec 24, 55; m 77; c 2. *Educ:* Rensselaer Polytech Inst, BS, 77, PhD(mat eng), 82. *Honors & Awards:* Presidential Young Investr Award, NSF; Silver Medal, Am Soc Metals Int. *Prof Exp:* Instr mat eng, Rensselaer Polytech Inst, 80-81; Nat Res Coun res fel, Nat Bur Stand, 82-84, metallurgist, 84-88. *Concurrent Pos:* Vis scientist, Inst Theoret Physics, Univ Calif, Santa Barbara; vis prof, Groupe de Physique des Solides, Universite Paris VII. *Mem:* Am Soc Metals; AAAS; Am Inst Mining Metall & Petrol Engrs; Am Phys Soc; Sigma Xi. *Res:*

First order solid-solid and solid-liquid phase transformations, specifically the kinetics of morphological development accompanying the phase transformation process. *Mailing Add:* 369 Ridge Ave Winnetka IL 60093-2517

**VOORHESS, MARY LOUISE,** PEDIATRICS, ENDOCRINOLOGY. *Current Pos:* RETIRED. *Personal Data:* b Livingston Manor, NY, June 2, 26. *Educ:* Univ Tex, BA, 52; Baylor Univ, MD, 56. *Prof Exp:* From intern to resident pediat, Albany Med Ctr, NY, 56-59; res fel pediat endocrinol & genetics, Upstate Med Ctr, State Univ NY, 59-61, from asst prof to prof pediat, 61-76, prof pediats, 76-91, emer prof, 91- *Concurrent Pos:* Nat Cancer Inst res grant, 62-69, career develop award, 61-71; consult pediat, Roswell Park Mem Inst, Buffalo, 78-90; mem, Nat Adv Environ Health Sci Coun, 80-83. *Mem:* Endocrine Soc; Am Acad Pediat; Lawson Wilkins Pediat Endocrine Soc; Am Pediat Soc; fel AAAS. *Res:* Pediatric endocrinology; catecholamine metabolism in children; growth disorders in children. *Mailing Add:* Children's Hosp 219 Bryant St Buffalo NY 14222. *Fax:* 716-878-7814

**VOORHIES, JOHN DAVIDSON,** SURFACE CHEMISTRY. *Current Pos:* DIR & CHIEF EXEC OFFICER, ENVIRON ANALYSIS CORP, 82- *Personal Data:* b Hartford, Conn, Nov 26, 33; m 59. *Educ:* Princeton Univ, AB, 55, MA, 57, PhD(chem), 58. *Prof Exp:* Res chemist, Am Cyanamid Co, 58-62, sr res chemist, 62-64, group leader, 64-71, sr res scientist, 71-82, specialist, safety & environ control, 78-81. *Concurrent Pos:* Vis scholar, Dept Chem Eng, Stanford Univ, 70-71. *Mem:* AAAS; Am Chem Soc; Electrochem Soc. *Res:* Electrochemistry; electrochemical power sources; electrochemistry of organic compounds; electroanalytical techniques; chronopotentiometry; polarography; coulometry; interfacial chemistry; heterogeneous catalysis; hydrotreating catalysts; water analysis. *Mailing Add:* 14 Harrison Ave New Canaan CT 06840-5801

**VOORHIES, MICHAEL REGINALD,** VERTEBRATE PALEONTOLOGY. *Current Pos:* assoc cur, 75-80, PROF GEOL, UNIV NEBR, 77-, CUR FOSSIL VERT, STATE MUS, 80- *Personal Data:* b Orchard, Nebr, June 17, 41; m 68; c 2. *Educ:* Univ Nebr, BS, 62; Univ Wyo, PhD(geol), 66. *Prof Exp:* From asst prof to assoc prof geol, Univ Ga, 66-75. *Mem:* Paleont Soc; Soc Vert Paleont; Soc Study Evolution; Soc Syst Zool; Sigma Xi. *Res:* Taphonomy and population dynamics of Cenozoic mammals; community evolution; neogene stratigraphy of the Great Plains. *Mailing Add:* 2736 Ossa Wintna Dr Orchard NE 68764

**VOORHOEVE, RUDOLF JOHANNES HERMAN,** SURFACE CHEMISTRY, PHYSICAL INORGANIC CHEMISTRY. *Current Pos:* CORP VPRES TECHNOL, GREAT LAKES CHEM CORP, 90- *Personal Data:* b Sentang, Sumatra, Indonesia, Oct 4, 38; m 62, 68, 75; c 5. *Educ:* Delft Univ Technol, Ing, 61, Dr(organosilicon & catalytic chem), 64. *Prof Exp:* Instr organosilicon & catalysis chem, Delft Univ Technol, 61-64; res chemist, Nat Defense Res Orgn, 64-66; res chemist, Koninklyke/Shell Lab, Amsterdam, 66-68; mem tech staff, Bell Labs, 68-80; tech dir, Res & Develop Ctr, Hoechst Celanese Advan Technol Group, Corpus Christi, Tex, 80-90. *Mem:* Am Chem Soc; Am Phys Soc; Mat Res Soc (pres, 79). *Res:* Organosilicon chemistry, especially direct synthesis of organohalosilanes; heterogeneous catalysis, studies by gas-solid kinetics, mechanistic studies; gas-solid reactions for chemical vapors deposition, molecular beams; process studies; commodity and intermediate chemicals; product research; flame retardant specialty chemicals; pharmaceutical intermediates. *Mailing Add:* 3025 Courthouse Dr Apt 1C West Lafayette IN 47906-1038

**VOOS, JANE RHEIN,** MICROBIOLOGY. *Current Pos:* from asst prof to assoc prof biol sci, 68-75, asst to dean, 71-72, chmn dept, 72-84, prof, 75-80, ASST TO VPRES ACAD AFFAIRS, WILLIAM PATERSON COL, 84- *Personal Data:* b Nuremberg, Ger, Oct 2, 27; m 50; c 3. *Educ:* Hunter Col, BA, 52; Columbia Univ, PhD(biol sci), 68. *Prof Exp:* Res bacteriologist, Bellevue Hosp, NY, 53-54; instr biol, Stern Col Women, 56-58. *Mem:* AAAS; Bot Soc Am; Mycol Soc Am. *Res:* Electron microscopy of spores and modern pollens. *Mailing Add:* 28 Wenonah Ave Rockaway NJ 07866

**VOPAT, WILLIAM A,** MECHANICAL ENGINEERING. *Current Pos:* from instr to prof, Sch Eng & Sci, 32-76, head, Dept Mech Eng, 48-69, dean, Sch Eng & Sci, 69-76, EMER PROF MECH ENG & EMER DEAN, SCH ENG & SCI, 76- *Personal Data:* b New York, NY, Mar 8, 10; m 35; c 2. *Educ:* Cooper Union, BS, 31; Univ Mich, MSE, 37. *Hon Degrees:* ME, Cooper Union, 39. *Prof Exp:* Asst sales refrig engr, Lynbrook, NY, 31-32. *Concurrent Pos:* Consult ed, McGraw-Hill Pub Co, Inc, 38-45; asst engr, Kennedy Van Saun Mfg Co, 42; consult, NY Civil Serv Comn. *Mem:* Am Soc Mech Engrs; Am Soc Eng Educ. *Res:* Applied energy conversion; steam and gas turbines; power station engineering and economy. *Mailing Add:* 150 Park Blvd Malverne NY 11565

**VORA, MANU KISHANDAS,** CHEMICAL ENGINEERING, QUALITY MANAGEMENT. *Current Pos:* mem tech staff, Holmdel, NJ, 83-84, mem tech staff, 84-93, DIST MEM TECH STAFF, AT&T BELL LABS, NAPERVILLE, ILL, 93-; PRES & DIR, BLIND FOUND FOR INDIA, 89-; CUSTOMER SATISFACTION MGR, LUCENT TECHNOL, 95- *Personal Data:* b Bombay, India, Oct 31, 45; m 74, Nila N Kothari; c Ashish & Anand. *Educ:* Hindu Univ, BSChemE, 68; Ill Inst Tech, Chicago, MSChemE, 70, PhD(chem), 75; Keller Grad Sch Mgt, MBA, 85. *Honors & Awards:* Joe Lisy Qual Award, Am Soc Qual Control, 94. *Prof Exp:* Res assoc, Inst Gas Tech, Chicago, 76-77, chem engr, 77-79, eng supvr, 79-82. *Concurrent Pos:* Trustee, Avery Coonley Sch, Downers Grove, Ill, 87091; qual consult, Naperville, 89-, Milwaukee, 90-; dir, Nat Educ Qual Initiatives, Inc, Milwaukee, 91, fel, 92;

mem steering comt, Ill Mfg Team Excellence Award, 93-, chief judge, 93- *Mem:* Am Chem Soc; Am Inst Chem Engrs; Sigma Xi; fel Am Soc Qual Control; fel Nat Educ Qual Initiative. *Res:* Chemical engineering; customer satisfaction-manage customer surveys from international switching customers. *Mailing Add:* Lucent Technol 2600 Warrenville Rd Lisle IL 60532. *E-Mail:* mvora@lucent.com

**VORCHHEIMER, NORMAN,** POLYMER CHEMISTRY. *Current Pos:* RETIRED. *Personal Data:* b Thungen, Ger, Sept 10, 35; US citizen; m 67; c 3. *Educ:* Brooklyn Col, BS, 57; Polytech Inst Brooklyn, PhD(org chem), 62. *Prof Exp:* Res chemist textile fibers, E I du Pont de Nemours & Co, 62-67; sr res chemist polymer synthesis, Betz Labs Inc, 67-70; exec vpres, Shasta Fund Inc, 70-71; sr res chemist, Betz Labs Inc, 71-73, group leader, 73-77, supvr polymer synthesis, 77-80, sect head synthesis-polymer appln, 80-82, mgr, synthesis-pilot plant-water-wastewater res, 82-86, res fel, 86-94. *Concurrent Pos:* Consult, 94- *Mem:* Am Chem Soc; Royal Soc Chem. *Res:* Water-soluble polymers. *Mailing Add:* PO Box 403 Buckingham PA 18912

**VORE, MARY EDITH,** TOXICOLOGY, PHARMACOLOGY. *Current Pos:* from asst prof to assoc prof, 78-86, PROF PHARMACOL, COL MED, UNIV KY, 86-, PROF & DIR, GRAD CTR TOXICOL, 94- *Personal Data:* b Guatemala City, Guatemala, June 27, 47; US citizen; m 76, Edgar Iwamoto; c Kenneth & Daniel Iwamoto. *Educ:* Asbury Col, BA, 68; Vanderbilt Univ, PhD(pharmacol), 72. *Prof Exp:* Fel, Dept Biochem & Drug Metab, Hoffmann-LaRoche Inc, 72-74; asst prof toxicol, Dept Pharmacol, Univ Calif Med Ctr, San Francisco, 74-78. *Concurrent Pos:* prin investr, NIH, 79-95, Pharmacol Study Sect, 83-87; coun, Nat Inst Environ Health Sci, 91-95. *Mem:* Am Soc Pharmacol & Exp Therapeut (secy-treas, 87-88); Soc Toxicol; Am Asn Study Liver Dis. *Res:* Mechanisms of organic anion transport across the liver; regulation by prolactin, estrogens and environmental pollutants; hepatic drug elimination in pregnancy. *Mailing Add:* Dept Pharmacol Univ Ky Med Sch Lexington KY 40536. *Fax:* 606-323-1981

**VOREADES, DEMETRIOS,** APPLIED PHYSICS, SEMICONDUCTOR DEVICE CHARACTERIZATION. *Current Pos:* CO-FOUNDER, SMARTWARE INTEL SOFTWARE FOR QUAL MGT, 93- *Personal Data:* b Athens, Greece, Dec 8, 42; m 76, Eileen F Dockman; c Noah & Cleo. *Educ:* Univ Athens, dipl physics, 66; Univ Chicago, MS, 70, PhD(physics), 76. *Prof Exp:* Res asst physics, Univ Athens, 67-68; teaching asst, Univ Chicago, 68-70, res asst, Enrico Fermi Inst, 70-75; res fel biol, Calif Inst Technol, 75-77; syst mgr cytol, Obstet & Gynec Lying-In Hosp, Chicago, 77-78; assoc biophysicist biol, Brookhaven Nat Lab, 78-79; sr engr, Burroughs Corp, 79-81; sr staff physicist, Hughes Aircraft, 81-93. *Mem:* Am Phys Soc; Inst Elec & Electronics Engrs. *Res:* Scanning transmission electron microscopy as analytical tool in biology, physics and materials science; ion implantation; semiconductor devices. *Mailing Add:* 2323 Broadway Suite 102 San Diego CA 92102

**VORHAUS, JAMES LOUIS,** MANAGEMENT OF MICROWAVE COMPONENT PRODUCT DEVELOPMENT. *Current Pos:* prod line mgr, Microwave Power Prod, 87-92, ENG MGR, AVANTEK INC, 92- *Personal Data:* b St Louis, Mo, Aug 2, 50; m 75, Carol Brandt; c Daniel, David & Sarah. *Educ:* Lehigh Univ, BS, 72; Univ Ill, Champaign-Urbana, MS, 74, PhD(physics), 76. *Honors & Awards:* Microwave Prize, Inst Elec & Electronics Engrs, 86. *Prof Exp:* Res asst low temp physics, Dept Physics, Univ Ill, Champaign-Urbana, 72-76; sr scientist device physics, Res Div, Raytheon Co, 76-85; dir opers, Solid State Microwave Group, Epsco, Inc, 85-87. *Concurrent Pos:* Indust consult, Dept Defense. *Mem:* Am Phys Soc; Inst Elec & Electronics Engrs. *Res:* Design, fabrication and evaluation of galium arsenide monolithic microwave integrated circuits. *Mailing Add:* 829 Santa Rita Rd Los Altos CA 94022

**VORHEES, CHARLES V,** NEUROTOXICOLOGY. *Current Pos:* Fel res scholar, Children's Hosp Res Found, 76-78, asst prof, 78-82, asst prof, Dept Pediat, 82-88, PROF PEDIAT & DEVELOP BIOL & ENVIRON HEALTH, CHILDREN'S HOSP RES FOUND, CINCINNATI, 88- *Personal Data:* b Columbus, Ohio, Oct 9, 48; m 82, Elizabeth Mollnow; c Darcy, Collin, Ashley & Lauren. *Educ:* Univ Cincinnati, BA, 71; Vanderbilt Univ, MA, 73, PhD(psychopharmacol), 77. *Honors & Awards:* Eli Lilly Distinguished Lectr, 90. *Concurrent Pos:* Prof neuroscience, Univ Cincinnati. *Mem:* Behav Teratology Soc (pres, 84-85); Teratology Soc; AAAS; Soc Neurosci; Am Psychol Soc; Soc Toxicol. *Res:* Behavioral birth defects; psychoactive drugs and food additives as possible causes of mental retardation or other learning or emotional problems caused by early (usually prenatal) exposure to these agents; developmental neurotoxicology. *Mailing Add:* 5447 Brookstone Dr Cincinnati OH 45230. *Fax:* 513-475-3912; *E-Mail:* vorheecv@ucbeh.san.uc.edu

**VORHERR, HELMUTH WILHELM,** OBSTETRICS & GYNECOLOGY, PHARMACOLOGY. *Current Pos:* assoc prof, 68-71, PROF OBSTET, GYNEC & PHARMACOL, UNIV NMEX, 71-, DIR, BREAST CLIN, SCH MED, 79- *Personal Data:* b Alzey, WGer, Feb 6, 28; m 55; c 2. *Educ:* Univ Mainz, MD, 55. *Prof Exp:* Mem staff obstet & gynec, Univ Frankfurt, 62-65; res pharmacologist, Cedars-Sinai Med Ctr, Los Angeles, Calif, 65-68. *Concurrent Pos:* Damon Runyon Mem Fund res fel, Cedars-Sinai Med Ctr & Univ Calif, Los Angeles, 65-66, NIH spec fel, 66-67; asst prof, Sch Med, Univ Calif, Los Angeles, 66-68. *Mem:* Am Fedn Clin Res; Am Soc Pharmacol & Exp Therapeut; Soc Gynec Invest. *Res:* Effects of sex steroid hormones on reproductive tissues; factors influencing embryonic/fetal growth; lactation; pathobiology of breast cancer. *Mailing Add:* 915 Stanford Dr NE Rm 127 Albuquerque NM 87131

**VORHIES, MAHLON WESLEY,** VETERINARY PATHOLOGY. *Current Pos:* DIR & DEPT HEAD, COL VET MED, KANS STATE UNIV, MANHATTAN, 86- *Personal Data:* b Fairfield, Iowa, June 26, 37; m 59, Ilene L Hoffman; c Susan R & Robert. *Educ:* Iowa State Univ, DVM, 62; Mich State Univ, MS, 67. *Honors & Awards:* E P Pope Award, Am Asn Vet Diagnosticians. *Prof Exp:* Vet pvt pract, Riverside, Iowa, 62-64; vet pathologist, Iowa State Univ, Ames, 62-72; vet pathologist, dir & dept head, SDak State Univ, Brookings, 72-86. *Concurrent Pos:* Consult, NIH, Commonwealth, Pa, Winrock Int Hq, USDA; clin instr, Mich State Univ, East Lansing, 64-67. *Mem:* Am Asn Avian Pathologists; US Animal Health Asn; Am Asn Vet Lab Diagnosticians; Am Vet Med Asn; Acad Vet Consult. *Res:* Veterinary medicine; veterinary pathology. *Mailing Add:* Col Vet Med Kans State Univ Manhattan KS 66506

**VORHIS, ROBERT C,** HYDROGEOLOGY, LARGER FORAMINIFERA. *Current Pos:* CONSULT GEOL, 83- *Personal Data:* b Covington, Ohio, Aug 31, 17; m 47, Monique Camus; c Grace L (Rembert) & Chilton Van. *Educ:* Ohio Wesleyan Univ, BA, 39; Univ Iowa, MS, 41. *Prof Exp:* Geologist, US Geol Surv, 46-74, Near East Found, Tanzania, 76-79 & Dimpex Co, Upper Volta, 80-83; geologist, Near East Found, Tanzania, 76-79; geologist Dimpex Co, Upper Volta, 80-83. *Concurrent Pos:* Mem, Hydrol Panel, Comt Alaskan Earthquake, Nat Acad Sci, 64-70. *Mem:* Geol Soc Am. *Res:* Worldwide hydrologic effects of the Alaskan earthquake of 1964; synonomy of the American larger foraminifera; geology of the Georgia coastal plain. *Mailing Add:* 1560 Stoneleigh Hills Rd Lithonia GA 30058-5631

**VORIS, HAROLD K,** HERPETOLOGY. *Current Pos:* asst to dir, Field Mus Natural Hist, 83-84, head div, 84, chmn, Dept Zool, 85, vpres collections & res, 85-89, CUR, FIELD MUS NATURAL HIST, 73- *Personal Data:* b Chicago, Ill, Oct 5, 40. *Educ:* Hanover Col, BA, 62; Univ Chicago, PhD(biol), 69. *Prof Exp:* Instr biol, Yale Univ, 67-69; asst prof, Dickinson Col, 69-73. *Concurrent Pos:* Assoc prog dir, Syst Biol Prog, NSF, 81-82. *Mem:* Am Soc Ichthyol & Herpet; Soc Syst Zool; Ecol Soc Am; Soc Study Evolution. *Res:* Evolution and systematics; ecology; sea snake ecology and systematics; rain forest ecosystems; numerical taxonomy. *Mailing Add:* 1500 W Juneway Terr Chicago IL 60626

**VOROSMARTI, JAMES, JR,** OCCUPATIONAL MEDICINE, DIVING PHYSIOLOGY. *Current Pos:* CONSULT, OCCUP MED, 86- *Personal Data:* b Palmerton, Pa, Oct 18, 35; c 3. *Educ:* Lafayette Col, AB, 57; Jefferson Med Col, MD, 61. *Honors & Awards:* Shilling Award, Undersea & Hyperbaric Med Soc, 87. *Prof Exp:* Fel, State Univ NY, Buffalo, 70-72; exchange med officer, Royal Naval Physiol Lab, Royal Naval Inst Naval Med, Gosport, Eng & Off Naval Res, London, 72-75; dep dir, Naval Med Res Inst, Bethesda, 75-78, prog mgr diving med, Naval Med Res & Develop Command, 78-80, cmndg officer, 80-83; asst to undersecy defense, Res & Eng, 83-86. *Mem:* Fel Am Col Physicians; fel Am Col Prev Med; fel Am Acad Family Med; Am Physiol Soc; fel Am Acad Occup Med; Undersea & Hyperbaric Med Soc (pres, 77-78). *Res:* Physiology of high pressure, unusual mesr gases and respiratory physiology. *Mailing Add:* 16 Orchard Way S Rockville MD 20854

**VORST, JAMES J,** AGRONOMY, CROP ECOLOGY. *Current Pos:* MEM FAC, DEPT AGRON, PURDUE UNIV, LAFAYETTE, 69- *Personal Data:* b Cloverdale, Ohio, Mar 20, 42; m 66; c 3. *Educ:* Ohio State Univ, BS, 64, MS, 66; Univ Nebr, PhD(agron), 69. *Prof Exp:* Teaching asst agron, Ohio State Univ, 64-66; instr, Univ Nebr, 66-69. *Mem:* Am Soc Agron; Crop Sci Soc Am; Sigma Xi; Ctr Appln Sci & Technol. *Res:* Crop production and physiology; cropping systems; teaching methods in agronomy. *Mailing Add:* Dept Agron Purdue Univ West Lafayette IN 47907-1968

**VORTMAN, L(UKE) J(EROME),** PHYSICS, ENGINEERING. *Current Pos:* RETIRED. *Personal Data:* b Springfield, Ill, Apr 18, 20; m 46. *Educ:* Univ Ill, BS, 47, MS, 49. *Prof Exp:* Mem tech staff, Sandia Labs, 49-83, distinguished mem tech staff, 83-87. *Concurrent Pos:* Mem adv comt civil defense, Nat Acad Sci, 61-73, chmn, Protective Struct Subcomt, 65-66 & blast & thermal effects subcomt, 66-70, mem, phys effects subcomt Supersonic Transport, 66-71; consult, Boeing Co, 64. *Mem:* AAAS; Am Nuclear Soc. *Res:* Effects of nuclear and chemical explosions in air and underground; peaceful uses of nuclear explosives; protective construction. *Mailing Add:* 933 McDuffie Circle NE Albuquerque NM 87110

**VOS, BERT JOHN,** toxicology, for more information see previous edition

**VOS, KENNETH DEAN,** PHYSICAL CHEMISTRY. *Current Pos:* PRES, PALMER HOUSTON, INC & UDSCO, INC. *Personal Data:* b Oskaloosa, Iowa, Nov 13, 35; m 96, Claude-Marie Halbritter; c Julie E & Peter D. *Educ:* Cent Col, Iowa, BA, 57; Mich State Univ, PhD(phys chem), 63. *Honors & Awards:* First Charles E Allderdice Jr Award, Chem Specialties Mfrs Asn. *Prof Exp:* Res asst chem, Los Alamos Sci Lab, 60; staff assoc, John Jay Hopkins Lab, Gen Atomic Div, Gen Dynamics Corp, Calif, 63-68; sr res chemist, S C Johnson & Son, Inc, 68-72, supvr pressurized prod res sect, 72-76, prod safety dir, 76-78, phys sci mgr & prod safety dir, 78-82, dir regulatory affairs, 82-87. *Mem:* AAAS; Am Chem Soc; Am Phys Soc; NY Acad Sci. *Res:* Physical chemistry, electron paramagnetic presonance of metalamines and free radicals; semiconductor and high polymer chemistry biomedical research; fine particle and aerosol research; toxicology; product safety; Environment Protection Agency, Food & Drug Admin, USDA, Consumer Product Safety Commision, Bur Alcohol, Tobacco and Firearms regulations. *Mailing Add:* Palmer Houston Inc 8226 Kerr St Houston TX 77029-3908. *Fax:* 713-672-5637

**VOSBURG, DAVID LEE,** STRATIGRAPHY. *Current Pos:* asst prof, 66-67, ASSOC PROF GEOL, ARK STATE UNIV, 67- *Personal Data:* b Enid, Okla, Dec 24, 30; m 60; c 2. *Educ:* Phillips Univ, BS, 52; Univ Okla, MS, 54, PhD(geol), 63. *Prof Exp:* From instr to asst prof geol, Univ RI, 60-65; asst prof & chmn dept, Phillips Univ, 65-66. *Mem:* Am Asn Petrol Geol. *Res:* Occurrence and distribution of subsurface evaporites within shelf sediments related to the Permian Basin, especially economic potential and stratigraphic relations. *Mailing Add:* Dept Chem Ark State Univ Main Campus PO Box 419 State University AR 72467-0419

**VOSBURGH, KIRBY GANNETT,** APPLIED PHYSICS, EXPERIMENTAL PHYSICS. *Current Pos:* physicist, Gen Elec Co, 72-77, mgr, Signal Electronic Systs, Corp Res & Develop, 77-79, mgr electronic mat, 79-80, mgr silicon processing, 80-84, mgr, Very-Large-Scale Integration Technol Lab, 84-87, mgr, Electronic Mat Lab, 88-89, mgr, Appl Physics Lab, 89-93, mgr, Imaging & Visualization Lab, 93-95, MGR, ELECTRONIC SYST LAB, GEN ELEC CO, 95- *Personal Data:* b Pasadena, Calif, May 27, 44; m 67, Kaye Barber; c Jennett & Kirby. *Educ:* Cornell Univ, BS, 65, MS, 67; Rutgers Univ, PhD(physics), 71. *Prof Exp:* Res asst appl physics, Cornell Univ, 65-67; mem tech staff accelerator physics, Princeton-Penn Accelerator, Princeton Univ, 67-68; res fel physics, Rutgers Univ, 68-71; mem tech staff & asst to dir particle physics, Princeton Particle Accelerator, Princeton Univ, 71-72. *Mem:* Am Phys Soc; Inst Elec & Electronics Engrs. *Res:* Electronic materials; electronic systems, devices and peripherals; medical diagnostic imaging (nuclear magnetic resonance, xray, nuclear); electron optics, lamps & lighting systems; computer graphics; computer imaging. *Mailing Add:* Corp Res & Develop Gen Elec Co PO Box 8 Schenectady NY 12301. *E-Mail:* vosburgh@crd.ge.com

**VOSHALL, ROY EDWARD,** ELECTRICAL ENGINEERING. *Current Pos:* PROF ELEC ENG, GANNON UNIV, 89- *Personal Data:* b Beacon, NY, May 29, 33; m 56; c 2. *Educ:* Carnegie Inst Technol, BS, 56, MS, 57, PhD, 61. *Prof Exp:* From instr to asst prof elec eng, Carnegie Inst Technol, 57-63, lectr, 63-69; sr res scientist, Westinghouse Elec Corp, 63-76, fel engr, Res Labs, 76-89. *Mem:* Inst Elec & Electronics Engrs; Am Phys Soc; Sigma Xi. *Res:* Electrical gaseous discharges; plasma physics; magnetohydrodynamics; vacuum arcs; vacuum breakdown. *Mailing Add:* 106 Walten Pt Erie PA 16511-3302

**VOSKO, SEYMOUR H,** theoretical physics; deceased, see previous edition for last biography

**VOSS, ANNE COBLE,** FOOD SCIENCE & NUTRITION. *Current Pos:* therapeut dietician & clin instr dietetics, 69-70, grad res assoc, Dept Food Sci & Technol, 80-84, RES ASSOC NUTRIT, DEPT MED BIOCHEM, OHIO STATE UNIV, 85-; CLIN RES ASSOC, ABBOTT LABS, ROSS PRODS DIV. *Personal Data:* b Richmond, Ind, Aug 22, 46; m 69, Harold L; c 3. *Educ:* Ohio State Univ, BS, 68, PhD(food sci & nutrit), 84. *Prof Exp:* Clin dietician, Johns Hopkins Hosp, 68-69; regist dietitian, US Army Clins, Ger, 70-75 & pvt pract, 75-78; proj dir, Nutrit Educ, Ohio Dept Educ, 79-80. *Concurrent Pos:* Consult, Ohio Dent Asn, 86- & Am Dent Asn Dent Health, 88-; lectr, Dept Food Sci & Technol, Col Dent & Pharm, 87-; adj asst prof, Col Human Ecol, Ohio State Univ, 87- & Col Nursing, Otterbein Col, 90- *Mem:* Sigma Xi; Am Dietetic Asn; Am Diabetes Asn; NY Acad Sci. *Res:* Fatty acid metabolism particularly desaturation and chain elongation using diabetic model. *Mailing Add:* Ross Prods 105650 RP3-2 625 Cleveland Ave Cleveland OH 43215-1724

**VOSS, CHARLES HENRY, JR,** ELECTRICAL ENGINEERING, BIOENGINEERING. *Current Pos:* assoc prof, 62-67, PROF, LA STATE UNIV, 67-, UNDERGRAD COORDR, ELEC & COMPUT ENG DEPT, 84- *Personal Data:* b Kiangyen, China, Sept 28, 26; US citizen; m 54, Elizabeth A Brown; c Elizabeth A & Charles H III. *Educ:* La State Univ, BS, 49, MS, 56; NC State Univ, PhD(elec eng), 63. *Prof Exp:* Engr, WJBO-WBRL-FM, 51-53; div transmission engr, Southern Bell Tel Co, 53-54; instr elec eng, La State Univ, 54-56 & NC State Univ, 58-61. *Concurrent Pos:* Res Coun fac fel, 65; Delta Regional Primate Ctr consult, 66-70; F J Haydel Jr Kiaser Aluminum prof, 90. *Mem:* Sigma Xi. *Mailing Add:* 5823 Clematis Dr Baton Rouge LA 70808

**VOSS, DONALD E,** PLASMA, ELECTROMAGNETIC & NUCLEAR SCIENCE. *Current Pos:* FOUNDER & PRES, VOSS SCI. *Educ:* Case Inst Technol, BS, 74; Princeton Univ, PhD(plasma physics), 80. *Prof Exp:* Scientist, Lewis Res Ctr, NASA, 74-76; supvr, GHz-bandpass Prompt Diag Systs Underground Nuclear Explosive Tests, Lawrence Livermore Nat Lab; head proj team, Harry Diamond Lab, Adelphi, Md; prin investr, AFWL HPM Exp Prog, 85-88. *Mem:* Am Phys Soc; Inst Elec & Electronics Engrs. *Res:* Plasma, electromagnetic and nuclear science; author of more than 60 technical reports and publications. *Mailing Add:* Voss Sci 418 Washington St SE Albuquerque NM 87108

**VOSS, EDWARD GROESBECK,** TAXONOMIC BOTANY, NOMENCLATURE. *Current Pos:* Asst syst bot, Biol Sta, Univ Mich, Ann Arbor, 49, bot, 50-51, Biol Sta, 51-53, res assoc, bot gardens, 54, res asst, Metab Res Lab, Univ Hosp, 54-56, res assoc herbarium, 56-61, from asst prof to assoc prof bot, 60-69, cur herbarium, 61-96, prof bot, 69-96, EMER CUR VASCULAR PLANTS & EMER PROF BOT, UNIV MICH, ANN ARBOR, 96- *Personal Data:* b Delaware, Ohio, Feb 22, 29. *Educ:* Denison Univ, BA, 50; Univ Mich, MA, 51, PhD(bot), 54. *Honors & Awards:* Gleason Award, NY Bot Garden, 86. *Concurrent Pos:* Ed, Mich Botanist, 62-76; secy gen comt on bot nomenclature, 69-87, secy ed comt, Int Code Bot

Nomenclature, 69-81, chmn ed comt, 81-87; vice rapporteur, Bur Nomenclature, Int Bot Cong, 69 & 75, rapporteur, 81. *Mem:* Am Soc Plant Taxon; Lepidop Soc; Int Asn Plant Taxon; Soc Hist Natural Hist; fel Linnean Soc London. *Res:* Floristics; vascular flora and vegetational history of Great Lakes region; history of biology; nomenclature; Lepidoptera of Michigan; natural areas in Michigan. *Mailing Add:* Herbarium North Univ Bldg Univ Mich Ann Arbor MI 48109-1057. *E-Mail:* egvoss@umich.edu

**VOSS, EDWARD WILLIAM, JR,** IMMUNOCHEMISTRY, MOLECULAR BIOLOGY. *Current Pos:* from asst prof to assoc prof immunochem, 67-74, dir, Cell Sci Ctr, 88-94, PROF MICROBIOL, UNIV ILL, URBANA, 74-, JUBILEE PROF, 90-, JAMES R MARTIN UNIV SCHOLAR, 94- *Personal Data:* b Chicago, Ill, Dec 2, 33; m 58, 74, Virginia Hellman; c Valerie & Cathleen. *Educ:* Cornell Col, AB, 55; Univ Ind, Indianapolis, MS, 64, PhD(immunol), 66. *Honors & Awards:* Nat Lupus Hall of Fame, Am Lupus Soc, Fluer-de-Lis Award, Community Serv Award; E I DuPont Educ Award. *Prof Exp:* USPHS fel, Sch Med, Wash Univ, 66-67. *Concurrent Pos:* Fac fel sci, NSF, 75; vis prof microbiol, Ore State Univ, 77, Dept Biochem, Molecular Biol & Cell Biol, Northwestern Univ, 85; assoc appointment, Ctr Advan Study, 81-88; vis scholar, Univ Utah, Salt Lake City, 84-85; hon bd mem, Cent Ill Chap, Am Lupus Soc, 86-; mem comt rev, USP, 90-95; vis prof, Univ Hawaii, 92. *Mem:* AAAS; Am Asn Immunol; Sigma Xi; Protein Soc; Fedn Am Scientists; Am Soc Biochemists; Am Chem Soc; NY Acad Sci; Am Soc Biochem & Molecular Biol; Am Inst Chemist. *Res:* Antibody structure-function studies utilizing the fluoresiem hapten group and the immunochemistry and immunogenetics of the autoimmune syndrome systemic lupus erythematosus; biotechnology. *Mailing Add:* Dept Microbiol 601 S Goodwin B103 Chem & Life Sci Lab Univ Ill Urbana IL 61801. *Fax:* 217-244-6697

**VOSS, GUSTAV-ADOLF,** PHYSICS. *Current Pos:* LEADER, MACHINE DIV, DEUTSHES ELKTRONON SYNCHROTON, GER, 73- *Personal Data:* b 29. *Educ:* Tech Univ Berlin, Charlottenburg, PhD. *Hon Degrees:* Dr, Univ Heidelberg. *Honors & Awards:* Robert R Wilson Prize, Am Phys Soc, 94. *Prof Exp:* Asst dir, Harvard Univ, 59-73. *Mailing Add:* Deutsches Elektronon-Synchroton Notkestrasse 85 22607 Hamburg Germany

**VOSS, HENRY DAVID,** ATMOSPHERIC PHYSICS, SPACE SCIENCES. *Personal Data:* b Evergreen Park, Ill, Jan 5, 50; m 73; c 4. *Educ:* Ill Inst Technol, BS, 72; Univ Ill, Urbana-Champaign, MS, 74, PhD(elec eng), 77. *Prof Exp:* Res assoc, Aeronomy Lab, Univ Ill, 77-79; res scientist, Lockheed Palo Alto Res Lab, 79-94. *Concurrent Pos:* Consult prof elec, Urbana, 76-78. *Mem:* Am Geophys Union; Inst Elec & Electronics Engrs. *Res:* Upper atmosphere and ionosphere investigations; plasma physics; energetic particles in the magnetosphere and their global precipitation patterns on the atmosphere; rocket-borne instrumentation development; thermal physics; satellite instrumentation development. *Mailing Add:* 8651 E 700th S Upland IN 46989

**VOSS, JAMES LEO,** ANIMAL PHYSIOLOGY. *Current Pos:* From instr to assoc prof med & surg, 58-71, head dept, 75- 86, PROF CLIN SCI, COLO STATE UNIV, 72-, DEAN, COL VET MED & BIOMED SCI, 86- *Personal Data:* b Grand Junction, Colo, Apr 7, 34; m 54; c 3. *Educ:* Colo State Univ, BS, 56, DVM, 58, MS, 65. *Mem:* Am Vet Med Asn; Soc Study Reproduction; Am Soc Animal Sci; Am Asn Equine Practioners. *Res:* Equine reproduction; sexual behavior; artificial insemination; spermatogenesis; female reproductive cycle; ova transfer; pregnancy maintenance and control of ovulation. *Mailing Add:* 15240 Red Feather Lakes Rd Livermore CO 80536-9608

**VOSS, KENNETH EDWIN,** COLLOID SCIENCE. *Current Pos:* from res chemist to sr 79-81, GROUP LEADER, NEW BUS RES, ENGELHARD CORP, 81- *Personal Data:* b Hastings, Nebr, Nov 12, 46; m 79; c 2. *Educ:* Univ Nebr, Lincoln, BSc, 69; Kans Univ, PhD(inorg chem), 75. *Prof Exp:* Fel res staff, Iowa State Univ, 74-76. *Mem:* Am Chem Soc; Am Ceramic Soc; Mat Res Soc. *Res:* Advanced materials, particularly ceramics, ceramic composites and coatings; inorganic compounds, industrial minerals and chemicals; characterization of physical, chemical and colloidal properties for applications as catalysts, pigments and sorbents. *Mailing Add:* Engelhard Corp 101 Wood Ave Iselin NJ 08830-0770

**VOSS, PAUL JOSEPH,** OPERATIONS RESEARCH, SYSTEMS DESIGN. *Current Pos:* Assoc physicist, 69-75, SR PHYSICIST, APPL PHYSICS LAB, JOHNS HOPKINS UNIV, 75- *Personal Data:* b Chicago, Ill, March 10, 43; div; c 2. *Educ:* Syracuse Univ, BS, 69; Johns Hopkins Univ, MS, 72. *Concurrent Pos:* Facil mgr, Guidance Syst Eval Lab, 83-; chmn, Aegis Scenario Cert Comt, 85- *Res:* Analysis and simulation of missile and radar processing systems. *Mailing Add:* 5635 Harpers Farm Rd Columbia MD 21044

**VOSS, REGIS D,** SOIL FERTILITY. *Current Pos:* from asst prof to assoc prof, 64-66, PROF AGRON, IOWA STATE UNIV, 69- *Personal Data:* b Cedar Rapids, Iowa, Jan 4, 31; m 56, Margaret Mitchell; c Lori, John & David. *Educ:* Iowa State Univ, BS, 52, MS, 60, PhD(soil fertil), 62. *Honors & Awards:* Agron Exten Educ Award, Am Soc Agron, 84, Agron Achievement Award-Soils, 89, Werner L Nelson Award, Diag Yield Limiting Factors, 92. *Prof Exp:* Res asst soil fertil, Iowa State Univ, 57-62; agriculturist, Test Demonstration Br, Tenn Valley Authority, 62-64. *Concurrent Pos:* Vis prof, Univ Ill, 70-71; consult, Int Maize & Wheat Improv Ctr, Arg, 71; mem bd dirs, Am Soc Agron, 77-78 & Soil Sci Soc Am, 80-83; leader, Agron Exten, Iowa State Univ, 83-96. *Mem:* Fel AAAS; fel Am Soc Agron; fel Soil Sci Soc Am. *Res:* Effect of uncontrolled factors on the response of field crops to applied fertilizers by using biological statistical methods. *Mailing Add:* Dept Agron Iowa State Univ Ames IA 50011-1010

**VOSS, RICHARD FREDERICK,** NOISE, JOSEPHSON JUNCTIONS. *Current Pos:* RES STAFF MEM, THOMAS J WATSON RES LAB, IBM, 75- *Personal Data:* b St Paul, Minn, Aug 27, 48. *Educ:* Mass Inst Technol, BS, 70; Univ Calif, Berkeley, PhD(physics), 75. *Honors & Awards:* Siefert Mem Lectr. *Mem:* Am Phys Soc; Sigma Xi. *Res:* Thermal and quantum mechanical limitations to physical devices, particularly Josephson Junctions; one-over-F noise and connection with music; computer generation and display of fractal objects; fractal characterization and analysis. *Mailing Add:* 18 Choate Lane Pleasantville NY 10570-2703. *Fax:* 914-945-4421

**VOSSEN, JOHN LOUIS,** PHYSICS. *Current Pos:* STAFF, JOHN VOSSEN & ASSOC, 86- *Personal Data:* b Philadelphia, Pa, Apr 4, 37; m 63; c 2. *Educ:* St Joseph's Col, Pa, 58. *Honors & Awards:* Achievement Awards, RCA Labs, 68, 69 & 71; Nerken Award, Am Vacuum Soc, 85. *Prof Exp:* Engr, RCA Semiconductor & Mat Div, RCA Labs, 58-62, group leader thin-film physics, RCA Advan Commun Lab, 62-65, mem tech staff, Process Res Lab, David Sarnoff Res Ctr, 65-78, head thin-film technol, 78-86. *Mem:* Am Vacuum Soc (pres, 80); Am Phys Soc; Electrochem Soc; Am Inst Physics. *Res:* Study of the methods by which the properties of thin films may be controlled or etched; principally sputtering, ion plating, plasma anodization, evaporation, plasma deposition and etching; thin film technology. *Mailing Add:* 1012 Sunset Ridge Bridgewater NJ 08807

**VOSTAL, JAROSLAV JOSEPH,** PHARMACOLOGY, TOXICOLOGY. *Current Pos:* HEAD, BIOMED SCI DEPT, GMC RES LABS, 77- *Personal Data:* b Prague, Czech, Mar 17, 27; m 52; c 4. *Educ:* Charles Univ, Prague, MD, 51; Czech Acad Sci, PhD(med sci), 61. *Prof Exp:* Physician, Regional Inst Nat Health, Jihlava, Czech, 51-55; vis scientist, Nat Inst Pub Health, Stockholm, Sweden, 67-68; assoc prof pharmacol & toxicol, Sch Med, Univ Rochester, 68-77, assoc prof prev med & commun health, 69-77. *Concurrent Pos:* Mem, Permanent Comn & Int Asn Occup Health, 66-, mem, Int Subcomt Toxicol Metals, 69-; chmn, Panel Fluorides, Nat Acad Sci-Nat Res Coun, 70-71, mem, Comt Biol Effects Atmospheric Pollutants, 70- *Mem:* AAAS; Am Soc Pharmacol & Exp Therapeut; Fedn Am Soc Exp Biol; Soc Toxicol. *Res:* Pharmacology of organomercurial compounds; toxicology of heavy metals and inorganic poisons, inter-species differences in pharmacokinetics and biotransformation of toxic substances. *Mailing Add:* EHAC 6360 Hills Dr Bloomfield Hills MI 48301. *Fax:* 313-644-6527, 313-947-1413

**VOTAW, CHARLES ISAC,** MATHEMATICS. *Current Pos:* RETIRED. *Personal Data:* b Farris, Okla, Jan 3, 33; m 56; c 2. *Educ:* Okla State Univ, BS, 57; NTex State Univ, MS, 67; Univ Kans, PhD(math), 71. *Prof Exp:* Staff mem, Sandia Corp, 57-60; mkt engr, Raytheon Co, 60-62; prod engr, Tex Instruments, 62-65; prod & test engr, Hunt Electronics, 65-66; prof math, Ft Hays State Univ, 71-96. *Mem:* Math Asn Am; Soc Indust & Appl Math; Am Math Soc. *Res:* Topology; applied mathematics. *Mailing Add:* Dept Math Ft Hays State Univ 600 Park St Hays KS 67601-4099

**VOTAW, ROBERT BARNETT,** BIOSTRATIGRAPHY, PALEOECOLOGY. *Current Pos:* asst prof, Ind Univ Northwest, 71-77, dept chmn, 73-76, asst dean facs, 76-77, dept chmn, 82-88, ASSOC PROF GEOL, IND UNIV NORTHWEST, 77- *Personal Data:* b Cincinnati, Ohio, Oct 19, 39; m 84; c 4. *Educ:* Ind Univ, BS, 62, MA, 64; Ohio State Univ, PhD(geol), 71. *Prof Exp:* Geologist, Standard Oil Co, Calif, 64-68. *Mem:* Geol Soc Am; Paleontol Soc. *Res:* Conodont biostratigraphy of the Ordovician rocks of the North American midcontinent; paleoecology of the middle and upper Ordovician rocks of the North American midcontinent. *Mailing Add:* Dept Geosci Ind Univ Northwest 3400 Broadway Gary IN 46408

**VOTAW, ROBERT GRIMM,** BIOCHEMISTRY, MEDICAL EDUCATION. *Current Pos:* instr biochem, Univ Conn, 67-70, asst prof, 70-77, assoc dean med educ, 74-77, ASST PROF RES HEALTH EDUC & DIR COMPUT BASED EDUC, SCH MED, UNIV CONN, 77- *Personal Data:* b St Louis, Mo, Sept 13, 38; m 61; c 3. *Educ:* Wesleyan Univ, BA, 60; Case Western Reserve Univ, PhD(microbiol), 66. *Prof Exp:* Instr microbiol, Sch Med, Case Western Res Univ, 66-67. *Mem:* AAAS; Am Soc Microbiol; Am Chem Soc; Am Asn Med Cols. *Res:* Medical education; computer based education; use of simulation of teaching and assessing complex behavior, clinical problem solving. *Mailing Add:* 390 Middle Rd Farmington CT 06032

**VOTH, DAVID RICHARD,** PARASITOLOGY, INVERTEBRATE ZOOLOGY. *Current Pos:* from asst prof to assoc prof, 71-79, PROF BIOL, METROP STATE COL, DENVER, 79- *Personal Data:* b St Cloud, Minn, July 11, 41; m 69; c 2. *Educ:* Univ NDak, BS, 63, MS, 65; Ore State Univ, PhD(zool), 71. *Prof Exp:* Asst prof biol, Haile Selassie I Univ, 66-68. *Mem:* Am Soc Parasitologists; Am Fedn Teachers. *Res:* Helminth taxonomy, ecology and natural history. *Mailing Add:* Biol Dept Box 53 Metrop State Col Denver PO Box 173362 Denver CO 80217-3362

**VOTH, HAROLD MOSER,** PSYCHIATRY. *Current Pos:* STAFF PSYCHIATRIST, MENNINGER FOUND, 57-; CHIEF OF STAFF, VET ADMIN HOSP, TOPEKA, 80- *Personal Data:* b Newton, Kans, Dec 29, 22; m 46; c 3. *Educ:* Washburn Univ, BS, 43; Univ Kans, MD, 47; Menninger Sch Psychiat, MD(psychiat), 52. *Honors & Awards:* William Porter Award, Am Asn Mil Surgeons, 79. *Prof Exp:* Asst sect chief, Vet Admin Hosp, Topeka, Kans, 52-53, asst chief, Acute Intensive Treatment Sect, 53-54, chief women's neuropsychiat serv, 54-57. *Concurrent Pos:* Mem fac, Menninger Sch Psychiat, 55-; NIMH res grant, Menninger Found, 63-72; examr, Am Bd Psychiat & Neurol, 70-71; consult, Walter Reed Army Med Ctr, 72-; assoc chief psychiat for educ, Vet Admin Hosp, Topeka, Kans, 75-; rear admiral, Med Corps, USNR. *Mem:* Fel AAAS; fel Am Psychiat Asn; Am Col Psychoanal. *Res:* Personality organization; psychotherapy; the study of autokinesis as a research and clinical instrument. *Mailing Add:* 901 Garfield Vet Admin Hosp Topeka KS 66606-1670

**VOTRUBA, JAN,** PHYSICS. *Current Pos:* PHYSICIST, FONAR CORP, 82- *Personal Data:* b Nov 14, 38; US citizen. *Educ:* Tech Univ Prague, Czech, Dipl Ing, 61; Czech Acad Sci, PhD(physics), 68. *Prof Exp:* Physicist, Inst Physics, Prague, 63-69, 70-79 & 80-82 & Brookhaven Nat Lab, 79-80. *Concurrent Pos:* Dir, Radio Frequency Technol, dept head, & sr systs engr, Fonar Corp, 82- *Mem:* NY Acad Sci. *Res:* Microwave electronics; accelerator physics; medical physics; high frequency superconductivity; vacuum technology; experimental physics; magnetic resonance imaging. *Mailing Add:* Fonar Corp 110 Marcus Dr Melville NY 11747

**VOTTA, FERDINAND, JR,** CHEMICAL ENGINEERING. *Current Pos:* RETIRED. *Personal Data:* b Providence, RI, June 8, 16; m 47, Lucile H Spooner; c Ruth L (Labriole, deceased) & Richard F. *Educ:* Univ RI, BS, 39, MS, 41; Yale Univ, DEng, 58. *Prof Exp:* Develop engr, Allied Chem & Dye Corp, 41-43; res engr, Manhattan Proj, Columbia, 44-46; from instr to prof chem eng, Univ RI, 46-81. *Mem:* Am Inst Chem Engrs; Sigma Xi; Am Soc Eng Educ. *Res:* Thermodynamics; heat and mass transfer. *Mailing Add:* 2294 Kingstown Rd Kingston RI 02881

**VOUGHT, ELDON JON,** TOPOLOGY. *Current Pos:* PROF MATH, CALIF STATE UNIV, CHICO, 70- *Personal Data:* b Chicago, Ill, May 21, 35; m 59, Patricia; c 4. *Educ:* Manchester Col, AB, 57; Univ Mich, Ann Arbor, MA, 58; Univ Calif, Riverside, PhD(math), 67. *Prof Exp:* Instr math, Pomona Col, 60-61; assoc prof math, Calif State Polytech Univ, Pomona, 61-70. *Concurrent Pos:* NSF res fel, 71-73; vis prof math, Ariz State Univ, 75-76, 84; mathematician, Lockheed Aircraft Co, 77-88; vis prof math, Univ Richmond, 89-90. *Mem:* Am Math Soc; Math Asn Am. *Res:* The study of the invariance of various topological properties of compact, connected metric spaces under certain types of continuous functions, for example, local homeomorphisms, confluent and refinable functions. *Mailing Add:* Dept Math Calif State Univ Chico CA 95929-0001

**VOUGHT, ROBERT HOWARD,** physics; deceased, see previous edition for last biography

**VOURNAKIS, JOHN NICHOLAS,** BIOPHYSICS, MOLECULAR BIOLOGY. *Current Pos:* SR VPRES, GENMAN INC, 90- *Personal Data:* b Cambridge, Ohio, Dec 1, 39; m 61; c 1. *Educ:* Albion Col, BA, 61; Cornell Univ, PhD(chem), 68. *Prof Exp:* Nat Acad Sci exchange fel, Inst Org Chem & Biochem, Prague, Czech, fall 68; NIH fel biol, Mass Inst Technol, 69-71, res assoc, 71-72; res assoc, Harvard Univ, 72-73; prof biol, Syracuse Univ, 73-85; dir, Molec Genetics Corp, Dartmouth Univ, 85-87; dir, Sci Affairs, Molecular Therapeut, Inc, 86-88; vpres sci, Venax Corp, 88-90. *Concurrent Pos:* Vis assoc prof, Amherst Col, 70-71; NIH res grant gen med, 75; dir, Genetic Eng, Bristol Myers Co, 82-83; consult, Bolt, Beranek & Newman, 81; Bristol Myers Co, 81, Nat Itellenic Biotech Co, Diohellas, 83 84; chmn, sci adv bd, Chitin Co, Inc, 85-88. *Mem:* Biophys Soc; Soc Develop Biol; AAAS. *Res:* Secondary and tertiary structure of eukaryotic mRNA; structure of mapping techniques using enzymes as probes; secondary structure of rRNA; anti-caner drug-DNA interactions; human genome analysis; gene finding technology. *Mailing Add:* 6 Carriage Lane Hanover NH 03755-4700

**VOUROS, PAUL,** ANALYTICAL CHEMISTRY, ORGANIC CHEMISTRY. *Current Pos:* sr scientist, Inst Chem Anal, 74-79, assoc prof, 79-85, PROF CHEM, NORTHEASTERN UNIV, 85- *Personal Data:* b Thessaloniki, Greece, Apr 1, 38; US citizen; m 65; c 2. *Educ:* Wesleyan Univ, BA, 61; Mass Inst Technol, PhD(chem), 65. *Prof Exp:* Staff scientist, Tech Opers, Inc, 66-67; proj mgr, 67-68; asst prof chem, Inst Lipid Res, Col Med, Baylor Univ, 68-74. *Mem:* Am Chem Soc; Sigma Xi; Am Soc Mass Spectrometry. *Res:* Organic mass spectrometry; mass spectrometry of biological compounds; gas chromatography-mass spectrometry; photographic ion detection; applications of chromatography and mass spectrometry to forensic problems; high performance liquid chromatography-mass spectrometry. *Mailing Add:* 260 Annursnac Hill Rd Concord MA 01742-5409

**VOURVOPOULOS, GEORGE,** NUCLEAR PHYSICS, APPLICATIONS OF NUCLEAR METHODS. *Current Pos:* PROF PHYSICS, WESTERN KY UNIV, 84- *Personal Data:* b June 11, 36; US citizen; m 63; c 3. *Educ:* Nat Univ Athens, BS, 58; Fla State Univ, MS, 65, PhD(physics), 67. *Prof Exp:* From assoc prof to prof physics, Fla A&M Univ, 67-76, chmn dept, 74-76; dir, Tandem Accelerator Lab, Greek Atomic Energy Comn, 76-83; vis prof, Vanderbilt Univ, 83-84. *Concurrent Pos:* Res fel, Israel Inst Technol, 69-70; Res Corp grant, Fla A&M Univ, 71-76, NSF grant, 72-74, 84-88. *Mem:* Am Phys Soc; Sigma Xi. *Res:* Nuclear reactions; applications of nuclear techniques. *Mailing Add:* 1713 Single Tree Ct Bowling Green KY 42103. *Fax:* 502-745-5062; *E-Mail:* vour@wku.edu

**VOUTSAS, ALEXANDER MATTHEW (VOUTSADAKIS),** TECHNOECONOMIC MANAGEMENT, AIRCRAFT AEROSPACE CONSULTANT. *Current Pos:* PRES, A VOUTSAS ASSOCS INC. *Personal Data:* b New York, NY, Mar 26, 23; div; c Alexandros & John. *Educ:* Rensselaer Polytech Inst, BAeE, 44; Northwestern Univ, Naval Acad, MS, 45; Harvard Grad Bus Sch, AMP, 69; Century Univ, Calif, PhD(eng), 85. *Prof Exp:* Aerodynamicist transonic windtunnel, Ames Labs, NASA, 45-46, XP-92, F102 delta wing, Gen Dynamics-Convair, San Diego, Calif, 47-48; proj aerodynamicist, Hermes Intercontinental Ballistic Missile, Gen Elec Co, Schenectady, NY, 48-51; aerodynamicist rigel missile (pre polaris), Grumman Corp, Bethpage, NY, 51-52; proj design engr terrapin NASA res iono rocket, Repub Aviation Corp, Hicksville, NY, 52-56; res & develop syst mgr atlas-titan intercontinental ballistic missile inertial guidance syst, Am

Bosch Arma Corp, Garden City, NY, 56-61; mgr mkt commun & aerospace syst, Int Tel & Tel Corp, NY, 62-67; pres adv aerospace, Hellenic Aerospace Indust, Ltd, Greece, 80-91. *Concurrent Pos:* Guest comt mem, US Naval Bur Ordnance Comt Aerobalastics, 49-; lectr, Am Mgr Asn NY, 68-69; mkt consult, ITT Fed Elec Corp NY, 67-73; indust develop consult & pres adv, Motor Oil Hellas Ltd, NY & Greece, 69-73; pres, A Voutsas Assoc, aerospace & indust tech consult, 73-; bd dirs, Am Acad Greece, 76-78; consult aeronaut, aerospace & bus indust mgt. *Mem:* Assoc fel Am Inst Aeronaut & Astronaut; fel Brit Interplanetary Soc. *Res:* Inventor pioneer of ultrasonic theory and equipment for diagnosis of materials fatigue and cancer growths and its cure; vibrating string accelerometer, Apollo 17 lunar mission gravimeter theory and equipment; author or coauthor of a number of publications. *Mailing Add:* Kalliga 21 Athens 114-73 Greece. *Fax:* 1-6462513

**VO-VAN, TRUONG,** THIN FILMS PHYSICS, OPTICAL INSTRUMENTATION. *Current Pos:* PROF PHYSICS, UNIV MONCTON, 76-, ASSOC VPRES RES, 95- *Personal Data:* b Saigon, Viet-Nam, Dec 3, 48; m 71, My-Lien Vu; c Nha-Thy & Tam-Ca. *Educ:* Polytech Col Montreal, BScA, 70; Univ Moncton, MSc, 72; Univ Toronto, PhD(physics), 76. *Concurrent Pos:* Nat Res Coun Can Grant, 76-, Regional Develop Prog grant, 76-, Coun Res, Univ Moncton, 76-, Energy Mines Resources Can & Com & Technol NB; pres, Optical Physics Div, Can Asn Physicians, 93-94. *Mem:* Optical Soc Am; Can Asn Physicists; Can-Fr Asn Advan Sci. *Res:* Experimental solid state physics; specialization in thin films; optical properties of solids, spectroscopy and optics; solar energy applications; thin film metrology. *Mailing Add:* Dept Physics Univ Moncton Moncton NB E1A 3E9 Can. *Fax:* 506-858-4279

**VOXMAN, WILLIAM L,** TOPOLOGY. *Current Pos:* asst prof to assoc prof, 70-76, PROF MATH, UNIV IDAHO, 76- *Personal Data:* b Iowa City, Iowa, Feb 1, 39; m 63; c 2. *Educ:* Univ Iowa, BA, 60, MS, 63, PhD(math), 68. *Prof Exp:* Latin Am teaching fel & prof math, Univ Chile, 68-69; prof, Concepcion Univ, 69; Fulbright travel grant & prof, State Tech Univ, Chile, 69-70. *Concurrent Pos:* Latin Am teaching fel & prof math, Nat Polytech Sch, Quito, Ecuador, 74-76. *Mem:* Am Math Soc; Sigma Xi. *Res:* General topology, especially upper semicontinuous decompositions of topological spaces. *Mailing Add:* Univ Idaho 1118 King Rd Moscow ID 83843-4199

**VOYTUK, JAMES A,** SCIENCE EDUCATIONAL, S&E HUMAN RESOURCE POLICY. *Current Pos:* SR PROJ DIR, NAT RES COUN, 89- *Personal Data:* b Pittsburg, Pa, July 5, 36; m 73, Elizabeth Campbell. *Educ:* Carnegie Inst Technol, BS, 58, MA, 59, PhD(math), 63. *Prof Exp:* Asst prof math, Western Res Univ, 62-66; from asst prof to assoc prof math, Rensselaer Polytech, 66-85; assoc exec dir, Am Math Soc, 85-89. *Concurrent Pos:* Exec officer, Dept Math, Rensselaer Polytech, 73-85. *Mem:* AAAS; Sigma Xi; Soc Indust & Appl Math. *Res:* Studies of educational and professional development of scientific personnel; mathematics. *Mailing Add:* Nat Res Coun 2101 Constitution Ave NW Washington DC 20418. *Fax:* 202-334-2753; *E-Mail:* jvoytuk@nas.edu

**VOYVODIC, LOUIS,** HIGH ENERGY PHYSICS. *Current Pos:* PHYSICIST, FERMI NAT ACCELERATOR LAB, 72- *Personal Data:* b Yugoslavia, Oct 22, 21; US citizen; m 51; c 5. *Educ:* McGill Univ, BSc, 43, PhD(physics), 48. *Prof Exp:* Physicist cosmic rays, Nat Res Coun Can, 48-56; tech proj dir radiation physics, Isotope Prod Ltd Can, 56-58; physicist, Armour Res Found, Ill Inst Technol, 58-60; physicist, Argonne Nat Lab, 62-72. *Mem:* Am Inst Physics; Am Phys Soc; Fedn Am Scientists. *Res:* Interactions of elementary particles at high energies, particularly as studied by optical track chamber techniques, and development of improved detection techniques. *Mailing Add:* 707 S Monroe St Hinsdale IL 60521

**VOZOFF, KEEVA,** EXPLORATION GEOPHYSICS, ENGINEERING GEOPHYSICS. *Current Pos:* DIR, HARBOUR DOM GMBH; PROF GEOPHYS, INST GEOPHYS-METEOROL, UNIV COLOGNE, GER, 89-; ADJ PROF GEOPHYS, CURTIN UNIV, AUSTRALIA; DIR HARBOUR DOM PTY LTD. *Personal Data:* b Minneapolis, Minn, Jan 26, 28; m 57, Elizabeth Philp; c Jennifer (Middleton), Nancy, Stephen & Andrew. *Educ:* Univ Minn, BPhys, 49; Pa State Univ, MSc, 51; Mass Inst Technol, PhD(geophys), 56. *Honors & Awards:* Humboldt Prize. *Prof Exp:* Geophysicist, Nucom-McPhar Geophys, Ltd, 55-58; assoc prof geophys, Univ Alta, 58-64; vpres, Geosci Inc, Mass, 64-69; consult, 69-72; prof geophys, Macquarie Univ, 72-94. *Concurrent Pos:* Mem earth sci ad hoc comt, Soviet-Australian Coop, 74-75; Hearst vis prof, Univ Calif, Berkeley, 78-80. *Mem:* Hon mem Australian Soc Explor Geophysicists (pres, 76-77); Am Geophys Union; Europ Asn Explor Geophys; Petrol Explor Soc Australia; fel Australian Acad Technol Sci & Eng; hon mem Soc Explor Geophysicists; hon fel Asn Explor Geophysicists India; Am Asn Petrol Geologists. *Res:* Electrical and electromagnetic methods of determining earth structure and composition; natural electromagnetic fields; characterization of geological bodies on basis of physical properties. *Mailing Add:* Harbor Dam Pty Ltd PO Box 596 North Sydney NSW 2109 Australia. *Fax:* 61-2-9922-1383; *E-Mail:* harbourd@ozemail.com.au

**VRADIS, GEORGE CHRIS,** FLUID MECHANICS & HEAT TRANSFER, NON-NEWTONIAN FLUIDS & RHEOLOGY. *Current Pos:* Instr, 86-87, asst prof, 88-94, ASSOC PROF MECH ENG, POLYTECH UNIV, 94- *Personal Data:* b Thessaloniki, Greece, Apr 12, 57; m 92, Sandra Demopoulos; c Emanuella & Christopher. *Educ:* Nat Tech Univ, Athens, Greece, BS, 81; Polytech Univ, MS, 82, PhD(mech eng), 86. *Honors & Awards:* Ralph Teetor Award, Soc Automotive Engrs, 94. *Concurrent Pos:* Prin investr, Gas Res Inst, NY Gas, Long Island Lighting Co, BV, Exxon & H-P, 91-; chmn, Long Island Sect, Am Soc Mech Engrs, 92-94, vchmn coord group, 96-98; proj mgr, NY Gas Group, 96-97. *Mem:* Am Soc Mech Engrs; Sigma Xi; Am Soc Elec Engrs; Soc Automotive Engrs. *Res:* Computational and experimental fluid mechanics and heat transfer with emphasis in incompressible flows, viscous flows, separated flows; non-Newtonian fluid mechanics and heat transfer; flow measurement; energy systems. *Mailing Add:* 179 N Kentucky Ave North Massapequa NY 11758

**VRANA, NORMAN M,** ELECTRICAL ENGINEERING. *Current Pos:* assoc prof, 66-75, PROF ELEC ENG, CORNELL UNIV, 75- *Personal Data:* b Hudson Heights, NJ, Feb 16, 20; m 42; c 4. *Educ:* NY Univ, BEE, 47; Cornell Univ, MEE, 51. *Prof Exp:* Sr engr, ADT Co, NY, 40-49; assoc prof elec eng, Cornell Univ, 49-57; sr res engr, Autonetics Co, Calif, 57-58; assoc prof elec eng, Cornell Univ, 58-65; res & develop engr, Hewlett Packard Co, Colo, 65-66. *Concurrent Pos:* Commun engr & seminar consult, NY Tel Co, 62-65; consult, Frankford Arsenal, Pa, 68-71 & Ballistics Res Lab, Md, 70- *Mem:* Inst Elec & Electronics Engrs. *Res:* Hybrid computer simulation and computation; communication and instrumentation; electronic design and development; computer and digital systems. *Mailing Add:* 1296 Ellis Hollow Rd Ithaca NY 14850

**VRANIC, MLADEN,** PHYSIOLOGY, ENDOCRINOLOGY. *Current Pos:* Fel, Univ Toronto, 63-65, from asst prof to assoc prof, 65-72, chmn, Dept Physiol, 91-95, PROF PHYSIOL, FAC MED, UNIV TORONTO, 72-, PROF MED, 78- *Personal Data:* b Zagreb, Yugoslavia, Apr 3, 30; Can citizen; m 83; c 3. *Educ:* Univ Zagreb, MD, 55, DSc (physiol), 62; FRCP(C), 86. *Hon Degrees:* MD, Karolinska Inst Med Fac, Swed, 92. *Honors & Awards:* Vuk Vrhovac Mem Lectr, Univ Zagreb, Croatia, 77; Upjohn Lectr, Univ Ottawa, Can, 80; Inaugural Banting & Best Mem Lectr, Madrid, Spain, 85; Pfizer Lectr, Clin Res Inst, Univ Montreal, 85; R Kroc Lectr, Sch Med, Univ Southern Calif, 91; Banting Medal & Lectr for Distinguished Sci Achievement, Am Diabetes Asn, 91; Mizuno Inaugural Lectr & Award, Osaka Univ, 92; Solomon A Berson Distinguished Lectr, Am Phys Soc, 95; Novo Nordisk Lectr, Karolinska Inst, Stockholm, 95. *Concurrent Pos:* Mem, Inst Med Sci, Univ Toronto, 73-, Inst Biomed Elec & Eng, 73-78, sen res comt, 80-82; fac scholar, Josia Macy Fedn, Univ Geneva, 76; invited prof, Univ Geneva, 76-77; assoc ed, Metab & Can J Phys & Pharm, 76-82, Am J Physiol, 82-89; vis res fel & invited prof, Merton Col, Univ Oxford, Eng, 86; fel, Merton Col, Oxford, 86; hon vis prof, Fac Med, Univ Zagreb, 87; Killam res fel, 88, 89; chmn, Coun Exercise, Am Diabetes Asn, 89-91; foreign adj prof, Karolinska Inst, Stockholm, 92-; Poll vis scholar, Univ Wash, Seattle, 95. *Mem:* Endocrine Soc; Can Diabetes Asn; Am Diabetes Asn; Can Physiol Soc; Am Physiol Soc; fel Royal Col Physicians & Surg; Int Diabetes Fed; NY Acad Sci; Europ Asn Study Diabetes; Can Soc Clin Res. *Res:* Metabolic and neuroendocrine regulations in physiology and diabetes tracer methodology; exercise and stress; indirect effects of insulin; regulation of glucose transport on molecular, cellular and integrative levels; effects of hyperglycemia and hypoglycemia; 227 publications in field. *Mailing Add:* Univ Toronto Fac Med Dept Physiol Med Sci Bldg 1 King's Col Circle Toronto ON M5S 1A8 Can. *Fax:* 416-978-4940; *E-Mail:* mladen.vranic@utoronto.ca

**VRATSANOS, SPYROS M,** BIOCHEMISTRY, ORGANIC CHEMISTRY. *Current Pos:* res assoc, 63-65, ASST PROF MICROBIOL, COL PHYSICIANS & SURGEONS, COLUMBIA UNIV, 65- *Personal Data:* b Athens, Greece, Apr 10, 20; US citizen; m 58; c 2. *Educ:* Univ Athens, dipl chem, 50; Adelphi Univ, MS, 56; Fordham Univ, PhD(enzymol, org chem), 61. *Prof Exp:* Asst prof biochem, Adelphi Univ, 61-63. *Mem:* Am Chem Soc; Neuberg Socl Harvey Soc; Sigma Xi. *Res:* Organophosphorous compounds; origin of life on the earth; proteins; active sites of enzymes; conversion of light energy to chemical signals; chemistry of vision; immunochemistry. *Mailing Add:* 11 Chadwick Rd Syosset NY 11791-6508

**VRBA, FREDERICK JOHN,** ASTRONOMY. *Current Pos:* STAFF ASTRONR, FLAGSTAFF STA, NAVAL OBSERV, 76- *Personal Data:* b Cedar Rapids, Iowa, May 25, 49; m 71, Sheryl L; c Marya K & Sarah E. *Educ:* Univ Iowa, BA, 71; Univ Ariz, PhD(astron), 76. *Honors & Awards:* Simon Newcomb Award, US Naval Observ, 87. *Mem:* Sigma Xi; Am Astron Soc; Int Astron Union. *Res:* Infrared, optical, and polarimetric observations of young stars, dark nebulae, and the general interstellar medium; optical and infrared investigations of Gamma-ray bursts. *Mailing Add:* Naval Observ Flagstaff Sta Box 1149 Flagstaff AZ 86002. *Fax:* 520-774-3626; *E-Mail:* fjv@nofs.navy.mil

**VRBANAC, JOHN JAMES,** MASS SPECTROMETRY, DRUG METABOLISM. *Current Pos:* RES SCIENTIST, UPJOHN CO, 88- *Personal Data:* b Grand Rapids, Mich, Jan 30, 49; m 91; c 1. *Educ:* Mich State Univ, BS, 72, PhD(pharmacol), 84. *Prof Exp:* Asst prof pharmacol, Med Univ SC, 84-88. *Concurrent Pos:* Consult, Ciba-Geigy Corp, 88-89. *Mem:* Am Soc Mass Spectrometry; Am Chem Soc. *Res:* Use of mass spectrometry to solve qualitative and quantitative problems in medicine and biology. *Mailing Add:* Pharmacia & Upjohn Inc OU 7256-300-161 Kalamazoo MI 49007

**VREBALOVICH, THOMAS,** SPACE PHYSICS, FLUID MECHANICS. *Current Pos:* mem coun sci & technol affairs, Am Embassy, New Delhi, India, 75-80, MEM COUN SCI & TECHNOL AFFAIR, AM EMBASSY, CAIRO, EGYPT, 80- *Personal Data:* b Los Angeles, Calif, July 10, 26; m 51; c 2. *Educ:* Calif Inst Technol, BS, 48, MS, 49, PhD(aeronaut eng), 54. *Honors & Awards:* Fairbanks Mem Award, Soc Photog Instrumentation Engrs, 66; NASA Group Achievement Award for Mariner Mars 71 proj. *Prof Exp:* From res scientist to sr res scientist, Jet Propulsion Lab, Calif Inst Technol, 52-61, res specialist, 61-62, Ranger proj scientist, 63-65, group supvr photosci, 65-66, Surveyor assoc proj scientist, 65-67, div rep space sci, 66-67, Voyager landed capsule syst scientist, 67-68, on leave, 68-70, Sci Recommendation Chief,

Mariner Mars 1971 Proj, 70-73, mission sci coordr, Mariner Jupiter Saturn Proj, 73-74, mgr res, 74-75. *Concurrent Pos:* Instr, Univ Southern Calif, 56 & Univ Calif, Los Angeles, 57; consult, Flow Corp, 66-; vis prof aeronaut, Indian Inst Technol, Kanpur, 68-70; mem bd gov, Photog Art & Sci Found, 72-; mem bd dir, US Educ Found, India, 75. *Mem:* Am Inst Aeronaut & Astronaut; Sigma Xi; Am Phys Soc; Explorers Club. *Res:* Supersonic aerodynamics; space photography and science. *Mailing Add:* 4265 Marina City Dr PH12 Marina Del Rey CA 90292

**VREDEVELD, NICHOLAS GENE,** PLANT PATHOLOGY, MICROBIOLOGY. *Current Pos:* from asst prof to assoc prof, 64-84, PROF BIOL, UNIV TENN, CHATTANOOGA, 84- *Personal Data:* b Hudsonville, Mich, May 5, 29; m 53; c 2. *Educ:* Calvin Col, AB, 51; Mich State Univ, MS, 55, PhD(plant path), 65. *Prof Exp:* Biochemist, St Lawrence Hosp, Lansing, Mich, 62-64. *Mem:* Am Phytopath Soc. *Res:* Fungicides and fungus physiology, environmental effect on plant disease distribution; effect of microbiol toxins on plants, whole and in tissue culture; animal cell culture (lymphocytes). *Mailing Add:* Dept Biol Univ Tenn Chattanooga TN 37401-2598

**VREDEVOE, DONNA LOU,** IMMUNOTOXICOLOGY, TUMOR IMMUNOLOGY & NEUROIMMUNOLOGY. *Current Pos:* Instr bact, Univ Calif, 63, asst res immunologist, 64-67, asst prof nursing res, 67-70, consult lab nuclear med & radiation biol, 67-80, assoc prof 70-76, dir space planning, Cancer Ctr, 74-90, assoc dean, 76-78, chmn, Allied Sci Sect, 79-88, actg assoc dean, Sch Nursing, 85-86, PROF NURSING RES, UNIV CALIF, LOS ANGELES, 76-; ACT DEAN, 95-96. *Personal Data:* b Ann Arbor, Mich, Jan 11, 38; m 62; c 1. *Educ:* Univ Calif, Los Angeles, BA, 59, PhD(microbiol), 63. *Concurrent Pos:* USPHS fel microbiol, Stanford Univ, 63-64; res grants, Calif Inst Cancer Res, Univ Calif, Cancer Res Coord Comt, Am Cancer Soc, Calif Div & Nat Am Cancer Soc, US Dept Energy & USPHS. *Mem:* Am Asn Immunol; Am Soc Microbiol; Am Asn Cancer Res; Sigma Xi; Nat League Nursing (vpres, 79-81). *Res:* Serotyping for human kidney transplantation; delayed hypersensitivity; immunosuppression; immunotherapy; tumor immunology; mouse lymphoma; effects of metallic ions on the immune response; carcinogenesis; immunology of heart failure. *Mailing Add:* Sch Nursing Ctr Health Sci Univ Calif PO Box 951702 Los Angeles CA 90095-1702. *E-Mail:* dvredevo@sonnet.ucla.edu

**VREDEVOE, LAWRENCE A,** ANESTHESIOLOGY. *Current Pos:* mem staff med training, Sch Med, Univ Calif, San Francisco, 72-75, surg resident, 75-77, head & neck surg resident, 77-78, anesthesiol resident, 78-80, ASST PROF ANESTHESIOL, CTR HEALTH SCI, UNIV CALIF, LOS ANGELES, 80-; CHIEF, DEPT ANESTHESIOL, SAINT JOHN'S HOSP, SANTA MONICA, CALIF, 84- *Personal Data:* b Ann Arbor, Mich, Aug 2, 40; m 66; c 2. *Educ:* Univ Calif, Los Angeles, BA, 62, MA, 64, PhD(physics), 66; Univ Calif, San Francisco, MD, 75. *Prof Exp:* Mem tech staff theoret physics, Sci Ctr, NAm Rockwell Corp, Calif, 66-70; assoc prof physics, Ind Univ, Bloomington, 70-72. *Mem:* AMA; Am Soc Anesthesiologists; Am Phys Soc. *Mailing Add:* 2118 Wilshire Blvd Suite 230 Santa Monica CA 90403

**VREELAND, JOHN ALLEN,** PHYSICS. *Current Pos:* PROF NUCLEAR ENG, SCH ENG, CALIF STATE UNIV, SACRAMENTO, 69- *Personal Data:* b Orlando, Fla, Jan 6, 25; m 52; c 2. *Educ:* Presby Col, BS, 49; Univ Wis, MA, 51, PhD(physics), 56. *Prof Exp:* Asst physicist, Univ Wis, 50-55; fel scientist, Atomic Power Div, Westinghouse Elec Corp, 55-60; sr nuclear specialist, Rocketdyne Div, NAm Aviation, 60-62; mgr nuclear anal dept, nuclear rocket opers, Aerojet-Gen Corp, 62-69. *Concurrent Pos:* Lectr, Univ Calif, 60-; consult, Univ Fla, 62; mem Atomic Indust Forum. *Mem:* Am Physics Soc; Am Nuclear Soc; Am Inst Aeronaut & Astronaut; Sigma Xi. *Res:* Reactor physics; nuclear structure; analysis and detection of nuclear transport phenomena; systems analysis related to nuclear power plant design. *Mailing Add:* 4901 Shamrock Dr Fair Oaks CA 95628-5248

**VREELAND, THAD, JR,** MATERIALS SCIENCE. *Current Pos:* Res fel mech eng, Calif Inst Technol, 52-54, from asst prof to assoc prof, 54-63, assoc prof mat sci, 63-67, prof, 68-91, EMER PROF MAT SCI, CALIF INST TECHNOL, 91- *Personal Data:* b Portland, Ore, Oct 20, 24; m 48, Mary J Badour; c Michael C, Terry P & Janet A. *Educ:* Calif Inst Technol, BS, 49, MS, 50, PhD(mech eng), 52. *Concurrent Pos:* Consult, indust & govt labs. *Res:* Dynamic powder consolidation; crystal analysis by x-ray rocking curves; plastic deformation of crystals; dislocation dynamics. *Mailing Add:* Eng & Appl Sci 128-95 Calif Inst Technol 1201 E Calif Blvd Pasadena CA 91125

**VREELAND, VALERIE JANE,** CELL BIOLOGY, CARBOHYDRATE BIOCHEMISTRY. *Current Pos:* fel carbohydrate immunocytochem, 74-78, RES BOTANIST DEVELOP BIOL, DEPT BOT, UNIV CALIF, BERKELEY, 78- *Personal Data:* b Brooklyn, NY, Oct 15, 43; m 73; c 2. *Educ:* Lake Forest Col, BA, 65; Stanford Univ, MA, 67, PhD(biol sci), 71. *Prof Exp:* Fel carbohydrate immunochem, Univ Trondheim, Norway, 71; fel marine pollution, Woods Hole Oceanog Inst, 72-73. *Concurrent Pos:* Lectr, dept biol, Univ Calif, Berkeley, 75, res assoc, Los Angeles, 75-78; res assoc, biol dept, Univ Calif, Los Angeles, 75-78. *Mem:* Am Soc Cell Biol; Am Soc Plant Physiol; Phycol Soc Am; Int Phycol Soc. *Res:* Cell wall carbohydrate production and developmental modifications investigated in a brown algal embryo system; monoclonal antibodies and carbohydrate hybridization probes utilized as molecular markers for important carbohydrate structures. *Mailing Add:* Dept ESPM Hilgard Hall Univ Calif Berkeley CA 94720-5099. *Fax:* 510-642-4995

**VREMAN, HENDRIK JAN,** NEONATAL JAUNDICE. *Current Pos:* res assoc med, Vet Admin Hosp, 75-80, lab dir, Gen Clin Res Ctr, 80-82, SR RES SCIENTIST & LAB DIR, NEONATAL METAB LAB, SCH MED, STANFORD UNIV, 82-, CORE LAB DIR, PEDIAT SUBCOMT, GEN CLIN RES CTR, 87- *Personal Data:* b Soest, Neth, Jan 22, 39; US citizen; m 64, Pietje de Groot; c Shirley & Gerrit J. *Educ:* Univ NC, Chapel Hill, BA, 68; Univ Wis-Madison, PhD(bot), 73. *Prof Exp:* Lab asst dairy chem & bact, United Gooi Dairies, Hilversum, Neth, 56-57; anal chemist vet med, Lab Med Vet Med, Univ Utrecht, 57-60; anal chemist pub health, Pharmaceut & Toxicol Lab, Nat Inst Pub Health, Utrecht, Neth, 60-62; res technician biochem, E R Johnson Found, Univ Pa, 62-64; res technician physiol & pharmacol, Duke Univ, 64-68; res asst bot, Inst Plant Develop, Univ Wis-Madison, 68-73; Nat Res Coun res assoc, Western Regional Res Ctr, Agr Res Serv, USDA, Calif, 73-75. *Concurrent Pos:* Consult, Trace Anal, Inc, Menlo Park, Calif, 82-, Natus Med, Inc, San Carlos, Calif, 91- & Transducer Res, Inc, Naperville, Ill, 93-95, Reflect Sci, Inc, 96- *Mem:* AAAS; Am Soc Photobiol; Oxygen Soc; Int Soc Free Radical Res. *Res:* Role of cytokinins in plant growth and development; isolation, separation, identification of naturally occurring cytokinins; plant cell and tissue cultures; acetate metabolism in humans with chronic renal failure; zinc nutrition; atherosclerosis; carbohydrate metabolism; diabetes mellitus in human subjects; neonatal jaundice; metabolism of heme; biological production of carbon monoxide; photosensitizers in medicine; lipid peroxidation; metalloporphyrins in medicine; development of analytical and medical devices. *Mailing Add:* Dept Pediat Stanford Univ Med Ctr S214 Stanford CA 94305-5119. *Fax:* 650-725-7724; *E-Mail:* henkvreman.hf.txg@forsythe.stanford.edu

**VRENTAS, CHRISTINE MARY,** POLYMER RHEOLOGY, DIFFUSION IN POLYMERS. *Current Pos:* Asst prof, 81-83, from adj asst prof to adj assoc prof, 83-90, ADJ PROF CHEM ENG, PA STATE UNIV, 90- *Personal Data:* b Chicago, Ill, June 16, 53; m 75, James S; c 2. *Educ:* Ill Inst Technol, BS, 75; Northwestern Univ, MS, 77, PhD(chem eng), 81. *Mem:* Am Inst Chem Engrs; Soc Rheology. *Res:* Transport phenomena in fluids, primarily polymeric materials; polymer rheology (development of constitutive equations and material properties measurement); theoretical studies of polymer-solvent diffusion and sorption. *Mailing Add:* Dept Chem Eng Pa State Univ University Park PA 16802. *Fax:* 814-865-2574

**VRENTAS, JAMES SPIRO,** DIFFUSION IN POLYMERS, POLYMER RHEOLOGY. *Current Pos:* prof, 80-85, DOW PROF CHEM ENG, PA STATE UNIV, 85. *Personal Data:* b Danville, Ill, Apr 14, 36; m 75, Christine Jarzebski; c 2. *Educ:* Univ Ill, BS, 58; Univ Del, MChE, 61, PhD(chem eng), 63. *Honors & Awards:* William H Walker Award, Am Inst Chem Engrs, 81, Charles M A Stine Mat Eng & Sci Award, 89. *Prof Exp:* Res engr, Dow Chem Co Mich, 63-72; from asst prof to prof, Ill Inst Technol, 72-80- *Mem:* Am Inst Chem Engrs; Am Chem Soc; Sigma Xi. *Res:* Transport phenomena; fluid mechanics; diffusion; applied mathematics; polymer science. *Mailing Add:* Dept Chem Eng Pa State Univ University Park PA 16802. *Fax:* 814-865-2574

**VRIELAND, GAIL EDWIN,** INDUSTRIAL CHEMISTRY. *Current Pos:* Res specialist, 63-80, RES ASSOC CHEM, CENT RES LAB, DOW CHEM CO, 80- *Personal Data:* b Grand Rapids, Mich, Jan 4, 38; m 63; c 3. *Educ:* Calvin Col, AB, 59; Northwestern Univ, PhD(chem), 63. *Mem:* Am Chem Soc; Sigma Xi. *Res:* Heterogeneous catalysis and high temperature vapor phase reaction including oxidations and hydrocyanation. *Mailing Add:* 1420 Crescent Dr Midland MI 48640-3315

**VRIESEN, CALVIN W,** ORGANIC POLYMER CHEMISTRY, ORGANIC CHEMISTRY. *Current Pos:* res chemist, Thiokol Corp, Elkton, Md, 58-62, staff chemist, 62-68, sr scientist, 68-74, GROUP SUPVR, THIOKOL CORP, ELKTON, MD, 74- *Personal Data:* b Elkhart Lake, Wis, Aug 31, 16; m 41; c 2. *Educ:* Univ Minn, BS, 39, MS, 47; Purdue Univ, PhD(org chem), 52. *Honors & Awards:* Aerospace Scientist of Yr Award, Am Inst Aeronaut & Astronaut, 67. *Prof Exp:* Assoc prof chem, Ill Col, 47-49; res chemist, Chattanooga Nylon Plant, E I du Pont de Nemours & Co, 52-56, Chambers Works, 56-58. *Mem:* Am Chem Soc; Sigma Xi. *Res:* Condensation, cationic, anionic polymerization; synthesis of new binders, oxidizers, coolants for solid rocket propellants. *Mailing Add:* 12 Mitchell Circle Brookside Newark DE 19713-2522

**VRIJENHOEK, ROBERT CHARLES,** EVOLUTIONARY BIOLOGY. *Current Pos:* from asst prof to assoc prof zool, 74-84, prof biol, 84-, PROF GENETICS & DIR, CTR THEORET GENETICS, RUTGERS UNIV, NEW BRUNSWICK. *Personal Data:* b Rotterdam, Neth, Mar 13, 46; US citizen; m 68; c 2. *Educ:* Univ Mass, BA, 68; Univ Conn, PhD(zool), 72. *Prof Exp:* Asst prof biol, Southern Methodist Univ, 72-74. *Concurrent Pos:* NSF grants, 74, 76, 77, 79, 82, 85, 87, 89,93 & 96; mem, Pop Biol & Physiol Ecol Panel, NSF, 78-81; mem, Conf Biol Diversity, US Dept State, 81; mem coun, Am Genetics Asn, 81-83, 85-, assoc ed, Evolution; ed, Evolution, 87-90; assoc ed, Conserv Biol, 87-; NIH grant, 95. *Mem:* Soc Study Evolution; Am Soc Ichthyol & Herpetol; Genetics Soc Am; Am Genetic Asn; Am Soc Naturalists; Am Soc Persatologist; Soc Conserv Biol. *Res:* Population genetic studies of evolutionary relationships and genetic variation in fishes, snails and parasitic helminths; the effects of various sexual and asexual mating systems on the genetic structure and evolutionary potential of populations. *Mailing Add:* 3 Woodland St Whitehouse Station NJ 08889

**VROMAN, HUGH EGMONT,** BIOCHEMISTRY. *Current Pos:* RETIRED. *Personal Data:* b Detroit, Mich, Apr 18, 28; m 59, Antonia Compton; c R G (Jones). *Educ:* Univ Md, BS, 50, PhD(zool), 62. *Prof Exp:* Biologist, Nat Heart Inst, 57-58, biochemist, 58-61; res biologist, Insect Physiol Lab, Agr

Res Serv, USDA, 61-66; biochemist, Dept Dermat, Sch Med, Univ Miami, 66-69; prof biol, Claflin Col, 69-76, actg chmn dept biol, 71-73; from asst prof to prof biol, Cleveland State Community Col, 76-90. *Mem:* AAAS; Entom Soc Am; Am Soc Zool; Brit Biochem Soc; Am Inst Biol Sci. *Res:* Cholesterol metabolism; lipid biosynthesis by insects; insect hormones; sterol metabolism by insects; lipid biosynthesis and metabolism in skin. *Mailing Add:* 3840 Sycamore Dr NW Cleveland TN 37312

**VROMAN, LEO,** PHYSIOLOGY, BIOPHYSICS. *Current Pos:* SR RES SCIENTIST, CHEM ENG DEPT, COLUMBIA UNIV, 87- *Personal Data:* b Gouda, Holland, Apr 10, 15; nat US; m 47, Georgine M Sanders; c Geraldine E (Griffin) & Peggy Ann (Gracy). *Educ:* Jakarta Med Col, Indonesia, Drs, 41; Univ Utrecht, PhD(animal physiol), 58. *Hon Degrees:* PhD, Ryks Univ Groningen, Neth, 89. *Honors & Awards:* Clemson Award for Basic Sci in Biomater Res, 86; Silver Medal, Neth Royal Acad Sci, 87. *Prof Exp:* Asst zool, anat & physiol, Jakarta Med Col, 41; res assoc, St Peter's Gen Hosp, New Brunswick, NJ, 46-55; asst, Mt Sinai Hosp, New York, 56-58; sr physiologist, Stress-Tension Proj, Dept Animal Behav, Am Mus Natural Hist, 58-61; biochemist, Vet Admin Hosp, Brooklyn, 61-78, res career scientist, 78-86; assoc prof, Biophys Dept, State Univ NY, Downstate Med Ctr, 77-87. *Mem:* Fel NY Acad Sci; fel NY Acad Med. *Res:* Behavior of blood at interfaces; biomaterials. *Mailing Add:* 2365 E 13th St Apt 6U Brooklyn NY 11229

**VROOM, ALAN HEARD,** INSTRUMENTATION, MATERIALS SCIENCE. *Current Pos:* CHMN, STARCRETE TECHNOL INC, 96- *Personal Data:* b Montreal, Que, Can, Oct 5, 20; m 43, 84, Pauline Ritchie; c Richard & Christopher. *Educ:* McGill Univ, BSc, 42, PhD(phys chem), 45. *Prof Exp:* Nat Res Coun Can, 44-46; asst dir res pulp & paper, Fraser Co, Ltd, 46-49; Hibbert Mem fel & hon lectr, McGill Univ, 50; res fel bark chem, Pulp & Paper Res Inst Can, 50-51; asst chief, Appl Chem Sect, Weyerhaeuser Timber Co, 51-52, chief, Appl Physics Sect, 52-54 & Appl Chem Sect, 54; asst dir res, Consol Paper Corp, Ltd, 55-56, dir res, 56-67, dir res & develop, Consol-Bathurst Ltd, 67-71; spec consult, Nat Res Coun Can, 71-73; pres, Sulfurcrete Prods, Inc, 73-96. *Concurrent Pos:* Consult, Pulp & Paper Res Inst, Can, 51-54; pres, Vroom Concrete Inc, 93-95. *Mem:* Am Concrete Inst; fel Chem Inst Can; Can Soc Chem Eng; Am Soc Testing & Mat. *Res:* Bark chemistry; pulp and paper; wood and fiber technology; sulfur utilization; development of new sulfur-based construction materials, primarily sulfur concrete. *Mailing Add:* 10728 Willowfern Dr SE Calgary AB T2J 1R4 Can. *Fax:* 403-278-6779; *E-Mail:* vrooma@sthrcrete.com

**VROOM, DAVID ARCHIE,** POLYMER ENGINEERING, RADIATION TECHNOLOGY. *Current Pos:* tech dir corp res & develop process eng, Raychem Corp, 81-84, mfg mgr, HTG Group, 85-87, dir radiation serv, 87-95, MGR, CORP MFG SUPPORT, RAYCHEM CORP, 95- *Personal Data:* b Vancouver, BC, Sept 12, 41; m 69, Anna Stravers; c Peter. *Educ:* Univ BC, BSc, 63, PhD(phys chem), 67. *Prof Exp:* Nat Res Coun Can overseas fel, 67-68; staff chemist, Atomic Physics Br, Gulf Radiation Technol Div, Gulf Energy & Environ Systs, 68-73; prin scientist, IRT Corp, 73-77, mgr atomic physics dept, 77-81. *Mem:* Am Phys Soc; Am Chem Soc. *Res:* Photoionization and photoelectron spectroscopy; electron impact studies of excitation; dissociation and ionization; low energy ion neutral reactions and pulse radiolysis studies; polymer processing; polymer physics; radiation technology; accelerator technology. *Mailing Add:* 300 Constitution Dr Raychem Corp Mail Stop 106/6613 Menlo Park CA 94025. *E-Mail:* dvroom@raychem.com

**VRSCAY, EDWARD ROBERT,** FRACTAL ANALYSIS, FRACTAL COMPRESSION METHODS. *Current Pos:* from asst prof to assoc prof, 86-94, PROF, DEPT APPL MATH, UNIV WATERLOO, CAN, 94- *Personal Data:* b Grimsby, Ont, May 9, 53; m 81, Rosemary Anne Radvak; c Robert Andrej. *Educ:* Univ Waterloo, BSc, 75, MMath, 77, PhD(appl math), 84. *Prof Exp:* Nat Sci & Eng Res Coun Can postdoctoral fel, Sch Math, Ga Inst Technol, 84-85. *Concurrent Pos:* Vis asst prof, Sch Math, Ga Inst Technol, 84-86; Nat Sci & Eng Res Coun Can Univ res fel, Dept Appl Math, Univ Waterloo, 86-96; vis prof, Sch Appl Math, Italy, 89; vis mem dynamical systs theory, Fields Inst Res Math Sci, Waterloo, 92-93. *Mem:* Can Appl Math Soc; Soc Indust & Appl Math; Planetary Soc; Inst Elec & Electronics Engrs. *Res:* Applied dynamical systems theory; iterated mappings; mathematical theory of fractal and fractal-wavelet transforms and their applications to signal and image compression and representation; classical limiting procedures in quantum mathematics, especially in perturbation methods and coherent states. *Mailing Add:* Dept Appl Math Univ Waterloo Waterloo ON N2L 3G1 Can. *Fax:* 519-746-4319; *E-Mail:* ervrscay@links.uwaterloo.ca

**VU, QUAT THUONG,** MODELING & SIMULATIONS. *Current Pos:* SR STAFF ENGR, INTEL CORP, 90- *Personal Data:* b Vietnam, 1944; US citizen; m 73, Lethuy Phan; c Hien T & Duc T. *Educ:* Univ Ky, BS, 65; Calif Inst Technol, MS, 67, PhD(elec eng), 70. *Prof Exp:* Dean, Minh Duc Univ Col Eng, 71-75. *Res:* On-chip interconnect modeling and simulations, system modeling and performance; granted 2 patents. *Mailing Add:* Intel Corp 3065 Bowers Ave Santa Clara CA 95052. *E-Mail:* quattvu@ccm.sc.intel.com

**VUCHIC, VUKAN R,** TRANSPORTATION ENGINEERING, URBAN TRANSPORTATION SYSTEMS. *Current Pos:* asst prof civil eng-transp, Union Pub Transp Found, 67-70, assoc prof, 70-75, prof, 75-90, chair transp eng, 90, PROF TRANSP ENG, DEPT SYST ENG, UNIV PA, 90- *Personal Data:* b Belgrade, Yugoslavia, Jan 14, 35; US citizen; m 60, Radmila Zeljic; c Monika, Boris, Lili & Victor. *Educ:* Univ Belgrade, dipl transp eng, 60; Univ Calif, Berkeley, MEng, 65, PhD(civil eng, transp), 66. *Hon Degrees:* MA,

Univ Pa, 71. *Honors & Awards:* Friedrich Lehner Medal, Munich, Ger, 82. *Prof Exp:* Planning engr, Hamburger Hochbahn AG, Ger, 60-61; asst & prin engr, Wilbur Smith & Assocs, Conn, 61-63. *Concurrent Pos:* Mem, Transp Res Bd, Nat Acad Sci-Nat Res Coun; consult, Off Technol Assessment, US Cong, 75, Fed Transit Admin, US Dept Transp, 91; vis prof, Stellenbosch Univ, SAfrica, 81-83 & 93; consult transp systs planning, Belgrade, Edmonton, Lima, Rome, NY, Philadelphia, Toronto & San Francisco. *Mem:* Am Soc Civil Engrs; Inst Transp Engrs; assoc mem Int Union Pub Transp; Asn Transp & Commun Eng & Technicians Yugoslavia; foreign mem Serbian Acad Sci & Arts. *Res:* Transportation policy, analysis, economics, systems definition, operation, evaluation and facilities; public transportation systems, rail transit; city planning and urban development; urban transportation planning, design and operations; traffic engineering; highway, street and transit network design; transportation in developing countries. *Mailing Add:* Dept Syst Eng Towne Bldg Univ Pa Philadelphia PA 19104-6315. *Fax:* 215-573-2065; *E-Mail:* vuchic@eniac.seas.upenn.edu

**VUCICH, M(ICHAEL) G(EORGE),** ELECTROCHEMISTRY, LUBRICATION. *Current Pos:* RETIRED. *Personal Data:* b Bower Hill, Pa, Oct 30, 26; m 57, Rosetta M Ciotti; c Michael, Rosanne, Robert & Richard. *Educ:* US Merchant Marine Acad, BS, 48; Carnegie Inst Technol, BS, 52. *Prof Exp:* From chem engr to res chem engr, Weirton Steel Co Div, Nat Steel Corp, 52-58, res engr, 58-59, sr res engr, 59-73, res assoc, 73-74, supvr corrosion & lubrication res, Res & Develop Dept, 74-85, sr scientist, 86-91, mgr process res & technol, 91-92. *Concurrent Pos:* Consult steel strip coatings & electrochem methods. *Mem:* Electrochem Soc; Nat Asn Corrosion Engrs; Am Electroplaters & Surface Finishers; Asn Iron & Steel Engrs. *Res:* Electrodeposition; surface chemistry and corrosion; lubrication; cold reduction; electrocoating. *Mailing Add:* 115 Forest Rd Weirton WV 26062

**VUCKOVIC, VLADETA,** MATHEMATICS. *Current Pos:* asst prof, 63-66, assoc prof, 66-89, EMER PROF MATH, UNIV NOTRE DAME, 89- *Personal Data:* b Aleksinac, Yugoslavia, Mar 30, 23; m 54; c 2. *Educ:* Univ Belgrade, MS, 49; PhD(math), Serbian Acad Sci, 53. *Prof Exp:* Instr math, Univ Belgrade, 49-52; sci collabr, Math Inst, Serbian Acad Sci, 52-54; prof math, Teacher Inst, Zrenjanin, Yugoslavia, 54-60; from asst prof to assoc prof, Univ Belgrade, 60-63. *Mem:* Math Asn Am; Asn Symbolic Logic. *Res:* Foundations of mathematics; mathematical analysis; summability of divergent series and integrals; theory of recursive functions. *Mailing Add:* 2754 Southridge Dr South Bend IN 46614

**VUILLEMIN, JOSEPH J,** GENERAL PHYSICS. *Current Pos:* asst prof, 66-70, assoc prof, 70-81, PROF PHYSICS, UNIV ARIZ, 81- *Personal Data:* b Waco, Tex, July 22, 34; m 57; c 3. *Educ:* Univ Tex, BS, 56; Baylor Univ, MS, 57; Univ Chicago, PhD(physics), 65. *Prof Exp:* NSF fel, Cambridge Univ, 65-66. *Concurrent Pos:* Sci res coun fel, Univ Bristol, 74-75; vis scientist, Nat High Magnetic Field Lab, 96-97. *Mem:* Am Phys Soc. *Res:* Electronic structure of metals and low temperature physics. *Mailing Add:* Dept Physics Univ Ariz Bldg 81 Tucson AZ 85721

**VUILLEUMIER, FRANCOIS,** POPULATION BIOLOGY, BIOGEOGRAPHY. *Current Pos:* assoc cur, 74-79, chmn, 87-92, CUR ORNITH, AM MUS NATURAL HIST, 79- *Personal Data:* b Berne, Switz, Nov 26, 38; m 64, 72, 83, Rebecca Branch; c Alexis B, Claire A & Isabelle. *Educ:* Univ Geneva, Lic nat sci, 61; Harvard Univ, PhD(biol), 67. *Prof Exp:* From instr to asst prof biol, Univ Mass, Boston, 66-71; prof zool & dir inst animal ecol, Univ Lausanne, 71-72; res fel marine biol, Biol Sta Roscoff, France, 72-73; vis prof, Lab Ecol, Ecole Normale Superieure, Univ Paris, 73-74. *Concurrent Pos:* Am Mus Natural Hist Chapman fel, 67-68; vis prof, Univ Andes, Merida, Venezuela, 81. *Mem:* Fel AAAS; fel Am Ornith Union; Soc Study Evolution; Soc Syst Zool; Am Soc Naturalists; Ecol Soc Am; corresp mem Soc Ornith France; Am Birding Asn. *Res:* Avian migration; avian speciation in South American Andes and in Patagonia; biogeography; patterns of species diversity in continental habitats; ecological genetics of marine molluscs; community ecology; evolution ornithology; southern hemisphere biogeography. *Mailing Add:* Am Mus Natural Hist Central Park W at 79th St New York NY 10024. *Fax:* 212-769-5759

**VUKASOVICH, MARK SAMUEL,** CORROSION PROTECTION, CORROSION INHIBITORS. *Current Pos:* CONSULT CORROSION PROTECTION & CORROSION INHIBITORS, 88- *Personal Data:* b Detroit, Mich, Dec 6, 27; m 53, 70, Sally J Niles; c John, Mark, Christian, Denise (Brazzel) & Nancy (Necker). *Educ:* Wayne State Univ, BS, 51, MS, 53. *Honors & Awards:* Wilbur Deutsch Mem Award, Soc Tribologists & Lubrication Engrs, 86. *Prof Exp:* Res scientist, Chrysler Corp, 53-60; dept head, Horizons Res Inc, 60-64; res mgr Sherwin Williams Co, 64-67; dir res & develop, Kerr Mfg Co, 67-69; dir technol, Climax Molybdenum Co, 70-88. *Concurrent Pos:* Part-time fac, Corrosion Protection, Chem Eng Dept, Wayne State Univ, 90- *Mem:* Nat Asn Corrosion Engrs; Soc Tribologists & Lubrication Engrs; Am Chem Soc; Fedn Soc Coating Technol. *Res:* Corrosion inhibition; corrosion protection; pigment synthesis; fiber reinforced composities; fiber optics; microencapsulated products; electronic materials; lubrication; author or co-author 20 journal articles, 16 US patents, three books. *Mailing Add:* 1457 Woodland Dr Ann Arbor MI 48103. *Fax:* 313-769-7894

**VUKOV, RASTKO,** ORGANIC & POLYMER CHEMISTRY, CHEMISTRY & PHYSICAL CHEMISTRY OF SURFACTANTS. *Current Pos:* DIR RES & DEVELOP, RHONE-POULENE SURFACTANTS & SPECIALTIES, CRANBURY, NJ, 90- *Personal Data:* b Belgrade, Yugoslavia, June 23, 42; Can citizen; m 66, Vesna Trifunovic; c Tamara & Ivana. *Educ:* Univ Belgrade, BSc, 65; Univ Alta, PhD(chem), 72. *Prof Exp:* Res scientist, Raylo Chem Ltd,

72-76, proj mgr, 76-78, dir indust res, 78-80, mgr contract res, 80-82; sci adv, Polysar Ltd, Can, 82-84; mgr Resins Res & Develop, Nacan Prod Ltd, Can, 84-86; tech dir, Alkaril Chem Ltd, Can, 86-90, vpres, 87-90. *Mem:* Can Inst Chem; Am Chem Soc; Sigma Xi. *Res:* Investigation of the micro-structure of polymers; studies of polymer reactions; synthesis of novel monomers, antioxidants and cross-linking agents, preparation and characterization of specialty polymers; development of structure-properties correlations for polymers; systheses and analysis of surface active agents and infestigation of their properties, process development. *Mailing Add:* 569 Sayre Dr Princeton NJ 08540

**VUKOVICH, FRED MATTHEW,** DYNAMIC METEOROLOGY, PHYSICAL OCEANOGRAPHY. *Current Pos:* CHIEF ATMOSPHERIC SCIENTIST, SCI APPLICATIONS INT CORP. *Personal Data:* b Chicago, Ill, July 13, 39; m 66; c 4. *Educ:* Parks Col Aeronaut Technol, St Louis, BS, 60; St Louis Univ, MS, 63, PhD(meteorol), 66. *Prof Exp:* Res meteorologist, Meteorol Res Inc, 63-64; res meteorologist, Res Triangle Inst, 55-68, supvr, 68-71, sr scientist, 71-74, mgr, Geosci Dept, 74-85, dir, 85-90, prin scientist, Atmospheric Sci Dept, 90-91. *Concurrent Pos:* Assoc prof, Duke Univ, 67-77; adj fac, adv & res, Col William & Mary, 92-; adj fac meterol, Univ NC, Chapel Hill, 93- *Mem:* Am Meteorol Soc. *Res:* Dynamic meteorology of urban atmosphere; physical oceanographic studies on continental shelf, Gulf Stream, and Gulf of Mexico; dynamics of synoptic-scale pollution; satellite meteorology and oceanography; tropical meteorology; global climate studies; cloud modelling; global ozone analysis using satellite remote sensing data. *Mailing Add:* Sci Applns Int Corp 615 Oberlin Rd Ste 300 Raleigh NC 27605

**VUKOVICH, ROBERT ANTHONY,** CLINICAL PHARMACOLOGY, CLINICAL RESEARCH. *Current Pos:* CHIEF EXEC OFFICER & PRES, ROBERTS PHARMACEUT CORP, 83- *Personal Data:* b Hoboken, NJ, Aug 6, 43; m 65; c 3. *Educ:* Allegheny Col, BS, 65; Jefferson Med Col, PhD(pharm), 69. *Honors & Awards:* Fel, Am Col Clin Pharmacol. *Prof Exp:* Clin res scientist clin pharmacol, Warner-Lambert Res Inst, 69-70; assoc dir, Med Res, USV Labs, 70-71; dir, Clin Pharmacol, The Sqiubb Inst Med Res, 72-79; dir, Clin Res, Div Develop Therapeut, Res & Develop Div, Revlon Health Care Group, 79-83. *Mem:* Am Soc Clin Pharmacol & Therapeut; Am Soc Pharmacol & Exp Therapeut; NY Acad Sci; fel Am Col Clin Pharmacol; AMA; AAAS; Parental Drug Asn; Sigma Xi; Royal Soc Med. *Res:* Clinical pharmacology; clinical research; new drug development; cardiovascular; inflammatory, infectious diseases; oncology; endocrinology; urology; pain management. *Mailing Add:* Roberts Pharmaceut Corp Meridan Ctr III 4 Industrial Way W Eatontown NJ 07724-2270. *Fax:* 732-389-1014

**VULLIEMOZ, YVONNE,** BIOCHEMICAL PHARMACOLOGY. *Current Pos:* Res assoc, Col Physicians & Surgeons, Columbia Univ, 69-77, asst prof, 77-84, assoc res scientist, 84-89, RES SCIENTIST, COL PHYSICIANS & SURGEONS, COLUMBIA UNIV, 90 *Personal Data:* b Switz, US citizen. *Educ:* Univ Lausanne, Switz, PharmD, 58; Univ Paris, France, PhD(pharmacol), 69. *Mem:* Am Soc Pharmacol & Exp Therapeut. *Res:* Pharmacology of the autonomic nervous system. *Mailing Add:* Anesthesiol Dept Columbia Col Physicians & Surgeons 630 W 168th St New York NY 10032-3702. *Fax:* 212-305-3204

**VULLO, WILLIAM JOSEPH,** ORGANIC CHEMISTRY. *Current Pos:* mem staff, environ protection oper, 80, MGR ENVIRON & LAB SERV, GEN ELEC CO, 85- *Personal Data:* b Buffalo, NY, June 14, 33; m 59; c 2. *Educ:* Univ Buffalo, BA, 55; Northwestern Univ, PhD(org chem), 59. *Prof Exp:* Instr gen chem, Northwestern Univ, 59; sr chemist, Hooker Chem Corp, 59-69; mgr textile res, Mohasco Industs, 69-79. *Mem:* Am Chem Soc; Am Asn Textile Chem & Colorists; Sigma Xi. *Res:* Organometallic chemistry; organic reaction mechanisms; metal conversion coatings and treatments; cellulose reactive chemicals; organic phosphorus and fluorine chemistry; fire retardants; textile chemicals and finishes; environmental sciences. *Mailing Add:* 24 Velina Dr Burnt Hills NY 12027-9724

**VUREK, GERALD G,** BIOMEDICAL ENGINEERING, ELECTRICAL ENGINEERING. *Current Pos:* Elec engr, Instrument Sect, NIH, 57-59, develop engr, Instrument Eng & Develop Br, 61-63, sr investr, Lab Tech Develop, 63-83, SR SCIENTIST, NAT HEART INST, 83-; ASSOC RES FEL, ABBOTT LABS. *Personal Data:* b San Francisco, Calif, May 7, 35; m 59, Ruth K Hall; c 1. *Educ:* Calif Inst Technol, BS, 56; Stanford Univ, MS, 57, Engr & MS, 61, PhD(physiol), 64. *Concurrent Pos:* Vpres, Joint Comt Eng in Med & Biol, 66, treas, 67-68, gen chmn ann conf, 70. *Mem:* AAAS; Inst Elec & Electronics Engrs; Biomed Eng Soc; Int Soc Optical Eng; Optical Soc Am. *Res:* Instrument and methods development for biochemical analysis; microchemical analysis instrumentation; cardiac anaphylaxis; microimmunochemistry; artificial circulatory support devices; in vivochemical sensors. *Mailing Add:* Abbott Labs 755 Jarvis Dr Morgan Hill CA 95037

**VUSKOVIC, LEPOSAVA,** ATOMIC INTERACTIONS WITH ELECTRONS & FIELDS IN GROUND & EXCITED STATES. *Current Pos:* FAC, PHYSICS DEPT, OLD DOMINION UNIV. *Personal Data:* b Lesnica, Yugoslavia, Apr 23, 41; m 87; c 3. *Educ:* Univ Belgrade, Yugoslavia, dipl physics/chem, 63, MS, 68, PhD(physics), 72. *Prof Exp:* Res fel physics, Inst Physics, Univ Belgrade, Yugoslavia, 64-73, res scientist, 73-78, head, Atomic Physics Lab, 75-78, assoc prof physics, 80-85, dir, Atomic Laser & High Energy Physics Div, 81-85; assoc prof, Univ Arts, Belgrade, Yugoslavia, 73-85; assoc prof physics, NY Univ, 85- *Concurrent Pos:* Mem, Gen Comn, Int Conf Physics, Int Conf Physics of Electronic & Atomic Collisions, 77-81; sr res assoc, Nat Res Coun/NASA Jet Propulsion Lab, Pasadena, Calif, 78-80. *Mem:* Am Phys Soc; Europ Phys Soc; Yugaslav Phys Soc. *Res:* Experimental

research in atomic beam collision physics; scattering studies, particularly measurements that describe fundamental interactions between electrons and atomic and molecular species and clusters, including collision in the presence of laser fields. *Mailing Add:* Physics Dept Old Dominion Univ 1040 W 45th St Norfolk VA 23529. *Fax:* 757-683-5676

**VYAS, BRIJESH,** INDUSTRIAL & MANUFACTURING ENGINEERING, METALLURGY & PHYSICAL METALLURICAL ENGINEERING. *Current Pos:* mem tech staff, 80-89, SUPVR, BELL LABS, 89- *Personal Data:* b Feb 7, 48. *Educ:* Indian Inst Technol, Bombay, India, BTech, 71; State Univ NY, Stony Brook PhD(mat sci), 75. *Honors & Awards:* Sam Tour Award, Am Soc Testing & Mat, 82. *Prof Exp:* Assoc mem tech staff, Brookhaven Nat Lab, Upton, NY, 75-80. *Concurrent Pos:* Vis prof, Tech Univ Denmark, Lyngby, 82. *Mem:* Electrochem Soc. *Res:* Energy conversion technologies primarily advanced batteries; erosion and corrosion of materials specially localized corrosion. *Mailing Add:* Bell Labs Lucent Technol Rm IE-247 600 Mountain Ave Murray Hill NJ 07974-2070. *Fax:* 908-582-2521; *E-Mail:* bry@bell-labs.com

**VYAS, GIRISH NARMADASHANKAR,** IMMUNOLOGY, GENETICS. *Current Pos:* lectr immunol, Univ Calif, San Francisco, 67-69, asst prof path, 69-73, dir, Blood Bank, 69-87, assoc prof, 73-77, PROF LAB MED & DIR TRANSFUSION RES, SCH MED, UNIV CALIF, SAN FRANCISCO, 77- *Personal Data:* b Aglod, India, June 11, 33; m 62, Devi; c Jay & Kris. *Educ:* Univ Bombay, BSc, 54, MSc, 57, PhD(microbiol), 64. *Honors & Awards:* Julliard Prize, Int Soc Blood Transfusion, 69. *Prof Exp:* Asst res officer, Blood Group Ref Ctr, Indian Coun Med Res, Bombay, 57-64; officer-in-chg, Bombay Munic Blood Ctr, King Edward Mem Hosp, India, 64-65. *Concurrent Pos:* Jr res fel hemat, J J Hosp, Bombay, India, 56-57; fel genetics, Western Res Univ, 65-67; Fulbright scholar, Pasteur Inst, 80. *Mem:* AAAS; Am Asn Immunol; Am Soc Microbiol; Am Soc Hemat. *Res:* Microbiology; blood group serology; immunogenetics; blood banking; viral hepatitis; transfusion and circulatory physiology; genetics of gamma globulin and its structure; molecular biology of transfusion transmitted viral infections causing aids and hepatitis. *Mailing Add:* Univ Calif Rm S555 San Francisco CA 94143-0134

**VYAS, REETA,** QUANTUM OPTICS, LASER THEORY. *Current Pos:* vis asst prof, Univ Ark, 84-88, res asst prof physics, 88-89, asst prof, 89-94, ASSOC PROF PHYSICS, UNIV ARK, 94- *Personal Data:* b Gujarat, India, May 25, 53; m 82, Surendra P Singh; c Savith R Chauhan. *Educ:* Banaras Hindu Univ, BSc, 73 & MSc, 75; State Univ NY, Buffalo, PhD(physics), 84. *Prof Exp:* Jr res fel, Coun Sci & Indust Res, India, 76-78; teaching asst, State Univ NY, Buffalo, 79-81, Univ grad fel, 81-83, postdoctoral res assoc physics, 85. *Concurrent Pos:* Hon lectr, Banaras Hindu Univ, India, 76; vis prof, Fed Univ da Pariaba, Joao Pessoa, Brazil, 92 & 96, Inst Quantum Physics, San Carlos USP, Brazil, 94. *Mem:* Am Phys Soc; Optical Soc Am. *Res:* Nonclassical effects and quantum statistics of light matter interactions; author of 50 scientific articles. *Mailing Add:* Physics Dept Univ Ark Fayetteville AR 72701. *Fax:* 501-575-4580; *E-Mail:* rvyas@comp.uark.edu

**VYBORNY, CARL JOSEPH,** RADIOLOGY, MEDICAL PHYSICS. *Current Pos:* Res assoc radiol physics, Univ Chicago, 78-80, resident physician radiol, 80-84, asst prof, 84-85, CLIN ASSOC PROF RADIOL, UNIV CHICAGO, 85- *Personal Data:* b Oak Park, Ill, Nov 23, 50; m 75; c 1. *Educ:* Univ Ill, Chicago, BS, 72, Urbana, MS, 73; Univ Chicago, PhD(radiol), 76, MD, 80. *Honors & Awards:* Eastman Kodak Sci Award, 76; Itek Award, 79; Andrew W Mellon Found Fel Award, 84. *Mem:* Am Asn Phys Med; Radiol Soc NAm; Am Col Radiol; AMA. *Res:* Applications of computer methods to radiologic diagnosis; chest radiography; mammography. *Mailing Add:* Suburban Radiologists PO Box 415 Western Springs IL 60558-0415

**VYDELINGUM, NADARAJEN AMEERDANADEN,** METABOLISM, CELL BIOLOGY. *Current Pos:* ASST ATTEND BIOCHEM, MEM SLOAN-KETTERING CANCER CTR, NY, 86-, DIR RES METAB & CANCER, 86- *Personal Data:* b Mauritius Plaines Wilhems Curepipe, June 1, 45; US citizen; m 71, Rosemary Dowland; c Eric & Naomi. *Educ:* Univ London, BSc, 72, MSc, 74, PhD(clin biochem), 79; Inst Biol, MIBiol, 90. *Prof Exp:* Res assoc endocrinol & metab, St Mary's Med Sch, Univ London, UK, 74-77; from instr to asst prof med & pharmacol, Med Col Wis, Milwaukee, 77-86, assoc dir, Core Res Facil, 79-86. *Concurrent Pos:* Prin investr, Am Heart Asn, 79-81, Am Diabetes Asn, 82-84, NIH, 85-88; adj asst prof biochem & cell biol, Univ Wis-Milwaukee, 79-82, lectr, 79-82; ad hoc reviewer, sci jour, 80-; peer reviewer, Health Sci Consortium, 84-, Am Diabetes Asn, 85-90; asst lab mem metab & cancer, Mem Sloan-Kettering Cancer Ctr, New York, 86-; health sci adminr, NIH, 91-; lectr, Johns Hopkins Univ, 94- *Mem:* Am Diabetes Asn; Am Soc Biochem & Molecular Biol; Am Inst Nutrit; Biochem Soc UK; Am Asn Cancer Res; Inst Biol UK. *Res:* Biochemical and molecular mechanisms responsible for the alteration of lipid and carbohydrate metabolism in cancer cachexia. *Mailing Add:* NIH 2A07 Westwood Bldg 5333 Westbard Ave Bethesda MD 20892

**VYE, MALCOLM VINCENT,** HEMATOLOGY, PATHOLOGY. *Current Pos:* ASST PROF PATH, MED SCH, NORTHWESTERN UNIV, EVANSTON, 71- *Personal Data:* b Gary, Ind, Feb 17, 36; m 60; c Jerome. *Educ:* Marquette Univ, MD, 61. *Prof Exp:* Asst instr, Col Med, Univ Ill, 62-64, from instr to asst prof path, 64-66 & 68-71. *Concurrent Pos:* Mem staff, Armed Forces Inst Path; assoc pathologist, Evanston Hosp, 71-89, vchmn, Dept Path, 89- *Mem:* AAAS; Am Soc Clin Path; Col Am Pathologists. *Res:* Hematology laboratory methodology. *Mailing Add:* Dept Path & Lab Med Evanston Hosp 2650 Ridge Ave Evanston IL 60201. *E-Mail:* maconmac@merle.acns.nwu.edu

# W

**WAACK, RICHARD,** PHYSICAL CHEMISTRY, POLYMER CHEMISTRY. *Current Pos:* MGR DEVELOP LAB, POLAROID CORP, WALTHAM, MD 69- *Personal Data:* b Syracuse, NY, May 18, 31; m 60. *Educ:* State Univ NY, BS, 53, MS, 54, PhD, 58. *Prof Exp:* Tech serv rep, Dow Chem Co, Mich, 54-56; chemist, Solvay Process Div, Allied Chem Co, NY, 58-59; res chemist, Eastern Res Lab, Dow Chem Co, Mich, 59-60, res chemist, Phys Res Lab, 67-69. *Mem:* Am Chem Soc; Soc Photog Sci & Eng. *Res:* Polymer synthesis; spectroscopy; ionic polymerization mechanisms; photographic science; silver halide emulsion technology; colloidal processes; water soluble polymers; diffusion processes. *Mailing Add:* 19 Morrill Dr Wayland MA 01778-4709

**WAAG, CHARLES JOSEPH,** GEOLOGY. *Current Pos:* FAC, BOISE STATE UNIV. *Personal Data:* b Oct 25, 31; US citizen; m 56; c 1. *Educ:* Univ Pittsburgh, BS, 56, MS, 58; Univ Ariz, PhD(geol), 68. *Prof Exp:* Sr geologist, Orinoco Mining Co, US Steel Corp, 58-63; sr geologist, Va Div Mineral Resources, 63-64; asst & lectr, Univ Ariz, 64-68; asst prof, 68-71, assoc prof geol, Ga State Univ, 71- *Concurrent Pos:* Consult hydrogeol, 69- *Mem:* Geol Soc Am. *Res:* Glaciers as models in structural geology; gravity tectonics attendant to mantled gneiss domes in the Basin and Range Province. *Mailing Add:* Dept Geol & Geophys Boise State Univ 1910 University Dr Boise ID 83725-0001

**WAAG, ROBERT CHARLES,** ELECTRICAL ENGINEERING, ACOUSTICS. *Current Pos:* ASSOC PROF ELEC ENG & RADIOL, UNIV ROCHESTER, 69- *Personal Data:* b Upper Darby, Pa, Oct 8, 38; m 61; c 2. *Educ:* Cornell Univ, BEE, 61, MS, 63, PhD(commun), 65. *Prof Exp:* Mem tech staff, Sandia Sci Labs, 65-66; proj officer commun, Rome Air Develop Ctr, USAF, 66-69. *Concurrent Pos:* NSF grant, 75-; Career Develop Award, NIH, 76- *Mem:* Inst Elec & Electronics Engrs; Acoust Soc Am; Am Inst Ultrasound Med. *Res:* Apply principles of physics and signal processing along with computer-based technology to improve imaging in diagnostic ultrasound and to characterize materials from measurements of ultrasonic scattering. *Mailing Add:* Dept Radiol Univ Rochester Med Ctr Box 648 601 Elmwood Ave 3-4314 Rochester NY 14627

**WAAGE, JONATHAN KING,** BEHAVIORAL ECOLOGY. *Current Pos:* From instr to assoc prof, 72-90, PROF BIOL, BROWN UNIV, 90- *Personal Data:* b Pueblo, Colo, July 27, 44; m 88. *Educ:* Princeton Univ, AB, 66; Univ Mich, PhD(zool), 71. *Mem:* Am Soc Naturalists; Soc Study Evolution; Animal Behav Soc; Ecol Soc Am; Societas Internationalis Odonatologics. *Res:* Evolutionary and ecological determinants of reproductive behavior in odonates and other insects; manipultive and comparative field studies of sexual selection, including sperm competition and mating systems. *Mailing Add:* Biol Box G-W208 Brown Univ Providence RI 02912-0001

**WAAGE, KARL MENSCH,** GEOLOGY. *Current Pos:* RETIRED. *Personal Data:* b Philadelphia, Pa, Dec 17, 15; m 42; c 2. *Educ:* Princeton Univ, AB, 39, MA, 42, PhD(geol), 46. *Prof Exp:* From instr to prof geol, Yale Univ, 46-86, chmn, Dept Geol-Geophys, 73-76, dir, Peabody Mus, 79-82, cur invert paleont, 46-86. *Concurrent Pos:* Geologist, US Geol Surv, Washington, DC, 42-59. *Mem:* Fel Geol Soc Am; Paleont Soc; fel AAAS. *Res:* Field exploration for non-metalliferous deposits; stratigraphic geology and paleontology of cretaceous of western interior. *Mailing Add:* Peabody Mus Natural Hist Yale Univ 170 Whitney Ave New Haven CT 06520

**WAALAND, IRVING T,** AERONAUTICAL DESIGN. *Current Pos:* AEROSPACE DESIGN CONSULT, 93- *Personal Data:* b Brooklyn, NY, July 2, 27; m 61, Helen Katz; c Ted, Neil, Elizabeth, Scotty & Diane. *Educ:* NY Univ, BAe, 53. *Honors & Awards:* Aircraft Design Award, Am Inst Aeronaut & Astronaut, 89 & Aircraft Design Cert Merit, 89; Leslie E Simon Award, Am Defense Preparedness Asn, 90; Wright Bros Lectr, Am Inst Aeronaut & Astronaut, 90; Eng Leadership Award, Soc Automotive Engrs, 93. *Prof Exp:* Proj aerodynamicist & proj engr, Grumman Aerospace Corp, 53-74; proj dir, Northrop Corp, 74-75, eng mgr var classified progs, 75-78, prog mgr B-2 concept develop, 79-80, vpres dep prog mgr, 81-83, vpres eng 83-86, vpres ATA prog mgr, 86-88, chief designer, 88-91. *Concurrent Pos:* Ad hoc mem, Naval Studies Bd, Nat Acad Sci & Aeronaut Facil Bd, NASA. *Mem:* Nat Acad Eng; fel Am Inst Aeronaut & Astronaut. *Res:* Advanced concept development and system synthesis; multi-discipline team building; program or engineering management; low observables; aeropropulsion; stability and control; avionics; sensors; author of various publications; granted 1 patent. *Mailing Add:* 65 Rollingwood Dr Rolling Hills Estates CA 90274-2425

**WAALAND, JOSEPH ROBERT,** ALGOLOGY, CYTOLOGY. *Current Pos:* From asst prof to assoc prof, 69-80, PROF BOT, UNIV WASH, 83-, ASSOC CHMN, 87- *Personal Data:* b San Mateo, Calif, Feb 22, 43; m 69; c 1. *Educ:* Univ Calif, Berkeley, BA, 66, PhD(bot), 69. *Mem:* Brit Phycol Soc; Phycol Soc Am; Int Phycol Soc; Marine Biol Asn UK. *Res:* Development, cytology and ecology of algae; aquaculture of marine algae. *Mailing Add:* 7029 18th Ave NE Seattle WA 98115

**WAALKES, T PHILLIP,** public health, for more information see previous edition

**WABECK, CHARLES J,** FOOD SCIENCE. *Current Pos:* prof poultry prod, 69-76, PROF POULTRY SCI, UNIV MD, COLLEGE PARK, 76- *Personal Data:* b Montague, Mass, July 16, 38; m 64; c 2. *Educ:* Univ Mass, BS, 62; Univ NH, MS, 64; Purdue Univ, PhD(food sci), 66. *Prof Exp:* Res assoc poultry & frozen foods, Armour & Co, 66-69; dir res frozen foods, Ocoma Foods Co, Nebr, 69. *Mem:* Inst Food Technologists; Poultry Sci Asn. *Res:* Research and development; quality control; frozen foods; poultry and meat products. *Mailing Add:* 4592 Nutters Crossroad Salisbury MD 21804

**WABER, JAMES THOMAS,** ATOMIC PHYSICS, SOLID STATE PHYSICS. *Current Pos:* RETIRED. *Personal Data:* b Chicago, Ill, Apr 8, 20; m 51; c 3. *Educ:* Ill Inst Technol, BS, 41, MS, 43, PhD(metall), 46. *Honors & Awards:* Turner Prize, Electrochem Soc, 47; Whitney Prize, Nat Asn Corrosion Engrs, 63. *Prof Exp:* Res assoc, Ill Inst Technol, 46, asst prof chem, 46-47; assoc metallurgist, Los Alamos Sci Lab, 47-49, staff mem, 49-66; prof mat sci, Northwestern Univ, Evanston, 67-85; prof physics, Mich Tech Univ, 85- *Concurrent Pos:* NSF sr fel, Univ Birmingham, 60-61; chmn, Comt Alloy Phases, past chmn, Nuclear Metall Comt & mem, Exec Comt, Inst Metals Div, NY; partic, Robert A Welch Found Conf Chem Res XIII Mendeleev Centennial-The Transuranium Elements; Alexander von Humboldt Found sr scientist award, Bonn, WGer; prof physics, Mich Technol Univ, Houghton. *Mem:* Am Soc Metals; Electrochem Soc; Am Inst Mining, Metall & Petrol Engrs; Nat Asn Corrosion Engrs; fel Am Phys Soc. *Res:* Corrosion and oxidation of metals; relativistic self-consistent field Dirac-Slater and Hartree-Fock calculations for atoms and ions; energy band calculations; chemistry and physics of superheavy elements; positron annhilation in metals. *Mailing Add:* 2651 Caminoto Carlitos Santa Fe NM 87501

**WACHENFELD, TIMOTHY H,** AERONAUTICAL ENGINEERING. *Current Pos:* GEN MGR, GEN ELEC AIRCRAFT ENGINES. *Honors & Awards:* Leadership Qual Mgt Award, Am Inst Astronaut & Aeronaut, 94. *Mailing Add:* GE Aircraft Engines 1 Neuman Way PO Box 156301 J101 Cincinnati OH 45215-6301

**WACHHOLZ, BRUCE WILLIAM,** RADIATION BIOLOGY. *Current Pos:* STAFF, NAT CANCER INST, BETHESDA, MD. *Personal Data:* b Chicago, Ill, Aug 16, 36; m 63; c 1. *Educ:* Valparaiso Univ, BA, 58; Univ Rochester, MS, 59, PhD(radiation biol), 67. *Prof Exp:* Sr res scientist, Pac Northwest Labs, Battelle Mem Inst, 66-71; radiation biologist, Off Health & Environ, Energy Res & Develop Admin, 71- *Mem:* AAAS; Am Phys Soc; Radiation Res Soc; NY Acad Sci; Geront Soc. *Res:* Pathological, physiological and endocrinological effects of radiation; metabolism and toxicity of radionuclides; gerontology. *Mailing Add:* 21031 Miracle Dr Gaithersburg MD 20882

**WACHMAN, HAROLD YEHUDA,** SURFACE PHYSICS, COMBUSTION AT ZERO-G. *Current Pos:* vis prof, 63-64, assoc prof, 64-69, PROF AERONAUT & ASTRONAUT, MASS INST TECHNOL, 69-, CHMN, GRAD DIV DEPT AERONAUT & ASTRONAUT, 76- *Personal Data:* b Tel Aviv, Israel, Dec 2, 27; nat US; m 54; c 3. *Educ:* City Col New York, BS, 49; Univ Mo, MA, 52, PhD(phys chem), 57. *Prof Exp:* Specialist chem physics, Aerosci Lab, Gen Elec Co, 57-63. *Concurrent Pos:* Consult, Space Sci Lab, Gen Elec Co; vis sr res fel, Jesus Col, Oxford Univ, 72-73. *Mem:* Sigma Xi; Am Inst Aeronaut & Astronaut. *Res:* Rarefied gas phenomena; adsorption; high temperature chemical equilibrium studies; gas surface interactions; nucleation phenomena; spacecraft-environment interactions; molecular dynamics computations. *Mailing Add:* 10 Diamond Rd Mass Inst Technol Lexington MA 02173-1622

**WACHMAN, MURRAY,** MATHEMATICS. *Current Pos:* assoc prof, 67-73, PROF MATH, UNIV CONN, 73-, ASSOC DEPT HEAD, 90- *Personal Data:* b Tel Aviv, Israel, Feb 1, 31; US citizen; m 58, Helene Leibowitz; c Elliot, Ronald & Adina. *Educ:* Brooklyn Col, BA, 53; NY Univ, MS, 56, PhD(math), 61. *Prof Exp:* Math analyst, Repub Aviation Corp, 57-59; appl mathematician, Gen Elec Co, 59-63, consult mathematician, 63-65, group leader appl math, 65-67. *Concurrent Pos:* Consult, Missile & Space Div, Gen Elec Co, 67-69, Naval Underwater Systs Ctr, 84-96. *Mem:* Am Math Soc; Soc Indust & Appl Math. *Res:* fluid mechanics; biological and economic models. *Mailing Add:* Dept Math Univ Conn Storrs CT 06268. *Fax:* 860-486-4238; *E-Mail:* wachman@uconnvm.uconn.edu

**WACHNIK, RICHARD ANDRE,** CONDENSED MATTER PHYSICS, SEMICONDUCTOR DEVICES. *Current Pos:* vis scientist, Res Div, 85-87, ADV SR ENGR, MICROELECTRONICS DIV, IBM, 87- *Personal Data:* b Cambridge, Mass, Feb 22, 54. *Educ:* Mass Inst Technol, BS, 77; Univ Pa, PhD(mat sci & eng), 82. *Prof Exp:* Electronics engr, Semiconductor Mat & Process Div, Nat Inst Stand & Technol, 82-85. *Mem:* Am Phys Soc; Inst Elec & Electronics Engrs. *Res:* Reliability physics of integrated circuits; electromigration; stress migration; dielectric breakdown; semiconductor device physics; development of reliable integrated circuit designs and processes; graphite compounds. *Mailing Add:* IBM Microelectronics Div AR1 E Fishkill Fac Hopewell Junction NY 12533

**WACHS, ALAN LEONARD,** PROCESS ENGINEERING & DEVELOPMENT, QUALITY ASSURANCE. *Current Pos:* PROCESS ENGR, MULTI-ARC, INC, 97- *Personal Data:* b Kalamazoo, Mich, Oct 25, 59. *Educ:* Cornell Univ, AB, 81; Univ Ill, Urbana-Champaign, MS, 82, PhD(physics), 87. *Prof Exp:* Teaching asst, Univ Ill, Urbana-Champaign, 81-82, assoc res asst physics, 82-86; postdoc res assoc, Lawrence Livermore Nat Lab, 86-89; mem res staff, Oakridge Nat Lab, 89-91, qual assurance specialist, 91-96. *Concurrent Pos:* Summer res assoc, Brookhaven Nat Lab,

80. *Mem:* Am Vacuum Soc; Am Phys Soc; AAAS; Am Soc Qual Control. *Res:* Process development; property process relationships; continuous quality improvement. *Mailing Add:* 7301 Georgetown Rd Suite 201 Indianapolis IN 46260

**WACHS, GERALD N,** DERMATOLOGY. *Current Pos:* PVT PRACT DERMAT & COSMETIC SURG, 82- *Personal Data:* b Chicago, Ill, Nov 5, 37; m 62; c 4. *Educ:* Univ Ill, BS, 58, MD, 62; Am Bd Dermat, dipl, 68. *Prof Exp:* Intern med, Michael Reese Hosp, Ill, 62-63; resident dermat, Univ Calif, 63-65, chief resident, 65-66; mem dept clin invest, Schering-Plough Corp, Kenilworth, NJ, 66-67, from asst med dir to assoc med dir, 67-74, dir new prod planning, 74-78, sr assoc med dir, 78-82; pres, bd health, Millburn, NJ, 84-90. *Concurrent Pos:* Clin asst dermatologist, St Vincent's Hosp, NY, 67-85; attend staff dermatologist, Mary Manning Walsh Home, NY, 71-81; attend staff, St Barnabas Med Ctr, Livingston, NJ; team dermatologist, NJ Nets, NJ Devils. *Mem:* Fel Am Col Physicians; fel Am Acad Dermat; fel Am Col Allergists; Int Soc Trop Dermat; Am Acad Allergy. *Res:* Clinical investigation of drugs in dermatology, allergy and ophthamology; development of new concepts in approaching the therapy of difficult clinical diseases in dermatology, allergy and ophthamology. *Mailing Add:* Assoc Derm & Surg 116 Millburn Ave Millburn NJ 07041-1919

**WACHS, MELVIN WALTER,** ENERGY CONSERVATION & STUDIES, ENVIRONMENTAL & PUBLIC HEALTH APPLICATIONS. *Current Pos:* prof, Adv Prog Govt Studies, 65-92, EMER PROF ADMIN, UNIV OKLA, 92-; EMER PROF BUS ADMIN, CENT MICH UNIV, 92- *Personal Data:* b Detroit, Mich, 1933. *Educ:* Univ Mich, BA, 52, MA, 54; Indust Col Armed Forces, MA & cert, 60; Am Univ, PhD(sci policy & admin), 68; Nat Defense Univ, MA & cert, 84. *Honors & Awards:* Int Medal of Honor, Museu de Baleen (Pres), Portugal, 83. *Prof Exp:* Asst prof Polit Sci & chmn, Asia Prog, Western Mich Univ, 59-62; assoc dir, Exec Inst, Off Career Develop, US Civil Comn, 62-64, Educ Resources, 64-66; planning-prog-budgeting & mgt info systs coord & chief, Planning Br, NIMH, USPHS, HEW, 66-68; dir, Community Develop Training Div, HUD, 68-72, sr prog officer, Community Planning & Develop, 72-82, dir, Intergovt Progs Div, 82-91, sr housing specialist, 91-93. *Concurrent Pos:* Consult, Off Sci & Technol, Exec Off Pres, 63-72, staff dir & mem, President's Comt Fed Labs, 63-72; mem, Fed Interagency Comn Sci & Eng, 64-78, Fed Interagency Coun Educ, 64- & var other groups & councils, 64-; prof pub admin, Maritime Col, State Univ NY, 67-68 & vis prof, Cent Mich Univ, 69-; energy coordr, Housing & Urban Develop, 73-84; Coastal Zone mgt coordr, Off Environ & Energy, 78-82. *Mem:* AAAS; NY Acad Sci; Am Acad Polit & Social Sci. *Res:* Technology transfer; science and public policy; energy conservation; industrial energy and environmental applications; public health policy and education. *Mailing Add:* 4832 Drummond Ave Chevy Chase MD 20815

**WACHSBERGER, PHYLLIS RACHELLE,** CELL BIOLOGY. *Current Pos:* INSTR, DEPT RADIATION ONCOL, THOMAS JEFFERSON UNIV, 86- *Personal Data:* b New York, NY; m 67; c 2. *Educ:* City Univ New York, BS, 64; Med Col Pa, PhD(physiol & biophys), 71. *Prof Exp:* Res instr muscle biophys, Dept Physiol & Biophys, Med Col Pa, 70-71; res assoc muscle biophys, Dept Anat, Univ Pa, 73-82; lectr biol, Bryn Mawr Col, 83-86. *Concurrent Pos:* NIH fel, Dept Anat, Univ Pa, 71-73; asst prof physiol & biophys, Hahnemann Med Col & Hosp, Philadelphia, 77-81; vis asst prof, Haverford Col, 84. *Mem:* Biophys Soc; AAAS; Am Inst Biol Sci; Sigma Xi; NAm Hypothermia Group; Am Soc Cell Biol. *Res:* Studies of the self assembly of synthetic vertebrate smooth muscle myosin filaments; comparative studies of molecular substructure of myosin filaments from various muscle types; immunochemical studies of the Myosin Crossbridge; identification of monsclonal antibodies raised to myosin and other myofibrillar proteins; effect of hyperthermia on cytoskeleton and nuclear matrix in mammalian cells. *Mailing Add:* 418 Newtown Rd Berwyn PA 19312-2082. *Fax:* 215-955-2052

**WACHSMAN, JOSEPH T,** MICROBIOLOGY, BIOCHEMISTRY. *Current Pos:* CONSULT, 91- *Personal Data:* b New York, NY, July 25, 27; m 60; c 1. *Educ:* NY Univ, AB, 48; Univ Calif, PhD(microbiol), 55. *Prof Exp:* USPHS fel, Brussels, Belg, 55-57; from asst prof to assoc prof microbiol, Univ Ill, Urbana-Champaign, 57-85; dir res, Touch Sci Inc, 89-91. *Concurrent Pos:* USPHS res career develop award, 62- *Mem:* Am Soc Microbiol. *Res:* Biochemistry and molecular biology of mammalian cells; unique properties of malignant cells-emphasis on the plasminogen activator associated with transformed cells-nucleic acid synthesis and repair. *Mailing Add:* NIEHS, NIH (B3-09) PO Box 12233 Research Triangle Park NC 27702. *Fax:* 919-541-1460

**WACHSPRESS, EUGENE LEON,** NUMERICAL ANALYSIS, ITERATIVE SOLUTION OF LARGE SYSTEMS. *Current Pos:* RETIRED. *Personal Data:* b New York, NY, Apr 17, 29; m 52, Natalie; c 3. *Educ:* Cooper Union, BME, 50; Union Col, BS, 56; Rensselaer Polytech Inst, PhD(math), 68. *Hon Degrees:* Dr, Univ Libre de Bruxelles, Belg, 85. *Prof Exp:* Nuclear engr, Knolls Atomic Power Lab, Gen Elec, 52-65, mathematician, 65-70, consult mathematician, 71-85; prof math, Univ Tenn, Knoxville, 83-91; consult mathematician, GE Nuclear Energy Div, San Jose, Calif, 92-94; lectr, Nuclear Eng Dept, Univ Calif, Berkeley, 95. *Concurrent Pos:* Vis fel numerical anal, Univ Dundee, Scotland, 70-71; ed, Comput & Math with Appln, 75- & J Applied Math Lett, 87-; numerical analyst, Res Inst Tallahassee, 85-86; vis fel, Electromech Br, Gen Elec, 86; consult, Supercomput Comput. *Mem:* Fel Am Nuclear Soc; Soc Indust & Appl Math. *Res:* Numerical solution of large linear systems; finite element basis function construction for complex geometry using algebraic-geometry foundations; numerical linear algebra; alternating direction implicit iteration theory and application; reactor physics computation. *Mailing Add:* 9802 Montego Ct Windsor CA 95492

**WACHTEL, ALLEN W,** CELL BIOLOGY, CYTOLOGY. *Current Pos:* from asst prof to assoc prof zool, 63-72, PROF BIOL, UNIV CONN, 72- *Personal Data:* b New York, NY, Aug 13, 25; m 46, 61; c 2. *Educ:* Columbia Univ, BS, 53, MA, 54, PhD(zool), 62. *Prof Exp:* Res asst cell biol, Cell Res Lab, Mt Sinai Hosp, NY, 56-63. *Mem:* Am Soc Cell Biol; Electron Micros Soc Am; Histochem Soc. *Res:* Histochemistry; cytology of electric organs; receptor structure. *Mailing Add:* 167 Daleville Rd Willington CT 06279

**WACHTEL, STEPHEN SHOEL,** EMBRYO TRANSFER. *Current Pos:* dir res, Ctr Reprod & Biol, 84-87, prof physiol & biophys, 85-86, PROF OBSTET & GYNEC & DIR, IMMUNOGENETICS LAB, DEPT OBSTET & GYNEC, UNIV TENN, MEMPHIS, 87-, CHIEF RES REPRODUCTIVE GENETICS LABS, 88- *Personal Data:* b Philadelphia, Pa, June 17, 37; m 62; c 2. *Educ:* Kenyon Col, Ohio, AB, 59; Univ Pa, PhD(biol), 71. *Honors & Awards:* Zurkow lectr, Univ Pa, 81; John Lattimer lectr, Am Acad Pediat, 78; Pres Lectr, Obstet Soc Philadelphia, 83. *Prof Exp:* Assoc immunogenetics, Sloan-Kettering Inst, 75-78, assoc mem, 78-81; assoc prof immunol, Cornell Univ Med Col, 77-81, assoc res prof pediat, 82-84. *Concurrent Pos:* NIH res career develop award, 75-80; prin investr, NIH res grants, 76-; co-investr, Pop Coun grant, 77-78; ad hoc consult, NIH, 82-, 92 & 95; chmn, AIBS-NOAD rev panel Molecular Genetics, 94; keynote speaker, N Am Soc Pediat Adolesc Gynecol, Genetics Soc Can, 95. *Mem:* Am Soc Reprod Med; Am Asn Immunologists; Int Embryo Transfer Soc; Am Col Med Genetics; Am Soc Immunol Reproduction; Soc Gynec Invest; Am Soc Human Genetics. *Res:* Fetal cells in maternal blood; immunogenetics of tissue transplantation; sex predetermination in bovine embryo transfer; serological analysis of epidermal cell antigens; H-Y antigen, biology of sex determination. *Mailing Add:* Dept Obstet & Gynec Univ Tenn 853 Jefferson Ave Rm SB-10 Memphis TN 38103. *Fax:* 901-576-8476; *E-Mail:* swachtel@utmem1.utmem.edu

**WACHTELL, GEORGE PETER,** PHYSICS. *Current Pos:* RETIRED. *Personal Data:* b New York, NY, Mar 18, 23; div; c 2. *Educ:* Princeton Univ, PhD(physics), 51. *Prof Exp:* Mem staff, Radiation Lab, Mass Inst Technol, 43-45; asst, Princeton Univ, 45-51; prin scientist, Energy Eng Lab, Franklin Res Ctr, Philadelphia, 51-88. *Res:* Optics; supersonics; heat transfer; fluid dynamics. *Mailing Add:* Kings Hwy Towers Apt D-209 Maple Shade NJ 08052

**WACHTELL, RICHARD L(LOYD),** ENGINEERING. *Current Pos:* PRES, METALOGOS, 90- *Personal Data:* b New York, NY, Feb 18, 20; m 41, Clara Hirsch; c Nancy. *Educ:* Columbia Univ, BS, 41. *Prof Exp:* Asst metallurgist, Repub Aviation Corp, NY, 42-46; metall engr, Tech Serv Sect, Res Lab, Air Reduction Co, 46-48; supvr metallog lab, Am Electro-Metals Corp, 48-49, proj engr, 49-51, asst tech dir, 51-52; chief metallurgist, Chromalloy Corp, 52-54, tech dir, 54-60, vpres & gen mgr, Chromalloy Div, 60-63, vpres, 63-68, proc, 63-76, pres, Turbine Support Div, 66-76, pres res & tech div & mem bd dirs, 68-71, exec vpres technol, 71-76, div pres & res tech div & mem bd dirs, 68-71, exec vpres Chromalloy Metal Tectonics, 77-80, chmn bd, 80-85. *Concurrent Pos:* Consult metall, 85- *Mem:* Am Soc Metals; Am Ord Asn; Am Inst Mining, Metall & Petrol Engrs; Am Iron & Steel Inst; Minerals, Metals & Mat Soc. *Res:* High temperature metallurgy, especially refractory metals and super-alloys and their protection from oxidation damage; coatings by diffusion; metallurgy techniques; intermetallic systems for high temperature service. *Mailing Add:* Metalogos Tuxedo Park NY 10987

**WACHTER, RALPH FRANKLIN,** biochemistry, virology; deceased, see previous edition for last biography

**WACHTMAN, JOHN BRYAN, JR,** SOLID STATE SCIENCE. *Current Pos:* dir, 83-88, SUSMAN PROF CERAMICS RES, CTR CERAMICS RES, RUTGERS UNIV, 88- *Personal Data:* b Conway, SC, Feb 6, 28; m 55. *Educ:* Carnegie Inst Technol, BS, 48, MS, 49; Univ Md, PhD(physics), 61. *Honors & Awards:* Silver Medal, Dept Com, 60, Gold Medal, 71; Sosman Mem Lectr Award, Am Ceramic Soc, 74; Stratton Award, Nat Bur Stand, 75; Hobart N Kramer Award, 78; Orton Mem Lectr, 81; Dorn Mem Lectr, 81; Nat Mat Achievement Award, Int Acad Ceramics, 86; Arthur L Fredburg Lectr, Int Acad Ceramics, 89. *Prof Exp:* Physicist, Nat Bur Stand, 51-62, chief, Phys Properties Sect, 62-68, chief, Inorg Mat Div, 68-78, dir, Ctr Mat Sci, 78-83. *Concurrent Pos:* Ed, Ceramics & Glass, 68- & Sci & Technol, 68-; trustee, Edward Orton, Jr Ceramic Found, 70-82; mem ceramic eng adv bd, Univ Ill Urbana, 73-76, Alfred Univ, 74-82, Pa State Univ, 76-83, Northwestern Univ, 77, & Mass Inst Technol,78-82; prog mgr mat, Off Technol Assessment, US Cong, 74-75; mem adv coun ceramics, Univ NY, Alfred, 74-80; mem mat dept adv comt, State Univ NY, Stonybrook, 79; lectr, Johns Hopkins Univ, 81; mem, Policy Comt, Nat Acad Eng, 82-85 & chmn, Comt Mem, 83; mem, Comt High Technol Ceramics Japan, Nat Res Coun, 83-84, Comt Sci & Technol Implications Processing Strategic Mat, 84-85, Subcomt Advan Mat, Comt Future Chem Eng, 85, Comt Mat Eng Res Bd, 85 & Comt Res Opportunities Mat Res, 87; ed, Am Ceramic Soc, 88- *Mem:* Nat Acad Eng; fel Am Ceramic Soc (pres, 78-79); fel Am Phys Soc; Nat Inst Ceramic Engrs; Fedn Mat Socs (secy/treas, 73, pres-elect, 74, pres, 75); Am Soc Metals Inc; Am Asn Crystal Growth; Am Chem Soc; AAAS; Mat Res Soc. *Res:* Mechanical properties and effective utilization of inorganic materials; composites; thin films; microporous ceramic composites; tribology; superconducting ceramics; national materials policy; author of various publications. *Mailing Add:* 208 Cedar Ridge Lane Conway SC 29526

**WACK, PAUL EDWARD,** NUCLEAR PHYSICS. *Current Pos:* from asst prof to prof, 49-86, head dept, 66-73, EMER PROF PHYSICS, UNIV PORTLAND, 86- *Personal Data:* b Council Bluffs, Iowa, Apr 28, 19; m 52, Mary E Van Hoomissen; c Paul, Edwin, Ellen & Mary. *Educ:* Creighton Univ, AB, 41; Univ Notre Dame, MS, 42, PhD(physics), 47. *Honors & Awards:*

Culligan Award, 61. *Prof Exp:* Asst physics, Univ Notre Dame, 41-43, instr, 43-46; res assoc, Off Naval Res, 46-47; dir dept physics, Creighton Univ, 47-49. *Concurrent Pos:* Res assoc, Off Rubber Res, 43-45; res assoc, Gen Tire Co, 45-46. *Mem:* Am Phys Soc; Am Asn Physics Teachers. *Res:* Electron optics; stress relaxation, low temperature behavior, equation of state and electrical conductivity of natural and synthetic rubbers; nuclear spectroscopy. *Mailing Add:* Dept Physics Univ Portland Portland OR 97203

**WACKER, GEORGE ADOLF,** METALLURGY, CORROSION. *Current Pos:* metallurgist, Naval Ship Res & Develop Ctr, 68-71, head metal physics br, 71-77, head, high temperature alloys br, 77-78, HEAD, METALS DIV, NAVAL SHIP RES & DEVELOP CTR, 79- *Personal Data:* b New York, NY, Aug 18, 39; m 63; c 2. *Educ:* Polytech Inst, Brooklyn, BSMetE, 62, MSMetE, 64. *Prof Exp:* Foundry metallurgist, Naval Appl Sci Lab, 62, phys metallurgist, 63-65 & Marine Eng Lab, 65-67. *Mem:* Am Soc Metals; Am Soc Testing & Mat; Nat Asn Corrosion Engrs; Sigma Xi. *Res:* Effects of the marine environment on metals and alloys; physical metallurgy of engineering materials used in saline environments; effects of elevated temperature corrosive environments on engineering materials. *Mailing Add:* 1128 Rutlandview Dr Davidsonville MD 21035

**WACKER, WALDON BURDETTE,** IMMUNOLOGY, MICROBIOLOGY. *Current Pos:* from asst prof to assoc prof microbiol, 59-80, prof ophthal res, 80-85, EMER PROF, UNIV LOUISVILLE, 85- *Personal Data:* b Garrison, NDak, Aug 13, 23; m 55, Priscilla Johnson; c Dennis, Janet, Nancy & Steven. *Educ:* Wash Univ, AB, 49; Univ Mich, MS, 51; Ohio State Univ, PhD(bact), 57. *Honors & Awards:* Am Uveitis Soc Award, 88; Proctor Medal, 91. *Prof Exp:* Res assoc virol, Ohio State Univ, 58-59. *Concurrent Pos:* NIH career develop award, Univ Louisville, 62-69, NIH res grant, 62-85. *Mem:* Asn Res Vision & Ophthal; Sigma Xi; Am Uveitis Soc. *Res:* Autoimmune disease; immunopathology; uveitis. *Mailing Add:* 7320 Keisler Way Louisville KY 40222

**WACKER, WARREN ERNEST CLYDE,** MEDICINE, BIOCHEMISTRY. *Current Pos:* PROF HYG, HARVARD UNIV, 71- *Personal Data:* b Brooklyn, NY, Feb 29, 24; m 48, Ann R MacMillan; c Margaret (Morrisey) & John F. *Educ:* George Washington Univ, MD, 51; Harvard Univ, MS, 68. *Prof Exp:* Intern, George Washington Univ Hosp, 51-52, resident, 52-53; resident, Peter Bent Brigham Hosp, 53-55; res fel biophys, Harvard Med Sch & Peter Bent Brigham Hosp, 55-57; from instr to assoc prof med, Harvard Med Sch, 57-71. *Concurrent Pos:* Nat Found Infantile Paralysis fel, 55-57; investr, Howard Hughes Med Inst, 57-68. *Mem:* Am Soc Biol Chemists; Am Soc Clin Invest; Biochem Soc; Am Chem Soc; Am Col Physicians. *Res:* Biochemistry of metals; studies of metalloenzymes; use of enzymatic methods in diagnoses; analytical chemistry of metals in biological material. *Mailing Add:* 91 Glen Rd Apt NC-1 Brookline MA 02146-7764

**WACKER, WILLIAM DENNIS,** STATISTICS. *Current Pos:* PROF MATH, PARKS COL, ST LOUIS UNIV, 91- *Personal Data:* b St Louis, Mo, Dec 5, 41; m 73, Betsy Koons; c Daniel W & Mark W. *Educ:* Wash Univ, BS, 64, MS, 67, DSc(probability), 71. *Mem:* Am Statist Asn. *Res:* Application of optimization theory and statistics to real world problems. *Mailing Add:* Dept Math Parks Col St Louis Univ Cahokia IL 62206. *Fax:* 618-332-6802; *E-Mail:* wackerd@slu.edu

**WACKERLE, JERRY DONALD,** PHYSICS, MATHEMATICS. *Current Pos:* Staff mem, 56-64, ASST GROUP LEADER, UNIV CALIF, LOS ALAMOS SCI LAB, 64- *Personal Data:* b Edna, Kans, May 21, 30; m 49; c 4. *Educ:* Univ Kans, BS, 51, MS, 54, PhD(physics), 56. *Concurrent Pos:* Adj prof physics, Univ NMex, 58-68. *Mem:* Am Phys Soc; AAAS. *Res:* Shock wave physics and equation of state; initiation and detonation of chemical explosives. *Mailing Add:* 1295 41st St Los Alamos NM 87544. *Fax:* 505-667-6372

**WACKERNAGEL, HANS BEAT,** ASTRODYNAMICS, DATA PROCESSING. *Current Pos:* astronr, Proj Spacetrack, Air Force Cambridge Res Labs, Mass, 58-59, 496L Syst Proj Off, 60-61, First Aerospace Control Squadron, Ent AFB, Colo, 61-62, Ninth Aerospace Defense Div, 62-68 & Fourteenth Aerospace Force, 68-73, comput specialist, Hq NAm Air Defense, 73-75, opers res analyst, Second Commun Squadron, Buckley Air Nat Guard Base, 75, mathematician, 75-79, physicist, Hq NAm Air Defense, Peterson AFB, Colo, 79, opers res analyst, GS-14, Hq Air Force Space Com, 83-86 & sr mathematician, 86-89, sr mathematician, GS-15, Hq Air Force Space Com, Colo Springs, 89-90, CONSULT, AEROSPACE ENG, 90- *Personal Data:* b Basel, Switz, Aug 31, 31; US citizen; m 74, Irene E Chavez; c 4. *Educ:* Univ Basel, PhD(astron), 58. *Honors & Awards:* Meritorious Civil Serv Award, 88; Outstanding Civilian Career Serv Award, 90. *Prof Exp:* Observer, Observ Neuchatel, 53-54; res asst, Observ Basel, 55-58. *Concurrent Pos:* Lectr, Dept Math, Univ Colo, Colo Springs, 64-72, Dept Eng, Navig Space, 90-; astron, GS-14, Hq 14th Aerospace Force, Colo Springs, 66-73. *Mem:* Am Astron Soc; fel Brit Interplanetary Soc; Swiss Astron Soc; Int Astron Union. *Res:* Design and evaluation of advanced space defense systems; applied celestial mechanics. *Mailing Add:* 51 Broadmoor Hills Dr Colorado Springs CO 80906-4355

**WACKERS, FRANS J TH,** CARDIOLOGY, NUCLEAR CARDIOLOGY. *Current Pos:* asst prof, 77-81, assoc prof, 84-86, PROF DIAG RADIOL & MED, YALE UNIV, 86- *Personal Data:* b Echt, Neth, May 29, 39; m 72, Marjan Meyer; c Michiel & Paul. *Educ:* Univ Amsterdam, Neth, MD & PhD(path), 70. *Hon Degrees:* MA, Yale Univ, 86. *Honors & Awards:* Rascar Award, Univ Maastricht, Neth, 88; Herrman Blumgart Award, Soc Nuclear

Med, 95. *Prof Exp:* Consult cardiol, Univ Amsterdam, Neth, 77; assoc prof, Univ Vt, Burlington, 81-84. *Concurrent Pos:* Dir cardiovasc nuclear imaging, Yale Univ, 84-, dir exercise lab, 85-; consult, DuPont, 81-, Mallinchrodt, 92-, Medco, 93- *Mem:* Fel Am Col Cardiol; Am Heart Asn; Soc Nuclear Med (pres, 92-93); Am Soc Nuclear Cardiol (pres, 94-95). *Res:* Evaluating the use of radionuclide imaging in patients with acute or chronic heart disease. *Mailing Add:* Yale Univ Sch Med 333 Cedar St-TE2 New Haven CT 06520-8042. *Fax:* 203-737-2160; *E-Mail:* frans_wackers@qm.yale.edu

**WADA, GEORGE,** ELECTRICAL ENGINEERING. *Current Pos:* STAFF SCIENTIST, HUGHES AIRCRAFT CORP, 80- *Personal Data:* b Lomita, Calif, Oct 18, 27; m 58; c 2. *Educ:* Calif Inst Technol, BS, 54; Stanford Univ, MS, 55, PhD(elec eng), 58. *Prof Exp:* Res assoc elec eng, Stanford Univ, 55-58; mem tech staff, Devices Dept, Watkins-Johnson Co, 58-80. *Mem:* Inst Elec & Electronics Engrs. *Res:* Microwave electron tubes and devices. *Mailing Add:* 300 Zagora Dr Danville CA 94506

**WADA, JAMES YASUO,** LASERS, PLASMA PHYSICS. *Current Pos:* Sect head, Elec-Gasdyn Lasers, Hughes Res Labs, Malibu, 56-74, SR SCIENTIST & DEPT MGR, HUGHES SPACE-COMMUN GROUP, LOS ANGELES, 74- *Personal Data:* b Lomita, Calif, May 15, 34; m 57; c 4. *Educ:* Univ Calif, Los Angeles, BS, 56; Univ Southern Calif, MS, 58, PhD(elec eng), 63. *Concurrent Pos:* Lectr, Univ Southern Calif, 64, asst prof, 64-66. *Mem:* Inst Elec & Electronics Engrs; Sigma Xi. *Res:* High power lasers and optics; physical optics; microwave tubes; electromagnetic theory; space communications. *Mailing Add:* 7401 Asman Ave Canoga Park CA 91307-1707

**WADA, JUHN A,** MEDICINE, NEUROLOGY. *Current Pos:* res assoc neurol, Health Sci Ctr Hosp, Univ BC, 57-59, asst prof neurol res & psychiat & chief labs EEG & neurophysiol, 60-63, assoc prof med neurol & dir EEG labs, 63-70, RROF NEUROL SCI & NEUROL, UNIV BC & DIR NEUROL & EEG DEPT, HEALTH SCI CTR HOSP, 70-, ATTEND NEUROLOGIST & DIR, SEIZURE INVEST UNIT, 80- *Personal Data:* b Tokyo, Japan, Mar 28, 24; nat Can; m 56, Mary M; c Kent & Eileen. *Educ:* Hokkaido Imp Univ, Japan, MD, 45, DMedSci, 51; FRCPS(C), 72. *Honors & Awards:* William G Lennox Lectr, Am Epilepsy Soc, 81; Wilder Penfield Award, Can League Against Epilepsy, 88; Order of Can, 92; Order of Japan, 95. *Prof Exp:* Asst prof neurol & psychiat, dir labs exp neurol & brain surgeon-in-chief, Univ Hosps, Hokkaido Imp Univ, Japan, 52-57. *Concurrent Pos:* Fel, Univ Minn, 54-55 & Montreal Neurol Inst, McGill Univ, 55-56; Can Med Res Coun assoc, 66; attend neurologist & assoc dir EEG dept, Vancouver Gen Hosp. *Mem:* Am Electroencephalog Soc; Am Epilepsy Soc; fel Am Acad Neurol; Can Neurol Soc; Can Soc Electroencephalog; Epilepsy Int Cong Vancouver (pres, 78); Can League Against Epilepsy (pres, 77-79); Am & E G Soc (pres, 85-88); Am Epilepsy Soc (pres, 88-89). *Res:* Neurological mechanism of human behavior; epilepsy; electrical activity of brain; cerebral speech function. *Mailing Add:* Dept Neurol Sci & Neurol Univ BC Hosp 2255 Wesbrook Mall Vancouver BC V6T 2B5 Can. *Fax:* 604-822-7664

**WADA, WALTER W,** PHYSICS. *Current Pos:* PROF PHYSICS, OHIO STATE UNIV, 64- *Personal Data:* b Loomis, Calif, Feb 26, 19; m 46; c 4. *Educ:* Univ Utah, BA, 43; Univ Mich, MA, 46, PhD, 51. *Prof Exp:* Physicist nucleonics div, US Naval Res Lab, 51-62. *Concurrent Pos:* Lectr, Univ Md, 51-62; vis prof, Northwestern Univ, 62-64. *Mem:* Fel Am Phys Soc. *Res:* Quantum theory of fields and applications in electrodynamics; theoretical high energy physics. *Mailing Add:* Dept Physics Ohio State Univ 174 W 18th Ave Columbus OH 43210

**WADDELL, CHARLES NOEL,** PHYSICS. *Current Pos:* RETIRED. *Personal Data:* b Omaha, Nebr, Nov 11, 22; m 45; c 6. *Educ:* Univ Calif, BA, 50, PhD(physics), 58. *Prof Exp:* Assoc physics, Univ Calif, 50-52, physicist, Radiation Lab, 52-58; from asst prof to emer prof physics, Univ Southern Calif, 58-92. *Mem:* Am Phys Soc. *Res:* Nuclear reaction mechanisms; semiconductor physics, ion implantation and optical properties. *Mailing Add:* 17025 Willton Pl Torrance CA 90504

**WADDELL, HENRY THOMAS,** BOTANY. *Current Pos:* PROF BIOL, LAMAR UNIV, 63- *Personal Data:* b Wilson, Ark, Apr 19, 18; m 45; c 2. *Educ:* Peabody Col, BS, 49, MA, 51; Univ Fla, PhD(plant path), 59. *Prof Exp:* Asst prof biol, Martin Br, Univ Tenn, 49-56; assoc prof, Peabody Col, 59-63. *Mem:* AAAS; Am Phytopath Soc; Mycol Soc Am; Sigma Xi. *Res:* Plant pathology; mycology. *Mailing Add:* 965 Dowlen Rd Beaumont TX 77706

**WADDELL, KIDD M,** LIMNOLOGY, GEOCHEMISTRY. *Current Pos:* Anal chemist, Qual Water Br, 62-66, hydrologist, Water Res Div, 66-84, SUPVR HYDROLOGIST, WATER RES DIV, US GEOL SURV, 84- *Personal Data:* b Roby, Tex, June 23, 37; m 83; c 3. *Educ:* Univ Tex, El Paso, BS, 61, BS, 62; Univ Utah, MS, 71. *Res:* Propose, plan and manage hydrologic and limnologic investigations; remedial investigations at contaminated sites; modeling of ground and surface water including water quality. *Mailing Add:* 6544 S Rothmoor Dr Salt Lake City UT 84121

**WADDELL, ROBERT CLINTON,** PHYSICS. *Current Pos:* From instr to prof, 48-81, EMER PROF PHYSICS, EASTERN ILL UNIV, 81- *Personal Data:* b Mattoon, Ill, Aug 15, 21; m 60; c 3. *Educ:* Eastern Ill Univ, BS, 47; Univ Ill, MS, 48; Iowa State Univ, PhD(physics), 55. *Concurrent Pos:* Res asst, Iowa State Univ, 53-55. *Mem:* Int Res Group Physics Teaching; Sigma Xi. *Res:* Physics education. *Mailing Add:* 9 Circle Dr Charleston IL 61920

**WADDELL, THOMAS GROTH,** BIO-ORGANIC CHEMISTRY. *Current Pos:* from asst prof to assoc prof, 71-81, PROF CHEM, UNIV TENN, CHATTANOOGA, 81- *Personal Data:* b Madison, Wis, July 29, 44. *Educ:* Univ Wis-Madison, BS, 66; Univ Calif, Los Angeles, PhD(org chem), 69. *Prof Exp:* Scholar org chem, Univ Calif, Los Angeles, 69; NIH res fel, Univ Calif, Berkeley, 70-71. *Concurrent Pos:* Vis prof, Univ Denver, 80. *Mem:* Am Chem Soc; Am Soc Pharmacog. *Res:* Chemical evolution; chemical constituents of medicinal plants; organic reactions. *Mailing Add:* Dept Chem Univ Tenn Chattanooga TN 37403

**WADDELL, WALTER HARVEY,** SURFACE SPECTROSCOPY. *Current Pos:* SR STAFF CHEMIST, EXXON CHEM, 96- *Personal Data:* b Chicago, Ill, Sept 26, 47. *Educ:* Univ Ill, Chicago, BS, 69; Univ Houston, PhD(chem), 73. *Honors & Awards:* Sparks-Thomas Award, Rubber Div, Am Chem Soc. *Prof Exp:* Res assoc chem, Columbia Univ, 73-75; from asst prof to assoc prof chem, Carnegie-Mellon Univ, 79-83; sect head, Goodyear Tire & Rubber, 83-90; scientist, PPG Indust, 90-96. *Concurrent Pos:* NIH res fel, Nat Eye Inst, 75. *Mem:* Am Chem Soc. *Res:* Spectroscopic and mechanistic investigations of tire compound chemical interactions; surface characterizations of polymers; compounding with butyl rubber and derivatives; polymer filler interactions; adhesion, precipitated silica. *Mailing Add:* 4923 Orange Tree Dr Pasadena TX 77505. *E-Mail:* walter.h.waddell@exxon.sprint.com

**WADDELL, WILLIAM JOSEPH,** PHARMACOLOGY, TOXICOLOGY. *Current Pos:* PROF PHARMACOL & TOXICOL & CHMN DEPT, UNIV LOUISVILLE, 77- *Personal Data:* b Commerce, Ga, Mar 16, 29; m 74; c 4. *Educ:* Univ NC, AB, 51, MD, 55. *Prof Exp:* From asst prof to assoc prof pharmacol, Univ NC, Chapel Hill, 58-71, assoc prof oral biol, 67-69, prof oral biol & assoc dir dent res ctr, 69-72, assoc div dir, Ctr Res Pharmacol & Toxicol, 66-67; prof pharmacol, Univ Ky, 72-77. *Concurrent Pos:* USPHS res fel, Univ NC, Chapel Hill, 55-58; NIH spec fel, Royal Vet Col, Sweden, 65-66. *Mem:* Teratology Soc; Soc Toxicol; Am Soc Pharmacol & Exp Therapeut; Soc Exp Biol & Med; Am Physiol Soc; Acad Toxicol Sci. *Res:* Intracellular pH; teratogenic agents, carcinogenic agents. *Mailing Add:* Dept Pharmacol & Toxicol Univ Louisville Health Sci Ctr Louisville KY 40292. *Fax:* 502-852-7868; *E-Mail:* wjwadd01@ulkyvx.louisville.edu

**WADDEN, RICHARD ALBERT,** ENVIRONMENTAL HEALTH, ENVIRONMENTAL ENGINEERING. *Current Pos:* asst dir, Environ Health Resource Ctr, 72-74, from asst prof to assoc prof, 72-79, PROF ENVIRON HEALTH SCI, SCH PUB HEALTH, UNIV ILL, 79-, DIR, OFF TECHNOL TRANSFER, CTR SOLID WASTE MGT & RES, 87- *Personal Data:* b Sioux City, Iowa. *Educ:* Iowa State Univ, BS, 59; NC State Univ, MS, 62; Northwestern Univ, PhD(chem, environ eng), 72. *Prof Exp:* Develop engr, Linde Co, Tonawanda, NY, 59-60; engr, Humble Oil & Refining Co, Houston, 62-65; instr chem & mech eng, Pahlavi Univ, Iran, 65-67; tech adv, Ill Pollution Control Bd, Chicago, 71-72. *Concurrent Pos:* Adv, Northeastern Ill Planning Comn, 73-76; lectr, Nat Safety Coun, 74-76 & Nat Inst Safety & Health, 74-76; mem task force hazardous mat in environ, Am Pub Health Asn, 75-77; vis scientist, Japanese Nat Inst Environ Studies, 78-79, invited scientist, 83, 84 & 88; mem, prog rev comt indoor air pollution, personal exposure, atmospheric chemistry & physics progs, US Environ Protection Agency; consult, Beijer Inst Energy & Environ, Swed Acad Sci, Off Toxic Substances, Environ Protection Agency; dir environ & occup health sci, 84-86 & 88-; reviewer, NSF Japan Prog; dipl, Am Acad Environ Eng & Am Acad Indust Hyg. *Mem:* Am Inst Chem Engrs; Am Chem Soc; Air Pollution Control Asn; Am Acad Environ Engrs; Am Acad Indust Hyg; Am Indust Hyg Asn. *Res:* Characterization and modeling of air pollution in inside and outside environments; fine particle modeling and measurements; ozone episode detection; methodologies for predicting pollution source impacts on human health; air pollution source-receptor modeling; engineering control of workplace hazards. *Mailing Add:* Univ Ill Sch Pub Health-M/C 922 2121 W Taylor St Chicago IL 60612

**WADDEN, THOMAS ANTONY,** PSYCHIATRY, NUTRITION. *Current Pos:* PROF PSYCHIAT, UNIV PENN, 93- *Personal Data:* b Richmond, Va, Sept 3, 52; m 84; c 2. *Educ:* Brown Univ, AB, 75; Univ NC, Chapel Hill, PhD(psychol), 81. *Honors & Awards:* New Res Award, Asn Advan Behav Ther, 86. *Prof Exp:* NIMH traineeship, Univ NC, 76-78; from instr to assoc prof psychol psychiat, Sch Med, Univ Pa, 81-91; prof, Syracuse Univ, 92-93. *Concurrent Pos:* Prin investr, Res Scientist Award, Behav Treatment Obese Children & Adults, NIMH, 87-; assoc ed, Ann Behavior Med, 91- *Mem:* Am Psychol Asn; Soc Behav Med; Asn Advan Behav Ther; NAm Asn Study Obesity. *Res:* Causes and treatment of obesity; short- and long-term effects of caloric restriction and weight loss on metabolic rate; long-term use of behavior therapy to improve the maintenance of weight loss. *Mailing Add:* Dept Psychiat Univ Penn 3600 Market St Philadelphia PA 19104

**WADDILL, VAN HULEN,** ENTOMOLOGY. *Current Pos:* From asst prof to assoc prof, 75-88, PROF ENTOM, AGR RES & EDUC CTR, INST FOOD & AGR SCI, UNIV FLA, 88-, CTR DIR, 88- *Personal Data:* b Brady, Tex, Aug 24, 47; m 69. *Educ:* Tex A&M Univ, BS, 70, MS, 71; Clemson Univ, PhD(entom), 74. *Concurrent Pos:* Coun, Arg Sci & Technol. *Mem:* Entom Soc Am. *Res:* Management of insect pests of vegetables. *Mailing Add:* 6409 64th Way West Palm Beach FL 33409

**WADDINGTON, CECIL JACOB,** PHYSICS, ASTROPHYSICS. *Current Pos:* assoc prof, 62-68, PROF, SCH PHYSICS & ASTRON, UNIV MINN, MINNEAPOLIS, 68- *Personal Data:* b Cambridge, Eng, July 6, 29; m 56. *Educ:* Bristol Univ, BSc, 52, PhD(physics), 55. *Honors & Awards:* Except Sci Achievement Medal, NASA. *Prof Exp:* Royal Soc McKinnon res studentship physics, Bristol Univ, 56-59, lectr, 59-62. *Concurrent Pos:* Res assoc & lectr, Univ Minn, 57-58; Nat Acad Sci sr fel, Goddard Space Flight Ctr, Md, 61; sr vis fel, Imp Col, Univ London, 72-73; mem, Cosmic Ray Comn, Int Union Pure & Appl Physics, 72-78. *Mem:* AAAS; fel Am Phys Soc; Am Astron Soc; Int Astron Union. *Res:* Physics and astrophysics of relativistic heavy ions, using detectors exposed on balloons and satellites to the cosmic radiation and to beams of ions accelerated by machines. *Mailing Add:* Sch Physics & Astron Univ Minn 116 Church St SE Minneapolis MN 55455. *Fax:* 612-626-2029; *E-Mail:* wadd@physics.spa.umn.edu

**WADDINGTON, DONALD VAN PELT,** NITROGEN FERTILIZERS, TURFGRASS MANAGEMENT. *Current Pos:* asst prof soil technol, 65-68, from assoc prof to prof soil sci, 68-91, EMER PROF, PA STATE UNIV, UNIV PARK, 92- *Personal Data:* b Norristown, Pa, Dec 31, 31; m 55, Caroline H Wicker; c Mary, James, Lauretta, Katherine, David & Douglas. *Educ:* Pa State Univ, BS, 53; Rutgers Univ, MS, 60; Univ Mass, PhD(agron), 64. *Honors & Awards:* Fred V Grau Turfgrass Sci Award, Crop Sci Soc Am, 93. *Prof Exp:* Asst chemist, Eastern States Farmer's Exchange, Inc, 56-57; instr agron, Univ Mass, 60-65. *Concurrent Pos:* Assoc ed, Crop Sci, Crop Sci Soc Am, 86-88; ed, Turfgrass Monograph, Am Soc Agron, 86-92. *Mem:* Fel Am Soc Agron; Soil Sci Soc Am; Int Soil Sci Soc; Soil & Water Conserv Soc; Int Turfgrass Soc; Crop Sci Soc Am. *Res:* Soil physical properties, especially soil modification for turfgrass; turfgrass nutrition; controlled-release fertilizers; impact attenuation and traction on athletic field surfaces. *Mailing Add:* 115 Pine Tree Ave Boalsburg PA 16827

**WADDINGTON, JOHN,** WEEDS, FORAGE CROPS. *Current Pos:* RETIRED. *Personal Data:* b Manchester, Eng, Mar 15, 38; Can citizen; m 66; c 1. *Educ:* Univ Leeds, Eng, BSc, 60; Univ Man, MSc, 62, PhD(agron), 68. *Prof Exp:* Res scientist forage crops, Res Br, Agr Can, 68-96. *Mem:* Agr Inst Can. *Res:* Forage crops management, particularly establishment, weed control, plant competition and effects of weather on yield and quality of hay and seed. *Mailing Add:* 3278 Boucherie Rd Kelowna BC V1Z 2H2 Can

**WADDINGTON, RAYMOND,** case technology, human-computer interaction, for more information see previous edition

**WADDLE, BRADFORD AVON,** AGRONOMY, PLANT BREEDING. *Current Pos:* asst agron & Altheimer chair cotton, Agr Exp Sta, Univ Ark, 51-56, assoc, 56-59, prof agron & Altheimer chair cotton res, 59-74, distinguished prof & Altheimer chair cotton, 74-86, EMER DISTINGUISHED PROF & ALTHEIMER CHAIR COTTON, UNIV ARK, FAYETTEVILLE, 86- *Personal Data:* b Tex, Jan 26, 20; m 45. *Educ:* Agr & Mech Col, Tex, BS, 42, MS, 50; Purdue Univ, PhD(plant breeding), 54. *Prof Exp:* Instr, Hunt County Voc Scho, Tex, 46-47; jr agronomist, Greenville Cotton Sta, USDA, 48; instr cotton breeding, Agr Exp Sta, Univ Tex A&M, 50. *Mem:* Am Soc Agron; Am Genetic Asn. *Res:* Cotton breeding and genetics, especially breeding for resistance to disease and insects. *Mailing Add:* 1600 Cherokee Circle Harrison AR 72601-3106

**WADE, ADELBERT ELTON,** PHARMACOLOGY, BIOCHEMISTRY. *Current Pos:* from asst prof to assoc prof, 59-67, PROF PHARMACOL, UNIV GA, 67-, HEAD DEPT, 68- *Personal Data:* b Hilliard, Fla, Apr 29, 26; m 50; c 2. *Educ:* Univ Fla, BS, 54, MS, 56, PhD(pharmacol), 59. *Prof Exp:* Asst chemother, Univ Fla, 54-56, asst biochem, 56-57, asst chemother, 57-59. *Mem:* Am Asn Cols Pharm; Soc Exp Biol & Med; Am Soc Pharmacol & Exp Therapeut; Int Soc Biochem Pharmacol; Sigma Xi. *Res:* Influence of diet and drugs on mixed-function oxidases; effects of diet on drug and carcinogen metabolism. *Mailing Add:* 180 Weatherly Woods Dr Winterville GA 30683

**WADE, ADRIAN PAUL,** FLOW INJECTION ANALYSIS, CHEMICAL ACOUSTIC EMISSION. *Current Pos:* CONSULT, WADE RES 94-; BCRI ASSOC, BC RES INST, VANCOUVER BC, 94- *Personal Data:* b Amersham, UK, Apr 7, 60; m 82, Susan Nash; c Toby, Andrew, Sam & Rebecca. *Educ:* Southampton Univ, UK, BSc, 81; Univ Wales, UK, PhD(anal chem), 85. *Prof Exp:* Extra-mural res assoc expert systs, Brit Petrol Res Ctr, Univ Col Swansea, 84-85; res chemist & comput scientist expert systs, Brit Petrol Res Ctr, Sunbury-on-Thames, UK, 85-87; asst prof chem, Univ BC, 87-94. *Concurrent Pos:* Vis res assoc anal chem, Mich State Univ, 85-87; corresp ed, J Automatic Chem, 90-; fac assoc, Pulp & Paper Res Inst Can, 90-; affil, Pulp & Paper Ctr, Univ BC, 90- *Mem:* Royal Soc Chem; fel Inst Analysts & Programmers; Asn Anal Chemists; Chem Inst Can; Can Soc Chem; Can Pulp & Paper Asn Tech Sect. *Res:* Flow injection analysis; chemical acoustic emission; chemometrics; expert systems; author of over 50 publications. *Mailing Add:* 11551 Kingfisher Dr Unit 30 Richmond BC V7E 3N5 Can. *Fax:* 604-275-3952; *E-Mail:* adrian__wade@msn.com

**WADE, CAMPBELL MARION,** ASTRONOMY. *Current Pos:* res assoc, 60-66, SCIENTIST, NAT RADIO ASTRON OBSERV, 66- *Personal Data:* b Elizabethtown, Ky, Nov 25, 30; m 56, 78; c 4. *Educ:* Harvard Univ, AB, 54, AM, 55, PhD(astron), 57. *Prof Exp:* Res officer, Div Radiophysics, Commonwealth Sci & Indust Res Orgn, Australia, 57-59. *Concurrent Pos:* Adv ed, Soviet Astron, Am Inst Physics, 69- *Mem:* Am Astron Soc; Int Astron Union. *Res:* Galactic and extragalactic radio astronomy. *Mailing Add:* 1224 Apache Dr Socorro NM 87801-4435

**WADE, CHARLES GARY,** ORGANIC & INORGANIC CHEMISTRY. *Current Pos:* sr chemist, 68-74, res chemist, 74-76, supvr, 76-83, sr res scientist & team leader, 83-85, TECH MGR & LICENSING, ATLAS POWDER CO, 85- *Personal Data:* b Spring City, Pa, Dec 8, 38; m 64; c 2.

*Educ:* Ursinus Col, BS, 60; Univ Del, MS, 68. *Honors & Awards:* IR 100 Award, Ind Res Mag, 77. *Prof Exp:* Chemist, Abex Corp, 66-68. *Concurrent Pos:* Chmn, Am Chem Soc, 85. *Mem:* Am Chem Soc. *Res:* Water based explosives based on emulsion technology. *Mailing Add:* 74 Maple Ave Lehighton PA 18235

**WADE, CHARLES GORDON,** POLYMER CHEMISTRY, PHYSICAL CHEMISTRY. *Current Pos:* mgr mat anal, 87-88, mgr poly char, 88-90, mgr tech staff, 90-93, MGR MAT ANALYSIS CHAIR, IBM ALMADEN RES CTR, 93- *Personal Data:* b Griggsville, Ill, Apr 5, 37; m 64. *Educ:* Southern Ill Univ, BA, 60; Mass Inst Technol, PhD(phys chem), 65. *Prof Exp:* Res assoc chem, Enrico Fermi Inst Nuclear Studies, Univ Chicago, 65-67; from asst prof to assoc prof chem, Univ Tex, Austin, 67-80; appln scientist, IBM Instruments, Inc, 80-82, mgr nuclear magnetic resonance, 82-83, mgr magnetics, 83-85, mgr WCoast Opers, 85-87. *Mem:* Am Phys Soc; Am Chem Soc; Sigma Xi; AAAS. *Res:* Nuclear magnetic resonance in biological systems; nuclear magnetic resonance in polymers; computer controlled instrumentation; properties of liquid crystals; fluorescence of carcinogens; chemical carcinogenesis; structure and diffusion in membrane systems; spectroscopic studies of biological systems. *Mailing Add:* 136 Mary Way Los Gatos CA 95032-4841. *Fax:* 408-927-3310; *E-Mail:* cwade@almaden.ibm.com

**WADE, CLARENCE W R,** ORGANIC CHEMISTRY. *Current Pos:* FAC, DEPT PHARMACOL, HOWARD UNIV, WASHINGTON, DC. *Personal Data:* b Laurinburg, NC, Mar 31, 27; m 55; c 1. *Educ:* J C Smith Univ, BS, 48; Tuskegee Inst, MS, 50; Georgetown Univ, PhD(org chem), 65. *Prof Exp:* From instr to asst prof chem, St Augustine's Col, 50-57; from chemist to res chemist, Nat Bur Stand, 57-66; res chemist, US Army Med & Biomech Lab, Walter Reed Army Med Ctr, 66-68, chief, Synthesis Br, 68-70, chief mat & applns div, 70-72, chief, Mat & Applns Div, 72-76, sr res chemist, 76-, proj area mgr chem systs, 80- *Concurrent Pos:* Consult, Nat Heart Inst, 68-70; adj prof chem, Univ DC, 75-; prof orthop res, Howard Univ, 77-79. *Mem:* AAAS; Am Chem Soc; NY Acad Sci; Asn Off Anal Chemists. *Res:* Development of inert or degradable implant materials, tissue and bone adhesives, sutures, tendons, vascular tubes, wound and burn dressings, bone repair polymers; mechanisms of implant degradation. *Mailing Add:* 1736 Buchanan St NE Washington DC 20017-3123

**WADE, DALE A,** WILDLIFE MANAGEMENT. *Current Pos:* RETIRED. *Personal Data:* b Buffalo, SDak, May 23, 28; m 53; c 5. *Educ:* SDak State Univ, BS, 69, PhD(animal sci), 72. *Prof Exp:* Mem staff mammal control, US Fish & Wildlife Serv, 62-65; wildlife specialist, Colo State Univ, 72-74, Univ Calif, Davis, 74-78; wildlife specialist, Tex A&M Univ, San Angelo, 78-86; dir Nat Tech Support Staff, ADC-APHIS-USDA, 86-90. *Concurrent Pos:* Consult, US Environ Protection Agency & US Dept Agr, Various State Agencies, 70-85. *Mem:* Sigma Xi; AAAS; Am Inst Biol Sci; Soc Range Mgt; Wildlife Soc; Am Soc Testing & Mat; Nat Parks & Conserv Asn; Coun Agr Sci & Tech. *Res:* Evaluation of biological, economic conflicts and possible solutions in human, wildlife and agricultural relationships. *Mailing Add:* 8610 Bonita Pl Cheyenne WY 82009

**WADE, DAVID ROBERT,** BIOCHEMISTRY. *Current Pos:* ASSOC PROF PHYSIOL, SCH MED, SOUTHERN ILL UNIV, 74- *Personal Data:* b London, Eng, May 25, 39; m 62; c 3. *Educ:* Univ Cambridge, BA & MA, 63, PhD(biochem), 67. *Prof Exp:* Res assoc physiol, Col Med, Pa State Univ, 67-69; Bank Am Giannini fel biochem, Sch Med, Univ Calif, Davis, 69-71; USPHS grant metab regulation & asst prof physiol, Col Med, Pa State Univ, 71-74. *Res:* Metabolic regulation. *Mailing Add:* Dept Physiol Southern Ill Univ Sch Med PO Box 19230 Springfield IL 62794-9230

**WADE, EARL KENNETH,** PLANT PATHOLOGY. *Current Pos:* asst potato cert serv, 46-50, prof plant path, 69-79, EXTEN PLANT PATHOLOGIST, UNIV WIS-MADISON, 50-, EMER PROF PLANT PATH, 79- *Personal Data:* b Toledo, Iowa, July 13, 14; m 47; c 3. *Educ:* Univ Wis, BS, 38, MS, 50. *Prof Exp:* Instr high sch, Wis, 38-42. *Mem:* Am Phytopath Soc; Am Potato Asn. *Res:* Vegetable and fruit diseases. *Mailing Add:* 5007 Marathon Dr Madison WI 53705

**WADE, GLEN,** ENGINEERING PHYSICS. *Current Pos:* PROF ELEC ENG, UNIV CALIF, SANTA BARBARA, 66- *Personal Data:* b Ogden, Utah, Mar 19, 21; m 45; c 4. *Educ:* Univ Utah, BS, 48, MS, 49; Stanford Univ, PhD, 54. *Honors & Awards:* Nat Electronics Conf Ann Award, 59. *Prof Exp:* Electronic scientist, US Naval Res Labs, Washington, DC, 49-50; res assoc, Microwave Lab, Gen Elec Co, 55; mem sr staff, Electronics Labs, Stanford Univ, 55-60, assoc prof elec eng, 58-60; asst gen mgr, Res Div, Raytheon Co, Mass, 60-63; dir sch elec eng & J Preston Levis prof eng, Cornell Univ, 63-66. *Concurrent Pos:* Consult, Gen Elec Co, 55-58, Diamond Ord Fuze Labs, 57-60, Zenith Radio Corp, 57-60, 63-73 & EG&G, Inc, 66-79, Innovision, 87-, Wiley Publ Co, 84-; ed, Trans on Electron Devices, Inst Elec & Electronics Engrs, 61-71 & J Quantum Electronics, 65-67; ser ed, Harcourt, Brace & World, Inc, 64-70; consult mem adv group electron devices, Comt of Dept Defense, 66-74; Japan Soc Promotion of Sci vis prof award, Univ Tokyo, 71; Fulbright-Hays fel, Spain, 72-73; ed, Proc of Inst Elec & Electronics Engrs, 77-80; Taiwanese Nat Sci Coun spec chair award, Nat Taiwan Univ, 80-81; UN vis prof, Nanjing Inst Technol, 86; lectr, Taiwanese Nat Sci Coun, 88; UN vis prof, Southeast Univ China, 89. *Mem:* Am Phys Soc; Inst Elec & Electronics Engrs; Sigma Xi. *Res:* Physical and quantum electronics; ultrasonics; optical systems. *Mailing Add:* Dept Elec & Comp Eng Univ Calif Santa Barbara CA 93106

**WADE, JAMES B,** PHYSIOLOGY, MEMBRANE STRUCTURE. *Current Pos:* PROF PHYSIOL, SCH MED, UNIV MD, 83- *Educ:* Princeton Univ, PhD(biol), 72. *Mailing Add:* Dept Physiol Univ Md Sch Med 660 W Redwood St Baltimore MD 21201-1041. *Fax:* 410-706-8341

**WADE, JAMES JOSEPH,** MEDICINAL CHEMISTRY, PHARMACEUTICALS RESEARCH & DEVELOPMENT. *Current Pos:* sr med chemist, Riker Labs, 3M Co, 73-76, res specialist, 76-83, sr res specialist, 3M Pharmaceut Div, 83-87, mgr chem, 87-91, LAB MGR DRUG DISCOVERY, 3M PHARMACEUT DIV, 3M CO, 91- *Personal Data:* b St Paul, Minn, Jan 7, 46; m 70, Elizabeth Weber; c Daniel, Michael & Kristin. *Educ:* Col St Thomas, BA, 68; Univ Minn, PhD(org chem), 72. *Prof Exp:* NIH fel org chem, Univ Rochester, 72-73. *Mem:* Am Chem Soc; Int Soc Heterocyclic Chem. *Res:* Discovery and preclinical development of novel anti-asthmatic and immunomodulator drug candidates. *Mailing Add:* 1385 N Hallmark Ave Oakdale MN 55128-5935. *E-Mail:* jjwade@mmm.com

**WADE, LEROY GROVER, JR,** ORGANIC SYNTHETIC METHODS. *Current Pos:* PROF CHEM, WHITMAN COL, 89- *Personal Data:* b Jacksonville, Fla, Oct 8, 47; m 96, Patricia Andrews; c Christine E & Jennifer D. *Educ:* Rice Univ, BA, 69; Harvard Univ, AM, 70, PhD(chem), 74. *Prof Exp:* From asst prof to assoc prof chem, Colo State Univ, 74-89. *Mem:* Am Chem Soc; AAAS; Sigma Xi; Am Acad Forensic Sci. *Res:* Organic chemistry; organic synthesis; chemical education; author of organic chemistry textbooks. *Mailing Add:* Chem Dept Whitman Col Walla Walla WA 99362

**WADE, MICHAEL GEORGE,** KINESIOLOGY & HUMAN FACTORS ENGINEERING, AGING & MOTOR CONTROL. *Current Pos:* DIR & PROF, SCH KINESIOL, PROF KINESIOL, CTR RES ON LEARNING, PERCEPTION & COGNITION, UNIV MINN, 86- *Personal Data:* b Watford, Eng, Nov 5, 41; c 4. *Educ:* Loughborough Col, DLC, 63; Univ Ill, MS, 68, PhD(kinesiology & human factors), 70. *Prof Exp:* Lectr phys educ, Univ Guelph, Can, 65-66; asst prof, Inst Child Behav & Develop, Univ Ill, 66-70, from asst prof to assoc prof, leisure studies & spec educ, 70-81; prof phys educ, Southern Ill Univ, 81-86. *Mem:* NAm Soc Psychol Sport & Phys Activ; Am Asn Ment Deficiency; fel Am Acad Phys Educ; fel Am Asn Ment Retardation; fel Am Acad Kinesiol; fel Am Acad Mental Retardation. *Res:* Motor behavior and developmental disabilities and problems of control and coordination; mental retardation; play behavior of children; biorhythms; aging research. *Mailing Add:* Sch Kinesiol & Leisure Studies Univ Minn 110 Cooke Hall 1900 University Ave Minneapolis MN 55455. *Fax:* 612-626-7700; *E-Mail:* mwade@maroon.umu.edu

**WADE, MICHAEL JAMES,** TOXICOLOGY, NUTRITIONAL TOXICOLOGY. *Current Pos:* SR TOXICOLOGIST, CALIF ENVIRON PROTECTION AGENCY, 85- *Personal Data:* b Salt Lake City, UT, May 18, 42; m 71. *Educ:* Univ Utah, BS, 64, MS, 67; Wash Univ, PhD(molecular biol), 71. *Prof Exp:* Res assoc biophysics, Max-Planck Inst Med Res, Heidelberg, Ger, 72-73, chem, Boston Univ, 73-75; fel toxicol, Univ Calif, San Francisco, 75-76; staff scientist, Life Sci Res Off, Fedn Am Soc Exp Biol, 76-78; rev scientist toxicol, US Food & Drug Admin, 78-85. *Mem:* Am Col Toxicol; Soc Toxicol & Environ Chem; Am Chem Soc. *Mailing Add:* Wade Res Inc 110 Holly Rd Marshfield MA 02050-1724

**WADE, MICHAEL JOHN,** POPULATION BIOLOGY, POPULATION GENETICS. *Current Pos:* From asst prof to assoc prof, 82-87, chair, 91-97, PROF BIOL, UNIV CHICAGO, 87- *Personal Data:* b Evanston, Ill, Oct 21, 49; m 87, Debra Rush; c Catherine, Megan & Travis. *Educ:* Boston Col, BA, 71; Univ Chicago, PhD(theoret biol), 75. *Concurrent Pos:* Res career develop award, NIH, 81-86. *Mem:* Am Soc Naturalists; Soc Study Evolution; Soc Study Pop Ecol; Genetics Soc Am. *Res:* Role of population structure in evolution; evolution of social behaviors; speciation genetics and development. *Mailing Add:* Dept Ecol & Evolution Univ Chicago 1101 E 57th St Chicago IL 60637-1455

**WADE, PETER ALLEN,** ORGANIC CHEMISTRY. *Current Pos:* asst prof, 76-87, ASSOC PROF CHEM, DREXEL UNIV, 87- *Personal Data:* b Taunton, Mass, Nov 12, 46; m 67; c 2. *Educ:* Lowell Technol Inst, BS, 68; Purdue Univ, PhD(org chem), 73. *Prof Exp:* Fel org chem, Univ Groningen, Neth, 73-74; IBM fel, Harvard Univ, 74-76. *Mem:* Am Chem Soc. *Res:* New synthetic methods; cycloaddition reactions; reactive intermediates; strained rings; carbohydrates. *Mailing Add:* Dept Chem Drexel Univ Philadelphia PA 19104-2875

**WADE, PETER CAWTHORN,** MEDICINAL CHEMISTRY, ORGANIC CHEMISTRY. *Current Pos:* EXCITON INC, DAYTON, OHIO, 88- *Personal Data:* b Washington, DC, Feb 15, 44; m 66, Tamara Chaikowski; c Douglas. *Educ:* Middlebury Col, AB, 66; Univ Wash, PhD(org chem), 71. *Prof Exp:* Res scientist, Squibb Inst Med Res, 71-80; res assoc, Diamond Shamrock Corp, 80-83; sr chemist, Exciton Inc, Dayton, Ohio, 83-88; sr chemist, Orsynex, Inc, Columbus, Ohio, 88- *Mem:* Am Chem Soc. *Res:* Anxiolytic, antidepressive, neuroleptic and anti-inflammatory, anti-hypertensive and anthelmintic agents; heterocyclic chemistry; fluorescent dyes; bulk manufacturing (fine organics). *Mailing Add:* 372 Nutt Rd Dayton OH 45458

**WADE, RICHARD ARCHER,** BIOLOGICAL OCEANOGRAPHY. *Current Pos:* MARINE ECOLOGIST, US FISH & WILDLIFE SERV, 75- *Personal Data:* b Fitchburg, Mass, Aug 16, 30; m 70; c 2. *Educ:* Univ Miami, BS, 56, MS, 62, PhD(biol oceanog), 68. *Prof Exp:* Marine scientist, Ayerst

Labs, Div Am Home Prod Corp, 66-68; head dept ecol & pollution, Va Inst Marine Sci, 68-69; chief lab, Environ Protection Agency, Fed Water Qual Admin, 68-69 & 70-71; exec secy, Sport Fishing Inst, 71-72; exec dir, Am Fisheries Soc, 72-75. *Concurrent Pos:* Consult, NIH Pesticide Proj, Univ Miami, 66-68; mem, Water Qual Mgt Comt, US Govt Interagency Group, 68-69; mem res subcomt, Fed Comt Pest Control, 68; clin res assoc, Med Univ SC, 70-71; mem, Subcomt Marine Water Qual Criteria, Nat Acad Sci, 71; treas, Sport Fishing Res Found, 71-72. *Mem:* Am Fisheries Soc; Am Soc Ichthyol & Herpet; Gulf & Caribbean Fisheries Inst; Marine Technol Soc. *Res:* Coastal ecosystems of the United States, including dredge disposal, offshore oil and gas development, development of deepwater ports, power plant construction and operation; marine and estuarine water quality problems. *Mailing Add:* 2310 15th St Alamogordo NM 88310

**WADE, RICHARD LINCOLN,** environmental toxicology, environmental engineering, for more information see previous edition

**WADE, ROBERT HAROLD,** ORGANIC CHEMISTRY, POLYMER CHEMISTRY. *Current Pos:* RETIRED. *Personal Data:* b Opportunity, Wash, Sept 16, 20; m 44, Dorothy Talen; c Diane (Williams) & Debra (Frese). *Educ:* Univ Wash, BS, 46, PhD(chem), 51. *Prof Exp:* Res chemist, M W Kellog Co Div, Pullman, Inc, 51-57; org chemist & proj leader, Stanford Res Inst, 57-63; sr res scientist, US Naval Undersea Ctr, 63-83. *Res:* Synthesis of polynuclear aromatic compounds; high temperature metal-chelate polymers; physical and chemical fate of fluoride in plants; synthesis and properties of water soluble and friction reducing polymers; marine natural products. *Mailing Add:* 7810 Golfcrest Dr San Diego CA 92119

**WADE, THOMAS EDWARD,** SOLID STATE MICROELECTRONICS, VLSI MULTILEVEL INTERCONNECTIONS SYSTEMS. *Current Pos:* actg dir, Ctr Microelectronics Design & Test, Univ SFla, 86-87, assoc dean res, Col Eng, 85-93, exec dir, Ctr Eng Develop & Res, 85-93, RES PROF, UNIV SFLA, 93-, CERT RES ADMINR, 93- *Personal Data:* b Jacksonville, Fla, Sept 14, 43; m 66, Ann E Chitty; c Amy R, Nathan T & Laura A. *Educ:* Univ Fla, BSEE, 66, MSEE, 69, PhD(microelectronics), 74. *Honors & Awards:* Centennial Cert Award, Am Soc Eng Educ, 92, Second Century Cert, 93. *Prof Exp:* Asst prof elec eng, Univ Fla, 74-76; prof elec eng & dir, Microelectron Res Lab, Miss State Univ, 76-85. *Concurrent Pos:* Solid State Circuit Specialist, Appl Micro Circuit Corp, San Diego, Calif, 81; res scientist, NASA, Marshall Space Flight Ctr, Huntsville, 83 & 84; consult, 82-92; dir, Eng Indust Exp Sta, Univ SFla, 85-93; bd dirs, Eng Res Coun, Am Soc Eng Educ; chmn, External Rel Comt, Soc Res Adminr, 87-89; educ comt, Int Soc Hybrid Microelectronics, 80-84; gen chmn, Very-Large-Scale Integration Multilevel Interconnection Conf, 84-, Dielectrics Ultra-Large-Scale Integration Multilevel Interconnection Conf, 94- *Mem:* Am Soc Eng Educ; Soc Res Adminr; Am Vacuum Soc; Nat Coun Univ Res Adminr; Nat Soc Prof Engrs; Int Elec & Electronics Engrs. *Res:* Technical specialization in solid state microelectronics and related topics; very large scale integration multilevel interconnection systems; fluctuation phenomena (electronic noise) in semiconductors and solid state devices; solid state device and related materials fabrications and characterizations; novel research administration techniques. *Mailing Add:* 5316 Witham Ct E Tampa FL 33647-1026. E-Mail: wade@sunburn.eng.usf.edu

**WADE, WILLIAM H,** PHYSICAL CHEMISTRY, PETROLEUM ENGINEERING. *Current Pos:* res scientist, Univ Tex, Austin, 58-61, from asst prof to assoc prof, 61-72, chmn dept, 74-80, PROF CHEM, UNIV TEX, AUSTIN, 72- *Personal Data:* b San Antonio, Tex, Nov 3, 30; wid. *Educ:* St Mary's Univ, Tex, BS, 51; Univ Tex, PhD(chem), 55. *Prof Exp:* Res scientist, Univ Calif, Berkeley, 55-58. *Mem:* Am Chem Soc; Soc Petrol Engrs. *Res:* Surface chemistry; emulsions; surfactants for enhanced oil recovery. *Mailing Add:* Dept Chem Univ Tex Austin TX 78712-1104

**WADE, WILLIAM HOWARD,** ENTOMOLOGY, PHYTOPATHOLOGY. *Current Pos:* RETIRED. *Personal Data:* b Stoughton, Wis, Apr 18, 23; m 43; c 1. *Educ:* Univ Calif, BS, 50, PhD(entom), 56. *Prof Exp:* Res & teaching asst, Univ Calif, 50-53; mgr tech serv & prod prom, Agr Chem Div, FMC Corp, 53-72, mgr develop, 72-75, mgr tech serv, Agr Chem Group, 75-85. *Mem:* Entom Soc Am; Sigma Xi. *Res:* Insect biology; field evaluation of pesticides; investigation of pesticide related problems. *Mailing Add:* 214 W Andrews Fresno CA 93705

**WADE, WILLIAM RAYMOND, II,** MATHEMATICS, HARMONIC ANALYSIS. *Current Pos:* From asst prof to assoc prof, 68-78, PROF MATH, UNIV TENN, KNOXVILLE, 78-, ASSOC HEAD, 94- *Personal Data:* b Los Angeles, Calif, Oct 28, 43; m 65; c 2. *Educ:* Univ Calif, Riverside, BA, 65, MA, 66, PhD(math), 68. *Concurrent Pos:* Consult, Oak Ridge Nat Lab, 69-76; vis assoc prof math, Univ Southern Calif, 77; Fulbright prof, Moscow State Univ, 77-78, Indian Statist Inst Bangalore, India, 83; res grantee, NSF, 78-79, 84-86 & 88-91; vis prof math, Eotvos Univ, Hungary, 85. *Mem:* Am Math Soc; Math Asn Am; Hungarian Acad Sci. *Res:* Fourier analysis on groups; Haar and Walsh series; sets of uniqueness; harmonic analysis of p-series fields; transform theory. *Mailing Add:* Dept Math Univ Tenn Knoxville TN 37996. *Fax:* 423-974-6576; *E-Mail:* wade@novell.math.utk.edu

**WADELIN, COE WILLIAM,** ANALYTICAL CHEMISTRY. *Current Pos:* RETIRED. *Personal Data:* b Dover, Ohio, Aug 18, 27; m 50; c Jeffrey. *Educ:* Mt Union Col, BS, 50; Purdue Univ, MS, 51, PhD, 53. *Prof Exp:* Res chemist, Goodyear Tire & Rubber Co, Akron, Ohio, 53-65, sect head anal chem, 65-75, sect head spectros, 75-77, mgr anal sci & technol, Fiber & Polymer Res &

Develop Div, 77-87. *Concurrent Pos:* Fel, Ctr Advan Eng Study, Mass Inst Technol, 68-69. *Mem:* Am Chem Soc. *Res:* Analysis of polymers and organic chemicals; absorption spectroscopy. *Mailing Add:* 1195 Inverness Lane Stow OH 44224-2290

**WADELL, LYLE H,** ANIMAL BREEDING, DATA PROCESSING MANAGEMENT. *Current Pos:* Res assoc animal breeding res, 59-60, res animal geneticist, 60-61, admin supvr comput ctr mgt, 61-66, DIR COMPUT CTR MGT, CORNELL UNIV, 66 - *Personal Data:* b Elsie, Mich, Mar 7, 34; div; c 5. *Educ:* Mich State Univ, BS, 55, MS, 57; Iowa State Univ, PhD(animal breeding, statist, genetics), 59. *Res:* Computing center management; data processing techniques; statistics. *Mailing Add:* 468 Auburn Ave Groton NY 13073

**WADEY, WALTER GEOFFREY,** PHYSICS. *Current Pos:* RETIRED. *Personal Data:* b Whangarei, NZ, Sept 9, 18; nat US; m 45; c 3. *Educ:* Univ Mich, BSc, 41, MA, 42, PhD(physics), 47. *Prof Exp:* Res assoc, Radio Res Lab, Harvard Univ, 43-45; instr physics, Yale Univ, 47-50, asst prof, 50-56; prof, Southern Ill Univ, 56-57; mgr sci prog, Remington Rand Univac Div, Sperry Rand Corp, 57-58, tech coordr, 59; physicist, Hughes Aircraft Co, 59-60; mgr advan electromech develop dept, Univac Div, Sperry Rand Corp, 60-62; chief scientist, Bowles Eng Corp, 62-63 & Wash Tech Assocs, 63-64; sr scientist, Opers Res, Inc, Silver Spring, MD, 64-84. *Mem:* AAAS; Am Phys Soc; Asn Comput Mach; Opers Res Soc Am; Marine Technol Soc. *Res:* Experimental nuclear physics; nuclear spectroscopy; linear electron accelerators; electronics; computer programming and arithmetics; fluid mechanics; electromechanical design; fluid-amplifier technology; operations research; systems analysis; anti-submarine warfare; information systems. *Mailing Add:* 6 Greenfield Lane Scituate MA 02066-4506

**WADGAONKAR, DILIP BHANUDAS,** FORMULATION DEVELOPMENT & DESIGN OF NEW DRUGS, FORMULATION OPTIMIZATION. *Current Pos:* SR RES SCIENTIST, AM CYANAMID CO, 85- *Personal Data:* b Pachora, India, Aug 8, 52; m 77, Sunanda N Mehendale; c Sunil & Ajay. *Educ:* Bombay Univ, BPharm, 74, MPharm, 77; Purdue Univ, MS; 80; Rutgers Univ, PhD(pharmaceut), 91. *Prof Exp:* Res scientist, Block Drug Co, 80-85. *Mem:* Am Asn Pharmaeut Scientists; Am Pharmaceut Asn. *Res:* Formulation and process development of new clinical entities; dosage form design and evaluation, solid state moisture interaction with pharmaceuticals; formulation and process optimization. *Mailing Add:* 26 Madison Hill Rd Suffern NY 10901. *Fax:* 914-732-5580

**WADKE, DEODATT ANANT,** PHYSICAL PHARMACY. *Current Pos:* PHARMACEUT CONSULT, 94- *Personal Data:* b July 7, 38; US citizen; m 67, Rupa G Gavankar; c Sagar & Samir. *Educ:* Banaras Hindu Univ, BPharm, 61; Ohio State Univ, MS, 63; State Univ NY, Buffalo, PhD(pharmaceut), 67. *Prof Exp:* Res assoc formulations, Merck Sharpe & Dohme Res Labs, 66-69; res investr pharmaceut res & develop, Bristol-Myers Squibb Pharmaceut Res Inst, New Brunswick, 69-71, sr res investr, 72-73, head, Preformulation Studies Sect, 73-76, head, Solid Formulation Develop Sect, 76-79, asst dir pharm res & develop, 79-85, dir pharmaceut res & develop, 85-93. *Mem:* Am Asn Pharmaceut Scientists; Controlled Release Soc. *Res:* Thermodynamics of dissolution, solubilization and absorption; dissolution of polyphase systems; drug stability; pharmacokinetics. *Mailing Add:* 2 Delaware Rim Dr Yardley PA 19067-2603. *Fax:* 215-321-6294

**WADKINS, CHARLES L,** BIOCHEMISTRY. *Current Pos:* chmn dept, 66-80, PROF BIOCHEM, MED CTR, UNIV ARK, LITTLE ROCK, 66- *Personal Data:* b Joplin, Mo, May 8, 29; m 52; c 2. *Educ:* Univ Kans, AB, 51, PhD(biochem), 56. *Prof Exp:* Instr biochem, Univ Kans, 55-56; fel biochem, Sch Med Johns Hopkins Univ, 56-57; from instr to assoc prof, 57-66. *Concurrent Pos:* USPHS sr res fel, 59-64; mem adv panel, NSF; planning officer, Nat Inst Aging, NIH, 80-82. *Mem:* Am Chem Soc; Am Soc Biol Chemists; Brit Biochem Soc. *Res:* Biological oxidation reactions; oxidative phosphorylation; mechanism and control of biological calcification reactions. *Mailing Add:* 32218 Sandpiper Dr Orange Beach AL 36561

**WADLEIGH, CECIL HERBERT,** plant physiology, resource conservation; deceased, see previous edition for last biography

**WADLEIGH, KENNETH R(OBERT),** MECHANICAL ENGINEERING. *Current Pos:* From instr to prof, Mass Inst Technol, 46-, dean student affairs, 61-69, vpres, 69-, dean, Grad Sch, 75-, EMER PROF MECH ENG, MASS INST TECHNOL. *Personal Data:* b Passaic, NJ, March 27, 21; m 48; c 2. *Educ:* Mass Inst Technol, SM & SB, 43, ScD, 53. *Hon Degrees:* MA, Univ Cambridge, Eng, 54. *Honors & Awards:* Goodwin Medal, 52; Bronze Beaver Award, Mass Inst Technol, 69. *Concurrent Pos:* Lectr, Univ Cambridge, Eng, 53-54. *Res:* Applied thermodynamics; fluid mechanics; two-phase flows. *Mailing Add:* 187 Seaview Ave Swansea MA 02777

**WADLEY, MARGIL WARREN,** ENVIRONMENTAL SCIENCES, ATMOSPHERIC SCIENCES. *Current Pos:* ADJ LECTR, CHAPMAN UNIV, CALIF, 93- *Personal Data:* b Cisco, Tex, Dec 4, 31; m 66; c 1. *Educ:* Southern Nazarene Univ, BS, 53; Okla State Univ, MS, 60; Purdue Univ, PhD(inorg chem), 63. *Prof Exp:* Sr chemist, Autonetics Div, NAm Aviation, Inc, 63-64 & Korad Dept, Union Carbide Corp, 64-65; sr res engr, Autonetics Div, NAm Aviation, Inc, 65 & 66-69 & Space Systems Div, Rockwell Int, Inc, 65-66; environ scientist, Southern Calif Air Pollution Control Dis, 69-71, prin chemist, 71-75, supv chemist, 75-77; prin chemist, S Coast Air Qual Mgt Dist, 85-93. *Concurrent Pos:* Mem bd, Henry George Sch Soc Sci, Los Angeles. *Mem:* Am Chem Soc; Sigma Xi; Am Sci Affil; Air & Waste Mgt Asn. *Res:* Size and mass distribution of airborne particulate matter and associated visibility relationships. *Mailing Add:* 520 E Riverdale Ave Orange CA 92865

**WADLINGTON, WALTER J,** CHILDRENS HEALTH CARE, LEGAL RESPONSES TO BIOMEDICAL TECHNOLOGY. *Current Pos:* JAMES MADISON PROF LAW, LAW SCH, UNIV VA, 70-, PROF LEGAL MED, MED SCH, 79- *Personal Data:* m 55, Ruth Hardie; c Claire, Charlotte (Griffith), Susan & Derek. *Educ:* Duke Univ, AB, 51; Tulance Univ, LLB, 54. *Concurrent Pos:* Prog dir, Med Malpractice Prog, Roert Wood Johnson Found, 85-91; mem, Comt Impact Med Prof Liability Delivery Maternal & Child Health Care, Inst Med, 87-89, Comt Legal & Ethical Issues Woman Clin Trials, 90-93. *Mem:* Inst Med-Nat Acad Sci; Am Law Inst. *Res:* Legal problems of reproductive technology; children's health care. *Mailing Add:* 1620 Keith Valley Rd Charlottesville VA 22901. *Fax:* 804-924-7536

**WADLOW, DAVID,** BIOMEDICAL SENSORS, GAS HANDLING. *Current Pos:* sr engr, 78-88, LEAD ENGR, BOC GROUP TECH CTR, 88- *Personal Data:* b London, Eng, 1950. *Educ:* Univ Manchester, UK, BSc, 71; Univ Leicester, UK, MSc, 72; Univ Reading, UK, PhD(electrogas dynamics), 84. *Prof Exp:* Res assoc, Dept Eng & Cybernet, Univ Reading, UK, 73-76 & Cryog Ctr, Stevens Inst Technol, 76-78. *Mem:* Inst Physics. *Res:* Sensors, including new technologies in gas flow measurement and gas composition measurement; mass spectrometry and visible emission spectroscopy; biomedical instrumentation. *Mailing Add:* 44 Smithfield Ct Apt 8 Basking Ridge NJ 07920

**WADMAN, W HUGH,** chemistry, biochemistry, for more information see previous edition

**WADSWORTH, DALLAS FREMONT,** PLANT PATHOLOGY. *Current Pos:* RETIRED. *Personal Data:* b Arcadia, Okla, Mar 2, 22; c 1. *Educ:* Okla State Univ, BS, 48, MS, 49; Univ Calif, PhD(plant path), 66. *Prof Exp:* From asst prof to prof bot & plant path, Okla State Univ, 71-85. *Mem:* Am Phytopath Soc. *Res:* Diseases of peanuts; plant virology. *Mailing Add:* 111 Cherry Hills Rockport TX 78382

**WADSWORTH, FRANK H,** FORESTRY. *Current Pos:* STAFF MEM, INST TROP FORESTRY, US FOREST SERV, 42- *Personal Data:* b Chicago, Ill, Nov 26, 15; m 41, 84, Isaber Colorado; c Robert, Frank (deceased), Clara, Sylvia & Isabot (Fernandez). *Educ:* Univ Mich, BSF & MF, 37, PhD(forestry), 50. *Honors & Awards:* Fernow Award, Am Forestry Asn, 73; Gulf Cons Award, 85. *Prof Exp:* Forester, SW Forest & Range Exp Sta, Flagstaff, Ariz, 38-41. *Concurrent Pos:* Consult 20 trop countries, 49-80. *Mem:* Soc Am Foresters; Int Soc Trop Foresters. *Res:* Multiple forest land use and management, silviculture, growth and yield of naturally regenerated forests and timber plantations in the humid tropics. *Mailing Add:* PO Box 25000 Rio Piedras PR 00928-5000. *Fax:* 787-766-6302

**WADSWORTH, HARRISON M(ORTON),** INDUSTRIAL ENGINEERING, STATISTICS. *Current Pos:* PRES, HARRISON M WADSWORTH & ASSOC INC, 91- *Personal Data:* b Duluth, Minn, Aug 20, 24; m 50, Irene Hawkins; c Harrison & Alice. *Educ:* Ga Inst Technol, BInd Eng, 50, MS, 55; Case Western Res Univ, PhD(statist), 60. *Honors & Awards:* Brumbaugh Award, Am Soc Qual Control, 71, Austin Bonis Award, 85, Howard P Jones Medal, 86; Shewhart Medal, 89. *Prof Exp:* Indust engr, Steel Heddle Mfg Co, SC, 52-54; qual control engr, Nat Carbon Co, 54-56; asst prof mech eng, Mich State Univ, 56-57; instr & res assoc statist, Case Western Res Univ, 57-60; from assoc prof to prof indust eng, Ga Inst Technol, 64-91. *Concurrent Pos:* Consult statist, Lockheed-Ga Co, 66-70; NSF grant, exp design course for eng profs, Univ Wis, 66; Orgn Econ Coop & Develop consult, Mid East Tech Univ, Ankara, 67-68; ed, J Quality Technol, 79-82; consult, qual control & statist. *Mem:* Fel Am Soc Qual Control; Inst Indust Eng; Am Statist Asn; Sigma Xi. *Res:* Economics of statistical sampling plans; design of experiments; quality control; reliability; quality management. *Mailing Add:* 660 Valley Green Dr NE Atlanta GA 30342. *Fax:* 404-250-1493; *E-Mail:* hwadswor@lsye.gatech.edu

**WADSWORTH, JEFFREY,** METALLURGY. *Current Pos:* MGR, METALL DEPT, LAWRENCE LIVERMORE NAT LABS, 92- *Personal Data:* b Hamburg, WGer, May 12, 50; US citizen; m 76; c 2. *Educ:* Sheffield Univ, Eng, BMetall, 72, PhD(metall), 75. *Hon Degrees:* DMet, Sheffield Univ, 90. *Honors & Awards:* Metallurgica Aparecida Medal; Brunton Medal. *Prof Exp:* Fel metall, Stanford Univ, 76-78, res assoc, 78-81; mgr, Metall Dept, Lockheed Res & Develop Div, 81-92. *Concurrent Pos:* Ed, Sheffield Univ Metall Soc J, 74; consult prof, Dept Mat Sci, Stanford Univ, 81- *Mem:* Am Inst Mining, Metall & Petrol Engrs; Fel Am Soc Metals; Am Ceramic Soc; Mat Res Soc. *Res:* Research into the physical and mechanical properties of metals and non-metals with an emphasis on materials of significant technological importance. *Mailing Add:* Texas Instruments Box 405 MS 3423 Lewisville TX 75067

**WADSWORTH, MILTON E(LLIOT),** ELECTROCHEMISTRY, EXTRACTIVE METALLURGY. *Current Pos:* from instr to prof, Univ Utah, 48-83, chmn dept, 55-66 & 74-76, assoc dean, Col Mines & Mineral Industs, 76-83, dean, Col Mines & Earth Sci, 83-91, distinguished prof, 83-96, DISTINGUIS HED EMER PROF METALL ENG, UNIV UTAH, 96- *Personal Data:* b Salt Lake City, Utah, Feb 9, 22; m 43; c 6. *Educ:* Univ Utah, BS, 48, PhD(metall), 51. *Hon Degrees:* Dr, Univ Liege Belgium 79; Deng, Colo Sch Mines, 91. *Honors & Awards:* Warren Lectr, Sch Mines & Metall, Univ Minn, 62; James Douglas Gold Medal Award, Am Inst Mining, Metall & Petrol Engrs, 78, Mineral Indust Educ Award, 81; Henry Crumb Lectr, 79; Antoine M Gaudin Award, Soc Mining Engrs, Am Inst Mining, Metall, & Petrol Engrs, 84 & Educ Award, Metall Soc, 89. *Concurrent Pos:* Milton E Wadsworth fel, Univ Utah, 65-, dir, Utah Mining & Minerals Resources Res Inst, 79-80; vis prof, Dept Metall, Univ BC, 67-68 & US Steel Res Lab, Pa; lectr, Extractive Metall Div, Am Inst Mining, Metall & Petrol Engrs, 69; consult, numerous insts; sci adv, US Bur Mines Metall Res Ctr, Salt Lake City Sta, 72-79; mem bd dirs, Am Chemet Corp, 83-, Tech Res Assocs, 85- & Utah Biores Inc, 85-, Utah Geol & Mineral Surv, 88-91; mem, Comt Mineral Resources, Nat Asn State Univs & Land-Grant Cols, 82-83, Future Iron & Steel Prod Adv Comt, Geneva Steel, 89. *Mem:* Nat Acad Eng; Am Inst Mining, Metall & Petrol Engrs (pres, 91); Am Soc Eng Educ; Can Metals Soc; fel Am Soc Metals Int; Am Chem Soc; Sigma Xi; Electrochem Soc; Can Inst Mining & Metall. *Res:* Surface chemistry of mineral systems in mineral dressing and extractive metallurgy processes; hydrometallurgy; intermediate temperature processing such as roasting, decomposition and reduction; application of reaction rate kinetics in determination of mechanisms in extractive metallurgy processes and electrochemistry as applied to metals extraction; author of numerous publications. *Mailing Add:* Dept Metall & Metall Eng Univ Utah 412 WBB Salt Lake City UT 84112. *Fax:* 801-581-4937; *E-Mail:* mwads@mines.utah.edu

**WADSWORTH, SCOTT,** IMMUNOLOGY. *Current Pos:* SR RES SCIENTIST IMMUNOL, IMMUNOL BIOL RES INST, 92- *Personal Data:* b Syracuse, NY, Oct 18, 58. *Educ:* Hamilton Col, BA, 80; Univ Del, MS, 83; Univ Pa, PhD(immunol), 89. *Prof Exp:* Fel immunol, NIH, 89-92. *Mem:* Am Asn Immunologists. *Res:* Immunology. *Mailing Add:* Dept Immunol R W Johnson Pharmaceut 1000 Rte 1025 Raritan NJ 08869

**WADSWORTH, WILLIAM BINGHAM,** PETROLOGY OF GRANITES, STATISTICS IN GEOLOGY. *Current Pos:* assoc prof, 72-78, PROF GEOL, WHITTIER COL, 78- *Personal Data:* b Cortland, NY, Dec 4, 34; m 62, Martha K Nakao; c W Bryan & Kyle E. *Educ:* Brown Univ, AB, 57; Northwestern Univ, MS, 62, PhD(geol). 66. *Prof Exp:* Asst prof, Univ SDak, 63-66; from asst prof to assoc prof, Idaho State Univ, 66-72. *Concurrent Pos:* NSF Sci fac fel, Pomona Col, 71-72; chmn, Geol Dept, Whittier Col, 73-85 & 87-90, interim dean fac, 85-86, fac master, 90-93. *Mem:* Am Asn Geol Teachers; Am Geophys Union; Am Mineral Soc; fel Geol Soc Am; Int Asn Math Geol; Mineral Asn Can. *Res:* Petrology of the Cornelia porphyry-copper stock at Ajo, Arizona; x-ray diffraction methods in modal analysis of granites; computer applications in geology; mapping jurassic rocks of the Mojave Desert. *Mailing Add:* Dept Geol Whittier Col 1306 Philadelphia St Whittier CA 90601-4446. *Fax:* 562-693-6117; *E-Mail:* wwadsworth@whittier.edu

**WADSWORTH, WILLIAM STEELE, JR,** ORGANIC CHEMISTRY. *Current Pos:* RETIRED. *Personal Data:* b Hartford, Conn, May 6, 27; m 56; c 4. *Educ:* Trinity Col, Conn, BS, 50, MS, 52; Pa State Univ, PhD(chem), 56. *Prof Exp:* Res chemist, Rohm & Haas Co, 56-63; assoc prof chem, SDak State Univ, 63-68, prof, 68-94. *Mem:* Am Chem Soc; Sigma Xi. *Res:* New reactions and mechanisms in organic chemistry; heterocyclic and organophosphorus chemistry. *Mailing Add:* 1320 Trail Ridge Circle Brookings SD 57006

**WADT, WILLARD ROGERS,** THEORETICAL CHEMISTRY. *Current Pos:* DEP DIV LEADER, LOS ALAMOS NAT LAB, 87- *Personal Data:* b Bayonne, NJ, Jan 6, 49. *Educ:* Williams Col, BA, 70; Calif Inst Technol, PhD(chem), 75. *Prof Exp:* Sr res chemist, Mound Lab, Monsanto Res Corp, 74-76; mem staff, Los Alamos Nat Lab, 76-81, dep group leader & proj mgr, 81-85; vpres, BioDesign, Inc, 86. *Mem:* Am Chem Soc; AAAS. *Res:* Ab initio electronic structure theory of molecules; electronic transition lasers; molecular photochemistry; mesic molecules; atmospheric chemistry. *Mailing Add:* QP MS M722 Los Alamos Nat Lab Los Alamos NM 87545-0001

**WAECHTER-BRULLA, DARYLE A,** BIOLOGY FOR NON-SCIENTISTS, SCIENCE & TECHNOLOGY IN SOCIETY. *Current Pos:* asst prof, 90-96, ASSOC PROF BIOL, UNIV WIS-WHITEWATER, 96- *Personal Data:* b Chicago, Ill, Mar 16, 58; m 83, William J Brulla; c 2. *Educ:* Ill State Univ, BS, 79, Univ Ill, MS, 82, PhD(microbiol), 88. *Prof Exp:* Fel, Calif Inst Technol, 88-90. *Mem:* Am Soc Microbiol; AAAS. *Res:* Genetic regulation of bacterial metabolic activities with bioremediation value, and other examples of bacterial ecology. *Mailing Add:* Dept Biol Univ Wis-Whitewater 800 W Main St Whitewater WI 53190. *E-Mail:* waechted@uwwvax.uww.edu

**WAELSCH, SALOME GLUECKSOHN,** GENETICS, DEVELOPMENTAL BIOLOGY. *Current Pos:* from assoc prof to prof anat, Albert Einstein Col Med, 55-63, prof, 55-88, chmn, Dept Genetics, 63-76, DISTINGUISHED EMER PROF GENETICS, ALBERT EINSTEIN COL MED, 88- *Personal Data:* b Ger, Oct 6, 07; nat US; m 2. *Educ:* Univ Freiburg, PhD(zool), 32. *Honors & Awards:* Nat Medal Sci, 93. *Prof Exp:* Res assoc & lectr zool, Columbia Univ, 36-55. *Mem:* Nat Acad Sci; Am Acad Arts & Sci; Am Asn Anatomists; Genetics Soc Am; Soc Develop Biol; Am Soc Zoologists. *Res:* Developmental and mammalian genetics; role and control of genes in differentiation. *Mailing Add:* Dept Molecular Genetics Albert Einstein Col Med 1300 Mars Park Ave Bronx NY 10461

**WAESCHE, R(ICHARD) H(ENLEY) WOODWARD,** AEROSPACE SCIENCE. *Current Pos:* SR SCIENTIST, SCI APPL INT CORP, 93- *Personal Data:* b Baltimore, Md, Dec 20, 30; m 57, Lucy S White; c Russell & Ann. *Educ:* Williams Col, BA, 52; Princeton Univ, MA, 62, PhD(aerospace & mech sci), 65. *Prof Exp:* Intermediate scientist, Redstone Arsenal Res Div, Rohm & Haas Co, Ala, 54-59, scientist, 64-66; asst in res aerospace sci, Princeton Univ, 61-64, res aidc, 64; sr res engr, Propulsion Appl, United Technol Res Ctr, 66-81; prin scientist technol, Atlantic Res Corp, 81-92. *Concurrent Pos:* Consult, Goodyear Aircraft Corp, 59, Princeton Univ, 64-65, Nat Res Coun, 85-86, Defense Advan Res Projs Agency, 88- & Directed

Technologies, Inc, 89-, Atlantic Res Corp, 92-, Battelle, 92-; assoc ed, J Spacecraft & Rockets, Am Inst Aeronaut & Astronaut, 75-80, ed-in-chief, 80-86, J Propulsion & Power, 86- *Mem:* Am Phys Soc; fel Am Inst Aeronaut & Astronaut; Combustion Inst. *Res:* Combustion related to chemical propulsion, rockets, ramjets, ducted rockets and guns; management of propulsion-related programs; optical spectroscopy; ablation heat transfer; fuel-spray atomization and combustion in a ramjet environment. *Mailing Add:* Sci Appl Int Corp 1710 Goodridge Dr McLean VA 22102. *Fax:* 703-821-4466; *E-Mail:* woodward_waesche@cpmx.saic.com

**WAFFLE, ELIZABETH LENORA,** PARASITOLOGY, INVERTEBRATE ZOOLOGY. *Current Pos:* asst prof, 68-77, ASSOC PROF BIOL, EASTERN MICH UNIV, 77- *Personal Data:* b Marion, Iowa, Feb 14, 38. *Educ:* Cornell Col, BA, 60; Univ Iowa, MS, 63; Iowa State Univ, PhD(parasitol), 67. *Prof Exp:* Assoc prof biol, Armstrong State Col, 66-67; asst prof, Iowa Wesleyan Col, 67-68. *Concurrent Pos:* Consult, Parasitol Prog, Ann Arbor Biol Ctr, 70-82. *Mem:* Am Soc Parasitol; Am Mosquito Control Asn; Wildlife Dis Asn. *Res:* Dog heartworm and other parasites of dogs; parasites of fish; mosquitoes feeding habits in relation to disease transmission; marine biology; entomology. *Mailing Add:* Dept Biol Eastern Mich Univ 316 Mark Jeffersen Ypsilanti MI 48197-2211

**WAGENAAR, RAPHAEL OMER,** DAIRY BACTERIOLOGY. *Current Pos:* sect leader microbiol, Food Develop Dept, 56-62, res assoc microbiol, food develop activ, Tech Ctr, 62-83, CONSULT, GEN MILLS, INC, 84- *Personal Data:* b Spokane, Wash, Jan 9, 16; wid; c 2. *Educ:* Wash State Univ, BS, 42, MS, 47; Univ Minn, PhD(dairy bact), 51. *Prof Exp:* Asst dairy bact, Univ Minn, 49-51; res assoc, Food Res Inst, Univ Chicago, 51-56. *Mem:* Am Soc Microbiol; Am Dairy Sci Asn; Inst Food Technologists; Sigma Xi. *Res:* Bacterial food poisoning; lactic acid bacteria; effect of irradiation on bacterial spores and toxins; psychrophilic bacteria causing food spoilage. *Mailing Add:* 1493 Fulham St St Paul MN 55113

**WAGENBACH, GARY EDWARD,** PARASITOLOGY, ZOOLOGY. *Current Pos:* from asst prof to assoc prof, 69-82, PROF BIOL, CARLETON COL, 82- *Personal Data:* b Barron, Wis, Mar 24, 40; m 60, Linda Jane Elkin; c Jeff, Paul & Brian. *Educ:* Univ Wis-River Falls, BS, 62; Univ Wis-Madison, MS, 64, PhD(zool), 68. *Prof Exp:* NIH proj assoc, Univ Wis-Madison, 68-69. *Concurrent Pos:* Vis prof, Stanford Univ, 80; prin investr, Marine Biol Lab, Woods Hole, 83-88, Univ Wash, Seattle, 89-; Carleton Foreign Study Prog, Australia. *Mem:* Sigma Xi. *Res:* Biology of parasites, especially digenetic trematodes and gregarines; biology of freshwater mussels. *Mailing Add:* Dept Biol Carleton Col Northfield MN 55057. *E-Mail:* gwagenba@carleton.edu

**WAGENET, ROBERT JEFFREY,** SOIL PHYSICS, SOIL CHEMISTRY. *Current Pos:* PROF SOIL, CROP & ATMOSPHERIC SCI, CORNELL UNIV, ITHACA, 82-, CHMN DEPT, 87- *Personal Data:* b Pittsburg, Calif, Aug 10, 50. *Educ:* Univ Calif, Davis, BS, 71, PhD(soil sci), 75; Univ Okla, MS, 72. *Honors & Awards:* Honor Award, Soil Conserv Soc Am, 89. *Prof Exp:* Staff res assoc, Univ Calif, Davis, 73-74, water scientist, 74-75; from asst prof to assoc prof soil sci, Utah State Univ, 76-82. *Mem:* Am Soc Agron; Am Geophys Union; Sigma Xi; fel Soil Sci Soc Am; Int Soil Sci Soc. *Res:* Simulation modeling of soil water and solutes including description of transient nitrogen and pesticide fluxes under field conditions; utilization and improvement of salt-affected soils and saline waters. *Mailing Add:* Cornell Univ 1014 Bradford Hall Ithaca NY 14853-0001

**WAGENKNECHT, BURDETTE LEWIS,** BOTANY. *Current Pos:* PROF BIOL & HEAD DEPT, WILLIAM JEWELL COL, 68- *Personal Data:* b Cotter, Iowa, Sept 9, 25; m 51; c 4. *Educ:* Univ Iowa, BA, 48, MS, 54; Univ Kans, PhD(bot), 58. *Prof Exp:* Instr biol & phys sci, Franklin Col, 54-55; asst bot, Univ Kans, 57-58; hort taxonomist, Arnold Arboretum, 58-61; from asst prof to assoc prof biol, Norwich Univ, 61-68. *Mem:* AAAS; Am Inst Biol Sci; Am Boxwood Soc. *Res:* Floristics of Washington County, Iowa; Heterotheca; taxonomy of cultivated wood plants; registration of cultivars in the genus Buxus. *Mailing Add:* 458 N Leonard St Liberty MO 64068

**WAGENKNECHT, JOHN HENRY,** ORGANIC CHEMISTRY, ELECTROCHEMISTRY. *Current Pos:* CONSULT & TECHNOL BROKER, CEDAR HILL, LLC, 94- *Personal Data:* b Washington, Iowa, Jan 30, 39; m 60, Joan Schilthuis; c 3. *Educ:* Monmouth Col, AB, 60; Univ Iowa, PhD(chem), 64. *Prof Exp:* Sr res chemist, Monsanto Co, 64-70, res specialist, 70-74, sci fel & mgr, 74-93. *Concurrent Pos:* Div Ed, J Electrochem Soc, 84-90; div secy-treas, Electrochem Soc, 77-79, vchmn, 79-81, chmn, 81-83. *Mem:* Electrochem Soc; Int Soc Electrochem; Am Chem Soc. *Res:* Synthesis of organic chemicals by electrochemistry; electroanalytical chemistry; electrical discharge chemistry; scale-up of electro-organic processes; sensors; displays; technology assessment. *Mailing Add:* Cedar Hill LLC 7510 Horseplay Lane Cedar Hill MO 63016. *Fax:* 314-285-2522; *E-Mail:* jhwagen@aol.com

**WAGER, JOHN FISHER,** ELECTRICAL ENGINEERING. *Current Pos:* asst prof, 84-89, ASSOC PROF ELEC ENG, ORE STATE UNIV, 89- *Personal Data:* b Glendale, Calif, Jan 22, 53; m 75; c 1. *Educ:* Ore State Univ, BS, 77; Colo State Univ, MS, 78, PhD(elec eng), 81. *Prof Exp:* Mem tech staff, Hughes Res Lab, 82-84. *Mem:* Am Vacuum Soc; Inst Elec & Electronics Engrs. *Res:* Electrical characterization, modeling and exploratory materials development of alternating current thin film electroluminescent devices for flat panel displays; electrical characterization and atomistic thermodynamic modeling of compound semiconductor defects. *Mailing Add:* Dept Elec & Comput Eng Ore State Univ Corvallis OR 97331

**WAGER-PAGE, SHIRLEY A,** NUTRITION. *Current Pos:* Fel, 88-90, RES SCIENTIST NUTRIT, MONEL CHEM SENSES CTR, USDA, 91- *Personal Data:* b Sleepy Eye, Minn. *Educ:* Univ Minn, BS, 81, MS, 84, PhD(nutrit), 88. *Mem:* Am Soc Neurosci; Am Inst Nutrit. *Res:* Nutrition. *Mailing Add:* Monel Chem Senses Ctr USDA 3500 Market St Phildelphia PA 19104

**WAGGENER, ROBERT GLENN,** MEDICAL PHYSICS, BIOPHYSICS. *Current Pos:* asst prof, 68-72, ASSOC PROF RADIOL, MED SCH, UNIV TEX, SAN ANTONIO, 72-, ASSOC PROF DIAG & ROENTGENOL, 77- *Personal Data:* b Benton, Ky, June 12, 32; m 59; c 2. *Educ:* Univ Tex, Austin, BA, 54, MA, 63; Univ Tex, Houston, PhD(biophys), 67; Am Bd Radiol, cert, 72. *Prof Exp:* Res asst physics, Nuclear Physics Lab, Balcones Res Ctr, Univ Tex, Austin, 60-61; pres, Nucleonics Res & Develop Corp, Tex, 61-63; radiol health specialist, Tex State Health Dept, 63-64; Nat Cancer Inst fel physics, Univ Tex M D Anderson Hosp & Tumor Inst Houston, 67-68. *Concurrent Pos:* Consult, Brooke Army Med Ctr, Ft Sam Houston, Tex, 71- *Mem:* Am Asn Physicists in Med; Biophys Soc; Am Col Radiol; Soc Nuclear Med; Radiol Soc NAm. *Res:* Measurement of x-ray spectra; calculation of information content in diagnostic x-rays; dosimetry and measurement of ionizing radiation; computerized tomography. *Mailing Add:* Dept Radiol Med Sch Radiol Med Phys Div Univ Tex 7703 Floyd Curl Dr San Antonio TX 78284-6200

**WAGGENER, RONALD E,** RADIOLOGY. *Current Pos:* ASSOC PROF RADIOL, UNIV NEBR MED CTR, OMAHA, 58- *Personal Data:* b Green River, Wyo, Oct 6, 26; m 48; c 4. *Educ:* Univ Nebr, BS, 49, MS, 53, MD, 54, PhD, 57; Am Bd Radiol, dipl, 59. *Concurrent Pos:* Radiotherapist, Methodist Hosp, 59- *Mem:* Am Asn Cancer Res; Radiol Soc NAm; Royal Soc Med; Brit Inst Radiol; fel Am Col Radiol. *Res:* Biological effects of radiation stressing the hematological effects of ionizing rays. *Mailing Add:* 1227 S 109th St Omaha NE 68144-1813

**WAGGENER, THOMAS BARROW,** PEDIATRICS, BIOENGINEERING. *Current Pos:* PRES, PHYSIO ANALYTICS, 94- *Personal Data:* b Alvin, Tex, Apr 15, 51; c 2. *Educ:* Harvard Univ, PhD(bioeng), 79. *Prof Exp:* Fel, Cardiovasc Res Inst, Univ Calif, San Francisco, 79-81; instr pediat & eng, Harvard Med Sch, 81-85; asst prof pediat, New Eng Med Ctr, 85-92, dir, Pediat Diag Serv, 92-94. *Mem:* Am Physiol Soc; Inst Elec & Electronics Engrs. *Res:* Physiological control system analysis; respiratory control in infants and adults; apnea of prematurity and sudden infant death syndrome; physiological effects of hypoxia. *Mailing Add:* 24 Wyoming Rd Newton MA 02160

**WAGGENER, THOMAS RUNYAN,** FOREST ECONOMICS, POLICY ANALYSIS. *Current Pos:* Asst prof, Univ Wash, 67-71, chmn, Mgt & Soc Sci Div, 72-75, assoc prof, 71-78, PROF FOREST ECON, COL FOREST RESOURCES, UNIV WASH, 78-, ASSOC DEAN INSTR, 78- *Personal Data:* b Indianapolis, Ind, July 20, 38; m 64; c 2. *Educ:* Purdue Univ, BSF, 62; Univ Wash, MF, 63, MA, 65, PhD(forest econ), 66. *Concurrent Pos:* Assoc coordr course in trop forestry, Orgn Trop Studies, Inc, Costa Rica & Honduras, 68 & 71; economist & analyst, Pub Land Law Rev Comn, DC, 68-69. *Mem:* Am Econ Asn; Soc Am Foresters; Sigma Xi. *Res:* Natural resources economics and analysis of economic impact of resource management policies; regional economic analysis; industrial organization and market structure; forest policy. *Mailing Add:* Col Forest Resources Univ Wash Box 352100 Seattle WA 98195

**WAGGLE, DOYLE H,** CEREAL CHEMISTRY. *Current Pos:* process res chemist, 67-68, mgr process res, 68-72, DIR RES & DEVELOP, VENTURE MGT, RALSTON PURINA CO, 72-, DIV VPRES, 78- *Personal Data:* b Osborne, Kans, Aug 11, 39; m 60; c 2. *Educ:* Ft Hays Kans State Col, BS, 61; Kans State Univ, MS, 63, PhD(milling indust), 66. *Prof Exp:* Res asst feed technol, Kans State Univ, 65-66, res assoc, 66-67. *Mem:* Am Asn Cereal Chemists; Inst Food Technologists; Am Chem Soc. *Res:* Chemistry of processes related to foods and feeds. *Mailing Add:* 348 Rieth Terr St Louis MO 63122

**WAGGONER, EUGENE B,** geology engineering; deceased, see previous edition for last biography

**WAGGONER, JACK HOLMES, JR,** THEORETICAL PHYSICS. *Current Pos:* from asst prof to assoc prof, 61-94, ASSOC EMER PROF PHYSICS, HARVEY MUDD COL, 94- *Personal Data:* b Pittsburgh, Pa, Sept 4, 27; m 61, Anne Bowers. *Educ:* Ohio State Univ, BS, 49, PhD(physics), 57. *Prof Exp:* Asst photochem, Res Found, Ohio State Univ, 49-53, asst physics, 53-55 from inst to asst prof & res assoc 58-59, from prof assoc supvr to prof supvr, 59; asst prof, Univ Calif, Riverside, 59-61. *Concurrent Pos:* Vis assoc, Calif Inst Technol, 67-68. *Mem:* AAAS; Am Phys Soc; Am Inst Physics; Am Asn Physics Teachers. *Res:* Methods of theoretical physics; theory of molecular spectroscopy. *Mailing Add:* Dept Physics Harvey Mudd Col 301 E 12th St Claremont CA 91711

**WAGGONER, JAMES ARTHUR,** NUCLEAR PHYSICS. *Current Pos:* PHYSICIST, SCHLUMBERGER WELL SERVS, 71- *Personal Data:* b West Lafayette, Ind, Dec 31, 31; m 53; c 4. *Educ:* Univ Ill, BS, 53; Cornell Univ, PhD(exp physics), 60. *Prof Exp:* Physicist, Lawrence Radiation Lab, Univ Calif, 60-70, Physics Int Co, Calif, 71 & Maxwell Labs, 71. *Concurrent Pos:* Consult, NASA. *Mem:* Am Phys Soc. *Res:* Lunar and planetary surface composition analysis using neutron inelastic scattering; Van Allen zone charged particles; geophysical instrumentation. *Mailing Add:* 849 Pecanwood Lane Houston TX 77024

**WAGGONER, PAUL EDWARD,** CLIMATOLOGY. *Current Pos:* From asst to assoc plant pathologist, Conn Agr Exp Sta, 51-56, chief dept soils & climat, 56-69, vdir, 69-71, dir, 72-87, DISTINGUISHED SCIENTIST, CONN AGR EXP STA, 87- *Personal Data:* b Appanoose Co, Iowa, Mar 29, 23; m 45, Barbara Lockerbie; c Jon V & Daniel M. *Educ:* Univ Chicago, SB, 46; Iowa State Col, MS, 49, PhD, 51. *Honors & Awards:* Am Meteorol Soc Award, 67; Anton de Bary Medal, German Phytomed Soc, 96. *Concurrent Pos:* Guggenheim fel, 63; lectr, Yale Univ, 62- *Mem:* Nat Acad Sci; fel Am Phytopath Soc; fel Am Meteorol Soc; fel Am Soc Agron; Coun Sci Food Agr. *Res:* Agriculture; plant pathology; effect of environment on plants, especially plant diseases; water resources. *Mailing Add:* Conn Agr Exp Sta PO Box 1106 New Haven CT 06504-1106. *Fax:* 203-789-7232; *E-Mail:* agwagg@caes.state.ct.us

**WAGGONER, PHILLIP RAY,** DEVELOPMENTAL BIOLOGY. *Current Pos:* FAC, DEPT ANAT, SCH MED, UNIV MIAMI. *Personal Data:* b Parkersburg, WVa, Apr 4, 43; m 67; c 2. *Educ:* WVa Univ, BS, 65, MS, 68, PhD(genetics & develop biol), 72. *Prof Exp:* Instr biol, Fairmont State Col, 68 & WVa Univ, 68-69; asst prof anat, Wayne State Univ, 72- *Mem:* Am Asn Anat; AAAS; Sigma Xi. *Res:* Development of the vertebrate eye. *Mailing Add:* Dept Anat Sch Med Univ Miami PO Box 016960 Miami FL 33101

**WAGGONER, RAYMOND C,** CHEMICAL ENGINEERING. *Current Pos:* assoc prof, 65-79, PROF CHEM ENG, UNIV MO, ROLLA, 79- *Personal Data:* b Louisville, Ky, Feb 13, 30; m 54, Barbara Maynard; c 3. *Educ:* Univ Louisville, BChE, 52; Tex A&M Univ, MEng, 61, PhD(chem eng), 64. *Prof Exp:* Prod control engr & sr prod control engr, Dow Chem Co, 56-61; res asst chem engr, Tex A&M Univ, 61-64; sr engr, Humble Oil & Refining Co, 64-65. *Concurrent Pos:* Res engr, Savannah River Lab, E I du Pont de Nemours & Co Inc, 81-82. *Mem:* Am Inst Chem Engrs; Am Chem Soc; Instrument Soc Am. *Res:* Distributed control micro processor based instruments for laboratory pilot scale and process plant operations; advanced algorithms for on line control applications particularly stage wise separation processes such as distillation and air stripping. *Mailing Add:* Dept Chem Eng Univ Mo Rolla MO 65401. *Fax:* 573-341-4377; *E-Mail:* rcw@shuttle.cc.umr.edu

**WAGGONER, RAYMOND WALTER,** PSYCHIATRY, NEUROLOGY. *Current Pos:* from asst prof to assoc prof neurol, Med Sch, Univ Mich, Ann Arbor, 29-36, from asst neurologist to neurologist, Univ Hosp, 29-36, chmn, Dept Psychiat, Med Sch, 37-70, prof psychiat & dir, Neuropsychiat Inst, 37-70, EMER PROF PSYCHIAT & EMER DIR, NEUROPSYCHIAT INST, MED SCH, UNIV MICH, ANN ARBOR, 70- *Personal Data:* b Carson City, Mich, Aug 2, 01; m 30, Marion Donnelly; c Raymond W Jr & Karen (Kitcher). *Educ:* Univ Mich, MD, 24; Univ Pa, ScD, 30. *Honors & Awards:* E B Bowis Award, Am Col Psychiat, 68. *Prof Exp:* Intern, Harper Hosp, Detroit, 24-25; resident, Philadelphia Orthop Hosp & Infirmary Nerve Dis, 25-26; lab intern, Pa Hosp, Philadelphia, 26; adv to Gen Hershev, Selective Serv, 43-48. *Concurrent Pos:* Consult, spec comt rights ment illness, Am Bar Found, 59-66, indust personnel security, Dept Defense, 48-60, Surgeon-Gen, US Army, Selective Serv Syst, Peace Corps, Vet Admin & Social Security Admin, 43-50; mem med adv bd, Social Security Admin, 65-; adv comt, Nat Paraplegic Found; mem test comt psychiat, Nat Bd Med Examr, 65-70; mem, Res Socs Coun, 70-73; vpres bd trustees, Mich Inst Pastoral Care; consult & bd mem, Reproductive Biol Res Found, 70-; consult, Mich State Dept Ment Health, 74-; distinguished vis prof psychiat, Univ Louisville, 74- *Mem:* Fel AAAS; Am Acad Psychoanal; fel Am Col Psychiat (vpres, 64-65, pres elect, 65-66, pres, 66-67); Am Geriat Soc; fel Am Psychiat Asn (vpres, 60-61, pres elect, 68-69, pres, 69-70). *Res:* Personality studies in chorea; the convulsive state; myopathies; psychotherapy; administration. *Mailing Add:* 3333 Geddes Rd Ann Arbor MI 48105

**WAGGONER, WILBUR J,** MATHEMATICS. *Current Pos:* RETIRED. *Personal Data:* b Sutherland, Iowa, May 28, 24; m 46; c 3. *Educ:* Buena Vista Col, BA, 47; Drake Univ, MSE, 50; Univ Wyo, EdD, 56. *Prof Exp:* Prin, coach & teacher high sch, 47-51; supt twp sch, 51-55; asst, Univ Wyo, 55-56; from asst prof to prof, Cent Mich Univ, 56-87, actg dean, Sch Grad Studies, 73-75, emer prof math, 87. *Mem:* Am Statist Asn; Nat Coun Teachers Math. *Res:* Statistics. *Mailing Add:* 417 West Dr Mt Pleasant MI 48858

**WAGGONER, WILLIAM CHARLES,** PHYSIOLOGY, TOXICOLOGY. *Current Pos:* AT R & D THOMPSON MED COL, NEW YORK, NY. *Personal Data:* b Alma, Mich, Jan 18, 36; m 80; c 8. *Educ:* Hope Col, AB, 58; Mich State Univ, MS, 61, PhD(physiol), 63. *Prof Exp:* Teaching fel physiol & pharmacol, Med Sch, Mich State Univ, 60-63; res physiologist, Colgate-Palmolive Res Ctr, 63-64, res projs coordr oral health, 64-66; asst dir med res, Unimed, Inc, 66-70; assoc dir med serv & govt affairs, Wallace Pharmaceut, NJ, 70-74; mgr med & regulatory affairs, 74-80, dir govt affairs, Baby Prod Co, Johnson & Johnson, 80- *Concurrent Pos:* Consult fac mem, Inst Clin Toxicol, 74- *Mem:* Am Physiol Soc; fel Am Acad Clin Toxicol; Soc Toxicol. *Res:* Clinical toxicology and pharmacology. *Mailing Add:* 10 Apgar Way Lebanon NJ 08833. *Fax:* 908-236-2027

**WAGGONER, WILLIAM HORACE,** INORGANIC CHEMISTRY. *Current Pos:* asst prof, 52-59, ASSOC PROF INORG CHEM, UNIV GA, 59- *Personal Data:* b Ravenna, Ohio, June 8, 24; m 46; c 1. *Educ:* Hiram Col, AB, 49; Western Reserve Univ, MS, 51, PhD(chem), 53. *Prof Exp:* Asst chem, Hiram Col, 48-49. *Mem:* Am Chem Soc. *Res:* Solubilities in non-aqueous systems; history of chemistry; spectral properties of inorganic materials. *Mailing Add:* 160 University Dr Athens GA 30605

**WAGH, MEGHANAD D,** PARALLEL PROCESSING, DIGITAL SYSTEM DESIGN. *Current Pos:* ASSOC PROF COMPUT ENG, LEHIGH UNIV, 84- *Personal Data:* b Bombay, India, Sept 23, 48; m 75; c 2. *Educ:* Indian Inst Technol, Bombay, BTech, 71, PhD(elec eng), 77. *Prof Exp:* Asst prof elec eng, Old Dom Univ, 80-84. *Mem:* Inst Elec & Electronics Engrs Comput Soc; Inst Elec & Electronics Engrs Speech & Signal Processing Soc. *Res:* Interdependence between parallel algorithms and parallel architectures; optimal parallel algorithms for realistic architectural overheads; new architectures matching algorithmic skeletons. *Mailing Add:* Dept Elec Eng & Comput Sci Lehigh Univ 19 Memorial Dr W Bethleham PA 18015. *E-Mail:* mdwo@lehigh.edu

**WAGH, PREMANAND VINAYAK,** biochemistry, for more information see previous edition

**WAGLE, GILMOUR LAWRENCE,** PHARMACOLOGY. *Current Pos:* RETIRED. *Personal Data:* b Staten Island, NY, Nov 17, 22; m 49; c 3. *Educ:* Wagner Col, BS, 50; Rutgers Univ, MS, 56; Princeton Univ, MA, 59, PhD(biol), 60. *Prof Exp:* Pharmacologist, Res Dept, Ciba Pharmaceut Prod, Inc, NJ, 48- 61; sr pharmacologist, Chas Pfizer & Co, 61-64; asst to dir res admin, Toxicol Res Sect, Am Cyanamid Co, 64-72, asst dir, Med Controls Br, Off Govt Controls, 72-77, dir, Sci Compliance Qual Assurance Dept, 77-79, res toxicologist, Environ Serv Div, 80, mgr med regulatory surveillance, Med Res Div, Lederle Labs, 81-85,. *Concurrent Pos:* Drug Regulatory Affairs, Qual Assurance Drug Res & Develop; consult. *Mem:* Soc Toxicol; Fedn Am Scientists. *Res:* Cardiovascular, renal and central nervous system pharmacology; government regulatory affairs; toxicology; quality assurance. *Mailing Add:* 18 Woodtrace Circle Greenville SC 29615

**WAGLE, ROBERT FAY,** FORESTRY, BOTANY. *Current Pos:* assoc prof watershed mgt, 57-69, PROF WATERSHED MGT & WATERSHED SPECIALIST, UNIV ARIZ, 69- *Personal Data:* b Jamestown, NDak, Sept 3, 16. *Educ:* Univ Minn, BS, 40; Univ Wash, MF, 55; Univ Calif, PhD(bot), 58. *Prof Exp:* Asst forestry, Univ Wash, 47-48; logging engr, Shasta Plywood Co, Calif, 48-49; sr lab asst, Univ Calif, 49-54; asst, Calif Forest & Range Exp Sta, US Forest Serv, 54-57. *Concurrent Pos:* Consult fire & silvicult, Univ Nev, 64, wood technol, Tucson Power, Indust Res Inst, World Bank, forest res, Yeman, Arabia, pulp wood availability, SW Wilburt Assoc, fire & forest regeneration & forestry educ, Ft Apache Indian Reservation, Bur Indian Affairs, Az,. *Mem:* Fel AAAS; Soc Am Foresters; Ecol Soc Am. *Res:* Silvics, genetics, ecology and silviculture; plant variation and its relationship to environment; nutrient and water relationships of wildland plants; effects of fire on plants and their environments; growth and variation in containerized pine seedling; effect of nutrients and mycorrhizae on containerized pine seedling growth, and root/shoot ratios and field survival; tree species for ornamentals and Christmas trees in the southwest. *Mailing Add:* 5612 N El Sirio Dr Tucson AZ 85704

**WAGLE, SHREEPAD R,** PHARMACOLOGY. *Current Pos:* from res assoc to asst prof, 60-65, assoc prof, 65-68, dir, Grad Progs, 68-80 PROF PHARMACOL, SCH MED, IND UNIV, INDIANAPOLIS, 68- *Personal Data:* b Bombay, India, Jan 1, 31; nat US; m 62; c 3. *Educ:* Univ Bombay, BS, 52, MS, 55; Univ Ill, PhD(biochem, nutrit), 59. *Prof Exp:* Res chemist, Haffkine Inst, India, 52-55; asst, Univ Ill, 55-59; res chemist, Sigma Lab, India, 60. *Concurrent Pos:* Fulbright Award. *Mem:* Am Cancer Soc; Am Inst Nutrit; Soc Exp Biol & Med; Am Diabetes Asn; Am Soc Pharmacol & Exp Therapeut; Am Soc Biochem & Molecular Biologists. *Res:* Cofactors in protein and RNA biosynthesis; role of hormones and nutritional factors in protein synthesis and cancer cells; protein kinases; lipases and cyclic adenosine monophosphates; metabolism of isolated liver parenchymal and sinusoidal cells; hepatic carcinogens and eicosanoids. *Mailing Add:* Dept Pharmacol & Toxicol Ind Univ Sch Med 635 Barnhill Dr Indianapolis IN 46205. *Fax:* 317-274-1560

**WAGLEY, PHILIP FRANKLIN,** MEDICINE. *Current Pos:* Instr med, 45-47 & 49-64, asst prof, 64-74, ASSOC PROF MED, JOHNS HOPKINS UNIV, 74- *Personal Data:* b Mineral Wells, Tex, Feb 5, 17; m 53. *Educ:* Southern Methodist Univ, BS, 38; Johns Hopkins Univ, MD, 43; Am Bd Internal Med, dipl. *Concurrent Pos:* Am Col Physicians res fel, Harvard Med Sch, 47-48; Nat Res Coun fel med sci, Mass Inst Technol, 48-49. *Mem:* Am Clin & Climat Asn; fel Am Col Physicians; Am Thoracic Soc; Am Soc Hemat. *Res:* Chest disease. *Mailing Add:* 21 Meadow Rd Baltimore MD 21212

**WAGMAN, GERALD HOWARD,** MICROBIAL BIOCHEMISTRY, TECHNICAL MANAGEMENT. *Current Pos:* RETIRED. *Personal Data:* b Newark, NJ, Mar 4, 26; m 48, Rhoda Kirschner; c Jan D & Neil M. *Educ:* Lehigh Univ, BS, 46; Va Polytech Inst, MS, 47. *Prof Exp:* Tech asst antibiotics, Squibb Inst Med Res, 47-49, electronics, 49-54, microbial biochemist, 54-57; from assoc biochemist to sr biochemist, Schering-Plough Corp, 57-69, sect leader, 69-70, mgr antibiotics dept, 70-74, assoc dir microbiol sci-antibiotics, 74-77, assoc dir, Microbiol Sci/Screening Lab, 77-78, dir, Microbiol Strain Lab, 79-85, prin scientist, 85-89, mgr, Libr Info Ctr, Schering-Plough Res Inst, 89-93. *Concurrent Pos:* Mem adv bd, Nat Cert Comn, Chem & Chem Eng, 85-88; chartered chemist, Gt Brit. *Mem:* AAAS; Am Chem Soc; Am Soc Microbiol; fel Am Inst Chemists; Sigma Xi; Royal Soc Chem. *Res:* Antibiotics, especially isolation, identification and evaluation; strain development; fermentation biosynthesis and development; isolation and identification of natural products; author and editor of four books on isolation, separation and purification of natural products, numerous patents, publications and presentations in field. *Mailing Add:* 17 Crommelin Ct East Brunswick NJ 08816-2406. *E-Mail:* k2ewa@aol.com

**WAGNER, ALBERT FORDYCE,** CHEMICAL PHYSICS. *Current Pos:* Presidential intern, 72-74, asst chemist, 74-77, CHEMIST, CHEM DIV, ARGONNE NAT LAB, 77- *Personal Data:* b Rochester, NY, Feb 3, 45; m 69; c 2. *Educ:* Boston Col, BS, 66; Calif Inst Technol, PhD(chem), 72. *Mem:* Am Inst Physics; Am Phys Soc; Am Chem Soc. *Res:* Theory and modeling of chemical reactions. *Mailing Add:* 10243 Hickory Dr Orland Park IL 60462-3541

**WAGNER, ANDREW JAMES,** METEOROLOGY, CLIMATOLOGY. *Current Pos:* Res meteorologist, Extended Forecast Div, Weather Bur, Climate Anal Ctr, Nat Weather Serv, Nat Oceanic & Atmospheric Admin, 65-69, res meteorologist forecasting & interpretation, 69-72, meteorologist long range prediction group, 72-78, meteorologist, Dept Com, 78-89, SR FORECASTER, PREDICTION BR, CLIMATE ANALYSIS CTR, NAT WEATHER SERV, NAT OCEANIC & ATMOSPHERIC ADMIN, 90- *Personal Data:* b Greenwich, Conn, Apr 12, 34; m 69; c Jonathan & Nathaniel. *Educ:* Wesleyan Univ, BA, 56; Mass Inst Technol, MS, 58. *Mem:* Am Meteorol Soc; Royal Meteorol Soc; Am Geophys Union; Am Sci Affil; Nat Weather Asn; Asn Am Weather Observers. *Res:* Understanding and predicting statistical and dynamical relationships of monthly and seasonal weather patterns over the northern hemisphere with aim to better predict them; authored articles in professional journals. *Mailing Add:* Rm 604 World Weather Bldg Climate Prediciton Ctr W/NP51 Washington DC 20233. *Fax:* 301-763-8395

**WAGNER, ARTHUR FRANKLIN,** ORGANIC CHEMISTRY. *Current Pos:* SR RES FEL ORG CHEM, MERCK SHARP & DOHME RES LABS, 65- *Personal Data:* b Jersey City, NJ, Oct 25, 22; m 45; c 3. *Educ:* Princeton Univ, AB, 48, MA, 49, PhD(org chem), 51. *Mem:* Am Chem Soc. *Res:* Synthetic organic chemistry in natural products, isolation, structure determination and synthesis of vitamins and cofactors; synthesis of benzimidazoles; synthesis of peptides, biopolymers and immobilized biopolymers; B-lactam antibiotic synthesis; nucleoside and nucleotide synthesis. *Mailing Add:* 24 Sturges Way Princeton NJ 08540-5335

**WAGNER, BERNARD MEYER,** PATHOLOGY. *Current Pos:* CLIN PROF PATH, COLUMBIA UNIV, 68-; DIR LABS, BEEKMAN DOWNTOWN HOSP, NY, 71-; DEP DIR, NATHAN KLINE RES INST, RES PROF, UNIV SCH MED, NY, 86- *Personal Data:* b Philadelphia, Pa, Jan 17, 28; m 51; c 3. *Educ:* Hahnemann Med Col, MD. *Honors & Awards:* Hon mem, Am Col Vet Pathologists, 85; fel, Royal Col Pathologists, London, 86. *Prof Exp:* Dir exp path labs, Hahnemann Med Col, 54-55; asst prof path, Med Sch & Grad Sch Med, Univ Pa, 56-58; assoc prof path & Robert L King chair cardiovasc res, Sch Med, Univ Wash, 58-60; prof path & chmn dept, New York Med Col, 60-67, clin prof, 67-68. *Concurrent Pos:* Dazian Found Med Res fel, Hahnemann Med Col, 53, Am Heart Asn Southeast Pa fels, 54-55; asst vis chief serv, Philadelphia Gen Hosp, 54-58; pathologist & dir path, Children's Hosp, Philadelphia, 55-58; lectr, Philadelphia Col Pharm, 56-58; attend pathologist, Vet Admin Hosp, 58-; Burroughs Wellcome Fund travel grant & spec investr, Hosp Sick Children, London, Eng, 59; vpres, Warner Lambert Res Inst, 67-; dir labs, Francis Delafield Hosp, 68-71; ed-in-chief, Human Path, 73-88; assoc ed, Conn Tissue Res, 74-80, J Environ Path & Toxicol, 76-80; dir labs, Overlook Hosp, Summit, NJ, 76-86. *Mem:* Am Soc Exp Path; Soc Pediat Res; Fedn Am Soc Exp Biol; Am Asn Path & Bact; Am Rheumatism Asn; fel Royal Col Pathologists Eng. *Res:* Diseases of connective tissue; rheumatic heart disease; toxicology; comparative pathology. *Mailing Add:* Wagner Assoc Inc Suite 208 343 Millburn Ave Millburn NJ 07041

**WAGNER, C(HRISTIAN) N(IKOLAUS) J(OHANN),** PHYSICAL METALLURGY, MATERIALS SCIENCE. *Current Pos:* prof eng & appl sci, Univ Calif, Los Angeles, 70-91, chmn, Mat Dept, 74-79, asst dean undergrad studies, 82-85, EMER PROF ENG & APPL SCI, UNIV CALIF, LOS ANGELES, 91- *Personal Data:* b Saarbruecken-Dudweiler, Ger, Mar 6, 27; US citizen; m 52; c 3. *Educ:* Univ Saarland, Lic es sc, 51, Dipl Ing, 54, Dr rer nat, 57. *Honors & Awards:* Humboldt Award, 89. *Prof Exp:* Asst x-ray metall, Inst Metall Res, Univ Saarland, 53-55, 57-58, res asst phys metall, 59; from asst prof to assoc prof eng & appl sci, Yale Univ, 59-70. *Concurrent Pos:* Vis prof, Univ Saarbrucken, 79-80. *Mem:* Am Soc Metals; Am Phys Soc; Am Crystallog Asn; Am Inst Mining, Metall & Petrol Engrs; Mat Res Soc. *Res:* Diffraction studies including x-rays, neutrons, electrons of amorphous materials and liquids, plastic deformation and transformation in alloys, thin films, and biomaterials. *Mailing Add:* Mat Dept 6531 Boelter Hall Univ Calif Los Angeles CA 90095-1595

**WAGNER, CARL E,** ARTIFICIAL INTELLIGENCE, PLASMA ENGINEERING. *Current Pos:* PRIN SCIENTIST, JAYCOR INC, 87- *Personal Data:* b NJ, July 10, 40; m 79; c 2. *Educ:* Mass Inst Technol, SB, 61, ScD(plasma physics), 70. *Prof Exp:* Physicist, US Naval Res Lab, 70-75; sr physicist, Sci Appl Inc, 75-81; head physicist, Int Nuclear Energy Systs Co, 81-84; sr physicist, TRW Inc, 84-87. *Concurrent Pos:* Consult, Sci Appl Inc, 81 & Energy Appl & Systs Inc, 84-85; adj prof, Calif State Univ, 86. *Mem:* Am Phys Soc; Am Asn Artificial Intel; Sigma Xi. *Res:* Development of expert system simulations; tokamak fusion reactor engineering; computational and theoretical plasma physics. *Mailing Add:* PO Box 9103 Rancho Santa Fe CA 92067

**WAGNER, CARL GEORGE,** MATHEMATICS. *Current Pos:* From asst prof to assoc prof, 69-81, PROF MATH, UNIV TENN, KNOXVILLE, 81- *Personal Data:* b Newark, NJ, Sept 26, 43. *Educ:* Princeton Univ, AB, 65; Duke Univ, PhD(math), 69. *Concurrent Pos:* Fel, Ctr Advan Study Behav Sci, Stanford, 78-79. *Mem:* Soc Indust & Appl Math. *Res:* Combinatorics; decision theory. *Mailing Add:* Dept Math Univ Tenn Knoxville TN 37996-1300

**WAGNER, CHARLES EUGENE,** MORPHOLOGY. *Current Pos:* RETIRED. *Personal Data:* b Memphis, Tenn, June 21, 23; wid; c Martin, David & Paul. *Educ:* Princeton Univ, AB, 47; Ind Univ, PhD(zool), 54. *Prof Exp:* Asst zool, Ind Univ, 48-50; from instr to prof anat, Sch Med, Univ Louisville, 52-88, from asst dean to assoc dean, 61-74. *Concurrent Pos:* Vis prof, Univ Nottingham, 74-75. *Mem:* Sigma Xi; Am Asn Clin Anatomists. *Res:* Experimental morphology; regeneration; movements at synovial joints. *Mailing Add:* 506 Fairlawn Rd Louisville KY 40207-3658

**WAGNER, CHARLES ROE,** organic chemistry, for more information see previous edition

**WAGNER, CLIFFORD HENRY,** STATISTICS, COMPUTER SCIENCE. *Current Pos:* asst prof math, 78-82, ASSOC PROF MATH & COMPUT SCI, PA STATE UNIV, HARRISBURG, 83- *Personal Data:* b Cincinnati, Ohio. *Educ:* Univ Cincinnati, AB, 67; Univ Mich, AM, 68; State Univ NY, Albany, PhD(math), 73. *Honors & Awards:* Allendoerfer Award, Math Asn Am, 83. *Prof Exp:* Asst prof math, Fitchburg State Col, 73-78. *Mem:* Math Asn Am; Nat Coun Teachers Math; Int Asn Statist Educ; Int Statist Inst; Asn Comput Mach. *Res:* Applied mathematics; statistics; computer graphics; iterative methods; probability theory; medical applications. *Mailing Add:* Pa State Univ Harrisburg Middletown PA 17057. *E-Mail:* w44@psuvm.psu.edu

**WAGNER, CONRAD,** BIOCHEMISTRY, NUTRITION. *Current Pos:* from asst prof to assoc prof biochem, 61-75, PROF BIOCHEM, SCH MED, VANDERBILT UNIV, 75- *Personal Data:* b Brooklyn, NY, Nov 1, 29; m 53; c 2. *Educ:* City Col New York, BA, 51; Univ Mich, MS, 52, PhD(biochem), 56. *Honors & Awards:* Borden Award, Am Inst Nutrit, 83. *Prof Exp:* USPHS fel biochem, NIH, 59-61. *Concurrent Pos:* Res biochemist, Vet Admin Hosp, 61-68, chief biochem res, 68-, assoc chief of staff res, 74- *Mem:* Am Soc Biol Chemists; Am Inst Nutrit. *Res:* Gluconeogenesis from lipid in Tetrahymena pyriformis; regulation of tryptophan-niacin relation in animals and microorganisms; sulfonium compounds and one carbon metabolism in bacteria; role and function of natural folate coenzymes; characterization of folate binding proteins; cellular transport of folate and other cofactors; nutritional biochemistry; nutrition and cancer. *Mailing Add:* Dept Biochem Vanderbilt Univ & VA Med Ctr 620 Light Hall Nashville TN 37231-0146. *Fax:* 615-322-4349

**WAGNER, DANIEL HOBSON,** MATHEMATICS. *Current Pos:* RETIRED. *Personal Data:* b Jersey Shore, Pa, Aug 24, 25; m 49, Mary E Wertz; c David H, Christopher D, Thomas J & Elizabeth A. *Educ:* Haverford Col, BS, 47; Brown Univ, PhD(math), 51. *Prof Exp:* Mem sci staff, Opers Eval Group, Mass Inst Technol, 51-56; supvr math anal, Burroughs Corp, 56-58; partner, Kettelle & Wagner, 58-63, pres, Daniel H Wagner Assocs, 63-86. *Concurrent Pos:* Chmn, Electronics Reliability Task Group, Off Asst Secy Defense Res & Eng, 56; lectr, Swarthmore Col, 58 & Univ Pa, 58 & 61-62; mem, Comt Appl Math Training, Nat Acad Sci-Nat Res Coun, 77-78; vis prof, Naval Postgrad Sch, Monterey, Calif, 88-89, US Naval Acad, 89-91. *Mem:* Am Math Soc; Opers Res Soc Am; Soc Indust & Appl Math; Math Asn Am; Inst Mgt Sci. *Res:* Operations research; constrained optimization; measurable set-valued functions. *Mailing Add:* 36 Laurel Circle Malvern PA 19355-2912

**WAGNER, DAVID DARLEY,** INTESTINAL ECOLOGY, INTESTINE FUNCTION. *Current Pos:* reviewing staff scientist metab drugs, Div Drugs Avian Species, Food & Drug Admin, 77-79, biores monitoring prog mgr toxicol, Off Sci Eval, 79-80, chief, Div Vet Res, 80-93, DIR, DIV ANIMAL RES, ANIMAL NUTRIT & BIOL BR CTR VET MED, FOOD & DRUG ADMIN, 93- *Personal Data:* b Ft Riley, Kans, Sept 27, 44; m 71; c 2. *Educ:* Univ Md, BSc, 72, MSc, 74, PhD(nutrit), 77. *Prof Exp:* Res assoc microbiol, Dept Food Sci, NC State Univ, 77. *Mem:* Sigma Xi; Am Soc Animal Sci; Poultry Sci Asn. *Res:* Effects of diet composition on intestine microecology; intestine digestive and absorptive function; intestine mucosal integrity and diet plus drug interactions. *Mailing Add:* Food & Drug Admin Div Animal Res Off Sci 8401 Muirkirk Rd Laurel MD 20708

**WAGNER, DAVID HENRY,** TAXONOMY, COLLECTIONS MANAGEMENT. *Current Pos:* Asst prof, 76-82, DIR & CUR, HERBARIUM, UNIV ORE, 76-, ASSOC PROF BIOL, 82- *Personal Data:* b Detroit, Mich, Aug 18, 45. *Educ:* Univ Puget Sound, BA, 68; Wash State Univ, MS, 74, PhD(bot), 76. *Concurrent Pos:* Pres, Mount Pisgah Arboretum, 79-81 & 83-85, vpres, 81-83; pres, Eugene Natural Hist Soc, 88-89 & 90- *Mem:* Int Asn Plant Taxon; Bot Soc Am; Am Bryological & Lichenological Soc; Am Soc Plant Taxonomists; Am Fern Soc; Brit Pteridological Soc. *Res:* Floristics of Pacific Northwest (especially Pteridophyta & Hepaticae); reproductive biology of ferns and flowering plants; cytology of fern hybrids; community phenology; endangered species management. *Mailing Add:* Biol Dept Univ Ore Eugene OR 97403-1210

**WAGNER, DAVID KENDALL,** SEMICONDUCTOR LASERS, EPITAXIAL GROWTH OF SEMICONDUCTORS. *Current Pos:* SR ENG MGR, POLAROID CORP, 93- *Personal Data:* b Berkeley, Calif, Aug 7, 45; m 90, Naomi Dyo; c Samuel C. *Educ:* Pomona Col, BA, 67; Cornell Univ, PhD(physics), 72. *Prof Exp:* Res assoc physics, Lab Atomic & Solid State Physics, 72-78, sr res assoc, Sch Elec Eng, Cornell Univ, 78-85; prin scientist, McDonnell Douglas Corp, 85-87; laser eng mgr, Advan Optoelectronics, 87-91, prin scientist, 91-92. *Concurrent Pos:* Asst dir, Cornell Prog Submicrometer Struct, Nat Res & Resource Facil Submicrometer Struct, 82-85, vis scientist, Sch Elec Eng, Cornell Univ, 85- *Mem:* Am Phys Soc; Inst Elec & Electronics Engrs; Int Soc Optical Eng. *Res:* Investigation of electronic scattering mechanisms in metals; epitaxy of compound semiconductor thin films by metalorganic chemical vapor deposition; short wavelength semiconductor lasers; photovolatic energy conversion. *Mailing Add:* Polaroid Corp 1 VP Land Rd MS N1-IC Norwood MA 02062

**WAGNER, DAVID LOREN,** ENGINEERING PHYSICS. *Current Pos:* From asst prof to assoc prof, 70-75, CHMN, DEPT PHYSICS, EDINBORO STATE COL, 72-, PROF, 75- *Personal Data:* b Erie, Pa, Nov 19, 42; m 64; c 1. *Educ:* Case Western Res Univ, BS, 64, MS, 66, PhD(physics), 70. *Concurrent Pos:* NSF acad year exten grant, 71-73, student sci training grant, 75, teacher grant, 78, robotics training, 86, research grant, 86. *Mem:* Am Asn Physics Teachers; AAAS. *Res:* Fermi surface of metals and semi-metals. *Mailing Add:* Dept Physics Edinboro Univ Edinboro PA 16444-0001

**WAGNER, EDWARD D,** PARASITOLOGY. *Current Pos:* RETIRED. *Personal Data:* b Eureka, SDak, June 28, 19; m 42, Ellen Greenway; c Patrice, Lynette & Edward G. *Educ:* Walla Walla Col, BA, 42; Wash State Univ, MS, 45; Univ Southern Calif, PhD, 53. *Prof Exp:* Instr biol, Atlantic Union Col, 45-47 & Andrews Univ, 47-49; assoc, Univ Southern Calif, 50-52; head dept parasitol, Sch Trop & Prev Med, Loma Linda Univ, 50-59, from instr to prof microbiol, Sch Med, 53-88. *Res:* Schistosomiasis; parasite therapy; helminths. *Mailing Add:* 10961 Desert Lawn Dr No 164 Calimesa CA 92320

**WAGNER, EDWARD KNAPP,** ANIMAL VIROLOGY, BIOCHEMISTRY. *Current Pos:* asst prof, 70-75, assoc prof, 75-80, PROF VIROL, UNIV CALIF, IRVINE, 80- *Personal Data:* b Akron, Ohio, May 4, 40; m 61; c 2. *Educ:* Univ Calif, Berkeley, BA, 62; Mass Inst Technol, PhD(biochem), 67. *Prof Exp:* Helen Hay Whitney Found fel, Univ Chicago, 67-70. *Concurrent Pos:* Nat Cancer Inst res grant, 70- *Mem:* AAAS; Am Soc Microbiol; Tissue Cult Asn; Am Soc Biol Chemists; Am Soc Cell Biol. *Res:* Control of gene action in animal virus infection; mechanism of viral carcinogenesis; control of information transfer between nucleus and cytoplasm in eucaryotic cells. *Mailing Add:* Prog Animal Virol Univ Calif Irvine CA 92717-0001. *Fax:* 714-856-8551; *E-Mail:* ewagner@uci.edu

**WAGNER, ERIC G,** MATHEMATICS. *Current Pos:* RETIRED. *Personal Data:* b Ossining, NY, Oct 1, 31; m 60; c 3. *Educ:* Harvard Univ, BA, 53; Columbia Univ, MA, 59, PhD(math), 63. *Prof Exp:* Tech engr, IBM Corp, 53-54, assoc engr switching theory, 56-58, res staff mem, T J Watson Res Ctr, 58-93. *Concurrent Pos:* Lectr, NY Univ, 64-65, adj asst prof, 65-66; sr vis res fel, Queen Mary Col, Univ London, 73-74. *Mem:* Am Math Soc; Asn Comput Mach; Asn Symbolic Logic; NY Acad Sci; Europ Asn Theoret Comput Sci. *Res:* Computability theory and category theory with emphasis on their relationship to computer science; theory of programming languages. *Mailing Add:* Old Albany Post Rd R2 Box 117 Garrison NY 10524

**WAGNER, EUGENE ROSS,** RADIOCHEMISTRY. *Current Pos:* Chemist, Spec Assignment Prog, Dow Chem Co, 63-64, Dow Human Res & Develop Labs, Pitman-Moore Div, 64-67, sr res chemist, 67-72, res specialist chem biol res, 72-75, sr res specialist, Midland, Mich, 75-78, sr res specialist, pharmaceut chem, 78-80, sr res specialist, Merrell Dow, 81-88, SR RES SCIENTIST, MARION MERRELL DOW RES INST, 89-, HEAD, RADIOCHEM LAB. *Personal Data:* b Monroe, Wis, Nov 21, 37; m 58, Betty Daley; c Amy & Paul. *Educ:* Univ Wis, BS, 59, PhD(org chem), 64. *Mem:* Am Chem Soc; Int Isotope Soc. *Res:* Radiolabeling of new drug candidates. *Mailing Add:* 36 McCormack Trail Milford OH 45150

**WAGNER, EUGENE STEPHEN,** BIOLOGICAL CHEMISTRY, PHYSICAL CHEMISTRY. *Current Pos:* from asst prof to assoc prof, 71-79, PROF MED EDUC & CHEM, MUNCIE CTR MED EDUC, BALL STATE UNIV, 79- *Personal Data:* b Gary, Ind, Mar 30, 34; m 62; c 3. *Educ:* Ind Univ, BS, 59; Purdue Univ, PhD(chem), 64. *Prof Exp:* Instr chem, Purdue Univ, 62-64; sr phys chemist, Eli Lily & Co, Ind, 64-71. *Mem:* Am Chem Soc. *Res:* Interactions of antibiotics and ascorbic acid with constituents of blood. *Mailing Add:* Ctr Med Educ Ball State Univ Muncie IN 47306-1099

**WAGNER, FLORENCE SIGNAIGO,** BOTANY. *Current Pos:* from res asst to sr res assoc bot, 61-76, assoc res scientist, 76-93, RES SCIENTIST, DEPT BIOL & HERBARIUM, UNIV MICH, ANN ARBOR, 93- *Personal Data:* b Birmingham, Mich, Feb 18, 19; m 48, Warren H Jr; c Warren C & Margaret F. *Educ:* Univ Mich, Ann Arbor, AB, 41, MA, 43; Univ Calif, Berkeley, PhD(bot), 52. *Honors & Awards:* Investigadora Asociada ad hon en Citologia, Museo Nacional de Costa Rica. *Prof Exp:* Res asst soc sci, Off Coordr Inter-Am Affairs, 43-45 & Off Strategic Serv, 45. *Concurrent Pos:* Lectr, Univ Ctr Adult Educ, Ann Arbor, 71-78; adj lectr, Univ Mich, 86. *Mem:* Am Fern Soc (vpres, 84-85, pres, 86-87); Brit Pteridological Soc; Bot Soc Am; Am Soc Plant Taxonomists; Int Asn pteridologists; Int Orgn Plant Biosystematists. *Res:* Analysis of chromosomal behavior in ferns and fern hybrids and comparative studies of their morphology. *Mailing Add:* Dept Biol Univ Mich Ann Arbor MI 48109-1048. *Fax:* 313-647-0884; *E-Mail:* fwagn@umich.edu

**WAGNER, FRANK A, JR,** ORGANIC CHEMISTRY. *Current Pos:* From chemist to sr res chemist, Am Cyanamid Co, 58-77, group leader, 77-85, sr group leader, 85-91, MGR, AM CYANAMID CO, 91- *Personal Data:* b New Haven, Conn, Apr 19, 32; m 61, Maria Carangelo; c Frank III, Anthony R, Stefan H & Nicholas A. *Educ:* Yale Univ, BS, 58; Rutgers Univ, PhD(org chem), 68. *Mem:* Am Chem Soc; AAAS. *Res:* Preparation of compounds as agricultural pesticides; design of procedures for large-scale syntheses; management of large-scale preparations laboratory, chemical pilot plant and plastics extrusion plant. *Mailing Add:* Am Cyanamid Co PO Box 400 Princeton NJ 08543-0400. *Fax:* 609-275-3570

**WAGNER, FRANK S, JR,** ORGANIC CHEMISTRY. *Current Pos:* RETIRED. *Personal Data:* b Temple, Tex, Aug 26, 25; m 53; c 5. *Educ:* SW Tex State Col, BA & MA, 47. *Prof Exp:* Assoc prof chem, Schreiner Inst, Tex, 48-50; analyst, Celanese Corp, 50-52, group leader, 52-53, librn, 53-65, head info ctr, Tech Ctr, Celanese Chem Co, 65-83. *Concurrent Pos:* Organizer, Nandina Corp, 84- *Mem:* AAAS; Am Chem Soc; Spec Libr Asn; Egypt Explor Soc. *Res:* Application of machine methods to critical literature reviews and commerical intelligence activities; writing of encyclopedic reviews. *Mailing Add:* 834 Oak Park Ave Corpus Christi TX 78408

**WAGNER, FREDERIC HAMILTON,** BIOLOGY. *Current Pos:* assoc prof, 61-66, assoc dean, Col Natural Resources, 70-77, PROF WILDLIFE RESOURCES, UTAH STATE UNIV, 66-, ASSOC DEAN, COL NATURAL RESOURCES, 77- *Personal Data:* b Corpus Christi, Tex, Sept 26, 26; m 49; c 2. *Educ:* Southern Methodist Univ, BS, 49; Univ Wis, MS, 53, PhD(wildlife mgt, zool), 61. *Honors & Awards:* Award, Wildlife Soc, 68. *Prof Exp:* Refuge asst, US Fish & Wildlife Serv, 45; asst zool & bot, Southern Methodist Univ, 46-49; asst wildlife mgt, Univ Wis, 49-51; res fel, Wildlife Mgt Inst, 51; res biologist, Wis Conserv Dept, 52-58; asst prof wildlife resources, Utah State Univ, 58-59; res biologist, Wis Conserv Dept, 59-61. *Concurrent Pos:* Dir Desert Biomed, US-Int Biol Prog & mem US Exec Comt, Int Biol Prog, 71-74; mem comt predator control, President's Coun Environ Qual, 71. *Mem:* Ecol Soc Am; Am Soc Mammal; Wildlife Soc; Am Inst Biol Sci; Cooper Ornith Soc; Sigma Xi. *Res:* Vertebrate population ecology, especially population dynamics, limiting factors and homeostatic mechanisms; wildlife management; conservation of natural resources; systems ecology. *Mailing Add:* Col Nat Res UMC 5200 Utah State Univ Logan UT 84322-5200

**WAGNER, FREDERICK WILLIAM,** BIOCHEMISTRY. *Current Pos:* asst prof biochem & nutrit, 68-73, assoc prof, 73-80, PROF, DEPT AGR BIOCHEM, UNIV NEBR, LINCOLN, 80- *Personal Data:* b Erie, Pa, Feb 4, 40; m 65; c 2. *Educ:* Southwest Tex State Col, BSc, 62; Tex A&M Univ, PhD(biochem), 66. *Prof Exp:* USAF res assoc, Brooks, AFB, 66-67; res fel biochem & biophys, Tex A&M Univ, 67-68. *Concurrent Pos:* Vis prof, Biophys Res Lab, Med Sch, Harvard Univ, Boston, 81-82. *Mem:* Sigma Xi. *Res:* Structure and function of proteins with special emphasis on proteolytic enzymes. *Mailing Add:* RR 1 Dept Biochem Walton NE 68461-9801. *Fax:* 402-472-4673

**WAGNER, GEORGE HOYT,** GEOLOGY, CHEMISTRY. *Current Pos:* CONSULT RES & DEVELOP, 71- *Personal Data:* b Mulberry, Ark, Dec 28, 14; m 39, Elizabeth Galer; c Carl B, George H Jr & Holly R. *Educ:* Univ Ark, BS, 37, MS, 74; Univ Iowa, MS, 39, PhD(phys chem), 41. *Honors & Awards:* Schoellkopf Medal, Am Chem Soc, 60. *Prof Exp:* Chemist, Univ Ark, 35-37; asst chem, Univ Iowa, 37-41; res chemist, Linde Div, Union Carbide Corp, 41-47, head div phys chem, 47-51, asst to supt, 51-53, res supvr, 53-55, mgr res, 55-59, dir, 59-64, mgr develop, 64-65, dir res, Mining & Metals Div, 65-66, vpres, 66-70, ferroalloy div, 70-71. *Concurrent Pos:* Adj prof, Univ Ark, 74- *Mem:* Am Chem Soc; Geol Soc Am; AAAS; Am Geophys Union. *Res:* Synthetic lubricants; corrosion inhibition; organometallics; geochemistry, economic geology and atmospheric chemistry. *Mailing Add:* Box 144 Fayetteville AR 72702

**WAGNER, GEORGE JOSEPH,** PLANT PHYSIOLOGY, ENVIRONMENTAL SCIENCES. *Current Pos:* assoc prof, 83-87, PROF, DEPT AGRON, UNIV KY, 87- *Personal Data:* b Buffalo, NY, Sept 15, 43; m 70; c 3. *Educ:* State Univ NY, Buffalo, BA, 70, MA, 71, PhD(biol), 74. *Prof Exp:* Res assoc, Brookhaven Nat Lab, 74-77, assoc scientist plant biochem, 79-83. *Mem:* Am Soc Plant Physiologists; AAAS; Phytochem Soc NAm; Soc Environ Geochem & Health. *Res:* Study of the physiology and biochemistry of the mature plant cell vacuole, the mechanisms of solute accumulation and the fate of heavy metals in plants; mechanisms of secretion in plants. *Mailing Add:* Agron Dept Univ Ky Lexington KY 11973. *Fax:* 606-323-1952; *E-Mail:* gwagner@ca.uky.edu

**WAGNER, GEORGE RICHARD,** SOLID STATE PHYSICS. *Current Pos:* Sr engr, 65-73, fel scientist physics, 74-89, MGR SUPERCONDUCTOR MAT & ELECTRONICS, SCI & TECHNOL CTR, WESTINGHOUSE ELEC CORP, 89- *Personal Data:* b Chicago, Ill, Nov 12, 33; m 54; c 3. *Educ:* Univ Ill, Urbana, BS, 60; Carnegie-Mellon Univ, MS, 62, PhD(physics), 65. *Mem:* Am Phys Soc. *Res:* Superconductor electronics, materials and devices. *Mailing Add:* 3625 Forbes Trail Dr Murrysville PA 15668. *Fax:* 412-256-1348

**WAGNER, GERALD C,** BIOCHEMISTRY, PROTEIN STRUCTURE & FUNCTION. *Current Pos:* AFFIL FAC CHEM, PARKLAND COL, CHAMPAIGN, ILL, 91- *Personal Data:* b Oct 17, 48. *Educ:* Univ Ill, Chicago, BSc, 70, PhD(chem,), 75. *Prof Exp:* Res scientist biochem, Univ Ill, Urbana, 75-84, physics, 84-89, mat sci, 90-91. *Concurrent Pos:* NIH fel, 75-77; NSF fel, 77-78. *Mem:* Am Chem Soc; Am Soc Biochem & Molecular Biol; Biophys Soc; AAAS. *Res:* Biochemistry, protein structure, dynamics, and function; computer technology in education and research. *Mailing Add:* 308 N Prairie St Apt 402 Champaign IL 61820-3449

**WAGNER, GERALD GALE,** IMMUNOLOGY, IMMUNOPARASITOLOGY. *Current Pos:* assoc prof, 77-86, PROF VET MICROBIOL & PARASITOL, TEX A&M UNIV, 86- *Personal Data:* b Plainview, Tex, June 3, 41; m 62; c 2. *Educ:* Tex Tech Col, BS, 63; Univ Kans, MA, 65, PhD, 68. *Prof Exp:* Microbiologist, Immunol Div, Plum Island Animal Dis Lab, 68- 71, microbiologist, Coop Res Div, EAfrican Vet Res

Orgn, USDA, 71-77. *Concurrent Pos:* Nat Acad Sci-Agr Res Serv res fel, Plum Island Animal Dis Lab, 68-70; tech adv, Interam Inst for Coop in Agr for Animal Health Projs in Mex, 80-84; subcomt foreign animal dis & ectoparasite diag & res, Bd Agr, Nat Acad Sci-Nat Res Coun, 82-84; consult, rev trypanosomiasis res & training, UN Develop Prog, 84; coordr int progs, Col Vet Med, Tex A&M Univ, 89- *Mem:* Fedn Am Soc Exp Biol; Am Soc Microbiol; Am Asn Immunol; Am Soc Parasitol. *Res:* Pathogenesis of protozoal infections in domestic animals; cellular effector mechanisms of immunity. *Mailing Add:* Dept Vet Pathobiol Tex A&M Univ College Station TX 77843-4467. *Fax:* 409-862-1147; *E-Mail:* gwagner@cvm.tamu.edu

**WAGNER, GERALD ROY,** ORGANIC CHEMISTRY, GEOLOGY. *Current Pos:* res chemist, Erie Community Col, 61-66, asst prof, 66, head dept, 66-72, PROF CHEM, ERIE COMMUNITY COL, 66- *Personal Data:* b Evansville, Ind, Feb 14, 28; m 50; c 2. *Educ:* Mt Union Col, BS, 50; Univ Ark, MS, 52. *Prof Exp:* Res chemist, Com Solvents Corp, NY, 52-53, Olin Mathieson Chem Corp, 53-55 & Nat Aniline Div, Allied Chem Corp, 55-61. *Mem:* Am Chem Soc; Nat Asn Geol Teachers; Am Inst Chemists. *Res:* Geological education; chemical education. *Mailing Add:* 152 Park Forest Dr Williamsville NY 14221

**WAGNER, GUNTER PAUL,** POPULATION GENETICS. *Current Pos:* PROF BIOL, YALE UNIV, 91- *Personal Data:* b Vienna, Austria, May 28, 54; m 85, Michaela Hauser; c Veronika & Nikolas. *Educ:* Univ Vienna, PhD(zool), 79. *Hon Degrees:* MA, Yale Univ, 92. *Honors & Awards:* MacArthur Prize, MacArthur Found, 92. *Prof Exp:* Researcher, Max Planck Inst Biophys Chem, 79-81, Univ Gottingen, 81-82 & Max Planck Inst Develop Biol, 82-85; asst prof, Univ Vienna, 85-90, dozent evolutionary theory, 90-92. *Concurrent Pos:* Vis prof biol, Northwestern Univ, 87-88, Univ Bazel, Switz, 91; assoc ed, Evolution, 94-; chair, Dept Ecol & Evolutionary Biol, 97- *Mem:* AAAS; Soc Study Evolution; Soc Syst Biol; Europ Soc Evolutionary Biol. *Res:* Origin of complex adaptations; developmental biology with evolutionary biology and the mathematical theory of complex system. *Mailing Add:* Dept Ecol & Evolutionary Biol Yale Univ New Haven CT 06520-8104. *Fax:* 203-432-6988; *E-Mail:* gpwag@peaplant.biology

**WAGNER, HANS,** FOREIGN LANGUAGES. *Current Pos:* CORP TRANSLR & INT SCI LIAISON, 88- *Personal Data:* b July 19, 32; US citizen; m 60; c 2. *Educ:* Univ Iowa, BS, 55; Pa State Univ, PhD(chem), 59. *Prof Exp:* Sr res investr, G D Searle & Co, 59-70, group leader chem, 70-76, sr scientist, 76-84, asst dir clin res, 84-87; sci consult, Regis Chem Co, 87-88. *Mem:* Am Chem Soc. *Res:* Dipolar cycloadditions; mesoionic compounds; heterocyclic azido compounds. *Mailing Add:* PO Box 3348 Estes Park CO 80517

**WAGNER, HARRY HENRY,** FISH BIOLOGY, ECOLOGY. *Current Pos:* RETIRED. *Personal Data:* b San Diego, Calif, Jan 10, 33; m 56; c 3. *Educ:* Humboldt State Col, BS, 55; Ore State Univ, MS, 59, PhD(fisheries), 70. *Prof Exp:* Fishery res biologist & physiol ecologist, Ore Dept Fish & Wildlife, 59-68, fishery res coordr, 69-73, res supvr, 73-78, asst chief, 79-82, chief, Fisheries Div, 83-89; planning assoc, NW Power Planning Coun, 90-94. *Concurrent Pos:* Courtesy assoc prof, Ore State Univ, 59- *Mem:* Am Fisheries Soc. *Res:* Parr-smolt transformation of anadromous salmonids. *Mailing Add:* 12340 Big Fir Ct NW Portland OR 97229

**WAGNER, HARRY MAHLON,** MATHEMATICS. *Current Pos:* RETIRED. *Personal Data:* b Iola, Kans, June 1, 24; m 44, Mary L Jones; c Christopher M, Derrick A, Jon D, Marc D (deceased) & Margaret E (Thompson). *Educ:* Naval Postgrad Sch, BS, 54; Kans State Teachers Col, MS, 64; Univ Ark, EdD(higher educ), 69. *Prof Exp:* Instr math, John Brown Univ, 64-67; res grad asst psychol, Univ Ark, 67-69; from asst prof to assoc prof math, Cameron Univ, 69-90. *Mem:* Math Asn Am. *Mailing Add:* 307 NW Tanglewood Lane Lawton OK 73505-5317

**WAGNER, HARVEY ARTHUR,** ENGINEERING. *Current Pos:* RETIRED. *Personal Data:* b Ann Arbor, Mich, Jan 2, 05; m 29. *Educ:* Univ Mich, BS, 27; Lawrence Inst Technol, DEng, 69. *Honors & Awards:* Cert Pub Serv, Fed Power Comn, 64; Sesquicentennial Award as Outstanding Exec & Nuclear Power Consult, Univ Mich, 67. *Prof Exp:* Mem staff, Procter & Gamble Co, 27-28; mem staff, Detroit Edison Co, 28-69, exec vpres, 69-70; vchmn & dir, Overseas Adv Assocs, Inc, 74-96. *Concurrent Pos:* Trustee, Nat Sanit Found, 65-84; consult engr, 70-; chmn, Comt Nuclear Fuels & Comt Advan Projs, Edison Elec Inst; mem, Tech & Eng Comt, Power Reactor Develop Co & Atomic Power Develop Assocs, Inc; vchmn, Econ Comt, Atomic Power Develop Assocs. *Mem:* Nat Acad Eng; fel Am Soc Mech Engrs; fel Am Nuclear Soc. *Res:* Power engineering and management; author of over 60 publications. *Mailing Add:* 932 Trombley Rd Grosse Pointe MI 48230

**WAGNER, HENRY GEORGE,** NEUROSCIENCES, AEROSPACE MEDICINE. *Current Pos:* dir intramural res, 66-74, actg chief lab neurophysiol, 76-80, CHIEF SECT NEURONAL INTERACTIONS, LAB NEUROPATH & NEUROANAT SCI, NAT INST NEUROL, COMMUN DIS & STROKE, 74- *Personal Data:* b Washington, DC, Sept 13, 17; m 45; c 3. *Educ:* George Washington Univ, AB, 39, MD, 42; Univ Pa, cert ophthal, 49. *Prof Exp:* Intern, Nassau Hosp, Brooklyn, NY, 42-43, med officer, Naval Med Sch, Md, 43, flight surgeon, Sch Aviation Med, Naval Air Sta, Fla, 43-44, flight surgeon, Naval Air Base, Guam, 44-45, flight surgeon, Naval Air Sta, Tex, 45-46, asst supt aeromed equip lab, Naval Air Exp Sta, Pa, 46-48, med res investr, Naval Med Res Inst, Md, 51-54, sr med officer, USS Valley Forge, 54-56, head physiol div, Naval Med Res Inst, 56-60, cmndg officer, 60-61, exec officer, 61-64, actg dir physiol sci dept, 61-64, dir aerospace crew

equip lab, Naval Air Eng Ctr, Pa, 64-66. *Concurrent Pos:* Fel biophys, Johns Hopkins Univ, 49-51, hon prof, 58-64; mem vision comt, hearing & bioacoust, Nat Acad Sci-Nat Res Coun; vis prof ophthal, Duke Univ, 76-85. *Mem:* AAAS; Am Physiol Soc; Soc Neurosci; Am Col Prev Med; AMA; Int Brain Res Orgn. *Res:* Neuroscience of the visual system; pathophysiology of stroke. *Mailing Add:* Health Sci Em Stroke Br NINDS NIH Bethesda MD 20892

**WAGNER, HENRY N, JR,** INTERNAL MEDICINE, NUCLEAR MEDICINE. *Current Pos:* From asst prof med & radiol to assoc prof med, radiol & radiol sci, Sch Med, 59-67, assoc prof med, 67-68, PROF RADIOL SCI & RADIOL, SCH MED & SCH HYG & PUB HEALTH, JOHNS HOPKINS UNIV, 67-, DIR, DIV NUCLEAR MED, 65-, PROF MED, 68-, DIR, DIV RADIATION HEALTH SCI, 77- *Personal Data:* b Baltimore, Md, May 12, 27; m 51; c Nick, Mark, Randy & Anne. *Educ:* Johns Hopkins Univ, AB, 48, MD, 52; Univ Gottingen, PhD; Univ Brussels, PhD. *Hon Degrees:* DSc, Washington Col. *Honors & Awards:* George Hevesy Medal, 76; Nuclear Pioneer, Soc Nuclear Med, 83; Sci Achievement Award, Am Med Asn, 91. *Mem:* Inst Med-Nat Acad Sci; Asn Am Physicians; Am Soc Clin Invest; Soc Nuclear Med (past pres); World Fedn Nuclear Med & Biol (past pres); Inst Med; AMA; Am Fedn Clin Res (past pres); Am Col Physicians. *Mailing Add:* Div Radiation Health Sci Johns Hopkins Sch Hyg & Pub Health 615 N Wolfe St Baltimore MD 21205

**WAGNER, HERMAN LEON,** POLYMER CHEMISTRY. *Current Pos:* RETIRED. *Personal Data:* b New York, NY, Mar 21, 21; m, Elaine Feinberg; c Nancy. *Educ:* City Col New York, BS, 42; Polytech Inst Brooklyn, MS, 46; Cornell Univ, PhD(Chem), 50. *Prof Exp:* Chemist, SAM Labs, Manhatten Proj, Columbia Univ, 42-46; res assoc, Cornell Univ, 50-51; phys chemist, E I du Pont de Nemours & Co, 51-55, M W Kellog Co, 55-57 & Celanese Corp Am, 57-68; res chemist, Nat Bur Stand, 68-87; sr scientist, Atlantic Res Corp, 87-91. *Mem:* Am Chem Soc. *Res:* Physical chemistry of high polymers; dilute solution properties; characterization of high polymers; thermal analysis; composites; melt rheology; fibers; gel permeation chromatography; correlation of molecular structure with physical properties; low shear viscosity of ultra high molecular weight polyethylene solutions. *Mailing Add:* 12038 Gatewater Dr Potomac MD 20854

**WAGNER, J ROBERT,** TEXTILES & NONWOVENS, PAPER. *Current Pos:* prof & dir textile & apparel res, 66-, EMER PROF, PHILADELPHIA COL TEXTILES & SCI, 96-; CONSULT, J ROBERT WAGNER & ASSOC, 96- *Personal Data:* b Philadelphia, Pa, Jan 8, 32; m 57; c 2. *Educ:* Philadelphia Col Textiles & Sci, BS, 57; NC State Univ, Raleigh, MS, 66; Univ Leeds, MPhil, 78. *Honors & Awards:* Leadership & Serv Award, Tech Asn Pulp & Paper Indust, 90. *Prof Exp:* Mgr res, Formex Co, Huyck Corp, 57-65. *Concurrent Pos:* Consult, J Robert Wagner Co, 66-; div chmn, Tech Asn Pulp & Paper Indust, 83-85. *Mem:* Fel Tech Asn Pulp & Paper Indust; Int Nonwovens & Disposables Asn; Am Asn Textile Chemists & Colorists. *Res:* Development of first synthetic Fourdrinier fabric, inside press fabric, open mesh dryer fabric, thermally bounded polypropylene nonwoven diaper cover stock and nonwoven fabric for space shuttle astronaut spacesuits. *Mailing Add:* 2996 Runnymede Dr Norristown PA 19401-2279

**WAGNER, JAMES BRUCE, JR,** MATERIALS SCIENCE. *Current Pos:* dir, 80-84, PROF, CTR SOLID STATE SCI, ARIZ STATE UNIV, 77- *Personal Data:* b Hampton, Va, July 28, 27; m 51; c 3. *Educ:* Univ Va, BS, 50, PhD(chem), 55. *Honors & Awards:* Found Res Award, Aluminum Co Am, 86; Outstanding Achievement Award of High Temperature Mat Div, Electrochem Soc, 86. *Prof Exp:* Fel metall, Mass Inst Technol, 54-56; asst prof, Pa State Univ, 56-58 & Yale Univ, 58-62; assoc prof, Northwestern Univ, 62-65, prof mat sci, 65-77, dir, Mat Res Ctr, 72-76. *Concurrent Pos:* Ford Found resident engr pract, Semiconductor Prod Div, Motorola, Inc, Ariz, 68-69; lectr, Univ Nacional del Sur, Argentina, 81; fel Japan Soc Promotion Sci, Nagoya Univ, 83; regents prof, Ariz State Univ, 89. *Mem:* Am Phys Soc; Am Inst Mining Metall & Petrol Eng; hon men Electrochem Soc (pres, 83-84); Solid State Ionics Soc; Asian Solid State Ionics. *Res:* Oxidation of metals; thermodynamics and transport properties of compound semiconductors; solid electrolytes. *Mailing Add:* 5418 E Wonderview Rd Phoenix AZ 85018

**WAGNER, JAMES W,** EXPERIMENTAL MECHANICS. *Current Pos:* from asst prof to assoc prof, 84-93, PROF & CHMN, DEPT MAT SCI & ENG, JOHNS HOPKINS UNIV, 93- *Personal Data:* b July 12, 53; c 2. *Educ:* Univ Del, BS, 75; Johns Hopkins Univ, MS, 78, PhD(mat sci & eng), 84. *Prof Exp:* Electronics engr, Ctr for Devices & Radiol Health, Food & Drug Admin, 75-84. *Concurrent Pos:* Alan Berman res grant, USN Naval Res Lab, 86; R E Peterson grant, Soc Exp Mech, 87-89. *Mem:* Sigma Xi; Am Soc Nondestructive Eval; Biomed Eng Soc; Inst Elec & Electronics Engrs; Lasers & Electro-Optics Soc; Mat Res Soc; Optical Soc Am; Soc Exp Mech; Int Soc Optical Eng. *Res:* Optical nondestructive testing and characterizations of materials properties especially holographic, interferometric and related techniques; biomaterials, electro-optic systems; contributed numerous articles to publications. *Mailing Add:* Dept Mat Sci & Eng Johns Hopkins Univ Baltimore MD 21218

**WAGNER, JEAMES ARTHUR,** ENVIRONMENTAL PHYSIOLOGY. *Current Pos:* from asst res to assoc res, 71-84, RES PHYSIOL, UNIV CALIF, SANTA BARBARA, 84- *Personal Data:* b New Praque, Minn, Sept 5, 44; div; c 1. *Educ:* St Johns Univ, BSc, 66; Univ SDak, MA, 67; Univ Western Ont, 70. *Prof Exp:* Asst prof physiol, Ind Univ, Bloomington, 69-71. *Concurrent Pos:* Prog chmn, Int Symposium, Univ Calif, Santa Barbara, 77; lectr, Westmont Col, 77, Univ Calif, Santa Barbara, 71-; prin investr, NIH, 79-; co-prin investr, Calif ARB, 83-85, HEI, 84- *Mem:* AAAS; Am Col Sports

Med; Am Physiol Soc; Fedn Am Scientists; NY Acad Sci. *Res:* Environmental and cardiorespiratory physiology, specifically physiological response differences to environmental stressors that are related to age and gender; physiological responses to heat, cold, altitude, air pollution and exercise stressors. *Mailing Add:* 1334 Kenwood Rd Santa Barbara CA 93109

**WAGNER, JOEL H,** AEROSPACE ENGINEERING. *Current Pos:* RESEARCHER, UNITED TECHS, 77- *Educ:* Iowa State Univ, BS, 76, MS, 77. *Honors & Awards:* Gas Turbine Award, Am Soc Mech Engrs, 91. *Res:* Heat Transfer in rotating systems; prediction of turbine component erosion; axial fan aerodynamics and noise; compressor and turbine aerodynamics and effects of rotation on internal cooling of gas turbine blades. *Mailing Add:* United Techs Res Ctr 411 Silver Ln Hartford CT 06118-1104

**WAGNER, JOHN ALEXANDER,** ENTOMOLOGY. *Current Pos:* BIOLOGIST, DEPT EDUC, FIELD MUS, 88- *Personal Data:* b Kansas City, Mo, Feb 9, 35; m 63, 86, Dru Radosevich; c Michael, James & Jordan. *Educ:* Northwestern Univ, BS, 57, MS, 59, PhD(biol), 62. *Prof Exp:* Mem fac, Kendall Col, 62-88, prof biol & Sci, 80-88. *Concurrent Pos:* Assoc, Dept Zool, Div Insects, Field. *Mem:* Am Inst Biol Sci; Xerces Soc; Coleopterists Soc; Nature Conservancy; Nat Sci Teachers Asn; Sigma Xi. *Res:* Coleoptera, family Pselaphidae, especially nearctic and neotropics. *Mailing Add:* Dept Educ Field Mus Roosevelt Rd Lake Shore Dr Chicago IL 60605-2496. *E-Mail:* wagner@fmppr.fmnh.org

**WAGNER, JOHN EDWARD,** CIVIL ENGINEERING, EARTH SCIENCES. *Current Pos:* SR CIVIL ENGR, ANALYTICAL SERV, INC, ARLINGTON, VA, 84- *Personal Data:* b Springfield, Mo, Oct 11, 27; m 50, Louise; c 2. *Educ:* US Mil Acad, BS, 50; Univ Ill, MS, 59, PhD(civil eng), 61; George Washington Univ, MBA, 80. *Prof Exp:* Instr, US Army Eng Sch, Ft Belvoir, Va, 52-53, asst proj engr, Eng Dist, Little Rock, Ark, 53-54, co comdr & staff engr, VII Corps, Europe, 55-58, res engr soil mech, Waterways Exp Sta, Miss, 60-63, staff engr adv, Army Repub Vietnam, 63, dep dir, Nuclear Cratering Group, Lawrence Radiation Labs, Calif, 64-65, chief engr br, Test Command, Defense Atomic Support Agency, NMex, 65-67, comdr & dir, Cold Regions Res & Eng Lab, NH, 67-70, staff engr, First Field Force, Vietnam, 70-71, comdr & dir, Engr Topographic Labs, Ft Belvoir, Va, 71-74, dep dir res, Off Dep Chief Staff, Res Develop & Acquisitions, 74-77, asst for conserv, Off Secy Defense, 77-79, dep div eng, NAtlantic Div, Corps Engrs, 79-81; exec secy, UN Nat Comt Rock Mech & Tunneling Technol, Nat Acad Sci, 81-84, sr staff officer, Bd Army Sci & Technol, 84. *Concurrent Pos:* Consult deep underground construct, Anal Serv, Inc, Va, 82-84. *Mem:* Sigma Xi; fel Am Soc Civil Engrs; Nat Soc Prof Engrs; Soc Am Mil Engrs. *Res:* Soil mechanics especially arching of soils and slope stability; all areas of Army funded research; cold regions research and topographic sciences. *Mailing Add:* 3229 First Pl N Arlington VA 22201-1038. *Fax:* 703-243-2925; *E-Mail:* wagnerje@erols.com

**WAGNER, JOHN PHILIP,** SEPARATIONS SCIENCES, COMBUSTION-FLAMMABILITY. *Current Pos:* assoc dir & res engr, Food Protein Res & Develop Ctr, Tex Eng Exp Sta, 83-90, assoc prof, Dept Indust Eng, 85-89, ASSOC PROF, DEPT NUCLEAR ENG, TEX A&M UNIV, 89-, ASSOC DIR & RES ENGR, ENG BIOSCI RES CTR, 90- *Personal Data:* b Trenton, NJ, Feb 29, 40; m 69; c 2. *Educ:* St Joseph's Univ, BS, 61; Johns Hopkins Univ, MS, 64, PhD(chem eng), 66. *Prof Exp:* Res asst, Dept Chem, Johns Hopkins Univ, 61-62, assoc chemist, Appl Physics Lab, 62, res fel, Dept Chem Eng, 62-66, sr engr, Appl Physics Lab, 66-72. *Concurrent Pos:* Res asst, RCA Labs, Princeton, NJ, 61; sr res engr, Factory Mutual Res Corp, Norwood, Mass, 72-73; res supv, Gillette Res Inst, 73-78, group leader, 78; staff engr, Exxon Res & Eng Co, 78-83, sr staff engr, 83; consult, Lawrence Livermore Nat Lab, Exxon Co, Englehard Industs, Gillette Res Inst, Liberty Mutual & Champion Int; mem, Environ Comt, Am Oil Chemists Soc, 85-86; co-guest ed, spec ed Bioresource Technol, 91. *Mem:* Am Inst Chem Engrs; Am Chem Soc; Am Soc Eng Educ; Asn Advan Indust Crops. *Res:* Advanced electrically enhanced separations in two and three- phase systems; process engineering involving biomaterials, petrochemicals and oily sludges; combustion/flammability characteristics of plastics and wood derived products; electrostatics; fire and gas sensor technology; author of numerous publications in science journals; awarded three US patents. *Mailing Add:* Food Protein Res & Develop Ctr Tex A&M Univ FM Box 183 College Station TX 77840-1852. *Fax:* 409-845-6443

**WAGNER, JOSEPH EDWARD,** LABORATORY ANIMAL SCIENCE. *Current Pos:* PROF VET MED, COL VET MED, UNIV MO, COLUMBIA, 69- *Personal Data:* b Dubuque, Iowa, July 29, 38; m 59; c Lucinda, Pamela, Jennifer & Douglas. *Educ:* Iowa State Univ, DVM, 63; Tulane Univ, MPH, 64; Univ Ill, Urbana, PhD, 67. *Honors & Awards:* Charles River Prize; Beecham Award Res Excellence. *Concurrent Pos:* Animal Resources Adv Comt, Div Res Resources, NIH, 80-84. *Mem:* Am Vet Med Asn; Am Asn Lab Animal Sci; Am Col Lab Animal Med; Am Soc Lab Animal Practitioners. *Res:* Pathogenesis and etiology of naturally occurring diseases of animals used in human health related research. *Mailing Add:* W213 Vet Path Univ Mo Columbia MO 65211

**WAGNER, LAWRENCE CARL,** HIGH TEMPERATURE CHEMISTRY, INSULATED CONDUCTORS FAILURE ANALYSIS. *Current Pos:* sr mem tech staff, 76-79, MGR, DEVICE ANALYSIS LAB, TEX INSTRUMENTS, 79- *Personal Data:* b Campbellsport, Wis, Dec 28, 46. *Educ:* Marquette Univ, BS, 68; Purdue Univ, PhD(chem), 74. *Prof Exp:* Appointee chem div, Argonne Nat Lab, 74-76. *Mem:* Am Chem Soc; Am Soc Mass Spectrometry; Sigma Xi; Inst Elec & Electronics Engrs; Am Soc Metall. *Res:* High temperature mass spectrometry; photoelectron spectrometry; diffusion controlled processes; scanning electron microscopy; semiconductor failure analysis. *Mailing Add:* 4405 Brigade Ct Plano TX 75024-5431

**WAGNER, MARTIN GERALD,** POLYMER SCIENCE, RHEOLOGY. *Current Pos:* SR ENG ASSOC, RES & DEVELOP LAB, E I DU PONT DE NEMOURS & CO, INC, 66- *Personal Data:* b New York, NY, Mar 19, 42; m 65, Aylene Parker; c 3. *Educ:* Cooper Union, BChE, 62; Northwestern Univ, Evanston, MS, 64, PhD(chem eng), 67. *Mem:* Am Inst Chem Engrs; Soc Rheology; Am Chem Soc. *Res:* Polymer processing; polymerization technology. *Mailing Add:* DuPont Cent Res DuPont Exp Sta PO Box 80323 Wilmington DE 19880-0323

**WAGNER, MARTIN JAMES,** BIOCHEMISTRY, SCIENCE EDUCATION. *Current Pos:* from asst prof to prof, 58-92, chmn dept, 58-87, EMER PROF BIOMED SCI, BAYLOR COL DENT, 92- *Personal Data:* b Independence, Kans, Oct 4, 31; m 53; c 3. *Educ:* Pittsburg (KS) State Univ, BS, 54; Ind Univ, PhD(biochem), 58. *Prof Exp:* Asst chem, Ind Univ, 54-58. *Mem:* Am Chem Soc; Int Asn Dent Res; Sigma Xi; Am Asn Dent Schs. *Res:* Intermediary metabolism of inorganic fluoride ion; trace element nutrition; toxicology of trace elements; microcomputer applications in education. *Mailing Add:* 9541 Angleridge Rd Dallas TX 75238-1803

**WAGNER, MELVIN PETER,** ORGANIC CHEMISTRY, POLYMER CHEMISTRY. *Current Pos:* RETIRED. *Personal Data:* b Nebr, Nov 16, 26; m 53; c 5. *Educ:* Creighton Univ, BS, 49, MS, 52; Univ Akron, PhD(polymer chem), 60. *Prof Exp:* Res chemist, Barberton Lab, Chem Div, PPG Industs, 52-60, sr res chemist, 60-64, supvr rubber chem res, 64-78, res scientist, 78-90. *Concurrent Pos:* Fel PPG Collegium Industs. *Mem:* Am Chem Soc; Am Soc Testing & Mat; Soc Plastic Engrs. *Res:* High polymers; rubber reinforcement; vulcanization. *Mailing Add:* 416 Forest Lane Wadsworth OH 44281

**WAGNER, MICHAEL R,** AGRICULTURE, FORESTRY. *Current Pos:* PROF, SCH FORESTRY, NORTHERN ARIZ UNIV. *Educ:* Univ Wis-Madison, PhD(entom), 80. *Concurrent Pos:* Fulbright grantee agr, Forestry Res Inst Ghana, 96. *Mem:* Soc Am Foresters; Entom Soc Am. *Res:* Companion planting to reduce insect damage on a West African tropical tree species. *Mailing Add:* Sch Forestry Northern Ariz Univ Flagstaff AZ 86011

**WAGNER, MORRIS,** bacteriology & gnotobiology, immunology; deceased, see previous edition for last biography

**WAGNER, NEAL RICHARD,** TOPOLOGY. *Current Pos:* From asst prof to assoc prof math, El Paso, 69-79, PROF COMPUT SCI, UNIV TEX, SAN ANTONIO, 79- *Personal Data:* b Topeka, Kans, May 4, 40; m 71. *Educ:* Univ Kans, AB, 62; Univ Ill, Urbana-Champaign, AM, 64, PhD(math), 70. *Concurrent Pos:* Vis assoc prof comput sci, Univ Houston, Tex, 79-81 & Drexel Univ, Philadelphia, 81-; consult modern cryptography, 81- *Mem:* Am Math Soc; Math Asn Am. *Res:* Computer sciences in general; computer systems; theory; real-time simulation of NASA space shuttle. *Mailing Add:* Math & Comput Sci Dept Univ Tex San Antonio TX 78285-0664

**WAGNER, NORMAN KEITH,** MICROMETEOROLOGY. *Current Pos:* asst prof, 66-70, dir, Atmospheric Sci Group, 72-76, ASSOC PROF METEOROL, UNIV TEX, AUSTIN, 70- *Personal Data:* b Longview, Wash, Oct 3, 32; m 54; c 2. *Educ:* Univ Wash, BS, 54, MS, 56; Univ Hawaii, PhD(meteorol), 66. *Prof Exp:* Instr meteorol, Univ Tex, 56-57 & 58-63, res meteorologist, 57-58; asst prof meteorol, Univ Hawaii, 65, res researcher, 65-66. *Concurrent Pos:* Vis prof, Univ Okla, 73 & 75. *Mem:* Am Meteorol Soc. *Res:* Micrometeorology; atmospheric boundary layer. *Mailing Add:* 7906 Havenwood Dr Austin TX 78759-8921

**WAGNER, ORVIN EDSON,** COHERENT WAVE BEHAVIOR IN PLANTS, WAVES IN PLANTS & ELSEWHERE. *Current Pos:* PRES, WAGNER RES LAB, ROGUE RIVER, ORE, 74- *Personal Data:* b Los Angeles, Calif, Jan 23, 30; m 77, Claudia May Eells; c Raymond, Michael & Kimberly. *Educ:* Walla Walla Col, BA, 53, BS, 57; Ariz State Univ, MS, 63; Univ Tenn, PhD(physics), 68. *Prof Exp:* Teaching & res asst physics, Ariz State Univ, 59-60; Scientist, Lockheed Res Lab, Palo Alto, Calif, 61-62; instr physics, Walla Walla Col, College Place, Wash, 62-64; fel, Oak Ridge Nat Lab, 68-69; asst prof physics, Calif State Polytech Univ, San Luis Obispo, 69-74. *Concurrent Pos:* Consult, Wagner Electronic Prods, 69-; lectr, Rogue Community Col, Grant Pass, Ore, 74-79. *Mem:* Sigma Xi; Am Phys Soc. *Res:* Wave behavior in plants and application of this theory to the solar system; author of nine articles and two books on w-wave behavior in plants and the solar system. *Mailing Add:* Wagner Res Lab 2645 Sykes Creek Rd Rogue River OR 97537. *Fax:* 541-582-4138; *E-Mail:* oedphd@chatlink.com

**WAGNER, PATRICIA ANTHONY,** NUTRITIONAL SCIENCES. *Current Pos:* asst prof, 75-80, ASSOC PROF HUMAN NUTRIT, UNIV FLA, 80- *Personal Data:* b Kirksville, Mo, Nov 26, 37; m 59; c 2. *Educ:* Northeast Mo State Teachers Col, BS, 59; Univ Wis-Madison, MS, 73, PhD(nutrit sci, biochem), 75. *Prof Exp:* Teacher home econ, Mo Pub Sch Syst, 59-69; res asst & NIH trainee nutrit sci, Univ Wis-Madison, 69-75. *Concurrent Pos:* Prin investr, NIH-Nat Inst Aging res grant, 77-80 & Area Agency Aging, Older Am Nutrit Proj, 81; co-prin investr, USDA-Sci & Educ Admin grant, 78-81. *Mem:* Sigma Xi; Am Inst Nutrit; Am Soc Clin Nutrit; Proc Soc Exp Biol & Med. *Res:* Human nutrition; trace element requirements and metabolism; community nutritional assessment; nutrition and aging; nutrition in international development particularly in subsaharan Africa. *Mailing Add:* 1510 NW 35th Terr Gainesville FL 32605-4832

**WAGNER, PETER EWING,** PHYSICS, ENVIRONMENTAL ENGINEERING. *Current Pos:* PROVOST & PROF PHYSICS & ELEC ENG, STATE UNIV NY, BINGHAMTON, 89- *Personal Data:* b Ann Arbor, Mich, July 4, 29; m 51; c 2. *Educ:* Univ Calif, AB, 50, PhD(physics), 56. *Prof Exp:* Asst, Univ Calif, 50-56; physicist, Westinghouse Res Labs, 56-59; from assoc prof to prof elec eng, Johns Hopkins Univ, 59-73; prof & dir, Ctr Environ & Estuarine Studies, Univ Md, 73-80; prof physics, Univ Ala, 80-81; acad vchancellor & prof physics, Univ Miss, 81-84; provost & prof physics & elec eng, Utah State Univ, 84-89. *Concurrent Pos:* Consult, Radiation Lab & Carlyle Barton Lab, Johns Hopkins Univ, 59-65, Westinghouse Elec Corp, 59-66, Am Cyanamid Co, 64-70 & US Army, 69-70; Guggenheim fel, 66-67; physicist, Appl Physics Lab, Johns Hopkins Univ, 71; spec proj engr, State of Md, 71-72; exec secy, Md Power Plant Siting Adv Comt, 72-75. *Mem:* AAAS; Am Phys Soc; Sigma Xi. *Res:* Solid state physics; paramagnetic resonance; microwave acoustics; static electrification; environmental measurements. *Mailing Add:* Physics & Elec Eng Dept Binghamton Univ Binghamton NY 13902-6000

**WAGNER, PETER J,** PHYSICAL ORGANIC CHEMISTRY, PHOTOCHEMISTRY. *Current Pos:* from asst prof to assoc prof, 65-70, PROF CHEM, MICH STATE UNIV, 70- *Personal Data:* b Chicago, Ill, Dec 25, 38; m 63, Mary Kelly; c 6. *Educ:* Loyola Univ, Ill, BS, 60; Columbia Univ, MA, 61, PhD(chem), 63. *Prof Exp:* Res assoc chem, Columbia Univ, 63-64; NSF fel, Calif Inst Technol, 64-65. *Concurrent Pos:* Sloan fel, 68-70; NSF sr fel, Univ Calif, Los Angeles, 71-72; consult, Hercules, Inc, 73-77; assoc ed, J Am Chem Soc, 75-86; Guggenheim fel, 83-84. *Mem:* Sigma Xi; Am Chem Soc; InterAm Photochemistry Soc. *Res:* Mechanisms of free radical and photochemical reactions; electronic energy transfer; photoexcited polyfunctional molecules. *Mailing Add:* Dept Chem Mich State Univ East Lansing MI 48823. *Fax:* 517-353-1793; *E-Mail:* wagner@msucem.bitnet

**WAGNER, RAYMOND LEE,** ASTRODYNAMICS, SYSTEMS ENGINEERING. *Current Pos:* mgr advan systs, 90-95, PRIN ENG SPECIALIST, ADV TECHNOL PROG, BOEING NAM, 95- *Personal Data:* b Kansas City, Mo, Aug 21, 46; m 69, Cheri; c Richard & Derek. *Educ:* Rice Univ, BA, 68; Univ Tex, Austin, PhD(astron), 72. *Prof Exp:* Asst prof astron, Univ Wash, 72-74; asst prof astron & physics, La State Univ, Baton Rouge, 74-79; software engr, Ford Aerospace, 79-82, prin software engr, 82-83, supvr, 83-86, prog mgr, 86-89, dept mgr, 89-90. *Concurrent Pos:* Fac assoc, Univ Colo, 83-84. *Mem:* Fel Am Inst Aeronaut & Astronaut; Sigma Xi; Int Astron Union; Nat Mil Intel Asn; Armed Forces Commun & Electronics Asn. *Res:* Formal methods; system security and integrity; astrodynamics; command and control; information warfare; object-oriented software design. *Mailing Add:* Boeing NAm PO Box 3105 MS/DF07 Anaheim CA 92803-3105. *Fax:* 714-762-2007; *E-Mail:* raymond.l.wagner@boeing.com

**WAGNER, RICHARD CARL,** MATHEMATICS. *Current Pos:* From asst prof to assoc prof, 68-79, PROF MATH, FAIRLEIGH DICKINSON UNIV, 79- *Personal Data:* b Orange, NJ, Sept 25, 41. *Educ:* Rutgers Univ, AB, 63; Univ Chicago, MS, 64, PhD(math), 68. *Mem:* Asn Comput Mach; Am Math Soc; Math Asn Am; London Math Soc. *Res:* Quadratic forms; algebraic k-theory. *Mailing Add:* Dept Math Fairleigh Dickinson Univ Madison NJ 07940

**WAGNER, RICHARD JOHN,** SOLID STATE PHYSICS. *Current Pos:* Mem tech staff eng, Hughes Aircraft Co, 58-68, staff physicist, 68-69, sr tech staff asst physics, 69-71, sr staff physicist, 71-75, sr scientist, 75-78, dept mgr, Receiver Dept, 78-80, asst lab mgr, Microwave Systs Lab, 80-90, SR DIV STAFF MGR, MICROWAVE DIV, HUGHES AIRCRAFT CO, 90- *Personal Data:* b Barnesville, Minn, Jan 13, 36; m 58; c 2. *Educ:* St John's Univ, Minn, BS, 58; Univ Calif, Los Angeles, MS, 60, PhD(physics), 66. *Concurrent Pos:* Teaching asst, Univ Calif, Los Angeles, 61-63, res asst, 63-66, asst res physicist, 66-67. *Mem:* Am Phys Soc. *Res:* Solid state physics, particularly as applicable to solid state microwave devices. *Mailing Add:* 8059 Dunfield Ave Los Angeles CA 90045. *Fax:* 310-334-1820

**WAGNER, RICHARD LLOYD,** POLYMER CHEMISTRY, PHOTOCHEMISTRY. *Current Pos:* RETIRED. *Personal Data:* b Manitowoc, Wis, May 30, 34; div; c 5. *Educ:* Univ Wis-Madison, BS, 60. *Prof Exp:* Chemist, Hercules Res Ctr, Hercules Inc, 60-65, res chemist & proj leader mat sci & appl res, 66-71, sr venture analyst, New Enterprise Dept, 71-73, supvr mkt serv, 73-75, mgr eng & develop, Graphic Systs Div, Org Dept, 75-78, mgr, Develop Dept, 78-85, vpres technol, MICA Corp, 85-87, mgr, com develop, 87-89, dir licensing, 89-94. *Mem:* Am Chem Soc. *Res:* Applications research and product development work related to uses of company products in graphic arts areas and other commercially important areas; product and market development with photochemical systems in graphic arts uses; chemical and equipment systems for graphic arts products involving photopolymers. *Mailing Add:* 1 Wellington West Dr Hockessin DE 19707-1014

**WAGNER, RICHARD LORRAINE, JR,** PHYSICS, MATHEMATICS. *Current Pos:* LOS ALAMOS NAT LAB, 96- *Personal Data:* b Oklahoma City, Okla, July 7, 36; m 58, Virginia Raymond; c 3. *Educ:* Williams Col, BA, 58; Univ Utah, PhD(physics), 63. *Prof Exp:* Student teacher & res asst physics, Univ Utah, 58-63; physics & defense res, Lawrence Livermore Lab, 63-75, assoc dir, 76-81; asst secy defense, Atomic Energy, Dept Defense, 81-86; chief scientist, Kaman Sci Corp, 86-96. *Concurrent Pos:* Mem, Advan Res Projs Agency-Defense Nuclear Agency Long Range Res & Develop Panel, 73-74, Joint Strategic Target Planning Staff Sci Adv Group, Joint Chiefs of Staff, Offutt AFB, Nebr, 73-79, US Army Sci Adv Panel, 76-78 & Defense Sci Bd, Off Under Secy Defense, 79-81. *Mem:* Am Phys Soc; AAAS. *Res:* Cosmic rays; high energy physics; nuclear explosive design; weapons effects; antiballistic missile system studies; defense technology strategy. *Mailing Add:* 1003 Congress Lane McLean VA 22101

**WAGNER, RICHARD S(IEGFRIED),** MATERIALS SCIENCE, SOLID STATE & ENGINEERING PHYSICS. *Current Pos:* RETIRED. *Personal Data:* b Wels, Austria, July 3, 25; m 57; c 4. *Educ:* Vienna Tech Univ, MS, 51; Harvard Univ, MS, 57, PhD(appl physics), 59. *Honors & Awards:* C Mathewson Gold Medal, Am Inst Mining, Metall & Petrol Engrs, 66. *Prof Exp:* Mem tech staff mat sci, AT&T Bell Tel Labs, 59-90, dept head, 70-90. *Concurrent Pos:* Consult, US Dept Energy. *Mem:* AAAS; Am Inst Mining, Metall & Petrol Engrs; Am Phys Soc; Electrochem Soc; Am Vacuum Soc; Sigma Xi. *Res:* Physical metallurgy; solidification; crystal growth; defects in solids; vapor phase reactions; semiconductor device and magnetic bubble device technology development; technology development Silicon VLS1 and VLS1 devices. *Mailing Add:* 161 Peachcrest Rd Bernardsville NJ 07974

**WAGNER, ROBERT ALAN,** COMPUTER SCIENCE. *Current Pos:* ASSOC PROF COMPUT SCI, DUKE UNIV, 78- *Personal Data:* b Philadelphia, Pa, Mar 25, 41; m 93, Virginia Cornelius. *Educ:* Mass Inst Technol, BS, 62; Carnegie-Mellon Univ, PhD(comput sci), 69. *Prof Exp:* Programmer, Rand Corp, 62-65; asst prof comput sci, Cornell Univ, 68-71; assoc prof systs & info sci, Vanderbilt Univ, 71-78. *Mem:* Soc Indust & Appl Math; Asn Comput Mach; Sigma Xi. *Res:* Algorithms, especially techniques for constructing optimal algorithms; application of dynamic programming to computer-suggested problems; programming languages; operating systems. *Mailing Add:* 1416 Meadow Wind Lane Hillsborough NC 27278-7334

**WAGNER, ROBERT E(ARL),** CHEMICAL ENGINEERING. *Current Pos:* RETIRED. *Personal Data:* b Baltimore, Md, July 30, 20; m 49; c 3. *Educ:* Drexel Inst, BS, 46; Princeton Univ, MS, 48, PhD(chem eng), 55. *Prof Exp:* Lab asst chem, E I du Pont de Nemours & Co, 39-41 & Lever Bros Co, 41-42; thermodynamist, Glenn L Martin Co, 46; from asst prof to prof chem eng, Worcester Polytech Inst, 49-88. *Concurrent Pos:* Consult, New Eng Gas & Elec Asn. *Mem:* Am Chem Soc; Am Inst Chem Engrs; Sigma Xi. *Res:* Distillation; vapor liquid equilibria. *Mailing Add:* 41 North St Shrewsbury MA 01545

**WAGNER, ROBERT EDWIN,** ORGANIC CHEMISTRY. *Current Pos:* res chemist, 53-60, TECH SERV SUPVR, EXP STA LAB, E I DU PONT DE NEMOURS & CO, INC, 60- *Personal Data:* b Akron, Ohio, May 5, 20; m 52; c 2. *Educ:* Mass Inst Technol, SB, 42; Princeton Univ, MA, 49, PhD(chem), 51. *Prof Exp:* Jr technologist, Shell Oil Co, 43-47. *Concurrent Pos:* Mem, Nat Defense Res Comt, 42. *Res:* Cellulose and polymer chemistry. *Mailing Add:* 441 Burnt Mill Rd Chadds Ford PA 19317

**WAGNER, ROBERT G,** SOLID STATE PHYSICS, DIGITAL IMAGE ANALYSIS. *Current Pos:* res asst solid state physics, McDonnell Douglas Corp, 60-66, from res scientist to assoc scientist, 66-71, sr group engr electronics, 71-76, sr tech specialist, 76-81, PRIN TECH SPECIALIST, MCDONNELL DOUGLAS CORP, 81- *Personal Data:* b Kansas City, Mo, Apr 2, 34; m 57; c 3. *Educ:* Grinnell Col, AB, 56; Univ Mo, MS, 60, PhD(physics), 66. *Prof Exp:* Res engr, NAm Aviation, Inc, 56-58. *Concurrent Pos:* Asst prof, Univ Mo, St Louis, 71- *Mem:* AAAS; Inst Elec & Electronics Engrs; Am Phys Soc; Sigma Xi. *Res:* Thins films; device physics. *Mailing Add:* 7052 Kingsbury Blvd St Louis MO 63130

**WAGNER, ROBERT G,** PARTICLE PHYSICS DETECTORS, ELECTROWEAK INTERACTIONS. *Current Pos:* Fel, 77-80, asst physicist, 80-82, PHYSICIST, ARGONNE NAT LAB, 82- *Personal Data:* b Freeport, Ill, Sept 14, 50; c 2. *Educ:* Univ Ill, BS, 72, MS, 74, PhD(physics), 78. *Mem:* Am Phys Soc. *Res:* Hadron collider; detector physics. *Mailing Add:* Bldg 362 Rm E-285 Argonne Nat Lab 9700 S Cass Ave Argonne IL 60439-4815. *Fax:* 630-252-5782

**WAGNER, ROBERT H,** BIOCHEMISTRY. *Current Pos:* res assoc path & instr biochem, Univ NC, Chapel Hill, 53-56, asst prof path & biochem, 57-61, assoc prof, 61-67, prof path, 67-86, prof biochem, 72-86, EMER PROF PATH & BIOCHEM, SCH MED, UNIV NC, CHAPEL HILL, 86- *Personal Data:* b Peru, Ind, Aug 11, 21; m 45, Jean Linde; c Sibyl, Lucy, John, Virginia, Jean & Elsbeth. *Educ:* DePauw Univ, AB, 43; Univ Cincinnati, PhD(biochem), 50. *Honors & Awards:* Muray Thelin Hemophilia Award; Int Prize Fr Asn Hemophilia; Karl Handsteiner Award; James Patterson Award. *Prof Exp:* Asst, DePauw Univ, 43-44; asst, Res Found, Children's Hosp, 46-50. *Concurrent Pos:* USPHS sr fel, Univ Chapel Hill, 59-63, res career develop fel, 64-69. *Mem:* Fel AAAS; Am Chem Soc; Am Soc Biochem & Molecular Biol; Am Inst Chemists; Am Soc Exp Path; Sigma Xi. *Res:* Plasma proteins; enzymes; blood clotting; antihemophilic factors. *Mailing Add:* 311 Burlage Circle Chapel Hill NC 27514

**WAGNER, ROBERT PHILIP,** GENETICS. *Current Pos:* from asst prof to prof, 45-77, EMER PROF ZOOL, UNIV TEX, AUSTIN, 77- *Personal Data:* b New York, NY, May 11, 18; m 47; c 3. *Educ:* City Col New York, BS, 40; Univ Tex, PhD(genetics), 43. *Prof Exp:* Instr zool, Univ Tex, 43-44; res biologist, Nat Cotton Coun, Dallas, 44-45. *Concurrent Pos:* Nat Res Coun fel, Calif Inst Technol, 46; Guggenheim fel, 57; mem genetics panel, NSF, 61-64 & prog projs comt, 64-68 & Genetics Training Grant Comt, Nat Inst Gen Med Sci, 70-73; consult, Los Alamos Nat Lab, 78-; vis prof, Ind Univ, 62- & Univ Tex, Austin, 88- *Mem:* Fel AAAS; Soc Study Evolution; Genetics Soc Am (secy, 65-66, vpres, 70, pres, 71); Am Soc Biochem & Molecular Biol; Am Soc Human Genetics; Am Genetics Asn. *Res:* Chromosome structure and function. *Mailing Add:* 313 Los Arboles Dr Santa Fe NM 87501-1242

**WAGNER, ROBERT RODERICK,** VIROLOGY, MICROBIOLOGY. *Current Pos:* prof microbiol & chmn dept, 67-97, Marion McNulty Weaver prof oncol, 84-97, EMER PROF MICROBIOL, UNIV VA, 97- *Personal Data:* b New York, NY, Jan 5, 23; m 67, Mary E Burke. *Educ:* Yale Univ, MD, 46. *Prof Exp:* Intern med, New Haven Hosp, 46-47, asst resident, 49-50; instr med, Yale Univ, 51-53, asst prof, 53-55; from asst prof to prof microbiol, Johns Hopkins Univ, 56-67, from asst dean to assoc dean med fac, 57-63. *Concurrent Pos:* USPHS fel, Nat Inst Med Res, London, 50-51; vis fel, All Souls Col, Oxford Univ, 67; vis scientist, Dept Path, Oxford Univ, 67, Chinese Acad Med Sci, 82; ed-in-chief, J Virol, 66-82; consult, NIH, NSF & Am Cancer Soc; Josiah Macy Jr Found Fac Scholar, Oxford Univ, 75-76; distinguished US scientist award, Alexander von Humboldt Found, 83; vis prof, Univ Giessen & Univ Wuerzburg, 83 & 91; dir, Cancer Ctr, 84-94. *Mem:* Am Soc Microbiol; Am Soc Clin Invest; Asn Am Med Cols; Asn Am Physicians; Am Soc Biol Chemists; Am Soc Virol (pres, 84-85). *Res:* Biochemistry of viruses; molecular and cell biology; cancer research. *Mailing Add:* Dept Microbiol Sch Med Univ Va Box 441 Charlottesville VA 22908. *Fax:* 804-982-1071; *E-Mail:* rrw@virginia.edu

**WAGNER, ROBERT THOMAS,** NUCLEAR PHYSICS. *Current Pos:* RETIRED. *Personal Data:* b Winona, Minn, July 15, 23; m 66, Margaret Watson; c George, Lynne & Ron. *Educ:* US Mil Acad, BS, 46; Univ Va, PhD(nuclear physics), 55. *Prof Exp:* Staff mem, Los Alamos Sci Lab, 55-64; prof physics, St Mary's Col, Minn, 64-66; chief tech develop div, Nike-X Syst Off, US Army, 66-67; prof & head physics dept, Northern Mich Univ, 67-75; dean fac, Sch Sci & Math, Univ Southern Colo, 75-78; acad dean, NMex Military Inst, 78-86; radiologic physicist, Radiol Dept, Eastern NMex Med Ctr, Roswell, NMex, 88-93. *Mem:* Sigma Xi. *Res:* Ferroelectric ceramics; particle accelerators; fission physics; nuclear decay schemes; neutron and x-ray transport and diffusion; theoretical mechanics; scintillation radiation detectors. *Mailing Add:* 2609 Sherrill Lane Roswell NM 88201

**WAGNER, ROGER CURTIS,** CELL BIOLOGY. *Current Pos:* asst prof biol sci, 74-77, PROF LIFE & HEALTH SCI, UNIV DEL, 77- *Personal Data:* b Aitkin, Minn, May 14, 43; m 68; c 2. *Educ:* Hamline Univ, BS, 65; Ohio Univ, MS, 67; Univ Minn, Minneapolis, PhD(cell biol), 71. *Honors & Awards:* Res Career Develop Award. *Prof Exp:* Teaching asst zool, anat & hist, Ohio Univ, 65-67; teaching asst biol & physiol, Univ Minn, Minneapolis, 67-68, res asst electrophysiol, St Paul; fel cell biol, Med Sch, Yale Univ, 71-74. *Concurrent Pos:* Nat Heart Lung & Blood Inst, 76-88. *Mem:* AAAS; Am Soc Cell Biol; Biophys Soc; Am Inst Biol Sci; Microcirculatory Soc Am. *Res:* Mechanism and function of macropinocytosis and micropinocytosis in mammalian cells; biomembranes; cell and molecular biology; histology; electron microscopy. *Mailing Add:* Biol Univ Del 112 Wolf Hall Newark DE 19717-0001. *Fax:* 302-451-2281

**WAGNER, ROSS IRVING,** SYNTHETIC INORGANIC & ORGANOMETALLIC CHEMISTRY. *Current Pos:* RETIRED. *Personal Data:* b Los Angeles, Calif, Apr 8, 25; m 49, Janet Struble; c Kathryn, Laurel & Glen. *Educ:* Univ Calif, Los Angeles, BS, 47; Univ Southern Calif, MS, 50, PhD(chem), 53. *Prof Exp:* Asst chem, Univ Southern Calif, 49-53; sr res chemist, Am Potash & Chem Corp, 53-63; mem tech staff, Rocketdyne Div, Rockwell Int, 63-90. *Mem:* Am Chem Soc. *Res:* Chemistry of boron and phosphorus sulfur and fluorine. *Mailing Add:* 4943 Queen Victoria Rd Woodland Hills CA 91364-4755

**WAGNER, SIGURD,** SEMICONDUCTORS APPLICATION. *Current Pos:* PROF ELEC ENG, PRINCETON UNIV, 80- *Personal Data:* b Gaenserndorf, Austria, Nov 13, 41. *Educ:* Univ Vienna, Austria, PhD(phys chem), 68. *Prof Exp:* Fel metall eng, Ohio State Univ, 69-70; mem tech staff semiconductor res, Bell Labs, 70-78; chief, Photovoltaic Res Br, Solar Energy Res Inst, 78-80. *Mem:* Inst Elec & Electronics Engrs; fel Am Phys Soc; Mat Res Soc; Electrochem Soc. *Res:* Preparation and properties of new semiconductors and their application to devices; new semiconductors for solar cells. *Mailing Add:* Dept Elec Eng Princeton Univ Princeton NJ 08544. *Fax:* 609-258-6379; *E-Mail:* wagner@tiger.princeton.edu

**WAGNER, THOMAS CHARLES GORDON,** ELECTRICAL ENGINEERING. *Current Pos:* PRES, TCG INC, 73- *Personal Data:* b Pittsburgh, Pa, Jan 9, 16; m 42; c 3. *Educ:* Harvard Univ, SB, 37; Univ Md, MA, 40, PhD(math), 43. *Prof Exp:* With W Jett Lauck, DC, 37-38; asst mathematician, Univ Md, College Park, 38-40, instr, 40-45, prof elec eng, 46-76. *Concurrent Pos:* Consult, Washington Inst Technol, Md, 40-46, Minneapolis-Honeywell Regulator Co, 47-59, Litton Industs, Inc, 59-62, Keltec Industs, Inc, 62-67 & Aero Geo Astro Div, Aiken Industs, Inc, 67-80. *Mem:* Inst Elec & Electronics Engrs; Sigma Xi. *Res:* Circuit analysis; timing devices; topology of networks. *Mailing Add:* 201 W Montgomery Ave Rockville MD 20850-2804

**WAGNER, THOMAS EDWARDS,** BIOCHEMISTRY, ENDOCRINOLOGY. *Current Pos:* from asst prof to assoc prof, 70-78, PROF, DEPT CHEM & BIOCHEM, OHIO UNIV, 78-, PROF, DEPT ZOOL & BIOMED SCI, 82-, DIR, MAMMALIAN RECOMBINANT GENETICS INST, 82- *Personal Data:* b Cleveland, Ohio, Nov 29, 42; m 66, 90; c 3. *Educ:* Princeton Univ, AB, 64; Northwestern Univ, PhD(biochem), 66. *Prof Exp:* Asst prof chem, Wellesley Col, 66-67; asst prof biochem, Med Col, Cornell Univ, 67-70. *Concurrent Pos:* Petrol Res Fund grant, 67-70; assoc endocrinol, Sloan-Kettering Inst Cancer Res, 68-70; prof & chmn, Grad Prog Molecular & Cell Biol, Ohio Univ, 82-86, dir, Edison Animal Biotechnol Ctr, 84-89, sci dir, 89-; sr vis fel, Animal Res Ctr, Cambridge Univ, 82; sci rev panelist, Nat Res Coun, 83-; distinguished lectr, Univ Tenn, 84 & Boyce Thompson Inst Plant Res, Cornell Univ, 87; mcm, Comt Maintaining Global Genetic Resources, Nat Acad Sci, 86. *Mem:* Am Chem Soc. *Res:* Author of 158 publications. *Mailing Add:* Dept Chem Ohio Univ 102 Wilson West Green Athens OH 45701-2979

**WAGNER, TIMOTHY KNIGHT,** solid state physics, for more information see previous edition

**WAGNER, WARREN HERBERT, JR,** BOTANY, PTERIDOLOGY. *Current Pos:* from instr to assoc prof, Univ Mich, Ann Arbor, 51-61, prof bot & natural resources, 61-91, dir, Bot Gardens, 66-71, CUR HERBARIUM, UNIV MICH, ANN ARBOR, 62-, EMER PROF BOT & NATURAL RESOURCES, 91- *Personal Data:* b Washington, DC, Aug 29, 20; m 48, Florence S; c Warren C & Margaret F. *Educ:* Univ Pa, AB, 42; Univ Calif, PhD, 50. *Honors & Awards:* Merit Award, Bot Soc Am, 78; Asa Gray Award, Am Soc Plant Taxon, 90. *Prof Exp:* Res fel, Harvard Univ, 50-51. *Concurrent Pos:* Mem, Ad Hoc Comt Plant Taxon, Nat Acad Sci, 56-57, Plant Sci Planning Comt, 64-65, dep bot, Subcomt Syst Biogeog, US Nat Comt, Int Biol Prog, 65-68; trustee, Cranbrook Inst Sci, 63-78; mem, Fairchild Trop Garden Res Comt, 66-69; mem, Smithsonian Inst Coun, 67-72, US Nat Mus Natural Hist coun, 90-, Panel Syst Biol, NSF; consult mem, Int Union Conserv Nature & Natural Resources, 72-; hon mem, Smithsonian Coun, Curado Asn ad hon Herbario Nacional de Costa Rica; vis prof, Univ Hawaii, 87, Harvard Univ, 91. *Mem:* Nat Acad Sci; fel AAAS (secy, 63-67); Soc Study Evolution (vpres, 66, pres, 72); Am Soc Plant Taxon (pres, 66); Am Fern Soc (secy, 51-53, pres, 70-71; Bot Soc Am (vpres, 72, pres, 77); Am Acad Arts & Sci; Int Asn Pteridologists (vpres, 83-87, pres, 88-93). *Res:* Morphology, life cycles, evolution and systematics of vascular plants, especially pteridophytes; science education; biology of higher plants, especially ferns; phylogenetic theory; systematics and evolution; methods of determining phylogeny; reticulate speciation; principles of systematics; ferns of Hawaii and North America; morphology and lifecycles. *Mailing Add:* 2111 Melrose Ave Ann Arbor MI 48104-4067. *Fax:* 313-747-0889; *E-Mail:* usergcks@umich.edu

**WAGNER, WARREN L,** BOTANY, TAXONOMY. *Current Pos:* assoc cur, 88-91, CUR PACIFIC BOT, NAT MUS NATURAL HIST, SMITHSONIAN INST, WASHINGTON, DC, 91-, CHMN, DEPT BOT, 92- *Personal Data:* b Las Cruces, NMex, Feb 8, 50; m 93, Lucy Julian; c Anthony J & Eleanor R. *Educ:* Univ NMex, BS, 73, MS, 77; Washington Univ, St Louis, PhD(biol), 81. *Honors & Awards:* Engler Silver Medal, Int Asn Plant Taxon, 93; Robert Allerton Award, Nat Bot Garden, 95. *Prof Exp:* Postdoctoral fel, Asn Mo Botanical Garden, St Louis, 81-82; asst res botanist, Bishop Mus, Honolulu, HI, 82-84, assoc, 84-88. *Concurrent Pos:* Res affil, Harold L Lyon Arboretum, Honolulu, 83-, Dept Bot, Bishop Mus Honolulu, 88-; res assoc, Nat Trop Bot Garden, Lawai, HI, 90-; adj prof, Dept Bot, Duke Univ, 92- *Mem:* Am Soc Plant Taxonomists; Soc Study Evolution; Bot Soc Am; Int Asn Plant Taxon; Sigma Xi; AAAS. *Res:* Biosystematic, taxonomic, and phylogenetic studies, especially monographs floras and nomenclature; classification phylogeny and biogeography of Pacific Island floras contributing to understanding island biodiversity, evolution and therefore conservation. *Mailing Add:* Dept Bot Nat Mus Natural Hist 10th & Constitution Ave NW MRC-166 Washington DC 20560. *Fax:* 202-786-2517; *E-Mail:* wagner.warren@nmnh.si.edu

**WAGNER, WILLIAM CHARLES,** ENDOCRINOLOGY, EDUCATION ADMINISTRATION. *Current Pos:* NAT PROG LEADER VET MED, USDA, WASHINGTON, DC, 93- *Personal Data:* b Elma, NY, Nov 12, 32; m 54; c 4. *Educ:* Cornell Univ, DVM, 56, PhD(physiol), 68. *Prof Exp:* Res vet, Col Vet Med, Cornell Univ, 57-65, fel physiol, Dept Animal Sci, 65-68; from asst prof to prof physiol, Col Vet Med, Iowa State Univ, 68-77; prof & head, Dept Vet Biosci, Col Vet Med, Univ Ill, 77-90, assoc dean res, 90-93. *Concurrent Pos:* Vis prof, Inst Physiol, Tech Univ Munich, WGer, 73-74; consult, Res Adv Bd, Morris Animal Found, 78-81; Alexander von Humboldt scientist award, 73; Fulbright sr res prof, Inst Tierzucht, WGer, 84-85; mem, Exec Comt, Int Cong Animal Reproduction & Artificial Insemination, 84-, pres, 88-; Am Vet Med Assoc, Coun Educ, 87-93; prog vet sci, USDA-CSRS, 90-91. *Mem:* Am Col Theriogenology (pres, 77-78); Am Physiol Soc; Am Vet Med Asn; Am Soc Animal Sci; Soc Study Reproduction. *Res:* Physiology of parturition and the postpartum female, especially in regard to ruminants; placental hormone synthesis and leucocyte function. *Mailing Add:* USDA-CSREES 1400 Independence Ave Stop 2220 Washington DC 20250-2220. *E-Mail:* w_wagner1@uiuc.edu

**WAGNER, WILLIAM EDWARD, JR,** CLINICAL PHARMACOLOGY. *Current Pos:* RETIRED. *Personal Data:* b New York, NY, June 17, 25; m 63; c 2. *Educ:* Princeton Univ, BA, 45; Columbia Univ, MD, 50; Am Bd Family Pract, dipl, 70, 77 & 83. *Prof Exp:* Instr clin med, Med Sch, NY Univ, 60-77; assoc clin prof med, Med Sch, Col Physicians & Surgeons, Columbia Univ, 77-96. *Concurrent Pos:* Sr fel clin pharmacol, Pharmaceut Div, Ciba-Geigy Corp, 51-96; Attending staff, Overlook Hosp, 62; secy, FPD, 76- *Mem:* AMA; Am Soc Clin Pharmacol & Therapeut; fel Am Acad Family Pract. *Res:* Drug metabolism; pharmacokinetics; biopharmaceuticals. *Mailing Add:* 3301 Valley Rd Basking Ridge NJ 07920

**WAGNER, WILLIAM FREDERICK,** CHEMISTRY. *Current Pos:* from instr to prof, 49-83, chmn dept, 65-68 & 76-82, EMER PROF CHEM, UNIV KY, 83- *Personal Data:* b Canton, Mo, Sept 13, 16; m, Jean Rosselot; c Jennie, Lenore & Russell. *Educ:* Culver-Stockton Col, AB, 38; Univ Chicago, SM, 40; Univ Ill, PhD(anal chem), 47. *Prof Exp:* Asst chemist, State Geol Surv, Ill, 40-45; asst chem, Univ Ill, 45-47; asst prof, Hanover Col, 47-49. *Mem:* AAAS; Am Chem Soc. *Res:* X-ray applied to chemical analysis; solvent extraction of metal chelates; thermal methods of analysis. *Mailing Add:* Dept Chem Univ Ky Lexington KY 40506

**WAGNER, WILLIAM GERARD,** THEORETICAL PHYSICS, INTELLIGENT SYSTEMS. *Current Pos:* assoc prof, 66-69, PROF PHYSICS & ELEC ENG, UNIV SOUTHERN CALIF, 69-, DEAN, 73- *Personal Data:* b St Cloud, Minn, Aug 22, 36; m 68; c Mary, Robert, David & Anne. *Educ:* Calif Inst Technol, BS, 58, PhD(physics), 62. *Prof Exp:* Mem tech staff, Res Labs, Hughes Aircraft Co, 60-65, sr staff physicist, 65-70. *Concurrent Pos:* Consult, Rand Corp, 60-65; Tolman res fel theoret physics, Calif Inst Technol, 62-65, lectr, 63-65; asst prof, Univ Calif, Irvine, 65-66; consult, Janus Mgt Corp, 70-71, Croesus Capital Corp, 71-74 & Financial Horizons, Inc, 74-; chmn bd, Malibu Securities Corp, 72-; dean, Div Natural Sci & Math, Col Lett, Arts & Sci, Univ Southern Calif, 73-87, spec asst, Acad Record Serv, 75-81; dean, Interdisciplinary Progs, 87-89. *Mem:* Sigma Xi; Asn Comput Mach. *Res:* Neuroscience; informatics; computer applications. *Mailing Add:* 2828 Patricia Ave Los Angeles CA 90064-4425. *E-Mail:* wwagner@mizar.usc.edu

**WAGNER, WILLIAM JOHN,** SOLAR PHYSICS, SOLAR-TERRESTRIAL PHYSICS. *Current Pos:* SOLAR PHYSICS DISCIPLINE SCIENTIST, SPACE PHYSICS DIV, OFF SPACE SCI & APPLN, NASA HQ, 90- *Personal Data:* b Gary, Ind, Mar 29, 38; m 62; c 5. *Educ:* John Carroll Univ, BS, 60, MS, 62; Univ Colo, PhD(astro-geophys), 69. *Prof Exp:* Sr physicist, 62-64, sci eng fel, Rocketdyne Div, NAm Aviation, Inc, 64-69; astrophysicist & Big Dome facil sect chief, Sacramento Peak Observ, Air Force Geophys Lab, 69-76; SMM coronagraph-polarimeter exp scientist, Nat Oceanic & Atmospheric Admin, 76-81, staff scientist, High Altitude observ, Nat Ctr Atmospheric Res, 81-84, physicist, Space Environ Lab, 84- 90. *Concurrent Pos:* Mem sub comn solar physics, Comt Space Res, 81-; responsible scientist GOES Solar X-ray Imager, 85-90, Solar X- ray Physics, proj leader, 86-90; prog scientist SMM, Stand Occup Safety & Health Admin, Solar-A, Orbiting Space Lab, 90- *Mem:* Fel AAAS; Int Astron Union; Am Astron Soc; Am Phys Soc; Am Geophys Union. *Res:* Observational research concerning solar physics, solar activity, the corona and solar wind; solar-terrestrial physics; spectroscopy. *Mailing Add:* Code SR NASA Hq Washington DC 20546. *Fax:* 202-358-3987

**WAGNER, WILLIAM S,** ELECTRICAL ENGINEERING. *Current Pos:* Instr, 61-67, ASST PROF ELEC ENG, UNIV CINCINNATI, 67- *Personal Data:* b Cincinnati, Ohio, Apr 8, 36; m 65. *Educ:* Univ Ky, BS, 59; Case Western Res Univ, MS, 61; Univ Cincinnati, PhD, 67. *Concurrent Pos:* Ford Found yr in residency prog grant, 68-69. *Res:* Nonlinear system analysis; network synthesis; electronics; control systems. *Mailing Add:* Dept Phys Sci Northern Ky Univ University Dr Newport KY 41076-1448

**WAGNER, WILLIAM SHERWOOD,** MAN-MADE FIBERS. *Current Pos:* CONSULT, 90- *Personal Data:* b Mora, Minn, Sept 21, 28; m 62, Elaine Stone. *Educ:* Univ Minn, BChem, 49; Univ Mo, PhD(org chem), 52. *Prof Exp:* Sr res chemist, Chemstrand Corp, Ala, 52-59; mgr org res paper prod, Fiber Prod Res Ctr, Inc, 59-62, asst dir paper prod, 62-63; res assoc, Celanese Res Co, 63-65, head spinning res sect, 65-70, group mgr, Hoechst Corp, 70-71, mgr res & labs, 71-72, dir develop, 72-81, dir fiber technol, Hoechst Fibers Indust Div, 81-88, sr tech assoc, Hoechst Celanese Corp, 88-90. *Mem:* Am Chem Soc. *Res:* Synthetic fibers; polymers; organic synthesis; polymer synthesis and properties, processes for forming and treating fibers, fiber properties. *Mailing Add:* 696 Perrin Dr Spartanburg SC 29307-2458

**WAGNER, WILTZ WALKER, JR,** PULMONARY PHYSIOLOGY. *Current Pos:* assoc prof physiol, biophys & anesthesia, 85-90, V K STOELTING PROF ANESTHESIOL, SCH MED, IND UNIV, 90- *Personal Data:* b New Orleans, La, July 7, 39; m 67; c 1. *Educ:* Colo State Univ, PhD(physiol), 74. *Prof Exp:* Res fel physiol, Med Ctr, Univ Colo, Denver, 60-67, res assoc, 67-74, instr, 74-80, asst prof med, 80-85. *Concurrent Pos:* Site vis, NIH, 74; consult, Med Sch, Univ Calif, Los Angeles, 74 & Univ Calif, La Jolla, 75, Med Sch, Univ Calif, San Francisco, 70 & 79, Harvard Med Sch, Boston, 79 & 84. *Mem:* Fel Royal Micros Soc; Sigma Xi; Am Physiol Soc; Microcirc Soc; Am Heart Asn. *Res:* Pulmonary microcirculation using methods for direct visualization of capillary perfusion in vivo; capillary control mechanisms and functional implications in health and disease; collateral ventilation and relation to ventilation-perfusion balance; athletic amenorrhea. *Mailing Add:* Dept Physiol & Biophys Sch Med Ind Univ 635 Barn Hill Dr Rm 345 Indianapolis IN 46202-5120

**WAGNER-BARTAK, CLAUS GUNTER JOHANN,** MOLECULAR PHYSICS, AEROSPACE ENGINEERING. *Current Pos:* VPRES, ENERGY DYNAMICS INC, 83-; PRES, STRUCT BIOLS, INC, 88- *Personal Data:* b Munich, Ger, Sept 9, 37: Ger & Can citizen; m 69, Marlene Reich; c Natalie, Nicholas & Nadine. *Educ:* Ludwig Maximilian Univ, Munich, BSc, 62, MSc, 66, DrRerNat, 69. *Honors & Awards:* Pub Serv Medal, NASA, 82; Joseph F Engelberger Award, Robotics Int, 86; Eng Medal, Asn Prof Eng Ont, 82. *Prof Exp:* Res scientist, Univ Munich, 66-69; proj scientist, aerospace technol, Messerschmitt-Boelkow-Blohm, 69-74, eng mgr & proj mgr, 69-74; proj mgr, Spar Aerospace Ltd, 74-80, vpres, 80-83. *Concurrent Pos:* Consult, Mgt, Bus & Technol. *Mem:* Am Inst Aeronaut & Astronaut; Aerospace Med Asn; Am Phys Eng Orgn. *Res:* Applied and theoretical physics; science; biology; biotechnology; material science and applications in medicine and biology; science and society technology assessments; new technology developments; robotics; radiology. *Mailing Add:* 4092 Lee Hwy Arlington VA 22207-3160

**WAGONER, DALE E,** GENETICS, BIOLOGY. *Current Pos:* from teaching lab specialist to sr teaching lab specialist, 88-93, ASST NATURAL SCI, NEW COL, UNIV SFLA, 93- *Personal Data:* b Niagara Falls, NY, Oct 12, 36; m 74, Lorraine J Samuel; c Lisa M, Libra M & Justin D. *Educ:* Ind Univ, AB(music) & AB(zool), 59, MA, 64, PhD(genetics), 65. *Prof Exp:* Res asst Drosophila genetics, H J Muller Lab, Ind Univ, 60; res geneticist, Metab & Radiation Res Lab, USDA, 64-75; prof biol, Maharishi Int Univ, 75-83. *Concurrent Pos:* From asst prof to assoc prof entom, Grad Fac, NDak State Univ, 68-75. *Mem:* Sigma Xi; Am Genetic Asn. *Res:* Basic formal genetics of house flies; karyotype-linkage group relationship; insect control by the use of genetic mechanisms, such as chromosomal translocation, meiotic drive, hybrid sterility, cytoplasmic incompatability, compound chromosomes and conditional lethal mutations; aging and oxygen consumption research in practitioners of the transcendental meditation and TM Sidhis Program. *Mailing Add:* 4427 Violet Ave Sarasota FL 34233-1826. *Fax:* 941-921-3158; *E-Mail:* wagdl@family-net.org

**WAGONER, DAVID EUGENE,** EXPERIMENTAL HIGH ENERGY PHYSICS, HADRO-PRODUCTION RESEARCH. *Current Pos:* assoc prof, 88-96, PROF, PRAIRIE VIEW A&M UNIV, 96- *Personal Data:* b Clarinda, Iowa, July 8, 49; m 82. *Educ:* Iowa State Univ, BS, 71; Cornell Univ, MS, 78, PhD(exp physics), 81. *Prof Exp:* Teaching asst, Dept Physics, Cornell Univ, 75-76, res asst, Lab Nuclear Studies, 76-81; res assoc, Dept Physics, Fermi Nat Accelerator Lab, 81-85; assoc res prof, Dept Physics, Fla A&M Univ, 85-88. *Concurrent Pos:* Co-prin investr, Fla A&M Univ, 86-88; co-prin investr, Prairie View A&M Univ, 88- *Mem:* Am Phys Soc; AAAS; Inst Elec & Electronics Engrs. *Res:* Hadronic production of charmonium states and direct phaton processes; Monte Carlo computer simulations; operation and analysis of large electromagnetic calorimeter; hadronic production of beauty mesons; study of massive dimuon states. *Mailing Add:* Dept Physics Box 488 Prairie View A&M Univ Prairie View TX 77446-0488

**WAGONER, GLEN,** PHYSICS, INSTRUMENT DESIGN. *Current Pos:* RETIRED. *Personal Data:* b Terreton, Idaho, July 28, 27; m 52, Julia Thornton; c Ann T. *Educ:* Idaho State Col, BS, 49; Univ Chicago, MS, 52; Univ Calif, PhD(physics), 57. *Prof Exp:* Physicist, Res Labs, Union Carbide Corp, 57-85. *Concurrent Pos:* Prof lectr, Case Inst Technol, 59-61; staff lectr, Baldwin Wallace Col, 84- *Mem:* Am Phys Soc. *Res:* Solid state physics; magnetic resonance; electronics; electric arcs; thermal conductivity of carbon fibers. *Mailing Add:* 26564 Lake Rd Bay Village OH 44140

**WAGONER, ROBERT H,** SHEET METAL FORMING, FINITE ELEMENT MODELLING. *Current Pos:* assoc prof, 83-86, chair, 92-96, PROF, DEPT MAT SCI & ENG, OHIO STATE UNIV, COLUMBUS, 86-, DIR, CTR ADVAN MAT & MFG AUTOMOTIVE COMPONENTS, 94- *Personal Data:* b Columbus, Ohio, Jan 8, 52; m 80, Robyn K O'Donnell; c Erin A & Amy J. *Educ:* Ohio State Univ, BS, 74, MS, 75, PhD(metall eng), 76. *Honors & Awards:* Robert Lansing Hardy Gold Medal, Metall Soc, 81, Champion H Mathewson Gold Medal, 88; Pres Young Investr, NSF, 84. *Prof Exp:* Res scientist, Physics Dept, Gen Motors Res Labs, 77-80, staff res scientist, 80-83. *Concurrent Pos:* NSF fel, Univ Oxford, 76-77, sheet forming coordr, Ctr Net Shape Mfg, 88-91; Maitre de Rechercle, Ecole des Mines de Paris, 90-91. *Mem:* Nat Acad Eng; Am Soc Mech Engrs; Soc Automotive Engrs; fel Am Soc Metals Int; Mat Res Soc; Metall Soc; Am Inst Mining, Metall & Petrol Engrs; Minerals, Metals & Mat Soc (vpres, 96-97, pres, 97-98). *Res:* Metal elasticity and plasticity; sheet metal forming; deformation testing, dislocation modelling; mechanical equation of state studies; finite element modelling. *Mailing Add:* Dept Mat Sci Eng 2041 College Rd Columbus OH 43210-1179. *Fax:* 614-292-6530; *E-Mail:* wagoner.2@osu.edu

**WAGONER, ROBERT VERNON,** THEORETICAL ASTROPHYSICS, COSMOLOGY. *Current Pos:* assoc prof, 73-77, PROF PHYSICS, STANFORD UNIV, 77- *Personal Data:* b Teaneck, NJ, Aug 6, 38; m 63, 87; c 2. *Educ:* Cornell Univ, BME, 61; Stanford Univ, MS, 62, PhD(physics), 65. *Prof Exp:* Res fel physics, Calif Inst Technol, 65-68, Sherman Fairchild distinguished scholar, 76; from asst prof to assoc prof astron, Cornell Univ, 68-73. *Concurrent Pos:* Sloan res fel, 69-71; Guggenheim fel, 79; George Ellery Hale distinguished vis prof, Univ Chicago, 78; mem comt space astron & astrophys, Nat Acad Sci, 79-82, physics surv comt & theory study panel, Space Sci Bd, Nat Res Coun, 80-86, prog adv comt, Ctr Particle Astrophys, 90, Nat Sci & Eng Res Coun Grant Selection Comt, Can, 90-93; prin investr, NSF & NASA. *Mem:* Fel Am Phys Soc; Int Astron Union; Am Astron Soc. *Res:* Astrophysics of compact objects and supernovae; cosmology; gravitation theory. *Mailing Add:* Dept Physics MC 4060 Stanford Univ Stanford CA 94305. *Fax:* 650-725-6544; *E-Mail:* wagoner@leland.stanford.edu

**WAGONER, RONALD LEWIS,** MATHEMATICS. *Current Pos:* Asst prof, 69-74, assoc prof, 74-77, PROF MATH, CALIF STATE UNIV, FRESNO, 77- *Personal Data:* b Fairfield, Calif, Aug 4, 42; m 60; c 2. *Educ:* Fresno State Col, BA, 65, MA, 66; Univ Ore, PhD(math), 69. *Concurrent Pos:* Math specialist, Fresno City Unified Sch Dist, 70-71. *Res:* Ring theory: associative rings with identity. *Mailing Add:* Dept Math Calif State Univ 5245 N Baker Fresno CA 93740-0001

**WAGREICH, PHILIP DONALD,** MATHEMATICS & SCIENCE EDUCATION, PURE MATHEMATICS. *Current Pos:* assoc prof, 73-80, PROF, UNIV ILL, CHICAGO, 80-, DIR, INST MATH & SCI EDUC, 96- *Personal Data:* b New York, NY, July 25, 41; m 90, Lorraine Owles; c Heidi, Ian, Amy & Alexander. *Educ:* Brandeis Univ, BA, 62; Columbia Univ, PhD(math), 67. *Honors & Awards:* Excellece Integrated Math & Sci Award, Sch Sci & Math Asn, 92. *Prof Exp:* Lectr math, Brandeis Univ, 66-68; asst prof, Univ Pa, 68-73. *Concurrent Pos:* Off Naval Res fel, 68-69; mem, Inst Advan Study, 68-70; NSF res grants, 74-; co-dir, Teaching Integrated Math & Sci Proj, 85-, Math & Educ Reform Network, 88-, Inst Math & Sci Educ, Univ Ill, Chicago, 90- *Mem:* Am Math Soc; Math Asn Am; Sch Sci & Math Asn; Nat Coun Teachers Math. *Res:* Development of curricula and programs to improve mathematics and science education. *Mailing Add:* Inst Math & Sci Educ Univ Ill M/C 250 2075 SEL 950 S Halsted St Chicago IL 60607-7019. *E-Mail:* wagreich@uic.edu

**WAGSTAFF, DAVID JESSE,** TOXICOLOGY. *Current Pos:* toxicologist, 73-77, epidemiologist, 77-92, TOXICOLOGIST, FOOD & DRUG ADMIN, 92- *Personal Data:* b Lehi, Utah, Feb 22, 35; m 63, Ann Taft; c David, Andrew & Terry. *Educ:* Utah State Univ, BS, 59, PhD(toxicol), 70; Cornell Univ, DVM, 62. *Prof Exp:* Vet epidemiologist, USPHS, 62-64 & 65-66; vet meat inspector, USDA, 64-65; asst prof toxicol, Univ Mo, Columbia, 69-73. *Concurrent Pos:* NIH fel toxicol, Utah State Univ, 66-69; mem, Am Bd Vet Toxicol. *Mem:* Soc Toxicol; Am Col Vet Toxicol; Am Vet Med Asn; Sigma Xi. *Res:* Induction of liver microsomal enzymes; drug toxicity; environmental contaminants; toxicants in natural foods; interaction of toxicology with other fields; toxicant interactions; poisonous plants; food safety epidemiology. *Mailing Add:* 10405 45th Pl Beltsville MD 20705

**WAGSTAFF, SAMUEL STANDFIELD, JR,** COMPUTATIONAL NUMBER THEORY. *Current Pos:* assoc prof, 83-92, PROF COMPUT SCI, PURDUE UNIV, 92- *Personal Data:* b New Bedford, Mass, Feb 21, 45; m 88, Cheryl Pemberton. *Educ:* Mass Inst Technol, BS, 66; Cornell Univ, PhD(math), 70. *Prof Exp:* Instr math, Univ Rochester, 70-71; vis mem, Inst Advan Study, 71-72; vis lectr, Univ Ill, 72-75, asst prof math, 75-81; assoc prof statist & comput sci, Univ Ga, 81-83. *Mem:* Am Math Soc; Math Asn Am; Soc Actuaries. *Res:* Factoring; primality testing; diophantine equations; computational complexity. *Mailing Add:* Dept Comput Sci Purdue Univ West Lafayette IN 47907-1398. *E-Mail:* ssw@cs.purdue.edu

**WAH, BENJAMIN WAN-SANG,** TEACHER LEARNING PROJECT, ALGORITHMS. *Current Pos:* Assoc prof, Dept Elec & Comput Eng & Coord Sci Lab, 85-89, PROF, DEPT ELEC & COMPUT ENG, RES PROF, COORD SCI LAB, & BECKMAN INST, RES ASSOC, COMPUT SCI DEPT, UNIV ILL, URBANA, 89- *Personal Data:* nat US; m, Christine Hai-Ling; c Catherine Lih-Lian & Elaine Ying-Lian. *Educ:* Columbia Univ, BS, 74, MS, 75, Univ Calif, Berkeley, MS, 76, PhD(eng), 79. *Concurrent Pos:* McKay vis prof, Univ Calif, Berkeley, 94. *Mem:* Inst Elec & Electronics Engrs. *Res:* Techniques for the automated creation of heuristics project to automate learning and generalization of new heuristics for knowledge-learn application problems. *Mailing Add:* Coordinated Sci Lab-Univ Ill 1308 W Main St Urbana IL 61801-2307

**WAH, THEIN,** MECHANICS, STRUCTURAL ENGINEERING. *Current Pos:* RETIRED. *Personal Data:* b Rangoon, Burma, Apr 11, 19; nat US; m 52; c 3. *Educ:* Univ Rangoon, BS, 41; Univ Utah, MS, 48; Harvard Univ, MS, 49; Univ Ill, PhD(eng), 53. *Prof Exp:* Asst engr, Burma Rwy, 41-47; bridge designer, State Div Hwys, Ill, 52-53; asst prof civil eng & mech, Lehigh Univ, 53-54 & Univ Conn, 54-57; sr res engr, Southwest Res Inst, Tex, 57-61, staff scientist, 62-71; prof civil & mech eng, Tex A&I Univ, 71-84. *Concurrent Pos:* Vis prof, Indian Inst Technol, Kharagpur, 61-62; eng consult, San Antonio, Tex, 84- *Mem:* Am Soc Mech Engrs. *Res:* Elasticity; plasticity; vibrations; creep; thermoelasticity. *Mailing Add:* 6821 Stonykirk San Antonio TX 78240

**WAH, YAU WAI,** CHARGE CONJUGATE-PARITY VIOLATION, KAON RARE DECAY. *Current Pos:* Robert McCormick fel, 84-88, asst prof, 88-93, ASSOC PROF PHYSICS, UNIV CHICAGO, 93- *Personal Data:* b Kowloon, Hong Kong, Dec 7, 55; m 93, Annie Wong; c Benny. *Educ:* Univ Calif, Los Angeles, BSc, 77; Yale Univ, PhD(physics), 83. *Mem:* Am Phys Soc. *Res:* Perform high energy physics experiments to investigate the fundamental question of charge parity violation in neutral Kaon decay. *Mailing Add:* Univ Chicago 5640 S Ellis Ave Chicago IL 60637

**WAHAB, JAMES HATTON,** MATHEMATICS. *Current Pos:* head dept, Univ SC, 68-73, dir undergrad studies math, 77-80, prof math, 68-84, VIS PROF MATH, UNIV SC, 84- *Personal Data:* b Bridgeton, NC, Aug 29, 20; m 47; c 2. *Educ:* Col William & Mary, BS, 40; Univ NC, AM, 50, PhD(math), 51. *Prof Exp:* Instr math & eng, Norfolk Div, Col William & Mary, 40-42 & 46-47, asst prof, 47-48; instr math, Univ NC, 50-51; from asst prof to assoc prof, Ga Inst Technol, 51-58; prof, La State Univ, 58-61, chmn dept, 60-61; prof, NC State Col, 61-63; prof & chmn dept, Univ NC, Charlotte, 63-68, actg acad dean, 64-68. *Mem:* Am Math Soc; Math Asn Am. *Res:* Irreducibility of legendre polynomials; algebra; statistics; numerical analysis. *Mailing Add:* 10902 Regent Circle Naples FL 33942

**WAHBA, ALBERT J,** BIOCHEMISTRY. *Current Pos:* PROF & CHMN, DEPT BIOCHEM, MED CTR, UNIV MISS, 77- *Personal Data:* b Alexandria, Egypt, Feb 27, 38; US citizen; m 65; c 3. *Educ:* Univ Calif, Berkeley, AB, 51; Univ Tex, MA, 54; Tufts Univ, PhD(biochem & pharamacol), 61. *Prof Exp:* Instr, Dept Biochem, Sch Med, NY Univ, 63, asst prof, 63-65, assoc prof, 66-69; prof & dir biochem, Lab Molecular Biol, Can, 70-77. *Concurrent Pos:* Jane Coffin Childs Fund med res fel, Dept Biochem, Sch Med, NY Univ, 62; vis scientist, Salk Inst Biol Studies, 66; Med Res Coun Assoc, Can, 70-77. *Mem:* Am Soc Biol Chemists; AAAS; Sigma Xi; Am Chem Soc; Am Soc Microbiol. *Res:* Nucleic acids and protein synthesis; molecular mechanisms and regulation during early embryonic development; transcriptional and translated control of gene expression during development of brine shrimp Artemia embryos; author or coauthor of over 70 publications. *Mailing Add:* Dept Biochem Med Ctr Univ Miss Jackson MS 39216-4505. *Fax:* 601-984-1501; *E-Mail:* wahba@fiona.umsmed.edu

**WAHBA, GRACE,** MATHEMATICAL & APPLIED STATISTICS. *Current Pos:* from asst prof to prof, 67-87, JOHN BASCOM PROF STATIST, UNIV WIS-MADISON, 87- *Personal Data:* b Washington, DC. *Educ:* Cornell Univ, BA, 56; Univ Md, College Park, MA, 62; Stanford Univ, PhD(math statist), 66. *Honors & Awards:* Parzen Prize Creativity Award, NSF; Neyman Lectr; Plenary Lectr, Soc Indust & Appl Math. *Prof Exp:* Res mathematician, Opers Res, Inc, 57-61; systs analyst, IBM Corp, 61-66; res assoc math statist, Stanford Univ, 66-67. *Concurrent Pos:* Vis prof, Oxford Univ, Weizmann Inst, Technion, Commonwealth Sci & Indust Res Orgn & Yale Univ. *Mem:* Fel Inst Math Statist; fel Am Statist Asn; Am Math Soc; Soc Indust & Appl Math; fel AAAS; fel Int Statist Inst; Am Meteor Soc. *Res:* Statistical model building; inverse problems; multivariate function estimation; numerical weather prediction and reanalysis; climate, risk factor estimation and biostatistical modeling; supervised machine learning. *Mailing Add:* Statist Univ Wis 1210 W Dayton St Madison WI 53706

**WAHL, A(RTHUR) J,** ELECTRICAL ENGINEERING. *Current Pos:* RETIRED. *Personal Data:* b Saxman, Kans, Feb 5, 20; m 50; c 2. *Educ:* Univ Kans, BS, 42; Princeton Univ, PhD(elec eng), 50. *Prof Exp:* Mem tech staff, Bell Tel Labs, 53-56, supvr semiconductor device develop, 56-83. *Mailing Add:* 1618 Meadowlark Rd Reading PA 19610

**WAHL, ARTHUR CHARLES,** NUCLEAR FISSION. *Current Pos:* assoc prof, 49-53, Farr prof radiochem, 53-83, EMER PROF CHEM, WASH UNIV, 83- *Personal Data:* b Des Moines, Iowa, Sept 8, 17; m 43, Mary McCauley; c Nancy (Miegel). *Educ:* Iowa State Univ, BS, 39; Univ Calif, PhD(chem), 42. *Honors & Awards:* Am Chem Soc Award, 66; Humboldt Award, 77. *Prof Exp:* Res assoc, Manhattan Proj, Univ Calif, 42-43, group leader, Los Alamos Sci Lab, 43-46. *Concurrent Pos:* Consult, Los Alamos Nat Lab, 50-93, guest scientist, 93-; NSF fel, 67. *Mem:* Am Chem Soc. *Res:* Nuclear-charge distribution in fission; rapid electron-transfer reactions. *Mailing Add:* 1550 Los Pueblos Los Alamos NM 87544

**WAHL, FLOYD MICHAEL,** GEOCHEMISTRY. *Current Pos:* EXEC DIR, GEOL SOC AM, 82- *Personal Data:* b Hebron, Ind, July 7, 31; m 53, Dorothy Daniel; c Timothy, David, Jeffrey & Kathryn. *Educ:* DePauw Univ, AB, 53; Univ Ill, MA, 57, PhD(mineral & geochem), 58. *Prof Exp:* Instr geol, Univ Ill, Urbana, 58-59, res asst prof, 59-60, from asst prof to assoc prof, 60-69; prof & chmn dept, Univ Fla, 69-73, prof geol, 70-82, dir div phys sci & math, 71-73, assoc dean, grad sch & assoc dir res, 73-79 & 80-81, actg dean grad study & res, 79-80. *Mem:* Fel Geol Soc Am; Mineral Soc Am; Clay Minerals Soc; Am Inst Prof Geologists; Am Geophys Union; Soc Econ Paleont & Mineral. *Res:* Clay mineralogy and sedimentary geochemistry; development of mineral resources; chemical alteration and those factors that lead to and control element concentration; phase changes in minerals at elevated temperatures. *Mailing Add:* Geol Soc Am PO Box 9140 Boulder CO 80301

**WAHL, GEORGE HENRY, JR,** STRUCTURAL CHEMISTRY, CHEMICAL SAFETY. *Current Pos:* from asst prof to assoc prof, 64-75, PROF ORG CHEM, NC STATE UNIV, 75- *Personal Data:* b New York, NY, Sept 17, 36; m 58; c 3. *Educ:* Fordham Univ, BS, 58; NY Univ, MS, 61, PhD(org chem), 63. *Honors & Awards:* Sigma Xi Res Award, 74. *Prof Exp:* Res chemist, Pittsburgh Plate Glass Chem Co, Ohio, 58-59; NIH res fel org chem, Cornell Univ, 63-64. *Concurrent Pos:* Guest prof, Swiss Fed Inst, Zurich, 73-74; consult, Environ Protection Agency, 78- *Mem:* Am Chem Soc. *Res:* Organic stereochemistry; nuclear magnetic resonance spectroscopy; mass spectrometry; synthesis of unusual structures for physical investigation; synthesis and structure of adamantane and biphenyl derivatives. *Mailing Add:* Dept Chem NC State Univ Box 8204 Raleigh NC 27695-8204. *Fax:* 919-515-5079; *E-Mail:* george_wahl@ncsu.edu

**WAHL, JONATHAN MICHAEL,** MATHEMATICS. *Current Pos:* from asst prof to assoc prof, 73-81, PROF MATH, UNIV NC, CHAPEL HILL, 81- *Personal Data:* b Washington, DC, Jan 29, 45; m 70; c 1. *Educ:* Yale Univ, BS & MA, 65; Harvard Univ, PhD(math), 71. *Prof Exp:* Instr math, Univ Calif, Berkeley, 70-72; vis, Inst Advan Study, Princeton Univ, 72-73, 79. *Concurrent Pos:* NSF res grant, 71- *Mem:* Am Math Soc. *Res:* Singularities; deformation theory; algebraic geometry. *Mailing Add:* Dept Math Univ NC Chapel Hill NC 27599-3250

**WAHL, PATRICIA WALKER,** BIOSTATISTICS. *Current Pos:* head programmer, Univ Wash, 64-66, instr biostatist, 71-73, asst prof, 74-85, PROF BIOSTATIST, UNIV WASH, 85-, ASSOC DEAN, SCH PUB HEALTH, 85- *Personal Data:* b La Grande, Ore, Dec 6, 38; m 63; c 1. *Educ:* San Jose State Univ, BA, 60; Univ Wash, PhD(biostatist), 71. *Prof Exp:* Res analyst comput programming, Lockheed Missiles, Lockheed Aircraft Corp, 60-62; systs analyst, Control Data Corp, 63-64. *Mem:* Am Statist Asn; Biomet Soc. *Res:* Use of regression analysis and other multivariate statistical techniques for exploratory data analysis; effect on classification by discriminant analysis when model assumptions fail. *Mailing Add:* Dept Biostatist Box 35-7230 Univ Wash Seattle WA 98195

**WAHL, SHARON KNUDSON,** IMMUNOLOGY. *Current Pos:* fel cellular immunol, Nat Inst Dent Res, 72-74, staff fel humoral immunity, 74-75, sr staff fel humoral immunity, 75-76, res microbiologist, 76-83, CHIEF, CELLULAR IMMUNOL, NAT INST DENT RES, 83- *Personal Data:* b Mt Vernon, Wash, Mar 16, 45; m 71, Larry M; c Allison M & Christopher L. *Educ:* Pac Lutheran Univ, BS, 67; Univ Wash, PhD(biol struct), 71. *Honors & Awards:* NIH Director's Award, 85; Howard & Martha Holley Res Prize Rheumatol, 90. *Prof Exp:* Fel path, Sch Med, Univ Wash, 71-72. *Concurrent Pos:* Preceptor, PRAT fel; lectr, grad course, FAES; vis prof, Cleveland Clin, 85; mem, Subcomt Joint Adv-Comt Clin Hyperbaric Med Res. *Mem:* Am Asn Immunol; Am Fedn Clin Res; AAAS; Wound Healing Soc; Soc Leukocyte Biol; Inflammation Res Asn. *Res:* Mechanisms of activation and characterization of T and B lymphocyte participation in cellular immune reactions and effect of immunosuppressive agents on these responses; influence of immune system on connective tissue metabolism; monocyte phenotype and function in inflammation and disease; immunomodulation by transforming growth factor beta; polypeptide growth factors. *Mailing Add:* Nat Inst Dent Res Bldg 30 Convent Dr MSC 4352 Bethesda MD 20892-4352. *Fax:* 301-402-1064

**WAHL, WERNER HENRY,** NUCLEAR CHEMISTRY, RADIOCHEMISTRY. *Current Pos:* VPRES SCI & TECHNOL, VENTURE/GROWTH FUNDING LTD, DETROIT, MICH, 89- *Personal Data:* b Buffalo, NY, Oct 1, 30; m 51; c 2. *Educ:* Univ Buffalo, BA, 54; Purdue Univ, MS, 56, PhD(phys inorg chem), 57. *Prof Exp:* Chem operator, Pathfinder Chem Corp, 49; asst, Linde Co Div, Union Carbide Co, 51-53; asst, Durez Plastics, Inc, 53; asst chem, Purdue Univ, 54-57; res chemist, Union Carbide Nuclear Corp, 57-61, group leader, 61-65, asst mgr res, 65-66, dir radiopharmaceut, Neisler Labs, Inc, Union Carbide Corp, NY, 66-69; dir opers, Mallinckrodt/Nuclear, Mo, 69-70; vpres & gen mgr, Amersham-Searle Corp, Ill, 70, exec vpres, 71, pres, 71-75; vpres new bus develop, Searle Diag, Inc, 75-78; pres, Nuclear Diagnostics, Inc, 78-88. *Concurrent Pos:* Asst chem, Univ Buffalo, 53. *Mem:* Fel AAAS; Am Chem Soc; Am Asn Physicists Med; Clin Radio Assay Soc; fel Am Inst Chem. *Mailing Add:* 1911 Wakerobin Dr Bloomfield Hills MI 48302-1285

**WAHLBECK, PHILLIP GLENN,** HIGH TEMPERATURE CHEMISTRY & SUPERCONDUCTIVITY, SURFACE CHEMISTRY. *Current Pos:* chmn dept, 72-78, PROF CHEM, WICHITA STATE UNIV, 72-; ASSOC, NAT INST AVIATION RES, 88- *Personal Data:* b Kankakee, Ill, Mar 29, 33; m 56, Donna G Frost; c Debra (Cappella), Paul & Beth (Rakow). *Educ:* Univ Ill, BS, 54, PhD(chem), 58. *Prof Exp:* Asst chem, Univ Ill, 54-58; res assoc, Univ Kans, 58-60; from instr to assoc prof, Ill Inst Technol, 60-72. *Concurrent Pos:* Vis prof, Tech Univ Norway, 70, 78 & 82; vis scientist, Los Alamos Nat Lab, 91- *Mem:* Am Sci Affil; Metall Soc; Am Chem Soc; Mat Res Soc. *Res:* Molecular beams; thermodynamics at high temperatures; transition metal hydrides, oxides, selenides and tellurides; vapor pressure measurements; effusion of gases; gas-surface interactions adsorption phenomena; mean residence times; surface diffusion; spatial distributions of restituted molecules; high temperature superconductors. *Mailing Add:* Dept Chem Wichita State Univ Wichita KS 67260-0051. *Fax:* 316-978-3431; *E-Mail:* pgwahlbe@ twsuvm.uc.twsu.edu

**WAHLE, RICHARD ANDREAS,** BEHAVIORAL ECOLOGY, MARINE ECOLOGY. *Current Pos:* VIS SCIENTISTS & TEACHER ANIMAL BEHAV & GEN ZOOL, UNIV RI, 92- *Personal Data:* m 83, Carol Lariviere; c Thomas & Ryan. *Educ:* Univ NH, BS, 77; San Francisco State Univ, MS, 82; Univ Maine, PhD(zool), 90. *Prof Exp:* Res assoc, Brown Univ, 90-92. *Concurrent Pos:* Consult, Narragansett Bay Proj, 90-91 & US Nat Park Serv, 91-93; lectr zool, Univ RI, 91. *Mem:* Ecol Soc Am; AAAS; Crustacean Soc. *Res:* Processes affecting the fate of cohorts in marine populations before and after larval settlement. *Mailing Add:* Bigelow Lab Ocean Sci McKown Point West Boothbay Harbor ME 04575. *Fax:* 401-792-4256; *E-Mail:* rwahle@ uriacc.uri.edu

**WAHLERT, JOHN HOWARD,** VERTEBRATE PALEONTOLOGY. *Current Pos:* Curatorial asst vert paleont, 72-77, assoc, 76-81, RES ASSOC, DEPT VERT PALEONT, AM MUS NATURAL HIST, 81- *Personal Data:* b New York, NY, May 12, 43; m 69, Katherine B Herrlich; c Emily, Sarah & Colin. *Educ:* Amherst Col, BA, 65; Harvard Univ, MA, 66, PhD(geol), 72. *Concurrent Pos:* Vis asst prof biol, Franklin & Marshall Col, 77-78, cur mammal, North Mus, 78-81; asst prof biol, Millersville State Col, 80-81; asst prof biol, Baruch Col, 81-86, prof, 89; mem doctoral fac, Grad Sch & Univ Ctrs Prog Biol, City Univ New York, 87- *Mem:* Soc Vert Paleont; Am Soc Mammal. *Res:* Cenozoic rodents and their anatomy, taxonomy and phylogeny. *Mailing Add:* Dept Vert Paleont Am Mus Natural Hist New York NY 10024. *E-Mail:* wahlert@amnh.org

**WAHLGREN, MORRIS A,** ENVIRONMENTAL CHEMISTRY. *Current Pos:* asst chemist, Chem Div, Argonne Nat Lab, 61-66, assoc chemist, 66-72, chemist, Radiol & Environ Res Div, 72-80, chemist, Chem Tech Div, 80-87, CHEMIST, ENVIRON, SAFETY & HEALTH DIV, ARGONNE NAT LAB, 87- *Personal Data:* b Wildrose, NDak, May 31, 29; m 55; c 3. *Educ:* Jamestown Col, BS, 51; Univ Mich, PhD(chem), 61. *Prof Exp:* Radiochemist, Atomic Energy Div, Phillips Petrol Co, Idaho, 53-56. *Mem:* AAAS; Am Chem Soc; fel Am Inst Chemists. *Res:* Nuclear and analytical chemistry; radiochemical separations; chemical limnology; behavior of artificial radionuclides in the Great Lakes; radiochemical bioassay. *Mailing Add:* 1278 Fellows St St Charles IL 60174

**WAHLIG, MICHAEL ALEXANDER,** ENERGY CONVERSION. *Current Pos:* PHYS SCIENTIST, WEAPONS RES DIV, OAKLAND OPERS OFF, DEPT ENERGY, 92- *Personal Data:* b New York, NY, Oct 21, 34; m 56, Joyce McKenna; c Beverly, Kathleen, Wendy & Ronald. *Educ:* Manhattan Col, BS, 55; Mass Inst Technol, PhD(physics), 62. *Prof Exp:* Res assoc physics, Mass Inst Technol, 62-66; res staff physics, Lawrence Berkeley Lab, Univ Calif, Berkeley, 66-72, mem res staff energy conversion & energy conserv, Energy & Environ Div, 72-91. *Res:* Research, development and analysis of conversion and use of thermal energy for providing cooling and heating; energy conservation in building energy systems; program management and oversight. *Mailing Add:* Dept Energy Oakland Opers Off Lawrence Livermore Nat Lab PO Box 808 Livermore CA 94550. *E-Mail:* wahlig2@llnl.gov

**WAHLS, HARVEY E(DWARD),** FOUNDATION ENGINEERING, SOIL MECHANICS. *Current Pos:* from asst prof to assoc prof, 60-69, PROF CIVIL ENG, NC STATE UNIV, 69-, ASSOC HEAD DEPT, 84- *Personal Data:* b Evanston, Ill, Aug 8, 31; m 60, Margaret Waggoner; c Richard & Nancy. *Educ:* Northwestern Univ, BS, 54, MS, 55, PhD(civil eng), 61. *Prof Exp:* From instr to asst prof civil eng, Worcester Polytech Inst, 55-60. *Concurrent Pos:* Instr, Northwestern Univ, 57-59; consult, Transp Res Bd, 70-71, 80-83 & 88-90; chmn, Am Soc Civil Engrs, Geotech Eng Div, 82-83. *Mem:* Am Soc Civil Engrs; Am Soc Testing & Mat; Am Soc Eng Educ; Int Soc Soil Mech & Found Engrs (secy, 85-); Transp Res Bd; Asn Soil & Found Engrs. *Res:* Consolidation theory for cohesive soils; settlement analysis; compaction process and the behavior of compacted soils; soil dynamics; tolerable settlement of structures. *Mailing Add:* Dept Civil Eng NC State Univ Box 7908 Raleigh NC 27695-7908. *Fax:* 919-515-7908; *E-Mail:* wahls@ eos.ncsu.edu

**WAHLSTROM, ERNEST E,** GEOLOGY. *Current Pos:* RETIRED. *Personal Data:* b Boulder, Co, Dec 30, 09. *Educ:* Univ Colo, BS, 31; Harvard Univ, MS, 36, PhD, 39. *Prof Exp:* Prof geol, Univ Colo, 36-78. *Mem:* Geol Soc Am; Mineral Soc Am; Soc Econ Geologists; Am Inst Petrol Geologists. *Mailing Add:* 2522 174th Ave NE Redmond WA 98052

**WAHLSTROM, LAWRENCE F,** MATHEMATICS. *Current Pos:* PROF MATH & CHMN DEPT, UNIV WIS-EAU CLAIRE, 48- *Personal Data:* b Aurora, Wis, Feb 4, 15; m 38; c 2. *Educ:* Lawrence Col, BA, 36; Univ Wis, MA, 37, PhD(math educ), 50. *Prof Exp:* Pub sch teacher, Ill, 37-41, chmn dept math, jr high sch, 41-45; chmn dept, Elgin Acad, 45-47; asst, Univ Wis, 47-48. *Concurrent Pos:* NSF fac sci grant, 57-58. *Mem:* Math Asn Am. *Res:* Geometry. *Mailing Add:* 110 Skyline Dr Eau Claire WI 54703-5920

**WAHLSTROM, RICHARD CARL,** ANIMAL SCIENCE. *Current Pos:* assoc prof animal husb, 52-59, head dept, 60-67, PROF ANIMAL HUSB, SDAK STATE UNIV, 59- *Personal Data:* b Craig, Nebr, Feb 13, 23; m 47; c 3. *Educ:* Univ Nebr, BS, 48; Univ Ill, MS, 50, PhD(animal nutrit), 52. *Honors & Awards:* Animal Mgt Award, Am Soc Animal Sci, 76. *Prof Exp:* Asst animal husb, Univ Ill, 48-51; res assoc nutrit, Merck Inst Therapeut Res, 51-52. *Concurrent Pos:* Vis prof, Univ Nottingham & Nat Inst Res, Dairying, Eng, 74-75. *Mem:* Am Soc Animal Sci; Am Inst Nutrit. *Res:* Swine nutrition; antibiotics; selenium poisoning; protein levels and amino acid requirements; high protein cereals; mineral nutrition; by-product feeds. *Mailing Add:* 1817 Garden Sq Brookings SD 57006

**WAHNSIEDLER, WALTER EDWARD,** CHEMICAL PHYSICS. *Current Pos:* TECH SPECIALIST, CHEM SYST DIV, ALUMINUM CO AM, 75- *Personal Data:* b Ind, Jan 23, 47; m 69, Sandra Oldham; c Brooke. *Educ:* Purdue Univ, BS, 67, PhD(chem physics), 75. *Prof Exp:* Vis scholar mat sci, Northwestern Univ, 74. *Mem:* Am Chem Soc; Sigma Xi; Inst Elec & Electronics Engrs. *Res:* Theoretical solid state studies; numerical modelling of chemical processes; properties of oxides; aluminum smelting; environmental impact of industry; fluid state modeling. *Mailing Add:* 16 Oakwood Terr Oakmont PA 15139-1016. *Fax:* 412-337-4063; *E-Mail:* walt@ convex_csd.al.alcoa.com

**WAHR, JOHN CANNON,** PHYSICS. *Current Pos:* RETIRED. *Personal Data:* b Ann Arbor, Mich, Apr 2, 26; m 49; c 2. *Educ:* Univ Mich, BSE, 48, MS, 49, PhD(physics), 53. *Prof Exp:* Asst, Univ Mich, 48-49; physicist, Cent Res, Dow Chem Co, 53-80. *Mem:* AAAS; Am Phys Soc; Optical Soc Am. *Res:* Quantum electronics; holography; atomic and molecular physics; surface physics. *Mailing Add:* 1570 Blue Sage Ct Boulder CO 80303

**WAHRHAFTIG, AUSTIN LEVY,** MASS SPECTROMETRY. *Current Pos:* from asst prof to prof, 47-87, EMER PROF CHEM, UNIV UTAH, 87- *Personal Data:* b Sacramento, Calif, May 5, 17; m 57. *Educ:* Univ Calif, AB, 38; Calif Inst Technol, PhD(phys chem), 41. *Prof Exp:* Fel, Calif Inst Technol, 41-45; res chemist, Dr W E Williams, 45-46; univ fel, Ohio State Univ, 46-47. *Concurrent Pos:* Vis prof, Latrobe Univ, Australia, 72 & 80. *Mem:* AAAS; Am Chem Soc; Am Phys Soc; Am Soc Mass Spectrometry. *Res:* Molecular spectra; mass spectrometry; kinetics of gas-phase ion reactions; dense (supercritical) gas chromatography. *Mailing Add:* 2239 Logan Ave Salt Lake City UT 84108-2714

**WAHRHAFTIG, CLYDE (ADOLPH),** geology; deceased, see previous edition for last biography

**WAI, CHIEN MOO,** GEOCHEMISTRY, ENVIRONMENTAL CHEMISTRY. *Current Pos:* from asst prof to assoc prof chem & geol, 69-78, PROF CHEM, UNIV IDAHO, 78- *Personal Data:* b China, Aug 8, 37; m 65; c 2. *Educ:* Nat Taiwan Univ, BS, 60; Univ Calif, Irvine, PhD(chem), 67. *Prof Exp:* Fel, Univ Calif, Los Angeles, 66-69. *Concurrent Pos:* Vis assoc prof, Inst Geophys & Planetary Physics, Univ Calif, Los Angeles, 82-83; scientist in residence, Argonne Nat Lab, 82-83. *Mem:* AAAS; Am Chem Soc; Geochem Soc. *Res:* Chemical effects of nuclear transformation; origin of meteorites; heavy metal pollution. *Mailing Add:* Dept Chem Univ Idaho Moscow ID 83844-2343

**WAI, WING-KIN,** nuclear magnetic resonance, electronics, for more information see previous edition

**WAIBEL, PAUL EDWARD,** POULTRY NUTRITION. *Current Pos:* res assoc, 54-55, from asst prof to assoc prof, 55-64, PROF POULTRY NUTRIT, UNIV MINN, ST PAUL, 64- *Personal Data:* b Hawthorne, NJ, June 22, 27; m 71; c 3. *Educ:* Rutgers Univ, BS, 48; Univ Wis, MS, 51, PhD(poultry nutrit, biochem), 53. *Honors & Awards:* Nat Turkey Fedn Res Award; Am Feed Manufacturers Poultry Nutrit Res Award. *Prof Exp:* Teaching asst poultry husb, Univ Wis, 49-53; res assoc poultry nutrit, Cornell Univ, 53-54. *Mem:* Am Inst Nutrit; Poultry Sci Asn; NY Acad Sci. *Res:* Nutrition of turkeys. *Mailing Add:* Dept Animal Sci 122 Peters Hall Univ Minn 1404 Gortner Ave St Paul MN 55108-6160. *Fax:* 612-625-5789

**WAID, MARGARET COWSAR,** APPLIED MATHEMATICS. *Current Pos:* SUPVR ELECTRO-MECH RES, HALLIBURTON ENERGY SERV, 90- *Personal Data:* b Baton Rouge, La, Feb 21, 41; m 63; c 2. *Educ:* La State Univ, Baton Rouge, BS, 61, MS, 63; Tex Tech Univ, PhD(math), 71. *Prof Exp:* Asst prof math, DC Teachers Col, 71-72; assoc prof, Univ Del, 72-81; sr develop engr, Schlumberger Well Serv, 81; supvr, s/w & anal, NL Sperry Sun, 84, mgr prod serv, 84-87; mgt consult, Waid Consult Serv, 87-90. *Concurrent Pos:* Vis assoc prof math, Univ Tex, 79-80. *Mem:* Soc Indust & Appl Math; Soc Petrol Engrs; Soc Prof Well Log Analysts; Nat Asn Corrosion Engrs. *Res:* Partial differential equations, including applications to fluid flow through porous media analysis; applications to well log analysis, especially pressure measurements and production logging. *Mailing Add:* 3103 Hollow Creek Ct Houston TX 77082-3514

**WAID, REX A(DNEY),** ELECTRICAL ENGINEERING. *Current Pos:* asst prof, 66-76, PROF ELEC ENG, UNIV MO, COLUMBIA, 76- *Personal Data:* b Dardanelle, Ark, Jan 14, 33; m 59; c 3. *Educ:* William Jewell Col, BA, 54; Univ Mo-Columbia, BS, 58, MS, 59; Univ Wis-Madison, PhD(elec eng), 68. *Prof Exp:* From instr to asst prof elec eng, Univ Mo, Columbia, 59-63; asst prof, Univ Wis-Madison, 65-66. *Concurrent Pos:* Consult, Univ Mo Network Analyzer, 62-63. *Mem:* Inst Elec & Electronics Engrs; Am Soc Eng Educ; Simulation Coun. *Res:* Pattern recognition; data acquisition and processing; computer design and development. *Mailing Add:* 2304 Ridgefield Rd Columbia MO 65203

**WAID, TED HENRY,** CHEMICAL ENGINEERING, ORGANIC CHEMISTRY. *Current Pos:* PRES, CHEMOR INC, 65- *Personal Data:* b Warsaw, Poland, Mar 28, 25; Can citizen; m 58, Andree Siksou; c Philip & Patrick. *Educ:* Univ Caen, BSc, 50, BEng, 51; McGill Univ, PhD(org chem), 57. *Prof Exp:* Chemist, Sherwin-Williams Co, Can, 52-53; sr res chemist, Monsanto Can Ltd, 57-60, res group leader surface finishes, 60-64, develop specialist, 64-65. *Concurrent Pos:* Mem Can Govt Specifications Bd, 63- *Mem:* Am Chem Soc; Sigma Xi; Am Concrete Inst. *Res:* Syntheses of nitrogen containing steroids, chloromethylated aromatic hydrocarbons, aromatic polyamides and sulphur containing heterocyclic compounds; chemical coatings and adhesives; polymer chemistry. *Mailing Add:* 6160 Bernard Mergler Cr Montreal PQ H3X 4A5 Can. *Fax:* 514-935-4870

**WAIDELICH, D(ONALD) L(ONG),** ELECTROMAGNETIC FIELDS. *Current Pos:* from instr to prof, Univ Mo, Columbia, 38-85, assoc dir eng exp sta, 54-58, chmn dept, 60-61, EMER PROF ELEC ENG, UNIV MO, COLUMBIA, 85- *Personal Data:* b Allentown, Pa, May 3, 15; m 39, Florence Bennethum; c Ann (Ross). *Educ:* Lehigh Univ, BS, 36, MS, 38; Iowa State Univ, PhD(elec eng), 46. *Honors & Awards:* Res Award, Sigma Xi, 77; Excellence Award, Inst Elec & Electronics Engrs, 85. *Prof Exp:* Asst, Lehigh Univ, 36-38. *Concurrent Pos:* Elec engr, US Naval Ord Lab, 44-45; Fulbright grant & vis prof, Univ Cairo, 51-52; Fulbright res grant, Univ Australia, 61-62; vis prof, Univ NSW, 61-62; consult, USN Electronics Lab, 49-52, UNESCO, Egypt, 52, Argonne Nat Lab, 53-56, 65-72, Bendix Aviation Corp, 57, Int Tel & Tel Co Labs, 58-59, Midwest Res Inst, 60-61, Goddard Space Flight Ctr, NASA, 62-67, US Naval Underwater Systs Ctr, 71, Hughes Aircraft Co, 72-88 & McDonnell Douglas Corp, 83-85. *Mem:* Am Soc Eng Educ; Nat Soc Prof Engrs; fel Inst Elec & Electronics Engrs; Am Soc Nondestructive Testing; Electrostatic Soc Am. *Res:* Electromagnetic fields; nondestructive testing; pulsed electromagnetic waves in metals and dielectrics; antennae for communication satellites; mathematical transforms. *Mailing Add:* Dept Elec Engr Univ Mo 333 West Eng Bldg Columbia MO 65211

**WAIFE, SHOLOM OMI,** INTERNAL MEDICINE, MEDICAL EDUCATION. *Current Pos:* RETIRED. *Personal Data:* b New York, NY, Feb 20, 19; m 42; c 2. *Educ:* Johns Hopkins Univ, AB, 40; NY Univ, MD, 43; Am Bd Internal Med, dipl, 51. *Prof Exp:* Res assoc med, Sch Med, Yale Univ, 45; resen resident physician, Long Island Col Hosp, 45-46; asst med, Med Sch, Johns Hopkins Univ, 46-48; instr, Sch Med, Univ Pa, 48-52; assoc, Sch Med, Ind Univ, Indianapolis, 52-60, asst prof, 60-68, assoc prof med, 68-81; dir med serv div, Res Lab, Eli Lilly & Co, 64-81. *Concurrent Pos:* Ed-in-chief, Am J Clin Nutrit, 52-62; head med educ dept, Eli Lilly & Co, 52-64; co-ed, Perspectives Biol & Med, 58-64. *Mem:* Am Diabetes Asn; Am Med Writers' Asn; fel Am Col Physicians; Am Fedn Clin Res. *Res:* Metabolism; diabetes; obesity; vitamins. *Mailing Add:* Seaview F 9150 SE Riverfront Terr Tequesta FL 33469

**WAILES, JOHN LEONARD,** PHARMACY. *Current Pos:* RETIRED. *Personal Data:* b Loveland, Colo, Oct 9, 23; m 47; c 3. *Educ:* Univ Colo, BS, 47, MS, 50, PhD(pharm), 54. *Prof Exp:* Chemist, US Food & Drug Admin, 47-48; pharmacist, Park-Hill Drug Co, Colo, 48-50; instr pharm, Univ Colo, 50-54; from asst prof to prof pharm, Univ Mont, 43-85. *Concurrent Pos:* USPHS grant, 59; with Merck Sharp & Dohme Div, Merck & Co, Colo, 51-54. *Mem:* Am Pharmaceut Asn; Asn Cols Pharm. *Res:* Respiration of mold and yeast in the presence and absence of inhibitors and antagonists using the Warburg apparatus; preservation of pharmaceutical products; synergism and antagonism of various preservatives and their possible inactivation; complexing of macromolecules. *Mailing Add:* 1525 34th St Missoula MT 59801

**WAINBERG, MARK ARNOLD,** AIDS, CANCER. *Current Pos:* STAFF INVESTR AIDS RES, LADY DAVIS INST MED RES, JEWISH GEN HOSP, MONTREAL, 74-; PROF MED, MCGILL UNIV. *Personal Data:* b Montreal, Que, Apr 21, 45; m 69; c 2. *Educ:* McGill Univ, BSc, 66; Columbia Univ, PhD(microbiol), 72. *Prof Exp:* Lectr immunol, Hebrew Univ-Hadassah Med Sch, 72-74. *Concurrent Pos:* Europ Molecular Biol Orgn res fel, 72-74; Que Med Res Coun res scholar, 75-; Nat Cancer Inst Can res grant, 75-; researcher, Dept Microbiol & Immunol, Univ Montreal, 75- *Mem:* Am Soc Microbiol; Sigma Xi; Can Soc Immunol; NY Acad Sci; Can Oncol Soc. *Res:* Virus-induced immune suppression; transmission and growth of HIV virus in aquired immune deficiency syndrome (AIDS); viral gene expression at different stages of retrovirus-induced tumor growth. *Mailing Add:* Jewish Gen Hosp McGill Univ 3755 Cote Ste Catherine Rd Montreal PQ H3T 1E2 Can. *Fax:* 514-340-7502

**WAINE, MARTIN,** PHYSICS. *Current Pos:* dir eng, 79-80, vpres, 81-82, PRES, GENERAL CLUTCH CORP, 82- *Personal Data:* b Berlin, Ger, Apr 8, 33; US citizen; m 63; c 2. *Educ:* Columbia Univ, BS, 58; Yale Univ, MS, 59, PhD(physics), 65. *Prof Exp:* Asst prof physics, Mt Holyoke Col, 64-70; prin engr, MRC Corp, Md, 71-72; chief engr, Diamondex Enterprises Inc, 72-74; vpres mfg, Evershield Prod Inc, 74-75; prin engr, MRC Corp, 75-79. *Res:* Dynamic nuclear orientation; nuclear magnetic resonance; instrumentation and control theory. *Mailing Add:* Gen Clutch Corp 200 Harvard Ave Stamford CT 06902

**WAINER, ARTHUR,** BIOCHEMISTRY. *Current Pos:* PROF CHEM, EDINBORO STATE COL, 70-, CHMN DEPT, 80- *Personal Data:* b Cincinnati, Ohio, Jan 28, 38; m 57; c 3. *Educ:* Univ Miami, BS, 57; Univ Fla, PhD(biochem), 61. *Prof Exp:* Instr biochem, Univ Fla, 61-62; from instr to assoc prof, Bowman Gray Sch Med, 62-70. *Mem:* AAAS; Am Chem Soc; Am Soc Biol Chemists; Am Asn Clin Chemists. *Res:* Sulfur amino acid metabolism, ion exchange column chromatography. *Mailing Add:* Dept Biol & Health Servs Edinboro Univ Edinboro PA 16444-0001

**WAINERDI, RICHARD E(LLIOTT),** NUCLEAR ACTIVATION ANALYSIS. *Current Pos:* PRES, TEX MED CTR, 84- *Personal Data:* b New York, NY, Nov 27, 31; m 56; c 2. *Educ:* Univ Okla, BS, 52; Pa State Univ, MS, 55, PhD, 58. *Hon Degrees:* LLD, St Thomas Univ, 91. *Honors & Awards:* George Henesy Medal, 77. *Prof Exp:* Jr exploitation engr, Shell Oil Co, 52; asst petrol eng, Pa State Univ, 53-55; coordr nuclear activities, Dresser Industs, Inc, 56-57; assoc prof petrol & nuclear eng, Tex A&M Univ, 57-61, supvr training reactor facil & radiol safety off, 57-58, head nuclear sci ctr, Eng Exp Sta, 57-59, head activation anal res lab, 58-77, asst to dean eng, 59-62, prof chem eng, 61-77, assoc dean eng, 62-72, assoc vpres acad affairs, 72-77; sr vpres & dir spec proj, 3D/Int, Inc, 77-82; pres, Gulf Res & Develop Co, 82-84. *Mem:* Am Nuclear Soc; Am Chem Soc; Soc Petrol Engrs. *Res:* Activation analysis and isotope utilization. *Mailing Add:* 406 Jesse Jones Library Tex Med Ctr Houston TX 77030-5382

**WAINFAN, ELSIE,** BIOCHEMISTRY. *Current Pos:* assoc investr, 68-80, INVESTR, NY BLOOD CTR, 80-; ASSOC SCIENTIST, SLOAN-KETTERING INST CANCER RES, 77- *Personal Data:* b New York, NY, Aug 2, 26; m 47; c 2. *Educ:* City Col New York, BS, 47; Univ Southern Calif, PhD(biochem), 54. *Prof Exp:* Res technician, NY Psychiat Inst, 47-49; USPHS fel, Med Sch, Univ Ore, 55-56; res assoc biochem, Cornell Univ, 56-59; res assoc, Col Physicians & Surgeons, Columbia Univ, 59-67; asst prof, Univ Southern Calif, 67-68. *Mem:* Am Chem Soc; Am Soc Biol Chemists; Am Soc Microbiologists; Am Asn Cancer Res. *Res:* Carcinogenesis, nucleic acids, enzymes; metabolic inhibitors. *Mailing Add:* 8-10 119th St College Point NY 11356-1032

**WAINGER, STEPHEN,** HARMONIC ANALYSIS. *Current Pos:* PROF MATH, UNIV WIS, 67- *Educ:* Univ Chicago, PhD(math), 61. *Mailing Add:* Dept Math Univ Wis 430 Lincoln Dr Madison WI 53706-1313

**WAINWRIGHT, JOHN,** APPLIED MATHEMATICS. *Current Pos:* From asst prof to assoc prof, 53-80, PROF MATH, UNIV WATERLOO, 81- *Personal Data:* b Sheffield, Eng, Jan 23, 43. *Educ:* Univ SAfrica, PhD(math), 67. *Mem:* Am Math Soc; Soc Indust & Appl Math. *Mailing Add:* Dept Math Univ Waterloo Waterloo ON N2L 3G1 Can

**WAINWRIGHT, LILLIAN K (SCHNEIDER),** GENETICS. *Current Pos:* RETIRED. *Personal Data:* b Brooklyn, NY, June 30, 23; m 52; c 2. *Educ:* Brooklyn Col, BA, 43; Columbia Univ, MA, 51, PhD(zool), 56. *Prof Exp:* Res asst zool, Columbia Univ, 43-52; from asst prof to prof, Mt St Vincent Univ, 57-70, emer prof biol, 70-88, chmn dept, 79-88. *Mem:* Genetics Soc Am; Can Soc Cell Biol; Sigma Xi; Can Fedn Biol Soc. *Res:* Organ cultures as models of tissues in vivo; control of the diurnal cycle of NAT activity in the chick pineal gland. *Mailing Add:* Torrington Dr Halifax NS B3M 1Y5 Can

**WAINWRIGHT, RAY M,** ELECTRICAL ENGINEERING. *Current Pos:* STAFF ELEC ENGR, STEARNS ROGER , 74- *Personal Data:* b Deep River, Iowa, July 24, 13; m 52; c 3. *Educ:* Mont State Univ, BSEE, 36; Univ Ill, MSEE, 49. *Prof Exp:* Asst elec engr, Mont Power Co, 36-38; elec engr, Mont-Dakota Utilities Co, 38-42, res engr, 45-46; res engr, US Signal Corps, 42-45; from asst prof to assoc prof elec eng, Univ Ill, 46-56; dir eng, Good-All Elec Mfg Co, 56-61; mgr res, Capacitor Div, TRW, Inc, 61-63; prof elec eng, Colo State Univ, 63-66; prof elec eng & coordr continuing educ, Univ Denver, 66-74. *Mem:* Nat Asn Corrosion Engrs; sr mem Inst Elec & Electronics Engrs. *Res:* Cathodic protection; reliability engineering; engineering economy. *Mailing Add:* United Engrs & Constructors PO Box 5888 Denver CO 80217

**WAINWRIGHT, STANLEY D,** NEUROCHEMISTRY, BIOLOGICAL CLOCKS. *Current Pos:* RETIRED. *Personal Data:* b Hull, Eng, Apr 15, 27; Can citizen; m 52, Lillian; c David S & Peter F. *Educ:* Cambridge Univ, BA, 47; Univ London, PhD(biochem), 50. *Prof Exp:* Brit Med Res Coun exchange scholar biochem, Physiol Microbiol Serv, Pasteur Inst, Paris, 50-51; res assoc microbial genetics, Columbia Univ, 51-52; Nat Res Coun Can & Atomic Energy Can, Ltd fel, Biol Div, Atomic Energy Can, Ltd, 52-55; res assoc microbial physiol, Yale Univ, 55-56; from res asst prof & Med Res Coun assoc biochem to res assoc prof & Med Res Coun assoc, Dalhousie Univ, 56-64, prof biochem, 65-92. *Concurrent Pos:* Career investr, Med Res Coun, 65- *Mem:* AAAS; Can Biochem Soc. *Res:* Biochemical neuroendocrinology of the developing chick pineal gland. *Mailing Add:* Dept Biochem Fac Med Dalhousie Univ Halifax NS B3H 3J5 Can

**WAINWRIGHT, STEPHEN ANDREW,** BIOMECHANICS. *Current Pos:* from assoc prof tp prof zool, 76-85, JAMES B DUKE PROF ZOOL, DUKE UNIV, 85-; ADJ PROF, SCH DESIGN, NC STATE UNIV, 83- *Personal Data:* b Indianapolis, Ind, Oct 9, 31; m 56; c 4. *Educ:* Duke Univ, BS, 53; Univ Cambridge, BA, 58, MA, 63; Univ Calif, Berkeley, PhD(zool), 62. *Prof Exp:* NSF fel med physics, Karolinska Inst, Sweden, 62-63; NSF fel biol, Woods Hole Oceanog Inst, 63-64. *Mem:* Soc Exp Biol UK; Marine Biol Asn UK; Sigma Xi; Am Soc Biomech (pres), 81); Am Soc Zoologists (pres), 88). *Res:* Functional morphology and mechanics of supportive systems of animals and plants from the macromolecular through the organism levels of organization. *Mailing Add:* Dept Zool Duke Univ Durham NC 27706

**WAINWRIGHT, THOMAS EVERETT,** PHYSICS. *Current Pos:* STAFF PHYSICIST, LAWRENCE LIVERMORE LAB, UNIV CALIF, 54- *Personal Data:* b Seattle, Wash, Sept 22, 27; m 59; c 5. *Educ:* Mont State Col, BS, 50; Univ Notre Dame, PhD(physics), 54. *Honors & Awards:* Lawrence Award, US AEC, 73. *Prof Exp:* Instr physics, Univ Notre Dame, 53-54. *Mem:* Fel Am Phys Soc; Am Geophys Union; Am Phys Soc. *Res:* Statistical mechanics; applied physics. *Mailing Add:* 220 Grover Lane Walnut Creek CA 94596

**WAINWRIGHT, WILLIAM LLOYD,** ENGINEERING. *Current Pos:* ASSOC PROF MECH, UNIV COLO, BOULDER, 64- *Personal Data:* b Fostoria, Ohio; m 51; c 4. *Educ:* Purdue Univ, West Lafayette, BS, 51, MS, 54; Univ Mich, Ann Arbor, PhD(eng mech), 58. *Prof Exp:* Assoc prof mech, US Naval Postgrad Sch, 58-61; res asst, Univ Calif, Berkeley, 61-63, asst prof, 63-64. *Mem:* AAAS; Soc Eng Sci; Sigma Xi. *Res:* Continuum mechanics. *Mailing Add:* 4305 Chippewa Dr Boulder CO 80303

**WAIS DE BADGEN, IRENE RUT,** LIMNOLOGY. *Current Pos:* Asst researcher, 78-81, main researcher, 81-87, HEAD, LIMNOL DEPT, NAT MUS NATURAL HIST & NAT INST NATURAL SCI RES, 87- *Personal Data:* b Buenos Aires, Arg, May 24, 57; m 80, Javier Martin; c Ezequiel D, Natalia A & Ivan M. *Educ:* Nat Col Buenos Aires Univ, BA, 73, Lic(biol), 78. *Concurrent Pos:* Consult, Hidronor SAm, Buenos Aires, 79-81, Entidad Binacional Yacyreta, 89-90; vis prof, Univ Austral, Chile, 83, Ctr Invest, Aguas, 85, Fundacion Vida Silvestre, Argentina, 87; coordr, Int Pihithrobiologists, Buenos Aires, 84-, Prog Environ Educ, 89- *Mem:* Nat Coun Sci & Tech Res. *Mailing Add:* Anasco 1792 Buenos Aires 1416 Argentina

**WAISMAN, JERRY,** PATHOLOGY. *Current Pos:* DIR LAB, UNIV HOSP, MED CTR, NY UNIV, 81- *Personal Data:* b Borger, Tex, Sept 14, 34; m 58; c 3. *Educ:* Univ Tex, BA, 56, MD, 60. *Prof Exp:* Pathologist & chief lab div path, USAF Hosp, Sheppard AFB, Tex, 62-64; fel path, Univ Utah, 64-65, instr path, 65-68; from asst prof to assoc prof, Univ Calif, Los Angeles, 68-76, prof path, 76-81. *Concurrent Pos:* Attend physician, Ft Douglas Vet Admin Hosp, Salt Lake City, 67, part-time sr physician, 67-68; consult, Sepulveda Vet Admin Hosp, 76-81, NY Vet Admin Med Ctr, 82- *Mem:* Int Acad Path; Am Asn Path; Electron Micros Soc Am; Am Soc Cytol. *Res:* Ultrastructure of benign and malignant neoplasms; fine needle aspiration of tumors. *Mailing Add:* Dept Path Med Ctr NY Univ 560 First Ave UH466 New York NY 10016. *Fax:* 212-263-7916

**WAISMAN, JOSEPH L,** METALLURGICAL ENGINEERING, MATERIALS SCIENCE. *Current Pos:* PVT CONSULT, 90- *Personal Data:* b Racine, Wis, Mar 10, 19; m 52; c 1. *Educ:* Univ Ill, MetE, 40; Univ Calif, Los Angeles, PhD(eng), 69. *Prof Exp:* Asst chief metallurgist, Douglas Aircraft Co, Calif, 45-57; western mgr, Tatnall Measuring Systs Div, Budd Co, 57-59; chief metallurgist, Douglas Aircraft Co, Calif, 59-60, chief mat res & prod methods, 60-62, asst chief engr, Missiles & Space Systs, 62-64, asst dir res & develop, 64-66, dir, 66-67, dir res & develop, McDonnell Douglas Astronaut Co, Huntington Beach, 67-68, dir res & develop, 68-73, dir advan prod applns, 73-80, dir cryogenic insulation prog, 80-81, dir energy prog, 81-84, consult, McDonnell Douglas Astronaut Co West, 84-85; consult, Southern Calif Edison Co, 91-93. *Concurrent Pos:* Consult, Metals Adv Bd, NSF, 63-66. *Mem:* Fel Am Soc Metals; assoc fel Am Inst Aeronaut & Astronaut; Soc Exp Stress Analysis; Am Inst Mining, Metall & Petrol Engrs; Am Soc Testing & Mat. *Res:* Fatigue of metals; stress corrosion cracking; residual stresses; cold fusion. *Mailing Add:* 25 Redwood Tree Lane Irvine CA 92714

**WAISS, ANTHONY C, JR,** organic chemistry, natural products, for more information see previous edition

**WAIT, DAVID FRANCIS,** METROLOGY. *Current Pos:* PHYSICIST, NAT BUR STAND, 63- *Personal Data:* b Sidney, Nebr, Sept 28, 33; div; c 4. *Educ:* Colo State Univ, BS, 55, MS, 57; Univ Mich, PhD(physics), 63. *Prof Exp:* Instr & res asst physics, Univ Mich, 62-63; sr scientist, Laser Systs Ctr, Lear Siegler, Inc, 63. *Mem:* Sigma Xi; Inst Elec & Electronics Engrs; Microwave Theory & Tech Soc. *Res:* Noise in communications; radiometers; microwave cryogenic noise standards. *Mailing Add:* 2795 Iliff St Boulder CO 80303-7019

**WAIT, JAMES RICHARD,** GEOENVIRONMENTAL SCIENCE. *Current Pos:* prof elec eng & geosci, 80-89, EMER REGENTS PROF ELEC ENG, UNIV ARIZ, 89-, ADJ PROF GEOL ENG, 95- *Personal Data:* b Ottawa, Can, Jan 23, 24; US citizen; m 51, Gertrude Norman; c Laura & George. *Educ:* Univ Toronto, BASc, 48, MASc, 49, PhD(elec eng), 51. *Honors & Awards:* Flemming Award, US Chamber Com, 64; Harry Diamond Award, Inst Elec & Electronics Engrs, 64, Centennial Award, 84, Geosci & Remote Sensing Soc Award, 85, Antennas & Propagation Soc Distinguished Achievement Award, 90, Heinrich Hertz Medal, 92; Res & Achievement Award, Nat Oceanic & Atmospheric Admin, 73; Van der Pol Gold Medal, Int Union Radio Sci, 78. *Prof Exp:* Radio Physics Lab, Ottawa, Can, 52-55; consult appl physics, US Dept Com, Boulder, Co, 55-80. *Concurrent Pos:* Mem nat comt, Int Union Radio Sci, 58-61 & 65-68, secy, US Nat Comt, 75-78; adj prof elec eng, Univ Colo, Boulder, 61-83, fel, Coop Inst Res Environ Sci, 68-80; co-ed, Int Series Monographs Electromagnetic Waves, Inst Elec Engrs, London, 75-; mem, Electromagnetic Lab, Univ Ariz, 83-90. *Mem:* Nat Acad Eng; fel Inst Elec Engrs; Am Geophys Union; fel Inst Elec & Electronics Engrs; Int Union Radio Sci; hon mem Soc Explor Geophysicist. *Res:* Applications of electromagnetic theory to problems in geophysics and telecommunications. *Mailing Add:* 2210 E Waverly Tucson AZ 85719-3848

**WAIT, JOHN V,** ELECTRONICS ENGINEERING. *Current Pos:* assoc prof, 66-71, PROF ELEC ENG, UNIV ARIZ, 71- *Personal Data:* b Chicago, Ill, Oct 1, 32; m 61, Sharon Godfrey; c Katherine & Kira. *Educ:* Univ Iowa, BSEE, 55; Univ NMex, MSEE, 59; Univ Ariz, PhD, 63. *Prof Exp:* Res engr, RCA Labs, 55; instr, Univ NMex, 57-59; res engr & instr, Univ Ariz, 59-63; asst prof, Univ Calif, Santa Barbara, 63-64; assoc prof grad eng educ syst, Univ Fla, 64-66. *Mem:* Inst Elec & Electronics Engrs; Soc Comput Simulation. *Res:* Electronics; computers; signal processing. *Mailing Add:* 7079 E Acoma St Tucson AZ 85715

**WAIT, SAMUEL CHARLES, JR,** PHYSICAL CHEMISTRY. *Current Pos:* from asst prof to assoc prof chem, Rensselaer Polytech Inst, 61-71, asst dean, Sch Sci, 72-74, actg dean, 78-80 & 88-89, PROF CHEM, RENSSELAER POLYTECH INST, 71-, ASSOC DEAN SCH SCI, 74- *Personal Data:* b Albany, NY, Jan 26, 32; m 57, Carol D Petrie; c Robert J & Alison R. *Educ:* Rensselaer Polytech Inst, BS, 53, MS, 55, PhD(chem), 56. *Prof Exp:* Fulbright fel, Univ Col, London, 56-57; asst lectr chem, 57-58; res fel, Univ Minn, 58-59; asst prof, Carnegie Inst Technol, 59-60; chemist, Nat Bur Stand, 60-61. *Concurrent Pos:* Mem adv coun sci & math, Schenectady Co Community Col, 75-, chmn, 76-78; mem, Schenectady Co Fire Adv Bd, 76-81, vchmn, 78; mem bd fire comnrs, Niskayuna Dist Two, 78-84; mem bd trustees, Dudley Observ, 80-, pres trustees, 91-; mem, Schenectady Co Hazardous Mat Team, 91- *Mem:* Am Chem Soc; Optical Soc Am; Coblentz Soc; Sigma Xi. *Res:* High resolution ultraviolet, infrared and Raman spectroscopy; asymmetric rotor theory and calculation; molecular orbital theory; vibrational and fine structural analyses; theoretical methods; simple and polyatomic systems. *Mailing Add:* Rensselaer Polytech Inst Sch Sci 110 Eighth St Troy NY 12180-3590. *Fax:* 518-276-2825; *E-Mail:* waitsc@rpi.edu

**WAITE, LEONARD CHARLES,** PHARMACOLOGY. *Current Pos:* From asst prof to assoc prof, 70-79, PROF PHARMACOL, SCH MED, UNIV LOUISVILLE, 79- *Personal Data:* b Reynoldsville, Pa, Sept 10, 41; m 60, Edith Kirkwood; c Karen, Kenny & Kathy. *Educ:* Alderson-Braddus Col, BS, 65; WVa Univ, MS, 67; Univ Mo, Columbia, PhD(pharmacol), 69. *Mem:* Endocrine Soc; Am Soc Pharmacol & Exp Therapeut. *Res:* Endocrinology; physiology; calcium metabolism. *Mailing Add:* Dept Pharmacol Sch Med Univ Louisville 2301 S Third St Louisville KY 40292-0001. *Fax:* 502-852-7868

**WAITE, MOSELEY,** BIOCHEMISTRY, ORGANIC CHEMISTRY. *Current Pos:* From asst prof to assoc prof, 67-76, PROF BIOCHEM, BOWMAN GRAY SCH MED, WAKE FOREST UNIV, 76-, CHMN, 78-, ASSOC MED, PULMONARY SECT, 89- *Personal Data:* b Durham, NC, Oct 22, 36; m 59; c 3. *Educ:* Rollins Col, BS, 58; Duke Univ, PhD(biochem), 63. *Concurrent Pos:* Am Cancer Soc fel biochem, Duke Univ, 62-65; Am Heart Asn advan fel, Univ Utrecht, 65-67; grants, Am Heart Asn, 66-69, USPHS, 67-81 & NC Heart Asn, 70-73; USPHS res career develop award, 73-78 & Environ Protection Agency, 80-82. *Mem:* AAAS; Am Chem Soc; Am Soc Biol Chemists. *Res:* Phospholipid and fatty acid metabolism; enzyme purification and characterization; relation of metabolism of lipids to certain morphological changes, especially mitochondrion; prostaglandin synthesis; phospholipid; prostaglandins. *Mailing Add:* Dept Biochem Sch Med Wake Forest Univ Winston-Salem NC 27157-1016. *Fax:* 919-716-7671

**WAITE, PAUL J,** CLIMATOLOGY. *Current Pos:* CLIMATE CONSULT, 88- *Personal Data:* b New Salem, Ill, June 21, 18; m 43, 90, Mildred Keever; c Lawrence W & Carolyn (Bojarra). *Educ:* Western State Univ, BEd, 40; Univ Mich, MS, 66. *Honors & Awards:* Group Achievement Award, NASA, 79. *Prof Exp:* Teacher & coach, Ill schs, 38-39 & 40-42; meteorologist, USAF, 42-46; coach & instr, Ill High Schs, 46-48; meteorologist & climatologist, Nat Weather Bur, 48-74; dep mgr Lacie Proj, Environ Data Serv, 74-76; climatologist, Iowa Dept Agr, 76-88. *Concurrent Pos:* Collabr, Agr Clin, Iowa

State Univ, 59-73; adj prof geol & geog, Drake Univ, 70-74 & 76-88; pres, Iowa Sci Acad, 86-87. *Mem:* Am Asn State Climatologists (pres, 77-78); Am Meteorol Soc. *Res:* Iowa storm climatology; agricultural climatology; climatology for decision making and descriptive climatology; approximately 100 professional and popular articles, reviews and books published. *Mailing Add:* 6657 NW Timberline Dr Des Moines IA 50313-5436

**WAITE, PETER DANIEL,** FACIAL RECONSTRUCTION, FACIAL COSMETIC SURGERY. *Current Pos:* ASSOC PROF DENT & MED, UNIV ALA, BIRMINGHAM, 85-, CHMN, DEPT ORAL SURG & PROG DIR, DEPT ORAL MAXILLO FACIAL SURG, 93- *Personal Data:* b Feb 20, 54; m 77, Sallie Babcock; c Allison, Eric & Jonathan. *Educ:* Graceland Col, BS, 75; Univ Minn, MPH, 76, DDS, 79; Univ Ala, MD, 83. *Honors & Awards:* Fred Henny Award, 85. *Concurrent Pos:* Consult, Cleft Palate Clin, Univ Ala, 85-, Sleep Disorder Clin, 86-, Craniofacial Clin, 89-; vis prof surg, Frei Univ, Berlin, 90- *Mem:* Am Dent Asn; AMA; Am Asn Oral Maxillofacial Surg. *Res:* Oral maxillofacial surgery to improve facial recostruction; surgical fixation device, bone physiology, improve masticatory and airway function.; surgical cure of obstructive sleep apnea; simultaneous cosmetic surgery and orthognathic surgery. *Mailing Add:* Fac Surg & Oral Surg Sch Med Univ Ala 1717 Seventh Ave Birmingham AL 35294. *Fax:* 205-934-9283

**WAITE, PRESTON JAY,** MATHEMATICAL STATISTICS. *Current Pos:* CHIEF, DEMOG STATIST METHODS DIV, US DEPT COM, 89- *Personal Data:* b Logan, Utah, Apr 4, 46. *Educ:* Utah State Univ, BS, 70, MA, 71. *Mem:* Am Statist Asn; Int Field Dir Asn; Pop Asn Am. *Mailing Add:* US Dept Com Bur Census Fed Ctr Suitland MD 20233

**WAITE, WILLIAM MCCASTLINE,** PROGRAMMING LANGUAGES, SOFTWARE. *Current Pos:* from asst prof to assoc prof, 66-75, PROF ELEC ENG, UNIV COLO, BOULDER, 75- *Personal Data:* b New York, NY, Jan 14, 39; m 60; c 1. *Educ:* Oberlin Col, AB, 60; Columbia Univ, MS, 62, PhD(elec eng), 65. *Prof Exp:* Res asst, Electronics Res Labs, Columbia Univ, 62-65; NSF fel, 65-66. *Concurrent Pos:* Vis lectr, Dept Info Sci, Monash Univ, Australia, 70-71; temp res assoc, Culham Lab, UK Atomic Energy Auth, Eng, 71; ed, Spec Interest Group Oper Systs, Asn Comput Mach, 72-; mem staff, Inst Informatik, Univ Karlsruhe, Ger, 80; vis lectr, Melbourne Univ, Australia, 77, 82 & 88; chmn, Int Fed Info Processing Working Group 2.4, 83-90; adj prof, Queensland Univ Technol, 94; vis fel, Australian Nat Univ, 96; vis prof, Univ Nacional de San Luis, Argentia, 96. *Mem:* Asn Comput Mach. *Res:* Programming languages and software system design. *Mailing Add:* Elec Eng Univ Colo Campus Box 425 Boulder CO 80309-0425

**WAITER, SERGE-ALBERT,** MATHEMATICS, GAS DYNAMICS. *Current Pos:* CONSULT & LECTR. *Personal Data:* b Paris, France, Feb 8, 30; US citizen; c 1. *Educ:* Univs Lille & Paris, Lic es Sci, 51; Univ Paris, Dr es Sci, Univ Paris, 54. *Prof Exp:* Res engr, Off Aeronaut & Astronaut Res, France, 49-51; flight test engr, Fouga Aircraft, 51-53; mgr, Prototype Dept, Sud Aviation, 53-59; res scientist plasma physics, Eng Ctr, Univ Southern Calif, 59-62; prin sr scientist, Space Div, NAm Rockwell Corp, 62-88; scientist, Dassault Aviation, 88-92. *Mem:* Assoc fel Am Inst Aeronaut & Astronaut; Sigma Xi; Soc Civil Engrs France. *Res:* Fluid dynamics; plasma physics; space sciences. *Mailing Add:* 801 S Crest Vista Dr Monterey Park CA 91754. *Fax:* 626-284-4370

**WAITES, ROBERT ELLSWORTH,** entomology, for more information see previous edition

**WAITHE, WILLIAM IRWIN,** CELL PHYSIOLOGY, CARCINOGEN METABOLISM. *Current Pos:* RETIRED. *Personal Data:* b New York, NY, May 3, 37; m 58, 74; c 6. *Educ:* St Francis Col, BS, 58; NY Univ, MS, 63, PhD(cell biol), 69. *Prof Exp:* Res asst med genetics, Sch Med, NY Univ, 58-66; res assoc immunol & cell biol, Mt Sinai Sch Med, City Univ NY, 66-68; instr genetics, 68-71; from asst prof to assoc prof med, Fac Med, Univ Laval, 77-92. *Concurrent Pos:* Scholar, Med Res Coun Can, 71-76. *Mem:* Can Biochem Soc; Can Soc Cell Biol. *Res:* Regulation of growth by nuclear and cytoplasmic proteins; biochemical mechanisms controlling lymphocyte activation in vitro; carcinogen metabolism by human lymphocytes; cytochrome P-450, enzymatic activity and gene expression in lymphocytes; Epstein-Barr virus transformed lymphocyte cell lines. *Mailing Add:* 230 Wright Ave Toronto ON M6R 1L3 Can

**WAITKINS, GEORGE RAYMOND,** PHYSICAL CHEMISTRY. *Current Pos:* RETIRED. *Personal Data:* b Glasgow, Scotland, Feb 28, 11; nat US; m 37; c 2. *Educ:* Syracuse Univ, 33, MS, 34, PhD(chem), 38. *Prof Exp:* Res engr, Battelle Mem Inst, 38-43; chemist, Mutual Chem Co Am, 43; chem supvr, Can Copper Refiners, Ltd, Que, 44-45; res chemist, Calco Div, Am Cyanamid Co, 45-52; asst mgr res dept, Am Zinc Lead & Smelting Co, 52-62; phys chemist, Mattin Labs, Mearl Corp, Ossining, 62-76. *Mem:* Am Chem Soc; Am Inst Chemists; AAAS; Sigma Xi. *Res:* Inorganic, organic and nacreous pigments; crystal growth. *Mailing Add:* 1 Hughes St Croton-on-Hudson NY 10520

**WAITS, BERT KERR,** MATHEMATICS, MATHEMATICS EDUCATION. *Current Pos:* Asst to chmn, Dept Math, 65-69, from asst prof to prof, 69-92, EMER PROF MATH, OHIO STATE UNIV, 92- *Personal Data:* b New Orleans, La, Dec 21, 40; m 63, Barbara Finley; c David & Jeffrey. *Educ:* Ohio State Univ, BSc, 62, MSc, 64, PhD(math educ), 69. *Concurrent Pos:* Mem, Nat Coun Teachers Math, Curric & Eval Stand Sch Math; dir, Math Placement Testing Prog, Ohio Early Col, 78-; co-founder, T-Cubed Prog.

*Mem:* Math Asn Am; Nat Coun Teachers Math. *Res:* Mathematics education; individualized instruction at the college level; micro-compter applications of pre-calculus and calculus; curriculum revision and graphing software. *Mailing Add:* Dept Math Ohio State Univ 231 W 18th Ave Columbus OH 43210

**WAITZ, JAY ALLAN,** CHEMOTHERAPY. *Current Pos:* RETIRED. *Personal Data:* b Elizabeth, NJ, Nov 26, 35; m 60; c 2. *Educ:* Univ Idaho, BS, 57, MS, 59; Univ Ill, PhD(parasitol), 62. *Prof Exp:* Assoc res parasitologist, Parke, Davis & Co, 62-65; res parasitologist, 65-66; sr microbiologist, Schering Corp, 66-68, sect head, 69-70, mgr chemother dept, 70-73, assoc dir microbiol, 73-77, dir antibiotic res, 77-81, vpres microbiol res, 81-82; pres, DNAX Res Inst, 82-92. *Mem:* Am Soc Microbiol. *Res:* Chemotherapy of parasitic, bacterial and fungal diseases. *Mailing Add:* c/o N McFarland, DNAX Research Inst 901 California Ave Palo Alto CA 94304

**WAITZMAN, MORTON BENJAMIN,** PHYSIOLOGY, BIOCHEMISTRY. *Current Pos:* assoc prof & dir, Lab Ophthal Res, Emory Univ, 62-68, asst prof, Dept Physiol, 62-67, prof & dir, Lab Ophthal Res, 68-91, EMER PROF & CONSULT, DEPT OPHTHAL, EMORY UNIV, 91- *Personal Data:* b Chicago, Ill, Nov 8, 23; m 49, Aviva Shedroff; c Sherri, Brad & Rhonda. *Educ:* Univ Miami, BS, 48; Univ Ill, MS, 50, PhD(physiol), 53. *Honors & Awards:* Numerous Hon Invited Lectureships. *Prof Exp:* Res asst physiol, Univ Ill, 51-54; res assoc, Dept Pharmacol & Lab Res Ophthal, Sch Med, Western Res Univ, 54-56, instr, 56-59, asst prof ophthal res & pharmacol & dir lab res ophthal, 59-62; sci & clin invest dir, Grady Eye Clins, 81-91. *Concurrent Pos:* Chair, Tech Adv Comt Clean Air, 70-71; extensive teaching at undergrad, grad & prof levels. *Mem:* AAAS; Asn Res Vision & Ophthal; Am Physiol Soc; NY Acad Sci; Sigma Xi. *Res:* Ophthalmic research; metabolic and hormonal aspects of aqueous humor and cerebrospinal fluid production; glaucoma; metabolic aspects of diabetes mellitus; neuro-chemistry; autonomic nature of ocular extracts; numerous major publications and chapters. *Mailing Add:* 1137 Mason Woods Dr NE Atlanta GA 30329. *Fax:* 404-634-5586; *E-Mail:* mwaitzm@emory.edu

**WAIWOOD, KENNETH GEORGE,** MARINE FISH AQUACULTURE. *Current Pos:* RES SCIENTIST MARINE FISH AQUACULT, FISHERIES & OCEANS, 77- *Personal Data:* b St Boniface, Man, Feb 12, 47; m 72, Brenda Perkins. *Educ:* Sir George Williams Univ, BSc, 68; Queen's Univ, MSc, 72; Univ Guelph, PhD(zool), 77. *Concurrent Pos:* Adj prof, Univ New Brunsard, Univ Maine, Mem Univ, Nfld. *Mem:* Can Soc Zoologists; Aquacult Asn Can. *Res:* Eco-physiology of marine fishes in support of aquaculture; bioenergetics; physiology of reproduction, feeding and growth; barval rearing and juvenile production. *Mailing Add:* Dept Fisheries & Oceans St Andrews Biol Sta St Andrews NB E0G 2X0 Can. *Fax:* 506-529-5862; *E-Mail:* kwaiwood@sta.ufo.ca

**WAJDA, EDWARD STANLEY,** PHYSICS, SEMICONDUCTOR DEVICES. *Current Pos:* RETIRED. *Personal Data:* b Schenectady, NY, Oct 31, 24; m 50, Sophie Krempa; c Mary J & Susan A. *Educ:* Union Col, NY, BS, 45; Cornell Univ, MS, 48; Rensselaer Polytech Inst, PhD(physics), 53. *Prof Exp:* Instr physics, Amherst Col, 46-47; sr physicist & proj mgr, IBM Corp, 55-86; instr, Union Col, NY, 48-49, asst prof, 53-55. *Mem:* Inst Elec & Electronics Engrs; Sigma Xi. *Res:* Solid state physics; semiconductors mat & devices. *Mailing Add:* 39 Spy Hill Poughkeepsie NY 12603

**WAJDA, ISABEL,** pharmacology, neurochemistry, for more information see previous edition

**WAKAYAMA, EDGAR JUNRO,** BIOSYNTHESIS & METABOLISM LICOSANOIDS IN INSECTS. *Current Pos:* from asst prof to assoc prof, 79-91, ASSOC PROF & CHAIRPERSON, CLIN LAB SCI, UNIV NEV, 91- *Personal Data:* b Manzanar, Calif, Mar 22, 43; m 68, June; c Lisa A & Liane K. *Educ:* Northeastern Univ, BA, 67; Univ Ore, MS, 71; Univ Nev, PhD(biochem), 85. *Prof Exp:* Asst prof, Clin Lab Sci, Health Sci Ctr, Univ Okla, 78-79. *Concurrent Pos:* Adj asoc prof biochem, Univ Nev, 85-91. *Mem:* Am Asn Clin Chemists; fel Nat Acad Clin Biochemists; fel Am Inst Chemists; Sigma Xi; Nat Registry Clin Chem; Am Chem Soc. *Res:* Biosynthesis and metabolism licosanoids in insects. *Mailing Add:* Dept Clin Lab Sci Univ Nev Box 453018 4505 Maryland Pkwy Las Vegas NV 89154-3018. *Fax:* 702-895-3872

**WAKAYAMA, YOSHIHIRO,** NEUROLOGY, MYOLOGY. *Current Pos:* assoc prof neurol, 80-89, PROF NEUROL, SCH MED, SHOWA UNIV, 89- *Personal Data:* b Oogaki City, Japan, Apr 30, 45; m 71; c 2. *Educ:* Nagoya Univ, MD, 76, PhD(med sci), 81. *Prof Exp:* Myology fel, Muscular Dystrophy Asn Am, 76-79; asst prof res, Sch Med, Univ Pa, 79. *Mem:* Japanese Soc Neurol; Am Acad Neurol; Am Soc Cell Biol; Am Asn Neuropathologists; Am Neurol Asn. *Res:* Ultrastructural investigations of muscle and plasma membrane associated cytoskeletons of dystrophic skeletal muscles by using cytochemical, immunoelectron microscopic and freeze etching electron microscopic techniques. *Mailing Add:* Div Neurol Dept Med Showa Univ Fujigaoka Hosp 1-30 Fujigaoka Midori-ku Yokohama 227 Japan. *Fax:* 81-045-974-2204

**WAKE, DAVID BURTON,** EVOLUTIONARY BIOLOGY. *Current Pos:* assoc prof zool, Univ Calif, Berkeley, 69-73, assoc cur, Mus Vert Zool, 69-71, prof zool, 73-89, John & Margaret Gompertz endowed chair, 91, DIR, MUS VERT ZOOL, UNIV CALIF, BERKELEY, 71-, CUR HERPET, 73-, PROF INTEGRATIVE BIOL, 89- *Personal Data:* b Webster, SDak, June 8, 36; m

62, Marvalee Hendricks; c Thomas A. *Educ:* Pac Lutheran Univ, BA, 58; Univ Southern Calif, MSc, 60, PhD(biol), 64. *Honors & Awards:* Quantrell Award, Univ Chicago, 67. *Prof Exp:* Asst biol, Univ Southern Calif, 58-59, head lab assoc, 62-63, instr, 63-64; instr anat & biol, Univ Chicago, 64-66, asst prof, 66-69. *Concurrent Pos:* Fel, John Simon Guggenheim Mem Found, 81-82; mem, Bd Biol, Nat Res Coun, 86-92. *Mem:* Fel AAAS; Am Soc Ichthyologists & Herpetologists; Soc Syst Zool; Am Soc Zoologists (pres, 93); Soc Study Evolution (pres, 83); Am Soc Naturalists (pres, 89); Am Philol Soc. *Res:* Functional, developmental and evolutionary morphology; evolution, systematics and zoogeography of modern Amphibia, with emphasis on salamanders; evolutionary theory. *Mailing Add:* 999 Middlefield Rd Berkeley CA 94708-1509. *E-Mail:* wakelab @uclink4.berkeley.edu

**WAKE, MARVALEE H,** VERTEBRATE BIOLOGY. *Current Pos:* lectr, Univ Calif, 69-73, from asst prof to prof zool, 73-89, assoc dean, Col Lett & Sci, 75-78, chmn, Dept Zool, 85-89, chmn, Dept Int Biol, 89-91, PROF INTEGRATIVE BIOL, UNIV CALIF, BERKELEY, 89- *Personal Data:* b Orange, Calif, July 31, 39; m 62, David B; c Thomas A. *Educ:* Univ Southern Calif, BA, 61, MS, 64, PhD(biol), 68. *Prof Exp:* Teaching asst biol, Univ Ill, Chicago, 64-66, instr, 66-68, asst prof, 68-69. *Concurrent Pos:* Prin investr, NSF, 77-; vis prof, Univ Bremen, 82, Univ Paris VII, 89; chair, US Nat Comn, Int Union Biol Scientists, 92-94, secy gen, 94-; trustee, Calif Acad Sci, 92-; secy gen, Third World Cong Herpet, 94-; mem, Bd Sustainable Develop, Nat Res Coun, Nat Acad Sci, 95-; chair-elect, Sect Biol Sci, AAAS, 97- *Mem:* Fel AAAS; Am Soc Zoologists; Am Soc Ichthyologists & Herpetologists (pres, 84); Soc Study Evolution; Soc Study Amphibians & Reptiles. *Res:* Evolution of vertebrates; morphology; reproductive biology; development. *Mailing Add:* Dept Integrative Biol Univ Calif Berkeley CA 94720-3140. *Fax:* 510-643-6264

**WAKEFIELD, ERNEST HENRY,** ELECTRICAL ENGINEERING. *Current Pos:* PRES, LINEAR ALPHA, INC, 62-; CHMN, THIRD WORLD ENERGY INST INT, 78-; CHMN, INT INST MGT & APPROPRIATE TECHNOL FOR EMERGING NATIONS, 81- *Personal Data:* b Vermilion, Ohio, Feb 11, 15; wid; c Ann & John. *Educ:* Univ Mich, BS, 38, MS, 39, PhD, 52. *Prof Exp:* Instr elec eng, Univ Tenn, 39-41; assoc physicist, Mass Inst Technol, 42; assoc physicist, Manhattan Proj, Chicago, 43-46; pres, RCL, Inc, 46-62 & RCL Calif, Inc, 59-62. *Concurrent Pos:* Hon prof, Cent Univ Ecuador, 58; dir, Atomic Indust Forum, 60-62; pres, Evanston Bd Educ, 66-67. *Res:* Data processing systems; electronic controls; technology for third world; electric vehicle design. *Mailing Add:* 2300 Noyes Ct Evanston IL 60201

**WAKEFIELD, LUCILLE MARION,** NUTRITION. *Current Pos:* CHMN, DEPT FOOD & NUTRIT, UNIV NC, GREENSBORO, 79- *Personal Data:* b Dayville, Conn, June 13, 25. *Educ:* Univ Conn, BS, 49, MS, 56; Ohio State Univ, PhD(nutrit), 65. *Prof Exp:* Intern dietetics, Mt Auburn Hosp, 49-50; therapeut dietitian, New Brit Gen Hosp, 50-52, admin dietitian, 52-53; dir dietetics, Auburn Mem Hosp, 53-57; asst prof food & nutrit, Univ Vt, 57-65, head, Dept Nutrit & Inst Mgt, 62-65; prof foods & nutrit & head dept, Kans State Univ, 65-75 & Fla State Univ, 75-79. *Concurrent Pos:* Int work in India, Mexico & Morroco. *Mem:* AAAS; fel Am Inst Chemists; Am Dietetic Asn; Am Pub Health Asn; Am Inst Nutrit; Am Col Nutrit. *Res:* Nutritional, sociological, psychological aspects of humans and their body composition as it relates to population groups and nutritional status; clinical nutrition and community health problems; nutrition in aging; food patterning. *Mailing Add:* 2810 Kilkierane Dr Tallahassee FL 32308

**WAKEFIELD, ROBERT CHESTER,** AGRONOMY. *Current Pos:* from asst prof to assoc prof agron, 54-65, chmn dept, 61-70, PROF AGRON, UNIV RI, 65- *Personal Data:* b Providence, RI, Sept 14, 25; m 49; c 3. *Educ:* Univ RI, BS, 50; Rutgers Univ, MS, 51, PhD, 54. *Prof Exp:* Res assoc farm crops, Rutgers Univ, 51-54. *Res:* Crop ecology; landscape ecology. *Mailing Add:* 850 Usquepaugh Rd West Kingston RI 02892

**WAKEFIELD, SHIRLEY LORRAINE,** other engineering, for more information see previous edition

**WAKEFIELD, TROY, JR,** ACADEMIC ADMINISTRATION, NUTRITIONAL STATUS ASSESMENT. *Current Pos:* dir, Int Food & Agr Develop, 82-89, RES DIR, TENN STATE UNIV, 87-, DEAN, 89- *Personal Data:* b Tipton Co, Tenn, Nov 20, 48. *Educ:* Tenn State Univ, BS, 70, MS, 72; Univ Tenn, PhD(human nutrit), 79. *Prof Exp:* Biol res asst, Natick Labs, 72-74. *Concurrent Pos:* Prin investr, Coop Agr Res Prog, Tenn State Univ, 79-87; consult, Bd Int Sci & Tech Int Develop, Nat Acad Sci, 87; mem, Nat Comt, Int Sci & Educ, 90- *Mem:* Am Inst Nutrit; AAAS; Asn Res Dir; Inst Food Technol; Soc Int Nutrit Res; Nat Asn State Univs. *Res:* Nutritional status assesment using anthropometric, biochemical, clinical & dietary methods; nutrition and growth in children; lipid and lipoprotein metabolism; international nutrition and diet related health of children; poultry nutrition; research administration. *Mailing Add:* 3500 John A Merritt Blvd Nashville TN 37203

**WAKEHAM, HELMUT,** PHYSICAL CHEMISTRY. *Current Pos:* RETIRED. *Personal Data:* b Hamburg, Ger, Apr 15, 16; US citizen; m 39; c 3. *Educ:* Univ Nebr, BA, 36, MA, 37; Univ Calif, PhD(phys chem), 39. *Prof Exp:* Asst chem, Univ Nebr, 36-37; asst, Univ Calif, 37-39; res chemist, Stand Oil Co, Calif, 39-41; res chemist, Southern Regional Res Lab, USDA, 41-47; from res assoc to proj head & dir res, Chem Physics Sect, Textile Res Inst, NJ, 49-56; dir, Ahmedabad Textile Industs Res Asn, India, 56-58; staff asst to vpres & chief opers & subsidiaries, Res Ctr, Philip Morris, Inc, 58-60, dir,

Res Ctr, 60-61, vpres res & develop, 61-82. *Concurrent Pos:* Mem, Tobacco Working Group, 68-76; mem, Nat Cancer Plan, 71; mem bd dir, Indust Res Inst, Inc, 71-72; Va Laureat Technol. *Mem:* Fel AAAS; Am Chem Soc; Fiber Soc; Soc Rheol; fel Am Inst Chemists. *Res:* Agricultural and food chemistry; technical management. *Mailing Add:* 8905 Norwick Rd Richmond VA 23229-7715

**WAKELAND, WILLIAM RICHARD,** ELECTRICAL ENGINEERING, CONTROL SYSTEMS. *Current Pos:* RETIRED. *Personal Data:* b Mound City, Ill, Nov 14, 21; m 45; c 4. *Educ:* US Naval Acad, BS, 43; US Naval Postgrad Sch, BS, 50, MS, 51; Univ Houston, PhD(elec eng), 68. *Prof Exp:* Dir astronaut directorate, Naval Missile Ctr, Point Mugu, Calif, 61-62; mgr Gemini-agena develop, Manned Spacecraft Ctr, NASA, Houston, 62-64; dir aeronaut elec dept, Naval Air Develop Ctr, Pa, 64-65; instr, Univ Houston, 65-68; from asst prof to assoc prof, Trinity Univ, Tex, 68-78; prof & head, Elec Eng Dept, Lamar Univ, 78-92. *Mem:* Inst Elec & Electronics Engrs; Nat Soc Prof Engrs; Am Soc Eng Educ. *Res:* Control system design; optimal design; weighting factor for quadratic performance index. *Mailing Add:* 6303 Royal Ridge San Antonio TX 78239

**WAKELEY, JAMES STUART,** WILDLIFE ECOLOGY, WETLAND DELINEATION. *Current Pos:* wildlife biologist, 86-91, RES WILDLIFE BIOLOGIST, US ARMY ENGR WATERWAYS EXP STA, 91- *Personal Data:* b Raleigh, NC, July 8, 50; m 73, Lillian Donley; c Ellen. *Educ:* Univ Calif, Santa Barbara, BA, 71; Univ Maine, MS, 73; Utah State Univ, PhD(wildlife ecol), 76. *Prof Exp:* From asst prof to assoc prof wildlife ecology, Pa State Univ, 76-86. *Mem:* Wildlife Soc; Am Ornithologists' Union; Ecol Soc Am; Cooper Ornith Soc; Soc Wetland Scientists. *Res:* Ecology and management of game and nongame birds; applied population biology; wetland ecology. *Mailing Add:* US Army Engrs Waterways Exp Sta 3909 Halls Ferry Rd Vicksburg MS 39180-6199. *Fax:* 601-634-4016

**WAKELIN, DAVID HERBERT,** METALLURGICAL ENGINEERING. *Current Pos:* MGR, DEVELOP ENG, PRIMARY, LTV STEEL CO, 84- *Personal Data:* b Southampton, Eng, Dec 8, 40; US citizen; m 66, Janet Cobb; c Sarah & Nigel. *Educ:* Univ London, BSc, 62, ARSM, 62, PhD(eng metall) & DIC, 66. *Prof Exp:* From res engr to sr res engr, Graham Res Lab, Jones & Laughlin Steel Corp, 66-70, res assoc metall, 70-74, develop engr ironmaking, 74-79, suprvr ironmaking eng, Graham Res Lab, Jones & Laughlin Steel Corp, 79-84. *Concurrent Pos:* Secy, Ironmaking Div, Iron & Steel Soc, 92-93, vchmn, 93- *Mem:* Am Inst Mining, Metall & Petrol Engrs; Iron & Steel Soc; Asn Iron & Steel Engrs. *Res:* Primary steelmaking processes and energy requirements. *Mailing Add:* LTV Steel Co Technol Ctr 6801 Brecksville Rd Independence OH 44131. *Fax:* 216-642-7288

**WAKELYN, PHILLIP JEFFREY,** TEXTILE CHEMISTRY. *Current Pos:* mgr environ health & safety, 73-96, SR SCIENTIST, NAT COTTON COUN, 97- *Personal Data:* b Akron, Ohio, Apr 29, 40. *Educ:* Emory Univ, BS, 63; Ga Inst Technol, MS, 68; Univ Leeds, PhD, 71. *Prof Exp:* Res chemist, Fibers Div, Dow Chem Co, 63-66 & Dow-Badische Co, 66-67; res assoc textile chem, Textile Res Ctr, Tex Tech Univ, 71-73, head chem res, 73. *Concurrent Pos:* Lectr textile chem, Tex Tech Univ, 72-73, adj prof chem eng, 74-78. *Mem:* Am Chem Soc; Sigma Xi; Am Asn Textile Chemists & Colorists; NY Acad Sci; assoc mem Brit Textile Inst; Am Oil Chem Soc; Nat Fire Protection Asn; Am Soc Testing & Mats. *Res:* Physical and chemical properties of textile fibers; dyeing and finishing of textile materials; fire retardants and flammability of textiles; chemistry of cotton and wool; environmental, industrial health and safety, consumer problems; cotton dust and occupational diseases, formaldehyde, toxic chemicals, air, water and solid waste pollutants. *Mailing Add:* Nat Cotton Coun 1521 New Hampshire Ave NW Washington DC 20036. *Fax:* 202-483-4040; *E-Mail:* pwakelyn @cotton.org

**WAKEMAN, CHARLES B,** ELECTRONICS. *Current Pos:* RETIRED. *Personal Data:* b New Haven, Conn, Aug 4, 27; m 48; c 3. *Educ:* Yale Univ, BE, 50, ME, 52, PhD(elec eng), 55. *Prof Exp:* Res engr, Magnetics Inc, 55-57, dir res & develop, 57-61, vpres res & develop, 61-62; dir electronics res, Corning Glass Works, 62-66, dir phys res, 66-72, dir corp develop, 72-74, dir res & develop Europe, 74-78, dir tech & admin serv, 78-80; vpres res & develop, Siecor Corp, 80-85, pres, 85-86. *Mem:* AAAS; Inst Elec & Electronics Engrs; Sigma Xi. *Res:* Magnetic domain effects in highly rectangular hysteresis loop magnetic materials of interest in magnetic switching, memory and similar devices. *Mailing Add:* PO Box 300 Hickory NC 28603-0300

**WAKEMAN, DONALD LEE,** ANIMAL HUSBANDRY. *Current Pos:* instr, Univ Fla, 55-57, asst prof, asst animal husbandman, Agr Exp Sta, 57-67, assoc prof, 67-75, PROF ANIMAL SCI, UNIV FLA, 75-, ASSOC ANIMAL HUSBANDMAN, AGR EXP STA, 67- *Personal Data:* b Lebanon, Mo, Nov 17, 29; m 50; c 3. *Educ:* Okla State Univ, BSA, 51; Univ Fla, MSA, 55. *Prof Exp:* Instr animal sci, Univ Tenn, 51. *Mem:* Am Soc Animal Sci. *Res:* Animal production and nutrition; beef cattle production. *Mailing Add:* Dept Animal Sci Univ Fla PO Box 110910 Gainesville FL 32611-0910

**WAKEMAN, JOHN MARSHALL,** FISH & WILDLIFE SCIENCES. *Current Pos:* PROF ANIMAL PHYSIOL, LA TECH UNIV, 79- *Personal Data:* b Victoria, Australia, June 12, 37; m 70; c 2. *Educ:* Southern Ill Univ, BS, 73; Univ Ala, MS, 75; Univ Tex, Austin, PhD(zool), 78. *Prof Exp:* Res scientist, Univ Tex, 78-79. *Concurrent Pos:* Res scientist, Marine Consortium, La Tech Univ, 80 & Marine Sci Inst, Univ Tex, Austin, 81. *Mem:* Sigma Xi; Am Fisheries Soc; Gulf Estuarine Res Soc. *Res:*

Swimming energetics and physiological responses of fishes with respect to salinity variations and to environmental pollutants; spawning and culture of marine fishes; closed-system aquaculture and mariculture. *Mailing Add:* Dept Biol Sci La Tech Univ 305 Wisteria St Ruston LA 71272-0001

**WAKIL, SALIH J,** BIOCHEMISTRY. *Current Pos:* prof biotechnol, 86-95, PROF BIOCHEM & CHMN DEPT, BAYLOR COL MED, 71-, LODWICK T BOLIN PROF, 84- *Personal Data:* b Kerballa, Iraq; nat US; m 52, Fawzia Al-Bahrani; c Sonya, Aida, Adil & Youssef. *Educ:* Am Univ Beirut, BSc, 48; Univ Wash, PhD(biochem), 52. *Honors & Awards:* Paul Lewis Award, Am Chem Soc, 67; Kuwait Prize, Kuwait Found Advan Sci, 88; Distinguished Serv Award, Arab Am Med Asn, 90-; Supelco Res Award, Am Oil Chem Soc, 93. *Prof Exp:* Res assoc, Inst Enzyme Res, Univ Wis, 52-56, asst prof, 56-59; from asst prof to prof biochem, Sch Med, Duke Univ, 59-71. *Concurrent Pos:* Vis prof, Pasteur Inst Paris, 68-69; John Simon Guggenheim fel, 68-69; ad hoc mem, Physiol Study Sect, NIH, 71; mem metab biol panel, NSF, 71-74; pres, Asn Med Sch Dept Biochem, 88-89. *Mem:* Nat Acad Sci; Am Soc Biochem & Molecular Biol; Sigma Xi; Am Soc Cell Biol; Am Soc Microbiol; Am Chem Soc; fel Am Acad Microbiol. *Res:* Genetic and metabolic control of fatty acid biosynthesis. *Mailing Add:* Dept Biochem Baylor Col Med 1 Baylor Plaza Houston TX 77030. *Fax:* 713-796-9438; *E-Mail:* swakil@bcm.tmc.edu

**WAKIMOTO, BARBARA TOSHIKO,** DEVELOPMENTAL GENETICS, CYTOGENETICS. *Current Pos:* ASST PROF DEVELOP BIOL, UNIV WASH, 85- *Personal Data:* b Phoenix, Ariz, July 22, 54. *Educ:* Ariz State Univ, BS, 76; Ind Univ, PhD(genetics), 81. *Prof Exp:* Res asst, Carnegie Inst Wash, 81-84. *Concurrent Pos:* Prin investr, Dept Zool, Univ Wash, 85- *Mem:* Genetics Soc Am; Develop Biol Soc. *Res:* Importance of chromosome structure for the expression of genes during development of Drosophila. *Mailing Add:* Dept Zool NJ-15 Univ Wash 3900 7th Ave NE Seattle WA 98195-0001

**WAKSBERG, ARMAND L,** LASERS, COMMUNICATIONS. *Current Pos:* CONSULT, 95- *Personal Data:* b Paris, France; Can citizen; m 60; c 1. *Educ:* McGill Univ, BS, 56, MS, 60. *Prof Exp:* Scientist, Canadair, Ltd, 56-58 & Can Aviation Electronics, 60-63; sr scientist, Res Dept, RCA Ltd, 63-77; dir laser & electro-optics, MPB Technologies, 77-95. *Concurrent Pos:* Chmn, Div Optics, Can Asn Physicists. *Mem:* Sr mem Inst Elec & Electronics Engrs; Can Asn Physicists. *Res:* Lasers, including sidelight spectroscopy, laser noise and phase locking phenomena; laser communications and propagation; laser systems; laser receivers. *Mailing Add:* 29 Stonecrest Dr Dollard-Des-Ormeaux PQ H9B 1N6 Can

**WAKSBERG, JOSEPH,** APPLIED STATISTICS. *Current Pos:* vpres, 73-91, CHMN BD, WESTAT INC, 91- *Personal Data:* b Kielce, Poland, Sept 20, 15; US citizen; m 41, Roslyn Karr; c Arlene & Mark. *Educ:* City Col New York, BS, 36. *Prof Exp:* Jr mathematician, USN Dept, 37-38; asst proj dir math, US Works Proj Admin, 38-40; asst proj dir, US Bur Census, 40-59, asst chief construction statist div, 59-63, chief statist methods div, 63-71, assoc dir statist, Bur, 72-73. *Concurrent Pos:* Instr statist, USDA Grad Sch, 63-73; consult, CBS News, 66- *Mem:* Fel Am Statist Asn; Int Statist Inst; Int Asn Surv Statist. *Res:* Sample design for surveys; research in survey methodology, especially sampling and response errors. *Mailing Add:* 6302 Tone Dr Bethesda MD 20817. *Fax:* 301-294-2034

**WAKSMAN, BYRON HALSTEAD,** NEUROSCIENCES. *Current Pos:* VIS SCIENTIST NEUROL, HARVARD UNIV, 90- *Personal Data:* b New York, NY, Sept 15, 19; m 44, Joyce Robertroy; c Nan & Peter. *Educ:* Swarthmore Col, BA, 40; Univ Pa, MD, 43. *Honors & Awards:* Charcot Award, Int Fedn Mult Sclerosis Socs, 93. *Prof Exp:* Intern, Michael Reese Hosp, Ill, 44; res assoc neuropath, Harvard Med Sch, 49-52, assoc bact & immunol, 52-57, asst prof, 57-63; prof microbiol, Yale Univ, 63-74, prof path, 74-78, adj prof path & biol, 79-89; vpres res & med progs, Nat Mult Sclerosis Soc, 80-89. *Concurrent Pos:* Fel, Mayo Clin, 46-48; NIH fel, Columbia Univ, 48-49; res fel neuropath, Mass Gen Hosp, 49-52, assoc bacteriologist, 52-63; consult assoc bacteriologist, Mass Eye & Ear Infirmary, 57-63; mem microbiol fels panel, NIH, 61-64, mem study sect B on allergy & immunol, 65-69; mem res rev panel, Nat Multiple Sclerosis Soc, 61-66; mem expert adv panel immunol, WHO, 63-68; chmn dept microbiol, Yale Univ, 64-70 & 72-74; adj prof path, NY Univ, 79-; dir, sci writing fels prog, Marine Biol Lab, Woods Hole, 90-95; Humboldt prof neuroimmunol, Max Planck Inst Psychiat, Munich, Ger, 91-93; dir, EICOS prog for sci journalists, Max Planck Inst Psychiat, Munich, 92-95. *Mem:* Fel AAAS; Am Asn Immunol (secy-treas, 61-64, pres, 70-71); Am Acad Microbiol; Am Neurol Asn; Am Acad Neurol; Am Soc Investigative Path; Am Acad Arts & Sci. *Res:* Role of thymus and lymphocytes in immune responses; immunologic tolerance; delayed hypersensitivity; mechanism of action of suppressor T-cells, lymphokines; experimental autoimmune diseases; neuroimmunology; demyelinative diseases; public understanding of science. *Mailing Add:* 300 E 54th St Apt 5K New York NY 10022. *Fax:* 212-263-8211; *E-Mail:* waksman@is2.nyu.edu

**WALASZEK, EDWARD JOSEPH,** PHARMACOLOGY. *Current Pos:* from asst prof to assoc prof, 57-62, chmn dept, 64-92, PROF PHARMACOL, MED CTR, UNIV KANS, KANSAS CITY, 62- *Personal Data:* b Chicago, Ill, July 4, 27; m 55, Sophie Ignarshi; c Edward Jr & Sheila. *Educ:* Univ Ill, BSc, 49; Univ Chicago, PhD(pharmacol), 53. *Hon Degrees:* MD, Univ Helsinki, 90. *Honors & Awards:* Bela Issekutz Medal, Hungarian Acad Sci; Pharmaceut Award, Polish Acad Sci; Recognition Award, Nat Drug Inst, Poland. *Prof Exp:* Asst prof neurophysiol & biochem, Univ Ill, 55-56. *Concurrent Pos:* Res fel, Univ Edinburgh, 53-55; USPHS spec res fel, 56-61, res career develop award, 61-63, res career award, 63-64; mem health study sect med chem, NIH, 62-66, mem res career award study sect, Nat Inst Gen Med Sci, 66-70; consult, Cutter Labs, 62-70, Alza Pharmaceut, 68-80, Inter X Corp, 73-81; mem adv coun, Int Union Pharmacol, 72-76; mem comt teaching of sci, Int Coun Sci Unions, 72-78; mem, Health Study Sect Pharmacol-Toxicol, 74-78; UN consult, China Develop Prog; consult, USSR through Ministry Health, Comput Med Educ; chmn, teaching comn, Int Union Pharmacol, 75-84. *Mem:* AAAS; Am Chem Soc; Soc Neurosci; Am Soc Pharmacol & Exp Therapeut; fel Am Col Clin Pharmacol; foreign mem Finnish Acad Sci; hon mem Hungarian Pharmacol Soc; hon mem Finnish Pharmacol Soc. *Res:* Pharmacologically active polypeptides; neurohumoral substances; naturally-occurring biogenic amines; pharmacology and physiology of the central nervous system. *Mailing Add:* Dept Pharmacol Med Ctr Univ Kans Kansas City KS 66103. *Fax:* 913-588-7501; *E-Mail:* ewalasze@kumc.edu

**WALASZEK, ZBIGNIEW,** CANCER PREVENTION & TREATMENT, CARDIOVASCULAR DISEASE PREVENTION & TREATMENT. *Current Pos:* ASSOC SCIENTIST & CHIEF, LAB BIO-ORG & NATURAL PROD CHEM, BIOMED HORIZONS INST, 95- *Personal Data:* b Dabrowa Tarnowska, Poland, Apr 14, 40; m, Margaret Hanausek; c Martin K. *Educ:* Silesia Tech Univ, Gliwice, Poland, MS, 62, PhD(bio-org chem), 72. *Honors & Awards:* Award for Studies RNA Synthesis, Polish Acad Sci, 83. *Prof Exp:* Postdoctoral fel, Dept Chem, Ohio State Univ, 74-75, res scientist, Dept Physiol Chem & Comprehensive Cancer Ctr, 82-86; sr lectr org chem, Silesia Tech Univ, 76-77; asst prof biochem, Inst Oncol, Poland, 77-81, M D Anderson Cancer Ctr, Univ Tex, 86-94. *Concurrent Pos:* Prin investr, Am Inst Cancer Res, 86-87 & 92-94; prin investr, NIH, 88-, consult, 92-; mem fac, Health Sci Ctr, Univ Tex, 90-95; consult, Am Inst Biol Sci, 93- *Mem:* Am Asn Cancer Res; Am Soc Biochem & Molecular Biol; Europ Asn Cancer Res; Int Soc Prev Oncol; AAAS; Am Chem Soc. *Res:* Mechanistic studies on the effect of various anti-cancer agents on the induction and growth of tumors in different animal models; prevention and treatment of cancer and cardiovascular diseases. *Mailing Add:* 908 NE Loop 230 PO Box 695 Smithville TX 78957

**WALAWENDER, MICHAEL JOHN,** PETROLOGY, GEOLOGY. *Current Pos:* asst prof geol, 72-77, ASSOC PROF GEOL, SAN DIEGO STATE UNIV, 77- *Personal Data:* b Auburn, NY, Dec 16, 39; m 67. *Educ:* Syracuse Univ, BS, 65; SDak Sch Mines & Technol, MS, 67; Pa State Univ, University Park, PhD(petrol), 72. *Prof Exp:* Res asst mineral, SDak Sch Mines & Technol, 65-67; asst petrol, Pa State Univ, University Park, 67-72. *Mem:* Geol Soc Am. *Res:* Igneous and metamorphic petrology; mineralogy; planetology. *Mailing Add:* Dept Geol San Diego State Univ San Diego CA 92182-0001

**WALBA, DAVID MARK,** ORGANIC CHEMISTRY. *Current Pos:* from asst prof to assoc prof, 77-87, PROF CHEM, UNIV COLO, BOULDER, 87- *Personal Data:* b Oakland, Calif, June 29, 49; m 81, Cassandra B Geneson; c Paul E (Geneson). *Educ:* Univ Calif, Berkeley, BS, 71; Calif Inst Technol, PhD(chem), 75. *Prof Exp:* Fel, Univ Calif, Los Angeles, 75-77. *Concurrent Pos:* Fel, A P Sloan Found; Camille & Henry Dreyfus Teacher-Scholar. *Mem:* Am Chem Soc; Sigma Xi. *Res:* Topological stereochemistry; organic photonic materials. *Mailing Add:* Dept Chem Univ Colo Boulder CO 80309-0215. *Fax:* 303-492-5894; *E-Mail:* walba@colorado.edu

**WALBA, HAROLD,** ORGANIC CHEMISTRY. *Current Pos:* From instr to assoc prof, 49-58, chmn dept, 61-64, PROF CHEM, SAN DIEGO STATE UNIV, 58- *Personal Data:* b Chelsea, Mass, Mar 10, 21; m 46; c 2. *Educ:* Univ Mass, BS, 46; Univ Calif, PhD(chem), 49. *Mem:* AAAS; Am Chem Soc; The Chem Soc; Sigma Xi. *Res:* Substituent effects and their transmission in organic molecules; tautomerism; acid-base strengths. *Mailing Add:* 3870 Carancho St La Mesa CA 91941-7606

**WALBERG, CLIFFORD BENNETT,** CLINICAL CHEMISTRY. *Current Pos:* Asst prof path, 69-76, CLIN CHEMIST, TOXICOL LAB, LOS ANGELES COUNTY-UNIV SOUTHERN CALIF MED CTR, 57-, ASSOC PROF PATH, SCH MED, UNIV SOUTHERN CALIF, 76- *Personal Data:* b Watkins, Minn, Feb 24, 15; m 46; c 4. *Educ:* Univ Sask, BS, 39; Univ Southern Calif, AB, 43, MS, 45, PhD(biochem), 57. *Mem:* Am Asn Clin Chem. *Res:* Clinical biochemistry; toxicology. *Mailing Add:* 364 W Spazier Ave Burbank CA 91506

**WALBORG, EARL FREDRICK, JR,** BIOCHEMISTRY. *Current Pos:* CONSULT, 85- *Personal Data:* b Chicago, Ill, Nov 13, 35; m 58; c 3. *Educ:* Austin Col, BA, 58; Baylor Univ, PhD(biochem), 62. *Prof Exp:* Asst biochemist & asst prof biochem, M D Anderson Hosp & Tumor Inst, Houston, 65-70, assoc prof biochem, 70-73, assoc biochemist & chief sect protein struct, 70-77, prof biochem, 73-77; prof biochem, Univ Tex Syst Cancer Ctr, Sci Park Res Div, Smithville, 77-85; mem grad fac, Univ Tex Grad Sch Biomed Sci, Houston, 70-85. *Concurrent Pos:* USPHS res fel physiol chem, Univ Lund, 62-65; Eleanor Roosevelt Int Cancer fel biochem, Neth Cancer Inst, Amsterdam, 74; consult, 85- *Mem:* AAAS; Am Chem Soc; fel Am Inst Chem; Am Asn Cancer Res; Am Soc Biol Chem. *Res:* Chemistry of the cell-surface, glyoproteins, hepatocarcinogenesis. *Mailing Add:* PO Box 727 Dermigen Inc Smithville TX 78957-0727. *Fax:* 512-237-3439

**WALBORN, NOLAN REVERE,** ASTRONOMY. *Current Pos:* STAFF ASTRONR, SPACE TELESCOPE SCI INST, 84- *Personal Data:* b Bloomsburg, Pa, Sept 30, 44; m 75; c 1. *Educ:* Gettysburg Col, BA, 66; Univ Chicago, PhD(astron, astrophys), 70. *Prof Exp:* Fel, Yerkes Observ, Univ Chicago, 71 & David Dunlap Observ, Univ Toronto, 71-73; staff astronr, Cerro Tololo Inter-Am Observ, 73-81; nat res coun sr res assoc, Goddard Space Flight Ctr, NASA, 82-84. *Mem:* Am Astron Soc; Can Astron Soc; Int

Astron Union; Astron Soc Pac. *Res:* Stellar spectroscopy; spectral classification; early-type stars; galactic structure; interstellar lines; Magellanic Clouds. *Mailing Add:* Space Telescope Sci Inst 3700 San Martin Dr Baltimore MD 21218

**WALBORSKY, HARRY M,** ORGANIC CHEMISTRY. *Current Pos:* from asst prof to assoc prof chem, 50-59, PROF CHEM, FLA STATE UNIV, 59- *Personal Data:* b Lodz, Poland, Dec 25, 23; nat US; m 53; c 4. *Educ:* City Col New York, BS, 45; Ohio State Univ, PhD(chem), 49. *Honors & Awards:* Alexander von Humboldt Sr Scientist Award, 88. *Prof Exp:* Res assoc, Calif Inst Technol, 48; res assoc, Atomic Energy Proj, Univ Calif, Los Angeles, 49-50. *Concurrent Pos:* USPHS fel, Basel, Switz, 52-53; R O Lawton distinguished prof, 80. *Mem:* Am Chem Soc; Royal Soc Chem. *Res:* Small ring compounds; organometallics; asymmetric synthesis; electrolytic and dissolving metal reductions; synthetic methods. *Mailing Add:* Dept Chem Fla State Univ Tallahassee FL 32306

**WALBOT, VIRGINIA ELIZABETH,** PLANT GENETICS. *Current Pos:* PROF BIOL SCI, STANFORD UNIV, 80- *Personal Data:* US citizen. *Educ:* Stanford Univ, AB, 67; Yale Univ, MPhil, 69, PhD(biol), 72. *Prof Exp:* NIH fel, Univ Ga, 72-75; asst prof biol, Washington Univ, 75-80. *Mem:* AAAS; Bot Soc Am; Soc Develop Biol; Am Soc Plant Physiol; Sigma Xi. *Res:* Plant molecular biology and development; genetics; botany. *Mailing Add:* Dept Biol Sci Stanford Univ Gilbert Hall Stanford CA 94305-9991

**WALBRICK, JOHNNY MAC,** INDUSTRIAL ORGANIC CHEMISTRY. *Current Pos:* res chemist, Res Labs, Merichem Co, 70-74, mgr res, 73-77, dir res, 77-89, VPRES, RES & DEVELOP, MERICHEM CO, 89- *Personal Data:* b Wichita Falls, Tex, Sept 14, 41; m 64, Elaine Reichert; c Kevin & Kelly. *Educ:* Midwestern Univ, BS, 63; Univ Fla, PhD(chem), 67. *Prof Exp:* NSF fel, Univ Fla, 67-68. *Mem:* Am Chem Soc; Chem Marketing Res Asn; Indust Res Inst; Com Develop Asn. *Res:* Mechanism of electroorganic reaction processes; new industrial processes for organic chemicals. *Mailing Add:* Merichem Co 4800 Tex Com Tower Houston TX 77002

**WALBURG, H E,** VETERINARY MEDICINE. *Current Pos:* CONSULT, 83- *Personal Data:* b Newark, NJ, Feb 6, 32; m 54; c 4. *Educ:* Dartmouth Col, AB, 53; Va Polytech Inst, MS, 58; Univ Ga, DVM, 58; Univ Ill, PhD(radiobiol), 61. *Honors & Awards:* Animal Care Panel Res Award, 65. *Prof Exp:* Biologist, 61-73, dir, Comp Animal Res Lab, Oak Ridge Nat Lab, 73-83. *Mem:* Radiation Res Soc; Geront Soc; Am Asn Cancer Res; Am Vet Med Asn. *Res:* Radiation carcinogenesis and radiation induced life-shortening and aging. *Mailing Add:* 921 Knob Creek Blvd Seymour TN 37865

**WALBURN, FREDERICK J,** BIOMEDICAL ENGINEERING. *Current Pos:* Res bioengr, 82-90, dir corp res develop, 90-91, PRIN INVESTR, RES DIV, MIAMI HEART INST, 91- *Personal Data:* b Cumberland, Md, Feb 7, 51. *Educ:* Va Polytech Inst, BS, 73, MS, 75, PhD(eng sci & mech), 79. *Concurrent Pos:* Adj prof bioeng, Univ Miami, 82- *Mem:* Biomed Eng Soc; Am Soc Mech Engr; Am Heart Asn; Inst Elec & Electronics Engrs; Soc Clin Trials. *Mailing Add:* 2000 N Rio De Flag Flagstaff AZ 86004

**WALCH, HENRY ANDREW, JR,** MYCOLOGY. *Current Pos:* from instr to assoc prof microbiol, 55-64, chmn dept, 60-64 & 72-75, PROF MICROBIOL, SAN DIEGO STATE UNIV, 64- *Personal Data:* b Minneapolis, Minn, June 3, 22; m 53; c 2. *Educ:* Univ Calif, Los Angeles, BA, 50, PhD(microbiol), 54. *Prof Exp:* Mycol technician, Univ Calif, Los Angeles, 50-54, res asst, 54-55. *Concurrent Pos:* Res grants, San Diego Imp Counties Tuberc & Respiratory Health Asn, 57-72 & Respiratory Dis Asn Calif, 72-73; consult & lectr, Sharp Mem Hosp, San Diego, 58- & US Naval Hosp, 64-; consult, Palomar Mem Hosp, Escondido, Calif; NIH spec fel, Mycol Unit, Commun Dis Ctr, Atlanta, Ga. *Mem:* Am Soc Microbiol; Mycol Soc Am; Am Inst Biol Sci; AAAS; Sigma Xi. *Res:* Human and animal pathogenic fungi, particularly virulence factors, immunology and ecology. *Mailing Add:* 4605 El Cerrito Dr San Diego CA 92115-3746

**WALCHLI, HAROLD E(DWARD),** COMPUTER SYSTEMS SOFTWARE, RADIOACTIVE MATERIALS TRANSPORT. *Current Pos:* PRES, HAL-COM ASSOCS, ENG COMPUTER CONSULTS, 80- *Personal Data:* b Warren, Pa, Nov 13, 22; m 45, Ruth Klenck; c Gary E & James D. *Educ:* Pa State Univ, BS, 44; Univ Tenn, MS, 54. *Prof Exp:* Field engr, Bell Tel Co, Pa, 41; instr preradar, Pa State Univ, 42-43, staff asst elec eng, 43, asst instr physics, 43-44; asst engr, Tenn Eastman Corp, 44-47; engr, Carbide & Carbon Chem Co, 47-55; asst to tech dir, Westinghouse Elec Corp, 56-57, mgr eng serv, Atomic Power Dept, 57-58, asst proj mgr, Yankee Atomic Plant Proj, 58-60, fuel serv supvr, 60-64, fuel serv mgr, Nuclear Fuel Div, 64-71, mgr & adv engr, pressurized water reactor systs, Nuclear Servs Dept, Nuclear Energy Systs, 71-77, mgr strategic progs, Nuclear Serv Div, 77-80, facil & financial planning, fel engr data & commun serv, 80-86, Info Ctr Consult, microcomput specialist, Water Reactor Div, 83-86. *Concurrent Pos:* Am Soc Sci Inst N14 Transp Stand, 60-; Am Soc Mech Engrs Y-32 Drafting Stand, 61-88; Chmn, Adv Comt Radioactive Mat, Hazardous Substances Transp Bd, Commonwealth Pa, 72-77. *Mem:* Am Soc Mech Engrs; Inst Elec & Electronics Engrs; Inst Nuclear Mat Mgt. *Res:* Nuclear magnetic resonance spectroscopy; electronic circuit design; radioactive materials transport; nuclear materials management; engineering management; computerized data communications; atomic plant design and construction; atomic fuel cycle services; microprocessor equipment applications; engineering and business applications software; measurement of nuclear magnetic moment of rare isotopes found sparsely in nature. *Mailing Add:* 1329 Foxboro Dr Monroeville PA 15146

**WALCOTT, BENJAMIN,** COMPARATIVE PHYSIOLOGY. *Current Pos:* asst prof, 72-79, ASSOC PROF NEUROBIOL & BEHAVIOR, STATE UNIV NY, STONY BROOK, 79-, ASSOC PROVOST, 87- *Personal Data:* b Boston, Mass, May 31, 41; m 72, Rosalind Bennett. *Educ:* Harvard Univ, BA, 63; Univ Ore, PhD(biol), 68. *Prof Exp:* USPHS physiol trainee, Univ Ore, 64-67, instr biol, 67-68; vis res fel biol, Res Sch Biol Sci, Australian Nat Univ, 69-71, fel biol, 71-72. *Mem:* Am Soc Cell Biol; Asn Res Vision & Ophthal; Soc Gen Physiol; Biophys Soc; Soc Neurosci. *Res:* Neural control of tear glands and of the cells of the immune system within the tear glands; innervation density by autonomic nervous system of heart, tear gland, gut and other tissues. *Mailing Add:* Dept Neurobiol Health Sci Ctr State Univ NY Stony Brook NY 11794. *E-Mail:* benjamin.walcott@sunysb.edu

**WALCOTT, CHARLES,** BEHAVIORAL PHYSIOLOGY. *Current Pos:* RETIRED. *Personal Data:* b Boston, Mass, July 19, 34; m 76, Jane Taylor; c Thomas S & Samuel C. *Educ:* Harvard Univ, AB, 56; Cornell Univ, PhD, 59. *Prof Exp:* Asst, Cornell Univ, 56-58; res fel biol, Harvard Univ, 59-60, asst prof appl biol, Div Eng & Appl Physics, 60-65; asst prof biol, Tufts Univ, 65-67; assoc prof biol, State Univ NY, Stony Brook, 67-74, actg dir, Ctr Curriculum Develop, 67-71, chmn, Dept Cellular & Comp Biol, 71-76; prof biol, State Univ NY, Stony Brook, 74-81; prof biol, Cornell Univ, 81-95, exec dir, 81-93, Louis Aggasiz Fuertes Dir, Lab Ornith, 93-95. *Concurrent Pos:* Dir, Natural Sci TV Proj, 59-60; dir elem sci study, Educ Develop Ctr, Inc, 65-67; dir, Content Res 3-2-1 Contact, Children's Television Workshop, 78-80. *Mem:* AAAS; Soc Exp Biol; Animal Behav Soc; Sigma Xi. *Res:* Animal orientation and navigation; animal acoustic communication. *Mailing Add:* W255 Mudd Hall Cornell Univ Ithaca NY 14853. *Fax:* 607-254-4308; *E-Mail:* w38@cornell.edu

**WALCZAK, HUBERT R,** MATHEMATICS. *Current Pos:* Asst prof, 63-72, assoc prof, 72-77, PROF MATH, COL ST THOMAS, 77- *Personal Data:* b South Saint Paul, Minn, Jan 21, 34; m 61; c 3. *Educ:* Col St Thomas, BA, 55; Univ Minn, PhD(math), 63. *Mem:* Math Asn Am. *Res:* Analysis and quasiconformal mappings. *Mailing Add:* Dept Math Univ St Thomas 2115 Summit Ave St Paul MN 55105

**WALD, ALVIN STANLEY,** HOSPITAL DESIGN, HOSPITAL SYSTEMS MANAGEMENT. *Current Pos:* SR RES SCIENTIST, COL PHYSICIANS & SURGEONS, COLUMBIA UNIV, 78- *Personal Data:* b New York, NY, May 17, 34; m 77; c 2. *Educ:* Cooper Union, BEE, 55; Polytech Inst Brooklyn, MEE, 61; NY Univ, PhD(biomed eng), 74. *Prof Exp:* Sr engr, Bulova Res Develop Labs, 61-64; biomed eng res scientist & asst prof exp neurosurg, Dept Neurosurg, Med Ctr, NY Univ, 64-78. *Concurrent Pos:* Instr, Sch Respiratory Ther, NY Univ-Bellevue Hosp, 68-81; NY State Health Res Coun grant, 76-77; mem, Comt Construct Exam Cert Clin Engrs, Am Bd Clin Eng, 77; mem, Neurol Device Panel, Bur Med Devices, Food & Drug Admin, 78-81; rep, Med Devices Stand Mgt Bd & Med Device Comt, Am Nat Stand Inst, 79-83; tech specialist, Physiol Monitoring Comt, Univ Hosp, State Univ NY, Stony Brook, 80; mem, Hosp Comt, Long-Range Planning Comt, Columbia Presby Med Ctr, 82-; ed, Eng in Med & Biol Mag, Inst Elec & Electronics Engrs, 84- *Mem:* AAAS; Am Physiol Soc; NY Acad Sci; Asn Advan Med Instrumentation; Inst Elec & Electronics Engrs. *Res:* Development and application of modern technology to health care needs. *Mailing Add:* Dept Anesthesiol Col Physicians & Surgeons Columbia Univ 630 W 168th St New York NY 10032-3702

**WALD, ARNOLD,** GASTROENTEROLOGY, INTERNAL MEDICINE. *Current Pos:* from asst prof to assoc prof, 78-91, PROF MED, SCH MED, UNIV PITTSBURGH, 91-, ASSOC CHIEF, DIV GASTROENTEROL & NEPATOLOGY, MED CTR, 93- *Personal Data:* b New York, NY, June 10, 42; m 66, Ellen Rashkow; c Elissa K & Eric L. *Educ:* Colgate Univ, BA, 64; State Univ NY, MD, 68. *Prof Exp:* From instr to asst prof med, Sch Med, Johns Hopkins Univ, 75-78. *Concurrent Pos:* Head, Gastroenterol Unit, Montefiore Univ Hosp, Pittsburgh, 83-93. *Mem:* Am Gastroenterol Asn; Am Fedn Clin Res; Am Motility Soc; fel Am Col Gastroenterol. *Res:* Disorders of gastrointestinal motor function (motility); behavioral modification of gastrointestinal function. *Mailing Add:* GI Div Univ Pittsburgh Med Ctr 200 Lothrop St Pittsburgh PA 15213. *Fax:* 412-648-9376; *E-Mail:* wald@novell2.dept-med.pitt.edu

**WALD, FRANCINE JOY WEINTRAUB,** PHYSICS, SCIENCE EDUCATION. *Current Pos:* sci consult physics & biol, 72-75, SCI INSTR, FRIENDS SEM, 75-, CHAIRPERSON, DEPT SCI, 76- *Personal Data:* b Brooklyn, NY, Jan 13, 38; m 64, Bernard J Wald; c David & Kevin. *Educ:* City Col New York, BEE, 60; Polytech Inst Brooklyn, MS, 62, PhD(chem physics), 69. *Prof Exp:* Engr solid state physics, Remington Rand Univac Div, 60; instr physics, Polytech Inst Brooklyn, 62-64, adj res assoc, 69-70. *Concurrent Pos:* Lectr phys sci, NY Community Col, 69 & 70. *Mem:* Am Phys Soc; Sigma Xi; Am Asn Physics Teachers; Nat Sci Teachers Asn; Asn Teachers Independent Schs; NY Acad Sci; AAAS. *Res:* Investigating how children of various ages respond to science, particularly physics, how they assimilate the concepts and language encountered; gender issues in science education. *Mailing Add:* 520 La Guardia Pl New York NY 10012-1426. *Fax:* 212-979-5034; *E-Mail:* waldf@acfcluster.nyu.edu

**WALD, FRITZ VEIT,** SOLID STATE CHEMISTRY, MATERIALS SCIENCE. *Current Pos:* sr scientist, Tyco Labs Inc, Mobil Solar Energy Corp, 63-69, head, Mat Sci Dept, Corp Technol Ctr, 69-75, assoc tech dir, 75-80, dir res, 81-87, sr sci adv, 88-93, SR SCI ADV & MGR, ASE AMERICAS INC, 94- *Personal Data:* b Dieringhausen, WGer, Apr 28, 33; m 59, Doris Herberg; c Kristin D, Andrea E & Katja F. *Educ:* Sch Tech Chem, Cologne, Ger, BS, 55. *Honors & Awards:* Indust Res Award, 70. *Prof Exp:*

Tech chemist, Ed Doerrenberg Soehne, Steelworks Ruenderoth, WGer, 55-57; res asst metall & solid state chem, Philips Cent Lab Aachen, 57-61; res metallurgist, Frigistors Ltd Que, Can, 61-63. *Concurrent Pos:* Mem bd dirs, Radiation Monitoring Devices Inc, 76-; mem bd vis, Sch Eng, Duke Univ, 85-95. *Mem:* Metall Soc; Am Inst Mining, Metall & Petrol Engrs; fel Am Inst Chemists; Mat Res Soc. *Res:* Solid state chemistry; electronic materials; photovoltaic solar energy conversion; crystal growth. *Mailing Add:* ASE Americas Inc 4 Suburban Park Dr Billerica MA 01821-3980. *Fax:* 508-358-4476; *E-Mail:* fvw@msu.com

**WALD, GEORGE,** biochemistry, molecular biology; deceased, see previous edition for last biography

**WALD, MILTON M,** CHEMISTRY. *Current Pos:* RETIRED. *Personal Data:* b San Francisco, Calif, Oct 29, 25; m 56; c 2. *Educ:* Univ Calif, Los Angeles, BS, 49; Univ Southern Calif, PhD(chem), 54. *Prof Exp:* Res assoc, Brookhaven Nat Lab, 54-56; chemist, Shell Develop Co, 56-88. *Mem:* Am Chem Soc. *Res:* Organic and catalytic chemistry; petroleum chemistry. *Mailing Add:* 10706 Holly Springs Dr Houston TX 77042

**WALD, NIEL,** PUBLIC HEALTH, RADIATION MEDICINE. *Current Pos:* assoc res prof, Univ Pittsburgh, 58-60, from assoc prof to prof radiation health, Grad Sch Pub Health, 60-76, chmn, Dept Radiation Health, 69-76 & 77-89, Dept Occup Health, 75-76 & Dept Indust Environ Health Sci, 76-77, PROF RADIOL, SCH MED, UNIV PITTSBURGH, 65-, PROF HUMAN GENETICS, GRAD SCH PUB HEALTH, 91-, PROF ENVIRON & OCCUP HEALTH, 92- *Personal Data:* b New York, NY, Oct 1, 25; m 53, Lucienne Hill; c David & Phillip. *Educ:* Columbia Univ, AB, 45; NY Univ, MD, 48. *Prof Exp:* Intern & resident med affiliated hosps, NY Univ, 48-49, 50-52; sr hematologist & head radioisotope lab, Atomic Bomb Casualty Comn, Japan, 54-57; head biologist, Health Physics Div, Oak Ridge Nat Lab, 57-58. *Concurrent Pos:* Fel immunohemat, NY Univ affiliated hosps, 49-50; asst prof med, Sch Med, Univ Pittsburgh, 58-65; mem, Pa Governor's Adv Comt Atomic Energy Develop & Radiation Control, 66-84, chmn, 74-76; consult, Div Oper Safety, US AEC, 68-75, Div Compliance, 69-75, US Navy Submarine & Radiation Med Div, 73-, US Energy Res & Develop Admin, 75-77, US Nuclear Regulatory Comn, 75- & US Dept Energy, 78-80; mem, Nat Coun Radiation Protection, 70-82, consociate mem, 82-, US Nuclear Regulatory Comn Adv Panel Decontamination, Three Mile Island-2 Reactor Facil, 83-93; mem, Pa Adv Comt Low Level Radioactive Waste Disposal, 85-; vis Am prof, Royal Soc Med, UK, 86; US mem, Working Group Health Effects, US-USSR Joint Coordr Comt, Civilian Nuclear Reactor Safety, 89-92. *Mem:* Health Physics Soc (pres, 73-74); Radiation Res Soc; Environ Mutagen Soc; Soc Human Genetics; AMA; Am Col Occup & Environ Med. *Res:* Diagnosis and treatment of radiation injury; health physics; cytogenetics. *Mailing Add:* A-744 Grad Sch Pub Health Univ Pittsburgh Pittsburgh PA 15261. *Fax:* 412-624-7534, 624-3040; *E-Mail:* wald@vms.cis.pitt.edu

**WALD, ROBERT MANUEL,** THEORETICAL PHYSICS. *Current Pos:* res assoc, 74-76, from asst prof to assoc prof, 76-85, PROF PHYSICS, UNIV CHICAGO, 85- *Personal Data:* b New York, NY, June 29, 47; m 88, Barbara Anderson; c Sarah & Kristina. *Educ:* Columbia Univ, AB, 68; Princeton Univ, PhD(physics), 72. *Prof Exp:* Res assoc physics, Univ Md, 72-74. *Mem:* Am Phys Soc. *Res:* General relativity and gravitation; black holes; quantum field theory in curved spacetime. *Mailing Add:* Enrico Fermi Inst Univ Chicago Chicago IL 60637

**WALDBAUER, EUGENE CHARLES,** NATURAL HISTORY. *Current Pos:* From asst prof to assoc prof, 56-69, PROF BIOL, STATE UNIV NY COL CORTLAND, 69- *Personal Data:* b Philadelphia, Pa, July 4, 26; m 56; c 5. *Educ:* East Stroudsburg State Col, BS, 52; Pa State Univ, MS, 56; Cornell Univ, PhD(wildlife biol, natural hist & parasitol), 66. *Mem:* Wilderness Soc. Sigma Xi. *Res:* Flora of Cortland County, New York; pollen analysis of central New York bogs; ferns and lycopodiums of central New York. *Mailing Add:* 6 Westfield Park Cortland NY 13045

**WALDBAUER, GILBERT PETER,** ENTOMOLOGY. *Current Pos:* Asst, 53-58, from instr to assoc prof, 58-71, PROF ENTOM, UNIV ILL, URBANA, 71- *Personal Data:* b Bridgeport, Conn, Apr 18, 28; m 55, Stephanie Stiefel; c Gwen R & Susan M. *Educ:* Univ Mass, BS, 53; Univ Ill, MS, 56, PhD, 60. *Concurrent Pos:* Sr scientist, Int Rice Res Inst, Los Banos, Phillipines, 78-79; USAID consult, Pakistan Agr Res Coun, 85. *Mem:* Sigma Xi; Entom Soc Am; Ecol Soc Am. *Res:* Ecology, behavior and physiology of insects; mimicry. *Mailing Add:* Dept Entom 320 Morrill Hall Univ Ill Urbana IL 61801

**WALDBILLIG, RONALD CHARLES,** MEMBRANE BIOPHYSICS, ELECTRO-OPTICAL DIELECTRICS. *Current Pos:* ASST PROF BIOPHYS, PHYSIOL DEPT, MED BR, UNIV TEX, 76- *Personal Data:* b Iron Mountain, Mich, Mar 17, 43; m 61; c 2. *Educ:* Northern Mich Univ, BS, 67; Univ Rochester, PhD(neurobiol), 73. *Prof Exp:* Res fel, Anat Dept, Duke Univ, 74-76. *Mem:* Biophys Soc; AAAS. *Res:* Molecular and physical aspects of membrane function and structure; electrical and optical analysis of the insulating characteristics of single lipid bilayer membranes. *Mailing Add:* 9718 Goldstone Lane Spring TX 77379

**WALDE, RALPH ELDON,** MATHEMATICS. *Current Pos:* ASST PROF MATH, TRINITY COL, CONN, 72- *Personal Data:* b Perham, Minn, Mar 8, 43; div; c 2. *Educ:* Univ Minn, Minneapolis, BA, 64; Univ Calif, Berkeley, PhD(math), 67. *Prof Exp:* Asst prof math, Univ Minn, Minneapolis, 67-72. *Mem:* Am Math Soc; Math Asn Am; Asn Comput Mach. *Res:* Lie algebras; non-associative algebras. *Mailing Add:* Eng & Comp Sci Dept Trinity Col Hartford CT 06106

**WALDEN, CLYDE HARRISON,** SCIENCE ADMINISTRATION. *Current Pos:* DIR PROCESS TECHNOL, KAISER ALUMINUM & CHEM CORP, 64- *Personal Data:* b Kansas City, Mo, Dec 19, 21; m 46; c 3. *Educ:* William Jewell Col, BA, 42; Univ Colo, MS, 46, PhD(phys chem), 49. *Prof Exp:* Mgr uranium accountability, Mallinckrodt Chem Co, 48-51; sr scientist sec recovery oil, Phillips Petrol Co, 51; mgr qual control, Nat Lead Co, Ohio, 51-57; dir qual control, Gen Tire & Rubber Co, 57-64. *Mem:* Am Chem Soc; fel Am Soc Qual Control. *Res:* Administration of technical and engineering functions; heats of chemical reactions. *Mailing Add:* 515 Silver Lake Dr Danville CA 94526

**WALDEN, DAVID BURTON,** PLANT GENETICS, CYTOGENETICS. *Current Pos:* from asst prof to assoc prof, 61-71, actg chmn dept, 71-73, PROF PLANT SCI, UNIV WESTERN ONT, 71- *Personal Data:* b New Haven, Conn, Mar 29, 32; c 2. *Educ:* Wesleyan Univ, BA, 54; Cornell Univ, MSc, 58, PhD(genetics), 59. *Prof Exp:* Fel bot, Ind Univ, 59-61. *Concurrent Pos:* Vis prof, Dept Genetics, Univ Birmingham, 73-74 & 81 & Dept Genetics & Develop & Dept Agron, Univ Ill, 74; pres, Biol Coun Can, 74-75; assoc ed, Can J Genetics & Cytol, 78-81; secy-gen, 16th Int Genetics Cong. *Mem:* AAAS; Crop Sci Soc Am; Genetics Soc Am; Genetics Soc Can (pres, 81-83); Int Genetics Fedn (pres, 88-). *Res:* Pollen biology; corn genetics; plant and human cytogenetics; somatic cell genetics; heat shock and stress proteins. *Mailing Add:* Dept Plant Sci Fac Sci Western Sci Ctr Univ Western Ont London ON N6A 5B9 Can

**WALDEN, JACK M,** ELECTRICAL ENGINEERING, COMPUTER SCIENCE. *Current Pos:* SECT TECH DIR, FISCAL INFO COLO, INC, 78- *Personal Data:* b Sheridan, Wyo, July 1, 22; m 46; c 5. *Educ:* SDak Sch Mines & Technol, BS, 44; Okla State Univ, MS, 62, PhD(eng), 65. *Prof Exp:* Chief engr, Midnight Sun Broadcasting, Alaska, 48-53; vpres & tech dir, Northern TV, Inc, 53-60; from instr to assoc prof elec eng, Okla State Univ, 60-69; eng group leader, Calculator Prod Div, Hewlett-Packard Co, 69-78. *Mem:* Sr mem Inst Elec & Electronics Engrs; Asn Comput Mach. *Res:* Computer logic design; computer programming of operating systems and compilers; engineering applications of computers; computer-aided instruction. *Mailing Add:* 2507 Lake Dr Loveland CO 80538

**WALDEN, ROBERT HENRY,** SEMICONDUCTORS, OPTOELECTRONIC INTEGRATED CIRCUITS. *Current Pos:* sr proj engr, Hughes Aircraft Co, 78-80, sect head, 80-81, mgr tech dept, 81-83, sr scientist, 83-85, SR STAFF ENGR, HUGHES RES LABS, 85- *Personal Data:* b New York, NY, May 24, 39; div; c 2. *Educ:* NY Univ, BES, 62, MEE, 63, PhD(eng sci), 66. *Honors & Awards:* Hughes Res Lab outstanding achievement award, 87. *Prof Exp:* Mem tech staff, Bell Tel Labs Inc, 66-78. *Mem:* Inst Elec & Electronics Engrs. *Res:* Optoelectronic integrated circuits, InP-based heterostructures; analog-to-digital conversion, sigma delta modulators; sub-micrometer III-V integrated circuits and device modelling; MOS, H8T device physics. *Mailing Add:* Hughes Res Labs 3011 Malibu Canyon Rd 254/R155 Malibu CA 90265

**WALDERN, DONALD E,** ANIMAL NUTRITION, BIOCHEMISTRY. *Current Pos:* RETIRED. *Personal Data:* b Lacombe, Alta, June 8, 28; m 53; c 4. *Educ:* Univ BC, BSA, 51, MSA, 54; Wash State Univ, PhD(nutrit, biochem), 62. *Prof Exp:* Res scientist, Exp Sta, Can Dept Agr, 53-57 & 61-62; assoc prof dairy nutrit, Wash State Univ, 62-67; res scientist, West Region Res Br, Agr Can, 67-73, dir, Res Sta, 73-78, prog specialist, 78-80, dir, Lacombe Res Sta, 80-89. *Concurrent Pos:* Coordr, Agr Res Progs, WCan. *Mem:* Am Dairy Sci Asn; Am Soc Animal Sci; Agr Inst Can; Can Soc Animal Sci. *Res:* Nutritive value of forages and cereal grains for dairy and beef cattle; complete feeds for dairy cows and early weaned calves; relationship of blood biochemical parameters to performance factors in dairy and beef cows; nutritional management systems for beef cows grazing grassland and forested rangeland. *Mailing Add:* Box 14 Site 75 RR 2 Summerland BC V0H 1Z0 Can

**WALDHAUER, F D,** engineering; deceased, see previous edition for last biography

**WALDHAUSEN, JOHN ANTON,** SURGERY. *Current Pos:* PROF SURG, HERSHEY MED CTR, PA STATE UNIV COL MED, 70- *Personal Data:* b New York, NY, May 22, 29; m 57; c 3. *Educ:* Col Great Falls, BS, 50; St Louis Univ, MD, 54. *Prof Exp:* Intern, Johns Hopkins Hosp, Baltimore, 54-55, resident, 56-57; surgeon, Nat Heart Inst, Md, 57-59; resident, Hosp, Univ Pa, 59-60; resident, Med Ctr, Ind Univ, Indianapolis, 60-62, instr surg, Sch Med, 62-63, asst prof, 63-66; assoc prof, Sch Med, Univ Pa, 66-70. *Concurrent Pos:* Surg res fel, Johns Hopkins Hosp, Baltimore, Md, 55-56; NIH career develop award, Sch Med, Ind Univ, Indianapolis, 63-66; assoc surgeon, Children's Hosp, Philadelphia, 66-70 & Hosp Univ Pa, 66-70; chmn, Dept Surg, Pa State Univ, 69-94, interim provost & dean, Col Med, 72-73, John W Oswald prof surg, Hershey Med Ctr, 84-94, exec dir univ physicians, 93-96; mem surg study sect B, NIH, 74-78; mem, Anesthesia Grant Comt, Nat Inst Gen Med Sci, NIH, 70-73; chmn, Coronary Artery Dis Opers Comt, Vet Admin Coop Study, 75-; mem, Pvt Doctors Am Collab Study, Harvard Sch Pub Health, 79-82; dir, Am Bd Surg, 85; ed, J Thoracic & Cardiovasc Surg, 94- *Mem:* Soc Univ Surg; Am Col Cardiol (secy, 81-82); Am Asn Thoracic Surg; Am Col Surgeons; Am Surg Asn (first vpres, 85-86); Am Physiol Soc; fel AAAS. *Res:* Effects of operative repair of congenital heart defects on pulmonary circulation; newer methods in repair of congenital heart defects; effects of cardiac surgery on ventricular function. *Mailing Add:* J Off-Dept Surg Pa State Univ Col Med Milton S Hershey Med Ctr PO Box 850 Hershey PA 17033. *Fax:* 717-531-4729

**WALDINGER, HERMANN V,** THEORY OF INFINITE GROUPS. *Current Pos:* ASSOC PROF MATH, POLYTECH UNIV, 61- *Personal Data:* b Vienna, Austria, June 17, 23; US citizen; m 48, Renee Kessler; c Roger & Ellen. *Educ:* Pomona Col, BA, 43; Brown Univ, MS, 44; Columbia Univ, PhD(math), 51. *Prof Exp:* Res engr, Repub Aviation Corp, 45-46; appl mathematician, M W Kellogg Co, 46-53; sr mathematician, Nuclear Develop Corp Am, 53-59; sr scientist, Repub Aviation Corp, 59-61. *Mem:* AAAS; Am Math Soc; Math Asn Am; Sigma Xi. *Res:* Calculus; structure of finitely presented infinite groups. *Mailing Add:* 600 Maitland Ave Teaneck NJ 07666-2201

**WALDINGER, RICHARD J,** COMPUTER SCIENCE. *Current Pos:* Res mathematician, 69-76, sr comput scientist, 76-81, PRIN SCIENTIST, ARTIFICIAL INTEL CTR, SRI INT, 81- *Personal Data:* b Brooklyn, NY, Mar 1, 44; m 75, Frances Bell; c Rachel & Evan. *Educ:* Columbia Univ, AB, 64; Carnegie-Mellon Univ, PhD(comput sci), 69. *Concurrent Pos:* Vis instr, Stanford Univ, 73, vis scholar, 79-85, consult prof, 85-; NSF grants. *Mem:* Fel Am Asn Artificial Intel; Asn Automatic Reasoning. *Res:* Artificial intelligence; automatic program synthesis; automated theorem proving; planning; formal methods in software engineering. *Mailing Add:* Artificial Intel Ctr 333 Ravenswood Ave SRI Int Menlo Park CA 94025. *E-Mail:* waldinger@al.sri.com

**WALDMAN, ALAN S,** MAMMALIAN CELL TRANSFECTION. *Current Pos:* ASST PROF BIOCHEM & MOLECULAR BIOL, SCH MED, IND UNIV, 89- *Personal Data:* b Bronx, NY, Aug 15, 59; m 85. *Educ:* State Univ NY, Albany, BS, 80; Johns Hopkins Univ, PhD(biochem), 85. *Prof Exp:* Fel, Sch Med, Yale Univ, 85-89. *Concurrent Pos:* Ad hoc reviewer, Molecular & Cellular Biol, 89-, J Molecular Biol, 89-, Somatic Cell & Molecular Genetics, 89-, Biotech, 90-, Proc Nat Acad Sci, 91- *Mem:* Am Soc Biochem & Molecular Biol; Sigma Xi. *Res:* Basic mechanisms of homologous recombination, genetic rearrangements, in mammalian cells, using molecular genetics as well as biochemical approaches. *Mailing Add:* Dept Biol Sci Univ SC CLS Rm 401 Columbia SC 29208. *Fax:* 803-777-4002; *E-Mail:* awaldman@biol.scarolina.edu

**WALDMAN, BARBARA CRISCUOLO,** GLYCOSYLATION, CELL BIOLOGY. *Personal Data:* b Bethesda, Md, Jan 24, 56; m 85. *Educ:* Va Polytech Inst & State Univ, BS, 78; Johns Hopkins Univ, PhD(biochem), 85. *Prof Exp:* Fel pharmacol, Yale Univ Sch Med, 85-89, assoc therapeut radiol, 89; asst scientist, Ind Univ Sch Med, 89-92. *Concurrent Pos:* Asst mem, Walther Oncol Ctr, 89-92. *Mem:* Am Soc Cell Biol; Am Soc Biochem & Molecular Biol; Sigma Xi; Am Chem Soc. *Res:* Regulation of glycosylation in mammalian cells; biosynthesis of asparagine-linked glycoproteins and nucleotide-sugar transport into the Golgi apparatus; protein trafficking. *Mailing Add:* Dept Biol Sci CLS 307 Univ SC Columbia SC 29208. *Fax:* 803-777-4002; *E-Mail:* bwaldman@biol.sc.edu

**WALDMAN, GEORGE D(EWEY),** AERONAUTICAL ENGINEERING. *Current Pos:* CONSULT, 87- *Personal Data:* b Hartford, Conn, Aug 5, 32. *Educ:* Trinity Col, BS, 54; Brown Univ, MS, 57, PhD(appl math), 59. *Prof Exp:* Scientist, Textron Defense Syst, 59-87. *Mem:* Am Inst Aeronaut & Astronaut. *Res:* Theory of flows at high speeds; pressure and heat transfer distributions over reentering vehicles; aerodynamic stability and control; multiphase flows and pollution. *Mailing Add:* 511 West St Reading MA 01867

**WALDMAN, JEFFREY,** ALUMINUM ALLOY RESEARCH, THERMAL MECHANICAL PROCESSING. *Current Pos:* LECTR & ASST DEPT HEAD, DEPT MAT ENG, DREXEL UNIV, 95- *Personal Data:* b Philadelphia, Pa, Jan 10, 41; m 62, Judith Shulman; c Stacey, Jonathan & Karen. *Educ:* Drexel Univ, BS, 63; Mass Inst Technol, ScD(metall), 67. *Prof Exp:* Mat engr, US Army Armament Res & Develop, 77-83; br chief, Naval Air Warfare Ctr, 83-95. *Concurrent Pos:* Vis scientist, Light Metals Res Inst, Novara, Italy, 71; adj prof, Drexel Univ, 75-; mem, Mfg Tech Adv Group Metals Subcomt, Dept Defense, 76-85, Nat Mat Adv Bd Panel Aluminum Powder Metall Alloys, 82-83, Agard Struct & Mat Panel, NATO, 87- & Aerospace Mat Conf, Am Soc Metals, 90-; res adv, Nat Res Coun, 78-95 & Off Naval Technol, 85-95; AIA Metallic Structures Comt, 92-95. *Mem:* Fel Am Soc Metals; Metall Soc. *Res:* Advanced metals and alloys for aircraft, such as aluminum-lithium alloys, thermal mechanical processing, as well as metal matrix and ceramic matrix composites. *Mailing Add:* 3894 Donna Dr Huntingdon Valley PA 19006

**WALDMAN, JOSEPH,** OPHTHALMOLOGY. *Current Pos:* Prof, 30-80, EMER PROF OPHTHAL, JEFFERSON MED COL, 30- *Personal Data:* b Philadelphia, Pa, May 12, 06; c 3. *Educ:* Jefferson Med Col, MD, 30; Am Bd Ophthal, dipl, 35. *Mem:* AMA. *Mailing Add:* 404 Meadowbrook Lane Erdenheim PA 19038-8225

**WALDMAN, L(OUIS) A(BRAHAM),** NUCLEAR REACTOR TECHNOLOGY. *Current Pos:* RETIRED. *Personal Data:* b Toledo, Ohio, Oct 13, 29; m 61; c 2. *Educ:* Univ Toledo, BS, 51; Carnegie Inst Technol, MS, 56; Univ Pittsburgh, PhD(chem eng), 64. *Prof Exp:* Student-employee, Oak Ridge Sch Reactor Tech, Oak Ridge Nat Lab, Union Carbide & Carbon Chem Corp, 51-52; fel engr, Bettis Atomic Power Lab, Westinghouse Elec Corp, 52-94. *Concurrent Pos:* Lectr, Carnegie Inst Technol, 65-66. *Mem:* Am Inst Chem Engrs; Am Nuclear Soc. *Res:* Heat and mass transfer; corrosion; erosion; fretting wear; release, transport and deposition of fission products from nuclear fuels; material and fuel element development for nuclear reactors. *Mailing Add:* 6550 Lilac St Pittsburgh PA 15217

**WALDMAN, LEWIS K,** CARDIAC MECHANICS & DYNAMICS. *Current Pos:* Fel, 83-85, ASST PROF, DEPT MED, UNIV CALIF, SAN DIEGO, 85- *Personal Data:* b Plainfield, NJ, Sept 20, 52. *Educ:* Northwestern Univ, BS, 74; Univ Calif, San Diego, MS, 77, PhD(bioeng), 82. *Mem:* Am Soc Mech Engrs; Biomed Eng Soc; Am Soc Biomech. *Mailing Add:* Dept Med 0613J Univ Calif San Diego La Jolla CA 92093-0613

**WALDMAN, ROBERT H,** microbiology; deceased, see previous edition for last biography

**WALDMANN, THOMAS A,** MEDICINE, IMMUNOLOGY. *Current Pos:* clin assoc, Nat Cancer Inst, 56-58, sr investr, Metab Br, 59-65, head, Immunophysiol Sect, 65-73, CHIEF, METAB BR, NAT CANCER INST, 71- *Personal Data:* b New York, NY, Sept 21, 30; m 58; c 3. *Educ:* Univ Chicago, AB, 51; Harvard Univ, MD, 55. *Hon Degrees:* DSc, Debrecen, Hungary, 90. *Honors & Awards:* Michael Heidelberger lectr, Columbia Univ; Irvin Strasberger lectr, Cornell Univ; Lucy Klein Mem lectr, Northwestern Univ; Merril lectr, Thomas Jefferson Univ; Phillips McMaster Mem lectr, Rockefeller Univ; Bela Schick Award, Am Col Allergists; Henry M Stratton Medal, Am Soc Hemat; Larry S Bernton Award, Allergy Soc; Kroc Honor Award, Am Asn Physicians; G Burroughs Mider Award, NIH; Ciba-Geigy Drew Award; Lila Gruber Prize; Artois-Baillet LaTour Health Prize; Bristol-Myers-Squib Cancer Prize; Milken Prize Cancer Res. *Prof Exp:* Intern, Mass Gen Hosp, 55-56. *Concurrent Pos:* Am Heart Asn fel, Nat Cancer Inst, 58-59; mem, Nat Cancer Plan Comt, 72; consult, Fed Trade Comn & WHO; assoc ed, J Immunol. *Mem:* Inst Med-Nat Acad Sci; Am Asn Immunologists; Am Soc Clin Invest; Asn Am Physicians; Am Physiol Soc; fel Am Soc Microbiologists; hon fel Am Acad Allergy & Immunol; fel AAAS; Sigma Xi; Am Acad Arts & Sci. *Res:* Factors controlling the human immune responses; discovery of the diseases intestinal lymphangiectasia, allergic enteropathy and familial hypercatabolic hypoproteinemia; new mechanisms of human disease including abnormalities of suppressor and helper t-cells in the pathogenesis of primary immune deficiency disease, immunodeficiency associated with cancer and autoimmune disease; molecular analysis of immunoglobulen and t-cell receptor rearrangement; interleukin-2 receptor. *Mailing Add:* Metab Br Nat Cancer Inst Bldg 410 Bethesda MD 20892-1374

**WALDO, GEORGE VAN PELT, JR,** ENGINEERING PHYSICS. *Current Pos:* PHYSICIST, CARDEROCK DIV, NAVAL SURFACE WARFARE CTR, MD, 62-, PRIN INVESTR, 70- *Personal Data:* b Montgomery, Ala, July 20, 40; m 66, Nancy Hershberger. *Educ:* Johns Hopkins Univ, AB, 61; Univ Md, PhD(physics), 72. *Mem:* Am Phys Soc; Sigma Xi. *Res:* Statistical mechanics of phase transitions; cavitation induced by shock waves; interaction of shock waves with structures; monte-carlo simulation of ship vulnerability; perturbation theory of phase transitions; underwater explosions. *Mailing Add:* Carderock Div Naval Surface Warfare Ctr Code 67-2 Bethesda MD 20084

**WALDO, WILLIS HENRY,** INORGANIC CHEMISTRY. *Current Pos:* RETIRED. *Personal Data:* b Detroit, Mich, Sept 27, 20; m 49; c 5. *Educ:* Washington & Jefferson Col, BS, 42; Univ Md, MS, 50. *Prof Exp:* Chemist, E I du Pont de Nemours & Co, 42-45; chemist, Socony Vacuum Oil Co, 45-46; asst chem, Univ Md, 46-49; tech ed, Monsanto Chem Co, 49-60, admin mgr agr div, Monsanto Co, 60-77, ed, Monsanto Tech Rev, 56-77; opers mgr, Indust Res Inst, Res Corp, St Louis, 77-80. *Concurrent Pos:* Mem, Nat Acad Sci-Nat Res Coun Comt Mod Methods Handling Chem Info, 62-66; lectr, Southern Ill Univ, Edwardsville, 72-74. *Mem:* Soc Tech Commun; Am Chem Soc; Sigma Xi; Am Soc Info Sci. *Res:* Chromium complexes; sulfur; machine documentation. *Mailing Add:* 49 Los Palos Dr San Luis Obispo CA 93401

**WALDREN, CHARLES ALLEN,** BIOPHYSICS. *Current Pos:* Chemist, Med Ctr, Univ Colo, 60-61, fel, 61-65, rest tech III, 65-67, instr, 67-75, ASST PROF BIOPHYS & GENETICS, MED CTR, UNIV COLO, 75-; SR FEL, ELEANOR ROOSEVELT INST CANCER RES, 74-; ASSOC PROF, DEPT RADIOL, UNIV COLO HEALTH SCI CTR, 80- *Personal Data:* b Syracuse, Kans, June 2, 34; m 61; c 3. *Educ:* Univ Colo, Boulder, BA, 59; Univ Colo Med Ctr, Denver, MS, 65, PhD(biophys), 72. *Concurrent Pos:* Vis scientist & fel, CRC DNA Repair Unit, Univ Cambridge, 72-73, 75-76, 81 & 85. *Mem:* Sigma Xi; Am Soc Cell Biol; Cancer Res Soc; Radiation Res Soc; Tissue Cult Asn; AAAS. *Res:* Genetic-biochemical-molecular biological analysis of mutagenesis and repair mechanisms in somatic mammalian cells; relationship to human developmental disease. *Mailing Add:* Dept Radiol Health Sci Colo State Univ Box MRB Ft Collins CO 80523-0001. *Fax:* 970-491-0623

**WALDREP, ALFRED CARSON, JR,** ORAL SURGERY, DENTISTRY. *Current Pos:* RETIRED. *Personal Data:* b Orange, Tex, Apr 17, 23; m 46, Dorothy Turcan; c Alfred, Debi, Douglas & Donald. *Educ:* Loyola Univ, La, DDS, 46; Baylor Univ, BS, 59, MS, 61; Am Bd Oral & Maxillofacial Surg, dipl, 63. *Prof Exp:* Oral surgeon, Valley Forge Gen Hosp, Valley Forge Pa Hq, US Army, San Antonio, Tex, 46-54, dent surgeon, Task Force 7, Cent Pac, 54-55, chief hosp surg dent, US Army Hosp, Ft Polk, La, 55-58, resident oral surg, Hosp, Baylor Univ, 58-59, resident, Brooks Army Med Ctr, 59-61, consult, US Army Med Area, Stuttgart, Ger, 61-64, chief host dent, US Army Hosp, Ft Polk, La, 64-68; asst dean extramural affairs, Col Dent Med, Univ SC, 76-77, asst dean curric & extramural affairs, 77-85, prof oral surg, 68-85. *Concurrent Pos:* Fel, Hosp, Baylor Univ, 58-59 & Brooks Army Med Ctr, 59-61; consult, Vet Admin Hosp, Charleston, SC, 68-, US Navy Hosp, 69-85 & SC Dept Corrections, 69-85; coordr dent activ, SC Area Health Educ Ctr, 72-85, Dept HEW, Washington, 82-85. *Mem:* Am Dent Asn; Am Soc Oral Surg; assoc mem Brit Asn Oral Surg; Am Soc Maxillofacial Surg. *Res:* Dental education; precautions for patients on drug therapy; oral surgery for patients on anticoagulant therapy. *Mailing Add:* 79 Mariners Cay Dr Box 1018 Folly Beach SC 29439

**WALDREP, THOMAS WILLIAM,** PLANT PHYSIOLOGY. *Current Pos:* RES SCIENTIST, LILLY RES LABS, ELI LILLY & CO, 69- *Personal Data:* b Madison, Fla, Feb 14, 34; m 55; c 2. *Educ:* Univ Fla, BSA, 61; Univ Ky, MSA, 63; NC State Univ, PhD(crop sci), 67. *Prof Exp:* Instr crop sci, NC State Univ, 66-67, asst prof, 67-69. *Mem:* Weed Sci Soc Am. *Res:* Basic and applied research in plant physiology; growth regulators and herbicides; herbicide research. *Mailing Add:* 1501 Chapman Dr Greenfield IN 46140

**WALDRON, ACIE CHANDLER,** AGRONOMY, ENTOMOLOGY. *Current Pos:* exten specialist pesticides chem & state coordr agr chem, 66-77, COORDR, NCENT REGION PESTICIDE IMPACT ASSESSMENT PROG, OHIO AGR RES & DEVELOP CTR, OHIO STATE UNIV, 77-, PESTICIDE COORDR & COORDR PETICIDE APPLICATOR TRAINING, OHIO COOP EXTEN SERV, 89- *Personal Data:* b Malad, Idaho, Feb 4, 30; m 57; c 5. *Educ:* Brigham Young Univ, BSc, 57; Ohio State Univ, MSc, 59, PhD(agron), 61. *Prof Exp:* Res asst agron, Agr Exp Sta, Ohio State Univ, 57-61; develop chemist, Agr Div, Am Cyanamid Co, NJ, 61-66. *Concurrent Pos:* State IR-4 rep, Ohio State Univ & Ohio Agr Res & Develop Ctr, 73-; pesticide appln educ training coordr, Ohio Coop Exten Serv, 75-77. *Mem:* Am Chem Soc; Am Soc Agron; Coun Agr Sci & Technol; Soil Sci Soc Am; Entom Soc Am. *Res:* Pesticide residue chemistry; pesticide residues in plant and animal crops, in soil and water; pesticide safety; administration of regional research for pesticide impact assessment; chemistry of organic nitrogen and phosphorous in soil organic matter. *Mailing Add:* 4220 Lyon Dr Columbus OH 43220

**WALDRON, CHARLES A,** ORAL PATHOLOGY. *Current Pos:* RETIRED. *Personal Data:* b Minneapolis, Minn, July 16, 22; m 43; c 2. *Educ:* Univ Minn, DDS, 45, MSD, 51; Am Bd Oral Path, dipl, 52. *Prof Exp:* From asst prof to prof path, Sch Dent, Wash Univ, 50-57; prof path, Sch Dent, Emory Univ, 57-82. *Concurrent Pos:* Consult, Vet Admin Hosp, Ga, 57 & Dent Intern Prog, Ft Benning, 59; mem med bd dirs, Am Bd Oral Path, 59-70; sci adv bd consult, Armed Forces Inst Path, 70-75. *Mem:* Am Dent Asn; fel Am Col Dent; Am Acad Oral Path (pres, 59, ed, 70-76). *Res:* Oral tumors; diagnostic oral pathology. *Mailing Add:* 1197 Hunters Dr Stone Mountain GA 30083

**WALDRON, HAROLD FRANCIS,** APPLIED CHEMISTRY. *Current Pos:* CONSULT, PROCESS & CORROSION CHEM, H F WALDRON ASSOCS, 90- *Personal Data:* b Manchester, Ohio, Sept 24, 29; m 49, Edna M Potts; c Mary E (Cook). *Educ:* Capital Univ, BS, 52; Purdue Univ, West Lafayette, MS, 54. *Prof Exp:* Chemist, Uranium Div, Mallinckrodt Chem Works, Mallinckrodt, Inc, 54-62, supvr anal methods develop, 62-66, supvr anal res, Opers Div, 66-67, res group leader, Indust Chem Div, 67-69, res mgr chem group, 69-73, res & develop mgr, 73-75, res assoc, 75-78, res fel, 78-89. *Mem:* Am Chem Soc; Nat Asn Corrosion Eng. *Res:* Chemical analytical methods, especially the use of vacuum techniques and complex ion formation; design and application of electronic instrumentation; chemical corrosion and materials selection; process chemistry research and development. *Mailing Add:* 6 Garden Lane Kirkwood MO 63122

**WALDRON, HOWARD HAMILTON (HANK),** APPLIED GEOLOGY, EARTHQUAKE HAZARDS & GEOLOGIC HAZARDS. *Current Pos:* RETIRED. *Personal Data:* b Nampa, Idaho, Nov 6, 17; m 43, Harriet Clough; c Bruce, Kathleen & Anne. *Educ:* Univ Wash, BS, 40. *Prof Exp:* Photogrammetrist, US Hydrographic Off, Washington, DC, 42-46; geologist, US Geol Surv, 46-73; staff consult geol, Shannon & Wilson, Inc, 73-97. *Concurrent Pos:* Tech adv, Geol Surv Indonesia, 60-62, Costa Rica, 64 & Colo Eng Coun, 65-73; eng geol consult & adv, AEC, 67-72 & Vet Admin, 71-73; mem, Earthquake Eng Res Inst; consult geol, 80- *Mem:* Asn Eng Geol; fel Geol Soc Am; Am Soc Civil Eng; Sigma Xi. *Res:* Engineering geology; areal and glacial geology of Pacific Northwest; urban and environmental geology; geologic volcanic and earthquake hazards evaluations. *Mailing Add:* 50 Beach Dr Nordland WA 98358-9602

**WALDRON, INGRID LORE,** PSYCHOSOMATIC MEDICINE. *Current Pos:* ASSOC PROF BIOL, UNIV PA, 68- *Personal Data:* b Nyack, NY, Dec 8, 39; c 2. *Educ:* Radcliffe Col, AB, 61; Univ Calif, Berkeley, PhD(biol), 67. *Prof Exp:* NSF fel, Univ Cambridge, 67-68. *Concurrent Pos:* NIH grant, Univ Pa, 69-72; social security grant, Univ Pa, 79-80; res assoc, Pop Studies Ctr & adj assoc prof psychol, Univ Pa, 82-; regional ed, Social Sci & Med, 83-88, adv ed, 88- *Mem:* Pop Asn Am. *Res:* Human biology; sex differences; social and psychological origins of disease; employment and women's health. *Mailing Add:* Dept Biol Univ Pa Philadelphia PA 19104

**WALDRON, KENNETH JOHN,** ROBOTICS, MACHINE DESIGN. *Current Pos:* MEM FAC, DEPT MECH ENG, OHIO STATE UNIV, 80-, NORDHOLT PROF, 84-, DEPT CHMN, 93- *Personal Data:* b Sydney, Australia, Feb 11, 43; m 68; c 3. *Educ:* Univ Sydney, BE, 64, MEngSci, 65; Stanford Univ, PhD(mech eng), 69. *Honors & Awards:* Ralph R Teetor Award, Soc Automotive Engrs, 77; Leonardo Da Vinci Award, Am Soc Mech Engrs, 88, Machine Design Award, 94. *Prof Exp:* Res asst mech eng, Stanford Univ, 65-68, actg asst prof, 68-69; from lectr to sr lectr, Univ NSW, 69-74; assoc prof, Univ Houston, 74-80. *Concurrent Pos:* Tech ed, Trans J Mechanisms, Transmissions & Automation in Design, Am Soc Mech Engrs, 88-92. *Mem:* Fel Am Soc Mech Engrs; Soc Automotive Engrs; Sigma Xi; Soc Mfg Engrs; Am Soc Eng Educ. *Res:* Mechanism kinematics; manipulator design and control; design of mobile robotic systems; computer-aided mechanism design. *Mailing Add:* Dept Mech Eng Ohio State Univ Columbus OH 43210

**WALDRON, MANJULA BHUSHAN,** DEAFNESS, TECHNOLOGY FOR SOCIETY. *Current Pos:* from asst prof to assoc prof, 80-89, PROF BIOMED ENG, OHIO STATE UNIV, 89- *Personal Data:* b Allahabad, India, Aug 17, 43; US citizen; m, Kenneth; c Andrew, Lalitha & Paul. *Educ:* Univ Delhi, India, BS, 62; Indian Inst Sci Eng, Bangalore, BE, 65; Stanford Univ, MS 68, PhD(elec eng), 71. *Honors & Awards:* Flugge-Lotz Lecturer in Eng Award, 83. *Prof Exp:* Instr, Dept Solid State Electronics, Sch Elec Eng, Univ NSW, Kensington, Australia, 70-74; instr, Elec Eng Dept, Univ Houston, 74-75, asst prof, 75-79; lectr math, Univ Delhi, India, 66-72, reader, 72-79, prof, 79-88. *Concurrent Pos:* Vis asst prof, Dept Elec Eng, Univ Md, 73; vis assoc prof, Design Div, Dept Mech Eng & Elec Eng, Stanford Univ, Calif, 86-87. *Mem:* Am Soc Eng Educ; Asn Comput Mach; Am Asn Artificial Intel; Inst Elec & Electronics Engrs; Biomed Eng Soc; Sigma Xi. *Res:* Actively developing technology for health care and deaf persons; applying artificial intelligence and neural network technology to integrated engineering design; rate distortion and response designs; published 100 research papers and authored 21 books; author of over 75 papers in engineering, research design and teaching. *Mailing Add:* Biomed Eng 270 Bevis Hall Ohio State Univ 1080 Carmack Rd Columbus OH 43210-1002. *Fax:* 504-482-1561

**WALDROP, FRANCIS N,** MEDICINE. *Current Pos:* RETIRED. *Personal Data:* b Asheville, NC, Oct 5, 26; m 50; c 2. *Educ:* Univ Minn, AB, 46; George Washington Univ, MD, 50. *Honors & Awards:* Vestermark Award, Am Psychiat Asn, 80. *Prof Exp:* Intern med, Univ Hosp, George Washington Univ, 50-51; resident psychiat, US Dept HEW, 51-54, med officer, 54-59, assoc dir res, 59-65, dir prof training psychiat, 63-71, dir, Clin & Behav Studies Res Ctr, St Elizabeth's Hosp, 65-79, dep adminr, Alcohol, Drug Abuse & Ment Health Admin, 75-79. *Concurrent Pos:* Clin asst prof, George Washington Univ, 62-65, clin assoc prof, 65-; spec asst res & training, NIMH, 66-68, dep dir, Nat Ctr Ment Health Serv, Training & Res, 68-71, from assoc dir to dir, Div Manpower & Training Progs, 71-75. *Mem:* AAAS; AMA; fel Am Psychiat Asn. *Res:* Clinical psychiatry; psychopharmacology; drug dependence; basic biological sciences in relation to psychiatric disorders. *Mailing Add:* 1775 Elton Rd Silver Spring MD 20903

**WALDROP, MORGAN A,** SOLID STATE PHYSICS, ATOMIC PHYSICS. *Current Pos:* SR RES PHYSICIST, PHILLIPS PETROL CO, 63- *Personal Data:* b Ft Worth, Tex, Jan 8, 37. *Educ:* Rice Inst, BA, 59, MA, 62, PhD(physics), 64. *Mem:* Am Phys Soc. *Res:* Nuclear magnetic and electron paramagnetic resonance in solids; atomic aspects of heterogeneous catalysis. *Mailing Add:* 1330 Melmart Dr SE Bartlesville OK 74006

**WALDROUP, PARK WILLIAM,** NUTRITION, BIOCHEMISTRY. *Current Pos:* from asst prof to assoc prof, 66-75, PROF POULTRY NUTRIT, UNIV ARK, FAYETTEVILLE, 75- *Personal Data:* b Maryville, Tenn, Oct 17, 37; m 61; c 3. *Educ:* Univ Tenn, Knoxville, BS, 59; Univ Fla, MS, 62, PhD(nutrit, biochem), 65. *Honors & Awards:* Nat Broiler Coun Award, 80. *Prof Exp:* Res assoc poultry nutrit, Univ Fla, 64-65, asst prof, 65-66. *Mem:* Poultry Sci Asn; Am Inst Nutrit; Animal Nutrit Res Coun. *Res:* Studies concerned with nutrient requirements of poultry in terms of nutrient balance and interrelationships of nutrients; effects of processing on nutritive value of feeds. *Mailing Add:* Dept Poultry Sci Univ Ark Fayetteville AR 72701

**WALDSTEIN, SHELDON SAUL,** INTERNAL MEDICINE, ENDOCRINOLOGY & METABOLISM. *Current Pos:* from clin asst to assoc prof, 51-66, PROF INTERNAL MED, MED SCH, NORTHWESTERN UNIV, CHICAGO, 66- *Personal Data:* b Chicago, Ill, June 23, 24; m 52; c 3. *Educ:* Northwestern Univ, BS, 46, MD, 47, MS, 51; Am Bd Internal Med, dipl. *Prof Exp:* Intern & resident internal med, Cook Co Hosp, 47-51. *Concurrent Pos:* Res assoc, Hektoen Inst & assoc attend physician, Cook Co Hosp, 54-57, attend physician, 57-69, chief, Northwestern Med Div, 59-62, class dir dept med, 62-64, chmn dept med, 64-69; exec dir, NSuburban Asn Health Resources, Northbrook, 69-72; dir, Northwestern Univ Med Asn, 74-77; exec dir, Cook Co Grad Sch Med, 77- *Mem:* Endocrine Soc; AMA; Am Col Physicians; Am Fedn Clin Res; Cent Soc Clin Res. *Res:* Endocrinology. *Mailing Add:* 541 N Fairbanks Ct Chicago IL 60611

**WALECKA, JOHN DIRK,** THEORETICAL PHYSICS. *Current Pos:* NSF fel, Stanford Univ, 59-60, from asst prof to assoc prof physics, 60-66, assoc dean humanities & sci, 70-72, chmn acad senate, 73-74, chmn, Dept Physics, 77-82, PROF PHYSICS, STANFORD UNIV, 66- *Personal Data:* b Milwaukee, Wis, Mar 11, 32; m 54; c 3. *Educ:* Harvard Col, BA, 54; Mass Inst Technol, PhD(physics), 58. *Prof Exp:* NSF fel, Europ Orgn Nuclear Res, Switz, 58-59. *Concurrent Pos:* A P Sloan Found fel, 62-66; mem sci prog adv comts, Bates Linac, Mass Inst Technol, 71-76, Nevis Cyclotron, Columbia Univ, 71-76, & Los Alamos Meson Physics Facil, 74-76; mem ad hoc panel future nuclear sci, Nat Res Coun-Nat Acad Sci, 75-77; mem, Nuclear Sci Adv Comt, 77; mem vis comt, Lab Nuclear Sci, Nat Inst Technol, 80- *Mem:* Fel Am Phys Soc. *Res:* Nuclear structure; high energy physics. *Mailing Add:* MS12H2 CEBAF 12000 Jefferson Ave Newport News VA 23606

**WALENGA, RONALD W,** ARACHIDONIC ACID METABOLISM, AIRWAY INFLAMMATION. *Current Pos:* ASSOC PROF, PEDIAT & PHYSIOL, SCH MED, CASE WESTERN RES UNIV, CLEVELAND, OHIO, 89- *Personal Data:* b New York, NY, Sept 25, 46; m 72, Kristen L Johnson; c Andrew & Jenna. *Educ:* Antioch Col, BS, 68; Univ Mich, PhD(biochem), 74. *Prof Exp:* Asst prof pediat, State Univ NY Health Sci Ctr, Syracuse, 81-89; assoc prof, Temple Univ Sch Med, 87-89. *Mem:* Am Asn Pathologists; NY Acad Sci. *Res:* Regulation of cyclooxygenase expression in airway epithelial cells; role of eicosonoids in airway diseases such as CF and asthma. *Mailing Add:* Biomed Res Bldg 8th Floor Admin 2109 Adobert Rd Cleveland OH 44106-4948. *Fax:* 216-368-4582; *E-Mail:* rxw13@po.cwru.edu

**WALERIAN, SZYSZKOWSKI,** FINITE ELEMENT METHODS IN APPLIED MECHANICS, MECHANICS OF TIME-DEPENDENT MATERIALS. *Current Pos:* PROF, DEPT MECH ENG, UNIV SASK, 91- *Personal Data:* b Ludwigsburg, Ger, Aug 10, 45; Can citizen; m 72, Ewa Kotlarek; c Jack & Anita. *Educ:* Univ Warsaw, Poland, MSc, 69, PhD(struct stability), 74. *Prof Exp:* From asst prof to assoc prof struct mech, Aeronaut Technol & Appl Mech Dept, Univ Warsaw, 74-82; vis prof ice mech, Univ Calgary, 82-86, assoc prof time-dependent mat, 86-91. *Mem:* Am Acad Mech; Am Soc Mech Engrs; Soc Eng Sci; Int Asn Shell & Spatial Struct. *Res:* Computer aided structural analysis; mechanics of composite thin-walled structures; structural optimization; modeling of visco-elasto-plastic and brittle materials; stability and dynamics of large flexible structures; holographic interferometry in strain-stress measurements. *Mailing Add:* Dept Mech Eng Univ Sask Saskatoon SK S7W 5A9 Can. *Fax:* 306-966-8710

**WALES, CHARLES E,** educational engineering, for more information see previous edition

**WALES, DAVID BERTRAM,** COMBINATORICS, FINITE MATHEMATICS. *Current Pos:* Bateman res fel, Calif Inst Technol, 67-68, from asst prof to assoc prof, 68-77, assoc dean, 76-80, dean, 80-84, PROF MATH, CALIF INST TECHNOL, 77-, EXEC OFFICER MATH, 85- *Personal Data:* b Vancouver, BC, July 31, 39; m 61; c 2. *Educ:* Univ BC, BSc, 61, MA, 62; Harvard Univ, PhD(math), 67. *Mem:* Am Math Soc. *Res:* Representation theory of finite groups; combinatorics. *Mailing Add:* Calif Inst Technol Pasadena CA 91125-0001

**WALES, WALTER D,** PHYSICS. *Current Pos:* From instr to assoc prof, 59-72, chmn dept, 73-82, PROF PHYSICS, UNIV PA, 72- *Personal Data:* b Oneonta, NY, Aug 2, 33; m 55; c 2. *Educ:* Carleton Col, BA, 54; Calif Inst Technol, MS, 55, PhD(physics), 60. *Concurrent Pos:* Assoc dir, Princeton Pa Accelerator, 68-71; physicist, AEC, 72-73. *Mem:* Am Phys Soc. *Res:* Particle physics. *Mailing Add:* Dept Physics Univ Pa Philadelphia PA 19104

**WALFORD, ROY LEE, JR,** PATHOLOGY. *Current Pos:* from asst prof to prof path, 54-70, PROF PATH & HEMATOPATH, SCH MED, UNIV CALIF, LOS ANGELES, 70- *Personal Data:* b San Diego, Calif, June 29, 24; m 50; c 3. *Educ:* Univ Chicago, BS, 46, MD, 48. *Honors & Awards:* Kleemeier Award, Gerontol Soc Am, 80; Res Award, Am Aging Asn, 80; Henderson Award, Am Geriat Soc, 82. *Prof Exp:* Intern, Gorgas Hosp, CZ, 50-51; resident path, Vet Admin Hosp, Los Angeles, 51-52; chief lab, Chanute AFB Hosp, Ill, 52-54. *Concurrent Pos:* Attend physician, Brentwood Vet Admin Hosp, 55-56; consult, Los Angeles Harbor Gen Hosp, 59-70, Space Biopheres Ventures, 82- *Mem:* Am Soc Exp Path; Am Asn Path & Bact; Geront Soc Am. *Res:* Hematologic pathology; immunology of the white blood cell; space biology; gerontology. *Mailing Add:* 903 Pacific Ave Venice CA 90291

**WALGENBACH, DAVID D,** ENTOMOLOGY, AGRONOMY. *Current Pos:* FAC, UNIV MINN, 89- *Personal Data:* b Marshall, Minn, Sept 4, 37; m 61; c 4. *Educ:* Iowa State Univ, BS, 59; Univ Wis-Madison, MS, 62, PhD(entom), 65. *Prof Exp:* Asst prof biol, Stout State Univ, 64-65; field tech specialist entom, Chevron Chem Co, 65-66, crop specialist, Agr Chem Res, 66-67, sr res specialist, 67-73; mem fac, Dept Entom & Zool, SDak State Univ, 73-89. *Mem:* AAAS; Entom Soc Am; Am Soc Agron. *Res:* Foreward agricultural chemical research; plant physiology. *Mailing Add:* 29351 128th St Waseca MN 56093

**WALGENBACH-TELFORD, SUSAN CAROL,** NEURAL CONTROL OF CIRCULATION, SMALL INTESTINAL TRANSPLANTATION. *Current Pos:* RES PHYSIOLOGIST, VET ADMIN MED CTR, MILWAUKEE, WIS, 84-; ASST CLIN PROF ANESTHESIOL & PHYSIOL, MED COL WIS, 88- *Personal Data:* b Sacramento, Calif, June 29, 52; m 83; c 2. *Educ:* Univ Calif, BS, 74, PhD(physiol), 79. *Prof Exp:* Postgrad res physiol, Univ Calif, Davis, 76-79; NIH fel physiol, Mayo Grad Sch Med, Minn, 79-82, instr, 81-83; res assoc physiol, Mayo Clin, Rochester, Minn, 82-83; asst prof anesthesiol, Med Col Wis, Milwaukee, 83-88, asst prof physiol, 84-88. *Concurrent Pos:* Prin investr, new fac award, Med Col Wis, 83-84, Am Heart Asn, 84-85, NIH new investr award, 84-87 & Vet Admin merit award, 87-90; mem, Coun Circulation, Am Heart Asn. *Mem:* Am Physiol Soc; AAAS. *Res:* Neural control of the circulation, specifically the role of baroreflexes and chemoreflexes in the regulation of circulation during exercise and environmental stress; secondary interest in physiology of small intestinal transplantation. *Mailing Add:* Res Serv 151 Med Col Wis Vet Admin Med Ctr Milwaukee WI 53295

**WALHOUT, JUSTINE I SIMON,** SCIENCE EDUCATION, EDUCATIONAL POLICY. *Current Pos:* from asst prof to assoc prof, 56-89, prof & chair, 89-96, EMER PROF CHEM, ROCKFORD COL, 96- *Personal Data:* b Aberdeen, SD, Dec 11, 30; m 58, Donald; c Mark, Timothy, Lynne & Peter. *Educ:* Wheaton Col, BS, 52; Northwestern Univ, PhD(org chem), 56. *Prof Exp:* Instr chem, Wright Br, Chicago City Jr Col, 55-56. *Concurrent Pos:* Consult, Pierce Chem Co, 68-69; mem, Ill State Bd Educ, Gubernatorial Appointee, 74-81; mem, Testing Comt, Am Chem Soc, 87-94, counr, 93- *Mem:* Am Chem Soc; Sigma Xi; Midwest Asn Chem Teachers Lib Arts Cols. *Res:* High temperature studies of nitrogen heterocyclic compounds; educational research and papers in nurses education in chemistry; literature research and writings of trimethylsilylation reactions. *Mailing Add:* Dept Chem Rockford Col Rockford IL 61108-2393. *Fax:* 815-226-4119

**WALI, KAMESHWAR C,** THEORETICAL PHYSICS. *Current Pos:* chmn dept, 86-89, PROF PHYSICS, SYRACUSE UNIV, 69- *Personal Data:* b Bijapur, India, Oct 15, 27; m 52, Kashi; c Alaka, Achala & Monona. *Educ:* Univ Bombay, BSc, 48; Benares Hindu Univ, MSc, 52, MA, 54; Univ Wis, PhD(theoret physics), 59. *Prof Exp:* Res assoc theoret physics, Univ Wis, 59-60 & Johns Hopkins Univ, 60-62; from asst physicist to sr physicist, Argonne Nat Lab, 62-69. *Concurrent Pos:* Co-ed, Int Conf Weak Interactions, Argonne Nat Lab, 65; vis mem, Inst Advan Sci Study, Bures-sur-Yvette, France, 71-72, 75-76, 79-80, 83-84, 90; co-ed, Int Symp Nucleon-Nucleon Annihilations, Syracuse, 75; vis scientist, Int Inst Theoret Physics, Trieste, Italy, 67; ed, Proceedings of eight workshop on grand unification, Syracuse Univ, NY, 87. *Mem:* Am Phys Soc; Sigma Xi; Int Soc Gen Relativity & Gravitation. *Res:* Elementary particles; high energy physics; higher symmetries; grand unified theories; non-commutative geometry. *Mailing Add:* Dept Physics Syracuse Univ Syracuse NY 13244-1130. *Fax:* 315-443-9103; *E-Mail:* wali@uhep.phy.syr.edu

**WALI, MOHAN KISHEN,** PLANT ECOLOGY, ENVIRONMENTAL SCIENCE & POLICY. *Current Pos:* dir, Sch Natural Resources & assoc dean, Col Agr, 90-93, PROF, SCH NATURAL RESOURCES, OHIO STATE UNIV, 90- *Personal Data:* b Srinagar, India, Mar 1, 37; m 60, Sarla Safaya; c Pamela & Promod. *Educ:* Univ Jammu & Kashmir, India, BSc, 57; Allahabad Univ, MSc, 60; Univ BC, PhD(plant ecol), 69. *Honors & Awards:* B C Gamble Award, 77. *Prof Exp:* Demonstr bot, S P Col, Srinagar, India, 61-63, lectr, 63-65; teaching asst biol, Univ BC, 66-67, teaching asst plant ecol, 68-69; asst prof, Univ NDak, 69-73, assoc prof, 73-79, spec asst univ pres, 77-82, prof biol, 79-82; prof, State Univ NY, Syracuse, 83-89, dir, Grad Prog Environ Sci, 83-85. *Concurrent Pos:* Res asst, Nat Res Coun Can, 67-69; dir, Proj Reclamation, 75-82; sr ed, Reclamation Rev, 76-81, chief ed, Reclamation & Revegetation res, 82-85; courtesy prof, Dept Agron, Dept Plant Biol, Sch Pub Policy & Mgt, 91- *Mem:* AAAS; fel Nat Acad Sci India; Am Inst Biol Sci; Brit Ecol Soc; Am Soc Agron; Ecol Soc Am; Soc Am Foresters. *Res:* Environmental science; influence of water, nutrients, temperature and light on plant populations and communities; nutrient cycling; ecosystem model building; soil-plant relationship; pollution; phytosociology; systems approach to the reclamation of mined areas; ecosystem restoration/rehabilitation; sustainable development; environmental policy. *Mailing Add:* Sch Natural Resources Ohio State Univ 2021 Coffey Rd Columbus OH 43210-1085. *Fax:* 614-292-7432

**WALIA, AMRIK SINGH,** IMMUNOLOGY, CHEMISTRY. *Current Pos:* tumor immunologist, 75-77, ASST RES PROF, DEPT SURG, SCH MED, UNIV ALA, 80-; PVT CONSULT, BIRMINGHAM, ALA, 91- *Personal Data:* b Punjab, India, Aug 6, 47; m 74; c 2. *Educ:* Punjab Univ, BS, 65; Meerut Univ, MS, 68; Loyola Univ, PhD(chem), 75. *Honors & Awards:* Inst Cancer Res Technol Trans Award, Int Union Against Cancer, 78. *Prof Exp:* Lectr chem, GMN Col, Ambala India, 68-70; instr, Loyola Univ, 74-75; chief alcoholism res, Vet Admin Med Ctr, 82-91. *Concurrent Pos:* Fel, Univ Ala Cancer Ctr, 77-78; NIH fel, Nat Cancer Inst, 78-80. *Mem:* AAAS; Am Chem Soc; Sigma Xi; Am Asn Immunologists; NY Acad Sci; Int Soc Immunopharmacol; Res Soc Alcholism. *Res:* Immune response to polyoma induced tumors, IgG, IgM, and C3 receptors for T cells; biological and biochemical characterization of C3 receptors; effect of alcohol on immune functions. *Mailing Add:* 4605 Round Forest Dr Birmingham AL 35213

**WALIA, JASJIT SINGH,** ORGANIC CHEMISTRY. *Current Pos:* assoc prof, 66-73, PROF CHEM, LOYOLA UNIV, LA, 73- *Personal Data:* b Lahore, India, Mar 19, 34; nat US; m 66, Parveen; c Sunila & Suneeta. *Educ:* Univ Punjab, India, BS(hons), 55, MS(hons), 56; Univ Southern Calif, PhD(org chem), 60. *Honors & Awards:* Prof Prem Singh Medal, 55; Dux Academicus Award, 82. *Prof Exp:* Res assoc org chem, Univ Southern Calif, 60; res assoc, Mass Inst Technol, 60-61; lectr, Benaras Hindu Univ, 62-66. *Mem:* Am Chem Soc; Royal Soc Chem; Sigma Xi. *Res:* New reactions of organic nitrogen compounds; new synthetic reactions; novel heterocyclization reactions; carbanion chemistry; cyanide ion-catalyzed reactions; mechanism of reactions; new compounds of potential therapeutic and/or other commercial importance. *Mailing Add:* Dept Chem Loyola Univ New Orleans LA 70118. *Fax:* 504-865-3269; *E-Mail:* walia@musiic.loyno.edu

**WALING, J(OSEPH) L(EE),** STRUCTURAL ENGINEERING. *Current Pos:* from asst prof to assoc prof eng mech, Purdue Univ, 45-54, prof eng sci, 54-55, prof struct eng, 55-83, from asst dean to assoc dean, Grad Sch, 60-82, dir, Div Sponsored Progs, 66-83, EMER PROF CIVIL ENG, PURDUE UNIV, 83-, EMER DIR, DIV SPONSORED PROGS, 83- *Personal Data:* b Brook, Ind, Mar 17, 16; m 42; c 4. *Educ:* Purdue Univ, BS, 38, MSE, 40; Univ Ill, PhD, 52. *Prof Exp:* Asst appl mech, Purdue Univ, 38-40, instr, 40-41; naval architect, Norfolk Navy Yard, 41-45. *Concurrent Pos:* Mem Nat Coun Univ Res Adminr. *Mem:* AAAS; Am Soc Civil Engrs; Am Soc Eng Educ; Am Concrete Inst; Int Asn Shell Struct. *Res:* Photoelasticity; structural mechanics; reinforced concrete; shell structures. *Mailing Add:* 3731 Capilano Dr West Lafayette IN 47906

**WALKENBACH, RONALD JOSEPH,** PHARMACOLOGY. *Current Pos:* lab investr, 78-81, EXEC DIR, EYE RES FOUND, COLUMBIA, 81- *Personal Data:* b Herman, Mo, Mar 15, 48; m 84, DeAnna M Roemer. *Educ:* Quincy Col, Ill, BS, 70; Univ Mo, Columbia, PhD(pharm), 75. *Prof Exp:* Fel, Univ Va, Charlottesville, 75-77, Univ Mo, Columbia, 77-78. *Concurrent Pos:* Prin investr, Nat Eye Inst, NIH, 78- *Mem:* AAAS; Asn Res Vision & Ophthal. *Res:* Pharmacology. *Mailing Add:* 919 Bourn Ave Columbia MO 65203

**WALKENSTEIN, SIDNEY S,** DRUG METABOLISM. *Current Pos:* RETIRED. *Personal Data:* b Philadelphia, Pa, Dec 21, 20; m 46; c 1. *Educ:* Temple Univ, BS, 42, AM, 50, PhD(biochem), 53. *Prof Exp:* Biochemist, Mold Metab, Pitman-Dunn Labs, 52-53; chief radiochemist drug metab, Wyeth Inst Med Res, 53-58; pharmaceut specialist, Union Burma Appl Res Inst, 58-60; sr res scientist, Wyeth Labs, Inc, 60-62, mgr radiochem sect, 62-67; assoc dir biol res, Smith Kline & Fr Labs, 67-83. *Concurrent Pos:* Consult, Burma pharmaceut indust, 58-60. *Mem:* Am Soc Pharmacol & Exp Therapeut; Am Pharmaceut Asn; Int Soc Biochem Pharmacol; NY Acad Sci. *Res:* Metabolism of aldehydes and fatty acids; effects of toxins on yeast respiration; pantothenate-deficient yeast metabolism; utilization of hydrocarbons by molds; biotransformation and physiological disposition of isotopically-labeled drugs; medicinal plants; mechanism of drug action; trace drug analysis; pharmacokinetics; biopharmaceutics. *Mailing Add:* 804 N 29th St Philadelphia PA 19130

**WALKER, A EARL,** medicine, neurological surgery; deceased, see previous edition for last biography

**WALKER, ALAN,** INORGANIC CHEMISTRY. *Current Pos:* PROF CHEM, UNIV TORONTO, 65- *Personal Data:* b Bridlington, Eng, Apr 30, 37; m 62; c 2. *Educ:* Univ Nottingham, BSc, 59, PhD(inorg chem), 62. *Prof Exp:* res fel inorg chem, Dept Indust & Sci Res, Univ Nottingham, 62-63; resident res assoc fel chem, Argonne Nat Lab, 63-65. *Concurrent Pos:* Natural Sci & Eng Res Coun Can res grant, 65- *Mem:* Fel Royal Soc Chem. *Res:* Nonaqueous solvent chemistry, particularly of nitrates; inorganic spectroscopy; reactions of coordinated ligands to platinum group metals. *Mailing Add:* Dept Chem Univ Toronto Scarborough ON M1C 1A4 Can

**WALKER, ALAN KENT,** agronomy, for more information see previous edition

**WALKER, ALTA SHARON,** PLANETOLOGY, GEOMORPHOLOGY. *Current Pos:* RES GEOLOGIST, US GEOL SURV, 79- *Personal Data:* b Ogdensburg, NY, Apr 28, 42. *Educ:* Syracuse Univ, BA, 64; Univ Minn, MS, 71; Rice Univ, PhD(geol), 77. *Prof Exp:* Geologist, Tetra Tech, Inc, 77-78, Nat Air & Space Mus, Smithsonian Inst, 78-79. *Concurrent Pos:* Adj prof, George Mason Univ, Fairfax, Va, 89- *Mem:* Am Geophys Union; Sigma Xi; Geol Soc Am. *Res:* Use of remotely sensed data to evaluate mineral resources, to analyze eolian and fluvial regimes and to assess paleoclimate indicators in arid environments; photogeology of the Galilean satellites. *Mailing Add:* 11743 Ledura Ct No 103 Reston VA 22091

**WALKER, AMEAE M,** PROLACTIN MODIFICATION, CELL BIOLOGY. *Current Pos:* Asst prof, 79-86, ASSOC PROF BIOMED SCI, UNIV CALIF, RIVERSIDE, 86- *Personal Data:* b Epsom, Eng, Oct 29, 51; m 82; c 4. *Educ:* Univ Liverpool, PhD(cell biol), 76. *Honors & Awards:* Fac Res lectr, Kitasato Univ, Japan, 93. *Concurrent Pos:* Ad hoc reviewer, NSF, NIH & USDA grants; prin investr, var res grants; teacher, med histol; vchair, Prolactin Gordon Conf, 94. *Mem:* Am Soc Cell Biol; Endocrine Soc; Brit Soc Cell Biol. *Res:* Protein secretion; cell endocrinology; growth factors. *Mailing Add:* Div Biomed Sci Univ Calif Riverside CA 92521-0121. *Fax:* 909-787-5504

**WALKER, ARTHUR BERTRAM CUTHBERT, JR,** SPACE PHYSICS, ASTRONOMY. *Current Pos:* Mem tech staff, Space Physics Lab, Aerospace Corp, Stanford Univ, 65-68, staff scientist, 68-70, sr staff scientist, 70-72, dir, Space Astron Proj, 72-73, ASSOC PROF APPL PHYSICS, STANFORD UNIV, 74-, ASSOC DEAN GRAD STUDIES, 75- *Personal Data:* b Cleveland, Ohio, Aug 24, 36; m 59; c 1. *Educ:* Case Inst Technol, BS, 57; Univ Ill, Urbana, MS, 58, PhD(physics), 62. *Concurrent Pos:* Mem exec comt, Inst Plasma Res, Stanford Univ, 75-, chmn, Astron Course Prog, 76- *Mem:* Sigma Xi; Am Phys Soc; Am Geophys Union; Am Astron Soc; Int Astron Union. *Res:* Solar physics; solar coronal structure; solar x-rays; solar abundances; high energy astrophysics; stellar x-ray sources; interstellar medium; physics of the upper atmosphere. *Mailing Add:* Stanford Univ CSSA ERL 310 Stanford CA 94305. *Fax:* 650-725-2333

**WALKER, AUGUSTUS CHAPMAN,** TECHNICAL MANAGEMENT, EDUCATION ADMINISTRATION. *Current Pos:* consult & dir, Off Post-Col Prof Educ, 75-80, SR LECTR ENG MGT, CARNEGIE-MELLON UNIV, 74-; PRES, EFFECTIVE RES, PITTSBURGH, 73- *Personal Data:* b Brooklyn, NY, Oct 2, 23; m 47; c 4. *Educ:* Harvard Univ, BS, 48. *Honors & Awards:* Award, Am Inst Chem Engrs, 63. *Prof Exp:* Asst biochemist, Thanhauser Lab, New Eng Med Ctr, 48-51; res chemist high polymers, Cryovac Div, W R Grace Co, 52-57; res assoc, Plastics Lab, Mass Inst Technol, 57-58; lectr, Lowell Technol Inst, 57-59, asst prof chem, 58-59; consult, group leader, sect chief & asst to gen mgr, Res & Adv Develop Div, Avco Corp, 59-65; dir res, Polymer Corp, Pa, 65-70; dir res, Resin Products Div, PPG Indust, Inc, 70-73. *Mem:* Am Chem Soc; Inst Elec & Electronics Engrs; Am Soc Eng Educ; Sigma Xi. *Res:* Writer and lecturer subjects include methods of managing technical activities; training scientists and engineers; problem solving in science and technology. *Mailing Add:* 2297 Colony Ct Pittsburgh PA 15237-1554

**WALKER, BAILUS,** PUBLIC HEALTH. *Current Pos:* PROF ENVIRON & OCCUP HEALTH & ASSOC DIR ENVIRON & OCCUP CANCER, COL MED, HOWARD UNIV, WASHINGTON, DC, 94- *Educ:* Univ Mich, MPH, 59; Univ Minn, PhD(occup & environ health), 75. *Honors & Awards:* Distinguished Health Scientist Award, Nat Environ Health Asn, 72; Browning Prize Dis Prev, 78; Gaylord W Anderson Mem Lectr, Univ Minn, 86; Ruth Webb Mem Lectr Award, Am Pub Health Asn, 86, Hildrus A

Poindexter Award, 88; Thomas Parren Distinguished Lectr, Univ Pittsburgh, 87; Wilbur D Mills Distinguished Health Policy Lectr, 88. *Prof Exp:* Environ health scientist & adminr, Environ Health Serv, Washington, DC, 71-79; dir, Occup Health Stand, US Dept Labor, 79-81; comnr pub health, Commonwealth Mass, 83-87; prof pub health policy/mgt & prof environ health & toxicol, State Univ NY, Albany, 87-90; prof, Dept Occup & Environ Health & Dean, Col Pub Health, Health Sci Ctr, Univ Okla, 90-94. *Concurrent Pos:* Head, US Exchange Mission to Japan, Collab US-Japanese efforts in occup med, 80; state dir pub health, Mich Dept Pub Health, 81-83; adj prof, Univ Mich, 81-, Boston Univ, 83-, Mass Univ, 84-; vis prof, Sch Pub Health, Harvard Univ, 86-; mem, Physicians Human Rights Mission, SKorea, 87; mem, Mozambique Health Assessment Mission, 88; mem, Secy's Coun Health Prom & Dis Prev, US Dept Health & Human Serv; mem, Comn Study Future Pub Health US, Nat Acad Sci; co-dir, Ctr Health Policy Res & Develop, Univ Okla Health Sci Ctr & Ctr Epidemiol Res, 90-94. *Mem:* Inst Med-Nat Acad Sci; fel Royal Soc Health; Am Pub Health Asn (pres, 87-88). *Res:* Physical, chemical and biological hazards in macroenvironments; author of numerous publications. *Mailing Add:* Cancer Ctr Howard Univ 2041 Georgia Ave Washington DC 20060. *Fax:* 202-667-1686

**WALKER, BENNIE FRANK,** PHYSICAL CHEMISTRY. *Current Pos:* from asst prof to assoc prof, 68-79, PROF CHEM, STEPHEN F AUSTIN STATE UNIV, 79- *Personal Data:* b Mt Pleasant, Tex, Sept 19, 37. *Educ:* Sam Houston State Col, BS, 59, MA, 62; Univ Tex, Austin, PhD(phys chem), 70. *Prof Exp:* Instr chem, Sam Houston State Col, 59-62. *Mem:* Am Chem Soc. *Res:* Kinetics; hydrogen bonding; applications of computers in chemistry. *Mailing Add:* Box 13006 Stephen F Austin State Univ Nacogdoches TX 75962-3006

**WALKER, BILLY KENNETH,** LARGE SOFTWARE SYSTEMS, PROGRAM CORRECTNESS. *Current Pos:* assoc prof, 83-87, PROF & CHMN, DEPT COMPUTER SCI, E CENT UNIV, 87- *Personal Data:* b Canyon, Tex, June 17, 46; m 80. *Educ:* WTex State Univ, BS, 68; Tex Tech Univ, MS, 70, PhD(math), 74. *Prof Exp:* Asst prof comput sci, WTex State Univ, 75-76, Amarillo Col, 76-79, Univ Okla, 79-83. *Mem:* Asn Comput Mach; sr mem Inst Elec & Electronics Engrs; Am Math Soc; Math Asn Am. *Res:* Author of three textbooks; author of more than 50 papers. *Mailing Add:* Dept Comput Sci E Cent Univ Ada OK 74820-6899

**WALKER, BRUCE DAVID,** IMMUNOLOGY. *Current Pos:* ASSOC PROF MED, HARVARD MED SCH, 88- *Personal Data:* b Champaign, Ill, Apr 18, 52; m 82; c 2. *Educ:* Univ Colo, BS, 76; Case Western Res Univ, MD, 80. *Mem:* Am Asn Immunologists; Am Soc Clin Invest. *Res:* HIV-1-specific cytoxic 7 lymphocytes; hepatitis c virus immunology. *Mailing Add:* Harvard Univ Mass Gen Hosp 55 Fruit St Boston MA 02114-2621. *Fax:* 617-726-7416

**WALKER, BRUCE EDWARD,** ANATOMY. *Current Pos:* PROF ANAT, MICH STATE UNIV, 75- *Personal Data:* b Montreal, Que, June 17, 26; m 48, Lois C McCuaig; c Brian, Dianne, Donald & Susan. *Educ:* McGill Univ BSc, 47, MSc, 52, PhD(genetics), 54; Univ Tex, MD, 66. *Prof Exp:* Lectr anat, McGill Univ, 54-57; from asst prof to assoc prof, 67-75. *Mem:* Am Asn Anat; Teratology Soc; Am Asn Cancer Res. *Res:* Experimental teratology; carcinogenesis. *Mailing Add:* Dept Anat Mich State Univ East Lansing MI 48824-1316

**WALKER, CAROL L,** MATHEMATICS. *Current Pos:* from asst prof to assoc prof, 64-72, dept head, 79-93, PROF MATH, NMEX STATE UNIV, 72- *Personal Data:* b Martinez, Calif, Aug 19, 35; m 62, Elbert A; c Diana, David, Daniel & Elaine. *Educ:* Univ Colo, BME, 57; NMex State Univ, MS, 61, PhD(math), 63. *Prof Exp:* Mem math, Inst Advan Study, 63-64. *Concurrent Pos:* NSF fel, 63-64, NSF grants, 64-72. *Mem:* Am Math Soc; Math Asn Am; Asn Women Math. *Res:* Algebra, primarily Abelian group theory, homological algebra and category theory. *Mailing Add:* Col Arts & Sci NMex State Univ Las Cruces NM 88003-0105. *Fax:* 505-646-6096; *E-Mail:* hardy@nmsu.edu

**WALKER, CEDRIC FRANK,** NEUROPROSTHESES, MICROPROCESSORS. *Current Pos:* asst prof, 77-82, assoc prof, 82-91, PROF BIOMED ENG & CHMN, TULANE UNIV, 91- *Personal Data:* b Los Angeles, Calif, Jan 26, 50; m 85, Julia Ingraham; c Jacob & Benjamin. *Educ:* Stanford Univ, BS, 72, MS, 72; Duke Univ, PhD(biomed eng), 78. *Prof Exp:* Res assoc, Div Neurosurg, Duke Med Ctr, 77. *Concurrent Pos:* Adj prof, Dept Orthop Surg & Dept Psychiat & Neurol, Tulane Univ, 78-; prin investr, NSF, 78-80 & Nat Inst Neurol & Comn Dis & Stroke, NIH, 82-85. *Mem:* Am Soc Eng Educ; fel Inst Elec & Electronics Engrs. *Res:* Neuroprosthetic devices, particularly for cerebellar stimulation; bioeffects of low frequency electromagnetic fields; electrical injuries. *Mailing Add:* Dept Biomed Eng Tulane Univ New Orleans LA 70118-5698. *Fax:* 504-862-8779; *E-Mail:* cedric.walker@tulane.edu

**WALKER, CHARLES A(LLEN),** CHEMICAL ENGINEERING. *Current Pos:* from instr to prof, Yale Univ, 42-84, master, Berkeley Col, 59-69, dept chmn, 74-76 & 81-84, EMER PROF CHEM ENG, YALE UNIV, 84- *Personal Data:* b Wise Co, Tex, June 18, 14; m 42, Bernice Rolf; c Allen R, John L & Laurence G. *Educ:* Univ Tex, BSChE, 38, MSChE, 40; Yale Univ, DEng, 48. *Prof Exp:* Asst prof chem, Tex Col Arts & Indust, 40-41 & Univ Ark, 41-42. *Concurrent Pos:* Mem adv bd, Petrol Res Fund, 70-72, chmn, 72-81. *Mem:* AAAS; Am Chem Soc; Sigma Xi; Am Soc Eng Educ; Am Inst Chem Engrs. *Res:* Water quality control; technology and the social sciences; role of the social sciences in energy policy; nuclear waste management. *Mailing Add:* 313-A Mason Lab Yale Univ Box 208286 New Haven CT 06520-8286

**WALKER, CHARLES R,** BIOCHEMISTRY, FISH BIOLOGY. *Current Pos:* RETIRED. *Personal Data:* b Chicago, Ill, Dec 18, 28; m 50; c 4. *Educ:* Southern Ill Univ, BA, 51, MA, 52. *Prof Exp:* Biochemist & fishery biologist, Mo Conserv Comn, 52-61; biochemist, Fish Control Lab, US Fish & Wildlife Serv, 61-67, chief br pest control res, Div Fishery Res, 67-72, chief off environ assistance, 72-75, sr environ scientist, 75-81; consult environ contaminants & toxicol, 81. *Concurrent Pos:* Consult fishery biol, hazardous mat, pesticides & pond cult, 54-82; lectr, Viterbo Col, 64-65; instr, USDA Grad Sch, 69-; mem adj fac environ systs mgt, Am Univ, 75- *Mem:* Am Chem Soc; Am Fisheries Soc; Weed Sci Soc Am; Am Soc Testing & Mat; Am Soc Limnol & Oceanog. *Res:* Fishery research; aquatic ecology, fish-pesticide relationships; pollution biology; pond culture; aquatic herbicides; toxicity; efficacy residues of drugs and pest control agents for fisheries; analytical chemistry; limnology; soil science; environment impact statements control; environmental impact assessments; biological testing methods and hazard assessment of toxic substances; monitoring environmental contaminants. *Mailing Add:* 29304 NW 182nd Terr Alachua FL 32615-9801

**WALKER, CHARLES THOMAS,** SOLID STATE PHYSICS. *Current Pos:* STAFF, 3M CO. *Personal Data:* b Chicago, Ill, Sept 5, 32; m 73; c 3. *Educ:* Univ Louisville, AB, 56, MS, 58; Brown Univ, PhD(physics), 61. *Prof Exp:* Res asst physics, Brown Univ, 58-60; res assoc, Cornell Univ, 61-63; asst prof, Northwestern Univ, Evanston, 63-67, assoc prof, 67-71, chmn dept, Ariz State Univ, 81-85, prof physics, 71- *Concurrent Pos:* Guggenheim fel, Oxford Univ, 67-68; vis prof, Munich Tech Univ, 71; consult, Motorola, Inc, 74-; vis prof, Univ Sao Paulo, 76 & Univ Regensburg, 77; dir, Ctr Solid State Sci, Ariz State Univ, 76-78; Alexander von Humboldt fel, Max-Planck Inst, Stuttgart, 78-79. *Mem:* AAAS; fel Am Phys Soc; Am Asn Physics Teachers. *Res:* Light scattering; lattice dynamics and impurity studies in solids; magnetism. *Mailing Add:* Corp Res Lab 3M Co Bldg 201-2S-05 St Paul MN 55144-1000

**WALKER, CHARLES WAYNE,** DEVELOPMENTAL BIOLOGY. *Current Pos:* asst prof, 76-80, ASSOC PROF EMBRYOL INVERTEBRATES, UNIV NH, 80- *Personal Data:* b Oberlin, Ohio, Mar 27, 47; m 69. *Educ:* Miami Univ, BA, 69; Cornell Univ, MS, 73, PhD(invertebrate zool), 76. *Prof Exp:* Lectr embryol, Cornell Univ, 75-76. *Concurrent Pos:* Hubbard Fund grant, 78-80, NSF grant, 80-81, NATO grant, 80-81. *Mem:* Am Soc Zoologists; Sigma Xi; Soc Develop Biol; Int Soc Invertebrate Reproduction. *Res:* Physiological and ultrastructural aspects of cellular interaction during spermatogenesis and regeneration; comparative aspects of invertebrate development. *Mailing Add:* Dept Zool Univ NH Durham NH 03824

**WALKER, CHERYL LYN,** CARCINOGENESIS, CELL BIOLOGY. *Current Pos:* SCIENTIST I, DEPT CELLULAR & MOLECULAR TOXICOL, CHEM INDUST INST TOXICOL, UNIV TEX, 88- *Personal Data:* b Portland, Ore, July 7, 55; m; c 2. *Educ:* Univ Colo, BA, 77; Univ Tex, PhD(cell biol), 84. *Prof Exp:* Staff fel, Lab Pulmonary Pathobiol, Nat Inst Environ Health Sci, NIH, 84-87, sr staff fel, 87-88. *Concurrent Pos:* Consult, BioSearch Labs Inc, Arlington, Tex, 73-77; coordr, Chem Indust Inst Toxicol Summer Student Intern Prog, 89-90; adj asst prof, Path, Univ NC, 89-, Toxicol, NC State Univ, 91-; mem, Pub Commun Comt, Soc Toxicol, 91-93, Small Bus Innovation Res Concept Rev Panel, NIH, Biol Models & Mat Resources Prog Study Sect, Sci Rev Panel, Nat Inst Environ Health Sci, prog comt, Am Asn Cancer Res, 91-92. *Mem:* Am Soc Cell Biol; Am Asn Cancer Res; Soc Toxicol; AAAS. *Res:* Molecular mechanisms of chemical carcinogenesis with emphasis on oncogenes and tumor suppressor genes involved in renal cell carcinoma and mesothelioma; current investigations utilize rodent models for renal carcinogenesis and in vitro and in vivo studies on mesothelial cell transformation; numerous publications. *Mailing Add:* Dept Carcinogenesis MD Anderson Cancer Ctr Univ Tex PO Box 389 Smithville TX 78957. *Fax:* 512-237-2475

**WALKER, CHRISTOPHER BLAND,** PHYSICS. *Current Pos:* RES PHYSICIST, ARMY MAT & MECH RES CTR, 63- *Personal Data:* b Lakeland, Fla, July 25, 25; m 61; c 3. *Educ:* Davidson Col, BS, 48; Mass Inst Technol, PhD(physics), 51. *Prof Exp:* Fulbright scholar, France, 51-52; instr physics, Mass Inst Technol, 52-53; from asst prof to assoc prof, Inst Metals, Chicago, 53-63. *Concurrent Pos:* Guggenheim fel, 63-64. *Mem:* Am Phys Soc; Am Crystallog Asn; Fr Soc Mineral & Crystallog. *Res:* X-ray diffraction; imperfections in crystals; thermal vibrations; neutron inelastic scattering. *Mailing Add:* 22 Baskin Rd Lexington MA 02173

**WALKER, DAN B,** PLANT ANATOMY & DEVELOPMENT. *Current Pos:* asst prof biol, 78-85, dir sci educ, 85-86, RES SCIENTIST, CTR STUDY EVOLUTION & ORIGIN LIFE, UNIV CALIF, LOS ANGELES, 85-; PROF & ASSOC DEAN, SAN JOSE STATE UNIV, 86- *Personal Data:* b Connersville, Ind, Apr 18, 45. *Educ:* Ind Univ, Bloomington, AB, 68; Univ Calif, Berkeley, PhD(bot), 74. *Prof Exp:* Lectr bot, Univ Calif, Berkeley, 73-74; asst prof bot, Univ Ga, 74-78. *Mem:* Sigma Xi; AAAS; Bot Soc Am; Am Soc Plant Physiologists; Soc Develop Biol. *Res:* Investigations of structure-function and developmental problems at the cellular level in higher plants, especially on the mechanisms of intercellular communication and pattern formation in plants. *Mailing Add:* Dept Biol Sci San Jose State Univ San Jose CA 95192-0100

**WALKER, DANIEL ALVIN,** SEISMOLOGY. *Current Pos:* RETIRED. *Personal Data:* b Cleveland, Ohio, Dec 18, 40; m 70; c 4. *Educ:* John Carroll Univ, BS, 63; Univ Hawaii, MS, 65, PhD(geophys), 71. *Prof Exp:* Res asst seismol, Hawaii Inst Geophys, Univ Hawaii, 63-68, jr seismologist, 69-71, asst geophysicist, 72-76, assoc geophysicist, 76-88, seismologist, 88-96. *Mem:* Seismol Soc Am; Am Geophys Union; AAAS. *Res:* Tsunami research; seismicity of ridge systems; fluctuations in global seismicity. *Mailing Add:* Hawaii Inst Geophys Univ Hawaii 2525 Correa Rd Honolulu HI 96822. *Fax:* 808-956-3188

**WALKER, DAVID,** PETROLOGY. *Current Pos:* PROF, LAMONT-DOHERTY GEOL OBSERV, 82- *Personal Data:* b Troy, New York, NY, Aug 9, 46; m 80, Celia M Nicholson; c 3. *Educ:* Oberlin Col, AB, 68; Harvard Univ, AM, 70, PhD(geol), 72. *Honors & Awards:* F W Clarke Medal, Geochem Soc, 75; Arthur L Day Medal, Geol Soc Am, 94. *Prof Exp:* Lectr geol, Harvard Univ, 73-74, res fel geophys, 72-77, sr res assoc, 78-82. *Mem:* Fel Geol Soc Am; fel Am Geophys Union; Geochem Soc; Mineral Soc Am; Meteoritical Soc. *Res:* General geology with specialty in petrology, particularly experimental petrology. *Mailing Add:* Lamont-Doherty Earth Observ Columbia Univ Palisades NY 10964. *Fax:* 914-365-8155; *E-Mail:* dwalker@ldeo.columbia.edu

**WALKER, DAVID CROSBY,** RADIATION CHEMISTRY, NUCLEAR CHEMISTRY. *Current Pos:* from asst prof to assoc prof, 64-75, PROF CHEM, UNIV BC, 75- *Personal Data:* b York, Eng, June 16, 34; m 78, Gale Young; c J Worsley, S Crofts & E Walker. *Educ:* Univ St Andrews, BSc, 55, Hons, 56; Univ Leeds, PhD(chem), 59. *Hon Degrees:* DSc, Univ St Andrews, 74. *Honors & Awards:* Miller Prize, 56; Irvine Chem Medal, 56. *Prof Exp:* Fel chem, Nat Res Coun Can, 59-61; res lectr, Univ Leeds, 61-64. *Concurrent Pos:* Vis prof, Univ Leeds, Paris & JSPS, 81. *Mem:* Fel Chem Inst Can; fel Royal Soc Chem; Am Chem Soc; Am Inst Physics; Radiation Res Soc. *Res:* Radiation chemistry of water and organic liquids; muonium chemistry; solvated electron studies in polar liquids; origins of optical activity in nature; kinetic isotope effects in chemistry. *Mailing Add:* Dept Chem Univ BC Vancouver BC V6T 1Z1 Can. *Fax:* 604-822-2847; *E-Mail:* walker@erich.triumf.ca

**WALKER, DAVID HUGHES,** RICKETTSIOLOGY, MICROBIAL PATHOGENESIS. *Current Pos:* PROF & CHMN, DEPT PATH, UNIV TEX MED BR, 87- *Personal Data:* b Nashville, Tenn, May 31, 43; m 68; c 2. *Educ:* Davidson Col, BA, 65; Vanderbilt Univ, MD, 69. *Prof Exp:* Resident path, Peter Bent Brigham Hosp, 69-73; USPHS surgeon virol, Ctr Dis Control, 73-75; from asst prof to prof path, Univ NC, 75-87. *Concurrent Pos:* Fel, Med Sch, Harvard Univ, 71-73; clin asst prof, Med Sch, Emory Univ, 74-75; prin investr, NIH grants, 79-82, 84- & 85-88, NIH contract, 79-82 & US Army Med Res & Develop Command contract, 83-86. *Mem:* Infectious Dis Soc Am; Am Soc Rickettsiology & Rickettsial Dis (vpres, 88); Am Asn Pathologists; Am Soc Trop Med & Hyg; Int Acad Pathologists; Soc Pediat Path. *Res:* Molecular rickettsiology, immunity to rickettsiae, rickettsial pathogenesis and diagnosis; role of proteases in infectious disease pathogenesis, and respiratory syncytial virus pathogenesis and antiviral treatment; tropical medicine, arenaviruses and hemorrhagic fevers, particularly Lassa fever; ecology of diseases; treatment and pathogenesis of Pheumocystis infections. *Mailing Add:* 301 University Blvd Galveston TX 77555-0609. *Fax:* 409-772-2500

**WALKER, DAVID KENNETH,** COMPUTER INTERFACING, INTERACTIVE VIDEO LEARNING. *Current Pos:* from asst prof to assoc prof, 71-80, PROF PHYSICS, WAYNESBURG COL, 81- *Personal Data:* b Youngstown, Ohio, Apr 4, 43; m 67. *Educ:* Pa State Univ, University Park, BS, 65; WVa Univ, MS, 68, PhD(physics), 71. *Prof Exp:* Instr physics, WVa Univ, 69-71. *Mem:* Asn Comput Mach; Math Asn Am; Am Asn Physics Teachers. *Res:* Computer applications in science; laboratory interfacing; interactive videodisc learning; hard disk organization and management systems. *Mailing Add:* RR 5 Waynesburg PA 15370

**WALKER, DAVID N,** PLASMA PHYSICS, SPACE PLASMA RESEARCH. *Current Pos:* PHYSICIST, NAVAL RES LAB, 77- *Personal Data:* b Yuba City, Calif, Aug 17, 43; m 68; c 2. *Educ:* Univ Md, BS, 65; Univ NH, MA, 72, PhD(physics), 75. *Prof Exp:* Engr, McDonnell-Douglas Corp, 66-67; assoc engr, Elec Assoc Inc, 68-70; instr physics, Univ NH, 70-75; analyst, Anal Servs Inc, 75-77. *Mem:* Am Phys Soc; Am Geophys Union; Am Acad Sci. *Res:* Plasma physics as related to space plasma. *Mailing Add:* Plasma Physics Div Naval Res Lab 4555 Overlook Ave Washington DC 20375. *Fax:* 202-767-3869

**WALKER, DAVID RUDGER,** POMOLOGY. *Current Pos:* assoc prof, 60-65, PROF PLANT SCI, UTAH STATE UNIV, 65- *Personal Data:* b Ames, Iowa, Sept 15, 29; m 48; c 10. *Educ:* Utah State Univ, BS, 51, MS, 52; Cornell Univ, PhD, 55. *Honors & Awards:* Shepard Award, Am Pomol Soc; Stark Award, Am Soc Hort Sci. *Prof Exp:* From asst prof to assoc prof hort, NC State Univ, 55-60. *Mem:* Fel Am Soc Hort Sci; Am Pomol Soc; fel AAAS. *Res:* Plant hardiness; mineral nutrition; growth substances; rootstocks. *Mailing Add:* 429 Blvd Logan UT 84321

**WALKER, DAVID TUTHERLY,** MATHEMATICS. *Current Pos:* RETIRED. *Personal Data:* b Huntington, WVa, July 10, 22; m 57; c 1. *Educ:* Wofford Col, BS, 49; Univ Ga, MS, 51, PhD, 55. *Prof Exp:* Instr, Univ SC, 53-54; from asst prof to prof math, Memphis State Univ, 67-87. *Mem:* Sigma Xi. *Res:* Mathematical analysis; modern algebra; theory of numbers; geometry. *Mailing Add:* 4344 Tuckahoe Rd Memphis TN 38117-3010

**WALKER, DENNIS KENDON,** BOTANY. *Current Pos:* Asst prof, 65-70, assoc prof, 70-76, PROF BOT, HUMBOLDT STATE UNIV, 76- *Personal Data:* b Sacramento, Calif, Aug 1, 38; m 60; c 4. *Educ:* Humboldt State Col, BA, 60; Univ Calif, Davis, MS, 64, PhD(bot), 66. *Mem:* Electron Micros Soc Am. *Res:* Plant morphology; developmental plant anatomy and plant ultrastructure, specifically the ultrastructure of differentiating elements of vascular tissues. *Mailing Add:* Dept Bot Humboldt State Univ 1 Harps St Arcata CA 95521-8299

**WALKER, DON WESLEY,** NEUROSCIENCE, NEUROPHARMACOLOGY. *Current Pos:* Asst prof, 70-75, assoc prof, 75-80, PROF NEUROSCI & PSYCHOL, UNIV FLA, 80-; RES CAREER SCIENTIST, VET ADMIN HOSP, GAINESVILLE, 83- *Personal Data:* b Ft Worth, Tex, July 30, 42; m 64; c 2. *Educ:* Univ Tex, Arlington, BA, 64; Tex Christian Univ, MA & PhD(psychol), 68. *Concurrent Pos:* NH training grant, Col Med, Univ Fla, 68-70, NIH res grant neurosci, 72-; Vet Admin res fund grant, Vet Admin Hosp, Gainesville, 70-, res investr, 70-83. *Mem:* AAAS; Soc Neurosci; Res Soc Alcoholism. *Res:* Neurobiology of alcoholism; chronic effects of ethanol on the brain. *Mailing Add:* Dept Neurosci Univ Fla Col Med 1 Miller Health Ctr Gainesville FL 32610-3000

**WALKER, DONALD I,** analytical chemistry, chemical microscopy, for more information see previous edition

**WALKER, DUARD LEE,** VIROLOGY, MICROBIOLOGY. *Current Pos:* assoc prof, Univ Wis-Madison, 52-59, prof med microbiol, Med Sch, 59-88, chmn dept, 70-76 & 81-88, PAUL F CLARK, UNIV WIS-MADISON, 88- *Personal Data:* b Bishop, Calif, June 2, 21; m 45, Dorothea V McHenry; c Douglas K, Donna I, David C & Diane S. *Educ:* Univ Calif, Berkeley, AB, 43, MA, 47; Univ Calif, San Francisco, MD, 45; Am Bd Med Microbiol, dipl. *Prof Exp:* Asst resident physician internal med, Stanford Univ Serv, San Francisco Hosp, 50-52. *Concurrent Pos:* Nat Res Coun fel, Rockefeller Inst, NY, 47-49; USPHS fel, George Williams Hooper Found, Univ Calif, San Francisco, 49-50, res assoc, 50-51; consult, Naval Med Res Unit 4, Great Lakes, Ill, 58-74; mem, Microbiol Training Comt, Nat Inst Gen Med Sci, 66-70; mem, Nat Adv Allergy & Infectious Dis Coun, 70-74, Study Group Papovaviridae, Int Comt Taxon Viruses, 76-87, Adv Comt Blood Prog Res, Am Red Cross, 78-79 & bd sci adv, Delta Regional Primate Ctr, Tulane Univ, 80-83; mem, Vaccines & Related Biol Prod Adv Comt, US Food & Drug Admin, 85-89; mem, Behring Diag Award Comt, Am Soc Microbiol, 86-89, Am Type Cult Adv Comt, 86-93. *Mem:* Nat Acad Sci; Am Soc Microbiol; fel Am Acad Microbiol; Am Soc Virol; fel Infectious Dis Soc Am; Am Asn Immunol. *Res:* Persistent and chronic viral infections; host response to viral infection; biology of human polyomaviruses. *Mailing Add:* Dept Microbiol & Immunol Med Sch Univ Wis Madison WI 53706. *Fax:* 608-262-8418

**WALKER, EARL E,** MANUFACTURING. *Current Pos:* PRES, CARR LANE MFG CO, 55- *Personal Data:* b St Louis, Mo, Feb 12, 21; m 42, Myrtle Agnew; c Mary, Tom, Nancy & Peggy. *Honors & Awards:* Eli Whitney Award, Soc Mfg Engrs, 91. *Prof Exp:* Welder, Curtis-Wright Aircraft Co, 41-49; welder, McDonnell-Douglas Aircraft Co, 49-51, Foreman, 51-53; pres, S N W Welding 52-53, Coeur Lane Mfg Co, 53-55. *Concurrent Pos:* Fel, Soc Mfg Engrs, 93. *Mailing Add:* Carr Lane Mfg Co 4200 Carr Lane Ct St Louis MO 63119-2129

**WALKER, EDWARD BELL MAR,** PHOTOCHEMISTRY, PHOTOBIOLOGY. *Current Pos:* asst prof, 81-85, ASSOC PROF BIOCHEM, WEBER STATE COL, 85- *Personal Data:* b Ogden, Utah, Mar 19, 52; m 75, Cheri; c Brian & Jeffrey. *Educ:* Weber State Col, BA, 76; Tex Tech Univ, PhD(chem), 80. *Honors & Awards:* Gov Medal for Sci & Technol, 92. *Prof Exp:* Grad student chem, Tex Tech Univ, 76-80; scholar biochem pharm, Stanford Univ Med Ctr, 80-81. *Mem:* Am Soc Photobiol; Am Chem Soc; Am Soc Plant Physiologists; Sigma Xi. *Res:* Photochemistry and photobiology, particularly the mechanisms of photoreception in both plants and animals; isolation and characterization of natural products. *Mailing Add:* Dept Chem 2503 Weber State Col Ogden UT 84408-0001

**WALKER, EDWARD JOHN,** SOLID STATE PHYSICS. *Current Pos:* RETIRED. *Personal Data:* b Detroit, Mich, Apr 16, 27; m 60; c 1. *Educ:* Univ Mich, BSE, 49; Yale Univ, PhD(physics), 60. *Prof Exp:* Asst electronics, Tube Lab, Nat Bur Stand, 49-53; physicist, Res Ctr, IBM Corp, 60-87. *Res:* Semiconductor physics. *Mailing Add:* Spring Valley Rd Ossining NY 10562

**WALKER, EDWARD ROBERT,** METEOROLOGY. *Current Pos:* RETIRED. *Personal Data:* b Winnipeg, Man, July 29, 22; m 54, Sarah McCombie; c 3. *Educ:* Univ Man, BSc, 43; Univ Toronto, MA, 49; McGill Univ, PhD(meteorol), 61. *Prof Exp:* Meteorologist, Meteorol Serv Can, 43-59; res asst meteorol, McGill Univ, 59-60; res micrometeorologist, Defence Res Bd, Can, 61-67; Arctic res meteorologist, Can Dept Environ, 67-78. *Concurrent Pos:* Environ consult, 78-85. *Mem:* Am Meteorol Soc; Royal Astron Soc Can; fel Royal Meteorol Soc. *Res:* Arctic meteorology; oceanography. *Mailing Add:* 3350 Woodburn Ave Victoria BC V8P 5C1 Can

**WALKER, ELBERT ABNER,** MATHEMATICS. *Current Pos:* CONSULT, 89- *Personal Data:* b Huntsville, Tex, Mar 11, 30; m 51; c 4. *Educ:* Sam Houston State Col, BA, 50, MA, 52; Univ Kans, PhD(math), 55; Colo State Univ, MS, 78. *Prof Exp:* High sch teacher, Tex, 50-52; mathematician, US Dept Defense, Washington, DC, 55-56; asst prof math, Univ Kans, 56-57; from asst prof to prof math, NMex State Univ, 57-87; prog officer, NSF, 87-89. *Mem:* Am Math Soc; Math Asn Am; Am Statist Asn; Sigma Xi. *Res:* Abelian group theory; category theory; ring theory; statistics. *Mailing Add:* Dept Math Sci NMex State Univ Las Cruces NM 88003-0105

**WALKER, ELIZABETH REED,** HUMAN ANATOMY. *Current Pos:* technologist electron micros, 67-71, lectr human anat, 74-75, INSTR HUMAN ANAT, WVA UNIV, 75- *Personal Data:* b Rochester, Pa, July 2, 41; m 67; c 1. *Educ:* Mich State Univ, BA, 63; WVa Univ, MS, 71, PhD(human anat), 75. *Prof Exp:* Res asst microbiol, Rockefeller Univ, 64-66. *Res:* Investigation of rheumatology by transmission and scanning electron

microscopy, particularly pathogenesis of rheumatoid arthritis and other connective tissue diseases, and pulmonary research, with emphasis on macrophage uptake of respirable mineral particulates. *Mailing Add:* Dept Anat Sch Med WVa Univ Morgantown WV 26506

**WALKER, ERIC A(RTHUR),** acoustical engineering; deceased, see previous edition for last biography

**WALKER, FRANCIS EDWIN,** AGRICULTURAL ECONOMICS. *Current Pos:* RETIRED. *Personal Data:* b Morris, Ill, Nov 29, 31; m 51; c 3. *Educ:* Univ Ill, BS, 54, MS, 58, PhD(agr econ), 60. *Prof Exp:* Asst prof agr econ, Purdue Univ, 60-61; form asst prof to prof agron econ, Ohio State Univ, 68-92. *Mem:* Am Statist Asn; Am Agr Econ Asn. *Res:* International trade policy; interregional competition. *Mailing Add:* 40 Mainsail Dr Salem SC 29676

**WALKER, FRANCIS H,** ORGANIC CHEMISTRY. *Current Pos:* Chemist, 60-76, sr res chemist, 76-90, PRIN RES CHEMIST, 90- *Personal Data:* b San Francisco, Calif, Jan 15, 36; m 66, Barbara Lyons; c Suzanne & Holly. *Educ:* Stanford Univ, BS, 58, MS, 60. *Res:* Organic synthesis of agricultural chemicals; metabolite synthesis and identification of metabolites of pesticides. *Mailing Add:* Zeneca Ag Prod 1200 S 47th St Richmond CA 94804. *Fax:* 510-231-1284

**WALKER, FREDERICK,** POLYMER CHEMISTRY. *Current Pos:* LOAD APPLICATIONS CHEMIST, AIR PRODS, 91- *Personal Data:* b Woodbury, NJ, Jan 1, 54; m 79; c 2. *Educ:* Bloomfield Col, BA, 76; Yale Univ, MS, 78, PhD(org chem), 82. *Prof Exp:* Sr scientist, Rohm & Haas, 82-88; res dir, Akzo Coatings, Inc, 88-91. *Concurrent Pos:* Chmn, Great Lakes Polymer Conf, 91- *Mem:* Am Chem Soc; Fedn Socs Coatings Technol. *Res:* Synthesis of solution polymers, nonaqueous dispersions, and acrylic latexes for use in coatings and related applications. *Mailing Add:* Air Prods Inc 7201 Hamilton Blvd Allentown PA 18195-1501

**WALKER, FREDERICK JOHN,** THROMBOEMBOLIC DISEASE, AUTOIMMUNE DISEASE. *Current Pos:* SCI DIR, AM RED CROSS, 86-; PROF MED, LAB MED, UNIV CONN, 86- *Personal Data:* b Salamanca, NY, Sept 2, 50; m 79, Edith Fend; c Matthew, Nicholas & Elizabeth. *Educ:* Univ Calif, San Diego, BA, 72; Univ Wis, PhD(biochem), 76. *Prof Exp:* Fel, Univ Okla, 76-79; assoc prof biochem, Ind Univ, 79-86. *Mem:* Am Chem Soc; Protein Soc; Am Soc Biochem & Molecular Biol; AAAS. *Res:* Studies on the causes of thromboembolic disease through alterations in natural regulators of blood coagulation and autoimmune disease. *Mailing Add:* Am Red Cross 209 Farmington Ave Farmington CT 06010-1911. *Fax:* 860-676-8093

**WALKER, GENE B(ERT),** ELECTRICAL ENGINEERING. *Current Pos:* from asst prof to assoc prof, 67-77, assoc dean eng, 79-92, PROF ELEC ENG, UNIV OKLA, 77- *Personal Data:* b Gladewater, Tex, Feb 24, 32; m 56; c Janet, Karen, Gene B Jr & Christopher A. *Educ:* Univ Tex, BS, 59, MS, 62, PhD(elec eng), 64. *Prof Exp:* Res engr, Elec Eng Res Lab, Univ Tex, 59-64; sr res engr, Southwest Res Inst, 64-67. *Concurrent Pos:* Consult, Nat Severe Storms Lab, Nat Oceanic & Atmospheric Admin, 69-78. *Mem:* Inst Elec & Electronics Engrs; Sigma Xi. *Res:* Radio wave propagation; radio direction finding; radar sounding of troposphere; acoustic sounding of the troposphere. *Mailing Add:* 2408 Cypress Ave Norman OK 73072-6844. *Fax:* 405-325-7066

**WALKER, GEORGE EDWARD,** THEORETICAL NUCLEAR PHYSICS. *Current Pos:* from asst prof to assoc prof, 70-76, from assoc vpres res/dean grad sch to vpres res/dean grad sch, 89-96, PROF PHYSICS, IND UNIV, BLOOMINGTON, 76-, CHAIRPERSON, 86- *Personal Data:* b Chillicothe, Ohio, Nov 5, 40; m 64, Erika Bopp; c Elizabeth, Patricia & Christopher. *Educ:* Wesleyan Univ, BA, 62; Case Western Res Univ, MS, 64, PhD(physics), 66. *Prof Exp:* Res assoc physics, Los Alamos Sci Lab, 66-68; res assoc, Stanford Univ, 68-70. *Concurrent Pos:* Vis staff mem, Los Alamos Sci Lab, 68- *Mem:* Fel Am Phys Soc; Am Asn Physics Teachers. *Res:* Nuclear theory; electron scattering; meson-nucleus interactions; nucleon-nucleus interactions; strangeness exchange interactions. *Mailing Add:* Bryan Hall No 104 Ind Univ Bloomington IN 47405. *Fax:* 812-855-6396

**WALKER, GLENN KENNETH,** CELL BIOLOGY, PROTOZOOLOGY. *Current Pos:* from asst prof to assoc prof, 76-85, PROF BIOL, EASTERN MICH UNIV, 85- *Personal Data:* b South Weymouth, Mass, May 15, 48. *Educ:* Univ Mass, Amherst, BS, 70; Northern Ariz Univ, MS, 72; Univ Md, Col Park, PhD(cell biol), 75. *Prof Exp:* Teaching asst biol, Northern Ariz Univ, 70-72; teaching asst zool, cell biol & protozool, Univ Md, College Park, 72-75; NIH res fel, Cell Chem Lab, Univ Mich, Ann Arbor, 75-76. *Concurrent Pos:* Adj prof, Med Sch, Univ Mich, 82-; consult, Occup Safety & Health Admin, 82- *Mem:* Am Micros Soc; Sigma Xi. *Res:* Examination of the molecular mechanisms associated with pathologies which may represent abnormalities in skeletal muscle differentiation; ultrastructural and cytochemical examination of protozoan encystment and differentiation. *Mailing Add:* Dept Biol Eastern Mich Univ 316 Mark Jefferson Ypsilanti MI 48197-2211

**WALKER, GORDON ARTHUR HUNTER,** ASTROPHYSICS. *Current Pos:* assoc prof, 69-74, dir inst astron & space sci, 72-78, PROF, UNIV BC, 74- *Personal Data:* b Kinghorn, Scotland, Jan 30, 36; m 62; c 2. *Educ:* Univ Edinburgh, BSc, 58; Univ Cambridge, PhD(astrophys), 62. *Prof Exp:* Nat Res

Coun fel astrophys, Dept Mines & Technol Surv, Dom Astrophys Observ, 62-63, res scientist II, 63-69. *Mem:* Can Astron Soc; fel Royal Soc Can; Am Astron Soc. *Res:* Interstellar materials, particularly interstellar dust; early type stars, their distance, luminosity and rotational velocities; telescope auxilliary instrumentation; low light level multichannel detection systems. *Mailing Add:* Dept Geophys & Astron Univ BC Rm 325 6224 Agr Rd Vancouver BC V6T 1Z1 Can. *Fax:* 604-822-6047

**WALKER, GRAYSON HOWARD,** STATISTICAL MECHANICS, CHEMICAL PHYSICS. *Personal Data:* b North Wilkesboro, NC, Dec 9, 38; m 71. *Educ:* Univ NC, BS, 61; Univ Ill, MS, 62; Ga Inst Technol, PhD(physics), 69. *Prof Exp:* From instr to prof physics, Clark Col, 67-77; prof, Univ Tenn, Chattanooga, 77-81, Univ Chattanooga Found prof physics & dir, Environ Studies Prog, 81-93. *Mem:* Am Phys Soc; Am Meteorol Soc; Am Asn Physics Teachers. *Res:* Applications of the methods of statistical physics to problems in chemical physics, atmospheric research, planetary atmospheres; nonlinear systems. *Mailing Add:* 221 S Palisades Dr Signal Mountain TN 37377

**WALKER, GRAYSON WATKINS,** ELECTROCHEMISTRY, MINERAL PROCESSING. *Current Pos:* res chemist, 80-83, SUPVRY RES CHEMIST, US BUR MINES, AVONDALE, MD, 83- *Personal Data:* b Norfolk, Va, Feb 10, 44; m 70; c 1. *Educ:* Va Polytech Inst, BS, 67; Am Univ, MS, 79, PhD(phys chem), 81. *Prof Exp:* Res chemist, Mobility Equip Res & Develop Ctr, US Army, Ft Belvoir, Va, 67-80. *Concurrent Pos:* Adj prof, Chem Dept, Am Univ, Washington, DC, 84-85. *Mem:* Am Inst Mining Engrs; Electrochem Soc; Sigma Xi; Am Chem Soc. *Res:* Surface chemistry of mineral flotation systems; electrochemistry of sulfide minerals; kinetics of fuel cell reactions on platinum electrodes; new electrolytes for acid fuel cell systems. *Mailing Add:* 1407 Key Dr Alexandria VA 22302

**WALKER, GUSTAV ADOLPHUS,** BIOCHEMISTRY, MICROBIOLOGY. *Current Pos:* RES SCIENTIST, UPJOHN CO, 77- *Personal Data:* b Locust Grove, Ga, Dec 5, 44; m 70; c 2. *Educ:* Clark Col, BS, 67; Purdue Univ, PhD(biochem), 74. *Prof Exp:* NIH fel, 74-76 & Med Sch, St Louis Univ, 76-77. *Mem:* Am Chem Soc; Am Soc Microbiologists; AAAS. *Res:* Protein chemistry; assay design and development of pharmaceutical products, including liquid chromatography, electrophoresis, and spectrophotometric techniques. *Mailing Add:* 5125 Midfield Kalamazoo MI 49001-3298

**WALKER, HARLEY JESSE,** COASTAL MORPHOLOGY, COASTAL ENGINEERING. *Current Pos:* from asst prof to prof, La State Univ, 60-77, chmn dept, 62-71, Boyd prof, 77-84, EMER BOYD PROF GEOG, LA STATE UNIV, 84-; ADV PROF, EAST CHINA NORMAL UNIV, 89- *Personal Data:* b Bushnell, Mich, July 4, 21; m 53, Rita Hays; c Winona, Angela & Tia. *Educ:* Univ Calif, Berkeley, BA, 47, MA, 54; La State Univ, Baton Rouge, PhD(geog), 60. *Hon Degrees:* Doctorate, Univ Uppsala, Sweden, 86. *Honors & Awards:* Hon Award, Asn Am Geogrs, 77, First Distinguished Career Award in Geomorphol, 89, First R J Russell Award in Coastal Geog, 91. *Prof Exp:* From asst prof to assoc prof geog, Ga State Univ, Atlanta, 50-59, chmn dept 53-59; res geogr, Off Naval Res, Wash, DC, 59-60. *Concurrent Pos:* Vis prof, Univ Calif, Berkeley, 67, Univ Hawaii, Manoa, 80, 85 & 88 & Tsukuba Univ, Japan, 81; liaison scientist, Off Naval Res, London, 68-69; vchmn, Comn Coastal Environ, 76-84; mem geog sci bd, Nat Acad Sci, 78-82; grant, Japan Found, 77-78, fel, 79; chmn, US Nat Comt, Int Geog Union-Nat Acad Sci, 80-84; consult, N Slope Bor; first hon fel, Int Asn Geomorphologists, 89; hon chair, Taiwan Res Coun, 90. *Mem:* Fel Arctic Inst NAm; Asn Am Geogrs; Coastal Soc; fel AAAS; Brit Geomorphol Res Group; Japanese Geomorphol Union; Am Geophys Union; Am Quaternary Asn. *Res:* Morphologic, hydrologic and nearshore oceanographic research on Arctic coasts; morphologic and human modification studies of Oriental shorelines. *Mailing Add:* Dept Geog La State Univ Baton Rouge LA 70803-4105. *Fax:* 504-388-2912; *E-Mail:* hwalker@unix1.sncc.lsu.edu

**WALKER, HARRELL LYNN,** PLANT PATHOLOGY, BIOLOGICAL CONTROL. *Current Pos:* PROF BOT, LA TECH UNIV, 87- *Personal Data:* b Minden, La, May 14, 45; wid; c 2. *Educ:* La Tech Univ, BS, 66; Univ Ky, MS, 69, PhD(plant path), 70. *Prof Exp:* Plant pathologist, Plant Indust Div, Ala Dept Agr, 74-75, asst dir, 75-76; res plant pathologist, Southern Weed Sci Lab, Sci & Educ Admin, USDA, 76-84; dir, La Res Sta, Mycogen Corp, 84-87. *Mem:* Am Phytopath Soc; Weed Sci Soc Am; Sigma Xi. *Res:* Biological control of weeds. *Mailing Add:* Dept Biol Sci La Tech Univ PO Box 3179 TS Ruston LA 71272-0001

**WALKER, HOMER FRANKLIN,** NUMERICAL ANALYSIS, SCIENTIFIC & STATISTICAL COMPUTING. *Current Pos:* PROF MATH, UTAH STATE UNIV, 85- *Personal Data:* b Beaumont, Tex, Sept 7, 43; m 84, Elizabeth Thompson; c Benjamin & John. *Educ:* Rice Univ, BA, 66; NY Univ, MS, 68, PhD(math), 70. *Prof Exp:* From asst prof to assoc prof math, Tex Tech Univ, 70-74; vis assoc prof, 74-75, assoc prof, 75-80; prof math, Univ Houston, 80-85. *Concurrent Pos:* Vis assoc prof, Univ Denver, 73-74; vis assoc prof comput sci, Cornell Univ, 78; consult, Lawrence Livermore Nat Lab, 79-, Sandia Nat Lab, 95-; vis prof math, Univ NMex, 81-82; vis prof comput sci, Yale Univ, 89-; vis scholar, Rice Univ, 93-94. *Mem:* Soc Indust & Appl Math; Am Math Soc. *Res:* Numerical analysis scientific computing; partial differential equations; statistical computing. *Mailing Add:* Dept Math & Statist Utah State Univ Logan UT 84322-3900

**WALKER, HOMER WAYNE,** FOOD MICROBIOLOGY. *Current Pos:* from asst prof to prof, 55-90, EMER PROF FOOD TECHNOL, IOWA STATE UNIV, 90- *Personal Data:* b Saxonburg, Pa, May 22, 25; m 63; c 1. *Educ:* Pa State Univ, BS, 51; Univ Wis, MS, 53, PhD(bact), 55. *Prof Exp:* Asst bact, Univ Wis, 51-55. *Concurrent Pos:* Fulbright fel, Denmark, 77. *Mem:* Am Soc Microbiol; fel Inst Food Technologists; AAAS; Int Asn Milk, Food & Environ Sanit; Brit Soc Appl Bact. *Res:* Resistance of bacterial spores to heat and chemicals; bacterial toxins; antibiotics in foods and use as preservatives; microbiology of processed poultry and meats; sanitary bacteriology of food and water; mycotoxins. *Mailing Add:* 1513 Harding Ames IA 50010-5247

**WALKER, HOWARD DAVID,** biochemistry; deceased, see previous edition for last biography

**WALKER, HUGH S(ANDERS),** MECHANICAL ENGINEERING, APPLIED MECHANICS. *Current Pos:* res asst, 60-64, from instr to assoc prof, 64-76, PROF MECH ENG, KANS STATE UNIV, 76-; ASSOC DIR, INST COMPUT RES IN ENG, 69- *Personal Data:* b Mooringsport, La, July 31, 35; m 58; c 4. *Educ:* La State Univ, BS, 57, MS, 60; Kans State Univ, PhD(mech eng), 65. *Prof Exp:* Instr eng mech, La State Univ, 57-60. *Concurrent Pos:* NSF res grant, 66-67. *Mem:* Am Soc Mech Engrs; Am Inst Aeronaut & Astronaut; Soc Exp Stress Analysis; Am Soc Eng Educ. *Res:* Analytical and experimental investigations in stress analysis, vibrations and acoustics; numerical analysis and computer techniques. *Mailing Add:* Dept Mech Eng Kans State Univ Durland Hall Manhattan KS 66506-5106

**WALKER, IAN GARDNER,** BIOCHEMISTRY, CELL BIOLOGY. *Current Pos:* RETIRED. *Personal Data:* b Saskatoon, Sask, Apr 20, 28; m 52, 80; c 4. *Educ:* Univ Sask, BA, 48; Univ Toronto, MA, 51, PhD(biochem), 54. *Prof Exp:* Defense sci serv officer, Defence Res Med Labs, Toronto, 54-60, spec lectr, Fac Pharm, Univ Toronto, 54-62; from asst prof to assoc prof, Cancer Res Lab & Dept Biochem, Univ Western Ont, 66-74, prof biochem, 74-93. *Concurrent Pos:* Nat Cancer Inst Can fel, Ont Cancer Inst, 60-62; Eleanor Roosevelt Int Cancer fel, 68-69; Stanford Univ, 81; Erasmus Univ, Rotterdam, 87-88. *Mem:* Am Asn Cancer Res; Can Biochem Soc; Can Soc Cell Biol. *Res:* Biochemistry of nucleic acids, cell division, anticancer agents; biochemistry and toxicology of omega-fluorinated compounds; toxicity of oxygen at high pressures; excision repair. *Mailing Add:* 1283 Santa Maria Pl Victoria BC V8Z 6S5 Can. *E-Mail:* igwalker@tnet.net

**WALKER, IAN MUNRO,** INORGANIC CHEMISTRY. *Current Pos:* asst prof, 68-73, ASSOC PROF CHEM, YORK UNIV, 73- *Personal Data:* b Toronto, Ont, Aug 18, 40; US citizen; m 66. *Educ:* Bowdoin Col, BA, 62; Brown Univ, PhD(chem), 67. *Prof Exp:* NIH fel chem, Univ Ill, Urbana, 67-68. *Mem:* Am Chem Soc. *Res:* Structure of ion aggregates in solution, single crystal near infrared spectroscopy. *Mailing Add:* Dept Chem York Univ 4700 Keele St Downsview ON M3J 1P6 Can

**WALKER, IAN RICHARD,** PALAEOLIMNOLOGY, PALAEOCLIMATOLOGY. *Current Pos:* PROF AQUATIC ECOL, OKANAGAN UNIV COL, 91- *Personal Data:* b Sherbrooke, Que, Nov 6, 58; m 92, Linda M Newall; c Emma J. *Educ:* Mt Allison Univ, BSc, 80; Univ Waterloo, MSc, 82; Simon Fraser Univ, PhD(biol sci), 88. *Prof Exp:* Lectr native flora, Mt Allison Univ, 82-83; fel biol, Queens Univ, 88-90, adj prof limnol, 90-91. *Concurrent Pos:* Adj prof biol sci, Simon Fraser Univ, 92-; hon res assoc zool, Univ BC, 92-; guest prof, Univ Bern, Switz, 96-97. *Mem:* Int Soc Limnologists; Am Soc Limnol & Oceanog; Soc Can Limnologists; Can Quaternary Asn; NAm Benthological Soc. *Res:* Development of chironomid fossils as quantitative indicators of palaeoenvironments. *Mailing Add:* Dept Biol Okanagan Univ Col North Kelowna Campus Kelowna BC V1V 1V7 Can

**WALKER, J CALVIN,** NUCLEAR PHYSICS, SOLID STATE PHYSICS. *Current Pos:* from asst prof to assoc prof, 63-70, PROF PHYSICS, JOHNS HOPKINS UNIV, 70-, CHMN, 87- *Personal Data:* b Mooresville, NC, Jan 16, 35; m 58; c 3. *Educ:* Harvard Univ, AB, 56; Princeton Univ, PhD(physics), 61. *Prof Exp:* Instr physics, Princeton Univ, 61-62; fel, Atomic Energy Res Estab, Harwell, Eng, 62-63. *Concurrent Pos:* Alfred P Sloan Found fel, 66-68; Shaw Travelling fel, Harvard, 57. *Mem:* Fel Am Phys Soc; NY Acad Sci. *Res:* Atomic beam studies of radioactive nuclei; solid state and nuclear studies using gamma resonance techniques. *Mailing Add:* Dept Physics & Astron Johns Hopkins Univ Baltimore MD 21218. *Fax:* 410-516-7239

**WALKER, J KNOX,** INSECT MANAGEMENT IN COTTON. *Current Pos:* RETIRED. *Personal Data:* b Bryan, Tex, Nov 16, 27; m 51; c 5. *Educ:* Agr & Mech Col, Tex, BS, 50, MS, 56. *Prof Exp:* From instr to prof entom, Tex A&M Univ, 53-93. *Mem:* Entom Soc Am. *Res:* Management systems for insects in cotton. *Mailing Add:* 105 College View St Bryan TX 77801

**WALKER, JACK L,** REMOTE SENSING, INFORMATION PROCESSING TECHNOLOGY. *Current Pos:* res engr, Environ Res Inst Mich, 64-79, assoc dir, Radar Div, 79-82, dir, Infrared & Optics Div, 82-86, exec vpres & dir, Tech Opers, 86-95, VPRES & CHIEF SCIENTIST, ENVIRON RES INST MICH, 95- *Educ:* Mass Inst Technol, BS, 62; Univ Mich, MS, 67, PhD(elec & comput eng), 74. *Prof Exp:* Jr engr, Gen Elec, 60-61; engr, Bendix Systs Div, 62-64. *Concurrent Pos:* Bd govs, Inst Elec & Electronics Engrs Aerospace & Electrons Systs Soc. *Mem:* Nat Acad Eng; fel Inst Elec & Electronics Engrs. *Res:* Remote sensing and information processing technology with applications for defense, industry, and the environment. *Mailing Add:* Environ Res Inst Mich PO Box 134001 Ann Arbor MI 48113-4001

**WALKER, JAMES BENJAMIN,** BIOCHEMISTRY. *Current Pos:* PROF BIOCHEM, RICE UNIV, 64- *Personal Data:* b Dallas, Tex, May 15, 22; m 56; c 3. *Educ:* Rice Inst, BS, 43; Univ Tex, MA, 49, PhD(biochem), 52. *Prof Exp:* Res scientist, Biochem Inst, Univ Tex, 52-55; Nat Cancer Inst fel biochem, Univ Wis, 55-56; from asst prof to assoc prof, Baylor Col Med, 56-64. *Concurrent Pos:* USPHS sr res fel, 57-64. *Mem:* Am Soc Biol Chemists; Am Chem Soc; Am Soc Microbiol. *Res:* Enzymes involved in biosynthesis of creatine and certain antibiotics especially gentamicin, spectinomycin and streptomycin and their regulation; physiological effects of introduction of synthetic phosphagens into brain, heart, muscle and tumor cells; feedback repression during embryonic development. *Mailing Add:* Dept Biochem William Marsh Rice Univ PO Box 1892 Houston TX 77251-1892. *Fax:* 713-285-5154

**WALKER, JAMES CALLAN GRAY,** ATMOSPHERIC CHEMISTRY & EVOLUTION. *Current Pos:* assoc dir, Space Physics Res Lab, 80-85, PROF ATMOSPHERIC SCI, UNIV MICH, 80- *Personal Data:* b Johannesburg, SAfrica, Jan 31, 39; m 59, 82; c 4. *Educ:* Yale Univ, BS, 60; Columbia Univ, PhD(geophys), 64. *Prof Exp:* Res assoc aeronomy, Inst Space Studies, NY, 64-65; res fel, Queen's Univ, Belfast, 65-66; res assoc, Goddard Space Flight Ctr, NASA, 66-67; asst prof geol, Yale Univ, 67-70, assoc prof geophys, 70-74; sr res assoc, Nat Astron & Ionosphere Ctr, 74-80. *Concurrent Pos:* Adj asst prof, NY Univ, 64-65; mem, Comt Solar Terrestrial Res, Geophys Res Bd, Nat Acad Sci, 71-76 & Comt Planetary & Lunar Exploration, Space Sci Bd, 77-78; assoc ed, J Geophys Res, 74-76; mem, Int Comn Planetary Atmospheres & Evolution, 78-; mem, Comt Planetary Biol & Chem Evolution, Space Sci Bd, 79-82; mem, Atmospheric Sci Adv Comt, NSF, 80-83; mem, Planetary Atmospheres Mgt Oper Working Group, NASA, 81-85; assoc ed, EOS, 88- *Mem:* AAAS; fel Am Geophys Union; Sigma Xi; Am Asn Univ Professors; Fedn Am Scientists; Int Soc Study Origin Life; Geol Soc Am. *Res:* Aeronomy; atmospheric physics; ionospheric physics; evolution of the atmosphere. *Mailing Add:* Univ Mich 2455 Hayward Ann Arbor MI 48109-1063

**WALKER, JAMES DAVID ALLAN,** FLUID MECHANICS & HEAT TRANSFER, APPLIED MATHEMATICS. *Current Pos:* assoc prof, 78-83, PROF MECH ENG, LEHIGH UNIV, 83- *Personal Data:* b Hamilton, Ont, Can, Oct 17, 45; US citizen; m 66, Margaret Elizabeth Cooper; c James C & Neal S. *Educ:* Univ Western Ont, Can, BA, 67, MS, 68, PhD(appl math), 71. *Honors & Awards:* Sr Scientist Award, Alexander von Humboldt Found, Ger 94. *Prof Exp:* Asst prof mech eng, Purdue Univ, 73-78. *Concurrent Pos:* Chmn, Fluid Dynamics Tech Comt, Am Inst Aeronaut & Astronaut, 93-96. *Mem:* Fel Am Phys Soc; assoc fel Am Inst Aeronaut & Astronaut. *Res:* Fluid mechanics and heat transfer; numerical methods and applied mathematics with aerospace applications. *Mailing Add:* 2529 Black River Rd Bethlehem PA 18015. *Fax:* 610-758-4041; *E-Mail:* jdw3@lehigh.edu

**WALKER, JAMES ELLIOT CABOT,** INTERNAL MEDICINE. *Current Pos:* prof med & soc, Univ Conn, 65-67, prof clin med & health care & chmn dept, 67-71, prof med & chmn, Dept Community Med & Health Care, 71-86, PROF MED & ASSOC DIR TRAVELERS CTR AGING, SCH MED, UNIV CONN, 87- *Personal Data:* b Bryn Mawr, Pa, Sept 28, 26; m 65, Audry Crouder; c James E C Jr & Holly (Burnwell). *Educ:* Williams Col, BA, 49; Univ Pa, MD, 53; Harvard Univ, MS, 66. *Prof Exp:* Intern, Univ Wis Hosp, 53-54; resident med, Univ Mich Hosp, 54-55; res fel, Harvard Med Sch, 57-60; sr resident, Peter Bent Brigham Hosp, 59-60, asst to assoc dir ambulatory serv, 60-65. *Concurrent Pos:* Mass Heart Asn fel, 58-59; Commonwealth Fund traveling fel, 65-66; from instr to lectr, Harvard Med Sch, 60-66; dir div med care res, Dept Med, Peter Bent Brigham Hosp, 63-66; chief med serv, Univ Conn Health Ctr, McCook Div & actg chief med serv, Vet Admin Hosps, Newington, Univ Conn, 69-71; pres, Can Am Health Coun, 79-87; dir, Ctr Int Community Health Studies, 81-86; dir, Geriat Assessment Clin, 89- *Mem:* AAAS; Asn Am Med Cols; fel Am Col Physicians; Am Fedn Clin Res; fel Am Geriat Soc. *Res:* Pulmonary physiology; airway temperatures; delivery of health care services; responsibilities of medical education and the university to medical care and society. *Mailing Add:* Health Ctr Travelers Ctr Aging Univ Conn Farmington CT 06032. *Fax:* 860-679-1307

**WALKER, JAMES FREDERICK,** physiology, histology, for more information see previous edition

**WALKER, JAMES FREDERICK, JR,** NUCLEAR THEORY, INTERMEDIATE ENERGY REACTIONS. *Current Pos:* asst prof, 68-74, ASSOC PROF PHYSICS, UNIV MASS, AMHERST, 74- *Personal Data:* b Minneapolis, Minn, July 22, 37; m 59; c 3. *Educ:* Univ Minn, BPhys, 59, MS, 61, PhD(physics), 64. *Prof Exp:* Asst res scientist, NY Univ, 64-66; mem res staff, Mass Inst Technol, 66-68. *Mem:* Am Phys Soc. *Res:* Pion interactions with nuclei; nuclear reaction theories. *Mailing Add:* Nuclear Physics Group Univ Mass LGRT Amherst MA 01003. *Fax:* 413-545-0648

**WALKER, JAMES HARRIS,** SPECTRORADIOMETRY, RADIOMETRIC PHYSICS. *Current Pos:* Physics technician optical pyrometry, Nat Bur Stand, 65-69, PHYSICIST RADIOMETRY, NAT INST STAND & TECHNOL, 70- *Personal Data:* b Washington, DC, Oct 13, 44; m 69, Jacqueline C Cormack; c James D & Kristin M. *Educ:* Univ Md, BS, 70. *Concurrent Pos:* Consult. *Mem:* Optical Soc Am. *Res:* Metal freezing point blackbodies; solar ultraviolet measurements; low background irradiation measurements. *Mailing Add:* 19157 St Johnsbury Lane Germantown MD 20876-1639

**WALKER, JAMES JOSEPH,** THEORETICAL PHYSICS. *Current Pos:* GROUP LEADER NEUTRON PHYSICS, LOS ALAMOS SCI LAB, J-16, 75- *Personal Data:* b Philadelphia, Pa, Dec 29, 33; m 57; c 3. *Educ:* Univ NMex, BS, 59; Univ SC, PhD(physics), 65. *Prof Exp:* Gen mgr, EG&G, Inc, NMex, 65-75. *Mem:* Sigma Xi. *Res:* Integral equations; holography; nuclear physics. *Mailing Add:* AM Paro Corp 2687 Santa Fe NM 87504

**WALKER, JAMES KING,** PARTICLE PHYSICS. *Current Pos:* PROF, UNIV FLA, 85- *Personal Data:* b Greenock, Scotland, Oct 9, 35; m 60; c 2. *Educ:* Glasgow Univ, BSc, 57, PhD(physics), 60. *Honors & Awards:* Kelvin Award, Exp Physics, 60. *Prof Exp:* Res scientist, Advan Training Sch, Paris, 60-62; res assoc physics, Harvard Univ, 62-64, from asst prof to assoc prof, 64-69; scientist, Nat Accelerator Lab, 69-84. *Concurrent Pos:* Consult, Pilot Chem Co, 67-69. *Res:* Electromagnetic and weak properties and structure of elementary particles; elementary particle physics. *Mailing Add:* Physics Dept Univ Fla PO Box 118440 Gainesville FL 32611-8440

**WALKER, JAMES MARTIN,** HERPETOLOGY. *Current Pos:* Assoc prof, 65-76, PROF ZOOL, UNIV ARK, FAYETTEVILLE, 76- *Personal Data:* b Jonesboro, La, Oct 21, 38; m 61; c 2. *Educ:* La Polytech Inst, BS, 60, MS, 61; Univ Colo, PhD(zool), 66. *Mem:* Am Soc Ichthyologists & Herpetologists; Herpetologists League. *Res:* Reptiles and amphibians of North America, with special interest in the ecology and systematics of lizards of the genus Cnemidophorus of the family Teiidae. *Mailing Add:* Dept Zool Univ Ark SCEN 632 Fayetteville AR 72701-1202

**WALKER, JAMES RICHARD,** PHYSIOLOGY. *Current Pos:* RETIRED. *Personal Data:* b Boise, Idaho, Feb 26, 33; m 61; c 3. *Educ:* Ariz State Univ, BS, 56; Univ Miss, PhD(physiol), 65. *Prof Exp:* Instr, Univ Tex Med Br, Galveston, 65-66, asst prof physiol, 66-93, asst dir, Integrated Functional Lab, 74-93. *Concurrent Pos:* Mem staff, Commun Sci Lab, Univ Fla, 72-73. *Mem:* Acoust Soc Am; Am Inst Physics. *Res:* Mathematical modelling of physiological systems. *Mailing Add:* 616 W Peach Fredericksburg TX 78624

**WALKER, JAMES ROY,** MICROBIOLOGY. *Current Pos:* from asst prof to assoc prof, 67-78, chmn dept, 81-93, PROF MICROBIOL, UNIV TEX, AUSTIN, 78- *Personal Data:* b Chestnut, La, Nov 8, 37; m 59, Barbara A Fess; c James B & Melinda L. *Educ:* Northwestern State Col, La, BS, 60; Univ Tex, PhD(microbiol), 63. *Prof Exp:* Nat Cancer Inst fel biochem sci, Princeton Univ, 65-67. *Concurrent Pos:* NIH res career develop award, 71-76; res assoc dept chem, Harvard Univ, 72-73; res grants, NIH, NSF & Am Cancer Soc. *Mem:* Am Soc Microbiol. *Res:* Microbial genetics; regulation of cell division; mechanism of DNA replication. *Mailing Add:* Dept Microbiol Univ Tex Austin TX 78712-1026

**WALKER, JAMES WILLARD,** EVOLUTIONARY BIOLOGY. *Current Pos:* From asst prof to assoc prof, 69-83, PROF BOT, UNIV MASS, AMHERST, 83-, HEAD DEPT, 86- *Personal Data:* b Taylor, Tex, Mar 23, 43; m 73; c 2. *Educ:* Univ Tex, Austin, BA, 64; Harvard Univ, PhD(biol), 70. *Honors & Awards:* George R Cooley Award, Am Soc Plant Taxon, 72. *Mem:* AAAS; Bot Soc Am; Am Soc Plant Taxon; Am Inst Biol Sci; Linnean Soc London. *Res:* Angiosperm systematics; morphology, phylogeny and evolution of primitive angiosperms; pollen morphology of primitive dicots. *Mailing Add:* Dept Bot Univ Mass Amherst MA 01003-0002

**WALKER, JAMES WILSON,** mathematical statistics, for more information see previous edition

**WALKER, JEAN TWEEDY,** MICROBIAL GENETICS, ELECTRON MICROSCOPY. *Current Pos:* asst res scientist, 72-75, ASSOC RES SCIENTIST, UNIV IOWA, 75- *Personal Data:* b Dublin, Ireland, Mar 3, 44; m 72. *Educ:* Trinity Col, Ireland, BA, 65; Univ Reading, Eng, PhD(microbiol), 71. *Prof Exp:* Res demonstr, Univ Reading, 65-67; from asst prof to assoc prof, Trinity Col, 67-72. *Mem:* Soc Gen Microbiol; Am Soc Microbiol; Royal Micros; Genetics Soc Am. *Res:* Bacterial and phage genetics and molecular biology; morphogenesis of phage; plasmids. *Mailing Add:* 335 Lucon Dr Iowa City IA 52246

**WALKER, JEARL DALTON,** OPTICS. *Current Pos:* Chmn, 85-89, from asst prof to assoc prof, 73-81, PROF PHYSICS, CLEVELAND STATE UNIV, 81- *Personal Data:* b Pensacola, Fla, Jan 20, 45; m 84; c 4. *Educ:* Mass Inst Technol, BS, 67; Univ Md, PhD(physics), 73. *Concurrent Pos:* Mem staff, Sci Am, 77-90. *Mem:* Am Asn Physics Teachers. *Res:* General physics. *Mailing Add:* Dept Physics Cleveland State Univ Cleveland OH 44115. *Fax:* 216-687-2424

**WALKER, JERRY ARNOLD,** SYNTHETIC ORGANIC CHEMISTRY. *Current Pos:* res chemist, 75-83, res mgr, 83-92, QUAL ASSURANCE/ QUAL CONTROL RES MGR, UPJOHN CO, 92- *Personal Data:* b Olney, Ill, Mar 4, 48; m 76. *Educ:* Univ Ill, BS, 69; Mass Inst Technol, PhD(org chem), 73. *Prof Exp:* Fel org chem, Univ Calif, Los Angeles, 73-74 & Calif Inst Technol, 74-75. *Mem:* Am Chem Soc; Royal Soc Chem; Int Soc Pharm Eng; Am Soc Qual Control. *Res:* Research and development of methods for the synthesis of biologically active compounds. *Mailing Add:* Pharmacia & Upjohn 1800-91-2 Kalamazoo MI 49001

**WALKER, JERRY C,** AGRONOMY, TOXICOLOGY. *Current Pos:* RETIRED. *Personal Data:* b El Paso, Tex, Feb 20, 38; m 55; c 3. *Educ:* Pan Am Univ, BA, 64; Clemson Univ, PhD(agron), 69. *Prof Exp:* Plant sci rep, Lilly Res Labs, 69-73, regional res rep, 73-75, regional res mgr, 75-79, res dir, 79-82, head, 82-83, dir, 83-86, dir toxicol, 86-93. *Mem:* Am Soc Agron; Soil Sci Soc Am; Weed Sci Soc Am; Coun Agr Sci & Technol; Am Chem Soc. *Res:* Agrichemical product development. *Mailing Add:* 2700 S 275 E Greenfield IN 46140

**WALKER, JERRY TYLER,** PLANT PATHOLOGY & PLANT NEMATOLOGY, TREE DISEASES. *Current Pos:* assoc prof, 69-79, head dept, Agr Exp Sta, Ga Sta, 79-91, PROF PLANT PATH, UNIV GA, 79- *Personal Data:* b Cincinnati, Ohio, Sept 7, 30; m 53, Mary Bridges; c Ann & Robert. *Educ:* Miami Univ, Ohio, BA, 52; Ohio State Univ, MSc, 57, PhD, 60. *Honors & Awards:* Porter Henegar Mem Award Hort Res. *Prof Exp:* Asst, Ohio State Univ, 55-59, asst agr exp sta, 59-61; plant pathologist, Brooklyn Bot Garden, 61-69. *Concurrent Pos:* Actg chmn res, Kitchawan Lab, NY, 67-69. *Mem:* Am Phytopath Soc; Soc Nematol; Int Soc Arboriculture; Sigma Xi. *Res:* Phytonematology, including control; diseases of ornamentals; air pollution effects on plants. *Mailing Add:* Dept Plant Path Ga Sta Agr Exp Sta Univ Ga Griffin GA 30223-1797. *Fax:* 770-228-7305

**WALKER, JOAN MARION,** CARTILAGE ARTICULATIONS, EXERCISE & AGING. *Current Pos:* dir, Phys Ther Sch, 86-94, PROF, DALHOUSIE UNIV, 94-, JOINT APPOINTMENT, DEPT ANAT. *Personal Data:* b New Plymouth, NZ, May 21, 37; NZ & Can citizen. *Educ:* Univ Man, BPT, 71, MA, 73; McMaster Univ, PhD(med sci), 77. *Honors & Awards:* Marion Williams Award Res Phys Ther, Am Phys Ther Asn, 94; Helen J Hislop Award, 94. *Prof Exp:* Lectr phys ther, Univ Toronto, 63-66, Univ Witwatersrand, 66-69, Univ Man, 70-71; lectr anat, McMaster Univ, 73-76; from asst prof to assoc prof, Dept Phys Ther, Univ Southern Calif, 78-86. *Mem:* Am Phys Ther Asn; Can Physiother Asn; AAAS; Am Asn Anatomists; Can Asn Anatomists; Sigma Xi. *Res:* Aging mechanisms in synovial joints including range of motion studies, interaction exercise/aging articular cartilage; postpolio sequelae. *Mailing Add:* Sch Phys Ther Forrest Bldg 5869 University Dr Halifax NS B3H 3J5 Can. *Fax:* 902-494-1941; *E-Mail:* jmwalker@is.dal.ca

**WALKER, JOHN ERNEST,** MOLECULAR BIOLOGY. *Current Pos:* staff scientist, 74-82, SR SCIENTIST, LAB MOLECULAR BIOL, MED RES COUN, 82- *Personal Data:* b Halifax, Eng, Jan 7, 41; m 63, Christina J Westcott; c 2. *Educ:* Oxford Univ, MA, DPhil, 69. *Honors & Awards:* Nobel Prize in Chem, 97; Johnson Found Prize, Univ Pa, 94; Ciba Medal & Prize, Biochem Soc, 96. *Prof Exp:* Vis res fel, Univ Wis, 69-71; NATO res fel, Nat Ctr Sci Res, Gif-sur-Yvette, France, 71-72; Europ Molecular Biol Orgn fel, Pasteur Inst, Paris, 72-74. *Mem:* Royal Soc London. *Res:* Elucidation of the enzymatic mechanism underlying the synthesis of adenosine triphosphate. *Mailing Add:* Med Res Coun Lab Molecular Biol Hills Rd Cambridge CB2 2QH England

**WALKER, JOHN J,** ORGANIC CHEMISTRY. *Current Pos:* DIR RES & DEVELOP, I SCHNEID, 81- *Personal Data:* b Alma, Nebr, July 4, 35; m 60. *Educ:* Univ Nebr, Lincoln, BS, 58; Atlanta Univ, MS, 68; Ga Inst Technol, PhD(org chem), 73. *Prof Exp:* Instr, Ga Inst Technol, 70-73; tech dir, Dettelbach Chem Corp, 73-81. *Concurrent Pos:* Adj prof, DeKalb Community Col, 73- *Mem:* Am Chem Soc; fel Am Inst Chemists; AAAS. *Res:* Synthesis of physiologically active barbiturates. *Mailing Add:* 2952 Greenrock Trail Doraville GA 30340-5007

**WALKER, JOHN LAWRENCE, JR,** PHYSIOLOGY. *Current Pos:* asst prof, 66-71, assoc prof, 75-76, PROF PHYSIOL, UNIV UTAH, 76- *Personal Data:* b Whitewater, Wis, Dec 12, 31; m 56; c 2. *Educ:* Univ Wis, BS, 56; Duke Univ, MA, 58; Univ Minn, Minneapolis, PhD(physiol), 63. *Prof Exp:* Instr physiol, Univ Minn, Minneapolis, 62-64, asst prof, 64-65. *Concurrent Pos:* USPHS fel, 64-66, res grant, 66. *Mem:* Am Physiol Soc. *Res:* Mechanism of movement of ions and molecules through membranes, especially permeation of ions and electrical properties of membranes; ion selective microelectrodes. *Mailing Add:* Dept Physiol Univ Utah 410 Chipeta Res Park Salt Lake City UT 84108-1209. *Fax:* 801-581-3476

**WALKER, JOHN MARTIN,** WATER POLLUTION, SOIL SCIENCE. *Current Pos:* regional sci adv wastewater, sludge & soil, Off Res & Develop, 75-77, PHYS SCIENTIST, OFF WATER PROGS OPERS, US ENVIRON PROTECTION AGENCY, 77- *Personal Data:* b Norfolk, Va, July 6, 35; m 55; c 2. *Educ:* Rutgers Univ, BS, 57, MS, 59, PhD(agron), 61. *Prof Exp:* Asst soil fertility and plant nutrit, Purdue Univ, 57-60; NATO fel soil chem, Rothamsted Exp Sta, Eng, 61-62; res soil scientist, Soils Lab Plant Indust Sta, Soil & Water Conserv Res Div, Agr Res Serv, USDA, 63-72, soil scientist, Biol Waste Mgt Lab, 72-74, actg chief, 75. *Concurrent Pos:* Adj prof, Dept Crop & Soil Sci, Mich State Univ, 75-77. *Mem:* Fel AAAS; Am Soc Agron; Soil Sci Soc Am; Int Soc Soil Sci; Water Pollution Control Fedn. *Res:* Utilization of sewage sludge and wastewater treatment and use on land; soil temperature effects on movement and uptake of water and ions; plant response to controlled environments. *Mailing Add:* Off Water Environ Protection Agency 401 M St Washington DC 20460

**WALKER, JOHN NEAL,** AGRICULTURAL & ENVIRONMENTAL ENGINEERING. *Current Pos:* RETIRED. *Personal Data:* b Erie, Pa, Feb 19, 30; m 54; c 2. *Educ:* Pa State Univ, BS, 51, MS, 58; Purdue Univ, PhD(agr eng), 61. *Prof Exp:* Exten agr engr, Pa State Univ, 54-58; asst agr eng, Purdue Univ, 58-60; from asst prof to prof, Univ Ky, 60-90, dept chmn, 74-81, actg

dir, Inst Mining & Minerals Res, 81-84, assoc dean, Col Agr, 84-90 & Col Eng, 90-96. *Concurrent Pos:* Vis scientist, Nat Inst Agr Eng, Eng, 70. *Mem:* Fel Am Soc Agr Eng; Am Soc Eng Educ. *Res:* Environmental and structural problems associated with plant and animal structures, especially greenhouse problems. *Mailing Add:* 1200 Glen Crest Lexington KY 40502-2800

**WALKER, JOHN ROBERT,** ENTOMOLOGY, RESEARCH ADMINISTRATION. *Current Pos:* RETIRED. *Personal Data:* b Newbern, Tenn, Nov 27, 31; m 55; c 1. *Educ:* La State Univ, BS, 55, MS, 59; Iowa State Univ, PhD(entom), 62. *Prof Exp:* From asst prof to assoc prof entom, La State Univ, Baton Rouge, 62-93, asst to vpres res, 66-68, asst to vpres instr & res, 66-80, asst vpres acad affairs, 80-85, actg vpres acad affairs, Univ Syst, 85-93. *Mem:* AAAS; Entom Soc Am; Nat Conf Advan Res; Nat Coun Univ Res Adminr; Sigma Xi. *Res:* Effects of ionizing radiations on reproductive system of insects. *Mailing Add:* 1120 Rodney Dr Baton Rouge LA 70808

**WALKER, JOHN SCOTT,** MAGNETOHYDRODYNAMICS, MATERIALS PROCESSING. *Current Pos:* from asst prof to assoc prof, Univ Ill, 71-78, asst dean, Col Eng, 80-81, prof, Dept Theoret & Appl Mech, 78-88, PROF, DEPT MECH & INDUST ENG, UNIV ILL, 88- *Personal Data:* b Washington, DC, May 25, 44; m 70. *Educ:* Webb Inst Naval Archit, BS, 66; Cornell Univ, PhD(fluid mech), 70. *Prof Exp:* Res assoc, Cornell Univ, 70-71. *Concurrent Pos:* NSF grants, 73-; consult, Oak Ridge Nat Lab, 78-80, IBM Res Lab, 81, Westinghouse Res & Develop Ctr, 81-83 & Monsanto Elec Mat Co, 83-85; Dept Energy contract, 84-; Dept Defense contract, 86-92; Nat Ctr Composite Mat Res, 86-91. *Mem:* Am Acad Mech; Am Soc Mech Engrs; Am Phys Soc; Minerals Metals & Mats Soc; Am Asn Crystal Growth. *Res:* Growth of crystals for electronics; design of homopolar machines; fusion reactor thermal hydraulics; metallurgical applications of magnetohydrodynamics. *Mailing Add:* Dept Mech & Indust Eng 140 Mech Eng Bldg 1206 W Green St Urbana IL 61801

**WALKER, JOSEPH,** ANALYTICAL CHEMISTRY, ORGANIC CHEMISTRY. *Current Pos:* RETIRED. *Personal Data:* b Rockford, Ill, Dec 28, 22; m 44, June Enerson; c Joseph, Amy, Richard & Jeanne. *Educ:* Beloit Col, BS, 43; Univ Wis, MS, 48, PhD(chem), 50. *Prof Exp:* Sr res chemist, Res Ctr, Pure Oil Co, Ill, 50-51, proj technologist, 51-56, sect supvr phys chem, 56-58, dir anal res & serv div, 58-64, res coordr, 64-65, dir res, 65-66, assoc dir res, 66-78, vpres, Chem Res Dept, Union Oil Co Calif, Brea, 78-85. *Mem:* Am Chem Soc; Am Petrol Inst; Am Soc Testing & Mat. *Res:* Petroleum technology; analysis of petroleum products; petrochemicals research; fuels development; petroleum research administration; petroleum research management (analytical, petrochemical and corrosion research). *Mailing Add:* 406-A Pasadena Court San Clemente CA 92672-5479

**WALKER, KEITH GERALD,** ATOMIC PHYSICS, MOLECULAR PHYSICS. *Current Pos:* instr physics, 65-67, from asst prof to assoc prof, 67-72, PROF PHYSICS, BETHANY NAZARENE COL, 72- *Personal Data:* b Carthage, Mo, Aug 22, 41; m 63; c 2. *Educ:* Bethany Nazarene Col, BS, 63; Ohio State Univ, MS, 66; Univ Okla, PhD(physics), 71. *Prof Exp:* Technician, State Ohio, summer 64. *Mem:* Am Asn Physics Teachers; Optical Soc Am; Am Phys Soc. *Res:* Electron-atom impact and resulting cross-sections. *Mailing Add:* Dept Physics Point Loma Nazarene Col 3900 Lomaland Dr San Diego CA 92106

**WALKER, KELSEY, JR,** theoretical gas dynamics, applied mathematics, for more information see previous edition

**WALKER, KENNETH MERRIAM,** biology, for more information see previous edition

**WALKER, KENNETH RUSSELL,** STRATIGRAPHY, PALEOECOLOGY. *Current Pos:* From asst prof to prof, 68-82, head dept, 77-87, CARDEN PROF GEOL, UNIV TENN, KNOXVILLE, 82- *Personal Data:* b Spartanburg, SC, June 21, 37; div; c 3. *Educ:* Univ NC, Chapel Hill, BS, 59, MS, 64; Yale Univ, MPh, 67, PhD(paleoecol), 69. *Concurrent Pos:* Spec publ co-ed, Paleont Soc, 82; pres, SE Sect Paleont Soc, 84-85; vchmn, SE Sect Paleont Soc, 82 & Geol Soc Am, 85; NSF panel mem, 90-93. *Mem:* Paleont Soc; Am Asn Petrol Geol; Soc Econ Paleont & Mineral; Geol Soc Am; Int Asn Sedimentologist. *Res:* Cambro-Ordovician problems; Holocene and ancient carbonate environments; carbonate geochemistry; ancient marine organic communities; lower paleozoic paleoenvironments; trophic relationships in organic communities; invertebrate paleontology; sedimentology. *Mailing Add:* Dept Geol Sci Univ Tenn 1345 Circle Park Knoxville TN 37996-0001

**WALKER, LARRY,** RENAL PHARMACOLOGY, SCREENING OF NATURAL PRODUCTS FOR BIOLOGICAL ACTIVITIES. *Current Pos:* res asst prof, Res Inst Pharmaceut Sci, Univ Miss, 81-86, asst prof, Dept Pharmacol, Sch Pharm, 85-86, actg asst dir biol sci, 86-88, RES ASSOC PROF, RES INST PHARMACEUT SCI & ASSOC PROF DEPT PHARMACOL, UNIV MISS, 86-, PROG COORDR, DRUG DISCOVERY & DEVELOP PROG, 92- *Personal Data:* b Martin, Tenn, Nov 23, 50; m, Patricia Davis; c Brian, Cory, Dani, Zack & Carrie. *Educ:* Oglethorpe Univ, BA, 72; Southern Sch Pharm, BS, 75; Vanderbilt Univ, PhD(pharmacol), 79. *Prof Exp:* Fel, Marg-Fisher-Bosch Inst Clin Pharmacol, WGer, 79, Dept Physiol; Sigma Xi; Soc Toxicol; Am Col Clin Pharmacol; Am Asn Lab Animal Sci. *Res:* Direct a biological screening program in drug discovery with a focus on new drugs from natural sources, especially plants. *Mailing Add:* Res Inst Pharmaceut Sci Miss Sch Pharm Oxford MS 38677-9999

**WALKER, LAURENCE COLTON,** SILVICULTURE, NATURAL RESOURCE POLICY. *Current Pos:* prof forestry & dean sch, 63-76, Hunt prof, 76-88, EMER PROF, STEPHEN F AUSTIN STATE UNIV, 88- *Personal Data:* b Washington, DC, Sept 8, 24; m 48, Anne Sinclair; c Janet, Stephen, Wendy & Jean. *Educ:* Pa State Univ, BS, 48; Yale Univ, MF, 49; State Univ NY, PhD(silvicult, soils), 53. *Honors & Awards:* William T Hornaday Gold Medal for Distinguished Serv in Conserv, 86. *Prof Exp:* Forester, US Forest Serv, 48-51; asst, State Univ NY Col Forestry, Syracuse, 51-53; res forester, US Forest Serv, 53-54; prof silvicult res, Univ Ga, 54-63. *Concurrent Pos:* Consult, Nat Plant Food Inst, & USAID; consult forest indust, surface-mining indust, educ insts & Int Exec Serv Corps. *Mem:* Fel AAAS; fel Soc Am Foresters; fel Am Sci Affil. *Res:* Silvicides for hardwood control; soil-water relationships in forests; forest fertilization; natural resource policy; technology transfer; transferring technical information for ready use by professional foresters and laymen; international forestry relationships; author of nine books. *Mailing Add:* Sch Forestry Stephen F Austin State Univ Nacogdoches TX 75962-6109. *Fax:* 409-468-2489

**WALKER, LELAND J,** QUALITY ASSURANCE, RESEARCH ADMINISTRATION. *Current Pos:* RETIRED. *Personal Data:* b Fallon, Nev, Apr 18, 23; m 46, Margaret; c Thomas, Peggy & Timothy. *Educ:* Iowa State Univ, BS, 44. *Hon Degrees:* PhD, Mont State Univ, 83. *Honors & Awards:* Grinter Award, Accrediting Bd Eng & Technol, 84; Truesdail Award, Am Coun Independent Labs, 85. *Prof Exp:* Lieutenant, USN, 44-46, lieutenant comdr, Civil Eng Res Lab, 51-53; mat engr, US Bur Reclamation, 46-51, construct engr, 53-55; vpres, Wenzel & Co Consult Eng, 55-58; chmn bd, Northern Eng & Testing Co, 58-88. *Concurrent Pos:* Dir, Mont Power Co, Entech Cos, Sletten Construct Co, Advan Technol Inst; pres, McLaughlin Res Inst, 89-92. *Mem:* Nat Acad Eng; fel AAAS; fel Am Consult Engrs Coun; fel Am Soc Civil Engrs; fel Accrediting Bd Eng & Technol (pres, 76-77); fel Am Coun Indust Labs. *Mailing Add:* Consult Engr PO Box 7425 Great Falls MT 59406

**WALKER, LEROY HAROLD,** MATHEMATICS, COMPUTER SCIENCE. *Current Pos:* SYST ANALYST, DESERET GENERATION & TRANSMISSION COOP. *Personal Data:* b Union, Utah, Sept 24, 33; m 63, Eunice Davidson; c James, Anne & Adrianne. *Educ:* Univ Utah, BS, 55; Mass Inst Technol, SM, 57, EE, 58; Univ Calif, Los Angeles, PhD(math), 68. *Prof Exp:* Res assoc opers res ctr, Mass Inst Technol, 58-60; asst prof math, Brigham Young Univ, 68-73; sr programmer & analyst, Univ Utah, 73-81. *Concurrent Pos:* Fac res fel, Brigham Young Univ, 69-70. *Mem:* Inst Math Statist; Math Asn Am; Am Math Soc; Asn Comput Mach. *Res:* Stopping rules for stochastic processes. *Mailing Add:* Deseret Generation & Transmission Coop 594 E 6170 S Murray UT 84107-7478. *E-Mail:* lhwalker@acm.com

**WALKER, LOREN HAINES,** HIGH POWER ELECTRONICS, AC MOTOR DRIVES. *Current Pos:* RETIRED. *Personal Data:* b Bartow, Fla, Sept 25, 36; m 61, Barbara G Doss; c 3. *Educ:* Univ Fla, BEE, 58; Mass Inst Technol, MS, 61. *Honors & Awards:* IR 100 Award, Indust Res Inc, 74. *Prof Exp:* Design engr, Spec Control Dept, Gen Elec Co, 58-60, sr design engr, 61-70; develop engr, Exide Power Systs, Div ESB Inc, 70-72; elec engr res & develop, Gen Elec Corp, 72-76, consult eng, Drive Systs Dept, 76-79. *Mem:* Fel Inst Elec & Electronics Engrs; Indust Appln Soc; Power Eng Soc; Power Electronics Soc. *Res:* Development, design and research of solid state power conversion equipment including variable frequency drives, cycloconverters, un-interruptible power supplies, power conversion for utility energy storage and reactive power controllers; granted 54 US patents. *Mailing Add:* 2823 Titleist Dr Salem VA 24153. *Fax:* 540-389-0744

**WALKER, M LUCIUS, JR,** MECHANICAL ENGINEERING. *Current Pos:* from asst prof to assoc prof eng, Harvard Univ, 63-68, asst dean, 65-66, actg head dept, 66-67, head, 67-68, assoc dean, Sch Eng, 73-74, actg dean, 77-78, PROF MECH ENG, HOWARD UNIV, 70-, DEAN, SCH ENG, 78- *Personal Data:* b Washington, DC, Dec 16, 36; m 60; c 2. *Educ:* Howard Univ, BSME, 57; Carnegie Inst Technol, MSME, 58, PhD(mech eng), 66. *Prof Exp:* Teaching asst, Carnegie Inst Technol, 57-58; instr eng, Howard Univ, 58-59 & Carnegie Inst Technol, 61-63. *Concurrent Pos:* Vis sr staff mem, Int Res & Technol Corp, Washington, DC, 69-70; Ford teaching fel, Carnegie Inst Technol; mem eng manpower comn, Accrediting Bd Eng & Technol & Biotechnol Resources Rev Comt, Nat Inst Health, 72-; mem bd trustees, Carnegie-Mellon Univ. *Mem:* Sigma Xi; NY Acad Sci; Am Soc Mech Engrs; Am Soc Eng Educ. *Res:* New transportation systems planning and economics; cardiovascular mechanics. *Mailing Add:* Sch Eng Howard Univ 2400 Sixth St NW Washington DC 20059-0001

**WALKER, MARY CLARE,** HISTOCOMPATIBILITY TESTING, HUMAN MONOCLONAL ANTIBODIES. *Current Pos:* ASSOC PROF IMMUNOL & DIR, HISTOCOMPATIBILITY LAB, IMMUNOL RES CTR, INST ARMAND-FRAPPIER, UNIV QUE, 81- *Personal Data:* b San Francisco, Calif. *Educ:* Univ Tex, El Paso, BS, 67; NY Univ, PhD(med sci), 75. *Prof Exp:* Res asst biochem, Res Inst, Hosp Joint Dis, Mt Sinai Sch Med, 68-69; adj lectr biol, Bernard Baruch Col, City Univ New York, 74-75; fel immunol, Dept Path, Sch Med, NY Univ, 75-80, res asst prof, 80-81. *Concurrent Pos:* Vis scientist trainee, Tissue Typing Lab, Mem Sloan-Kettering Cancer Ctr, 81-82; mem, Nat Health Res & Develop Prog Rev Comt, Health & Welfare Can, 84- *Mem:* Am Asn Immunologists; Am Soc Histocompatibility & Immunogenetics; Can Soc Immunol; NY Acad Sci. *Res:* Production of human monoclonal antibodies against histocompatibility locus antigens; primary and secondary in vitro immunization of human B lymphocytes; chemotherapy of AIDS. *Mailing Add:* Div AIDS Vaccine Res Dev Br NIAID NIH 6003 Executive Blvd Rockville MD 20892-0001. *Fax:* 301-402-1506

**WALKER, MARY W,** NEURO-PHARMACOLOGY. *Current Pos:* SCIENTIST NEURO-PHARMACOL, SYNAPTIC TECH PHARMACEUT, 92- *Personal Data:* b Evanston, Ill, Sept 12, 60. *Educ:* Loyola Univ, BS; Univ Chicago, PhD(pharmacol), 88. *Prof Exp:* Fel pharmacol, NIH, 88-92. *Mem:* AAAS; Am Soc Cell Biol. *Res:* Neuro-pharmacology. *Mailing Add:* Synaptic Pharmaceut 215 College Rd Paramus NJ 07602

**WALKER, MERLE F,** ASTRONOMY. *Current Pos:* from asst astronr to assoc astronr, 57-71, PROF ASTRON & ASTRONR, LICK OBSERV, UNIV CALIF, SANTA CRUZ, 71- *Personal Data:* b Pasadena, Calif, Mar 3, 26; m 59; c 1. *Educ:* Univ Calif, AB, 49, PhD(astron), 52. *Honors & Awards:* Helen B Warner Prize Astron, Am Astron Soc, 58. *Prof Exp:* Asst astron, Univ Calif, 49-52, jr res astronr, 55-56; Carnegie fel, Mt Wilson & Palomar Observ, 52-54; res assoc, Yerkes Observ, Univ Chicago, 54-55; instr, Warner & Swasey Observ, Case Inst Technol, 56-57. *Concurrent Pos:* Sr resident astronr, Cerro Tololo Interam Observ, 68-69. *Mem:* Int Astron Union; Am Astron Soc; Sigma Xi. *Res:* Photoelectric photometry of short period variable stars; photoelectric magnitudes and colors of stars; stellar spectra and radial velocities; electronic image intensification; astronomical seeing and observatory sites. *Mailing Add:* Lick Observ Univ Calif Santa Cruz CA 95064

**WALKER, MICHAEL BARRY,** PHYSICS. *Current Pos:* Fel, 66-68, from asst to assoc prof, 68-77, PROF PHYSICS, UNIV TORONTO, 77- *Personal Data:* b Regina, Sask. *Educ:* McGill Univ, BEng, 61; Oxford Univ, PhD, 65. *Honors & Awards:* Herzberg Medal, 77. *Mem:* Can Asn Physicists; Am Phys Soc. *Res:* Theoretical solid state physics. *Mailing Add:* Dept Physics Univ Toronto Toronto ON M5S 1A7 Can. *Fax:* 416-978-2537; *E-Mail:* walker@physics.utoronto.ca

**WALKER, MICHAEL DIRCK,** NEUROSURGERY. *Current Pos:* DIR, STROKE & TRAUMA PROG, NAT INST NEUROL & COMMUN DIS & STROKE, NIH, 80- *Personal Data:* b New York, NY, Jan 24, 31; m 53; c 3. *Educ:* Yale Univ, BA, 56; Boston Univ, MD, 60. *Prof Exp:* Intern surg, Mass Mem Hosps, 60-61; resident neurosurg, Boston City Hosp & Lahey Clin, 61-65; sr investr pharmacol, Nat Cancer Inst, 65-67; chief sect neurosurg, Baltimore Cancer Res Ctr, 67-80, chief ctr, 71-80. *Concurrent Pos:* Chmn, Brain Tumor Study Group, 67; assoc dir, Div Cancer Treatment, Nat Cancer Inst, 73-; assoc prof neurosurg, Sch Med, Univ Md, 73-; asst prof neurol surg, Sch Med, Johns Hopkins Univ, 74- *Mem:* Am Asn Cancer Res; Am Acad Neruol; Am Soc Clin Oncol; Cong Neurol Surg; NY Acad Sci; Sigma Xi. *Res:* Neurological surgery; analysis and treatment of human brain tumors with cytotoxic agents able to penetrate the blood-brain barrier. *Mailing Add:* Div Stroke & Trauma & Neurodegenerative Dis Nat Inst Neurol Dis & Stroke Fed Bldg Rm 8A08 Bethesda MD 20892

**WALKER, MICHAEL SIDNEY,** PHOTOPHYSICS. *Current Pos:* scientist res labs, 67-71, mgr, 71-91, MFR SITE MGR, XEROX CORP, 91- *Personal Data:* b Hull, Eng, Sept 13, 40; m 66; c 2. *Educ:* Univ Sheffield, BS, 62, PhD(chem), 65. *Prof Exp:* AEC fel, Dept Chem, Univ Minn, Minneapolis, 65-67. *Mem:* Inst Elec & Electronics Engrs. *Res:* Photophysics of organic molecules including semiconductors and photoconductors; materials characterization. *Mailing Add:* 800 Philips Rd Bldg Z18-085 Webster NY 14580

**WALKER, MICHAEL STEPHEN,** ENGINEERING & SOLID STATE PHYSICS. *Current Pos:* SR STAFF SCIENTIST ADVAN DEVELOP & SYSTS, MAGSTREAM, INTERMAGNETICS GEN CORP, 76-, TECH DIR, 76- *Personal Data:* b Detroit, Mich, Dec 16, 39; m 70; c 2. *Educ:* Mass Inst Technol, BS, 61; Carnegie Inst Technol, MS, 64; Carnegie Mellon Univ, PhD(physics), 71. *Prof Exp:* Sr engr, Westinghouse Elec Corp, 61-75. *Mem:* Am Phys Soc; Inst Elec & Electronics Engrs; Soc Mining Engrs. *Res:* Research and development on superconducting materials and devices, including the development of niobium-tin multifilament conductors and superconducting magnets for machinery, energy storage and for plasma confinement for fusion devices; mineral separation with magnetic fluids. *Mailing Add:* Intermagnetics Gen Corp PO Box 461 Latham NY 12110-0461

**WALKER, NATHANIEL,** forest management, forest economics; deceased, see previous edition for last biography

**WALKER, PETER ROY,** BIOCHEMISTRY, MOLECULAR BIOLOGY. *Current Pos:* RES OFFICER BIOL, NAT RES COUN, 75- *Personal Data:* b Batley, Eng, Nov 24, 45; m 81; c 1. *Educ:* Univ Sheffield, BSc Hons, 67, PhD(biochem), 70. *Prof Exp:* Damon Runyon Mem Fund fel oncol, McArdle Lab, Univ Wis, 70-73; hon lectr biochem, Univ Sheffield, 73-75. *Concurrent Pos:* Med Res Coun grant, Brit Empire Cancer Campaign grant & Wellcome Found grant, Univ Sheffield, 73-75. *Res:* Mechanisms of gene expulsion; changes in chromosome structure and action of transcription factors; molecular and cell biological aspect of cell growth and cell death. *Mailing Add:* Apoptosis Res Inst Biol Sci Group Nat Res Coun Can Bldg M54 Montreal Rd Ottawa ON K1A 0R6 Can

**WALKER, PHILIP L(EROY), JR,** MATERIALS SCIENCE. *Current Pos:* from asst prof to assoc prof, Pa State Univ, University Park, 52-55, head dept fuel technol, 54-59, chmn div mineral technol, 59-65, head dept mat sci, 67-78, prof fuel technol, 55-74, Evan Pugh prof mat sci, 74-83, EMER PROF, PA STATE UNIV, UNIVERSITY PARK, 83- *Personal Data:* b Baltimore, Md, Jan 10, 24; m 49; c 3. *Educ:* Johns Hopkins Univ, BS, 47, MS, 48; Pa State Univ, PhD(fuel technol), 52. *Honors & Awards:* Henry H Storch Award, Am

Chem Soc, 69; George Skakel Mem Award, 71. *Prof Exp:* Control chemist, Lever Bros Co, 48-49. *Concurrent Pos:* Chmn, Am Carbon Comt, 62-70; ed, Chem Physics of Carbon, 62-81; assoc ed, Carbon, 64-81. *Mem:* Am Chem Soc; Am Phys Soc; Am Carbon Soc; Sigma Xi. *Res:* Catalysis; adsorption; kinetics; crystal growth; solid state chemistry; heterogeneous reactions; pollution control; carbon and coal science. *Mailing Add:* 223 Acad Projs Pa State Univ University Park PA 16802-2302

**WALKER, RAYMOND JOHN,** SPACE PHYSICS. *Current Pos:* from asst researcher to assoc researcher, 77-84, RESEARCHER GEOPHYS, UNIV CALIF, LOS ANGELES, 84- *Personal Data:* b Los Angeles, Calif, Oct 26, 42. *Educ:* San Diego State Univ, BA, 64; Univ Calif, Los Angeles, MS, 69, PhD(planetary & space physics), 73. *Honors & Awards:* Edward A Flinn III Award, Am Geophys Union, 96. *Prof Exp:* Res assoc physics, Univ Minn, Minneapolis, 73-77. *Concurrent Pos:* Mem, Comt Data Mgt & Comput, Space Sci Bd, Nat Res Coun, 81-86, Comt Geophys Data, Comn Phys Sci, Math & Res, 84-87, Comt NASA Info Systs, Bd Telecommun & Comput Appln, Comn Eng & Tech Systs, 86, Comt Solar & Space Physics, Space Studies Bd, Nat Res Coun, 90-93; chair, Catalog Interoperability adv, NASA, 88-94, mgr, Planetary Plasma Interactions Node, Planetary Data Syst, 89-, chair, Steering Comt Space Physics Data Syst, 91-93, proj scientist, Planetary Data Syst, 92-96. *Mem:* Am Geophys Union; AAAS; Am Astron Soc. *Res:* Magnetospheric physics; the magnetospheres of the earth and Jupiter; the dynamics of charged particles in the magnetosphere; numerical studies of magnetospheric convection; quantitative modeling of magnetospheric magnetic fields; organization and analysis of multi-parameter satellite data sets; magnetohydrodynamic simulation of magnetospheric processes; data management. *Mailing Add:* 11053 Tennessee Ave Los Angeles CA 90064. *Fax:* 310-206-8042; *E-Mail:* rwalker@igpp.ucla.edu

**WALKER, RICHARD BATTSON,** BOTANY. *Current Pos:* From instr to assoc prof, Univ Wash, 48-60, chmn dept, 62-71, dir biol educ, 75-82, prof, 60-87, EMER PROF BOT, UNIV WASH, 87- *Personal Data:* b Tennessee, Ill, Oct 24, 16; m 40; c 3. *Educ:* Univ Ill, BS, 38; Univ Calif, PhD(bot), 48. *Mem:* AAAS; Ecol Soc Am; Bot Soc Am; Am Soc Plant Physiologists. *Res:* Mineral nutrition and water relations of conifers; comparative calcium-magnesium nutrition; iron nutrition. *Mailing Add:* Dept Bot Box 351330 Univ Wash Seattle WA 98195. *Fax:* 206-543-3262

**WALKER, RICHARD DAVID,** CIVIL ENGINEERING. *Current Pos:* from instr to prof civil eng, Va Polytech Inst & State Univ, 57-96, actg head dept, 69-70, head dept, 70-83, EMER PROF CIVIL ENG, VA POLYTECH INST & STATE UNIV, 96- *Personal Data:* b Washington, DC, Feb 19, 31; m 53, Alice Patricia Davis; c Patricia, Jean & Sheryl. *Educ:* Univ Md, BS, 53; Purdue Univ, MSCE, 55, PhD(civil eng), 61. *Prof Exp:* Asst civil eng, Purdue Univ, 53-55, instr, 55-61. *Mem:* Am Soc Civil Engrs; Am Soc Eng Educ; Am Soc Testing & Mat. *Res:* Highway materials; durability of concrete, design of flexible pavements; lime-stabilization; identification of aggregates causing poor concrete performance when frozen. *Mailing Add:* 701 Broce Dr NW Blacksburg VA 24060

**WALKER, RICHARD E,** CHEMICAL ENGINEERING, RHEOLOGY. *Current Pos:* RETIRED. *Personal Data:* b Cincinnati, Ohio, Dec 24, 23; m 46; c 2. *Educ:* Purdue Univ, BS, 45; Bucknell Univ, MS, 48; Iowa State Col, PhD(chem eng), 52. *Prof Exp:* Res chem engr, Stand Register Co, 46-47; from asst to instr, Bucknell Univ, 47-48; res assoc, Iowa Eng Exp Sta, 48-52; res engr, Jersey Prod Res Co, Stand Oil Co NJ, 52-63; prof chem eng, Lamar Univ, 63-92. *Mem:* Am Inst Chem Engrs; Am Inst Mining, Metall & Petrol Engrs; Soc Rheology. *Res:* Means of drilling for and producing oil; rheology of elastic and non-elastic liquids; non-Newtonian flow applications. *Mailing Add:* RR 2 No 127 Clifton TX 76634

**WALKER, RICHARD FRANCIS,** gerontology, reproductive endocrinology, for more information see previous edition

**WALKER, RICHARD IVES,** IMMUNOMODULATION, NUCOSAL IMMUNITY. *Current Pos:* DIR, INT VACCINE, ANTEBIOLOGICS, 93- *Personal Data:* b Portsmouth, Va, Nov 2, 42; m 67; c 2. *Educ:* Tex Christian Univ, BS, 69, MS, 68; Univ NH, PhD, 73. *Prof Exp:* Microbiologist, Naval Radiol Defense Lab, 68-69; head, Bacteriol Div, Naval Med Res Unit Two, 69-71; microbiologist, Armed Forces Radiobiol Res Inst, 73-78; microbiologist, Naval Med Res Inst, 78-79, head, Enteric Dis Div, 80, head, Med Microbiol Br, 80-82, dep dir, Infectious Dis, 82-84; dep dir, Armed Forces Radiobiol Res Inst, 84-88; dir, Infectious Dis, Naval Med Res Inst, 88-91, sci adv, Nat Prog Off, 91-93, dir, Vaccine Res Microcarb, 93. *Mem:* Am Soc Microbiol; Soc Intestinal Microbiol Ecol & Dis; Sigma Xi. *Res:* Management of opportunistic infections and protection against enteric infections; understanding mechanisms and use of immunomodulators and means to enhance nucosal immunity. *Mailing Add:* 120 Briscoe St Gaithersburg MD 20878

**WALKER, RICHARD V,** MEDICAL BACTERIOLOGY, IMMUNOLOGY. *Current Pos:* RETIRED. *Personal Data:* b Pueblo, Colo, Mar 8, 18; m 45; c 3. *Educ:* Univ Calif, Berkeley, BS, 49, MPH, 52, PhD(bact), 60. *Prof Exp:* Assoc & instr, Pub Health Lab, Sch Pub Health, Univ Calif, Berkeley, 49-57; from grad res immunologist to asst res immunologist, George Williams Hooper Found, Med Ctr, Univ Calif, San Francisco, 57-65; asst res immunologist, Nat Ctr Primate Biol, Univ Calif, Davis, 65-67; assoc prof zool, Ohio Univ, 67-88. *Mem:* Am Soc Microbiol. *Res:* Bacterial toxins; immunochemistry; fluorescent antibody; Salmonella-Shigella diagnosis. *Mailing Add:* 11 West Hills Dr Athens OH 45701

**WALKER, ROBERT BRIDGES,** THEORETICAL CHEMISTRY, CHEMICAL PHYSICS. *Current Pos:* appointee, 76-77, STAFF MEM, LOS ALAMOS NAT LAB, 77- *Personal Data:* b Houston, Tex, Sept 24, 46; m 71. *Educ:* La State Univ, New Orleans, BS, 68; Univ Tex, Austin, PhD(chem), 73. *Prof Exp:* Res assoc, James Franck Inst, Univ Chicago, 73-76. *Mem:* AAAS; Am Phys Soc. *Res:* Quantum reactive scattering of light atom-diatom systems; quantum and classical description of infrared multiple photon excitation dynamics of polyatomic molecules. *Mailing Add:* Group T-12 MS B268 PO Box 1663 Los Alamos Nat Lab Los Alamos NM 87545

**WALKER, ROBERT D(IXON), JR,** CHEMICAL ENGINEERING. *Current Pos:* prof, 44-82, EMER PROF, CHEM ENG, UNIV FLA, 82- *Personal Data:* b Atlanta, Ga, Mar 6, 12; m 35; c 3. *Educ:* Ga Inst Technol, BS, 35; Univ Fla, MS, 51. *Honors & Awards:* Sigma Xi, 46. *Prof Exp:* Res chemist, Eastman Kodak Co, NY, 35-44. *Mem:* Am Chem Soc; Electrochem Soc; Soc Petrol Engrs; Am Inst Chem Engrs. *Res:* Adsorption fractionation; electrochemistry and thermodynamics of fused salt systems; transport phenomena; electrochemical engineering; solubility and diffusion in biological systems; fuel cells; thermal batteries; enhanced oil recovery. *Mailing Add:* 4740 NW 20th Pl Gainesville FL 32605-3443

**WALKER, ROBERT HUGH,** PHYSICS. *Current Pos:* Asst prof physics, Univ Houston, 64-67, assoc dean, Col Arts & Sci, 73-74, dean, Col Natural Sci & Math, 74-82, interim chancellor, 82-83, vpres acad affairs, 84-87, exec vchmn, 88-90, ASSOC PROF PHYSICS, UNIV HOUSTON, 67- *Personal Data:* b O'Donnell, Tex, Sept 8, 35; m 55, Sherry Dean Gray; c Valerie (Harvcastle), Shannon, Rosalyn (Stewart) & Robert A. *Educ:* Tex Christian Univ, BS, 57, MS, 59; Mass Inst Technol, PhD(physics), 62. *Concurrent Pos:* Lectr, Baylor Col Med, 66-; consult, Int Inst Educ, 67-69; dean, Hilton Col, 93-94. *Mem:* Am Phys Soc; Am Asn Physics Teachers. *Res:* Theoretical physics; solid state physics; atomic physics. *Mailing Add:* 10930 Chimney Rock Houston TX 77096

**WALKER, ROBERT LEE,** PHYSICS. *Current Pos:* from asst prof to assoc prof, 49-59, PROF PHYSICS, CALIF INST TECHNOL, 59- *Personal Data:* b St Louis, Mo, June 29, 19; m 46. *Educ:* Univ Chicago, BS, 41; Cornell Univ, PhD(exp physics), 48. *Prof Exp:* Asst metall lab, Univ Chicago, 42-43; scientist, Los Alamos Sci Lab, 43-46; res assoc, Cornell Univ, 48-49. *Mem:* Am Phys Soc; Sigma Xi. *Res:* Photoproduction experiments and analyses; interaction of gamma rays with matter; high energy physics. *Mailing Add:* 200 Barbara St Frederick MD 21701-6210

**WALKER, ROBERT MOWBRAY,** SPACE PHYSICS. *Current Pos:* dir lab space physics, 66-73, MCDONNELL PROF PHYSICS, WASHINGTON UNIV, 66-, DIR, MCDONNELL CTR SPACE SCI, 75- *Personal Data:* b Philadelphia, Pa, Feb 6, 29; m 51, 73, Ghislaine Crozaz; c Eric & Mark. *Educ:* Union Univ, NY, BS, 50; Yale Univ, MS, 51, PhD(physics), 54. *Hon Degrees:* DSc, Union Univ, NY, 67; Dr, Univ Clermont-Ferrand, 75. *Honors & Awards:* Am Nuclear Soc Award, 64; Yale Eng Asn Award, 66; NASA Medal Except Sci Achievement, 70; E O Lawrence Award, AEC, 71; Lawrence Smith Medal, Nat Acad Sci, 91; Leonard Medal, Meteoritical Soc, 93. *Prof Exp:* Res assoc, Gen Elec Co, 54-66. *Concurrent Pos:* NSF sr fel, 62; vis prof, Univ Paris, 62-63 & Calif Inst Technol, 72; adj prof, Rensselaer Polytech Inst, 65-66; mem, Lunar Sample Anal Planning Team, 68-70 & Lunar Sample Rev Bd, 70-72; mem bd dirs, Vols Tech Assistance & Univs Space Res Asn, 69-71; mem, Lunar Sci Inst Adv Comt, 72-76, Space Sci Bd, Nat Sci, bd sci & tech for int develop, 74-77, comt lunar & planetary explor, 77-80; vis phys res lab, Ahmedabad, India & Inst Astron, Paris, 81; mem, Task Force Sci Uses Space Sta, NASA, 85-, meteorite working group, 85-88, chmn, 90-92, Planetary Geosci Strategy Comn, 86; mem, Org Comt Soc, Europ Sci Found, 89. *Mem:* Nat Acad Sci; fel Am Phys Soc; fel Meteoritical Soc; fel Am Geophys Union; Am Astron Soc; fel AAAS. *Res:* Radiation effects in solids; development of dielectric nuclear track detectors and their application to nuclear science; geochronology; space science; cosmic rays; meteorites; astrophysics; planetary surfaces; archeometry; laboratory studies of interplanetary dust and individual grains of interstellar dust found in primitive meteorites. *Mailing Add:* Dept Physics Washington Univ 1 Brookings Dr PO Box 1105 St Louis MO 63130. *Fax:* 314-935-4083; *E-Mail:* rmw@howdy.wustl.edu

**WALKER, ROBERT PAUL,** MATHEMATICS. *Current Pos:* DESIGNER, DEWBERRY DAVIS CO, 86- *Personal Data:* b Washington, DC, Mar 15, 43; m 65; c 2. *Educ:* Univ Md, BS, 65; Mass Inst Technol, PhD(math), 68. *Prof Exp:* Asst prof math, Univ NC, Chapel Hill, 68-73; prof & chmn dept, Talladega Col, 73-76; assoc prof & dir, Bowie State Col, 76-79; assoc dir, Syst Planning Corp, 79-86. *Mem:* Am Math Soc; Math Asn Am; Nat Asn Mathematicians. *Res:* Systems engineering, structured analysis and software systems design and development; operations research; strategic systems analysis. *Mailing Add:* 1724 S Pollard St Arlington VA 22204

**WALKER, ROBERT W,** ENVIRONMENTAL SCIENCES. *Current Pos:* instr, 64-65, asst prof, 65-74, ASSOC PROF ENVIRON SCI, UNIV MASS, AMHERST, 74- *Personal Data:* b Arlington, Mass, Mar 15, 33; m 59; c 1. *Educ:* Univ Mass, BS, 55, MS, 59; Mich State Univ, PhD(microbiol), 63. *Honors & Awards:* Co-recipient DIFCO Lab Award, Am Pub Health Asn, 79. *Prof Exp:* Hatch fel, 63-64. *Concurrent Pos:* Vis prof res, Univ Toulouse, France, 72-73, Univ Otago, Dunedin, NZ, 80, INSA Univ Toulouse, 90 & Univ El Salvador, San Salvador, 91. *Res:* Environmental microbiology; bioremediation. *Mailing Add:* Environ Sci Univ Mass French Hall Amherst MA 01003-0013

**WALKER, ROBERT WINN,** PHYSICAL CHEMISTRY. *Current Pos:* LECTR, PA STATE UNIV, 84- *Personal Data:* b Montgomery, Ala, Jan 5, 25; m 49, Genevieve Finneran; c Margaret, Nancy & Wynne. *Educ:* Auburn Univ, BS, 48; Mass Inst Technol, PhD(phys chem), 52. *Prof Exp:* Res chemist, Redstone Labs, Rohm & Haas Co, 52-53, group leader propellant res, 53-59, sect head phys & polymer chem, 59-65, lab head ion exchange appln res div, 65-73, mgr ion exchange res dept, 73-76, proj leader fluid process chem res, 76-83. *Mem:* Am Chem Soc; Am Inst Chemists. *Res:* Molecular structure; chemical thermodynamics; rocket propulsion; ion exchange resins; adsorbents; flocculants. *Mailing Add:* 6008 Cannon Hill Rd Ft Washington PA 19034-1802

**WALKER, ROGER GEOFFREY,** SEDIMENTOLOGY. *Current Pos:* from asst prof to assoc prof, 66-73, PROF GEOL, MCMASTER UNIV, 73- *Personal Data:* b London, Eng, Mar 26, 39; m 65, Gay Parsons; c 2. *Educ:* Oxford Univ, BA, 61, DPhil(geol), 64. *Honors & Awards:* Past Pres' Medal, Geol Asn Can, 75; Link Award, Can Soc Petrol Geologists, 83; R J W Douglas Mem Medal, 90; Judd A & Cynthia S Oualline Centennial Lectr, Univ Tex, Austin, 86; Francis J Pettijohn Medal, Soc Sedimentary Geol, 97. *Prof Exp:* NATO fel geol, Johns Hopkins Univ, 64-66. *Concurrent Pos:* Vis scientist, Denver Res Ctr, Marathon Oil Co, 73-74; Amoco Can Petrol Co, 82; distinguished lectr, Am Asn Petrol Geologists, 79-80; vis fel, Australian Nat Univ, 81; vis prof, Fed Univ Ouro Preto, Brazil, 87, 89, 90, 91, Fed Univ Rio Grande do Sul, Brazil, 92. *Mem:* hon mem Soc Econ Paleontologists & Mineralogists; Int Asn Sedimentol; Am Asn Petrol Geologists; Geol Asn Can; fel Royal Soc Can; Can Soc Petrol Geologists. *Res:* Sedimentary facies analysis; sedimentology of turbidites; quantitative basin analysis; sedimentology of Western Canadian Cretaceous clastic wedge. *Mailing Add:* Dept Geol McMaster Univ 1280 Main St W Hamilton ON L8S 4M1 Can. *Fax:* 905-522-3141

**WALKER, RUSSELL GLENN,** ASTRONOMY, INFRARED PHYSICS. *Current Pos:* ASSOC SCIENTIST, JAMIESON SCI & ENG, INC, 81- *Personal Data:* b Cincinnati, Ohio, May 3, 31; m 86, Nancy E Rensted; c Sandra J (Contreras) & Sharon L (Merchant). *Educ:* Ohio State Univ, BSc, 53, MSc, 54; Harvard Univ, PhD(astron), 67. *Honors & Awards:* Medal for Except Sci Achievement, NASA. *Prof Exp:* Staff scientist Fourier spectros, Block Assocs, 60-61; physicist infrared physics, Air Force Cambridge Res Labs, 61-66, chief, Infrared Physics Br, 67-75; astronr, Int Sci Sta, Jungfraujoch, Switz, 66-67; staff scientist astrophys, Ames Res Ctr, NASA, 75-81. *Concurrent Pos:* Consult, Smithsonian Astrophys Observ, 65-66 & TOM sub-group, Dir Defense Res & Eng Reentry Progs, 68-69; mem, Infrared Panel Astron Study Group, Nat Acad Sci, 71-72; mem, Space Sci Bd Infrared & Submillimeter Astron, 74-75, Sci Team Infrared Astron Satellite (IRAS), 77-84. *Mem:* Am Astron Soc; fel Optical Soc Am; Astron Soc Pac. *Res:* Infrared astronomy; cryogenically cooled telescopes and instruments for space research; infrared sky surveys, atmospheric infrared phenomena. *Mailing Add:* PO Box F1 Felton CA 95018

**WALKER, RUSSELL WAGNER,** ORGANIC CHEMISTRY, PHYSICAL CHEMISTRY. *Current Pos:* RETIRED. *Personal Data:* b Fredericktown, Ohio, Nov 14, 24; m 46; c 3. *Educ:* Ohio Wesleyan Univ, BS, 47; Ohio State Univ, PhD(org chem), 52. *Prof Exp:* Res assoc, Am Petrol Inst, 48-52; res chemist, Sinclair Res, Inc, 53-57, group leader, 57-60, div dir, 60-66, res dir, Sinclair Petrochem, Inc, 66-67, tech mgr, Sinclair Res, Inc, 67-68, vpres & dir assoc opers, Sinclair Petrochem, 68-69, mgr res & develop, Sinclair-Koppers Co, 69-74; dir res & develop, Arco Polymers Inc, 74-86. *Mem:* AAAS; Am Chem Soc; Indust Res Inst; Sigma Xi. *Res:* Relation of hydrocarbon structure to combustion characteristics; biodegradation and environmental pollution. *Mailing Add:* 109 Bartram Rd Savannah GA 31411-1369

**WALKER, RUTH ANGELINA,** ORGANIC CHEMISTRY, TEACHING. *Current Pos:* instr chem, Hunter Col, Bronx, 57-60, asst prof, 61-68, assoc prof, Lehman Col, 69-71, dir, Health Prof Inst, 77-78, prof chem, 71-84, assoc dean health professions, 79-84, EMER PROF, LEHMAN COL, CITY UNIV NEW YORK, 85- *Personal Data:* b New York, NY, July 11, 20. *Educ:* Vassar Col, BA, 42; Yale Univ, PhD(org chem), 45. *Honors & Awards:* Award, Am Asn Textile Chem & Colorists, 60. *Prof Exp:* Asst chem, Chas Pfizer & Co, NY, 45, Col Med, NY Univ, 45-50; sr res chemist, Celanese Corp Am, 50-56, Johnson & Johnson, 57. *Concurrent Pos:* Sigma Delta Epsilon grant-in-aid metal complexes hydroxyanthraquinones, Hunter Col, 63, Sigma Xi grant-in-aid res, 65, George N Shuster fel grant, 65, City Univ New York res grant, 65; chmn, Lehman Col Comt Curric, 68-77. *Mem:* Sigma Xi; Am Chem Soc; Sci Res Soc Am; Am Women Sci. *Res:* Synthesis of medicinal products; dyestuff synthesis; organometallic complexes of 1,4-dihydroxynathraquinones; methods of teaching; development of interdisciplinary programs to teach the team delivery of health care. *Mailing Add:* 3300 Darby Rd-Pine 7310 Quadrang Haverford PA 19041-1075

**WALKER, SHARON LESLIE,** SUSPENDED PARTICLE DETECTION, SEDIMENT TRANSPORT. *Current Pos:* OCEANOGR, PAC MARINE ENVIRON LAB, NAT OCEANIC & ATMOSPHERIC ADMIN, DEPT COM, 79- *Personal Data:* b Orange, NJ, May 7, 58. *Educ:* Univ Wash, BS, 81. *Mem:* Am Geophys Union. *Res:* Analysis of suspended particle size distributions; chemistry and transport of suspended particles in marine estuarine environments and in hydrothermal vent plumes. *Mailing Add:* Nat Oceanic & Atmospheric Admin PMEL-R-E-PM 7600 Sandpoint Way NE Bldg No 3 Seattle WA 98115

**WALKER, SHEPPARD MATTHEW,** PHYSIOLOGY, BIOPHYSICS. *Current Pos:* assoc prof, 49-62, prof, 62-74, EMER PROF PHYSIOL, SCH MED, UNIV LOUISVILLE, 74- *Personal Data:* b Perkinston, Miss, Feb 2, 09; m 32; c 1. *Educ:* Western Ky Univ, BS, 32, AM, 33; La State Univ, PhD(physiol), 41. *Prof Exp:* Instr biol, Perkinston Jr Col, 33-38; asst prof sci, Delta State Teachers Col, Miss, 41-42; from instr to asst prof physiol, Sch Med, Wash Univ, 42-49. *Concurrent Pos:* Mem, Spec Rev Muscle Contraction, 60 & 67; actg chmn, Dept Physiol & Biophys, Sch Med, Univ Louisville, 65-67. *Mem:* Soc Exp Biol & Med; Am Physiol Soc; Biophys Soc. *Res:* Muscle structure and function; development of fine structures in muscle fibers; neurophysiology. *Mailing Add:* Dept Physiol & Biophys Sch Med Health Sci Ctr Univ Louisville 1115A Louisville KY 40292

**WALKER, SYDNEY, III,** PSYCHIATRY, NEUROLOGY. *Current Pos:* DIR & DIAG NEUROPSYCHIATRIST, SOUTHERN CALIF NEUROPSYCHIAT INST, 74- *Personal Data:* b Chicago, Ill, Oct 4, 31. *Educ:* Univ Calif, Los Angeles, BA, 53; Univ Southern Calif, MS, 56; Boston Univ, MD, 64; Am Bd Psychiat & Neurol, dipl. *Prof Exp:* Intern surg, Presby St Lukes Hosp, Chicago, 64-65; resident neurosurg, Univ Pittsburgh Sch Med, 65; resident & teaching fel psychiat, Univ Pittsburgh Sch Med/Western Psychiat Inst, 65-66; resident psychiat, Neuropsychiat Inst, Univ Calif, Los Angeles, 66-68; resident neurol, Los Angeles Col Univ Southern Calif Med Ctr, 68-70; pvt pract neuropsychiatrist, La Jolla, Calif, 71-74. *Concurrent Pos:* Ed-in-chief, Neuropsychiat Bull, 76-; chmn bd dirs, Behav Neurol Int, 86- *Mem:* Fel Royal Soc Med; assoc mem Am Acad Neurol; assoc mem Am Psychiat Asn; Soc Biol Psychiat; World Fedn Neurol. *Res:* Psychiatry; neurosurgery. *Mailing Add:* Southern Calif Neuropsychiat Inst 6794 La Jolla Blvd La Jolla CA 92037

**WALKER, TERRY M,** COMPUTER SCIENCE. *Current Pos:* RETIRED. *Personal Data:* b Chicago, Ill, Dec 15, 38; m 60; c 2. *Educ:* Fla State Univ, BS, 61; Univ Ala, PhD(statist), 66. *Prof Exp:* Asst prof comput sci & economet, Ga State Col, 65-67; assoc prof comput sci, Univ Houston, 67-72; prof comput sci & head dept, Univ Southwestern La, 72-87. *Concurrent Pos:* Lectr & Ford Found consult, Atlanta, 66-67. *Mem:* Asn Comput Mach. *Res:* Simulation of industrial processes; computer programming languages. *Mailing Add:* 2163 D O-Pu-Hue Ct Kihei Maui HI 96753

**WALKER, THAD GILBERT,** LASER COOLING & TRAPPING OF ATOMS, SPIN EXCHANGE OPTICAL PUMPING. *Current Pos:* from asst prof to assoc prof, 90-97, PROF PHYSICS, UNIV WIS-MADISON, 97- *Personal Data:* b Boulder, Colo, Aug 5, 61; m 83, Michele Nichols; c Brent & Amy. *Educ:* Abilene Christian Univ, BS, 83; Princeton Univ, MA, 86, PhD(physics), 88. *Honors & Awards:* Nat Young Investr, NSF, 92. *Prof Exp:* Res assoc, Univ Colo, 88-90. *Concurrent Pos:* Alfred P Sloan res fel, Sloan Found, 91; David & Lucille Packard Sci & Engr Fel, Packard Found, 92; H I Romnes fel, Univ Wis-Madison, 96- *Mem:* Am Phys Soc. *Res:* Atomic collisions at ultracold temperatures; collisions involving excited states and applied laser fields; spin-exchange and spin-relaxation phenomena in optically pumped atomic vapors. *Mailing Add:* Dept Physics Univ Wis 1150 University Ave Madison WI 53706. *Fax:* 608-265-2334; *E-Mail:* walker@uwhuc0. physics.wsc.edu

**WALKER, THEODORE ROSCOE,** GEOLOGY, SEDIMENTARY PETROLOGY. *Current Pos:* RETIRED. *Personal Data:* b Madison, Wis, Feb 8, 21; m 49; c 4. *Educ:* Univ Wis, BS, 47, PhD, 52. *Prof Exp:* Asst geologist, State Geol Surv, Ill, 52-53; from asst prof to emer prof geol, Univ Colo, Boulder, 53-93, fac res lectr, 72-73, chmn, Dept Geol Sci, 72-75. *Concurrent Pos:* NSF sr fel, 62-63; Am Asn Petrol Geol distinguished lectr, 65. *Mem:* Geol Soc Am; hon mem Soc Econ Paleont & Mineral (pres, 82-83); Am Asn Petrol Geologists. *Res:* Sedimentation; sedimentary petrology. *Mailing Add:* 2805 16th St Boulder CO 80304

**WALKER, THERESA ANNE,** SCIENCE & TECHNOLOGY FOR ECONOMIC DEVELOPMENT. *Current Pos:* prin sci assoc, 88-90, MGR UNIV-INDUST PROGS, NY STATE SCI TECHNOL FOUND, 90- *Personal Data:* b Rantoul, Ill, Mar 26, 52. *Educ:* Eastern Ill Univ, BS, 73; Yale Univ, MPhil, 77, PhD(biochem), 80. *Prof Exp:* Sci & technol res asst, Ill Legis Coun, 80-81; dir res, Dept Obstet-Gynec, Quillen-Dishner Col Med, ETenn State Univ, 81-82; staff scientist, Ill Legis Res Unit, 82-85; dir, NY State Legis Comn Sci & Technol, 85-88. *Concurrent Pos:* Teaching asst, Dept Biol, Yale Univ, 74-76, res asst, 78-80; teaching asst, Dept Biochem, Quillen-Dishner Col Med, 80; guest lectr, ETenn State Univ, 80; adj asst prof, Dept Pharmacol, Sch Med, Southern Ill Univ, 84-85. *Mem:* Sigma Xi; AAAS; Am Chem Soc; Scientists' Inst Pub Info; Am Inst Biol Sci. *Res:* Science and technology for economic development. *Mailing Add:* 81 Seaman Ave Castleton NY 12033-1110

**WALKER, THOMAS EUGENE,** BIOCHEMISTRY, STABLE ISOTOPES. *Current Pos:* SR RES SPECIALIST, ISOTEC, INC, 88- *Personal Data:* b Glendale, Calif, Feb 1, 48; m 73, Robin Russell. *Educ:* Westmar Col, BA, 69; Univ Iowa, PhD(biochem), 74. *Prof Exp:* Res assoc, Mich State Univ, 74-75; fel, Los Alamos Nat Lab, 75-77, staff mem, 77-88. *Mem:* Am Chem Soc; Am Soc Biochem & Molecular Biol; AAAS. *Res:* The synthesis by chemical and biosynthetic techniques and nuclear magnetic resonance and mass spectral analysis of carbon 13, nitrogen 15, oxygen 17 and oxygen 18 enriched compounds of biological interest. *Mailing Add:* Isotec 3858 Benner Rd Miamisburg OH 45342-4304. *E-Mail:* isotec@isotec.com

**WALKER, THOMAS JEFFERSON,** BEHAVIORAL ECOLOGY, SYSTEMATICS. *Current Pos:* From asst prof to assoc prof biol sci & entom, 57-68, prof biol sci, 68-71, PROF ENTOM, UNIV FLA, 71- *Personal Data:* b Dyer Co, Tenn, July 24, 31; m 59, Jane Beck; c Rose A & William T. *Educ:* Univ Tenn, BA, 53; Ohio State Univ, MSc, 54, PhD(entom), 57. *Concurrent Pos:* Res assoc dept tropic res, NY Zool Soc, 66; res assoc, Fla State Collection Arthropods, 63-; ed, Fla Entomologist, 64-66. *Mem:* Fel AAAS; Entom Soc Am; Soc Study Evolution; Orthopterists Soc; Sigma Xi; Lepidopterist's Soc. *Res:* Acoustical behavior of insects; systematics, behavior, ecology and evolution of Gryllidae and Tettigoniidae; migratory behavior of butterflies. *Mailing Add:* PO Box 110620 Gainesville FL 32611-0620

**WALKER, WALDO SYLVESTER,** BOTANY. *Current Pos:* From asst prof to assoc prof biol, Grinnel Col, 58-68, assoc dean, 63-65, dean admin, 69-73, dean col, 73-80, PROF BIOL, GRINNEL COL, 68, EXEC VPRES, 80- *Personal Data:* b Fayette, Iowa, June 12, 31; m 52; c 2. *Educ:* Upper Iowa Univ, BS, 53; Univ Iowa, MS, 57, PhD(bot), 59. *Res:* Ultrastructure of plants; experimental morphology; plant physiology. *Mailing Add:* 1920 Country Club Rd Grinnell IA 50112

**WALKER, WARREN ELLIOTT,** OPERATIONS RESEARCH, PUBLIC POLICY ANALYSIS. *Current Pos:* SR POLICY ANALYST, RAND CORP, 77- *Personal Data:* b New York, NY, Apr 7, 42; div; c Carly, Luke & Hannah. *Educ:* Cornell Univ, BA, 63, MS, 64, PhD(opers res), 68. *Honors & Awards:* Lanchester Prize, Opers Res Soc Am, 74; Edelman Award, Inst Mgt Sci, 74 & 84; NATO Systs Sci Prize, 76. *Prof Exp:* Pres, Compuvisor, Inc, 68-70; sr opers res analyst & proj dir, NY City-Rand Inst, Rand Corp, 70-75; asst vpres, Chem Bank, 75-76; dep dir, Urban Acad, 76-77. *Concurrent Pos:* Consult, US Environ Protection Agency Off Solid Waste Mgt Progs, 68-72; adj prof opers res, Columbia Univ, 71-77; pres, Urbatronics Inc, 75-80; chmn, Los Angeles Prod Adv Comt, 85-88; vis prof, Delft Univ Technol, 88-89; staff mem, RAND Europe, 94- *Mem:* Inst Opers Res & Mgt Sci. *Res:* Applying quantitative methods to the analysis of public policy problems in the areas of water management, fire department deployment, the criminal justice system, military manpower, and transportation. *Mailing Add:* Rand 1700 Main St Santa Monica CA 90407-2138. *Fax:* 310-393-4818; *E-Mail:* warren@rand.org

**WALKER, WARREN FRANKLIN, JR,** ZOOLOGY. *Current Pos:* RETIRED. *Personal Data:* b Malden, Mass, Sept 27, 18; m 44; c 4. *Educ:* Harvard Univ, SB, 41, PhD(zool), 46. *Prof Exp:* Instr anat sch med, Boston Univ, 45-47; instr zool, Oberlin Col, 47-48, from asst prof to prof biol, 49-85, actg provost, 74-75, chmn dept, 67-74. *Mem:* AAAS; Am Asn Anat; Am Soc Zool; Soc Syst Zool; Am Soc Ichthyol & Herpet. *Res:* Herpetology of South America; vertebrate anatomy and evolution; myology; vertebrate locomotion. *Mailing Add:* PO Box 436 Ossipee NH 03864

**WALKER, WILBUR GORDON,** internal medicine, nephrology, for more information see previous edition

**WALKER, WILLIAM CHARLES,** SOLID STATE PHYSICS. *Current Pos:* from instr to prof, 55-91, chmn dept, 72-75, EMER PROF PHYSICS, UNIV CALIF, SANTA BARBARA, 91- *Personal Data:* b Santa Barbara, Calif, Aug 22, 28; m 51, Jane E Searl; c 3. *Educ:* Univ Calif, AB, 50; Univ Southern Calif, MS, 53, PhD(physics), 55. *Prof Exp:* Asst physics, Univ Southern Calif, 50-52, res assoc, 52-55. *Concurrent Pos:* Consult, Servomechanisms, Inc, 59-60; Nat Acad Sci-NASA fel, Goddard Space Flight Ctr, 63-64; consult, Sloan Technol, 68-74. *Mem:* AAAS; Am Phys Soc; Sigma Xi. *Res:* Solid state and ultraviolet spectroscopy; optical properties of solids; conducting polymers. *Mailing Add:* Dept Physics Univ Calif Santa Barbara CA 93106

**WALKER, WILLIAM COMSTOCK,** PAPER CHEMISTRY, PHYSICAL CHEMISTRY. *Current Pos:* RETIRED. *Personal Data:* b Milwaukee, Wis, July 6, 21; m 45, Althea George; c 2. *Educ:* Lehigh Univ, BS, 43, MS, 44, PhD(phys chem), 46. *Honors & Awards:* Silver Medal Award & Charles W Englehard Medallion, Tech Asn Pulp & Paper Indust, 82; Robert F Reid Award, Graphic Arts Tech Found, 87. *Prof Exp:* Inst res fel, Lehigh Univ, 46-47; dir, Nat Printing Ink Res Inst, 47-55, res asst prof chem, 53-55; res dir, Westvaco Corp, New York, NY, 55-65, tech asst to corp vpres res, 64-86. *Concurrent Pos:* Instr, Muhlenberg Col, 46-47. *Mem:* Am Chem Soc; Tech Asn Graphic Arts; Tech Asn Pulp & Paper Indust; Can Pulp & Paper Asn; Sigma Xi. *Res:* Printability of paper; novel crop systems; paper production technology; printing inks; adsorption of gases on solids; removal of sulfur oxides from flue gases. *Mailing Add:* One Springfield Pl Savannah GA 31411

**WALKER, WILLIAM DELANY,** PARTICLE PHYSICS. *Current Pos:* prof, 71-90, chmn dept, 75-81, J B DUKE PROF PHYSICS, DUKE UNIV, 90- *Personal Data:* b Dallas, Tex, Nov 23, 23; m 46, 75, Constance Kalbach; c Samuel D, Nancy (Davis) & Elizabeth (Schenkel). *Educ:* Rice Inst, BA, 44; Cornell Univ, PhD(cosmic ray physics), 49. *Prof Exp:* Physicist, US Naval Res Lab, 44-45; asst prof physics, Rice Inst, 49-51; lectr, Univ Calif, 51-52; asst prof, Univ Rochester, 52-54; from asst prof to prof, Univ Wis-Madison, 54-67, chmn dept, 64-66, Max Mason prof, 67-71. *Concurrent Pos:* Mem, High Energy Surv Comt, Nat Acad Sci, 64-65; Physics Panel, NSF, 64-67; User's Exec Comt, Fermilab, 72-75; chmn, Argonne User's Group, 64-66; chmn, User's Exec Comt, Fermilab, 73-74; mem bd dir, Oak Ridge Assoc Univ, 80-85; secy, Region 5, Univ Res Asn. *Mem:* Fel Am Phys Soc; Sigma Xi. *Res:* Strong interaction physics; technology of bubble chambers; technology of particle detection; particle phenomology. *Mailing Add:* Dept Physics Duke Univ PO Box 90305 Durham NC 27708. *Fax:* 919-660-2525

**WALKER, WILLIAM F(RED),** MECHANICAL ENGINEERING, BIOMEDICAL ENGINEERING. *Current Pos:* from asst prof to assoc prof, 65-75, PROF AEROSPACE ENG, RICE UNIV, 75-, CHMN, DEPT MECH ENG & MAT SCI, 76- *Personal Data:* b Sherman, Tex, Dec 1, 37; m 60; c 2. *Educ:* Univ Tex, BS, 60, MS, 61; Okla State Univ, PhD(mech eng), 66. *Prof Exp:* Aerodyn engr, Ling-Temco-Vought, Inc, 61-62. *Mem:* Am Inst Aeronaut & Astronaut; Am Soc Mech Engrs; Am Soc Artificial Internal Organs. *Res:* Compressible turbulent boundary layers; separated and reattached jet flows; transpiration and ablation cooling. *Mailing Add:* Eng Auburn Univ Auburn AL 36849-3501

**WALKER, WILLIAM HAMILTON,** CIVIL ENGINEERING, STRUCTURAL DYNAMICS. *Current Pos:* Res asst civil eng, Univ Ill, 56-61, from instr to assoc prof, 61-90, asst head dept, 73-76, ASSOC HEAD DEPT, UNIV ILL, URBANA, 86-, PROF CIVIL ENG, 90- *Personal Data:* b Brookline, Mass, Dec 28, 34; m 62, Shirley Ackerman; c John H & William F. *Educ:* Univ Mass, BS, 56; Univ Ill, Urbana, MS, 58, PhD(civil eng), 63. *Concurrent Pos:* Mem comt bridge dynamics, proj panels, Transp Res Bd, Nat Acad Sci, 65- *Mem:* Am Soc Civil Engrs; Am Soc Eng Educ; Am Asn Univ Professors; Sigma Xi. *Res:* Structural mechanics with emphasis on dynamics; dynamic response of bridges by means of field tests and computer analysis; earthquake engineering; fatigue and fracture metal structures. *Mailing Add:* Univ Ill 205 N Mathews Urbana IL 61801

**WALKER, WILLIAM J, JR,** RADIATION SAFETY MANAGEMENT, LOW LEVEL RADIOACTIVE WASTE MANAGEMENT. *Current Pos:* RADIATION SAFETY OFFICER, NIH, 88-, CHIEF, RADIATION SAFETY BR, 89- *Personal Data:* b Dec 13, 36; m, Belinda A McClary; c Donna L (Smith), Catherine A, William J III & David W. *Educ:* Va Mil Inst, BS, 58; Univ Kans, MS, 64; Univ Fla, PhD(environ eng), 71; Am Bd Health Physics, cert. *Prof Exp:* Base sanit & indust hyg eng, Castle AFB, Calif, 58-60; staff environ engr, High Wycombe, Eng, 60-62; res health physicist, Kirtland AFB, Albuquerque, NMex, 64-68; pres & prin consult, Physics Control Inc, 73-78; chief med physics, Malcolm Grow USAF Med Ctr, Andrew AFB, Washington, DC, 71-78; sect leader, Med & Acad Licensing Sect, US Nuclear Regulatory Comn, Washington, DC, 78-83; vpres, Med Div, RSO Inc, 83-84; sr vpres & chief scientist, Health Physics Serv, Inc, 85-88. *Concurrent Pos:* Regist prof engr, Civil & Sanit Eng, Vt, 68-; consult radiol physicist, Sacred Heart Hosp, 84-; US Nuclear Regulatory Comn, 89; sr consult, Inst Radiol Imaging Sci, Inc, 88-89; pres & chief operating officer, Radiopharmaceut Mat Ser Mat Serv Inc, 88; chmn bd & pres, Profound Paralysis Found, 92-; mem, Nuclear Med Sci Comt, Am Col Nuclear Physicians, Stand Nuclear Med Instrumentation Comt, Subcomt Nuclear Med Technol. *Mem:* Health Physics Soc; Sigma Xi. *Res:* Area of biomedical research radiation safety; internal dosimetry, low-level radioactive waste management and treatment technologies for mixed wastes. *Mailing Add:* 11928 Ropp Lane Lovettsville VA 20180. *Fax:* 301-496-3544

**WALKER, WILLIAM M,** SOIL FERTILITY, BIOMETRICS. *Current Pos:* from asst prof to prof, 66-88, EMER PROF BIOMET, UNIV ILL, URBANA, 88- *Personal Data:* b Savannah, Tenn, Sept 17, 28; m 51; c 4. *Educ:* Florence State Col, BS, 50; Univ Tenn, MS, 57; Iowa State Univ, PhD(soil fertil), 61. *Prof Exp:* Res assoc agron, Iowa State Univ, 57-61; asst agronomist, Univ Tenn, 61-66. *Mem:* Am Soc Agron; Coun Soil Testing & Plant Anal. *Res:* Application of biomathematics to soil-plant relationships. *Mailing Add:* Rte 2 PO Box 67 Skyline Yellville AR 72687

**WALKER, WILLIAM R,** CIVIL ENGINEERING, LAW. *Current Pos:* CONSULT, 92- *Personal Data:* b Lincoln, Nebr, June 8, 25; m 49, Loreta J Coe; c James, Jo Ellen & Michael. *Educ:* Univ Nebr, Lincoln, BSCE, 49, JD, 52; Univ NC, Chapel Hill, MSSE, 64. *Honors & Awards:* Julian Hinds Award, Am Soc Civil Engrs. *Prof Exp:* Dir, Water Resources Res Ctr, Va Polytech Inst & State Univ, 65-92. *Concurrent Pos:* Vis scholar, Bd Rivers & Harbors, CEngr, 70-71; mem exec bd, Univ Coun Water Resources. *Mem:* AAAS; Am Soc Civil Engrs; Am Soc Eng Educ; Water Fedn; Am Water Works Asn; Int Water Resources Asn. *Res:* Legal and institutional arrangements for management of water resources. *Mailing Add:* 1502 Greenwood Dr Blacksburg VA 24060. *Fax:* 540-231-6673; *E-Mail:* walkerwr@utvm1.cc.vt.edu

**WALKER, WILLIAM STANLEY,** IMMUNOLOGY. *Current Pos:* asst mem, Labs Virol & Immunol, 72-74, assoc mem, Div Immunol, 75-84, MEM DEPT IMMUNOL, ST JUDE CHILDREN'S RES HOSP, 84-, VCHMN, DEPT IMMUNOL, 90- *Personal Data:* b Glendale, Calif, Apr 21, 40; m 64, Mary E; c Heather M & Jennifer A. *Educ:* Univ Southern Calif, AB, 63, PhD(microbiol), 68. *Prof Exp:* Lectr bact, Univ Southern Calif, 64-65; sci officer first class, Dept Immunohaemat, Acad Hosp, State Univ Leiden, 71. *Concurrent Pos:* Fel immunol, Pub Health Res Inst City New York, Inc, 68-71. *Mem:* Soc Leukocyte Biol; Am Asn Immunologists; Am Soc Cell Biol. *Res:* Immunobiology of macrophages. *Mailing Add:* Dept Immunol St Jude Children's Res Hosp PO Box 318 Memphis TN 38105-2794

**WALKER, WILLIAM WALDRUM,** PHYSICS. *Current Pos:* from asst prof to prof, 67-94, EMER PROF PHYSICS, UNIV ALA, 94- *Personal Data:* b Alexander City, Ala, Jan 16, 33; m 58; c 3. *Educ:* Auburn Univ, BS, 55; Univ Va, MA, 57, PhD(physics), 59. *Prof Exp:* Asst prof physics, Col William & Mary, 59-60; physicist, Signal Res & Develop Lab, US Army, NJ, 60. *Concurrent Pos:* Radiation Safety Officer, Univ Ala, 84-94. *Mem:* Am Phys Soc; Am Asn Physics Teachers. *Res:* Positron life-times; low energy nuclear physics. *Mailing Add:* Dept Physics Univ Ala Tuscaloosa AL 35487. *Fax:* 205-348-5051; *E-Mail:* wwalker@ua1vm.ua.edu

**WALKIEWICZ, THOMAS ADAM,** NUCLEAR PHYSICS, SOLID STATE PHYSICS. *Current Pos:* ASSOC PROF PHYSICS, EDINBORO STATE COL, 70- *Personal Data:* b Erie, Pa, Dec 25, 39; m 62; c 3. *Educ:* Xavier Univ, Ohio, BS, 62; Pa State Univ, PhD(physics), 69. *Prof Exp:* Asst prof physics, East Stroudsburg State Col, 69; physicist, Picatinny Arsenal, NJ, 69-70. *Concurrent Pos:* AEC collab researcher, Oak Ridge Nat Lab, 71-77, consult, 75-76. *Mem:* Am Phys Soc; Am Asn Physics Teachers. *Res:* Experimental low-energy nuclear physics, especially gamma ray spectroscopy; neutron and charged particle reactions; experimental solid state physics, especially electrooptical and radiation effects in amorphous semiconductors. *Mailing Add:* Dept Physics Edinboro Univ Edinboro PA 16444

**WALKINGTON, DAVID L,** botany, for more information see previous edition

**WALKINSHAW, CHARLES HOWARD, JR,** PHYTOPATHOLOGY, MICROBIOLOGY. *Current Pos:* PRIN PLANT PATHOLOGIST, SOUTHERN FOREST EXP STA, US FOREST SERV, 73- *Personal Data:* b Blairsville, Pa, Nov 14, 35; m 57, 83; c 5. *Educ:* Univ Fla, BSA, 57; Univ Wis, PhD(plant path), 60. *Honors & Awards:* Super Serv Award, USDA, 72. *Prof Exp:* Asst plant path, Univ Wis, 57-60, proj assoc, 60-61, trainee biochem & path sch med, 61-63; plant pathologist, Southern Forest Exp Sta, US Forest Serv, Miss, 63-65; asst prof microbiol sch med, Univ Miss, 65-68; plant pathologist med support br, NASA-Manned Spacecraft Ctr, 68-73. *Mem:* AAAS; Am Phytopath Soc; Am Soc Cell Biol; Sigma Xi. *Res:* Plant diseases; plant tissue culture; fungus diseases of pines; biochemistry of plant diseases; agriculture in Lunar and Mars bases. *Mailing Add:* 11 E 65th St Savannah GA 31405

**WALKLING, ROBERT ADOLPH,** ACOUSTICS. *Current Pos:* ASSOC PROF PHYSICS, UNIV SOUTHERN MAINE, 69- *Personal Data:* b Philadelphia, Pa, Sept 11, 31; m 59, Julia (Robinson); c Andrew & Ellen. *Educ:* Swarthmore Col, BA, 53; Harvard Univ, SM, 54, PhD(acoustics), 62. *Prof Exp:* Res fel appl physics, Harvard Univ, 62-63; asst prof physics, Bowdoin Col, 63-69. *Mem:* AAAS; Acoust Soc Am; Audio Eng Soc; Am Sci Affiliation; Am Asn Physics Teachers; Sigma Xi. *Res:* Electroacoustics; noise and vibration; architectural and musical acoustics. *Mailing Add:* 34 Boody St Brunswick ME 04011

**WALKLING, WALTER DOUGLAS,** PHARMACY. *Current Pos:* sr scientist, McNeil Pharmaceut, 70-72, group leader, 72-76, sect head, Pharm Res Dept, 76-86, dir Pharmaceut Technol Dept, McNeil Pharmaceut, 86-90, DIR PHARMACEUT TECHNOL DEPT, R W JOHNSON, 90- *Personal Data:* b Baltimore, Md, Feb 27, 39; m 61, Carolyn Powell; c 2. *Educ:* Univ Md, BS, 61, MS, 63, PhD(pharm), 66. *Prof Exp:* Pharmacist, Yager Drug Co, 64-66; Nat Inst Gen Med Sci fel, Swiss Fed Inst Technol, 66-67; sr pharmaceut chemist, Eli Lilly & Co, 67-70. *Mem:* Fel Am Asn Pharmaceut Scientists; Controlled Release Soc; Am Chem Soc; Drug Info Asn. *Res:* Acquisition of drug delivery and pharmaceutical product technologies. *Mailing Add:* Pharmaceut Technol Dept R W Johnson Spring House PA 19477. Fax: 215-540-4683

**WALKUP, JOHN FRANK,** OPTICAL COMPUTING, DIGITAL IMAGE & SIGNAL PROCESSING. *Current Pos:* from asst prof to prof elec eng, 71-85, PW HORN PROF ELEC ENG, TEX TECH UNIV, 85- *Personal Data:* b Oakland, Calif, Feb 7, 41; m 65, Patricia A Hagbom; c Mary K, Amy C & Rebecca J. *Educ:* Dartmouth Col, BA, 62, BEE, 63; Stanford Univ, MS, 65, Engineer, 69, PhD(elec eng), 71. *Honors & Awards:* Halliburton Award, Tex Tech Univ, 80, 96; AT&T Found Award, Am Soc Eng Educ, 85; Fac Achievment Award El Paso Natural Gas Found, 95. *Prof Exp:* Res asst, Stanford Univ, 63-71. *Concurrent Pos:* Assoc, Gen Motors Res Labs, 62; assoc engr, Aerojet-Gen Corp, 63; consult, ESL, Inc, 74-76, Optics Technol, 74 & NSF, 75; vis scholar, Optical Sci Ctr, Univ Ariz, 82; assoc dean eng, Tex Tech Univ, 82-83; chmn, Educ Coun, Optical Soc Am, 87-88 & Gordon Res Conf Holography & Optical Info Processing, 91; mem, bd dir, Optical Soc Am, 87-88; vis prof, Stanford Univ, 92-93; mem, Nat Res Coun; sr associateship, Ames Res Ctr, NASA; topical ed, J Optical Soc Am, 92-94, Appl Optics, 95-98. *Mem:* Fel Inst Elec & Electronics Engrs; fel Optical Soc Am; Int Soc Optical Eng; Sigma Xi. *Res:* Basic and applied research in optical information processing, optical computing, statistical optics, digital image processing, neural networks and signal processing; optoelectronics. *Mailing Add:* Optical Systs Lab Dept Elec Eng Tex Tech Univ Lubbock TX 79409-3102

**WALL, CONRAD, III,** BIOENGINEERING. *Current Pos:* ASSOC PROF, DEPT OTOLARYNGOL, HARVARD MED SCH & MASS INST TECHNOL, 87-; DIR, DEPT VESTIBULAR LAB, MASS EYE & EAR INFIRM, 87- *Personal Data:* b Boston, Mass, June 13, 39; m 61; c 2. *Educ:* Tulane Univ, BS, 62, MS, 68; Carnegie-Mellon Univ, PhD(bioeng), 75. *Prof Exp:* Proj officer elec eng, US Army AV Labs, 63-65; mem tech staff appl physics, Boeing Co, 65-70; NIH res assoc sensory physiol, Dept Otolaryngol, Med Sch, Univ Pittsburgh, 75-77, sci dir, Human Vestibular Lab, 76-87. *Mem:* Soc Neurosci; Inst Elec & Electronics Engrs; Barany Soc; Sigma Xi. *Res:* Information processing in the vestibular and visual systems; digital signal processing of clinical and experimental sensory systems data. *Mailing Add:* 19 Joy St No 2 Boston MA 02114

**WALL, DONALD DINES,** COMPUTER SCIENCES. *Current Pos:* RETIRED. *Personal Data:* b Kansas City, Mo, Aug 13, 21; m 43; c 3. *Educ:* Univ Calif, PhD(math), 49. *Prof Exp:* Instr, Santa Barbara Col, 49-51; appl sci rep, IBM Corp, 51-74, mkt analyst, 74-81; pres, Datamaps Consult Co, 81- *Mem:* Math Asn Am. *Res:* Number theory; computing machines. *Mailing Add:* 1861 Clairmont Rd Decatur GA 30033

**WALL, EDWARD THOMAS,** ELECTRICAL ENGINEERING, CONTROL SYSTEMS. *Current Pos:* assoc prof, 66-73, PROF ELEC ENG, UNIV COLO, DENVER, 66- *Personal Data:* b Brooklyn, NY, May 16, 20; m 47; c 4. *Educ:* Purdue Univ, West Lafayette, BS, 47; Lehigh Univ, MS, 49; Univ Denver, PhD(elec eng), 67. *Prof Exp:* Instr elec eng, Univ Maine, 49; engr, Pac Gas & Elec Co, 49-51; asst prof, Calif State Polytech Univ, 51-54; analytical engr, Gen Elec Co, 54-57; staff engr, Martin-Marietta Corp, 57-64; res elec engr, US Bur Reclamation, 64-66. *Concurrent Pos:* NSF grants, Univ Colo, Denver, 68-71. *Mem:* AAAS; Inst Elec & Electronics Engrs; Sigma Xi. *Res:* Adaptive control system design, digital control systems with application to aerospace systems; nonlinear control systems; power system analysis. *Mailing Add:* 6055 S Manaco Way Englewood CO 80211-4431

**WALL, FREDERICK THEODORE,** STATISTICAL MECHANICS. *Current Pos:* RETIRED. *Personal Data:* b Chisholm, Minn, Dec 14, 12; m 40; c 2. *Educ:* Univ Minn, BCh, 33, PhD(chem), 37. *Honors & Awards:* Am Chem Soc Award, 45. *Prof Exp:* Univ Ill, Urbana, 37-64, dean grad col, 55-63; prof chem & chmn dept, Univ Calif, Santa Barbara, 64-66, vchancellor res, 65-66; vchancellor grad studies & res & prof chem, Univ Calif, San Diego, 66-69, adj prof chem, 82-91; exec dir, Am Chem Soc, 69-72; prof, Rice Univ, 72-78; lectr chem, San Diego State Univ, 79-82. *Mem:* Nat Acad Sci; AAAS; Am Acad Arts & Sci; Am Chem Soc; Am Phys Soc; Finnish Chem Soc. *Res:* Physical chemistry of macromolecular configurations; Monte Carlo methods applied to physical chemistry. *Mailing Add:* 2468 Via Viesta La Jolla CA 92037

**WALL, GEORGE C,** PLANT PATHOGENIC VIRUSES & VIROIDS, PLANT PATHOGENIC BACTERIA. *Current Pos:* ASSOC PROF PLANT PATH, UNIV GUAM, 86- *Educ:* Univ Calif, Berkeley, BS, 73; Tex A&M Univ, PhD(plant path), 86. *Prof Exp:* Instr, Univ El Salvador, 74-75; researcher, Nat Ctr Agr Technol, El Salvador, 75-80; res assoc, Tex A&M Univ, 83-86. *Concurrent Pos:* Instr, PanAm Sch Agr, Honduras, 85. *Mem:* Am Phytopath Soc. *Res:* Coconut viroid work, detection and management; taro leaf blight; screening for resistance to cucurbit viruses; detection and management of papaya viruses; cross-protection research on zucchini and papaya viruses. *Mailing Add:* CALS/AES Univ Guam Mangilao GU 96923. Fax: 671-734-4600

**WALL, GREGORY JOHN,** SOIL SCIENCE. *Current Pos:* SOIL SCIENTIST, AGR CAN, 73- *Personal Data:* b Toronto, Ont, Aug 16, 44; m 68; c 3. *Educ:* Univ Guelph, BSA, 67, MSc, 69; Ohio State Univ, PhD(soil sci), 73. *Prof Exp:* Res officer soil sci, Agr Can, 67-70; teaching asst agron, Ohio State Univ, 70-71, res assoc soil mineral, 71-73. *Mem:* Can Soc Soil Sci; Am Soc Agron; Int Asn Great Lakes Res; Int Soc Soil Sci; Soil Conserv Soc Am. *Res:* Sources and magnitude of water pollution by sediment in agricultural regions; mineralogy and exchange properties of fluvial sediments; variability of soil physical and engineering properties in the mineralogy of soils; interpretation of soil survey data. *Mailing Add:* 12 Princeton Pl Guelph ON N1G 3S4 Can

**WALL, JOHN HALLETT,** MICROPALEONTOLOGY. *Current Pos:* res scientist, 74-93, EMER RES SCIENTIST, GEOL SURV CAN, 93- *Personal Data:* b St Stephen, NB, Aug 10, 24; m 61, Margery Rowbotham; c James. *Educ:* Univ NB, BSc, 45; Univ Alta, MSc, 51; Univ Mo, PhD(geol), 58. *Prof Exp:* Asst geologist, NB Dept Mines, 43 & Geol Surv Can, 44; jr geologist, Imp Oil Ltd, 45-46, subsurface geologist & micropaleontologist, 47-51; subsurface geologist, J C Sproule & Assocs, Explor Consults, 52; micropaleontologist, Calif Stand Co, 53; res officer, Res Coun Alta, 57-74. *Concurrent Pos:* Lectr geol, Univ Alta, 60-72. *Mem:* Fel Geol Soc Am; Soc Sedimentary Geol; Paleont Soc; fel Geol Asn Can; Can Soc Petrol Geologists; Paleont Res Inst. *Res:* Mesozoic microfossils of western and arctic Canada. *Mailing Add:* 103 Edgeview Dr NW Calgary AB T3A 4W9 Can

**WALL, JOSEPH S,** BIOPHYSICS. *Current Pos:* assoc biophysicist, 73-78, BIOPHYSICIST, DEPT BIOL, BROOKHAVEN NAT LAB, 78- *Personal Data:* b Madison, Wis, Nov 17, 42. *Educ:* Univ Wis-Madison, BS, 64; Univ Chicago, PhD(biophys), 71. *Honors & Awards:* Lawrence Award, US Dept Energy, 88. *Prof Exp:* Fel biophys, Univ Chicago, 71-73. *Mem:* AAAS; NY Acad Sci; Electron Micros Soc Am. *Res:* Development and biological application of the high resolution scanning transmission electron microscope. *Mailing Add:* Dept Biol Brookhaven Nat Lab Upton NY 11973

**WALL, JOSEPH SENNEN,** BIOCHEMISTRY, PROTEIN CHEMISTRY. *Current Pos:* head chem reactions & structure invests, 56-72, res leader, 72-83, RES CHEMIST, CEREAL PROTEINS RES UNIT, CEREAL SCI & FOODS LAB, NORTHERN REGIONAL RES CTR, USDA, PEORIA, ILL, 83- *Personal Data:* b Chicago, Ill, June 2, 23; m 50; c 3. *Educ:* Univ Chicago, BS, 46, MS, 49; Univ Wis, PhD(biochem), 52. *Prof Exp:* Instr chem, Lincoln Col, 47-49; asst biochem, Univ Wis, 50-52; instr pharmacol sch med, NY Univ, 52-56. *Mem:* AAAS; Am Chem Soc; Am Soc Biol Chemists; Am Asn Cereal Chemists; Inst Food Technologists. *Res:* Mechanism of nitrogen fixation by bacteria; isolation of natural products; hormonal regulation of carbohydrate metabolism in mammals; protein chemistry; cereal chemistry; nutrition; enzymology. *Mailing Add:* 8606 N Servite Dr Milwaukee WI 53223-2514

**WALL, LEONARD WONG,** PHYSICS. *Current Pos:* PROF PHYSICS, CALIF POLYTECH STATE UNIV, 69- *Personal Data:* b Tallulah, La, Nov 7, 41; m 68; c 3. *Educ:* La Tech Univ, BS, 63; Iowa State Univ, PhD(physics), 69. *Prof Exp:* Vis asst prof, Univ Kans, 68-69. *Mem:* Am Phys Soc; Am Asn Physics Teachers; AAAS; Sigma Xi. *Res:* Physics of energy; energy usage in buildings; passive solar. *Mailing Add:* 2862 Prefumo Canyon Rd San Luis Obispo CA 93405

**WALL, MONROE ELIOT,** BIOCHEMISTRY, MEDICINAL CHEMISTRY. *Current Pos:* head natural prod lab, Res Triangle Inst, 60-66, dir chem & life sci lab, 66-71, vpres phys & life sci div, 71-83, CHIEF SCIENTIST, RES TRIANGLE INST, 83- *Personal Data:* b Newark, NJ, July 25, 16; m 41, Marian Strelitz; c Michael A & Marth S (Nebb). *Educ:* Rutgers Univ, BS, 36, MS, 38, PhD(biochem), 39. *Hon Degrees:* Dr, Uppsala Univ, Sweden, 87. *Honors & Awards:* Walter Harrung Mem lect, Univ NC, Col Pharm, 77; Eber Lect Award, Univ Ill, Col Pharm, 83; Res Achievement Award, Am Pharmacog Soc, 90; Bruce F Cain Mem Award, Am Asn Cancer Res, 94. *Prof Exp:* Chemist, NJ Exp Sta, 39-40; res chemist, Wallerstein Labs, 40; res assoc, Barrett Co, 41; from asst chemist to supvr plant steroid units eastern regional res lab, Bur Agr & Indust Chem, USDA, 41-53, supvr eastern utilization res br, Agr Res Serv, 53-60. *Concurrent Pos:* Adj prof, NC State Univ, 62- & Univ NC, Chapel Hill, 66-; consult, NIH, 62- *Mem:* AAAS; Am Chem Soc; fel Am Asn Pharmaceut Scientists; Am Pharmacol Soc; Soc Econ Bot (pres, 75); hon mem Am Soc Pharmacog. *Res:* Plant chemistry; steroids; cancer chemotherapy; drug metabolism; chemistry and metabolism of cannabinoids. *Mailing Add:* PO Box 12194 Research Triangle Park NC 27709-2194

**WALL, ROBERT ECKI,** GEOPHYSICS. *Current Pos:* prog dir submarine geol & geophys, 70-75, head oceanog sect, 75-81, HEAD OCEAN SCI RES SECT, NSF, 81- *Personal Data:* b Aurora, Ill, Aug 1, 35; m 63; c 3. *Educ:* Carleton Col, AB, 57; Columbia Univ, PhD(geophys), 65. *Prof Exp:* Res assoc marine geophys, Lamont Geol Observ, Columbia Univ, 65-66; sci officer marine geol & geophys, Off Naval Res, 66-70. *Mem:* AAAS; Am Geophys Union; Geol Soc Am; Soc Explor Geophys. *Res:* Marine geophysics; geological oceanography. *Mailing Add:* 14 Coburn Hall 168 College Ave Univ Maine Orono ME 04469

**WALL, ROBERT GENE,** ORGANIC CHEMISTRY. *Current Pos:* RETIRED. *Personal Data:* b Mo, Nov 17, 37; m 64, Josephine Ong; c 3. *Educ:* Ore State Univ, BS, 61, MS, 63; Univ Wis-Madison, PhD(org chem), 66. *Prof Exp:* NIH fel, Univ Mich, Ann Arbor, 66-67; res chemist, Chevron Res Co, Richmond, Calif, 67-72; sr res chemist, 72-81, sr res assoc chemist, 81-90, sr staff scientist, 90-96. *Res:* Physical organic chemistry; catalysis and surfactants for enhanced oil recovery. *Mailing Add:* 2826 Wright Ave Pinole CA 94564-1040. *E-Mail:* rgjow@msn.com

**WALL, ROBERT LEROY,** medicine, for more information see previous edition

**WALL, RONALD EUGENE,** PLANT PATHOLOGY. *Current Pos:* RETIRED. *Personal Data:* b Dryden, Ont, Feb 19, 36; m 57; c 4. *Educ:* Ont Agr Col, BSA, 58; Univ Wis, PhD(plant path), 62. *Prof Exp:* Plant pathologist, Can Dept Agr, 62-66; plant pathologist, Can Forestry Serv, 66-73, res scientist, Dept Environ, 73-95. *Concurrent Pos:* Teacher forest path. *Mem:* Am Phytopath Soc; Can Phytopath Soc. *Res:* Decays of maturing plants; trunk rots of forest trees; diseases of conifer seedlings; diseases of forest weeds. *Mailing Add:* 586 Belson St Parksville BC V8P 1B5 Can

**WALL, THOMAS RANDOLPH,** MOLECULAR BIOLOGY, IMMUNOLOGY. *Current Pos:* asst prof, 72-78, assoc prof, 78-79, PROF MICROBIOL & IMMUNOL, SCH MED, UNIV CALIF, LOS ANGELES, 79- *Personal Data:* b Lakeland, Fla, Mar 23, 43; m; c 2. *Educ:* Univ SFla, AB, 65; Ind Univ, PhD(microbiol), 70. *Prof Exp:* Res assoc cell & molecular biol, Columbia Univ, 70-72. *Concurrent Pos:* Damon Runyon Mem Fund Cancer Res fel, Columbia Univ, 70-72; mem, Molecular Biol Inst, Univ Calif, Los Angeles, 72-; founder & dir, INGENE Inc, Santa Monica, Calif, 80-; sci adv bd, FMC Bio Products; mem sci adv bd, XOMA Corp. *Mem:* Am Soc Microbiol; Am Asn Immunologists. *Res:* Expression and regulation of genes in eukaryotic cells; molecular analysis of the expression and control of genes in lymphocytes; developmental control of the immune response. *Mailing Add:* Molecular Biol Inst Univ Calif Los Angeles CA 90024. *Fax:* 310-206-7286

**WALL, WILLIAM JAMES,** entomology, for more information see previous edition

**WALLACE, ALEXANDER CAMERON,** MEDICINE, PATHOLOGY. *Current Pos:* dir, Cancer Res Lab, Univ Western Ont, 61-65, head, Dept Path, 65-74, prof, Fac Med, 65-87, EMER PROF PATH, UNIV WESTERN ONT, 87- *Personal Data:* b St Thomas, Ont, Aug 27, 21; m 48, Ruth Brazil; c Kathry, Ann, David & Jane. *Educ:* Univ Western Ont, BA, 47, MD, 48; FRCP(C), 72. *Prof Exp:* Clin intern, Victoria Hosp, London, Ont, 48-49; intern path, New Haven Hosp, 49-51; resident, 51-52; lectr med res, Univ Western Ont, 52-53, asst prof, 53-55; assoc prof path, Univ Man, 55-61. *Concurrent Pos:* Markle Found scholar, 52-57; pathologist, Winnipeg Munic Hosp, 55-61; mem res adv comt, Nat Cancer Inst Can, 60-68, dir, 69-80; consult, Westminster Hosp, London, 63-78; pathologist, Univ Hosp, London, 72- *Mem:* Fel Am Col Physicians; Can Asn Path; Int Acad Path. *Res:* Cancer; biology of neoplasia; metastases; renal pathology; immunopathology. *Mailing Add:* 19 King St Unit 1001 London ON N6A 5N8 Can

**WALLACE, ALFRED THOMAS,** ENVIRONMENTAL ENGINEERING. *Current Pos:* assoc prof, 67-72, PROF CIVIL ENG, UNIV IDAHO, 72- *Personal Data:* b Cranford, NJ, Nov 26, 35; m 58; c 3. *Educ:* Rutgers Univ, BS, 59, Univ Wis, MS, 60, PhD(sanit eng), 65. *Prof Exp:* Asst engr, Triangle Conduit & Cable Co, 57-58 & Am Oil Co, 60-62; instr sanit eng, Univ Wis, 62-65; asst prof environ eng, Clemson Univ, 65-67. *Concurrent Pos:* Lectr,

Calumet Ctr, Purdue Univ, 60-62. *Mem:* Am Water Works Asn; Water Pollution Control Fedn; Am Soc Civil Engrs. *Res:* Unit operations of environmental engineering; industrial wastes; ground water pollution. *Mailing Add:* Dept Civil Eng Univ Idaho Moscow ID 83844-1022

**WALLACE, ALTON SMITH,** OPERATIONS RESEARCH. *Current Pos:* assoc dir, 75-87, DIR, SYST PLANNING CORP, VA, 87- *Personal Data:* b New Bern, NC, Jan 3, 44; m 69; c 2. *Educ:* NC A&T State Univ, BS, 66; Pa State Univ, MS, 68; Univ Md, PhD(math), 74. *Prof Exp:* Eng officer, US Army Corps Engrs, 68-70; sr scientist, BDM Corp, Va, 73-75. *Mem:* Asn US Army; Armed Forces Commun Electronics Asn. *Res:* Development of military weapons systems and surveillance systems; test and evaluation of systems; survivability assesments; weapons effectiveness. *Mailing Add:* 11803 Maher Dr Ft Washington MD 20744-5936

**WALLACE, ANDREW GROVER,** INTERNAL MEDICINE, CARDIOVASCULAR PHYSIOLOGY. *Current Pos:* DEAN, DARTMOUTH MED SCH, VPRES HEALTH AFFAIRS, DARTMOUTH COL, 90- *Personal Data:* b Columbus, Ohio, Mar 22, 35; m 57, Kathleen Barrick Altvater; c Andrew, Mike & Kacie. *Educ:* Duke Univ, BS, 58, MD, 59; Am Bd Internal Med, dipl. *Honors & Awards:* Alan Gregg Mem Lectr, Am Asn Med Col, 96. *Prof Exp:* Intern med, Med Ctr, Duke Univ, 59-60, asst resident, 60-61; investr cardiovasc physiol, Nat Heart Inst, 61-63; chief resident med, Duke Univ, 63-64, assoc, 64-65, from asst prof to assoc prof, 65-70, dir, Cardiac Intensive Care Unit, 65-70, prof med, asst prof physiol, asst dir grad med educ & chief, Cardiol Div, Med Ctr, 70-90, assoc vpres & chief exec officer, Med Ctr, 81-90. *Concurrent Pos:* Fel cardiol, Duke Univ, 61; Markle scholar acad med, 65-70; USPHS career develop award, 65-70; dir, Lab Corp Am, 95-, Welch Allyn, Inc, 96- *Mem:* Inst Med-Nat Acad Sci; Am Heart Asn; Am Fedn Clin Res; AAAS; Am Soc Clin Invest; Am Soc Internal Med; Am Physiol Soc; Soc Med Admin (secy, 95-); Biomed Eng Soc. *Res:* Cardiology; electrocardiology; electrophysiology of the heart; coronary heart disease; exercise physiology. *Mailing Add:* Off Dean Dartmouth Med Sch Hanover NH 03755-3833

**WALLACE, ANDREW HUGH,** MATHEMATICS. *Current Pos:* prof, 65-86, EMER PROF MATH, UNIV PA, 86- *Personal Data:* b Glasgow, Scotland, June 14, 26. *Educ:* Univ Edinburgh, MA, 46; St Andrews Univ, PhD(math), 49. *Prof Exp:* Asst lectr math, Univ Col, Dundee, 46-49, lectr, 49-50; Commonwealth Fund fel, Univ Chicago, 50-52; lectr, Univ Col, Dundee, 52-53; from lectr math to sr lectr, Univ Col, NStaffordshire, 53-57; asst prof, Univ Toronto, 57-59; from asst prof to prof, Indu Univ, 59-64; grant in aid, Inst Advan Study, 64-65. *Concurrent Pos:* Vis prof & assoc dir, Univ Pa Group, Palhavi Univ, Iran, 71-72. *Mem:* Am Math Soc; Can Math Cong; London Math Soc. *Res:* Algebra; algebraic geometry and topology. *Mailing Add:* Ano Daratso Chania Crete 73100 Greece

**WALLACE, ARTHUR,** PLANT NUTRITION, PLANT PHYSIOLOGY. *Current Pos:* Prof plant nutrit, Univ Calif, Los Angeles, 49-89, chief, Div Environ Biol, 66-72, asst chief, 72-79, EMER PROF PLANT NUTRIT, UNIV CALIF, LOS ANGELES, 89- *Personal Data:* b Bear River, Utah, Jan 4, 19; m 43; c 4. *Educ:* Utah State Univ, BS, 43; Rutgers Univ, PhD, 49. *Mem:* Am Soc Plant Physiol; Am Chem Soc; Am Soc Hort Sci; fel Am Soc Agron; fel Soil Sci Soc Am. *Res:* Inorganic plant nutrition and related physiology; major cations, nitrogen and micronutrient elements including their supply to plants by synthetic chelating agents; comparative mineral nutrition of plants; ecophysiology; trace element toxicity; soil conditioners; composting. *Mailing Add:* 10215 Clematis Ct Los Angeles CA 90077

**WALLACE, BRUCE,** GENETICS. *Current Pos:* prof biol, 81-82, distinguished prof, 83-94, DISTINGUISHED EMER PROF, VA POLYTECH INST & STATE UNIV, 94- *Personal Data:* b McKean, Pa, May 18, 20; m 45, Miriam Covalla; c 2. *Educ:* Columbia Univ, AB, 41, PhD(genetics), 49. *Prof Exp:* Res assoc, Dept Genetics, Carnegie Inst, 47-49; res assoc, LI Biol Asn, 49-58; from assoc prof to prof genetics, Cornell Univ, 58-81. *Concurrent Pos:* Humboldt preistrager, 86-87. *Mem:* Nat Acad Sci; Genetics Soc Am (secy, 68-70, pres, 74); Am Acad Arts & Sci; Am Soc Naturalists (secy, 56-58, pres, 70); AAAS; Soc Study Evolution (pres, 74); Am Genetics Asn (pres, 90). *Res:* Population dynamics and speciation of Drosophila; environmental literacy. *Mailing Add:* Dept Biol Va Polytech Inst & State Univ Blacksburg VA 24061. *Fax:* 540-231-9307

**WALLACE, C(HARLES) E(DWARD),** ENGINEERING MECHANICS, PHYSICS. *Current Pos:* asst prof eng sci, Ariz State Univ, 58-59, from assoc prof to prof & chmn dept, 59-67, prof eng mech & mat & chmn dept, 67-74, prof & chmn aerospace eng & eng sci, 74-82, prof mech & aerospace, 82-87, PROF & ASST DEAN, COL ENG & APPL SCI, ARIZ STATE UNIV, 87- *Personal Data:* b Portland, Ore, Apr 19, 29; m 65; c 2. *Educ:* Lewis & Clark Col, BS, 51; Ore State Univ, MS, 54; Stanford Univ, PhD(eng mech), 59. *Prof Exp:* Engr, Douglas Aircraft Co, 53-55. *Concurrent Pos:* Consult, Gen Elec Co, 59 & NAm Aviation, Inc, 60-; Nat Res Coun sr resident res associateship, NASA-Langley Res Ctr, 68-69. *Mem:* Am Inst Aeronaut & Astronaut; Acoust Soc Am; Am Soc Eng Educ; Am Acad Mech. *Res:* Plasticity of anisotropic materials; thermoelasticity of plates; vibration of aircraft structure; acoustic fatigue and damping; community noise control; radiation resistance. *Mailing Add:* Col Eng Ariz State Univ PO Box 876106 Tempe AZ 85287-6106

**WALLACE, CARL J,** CHEMICAL ENGINEERING. *Current Pos:* TECH PROG INTEGRATOR, SOLAR ENERGY RES INST, 88- *Personal Data:* b Lane's Prairie, Mo, Feb 11, 38; m 61; c 3. *Educ:* Univ Mo, Rolla, BS, 61, MS, 62, PhD(chem eng), 66. *Prof Exp:* Teaching asst chem, Sch Mines, Univ Mo, Rolla, 61-62, 63-64 & 65-66; from asst prof to assoc prof chem eng, SDak Sch Mines & Technol, 66-75; group leader, Jet Propulsion Lab, Calif Inst Technol, 75-80; detailee, US Dept Energy, 80-83; tech staff, Argonne Nat Lab, 84-88. *Concurrent Pos:* Lectr, NSF Summer Inst, 67; NSF res initiation grant, 69-70. *Mem:* Am Inst Chem Engrs; Am Chem Soc; Am Soc Eng Educ; AAAS; Sigma Xi. *Res:* Biochemical engineering; chemical processing by ultraviolet and ultrasonic energy; bioconversion; energy recovery from wastes; environmental engineering. *Mailing Add:* 907 Sixth St SW Apt 303 C Washington DC 20024-3817

**WALLACE, CHESTER ALAN,** stratigraphy, sedimentary petrology, for more information see previous edition

**WALLACE, CRAIG KESTING,** MEDICINE, RESEARCH ADMINISTRATION. *Current Pos:* RETIRED. *Personal Data:* b Woodbury, NJ, Dec 4, 28; m 60; c 3. *Educ:* Princeton Univ, AB, 50; NY Med Col, MD, 55. *Prof Exp:* Clin investr, US Naval Med Res Unit, Taiwan, 60-63; instr med, Jefferson Med Col Hosp, 60-64; from asst prof to assoc prof, Sch Med & Sch Hyg & Pub Health, Johns Hopkins Univ, 64-72 & Ctr Med Res & Training Calcutta India, 64-72; cmndg officer, US Naval Med Res Unit Ethiopia, 72-76, prog mgr infectious dis, Naval Med Res & Develop Command, 76-78, chief internal med, Camp Pendleton, 78-80, dir clin serv, Naval Regional Med Ctr, Jacksonville, Fla, 80-82, cmdg officer, US Naval Med Res Unit, Egypt, 80-84; dir, Fogarty Int Ctr, NIH, 84-87, assoc dir int res, 84-93; head adm, Conf WHO, 91-93. *Concurrent Pos:* Adv & consult, WHO , 62-; consult, Magee Mem Hosp Philadelphia, Pa, 63-64; physician & consult, Vet Admin Hosp, Perry Point, Md, 67-72; mem Bact & Mycol Study Sect, NIH, 68-72, chmn, 71-72; physician Good Samaritan Hosp, Baltimore, Md, 69-72; ed bd & correp ed, Ethiopian Med J, 74-; clin assoc prof med, Uniformed Servs Univ Sci, 77-; mem, sci adv bd, Leonard Wood Mem Liploser Found, 84-88; physician, Good Samaritan Hosp, Baltimore, 69-72; dir, John E Fogarty Int Ctr Advan Study Health Sci, NIH, 84-87. *Mem:* AAAS; fel Am Col Physicians; Infectious Dis Soc Am; Am Soc Microbiol; Royal & Am Soc Trop Med & Hyg; Royal Soc Trop Med & Hyg. *Res:* Pathophysiology and treatment of infectious diseases, especially in the areas of tropical enteric infections; physician training and research in international medicine. *Mailing Add:* 14844 Dufies Dr North Potomac MD 20878

**WALLACE, DAVID H,** BACTERIAL FERMENTATIONS. *Current Pos:* MICROBIOLOGIST, NEW ENG BIOLABS, 80- *Personal Data:* b Cambridge, Mass, May 15, 37; m 63, Jessie Young. *Educ:* Harvard Univ, AB, 58; Mass Inst Technol, SM, 63, ScD(food sci & eng), 66. *Prof Exp:* Dep dir, New Eng Enzyme Ctr, Tufts Univ, 66-80. *Mem:* Sigma Xi. *Res:* Carry out large scale culture of microorganisms, optimize growth conditions and improve methods for large scale purification. *Mailing Add:* 61 Donizetti St Wellesley MA 02181

**WALLACE, DAVID LEE,** STATISTICS, DATA ANALYSIS. *Current Pos:* from asst prof to prof statist, 54-95, EMER PROF STATIST, UNIV CHICAGO, 95- *Personal Data:* b Homestead, Pa, Dec 24, 28; m 55, Anna Mary Adams; c Margaret, Kathryn & Edward. *Educ:* Carnegie Inst Technol, BS, 48, MS, 49; Princeton Univ, PhD(math), 53. *Prof Exp:* Res mathematician, Mass Inst Technol, 53-54. *Concurrent Pos:* Fel, Ctr Advan Study Behav Sci, 60-61; mem comput & biomath sci study sect, NIH, 70-74. *Mem:* Fel Am Statist Asn; Inst Math Statist; Biometric Soc; fel Royal Statist Soc. *Res:* Theoretical statistics; computer methods. *Mailing Add:* Dept Statist Univ Chicago 5734 S University Ave Chicago IL 60637-1514

**WALLACE, DENNIS D,** ENVIRONMENTAL STATISTICS, AIR POLLUTION CONTROL. *Current Pos:* ASST PROF BIOSTATIST, DEPT PREVENTIVE MED, MED CTR, UNIV KANS, 96- *Personal Data:* b Salina, Kans, Sept 19, 49; m 92, Carol J Athey. *Educ:* Univ Kans, BS, 71; Univ Mo, Kans City, MS, 77; Univ NC, PhD(biostatist), 93. *Prof Exp:* Math teacher, Kans City, Mo Sch Dist, 71-74; asst & assoc environ scientist, Midwest Res Inst, 74-84, sr environ scientist, 84-93, prin environ statistician, 93-94; asst prof biostat, Univ Ala, Birmingham, 94-96. *Concurrent Pos:* Adj lectr math, Univ Mo, Kansas City, 79-85. *Mem:* Air & Waste Mgt Asn; Am Statist Asn; Biomet Soc. *Res:* Actively involved in studies on the characterization and control of air pollution and hazardous waste; the statistical analyses of air pollution and environmental health data. *Mailing Add:* Dept Prev Med 3901 Rainbow Blvd Univ Kans Med Ctr Kansas City KS 66160. *Fax:* 913-588-2780; *E-Mail:* dwallac1@kumc.edu

**WALLACE, DONALD HOWARD,** PLANT GENETICS. *Current Pos:* Asst plant breeding, Cornell Univ, 53-55 & 57, actg asst prof plant breeding & veg crops, 55-57, from asst prof to assoc prof, 58-71, PROF PLANT BREEDING & VEG CROPS, CORNELL UNIV, 71- *Personal Data:* b Driggs, Idaho, June 27, 26; m 49; c Conley D, Russell W, Patricia A, Paulette & Carol J. *Educ:* Utah State Agr Col, BS, 53; Cornell Univ, PhD(plant breeding), 58. *Honors & Awards:* Campbell Award, 70; Asgrow Award, 81. *Concurrent Pos:* Vis prof, Univ Philippines, Los Bonos, 68-69, Mich State Univ, 78-79. *Mem:* Fel Am Soc Hort Sci; Crop Sci Soc Am; Am Soc Plant Physiol; fel AAAS. *Res:* Development of hybrid and improved varieties of vegetables; physiological genetics of crop yield. *Mailing Add:* Dept Plant Breeding Cornell Univ Ithaca NY 14853

**WALLACE, DONALD MACPHERSON, JR,** MECHANICAL ENGINEERING. *Current Pos:* PROF MECH ENG, NORWICH UNIV, 62- *Personal Data:* b Montclair, NJ, June 24, 34. *Educ:* Univ Vt, BSME, 60; Univ Ill, Urbana, MS, 62; Columbia Univ, EngScD(mech eng), 68. *Prof Exp:* Instr mech eng, Univ Ill, 60-62. *Concurrent Pos:* Engr, Allis-Chalmers Corp, 73-74. *Mem:* Am Soc Mech Engrs; Am Soc Eng Educ; Sigma Xi. *Res:* Kinematics of spatial mechanisms. *Mailing Add:* Dept Mech Eng Norwich Univ 655 S Main St Northfield VT 05663

**WALLACE, DOUGLAS CECIL,** MITOCHONDRIAL GENETICS. *Current Pos:* prof biochem, Emory Univ, 83-90, dir, Ctr Genetics & Molecular Med, 90-92, prof & chmn, Dept Genetics & Molecular Med, 92-96, PROF BIOCHEM & PROF ANTHROP, EMORY UNIV, 83-, ROBERT W WOODRUFF PROF MOLECULAR GENETICS & DIR, CTR MOLECULAR MED, 93- *Personal Data:* b Cumberland, Md, Nov 6, 46. *Educ:* Cornell Univ, BS, 68; Yale Univ, MPh, 72, PhD(microbiol & human genetics), 75; Am Bd Med Genetics, dipl, 89 & 93. *Honors & Awards:* William Allan Award, Am Soc Human Genetics, 94; Albert L Lehninger Lect, Sch Med, John Hopkins Univ, 96; Annie W Riecker Lect, Univ Ariz, 96; Melvin V Simpson Lect, State Univ NY, Stony Brook, 97. *Prof Exp:* Res microbiologist, Northwestern Water Hyg Lab, USPHS, Gig Harbor, Wash, 68-70; NIH fel, Sch Med, Yale Univ, 75-76; asst prof genetics, Sch Med, Stanford Univ, 76-83. *Concurrent Pos:* Mellon Found fel, Stanford Univ, 78-79; Hume fac scholar, 81-82; chairperson & sr ed, Mitochondrial DNA Comt, Int Human Genome Orgn, 93- *Mem:* Nat Acad Sci; Sigma Xi; Am Soc Microbiol; AAAS; Am Soc Human Genetics; Am Acad Microbiol. *Res:* Genetics, biogenesis and phylogenetic relationships of mammalian mitochondria; author of numerous publications. *Mailing Add:* Dept Gen & Mol Med Emory Univ Sch Med 1462 Clifton Rd Suite 420 Atlanta GA 30322

**WALLACE, DOUGLAS WILLIAM ROY,** TRANSIENT TRACERS IN THE OCEAN, OCEAN CARBON CYCLE. *Current Pos:* from asst scientist to assoc scientist, 87-92, SCIENTIST, BROOKHAVEN NAT LAB, 92- *Personal Data:* b Ashby-de-la-Zouch, UK, Jan 2, 59; Brit & Can citizen; m, Julie LaRoche. *Educ:* Univ East Anglia, BSc(Hons), 78; Dalhousie Univ, PhD(chem oceanog), 85. *Prof Exp:* Ed asst, Aquatic Sci & Fisheries Abstracts, 78-80; Vis fel, Bedford Inst Oceanog, 86-87. *Concurrent Pos:* Adj prof, Marine Sci Res Ctr, 92-; tech dir, Dept Energy Global Surv Carbon-Dioxide in Oceans, 93- *Mem:* Oceanog Soc; Am Geophys Union. *Res:* oceanic uptake of fossil fuel carbon-dioxide; oceanic distribution of anthropogenic tracers and natural halocarbons; cycling of carbon-dioxide and oxygen on continental shelves; air-sea gas exchange. *Mailing Add:* Brookhaven Nat Lab Bldg 318 PO Box 5000 Upton NY 11973. *Fax:* 516-282-3246; *E-Mail:* wallace@bnlux1.bnl.gov

**WALLACE, EDITH WINCHELL,** SPERMATOGENESIS, ENDOCRINOLOGY. *Current Pos:* PROF BIOL, WILLIAM PATERSON COL, NJ, 68- *Personal Data:* b Jersey City, NJ, Oct 3, 35; m; c 3. *Educ:* Montclair State Col, BA, 56, MA, 61; Rutgers Univ, PhD(zool), 69. *Prof Exp:* Instr biol, Westwood Bd Educ, NJ, 56-61; instr sci, Englewood Hosp Sch Nursing, 65-68. *Mem:* AAAS; NY Acad Sci; Soc Study Reproduction. *Res:* Morphological, histological, transmission electron microscope and physiological investigations in selenium and zinc deficient rodents of the roles of these trace elements in spermatogenesis. *Mailing Add:* 19 Iris Circle Glen Rock NJ 07452-3428

**WALLACE, EDWIN GARFIELD,** ORGANIC CHEMISTRY. *Current Pos:* RETIRED. *Personal Data:* b Akron, Ohio, Jan 27, 17; m 44, Elvera Langbein; c Barbara, Carolyn, Melanie, Bruce, David & Charles. *Educ:* Univ Miami, Ohio, AB, 38; Ohio State Univ, PhD(chem), 42. *Prof Exp:* Res chemist, Eastman Kodak Co, NY, 42-47; res chemist, US Naval Ord Test Sta, Calif, 47-48; res chemist & group leader, Shell Chem Corp, 48-54; from asst to vpres res to mgr chem res, Western Res Ctr, Stauffer Chem Co, 54-65, lab dir, 65-67, sr res assoc, 67-82. *Concurrent Pos:* Chmn, Calif Sect, Am Chem Soc, 79. *Mem:* Am Chem Soc. *Res:* Agricultural chemicals; industrial organic chemicals and products; polymers; fluorine chemicals. *Mailing Add:* 133 Sleepy Hollow Lane Orinda CA 94563

**WALLACE, F BLAKE,** AEROSPACE, MECHANICAL ENGINEERING. *Current Pos:* RETIRED. *Personal Data:* b Phoenix, Ariz, Jan 10, 33. *Educ:* Calif Inst Technol, BMechE, 55; Ariz State Univ, MS, 63, PhD, 67. *Prof Exp:* Design engr, Pratt & Whitney, E Hartford, Conn, 55-59; chief engr advan tech, Garrett Corp, Phoenix, 59-80; mgr advan plans & progress, Aircraft Eng & Aircraft Engine Groups GE, Evandale, Ohio, 81-83; gen mgr, Allison Div, Gen Motors, Indianapolis, In, 83-95. *Mem:* Fel Am Inst Aeronaut & Astronaut; US Advan Ceramic Asn. *Res:* Aircraft engineering; aerospace engineering; mechanical engineering; ceramic engineering. *Mailing Add:* 8409 Bay Colony Dr Indianapolis IN 46234

**WALLACE, FRANKLIN GERHARD,** parasitology; deceased, see previous edition for last biography

**WALLACE, FREDERIC ANDREW,** PHYSICAL CHEMISTRY, ANALYTICAL CHEMISTRY. *Current Pos:* GROUP LEADER PHYS & ANALYTICAL CHEM RES, CENT ANALYSIS LAB, RES DIV, POLAROID CORP, 67- *Personal Data:* b Boston, Mass, Apr 28, 33; m 54; c 2. *Educ:* Harvard Univ, AB, 58; Calif Inst Technol, MS, 60; Tufts Univ, PhD(chem), 67. *Concurrent Pos:* Chemist, Monsanto Chem Co, 70-74. *Mem:* Am Chem Soc. *Res:* Investigations of structure and bonding of organo-silver complexes and salts; measurement of stability constants, and solubility products of same; chemical analysis and method development for photographic chemicals. *Mailing Add:* 53 Eaton Rd Framingham MA 01701-2727

**WALLACE, GARY DEAN,** PLANT SYSTEMATICS, PLANT ANATOMY. *Current Pos:* STAFF, RANCHO SANTA ANA BOT GARDEN. *Personal Data:* b Pasadena, Calif, Jan 4, 46; m 77; c 2. *Educ:* Calif State Univ, BA, 67, MA, 72; Claremont Grad Sch, PhD(bot), 75. *Prof Exp:* Biologist, Los Angeles Count Aboretum, 75-81; assoc cur & botanist, Natural Hist Mus, Los Angeles, 82- *Concurrent Pos:* Exten Instr, Univ Calif, Los Angeles, 76- *Mem:* Am Soc Plant Taxonomists; Int Asn Plant Taxonomy; Bot Soc Am; AAAS; Asn Trop Biol; Sigma Xi. *Res:* Taxonomy of the monotropoidese (ericpase); checklist of the flora of the offshore islands of Southern California; ecological word anatomy of arctostaphylos (ericpase). *Mailing Add:* Rancho Santa Ana Bot Garden 1500 N College Ave Claremont CA 91711-3157

**WALLACE, GARY OREN,** ECOLOGY. *Current Pos:* ASST PROF BIOL, MILLIGAN COL, 67-68 & 71- *Personal Data:* b Stewart Co, Tenn, Apr 2, 40; m 62; c 2. *Educ:* Austin Peay State Univ, BS, 62; Univ Tenn, MS, 64, PhD(zool), 70. *Prof Exp:* Teacher biol, Maryville Col, 64-65. *Concurrent Pos:* Ed, The Migrant, 71-81. *Mem:* Wilson Ornith Soc; Nat Audubon Soc; Sigma Xi. *Res:* Abundance and distribution of certain bird populations. *Mailing Add:* Dept Sci Milligan Col Milligan College TN 37682-0009

**WALLACE, GERALD WAYNE,** ANALYTICAL CHEMISTRY, PHYSICAL CHEMISTRY. *Current Pos:* RETIRED. *Personal Data:* b Sault Ste Marie, Mich, July 20, 33; m 54; c 3. *Educ:* Univ Mich, BS, 55; Purdue Univ, MS, 57, PhD(anal chem), 59. *Prof Exp:* Sr chemist, Esso Res & Eng Co, 59-60; sr anal chemist, Eli Lilly & Co, 60-65; res scientist, 65-67, head anal develop phys, 67-71, dir, Phys Chem Res Div, 71-79, dir pharmaceut res, 79-80, dir anal develop, 80-92. *Concurrent Pos:* USP Comt Rev. *Mem:* Am Chem Soc; AAAS. *Res:* Spectroscopy; fluorescence; photochemistry. *Mailing Add:* 190 Channel Ct Marco Island FL 33937-4716

**WALLACE, GORDON DEAN,** MICROBIOLOGY. *Current Pos:* PRES, BIO-BRITE, 89- *Personal Data:* b Los Angeles, Calif, Dec 17, 27; m 52; c 2. *Educ:* Colo State Univ, BS, 52, DVM, 54; Univ Calif, MPH, 62. *Honors & Awards:* McCallam Award, Asn Mil Surgeons US, 83. *Prof Exp:* Epidemiologist, Commun Dis Ctr, USPHS, 54-61; med researcher, 61-79, asst sci dir, 78-83, sr policy analyst, Exec Off Pres, Off Sci & Technol Policy, 83-84, assoc sci dir, actg dep dir & sci dir, Nat Inst Allergy & Infectious Dis, 84-86; sr assoc, Ling Technol, 86-87; pres, WBA, 87-91. *Concurrent Pos:* Consult infectious dis, Tripler Us Army Hosp, Childrens Hosp & Queens Med Ctr, Honolulu, Hawaii, 61-78; assoc clin prof trop med & med microbiol, Sch Med, Univ Hawaii, 70-78; counr, Am Soc Trop Med & Hyg, 77-81, sci prog chmn, 81-83; guest instr, Georgetown Univ, 83-84; mem competetive grants policy adv comt, USDA, 83-85; pres, NIH Alumni Asn, 90-91. *Mem:* Fel AAAS; Am Soc Trop Med & Hyg. *Res:* Epidemiology of infectious diseases, including eosinophilic meningitis, influenza and toxoplasmosis. *Mailing Add:* 7315 Wisconsin Ave Suite 900 E Bethesda MD 20814

**WALLACE, GORDON THOMAS,** CHEMICAL OCEANOGRAPHY, ATMOSPHERIC CHEMISTRY. *Current Pos:* dir, Environ Sci Prog, 90-93, ASSOC PROF ENVIRON SCI, UNIV MASS, 82- *Personal Data:* b Chicago, Ill, Sept 22, 42; m 69; c 2. *Educ:* Antioch Col, BS, 65; Univ RI, PhD(oceanog), 76. *Prof Exp:* Anal chemist, Geigy Chem Corp, 62-63; chemist, Naval Res Lab, 63-69; res asst, Univ RI, 72-76; res assoc, Skidaway Inst Oceanog, 75-76, asst prof, 76-82. *Concurrent Pos:* Consult, Amos T Shaler Inc, 73-74, Knoll Atomic Power Labs; adj asst prof, Ga Inst Technol, 78-88. *Mem:* Am Soc Limnol & Oceanog; AAAS; Am Geophys Union; Estaurin Res Fed; Am Chem Soc. *Res:* Biogeochemistry of metals in the marine environment; trace metal-organic interactions; chemical fractionation at the sea-air interface; waste disposal in coast-marine environment. *Mailing Add:* Environ Sci Prog Univ Mass Boston 100 Marress Blvd Boston MA 02125

**WALLACE, GRAHAM FRANKLIN,** SOFTWARE ENGINEERING, SOFTWARE DEVELOPMENT. *Current Pos:* SYSTS ENG SPECIALIST, LOCKHHEED MARTIN MISSILES & SPACE, 97- *Personal Data:* b Santa Rosa, Calif, Mar 27, 35; m 59; c 2. *Educ:* Pomona Col, BA, 57; Univ Calif, Berkeley, MA, 60. *Prof Exp:* Mathematician, Math Sci Dept, SRI Int, 60-64, res mathematician, 64-66, asst mgr admin, 66-70, sr systs programmer, Info Sci Lab, 70-74, sr res engr, Systs Tech Lab, Stanford Res Inst, 74-84, sr res engr, Spec Commun Systs Lab, 84-94. *Concurrent Pos:* Chmn seventh symposium gaming & chmn steering comt, Nat Gaming Coun, 68; vchmn tech prog eight int conf, Inst Elec & Electronics Engrs Comput Soc, 74. *Mem:* AAAS; Sigma Xi. *Res:* Development of computer software; design, analysis and evaluation of computer-based information systems. *Mailing Add:* 1707 Equestrian Dr Pleasanton CA 94588-2622

**WALLACE, HAROLD DEAN,** ANIMAL NUTRITION. *Current Pos:* RETIRED. *Personal Data:* b Walnut, Ill, June 8, 22; m 45; c 4. *Educ:* Univ Ill, BS, 45, MS, 47; Cornell Univ, PhD(animal nutrit), 50. *Honors & Awards:* Am Feed Mfrs Award, 62. *Prof Exp:* From asst prof to prof animal nutrit, Univ Fla, 50-84, chmn, 76-84. *Mem:* AAAS; Am Soc Animal Sci; Am Dairy Sci Asn; Am Inst Nutrit. *Res:* Swine nutrition; vitamins; antibiotics; amino acids; carcass quality. *Mailing Add:* 1812 SW 36th Pl Gainesville FL 32608

**WALLACE, HELEN M,** PUBLIC HEALTH. *Current Pos:* PROF, GRAD SCH PUB HEALTH, SAN DIEGO STATE UNIV, 80- *Personal Data:* b Hoosick Falls, NY, Feb 18, 13. *Educ:* Wellesley Col, AB, 33; Columbia Univ, MD, 37; Harvard Univ, MPH, 43. *Prof Exp:* NY Dept Health, 43-55; prof prev med, NY Med Col, 55-56; prof maternal & child health, Univ Minn, 56-59; chief child health studies, US Children's Bur, 59-62; prof maternal, child & family health, Sch Pub Health, Univ Calif, Berkeley, 62-80. *Concurrent Pos:* WHO traveling fel, 57; consult, WHO, Uganda, 61, Philippines, 66, India, 68 & 69, Turkey, 69, Geneva, 70 & 74 & Iran, 72; Ford Found consult, Sch Pub Health, Univ Antioquaia, Colombia, 71; consult, Health Bur, Panama Canal Co, 72, India, Thailand, Burma & Ceylon, 75; dir, Uganda Prog, Univ Calif, India & Thailand, 81, Nepal, 83 & Burma, 85, China, 87, Zimbabwe, 84-87, India, 91. *Mem:* Asn Teachers Maternal & Child Health (pres); Am Pub Health Asn; Am Acad Pediat. *Res:* Maternal and child health; author of 325 publications and 10 books. *Mailing Add:* San Diego State Univ 850 State St San Diego CA 92101

**WALLACE, HERBERT WILLIAM,** BIOCHEMISTRY, SURGERY. *Current Pos:* assoc, Univ Pa, 66-70, from asst prof to assoc prof surg & assoc prof physiol, Sch Med, 70-79, assoc prof bioeng, Col Eng & Appl Sci, 74-76, PROF SURG & PHYSIOL, SCH MED & PROF BIOENG, COL ENG & APPL SCI, UNIV PA, 76-; RES ASSOC, DIV CARDIOL, PHILADELPHIA GEN HOSP. *Personal Data:* b Brooklyn, NY, Dec 11, 30; m 54; c 3. *Educ:* Harvard Univ, AB, 52; Tufts Univ, MD, 56, MS, 60; Wharton Sch Univ Pa, MBA, 81. *Prof Exp:* Asst attend surgeon, Elmhurst Gen Hosp Div, Mt Sinai Hosp, 65-66. *Concurrent Pos:* Res fel, Nat Heart Inst, 58-59; teaching fel surg, Sch Med, Univ Pittsburgh, 61-62; Am Thoracic Soc fel, 62-65; John Polachek Found Med Res fel, Div Cardio-Thoracic Surg, Mt Sinai Hosp, NY, 65-66; asst surgeon, Grad Hosp, Univ Pa, 66-74, assoc surg, 74-, assoc dir, Gen Clin Res Ctr, 67-70, actg dir, 70-73. *Mem:* AAAS; Asn Acad Surg; Am Chem Soc; Am Col Surg; Am Fedn Clin Res; Sigma Xi. *Res:* Biochemistry and physiology of extracorporeal circulation and respiration; lung metabolism; hemoglobin; artificial red cell; cardiac metabolism; cancer immunology; management and marketing of medical services. *Mailing Add:* 255 Harrogate Rd Wynnewood PA 19096-3131

**WALLACE, JACK E,** BIOCHEMICAL PATHOLOGY, ANALYTICAL TOXICOLOGY. *Current Pos:* from asst prof to assoc prof, 72-79, PROF PATH, HEALTH SCI CTR, UNIV TEX, SAN ANTONIO, 79- *Personal Data:* b Harrisburg, Ill, Jan 5, 34; m 55, Verta A Standerfur; c Michael & Kimberly. *Educ:* Univ Southern Ill, BA, 55, MA, 57; Purdue Univ, PhD(biochem), 62. *Honors & Awards:* Alexander O Gettler Award in Forensic Toxicol, 91. *Prof Exp:* Instr chem, Univ Southern Ill, 55-57; instr biochem, Purdue Univ, 59-61; chemist anal lab, State Chemist's Lab, Ind, 57-59; chief forensic toxicol br, USAF Sch Aerospace Med, 61-72. *Concurrent Pos:* Consult, Army Med Lab, Ft Sam Houston, Tex, Audie Murphy Vet Admin Hosp, San Antonio, Tex, Wilford Hall USAF Med Ctr, Lackland AFB, Tex, & Harris Med Labs, Ft Worth, Tex, SW Res Inst, San Antonio, Tex, Drug Abuse Testing Prog, Nat Inst Drug Abuse; inspector, Matrix Technologies, Houston, Tex; sci dir, Precision Anal Labs, San Antonio, Tex, 90-; consult, Nichols Inst, Dallas, 90-92. *Mem:* Sr mem Am Chem Soc; fel Am Inst Chem; fel Am Acad Forensic Sci; Am Acad Clin Toxicol; Am Asn Clin Chemists; fel Nat Acad Clin Biochem. *Res:* Forensic toxicology; drug metabolism; drug analysis in biological specimens; pharmacology; clinical chemistry; biochemical pathology; author of over 150 publications in various scientific journals. *Mailing Add:* Dept Path Health Sci Ctr Univ Tex 7703 Floyd Curl Dr San Antonio TX 78284-6200

**WALLACE, JAMES,** optics, fluid mechanics; deceased, see previous edition for last biography

**WALLACE, JAMES BRUCE,** ENTOMOLOGY, HYDROBIOLOGY. *Current Pos:* asst prof, 67-71, assoc prof, 71-77, MEM STAFF, INST COL, UNIV GA, 69-, PROF ENTOM, 77- *Personal Data:* b Williamsburg Co, SC, Mar 2, 39; m 62; c 1. *Educ:* Clemson Univ, BS, 61; Va Polytech Inst, MS, 63, PhD(entom), 67. *Prof Exp:* Res asst entom, Va Polytech Inst, 61-66. *Concurrent Pos:* Environ Protection Agency res grant, Univ Ga, 68-72; NSF res grant, 74-88; vis scientist, Univ Lund, Sweden, 80. *Mem:* AAAS; Ecol Soc Am; Am Entom Soc; NAm Benthol Soc. *Res:* Stream ecology; aquatic entomology; secondary production of invertebrates. *Mailing Add:* Dept Entom Univ Ga 1180 E Broad St Athens GA 30601-3040

**WALLACE, JAMES D,** ELECTRICAL ENGINEERING. *Current Pos:* RETIRED. *Personal Data:* b Miss, Mar 6, 04. *Educ:* Univ Miss, BA, 25, MA, 27. *Prof Exp:* Electronic scientist, radio physicist, consult, Naval Res Lab, 28-66. *Mem:* Fel Inst Elec & Electronics Engrs. *Res:* Military communication with voice communication; teletype and data transmission. *Mailing Add:* 3501 Bayshore Blvd Apt 803 Tampa FL 33629

**WALLACE, JAMES M,** TURBULENT FLOW. *Current Pos:* from asst prof to assoc prof, Univ Md, Col Park 75-83, asst provost, 85-86, asst dean, 86-87, PROF MECH ENG, UNIV MD, COL PARK, 83-, ASSOC CHAIR, 93- *Personal Data:* b Augusta, Ga, Aug 11, 39; m 84, Barbara K; c James C. *Educ:* Ga Inst Technol, BCE, 62; MSc, 64; Oxford Univ, PhD(eng sci), 69. *Prof Exp:* Hydraul engr, Harza Eng Co, 64-65 & Sir William Halcrow & Partners, London, 65-66; res scientist, Max-Planck Inst, 69-75. *Concurrent Pos:* Vis asst prof, Ohio State Univ, 71-73. *Mem:* Fel Am Phys Soc. *Res:* Interaction of science and technology with society; physics of turbulent flow. *Mailing Add:* Dept Mech Eng Univ Md College Park MD 20742. *Fax:* 301-314-9477; *E-Mail:* wallace@eng.umd.edu

**WALLACE, JAMES ROBERT,** HYDROLOGY, FLUID MECHANICS. *Current Pos:* asst prof, 66-69, ASSOC PROF CIVIL ENG, GA INST TECHNOL, 69- *Personal Data:* b Magnolia, Ark, Nov 9, 38; m 63; c 3. *Educ:* Ga Inst Technol, BCivE, 61, MS, 63; Mass Inst Technol, ScD, 66. *Prof Exp:* Res asst civil eng, Mass Inst Technol, 62-66. *Mem:* Am Geophys Union; Am Soc Civil Engrs. *Res:* Flow of fluids in open channels; design and operation of water resource systems; computer simulation of hydrologic processes. *Mailing Add:* 2680 Peppermint Dr Tucker GA 30084

**WALLACE, JAMES WILLIAM, JR,** PLANT PHYSIOLOGY BIOCHEMISTRY, BIOLOGICAL PHOTOGRAPHY. *Current Pos:* from asst to assoc prof, 67-77, PROF BIOL, WESTERN CAROLINA UNIV, 78- *Personal Data:* b Cincinnati, Ohio, July 31, 40; m 62; c 2. *Educ:* Miami Univ, BS, 62, MS, 64; Univ Tex, Austin, PhD(plant biochem), 67. *Prof Exp:* Technician, Kimberly-Clarke Corp, 62. *Concurrent Pos:* Secy, Phytochem Soc NAm, 71-74, ed-in-chief, 74-76; fac exchange prog, People's Repub China, 84; sr res fel, NZ Nat Res Adv Coun, 76-77; chmn, Southeastern Sect, Bot Soc Am, 82-85, Phytochem Sect, 85-87; biol photogr, Lobdell & Assoc, Anchorage, Alaska; chmn fac, Western Carolina Univ, 88-92. *Mem:* Sigma Xi; Bot Soc Am; Phytochem Soc NAm (secy, 71-74); Explorers Club; Am Fern Soc. *Res:* Flavonoids, biosynthesis, physiology and distribution; biological photography. *Mailing Add:* Dept Biol Western Carolina Univ Cullowhee NC 28723. *Fax:* 704-227-7647

**WALLACE, JOHN F(RANCIS),** METALLURGY, FOUNDRY TECHNOLOGY. *Current Pos:* from assoc prof to prof, 54-80, dir NASA-CCDS, 87-90, CHMN, DEPT METALL & MAT SCI, CASE WESTERN RES UNIV, 74-, REP STEEL PROF METALL, 80- *Personal Data:* b Boston, Mass, Oct 26, 19; wid; c 3. *Educ:* Mass Inst Technol, BS, 41, MS, 53. *Honors & Awards:* Pangborn Gold Medal, Foundrymen's Soc, 62; Nyselius Award, Am Die Casting Inst, 67; Gold Medal, Gray & Ductile Iron Founders' Soc, 70; Howard Taylor Award, Am Foundry Men's Soc, 81; Doehler Award, Am Die Casting Inst, 84. *Prof Exp:* Asst metallurgist, Watertown Arsenal, Mass, 41-42, metallurgist, 46-47, sr metallurgist, 47-52, prin metallurgist, 52-54. *Concurrent Pos:* Consult, 55; Hoyt Mem lectr, Am Foundrymen's Soc, 75. *Mem:* Foundrymen's Soc; fel Am Soc Metals; Am Inst Mining, Metall & Petrol Engrs; Soc Die Casting Engrs; Sigma Xi. *Res:* Cast metals; control of casting processes, including solidification behavior, gating, rising, mold selection and behavior; die casting; heat treatment of metals; welding; metal forming and mechanical behavior of metals. *Mailing Add:* Metallurgy 10900 Euclid Case Western Res Univ Cleveland OH 44106

**WALLACE, JOHN LAWRENCE,** IMMUNOPHYSIOLOGY. *Current Pos:* assoc prof, 89-93, PROF, UNIV CALGARY, 93- *Personal Data:* b Toronto, Ont, Sept 25, 56; m 87, Beth C Chin; c Alexandra E & Meredith E. *Educ:* Queens Univ, Ont, BSc, 79, MSc, 80; Univ Toronto, PhD, 83. *Prof Exp:* Fel, Wellcome Res Found, Beckenham, Eng, 84-86; asst prof, Queens Univ, Ont, 86-89. *Res:* Immunology; physiology. *Mailing Add:* Dept Pharmacol Univ Calgary 3330 Hosp Dr NW Calgary AB T2N 1N4 Can

**WALLACE, JOHN M, JR,** electrical engineering; deceased, see previous edition for last biography

**WALLACE, JOHN MICHAEL,** METEOROLOGY. *Current Pos:* From asst prof to assoc prof, 66-77, PROF ATMOSPHERIC SCI, UNIV WASH, 77- *Personal Data:* b Flushing, NY, Oct 28, 40; c 3. *Educ:* Webb Inst Naval Archit, BS, 62; Mass Inst Technol, PhD(meteorol), 66. *Honors & Awards:* Macelwane Award, Am Geophys Union, 72; Meisinger Award, Am Meteorol Soc, 75, Rossby Medal, 93. *Concurrent Pos:* Adj assoc prof environ studies, Univ Wash, 73-; dir, Joint Inst Study Atmosphere & Ocean, 80-; chair, Dept Atmospheric Sci, 83-88. *Mem:* Nat Acad Sci; Am Geophys Union; Am Meteorol Soc. *Res:* General circulation; climate dyanamics. *Mailing Add:* Dept Atmospheric Sci AK-40 Univ Wash Seattle WA 98195-0001. *E-Mail:* wallace@atmos.washington.edu

**WALLACE, JON MARQUES,** PLASMA PHYSICS. *Current Pos:* STAFF MEM, LOS ALAMOS NAT LAB, 73- *Personal Data:* b Pensacola, Fla, Dec 21, 43; m 70; c 2. *Educ:* Univ Calif, Berkeley, AB, 66; Harvard Univ, PhD(physics), 71. *Prof Exp:* Fel physics, Univ Md, 71-73. *Mem:* Am Phys Soc. *Res:* Laser-plasma interactions; transport theory; hydrodynamics; inertial confinement fusion; cosmic ray theory; nuclear scattering theory. *Mailing Add:* Los Alamos Nat Lab MS B259 Los Alamos NM 87545

**WALLACE, KENDALL B,** BIOCHEMICAL MECHANISMS, COMPARATIVE TOXICOLOGY. *Current Pos:* ASST PROF PHARMACOL & TOXICOL, UNIV MINN, 81-, DIR, CHEM TOXICOL RES CTR, DULUTH SCH MED, 85- *Personal Data:* Alpena, Mich, May 3, 53. *Educ:* Mich State Univ, PhD(physiol), 79. *Mem:* Int Soc Xenobiotics; Soc Environ Toxicol & Chem. *Mailing Add:* Dept Pharmacol Sch Med Univ Minn Duluth MN 55812-2403

**WALLACE, KYLE DAVID,** MATHEMATICS. *Current Pos:* asst prof, 70-75, assoc prof, 75-80, PROF MATH, WESTERN KY UNIV, 80- *Personal Data:* b Nancy, Ky, Apr 3, 43; m 64; c 2. *Educ:* Eastern Ky State Col, BS, 63; Vanderbilt Univ, MS, 65, PhD(math), 70. *Prof Exp:* Instr math, Easten Ky Univ, 65-67. *Mem:* Math Asn Am. *Res:* Infinite Abelian groups; structure and classification of groups. *Mailing Add:* 1327 Western Ave Bowling Green KY 42104-3351

**WALLACE, LANCE ARTHUR,** HUMAN EXPOSURE ASSESSMENT, RELATION OF EXPOSURE TO BODY BURDEN. *Current Pos:* MEM STAFF ENVIRON SCI, US ENVIRON PROTECTION AGENCY, 77- *Personal Data:* b San Francisco, Calif, Dec 29, 38; m 64, 75; c 2. *Educ:* Univ Wash, BA, 59; City Univ NY, PhD(physics), 73. *Prof Exp:* Asst prof physics & astron, Rose-Hulman Inst Technol, 73-75; staff assoc, Nat Acad Sci, 75-77. *Concurrent Pos:* Vis prof, Sch Pub Health, Harvard Univ, 84-86. *Mem:* AAAS; Am Cancer Soc. *Res:* Measurement of human exposure to environmental pollutants and associated body burden; development of personal air quality monitors for volatile organic compounds, carbon monoxide, respirable particles and pesticides; large scale (100-1000 persons) field studies of exposure. *Mailing Add:* 11568 Woodhollow Ct Reston VA 20191

**WALLACE, LARRY J,** ORTHOPEDIC SURGERY, SPINE SURGERY. *Current Pos:* assoc prof, 72-74, PROF ORTHOP SURG, UNIV MINN, 74- *Personal Data:* b South Lyon, Mich, Sept 17, 37; m 58, Eileen M Stickler; c Steven, Cheryl & Kathryn. *Educ:* Mich State Univ, BS, 60, DVM, 62, MS, 64; Am Col Vet Surgeons, dipl, 70. *Prof Exp:* Asst instr surg & intern med, Mich State Univ, 62-63; asst prof exp path, Lab Animal Med, Univ Fla, 63-66; asst prof surg, Kans State Univ, 66-69, assoc prof, 69-72. *Concurrent Pos:* Dir surg residencies, Col Vet Med, Univ Minn, 72-87, head, Div Small Animal Surg, 73-78 & 84-87; consult vet, Cardiac Pacemakers, Inc, St Paul, 78-87; lectr orthop surg, Ohio State Univ, 82; mem, Comt Vet Tech Educ & Activ, Am Vet Med Asn, 92- *Mem:* Am Col Vet Surg (vpres, 76-77, pres 78-79); Am Vet Med Asn; Am Animal Hosp Asn; Vet Orthop Soc; Sigma Xi; Am Asn Vet Clinicians. *Res:* Joint transplantation; bone grafting; bone healing; methods for the fixation of fractures; arthritis; reconstructive surgery; joint prostheses; growth deformities of bone; hip dysplasia; bone banking; bone infections; experimental surgery; spine surgery. *Mailing Add:* 233 17th Ave NW New Brighton MN 55112-7169. *Fax:* 612-624-0751

**WALLACE, MARION BROOKS,** ENTOMOLOGY. *Current Pos:* RETIRED. *Personal Data:* b Mankato, Minn, Dec 17, 17; m 36, 75; c 1. *Educ:* Univ Minn, BA, 47, MS, 50, PhD(zool), 54. *Prof Exp:* Res fel, Univ Minn, St Paul, 54-56, from instr to assoc prof, 56-71, prof entom, 71-86. *Mem:* NY Acad Sci; Entom Soc Am; Soc Invert Path; Am Soc Zoologists; Tissue Cult Asn. *Res:* Insect tissue culture; physiology of intracellular symbiotes; infectious diseases; nutrition and development of insects. *Mailing Add:* 2603 Cohansey St Roseville MN 55113

**WALLACE, MICHAEL DWIGHT,** process control engineering, chemical engineering, for more information see previous edition

**WALLACE, PAUL FRANCIS,** surface chemistry, for more information see previous edition

**WALLACE, PAUL WILLIAM,** MECHANICAL ENGINEERING, MANUFACTURING ENGINEERING. *Current Pos:* GEN MGR, INGERSOLL RAND, 93- *Personal Data:* b Cork, Ireland, Dec 27, 36, US citizen; m 64, Margaret Malone; c Karen, Ian, Michael & David. *Educ:* Col Technol, Dublin, BS, 58; Univ Salford, MS, 62; Univ Bristol, PhD(mech eng), 65; Irish Mgt Inst, Gen Mgt Dipl, 72; Univ Dublin, MA, 81. *Honors & Awards:* James Clayton Prize, Inst Mech Eng, 85. *Prof Exp:* Engr, Unidare Ltd, Dublin, 58-60; res asst, Univ Salford, 60-62; res engr, Univ Bristol, 62-65; res metallurgist, IIT Res Inst, Chicago, 65-68; mgr, Mat Develop, SPS Technol, 68-69, mgr, Irish Lab, 70-76, dir res & develop, 76-80, vpres eng, 83-85, pres, Assembly Systs Div, 85-93. *Concurrent Pos:* Prof & head, Dept Mech Eng, Trinity Col, Dublin, Ireland, 80-82. *Mem:* Inst Mech Engrs, London; Am Soc Mech Engrs; Soc Mfg Eng. *Res:* Mechanics; metallurgy; machine tools; metal working; automatic control; adhesive and mechanical fastening. *Mailing Add:* Ingersoll-Rand Fastner Tightening Syst 8 Bartles Corner Pl Suite 101 Flemington NJ 08822

**WALLACE, PHILIP RUSSELL,** SOLIDS IN STRONG MAGNETIC FIELDS, PHILOSOPHY OF QUANTUM MECHANICS. *Current Pos:* from assoc prof to prof appl math, McGill Univ, 46-61, dir, Inst Theoret Physics, 66-70, MacDonald prof, 72-81, PROF PHYSICS, MCGILL UNIV, 61-, EMER PROF APPL MATH, 82- *Personal Data:* b Toronto, Ont, Apr 19, 15; m 40, Jean E Young; c Michael D, Kathryn J & Robert P. *Educ:* Univ Toronto, BA, 37, MA, 38, PhD, 40. *Prof Exp:* Instr math, Univ Cincinnati, 40-42; instr, Mass Inst Technol, 42; assoc res physicist, Atomic Energy Div, Nat Res Coun, Can, 43-46. *Concurrent Pos:* Vis scientist, Dept Theoret Physics, Oxford, 65-66 & 73; mem comn higher educ, Super Coun Educ, Que, 70-73; mem grant selection comt physics, Nat Res Coun Can, 71-74; vis prof, Univ Paul Sabatier, Toulouse, France, 72-73 & 81-82; ed, Can J Physics, 72-80; mem, Int Adv Comt, Int Conf Semiconductors Edinburgh, 78, Kyoto, 80, Montpellier, 82; prin, Sci Col, Concordia Univ, 84-87. *Mem:* Am Phys Soc; Am Asn Physics Teachers; Can Asn Physicists; Europ Phys Soc; fel Royal Soc Can; NY Acad Sci; hon fel Nat Acad Sci India. *Res:* Theoretical physics: relativity, solid state, semiconductors; physics of semiconductors and semimetals in intense magnetic fields; radar meteorology; foundations of quantum mechanics. *Mailing Add:* 104-1039 Linden Ave Victoria BC V8V 4H3 Can. *E-Mail:* 104-prw@islandnet.com

**WALLACE, RAYMOND HOWARD, JR,** GEOPRESSURED-GEOTHERMAL ENERGY RESEARCH, CONTINENTAL SCIENTIFIC DRILLING TECHNOLOGY. *Current Pos:* geologist, US Geol Surv, 66-69, hydrologist, 69-74, res proj chief, 75-83, geothermal liaison, 84-87, LIAISON, HIGH-LEVEL RADIOACTIVE WASTE MGT, US GEOL SURV, 87- *Personal Data:* b Columbus, Ga, July 29, 36; m 58, Katharine Ritter; c Raymond H III & M Haviland. *Educ:* Fla State Univ, BS, 60; La State Univ, MS, 66. *Honors & Awards:* Super Serv Award, Dept Interior, 82. *Prof Exp:* Res asst, La Water Resources Res Inst, 65-66. *Concurrent Pos:* Geol consult, 65; teaching asst phys geol, La State Univ, 64-65; geologist-trainee, Gulf Oil Corp, 64; dep chief, Gulf Coast Hydrosci Ctr, US Geol Surv, 74-83; geothermal tech adv, US Dept Energy, 75-, geothermal prog mgr, 84-87; mem, Task Force Non-Conventional Gas, Fed Energy Regulatory Comn, 75-78 & Hydrocarbon Geosci Res Coord Comt, Dept Energy, 88-89; sci tech adv & mgr, Nat Continental Sci Drilling, US Geol Surv & Dept Energy, 84- *Mem:* Geol Soc Am; Am Asn Petrol Geologists; Sigma Xi. *Res:* Deep-basin hydrogeologic research and geothermal resources; scientific drilling activities related to geothermal resources and geologic disposal of radioactive wastes; author of 28 publications. *Mailing Add:* 6663 Tennyson Dr McLean VA 22101-5716

**WALLACE, RICHARD KENT,** NUCLEAR ASTROPHYSICS, RADIATION HYDRODYNAMICS. *Current Pos:* MEM STAFF, LOS ALAMOS NAT LAB, 81- *Personal Data:* b Washington, DC, Jan 29, 54; m 76; c 1. *Educ:* La State Univ, Baton Rouge, BS, 75; Univ Calif, Santa Cruz, MS, 77, PhD(astrophys), 81. *Mem:* Am Astron Soc. *Res:* Basic thermonuclear burn physics; laser fusion target physics; applications to astrophyscics includes nucleosynthesis and nuclear sources for novae, supernovae and x- and gamma-ray bursts. *Mailing Add:* 25 Los Arboles Dr Los Alamos NM 87544

**WALLACE, ROBERT B,** PSYCHOBIOLOGY, NEUROANATOMY. *Current Pos:* from asst prof to assoc prof, 68-80, chair, Dept Psychol, 86-91, PROF PSYCHOL & BIOL, UNIV HARTFORD, 80-, CHAIR, DEPT BIOL, 94- *Personal Data:* b Stoneham, Mass, Jan 16, 37. *Educ:* Boston Univ, AB, 60, AM, 61, PhD(psychol), 66. *Prof Exp:* Instr psychol, 66-67, lectr, 67-68. *Concurrent Pos:* Res assoc, Mass Inst Technol, 66-68 & Inst Living, 71-; consult, Dept Biol Sci, Purdue Univ, 68-70; vis assoc prof, Univ Conn Health Ctr, 74-77, res assoc, 78; dir, Neurosci Prog, Univ Hartford, 76- *Mem:* AAAS; Am Asn Anat; Soc Neurosci; Psychonomic Soc; NY Acad Sci; Am Psychol Soc; Europ Soc Comp Endocrinol; Int Neuropsychol Soc; Int Brain Res Orgn; Sigma Xi. *Res:* Relation of central nervous system structure to behavior; plasticity of mammalian nervous system; postnatal neurogenesis; neural transplantation. *Mailing Add:* Univ Hartford Dept Psychol 200 Bloomfield Ave West Hartford CT 06117. *Fax:* 860-768-5292; *E-Mail:* rwallace@uhavax.hartford.edu

**WALLACE, ROBERT EARL,** GEOLOGY. *Current Pos:* RETIRED. *Personal Data:* b New York, NY, July 16, 16; m 45; c 1. *Educ:* Northwestern Univ, BS, 38; Calif Inst Technol, MS, 40, PhD(struct geol, vert paleont), 46. *Honors & Awards:* Medal, Seismol Soc Am, 89. *Prof Exp:* Geologist, US Geol Surv, 42-70, chief, Southwestern Br, 60-65, regional geologist, 70-73, chief scientist, Off Earthquake Studies, 73-87. *Concurrent Pos:* From asst prof to assoc prof, Wash State Univ, 46-51; vis lectr, Stanford Univ, 60; mem comt seismol, Nat Acad Sci-Nat Res Coun; chmn, US/USSR Environ Agreement, US Working Group Earthquake Prediction; mem eng criteria rev bd, San Francisco Bay Conserv & Develop Comn, 78-, chmn, 81-90. *Mem:* Fel Geol Soc Am; Soc Econ Geol; Seismol Soc Am; Earthquake Eng Res Inst; fel AAAS. *Res:* Active faults; tectonics; earthquakes; engineering geology and environment; mineral deposits. *Mailing Add:* 240 Cervantes Rd Portola Valley CA 94028

**WALLACE, ROBERT WILLIAM,** SCIENCE EDUCATION, ENVIRONMENTAL CHEMISTRY. *Current Pos:* ASST PROF CHEM, BENTLEY COL, 72- *Personal Data:* b Central Falls, RI, Jan 1, 43; m 65; c 2. *Educ:* Providence Col, BS, 64; Niagara Univ, MS, 66; Boston Univ, PhD(chem), 73. *Mem:* Am Chem Soc; AAAS. *Res:* Air and water quality as well as the quality of consumer products, including chemical composition versus the list of ingredients. *Mailing Add:* 19 Coolidge Ave Westford MA 01886-1807

**WALLACE, ROBIN A,** REPRODUCTIVE BIOLOGY. *Current Pos:* PROF ANAT & CELL BIOL, WHITNEY LAB, ST AUGUSTINE, 84- *Personal Data:* b Chicago, Ill, Nov 11, 33; m 55, 84; c 2. *Educ:* Columbia Univ, BA, 55, PhD(zool), 61. *Prof Exp:* Res assoc, Sloan-Kettering Inst, NY, 57; consult, Oak Ridge Nat Lab, 60-61, USPHS fel, 61-63, staff mem biol div, 63-81; vis prof, Anat Dept, Col Med, Univ Fla, Gainesville, 81-84. *Concurrent Pos:* Vis investr, Nat Res Coun Can, 63-64; mem, Marine Biol Lab Corp; dir reprod biol prog, Marine Biol Lab, Woods Hole, 74 & 75; co-ed, Develop Biol, 72-74; mem develop biol panel, NSF, 75-76. *Mem:* AAAS; Am Soc Biochem Molecular Biol; Soc Develop Biol; Fedn Am Sci; Am Soc Ichthyol Herpetol; Int Soc Develop Biol. *Res:* Comparative biochemical studies on yolk proteins and the mechanisms of oocyte growth in vertebrates. *Mailing Add:* Whitney Lab 9505 Ocean Shore Blvd St Augustine FL 32086-8623

**WALLACE, RONALD GARY,** GEOMORPHOLOGY, PETROLEUM GEOLOGY. *Current Pos:* PROF GEOL & CHMN DEPT, EASTERN ILL UNIV, 70- *Personal Data:* b Cadiz, Ohio, July 6, 38; m 65; c 2. *Educ:* Kent State Univ, BS, 61; Ohio State Univ, MS, 64, PhD(geol), 67. *Prof Exp:* Petroleum geologist, Stand Oil Co, Tex, 67-69; asst prof geol, Ohio State Univ, 69-70. *Mem:* Am Asn Petrol Geol. *Res:* Alpine mass movement; strip mine erosion. *Mailing Add:* Dept Geog & Geol Eastern Ill Univ 600 Lincoln Ave Charleston IL 61920-3011

**WALLACE, RUSSELL JOHN,** PLASMA PHYSICS. *Current Pos:* RES SCIENTIST, LAWRENCE LIVERMORE NAT LAB. *Honors & Awards:* Excellence in Plasma Physics Award, Am Physics Soc, 95. *Mailing Add:* Lawrence Livermore Nat Lab MS L482 PO Box 808 Livermore CA 94550

**WALLACE, SIDNEY,** RADIOLOGY. *Current Pos:* assoc prof, 66-69, prof, 69-80, ASHBEL SMITH PROF RADIOL, M D ANDERSON HOSP & TUMOR INST, UNIV TEX, HOUSTON, 80- *Personal Data:* b Philadelphia, Pa, Feb 26, 29; c 3. *Educ:* Temple Univ, BA, 49, MD, 54; Am Bd Radiol, dipl, 62. *Prof Exp:* Intern, Philadelphia Gen Hosp, 54-55; resident radiol, Hosp, Jefferson Med Col, 59-62, from instr to asst prof, Col, 62-66. *Concurrent Pos:* Fel radiol, Univ Lund, 63-64. *Mem:* AMA; Am Col Radiol; Int Soc Lymphology. *Res:* Lymphangiography and angiography. *Mailing Add:* M D Anderson Cancer Ctr Univ Tex 1515 Holcomb Blvd Houston TX 77030-4009

**WALLACE, STEPHEN JOSEPH,** THEORETICAL NUCLEAR PHYSICS. *Current Pos:* from asst prof to assoc prof, 74-82, PROF PHYSICS, UNIV MD, COLLEGE PARK, 82-, CHAIR, PHYSICS DEPT, 94- *Personal Data:* b Youngstown, Ohio, May 10, 39; m 61; c 2. *Educ:* Case Inst Technol, BS, 61; Univ Wash, MS, 69, PhD(physics), 71. *Prof Exp:* Res engr, Boeing Co, 61-68; res asst physics, Univ Wash, 68-71; res assoc, Univ Fla, 71-72 & Harvard Univ, 72-74. *Concurrent Pos:* Donders chmn, Univ Utricht, 88; Scheinbrun vis prof, Hebrew Univ, 88. *Mem:* Am Phys Soc. *Res:* Relativistic dynamics of nuclei; relativistic bound states; electromagnetic interactions. *Mailing Add:* Dept Physics Univ Md College Park MD 20742

**WALLACE, STEWART RAYNOR,** ECONOMIC GEOLOGY, METALS. *Current Pos:* CONSULT, 76- *Personal Data:* b Freeport, NY, Mar 31, 19; div; c William D & Margaret B. *Educ:* Dartmouth Col, BA, 41; Univ Mich, MS, 48, PhD(geol), 53. *Honors & Awards:* D C Jackling Award, Am Inst Mining, Metal & Petrol Engrs, 74; Distinguished Mem, Soc Mining Engrs, 84. *Prof Exp:* Geologist, US Geol Surv, 48-55; resident geologist, Climax Molybdenum Co, 55-58, chief geologist, 58-64, chief geol & explor, 64-69; pres & dir explor, Mine Finders, Inc, 70-75. *Mem:* Geol Soc Am; Am Inst Mining, Metall & Petrol Engrs; Soc Econ Geol (pres, 93). *Res:* Geophysical properties of upper crust and composition of near-surface lithologics relative to genesis of high grade climax-type molybdenum orebodies unique to Colorado; relation of precambrian and tertiary tectonic features to causative magma generation and distribution of deposits. *Mailing Add:* 8700 W 14th Ave Lakewood CO 80215

**WALLACE, SUSAN SCHOLES,** MOLECULAR BIOLOGY, BIOPHYSICS. *Current Pos:* PROF & CHAIRPERSON MICROBIOL & MOLECULAR GENETICS, UNIV VT, 88- *Personal Data:* b Brooklyn, NY, Jan 10, 38; c 3. *Educ:* Marymount Col, NY, BS, 59; Univ Calif, Berkeley, MS, 61; Cornell Univ, PhD(biophys), 65. *Honors & Awards:* Aaron Bendich Award, 84. *Prof Exp:* USPHS fel, Columbia Univ, 65-67; instr biol sci, Lehman Col, 67-68, asst prof, 69-73, assoc prof, 73-76; from assoc prof to prof microbiol, NY Med Col, 76-88. *Concurrent Pos:* City Univ New York res grant, Lehman Col, 68-76, NIH res grant, 72-; vis prof, Albert Einstein Col Med, 74-75; scholar, Am Cancer Soc, 74-75; mem, NIH Radiation Study Sect, 77-81; Dept Energy res grant, 77- *Mem:* AAAS; Biophys Soc; Radiation Res Soc (pres, 91-92); Am Soc Microbiologists; Am Soc Biol Chemists; Am Soc Photobiol. *Res:* Quantitation and repair of DNA damage in bacteria and bacteriophages; in vivo and in vitro processing and repair of ionizing radiation and oxidative DNA damage. *Mailing Add:* Dept Microbiol Univ Vt Stafford Hall Burlington VT 05405-0001. *Fax:* 802-656-8749

**WALLACE, SUSAN ULMER,** CROP PHYSIOLOGY. *Current Pos:* From asst prof to assoc prof, 80-90, PROF AGRON, CLEMSON UNIV, 90- *Personal Data:* b Demopolis, Ala, Jan 31, 52; m 81. *Educ:* Univ Ala, BS, 73, MS, 75; Iowa State Univ, PhD(agron), 79. *Mem:* Am Soc Agron; Crop Sci Soc Am; Am Soc Plant Physiologists. *Res:* Production-oriented physiology of soybeans and other field crops; crop plant tolerance to environmental stress. *Mailing Add:* Dept Agron & Soils Clemson Univ Clemson SC 29634-0001

**WALLACE, TERRY CHARLES, SR,** MATERIALS CHEMISTRY, CHEMICAL TECHNOLOGY. *Current Pos:* RETIRED. *Personal Data:* b Phoenix, Ariz, May 18, 33; m 55, Jeannette Owens; c Terry C Jr, Randall J, Timothy A, Janice (Crabtree) & Sheryl (Parra). *Educ:* Ariz State Univ, BS, 55; Iowa State Univ, PhD(phys chem), 58. *Honors & Awards:* Fed Lab Consortium Award, 88. *Prof Exp:* Mem staff, Los Alamos Nat Lab, Univ Calif, 58-70, alt group leader, 70-79, group leader, 79-83, assoc div leader, 83-87, prog mgr, 87-88, tech prog coordr, 88-91, assoc mem staff, 91-93; consult, Sci Applns Int Corp, 94-95. *Concurrent Pos:* Chief tech projs br, Environ Test Div, Dugway Proving Ground, 59-61; consult, Hercules Aerospace, 91-92; EG&G, Idaho, 92. *Mem:* AAAS; Am Chem Soc; fel Am Inst Chem. *Res:* Structural properties and mass transport of materials at high temperature; materials synthesis; materials characterization; high temperature thermodynamics; chemical vapor deposition; modeling of high temperature chemical processes. *Mailing Add:* 146 Monte Rey S Los Alamos NM 87544. *Fax:* 505-672-0068; *E-Mail:* wallace@trail.com

**WALLACE, TERRY CHARLES, JR,** SEISMOLOGY, CRUSTAL DYNAMICS. *Current Pos:* From asst prof to assoc prof, 88-92, PROF SEISMOL, DEPT GEOSCI, UNIV ARIZ, 92-, PROF, APPL MATH PROG, 92- *Personal Data:* b Ames, Iowa, June 30, 56; m 88, Michelle Hall; c David. *Educ:* NMex Inst Mining Technol, BS(geophys) & BS(math), 78; Calif Inst Technol, MS, 80, PhD(geophys), 83. *Honors & Awards:* James B Macelvane Medal, Am Geophys Union, 92. *Concurrent Pos:* Cur, Univ Ariz, Mineral Mus, 85-; vpres, Mineral Rec, 92-94. *Mem:* Seismog Soc Am; Am Geophys Union; AAAS. *Res:* Computational Seismology; global crustal structure; explosion source physics; tectonics. *Mailing Add:* Dept Geosci Univ Ariz Bldg 77 Tucson AZ 85721

**WALLACE, THOMAS PATRICK,** physical chemistry, polymer science, for more information see previous edition

**WALLACE, TRACY I,** INTERNAL MEDICINE. *Current Pos:* FAC, DEPT INTERNAL MED, TEX A&M UNIV. *Personal Data:* b Irvine, Ky, Nov 20, 24; m 51; c 3. *Educ:* Univ Ky, BS, 46; Univ Cincinnati, MD, 49. *Prof Exp:* Staff physician, Vet Admin Hosp, McKinney, Tex, 55-57, asst chief med serv, Temple Vet Admin Hosp, 57-59, chief med serv, 61- *Mem:* AMA. *Res:* Adrenal function in patients with pulmonary emphysema and other hypoxic states. *Mailing Add:* 3609 Deer Trail Vet Admin Hosp Temple TX 76504

**WALLACE, VICTOR LEW,** OPERATING SYSTEMS, GRAPHICS. *Current Pos:* chmn, 76-84, PROF COMPUT SCI, UNIV KANS, 76- *Personal Data:* b Brooklyn, NY, Mar 20, 33; m 62, Mary Jamieson; c Robert & Andrew. *Educ:* Polytech Inst Brooklyn, BS, 55; Univ Mich, PhD(elec eng), 69. *Prof Exp:* Mem tech staff syst eng, Bell Tel Labs, 55-56; mathematician-programmer, IBM Corp, 56-57; instr elec eng, Univ Mich, 57-62; assoc res scientist, 62-69; assoc prof comput sci, Univ NC, 69-76. *Concurrent Pos:* Vis scientist, Imp Col, Univ London, 70. *Mem:* Asn Comput Mach; Inst Elec & Electronics Engrs; Int Ref Orgn Forensic Med & Sci; Am Asn Univ Professors; Sigma Xi. *Res:* Computer system modeling; operating system theory; computer graphics software; man-machine interface in computer-aided design; queueing theory. *Mailing Add:* 1509 Massachusetts St Lawrence KS 66044. *E-Mail:* wallace@ukans.edu

**WALLACE, VOLNEY,** AGRICULTURAL CHEMISTRY, ANALYTICAL CHEMISTRY. *Current Pos:* RETIRED. *Personal Data:* b Idaho Falls, Idaho, Oct 9, 25; m 53; c 5. *Educ:* Univ Idaho, BS, 46; Purdue Univ, MS, 49, PhD(agr chem), 53. *Prof Exp:* Asst agr chem, Purdue Univ, 47-53; res assoc, Wash State Univ, 53-55; asst prof biochem, SDak State Col, 55-61; res chemist, Dugway Proving Ground, 61-90. *Res:* Agricultural and analytical chemistry. *Mailing Add:* 72 W 61 S Murray UT 84107

**WALLACE, WILLIAM,** MATERIALS ENGINEERING, METALLURGY. *Current Pos:* assoc res officer, Nat Res Coun Can, 67-70, assoc res officer, 70-76, head, Mat Sect, 76-81, HEAD, STRUCT & MAT LAB, NAT AERONAUT ESTAB CAN, NAT RES COUN CAN, 81-, DIR, STRUCT & MAT LAB, INST AEROSPACE RES, 92-, DIR, STRUCT MAT & PROPULSION LAB, 93- *Personal Data:* b Manchester, Eng, Oct 15, 40, Can citizen; m 64, Monica Elizabeth; c 3. *Educ:* Manchester Univ, BSc, 63; Victoria Univ Manchester, PhD(metall), 66. *Honors & Awards:* Dofasco Award for Mat Eng, Can Inst Mining & Metall. *Prof Exp:* Lectr, John Dalton Col Technol, 66-67. *Concurrent Pos:* Hon adj prof, Dept mech & Aeronaut Eng, Carleton Univ, Ottawa, Dept Mech Eng, Univ Toronto, Ont; mem adv group aerospace res & develop, NATO, mat panel, chmn, 83-84. *Mem:* Fel Inst Mat UK; fel Am Soc Mining Metall & Petrol Engrs; fel Can Aerospace Inst; Can Asn Composite Structures & Mat; fel Can Aeronautics & Space Inst. *Res:* Metal processing; powder metallurgy; isothermal and superplastic forging; mechanical behavior, creep, fatigue, and fracture; airframe and engine structural technology; corrosion; aerospace structural engineering. *Mailing Add:* Struct Mat & Propulsion Lab NRC Inst Aerospace Res Montreal Rd Ottawa ON K1A 0R6 Can. *Fax:* 613-990-7444; *E-Mail:* bill.wallace@nrc.ca

**WALLACE, WILLIAM DONALD,** SOLID STATE PHYSICS. *Current Pos:* asst prof, 70-74, ASSOC PROF PHYSICS, OAKLAND UNIV, 74- *Personal Data:* b Detroit, Mich, Sept 19, 33; m; c 2. *Educ:* Eastern Mich Univ, BA, 55; Univ Md, College Park, MS, 60; Wayne State Univ, PhD(physics), 66. *Prof Exp:* Asst prof physics, Eastern Mich Univ, 59-62; res asst, Cornell Univ, 67-70. *Concurrent Pos:* Leverhulme vis fel, Univ Essex, 66-67. *Mem:* Am Phys Soc; Am Asn Physics Teachers. *Res:* Ultrasonic properties and magnetic properties of solids; amorphous materials and low temperature physics. *Mailing Add:* 70 Poplar St Wyandotte MI 48192

**WALLACE, WILLIAM EDWARD,** MATERIALS SCIENCE, RARE EARTHS. *Current Pos:* PROF APPL SCI & ENG, CARNEGIE-MELLON UNIV, 83- *Personal Data:* b Fayette, Miss, Mar 11, 17; m 47; c 3. *Educ:* Miss Col, BA, 36; Univ Pittsburgh, PhD(chem), 41. *Honors & Awards:* Morley Award, 83; Rare Earth F Spedding Award. *Prof Exp:* Asst, Univ Pittsburgh, 36-40; Carnegie Found fel, 40-42, sr res fel, 42-44; res assoc, Ohio State Univ, 44-45; from asst res prof to assoc res prof chem, Univ Pittsburgh, 45-53, chmn dept, 63-77, distinguished serv prof, 77-83, prof chem, 53-82. *Concurrent Pos:* Guggenheim fel, 54; consult numerous industs & govt agencies; pres, Adv Mat Corp, 84-93. *Mem:* Fel AAAS; Am Chem Soc; Sigma Xi. *Res:* Magnetic behavior and hydrogen absorption of intermetallic compounds containing lanthanides; high energy permanent magnets. *Mailing Add:* 201 Pinecrest Dr Pittsburgh PA 15237

**WALLACE, WILLIAM EDWARD, JR,** ENVIRONMENTAL HEALTH, RESPIRABLE PARTICLE SURFACE ANALYSIS & TOXICOLOGY. *Current Pos:* RES PHYSICIST & AEROSOL RES TEAM LEADER, DIV RESPIRATORY DIS STUDIES, NAT INST OCCUP SAFETY & HEALTH, 80-; RES ADV, NAT RES COUN, 90- *Personal Data:* b Charleston, WVa, Sept 25, 42; m 70, Elisabeth Fehl; c Sarah & David. *Educ:* WVa Univ, BS, 63, MS, 67, PhD(physics), 69. *Prof Exp:* Nat Res Coun-US Bur Mines res assoc, Morgantown Energy Res Ctr, US Bur Mines, 70-71, res physicist, 71-74; res physicist-asst dir, Morgantown Energy Technol Ctr, US Dept Energy, 75-80. *Concurrent Pos:* Adj prof, Dept Chem Eng, WVa Univ, 82- & Col Mineral & Energy Resources, 90-, grad fac, Col Eng, 88-; comt mem, Nat Res Coun, 82; monograph workshop mem, WHO-Int Agency Res Cancer, 83. *Mem:* Sigma Xi. *Res:* Spectroscopic methods development and bioassay methods development for analysis of respirable particle toxicity and pulmonary response. *Mailing Add:* Nat Inst Occup Safety & Health 1095 Willowdale Rd MS-3030 Morgantown WV 26505

**WALLACE, WILLIAM J,** PHYSICAL CHEMISTRY. *Current Pos:* from asst prof to assoc prof, Muskingum Col, 63-72, actg chmn dep, 68-69, chmn dept, 79-80 & 85-89, coordr, Sci Div, 72-76, PROF INORG & PHYS CHEM, MUSKINGUM COL, 72- *Personal Data:* b Knoxville, Tenn, July 27, 35; m 58; c 2. *Educ:* Carson-Newman Col, BS, 56; Purdue Univ, PhD(inorg chem), 61. *Prof Exp:* Asst prof inorg chem, Univ Miss, 60-63. *Concurrent Pos:* Res grants, Res Corp, 61-63 & Am Acad Arts & Sci, 62-63; dir, NSF Res Partic High Sch Teachers, 66, 67 & 68; res fel with P S Braterman, Univ Glasgow, 70-71; fac fel & res grants, Lewis Res Ctr, NASA, 78-80; vis fac fel, Fla State Univ, R J Clark, 87, 88 & 90. *Mem:* Am Chem Soc; Sigma Xi. *Res:* Study of systems using polyether solvents with inorganic compounds, especially solubility, reaction and spectral phenomena; iron carbonyl reactions with Lewis bases; electrocatalysis of chronium; reduction in flow cell; super conductor synthesis. *Mailing Add:* 177 N Liberty St New Concord OH 43762-9701

**WALLACE, WILLIAM JAMES LORD,** PHYSICAL CHEMISTRY. *Current Pos:* RETIRED. *Personal Data:* b Salisbury, NC, Jan 13, 08; m 29; c 1. *Educ:* Univ Pittsburgh, BS, 27; Columbia Univ, AM, 31; Cornell Univ, PhD(phys chem), 37; Livingstone Col, LLD, 59; Concord Col, LHD, 70; Alderson Broaddus Col, DSc, 71. *Honors & Awards:* Outstanding Civilian Serv Medal, Dept Army, 72; Annual Award, Educ Comn States, 75. *Prof Exp:* Instr chem, Livingston Col, 27-32; instr, Lincoln Univ, Mo, 32-33; from instr to prof, WVa State Col, 33-75, actg admin asst to pres, 44-45, admin asst, 45-50, actg pres, 52-53, pres, 53-73, emer pres, 73- *Concurrent Pos:* Mem, Kanawha County Pub Libr Bd, 68- *Mem:* Am Chem Soc; Sigma Xi. *Res:* Freezing points of aqueous solutions of alpha amino acids; teaching problems in general chemistry. *Mailing Add:* PO Box 417 Institute WV 25112-0417

**WALLACH, EDWARD ELIOT,** OBSTETRICS & GYNECOLOGY, REPRODUCTIVE ENDOCRINOLOGY. *Current Pos:* prof & chmn, Dept Gynec & Obstet, 84-94, J DONALD WOODRUFF PROF GYNEC, DEPT GYNEC & OBSTET, JOHNS HOPKINS SCH MED, 94- *Personal Data:* b Brooklyn, NY, Oct 8, 33; m 56, Joanne Wallach; c Paul & Julie. *Educ:* Swarthmore Col, BA, 54; Cornell Univ, MD, 58; Nat Bd Med Examr, dipl, 59; Am Bd Obstet & Gynec, dipl, 66, dipl reproductive endocrinol, 75. *Hon Degrees:* MA, Univ Pa, 70. *Honors & Awards:* Serono lectr, Am Fertil Soc, 84; Robert B Greenblatt lectr, Med Col Ga, 88; Isadore Seigel Mem lectr, Univ Md, 91; Alvin F Goldfarb Lectr, Vanderbilt Univ, 96. *Prof Exp:* Intern internal med, Cornell Med Div, Bellevue Hosp, NY, 58-59; resident obstet & gynec, Kings Co Hosp, 59-63; surgeon, Div Indian Health & chief, Indian Hosp, USPHS, Tuba City, Ariz, 63-65; assoc, Sch Med, Univ Pa, 65-66, from asst prof to prof, 66-84. *Concurrent Pos:* Res fel reproductive physiol, Worcester Found Exp Biol, 61-62; Josiah Macy Jr Found fel, 65-, Lalor Found fel, 67-69; dir obstet & gynec, Pa Hosp, 71-84; consult, US Naval Hosp, Philadelphia, 74-84; vis prof, Dept Obstet & Gynec, Kyoto Univ Med Sch, Japan, 81-82 & 87; mem, Pop Res Comt, Nat Inst Child Health & Develop, 86-90; prof, joint appt, Dept Pop Dynamics & Sch Hyg & Pub Health, John Hopkins Univ, 91-93. *Mem:* Inst Med-Nat Acad Sci; Soc Gynec Invest (pres, 86-87); Am Fertil Soc (pres, 85-86); Soc Study Reproduction; Endocrine Soc; AAAS; Am Asn Hist Med; Am Col Surgeons; Asn Planned Parenthood Physicians; Am Col Obstetricians & Gynecologists; Am Gynec & Obstet Soc. *Res:* Reproductive biology; ovarian physiology; gynecologic endocrinology; infertility; family planning; periovulatory interval-follicle maturation, mechanism of ovulation, attainment of oocyte maturity and corpus luteum formation. *Mailing Add:* Johns Hopkins Hosp 600 N Wolfe St Houck 201 Baltimore MD 21287-1201

**WALLACH, JACQUES BURTON,** MEDICINE, PATHOLOGY. *Current Pos:* From instr to asst prof, 54-59, VIS ASST PROF PATH, ALBERT EINSTEIN COL MED, 59-; CLIN PROF PATH, HEALTH SCI CTR, STATE UNIV NY, BROOKLYN, 79- *Personal Data:* b New York, NY, Jan 25, 26; m 53, Doris Foss; c Kim, Lisa (Auteri) & Tracy. *Educ:* Long Island Col Med, MD, 47; Am Bd Path, dipl, 55. *Concurrent Pos:* Resident fel & asst pathologist, Queens Gen Hosp Ctr, NY, 48-55; asst vis pathologist, Bronx Munic Hosp Ctr, 54-59; consult, NY Zool Park, 54-84; vis asst prof, Rutgers Med Sch, Col Med & Dent NJ, 69-72, vis assoc prof, 72-; fel, Nat Libr Med, Comput Med, Mt Sinai Sch Med, New York, NY, 78-79; hon prof, Nat Univ Ica, Peru, 81. *Mem:* Fel Am Soc Clin Path; fel Col Am Path; fel Am Col Physicians; NY Acad Sci; fel NY Acad Med. *Res:* Rheumatic heart disease; clinical pathology; comparative pathology; computers in interpretative medical laboratory reporting. *Mailing Add:* 10 Ashbourne Dr Cranbury NJ 08512-4655

**WALLACH, MARSHALL BEN,** NEUROPHARMACOLOGY. *Current Pos:* staff researcher II, Syntex Res, 73-76, sr staff researcher, 76-79, prin scientist, 79-83, head dept neuropharmacol, 83-86, MGR BIOL INFO, SYNTEX RES, 87- *Personal Data:* b Buffalo, NY, June 15, 40; m 63; c 3. *Educ:* Columbia Univ, BS, 62; Univ Minn, PhD(pharmacol), 67. *Prof Exp:* Assoc res scientist neuropharmacol, Dept Psychiat, Med Ctr, NY Univ, 68-70, res scientist, 70-71, instr, 71-72. *Concurrent Pos:* Consult, New York City Rand Inst, 71-72. *Mem:* AAAS; Am Soc Exp Pharmacol & Therapeut; Western Pharmacol Soc; Soc Neurosci. *Res:* Models of psychiatric and neurological diseases; electrophysiology of sleep; neurohumoral mechanisms; anorexigens; antidepressants; neuroleptics; analgesics; antiparkinsonian agents; anticonvulsants; antitussives and psychotomimetic agents. *Mailing Add:* 648 Towle Pl Palo Alto CA 94306. *Fax:* 650-855-5627

**WALLACH, STANLEY,** MEDICINE. *Current Pos:* chief med, Bay Pines Vet Admin Med Ctr, 83-90, PROF MED & ASSOC CHMN DEPT, COL MED, UNIV SFLA, 83- *Personal Data:* b Brooklyn, NY, Dec 10, 28; m 54, 73; c 8. *Educ:* Cornell Univ, AB, 48; Columbia Univ, MA, 49; State Univ NY, MD, 53. *Honors & Awards:* Hektoen Silver Award, AMA, 59; John B Johnson Award, Paget's Dis Found, 89. *Prof Exp:* Intern med, Univ Med Serv, Kings Co Hosp, Brooklyn, 53-54; resident, Col Med, Univ Utah, 54-56; clin & res fel, Mass Gen Hosp, 56-57; from instr to prof, NY Downstate Med Ctr, State Univ NY, 57-73, prog dir, USPHS Clin Res Ctr, 66-73; prof med & assoc chmn dept, Albany Med Col, 73-83; chief med, Albany Vet Admin Med Ctr, 73-83. *Concurrent Pos:* Vis physician, Kings Co Hosp, Brooklyn, 57-73; career scientist, Health Res Coun City New York, 61-71; consult, St Johns Episcopal Hosp, Brooklyn, 65-73; attend physician, State Univ Hosp, Brooklyn, 66-73; consult & lectr, US Naval Hosp, St Albans, NY, 66-73; res collabr, Med Dept, Brookhaven Nat Lab, 69-81; attend physician, Albany Med Ctr, 73-83; chmn, Med Adv Panel, Paget's Dis Found, mem bd dirs, 90- *Mem:* Asn Am Phys; Am Soc Clin Invest; fel Am Col Pharmacol; Am Soc Bone & Mineral Res; fel Am Col Nutrit (vpres, 83-85, pres-elect, 85-87, pres, 87-); Am Soc Magnesium Res. *Res:* Endocrine and metabolic diseases; radioisotopes; calcium, magnesium, trace element and mineral metabolism; metabolic bone disease. *Mailing Add:* 301 E 75th St Apt 18E New York NY 10021

**WALLACH, STEVEN J,** ELECTRICAL ENGINEERING, COMPUTER DESIGN. *Current Pos:* CHIEF TECHNOL OFFICER, CONVEX DIV, HEWLETT PACKARD, 82- *Personal Data:* b Brooklyn, NY, Sept 25, 45. *Educ:* Brooklyn Polytech, BS, 66; Univ Pa, MS, 68. *Mem:* Nat Acad Eng. *Mailing Add:* 3000 Waterview Pkwy Richardson TX 75080. *Fax:* 972-497-3331; *E-Mail:* wallach@convex.wp.com

**WALLACH, SYLVAN,** MATHEMATICS. *Current Pos:* chmn dept math, 62-72, PROF MATH, C W POST COL, LONG ISLAND UNIV, 62- *Personal Data:* b San Antonio, Tex, Jan 9, 14; m 38; c 5. *Educ:* Rutgers Univ, BS, 34; Johns Hopkins Univ, PhD(math), 48. *Prof Exp:* Chemist Mass & Waldstein Co, NJ, 36-38; patent examr, US Patent Off, Washington, DC, 38-42; indust analyst, War Prod Bd, 42-45; instr math, Johns Hopkins Univ, 48-49; sr scientist atomic power div, Westinghouse Elec Corp, 49-52; sr scientist, Walter Kidde Nuclear Labs, Inc, 52-57; asst proj mgr, Gibbs & Cox, Inc, 57-61. *Mem:* AAAS; Am Math Soc; Math Asn Am. *Mailing Add:* 101 Central Park W New York NY 10023

**WALLACK, PAUL MARK,** INDUSTRIAL ENGINEERING. *Current Pos:* PRES, WALCO CONSULT, INC, 88- *Personal Data:* b Girard, Kans, Aug 3, 27; m 50, 80; c 6. *Educ:* Univ Tulsa, BS, 50; Okla State Univ, MS, 56, PhD(indust eng), 67. *Prof Exp:* Div engr, Pure Oil Co, 50-55; supvr, Sandia Labs, 56-59; asst prof, Ariz State Univ, 59-62; assoc prof, Kans State Univ, 62-64; supvr, Space Div, Rockwell Corp, 64-67; staff specialist, Autonetics Div, 67-69; mgr prod eng, 69-74; mgr indust eng, Admiral Div, 74-75, staff specialist, Strategic Systs Div, 76-78, mgr advan mfg, Autonetics Strategic Systs Div, 78-84, eng staff specialist, Strategic Defense & Electro-Optical Systs Div, 84-87, prod oper specialist, Satellite & Space Electronics Systs Div, Rockwell Int, 87-88. *Concurrent Pos:* Consult, Sandia Corp, 63; lectr, Calif State Univ, Fullerton, 72-74 & 79-80; lectr, Prod Opers Mgmt, Univ Calif, Irvine, 88. *Mem:* Inst Indust Engrs. *Res:* Production design economics and forecasting; sources and statistics associated with inspector error; organization behavior and the management process. *Mailing Add:* 2306 Arbutus St Newport Beach CA 92660. *E-Mail:* drsk62a@prodigy.com

**WALLANDER, JEROME F,** FOOD SCIENCE, BIOCHEMISTRY *Current Pos:* Sr scientist, Mead Johnson Nutritionals, 67-71, assoc dir food prod develop, Mead Johnson & Co, 71-89, DIR, NUTRIT PROD DEVELOP, MEAD JOHNSON NUTRITIONALS, 90- *Personal Data:* b Cato, Wis, Aug 29, 39; m 65; c 3. *Educ:* Univ Wis, BS, 62, MS, 65, PhD(food sci), 68. *Mem:* Sigma Xi; Am Dairy Sci Asn; Inst Food Technol; Am Chem Soc. *Res:* Milk lipase and milk protein studies. *Mailing Add:* 714 S Willow Rd Evansville IN 47714

**WALLBANK, ALFRED MILLS,** VIROLOGY. *Current Pos:* RETIRED. *Personal Data:* b Farmington, Mich, May 13, 25; wid. *Educ:* Mich State Univ, BS, 48, MS, 53, PhD, 57. *Prof Exp:* Bacteriologist, Barry Labs, Inc, Mich, 48-50; bacteriologist, Blood Sterilization Proj, Henry Ford Hosp, Detroit, 50-52; asst microbiol & pub health, Mich State Univ, 53-56; res assoc & microbiologist, Duke Univ, 56-59; res asst prof microbiol & virologist, Sch Vet Med, Univ Pa, 59-66; head dept virol, Va Inst Sci Res, 66-67; assoc prof microbiol, Med Col, Univ Man, 67-90. *Mem:* Am Soc Microbiol; Am Asn Cancer Res; Can Col Microbiologists; Tissue Cult Asn; Am Acad Microbiol; Sigma Xi. *Res:* Virucides, disinfectants and biohazards. *Mailing Add:* 23 River Rd Winnipeg MB R2M 3Z1 Can

**WALLBRUNN, HENRY MAURICE,** ZOOLOGY. *Current Pos:* asst prof biol, 51-62, ASSOC PROF ZOOL, UNIV FLA, 63- *Personal Data:* b Chicago, Ill, Apr 30, 18; m 53; c 4. *Educ:* Univ Chicago, BS, 40, PhD, 51. *Prof Exp:* Instr zool, Univ Chicago, 50. *Concurrent Pos:* Fel statist & zool, Univ Chicago, 53-54. *Mem:* Genetics Soc Am; Soc Study Evolution. *Res:* Genetics; genetics and evolution of orchids. *Mailing Add:* 7016 NW 20th Pl Gainesville FL 32605

**WALLCAVE, LAWRENCE,** BIOCHEMISTRY. *Current Pos:* RETIRED. *Personal Data:* b Schenectady, NY, Apr 21, 26; m 65. *Educ:* Univ Calif, Berkeley, BS, 48; Calif Inst Technol, PhD, 53. *Prof Exp:* Assoc prof biochem, Eppley Inst Med Ctr, Univ Nebr, Omaha, 68-74, res prof, 74-81; consult, Calsec Consults, Inc, Berkeley, Calif, 81- *Res:* Chemical carcinogenesis; analytical biochemistry. *Mailing Add:* 6578 Birch Dr Santa Rosa CA 95404

**WALLE, THOMAS,** DRUG METABOLISM. *Current Pos:* from asst prof to assoc prof, 72-78, PROF PHARMACOL, MED UNIV SCI, 78- *Personal Data:* b Sweden, Sept 20, 38; m, U Kristina; c Jens P. *Educ:* Royal Inst Pharmacol, Sweden, BS, 65, PhD(bioanal chem), 68. *Prof Exp:* Asst prof, Univ Cincinnati, 70-72. *Mem:* Am Soc Pharmacol; Am Chem Soc; Am Soc Clin Pharmacol Ther. *Res:* Drug metabolism; carcinogenesis; sulfotransferases; stereochemistry; flavonoids; chemoprevention. *Mailing Add:* Dept Pharmacol Med Univ SC 171 Ashley Ave Charleston SC 29425-2251. *Fax:* 803-792-2475; *E-Mail:* tom__walle@smtpgw.musc.edu

**WALLEIGH, ROBERT S(HULER),** ELECTRICAL ENGINEERING. *Current Pos:* CONSULT, INST ELEC & ELECTRONICS ENGRS, 79- *Personal Data:* b Washington, DC, Mar 31, 15; m 38, Catherine Coulon; c Margaret (Shaffer) & Catherine (Carnevale). *Educ:* George Washington Univ, BS, 36. *Honors & Awards:* Gold Medal, Dept Com, 67. *Prof Exp:* Test engr, Gen Elec Co, 36-37; lighting & power apparatus specialist, Gen Elec Supply Corp, DC, 37-38; rating exam, US Civil Serv Comn, 38-39, secy, Bd US Civil Serv Exam, US Pub Rd Admin, 39-43; elec engr, Lab, Nat Bur Stand, 43, phys sci adminr, 43-53; phys sci adminr, Diamond Ord Fuze Labs, Ord Corps, US Dept Army, 53-55; assoc dir admin, Nat Bur Stand, 55-74, actg dep dir, 75-78, sr adv int affairs, 78-79. *Mem:* AAAS; Inst Elec & Electronics Engrs. *Res:* Radio; illumination engineering; electric apparatus and machinery; electronics management. *Mailing Add:* 5701 Springfield Dr Bethesda MD 20816-1237

**WALLEN, CLARENCE JOSEPH,** MATHEMATICS. *Current Pos:* Instr math, Loyola Marymount Univ, 46-48 & 56-57, from asst prof to assoc prof, 57-70, chmn dept, 70-73, PROF MATH, LOYOLA MARYMOUNT UNIV, LOS ANGELES, 70-, MEM BD TRUSTEES, 67- *Personal Data:* b Phoenix, Ariz, Oct 17, 16. *Educ:* St Louis Univ, BA, 45, MS, 46, PhD(math), 56; Alma Col, STL, 52. *Mem:* AAAS; Am Math Soc; Math Asn Am; Sigma Xi. *Res:* Limit theory in mathematics. *Mailing Add:* Dept Math PO Box 45041 Los Angeles CA 90045

**WALLEN, CYNTHIA ANNE,** EXPERIMENTAL THERAPEUTICS, CELL KINETICS. *Current Pos:* FAC, DEPT RADIOL, BOWMAN GRAY SCH MED, NC. *Personal Data:* b Asheville, NC, June 27, 52; m 80; c 2. *Educ:* Univ NC, Greensboro, BA, 74; Univ Rochester, MS, 78, PhD(biophys), 80. *Prof Exp:* Res assoc exp therapeut, Dept Radiol, Univ Utah, 80-82, res asst prof, 82-84; asst scientist radiation biophys, Univ Kans, 84- *Concurrent Pos:* Fel, Univ Utah, 80-81. *Mem:* Radiation Res Soc; Sigma Xi; Soc Anal Cytologists; Cell Kinetics Soc; Am Asn Cancer Res; NAm Hyperthermia Group. *Res:* The regulation of cell proliferation within tumors and the influence a cell's proliferative status has on determining its response to various treatment modalities such as x-ray, heat and nitro sources and their combinations. *Mailing Add:* Dept Radiol Bowman Gray Sch Med Ctr 300 S Hawthorne Blvd Winston Salem NC 27157-0002

**WALLEN, DONALD GEORGE,** ECOLOGY, ALGAL PHYSIOLOGICAL ECOLOGY. *Current Pos:* Asst prof, 70-75, ASSOC PROF BIOL, UNIV WINDSOR, 75- *Personal Data:* b Ont, Can, July 6, 33; m 65; c 2. *Educ:* Dalhousie Univ, BS, 61, MEd, 62; Simon Fraser Univ, MS, 67, PhD(algal physiol & ecol), 70. *Mem:* Am Soc Limnol & Oceanog; Phycol Soc Am; Can Soc Plant Physiol; Int Asn Theoret Appl Limnol. *Res:* Interrelationship between light quality, intensity and temperature on growth, photosynthesis and metabolism of algae; toxic substances, chromium and other heavy metal effects on growth and photosynthesis of diatoms, and phytoplankton assemblages in lakes Erie and St Clair; heterotrophic utilization of amino acids by algae. *Mailing Add:* Dept Biol Sci Univ Windsor Windsor ON N9B 3P4 Can

**WALLEN, LOWELL LAWRENCE,** BIO-ORGANIC CHEMISTRY. *Current Pos:* RETIRED. *Personal Data:* b Rockford, Ill, May 22, 21; m 49, Charlotte Broman; c Peter & Timothy. *Educ:* Wheaton Col, Ill, BS, 44; Univ Ark, MS, 48; Iowa State Col, PhD, 54. *Prof Exp:* Asst chemist, Goodyear Tire & Rubber Co, Ohio, 44-46; asst, Univ Ark, 46-48; asst, Iowa State Col, 51-54; biochemist, Northern Regional Res Ctr, USDA, 54-83; lab instr, Bradley Univ, 86-93. *Mem:* Am Chem Soc; Coblentz Soc; Am Oil Chem Soc. *Res:* Chemistry of fermentation products; microbiological type reactions; oxidation; reduction; fermentations; chemical structure elucidation; bio-organic chemistry; infrared spectroscopy; fatty acid chemistry; mycotoxin chemistry. *Mailing Add:* 2929 N Gale Ave Peoria IL 61604-2437

**WALLEN, STANLEY EUGENE,** dairy science, food safety, for more information see previous edition

**WALLENDER, WESLEY WILLIAM,** IRRIGATION ENGINEERING, WATER SCIENCE. *Current Pos:* PROF WATER SCI & IRRIG ENG, UNIV CALIF, DAVIS, 82- *Personal Data:* b Bismark, NDak, Feb 16, 54; m 78; c 2. *Educ:* Ore State Univ, BS, 76; Univ Calif, Davis, MS, 78; Utah State Univ, BS, 81, PhD(agr & irrigational eng), 82. *Prof Exp:* Consult eng, irrig, Keller Eng, 80-82. *Concurrent Pos:* Consult engr, 80- *Mem:* Am Soc Agr Engrs; Am Geophys Union; Sigma Xi. *Res:* Surface irrigation hydraulic modeling with stochastic inputs; spatial variability of infiltration characteristics related to optimization within environmental constraints; sprinkle irrigation hydraulics and optimization; volume variance relations on sampling. *Mailing Add:* 4208 Calmia Pl Davis CA 95616-5224

**WALLENFELDT, EVERT,** FOOD SCIENCE. *Current Pos:* prof dairy indust & food sci, 38-70, EMER PROF FOOD SCI, UNIV WIS-MADISON, 70- *Personal Data:* b Stanton, Iowa, June 26, 04; m 28, Ilma Zernpel; c 2. *Educ:* Iowa State Col, BS, 26; Cornell Univ, MS, 29. *Prof Exp:* Instr high sch, Wis, 26-28; dairy fieldman, Borden Farm Prod Co, Ill, 29-31, supvr spec prod & tech probs, 31-34; supvr, Borden-Wieland Co, 34-37; res bacteriologist, Borden Co, 37-38. *Mem:* AAAS; Am Dairy Sci Asn; Nat Environ Health Asn; Int Asn Milk, Food & Environ Sanitarians. *Res:* Market milk; butter manufacturing; concentrated milks and related products. *Mailing Add:* 6209 Mineral Pt Rd Madison WI 53705

**WALLENFELS, MIKLOS,** MECHANICAL ENGINEERING. *Current Pos:* Engr, 59-62, res engr, 62-69, ASSOC ENGR, YERKES RES & DEVELOP, E I DU PONT DE NEMOURS & CO, INC, 69- *Personal Data:* b Budapest, Hungary, July 14, 34; US citizen; m 57; c 2. *Educ:* Budapest Tech Univ, BS, 56; Univ Buffalo, MS, 62. *Mem:* Soc Plastics Engrs. *Res:* Process development for manufacturing and coating thermoplastic films. *Mailing Add:* 1329 Corridae St Carlsbad CA 92009

**WALLENMEYER, WILLIAM ANTON,** HIGH ENERGY PHYSICS. *Current Pos:* RETIRED. *Personal Data:* b Evansville, Ind, Feb 3, 26; m 52, Diane M Hankins; c Wendy S (Kauffman), Jon D, Ann R (Ellis) & Timothy D. *Educ:* Purdue Univ, BS, 50, MS, 54, PhD(physics), 57. *Hon Degrees:* DSc, Purdue Univ, 89. *Prof Exp:* Asst physics, Purdue Univ, 50-54 & 56; jr res assoc high energy particle interactions, Brookhaven Nat Lab, 54-55; asst prof physics, Wabash Col, 55-56; physicist, Midwestern Univs Res Asn, Wis, 56-60, div dir particle accelerators, 60-62; physicist res div, US AEC, 62-64, dir high energy physics, 64-75; dir high energy physics, US Energy Res & Develop Admin, 75-77; dir high energy physics, Dept Energy, 77-87, assoc dir high energy & nuclear physics, Dept Energy, 85-86; pres, Southeastern Univ Res Asn, 87-92; spec asst to pres, Univ Res Asn, 93- *Mem:* Fel AAAS; fel Am Phys Soc. *Res:* Elementary particle physics; accelerator physics; science management and administration. *Mailing Add:* 1204 Azelia Dr Rockville MD 20850

**WALLENSTEIN, MARTIN CECIL,** EPILEPSY, THERMOREGULATION. *Current Pos:* ASSOC PROF PHYSIOL, NY UNIV, 78- *Educ:* Univ Pa, PhD(physiol), 74. *Mailing Add:* Dept Physiol Dent Ctr NY Univ 421 First Ave New York NY 10010-4001

**WALLENTINE, MAX V,** FARM & RANCH MANAGEMENT, DAIRY MANAGEMENT. *Current Pos:* dir agr sta, Brigham Young Univ, 68-96, assoc dean col biol & agr, 71-82, chmn, Animal Sci, 85-88, PROF MEAT & ANIMAL SCI, BRIGHAM YOUNG UNIV, 67-, EMER PROF ANIMAL SCI, 96- *Personal Data:* b Paris, Idaho, Apr 19, 31; m 53, Gay Winters; c 9. *Educ:* Utah State Univ, BS, 55; Cornell Univ, MS, 56, PhD(animal sci & physiol), 60. *Prof Exp:* Asst animal sci, Cornell Univ, 55-56 & 58-60, res assoc meat sci, 60-61; asst prof meat & animal sci, Purdue Univ, 58-60. *Concurrent Pos:* Consult, Algerian Govt, 68-70; vis prof animal sci, Massey Univ, NZ, 91. *Mem:* Am Meat Sci Asn; Sigma Xi; Am Soc Am Sci. *Res:* Ultrasonic evaluation of live meat animals; carcass effects from stilbestrol and pelleted roughages; early breeding of ewe lambs; effects of nutritional level; alfalfa silage (plastic bags) quality and effect on milk production. *Mailing Add:* 392 Widstoe Bldg Brigham Young Univ Provo UT 84602. *E-Mail:* mwallent@ acdl.byu.edu

**WALLER, BRUCE FRANK,** CARDIOVASCULAR PATHOLOGY, CARDIOLOGY. *Current Pos:* prof, 82-89, CLIN PROF PATH & MED, SCH MED, IND UNIV, INDIANAPOLIS, 89-; CARDIOLOGIST, NASSER, SMITH & PINDERTON, 89-; DIR CARDIOVASC PATH REGISTRY ST, VINCENT HOSP, 89- *Personal Data:* b Austin, Minn, Oct 18, 47; m; c 4. *Educ:* Luther Col, Decorah, Iowa, BA, 69; Univ Minn, Minneapolis, MD, 73, MS, 76. *Prof Exp:* Staff assoc, Path Br, Nat Heart, Lung & Blood Inst, NIH, Bethesda, Md, 78-82; clin asst & prof med, Sch Med, Georgetown Univ, 78-82. *Concurrent Pos:* Res assoc, Krannert Inst Cardiol, 82-89. *Mem:* Am Col Cardiol; Am Heart Asn; Am Col Physicians; Am Col Chest Physicians; Int Acad Path; Am Col Sports Med. *Res:* Cardiovascular research; angioplasty and valvular heart disease; sudden death in athletes. *Mailing Add:* 8333 Naab Rd Suite 400 Indianapolis IN 46260. *Fax:* 317-871-6019

**WALLER, COY WEBSTER,** PHARMACEUTICAL CHEMISTRY, DRUGS OF ABUSE. *Current Pos:* from assoc dir to dir, Res Inst Pharmaceut Sci & prof pharm, 68-79, RES PROF, UNIV MISS, 79- *Personal Data:* b Dover, NC, Feb 25, 14; m 45, Beverly Brawn; c James, David, Deborah & Elizabeth. *Educ:* Univ NC, BS, 37; Univ Buffalo, MS, 39; Univ Minn, PhD(pharmaceut chem), 42. *Prof Exp:* Instr pharm, State Col Wash, 42-44; dir org chem, Lederle Labs, Am Cyanamid Co, 44-57; dir chem res, Mead Johnson & Co, 57-61; vpres res, Res Ctr, 61-68. *Mem:* Am Chem Soc; Am Pharmaceut Asn; Royal Soc Chem; Sigma Xi; fel Am Inst Chemists. *Res:* Structural determination of natural organic compounds; tetracyclines and other antibiotics; synthesis of folic acid; marijuana and cocaine. *Mailing Add:* Univ Miss Sch Pharm University MS 38677

**WALLER, DAVID PERCIVAL,** ORGANIC CHEMISTRY, PHOTOGRAPHIC CHEMISTRY. *Current Pos:* from asst scientist to assoc scientist chem, Polaroid Corp, 65-74, scientist, 74-80, sr scientist chem, 80-87, res assoc, 87-94, res fel, 94-97, MGR ORG CHEM, POLAROID CORP, 97- *Personal Data:* b Buffalo, NY, Jan 18, 43; m 78; c 3. *Educ:* Tex Christian Univ, BS, 64; Northeastern Univ, MS, 75. *Prof Exp:* Res asst chem, Res Found, Tex Christian Univ, 64-65. *Mem:* Am Chem Soc; Royal Soc Chem. *Res:* Organic synthesis; novel photographic systems; dye chemistry. *Mailing Add:* 31 Coolidge Ave Lexington MA 02173

**WALLER, DONALD MACGREGOR,** PLANT ECOLOGY, POPULATION BIOLOGY. *Current Pos:* from asst prof to assoc prof, 78-89, PROF BOT, UNIV WIS-MADISON, 90- *Personal Data:* b Northampton, Mass, Oct 15, 51; m, Caitlyn Allen; c 1. *Educ:* Amherst Col, AB, 73; Princeton Univ, PhD(biol), 78. *Prof Exp:* Asst instr biol, Princeton Univ, 74-75. *Concurrent Pos:* Res fel bot, Gray Herbarium, Harvard Univ, 77-78; Humboldt scholar, 88. *Mem:* Bot Soc Am; Soc Study Evolution (vpres, 91-93); Sigma Xi; Soc Conserv Biol; Ecol Soc Am. *Res:* Ecology; competitive and reproductive strategies of plants; evolution; adaptive significance of various breeding systems of plants; demography and genetics of rare plants. *Mailing Add:* Dept Bot Birge Hall Univ Wis 430 Lincoln Dr Madison WI 53706-1381

**WALLER, FRANCIS JOSEPH,** ORGANIC CHEMISTRY, INDUSTRIAL ORGANIC CHEMISTRY. *Current Pos:* res assoc, 88-93, SR RES ASSOC, CORP SCI & TECH CTR, AIR PROD & CHEM INC, 93-, GROUP HEAD, 94- *Personal Data:* b Rome, NY, Mar 12, 43; m 69, Patricia Letchko. *Educ:* Niagara Univ, BS, 65; Univ Vt, PhD(org chem), 70. *Prof Exp:* Res investr low temperature kinetics, St Louis Univ, 70-71; vis asst prof org chem, St Lawrence Univ, 71-72; asst prof, Simmons Col, 72-74; res chemist, Polymer Prod Dept & Petrochem Dept, E I du Pont de Nemours & Co, Inc, 74-79, staff scientist, 79-82, proj leader, Cent Res & Develop Dept, 82-88. *Concurrent Pos:* Adj prof, Lehigh Univ, 93- *Mem:* AAAS; Am Chem Soc; NAm Catalysis Soc. *Res:* Homogeneous catalysis; chemical process assessment; perfluorinated ion-exchange polymers; syn-gas and carbonylation technology; photochemistry; industrial organic chemistry; organic chemistry. *Mailing Add:* Air Prod & Chem Inc 7201 Hamilton Blvd Allentown PA 18195-1501. *Fax:* 610-481-7719; *E-Mail:* wallerfj@apci.com

**WALLER, GEORGE ROZIER, JR,** BIOCHEMISTRY. *Current Pos:* from asst prof to prof, 56-68, asst dir, Agr Exp Sta, 69-76, EMER PROF BIOCHEM, OKLA STATE UNIV, 88- *Personal Data:* b Clinton, NC, July 14, 27; m 47, Hilda M Lominac; c Anne M, Rebecca J & Catherine I. *Educ:* NC State Univ, BS, 50; Univ Del, MS, 52; Okla State Univ, PhD(biochem), 61. *Honors & Awards:* Seydell-Woolley lectr, Ga Inst Technol, 68. *Prof Exp:* Instr agr & biol chem, Univ Del, 50-53; res chemist, Imp Paper & Color Div, Hercules Powder Co, NY, 53-56. *Concurrent Pos:* NIH fel, Nobel Med Inst & Karolinska Inst, Sweden, 63-64; pres, Midcontinent Environ Ctr Asn, 69-75; mem, Okla Environ Qual Task Force & Gov Task Force Recommending Sci Policy Struct State Okla, 70; sabbatical leave, Swed Food Inst, Univ Zurich & Univ London, 78, Inst Bot, Academia Sinica, Taipei, 91-92; mgr nat prod meeting, Phytochem Soc NAm & Am Soc Pharmacog, 78; ed, Mass Spectrometry Rev, 81-83, founding ed, 84; head, USA team for USA & Taiwan sem, NSF, Bilateral Sci Meeting, 82 & 88; mgr nat prod meeting, Phytochem Soc NAm & Am Soc Pharmacog, 78; Nat Chung Hsing Univ, Taichung, Taiwan, 94-95. *Mem:* Am Soc Biol Chemists; Am Soc Mass Spectrometry; Am Chem Soc; Phytochem Soc NAm (pres, 78-79); Sigma Xi; Int Allelopathy Soc (pres, 96-). *Res:* Plant biochemistry, autotoxicity and allelopathy in plants; biochemical applications of mass spectrometry; author of numerous publications. *Mailing Add:* Dept Biochem & Molecular Biol Okla State Univ Stillwater OK 74074. *Fax:* 405-744-7799

**WALLER, GORDON DAVID,** APICULTURE. *Current Pos:* RETIRED. *Personal Data:* b Gale, Wis, July 19, 35; m 59; c 2. *Educ:* Wis State Univ-River Falls, BS, 59; Utah State Univ, MS, 67, PhD(entom, statist), 73. *Prof Exp:* Sci teacher, Pub Schs, Wis, 62-64; res entomologist, Carl Hayden Bee Res Ctr, Agr Res Serv, USDA, 67-89; adj prof entom, Univ Ariz, 69-89. *Mem:* Int Bee Res Asn; Entom Soc Am; Int Comn Bee Bot; Int Union Study Social Insects; Am Soc Agron. *Res:* Applied pollination ecology with special emphasis on honey bee responses to olfactory and gustatory stimuli and the evaluation of foraging behavior of honey bees subjected to different management practices; protecting honey bees from insecticides. *Mailing Add:* S 10010 County Rd Augusta WI 54722

**WALLER, HARDRESS JOCELYN,** AUDITORY SYSTEM, ELECTROPHYSIOLOGY. *Current Pos:* ASSOC PROF NEUROSCI, MED COL OHIO, 73- *Personal Data:* b San Diego, Calif, Aug 27, 28; m 53, Gertrude Gearhart; c Andrew Jocelyn & Bonnie Jo. *Educ:* San Diego State Col, AB, 50; Univ Wash, PhD(physiol), 57. *Prof Exp:* From instr to assoc prof physiol, Albert Einstein Col Med, Yeshiva Univ, 58-73. *Mem:* Soc Neurosci; AAAS; Am Physiol Soc; Sigma Xi; Asn Otolarngol. *Res:* Electrical activity of central nervous system; organization of cochlear nucleus in brain slices. *Mailing Add:* Dept Neurol Surg Med Col Ohio CS 10008 Toledo OH 43699. *Fax:* 419-381-3096; *E-Mail:* hwaller@gemini.mco.edu, hwaller@glasscity.net

**WALLER, JAMES R,** microbiology, biochemistry, for more information see previous edition

**WALLER, JOHN WAYNE,** ELECTRICAL ENGINEERING, ELECTRONICS. *Current Pos:* From asst prof to assoc prof elec eng, 64-88, ASSOC DEPT HEAD, UNIV TENN, KNOXVILLE, 83- *Personal Data:* b Johnson City, Tenn, Dec 15, 37; m; c 3. *Educ:* Univ Tenn, PhD(eng sci). *Concurrent Pos:* Vis prof, Ga Tech, 74-75. *Res:* Circuits; non-majors courses. *Mailing Add:* Dept Elec Eng Univ Tenn Knoxville TN 37996-2100

**WALLER, JULIAN ARNOLD,** MEDICINE, PUBLIC HEALTH. *Current Pos:* prof community med, Univ Vt, 68-72, prof & chmn, Dept Epidemiol & Environ Health, 72-79, prof, 79-95, EMER PROF MED, UNIV VT, 95- *Personal Data:* b New York, NY, Apr 17, 32; m 56, Elsa Neipris; c Naomi & Seth. *Educ:* Columbia Univ, AB, 53; Boston Univ, MD, 57; Harvard Univ, MPH, 60; Am Bd Prev Med, dipl, 65. *Honors & Awards:* Int Asn Accident & Traffic Med Award, 78; A J Mirkin Award, Asn Advan Automotive Med, 87; Injury Control Sect Award, Am Pub Health Asn, 89; Award Merit, Asn Adran Automotive Med, 94. *Prof Exp:* Intern, Mary Fletcher Hosp, Burlington, Vt, 57-58; resident, Contra Costa Health Dept, Calif, 58-59; regional consult chronic dis & voc rehab, USPHS, 60-62; resident, Calif Dept Pub Health, 62, coordr accident prev, 62-63, med officer occup health, 64-66, med officer chronic dis, 66-67, chief emergency health serv, 68. *Concurrent Pos:* Consult, US Dept Transp, 67-80, Vt State Health Dept, 68-78 & Vt Dept Ment Health, 70-76; mem, Safety & Occup Health Study Sect, Dept HEW, 68-71; mem, Nat Hwy Safety Adv Comt, 69-72 & Nat Motor Vehicle Safety Adv Coun, 74-77; mem, Nat Res Coun Comt Trauma Res, 84-85, Expert Panel Accident Prev, WHO, 85-; bd dir, Consumers Union US, 86- *Mem:* Fel Am Pub Health Asn; fel Am Col Epidemiol; fel Am Col Prev Med; fel Asn Advan Automotive Med (pres), 74). *Res:* Epidemiology and control of highway and non-highway injury; epidemiology and control of problem drinking; health hazards to visual artists. *Mailing Add:* 2670 Tamalpais Ave El Cerrito CA 94530

**WALLER, MICHAEL HOLTON,** PAPERMAKING, PROCESS CONTROL. *Current Pos:* PROF, PAPER SCI & ENG DEPT, MIAMI UNIV, OHIO, 79- *Personal Data:* b Buffalo, NY, Mar 7, 42; m 66, Marcia; c 3. *Educ:* Rensselaer Polytech Inst, BME, 63; Mass Inst Technol, SM, 64, ME, 66. *Prof Exp:* Exec officer, D&PS, Aberdeen Proving Ground, Md, 66-68; paper making engr, Procter & Gamble, 68-77, sr engr, 77-79. *Concurrent Pos:* Lectr, Univ Manchester Inst Sci Technol, 86. *Mem:* Tech Asn Pulp & Paper Industs; Instrument Soc Am; Int Fedn Automatic Control. *Res:* Computer simulation of vacuum & thermal dewatering processes for paper; process control schemes for time-delay processes. *Mailing Add:* Miami Univ Oxford OH 45056. *Fax:* 513-529-3841; *E-Mail:* mhwaller@miamiu.acs. muohio.edu

**WALLER, RAY ALBERT,** STATISTICS. *Current Pos:* EXEC DIR, AM STATIST ASN, 95- *Personal Data:* b Grenola, Kans, Mar 4, 37; m 60, Carolyn A McCoy; c Lance A & Jay A. *Educ:* Southwestern Col, BA, 59; Kans State Univ, MS, 63; Johns Hopkins Univ, PhD(math statist), 67. *Prof Exp:* Instr math, St John's Sch, PR, 60-61; asst prof, Towson State Col, 66-67; from asst prof to assoc prof statist, Kans State Univ, 67-74; tech staff mem & mgr, Los Alamos Nat Lab, 74-93. *Concurrent Pos:* Consult, White Sands Missile Range, 68-72. *Mem:* Fel Am Statist Asn; Int Statist Inst. *Res:* Bayesian inference and reliability estimation. *Mailing Add:* 6201 Elati Ct Alexandria VA 22310. *E-Mail:* ray@amstat.org

**WALLER, RICHARD CONRAD,** CHEMICAL ENGINEERING, PHYSICAL CHEMISTRY. *Current Pos:* CONSULT, 80- *Personal Data:* b Victory, Wis, Sept 24, 15; m 36, 48; c 5. *Educ:* Wash State Univ, BS, 38; Iowa State Univ, PhD(phys chem), 42. *Prof Exp:* Res chemist, E I du Pont de Nemours & Co, Inc, 42-48; res scientist fibers, Goodyear Tire & Rubber Co, 48-53, sect head polymer, 53-58, mgr, 58-65, dir res & develop polymer, 65-76, vpres res, 76-80. *Res:* Polymer; fiber. *Mailing Add:* 123 Leland St SE Port Charlotte FL 33952

**WALLER, ROGER MILTON,** GROUNDWATER GEOLOGY. *Current Pos:* RETIRED. *Personal Data:* b Taylor, Wis, Dec 30, 26; m 55, Ruth Pariser; c Elizabeth, Janet & Nancy. *Educ:* Univ Wis, BS, 50; Univ Ariz, MS, 69. *Prof Exp:* Jr comput seismic explor, NMex-Tex, Nat Geophys Co, 50-51; groundwater geologist, Calif Dist, US Geol Surv, 51-54, admin/res hydrologist, Alaska Dist, 55-63, res hydrologist, Alaska Earthquake Effects, 64-65, hydrologist, NY Dist, 66-68 & 73-86, Great Lakes Basin groundwater coordr, Madison, Wis, 68-71, assoc dist chief, Ohio Dist, 72-73. *Concurrent Pos:* Mem, Hydrol Panel, Comt Alaska Earthquake, 64-74; consult, 87- *Mem:* Fel Geol Soc Am; Am Geophys Union; Nat Ground Water Asn. *Res:* Groundwater occurence in glacial deposits. *Mailing Add:* Univ Minn 115 Green Hall Whitehall WI 54773

**WALLER, STEVEN SCOBEE,** RANGE SCIENCE, PLANT ECOLOGY. *Current Pos:* assoc prof, 78-84, PROF RANGE SCI, UNIV NEBR, 84- *Personal Data:* b Indianapolis, Ind, Aug 29, 47; m 70; c 3. *Educ:* Purdue Univ, BSc, 70; Tex A&M Univ, PhD(range sci), 75. *Honors & Awards:* Serv Award, Soc Range Mgt, 88. *Prof Exp:* Res asst, Tex A&M Univ, 71-73, teaching asst, 73-74, res fel, 74-75; asst prof, SDak State Univ, 75-77, asst to dir resident instr & asst prof, 77-78. *Concurrent Pos:* Assoc ed, J Range Mgt, 82-84; chmn, Range Sci Educ Coun, 85; regional coordr, NCent Region, LISA Prog, 89- *Mem:* Soc Range Mgt; Sigma Xi; Nat Asn Cols & Teachers Agr. *Res:* Development of successful range improvement practices within the field of range science. *Mailing Add:* 6820 Crooked Creek Ct Lincoln NE 68516

**WALLER, THOMAS RICHARD,** MALACOLOGY, INVERTEBRATE PALEONTOLOGY. *Current Pos:* Assoc cur, 66-74, CUR & RES SCIENTIST CENOZOIC MOLLUSCA, SMITHSONIAN INST, 74- *Personal Data:* b Chicago, Ill, July 18, 37; m 59; c 2. *Educ:* Univ Wis, BS, 59, MS, 61; Columbia Univ, PhD(geol), 66. *Mem:* AAAS; Paleont Soc; Soc Syst Biol; Am Malacological Union; Nat Shellfisheries Asn; Paleont Res Inst; Unitas Malacologia. *Res:* Cenozoic and living mollusca; evolution; zoogeography; bivalve morphology, development and phylogeny; upper Cenozoic biostratigraphy of eastern North America and Caribbean. *Mailing Add:* Dept Paleobiol MRC-121 Smithsonian Inst Washington DC 20560

**WALLERSTEIN, DAVID VANDERMERE,** APPLIED MECHANICS, SYSTEMS ANALYSIS. *Current Pos:* SR STAFF ENGR, MACNEAL-SCHWENDLER CORP, 82- *Personal Data:* b New York, NY, Nov 19, 37; m 72; c 1. *Educ:* Mich Technol Univ, BS, 60, MS, 61, PhD(eng mech), 69. *Prof Exp:* Design specialist, Lockheed Calif Co, 69-71; asst prof res, Va Polytech Inst, 71-72; sr opers res specialist, Lockheed Calif Co, 72-81. *Concurrent Pos:* Adj assoc prof aerospace eng, Univ Southern Calif, 82- *Mem:* Am Inst Mining, Metall & Petrol Engrs. *Res:* Structuring of engineering systems into mathematical models; development of solutions that yield optimal values of system measures of desirability; finite element analysis. *Mailing Add:* 667 W California Blvd Pasadena CA 91105

**WALLERSTEIN, EDWARD PERRY,** OPTICAL SYSTEM DESIGN. *Current Pos:* CONSULT, 91- *Personal Data:* b New York, NY, May 23, 28; m 51; c 3. *Honors & Awards:* IR 100 Award, Indust Res & Develop, 79, 87 & 88. *Prof Exp:* Engr, Perkin-Elmer Corp, 51-55; res asst, Phys Res Labs, Boston Univ, 55-58; engr, Itek Corp, 58-60; founder & exec, Diffraction Limited, Inc, 60-69; mgr systs group, Valtec Corp, 70-74; group leader/proj engr, Lawrence Livermore Nat Lab, 74-90, dep assoc prog leader/group leader, 90-91. *Concurrent Pos:* Consult design optical systs, 55- *Mem:* Optical Soc Am; Soc Photo-Optical Instrumentation Engrs; Int Soc Optical Eng. *Res:* Design and manufacture of advanced high precision optical systems for reconnaisance, astronomy and laser fusion; large aperture frequency conversion with nonlinear materials; numerous articles in optical industry journals. *Mailing Add:* 1742 Beachwood Way Pleasanton CA 94566

**WALLERSTEIN, GEORGE,** ASTRONOMY. *Current Pos:* chmn, Astron Dept, 65-80, PROF ASTRON, UNIV WASH, 65- *Personal Data:* b New York, NY, Jan 13, 30. *Educ:* Brown Univ, AB, 51; Calif Inst Technol, PhD, 58. *Prof Exp:* From instr to assoc prof astron, Univ Calif, Berkeley, 58-64. *Mem:* Am Astron Soc; Royal Astron Soc; Arctic Inst NAm; Astron Soc Pac; fel AAAS. *Res:* Spectra of variable stars; abundances of the elements in stellar atmospheres; interstellar absorption lines. *Mailing Add:* Dept Astron Univ Wash Seattle WA 98195. *Fax:* 206-685-0403

**WALLERSTEIN, RALPH OLIVER, JR,** hematology, oncology; deceased, see previous edition for last biography

**WALLERSTEIN, ROBERT SOLOMON,** PSYCHIATRY, PSYCHOANALYSIS. *Current Pos:* clin prof psychiat, Sch Med & Langley-Porter Psychiat Inst, Univ Calif, San Francisco, 67-75, prof & chmn dept psychiat, Sch Med & Dir, Langley Porter Inst, 75-85, prof, 85-91, EMER PROF PSYCHIAT, UNIV CALIF, SAN FRANCISCO, 91- *Personal Data:* b Berlin, Ger, Jan 28, 21; US citizen; m 47, Judith Saretsky; c Michael, Nina & Amy. *Educ:* Columbia Univ, BA, 41, MD, 44. *Honors & Awards:* Heinz Hartmann Award, NY Psychoanal Inst, 68; J Elliott Royer Award, Univ Calif, 73; Outstanding Achievement Award, Northern Calif Psychiat Soc, 87; Gold Medal Award, Mt Airy Found, 90; Mary S Sigourney Award, 91. *Prof Exp:* Intern med, Mt Sinai Hosp, NY, 44-45, asst resident, 45-46, resident, 48; resident psychiat, 49; resident, Vet Admin Hosp, Topeka, Kans, 49-51, chief psychosom sect, 51-53; assoc dir, Dept Res, Menninger Found, Kans, 54-65, dir dept, 65-66; chief, Dept Psychiat, Mt Zion Hosp, San Francisco, 66-78. *Concurrent Pos:* Lectr psychiat, Menninger Sch Psychoanal, Kans, 51-66; lectr, Topeka Inst Psychoanal, 59-66, training & supv analyst, 65-66; fel, Ctr Advan Studies Behav Sci, Stanford, Calif, 64-65 & 81-82; training & supv analyst, San Francisco Psychoanal Inst, 66-; mem res sci career develop comn, NIMH, 66-70, chmn, 68-70; vis prof psychiat, Sch Med, La State Univ & New Orleans Psychoanal Inst, 72-73 & Sch Med, Pahlavi Univ, Iran, 77; fel, Rockefeller Found Study Ctr, Bellagio, Lake Como, Italy, 92. *Mem:* Am Psychoanal Asn (pres, 71-72); Int Psychoanal Asn (vpres, 77-85, pres, 85-89, past-pres, 89-93); fel Am Psychiat Asn; fel Am Col Physicians; fel Am Orthopsychiat Asn. *Res:* Psychotherapy research, especially the processes and outcomes of psychoanalytic therapy; supervision processes; alcoholism; psychosomatic medicine. *Mailing Add:* 290 Beach Rd Belvedere Tiburon CA 94920-2472. *Fax:* 415-388-1225

**WALLES, WILHELM EGBERT,** ORGANIC CHEMISTRY, POLYMER CHEMISTRY. *Current Pos:* pres & chief exec officer, 90-93, CHMN, COALITION TECHNOL, LTD, 93- *Personal Data:* b Enschede, Neth, May 25, 25; nat US; m 51, Carolina A Walles; c Irene C, Eric W, Frand E, Rosalinde C & Willem E. *Educ:* Univ Amsterdam, MSc, 48, PhD(org chem, physics), 51, DSc, 53. *Honors & Awards:* IR 100 Award, 74; Centurion Award, 88. *Prof Exp:* Asst indust res, Univ Amsterdam, 49-51, Nat Res Coun Can fel, 51-53; dir res, N V Neth Refining Co, 53-55; assoc scientist, Dow Chem Co, 55-67, sr assoc res scientist plastics, Cent Res Lab, 67-89. *Concurrent Pos:* Chmn, Terra Environ Technol, Inc. *Mem:* Am Chem Soc. *Res:* Synthesis and physical properties of high polymers; surface reactions of polymers; polymolecular complexes; magneto-organic chemistry; aerosol physics; surface chemistry of plastic films, fibers and articles; novel technical approaches toward environmental problems; granted over 120 US patents. *Mailing Add:* 6648 N River Rd Freeland MI 48623-9202

**WALLEY, WILLIS WAYNE,** ZOOLOGY, ECOLOGY. *Current Pos:* PROF BIOL & CHMN DEPT, DELTA STATE UNIV, 79- *Personal Data:* b Brooklyn, Miss, July 26, 34; m 66, Kathleen Mason; c James Brian & William Todd. *Educ:* Southern Miss Univ, BS, 56; Miss State Univ, MS, 61, PhD(zool), 65. *Prof Exp:* Pub sch teacher, Miss, 56-61; asst prof biol, Southeastern La Col, 64-68; prof biol & chmn dept & chmn div III, Belhaven Col, 68-79. *Mem:* AAAS; Am Inst Biol Sci; Nat Audubon Soc; Sigma Xi. *Res:* Absorption, metabolism and excretion of chlorinated hydrocarbons in birds; in vitro metabolism of dichloro-diphenyl-trichloro-ethane by various tissues of the common grackle; biogeochemical cycling of boron; site fertility and primary production in hydrosoils. *Mailing Add:* Dept Biol Delta State Univ Cleveland MS 38733. *Fax:* 601-846-4016; *E-Mail:* wwalley@dsu.deltast.edu

**WALLICK, EARL TAYLOR,** BIOLOGICAL CHEMISTRY. *Current Pos:* from asst prof to assoc prof, 77-85, PROF PHARMACOL & CELL BIOPHYS, COL MED, UNIV CINCINNATI, 86- *Personal Data:* b Monticello, Ark, Jan 11, 38; m 62; c 2. *Educ:* Miss State Univ, BS, 60, MS, 62; Rice Univ, PhD(org chem), 66. *Prof Exp:* Res chemist, Dacron Res Lab, E I du Pont de Nemours & Co, Inc, 66-67; assoc prof chem, King Col, 67-71; trainee myocardial biol, Baylor Col Med, 71-73, instr cell biophys, 73-76, asst prof, 76-77. *Concurrent Pos:* Mem, Pharmacol Study Sect, NIH. *Mem:* Am Chem Soc; Am Soc Pharmacol & Exp Therapeut. *Res:* Isotope effects; cardiac glycosides, adenosine triphosphatase. *Mailing Add:* Dept Pharmacol & Cell Biophys Col Med Univ Cincinnati Cincinnati OH 45267-0575

**WALLICK, GEORGE CASTOR,** PHYSICS. *Current Pos:* sr res technologist appl math, 51-59, RES ASSOC, FIELD RES LAB, MOBIL RES & DEVELOP CORP, DALLAS, 59- *Personal Data:* b Grand Rapids, Mich, July 2, 23; m 45; c 2. *Educ:* Univ Mich, BS, 43, MS, 46, PhD(physics), 52. *Prof Exp:* Radio engr radar res & develop, US Naval Res Lab, 44-45. *Mem:* Am Phys Soc; Am Asn Physics Teachers. *Res:* Petroleum production; flow of fluids through porous media; non-Newtonian flow; heat transfer; numerical analysis; computer programming and utilization; geophysics; underground coal gasification. *Mailing Add:* 518 Towne Pl Duncanville TX 75116

**WALLIN, JACK ROBB,** plant pathology, for more information see previous edition

**WALLIN, JOHN DAVID,** NEPHROLOGY, RENAL PHYSIOLOGY. *Current Pos:* CHIEF NEPHROLOLGY & PROF INTERNAL MED, SCH MED, LA STATE UNIV, 90- *Personal Data:* b Pasadena, Calif, June 30, 37; m 59; c 2. *Educ:* Stanford Univ, BS, 58; Sch Med, Yale Univ, MD, 62. *Prof Exp:* Intern & resident med, Naval Regional Med Ctr, PR, 62-66, chief med, 66-70; res fel nephrology, Southwest Med Sch, Univ Tex, 70-72; dir clin invest, Naval Regional Med Ctr, Calif, 72-78; chief nephrology & prof internal med, Sch Med, Tulane Univ, 78-90. *Concurrent Pos:* Instr internal med, Univ PR, 67-70; chief nephrology, Vet Admin Hosp, New Orleans, 78-81. *Mem:* Fel Am Col Physicians; Am Soc Nephrology; Am Fedn Clin Res; Int Soc Nephrol; Am Soc Hypertension. *Res:* Examination of homeostasis of water metabolism with specific reference to control of vasopresion release from hypophysis and its end organ effects in renal tubule; effects of hypertension on renal function and progression of renal failure. *Mailing Add:* Dept Med Sch Med La State Univ 1542 Tulane Ave New Orleans LA 70112

**WALLIN, RICHARD FRANKLIN,** TOXICOLOGY, MEDICAL DEVICE EVALUATION. *Current Pos:* sci dir, 77-78, vpres & sci dir, 78-81, PRES, N AM SCI ASSOCS, INC, 81- *Personal Data:* b Chicago, Ill, Jan 31, 39; m 61; c 2. *Educ:* Univ Ill, BS, 61, DVM, 63, MS, 64, PhD(vet med sci), 66. *Prof Exp:* Physiologist, McDonnell Aircraft Corp, 66-67; sr res pharmacologist, Baxter Labs, Inc, Morton Grove, 67-70, dir res admin, 70-72, actg dir pharm & microbiol res, 72-73, assoc dir pharmacol res, 73-77. *Concurrent Pos:* NIH fel, 63-66; adj assoc prof, Med Col Ohio; lectr & course dir, Ctr Prof Advan, East Brunswick, NJ; mem, USP Adv Comt. *Mem:* Am Vet Med Asn; Parenteral Drug Asn; Am Asn Lab Animal Sci; Soc Biomat. *Res:* Biomaterials; medical devices; biocompatibility of materials. *Mailing Add:* 29969 St Andrews Rd Perrysburg OH 43551

**WALLING, CHEVES (THOMSON),** PHYSICAL ORGANIC CHEMISTRY, FREE RADICAL REACTIONS. *Current Pos:* distinguished prof, 70-91, EMER PROF, UNIV UTAH, 91- *Personal Data:* b Evanston, Ill, Feb 28, 16; m 40, Jane Ann Wilson; c Hazel, Rosalind, Cheves, Janie & Barbara. *Educ:* Harvard Univ, BA, 37; Univ Chicago, PhD(org chem), 39. *Honors & Awards:* James Flack Norris Award, Am Chem Soc, 70, Lubrizol Award in Petrol Chem, 84. *Prof Exp:* Res chemist, Jackson Lab, E I DuPont de Nemours & Co, 39-42 & Gen Labs, US Rubber Co, 43-49; res assoc, Lever Bros Co, 49-52; prof chem, Columbia Univ, 52-70, chmn dept, 63-66. *Concurrent Pos:* Tech aide, Comt Med Res, Off Sci Res & Develop, 45-46; chmn, Div Chem & Chem Technol, Nat Res Coun, 72-73; ed, J Am Chem Soc, 75-81. *Mem:* Nat Acad Sci; Am Acad Arts & Sci; AAAS; Am Chem Soc. *Res:* Organic reaction mechanisms; free radical reactions; polymerization; peroxides and autoxidation. *Mailing Add:* Box 537 Jaffrey NH 03452

**WALLING, DERALD DEE,** MATHEMATICAL MODELING. *Current Pos:* from assoc prof to prof, 66-92, EMER PROF MATH, TEX TECH UNIV, 92-; SR OPERS RES ANALYST, AUTOMATION RES SYSTS, 91- *Personal Data:* b Granger, Iowa, Feb 14, 37; m 58, Elizabeth Harris; c Jeffrey V, Gerald N, Lizann R & Suzette Y. *Educ:* Iowa State Univ, BS, 58, MS, 61, PhD(math), 63. *Prof Exp:* Mathematician, Ames Lab, US AEC, 62-63; asst prof math, Univ Ariz, 63-66. *Res:* Psychophysics; mathematics sociology; statistics; probability. *Mailing Add:* 662 S Avenida del Sol Sierra Vista AZ 85635-6723. *Fax:* 520-459-2189

**WALLINGFORD, ERROL E(LWOOD),** COMMUNICATIONS. *Current Pos:* RETIRED. *Personal Data:* b Ottawa, Ont, Jan 25, 28; m 54; c 3. *Educ:* Carleton Col, BSc, 53; Univ Ottawa, MSc, 61. *Prof Exp:* Inspector, Dept Nat Defense Inspection Servs, 52-57; lectr physics, Waterloo Col, 57-58; from lectr to asst prof, Royal Mil Col Can, 61-68, assoc prof elec eng, 68-88. *Concurrent Pos:* Defence Res Bd Can grants, 65- *Mem:* Inst Elec & Electronics Engrs. *Res:* Primary source redundancy identification; removal and replacement using secondary source data to maintain a block code structure; method applicable to both first and second order redundancies. *Mailing Add:* RR 1 Sydenham ON K0H 2T0 Can

**WALLINGFORD, JOHN STUART,** PHYSICS. *Current Pos:* assoc prof, 70-75, PROF PHYSICS, PEMBROKE STATE UNIV, 75- *Personal Data:* b El Paso, Tex, Apr 13, 35; m 70; c 2. *Educ:* Univ Minn, Minneapolis, BPhys, 61; Fla State Univ, MS, 66, PhD(physics), 67. *Prof Exp:* Instr physics, Fullerton Jr Col, 61-62 & Cerritos Col, 62-63; asst, Fla State Univ, 63-66; from asst prof to assoc prof, Fla A&M Univ, 66-69; vis assoc prof, Temple Univ, 69-70. *Mem:* Am Asn Physics Teachers; Am Inst Physics. *Res:* Consequences of general relativity theory; making science interesting and accessible to all; hydrolysis of organic wastes; computer assisted tomography (reconstruction techniques); linear programming (simplex algorithm Kachiyan's algorithm); personal (micro-) computer programming and interfacing. *Mailing Add:* 5408 Simmons Dr Lumberton NC 28358

**WALLINGTON, TIMOTHY JOHN,** CHEMISTRY OF AIR POLLUTION, ATMOSPHERIC DEGRADATION OF VOLATILE COMPOUNDS. *Current Pos:* SR RES SCIENTIST, FORD MOTOR CO, 87- *Personal Data:* b Northampton, Eng, Nov 4, 58. *Educ:* Univ Oxford, BA, 81, PhD(atmospheric chem), 84. *Hon Degrees:* MA, Oxford Univ, 84. *Prof Exp:* Res chemist, Statewide Air Pollution Res Ctr, Univ Calif, Riverside, 84-86; vis scientist, Nat Bur Stand, 86-87. *Mem:* Royal Soc Chem; Am Chem Soc. *Res:* Elucidation of the kinetics and mechanisms of key atmospheric reactions to establish the environmental impact of the release of volatile compounds into the atmosphere. *Mailing Add:* 306 Montgomery Ann Arbor MI 48103-4115. *Fax:* 313-594-2923; *E-Mail:* twalling@smail.srl.ford.com

**WALLIS, CLIFFORD MERRILL,** ELECTRONICS, RADIO ENGINEERING. *Current Pos:* from instr to prof elec eng, 28-70, chmn dept, 47-68, EMER PROF ELEC ENG, UNIV MO, COLUMBIA, 70- *Personal Data:* b Waitsfield, Vt, Mar 7, 04; m 28; c 2. *Educ:* Univ Vt, BS, 26; Mass Inst Technol, MS, 28; Harvard Univ, ScD(eng), 41. *Prof Exp:* Mem staff eng training course, Gen Elec Co, Mass, 26-28. *Concurrent Pos:* Res assoc, Underwater Sound Lab, Harvard Univ, 44-45; mem & vchmn, Nat Res Comt, Am Inst Elec Engrs, 58-59; Fulbright lectr, Ankara, 60-61, award, Taiwan, 67-68; dir prof develop, USN Underwater Systs Ctr, Conn, 70-72. *Mem:* Am Soc Eng Educ; fel Inst Elec & Electronics Engrs. *Res:* Rectifier analysis; half wave gas rectifier circuits; single phase full wave rectifier circuits; current division in tetrode and pentode power tubes; low frequency constant time delay lines; solid state theory of semiconductors. *Mailing Add:* PO Box 750 Moretown VT 05660

**WALLIS, DONALD DOUGLAS JAMES H,** IONOSPHERIC PHYSICS. *Current Pos:* res assoc, 76-81, RES OFFICER SPACE PHYS, NAT RES COUN CAN, 81- *Personal Data:* b Brandon, Man, Apr 20, 43. *Educ:* Univ Alta, Calgary, BSc, 65; Univ Calgary, MSc, 68; Univ Alaska, PhD(geophys), 74. *Prof Exp:* Fel geophys, Univ Alta, 73-75; res assoc geophys, Univ Calgary, 75-76. *Mem:* Can Asn Physicists; Am Geophys Union. *Res:* Auroral spectroscopy; ionospheric winds and currents; atmospheric changes; magnetospheric physics. *Mailing Add:* 2340 Briar Hill Dr Ottawa ON K1H 7A9 Can

**WALLIS, GRAHAM B,** ENGINEERING. *Current Pos:* from asst prof to assoc prof, 62-72, interim dean, 94-95, PROF ENG, DARTMOUTH COL, 72- *Personal Data:* b Rugby, Eng, Apr 1, 36; m 59, Suzanne White; c Iain, Tasha, Peter & Jeremy. *Educ:* Cambridge Univ, BA, 57, MA, 61, PhD(eng), 61; Mass Inst Technol, SM, 59. *Honors & Awards:* Ludwig Mond Prize, Inst Mech Engrs, 62; Moody Award, Am Soc Mech Engrs, 71 Centennial Award & Medal, 80, Fluid Eng Award, 94. *Prof Exp:* Res fel, UK Atomic Energy Authority, 59-62. *Concurrent Pos:* Sr vis res fel, Heriot-Watt Univ, 64; vis reader, Univ Warwick, 70-71. *Mem:* Am Soc Mech Engrs. *Res:* Two-phase and multicomponent flow; heat and mass transfer; boiling and condensation. *Mailing Add:* Dept Eng Sci Dartmouth Col Hanover NH 03755-8000. *E-Mail:* graham.b.wallis@dartmouth.edu

**WALLIS, JAMES RICHARD,** FLOOD & DROUGHT FREQUENCY ANALYSIS, REGIONALIZATION TECHNIQUES. *Current Pos:* VIS PROF, YALE UNIV, 96- *Personal Data:* b Montreal, Que, Mar 18, 28; US citizen; m 76. *Educ:* Univ NB, BSc, 50; Ore State Univ, MSc, 54; Univ Calif, Berkeley, PhD(soil morphol), 65. *Honors & Awards:* Horton Award, Am Geophys Union, 65. *Prof Exp:* Adv, Arno River Flood Study Group, 73-75; prof consult, Inst Hydrol, 83-84; res staff mem, Phys Sci Dept, IBM, 67-73, Gen Sci Dept, 75-83, res staff mem, Dept Math Sci, Thomas J Watson Res Ctr, 84-96. *Concurrent Pos:* Charles E Bullard fel, Harvard Univ, 66; chmn, working group stochastic hydrol, Int Asn Hist Sci, 75-78; mem, US Nat Comt, Int Union Geodesy & Geophys, Nat Acad Sci; mem, Comt Assessment Tech, Estimating Probabilities Extreme Floods, Nat Res Coun, 83-86 & 86-88, water sci & technol bd, 88-91; Comt Regional Assessment Potential For Ground Water Contamination, 90-92, rep, US Nat Comt Global Climate Control; mem, US Nat Drought Atlas Team, 91-93. *Mem:* Fel Am Geophys Union (pres, 80-82); Europ Geophys Union; AAAS; Sigma Xi; Brit Hydrol Soc. *Res:* Statistical modeling of hydrologic and environmental problems from flood frequency analysis to forest growth modeling. *Mailing Add:* Sch Forestry & Environ Studies Yale Univ 205 Prospect New Haven CT 06511. *E-Mail:* james.wallis@yale.edu

**WALLIS, PETER MALCOLM,** BIOGEOCHEMISTRY. *Current Pos:* PRES, HYPERION RES LTD, 90- *Personal Data:* b London, Eng, May 9, 52; Can citizen; m 76; c 3. *Educ:* Univ Toronto, BSc, 74; Univ Waterloo, MSc, 75, PhD(biol), 78. *Honors & Awards:* E E Ballantyne Award Environ Res, 86. *Prof Exp:* Fel, Kananaskis Ctr, Univ Calgary, 78-79, res assoc, 79-80, prof assoc, 80-90. *Mem:* NAm Benthological Soc; Soc Int Limnol; Freshwater Biol Asn; Sigma Xi; Wildlife Dis Asn; Am Soc Microbiol. *Res:* Microbiology; biogeochemistry; chemical evolution of groundwater; host reservoirs and transmission of giardiasis; survival of pathogens in the environment. *Mailing Add:* Med Hat Col 299 College Dr Medicine Hat AB T1A 3Y6 Can

**WALLIS, RICHARD FISHER,** SOLID STATE PHYSICS. *Current Pos:* prof, 69-93, chmn dept, 72-75 & 80-83, EMER PROF PHYSICS, UNIV CALIF, IRVINE, 93- *Personal Data:* b Washington, DC, May 14, 24; m 55, Mary C Williams; c Maria F & Sylvia C. *Educ:* George Washington Univ, BS, 45, MS, 48; Cath Univ, PhD(chem), 52. *Honors & Awards:* Pure Sci Award, Naval Res Lab, 64. *Prof Exp:* Fel, Inst Fluid Dynamics, Univ Md, 51-53; chemist, Appl Physics Lab, Johns Hopkins Univ, 53-56; physicist, US Naval Res Lab, 56-58, from actg head to head, Semiconductors Br, 58-66; prof physics, Univ Calif, Irvine, 66-67; head, Semiconductors Br, US Naval Res Lab, 67-69. *Concurrent Pos:* Consult, Res Labs, Gen Motors Corp, 58-79, US Naval Res Lab, 69-79. *Mem:* Fel Am Phys Soc; AAAS. *Res:* Quantum and statistical mechanics; solid state theory; lattice dynamics; surface excitations; nonlinear phenomena; semiconductor physics. *Mailing Add:* Dept Physics Univ Calif Irvine CA 92697

**WALLIS, ROBERT L,** PHYSICS. *Current Pos:* From asst prof to assoc prof, 62-75, CHMN DEPT, BALDWIN-WALLACE COL, 70-, PROF PHYSICS, 75- *Personal Data:* b Sheridan, Wyo, Sept 22, 34; m 60; c 2. *Educ:* Univ Colo, BA, 56, MA, 58, PhD(physics), 62. *Mem:* AAAS; Am Phys Soc; Am Asn Physics Teachers; Sigma Xi. *Res:* Educational techniques. *Mailing Add:* Dept Physics Baldwin-Wallace Col 275 Eastland Rd Berea OH 44017

**WALLIS, RONALD ALBERT,** HEAT TRANSFER, COMPUTER MODELLING. *Current Pos:* MGR RES & DEVELOP, WYMAN GORDON FORGINGS, INC, TEX, 95- *Personal Data:* m 80, Kimberly Ann Gibson; c Sarra May, Evan Trevor & Ainsley Ann. *Educ:* Derby Univ, Eng, HND, 73; Cranfield Inst Technol, MSc, 75, PhD(mech eng), 91. *Prof Exp:* Scientist, Coal Res Estab, Nat coal Bd, Eng, 78-80; sr develop engr, Teesside Labs, Brit Steel, Eng, 80-82; sr res engr, Graham Res Lab, J & L Steel, Pa, 82-85; sr scientist, Cameron Iron Works, Tex, 85-90; mgr thermal eng, Cameron Forged Prod Div, Cooper Indust, Tex, 90-95. *Concurrent Pos:* Bd mem, Am Soc Mat, 90- *Mem:* Inst Energy; Coun Eng Inst; Iron & Steel Soc; Am Soc Mat; Minerals, Metals & Mat Soc. *Res:* Computer modeling of the heat treatment process such as quenching prediction of fluid flow, cooling rates and residual stresses in components; furnace modelling, heat treatment and steel reheating furnaces. *Mailing Add:* Wyman Gordon Forgings Houston Opers PO Box 40456 Houston TX 77240. *Fax:* 281-856-3315

**WALLIS, THOMAS GARY,** PHOTOGRAPHIC SCIENCE. *Current Pos:* res chemist, 76-86, TECH MGR, EASTMAN KODAK CO, 86- *Personal Data:* b Paducah, Ky, 48; m 69; c 2. *Educ:* Murray State Univ, BA, 70; Duke Univ, PhD(org chem), 74. *Prof Exp:* Assoc chemist, Ohio State Univ, 74-76. *Mem:* Soc Motion Picture & TV Engrs. *Res:* Synthesis of photographically active compounds; image structure improvement in color films; new motion picture color films. *Mailing Add:* 608 El Mar Dr Rochester NY 14616

**WALLIS, W ALLEN,** ECONOMICS, STATISTICS. *Current Pos:* RESIDENT SCHOLAR, AM ENTERPRISE INST, 89- *Personal Data:* b Philadelphia, Pa, Nov 5, 12; wid; c Nancy W (Ingling) & Virginia W (Cates). *Educ:* Univ Minn, AB, 32. *Hon Degrees:* DSc, Hobart & William Smith Cols, 73; LLD, Roberts Wesleyan Col, 73 & Univ Rochester, 84; LHD, Grove City Col, 75; Dr Soc Sci, Francisco Marroquin Univ, Guatemala, 92. *Honors & Awards:* Wilks Mem Award, Am Statist Asn, 80. *Prof Exp:* Instr econ, Dept Econ, Yale Univ, 37-38; from asst prof to assoc prof, Stanford Univ, 38-46; prof statist & econ, Grad Sch Bus, Dept Econ & Dept Statist, Univ Chicago, 46-62, chmn, Dept Statist, 49-57, dean, Grad Sch Bus, 56-62; prof econ, statist, pres/chancellor & trustee, Univ Rochester, 62-82; under secy econ affairs, US State Dept, 82-89. *Concurrent Pos:* Consult, Rand Corp, 46-66; pres, Nat Comn Study Nursing & Nursing Educ, 67-70; mem, Adv Coun Higher Educ, NY State Dept Educ, 70-78; chmn, Adv Comt Social Security Studies, Am Enterprise Inst, 76-82; subcomt postperformance eval res, Nat Acad Sci, 81-82; W Allen Wallis prof, Univ Chicago, 82, Univ Rochester, 92 & W Allen Wallis Inst Polit Econ. *Mem:* Fel AAAS; fel Am Acad Arts & Sci; Am Econ Asn; fel Am Statist Asn (pres, 65). *Res:* Author or co-author of ten books and monographs and 55 articles on statistics, economics, high education, and international relations. *Mailing Add:* Am Enterprise Inst 1150 17th St NW Washington DC 20036. *Fax:* 202-862-7178

**WALLIS, WALTER DENIS,** COMBINATORIAL DESIGNS, GRAPH THEORY. *Current Pos:* PROF MATH, SOUTHERN ILL UNIV, 85- *Personal Data:* b Sydney, NSW, Australia, June 26, 41. *Educ:* Univ Sydney, BSc, 63, PhD(pure math), 68. *Prof Exp:* Lectr math, La Trobe Univ, 67-70; from lectr to assoc prof math, Univ Newcastle, 70-85. *Concurrent Pos:* Vis prof, Univ Waterloo, 72 & 78, Univ Man, 73, Univ Surrey, 76 & Simon Fraser Univ, 84-85; ed, J Combinatorial Math & Comput, 87-; vis prof, Curtin Univ Technol, 88. *Mem:* Am Math Soc; Math Asn Am; Soc Indust Appl Math; Inst Combinatorics Appln; Combinatorics Math Soc Australia. *Res:* Combinatorial mathematics including graph theory and experimental designs. *Mailing Add:* Math Dept Southern Ill Univ Carbondale IL 62901-4408. *Fax:* 618-453-5300; *E-Mail:* ga3506@siucvmb.bitnet

**WALLMAN, JOSHUA,** NEUROBIOLOGY. *Current Pos:* from asst prof to assoc prof, 74-85, PROF BIOL, CITY COL NEW YORK, 86- *Personal Data:* b New York, NY, July 4, 43. *Educ:* Harvard Univ, AB, 65; Tufts Univ, PhD(biol), 72. *Prof Exp:* Fel neurophysiol, Inst Animal Behav, Rutgers Univ, 72-74. *Concurrent Pos:* NIH fel, 72-73; res grants, Nat Eye Inst, NIH, 78-81 & 81-, NSF, 85-86; mem, Working Group on Myopia, Nat Res Coun, Integrative Neural Sci Panel, NSF, 84-87. *Mem:* Asn Res Vision Ophthal; Soc Neurosci; Sigma Xi. *Res:* Neurophysiology of the accessory optic system; physiological and behavioral studies of the development of the oculomotor and visual systems in birds; studies on experimentally-induced myopia; regulation of growth of the eye. *Mailing Add:* Dept Biol City Col New York 160 Convert Ave New York NY 10031-9101

**WALLMARK, J(OHN) TORKEL,** ELECTRONICS. *Current Pos:* RETIRED. *Personal Data:* b Stockholm, Sweden, June 4, 19; m 49; c 2. *Educ:* Royal Inst Technol, Sweden, Civilingenjor, 44, Techn lic, 47, Techn dr, 53. *Honors & Awards:* L J Wallmark Award, Royal Acad Sci Sweden, 54; Polhem Award, Sweden Eng Soc, 82; Cedergren Medal, Royal Inst Tech, 85. *Prof Exp:* Asst electronics, Royal Inst Technol, Sweden, 44; engr, A B Stand Radio Mfg Co, Stockholm, 44-45; asst electronics, Royal Inst Technol, Sweden, 45-47; trainee, RCA Labs, 47-48; asst electronics, Royal Inst Technol, 49-53; res engr, RCA Labs, 53-68; prof electronics, Chalmers Univ Technol, Sweden, 68-90. *Concurrent Pos:* Secy, State Tech Res Coun, Stockholm, 50-51; res engr, Elektrovarme Inst, Sweden, 52-53; consult, Royal Swed Air Force, 52-53; prof, Chalmers Univ Technol, 64-66. *Mem:* Am Phys Soc; fel Inst Elec & Electronics Engrs; Royal Swed Acad Eng Sci; Royal Swed Acad Sci; fel AAAS. *Res:* Integrated circuits; solid state devices. *Mailing Add:* Chalmers Univ Sjoallen 5 Kungsbacka 43431 Sweden

**WALLNER, STEPHEN JOHN,** PLANT PHYSIOLOGY. *Current Pos:* ASSOC PROF PLANT PHYSIOL, COLO STATE UNIV, 80- *Personal Data:* b Sioux Falls, SDak, Mar 22, 45; m 69; c 2. *Educ:* SDak State Univ, BS, 67, MS, 69; Iowa State Univ, PhD(plant physiol), 73. *Prof Exp:* Plant physiologist, US Army Natick Labs, 73-75; asst prof hort physiol, Pa State Univ, University Park, 75-80. *Mem:* Am Soc Plant Physiologists; Am Inst Biol Sci; Sigma Xi; AAAS; Int Asn Plant Tissue Cult. *Res:* Postharvest physiology, especially involving cell wall changes during fruit ripening. *Mailing Add:* Hort Dept Pa State Univ 102 Tyson Bldg University Park PA 16802-4200

**WALLNER, WILLIAM E,** ENTOMOLOGY, PLANT PATHOLOGY. *Current Pos:* RES PROJ LEADER, FOREST INSECT & DIS LAB, US FOREST SERV, 76- *Personal Data:* b Greenfield, Mass, Nov 25, 36; m 64, Amada Ober; c Christine & Abbie. *Educ:* Univ Conn, BS, 59; Cornell Univ, PhD, 65. *Prof Exp:* Res asst entom, Cornell Univ, 59-65; exten entomologist, Mich State Univ, 65-76, assoc prof entom, 69-74, prof, 74-76. *Concurrent Pos:* Vis scientist, USSR, 81, 83, 88, 89, 90, 91, 92 & 93, China, 82; lectr forestry, Yale Univ. *Mem:* Entom Soc Am; Soc Am Foresters; Sigma Xi. *Res:* Biology and control of forest ornamental and plantation insects with emphasis on population suppression and pest management of insects for forest-recreational areas; gypsy moth; biolcology of forest insects with emphasis on biological control and population dynamics; recent research centers on gypsy moth and insects associated with acid rain deposition; outbreak insects especially the lepidoptera. *Mailing Add:* Forest Insect & Dis Lab US Forest Serv Hamden CT 06514. *Fax:* 203-230-4315

**WALLRAFF, EVELYN BARTELS,** MICROBIOLOGY, IMMUNOLOGY. *Current Pos:* RETIRED. *Personal Data:* b Chicago, Ill, Oct 21, 20. *Educ:* Rosary Col, BS, 40; Univ Chicago, MS, 42; Univ Ariz, PhD(virol, immunol), 61. *Prof Exp:* Res technician bact & immunol, Univ Chicago & Zoller Dent Clin, 41-43; res microbiologist, Vet Admin Hosp, 61-71; res assoc microbiol & med technol, Univ Ariz, 70-87; prof microbiol & Life Sci, Pima Col, 72-87. *Concurrent Pos:* Consult, Vet Admin Hosp, Tucson, 71- *Mem:* AAAS; Am Soc Microbiol; Am Asn Immunol; Reticuloendothelial Soc; Am Thoracic Soc. *Res:* Coccidioidinn hypersensitivity used for study of mechanisms of delayed hypersensitivity in man; cellular and transplantation immunology; anti-macrophage serum. *Mailing Add:* 2708 E Mabel St Tucson AZ 85716

**WALLS, KENNETH W,** IMMUNOLOGY, PARASITOLOGY. *Current Pos:* Lab chief parasitol & mycol serol, 55-59, lab chief toxoplasmosis, 59-66, CHIEF, PARASITOL SEROL UNIT, CTR DIS CONTROL, 66- *Personal Data:* b Ft Lauderdale, Fla, Dec 4, 28; m 56. *Educ:* Ind Univ, AB, 49 & 50; Univ Mich, MS, 52, PhD(bact), 55. *Mem:* AAAS; Am Soc Trop Med & Hyg. *Res:* Immunology, serology and epidemiology of parasitic diseases with special emphasis on toxoplasmosis and related diseases. *Mailing Add:* 4006 Northlake Creek Ct Tucker GA 30084

**WALLS, NANCY WILLIAMS,** BACTERIOLOGY. *Current Pos:* asst res biologist, Ga Inst Technol, 59-61, res asst prof, 62-67, sr res biologist, 67-69, actg dir sch biol, 69-70, ASSOC PROF BIOL, GA INST TECHNOL, 69- *Personal Data:* b Johnstown, Pa, Sept 19, 30; div. *Educ:* Univ Mich, BS, 52, MS, 53, PhD(bact), 59. *Prof Exp:* Instr bact, Emory Univ, 58-59. *Mem:* AAAS; Am Soc Microbiol; Radiation Res Soc; Am Inst Biol Sci; NY Acad Sci; Sigma Xi. *Res:* Physiology of Clostridium botulinum; marine microbial ecology; anaerobic bacterial spores; mechanisms of bacterial toxin formation; behavioral mechanisms of sea turtles. *Mailing Add:* Sch Biol Sci Ga Inst Technol 225 North Ave NW Atlanta GA 30332-0001

**WALLS, ROBERT CLARENCE,** BIOMETRICS & BIOSTATISTICS, STATISTICS. *Current Pos:* from asst prof to assoc prof, 66-77, head, 77-82, PROF BIOMET, UNIV ARK MED SCI, LITTLE ROCK, 82- *Personal Data:* b Batesville, Ark, Mar 9, 34; m 66; c 3. *Educ:* Harding Univ, BS, 59; Univ Ark, MS, 61; Okla State Univ, PhD(statist), 67. *Prof Exp:* Mathematician, Res & Technol Dept, Texaco Inc, 61-64. *Mem:* Am Statist Asn; Soc Clin Trials; Biomet Soc; Sigma Xi. *Res:* Health services research; mathematical models in biology and medicine. *Mailing Add:* Div Biomet No 585 Univ Ark Med Sci 4301 W Markham St Little Rock AR 72205-7101

**WALMSLEY, FRANK,** INORGANIC CHEMISTRY, SCIENCE EDUCATION. *Current Pos:* From asst prof to prof, 62-87, EMER PROF CHEM, UNIV TOLEDO, 87- *Personal Data:* b New Bedford, Mass, June 26, 35; m 59; c 2. *Educ:* Univ NH, BS, 57; Univ NC, Chapel Hill, PhD(chem), 62. *Concurrent Pos:* Vis prof, Mich State Univ, 79-80; lectr, Univ Tex, San Antonio, 87-89, 91, 93 & 95-96, Trinity Univ, 89- *Mem:* Am Chem Soc; Royal Soc Chem; Am Sci Affil; Sigma Xi. *Res:* Spectral and magnetic properties of coordination compounds; heteropolyions; author, general and inorganic chemistry. *Mailing Add:* 8311 Kingsway San Antonio TX 78250-2429

**WALMSLEY, IAN ALEXANDER,** NONLINEAR OPTICS, QUANTUM OPTICS. *Current Pos:* asst prof, 88-93, ASSOC PROF OPTICS, UNIV ROCHESTER, 94- *Personal Data:* b Manchester, Eng, Jan 13, 60. *Educ:* Univ London, BSc, 80; Univ Rochester, PhD(optics), 86. *Prof Exp:* Res assoc, Cornell Univ, 86-87. *Concurrent Pos:* NSF presidential young investr, 90. *Mem:* Optical Soc Am; Am Phys Soc. *Res:* Nonlinear and quantum optics, especially ultrafast phenomena in these areas. *Mailing Add:* Inst Optics Univ Rochester 601 Elmwood Ave Rochester NY 14627. *Fax:* 716-244-4936; *E-Mail:* walmsley@optics.optics.rochester.edu

**WALMSLEY, JUDITH ABRAMS,** INORGANIC CHEMISTRY, BIOPHYSICAL CHEMISTRY. *Current Pos:* asst prof, 87-93, ASSOC PROF CHEM, UNIV TEX, SAN ANTONIO, 93- *Personal Data:* b Oak Park, Ill, Feb 6, 36; m 59, Frank; c Katherine & Susan. *Educ:* Fla State Univ, BA, 58; Univ NC, Chapel Hill, PhD(chem), 62. *Prof Exp:* Res scientist chem,

Owens-Ill, Inc. 63-66; vis res assoc, Univ Toledo, 73-75, asst prof chem, 81-82, sr res assoc chem, 74-87. *Mem:* Am Chem Soc; AAAS; Sigma Xi; Asn Women Sci. *Res:* Chemistry of metal complexes of biological significance; transition metal and post-transition metal complexes of organophosphorus ligands; self-association of hydrogen-bonding molecules; solute-solvent interactions; properties of nucleotides in solution. *Mailing Add:* Div Earth & Phys Sci Univ Tex San Antonio TX 78249-0663. *Fax:* 210-458-4469

**WALMSLEY, PETER N(EWTON),** CHEMICAL ENGINEERING. *Current Pos:* PRES, AMT MGT, INC, 89- *Personal Data:* b Oldham, Eng, Mar 11, 36; m, Patricia D Coupe; c Hilary, Jane & Alix. *Educ:* Univ Manchester, BScTech, 57, PhD(chem eng), 60. *Prof Exp:* Engr, Sabine River Works, E I du Pont de Nemours & Co, Inc, 60-63, engr, Plastics Dept, Exp Sta, 63-67, sr res engr, 67-70, res supvr, 70-74, sr res supvr, 74-75, prin consult, Corp Plans Dept, 75-79, mgr acquisitions & divestitures, Corp Plans Dept, 79-89. *Concurrent Pos:* Dir, Oxford Molecular Inc, Brunswick Technol, Ultra Optic Inc, Automated Dynamics Inc, Katrina Inc, TPL Inc, Toramaya Inc & ACSI Inc. *Mem:* Am Inst Chem Engrs; Soc Advan Mat & Process Eng. *Mailing Add:* 10929 Wickshire Way North Bethesda MD 20852

**WALNE, PATRICIA LEE,** CELL BIOLOGY, PHYCOLOGY. *Current Pos:* from asst prof to assoc prof, 66-73, PROF BOT, UNIV TENN, KNOXVILLE, 73-, BENWOOD DISTINGUISHED PROF, 85- *Personal Data:* b Newark, NJ, Nov 27, 32. *Educ:* Hanover Col, BS, 54; Ind Univ, MS, 59; Univ Tex, PhD(phycol, cell biol), 65. *Honors & Awards:* Darbaker Prize, Bot Soc Am, 78. *Prof Exp:* Res fel, Cell Res Inst, Univ Tex, 65-66. *Concurrent Pos:* Ed, Phycol Soc Am Newslett, 66-69; consult, Biol Div, Oak Ridge Nat Lab, 66-74; Fulbright sr res scholar Denmark, Inter-country Exchange, Turkey & WGer; prin investr res grants, NSF, 68-, adv panel, 76-78; Am Asn Univ Women sr fel, 74-75; vis res prof, Univ Copenhagen, 76, 77, 82, CNR Inst Biophys, Pisa, 93, Nencki Inst Exp Biol, Warsaw, 81, 87, 93; Nat Acad Sci US Exchange Scientist Poland, 83; Adv panel life sci, 78-80, chair, 81, area adv panel, WEurop/Scand, 86-88, coun int exchange scholars; int org comt, 2nd Int Phycol Cong, Copenhagen, Denmark, 85. *Mem:* Am Soc Cell Biol; Int Soc Evolutionary Protistology; Phycol Soc Am (secy, 69-72, vpres, 73, pres, 74); Electron Micros Soc Am; Int Phycol Soc; Brit Phycol Soc; Soc Protozoologists; fel AAAS. *Res:* Cell biology and experimental phycology; ultrastructure and development of algae; photoresponse and sensory transduction in algal flagellates; biomineralization, especially of extracellular matrices; systematic and evolutionary biology. *Mailing Add:* Dept Bot Univ Tenn Knoxville TN 37996-1100. *Fax:* 423-974-0978; *E-Mail:* walne@utkvx.utk.edu

**WALNUT, THOMAS HENRY, JR,** QUANTUM CHEMISTRY. *Current Pos:* from asst prof to assoc prof, 52-63, PROF CHEM, SYRACUSE UNIV, 63- *Personal Data:* b Philadelphia, Pa, May 22, 24; m 70; c 2. *Educ:* Harvard Univ, AB, 47; Brown Univ, PhD(chem), 51. *Prof Exp:* Instr, Inst Study Metals, Univ Chicago, 50-52. *Mem:* Am Chem Soc; Am Phys Soc. *Res:* Magnetic susceptibility of molecules; quantum chemistry; magnetic vibrational circular dichroism. *Mailing Add:* Dept Chem Syracuse Univ Syracuse NY 13244-0001

**WALOGA, GERALDINE,** NEUROBIOLOGY. *Current Pos:* res assoc, 79-80, asst prof, 80-87, ASSOC PROF PHYSIOL, BOSTON UNIV, SCH MED, 87- *Personal Data:* b Warrenton, NC, June 17, 46. *Educ:* Northwestern Univ, BA, 68; Purdue Univ, PhD(biol sci), 75. *Prof Exp:* Res assoc, Harvard Univ, 75-77 & State Univ NY, Stony Brook, 77-79. *Mem:* Asn Res Vision & Ophthal; Biophys Soc. *Res:* Interactions of cyclic nucleotides, calcium ions and the inositol polyphosphates in excitation and adaption of vertebrate photoreceptors; electrophysiology of human retinoblastoma cells. *Mailing Add:* Dept Diabetes & Metabolism Sch Med Boston Univ 80 E Concord St Boston MA 02118. *Fax:* 617-638-4273

**WALPER, JACK LOUIS,** GEOLOGY. *Current Pos:* RETIRED. *Personal Data:* b Excel, Alta, Nov 29, 16; nat US; m 43. *Educ:* Univ Okla, BS, 47, MS, 49; Univ Tex, PhD(geol), 58. *Prof Exp:* Asst geol, Univ Okla, 47-48; asst prof, Univ Tulsa, 48-54; instr, Univ Tex, 55-58; assoc prof, Univ Tulsa, 58-63; prof geol, Tex Christian Univ, 63-81. *Concurrent Pos:* Consult & mem bd dirs, Tex Archit Aggregate Co & Empresa Centro Americana, 74- *Mem:* Am Geophys Union; Asn Eng Geologists; Am Asn Petrol Geologists; Geol Soc Am; Nat Asn Geol Teachers. *Res:* Field exploration; tectonics, especially Central American tectonics. *Mailing Add:* 6517 Wrigley Way Ft Worth TX 76133

**WALPERT, GEORGE W,** CHEMICAL ENGINEERING. *Current Pos:* mgr mat eng, 64-68, MGR OPERS REV STAFF, XEROX CORP, ROCHESTER, 68- *Personal Data:* b Monett, Mo, Dec 10, 24; m 48; c 6. *Educ:* Mo Sch Mines, BS, 47; Univ Colo, MS, 51, PhD(chem eng), 54. *Prof Exp:* Chem engr, Koppers Co, Inc, 47-50; sr engr, Monsanto Chem Co, 53-57; group leader atomic fuel recovery, Phillips Petrol Co, 57-58; dir res, Wigton Develop Lab, 58-59; mgr process develop, Kordite Co Div, Nat Distillers & Chem Corp, 59-62, USI Film Prod Div, 62-63 & Kordite Co Div, Socony Mobil Oil Co, Inc, 63-64. *Mem:* Am Chem Soc; Soc Plastics Engrs. *Res:* Process and materials development in fields of coal byproducts, plastics and intermediates, pure metals, packaging materials and consumables for office machinery. *Mailing Add:* 3471 Rutgers Rd Bethlehem PA 18017

**WALPOLE, JONATHAN,** COMPUTER SCIENCE. *Current Pos:* ASSOC PROF, DEPT COMPUT SCI & ENG, ORE GRAD INST SCI & TECHNOL. *Personal Data:* b Peterborough, Eng, Sept 20, 61. *Educ:* Lancaster Univ, PhD(comput sci), 87. *Concurrent Pos:* Mem, Data Intensive Syst Ctr & Distributed Syst Res Group. *Res:* Tools for specializing systems

software; quality specification and adaptive resource management for distributed multimedia systems; migration and integrated scheduling tools for parallel processing on networks of shared heterogeneous computers. *Mailing Add:* Dept Comput Sci & Eng Ore Grad Inst Sci & Technol Portland OR 97291-1000. *Fax:* 503-690-1553; *E-Mail:* walpole@cse.ori.edu

**WALRADT, JOHN PIERCE,** FLAVOR & FRAGRANCE CHEMISTRY, LABORATORY AUTOMATION. *Current Pos:* Sr chemist, Flavor Res, Int Flavors & Fragrances, Inc, 69-71, proj leader, 71-73, group leader, Flavor Res, Anal Chem, 73-76, sr group leader, Instrumental Anal, 76-85, mgr, 85-87, DIR, RES & DEVELOP ADMIN, INT FLAVORS & FLAGRANCES, INC, 87- *Personal Data:* b Caldwell, Idaho, Feb 12, 42; m 64, Anne Frazier; c Daniel, Michael, James & Elizabeth. *Educ:* Univ Idaho, BS, 65; Ore State Univ, MS, 67, PhD(food sci), 69. *Mem:* Am Chem Soc; Inst Food Technologists. *Res:* Analytical chemistry; laboratory automation; robotics; flavor chemistry, gas chromatography, natural component identification; research facilities management. *Mailing Add:* Int Flavors & Fragrances Inc 1515 Hwy 36 Union Beach NJ 07735-3500

**WALRAFEN, GEORGE EDOUARD,** STRUCTURE WATER, STRUCTURE GLASSES. *Current Pos:* prof, 75-96, EMER PROF CHEM, HOWARD UNIV, 97- *Personal Data:* b Topeka, Kans, May 18, 29; m 60. *Educ:* Univ Kans, BS, 51, MS, 57, PhD (chem), 59. *Prof Exp:* Mem tech staff phys chem, AT&T Bell Labs, 60-75. *Concurrent Pos:* Prof phys chem, Univ Marburg, 72-73. *Mem:* Sigma Xi; Am Phys Soc. *Res:* Roman and infrared spectroscopy of water; aqueous solutions, glasses, optical fibers. *Mailing Add:* Chem Dept Howard Univ 525 College St NW Washington DC 20059-0001

**WALSBERG, GLENN ERIC,** ENVIRONMENTAL PHYSIOLOGY, BIOPHYSICAL ECOLOGY. *Current Pos:* from asst prof to assoc prof zool, 78-89, PROF ZOOL, ARIZ STATE UNIV, 89- *Personal Data:* b Long Beach, Calif, June 25, 49; m 74; c 2. *Educ:* Calif State Univ, BS, 71; Univ Calif, Los Angeles, PhD(biol), 75. *Prof Exp:* NIH fel, Wash State Univ, 76-78. *Concurrent Pos:* Ed, The Condor, 90- *Mem:* Am Ornithologists' Union; Ecol Soc Am; Cooper Ornith Soc; Am Soc Zoologists; Sci Res Soc NAm; AAAS. *Res:* Avian ecological energetics; physiological and biophysical ecology of birds and mammals; desert ecology; avian physiology. *Mailing Add:* Dept Zool Ariz State Univ Box 871501 Tempe AZ 85287-1501

**WALSER, ARMIN,** MEDICINAL CHEMISTRY. *Current Pos:* sr chemist, Nutley, NJ, 64-66, Basel, Switz, 66-69 & Nutley, NJ, 69-72, res fel med chem, 72-74, group chief med chem, 74-79, SR RES FEL, HOFFMANN-LA ROCHE, INC, 79- *Personal Data:* b Walzenhausen, Switz, Apr 6, 37; m 57; c 3. *Educ:* Swiss Fed Inst Technol, Dipl Ing Chem, 60, PhD(org chem), 63. *Prof Exp:* Fel org chem, Stanford Univ, 63-64. *Mem:* Am Chem Soc. *Res:* Synthesis of new compounds of potential pharmaceutical interest, in particular compounds acting on central nervous system. *Mailing Add:* 5900 N Camino Miraval Tucson AZ 85718-4106

**WALSER, MACKENZIE,** MEDICINE. *Current Pos:* from asst prof to assoc prof, 57-70, PROF MED & PHARMACOL, SCH MED, JOHNS HOPKINS UNIV, 70-, PHYSICIAN, JOHNS HOPKINS HOSP, 60- *Personal Data:* b New York, NY, Sept 19, 24; m 88, Elizabeth Gearon; c Karin, Jennifer, Cameron & Eric. *Educ:* Yale Univ, BA, 44; Columbia Univ, MD, 48; Am Bd Internal Med, dipl, 56. *Honors & Awards:* Exp Therapeut Award, Am Soc Pharmacol & Exp Therapeut, 75; Herman Award, Am Soc Clin Nutrit, 88; Addis Award, Int Soc Renal Nutrit & Metabol, 84. *Prof Exp:* Intern med, Mass Gen Hosp, 48-49, asst resident, 49-50; from instr to asst prof, Southwestern Med Sch, Univ Tex, Dallas, 50-52; investr, Nat Heart Inst, 54-57. *Concurrent Pos:* Resident, City-Co Hosp, Dallas, Tex, 50-52. *Mem:* Am Physiol Soc; Am Soc Clin Invest; Am Soc Pharmacol & Exp Therapeut; Am Inst Nutrit; Asn Am Physicians; Am Soc Clin Nutrit. *Res:* Medical, physiological, and pharmacological aspects of electrolyte and amino acid metabolism and renal function. *Mailing Add:* Dept Pharmacol Sch Med Johns Hopkins Univ 725 Wolfe St Baltimore MD 21205-2105

**WALSER, RONALD HERMAN,** HORTICULTURE, PLANT PHYSIOLOGY. *Current Pos:* assoc prof agron, 80-91, PROF AGRON, BRIGHAM YOUNG UNIV, 91- *Personal Data:* b Juarez, Mex, Jan 24, 44; m 67; c 5. *Educ:* Brigham Young Univ, BS, 68; Utah State Univ, PhD(crop physiol), 75. *Prof Exp:* Mgr res & develop, Hyponex Co, 75-76; asst prof, Univ Ky, 76-78; asst prof hort, Tex Tech Univ, 78-80. *Mem:* Am Soc Hort Sci. *Res:* Environmental physiology of fruits and vegetables. *Mailing Add:* Dept Agron Brigham Young Univ 275 Widb Bldg Provo UT 84062-1049

**WALSH, ARTHUR CAMPBELL,** GERIATRIC PSYCHIATRY, ALZHEIMERS DISEASE. *Current Pos:* PRES, CTR SENILITY STUDIES, 80- *Personal Data:* b Vancouver, BC, Dec 21, 19; US citizen; m 44, Bernice M Hessom; c 3. *Educ:* Univ Alta, MD, 43. *Prof Exp:* Family med pract, 45-64; fel psychiat, Western Psychiat Inst & Clin, Univ Pittsburgh, 64-67, clin asst prof, 68-90. *Concurrent Pos:* Pvt pract adult psychiat, 68-; psychiat consult, Vet Admin Hosp, Pittsburgh, 70-88; staff psychiatrist, Woodville State Hosp, 75-86. *Mem:* Am Psychiat Asn; AMA; Am Asn Geriat Psychiat; Am Geriat Soc. *Res:* Treatment program for dementia, including Alzheimer's disease; combining psychiatric therapy with medicine to improve the blood flow to the brain; legal aspects of dementia, such as competency to make a will and abnormal behavior; author of over 20 publications and two books. *Mailing Add:* Ctr Senility Studies 161 N Dithridge St Pittsburgh PA 15213

**WALSH, CHARLES JOSEPH,** NUCLEOLI, FLAGELLA. *Current Pos:* Asst prof, 73-78, ASSOC PROF BIOL SCI, UNIV PITTSBURGH, 79- *Personal Data:* b July 30, 40; m 62; c 2. *Educ:* San Diego State Univ, BS, 63; Univ Calif, Riverside, PhD(cell biol), 68. *Mem:* Am Soc Cell Biol. *Res:* Cell differentiation; regulation of gene expression; biology of cilia and flagella, naegleria biology; biology of the nucleolus. *Mailing Add:* Dept Biol Sci Univ Pittsburgh Pittsburgh PA 15260-0001. *Fax:* 412-624-4759; *E-Mail:* cwalsh@vms.cis.pitt.edu

**WALSH, CHRISTOPHER THOMAS,** BIOCHEMISTRY. *Current Pos:* David Wesley Gaiser prof, 87-91, chmn, Dept Biol Chem & Molecular Pharmacol, 87-95, HAMILTON KUHN PROF, MED SCH, HARVARD UNIV, 91- *Personal Data:* b Boston, Mass, Feb 16, 44; m 66; c 1. *Educ:* Harvard Univ, BA, 65; Rockefeller Univ, PhD(life sci), 70. *Honors & Awards:* Eli Lilly Award, 79; Baker Lectr, Univ Calif, Santa Barbara, 83; Lutz Lectr, Univ Va, 85; Troy C Daniels Lectr, Univ Calif, San Francisco, 86; Edward E Smissman Lectr, Univ Kans, 86; Guthikonda Lectr, Columbia Univ, 86; Ida Beam Lectr, Univ Iowa, 87; Nelson Leonard Lectr, Univ Ill, 89; Melvin Calvin Lectr, Univ Calif, Berkeley, 89; Dauben Lectr, Univ Wash, 90; David Green Lectr, Univ Wis, 90; Ty Shen Lectr, Mass Inst Technol, 91; Calbiochem Lectr, Univ Calif, San Diego, 91; Williams Lectr, Stanford Univ, 91; Bayer Lectr, Yale Med Sch, 92. *Prof Exp:* Helen Hay Whitney Found fel, Brandeis Univ, 70-72; from asst prof to prof chem & biol, Mass Inst Technol, 72-87, assoc dir, Whitaker Col Mgt, 79-82, Uncas & Helen Whitaker prof, 80-85, Karl Taylor Compton prof, 85-87, chmn, Chem Dept, 82-87. *Concurrent Pos:* Alfred P Sloan Found fel, 75-77; consult, Merck, Sharp & Dohme Res Labs, 75-81, Monsanto Corp Res Labs, 80-81, Johnson & Johnson, 82-83, Hoffman LaRoche, 82-, Genzyme & Bioinfo Assocs, 83-, Firmenich, SA, 86-90, Enzymatics, 88- & Biotage, 89-91; Camille & Henry Dreyfus teacher-scholar grant, 76-80; mem, Panel Res Grants Study, NSF, 77-79, Panel Study Sect Biochem, NIH, 78-82, Gen Med Coun, NIH, 83-85 & Chemal Rev Group, WHO, 84-86; biol sect ed, Ann Reports Med Chem, 78-80; co-chmn, Gordon Res Conf Enzymes, Coenzymes & Molecular Biol, 78 & Conf Methanogenesis, 84; chmn, Study Sect Biochem, NIH, 82-; assoc ed, Ann Rev Biochem, 90-; pres, Dana-Farber Cancer Inst, 92-95; bd dirs, Asn Am Cancer Inst, 93-96, Leukosite, 96-, Diacrin, 97- *Mem:* Nat Acad Sci; Inst Med-Nat Acad Sci; Am Acad Arts & Sci; Am Soc Biol Chemists; Am Chem Soc; Am Soc Microbiol. *Res:* Enzymatic reaction mechanisms, phosphoryl and pyrophosphoryl transfers; flavin-dependent enzymes; membrane biochemistry and mechanism of active transport; chemistry of energetic intermediate in biological systems; enzyme stereochemistry, molecular toxicology; signal transduction; mechanism of action of antiinfective agents and of immuno-suppressive agents. *Mailing Add:* Dept Biol Chem & Molecular Pharmacol Harvard Med Sch 240 Longwood Ave LHRRB Rm 301A Boston MA 02115

**WALSH, DAVID ALLAN,** STRUCTURE BASED DRUG DESIGN, DRUG SYNTHESIS. *Current Pos:* exec dir chem, 92-94, VPRES CHEM & DRUG DEVELOP & QUAL MGT, BIOCRYST PHARMACEUT INC, 97- *Personal Data:* b Schenectady, NY, Aug 3, 45; m 67, Judith E Levko; c Alicia & Karyn. *Educ:* Clarkson Col Tech, NY, BS, 67; Univ NH, MS, 70, PhD(org chem), 73. *Prof Exp:* NIH fel, Dept Med Chem, Sch Pharm, Univ Kans, 73-74; sr res chemist, A H Robins Co, 74-79, group mgr, 79-90; sr process chemist, Nutrasweet, 90-92. *Concurrent Pos:* Consult pharmaceut indust. *Mem:* Am Chem Soc; Int Soc Heterocydic Chem; NY Acad Sci; AAAS. *Res:* Synthesis of new nonsteroidal anti-inflammatory agents; synthesis of various nitrogen-containing heterocydes including piperidines, pyrrolidines, isoquinolines, and quinolines; synthesis of novel antiallergy agents; synthesis of enzyme inhibitors useful as drug candidates. *Mailing Add:* Biocryst Pharmaceut Inc 2190 Parkway Lake Dr Birmingham AL 35244. *Fax:* 205-444-4640

**WALSH, DON,** PHYSICAL OCEANOGRAPHY, OCEAN ENGINEERING. *Current Pos:* PRES, INT MARITIME INC, 76- *Personal Data:* b Berkeley, Calif, Nov 2, 31; m 62, Joan A Betzmer; c Kelly Elizabeth. *Educ:* US Naval Acad, BS, 54; Tex A&M Univ, MS, 67, PhD(oceanog), 68; San Diego State Col, MA, 68. *Prof Exp:* Officer-in-chg bathyscaphe Trieste, Navy Electronics Lab, USN, San Diego, Calif, 58-62, prin investr remote sensor oceanog proj, Tex A&M Univ, 65-68, sci liaison officer ocean eng, Submarine Develop Group One, San Diego, 69-70, spec asst to Asst Secy Navy Res & Develop, Navy Dept, Washington, DC, 70-73, dep dir, Navy Labs, Hq Naval Mat Command, 74-75; prof ocean eng & dir, Inst Marine & Coastal Studies, Univ Southern Calif, 75-83. *Concurrent Pos:* Partic, Deep Freeze, Antarctic, 71; fel, Woodrow Wilson Int Ctr Scholars, Smithsonian Inst, 72-74; mem, US Adv Comt, Eng Comt Ocean Resources, Nat Acad Eng, 72-82; dir, US Naval Inst, 74-75; ed, Marine Technol Soc J, 75-80; chmn, Comt Aquacult, Nat Res Coun, 76-78; pres & mem bd dirs, Int Maritime, Inc, 76-; mem, State Dept Law of Sea Adv Group, 79-83, Nat Adv Comt Oceans & Atmosphere, 79-86; mem, Comt Maritime Indust Opportunities & requirements for develop ocean resources, Nat Res Coun, Nat Acad Sci, 78-80; mem, Space Appln Adv Comt, NASA, 83-86, mem bd govs, Calif Maritime Acad, 85-95 & Marine bd, Nat Res Coun, 90-94; dir, Deep Ocean Eng, 89-; dir, Explorers Club, 93-96 & 97- *Mem:* AAAS; Am Soc Naval Engrs; hon life mem & fel Marine Technol Soc (vpres, 75-79); Soc Naval Architects & Marine Engrs; hon life mem & fel Explorers Club; fel Royal Geog Soc Eng. *Res:* Application of deep submersibles to ocean sciences; deep ocean engineering research and development; application of remote sensors to oceanography; ocean resource planning and policy; author of numerous publications. *Mailing Add:* Int Maritime Inc HC-86 Box 101 Myrtle Point OR 97458. *Fax:* 541-572-4041; *E-Mail:* 1m142north@aol.com

**WALSH, EDWARD JOHN,** INORGANIC CHEMISTRY, POLYMER CHEMISTRY. *Current Pos:* MGR MAT DEVELOP, WESTINGHOUSE & MGR, ENVIRON CONTROL, ABB POWER T&D CO, ENVIRONMENTALIST, ENVIRON RES CTR. *Personal Data:* b Brooklyn, NY, Aug 29, 42; m 64, Mary Delong; c 3. *Educ:* Franklin & Marshall Col, BA, 64; Middlebury Col, MS, 66; Pa State Univ, University Park, PhD(inorg chem), 70. *Prof Exp:* Asst prof chem, Pa State Univ, Shenango Valley Campus, 70- *Mem:* Am Chem Soc; Chem Soc; sr mem Inst Elec & Electronics Engrs. *Res:* Phosphazene derivatives; germazanes; trace elements in water aseneazenes; pcb's and fire resistant products; environmental management. *Mailing Add:* 4712 Cedarfield Dr Raleigh NC 27606. *Fax:* 919-856-2448

**WALSH, EDWARD JOSEPH,** ELECTRICAL ENGINEERING, RADIO OCEANOGRAPHY. *Current Pos:* aerospace technologist, Electronics Res Ctr, 67-70, AEROSPACE TECHNOLOGIST, NASA & GODDARD SPACE FLIGHT CTR, WALLOPS FLIGHT FACIL, 70- *Personal Data:* b Woonsocket, RI, June 13, 41; m 73; c 1. *Educ:* Northeastern Univ, BS, 63, PhD(elec eng), 67. *Prof Exp:* Instr elec eng, Northeastern Univ, 66-67. *Concurrent Pos:* Mem, Comn F, Union Radio Sci Int. *Mem:* Inst Elec & Electronics Engrs. *Res:* Electromagnetic theory; radio wave propagation and scattering; radio oceanography; radar altimetry. *Mailing Add:* NASA/Goddard Space Flight Ctr Wallops Flight Facil E 106 Wallops Island VA 23337

**WALSH, EDWARD JOSEPH, JR,** ORGANIC CHEMISTRY. *Current Pos:* from asst prof to prof, 68-86, DEPT CHMN, ALLEGHENY COL, 70-, PAUL E HILL PROF CHEM, 86- *Personal Data:* b Philadelphia, Pa, Aug 2, 35; m 78, Kirsten Peterson; c Shioban. *Educ:* State Univ NY, Albany, BS, 60; Univ NH, PhD(chem), 64. *Prof Exp:* Teaching asst, State Univ NY, Albany, 60-61. *Concurrent Pos:* NSF sci fac grant, Mass Inst Technol, 69-70. *Mem:* Am Chem Soc. *Res:* Free radical reactions involving the acyl radical; free radical reactions of certain organotin hydrides. *Mailing Add:* Allegheny Col PO Box 166 Meadville PA 16335-3902

**WALSH, EDWARD KYRAN,** ENGINEERING SCIENCE, APPLIED MECHANICS. *Current Pos:* assoc prof, 70-74, PROF ENG SCI, UNIV FLA, 74- *Personal Data:* b Philadelphia, Pa, Feb 19, 31; m 52; c 6. *Educ:* Union Col, BME, 63; Brown Univ, PhD(appl math), 67. *Prof Exp:* Engr, Mech Technol Inc, 62-63; res fel, Mellon Inst Sci, 66-68; asst prof civil eng, Carnegie-Mellon Univ, 67-70. *Concurrent Pos:* Consult, Gen Eng & Consult Lab, Gen Elec Co, 64-65, Sandia Labs, Albuquerque, 69-82, Vet Admin Hosp, Richmond, 80- *Mem:* Soc Natural Philos. *Res:* Continuum mechanics; dynamic material response; wave propagation; bioengineering. *Mailing Add:* Dept Eng Sci Univ Fla Gainesville FL 32611-2002

**WALSH, EDWARD NELSON,** SYNTHETIC INORGANIC & ORGANOMETALLIC CHEMISTRY. *Current Pos:* CONSULT, 86- *Personal Data:* b Chicago, Ill, Nov 22, 25; m 50; c 2. *Educ:* Ill Inst Technol, BS, 48, PhD, 65; DePaul Univ, MS, 52. *Prof Exp:* Chemist, Swift & Co, Ill, 48-51 & Victor Chem Works, 51-59; supvr org res, 59-63, Dobbs Ferry, mgr chem res, 63-65, mgr chem prod develop sect, 65-69, sr sect mgr org res, 69-75, mgr chem dept, 75-83, sr scientist, Stauffer Chem Co, Dobbs Ferry, 83-85, adj lectr, 85-86; asst prof, St Peters Col, Jersey City, NJ, 86-89. *Mem:* AAAS; Am Chem Soc; Sigma Xi. *Res:* Organophosphorus compounds; agricultural chemicals; solvents; surfactants; flame retardants; synthetic lubricants; pharmaceutical intermediates; organometallics; photochemistry; catalysts; inorganic phosphorus compounds. *Mailing Add:* 33 Concord Dr New City NY 10956

**WALSH, GARY LYNN,** AIR POLLUTION, ENVIRONMENTAL SCIENCES. *Current Pos:* admin asst to air pollution control officer, Lincoln Lancaster Co Health Dept, 72-74, supvr, Air Pollution Control Sect, 74-79, asst chief, 79-84, chief, 84-89, ENVIRON ENGR AIR QUAL, DIV ENVIRON HEALTH, LINCOLN LANCASTER CO HEALTH DEPT, 89- *Personal Data:* b Fremont, Nebr, June 30, 40; m 64. *Educ:* Midland Lutheran Col, BS, 62; Univ Nebr, MS, 65; Univ SDak, PhD(zool), 69. *Prof Exp:* Asst prof zool, Ind Univ Northwest, 69-70; air pollution control chief, Michigan City, Ind, 70-72. *Mem:* Air Pollution Control Asn. *Res:* Role of vitamin B12, biotin and thiamine on seasonal fluctuations of euglenophyte populations; taxonomy of Antarctic freshwater and soil amoeba. *Mailing Add:* 6050 Normal Blvd Lincoln NE 68506-2764

**WALSH, GERALD MICHAEL,** PHARMACOLOGY. *Current Pos:* EXEC DIR BIOL SCI, BIOCRYST PHARMACEUT INC. *Personal Data:* b Portland, Ore, Sept, 1, 44; m 70; c 5. *Educ:* Univ Santa Clara, BS, 66; Ore State Univ, PhD(pharmacol), 71; John Marshall Law Sch, JD, 84. *Prof Exp:* Res asst pharmacol, Ore State Univ, 67-69; asst prof, Univ Ga, 70-74; asst prof res med, Sch Med, Univ Okla, 74-76; staff scientist, Alton Ochsner Med Found, 76-78; mgr cardiovasc pharmacol, Baxter-Travenol, 78-81; group leader, Dept Pharmacol, G D Searle & Co, 81- *Concurrent Pos:* NIH instnl res grant, 81-; Ochsner Found, 76-79. *Mem:* Am Soc Pharmacol & Exp Therapeut; Soc Exp Biol Med. *Res:* Cardiovascular pharmacology and toxicology; hypertension. *Mailing Add:* Biocryst Pharmaceut Inc 2190 Parkway Lake Dr Birmingham AL 35244

**WALSH, JAMES ALOYSIUS,** ORGANOSULFUR CHEMISTRY. *Current Pos:* from asst prof to assoc prof, 63-73, chmn dept, 69-72, 77-81, PROF CHEM, JOHN CARROLL UNIV, 73- *Personal Data:* b Brooklyn, NY, Dec 15, 33; m 60. *Educ:* Fordham Univ, BS, 55; Purdue Univ, MS, 58, PhD(org chem), 63. *Prof Exp:* Instr chem, Purdue Univ, 60-63. *Concurrent Pos:* Res assoc, Univ Calif, Santa Cruz, 73; summer res consult, Diamond Shamrock Corp, 80; vis prof, Ohio State Univ, 84. *Mem:* Am Chem Soc; Sigma Xi. *Res:* Chemistry of organo-sulfur compounds, especially sulfoxides and derivatives of sulfurtrioxide; phthalocyanines. *Mailing Add:* Dept Chem John Carroll Univ North Park & Miramar Cleveland OH 44118

**WALSH, JAMES PAUL,** ocean engineering; deceased, see previous edition for last biography

**WALSH, JOHN BREFFNI,** radar systems, operation analysis, for more information see previous edition

**WALSH, JOHN E,** CLIMATE CHANGE, ARCTIC & ANTARCTIC POLAR CLIMATE. *Current Pos:* PROF ATMOSPHERIC SCI, UNIV ILL, 74- *Personal Data:* b Philadelphia, Pa, Aug 9, 48; m 71, Laura Lynn; c Rachel & Emily. *Educ:* Dartmouth Col, BA, 70; Mass Inst Technol, PhD(meteorol), 74. *Concurrent Pos:* Vis scientist, Nat Ctr Atmospheric Res, 76-77; chair, Comt Polar Meteorol, Am Meteorol Soc, 80-81; chair arctic marine sci, Off Naval Res, 86; vis prof, Naval Postgrad Sch, 86-87 & Univ Alaska, 92-96; mem, Climate Res Comt, Nat Res Coun, 89-92. *Mem:* Fel Am Meteorol Soc; Am Geophys Union; AAAS. *Res:* Climate change, as affected by processes in polar regions; variability of sea ice; frequency and intensity of severe weather events in context of global climate change. *Mailing Add:* 105 S Gregory Ave Urbana IL 61801. *Fax:* 217-244-4393; *E-Mail:* walsh@atmos.uiuc.edu

**WALSH, JOHN EDMOND,** ELECTRON BEAMS, RADIATION & ACCELERATORS. *Current Pos:* from asst prof to assoc prof, 68-79, PROF PHYSICS, DARTMOUTH COL, 79-, FRANCIS & MILDRED SEARS PROF PHYSICS, 89-, ASSOC DEAN FAC SCI, 94- *Personal Data:* b New York, NY, Aug 20, 39; m 66; c 3. *Educ:* NS Tech Col, BSc, 62; Columbia Univ, MSc, 65, DSc, 68. *Prof Exp:* Res engr, US Army Signal Res & Develop Lab, Ft Monmouth, 62-65. *Mem:* Fel Am Phys Soc; Sigma Xi; Optical Soc Am. *Res:* Millimeter and submillimeter radiation sources; free electron lasers theory and experiment; radio frequency accelerators; far infrared spectrosonic techniques. *Mailing Add:* Dept Physics Dartmouth Col Hanover NH 03755

**WALSH, JOHN H,** INTERNAL MEDICINE, GASTROENTEROLOGY. *Current Pos:* PROF MED, SCH MED, UNIV CALIF, LOS ANGELES, 78- *Personal Data:* b Jackson, Miss, Aug 22, 38; m 89, Mary C Territo; c Harley & Courtney. *Educ:* Vanderbilt Univ, BA, 59, MD, 63. *Honors & Awards:* Fiterman/Kirsmer Prize, Am Gastroenterol Asn. *Concurrent Pos:* Dir, CURE Gastroenteric Biol Ctr. *Mem:* Am Soc Clin Invest; Am Physiol Soc; Asn Am Physicians; Am Gastroenterol Asn; Endocrine Soc. *Res:* Study hormones and receptors involved in regulation of gastric secretion and pathophysiology of peptic ulcer. *Mailing Add:* Univ Calif 247 S Carmelina Ave Los Angeles CA 90049-3903. *Fax:* 310-312-9279

**WALSH, JOHN HERITAGE,** ENERGY & ENVIRONMENT INTERFACE, CARBON DIOXIDE & CLIMATE CHANGE. *Current Pos:* PVT PRACT, ENERGY ADV, 85- *Personal Data:* b Montreal, Que, Jan 3, 29; m 58, Barbara Magee; c D'Arcy & John. *Educ:* McGill Univ, BEng, 50, MEng, 51; Mass Inst Technol, ScD, 55. *Honors & Awards:* Airey Award, Can Inst Mining & Metall, 68, Coal Award, 89; Joseph Beck Award, Int Steel Soc, 78. *Prof Exp:* Res scientist, Dept Energy, Mines & Resources, 55-80, sr adv, Coal, 80-85. *Concurrent Pos:* Fr grant fel, study Fr steel indust, 58; ed/publ, Can Metall Quart, 62-68; Imp Oil Ltd lectr, Univ Western Ont, 83. *Mem:* Fel Am Soc Metals; fel Can Inst Inst Mining & Metall; Am Inst Mining, Metall & Petrol Engrs; Int Asn Energy Economists. *Res:* Application of fossil fuels under conditions of a limit of carbon dioxide emissions; technical and policy aspects; thermodynamics; material properties. *Mailing Add:* 19 Lambton Ave Ottawa ON K1M 0Z6 Can. *E-Mail:* dwalsh@magi.com

**WALSH, JOHN JOSEPH,** ECOLOGY, OCEANOGRAPHY. *Current Pos:* grad res prof, 84-91, DISTINGUISHED RES PROF MARINE SCI, UNIV SFLA, 91- *Personal Data:* b Cambridge, Mass, Sept 11, 42; m 69. *Educ:* Harvard Univ, AB, 64; Univ Miami, MS, 68, PhD(marine sci), 69. *Honors & Awards:* Gold Medal Sci, Univ de Liege, 80. *Prof Exp:* Fel, Univ Wash, 69-70, res asst prof oceanog, 70-75; head div oceanog sci, Brookhaven Nat Lab, 75-84. *Mem:* AAAS; Am Soc Limnol & Oceanog. *Res:* Shelf ecosystems; systems analysis; statistics; phytoplankton ecology; mathematical models; theoretical ecology. *Mailing Add:* Univ SFla Marine Sci 140 Seventh Ave S St Petersburg FL 33701-5016

**WALSH, JOHN JOSEPH,** CARDIOLOGY. *Current Pos:* RETIRED. *Personal Data:* b New York, NY, July 31, 24; m, Dorothy B Ray; c Maureen, John J & Kathleen. *Educ:* Long Island Col Med, MD, 48; Am Bd Internal Med, dipl, 58. *Prof Exp:* Intern, USPHS Hosp, NY, 48-49, resident med, Seattle, Wash, 51-54, asst chief med, New Orleans, La, 54-56, dep chief, 56; from instr med to asst prof clin med, Tulane Univ, 57-60, dean, Sch Med & coordr health serv, 68-69, prof med, Sch Med, 60-89, vpres health affairs, 69-89, chancellor med ctr, 72-89. *Concurrent Pos:* Fel cardiol, Sch Med, Tulane Univ, 57-58, instr, 55-; vis physician, Charity Hosp, 55-; chief res activ, USPHS, 58-64, chief med, 63-64, med officer in-chg, 64-66, dir, Div Direct Health Serv, 66-68, asst surgeon gen. *Mem:* Am Thoracic Soc; AMA; fel Am Col Cardiol; fel Am Col Physicians; fel Am Col Chest Physicians. *Res:* Cardiopulmonary diseases with emphasis on cardiomyopathics. *Mailing Add:* 24 Orphem Ave Metairie LA 70005

**WALSH, JOHN M,** PHYSICS, CONTINUUM DYNAMICS. *Current Pos:* mem staff, 74-88, LAB ASSOC, LOS ALAMOS NAT LAB, 88 - *Personal Data:* b Wichita Falls, Tex, Nov 6, 23; m 52; c 3. *Educ:* Univ Tex, BS, 47, PhD(physics), 50. *Honors & Awards:* Shock Compression Award, Am Phys Soc, 87. *Prof Exp:* Staff mem, Los Alamos Sci Lab, 50-60; staff mem, Gen Atomic Div, Gen Dynamics Corp, 60-67; mgr continuum mech div, Systs Sci & Software, 67-74. *Mem:* Am Phys Soc. *Res:* Shock hydrodynamics; shock wave physics; properties of materials at extreme pressures; experimental, theoretical and numerical work in these areas and supervision of groups so involved; fluid dynamics. *Mailing Add:* Rt 1 Box 198A Santa Fe NM 87501

**WALSH, JOHN PAUL,** ORGANIC CHEMISTRY. *Current Pos:* RES MGR, ADCO CHEM CO, 92- *Personal Data:* b Rochester, NY, Dec 29, 42; c 2. *Educ:* Purdue Univ, Lafayette, BS, 64; Univ Wis-Madison, MS, 66; Univ Tex, Austin, PhD(org chem), 70. *Prof Exp:* Sr res chemist, Org Res Dept, Pennwalt Corp, Pa, 69-74; res chemist, Para-Chem Inc, 74-76; sr appl chemist, Celanese Chem Co, Inc, 76-86; Chemist, BASF Corp, 86-91. *Mem:* Am Chem Soc. *Res:* Organic synthesis; organosulfur, nitrogen and phosphorus; alkyds; polyesters; urea-formaldehyde resins; rosins. *Mailing Add:* 295 Whippany Rd Whippany NJ 07981-1941

**WALSH, JOHN RICHARD,** INTERNAL MEDICINE. *Current Pos:* head, Div Geront, 78-92, dir, Ore Geriat Educ Ctr, 89-94, PROF MED, MED SCH, UNIV ORE, 60- *Personal Data:* b San Francisco, Calif, Aug 22, 20; m 44, Nellie K Netherola; c 5. *Educ:* Creighton Univ, BS, 43, MD, 45, MSc, 51; Am Bd Internal Med, dipl, 53. *Honors & Awards:* Milo D Leavitt Mem Lectr Award, Am Geriat Soc, 90. *Prof Exp:* Actg asst med, Sch Med, Creighton Univ, 51-52, asst, 52-53, from instr to assoc prof, 53-57, prof & dir dept, 57-60. *Concurrent Pos:* Ward physician, Vet Admin Hosp, Omaha, Nebr, 51-52, asst chief med serv, 52-53, actg chief, 53-54, chief, 54-56; assoc, Col Med, Univ Nebr, 53-55, asst prof, 55-56; chief, Portland, Ore, 60-78, actg chief radioisotope serv, 62-70. *Mem:* Am Fedn Clin Res; fel Am Col Physicians; Am Geriatrics Soc. *Res:* Hematology. *Mailing Add:* Health Sci Ctr Sch Med Univ Ore 3181 SW Jackson Park Rd Portland OR 97201-3011. *Fax:* 503-220-3471

**WALSH, JOHN THOMAS,** ANALYTICAL CHEMISTRY. *Current Pos:* RES CHEMIST, STATE RI DEPT TRANSP LABS, 86- *Personal Data:* b Lincoln, RI, Dec 23, 27; m 52; c 3. *Educ:* Providence Col, BS, 50; Univ RI, MS, 52, PhD(chem), 65. *Prof Exp:* Res chemist, Rumford Chem Works, RI, 52-54; res chemist, US Army Natick Labs, 54-86. *Mem:* Am Chem Soc; Am Soc Testing & Mat. *Res:* Analytical instrumentation research in the areas of gas chromatography and mass spectrometry; applications have been the composition study of natural products such as foods and biologicals; investigation of toxic pollutants in air, water and solid wastes by analytical methods of gas and liquid chromatography and mass spectrometry; fourier transform infrared spectroscopy as an area of analytical instrumentation research; bacterial degradation products of military materials such as foods, clothing and munitions; investigation of tricothecene mycotoxins by analytical methods of gas and liquid chromatography and mass spectronmetry; investigation of protective coating materials via fourier transform IR spectroscopy and gas chromatography. *Mailing Add:* 15 Ridgeland Dr Cumberland RI 02864

**WALSH, JOHN V,** MEMBRANE PHYSIOLOGY. *Current Pos:* Assoc prof, 81-86, PROF PHYSIOL, SCH MED, UNIV MASS, 86- *Personal Data:* b Okla, Dec 11, 42. *Educ:* Harvard Univ, MD, 70. *Mem:* Soc Neurosci; Am Physiol Soc; Biophys Soc; AAAS. *Mailing Add:* Dept Physiol Sch Med Univ Mass 55 Lake Ave N Worcester MA 01655

**WALSH, JOSEPH BROUGHTON,** GEOLOGY, GEOPHYSICS. *Current Pos:* res assoc geol & geophys, 63-72, SR RES SCIENTIST, DEPT EARTH & PLANETARY SCI, MASS INST TECHNOL, 72- *Personal Data:* b Utica, NY, Sept 5, 30; m 62; c 1. *Educ:* Mass Inst Technol, SB, 52, SM, 54, ME, 56, ScD(mech eng), 58. *Prof Exp:* Engr, Foster Miller Assocs, Inc, 57-59, A-b DeLaval Ljungstrom Angturbin, 59-60 & Woods Hole Oceanog Inst, 60-63; part-time vis prof, 63-64. *Res:* Theoretical analysis of various properties of rock, especially strength, elastic moduli and seismic attenuation, and analysis of how these properties should affect behavior in situ. *Mailing Add:* Box 22 Adamsville RI 02801

**WALSH, KENNETH ALBERT,** CHEMICAL METALLURGY, CERAMICS. *Current Pos:* RETIRED. *Personal Data:* b Yankton, SDak, May 23, 22; m 44, Dorothy Thompson; c Jeanne K, Kenneth A, David B, Rhonda J & Leslie G. *Educ:* Yankton Col, BA, 42; Iowa State Univ, PhD(chem), 50. *Prof Exp:* Asst prof chem, Iowa State Univ, 50-51; mem staff, Los Alamos Sci Lab, 51-57; supvr inorg chem res, Int Minerals & Chem Corp, 57-60; assoc dir technol, Brush Wellman Inc, Elmore, 60-86. *Concurrent Pos:* Consult, 86- *Mem:* Soc Mining Engrs; Am Chem Soc; Int Am Soc Metals. *Res:* Beryllium metal extraction; role of trace elements in properties of beryllium; beryllium chemicals, ecology, and electronic materials. *Mailing Add:* 2106 Kensington Dr Tyler TX 75703-2232

**WALSH, KENNETH ANDREW,** BIOCHEMISTRY, PROTEIN SCIENCE. *Current Pos:* res instr, 59-62, from asst prof to assoc prof, 62-65, PROF BIOCHEM, UNIV WASH, 69-, CHAIR BIOCHEM, 90- *Personal Data:* b Sherbrooke, Que, Aug 7, 31; m 53, Deirdre Clarke; c Andrew, Michael & Erin. *Educ:* McGill Univ, BSc, 51; Purdue Univ, MS, 53; Univ Toronto, PhD, 59. *Prof Exp:* Jr res officer, Nat Res Coun Can, 53-55. *Mem:* Am Soc Biol Chemists; Protein Soc. *Res:* Structure and function of proteins; mechanisms of zymogen activation and protease action; amino acid sequence and protein conformation; molecular evolution; domain structure of regulated proteins; mass spectrometry of proteins. *Mailing Add:* Dept Biochem Univ Wash Box 357350 Seattle WA 98195. *Fax:* 206-685-9231; *E-Mail:* walsh@u.washington.edu

**WALSH, LEO MARCELLUS,** SOIL FERTILITY, SOIL SCIENCE. *Current Pos:* Asst prof & exten specialist, Univ Wis-Madison, 59-64, assoc prof, 64-68, prof soils, 68-91, chmn, 72-79, dean, Col Agr & Life Sci, 79-91, PROF EXTEN SOIL SCI, UNIV WIS-MADISON, 91- *Personal Data:* b Moorland, Iowa, Jan 16, 31; m 58. *Educ:* Iowa State Univ, BS, 52; Univ Wis, MS, 57, PhD(soils), 59. *Concurrent Pos:* Mem, Comn Consumer Needs & Opportunities, Bd Agr, Nat Res Coun; bd dirs, Nat Nonpoint Source Inst, secy & treas, 85. *Mem:* Fel Soil Sci Soc Am (pres, 79); fel AAAS; fel Am Soc Agron; Soil Conserv Soc Am. *Res:* Use of nitrogen and sulfur fertilizers; use of zinc, manganese and other micronutrients; soil fertility, especially for corn and other cash crops; disposal of wastes on agricultural land; soil conservation; water quality as influenced by agricultural practices. *Mailing Add:* Dept Soil & Sci Univ Wis 1525 Observatory Dr Madison WI 53706

**WALSH, MICHAEL PATRICK,** MUSCLE BIOCHEMISTRY, CELL REGULATION. *Current Pos:* from asst prof to assoc prof, 82-90, PROF BIOCHEM, DEPT MED BIOCHEM, UNIV CALGARY, 90- *Personal Data:* b Liverpool, Eng, Feb 20, 51; Brit & Can citizen; m 72, Mary Lynch; c Katy & Emma. *Educ:* Univ Col, Dublin, BSc, 74; Univ Manitoba, PhD(biochem), 78. *Honors & Awards:* Ayerst Award, Can Biochem Soc, 90; EWR Steacie Prize, 90. *Prof Exp:* Teaching fel, Nat Ctr Sci Res, Montpellier, France, 78-80; res assoc, Dept Nutrit & Food Sci, Univ Ariz, 80-82. *Concurrent Pos:* Vis scientist, Lab Molecular Biol, Med Res Coun, Cambridge, Eng, 88-89; consult, Upstate Biotechnol, Inc, 92- *Mem:* Am Soc Biochem & Molecular Biol; Biophys Soc; Biochem Soc UK; Can Soc Biochem & Molecular Biol (vpres, 93-94). *Res:* Study of the biochemical mechanisms involved in the regulation of smooth muscle contraction, particularly protein phosphorylations; study of calcium-binding proteins and their involvement in the physiological regulation of the activities of various enzymes. *Mailing Add:* Dept Med Biochem Univ Calgary 3330 Calgary AB T2N 4N1 Can. *Fax:* 403-283-1841; *E-Mail:* walsh@acs.ucalgary.ca

**WALSH, NICOLAS EUGENE,** PHYSICAL MEDICINE & REHABILITATION, PAIN MANAGEMENT. *Current Pos:* from asst prof to assoc prof, 82-89, PROF & CHMN, DEPT REHAB MED, HEALTH SCI CTR, UNIV TEX, SAN ANTONIO, 89- *Personal Data:* b Minneapolis, Minn, July 1, 47; m 73, Wendy Sarah; c Meghan Kathleen, Rorey Marie, Katlin Courtney & Alaine Landy. *Educ:* USAF Acad, BS, 69; Marquette Univ, MS, 74; Univ Colo, MD, 79. *Honors & Awards:* Richard & Hinda Rosenthal Found Award, Am Acad Pain Mgt & Res, 91. *Prof Exp:* Asst prof, Marquette Univ, 72-72. *Concurrent Pos:* Mem bd dirs, Archives Phys Med & Rehab, 90-, ed chief, 94-; mem bd dirs, Am Bd Phys Med & Rehab, 93-, secy, 95- *Mem:* Asn Acad Physiatrists (pres-elect, 95-96, pres 97-). *Mailing Add:* Dept Rehab Med Health Sci Ctr Univ Tex 7703 Floyd Curl Dr San Antonio TX 78284-7798. *Fax:* 210-567-5354; *E-Mail:* walshn@uthscsa.edu

**WALSH, PATRICK C,** UROLOGY, ENDOCRINOLOGY. *Current Pos:* DAVID HALL MCCONNELL PROF & DIR, DEPT UROL, JOHNS HOPKINS UNIV SCH MED, 74-, UROLOGIST-IN-CHIEF, JAMES BUCHANAN BRADY UROL INST, 74- *Personal Data:* b Feb 13, 38. *Educ:* Case Western Res Univ, AB, 60, MD, 64; Am Bd Urol, cert. *Honors & Awards:* First Prize Lab Res, Am Urol Asn, 70, First Prize Clin Res, 74, Gold Cystoscope Award, 78, William R Smart Film Award, 85, Triennial Eugene Fuller Prostate Award, 86, Hugh Hampton Young Award, 96; Grand Officer Order Leopold, Kingdom Belg, 92; Ellen Browning Scripps Soc Medal, 93; Ramon Guiteras Lectr, Am Urol Asn, 93; Barringer Medal, Am Asn Genitourinary Surgeons, 95; Charles F Kettering Medal, Gen Motors Cancer Res Found, 96. *Prof Exp:* Intern surg, 64-65, Peter Bent Brigham Hosp, Boston, jr asst resident surg, 65-66; asst resident pediat surg, Children's Hosp Med Ctr, Boston, 66-67; resident urol, Univ Calif, Los Angeles, 67-71; urologist, Naval Hosp, San Diego, 71-73. *Concurrent Pos:* Fel endocrinol, Univ Calif Sch Med, Los Angeles, Harbor Gen Hosp Campus, 68-70; asst clin prof surg/urol, Univ Calif, San Diego, 71-73; vis asst prof med, Div Metabol, Univ Tex Southwestern Med Sch, 73-74; consult, Naval Hosp, Md, 74-96, Nat Cancer Inst, NIH, Md, 74-89, HEW, NIH Clin Ctr, Md, 74-89, Baltimore City Hosps, 74-84, Good Samaritan Hosp, Md, 74-85, Dept Army, Walter Reed Hosp, Washington, DC, 75-96, Am Urol Asn Continuing Educ Comt, 75-78, Food & Drug Admin, Md, 75-83 & St Joseph's Hosp, Md, 75-86; asst ed, J Urol, 74-86; Dornier Innovative res award, Am Found Urol Dis, 94. *Mem:* Inst Med-Nat Acad Sci; Am Asn Genito-Urinary Surgeons; Am Surg Asn; Am Urol Asn; Am Fertil Soc; Am Soc Andrology; Clin Soc Genito-Urinary Surgeons; Endocrine Soc; fel Am Col Surgeons; Soc Univ Surgeons; Soc Urol Oncol. *Res:* Nuclear localization of androgen receptors in the prostate; balloon occlusion of varicocles; stage A prostate cancer; autosomal dominant inheritance of Peyronie's disease; nerve-sparing radical prostatectomy for preservation of sexual function; cavernous nerve grafts to restore erectile function; contributed articles to professional journals. *Mailing Add:* James Buchanan Brady Urol Inst Baltimore MD 21287-2101

**WALSH, PATRICK NOEL,** HIGH TEMPERATURE CHEMISTRY, METAL & CERAMIC COATINGS. *Current Pos:* RETIRED. *Personal Data:* b New York, NY, Dec 7, 30; m 62; c 5. *Educ:* Fordham Univ, BS, 51, MS, 52, PhD(chem), 56. *Prof Exp:* Res assoc high temperature chem, Ohio State Univ, 56-60; mem staff, Union Carbide Res Inst, NY, 60-66 & Space Sci & Eng Lab, 66-68, res assoc, Linde Div, 68-81, consult, Coatings Serv Dept, Union Carbide Corp, 82-93. *Mem:* Am Soc Metals; Electrochem Soc; Am Chem Soc. *Res:* Thermodynamics and kinetics of high temperature chemical processes; formulation, deposition and analysis of wear-resistant coatings. *Mailing Add:* 3234 Lincoln Ct Indianapolis IN 46228

**WALSH, PETER,** PHYSICS. *Current Pos:* PROF PHYSICS & ELEC ENG, FAIRLEIGH DICKINSON UNIV, 63- *Personal Data:* b New York, NY, Aug 21, 29; m 52; c 5. *Educ:* Fordham Univ, BS, 51; NY Univ, MS, 53, PhD(physics), 60. *Honors & Awards:* Outstanding Res Award, Picatinny Arsenal, 72 & 73. *Prof Exp:* Sr scientist, Westinghouse Lamp Div, NY, 51-61; instr physics & math, eve sch, Wagner Col, 57-63; supvr physics res, Am Stand Res Lab, NJ, 61-63. *Concurrent Pos:* Dir, NSF Undergrad Partic Prog, Fairleigh Dickinson Univ, 63-; consult, S-F-D Labs, 63-66, Am Stand, 63, Belock Instr, 63-64, Nuclear Res Assocs, 64-65, Thiokol Chem, 64, US Army Res Off, 64-71, 77, 80, Curtiss Wright Corp, 65, Singer Corp, 68, Picatinny Arsenal, 70-74, Corning Glass, 71, Columbus Labs, Battelle Mem Inst, 74-75, Duro Test Corp, 76-89, Xerox Corp, 79-83, Mass Inst Technol, 80, Polaroid, 81 & 84, Peak Systs & Vet Admin, 85, Valore McAllister, 87, Qwest, 88-; vis res scientist, Mass Inst Technol, 77; vis prof, Univ Sheffield, 78 & 79, Univ Genova, 84 & Stanford Univ, 84 & 85; NASA fel, 80, 83 & 87; Nat Res Lab fel, 81, 82, 86, 88 & 90; invited speaker for various asn, 70-90; Res Award, DOA, 75. *Mem:* AAAS; Am Phys Soc; Optical Soc Am; Mat Res Soc. *Res:* Optics; amorphous semiconductors; lasers; quantum physics; plasmas; artificial intelligence; super conductivity. *Mailing Add:* 40 St Joseph's Dr Stirling NJ 07980

**WALSH, PETER NEWTON,** HEMATOLOGY. *Current Pos:* asst prof, 72-74, ASSOC PROF INTERNAL MED, HEALTH SCI CTR, TEMPLE UNIV, 75- *Personal Data:* b Chicago, Ill, Apr 16, 35; m 58, Marion E Knight; c Theodore S, Kathleen V & Elizabeth K. *Educ:* Amherst Col, BA, 57; Washington Univ, MD, 61; Oxford Univ, DPhil(med), 72; Am Bd Internal Med, dipl, 68. *Honors & Awards:* First Int Prize, Viviana Luckhaus Found, Arg, 72; Jane Nugent Cochems Prize, Univ Colo Sch Med, 74. *Prof Exp:* Intern internal med, Barnes Hosp, St Louis, 61-62, resident, 62-63; fel hemat, Sch Med, Wash Univ, 63-69; res fel blood coagulation, Oxford Haemophilia Ctr, Churchill Hosp, 69-72. *Concurrent Pos:* Sr resident, Palo Alto Stanford Hosp, 64-65; chief resident, Sch Med, Wash Univ, 65-66; asst physician, Barnes Hosp, 65-66; med liaison officer, Nat Heart Inst, 66-69; NIH res fel, 69-72; hon sr registr med, United Oxford Hosps, 69-72; assoc ed, Thrombosis et Diathesis Haemorrhagica, 76-; mem, Exec Comt Coun Thrombosis, Am Heart Asn. *Mem:* Int Soc Thrombosis & Haemostasis; Am Physiol Soc; Soc Exp Med & Biol; Am Soc Clin Invest; Am Soc Biochem Molecular Biol. *Res:* Role of blood platelets in blood coagulation, hemostasis and thrombosis; coagulation factor biochemistry; mechanisms of binding of coagulation factors to platelets; role of platelet coagulant activities in thrombosis. *Mailing Add:* Med Biochem Thrombosis Res Temple Univ 3400 N Broad St Philadelphia PA 19140. *Fax:* 215-707-2783

**WALSH, RAYMOND ROBERT,** PHYSIOLOGY. *Current Pos:* prof & chmn dept, 72-88, EMER PROF BIOL, ST LOUIS UNIV, 88- *Personal Data:* b Denver, Colo, Apr 9, 25; m 52; c 6. *Educ:* Cornell Univ, AB, 50, PhD(zool), 53. *Prof Exp:* Assoc res physiologist, Brookhaven Nat Lab, 53-55; from instr to assoc prof physiol, Sch Med, Univ Colo, Denver, 55-71; prof, Sch Dent, Southern Ill Univ, 71-72. *Mem:* Am Physiol Soc; Am Soc Zoologists; Soc Exp Biol & Med; Sigma Xi. *Res:* Neurobiology; comparative physiology. *Mailing Add:* 112 Hollyhock Lane Edwardsville IL 62025-4227

**WALSH, ROBERT JEROME,** SEMICONDUCTOR MATERIALS, CHEMO-MECHANICAL POLISHING. *Current Pos:* RETIRED. *Personal Data:* b Chicago, Ill, Jan 12, 29; div; c 3. *Educ:* Univ Wis, BS, 50. *Prof Exp:* Res engr, Monsanto Co, 51-55, sr res engr, 55-58, res group leader, 58-62, sr res group leader, 62-70, fel, 70-81, sr fel, 81-85. *Res:* Semiconductor materials technology including growth of single crystals, epitaxial deposition, damage free polished surfaces and ultracleaning of surfaces, ultraflat sicicon wafers; ultraflat silicon wafers. *Mailing Add:* 356 Sudbury Lane Ballwin MO 63011-2470

**WALSH, ROBERT MICHAEL,** PHYSICAL CHEMISTRY. *Current Pos:* RETIRED. *Personal Data:* b Wilmington, Del, Jan 28, 38; m 61; c Elizabeth (Conaty), Maura (Dinenberg), Michael R & Christopher D. *Educ:* Univ Del, BS, 60; Univ Calif, Berkeley, PhD(chem), 65. *Prof Exp:* Res chemist, Hercules Inc, 65-72, sr res chemist, 72-80, res scientist, 80-85, res assoc, 85-90, corp mgr technol, 90-92, dir corp res, 92-95. *Concurrent Pos:* Tech dir, Esgraph, 85-86. *Mem:* Licensing Exec Soc; Am Chem Soc; Sigma Xi; Technol Transfer Soc. *Res:* Photoprocesses in materials; photographic systems; polymer systems. *Mailing Add:* 1800 Mount Salem Lane Wilmington DE 19806. *E-Mail:* rmwalsh@earthlink.net

**WALSH, ROBERT R(EDDINGTON),** ELECTRICAL ENGINEERING, PHYSICS. *Current Pos:* RETIRED. *Personal Data:* b Wilmington, Del, Nov 4, 27. *Educ:* St Mary's Col, Md, AB, 53. *Prof Exp:* Engr, E I du Pont de Nemours & Co, 54-59, res engr, 59-60; asst to dir appl physics, All Am Eng Co, 60-61, dir, Mkt & Prod Develop Div, 61-63, dir res, 63-66; exec vpres & gen mgr, Technidyne, Inc, 67-71; pub rels asst, 71-72; electronics consult, Advan Technol Prod, Inc, Newark, 73-76; tech planning staff mem, Wilmington Trust Co, 76-79, asst vpres tech planning, 80-87, asst vpres tech servs admin, 88-92. *Concurrent Pos:* Chief engr, Reynolds Broadcasting Co, 57-60; teacher, Adult Prog, Wilmington Pub Schs, 56-60; consult, 93- *Mem:* Inst Elec & Electronics Engrs; AAAS; NY Acad Sci. *Res:* Circuit logic; systems; automata; memory and computing circuits; design of cybernetic systems; instruments for medical applications and devices and systems for instrumentation, control and automation of industrial processes; engineering applications of lasers; data and communication networks; energy management. *Mailing Add:* PO Box 1228 Rodney Sq Sta Wilmington DE 19899

**WALSH, ROBIN,** CHEMISTRY. *Current Pos:* PROF CHEM & SCI FAC, UNIV READING ENG. *Honors & Awards:* Frederic Stanley Kipping Award, Am Chem Soc, 94. *Mailing Add:* Sci Fac Univ Reading Reading RG6 2AH England

**WALSH, SCOTT WESLEY,** PERINATAL PHYSIOLOGY, REPRODUCTIVE ENDOCRINOLOGY. *Current Pos:* PROF, DEPT OBSTET & GYNEC, MED COL VA, VA COMMONWEALTH UNIV, 90- *Personal Data:* b Wauwatosa, Wis, July 23, 47; m 94, Margaret Dahmus. *Educ:* Univ Wis-Milwaukee, BS, 70; Univ Wis-Madison, MS, 72, PhD(endocrinol, reproductive physiol), 75. *Prof Exp:* Asst prof physiol, Sch Med Univ NDak, 75-76; asst scientist perinatal physiol, Ore Regional Primate Res Ctr, 76-80; asst prof, Dept Physiol, Health Sci Ctr, Sch Med, Univ Ore, 78-80, Mich State Univ, 80-85; assoc prof, Dept Obstet & Gynec, Univ Tex Med Sch, 85-90. *Mem:* Soc Study Reproduction; Sigma Xi; Endocrine Soc; Am Physiol Soc; Soc Gynec Invest; Oxygen Soc; Int Soc Study Hypertension Pregnancy. *Res:* Endocrine functions of the primate placenta as they relate to hypertension in pregnancy (preeclampsia) and regulation of placental blood flow; placental production rates of prostacyclin, thromboxane, and lipid peroxides and their effects on placental blood flow; placental antioxidants, human placental tissues are studied in vitro. *Mailing Add:* Dept Obstet & Gynec Med Col Va PO Box 980034 Richmond VA 23298-0034

**WALSH, STEPHEN G,** BIOCHEMISTRY. *Current Pos:* patent examiner, 90-96, SUPERVISORY PATENT EXAMR, US PATENT & TRADEMARK OFF, 96- *Personal Data:* b Brooklyn, NY, Apr 23, 47. *Educ:* Cath Univ Am, BA, 69; State Univ NY, Buffalo, MA, 80, PhD(biochem), 81. *Prof Exp:* Teacher sci & math, St Thomas Community Sch, 69-73; teacher chem, La Salle Acad, 73-77; asst prof, Col Mt St Vincent, 81-87; mem staff, Bur Patents & Trademarks, 87-90. *Mem:* AAAS; Am Chem Soc; Sigma Xi. *Res:* Protein chemistry and immunochemistry of venom allergens investigated by biochemical and immunochemical methods. *Mailing Add:* 1712 N Monroe St Arlington VA 22207

**WALSH, TERESA MARIE,** rheology, for more information see previous edition

**WALSH, THOMAS DAVID,** CHEMISTRY. *Current Pos:* asst prof, 70-72, ASSOC PROF CHEM, UNIV NC, CHARLOTTE, 72- *Personal Data:* b Chicago, Ill, Oct 30, 36; m 87; c 2. *Educ:* Univ Notre Dame, AB, 58; Univ Calif, PhD(chem), 62. *Prof Exp:* Asst prof chem, Univ Ga, 62-67; vis asst prof, Ohio State Univ, 67-68; assoc prof, Univ SDak, 68-70. *Concurrent Pos:* NSF postdoctoral fel, Calif Inst Technol, 61-62; Danforth Found assoc, 64-; res assoc, Univ NC, Chapel Hill, 69-70. *Mem:* Am Chem Soc. *Res:* Organic reaction mechanisms; computer-aided instruction. *Mailing Add:* Dept Chem UNCC Sta Univ NC Charlotte NC 28223-0001

**WALSH, WALTER MICHAEL, JR,** SOLID STATE PHYSICS. *Personal Data:* b Los Angeles, Calif, July 28, 31; m 56; c 2. *Educ:* Harvard Univ, AB, 54, AM, 55, PhD(physics), 58. *Prof Exp:* Res fel solid state physics, Harvard Univ, 58-59; mem tech staff, Bell Labs, 59-67 & 77, dept head, 67-77, head, Solid State & Physics Metals Res Dept, 67-77. *Mem:* Fel Am Phys Soc; Am Phys Soc. *Res:* Experimental physics of solids using microwave resonance techniques; effects of pressure and temperature on solids; resonance and wave propagation phenomena in metals and organic conductors. *Mailing Add:* 18 Browning Dr Livingston NJ 07039

**WALSH, WILLIAM ARTHUR,** ICHTHYOLOGY. *Current Pos:* RES BIOLOGIST, OCEANIC INST, WALMANALO, HAWAII, 86- *Personal Data:* b Manchester, Conn, June 28, 54. *Educ:* Fairfield Univ, BS, 77; Univ Conn, MS, 83, PhD(ecol), 86. *Mem:* Am Fisheries Soc; Am Soc Ichthyologists & Herpetologists. *Res:* Effects of abiotic factors on the ecology and physiology of early life stages of marine fishes. *Mailing Add:* 1524 Aalapapa Dr Kailua HI 96734

**WALSH, WILLIAM J,** CHEMICAL & NUCLEAR ENGINEERING. *Current Pos:* MEM STAFF, DIAMOND SHAMROCK CORP, 77- *Personal Data:* b Saginaw, Mich, Oct 2, 36; m 62; c 5. *Educ:* Notre Dame Univ, BS, 58; Univ Mich, MS, 60, MS, 61; Iowa State Univ, PhD(chem eng), 64. *Prof Exp:* Res asst, Univ Mich Res Inst, 58-61 & Inst Atomic Res, Ames, Iowa, 61-64; assoc engr, Argonne Nat Lab, 64-77. *Mem:* Am Inst Chem Engrs; Inst Elec & Electronics Engrs. *Res:* High temperature battery development; nuclear fuels reprocessing; liquid metal distillation, nuclear criticality; radiotracer experiments; mass transfer; heat transfer; high vacuum experiments; fast breeder reactor design and economics. *Mailing Add:* PO Box 889 Alamo CA 94507-0889

**WALSH, WILLIAM K,** TEXTILE CHEMISTRY, CHEMICAL ENGINEERING. *Current Pos:* asst prof, NC State Univ, 67-72, assoc prof, 72-77, prof textile chem, 77-80, asst dean res, Sch Textiles, 80-81, ASSOC DEAN, RES & GRAD EDUC, SCH TEXTILES, NC STATE UNIV, 81- *Personal Data:* b Columbus, Ohio, Sept 29, 32; m; c 1. *Educ:* Univ SC, BS, 54; NC State Univ, PhD(chem eng), 67. *Prof Exp:* Engr, Celanese Corp Am, SC, 59-60. *Mem:* AAAS; Am Chem Soc; Am Asn Textile Chemists & Colorists; Fiber Soc. *Res:* Applications of ionizing radiation to textile chemistry; radiation graft copolymerization, cross-linking, mechanical properties of textiles; physical and surface chemistry of polymers. *Mailing Add:* 572 Cross Creek Rd Auburn AL 36830-3417

**WALSKE, M CARL,** PHYSICS. *Current Pos:* RETIRED. *Personal Data:* b Seattle, Wash, June 2, 22; m 46, E Marjorie Nelson; c C Susan, Steven C & Carol A. *Educ:* Univ Wash, BS, 44; Cornell Univ, PhD(physics), 51. *Prof Exp:* Mem staff, Los Alamos Sci Lab, 51-55, asst leader, Theoret Div, 55-56; dep res dir, Atomics Int Div, NAm Aviation, Inc, 56-59; mem, Conf Suspension Nuclear Tests, US Deleg, Geneva, Switz, 59-61; sci rep, AEC, London, Eng,

61-62; theoret physicist, Rand Corp, 62-63; sci attache, US Missions to NATO & Orgn Econ Coop & Develop, Paris, France, 63-65; staff mem, Los Alamos Sci Lab, 65-66; asst to secy defense for atomic energy & chmn, Mil Liaison Comt, US Dept Defense, 66-73; pres, Atomic Indust Forum Inc, 73-87. *Concurrent Pos:* Consult, Los Alamos Sci Lab, 56-59 & 62-63. *Mem:* Am Phys Soc; fel Am Nuclear Soc; Explorers Club; Sigma Xi. *Res:* Nuclear and reactor physics. *Mailing Add:* PO Box 370 Silverdale WA 98383-0370

**WALSTAD, JOHN DANIEL,** FOREST PROTECTION. *Current Pos:* ASSOC PROF FOREST VEG MGT, ORE STATE UNIV, 80- *Personal Data:* b Minneapolis, Minn, Aug 22, 44; m 66; c 2. *Educ:* Col William & Mary, BS, 66; Duke Univ, MF, 68; Cornell Univ, PhD(entom), 71. *Prof Exp:* Forest scientist, Weyerhaeuser Co, 71-76, admin asst res, 76-77, res mgr forestry, 77-80. *Mem:* Soc Am Foresters; Weed Sci Soc Am; Entom Soc Am; AAAS. *Res:* Forest vegetation management. *Mailing Add:* Dept Forestry Ore State Univ 140 Peavy Hall Corvallis OR 97331-5710

**WALSTEDT, RUSSELL E,** solid state physics, for more information see previous edition

**WALSTON, DALE EDOUARD,** MATHEMATICS. *Current Pos:* Asst prof, 61-72, ASSOC EMER PROF MATH, UNIV TEX, AUSTIN, 72- *Personal Data:* b Woodsboro, Tex, Dec 1, 30. *Educ:* Tex A&M Univ, BA, 52; Univ Tex, MA, 59, PhD(math), 61. *Concurrent Pos:* Consult, Manned Space Ctr, NASA, 66. *Res:* Numerical solution of differential equations. *Mailing Add:* Box 1253 Dripping Springs TX 78620

**WALSTON, WILLIAM H(OWARD), JR,** MECHANICAL ENGINEERING. *Current Pos:* From asst prof to assoc prof mech eng, 65-84, ASSOC CHAIR, UNIV MD, COLLEGE PARK, 84- *Personal Data:* b Salisbury, Md, Apr 13, 37; m 62; c 2. *Educ:* Univ Del, BME, 59, MME, 61, PhD(appl sci), 64. *Mem:* Am Soc Mech Engrs; Am Soc Eng Educ. *Res:* Signal propagation; shock and vibrations analysis; applied mathematics; design; automotive drag reduction, acoustics, noise control. *Mailing Add:* Dept Mech Eng Univ Md College Park MD 20742

**WALSTROM, ROBERT JOHN,** ENTOMOLOGY. *Current Pos:* PROF ENTOM, SDAK STATE UNIV, 55- *Personal Data:* b Omaha, Nebr, Apr 24, 22; m 44; c 2. *Educ:* Univ Nebr, BS, 47, MS, 49; Iowa State Univ, PhD, 55. *Prof Exp:* State entomologist, State Dept Agr & Inspection, Nebr, 48-50; exten entomologist, Iowa State Univ, 50-55. *Mem:* AAAS; Entom Soc Am. *Res:* Control of beneficial and injurious legume insects; apiculture. *Mailing Add:* 1409 First St Brookings SD 57006

**WALT, ALEXANDER JEFFREY,** surgery; deceased, see previous edition for last biography

**WALT, MARTIN,** SPACE PLASMA PHYSICS, GEOPHYSICS. *Current Pos:* CONSULT PROF, STANFORD UNIV, 85- *Personal Data:* b West Plains, Mo, June 1, 26; m 50, Mary Thompson; c Susan M, Stephen M, Anne E & Patricia R. *Educ:* Calif Inst Technol, BS, 50; Univ Wis, MS, 51, PhD(physics), 53. *Prof Exp:* Mem staff, Los Alamos Sci Lab, 53-56; mem sci staff, Lockheed Missiles & Space Co, 56-65, mgr physics, 65-71, dir phys sci, 71-84, dir res, 84-93. *Concurrent Pos:* Mem, Panel Nuclear Physics, 70-72, comt solar terrestrial res, Nat Acad Sci, 83-89; mem adv comt, Space Sci Lab, Univ Calif, Berkeley, 72-76, mem sci & educ adv comt, Lawrence Berkeley Lab, 82-92; mem space & earth sci adv comt, NASA, 84-88; mem exec comt, 87-89, mem governing bd, 86-95, Am Inst Phyics; bd overseers, Superconducting Supercollider, 89-94; mem adv comt, Ctr Particle Astrophysics, Univ Calif, Berkeley, 89- *Mem:* Fel Am Phys Soc; fel Am Geophys Union; AAAS. *Res:* Experiments and theory of interaction of fast neutrons with nuclei; space research, including measurements and theory on geomagnetically trapped radiation belts, aurora and cosmic rays; diffusion of ions and electrons in plasmas. *Mailing Add:* 12650 Viscaino Ct Los Altos Hills CA 94022. *E-Mail:* walt@nova.stanford.edu

**WALTAR, ALAN EDWARD,** FAST REACTORS, SAFETY. *Current Pos:* adv eng, 77-79, MGR, REACTOR & PHYSICS APPL PHYSICS & SAFETY, WESTINGHOUSE HANFORD CO, 79- *Personal Data:* b Chehalis, Wash, July 10, 39; m 61; c 4. *Educ:* Univ Wash, BS, 61; MIT, MS, 62; Univ Calif Berkeley, PhD(eng sci), 66. *Prof Exp:* Sr res sci, fast reactor modeling, Battelle Northwest, 66-72; mgr reactor dynamics, Westinghouse Hanford Co, 72-76; vis prof heat transfer fast reactors, Univ Va, 76-77. *Concurrent Pos:* Chmn, Prog Comt, Nuclear Reactor Safety Div, Am Nuclear Soc, 78-80, Richland Sect, 82-83, Tech Prog Comt, 82-85, Bylaws & Rules Comt, ANS, 84-86, Nuclear Reactor Safety Div, 86-87, Tech Prog Comt, 86-88; instr, Power Reactors Short Course on Fast Breeder Reactors, Joint Ctr Grad Study, 81-82 & 83, Short Course Fast Breeder Reactors, Los Alamos, Nat Lab, 83-84. *Mem:* Am Nuclear Soc (chair, Nuclear Reactor Safety Div, 86-87, Bylaws & Rules Comt, 84-86); Am Assoc Adv Sci. *Res:* Development of computational models to describe the intrinsic safety response of fast breeder reactors during off normal conditions; wide range energy transformation systems. *Mailing Add:* 1617 Sunset St Richland WA 99352

**WALTCHER, AZELLE BROWN,** GEOMETRY, LOGIC. *Current Pos:* from instr to prof, 52-92, teaching fel, New Col, 61-72, EMER PROF MATH, HOFSTRA UNIV, 92- *Personal Data:* b New York, NY, Mar 27, 25; m 55, Irving; c Jeffrey S & Daniel R. *Educ:* Barnard Col, BA, 45; Columbia Univ,

MA, 46; NY Univ, PhD(math, educ), 54. *Prof Exp:* Asst math, Barnard Col, Columbia Univ, 45-46; instr, Hollins Col, 46-48; teacher, Calhoun Sch, NY, 48-52. *Concurrent Pos:* Mem fac, Sarah Laurence Col, 53-55. *Mem:* Am Math Soc; Math Asn Am. *Res:* Logic and foundations of mathematics. *Mailing Add:* 84-19 Kent St Jamaica Estates NY 11432

**WALTCHER, IRVING,** POLYMER CHEMISTRY. *Current Pos:* asst prof, 55-58, ASSOC PROF CHEM, CITY COL NEW YORK, 58, DEP CHMN DEPT, 74- *Personal Data:* b Newport, RI, Mar 6, 17. *Educ:* Univ RI, BS, 38; Duke Univ, MA, 40; Ohio State Univ, PhD(org chem), 47. *Prof Exp:* Chemist, War Ord Dept, Ala, 41-42; res chemist, B F Goodrich Co, Ohio, 42-44; asst org chem, Res Found, Ohio State Univ, 44-47; res assoc chem, Polytech Inst Brooklyn, 47-48; assoc prof, State Univ NY Col Forestry, Syracuse, 48-55. *Mem:* Am Chem Soc. *Res:* Selective hydrogenation of acetylenes; preparation and characterization of graft copolymers. *Mailing Add:* 8419 Kent St Jamaica NY 11432-5832

**WALTENBAUGH, CARL,** IMMUNOGENETICS, REGULATION OF IMMUNE RESPONSE. *Current Pos:* asst prof, 79-84, ASSOC PROF MICROBIOL & IMMUNOL, SCH MED, NORTHWESTERN UNIV, 84- *Personal Data:* b Canton, Ohio, July 17, 48; m 73; c 3. *Educ:* Baldwin-Wallace Col, Berea, Ohio, BS, 70; Univ Ill Med Ctr, Chicago, MS, 73, PhD(immunol), 75. *Prof Exp:* Res fel, 75-77; instr path, Sch Med, Harvard Univ, 77-79. *Mem:* Soc Develop Biol; Sigma Xi; Am Asn Immunologists; Reticuloendothelial Soc. *Res:* Immunogenetic regulation of the immune response by suppressor T cells and their soluble factors; development of monoclonal antibodies and cell lines. *Mailing Add:* Dept Microbiol-Immunol Northwestern Univ Sch Med 303 E Chicago Ave Chicago IL 60611-3072. *Fax:* 312-503-1339; *E-Mail:* cwalten@casbah.acns.nws.edu

**WALTER, CARLTON H(ARRY),** ELECTRICAL ENGINEERING, PHYSICS. *Current Pos:* MGR, ANTENNA SYSTS PROD, TRW, 83- *Personal Data:* b Willard, Ohio, July 22, 24; m 48; c 2. *Educ:* Ohio State Univ, BEE, 48, MS, 51, PhD(elec eng), 57. *Prof Exp:* Res assoc, Ohio State Univ, 48-54, from instr to assoc prof, 54-65, asst supvr lab, 54-57, assoc supvr, 57-69, prof elec eng, Electro Sci Lab, 65-83, tech area dir antennas, 69-83. *Concurrent Pos:* Mem bd dirs, Ladar Systs, Inc, 64-71. *Mem:* Fel Inst Elec & Electronics Engrs. *Res:* Microwave, traveling wave, Luneberg lens and electrically small antennas. *Mailing Add:* 13208 Tining Dr Poway CA 92064-1223

**WALTER, CHARLES FRANK,** BIOCHEMISTRY, TECHNICAL AND PATENT LAW. *Current Pos:* PATENT & TRADEMARK ATTY, 79- *Personal Data:* b Sarasota, Fla, June 19, 36. *Educ:* Ga Inst Technol, BS, 57; Fla State Univ, MS, 59, PhD(chem), 62; Univ Houston, JD, 79, *Prof Exp:* NIH fel, Med Sch, Univ Calif, San Francisco, 62-64; from asst prof to assoc prof biochem, Med Sch, Univ Tenn, Memphis, 64-70; assoc prof biomath & biochem, M D Anderson Hosp & Tumor Inst, Univ Tex, Houston, 70-74; prof chem eng, Univ Houston, 74-77; dir, Prog on Law & Technol, Univ Park Law Ctr, Univ Houston, 83-85. *Concurrent Pos:* NIH career develop award, Med Sch, Univ Tenn, Memphis, 65-70. *Mem:* Biophys Soc; Soc Math Biol; Am Soc Biol; Chem Fed Soc Exp Biol; Am Bar Asn; Tex Bar Asn. *Res:* Information science; biological control; enzyme mechanisms and kinetics; data bases; communications; real-time computer applications; cognitive processes and models; artificial intelligence and expert systems; cybernetics of law and science; impact of technological developments; societal regulation of science and technology; ethics in scientific research. *Mailing Add:* 9131 Timberside Houston TX 77025. *Fax:* 713-667-5201

**WALTER, CHARLES ROBERT, JR,** ORGANIC CHEMISTRY. *Current Pos:* chmn dept, 66-83, prof chem, 66-87, EMER PROF CHEM, GEORGE MASON UNIV, 88- *Personal Data:* b Charlottesville, Va, Oct 31, 22; m 50, Marjorie Johnson; c Margaret, John & Elizabeth. *Educ:* Univ Va, BA, 43, PhD(chem), 49. *Prof Exp:* Res asst chem, Univ Ill, 49-50; asst prof, Univ NC, 50-52; sr res chemist, Nitrogen Div, Allied Chem Corp, 52-58, supvry res chemist, 58-60, mgr res, 60-66. *Mem:* Am Chem Soc. *Res:* Synthetic organic chemistry; Diels-Alder reaction of quinoneimides; industrial process development; organic nitrogen chemicals; vapor phase catalysis; chlorination of olefins. *Mailing Add:* 4221 SE Eighth Ave Cape Coral FL 33904

**WALTER, CHARLTON M,** INFORMATION SCIENCE, SIGNAL DATA ANALYSIS. *Current Pos:* CONSULT, APPL RES CONSULTS, INC, 80- *Personal Data:* b Altoona, Pa, July 1, 23; m 47; c 2. *Educ:* Columbia Univ, BA, 49; Harvard Univ, MA, 51. *Prof Exp:* Mathematician, Commun Lab, USAF Cambridge Res Ctr, 51-54, chief simulation & eval br, Comput & Math Sci Lab, 54-63, chief dynamic processes br, Data Sci Lab, 63-70, chief multisensor processing br, Data Sci Lab, USAF Cambridge Res Labs, 70-73, chief anal & simulation br, Comput Ctr, 73-76; sr systs analyst, dir res servs, USAF Geophys Lab, 76-79. *Mem:* AAAS; Inst Elec & Electronics Engrs; Soc Gen Syst Res. *Res:* Development of interactive, computer-based, display-oriented signal processing systems, with applications to environmental sensor data collection; statistical data reduction; dynamic modelling; simulation and systems evaluation. *Mailing Add:* 58 Conant Rd Lincoln MA 01773

**WALTER, DONALD K,** ENERGY CONSERVATION. *Current Pos:* CONSULT, 93- *Personal Data:* b Philadelphia, Pa, May 28, 31; m 63; c 1. *Educ:* Drexel Inst Technol, BS, 53; Drexel Univ, MS, 66. *Prof Exp:* Chief opers, facil engr, 1st Cav Div, US Army, 59-60, resident engr, Area Off, Warren AFB, 60-61, real estate & facil engr, HQ Area Command, Vietnam, 66-67, chief supply, Engr Command, 67-69, facil engr, Wuertzberg, Ger,

69-71 & Ft Detrick, Md, 71-73; asst prof mil sci & tactics, Drexel Univ, 61-66; city engr, Annapolis, Md, 73-75; dir, Dept Energy, 75-93. *Mem:* Am Soc Mech Engrs; Nat Soc Prof Engrs; Soc Am Mil Engrs; Am Soc Testing & Mats. *Res:* Management of programs related to productive use of municipal solid waste and energy conservation in municipal functions; conservation technologies including mechanical processing for solid fuels and recyclable materials, thermochemical conversion for steam, gaseous or liquid fuels and biochemical conversion for gaseous or liquid fuels; energy from municipal waste; management of programs on industrial waste materials utilization, conversion and reduction; programs on solar industrial applications to include hazardous wastes detoxification, solar industrial heat and application of high photon and heat fluxes to industrial processes. *Mailing Add:* 289 Marlinspike Dr Severna Park MD 21146

**WALTER, EDWARD JOSEPH,** geophysics, for more information see previous edition

**WALTER, EUGENE LEROY, JR,** MEDICAL MICROBIOLOGY, VIROLOGY. *Current Pos:* RETIRED. *Personal Data:* b St Thomas, VI, Aug 14, 22; m 64; c 4. *Educ:* Univ Calif, Los Angeles, BA, 47; Univ Southern Calif, MS, 58; Univ Wis, PhD(med microbiol), 64. *Prof Exp:* Eng asst, Los Angeles Bur Standard, 47-51; microbiologist, Epidemic Dis Control Unit, Pearl Harbor, 51-56; med microbiologist med res units, Berkeley, Calif, Great Lakes, Ill, Cairo, Egypt, Washington, DC, 56-69; health sci adminr, Nat Heart Blood & Lung Inst, NIH, 71-87. *Concurrent Pos:* Instr bact, US Navy Hosp Corps Sch, 53-54. *Mem:* Am Soc Microbiol. *Res:* Bacteriophage; papilloma virus; infectious hepatitis diagnosed by fluorescent antibody; latent herpes simplex virus; leptospirosis; environmental engineering; health science administration. *Mailing Add:* 8410 Post-Oak Rd Potomac MD 20854-3480

**WALTER, EVERETT L,** MATHEMATICS. *Current Pos:* assoc prof, 62-68, PROF MATH, NORTHERN ARIZ UNIV, 68- *Personal Data:* b Rensselaer, Ind, July 1, 29; m 51; c 4. *Educ:* Ariz State Univ, BS, 51; NMex State Univ, MS, 57, PhD(math), 61. *Prof Exp:* Dir comput, Army Field Forces, Ft Bliss, Tex, 54-56; instr math, NMex State Univ, 56-60; res mathematician, White Sands Missile Range, 61-62. *Mem:* Math Asn Am; Am Math Soc. *Res:* Functional analysis. *Mailing Add:* Dept Math 609 Wiliams Rd Flagstaff AZ 86011-0001

**WALTER, F JOHN,** LOW TEMPERATURE NUCLEAR ALIGNMENT & POLARIZATION, NUCLEAR PHYSICS. *Current Pos:* PRES, INSTRAPEC INC, 85- *Personal Data:* b 1931; c 4. *Educ:* Kans State Univ, BS, 53; Univ Tenn, MS, 58, PhD(physics), 65. *Prof Exp:* Develop engr, Reactor Exp Eng Div, ORNL, 53-57, res assoc, Physics Div, 57-64; chief physicst Div Nuclear, RIDL, chief, 64-65, dir semiconductor res & develop, ORTEC Inc, 66-71, res & develop, 71-73, vpres & tech dir, 73-76; vpres & gen mgr, Phys Sci Dir, Egg Ortec, 76-77, vpres, asst gen mgr & dir, Detection Div, 77-80; pres, Waltec Inc, 80-82; mgr, Semiconductor Div, Tennelec Inc, 82-85. *Concurrent Pos:* Develop dir, portable gold analyzer, SAfrica Chamber Mines; admin comnr, Nuclear & Plasma Sci Soc, 80-, chmn, Nuclear Instruments & Detectors Comn, proj engr, Nuclear Instruments Stand, asst prog chmn, Semiconductor & Scintillation Counter & Nuclear Sci Symp; prog chmn, Nuclear Sci Symp, Inst Elec & Electronics Engrs & Nuclear & Plasma Sci Soc, 80, fel review comt, 82-, proj leader video teaching pilot prog, Educ & Continued Prof Develop, mem, Environ Instructing & Montoring; Nuclear & Plasma Sci Soc rep, Coun Ocean Eng, Inst Elec & Electronics Engrs-Coun Ocean Eng; delegate, nuclear instruments & detection comt, Int Electro Tech Comn, 80-; tech dir, Life Sci Prog, ORTEC. *Mem:* Fel Inst Elec & Electronics Engrs; Nuclear & Plasma Sci Soc; Sigma Xi; Am Phys Soc. *Res:* Author and co-author of more than 40 papers on semiconductor radiation detectors, nuclear instrumentation, cryogenics, kinetics and kinematics of heavy nuclei decay and fission. *Mailing Add:* Intraspec Inc PO Box 4579 Oak Ridge TN 37831-4579

**WALTER, GILBERT G,** ANALYSIS & FUNCTIONAL ANALYSIS, BIOMATHEMATICS. *Current Pos:* PROF MATH, UNIV WIS-MILWAUKEE, 61- *Personal Data:* b Ottawa, Ill, Nov 24, 30; m 58; c 3. *Educ:* Gen Motors Inst, BIE, 53; NMex State Univ, BSEE, 56; Univ Wis, MS, 59, PhD(math), 62. *Prof Exp:* Proj engr, AC Electronics Div, Gen Motors Corp, 56-57. *Concurrent Pos:* Vis prof, Univ Calif, San Diego, 65-66, Univ Agraria, Lima, Peru, 68-69, Univ Costa Rica, 78, Imp Col, London, 80, Univ Nac Auto Mex, Mexico City, 81, Univ Calif, Davis, 82, Calif Polytech Univ, San Luis Obispo, 85, Univ Del, 88. *Mem:* Am Math Soc; Math Asn Am; Inst Math Statist; Soc Indust & Appl Math. *Res:* Mathematical analysis: generalized functions, sampling theorems; statistics: density estimation, empiric Bayes estimation; biomathematics; compartmental models and fisheries models. *Mailing Add:* Math Dept Univ Wis Box 415 Milwaukee WI 53201-0413. *Fax:* 414-229-4907

**WALTER, GORDON H,** METALLURGY. *Current Pos:* RETIRED. *Educ:* Ill Inst Technol, BS. *Prof Exp:* Mgr mat tech & stand, agr & components eng, JI Case Co. *Concurrent Pos:* Staff mem mat spec develop, Int Harvester, metal res, mat engr, Agr Group, mgr, metals res. *Mem:* Am Soc Metals; Am Soc Agr Engrs; Soc Automotive Engrs. *Res:* Materials specifications development; agricultural and components engineering. *Mailing Add:* 512 Lucerne Dr DeKalb IL 60115-4734

**WALTER, HARRY,** BIOCHEMISTRY, CELL BIOLOGY. *Current Pos:* RES CHEMIST, LAB CHEM BIOL, VET AFFAIRS MED CTR, LONG BEACH, CALIF, 62-, RES CAREER SCIENTIST, 78- *Personal Data:* b Vienna, Austria, May 15, 30; m, Marie Willett; c Heidi, Martin & Paula. *Educ:*

City Col NY, BS, 51; Ind Univ, MS, 53, PhD(biochem), 55. *Prof Exp:* Teaching asst chem, Ind Univ, 51-52, res asst biochem, 52-55, res assoc, 55-57; prin scientist, Vet Admin Hosp, Brooklyn, NY, 57-62. *Concurrent Pos:* Asst clin prof, Dept Biol Chem, Sch Med, Univ Calif, Los Angeles, 62-75; vis scientist, Univ Umea, Sweden, 66&69, Univ Lund, Sweden, 76; clin prof, Dept Physiol, Col Med, Univ Calif, Irvine, 75-79, prof in residence, Dept Physiol & Biophys, 79-89; distinguished vis, Univ London, 89. *Mem:* Am Soc Biochem & Molecular Biol; Am Soc Cell Biol; Biophys Soc; Swed Soc Biochem & Molecular Biol. *Res:* Characterization of membrane surface properties by cell partitioning in two-polymer aqueous phase systems; factors in cell partitioning. *Mailing Add:* 2715 Ordway St NW Washington DC 20008-5038. *Fax:* 562-494-5675

**WALTER, HARTMUT S,** BIOGEOGRAPHY, ORNITHOLOGY. *Current Pos:* actg asst prof, Univ Calif, Los Angeles, 72-73, asst prof, 73-74, assoc prof biogeog, 74-80, PROF GEOG, UNIV CALIF, LOS ANGELES, 80- *Personal Data:* b Stettin, Ger, July 13, 40; m 69; c 2. *Educ:* Univ Bonn, Dr rer nat(bird ecol), 67. *Honors & Awards:* Hoerlein Prize, Ger Biol Asn, 60. *Prof Exp:* Harkness fel geog, Univ Calif, Berkeley, 67-68 & Univ Chicago, 68; assoc regional expert ecol & conserv for Africa, UNESCO Field Sci Off, Nairobi, Kenya, 70-72. *Mem:* AAAS; Am Ornith Union; Cooper Ornith Soc; Soc Conserv Biol. *Res:* Island biogeography; evolutionary ecology; raptor ecology; wildlife conservation; design and management of nature reserves and national parks; conservation biology; geography of extinction. *Mailing Add:* Dept Geog Univ Calif PO Box 951524 Los Angeles CA 90095-1524. *Fax:* 310-206-5976; *E-Mail:* walter@geog.ucla.edu

**WALTER, HENRY ALEXANDER,** ORGANIC CHEMISTRY. *Current Pos:* CONSULT CHEMIST, CATAUMET, MASS, 76- *Personal Data:* b Muehlhausen, Ger, Jan 8, 12; nat US; m 39; c 4. *Educ:* Univ Heidelberg, dipl, 39. *Prof Exp:* Res chemist, Plaskon Co, 39-42; asst prof chem, Univ Mo, 42-44; res specialist, Monsanto Chem Co, 44-62; sr scientist, Plastic Coating Corp, Scott Paper Co, 62-71, consult, Scott Graphics, Inc, 71-76. *Concurrent Pos:* Assoc mem, Woodshole Oceanog Inst. *Mem:* AAAS; Am Chem Soc; NY Acad Sci. *Res:* Polymer chemistry; technical information services; patent liaison. *Mailing Add:* 42 Timber Ridge Savannah GA 31404

**WALTER, HENRY CLEMENT,** ORGANIC CHEMISTRY. *Current Pos:* RES CHEMIST, EXP STA, E I DU PONT DE NEMOURS & CO, INC, 46- *Personal Data:* b Boston, Mass, Sept 12, 19; m 54; c 6. *Educ:* Mass Inst Technol, SB, 41, PhD(org chem), 46. *Prof Exp:* Asst, Mass Inst Technol, 42-43 & 44-45. *Mem:* Am Chem Soc. *Res:* Elastomers; adhesives. *Mailing Add:* 310 Hampton Rd Sharpley Wilmington DE 19803-2420

**WALTER, JOHN FITLER,** APPLIED PHYSICS, ELECTRO-OPTICS. *Current Pos:* PHYSICIST, APPL PHYSICS LAB, JOHNS HOPKINS UNIV, 70- *Personal Data:* b Philadelphia, Pa, Mar 19, 43; m 68, Gail Konhaus; c John F III, Katharine J & Andrew B. *Educ:* Drexel Univ, BSEE, 66, MS, 68, PhD(physics), 70. *Concurrent Pos:* Prog Area Mgr, Strike Warfare. *Mem:* Am Defense Prep Asn; Am Inst Aeronaut & Astronaut; Cruise Missiles Asn. *Res:* Electro-optics applications to missile navigation and control; laser physics with applications to missile guidance. *Mailing Add:* Appl Physics Lab Johns Hopkins Rd Laurel MD 20723-6099

**WALTER, JOHN HARRIS,** ALGEBRA. *Current Pos:* assoc prof, 61-66, PROF MATH, UNIV ILL, URBANA, 66- *Personal Data:* b Los Angeles, Calif, Dec 14, 27; m 55; c 3. *Educ:* Calif Inst Technol, BS, 51; Univ Mich, MS, 53, PhD, 54. *Prof Exp:* From instr to asst prof math, Univ Wash, 54-61. *Concurrent Pos:* NSF fel, 57-58; vis asst prof, Univ Chicago, 60-61, vis assoc prof, 65-66; res assoc, Harvard Univ, 67-68 & Cambridge Univ, 72-73. *Mem:* Am Math Soc. *Res:* Finite groups; classical groups; representation theory. *Mailing Add:* 2211 Valleybrook Champaign IL 61821

**WALTER, JOSEPH DAVID,** ENGINEERING MECHANICS, MECHANICAL ENGINEERING. *Current Pos:* dir res, 89-90, DIR RES & ENG, BRIDGESTONE/FIRESTONE INC, 90- *Personal Data:* b Merchantville, NJ, July 6, 39; m 62; c 3. *Educ:* Va Polytech Inst, BS, 62, MS, 64, PhD(eng mech), 66; Univ Akron, MBA, 85. *Prof Exp:* Asst, Va Polytech Inst, 65-66; res physicist, Cent Res Labs, Firestone Tire & Rubber Co, 66-69, mgr physics & math res, 69-74, asst dir, 74-89. *Concurrent Pos:* Adj prof, Dept Mech Eng, Univ Akron, 75- *Mem:* Am Chem Soc; Accreditation Bd Eng & Technol; Am Soc Mech Engrs; Soc Automotive Engrs. *Res:* Composite materials; polymer physics; stress analysis; tire mechanics. *Mailing Add:* 343 Barnstable Rd Akron OH 44313

**WALTER, JOSEPH L,** INORGANIC CHEMISTRY. *Current Pos:* ASSOC PROF INORG CHEM, UNIV NOTRE DAME, 60- *Personal Data:* b Braddock, Pa, Jan 23, 30. *Educ:* Duquesne Univ, BS, 51; Univ Pittsburgh, PhD(chem), 55. *Concurrent Pos:* NIH fels, 62-70; AEC fel, 63-67. *Mem:* Am Chem Soc; Soc Appl Spectros; Am Asn Med Col. *Res:* Normal coordinate analysis of inorganic coordination compounds using the Urey-Bradley Force Field calculations and the thermodynamic studies of metal chelate formation. *Mailing Add:* Dept Chem & Biochem Univ Notre Dame Notre Dame IN 46556

**WALTER, LOUIS S,** GEOCHEMISTRY. *Current Pos:* geochemist, Goddard Space Flight Ctr, NASA, 63-73, asst div chief, Earth Sci Div, 73-74, chief, Earth Surv Appln Div, 74-92, ASSOC DIR EARTH SCI, GODDARD SPACE FLIGHT CTR, NASA, 92- *Personal Data:* b New York, NY, Aug 11, 33; m 57; c 2. *Educ:* City Col New York, BS, 54; Univ Tenn, MS, 55; Pa

State Univ, PhD(geochem), 60. *Prof Exp:* Res fel geochem, Pa State Univ, 60-62; res assoc, Nat Acad Sci, 62-63. *Mem:* Am Geophys Union; Geochem Soc; Mineral Soc Am; Meteoritical Soc; Sigma Xi. *Res:* Experimental petrology and mineralogy; crystal chemistry; phase equilibria; petrography; electron microprobe analyses; planetology; theoretical petrology; application of remote sensing to agriculture, geology; use of geophysical measurements from space for tectonic studies and oil and mineral exploration. *Mailing Add:* 1903 Allanwood Pl Silver Spring MD 20906-1180

**WALTER, MARTIN EDWARD,** DUALITY BETWEEN GEOMETRY & ALGEBRA. *Current Pos:* from asst prof to assoc prof, 73-84, PROF MATH, UNIV COLO, BOULDER, 84- *Personal Data:* b Lone Pine, Calif, Jan 26, 45; m 67; c 1. *Educ:* Univ Redlands, Calif, BS, 66; Univ Calif, Irvine, MA, 68, PhD(math), 71. *Prof Exp:* Fel math, Univ Calif, Los Angeles, 70-71; res assoc, Queens Univ, Kingston, Can, 71-73. *Concurrent Pos:* Prin investr, NSF, 73-85; fel, Univ Pa, 77; fel, Univ Calif, Berkeley, 78; vis prof math, Univ Trondheim, Norway, 82; res fel math sci, Res Inst, Berkeley, 84; NSF fel; Woodrow Wilson fel; Alfred P Sloan fel. *Mem:* Am Math Soc; Math Asn Am; AAAS. *Res:* Duality between geometry and algebra with application to physics and other branches of mathematics. *Mailing Add:* Univ Colo Campus Box 395 Boulder CO 80309-0395

**WALTER, PAUL HERMANN LAWRENCE,** INORGANIC CHEMISTRY. *Current Pos:* from asst prof to assoc prof, Skidmore Col, 67-78, chmn dept, 75-85, prof chem, 78-96, EMER PROF, SKIDMORE COL, 96- *Personal Data:* b Jersey City, NJ, Sept 22, 34; m 56, Grace L Carpenter; c Marjorie & Katherine (Bousquet). *Educ:* Mass Inst Technol, SB, 56; Univ Kans, PhD(inorg chem), 60. *Prof Exp:* Res chemist, Cent Res Dept, E I du Pont de Nemours & Co, 60-66, col rels rep, Employee Rels Dept, 66-67. *Concurrent Pos:* Guest, Univ Stuttgart, 64-65; mem bd dirs, Am Chem Soc, 91-, chmn, 93-95. *Mem:* AAAS; Am Chem Soc (pres elect, 97, pres, 98); fel Chem Inst Can; fel Am Inst Chemists; Am Asn Univ Profs (pres, 84-86); hon mem Soc Chem Mex. *Res:* Solid state inorganic chemistry; chemical education; rhenium chemistry; inorganic analytical chemistry; environmental chemistry. *Mailing Add:* Dept Chem Skidmore Col Saratoga Springs NY 12866. *Fax:* 518-581-0767; *E-Mail:* pwalter@skidmore.edu

**WALTER, REGINALD HENRY,** food chemistry, for more information see previous edition

**WALTER, REUBEN,** ORGANIC CHEMISTRY. *Current Pos:* PROF CHEM, TARLETON STATE UNIV, 77- *Personal Data:* b Slaton, Tex, Mar 23, 46. *Educ:* Tex Lutheran Col, BS, 68; Tex Christian Univ, MAT, 72, PhD(chem), 74. *Prof Exp:* Teacher chem, Navarro Col, Colo, 75-77. *Mem:* Am Chem Soc; Sigma Xi; AAAS. *Mailing Add:* Dept Phys & Environ Sci Tarleton State Univ Stephenville TX 76402

**WALTER, RICHARD L,** NUCLEAR PHYSICS. *Current Pos:* from asst prof to assoc prof, 62-74, PROF PHYSICS, DUKE UNIV, 74- *Personal Data:* b Chicago, Ill, Nov 1, 33; m 58, Carol Goethals; c Timothy, Susan & Matthew. *Educ:* St Procopius Col, BS, 55; Univ Notre Dame, PhD(physics), 60. *Prof Exp:* Res assoc nuclear physics, Univ Wis, 59-61, instr physics, 61-62. *Concurrent Pos:* Vis prof, Max Planck Inst Nuclear Physics, Heidelberg, Ger, 70-71; Fulbright res fel, 70-71; vis scientist, Los Alamos Sci Lab, 75; vis prof, Tsinghua Univ, Beijing, Peoples Repub China, 88, 91, 94, 95 & 96. *Mem:* Am Phys Soc; Sigma Xi. *Res:* Neutron physics; polarization of nucleons produced in reactions; scattering of polarized nucleons; low energy accelerator physics; studies involving trace metals in the environment. *Mailing Add:* Dept Physics Duke Univ Durham NC 27708-0305. *Fax:* 919-660-2634; *E-Mail:* walter@tunl.duke.edu

**WALTER, RICHARD WEBB, JR,** MICROBIAL BIOCHEMISTRY, FERMENTATION. *Current Pos:* sr res biochemist, Dow Chem Co, 74-80, res leader, 80-85, develop leader, 85-89, DEVELOP ASSOC, DOW CHEM CO, 89- *Personal Data:* b West Chester, Pa, Oct 5, 44; m 67, Christine Tobias; c Jonathon B & Jessica B. *Educ:* Pa State Univ, BS, 66; Mich State Univ, PhD(biochem), 72. *Prof Exp:* Fel biochem, Univ Colo Med Ctr, Denver, 72-74. *Concurrent Pos:* Chairperson, Am Stand Testing Mat, 90. *Mem:* Am Soc Microbiol; Am Chem Soc; Am Soc Testing & Mat; Soc Indust Microbiol. *Res:* Biochemical transformation and synthesis of sterospecific molecules that are of interest to both the chemical and pharmaceutical industries and are difficult to synthesize by normal chemical means; fermentation process design and optimization; structure activity, relationship for antimicrobials; development of new industrial antimicrobials; mechanism of action studies. *Mailing Add:* 26 Lexington Ct Midland MI 48642. *Fax:* 517-616-7496; *E-Mail:* rwwalter@dow.com

**WALTER, ROBERT IRVING,** PHYSICAL ORGANIC CHEMISTRY. *Current Pos:* prof, 68-90, EMER PROF CHEM, UNIV ILL, CHICAGO, 90- *Personal Data:* b Johnstown, Pa, Mar 12, 20; m 93, Frieda Asghari. *Educ:* Swarthmore Col, AB, 41; Johns Hopkins Univ, MA, 42; Univ Chicago, PhD(chem), 49. *Prof Exp:* Asst, Swarthmore Col, 40-41 & Johns Hopkins Univ, 41-42; res chemist, Wyeth, Inc, 42-44; instr chem, Univ Colo, 49-51; from res asst prof to res assoc prof, Rutgers Univ, 51-53; instr chem, Univ Conn, 53-55; assoc physicist, Brookhaven Nat Lab, 55-56; from asst prof to prof chem, Haverford Col, 56-68. *Concurrent Pos:* NSF fac fel, 60-61; vis prof, Stanford Univ, 67; acad guest, Inst Phys Chem, Univ Zurich, 75-76; US Nat Acad Sci exchange vis, Romania, 82 & 88. *Mem:* Fel AAAS; Am Chem Soc; Sigma Xi. *Res:* Equilibria in porphyrin systems; preparation and properties of stable organic free radicals; mechanisms in heterogeneous catalysis. *Mailing Add:* Dept Chem 845 W Taylor St Chicago IL 60607

**WALTER, ROBERT JOHN,** CELL MOTILITY, TUMOR IMMUNOLOGY. *Current Pos:* SR SCIENTIFIC OFF, HEKTOEN INST, 88-; DIR, DIV SURG RES, COOK CO HOSP, 93- *Personal Data:* b Cleveland, Ohio, Nov 15, 50; m 73; c 2. *Educ:* Ohio State Univ, BS, 72; Case Western Res Univ, PhD(anat & cell biol), 78. *Prof Exp:* Asst prof cell biol, Univ Ill, 80-87; adj assoc prof anat, Loyola Univ, 87-93. *Concurrent Pos:* Vis scientist, Dept Path, Univ Mich, 88 & Univ Pavia, 90; fel, Am Cancer Soc & NIH. *Mem:* Am Soc Cell Biol; AAAS; Soc Leukocyte Biol. *Res:* Cell motility research with specific interests in leukocyte chemotaxis receptors, the role of cytoskeleton in cell locomotion, and abnormal chemotaxis as in Kartagener's syndrome and in tumor patients; hormonal effects on the immune system and tumors. *Mailing Add:* Dept Surg Hektoen Inst Cook City Hosp 625 S Wood St Chicago IL 60612-3810. *Fax:* 312-738-3102

**WALTER, RONALD BRUCE,** NUCLEIC ACID CHEMISTRY, MOLECULAR GENETIC. *Current Pos:* ASST PROF GENETICS & MOLECULAR BIOL, SOUTHWEST TEX STATE UNIV, 88- *Personal Data:* b South Bend, Ind, July 15, 57; m 87. *Educ:* Fla State Univ, BS, 79, MS, 81, PhD(molecular genetic), 85. *Honors & Awards:* Arnold Ravin Award, 84. *Prof Exp:* Res assoc, Environ Res Coun, Nat Res Coun, Environ Protection Agency, 85-87; fel, Syst Cancer Ctr, Univ Tex, 87-88, res assoc, 88. *Concurrent Pos:* Adj res assoc, Cancer Ctr Sci Park Res Div, Univ Tex, 88-; res assoc award, Nat Res Coun. *Mem:* Am Soc Microbiol. *Res:* Molecular mechanisms of DNA repair in prokaryotes particularly with the bacterium Haemophilus influenzae; evolution of DNA repair enzymes from lower vertebrates to mammals by genetic mapping of homologous genes in fish. *Mailing Add:* Dept Biol SW Tex State Univ San Marcos TX 78666-4602

**WALTER, THOMAS JAMES,** organic chemistry, for more information see previous edition

**WALTER, TREVOR JOHN,** biochemistry, for more information see previous edition

**WALTER, WILBERT GEORGE,** NATURAL PRODUCTS, MEDICINAL CHEMISTRY. *Current Pos:* RETIRED. *Personal Data:* b Lingle, Wyo, Nov 16, 33; m 55; c 2. *Educ:* Univ Colo, BA, 55, BS & MS, 58; Univ Conn, PhD(pharmaceut chem), 62. *Prof Exp:* Asst, Univ Colo, 55-58; asst, Univ Conn, 58-61, spec res technologist, 60; res assoc pharmacog & asst prof pharmaceut chem, Sch Pharm, Univ Tenn, 61-63; assoc prof, Sch Pharm, Univ Miss, 63-68; chmn dept, Med Univ SC, 68-77, prof med chem, Col Pharm, 68-93. *Mem:* Am Pharmaceut Asn; Am Soc Pharmacog; Am Chem Soc; Soc Econ Bot. *Res:* Organic medicinal chemistry; natural product chemistry. *Mailing Add:* 721 Oak Marsh Dr Mt Pleasant SC 29464

**WALTER, WILLIAM ARNOLD, JR,** epidemiology, for more information see previous edition

**WALTER, WILLIAM MOOD, JR,** FOOD SCIENCE. *Current Pos:* asst prof, 65-70, assoc prof, 70-77 PROF FOOD SCI, NC STATE UNIV, 77- RES CHEMIST, AGR RES SERV, USDA, 65- *Personal Data:* b Sumter, SC, Nov 20, 36; m 59; c 1. *Educ:* The Citadel, BS, 58; Univ Ga, PhD(org chem), 63. *Prof Exp:* Res asst, Univ Ga, 60-63. *Mem:* Am Chem Soc; Inst Food Technologists; Sigma Xi. *Res:* Effect of processing and storage on organic constituents of food; emphasis on quality and nutritional value of processed foods. *Mailing Add:* 2128 Cowper Dr Raleigh NC 27608-1324

**WALTER, WILLIAM TRUMP,** ELECTROPHYSICS. *Current Pos:* PRES, LASER CONSULTS, INC, 68- *Personal Data:* b Jamaica, NY, Dec 28, 31; m 60, Susan Tallman; c William, Todd, Bruce & Elizabeth. *Educ:* Middlebury Col, AB, 53; Mass Inst Technol, PhD(physics), 62. *Prof Exp:* Res asst, Res Lab Electronics, Mass Inst Technol, 59-62; sr scientist, TRG, Inc, 62-67; res scientist, Polytech Inst NY, 67-79, res assoc prof, 79-84; prin staff engr, Ail Systs Inc, Subsid, Eaton Corp, 84-95. *Concurrent Pos:* Guest, Res Lab Electronics, Mass Inst Technol, 62-63. *Mem:* Optical Soc Am; NY Acad Sci; Soc Photo-Optical Instrumentation Engrs; Am Asn Physics Teachers; AAAS; Air Waste Mgt Asn. *Res:* Remote detection of molecules in the atmosphere and wave-matter interactions; metal vapor lasers; laser research, development and applications; gas discharges; atomic physics; resonance phenomena in dilute gases, including optical pumping, orientation and nuclear magnetic resonance; optical and radiofrequency spectroscopy; infrared and electro-optics. *Mailing Add:* 344 W Hills Rd Huntington NY 11743. *Fax:* 516-424-0422; *E-Mail:* lcinc@pb.net

**WALTERBOS, RENE A M,** ASTRONOMY, THEORETICAL PHYSICS. *Current Pos:* Hubble fel, 90-91, res asst prof, 91-96, DEPT HEAD & ASSOC PROF ASTRON, NMEX STATE UNIV, 96- *Educ:* Univ Leiden, BA, 79, MS, 82, PhD(astron), 86. *Prof Exp:* Post-doctoral res assoc, Inst Advan Study, Princton Univ, 86-87; Astron Dept, Univ Calif, Berkeley, 87-90. *Concurrent Pos:* Vis asst prof physics, Univ Calif, Davis, 89-90. *Mem:* Int Astron Union; Am Astron Soc; Neth Astron Soc. *Res:* Structure and evolution of galaxies; properties of the diffuse interstellar medium in galaxies; interaction of massive stars with the interstellar medium in galaxies. *Mailing Add:* Astron Dept NMex State Univ Box 30001 Dept 4500 Las Cruces NM 88003

**WALTERS, ALLAN N,** ANALYSIS OF EXPLOSIVES & THEIR RESIDUE IN BOMB CASES, ANALYSIS OF FIRE DEBRIS FOR ACCELERANTS IN SUSPECTED ARSON CASES. *Current Pos:* SR FORENSIC CHEMIST, FORENSIC & TECH SERV DIV, US POSTAL INSPECTION SERV, 92- *Educ:* Univ Rochester, BS, 67; SDak Sch Mines & Techol, MS, 72. *Prof Exp:* Forensic chemist, Monroe Co Pub Safety Lab, Rochester, 77-88; forensic chemist, Bur Alcohol Tobacco & Firearms, Nat Lab Ctr, 88-92. *Mem:* Am Chem Soc. *Res:* Developing new methods and improving existing methods for the anaylsis of fire debris, accelerants, explosives and explosive residue using instrumental methods. *Mailing Add:* Forensic & Tech Servs 22433 Randolph Dr Dulles VA 20104-1000

**WALTERS, CARL JOHN,** SYSTEMS ECOLOGY. *Current Pos:* assoc prof, 69-82, PROF ZOOL & ANIMAL RESOURCE ECOL, UNIV BC, 82- *Personal Data:* b Albuquerque, NMex, Sept 14, 44. *Educ:* Humboldt State Col, BS, 65; Colo State Univ, MS, 67, PhD(fisheries), 69. *Prof Exp:* Res asst fisheries biol, Colo Coop Wildlife Unit, Colo State Univ, 66-67, NSF fel, 67-69, consult, 68-70. *Concurrent Pos:* Can Depts Environ & Fisheries consult, 71-; res scholar, Int Inst Appl Systs Anal, Austria, 74-75, 82-83. *Res:* Dynamics of ecological communities; application of mathematical models and computer simulation techniques to problems in resource ecology; adaptive management of renewable resources. *Mailing Add:* Dept Zool Univ BC 6270 Univ Blvd Vancouver BC V6T 1Z4 Can

**WALTERS, CAROL PRICE,** NEWBORN & PRENATAL SCREENING. *Current Pos:* From res assoc med to res assoc prof med, 72-85, res assoc prof pediat, 85-93, ASSOC PROF PEDIAT, COL MED, UNIV VT, 93- *Personal Data:* b Lansing, Mich, Oct 15, 41; m 88, David L; c Jennifer (Smith). *Educ:* Albion Col, AB, 63; Univ Vt, PhD(physiol), 72. *Concurrent Pos:* Dir, Vt Alpha-Fetoprotein Prenatal Screening Prog, 81-; coordr, Vt Newborn Screening Prog, 89- *Mem:* Sigma Xi; Int Soc Oncodevelop Biol & Med; Am Asn Cancer Res. *Res:* Investigation of the physicochemistry and metabolism of the carcino-embryonic protein alpha-fetoprotein and its molecular variants in sera of fetal and hepatoma-bearing rats and also in human maternal serum and amniotic fluid in the presence of fetal malformations. *Mailing Add:* Vt Newborn Screening Prog 1 Mill St Suite 3-3 Burlington VT 05401. *Fax:* 802-860-7542; *E-Mail:* cwalters@salus.uvm.med.edu

**WALTERS, CHARLES PHILIP,** ASTROGEOLOGY. *Current Pos:* from asst prof to prof, 45-86, EMER PROF GEOL, KANS STATE UNIV, 86- *Personal Data:* b Kansas City, Mo, May 1, 15; m 36, Esther W Sayre; c John, Maryellen & Joan. *Educ:* Kans State Univ, BS, 36, MS, 38; Cornell Univ, PhD, 57. *Prof Exp:* Asst geologist, Continental Oil Co, 44-48. *Concurrent Pos:* Ford Found fac fel, 51-52; mem comt exam natural sci test & geol subj matter test, Educ Testing Serv, 62-70. *Mem:* AAAS; Am Asn Petrol Geologists; Am Quaternary Asn; Meteoritical Soc; Sigma Xi. *Res:* Structural and tectonic geology; geophysics; planetology; environmental geology; deterioration of Kansas salt beds; tektites from cryptovolcanic eruptions; paleoclimatology; climate change. *Mailing Add:* 2101 Meadowlark Rd Manhattan KS 66502-4556

**WALTERS, CHARLES SEBASTIAN,** FORESTRY. *Current Pos:* RETIRED. *Personal Data:* b Detroit, Mich, Aug 18, 13; m 39; c 2. *Educ:* Purdue Univ, BS, 38; Yale Univ, DFor, 57. *Prof Exp:* Asst, Tenn Valley Authority, 40 & Univ Ill, 40-41; proj forester, Timber Prod War Proj, Ill, 41-45; asst chief wood technol & utilization in forestry, Univ Ill, Urbana, 45-47, from asst prof to assoc prof, 47-57, prof, 57-79; consult, 79-81. *Concurrent Pos:* Consult, Indonesia, 71; adv, Nat Bur Stand, 71-78; mem standing comt hardboard, US Bur Stand, 74-78. *Mem:* AAAS; Sigma Xi; Forest Prod Res Soc; Soc Wood Sci & Technol; Am Soc Testing & Mat. *Res:* Technology of wood and its use; wood preservation. *Mailing Add:* 101 W Windsor Rd Urbana IL 61801-6663

**WALTERS, CRAIG THOMPSON,** LASER EFFECTS, MATERIALS PROCESSING. *Current Pos:* From res physicist to sr physicist, Battelle Mem Inst, 63-71, assoc fel plasma physics, 71-73, sr researcher laser effects, 73-75, assoc sect mgr laser effects & electromagnetics, 75-87, RES LEADER, LASER EFFECTS CTR, BATTELLE COLUMBUS LABS, BATTELLE MEM INST, 87- *Personal Data:* b Columbus, Ohio, July 23, 40; m 62, Judith Claire; c Deron. *Educ:* Ohio State Univ, BS & MS, 63, PhD(physics), 71. *Honors & Awards:* NASA Tech Brief Award, 69. *Concurrent Pos:* Mem adv panel laser-supported absorption waves, Defense Advan Proj Agency, 74; mem adv group sensor susceptibility, Forum Mil Appln Directed Energy, 89-90. *Mem:* Am Phys Soc; Optical Soc Am; Sigma Xi; Int Soc Optical Eng. *Res:* Interaction of intense laser beams with materials; study of effects of laser generated shocks; laser processing of materials; design of solid-state lasers; beam conditioning optics and optical instruments. *Mailing Add:* 2353 Cambridge Blvd Columbus OH 43221-4111

**WALTERS, CURLA SYBIL,** IMMUNOLOGY, MICROBIOLOGY. *Current Pos:* MEM STAFF, DEPT MED, HOWARD UNIV HOSP, 77- *Personal Data:* b Jamaica, June 3, 29; c 1. *Educ:* Andrews Univ, BA, 61; Howard Univ, MSc, 64; Georgetown Univ, PhD(microbiol & immunol), 69. *Prof Exp:* From instr to asst prof immunol, Med Ctr, Univ Colo, Denver, 71-74; assoc prof, Dept Med, Med Ctr, Howard Univ, 74-77. *Concurrent Pos:* Am Asn Univ Women fel, Karolinska Inst, Sweden, 69-70; NIH training grant, Med Ctr, Univ Colo, 71; mem study sect, NIH, 81-85 & Nat Kidney Found. *Mem:* Am Soc Microbiologists; Am Asn Immunol; Sigma Xi. *Res:* Basic and tumor immunology. *Mailing Add:* Howard Univ Col Med Rm 3F03 Howard Univ Hosp 2041 Georgia Ave NW Washington DC 20060-0001

**WALTERS, DEBORAH K W,** COMPUTER VISION, VISUAL PSYCHOPHYSICS. *Current Pos:* vis asst prof visual psycho-physics, Dept Psychol, 81-83, ASSOC PROF COMPUT SCI & ADJ PROF PSYCHOL, STATE UNIV NY, BUFFALO, 83- *Personal Data:* b Baltimore, Md, June 14, 51. *Educ:* Guilford Col, AB, 73; Univ Birmingham, Eng, MSc, 78, PhD(neurocommun), 80. *Prof Exp:* Physicist med image processing, King's Col Hosp & Med Sch, Eng, 73-76; teaching fel exp neurol, Med Sch, Univ Birmingham, Eng, 79-81. *Mem:* Inst Elec & Electronics Engrs; Cognitive Sci Soc; Am Asn Artificial Intel; Int Soc Optical Eng; Am Asn Comput Mach; Int Soc Neural Networks. *Res:* Computer vision; the early stages of visual processing; development of algorithms based on human psychophysics and neurophysiology; geometrical considerations; inferences about the regularities in the physical world; parallel computations. *Mailing Add:* Dept Comput Sci State Univ NY 226 Bell Hall Buffalo NY 14260-0001

**WALTERS, DOUGLAS BRUCE,** LABORATORY HEALTH & SAFETY, INDUSTRIAL HYGIENE. *Current Pos:* tech progs mgr chem, 77-80, HEAD, LAB HEALTH & SAFETY, NAT TOXICOL PROG, NAT INST ENVIRON HEALTH SCI, HEALTH HUMAN SERV, NIH, 80- *Personal Data:* b Brooklyn, NY, Apr 6, 42; c Patricia J. *Educ:* Long Island Univ, BS, 63, MS, 65; Univ Ga, PhD(chem), 71. *Honors & Awards:* Nat Award Outstanding Contrib Sci & Technol Chem Health & Safety, Am Chem Soc, 89. *Prof Exp:* Food chemist, A&P, NY, 62-64; res chemist, Farbewerke Hoechst A G, Frankfurt, Ger, 65, US Environ Protection Agency, Athens, Ga, 69-71 & USDA, 71-77. *Concurrent Pos:* Adj assoc prof, Col Pub Health, Old Dominion Univ, 90-94. *Mem:* Am Chem Soc; Am Indust Hyg Asn. *Res:* Chemical health and safety; human factors; ergonomics; laboratory health and safety; safety engineering; laboratory and equipment design; safety and health; health and safety aspects of toxicology testing; safe handling chemical carcinogens; waste disposal of hazardous chemicals; industrial hygiene. *Mailing Add:* Nat Inst Environ Health Sci PO Box 12233 Research Triangle Park NC 27709. *E-Mail:* walters@niehs.nch.gov

**WALTERS, EDWARD ALBERT,** CHEMICAL DYNAMICS, QUANTUM CHEMISTRY. *Current Pos:* from asst prof to assoc prof, 68-74, PROF CHEM, UNIV NMEX, 85- *Personal Data:* b Whitefish, Mont, Jan 2, 40; m 64; c 3. *Educ:* Pac Lutheran Univ, BS, 62; Univ Minn, Minneapolis, PhD(org chem), 66. *Honors & Awards:* Lee Irving Smith Award, 66. *Prof Exp:* Res assoc chem, Cornell Univ, 66-68. *Concurrent Pos:* Res Corp grant, Univ NMex, 69-70, NSF grant, 69-72; sabbatical, Univ Kent, Canterbury, 75, MPI für Strömungsforshung, Göttingen, 76, Brookhaven Nat Lab, 84. *Mem:* AAAS; Am Vacuum Soc; Am Chem Soc. *Res:* Vacuum ultra violet spectroscopy; kinetic isotope effects; potential energy surfaces for reactive collisions; photoionization mass spectrometry of cluster molecules; extinguishment of flames. *Mailing Add:* Dept Chem Univ NMex Albuquerque NM 87131. *Fax:* 505-277-2609; *E-Mail:* walters@unm.edu

**WALTERS, FRED HENRY,** ANALYTICAL CHEMISTRY. *Current Pos:* ASSOC PROF, UNIV SOUTHWESTERN LA, 79- *Personal Data:* b Owen Sound, Ont, Aug 8, 47. *Educ:* Univ Waterloo, BSc, 71; Univ Mass, PhD(chem), 75. *Prof Exp:* Res asst, Toronto Gen Hosp, Kitchener Waterloo Hosp & Ashland Oil Can, 66-71; res assoc chem, Univ Windsor, 75-76; asst prof, Quinnipiac Col, Hamden, Conn, 76-79. *Mem:* Nat Asn Corrision Engrs; Am Chem Soc; Sigma Xi. *Res:* Chemometrics and statistics; high pressure liquid chromatography; corrosion. *Mailing Add:* Dept Chem No 44370 Univ Southwestern La Lafayette LA 70504. *E-Mail:* fhw1207@usl.edu

**WALTERS, GEOFFREY KING,** ATOMIC PHYSICS. *Current Pos:* prof physics, Rice Univ, 63-64, actg dean sci & eng, 68-69 & 72-73, chmn dept physics, 73-77, dean nat sci, 80-87, PROF PHYSICS & SPACE SCI, RICE UNIV, 64- *Personal Data:* b Baton Rouge, La, Aug 23, 31; m 54, Jeanette Long; c Terry L, Jeffrey K & Gina L. *Educ:* Rice Univ, BA, 53; Duke Univ, PhD(physics), 56. *Prof Exp:* NSF fel, Duke Univ, 56-57; br mgr & physicist, Tex Instruments, Inc, 57-62, corp res assoc, 62-63. *Concurrent Pos:* Actg chief fire technol div, Nat Bur Stand, 71-72; Guggenheim Found fel, Stanford Univ, 77-78; vis prof, Col de France, 87 & Univ Tex, Austin, 89-90. *Mem:* Fel AAAS; fel Am Phys Soc; Am Geophys Union. *Res:* Magnetic resonance; low temperature, solid state, atomic collisions and reactions; surface physics; optical pumping and dynamic nuclear orientation; solar-terrestrial relationships; radio-astronomy. *Mailing Add:* Dept Physics Rice Univ Box 1892 Houston TX 77251

**WALTERS, HUBERT JACK,** plant pathology; deceased, see previous edition for last biography

**WALTERS, JACK HENRY,** OBSTETRICS, GYNECOLOGY. *Current Pos:* RETIRED. *Personal Data:* b Toronto, Ont, Apr 2, 25; m 49; c 3. *Educ:* Univ Western Ont, BA, 46, MD, 51; FRCPS(C), 57; FRCOG, 67. *Prof Exp:* Chief, Dept Obstet & Gynec & dir cytol, St Joseph's Hosp, London, Ont, 58-73; prof obstet & gynec, Univ Western Ont, 66-73; prof obstet & gynec & chmn dept, Med Col Ohio, 73-78; prof & chmn, Dept Obstet & Gynec, Univ Ottawa, 78- *Concurrent Pos:* Can Cancer Soc McEachern traveling fel, 56-57; chief obstet & gynec, Ottawa Gen Hosp, 78- *Mem:* Can Med Asn; Soc Obstet & Gynec Can; Am Soc Cytol; fel Am Col Obstet & Gynec. *Res:* Gynecological, particularly hormonal cytology; screening programs; perinatal mortality, particularly statistical research in computer programs; manpower studies; obstetrics-gynecology health care; delivery systems. *Mailing Add:* Univ Ottawa Ontario ON Can

**WALTERS, JAMES CARTER,** GLACIAL & PERIGLACIAL GEOMORPHOLOGY. *Current Pos:* From asst prof to assoc prof, 75-89, PROF GEOL, UNIV NORTHERN IOWA, 89-, DEPT HEAD, DEPT EARTH SCI, 95- *Personal Data:* b Zeeland, Mich, June 27, 48; m 71, Bonnie Kuhlman; c Jennifer & Kyle. *Educ:* Grand Valley State Col, Mich, BA, 70; Rutgers Univ, MPhil, 73, PhD(geol), 75. *Prof Exp:* Teach fel, Fairleigh Dickinson Univ, Madison, NJ, 74-75. *Concurrent Pos:* Res assoc, Ctr Northern Studies, 75-87; co-prin investr, Nat Park Serv, Interior & Western Alaska, 78-79; vis prof, Middlebury Col, 80, Univ Vt, 81-82; consult, Northern Tech Serv, Anchorage, Alaska, 83, Cold Regions Res & Eng Lab, US Army Corps Engrs, 89-96. *Mem:* Fel Geol Soc Am; Am Quaternary Asn; Nat Asn Geol Teachers; Sigma Xi. *Res:* Quaternary geology; glacial and periglacial geomorphology; arctic studies. *Mailing Add:* Dept Earth Sci Univ Northern Iowa Cedar Falls IA 50614-0335. *Fax:* 319-273-7124; *E-Mail:* james.walters@uni.edu

**WALTERS, JAMES VERNON,** CIVIL ENGINEERING, SANITARY ENGINEERING. *Current Pos:* RETIRED. *Personal Data:* b Dublin, Ga, May 13, 33; m 55; c 2. *Educ:* Ga Inst Technol, BCE, 55, MS, 58; Univ Fla, PhD(sanit eng), 63. *Prof Exp:* Res asst, State Hwy Dept Ga, 55-56; jr asst & asst sanit engr, Atlanta Regional Off, USPHS, 56-59; from asst prof to prof civil eng, Univ Ala, Tuscaloosa, 59-94. *Concurrent Pos:* Ford Found eng resident, Southern Kraft Div, Int Paper Co, 66-67; mem, Univ Ala Environ Inst Waste Mgt Studies, 84- *Mem:* Am Chem Soc; Am Soc Civil Engrs; Am Water Works Asn; Tech Asn Pulp & Paper Indust; Water Pollution Control Asn; Air Pollution Control Asn; Sigma Xi. *Res:* Water supply and sewerage; water, sewage and industrial waste treatment; hydrology; sanitary nematology; hazardous waste management. *Mailing Add:* 1218 27th Ave E Tuscaloosa AL 35404

**WALTERS, JOHN PHILIP,** ANALYTICAL CHEMISTRY, SPECTROSCOPY. *Current Pos:* asst prof, 65-72, PROF ANALYTICAL CHEM, UNIV WIS-MADISON, 72- *Personal Data:* b Elgin, Ill, July 4, 38; m 61; c 2. *Educ:* Purdue Univ, BS, 60; Univ Ill, Urbana, PhD(chem), 64. *Honors & Awards:* Am Chem Soc Award Chem Instrumentation; Meggers Award; Lester W Strock Award. *Prof Exp:* Res assoc spectros, Univ Ill, Urbana, 64-65. *Mem:* Soc Appl Spectros; Am Soc Testing & Mat; Am Chem Soc; fel AAAS. *Res:* Time-resolved emission spectroscopy; mechanisms of spectroscopic discharges; spectrochemical methods and instrumentation; computers and lab information management. *Mailing Add:* 1204 Woodland Trail Northfield MN 55057-5246

**WALTERS, JOHN PHILIP,** POLYMER STABILIZATION, FIBER EXTRUSION. *Current Pos:* supvr, 93-95, MGR, AMOCO FABRICS & FIBERS CO, AUSTELL, GA, 95- *Personal Data:* b Manhattan, Kans, Sept 26, 41; m 63, Karen L Toburen; c Anne, Matthew, Joshua & Nathaniel. *Educ:* Kans State Univ, BS, 63; Iowa State Univ, PhD(phys chem), 68. *Prof Exp:* Res chemist, Phillips Petrol Co, Okla, 68-70, Phillips Fibers Corp, Greenville, SC, 70-76 & Phillips Petrol Co, 76-78, sr res chemist, 78-86, Phillips Fibers Corp, Greenville, SC, 86-92, supvr, 92-93. *Mem:* Am Chem Soc; Sigma Xi; Soc Polymer Eng; Fiber Soc. *Res:* Polymer stabilization; fiber extrusion; color science. *Mailing Add:* 3000 Ashland Ct Marietta GA 30064

**WALTERS, JUDITH R,** NEUROPHARMACOLOGY, NEUROPHYSIOLOGY. *Current Pos:* SECT CHIEF, NAT INST NEUROL DIS & STROKE, NIH, 81- *Personal Data:* James R, Gregory S & Douglas P. *Educ:* Yale Univ, PhD(pharmacol), 72. *Prof Exp:* Asst prof, Dept Psychiat, Sch Med, Yale Univ. *Mem:* Soc Neurosci; Am Soc Pharmacol & Exp Therapeut. *Res:* Basal ganglia function. *Mailing Add:* NINDS NIH Bldg 10 Rm 5C106 Bethesda MD 20892-0001

**WALTERS, KENNETH,** APPLIED MATHEMATICS. *Current Pos:* from lectr to sr lectr, 60-70, reader, 70-73, PROF, UNIV COL WALES, 73- *Personal Data:* b Swansea, Wales, Sept 14, 34; m 63, Mary Ross Eccles; c Jeremy R, Jonathan M & Josephine J. *Educ:* Univ Col Swansea, BSc, 56, MSc, 57, PhD, 59. *Hon Degrees:* DSc, Univ Col Swansea, 84. *Honors & Awards:* Gold Medal Brit Soc Rheology, 84. *Prof Exp:* Res assoc, Brown Univ, 59; asst prof, San Diego State Col, 60. *Mem:* Foreign assoc Nat Acad Eng; fel Royal Soc. *Mailing Add:* 8 Peny Graig Aberystwyth Dyfed SY23 2JA Wales

**WALTERS, LEE RUDYARD,** ORGANIC CHEMISTRY. *Current Pos:* ASST PROF CHEM, LAFAYETTE COL, 59- *Personal Data:* b New York, NY, Jan 20, 28; m 50; c 2. *Educ:* Bucknell Univ, BS, 54; Univ Kans, PhD(chem), 58. *Prof Exp:* Asst org chem, Univ Kans, 55-58; res chemist, Atlas Powder Co, Del, 58-59. *Mem:* Am Chem Soc. *Res:* Nitrogen heterocyclic and organometallic compounds; chemistry of natural products. *Mailing Add:* 317 W Lafayette St Lafayette Col Easton PA 18042-1768

**WALTERS, LEON C,** MATERIALS SCIENCE, METALLURGICAL ENGINEERING. *Current Pos:* assoc metall eng, Argonne Nat Lab, Idaho, 69-73, mgr reactor & mfg mat support sect & metall engr, Fuels & Mat Dept, 73-78, assoc dir, 78-85, ASSOC DIR INTEGRAL FAST REACTOR PROG, EBR-II PROJ, ARGONNE NAT LAB, IDAHO, 85- *Personal Data:* b Butte, Mont, Jan 6, 40; m 61; c 3. *Educ:* Purdue Univ, BS, 61, MS, 63, PhD(mat sci, metall eng), 66. *Prof Exp:* Staff mem, Sandia Labs, 66-69. *Mem:* Am Inst Mining, Metall & Petrol Engrs; Am Soc Metals; Am Nuclear Soc. *Res:* Formation and diffusion of point defects in compounds; effects of irradiation on the mechanical properties of metals; fabrication and performance of fast reactor metallic fuels. *Mailing Add:* 5029 Gleneagle Rd Idaho Falls ID 83401

**WALTERS, LESTER JAMES, JR,** GEOCHEMISTRY, ENVIRONMENTAL CHEMISTRY. *Current Pos:* DIR TECH SERV, PSM INT, INC, 92- *Personal Data:* b Tulsa, Okla, June 3, 40; m 67, Lynn Hager; c Kristin & David. *Educ:* Univ Tulsa, BS, 62; Mass Inst Technol, PhD(geochem), 67. *Prof Exp:* Res scientist, Marathon Oil Co, 67-69; tech assistance expert, Int Atomic Energy Agency, 69; from asst prof to prof geol, Bowling Green State Univ, 70-81; from prin res scientist to sr prin res geologist, Arco Oil & Gas Co, 87-91. *Mem:* Am Chem Soc; Am Asn Petrol Geologists; Geochem Soc; Soc Explor Paleontologists & Mineralogists. *Res:* Advanced chemical fingerprint analysis of petroleum fuels; geochemistry of metals in the surficial environment. *Mailing Add:* 2804 Glencliff Dr Plano TX 75075. *E-Mail:* twowells@aol.com

**WALTERS, LOWELL EUGENE,** ANIMAL SCIENCE. *Current Pos:* RETIRED. *Personal Data:* b Freedom, Okla, Jan 13, 19; m 42; c 2. *Educ:* Okla State Univ, BS, 40; Univ Mass, MS, 42; Okla State Univ, PhD(animal nutrit), 53. *Honors & Awards:* Meritorious Serv Award, Am Meat Sci Asn, R C Pollock Award; Don M Tyler Award; Distinguished Serv Award, Am Soc Animal Sci. *Prof Exp:* Instr animal husb, La State Univ, 42-44; asst prof, Univ Mass, 44-46; from asst prof to prof animal husb, Okla State Univ, 58-93. *Mem:* Am Meat Sci Asn; fel Am Soc Animal Sci. *Res:* Meats; beef quality; carcass composition of beef, pork and lamb; potassium 40 techniques in live animal and carcass evaluation; growth and performance in slaughter livestock; systems analysis methods as applied to efficient beef production. *Mailing Add:* 2128 W3 Stillwater OK 74074

**WALTERS, MARIAN R,** CELLULAR & MOLECULAR ENDOCRINOLOGY. *Current Pos:* from asst prof to assoc prof, 80-90, PROF ENDOCRINOL, DEPT PHYSIOL, SCH MED, TULANE UNIV, 90-, PROF, MOLECULAR & CELLULAR BIOL INTERDISCIPLINARY PROG, 90- *Personal Data:* b Washington, DC, May 27, 48. *Educ:* Millsaps Col, BS, 70; Univ Houston, MS, 72, PhD(biol & physiol), 75. *Prof Exp:* Fel, Dept Cell Biol, Baylor Col Med, 76-79; fel, Dept Biochem, Univ Calif, 79-80, asst res biochemist, 80. *Concurrent Pos:* Mem grad fac, Sch Med, Tulane Univ, 83-, dir grad studies, Dept Physiol, 88-, chmn gen med fac, 93-94; vis scientist, Cent Res Unit, Hoffmann-LaRoche, Basel, Switz, 90. *Mem:* Am Soc Bone & Mineral Res; Am Physiol Soc; Am Soc Biol Chem & Molecular Biol; Endocrine Soc; Int Cong Calcium Regulating Hormones. *Res:* Cellular and molecular endocrinology; steroid hormone receptors: structure and function; mechanism of action of 1,25-dihydroxyvitamin D3; role of 1,25-dihydroxyvitamin D3 in intracellular calcium homoeostasis; calmodulin acceptor proteins induced by 1,25-dihydroxvitamin D; calcium binding proteins: expression and function; protein Kinase C in 1,25-dihydroxyvitamin D signal transduction. *Mailing Add:* Dept Physiol SL 39 Med Ctr Tulane Univ 1430 Tulane Ave New Orleans LA 70112. *Fax:* 504-584-2675

**WALTERS, MARK DAVID,** ELECTRONICS ENGINEERING. *Current Pos:* MEM TECH STAFF, CTR MICROELECTRONICS, MCNC, 86- *Personal Data:* b Washington, DC, July 8, 59; m 83; c 1. *Educ:* Univ NC, Chapel Hill, BA, 81; Univ Va, Charlottesville, MS, 86; NC State Univ, Raleigh, PhD(mat sci), 89. *Prof Exp:* Teaching asst physics, Dept Physics, Univ Va, 83-84, res asst, Dept Mat Sci, 84-86. *Mem:* Mat Res Soc; Minerals, Metals & Mat Soc; Sigma Xi; Electrochem Soc. *Res:* Study of radiation-induced defects in the gate insulators of field effect transistors; developed models of defect distributions and generation mechanisms, and performed experimental studies in association with these models. *Mailing Add:* 103 Cricket Ground Durham NC 27707

**WALTERS, MARTHA I,** clinical chemistry, for more information see previous edition

**WALTERS, RANDALL KEITH,** mathematics, computer science, for more information see previous edition

**WALTERS, RICHARD FRANCIS,** INFORMATION SCIENCE, MEDICAL EDUCATION. *Current Pos:* RETIRED. *Personal Data:* b Teleajen, Romania, Aug 30, 30; US citizen; m 52, Shipley Newlin; c Leslie W (Tuomi) & David T. *Educ:* Williams Col, BA, 52, Univ Wyo, MA, 53; Univ Bordeaux, dipl natural sci, 55; Stanford Univ, PhD(geol), 57. *Prof Exp:* Res geologist, Humble Oil & Ref Co, 56-67; from asst prof to prof community health, Univ Calif, Davis, 67-83, prof elec & comput eng, 80-83, prof & chmn, Div Comput Sci, 83-89. *Concurrent Pos:* Fel, Col Med Informatics. *Mem:* Asn Am Med Sys & Informatics; Biomed Eng Soc; Asn Comput Mach; sr mem Inst Elec & Electronics Engrs. *Res:* High level language support of networked distributed data bases on heterogeneous systems; machine-independent implementation of high-level languages; computer support of medical records; distance learning. *Mailing Add:* Dept Comput Sci Univ Calif Davis CA 95616. *Fax:* 530-752-4767

**WALTERS, ROBERT F,** HYDROLOGY & WATER RESOURCES. *Current Pos:* PRES, WALTERS DRILLING CO, INC, 51- *Personal Data:* b Rochester, NY, July 15, 14; m 48, Margaret Robbins; c 4. *Educ:* Univ Rochester, BSc, 36, MSc, 38; Johns Hopkins Univ, PhD(geol), 46. *Honors & Awards:* President's Award, Am Asn Petrol Geologists, 46; John C Frye Award in Environ Geol, Geol Soc Am, 93. *Prof Exp:* Res geol, Gulf Oil Corp, Tulsa, 40-48; geologist, Heathman Drilling Co, 48-51. *Concurrent Pos:* Assoc ed, Am Asn Petrol Geologists, 65; consult drilling & coring, Nuclear Div Oak Ridge Nat Lab, Union Carbide Corp, 70-79 & Off Nuclear Waste Isolation, Battelle Mem Inst, 78-82; consult salt & subsidence ind, Vulcan Mat Co, 76- *Mem:* Sigma Xi; Am Geophys Union; hon mem Am Asn Petrol Geologists; Geol Soc Am; Soc Econ Geologists. *Res:* Movement of fluids through rocks; migration of oil and gas; dissolution of carbonate rocks(karst, paleo karst) and salt beds; paleohydrology of Cambro-Ordovician and Precambrian rocks underlying Kansas. *Mailing Add:* 100 S Main St Suite 420 Wichita KS 67202. *Fax:* 316-265-8705

**WALTERS, ROLAND DICK,** orthodontics, for more information see previous edition

**WALTERS, RONALD ARLEN,** BIOCHEMISTRY, RADIOBIOLOGY. *Current Pos:* dep group leader, Los Alamos Nat Lab, Univ Calif, 80-81, group leader, 82-84, from asst to assoc dir chem, earth & life sci, 85-86, asst to assoc dir res, 86-89, prog dir biol & environ res, 89-93, STAFF MEM BIOCHEM, LOS ALAMOS NAT LAB, UNIV CALIF, 67-, ASSOC LAB DIR, PAC NW NAT LAB, 93- *Personal Data:* b Greeley, Colo, Apr 25, 40; m 69, Geraldine J Huck; c Christian Grant & Colin Jeremy. *Educ:* Colo State Univ, BS, 62, MS, 64, PhD(radiation biol), 67. *Prof Exp:* Engr radiation biol, Gen Elec Co, 62-63. *Mem:* AAAS; Am Chem Soc; Am Soc Biochem & Molecular Biol; Radiation Res Soc; Am Soc Cell Biol. *Res:* Cellular biology; gene structure and function; trace metal metabolism; radiation biology; genomics. *Mailing Add:* Battelle Pac NW Nat Lab Life Sci Ctr K1-50 Richland WA 99352. *Fax:* 509-375-3686; *E-Mail:* ra__walters@pnl.gov

**WALTERS, THOMAS RICHARD,** PEDIATRICS, HEMATOLOGY. *Current Pos:* RETIRED. *Personal Data:* b Milwaukee, Wis, May 9, 29; m 84. *Educ:* Marquette Univ, MD, 54. *Prof Exp:* Instr pediat, Stanford Univ, 61-62; asst prof, Univ Kans Med Ctr, Kansas City, 62-67; assoc prof, Univ Tenn, Memphis, 67-71; assoc prof, NJ Med Sch, 71-76, prof pediat & dir div hemat-oncol, 76-90. *Concurrent Pos:* Assoc mem hemat, St Jude Children's Res Hosp, Memphis, 67-71. *Mem:* Am Soc Hemat; Am Acad Pediat. *Res:* Mechanisms of tumor growth. *Mailing Add:* UMDNJ NJ Med Sch 185 S Orange Ave Newark NJ 07103-2714

**WALTERS, VIRGINIA F,** PHYSICS. *Current Pos:* RETIRED. *Personal Data:* b New York, NY, May 26, 25; m 45; c 2. *Educ:* Smith Col, AB, 47; Western Reserve Univ, MA, 58, PhD(physics), 65. *Prof Exp:* Physicist, DeMornay Budd, Inc, 47-49; res asst microwave components, Radiation Lab, Columbia Univ, 49-50; lectr elem physics, Adelphi Col, 50-51; physicist, Servo Corp Am, 51; asst physics, Western Res Univ, 54-65, fel, 65-66; asst prof, Cleveland State Univ, 66-67; res physicist, Carnegie-Mellon Univ, 67-68; asst prof phys sci, Point Park Col, 68-69; teacher physics & math, Western Reserve Acad, 69-74; lectr physics, Cleveland State Univ, 75-80. *Concurrent Pos:* Vis asst prof, Dept Physics, Cleveland State Univ, 77-81. *Mem:* Am Phys Soc; Am Asn Physics Teachers. *Res:* Positron annihilation; nuclear instrumentation. *Mailing Add:* 105 S Beach Rd South Burlington VT 05403

**WALTERS, WILLIAM BEN,** NUCLEAR CHEMISTRY, ASTROPHYSICS. *Current Pos:* assoc prof, 70-77, PROF CHEM, UNIV MD, COL PARK, 77- *Personal Data:* b Highland, Kans, Apr 26, 38; m 62; c 2. *Educ:* Kans State Univ, BS, 60; Univ Ill, PhD(chem), 64. *Prof Exp:* Res assoc chem, Mass Inst Technol, 64-65, asst prof, 65-70. *Concurrent Pos:* Vis prof physics, Katolieke Univ Leuven, Belg, 78; Guggenheim fel, Clarendon Lab, Oxford, 86-87. *Mem:* Am Chem Soc; Am Phys Soc. *Res:* Radioactive decay; nuclear spectroscopy; new isotopes and isomers; nuclear reactions; nuclear orientation; nuclear structure; neutron-capture gamma-ray spectroscopy; gamma-gamma angular correlations; in-beam gamma ray spectroscopy. *Mailing Add:* Dept Chem Univ Md College Park MD 20742. *Fax:* 301-314-9121; *E-Mail:* ww3@umail.umd.edu

**WALTERS, WILLIAM LE ROY,** PRE-COLLEGE SCIENCE & MATH EDUCATION. *Current Pos:* From asst prof to prof physics, Univ Wis-Milwaukee, 61-68, assoc dean sci, Col Lett & Sci, 65-68, exec asst chancellor, 68-70, actg dean, Col Appl Sci & Eng, 70, vchancellor, 71-81, assoc dir, Ctr Math/Sci Educ Res, 86-95, EMER PROF, UNIV WIS-MILWAUKEE, 95- *Personal Data:* b Racine, Wis, Mar 30, 32; m 55; c 4. *Educ:* Univ Wis, BS, 54, MS, 58, PhD(physics), 61. *Concurrent Pos:* Exec Comt, Coun Acad Affairs, Nat Asn State Univs & Land-Grant Cols, 76-79, chmn coun, 78. *Mem:* AAAS; Am Asn Physics Teachers. *Res:* Science education; science communications. *Mailing Add:* Univ Wis Milwaukee WI 53201

**WALTHER, ADRIAAN,** OPTICS. *Current Pos:* PROF PHYSICS, WORCESTER POLYTECH INST, 72- *Personal Data:* b The Hague, Holland, Apr 22, 34; m 60, Trudy C Huygen; c 2. *Educ:* Delft Univ Technol, PhD(physics), 59. *Prof Exp:* Mem res staff, Diffraction Ltd Inc, 60-72. *Concurrent Pos:* Am Optical vis prof, Worcester Polytech Inst, 68-69. *Mem:* Fel Optical Soc Am; Neth Phys Soc. *Res:* Geometrical and physical optics. *Mailing Add:* 20 Whittier Dr Acton MA 01720. *E-Mail:* awalther@wpi.wpi.edu

**WALTHER, ALINA,** PLANT PHYSIOLOGY, PLANT ECOLOGY. *Current Pos:* RETIRED. *Personal Data:* b Rosenthal, USSR, Aug 15, 23; Can citizen. *Educ:* Sir George Williams Univ, BCom, 53, BSc, 61; McGill Univ, MSc, 63; Univ Toronto, PhD(plant physiol), 68. *Prof Exp:* Spec lectr, Univ Regina, 67-68, from asst prof to emer prof biol, 68-92. *Mem:* AAAS; Phytochem Soc NAm; Am Soc Plant Physiologists; Can Soc Plant Physiologists; Ecol Soc Am. *Res:* Plant senescence, especially metabolic changes in developing and senescing sunflower cotyledons and leaves; seed production and germination in native prairie plants (opuntia polyacantha and glycyrrhiza lepiolola); betalaines in emergent cactus seedlings. *Mailing Add:* 30 Bell St Regina SK S4S 4B6 Can

**WALTHER, FRANK H,** MINERALOGY. *Current Pos:* RETIRED. *Personal Data:* b Williamsport, Pa, Aug 4, 30; m 54; c 3. *Educ:* Franklin & Marshall Col, BSc, 52. *Prof Exp:* Mgr mineral res, Harbison-Walker Refractories, 56-72, mgr res, 72-78, dir res, 78. *Mem:* Fel Am Ceramic Soc. *Res:* Mineralogical aspects of refractory technology. *Mailing Add:* HC 64 Box 397 Trout Run PA 17771

**WALTHER, FRITZ R,** ANIMAL BEHAVIOR. *Current Pos:* prof, 70-83, EMER PROF WILDLIFE, TEX A&M UNIV, 84- *Personal Data:* b Chemnitz, Ger, Sept 8, 21; m 52, Elizabeth M Mueller; c Senta M Fanzott. *Educ:* Univ Frankfurt, BS, 44, MS, 56, PhD(zool), 63. *Prof Exp:* Teacher, Fed Ministry Educ, Ger, 51-59; sci dir res & admin, Opel Zoo, 60-63; res scientist, Zurich Zool, Switz, 64, Serengeti Nat Park, Tanzania, 65-67 & 74-75 & Etosha Nat Park, Namibia, 78; assoc prof zool, Univ Mo, Columbia, 67-70. *Concurrent Pos:* Grants, Ger Res Soc, 63, Gertrud Ruegg Found, 64 & 67, Fritz Thyssen Found, 65-67 & 74-75, Res Coun Univ Mo, 69-70, Smithsonian Foreign Currency, 70-72 & Caesar Kleberg Found, 74-75, 78. *Res:* Ethology of game animals, especially horned ungulates. *Mailing Add:* Dorsstr 22 56269 Diedorf-Wienau Germany

**WALTHER, HERBERT,** PHYSICS. *Current Pos:* PROF PHYSICS, UNIV MUNICH, 75-; DIR, MAX-PLANCK INST QUANTUM OPTICS, GER, 81- *Personal Data:* b Ludwigshafen, Ger, Jan 19, 35; m 62, Margot Groschel; c Thomas & Ulrike. *Educ:* Univ Heidelberg, dipl, 60, PhD, 62; Tech Univ Hannover, Habilitation, 68. *Hon Degrees:* Dr, Univ Moscow, 91, Univ Hannover, 94. *Honors & Awards:* Max Born Prize, Ger Phys Soc, 78; Stanley H Klosk Lectr, NY Univ, 85; Guass Medal, 89; Charles Hard Townes Award, Optical Soc Am, 90; Loeb Lectr, Harvard Univ, 90; King Faisal Prize Physics, 93; Michelson Medal, Franklin Inst, 93; Celsius Lectr, Uppsala Univ, 94; Muller Lectr, Pa State Univ, 96; Humboldt Medal, 97; James Franck Mem Lectr, Jerusalem, 97. *Prof Exp:* Postdoctoral fel, Univ Heidelberg, 62-63; sci asst, Univ Hannover, 63-68, lectr, 68-69; guest scientist, Lab Aime Cotton, Nat Ctr Sci Res, 69; vis fel, Joint Inst Lab Astrophys, Univ Colo, 70; prof, Univ Bonn, 71, Univ Cologne, 71-75. *Concurrent Pos:* Mem senate & coun, NSF, Fed Repub Ger, 78-84; bd dirs, Ger Phys Soc, 79-82; hon prof, Acad Sinica, China, 80; mem planning comt, Max-Planck Soc, 82-86, vpres, 91-96; chmn, Comn Atomic & Molecular Physics, Int Union Pure & Appl Physics, 84-87. *Mem:* Fel Optical Soc; Europ Phys Soc; Ger Phys Soc; foreign hon mem Am Acad Arts & Sci; Bavarian Acad Sci; hon mem Romanian Acad; Acad Europaea. *Res:* Investigation of the radiation-matter interaction with special emphasis on quantum phenomena and experiments with single atoms. *Mailing Add:* Egenhoferstr 7a 81243 Munich Germany. *Fax:* 32905-710; *E-Mail:* herbert.walther@mpq.mpg.de

**WALTHER, JAMES EUGENE,** CHEMICAL ENGINEERING. *Current Pos:* res engr, 62-70, SR RES ENGR, CROWN ZELLERBACH CORP, CAMAS, 70- *Personal Data:* b Spokane, Wash, May 16, 32; m 54; c 2. *Educ:* Univ Wash, BS, 54; Univ Ill, Urbana, MS, 56, PhD(chem eng), 57. *Prof Exp:* Res engr, Stand Oil Co Calif, 57-62. *Mem:* Am Inst Chem Engrs; Am Chem Soc. *Res:* Air pollution control from pulp and paper industry; instrumentation development for air pollution control. *Mailing Add:* 19610 NW 30th Ave Ridgefield WA 98642

**WALTHER, JOSEPH EDWARD,** GASTROENTEROLOGY. *Current Pos:* clin asst prof, 48-93, EMER CLIN ASST PROF MED, IND UNIV SCH MED, INDIANAPOLIS, 93-; PRES & CHIEF EXEC OFFICER, WALTHER CANCER INST, 56- *Personal Data:* b Indianapolis, Ind, Nov 24, 12; wid; c Mary A (Margolis), Karl, Joanne (Landman), Suzanne (Conran), Diane (Paczesny) & Kurt. *Educ:* Ind Univ, BS & MD, 36; Am Bd Internal Med, dipl. *Honors & Awards:* Weiss Award, Am Col Gastroenterol, 88. *Prof Exp:* Intern, Meth Hosp & St Vincent Hosp, Indianapolis, 36-37; physician & surgeon, US Engrs/Pan Am Airways, Midway Islands, 37-38; chief resident & med dir, Wilcox Mem Hosp, Lihue, Hawaii, 38-40. *Concurrent Pos:* Internist & gastroenterologist, Mem Clin, Indianapolis, 47-83, med dir, pres & chief exec officer, 47-; deleg, AMA, 70-86. *Mem:* Master Am Col Gastroenterol (pres, 70-71); AMA. *Res:* Internal medicine. *Mailing Add:* 3266 N Meridian St Indianapolis IN 46208-5838

**WALTKING, ARTHUR ERNEST,** ANALYTICAL CHEMISTRY, FOOD CHEMISTRY. *Current Pos:* Asst chemist, CPC Int Inc, 59-64, chemist, 64-66, group leader anal res, 66-72, sect head anal serv, 72-79, assoc res scientist, Best Foods Div, 79-84, PRIN MAT SCIENTIST, CPC INT INC, 84- *Personal Data:* b New York, NY, Nov 7, 37; m 61, Kathryn M Schraut; c Claire & Adrienne. *Educ:* Lehigh Univ, BA, 59. *Honors & Awards:* Golden Peanut Award, Nat Peanut Coun, 71. *Prof Exp:* Tech asst, Durkee Foods, 57- *Concurrent Pos:* Assoc referee oxidized oils, Asn Off Analytical Chemists, 71-83 & 85-86; chmn, Hydraul Oil Comt, Am Oil Chemists Soc, 71-75, Biochem Methodology Comt, 73-76, Flavo Nomenclature Comt, 75-79, Mycotoxin Comt, 78-79 & Phys Methodology Com, 88-; co-founder & pres, NY & NJ Regional Sect, 88-90, chmn, Foods I Comt, 80-88, rep, Am Oil Chemists Soc, Joint Am Oil Chemists Soc-Asn Off Analytical Chemists-Am Asn Cereal Chemists, Comt Mycotoxins, 75-90; US rep, comn oils, fats & derivatives, Int Union Pure & Appl Chem, 78-91. *Mem:* Am Oil Chemists Soc; fel Asn Anal Chemists. *Res:* Development of analytical methodology for analysis of food products for mycotoxins, flavor volatiles, texture, rheological properties, essential fatty acids and polymers derived from oxidation or heat abuse of vegetable oils. *Mailing Add:* Best Foods Tech Ctr 150 Pierce St Box 6710 Somerset NJ 08873-6710

**WALTMAN, PAUL ELVIS,** DIFFERENTIAL EQUATIONS, MATHEMATICAL BIOLOGY. *Current Pos:* PROF MATH, EMORY UNIV, ATLANTA, 83- *Personal Data:* b St Louis, Mo, Oct 17, 31; m 53, Ruth J Major; c Frederick J, Paul D & Robert B. *Educ:* St Louis Univ, BS, 52; Baylor Univ, MA, 54; Univ Mo, MA, 60, PhD(math), 62. *Prof Exp:* Staff mem, Mitre Corp, 62-63 & Sandia Corp, 63-65; from asst prof to prof, Univ Iowa, 65-83. *Mem:* Soc Indust & Appl Math. *Res:* Ordinary differential equations; modeling biological phenomena. *Mailing Add:* Dept Math & Comput Sci Emory Univ Atlanta GA 30322. *Fax:* 404-727-5611; *E-Mail:* waltman@mathcs.emory.edu

**WALTMANN, WILLIAM LEE,** MATHEMATICS. *Current Pos:* assoc prof, 64-72, chmn dept, 71-94, PROF MATH, WARTBURG COL, 72- *Personal Data:* b Cedar Falls, Iowa, July 5, 34; m 58, Carol A Johnson; c Karen, Ronald & Diane. *Educ:* Wartburg Col, BA, 56; Iowa State Univ, MS, 58, PhD(math), 64. *Prof Exp:* Instr math, Wartburg Col, 58-61 & Iowa State Univ, 63-64. *Mem:* Math Asn Am; Soc Indust & Appl Math. *Res:* Inversion of matrices; non-associative rings; tridiagonalization of matrices. *Mailing Add:* Dept Math Comput Sci & Physics Wartburg Col Waverly IA 50677. *Fax:* 319-352-8606

**WALTON, ALAN GEORGE,** BIOPHYSICAL CHEMISTRY. *Current Pos:* PRES, UNIV GENETICS CO, 81- *Personal Data:* b Birmingham, Eng, Apr 3, 36; m 77; c 4. *Educ:* Univ Nottingham, BSc, 57, PhD(chem), 60, DSc(biophys chem), 73. *Prof Exp:* Res assoc chem, Ind Univ, 60-62; from asst prof to assoc prof macromolecular sci, Case Western Res Univ, 62-71, prof, 71-81. *Concurrent Pos:* Vis lectr, Harvard Med Sch, 71; mem, Pres Task Force Sci & Technol Policy, 75-76. *Mem:* NY Acad Sci; Am Chem Soc; Biophys Soc. *Res:* Conformation and structure of synthetic biopolymers and fibrous proteins; molecular hematology; cell adhesion; genetic engineering; cartilage research; drug release. *Mailing Add:* 17 Walnut Lane Weston CT 06883

**WALTON, ANTHONY WARRICK,** PHYSICAL SEDIMENTOLOGY, DIAGENESIS. *Current Pos:* asst prof geol, 75-78, ASSOC PROF GEOL, UNIV KANS, 78-, CHMN GEOL, 87- *Personal Data:* b Mt Holly, NJ, Apr 10, 43; m 69, Ann V Kershner; c Steven R & Susan E. *Educ:* Lafayette Col, BA, 65; Univ Tex, Austin, MA, 68, PhD(geol), 72. *Prof Exp:* asst prof geol, Vanderbilt Univ, 72-75. *Concurrent Pos:* Res assoc, Bureau Econ Geol, Univ Tex, Austin, 73 & 75 & 76; geologist, Conoco, 74; res assoc, Kans Geol Surv, 83 & 86. *Mem:* Geol Soc Am; Soc Econ Paleontologists & Mineralogists; Int Asn Sedimentologists; Am Asn Petrol Geologists. *Res:* Sedimentology, especially deposition and diagenesis of siliciclastic sediments; oil reservoir characterization; deposition of volcaniclastic sediments by lahars and fluvial processes; diagenesis of volcaniclastics. *Mailing Add:* Dept Geol Univ Kans Lawrence KS 66045-0001

**WALTON, BARBARA ANN,** VERTEBRATE EMBRYOLOGY, HISTOLOGY. *Current Pos:* ASST PROF BIOL, UNIV TENN, CHATTANOOGA, 70- *Personal Data:* b Baltimore, Md, Mar 30, 40; m 70. *Educ:* Ind Univ Pa, BSEd, 62; Univ Okla, MNatSci, 66, PhD(zool), 70. *Prof Exp:* Teacher, Franklin Twp Sch Dist, Pa, 62-63 & Bethel Park Jr High Sch, 63-65. *Mem:* Am Inst Biol Sci; Am Soc Zoologists. *Res:* Development of the chicken embryo following x-irradiation and application of other teratogens; histology and histochemistry of embryonic development. *Mailing Add:* Dept Biol Univ Tenn 615 McCallie Ave Chattanooga TN 37403-2504

**WALTON, BRYCE CALVIN,** PARASITOLOGY. *Current Pos:* CONSULT, 83- *Personal Data:* b Lead, SDak, June 5, 23; m 46, Elmira Blumhardt; c Laurel, Judith, Thomas & Raquel. *Educ:* Univ Southern Calif, AB, 48, MS, 50; Univ Md, PhD(zool, parasitol), 56. *Prof Exp:* US Army, 50-, res parasitologist, Walter Reed Army Inst Res, 52-56, chief dept med zool, 406th Med Gen Lab, 56-59, parasitologist, Third Army Med Lab, 59-62, chief parasitic dis sect, Middle Am Res Unit, 62-65, cmndg officer, Med Res Unit, Panama, CZ, 65-69 & US Army Res & Develop Group Far East, 69-72, cmndg officer, Army Med Res Unit-Panama, 72-76; regional adv parasitic dis, Pan Am Health Orgn-WHO, 76-82. *Concurrent Pos:* Adj res assoc, Gorgas Mem Lab, Panama, 62-69, 72-76; prof Ad Honorem, Univ Panama Fac Med, 67-69; WHO Expert Comt, Parasite Dis, 87-; chmn, Comn Ed, Pan Am Health Orgn, 90-94. *Mem:* Am Soc Trop Med & Hyg; fel Royal Soc Trop Med & Hyg; Am Micros Soc; Am Soc Parasitol; fel Am Acad Microbiol. *Res:* American trypanosomiasis and leishmaniasis; toxoplasmosis; immuno-diagnosis of parasitic disease; systematics; international public health. *Mailing Add:* 779 Barlow Dr Lake Heritage Gettysburg PA 17325-8968. *Fax:* 717-337-3506

**WALTON, CHARLES ANTHONY,** pharmacy, pharmacology, for more information see previous edition

**WALTON, CHARLES MICHAEL,** TRANSPORTATION ENGINEERING, POLICY PLANNING. *Current Pos:* from asst prof to assoc prof, Univ Tex, Austin, 71-83, prof civil eng, 83-87, Bess Harris Jones Centennial Prof natural resource policy studies, 87-91, chmn civil eng, 88-96, Paul D & Betty Robertson Meek Centennial prof eng, 91-93, ERNEST H COCKRELL CENTENNIAL CHAIR ENG, UNIV TEX, AUSTIN, 93- *Personal Data:* b Hickory, NC, June 28, 41; m 63, Betty Hughes; c 4. *Educ:* Va Mil Inst, BS, 63; NC State Univ, MCE, 69, PhD(civil eng), 71. *Honors & Awards:* Harland Bartholomew Award, Am Soc Civil Engrs, 87; Frank M Masters Transp Eng Award, Am Soc Civil Engrs, 87; James Laurie Prize, 92. *Prof Exp:* Asst civil eng, NC State Univ, 67-71. *Concurrent Pos:* Chmn exec comt, Transp Res Bd, Nat Acad Sci-Nat Res Coun; mem exec comn, Urban Transp Div, Am Soc Civil Engrs, 81-; assoc dir, Ctr Transp Res, Univ Tex,

Austin, 80-88. *Mem:* Nat Acad Eng; Inst Transp Engrs; Transp Res Bd; Am Soc Civil Engrs; Intelligent Transp Soc Am; Int Road Fedn. *Res:* Transportation and land use planning; traffic safety; application of light rail transit; truck use of highways; truck size and weight issues; public/private participation in transportation; intelligent transportation systems; commercial vehicle operations. *Mailing Add:* ECJ Hall Suite 6-3 Univ Tex Austin TX 78712. *Fax:* 512-471-4995; *E-Mail:* cmwalton@mail.utexas.edu

**WALTON, DANIEL C,** PLANT BIOCHEMISTRY, PLANT PHYSIOLOGY. *Current Pos:* RETIRED. *Personal Data:* b Philadelphia, Pa, May 16, 34; m 60; c 2. *Educ:* Univ Del, BS, 55; State Univ NY Col Forestry, Syracuse Univ, PhD(plant physiol), 62. *Prof Exp:* Chem engr, E I du Pont de Nemours & Co, 55-58; fel, Univ Tex, 62-63; from asst prof to prof, State Univ NY Col Forestry, Syracuse, 63-92, emer prof biochem, 92. *Concurrent Pos:* Vis mem, Dept Bot, Univ Col Wales, 71-72 & 78-79. *Mem:* AAAS; Am Chem Soc; Plant Growth Regulator Soc; Am Soc Plant Physiologists. *Res:* Seed germination; plant growth regulation. *Mailing Add:* 730 Myakka Rd Sarasota FL 34240

**WALTON, DEREK,** CONDENSED MATTER PHYSICS. *Current Pos:* assoc prof, 68-74, prof physics, 74-95, EMER PROF PHYICS, MCMASTER UNIV, 95- *Personal Data:* b Sao Paulo, Brazil, Mar 1, 31; nat US; m 54; c 4. *Educ:* Univ Toronto, MSc, 54; Harvard Univ, PhD(appl physics), 58. *Prof Exp:* Asst res engr, Univ Calif, 57-58; sr physicist, Convair Div, Gen Dynamics Corp, 58-60; res assoc eng physics, Cornell Univ, 60-62; physicist, Oak Ridge Nat Lab, 62-68. *Mem:* Fel Am Phys Soc. *Res:* Experimental research in orientational glasses, spin glasses and glasses in general using light scattering and magnetic techniques; physics applied to archaeology and geomagnetism. *Mailing Add:* Dept Physics McMaster Univ 1280 Main St W Hamilton ON L8S 4L8 Can

**WALTON, GEORGE,** ANALYTICAL & PHYSICAL CHEMISTRY, FORENSIC SCIENCE. *Current Pos:* DIR, TURQUITE MINERALS ASSAY LAB, 80- *Personal Data:* b Edmunton, Eng, Aug 14, 14; nat US; m 49, Maverne Sparks; c Charles Ronald. *Educ:* San Diego State Col, AB, 36; Columbia Univ, MA, 39, PhD(phys chem), 41. *Prof Exp:* Asst, Columbia Univ, 40-41, Manhattan proj, 41; asst prof chem, Col Pharm, Univ Cincinnati, 41-44, assoc prof, 46-47; consult chemist, 47-50; sr res chemist, Drackett Co, 50-52, tech adminr, 52-57, sr scientist, 57-62; geochem prospecting, 62-66; asst dir, Southwestern NMex Media Ctr, Western NMex Univ, 66-68, from asst prof to assoc prof phys sci, 68-80. *Concurrent Pos:* Consult precious metals recovery & analysis. *Mem:* Am Acad Forensic Sci. *Res:* X-ray crystallography applied to chemical problems; paper chromatography of metal ions; silver in ores by atomic absorption spectroscopy; precious metals recovery and analysis; recovery of precious metals from scrap; research in solvent-bleed forgery; barite ore processing; granted many patents. *Mailing Add:* 1312 S Silver Ave Deming NM 88030

**WALTON, GERALD STEVEN,** PLANT PATHOLOGY. *Current Pos:* From asst plant pathologist to assoc plant pathologist, 61-77, PLANT PATHOLOGIST, CONN AGR EXP STA, 77- *Personal Data:* b Kansas City, Kans, July 23, 35; m 56; c 5. *Educ:* Wabash Col, AB, 57; Rutgers Univ, PhD(plant path), 61. *Mem:* Am Phytopath Soc. *Res:* Nature of resistance to plant diseases, methods of disease control and determination of causal factor of a disease when unknown. *Mailing Add:* 285 Hillfield Rd Hamden CT 06518

**WALTON, HAROLD FREDERIC,** ANALYTICAL CHEMISTRY. *Current Pos:* from asst prof to prof, 47-82, chmn dept, 62-66, EMER PROF CHEM, UNIV COLO, BOULDER, 83-, SR RES ASSOC, COOP INST RES ENVIRON SCI, 83- *Personal Data:* b Tregony, Eng, Aug 25, 12; nat US; wid; c James, Elizabeth & Daniel. *Educ:* Oxford Univ, BA, 34, PhD(chem), 37. *Honors & Awards:* Dal Nogare Award in Chromatography, 88. *Prof Exp:* Procter vis fel, Princeton Univ, 37-38; res chemist, Permutit Co, 38-40; from instr to asst prof chem, Northwestern Univ, 40-46. *Concurrent Pos:* Vis Fulbright-Hays lectr, Trujillo, 66-67 & 70 & Lima, 66-67; vis prof, Pedag Inst, Caracas, Venezuela, 72; hon prof, Univ San Marcos & Univ Trujillo, Peru. *Mem:* AAAS; Am Chem Soc; Royal Soc Chem; corresp mem Chem Soc Peru. *Res:* Ion exchange; chromatography. *Mailing Add:* Univ Colo Campus Box 215 Boulder CO 80309

**WALTON, HAROLD V(INCENT),** AGRICULTURAL ENGINEERING. *Current Pos:* RETIRED. *Personal Data:* b Christiana, Pa, June 17, 21; m 46, Velma Braun; c H Richard, Marilyn W (Friedersdorf) & Carol A. *Educ:* Pa State Univ, BS, 42, MS, 50; Purdue Univ, PhD, 61. *Prof Exp:* Engr, Gen Elec Co, 43-45; prof agr eng, Pa State Univ, 47-62; prof, Univ Mo, Columbia, 62-76, chmn dept, 62-69, prof & chief party, India Contract, 69-71; prof agr eng & head dept, Pa State Univ, University Park, 76-85. *Mem:* fel Am Soc Agr Engrs. *Res:* Physical properties of poultry egg and meat products. *Mailing Add:* 291 E McCormick Ave State College PA 16801

**WALTON, HARRIETT J,** MATHEMATICS. *Current Pos:* from asst prof to assoc prof, 54-81, PROF MATH, MOREHOUSE COL, 81- *Personal Data:* b Claxton, Ga, Sept 19, 33; m 58; c 4. *Educ:* Clark Col, AB, 52; Howard Univ, MS, 54; Syracuse Univ, MA, 57; Ga State Univ, PhD(math educ), 79. *Prof Exp:* Instr math, Hampton Inst, 54-55, asst prof, 57-58. *Concurrent Pos:* Proj dir, Atlanta Univ, 70-73 & Atlanta Univ Ctr, Inc, 81-82. *Mem:* Math Asn Am; Nat Asn Math (secy/treas, 80-). *Res:* Remediation in mathematics at the college level. *Mailing Add:* Dept Math Morehouse Col PO Box 73 830 Westview Dr SW Atlanta GA 30314-0104. *Fax:* 404-681-2800, Ext 2451

**WALTON, HENRY MILLER,** ORGANIC CHEMISTRY. *Current Pos:* RETIRED. *Personal Data:* b Frankfurt am Main, Ger, May 7, 12; nat US; m 50, Norma L Horn; c 2. *Educ:* Univ Frankfurt, PhD(philos), 34; Univ Chicago, PhD(org chem), 38. *Prof Exp:* Res chemist, Continental Carbon Co, NY, 39; Chas Pfizer & Co fel, Columbia Univ, 40-42; sr res chemist, Warner Inst Therapeut Res, 43-47; group leader fundamental res lab, Nat Dairy Res Labs, Inc, 47-57; sr res chemist, A E Staley Mfg Co, 57-61, res assoc, 61-69, patent chemist, 69-72; patent consult, 72-74; prof philos, Richland Community Col, 74-75. *Mem:* Am Chem Soc; Am Philos Asn; Philos Sci Asn. *Res:* Vitamins A and E; unsaturated aliphatics; condensation polymers; free radical polymerization reactions; starches; sugars; enzymes; immobilized enzymes; philosophy of science. *Mailing Add:* 2960 N Lake Shore Dr Apt 2808 Chicago IL 60657

**WALTON, JAMES STEPHEN,** VIDEO-BASED QUANTIFICATION OF MOTION, HIGH-SPEED PHOTOGRAPHY & VIDEOGRAPHY FOR MOTION MEASUREMENTS. *Current Pos:* PRES & OWNER, 4D VIDEO, 88- *Personal Data:* b Kingston-upon-Thames, Surrey, Eng, Nov 27, 46, US citizen; m 74, Dorcas A Graham; c Kirstyn Amy & Lars Timothy. *Educ:* Carnegie Col Phys Educ, Leeds, Eng, DPE, 68; cert educ, 68, Mich State Univ, East Lansing, MA, 70; Stanford Univ, MS, 76; Pa State Univ, PhD(biomech), 81. *Prof Exp:* Teacher math & phys ed, Gaynesford High Sch, Eng, 69-70; teaching & res asst kinesiology, Biomech Lab, Pa State Univ, 70-74; teaching asst, Dept Appl Mech, Stanford Univ, 74-76; dir eng, Computerized Biomech Anal Inc, 79; assoc sr res scientist, Biomed Sci Dept, Gen Motors Res Labs, 79-81, sr res scientist, 81-85; sr software engr, Motion Anal Corp, 85-86, mgr applns eng & prod planning, 86-87, vpres applns eng, 87-88. *Concurrent Pos:* Tech adv, Dept Biomech, Mich State Univ, 85-; investr, Lockheed Eng Mgt Serv Co, NASA, White Sands Test Facil, 86; res consult, 3M Corp, 88, Ames Res Ctr, NASA, Moffett Field, Calif, 88, Western Digital Corp, San Jose, Calif, 88, McDonnell Douglas Corp, St Louis, 88, Ford Motor Co, Mich, 88. *Mem:* Am Acad Forensic Sci; AAAS; Am Col Sports Med; Am Soc Biomech; Am Soc Mech Engrs; Am Soc Photogram & Remote Sensing; Digital Equip Comput User's Soc; Human Factors Soc; Int Soc Biomech; Sigma Xi; Soc Photo-Optical Instrumentation Engrs; NY Acad Sci; Inst Soc Biomech Sports; hon fel Brit Asn Phys Training. *Res:* Design and development and application of hardware and software for quantifying motion by means of imaging techniques, including high-speed cinematography and videography and strobe photography; two- and three-dimensional measurements; contributed articles to professional journals. *Mailing Add:* 825 Gravenstein Hwy N Suite 4 Sebastopol CA 95472. *Fax:* 707-829-3527; *E-Mail:* jim@4dvideo.com

**WALTON, JAY R,** SOLID MECHANICS, VISCOELASTICITY. *Current Pos:* From asst prof to assoc prof, 73-86, PROF MATH, TEX A&M UNIV, 86-, PROF AEROSPACE ENG, 90- *Personal Data:* b Gary, Ind, Aug 24, 46; m 84; c 2. *Educ:* DePauw Univ, BA, 68; Ind Univ, MA, 70, PhD(math), 73. *Concurrent Pos:* Vis assoc prof, Math Res Ctr, Univ Wis, 79-80; vis Sci Eng Res Coun res fel, Inst Computational Math, Brunel Univ, Eng, 87-88. *Mem:* Am Acad Mech; Am Math Soc; Am Soc Mech Engrs; Math Asn Am; Soc Indust & Appl Math. *Res:* Solid mechanics, especially viscoelasticity and fractures; applied mathematics, especially integral equations, partial differential equations numerical methods. *Mailing Add:* Math Dept Tex A&M Univ College Station TX 77843-3368

**WALTON, JOHN JOSEPH,** ATMOSPHERIC PHYSICS. *Current Pos:* RETIRED. *Personal Data:* b Sterling, Ill, Aug 25, 34; m 59; c 2. *Educ:* Northwestern Univ, BS, 56; Univ Kans, PhD(physics), 61. *Prof Exp:* Physicist, Lawrence Radiation Lab, Lawrence Livermore Lab, 61-72, physicist, 72-93. *Concurrent Pos:* Lectr appl sci, Univ Calif, 67-71. *Res:* Regional and global atmospheric modeling with emphasis on transport processes. *Mailing Add:* 5629 Shoshoni Pass Pinckney MI 48169-9392

**WALTON, JONATHAN DODGSON,** PLANT-MICROBE INTERACTIONS, PLANT MOLECULAR BIOLOGY. *Current Pos:* Assoc prof, 87-97, PROF BOT & PLANT PATH, MICH STATE UNIV, 97- *Personal Data:* b New Haven, Conn, June 16, 53. *Educ:* Univ Calif, Santa Cruz, BA, 75; Cornell Univ, MS, 78; Stanford Univ, PhD(biol sci), 82. *Concurrent Pos:* Vis prof, Univ Naples, 97. *Mem:* Am Soc Plant Physiologists; Am Phytopath Soc; AAAS; Int Soc Plant Microbe Interactions. *Res:* Molecular genetics and biochemistry of plant pathogenesis; biosynthesis of host-selective toxins; cyclic peptides and other secondary metabolites; cell wall degrading enzymes from fungi. *Mailing Add:* Dept Energy Plant Res Lab Mich State Univ East Lansing MI 48824-1312. *Fax:* 517-353-9168; *E-Mail:* walton@pilot.msu.edu

**WALTON, KENNETH NELSON,** MEDICINE. *Current Pos:* chmn, Dept Urol, 69-80, LOUIS MCDONALD ORR PROF SURG, SCH MED, EMORY UNIV, 69- *Personal Data:* b Winnipeg, Man, May 1, 35; US citizen; c 4. *Educ:* Univ Man, MD, 59; Am Bd Urol, dipl, 68. *Prof Exp:* Intern, Winnipeg Gen Hosp, 59-60, resident surg & path, 60-61; jr asst resident urol, Johns Hopkins Hosp, 61-62, res fel, 62-63, sr asst resident, 63-64, co-head resident, 64-65; from instr to asst prof urol, Dept Surg, Med Ctr, Univ Ky, 65-69, chmn div urol, 68-69. *Concurrent Pos:* Am Cancer Soc res fel, 63-64. *Mem:* Am Col Surgeons; AMA; Am Soc Nephrology; Am Urol Asn; Pan-Am Med Asn; Sigma Xi. *Res:* Kidney transplants; factors influencing renal oxygen consumption; effect of hypothermia and the inhibition of the tubular transport of sodium; difference in carbohydrate metabolism between prostatic cancers which are endocrine sensitive and those which are not. *Mailing Add:* 1938 Peachtree Rd NW No 306 Atlanta GA 30309-1252

**WALTON, MARK ALLAN,** CONFORMAL FIELD THEORY. *Current Pos:* ASST PROF PHYSICS, UNIV LETHBRIDGE, 91- *Educ:* Dalhousie Univ,BS, 81; McGill Univ, MS, 83, PhD(physics), 87. *Prof Exp:* Nat Sci & Eng Res Coun Can fel, Stanford Univ, 87-89; fel, Univ Laval, 89-90. *Mem:* Can Asn Physicists. *Res:* Theoretical physics. *Mailing Add:* Physics Dept Univ Lethbridge 4401 University Dr Lethbridge AB T1K 3M4 Can. *E-Mail:* walton@hg.uleth.ca

**WALTON, MATT SAVAGE,** GEOLOGY. *Current Pos:* prof, 73-86, EMER PROF GEOL, UNIV MINN, 86-; CONSULT GEOL, 86- *Personal Data:* b Lexington, Ky, Sept 16, 15; m 39, 69, 70; c 5. *Educ:* Univ Chicago, BA, 36; Columbia Univ, MA, 46, PhD(geol), 51. *Prof Exp:* Geologist, US Geol Surv, 41-47; from instr to assoc prof geol, Yale Univ, 48-64; independent consult, 64-73. *Concurrent Pos:* Geologist, NY State Geol & Natural Hist Surv, 48-58; regents lectr, Univ Calif, Los Angeles, 71-73; dir, Minn Geol Surv, 73-86. *Mem:* Geol Soc Am. *Res:* Petrology and tectonic development of ultrabasic granite and high grade unitamorphic rocks, especially in the Adirondack mountains of New York and in Minnesota; aquifer thermal energy storage and environmental geology; geological survey program, heavy construction site investigations and underground construction. *Mailing Add:* 30 Crocus Pl St Paul MN 55102

**WALTON, PETER DAWSON,** PLANT BREEDING. *Current Pos:* chmn dept, 75-80, PROF PLANT SCI, UNIV ALTA, 69- *Personal Data:* b Leeds, Eng, Oct 18, 24; Can citizen; m 49; c 4. *Educ:* Univ Durham, BSc, 49, MSc, 53; Univ Lancaster, PhD(pop genetics), 61. *Prof Exp:* Plant breeder, Res Div, Ministry Agr, Sudan, 50-55; sr plant breeder, Empire Cotton Growing Corp, 55-63; lectr agr & bot, Ahmadu Bello Univ, Nigeria, 63-67; assoc prof plant sci, Univ Sask, 67-69. *Mem:* Brit Inst Biol; Am Soc Agron; Genetics Soc Can; Am Forage & Grassland Coun; fel Royal Soc Arts. *Res:* Forage crop breeding with special reference to the study of genotype by environment interaction. *Mailing Add:* 14204 57th Ave Edmonton AB T6H 1B3 Can

**WALTON, RAY DANIEL, JR,** CHEMICAL & NUCLEAR ENGINEERING, OPERATIONS RESEARCH & NUCLEAR WASTE MANAGEMENT. *Current Pos:* PROG MGR, ARGONNE NAT LAB, 86- *Personal Data:* b Ogden, Utah, Jan 26, 21; wid; c Rodney, Scott, Eric, Kip, Trudy & James. *Educ:* Ore State Univ, BS, 43, MS, 48. *Prof Exp:* Chem engr, Hanford Labs, Gen Elec Co, 47-56; chem engr, Idaho Opers Off, US AEC, 56-60, tech analyst, Div Opers Analysis & Forecasting, 60-64; chem engr, Int Atomic Energy Agency, 64-66; chief eng br, Div Oper Anal & Forecasting, US AEC, 66-70, mat & process control engr, Div Waste & Scrap Mgt, 70-71, chem engr, Develop Br, Div Waste Mgt & Transp, 71-74; proj engr, US Energy Res & Develop Admin, 74-77; actg chief, Technol Br, Div Waste Prod, US Dept Energy, 77-78, eng prog mgr, Technol Div, Off Defense Waste & Transp, 79-86. *Concurrent Pos:* Leader, Int Atomic Energy Agency Nuclear Power Mission, Turkey; vchmn, Nuclear Eng Div, Am Inst Chem Engrs, 76, chmn, 77, prog chmn, 78. *Mem:* Am Sci Affiliation; Am Inst Chem Engrs; AAAS. *Res:* Technical and economic aspects of the nuclear fuel cycle, irradiated reactor fuel processing and disposal of radioactive waste; initiation, funding, direction, evaluation and management of nuclear waste management research and development projects. *Mailing Add:* 19205 Germantown Rd Germantown MD 20874. *Fax:* 301-990-1929

**WALTON, ROBERT BRUCE,** MICROBIOLOGY. *Current Pos:* RETIRED. *Personal Data:* b Jersey City, NJ, Nov 30, 15; m 39, Audrey B Brown; c Wendy A (Reichenbach), Bobette S (Chase), Sheryl W & Scott W. *Educ:* Rutgers Univ, BSc, 48, PhD(microbiol), 53. *Prof Exp:* From asst res microbiologist to assoc, Merck Sharp & Dohme Res Labs, 40-53, sr res microbiologist, 53-78, res fel, 78-81. *Res:* Antibiotics; vaccines; immunology; microbial nutrition and physiology; fermentations; actinophage. *Mailing Add:* 798 Central Ave Rahway NJ 07065

**WALTON, ROBERT EUGENE,** ANIMAL BREEDING, ANIMAL GENETICS. *Current Pos:* PRES & CHIEF EXEC OFFICER, GRACE ANIMAL SERV, 89-; CHMN, AGRACETUS, 90- *Personal Data:* b Shattuck, Okla, Jan 15, 31; m 59; c 3. *Educ:* Okla State Univ, BS, 52, MS, 56; Iowa State Univ, PhD, 61. *Honors & Awards:* Nat Agribus Award, Nat Agri-Mkt Asn, 85. *Prof Exp:* Farm mgr, Westhide Farms, Eng, 53-54; asst prof dairy sci, Univ Ky, 58-62; geneticist, Am Breeders Serv, 68, pres & chief exec officer, 68-88. *Concurrent Pos:* Mem prog mgt develop, Harvard Univ, 70. *Mem:* Am Soc Animal Sci; Am Dairy Sci Asn; Biomet Soc; Nat Asn Animal Breeders (pres, 72-74). *Res:* Application of genetical and statistical tools to problems of animal breeding and improvement; estimation of parameters of domestic large animal populations; genetic evaluation of dairy sires. *Mailing Add:* 4066 Vinburn Rd De Forest WI 53532

**WALTON, RODDY BURKE,** NUCLEAR PHYSICS. *Current Pos:* STAFF MEM, LOS ALAMOS SCI LAB, 67- *Personal Data:* b Goldthwaite, Tex, Dec 9, 31; m 61; c 2. *Educ:* Tex A&M Col, BS, 52; Univ Wis, MS, 54, PhD(nuclear physics), 57. *Prof Exp:* Nuclear res officer, Air Force Weapons Lab, 57-59; staff physicist, Gen Atomic Div, Gen Dynamics Corp, 59-67. *Mem:* Am Phys Soc; Inst Nuclear Mat Mgt; fel Am Nuclear Soc. *Res:* Neutron physics; photonuclear research; positron production with an electron linear accelerator; delayed gamma rays and delayed neutrons from fission; non-destructive assay applications; neutral particle beam applications. *Mailing Add:* 141 Monte Rey Dr S Los Alamos NM 87544

**WALTON, THEODORE ROSS,** CONDUCTIVE POLYMERS, THERMAL STABLE POLYMERS. *Current Pos:* RETIRED. *Personal Data:* b Takoma Park, Md, Feb 26, 31; m 56, Virginia Gough; c Rebecca Jean, Michael Edward, Jame Paul & Kathleen Patricia. *Educ:* Univ Md, BS, 55; Ohio State Univ, PhD(org chem), 60. *Prof Exp:* Proj dir chem, Atlantic Res Corp, 60-63; res chemist, Author W Sloan Found Va, 63-64; res chemist, US Naval Res Lab, Washington, DC, 64-90, actg sect head, Coating Sect, 90-91. *Res:* Organic and polymer synthesis and chemistry; thermally stable organic polymers; electrical conducting organic polymers; organic non-linear optical materials; rocket motor case thermal insulation and material compatibility; fire retardant coating systems; water based paints; adhesive bonding. *Mailing Add:* 8919 Moreland Lane Annandale VA 22003

**WALTON, THOMAS EDWARD,** VIROLOGY, ARBOVIROLOGY. *Current Pos:* res leader, USDA, Denver, Colo, 64-85, vet med officer, 72-74, res leader, Arthropod-Borne Animal Dis Res Lab, Laramie Wyo, 86-92, NAT PROG LEADER ANIMAL HEALTH, AGR RES SERV, USDA, BELTSVILLE, 92- *Personal Data:* b McKeesport, Pa, Dec 2, 40; m 87; c 3. *Educ:* Purdue Univ, DVM, 64; Cornell Univ, PhD(microbiol), 68. *Prof Exp:* Res vet microbiol, NIH, Nat Inst Allergy & Infectious Dis, USPHS, Maru, 68-72. *Concurrent Pos:* Affil fac, Dept Microbiol, Colo State Univ, 75-; adj prof, Dept Vet Sci, Univ Wyo, 86-; chair, Exec Coun, Am Comn Arthropod-Borne Viruses. *Mem:* Am Vet Med Asn; Am Soc Trop Med Hyg; Am Soc Trop Vet Med (secy, 91-); Soc Vector Ecologists; Am Biol Safety Asn. *Res:* Diagnosis and control of arthropod borne virus diseases of livestock; author or co-author of over 85 publications. *Mailing Add:* Nat Prog Staff Bldg 005 Rm 203 Agr Res Serv USDA Beltsville MD 20705

**WALTON, THOMAS PEYTON, III,** surgery, for more information see previous edition

**WALTON, VINCENT MICHAEL,** SPACECRAFT & POINTING PAYLOAD, ALTITUDE CONTROL. *Current Pos:* mem tech staff, 75-80, MEM STAFF, TRW SYSTS GROUP, 80- *Personal Data:* b Spokane, Wash, Oct 23, 49. *Educ:* Univ Wash, BS, 73, MS, 75. *Prof Exp:* Mem tech staff, Boeing Aerospace Co, 73-75. *Mem:* Am Inst Aeronaut & Astronaut; Inst Elec & Electronics Engrs. *Res:* Systems engineering; design, analysis and simulation of automatic control sytems for spacecraft; orbitor gimballed payloads; gimballed optical pointer trackers; laser hot antoalignment. *Mailing Add:* 302 SW 325 PL Federal Way WA 98023

**WALTON, WARREN LEWIS,** ORGANIC CHEMISTRY. *Current Pos:* CONSULT, 79- *Personal Data:* b La, Dec 13, 14; m 43; c 3. *Educ:* Millsaps Col, BS, 35; La State Univ, MS, 37; Univ Ill, PhD, 41. *Prof Exp:* Br chemist, Coca-Cola Co, 37-38; res & develop chemist, Hercules Co, 41-46; res & develop chemist silicone synthesis, Gen Elec Co, NY, 46-50, head analytical unit, Insulating Mat Dept, 50-69, instrumental analytical chemist, 50-71; consult analytical chemist, Schenectady Chem Co, 78-79. *Mem:* Am Chem Soc; fel Am Inst Chemists. *Res:* Infrared spectroscopy; microscopy, gas and gelpermeation chromatography, nuclear magnetic resonance spectroscopy. *Mailing Add:* PO Box 1564 Hammond LA 70404

**WALTON, WILLIAM RALPH,** GEOLOGICAL OCEANOGRAPHY. *Current Pos:* PROF, NORTHWESTERN UNIV, 85- *Personal Data:* b Ft Worth, Tex, Apr 11, 23; m 49; c 2. *Educ:* Amherst Col, BA, 49; Univ Calif, MS, 52, PhD(oceanog), 54. *Honors & Awards:* Pres Award, Am Asn Petrol Geol, 57. *Prof Exp:* Paleoecologist, Gulf Res & Develop Co, 53-57; paleoecologist & sedimentologist, Pan Am Petrol Corp, 57-60, div consult geologist, 60-63, geol & geochem res dir, Amoco Prod Co, Okla, 63-73, chief geologist, 73-75, chief geologist, Amoco Int Oil Co, Ill, 75-81, explor mgr, 77-81. *Concurrent Pos:* Distinguished lectr, Am Asn Petrol Geologists, 72-73; mem offshore explor & prod task group, Nat Petrol Coun Comt Ocean Petrol Resources, 74. *Mem:* Soc Econ Paleontologists & Mineralogists; Geol Soc Am; Paleont Soc; Am Asn Petrol Geologists. *Res:* Biostratigraphy of gulf coast tertiary; paleoecology, marine geology and sedimentology. *Mailing Add:* 116 S Sager Valparaiso IN 46383

**WALTRUP, PAUL JOHN,** ENGINEERING, MATERIALS SCIENCE. *Current Pos:* Fel, Johns Hopkins Univ, 71-72, sr staff engr, 72-74, sect supvr, 74-82, GROUP SUPVR, APPL PHYSICS LAB, JOHNS HOPKINS UNIV, 83- *Personal Data:* b Baltimore, Md, June 12, 45; c 2. *Educ:* Univ Md, BS, 67, MS, 68; Va Polytech Inst, PhD(aeronaut eng), 71. *Honors & Awards:* Young Engr Award, Am Inst Aeronaut & Astronaut, 74. *Concurrent Pos:* Consult, McGraw Hill Info Systs, 77-82, Off Naval Res, 84-88; instr, Univ Md, 78-89; adj prof, Va Polytech Inst, 82-89. *Mem:* Assoc fel Am Inst Aeronaut & Astronaut; Combustion Inst; AAAS. *Res:* Ramjet-Scramjet propulsion. *Mailing Add:* Appl Physics Lab Rm 1E236 Johns Hopkins Univ John Hopkins Rd Laurel MD 20723

**WALTZ, ARTHUR G,** NEUROLOGY, CEREBROVASCULAR DISEASES. *Current Pos:* RETIRED. *Personal Data:* b Irwin, Pa, Feb 14, 32; m; c 3. *Educ:* Univ Mich, BS, 52, MD, 55; Am Bd Psychiat & Neurol, dipl neurol, 62. *Prof Exp:* Rotating intern, Hosp Univ Pa, 55-56; asst resident neurol, Neurol Unit, Boston City Hosp, Mass, 56-57; sr resident, 57-58; res assoc, Sch Med, Wayne State Univ, 58-59, instr, 59; from instr to assoc prof, Mayo Grad Sch Med, Univ Minn, 62-71; prof neurol, Med Sch, Univ Minn, Minneapolis, 71-74; chmn, Dept Neurol, Pac Med Ctr, 75-81; clin prof neurol, Univ Calif, 81-90. *Concurrent Pos:* Teaching fel neurol, Harvard Med Sch, 56-58; asst to staff neurol, Mayo Clin, 61, consult, 62-71; adj prof neurol, Univ Pac, 75-80; fel stroke coun, Am Heart Asn. *Mem:* Fel Am Acad Neurol; Am Neurol Asn; Asn Res Nerv & Ment Dis; Sigma Xi. *Res:* Cerebral circulation, including blood flow, microcirculation and fluid balance, in normal and ischemic brain. *Mailing Add:* 1104 Ben Franklin Dr Apt 716 Sarasota FL 34236-2223

**WALTZ, DAVID LEIGH,** APPLICATIONS OF MASSIVELY PARALLEL COMPUTERS TO VERY LARGE DATABASES, MEMORY-BASED REASONING & LEARNING. *Current Pos:* VPRES, COMPUT SCI RES, NEC RES INST, 93- *Personal Data:* b Boston, Mass, May 28, 43; m 70, Bonnie E Freedson; c Vanessa L & Jeremy B. *Educ:* Mass Inst Technol, SB, 65, SM, 68, PhD(elec eng), 72. *Prof Exp:* Prof comput eng, Univ Ill, Urbanna, 73-84; prof comput sci, Brandeis Univ, 84-93. *Concurrent Pos:* Dir, Advan Info Systs, Thinking Mach Corp, 84-93; mem, Ctr Complex Systs, Brandeis Univ, 91-, adj prof comput sci, 93- *Mem:* Cognitive Sci Soc; Asn Comput Mach; Spec Interest Group Artificial Intel (pres, 77-80); fel An Asn Artificial Intel; Inst Elec & Electronics Engrs; Asn Comput Linguistics; Sigma Xi. *Res:* Constraint propagation for computer vision, machine learning, memory-based reasoning and massively parallel artificial intelligence; research and development management of text retrieval and database mining products; contributions to natural language processing and computational biology applications. *Mailing Add:* NEC Res Inst 4 Independence Way Princeton NJ 08540. *E-Mail:* waltz@research.nj.nec.com

**WALTZ, RONALD EDWARD,** PHYSICS. *Current Pos:* SR TECH ADV, GEN ATOMICS, SAN DIEGO, CA, 75- *Personal Data:* b Indianapolis, Ind, Nov 21, 43; m 67, Candace Dumlao; c Justin & Jonathan. *Educ:* Purdue Univ, BS, 66; Univ Chicago, PhD(physics), 70. *Prof Exp:* Fel, NSF, Europ Orgn Nuclear Res, Geneva, Switz, 71-72; res assoc, Ctr Theoret Physics, Mass Inst Technol, 72-73; sr scientist, Visidyne Inc, Burlington, Ma, 73-74. *Concurrent Pos:* Adj prof physics, Univ Calif, San Diego, 86; vis prof, Joint Inst Fusion Theory, Nagoya Univ, Japan, 86; vis fel, Australian Nat Univ. *Mem:* Fel Am Phys Soc. *Res:* Theory and simulation of turbulence in fusion plasmas and the phenomenology of tokamak confinement experiments. *Mailing Add:* Gen Atomics 13-303 PO Box 85608 San Diego CA 92186. *Fax:* 619-455-3586; *E-Mail:* waltz@gav.gat.com

**WALTZ, WILLIAM LEE,** PHOTOCHEMISTRY, RADIATION CHEMISTRY. *Current Pos:* from asst prof to assoc prof, 69-80, head, Dept Chem, 89-94, PROF CHEM, UNIV SASK, 80- *Personal Data:* b Berkeley, Calif, June 3, 40; m 63; c 2. *Educ:* Miami Univ, BS, 62; Northwestern Univ, PhD(phys inorg chem), 67. *Prof Exp:* Res assoc chem, Univ Southern Calif, 66-68; sr chemist, Cent Res Lab, 3M Co, Minn, 68-69. *Concurrent Pos:* Vis assoc prof chem, Ohio State Univ, 77-78; guest scientist, Hahn-Meitner Inst Nuclear Res, West Berlin, Ger, 78-82, 84-85 & 87-95. *Mem:* Sigma Xi; Am Chem Soc; fel Can Inst Chem. *Res:* Inorganic materials. *Mailing Add:* Dept Chem Univ Sask 110 Science Pl Saskatoon SK S7N 5C9 Can. *Fax:* 306-966-4730; *E-Mail:* waltz@sask.usask.ca

**WALTZER, WAYNE C,** RENAL TRANSPLANTATION, RECONSTRUCTIVE UROLOGICAL SURGERY. *Current Pos:* from instr surg to asst prof surg & urol, 79-84, assoc prof surg & urol, 84-89, PROF SURG & UROL, STATE UNIV NY, STONY BROOK, 89-, CHMN, DEPT UROL, 93- *Personal Data:* b Brooklyn, NY, Apr 18, 48; m 86, Arlene Kaelber; c 2. *Educ:* Pa State Univ, BA, 69; Univ Pittsburgh Sch Med, MD, 73; NY Univ MBA, 91. *Prof Exp:* Intern, internal med, Presby Univ Hosp, Pa, 73-74, resident, 74-75, resident urol surg, 75-78; fel renal transplant, Mayo Clin Rochester, Minn, 78-79. *Concurrent Pos:* Asst ed, Transplantation Proceedings, 80-; consult, J Urol, 87-; consult urol, 93- *Mem:* Sigma Xi; Am Soc Transplant Surgeons; Am Col Surgeons; Am Urol Asn; Soc Univ Urologists; Asn Acad Surg; Nat Kidney Found. *Res:* Immunological monitoring of renal transplant recipient with specific emphasis on the lymphocyte subpopulations in blood and renal allograft; immunological aspects of urologic malignancy. *Mailing Add:* Surg Dept Health Sci Ctr State Univ NY Stony Brook NY 11794-0001. *Fax:* 516-444-7620

**WALUM, HERBERT,** MATHEMATICS. *Current Pos:* asst prof, 64-71, ASSOC PROF MATH, OHIO STATE UNIV, 71- *Personal Data:* b Bremerton, Wash, Aug 14, 36; m 59; c 2. *Educ:* Reed Col, BA, 58; Univ Colo, PhD(math), 62. *Prof Exp:* Asst prof math, Harvey Mudd Col, 62-64. *Mem:* Am Math Soc; Math Asn Am; Sigma Xi. *Res:* Number theory. *Mailing Add:* 3276 Milton Ave Columbus OH 43202-1069

**WALVEKAR, ARUN GOVIND,** APPLIED MATHEMATICS, OPERATIONS RESEARCH. *Current Pos:* FAC, DEPT INDUST ENG, NORTHERN NMEX COMMUNITY COL, EL RITO. *Personal Data:* b Belgaum, India, May 7, 42. *Educ:* Univ Bombay, BE, 63 & 64; Ill Inst Technol, MS, 66, PhD(opers res), 67. *Prof Exp:* Instr math, Northeastern Ill State Col, 67-68; asst prof indust eng, Tex Tech Univ, 68-71, assoc prof Indust Eng & Statist, 71- *Mem:* Opers Res Soc Am; Am Inst Indust Engrs. *Res:* Multistage decision processes; calculus of variations; complex variables. *Mailing Add:* 62 Guillama Subdivision New Santa Rita San Miguel Bulaacan 3011 Philippines

**WALZ, ALVIN EUGENE,** PHYSICAL CHEMISTRY, ANALYTICAL CHEMISTRY. *Current Pos:* chmn dept, 66-86, PROF CHEM, CALIF LUTHERAN COL, 63- *Personal Data:* b Hot Springs, SDak, Jan 12, 19. *Educ:* Northern State Teachers Col, BS, 43; Univ Iowa, MS, 45, PhD(phys chem), 50. *Prof Exp:* Teacher, high sch, Iowa, 43-48; from asst prof to prof chem, Mankato State Col, 50-63. *Mem:* AAAS; Am Chem Soc; Sigma Xi. *Res:* Reaction rates; electron affinity; methyl stibine. *Mailing Add:* 119 Sirius Circle Thousand Oaks CA 91360

**WALZ, DANIEL ALBERT,** PHYSIOLOGY, BIOCHEMISTRY. *Current Pos:* Instr, 73-74, from asst prof to assoc prof, 74-79, PROF PHYSIOL, WAYNE STATE UNIV, 83- *Personal Data:* b Rochester, NY, July 30, 44; m 66; c 3. *Educ:* St John Fisher Col, BS, 66; Wayne State Univ, PhD(physiol), 73. *Mem:* Am Chem Soc; Int Soc Thrombosis & Hemostasis; Am Heart Asn; AAAS; Am Soc Biol Chem. *Res:* Properties of macromolecules; protein structure; coagulation biochemistry. *Mailing Add:* Wayne State Univ 540 E Canfield Detroit MI 48201-1908

**WALZ, DONALD THOMAS,** PHARMACOLOGY. *Current Pos:* RETIRED. *Personal Data:* b Newark, NJ, Oct 25, 24; m 59; c 3. *Educ:* Upsala Col, BS, 50; Rutgers Univ, MS, 51; Georgetown Univ, PhD(pharmacol), 59. *Prof Exp:* Jr pharmacologist, Hoffmann-La Roche, Inc, 51-55; sr investr pharmacol, Smithkline & Fr Labs, 60-68, from asst dir to assoc dir pharmacol, 68-77, assoc dir res, 77- *Concurrent Pos:* Nat Inst Neurol Dis & Blindness fel, Sch Med, Georgetown Univ, 59-60. *Mem:* AAAS; Am Diabetes Asn; Am Soc Pharmacol & Exp Therapeut; Acad Pharmaceut Sci; Fedn Am Socs Exp Biol; Sigma Xi. *Res:* Biochemical neuropharmacology metabolism; carbohydrate metabolism; cardiovascular-autonomic pharmacology. *Mailing Add:* 14 Pilgrim Lane Drexel Hill PA 19026

**WALZ, FREDERICK GEORGE,** BIOCHEMISTRY, MOLECULAR BIOLOGY. *Current Pos:* res assoc prof, 77-83, RES PROF MOLECULAR PATH, COL MED, NORTHEAST OHIO UNIV, 83-; PROF CHEM, KENT STATE UNIV, 82- *Personal Data:* b Brooklyn, NY, May 11, 40; m 62, Julia Peebles; c Jacquelin, Frederick, Jennifer, Judith, Rebecca, Andrew & Matthew. *Educ:* Manhattan Col, BS, 62; State Univ NY Downstate Med Ctr, PhD(biochem), 66. *Prof Exp:* NIH res fel biochem, Cornell Univ, 66-68; asst prof, State Univ NY, Albany, 68-75; from asst prof to assoc prof chem, Kent State Univ, 75-82. *Concurrent Pos:* NSF res grant, State Univ NY Albany, 69-75 & Kent State Univ, 76-80, 81-84; NIH res grant, 89-93. *Mem:* Am Soc Biochem; Am Chem Soc. *Res:* Genetics, regulation and evolution of cytochromes P-450, liver endoplasmic reticulum proteins, albumin secretion; ribonuclease mechanisms and substrate recognition. *Mailing Add:* Dept Chem Kent State Univ Kent OH 44242-0002. *Fax:* 330-672-3816; *E-Mail:* fwalz@kentvm.kent.edu

**WAMBOLD, JAMES CHARLES,** MECHANICAL ENGINEERING, ENGINEERING MECHANICS. *Current Pos:* RETIRED. *Personal Data:* b Emmaus, Pa, Nov 24, 32; m 60; c 4. *Educ:* Pa State Univ, BS, 59; Carnegie Inst Technol, MS, 60; Univ NMex, PhD(mech eng), 67. *Honors & Awards:* Kummer Lect Award, Am Soc Testing & Mat, 82, Outstanding Achievement Award, 89. *Prof Exp:* Staff mem, Sandia Corp, 58-62; instr mech eng, Univ NMex, 62-67; from asst prof to prof mech eng, Pa State Univ, 67-92, dir automotive safety, 81-92, emer prof, 92. *Concurrent Pos:* Aircraft mech consult to indust & lawyers; US expert, Vehicle-Surface Interaction Comt 1, Permanent Int Asn Road Congresses. *Mem:* Fel Am Soc Mech Engrs; Am Soc Eng Educ; Am Soc Testing & Mat. *Res:* Random signal processing; roughness effects on vehicle performances; application of solid mechanics to engineering design; modeling of physical systems for computer solution and control system design. *Mailing Add:* PO Box 1277 State College PA 16804

**WAMPLER, D EUGENE,** PROTEIN CHEMISTRY. *Current Pos:* SR RES FEL, MERCK RES LABS, 77- *Personal Data:* b Shanxi, China, July 24, 35; US citizen; m 61; c 3. *Educ:* Bridgewater Col, BA, 59; Mich State Univ, MS, 61 & PhD(biochem), 63. *Prof Exp:* Asst prof, dept biochem, Univ Conn Sch Med, 68-75; sr scientist, Bio Gant Corp, 75-76; res specialist, Dept Biochem, Mich State Univ, 76-77. *Mem:* Am Soc Biochem & Molecular Biol; Am Chem Soc; AAAS. *Res:* Protein isolation from natural sources and recombinant-DNA microorganisms; vaccine formulation; biochemical process research and development. *Mailing Add:* Merck Co Inc WP28 B-231 West Point PA 19486. *Fax:* 215-661-3121

**WAMPLER, E JOSEPH,** astronomy, for more information see previous edition

**WAMPLER, FRED BENNY,** PHYSICAL CHEMISTRY, PHOTOCHEMISTRY. *Current Pos:* staff mem, Los Alamos Nat Lab, 74-79, asst group leader, 79-81, dep group leader, 81-82, group leader, 82-94, DEP DIV DIR, LOS ALAMOS NAT LAB, 94- *Personal Data:* b Kingsport, Tenn, Apr 2, 43; m 84, Elvira L Martinez; c Valerie, Kevin & Susan. *Educ:* Univ Tenn, Knoxville, BS, 65; Univ Mo, Columbia, PhD(phys chem), 70. *Prof Exp:* Fel phys chem, Ohio State Univ, 70-72; sr scientist, Allison Div, Gen Motors Corp, 72-74. *Concurrent Pos:* Lectr, Butler Univ, Indianapolis, Ind, 73-74. *Mem:* Am Chem Soc; Inter-Am Photochem Soc. *Res:* Kinetics; application of lasers to chemical problems; energy transfer; laser spectroscopy; atmospheric chemistry; optical instrumentation. *Mailing Add:* 708 Avenida Castellano Santa Fe NM 87501

**WAMPLER, JESSE MARION,** NUCLEAR GEOCHEMISTRY, GEOCHRONOLOGY. *Current Pos:* from asst prof to prof geophys sci, 65-89, assoc dir, 84- 89, ASSOC PROF, SCH EARTH & ATMOSPHERIC SCI, GA INST TECHNOL, 90- *Personal Data:* b Harrisonburg, Va, Oct 31, 36; m 62; c 2. *Educ:* Bridgewater Col, BA, 57; Columbia Univ, PhD(geochem), 63. *Prof Exp:* Res asst geochem, Lamont Geol Observ, NY, 60-63; res assoc, Brookhaven Nat Lab, 63-65. *Mem:* Geochem Soc; Am Geophys Union; Sigma Xi; Nat Asn Geol Teachers; Int Asn Geochem & Cosmochem. *Res:* Nuclear geochemistry; geochemistry of argon and potassium; potassium-argon geochronology; lead isotope geochemistry; geochemistry of natural radionuclides. *Mailing Add:* Sch Earth & Atmospheric Sci Ga Inst Technol Atlanta GA 30332-0340

**WAMPLER, JOE FORREST,** MATHEMATICS, STATISTICS. *Current Pos:* RETIRED. *Personal Data:* b Chanute, Kans, Dec 13, 26; m 49, Doris Barsby; c David & Dean. *Educ:* Univ Kans, AB, 50, MA, 52; Univ Nebr, PhD, 67. *Prof Exp:* Instr math, York Col, 51-54, registrar, 53-54; assoc prof math, Nebr Wesleyan Univ, 54-66, head dept 54-83, chmn div natural sci, 71-76, actg chair, 88-89, prof math, 66-92. *Concurrent Pos:* Woods Found grant, 60-61; NSF coop teacher develop grant, 66. *Mem:* Math Asn Am (secy-treas, 91-94); Nat Coun Teachers Math; Am Asn Univ Professors. *Res:* Liouville's methods; use of various measures of aptitude to predict achievement in college mathematics; statistics; number theory; author of three publications. *Mailing Add:* Dept Math Nebr Wesleyan Univ 5000 St Paul Ave Lincoln NE 68504-2796

**WAMPLER, JOHN E,** COMPUTER AUTOMATION, ANALYTICAL SPECTROSCOPY. *Current Pos:* PROF BIOCHEM, UNIV GA, 82- *Educ:* Univ Tenn, PhD(biochem), 69. *Concurrent Pos:* Ed, Anal Instrumentation. *Res:* Stimulus response coupling in single living animal cells; studies of computation approaches to biochemical problems. *Mailing Add:* Dept Biochem Univ Ga Athens GA 30602-7229

**WAMSER, CARL CHRISTIAN,** ORGANIC CHEMISTRY, PHOTOCHEMISTRY. *Current Pos:* assoc prof, 83-86, PROF CHEM, PORTLAND STATE UNIV, 86- *Personal Data:* b New York, NY, Aug 10, 44; m, Laurie A Schmidt; c Scott, Kimberly & Zoe. *Educ:* Brown Univ, ScB, 66; Calif Inst Technol, PhD(chem), 70. *Prof Exp:* USAF Off Sci Res-Nat Res Coun fel, Harvard Univ, 69-70; from asst prof to prof chem, Calif State Univ, Fullerton, 70-83. *Concurrent Pos:* Vis assoc prof, Univ Southern Calif, 75-76; res fel, Univ Calif, Berkeley, 80; vis prof, Univ Hawaii, 81, Reed Col, 89-90, Ecole Polytech Federale Lausanne, Switz, 92; adj prof, Ore Grad Inst, 87- *Mem:* Am Chem Soc; Inter-Am Photochem Soc. *Res:* Solar energy conversion by artificial photosynthesis; photochemistry of polymeric porphyrin films. *Mailing Add:* Dept Chem Portland State Univ Portland OR 97207-0751. *E-Mail:* wamserc@pdx.edu

**WAMSER, CHRISTIAN ALBERT,** INORGANIC CHEMISTRY. *Current Pos:* RETIRED. *Personal Data:* b Long Island City, NY, July 15, 13; m 40, Madeline G Miller; c Carl C & Christina (Trautman). *Educ:* Cooper Union, BS, 34. *Prof Exp:* Anal chemist, J F Jelenko & Co, Inc, NY, 34-41; supvr anal group, Gen Chem Div, Allied Chem Corp, 41-48; res chemist, Vitro Corp Am, NJ, 53-62; res chemist, Gen Chem Div, Allied Chem Corp, 62-65, res scientist, 65-69, res scientist, Syracuse Tech Ctr, 69-74, res assoc, Indust Chem Div, 74-78. *Concurrent Pos:* Consult, Allied Chem Corp, 78-86. *Mem:* Am Chem Soc. *Res:* Industrial inorganic chemistry, uranium, fluorine, chromium and aluminum compounds. *Mailing Add:* 207 Rebhahn Dr Camillus NY 13031-1919

**WAMSLEY, W(ELCOME) W(ILLARD),** CHEMICAL ENGINEERING. *Current Pos:* RETIRED. *Personal Data:* b Leavenworth, Wash, July 18, 25; m 47; c 3. *Educ:* Univ Wash, BS, 49, PhD(chem eng), 53. *Prof Exp:* Instr, Univ Wash, 51-53; chem engr, E I du Pont de Nemours & Co Inc, 53-60, tech supvr, 60-61, sr tech supvr, 61-64, spec asst, 64-65, supt process control, 65-75, asst plant mgr, 75-80, plant mgr, 80-83, raw mats mgr, 83-85. *Mem:* Am Chem Soc; assoc Am Inst Chem Engrs; Sigma Xi. *Res:* Heat transfer; gas-solid fluidization; coating and drying of photographic emulsions. *Mailing Add:* 114 Marlbrooke Way Kennett Square PA 19348-1720

**WAN, FREDERIC YUI-MING,** SOLID MECHANICS. *Current Pos:* assoc dean, Col Arts & Sci, 88-92, PROF MATH, UNIV WASH, 83-, CHMN, APPL MATH DEPT, 84-, VCHANCELLOR RES, DEAN GRAD STUDIES & PROF MECH & AEROSPACE ENG. *Personal Data:* b Shanghai, China, Jan 7, 36; US citizen; m 60, Julia Chang. *Educ:* Mass Inst Technol, SB, 59, SM, 63, PhD(math), 65. *Honors & Awards:* Arthur Beaumont Distinguished Serv Award, Can Appl Maths Soc. *Prof Exp:* Staff mem struct mech, Lincoln Lab, Mass Inst Technol, 59-62, staff assoc, 62-65, from instr to assoc prof appl math, 65-74; prof math & dir, Inst Appl Math & Statist, Univ BC, 74-83. *Concurrent Pos:* Sloan Found fel, 73; Killam sr fel, Univ BC, 79-80; vis fel econ, Mass Inst Technol; vis assoc appl mech, Calif Technol; consult, indust & govt agencies; div dir, Div Math Sci, NSF, 93-94. *Mem:* Fel Am Soc Mech Eng; Soc Indust & Appl Math; Can Math Soc; Can Appl Math Soc (pres, 83-84); fel Am Acad Mech (secy fels, 84-89, pres, 92-93); fel AAAS. *Res:* Classical elasticity; shell theory; random vibrations; stochastic ordinary and partial differential equations; natural resource economics; bio-mathematics. *Mailing Add:* 155 Admin Univ Calif Irvine CA 92697-3175. *Fax:* 714-824-2095; *E-Mail:* fwan@uci.edu

**WAN, JEFFREY KWOK-SING,** PHYSICAL CHEMISTRY. *Current Pos:* from asst prof to assoc prof, 66-74, PROF CHEM, QUEEN'S UNIV, 74- *Personal Data:* b Hong Kong, June 4, 34; m 62; c 2. *Educ:* McGill Univ, BSc, 58; Univ Alta, PhD(phys chem), 62. *Prof Exp:* Fel, Univ Alta, 62-63; asst res chemist, Univ Calif, 63-65; Nat Res Coun Can fel chem, 65-66. *Concurrent Pos:* Hon prof, Univ Lanzhou, China, 81-; pres, W & Y Consults Kingston Ltd, Can, 82- *Mem:* Chem Inst Can. *Res:* Photochemistry and electron paramagnetic resonance spectroscopy; microwave induced catalysis. *Mailing Add:* Dept Chem Queen's Univ Kingston ON K7L 3N6 Can

**WAN, PETER J,** PROCESS DEVELOPMENT, METHODS DEVELOPMENT. *Current Pos:* res leader, 90-93, LEAD SCIENTIST, SOUTHERN REGIONAL RES CTR, AGR RES SERV, USDA, 93- *Personal Data:* b Shantong, China, Jan 1, 29, 43; US citizen; m 70, Catherina; c Anne & Ellen. *Educ:* Cheng-Kung Univ, China, BSE, 65; Ill Inst Technol, MS, 70; Tex A&M Univ, PhD(phys chem), 73. *Prof Exp:* Fel, Chem Dept, Tex A&M Univ, 74-75, proj leader & asst res chemist, Res & Develop Ctr Food Protein, 75-79; sr res chemist, Best Foods, CPC Int, 79-80; res assoc, Anderson Clayton Foods, 80-83, mgr, 83-84, dir, 84-87; technol mgr, Kraft Inc, 87-90. *Mem:* Inst Food Technologists; Am Oil Chemists Soc; Am Chem Soc; Am Inst Chem Engrs. *Res:* Improve and assure the quality of product; improve process efficiency; develop new methods, new processes and new products. *Mailing Add:* USDA ARS S Reg Res Ctr Box 19687 1100 Robert Lee Blvd New Orleans LA 70179-0687. *E-Mail:* pwan@nola.srrc.usda.gov

**WAN, YIEH-HEI,** TOPOLOGY, APPLIED MATHEMATICS. *Current Pos:* From asst prof to assoc prof, 73-84, PROF MATH, STATE UNIV NY, BUFFALO, 84- *Personal Data:* b China, Feb 17, 47; m 75. *Educ:* Nat Taiwan Univ, BS, 68; Univ Calif, Berkeley, PhD(math), 73. *Res:* Application of global analysis to the study of general competitive equilibrium theory in mathematical economics; bifurcation theory for dynamical systems. *Mailing Add:* Dept Math State Univ NY 231 S Diefendorf Hall Buffalo NY 14214-3093

**WANAMAKER, DIANA,** AGRICULTURE BUSINESS & MANAGEMENT. *Current Pos:* GROUP LEADER, DAIRY & IMPORT POLICIES, 90- *Personal Data:* b New York, NY. *Educ:* George Washington Univ, BA & MA. *Mailing Add:* Stop 1021 12th Independence Ave SW Washington DC 20250-1021

**WANAT, STANLEY FRANK,** ORGANIC CHEMISTRY, POLYMER CHEMISTRY. *Current Pos:* res & develop mgr graphic arts chem, PPD Div, 73-93, RES ASSOC, AZ-PHOTORESIST PROD DIV, HOECHST CELANESE CORP, 93- *Personal Data:* b Nanticoke, Pa, Dec 31, 39; m 64; c 2. *Educ:* Rutgers Univ, AB, 63; Seton Hall Univ, MS, 69, PhD(org chem), 71. *Prof Exp:* Develop chemist agr chem, Shell Chem Co, 64-65; instr chem & math, Union County Col Syst, NJ, 65-67; process develop chemist agr chem, Ciba-Geigy Corp, 67-70; asst, Seton Hall Univ, 70-71; instr org chem, Upsala Col, 71-73. *Concurrent Pos:* Teacher chem, Union Co Schs, 71-73. *Mem:* Am Chem Soc; Soc Photog Instrument Eng. *Res:* Development of photosensitive lithographic products, printing plates, color proofing systems and chemicals; study of surface chemistry of substrates suitable for coating lithographic materials; coating technology; polymer modification for lithographic use; resin development for photoresists. *Mailing Add:* 3 Frances Lane Scotch Plains NJ 07076

**WAND, MITCHELL,** PROGRAMMING LANGUAGES, SEMANTICS. *Current Pos:* PROF COMPUT SCI, COL COMPUT SCI, NORTHEASTERN UNIV, BOSTON, 85- *Personal Data:* b Philadelphia, Pa, Nov 6, 48; m 70; c 3. *Educ:* Mass Inst Technol, SB, 69, PhD(math), 73. *Prof Exp:* Prof comput sci, Ind Univ, 73-85. *Concurrent Pos:* Vis prof, Brandeis Univ, 84-85; vis scientist, Lab Comput Sci, Mass Inst Technol, 84-86. *Mem:* Asn Comput Mach; Europ Asn Theoret Comput Sci. *Res:* Semantics of programming languages; programming theory; logic; algebra. *Mailing Add:* Northeastern Univ 360 Huntington Ave No 161 CN Boston MA 02115. *E-Mail:* wand@ccs.neu.edu

**WANDER, JOSEPH DAY,** ORGANIC CHEMISTRY, AIR POLLUTION CONTROL TECHNOLOGY. *Current Pos:* FUELS CHEMIST, USAF, TYNDALL AFB, 86- *Personal Data:* b Columbus, Ohio, July 20, 41; m 67, Rosemary Casey; c Lucrezia, Ezekiel & Jeremiah. *Educ:* Case Inst Technol, BS, 63; Ohio State Univ, PhD(chem), 70. *Prof Exp:* Res fel chem, Tulane Univ, 70-71, La State Univ, Baton Rouge, 71-72 & Ohio State Univ, 72-74; dir, Charles B Stout Neurosci Lab, Univ Tenn Ctr Health Sci, Memphis, 74-77; asst prof chem, Univ Ga, 78-84 & Columbus Col, Ga, 85-86. *Mem:* Am Chem Soc; Sigma Xi; Air & Waste Mgt Asn. *Res:* Air pollution control technology for industrial ventilation and combustion systems. *Mailing Add:* AL/EQS 139 Barnes Dr Suite 2 Tyndall AFB FL 32403-5323. *E-Mail:* joe_wander@ccmail.aleq.tyndall.af.mil

**WANDERER, PETER JOHN, JR,** SUPERCONDUCTING ACCELERATOR MAGNETS. *Current Pos:* assoc scientist, 75-78, SCIENTIST HIGH ENERGY PHYSICS, BROOKHAVEN NAT LAB, 78- *Personal Data:* b Monroe, La, Aug 5, 43; m 72; c 3. *Educ:* Univ Notre Dame, BS, 65; Yale Univ, PhD(physics), 70. *Prof Exp:* Res assoc high energy physics, Lab Nuclear Studies, Cornell Univ, 70-73 & Univ Wis-Madison, 73-75. *Mem:* Am Phys Soc. *Res:* Construction of high field superconducting magnets for the RHIC accelerator. *Mailing Add:* Bldg 902B Brookhaven Nat Lab Upton NY 11973. *Fax:* 516-282-2190; *E-Mail:* wanderer@bnl.gov

**WANDS, RALPH CLINTON,** toxicology, industrial hygiene; deceased, see previous edition for last biography

**WANE, MALCOLM T(RAFFORD),** MINING ENGINEERING. *Current Pos:* assoc, 53-59, from asst prof to assoc prof, 59-69, PROF MINING, COLUMBIA UNIV, 69- *Personal Data:* b Pittston, Pa, Jan 2, 21; m 46; c 1. *Educ:* Lehigh Univ, BS, 50, Columbia Univ, MS, 54. *Prof Exp:* Res technician & mineral engr, US Steel Corp, 50-53. *Concurrent Pos:* NSF fac fel, Royal Sch Mines, 65-66; consult geologist, New York City Transit Authority & New York City Bd Water Resource Develop. *Mem:* Am Inst Mining, Metall & Petrol Engrs. *Res:* Rock mechanics; failure of brittle solids; earth vibration and blasting problems. *Mailing Add:* 38 Mile Rd Suffern NY 10901

**WANEBO, HAROLD,** SURGICAL ONCOLOGY, IMMUNOLOGY. *Current Pos:* CHMN SURG, ROGER WILLIAM HOSP, PROVIDENCE, 87- *Educ:* Univ Colo, MD, 61. *Prof Exp:* Prof surg & chief, Div Surg Oncol, Univ Va, 77-87. *Mailing Add:* Dept Surg Brown Univ 825 Chalkstone Ave Providence RI 02908

**WANER, JOSEPH LLOYD,** VIROLOGY. *Current Pos:* assoc prof, 80-88, PROF PEDIAT, SCH MED, UNIV OKLA, 88-; DIR CLIN VIROL/SEROL, CHILDREN'S HOSP OKLA, 80- *Personal Data:* b Detroit, Mich, Feb 4, 42; m 71, Elizabeth; c Mark & Jeffrey. *Educ:* Loyola Univ Chicago, BS, 64, MS, 66, PhD(microbiol), 69. *Prof Exp:* Res fel, Harvard Sch Pub

Health, 69-71, res assoc, 71-74, from asst prof to assoc prof, Trop Pub Health, 74-80. *Concurrent Pos:* Vis prof, Sch Pub Health, Teheran Univ, Iran, 76; ed, Newslett Pan Am Group Rapid Viral Diag, 85-; sect ed, Manual Clin Microbiol, 94; numerous lectr. *Mem:* Am Soc Microbiol; fel Am Acad Microbiol; Pediat Infant Dis Soc. *Res:* Rapid diagnosis of viral infections; immunity to human cytomegalovirus. *Mailing Add:* Dept Pediat Col Med Univ Okla PO Box 26901 Oklahoma City OK 73126-0901. *Fax:* 405-271-3967; *E-Mail:* joseph-waner@uokhsc.edu

**WANG, ALBERT SHOW-DWO,** APPLIED MECHANICS, COMPOSITE MATERIALS. *Current Pos:* from asst prof to assoc prof, 67-77, PROF APPL MECH, DREXEL UNIV, 77- *Personal Data:* b Chifoo, China, July 13, 37; m 67; c 2. *Educ:* Univ Taiwan, BS, 59; Univ Nev, MS, 63; Univ Del, PhD(aerospace eng), 67. *Concurrent Pos:* Fel, Univ Del, 67. *Concurrent Pos:* Consult, Lockheed Corp, Lawrence Livermore Lab & Gen Motors Corp; res fel, Acad Sci, 83; vis scientist, Air Force Off Sci Res, 86-87. *Mem:* Am Soc Mech Engrs; Am Soc Testing & Mat; Soc Advan Mat & Process Eng. *Res:* Stress analysis of composite materials, including failure, fracture, fatigue and reliability. *Mailing Add:* Dept Mech Eng Drexel Univ 3141 Chestnut St Philadelphia PA 19104-2875

**WANG, ALLAN ZU-WU,** CELL MEMBRANE & CELL-TO-EXTRACELLULAR MATRIX-INTERACTION, CHEMOTAXIS & INVASION OF CANCER CELLS & RHEUMATOID SYNOVICYTES. *Current Pos:* actg sci dir, 90-91, DIR RES & SR FAC SCIENTIST, DEPT MED, WESTERN PA HOSP FOUND RES INST, 90- *Personal Data:* b Shanghai, China, June 1, 39; m 68, Jane Chen Qin-Yu; c George Q. *Educ:* Shanghai Med Univ, MD, 62; Chinese Acad Sci, PhD(cancer biol & pharmacol), 66. *Honors & Awards:* Int Dir Distinguished Leadership Award, Am Biog Inst, 87. *Prof Exp:* Res assoc, Chinese Acad Sci, 66-80; fel, Imp Cancer Res Fund Labs, 80-82; assoc res scientist, Syst Cancer Ctr, Univ Tex, 82-83; assoc prof & lab chief, Chinese Acad Sci, 83-85; vis assoc prof, Med Col Pa, 86-87; Stanley Reimann scientist, Fox Chase Cancer Ctr, 87-90. *Concurrent Pos:* Consult, Shanghai Biotechnol Ctr, 84-85, China Sci & Technol Univ, 84-85, Inst Molecular Med, Zhejian Traditional Med Univ, 85; coun mem, Inst Animal Use & Care Comt, Western Pa Hosp Found, 90- *Mem:* Inflamation Res Asn; Am Soc Cell Biol; Am Asn Cancer Res; AAAS; Brit Soc Cell Biol; Brit Asn Cancer Res. *Res:* Chemotactic and invasive migration of rheumatoid synoviocytes and cancer cells; renal epithelial membrane polarity and ion transport; development of model system for pathophysiological and pharmacological studies of tumor, rheumatoid arthritis and alzheimer's disease based on the aboved mentioned research; technologies of digital live cell imaging and 3-dimensional reconstruction. *Mailing Add:* 4800 Friendship Ave Daly Bldg No 233 Pittsburgh PA 15224. *Fax:* 412-578-4839

**WANG, AN-CHUAN,** IMMUNOGENETICS. *Current Pos:* assoc prof, 75-76, PROF IMMUNOL, MED UNIV SC, 76-; CONSULT, 86- *Personal Data:* b Tsing Tao City, China, Dec 28, 36; m 65; c 2. *Educ:* Nat Taiwan Univ, BS, 59; Univ Tex, PhD(genetics), 66. *Prof Exp:* Sec teacher, Taiwan, 61; res assoc genetics, Univ Tex, 66-67; asst prof genetics, Med Ctr, Univ Calif, San Francisco, 70-72, assoc prof microbiol & assoc researcher med, 72-75. *Concurrent Pos:* Fel, Med Ctr, Univ Calif, San Francisco, 67-70; USPHS & NSF res grants, 70-; USPHS career development award, 74; Am Cancer Soc fac res award, 74-79; adv ed, Immunochem, 78- *Mem:* AAAS; Am Soc Human Genetics; Genetics Soc Am; Am Asn Immunol. *Res:* Biochemical and genetical analyses of human plasma proteins, with special emphasis on immunoglobulins; immunology. *Mailing Add:* Dept Microbiol & Immunol Med Univ SC 171 Ashley Ave Charleston SC 29425-2230. *Fax:* 803-792-2464

**WANG, ANDREW H-J,** BIOPHYSICAL CHEMISTRY, STRUCTURAL BIOLOGY. *Current Pos:* PROF, DEPT PHYSIOL & BIOPHYS, UNIV ILL, URBANA-CHAMPAIGN, 88- *Personal Data:* b Taipei, Taiwan, Nov 29, 45; US citizen; m 68; c 3. *Educ:* Nat Taiwan Univ, BS, 67, MS, 70; Univ Ill, Urbana, PhD(chem), 74. *Prof Exp:* Res assoc, Dept Biol, Mass Inst Technol, 74-80, res scientist, 80-82, prin res scientist, 82-85, sr res scientist, 85-88. *Mem:* Am Chem Soc; Am Crystallog Asn; AAAS; Am Soc Biochem Molecular Biol; Am Inst Chem. *Res:* Molecular structure of biological macromolecules; structure-function relationship of proteins and nucleic acids; x-ray crystallography. *Mailing Add:* Dept Cell & Struct Biol Univ Ill 506 Morrill Hall Urbana IL 61801

**WANG, BAOLIANG (BOB),** POLARIZATION MODULATION SPECTROSCOPY, DOUBLE MODULATION INFRARED SPECTROSCOPY. *Current Pos:* APPLN SCIENTIST, HINDS INSTRUMENTS INC, 95- *Personal Data:* b Shijiazhuang, Hebei, China, Jan 9, 63; m 87, Haiying Li; c George. *Educ:* Nankai Univ, BS, 82; MS, 85; Univ Ill, PhD(phys chem), 93. *Prof Exp:* Lectr inorg chem, Hebei Teachers Univ, China, 85-88; postdoctoral res assoc, Univ Ill, Chicago, 94. *Mem:* Am Chem Soc; Soc Appl Spectros; Soc Photo-Instrumentation Engrs. *Res:* Develop polarization modulation spectroscopy methods, such as vibrational circular dichrosim and magnetic vibrational circular dichrosim; design and test optical systems for detecting chiral molecules and other polarization sensitive samples. *Mailing Add:* Hinds Instruments 3175 NW Aloclek Dr Hillsboro OR 97124. *Fax:* 503-690-3000; *E-Mail:* bwang@hindspem.com

**WANG, BIN,** WAVE & INSTABILITY, TROPICAL METEOROLOGY & CLIMATE DYNAMICS. *Current Pos:* from asst prof to assoc prof, 87-92, PROF, DEPT METEOROL, UNIV HAWAII, 92- *Personal Data:* b Qingdao, China, Oct 25, 44; US citizen; m 71, Joanne; c Datong & Stuart. *Educ:* Qingdao Ocean Univ, BS, 66; Univ Sci & Technol, China, MS, 82; Fla

State Univ, PhD(geophys fluid dynamics), 84. *Prof Exp:* Vis scientist geophys fluid dynamics, Geophys Fluid Dynamics Prog, Princeton Univ, 84-86. *Concurrent Pos:* Sr fel, Joint Inst Marine & Atmospheric Res, Univ Hawaii, Nat Oceanic & Atmospheric Admin, 88-; guest prof, Ocean Univ Qingdao, Peoples Repub China, 90-, First Inst Oceanog, State Oceanic Admin, 89-, Chinese Acad Meteorol Scis, 91- & Nat Climate Ctr China, 94- *Mem:* Am Meteorol Soc; Am Geophys Soc; Royal Meteorol Soc. *Res:* Atmospheric, oceanic wave and instability; tropical cyclones; monsoons; El Nino southern oscillation; intraseasonal oscillation. *Mailing Add:* 1068 Kaupaku Pl Honolulu HI 96825. *Fax:* 808-956-2877; *E-Mail:* bwang@soest.hawaii.edu

**WANG, BINGHE,** ARTIFICIAL ENZYME DEVELOPMENT, ENZYME INHIBITION. *Current Pos:* ASST PROF MED CHEM, UNIV OKLA, 94- *Personal Data:* b Beijing, China, May 25, 62; m, Siming Liu; c Anne Y. *Educ:* Beijing Med Univ, BS, 82; Univ Kans, MS, 87, PhD(med chem), 91. *Prof Exp:* Fel, Univ Ariz, 92, Univ Kans, 92-93. *Mem:* Am Chem Soc. *Res:* Artificial enzyme development; design and synthesis of enzyme inhibitors as potential antibiotics; peptide chemistry. *Mailing Add:* Chem Dept NC State Univ Raleigh NC 27695-8204

**WANG, BOSCO SHANG,** TUMOR IMMUNOLOGY, IMMUNOENDOCRINOLOGY. *Current Pos:* PRIN RES SCIENTIST, AM CYANAMID CO, 81- *Personal Data:* b Shang-hai, China, Aug 30, 47; US citizen; m 72; c 2. *Educ:* Fu-Jen Cath Univ, BS, 69; Mich State Univ, MS, 73; Boston Univ, PhD(microbiol), 76. *Honors & Awards:* Wilson Stone Mem Award, M D Anderson Hosp & Tumor Inst, Tex Cancer Ctr, 77. *Prof Exp:* Postdoctoral path, Harvard Med Sch, 76-77, instr, 77-79, asst prof, 79-81. *Mem:* Am Asn Immunologists. *Res:* Immunologic regulation of endocrine systems. *Mailing Add:* Am Cyanamid Co PO Box 400 Princeton NJ 08540-0400. *Fax:* 609-799-1842

**WANG, C(HIAO) J(EN),** AERONAUTICS, MECHANICAL ENGINEERING. *Current Pos:* DIR, OFF ADVAN ENG, ADVAN RES PROJS AGENCY, US DEPT DEFENSE, DC, 66- *Personal Data:* b China, Mar 24, 18; nat US; m 45; c 1. *Educ:* Chiao Tung Univ, China, BS, 42; Mass Inst Technol, MSME, 46; Johns Hopkins Univ, PhD, 53. *Prof Exp:* Instr, Johns Hopkins Univ, 49-53; res & eng specialist, NAm Aviation, Inc, 53-56; assoc mgr aerophys dept & mgr propulsion systs dept, Space Technol Labs, Inc, 56-60; head propulsion dept & dir advan studies, Aerospace Corp, 60-65; dep dir combined arms res off, Booz-Allen Appl Res, Inc, Kans, 65-66. *Res:* Aeronautical and space science and technology; systems analysis; operations research. *Mailing Add:* 1300 Army-Navy Dr Arlington VA 22202

**WANG, CARL C T,** ELECTRICAL ENGINEERING. *Current Pos:* PRES, MED INSTRUMENTATION DEVELOP LABS INC, 91- *Personal Data:* b Hankow, China, Dec 2, 35; m 63; c 3. *Educ:* Univ Ill, BS, 58, MS, 59, PhD(elec eng), 64. *Prof Exp:* Res asst plasma physics, Univ Ill, 60, res asst microwave, 60-64; mem res staff electron-optics, T J Watson Res Ctr, Int Bus Mach Corp, 64-67; res assoc biomed eng & elec engr, Columbia Univ, 67-69; sr engr, Micro-Bit Corp, 69-75; vpres eng, Berkeley Bio-Eng, Inc, 75-79; vpres eng, Cooper Med Device Corp, 79-81; pres, Med Instrument Develop Labs Inc, 81-85; vpres res, Alcon Surg Instrument, 85-90. *Concurrent Pos:* Tech consult, NIMH, 68-75, NEI, 84-85, Univ Calif, Los Angeles, 83-84, Univ Southern Calif, 82-83. *Mem:* Inst Elec & Electronics Engrs; Am Acad Ophthal; Sigma Xi; Asn Res in Vision & Ophthal; Chinese-Am Ophthal Soc; World Eye Found. *Res:* Laser; ultra-microwave; electromagnetohydrodynamics; electron-optics; display systems; man-machine systems; physical electronics; physiological system simulation; bio-medical instrumentation. *Mailing Add:* Med Instrumentation Develop Labs Inc 14477 Catalina St San Leandro CA 94577

**WANG, CHANG-YI,** APPLIED MATHEMATICS. *Current Pos:* from asst prof to assoc prof math, 69-77, PROF MATH, PHYSIOL & MECH ENG, MICH STATE UNIV, 77- *Personal Data:* b Kweichow, China, Aug 26, 39; US citizen; m 66; c 3. *Educ:* Nat Taiwan Univ, BS, 60; Mass Inst Technol, MS, 63, PhD, 66. *Prof Exp:* Fel appl math, Calif Inst Technol, 66-67, assoc appl math, Jet Propulsion Lab, 67-68; asst prof math, Univ Calif, Los Angeles, 68-69. *Concurrent Pos:* Vis prof, Nat Taiwan Univ, 71-72 & 84-85, Nat Tsing Hua Univ, 84-85. *Mem:* Soc Indust & Appl Math; Am Soc Mech Engrs. *Res:* Fluid mechanics; elasticity; biomathematics. *Mailing Add:* Dept Math Mich State Univ East Lansing MI 48824-0001

**WANG, CHAO CHEN,** ENGINEERING PHYSICS. *Current Pos:* PRES & DIR INDUST RES, INDUST TECHNOL RES INST, 73- *Personal Data:* b Changchow, Kiangsu, China, Oct 20, 14; US citizen; m 47; c 1. *Educ:* Chiao Tung Univ, Shanghai, China, 36; Harvard Univ, SM, 38, ScD, 40. *Prof Exp:* Proj engr microwave, Westinghouse Elec, 41-44; res engr, head dept eng electronics & chief scientist, div beams & laser, Sperry Corp, 45-73. *Concurrent Pos:* Vis prof, Cornell Univ, 60-61. *Mem:* Am Phys Soc; Inst Elec & Electronics Engrs; AAAS. *Res:* Microwave tubes for radar during World War II; high density electron beam control and focusing pioneered laser ring gyro development, electromagnetic wave propagation and interaction with electron beams; high power klystron development for radar and for linear accelerator. *Mailing Add:* Indust Tech Res Inst Holmdel NJ 07733

**WANG, CHAO-CHENG,** MECHANICS. *Current Pos:* prof, 69-79, chmn, Math Sci Dept, 83-89, NOAH HARDING PROF MATH SCI & PROF, MECH ENG DEPT, RICE UNIV, 79-, CHMN, MECH ENG & MAT SCI DEPT, 91- *Personal Data:* b China, July 20, 38; US citizen; m 63, Sophia C; c Ferdinand T & Edward T. *Educ:* Nat Taiwan Univ, BS, 59; Johns Hopkins Univ, PhD(mech), 65. *Prof Exp:* From asst prof to assoc prof mech, Mech

Dept, Johns Hopkins Univ, 66-69. *Concurrent Pos:* Prof, Mech Eng Dept, Rice Univ, 79- *Mem:* Soc Natural Philos; Am Acad Mech; Am Soc Mech Eng. *Res:* Continuum mechanics; applied mathematics; mechanical engineering. *Mailing Add:* Mech Eng & Mat Sci Dept Rice Univ Houston TX 77251-1892. *Fax:* 713-285-5423; *E-Mail:* ccwang@rice.edu

**WANG, CHARLES C(HEN-DING),** OPTICS, PHYSICS. *Current Pos:* PRES, PENINSULA TECHNOL INC, 87- *Personal Data:* b Hankow, China, Sept 4, 33; m 61; c 3. *Educ:* Taiwan Col Eng, BS, Brown Univ, MS, 58; Stanford Univ, PhD, 60. *Prof Exp:* Asst prof elec eng, Univ Wash, 60-63; res specialist, Philco Res Lab, 63-65; prin res assoc scientist, Ford Sci Lab, 66-68, staff scientist, 68-77, prin res scientist, 77-87. *Concurrent Pos:* Adj prof elec eng, Wayne State Univ, 76-87; adj prof physics, Univ Mich, 81- *Mem:* Fel Am Phys Soc; Inst Elec & Electronics Engrs. *Res:* Nonlinear optics, quantum electronics; laser spectroscopy; atomic and molecular physics; detection of oxygen hydrogen in the atmosphere. *Mailing Add:* Box 25-0463 Franklin MI 48025. *Fax:* 248-851-1477

**WANG, CHARLES P,** OPTICS, AUTOMATION & ROBOTICS. *Current Pos:* PRES, OPTODYNE INC, 86- *Personal Data:* b Shanghai, China, Apr 26, 37; m 63, Lily Lee. *Educ:* Nat Taiwan Univ, Taiwan, BS, 59; Tsinghua Univ, Taiwan, MS, 61; Calif Inst Technol, PhD(aeronaut), 67. *Prof Exp:* Lectr appl math, Nat Taiwan Univ, 61-62; mem tech staff aronaut, Bellcom Inc, 67-69; sr scientist quantum elec, Aerospace Corp, 74-86. *Concurrent Pos:* Adj prof eng physics, Univ Calif, San Diego, 74-88; assoc ed, Am Inst Aeronaut & Astronaut, 80-84. *Mem:* Fel Optical Soc Am; Am Inst Aeronaut & Astronaut; Soc Optical & Quantum Electronics; Chinese Am Engr & Scientists. *Res:* Research on laser applications in fluid mechanics and quantum electronics; successfully developed a CW 150 W Argon-Ion Laser, discharge excimer laser, stable chemical laser, optical phase arrays for higher power chemical lasers; laser doppler displacement meter. *Mailing Add:* Optodyne Inc 1180 Mahalo Pl Compton CA 90220. *Fax:* 310-635-6301

**WANG, CHARLES T P,** physics; deceased, see previous edition for last biography

**WANG, CHEN-SHOW,** SOLID STATE PHYSICS, QUANTUM ELECTRONICS. *Current Pos:* mgr res & develop, 79-82, dir, 82-84, VPRES RES & DEVELOP, GEN OPTRONICS CORP, 84- *Personal Data:* b Taiwan; US citizen; c 3. *Educ:* Nat Taiwan Univ, BS, 59; Univ Iowa, MS, 64; Univ Calif, San Diego, PhD(physics), 68. *Prof Exp:* Fel physics, Univ Calif, San Diego, 68-69; res fel, Harvard Univ, 69-72; from asst prof to assoc prof physics, Bartol Res Found, Univ Del, 72-79. *Mem:* Am Phys Soc; Sigma Xi; NY Acad Sci. *Res:* Solid state physics and quantum electronics, surface physics, lattice dynamics, nonlinear optics laser light scattering, solid state lasers, gas lasers and semiconductor lasers. *Mailing Add:* 58 Mt Horeb Rd Warren NJ 07059

**WANG, CHIA PING,** NUCLEAR PARTICLE & RADIATION PHYSICS, THERMAL PHYSICS. *Current Pos:* RES PHYSICIST, SCI & ADVAN TECHNOL DIR, US ARMY NATICK RES & DEVELOP CTR, 75- *Personal Data:* b Philippines; US citizen. *Educ:* Univ London, BSc, 50; Univ Malaya, MSc, 51; Univs Malaya & Cambridge, PhD(physics), 53. *Hon Degrees:* DSc, Univ Singapore, 72. *Honors & Awards:* Outstanding Performance Award, Dept Army, Qual Increase Award. *Prof Exp:* Asst lectr, Univ Malaya, 51-53; from assoc prof physics to prof, Nankai Univ, 54-58, head, Electron Physics & Electronics Div, 55-58; head, Electroph Div, Lanchow Atomic Proj, 58; sr lectr, prof & actg head, Depts Physics & Math, Hong Kong Univ & Chinese Univ Hong Kong, 58-63; res assoc, Lab Nuclear Studies, Cornell Univ, 63-64; assoc prof space sci & physics, Cath Univ, 64-66; assoc prof physics, Case Inst Technol & Case Western Res Univ, 66-70; vis scientist & vis prof, Univs Cambridge & Louvain, US Naval Res Lab, Univ Md & Mass Inst Technol, 70-75. *Concurrent Pos:* Mem, Steering Comt, Nuclear Physics Div, Nankai Univ, 56-58; US Army Natick Res & Develop Ctr, 93- *Mem:* Am Phys Soc; Inst Physics London; AAAS; Sigma Xi; NY Acad Sci; Am Nuclear Soc. *Res:* Nuclear particle physics; cosmic radiation; neutrinos; space physics; nucleon sub-structure; ultra-high energy particle production; quantum electrodynamics and quantum fields, quantum electronics; dosimetry; laser physics; nonlinear optics; thermal physics; microwaves. *Mailing Add:* 28 Hallett Hill Rd Weston MA 02193

**WANG, CHIA-LIN JEFFREY,** CHEMISTRY. *Current Pos:* SR RES CHEMIST, MED DEPT, DUPONT MERCK CO, 91- *Personal Data:* b China, June 24, 49; m 73. *Educ:* Nat Taiwan Univ, BS, 71; Univ Pittsburgh, PhD(chem), 77. *Prof Exp:* Res assoc, Dept Chem, Univ Pittsburgh, 77 & Harvard Univ, 78-79; res chemist, cent res & develop dept, E I DuPont de Nemours & Co, Inc, 79-85, sr res chemist, Med Dept, 85-90. *Mem:* Am Chem Soc. *Res:* Synthesis of medicinally interesting compounds. *Mailing Add:* 4th Flr No 181 Chinsan S Rd Sec 2 Taipei Taiwan

**WANG, CHIEN BANG,** FILTRATION, FLUID & PARTICLE SEPARATION. *Current Pos:* Res chem engr, 69-71, sr res chem engr, 72-85, RES ASSOC, EASTMAN CHEM DIV, EASTMAN KODAK CO, 85- *Personal Data:* b China, Oct 10, 41; m 70; c 2. *Educ:* Nat Taiwan Univ, BS, 62; Kans State Univ, MS, 65; Univ Wis, PhD(chem eng), 69. *Mem:* Am Filtration Soc; Fiber Soc. *Res:* Filtration and fluid/particle separtaion processes; process and product development of synthetic fibers. *Mailing Add:* 2313 Oxford Ct Kingsport TN 37660. *Fax:* 423-229-4558

**WANG, CHIEN YI,** POSTHARVEST PHYSIOLOGY, HORTICULTURE. *Current Pos:* RES HORTICULTURIST, USDA, 76- *Personal Data:* b Kaoshiung, Taiwan, Nov 22, 42; US citizen; m 68, Shiow Y Shyr; c Jean & Ken. *Educ:* Nat Taiwan Univ, BS, 64; Ore State Univ, PhD(hort), 69. *Prof Exp:* Res asst fruits, Ore State Univ, 65-69; res assoc, Mid-Columbia Exp Sta, 69-76. *Concurrent Pos:* Chairperson, Postharvest Work Group, Am Soc Hort Sci. *Mem:* Fel Am Soc Hort Sci; Int Soc Hort Sci. *Res:* Postharvest physiology of horticultural crops; basic and applied problems concerning physiological and pathological deterioration and quality maintenance of fruits, vegetables and flowers after harvest. *Mailing Add:* Bldg 002 USDA Beltsville MD 20705

**WANG, CHIH CHUN,** MATERIALS SCIENCE, PHYSICAL CHEMISTRY. *Current Pos:* mem tech staff solid state mat res, 63-73, FEL TECH STAFF, RCA LABS, DAVID SARNOFF RES CTR, RCA CORP, PRINCETON, 73- *Personal Data:* b Peking, China, Oct 9, 32; m 59; c 3. *Educ:* Nat Taiwan Univ, BSc, 55; Kans State Univ, MSc, 59; Colo State Univ, PhD(phys chem), 62. *Prof Exp:* Res assoc, High Temp Phys Chem Res Lab, Univ Kans, 62-63. *Mem:* Am Chem Soc; Electrochem Soc; Am Phys Soc. *Res:* Electronic materials; thin films; crystal growth; chemical vapor deposition; high pressure and high temperature chemistry; thermodynamics; x-ray crystallography; vidicon materials and devices; tribology. *Mailing Add:* Am Lumi Cranbury Plaza Bldg B 2525 Rte 130 Cranbury NJ 08512-0515

**WANG, CHIH HSING,** RADIOCHEMISTRY. *Current Pos:* From asst prof to prof chem, Ore State Univ, 51-85, dir, Radiation Ctr, 62-85, dir, Inst Nuclear Sci & Eng, 64-85, head, Dept Nuclear Eng, 74-85, EMER PROF & DIR, RADIATION CTR, ORE STATE UNIV, 85- *Personal Data:* b Shanghai, China, Sept 20, 17; nat US; m 58; c 1. *Educ:* Shantung Univ, China, BS, 37; Ore State Univ, MS, 47, PhD(chem), 50. *Concurrent Pos:* Consult, NSF, 65-69; chmn, Ore Nuclear & Thermal Energy Coun, 72-73. *Mem:* Fel AAAS; Am Chem Soc; Am Soc Biol Chem; Am Soc Plant Physiol; fel Am Nuclear Soc. *Res:* Nuclear education; radiotracer methodology; energy analysis. *Mailing Add:* 3110 Chintimini Ave SW Corvallis OR 97333-1532

**WANG, CHIH-CHUNG,** METALLURGY. *Current Pos:* CONSULT, MAT TECHNOL, 95- *Personal Data:* b Wusih, China, Mar 8, 22; US citizen; m 95, Yinxu Xie; c Clement & Cheryl. *Educ:* Chiao-Tung Univ, BS, 45; Ill Inst Technol, MS, 50; Mass Inst Technol, DSc, 53. *Prof Exp:* Sr engr, Sylvania Elec Prod, Inc, 53-55; dir, Mat & Metall Dept, Clevite Transistor Prod, Inc, 55-63; staff scientist, Ledgemont Lab, Kennecott Copper Corp, 63-78, mgr metal prod, Lexington Develop Ctr, 78-80; chief metallurgist, Duracell Inc, 81-95. *Concurrent Pos:* Consult, Advan Pos Systems Inc & Lithium Battery Plan, Duracell Inc, 96- *Mem:* Am Inst Mining, Metall & Petrol Engrs; Am Soc Metals; Electrochem Soc. *Res:* Solidification of metals; crystal growing; materials research; extractive metallurgy; electroplating; recycling of metals; battery materials and technology. *Mailing Add:* 9 Gould Rd Lexington MA 02173. *E-Mail:* duraccw@aol.com

**WANG, CHIH-LUEH ALBERT,** CONTRACTILE PROTEINS, FLUORESCENCE SPECTROSCOPY. *Current Pos:* fel, Boston Biomed Res Inst, 79-82, res assoc, 82-84, staff scientist, 84-88, prin scientist, 88-92, SR SCIENTIST, BOSTON BIOMED RES INST, 92- *Personal Data:* b Chia-yi, Taiwan, China, June 22, 50; US citizen; m 75, Li-Wen Chang; c Chi-An & Chi-Fong. *Educ:* Nat Taiwan Univ, BS, 71; Ohio State Univ, PhD(chem), 78. *Mem:* Am Chem Soc; Biophys Soc; Am Soc Biochem & Molecular Biol; Soc Chinese Bioscientists Am. *Res:* Structure and function of regulatory proteins in smooth muscle; calcium-binding proteins; application of rare earth ions in biological systems. *Mailing Add:* Dept Muscle Boston Biomed Res Inst 20 Staniford St Boston MA 02114. *Fax:* 617-523-6649; *E-Mail:* wang@bbri.eri. harvard.edu

**WANG, CHI-HUA,** ORGANIC CHEMISTRY. *Current Pos:* assoc prof, 68-70, PROF CHEM, UNIV MASS, HARBOR CAMPUS, 70- *Personal Data:* b Peking, China, Apr 18, 23; m 49, Nancy Yang; c Fong. *Educ:* St John's Univ, China, BS, 45; Cath Univ, China, MS, 47; St Louis Univ, PhD(org chem), 51. *Prof Exp:* Fel, Brandeis Univ, 51-53, from instr to assoc prof chem, 53-62; sr chemist, Arthur D Little, Inc, 62-64; assoc prof chem, Wellesley Col, 64-68. *Concurrent Pos:* Vis prof chem, Chinese Acad Sci, 83, 85 & 87. *Mem:* Am Chem Soc; Sigma Xi. *Res:* Chemistry of free radicals in solution; mechanism of organic reactions. *Mailing Add:* Dept Chem Univ Mass Harbor Campus 100 Morrisey Blvd Boston MA 02125-3393

**WANG, CHIN HSIEN,** LASER LIGHT SCATTERING FROM CONDENSED MEDIA. *Current Pos:* MD CLARK DISTINGUISHED PROF CHEM, UNIV NEBR, 89-, ADJ PROF PHYSICS, 91- *Personal Data:* b Taiwan, Sept 4, 39; US citizen; m 63, Lirong R; c Nancy, Jenny, Elaine & Wilson. *Educ:* Nat Taiwan Univ, BS, 61; Utah State Univ, MS, 64; Mass Inst Technol, PhD(phys chem), 67. *Prof Exp:* Mem tech staff, Bell Tel Labs, 67-69; from asst prof to prof chem, Univ Utah, 69-89, adj prof, Dept Mat Sci & Eng, 81-93, adj prof chem, 90-93. *Concurrent Pos:* Adj asst prof elec eng, Univ Utah, 70-75, chmn, Chem Physics Prof, 83-89; petrol res fund grant, 70-78; Res Corp grant, 72-73; Alfred P Sloan Found res fel, 73-77; Off Naval Res grants, 74-; NSF grants, 76-91; Alexander von Humboldt fel, 77-78; US sr scientist award, WGer, 83-84; mem, Adv Comt Ctr Mat Res & Anal, Univ Nebr, 89-, coodr, Phys Chem Div, 96- *Mem:* Fel Am Phys Soc; Am Chem Soc; AAAS; Sigma Xi. *Res:* Light scattering and Raman spectroscopy; polymer physics; statistical mechanics; relaxation and orientation behavior of polymer chairs in solution and in bulk; studies of the glass transition phenomena in supercooled liquids and solids using light scattering and non-equilibrium statistical mechanics. *Mailing Add:* Dept Chem Univ Nebr Lincoln NE 68588-0304. *Fax:* 407-472-9402; *E-Mail:* chwang@unlinfo.unl. edu

**WANG, CHING CHUNG,** BIOCHEMISTRY, PARASITOLOGY. *Current Pos:* PROF CHEM & PHARMACEUT CHEM, SCH PHARM, UNIV CALIF, SAN FRANCISCO, 81- *Personal Data:* b Peking, China, Feb 10, 36; m 63, Alice; c Charlotte. *Educ:* Nat Taiwan Univ, BS, 58; Univ Calif, Berkeley, PhD(biochem), 66. *Honors & Awards:* Burroughs Wellcome Molecular Parasitol Award, 83. *Prof Exp:* Fel biochem, Col Physicians & Surgeons, Columbia Univ, 66-67; res assoc, Princeton Univ, 67-69; sr res biochemist, Merck Inst Therapeut Res, 69-72, from res fel to sr res fel, 72-78, sr investr, 78-81. *Concurrent Pos:* Dir, Inst Molecular Biol, Academia Sinica, Taiwan, 91-93. *Mem:* Am Soc Biochem & Molecular Biol; fel AAAS. *Res:* Biochemistry and development of protozoan parasites; invertebrate neurobiology; antiparasitic chemotherapy. *Mailing Add:* 22 Miraloma Dr San Francisco CA 94127. *Fax:* 415-476-3382

**WANG, CHING YUNG,** IMMUNOLOGY, BIOCHEMISTRY. *Current Pos:* Assoc mem res, 76-84, STAFF MEM BIOCHEM, MICH CANCER FOUND, 84- *Personal Data:* b Taipei, Taiwan, Feb 26, 41. *Educ:* Taiwan Univ, BS, 64; Auburn Univ, PhD(biochem), 70. *Mem:* Am Soc Pharmacol & Exp Therapeut; Am Asn Cancer Res; Soc Toxicol. *Res:* Immunology; biochemistry. *Mailing Add:* 110 E Warren Ave Detroit MI 48201-1379

**WANG, CHING-PING SHIH,** THEORETICAL SOLID STATE PHYSICS. *Current Pos:* asst prof, 79-85, ASSOC PROF, DEPT PHYSICS, UNIV MD, 85- *Personal Data:* b Shanghai, China, Feb 16, 47; c Eric. *Educ:* Tung-Hai Univ, Taiwan, BS, 69; La State Univ, Baton Rouge, MS, 71, PhD(physics), 74. *Prof Exp:* Res assoc physics, Dept Physics & Astron, La State Univ, Baton Rouge, 74-76; res assoc physics, Dept Physics & Astron, Northwestern Univ, Evanston, 76-79. *Concurrent Pos:* Off Naval Res contract, 79-88; NSF grant, 85-92; consult, Naval Res Lab, 85- *Mem:* Am Phys Soc. *Res:* Electronic structure and other properties of high temperature superconductors, of heavy fermion superconductors, of ferromagnetic metals, of magnetic metal surfaces with absorbed atoms and of semiconductors. *Mailing Add:* 2 Holly Leaf Ct Bethesda MD 20817

**WANG, CHI-SUN,** BIOCHEMISTRY. *Current Pos:* Staff scientist, 74-75, asst mem, 75-82, ASSOC MEM, OKLA MED RES FOUND, 82- *Personal Data:* b Shanghai, China, Oct 8, 42; m 73; c 1. *Educ:* Nat Taiwan Univ, BS, 66; Univ Okla, PhD(biochem), 71. *Honors & Awards:* Eason Award, 77; Merrick Award, 81. *Concurrent Pos:* Adj assoc prof, Dept Biochem & Molecular Biol, Sch Med, Univ Okla, 85- *Mem:* Sigma Xi; Am Chem Soc; AAAS; Am Soc Biochem & Molecular Biol; Am Oil Chemists Soc. *Res:* Lipoprotein lipase; bile salt-activated lipase; tissue lipases. *Mailing Add:* 825 NE 13th St Oklahoma City OK 73104

**WANG, CHIU-CHEN,** RADIATION ONCOLOGY, SUBSPECIALITY HEAD & NECK CANCER MANAGEMENT. *Current Pos:* asst radiol, Harvard Med Sch, 58-60, instr, 60-61, clin assoc, 62-67, asst clin prof, 68-69, asst prof, 69-70, from asst prof to assoc prof, 70-75, PROF RADIATION ONCOL, HARVARD MED SCH, 75-; RADIATION ONCOLOGIST & HEAD CLIN SERV, MASS GEN HOSP, 73- *Personal Data:* b Canton, China, Nov 5, 22; US citizen. *Educ:* Nat Kwei-Yang Med Col, China, MD, 48; Am Bd Radiol, dipl, 53. *Hon Degrees:* MA, Harvard, 90. *Prof Exp:* Rotation intern, Canton Hosp, China, 47-48, asst resident med, 48-49; intern, Univ Hosp, Syracuse, NY, 49-50; asst resident radiol, Mass Gen Hosp, Boston, 50-51, resident, 52, clin fel, 53-56. *Concurrent Pos:* Damon Runyon res grant, Donner Lab, Univ Calif, Berkeley, 61-62; consult radiologist, Lawrence Berkeley Lab, Univ Calif, Berkeley, 62-65 & Mass Eye & Ear Infirmary, Emerson Hosp, Mass, 62-; guest examr, Am Bd Radiol, 66 & 94. *Mem:* Fel Am Col Radiol; Am Soc Therapeut Radiol & Oncol; AMA. *Res:* Clinical radiation oncology. *Mailing Add:* Dept Radiation Oncol Mass Gen Hosp Boston MA 02114. *Fax:* 617-726-3603

**WANG, CHRISTINE A,** ELECTRONIC MATERIALS. *Current Pos:* STAFF SCIENTIST, LINCOLN LAB, MASS INST TECHNOL, 84- *Personal Data:* b Providence, RI, Sept 20, 55; m 80; c 2. *Educ:* Mass Inst Technol, SB, 77, SM, 78, PhD(electronic mat), 84. *Mem:* Am Asn Crystal Growth; Mat Res Soc; Inst Elec & Electronics Engrs. *Res:* Development of III-V semiconductors for diode lasers; uniformity, controllability, and reproducibility for an epitaxial process for optoelectronic devices; diode lasers and short wavelength lasers; author of over 60 publications and 4 patents. *Mailing Add:* Lincoln Lab Mass Inst Technol 244 Wood St Lexington MA 02173

**WANG, CHU PING,** COMPUTER SYSTEMS, INFORMATION SCIENCE. *Current Pos:* res staff mem, San Jose Res Lab, 68-76, RES STAFF MEM, THOMAS J WATSON RES CTR, IBM CORP, 76- *Personal Data:* b China, Mar 25, 31; m 61; c 3. *Educ:* Taiwan Univ, BSc, 54; Univ Toronto, MASc, 56; Stanford Univ, PhD(microwave electronics), 61. *Prof Exp:* Asst prof elec eng, San Jose State Col, 60-61; res staff mem, Thomas J Watson Res Ctr, IBM Corp, 61-67; vis assoc prof, Wash Univ, 67-68. *Mem:* Inst Elec & Electronics Engrs. *Res:* Information system design and evaluation methodology; computer performance evaluation; data base organization. *Mailing Add:* 13815 Franklin Ave Flushing NY 11355

**WANG, CHUNG-CHING,** STATISTICAL GRAPHICS, STATISTICAL COMPUTING. *Current Pos:* asst prof, 91-96, ASSOC PROF STATIST, UNIV CENT FLA, 96- *Personal Data:* b Taiwan, China, Mar 19, 55; m 86, Yin Fang; c Jay-Shing, Jay-Ming & Jay-Yun. *Educ:* Chaio-Tung Univ, BS, 77; Mankato State Univ, MS, 86; Iowa State Univ, PhD(statisst), 91. *Prof Exp:* Consult, Inst Statist Asn. *Mem:* Am Statist Asn; Soc Indust & Appl Math; Internal Chinese Statistician Asn. *Res:* Meta-analysis; statistical computing; statistical graphics; intelligent data base. *Mailing Add:* 610 Sherburn Ct Orlando FL 32828. *E-Mail:* cwang@pegasus.cc.ucf.edu

**WANG, CHUN-JUAN KAO,** MYCOLOGY. *Current Pos:* from asst prof to assoc prof, 59-72, PROF BOT & MYCOL, COL ENVIRON SCI & FORESTRY, STATE UNIV NY, 72- *Personal Data:* b Mukden, China, Jan 10, 28; m 55; c 3. *Educ:* Nat Taiwan Univ, BS, 50; Vassar Col, MS, 52; Univ Iowa, PhD(mycol), 55. *Honors & Awards:* W H Weston Award for Excellence in Teaching Mycol, Mycol Soc Am, 90. *Prof Exp:* Asst, Univ Iowa, 52-55; res assoc, Clin Labs, Jewish Hosp, Cincinnati, Ohio, 55-58. *Concurrent Pos:* Instr, Sch Med, Univ Cincinnati, 57-58. *Mem:* Mycol Soc Am; Brit Mycol Soc; Sigma Xi; Int Soc Human & Animal Mycol; Asn Women Sci. *Res:* Medical mycology; ecology, ultrastructure and systematics of imperfect fungi (Hyphomycetes). *Mailing Add:* Col Environ Sci & Forestry State Univ NY 320 Bray Hall Syracuse NY 13210-2723. *Fax:* 315-470-6934

**WANG, DALTON T,** protein chemistry, for more information see previous edition

**WANG, DANIEL I-CHYAU,** CHEMICAL & BIOCHEMICAL ENGINEERING. *Current Pos:* from asst prof to prof biochem, 76-84, chevron prof chem eng, 85-95, DIR, BIOTECHNOL PROCESS ENG CTR, MASS INST TECHNOL, 85-, INST PROF CHEM ENG, 95- *Personal Data:* b Nanking, China, Mar 12, 36; US citizen; m 66; c 1. *Educ:* Mass Inst Technol, BS, 59, SM, 61; Univ Pa, PhD(chem eng), 63. *Honors & Awards:* Food, Pharmaceut & Bioeng Award, Am Inst Chem Engrs, Inst Lectr; M J Johnson Award, Am Chem Soc, D J Perlrahn Mem Lectr. *Prof Exp:* Process engr, US Army Biol Labs, 63-65. *Mem:* Nat Acad Eng; Am Inst Chem Engrs; Inst Food Technol; Am Soc Microbiol; Sigma Xi; Am Chem Soc; Am Acad Arts & Sci; Am Inst Med & Biol Eng. *Res:* Kinetics of biological systems; mass transfer in fermentation process; membrane processes; animal cell cultivation; protein purification; protein refolding. *Mailing Add:* 17 Pequosset Rd Belmont MA 02178. *Fax:* 617-253-2400; *E-Mail:* dicwang@mit.edu

**WANG, DAZONG,** advanced vehicle systems, computer aided engineering, for more information see previous edition

**WANG, DER-SHI,** TEXTILE ENGINEERING. *Current Pos:* pres & chief exec officer, 88-89, chem & chief exec officer, 89-90, DIR TEXTILE RES, VELCRO GROUP CORP, 91- *Personal Data:* b Taipei, Taiwan, Nov 28, 41; Can citizen; m 90, Pamela C Brooks. *Educ:* Taipei Inst Technol, dipl textile eng, 63; Leeds Univ, UK, dipl textile indust, 70, MSc, 72, PhD(textile indust), 76. *Prof Exp:* Assoc prof, Dept Textiles, Nat Taiwan Inst Technol, 76-80, chmn, 79-80. *Concurrent Pos:* Tech consult & res proj dir, China Textile Testing & Res Ctr, 76-80; res & develop mgr, Hung-Lung Indust Co, Taipei, 76-80; comt mem, China Stand Orgn, 76-80. *Mem:* Textile Inst UK; Soc Plastic Engrs; Can Soc Textile Sci; Textile Club; Can Textile Soc. *Res:* Evaluation of yarn (conventional and high tech polymer) properties for a specific end use, improving by design all weaving technology to produce specialty products; granted 1 US patent. *Mailing Add:* 54 Hardy Rd Bedford NH 03110

**WANG, DONG-PING,** PHYSICAL OCEANOGRAPHY, OCEAN MODEL. *Current Pos:* PROF, DEPT MARINE SCI, STATE UNIV NY, STONY BROOK, 85- *Personal Data:* b Shanghai, China, Sept 12, 48; m 75, Julia Wang; c Ronald & Joanne. *Educ:* Nat Tsing-Hua Univ, Taiwan, BS, 70; Univ Miami, PhD(oceanog), 75. *Prof Exp:* Res scientist, Johns Hopkins Univ, 76-79; oceanogr, Argonne Nat Lab, 80-84. *Concurrent Pos:* CNOC chair, Naval Postgrad Sch, 85; vis prof, Univ de les Illes Balears, Spain, 90 & Univ Tokyo, 92. *Mem:* Am Geophys Union. *Res:* Mixing and transport of materials inestuaries and coastal ocean; numerical ocean model and prediction. *Mailing Add:* Marine Sci Res Ctr State Univ NY Stony Brook NY 11794

**WANG, EDWARD YEONG,** SOLID STATE ELECTRONICS. *Current Pos:* prof, 79-, EMER PROF ELEC & COMPUT ENG, ARIZ UNIV, TEMPE. *Personal Data:* b Nantung, China, July 30, 33; m 60; c 3. *Educ:* Morningside Col, BS, 54; Purdue Univ, MS, 59; Tufts Univ, PhD(physics), 66. *Prof Exp:* Jr physicist, Nat Semiconductor Co, Ill, 54-56; assoc staff mem, Res Div, Raytheon Co, Mass, 59-61; sr res, Electronics Corp Am, 61-63 & Gen Motors Res Lab, Mich, 66-70; assoc prof elec eng, Wayne State Univ, 70-77, prof elec & comput eng, 77-79. *Mem:* Am Phys Soc; Inst Elec & Electronics Engrs. *Res:* Electrical and optical properties of solids; optoelectronics. *Mailing Add:* 5323 Royal View Dr Phoenix AZ 85018

**WANG, EUGENIA,** MOLECULAR BIOLOGY, BIOCHEMISTRY. *Current Pos:* FAC, LADY DAVIS INST, JEWISH GEN HOSP, 90- *Personal Data:* b Chungking, China, Feb 26, 45; US citizen; m 76; c 1. *Educ:* Nat Taiwan Univ, BSc, 66; Northern Mich Univ, MA, 69; Case Western Reserve Univ, PhD(cell biol), 74. *Prof Exp:* Res asst, Inst Zool, Acad Sinica, 66-67; teaching asst, Northern Mich Univ, 67-69; teaching fel, Case Western Res Univ, 69-74; postdoctoral fel, Virol Lab, Rockefeller Univ, 74-76, res assoc, 76-78, asst prof, 78-86; assoc prof, Dept Anat & Dept Med, McGill Univ, 87-90. *Concurrent Pos:* Scientist award, Med Res Coun Can, 88-; mem, Study Sect Aging Rev Comt, Nat Inst Aging, NIH, 90-; chairperson biol sci, Can Asn Geront, 90-91; ad hoc reviewer, Nat Cancer Inst, NIH, Med Res Coun Can & NSF; vis specialist, Inst Biomed Sci, Acad Sinica. *Mem:* Am Soc Cell Biol; NY Acad Sci; Geront Soc Am; Can Asn Geront. *Mailing Add:* Lady Davis Inst Jewish Gen Hosp 3755 Cote St Catherine Montreal PQ H3T 1E2 Can

**WANG, FRANCIS WEI-YU,** POLYMER SCIENCE. *Current Pos:* SUPVRY RES CHEMIST, POLYMERS DIV, NAT INST STAND & TECHNOL, 72- *Personal Data:* b Peikang, Taiwan, July 21, 36; US citizen; m 66, Susan Liao; c Anthony, Andrea & Edwin. *Educ:* Calif Inst Technol, BS, 61, MS, 62; Univ

Calif, San Diego, PhD(chem), 71. *Honors & Awards:* Bronze Medal Award, Dept Com, 85. *Prof Exp:* Chemist, Pac Soap Co, 62-66; USPHS fel, 71-72. *Mem:* Am Chem Soc; Am Phys Soc; Soc Plastics Engrs. *Res:* Photophysical processes in polymer molecules; diffusion in polymers; optical fiber sensors; polymer processing; biomaterials; tissue engineering. *Mailing Add:* Rm A143 Bldg 224 Polymers Div Nat Inst Stand & Technol Gaithersburg MD 20899

**WANG, FRANK FENG HUI,** MARINE GEOLOGY. *Current Pos:* MARINE GEOLOGIST, US GEOL SURV, 67-, EMER SCIENTIST, 95- *Personal Data:* b Hopeh, China, Mar 21, 24; nat US; m 58, Sandra H Tien; c Larry, Audrey & Albert. *Educ:* Nat Southwestern Assoc Univ, China, BS, 45; Univ Wash, PhD(geol), 55. *Prof Exp:* Asst geol, Nat Southwestern Assoc Univ, China, 45-46; instr, Nat Peking Univ, 46-48; asst, Univ Wash, 50-54; sedimentologist-stratigrapher, Western Gulf Oil Co, 54-57; res geologist, Gulf Res & Develop Co, 57-63; marine geologist, Int Minerals & Chem Corp, 64-67. *Concurrent Pos:* Spec consult, Chinese Petrol Corp, 58; vis scholar, Northwestern Univ, 64; tech adv, UN, 67-, spec adv & sr marine geologist, UN Develop Prog Regional Offshore Prospecting EAsia, 72-74, prin marine geologist, 74-; vchmn, Marine Geol Panel, US-Japan Coop Prog Natural Resources, 70-92 & chmn, 93-; consult prof, Sch Ocean, Earth Sci & Ocean Eng, Univ Hawaii, Honolulu, 97- *Mem:* Am Asn Petrol Geol; Am Geophys Union; Marine Technol Soc. *Res:* Marine mineral resources; ocean mining; regional climate and environmental changes in the Western Pacific; regional marine geology of eastern Asia. *Mailing Add:* US Geol Surv Off Marine Geol 345 Middlefield Rd Menlo Park CA 94025

**WANG, FRANKLIN FU-YEN,** materials science; deceased, see previous edition for last biography

**WANG, FREDERICK E,** NITINOL TECHNOLOGY, SUPERCONDUCTIVITY. *Current Pos:* PRES, INNOVATIVE TECHNOL INT, INC, 80- *Personal Data:* b She-Tou, Formosa, Aug 1, 32; US citizen; m 61; c 2. *Educ:* Memphis State Univ, BS, 56; Univ Ill, MS, 57; Syracuse Univ, PhD(phys chem), 60. *Prof Exp:* Fel, Harvard Univ, 60-61; res assoc metal alloys, Syracuse Univ, 61-63; chemist, US Naval Surface Weapons Ctr, 63-80. *Concurrent Pos:* Fulbright exchange lectr, 67-68. *Mem:* Am Phys Soc; Am Soc Metals; AAAS. *Res:* Metal and alloy physics; order-disorder phenomena; superconductivity; memory effect in alloy. *Mailing Add:* Innovative Technol Int Inc 10747-3 Tucker St Beltsville MD 20705

**WANG, GAN,** VIRTUAL REALITY & COMPUTER GRAPHICS, FLIGHT SIMULATION & REAL-TIME SYSTEMS. *Current Pos:* SR SYSTS ANALYST & ENGR, CAMBRIDGE RES ASSOCS, 95- *Personal Data:* m 89, Karen H Oiu. *Educ:* Harbin Inst Technol, BS, 81; George Mason Univ, MS, 87; Univ Va, PhD(elec eng), 91. *Prof Exp:* Systs engr, Environ Tectonics Corp, 91-95. *Concurrent Pos:* Consult, Environ Tectonics Corp, 95-96. *Res:* Software development in virtual reality and flight simulation; military mission planning and rehearsal; computer graphics. *Mailing Add:* 1430 Spring Hill Rd Suite 200 McLean VA 22102

**WANG, GARY T,** BIOORGANIC CHEMISTRY, BIOCHEMICAL PROBES. *Current Pos:* fel, 88-90, res scientist, Diag Div, 90-92, SR RES SCIENTIST, PHARMACEUT DIV, ABBOTT LABS, 92- *Personal Data:* b Gansu, China, Mar 7, 63; m 89, Pu Chen; c Andrew. *Educ:* Lanzhou Univ, China, BS, 82; Northwestern Univ, Evanston, MS, 84, PhD(chem), 87. *Prof Exp:* Res asst, Chem Dept, Northwestern Univ, 83-87; fel, Chem Dept, Syracuse Univ, 88. *Mem:* Am Chem Soc; AAAS; NY Acad Sci. *Res:* Organic/bioorganic chemistry and medicinal chemistry; elucidation of mechanisms of biological processes, particularly processes involving enzymes, antibodies etc; design and synthesis of tailored molecular entities for biomedical application as diagnostic probes or therapeutic agents. *Mailing Add:* Abbott Labs D-4CP Ap10 Abbott Park IL 60064

**WANG, GUANG TSAN,** VETERINARY MEDICINE, PARASITOLOGY. *Current Pos:* res vet, Am Cyanamid Co, 68-74, group leader parasitol discovery, 74-77, prog mgr, Agr Div, 77-81, dir animal indust res & develop, 81-90, sr prod develop mgr, Americas/Far East, 90-93, RES FEL, AGR RES DIV, AM CYANAMID CO, PRINCETON, 93- *Personal Data:* b Taiwan, China, Mar 6, 35; US citizen; m 62, Sue; c Albert & Thomas. *Educ:* Nat Taiwan Univ, DVM, 58; Univ Ill, Urbana, MS, 64, PhD(vet med sci), 68. *Prof Exp:* Vet, Taiwan Serum Vaccine Labs, 60-62; res asst parasitol, Univ Ill, 62-68. *Mem:* Am Soc Parasitol; Am Vet Med Asn; Am Asn Vet Parasitologists; World Poultry Sci Asn. *Res:* Toxicity and efficacy of anthelmintics, anticoccidials and antibiotics in domestic animals; industrial parasitic chemotherapy; research administration. *Mailing Add:* 41 Slayback Dr Princeton Junction NJ 08550

**WANG, GWO-CHING,** INTERFACE PHYSICS, ULTRATHIN FILM MAGNETISM. *Personal Data:* b Hu-Pei Prov, China, Oct 10, 46; c Victor Lu. *Educ:* Cheng Kung Univ, Taiwan, BS, 68; Northern Ill Univ, MS, 73; Univ Wis-Madison, PhD(mat sci), 78. *Honors & Awards:* Nottingham Prize, 78. *Prof Exp:* Teaching asst, Fu-Jen Univ, Taiwan, 68-69 & Univ Wyo, 69-71; res asst, Northern Ill Univ, 71-73, Univ Wis-Madison, 73-78; physicist, Nat Bur Stand, 78-80; physicist, Solid State Physics Div, Oak Ridge Nat Lab, 80-84. *Mem:* Fel Am Phys Soc; Mat Res Soc; Am Vacuum Soc. *Res:* Geometric properties of surfaces and interfaces; chemisorption, kinetics, and phase transitions using high resolution low energy electron diffraction; growth modes and magnetic properties of ultra thin ferromagnetic films. *Mailing Add:* Physics Dept Rensselaer Polytech Inst Troy NY 12180-3590. *Fax:* 518-276-6680; *E-Mail:* wangg@rpu.edu

**WANG, H E FRANK,** FLUID PHYSICS, SYSTEMS ENGINEERING. *Current Pos:* DEP GEN DIR, INDUST TECHNOL RES INST, TAIWAN, REPUB CHINA. *Personal Data:* b China, Oct 23, 29; US citizen; m 55, Ming-Min Mi; c Joseph & Joyce. *Educ:* Nat Taiwan Univ, BS, 52; Bucknell Univ, MS, 54; Brown Univ, PhD(gas dynamics), 59. *Prof Exp:* Res engr gas dynamics, Boeing Co, 58-60; mem tech staff & prog mgr acrophysics & systs eng, Aerospace Corp, 60-77, dir, Space Test Progs, 76-81, prin dir, 81-92. *Mem:* Assoc fel Am Inst Aeronaut & Astronaut. *Mailing Add:* 27241 Sunnyridge Rd Rolling Hills CA 90274

**WANG, HAI,** COMBUSTION SCIENCE & TECHNOLOGY, HIGH-TEMPERATURE CHEMICAL KINETICS. *Current Pos:* ASST PROF MECH ENG, UNIV DEL, 97- *Personal Data:* b Shanghai, China, Sept 23, 62; m, Jasna Tomic; c Neven. *Educ:* East China Inst Chem Technol, BEng, 84; Mich Technol Univ, MS, 86; Pa State Univ, PhD(fuel sci), 92. *Prof Exp:* Res assoc, Pa State Univ, 92-94; prof res staff, Princeton Univ, 94-96. *Mem:* Am Chem Soc; Combustion Inst. *Res:* Application of the principles and methods of quantum mechanics, statistical mechanics and aerosol dynamics to problems of combustion, combustion-generated pollutants, chemically reactive flows and nanoparticle synthesis. *Mailing Add:* Dept Mech Eng Univ Del Newark DE 19716. *Fax:* 302-831-3619; *E-Mail:* hwang@me.udel.edu

**WANG, HAIMIN,** ASTRONOMY. *Current Pos:* asst prof, 95-97, ASSOC PROF PHYSICS, NJ INST TECHNOL, 97- *Personal Data:* b China, June 19, 62. *Educ:* Nanjing Univ, China, BS, 82; Calif Inst Technol, PhD(astron), 88. *Honors & Awards:* NSF Career Award, 96. *Prof Exp:* Postdoctoral res fel, Calif Inst Technol, 88-89, scientist, 89-93, sr res fel, 93-95. *Mem:* Inst Astron Union; Am Astron Soc. *Mailing Add:* Dept Physics NJ Inst Technol Newark NJ 07102. *Fax:* 973-596-5794; *E-Mail:* haimin@solar.njij.edu

**WANG, HAO,** mathematics; deceased, see previous edition for last biography

**WANG, HENRY Y,** BIOCHEMICAL ENGINEERING, APPLIED BIOTECHNOLOGY. *Current Pos:* from asst prof to assoc prof, 79-89, PROF CHEM ENG, UNIV MICH, 89- *Personal Data:* b Shanghai, China, July 22, 51; m 84, Evangeline Cesar; c Stephanie. *Educ:* Iowa State Univ, BS, 72; Mass Inst Technol, SM, 74, PhD(biochem eng), 77. *Honors & Awards:* W M Peterson Award, Am Chem Soc, 74. *Prof Exp:* Eng assoc, Merck & Co, 77-78; sr scientist, Schering Plough, 78-79. *Concurrent Pos:* Vis prof, Univ BC, 85 & Osaka Univ, 93; sr vis scientist, Fermentation Res Inst, Japan, 86. *Mem:* Am Inst Chem Engrs; Am Chem Soc; Am Soc Microbiol; Soc Indust Microbiol; AAAS. *Res:* Biochemical engineering; cell culture engineering; fermentation technology; computer control of bioprocesses; environmental biotechnology. *Mailing Add:* 1215 Bardstown Trail Ann Arbor MI 48105-3291. *Fax:* 313-763-0459; *E-Mail:* hywang@eng.umich.edu

**WANG, HERBERT FAN,** GEOPHYSICS. *Current Pos:* from asst prof to assoc prof, 72-82, PROF GEOPHYS, UNIV WIS-MADISON, 82- *Personal Data:* b Shanghai, China, Sept 14, 46; US citizen; m 68, Rosemary Dugan; c Michelle, Melissa, Michael & Matthew. *Educ:* Univ Wis-Madison, BA, 66; Harvard Univ, AM, 68; Mass Inst Technol, PhD(geophys), 71. *Prof Exp:* Res assoc geophys, Mass Inst Technol, 71-72. *Concurrent Pos:* Geoscientist, Dept Energy, 80-81; physicist, Lawrence Livermore Nat Lab, 86-87; vis prof, State Univ NY, Albany, 89-90. *Mem:* Am Geophys Union. *Res:* Rock mechanics; groundwater, thermal and diffusion modeling. *Mailing Add:* Dept Geol 225 Weeks Hall Univ Wis 1215 W Dayton St Madison WI 53706-1692. *Fax:* 608-262-0693; *E-Mail:* wang@geology.wisc.edu

**WANG, HOWARD HAO,** NEUROSCIENCES, MOLECULAR PHARMACOLOGY. *Current Pos:* from asst prof to assoc prof, 70-82, PROF BIOL, STEVENSON COL, UNIV CALIF, SANTA CRUZ, 82- *Personal Data:* b Shanghai, China, Jan 24, 42; m 63; c 2. *Educ:* Calif Inst Technol, BS, 63; Univ Calif, Los Angeles, PhD(neurophysiol), 68. *Prof Exp:* USPHS fel, Univ Calif, Berkeley, 68-69; resident scientist, Neurosci Res Prog, Mass Inst Technol, 69-70. *Mem:* AAAS; Am Asn Anat; Biophys Soc; Soc Neurosci. *Res:* Mechanism of anesthetic action and drug-receptor interaction; effect of environmental chemicals on membrane structure and function; molecular and cellular mechanisms of brain function. *Mailing Add:* Biol UCSC Santa Cruz CA 95064. *Fax:* 408-459-3139; *E-Mail:* membio@cats.ucsc.edu

**WANG, HSIANG,** FLUID MECHANICS. *Current Pos:* VPRES, COASTAL & OFFSHORE ENG & RES, INC, 77-; CHMN & PROF COASTAL & OCEAN ENG, UNIV FLA, 82- *Personal Data:* b China, Jan 20, 36; m 64; c 3. *Educ:* Taiwan Univ, BS, 58; Univ Mass, MS, 63; Univ Iowa, PhD(fluid mech), 65. *Prof Exp:* Res asst fluid mech, Iowa Inst Hydraul Res, 62-63, res assoc, 63-65; res engr ocean, US Naval Civil Eng Lab, 65-67; mem tech staff, Nat Eng Sci Div, Fluor Corp Int, 67, mem sr staff, 67-69; sr engr, Tatra-Technol Inc, 69-70; from assoc prof civil eng to prof, Univ Del, 70-81, actg chmn, 78-79. *Concurrent Pos:* Vis prof, Tech Univ Braunschweig. *Mem:* Am Soc Civil Engrs; submarine wake study; offshore structure and offshore oil exploration; coastal and estuarine research; fluid mechanics and ocean engineering. *Mailing Add:* Coastal Oceanog Eng Dept Univ Fla 336 Weil Hall PO Box 116590 Gainesville FL 32611-6590

**WANG, HSIN-PANG,** COMPUTER ENGINEERING, COMPUTATIONAL MECHANICS. *Current Pos:* RES STAFF, GEN ELEC RES & DEVELOP CTR, 76- *Personal Data:* b Nanking, China, Apr 11, 46; US citizen; m 73; c 2. *Educ:* Cheng-Kung Univ, BS, 69; Univ Fla, MS, 72; Univ RI, PhD(mech eng), 76. *Honors & Awards:* Indust Res 100 Award, 83. *Concurrent Pos:* Prin investr, Intel Processing Mat, 88- *Mem:* Am Soc

Mech Engrs; Am Phys Soc. *Res:* Computer simulation of manufacturing processes; integration of CAE, CAD and CAM to improve the productivity and producibility; inter-relationship between product design and process development; intelligent processing of material. *Mailing Add:* Gen Elec Res & Develop Ctr PO Box 43 Schenectady NY 12301

**WANG, HSIOH-SHAN,** NEUROLOGY, NEUROPHYSIOLOGY. *Current Pos:* from asst prof to assoc prof, 66-75, PROF PSYCHIAT, MED SCH, DUKE UNIV, 75-, CHIEF PSYCHIAT DAY UNIT, DUKE UNIV HOSP, 71- *Personal Data:* b Shanghai, China, Sept 1, 28; US citizen; m 64; c 2. *Educ:* Taiwan Univ, Taipei, MB, 53; Am Bd Psychiat & Neurol, dipl, 66. *Prof Exp:* Assoc prof psychiat, Nat Defense Med Col, 61-63. *Concurrent Pos:* Chief neuropsychiat, Taiwan Vet Gen Hosp, 61-63; consult, var ment health ctr & hosps, 68-79; sr fel, Ctr Study Aging Human Develop, 75. *Mem:* Am Med Asn; fel Am Psychiat Asn; Am Geriat Soc; fel Geront Soc Am. *Res:* Mental health and mental disorders in the elderly; relationship between changes of brain function and behaviors associated with aging; noninvasive Xenon inhalation method for the determination of regional cerebral blood flow. *Mailing Add:* 2832 McDowell Rd Durham NC 27705

**WANG, HSUEH-HWA,** PHARMACOLOGY, PHYSIOLOGY. *Current Pos:* From assoc prof to prof, 70-90, EMER PROF PHARMACOL, COL PHYSICIANS & SURGEONS, COLUMBIA UNIV, 90- *Personal Data:* b Peiping, China, July 10, 23; US citizen; m 48, Shis-Hsun Ngai; c Mae, Janet & John. *Educ:* Nat Cent Univ, Nanking, China, MB, 46. *Honors & Awards:* Outstanding Woman Scientist, Am Women Sci, 91. *Concurrent Pos:* NY Heart fel, 53-54. *Mem:* AAAS; Am Physiol Soc; Am Soc Pharmacol & Exp Therapeut. *Res:* Coronary circulation; effects of endogenous mediators (prostaglandins, antidiuretic hormone, angiotensin) on peripheral circulation and blood pressure control. *Mailing Add:* 281 Edgewood Ave Teaneck NJ 07666

**WANG, HUEI-HSIANG LISA,** ENZYMOLOGY, PHARMACEUTICAL ANALYSIS. *Current Pos:* ASST PROF BIOCHEM, WINTHROP UNIV, 93- *Personal Data:* b Taiwan, July 11, 59; US citizen; m 84, Shen-Ling A; c Richard Y & Linda R. *Educ:* Nat Taiwan Univ, BS, 81, MS, 83; Univ Minn, PhD(pharmacog/biochem), 88. *Prof Exp:* Lectr, Univ Wis, 86-87; res assoc, Med Col Wis, 87-89; res scientist, Sandoz Pharmaceut, 89; assoc ed, Chem Abstr Serv, 90-93. *Mem:* Am Chem Soc. *Mailing Add:* 1076 Windermere Blvd Fishers IN 46038

**WANG, HWA-CHI,** AEROSOL PHYSICS, MICROCONTAMINATION. *Current Pos:* sr scientist, 84-92, ASSOC DIR RES, AIR LIQUIDE, 92- & CORP SCI COUN, 96- *Personal Data:* b Hsinchu, Taiwan, Nov 13, 55; US citizen; m 81, Pauline Chen; c Christine, Timothy & Jonathan. *Educ:* Nat Taiwan Univ, BS, 77; Univ Ill, Urbana, MS, 82, PhD(environ eng), 84. *Prof Exp:* Res assoc, Air & Indust Hyg Lab, 84-87. *Concurrent Pos:* Chmn, Semi Particle Task Force, 89-92; adj prof, Dept Environ Eng, Ill Inst Technol, 92-; chmn, Microcontamination Working Group, Am Asn Aerosol Res, 92-93; mem bd dirs, Midwest Chinese Environ Eng Sci Asn, 93-95. *Mem:* Am Asn Aerosol Res; Inst Environ Sci; Asn Aerosol Res; Semiconductor Equip & Mat Inst; Am Soc Testing & Mat; Europ Asn Aerosol Res. *Res:* Fine particle sampling, detection and removal in gas media; contamination control for semiconductor manufacturing, corrosion and development of standard test methods for ultrahigh purity components. *Mailing Add:* Am Air Liquide 5230 S East Ave Countryside IL 60525. *Fax:* 708-579-7833; *E-Mail:* hwa-chi. wang@airliquide.com

**WANG, JAMES C,** BIOCHEMISTRY, MOLECULAR BIOLOGY. *Current Pos:* prof, 77-88, MALLINCKRODT PROF, BIOCHEM & MOLECULAR BIOL, HARVARD UNIV, 88- *Personal Data:* b China, Nov 18, 36; m 61, Sophia S Hwang; c Janice S & Jessica A. *Educ:* Nat Taiwan Univ, BS, 59; Univ SDak, MA, 61; Univ Mo, PhD(chem), 64. *Hon Degrees:* MA, Harvard Univ, 77. *Honors & Awards:* Nat Acad Sci Award Molecular Biol, 83. *Prof Exp:* Res fel chem, Calif Inst Technol, 64-66; from asst prof to prof chem, Univ Calif, Berkeley, 66-77. *Concurrent Pos:* Mem biophys & biochem study sect, NIH, 72-76; mem adv comt physiol, cellular & molecular biol, NSF, 80-82; mem molecular biol study sect, NIH, 88-91, chair, 91-92. *Mem:* Nat Acad Sci; Biophys Soc; Am Acad Arts & Sci; Am Soc Biol Chem; AAAS. *Res:* Structures and functions of DNAs and enzymes involoved in DNA transactions. *Mailing Add:* Dept Molecular & Cell Biol Harvard Univ Cambridge MA 02138. *Fax:* 617-495-0758

**WANG, JAMES LI-MING,** ANALYSIS. *Current Pos:* From asst prof to assoc prof, 76-85, PROF MATH, UNIV ALA, 85- *Personal Data:* b Nan-King, China, June 25, 46; m, Ai-Shen Chao; c Ming, Ning & Ping. *Educ:* Brown Univ, PhD(math), 74. *Mem:* Fel Am Math Soc. *Mailing Add:* Dept Math Univ Ala PO Box 870350 Tuscaloosa AL 35487-0350

**WANG, JAMES TING-SHUN,** STRUCTURAL MECHANICS. *Current Pos:* from asst prof to prof eng mech, 61-86, prof civil eng, 86-92, EMER PROF ENG MECH, GA INST TECHNOL, 92- *Personal Data:* b Nanking, China, Feb 8, 31; US citizen; m 63, Elaine Woo; c Caroline W, Sophia W & Irene W. *Educ:* Nat Taiwan Univ, BS, 54; Univ Kans, MS, 58; Purdue Univ, PhD(civil eng), 61. *Honors & Awards:* Sr US Scientist Award, Alexander von Humboldt Found, Ger. *Prof Exp:* Instr eng mech, Univ Kans, 56-58. *Concurrent Pos:* Spec lectr, George Washington Univ, 63; consult, Lockheed-Ga Co, 65-66 & 76-87; aircraft develop engr specialist, 66-67. *Mem:* Am Soc Civil Engrs; Am Soc Eng Educ; Am Acad Mech; Sigma Xi. *Res:* Structural mechanics; analysis. *Mailing Add:* Sch Civil & Environ Eng Ga Inst Technol Atlanta GA 30332

**WANG, JASON TSONG-LI,** DATA & KNOWLEDGE MANAGEMENT SYSTEMS. *Current Pos:* ASST PROF & DIR, DATA & KNOWLEDGE ENG LAB, DEPT COMPUT & INFO SCI, NJ INST TECHNOL. *Educ:* NY Univ, PhD(comput sci), 91. *Mem:* NY Acad Sci; Asn Comput Mach; Inst Elec & Electronics Engrs; Am Asn Artificial Intel; Soc Indust & Appl Math. *Res:* Data and knowledge management systems, scientific and multimedia information retrieval, software development, pattern discovery and computational biology. *Mailing Add:* Dept Comput & Info Sci NJ Inst Technol University Heights Newark NJ 07102

**WANG, JAW-KAI,** AGRICULTURAL ENGINEERING, BIO-ENGINEERING. *Current Pos:* from asst prof to assoc prof agr eng, Univ Hawaii, 59-68, chmn dept, 64-75, prof agr eng, 68-96, PROF BIOSYST ENG, UNIV HAWAII, 96- *Personal Data:* b Nanjing, China, Mar 4, 32; div; c Angela Chia-chen, Dora Chia-chi & Lawrence Chia-Yen. *Educ:* Nat Taiwan Univ, BSAE, 53; Mich State Univ, MSAE, 56, PhD, 58. *Honors & Awards:* Engr of the Yr Award, ASAE, Pac Region, 76; Kishida Int Award, Am Soc Agr Engrs, 91. *Prof Exp:* Lectr farm mach, Prov Taoyaun Agr Inst, 54-55; asst farm processing, Mich State Univ, 55-58. *Concurrent Pos:* Consult, US Army, Okinawa, 65, Taiwan Sugar Co, 67, Int Rice Res Inst, 71, Pac Concrete & Rock Co, 74, USAID, 73, The World Bank, 81 & 82, ABA Int, 81-85, Univ Tankship, Del, 80 & 81, Food & Agr Orgn/UN, 83, County of Maui, 84 & US Dept State, 85; sr fel, Food Inst, East-West Ctr, 73-74; co-dir, Int Sci & Educ Coun, 79; vis assoc dir, Int Prog & Studies Off, Nat Asn State Univ & land-grant col, 79; vis prof, Nat Taiwan Univ, 64, Univ Calif, Davis, 80; mem, Expert Panel Agr Mechanization, Food & Agr Orgn, UN; pres, Aquacult Technol, Inc, 92; pres, Kona Bay Oyster & Shrimp Co, 96. *Mem:* Nat Acad Eng; fel Am Soc Agr Engrs; Chinese Soc Agr Engrs; World Mariculture Soc; Sigma Xi; Am Inst Med & Biol Eng; Nat Soc Prof Engrs. *Res:* Aquaculture production systems design, especially integrated production of oyster and shrimp; marine micro-algae production; extraction of antibacterial substances from marine micro-algae; pearl oyster. *Mailing Add:* Biosyst Engr Dept Univ Hawaii 3050 Mailu Way Rm 110 Gilmore Honolulu HI 96822. *Fax:* 808-956-9269; *E-Mail:* jawkai@hawaii.edu

**WANG, JEN YU,** METEOROLOGY. *Current Pos:* GEN MGR & PRES, MILIEU INFO SERVS INC, 89- *Personal Data:* b Foochow, China, Mar 3, 15; c 1. *Educ:* Fukien Christian Univ, China, BS, 38; Univ Chicago, cert, 54; Univ Wis, MS, 55, PhD(meteorol), 58. *Prof Exp:* Instr math & physics, Cols, China & Hong Kong, 38-42; prin meteorologist, Weather Bur, China, 42-47; assoc prof physics, Fukien Christian Univ, 47-50; asst meteorol, Weather Forecasting Res Ctr, Univ Chicago, 53-54; asst, Univ Wis, 54-57, res assoc, 57-60, asst prof, 60-64; from assoc prof to prof meteorol & dir, Environ Sci Inst, San Jose State Univ, 64-89. *Concurrent Pos:* Fel, United Bd Higher Educ Asia, US, 50-54; consult, 10th Weather Squadron, USAF, China, 45, US Weather Bur, Washington, DC, 58, AEC Proj, 65 & Stanford Res Inst, 66-67; pres, Milieu Info Serv, 71-, Blackwell Land Mgt Co, 74- & Sierra-Misco, Inc, 81- *Mem:* Am Meteorol Soc; Am Soc Agron; Int Soc Biometeorol; fel Am Geog Soc. *Res:* New techniques in the investigation of environmental relationships between animals and plants; agricultural meteorology; ecology; phenology; phytoclimatology; environmental assessment studies. *Mailing Add:* 1863 Shulman Ave San Jose CA 95124

**WANG, JERRY HSUEH-CHING,** BIOCHEMISTRY. *Current Pos:* AT DEPT BIOCHEM, UNIV CALGARY. *Personal Data:* b Nanking, China, Mar 12, 37; m 62; c 2. *Educ:* Nat Taiwan Univ, BSc, 58; Iowa State Univ, PhD(biochem), 65. *Prof Exp:* From asst prof to assoc prof, Univ Man, 66-78, prof biochem, Fac Med, 78- *Concurrent Pos:* Nat Res Coun Can fel biochem, 65-66; Med Res Coun scholar, 66- *Mem:* Can Biochem Soc; Am Soc Biol Chemists. *Res:* Quaternary structure and regulatory property of enzymes. *Mailing Add:* Dept Med Biochem Health Sci Ctr Univ Calgary 3330 Hospital Dr NW Calgary AB T2N 4N1 Can

**WANG, JI,** PIEZOELECTRICITY, VIBRATIONS OF PLATES. *Current Pos:* SR MEM TECH STAFF, EPSON PALO ALTO LAB, 95- *Personal Data:* b Huixian, Gansu, China, Nov 4, 62; m. *Educ:* Gansu Polytech Univ, BSc Eng, 83; Princeton Univ, MS, 93, PhD(civil eng), 96. *Prof Exp:* Res engr, 11th Inst Proj Planning & Res, Xi'an, China, 83-88; vis res staff, Argonne Nat Lab, 88-90. *Mem:* Sigma Xi; Inst Elec & Electronics Engrs. *Res:* Piezoelectricity theory and its applications in vibration analysis of crystal plates and quartz crystal resonators; finite element analysis of anisotropic and piezoelectric plates; wave propagation in piezoelectric plates and devices. *Mailing Add:* 3145 Porter Dr Suite 104 Palo Alto CA 94304-1224. *Fax:* 650-843-9106; *E-Mail:* jiwang@epal.com

**WANG, JI CHING,** ENGINEERING SCIENCE. *Current Pos:* from asst prof to assoc prof, 69-82, PROF MECH ENG, SAN JOSE STATE UNIV, 82- *Personal Data:* b Kobe, Japan, Nov 29, 38; m 71, Elaine T; c 2. *Educ:* Osaka Inst Technol, BS, 61; Univ Calif, Berkeley, MS, 65, PhD(mech eng), 69. *Prof Exp:* Design engr, Shinippon Koki, Japan, 61-62; res asst mech eng, Univ Calif, Berkeley, 64-66; res engr, Kaiser Eng, 66-67. *Concurrent Pos:* NSF grants, 70-71; consult, Ames Res Ctr, NASA, 70-71 & 74-91, res grants, 77-91; res engr, Ford Aerospace, 75-76; res grant, CONTECT, 84-91, Westinghouse, 89-91, Gen Elec, 91-94. *Mem:* Inst Elec & Electronics Engrs; Am Soc Mech Engrs; Am Soc Mfg Engrs. *Res:* System control engineering: theory and application of control theory in aircraft; robotics; process control. *Mailing Add:* 24815 Papaya St Hayward CA 94545. *Fax:* 408-924-3995

**WANG, JIA-CHAO,** SOLID STATE PHYSICS, THEORETICAL PHYSICS. *Current Pos:* STAFF MEM, SOLID STATE DIV, OAK RIDGE NAT LAB, 77- *Personal Data:* b China, Mar 17, 39; m 66; c 2. *Educ:* Tunghai Univ, BS, 62; Nat Chiao Tung Univ, Taiwan, MS, 65; Univ NC, PhD(physics), 73. *Prof*

*Exp:* Res assoc, Dept Physics & Astron, Univ NC, 73-75 & Wright-Patterson AFB, 75-77. *Concurrent Pos:* Res assoc, Nat Res Coun, 75-77. *Mem:* Am Phys Soc; Electrochem Soc; Sigma Xi; Sci Res Soc. *Res:* Solid electrolytes or superionic conductors; laser annealing of ion-implanted semiconductors; electronic density of states of disordered systems. *Mailing Add:* Oak Ridge Nat Lab Bldg 4500N MS 6185 Eng Div Oak Ridge TN 37831. *Fax:* 423-574-5788

**WANG, JIN TSAI,** INORGANIC CHEMISTRY, ANALYTICAL CHEMISTRY. *Current Pos:* RES CHEMIST, BIOPHARMACEUT RES BR, FOOD & DRUG ADMIN, WASHINGTON, DC, 87- *Personal Data:* b Inchon, Korea, Apr 7, 31; US citizen; m 58; c 2. *Educ:* Ore State Univ, BS, 57; Carnegie Inst Technol, PhD(chem), 68. *Prof Exp:* Instr, Pa State Univ, 68; from asst prof to assoc prof chem, Duquesne Univ, 77-87. *Concurrent Pos:* Vis scientist, NIH, 74, 79 & 85. *Mem:* Am Chem Soc; Soc Asian Comp Philos. *Res:* Infrared and polarographic studies of metal complexes. *Mailing Add:* Food & Drug Admin-HFD 424 200 C St SW Washington DC 20204

**WANG, JIN-LIANG,** FLAME RETARDANT POLYMERS, LATICES & COATINGS. *Current Pos:* PROJ LEADER, GREAT LAKES CHEM CORP, 88- *Personal Data:* b Chu-Nan, Taiwan, Aug 18, 37; US citizen; m, Grace Y Feng; c Lucy, Samuel & Eliza. *Educ:* Taipei Inst Technol, dipl, 58; Kent State Univ, MS, 66; Univ Akron, PhD(polymer chem), 71. *Prof Exp:* Sr chem engr, Hua-Min Paper Mill, Taiwan, 60-61; sr res chem engr, Taiwan Prov Tobacco & Wine Monopoly Bur, 61-63; sr res chemist, Res Div, Goodyear Tire & Rubber Co, 66-87. *Concurrent Pos:* Part-time teaching, Univ Akron, 71-86. *Mem:* Am Chem Soc; Sigma Xi. *Res:* Polymer synthesis compounding, characterization and applications; grafting of latices and polymers; crosslinked latices and polymers; compatibility and impact modification; block polymers; polymer addivitves; UV stabilized. *Mailing Add:* 2406 River Oaks Dr Lafayette IN 47905. *Fax:* 765-497-6304

**WANG, JOHN L,** BIOCHEMISTRY. *Current Pos:* assoc prof, 81-84, PROF BIOCHEM, MICH STATE UNIV, 85- *Personal Data:* b Hunan, China, Oct 1, 46. *Educ:* Rockefeller Univ, PhD(biochem), 73. *Mailing Add:* Dept Biochem Mich State Univ East Lansing MI 48824-1319. *Fax:* 517-353-9334

**WANG, JOHN LING-FAI,** physical chemistry, chemical metallurgy, for more information see previous edition

**WANG, JOHNSON C T,** PHYSICAL MATHEMATICS, ROCKET PROPULSIONS. *Current Pos:* SR ENG SPECIALIST, AEROSPACE CORP, 84- *Personal Data:* b Chia-yi, China, May 20, 38; US citizen; m, Jin-Chen C; c David J & Jaime J. *Educ:* Nat Taiwan Univ, BS & MS, 66; Mass Inst Technol, MS, 67; Purdue Univ, PhD(aeronaut & astronaut), 72. *Prof Exp:* Postdoctoral fel, Cornell Univ, 73-76; eng specialist, Garrett AiResearch, Phoenix, 76-78; mem tech staff, Los Alamos Nat Labs, 78-79; sr consult scientist, Avco Systs Div, 79-84. *Concurrent Pos:* Vis adj fac, Calif Inst Technol, 91- *Mem:* Soc Indust & Appl Math. *Res:* Development of computational algorithm and code for multi-dimensional compressible Navier-stokes equations; applications of the code to launch vehicles of complex configurations such as Titan IV and Delta II rockets. *Mailing Add:* 30926 Oceangrove Dr Rancho Palos Verdes CA 90275. *Fax:* 310-336-2098; *E-Mail:* wang@couriers.aero.org

**WANG, JOHNSON JENN-HWA,** COMPUTER SOLUTION OF ELECTROMAGNETIC PROBLEMS, ANTENNAS. *Current Pos:* sr res engr, 75-80, br head, 85-88, PRIN RES ENGR, GA INST TECHNOL, 80-, ADJ PROF, 88- *Personal Data:* b Hunan, China, Oct 24, 38; US citizen; m 68; c John & Michael. *Educ:* Nat Taiwan Univ, BS, 62; Fla State Univ, MS, 65; Ohio State Univ, PhD(elec eng), 68. *Prof Exp:* Prof staff mem, TRW Systs, 69-70; sr engr, Motorola, 70-73; mem tech staff, Tex Instruments, 73-75. *Concurrent Pos:* Pres, Wang-Tripp Corp, 91- *Mem:* Inst Elec & Electronics Engrs; Sigma Xi; Electromagnetics Acad; L'Union Radio Scientist Int. *Res:* Electromagnetic theory; numerical analysis using digital computers; antennas; scattering; bioelectromagnetics; electromagnetic radiation hazard; electromagnetic interference; electromagnetic compatibility; microwave imaging. *Mailing Add:* 445 Cove Dr Marietta GA 30067. *Fax:* 404-984-9045

**WANG, JON Y,** LASER RADAR TECHNOLOGY, INFRARED SYSTEM ENGINEERING. *Current Pos:* SCIENTIST ENG, HUGHES MISSILE SYSTS CO, 93- *Personal Data:* b Tainan, Taiwan, June 22, 43; US citizen; m 71; c 1. *Educ:* Nat Taiwan Univ, BS, 65; Mass Inst Technol, MS, 68; Purdue Univ, PhD(aerophys & astrophys), 71. *Prof Exp:* Sr res engr electro optics, Gen Dynamics Convair Div, 71-73; staff scientist, Sci Applns, Inc, 73-75; eng staff specialist electro optics, Gen Dynamics Convair Div, 75-93. *Mem:* Optical Soc Am; Am Inst Physics. *Res:* Electro-optics; atmospheric propagation; laser radar applications; sensor system modelings; publications in science journals. *Mailing Add:* Hughes Missile Systs Co Bldg No 847 MS B-7 PO Box 11337 Tucson AZ 85734

**WANG, JOSEPH,** CHEMISTRY. *Current Pos:* From asst prof to assoc prof, 80-88, PROF CHEM, NMEX STATE UNIV, 88- *Personal Data:* b Haifa, Israel; US citizen; m 76, Ruth; c Sharon. *Educ:* Israel Inst Technol, PhD(chem), 78. *Honors & Awards:* Heyrovsky Medal, Czech Repub, 94. *Concurrent Pos:* Chief ed, Electroanal. *Mem:* Am Chem Soc; Electrochem Soc; Soc Electroanal Chem. *Res:* Design and development of electrochemical sensors; author of 400 papers and 4 books. *Mailing Add:* Dept Chem NMex State Univ Las Cruces NM 88003

**WANG, JUI HSIN,** BIOCHEMISTRY & SUPERCONDUCTORS. *Current Pos:* EINSTEIN PROF SCI, STATE UNIV NY, BUFFALO, 72- *Personal Data:* b Peking, China, Mar 16, 21; nat US; wid; c Jane & Nancy. *Educ:* Nat Southwest Assoc Univ, China, BSc, 45; Wash Univ, PhD(chem), 49. *Hon Degrees:* MA, Yale Univ, 60. *Prof Exp:* Fel radiochem, Wash Univ, 49-51; res fel chem, Yale Univ, 51-52, res asst, 52-53, from instr to prof, 53-62, Eugene Higgins, prof chem & molecular biophysics, 62-72. *Concurrent Pos:* Guggenheim fel, Cambridge Univ, 60-61, Yale Univ, 71-72; mem biophys & biochem study sect, NIH, 65-69; Kennedy lectr, Washington Univ, 72; distinguished vis prof, Mich State Univ, 60, 69 & 80; mem Acad Sinica & sci adv, Inst Chem & Inst Biol Chem Acad Sinica. *Mem:* AAAS; Am Chem Soc; Am Soc Biol Chemists; Am Acad Ar; Am Phys Soc; Biophys Soc. *Res:* Diffusion in liquids; hemoglobin; mechanisms of enzyme action, particularly those related to oxidative phosphorylation, photosynthesis and ion-transport through biological membranes; electrochemistry; superconductivity; kinases; reverse transcriptases; antiviral agents. *Mailing Add:* NSM Complex State Univ NY Buffalo NY 14260-3000. *Fax:* 716-645-6949

**WANG, JUN,** NEURAL NETWORKS, CONTROL & MANUFACTURING SYSTEMS. *Current Pos:* asst prof, 90-93, ASSOC PROF INDUST TECHNOL, UNIV NDAK, 93- *Personal Data:* b Dalian, China, July 11, 54; m 84, Li Jin; c Shuo. *Educ:* Dalian Univ Technol, BS, 82, MS, 85; Case Western Res Univ, PhD(systs eng), 91. *Prof Exp:* Instr elec eng, Dalian Univ Technol, 85-86; teaching & res asst, Case Western Res Univ, 86-89; CAD programmer, Zagar, Inc, 89-90. *Concurrent Pos:* Prin investr, Exp Prog Stimulate Competitive Res, NSF, 92-95. *Mem:* Sr mem Inst Elec & Electronics Engrs; sr mem Inst Indust Engrs; Opers Res Soc Am; Int Neural Network Soc. *Res:* Theory, methodology and applications of artificial neural networks to electronic, control and manufacturing systems. *Mailing Add:* Univ NDak PO Box 7118 Grand Forks ND 58202-7118. *Fax:* 701-777-4320; *E-Mail:* jwang@plains.nodak.edu

**WANG, K P,** MINING ENGINEERING, METALLURGICAL ENGINEERING. *Current Pos:* PRES, K P WANG ASSOCS, 80- *Personal Data:* b China, Mar 11, 19; nat US; m 66, Rose Kwang; c Michael C. *Educ:* Yenching Univ, China, BS, 40; Mo Sch Mines, BS, 42; Columbia Univ, MS, 43, PhD(mining), 46; Int Col Armed Forces, res grad, 61. *Prof Exp:* Jr engr, Wah Chong Corp, 42 & Hudson Coal Co, 43-44; supvr, NJ Zinc Co, 44-45; engr, Warren Pipe & Foundry Corp, 46; chief engr & asst gen mgr, Ping-Hsing Coal Co, 46-48; prof, Peiyang Univ, 48; chief specialist int activ, US Bur Mines, 60-69, supvry phys scientist nonmetallic minerals, 70-75, supvry phys scientist Asia minerals, 75-80. *Concurrent Pos:* Prof mining engr, Mo Sch Mines, 61; part-time asst to sci adv, Dept Interior, 64-67; adj assoc prof, Krumb Sch Mines, Columbia Univ, 67-70; consult to UN, 69-71, Pennzoil, 80-84, Mitsubishi, 87-, Kreri Co, Korea. *Mem:* Am Inst Mining, Metall & Petrol Engrs; Sigma Xi. *Res:* Mineral economics; international natural resources, particularly in developing countries. *Mailing Add:* 1573 Warrington St Winter Springs FL 32708. *Fax:* 407-359-5898

**WANG, KANG-LUNG,** ELECTRICAL ENGINEERING, SEMICONDUCTOR PHYSICS & DEVICES. *Current Pos:* assoc prof, 79-82, PROF, ENG DEPT, UNIV CALIF, LOS ANGELES, 82- *Personal Data:* b China, July 3, 41; m 68; c 3. *Educ:* Cheng Kung Univ, Taiwan, BS, 64; Mass Inst Technol, MS, 66, PhD(elec eng), 70. *Prof Exp:* Res assoc, Div Sponsored Res, Mass Inst Technol, 70-71; asst prof elec eng, 71-72; scientist, Res & Develop Ctr, Gen Elec Co, 72-79. *Concurrent Pos:* Adj prof, Physics Dept, State Univ NY Albany; consult, Xerox Corp, El Segundo, Calif, Rockwell Int, Thousand Oaks, Calif, Jet Propulsion Lab, Calif Inst Technol & Hughes Aircraft, Areospace, Inc; Guggenheim Fel & Hon Prof, Xi'an Jiaotong Univ, Peoples Repub China. *Mem:* Inst Elec & Electronics Engrs; Am Phys Soc; Am Vacuum Soc; Sigma Xi. *Res:* Semiconductor physics and devices; quantum wells and superlattices; molecular beam epitaxy of SiGe and III-V; quantum effects in semiconductors. *Mailing Add:* 2024 Pier Ave Santa Monica CA 90405-5950

**WANG, KEN HSI,** NUCLEAR PHYSICS. *Current Pos:* asst prof, 66-69, ASSOC PROF PHYSICS, BAYLOR UNIV, 69- *Personal Data:* b Shanghai, China, July 4, 34; m 62; c 3. *Educ:* Int Christian Univ, Tokyo, BA, 58; Yale Univ, PhD(physics), 63. *Prof Exp:* Res fel physics, Harvard Univ, 63-66. *Concurrent Pos:* Assoc res scientist, Tex A&M Univ, 80-81. *Mem:* Am Phys Soc; Am Asn Physics Teachers. *Res:* Nuclear reaction and scattering. *Mailing Add:* Dept Physics Baylor Univ Waco TX 76798

**WANG, KUAN,** BIOCHEMISTRY, CELL BIOLOGY. *Current Pos:* ASSOC PROF CHEM, UNIV TEX, AUSTIN, 77- *Educ:* Yale Univ, PhD(biochem), 74. *Res:* Contracto proteins; muscle structure and function; cell motility. *Mailing Add:* Dept Chem Univ Tex Austin TX 78712. *Fax:* 512-471-4065; *E-Mail:* kw@emx.cc.utexas.edu

**WANG, KUO KING,** ENGINEERING. *Current Pos:* assoc prof, 70-77, PROF MECH ENG, CORNELL UNIV, 77- *Personal Data:* b Wutsin, China, Oct 8, 23; c 3. *Educ:* Nat Cent Univ, Nanking, BS, 47; Univ Wis-Madison, MS, 62, PhD(mech eng), 68. *Honors & Awards:* Blackall Award, Am Soc Mech Engrs, 68, William T Ennor Mfg Technol Award, 91; Adams Mem Award, Am Welding Soc, 76; Frederick W Taylor Res Medal, Soc Mfg Engrs, 87. *Prof Exp:* Engr, Taiwan Shipbuilding Corp, 47-57; mgr eng, Ingalls-Taiwan Shipbuilding Corp, 57-60; supvr shipbuilding, United Tanker Corp, 60-61; proj engr, Walker Mfg Co, 62-66; asst prof mech eng, Univ Wis-Madison, 68-70. *Concurrent Pos:* Consult, Xomox Corp, Gen Elec Co, TRW Inc, Polaroid Corp & Gillette Co; TRW fel mfg eng, TRW Found, 77; mem, Int Inst Prod Eng Res, 85- *Mem:* Nat Acad Eng; fel Am Welding Soc; fel Soc Mfg Engrs; fel Am Soc Mech Engrs; Am Soc Metals Int; Soc Plastics Engrs;

Polymer Processing Soc. *Res:* Materials processing; numerical control; author of over 100 publications and several book chapters; recipient of one patent. *Mailing Add:* Sch Mech Eng-Aero Eng Cornell Univ Upson Hall Ithaca NY 14853. *Fax:* 607-254-4588; *E-Mail:* kkwi@cornel.edu

**WANG, LAWRENCE CHIA-HUANG,** PHYSIOLOGY, ZOOLOGY. *Current Pos:* from asst prof to assoc prof, Univ Alta, 70-80, McCalla prof, 83-84, prof-in-residence, 84-85, PROF ZOOL, UNIV ALTA, 80- *Personal Data:* b Wusih, China, Apr 5, 40; m 66. *Educ:* Taiwan Norm Univ, BSc, 63; Rice Univ, MA, 67; Cornell Univ, PhD(physiol), 70. *Prof Exp:* Vis asst prof biol, Univ Ore, 69-70. *Concurrent Pos:* Operating grant, Nat Res Coun Can, 71-, Nat Defense Res Bd Can, 73-76 & Nat Defense Can, 80- *Mem:* AAAS; Can Soc Zool; Can Physiol Soc; Soc Cryobiol; Am Soc Zoologists; Int Hibernation Soc. *Res:* Physiology of temperature regulation; hypothermia and hibernation in mammals. *Mailing Add:* Dept Biol Sci Univ Alberta Edmonton AB T6G 2E9 Can

**WANG, LAWRENCE K,** WATER & WASTE WATER TREATMENT, HAZARDOUS WASTE DISPOSAL. *Current Pos:* vpres, 88-97, ACTG PRES, ZOREX CORP, 97- *Personal Data:* b China, Nov 20, 40; c 3. *Educ:* Nat Cheng Kung Univ, BE, 62; Univ Mo, Rolla, ME, 65; Univ RI, MS, 67; Rutgers Univ, PhD(environ eng), 72. *Honors & Awards:* Drinking Water Award, Taiwan, China, 86. *Prof Exp:* Res asst civil eng, Univ Mo, 65-66, environ eng, Univ RI, 66-67; res fel, Rutgers Univ, 67-70; civil engr, Hackensack Water Co, 70-71; proj mgr consult eng, Calspan Corp, 71-74; asst prof chem eng, Rennselaer Polytech Inst, 74-77; mech eng, Stevens Inst Technol, 77-81; dir environ eng, Lenox Inst Res, 81-88. *Concurrent Pos:* Sr sanit engr, NY State Dept Environ Conserv, 74-77; examr, Nat Coun Eng Examrs, 74-81; eng consult, US Environ Protection Agency, 77-81, Krofta Eng Corp, 80-; assoc ed, Pergamon Press, 78-81; chmn, Stand Method Subcomt, Am Water Works Asn, 80-85; vis prof, Nat Cheng Kung Univ, Taiwan, 82-86, Chekiang Univ, China, 86-; Water Oper Training Prog, New Eng Water Works Asn, 84-87; task group, Nat Sanit Found, 85-87. *Mem:* Am Acad Environ Engrs; Am Water Works Asn; Am Inst Chem Engrs (treas, 86-87); Nat Sanit Found; Overseas Environ Engrs & Scientists Asn (pres, 88-90). *Res:* Conducting research areas of drinking water, industrial wastes; domestic sewage, hazardous wastes, acid rain and cooling tower; authored 5 books and over 600 journal reports on environmental engineering; granted 3 US patents. *Mailing Add:* Zorex Corp 1223 People Ave Troy NY 12180

**WANG, LEON RU-LIANG,** STRUCTURAL ENGINEERING. *Current Pos:* chmn dept, 84-90, prof, 84-95, EMER PROF, OLD DOM UNIV, 95- *Personal Data:* b Canton, China, June 15, 32; US citizen; m 61, Joyce Tien; c 3. *Educ:* Cheng Kung Univ, Taiwan, BS, 57; Univ Ill, MS, 61; Mass Inst Technol, ScD(struct), 65. *Prof Exp:* Res asst struct eng, Mass Inst Technol, 61-65, res engr, 65; asst prof struct, Rensselaer Polytech Inst, 65-69, assoc prof, 69-80; prof civil eng, Univ Okla, 80-84. *Concurrent Pos:* Tech consult, Watervliet Arsenal, 66-80 & Nat Sci Coun, Taiwan, 75-; lectr, Am Inst Steel Construct, 69 & 71; NSF vis scientist, Cheng Kung Univ, Taiwan, 72-73; tech rev, NSF, 76-; vis scholar, Pub Works Res Inst, Japan, 81, Toyohashi Univ Technol, Japan, 86; adj prof, Dept Civil & Struct Eng, Hong Kong Univ Sci & Technol, 93-95. *Mem:* AAAS; Am Concrete Inst; Am Soc Civil Engrs; Am Soc Eng Educ; Chinese Inst Eng; Earthquake Eng Res Inst; Hong Kong Inst Engrs. *Res:* Structural mechanics; dynamics; stability; buckling; computer applications; model analysis; plate and shell theories; steel and reinforced concrete construction; earthquake engineering; lifeline earthquake engineering. *Mailing Add:* Civil Eng Dept Old Dom Univ Norfolk VA 23529-0241

**WANG, LING JUN,** LASER SPECTOSCOPY OF GASES & SURFACES, SCATTERING OF HIGHLY IONIZED HEAVY IONS. *Current Pos:* asst prof, 90-92, ASSOC PROF PHYSICS, UNIV TENN, CHATTANOOGA, 92- *Personal Data:* b Jian Xi, China, Dec 4, 46; US citizen; m 77, Bihua Liu; c Peter Z & Amy E. *Educ:* Southeastern Mass Univ, MS, 81; Univ Del, PhD(physics), 84. *Prof Exp:* Postdoctoral res assoc, Wesleyan Univ, 84-86, Oak Ridge Nat Lab, 86-87; res asst prof, Vanderbilt Univ, 87-90. *Concurrent Pos:* Adj prof physics, Fisk Univ, 89; vis prof, Battelle NW Lab, 90; vis scientist, Argonne Nat Lab, 91, Oak Ridge Nat Lab, 92, 95 & 96; fac researcher, Marshall Space Ctr, NASA, 97. *Res:* Spectroscopic studies of materials in gaseous and solid phases and materials manufactured in microgravity environments as compared to that manufactured on the earth. *Mailing Add:* Dept Phys Univ Tenn Chattanooga TN 37403. *Fax:* 423-755-4279; *E-Mail:* lingjun__wang@utc.edu

**WANG, LIN-SHU,** INTERNAL COMBUSTION ENGINES, ENERGY CONVERSION. *Current Pos:* From asst prof to assoc prof eng, 65-72, ASSOC PROF MECH ENG, STATE UNIV NY, STONY BROOK, 72- *Personal Data:* b Shanghai, China, Feb 14, 38; US citizen; m 65, Ming Liu; c 2. *Educ:* Univ Calif, Berkeley, PhD(eng), 66. *Concurrent Pos:* Vis mem, Ctr Earth & Planetary Physics, Harvard Univ, 72; founder & pres, Intercool Develop, Ltd, 87- *Mem:* Sigma Xi; Soc Automotive Engrs; Am Soc Mech Engrs. *Res:* Internal combustion engines; intercooled-supercharged power cycles; thermodynamics; turbulent fluid flow and atmospheric dynamics. *Mailing Add:* Dept Mech Eng State Univ NY Stony Brook NY 11794. *Fax:* 516-632-8544

**WANG, MARIAN M,** NUTRITION. *Current Pos:* ASSOC PROF NUTRIT, UNIV GA, 79- *Personal Data:* b Funkien, China, June 20, 28. *Educ:* Pa State Univ, PhD(nutrit), 60. *Mem:* Am Inst Nutrit; Inst Food Technologists; Am Dietary Asn. *Mailing Add:* Dept Food & Nutrit Univ Ga Dawson Hall Athens GA 30602. *Fax:* 706-542-5059

**WANG, MAW SHIU,** AGRONOMY, SPECTROCHEMISTRY. *Current Pos:* RETIRED. *Personal Data:* b Chang Hwa, Formosa, Nov 1, 25; m 51; c 3. *Educ:* Prov Agr Col, Formosa, BS, 51; Okla State Univ, MS, 56; Univ Ill, PhD, 59. *Honors & Awards:* Megger's Award, Soc Appl Spectros, 73. *Prof Exp:* Jr engr, Chem Lab, Pingtong Sugar Exp Sta, Formosa, 51-54; asst soil chem, Univ Ill, Urbana, 55-59, res assoc, 59-61; sr res chemist, Cent Res Dept, Monsanto Co, 61-68, res specialist, 68-77, fel, 78-91. *Concurrent Pos:* Adj prof, St Louis Univ, 70- *Mem:* Am Soc Testing & Mat; Soc Appl Spectros; Sigma Xi. *Res:* Emission spectroscopy; spectrochemical analysis of major and minor elements in agricultural material; traces in semiconductors and related materials; surface analysis, cleaning, and packaging of semiconductors. *Mailing Add:* 14037 Boxford Ct Chesterfield MO 63017-3452

**WANG, MICHAEL QUANLU,** AIR POLLUTION, TRANSPORTATION ENERGY. *Current Pos:* ENVIRON ENGR, ARGONNE NAT LAB, 93- *Personal Data:* b Baoji, Shanxxi, China, June 7, 61; m 87, Susan; c Jason. *Educ:* Beijing Agr Univ, China, BS, 82; Univ Calif, Davis, MS, 89, PhD(environ sci), 92. *Prof Exp:* Researcher, Oak Ridge Nat Lab, 91-92; asst res engr, Univ Calif, Davis, 92-93. *Mem:* Soc Automotive Engrs; Air & Waste Mgt Asn; Transp Res Bd. *Res:* Transportation-related air pollution and energy issues; long-term solutions to transportation air pollution and energy insecurity problems. *Mailing Add:* Argonne Nat Lab Bldg 362 Rm B215 Argonne IL 60439. *E-Mail:* mqwang@anl.gov

**WANG, MICHAEL RENXUN,** integrated optics, optoelectronic interconnects, for more information see previous edition

**WANG, MUHAO S,** ENVIRONMENTAL MANAGEMENT ENGINEERING. *Current Pos:* SR SANIT ENG, NY STATE DEPT ENVIRON CONSERV, 72- *Personal Data:* b China, Jan 29, 42; US citizen; m 68; c 3. *Educ:* Nat Cheng Kung Univ, China, BE, 65; Univ RI, MS, 68, Rutgers Univ, New Brunswick, PhD(environ eng), 72. *Prof Exp:* Civil engr, Sino-Am Eng Corp, 65-66; res asst environ eng, Univ RI, 66-68; res fel, Rutgers Univ, 68-72. *Concurrent Pos:* Consult, Calsban Corp, Buffalo, 71-74; dipl, Am Acad Environ Engrs; vis prof, Nat Cheng Kung Univ, Taiwan, 81-86 & Lenox Inst Res, Mass, 81-; ed, Humana Press, Clifton, NJ, 86- *Mem:* Overseas Chinese Environ Engrs & Scientists Asn; Asn Environ Eng Prof; Water Pollution Control Fedn; Chinese Inst Engrs. *Res:* Environmental management; stream pollution; industrial wastes; solid wastes; harzadous wastes. *Mailing Add:* 1 Dawn Dr Latham NY 12110

**WANG, NAI-SAN,** PULMINARY PATHOLOGY, DIAGNOSTIC ELECTRON MICROSCOPY. *Current Pos:* PROF PATH, UNIV CALIF, IRVINE, 90- *Personal Data:* b Changhua, Taiwan, Jan 20, 36; Can citizen; m 63, Ruey-Suey How; c Beatrice, Annabel, Arthur & Emily. *Educ:* Nat Taiwan Univ, MD, 60; McGill Univ, MS, 69, PhD(path), 71. *Prof Exp:* Teaching & res fel path, McGill Univ, 67-71, from asst prof to prof, 71-90. *Concurrent Pos:* Consult, Mesothelioma Ref Panel Can, Tumor Ref Ctr, 74-81. *Mem:* Am Asn Pathologists; Am Thoracic Soc; Can Thoracic Soc; Int Asn Pathologists. *Res:* Ultrastructural studies of the lung and pleura in normal and diseased conditions. *Mailing Add:* Dept Path Univ Calif Irvine Med Ctr 101 The City Dr Orange CA 92668. *Fax:* 714-456-5873; *E-Mail:* nwangt@uci.edu

**WANG, NANCY YANG,** ORGANIC CHEMISTRY. *Current Pos:* RETIRED. *Personal Data:* b Peiping, China, Jan 20, 26; m 49; c 1. *Educ:* Cath Univ, Peiping, BS, 45; St Louis Univ, MS, 51; Boston Univ, PhD(org chem), 65. *Prof Exp:* Fel biol, Mass Inst Technol, 64-65, fel nutrit, 65-66, res assoc chem, 66-68; res assoc, Retina Found, Boston Univ, 68-71; res assoc, Univ Mass, Boston, 71-73, lectr, 73-75, res assoc chem, 75-82. *Mem:* Sigma Xi. *Res:* Biochemistry and organic reaction mechanisms. *Mailing Add:* 106 Pleasant St Lexington MA 02173

**WANG, PAO-KUAN,** CLOUD PHYSICS, AEROSOL PHYSICS & TECHNOLOGY. *Current Pos:* from asst prof to assoc prof, 80-88, PROF METEOROL, UNIV WIS-MADISON, 88- *Personal Data:* b Tainan, Taiwan, Dec 1, 49; m 76, Li-Bi Tseng; c Lawrence C & Victor C. *Educ:* Nat Taiwan Univ, BS, 71; Univ Calif, Los Angeles, MS, 75, PhD(atmospheric sci), 78. *Honors & Awards:* Humboldt Sr Res Award, 93. *Prof Exp:* Res atmospheric physicist, Univ Calif, Los Angeles, 78-80, adj asst prof, 80. *Concurrent Pos:* Prin investr res projs, Environ Protection Agency, 81-, NSF, 82-, Dept Energy, 90-92; mem, Sci Rev Panel Atmospheric Physics & Chem, Environ Protection Agency, 82-; consult, Nelson Industs Inc, 87-; mem, Cloud Physics Comt, Am Meterol Soc, 90-, chmn, 91-93; S C Johnson Distinguished fel, 93; vis prof, Johannes Gutenberg Univ, Ger, 93, Nat Taiwan Univ, 93 & Mass Inst Technol, 97. *Mem:* Am Meteorol Soc; AAAS; Am Geophys Union; Am Asn Aerosol Res; Royal Meteorol Soc UK. *Res:* Aerosol physics; cloud and precipitation physics; atmospheric electricity; particle technology; cloud dynamics; atmospheric chemistry; historical climatology; aerosol filtration. *Mailing Add:* Dept Atmospheric & Oceanic Sci Univ Wis 1225 W Dayton St Madison WI 53706

**WANG, PAUL KENG CHIEH,** CONTROL OF DISTRIBUTED-PARAMETER SYSTEMS, MICROROBOTICS. *Current Pos:* assoc prof, 67-73, PROF ELEC ENG, UNIV CALIF, LOS ANGELES, 73- *Personal Data:* b Nanking, China, July 23, 34; US citizen. *Educ:* Calif Inst Technol, BS, 55, MS, 56; Univ Calif, Berkeley, PhD(elec eng), 60. *Prof Exp:* Mem res staff, Int Bus Mach Res Lab, San Jose, Calif, 59-64; asst prof elec eng, Univ Southern Calif, 64-67. *Concurrent Pos:* Vis res mem, Dept de Physique du Plasma et de la Fusion Control, Centre d'Etude Nucleaires, Fontenay-aux-Roses, France, 74; consult, Jet Propulsion Lab, Pasadena, Calif, 81-; hon vis prof, Dept Comput & Syst Sci, Nankai Univ, Tianjin, China,

84- *Mem:* Am Phys Soc; Am Math Soc; Inst Elec & Electronics Engrs; Soc Indust & Appl Math. *Res:* Theoretical and experimental studies on the control of distributed-parameter and nonlinear dynamical systems with applications to microrobotics, micro-electromechanical and hydrodynamic systems; nonlinear systems. *Mailing Add:* Dept Elec Eng Rm 66-147L Engr IV Univ Calif Los Angeles CA 90024. *E-Mail:* pkcwang@ee.ucla.edu

**WANG, PAUL SHYH-HORNG,** SYMBOLIC MATHEMATICAL COMPUTATION, NON-NUMERICAL ALGORITHMS. *Current Pos:* assoc prof, 77-81, PROF COMPUT SCI, KENT STATE UNIV 81-, DIR RES, INST COMPUT MATH, 85- *Personal Data:* b Shensi, China, Jan 11, 44; US citizen; m 84, Jennifer S Ko; c 2. *Educ:* Taiwan Nat Chung-hsing Univ, BS, 66; Mass Inst Technol, PhD(comput sci), 71. *Prof Exp:* From lectr to asst prof comput sci, Mass Inst Technol, 71-77. *Concurrent Pos:* Consult, Hewlett-Packard Labs, 86-; prin investr, NSF grants, 87-; chmn spec interest group on symbolic & algebraic manipulation, Asn Comput Mach, 87-; vis scientist, Sandia Nat Labs, Livermore, Calif, 94. *Mem:* Asn Comput Mach. *Res:* Making the digital computer a useful tool for scientific computations. *Mailing Add:* Dept Math & Comput Sci Kent State Univ Kent OH 44242-0001. *Fax:* 330-672-7824; *E-Mail:* pwang@cs.kent.edu

**WANG, PAUL WEILY,** SURFACES OF OPTICAL MATERIALS, PROCESSES TO MANUFACTURE OPTICAL MATERIALS. *Current Pos:* asst prof, 90-96, ASSOC PROF, DEPT PHYSICS & MAT RES INST, UNIV TEX, EL PASO, 96- *Personal Data:* b Kao-Hsiung, Taiwan, Nov 4, 51; m 79, Diana Chung-Chung Chow; c Agnes, Carol & Alfred. *Educ:* Nat Taiwan Normal Univ, BS, 74; State Univ NY, Albany, MS, 81, PhD(physics), 86. *Prof Exp:* Res assoc, Inst Studies Defects Solids, 86; res asst prof, Vanderbilt Univ, 86-90. *Concurrent Pos:* Hon prof, Dalian Inst Light Indust; consult, Medtex Commun Instruments Inc, 90- *Mem:* Am Physics Soc; Inst Studies Defects Solids; Photonics Soc Chinese-Am; Int Soc Optical Eng; Am Ceramic Soc; Mat Res Soc. *Res:* Stimulated luminescence in glasses by particle bombardments; adsorption and desorption of surfaces by electron spectroscopy and sims; sol-gel thin silicate film; aluminum oxide/aluminum nitride composite films. *Mailing Add:* Dept Physics & Mat Res Inst Univ Tex El Paso TX 79968. *Fax:* 915-747-5447; *E-Mail:* pwang@utep.edu

**WANG, PEIZHI,** STRUCTURE & FUNCTION OF PROTEIN & DNA, GENE REGULATIONS IN THE LEVELS OF REPLICATION TRANSCRIPTION & TRANSLATION. *Current Pos:* SR RES SCIENTIST, SKIRBALL INST BIOMOLECULAR MED, MED CTR, NY UNIV, 93- *Personal Data:* b Shanghai, China, Jan 30, 43; m 75, Dunrong Jiang; c Jieming. *Educ:* Fudan Univ, China, BS, 69; Univ Sci & Technol, China, PhD(molecular biol), 82. *Prof Exp:* Teaching asst, Univ Sci & Technol, China, 69-79, lectr, 80-82, assoc prof molecular biol, 87-89; fel, Univ Calif, Davis, 82-84; res assoc, Pub Health Res Inst, City Univ New York, 84-87, assoc scientist, 89-93. *Concurrent Pos:* Consult prof, Univ Sci & Technol, China, 89- *Mem:* China Soc Biochem; Am Soc Microbiol. *Res:* Structure and function of replication initiator protein and replication origin; control mechanisms in genetic replication, transcription and translation; protein engineering of industrial enzymes. *Mailing Add:* 62-54 97th Pl Apt 3J Rego Park NY 11374

**WANG, PENG,** immunology, for more information see previous edition

**WANG, PIE-YI,** FOOD ENGINEERING, MEAT SCIENCE. *Current Pos:* DIR PROCESS RES, SWIFT-ECKRICH INC, 85- *Personal Data:* b Chanhua, Taiwan, Feb 28, 40; nat US; m 68; c 2. *Educ:* Nat Taiwan Univ, BS, 63; Univ Hawaii, MS, 67; Michigan State Univ, PhD(agr eng), 70. *Prof Exp:* Res eng, Peter Eckroch & Sons, Inc, 70-74, sr eng, 74-80; mgr oper eng, Armour Foods, 80-81; mgr basic res, Eckrich & Sons Inc, 81-85. *Mem:* Am Soc Agr Eng; Inst Food Technologists. *Res:* Developing, planning and managing research and development activities on meat processing technologies, control and instrumentation, equipment development, physical and chemical properties of meats and transfer new technologies to operations. *Mailing Add:* Armor Swift-Eckrich 3131 Woodcreek Dr Downers Grove IL 60515

**WANG, PING CHUN,** ENGINEERING. *Current Pos:* PROF CIVIL ENG, POLYTECH INST NY, 63- *Personal Data:* b Kiangsu, China, Mar 10, 20; US citizen; m 55; c 2. *Educ:* Nat Cent Univ China, BS, 43; Univ Ill, MS, 48, PhD(eng), 51. *Prof Exp:* Engr, China Bridge Co, 43-47; struct designer, Ammann & Whitney Consult Engrs, 51-52; struct supvr, Seelye, Stevenson, Value & Knecht Consult Engrs, 52-60; assoc prof eng, Stevens Inst Technol, 60-63. *Concurrent Pos:* Dir & vpres, Omnidata Serv Inc, 71-72. *Mem:* Fel Am Soc Civil Engrs; Am Concrete Inst; Am Soc Eng Educ. *Res:* Discrete systems approach in structural mechanics. *Mailing Add:* 36 East Dr Garden City NY 11530

**WANG, PING-LIEH THOMAS,** POULTRY PRODUCT, FEED MILL PRODUCT. *Current Pos:* DIR QUAL ASSURANCE, B C ROGERS POULTRY INC, 83- *Personal Data:* b China, Nov 16, 46; m 75; c 2. *Educ:* Nat Chung-Hsing Univ, BS, 70; Miss State Univ, MS, 75; Tex A&M Univ, PhD(food technol), 82. *Mem:* Poultry Sci Asn; Inst Food Technologists. *Mailing Add:* B C Rogers Sons Inc PO Box A Morton MS 39117

**WANG, RICHARD HSU-SHIEN,** POLYMER DEGRADATION & STABILIZATION, PLASTICS ADDITIVES. *Current Pos:* res chemist, 68-74, prin res chemist, 74-93, RES ASSOC, EASTMAN CHEM CO RES LABS, GASTMAN CHEM CO, 93- *Personal Data:* b Qianshan, Anhui, China, Jan 2, 32; m 62, Josephine Sun; c Joseph K, Christine P & Dorothy

Y. *Educ:* Nat Taiwan Univ, BS, 56; Univ Ill, Urbana, MS, 61; Univ Kans, PhD(chem), 68. *Prof Exp:* Res asst soil chem, Nat Taiwan Univ, 58-59; res asst entomol, Nat Hist Surv Ill, 61-63. *Concurrent Pos:* Hon prof, Anhui Univ, China, 89. *Mem:* Am Chem Soc. *Res:* Polymer stabilization and synthesis of new antioxidants and light inhibitors for polymeric compositions; development of new polymer intermediates and improved synthetic methods for fine organic chemicals; synthesis and development of plastics additives. *Mailing Add:* 1414 Fairidge Dr Kingsport TN 37664

**WANG, RICHARD I H,** PHARMACOLOGY, INTERNAL MEDICINE. *Current Pos:* assoc prof pharmacol & med, 63-70, PROF CLIN PHARMACOL, MED COL WIS, 70-, ASSOC PROF MED, 77-; CHIEF, DRUG TREATMENT CTR, WOOD VET'S ADMIN CTR, 77- *Personal Data:* b Shanghai, China, Oct 12, 24; US citizen; m 58; c 2. *Educ:* St John's Univ, BS, 45; Utah State Univ, MS, 49; Univ Ill, PhD(pharmacol), 52; Northwestern Univ, MD, 55. *Prof Exp:* Intern, Presby Hosp, Chicago, Ill, 55-56; resident, Indianapolis Gen Hosp, Ind, 56-58; prin scientist, Roswell Park Mem Inst, 61-63. *Concurrent Pos:* Chief, Clin Pharmacol Serv, Wood Vet Admin Hosp, 63-, dir, Drug Abuse Treatment & Rehab Prog, 71-; consult physician, Milwaukee County Gen Hosp, 64-; attend physician, Milwaukee County Ment Health Ctr, 65- *Mem:* Am Soc Pharmacol & Exp Therapeut; Fedn Am Socs Exp Biol; Radiation Res Soc; Am Soc Clin Pharmacol & Therapeut. *Res:* Clinical pharmacology; radiation biology. *Mailing Add:* Dept Hosp Psychiat John L Doyne Hosp Box 196 Milwaukee WI 53226. *Fax:* 414-257-5241

**WANG, RICHARD J,** CELL BIOLOGY, AUTOIMMUNITY. *Current Pos:* from asst to assoc prof, 71-83, PROF BIOL, 83-, DIR, HUMAN MONOCLONAL ANTIBODY FAC, UNIV MO, COLUMBIA, 87- *Personal Data:* b Chungking, China, Oct 23, 41; US citizen; m 66, Grace; c Mike, Larry & Melanie. *Educ:* Harvard Univ, BA, 64; Univ Colo, PhD(biophys), 68. *Prof Exp:* Fel cell biol, NY Univ, 68-70; res assoc biol, Mass Inst Technol, 70-71. *Concurrent Pos:* NIH res career develop award, 72-77; biochem consult, Cancer Res Ctr, Columbia, Mo, 73-; res investr, Dalton Res Ctr, Univ Mo, Columbia, 74- *Mem:* Am Soc Cell Biol; Tissue Cult Asn; AAAS. *Res:* Biochemical genetics of human and mammalian cells in culture; regulatory mechanisms in autoimmunity. *Mailing Add:* Tucker Hall Univ Mo Columbia MO 65211-0001

**WANG, RICHARD RUEY-CHYI,** GENOME MAPPING, GENE TRANSFER. *Current Pos:* RES GENETICIST, USDA-AGR RES SERV, 83-, HON PROF, SHAANXI ACAD AGR SCI, 93- & CHINA AGR UNIV, 95- *Personal Data:* b Chongqing, Sichuan, China, Sept 1, 43; US citizen; m, Yeelan Ma; c Aaron E & Brian E. *Educ:* Nat Taiwan Univ, BS, 67; Rutgers Univ, MS, 71, PhD(plant genetics), 74. *Prof Exp:* Fel, Kans State Univ, 75-77; cytopathologist, Dekalb Agr Res, 77-82; res scientist, Int Plant Res Inst, 82-83. *Concurrent Pos:* Adj asst prof, Utah State Univ, 83-86, adj assoc prof, 86-; lead consult, UN Develop Prog, 93-94. *Mem:* Crop Sci Soc Am; Agron Soc Am; Genetics Soc Can; Asn Chinese Soil & Plant Scientists (secy-treas, 90-91, vpres, 91-92, pres, 92-93). *Res:* Characterize genomes in the tribe Triticeae; collect useful germplasm resources; transfer useful genes for cereal and forage improvement; identify, isolate and sequence genes controlling apomixis. *Mailing Add:* USDA-ARS-FRRL Utah State Univ Logan UT 84322-6300

**WANG, ROBERT T,** INORGANIC CHEMISTRY, PHYSICAL CHEMISTRY. *Current Pos:* asst prof, 70-76, ASSOC PROF CHEM, SALEM STATE COL, 76- *Personal Data:* b Chung King, China, Aug 3, 41; US citizen; m 68; c 2. *Educ:* Taiwan Cheng Kung Univ, BS, 62; Johns Hopkins Univ, PhD(chem), 68. *Prof Exp:* Fel inorg chem, Iowa State Univ, 68-70. *Concurrent Pos:* Consult, US Summit Corp, New York, NY, 72- *Mem:* Am Chem Soc. *Res:* The studies of kinetics and mechanisms of inorganic transition metal complexes reactions; synthesis of bioinorganic compounds. *Mailing Add:* Dept Chem & Physics Salem State Col Salem MA 01970-5348

**WANG, RU-TSANG,** physics of light scattering, microwave electronics, for more information see previous edition

**WANG, SAM S(HU) Y(I),** MECHANICAL ENGINEERING, HYDRAULIC ENGINEERING. *Current Pos:* from asst prof to assoc prof eng, 67-81, actg chmn, Dept Mech Eng, 82-83, PROF ENG, UNIV MISS, 81-, DIR, CTR COMPUTATIONAL HYDROSCI & ENG, 83-, FREDERICK A P BARNARD DISTINGUISHED PROF, 88- *Personal Data:* b Chungking, China, Sept 21, 36; m 66, Jine Yang; c David S & Susan S. *Educ:* Cheng Kung Univ, Taiwan, BSc, 59; Univ Rochester, MSc, 65, PhD(comput hydrodyn), 68. *Honors & Awards:* Ralph R Teetor Award, Soc Automotive Engrs, 75; Hydraul Res Achievement Award, Am Soc Civil Engrs, 88; Spec Award, Am Inst Aeronaut & Astronaut, 79. *Prof Exp:* Design engr, Yue Loong Motor Co Ltd, 60-61; asst mech, Cheng Kung Univ, 61-63; asst fluid mech, Univ Rochester, 63-64; asst aerospace sci, 64-67. *Concurrent Pos:* Res fel, Stanford Univ, 68; vis scientist, Johnson Space Ctr, NASA, 73-74 & Aero Propulsion Lab, USAF, 75-76; gen chmn & organizer, 3rd Int Conf Finite Elements in Water Resources, Univ Miss, 80; exec coun, Int Soc Comput Methods Eng, 80-84; tech prog co-chair, Fluid Dynamics, Plasmadynamics & Lasers Conf, Am Inst Aeronaut & Astronaut, 84; gen chmn, 3rd Int Symp River Sedimentation, 86 & Int Symp Sediment Transp Modeling, Am Soc Civil Engrs, 89; gen chmn, Int Conf Hydrosci & Eng, 93. *Mem:* Assoc fel Am Inst Aeronaut & Astronaut; Am Geophys Union; Am Soc Mech Engrs; hon mem Chinese Soc Theoret & Appl Mech; Int Asn Hydraul Res; Nat Soc Prof Engrs; Nat Geog Soc. *Res:* Fluid mechanics including hypersonic flow theory, boundary layer theory, hydrodynamic stability, magnetohydrodynamics, plasma physics and physics of fluids; computer simulation of river and coastal flows and sediment transports. *Mailing Add:* Ctr Comput Hydrosci & Eng Sch Eng Univ Miss University MS 38677. *Fax:* 601-232-7796; *E-Mail:* wang@hydra.cche.olemiss.edu

**WANG, SAN-PIN,** MEDICAL MICROBIOLOGY. *Current Pos:* vis assoc prof prev med, Sch Med, 64-66, assoc prof, 66-70, PROF PATHOBIOL, SCH PUB HEALTH & COMMUNITY MED, UNIV WASH, 70- *Personal Data:* b Taiwan, Nov 7, 20; m 46; c 5. *Educ:* Keio Univ, Japan, MD, 44; Univ Mich, MPH, 52. *Hon Degrees:* Dr Med Sci, Keio Univ, Japan, 59. *Prof Exp:* Asst bact, Sch Med, Keio Univ, Japan, 44-46; chief dept bact, Taiwan Prov Hyg Lab, 46-51; chief dept virol, Taiwan Serum Vaccine Lab, 52-58; med officer virus immunol, US Naval Med Res Unit, 58-64. *Mem:* Am Asn Path. *Res:* Biological products, rabies and smallpox vaccines; research on tropical diseases, rabies, influenza, encephalitis and trachoma. *Mailing Add:* 2050 182nd Ave NE Redmond WA 98052

**WANG, SHAO-FU,** theoretical physics, condensed matter physics; deceased, see previous edition for last biography

**WANG, SHIEN TSUN,** STRUCTURAL ENGINEERING, ENGINEERING MECHANICS. *Current Pos:* from asst prof to assoc prof, 69-83, dir grad studies, 80-84, PROF CIVIL ENG, UNIV KY, 83-, DIR GRAD STUDIES, 87- *Personal Data:* b Changsha, China, Aug 24, 38; m 69; c 2. *Educ:* Nat Taiwan Univ, BS, 60; Mich State Univ, MS, 64; Cornell Univ, PhD(struct eng), 69. *Honors & Awards:* Outstanding Civil Eng Prof Award, 85; Outstanding Achievement Eng Educ Award, Lincoln Arc Welding Found, 85. *Prof Exp:* Civil eng, Nat Taiwan Univ, 61-62 & Mich State Univ, 62-64; struct engr, Cornell Univ, 64-68, res assoc & instr, 68-69. *Concurrent Pos:* Fac res & teaching fels, Univ Ky, 70-72; NSF fel, Syracuse Univ, 71 & Ohio State Univ, 80; var consult work; chmn & mem, several Am Soc Civil Engrs Nat Comts; ed bd, J Thin Walled Struct. *Mem:* Am Soc Civil Engrs; Struct Stability Res Coun; Am Soc Eng Educ; Sigma Xi; Am Acad Mech. *Res:* Structural stability and post-buckling analysis; thin-walled and cold formed structures; computer aided design and computer graphics; damage and failure analysis; computer modeling and analysis of space and special structures; nonlinear structural analysis; finite element methods; metal structures. *Mailing Add:* Dept Civil Eng Univ Ky 210 Andersen Hall Lexington KY 40506. *Fax:* 606-257-4404

**WANG, SHOU-LING,** SHIP PROTECTION. *Current Pos:* RETIRED. *Personal Data:* b Shanghai, China, Oct 17, 24; nat US; m 86; Nilcea Muniz; c Michael, Lawrence & Caroline. *Educ:* St John's Univ, China, BS, 46; Yale Univ, ME, 48; Univ Ill, PhD(theoret & appl mech), 52. *Honors & Awards:* Meritorious Civilian Serv, Dept Navy, 85. *Prof Exp:* Designer, D B Steinman, 52-55; asst prof civil eng, Clarkson Univ, 55-57; assoc prof, Univ Mo, 57-60; vis assoc prof eng mech, NC State Univ, 60-67; struct engr, David Taylor Res Ctr, 67-78, head, Underwater Protection Group, 79-91. *Concurrent Pos:* Lectr weapon effects and ship protection, Mass Inst Technol, 76-91. *Res:* Structural dynamics; weapon effects; ship protection. *Mailing Add:* 9132 Kirkdale Rd Bethesda MD 20817

**WANG, SHU LUNG,** COMPUTER APPLICATIONS. *Current Pos:* ASSOC PROF INFO SYSTS, PACE UNIV, 86- *Personal Data:* b Sichuan, China, May 2, 25; m 47; c 2. *Educ:* Wash Univ, St Louis, BS, 49, MS, 50, DSc(chem eng), 53. *Prof Exp:* From asst prof to assoc prof chem eng, Kans State Univ, 52-57; sect head eng systs develop & dir comput lab, Linden Div, Tarrytown Tech Ctr, 57-66, mgr, Niagara Frontier Regional Comput Ctr, 66-69, mgr comput applns & sci, 69-83; consult, Advan Comput Technol, Union Carbide Corp, 84-85. *Mem:* Am Inst Chem Eng; Am Chem Soc; Inst Elec & Electronics Engrs Comput Soc; Asn Comput Mach; Am Asn Artificial Intel. *Res:* Applied artificial intelligence, information system development and data processing management; process control systems engineering; adsorption and cryogenic gas separation processes; vapor-liquid equilibrium data; knowledge based systems. *Mailing Add:* 21 Sunset Dr Ossining NY 10562-2101

**WANG, SOO RAY,** allergy, immunology, for more information see previous edition

**WANG, SUSAN S,** COMPUTER SCIENCE. *Current Pos:* ASST PROF COMPUT SCI, MILLS COL, 92- *Personal Data:* b Taipei, Taiwan, Feb 18, 61; US citizen. *Educ:* Mass Inst Technol, BS, 83; Princeton Univ, MA, 85, PhD(comput sci), 89. *Prof Exp:* Postdoctoral fel, Tokyo Res Lab, IBM, Japan, 88-89; lectr comput sci, Princeton Univ, 90. *Concurrent Pos:* Fac comput sci, Mills Summer Math Inst, 94. *Mem:* Asn Comput Mach; Inst Elec & Electronics Engrs; Am Asn Univ Women. *Res:* Design and analysis of efficient computer algorithms, parallel computation and compiling techniques; design and development of tools for very large scale integrated systems; emphasis on problem-solving methods, particularly those applicable to graph problems. *Mailing Add:* 5000 MacArthur Blvd Oakland CA 94613. *Fax:* 510-430-3314; *E-Mail:* wang@mills.edu

**WANG, TAITZER,** BIOCHEMISTRY. *Personal Data:* b Taiwan, Feb 2, 39; m 68; c 3. *Educ:* Nat Univ Taiwan, BS, 61; Rice Univ, PhD(org chem), 67. *Prof Exp:* Res asst prof cell biophys, Baylor Col Med, 75-77; from asst prof to assoc prof pharmacol & cell biophys, Col Med, Univ Cincinnati, 77-91. *Concurrent Pos:* Nat Inst Arthritis & Metab Dis res fel org chem, Fla State Univ, 67-69; US Dept Defense res fel inorg chem, Univ Ky, 69-71; Welch fel biochem, Baylor Col Med, 71-73; Welch fel, Rice Univ, 73-74; NIH spec res fel cell biophys, Baylor Col Med, 74-75. *Mem:* Am Chem Soc; AAAS; NY Acad Sci; Am Soc Biol Chemists & Molecular Biologists; Am Heart Asn; Biophys Soc. *Res:* Enzyme kinetics and synthetic chemistry; cell biophysics. *Mailing Add:* 450 Flemridge Ct Cincinnati OH 45231

**WANG, TAYLOR GUNJIN,** MICROGRAVITY SCIENCE & APPLICATION. *Current Pos:* CENT PROF & DIR, CTR MICROGRAVITY RES & APPLNS & APPL PHYSICS PROG, VANDERBILT UNIV, NASHVILLE, 88- *Personal Data:* b Shanghai, China, June 16, 40; m 65; Beverly Fung; c Kenneth & Eric. *Educ:* Univ Calif, Los Angeles, BS, 67, MS, 68, PhD, 71. *Honors & Awards:* Space Flight Medal, NASA, 85. *Prof Exp:* Mgr, Microgravity Sci & Applns Prog, Jet Propulsion Lab, Pasadena, Calif, 72-88, consult, 87-89. *Concurrent Pos:* Space shuttle astronaut-scientist, NASA, 83-85. *Mem:* Fel Acoust Soc Am; Am Inst Aeronaut & Astronaut; Am Phys Soc; Asn Space Explorers (pres, 88); Sigma Xi. *Res:* Utilize the extended zero-gravity environment provided by space to conduct both basic and applied research that cannot be performed on earth. *Mailing Add:* Vanderbilt Univ Sta B Box 1743 Nashville TN 37235. *Fax:* 615-343-8730; *E-Mail:* wangtg@vuse.vanderbilt.edu

**WANG, THEODORE JOSEPH,** PHYSICS. *Current Pos:* RETIRED. *Personal Data:* b Chicago, Ill, Dec 8, 06; m 36; c 2. *Educ:* Univ Ill, BS, 32, PhD(physics), 39. *Prof Exp:* Asst physics, Univ Ill, 35-39; physicist, Oakes Prod Corp, Ill, 39-40; fel, Univ Minn, 41; from instr to asst prof elec eng, Ohio State Univ, 42-48; physicist, Nat Bur Stand, 48-49; biophysicist, Nat Cancer Inst, 49-50; physicist, George Washington Univ, 50-52; asst prof physics, Univ Mass, 52-55; prof & head dept, SDak Sch Mines & Technol, 55-56; prof, Howard Univ, 56-59; analyst, Opers Res Off, Res Anal Corp, 59-62; prin scientist, Booz, Allen Appl Res, 62-66; dir, Inst Creative Studies, 67-88. *Concurrent Pos:* Consult physicist, 50-52; analyst, Opers Res Off, Johns Hopkins Univ, 57; analyst, Res Anal Corp, 57-58; prof, Howard Univ, 60-64; lectr, 64-88. *Res:* Radiation physics. *Mailing Add:* 4700 Essex Ave Chevy Chase MD 20815

**WANG, THEODORE SHENG-TAO,** RADIOPHARMACOLOGY, PHARMACEUTICAL CHEMISTRY. *Current Pos:* from asst prof to prof clin radiol & pub health, 78-95, PROF RADIOL, COL PHYSICIANS & SURGEONS, COLUMBIA UNIV, 95- *Personal Data:* b Oct 18, 30; US citizen, Aileen M P; c Angela & Christopher. *Educ:* Nat Mukden Med Col, China, BS, 52; Univ Nebr, Lincoln, MS, 58; Univ Md, Phd(med chem & pharmacol), 64. *Prof Exp:* Asst prof nuclear med, Dept Nuclear Med, Health Ctr, Univ Conn, Farmington, 74-76; chief radiopharmacist & sr staff assoc, Columbia-Presby Med Ctr, 76-78. *Concurrent Pos:* Head, Radiopharmaceut Chem Lab. *Mem:* Soc Nuclear Med; Am Chem Soc; NY Acad Sci; Am Pharmaceut Asn; AAAS; Int Asn Radiopharmacol; Am Col Nuclear Physicians. *Res:* Radiotracer labelling of monoclonal antibodies for tumor diagnostic imaging and therapy. *Mailing Add:* Columbia-Presby Med Ctr 622 W 168th St New York NY 10032

**WANG, THOMAS NIE-CHIN,** ELECTRICAL ENGINEERING, APPLIED MATHEMATICS. *Current Pos:* PRES, SYSTEC RES CTR, 89- *Personal Data:* b Shanghai, China, Feb 17, 38; m 67; c 2. *Educ:* Cheng Kung Univ, Taiwan, BSEE, 60; Univ NMex, MSEE, 64; Stanford Univ, PhD(elec eng), 70. *Prof Exp:* Res engr, Radio Physics Lab, Stanford Res Inst, 67- *Concurrent Pos:* Vis prof, Cheng Kung Univ, Taiwan, 71-72; mem, US Nat Comt, Comn 6, Int Union Radio Sci, Washington, DC, 72. *Mem:* Inst Elec & Electronics Engrs; Int Union Radio Sci. *Res:* Radiation and waves in scattering and diffraction of electromagnetic waves; propagation in magnetosphere and ionosphere. *Mailing Add:* 1294 Bedford Ct Sunnyvale CA 94087

**WANG, TING CHUNG,** MYOCARDIAL METABOLISM, ORGAN TRANSPLANTATION. *Current Pos:* ASSOC PROF SURG, SCH MED, TULANE UNIV, 82- *Educ:* Univ Minn, PhD(cell biol), 74. *Mailing Add:* 1430 Tulane Ave New Orleans LA 70112

**WANG, TING-I,** WEATHER INSTRUMENTATION, ATMOSPHERIC REMOTE SENSING. *Current Pos:* PRES, SCI TECHNOL, INC, 85- *Personal Data:* b Chekiang, China, Jan 11, 44. *Educ:* Nat Taiwan Univ, BA, 66; Dartmouth Col, MA, 70, PhD(radiophys), 73. *Prof Exp:* Vis fel & res assoc optical remote sensing, Coop Inst Res Environ Sci, Univ Colo, 73-75; physicist optical remote sensing, Wave Propagation Lab, Nat Oceanic & Atmospheric Admin, 75-82; staff scientist, Propagation Studies Satellite Commun, Comsat Labs, 82-84; div mgr, opto-electronics instrumentation, Dynamics Technol Inc, 84-85. *Mem:* Fel Optical Soc Am; Am Inst Physics; Am Geophys Union; Sigma Xi; sr mem Inst Elec & Electronics Engrs. *Res:* The use of optical effects to develop novel techniques of remote sensors to probe the atmosphere, including turbulence, wind and precipitation; propagation effects on satellite and terrestrial communication systems. *Mailing Add:* Sci Technol Inc 205 Perry Pkwy Gaithersburg MD 20877

**WANG, TING-TAI HELEN,** MOTOR OIL RESEARCH, CRUDE OIL RESEARCH. *Current Pos:* SR RES CHEMIST, PENNZOIL PROD CO, 84- *Personal Data:* b Taipei, Taiwan, May 31, 48; m; c 2. *Educ:* Nat Taiwan Univ, BS, 70; Vanderbilt Univ, MS, 73; Univ Houston, PhD(anal chem), 82. *Prof Exp:* Res chemist, Gulf Oil Chem Co, 81-82; res assoc anal & environ chem, Dept Environ Sci & Eng, Rice Univ, 83-84. *Concurrent Pos:* Chmn int rels, Southeastern Tex Sect, Am Chem Soc, 81- *Mem:* Am Chem Soc; Am Soc Mass Spectrometry. *Res:* Conduct motor oils, crude oils, base stocks and environmental related research using gas chromatography and mass spectrometry; liquid chromatography and mass spectrometry; high pressure liquid chromatography and other analytical separation and spectroscopy techniques. *Mailing Add:* 3810 Browning St Houston TX 77005

**WANG, TSEN CHEN,** ENVIRONMENTAL MONITORING, FATE, TRANSPORT, ASSIMILATION & REMEDIATION, WASTE & WASTE WATER TREATMENT, WASTE CONTROL & MINIMIZATION. *Current Pos:* chem engr, Dept Chem & Environ Eng, 73-85, chief chem engr, 85-91, DIR, HARBOR BR ENVIRON LAB, OCEANOG INST INC, 91- *Personal Data:* b Taiwan City, Taiwan, Apr 26, 43; m 70, Huei Li; c Clifford & Sean. *Educ:* Chun Yuan Univ, BS, 66; Univ Iowa, MS, 69, PhD(chem eng), 72. *Prof Exp:* Smithsonian fel, Smithsonian Inst, 72-73. *Concurrent Pos:* Cert water & waste treatment operator, Fla Dept Environ Protection, 76-; regist prof engr, Fla Eng Soc, 78-; cert chem engr & cert prof chemist, Am Inst Chemists, 89-, bd dir, 93-94; interdisciplinary comt mem, World Cult Coun, 90-; pres, Fla Inst Chemists, 90-91; adj prof, Indian River Community Col, 90-91, Fla Inst Technol, 91-; prog mgr, Ocean Eng Div, Am Soc Mech Engrs, 90-91. *Mem:* Am Inst Chem Engrs; Am Chem Soc; Am Inst Chemists; Am Water Works Asn; Am Soc Mech Engrs. *Res:* Environmental monitoring, contaminants fate and persistence, assimilation and degradation of contaminants in environment; water and waste water treatment, bioremediation, waste control and minimization; method development in environmental analysis and testing. *Mailing Add:* Harbor Br Environ 5600 US 1 N Ft Pierce FL 34946-7303. *Fax:* 561-465-2446

**WANG, TSUEY TANG,** POLYMER SCIENCE, MATERIALS SCIENCE. *Current Pos:* VIS PROF, DEPT MAT SCI & ENG, RUTGERS UNIV, BUSCH CAMPUS, 89- *Personal Data:* b Tainan, Taiwan, Nov 12, 32; US citizen; m 65, Mei-Tieh Lin; c David, Marjorie & Vanessa. *Educ:* Cheng Kung Univ, Taiwan, BSc, 55; Brown Univ, MSc, 61, PhD(appl mech), 65. *Prof Exp:* Asst prof, Polytech Univ NY, 65-67; distinguished mem tech staff, Bell Tel Labs, 67-88. *Concurrent Pos:* Foreign spec invited prof, Japan Ministry Educ, 92. *Mem:* Fel Am Phys Soc; Mat Res Soc; Am Acad Mech; NY Acad Sci. *Res:* Mechanical behavior of polymers; structures and properties; piezoelectricity in polymers; high temperature polymers; high performance composites; polymer blends. *Mailing Add:* Dept Chem Eng & Biochem Eng Rutgers Univ Piscataway NJ 08854

**WANG, TUNG YUE,** BIOCHEMISTRY. *Current Pos:* prof, 63-89, EMER PROF, DEPT BIOL SCI, STATE UNIV NY, BUFFALO, 89- *Personal Data:* b Peking, China, Oct 27, 21; US citizen; m 48. *Educ:* Nat CheKiang Univ, BSc, 42; Univ Mo, MA, 49, PhD(biochem), 51. *Prof Exp:* Res fel, Jewish Hosp, St Louis, 51-53; res assoc, Washington Univ, St Louis, 53-57, asst prof, 57-59, assoc prof, 59-63. *Mem:* Am Soc Biol Chemists; Am Soc Cell Biol; Am Chem Soc; AAAS. *Mailing Add:* 65 Autumnview Rd Buffalo NY 14221-1601

**WANG, VICTOR KAI-KUO,** PHYSICAL CHEMISTRY, INDUSTRIAL CHEMISTRY. *Current Pos:* res chemist, E I du Pont de Nemours & Co Inc, 73-80, sr res chemist, 81-84, tech mgr, 85-92, MARKET DEVELOP MGR, E I DU PONT DE NEMOURS & CO, INC, 92- *Personal Data:* b Quei-Chow, China, Mar 18, 44; m 69; c 2. *Educ:* Chung Yuan Col Sci & Eng, Taiwan, BS, 65; State Univ NY, Binghamton, MS, 68; Univ Minn, PhD(phys chem), 73. *Prof Exp:* Res asst phys chem, State Univ NY, Binghamton, 66-68; teaching assoc, Univ Minn, 68-73. *Mem:* Am Chem Soc. *Res:* Process research, kinetics and catalysis; printed wiring board fabrication and cleaning. *Mailing Add:* Electronics Dept E I du Pont de Nemours & Co Inc 14 T W Alexander Dr Research Triangle Park NC 27709. *Fax:* 919-248-5550

**WANG, VICTOR S F,** high performance polymeric matrix composites product development, engineering of specialty bearings for defense industry, for more information see previous edition

**WANG, WEI-E,** NUCLEAR CHEMISTRY, HEALTH PHYSICIST. *Current Pos:* RES ENGR NUCLEAR ENG, UNIV CALIF, BERKELEY, 93- *Personal Data:* m, Mila Lieu; c Sabrina. *Educ:* Tsing Hoa Univ, BS, 81, MS, 83; Univ Calif, Berkeley, PhD(nuclear eng), 93. *Res:* Thermodynamics of nuclear material; oxidation of alloys and oxides. *Mailing Add:* 1112B Eighth St No 20 Albany CA 94710. *Fax:* 510-643-9685; *E-Mail:* wangwei@ucbcmsa

**WANG, WEI-YEH,** BIOCHEMICAL GENETICS, PLANT PHYSIOLOGY. *Current Pos:* from asst prof to assoc prof, 75-87, PROF BOT, UNIV IOWA, 87- *Personal Data:* b Sian, China, Oct 10, 44; m 69; c 2. *Educ:* Nat Taiwan Univ, BS, 66; Univ Mo, Columbia, PhD(genetics), 72. *Prof Exp:* Fel genetics, Duke Univ, 72-75. *Concurrent Pos:* Vis prof, Carlsberg Lab, Copenhagen, 80-81. *Mem:* Genetics Soc Am; Am Soc Plant Physiologists; Sigma Xi. *Res:* Genetics, biochemistry and molecular biology of chlorophyll and heme biosynthesis. *Mailing Add:* Biol Sci Univ Iowa 138 Biol Bldg Iowa City IA 52242-1324

**WANG, WEN I,** ELECTRICAL ENGINEERING, APPLIED PHYSICS. *Current Pos:* PROF ELEC ENG & APPL PHYSICS, COLUMBIA UNIV, 87- *Personal Data:* b Taiwan, June 11, 53. *Educ:* Nat Taiwan Univ, BS, 75; Cornell Univ, ME, 79, PhD(elec eng), 81. *Prof Exp:* Res staff mem, Rockwell Int Sci Ctr, 81-82; res staff mem, IBM Res Ctr, 82-87. *Mem:* Am Phys Soc; Inst Elec & Electronics Engrs. *Res:* Solid state physics; molecular beam epitaxy. *Mailing Add:* Elec Eng Dept Columbia Univ 1320 Mudd Bldg New York NY 10027

**WANG, WILLIAM S Y,** LANGUAGE EVOLUTION. *Current Pos:* PROF, GRAD SCH, UNIV CALIF, 66- *Personal Data:* c 4. *Educ:* Univ Mich, PhD(ling), 60. *Concurrent Pos:* Prof lang eng, Dept Electronic Eng, City Univ Hong Kong, 95- *Res:* Evolution theory and language evolution; bringing engineering technology to simulate language behavior; author of 200 technical publications. *Mailing Add:* Univ Calif 2222 Piedmont Ave Berkeley CA 94720-2170. *E-Mail:* wsyw@socrates.berkeley.edu

**WANG, WUN-CHENG W(OODROW),** AQUATIC TOXICOLOGY. *Current Pos:* WATER QUAL SPECIALIST, US GEOL SURV, 91- *Personal Data:* b Taichung, China, Mar 10, 36; m 62; c 3. *Educ:* Nat Taiwan Univ, BS, 58, MS, 61; Univ Wis-Madison, PhD(water chem), 68. *Prof Exp:* from asst prof scientist to assoc prof scientist, Water Qual Sect, Ill State Water Surv, 67-80, prof scientist, 81-91. *Mem:* Soc Environ Toxicol & Chem; Am Soc Testing & Mat. *Res:* Bioassay; aquatic toxicology; ecotoxicology; toxicity tests. *Mailing Add:* US Geol Surv Stevenson Ctr Suite 129 720 Gracern Rd Columbia SC 29210. *Fax:* 803-750-6181; *E-Mail:* wwang@usgs.gov

**WANG, XIANG-DONG,** CAROTENOIDS & RETINOID, HUMAN CANCER & ANIMAL MODELS. *Current Pos:* researcher, 88-91, res scientist III, 91-93, RES SCIENTIST II, USDA HUMAN NUTRIT RES CTR AGING, TUFTS UNIV, 93-, ASST PROF, SCH NUTRIT SCI & POLICY, 93-, SCH MED, 93- *Personal Data:* b Lanzhou, China, Dec 7, 56; m 85, Connie Hu; c Karl. *Educ:* Beijing Med Univ, MD, 82; Tufts Univ, PhD(nutrit), 92. *Prof Exp:* Intern med, Peking Union Med Col Hosp, 81-82, resident, 83-86; res fel, Joslin Diabetes Ctr, Harvard Med Sch, 86-87, Brigham & Womens Hosp, 87-88. *Concurrent Pos:* Co-investr, NIH, 91-94; prin investr, Am Col Nutrit, 92-93, NIH, 95-97; Vis scientist, Mass Gen Hosp Cancer Res Ctr, Harvard Med Sch, 96. *Mem:* Am Soc Clin Nutrit; Am Soc Nutrit Sci. *Res:* Investigation on the role of carotenoids and retinoid in human nutrition and cancer. *Mailing Add:* 711 Washington St Boston MA 02111

**WANG, XIAO WU,** COMPUTER AIDED RESEARCH IN SCIENCE, DATA ANALYSIS & GRAPHICS PRESENTATION METHODS. *Current Pos:* PRES, POLY SOFTWARE INT INC, 94- *Personal Data:* b Hefei, Anhui, China, July 6, 58; m 82, Lin Hu; c Fanny, Kathy & Bill. *Educ:* NY Univ, PhD(physics), 90. *Prof Exp:* Res assoc, Brookhaven Nat Lab, 88-89; software engr, Micromath Inc, 90-92; chmn, Polysoft Ltd, 92-94. *Concurrent Pos:* Grantee, NIH, 94. *Mem:* Am Phys Soc; Asn Comput Mach. *Res:* Computational methods for mathematical and statistical analysis and graphical presentation. *Mailing Add:* 9845 S Geode Circle Sandy UT 84094. *Fax:* 801-485-0480; *E-Mail:* wang@polysoftware.com

**WANG, XINGWU,** SUPERCONDUCTIVE COMPONENTS, THIN FILMS. *Current Pos:* asst prof, 88-93, ASSOC PROF ELEC ENG, ALFRED UNIV, 93- *Personal Data:* b Hangzhou, China, Feb 19, 53; m 87, Changjiang Xu; c Changcheng J. *Educ:* Harbin Naval Eng Inst, BS, 78; Hangzhou Univ, MS, 81; State Univ NY, Buffalo, PhD(physics), 87. *Prof Exp:* Teacher elec eng, Hangzhou Naval Eng Sch, 78-81, teacher physics, Hangzhou Univ, 81-84; teaching asst physics, State Univ NY, Buffalo, 82-84, res asst, 84-87, res assoc elec eng, 87-88. *Concurrent Pos:* Prin investr, Ctr Advan Ceramic Technol, 88-, NY State Inst Superconductivity, 89-90 & NSF, Glass Res Ctr, 91 & 93-94; session chair, US-Japan Workshop Superconductivity, 89; abstractor, Am Soc Metal Int, 90-; reviewer, NY State Sci & Technol Found, 90; fac, Argonne Nat Lab, USAF, 92 & 93, prin investr, 93-94, vis scientist, 94. *Mem:* Inst Elec & Electronics Engrs; Am Phys Soc; Am Ceramic Soc; Mat Res Soc; AAAS; Am Soc Metal Int. *Res:* Superconductivity, superconductive electronics, bulk superconductors, physical properties of super conductors, low temperature physics, superfluidity; thin films by laser and plasma deposition technique, physisorption of films; bimodal switching in lasers, mean switching time; phase transitions, critical phenomena, mathematical physics; author of more than 50 publications, three patents issued. *Mailing Add:* Elec Eng Dept Alfred Univ Alfred NY 14802. *Fax:* 607-871-2348; *E-Mail:* fwangx.biguax.alfred.edu

**WANG, YANG,** CARDIOLOGY. *Current Pos:* dir cardiac catherization Labs, Univ Hosps, 60-85, from instr to assoc prof, 59-64, PROF MED, MED SCH, UNIV MINN, MINNEAPOLIS, 74- *Personal Data:* b Tangshan, China, May 12, 23; US citizen; m 66, Helen Huang; c 4. *Educ:* Nat Med Col Shanghai, MB; Harvard Univ, MD, 52; Am Bd Internal Med, dipl; Am Bd Cardiovasc Dis, dipl. *Prof Exp:* Intern & resident med, Mass Gen Hosp, 52-54 & 56-57. *Concurrent Pos:* P D White fel cardiol, Mass Gen Hosp, Boston, 57-58; fel physiol, Mayo Grad Sch Med, Univ Minn, 58-59; consult, Vet Admin Hosp, Minneapolis, 67; fel coun clin cardiol & circulation, Am Heart Asn; attend physician, Univ Minn Hosps, Minneapolis, 59- *Mem:* Fel AAAS; Am Fedn Clin Res; fel Am Col Physicians; Soc Exp Biol & Med; Asn Univ Cardiol; fel Am Col Cardiol. *Res:* Cardiovascular and exercise physiology; cardiac catheterization in humans; adult congenital heart disease. *Mailing Add:* Dept Med Univ Minn Hosps Box 83 Minneapolis MN 55455. *Fax:* 612-626-4411; *E-Mail:* wangx002@maroon.tc.umn.edu

**WANG, YAR-MING,** ELECTROCHEMISTRY. *Current Pos:* sr res engr, 79-84, STAFF RES ENGR, GEN MOTORS RES LABS, 84- *Personal Data:* b Taitung, Taiwan, Sept 22, 47; US citizen; m 75, Melody Sun; c Thomas & James. *Educ:* Nat Cheng-Kong Univ, Taiwan, BS, 68; Univ Mo, Rolla, PhD(metall eng), 75. *Prof Exp:* Plant engr, Taiwan Metal & Mining Corp, 69-70; teaching fel, Univ Mo, Rolla, 75-76, res asst prof metall eng, 76-77; res scientist, Sprague Elec Co, 78-79. *Mem:* Metall Soc Am Inst Mining, Metall & Petrol Engrs; Electrochem Soc; Nat Soc Corrosion Engrs. *Res:* Nonferrous chemical metallurgy; electrolytic processes; corrosion mechanism studies; battery research. *Mailing Add:* Phys Chem 5156 Callington Dr Troy MI 48098. *Fax:* 810-986-2244

**WANG, YA-YEN LEE,** mathematics, computer science; deceased, see previous edition for last biography

**WANG, YEN,** RADIOLOGY, NUCLEAR MEDICINE. *Current Pos:* Asst prof, 63-65, assoc prof, 65-75, CLIN PROF RADIOL, UNIV PITTSBURGH, 75-; DIR RADIOL, HOMESTEAD HOSP, 66-; DIR NUCLEAR MED, MAGEE-WOMENS HOSP, PITTSBURGH, 67-; PROF RADIOL, UNIV PA. *Personal Data:* b Dairen, China, Oct 21, 28; m 62. *Educ:* Nat Taiwan Univ, MD, 53; Univ Pa, DSc(med), 62. *Concurrent Pos:* Res fel, Picker Found Acad Sci, 61-63; vis scientist, Protein Found, 62-64; ed, Critical Rev Clin Radiol & Nuclear Med. *Mem:* AMA; Soc Nuclear Med; Am Roentgen Ray Soc; Am Physiol Soc; Am Radium Soc; Radiol Soc NAm. *Res:* Physiology; protein chemistry. *Mailing Add:* 1483 Flat Rock Rd Penn Valley PA 19072

**WANG, YEN CHU,** APPLIED SUPERCONDUCTIVITY. *Current Pos:* PROF ELEC ENG, HOWARD UNIV, 74- *Personal Data:* b China, Nov 25, 38. *Educ:* Cheng Kung Univ, Taiwan, BS, 60; Nat Chiao Tung Univ, MS, 62; NY Univ, PhD(elec eng), 69. *Prof Exp:* Mem tech staff, Hughs Aircraft Co, Torrance, CA, 69-70; proj engr, ADT Co, NY, 71-72; proj engr, Gen Microwave Corp, Farmingdale, Long Island, 72-74. *Mem:* Am Phys Soc; AAAS; Inst Electronic Commun Engrs Japan; Am Asn Physics Teachers; Math Asn Am. *Res:* Electromagnetic properties of high Tc superconductors; superconducting transistors and EM scattering. *Mailing Add:* Dept Elec Eng Howard Univ Washington DC 20059

**WANG, YI-MING,** SOLAR PHYSICS, HIGH-ENERGY ASTROPHYSICS. *Current Pos:* ASTROPHYSICIST, NAVAL RES LAB, 88- *Personal Data:* b Hong Kong, Aug 3, 50; US citizen. *Educ:* Mass Inst Technol, ScD, 76. *Prof Exp:* Res fel, Astron Ctr, Univ Sussex, 76-79 & Astronomische Inst, Univ Bonn, 79-86; assoc scientist, Appl Res Corp, 86-88. *Concurrent Pos:* Vis res fel, Max Planck Inst Astrophys, 83-84. *Mem:* Am Astron Soc; Int Astron Union. *Res:* Solar and interplanetary physics; high-energy astrophysics; astrophysical fluids; theoretical and numerical modelling; data analysis. *Mailing Add:* Code 7672W Naval Res Lab Washington DC 20375

**WANG, YI-TIN,** BIODEGRADATION & BIOTRANSFORMATION OF ENVIRONMENTAL POLLUTANTS, BIOLOGICAL PROCESSES FOR WASTE TREATMENT. *Current Pos:* asst prof, 86-90, ASSOC PROF, DEPT CIVIL ENG, UNIV KY, 91- *Personal Data:* b Taiwan, China, Jan 17, 52; US citizen; m, Yuh-Lang Doung; c Andrew & Jonathan. *Educ:* Nat Chung-Hsing Univ, BS, 74; Nat Taiwan Univ, MS, 76; Univ Del, MCE, 81; Univ Ill, Urbana, PhD(environ eng), 84. *Prof Exp:* Res assoc, Dept Civil Eng, Univ Ill, 84-85. *Mem:* Water Environ Fedn; Am Water Works Asn; Am Soc Civil Engrs; Asn Environ Eng Profs. *Res:* Evaluate the factors affecting biotransformation of toxic hexavalent chromium; biochemical mechanisms and genes involved in the transformation of toxic hexavalent chromium. *Mailing Add:* Dept Civil Eng 365 Civil Eng Bldg Univ Ky Lexington KY 40506. *Fax:* 606-257-4404; *E-Mail:* ywang@engr.uky.edu

**WANG, YUAN REAU,** DATA STRUCTURES & PROGRAMMING LANGUAGES, PATTERN RECOGNITION. *Current Pos:* assoc prof elec eng & comput sci, 77-82, chmn, Dept Elec Eng & Comp Sci, 85-96, PROF ELEC ENG & COMPUT SCI, TEX A&M UNIV, KINGSVILLE, 82- *Personal Data:* b Wuchang, China, June 3, 34; US citizen; m 61, Betty Yang; c Gary, Lisa, Alan & Jean. *Educ:* Nat Taiwan Univ, BS, 55; State Univ Iowa, MS, 60; Northwestern Univ, Evanston, PhD(comput sci), 67. *Prof Exp:* Develop engr, Hawthorne Works, Western Elec Co, Ill, 60-63; asst prof indust eng, Univ Pittsburgh, 67-70; assoc prof comput sci, Univ Nebr, Lincoln, 70-77. *Concurrent Pos:* Assoc consult, Comput Mgt Consults, Inc, Skokie, Ill, 68-69; res fel, NASA-ASEE summer fac prog, Manned Spacecraft Ctr, Houston, Tex, 70 & 85; sr prog lang researcher, US Army Comput Systs Command, Ft Belvoir, Va, 76-77; electronic engr, Lawrence Livermore Nat Lab, Summer Res Inst, 80. *Mem:* Inst Elec & Electronics Engrs; Asn Comput Mach; Am Soc Eng Educ. *Res:* Formal languages and its applications; switching and automata theory as applied in computer organization; author of numerous publications. *Mailing Add:* Campus Box 192 Tex A&M Univ Kingsville TX 78363

**WANG, YU-LI,** CYTO-SKELETON, MYOGENESIS. *Current Pos:* SR SCIENTIST, WORCESTER FOUND EXP BIOL, 87- *Educ:* Harvard Univ, PhD(biophys), 80. *Prof Exp:* Staff scientist, Immunol & Respiratory Med, Nat Jewish Ctr, 82-87. *Concurrent Pos:* Assoc prof, Dept Cell Biol, Univ Mass, 87- *Mailing Add:* Worcester Found Exp Biol 222 Maple Ave Shrewsbury MA 01545-2795. *Fax:* 508-842-3915

**WANG, YUNG-LI,** SOLID STATE PHYSICS. *Current Pos:* asst prof, 68-72, assoc prof, 72-77, PROF PHYSICS, FLA STATE UNIV, 77- *Personal Data:* b Canton, China, Jan 8, 37; m 63; c 1. *Educ:* Nat Taiwan Univ, BS, 59; Nat Tsing Hua Univ, Taiwan, MS, 61; Univ Pa, PhD(physics), 66. *Prof Exp:* Res assoc physics, Univ Pa, 66-67 & Univ Pittsburgh, 67-68. *Mem:* Am Phys Soc. *Res:* Many body theory of spin systems, magnetic phase transitions; crystal-field effects and impurities in magnetic systems. *Mailing Add:* Dept Physics Fla State Univ 600 W College Ave Tallahassee FL 32306. *Fax:* 850-644-6504

**WANGAARD, FREDERICK FIELD,** FOREST PRODUCTS. *Current Pos:* CONSULT, 76- *Personal Data:* b Minneapolis, Minn, Jan 3, 11; m 36, Lorraine M Crough; c Frederick F Jr, Walter C & David B. *Educ:* Univ Minn, BS, 33; State Univ NY, MS, 35, PhD(wood technol), 39. *Hon Degrees:* MA, Yale Univ, 52. *Honors & Awards:* Borden Chem Award, 73; Outstanding Achievement Medal, Univ Minn, 75; Distinguished Serv Award, Soc Wood Sci & Technol, 83; Golden Mem Award, Soc Am Foresters, 84. *Prof Exp:* Instr forestry, Univ Wash, 36-39, asst prof wood technol, 39-42; technologist, Forest Prod Lab, US Forest Serv, 42-45; from asst prof to prof forest prod, Yale Univ, 45-67; head dept wood & wood sci, Colo State Univ, 68-76. *Concurrent Pos:* Adv, Food & Agr Orgn, Philippines, 57; Fulbright res scholar, Norway, 58. *Mem:* Forest Prod Res Soc (pres, 75); Soc Am Foresters; Soc Wood Sci & Technol (pres, 64); Int Acad Wood Sci. *Res:* Thermal conductivity of wood; properties of wood in relation to growth; properties of tropical woods; plywood and laminated wood; technology of wood fibers; wood structure and properties. *Mailing Add:* 1609 Hillside Dr Ft Collins CO 80524

**WANGBERG, JAMES KEITH,** ENTOMOLOGY. *Current Pos:* FAC, PLANT SOIL INSECT SCI DEPT, UNIV WYO. *Personal Data:* b Oakland, Calif, Sept 6, 46. *Educ:* Humboldt State Col, Calif, BA, 69; Calif State Univ, Humboldt, MA, 73; Univ Idaho, PhD(entom), 76. *Prof Exp:* Vis instr, Tex Tech Univ, 75-76, asst prof entom, 76-81, assoc prof, 81- *Concurrent Pos:* Co-prin investr, Smithsonian Inst res grant, 78- *Mem:* AAAS; Entom Soc Am; Soc Range Mgt. *Res:* Rangeland entomology with emphasis on insects affecting native shrubs; gall insect biology. *Mailing Add:* Plant Soil Insect Sci Dept Univ Wyo Laramie WY 82071

**WANGE, RONALD LEROY,** SIGNAL TRANSDUCTION, T-CELL ACTIVATION. *Current Pos:* Res fel, Nat Inst Child Health & Human Develop, 91-96, INVESTR, NAT INST AGING, NIH, 96- *Personal Data:* b Lynwood, Calif, Oct 9, 62. *Educ:* Univ Calif, BS, 84; Vanderbilt Univ, PhD(pharmacol), 91. *Mem:* Am Soc Biochem & Molecular Biol; AAAS. *Res:* Molecular signals involved in t cell activation in response to engagement of specific cell surface receptors, and attempting to understand how the same stimuli induce different outcomes in t-cells isolated from aged animals, or that have become tolerized. *Mailing Add:* 3 Pooks Hill Rd No 215 Bethesda MD 20814. *E-Mail:* wanger@grc.nia.nih.gov

**WANGEMANN, ROBERT THEODORE,** BIOPHYSICS. *Current Pos:* RETIRED. *Personal Data:* b Rhinelander, Wis, Apr 27, 33; m 54; c 2. *Educ:* Univ Wis-Madison, BS, 55; Univ Rochester, MS, 64; Med Col Va, PhD(biophys), 74. *Prof Exp:* Pharmacist, Northgate Drugs & Southside Drugs, 55-57; med supply officer, US Army, 57-62, health physicist, 64-67, instr nuclear sci, 67-70, chief, Laser-Microwave Div, 73-77, dir radiation & environ sci, 77-78, consult, Off Surgeon Gen, 78-81, comdr, Environ Hyg Agency, 81-84; assoc prof & dir laser biophys, Uniformed Serv Univ, 84-86; exec dir, Inst Elec & Electronics Engrs Lasers & Electro-Optics Soc, 86- *Concurrent Pos:* Mem, Phys Agents Threshold Limit Value Comt, Am Conf Govt Indust Hygienists; Merit Rev Panel, Med Res & Develop Command, US Army; assoc ed, Health Physics Jour. *Mem:* AAAS; Bioelectromagnetics Soc; Health Physics Soc; Inst Elec & Electronics Engrs; Am Soc Asn Execs. *Res:* Biological effects of electromagnetic radiation; interactions of radio frequency and optical energy at the biomolecular level and the photochemical aspects of vision and optical radiation effects. *Mailing Add:* Lasers & Electro-optics Soc Inst Elec & Electronics Engrs 445 Hoes Lane Piscataway NJ 08854

**WANGENSTEEN, OVE DOUGLAS,** RESPIRATORY PHYSIOLOGY, MICROVASCULAR EXCHANGE. *Current Pos:* asst prof, 70-76, ASSOC PROF PHYSIOL, MED SCH, UNIV MINN, MINNEAPOLIS, 76-, ASSOC PROF PEDIAT, 89- *Personal Data:* b St Paul, Minn, Mar 15, 42; m 65; c 2. *Educ:* Univ Minn, Minneapolis, BS, 64, PhD(physiol), 68. *Prof Exp:* Res assoc physiol, Sch Med & Dent, State Univ NY, Buffalo, 68-70. *Concurrent Pos:* Vis prof, Anat Inst, Univ Bern, Switz, 80; consult, 3M Co, 86- *Mem:* Am Physiol Soc; Am Thoracic Soc; Microcirculatory Soc. *Res:* Respiratory and cardiovascular physiology; transcapillary exchange; lung fluid balance; transport across lung epithelia. *Mailing Add:* Dept Physiol 6-255 Millard Hall Univ Minn 435 Delaware St SE Minneapolis MN 55455-0347. *Fax:* 612-625-5149; *E-Mail:* wange001@maroon.tc.umu.edu

**WANGENSTEEN, STEPHEN LIGHTNER,** SURGERY. *Current Pos:* PROF & HEAD, DEPT SURG, UNIV ARIZ, 76- *Personal Data:* b Minneapolis, Minn, Aug 30, 33; m 56; c 4. *Educ:* Univ Minn, BA, 54, BS, 55; Harvard Univ, MD, 58. *Prof Exp:* Instr surg, Columbia-Presby Med Ctr, 64-65; from asst prof to prof surg, Univ Va, 67-76. *Concurrent Pos:* Vascular fel, Columbia-Presby Med Ctr, 58-59, USPHS fel, 60-63. *Mem:* Asn Acad Surg (vpres, 67-68); Soc Univ Surg; Am Surg Asn. *Res:* Gastrointestinal pathophysiology; circulatory shock; vascular surgery. *Mailing Add:* Univ SFla Vet Affairs 12901 Bruce B Downs Blvd Box 16 Tampa FL 33612

**WANGERSKY, PETER JOHN,** ECOLOGY. *Current Pos:* assoc prof chem, Dalhousie Univ, 65-68, prof oceanog, 68-93, chmn, Dept Oceanog, 77-80, ADJ PROF, DALHOUSIE UNIV; ADJ PROF, UNIV VICTORIA. *Personal Data:* b Woonsocket, RI, Aug 26, 27; m 59, Eleanor Dodge; c Charles, Russell & George. *Educ:* Brown Univ, ScB, 49; Yale Univ, PhD(zool), 58. *Prof Exp:* Marine chem technician, Scripps Inst, Univ Calif, 49-50; chemist, Chem Corps, US Dept Army, 50-51; chem oceanogr, US Fish & Wildlife Serv, 51-54; res asst prof marine sci, Marine Lab, Univ Miami, 58-61; res assoc, Bingham Oceanog Lab, Yale Univ, 61-65. *Concurrent Pos:* John Simon Guggenheim Found, 71-72; ed-in-chief, Marine Chem, 74-92. *Mem:* AAAS; Am Soc Limnol & Oceanog; Am Chem Soc; Ecol Soc Am; Am Nat Soc. *Res:* Mechanisms of marine sedimentation; chemical oceanography; organic metabolites in sea water; population dynamics. *Mailing Add:* Sch Earth & Ocean Sci Univ Victoria Victoria BC V8W 2V2 Can. *Fax:* 250-721-6200; *E-Mail:* wangers@ibm.net

**WANG-IVERSON, PATSY,** CELL BIOLOGY, LIPID BIOCHEMISTRY. *Current Pos:* ASST PROF BIOCHEM, MT SINAI SCH MED, 79- *Personal Data:* b Shanghai, China, Jan 6, 47; m 76; c 1. *Educ:* Mt Holyoke Col, BA, 68; Bowman Gray Sch Med, 70, PhD(biochem), 75. *Prof Exp:* Res asst enzyme, Burroughs Wellcome & Co, 70-71; fel bact & immunol, Sch Med, Univ NC, 75-77, fel cellular physiol & immunol, Rockefeller Univ, 77-79. *Concurrent Pos:* Mem, Coun Arteriosclerosis. *Mem:* Sigma Xi; NY Acad Sci; Am Soc Biol Chemists. *Res:* Human monocyte; macrophage function, specifically its contribution to lipoprotein metabolism. *Mailing Add:* 444 N Third St Philadelphia PA 19123-4107. *Fax:* 732-932-3477; *E-Mail:* patsy@dimacs.rutgers.edu

**WANGLER, ROGER DEAN,** CELL BIOLOGY, CARDIOVASCULAR PHYSIOLOGY. *Current Pos:* RES SCIENTIST, EISENHOWER MED CTR, 87-; FIFTH GRADE TEACHER, GERALD FORD ELEM SCH, 92- *Personal Data:* b Webster City, Iowa, June 3, 50; m 72; c 2. *Educ:* Iowa State Univ, BS, 72; Univ Iowa, PhD(anat), 81. *Prof Exp:* Res assoc & fel, Mich State Univ, 85-87. *Mem:* Am Physiol Soc. *Res:* Regulation of coronary blood flow; solute exchange across the coronary microvascular bed. *Mailing Add:* 74381 Santolina Dr Palm Desert CA 92260

**WANGLER, THOMAS P,** PHYSICS. *Current Pos:* MEM STAFF, LOS ALAMOS NAT LAB, 80- *Personal Data:* b Bay City, Mich, Aug 2, 37. *Educ:* Mich State Univ, BS, 58; Univ Wis, PhD(physics), 64. *Prof Exp:* Res assoc physics, Univ Wis, 64-65 & Brookhaven Nat Lab, 65-66; asst physicist, Argonne Nat Lab, 66-80. *Mem:* Am Phys Soc. *Res:* Accelerator physics; cosmic rays; environmental science; nuclear physics; Experimental high energy physics. *Mailing Add:* AOTI H817 Los Alamos Nat Lab PO Box 1663 Los Alamos NM 87545. *Fax:* 505-665-6590

**WANGSNESS, PAUL JEROME,** ANIMAL NUTRITION. *Current Pos:* from asst prof to prof nutrit, 72-89, head, Dept Dairy & Animal Sci, 81-89, PROF & DIR, COOP EXTEN, PA STATE UNIV, 89- *Personal Data:* b Madison, Wis, Mar 27, 44; m 67; c 2. *Educ:* Univ Wis-Madison, BS, 66; Iowa State Univ, PhD(nutrit & physiol), 71. *Honors & Awards:* Young Scientist Award, NE Am Soc Animal Sci, 81. *Prof Exp:* NDEA fel nutrit, Iowa State Univ, 66-69, NSF fel, 69-71. *Concurrent Pos:* Dir, Am Soc Animal Sci Bd, 88-90. *Mem:* Am Dairy Sci Asn; Am Soc Animal Sci; Am Inst Nutrit. *Res:* Regulatory mechanisms involved in the control of food intake and the regulation of energy balance in lean and obese animals. *Mailing Add:* 217 Agr Admin Bldg University Park PA 16802-0001. *Fax:* 814-863-7776

**WANGSNESS, ROALD KLINKENBERG,** THEORETICAL PHYSICS. *Current Pos:* acting head dept, 83-85, prof, 59-89, EMER PROF PHYSICS, UNIV ARIZ, 89- *Personal Data:* b Sleepy Eye, Minn, July 24, 22; m 44, Cleo Abbott; c Peter A A & Steven J. *Educ:* Univ Minn, BA, 44; Stanford Univ, PhD(physics), 50. *Prof Exp:* Asst physics, Univ Minn, 42-44; jr scientist, Los Alamos Sci Lab, 44-45; asst physics, Univ Minn, 45-46; asst physics, Stanford Univ, 46-48; asst prof, Univ Md, 50-51, prof, 53-59. *Concurrent Pos:* Physicist, Naval Ord Lab, Md, 51-59; assoc ed, Am J Physics, 83-85. *Mem:* Fel AAAS; fel Am Phys Soc; Sigma Xi; Am Asn Physics Teachers. *Res:* Nuclear induction; nuclear moments; ferrimagnetic resonance; anti-ferromagnetism; atomic spectra; electromagnetism. *Mailing Add:* 5035 E Scarlett St Tucson AZ 85711-4340. *Fax:* 520-325-8363; *E-Mail:* rkw@azstarnet.com

**WANI, JAGANNATH K,** STATISTICS. *Current Pos:* RETIRED. *Personal Data:* b Maharashtra, India, Sept 10, 34; m 59; c 3. *Educ:* Univ Poona, BSc, 58, Hons, 59, MSc, 60; McGill Univ, PhD(math statist), 67. *Prof Exp:* Lectr math, Col Agr, Dhulia, India, 60-61; res asst statist, Gokhale Inst Econ, Poona, India, 61-62; res asst math statist, McGill Univ, 62-65; asst prof math, Univ Lethbridge, 65-66; from asst prof to assoc prof, St Mary's Univ, NS, 66-69; assoc prof, Univ Calgary, 69-85, prof statist, 85-95, chmn dept, 92-95. *Concurrent Pos:* Nat Res Coun Can fel, St Mary's Univ & Univ Calgary, 67-72; Can Math Cong fel, McGill Univ, Queen's Univ & Univ Alta, 69-71. *Mem:* Am Statist Asn; Statist Soc Can. *Res:* Distribution theory and statistical inference. *Mailing Add:* Dept Math & Statist Univ Calgary 2500 University Dr NW Calgary AB T2N 1N4 Can

**WANI, MANSUKHLAL CHHAGANLAL,** STEROID SYNTHESIS, SYNTHESIS OF HETEROCYCLIC COMPOUNDS. *Current Pos:* PRIN SCIENTIST, RES TRIANGLE INST, NC, 62- *Personal Data:* b Nandubar, India, Feb 20, 25; US citizen; m 54, Ramila I Dalal; c Bankim M. *Educ:* Bombay Univ, BSc, 47, MSc, 50; Ind Univ, PhD(chem), 62. *Honors & Awards:* Bruce F Cain Mem Award, Am Asn Cancer Res, 94; Award Recognition, Nat Cancer Inst, 96. *Prof Exp:* Lectr chem, Bhavan's Col, Bombay, India, 51-58; res asst, Ind Univ, Bloomington, 58-61; res assoc, Univ Wis-Madison, 61-62. *Mem:* Am Chem Soc; Am Soc Pharmacog; Sigma Xi; AAAS; NY Acad Sci. *Res:* Isolation and characterization of biologically active compounds from natural sources; synthesis of anticancer, antifertility and iron chelating agents. *Mailing Add:* Res Triangle Inst PO Box 12194 Research Triangle Park NC 27709-2194. *Fax:* 919-541-6326; *E-Mail:* mcw@rti.org

**WANIEK, RALPH WALTER,** PHYSICS. *Current Pos:* CONSULT, 89- *Personal Data:* b Milan, Italy, June 1, 25; nat US; m 53; c 1. *Educ:* Univ Vienna, PhD(physics), 50. *Prof Exp:* Res assoc nuclear physics, Inst Radium Res, Univ Vienna, 48-50; asst prof physics & math, Newton Col, 50-56; sr physicist, Cambridge Electron Accelerator, Harvard Univ & Mass Inst Technol, 50-58; dir res, Plasmadyne Corp, 58-60; pres & dir res, Advan Kinetics, Inc, 60-89. *Concurrent Pos:* Res fel, Synchrocyclotron Lab, Harvard

Univ, 50-55; consult, Transistor Prod, Inc, 52-55 & Allied Res Assocs, 56-57; lectr, Boston Col, 56-58 & Exten, Univ Calif, Los Angeles, 59-67. *Mem:* Am Phys Soc; Am Inst Aeronaut & Astronaut; Inst Elec & Electronics Engrs. *Res:* Plasma, laser, space and nuclear physics; solid state; production of very intense magnetic fields; problems of space propulsion. *Mailing Add:* 1388 Pacific Ave Laguna Beach CA 92651

**WANIELISTA, MARTIN PAUL,** ENVIRONMENTAL ENGINEERING, WATER RESOURCES. *Current Pos:* From asst prof to assoc prof, 70-76, actg chmn, Dept Civil & Environ Eng, 78-94, PROF ENG & GORDON J BARNETT PROF ENVIRON SYSTS & MGT, FLA TECHNOL UNIV, 76-, DEAN, COL ENG, UNIV CENT FLA, 94- *Personal Data:* b Taylor, Pa, Dec 7, 41; m 66; c 1. *Educ:* Univ Detroit, BS, 64; Manhattan Col, MS, 65; Cornell Univ, PhD(environ eng), 71. *Concurrent Pos:* Dir, Environ Systs Eng Inst, 71-74; NSF grant, 72-73; pres, STE Inc, 73- *Mem:* Am Soc Civil Engrs; Am Soc Eng Educ; Asn Environ Eng Prof; Am Water Works Asn; Am Water Resources Asn. *Res:* Optimization models for water and solid waste systems; lake restoration; mathematical models of surface water systems; atmospheric pollution measurements and control methods. *Mailing Add:* Off Dean Col Eng Univ Cent Fla Box 162993 Orlando FL 32816-2993

**WANKAT, PHILLIP CHARLES,** SEPARATIONS. *Current Pos:* Assoc prof, Purdue Univ, 74-78, head freshman eng, 87-95, interim dir continuing eng educ, 96, PROF CHEM ENG, PURDUE UNIV, WEST LAFAYETTE, 78- *Personal Data:* b Oak Park, Ill, July 11, 44; m 80, Dorothy Richardson; c 2. *Educ:* Purdue Univ, West Lafayette, BS, 66; Princeton Univ, PhD(chem eng), 70; Purdue Univ, MS Ed, 82. *Honors & Awards:* Westinghouse Award, Am Soc Eng Educ, 84, Carlson Award, 90; Catalyst Award, Chem Mfrs Asn, 93; Separation Sci & Tech Award, Am Chem Soc, 94. *Concurrent Pos:* NSF eng grants, 72-; vis prof, ENSIC, Nancy, France, 83-84. *Mem:* Am Inst Chem Engrs; Am Chem Soc; Am Soc Eng Educ. *Res:* Separation techniques; adsorption distillation; pressure swing adsorption; chromatography; biochemical separations; combined fermentation-separation. *Mailing Add:* Sch Chem Eng Purdue Univ West Lafayette IN 47907-1283. *Fax:* 765-494-0805; *E-Mail:* Wankat@ecn.purdue.edu

**WANKE, SIEGHARD ERNST,** CHEMICAL ENGINEERING. *Current Pos:* from asst prof to assoc prof, 70-78, chmn dept, 85-90, PROF CHEM ENG, UNIV ALTA, 78- *Personal Data:* b Herrenstein, Ger, July 31, 42; Can citizen; m 69; c 3. *Educ:* Univ Alta, BSc, 64, MSc, 66; Univ Calif, Davis, PhD(chem eng), 69. *Prof Exp:* Engr, Chemcell Ltd, Alta, 65-66; res engr, Celanese Res Co, 69-70. *Mem:* Chem Inst Can; Can Soc Chem Eng; Am Inst Chem Engrs; Electron Micros Soc Am; Can. *Res:* Heterogeneous catalysis; supported metal catalysts; chemical kinetics; olefin polymerization. *Mailing Add:* Dept Chem & Mat Eng Univ Alta Edmonton AB T6G 2M7 Can

**WANLESS, HAROLD ROGERS,** SEDIMENTOLOGY, MARINE GEOLOGY. *Current Pos:* Res scientist, Univ Miami, 71-73, res asst prof, 73-75, asst prof, 75-81, ASSOC PROF MARINE GEOL, SCH MARINE & ATMOSPHERIC SCI, UNIV MIAMI, 81- *Personal Data:* b Champaign, Ill, Feb 14, 42; m 65; c 3. *Educ:* Princeton Univ, AB, 64; Univ Miami, MS, 68; Johns Hopkins Univ, PhD(geol), 73. *Mem:* Soc Econ Paleontologists & Mineralogists. *Res:* Environments and processes of modern coastal and shelf sediments; petrology and paleo-environmental reconstruction of ancient sedimentary rocks; fine-grained sediment dynamics; biotic influences on sediments; economic and environmental application. *Mailing Add:* Dept Marine Sci Univ Miami Coral Gables FL 33124

**WANN, ELBERT VAN,** GENETICS, PLANT BREEDING. *Current Pos:* RETIRED. *Personal Data:* b Grange, Ark, Dec 29, 30; m 50, Joyce N Sawyer; c Vivian L. *Educ:* Univ Ark, BS, 59, MS, 60; Purdue Univ, PhD(genetics), 62. *Honors & Awards:* Asgrow Award, Am Soc Hort Sci, 72. *Prof Exp:* Res assoc veg crops, Univ Ill, 62-63; geneticist, USDA, Agr Res Serv, 63-71, lab dir, US Veg Lab, 72-84, res leader, Scen Agr Res Lab, USDA, 84-97. *Mem:* Fel Am Soc Hort Sci; Am Soc Agron; Crop Sci Soc Am; Coun Agr Sci & Technol. *Res:* Genetics and breeding of sweet corn and tomatoes, as related to disease and insect resistance and the improvement of consumer quality. *Mailing Add:* USDA-ARS-SCARL PO Box 159 Hwy 3W Lane OK 74555

**WANNEMACHER, ROBERT, JR,** BIOCHEMISTRY, NUTRITION. *Current Pos:* SR BIOCHEMIST, PHYS SCI DIV, US ARMY MED RES INST INFECTIOUS DIS, 69- *Personal Data:* b Hackensack, NJ, Jan 12, 29; m 71. *Educ:* Wagner Col, BS, 50; Rutgers Univ, MS, 51, PhD(biochem, nutrit), 60. *Prof Exp:* From res asst to res assoc nutrit & biochem, Bur Biol Res, Rutgers Univ, 51-60, from asst res prof to assoc res prof, 60-69. *Mem:* AAAS; Am Inst Nutrit; Am Chem Soc; Biophys Soc; Soc Exp Biol & Med; Am Soc Biol Chem; Soc Toxicol; Int Soc Toxinol. *Res:* Protein and RNA metabolism; infectious diseases; regulatory mechanisms; endocrinology, cancer and radiation; toxicinology. *Mailing Add:* Army Med Res Inst Infect Dis Frederick MD 21702-5011. *Fax:* 301-619-2348

**WANNER, ADAM,** PULMONARY DISEASES, ASTHMA. *Current Pos:* PROF MED & CHIEF, PULMONARY DIV, UNIV MIAMI, 83- *Educ:* Univ Basil, Switz, MD, 66. *Mailing Add:* Dept Med Univ Miami Sch Med 4300 Alton Rd Miami Beach FL 33140. *Fax:* 305-674-2647

**WANNIER, PETER GREGORY,** RADIO ASTRONOMY. *Current Pos:* MEM TECH STAFF, SPACE PHYSICS & ASTROPHYS SECT, JET PROPULSION LAB, PASADENA, 83- *Personal Data:* b Iowa City, Iowa, Sept 14, 46; m 78; c 4. *Educ:* Stanford Univ, BS, 68; Princeton Univ,

PhD(astron), 75. *Prof Exp:* Tech consult radio astron, Bell Tel Labs, 74-75; asst prof astron & elec eng, Univ Mass, 75-76; from asst prof to assoc prof radio astron, Calif Inst Technol, 78-83. *Concurrent Pos:* Mem, Comn J, Int Union Radio Sci, 77-88; vis prof, Univ Gothenburg, Sweden, 86-87; mem, Comn 34, Int Astron Union, 86-88. *Mem:* Am Astron Soc; Int Astron Union. *Res:* Millimeter-wave and centimeter-wave studies of the interstellar medium, especially of dense clouds, with special interest in nuclear processing of material in the galaxy. *Mailing Add:* 5131 Gould Ave La Canada Flintridge CA 91011

**WANTLAND, EVELYN KENDRICK,** MATHEMATICS. *Current Pos:* RETIRED. *Personal Data:* b Suffolk, Va, June 22, 17; wid; c Lois K Dimmitt. *Educ:* Univ Ill, BA, 48, MA, 49, PhD(math), 58. *Prof Exp:* Asst, Univ Ill, 48-49; prof math, Ferrum Jr Col, 49-51; asst prof, Ill Wesleyan Univ, 51-57; asst prof, Kans State Univ, 57-62; assoc prof, Univ Miss, 62-64; prof math & head dept, Ill Wesleyan Univ, 64-76. *Mem:* Am Math Soc; Math Asn Am; Sigma Xi. *Res:* Complex variables. *Mailing Add:* 101 W Windsor Rd Urbana IL 61801

**WAPNIR, RAUL A,** BIOCHEMICAL NUTRITION, INTESTINAL PHYSIOLOGY. *Current Pos:* assoc prof biochem pediat, 73-80, head lab, Pediat Res, North Shore Univ Hosp, 73-91, PROF BIOCHEM PEDIAT, MED COL, CORNELL UNIV, 80-, HEAD, PERINATAL MED RES LAB, 91- *Personal Data:* b Buenos Aires, Arg, Jan 6, 30; US citizen; m 52; c 2. *Educ:* Univ Buenos Aires, Arg, MS, 53, PhD(chem), 54; Johns Hopkins Univ, Baltimore, MPH, 70. *Prof Exp:* Sr biochemist, Res Dept, Rosewood State Hosp, 63-70, co-dir, 70-73. *Concurrent Pos:* From asst to assoc prof pediat res, Univ Md Sch Med, 66-73; grants, NIH, 87-90 & 95-97, USDA, 88-91. *Mem:* Fel Am Col Nutrit; Am Soc Nutrit Sci; Soc Exp Biol & Med; NY Acad Sci. *Res:* Intestinal absorption research, as related to the transport of trace elements and electrolytes, using animal models of gastrointestinal diseases prevalent in childhood. *Mailing Add:* North Shore Univ Hosp Manhasset NY 11030. *Fax:* 516-562-1022; *E-Mail:* rwapnir@nshs.edu

**WAPPNER, REBECCA SUE,** PEDIATRICS, BIOCHEMICAL GENETICS. *Current Pos:* fel pediat metab & genetics, 73-75, from asst prof to assoc prof, 75-93, PROF PEDIAT, SCH MED, IND UNIV, INDIANAPOLIS, 93-, PROF MED GENETICS, 94- *Personal Data:* b Mansfield, Ohio, Feb 25, 44. *Educ:* Ohio Univ, BS, 66; Ohio State Univ, MD, 70; Am Bd Pediat, dipl, 75; Am Bd Med Genetics, dipl, 82. *Prof Exp:* Intern pediat, Children's Hosp, Columbus, Ohio, 70-71, resident, 71-72, asst chief resident, 72-73. *Mem:* Am Acad Pediat; Sigma Xi; Am Soc Human Genetics; Am Med Women's Asn; Soc Study Inborn Errors Metab; Soc Inherited Metab Dis. *Res:* Inborn errors of metabolism. *Mailing Add:* Dept Pediat Riley Rm 0907 Sch Med Ind Univ Indianapolis IN 46202-5225

**WARAVDEKAR, VAMAN SHIVRAM,** BIOCHEMISTRY, EXPERIMENTAL CANCER CHEMOTHERAPY. *Current Pos:* RETIRED. *Personal Data:* b Varavda, India, May 11, 14; nat US; m 60, Mazie F Duke; c Neil & Jay. *Educ:* Univ Bombay, MSc, 40, PhD(chem), 42. *Prof Exp:* Res assoc, V J Tech Inst, India, 42-45; res officer carcinogenesis, Tata Mem Hosp, Bombay, 45-48; prin investr, Georgetown Univ, 50-52; vis scientist, Nat Cancer Inst, 52-57; prof biochem, All-India Inst Med Sci, 57-58; chief, Biochem Br, Armed Forces Inst Path, 58-65; dir, Cancer Chemother Dept, Microbial Assocs, Inc, DC, 65-72; res chemist, Off Assoc Dir Drug Res & Develop, Div Cancer Treat, 72-73, res planning officer, Nat Cancer Inst, 73-, Off Assoc Dir Prof Prog Planning & Anal, 83. *Concurrent Pos:* Res fel chemother cancer, Nat Cancer Inst, 48-50; lectr, Grad Sch, Georgetown Univ, 50-55; adj prof, Dept Med, Georgetown Univ Med Ctr, 83-88. *Mem:* AAAS; Soc Exp Biol & Med; Am Soc Pharmacol & Exp Therapeut; Am Chem Soc; Am Asn Cancer Res; fel NY Acad Sci. *Res:* Cellular chemistry; metabolism; enzymology; fatty acid oxidation; protein synthesis; chemotherapy; cancer research. *Mailing Add:* 9479 Reichs Ford Rd Ijamsville MD 21754-9551

**WARBURTON, CHARLES E, JR,** POLYMER CHEMISTRY & PHYSICS. *Current Pos:* RES SCIENTIST, ROHM & HAAS CO, 67- *Personal Data:* b Holyoke, Mass, Nov 20, 41; m 66; c 4. *Educ:* Univ Mass, BChE, 63; Princeton Univ, MA, 65, PhD(chem eng), 67. *Prof Exp:* Fel, Textile Res Inst, 63-67. *Mem:* Sigma Xi. *Res:* Polymer chemistry and physics, adhesion, textile finishes, nonwoven binders, organic coatings, radiation cure coatings. *Mailing Add:* 915 Denston Dr Ambler PA 19002. *E-Mail:* rsscew@rohmhaas.com

**WARBURTON, DAVID LEWIS,** GEOCHEMISTRY, WATER RESOURCES. *Current Pos:* asst prof, 75-91, ASSOC PROF GEOL, FLA ATLANTIC UNIV, 91- *Personal Data:* b Hackensack, NJ, Aug 10, 47; m 75. *Educ:* Univ Calif, San Diego, BA, 69; Univ Chicago, PhD(geochem), 78. *Mem:* Am Geophys Union; AAAS; Mineral Soc Am; Sigma Xi; Geol Soc Am; Nat Asn Geol Teachers. *Res:* Inorganic pollution of water. *Mailing Add:* Dept Geol Fla Atlantic Univ PO Box 3091 Boca Raton FL 33431. *Fax:* 561-367-2745

**WARBURTON, DOROTHY,** HUMAN GENETICS, CYTOGENETICS. *Current Pos:* instr obstet & gynec, Columbia Univ, 68-69, assoc human genetics & develop, 69-71, asst prof human genetics & develop, 71-75, asst prof pediat, 74-75, PROF CLIN GENETICS PEDIAT, COL PHYSICIANS & SURGEONS, COLUMBIA UNIV, 75-; DIR GENETICS DIAG LAB, PRESBY HOSP, 69- *Personal Data:* b Toronto, Ont, Jan 12, 36; m 57; c 4. *Educ:* McGill Univ, BSc, 57, PhD(genetics), 61. *Prof Exp:* From res asst to res assoc human genetics, Montreal Children's Hosp & McGill Univ, 58-63; res assoc obstet & gynec, Col Physicians & Surgeons, Columbia Univ, 64-67;

dir genetics serv, St Luke's Hosp Ctr, 67-68. *Mem:* Am Soc Human Genetics. *Res:* Cytogenetics; congenital malformations; human embryonic and fetal death; human gene mapping. *Mailing Add:* Col Physicians & Surgeons Columbia Univ 630 W 168th St New York NY 10032

**WARBURTON, ERNEST KEELING,** NUCLEAR PHYSICS. *Current Pos:* assoc physicist, 61-63, physicist, 63-68, SR PHYSICIST, BROOKHAVEN NAT LAB, 68- *Personal Data:* b Worcester, Mass, Apr 26, 28; m 47; c 3. *Educ:* Miami Univ, BA, 49; Mass Inst Technol, SB, 51; Univ Pittsburgh, PhD(physics), 57. *Prof Exp:* From instr to asst prof physics, Princeton Univ, 58-61. *Concurrent Pos:* NSF fel, Oxford Univ, 63-64 & 68-69; consult, Lawrence Livermore Nat Lab; assoc ed, Phys Rev Letters, 82-87; Alexander von Humboldt Award, 88-89. *Mem:* Fel Am Phys Soc. *Res:* Theoretical and experimental investigations of nuclear structure. *Mailing Add:* 12 Harbor Hills Dr Port Jefferson NY 11777. *Fax:* 516-282-3000

**WARBURTON, WILLIAM KURTZ,** X-RAY DIFFRACTIONS FROM LIQUIDS, X-RAY DETECTOR & OPTICS. *Current Pos:* from asst res prof x-ray detectors to assoc res prof x-ray detectors, 84-85, RES ASSOC PROF RADIOL, UNIV SOUTHERN CALIF SCH MED, 87-; PRES X-RAY INSTRUMENT RES CONSULT, X-RAY INSTRUMENT ASN, 88- *Personal Data:* b Pasadena, CA, July 21, 42. *Educ:* Cornell Univ, BSE, 64, MSE, 66; Harvard Univ, MA, 65, PhD(physics) 72. *Prof Exp:* Res assoc nat sci, Div Eng & Appl Sci, Stanford Synchrotron Radiation Lab, 72-78 & Dept Mat Sci, 79, sr res assoc x-ray phys, 79-84. *Concurrent Pos:* Sr scientist x-ray instrument, Adv Res & Appln Corp, 87-88. *Mem:* Am Phys Soc; AAAS; Int Soc Optic Eng; Int Radiation Physics Soc. *Res:* Advanced x-ray instrumentation for x-ray research using synchrotron or laboratory sources, including x-ray optics, array detectors, and beamline components; x-ray scattering studies of structure of liquids, amorphous materials, and x-ray optical elements. *Mailing Add:* X-Ray Instrumentation Assoc 2513 Charleston Rd Suite 207 Mountain View CA 94043. *Fax:* 650-903-9887

**WARCHOL, MARK EDWARD,** SENSORY NEUROBIOLOGY. *Current Pos:* res assoc, 89-94, ASST PROF, DEPT OLARYNGOL-HNS, UNIV VA, 94- *Personal Data:* b Portland, Ore, June 6, 57. *Educ:* Univ Wash, BS, 81, Northwestern Univ, PhD(neurobiol), 89. *Mem:* AAAS; Soc Neurosci; Asn Res Otolaryngol. *Res:* Cellular mechanisms of regeneration in the auditory and vestibular systems; immune system influences on sensory development. *Mailing Add:* Dept Otolaryngol-HNS Sch Med Univ Va PO Box 396 Charlottesville VA 22908. *E-Mail:* markw@virginia.edu

**WARD, ANTHONY THOMAS,** PHYSICAL CHEMISTRY. *Current Pos:* MEM RES STAFF, XEROX CORP, 66- *Personal Data:* b London, Eng, Mar 9, 41; m 66, Sandra Elliott; c Teresa & Stephanie. *Educ:* Univ London, BSc, 62; Rensselaer Polytech Inst, MS, 64, PhD(phys chem), 66. *Mem:* Soc Photog Scientists & Engrs; Sigma Xi. *Res:* Design approaches; fabrication methods and spectroscopic characterization techniques for xerographic photoconductors and optical disk devices. *Mailing Add:* 934 Little Pond Way Webster NY 14580

**WARD, ARTHUR ALLEN, JR,** NEUROSURGERY. *Current Pos:* from asst prof to prof surg, 48-65, chmn dept, 65-81, PROF NEUROSURG, MED SCH, UNIV WASH, 65- *Personal Data:* b Manipay, Ceylon, Feb 4, 16; US citizen; m 41. *Educ:* Yale Univ, BA, 38, MD, 42. *Honors & Awards:* Lennox Award, 76. *Prof Exp:* Demonstr path, McGill Univ, 43, demonstr neurol & neurosurg, 44-45; asst physiol, Yale Univ, 45; asst, Ill Neuropsychiat Inst, 46; instr neurosurg, Univ Louisville, 46-48. *Concurrent Pos:* Fel, McGill Univ, 43. *Mem:* Soc Neurol Surg (pres, 74); Am Acad Neurol Surg (pres, 77-78); Am Epilepsy Soc (vpres, 49, pres, 72); Am Physiol Soc; Am EEG Soc (pres, 59-60). *Res:* Epilepsy; function of animal and human cerebral cortex; reticular formation of the midbrain. *Mailing Add:* Univ Wash N-S Med Seattle WA 98195

**WARD, BENJAMIN F, JR,** NEW CHEMICAL PRODUCT DEVELOPMENT, RESEARCH MANAGEMENT. *Current Pos:* Res chemist, Westvaco Corp, 69-72, res group leader, 72-74, prod develop mgr, 74-75, tech dir, 75-79, sr prod mgr, 79-83, RES DIR, CHARLESTON RES CTR, WESTVACO CORP, 83- *Personal Data:* b Yazoo City, Miss, Apr 23, 43; m 66; c 2. *Educ:* Rhodes Col, BS, 65; Univ NC-Chapel Hill, PhD(chem), 69. *Mem:* Am Chem Soc; Tech Asn Pulp & Paper Indust; Can Pulp & Paper Asn; Int Acad Wood Sci. *Res:* Pulping and bleaching technology; derivitization and utilization of the by-products of the paper industry; tall oil fatty acids, rosin, lignin and carbon. *Mailing Add:* Westvaco Corp PO Box 118005 North Charleston SC 29423-8005

**WARD, BENNIE FRANKLIN LEON,** THEORETICAL PHYSICS. *Current Pos:* assoc prof, 86-90, PROF PHYSICS, UNIV TENN, KNOXVILLE, 90- *Personal Data:* b Millen, Ga, Oct 19, 48. *Educ:* Mass Inst Technol, BS(physics) & BS(math), 70; Princeton Univ, MA, 71, PhD(physics), 73. *Prof Exp:* Instr physics, Princeton Univ, 73; res assoc physics, Stanford Linear Accelerator Ctr, Stanford Univ, 73-75; asst prof physics, Purdue Univ, West Lafayette, 75-78; staff engr, Intel Corp, 79-80; res specialist, 80-82, staff engr, Lockheed Missiles & Space Co, 82-84. *Concurrent Pos:* Vis scientist, Stanford Linear Accelerator Ctr, 78-, res assoc, 78. *Mem:* Am Phys Soc; Inst Elec & Electronics Engrs; NY Acad Sci; Sigma Xi; AAAS. *Res:* Pursues primarily renormalization-group-improved Yennie-Frantschi-Suura approach to high precision SU2L x U1; radiative corrections at SLC and LEP and new heavy particle production and decay at SLC and LEP type energies. *Mailing Add:* Physics/Astron Univ Tenn Knoxville TN 37996-1200. *E-Mail:* bflw@slacvm

**WARD, BESS B,** MARINE MICROBIAL ECOLOGY, BIOGEOCHEMISTRY OF AQUATIC SYSTEMS. *Current Pos:* asst prof, 89-91, assoc prof, 91-95, PROF OCEAN SCI, UNIV CALIF, SANTA CRUZ, 95-, CHAIR OCEAN SCI DEPT, 95- *Personal Data:* b Tonowanda, NY, Oct 6, 54. *Educ:* Mich State Univ, BS, 76; Univ Wash, MS, 79, PhD(oceanog), 82. *Honors & Awards:* G Evelyn Hutchinson Award, Am Soc Limnol & Oceanog, 97. *Prof Exp:* Researcher, Scripps Inst Oceanog, 82-84, asst res scientist, 84-89. *Concurrent Pos:* Prin investr, NSF, Dept Energy, Off Naval Res & NASA, 84-; vis scientist, Max Planck Inst Limnol, 93. *Mem:* Am Soc Limnol & Oceanog; Am Soc Microbiol; Oceanog Soc; Sigma Xi. *Res:* Focus on bacteria involved in the nitrogen cycle; use of molecular, isotopic and chemical methods to investigate bacterial transformations in marine and other aquatic environments; denitrification in oxygen minimum zones of the ocean; nitrification in Antarctic lakes; degradation by denitrifying bacteria in intertidal sediments; probes for denitrifying and nitrifying bacteria in aquatic environments. *Mailing Add:* Ocean Sci Dept Univ Calif Santa Cruz CA 95064. *Fax:* 408-459-4882; *E-Mail:* bbw@cats.ucsc.edu

**WARD, CALVIN HERBERT,** PLANT PATHOLOGY, PHYSIOLOGY. *Current Pos:* assoc prof biol, 66-70, PROF BIOL & ENVIRON SCI & CHMN, DEPT ENVIRON SCI & ENG, RICE UNIV, 70-, CO-DIR, NAT CTR GROUNDWATER RES, 79- *Personal Data:* b Strawberry, Ark, Mar 1, 33; m 54; c 3. *Educ:* NMex State Univ, BS, 55; Cornell Univ, MS, 58, PhD(plant path), 60; Univ Tex, MPH, 78. *Honors & Awards:* Group Achievement Award, STS-1 Shuttle Environ Effects Team, NASA, 81; Charles Porter Award, Soc Indust Microbiol, 86; Distinguished Serv Award, Soc Environ Toxicol & Chem, 90. *Prof Exp:* Res biologist, USAF Sch Aerospace Med, 60-63, plant physiologist, 63-65. *Concurrent Pos:* Grants, NASA, 63-66 & 70-, Environ Protection Agency, 66- & USAF, 68-70; mem environ biol adv panel, Am Inst Biol Sci, 66-71, chmn, 69-71, mem comt space shuttle impact eval, 74-; mem bd dirs, Southwest Ctr Urban Res, 69-, chmn, 77-78; mem life sci comt, NASA, 71-78; vis prof, Sch Pub Health, Univ Tex, Houston, 73-74, adj prof environ health, 74-; vpres, US Nat Comn, Int Water Resource Asn, 77-; ed-in-chief, Environ Toxicol & Chem, 81-; sr ed, J Indust Microbiol & Develop Indust Microbiol, 85-; mem, Expert Panel Res Needs & Opportunities at Federally-Supervised Hazardous Waste Sites, Coun Environ Qual, Exec Off Pres, 85-86; mem, Comt Multimedia Approaches to Pollution Control, Nat Acad Sci, 86-87, Environ Eng Comt, Sci Adv Bd, US Environ Protection Agency & Adv Comt Multiagency Hazardous Wastes Res, Nat Acad Sci, 87; mem bd dirs, Am Type Culture Collection, 87. *Mem:* AAAS; Am Phytopath Soc; Am Soc Microbiol; Soc Indust Microbiol (pres, 83-84); Int Water Resource Asn; Am Inst Biol Sci (pres, 84-85); Soc Environ Toxicol & Chem; Asn Ground Water Sci & Eng. *Res:* Algal and plant physiology; bioregeneration; environmental microbiology; ground water contamination and pollution control. *Mailing Add:* Depts Biol & Environ Sci & Eng Rice Univ 6100 Main St Houston TX 77005-1827

**WARD, CALVIN LUCIAN,** GENETICS. *Current Pos:* from instr to assoc prof zool, 52-78, PROF ZOOL, DUKE UNIV, 78- *Personal Data:* b Yancey, Tex, Jan 30, 28; m 66; c 2. *Educ:* Univ Tex, BA, 47, MA, 49, PhD(zool), 51. *Prof Exp:* AEC fel, Oak Ridge Nat Lab, 51-52. *Mem:* Genetics Soc Am; Soc Study Evolution. *Res:* Cytology and genetics of Drosophila; speciation. *Mailing Add:* Box 91000 Duke Univ Durham NC 27708

**WARD, CHARLES ALBERT,** MECHANICAL ENGINEERING, BIOMEDICAL ENGINEERING. *Current Pos:* From asst prof to assoc prof, 67-72, PROF MECH ENG, UNIV TORONTO, 77- *Personal Data:* b Bailey, Tex, May 28, 39; m 59. *Educ:* Univ Tex, Arlington, BSc, 62; Northwestern Univ, PhD(mech eng), 67. *Honors & Awards:* Robert W Angus Medal, Can Soc Mech Eng & Eng Inst Can, 88. *Concurrent Pos:* Res assoc, Hosp Sick Children, 72- *Res:* Surface and chemical kinetics; phase change and stability; biocompatibility of synthetic materials; complement activation. *Mailing Add:* 25 Borden St Toronto ON M5S 1A4 Can

**WARD, CHARLES EUGENE WILLOUGHBY,** COMPUTER SOFTWARE DESIGN. *Current Pos:* mem tech staff, AT&T Bell Labs, 79-84, TECH MGR, LUCENT TECHNOL, 84- *Personal Data:* b Madison, Wis, Sept 8, 38; m 61, Ann Langdon; c Carol & Douglas. *Educ:* Northwestern Univ, BS, 61; Mass Inst Technol, PhD(physics), 67. *Prof Exp:* Res assoc, Lab Nuclear Sci, Mass Inst Technol, 67-68; appointee, High Energy Physics Div, Argonne Nat Lab, 68-70, asst physicist, 70-73, physicist, 74-79. *Mem:* Am Soc Qual Control. *Res:* Managing computer software development for switching systems and other telecommunications applications. *Mailing Add:* Rm IH-6N-312 Lucent Technol 2000 N Naperville Rd Naperville IL 60566

**WARD, CHARLES RICHARD,** ENTOMOLOGY, AGRICULTURE. *Current Pos:* res assoc, 78-80, assoc prof, 78-85, PROF ENTOM, NMEX STATE UNIV, 85-, EXTEN ENTOMOLOGIST PEST MGT SPECIALIST, 80- *Personal Data:* b Tahoka, Tex, Mar 25, 40; m 61; c 2. *Educ:* Tex Tech Col, BS, 62, MS, 64; Cornell Univ, PhD(med entom), 68. *Honors & Awards:* Outstanding Contrib Award, Am Registry Prof Entomologists, 81. *Prof Exp:* From asst prof to assoc prof entom, Tex Tech Univ, 67-76; assoc prof, Tex Agr Exp Sta, 76; entom specialist, Consortium Int Develop, Bolivia, 76-78. *Concurrent Pos:* Consult, Consortium Int Crop Protection, Indonesia, 81, Dominican Repub, 88, Guatemala, 89, Ecuador, 90; chief, Consortium Int Develop, Honduras, 83-84, Trop Res & Develop, El Salvador, 89 & 90. *Mem:* Entom Soc Am; Am Registry Prof Entomologists. *Res:* Pest management research and extension; biology and control of ornamental, turf, cotton, alfalfa, pecan and range land pests; ecology of desert and grasslands insects; biological control; insects resistance to pesticides. *Mailing Add:* Entom Plant Path & Weed Sci Dept NMex State Univ 9301 Indian School Rd NE-201 Albuquerque NM 87112

**WARD, CHARLOTTE REED,** PHYSICAL CHEMISTRY, SCIENCE EDUCATION. *Current Pos:* RETIRED. *Personal Data:* b Lexington, Ky, Feb 19, 29; m 51; c Emma (Morris), Bess, Mark & Matthew. *Educ:* Univ Ky, BS, 49; Purdue Univ, MS, 51, PhD(phys chem), 56. *Prof Exp:* Instr gen sci, Ala Educ TV, Auburn Univ, 58-60, 61-62 & 63-72, from instr to assoc prof physics, 61-94. *Concurrent Pos:* Abstractor, Chem Abstr, 58-82; auth; pres state conf, Am Asn Univ Professors, 89-91, mem coun, 91-94, exec comt, 92-94. *Mem:* Am Asn Physics Teachers; Sigma Xi; Am Asn Univ Professors. *Res:* Molecular spectroscopy; development of physical science courses and textbooks, "hands-on" science for children. *Mailing Add:* 134 Norwood Ave Auburn AL 36830

**WARD, COLEMAN YOUNGER,** AGRONOMY, PHYSIOLOGY. *Current Pos:* prof agron & dept head, 79-83, PROF & TURF SPECIALIST, AUBURN UNIV, 83- *Personal Data:* b Millican, Tex, Sept 20, 28; m 47; c 3. *Educ:* Tex Tech Univ, BS, 50, MS, 54; Va Polytech Inst & State Univ, PhD(agron), 62. *Prof Exp:* Instr agricult, Eastern NMex Univ, 50-51; soil scientist, Soil Conserv Serv, USDA, 51-52; instr agron, Tex Tech Univ, 52-54; asst agronomist, Univ Fla, 54-55 & Va Agr Exp Sta, 55-61; from assoc prof to prof crop sci, Miss State Univ, 61-74; prof agron & chmn dept, Univ Fla, 74-80. *Concurrent Pos:* Biomass Res. *Mem:* Fel Am Soc Agron; Sigma Xi; Crop Sci Soc Am. *Res:* Physiology and ecology of turfgrasses and forage crops. *Mailing Add:* 3809 Heritage Pl Opelika AL 36801-7615

**WARD, CURTIS HOWARD,** PHYSICAL CHEMISTRY. *Current Pos:* assoc prof, 61-65, PROF CHEM, AUBURN UNIV, 65- *Personal Data:* b Round Bottom, Ohio, June 21, 27; m 51; c 4. *Educ:* Ind State Teachers Col, BS, 47; Univ Ky, MS, 50; Purdue Univ, PhD(phys chem), 54. *Prof Exp:* Res chemist, Linde Co Div, Union Carbide Corp, 53-57; assoc prof chem, Auburn Univ, 57-60; sr staff scientist, Avco Corp, 60-61. *Mem:* Am Chem Soc; Sigma Xi. *Res:* Thermodynamics; molecular spectroscopy; organometallic chemistry. *Mailing Add:* 134 Norwood Ave Auburn AL 36830

**WARD, DANIEL BERTRAM,** PLANT TAXONOMY. *Current Pos:* From asst prof to assoc prof, 58-75, PROF BOT, UNIV FLA, 75- *Personal Data:* b Crawfordsville, Ind, Mar 20, 28; m 56; c 4. *Educ:* Wabash Col, AB, 50; Cornell Univ, MS, 53, PhD(plant taxon), 59. *Mem:* Int Asn Plant Taxon; Am Soc Plant Taxonomists. *Res:* Vascular flora of Florida; methods of population analysis; preservation of endangered species. *Mailing Add:* 3165 MCC Bldg Gainesville FL 32611

**WARD, DARRELL N,** BIOCHEMISTRY. *Current Pos:* from asst biochemist to biochemist, Univ Tex, 55-82, head dept, 61-82, from chmn to pres grad fac, 78-80, MEM GRAD FAC, GRAD SCH BIOMED SCI, M D ANDERSON HOSP & TUMOR INST, UNIV TEX, HOUSTON, 61-, PROF BIOCHEM & ANIS J SORRELL PROF, DEPT BIOCHEM & MOLECULAR BIOL, 83- *Personal Data:* b Logan, Utah, Jan 22, 24; m 46, Afton Hall; c Kathleen, Pamela, Becky, Janeen, Alan, Melissa & Greg. *Educ:* Utah State Univ, BS, 49; Stanford Univ, MS, 51, PhD(biochem), 53. *Honors & Awards:* Ayerst Award, Endocrine Soc, 78. *Prof Exp:* Res assoc & instr biochem, Med Col, Cornell Univ, 52-55. *Concurrent Pos:* Asst prof, Univ Tex Dent Br, Houston, 56-60; from asst clin prof to assoc clin prof, Baylor Col Med, 56-62; mem reproductive biol study sect, NIH, 67-71, consult, Ctr Pop Res, 69-71; chmn, Biochem Endocrinol Study, NIH, 79-81; mem, gonadotropin subcomt, Nat Hormone & Pituitary Prog, 82- *Mem:* AAAS; Am Chem Soc; Am Asn Cancer Res; Am Soc Biol Chem; Endocrine Soc. *Res:* Protein purification; protein and peptide hormones; gonadotropins amino acid sequence; functional group substitution and effects of biological activity; biochemistry of glycoprotein hormones. *Mailing Add:* 4617 Tonawanda Dr Houston TX 77035-3717. *Fax:* 713-790-0329

**WARD, DAVID,** EXPERIMENTAL NUCLEAR PHYSICS. *Current Pos:* PHYSICIST, CHALK RIVER NUCLEAR LABS, ATOMIC ENERGY CAN, 68- *Personal Data:* b Wakefield, Eng, Aug 5, 40; Can citizen. *Educ:* Univ Birmingham, BSc, 61; Univ Manchester, PhD(nuclear physics), 65. *Prof Exp:* Fel nuclear physics, Univ Manchester, 65-66 & Univ Calif, Berkeley, 66-68. *Concurrent Pos:* Vis scientist nuclear physics, Univ Calif, Berkeley, 74-75; vis fel nuclear physics, Australian Nat Univ, 81-82. *Mem:* Am Phys Soc; Royal Soc Can. *Res:* Reactions and coulomb excitation with heavy ions; lifetimes and magnetic moments of short-lived nuclear states; atomic phenomena in nuclear physics; stopping powers for heavy ions. *Mailing Add:* 257 Maple Ave Pembroke ON K8A 1L7 Can

**WARD, DAVID ALOYSIUS,** MECHANICAL & NUCLEAR ENGINEERING. *Current Pos:* PRES, DAVID WARD ASSOC INC, 89- *Personal Data:* b Joliet, Ill, Nov 13, 30; m 53; c 9. *Educ:* Univ Ill, BSME, 53. *Prof Exp:* Res engr, Savannah River Lab, E I du Pont de Nemours & Co, Inc, 53-65, engr, Savannah River Plant, 65-67, sr supvr, 67-69, area supvr, 69-72, chief tech supvr, 72-75, supt, Reactor Technol Dept, 75-78, supt, Reactor & Reactor Mat Technol Dept, 78-80, res mgr nuclear eng, Savannah River Plant, 80-89. *Concurrent Pos:* Mem adv comt reactor safeguards, US Nuclear Regulatory Comn. *Mem:* Am Nuclear Soc. *Res:* Nuclear reactor heat transfer; hydraulics; safety analysis; engineering management. *Mailing Add:* 2108 Tisgah Rd North Augusta SC 29841

**WARD, DAVID CHRISTIAN,** VIROLOGY, BIOCHEMISTRY. *Current Pos:* ASST PROF MOLECULAR BIOPHYS & BIOCHEM, SCH MED, YALE UNIV, 71- *Personal Data:* b Sackville, NB, May 22, 41; m 62; c 1. *Educ:* mem Univ Nfld, BSc, 61; Univ BC, MSc, 63; Rockefeller Univ, PhD(biochem), 69. *Concurrent Pos:* Leukemia Soc Am fel, Imp Cancer Res Fund, Eng, 69-71. *Mem:* AAAS; Am Soc Microbiol. *Res:* Replication and genetic analysis of animal viruses; molecular cytogenetics and gene mapping; 3-D topography of DNA in interphase nuclei. *Mailing Add:* Dept Human Genetics Yale Univ Sch Med PO Box 208005 New Haven CT 06520-8005

**WARD, DAVID GENE,** NEUROPHYSIOLOGY, NEUROENDOCRINOLOGY. *Current Pos:* PROF, DIV SCI, MATH & ENG, MODESTO JR COL, 90- *Personal Data:* b Modesto, Calif, Feb 19, 49; div; c Jessica, John & Edward. *Educ:* Calif State Univ, Stanislaus, BA, 71; Univ Okla, PhD(neurosci), 74. *Prof Exp:* Fel biomed eng, Sch Med, Johns Hopkins Univ, 74-76, res assoc, 76-77, asst prof, 77-79; asst prof physiol, Sch Med, Univ Va, 79-82; dir physiol, H M Ward Mem Lab, 83-90. *Concurrent Pos:* Res career develop award, USPHS, 81; vis lectr, Calif State Univ, Stanislaus, 83- *Mem:* AAAS; Am Physiol Soc; NY Acad Sci; Soc Neurosci; Fedn Am Socs Exp Biol. *Res:* Central neural mechanisms responsible for control of circulation, blood pressure and fluid balance; neurophysiology; neuroendocrinology. *Mailing Add:* Div Sci Math & Eng Modesto Jr Col 435 College Ave Modesto CA 95350. E-Mail: david.ward@ccc-infonet

**WARD, DAVID MERCER,** COMMUNITY ECOLOGY. *Current Pos:* SR LECTR & DIR, RAMON SCI CTR, INST DESERT RES BEN GURION UNIV, 94- *Personal Data:* b Mombasa, Kenya, June 15, 61. *Educ:* Univ Natal S Africa, BSc, 83, BSc Hons, 84, PhD(zool), 87. *Prof Exp:* From fel to res assoc, Ben Gurion Univ, Israel, 88-92; fel & lectr biomet, Univ BC, 92-94. *Concurrent Pos:* Res assoc, Desert Res Inst, Namibia, 89-; consult, Israel Nature Res Authority, 91-93. *Mem:* Entom Soc Am; Am Arachnological Soc; Am Ornithologists Union; Cooper Ornith Soc. *Res:* Study the effects of phenotypic plasticity on the life histories of desert plants; community ecology of desert plants; coevolution, plant-animal interactions, herbivory. *Mailing Add:* Inst Desert Res Sede Boqer Israel. *Fax:* 972-7-6557829; *E-Mail:* bgumail.bgu.ac.il

**WARD, DONALD THOMAS,** FLIGHT TESTING, STABILITY & CONTROL. *Current Pos:* ASSOC PROF AEROSPACE ENG, TEX A&M UNIV, 81- *Personal Data:* b Sidney, Tex, Mar 18, 36; m 64; c 2. *Educ:* Univ Tex, Austin, BS, 58; Air Force Inst Technol, MS, 65; Miss State Univ, PhD(aerospace eng), 74. *Prof Exp:* Tactical fighter pilot, 474th Tactical Fighter Wing, Cannon AFB, USAF, NMex, 59-63, student test pilot, Empire Test Pilots Sch, Farnborough, Eng, 66, tactical fighter pilot, Air Force Adv Group, DaNang Air Base, Vietnam, 67-68, student, Air Command & Staff Col, Maxwell AFB, Calif, 69-71, & test pilot, Res & Develop Off, Air Force Flight Test Ctr, 75-76, staff officer, HQ Air Force Test Pilot Sch, Edwards AFB, Calif, 78-79, Comdr, 4950th Test Wing, Wright-Patterson AFB, Ohio, 79-81. *Concurrent Pos:* Lectr, Calif State Univ, Fresno, 78-79; consult, E-Systs, Inc, 84-87 & Lockheed-Ga Co, 85- *Mem:* Am Inst Aeronaut & Astronaut; Am Soc Eng Educ; Soc Exp Test Pilots; Am Astronaut Soc; Soc Flight Test Engrs. *Res:* Flight mechanics; flight test methods; control of aircraft and spacecraft; orbital mechanics. *Mailing Add:* Dept Aerospace Eng Tex A&M Univ College Station TX 77843-3141

**WARD, DOUGLAS ERIC,** OPTIMIZATION THEORY, NONSMOOTH ANALYSIS. *Current Pos:* Instr, 84-85, from asst prof to assoc prof, 85-95, PROF MATH, MIAMI UNIV, 95- *Personal Data:* b Wooster, Ohio, Aug 23, 57; m 82, Sherry L Longcor; c Timothy D, Rebekah E, Andrew C & Emily R. *Educ:* Haverford Col, BA, 79; Carnegie-Mellon Univ, MS, 81; Dalhousie Univ, PhD(math), 85. *Concurrent Pos:* Vis assoc prof, Dept Combinatorics & Optionization, Univ Waterloo, 91-92. *Mem:* Math Asn Am; Am Math Soc. *Res:* Optimization problems involving nondifferentiable functions; tangent cones; the calculus of generalized gradients; the application of these concepts in the formulation of optimality conditions. *Mailing Add:* Dept Math Miami Univ Oxford OH 45056-1641. *Fax:* 513-529-1493; *E-Mail:* dw86mthf@miamiu.acs.muohio.edu

**WARD, EDMUND WILLIAM BESWICK,** PLANT PATHOLOGY, MICROBIOLOGY. *Current Pos:* RETIRED. *Personal Data:* b Stockport, Eng, May 30, 30; m 53; c 3. *Educ:* Univ Wales, BSc, 52; Univ Alta, MSc, 54, PhD, 58. *Prof Exp:* Res officer, Can Dept Agr, Alta, 57-61, prin plant pathologist, London Res Ctr & head, Plant Path Lab, 61-93. *Mem:* Am Phytopath Soc; Can Soc Phytopath; Brit Soc Plant Path. *Res:* Physiology of fungi; disease resistance in plants. *Mailing Add:* 448 Regal Dr London ON N5Y 1J9 Can

**WARD, EDWARD HILSON,** INORGANIC CHEMISTRY, ANALYTICAL CHEMISTRY. *Current Pos:* RETIRED. *Personal Data:* b Milton, Fla, Sept 15, 30; m 54; c 2. *Educ:* Troy State Col, BS, 58; Univ Miss, PhD(chem), 63. *Prof Exp:* Fel chem, Fla State Univ, 63-65; from assoc prof to prof, Troy State Univ, 65-84, chmn, Dept Phys Sci, 70-89. *Mem:* Am Chem Soc. *Res:* Inorganic complexes; non-aqueous solvent systems; co-precipitation. *Mailing Add:* 129 Glenwood Ave Troy AL 36081-4513

**WARD, FRANCES ELLEN,** IMMUNOGENETICS. *Current Pos:* From instr to assoc prof, 67-73, PROF IMMUNOL, MED CTR, DUKE UNIV, 79-; DIR, TRANSPLANT LAB, DURHAM VET ADMIN HOSP, 93- *Personal Data:* b Freedom, Maine, Mar 21, 39. *Educ:* Clark Univ, AB, 61; Brown Univ, PhD(biol), 65. *Concurrent Pos:* NIH fel statist, Iowa State Univ, 66-67; dir, Transplant Lab, Durham Vet Admin Hosp, 69-79; assoc scientist, Wistar Inst, 80-81. *Mem:* Genetics Soc Am; AAAS; Transplantation Soc; Am Asn Clin Histocompatibility Testing; Am Asn Immunologists; Sigma Xi. *Res:* Genetics of the major human histocompatibility complex; immunogenicity of gene products of the major histocompatibility complex as measured by organ and tissue rejection. *Mailing Add:* Vet Admin Hosp Fulton St Durham NC 27705

**WARD, FRANK KERNAN,** ORGANIC CHEMISTRY, POLYMER CHEMISTRY. *Current Pos:* RETIRED. *Personal Data:* b Brockton, Mass, Jan 19, 31; m 56, Phoebe E Driscoll; c Katherine, Elizabeth & Francis. *Educ:* Boston Col, BS, 54; Mass Inst Technol, PhD(org chem), 58. *Prof Exp:* Res asst chem, Mass Inst Technol, 54-57; res chemist, Celanese Corp, 57-59; scientist, Avco Corp, 59-60, sr scientist, 60-61; from sr chemist to res chemist, Texaco Inc, Beacon, 61-67, group leader, 67-71, environ technologist, 71-78, from coordr to sr prog coordr, 78-90, mgr, 90-94. *Mem:* Sigma Xi; Am Chem Soc. *Res:* Synthetic polymer chemistry; organometallics; environmental affairs; fuel and lubricant additives; petrochemicals. *Mailing Add:* 17 Deerwood Dr Hopewell Junction NY 12533

**WARD, FRASER PRESCOTT,** ecology, veterinary medicine, for more information see previous edition

**WARD, FREDERICK ROGER,** MATHEMATICS. *Current Pos:* asst prof, 69-72, ASSOC PROF MATH, BOISE STATE UNIV, 72- *Personal Data:* b Cleveland, Miss, Oct 30, 40; m 64; c 2. *Educ:* Col William & Mary, BS, 62; Univ Colo, MS, 65; Va Polytech Inst & State Univ, PhD(math), 69. *Prof Exp:* Instr math, Va Polytech Inst & State Univ, 65-69. *Mailing Add:* Dept Math Boise State Univ 1910 Univ Dr Boise ID 83725-0001

**WARD, FREDRICK JAMES,** LIMNOLOGY, FISH BIOLOGY. *Current Pos:* RETIRED. *Personal Data:* b Alert Bay, BC, Jan 22, 28; m 56; c 3. *Educ:* Univ BC, BA, 52, MA, 57; Cornell Univ, PhD(conserv), 62. *Prof Exp:* Biologist, Int Pac Salmon Fisheries Comn, 52-57, proj supvr, 57-64; from asst prof to prof limnol & invert zool, Univ Man, 64-92, sr scholar. *Mem:* Am Fisheries Soc; Am Soc Limnol & Oceanog; Can Soc Wildlife & Fishery Biol; Int Asn Theoret & Appl Limnol. *Res:* Limnology, particularly secondary production; dynamics of Pacific salmon populations. *Mailing Add:* 51 MacAlester Bay Ft Garry MB R3T 2X6 Can

**WARD, GEORGE A,** analytical chemistry, for more information see previous edition

**WARD, GEORGE HENRY,** SYSTEMATIC BOTANY. *Current Pos:* from asst prof to prof, 54-80, Cornila H Dudley prof, 80-82, EMER PROF BIOL, KNOX COLL, ILL, 82- *Personal Data:* b Withrow, Wash, Nov 28, 16; m 46; c 2. *Educ:* State Col Wash, BS, 40, MS, 48; Stanford Univ, PhD(biol), 52. *Prof Exp:* Teacher, Wash High Sch, 40-42; asst bot & taxon, State Col Wash, 42 & 46-48; asst bot & biol, Stanford Univ, 48-52 & instr biol, 52-54, cur asst, Dudley Herbarium, 49. *Concurrent Pos:* Vis prof, Wash State Univ, 62, 64, 66 & 70. *Mem:* AAAS; Sigma Xi; Am Soc Plant Taxonomists. *Res:* Cyto-taxonomy of Artemisia; arctic flora; stripmine spoilbank ecology. *Mailing Add:* Box 195 Husum Washington WA 96823

**WARD, GERALD MADISON,** ANIMAL SCIENCE. *Current Pos:* prof animal sci, 61-88, EMER PROF, COLO STATE UNIV, 88- *Personal Data:* b Thorndike, Maine, Nov 2, 21; m 48; c 2. *Educ:* Univ Maine, BS, 47; Univ Wis, MS, 48; Wash State Univ, PhD(animal sci), 51. *Prof Exp:* Asst prof dairy sci, Univ Maine, 48-49; exten specialist, Kans State Univ, 51-52 & Wash State Univ, 52-53; from asst prof to assoc prof, Colo State Univ, 53-60; scientist, Los Alamos Sci Lab, Univ Calif, 60-61. *Concurrent Pos:* Head animal prod & health sect, Joint Div Food & Agr Orgn-Int Atomic Energy Agency, UN, Vienna, Austria, 68-70. *Mem:* AAAS; Am Dairy Sci Asn; Am Inst Nutrit; Am Soc Animal Sci. *Res:* Applications of radioisotope technique to animal nutrition; environmental problems of animal agriculture; nutrition of ruminant animals; systems analysis of livestock production. *Mailing Add:* 1301 Robertson St Ft Collins CO 80524

**WARD, GERTRUDE LUCKHARDT,** entomology; deceased, see previous edition for last biography

**WARD, HAROLD NATHANIEL,** MATHEMATICS. *Current Pos:* from asst prof to assoc prof, 67-82, PROF MATH, UNIV VA, 82- *Personal Data:* b Evanston, Ill, Apr 29, 36; m 59; c 3. *Educ:* Swarthmore Col, BA, 58; Harvard Univ, MA, 59, PhD(math), 62. *Prof Exp:* From instr to asst prof math, Brown Univ, 62-67. *Mem:* Am Math Soc; Math Asn Am; Soc Indust Appl Math. *Res:* Finite groups; representations of groups; coding theory. *Mailing Add:* Dept Math Math-Astro Bldg Univ Va Charlottesville VA 22903-3199

**WARD, HAROLD RICHARD,** ELECTRICAL ENGINEERING. *Current Pos:* RETIRED. *Personal Data:* b Lancaster, NY, July 31, 31; m 60; c 3. *Educ:* Clarkson Col Technol, BEE, 53; Univ Southern Calif, MSEE, 57. *Prof Exp:* Engr electronics, Hughes Aircraft Co, 53-54 & 56-57; res engr radar, Sylvania Elec Prod, 57-64; consult scientist radar, Raytheon Co, 64-92. *Mem:* Am Inst Elec & Electronics Engrs. *Res:* Radar system design. *Mailing Add:* 23 Hilltop Dr Bedford MA 01730

**WARD, HAROLD ROY,** ENVIRONMENTAL CHEMISTRY. *Current Pos:* from asst prof to assoc prof, 63-71, assoc dean, 76-80, PROF CHEM, BROWN UNIV, 71-, DIR, CTR ENVIRON STUDIES, 76- *Personal Data:* b Mt Vernon, Ill, Nov 3, 35. *Educ:* Southern Ill Univ, AB, 57; Mass Inst Technol, PhD(org chem), 61; Harvard Univ, JD, 75. *Prof Exp:* NSF fel, 61-62; NATO fel, 62-63. *Concurrent Pos:* Spec fel, Environ Protection Agency, 72-75. *Res:* Hazardous and solid waste management; environmental law; urban environmental issues. *Mailing Add:* Environ Studies Brown Univ Box 1943 Providence RI 02912

**WARD, HERBERT BAILEY,** APPLIED & ENVIRONMENTAL MICROBIOLOGY, FOSSIL FUEL BIOPROCESSING. *Current Pos:* RETIRED. *Personal Data:* b Texarkana, Tex; c 1. *Educ:* NTex State Univ, BS, 65, MS, 66; Univ Tex, Austin, PhD(bot), 71. *Prof Exp:* Asst biol, NTex State Univ, 63-66; instr, Univ Tex, Arlington, 66-67; res scientist II bot, Lab Algal Physiol, Univ Tex, Austin, 68-71; from asst prof to assoc prof biol, Univ Miss, 71-86, prof, 86- *Concurrent Pos:* Oak Ridge Assoc Univs fac res appointee, Oak Ridge Nat Lab, 84, consult, 85-; consult, US Dept Energy, 85-, EG&G Idaho, Inc, 87- *Mem:* Sigma Xi; Am Chem Soc; Am Soc Microbiol. *Res:* Fossil fuel bioprocessing; microbial bioconversions for fuels and chemicals; environmental microbiology. *Mailing Add:* 5242 Sagamore Ct New Port Richey FL 34655

**WARD, INGEBORG L,** PHYSIOLOGICAL PSYCHOLOGY. *Current Pos:* PROF PSYCHOL, VILLANOVA UNIV, 66- *Personal Data:* b R-tha, Ger, Aug 14, 40; US citizen; m 63; c 2. *Educ:* Westhampton Col, BS, 60; Tulane Univ, MS, 65, PhD(psychol), 67. *Concurrent Pos:* NSF res grant, 68-69; Nat Inst Child Health & Human Develop res grant, 70-85; mem ment health small grant comt, NIMH, res career develop award, 75-85; mem, Bio-Psychol Study Sect, NIH, 78-82; consult ed, Behav Neurosci, Physiol Psychol. *Mem:* Fel Am Psychol Asn; Soc Study Reproduction; AAAS. *Res:* Hormonal and environmental determinants of reproductive behavior, neural and pharmacological bases of sexual behavior. *Mailing Add:* Dept Psychol Villanova Univ Villanova PA 19085

**WARD, JAMES,** RADAR, SIGNAL PROCESSING. *Current Pos:* STAFF MEM ELEC ENG, LINCOLN LAB, MASS INST TECHNOL, 90- *Personal Data:* b Belleville, NJ, July 11, 64. *Educ:* Univ Dayton, BEE, 85; Ohio State Univ, MScEE, 87, PhD(elec eng), 90. *Prof Exp:* Res assoc elec eng, Ohio State Univ, 85-90. *Mem:* Inst Elec & Electronics Engrs; Sigma Xi. *Res:* Analysis of adaptive antenna array architectures and algorithms for radar and communication systems; signal processing; radar systems analysis; packet radio networks. *Mailing Add:* Lincoln Lab Mass Inst Technol M/S ANI-4F 244 Wood St Boston MA 02173

**WARD, JAMES ANDREW,** PHYSICAL CHEMISTRY, POLYMER CHEMISTRY. *Current Pos:* CHIEF POLYMER CHEMIST, BUCKMAN LABS, 79- *Personal Data:* b Pittsburgh, Pa, May 11, 38; m 66; c 6. *Educ:* St Vincent Col, BS, 60; Univ Notre Dame, PhD(phys chem), 64. *Prof Exp:* Res scientist radiation chem, Babcock & Wilcox Co, 64-65, Union Carbide Corp, 65-79. *Concurrent Pos:* Adj prof chem, Memphis State Univ. *Mem:* Am Chem Soc; Tech Asn Pulp & Paper Indust. *Res:* Hydrogels; water soluble polymers, water treatment, biocidal polymers; Polymers for paper mill applications. *Mailing Add:* Buckman Labs 1256 N McLean Blvd Memphis TN 38108. *E-Mail:* jaward@buckman.com

**WARD, JAMES AUDLEY,** MATHEMATICS, COMPUTER SCIENCE. *Current Pos:* RETIRED. *Personal Data:* b Timmonsville, SC, May 19, 10; m 35; c 3. *Educ:* Davidson Col, BA, 31; La State Univ, MS, 34; Univ Wis, PhD(math), 39. *Prof Exp:* Asst prof math, Davidson Col, 37-38 & Tenn Polytech Inst, 39-40; prof, Delta State Col, 40-42; from assoc prof to prof, Univ Ga, 46-49; prof, Univ Ky, 49-55; mathematician, USAF Missile Develop Ctr, 55-57, chief digital comput br, 57-59; spec asst to vpres, Univac Div, Sperry Rand Corp, 59-62; staff specialist electronic comput, Off Dir Defense Res & Eng, Dept Defense, 62-69; staff asst comput progs, Naval Sea Systs Command, 69-76. *Concurrent Pos:* Consult, Proj Scamp, Univ Calif, Los Angeles, 52 & Tube Turns, Ky, 53-55; consult, Appl Physics Lab, 76-78. *Mem:* Math Asn Am; Am Math Soc; Asn Comput Mach; sr mem Inst Elec & Electronics Engrs. *Res:* Digital computers; research in hardware and software; mathematical research in linear algebra and in numerical analysis. *Mailing Add:* 2726 Timbertrail Circle Tallahassee FL 32308-5747

**WARD, JAMES EDWARD, III,** MATHEMATICS. *Current Pos:* jr instr, Bowdoin Col, 66-68, from asst prof to assoc prof, 68-79, dir sr ctr, 71-76, chmn dept, 78-81, 86-89 & 93-95, dean col, 92-93, PROF MATH, BOWDOIN COL, 79- *Personal Data:* b Greenville, SC, Sept 20, 39; m 62, Mary L Parker; c James E, R Parker & Margaret. *Educ:* Vanderbilt Univ, BA, 61; Univ Va, MA, 64, PhD(math), 68. *Prof Exp:* Asst to pres, George Peabody Col, 61-62; teaching asst math, Univ Va, 62-64. *Concurrent Pos:* Consult, Va Union Univ, 68, Worcester State Col, 83, Mass Dept Educ, 83-89, The Trout Asn, 91-; Fulbright lectr, Nat Univ Lesotho, Africa, 89-90. *Mem:* Am Math Soc; Math Asn Am; Fulbright Asn; Soc Values High Educ; Am Asn Univ Profs; AAAS. *Res:* Jordan algebras of characteristic two; structure of two-groups. *Mailing Add:* Dept Math Bowdoin Col Brunswick ME 04011-2546

**WARD, JAMES VERNON,** STREAM ECOLOGY, LIMNOLOGY. *Current Pos:* PROF, DEPT BIOL, COLO STATE UNIV, 73- *Personal Data:* b Minneapolis, Minn, Mar 27, 40; m 63. *Educ:* Univ Minn, Minneapolis, BS, 63; Univ Denver, MS, 67; Univ Colo, PhD(limnol), 73. *Mem:* Am Soc Limnol & Oceanog; Soc Int Limnol, Ecol Soc Am; NAm Benthological Soc (pres, 87-88). *Res:* Stream ecology and limnology, especially aquatic macroinvertebrates and factors influencing their distribution and community structure; ground water ecology. *Mailing Add:* Dept Biol Colo State Univ Ft Collins CO 80523-0001

**WARD, JEFFREY STUART,** SILVICULTURE, AUTECOLOGY. *Current Pos:* ASST SCIENTIST, CONN AGR EXP STA, 87- *Personal Data:* b Cleveland, Ohio, May 28, 57; m 81, Lilian; c 3. *Educ:* Ohio State Univ, BS, 79, MS, 83; Purdue Univ, PhD(forest ecol), 87. *Prof Exp:* Res assoc forestry, Ohio State Univ, 79 & 82-83; forest exten, Peace Corps, Guatemala, 79-82;

grad instr, Purdue Univ, 83-87. *Mem:* Soc Am Foresters; Nat Areas Asn. *Res:* Influence of neighborhood competition and initial individual tree characteristics on individual tree development and survival; how the aggregate development of individual trees drives forest stand development. *Mailing Add:* 123 Huntington St New Haven CT 06504. *Fax:* 203-789-7232

**WARD, JERROLD MICHAEL,** VETERINARY PATHOLOGY. *Current Pos:* vet pathologist, 72-78, chief tumor path, Nat Toxicol Prog, 79-81, ACTG CHIEF, TUMOR PATH BR, CARCINOGENESIS TESTING PROG, NAT CANCER INST, 78- *Personal Data:* b New York, NY, Oct 29, 42; m 71. *Educ:* Cornell Univ, DVM, 66; Univ Calif, Davis, PhD(comp path), 70. *Prof Exp:* Res pathologist, Univ Calif, Davis, 66-68; vet pathologist, Environ Protection Agency, 70-72. *Mem:* Am Vet Med Asn; Int Acad Path. *Res:* Pathology; cancer research; hematopoietic pathology; rodent pathology. *Mailing Add:* 10513 Wayridge Dr Gaithersburg MD 20879

**WARD, JOHN EDWARD,** ORGANIC CHEMISTRY. *Current Pos:* from chief chemist paper chem lab to tech mgr foreign dept, NopCo Chem Co, NJ, 51-59, MANAGING DIR, HENKEL-NOPCO CHIMIE, SA, 59-, CHMN BD, NOPCO ITALIA SPA, 81- *Personal Data:* b Chicago, Ill, Feb 7, 23; m 46, Ada Lovinger; c Marianne, Elizabeth, Kitty, Johanna, Thomas & Andrew (deceased). *Educ:* Wabash Col, AB, 44; Lawrence Col, MS, 48, PhD, 51. *Prof Exp:* Res chemist, P H Glatfelter Co, Pa, 50-51. *Concurrent Pos:* Managing dir, Danlink Sa, 83- *Mem:* Am Chem Soc; Tech Asn Pulp & Paper Indust. *Res:* Pulp and paper technology, especially the production of pigment coated papers; market research, product development and international marketing of industrial chemical specialties, especially for the particular requirements of various European markets. *Mailing Add:* 24 Route de la Veveyse CH-1700 Fribourg Switzerland

**WARD, JOHN EVERETT, JR,** mycology, ecology, for more information see previous edition

**WARD, JOHN F,** RADIATION CHEMISTRY & BIOCHEMISTRY, RADIATION BIOLOGY. *Current Pos:* assoc res chemist, 69-79, assoc prof path, Sch Med, 74-78, PROF RADIOL, SCH MED, UNIV CALIF, SAN DIEGO, 78-, CHIEF RADIOBIOL, 80- *Personal Data:* b Blyth, Northumberland, Eng, Aug 26, 35; m 75, Elizabeth L Daugherty; c Julianne & Wendy E. *Educ:* Durham Univ, BSc, 56, PhD(radiation chem), 60. *Honors & Awards:* Weiss Medal, 95; Failla Award, 97. *Prof Exp:* Demonstr chem, Kings Col, Durham Univ, 60-62; asst res biophysicist, Lab Nuclear Med & Radiation Biol, Univ Calif, Los Angeles, 62-69. *Concurrent Pos:* Mem radiation study sect, NIH, 74-78 & 89-92; counr chem, Radiation Res Soc, 78-81; assoc ed, Radiation Res, 81-84, Ed Chief, 96- *Mem:* Royal Soc Chem; Radiation Res Soc (pres, 85-86); Asn Radiation Res. *Res:* Studies of radiation chemical destruction of biologically significant molecules; molecular mechanisms of cell killing; measurement of repair of DNA damage in mammalian cells. *Mailing Add:* Dept Radiol Univ Calif San Diego La Jolla CA 92093-0610. *Fax:* 619-534-0265; *E-Mail:* john__ward@som.bsb.ucsd.edu

**WARD, JOHN FRANK,** PHYSICS. *Current Pos:* assoc prof, 67-74, PROF PHYSICS, UNIV MICH, ANN ARBOR, 74- *Personal Data:* b London, Eng, May 14, 34; m 60; c 2. *Educ:* Oxford Univ, BA, 57, MA & DPhil(physics), 61. *Prof Exp:* From lectr to asst prof physics, Univ Mich, 61-64; Asn Elec Industs res fel, Oxford Univ & lectr, Wadham Col, Univ Oxford, 64-67. *Concurrent Pos:* Consult, Lear-Siegler Laser Systs Ctr, 62-64, Royal Radar Estab, 66, Photon Sources, 67- & KMS Fusion Inc, 81- *Mem:* Am Phys Soc; Sigma Xi. *Res:* Nonlinear optics; lasers. *Mailing Add:* Randall Physics Lab Univ Mich Ann Arbor MI 48109

**WARD, JOHN HENRY,** ATMOSPHERIC SCIENCE. *Current Pos:* FEL NUMERICAL WEATHER PREDICTION, NAT WEATHER SERV, 78- *Personal Data:* b Springfield, Mass, Oct 10, 50; c 2. *Educ:* Worcester Polytech Inst, BS, 73; Purdue Univ, MS, 75, PhD(atmospheric sci), 78. *Prof Exp:* Asst atmospheric sci, Purdue Univ, 73-78. *Concurrent Pos:* Ed, Nat Meteorol Ctr Monthly Performance Summary. *Mem:* Am Meteorol Soc; Sigma Xi. *Res:* Numerical weather prediction, particularly diagnostic evaluation of regional forecast systems and tropical hurricane forecasting. *Mailing Add:* Nat Weather Serv NP12 5200 Auth Rd Camp Springs MD 20674

**WARD, JOHN K,** ANIMAL NUTRITION. *Current Pos:* RETIRED. *Personal Data:* b Litchfield, Nebr, July 1, 27; m 53; c 3. *Educ:* McPherson Col, BS, 50; Kans State Univ, BS, 54, PhD, 61. *Prof Exp:* Asst animal husb, Okla State Univ, 54-56; asst prof agr, McPherson Col, 56-66; from assoc prof to prof animal sci, Univ Nebr, Lincoln, 67-88. *Res:* Beef cattle management. *Mailing Add:* 1208 Darlow Dr McPherson KS 67460

**WARD, JOHN WESLEY,** PHARMACOLOGY, DRUG DISCOVERY & DEVELOPMENT. *Current Pos:* RETIRED. *Personal Data:* b Martin, Tenn, Apr 8, 25; m 47, Martha Hendley; c Henry R, Judith C, Charles W & Richard L. *Educ:* George Washington Univ, BS & MS, 55; Georgetown Univ, PhD(pharmacol), 59. *Prof Exp:* Res assoc pharmacol, Hazleton Labs, Inc, 50-56, head dept pharmacol, 56-58, chief dept pharmacol & biochem, 58, res appln specialist, 59; prin pharmacologist, A H Robins Co, 59-60, dir pharmacol, 60-71, pharmacol develop, 71-72, toxicol, 73-77, dir good lab pracs, 77-78, biol res, 78-80, res, 80-81, vpres res, 82-89, vpres & gen mgr, Res & Develop Div, 89-90. *Concurrent Pos:* Lectr, Med Col Va, 60-65, affil assoc prof pharmacol, 82-90. *Mem:* AAAS; Am Chem Soc; Soc Toxicol; NY Acad Sci; Am Soc Pharmacol & Exp Therapeut; Sigma Xi; Int Soc Regulatory Toxicol & Pharmacol. *Res:* Structure-activity relationships; general pharmacodynamics; autonomics; toxicology. *Mailing Add:* 10275 Cherokee Rd Richmond VA 23235-1107

**WARD, JOHN WILLIAM,** ACTINIDE CHEMISTRY, METAL HYDRIDES. *Current Pos:* STAFF MEM, LOS ALAMOS NAT LAB, 56- *Personal Data:* b Moline, Ill, Oct 16, 29; m 52, 95, Arlene DeYoung; c William, David, Daniel & Michael. *Educ:* Augustana Col, Ill, BA, 52; Wash Univ, MA, 55; Univ NMex, PhD(phys chem), 66. *Honors & Awards:* Von Humboldt USA prize, 72. *Concurrent Pos:* Consult, US Army Nuclear Defense Lab, Edgewood Arsenal, 66-; sr fel, Alexander von Humboldt Found, Inst Transuranium Elements, Ger, 72-73; lab fel, Los Alamos Nat Lab, 83. *Mem:* Am Chem Soc; fel Am Inst Chem. *Res:* Vapor pressure theory; Monte Carlo computer simulation of experiment; metal hydrides; gas-surface reactions; chemistry of actinides. *Mailing Add:* 2833 Pueblo Bonito Santa Fe NM 87505. *Fax:* 505-665-8002

**WARD, JOHN WILLIAM,** PHYSICAL CHEMISTRY CATALYSIS, PETROLEUM PROCESSING. *Current Pos:* res scientist, Union Oil Co Calif, 63-66, sr res scientist, 66-70, res assoc, 70-77, sr res assoc, 77-79, staff consult, 79-87, SR STAFF CONSULT, UNION OIL CO CALIF, 87- *Personal Data:* b Wigan, Eng, Aug 4, 37; m 69, Margaret M; c 6. *Educ:* Univ Manchester, BSc, 59, MSc, 60; Cambridge Univ, PhD(phys chem), 62. *Honors & Awards:* Eugene Howdry Award Appl Catalysis, 85. *Prof Exp:* Res coun Alta Can fel, 62-63. *Mem:* Am Chem Soc; Catalysis Soc; Royal Soc Chem; Int Zeolite Asn. *Res:* Application of spectroscopic techniques to the study of surface chemistry and catalysis; heterogeneous catalysis; hydrocarbon conversions; petroleum processing, especially hydrotreating, hydrocracking and reforming petrochemical processing; molecular sieves and zeolites. *Mailing Add:* 19002 Gordon Lane Yorba Linda CA 92886. *Fax:* 714-577-1610

**WARD, JONATHAN BISHOP, JR,** GENETICS, TOXICOLOGY. *Current Pos:* sr res assoc human genetics, 74-78, asst prof, 78-87, ASSOC PROF GENETIC TOXICOL, MED BR, UNIV TEX, 87- *Personal Data:* b Tacoma, Wash, Oct 13, 43; m 69; c 3. *Educ:* Whitman Col, AB, 65; Univ Idaho, MS, 68; Cornell Univ, PhD(microbiol), 72. *Prof Exp:* Fel somatic cell genetics, Mass Gen Hosp, 72-74. *Concurrent Pos:* Prin investr, US Environ Protection Agency. *Mem:* AAAS; Sigma Xi; Environ Mutagen Soc; Soc Toxicol. *Res:* Mutagenicity of environmental chemicals in cultured mammalian cells; evaluation of chemical mutagens in animals; human population monitoring for genetic damage from environmental agents. *Mailing Add:* Med Br Univ Tex 2102 Ewing Hall 1110 Galveston TX 77555-1110. *Fax:* 409-772-9108; *E-Mail:* ward@beach.utmb.edu

**WARD, JOSEPH D,** ANALYSIS. *Current Pos:* From asst prof to assoc prof, 74-85, PROF MATH, TEX A&M UNIV, 85- *Personal Data:* b Boston, Mass, Dec 11, 46. *Educ:* Purdue Univ, PhD(math), 73. *Concurrent Pos:* Vis prof math, Univ Bonn, Ger, 76. *Mem:* Am Math Soc. *Res:* Approximation theory. *Mailing Add:* Dept Math Tex A&M Univ College Station TX 77843

**WARD, JOSEPH RICHARD,** CHEMISTRY. *Current Pos:* RES CHEMIST, US ARMY BALLISTIC RES LABS, ABERDEEN PROVING GROUND, 71- *Personal Data:* b Salt Lake City, Utah, Dec 7, 42. *Educ:* Univ Del, BS, 64; State Univ NY, Stony Brook, PhD(chem), 69. *Mem:* Am Chem Soc. *Res:* Erosion of gun barrels, combustion of solid propellants; effect of propellant combustion in the near-wake of supersonic projectiles. *Mailing Add:* 1332 Sweetbriar Lane Bel Air MD 21014

**WARD, KEITH BOLEN, JR,** BIOPHYSICS. *Current Pos:* LEADER, MACROMOLECULAR STRUCT & FUNCTION GROUP, LAB STRUCT MATTER, NAVAL RES LAB, 84- *Personal Data:* b Paducah, Tex, Feb 20, 43; m 74, Diane E Bowen; c Jenni D & Lucas D. *Educ:* Tex A&M Univ, BS, 65; Johns Hopkins Univ, PhD(biophys), 74. *Prof Exp:* Res assoc physics, Appl Res Lab, Gen Dynamics Corp, 65-66; Nat Res Coun res assoc, Lab Struct Matter, Naval Res Lab, 74-76; asst prof, 76-81, assoc prof chem, Univ Wis-Parkside, 82-84. *Concurrent Pos:* Adj assoc prof, chem, Cath Univ, Washington, DC, 90- *Mem:* AAAS; Am Crystallog Asn. *Res:* Study the structure and function of proteins by x-ray diffraction analysis; oxygen transport pigments; phospholipases; bioluminescent proteins. *Mailing Add:* 4509 Dartmoor Lane Alexandria VA 22310-1409

**WARD, KYLE, JR,** CELLULOSE CHEMISTRY, PULP & PAPER TECHNOLOGY. *Current Pos:* res assoc, Inst Paper Chem, 51-59, leader cellulose group, 59-66, chmn dept chem, 59-68, leader carbohydrate group & chmn sect org chem, 66-68, EMER PROF, INST PAPER CHEM, 68- *Personal Data:* b Beaumont, Tex, Sept 2, 02; wid. *Educ:* Univ Tex, BA & BS, 23; George Washington Univ, MS, 26; Univ Berlin, PhD(chem), 32. *Hon Degrees:* MS, Lawrence Univ, 68. *Honors & Awards:* Anselmo Payon Award. *Prof Exp:* Instr, Univ Tex, 23-24; jr chemist, Bur Chem & Soils, USDA, 24-28, collabr, 36-38, sr chemist, Southern Regional Res Lab, Bur Agr & Chem Eng, 38-41, prin chemist, Bur Agr & Indust Chem, 41-51; res chemist, Hercules Powder Co, 28-36. *Concurrent Pos:* Res chemist, Chem Found, 36-38; True Mem lectr, 63; consult, Joint Chiefs of Staff, 45 & Am Can Co, 73-75; mem, Am-Egyptian Chem Workshop, 77; Fulbright prof, Helsinki, 70. *Mem:* AAAS; fel Am Chem Soc; hon mem Fiber Soc; fel Tech Asn Pulp & Paper Indust; Am Soc Testing & Mat. *Res:* Cellulose and derivatives; terpenes and related fields; chlorination and oxidation; cotton fiber properties; textiles; high polymers; wood, pulp and paper. *Mailing Add:* The Heritage 2600 Heritage Woods Dr Apt A224 Appleton WI 54915-1409

**WARD, LAIRD GORDON LINDSAY,** INORGANIC CHEMISTRY. *Current Pos:* RETIRED. *Personal Data:* b Wellington, NZ, Dec 6, 31; US citizen. *Educ:* Univ NZ, BSc, 56, MSc, 57; Univ Pa, PhD(inorg chem), 61. *Prof Exp:* Res chemist, Fabrics & Finishes Dept, E I du Pont de Nemours &

Co, 61-63; res fel, Mellon Inst Sci, 63-64; res chemist, Int Nickel Co, Inc, NY, 64-71; res assoc chem, Univ Ga, 72; sr chemist, Colonial Metals, Inc, 72-74; res assoc & mem chem fac, Cend, Univ Del, 75-81; group leader res & develop, Johnson Matthey Inc, 75-94, sr process chemist, 84-90; process consult, Precious Metals Refiners Ltd, 91-93, Minerals Processing Res Lab, 92-93. *Concurrent Pos:* Consult noble & precious metals recycling representation, 95-; observer, Bd Dirs, Chem Heritage Found, Am Inst Chemists, 97. *Mem:* Am Chem Soc; Royal Soc Chem; fel Am Inst Chemists; SAfrican Chem Inst; Minerals, Metals & Mat Soc. *Res:* Hydrometallurgical and pyrometallurgical processes related to refining and recovery of platinum group metals; kinetics of release of carbon-14 and tritium labeled molecules from biosorbable polymers; synthesis of inorganic complexes, especially platinum group metals; organometallic chemistry with group five elements; inorganic pigment applications of non-stoichiometric transition metal oxides. *Mailing Add:* 7131 Shady Wood Lane Woodlands Village Orlando FL 32835-2724. *Fax:* 407-294-1307

**WARD, LAWRENCE MCCUE,** PSYCHOPHYSICS, ATTENTION. *Current Pos:* vis asst prof, 73-74, from asst prof to assoc prof, 74-88, PROF PSYCHOL, UNIV BC, 88- *Personal Data:* b Canton, Ohio, Dec 11, 44; div; c 3. *Educ:* Harvard Univ, AB, 66; Duke Univ, PhD(exp psychol), 71. *Prof Exp:* Asst prof psychol, Rutgers Univ, 70-73. *Concurrent Pos:* Consult, Dept Hwys, State NJ, 72; assoc, Acoust Eng, Vancouver, BC, 75-83; res fel, Harvard Univ, 78-79; consult, Transport Can, 89-91, Mestre Greve Asn, 92-93. *Mem:* AAAS; fel Am Psychol Asn; Psychonomic Soc; Int Soc Psychophysics; Can Psychol Asn; fel Am Psychol Soc. *Res:* Psychophysical scaling; psychophysical judgement; general systems theory; decision theory; attention; chaos theory. *Mailing Add:* Dept Psychol Univ BC Vancouver BC V6T 1Z4 Can. *Fax:* 604-822-6923; *E-Mail:* lward@cortex.psych.ubc.ca

**WARD, LAWRENCE W(ATERMAN),** APPLIED & FLUID MECHANICS. *Current Pos:* RETIRED. *Personal Data:* b Flushing, NY, Feb 21, 26; m 55, Grace Viard; c John, Charles & Anne. *Educ:* Univ Mich, BS, 48; Stevens Inst Technol, MS, 51, DSc(appl mech), 62. *Prof Exp:* Technician, Gibbs & Cox, Inc, NY, 48-50, res engr, 51-55; res engr, Stevens Inst Technol, 55-58; prof eng, Webb Inst Naval Archit, 58-87 & 93-97, asst dean, 87-93, prof eng, 93-97. *Concurrent Pos:* NSF sci fac fel, 65-66. *Mem:* Soc Naval Architects & Marine Engrs; Am Soc Naval Engrs; Am Soc Eng Educ; Ger Ship Bldg Soc; Sigma Xi. *Res:* Ship wave pattern and spectra; experimental determination of wave resistance from wave pattern; ship anti-rolling tanks; ship maneuvering; hull impact; wind effect on ships. *Mailing Add:* Dept Eng Webb Inst Naval Archit Glen Cove NY 11542-1398

**WARD, LEONARD GEORGE,** SYSTEMS DESIGN & SYSTEMS SCIENCE, POLYMER ENGINEERING. *Current Pos:* RETIRED. *Personal Data:* b Tupper Lake, NY, Mar 23, 30; m 50; c 2. *Prof Exp:* Design engr, Westinghouse Elec Corp, 50-54, Flight Refueling Inc, 54-59, Lockheed Aircraft Co, 59-60, Manovox Corp, 60-61 & Int Bus Mach, 61-62; sr mech engr, Sororan Eng Inc, 62-69; prin engr, GDI Inc, 69-72; adv develop engr, Storage Technol Corp, 72-93. *Concurrent Pos:* Pres, Ocean Edge Publ, 86- *Res:* Non impact and impact high speed printer design; forms transport; fusing systems; magnetic ink character recognition systems; print band technology; print hammer design; design for manufacturing/design for assembly; awarded nine US patents. *Mailing Add:* 2109 Royal Dr Melbourne FL 32904-9119

**WARD, LEWIS E, JR,** CONTINUUM THEORY, ORDERED SPACES. *Current Pos:* from assoc prof to prof math, 59-91, asst dean, Col Lib Arts, 66-68, EMER PROF MATH, UNIV ORE, 91- *Personal Data:* b Arlington, Mass, July 20, 25; m 49, Grace Jefferson; c Lawrence, Dinah & Michael. *Educ:* Univ Calif, AB, 49; Tulane Univ, MS, 51, PhD(math), 53. *Prof Exp:* Instr math, Univ Nev, 53-54; asst prof, Univ Utah, 54-56; mathematician, US Naval Ord Test Sta, Univ Calif, 56-59. *Mem:* Am Math Soc; Math Asn Am. *Res:* Topology, especially ordered spaces, fixed point theory and continuum theory. *Mailing Add:* Dept Math Univ Ore Eugene OR 97403. *E-Mail:* lward@darkwing.uoregon.edu

**WARD, LOUIS EMMERSON,** MEDICINE, RHEUMATOLOGY. *Current Pos:* RETIRED. *Personal Data:* b Mt Vernon, Ill, Jan 19, 18; m 42; c 4. *Educ:* Univ Ill, AB, 39; Harvard Univ, MD, 43; Univ Minn, MS, 49. *Prof Exp:* Consult, Sect Med, Mayo Clin, 50-83, chmn bd gov, 64-75; from instr med to prof clin med, Mayo Grad Sch Med, Univ Minn, 51-73, prof med, Mayo Med Sch, 73-83. *Mem:* Inst Med-Nat Acad Sci; Am Rheumatism Asn; AMA; Nat Soc Clin Rheumatology; Am Col Phys; Cent Soc Clin Res. *Res:* Rheumatic diseases. *Mailing Add:* 30 Raeburn Ct Port Ludlow WA 98365

**WARD, MELVIN A,** CANCER ETIOLOGY & PREVENTION. *Current Pos:* asst prof, 71-77, ASSOC PROF BIOL, HAWAII LOA COL, 77- *Personal Data:* b Tonkawa, Okla, June 4, 40; m 69, Sharon L Ulshoeffer; c Robert B & Alyssa E. *Educ:* Okla State Univ, BA, 62; Univ Hawaii, MS, 64, PhD(bot), 69. *Prof Exp:* Postdoctoral biochem, Univ Hawaii, 69-70; postdoctoral microbiol, Purdue Univ, 70-71. *Concurrent Pos:* Marc fac fel, Nat Cancer Inst, Cancer Ctr Hawaii, 78-79; coordr & adv, Pre-Med Studies Prog, 92- *Mem:* Assoc mem Sigma Xi; Nat Asn Adv Health Professions. *Res:* Polymerase chain reaction induced DNA amplification of HTLV-I; induction of adult T-cell leukemia; cancer etiology and prevention: mutagen testing and detection in human bodily fluids. *Mailing Add:* 1415 Kupau Pl Kailua HI 96734. *E-Mail:* melward@mail.lava.net

**WARD, MILTON HAWKINS,** MANAGED METHODS FOR PRODUCTIVITY IMPROVEMENT, ECONOMIC DEVELOPMENT IN FOREIGN COUNTRIES. *Current Pos:* co-chmn, 92-96, CHMN, PRES & CHIEF EXEC OFFICER, CYPRUS AMAX MINERALS CO, 96- *Personal Data:* b Bessemer, Ala, Aug 1, 32; m 52, Adele R; c Jeffrey R & Lisa A. *Educ:* Univ Ala, BS, 55, MS, 81; Univ NMex, MBA, 74. *Hon Degrees:* DEng, Colo Sch Mines, 94. *Honors & Awards:* Saunders Gold Medal, Soc Mining Engrs, 90, Daniel Jackling Award, 93. *Prof Exp:* Engr & supvr, San Manuel Copper Corp, 55-60; gen supt mines & div eng, Kerr McGee Corp, 60-66; gen mgr, United Nuclear-Homestake Partners, Homestake Mining, 66-70; vpres opers, Ranchers Explor & Develop Corp, 70-74; chmn & chief exec officer, PT Freeport Indonesia Inc, Freeport-McMoran Copper & Gold Inc, 74-92; pres & chief operating officer, Freeport McMoran Inc, 74-92. *Concurrent Pos:* Chmn, Am Mining Cong, 89-92, vchmn & dir, 92-; chmn, Bioenviron Ctr, Tulane Univ, 91-92; lectr, Am Mining Cong, Inst Mining Engrs & Mining Eng Gt Brit. *Mem:* Nat Acad Eng (pres, 93); Am Mining Cong; Mining & Metall Soc (pres, 81-83); Int Copper Asn. *Res:* Developing mining methods and processing practices for producing metals and minerals; cost reduction and productivity improvements in open pit and underground mining operations; in-situ and constructed facilities for clean and leaching of copper and uranium ores; design, layout and implementation methods for extracting ore from underground and open pit workings. *Mailing Add:* Cyprus Amax Minerals Co 9100 E Mineral Circle Englewood CO 80112. *Fax:* 303-643-5269; *E-Mail:* minard@cyprus.com

**WARD, OSCAR GARDIEN,** GENETICS, CYTOGENETICS. *Current Pos:* asst prof, 66-74, lectr, 74-77, ASSOC PROF BIOL SCI, UNIV ARIZ, 77- *Personal Data:* b Denver, Colo, Feb 16, 32; m 55; c 2. *Educ:* Univ Ariz, BS, 58, MS, 60; Purdue Univ, PhD(genetics), 66. *Prof Exp:* Instr biol, Purdue Univ, 60-64. *Concurrent Pos:* Fogarty sr int fel, Mex, 80. *Mem:* AAAS; Genetics Soc Am; Am Soc Human Genetics; Am Soc Mammalogists; Am Genetic Asn. *Res:* Plant and animal cytogenetics with emphasis on mammalian systems including man; chromosome identification by banding patterns with application to karyotype evolution; role of chromosomes during development; human cytogenetics. *Mailing Add:* Dept Ecol & Evolutionary Biol Univ Ariz 1600 E University Blvd Tucson AZ 85721-0001

**WARD, PAUL H,** OTOLARYNGOLOGY. *Current Pos:* PROF SURG & CHIEF HEAD & NECK SURG, CTR HEALTH SCI, UNIV CALIF, LOS ANGELES, 68- *Personal Data:* b Lawrence, Ind, Apr 24, 28; m 52; c 2. *Educ:* Anderson Col, AB, 53; Johns Hopkins Univ, MD, 57; Am Bd Otolaryngol, dipl, 62. *Prof Exp:* Intern, Henry Ford Hosp, Detroit, 57-58; resident otolaryngol, Univ Chicago, 58-61, NIH spec res fel, 61-62, asst prof, 62-64; assoc prof surg & chief div otolaryngol, Sch Med, Vanderbilt Univ, 64-68. *Concurrent Pos:* USPHS res grant, 63-69; Deafness Res Found res grant, 65-67; NIH res grant, 66-70; attend otolaryngologist, Nashville Metrop Gen Hosp, Tenn, 64-68; consult, Thayer Vet Admin Hosp, 64-68 & Surgeon Gen, USN, 74-; mem bd dirs, Bill Wilkerson Hearing & Speech Ctr, 64-68. *Mem:* AAAS; Am Otol Soc; Am Acad Ophthal & Otolaryngol; Am Laryngol Soc; Am Laryngol, Rhinol & Otolaryngol Soc; Sigma Xi. *Res:* Cochlear, vestibular and laryngeal physiology; temporal bone pathology; velopharyngeal corrective techniques; laryngeal and palatal reconstruction. *Mailing Add:* Sch Med Univ Calif Los Angeles CA 90024

**WARD, PETER A,** PATHOLOGY, IMMUNOLOGY. *Current Pos:* interim dean, 82-85, PROF & CHMN, DEPT PATH, SCH MED, UNIV MICH, 80- *Personal Data:* b Winsted, Conn, Nov 1, 34. *Educ:* Univ Mich, BS, 58, MD, 60. *Honors & Awards:* Borden Award, 60; Parke Davis Award Except Path, 71; Rous-Whipple Award, 96. *Prof Exp:* Intern med, Third Div, Bellevue Hosp, NY, 60-61; resident path, Hosp, Univ Mich, Ann Arbor, 61-63; res fel immunopath, Div Exp Path, Scripps Clin & Res Found, La Jolla, Calif, 63-65; chief immunobiol, Armed Forces Inst Path, Washington, DC, 65-71; prof path, Sch Med, Univ Conn, 71-80, chmn dept, 73-80. *Mem:* Nat Acad Sci-Inst Med; Am Asn Immunologists; Am Soc Clin Invest; Am Asn Path; Asn Am Physicians. *Res:* Immunopathology; inflammation; biological role of complement; antibody formation; immune complexes; oxygen radicals. *Mailing Add:* Dept Path Med Sch Univ Mich 1301 Catherine Rd Box 0602 Ann Arbor MI 48109-0602

**WARD, PETER LANGDON,** SEISMOLOGY, VOLCANOLOGY. *Current Pos:* geophysicist, US Geol Surv, 71-75, chief br seismol, 75, chief br earthquake mech & prediction, 75-77, coordr earthquake prediction prog, 77-78, GEOPHYSICIST SEISMOL, US GEOL SURV, 78- *Personal Data:* b Washington, DC, Aug 10, 43; m 65, 78, 96, Adrienne Baptiste; c Tonya Holyoke, Christopher Langdon, Taya Marlies & Nils Bjorn. *Educ:* Dartmouth Col, BA, 65; Columbia Univ, MA, 67, PhD(geophys), 70. *Honors & Awards:* Award of Excellence, Nat Asn Govt Communicators, 91; Pub Affairs Award, US Dept Interior, 90. *Prof Exp:* Asst seismol, Columbia Univ, 65-70, res scientist, 70-71. *Concurrent Pos:* Mem adv panel magma energy res, Sandia Labs, 74-82; mem, Earth Dynamics Adv Subcomt, NASA, 76-77; mem geophys prediction panel, Nat Acad Sci, 77-78. *Mem:* Int Asn Volcanol & Chem Earth's Interiors; AAAS; Am Geophys Union; Seismol Soc Am; Geol Soc Am. *Res:* Analysis of earthquakes related to volcanoes, geothermal areas and tectonic features; earthquake seismology; earthquakes and ground deformation near volcanoes; geothermal exploration with seismic techniques; seismic instrumentation; computer techniques; earthquake prediction and hazard reduction; relation of continental geology to plate tectonics. *Mailing Add:* US Geol Surv NCER 345 Middlefield Rd Menlo Park CA 94025. *E-Mail:* pward@usgs.gov

**WARD, PHILLIP WAYNE,** NAVIGATION SATELLITE RECEIVERS, DIGITAL SIGNAL PROCESSING OF SPREAD SPECTRUM SIGNALS. *Current Pos:* PRES, NAVWARD GPS CONSULT, 91- *Personal Data:* b Warren, Ark, June 10, 35; m 58, Nancy Cook; c Christopher, Stephen, Ivy (O'Malley) & Andrew. *Educ:* Univ Tex, El Paso, BS; Southern Methodist Univ, MS, 65. *Honors & Awards:* Colonel Thomas L Thurlow Award, Inst Navig, 89. *Prof Exp:* Lt, US Coast & Geod Surv, 58-60; mem tech staff, Mass Inst Technol Instrumentation Lab, 67-69; design engr, Tex Instruments Inc, 60-67, sr mem tech staff, 69-91. *Mem:* Inst Navig; sr mem Inst Elec & Electronics Engrs. *Res:* Development of advanced Navstar global positioning systems receivers for navigation using global positioning systems satellites used on a variety of Commercial and Department of Defense platforms; real time software; integrated circuit technology, digital signal processing; spread spectrum technology. *Mailing Add:* 9629 Covemeadow Dr Dallas TX 75238. *Fax:* 214-348-9447; *E-Mail:* pward@flash.net

**WARD, RAYMOND LELAND,** PHYSICAL CHEMISTRY. *Current Pos:* CHEMIST, LAWRENCE LIVERMORE NAT LAB, UNIV CALIF, 65- *Personal Data:* b San Pedro, Calif, Feb 12, 32; m 58, Margaret Foley; c Barbara, Mary, Michael & James. *Educ:* Univ Calif, BSc, 53; Washington Univ, St Louis, PhD(chem), 56. *Prof Exp:* Chemist, Lawrence Radiation Lab, Univ Calif, 56-64; NSF sr fel, Harvard Univ, 64-65. *Mem:* Am Chem Soc; Am Phys Soc. *Res:* Magnetic resonance studies of molecular interactions. *Mailing Add:* 3684 Arcadian Dr Castro Valley CA 94546-1150. *Fax:* 510-422-5424

**WARD, RICHARD FLOYD,** GEOLOGY. *Current Pos:* RETIRED. *Personal Data:* b New York, NY, July 5, 27; m 49; c 3. *Educ:* Bradley Univ, BS, 50; NY Univ, MS, 56; Bryn Mawr Col, PhD, 58. *Prof Exp:* Geologist, Del State Geol Surv, 54-58; assoc prof geol, Wayne State Univ, 59-87. *Mem:* Geol Soc Am; Geochem Soc. *Res:* Metamorphic and igneous petrology; evolution of crystalline terrains. *Mailing Add:* 22434 Melrose Ct Eastpointe MI 48021-2403

**WARD, RICHARD JOHN,** ANESTHESIOLOGY. *Current Pos:* RETIRED. *Personal Data:* b Seattle, Wash, Aug 7, 25; wid; c 3. *Educ:* Gonzaga Univ, BSc, 46; St Louis Univ, MD, 49; Seattle Univ, MEd, 72; Am Bd Anesthesiol, dipl. *Prof Exp:* Chief anesthesiol serv, Air Force Hosp, Weisbaden, Ger, 54-57; asst chief anesthesiol, Lackland AFB, 57-60, chief, 60-61; chief anesthesiol, Ballard Gen Hosp, 62-63; from instr to prof anesthesiol, Sch Med, Univ Wash, 63-90, chief staff, Univ Hosp, 77-79. *Concurrent Pos:* NIH res fel, 64-65; consult, Surgeon Gen, USAF, Europe, 54-57; chief surg res lab, Lackland AFB, 58-61; admin officer, Sch Med, Univ Wash, 66; consult, Madigan Gen Hosp, 72- *Mem:* AAAS; Am Soc Anesthesiol; AMA; Asn Mil Surg US; fel Am Col Anesthesiol. *Res:* Pharmacology and physiology of anesthetized man. *Mailing Add:* 2601 W Viemont Way W Seattle WA 98199

**WARD, RICHARD LEO,** virology, for more information see previous edition

**WARD, RICHARD S,** PSYCHIATRY, PEDIATRICS. *Current Pos:* assoc prof, 60-63, PROF PSYCHIAT, SCH MED, EMORY UNIV, 63-, ASSOC PROF PEDIAT, 76- *Personal Data:* b Beirut, Lebanon, Oct 9, 20; m 60, Adele Marie Zangosa; c Steven Henry, Charlotte C (Ford) & Richard Z. *Educ:* Amherst Col, BA, 42; Columbia Univ, MD, 45, cert, 57. *Prof Exp:* Clin dir, Child Guid Inst, Jewish Bd Guardians, NY, 56-61. *Concurrent Pos:* Rockefeller fel child psychiat, Babies Hosp, Columbia Univ, 48-50. *Mem:* Am Psychoanal Asn; Am Psychiat Asn; fel Am Orthopsychiat Asn; Am Acad Child Psychiat. *Res:* Child development; psychoanalysis. *Mailing Add:* 27 Lenox Pointe NE Atlanta GA 30324-3172

**WARD, ROBERT C,** OSTEOPATHY, BIOMECHANICS. *Current Pos:* preceptor, Col Osteop Med & asst prof family med, Mich State Univ, 70-71, prof family med & chmn dept, 72-74, prof med educ res & develop, 74-81, PROF BIOMECH, MICH STATE UNIV, 81-; STAFF MEM, LANSING GEN HOSP, 72- *Personal Data:* b Mt Clemens, Mich, Mar 9, 32; c 4. *Educ:* Kansas City Col Osteop Med, DO, 57. *Prof Exp:* Intern, Mt Clemens Gen Hosp, 57-58, staff mem family med, 58-71. *Concurrent Pos:* Off Med Educ fel, Mich State Univ, 72-73. *Mem:* Am Osteop Asn; Am Asn Study Headache; Am Acad Osteop; NAm Acad Musculoskeletal Med; Int Asn Study Pain. *Res:* Family medicine curriculum design; osteopathic therapeutics; community based medical education; stress management education; spinal radiography soft tissue mechanics. *Mailing Add:* Dept Osteop Manipulation Med E Fee Hall A439 EL Mich State Univ Col Osteopath Med East Lansing MI 48824

**WARD, ROBERT CARL,** ENVIRONMENTAL ENGINEERING, AGRICULTURAL ENGINEERING. *Current Pos:* Asst prof agr eng, Colo State Univ, 70-75, assoc prof, 75-80, actg head dept, 82-83, PROF AGR & CHEM ENG, COLO STATE UNIV, 80-, ASSOC DEAN, COL ENG, 86- *Personal Data:* b Swansea, Wales, July 4, 44; US citizen; m 66; c 3. *Educ:* Miss State Univ, BS, 66; NC State Univ, MS, 68, PhD(agr eng), 70. *Honors & Awards:* Durrell Award, 74; Gunlogson Award, Am Soc Agr Engrs, 76. *Concurrent Pos:* Guest researcher, Water Qual Inst, Denmark, 76; systs engr, US Environ Protection Agency, 77; consult, Water Qual Ctr, Hamilton, NZ, 83-84. *Mem:* Nat Water Well Asn; Water Pollution Control Fedn; Am Soc Agr Engrs; Am Water Resources Asn; Am Geophys Union; Am Soc Engr Educ. *Res:* Water quality management; design of water quality monitoring systems; on-site home sewage disposal; data use for regulatory water quality management. *Mailing Add:* Dept Agr & Chem Eng Colo State Univ Ft Collins CO 80523

**WARD, ROBERT CLEVELAND,** NUMERICAL ANALYSIS. *Current Pos:* res staff mem math, Oak Ridge Nat Lab, 74-77, head math res sect, 77-82, head math sci, 82-90, DIR ENG PHYS & MATH, OAK RIDGE NAT LAB, 90- *Personal Data:* b Sparta, Tenn, Dec 7, 44; m 65, Gayle Gillen; c Kimberly & Jonathan. *Educ:* Tenn Technol Univ, BS, 66; Col William & Mary, MS, 69; Univ Va, PhD(appl math), 74. *Prof Exp:* Mathematician, Langley Res Ctr, NASA, 66-74. *Mem:* Sigma Xi; AAAS; Soc Indust & Appl Math; Asn Comput Mach. *Res:* Developing, analyzing and improving numerical techniques in the areas of numerical linear algebra and scientific computing. *Mailing Add:* Dept Comput Sci Univ Tenn 107 Ayres Hall Knoxville TN 37996. *E-Mail:* wardrc@ornl.gov

**WARD, ROBERT T,** ZOOLOGY, CYTOLOGY. *Current Pos:* RETIRED. *Personal Data:* b Jersey City, NJ, Feb 7, 20; m 60. *Educ:* NJ State Teachers Col, AB, 42; Columbia Univ, MA, 52, PhD(zool), 60. *Prof Exp:* Res assoc zool, Columbia Univ, 52-57; asst prof anat, Downstate Med Ctr, State Univ NY, 60-79, assoc prof, 79- *Concurrent Pos:* NSF res grant, 62-66. *Mem:* AAAS; Electron Micros Soc Am; Am Soc Cell Biol; Am Asn Anat. *Res:* Electron microscopy; histochemistry. *Mailing Add:* 156 Glen Cannon Dr Pisgah Forest NC 28768-9611

**WARD, ROGER WILSON,** QUARTZ CRYSTAL RESONATORS & TRANSDUCERS. *Current Pos:* vpres eng, Quartztronics Inc, 83-90, PRES, QUARTZDYNE INC, SALT LAKE CITY, UTAH, 90- *Personal Data:* b Paris, Tex, Dec 2, 44; m 79, Kimberley E Lohman; c Eric & Tara. *Educ:* McMurry Col, BA, 67; Purdue Univ, MS, 69. *Prof Exp:* Mem tech staff, Hewlett-Packard, Palo Alto, Calif, 69-75; prod mgr, Litronix, Cupertino, Calif, 75-77; engr, Statek Corp, Orange, Calif, 77-79; vpres eng, Colo Crystal Corp, Loveland, Colo, 79-81; eng mgr, Motorola Inc, Ft Lauderdale, Fla, 81-83. *Mem:* Sr mem Inst Elec & Electronics Engrs; sr mem Inst Soc Am. *Res:* X-ray orientation of quartz crystals; SC-cut manufacturing; quartz resonator pressure transducers; photolithography on quartz wafers; over 15 patents and 26 publications on quartz crystal technology. *Mailing Add:* Quartzdyne Inc 1020 Atherton Dr C Salt Lake City UT 84123. *Fax:* 801-266-7985

**WARD, RONALD A(NTHONY),** MEDICAL ENTOMOLOGY. *Current Pos:* RETIRED. *Personal Data:* b New York, NY, Jan 25, 29; m 50, Harriet Arthur; c 2. *Educ:* Cornell Univ, BSc, 50; Univ Chicago, PhD(zool), 55; Univ London, MSc, 67. *Honors & Awards:* Medal of Honor, Am Mosquito Control Asn, 94. *Prof Exp:* Instr biol, Gonzaga Univ, 55-58; med entomologist, Walter Reed Army Inst Res, 58-94. *Concurrent Pos:* US Secy Army fel, London Sch Hyg & Trop Med, 66-67; res assoc, Smithsonian Inst, Washington, DC, 79-; ed, J Am Mosquito Control Asn, 81-96. *Mem:* Am Mosquito Control Asn; Royal Soc Trop Med & Hyg; Entom Soc Am. *Res:* Genetic and ecologic factors affecting susceptibility and resistance of arthropods to infectious agents; host adaptation of malaria parasites; mosquito biosystematics; mosquito control. *Mailing Add:* PO Box 12091 Silver Spring MD 20908

**WARD, RONALD WAYNE,** AGRICULTURAL ECONOMICS, ECONOMETRICS. *Current Pos:* assoc prof, 70-79, PROF ECON, DEPT FOOD & RESOURCE ECON, UNIV FLA, 79- *Personal Data:* b Johnson City, Tenn, Dec 17, 43; m 66, Geraldine Light. *Educ:* Univ Tenn, BS, 65; Iowa State Univ, MS, 67, PhD(econ & statist), 70. *Honors & Awards:* Qual of Res Award, Am Agr Econ Asn, 77, 79 & 80. *Prof Exp:* Res asst agr econ, Univ Tenn, 65; res asst, Iowa State Univ, 65-69; coop agent, USDA, 69-70. *Concurrent Pos:* Res economist, Fla Dept Citrus, 70-; USDA mkt struct res grant, Univ Fla, 71-72. *Mem:* Am Econ Asn; Am Agr Econ Asn. *Res:* Price analysis; marketing; advertising; market structures. *Mailing Add:* Dept Food & Resource Econ Univ Fla 1125 McCarty Hall Gainesville FL 32611-2002. *Fax:* 352-392-3646; *E-Mail:* ward@fred.ifas.ufl.edu

**WARD, RONALD WAYNE,** APPLIED SEISMOLOGY, EARTHQUAKE SEISMOLOGY. *Current Pos:* dir, Ctr Lithospheric Studies, 81-84, ASSOC PROF GEOPHYS, UNIV TEX, DALLAS, 74-; STAFF GEOPHYS, LA LAND EXPLOR, INC, 84- *Personal Data:* b Burbank, Calif, Sept 20, 44; m 76; c 1. *Educ:* Mass Inst Technol, BS, 66, PhD(geophys), 71. *Prof Exp:* Res scientist, Tex Instruments, Inc, 65; res geophysicist, Ray Geophys, Inc, Houston, Tex, 66, Geosci, Inc, 67 & Lincoln Lab, 68; sr res scientist geophys, Amoco Prod Co, Tulsa, Okla, 71-74. *Concurrent Pos:* Chmn, Tech Adv Comt Seismic Methods, Dept Energy, 77-; adv, External Proposal Rev Panel, US Geol Surv, 78-79, co-covener, Workshop Seismic Model Geysers-Clear Lake Geothermal Region, Pajaro Dunes, Calif, 79; distinguished lectr, Phillips Petrol Seminars, 80. *Mem:* Am Geophys Union; Soc Explor Geophysicists; Seismol Soc Am; Europ Asn Explor Geophysicists; AAAS. *Res:* Three-dimensional and long-range seismic reflection/refracion surveys of the earth's crust; development of new signal processing techniques; seismic modeling techniques, and seismic inversion techniques; seismic studies of geothermal areas, especially the attenuation of seismic waves; seismic velocity studies in partially melted rock. *Mailing Add:* La Land & Explor Inc 909 Poydras St Suite 3600 New Orleans LA 70112

**WARD, ROSCOE FREDRICK,** CIVIL ENGINEERING. *Current Pos:* PROF PAPER SCI & ENG, MIAMI UNIV, 83- *Personal Data:* b Boise, Idaho, Dec 5, 30; m 63, Julia Duffy; c Eric & David. *Educ:* Col Idaho, BA, 53; Ore State Col, BS, 59; Wash State Univ, MS, 61; Wash Univ, DSc(environ & sanit eng), 64; Environ Engrs Intersoc, dipl, 69. *Prof Exp:* Design engr, Stand Oil Co Calif, 59-60; asst prof civil eng, Univ Mo, Columbia, 63-65 & Robert Col, Istanbul, 65-67; assoc prof, Asian Inst Technol, Bangkok, 67-68; assoc prof civil eng & assoc dean sch eng, Univ Mass, Amherst, 68-75; br chief, Fuels from Biomass Systs Br, Dept Energy, 75-79; with UN/World Bank, 79-83. *Concurrent Pos:* Prof, Istanbul Tech Univ, 66-67; consult,

Democ, 66-67; prog mgr undergrad instrnl progs & res appl to nat needs, NSF, 72-73; prof civil eng, Bogazici Univ, Istanbul, 74-75; Fulbright prof, Univ Sao Paulo, Sao Carlos, Brazil, 86; scientist, CSIR - Div Forest Technol, Victoria, SAfrica, 90-91; Fulbright lectr, Agricult Res Inst, Nicosia, Cyprus, 90. *Mem:* Am Soc Civil Engrs. *Res:* Water supply, wastewater treatment, solid waste disposal and clean energy production from biomass. *Mailing Add:* Dept Paper Sci Miami Univ Oxford OH 45056-1618. *Fax:* 513-529-3841; *E-Mail:* wardrf@muohio.edu

**WARD, SAMUEL,** CELL BIOLOGY. *Current Pos:* DEPT HEAD & PROF MOLECULAR & CELLULAR BIOL, UNIV ARIZ, 89- *Personal Data:* b Los Angeles, Calif, Sept 29, 44; m 66; c 2. *Educ:* Princeton Univ, AB, 65; Calif Inst Technol, PhD(biochem), 71. *Prof Exp:* Tutor biochem sci, Harvard Col, 73-74; asst prof biol, Med Sch, Harvard Univ, 72-77; from assoc prof to prof biol, Johns Hopkins Univ, 77-89; mem staff, Dept Embryol, Carnegie Inst Washington, 77-89. *Concurrent Pos:* NSF fel, Med Res Coun Lab Molecular Biol, Cambridge, Eng, 70-71, NIH spec fel, 71-72. *Mem:* Am Soc Genetics; AAAS; Am Soc Cell Biol; Am Soc Develop Biol; Soc Nematologists. *Res:* Genetic control of cell structure and morphology; nematode sperm development; parasite molecular biology. *Mailing Add:* Dept Molecular & Cellular Biol Univ Ariz Life Sci S Bldg-R444 Tucson AZ 85721-0001. *Fax:* 520-621-3709

**WARD, SUSAN A,** respiratory physiology, for more information see previous edition

**WARD, THOMAS EDMUND,** NUCLEAR CHEMISTRY, NUCLEAR PHYSICS. *Current Pos:* sci adv, 91-94, SR SCI ADV, DEFENSE PROGS, US DEPT ENERGY, 94- *Personal Data:* b Los Angeles, Calif, Nov 10, 44; div, Marnie L; c 1. *Educ:* Northeastern State Col, BSEd, 65; Univ Ark, Fayetteville, MS, 69, PhD(nuclear chem), 71. *Prof Exp:* Res assoc nuclear chem, Brookhaven Nat Lab, 70-72; staff chemist, Dept Physics, Ind Univ, Bloomington, 72-85; assoc physicist, Dept Nuclear Energy & Advan Technol, Brookhaven Nat Lab, 85-88, physicist, 88-96. *Concurrent Pos:* Vis assoc chemist, Brookhaven Nat Lab, 72-75; vis fac mem, Dept Chem, Ind Univ, 81-85; mem, Synthesis Group Nat Space Coun, 90-91; sci & tech adv, Dept Energy Hq, 91- *Mem:* Am Chem Soc; Am Phys Soc; NY Acad Sci; Sigma Xi; Am Inst Chemists. *Res:* Nuclear spectroscopy and radioactive decay; intermediate energy nuclear reactions; pion production; cosmic rays; environmental nuclear chemistry; radiation effects. *Mailing Add:* 1200 N Nash St No 508 Arlington VA 22209. *Fax:* 516-282-7650; *E-Mail:* snead@bnl.gov

**WARD, THOMAS J(ULIAN),** CHEMICAL ENGINEERING, PROCESS CONTROL. *Current Pos:* from asst prof to assoc prof, 59-82, PROF CHEM ENG, CLARKSON UNIV, 82- *Personal Data:* b Amsterdam, NY, Aug 14, 30; m 67, Florence McCarthy; c Peter & Amy. *Educ:* Clarkson Univ BChE, 52; Univ Tex, MS, 56; Rensselaer Polytech Inst, PhD(chem eng), 59. *Prof Exp:* Chem engr, Carbide & Carbon Chem, Oak Ridge, Tenn, 52-53; design engr, E I du Pont de Nemours & Co, Wilmington, Del, 53; asst, Dr E J Weiss, Austin, Tex, 53-56; mem staff, Rensselaer Polytech Inst, 56-59. *Mem:* Am Inst Chem Engrs; Am Nuclear Soc; sr mem Instrument Soc Am. *Res:* Process control; optimization; design; ceramic materials; nuclear engineering. *Mailing Add:* Dept Chem Eng Clarkson Univ Box 5705 Potsdam NY 13699-5705

**WARD, TRUMAN L,** PHYSICS, PHYSICAL CHEMISTRY. *Current Pos:* Assoc physicist, 48-63, RES PHYSICIST, SOUTHERN REGIONAL LAB, AGR RES SERV, USDA, 63- *Personal Data:* b Ft Worth, Tex, Oct 21, 25; m 45; c 3. *Educ:* Tulane Univ, BS, 48. *Mem:* Am Chem Soc; Sigma Xi; fel Am Inst Chem; Am Asn Textile Chem & Colorists. *Res:* Physical properties of vegetable fats and oils; reaction mechanisms and kinetics; synthesis and reactions of thiorane and epoxy compounds; development of new instrumental procedures; glassification of cellulose; low temperature plasmas; polymers; ion exchanges. *Mailing Add:* 500 Walker St New Orleans LA 70124-3432

**WARD, WALLACE DIXON,** PSYCHOACOUSTICS. *Current Pos:* PROF OTOLARYNGOL & COMMUN DIS, UNIV MINN, MINNEAPOLIS, 62- & PROF ENVIRON HEALTH & PSYCHOL, 72- *Personal Data:* b Pierre, SDak, June 30, 24; m 49, Edith M Bystrom; c Edith M IV, Laurie E, Kathryn C & Holly L. *Educ:* SDak Sch Mines & Technol, BS, 44; Harvard Univ, PhD(exp psychol), 53. *Hon Degrees:* ScD, SDak Sch Mines & Technol, 71. *Honors & Awards:* Milver Medal in Psychol & Physiol Acoust, Musical Acoust & Noise, Acoust Soc Am, 91. *Prof Exp:* Asst scientist, Rosemount Res Ctr, Univ Minn, 49; asst, Harvard Univ, 49-53; res engr, Baldwin Piano Co, 53-54; res scientist, Cent Inst Deaf, 54-57; res assoc subcomt noise, Comt Conserv Hearing, Am Acad Ophthal & Otolaryngol, 57-62. *Concurrent Pos:* Fels, Acoust Soc Am, 61 & Am Speech & Hearing Asn, 66; chmn exec coun, Comt Hearing, Bioacoust & Biomech, Nat Acad Sci-Nat Res Coun, 71-73; consult, US Army, 71-88, Off Noise Abatement & Control, Environ Protection Agency, 72-73 & Air Transport Asn Am, 73-84; assoc ed, Int Audiol, 78-, J Acoust Soc Am, 84-86 & 91-93 & Music Perception, 84- *Mem:* Am Otol Soc; Acoust Soc Am (vpres, 86-87, pres, 88-89); Int Soc Audiol (vpres, 76-78, pres, 78-80); Am Audiol Soc (vpres, 73-75, pres, 76-77); Int Comt Biol Effects Noise; Soc Res Psychol Music & Music Educ. *Res:* Auditory fatigue and noise-induced hearing loss; musical perception; musical psychoacoustics. *Mailing Add:* 121 Lions Res Bldg 2001 Sixth St SE Minneapolis MN 55455. *Fax:* 612-626-9871; *E-Mail:* wardx003@staff.tc.umn.edu

**WARD, WALTER FREDERICK,** PHYSIOLOGY, ENDOCRINOLOGY. *Current Pos:* asst prof, 78-80, ASSOC PROF PHYSIOL, HEALTH SCI CTR, UNIV TEX, SAN ANTONIO, 80- *Personal Data:* b Darlington, Wis, June 23, 40; m 59, Patricia A Hauser; c Elizabeth A, Daniel H & Diane L. *Educ:* Univ Wis-Platteville, BSc, 64; Marquette Univ, PhD(physiol), 70. *Prof Exp:* USPHS fel, Brown Univ, 71-73; asst prof physiol, Col Med, Pa State Univ, 73-78. *Mem:* AAAS; Am Physiol Soc; fel Geront Soc Am. *Res:* Regulation of protein metabolism; mechanisms of hormone action; aging and protein metabolism; gerontology. *Mailing Add:* Dept Physiol Health Sci Ctr Univ Tex San Antonio TX 78284-7756. *Fax:* 210-567-4410; *E-Mail:* wardw@uthscsa.edu

**WARD, WILLIAM CRUSE,** SEDIMENTARY PETROLOGY. *Current Pos:* from asst prof to prof, 70-95, EMER PROF GEOL, UNIV NEW ORLEANS, 95- *Personal Data:* b Waco, Tex, Apr 26, 33; m 57; c 3. *Educ:* Univ Tex, Austin, BS, 55, MA, 57; Rice Univ, PhD(geol), 70. *Prof Exp:* Geologist, Humble Oil & Refining Co, 57-66. *Mem:* Soc Econ Paleontologists & Mineralogists; Am Asn Petrol Geologists. *Res:* Petrology and diagenesis of Quaternary limestones of eastern Yucatan; sandstone petrology and diagenesis. *Mailing Add:* 26328 Autumn Glen Boerne TX 78006

**WARD, WILLIAM FRANCIS,** PARASITOLOGY. *Current Pos:* asst prof, Rosemont Col, 57-66, from actg chmn dept to chmn dept, 64-72, chmn, Div Natural Sci & Math, 76-79 & 87-90, ASSOC PROF BIOL, ROSEMONT COL, 66- *Personal Data:* b Erie, Pa, June 19, 28. *Educ:* Gannon Col, BS, 50; Univ Notre Dame, MS, 55. *Prof Exp:* Instr biol, Col St Mary, Utah, 55-57. *Mem:* Am Soc Microbiol; Sigma Xi; AAAS; Am Soc Parasitol; Am Inst Biol Sci. *Res:* Interrelationships between intestinal parasites and the bacterial flora. *Mailing Add:* Dept Biol Rosemont Col Montgomery Ave Rosemont PA 19010-1699

**WARD, WILLIAM J, III,** CHEMICAL ENGINEERING. *Current Pos:* RES ENGR, GEN ELEC CO, 65- *Personal Data:* b Paterson, NJ, Oct 4, 39; m 62; c 2. *Educ:* Pa State Univ, BS, 61; Univ Ill, MS, 63, PhD(chem eng), 65. *Mem:* Nat Acad Eng; AAAS; Am Inst Chem Engrs. *Res:* Research and development of membrane separation processes; catalysis. *Mailing Add:* 1924 Hexam Rd Schenectady NY 12309. *Fax:* 518-387-6662

**WARDE, CARDINAL,** SOLID STATE PHYSICS, OPTICAL ENGINEERING. *Current Pos:* Asst prof, 74-79, ASSOC PROF ELEC ENG, MASS INST TECHNOL, 79- *Personal Data:* b Barbados, July 14, 45. *Educ:* Stevens Inst Technol, BSc, 69; Yale Univ, MPhil, 71, PhD(physics), 74. *Concurrent Pos:* Vinton Hayes fel, Mass Inst Technol, 75-76; prin investr, NSF grants, 76- & Air Force Off Sci Res grant, 77-; consult, Lincoln Lab, Mass Inst Technol, 77-, Rome Air Develop Ctr, 81- & Hamamatsu TV Co, Japan, 80-; State Univ NY res grant, 80-81. *Mem:* Optical Soc Am; Inst Elec & Electronics Engrs; Soc Photo-Optical Instrumentation Engrs. *Res:* Optical signal processing and storage devices; adaptive optical systems; optical properties of electron-beam-addressed materials. *Mailing Add:* Prof Rm 13-3102 Mass Inst Technol 77 Massachusetts Ave Cambridge MA 02139

**WARDELL, JAMES C,** theoretical physics, for more information see previous edition

**WARDELL, JOE RUSSELL, JR,** PHARMACOLOGY, PHYSIOLOGY. *Current Pos:* PRES, WARDELL ASSOCS, 86- *Personal Data:* b Omaha, Nebr, Nov 11, 29; m 52, 82, Doris Erway; c Michael, Susan & John. *Educ:* Creighton Univ, BS, 51; Univ Nebr, MSc, 59, PhD(pharmacol, physiol), 62. *Prof Exp:* Sr pharmacologist, Smith Kline & French Labs, 62-65, group leader pharmacol, 64-68, asst dir pharmacol, 68-71, assoc dir pharmacol & mission dir cardiopulmonary res area, 71-75, assoc dir biol res & mission dir cardiovasc res area, 75-78, sci dir new prod eval, res & mission dir cardiovasc res area, 78-81, dir new compound eval, 81-85, dept dir res & develop compound acquisitions, 85-86. *Mem:* AAAS; Am Chem Soc; NY Acad Sci; Am Soc Pharmacol & Exp Therapeut; Am Acad Allergy; Licensing Exec Soc. *Res:* Cardiovascular and respiratory pharmacology; immunopharmacology; autonomic pharmacology; regulation of biosynthesis and secretion of respiratory mucus. *Mailing Add:* Wardell Assocs 55 Thaynes Canyon Dr Park City UT 84060. *Fax:* 435-649-9323, 412-728-1048; *E-Mail:* jrwardell@sisna.com

**WARDELL, WILLIAM MICHAEL,** CLINICAL PHARMACOLOGY. *Current Pos:* VPRES & MED DIR, BOEHRINGER INGELHEIM PHARMACEUTICALS, INC, 83- *Personal Data:* b Christchurch, NZ, Nov 15, 38; m 65; c 2. *Educ:* Oxford Univ, BA, 61, DPhil(pharmacol), 64, BM & BCh, 67, DM, 73. *Honors & Awards:* Christopher Welch Prize Biol. *Prof Exp:* Intern med, Radcliffe Infirmary, Oxford, 67; intern med & surg, Dunedin Hosp, Univ Otago, NZ, 68; med res officer clin pharmacol & toxicol, NZ Med Res Coun, 69; lectr clin pharmacol, Univ Otago, Med Sch, NZ, 70; instr clin pharmacol, Univ Rochester, 71-73, from asst prof to assoc prof pharmacol, 73-83. *Concurrent Pos:* Hon clin asst, Otago Hosp Bd, Dunedin, NZ, 69-70; co-founder & dir, Ctr Study Drug Develop, Univ Rochester Med Ctr, 75-83. *Mem:* Am Soc Pharmacol & Exp Therapeut; Am Soc Clin Pharmacol & Therapeut; Am Col Clin Pharmacol; Australasian Soc Clin & Exp Pharmacol; AMA. *Res:* Design, methodology and analysis of drug studies in man; analgesic and hypnotic drugs in man; regulation and drug development; adverse drug reactions. *Mailing Add:* 1225 Fair Oaks Pkwy Ann Arbor MI 48104. *Fax:* 313-996-7659

**WARDEN, GLENN DONALD,** BURN SURGERY. *Current Pos:* PROF, DEPT SURG & DIR, DIV BURN SURG, UNIV CINCINNATI MED CTR, 85-; CHIEF-OF-STAFF, CINCINNATI UNIT, SHRINERS BURN INST. *Educ:* Univ Utah, MD, 68; Am Bd Surg, dipl. *Prof Exp:* Intern surg, Dept Surg, Univ Utah Med Ctr, Salt Lake City, 68-69, resident gen surg, 69-71 & 74-76; from instr to prof, Dept Surg, Intermountain Burn Ctr, Sch Med, Univ Utah, 76-85, dir, 77-85, Trauma Div, Dept Surg, 78-85, co-dir, Intensive Care Unit, 83-84. *Concurrent Pos:* Int hon prof surg, Third Mil Med Col, People's Repub China; fel renal transplantation, Nephrol Dept, Med Div Nephrol, Vet Admin Hosp, Salt Lake City, 70-71; critical care unit consult, Emergency Med Serv, Salt Lake City Dept Health, 77-85, bd dirs, Emergency Training Coun, 82-85; deleg, Utah Med Asn, 79-81; treas, Utah Soc Cert Surgeons, 81, pres, 82; burn consult, Handicapped Children's Serv, Utah State Dept Health, 81-85; mem univ senate, Univ Utah, 84-85; chmn fel comt, Surg Infection Soc, 86-88; bd dirs, Int Burn Found US, 92. *Mem:* Fel Am Col Surgeons (secy-treas, 84); Int Soc Burn Injuries; Int Soc Surg; Int Burn Found US; Pan-Pac Surg Asn; Pan-Am Med Asn; Am Burn Asn (secy, 87-90, 1st vpres, 90-91, pres-elect, 91-92, pres, 92-93); Transplantation Soc; Soc Leukocyte Biol; Am Asn Tissue Banks; Am Soc Transplant Surgeons; Am Soc Parental & Enteral Nutrit. *Res:* Burn injuries; surgery; nephrology; infections; transplantations. *Mailing Add:* 3229 Burnet Ave Cincinnati OH 45229-3095

**WARDEN, HERBERT EDGAR,** SURGERY, THORACIC SURGERY. *Current Pos:* assoc prof, 60-62, PROF SURG, MED CTR, WVA UNIV, 62- *Personal Data:* b Cleveland, Ohio, Aug 30, 20; m 58, Audrey E Flaten; c Karen E, Bradford E, Douglas E & Suzanne E. *Educ:* Washington & Jefferson Col, BS, 42; Univ Chicago, MD, 46; Am Bd Surg, dipl, 58; Bd Thoracic Surg, dipl, 63. *Honors & Awards:* Cert of Merit, AMA, 55 & 58, Hektoen Gold Medal, 57; Lasker Award, Am Pub Health Asn, 55. *Prof Exp:* Intern, Clin, Univ Chicago, 46-47; asst resident surg, Hosps, Univ Minn, 51-56, res asst, 53-55, res asst physiol, 55-56, clin instr surg, 55-57, chief resident, 56-57, instr surg, 57-60. *Concurrent Pos:* Coordr, USPHS Cardiovasc Surg Training Prog, Univ Minn, 56-60; consult, Anoka State Hosp, Minn, 58-59. *Mem:* Soc Univ Surgeons; Am Asn Thoracic Surgeons; Am Surg Asn; Soc Thoracic Surgeons; fel Am Col Surgeons; AMA; fel Am Col Cardiol. *Res:* Cardiovascular surgery and physiology. *Mailing Add:* Dept Surg WVa Univ 616 Schubert Pl Morgantown WV 26506-2330. *Fax:* 304-293-4711

**WARDEN, JOSEPH TALLMAN,** BIOPHYSICAL CHEMISTRY. *Current Pos:* from asst prof to assoc prof, 75-88, PROF CHEM, RENSSELAER POLYTECH INST, 88- *Personal Data:* b Huntington, WVa, Aug 7, 46; c 1. *Educ:* Furman Univ, BS, 68; Univ Minn, PhD(phys chem), 72. *Prof Exp:* Vis scientist biophys, State Univ Leiden, 72-73; chemist, Univ Calif, Berkeley, 73-75. *Concurrent Pos:* Vis prof, Univ Col, London, 81; Carnegie fel, Int Conf Educ Chem, 86. *Mem:* AAAS; Am Chem Soc; Am Soc Photobiol; Biophys Soc. *Res:* Electron spin resonance investigations of electron transfer components and mechanisms in photosynthesis and mitochondrial respiration; artificial intelligence applications in chemistry; photochemistry; solid state chemistry; microelectronics. *Mailing Add:* Dept Chem Rensselaer Polytech Inst Troy NY 12180-3590. *E-Mail:* wardej@rpi.edu

**WARDER, DAVID LEE,** CIVIL ENGINEERING. *Current Pos:* SR ENGR, ATEC ASSOCS, INC, 76- *Personal Data:* b Akron, Ohio, June 17, 40; m 63; c 2. *Educ:* Univ Akron, BSCE, 63; Mich State Univ, MS, 65, PhD(civil eng), 69. *Prof Exp:* Assoc prof civil eng, Tri-State Col, 69-73. *Mem:* Am Soc Civil Engrs; Int Soc Soil Mech & Found Engr. *Res:* Use of artificially frozen soil for temporary support; structure-foundation interaction. *Mailing Add:* 11344 Fieldstone Ct Carmel IN 46033

**WARDER, RICHARD C, JR,** MECHANICAL ENGINEERING. *Current Pos:* assoc prof, 68-72, PROF MECH & AEROSPACE ENG, UNIV MO, COLUMBIA, 72-, CHMN DEPT, 88- *Personal Data:* b Nitro, WVa, Sept 30, 36; m 81, M Dianne Forney; c Jennifer & Jeffrey. *Educ:* SDak Sch Mines & Technol, BS, 58; Northwestern Univ, MS, 59, PhD(mech eng, astronaut sci), 63. *Prof Exp:* Asst prof mech eng & astronaut sci, Northwestern Univ, 63-65; mgr energy processes res, Space Sci Labs, Litton Industs, Inc, Calif, 65-68. *Concurrent Pos:* Prof staff mem, NSF, 74-76. *Mem:* AAAS; Am Soc Eng Educ; Am Phys Soc; Am Inst Aeronaut & Astronaut; Am Soc Mech Engrs; Am Aerosol Res. *Res:* Aerosol and particulate mechanics; gas dynamics; indoor air quality. *Mailing Add:* Dean Herff Co Eng Univ Memphis Memphis TN 38152-0001. *Fax:* 573-884-5090; *E-Mail:* warder@ecvax2.ecn.missouri.edu

**WARDESKA, JEFFREY GWYNN,** INORGANIC CHEMISTRY, BIOINORGANIC CHEMISTRY. *Current Pos:* From asst prof to prof, 67-79, PROF CHEM, ETENN STATE UNIV, 79- *Personal Data:* b Irondale, Ohio, June 13, 41; m 65, Brenda Campbell; c Angela & Elisa. *Educ:* Mt Union Col, BSc, 63; Ohio Univ, PhD(inorg chem), 67. *Concurrent Pos:* Vis prof, Univ NH, 84-85. *Mem:* Am Chem Soc; Sigma Xi. *Res:* Coordination chemistry; reactions of coordination compounds of transition metals; aminoalcohol complexes; metal ion binding to metalloproteins. *Mailing Add:* 4 Bingham Ct Johnson City TN 37604-7120. *Fax:* 423-929-5835; *E-Mail:* r21jeff@etsu.etsu__tn.edu

**WARDLAW, JANET MELVILLE,** NUTRITION, HOME ECONOMICS. *Current Pos:* RETIRED. *Personal Data:* b Toronto, Ont, June 20, 24. *Educ:* Univ Toronto, BA, 46; Univ Tenn, MS, 50; Pa State Univ, PhD(nutrit), 63. *Honors & Awards:* Stuart's Branded Foods Ltd Award, Can Dietetic Asn, 71. *Prof Exp:* Dietition, Can Red Cross Soc, Toronto, 47-49; nutritionist, Mich Dept Health, 50-53 & Toronto Dept Pub Health, 53-56; asst prof nutrit, Fac Household Sci, Univ Toronto, 56-60 & 63-64, assoc prof, Fac Food Sci, 64-66; assoc dean-dean designate, Univ Guelph, 67-68, dean, 69-83, prof nutrit, Col

Family & Consumer Studies, 66-87, assoc vpres acad, 84-87. *Concurrent Pos:* Chmn bd gov, Int Develop Res Ctr, Ottawa, Can, 85-92; hon fel, Univ Guelph, 89. *Mem:* AAAS; Nutrit Soc Can; Can Dietetic Asn (treas, 65-67). *Res:* Sodium regulation during pregnancy; body composition and feeding frequency; community nutrition. *Mailing Add:* 20 Suffolk St W Guelph ON N1H 2H8 Can

**WARDLAW, NORMAN CLAUDE,** geology, for more information see previous edition

**WARDLAW, WILLIAM PATTERSON,** MATHEMATICS. *Current Pos:* asst prof, 72-84, ASSOC PROF MATH, US NAVAL ACAD, 84- *Personal Data:* b Los Angeles, Calif, Mar 3, 36; m 63; c 4. *Educ:* Rice Inst, BA, 58; Univ Calif, Los Angeles, MA, 64, PhD(math), 66. *Prof Exp:* Asst prof, Univ Ga, 66-72. *Mem:* Am Math Soc; Math Asn Am. *Res:* Lie algebras and Chevalley groups; universal algebra. *Mailing Add:* Dept Math US Naval Acad Annapolis MD 21402-5002

**WARDLE, CAROLINE ELIZABETH,** RESEARCH ADMINISTRATION, INFORMATION SCIENCE & SYSTEMS. *Current Pos:* prog dir cross disciplinary activ, 90-95, dep div dir comput & comput res, 95-96, DEP OFFICE HEAD, CROSS-DISCIPLINARY ACTIV, NSF, 96- *Personal Data:* b Leicester, Eng, Mar 1, 44; US citizen. *Educ:* London Univ, BSc, 65, PhD(math physics), 70. *Prof Exp:* Instr comput sci, Univ Nebr, Lincoln, 68-69; lectr, Hunter Col, Cent Univ NY, 69-70, asst prof, 70-75; assoc prof, Boston Univ, 75-91; assoc dean & prof info technol, Wang Inst Grad Studies, 80, dean & prof, 80-81; res adv, Nolan, Nortan & Co, 83-86. *Concurrent Pos:* Mem, Working Group Software Eng Model Curric, Inst Elec & Electronics Engrs, 81-82 & Task Force, Asn Comput Mach, 83-85; vis scientist, Sloan Sch Mgt, Mass Inst Technol, 82; guest researcher, Nat Inst Stand & Technol, 90- *Mem:* Asn Comput Mach; Inst Elec & Electronics Engrs. *Res:* Examining the use of software quality assurance and total quality management as vehicles for improving software systems quality; examined the use of software quality assurance and the adaption of total quality management to software development. *Mailing Add:* 4201 Wilson Blvd Arlington VA 22230. *Fax:* 703-306-0589; *E-Mail:* cwardle@nsf.gov

**WARDLE, JOHN FRANCIS CARLETON,** RADIO ASTRONOMY. *Current Pos:* from instr to assoc prof, 71-86, PROF ASTROPHYS, BRANDEIS UNIV, 86- *Personal Data:* b Hemel Hempstead, Eng, May 8, 45; m 71. *Educ:* Univ Cambridge, BA, 66; Univ Manchester, MSc, 68, PhD(radio astron), 69. *Prof Exp:* Res asst radio astron, Nat Radio Astron Observ, 69-71. *Mem:* Am Astron Soc; Royal Astron Soc. *Res:* Extragalactic radio astronomy; cosmology. *Mailing Add:* 226 Taunton St Waltham MA 02093

**WARD-MCLEMORE, ETHEL,** fortran programming, bibliographies of sedimentary basins of the appalachian-ouachita orogen & china; deceased, see previous edition for last biography

**WARDOWSKI, WILFRED FRANCIS, II,** HORTICULTURE. *Current Pos:* assoc prof, 69-80, PROF EXTEN SERV, CITRUS HARVESTING & HANDLING, CITRUS RES & EDUC CTR, UNIV FLA, 80- *Personal Data:* b Pontiac, Mich, May 23, 37; m 74; c 1. *Educ:* Mich State Univ, BS, 59, MS, 61, PhD(pomol), 66. *Prof Exp:* Foreman fruit prod, Blossom Orchard, Leslie, Mich, 61-63; midwest rep tech exten agr chem, Agr Div, Upjohn Co, 66-69. *Concurrent Pos:* Consult, UN Food & Agr Orgn develop prog, Bhutan, 80, Fed Nat de Cafe, Colombia, 82, Fed Agr Orgn, UN, China 82, 85, 86, 89, Citrus Packers, Honduras, 88, 89, 91, Citrus Growers, Brazil & Spain, 93. *Mem:* Am Soc Hort Sci. *Res:* Nutrition and histology of apples; agricultural chemicals research and development; harvesting and handling of fresh market citrus. *Mailing Add:* Citrus Res & Educ Ctr Univ Fla Lake Alfred FL 33850-2299. *Fax:* 941-956-4631; *E-Mail:* wfw@gnv.ifas.ufl.edu

**WARE, ALAN ALFRED,** PLASMA PHYSICS. *Current Pos:* SR RES SCIENTIST PLASMA PHYSICS, UNIV TEX, AUSTIN, 69- *Personal Data:* b Portsmouth, Eng, Dec 4, 24; US citizen; m 52; c 4. *Educ:* Imp Col, Univ London, BSc & ARCS, 44, PhD(physics) & DIC, 49. *Prof Exp:* Res asst plasma physics, Imp Col, Univ London, 47-51; sect leader, Res Lab, Assoc Elec Industs, UK, 51-63; consult, Gen Atomic, San Diego, 60-61; group leader plasma physics, Culham Lab, UK Atomic Energy Authority, 63-65; asst mgr res oper plasma physics, Aerojet Gen Corp, 65-69. *Concurrent Pos:* Consult, Los Alamos Sci Lab, 71- *Mem:* Am Phys Soc. *Res:* Theory of Tokamak plasmas in research aimed at controlled nuclear fusion power. *Mailing Add:* Dept Physics Univ Tex Austin TX 78712. *Fax:* 512-471-6715

**WARE, BRENDAN J,** ELECTRICAL POWER TRANSMISSION, SYSTEM ENGINEERING. *Current Pos:* Engr eng & res, 60-76, MGR, ELEC RES & DEVELOP DIV, AM ELEC POWER & SERV, COLUMBUS, OHIO, 76- *Personal Data:* b Dublin, Ireland, Aug 27, 32. *Educ:* Nat Univ Ireland, BE, 54; NJ Inst Technol, MSEE, 67. *Mem:* Fel Inst Elec & Electronics Engrs. *Mailing Add:* 2478 Bryden Rd Columbus OH 43209

**WARE, BUCK,** MATHEMATICAL ANALYSIS. *Current Pos:* PROF MATH, CALIF STATE UNIV, CHICO, 76- *Personal Data:* b Jan 1940. *Educ:* Univ Calif, Berkeley, BA; San Francisco State Univ, MS; Univ Calif, Santa Cruz, PhD. *Mem:* Am Math Soc. *Res:* Mathematical analysis. *Mailing Add:* Math Dept Calif State Univ Chico CA 95929-0525

**WARE, CARL F,** T-CELL MEDIATED IMMUNOLOGY. *Current Pos:* MEM & HEAD, DIV MOLECULAR IMMUNOL, LA JOLLA INST ALLERGY & IMMUNOL. *Personal Data:* b Fullerton, Calif, May 23, 51. *Educ:* Univ Calif, Irvine, BS, 74, PhD(molecular biol & biochem), 79. *Mem:* AAAS; Am Asn Immunologists. *Res:* Molecular immunopathogensis of T lymphocyte-virus interations; TNF/LT ligand-receptor superfamily; structure-function and signal transduction mechanisms. *Mailing Add:* Div Allergy LaJolla Inst Allergy & Immunol 10355 Sci Ctr Dr San Diego CA 92121. *Fax:* 619-678-4695; *E-Mail:* carl__ware@liai.org

**WARE, CAROLYN BOGARDUS,** neuroanatomy, physiological psychology, for more information see previous edition

**WARE, CHARLES HARVEY, JR,** chemical engineering, for more information see previous edition

**WARE, DONNA MARIE EGGERS,** PLANT TAXONOMY. *Current Pos:* HERBARIUM CUR VASCULAR PLANTS, COL WILLIAM & MARY, 69- *Personal Data:* b Springfield, Mo, Oct 1, 42; m 68. *Educ:* Southwest Mo State Col, BA, 64; Vanderbilt Univ, PhD(biol), 69. *Concurrent Pos:* NSF grant-in-aid, Highlands Biol Sta, NC, 70. *Mem:* Am Soc Plant Taxon. *Res:* Floristics; revisional and biosystematic taxonomy. *Mailing Add:* Herbarium Dept Biol Col William & Mary Millington Hall Williamsburg VA 23185

**WARE, FREDERICK,** PHYSIOLOGY, INTERNAL MEDICINE. *Current Pos:* Instr physiol, Univ Nebr, 53-56, instr internal med, 55-56, asst prof physiol & pharmacol, 60-62, assoc prof physiol & asst prof internal med, 62-70, PROF PHYSIOL, BIOPHYS & INTERNAL MED, COL MED, UNIV NEBR, OMAHA, 70- *Personal Data:* b Omaha, Nebr, June 16, 28; m 50, 78; c 5. *Educ:* Univ Nebr, BS, 49, MS, 53, PhD & MD, 56. *Mem:* Am Physiol Soc; Am Soc Nephrology; Int Soc Nephrology; Am Col Physicians; Am Soc Artificial Internal Organs. *Res:* Membrane electrophysiology of skeletal muscle and heart; principles of electrocardiography; biophysics of renal function. *Mailing Add:* 4242 Farnam St Omaha NE 68131-2850

**WARE, GEORGE HENRY,** PLANT ECOLOGY. *Current Pos:* DENDROLOGIST, MORTON ARBORETUM, 68-, RES GROUP ADMINR, 76-, RES FEL DENDROLOGY, 93- *Personal Data:* b Avery, Okla, Apr 27, 24; m 55, June Gleason; c David, Daniel, Patrick & John. *Educ:* Univ Okla, BS, 45, MS, 48; Univ Wis, PhD(bot), 55. *Prof Exp:* From asst prof to prof bot, Northwestern State Univ, 48-68; adminr, Urban Veg Lab, 85-93. *Mem:* Ecol Soc Am; Int Soc Arboricult; Soc Ecol Restoration. *Res:* ecology of swamp and floodplain forests; ecology of urban trees. *Mailing Add:* 573 59th Lisle IL 60532-3102. *Fax:* 630-719-2433

**WARE, GEORGE WHITAKER, JR,** ENTOMOLOGY. *Current Pos:* RETIRED. *Personal Data:* b Pine Bluff, Ark, Aug 27, 27; m 52; c 3. *Educ:* Univ Ark, BS, 51, MS, 52; Kans State Univ, PhD(entom), 56. *Prof Exp:* Assoc prof entom, Ohio State Univ, 56-66; prof entom & head dept, Univ Ariz, 67-83, assoc dir, Agr Exp Sta, 83-92. *Concurrent Pos:* Consult, Environ Protection Agency, Off Pesticide Progs Washington, USAID, Univ Calif, Berkeley, 78-79 & Nat Agr Chem Asn, 80-82; Coop States Res Serv, USDA; expert witness pesticide drift litigation, PR, Fla & Mass, 84-88; ed, Rev Environ Contamination & Toxicol. *Mem:* Entom Soc Am; Am Chem Soc; Soc Toxicol. *Res:* Insecticide toxicology; pesticide chemistry, metabolism and residues; application of pesticides; pesticide drift reduction. *Mailing Add:* 5794 E Camino Del Celador Tucson AZ 85750. *Fax:* 520-299-3735; *E-Mail:* gware@ag.arizona.edu

**WARE, GLENN OREN,** APPLIED STATISTICS, OPERATIONS RESEARCH. *Current Pos:* asst prof statist, 66-74, assoc prof forestry, 77-84, STA STATISTICIAN, EXP STA, UNIV GA, 74-, PROF FORESTRY, 85- *Personal Data:* b Athens, Ga, Dec 8, 41; m 67; c 2. *Educ:* Univ Ga, BSF, 63, PhD(forest biomet), 68; Yale Univ, MF, 64. *Prof Exp:* Res forester, Hudson Pulp & Paper Corp, 64-65. *Mem:* Soc Am Foresters; Biometrics Soc. *Res:* Application of mathematical and statistical techniques in the physical and biological sciences. *Mailing Add:* Sch Forest Resources Univ Ga 209 Conner Hall Athens GA 30602

**WARE, JAMES GARETH,** MATHEMATICS. *Current Pos:* assoc prof, 67-73, chmn dept, 68-90, PROF MATH, UNIV TENN, CHATTANOOGA, 73- *Personal Data:* b Baltimore, Md, Aug 19, 29; m 55; c 1. *Educ:* Duke Univ, BS, 50; George Peabody Col, MA, 51, PhD(math), 62. *Prof Exp:* Teacher, McCallie Sch, Tenn, 52-54 & 59-60, dept chmn, 60-65. *Mem:* Nat Coun Teachers Math; Am Asn Univ Professors; Math Asn Am. *Res:* Mathematics education; geometry. *Mailing Add:* 1071 Constitution Dr Chattanooga TN 37405

**WARE, JAMES H,** MATHEMATICAL STATISTICS. *Current Pos:* MEM FAC, DEPT BIOSTATIST, HARVARD SCH PUB HEALTH, 80- *Personal Data:* b Detroit, Mich, Oct 27, 41; m 72; c 1. *Educ:* Yale Univ, BA, 63; Stanford Univ, MA, 65, PhD(statist), 69. *Prof Exp:* Instr statist, Calif State Col, Hayward, 69-70; math statistician, NIH, 71-80. *Concurrent Pos:* Assoc ed, J Am Statist Asn, 73-75; adj prof statist, George Washington Univ, 75- *Mem:* Am Statist Asn; Biomet Soc. *Res:* Interest in the areas of nonparametric methods and sequential analysis; survival data analysis and methods for data analysis in clinical trials of chronic disease. *Mailing Add:* Dept Biostatist Harvard Sch Pub Health 677 Huntington Ave Boston MA 02115-6023

**WARE, JOHN E, JR,** PSYCHOLOGY. *Current Pos:* SR SCIENTIST, HEALTH INST, NEW ENG MED CTR, MASS, 88-, DIR, HEALTHCARE ASSESSMENT LAB, 89-; RES PROF, DEPT PSYCHIAT, TUFTS UNIV, 94- *Educ:* Pepperdine Univ, BA, 64, MA, 66; Southern Ill Univ, PhD(educ measurements & statist), 74. *Prof Exp:* Instr & res assoc, Dept Psychiat, Sch Med, Univ Southern Calif, 66-72, dir res, Postgrad Div, 69-71; asst prof & dir, Sch Med, Southern Ill Univ, Carbondale, 72-75; sr res psychologist, Behav Sci Dept & Health Sci Prog, Band Corp, Calif, 75-88. *Concurrent Pos:* Instr, Dept Psychol, Pepperdine Univ, Los Angeles, 66-72 & 76-78; adj prof & res adv, Clin Scholar's Prog, Sch Med & Pub Health, Univ Calif, Los Angeles, 76-88; prin investr, Med Outcomes Study, 84-; bd dirs, Asn Health Servs Res, 89-95; dir, Int Qual Life Assessment Proj, Health Inst, New Eng Med Ctr, Mass, 91-; adj prof, Dept Health & Social Behav, Harvard Sch Pub Health, 94- *Mem:* Inst Med-Nat Acad Sci; Asn Health Servs Res; Am Psychol Asn. *Res:* Health care services; patient satisfaction; health related quality of life. *Mailing Add:* New Eng Med Ctr 750 Washington St Box 345 Boston MA 02111

**WARE, KENNETH DALE,** FOREST BIOMETRICS, SURVEY SAMPLING. *Current Pos:* CONSULT, 88- *Personal Data:* b Webster Springs, WVa, Aug 30, 35; m 57, Mary A McClung; c Suzanne & Greg. *Educ:* WVa Univ, BS, 56; Yale Univ, MS, 57, PhD(biomet), 60. *Prof Exp:* Res forester, Northeastern Forest Exp Sta, US Forest Serv, 58-61; asst prof forestry, Iowa State Univ, 61-64, assoc prof, 65-68, prof, 69-71; chief mensurationist, Southeastern Forest Exp Sta, US Forest Serv, 71-88. *Concurrent Pos:* Vis scientist, NSF & Soc Am Forests; adj prof, Sch Forest Resources, Univ Ga, 71-; Tasman fel, Univ Canterbury, NZ, 84; vis fel, Australian Nat Univ, Canberra, 84. *Mem:* Soc Am Forests; Int Union Forestry Res Orgn. *Res:* Concepts and techniques for forest sampling, including surveys on successive occasions; special unequal probability procedures; multi-phase sampling structures and sampling for predicting forest growth and yield under timber management and for monitoring responses to management. *Mailing Add:* 195 Deerfield Rd Bogart GA 30622

**WARE, LAWRENCE LESLIE, JR,** medical microbiology; deceased, see previous edition for last biography

**WARE, ROGER PERRY,** ALGEBRA. *Current Pos:* assoc prof, 74-80, PROF MATH, PA STATE UNIV, 80- *Personal Data:* b San Francisco, Calif, Apr 2, 42; m 65; c 2. *Educ:* Univ Calif, Berkeley, AB, 65; Univ Calif, Santa Barbara, MA, 68, PhD(math), 70. *Prof Exp:* Asst prof math, Northwestern Univ, Evanston, 70-72 & Univ Kans, Lawrence, 72-74. *Concurrent Pos:* NSF grants, 71-72, 73, 74 & 76-82; vis prof math, Univ Calif, Berkely, 80-81; prin invest NSA grant, 88-89. *Mem:* Am Math Soc; Math Asn Am. *Res:* Quadratic forms; field theory. *Mailing Add:* Dept Math Pa State Univ University Park PA 16802-6401

**WARE, STEWART ALEXANDER,** PLANT ECOLOGY. *Current Pos:* From asst prof to assoc prof, 67-82, chmn dept, 76-82, PROF BIOL, COL WILLIAM & MARY, 82- *Personal Data:* b Stringer, Miss, Aug 20, 42; m 68. *Educ:* Millsaps Col, BA, 64; Vanderbilt Univ, PhD(biol), 68. *Concurrent Pos:* Ed, Jeffersonia, Va Bot Newslett, 69-74 & Va J Sci, 79-84; vis prof bot, Univ Ark, 84. *Mem:* Ecol Soc Am; Sigma Xi; Bot Soc Am; Torrey Bot Club; Int Asn Veg Sci. *Res:* Vegetation of the southeastern United States; Quercus systematics and ecology; physiological ecology of rock outcrop plants; ecology and distribution of Talinum. *Mailing Add:* Dept Biol Sci Univ Ark Fayetteville AR 72701

**WARE, VASSIE C,** RIBOSOMAL RNA, RNA PROCESSING. *Current Pos:* ASST PROF BIOL, LEHIGH UNIV, 85- *Educ:* Yale Univ, PhD(biol), 81. *Mailing Add:* Dept Biol Sci Lehigh Univ 111 Research Dr Bethlehem PA 18015-4732

**WARE, W(ILLIS) H(OWARD),** COMPUTER SCIENCE, HARDWARE SYSTEMS. *Current Pos:* head, Comput Sci Dept, Rand Corp, 51-71, dep vpres, 71-73, corp res staff, 73-92, CONSULT, RAND CORP, 92- *Personal Data:* b Atlantic City, NJ, Aug 31, 20; m 43; c 3. *Educ:* Univ Pa, BS, 41; Mass Inst Technol, SM, 42; Princeton Univ, PhD(elec eng), 51. *Honors & Awards:* Except Civilian Serv Medal, USAF, 79; Centennial Medal, Inst Elec & Electronics Engrs, 84; Nat Comput Syst Security Award, Nat Inst Stand & Technol & Nat Comput Security Ctr, 89; Comput Pioneer Award, Inst Elec & Electronics Engrs Comput Soc, 93; Pioneer Award, Electronic Frontier Found, 95. *Prof Exp:* Res engr, Hazeltine Electronics Corp, 42-46, Princeton Inst Advan Study, 46-51. *Concurrent Pos:* Chmn, HEW, Sec'y Adv Comn Automated Personal Data Systs, 71-73; mem & vchmn, Privacy Protection Study Comn, 75-77. *Mem:* Nat Acad Eng; fel AAAS; fel Inst Elec & Electronics Engrs; fel Asn Comput Mach. *Res:* Electronic digital computers; applications of computers to military and civil information processing problems; computer system research; societal impact of information technology. *Mailing Add:* RAND Corp 1700 Main St Santa Monica CA 90401. *E-Mail:* willis@rand.org

**WARE, WALTER ELISHA,** PHYSICS. *Current Pos:* DIV MGR, MISSION RES CORP, 80- *Personal Data:* b Jacksonville, Fla, June 1, 33; m 55; c 3. *Educ:* US Naval Acad, BS, 55; Univ Colo, PhD(physics), 62. *Prof Exp:* From instr to assoc prof physics, USAF Acad, 62-65, tenure assoc prof, 65-66; res scientist, Nuclear Technol Lab, Kaman Sci Corp, 66-80. *Concurrent Pos:* Proj consult, Kaman Nuclear, 62-66. *Mem:* Am Asn Physics Teachers; Inst Elec & Electronics Engrs. *Res:* Nuclear structure theory; effects of nuclear weapons; electromagnetic theory; quantum theory. *Mailing Add:* 14 Las Piedras Escondidas Colorado Springs CO 80904

**WARE, WILLIAM ROMAINE,** PHYSICAL CHEMISTRY. *Current Pos:* PROF CHEM, UNIV WESTERN ONT, 71- *Personal Data:* b Portland, Ore, June 13, 31; m 54. *Educ:* Reed Col, BA, 53; Univ Rochester, PhD, 58. *Prof Exp:* Res chemist, Parma Res Ctr, Union Carbide Corp, 57-60; res assoc chem, Univ Minn, Minneapolis, 61; from asst prof to assoc prof, San Diego State Col, 62-66; from assoc prof to prof, Univ Minn, Minneapolis, 67-71. *Mem:* Fel Chem Inst Can. *Res:* Molecular photochemistry and photophysics. *Mailing Add:* Dept Chem Univ Western Ont London ON N6A 5B9 Can

**WAREHAM, ELLSWORTH EDWIN,** thoracic surgery, for more information see previous edition

**WAREN, ALLAN D(AVID),** OPERATIONS RESEARCH, COMPUTER SCIENCE. *Current Pos:* chmn dept, Cleveland State Univ, 71-76, prof, 71-93, Interim dean, Col Bus Admin, 90-91, EMER PROF COMPUT & INFO SCI, CLEVELAND STATE UNIV, 93- *Personal Data:* b Toronto, Ont, Nov 23, 35; m 62, Marion Halligan; c David, Melissa, Melanie & Jessica. *Educ:* Univ Toronto, BASc, 60; Case Inst Technol, MS, 62, PhD(eng), 64. *Prof Exp:* Electronics engr, Electronic Res Div, Clevite Corp, 63-64, sr electronics engr, 64-66, staff engr, 66; from asst prof to assoc prof elec eng, Cleveland State Univ, 66-69; founder & pres, Com-Share Ltd, 69-71. *Concurrent Pos:* Consult, Cleveland Court Mgt Proj, Environ Econ, Gould & Cleveland Legal Firms; consult, Gould Inc Ocean Systs Div, 77-84, Cleveland Pub Utilities, 80, Sci Systs Inc, 80-84, Gould Elastomer Prods Div, 79-80, World Bank, 79 & PPG, 88-92, Rose Law Firm, 92-94 & LTV Steel, 91-96, Transat Corp, 96-; res grants, NSF, 75-78, Off Naval Res, 73-82, NASA, 80-83, Sci Assoc Inc, 85-87, State of Ohio, 88-89; vpres, Optimal Methods, Inc, 93- *Mem:* Asn Comput Mach; Inst Elec & Electronics Engrs; Math Program Soc. *Res:* Computer-aided design of engineering systems; optimization methods and mathematical programming; micro-computer software development; image processing. *Mailing Add:* Dept Comput & Info Sci Cleveland State Univ Cleveland OH 44115. *Fax:* 216-687-5448; *E-Mail:* waren@cis.csuohio.edu

**WARF, C CAYCE, JR,** MANGANESE CHEMICALS, CHEMICAL OXIDATION FOR WATER TREATMENT. *Current Pos:* TECH DIR, VULCAN CHEM TECHNOL INC, 97- *Personal Data:* b Lyle, Tenn, Apr 3, 46; m 73, Linda G Yarbrough; c Kenneth N & Patrick M. *Educ:* Delta State Univ, BS(chem) & BS(physics), 68; Univ Miss, MS, 72, PhD(chem), 79. *Prof Exp:* Res chemist, Ecusta Paper & Film Div, Olin Corp, 79-80, res assoc, 80-81, mgr, Olin Res Coun, 81-84, mgr lab, Olin Water Servs, 84-90; dir prod develop, Carus Chem Co, 90-91, dir lab, 91-92, mgr customer serv & mkt support, 92, dir health, safety & environ affairs, 92-96. *Mem:* Am Chem Soc; Am Water Works Asn. *Res:* Application of oxidation solutions to water treatment problems. *Mailing Add:* 1902 Channel Dr West Sacramento CA 95691-3477

**WARF, JAMES CURREN,** INORGANIC CHEMISTRY, NUCLEAR SCIENCE. *Current Pos:* from asst prof to prof, 48-84, EMER PROF CHEM, UNIV SOUTHERN CALIF, 84- *Personal Data:* b Nashville, Tenn, Sept 1, 17; m 65, Kyoko Sato; c Sandra, Curren & Barney. *Educ:* Univ Tulsa, BS, 39; Iowa State Univ, PhD(inorg chem), 46. *Prof Exp:* Jr chemist, Phillips Petrol Co, Okla, 40-41; instr chem, Univ Tulsa, 41-42; group leader, Manhattan Proj, Iowa State Univ, 42-47; Guggenheim fel, Univ Berne, 47-48. *Concurrent Pos:* Vis prof, Univ Indonesia, 57-59, Airlangga Univ, Indonesia, 62-64, Tech Univ Vienna, 69-70 & Nat Univ Malaysia, Kuala Lumpur, 74-75; consult, Jet Propulsion Lab, Calif Inst Technol, Hasanuddin Univ & Andalas Univ, Indonesia, 78-79, Nat Univ Malaysia, Sabah, 82-83. *Mem:* Am Chem Soc; Fedn Am Sci; Union Concerned Scientists. *Res:* Hydrides of heavy metals; chemistry in liquid ammonia; chemistry of europium and ytterbium; inorganic and analytical chemistry. *Mailing Add:* Dept Chem Univ Southern Calif Los Angeles CA 90089-1062. *Fax:* 213-661-1535; *E-Mail:* warf@chem1.usc.edu

**WARFEL, DAVID ROSS,** ORGANIC CHEMISTRY, POLYMER CHEMISTRY. *Current Pos:* NEW PROD SCIENTIST, WASHINGTON PENN PLASTIC CO, 86- *Personal Data:* b Pana, Ill, Sept 25, 42; m 65; c 2. *Educ:* Carthage Col, BA, 64; Univ Tenn, Knoxville, PhD(chem), 70; Univ Pittsburgh, MBA, 76. *Prof Exp:* Scientist polymer chem, Koppers Co, Inc, Monroeville, 69-74; sr scientist polymer chem, Arco/Polymers, Inc, Monroeville, 74, prin scientist, Arco Chem Co, 74-86. *Mem:* Am Chem Soc. *Res:* Polyolefin compound formulation. *Mailing Add:* PO Box 355 Meadow Lands PA 15347

**WARFEL, JOHN HIATT,** ANATOMY. *Current Pos:* RETIRED. *Personal Data:* b Marion, Ind, Mar 3, 16; m 42, Marjorie Wolfe; c Barbara A, Susan R & David B. *Educ:* Capital Univ, BSc, 38; Ohio State Univ, MSc, 41; Western Res Univ, PhD, 48. *Prof Exp:* Asst, Western Res Univ, 46-48; instr, State Univ NY, Buffalo, 49-54, assoc, 54-56, from asst prof to assoc prof anat, Sch Med, 56-86. *Mem:* Am Asn Anatomists; Sigma Xi. *Res:* Gross anatomy; author of two books. *Mailing Add:* 153 Walton Dr Buffalo NY 14226

**WARFIELD, CAROL LARSON,** TEXTILE CHEMISTRY, EDUCATIONAL & RESEARCH ADMINISTRATION. *Current Pos:* from asst prof to assoc prof textile sci, 77-90, coordr indust rels, 86-90, HEAD CONSUMER AFFAIRS, AUBURN UNIV, 82-, PROF TEXTILE SCI, 90- *Personal Data:* b Oldham, SDak, June 6, 41; m 62; c David, Alan & Paul. *Educ:* SDak State Univ, BS, 62; Univ Ill, Urbana, MS, 67, PhD(family econ), 77. *Prof Exp:* Teacher home econ, Bridgewater Pub Sch, SDak, 63, Rock Island Pub Sch, Ill, 63-65; instr textiles, Univ Ill, Urbana, 69-77. *Mem:* Sigma Xi; Am Asn Textile Chemists & Colorists; fel Textile Inst; fel Int Textile & Apparel Asn; Europ Int Bus Acad. *Res:* Consumer attitudes relating to textiles and textile regulation; end-use performance characteristics of textiles;

economic aspects of regulation, selection, use and care; upholstery fabric performance aspects and test method development; textile and apparel industry competitiveness; global retailing. *Mailing Add:* Auburn Univ 1108 Felton Lane Auburn AL 36830. *Fax:* 334-844-1340; *E-Mail:* awarfield@humsci.auburn.edu

**WARFIELD, GEORGE,** SOLID STATE ELECTRONICS, PHOTO VOLTAICS. *Current Pos:* CONSULT PHOTOVOLTAICS, 80- *Personal Data:* b Piombino, Italy, Apr 21, 19; nat US; m 45; c 3. *Educ:* Franklin & Marshall Col, BS, 40; Cornell Univ, PhD(physics), 49. *Prof Exp:* From asst prof to prof elec eng, Princeton Univ, 49-74; prof elec eng & exec dir, Inst Energy Conversion, Univ Del, 74-78; assoc dir technol dissemination, Solar Energy Res Inst, 78-80. *Mem:* Am Phys Soc; Inst Elec & Electronics Engrs. *Res:* Photovoltaic cells; solid state device physics; insulator electronics; behavior of electrons in insulators. *Mailing Add:* Box 2678 Hallock Rd 2 Vergennes VT 05491

**WARFIELD, J(OHN) N(ELSON),** SYSTEMS ENGINEERING, APPLIED MATHEMATICS. *Current Pos:* dir, Inst Info Technol, 84-86, DIR, INST ADVAN STUDY INTEGRATIVE SCI, GEORGE MASON UNIV, 87- *Personal Data:* b Sullivan, Mo, Nov 21, 25; m 48, Rosamond Howe; c Daniel, Nancy & Thomas. *Educ:* Univ Mo, AB & BSEE, 48; MSEE, 49; Purdue Univ, PhD, 52. *Honors & Awards:* Western Elec Fund Award, SAm Soc Eng Educ, 66; Outstanding Contrib Award, Man & Cybernet Soc, 77; Outstanding Contrib Award, Inst Elec & Electronics Engrs Systs, 77; Centennial Medal Award, 84; Spec Recognition Award, Int Soc Design & Process Sci, 95. *Prof Exp:* Instr elec eng, Univ Mo, 48; from instr to assoc prof, Pa State Univ, 49-55; from asst prof to assoc prof, Univ Ill, 55-57; assoc prof, Purdue Univ, 57-58; from assoc prof to prof, Univ Kans, 58-66; sr adv, Battelle Mem Inst, 66-74; chmn, Dept Elec Eng, Univ Va, 75-78, Harry Douglas Forsyth prof, 75-83, dir, Ctr Interactive Mgt, 81-83; sr mgr, Burroughs Corp, 83-84. *Concurrent Pos:* Consult, Ramo-Wooldridge Corp, 56-57, Sylvania Data Systs, 59-60, Wilcox Elec Co, 62-66, IBM Corp, 79-82, NSF, 79-, Coun Sci & Indust Res Ghana & Tech Inst Higher Learning Monterrey, Mex, 88-, Ford Motor Co, 93-; ed, Off J Inst Fedn Systs Res. *Mem:* Fel Soc Design & Process Sci; Int Soc Panetics; fel Inst Elec & Electronics Engrs; Asn Integrative Studies. *Res:* Interdisciplinary research methodology and modeling; science education; systems planning; environmental education; bureaucracy; design science; science of complexity; interactive management. *Mailing Add:* Inst Advan Study Integrative Sci George Mason Univ Module G Fairfax VA 22030-4444. *Fax:* 703-993-2996; *E-Mail:* jwarfiel@gmu.edu

**WARFIELD, PETER FOSTER,** POLYMER CHEMISTRY. *Current Pos:* RETIRED. *Personal Data:* b Rye, NY, Aug 4, 18; m 42; c Frederic Parkman, William Slogum & Ruth White. *Educ:* Hamilton Col, BS, 40; Univ Ill, MS, 41, PhD(org chem), 44. *Prof Exp:* Asst chem, Univ Ill, 42-44; res chemist, Bakelite Corp, NJ, 44-45; from res chemist to sr res chemist, Ansco Div, Gen Aniline & Film Corp, 45-49, develop specialist, 49-52; chemist, E I du Pont de Nemours & Co, Inc, 52-60, tech serv rep, 60-63, res chemist, 63-68, sr res chemist, 69-78, res assoc, Photo Prods Dept, 78-82. *Mem:* Am Chem Soc; Soc Photog Sci & Eng; Sigma Xi. *Res:* Hindered Grignard reactions; aliphatic polyamines; phenolic resins; synthetic peptides; restrainers for photographic gelatin; photographic emulsions; cyanine dyes; color photography; color formers; color processing; photopolymer printing plates. *Mailing Add:* 508 Birch Ave Westfield NJ 07090-3003

**WARFIELD, ROBERT WELMORE,** POLYMER CHEMISTRY, THERMODYNAMICS & MATERIAL PROPERTIES. *Current Pos:* chemist, 55-64, SR SCIENTIST, NAVAL SURFACE WEAPONS CTR, WHITE OAK, 64- *Personal Data:* b Asbury Park, NJ, Oct 11, 26; m 55, Mildred T Stewart; c Richard S & Garrett W. *Educ:* Univ Va, BS, 50. *Prof Exp:* Chemist, US Bur Mines, Md, 50-55. *Mem:* Am Chem Soc. *Res:* Patentee in field; chemistry and physics of the solid state of polymers; compressibility and electrical properties of polymers; transitions of polymers; polymerization kinetics; acoustic properties of polymers. *Mailing Add:* 22712 Ward Ave Hereford Hills Germantown MD 20876

**WARFIELD, VIRGINIA MCSHANE,** MATHEMATICAL ANALYSIS. *Current Pos:* LECTR MATH, UNIV WASH, 73-, DIR REMEDIAL MATH, 80- *Personal Data:* b Charlottesville, Va, Sept 30, 42; m 64; c 3. *Educ:* Bryn Mawr Col, AB, 63; Brown Univ, MA, 65, PhD(math), 71. *Prof Exp:* Seattle dir math, Spec Elem Educ Disadvantaged Proj, 70-73. *Mem:* Sigma Xi. *Res:* Stochastic integrals and stochastic control theory. *Mailing Add:* 1831 23rd Ave E Seattle WA 98112-2913

**WARGA, JACK,** OPTIMAL CONTROL THEORY, NONLINEAR ANALYSIS. *Current Pos:* prof, 66-93, EMER PROF MATH, NORTHEASTERN UNIV, 93- *Personal Data:* b Warsaw, Poland, Dec 5, 22; nat US; m 49, Faye Kleinman; c Charna R (Schakow) & Arthur D. *Educ:* Carleton Col, BA, 44; NY Univ, PhD(math), 50. *Prof Exp:* Assoc mathematician, Reeves Instrument Corp, 51-52; head, Comput Sect, Repub Aviation Corp, 52-53; sr mathematician & head math dept, Electrodata Div, Burroughs Corp, 54-56; fel, Weizmann Inst Sci, Israel, 56-57; sr staff mathematician & mgr math dept, Res & Adv Develop Div, Avco Corp, 57-66. *Concurrent Pos:* Ed, J Control & Optimization, Soc Indust & Appl Math, 62-89. *Mem:* Fel AAAS; Am Math Soc; Soc Indust & Appl Math. *Res:* Mathematical control theory; nonlinear analysis. *Mailing Add:* 233 Clark Rd Brookline MA 02146. *E-Mail:* warga@neu.edu

**WARGEL, ROBERT JOSEPH,** BIOCHEMISTRY, FOOD SCIENCE & TECHNOLOGY. *Current Pos:* group leader, 70-80, SR GROUP LEADER, KRAFT GEN FOODS, 80- *Personal Data:* b Evansville, Ind, Dec 24, 40; m 70. *Educ:* Univ Evansville, BA, 66; Northwestern Univ, PhD(chem), 70. *Prof Exp:* Chemist, City Evansville, Ind, 64-66 & Mead Johnson & Co, 66. *Mem:* Am Chem Soc; Am Soc Microbiol; Am Dairy Sci Asn; Inst Food Technologists. *Res:* Enzyme use in dairy products; biochemistry of cheese; metabolism of dairy culture; new product development and implementation; technical management; research administration. *Mailing Add:* 800 Rosewood Ave Winnetka IL 60093

**WARGO, PHILIP MATTHEW,** STRESS PHYSIOLOGY, ROOT PATHOLOGY & PHYSIOLOGY. *Current Pos:* res plant pathologist, 68-89, PROJ LEADER & PRIN PLANT PATHOLOGIST, USDA FOREST SERV, HAMDEN, CONN, 89- *Personal Data:* b Danville, Pa, Mar 1, 40. *Educ:* Gettysburg Col, BA, 62; Iowa State Univ, MS, 64, PhD(plant path), 66. *Honors & Awards:* Res Award, Int Soc Arboricult, 85. *Prof Exp:* Res scientist, US Army, Ft Detrich, Md, 66-68. *Mem:* Am Phytopath Soc; Soc Am Foresters. *Res:* Ecology, physiology of dieback/decline diseases; effects of stress on trees; stress-induced predisposition of trees to pathogens; Armillaria root disease-taxonomy and ecology; stress and root dynamics. *Mailing Add:* 3 Spring Brook Rd Wallingford CT 06492. *Fax:* 203-773-2183; *E-Mail:* fswa/s=wargolou=s24lo7a@mhs.attmail.com

**WARGOTZ, ERIC S,** BREAST & GYNECOLOGICAL PATHOLOGY, GENERAL SURGICAL PATHOLOGY. *Current Pos:* CHIEF PATH & MED LAB DIR, DOCTORS COMMUNITY HOSP, 90- *Personal Data:* b Akron, Ohio, Dec 28, 56. *Educ:* Rutgers Univ, BS, 78; Ohio State Univ, MD, 83. *Prof Exp:* Asst path, George Washington Univ Sch Med, 83-87, clin instr path, 87-89; assoc pathologist, Capital Med Labs, 89-90. *Concurrent Pos:* Callender-Binford fel gynec & breast path, Am Registry Path, Armed Forces Inst Path, 87-88; staff pathologist, Dept Gynec & Breast Path, 88-89; asst clin prof path, George Washington Univ Sch Med, 89- *Mem:* Int Soc Gynec Path; Am Soc Clin Pathologists; Int Acad Path; Col Am Pathologists; AMA. *Res:* Pathology of the human mammary gland; unusual benign neoplasms, clincopathological studies of various forms of mammary cancer including spindle cell neoplasms; pathology of the human ovary-steroid and molecular/DNA studies. *Mailing Add:* Doctors Community Hosp 8118 Good Luck Rd Lanham MD 20706-3595

**WARHOL, MICHAEL J,** SURGICAL PATHOLOGY, IMMUNOCYTOCHEMISTRY. *Current Pos:* HEAD, DEPT PATH, PA HOSP, 90- *Educ:* Univ Pittsburgh, MD, 69. *Prof Exp:* Assoc prof path, Sch Med, Harvard Univ, 85-90. *Mailing Add:* Dept Path Pa Hosp 800 Spruce St Philadelphia PA 19107

**WARING, GAIL L,** MOLECULAR & DEVELOPMENTAL BIOLOGY, GENETICS. *Current Pos:* Assoc prof, 84-89, PROF BIOL, MARQUETTE UNIV, 89- *Educ:* Univ Ore, PhD(biol), 74. *Honors & Awards:* Scientific Achievement Award, Sigma Xi. *Mem:* Fel AAAS; Am Soc Cell Biol; Soc Develop Biol; Genetics Soc Am. *Res:* Eggshell formation in drosophila; developmental regulation of gene expression incuding molecular strategies used to control the assembly of eggshell proteins into a highly ordered three dimensional structure. *Mailing Add:* Dept Biol Marquette Univ 530 N 15th Milwaukee WI 53233-2274

**WARING, GEORGE HOUSTOUN, IV,** ANIMAL BEHAVIOR, VERTEBRATE ZOOLOGY. *Current Pos:* From asst prof to assoc prof, 66-83, PROF ZOOL, SOUTHERN ILL UNIV, CARBONDALE, 83- *Personal Data:* b Denver, Colo, July 15, 39; m 62, Annmeredith Kenney; c Sari, G Houstoun & Heidi. *Educ:* Colo State Univ, BS, 62, PhD(zool), 66; Univ Colo, MA, 64. *Honors & Awards:* Exceptional Serv Award, Animal Behav Soc. *Concurrent Pos:* Guest prof, Univ Munich, 72-73; res prog dir, US Marine Mammal Comn, 74-75; chair, Pub Affairs Comt, Animal Behav Soc, 83-89, Orgn & Bylaws Comm, 89-, parliamentarian, 89-95; fel, Deutsche Forshungsgemeinschaft. *Mem:* Fel AAAS; Animal Behav Soc; Am Soc Mammal; Am Ornith Union; Int Soc Appl Ethology; Sigma Xi. *Res:* Communicative behaviors of vertebrates; equine behavior; vertebrate natural history; wildlife and behavioral ecology; marine mammal conservation and ethology; applied ethology of wildlife, pest species, and domestic animals; social behavior of birds and mammals. *Mailing Add:* Dept Zool Southern Ill Univ Carbondale IL 62901-6501. *Fax:* 618-453-2806; *E-Mail:* waring@siv.edu

**WARING, GEORGE O, III,** OPHTHALMOLOGY. *Current Pos:* ASSOC PROF OPHTHAL, EMORY UNIV, 79- *Personal Data:* b Buffalo, NY, Feb 21, 41; m 65; c 3. *Educ:* Wheaton Col, BS, 63; Baylor Med Col, MD, 67; Am Bd Ophthal, dipl, 78. *Honors & Awards:* Physician's Recognition Award, AMA, 76. *Prof Exp:* Sr asst surgeon, USPHS Indian Hosp, Winnebago, NB, 68-70; resident, Wills Eye Hosp, Philadelphia, Pa, 70-73, Heed fel, 73-74; asst prof ophthal, Univ Calif, Davis, 74-79. *Concurrent Pos:* Attend physician ophthal, Ship of Hope, Natal, Brazil, 72; consult, Vet Admin Hosp, Martinez, Calif, 74-79 & Travis AFB, Fairfield, Calif, 74-78; surg dir, Sacramento Valley Eye Bank, 75-79; res consult, Calif Comn Peace Officer Stand & Training, Sacramento, 76-78; chmn, Corneal & External Dis Sect, Found Systs Postgrad Educ Ophthal, 76- *Mem:* Am Acad Ophthal; Am Soc Contemporary Ophthal; Asn Res Vision & Ophthal; AMA. *Res:* Clinico-pathologic correlations in corneal diseases; corneal basement membrane; corneal lipid metabolism. *Mailing Add:* Emory Clin Ophthal 1365 B Clifton Rd NE Atlanta GA 30322

**WARING, RICHARD C**, PHYSICS. *Current Pos:* From instr to asst prof, 60-72, ASSOC PROF PHYSICS, UNIV MO, KANSAS CITY, 72- *Personal Data:* b Excelsior Springs, Mo, Mar 25, 36; m 62; c 3. *Educ:* William Jewell Col, BA, 58; Univ Ark, MS, 61. *Concurrent Pos:* Nat coun mem, Soc Physics Students, 76-82; dir, Math & Physics Inst, 84. *Mem:* Sigma Xi; Am Asn Physics Teachers. *Res:* Infrared reflectance spectroscopy. *Mailing Add:* 11706 Stockdale Rd Liberty MO 64068

**WARING, RICHARD H**, PLANT ECOLOGY. *Current Pos:* Asst prof, 63-72, PROF FOREST ECOL, ORE STATE UNIV, 76- *Personal Data:* b Chicago, Ill, May 17, 35; m 57; c 2. *Educ:* Univ Minn, St Paul, BS, 57, MS, 59; Univ Calif, Berkeley, PhD(bot), 63. *Concurrent Pos:* Dep dir, Coniferous Forest Biome, 73- *Mem:* AAAS; Ecol Soc Am. *Res:* Ecosystem analysis of watersheds; environmental classification; physiological ecology; plant-water relationships. *Mailing Add:* Dept Forestry Ore State Univ 140 Peavy Hall Corvallis OR 97331-5710

**WARING, ROBERT KERR, JR**, PIGMENT OPTICS, COLOR IMAGING. *Current Pos:* RETIRED. *Personal Data:* b Palmerton, Pa, Aug 18, 28; m 54, Judith Malin; c Sarah, Rebecca, Adam & Ann. *Educ:* Va Mil Inst, BS, 50; Yale Univ, PhD, 55. *Prof Exp:* Res physicist, E I du Pont de Nemours & Co, Inc, 55-85; develop physicist, D X Imaging, 87-91; physics teacher, Tower Hill Sch, 91-93. *Mem:* Am Phys Soc. *Res:* Measurement and interpretation of the optical properties of colored pigments; general color imaging; measurement and interpretation of the magnetic properties of assemblies of single domain ferromagnetic particles; development of color xerographic printing machines; electrostatics. *Mailing Add:* 14 Davenport Dr Downingtown PA 19335

**WARING, WILLIAM WINBURN**, PEDIATRICS. *Current Pos:* from instr to assoc prof, 57-65, lectr physiol, 66-80, PROF PEDIAT, SCH MED, TULANE UNIV, 65-, JANE B ARON PROF PEDIAT, 86- *Personal Data:* b Savannah, Ga, July 20, 23; m 52; c 5. *Educ:* Harvard Univ, MD, 47. *Prof Exp:* Intern pediat, Children's Hosp, Boston, Mass, 47-48; intern, Johns Hopkins Hosp, Md, 48-49, asst res, 49-50, chief res outpatient dept, 50-51, chief res, Hosp, 51-52. *Concurrent Pos:* Pulmonary dis adv comt, Nat Heart & Lung Inst, 71-73; vchmn gen med & sci adv coun, Cystic Fibrosis Found, 72-73; assoc ed, Am J Dis Children. *Mem:* Am Pediat Soc; Am Acad Pediat; Am Col Chest Physicians; Am Thoracic Soc (vpres, 72-73). *Res:* Respiratory disease and physiology in infants and children; cystic fibrosis. *Mailing Add:* Sch Med Tulane Univ 1430 Tulane Ave New Orleans LA 70112-2699

**WARING, WORDEN**, BIOMEDICAL ENGINEERING. *Current Pos:* assoc prof biomed eng, 69-72, prof, Schs Med & Eng, 72-82, EMER PROF, UNIV CALIF, DAVIS, 82- *Personal Data:* b Washington, DC, Jan 8, 15; m 49; c 1. *Educ:* Cornell Univ, BChem, 36; Mass Inst Technol, PhD(phys chem), 40. *Prof Exp:* Instr chem, Tulane Univ, 40-42, asst prof, 42-43; engr, Shell Develop Co, 43-53; engr opers res group, Arthur D Little, Inc, 53-54; chemist, Semiconductor Div, Raytheon Mfg Co, 54-58; head chem sect, Fairchild Semiconductor Corp, 58-64; prin investr human systs design ctr, Rancho Los Amigos Hosp, Downey, Calif, 64-69. *Mem:* AAAS; Biomed Eng Soc; Am Chem Soc; Electrochem Soc; Inst Elec & Electronics Engrs. *Res:* Thermodynamics; phase rule; industrial operations research; surface chemistry; diffusion; electrochemistry; biomedical engineering. *Mailing Add:* 27083 Patwin Rd Davis CA 95616

**WARINNER, DOUGLAS KEITH**, NUCLEAR ENGINEERING & THERMOSCIENCES, SYSTEMS ANALYSIS. *Current Pos:* mech engr, 75-85, MECH ENGR THERMOHYDRAUL, ARGONNE NAT LAB, 89- *Personal Data:* b Little Falls, Minn, Jan 20, 41; m 67, Kathleen T Tam; c Derek K & Sonja Anne. *Educ:* Univ Calif, Davis, BS, 65, MS, 68; Purdue Univ, PhD(mech eng), 73. *Prof Exp:* Teaching asst fluid mech, aerodyn & rocket propulsion, Univ Calif, Davis, 65-67; mech engr aerodyn, Naval Weapons Ctr, 67-68; teaching asst heat transfer & measurements, Purdue Univ, 69-71; asst prof thermosci, Fla Atlantic Univ, 71-75; prof & chairperson, Mech Eng, Mankato State Univ, 85-89. *Concurrent Pos:* Instr, Ill Inst Technol, 77-81; mem safety comn, US Dept Energy, 78-80; consult, missile propulsion, FMC Corp, 87-89. *Mem:* AAAS; Sigma Xi; Am Soc Mech Engrs; Am Soc Eng Educ. *Res:* Analytical study of the in-core behavior and atmospheric consequences of a nuclear research reactor meltdown or loss of coolant accident: prediction of the in core thermohydraulics (natural circulation and natural conversion) and the atmospheric dispersion and decay of nuclid. *Mailing Add:* Div RA 9700 S Cass Ave Bldg 208 Rm C-114 Argonne IL 60439. *Fax:* 630-252-4780; *E-Mail:* warinner@salt.ra.anl.gov

**WARITH, MOSTAFA ABDEL**, GEOENVIRONMENT, BIOREMEDIATION. *Current Pos:* ASST PROF, RYERSON POLYTECH UNIV, TORONTO, 95- *Personal Data:* b Sept 7, 53; Can citizen. *Educ:* Cairo Univ, BSc, 76; Ein Shams Univ, MSc, 81; McGill Univ, MEng, 83, PhD(environ eng), 87. *Prof Exp:* Engr, Constoga Rovers & Assocs, 88; proj dir, Golder Assocs, 90-95. *Concurrent Pos:* Lectr, Carleton Univ, 90. *Res:* Migration of contaminants in soil; clay liner design; bioremediation of organics in soil environment; absorption of organics on clay or organic soil. *Mailing Add:* 157 Marlborough Ave Ottawa ON K1N 8G1 Can

**WARITZ, RICHARD STEFAN**, INDUSTRIAL CHEMICALS, MECHANISMS OF TOXICITY OF CHEMICALS. *Current Pos:* PRES, BIOSANTE INT, INC, 93- *Personal Data:* b Portland, Ore, Apr 1, 29; m 50, Ruth E White; c Joyce, Sharon, Gary & Carol. *Educ:* Reed Col, BA, 51; Stanford Univ, PhD(chem), 57; Am Bd Toxicol, dipl, 80; Acad Toxicol Sci, dipl, 83. *Prof Exp:* Actg instr gen chem & biochem, Wash State Univ, 54-55; sr res chemist, E I du Pont de Nemours & Co, Inc, 56-62, sr res scientist,

62-64, sect chief inhalation toxicol, 64-70, res mgr, Biosci Group, 70-75; sr toxicologist, Hercules Inc, 75-77, mgr toxicol, 78-92. *Concurrent Pos:* Counr, Int Union Toxicol Soc, 84-85; vis assoc prof toxicol, Rutgers Univ, 93- *Mem:* Sigma Xi; Am Chem Soc; Am Indust Hyg Asn; Soc Toxicol (treas, 81-85); Am Col Toxicol; Am Conf Govt Indust Hygienists. *Res:* Pulmonary toxicology and pharmacology; biochemical measures of chemical exposure; mechanisms of toxic actions of chemicals; biological markers of chemical exposure; chemical isomerism and toxicity. *Mailing Add:* 2613 Turnstone Dr Brookmeade 2 Wilmington DE 19808-1638. *Fax:* 302-994-4490

**WARK, KENNETH, JR**, THERMODYNAMICS. *Current Pos:* RETIRED. *Personal Data:* b Indianapolis, Ind, Jan 2, 27; m 55; c 3. *Educ:* Purdue Univ, BS, 50, PhD(mech eng), 55; Univ Ill, MS, 51. *Prof Exp:* Res engr, Atlantic Refining Co, Tex, 51-53; assoc prof mech eng, Purdue Univ, West Lafayette, 55-96. *Concurrent Pos:* Consult, US Steel Corp, 57-58 & Rovac Corp, 76-78; NSF sci fac fel, Stanford Univ, 62-63. *Mem:* Am Chem Soc; Am Soc Eng Educ; Combustion Inst. *Res:* Alternative and innovative energy conversion systems. *Mailing Add:* Dept Mech Eng Purdue Univ West Lafayette IN 47907. *E-Mail:* wash@ecn.pmdue.edu

**WARKENTIN, BENNO PETER**, ENVIRONMENTAL MANAGEMENT, WATER QUALITY. *Current Pos:* head soil sci, 78-89, PROF, DEPT SOIL SCI, ORE STATE UNIV, CORVALLIS, 89- *Personal Data:* b Man, Can, June 21, 29; m 56; c 3. *Educ:* Univ BC, BSA, 51; Wash State Univ, MS, 53; Cornell Univ, PhD(soils), 56. *Prof Exp:* Nat Res Coun Can Overseas fel, Oxford Univ, 56-57; asst prof agr physics, McGill Univ, 57-62, assoc prof soil sci, 62-70, MacDonald Col, 70-78, dir environ studies, 72-75. *Mem:* Am Soc Agron; Can Soc Soil Sci (pres, 65-66); Int Soc Soil Sci; Int Water Res Asn. *Res:* Physical and chemical properties of clay minerals; physical properties of soils; water in clay soils; solid waste disposal; water quality; soil quality. *Mailing Add:* Dept Soil Sci Ore State Univ 3017 Agr Life Sci Corvallis OR 97331-7306

**WARKENTIN, JOHN**, ORGANIC CHEMISTRY. *Current Pos:* from asst prof to prof, 60-71, PROF CHEM, MCMASTER UNIV, 71- *Personal Data:* b Grunthal, Man, Aug 18, 31; m 57; c 3. *Educ:* Univ Man, BS, 54, MS, 55; Iowa State Univ, PhD(chem), 59. *Honors & Awards:* Syntex Award, 89. *Prof Exp:* Fel chem, Calif Inst Technol, 59 & Harvard Univ, 59-60. *Concurrent Pos:* Assoc ed, Can J Chem, 76-81. *Mem:* Am Chem Soc; Chem Inst Can. *Res:* Synthetic and mechanistic investigations in organic chemistry including carbenes, free radicals, and ylides. *Mailing Add:* Dept Chem McMaster Univ 1280 Main St W Hamilton ON L8S 4M1 Can

**WARLICK, CHARLES HENRY**, MATHEMATICS, COMPUTER SCIENCE. *Current Pos:* lectr comput sci & dir, 65-80, dir & sr lectr, Comput Ctr, 80-97, SPEC ASST TO PROVOST, UNIV TEX, AUSTIN, 97- *Personal Data:* b Hickory, NC, May 08, 30; m 58; c 1. *Educ:* Duke Univ, BS, 52; Univ Md, MA, 55; Univ Cincinnati, PhD(math), 64. *Prof Exp:* Mathematician, US Dept Army, 52-53; programmcr, Int Bus Mach Corp, 54; appl mathematician, Gen Elec Co, 55-57, supvr appl math, 57-62, supvr appl math & comput software develop, 63-65. *Concurrent Pos:* Vpres, VIM Users Orgn Control Data Corp 6000 Series Comput, 68-70, pres, 70-71. *Mem:* Asn Comput Mach. *Res:* Numerical solution of partial differential equations; fundamental solutions of finite difference equations; computer executive operating systems; algorithmic languages. *Mailing Add:* 4306 Oak Creek Dr Nacogdoches TX 75961-6563

**WARLTIER, DAVID CHARLES**, ANESTHESIOLOGY, CARDIOLOGY. *Current Pos:* Asst prof pharmacol, 78-82, assoc prof pharmacol & med, 82-88, PROF ANESTHESIOL, MED & PHARMACOL, VCHMN RES ANESTHESIOL, MED COL WIS, 88- *Personal Data:* b Hartford, Conn, Mar 28, 47; m 91, Marilyn Binder; c 4. *Educ:* Carroll Col, BS, 69; Med Col Wis, PhD(pharmacol), 76, MD, 82. *Hon Degrees:* DSc, Carroll Col, 91. *Concurrent Pos:* Staff anesthesiologist, Zablocki Vet Admin Med Ctr, 89-; adj prof biomed eng, Marquette Univ, 95- *Mem:* Am Physiol Soc; Soc Cardiovasc Anesthesiologists; Am Heart Asn; Am Soc Pharmacol & Exp Therapeut; Am Soc Anesthesiol; Asn Univ Anesthesiologists. *Res:* Physiology, pathophysiology and pharmacology of the coronary circulation; myocardial ischemia; influence of pharmacological agents on the coronary collateral circulation; angiogenesis; growth factors; cardioprotection. *Mailing Add:* Dept Anesthesiol MEB Med Col Wis 8701 Watertown Plank Rd Milwaukee WI 53226

**WARMAN, JAMES CLARK**, HYDROGEOLOGY. *Personal Data:* b Morgantown, WVa, May 27, 27; m 53, Eudora A Hedrick; c Lloyd C, Andrew E & Christopher L. *Educ:* WVa Univ, BA, 50, MS, 52. *Honors & Awards:* Ross L Oliver Award, Nat Water Well Asn, 74. *Prof Exp:* Geologist, US Geol Surv, 52-65; dir, Water Resources Inst, Auburn Univ, 65-88, assoc prof civil eng, 70-88; pres, Water Cycle Concepts, Inc, 88-93. *Concurrent Pos:* Grants, Auburn Univ, Water Resources Planning, US Water Resources Coun, 68-, Econ Pollution Abatement, US Dept Interior, 71-73 & Res Mgt, 72-74; mem work group hydrol maps, US Nat Comt Int Hydrol Decade, 70-73; consult, Study Nat Water Res Probs & Priorities, Univs Coun Water Resources, US Dept Interior, 71-72 & Harmon Eng, 75-; chmn tech div & vpres, Nat Water Well Asn, 71-72. *Mem:* Fel Am Water Resources Asn (pres, 76); Am Geophys Union; fel Geol Soc Am. *Res:* Occurrence and availability of ground water; water resources planning; research management; waste heat storage by injection into a confined aquifer. *Mailing Add:* 470 Cary Dr Auburn AL 36830

**WARMAN, PHILIP ROBERT,** SOIL BIOCHEMISTRY, SOIL FERTILITY. *Current Pos:* from asst prof to assoc prof, 81-87, PROF SOIL SCI, NS AGR COL, 87- *Personal Data:* b Jersey City, NJ, Aug 10, 46; Can citizen; m 88, T Renee Munro; c Beth M. *Educ:* Rutgers Univ, BSc, 68; Univ Guelph, MSc, 72, PhD(soil biochem), 77. *Honors & Awards:* Plant Food Inst Award, 68. *Prof Exp:* Lectr, Univ Guelph, 76-77; lectr, MacDonald Col, McGill Univ, 77-78, from auxiliary prof to asst prof, 78-81. *Concurrent Pos:* Consult & pres, Coastal BioAgresearch, Ltd, 84-97; hon res assoc, Dalhousie Univ, 88-; adj prof, McGill Univ, 93-; Forscheimer vis prof, Hebrew Univ, Jerusalem, 94-95. *Mem:* Coun Soil Testing & Plant Anal; Soil Sci Soc Am; Compost Coun Can; Can Soil Sci Soc; Am Soc Agron; Int Asn Optimization Plant Nutrit. *Res:* Effects of organic amendments and alternative fertilizers on soil chemistry, soil fertility, crop nutrition and crop production; effects of heavy metals on soils and crops; extraction and identification of soil organic, Nitrogen, Phosphorus and Sulfur compounds; compost production, quality and analysis. *Mailing Add:* NS Agr Col PO Box 550 Truro NS B2N 5E3 Can. *Fax:* 902-893-1404; *E-Mail:* pwarman@cox.nsac.ns.ca

**WARME, JOHN EDWARD,** PALEOECOLOGY, BASIN ANALYSIS. *Current Pos:* PROF GEOL, COLO SCH MINES, 79- *Personal Data:* b Los Angeles, Calif, Jan 16, 37; m 94, Judy O'Keefe; c Susan L & Jayne K (Bell). *Educ:* Augustana Col, Ill, BA, 59; Univ Calif, Los Angeles, PhD(geol), 66. *Prof Exp:* Fulbright scholar, Scotland, 66-67; W Maurice Ewing prof oceanog, Rice Univ, 67-79. *Concurrent Pos:* Consult, NSF Geol Prog, 79-83; mem, Nat Acad Sci/Nat Res Coun Prog Panel, 92-94; bd mem, Petrol Res Fund, Am Chem Soc, 94- *Mem:* Fel AAAS; Am Asn Petrol Geol; Int Asn Sedimentologists; Sigma Xi; fel Geol Soc Am; hon mem Soc Econ Paleontologists & Mineralogists (pres, 83-84). *Res:* Depositional systems; basin analysis and history; submarine bio-erosion by invertebrates; burrowing marine invertebrates and trace fossils; regional geological synthesis-Morocco, Algeria, Nevada, California, Colorado; modern and fossil reef ecology; carbonate rock environments and paleoenvironments; lagoonal and deep marine ecology and sedimentation; devonian impact deposit, Nevada. *Mailing Add:* Dept Geol Colo Sch Mines Golden CO 80401. *E-Mail:* jwarme@mines.edu

**WARME, PAUL KENNETH,** BIOCHEMISTRY. *Current Pos:* asst prof biochem, University Park, 72-79, RES DIR, INTERACTIVE DIV, PA STATE UNIV, 79- *Personal Data:* b Westbrook, Minn, Jan 23, 42; m 62; c 1. *Educ:* Univ Minn, Minneapolis, BCh, 64; Univ Ill, Urbana, PhD(biochem), 69. *Prof Exp:* Fel protein chem, Cornell Univ, 69-72. *Concurrent Pos:* NIH fel, Cornell Univ, 69-71. *Res:* Micro-computer software and hardware for laboratory use; computer applications in biochemistry. *Mailing Add:* Bio Anal Systs 444 E College Ave No 360 State College PA 16801

**WARNE, RONSON JOSEPH,** MATHEMATICS. *Current Pos:* PROF MATH, UNIV ALA, BIRMINGHAM, 69- *Personal Data:* b East Orange, NJ, June 14, 32; m 50. *Educ:* Columbia Univ, AB, 53; NY Univ, MS, 55; Univ Tenn, PhD(math), 59. *Prof Exp:* Asst & instr math, Univ Tenn, 55-59; asst prof, La State Univ, 59-63; assoc prof, Va Polytech Inst, 63-64; prof, WVa Univ, 64-69. *Res:* Algebraic theory of semigroups. *Mailing Add:* King Fahd Univ Petrol & Mining KFUPM No 1564 Dhahran 31261 Saudi Arabia

**WARNE, THOMAS MARTIN,** organic chemistry, petroleum chemistry, for more information see previous edition

**WARNER, ALDEN HOWARD,** DEVELOPMENTAL BIOLOGY. *Current Pos:* from asst prof to assoc prof, 65-72, head dept, 79-85, PROF BIOL, UNIV WINDSOR, 72- *Personal Data:* b Central Falls, RI, July 2, 37; c Helena (Perkins), William, Brenda (Blair) & Debra (Anderson). *Educ:* Univ Maine, BA, 59; Univ Southern Ill, MA, 61, PhD(physiol), 64. *Prof Exp:* USPHS fel biol & biochem, Biol Div, Oak Ridge Nat Lab, 64-65. *Concurrent Pos:* Consult, Biol Div, Oak Ridge Nat Lab, 74-75; res prof, Univ Windsor, 90-91; distinguished res fel, Univ Calif, Davis, 93. *Mem:* Am Soc Biochem & Molecular Biol; Soc Develop Biol; Can Soc Biochem, Cell & Molecular Biol. *Res:* Proteases and protease inhibitors and their control in development and the onset of muscular dystrophy; proteases and their control in development and the onset of muscular dystrophy. *Mailing Add:* Dept Biol Univ Windsor Windsor ON N9B 3P4 Can. *Fax:* 519-971-3609; *E-Mail:* warner1@ucc.uwindsor.ca

**WARNER, ANN MARIE,** THERAPEUTIC DRUG MONITORING, TOXICOLOGY. *Current Pos:* assoc prof, 85-97, ASSOC DIR, TOXICOL LAB, MED CTR, UNIV CINCINNATI, 85-, PROF TOXICOL, 97- *Personal Data:* b Denver, Colo, Mar 31, 44; m 68; c 1. *Educ:* Marymount Col, Kans, BS, 66; Univ Kans, PhD(med chem), 70; Am Bd Clin Chem, dipl, 77. *Honors & Awards:* Outstanding Speaker Award, Am Asn Clin Chem, 87. *Prof Exp:* NIH fel, Northeastern Univ, 71-73; assoc dir clin labs, Lahey Clin Med Ctr, 73-81; assoc prof path, Med Ctr, Univ PR, 81-85. *Concurrent Pos:* Lectr, Cardinal Cushing Col, 71-72. *Mem:* Clin Ligand Assay Soc; Am Asn Clin Chem. *Res:* Evaluation of biological versus chronological age in neonates; prodrugs. *Mailing Add:* 10868 Bromwell Lane Cincinnati OH 45249. *Fax:* 513-558-4176

**WARNER, BARRY GREGORY,** WETLAND ECOSYSTEMS. *Current Pos:* from res asst prof to res assoc prof, 85-91, assoc prof geog, 91-96, DIR, WETLANDS RES INST, UNIV WATERLOO, 91-, PROF GEOG, BIOL & ENVIRON SCI, 96- *Personal Data:* b Cambridge, Ont, July 20, 55. *Educ:* Univ Waterloo, BES, 78, MS, 80; Simon Fraser Univ, PhD, 84. *Prof Exp:* Fel, Nat Sci & Eng Res Coun Can, 84-85, res fel, 85-90. *Concurrent Pos:* Vis prof, Univ Neuchatel, 93; fel Swiss NSF, 93; chair, Can Nat Wetlands Working Group. *Mem:* Fel Geol Asn Can; Soc Wetland Scientists. *Res:* Wetland ecosystems; functional dynamics of natural, restored and constructed wetlands in northern hemisphere. *Mailing Add:* Dept Geog Univ Waterloo Waterloo ON N2L 3G1 Can. *Fax:* 519-746-0658; *E-Mail:* bwarner@watserv1,uwaterloo.ca

**WARNER, BERT JOSEPH,** CHEMICAL ENGINEERING. *Current Pos:* res technologist, Mobil Oil Corp, 55-58, sr res technologist, 58-64, eng assoc, 64-77, MGR RECOVERY PROCESSES, FIELD RES LAB, MOBIL OIL CORP, 78- *Personal Data:* b Ardmore, Okla, June 15, 25; m 52; c 2. *Educ:* Rice Univ, BS, 49. *Prof Exp:* Chem engr, Colombian Petrol Co, 50-53, petrol eng lab mgr, 53-55. *Mem:* Soc Petrol Engrs; Sigma Xi. *Res:* Hydrocarbon phase behavior, processing and production. *Mailing Add:* 504 Town Creek Dr Dallas TX 75232-1651

**WARNER, BRENT A,** SOLID STATE PHYSICS, CRYOGENICS ENGINEERING. *Current Pos:* AEROSPACE ENGR, GODDARD SPACE CTR, 85- *Personal Data:* b Charleston, WVa, Sept 17, 53. *Educ:* Col Wooster, BA, 75; Ohio State Univ, MS, 85. *Mem:* Am Phys Soc; Sigma Xi. *Res:* Magnetic shielding for a magnetic cooling system for satellite use. *Mailing Add:* Code 713 Goddard Space Flight Ctr Greenbelt MD 20771-0001

**WARNER, CAROL MILLER,** IMMUNOBIOLOGY, GENETICS. *Current Pos:* PROF BIOL, NORTHEASTERN UNIV, 88- *Personal Data:* b New York, NY, Sept 26, 46; c 2. *Educ:* Queens Col, NY, BA, 66; Univ Calif, Los Angeles, PhD(biochem), 70. *Prof Exp:* Fel, Yale Univ, 70-71; from asst prof to prof biochem, Iowa State Univ, 71-88. *Mem:* Soc Develop Biol; Fedn Am Scientists; Sigma Xi; Am Soc Biochem & Molecular Biol; Am Asn Immunologists. *Res:* Preimplantation mouse embryo development; major histocompatibility complex; gene mapping. *Mailing Add:* Dept Biol 414 Mugar Bldg Northeastern Univ 360 Huntington Ave Boston MA 02115. *Fax:* 617-373-3724; *E-Mail:* cmw@neu.edu

**WARNER, CECIL F(RANCIS),** MECHANICAL ENGINEERING. *Current Pos:* RETIRED. *Personal Data:* b Parker, Ind, June 13, 15; m 39; c 2. *Educ:* Purdue Univ, BS, 39, PhD(heat transfer), 45; Lehigh Univ, MS, 41. *Prof Exp:* Instr mech eng, Lehigh Univ, 40-42; from instr to prof mech eng, Purdue Univ, West Lafayette, 42-81. *Concurrent Pos:* Staff mem, Aerojet Gen Corp. *Mem:* Am Soc Mech Engrs; Air Pollution Control Asn. *Res:* Problems in air pollution; heat transfer; jet and rocket propulsion; heat transfer characteristics of liquid film cooling. *Mailing Add:* 2614-A Westminster Dr West Lafayette IN 47906-1438

**WARNER, CHARLES D,** ORGANIC CHEMISTRY. *Current Pos:* GROUP LEADER ANAL & ORG LABS, ARGUS, 92- *Personal Data:* b Mt Hope, WVa, Mar 25, 45; m 66; c 1. *Educ:* Univ Mo, Columbia, BS, 67, PhD(org chem), 71. *Prof Exp:* Asst prof chem, Mo Valley Col, 71-74; from asst prof to prof chem, Hastings Col, 74-92, head dept, 78-92. *Concurrent Pos:* Vis assoc prof, Eppley Inst Cancer Res, 83-84, Univ Md, Columbia, 86. *Mem:* Am Chem Soc; Sigma Xi; Am Soc Mass Spectrometry. *Res:* Organic chemistry mass spectrometry, gas-phase ion chemistry. *Mailing Add:* 22 Evian Path Ct Pl The Woodlands TX 77382

**WARNER, CHARLES ROBERT,** MATHEMATICS. *Current Pos:* asst prof, 64-69, ASSOC PROF MATH, UNIV MD, COLLEGE PARK, 69- *Personal Data:* b Aug 24, 31; Can citizen; m 71, Anne Woolever. *Educ:* Univ Toronto, BA, 55; Rochester Univ, MS, 57, PhD(math), 62. *Prof Exp:* Instr math, Univ Conn, 58-59; asst prof, Mich State Univ, 62-64. *Concurrent Pos:* Vis assoc prof, Univ Calif, Irvine, 70-71, vis prof, Mittag-Leffler Inst, Djursholm, Sweden, 77, Univ Paris, Orsay, 77-78 & Univ Lausanne, Switz, 78. *Mem:* Am Math Soc; Math Asn Am. *Res:* Banach algebras and harmonic analysis. *Mailing Add:* Dept Math Univ Md College Park MD 20742

**WARNER, CHARLES Y,** MECHANICAL ENGINEERING. *Current Pos:* SR ENGR, COLLISION SAFETY ENG, 81- *Personal Data:* b Pocatello, Idaho, Sept 4, 34. *Educ:* Brigham Young Univ, BES, 57, MS, 63; Univ Mich, PhD(mech eng), 66. *Prof Exp:* Design engr, Hewlett-Packard, Calif, 57; test prog engr, Nat Reactor Test Sta, Gen Elec Co, Idaho, 58; from instr to prof mech eng, Brigham Young Univ, 61-81. *Concurrent Pos:* Consult, Eimco Corp, Utah & Rich's Soft Cushion Bumper Co, 67- *Mem:* Am Soc Mech Engrs; Am Soc Eng Educ; Sigma Xi. *Res:* Automotive safety; heat transfer; engineering design. *Mailing Add:* 150 S Mountain Way Dr Orem UT 84058

**WARNER, DANIEL DOUGLAS,** NUMERICAL ANALYSIS. *Current Pos:* PROF MATH, CLEMSON UNIV, 80- *Personal Data:* b Mobile, Ala, Sept 1, 42; m 68; c 3. *Educ:* Ariz State Univ, BS, 65; Univ Calif, San Diego, PhD(math), 74. *Prof Exp:* Programmer, Process Comput Sect, Gen Elec Co, 63-65; comput analyst, Airesearch Corp, 66; mem tech staff, Bell Tel Labs, 74-80. *Mem:* Am Math Soc; Soc Indust & Appl Math; Asn Comput Mach. *Res:* Computational mathematics with emphasis on the numerical solution of ordinary and partial differential equations; design of algorithms for parallel computing. *Mailing Add:* Dept Math Sci Clemson Univ Martin Hall Clemson SC 29634-1907

**WARNER, DAVID CHARLES,** MATHEMATICAL PHYSICS, PLASMA PHYSICS. *Current Pos:* ASST PROF PHYSICS, COLUMBIA COL, MO, 78- *Personal Data:* b Granite City, Ill, Apr 27, 42; m 64. *Educ:* Univ Mo, Columbia, BS, 65, MS, 67, PhD(physics), 70. *Prof Exp:* Asst prof physics,

Lincoln Univ, 70-78. *Mem:* Am Asn Physics Teachers; Am Phys Soc. *Res:* Quantum kinetic equations of plasma physics; density matrix formalism applied to damping of plasma waves. *Mailing Add:* Dept Math/Physics Ore Inst Technol 3201 Campus Dr Klamath Falls OR 97601-8801

**WARNER, DON LEE,** HYDROGEOLOGY, GEOLOGICAL ENGINEERING. *Current Pos:* assoc prof, Univ Mo, Rolla, 69-72, prof geol eng, 72-81, dean, 81-93, EMER DEAN SCH MINES & METALL & EMER PROF GEOL ENG, UNIV MO, ROLLA, 92- *Personal Data:* b Norfolk, Nebr, Jan 4, 34; m 57, Patricia A Walker; c Mark & Scott. *Educ:* Colo Sch Mines, Geol Engr, 56, MSc, 61; Univ Calif, Berkeley, PhD(eng sci), 64. *Honors & Awards:* Sci Award, Nat Water Well Asn, 84. *Prof Exp:* Res geologist, R A Taft Sanit Eng Ctr, Ohio, 64-69. *Concurrent Pos:* Consult; ed, Ground Water & Ground Water Monitoring Rev, 80-85. *Mem:* Am Soc Testing & Mat; Geol Soc Am; Am Asn Petrol Geol; Am Inst Prof Geol; Nat Ground Water Asn; Soc Petrol Engrs. *Res:* Ground water protection and restoration. *Mailing Add:* 129 McNutt Hall Univ Mo Rolla MO 65401. *Fax:* 573-341-4192; *E-Mail:* warner@umr.edu

**WARNER, DONALD R,** ANIMAL HUSBANDRY, ANIMAL NUTRITION. *Current Pos:* RETIRED. *Personal Data:* b Winston, Mo, July 6, 18; m 45, Doris Reilly; c Carol, Mary & Don E. *Educ:* Univ Mo, BS, 42, MS, 49, PhD(animal nutrit & ed), 60. *Hon Degrees:* Hon Am Farmer Org Degree, Nat Future Farmers Am, 82. *Prof Exp:* Mem staff, Mo Agr Exten Serv, 45-47; instr animal husb, Univ Mo, 47-49; asst prof animal sci, Univ Nebr, 49-56; from asst prof to prof animal sci, Iowa State Univ, 60-87, emer prof, 87-88. *Concurrent Pos:* Livestock judging team coach, Iowa State Univ. *Mem:* Am Soc Animal Sci. *Res:* Swine feeding investigations; antibiotics; protein supplements for pigs on pasture and in dry lot; methods of feeding and effects on carcass value; bloat studies of sheep; breeding, feeding and management of sheep. *Mailing Add:* 1309 Glendale Ames IA 50011-5525

**WARNER, DONALD THEODORE,** BIOCHEMISTRY, PROTEIN CONFORMATION STUDIES. *Current Pos:* RETIRED. *Personal Data:* b Holland, Mich, Apr 7, 18; m 45, Ruth Vickland; c Robert & Nancy. *Educ:* Hope Col, AB, 39; Univ Ill, PhD(biochem), 43. *Honors & Awards:* Bond Award, Am Oil Chem Soc, 66. *Prof Exp:* Res chemist, Gen Mills, Inc, 43-52 & Upjohn Co, 52-82. *Concurrent Pos:* Invited sabbatical, City of Hope Nat Med Ctr, Duarte, Calif, 65-66. *Mem:* Am Chem Soc. *Res:* Amino acids; isolation and synthesis; amino acid diets; isolation and properties of threonine; organic synthesis, 1, 4 addition reactions; polysaccharides; peptide synthesis; protein conformation studies; antiasthmatic drugs. *Mailing Add:* 2723 Winchell Ave Kalamazoo MI 49008-2173

**WARNER, DWAIN WILLARD,** ZOOLOGY. *Current Pos:* PRES, TECHNOL SERV INDUST, INC; PRES, KASIMBA LTD. *Personal Data:* b Cottonwood Co, Minn, Sept 1, 17; m 40, 66, 85; c 5. *Educ:* Carleton Col, BA, 39; Cornell Univ, PhD(ornith), 47. *Prof Exp:* Lab asst bot, Carleton Col, 38-39; asst zoologist, Cornell Univ, 41, asst, 42-43 & 46, instr, 46-47; cur birds, Bell Mus Natural Hist, Univ Minn, Minneapolis, 47-87, from asst prof to prof zool, 47-87, environ dir, Belwin Outdoor Educ Lab, 83-89. *Mem:* Assoc Am Ornith Union; Cooper Ornith Soc; Wilson Ornith Soc; AAAS. *Res:* Birds of Mexico and New Caledonia; zoogeography; biology and ecology of avifauna; bird migration and habitat selection; population levels in declining habitats in tropical and temperate regions. *Mailing Add:* 2666 Sumac Ridge Rd White Bear Lake MN 55110

**WARNER, ELDON DEZELLE,** ENDOCRINOLOGY. *Current Pos:* from instr to assoc prof, Univ Wis-Milwaukee, 46-58, chmn dept, 56-58, 59-61 & 66-69, prof zool, 58-78, EMER PROF ZOOL, UNIV WIS-MILWAUKEE, 78- *Personal Data:* b Whitewater, Wis, Oct 5, 11; m 41, Jean M Downing; c David, Philip & Janet (Lay). *Educ:* Wis State Teachers Col, BEd, 32; Univ Wis, PhM, 38, PhD(zool), 41. *Prof Exp:* Asst prof sci, Adams State Teachers Col, 41-43. *Concurrent Pos:* NSF fel, 58-59; vis prof, Cornell Univ, Ithaca, NY, 64-65; vis prof, Univ Wis-Madison, 67-69. *Mem:* AAAS; Am Soc Zool. *Res:* Lower vertebrate endocrinology. *Mailing Add:* 7921 W Clarke Wauwatosa WI 53213

**WARNER, FRANK WILSON, III,** DIFFERENTIAL GEOMETRY, RIEMANNIAN GEOMETRY. *Current Pos:* assoc prof, 68-73, assoc dean, 92-95, PROF MATH, UNIV PA, 73-, DEP DEAN, SCH ARTS & SCI, 95- *Personal Data:* b Pittsfield, Mass, Mar 2, 38; m 58, Ada Woodward; c Bruce & Clifford. *Educ:* Pa State Univ, BS, 59; Mass Inst Technol, PhD(math), 63. *Prof Exp:* Instr math, Mass Inst Technol, 63-64; actg asst prof, Univ Calif, Berkeley, 64-65, asst prof, 65-68. *Concurrent Pos:* Guggenheim fel, 76-77. *Mem:* Am Math Soc; Math Asn Am; AAAS; Sigma Xi. *Res:* Differential geometry; research on the conjugate locus of a riemannian manifold; existence and conformal deformation of metrics with prescribed gaussian and scalar curvatures; great circle fibrations of spheres. *Mailing Add:* Dept Math Univ Pa Philadelphia PA 19104-6395. *E-Mail:* fwarner@math.upenn.edu

**WARNER, FREDERIC COOPER,** GEOMETRY. *Current Pos:* RETIRED. *Personal Data:* b Whitesboro, NY, Jan 28, 15; m 40, Idella Hill; c Judith W (Mairs) & Frederick R. *Educ:* Col Wooster, BA, 37; Univ Buffalo, MA, 50, PhD, 53. *Prof Exp:* Teacher high schs, NY, 37-46; instr math, Univ Buffalo, 46-53; from asst prof to prof, St Lawrence Univ, 53-80. *Mem:* Am Math Soc; Sigma Xi; Math Asn Am. *Res:* Operations research. *Mailing Add:* 10 Jay St Canton NY 13617

**WARNER, GARVIN L,** IMMUNOTOXICOLOGY, MOLECULAR TOXICOLOGY. *Current Pos:* MGR, IMMUNOTOXICOL SECT, DEPT BIOL EVAL, BRISTOL-MYERS SQUIBB CO, 93- *Personal Data:* b Albany, NY, June 9, 56; m 80, Margaret Wheeler. *Educ:* Colgate Univ, BA, 78; Albany Med Col Union Univ, PhD(microbiol & immunol), 86. *Prof Exp:* Fel, Univ Rochester Cancer Ctr, 80-89, res asst prof, 89-91. *Mem:* Sigma Xi; Am Asn Immunol; Soc Toxicol. *Res:* Assessment of drug safety of recombinant DNA derived protein therapeutics; mechanistic analysis of toxicity with special regard to effects on the immune system. *Mailing Add:* Bristol-Myers Squibb Co PO Box 4755 Syracuse NY 13221. *Fax:* 315-432-2172

**WARNER, H JACK,** FOOD TECHNOLOGY. *Current Pos:* food technologist develop, Beatreme Foods, 69-72, dir, Tech Serv, Spec Foods Div, 72-78, asst gen mgr, 79-83, GEN MGR, KERRY INGREDIENT, 83-, PRES 85- *Personal Data:* US citizen. *Educ:* Ohio State Univ, BS, 65. *Prof Exp:* Qual control mgr, Chung King Corp, 65-67; food inspector, US Army, 67-69. *Mem:* Inst Food Technol; Am Asn Cereal Chemists. *Res:* Spray dehydration of foods. *Mailing Add:* Kerry Ingredient 100 E Grand Ave Beloit WI 53511

**WARNER, HARLOW LESTER,** PLANT PHYSIOLOGY, PLANT BREEDING. *Current Pos:* SR SCIENTIST PLANT PHYSIOL, ROHM & HAAS CO, 69- *Personal Data:* b Greenport, NY, Aug 26, 42; m 63; c 3. *Educ:* Cornell Univ, BS, 64; Univ Idaho, MS, 66; Purdue Univ, PhD(plant physiol), 70. *Mem:* Am Soc Hort Sci; Am Soc Plant Physiologists. *Res:* Agricultural chemicals, specifically plant growth regulators and herbicides; plant growth regulators for developing hybrid seeds. *Mailing Add:* 111 Quince Dr Hatboro PA 19040

**WARNER, HAROLD,** BIOMEDICAL ENGINEERING, NUTRITION. *Current Pos:* clin asst prof psychiat, res prof biomed eng & chief, Biomed Eng Lab, 65-82, EMER PROF BIOMED ENG & CONSULT, EMORY UNIV, 82- *Personal Data:* b Philadelphia, Pa, June 6, 17; m 43, Ethel Bersh; c Carol W (Dougan) & Stephen D. *Prof Exp:* Chief engr, Microwave Div, Frankford Arsenal, 48-56, Teledynamics, Inc, 56-58; consult engr, Missile & Space Div, Gen Elec Corp, 58-65. *Mem:* Sigma Xi. *Res:* Application of electronics, physics and mechanics to the fields of reproductive biology, the neurosciences and psychology; role of nutrition in aging and disease. *Mailing Add:* 1891 Briarcliff Circle Apt A Atlanta GA 30329. *Fax:* 404-727-7845

**WARNER, HOMER R,** PHYSIOLOGY, BIOENGINEERING. *Current Pos:* RETIRED. *Personal Data:* b Salt Lake City, Utah, Apr 18, 22; m 46; c 6. *Educ:* Univ Utah, BA, 46, MD, 49; Univ Minn, PhD(physiol), 53. *Hon Degrees:* DSc, Brigham Young Univ, 71; Dr, Univ Linkoping, Sweden, 90. *Honors & Awards:* James E Talmage Sci Achievement Award, 68; Comput in Healthcare Pioneer Award, 90; Morris Collen Award, Am Col Med Informatics, 94. *Prof Exp:* Intern, Parkland Hosp, Dallas, 49-50; resident med, Univ Minn Hosp, 50-51; fel, Mayo Clin, 51-52 & Univ Minn, 52-53; res instr, Dept Internal Med, Univ Utah, 53-54, asst res prof, Dept Physiol, 57-64, prof & chmn, Dept Biophys & Bioeng, 64-73, res prof, Dept Surg, 66-83, prof & chmn, Dept Med Informatics, 73-96, spec asst info mgt to vpres health sci, 83-93, dir & chmn comput health sci, 93-96, chief info officer, Health Sci Ctr, 94-96. *Concurrent Pos:* Dir, Cardiovasc Lab, Latter-Day Saints Hosp, 54-70; estab investr, Am Heart Asn, 59-64; mem, Adv Comt Comput Res, NIH, 61-63, chmn, Comput Res Study Sect, 63-66; res career awardee, Nat Heart Inst, NIH, 62-83, mem, Heart Prog Proj Study Sect, 66-70; ed, Comput & Biomed Res, 66-; vis prof, Univ Hawaii, 68 & Univ Southern Calif, 72; mem, Pres Adv Comt Deploying Scientists & Engrs into Health Ctrs, 71; mem, Health Care Technol Study Sect, Nat Ctr Health Servs Res & Develop, 72-76; mem, Biomed Libr Rev Comt, Nat Libr Med, 82-86, chmn, Grant Rev Study Sect, 85-86; prin investr, Utah IAIMS Develop Proj, 85-89; pres, Am Col Med Informatics, 89-90; mem, Health Serv Res Dissemination Study Sect, Agency Health Care Policy & Res, Health & Human Servs, 93-96. *Mem:* Sr mem Inst Med-Nat Acad Sci; Am Physiol Soc; Am Col Med Informatics (pres, 89); Western Soc Clin Res; Am Med Informatics Soc. *Res:* Control of cardiovascular system; application of computers to medicine; author of over 200 scientific journals. *Mailing Add:* Dept Med Infomatics Sch Med Univ Utah AB193 Med Ctr Salt Lake City UT 84132

**WARNER, HUBER RICHARD,** AGING. *Current Pos:* DEP ASSOC DIR, BIOL AGING PROG, NAT INST AGING, BETHESDA, MD, 84- *Personal Data:* b Glendale, Ohio, May 16, 36; m 85; c 2. *Educ:* Ohio Wesleyan Univ, BA, 58; Mass Inst Technol, BS, 58; Univ Mich, PhD(biochem), 62. *Prof Exp:* NSF fel biochem, Mass Inst Technol, 62-64; from asst prof to assoc prof, Univ Minn, St Paul, 64-72, prof biochem, 72-84. *Concurrent Pos:* Vis prof, Karolinska Inst, Stockholm, 71-72, Univ Calif, Berkeley, 79. *Mem:* Am Soc Biochem & Molecular Biol; Geront Soc Am; AAAS. *Res:* Biochemistry of bacteriophage infection and replication; DNA repair; nucleotide metabolism. *Mailing Add:* Nat Inst Aging NIH GW Bldg Rm 2C231 Bethesda MD 20892. *Fax:* 301-402-0010

**WARNER, ISIAH MANUEL,** FLUORESCENCE SPECTROSCOPY, CHEMOMETRICS. *Current Pos:* PHILIP W WEST PROF CHEM, LA STATE UNIV, 92-, CHMN, DEPT CHEM, 94- *Personal Data:* b DeQuincy, La, July 20, 46; m 68, Della Blount-Warner; c Isiah Jr, Chideha & Edward. *Educ:* Southern Univ, BS, 68; Univ Wash, PhD(anal chem), 77. *Honors & Awards:* Pres Young Investr Award, 84; Percy Julian Award Outstanding & Significant Contrib in Res, Nat Orgn Black Chemists & Chem Engrs, 88; Charles Holmes Hesty Medal, Am Chem Soc, 92; Bennedetti-Pichler Award, Am Microchem Soc, 94; Procter & Gamble Award Continuing Support Educ & Diversity Analytical Chem, 96. *Prof Exp:* Res chemist, Battelle Northwest, 68-73; teaching asst chem, Univ Wash, 73-75, res asst, 75-77; asst prof chem, Tex A&M Univ, 77-82; from assoc prof to prof chem, Emory Univ, 82-87,

Samuel Chandler Dobbs prof analytical chem, 87-92. *Concurrent Pos:* Adv & consult, Perkin-Elmer Corp, 83-88, Packard Instruments, 84-85, Fla A&M Univ, 83-88 & Eli-Lilly, 88-89; prog officer analytical & surface chem, NSF. *Mem:* Am Chem Soc; AAAS; Nat Orgn Black Chemists & Chem Engrs; Soc Appl Spectros; Sigma Xi (secy, 84-86, 89); AAAS. *Res:* Develop and apply new and improved methods (chemical, mathematical and instrumental) for analysis of complex systems; development of novel fluorescence instrumentation and new data reduction strategies; improved multicomponent fluorescence analysis. *Mailing Add:* Dept Chem La State Univ 434 Choppin Hall Baton Rouge LA 70803. *Fax:* 504-388-3971; *E-Mail:* isiah.warner@chemgate.chem.lsu.edu

**WARNER, JAMES HOWARD,** BOTANY, PLANT ECOLOGY. *Current Pos:* ASSOC PROF BIOL, UNIV WIS-LA CROSSE, 63- *Personal Data:* b Angola, Ind, Dec 24, 38. *Educ:* Manchester Col, BS, 61; Univ Wis-Madison, MS, 63; Univ Utah, PhD(biol), 71. *Prof Exp:* Teaching asst bot, Univ Wis-Madison, 61-63. *Mem:* AAAS; Am Inst Biol Sci; Ecol Soc Am; Sigma Xi. *Res:* Development of indices of site quality in forest management and plant association. *Mailing Add:* 4071 Terrace Dr La Crosse WI 54601-7514

**WARNER, JOHN CHARLES,** MATERIALS DESIGN, HETEROCYCLIC SYNTHESIS. *Current Pos:* SCIENTIST, POLAROID CORP, 88- *Personal Data:* b Quincy, Mass, Oct 25, 62; m 85; c 2. *Educ:* Univ Mass, Boston, BS, 84; Princeton Univ, MA, 86, PhD(org chem), 88. *Concurrent Pos:* Lectr/instr, Univ Mass, Boston, 89- *Mem:* Am Chem Soc; Soc Imaging Sci & Technol. *Res:* Organic synthesis; heterocyclic chemistry; photographic chemistry; photochemistry; molecular recognition and self assembly; construction of multi-component organic materials based on non-covalent interactions; computational chemistry. *Mailing Add:* 47 Cedar St Norwood MA 02062-3104

**WARNER, JOHN DESHON,** AERONAUTICAL ENGINEERING. *Current Pos:* engr supersonic transp, Boeing Com Airplane Group, 68-74, chief engr prod develop, 78-82, vpres, 89-93, PRES, INFO & SUPPORT SERVS, BOEING CO, 93- *Personal Data:* b Glendale, Calif, Jan 4, 40. *Prof Exp:* Sloan fel, Stanford Grad Sch Bus, 76-77; prog mgr B-2, Mil Airplane Div, Defense & Space Group, 82-85. *Mem:* Nat Acad Eng; fel Royal Aeronaut Soc London; Soc Automotive Engrs. *Mailing Add:* Boeing Co PO Box 3707 MS 7A-49 Seattle WA 98124-2207. *Fax:* 425-865-2953; *E-Mail:* john.warner@pss.boeing.com

**WARNER, JOHN SCOTT,** CHROMATOGRAPHIC METHODS, ENVIRONMENTAL ANALYSIS. *Current Pos:* INDEPENDENT CONSULT, 91- *Personal Data:* b Woodstown, NJ, Oct 25, 28; m 61, Marilyn Stephenson; c Patricia, Elizabeth, Joanna & Kathleen. *Educ:* Rensselaer Polytech Inst, BS, 49; Cornell Univ, PhD(org chem), 52. *Prof Exp:* Anal chemist, Socony Vacuum Oil Co, 49; asst, Cornell Univ, 49-52; prin chemist, Columbus Labs, Battelle Mem Inst, 52-57, proj leader, 57-62, sr res chemist, 62-81, res leader, 81-90. *Mem:* Am Chem Soc. *Res:* Development of methods for determining petroleum, pesticides and other organic compounds in water, soil, tissues, sludge and solid wastes; application of chromatographic techniques, mass spectrometry, and supercritical fluid extraction in environmental analysis. *Mailing Add:* 3605 219th St SW Lynnwood WA 98036

**WARNER, JONATHAN ROBERT,** MOLECULAR BIOLOGY, CELL BIOLOGY. *Current Pos:* res assoc biochem, Albert Einstein Col Med, 64-65, from asst prof to assoc prof, 65-74, dir, Sue Golding Grad Sch, 72-83, prof biochem & cell biol, 74-83, PROF & CHMN, DEPT CELL BIOL, ALBERT EINSTEIN COL MED, 83- *Personal Data:* b New York, NY, Feb 19, 37; m 58, Nancy Heers; c 2. *Educ:* Yale Univ, BS, 58; Mass Inst Technol, PhD(biophys), 63. *Prof Exp:* Res assoc biophys, Mass Inst Technol, 63-64. *Concurrent Pos:* NSF fel, 64-65; career scientist, Health Res Coun, City New York, 65-72; Guggenheim fel, 71-72; Am Cancer Soc fac res award, 72-77; mem sci adv bd, Damon Runyon-Walter Winchell Cancer Fund, 73-77; mem molecular cytol study sect, NIH, 75-77, mem genetic basis dis rev comt, 85-90; mem sci adv comt, Am Cancer Soc, 81-84, 89-92; mem bd trustees, Cold Spring Harbor Lab, 87- *Mem:* Am Soc Biol Chemists; Am Soc Cell Biol; Am Soc Microbiol; NY Acad Sci; Harvey Soc (vpres, 87-88, pres, 88-89); RNA Soc. *Res:* Synthesis and assembly of ribosomes and its regulation in eucaryotic cells; ribosomal protein genes; transcription and processing of RNA nuclear-cytoplasmic interactions. *Mailing Add:* Dept Cell Biol Albert Einstein Col Med 1300 Morris Park Ave Bronx NY 10461-1975

**WARNER, KENDALL,** FISHERIES. *Current Pos:* regional fishery biologist, 52-68, chief res biologist, Fishery Div, 68-84, RES MGT SUPRV, MAINE DEPT INLAND FISHERIES & WILDLIFE, 84- *Personal Data:* b Westfield, Mass, Oct 2, 27; m 70, Sandra Noyes; c Kendra & Leanna. *Educ:* Univ Maine, BS, 50; Cornell Univ, MS, 52. *Honors & Awards:* Prof Award of Merit, Northeast Div, Am Fisheries Soc, 87, Pres Award, 94; T J Dirkham Award & Atlantic Salmon Restoration, 94. *Prof Exp:* Fishery aide, US Fish & Wildlife Serv, 50; asst fishery biol, Cornell Univ, 51-52. *Mem:* Am Fisheries Soc; fel Am Inst Fishery Res Biologists. *Res:* Fresh water fisheries; landlocked salmon; brook trout. *Mailing Add:* Fisheries Div Inland Fisheries & Wildlife 650 State St Bangor ME 04401-5654

**WARNER, KENNETH E,** HEALTH ECONOMICS. *Current Pos:* COL PROF PUB HEALTH, DEPT HEALTH MGT & POLICY, SCH PUB HEALTH, UNIV MICH, 95-; ASSOC DIR, CLIN SCHOLARS PROG, ROBERT WOOD JOHNSON FOUND. *Personal Data:* b 1947; m 77, Patricia Hilty; c Andrew & Peter. *Educ:* Dartmouth Col, AB, 68; Yale Univ,

MPhil, 70, PhD, 74. *Honors & Awards:* Surgeon General's Medallion, 89; Leadership Award, Am Pub Health Asn, 90. *Mem:* Inst Med-Nat Acad Sci; fel Asn Health Serv Res; Am Pub Health Asn; Soc Res Nicotine & Tobacco; Int Health Econ Asn. *Res:* Economic and policy aspects of disease prevention and health promotion; smoking and health; authored over 150 professional articles. *Mailing Add:* Dept Health Mgt & Policy Sch Pub Health Univ Mich 109 Observatory Ann Arbor MI 48109-2029. *Fax:* 313-764-4338; *E-Mail:* kwarner@umich.edu

**WARNER, LAURANCE BLISS,** NUCLEAR PHYSICS. *Current Pos:* PROG MGR, LOS ALAMOS NAT LAB, 77- *Personal Data:* b Brooklyn, NY, Dec 29, 31; m 52; c 3. *Educ:* Rensselaer Polytech Inst, BS, 53; Johns Hopkins Univ, MS, 58; Fla State Univ, PhD(physics), 62. *Prof Exp:* US Navy, 53-, instr physics & electronics, US Naval Acad, 56-58; terrier battery officer, USS Long Beach CGN-9, 62-64, exec officer, USS Benjamin Stoddert DDG-22, 64-66, physicist, Lawrence Radiation Lab, 66-69, weapons officer, USS Galveston CLG-3, 69-70, dir, Atomic Energy Div, Chief Naval Opers, Washington, DC, 70-77. *Concurrent Pos:* Instr physics, Fed City Col, Washington, DC, 71- *Mem:* Am Phys Soc. *Res:* Nuclear decay and reaction spectroscopy; deformed nuclei; fast electronics instrumentation; computer applications; neutron transport; radiative transfer; missile systems analysis; free electron lasers; advanced microwave sources. *Mailing Add:* 465 Camino Cereza Los Alamos NM 87544. *Fax:* 505-665-5739

**WARNER, LAWRENCE ALLEN,** geology, for more information see previous edition

**WARNER, MARLENE RYAN,** endocrinology, cancer research, for more information see previous edition

**WARNER, MONT MARCELLUS,** GEOLOGY. *Current Pos:* RETIRED. *Personal Data:* b Fillmore, Utah, Oct 9, 19; m 47. *Educ:* Brigham Youn Univ, AB, 47, MA, 49; Univ Iowa, PhD(geol), 63. *Prof Exp:* Geologist, Shell Oil Co, 49-55; consult petrol geol, La & Utah, 55-59; instr geol, Brigham Young Univ, 59-61; asst prof, Ariz State Univ, 63-67, res grant, 64-66; chmn, Dept Ecol, Boise State Col, 67-70, prof geol, 67-84. *Concurrent Pos:* Idaho state rep in geothermal matters, 70-72; res & legis work in geothermal resources, 70-72; mem exec comt & comt info educ, Geothermal Resources Coun, 70-72. *Mem:* Am Asn Petrol Geologists; Nat Asn Geol Teachers; Ecol Soc Am; Nat Inst Prof Geol. *Res:* Sedimentation; structural and petroleum geology. *Mailing Add:* 8916 W Brookview Dr Boise ID 83709

**WARNER, NANCY ELIZABETH,** PATHOLOGY. *Current Pos:* from assoc prof to prof path, Univ Southern Calif, 67-91, chmn dept, 72-83, assoc dean acad affairs, 77-91, EMER PROF PATH, UNIV SOUTHERN CALIF, 91- *Personal Data:* b Dixon, Ill, July 8, 23. *Educ:* Univ Chicago, SB, 44, MD, 49; Am Bd Path, dipl, 54. *Prof Exp:* From intern to asst resident path, Univ Chicago Clins, 49-50; resident, Cedars of Lebanon Hosp, Los Angeles, Calif, 53-54, asst pathologist, 54-58; from asst prof to assoc prof path, Univ Chicago, 58-65, dir, Lab Surg Path, Univ Clins, 59-65; assoc clin prof path, Univ Southern Calif, 65-66; assoc prof, Sch Med, Univ Wash, 66-67. *Concurrent Pos:* Assoc dir labs, Cedars-Sinai Med Ctr, Los Angeles, 65-66; chief pathologist, Women's Hosp, Los Angeles Co-Univ Southern Calif Med Ctr, 68-72, dir labs & path, 72-83, surgical pathologist, Norris Cancer Hosp, 83-91 & mem active staff, 83- *Mem:* Fel Col Am Pathologists; Endocrine Soc; Microcirculatory Soc; fel Am Soc Clin Pathologists; Sigma Xi. *Res:* Pathology of endocrine glands; comparative pathology of tumors of the gonads; pathology of preneoplastic lesions of the breast; microvasculature of tumors. *Mailing Add:* Dept Path Univ Southern Calif 2011 Zonal Ave Los Angeles CA 90033-1054

**WARNER, PETER,** MICROBIOLOGY. *Current Pos:* RETIRED. *Personal Data:* b Winnipeg, Man, Apr 22, 20; m 52, 78, Iona Maude Henderson; c Susanna, Janice, William, Sarah, Charlotte & Oenona. *Educ:* Univ London, MB & BS, 44, MD, 48, PhD(path), 51. *Prof Exp:* Asst pathologist, Bland-Sutton Inst Path, Middlesex Hosp, London, Eng, 46-52; pathologist, Winnipeg Gen Hosp, 53-54; assoc prof path, Fac Med, Univ Man, 54-55; head med res div, Inst Med Sci, Australia, 55-58; assoc prof med bact, Fac Med, Univ Man, 58-74; asst regional dir, Man Med Servs Br, Health & Welfare, Can, 74-81; dir, Environ Health, Man Govt, 81-86. *Concurrent Pos:* Brit Empire Cancer Campaign traveling scholar, Walter Reed Army Med Ctr, DC, 48-49; asst dep minister health, Man Govt, 67-71; chmn, Man Clean Environ Comn, 71-72; consult, Man Inst Tech; ed, Man Med Rev. *Mem:* Fel Am Acad Microbiol; fel Am Soc Clin Path; Can Soc Microbiol; Can Asn Path; Path Soc Gt Brit & Ireland. *Res:* Medical microbiology; experimental pathology; health administration. *Mailing Add:* 3202-55 Nassau Winnipeg MB R3L 2G8 Can

**WARNER, PHILIP MARK,** ORGANIC CHEMISTRY. *Current Pos:* chair, 88-93, PROF CHEM, NORTHEASTERN STATE UNIV, 88- *Personal Data:* b New York, NY, Nov 5, 46; m 93, Cynthia. *Educ:* Columbia Univ, BA, 66; Univ Calif, Los Angeles, PhD(chem), 70. *Prof Exp:* NSF fel, Yale Univ, 70-71; from instr to asst prof, Iowa State Univ, 71-77, assoc prof org chem, 77-86, prof chem, 86-88. *Mem:* Am Chem Soc; Royal Soc Chem. *Res:* Study of DNA binding interactions with small synthetic molecules, small peptides, and proteins; cleavage of DNA and peptides. *Mailing Add:* Dept Chem Northeastern Univ Boston MA 02115-5096

**WARNER, R(ICHARD) E(LMORE),** chemical engineering; deceased, see previous edition for last biography

**WARNER, RAY ALLEN,** EXPERIMENTAL NUCLEAR PHYSICS. *Current Pos:* sr res scientist analytical & nuclear res, 77-90, PROG MGR, OFF NAT SECURITY TECHNOL, PAC NORTHWEST LAB, 90- *Personal Data:* b Davis, Calif, May 5, 38; m 65. *Educ:* Univ Calif, Berkeley, BS, 61; Univ Calif, Davis, PhD(physics), 69. *Prof Exp:* Res assoc, Cyclotron Lab, Mich State Univ, 69-71, asst prof chem & physics, 72-77. *Concurrent Pos:* Tech adv, US Dept Energy Off Arms Control, 88-90. *Mem:* Am Phys Soc; AAAS. *Res:* Experiments in collective and intrinsic nuclear structure, parity mixing, beta strength functions, fission yields and properties of delayed neutron emitters; instrumentation for mass spectrometry radio-analytical chemistry; research into technology applicable to verification of compliance with arms control treaties. *Mailing Add:* 1234 W Acord Rd No A Benton City WA 99320

**WARNER, RAYMOND M, JR,** PHYSICS. *Current Pos:* RETIRED. *Personal Data:* b Barberton, Ohio, Mar 21, 22; m 48, 74; c 3. *Educ:* Carnegie Inst Technol, BS, 47; Case Univ, MS, 50, PhD(physics), 52. *Prof Exp:* Lab asst, Pittsburgh Plate Glass Co, Ohio, 41 & 42; lab instr physics, Carnegie Inst Technol, 43; jr physicist, Res Lab, Corning Glass Works, NY, 47-48; instr physics, Case Univ, 51-52; mem tech staff semiconductor device develop, Bell Tel Labs, Inc, NJ, 52-59; chief engr diode develop, Semiconductor Prod Div, Motorola, Inc, Ariz, 59-61, mgr mat res, 61-63, dir eng, 63-65; mgr metal-oxide-semiconductor devices prog, Semiconductor Components Div, Tex Instruments Inc, 65-67; US tech dir, Semiconductor Div, Int Tel & Telegraph Corp, Fla, 67-69; dir technol, Semiconductor Dept, Union Carbide Corp, Calif, 69-70; prof elec eng, Univ Minn, Minneapolis, 70-, chmn, Res Microelectronics Comt, 70-80. *Mem:* AAAS; fel Inst Elec & Electronics Engrs; Sigma Xi. *Res:* Semiconductor device physics and engineering; solid-state electronics; intergrated circuits. *Mailing Add:* 6136 Sherman Circle Minneapolis MN 55436

**WARNER, RICHARD CHARLES,** LANDFILL DESIGN, SEDIMENT CONTROL. *Current Pos:* exten specialist irrig, 80-81, asst prof, 81-86, ASSOC PROF POLLUTION CONTROL, AGR ENG DEPT, UNIV KY, 86- *Personal Data:* b Chicago, Ill, Sept 22, 47. *Educ:* Univ Ill, BS, 70; Clemson Univ, MS, 72, PhD(environ syst eng), 82. *Prof Exp:* Oper officer oceanog, USN, Lewes, Del, 74-75; res asst polit sci, Polit Sci Dept, Clemson Univ, 75-76, res asst pollution control, Environ Systs Eng, 76-79; hydrologist, US Geol Surv, 79-80. *Concurrent Pos:* Spec intel, USN, Keflavik, Iceland, 72-73; comput systs dir, 73-74, oceanog res officer, 73-74; consult, Nat Acad Sci, 84- *Mem:* Am Soc Agr Engrs (secy, 85). *Res:* Technology transfer in the water resources areas; hydrology; sediment control; landfill design, monitoring and modelling; irrigation; computer aided design. *Mailing Add:* Agr Eng Dept Rm 128 Univ Ky Lexington KY 40546-0276

**WARNER, RICHARD DUDLEY,** PLANETARY SCIENCE. *Current Pos:* asst prof, 80-85, ASSOC PROF GEOL, CLEMSON UNIV, 85-, ACTG DEPT HEAD, 86- *Personal Data:* b Pittsfield, Mass, Aug 3, 44; m 74; c 2. *Educ:* Mass Inst Technol, SB, 66; Stanford Univ, PhD(geol), 71. *Prof Exp:* Res assoc geol, Univ Md, 73-74; res assoc geol, Univ NMex, 74-80. *Concurrent Pos:* Resident res assoc, Goddard Space Flight Ctr, NASA, 71-73; NASA/Am Soc Eng Ed summer fac fel, 81, 82. *Mem:* Mineral Soc Am. *Res:* Petrology of lunar samples; petrology of terrestrial mafic and ultramafic rocks; experimental petrology; magnetic petrology. *Mailing Add:* Dept Earth Sci Clemson Univ Clemson SC 29632-0001

**WARNER, RICHARD G,** ANIMAL NUTRITION. *Current Pos:* RETIRED. *Personal Data:* b Washington, DC, Nov 1, 22; m 49; c 4. *Educ:* Ohio State Univ, BSc, 47, MS, 48; Cornell Univ, PhD(animal nutrit), 51. *Prof Exp:* Prof animal nutrit, Cornell Univ, 51-89. *Concurrent Pos:* Consult dairy nutrit, Empresa Brasileira Pesquisa Agropecuaria, Brazil. *Mem:* Am Soc Animal Sci; Am Dairy Sci Asn; Am Inst Nutrit. *Res:* Calf and ruminant nutrition; laboratory animal nutrition; food intake physiology. *Mailing Add:* 1483 Ellis Hollow Rd Ithaca NY 14850-9656

**WARNER, ROBERT COLLETT,** BIOCHEMISTRY. *Current Pos:* chmn dept, 69-77, prof, 69-84, EMER PROF MOLECULAR BIOL & BIOCHEM, UNIV CALIF, IRVINE, 84- *Personal Data:* b Denver, Colo, Aug 31, 13; m 36, 69, Estelle Prussin; c Peter, Jisho C & Victoria. *Educ:* Calif Inst Technol, BS, 35; NY Univ, MS, 37, PhD(biochem), 41. *Prof Exp:* Chemist protein chem, Eastern Regional Lab, USDA, Philadelphia, 41-46; from asst prof to prof biochem, Sch Med, NY Univ, 46-69. *Concurrent Pos:* Mem panel plasma, Nat Res Coun, 52-57; Guggenheim Mem Found fel, Carlsberg Lab, Copenhagen, Denmark, 58; mem study sect biophys & biophys chem, NIH, 60-64; chmn study sect biochem, 72-74; assoc ed, J Biol Chem, 68-72. *Mem:* Am Soc Biochem & Molecular Biol; Biophys Soc; Am Chem Soc. *Res:* Physical biochemistry of nucleic acids and proteins; mechanism of genetic recombination in small DNA containing bacteriophages; properties of circular DNA; kinetics of branch migration of DNA. *Mailing Add:* Dept Molecular Biol & Biochem Univ Calif Irvine CA 92697

**WARNER, ROBERT EDSON,** PARTICLE-PARTICLE CORRELATIONS, TOTAL REACTION CROSS SECTIONS. *Current Pos:* assoc prof, 65-72, dept chair, 90-93, PROF PHYSICS, OBERLIN COL, 72-, LONGMAN PROF NATURAL SCI, 95- *Personal Data:* b Pomeroy, Ohio, Apr 11, 31; m 86, Mary Ann Black; c Ruth (Berlow), Margaret (Bushee), Deborah (Blackburn) & Elizabeth. *Educ:* Antioch Col, BS, 54; Univ Rochester, PhD(physics), 59. *Prof Exp:* From instr to asst prof physics, Univ Rochester, 59-61; asst prof, Antioch Col, 61-63; from asst prof to assoc prof, Univ Man, 63-65; vis prof physics, Univ Mich, 93-94. *Concurrent Pos:* NSF sci fac fel, Oxford Univ, 71-72; vis prof, Mich State Univ, 80-81 & 95-96, Univ Notre Dame, 87-88. *Mem:* Am Phys Soc; Am Asn Physics Teachers. *Res:* Nuclear

scattering and reactions; nucleon-nucleon scattering; final-state interactions; angular correlations; reaction cross sections; radioactive nuclear beams. *Mailing Add:* Dept Physics Oberlin Col Oberlin OH 44074. *E-Mail:* fwarner@oberlin.edu

**WARNER, ROBERT JOHN,** REACTION CALORIMETRY, KINETICS & MECHANISMS OF POLYMERIZATION. *Current Pos:* SCIENTIST, S C JOHNSON POLYMER, 79- *Personal Data:* b Binghamton, NY, Jan 5, 51; m 75, Linda J Calvin; c Marie E & David M. *Educ:* Clarkson Univ, BS, 73, MS, 75, PhD(chem), 77. *Prof Exp:* Res assoc, Midland Macromolecular Inst, 77-79. *Mem:* Am Chem Soc; Am Inst Chem Engrs; AAAS; NY Acad Sci. *Res:* Measurement, modeling and simulation of industrial chemical processes using infrared, calorimetry and currently available mathematical and molecular modeling tools. *Mailing Add:* 5310 Crystal Lane Sturtevant WI 53177. *Fax:* 414-631-4039; *E-Mail:* rjwarner@scj.com

**WARNER, ROBERT LEWIS,** AGRONOMY, PLANT PHYSIOLOGY. *Current Pos:* from asst prof to assoc prof, 68-80, PROF AGRON, WASH STATE UNIV, 80- *Personal Data:* b Redwood Falls, Minn, June 16, 37; m 64; c 2. *Educ:* Univ Minn, BS, 62, MS, 64; Univ Ill, PhD(plant physiol & agron), 68. *Prof Exp:* Res asst agron, Univ Minn, 62-64 & Univ Ill, 64-68. *Mem:* Am Soc Agron; Am Soc Plant Physiol; Sigma Xi. *Res:* Factors involved in cold resistance of alfalfa; inheritance and physiological studies of nitrate reductase. *Mailing Add:* Crop & Soil Sci Wash State Univ Pullman WA 99164-6420

**WARNER, ROBERT RONALD,** MARINE ECOLOGY. *Current Pos:* PROF BIOL, UNIV CALIF, SANTA BARBARA, 75- *Personal Data:* b Long Beach, Calif, Oct 28, 46; c 3. *Educ:* Univ Calif, Berkeley, AB, 68, Univ Calif, San Diego, PhD(marine ecol), 73. *Prof Exp:* Fel biol, Smithsonian Trop Res Inst, 73-75. *Mem:* Soc Study Evolution; Ecol Soc Am; Am Soc Naturalists; Animal Behav Soc; Am Soc Ichthyologists & Herpetologists. *Res:* Reproductive strategies of marine organisms. *Mailing Add:* Dept Biol Sci Univ Calif 552 University Ave Santa Barbara CA 93106-0002

**WARNER, SETH L,** ALGEBRA. *Current Pos:* From res instr to assoc prof, 55-65, PROF MATH, DUKE UNIV, 65- *Personal Data:* b Muskegon, Mich, July 11, 27; m 62; c 3. *Educ:* Yale Univ, BS, 50; Harvard Univ, MA, 51, PhD(math), 55. *Concurrent Pos:* NSF fel, Inst Advan Study, 59-60; vis prof, Univ Paris, 64-65, Univ Oslo, 82-83; vis res prof, Reed Col, 70-71. *Mem:* Am Math Soc; Math Asn Am. *Res:* Topological algebra; abstract analysis. *Mailing Add:* Dept Math Duke Univ Box 90320 Durham NC 27708-0320

**WARNER, THOMAS CLARK, JR,** VIBRATION THEORY & APPLICATIONS, ENGINEERING EDUCATION & ADMINISTRATION. *Current Pos:* RETIRED. *Personal Data:* b Waterbury, Conn, Nov 20, 19; m 42, 84, Helen Borchers; c Anita L (Sause) & Thomas C III. *Educ:* Yale Univ, BE, 42; Mass Inst Technol, MS, 47. *Prof Exp:* Res & develop officer, USAF, Wright Patterson AFB, Ohio, 42-45 & Hq, Washington, DC, 47-52; chief develop engr, MB Electronics Div, Textron Inc, 52-62; chmn dept math, Univ New Haven, 62-64 & dept mech eng, 62-65, dean, Sch Eng, 65-77, prof mech eng, 65-84. *Concurrent Pos:* Adj prof math, Univ New Haven, 55, 62 & 84-90, Daytona Beach Community Col, 93-95; consult, MB Electronics Div, Textron Inc, 62-70. *Mem:* Am Soc Mech Engrs; Am Soc Eng Educ; Inst Environ Sci; Nat Soc Prof Engrs; Am Inst Aeronaut & Astronaut. *Res:* Vibration analysis and instrumentation; electro-mechanical design. *Mailing Add:* 41 Misty Falls Dr Ormond Beach FL 32174

**WARNER, THOMAS GARRIE,** BIOCHEMISTRY. *Current Pos:* asst res neuroscientist, 78-79, ASST PROF IN RESIDENCE, DEPT NEUROSCI, UNIV CALIF, 79- *Personal Data:* b El Paso, Tex, July 7, 48. *Educ:* Univ Tex, El Paso, BS, 70; Univ Calif, San Diego, PhD(chem), 75. *Prof Exp:* Res chemist, Scripps Inst Oceanog, 75-77; US Dept Pub Health fel, Neurosci Dept, Univ Calif, 77-78. *Mem:* Am Chem Soc; Am Oil Chemists Soc; AAAS. *Res:* Human biochemical genetics; lysosomal storage diseases; complex carbohydrates structure and function analysis and relation to disease states; chemical anthesis of lipids and phospholipids; hydrophobic enzymes. *Mailing Add:* Genetech Inc 460 Point San Bruno Blvd Bldg 5 Rm 1301 South San Francisco CA 94080-4918

**WARNER, VICTOR DUANE,** MEDICINAL CHEMISTRY. *Current Pos:* PROF MED CHEM & DEAN, COL PHARM, UNIV CINCINNATI, 85- *Personal Data:* b Coulee Dam, Wash, Sept 9, 43; m 68, Ann M Bowman; c Eric. *Educ:* Univ Wash, BS, 66; Univ Kans, PhD(med chem), 70. *Prof Exp:* Asst prof med chem, Col Pharm & Allied Health Sci, Northeastern Univ, 70-74, assoc prof, 74-80, prof, 80-81, actg chmn, Dept Med Chem & Pharmacol, 75-76, chmn, 76-79, actg dean, Col Pharm & Allied Health, 77-78, actg assoc provost, 78-79, assoc provost, 79-81; prof med chem & dean, Col Pharm, Univ PR, 81-85. *Mem:* Am Chem Soc; Am Pharmaceut Asn; Am Asn Cols Pharm. *Res:* Antibacterial agents for inhibition of dental plaque. *Mailing Add:* Col Pharm Univ Cincinnati Cincinnati OH 45267-0001. *Fax:* 513-558-4372

**WARNER, WALTER CHARLES,** POLYMER CHEMISTRY. *Current Pos:* sr res chemist, Gen Tire & Rubber Co, 49-55, group leader analysis & testing, 55-62, sect head, Tech Serv, 62-71, sect head, Phys Testing Res & Serv, 71-77, res ctr adminr, 78-80, HEAD, INFO CTR, GEN TIRE & RUBBER CO, 80- *Personal Data:* b Barberton, Ohio, June 2, 20; m 47; c 2. *Educ:* Oberlin Col, AB, 41; Case Western Res Univ, MS, 43, PhD(org chem), 50. *Prof Exp:* Chem engr, Firestone Tire & Rubber Co, 43-47. *Mem:* Am Chem Soc; Soc Rheology; Am Soc Testing & Mat; Spec Libraries Asn; Am Soc Info Sci; Sigma Xi. *Mailing Add:* 156 Colony Dr Hudson OH 44236-3314

**WARNER, WILLIAM,** OPIATE PHARMACOLOGY, PESTICIDE TOXICOLOGY. *Current Pos:* ASSOC PROF PHARMACOL, COL DENT, NY UNIV, 83- *Educ:* State Univ NY, PhD(pharmacol), 75. *Mailing Add:* 80-15 Grand Central Pkwy Jackson Heights NY 11370-1343

**WARNER, WILLIAM HAMER,** APPLIED MATHEMATICS. *Current Pos:* from asst prof to assoc prof mech, 55-68, prof aerospace eng & mech, 68-95, EMER PROF AEROSPACE ENG & MECH, UNIV MINN, MINNEAPOLIS, 95- *Personal Data:* b Pittsburgh, Pa, Oct 6, 29; m 57, Janet West; c Katherine P. *Educ:* Carnegie Inst Technol, BS, 50, MS, 51, PhD(math), 53. *Prof Exp:* Asst math, Carnegie Inst Technol, 50-53; res assoc appl math, Brown Univ, 53-55. *Mem:* Soc Indust & Appl Math; Am Math Soc; Math Asn Am; Soc Natural Philos. *Res:* Continuum mechanics; dynamic stability; energy methods; nonlinear systems; optimization of structures. *Mailing Add:* Dept Aerospace Eng & Mech Univ Minn 107 Akerman Hall 110 Union St SE Minneapolis MN 55455. *E-Mail:* warner@aem.umn.edu

**WARNER, WILLIS L,** MEDICINE. *Current Pos:* PRES, CONSULTS FOR HEALTHCARE, 79-; OWNER, GLB PUBLISHERS, 90- *Personal Data:* b Endicott, NY, Jan 28, 30. *Educ:* Syracuse Univ, BA, 50; State Univ NY, MD, 60. *Prof Exp:* Res investr biochem, US Naval Radiol Defense Lab, 52-55; intern, San Francisco Hosp, 60-61; resident obstet, St Mary's Hosp, San Francisco, 61-63; assoc clin res, Baxter Labs, Ill, 63-68, assoc dir clin res, 68-71; dir clin res-biol, Hoechst Pharmaceut, Inc, 71-75; dir clin res, Cutter Labs, Inc, 75-76, dir med opers, 77-79. *Concurrent Pos:* Ed, Plasma Forum, 79-81. *Mem:* Am Soc Pharmacol Therapeut; Am Soc Hemat; Am Asn Blood Banks; Am Heart Asn. *Res:* Clinical pharmaceutical. *Mailing Add:* 1028 Howard St No 503 San Francisco CA 94103. *Fax:* 415-243-0885

**WARNES, DENNIS DANIEL,** AGRONOMY, WEED SCIENCE. *Current Pos:* AGRONOMIST, WCENT EXP STA, UNIV MINN, MINNEAPOLIS, 69- *Personal Data:* b Stephen, Minn, June 14, 33; m 56; c 3. *Educ:* NDak State Univ, BSc, 55; Univ Minn, St Paul, MSc, 60; Univ Nebr, Lincoln, PhD(plant breeding), 69. *Prof Exp:* Technician agron, NDak State Univ, 51-55; teaching asst agron, Univ Minn, Minneapolis, 57-60; instr agron & outstate testing, Univ Nebr, Lincoln, 60-66, supvr, Mead Field Lab, 66-69. *Mem:* Am Soc Agron; Weed Sci Soc Am. *Res:* Variety testing, weed control, row spacing, plant population, disease and insect control in corn, soybeans, field beans, sunflowers, small grains and forage crops; principles of weed control with specific weeds. *Mailing Add:* 11 S Court St Morris MN 56267

**WARNES, RICHARD HARRY,** OPTICS, INSTRUMENTATION. *Current Pos:* STAFF MEM PHYSICS, LOS ALAMOS NAT LAB, 57- *Personal Data:* b Chicago, Ill, Apr 23, 33; m 55, Nancy Holderman; c William H & Linda J (Penaloza). *Educ:* DePauw Univ, BA, 55; Stanford Univ, MS, 57. *Mem:* Am Phys Soc. *Res:* Shock wave phenomena; dynamic equation of state; constitutive relations; optical instrumentation; instrumentation. *Mailing Add:* 299 La Cueva St Los Alamos NM 87544. *Fax:* 505-667-6301; *E-Mail:* rhw@lanl.gov

**WARNHOFF, EDGAR WILLIAM,** ORGANIC CHEMISTRY. *Current Pos:* from asst prof to prof, 62-93, EMER PROF CHEM, UNIV WESTERN ONT, 93- *Personal Data:* b Knoxville, Tenn, May 5, 29; m 56, Patricia C Reynolds; c Mark, Andrew & Rolf. *Educ:* Washington Univ, St Louis, AB, 49; Univ Wis, PhD(org chem), 53. *Honors & Awards:* Merck, Sharp & Dohme Lect Award, Chem Inst Can, 69. *Prof Exp:* Nat Res Coun fel, Birkbeck Col, Eng, 53-54; asst scientist, Nat Heart Inst, 54-57; NSF fel, Fac Pharm, Univ Paris, 57-58; res assoc chem, Mass Inst Technol, 58-59; asst prof, Univ Southern Calif, 59-62. *Concurrent Pos:* Mem ed adv bd, J Org Chem, 70-74 & Can J Chem, 75-77; ed, Can J Chem, 82-88. *Mem:* Am Chem Soc. *Res:* Organic nitrogen chemistry; mechanisms of organic reactions, especially alpha-substituted carbonyl compounds. *Mailing Add:* Dept Chem Univ Western Ont London ON N6A 5B7 Can. *Fax:* 519-661-3022

**WARNICK, ALVIN CROPPER,** PHYSIOLOGY OF REPRODUCTION. *Current Pos:* from asst to assoc physiologist, 53-62, physiologist, 62-90, EMER PROF ANIMAL SCI, UNIV FLA, 96- *Personal Data:* b Hinckley, Utah, Nov 15, 20; m 47, Barbara Webster; c John A, Barbara A & Mary W (Dargan). *Educ:* Utah State Agr Col, BS, 42; Univ Wis, MS, 47, PhD(physiol of reproduction), 50. *Prof Exp:* Asst animal husb & genetics, Univ Wis, 46-50; asst prof, Ore State Col, 50-53. *Concurrent Pos:* Animal physiologist, UNFAO, Balcarce, Arg, 63. *Mem:* Fel Am Soc Animal Sci; Am Soc Study Reproduction; Genetic Asn; Sigma Xi; Int Embryo Transfer Soc. *Res:* Physiology of reproduction; effect of nutrition on fertility; estrous synchronization; genetics of reproduction in farm animals. *Mailing Add:* 518 NW 36th St Gainesville FL 32607-2445

**WARNICK, JORDAN EDWARD,** NEUROPHARMACOLOGY. *Current Pos:* asst prof, 74-80, ASSOC PROF PHARMACOL & EXP THERAPEUT, DIR OFF STUDENT RES, SCH MED, UNIV MD, BALTIMORE CITY, 80- *Personal Data:* b Boston, Mass, Mar 21, 42; m 70, Hazel Cohen; c Meredith Nicole. *Educ:* Mass Col Pharm, BS, 63; Purdue Univ, Lafayette, PhD(pharmacol), 68. *Prof Exp:* USPHS trainee pharmacol, Sch Med, State Univ NY, Buffalo, 68-70 & spec awardee, 70-71, asst prof biochem pharmacol, Sch Pharm, 71-74. *Concurrent Pos:* Vis assoc prof physiol, Armed Forces Radiobiol Res Inst, Bethesda, MD, 85-86; vis prof neurosurg, Nat Taiwan Med Ctr, Taipei, Taiwan, 88. *Mem:* AAAS; NY Acad Sci; Am Soc Pharmacol & Exp Therapeut; Soc Neurosci; Soc Biophys; Soc Toxicol. *Res:* Physiology and pharmacology of muscular dystrophy and allied neuromuscular disorders; trophic influence of nerve on muscle; degeneration and regeneration in the peripheral and central nervous systems; pharmacology of neurotoxins; effects of psychoactive drugs on nicotinic receptor-channel complex, hypocampus and spinal cord; pharmacology of anticholinesterases, TRH and related peptides in the central nervous system disorders. *Mailing Add:* Off Stud & Res Sch Med Univ Md 685 W Baltimore St Baltimore MD 21201-1509. *E-Mail:* jwarnick@offsr.ab.umd.edu

**WARNICK, ROBERT ELDREDGE,** NUTRITION. *Current Pos:* lab technician chem anal, 59-60, res asst poultry res, 60-76, RES ASST PROF TURKEY RES, UTAH STATE UNIV, 76- *Personal Data:* b Pleasant Grove, Utah, July 10, 29; m 53; c 6. *Educ:* Brigham Young Univ, BS, 55; Utah State Univ, MS, 63, PhD(poultry nutrit), 70. *Prof Exp:* Agr inspector, Utah State Dept Agr, 58-59. *Mem:* Poultry Sci. *Res:* Nutrition and management of growing turkeys. *Mailing Add:* 310 S 400 E Ephriam UT 84627

**WARNICK, WALTER LEE,** ENVIRONMENTAL EFFECTS OF ACID RAIN. *Current Pos:* engr, 77-85, div dir, Prog Integration Analyisis Div, 85-96, DIR, OFF SCI & TECH INFO, US DEPT ENERGY, 96- *Personal Data:* b Baltimore, Md, May 31, 47; m 70, Metta A Nichter; c Ashlie C & Leah B. *Educ:* Johns Hopkins Univ, BS, 69; Univ Md, MS, 72, PhD(mech eng), 77. *Prof Exp:* Engr, Westinghouse Aerospace, 69-71 & US Naval Res Lab, 71- 77. *Concurrent Pos:* Mem, Aquatics Task Group, Nat Acid Precipitation Assessment Prog, 81-96. *Mem:* Am Soc Mech Engrs; Sigma Xi. *Res:* Critical examination of the causal chain linking human activities to environmental effects. *Mailing Add:* Off Sci & Tech Info US Dept Energy Off Washington DC 20585. *Fax:* 202-586-8054; *E-Mail:* walter.warnick@oer.doe.gov

**WARNKE, DETLEF ANDREAS,** EARTH SCIENCES. *Current Pos:* asst prof, Calif State Univ, 71-73, actg chmn dept, 73-74, assoc prof, 73-77, prof earth sci, 77-80, PROF GEOL SCI, CALIF STATE UNIV, HAYWARD, 80-, CHAIR, 94- *Personal Data:* b Berlin, Ger, Jan 29, 28; div; c 2. *Educ:* Freiburg Univ, dipl, 53; Univ Southern Calif, PhD(geol), 65. *Prof Exp:* Res asst geol, Aachen Tech Univ, 55-56; jr exploitation engr, Shell Oil Co, 57-58; res asst oceanog, Alan Hancock Found, 59-61; from res assoc to asst prof oceanog & geol, Fla State Univ, 65-71. *Concurrent Pos:* Exchange prof, Free Univ Berlin, 80-81; fac res partic, US Geol Surv, 85; Fulbright scholar, Free Univ, Berlin, 87-88. *Mem:* Am Geophys Union; Soc Econ Paleont & Mineral; Ger Geol Union; Geol Soc Am. *Res:* Marine geology; geomorphology; paleoceanography. *Mailing Add:* Dept Geol Sci Calif State Univ Hayward CA 94542. *Fax:* 510-885-2035; *E-Mail:* dwarnke@csuhayward.edu

**WARNOCK, DAVID GENE,** RENAL PHYSIOLOGY & TRANSPORT SYSTEMS. *Current Pos:* CHIEF, DIV NEPHROLOGY, UNIV ALA, 90- *Personal Data:* b Parkes, Ariz, Mai 5, 45. *Educ:* Univ Calif, San Francisco, MD, 70. *Prof Exp:* Assoc prof med & pharmacol, Univ Calif, San Francisco, 82-; chief, Nephrol Sect, Vet Admin Med Ctr, 83-90. *Mem:* AAAS; Am Physiol Soc; Am Soc Clin Invest; Am Soc Nephrology. *Mailing Add:* Div Nephrol Univ Ala UAB Sta Birmingham AL 35294-0007

**WARNOCK, JOHN E,** COMPUTER GRAPHICS. *Current Pos:* CHIEF EXEC OFFICER & CHMN, ADOBE SYSTS, 82- *Educ:* Univ Utah, BS, MS, PhD(elec eng). *Prof Exp:* Prin scientist, Xerox Palo Alton Res Ctr, 78-81. *Concurrent Pos:* Bd dirs, Netscape Commun Corp, Red Brick Systs, Evans & Sutherland; chmn bd, Tech Mus Innovation. *Mem:* Nat Acad Eng. *Res:* Innovator in the field of computer graphics; received 3 patents. *Mailing Add:* Adobe Systs 345 Park Ave San Jose CA 95110

**WARNOCK, JOHN EDWARD,** ZOOLOGY. *Current Pos:* from asst prof to assoc prof, Western Ill Univ, 64-72, prof biol, 72-87, dir, Inst Environ Mgt, 79-87, EMER PROF SCI, WESTERN ILL UNIV, 87- *Personal Data:* b Freeport, Ill, Aug 20, 32; m 55; c 2. *Educ:* Univ Ill, BS, 54; Univ Wis, MS, 58, PhD(zool), 63. *Prof Exp:* Field asst wildlife res, Ill Natural Hist Surv, 54 & Southern Ill Univ & Ill Natural Hist Surv, 54-55; res assoc, Ill Natural Hist Surv & Univ Ill, 62-64. *Mem:* Am Soc Mammal; Wildlife Soc; Sigma Xi. *Res:* Mammalogy; animal behavior; vertebrate ecology; ornithology; ecology of small mammal populations, especially the relationships of behavior, physiological condition, density and physical factors of the environment; biology and management of small game animals. *Mailing Add:* Dept Biol Sci Western Ill Univ Macomb IL 61455

**WARNOCK, LAKEN GUINN,** BIOCHEMISTRY. *Current Pos:* ASST PROF BIOCHEM, VANDERBILT UNIV, 64-; BIOCHEMIST, VET ADMIN HOSP, 64- *Personal Data:* b Newton Falls, Ohio, Apr 19, 28; m 53; c 2. *Educ:* Milligan Col, BS, 57; Vanderbilt Univ, PhD(biochem), 62. *Prof Exp:* Instr biochem, Okla State Univ, 62-64. *Concurrent Pos:* Consult, Interdept Comt Nutrit, Nat Defense Nutrit Surv, Lebanon, 61. *Mem:* Am Inst Nutrit. *Res:* Carbohydrate metabolism in vitamin deficiencies; vitamin nutriture in hemodialysis. *Mailing Add:* Sch Med Vanderbilt Univ 21st Ave S & Garland Nashville TN 37232

**WARNOCK, MARTHA I.,** PATHOLOGY, PULMONARY. *Current Pos:* prof path, 78-89, EMER PROF PATH, UNIV CALIF, SAN FRANCISCO, 89- *Personal Data:* b Detroit, Mich, July 19, 34; m 59; c 2. *Educ:* Oberlin Col, AB, 56; Harvard Univ, MD, 60. *Prof Exp:* From instr to prof path, Univ Chicago, 65-78. *Mem:* AAAS; Am Thoracic Soc; Int Acad Path. *Mailing Add:* HSW501 Univ Calif San Francisco CA 94143-0506

**WARNOCK, ROBERT G,** PARASITOLOGY. *Current Pos:* from asst prof to prof, 63-90, EMER PROF BIOL, WESTMINSTER COL, UTAH, 90- *Personal Data:* b Salt Lake City, Utah, Mar 28, 25; m 48; c 3. *Educ:* Univ Utah, BS, 49, MS, 51, PhD(parasitol), 62. *Hon Degrees:* DSc, Westminster Col, 90. *Prof Exp:* Instr biol, Univ Utah, 62-63. *Mailing Add:* 2941 Delsa Dr Salt Lake City UT 84124

**WARNOCK, ROBERT LEE,** MATHEMATICAL PHYSICS, ACCELERATOR THEORY. *Current Pos:* physicist, 87-95, VIS PHYSICIST, STANFORD LINEAR ACCELERATOR CTR, STANFORD UNIV, 95- *Personal Data:* b Portland, Ore, Feb 20, 30; m 59, Martha Lawall; c Andrew & Kevin. *Educ:* Reed Col, BA, 52; Harvard Univ, AM, 55, PhD(physics), 59. *Prof Exp:* Res assoc, Boston Univ, 59-60 & Univ Wash, Seattle, 60-62; from asst prof to prof theoret physics, Ill Inst Technol, 62-79. *Concurrent Pos:* Asst physicist, Argonne Nat Lab, 64-67, assoc physicist, 67-71; vis scientist, Int Ctr Theoret Physics, Italy, 67; vis prof, Imp Col, Univ London & Univ Bonn, 72; sci assoc, Inst Theoret Phys, Univ Groningen, 76; participating guest, Lawrence Berkeley Lab, 78-87; adj prof theoret physics, Ill Inst Technol, 79- *Mem:* Am Phys Soc; Soc Indust & Appl Math; Am Math Soc. *Res:* Accelerator theory; nonlinear mechanics; electromagnetic theory; nonlinear mathematical physics; elementary particles and fields. *Mailing Add:* SLAC-Bin 26 PO Box 4349 Stanford CA 94309. *Fax:* 650-926-4999; *E-Mail:* warnock@slac.stanford.edu

**WARPEHOSKI, MARTHA ANNA,** ORGANIC CHEMISTRY, POLYMER SCIENCE. *Current Pos:* SCIENTIST, UPJOHN CO, 81- *Personal Data:* b Wausau, Wis, Feb 22, 49; div. *Educ:* Mass Inst Technol, SB, 71, PhD(org chem), 77; Johns Hopkins Univ, MA, 75. *Prof Exp:* Res assoc biomat, Dept Mech Eng, Mass Inst Technol, 77-79. *Mem:* Am Chem Soc; Sigma Xi. *Res:* Biological responses to polymeric materials; properties and modifications of biopolymers; oxidation of organic molecules; chemiluminescence of organic molecules; organic synthesis; medicinal chemistry. *Mailing Add:* Pharmacia & Upjohn 7246-209-6 301 Henrietta St Kalamazoo MI 49001-0199

**WARR, WILLIAM BRUCE,** NEUROANATOMY. *Current Pos:* RES ASSOC & DIR, NEUROANAT LAB, BOYS TOWN NAT RES HOSP, 78-; PROF HUMAN COMMUN, SCH MED, CREIGHTON UNIV, 78- *Personal Data:* b Providence, RI, June 24, 33; wid; c 2. *Educ:* Brown Univ, BA, 57, MA, 58, PhD(physiol psychol), 63. *Prof Exp:* NIH fel neurophysiol & neuroanat, Eaton-Peabody Lab Auditory Physiol, Mass Eye & Ear Infirmary, 63-64, res assoc neurophysiol & neuroanat, 64-67; assoc prof anat, Sch Med, Boston Univ, 67-78. *Concurrent Pos:* Asst, Harvard Med Sch, 67. *Mem:* AAAS; Am Asn Anatomists. *Res:* Neuroanatomy of the auditory system; efferent innervation of the cochlea. *Mailing Add:* Boystown 555 W 30th St Omaha NE 68131

**WARREN, ALAN,** LABORATORY SAFETY. *Current Pos:* int mkt specialist, 72-75, mkt develop specialist, 76-77, RES & DEVELOP OPERS MGR, PQ CORP, 77- *Personal Data:* b Philadelphia, Pa, Dec 20, 36; m 73, Lorraine Benedetto. *Educ:* Univ Pa, BA, 58. *Prof Exp:* Res & develop chemist, Philadelphia Quartz Co, 58-63, tech serv rep, 63-66, res & develop scrv mgr, 66-70, tech serv specialist, 70-72. *Concurrent Pos:* Secy-treas, Synthetic Amorphous Silica & Silicate Indust Asn, 87-88, vchmn, 89-90, chmn, 91-92. *Mem:* Am Inst Chemists; Am Chem Soc; AAAS; Soc Res Adminr; Nat Asn Sci Mat Mgrs. *Res:* Properties and applications of soluble silicates and derivatives. *Mailing Add:* PO Box 17124 Philadelphia PA 19105-7124

**WARREN, BRUCE ALBERT,** pathology, for more information see previous edition

**WARREN, BRUCE ALFRED,** PHYSICAL OCEANOGRAPHY. *Current Pos:* Res asst phys oceanog, 62-63, from asst scientist to assoc scientist, 63-78, SR SCIENTIST, WOODS HOLE OCEANOG INST, 78- *Personal Data:* b Waltham, Mass, May 14, 37. *Educ:* Amherst Col, BA, 58; Mass Inst Technol, PhD(phys oceanog), 62. *Concurrent Pos:* Co-ed, J Phys Oceanog, 80-85. *Mem:* Am Geophys Union; Sigma Xi; Am Meteorol Soc. *Res:* Dynamics of ocean currents; water-mass structures; general ocean circulation. *Mailing Add:* Woods Hole Oceanog Inst Woods Hole MA 02543

**WARREN, CHARLES EDWARD,** ECOLOGY, FISH BIOLOGY. *Current Pos:* RETIRED. *Personal Data:* b Portland, Ore, Oct 26, 26; m 48; c 3. *Educ:* Ore State Col, BS, 49, MS, 51; Univ Calif, PhD(zool), 61. *Prof Exp:* From asst prof to assoc prof fisheries, Ore State Univ, 53-65, prof, 65-; gen coordr biol, Dept Fisheries & Wildlife, Oak Creek Lab, 57-87. *Concurrent Pos:* Actg head, Dept Fisheries & Wildlife, Ore State Univ, 70-74. *Mem:* Sigma Xi. *Res:* Water pollution biology; autecology; population ecology; community ecology; theoretical ecology; resource management; philosophy of science. *Mailing Add:* PO Box 8054 Black Butte Ranch Sisters OR 97759

**WARREN, CHRISTOPHER DAVID,** CARBOHYDRATE CHEMISTRY. *Current Pos:* res fel biol chem, Harvard Med Sch, 69-70, assoc, 70-73, prin assoc biol chem, 73-84, ASSOC PROF BIOL CHEM, HARVARD MED SCH, 84- *Personal Data:* b Luton, Eng, Apr 24, 38; m 66; c 2. *Educ:* Univ Sheffield, BS, 60, PhD(carbohydrate chem), 63; Royal Inst Chem, ARIC, 64. *Prof Exp:* Mem sci staff lipid & carbohydrate chem, Med Res Coun, Nat Inst Med Res, London, 63-69. *Concurrent Pos:* Res fel biochem, Mass Gen Hosp, 69-72, asst biochemist, 72-81, assoc biochemist, 82. *Mem:* Fel Royal Soc Chem; Asn Biol Chemists; AAAS; Soc Complex Carbohydrates; Am Chem Soc. *Res:* Structure, function, biosynthesis, and catabolism of glycoprotein glycans; role of envelope glycoproteins in the pathogenicity of HIV infection;

genetic diseases of complex carbohydrate metabolism; synthetic and natural inhibitors of glycoprotein processing; biochemistry of locoweed toxicosis; biosynthesis of glycosylphosphatidylinositol membrane anchors. *Mailing Add:* Shriver Ctr Ment Retardation 200 Trapello Rd Waltham MA 02254. *Fax:* 617-726-5651

**WARREN, CLAUDE EARL,** ELECTRICAL ENGINEERING. *Current Pos:* from asst prof to prof, 45-81, supvr res found, 46, EMER PROF ELEC ENG, OHIO STATE UNIV, 81- *Personal Data:* b Columbus, Ohio, Jan 11, 14; m 39; c 2. *Educ:* Ohio State Univ, BEE, 38; Mass Inst Technol, MS, 40. *Prof Exp:* Meter tester, Ohio Power Co, 38; asst, Mass Inst Technol, 38-40; engr cent sta, Westinghouse Elec Corp, Pa, 40-45. *Mem:* Sr mem Inst Elec & Electronics Engrs. *Res:* Analog computers; circuit theory. *Mailing Add:* Dept Elec Eng Ohio State Univ 2015 Neil Ave Columbus OH 43210

**WARREN, CLIFFORD A,** ELECTRICAL ENGINEERING. *Current Pos:* RETIRED. *Personal Data:* b Plainfield, NJ, Nov 6, 13. *Educ:* Cooper Union, BSEE, 36; Stevens Inst Technol, MSEE, 49. *Prof Exp:* Exec dir, Bell Tel Labs, Whippany, NJ, 31-76; dir bd, Plantronic, Santa Cruz, Calif, 77-87. *Mem:* Fel Inst Elec & Electronics Engrs. *Mailing Add:* 31 Evergreen Lane Watchung NJ 07060

**WARREN, CRAIG BISHOP,** PHYSICAL ORGANIC CHEMISTRY. *Current Pos:* group leader, Int Flavors & Fragrances, 75-77, sr group leader, 77-80, dir, 80-82, VPRES, INT FLAVORS & FRAGRANCES RES & DEVELOP, 82- *Personal Data:* b Philadelphia, Pa, Oct 21, 39; m 64; c 2. *Educ:* Franklin & Marshall Col, AB, 61; Villanova Univ, BS, 63; Cornell Univ, PhD(phys org chem), 70. *Prof Exp:* Fel prebiol evolution, Corp Res Dept, Monsanto Co, 68-69, sr res chemist, 69-73, res specialist, 73-75. *Mem:* Am Chem Soc; Sigma Xi; Soc Cosmetic Chem; Am Soc Testing & Mat; Indust Res Inst; Am Chemosensory Soc. *Res:* Structure-activity relationships of fragrance molecules; quantitative sensory evaluation of flavors and frangrances; neurochemistry of the olfactory system. *Mailing Add:* Int Flavors & Fragrances 1515 Hwy 36 Union Beach NJ 07735

**WARREN, DAVID HENRY,** earth sciences, applied economic & engineering geology, for more information see previous edition

**WARREN, DONALD W,** DENTISTRY. *Current Pos:* From asst prof to assoc prof dent, Sch Med, Univ NC, Chapel Hill, 63-69, prof dent surg, 69-80, prof dent ecol & chmn dept, 70-85, DIR, CRANIOFACIAL CTR, UNIV NC, CHAPEL HILL, 63-, KENAN PROF, 80-, RES PROF OTOLARYNGOL, 88- *Personal Data:* b Brooklyn, NY, Mar 22, 35; m 56; c 2. *Educ:* Univ NC, BS, 56, DDS, 59; Univ Pa, MS, 61, PhD(physiol), 63. *Hon Degrees:* Dr(odontol), Univ Kuopio, Finland, 91. *Honors & Awards:* Honors & Distinguished Serv Award, Am Cleft Palate-Craniofacial Asn. *Concurrent Pos:* Asst secy gen, Int Cong Cleft Palate, 66-69; consult, Joint Comt Dent & Speech Path-Audiol, Am Dent Asn & Am Speech & Hearing Asn, 67-71; pres, Am Cleft Palate Educ Found, 76-77. *Mem:* Am Dent Asn; Int Asn Dent Res; fel Am Speech & Hearing Asn; Am Cleft Palate Asn (vpres, 67-68, pres, 81-82). *Res:* Physiology of speech; effects of oral-facial disorders on the speech process; effects of breathing on facial morphology; effect of breathing on olfaction. *Mailing Add:* Sch Dent Univ NC CB 7450 Chapel Hill NC 27599-7450

**WARREN, DOUGLAS ROBSON,** OCCUPATIONAL MEDICINE, ENVIRONMENTAL MEDICINE. *Current Pos:* RETIRED. *Personal Data:* b Fenelon Falls, Ont, July 16, 16; m 42; c 1. *Educ:* Univ Toronto, MD, 41, dipl pub health, 47; Can Bd Occup Med, cert, 81. *Prof Exp:* Indust physician & consult, Can, 47-67; dir & partner, Indust Med Consult, Ltd, 67-85. *Concurrent Pos:* Assoc prof indust health, Sch Hyg, Univ Toronto, 67-75, spec lectr, Fac Med, 68-71 & 82-, mem staff hearing conserv course, Div Exten, 69-71; mem, Assoc Comt Sci Criteria Environ Qual, Nat Res Coun Can, 71-78; Can med dir, Occidental Life Calif, 71-81; chmn, Continued Educ Can Coun Occup Med, 75-; mem, Environ Qual Comt, Metrop Toronto Bd Trade, 75-81; exec secy, Occup Med Asn Can & Can Bd Occup Med, 82-90. *Res:* Industrial medicine, related occupational and environmental subjects; hearing conservation and noise control; administration studies related to sickness absence control; metals in the environment and health factors. *Mailing Add:* Lankin Lane PO Box 670 Fenelon Falls ON K0M 1N0 Can

**WARREN, DWIGHT WILLIAM, III,** ENDOCRINOLOGY, REPRODUCTION. *Current Pos:* From instr to assoc prof, 72-88, PROF PHYSIOL & BIOPHYS, UNIV SOUTHERN CALIF, 88- *Personal Data:* b Los Angeles, Calif, Dec 21, 42; m 65; c 1. *Educ:* Univ Calif, AB, 64; Univ Southern Calif, PhD(physiol), 72. *Concurrent Pos:* Consult, Amvac Chem Corp, 79-81; mem, Nat Res Serv sr fel, NIH, 80-81; Fulbright scholar, 90. *Mem:* Endocrine Soc; Soc Study Reproduction; Am Soc Andrology; AAAS; NY Acad Sci. *Res:* Development of the fetal testis and regulation of androgen production by this organ by both internal and external modulators. *Mailing Add:* Dept Physiol & Biophs Med Univ Southern Calif 1333 San Pablo St Los Angeles CA 90033

**WARREN, FRANCIS SHIRLEY,** AGRONOMY. *Current Pos:* RETIRED. *Personal Data:* b Winnipeg, Man, Oct 26, 20; m 43; c 6. *Educ:* Ont Agr Col, BSA, 46; Univ Minn, MSc, 48, PhD(plant genetics & path), 49. *Prof Exp:* Asst corn breeding, Univ Minn, 47-49; res officer, Exp Farm Can Dept Agr, Ont, 49-53, head forage & cereal sect, 53-66, res scientist, Forage Crops Sect, Cent Exp Farm, 66-86. *Mem:* Can Soc Agron; Agr Inst Can. *Res:* Cereal and forage crop production. *Mailing Add:* 45 Rockfield Crest Ottawa ON K2E 5L6 Can

**WARREN, GEORGE FREDERICK,** WEED SCIENCE. *Current Pos:* CONSULT AGR, 79- *Personal Data:* b Ithaca, NY, Sept 23, 13; m 44, Ann Fusek; c Stephen, Virginia & William. *Educ:* Cornell Univ, BS, 35, PhD(veg crops), 45. *Honors & Awards:* Campbell Award, Am Inst Biol Sci, 66; Gold Medal Award, Krakow Poland Hort Soc, 70; Meritorious Honor Award, USAID, 79. *Prof Exp:* Dist county agr agent, Maine, 35-38; asst nutrit veg crops, Cornell Univ, 38-42; asst prof hort, Univ Wis, 45-48; from assoc prof to prof hort, Purdue Univ, 49-79. *Concurrent Pos:* Exec comt mem, Coun Agr Sci & Technol, 75-76, pres, 77-78; hon mem, N Cent Weed Sci Soc. *Mem:* Fel AAAS; fel Weed Sci Soc Am (pres, 64-66); fel Am Soc Hort Sci; Weed Sci Soc Am; Sigma Xi. *Res:* Basis of selective action of herbicides; fate of herbicides in soil; control of weeds in crops. *Mailing Add:* 1130 Cherry Lane West Lafayette IN 47906

**WARREN, GEORGE HARRY,** microbiology, chemotherapy, for more information see previous edition

**WARREN, GUYLYN REA,** MOLECULAR BIOLOGY, ANIMAL GENOME MAPPING. *Current Pos:* res assoc vet res, Mont State Univ, 73-74, asst prof, 74-76, adj asst prof, 76-80, adj assoc prof chem, 80-89, ADJ ASSOC PROF ANIMAL & RANGE SCI, MONT STATE UNIV, 90- *Personal Data:* b Butte, Mont, Aug 16, 41. *Educ:* Mont State Col, BS, 63; Mont State Univ, PhD(genetics), 67. *Prof Exp:* NIH fel radiation repair, Palo Alto Med Res Found, Stanford Univ, 68-70, res assoc, 70-72. *Concurrent Pos:* Prin investr, USDA, 74-76 & 79-81, Mont Air Pollution Study, 78-80, Smelter Environ Res Assoc, 76-77, Proctor & Gamble, 79-81 & NIH Cancer Inst, 80-82; sci consult, Dept Energy, 77-78, NIH, 82-, Nat Inst Environ Health Sci, 83-86, Mont Agr Exp Sta, 90-93. *Mem:* Environ Mutagen Soc; AAAS; Int Soc Animal Genetics. *Res:* Pollution assessment by rapid microbial bioassays; natural products as mutagens or antimutagens; molecular mode of action of metals as mutagens; ovine genome mapping. *Mailing Add:* 4720 Buttleman Rd Willow Creek MT 59760

**WARREN, H(ERBERT) DALE,** ANALYTICAL CHEMISTRY, INORGANIC CHEMISTRY. *Current Pos:* from instr to asst prof, 63-74, ASSOC PROF CHEM, WESTERN MICH UNIV, 74- *Personal Data:* b Houston, Tex, Apr 8, 32; m 56, 82, Sharon Henry; c Christopher. *Educ:* Rice Univ, BA, 54; Univ Idaho, MS, 59; Ore State Univ, PhD(anal chem), 66. *Prof Exp:* Tech grad chem, Hanford Atomic Prod Oper, Gen Elec Co, Wash, 56-58, chemist II, 58, tech librn, 59; tech asst chem, Los Alamos Sci Lab, 61; res asst, Union Oil Res Ctr, Calif, 62. *Mem:* Am Chem Soc; Hist Sci Soc. *Res:* Organic reagents for spectrophotometric analysis; equilibrium constants of coordination compounds; extraction chromatography of inorganic systems; history of chemistry. *Mailing Add:* Dept Chem Western Mich Univ Kalamazoo MI 49008

**WARREN, HALLECK BURKETT, JR,** BACTERIOLOGY. *Current Pos:* RETIRED. *Personal Data:* b St Louis, Mo, Sept 3, 22; m 51, Miriam Rector; c John. *Educ:* Univ St Louis, BS, 43; Univ Ill, MS, 49, PhD(bact), 51. *Prof Exp:* Asst dairy bact, Univ Ill, 49-50; res microbiologist, Res Div, Abbott Labs, 51-57; head bact, Res Labs, Pet Inc, 57-68, mgr food sci & eng, 68-70; mgr food sci, Fairmont Foods Co, 70-72; mgr food sci, Interstate Brands Corp, 72-77, dir food sci & qual assurance, 77-78, vpres & dir tech serv, 78-84. *Mem:* Am Asn Cereal Chem; Am Soc Microbiol; Sigma Xi. *Res:* Microbial physiology of flavor components; bacteriology of foods and dairy products; antibiotic action, production and assay; food preservation. *Mailing Add:* 11021 W 96 Terr Shawnee Mission KS 66214

**WARREN, HAROLD HUBBARD,** ORGANIC CHEMISTRY. *Current Pos:* From instr to prof chem, 50-72, Halford R Clark prof, 72-84, EMER PROF CHEM, WILLIAMS COL, 84- *Personal Data:* b Derry, NH, July 5, 22. *Educ:* Univ NH, BS, 44, MS, 47; Princeton Univ, MA, 49, PhD(chem), 50. *Mem:* Fel AAAS; Am Chem Soc. *Res:* Determination of structure of natural products and synthesis and evaluation of structural variants. *Mailing Add:* 5807 Tidewood Ave Sarasota FL 34231

**WARREN, HARRY VERNEY,** GEOLOGY, MINERALOGY. *Current Pos:* RETIRED. *Personal Data:* b Anacortes, Wash, Aug 27, 04; m 34; c 2. *Educ:* Univ BC, BA, 26, BASc, 27; Oxford Univ, MSc, 28, DPhil, 29. *Hon Degrees:* DSc, Univ Waterloo, 75, Univ BC, 78; FRCGP, Gt Brit, 73. *Prof Exp:* Commonwealth Fund fel, Calif Inst Technol, 29-32; geochem adv, Placer Develop Ltd, Vancouver, 71-74; from lectr to prof, Univ BC, 32-71, prof mineral & petrol, 71- *Concurrent Pos:* Exec mem, BC & Yukon Chamber Mines, 39-, from vpres to pres, 39-54; exec mem, UN Asn Can, 48-, pres, 55-58. *Mem:* Fel Geol Soc Am; Am Inst Mining, Metall & Petrol Eng; fel Royal Soc Can; fel Geol Asn Can; Can Inst Mining & Metall; fel Inst Mining & Metall. *Res:* Lead and zinc deposits in southwestern Europe; precious and base metal relationships in western and North America; rarer metals; precious and base metal deposits of British Columbia; trace elements in relation to mineral exploration, epidemiology and biogeochemistry; relationship existing between geology and health. *Mailing Add:* 1575 Balsam St Apt 301 Vancouver BC V6K 3L7 Can

**WARREN, HERMAN LECIL,** PLANT PATHOLOGY. *Current Pos:* PROF, VA POLYTECH INST & STATE UNIV, 86- *Personal Data:* b Tyler, Tex, Nov 13, 32; m 63; c 3. *Educ:* Prairie View Agr & Mech Col, BS, 53; Mich State Univ, MS, 62; Univ Minn, St Paul, PhD(plant path), 69. *Prof Exp:* Res scientist plant path, Olin Mathieson Chem Corp, 62-67; plant pathologist, Agr Res Serv, USDA, 69-70; adj prof, Purdue Univ, 70-86. *Concurrent Pos:* From asst prof to prof, Purdue Univ, West Lafayette, 71-81; Commonwealth vis prof, Dept Plant Path Phys & Weed Sci, Va Polytech Inst & State Univ,

Blacksburg, Va, 87-88. *Mem:* Am Phytopath Soc; Mycol Soc Am. *Res:* Relationship of soilborne diseases to stalk rot of corn; survival mechanism of soilborne pathogens; effects of light and temperature on spore germination, growth and production of fungi; physiology of host parasites. *Mailing Add:* Dept Plant Path Physiol Weed Sci Va Polytech Inst & State Univ Blacksburg VA 24061-0001

**WARREN, HOLLAND DOUGLAS,** PHYSICS. *Current Pos:* RETIRED. *Personal Data:* b Wilkes Co, NC, July 31, 32; m 55, Nancy Wall; c Douglas, Jill & Karen. *Educ:* Wake Forest Col, BS, 59; Univ Va, MS, 61, PhD(nuclear physics), 63. *Honors & Awards:* I R Award, Res & Develop Magazine, 84. *Prof Exp:* Develop physicist, Celanese Corp Am, 63-64; sr physicist, Babcock & Wilcox Corp, 64-70, res specialist, 70-87, adv engr, 87-92, adv eng, B&W Nuclear Technol, 92-94. *Mem:* Am Phys Soc; Am Nuclear Soc. *Res:* Neutron spectroscopy; nuclear physics; nuclear instrumentation; neutron radiography; reactor instrumentation. *Mailing Add:* 207 Nottingham Circle Lynchburg VA 24502

**WARREN, J(OSEPH) E(MMET),** PETROLEUM ENGINEERING. *Current Pos:* CHMN, FRONTIER RESOURCES INT, 96- *Personal Data:* b Chicago, Ill, Aug 19, 26; wid; c 5. *Educ:* Univ Pittsburgh, BS, 51; Univ Pa, MS, 54, PhD(petrol eng), 60. *Honors & Awards:* Lucas Medal, Soc Petrol Engrs. *Prof Exp:* Res engr, Stanolind Oil & Gas Co, 51-52; res assoc petrol eng, Pa State Univ, 55-56; sect head reservoir eng appln, Gulf Res & Develop Co, 56-63; gen supt reservoirs, Kuwait Oil Co, 63-66; div dir prod, Gulf Res & Develop Co, Pa, 66-67; dept dir explor & prod, 67-70; vpres opers, Santa Fe Int Corp, 70-76; planning adv, Gulf Oil Corp, 76-83; consult petrol, 83-96. *Mem:* Nat Acad Eng; Soc Petrol Engrs; Inst Mgt Sci; Brit Inst Petrol. *Res:* Energy management; economics; production systems; computer applications; optimization methods; transportation. *Mailing Add:* 107 Nantucket Dr Pittsburgh PA 15238. *Fax:* 412-963-9506

**WARREN, JAMES C,** endocrinology, biochemistry, for more information see previous edition

**WARREN, JAMES DONALD,** MEDICINAL CHEMISTRY, SYNTHETIC ORGANIC CHEMISTRY. *Current Pos:* PROF, PARAMUS HIGH SCH, 87- *Personal Data:* b Ludlow, Mass, June 10, 48; m 74. *Educ:* Western New Eng Col, BS, 70; Brown Univ, PhD(chem), 74. *Prof Exp:* Nat Cancer Inst fel, Temple Univ, 73-74; sr res chemist, Lederle Labs, Am Cyanamid Co, 74-78 & Shulton Labs, 78-87. *Mem:* Am Chem Soc. *Res:* Organic synthesis and evaluation of antitumor drug candidates. *Mailing Add:* 40 W Nauraushaun Ave Pearl River NY 10965

**WARREN, JOEL,** cancer research; deceased, see previous edition for last biography

**WARREN, JOHN STANLEY,** GEOLOGY. *Current Pos:* SR SPECTROSCOPIST, DEPT APPL OPTICS, OMEGA OPTICAL, 80- *Personal Data:* b Ithaca, NY, Dec 19, 37; div; c 1. *Educ:* Cornell Univ, BA, 60; Stanford Univ, PhD(geol), 67. *Prof Exp:* Asst prof geol, Univ Cincinnati, 65-72; assoc prof geol, Thomas Jefferson Col, Grand Valley State Col, 72-79; vis fac, Evergreen State Col, 79-80; mem fac, Marlboro Col, 80-82. *Mem:* Paleont Soc; Sigma Xi; AAAS. *Res:* Invertebrate paleontology; micropaleontology; palynology. *Mailing Add:* RD 2 Box 768 East Putney VT 05346

**WARREN, KENNETH S,** tropical medicine; deceased, see previous edition for last biography

**WARREN, KENNETH WAYNE,** WATER TREATMENT, CRUDE OIL PROCESSING. *Current Pos:* sr engr, Natco, 71-80, sr staff engr, 80-82, dir res, develop & combustion eng, 82-90, vpres tech opers, 90-92, VPRES TECHNOL, NATCO, 92- *Personal Data:* b Dallas, Tex, Mar 23, 40; c 3. *Educ:* Baylor Univ, BS, 62, PhD(chem), 68. *Prof Exp:* Sr chemist, Texaco Inc, 68-71. *Mem:* Am Chem Soc; fel Am Inst Chemists; Am Inst Chem Engrs. *Res:* Water purification for both process use & disposal with emphasis on oil/water separation; crude oil processing for oil/water separation especially by electrostatic processes & removal of salt from crude oil; solvent/water separation in hydrometallurgical processes. *Mailing Add:* 2950 N Loop W No 750 Houston TX 77092-8814

**WARREN, LEONARD,** BIOCHEMISTRY, HISTORY OF SCIENCE. *Current Pos:* PROF, DEPT ANAT, UNIV PA, 63-; INST PROF, WISTAR INST, PHILADELPHIA, PA, 75- *Personal Data:* b Toronto, Can, Sept 23, 24; US citizen; m 47, Eve Ruth Yanofsky; c Daniel M, Katherine A & Suzanne E. *Educ:* Univ Toronto, BA, 47, MD, 51; Mass Inst Technol, PhD(biochem), 57. *Hon Degrees:* Dr, Univ Reims, France, 88. *Prof Exp:* Vis scientist biochem, NIH, 57-63. *Concurrent Pos:* Vis scientist, Pasteur Inst, Paris, France, 63-64 & 77-78 & Imp Cancer Res Fund, Eng, 70-71; prof, Am Cancer Soc, 64- *Mem:* Am Soc Biol Chem; Soc Gen Physiologists; Am Asn Cancer Res; Hist Sci Soc. *Res:* Glycoproteins of membrane, in normal and pathological cells (malignancy, metabolic and other diseases); changes in the structure of the carbohydrate groups of glycoproteins with changing conditions; multidrug resistance; lysomal enzymes secretion; history of science society. *Mailing Add:* Wistar Inst 36th & Spruce St Philadelphia PA 19104. *Fax:* 215-898-3868

**WARREN, LIONEL GUSTAVE,** PARASITOLOGY, MOLECULAR BIOLOGY. *Current Pos:* assoc prof med parasitol, 63-79, assoc prof trop med, 77-79, PROF MED PARASITOL & TROP MED, MED CTR, LA STATE UNIV, NEW ORLEANS, 79- *Personal Data:* b New York, NY, May 5, 26; m 52; c 3. *Educ:* Syracuse Univ, AB, 48, MA, 53; Johns Hopkins Univ, ScD, 57. *Prof Exp:* Res assoc biol, Rice Univ, 57-60; vis Int Atomic Energy Agency prof parasitol, Sci Res Inst, Caracas, Venezuela, 60-63. *Concurrent Pos:* USPHS grant, 64-70; scientist, Charity Hosp La, New Orleans, 67-; coordr grad studies, Dept Trop Med, La State Univ Med Ctr, 80-; Pfizer Latin Am grant, 81-82. *Mem:* Am Soc Parasitologists; Am Soc Trop Med & Hyg; Am Soc Cell Biol; Sigma Xi. *Res:* Carbohydrate and oxidative metabolism of endoparasitic animals; immunology of endoparasites; biochemistry of endemic amoebae and related organisms. *Mailing Add:* Dept Microbiol Med Ctr La State Univ 1901 Perdido St Box P6-1 New Orleans LA 70112

**WARREN, LLOYD OLIVER,** ENTOMOLOGY. *Current Pos:* RETIRED. *Personal Data:* b Fayetteville, Ark, Dec 27, 15; m 42; c 3. *Educ:* Univ Ark, BS, 47, MS, 48; Kans State Col, PhD, 54. *Prof Exp:* Instr & jr entomologist, Univ Ark, 47-51; instr entom, Kans State Univ, 53-54; from asst prof & asst entomologist to prof entom & entomologist, Univ Ark, Fayetteville, 54-73, dir, Ark Agr Exp Sta, 73-83. *Concurrent Pos:* Fulbright scholar, Yugoslavia, 72; Off Int Coop & Develop Rev Panel, Greece, 81; NSF Sem Panel, Seoul, Korea, 82. *Mem:* Entom Soc Am; Rice Working Tech Group. *Res:* Forest insects; apiculture. *Mailing Add:* 4333 Bridgewater Lane Fayetteville AR 72703

**WARREN, MCWILSON,** MALARIOLOGY, TROPICAL MEDICINE. *Current Pos:* EXEC DIR, COUN STATE & TERRITORIAL EPIDEMIOLOGISTS, 92- *Personal Data:* b Wayne Co, NC, Aug 29, 29; m 75, Mary Keany; c James R. *Educ:* Univ NC, BA, 51, MSPH, 52; Rice Univ, PhD(parasitol), 57. *Prof Exp:* From asst prof to assoc prof prev med & pub health, Sch Med, Univ Okla, 57-61, vchmn dept, 59-61, scientist, Lab Parasite Chemother, NIH & USPHS, 61-69, Far East Res Proj, Kuala Lumpur, Malaysia, 61-64; officer-in-chg, 63-64, officer-in-chg, Sect Cytol, Chamblee, Ga, 64-65; head sect chemother, Nat Inst Allergy & Infectious Dis, 66-69, parasitologist, Cent Am Malaria Res Sta, Ctr Dis Control, 69-74, scientist dir, 72-79, parasitologist, Vector Biol & Control Div, 74-79, dir, Sci Resource Prog, Ctr Infectious Dis, 85-92; dir, Cent Am Res Sta, El Salvador, 79-81; dir, WHO secretariat for malaria training & appl res, Bur Trop Dis, Kuala Lumpur, Malaysia, 82-85. *Concurrent Pos:* China Med Bd fel trop med, Cent Am, 57; consult var orgns, 66-; res assoc, Sch Trop Med & Hyg, Univ London, 67-68; adj prof, Sch Med, Tulane Univ, 78-; mem, Comt Malaria, Inst Med, 90-91; ed, Am J Trop Med & Hyg, 91- *Mem:* Am Soc Trop Med & Hyg; Am Soc Parasitol; Soc Protozool; Royal Soc Trop Med & Hyg; Am Mosquito Control Asn; Sigma Xi. *Res:* Ecology and immunity of the primate malarias; parasite physiology; pathophysiology of infectious disease agents; global and institutional epidemiology and human ecology; field studies on sero-epidemiology of malaria; genetics of malaria vectors; field problems in chemotherapy of malaria; biology of malaria parasites; technology for community participation in malaria control; training methodologies; management issues in Health Delivery Systems; edpidemiology; disease prevention methodologies; health systems management. *Mailing Add:* 2153 Kodiak Dr NE Atlanta GA 30345. *Fax:* 404-982-0576

**WARREN, MASHURI LAIRD,** SOLAR ENERGY, ENERGY EFFICIENT BUILDINGS & BUILDING CONTROLS. *Current Pos:* PROD MGR, ASI CONTROLS, 88- *Personal Data:* b Findlay, Ohio, Jan 12, 40; m 84; c 2. *Educ:* Ohio Wesleyan Univ, BA, 61; Univ Calif, Berkely, MA, 63, PhD(plasma physics), 68. *Prof Exp:* Asst prof physics, Calif State Univ, Hayward, 68-74; lectr, San Francisco State Univ, 76-78; sci writing, 74-78; staff scientist, Appl Sci Div, Lawrence Berkeley Lab, 78-88. *Mem:* Am Soc Heating, Refrig & Air Conditioning Engrs. *Res:* Solar energy physics; application computer for building energy conservation; control theory and application; computer simulation and analysis; building monitoring. *Mailing Add:* 3270 Theresa Lane Lafayette CA 94549

**WARREN, MITCHUM ELLISON, JR,** ORGANIC CHEMISTRY. *Current Pos:* CONSULT, WARREN ENTERPRISES, 79- *Personal Data:* b Paris, Tenn, Nov 10 34; m 61; c 2. *Educ:* Vanderbilt Univ, BA, 56, PhD(org chem), 63. *Prof Exp:* NIH fel, 63-66; asst prof chem, George Peabody Col, 66-71, assoc prof, 71-79. *Mem:* AAAS; Am Chem Soc. *Res:* Stereochemistry; optically active compounds; alkaloids. *Mailing Add:* 2500 Belmont Blvd Nashville TN 37212-5506

**WARREN, PAUL HORTON,** PLANETOLOGY, GEOCHEMISTRY & ASTROGEOLOGY. *Current Pos:* from asst res to assoc res, 83-93, RES GEOCHEM, UNIV CALIF, LOS ANGELES, 93- *Personal Data:* b Bay Shore, NY, July 19, 53; m 83, Bessie Fong; c Kien. *Educ:* State Univ NY, Oswego, BS, 75; Univ Calif, Los Angeles, PhD(geochem), 79. *Prof Exp:* Fel, Inst Geophys & Planetary Physics, Univ Calif, Los Angeles, 79; fel, Inst Meteoritics, Univ NMex, 79-83. *Concurrent Pos:* Vis prof, Univ Tokyo, 95-96. *Mem:* Fel Meteorit Soc; Mineral Soc Am; Planetary Soc; Geochem Soc; Geol Soc Am; Am Geophys Union. *Res:* Early igneous differentiation of the moon and planets; lunar samples; igneous meteorites; gabbroic-basaltic igneous rocks. *Mailing Add:* Inst Geophys & Planetary Physics Univ Calif 4875 Slichter Hall 405 Hilgard Los Angeles CA 90095-1567. *Fax:* 310-206-3051; *E-Mail:* warren@iapp.ucla.edu

**WARREN, PETER,** MATHEMATICS, COMPUTER SCIENCE. *Current Pos:* dir, Div Data Processing, 85-86, asst prof math, 70-74, ASSOC PROF MATH, UNIV DENVER, 74-, DEAN, UNIV COL, UNIV DENVER, 86- *Personal Data:* b New York, NY, Sept 30, 38; m 84. *Educ:* Univ Calif,

Berkeley, BA, 60; Univ Wis-Madison, MA, 65, PhD(math), 70. *Prof Exp:* Mem tech staff, IBM Nordic Labs, 61-63; invited fel theory of traffic control, Thomas J Watson Res Labs, 64; lectr math, Med Sch, Univ Wis-Madison, 65-66. *Concurrent Pos:* Statist consult, 73-; dir res, Energy Rec Inst, Colo, 78-82. *Mem:* Am Math Soc; Math Asn Am. *Res:* Probability theory; epidemiology; probability theory in Banach spaces; computer graphics. *Mailing Add:* Dean Univ Col Univ Denver 2327 Evans Ave Denver CO 80210-4749

**WARREN, REED PARLEY,** AUTOIMMUNITY, BIOLOGICAL RESPONSE MODIFIERS-IMMUNE-MODULATORS. *Current Pos:* res assoc prof immunol, 82-89, PROF IMMUNOL & BIOL, PERSONS WITH DISABILITIES, UTAH STATE UNIV, LOGAN, 89- *Personal Data:* b Price, Utah, May 6, 42; m 64, Wynema L Walker; c Clifford, Jennifer, Julia, Susan, Spencer & Meredith. *Educ:* Univ Utah, BS, 68, PhD(immunol), 73. *Honors & Awards:* Dwynn Thorne Award. *Prof Exp:* Res asst, Immunol Lab, Univ Utah, Salt Lake City, 69-73; postdoctorate & res assoc immunol, Sch Med, Univ Wash, Seattle, 73-79, res asst prof, 79-82; res scientist, Fred Hutchinson Cancer Res Ctr, Seattle, Wash, 73-82. *Concurrent Pos:* Prin investr, many grants from NIH & pvt sources, 73-; vis prof microbiol, Brigham Young Univ, Provo, Utah, 78; consult, Cell Technol Inc, Boulder, Colo, 83-, HyClone Labs, Logan, Utah, 83-, Pennwalt Corp, Rochester, NY, 84-88, Murdock Int, Springville, Utah, 89-90; mem, Rev Panel, NIMH, 88-; chmn, Inst Rev Bd, Utah State Univ, 88-90. *Mem:* Am Asn Immunol; Nat Autism Soc; AAAS; Inter-Am Soc Chemother. *Res:* Immunologic, viral and genetic studies in infantile autism; development of immune modulators for the treatment of viral infections, immune deficiencies and autoimmunity; more than 150 full-length articles and presentations at national meetings. *Mailing Add:* Ctr Persons with Disabilities Utah State Univ UMC 6895 Logan UT 84322. *Fax:* 435-797-2044; *E-Mail:* medlabecc@usu.edu

**WARREN, RICHARD HAWKS,** MATHEMATICS. *Current Pos:* SR SYSTS ANALYSIS, GEN ELEC CO, 80- *Personal Data:* b Binghamton, NY, Feb 16, 34; m 61; c 2. *Educ:* US Naval Acad, BS, 56; Univ Mich, Ann Arbor, MS, 64; Univ Colo, Boulder, PhD(math), 71. *Prof Exp:* Maintenance officer, USAF, 56-62, from instr to assoc prof math, USAF Acad, 64-69, dep dir, Appl Math Res Lab, Aerospace Res Lab, 72-75, res mathematician, Aerospace Med Res Lab, Wright-Patterson AFB, 76-77, chief, Appl Math Group, Air Force Flight Dynamics Lab, 75-76; assoc prof math, Univ Nebr, Omaha, 77-80. *Mem:* Math Asn Am; Am Math Soc. *Res:* Scheduling theory; operations research; finite mathematics; combinatorics; applied mathematics; complexity theory. *Mailing Add:* 1528 Green Hill Circle Berwyn PA 19312-1918

**WARREN, RICHARD JOSEPH,** ANALYTICAL CHEMISTRY. *Current Pos:* Analytical chemist, Smithkline & French Labs, 56-61, sr analytical chemist, 61-73, sr investr, 73-80, asst dir, 80-83, ASSOC DIR, SCI ADMIN, SMITHKLINE & FRENCH LABS, 83- *Personal Data:* b Lowell, Mass, Dec 25, 31; m 58; c 4. *Educ:* Merrimack Col, BS, 53; Univ Pa, MS, 58. *Mem:* Am Chem Soc; Soc Appl Spectros; AAAS. *Res:* Infrared, ultra violet and nuclear magnetic resonance spectroscopy; mass spectroscopy; x-ray diffraction. *Mailing Add:* 552 Walker Rd Wayne PA 19087-1419

**WARREN, RICHARD JOSEPH,** human genetics, cytogenetics, for more information see previous edition

**WARREN, RICHARD SCOTT,** PLANT PHYSIOLOGY. *Current Pos:* Sigma Xi grant-in-aid res, 70-71, ASST PROF BOT, CONN COL, 70- *Personal Data:* b Malden, Mass, Oct 21, 42; m 67. *Educ:* Defiance Col, BA, 65; Univ NH, MS, 68, PhD(plant sci), 70. *Mem:* AAAS; Bot Soc Am; Am Inst Biol Sci; Sigma Xi. *Res:* Physiological ecology of Halophytes; physiology of disease resistance. *Mailing Add:* Dept Bot Conn Col New London CT 06320

**WARREN, ROBERT HOLMES,** CELL BIOLOGY. *Current Pos:* asst prof biol struct, 71-75, ASSOC PROF ANAT, MED SCH, UNIV MIAMI, 75- *Personal Data:* b Austin, Tex, Feb 20, 41; div. *Educ:* Rice Univ, BA, 62, MA, 63; Harvard Univ, PhD(cell biol), 69. *Prof Exp:* NIH fels, Cambridge Univ, 69-70 & Univ Tex, Austin, 70-71. *Mem:* Am Soc Cell Biol; Soc Develop Biol. *Res:* Ultrastructural and biochemical basis of cell motility. *Mailing Add:* Univ Miami PO Box 016960 Miami FL 33101. *Fax:* 305-545-6166

**WARREN, S REID, JR,** ELECTRICAL ENGINEERING, RADIOLOGIC PHYSICS. *Current Pos:* From instr to prof elec eng, Univ Pa, 33-76, asst vpres eng, 54-73, prof radiol physics, Sch Med, 58-76, EMER PROF ELEC ENG & RADIOL, UNIV PA, 76- *Personal Data:* b Philadelphia, Pa, Jan 31, 08; m 30; c 2. *Educ:* Univ Pa, BS, 28, MS, 29, ScD, 37; Am Bd Radiol, dipl, 47. *Concurrent Pos:* Consult radiol physicist, Vet Admin, Pub Health Serv, Hosps, 36-70. *Mem:* Assoc fel Am Col Radiol; fel Inst Elec & Electronics Engrs; fel AAAS; Soc Hist Technol; Health Physics Soc; Hist Sci Soc; Am Asn Physicists Med. *Res:* Electric circuits and fields; radiologic physics. *Mailing Add:* 3300 Darby Rd Elm 3114 Haverford PA 19041

**WARREN, STEPHEN GEORGE,** SOLAR & INFRARED RADIATION, CLIMATES OF POLAR REGIONS. *Current Pos:* asst prof atmospheric sci & geophys, 82-87, assoc prof, 87-94, PROF ATMOSPHERIC SCI & GEOPHYS, UNIV WASH, 94- *Personal Data:* b Madison, Wis, Sept 20, 45. *Educ:* Cornell Univ, AB, 67; Harvard Univ, AM, 69, PhD(phys chem), 73. *Prof Exp:* Postdoctoral fel, Max-Planck Inst Med Res, Ger, 74-75; Brandeis Univ, 75-77, Nat Ctr Atmospheric Res, 78-79; res fel, Univ Colo, 80-81. *Concurrent Pos:* Vis scientist, Australian Antarctic Div, 88-89 & 96; sta sci leader, South Pole Sta, 92; consult, US-Russ Working Group Arctic Climate, 96- *Mem:* Am Meteorol Soc; Int Glaciological Soc; AAAS; Int Asn Meteorol & Atmospheric Sci. *Res:* Solar and infrared radiation processes in snow, clouds and sea ice; Antarctic climate; global cloud climatology. *Mailing Add:* Univ Wash Box 351640 Seattle WA 98195. *Fax:* 206-543-0308; *E-Mail:* sgw@atmos.washington.edu

**WARREN, STEPHEN THEODORE,** HUMAN MOLECULAR GENETICS, GENETIC DISEASE. *Current Pos:* from asst prof to assoc prof biochem, 85-93, PROF PEDIAT, SCH MED, EMORY UNIV, 85-, W P TIMMIE PROF HUMAN GENETICS, 93- *Personal Data:* b Mich, Nov 30, 53; m 78, Karen Pierce; c Thomas. *Educ:* Mich State Univ, BS, 76, PhD (human genetics), 81; Am Bd Med Genetics, dipl, 87. *Honors & Awards:* Basil O'Conner Award, March of Dimes Nat Found, 86, Albert E Levy Award, 87; NIH Merit Award, 96; William Rosen Res Award, Nat Fragile X Found, 96. *Prof Exp:* Res assoc genetics, Col Med, Univ Ill, 81-83, instr, 83-85. *Concurrent Pos:* collabr, Centre D'Etude de Polymorphisme Humain, 89-; mem, Human Genome Orgn, 91- *Mem:* Am Soc Human Genetics; Am Soc Biochem & Molecular Biol; Am Soc Microbiol; Genetics Soc Am; AAAS; Am Col Med Genetics. *Res:* Human molecular genetics; molecular analysis of the fragile X syndrome; X-linked genetic diseases particulary those mapping to Xq 28; trinudeotide repeat expansion mutations; mental retardation; genome analysis. *Mailing Add:* Dept Biochem Sch Med Emory Univ Atlanta GA 30322. *Fax:* 404-727-5408; *E-Mail:* swarren@bimcore.emory.edu

**WARREN, STEVEN EUGENE,** PHYSICAL ORGANIC CHEMISTRY, MASS SPECTROSCOPY. *Current Pos:* PROF ORG CHEM, SOUTHERN ADVENTIST UNIV, 82-, CHAIR, CHEM DEPT, 85- *Personal Data:* b Southbend, Ind, Nov 20, 49. *Educ:* Andrews Univ, BS, 71; Ariz State Univ, PhD(org chem), 78. *Prof Exp:* Res assoc, Univ Notre Dame, 79-81, fac assoc, 81. *Mem:* Am Chem Soc. *Res:* Synthesizing compounds of potential medical interest. *Mailing Add:* PO Box 1747 Collegedale TN 37315-1747. *Fax:* 423-238-2201; *E-Mail:* warren@southern.edu

**WARREN, WALTER R(AYMOND), JR,** CHEMICAL LASERS, EXPERIMENTAL FLUID DYNAMICS. *Current Pos:* PRES, PAC APPL RES, LOS ANGELES, 81- *Personal Data:* b New York, NY, Nov 25, 29; m 54, Austine R Dougherty; c Michael, Christopher, Walter, Austine, Susan, Richard, Jennifer, John, David & James. *Educ:* NY Univ, BSE, 50; Princeton Univ, MSE, 52, PhD(aeronaut eng), 57. *Prof Exp:* Asst aeronaut eng, Princeton Univ, 50-55; assoc res scientist, Missiles & Space Div, Lockheed Aircraft Corp, 55-56; mgr, Aeromech & Mat Lab, Missile & Space Div, Gen Elec Co, Pa, 56-68; dir, Aerophys Lab, Aerospace Corp, Los Angeles, 68-81. *Concurrent Pos:* Guggenheim fel, Princeton, 52-53; lectr, Univ Pa, 62-68; mem, Fluid Mech Subcomt, NASA, 70; chmn, Plasmadynamics Tech Comt, Am Inst Aeronaut & Astronaut, 71-72; assoc ed, Am Inst Aeronaut & Astronaut J, 72-74. *Mem:* Fel Am Inst Aeronaut & Astronaut. *Res:* High energy lasers; fluid dynamics; plasma dynamics; atmospheric entry; shock tube/tunnel and plasma jet development and application; lasers. *Mailing Add:* 6 Crestwind Dr Rancho Palos Verdes CA 90275. *Fax:* 310-544-0764; *E-Mail:* wrwarren@msn.com

**WARREN, WAYNE HUTCHINSON, JR,** ASTRONOMICAL & ASTROPHYSICAL DATA, COMPUTER APPLICATIONS. *Current Pos:* Nat Acad Sci res assoc, Goddard Space Ctr, 76-77, astronr, Sigma Data Serv Corp, 77-86, prin scientist, ST Systs Corp, Nat Space Sci Data Ctr, 86-92, PRIN SCIENTIST, HUGHES STX COPR, LAB ASTRON SOLAR PHYSICS, GODDARD SPACE FLIGHT CTR, 92- *Personal Data:* b Newark, NJ, Dec 11, 40; m 67; c 3. *Educ:* Fairleigh Dickinson Univ, BA, 68; Ind Univ, MS, 70, PhD(astron), 75. *Concurrent Pos:* Ed, Astron Data Ctr Bull, 80; mem, PACS Oversight Comt, Am Inst Physics, 88, Comt Info Retrieval, 92. *Mem:* Int Astron Union; Am Astron Soc; Astron Soc Pac; Royal Astron Soc; Int Amateur Prof Photoelec Photom Asn; Planetary Soc. *Res:* Computerized astronomical catalogs and retrieval systems; data archive management and dissemination; data center operations; astronomical photometry and spectrophotometry; astronomical documentation and literature. *Mailing Add:* Lab Astron Solar Physics Code 681 NASA Goddard Space Flight Ctr Greenbelt MD 20771. *E-Mail:* w3whw@gibbs.gsfe.nasa.gov

**WARREN, WILLIAM A,** biochemistry, for more information see previous edition

**WARREN, WILLIAM ERNEST,** APPLIED MATHEMATICS, ENGINEERING MECHANICS. *Current Pos:* ASSOC PROF CIVIL ENG, TEX A&M UNIV, 91- *Personal Data:* b Rochester, NY, Aug 11, 30; m 89, Cynthia Frank; c Thomas L & John W. *Educ:* Univ Rochester, BS, 56, MS, 59; Cornell Univ, PhD(eng mech), 62. *Prof Exp:* From instr to asst prof mech & mat, Cornell Univ, 57-62; staff mem, Solid Dynamics Res Dept, Sandia Labs, 62-91. *Concurrent Pos:* Mem, NMex House Rep, 71-78; chmn, Legis Sch Study Comt, 75-76. *Mem:* Am Inst Aeronaut & Astronaut; Am Math Soc; fel Am Soc Mech Engrs; Soc Indust & Appl Math; Am Acad Mech. *Res:* Plane elastic systems; thermal stress concentrations; electric field effects on solid dielectrics, particularly dielectric breakdown; wave propagation; solid-fluid interacting systems. *Mailing Add:* Dept Civil Eng Tex A&M Univ College Station TX 77843-3136. *Fax:* 409-845-6156; *E-Mail:* wew3410@acs.tamu.edu

**WARREN, WILLIAM WILLARD, JR,** NUCLEAR MAGNETIC RESONANCE. *Current Pos:* PROF PHYSICS, ORE STATE UNIV, 91- *Personal Data:* b Seattle, Wash, Nov 7, 38; m 65; c 2. *Educ:* Stanford Univ, BS, 60; Wash Univ, PhD(physics), 65. *Honors & Awards:* US Sr Scientist Award. *Prof Exp:* Asst res physicist, Univ Calif, Los Angeles, 65-68; mem tech staff, AT&T Bell Labs, 68-90. *Concurrent Pos:* Alexander von Humbold Found, 74. *Mem:* AAAS; fel Am Phys Soc; NY Acad Sci. *Res:* Application of nuclear magnetic resonance to the study of electronic structure and atomic dynamics of liquids and solids, especially metals and semiconductors under extreme temperature/pressure conditions; metal-nonmetal transitions in liquids; electronic transport properties of liquids; high Tc superconductivity. *Mailing Add:* Dept Physics Ore State Univ Weniger Hall 313 Corvallis OR 97331. *Fax:* 541-737-1683

**WARRICK, ARTHUR W,** SOIL PHYSICS, MATHEMATICS. *Current Pos:* asst prof, 67-71, assoc prof, 71-81, RES SCIENTIST, AGR EXP STA, UNIV ARIZ, 71-, PROF SOIL PHYSICS, 81- *Personal Data:* b Kellerton, Iowa, Dec 4, 40; m 62, Shan Brothers; c 3. *Educ:* Iowa State Univ, BS, 62, MS, 64, PhD(soil physics), 67. *Prof Exp:* Res assoc soil physics, Iowa State Univ, 66-67. *Mem:* Soil Sci Soc Am; Am Soc Agron; Am Geophys Union. *Res:* Drainage; soil water flow; porous media flow; potential theory. *Mailing Add:* Dept Soil Water & Environ Sci Univ Ariz Tucson AZ 85721-0001

**WARRICK, EARL LEATHEN,** PHYSICAL CHEMISTRY. *Current Pos:* RETIRED. *Personal Data:* b Butler, Pa, Sept 23, 11; m 40, Jean W Davis; c Nancy J & Catherine D. *Educ:* Carnegie Inst Technol, BS, 33, MS, 34, DSc, 43. *Hon Degrees:* DH, Saginaw Valley State Col, 84. *Honors & Awards:* Charles Goodyear Medal & Award, 76. *Prof Exp:* Asst, Mellon Inst Sci, 35-37, fel organosilicon chem, 37-46, sr fel, 46-56; asst dir res, Dow Corning Corp, 57-59, mgr hyper-pure silicon div, 59-62, gen mgr electronic prod div, 62-68, mgr new proj bus, 68-72, sr mgt consult, 72-76. *Concurrent Pos:* Lectr, Univ Pittsburgh, 47-48; interim dean sci & eng technol, Saginaw Valley State Col, 79-80 & 83-84. *Mem:* Am Chem Soc; Sigma Xi. *Res:* Glass composition; chemical kinetics; gas phase; organosilicon and radiation chemistry; physical chemistry of polymers. *Mailing Add:* 508 Crescent Dr Midland MI 48640

**WARRICK, PERCY, JR,** PHYSICAL ORGANIC CHEMISTRY. *Current Pos:* from asst prof to assoc prof, 63-77, PROF CHEM, WESTMINSTER COL, PA, 77- *Personal Data:* b South Bend, Ind, Aug 6, 35; m 61; c 2. *Educ:* Wabash Col, 57; Univ Rochester, PhD(org chem), 61. *Prof Exp:* Fel phys org chem, Univ Minn, 60-62; res assoc, Mass Inst Technol, 62-63. *Concurrent Pos:* Fel, Univ Utah, 70-71; vis prof, Univ Kent, Canterbury, Eng, 78-79. *Mem:* Am Chem Soc; Royal Soc Chem; Sigma Xi. *Res:* Mechanisms of reactions between metals and solutions; general-acid catalysis; relaxation kinetics; acid-base reactions in mixed solvents. *Mailing Add:* 2075 Mercer New Wilmington Rd New Wilmington PA 16142

**WARRINGTON, PATRICK DOUGLAS,** AQUATIC PLANTS DISTRIBUTION & ECOLOGY. *Current Pos:* res officer aerial satellite photog, 73-75, BIOLOGIST, BC GOVT, 75- *Personal Data:* b Winnipeg, Man, Mar 21, 42. *Educ:* Univ BC, BSc, 64, PhD(bot), 70. *Concurrent Pos:* Consult bot, 72-73. *Mem:* Asn Prof Biologists BC. *Res:* All aspects of the biology of aquatic plants; aquatic toxicology. *Mailing Add:* Water Qual Br Parliament Bldg Victoria BC V8V 1X5 Can. *E-Mail:* patwarr@pobox.com

**WARRINGTON, ROBERT O'NEIL, JR,** MECHANICAL ENGINEERING. *Current Pos:* PROF MECH ENG & DEPT HEAD, LA TECH UNIV, RUSTON, 83- *Personal Data:* b Sparta, Wis, Mar 13, 45; m 68, Anne Cabell; c Robert O III, Daniel S & Kristy C. *Educ:* Va Polytech Inst, BS, 67; Univ Tex, EL Paso, MS, 71; Mont State Univ, PhD(mech eng), 75. *Prof Exp:* From instr to assoc prof, Mont State Univ, Bozeman, 75-83. *Concurrent Pos:* Grantee, NSF, Exxon Found, Hewlett-Packard Corp, CE & Dept Energy, 75-; consult, Atlas Processing Co, Shreveport, 84- *Mem:* Am Soc Mech Engrs; Am Soc Eng Educ. *Res:* Mechanical engineering. *Mailing Add:* 700 Hundred Oaks Dr Ruston LA 71270

**WARRINGTON, TERRELL L,** PHYSICAL CHEMISTRY, BIOCHEMISTRY. *Current Pos:* ASST PROF CHEM, MICH TECHNOL UNIV, 67- *Personal Data:* b Baltimore, Md, June 5, 40; m 64. *Educ:* Yale Univ, BA, 61; Purdue Univ, PhD(phys chem), 66. *Mem:* Am Chem Soc. *Res:* Physical chemistry of biological macromolecules concentrating mainly on conformational studies. *Mailing Add:* Dept Chem & Chem Eng Mich Technol Univ Houghton MI 49931-1295

**WARSHAUER, STEVEN MICHAEL,** PALEOECOLOGY. *Current Pos:* SR GEOLOGIST, BRIT GAS, 89- *Personal Data:* b New York, NY, May 20, 45; c 2. *Educ:* Queens Col, NY, BA, 67; Univ Cincinnati, MS, 69, PhD(geol), 73. *Prof Exp:* Asst prof geol, WVa Univ, 72-77, assoc prof, 77-81; explor geologist, Tenneco Oil, 81-83, sr explor geologist, 83-89. *Concurrent Pos:* Consult, WVa Geol Econ Surv, Champlin Petrol, Dept Energy, Amoco Oil & US Geol Surv. *Mem:* Am Asn Petrol Geologists; Soc Econ Paleontologists & Minerologists; Sigma Xi. *Res:* Carbonate depositional models; multivariate statistical methods in analyzing geologic data. *Mailing Add:* Brit Gas 6634 Gentle Bend Dr Houston TX 77069

**WARSHAW, ISRAEL,** MATERIALS SCIENCE. *Current Pos:* CONSULT, 90- *Personal Data:* b Brooklyn, NY, Nov 30, 25; m 48. *Educ:* Alfred Univ, BA, 51; Pa State Univ, MS, 53, PhD, 61. *Prof Exp:* Sci aide & chem lab asst, Water Resources Br, US Geol Surv, 42-43, chem lab asst, Geochem & Petrol Br, 46-51, chemist, 51-53; asst geochem, Pa State Univ, 51-53 & 57-58; group leader, Glass Res Labs, Pittsburgh Plate Glass Co, 53-57; assoc res dir, Tem-Pres Res, Inc, Pa, 59-60; assoc prog dir, NSF, 60-63, dir eng mat prog, 63-71, actg dir, Eng Div, 71-74, dep dir, 72-76; phys sci adminr, Dept Energy, 77-90. *Concurrent Pos:* Lectr, Univ Pittsburgh, 56-57. *Res:* Phase equilibrium studies of silicate, aluminate and oxide systems at high temperatures and pressures; synthesis of refractory compounds, particularly those of the rare earths; silicate glasses; materials research. *Mailing Add:* 3703 Stewart Dr Chevy Chase MD 20815

**WARSHAW, JOSEPH B,** PEDIATRICS. *Current Pos:* chief pediat, 87-93, CHMN, DEPT PEDIAT, YALE UNIV, 87-, DEP PHYSICIAN-IN-CHIEF, CHILDREN'S HOSP, 93-, DEAN CLIN AFFAIRS & PROF PEDIAT, SCH MED, 95- *Personal Data:* b Miami, Fla, July 17, 36. *Educ:* Univ Fla, BS, 57; Duke Univ, MD, 61. *Honors & Awards:* David Smith Lectr, Western Soc Pediat Res, 86; United Cerebral Palsy Found Lectr, 88; Howland Lectr, Johns Hopkins Sch Med, 89; Townsend Lectr, Univ Rochester, 90, Richard Ham Lectr, 93; Helen S Jones Lectr, Mass Gen Hosp, 94. *Prof Exp:* Fac, Harvard Med Sch, 67-73; dir, Div Perinatal Med & prof pediat, obstet & gynec, Yale Med Sch, 73-82; George L MacGregor prof & chmn, Dept Pediat, Health Sci Ctr, Univ Tex, Dallas, 82-87. *Concurrent Pos:* Josiah Macy scholar, Univ Oxford, 79-80; mem adv coun, Nat Inst Child Health & Human Develop, NIH, 87-91; mem coun, Am Pediat Soc, 87-; mem sci adv bd, St Jude's Children's Res Hosp; trustee, Int Pediat Res Found; vis lectr, Univ Col Health Sci Ctr, 94; vis scholar, Develop Biol Unit, Dept Zool, Imp Cancer Res Ctr, Oxford Univ, 95. *Mem:* Inst Med-Nat Acad Sci; Am Soc Clin Invest; Asn Am Physicians; Soc Pediat Res (pres, 81-82); Am Pediat Soc; Am Soc Biol Chemists; Am Soc Cell Biol; fel Am Acad Pediat; Am Soc Develop Biol; Sigma Xi. *Res:* Developmental biology; neonatal and perinatal medicine. *Mailing Add:* Dept Pediat Sch Med Yale Univ 333 Cedar St New Haven CT 06250-8064

**WARSHAW, STANLEY I(RVING),** PRODUCT ENGINEERING, MATERIAL SCIENCE & STANDARDS. *Current Pos:* DIR STAND, NAT INST STAND & TECHNOL, 90- *Personal Data:* b Boston, Mass, Nov 5, 31; m 92, Wanda F Capato; c Karen B. *Educ:* Ga Inst Technol, BCerE, 57; Mass Inst Technol, ScD, 61. *Prof Exp:* Res asst, Ga Inst Technol, 56-57 & Mass Inst Technol, 57-61; sr res scientist, Raytheon Mfg Co, 61-64; res supvr, Ceramics & Metall Sect, Am Stand Inc, 64-68, mgr ceramic technol, Res & Develop Ctr, 68-69, mgr mat & chem dept, 69-72, gen mgr, Prod Develop & Eng Lab, 72-75; dir, Ctr Consumer Prod Technol, Nat Bur Stand, 75-80, dir, Off Stand Policy, 81-87, assoc dir indust & stand, 87-89. *Concurrent Pos:* Sr policy adv, Stand & Technol, 90- *Mem:* Sigma Xi; fel NY Acad Sci; Inst Elec & Electronics Engrs; Am Soc Testing & Mat; Am Soc Mech Engrs. *Res:* Product design; standards and conformity assessment. *Mailing Add:* Nat Inst Stand & Technol North Rm 326 Gaithersburg MD 20899. *Fax:* 301-963-2871; *E-Mail:* stanley.warshaw@nist.gov

**WARSHAW, STEPHEN I,** COMPUTATIONAL PHYSICS, AEROACOUSTICS. *Current Pos:* SR PHYSICIST, LAWRENCE LIVERMORE NAT LAB, UNIV CALIF, 68- *Personal Data:* b New York, NY, Mar 26, 39; m 64, Harriet Golden; c 2. *Educ:* Polytech Inst Brooklyn, BSc, 60; Johns Hopkins Univ, PhD(physics), 66. *Prof Exp:* Jr instr physics, Johns Hopkins Univ, 60-63, res asst, 63-66; res assoc, Univ Ill, Urbana-Champaign, 66-68. *Mem:* Am Phys Soc; Acoust Soc Am; Am Geophys Union. *Res:* Experimental low energy nuclear physics; computer modeling of hydrodynamic phenomena; theoretical atmospheric acoustics; computer code solutions to mathematical and physical problems; interpolation methods; ionospheric radio propagation theory and simulation; nuclear reaction applications; remote sensing research. *Mailing Add:* Lawrence Livermore Nat Lab L-59 Univ Calif PO Box 808 Livermore CA 94551. *E-Mail:* warshaw@llnl.gov, siw@well.com

**WARSHAWSKY, HERSHEY,** HISTOLOGY. *Current Pos:* from asst prof to assoc prof, 67-77, PROF ANAT, MCGILL UNIV, 77- *Personal Data:* b Montreal, Que, Feb 6, 38; m 60, Goldie Kaplansky; c Bryna F, Avrum S & Paul J. *Educ:* Sir George Williams Univ, BSc, 59; McGill Univ, MSc, 61, PhD(anat), 66. *Hon Degrees:* Dr Odont, Royal Dent Col, Aarhus, Denmark, 92. *Honors & Awards:* Res Oral Biol Award, Int Asn Dent Res, 92. *Prof Exp:* Lectr anat, McGill Univ, 63-66; res fel orthop res, Harvard Univ, 66-67. *Concurrent Pos:* Vis prof, Univ Sao Paulo, Royal Dent Col, Aarhus, Denmark, State Univ Compinas, Brazil, Univ Queensland, Brisbane, Australia. *Mem:* Am Asn Anat; Can Asn Anat. *Res:* Use of the enamel organ in the rat incisor as a model system for structural and radioautographic studies of secretory processes, cell renewal, mineralization and growth factor receptors. *Mailing Add:* Dept Anat & Cell Biol McGill Univ 3640 University St Montreal PQ H3A 2B2 Can. *Fax:* 514-398-5047

**WARSHAWSKY, JAY,** ELECTRICAL ENGINEERING. *Current Pos:* RETIRED. *Personal Data:* b Chicago, Ill, Mar 27, 27; m 54; c 3. *Educ:* Ill Inst Technol, BS, 48; Purdue Univ, MS, 50; Northwestern Univ, PhD(elec eng, biomed eng), 63. *Prof Exp:* Dir servomech sect, Cook Res Labs, 51-56; tech dir mech res div, Am Mach & Foundry Co & Gen Am Transp Corp, 56-65; dir res & develop, Fuller Co, GATX Corp, 65-77, vpres res & develop, 77-; assoc dir, Mgt Tech Group, Carnegie Mellon Res Inst, Carnegie Mellon Univ, 88-93. *Concurrent Pos:* Lectr, Grad Sch, Ill Inst Technol, 54, lectr, Med Sch, 63, res asst, 63. *Mem:* AAAS; Inst Elec & Electronics Engrs; Air Pollution Control Asn; Water Pollution Control Fedn; Instrument Soc Am; Sigma Xi. *Res:* Automatic control systems; analog and digital computers; electronic instrumentation; accommodation in the human eye; automatic focusing devices; physiological optics. *Mailing Add:* 3142 Woodlane Ave Orefield PA 18069-2330

**WARSHAY, MARVIN,** ELECTROCHEMICAL SYSTEMS, ENERGY TECHNOLOGY. *Current Pos:* res engr, Lewis Res Ctr, NASA, 62-78, mgr fuel cell proj, Dept Energy, 76-87, chief, Solar Dynamics & Thermal Mgt Br, 87-89, CHIEF, ELECTROCHEM TECHNOL BR, NASA, 89- *Personal Data:* b Tel Aviv, Israel, Jan 12, 34; US citizen; m 62; c 3. *Educ:* Rensselaer Polytech Inst, BChE, 55; Ill Inst Technol, MS, 57, PhD(chem eng), 60. *Prof Exp:* Res engr, Esso Res & Eng Co, 60-62. *Concurrent Pos:* Lectr, Cleveland State Univ, 67-, adj prof chem eng, 74- *Mem:* Am Chem Soc; Am Inst Chem Engrs; Electrochem Soc; Sigma Xi. *Res:* Drop motion; chemical reactions in nozzles; chemical reactions and colloidal phenomena in oil additive formation and in muffler corrosion; shock tubes; high temperature chemical kinetics of gases; electrochemical systems; batteries; fuel cells. *Mailing Add:* 3652 Latimore Rd Beachwood OH 44122

**WARSHEL, ARIEH,** CHEMICAL PHYSICS, MOLECULAR BIOLOGY. *Current Pos:* from asst prof to assoc prof, 76-84, PROF CHEM, UNIV SOUTHERN CALIF, 84- *Personal Data:* b Sde-Nahom, Israel, Nov 20, 40; m 66; c 2. *Educ:* Israel Inst Technol, BSc, 66; Wiezmann Inst Sci, MSc, 67, PhD(chem), 69. *Prof Exp:* Res assoc chem, Harvard Univ, 70-72; res assoc, Wiezmann Inst, 72-73, sr scientist, 73-74; vis scientist, Med Res Coun Lab Molecular Biol, Cambridge, Eng, 74-76. *Res:* Theoretical study of the early steps of the visual process; resonance Raman of large molecules; simulation of protein folding; simulation of enzymatic reactions; simulation of electron transfer reactions. *Mailing Add:* Dept Chem Univ Southern Calif Los Angeles CA 90089-0001

**WARSHOWSKY, BENJAMIN,** analytical chemistry; deceased, see previous edition for last biography

**WARSI, NAZIR AHMED,** MATHEMATICAL PHYSICS. *Current Pos:* prof physics & math, 64-66, PROF MATH, ATLANTA UNIV, 66-, ACTG CHMN DEPT, 70- *Personal Data:* b Sheopur, Uttar Pradesh, India, June 30, 39; m 66. *Educ:* St Andrew's Col, Gorakhpur, India, BSc, 57; Gorakhpur Univ, MSc, 59, PhD(shock wave), 61. *Prof Exp:* Asst prof math, Gorakhpur Univ, India, 59-63; assoc prof physics & math, Savannah State Col, 63-64. *Mem:* Am Math Soc; Tensor Soc. *Res:* Shock waves in ideal and magneto-gas-dynamic flows; nonlinear functional analysis; optimization. *Mailing Add:* Dept Comput Sci Clark Atlanta Univ 223 James Brawley SW Atlanta GA 30314-4358

**WARSI, ZAHIR U A,** APPLIED MATHEMATICS, FLUID DYNAMICS. *Personal Data:* b Uttar Pradesh, India, July 7, 36; m 58, Amina; c 5. *Educ:* Univ Lucknow, BSc, 54, MSc, 56, PhD(math), 65. *Honors & Awards:* Am Soc Eng Educ Res Award, 75; Von Karmen Inst Fluid Dynamics Award, 84. *Prof Exp:* Scientist, Cent Bldg Res Inst, Roorkee, India, 62-67; fel aerodyn, Miss State Univ, 67-70, from asst prof to prof, 70-80, Hearin-Hess prof aerospace eng, 89-90, 92-93 & 96. *Concurrent Pos:* Minna-James-Heineman Found. *Mem:* Sigma Xi; Am Inst Aeronaut & Astronaut; Am Acad Mech. *Res:* Analytical and numerical fluid dynamics; solutions of compressible and turbulent incompressible flow equations in general coordinates; mathematical theories in coordinate generation; turbulence modeling; continuum mech. *Mailing Add:* Dept Aerospace Eng Miss State Univ Drawer A Mississippi State MS 39762. *Fax:* 601-325-7730; *E-Mail:* warsi@ae.msstate.edu

**WARTELL, ROGER MARTIN,** BIOPHYSICS, MOLECULAR BIOLOGY. *Current Pos:* from asst prof to prof physics & biol & asst dir, Sch Physics, 74-86, CHAIR, SCH BIOL, GA INST TECHNOL, 90- *Personal Data:* b New York, NY, Feb 24, 45; m 68; c 2. *Educ:* Stevens Inst Technol, BSc, 66; Univ Rochester, PhD(physics), 71. *Prof Exp:* NIH fel & res assoc biochem, Univ Wis-Madison, 71-73. *Concurrent Pos:* Vis prof, Univ Wis-Madison, 78-79; NIH career develop award, 79-84; vis scholar, NIH, 86-87. *Mem:* Biophys Soc. *Res:* Conformational properties of DNA and RNA; influence of cooperative interactions; temperature gradient gel electrophoresis. *Mailing Add:* Sch Biol Ga Inst Technol Atlanta GA 30332

**WARTER, JANET KIRCHNER,** PALYNOLOGY, SCIENCE EDUCATION. *Current Pos:* RETIRED. *Personal Data:* b Greensburg, Pa, July 27, 33; m 62, Stuart L. *Educ:* Pa State Univ, BS, 55, MEd, 60; La State Univ, PhD(bot), 65. *Prof Exp:* Lectr bot, Calif State Col, Fullerton, 65-66; lectr geol, Calif State Univ, Long Beach, 66-68 & 70-93. *Concurrent Pos:* Res assoc, Los Angeles Co Mus Natural Hist. *Mem:* Am Asn Stratig Palynologists. *Res:* Tertiary palynology; Pleistocene seeds and pollen; archeological macro-plant analysis. *Mailing Add:* 17841 Still Harbor Lane Huntington Beach CA 92647-6440

**WARTER, STUART L,** ORNITHOLOGY, VERTEBRATE PALEONTOLOGY. *Current Pos:* from asst prof to assoc prof, 65-75, PROF BIOL, CALIF STATE UNIV, LONG BEACH, 75- *Personal Data:* b New York, NY, Apr 9, 34; m 62. *Educ:* Univ Miami, Fla, BS, 56, MS, 58; La State Univ, PhD(zool), 65. *Prof Exp:* Instr zool, La State Univ, 64-65. *Concurrent Pos:* Res assoc vert paleont, Los Angeles Co Mus Natural Hist, 66- *Mem:* Am Ornith Union; Cooper Ornith Soc; Wilson Ornith Soc; Soc Vert Paleont. *Res:* Avian paleontology, morphology and systematics; osteology and relationships of suboscine passerine birds. *Mailing Add:* Dept Biol Calif State Univ Long Beach 3702 Csulb Long Beach CA 90840-0004

**WARTERS, RAYMOND LEON,** MOLECULAR & CELLULAR BIOLOGY, RADIATION BIOLOGY. *Current Pos:* Nat Cancer Inst fel, 76-78, from res asst prof to res assoc prof, 78-86, assoc prof, 86-92, PROF RADIOL, UNIV UTAH, 92- *Personal Data:* b Atlanta, Ga, Nov 22, 45; m 78, LaNetta. *Educ:* Emory Univ, BA, 67; Fla State Univ, MS, 72, PhD(molecular & cellular biol), 76. *Concurrent Pos:* Assoc ed, Radiation Res, 90-94. *Mem:* Sigma Xi; Radiation Res Soc; Am Soc Cell Biol; AAAS; Am Cancer Soc. *Res:* Effect of enviromental agents, including radiations and chemicals, on molecular and cellular biology and biochemistry, especially with respect to the eukaryotic genetic apparatus. *Mailing Add:* Dept Radiol Univ Utah Col Med 50 N Medical Dr Salt Lake City UT 84132-0001. *Fax:* 801-581-2414; *E-Mail:* rwarters@rad.med.utah.edu

**WARTERS, WILLIAM DENNIS,** MICROWAVE ELECTRONICS. *Current Pos:* CONSULT, 89- *Personal Data:* b Des Moines, Iowa, Mar 22, 28; m 52, Margaret Reimer; c John B & William D Jr. *Educ:* Harvard Univ, AB, 49; Calif Inst Technol, MS, 50, PhD(physics), 53. *Hon Degrees:* LLD, Monmouth Col, 86. *Prof Exp:* Asst, Calif Inst Technol, 50-52; mem tech staff guided wave res, Bell Tel Labs, Inc, 53-61, head repeater res dept, 61-67, dir transmission systs res ctr, 67-69, exec dir tech, Staff Employ, Educ & Salary Admin Div, 69-70, dir, Millimeter Wave Syst Lab, 70-76, dir, Toll Transmission Lab, 76-80, dir, Satellite Transmission Lab, 80-83; asst vpres, Network Technol Res Lab, Bell Commun Res, Inc, 84-89. *Mem:* Am Phys Soc; fel Inst Elec & Electronics Engrs. *Res:* Multi-mode wave guides; millimeter waves; microwaves; transmission systems; communications satellites, fiber optics. *Mailing Add:* 236 Sunnyside Rd Lincroft NJ 07738

**WARTHEN, JOHN DAVID, JR,** NATURAL PRODUCT CHEMISTRY. *Current Pos:* RES CHEMIST, AGR RES SERV, USDA, 65- *Personal Data:* b Baltimore, Md, Mar 8, 39; m 69, Constance Mumma; c Jacqueline N & Angela M. *Educ:* Univ Md, BS, 60, PhD(pharmaceut chem), 66. *Mem:* Am Chem Soc. *Res:* Isolation and identification of phytochemicals; insect attractants, antifeedants, repellants and insecticides. *Mailing Add:* 4413 Rendale Ct Olney MD 20832-1829

**WARTIK, THOMAS,** INORGANIC CHEMISTRY. *Current Pos:* RETIRED. *Personal Data:* b Cincinnati, Ohio, Oct 1, 21; m 52; c 2. *Educ:* Univ Cincinnati, AB, 43; Univ Chicago, PhD(chem), 49. *Prof Exp:* From asst prof to prof chem & head dept, Pa State Univ, 50-71, dean col sci, 71-87. *Concurrent Pos:* Vis scientist, Radiation Lab, Univ Calif, 57, 59 & 61; mem, Fulbright selection comt chem, Nat Acad Sci-Nat Res Coun, 66-72, chmn, 70-72; mem adv bd, Am Chem Soc-Petrol Res Fund, 68-71; consult, Radiation Lab, Callery Chem Co, Koppers Co, Inc & NY Bd Regents, 73-74. *Mem:* Fel AAAS; Am Chem Soc. *Res:* Chemistry of boron and aluminum compounds; light metal hydrides; organometallic chemistry. *Mailing Add:* 120 Davey Lab University Park PA 16802-6302

**WARTOFSKY, LEONARD,** INTERNAL MEDICINE, ENDOCRINOLOGY. *Current Pos:* CHIEF ENDOCRINOL METAB SERV, WALTER REED ARMY MED CTR, WASHINGTON, DC, 76-; PROF MED & COORDR, ENDOCRINOL DIV, UNIFORMED SERV UNIV HEALTH SCI, 80- *Personal Data:* b New York, NY, July 14, 37; m 59; c 1. *Educ:* George Washington Univ, BS, 59, MS, 61, MD, 64. *Concurrent Pos:* Mem, endocrinol study sect, NIH, 77-85; gov, Am Col Physicians, 82-87; clin prof med, Georgetown Univ Sch Med, 84. *Mem:* Am Thyroid Asn (vpres); Am Col Physicians; Endocrine Soc; Am Soc Clin Invest; Am Fedn Clin Res. *Res:* Physiology of thyroid gland; pathophysiology of disorders of the thyroid. *Mailing Add:* Wash Hosp Ctr Chem Dept Med 110 Irving St NW Washington DC 20010-2975. *Fax:* 202-576-3787

**WARTZOK, DOUGLAS,** MARINE MAMMAL BEHAVIOR & ECOLOGY. *Current Pos:* ASSOC VCHANCELLOR & DEAN GRAD SCH, UNIV MO, ST LOUIS, 91- *Personal Data:* b Lansing, Mich, May 10, 42; m 66, Susan Gibson. *Educ:* Andrews Univ, BA, 63; Univ Ill, MS, 65; Johns Hopkins Univ, PhD(biophys), 71. *Prof Exp:* Asst prof pathobiol & pop biol, Johns Hopkins Univ, 72-78, assoc prof immunol & infectious dis, dis ecol, 78-84, dir, Div Ecol, 79-82; prof & chmn dept biol sci, Purdue Univ, Ind, 83-91. *Concurrent Pos:* Prin investr, NSF, Off Naval Res, NASA & var other orgns, 75-; invited expert, Int Coun Exploration of the Sea, 81; vis prof, Inst Marine Sci, Univ Alaska, 83; ed-in-chief, Marine Mammal Sci, 87-96, emer ed, 96- *Mem:* Soc Marine Mammal. *Res:* Physiological ecology, behavior, population structure and sensory physiology of marine mammals; sensory components of under-ice navigation of ringed seals; behaviors and movements of bowhead whales in response to industrial activities. *Mailing Add:* Grad Sch Univ Mo St Louis MO 63121-4499. *E-Mail:* sdwartz@umslvma.umsl.edu

**WARWICK, JAMES WALTER,** RADIO ASTRONOMY. *Current Pos:* mem sr sci staff, High Altitude Observ, 55-61, PROF ASTRO-GEOPHYS, UNIV COLO, BOULDER, 61- *Personal Data:* b Toledo, Ohio, May 22, 24; m 47, 66; c 6. *Educ:* Harvard Univ, AB, 47, AM, 48, PhD(astron), 51. *Prof Exp:* Asst prof astron, Wellesley Col, 50-52; mem res staff, Sacramento Peak Observ, 52-55. *Concurrent Pos:* Prin investr, Voyager Missions Planetary Radio Astron Exp, NASA, 73-88. *Mem:* Am Astron Soc; AAAS; Am Geophys Union. *Res:* Theoretical astrophysics; stellar and planetary magnetism; solar physics; solar-terrestrial physics. *Mailing Add:* 3845 E Northbrook Dr Boulder CO 80304

**WARWICK, SUZANNE IRENE,** PLANT TAXONOMY, POPULATION BIOLOGY. *Current Pos:* SR RES SCIENTIST, CTR LAND & BIOL RESOURCES RES, AGR CAN, 77- *Personal Data:* b Winnipeg Beach, Man, Dec 10, 52; m 91. *Educ:* Univ Man, BSc, 74; Univ Cambridge, Eng, PhD(bot), 77. *Concurrent Pos:* Adj prof, MacDonald Col, Univ McGill, 85-87 & Univ Ottawa, 85- *Mem:* Can Bot Asn; Am Bot Soc. *Res:* Crucifer taxonomy and molecular systematics; genetic diversity of cruciferous crops and wild allies. *Mailing Add:* Ctr Land & Biol Resources Res Agr Can K W Neatby Bldg CEF Ottawa ON K1A 0C6 Can. *Fax:* 613-759-1924; *E-Mail:* warwicks@em.agr.ca

**WARWICK, WARREN J,** PEDIATRICS, PULMONOLOGY. *Current Pos:* Med fel pediat, Univ Minn, Minneapolis, 55-57, med fel specialist, 59-60, from instr to assoc prof pediat, 60-78, PROF PEDIAT, UNIV MINN, MINNEAPOLIS, 78- *Personal Data:* b Racine, Wis, Jan 27, 28; m 52; c Anne (Coleman) & Marion. *Educ:* St Olaf Col, BA, 50; Univ Minn, MD, 54. *Concurrent Pos:* Alpha Omega Phi fel cardiovasc res, 55-57; Am Heart Asn res fel, 59-60; USPHS res career develop award, 61-66; mem, Ctr Prog Comt, Nat Cystic Fibrosis Res Found, 64-66, chmn, Med Care Comt, 66-71, Coop Study Comt, 71-72; mem exec bd, Sci-Med Comt, Int Cystic Fibrosis (Mucoviscidosis) Asn, 70-80; mem, Nat Data Registry Comt, Cystic Fibrosis Found, 72-86, Annalisa Marzotto chair Cystic fibrosis, 89. *Mem:* Am Pediat Soc; Soc Pediat Res; Am Soc Invest Path. *Res:* Pulmonary diseases; experimental pathology; immunology; cystic fibrosis; bioengineering; medical physics. *Mailing Add:* Dept Pediat Univ Minn PO Box 184 Minneapolis MN 55455

**WARZEL, L(AWRENCE) A(LFRED),** CHEMICAL ENGINEERING. *Current Pos:* AT DEPT PETROL & GEOL, UNIV OKLA, NORMAN. *Personal Data:* b Ft Scott, Kans, Sept 26, 25; m 50; c 3. *Educ:* Univ Tulsa, BS, 47; Univ Mich, MS, 52, PhD(chem eng), 55. *Prof Exp:* Res proj engr, Ethyl Corp, 47-51; res assoc, Eng Res Inst, Univ Mich, 53-55; theoret develop engr, Phillips Petrol Co, NY, 55-60, sect mgr, 60-65, tech rep proj develop, Int Dept, 65-68, sr proj mgr, NJ, 68-76, sr proj mgr, Okla, 76- *Mem:* AAAS; Am Chem Soc; Am Inst Chem Engrs. *Res:* Mass transfer; separations; systems engineering; phase equilibria; thermodynamics; mathematical analysis of engineering data and scale-up problems; international projects development. *Mailing Add:* PO Box 1131 Bartlesville OK 74005-1131

**WASA, KIYOTAKA,** CATHODIC SPUTTERING TECHNOLOGY. *Current Pos:* Researcher mat, Wireless Res Labs, Matsushita Elec, 60-75, sr researcher, Mat Res Labs, 76-81, chief researcher, Cent Res Labs, 81-83, res dir, 83-88, VPRES, MATSUSHITA ELEC CO LTD, 89-; DEP RES DIR, RES INST INNOVATIVE TECHNOL EARTH, 90- *Personal Data:* b Osaka, Japan, Feb 24, 37; m 66; c 1. *Educ:* Osaka Univ, Bachelor, 60, Dr(elec eng), 68. *Honors & Awards:* IR 100 Indust Award, 84. *Concurrent Pos:* Comt mem, Agency Sci & Technol, Japan, 81-86 & Ministry Int Trade & Indust, Japan, 89; vis prof, Osaka Univ, 85-89 & 90-91, Nagoya Univ, 89-90 & Osaka Prefecture Univ, 89-90. *Mem:* Fel Inst Elec & Electronics Engrs; Am Vacuum Soc; Mat Res Soc. *Res:* Developments of a cathodic sputtering technology as a material processing; production of thin film electronic devices, including saw devices and superconducting devices. *Mailing Add:* Central Research Lab Matsushita Elec Ind Co Ltd 3-15 Yagumo Nakamachi Moriguchi 570 Japan

**WASACZ, JOHN PETER,** ORGANIC CHEMISTRY. *Current Pos:* From asst prof to assoc prof, 69-82, chmn dept, 84-88, PROF CHEM, MANHATTAN COL, 82-, CHMN DEPT, 92- *Personal Data:* b Brooklyn, NY, Sept 11, 44; m 70, Mary C Perry; c John III, Mary C, Anthony & Catherine A. *Educ:* St John's Univ, NY, BS, 65; Univ Pa, PhD(org chem), 69. *Concurrent Pos:* Asst mgr, NY Sect, Am Chem Soc, 73-77, mgr, 77-84; NSF fac fel, Columbia Univ, 75-77; vis scholar, NY Univ, 80 & 88-89; dir-at-large, Sigma Xi, 83-88. *Mem:* Am Chem Soc; Sigma Xi. *Res:* Organic synthesis; photochemistry of heterocyclic molecules; synthesis of natural products. *Mailing Add:* Dept Chem Manhattan Col Bronx NY 10471. *Fax:* 718-862-7814

**WASAN, DARSH T,** CHEMICAL ENGINEERING. *Current Pos:* From asst prof to assoc prof & chmn dept, Ill Inst Technol, 71-87, actg dean eng, 87-88, vpres res & Technol, 88-91, provost & acad vpres, 91-96, PROF CHEM ENG, ILL INST TECHNOL, 70-, VPRES & MOTOROLA PROF, 96- *Personal Data:* b Sarai Salah Hazara, India, July 15, 38; m 66, Usha; c Ajay & Kern. *Educ:* Univ Ill, Urbana, BSChE, 60; Univ Calif, Berkeley, PhD(chem eng), 64. *Honors & Awards:* Western Elec Fund Award, Am Soc Eng Educ, 88, 3M Lectureship Award, Chem Eng Div, 91; Creativity Award, NSF, 88; E W Treile Award, Am Soc Chem Engrs, 89; Sydney Ross Lectr, 96; JJ Bickerman Lectr; Stearns Lectr, 91. *Concurrent Pos:* Consult, Inst Gas Technol, 65-, res inst, Ill Inst Technol, 66-, Chicago Bridge & Iron Co, 67-71, Ill Environ Protection Agency, 71-, Continental Can Co, 72-, Nelson Indust, 76-, Exxon Res & Eng Co, 77-, Stauffer Chem Co, 80-87 & ICI, Am, 88-; ed-in-chief, J Colloid & Interface Sci, 93. *Mem:* AAAS; Am Inst Chem Engrs; Am Chem Soc; Am Soc Eng Educ; Am Inst Physics; Fine Particle Soc; Soc Pheology. *Res:* Interfacial phenomena; particle science and technology; enhanced oil recovery; interfacial rheology; emulsions and foams; thin films. *Mailing Add:* 8705 Royal Swan Lane Darien IL 60561

**WASAN, MADANLAL T,** STATISTICS. *Current Pos:* From asst prof to assoc prof, 59-68, PROF MATH, QUEEN'S UNIV, ONT, 68- *Personal Data:* b Saraisaleh, WPakistan, July 13, 30; m 60; c 4. *Educ:* Univ Bombay, BA, 52, MA, 54; Univ Ill, PhD(statist), 60. *Concurrent Pos:* Vis assoc prof, Stanford Univ, 65 & Univ Bombay, 65-66; statist consult, Du Pont of Can, 62-65. *Mem:* Inst Math Statist. *Res:* Sequential estimation; stochastic approximation; stochastic processes and applied probability. *Mailing Add:* Dept Math/Statist Queen's Univ Kingston ON K7L 3N6 Can

**WASBAUER, MARIUS SHERIDAN,** ENTOMOLOGY. *Current Pos:* RETIRED. *Personal Data:* b Rockford, Ill, Sept 29, 28; m 69, Joanne Slansky; c Carol, David & Kevin. *Educ:* Univ Calif, Berkeley, BS, 51, PhD(syst entom), 61. *Prof Exp:* Instr prev med, US Army, 51-53; jr vector control specialist, Calif Dept Pub Health, 54; syst entomologist, Calif Dept Food & Agr, 59-85, sr insect biosystematist, 85-93. *Concurrent Pos:* Fel, Calif Acad Sci, 78-; res assoc, US Nat Mus, 80-, Univ Calif, Berkeley, 80-85 & Univ Calif, Davis, 93- *Res:* Biosystematics of aculeate wasps, especially families Mutillidae, Tiphiidae, Pompilidae. *Mailing Add:* PO Box 6820 Brookings OR 97415. *Fax:* 541-469-3152; *E-Mail:* wasb@harborside.com

**WASE, ARTHUR WILLIAM,** biochemistry; deceased, see previous edition for last biography

**WASER, NICKOLAS MERRITT,** POLLINATION ECOLOGY, POPULATION BIOLOGY. *Current Pos:* from asst prof to assoc prof, 79-90, PROF BIOL, UNIV CALIF, RIVERSIDE, 90- *Personal Data:* b Pasadena, Calif, June 28, 48; m 77. *Educ:* Stanford Univ, AB, 70; Univ Ariz, PhD(biol), 77. *Prof Exp:* Teaching fel, Univ Utah, 77-79. *Concurrent Pos:* Secy, Rocky Mountain Biol Lab, 82-90, trustee, 82-97. *Mem:* Soc Study Evolution; Ecol Soc Am; Bot Soc Am; Animal Behav Soc; Sigma Xi. *Res:* Plant sexual characteristics; behavior of animal pollinators and their influence on the ecology, genetics, and evolution of plant populations. *Mailing Add:* Dept Biol Univ Calif Riverside CA 92521-0427. *E-Mail:* waser@citrus.ucr.edu

**WASER, PETER MERRITT,** BEHAVIORAL ECOLOGY. *Current Pos:* asst prof, 75-80, ASSOC PROF BIOL, PURDUE UNIV, 80- *Personal Data:* b Pasadena, Calif, Dec 12, 45. *Educ:* Stanford Univ, BS, 68; Rockefeller Univ, PhD(biol), 74. *Prof Exp:* NIH fel, Rockefeller Univ, 74-75. *Concurrent Pos:* Grants, EAfrican Wildlife Soc, 74-75, Am Philos Soc, 76-77, NIMH, 77-78, NSF, 78- & NIH, 80-82. *Mem:* Animal Behav Soc; Int Primate Soc; Ecol Soc Am; AAAS; Am Soc Mammalogists; Sigma Xi. *Res:* Adaptive aspects of animal social behavior; animal communication; territoriality and resource use. *Mailing Add:* Dept Biol Sci Purdue Univ West Lafayette IN 47907

**WASFI, SADIQ HASSAN,** INORGANIC CHEMISTRY, ANALYTICAL CHEMISTRY. *Current Pos:* assoc prof, 79-84, PROF CHEM, DEL STATE UNIV, 84- *Personal Data:* b Basrah, Iraq, July 1, 37; m 68, Ellen O Schwarz; c Yasmine, Dahlia & Ammar. *Educ:* Univ Baghdad, BS, 61; Georgetown Univ, MS, 66, PhD(inorg chem), 71. *Prof Exp:* From lectr to asst prof chem, Col Sci, Basrah Univ, Iraq, 71-77; res assoc chem, Univ Hawaii, Manoa, 75-76; res assoc, Georgetown Univ, 77-78; assoc prof chem, Montgomery Col, Md, 78-79. *Concurrent Pos:* Prin investr, NIH, MBRS Grant, 87-; vis assoc prof, Georgetown Univ, 80-81. *Mem:* Am Chem Soc; Iraqi Chem Soc; Sigma Xi. *Res:* Transition metal complexes of organic thiols and disulfides; organic derivatives of heteropoly tungstates and molybdates; heteropoly tungstate and molybdate anions containing several transition metal ions; heteropoly oxometalate anions as antiviral agents; granted one patent. *Mailing Add:* Dept Chem Del State Univ Dover DE 19901. *E-Mail:* drswasfi@dsc.edu

**WASHA, GEORGE WILLIAM,** MECHANICS. *Current Pos:* Instr, Univ Wis-Madison, 30-40, chmn dept, 53-75, prof, 40-78, EMER PROF MECH, UNIV WIS-MADISON, 78- *Personal Data:* b Milwaukee, Wis, May 6, 09; m 34; c 3. *Educ:* Univ Wis, BS, 30, MS, 32, PhD(mech), 38. *Honors & Awards:* Wason Medal, Am Concrete Inst, 41 & 76. *Mem:* Fel Am Concrete Inst; hon mem Am Con Inst. *Res:* Durability, permeability and plastic flow of concrete; light weight agregates and concrete; vibrated concrete; masonry cements; properties of ferrous metals; concrete block. *Mailing Add:* 202 N Eau Claire Ave Apt 205 Madison WI 53705

**WASHBORN, SEAN,** SURFACE PHYSICS, MAN-MACHINE INTERACTIONS. *Current Pos:* LYLE V JONES PROF PHYSICS, DEPT PHYSICS & ASTRON, UNIV NC, CHAPEL HILL, 91-, PROF APPL SCI, 96- *Personal Data:* b Jacksonville, Fla, Apr 19, 55; m 81; c 3. *Educ:* Stetson Univ, BSc, 76; Duke Univ, PhD(physics), 82. *Prof Exp:* Res staff mem, IBM, TJ Watson Res Ctr, 82-91. *Mem:* Am Phys Soc. *Mailing Add:* Dept Physics & Astron Univ NC Chapel Hill NC 27599-3255. *E-Mail:* sean@physics.unc.edu

**WASHBURN, ALBERT LINCOLN,** GEOMORPHOLOGY, QUATERNARY GEOLOGY. *Current Pos:* prof, 67-76, EMER PROF GEOL, UNIV WASH, 76- *Personal Data:* b New York, NY, June 15, 11; m 35, B Tahoe Talbot; c Nuna C, Sila T & Lahn L. *Educ:* Dartmouth Col, AB, 35; Yale Univ, PhD(geol), 42. *Hon Degrees:* DSc, Univ Alaska, 81. *Honors & Awards:* Kirk Bryan Award, Geol Soc Am, 71; Medal, Univ Liege, Belg, 71; Medaille Andre H Dumont, Geol Soc Belg, 73; Distinguished Career Award, Geol Soc Am, 88; Dartmouth Col Pres Medal, 91; Vega Medal, Swed Soc Anthrop & Geog, 97. *Prof Exp:* Mem, Nat Geog Soc exped, Mt McKinley, 36; asst geologist, Boyd E Greenland exped, 37; geol invests, Can Arctic, 38-41, 49 & 81-; exec dir, Arctic Inst NAm, 45-51; dir snow, ice & permafrost res estab, Corps Engrs, US Army, 51-52; prof northern geol, Dartmouth Col, 53-59; prof geol, Yale Univ, 60-66. *Concurrent Pos:* Hon lectr, McGill Univ, 48-51; consult, Res & Develop Bd, 47-53 & CEngrs, US Army, 52-61; mem, US Nat Comt, Int Geophys Year, 53-59, Comt Polar Res, 58-59 & 63-73, Panel Glaciol, Nat Acad Sci, 59-65 & 67-71; geomorphol investrs, Greenland, 54-58, 60 & 64, Antarctica, 57-58; dir, Quaternary Res Ctr, Univ Wash, 67-76; vpres, Int Quaternary Union, 73-82; chmn bd, Polar Res, 78-81; mem, Geophys Inst Adv Bd, Univ Alaska, Fairbanks, 82-88; comn, US Arctic Res Comn, 85-88. *Mem:* Fel Am Geog Soc; hon mem Int Glaciol Soc; fel Geol Soc Am; Am Geophys Union; hon mem Arctic Inst NAm; fel Geol Asn Can; hon mem Int Quaternary Union; Am Quaternary Asn (pres, 70); corresp mem Geog Soc Finland; corres mem Geol Soc Belg. *Res:* Geocryology; periglacial studies. *Mailing Add:* Quaternary Res Ctr Univ Wash Box 351360 Seattle WA 98195

**WASHBURN, H BRADFORD, JR,** GEOGRAPHY, EXPLORATION. *Current Pos:* dir, 39-80, chmn corp, 80-85, HON DIR, MUS SCI, BOSTON, 85- *Personal Data:* b Cambridge, Mass, June 7, 10; m 40, Barbara T Polk; c Dorothy P, Edward H & Elizabeth B. *Educ:* Harvard Univ, AB, 33, AM, 60. *Hon Degrees:* PhD, Univ Alaska, 51; DSc, Tufts Univ, 57, Colby Col, 57, Northeastern Univ, 58, Univ Mass, 72 & Curry Col, 82; DFA, Suffolk Univ, 65; DHL, Boston Col, 74, Harvard Univ, 75; LLD, Babson Col, 80. *Honors & Awards:* Cuthbert Peek Award, Royal Geog Soc, 38; Burr Prize, Nat Geog Soc, 60 & 65, Alexander Graham Bell Award, 80, Centennial Award, 88; Gold Res Medal, Royal Scottish Geog Soc, 79. *Prof Exp:* Instr, Inst Geog Explor, Harvard Univ, 35-42. *Concurrent Pos:* Dir, Mountaineer in Alps, 26-31; explorer, Alaska Coast Range, 30-40; leader numerous expeds, 34-; lectr, Yukon Exped, Royal Geog Soc, London, 36-37, Grand Canyon Mapping, 76, Mus Imaging Technol, 89 & Mapping Mt Everest, Royal Geog Soc, London, 90; leader, Nat Geog Mapping Exped to Grand Canyon, 71-75; mem, US Nat Comn, UNESCO, 78; hon mem bd dirs, Swiss Found Alpine Res, 84- *Mem:* Nat Geog Soc; AAAS; Am Acad Arts & Sci; hon mem Am Geog Soc; Arctic Inst NAm; hon mem Chinese Asn Sci Expeds. *Res:* Cartography. *Mailing Add:* Science Park Boston MA 02114

**WASHBURN, JACK,** MATERIAL SCIENCE OF SEMICONDUCTOR MATERIALS. *Current Pos:* Res engr, Inst Eng Res, Univ Calif, 49-52, from instr to assoc prof metall, 52-61, prof mat sci & eng, 61-81, chmn dept, 67-70, EMER PROF, DEPT MAT SCI & MINERAL ENG & SR FAC SCIENTIST, LAWRENCE BERKELEY LAB, UNIV CALIF, BERKELEY, 81- *Personal Data:* b Mt Vernon, NY, Apr 30, 21; m 47, Trudy Gastelum; c JoAnn, Kenneth & Melissa. *Educ:* Univ Calif, BS, 49, MS, 50, PhD, 54. *Honors & Awards:* Mathewson Gold Medal, Am Inst Mining, Metall & Petrol Engrs, 56. *Concurrent Pos:* Sr fel, Univ Cambridge, 59-60, Univ Paris, 65; NSF fel, 59 & 65; res prof, Miller Inst Basic Res Sci, 61-62. *Mem:* Am Soc Metals; Am Inst Mining, Metall & Petrol Engrs; Mat Res Soc. *Res:* Relation between properties and structure of electronic materials, particularly the characterization and effects of crystal imperfections in semiconductors and at metal-semiconductor interfaces. *Mailing Add:* Dept Mat Sci & Mineral Eng Univ Calif Berkeley CA 94720

**WASHBURN, KENNETH W,** POULTRY GENETICS. *Current Pos:* assoc prof, 65-75, PROF POULTRY GENETICS, UNIV GA, 75- *Personal Data:* b Martinsville, Va, June 21, 37; m 59; c 2. *Educ:* Va Polytech Inst, BS, 59, MS, 62; Univ Mass, PhD(poultry), 65. *Honors & Awards:* Poultry Sci Jr Res Award, Poultry Sci Asn, 75. *Prof Exp:* Res asst poultry genetics, Va Polytech Inst, 60-62; instr, Univ Mass, 62-65. *Mem:* Poultry Sci Asn. *Res:* Genetic-nutrition interrelationships; compensatory growth; feed efficiency; egg shell strength; egg cholesterol; hemoglobins. *Mailing Add:* Dept Poultry Sci Univ Ga 1180 E Broad St Athens GA 30601-3040

**WASHBURN, LEE CROSS,** ORGANIC CHEMISTRY, RADIOPHARMACEUTICAL CHEMISTRY. *Current Pos:* RES ASSOC PROF, EUGENE L SAENGER RADIOISOTOPE LAB, UNIV CINCINNATI MED CTR, 91- *Personal Data:* b Paducah, Ky, Jan 10, 47; m 69, Linda C Shirk; c Angela L, Allison L & Trevor M. *Educ:* Murray State Univ, BA, 65; Vanderbilt Univ, PhD(org chem), 72. *Prof Exp:* Assoc scientist, Oak Ridge Assoc Univs, 72-77, scientist Radiopharmaceut Develop & Preclin Nuclear Med, Med & Health Sci Div, 77-90, actg dir, Nuclear Med Prog, Med Sci Div, 90-91. *Mem:* Soc Nuclear Med; Am Chem Soc; Int Asn Radiopharmacol. *Res:* Development of radiopharmaceuticals for diagnostic and therapeutic applications in nuclear medicine. *Mailing Add:* Eugene L Saenger Radioisotope Lab Univ Cincinnati Med Ctr 234 Goodman St Cincinnati OH 45267-0577. *Fax:* 513-558-0308

**WASHBURN, ROBERT HENRY,** STRATIGRAPHY, STRUCTURAL GEOLOGY. *Current Pos:* from asst prof to assoc prof, 66-77, PROF GEOL, JUNIATA COL, 77- *Personal Data:* b Lincoln, Nebr, Nov 27, 36; m 66. *Educ:* Univ Nebr, BS, 59, MS, 61; Columbia Univ, PhD(geol), 66. *Prof Exp:* Instr geol, Brooklyn Col, 64-66. *Mem:* AAAS; Geol Soc Am; Am Asn Petrol Geologists; Soc Econ Paleont & Mineral. *Res:* Paleozoic stratigraphy; structural geology of central Nevada and Pennsylvania. *Mailing Add:* Dept Geol Juniata Col Huntingdon PA 16653

**WASHBURN, ROBERT LATHAM,** MECHANICAL ENGINEERING, POLYMER ENGINEERING. *Current Pos:* RETIRED. *Personal Data:* b Malone, NY, June 22, 21; m 74; c 4. *Educ:* Clarkson Col Technol, BE, 47; Mass Inst Technol, MS, 48. *Prof Exp:* Chief engr design develop, Sklenar Furnace & Mfg Co, 46-47; mgr, Eng Tech Sect, E I du Pont de Nemours & Co, Inc, 48-53, asst supt, 53-55, supt, 55-58, sr supvr res & develop, 58-68 & Res Plastics Prod Div, 68- 72, supt, Res Lab, 68-72 & Polymer Prod Div, 72-78, sr supvr, Admin & Eng Res, 78-79, tech serv mgr, Plastics Mkt Molding Compounding & Extrusion, 79-82, Adhesives & Sealants, 82-83, sr tech consult, Warp Size Develop-Textiles, 83-90. *Mem:* Sigma Xi; Am Soc Mech Engrs; Tech Asn Pulp & Paper Indust. *Res:* Concept development, resultant program derivation, and subsequent engineering new polymer systems encompassing process, product and equipment; synthesis, rheology, morphology and conformational alterations such as orientation. *Mailing Add:* 3205 Landsdowne Dr Cardiff Wilmington DE 19810

**WASHBURN, SHERWOOD L,** PRIMATE BEHAVIOR. *Current Pos:* prof, 58-78, EMER UNIV PROF ANTHROP, UNIV CALIF, BERKELEY, 78- *Personal Data:* b Cambridge, Mass, Nov 26, 11. *Educ:* Harvard Univ, BA, 35, PhD(anthrop), 40. *Prof Exp:* Prof anat, Sch Med, Columbia Univ, 39-47; prof anthrop, Univ Chicago, 47-58. *Mem:* Nat Acad Sci; Am Anthrop Soc (pres, 62); AAAS. *Res:* Experimental analysis of behavior. *Mailing Add:* Dept Anthrop Univ Calif Kroeber Hall Rm 232 Berkeley CA 94720

**WASHBURN, WILLIAM H,** ANALYTICAL CHEMISTRY. *Current Pos:* RETIRED. *Personal Data:* b Milwaukee, Wis, Oct 14, 20; m 42; c 3. *Educ:* Univ Wis, BA, 41. *Prof Exp:* Chemist, Abbott Labs, 46-85. *Mem:* Soc Appl Spectros; Am Chem Soc; Coblentz Soc; Sigma Xi. *Res:* Infrared spectroscopy, materials purity and chemical structure analysis. *Mailing Add:* 120 E Hawthorne Ct Lake Bluff IL 60044

**WASHBURNE, STEPHEN SHEPARD,** ORGANIC CHEMISTRY. *Current Pos:* Asst prof, 67-73, asst chmn dept, 74-78, ASSOC PROF CHEM, TEMPLE UNIV, 73- *Personal Data:* b Hartford, Conn, Sept 6, 42; m 83, Betsy; c Matthew. *Educ:* Trinity Col, Conn, BS, 63; Mass Inst Technol, PhD(org chem), 67. *Concurrent Pos:* NSF fel, 64-66; NIH fel, 67; Fulbright sr lectr, Port, 80. *Mem:* Am Chem Soc. *Res:* Organosilicon chemistry; cancer chemotherapy; organometallic chemistry of the elements of group IV. *Mailing Add:* Dept Chem 016-00 Temple Univ Philadelphia PA 19122. *E-Mail:* swashbur@nimbus.temple.edu

**WASHINGTON, A EUGENE,** OBSTETRICS & GYNECOLOGY. *Current Pos:* PROF & CHAIR, DEPT OBSTET, GYNEC & REPRODUCTIVE SCI, UNIV CALIF, SAN FRANCISCO, 86- *Personal Data:* b Houston, Tex, 1950. *Educ:* Univ Calif, San Francisco, MD, 76; Am Bd Obstet & Gynec, dipl; Am Bd Gen Prev Med, dipl. *Prof Exp:* Intern, USPHS, Staten Island, NY, 76-77; resident prev med, Harvard Univ, 77-79; fel health policy, Inst Health, Univ Calif, San Francisco, 83-86. *Concurrent Pos:* Resident obstet & gynec, Stanford Univ, 86- *Mem:* Inst Med-Nat Acad Sci; AAAS; Am Pub Health Asn; Soc Epidemiol Res. *Mailing Add:* Univ Calif PO Box 0132 San Francisco CA 94143

**WASHINGTON, ARTHUR CLOVER,** DEVELOPMENTAL BIOLOGY. *Current Pos:* PROF CHEM, TENN STATE UNIV, 91- *Personal Data:* b Tallulah, La, Aug, 19, 39; m 62; c 3. *Educ:* Tex Col Tyler, BS, 61; Tuskegee Inst, Ala, MS, 63; Ill Inst Technol, PhD(biol), 71. *Prof Exp:* Res scientist plant path, Wash State Univ, 63-64; instr biol, Talladega Col, 65-67; assoc prof, Amundsen-Mayfair Col, 67-72; assoc prof, Langston Univ, Okla, 72-74; prof biochem, Prairie View A&M Univ, 74-91, dean, Grad Sch, 82-91. *Concurrent Pos:* Res scientist, Pfizer Chem Co, Conn, 66; univ admin trainee, Univ Wis-Exten, Madison, 73; prin investr, NSF res initiation award, 73-74, USDA Tri-Co Nutrit, Prairie View, 74-79, Robert A Welch Found award, 76- & NIH awards, 76-; sci develop consult, Paul Quinn Col, Tex, 76- *Mem:* Nat Inst Sci; Am Soc Microbiologists; AAAS; Sigma Xi. *Res:* Mechanisms which seem to regulate morphogenesis in the cellular slime mold, Dictyostelium discoideum; DNA, RNA folic acid and mitochondrial enzyme metabolism. *Mailing Add:* Biol Sci Tenn State Univ 3500 J A Merritt Blvd Nashville TN 37209-1561

**WASHINGTON, ELMER L,** PHYSICAL CHEMISTRY. *Current Pos:* from asst prof to assoc prof phys sci, Chicago State Univ, 69-77, dean natural sci & math, 72-74, prof chem & vpres res & develop, 76-80, dean, Col Arts & Sci, 74-76, actg vpres student affairs, 90-91, PROF CHEM, CHICAGO STATE UNIV, 80- *Personal Data:* b Houston, Tex, Oct 18, 35; m 60; c 2. *Educ:* Tex Southern Univ, BS, 57, MS, 58; Ill Inst Technol, PhD(thermodyn), 66. *Prof Exp:* Asst proj engr, Pratt & Whitney Aircraft Div, United Aircraft Corp, Conn, 65-67, res assoc, Advan Mat Res & Develop Lab, 67-69. *Mem:* Electrochem Soc; Am Chem Soc. *Res:* Thermodynamics of non-electrolytes; electrochemistry as related to fuel cell technology. *Mailing Add:* 221 Grant St Park Forest IL 60466-1013

**WASHINGTON, JAMES M(ACKNIGHT),** CHEMICAL ENGINEERING. *Current Pos:* res engr, 72-80, ASSOC SR ENGR, PHILIP MORRIS RES CTR, 80- *Personal Data:* b Hackensack, NJ, Dec 1, 38; m 56, 88; c 5. *Educ:* Clemson Univ, BS, 61; Va Polytech Inst, MS, 64, PhD, 69. *Prof Exp:* Asst prof chem eng, Univ NB, 65-66; res engr, E I du Pont de Nemours & Co, 66-68; sr scientist, Allied Chem Corp, 68-72. *Mem:* Am Inst Chem Engrs; Sigma Xi. *Res:* Chemical reactor engineering, particularly non-ideal mixing of fluids. *Mailing Add:* 2400 Stuts Lane Richmond VA 23236-1638

**WASHINGTON, JOHN A, II,** CLINICAL MICROBIOLOGY, CLINICAL PATHOLOGY. *Current Pos:* CHMN DEPT MICROBIOL, CLEVELAND CLIN FOUND, 86- *Personal Data:* b Istanbul, Turkey, May 29, 36; US citizen; m 59; c 3. *Educ:* Univ Va, BA, 57; Johns Hopkins Univ, MD, 61. *Prof Exp:* From intern to asst resident surg, Med Ctr, Duke Univ, 61-63; Nat Cancer Inst fel, 63-65; resident clin path, Clin Ctr, NIH, 65-67; assoc consult, Mayo Clin, 67-68, consult, 68-85, head sect clin microbiol, 71-85, assoc prof microbiol & lab med, Mayo Med Sch, 72-76, prof microbiol & lab med, 76-85. *Concurrent Pos:* Asst prof microbiol, Mayo Grad Sch Med, 70-72; ed, J Clin Microbiol, 74-75; ed, Antimicrobial Agents & Chemother, 81-; trustee, Am Bd Path, 89- *Mem:* Fel Am Soc Clin Path; Am Soc Microbiol; fel Am Col Physicians; fel Am Acad Microbiol; fel Infectious Dis Soc Am; fel Col Am Pathologists; fel Am Col Chest Physicians. *Res:* Antimicrobial agents; antimicrobial susceptibility tests; methodology in clinical bacteriology. *Mailing Add:* Dept Microbiol Cleveland Clin Found Clin Ctr 9500 Euclid Ave Cleveland OH 44195-0001

**WASHINGTON, LAWRENCE C,** MATHEMATICS, NUMBER THEORY. *Current Pos:* from asst prof to assoc prof, 77-86, PROF MATH, UNIV MD, 86- *Personal Data:* b Middlebury, Vt, June 14, 51; m 92, Susan Zengerle. *Educ:* Johns Hopkins Univ, BA & MA, 71; Princeton Univ, PhD(math), 74. *Prof Exp:* Asst prof, Stanford Univ, 74-77. *Concurrent Pos:* Alfred P Sloan fel, 79-81. *Mem:* Am Math Soc; Math Asn Am. *Mailing Add:* Dept Math Univ Md College Park MD 20742-0001. *E-Mail:* lcw@math.umd.edu

**WASHINGTON, WARREN MORTON,** meteorology; deceased, see previous edition for last biography

**WASHINGTON, WILLIE JAMES,** PLANT GENETICS, CYTOGENETICS. *Current Pos:* from asst prof to assoc prof, 73-82, PROF BIOL, CENT STATE UNIV, OHIO, 82- CHMN DEPT, 85- *Personal Data:* b Madison, Fla, Dec 26, 42; m 70. *Educ:* Fla A&M Univ, BS, 64; Univ Ariz,

MS, 66; Univ Mo-Columbia, PhD(plant genetics, cytogenetics), 70. *Prof Exp:* Asst prof biol, Tougaloo Col, 70-71 & Cent State Univ, Ohio, 71-72; D F Jones fel agron, NDak State Univ, 72-73. *Concurrent Pos:* Prin investr, Mutagenic-Teratological Potential Lab Solvents, Minority Biomed Support Prog, NIH, 80-83 & Minority Access to Res Careers Prog, 82-87. *Mem:* Orgn Black Scientists; Nat Inst Sci; Cent Asn Adv Health Prof; AAAS. *Res:* Genetic toxicology; assessment of genetic risks of exposure to environmental pollutants; application of genetical and cytogenetical analysis to the improvement of economic crops; mammalian tissue culture; environmental mutagenesis; genetics and cytogenetics of higher plants and animals. *Mailing Add:* Vpres Acad Affairs Cent State Univ Wilberforce OH 45384-9999

**WASHINO, ROBERT K,** ENTOMOLOGY, PUBLIC HEALTH. *Current Pos:* asst specialist, 65-67, assoc prof, 67-81, PROF ENTOM, UNIV CALIF, DAVIS, 81-, LECTR & ASST ENTOMOLOGIST, 67- *Personal Data:* b Sacramento, Calif, Mar 14, 32; m 56; c 3. *Educ:* Univ Calif, Berkeley, BS, 54; Univ Calif, Davis, MS, 56, PhD(entom), 67. *Prof Exp:* Assoc-sr specialist, Calif State Dept Pub Health, 59-65. *Concurrent Pos:* NIH grant, 71-73. *Mem:* Entom Soc Am; Am Soc Trop Med & Hyg; Am Mosquito Control Asn (vpres). *Res:* Studies regarding the various aspects of insect biology which affect their role as vectors of human and animal pathogens; sociological as well as entomological studies of mosquito pest problems. *Mailing Add:* 2224 Amador Ave Davis CA 95616

**WASHKO, FLOYD VICTOR,** VETERINARY PATHOLOGY. *Current Pos:* VET PATHOLOGIST, MERCK, SHARP & DOHME RES LABS, 54-, SR INVESTR, 74- *Personal Data:* b New Brunswick, NJ, Oct 17, 22; m 47; c 2. *Educ:* Mich State Univ, DVM, 44; Purdue Univ, MS, 48, PhD, 50. *Prof Exp:* Vet pract, NJ, 44-45; assoc prof vet sci, Purdue Univ, 46-53; mem staff, Plum Island Animal Dis Lab, USDA, 53-54. *Mem:* Am Vet Med Asn; NY Acad Sci; Am Asn Avian Pathologists; Am Asn Vet Lab Diagnosticians; US Animal Health Asn. *Res:* Brucellosis of swine and cattle; virus diseases of the bovine; veterinary therapeutics. *Mailing Add:* 523 Colonia Blvd Colonia NJ 07067

**WASHKO, WALTER WILLIAM,** AGRONOMY. *Current Pos:* RETIRED. *Personal Data:* b New Brunswick, NJ, July 29, 20; m 55; c 4. *Educ:* Rutgers Univ, BS, 41, MS, 47, Univ Wis, PhD(agron, bot), 58. *Prof Exp:* Agronomist, Tex Res Found, 47-53 & Eastern States Farmers Exchange, 53-64; ext agronomist & prof agron, Univ Conn, 64-88. *Mem:* Am Soc Agron; Am Inst Biol Sci; Sigma Xi. *Res:* Crop production. *Mailing Add:* 6 Turnpike Rd Ashford CT 06278

**WASHTON, NATHAN SEYMOUR,** SCIENCE EDUCATION & COMMUNICATIONS. *Current Pos:* coordr sci educ & teaching sci, 50-80, EMER PROF, QUEENS COL, CITY UNIV NEW YORK, 80- *Personal Data:* b New York, NY, Nov 9, 16; m 44, Sylvia Salitsky; c Gale (DuBrow), Ruth (Brown) & Laura (Orr). *Educ:* NY Univ, BS, 39, EdD, 50; Columbia Univ, MA, 41. *Honors & Awards:* Distinguished Serv, Nat Asn Res Sci Teaching, 58; Res Award, Libr Sci, 61. *Prof Exp:* Chmn sci, Newark Jr Col, 39-42; dir tech training, USAF, 42-45; teacher biol, chem & math, Rhodes Sch, 45-46; chmn sci, Rutgers Univ, 46-50. *Concurrent Pos:* Consult, NSF; vis prof, Univ PR, 48, Upsala Col, 48, Univ Hawaii, 62-63, Hebrew Univ, Jerusalem, 67 & Ben Gurion Univ, Israel, 79; educ consult, 80- *Mem:* Fel AAAS; Nat Asn Res Sci Teaching (vpres, 57, pres, 58); Nat Sci Teachers Asn; Am Educ Res Asn; Am Environ Sci Acad. *Res:* Seminars and workshops for faculty development in teaching of sciences for effectiveness; evaluation of college and medical faculty. *Mailing Add:* 10104 E Topaz Dr Scottsdale AZ 85258-1613

**WASI, SAFIA,** TRANSFUSION MEDICINE, ENDOTHELIAL CELL BIOLOGY. *Current Pos:* SR DIR SCI AFFAIRS, HEART & STROKE FOUND CAN, 93- *Personal Data:* b Simla, India; Can citizen. *Educ:* Univ Karachi, BSc(Hons), 56, MSc, 57; Wash Univ, MA, 60; Univ Toronto, PhD(biochem), 71. *Prof Exp:* Prof physics, Univ Karachi, 57-59 & 62-64; prof, Col Home Econs, Ford Found, Karachi, 62-64; res assoc, Dept Path, Univ Toronto, 64-66, teaching asst, Dept Biochem, 66-71, Dept Immunol, 67-69, fel, Dept Med Genetics, 71-73, asst prof, Dept Path, 75-81, asst prof, MRC Group Periodont Physiol, 81-88; res assoc, Univ Western Ont, London, 73-75; prof path, Chiropractor Col, 78-79; head, Protein Chem Lab, Nat Reference Lab, Can Red Cross Soc, 83-92, sci adv, 92-93. *Concurrent Pos:* Adj prof, Dept Microbiol & Immunol, Univ Ottawa, 91- *Mem:* Am Asn Cell Biol; Int Soc Thrombosis & Hemostasis; Am Heart Asn; NY Acad Sci; Can Atherosclerosis Soc; Can Biochem Soc. *Res:* Elucidation of the biochemical and molecular mechanisms of growth and regression of lymphatic vascular endothelial cell system; the inability of the lymphatic endothelium to grow into solid tumors and rheumatoid arthritis pannus. *Mailing Add:* Heart & Stroke Found Can 160 George St Suite 200 Ottawa ON K1N 9M2 Can. *Fax:* 613-241-3278; *E-Mail:* swasi@acadvm1.uottawa.ca

**WASIELEWSKI, MICHAEL ROMAN,** PHOTOSYNTHESIS, PHOTOCHEMISTRY. *Current Pos:* res assoc, Argonne Nat Lab, 75-76, asst chemist, 76-81, chemist, 81-91, SR CHEMIST, ARGONNE NAT LAB, 91-, GROUP LEADER, 93- *Personal Data:* b Chicago, Ill, June 7, 49; m 75; c 1. *Educ:* Univ Chicago, BS, 71, MS, 72, PhD(chem), 75. *Prof Exp:* Fel chem, Columbia Univ, 74-75. *Mem:* Am Chem Soc; Biophys Soc; Am Soc Photobiol. *Res:* Mechanism of the primary events of photosynthesis; light induced electron transfer reactions; biomimetic modelling of natural biophysical chemistry. *Mailing Add:* Chem Div Argonne Nat Lab 9700 S Cass Ave Argonne IL 60439-4831. *E-Mail:* wasielewski@anlchm.chm.anl.gov

**WASIELEWSKI, PAUL FRANCIS,** VEHICLE-BORNE COMPUTER APPLICATIONS. *Current Pos:* SCIENTIST, DEPT TRANSP RES, GEN MOTORS RES LAB, 69- *Personal Data:* b Bay Shore, NY, Oct 21, 41; m 67; c 3. *Educ:* Georgetown Univ, BS, 63; Yale Univ, MS, 65, PhD(physics), 69. *Mem:* Am Phys Soc. *Res:* Microcomputer-based automotive navigation and map display systems; traffic accident research; mathematical models of traffic flow. *Mailing Add:* 25474 Wareham Dr Huntington Woods MI 48070-1604

**WASILIK, JOHN H(UBER),** SOLID STATE PHYSICS, MICROWAVE ENGINEERING. *Current Pos:* PRIN, WASILIK ASSOC, SILVER SPRING, MD. *Personal Data:* b Franklin, NC, Feb 9, 25; m 51; c 6. *Educ:* Manhattan Col, BS, 47; Cath Univ Am, PhD(physics), 57. *Prof Exp:* Physicist, Nat Bur Stand, 50-67; physicist, Harry Diamond Labs, 67- *Mem:* Am Phys Soc; Inst Elec & Electronics Engrs. *Res:* Elastic and dielectric properties, their pressure and temperature dependence; associated loss mechanisms; excitons; microwave acoustics; lattice attenuation; theory and experiment; piezoelectricity; electrostriction; bulk and surface wave microwave acoustic delay lines; acousto-optics; fiber optics; operations research; strategic defense initiative; nuclear weapons effects. *Mailing Add:* 1307 Sarah Dr Silver Spring MD 20904. *Fax:* 301-394-2998

**WASKELL, LUCY A,** MEDICINE-ANESTHESIOLOGY, DRUG METABOLISM & BIOCHEMISTRY. *Current Pos:* PROF ANESTHESIOL, UNIV CALIF, SAN FRANCISCO, 79- *Personal Data:* b Radford, Va, Feb 1, 42; m 81. *Educ:* Columbia Univ, MD, 67; Univ Calif, Berkeley, PhD(molecular biol), 73. *Prof Exp:* Residency anesthesiol, Stanford Univ, 73-74. *Mem:* Am Chem Soc. *Res:* Molecular basis of the metabolism of drugs, especially anesthetics, by the enzyme cytochrome P-450. *Mailing Add:* Dept Anesthesia 129 Vet Admin Med Ctr 4150 Clement St San Francisco CA 94121-1598. *Fax:* 415-750-6946

**WASLEY, RICHARD J(UNIOR),** CIVIL ENGINEERING. *Current Pos:* RETIRED. *Personal Data:* b Oakland, Calif, June 24, 31; m 92, Liena M Boone; c Richard J, Anne W (Jones) & Pamela R. *Educ:* Univ Calif, Berkeley, BS, 54; Stanford Univ, MS, 58, PhD(civil eng), 60. *Honors & Awards:* Alfred Noble Prize, 62. *Prof Exp:* Sanit engr, Bur Sanit Eng, Calif Dept Pub Health, 55-56; civil engr, Alameda County Surveyor Off, 57; engr, Lawrence Livermore Lab, Univ Calif, 60-95. *Mem:* Fel Am Soc Civil Engrs; Nat Soc Prof Engrs; Am Soc Mech Engrs. *Res:* Dynamic mechanical properties of materials; elastic and viscoelastic waves; fluid mechanics; shock wave phenomena. *Mailing Add:* 4290 Colgate Way Livermore CA 94550

**WASLIEN, CAROL IRENE,** CLINICAL NUTRITION, NUTRITION ASSESSMENT. *Current Pos:* PROF PUB HEALTH NUTRIT, UNIV HAWAII, 90-, CHAIR, PUB HEALTH SCI DEPT. *Personal Data:* b Mayville, NDak, Sept 24, 40; m 80. *Educ:* Univ Calif, Santa Barbara, BA, 61; Cornell Univ, MS, 63; Univ Calif, Berkeley, PhD(nutrit), 68. *Prof Exp:* NIH res training fel, Vanderbilt Univ, Naval Med Res Unit-3, Egypt, 68-69; res assoc nutrit, Vanderbilt Univ, 69-72; assoc prof & head, Dept Nutrit & Foods, Auburn Univ, 72-77; chief, Nutrit Planning Proj, USAID, 77-79; exec dir, League Int Food Educ, 79-81; prof nutrit & food sci prog, Hunter Col, City Univ New York, 81-90. *Concurrent Pos:* Res consult, Biochem Dept, Vanderbilt Univ, 72-74; res consult & mem, Bd Dir, Universal Foods Corp, 80-; adj prof, Mt Sinai Sch Med, 80- *Mem:* Am Inst Nutrit; Am Dietetic Asn; Inst Food Tech; Am Pub Health Asn. *Res:* Human requirements for protein, vitamins and trace minerals; use of micro-organisms as food sources for man; nutrition assessment; nutrition program evaluation; international nutrition; geriatric nutrition. *Mailing Add:* Dept Pub Health Sci Univ Hawaii Sch Pub Health 1960 East-West Rd Honolulu HI 96822

**WASON, SATISH KUMAR,** PHYSICAL INORGANIC CHEMISTRY. *Current Pos:* tech dir & asst vpres, 85-87, vpres, 87-88, PRES, CHEM DIV, J M HUBER CORP, 88- *Personal Data:* b Lyallpur, India, Feb 24, 40; m 70; c 3. *Educ:* Univ Delhi, BSc, 59, MSc, 61; Cornell Univ, PhD(phys chem), 65. *Prof Exp:* Scientist, Coun Sci & Indust Res, New Delhi, India, 65-66; res assoc phys chem, Boston Univ, 66-67; res chemist, E I du Pont de Nemours & Co, Inc, Del, 67-69. *Mem:* Am Chem Soc; Soc Cosmetic Chemists; Sigma Xi; Soc Plastic Indust; Soc Plastic Engrs. *Res:* High temperature thermodynamic and spectroscopic studies; photochemistry and mercury photosensitized reactions; chemistry of synthetic silicas and silicates; surface chemistry, structure and applications of fine-particle synthetic silicas and silicates in paper, rubber, paints, plastics, dentifrices, cosmetics, pharmaceutical and specialty industries; structure and properties of kaolin products, zeolites, micas, hectorites, specialty minerals, fillers and extenders. *Mailing Add:* J M Huber Corp PO Box 310 Havre de Grace MD 21078

**WASOW, WOLFGANG RICHARD,** mathematics; deceased, see previous edition for last biography

**WASS, JOHN ALFRED,** STATISTICS, BIOCHEMISTRY. *Current Pos:* special opers, 91-93, MATH ANALYST, ABBOT LABS, 93- *Personal Data:* b Kyoto, Japan, Apr 14, 50; US citizen. *Educ:* Lake Forest Col, BA, 69; Northern Ill Univ, MS, 70; Southern Ill Univ, PhD(physiol), 74; Univ Cincinnati, BS, 77; Lake Forest Grad Sch, MBA, 87. *Prof Exp:* Clin microbiologist, N Chicago Vet Admin Hosp, 74-75; criteria mgr pharmacol & toxicol, Nat Inst Occup Safety & Health, 75-77; postdoctoral res assoc pharmacol & toxicol, Med Col Wis, 77-79; postdoctoral res assoc path, Univ Conn, 79-80; postdoctoral fel path, Univ Mich, 80-83; mgr oncol & immunol, Am Int Hosp, 83-86, dir res & develop, 86-91. *Concurrent Pos:* Treas, Vet Lab Asn, 89-; secy mid-west br, Tissue Culture Asn, 87-93. *Mem:* Am Physiol Soc; Am Asn Cancer Res; AAAS; Biophys Soc; Am Stat Asn. *Res:* Variance analysis in biochemical and electronic systems; statistical/mathematical modeling of biochemical/biophysical processes; computational algorithms. *Mailing Add:* Clin Chem 9AL Abbott Labs Abbott Park IL 60064. *Fax:* 847-937-2486; *E-Mail:* john.wass@add.ssw.abbott.com

**WASS, WALLACE M,** VETERINARY MEDICINE, VETERINARY SURGERY. *Current Pos:* prof vet clin sci & head dept, 64-83, PROF, VET CLIN SCI, IOWA STATE UNIV, 83- *Personal Data:* b Lake Park, Iowa, Nov 19, 29; m 53; c 4. *Educ:* Univ Minn, BS, 51, DVM, 53, PhD(vet med), 61. *Hon Degrees:* Vet Med, Nat Univ Colombia, 63. *Prof Exp:* From instr to asst prof vet med, Univ Minn, 58-63; res assoc lab animal med, Brookhaven Nat Lab, 63-64. *Mem:* Am Vet Med Asn. *Res:* Large animal medicine and surgery; metabolic diseases of domestic animals; bovine porphyria. *Mailing Add:* 2166 Ashmore Circle Ames IA 50014

**WASSARMAN, PAUL MICHAEL,** DEVELOPMENTAL BIOLOGY. *Current Pos:* AT DEPT CELL BIOL, MT SINAI SCH MED. *Personal Data:* b Milford, Mass, Mar 26, 40; m 60; c 4. *Educ:* Univ Mass, BS, 61, MS, 64; Brandeis Univ, PhD(biochem), 68. *Prof Exp:* Helen Hay Whitney Found fel, Molecular Res Coun Lab, Cambridge, Eng, 67-69; asst prof, Dept Biol Sci, Purdue Univ, 69-72; lectr & spec res fel, Harvard Med Sch & Rockefeller Found fel, 72-73; from asst prof to assoc prof, Dept Biol Chem, Harvard Med Sch, 73-85, full mem, 85-86; chmn, Dept Cell Develop Biol, Roche Inst Molecular Biol, 86- *Concurrent Pos:* Mem, Exec Comt, Prog Cell & Develop Biol, Harvard Med Sch, 75-85; bd tutors biochem sci, Harvard Univ, 75-82; mem, Molecular Cytol Study Sect, NIH, 78-82; ad hoc rev, Spec Study Sect, Nat Inst Child Health & Human Develop, 85-; adj prof, Dept Cell Biol, NY Univ Sch Med. *Mem:* Am Soc Biol Chem; Am Soc Cell Biol; Soc Develop Biol; AAAS. *Res:* Cellular and molecular mechanisms of early mammalian development. *Mailing Add:* Dept Cell & Develop Biol Mt Sinai Sch Med-1 Gustaveh Levy Pl New York NY 10129. *Fax:* 973-235-2839

**WASSEF, NABILA M,** LIPID BIOCHEMISTRY & IMMUNOLOGY, LIPSOMOLOGY. *Current Pos:* sr investr, 81-89, DEP CHIEF, MEMBRANE BIOCHEM BR, WALTER REED ARMY INST RES, 90- *Personal Data:* b Cairo, Egypt, Jan 1, 43; US citizen; m 73; c 1. *Educ:* Ain-Shams Univ, Cairo, Egypt, BSc, 63, MSc, 67, PhD(biochem), 74. *Prof Exp:* Instr biochem, Fac Sci, Ain-Shams Univ, 63-68; res assoc, US Naval Med Res Unit No 3, 68-73 & Dept Path, Univ Ky Sch Med, 74-76; asst prof pharmacol & biochem, NY Med Col, 77-80. *Mem:* Am Asn Immunologists; Soc Leukocyte Biol; AAAS. *Res:* Lipid biochemistry; prostaglandins and leukotrienes; lipid immunology; presentation of liposomal antigens by macrophages; development of liposomes as carriers of drugs and vaccines. *Mailing Add:* Dept Membrane Biochem Walter Reed Army Inst Res Med Ctr Washington DC 20307-5100. *Fax:* 202-576-0721

**WASSER, CLINTON HOWARD,** RANGE ECOLOGY & REVEGETATION. *Current Pos:* CONSULT, 80- *Personal Data:* b Phoenix, Ariz, Nov 11, 15; m 39; c 3. *Educ:* Univ Ariz, BS, 37; Univ Nebr, MS, 47; Colo State Univ, MF, 48. *Honors & Awards:* Frederic Renner Award, Soc Range Mgt, 89. *Prof Exp:* Res asst southwestern forest & range exp sta, US Forest Serv, 37-38; instr range sci & asst range mgt, Colo State Univ, 38-43, asst range conservationist, 43-47, from asst prof to assoc prof, 43-52, head, range sci dept, 47, actg head dept range mgt, 47-50, chief range conservationist & chief forestry & range mgt sect, Agr Exp Sta, 47-52, head, 50-57, dean, col forestry & natural resources, 52-69, prof, 52-80, pres, res found, 57-59; collabr, State Prod & Mkt Admin, Colo, US Forest Serv, 43-80, Rocky Mt Forest & Range Exp Sta, 54-; consult, Bowes & Hart, Inc, 47; agr res serv, USDA, 50-85; admin tech rep, McIntire Stennis Coop State Forestry Prog, 63-69; dir, int shortcourse Range Mgt & Forage Prod, 71-78. *Concurrent Pos:* Dir, Peace Corps Training Prog Firewood Prod, WAfrica, 85; consult, Bowes & Hart, Inc, 47; admin tech rep, McIntire Stennis Coop State Forestry Prog, 63-69. *Mem:* Soc Am Foresters; Soc Range Mgt (pres-elect, 64, pres, 65); AAAS; Ecol Soc Am; Sigma Xi. *Res:* Range management, ecology and seeding; alpine plant ecology; rangeland habitat type classification; author of several manuals of the ecology of plant materials suitable for revegetation purposes. *Mailing Add:* 1400 S Shields St Ft Collins CO 80521

**WASSER, RICHARD BARKMAN,** PAPER CHEMISTRY, PHYSICAL CHEMISTRY. *Current Pos:* RETIRED. *Personal Data:* b Oshkosh, Wis, Sept 26, 36; m 68, Pauline Ames; c Joan & Daniel. *Educ:* Univ Wis, BS, 59; Inst Paper Chem, MS, 61, PhD(paper chem), 64; Polytech Inst NY, MS, 85. *Prof Exp:* From res chemist to sr res chemist, Am Cyanamid Co, 64-73, proj leader paper chem, 73-78, mgr paper chem res & develop, 78-80, prin res scientist, 80-93; prin res Scientist, Cytec Industs, 94-97. *Mem:* Tech Asn Pulp & Paper Indust. *Res:* Physical chemistry of paper and its modification with chemical additives. *Mailing Add:* 7 Dock Rd SN Norwalk CT 06854

**WASSERBAUER, JOHN GILMARY,** optoelectronics engineering, solid state devices, for more information see previous edition

**WASSERBURG, GERALD JOSEPH,** GEOLOGY, GEOPHYSICS. *Current Pos:* from asst prof to assoc prof, Calif Inst Technol, 55-62, prof, 62-82, chmn Div, Geol & Planetary Sci, 87-89, JOHN D MACARTHUR PROF GEOL & GEOPHYS, DIV GEOL & PLANETARY SCI, CALIF INST TECHNOL, 82- *Personal Data:* b New Brunswick, NJ, Mar 25, 27; m 51, Naomi Z Orlick; c Charles D & Daniel M. *Educ:* Univ Chicago, BSc, 51, MS, 52, PhD(geol), 54. *Hon Degrees:* Dr, Free Univ Brussels, 85, Univ Paris, 86, Univ Chicago, 92; DSc, Ariz State Univ, 87. *Honors & Awards:* Arthur L Day Medal, Geol Soc Am, 70; Except Sci Achievement Award, NASA 70; J F

Kemp Medal, Columbia Univ, 73; Leonard Medal, Meteoritical Soc, 75; V M Goldschmidt Medal, Geochem Soc, 78; Jaeger-Hales lectr, Australian Nat Univ, 80; Harold Jeffreys lectr, Royal Astron Soc, 81; Arthur L Day Prize & lectr, Nat Acad Sci, 81, J Lawrence Smith Medal, 85; Ernst Cloos lectr, Johns Hopkins Univ, 84; Wollaston Medal, Geol Soc London, 85; Sr US Scientist Award, Alexander von Humboldt Found, 85; Harry H Hess Medal, Am Geophys Union, 85; Crafoord Medal, Royal Swed Acad, 86; Holmes Medal, Europ Union Geol, 87; Danz lectr, Univ Wash, 89; Goldschmidt Centennial lectr, Norweg Acad Sci & Lett, 89; Gold Medal, Royal Astron Soc, 91. *Prof Exp:* Res assoc, Inst Nuclear Studies, Univ Chicago, 54-55. *Concurrent Pos:* Vis prof, Univ Kiel, 60, Harvard Univ, 62, Univ Berne, 66 & Swiss Fed Inst Technol, 67; mem, Lunar Sample Analysis Planning Team, NASA, 67-74, Lunar Base Steering Comt, 84-85; adv, NASA, 68-88; chmn, Comt Planetary & Lunar Explor & mem, Space Sci Bd, Nat Acad Sci, 75-78; Vinton Hayes sr fel, Harvard, 80; Smithsonian Regents' fel, 82; Cecil H & Ida Green vis prof, Univ BC, 82. *Mem:* Nat Acad Sci; fel Am Geophys Union; Geol Soc Am; fel Am Acad Arts & Sci; Meteoritical Soc (vpres, 85, pres, 87, 88); Am Philos Soc; hon foreign fel Europ Union Geosci; foreign mem Norweg Acad Sci & Lett. *Res:* Geochemistry and geophysics and the application of the methods of chemical physics to problems in the earth sciences; determination of the time scales of nucleosynthesis; connection between the interstellar medium and solar material; time of formation of the solar system; chronology and evolution of the earth, moon and meteorites; establishment of dating methods using long-lived natural radio-activities; study of geologic and lunar processes using nuclear and isotopic effects as a tracer in nature; origin of natural gases; application of thermodynamic methods to geologic systems. *Mailing Add:* Arms Lab 170-25 Calif Inst Technol Pasadena CA 91125. *Fax:* 626-796-9823

**WASSERHEIT, JUDITH NINA,** MEDICAL RESEARCH. *Current Pos:* CHIEF, SEXUALLY TRANSMITTED DIS BR, NAT INST ALLERGY & INFECTIOUS DIS, NIH, 89- *Personal Data:* b Sept 2, 54. *Educ:* Princeton Univ, BA, 74; Harvard Med Sch, MD, 78; Johns Hopkins Univ, MPH, 89; Am Bd Internal Med, dipl, 83. *Prof Exp:* Co-dir, SE Asian Refugee Clin, Harborview Med Ctr, Univ Wash, Seattle & res fel infectious dis, 82-84; res physician infectious dis, Diarrhoeal Dis Res, Bangladesh, 84-86; asst prof, Dept Med, Div Infectious Dis, Johns Hopkins Univ, 86-89. *Concurrent Pos:* Asst chief, STD Clin Serv, Baltimore City Health Dept, 86-89, med dir, Druid STD Clin, 86-89 & fac STD training ctr, 86-89; mem steering comt, Task Force Prev & Mgt Infertil Human Reproduction Prog, WHO, 89-, Subcomt AIDS/STD Task Force, 90, res working group, Sexually Transmitted Dis Prog, 91, tech adv group, Women & AIDS Prog, Int Ctr Res Women, 91-; consult, Java & Bali Indonesia, Int Women's Health Coalition, 87, 88, 90, Cairo, Egypt, 89, Lusaka, Zambia, 89 & 91. *Mem:* Am Col Physicians; Am Soc Trop Med & Hyg; Am Med Women's Asn; Am Venereal Dis Asn; Nat Coun Int Health; Int AIDS Soc. *Res:* Prevention and management of infertility; sexually transmitted diseases. *Mailing Add:* 210 W 90th St New York NY 10024-1239

**WASSERMAN, AARON E,** FOOD CHEMISTRY. *Current Pos:* RETIRED. *Personal Data:* b Philadelphia, Pa, Dec, 28, 21; m 44, Mildred Kopaloff; c Harve J & Lee D. *Educ:* Philadelphia Col Pharm, BSc, 42, ScD(bact), 48; Mass Inst Technol, MSc, 47. *Honors & Awards:* Distinguished Res Award, Am Meat Sci Asn, 77; Distinguished Serv Award, Inst Food Technologists, 90; Super Serv Unit Award, USDA, 88. *Prof Exp:* Instr bact, Pa State Col Optom, 47; res assoc, Sharp & Dohme, Inc, 48-54; head, USDA, Meat Composition & Qual Invest, Meat Lab, 63-77, chemist & biochemist, Eastern Regional Res Ctr, 54-81, chief, Meat Lab, 77-81. *Concurrent Pos:* Ed, J Food Sci, 80-90. *Mem:* Am Meat Sci Asn; Am Chem Soc; fel Inst Food Technol. *Res:* Flavor chemistry; organoleptic and sensory evaluation of food products; isolation and identification techniques; food processing; meat technology; bacterial physiology and metabolism; food safety. *Mailing Add:* 2156 Conwell Ave Philadelphia PA 19115-2310

**WASSERMAN, AARON OSIAS,** VERTEBRATE ZOOLOGY. *Current Pos:* RETIRED. *Personal Data:* b New York, NY, Oct 15, 27; m 69; c 1. *Educ:* City Col New York, BS, 51; Univ Tex, PhD(zool), 56. *Prof Exp:* From asst prof to prof biol, City Col New York, 63-92; adj prof, William Paterson Col, 92-93. *Concurrent Pos:* Lectr, Univ Tex, 94-96. *Mem:* Sigma Xi. *Res:* Speciation problems in anuran amphibians; cytogenetics of anurans. *Mailing Add:* 40 IH-35 N Unit 11D3 Austin TX 78701-4332

**WASSERMAN, AARON REUBEN,** BIOCHEMISTRY. *Current Pos:* RETIRED. *Personal Data:* b Philadelphia, Pa, Apr 14, 32; div; c Joseph, Geoffrey & Sheila. *Educ:* Univ Pa, AB, 53; Univ Wis, MS, 57, PhD(biochem), 60. *Prof Exp:* Asst Univ Wis, 57-59; fel plant biochem, Johnson Found Med Physics, Univ Pa, 60-61, res assoc, Dept Chem, 61-62; fel, Enzyme Inst, Univ Wis-Madison & Dept Molecular Biol, Vanderbilt Univ, 63-65; from asst prof to assoc prof biochem, McGill Univ, 65-92. *Mem:* Can Biochem Soc. *Res:* Biomembranes; membrane proteins; cytochromes; bioenergetics; photosynthesis. *Mailing Add:* 4610 Mariette Ave Montreal PQ H4B 2G2 Can

**WASSERMAN, ALBERT J,** CLINICAL PHARMACOLOGY, INTERNAL MEDICINE. *Current Pos:* Instr, Med Col Va, 56-57, assoc, 57-60, from asst prof to assoc prof, 60-67, asst dean curric, 78-80, PROF MED & PHARMACOL, MED COL VA, 67-, ASSOC DEAN CURRIC, 80- *Personal Data:* b Richmond, Va, Jan 25, 28; m 48; c 3. *Educ:* Univ Va, BA, 47; Med Col Va, MD, 51. *Concurrent Pos:* Chief, Med Serv, Vet Admin Hosp, Richmond Va, 60-64. *Mem:* Am Col Physicians; Am Col Chest Physicians; Am Soc Clin Pharmacol & Therapeut; Am Fedn Clin Res. *Res:* Cardiovascular pharmacology; human pharmacology and drug trials. *Mailing Add:* Med Col Va Box 565 MCV Sta Richmond VA 23204-0565

**WASSERMAN, ALLEN LOWELL,** SOLID STATE PHYSICS. *Current Pos:* from asst prof to assoc prof, 65-83, PROF PHYSICS, ORE STATE UNIV, 84- *Personal Data:* b New York, NY, Dec 7, 34; m 58; c 2. *Educ:* Carnegie Inst Technol, BS, 56; Iowa State Univ, PhD(physics), 63. *Prof Exp:* Res assoc, Princeton Univ, 63-65. *Concurrent Pos:* Vis prof, Univ Sussex, Eng, 80, 87 & Univ Bristol, Eng, 90; vis res fel, Royal Soc, 90-91. *Mem:* Am Phys Soc; Sigma Xi. *Res:* Optical properties of solids; heavy fermians. *Mailing Add:* Dept Physics Ore State Univ Corvallis OR 97331-6507

**WASSERMAN, ARTHUR GABRIEL,** MATHEMATICS. *Current Pos:* asst prof, 68-70, assoc prof, 70-80, PROF MATH, UNIV MICH, ANN ARBOR, 80- *Personal Data:* b Bayonne, NJ, Nov 10, 38; m 64, 74; c 2. *Educ:* Mass Inst Technol, BS, 60; Brandeis Univ, PhD(math), 65. *Prof Exp:* Pierce instr math, Harvard Univ, 65-68. *Concurrent Pos:* Mem, Inst Advan Study, Princeton Univ, 71-72; vis prof, Unicamp, Campinas, Brazil, 80, Univ Oporto, Portugal, 81, Aarhus Univ, 84-85; managing partner, Diamond Venture Mgt, 88-91. *Mem:* Am Math Soc; Math Asn Am. *Res:* Topology; transformation groups; applied mathematics. *Mailing Add:* Dept Math E Hall Univ Mich Ann Arbor MI 48109-1109. *E-Mail:* awass@umich.edu

**WASSERMAN, BRUCE P,** ENZYME TECHNOLOGY, BIOLOGICAL MEMBRANES. *Current Pos:* From asst prof to assoc prof, 81-90, PROF FOOD SCI, RUTGERS UNIV, 90- *Personal Data:* b Brooklyn, NY, Aug 19, 53; m 84, Mary Lautzenheiser; c David. *Educ:* Rutgers Univ, BA, 75; Univ Mass, MS, 78, PhD(food sci), 79. *Honors & Awards:* Distinguished Scientist Award, Inst Food Technologists, 89. *Concurrent Pos:* Assoc ed, J Food Biochem. *Mem:* Am Soc Plant Physiologists; Inst Food Technologists; Am Chem Soc. *Res:* Starch struction, function and biosyntheses; plasma membrane enzyme complexes; cell wall polymer biogenesis. *Mailing Add:* Dept Food Sci Cook Col Rutgers Univ New Brunswick NJ 08903-0231

**WASSERMAN, DAVID,** POLYMER CHEMISTRY. *Current Pos:* sr res scientist, 64-68, PROJ LEADER, ETHICON, INC, 68- *Personal Data:* b New York, NY, Apr 6, 17; m 46; c 2. *Educ:* Brooklyn Col, AB, 37; Columbia Univ, PhD(org chem), 43. *Honors & Awards:* P B Hoffman Award for Res, Johnson & Johnson, Inc, 74. *Prof Exp:* Irvington Varnish & Insulator Co fel chem, Columbia Univ, 43-46; sr chemist, Irvinton Varnish & Insulator Div, Minn Mining & Mfg Co, 46-58, res assoc, Merck, Sharp & Dohme Res Div, 58-64. *Mem:* AAAS; NY Acad Sci; Am Chem Soc. *Res:* Synthetic polymers; organic synthesis; natural products; pharmaceutical chemistry; developed new synthetic absorbable suture. *Mailing Add:* 37 Cottage Lane Springfield NJ 07081-2302

**WASSERMAN, DONALD EUGENE,** ERGONOMICS, OCCUPATIONAL-HUMAN VIBRATION. *Current Pos:* CONSULT BIODYNAMICS, HUMAN VIBRATION & BIOMED ENG, 88- *Personal Data:* b New Haven, Conn, Apr 1, 39; m 67, Helen Schwartz; c Melissa & Sherri. *Educ:* Univ Conn, Storrs, BA, 62; NY Univ, MSEE, 71; Xavier Univ, MBA, 84. *Prof Exp:* Biomed proj engr, Mnemotron Div, Tech Measurements Corp, 62-63; sr biomed engr, Cambridge Instruments Co, 64; sr biomed proj & res engr, Perkin-Elmer Corp, 65-71; chief, Bioacoust & Occup Vibration Group, USPHS, Nat Inst Occup Safety & Health, Cincinnati, 71-84; dir, Eng & Opers & sr res investr, Nat Ctr Rehab Eng, Wright-State Univ, Dayton, 84-86; dir, Human Vibration Eng, Anatrol Corp, Cincinnati, 86-88. *Concurrent Pos:* Mem, Comt Hearing & Bioacoust, Nat Res Coun; consult, Am Conf Govt Indust Hygienists; reviewer, J Acoust Soc Am & J Occup Med. *Mem:* Int Stand Orgn; Am Nat Stand Inst. *Res:* Biomedical engineering; cardiovascular, peripheralvascular, neurological, ocular, auditory, muscle-skeletal, clinical chemistry, and rehabilitation engineering; biodynamics, biomechanics, and the effects of mechanical vibration on humans; author of 90 technical publications; holder of two US patents. *Mailing Add:* 7910 Mitchell Farm Lane Cincinnati OH 45242. *Fax:* 513-891-9084

**WASSERMAN, EDEL,** THEORETICAL CHEMISTRY, ORGANIC CHEMISTRY. *Current Pos:* assoc dir technol, 83-92, CHEM SCIENTIST, E I DUPONT DE NEMOURS & CO, INC, 80-, SCI ADV, CENT RES & DEVELOP, 93- *Personal Data:* b New York, NY, July 29, 32; m 55, Zelda L Rakovitz; c Stephen R & Diane C. *Educ:* Cornell Univ, BA, 53; Harvard Univ, AM, 54, PhD(chem), 59. *Prof Exp:* Mem tech staff, Bell Tel Labs, Inc, 57-76; prof chem, Rutgers Univ, 67-76; dir, Chem Res Ctr, Allied Chem, 76-78, & Corp Res Ctr, 78-80. *Concurrent Pos:* Vis prof, Cornell Univ, 62-63; adv ed, Chem Phys Lett, 68-79, J Am Chem Soc, 71-76 & Chem Rev, 82-; regent's lectr, Univ Calif, Irvine, 73. *Mem:* Am Chem Soc; Am Phys Soc. *Res:* Complex chemical systems. *Mailing Add:* 1904 Acad Pl Wilmington DE 19806-2135

**WASSERMAN, EDWARD,** PEDIATRICS. *Current Pos:* From clin asst to instr, NY Med Col, 51-54, asst, 54-55, clin assoc, 55-56, from asst prof to assoc prof, 56-64, PROF PEDIAT, NY MED COL, FLOWER & FIFTH AVE HOSPS, 64-, CHMN DEPT, 66- *Personal Data:* b New York, NY, Jan 13, 21. *Educ:* Johns Hopkins Univ, BA, 41; NY Med Col, MD, 46. *Concurrent Pos:* Mem pediat adv comt, Dept Health, New York, 64- *Mem:* Fel Am Fedn Clin Res; Am Acad Pediat. *Res:* Renal diseases. *Mailing Add:* NY Med Col Valhalla NY 10595

**WASSERMAN, FREDERICK E,** AVIAN BEHAVIORAL ECOLOGY. *Current Pos:* ASST PROF BIOL, BOSTON UNIV, 77- *Personal Data:* b New York, NY, Sept 19, 49; m 78; c 2. *Educ:* State Univ NY, Stony Brook, BS, 71; Univ Md, MS, 74, PhD(zool), 77. *Prof Exp:* Res asst, Smithsonian Inst, 75. *Concurrent Pos:* NSF grant, Orgn Trop Studies, 72; Harris Found grant,

74; Sigma Xi grant-in-aid res, 77; sr scientist, dept energy grant, 79-82; NIMH grant, 79-81 & 86-87; consult, Arthur D Little, Inc, 81-82. *Mem:* AAAS; Am Ornith Union; Animal Behav Soc; Am Soc Naturalists; Sigma Xi; Cooper Ornith Soc; Wilson Ornith Soc. *Res:* Functions of territoriality; ecological sources of selection; behavior of the white-throated sparrow and the rufous-sided towhee; effects of microwaves on birds; predatory relationship between birds and Lepidoptera; neuroendocrine correlates of aggression in birds. *Mailing Add:* Dept Biol Boston Univ 5 Cummington St Boston MA 02215

**WASSERMAN, GERALD STEWARD,** PSYCHOBIOLOGY, SENSORY CODING. *Current Pos:* PROF PSYCHOL, PURDUE UNIV, 75- *Personal Data:* b Brooklyn, NY, Nov 22, 37; m 62, Louise Mund; c Mark D & Rachel L. *Educ:* NY Univ, BA, 61; Mass Inst Technol, PhD(psychol), 65. *Prof Exp:* Fel electrophysiol, NIH, 65-67; from asst prof to assoc prof psychol, Univ Wis-Madison, 67-75. *Concurrent Pos:* Adv ed, Contemp Psychol, 81-87. *Mem:* Acoust Soc Am; Int Brain Res Orgn; fel Am Psychol; fel Optical Soc Am; Soc Neurosci. *Res:* Psychobiology of sensory coding with particular interest in natural and artificial receptor neurons. *Mailing Add:* Purdue Univ Dept Psychol Sci West Lafayette IN 47907-1364. *E-Mail:* codelab@psych.purdue.edu

**WASSERMAN, HARRY H,** ORGANIC CHEMISTRY. *Current Pos:* from instr to prof chem, Yale Univ, 48-62, dir grad studies, 60-62, chmn, Dept Chem, 62-65, dir Div Phys Sci, 72-75, Eugene Higgins prof, 82-91, EMER EUGENE HIGGINS PROF, DEPT CHEM, YALE UNIV, 91- *Personal Data:* b Boston, Mass, Dec 1, 20; m 47; c 3. *Educ:* Mass Inst Technol, BS, 41; Harvard Univ, MS, 42, PhD(org chem), 49. *Honors & Awards:* Catalyst Award, Chem Mfg Asn, 85; Aldrich Award, Am Chem Soc, 87. *Prof Exp:* Res asst, Off Sci Res & Develop, 45. *Concurrent Pos:* Guggenheim fel, 59-60; Am ed, Tetrahedron Lett, 60-; mem, Study Sect Med Chem, NIH, 62-66; mem, Postdoctoral Rev Panel, NSF, 63-65; vis lectr, Japanese Soc Prom Sci, 78; vis distinguished prof, Tex A&M Univ, 82; Arthur C Cope scholar, Am Chem Soc, 90. *Mem:* Nat Acad Sci; Am Acad Arts & Sci. *Res:* Natural products; reactions of organic systems with oxygen; cyclopropanones. *Mailing Add:* 192 Bishop St New Haven CT 06511-3718

**WASSERMAN, JACK F,** BIOMECHANICS & BIOACOUSTICS, AQUATIC SPORTS EQUIPMENT DEVELOPMENT. *Current Pos:* assoc prof, 79-85, PROF BIO MECH SIGNAL PROCESSING, DEPT ENG SCI & MECH, UNIV TENN, 85-, SHELL PROF, DEPT MECH & AERO ENG & ENG SCI. *Personal Data:* b Dayton, Ohio, July 29, 41; m 78, Betty McClain; c 3. *Educ:* Purdue Univ, BS, 64; Univ Cincinnati, MS, 71, PhD(mech eng & biomed acoust), 75. *Prof Exp:* Design engr, Gen Elec Co, 65-71; assoc dir, Stroke Res Lab, Univ Cincinnati, 75-79. *Concurrent Pos:* Adj assoc prof, Mech Eng Dept, Univ Cincinnati, 75-79; Vet Med, Univ Tenn; consult, Surg Appliances, Inc, 78-81, Patricia Neal Rehab Ctr, 80-81; prin investr, IBM, 82-83, Moore Mach Tool, 84, Electro-Optic, 84. *Mem:* Am Soc Mech Eng; Orthop Res Soc; Am Soc Biomech. *Res:* Finite element analysis, human vibration analysis; aquatic exercise equipment. *Mailing Add:* Dept Eng Sci & Mech Univ Tenn 310 Perkins Hall Knoxville TN 37996-2030

**WASSERMAN, JERRY,** INTERNATIONAL TRADE ISSUES. *Current Pos:* VPRES & DIR, ARTHUR D LITTLE, INC, 70- *Personal Data:* b Brooklyn, NY, Sept 22, 31; m 52, Maxine Kaplan; c Allen, David & Terri. *Educ:* City Col NY, BS, 51, MA, 53; Newark Col Eng, MSEE, 57. *Prof Exp:* Sales mgr, Lambda Electronics Corp, 61-67; gen mgr, Amerex Trading Corp, 67-69; pres, Intertrade Technol, Inc, 69-70. *Concurrent Pos:* Mem, Int Bus Coun, Electronics Industs Asn, 70-, Nat Asn Corp Dirs; dir, China Fund, 87- & Rosh Intel Systs, 88-93. *Res:* International trade issues, especially Far East and Israel; business issues faced by electronics and information industries. *Mailing Add:* 11 Winthrop Rd Lexington MA 02173. *Fax:* 617-498-7244

**WASSERMAN, KARLMAN,** PHYSIOLOGY, MEDICINE. *Current Pos:* CHIEF DIV RESPIRATORY DIS, HARBOR-UCLA MED CTR, TORRANCE, 67-; PROF MED, MED SCH, UNIV CALIF, LOS ANGELES, 72- *Personal Data:* b Brooklyn, NY, Mar 12, 27; m 53, Gail C; c 4. *Educ:* Upsala Col, BA, 48; Tulane Univ, PhD(physiol), 51, MD, 58. *Honors & Awards:* Walter B Cannon lectr & Award; Distinguished Scientist Award, Am Heart Asn. *Prof Exp:* Intern, Johns Hopkins Univ, 58-59; res fel med, Univ Calif, San Francisco, 59-61; asst prof med, Stanford Univ, 61-67, dir respiratory function lab & chest clin, 61-67; assoc prof, Med Sch, Univ Calif, Los Angeles, 67-72. *Mem:* Am Physiol Soc; Am Fedn Clin Res; Am Heart Asn; Am Thoracic Soc; Am Asn Physicians. *Res:* Respiratory, circulatory and renal physiology; respiratory disease. *Mailing Add:* Div Respiratory & Critical Care Physiol & Med Harbor UCLA Med Ctr 1000 W Carson St PO Box 405 Torrance CA 90509-9823

**WASSERMAN, LAWRENCE HARVEY,** PLANETARY ASTRONOMY. *Current Pos:* fel, 74-77, ASTRONR, LOWELL OBSERV, 77- *Personal Data:* b Bronx, NY, Oct 19, 45; m 70; c 3. *Educ:* Rensselaer Polytech Inst, BS, 67; Cornell Univ, MS, 71, PhD(astron), 73. *Prof Exp:* Res assoc astron, Lab Planetary Studies, Cornell Univ, 73-74. *Mem:* Am Astron Soc; Sigma Xi. *Res:* Studies of planets, satellites and asteroids by occultation techniques; astronomical image processing; photographic astrometry. *Mailing Add:* 1035 E Appalachian Rd Flagstaff AZ 86004

**WASSERMAN, LOUIS ROBERT,** HEMATOLOGY. *Current Pos:* prof med, Mt Sinai Sch Med, 66-72, chmn, Dept Clin Sci, 68-72, distinguished serv prof, 72-79, Albert A & Verg G List prof med hematology, 77-79, EMER PROF, MT SINAI SCH MED, 79- *Personal Data:* b New York, NY, July 11,

10; m 57, Julia Wheeler. *Educ:* Harvard Univ, AB, 31; Rush Med Col, MD, 35; Am Bd Internal Med, dipl, 46. *Prof Exp:* Intern, Michael Reese Hosp, 35-37; res fel, Mt Sinai Hosp, 37-39, clin asst, 40-42, adj physician physiol hemat, 47-50, assoc physician, 50-54, hematologist & dir dept hemat, 54-72. *Concurrent Pos:* Res fel, Donner Lab Med Physics, Univ Calif, 46-49, consult, Radiation Lab, 48-51; asst clin prof, Col Physicians & Surgeons, Columbia Univ, 51-60, assoc prof, 60-66; res collabr, Brookhaven Nat Lab, 60-72; chmn, Polycythemia Vera Study Group, Nat Cancer Inst, 67-, Nat Cancer Planning Comt, 72-73 & Cancer Control Comt, 72-73; diag rev adv group, 72-75; mem cancer treatment adv comt, 72-74 & chmn, 74-76. *Mem:* Fel Am Col Physicians; Int Soc Hemat (vpres, 70-74); Am Soc Hemat (vpres, 67-68, pres, 68-69); Asn Am Physicians; Am Asn Cancer Res. *Res:* Diseases of the blood; polycythemia vera study group; investigation of polycythemia vera and the myeloproliferative diseases. *Mailing Add:* Mt Sinai Sch Med 19 E 98th St Apt 5-B Box 1410 New York NY 10029

**WASSERMAN, MARTIN ALLAN,** pharmacology, for more information see previous edition

**WASSERMAN, MARTIN S,** CHILD PSYCHIATRY, PSYCHOANALYSIS. *Current Pos:* asst prof & assoc dir grad educ, Med Sch, 70-75, ASSOC CLIN PROF PSYCHIAT, UNIV SOUTHERN CALIF, 75-; SR FAC, LOS ANGELES PSYCHOANALYTIC SOC & INST, 88- *Personal Data:* b New York, NY, Jan 19, 38; m 63, 76, Francine Bartfield; c Gregory (deceased) & Eric. *Educ:* Columbia Col, AB, 59; State Univ NY Downstate Med Ctr, MD, 63. *Prof Exp:* Intern med, Albany Med Ctr, Union Univ, 64; resident psychiat, Kings County Gen Hosp, 64-67; instr, State Univ NY Downstate Med Ctr, 66-68; fel child psychiat, Univ Mich-Childrens Psychiat Hosp, 69-70. *Concurrent Pos:* Asst adj prof soc sci, Long Island Univ, 66-69; staff psychiatrist, Cath Charities, New York, 66-69; consult, Oper Headstart, Off Econ Opportunity, San Diego, Calif, 67-69, Ctr Forensic Psychiat, Mich, 69-70 & Bur Prisons, USPHS, 69-70; assoc, Los Angeles Psychoanal Soc & Inst, 70-75; dir & fac mem, Los Angeles Psychoanal Soc & Inst, 76-78, secy, 77-78; sr fac, LA Psychoanal Soc & Inst, 76-; psychiat consult, MGM, Columbia & 20th Century Fox Film Studios, 77-93. *Mem:* Fel Am Psychiat Asn; Am Col Psychiat; assoc Am Psychoanal Asn; Am Acad Child Psychiat. *Res:* College health; psychiatric education; socio-cultural factors in human development; film as developmental organizer; impact of coronary disease and the mind. *Mailing Add:* 510 E Channel Rd Santa Monica CA 90402

**WASSERMAN, MARVIN,** EVOLUTIONARY BIOLOGY. *Current Pos:* from asst prof to assoc prof, 62-67, PROF BIOL, QUEENS COL, NY, 67- *Personal Data:* b New York, NY, Feb 2, 29; m 64; c 2. *Educ:* Cornell Univ, BS, 50; Univ Tex, MA, 52, PhD(biol), 54. *Prof Exp:* Res assoc biol, Univ Tex, 56-60; sr lectr zool, Univ Melbourne, 60-62. *Mem:* Am Genetic Asn; Genetics Soc Am; Am Soc Naturalists; Soc Study Evolution. *Res:* Evolution and genetics of Drosophila; chromosomal polymorphism. *Mailing Add:* Biol Dept Queens Col Flushing NY 11367

**WASSERMAN, ROBERT II,** APPLIED MATHEMATICS. *Current Pos:* from asst prof to assoc prof, 57-70, prof math, 70-89, EMER PROF MATH, MICH STATE UNIV, 89- *Personal Data:* b Chicago, Ill, Jan 3, 23; m 48; c 1. *Educ:* Univ Chicago, BS, 43; Univ Mich, MS, 46, PhD(math), 57. *Prof Exp:* Aeronaut res scientist, Nat Adv Comt Aeronaut, 43-57. *Mem:* Am Math Soc; Math Asn Am. *Res:* Fluid mechanics. *Mailing Add:* Dept Math Mich State Univ East Lansing MI 48824-0001. *E-Mail:* wasser@math.msu.edu

**WASSERMAN, ROBERT HAROLD,** PHYSIOLOGY, BIOCHEMISTRY. *Current Pos:* assoc prof phys biol, NY State Col Vet Med, Cornell Univ, 57-63, prof physiol, 63-90, actg chmn dept physiol, 64, 71 & 75-76, chmn dept/sect physiol, Div Biol Sci, 83-87, JAMES LAW PROF PHYSIOL, COL VET MED, CORNELL UNIV, 90- *Personal Data:* b Schenectady, NY, Feb 11, 26; m 50, Marilyn Mintz; c Diane J, Arlene L & Judith R. *Educ:* Cornell Univ, BS, 49, PhD(nutrit), 53; Mich State Univ, MS, 51. *Honors & Awards:* Mead-Johnson Award Nutrit, Am Inst Nutrit, 69; Wise & Helen Burroughs lectr, Iona State Univ, 74; Andre Lichtwit Prize, Nat Inst Health & Med Res, Paris, 82; Merit Award, NIH, 88; Neuman Award, Am Soc Bone & Mineral Res, 90. *Prof Exp:* Asst bact, Mich State Univ, 49-50; asst animal nutrit, Cornell Univ, 51-53; res assoc biochem, Univ Tenn-AEC agr res prog, 53-55; sr scientist, Oak Ridge Inst Nuclear Studies, 55-57. *Concurrent Pos:* Lectr, Oak Ridge Inst Nuclear Studies, 57-59 & Int Atomic Energy Agency, Buenos Aires, 61; chmn, Conf Calcium & Strontium Transport, Cornell Univ, 62; Guggenheim fel, 64-65 & 72; vis fel, Inst Biol Chem, Denmark, 64-65; Orgn Econ Coop & Develop-NSF fel, 64-65; mem gen med B study sect, NIH, 68-72; consult, Dent Res Inst, NC Med & Dent Sch, Chapel Hill, 69; assoc ed, Calcified Tissue Res, 76-79; mem nutrit educ subcomt, Nat Nutrit Consortium, 77-; mem adv bd, Am Soc Bone & Mineral Res, 78-80; mem bd dirs, Cornell Vet, 81-90; mem, food & nutrit bd, Nat Acad Sci-Nat Res Coun, 84-87. *Mem:* Nat Acad Sci; Soc Exp Biol & Med; Am Physiol Soc; fel Am Inst Nutrit; Am Soc Bone & Mineral Res; AAAS. *Res:* Mechanisms by which various ions move across epithelial membranes particularly intestinal membranes; study of calcium, phosphorous, and action of vitamin D; macromolecules in intestinal mucosa that might be involved in ion movement. *Mailing Add:* Dept Physiol Cornell Univ 717 Vet Res Tower Ithaca NY 14853. *Fax:* 607-253-3851; *E-Mail:* rhwz@cornell.edu

**WASSERMAN, STANLEY,** APPLIED STATISTICS, SOCIAL SCIENCE. *Current Pos:* assoc prof, 82-88, PROF PSYCHOL, STATIST & SOCIOL, UNIV ILL, 88- *Personal Data:* b Louisville, Ky, Aug 29, 51; m 74, Sarah Wilson; c Andrew & Eliot. *Educ:* Univ Pa, BS & MA, 73; Harvard Univ, AM, 74, PhD(statist), 77. *Prof Exp:* Instr psychol, Harvard Univ, 76; vis instr urban

& pub affairs, Carnegie-Mellon Univ, 76-77; asst prof statics, Univ Minn, 77-82. *Concurrent Pos:* Res assoc social sci, Columbia Univ, 78; fel, Social Sci Res Coun, 78-79; co prin investr grants, NSF, 79, prin investr, 80-81, 85-89 & 93-; assoc ed, Sociol Methodology, 80-82, J Am Statist Asn, 87-, Psychometrika, 88-; dir, Math & Statist Consult Comt, 85-86 & 92-94; vis res fel, Univ Melbourne, 93. *Mem:* Am Sociol Asn; Am Statist Asn; Inst Math Statist; Royal Statist Soc; Sigma Xi; Psychomet Soc; AAAS. *Res:* Categorical data analysis; mathematical sociology; applied stochastic processes; mathematical psychology. *Mailing Add:* 1709 Pleasant St Urbana IL 61801-5830

**WASSERMAN, STEPHEN I,** INTERNAL MEDICINE. *Current Pos:* PROF MED & CHMN DEPT, MED CTR, UNIV CALIF, SAN DIEGO, 88- *Personal Data:* b Dec 17, 42; m 64, Linda Morgan; c Matthew & Zachary. *Educ:* Stanford Univ, BA, 64; Univ Calif, Los Angeles, MD, 68. *Prof Exp:* Assoc prof, Harvard Med Sch. *Concurrent Pos:* Mem bd dirs, Am Acad Allergy & Immunol, Am Bd Int Med & Am Bd Allergy & Immunol. *Mem:* Am Soc Clin Invest; Am Acad Allergy & Immunol (pres-elect); Am Asn Physicians; Am Bd Internal Med; Am Bd Allergy & Immunol. *Res:* Allergy; immunology. *Mailing Add:* Dept Med/8811-W Univ Calif San Diego Med Ctr 402 W Dickinson St San Diego CA 92103

**WASSERMAN, WILLIAM JACK,** ORGANIC POLYMER CHEMISTRY. *Current Pos:* INSTR CHEM, SEATTLE CENT COMMUNITY COL, 67- *Personal Data:* b New York, NY, Apr 27, 25; m 59, Harriet Marsh; c Wayland & Wyeth. *Educ:* Univ Calif, Los Angeles, BS, 47; Univ Southern Calif, MS, 50; Univ Wash, PhD(org chem), 54. *Prof Exp:* Asst prof chem, Humboldt State Univ, 54-57; sr res chemist, Martin-Marietta Corp, Wash, 57-62 & Truesdail Labs, Los Angeles, Calif, 62-63; asst prof chem, San Jose State Univ, 63-67. *Concurrent Pos:* Dir, NSF Inst Polymer Chem for Col Teachers, San Jose State Univ, 67 & NSF CAUSE proj, Ninety-Seattle Cent Community Col, 80-83; mem writing team, Am Chem Soc-NSF Chemtec Proj, 70-72; chmn, Puget Sound Sect, Am Chem Soc, 81, Nat Spring Meeting, 83; vis lectr, Chem Dept, Western Wash Univ, 89 & Univ Wash, 90, 91, 92; prog co-chair, Capilano Conf, Vancouver, 90, Two Year Col Chem Conf & Col Chem Can; counr, Nat Am Chem Soc, 90-; mem task force gen chem reform, Am Chem Soc, 92- *Mem:* Am Chem Soc; Sigma Xi. *Res:* Synthesis of condensation polymers; epoxies, polyesters, polyamides, polyurethanes; cross-linking agent synthesis and evaluation; aldol condensations with unsaturated ketones; grignard reactions of furan derivatives. *Mailing Add:* 1247 20th Ave E Seattle WA 98112-3530. *Fax:* 206-344-4390

**WASSERMAN, WILLIAM JOHN,** CELL BIOLOGY, DEVELOPMENTAL BIOLOGY. *Current Pos:* ASSOC PROF BIOL, LOYOLA UNIV CHICAGO, 94- *Personal Data:* b Toronto, Ont, Feb 27, 47. *Educ:* Univ Toronto, BSc, 69, MSc, 72, PhD(biol), 76. *Prof Exp:* Fel, Purdue Univ, 76-80; from asst prof to assoc prof, Univ Rochester, 80-91. *Concurrent Pos:* Prin investr, Univ Rochester, 81-94 & Loyola Univ Chicago, 94-; fel, NATO. *Mem:* AAAS; Am Soc Cell Biologists; Soc Develop Biol. *Res:* Determining the molecular mechanisms involved in controlling meiosis and mitosis, in oocytes and embryos. *Mailing Add:* Dept Biol Loyola Univ Lake Shore Campus Chicago IL 60626-0001. *Fax:* 773-508-3646; *E-Mail:* wwasser@orion.it.luc.edu

**WASSERMAN, ZELDA RAKOWITZ,** COMPUTATIONAL CHEMISTRY, MOLECULAR DESIGN. *Current Pos:* sr res scientist, 91-95, PRIN RES SCIENTIST, DU PONT MERCK PHARMACEUT CO, 95- *Personal Data:* b New York, NY, July 19, 35; m 55, Edel; c Stephen & Diane (Feldman). *Educ:* Radcliffe Col, AB, 56; Rutgers Univ, MS, 65. *Prof Exp:* Asst math, Mass Inst Technol, 56-57; mem tech staff, Bell Labs, 65-81; prin investr, E I du Pont de Nemours & Co, 81-90. *Mem:* Am Chem Soc; Asn Comput Mach. *Res:* Computational methods applied to design of pharmaceuticals, proteins and biomaterials. *Mailing Add:* Du Pont Merck Pharmaceut Co Exp Sta E500/3211 PO Box 80353 Wilmington DE 19880-0500. *E-Mail:* wasserzr@lldmpc.dnet.dupont.com

**WASSERMANN, FELIX EMIL,** EPIDEMIOLOGY, BIOMEDICAL ETHICS. *Current Pos:* from asst prof to assoc prof, 65-77, actg chmn dept, 70-76, PROF VIROL, NY MED COL, 77- *Personal Data:* b Bamberg, Ger, Aug 7, 24; US citizen; m 53; c 3. *Educ:* Univ Wis, BS, 49, MS, 50; NY Univ, PhD(microbiol), 57. *Prof Exp:* Res assoc microbiol, Univ Chicago, 58; asst virol, Pub Health Res Inst City New York, Inc, 58-60, from asst to assoc epidemiol, 60-65. *Mem:* Am Soc Microbiol; AAAS; NY Acad Med. *Res:* Virus-host cell interaction; viral genetics; epidemiology; biomedical ethics; medical ethics. *Mailing Add:* Dept Microbiol NY Med Col Valhalla NY 10595

**WASSERSUG, RICHARD JOEL,** EVOLUTIONARY BIOLOGY. *Current Pos:* assoc prod, 81-86, PROF ANAT, DALHOUSIE UNIV, 86- *Personal Data:* b Boston, Mass, Apr 13, 46; c 2. *Educ:* Tufts Univ, BS, 67; Univ Chicago, PhD(evolutionary biol), 73. *Prof Exp:* Asst prof syst & ecol & asst cur, Mus Natural Hist, Univ Kans, 73-74; asst prof anat & comt evolutionary biol, Univ Chicago, 74-81. *Mem:* Soc Study Evolution; Am Soc Ichthyologists & Herpetologists; AAAS; Ecol Soc Am; Am Soc Zoologists. *Res:* Adaptations of amphibian larvae, and of fish; studies on the evolution of complex life cycles and on the evolution of diversity. *Mailing Add:* Dept Anat Sir Charles Tupper Blvd Dalhousie Univ Halifax NS B3H 4H7 Can

**WASSHAUSEN, DIETER CARL,** SYSTEMATIC BOTANY. *Current Pos:* From asst cur to assoc cur dept bot, 69-76, CUR & CHMN DEPT BOT, MUS NATURAL HIST, SMITHSONIAN INST, 76- *Personal Data:* b Jena, Ger, Apr 15, 38; US citizen; m 61, Merrilee Locklin; c Lisa A & David B. *Educ:* George Washington Univ, BS, 63, MS, 66, PhD(bot), 72. *Honors & Awards:* Smithsonian Res Found awards, 74 & 75; Willdenow Medal, 79. *Mem:* Int Asn Plant Taxon; Am Soc Plant Taxon; Sigma Xi; AAAS; Am Inst Biol Sci. *Res:* Taxonomy of Acanthaceae and flowering plants of the New World tropics. *Mailing Add:* Dept Bot Mus Natural Hist Smithsonian Inst Washington DC 20560. *Fax:* 202-786-2563

**WASSMUNDT, FREDERICK WILLIAM,** ORGANIC CHEMISTRY. *Current Pos:* from instr to assoc prof, 58-92, EMER ASSOC PROF CHEM, UNIV CONN, 92- *Personal Data:* b Oak Park, Ill, Aug 6, 32; div; c Frederick W Jr. *Educ:* DePauw Univ, BA, 53; Univ Ill, PhD(chem), 56. *Prof Exp:* Instr chem, Univ Calif, 56-58. *Concurrent Pos:* Guest prof, Univ Heidelberg, 66-67; invited lectr, Chem Soc Heidelberg, 74; treas, 8th Biennial Conf Chem Educ, 82-85; nat treas, Phi Lambda Upsilon Hon Chem Soc, 84-90, nat pres, 90-96; consult, SmithKline Beecham, 90-91. *Mem:* Am Chem Soc; Royal Soc Chem; Sigma Xi. *Res:* Exploratory synthesis; reactions of organic nitrogen compounds; diazonium salts; bridged bicyclic compounds. *Mailing Add:* Dept Chem Univ Conn Storrs CT 06269-3060. *Fax:* 860-486-2981

**WASSOM, CLYDE E,** AGRONOMY. *Current Pos:* asst prof, 54-62, assoc prof, 62-76, PROF, KANS STATE UNIV, 76- *Personal Data:* b Osceola, Iowa, Feb, 6, 24; m 45; c 3. *Educ:* Iowa State Col, BS, 49, MS, 51, PhD(crop breeding), 53. *Prof Exp:* Technician agron, Iowa State Col, 47-51, res assoc, 51-54. *Concurrent Pos:* Temp staff mem, Int Ctr Improv Corn & Wheat, Mexico City, 67. *Mem:* Am Soc Agron. *Res:* Forage breeding; research and breeding for improvement of red clover and other legumes; corn breeding and genetics research. *Mailing Add:* 2407 Buena Vista Dr Manhattan KS 66502

**WASSON, JAMES A(LLEN),** PETROLEUM ENGINEERING. *Current Pos:* RETIRED. *Personal Data:* b Tyrone, Pa, July 5, 26; m 83; c 2. *Educ:* Pa State Univ, BS, 51 & 52, MS, 57. *Prof Exp:* Jr petrol engr, Humble Oil & Refining Co, Exxon, 56-58; asst prof petrol eng, La Polytech Inst, 58-60; from asst prof to assoc prof, WVa Univ, 60-80, chmn dept, 77-82, prof petrol eng, Col Mineral & Energy Resources, 80-96. *Concurrent Pos:* Staff res adv, US Dept Energy, Morgantown, WVa, 60-85. *Mem:* Am Inst Mining, Metall & Petrol Engrs. *Res:* Petroleum reservoir engineering; secondary recovery of oil; enhanced oil recovery. *Mailing Add:* 544 Lanceshire Lane State College PA 16803-1434

**WASSON, JAMES WALTER,** program management & project engineering, electronic systems integration, for more information see previous edition

**WASSON, JOHN R,** PHYSICAL CHEMISTRY, INORGANIC CHEMISTRY. *Current Pos:* PRES, ADVAN MAT, 89- *Personal Data:* b St Louis, Mo, Aug 22, 41; m 63; c 2. *Educ:* Univ Mo-Columbia, BS, 63, MA, 66; Ill Inst Technol, PhD(phys chem), 70. *Prof Exp:* Instr chem, Southern State Col, 65-66; asst prof chem, Univ Ky, 69-75; vis sr scientist, Univ NC, Chapel Hill, 75-78; dir, Chem Div, res dept, Lithium Corp Am, 78-81; pres, Kings Mountain Specialties, Inc, 81-82; pres, Syntheco Inc, 82-89. *Mem:* Am Chem Soc. *Res:* Transition metal complexes; polymers; electrolytes; specialty ceramics; inorganic synthesis. *Mailing Add:* Advan Mat 865 Pea Ridge Rd New Hill NC 27562-8947

**WASSON, JOHN TAYLOR,** COSMOCHEMISTRY, PLANETOLOGY. *Current Pos:* from asst prof to assoc prof, 64-72, PROF, UNIV CALIF, LOS ANGELES, 72- *Personal Data:* b Springtown, Ark, July 4, 34; m 60, Gudrun Hanewald; c 2. *Educ:* Univ Ark, BS, 55; Mass Inst Technol, PhD(nuclear chem), 58. *Honors & Awards:* Fel, Am Geophys Union; Leonard Medal, Meteoritical Soc, 92. *Prof Exp:* NSF fel tech physics lab, Munich Technol Univ, 58-59; res chemist geophys res directorate, Air Force Cambridge Res Labs, 59-63; NIH spec fel phys inst, Univ Berne, 63-64. *Concurrent Pos:* Guggenheim fel, Max Planck Inst Chem, 70-71. *Mem:* Am Geophys Union; Geochem Soc; Meteoritical Soc (pres, 79-80); Sigma Xi. *Res:* Composition and origin of the meteorites; major accretionary events on earth; geochemistry; solar nebula formation and evolution. *Mailing Add:* Inst Geophys Plan Phys Univ Calif Los Angeles CA 90095. *Fax:* 310-206-3051

**WASSON, L(OERWOOD) C(HARLES),** CORROSION SCIENCE, BIO-MEDICAL. *Current Pos:* PRES, L C WASSON CO, 74- *Personal Data:* b Denning, Ark, Feb 27, 09; m 36, 90, Jean E Vick; c 1. *Educ:* Univ Ark, BSEE, 33. *Prof Exp:* Shop foreman, Hydraul Lab, Tenn Valley Authority, 35-36; develop engr, Milwaukee Gas Specialty Co, 36-42, prod engr, 42-46, res engr, 46-48; asst chief engr, Durant Mfg Co, 48-49; elec res engr, A O Smith Corp, 49-52, dir, Electrochem Lab, 52-60, mat engr, 60-65, res scientist, 65-74. *Concurrent Pos:* Mem, Eng Med & Biol Group, Inst Elec & Electronics Engrs; nat dir, Nat Asn Corrosion Engrs Int, 58-61; consult, Aqua Dynamics Group Corp, Adamsville, Tenn, 87- *Mem:* Nat Asn Corrosion Engrs Int; Inst Elec & Electronics Engrs. *Res:* Cathodic protection theory and application; corrosion mechanisms and corrosion prevention techniques; electrochemistry of corrosion. *Mailing Add:* 8711 W Beloit Rd Apt 431 West Allis WI 53227. *Fax:* 414-771-4671

**WASSON, OREN A,** NUCLEAR PHYSICS. *Current Pos:* physicist, Nat Bur Stand, 73-78, PHYSICIST, NAT INST STAND & TECHNOL, 78- *Personal Data:* b Wooster, Ohio, Mar 27, 35; m 59, Anne Garcin; c David A & Douglas D. *Educ:* Col Wooster, BA, 57; Yale Univ, MS, 59, PhD(physics), 64. *Prof*

*Exp:* Res staff physicist, Yale Univ, 63-65; from res assoc physics to physicist, Brookhaven Nat Lab, 65-73. *Concurrent Pos:* Vis mem, Oak Ridge Nat Lab, 71-72; tech expert, Int Atomic Energy Agency, Greece, 75. *Mem:* AAAS; Am Phys Soc; Sigma Xi. *Res:* Experimental nuclear physics; neutron and photon reaction mechanisms; neutron cross sections and dosimetry. *Mailing Add:* 3713 Stoney Castle St Olney MD 20832-1331. *Fax:* 301-869-7682; *E-Mail:* wasson@enh.nist.gov

**WASSON, RICHARD LEE,** ORGANIC PROCESS CHEMISTRY, TECHNICAL MANAGEMENT. *Current Pos:* PVT SCI CONSULT, 90- *Personal Data:* b Farmington, Ill, May 19, 32; m 55, Neva Adams; c Nancy (Niemann) & Sue (Bohm). *Educ:* Univ Ill, BS, 53; Mass Inst Technol, PhD, 56. *Prof Exp:* Asst org chem, Mass Inst Technol, 53-56; sr res chemist, Monsanto Co, 56-63, res specialist, 63-66, res group leader, 66-71, mgr flavor-fragrance res, 71-76, mgr com develop, 76-77, mgr new prod/process res, 77-78, mgr technol planning, 78-80, dir technol support, 80-83; dir, Technol Planning & Eval, Indust Chem, G D Searle, 83-84, dir, chem develop, Health Care Div, 84-86, dir, develop, 86-89. *Mem:* Am Chem Soc; Am Inst Chem; NY Acad Sci. *Res:* Preparation and rearrangements of epoxides; halogenation and carboxylation of aromatic compounds; aromatic nitro compounds; basic condensations; organophosphate compounds; isolation and identification of natural products; food chemistry; organic analysis; environmental hazard assessment; process chemistry and scale up, biological research, technical management; peptide chemistry. *Mailing Add:* 8821 Hemingway Dr Crestwood MO 63126

**WASSON, W(ALTER) DANA,** COMPUTER SCIENCE, ELECTRICAL ENGINEERING. *Current Pos:* From asst prof to assoc prof elec eng, Univ NB, 58-70, head, comput sci dept, 69-74, dir, Comput Ctr, 64-74, PROF ELEC ENG, UNIV NB, FREDERICTON, 70- *Personal Data:* b NB, Apr 2, 34; m 59; c 2. *Educ:* Univ NB, BSc, 56; Mass Inst Technol, SM, 58; Univ Waterloo, PhD, 72. *Honors & Awards:* Bryden Jack Prize; EIC Prize. *Concurrent Pos:* Dir, Sch Comput Sci, Univ NB, Frederiction, 74-91, dean, fac comput sci, 91- *Mem:* Inst Elec & Electronics Engrs; Asn Prof Eng; Asn Comput Mach; Can Info Processing Soc; Pattern Recognition Soc. *Res:* Computer hardware and software; pattern recognition and active circuit analysis. *Mailing Add:* Dept Comput Sci Univ NB PO Box 4400 Fredericton NB E3B 5A3 Can

**WASTERLAIN, CLAUDE GUY,** EPILEPTOLOGY, CEREBRAL ISCHEMIA. *Current Pos:* assoc prof, 76-79, PROF NEUROL, UNIV CALIF, LOS ANGELES SCH MED, 79-, VCHMN DEPT, 76- *Personal Data:* b Courcelles, Belg, Apr 15, 35; US citizen; m 57, Anne; c 1. *Educ:* Univ Liege, CSc, 57, MD, 61; Free Univ Brussels, LSc, 69. *Honors & Awards:* Milken Family Found Award, Am Epilepsy Soc, 92. *Prof Exp:* Asst physiol, Univ Liege, Belg, 61-63; intern, Middlesex Mem Hosp, 63-64; resident neurol, NY Hosp, Cornell Univ Med Col, 64-67, from instr to assoc prof neurol, 69-76. *Concurrent Pos:* Chief neurol serv, Vet Admin Med Ctr, Sepulveda, Calif, 76- & Olive View Med Ctr, 88-89; attend neurologist, Univ Calif-Los Angeles Hosp, 79-; mem, Brain Res Inst, Univ Calif-Los Angeles, 77-; chief epilepsy res, Vet Admin Med Ctr, 76-; mem prof adv bd, Epilepsy Found Am, 79-, Nat Ataxia Found, 80-; chair Antiepileptic Drug Develop Comt, NIH, 86-88, res career develop award, 73-76. *Mem:* Am Neurol Asn; fel Am Acad Neurol; Am Soc Neurochem; Am Epilepsy Soc; Int Soc Neurochem. *Res:* Use biochemical and pharmacological methods to investigate how epilepsy is acquired, and how epileptic seizures or ischemia can damage the brain and impair its development. *Mailing Add:* Neurol Serv 127 Vet Admin Med Ctr Sepulveda CA 91343. *Fax:* 818-895-5801

**WASTI, KHIZAR,** TOXICOLOGY. *Current Pos:* toxicologist, 78-92, DIR, BUR TOXIC SUBSTANCES, VA STATE DEPT HEALTH, RICHMOND, 92- *Personal Data:* b Jan 27, 48; US citizen; m 76, Suraiya Zaidi; c Nylah F. *Educ:* Univ Punjab, Pakistan, BSc, 66; Univ Peshawar, MSc, 69; Marshall Univ, MS, 72; Univ Pa, PhD(chem), 76. *Prof Exp:* Sr lectr chem, Edwardes Col, Pakistan, 69-71; teaching asst, Marshall Univ, 71-72; teaching fel, Univ Pa, 73-75; res chemist, McNeil Labs, Ft Washington, Pa, 74, Campbell Soup Co, Camden, NJ, 74-75; proj mgr & sr info analyst, Toxicol Dept, Res Labs, Franklin Inst, 75-78. *Mem:* Am Col Toxicol; fel Am Inst Chemists; fel Royal Soc Chem. *Mailing Add:* Bur Toxic Substances Info Va State Dept Health PO Box 2448 Richmond VA 23218

**WASYLISHEN, RODERICK ERNEST,** CHEMISTRY. *Current Pos:* assoc prof, 82-86, PROF CHEM, DALHOUSIE UNIV, 86-, FAC SCI KILLAM PROF, 95- *Personal Data:* b Elk Point, Alta, July 6, 44; m 68, Valerie Burrows; c Stephen & Eric. *Educ:* Univ Waterloo, BSc, 68; Univ Man, MSc, 70, PhD(phys chem), 72. *Honors & Awards:* Gerhard Herzberg Award, Can Spectros Soc, 94. *Prof Exp:* Res fel, NIH, Bethesda, Md, 72-74; from asst prof to assoc prof chem, Univ Winnipeg, 74-82. *Concurrent Pos:* Vis prof, Univ Guelph, 80-81; Killam sr fel, Dalhousia Univ, 86-87; Can Coun Killiam fel, 95-97; ed, Can J Chem (Magnetic Resonance). *Mem:* Chem Inst Can; Am Chem Soc; Sigma Xi; Int Soc Magnetic Resonance; Spectros Soc Can. *Res:* Characterization of nuclear magnetic shielding, j-coupling and EFG tensors using single crystal nuclear magnetic resonsnace techniques; applications of high-resolution, multinuclear CP-MAS nuclear magnetic resonance spectroscopy in studying molecular structure and conformation. *Mailing Add:* Dept Chem Dalhousie Univ Halifax NS B3H 4J3 Can. *Fax:* 902-494-1310; *E-Mail:* rod@is.dal.ca

**WASYLKIWSKYJ, WASYL,** ELECTROMAGNETICS. *Current Pos:* AT DEPT ELEC ENG, GEORGE WASHINGTON UNIV. *Personal Data:* b Kowel, Ukraine, Feb 12, 35; US citizen; m 60; c 2. *Educ:* City Col New York, BEE, 57; Polytech Inst Brooklyn, MS, 65, PhD(elec eng), 68. *Honors &*

*Awards:* Spec Commendation Award, Inst Elec & Electronics Engrs Antennas & Propagation Soc, 72. *Prof Exp:* Microwave component design engr, Missiltron Inc, NY, 59-60; at Consult & Designers, NY, 60-62; sr tech specialist, ITT Defense Commun Div, Int Tel & Tel Corp, NJ, 62-69; mem tech staff, Inst Defense Anal, 69- *Concurrent Pos:* Consult, ITT Fed Labs, NJ, 63-65; prof lectr, George Washington Univ, 70-; mem comns B & C, Int Union Radio Sci. *Mem:* Inst Elec & Electronics Engrs. *Res:* Electromagnetic radiation and diffraction, guided wave and cavity theory; antenna theory, particularly antenna arrays; microwave technology, particularly parametric and solid state microwave devices. *Mailing Add:* Dept Elec Eng & Comp Sci George Washington Univ 2029 G St NW Washington DC 20006-4211

**WASYLYK, JOHN STANLEY,** GLASS TECHNOLOGY, CERAMIC SCIENCE. *Current Pos:* DIR INT CONSULT SERV, AGR INT, INC, 89- *Personal Data:* b Passaic, NJ, Feb 15, 42; m 69; c 2. *Educ:* Rutgers Univ, BS, BA, 64, PhD(ceramics sci), 70. *Prof Exp:* Pres & tech dir, Glass Container Indust Res Corp, 69-76; tech dir, Am Glass Res Inc, 76-86, dir res, 86-88, dir corp res, 88-89. *Mem:* Am Ceramic Soc; Am Soc Testing & Mat; Soc Glass Technol; Nat Inst Ceramic Engrs; Ger Glass Technol Soc. *Res:* Glass technology; heat transfer during forming and relation to workability; glass microanalysis; lubricating coatings on glass surfaces; glass strength; glass fracture analysis; statistical sampling methods; container production process improvements. *Mailing Add:* 107 Beverly Rd Butler PA 16001

**WAT, BO YING,** MEDICINE. *Current Pos:* From asst to assoc prof, 58-62, PROF PATH, SCH MED, LOMA LINDA UNIV, 62- *Personal Data:* b Honolulu, Hawaii, Feb 15, 25; m 48; c 4. *Educ:* Col Med Evangelists, MD, 49; Am Bd Path, dipl. *Mem:* Am Soc Clin Pathologists; AMA. *Mailing Add:* Dept Path Loma Linda Univ Box 546 Loma Linda CA 92354-0546

**WAT, EDWARD KOON WAH,** ORGANIC CHEMISTRY. *Current Pos:* res chemist, Cent Res Dept, 66-77, RES CHEMIST, BIOCHEM DEPT, EXP STA, E I DU PONT DE NEMOURS & CO, INC, 77- *Personal Data:* b Honolulu, Hawaii, Aug 27, 40; m 69; c 3. *Educ:* Univ Hawaii, BA, 62; Stanford Univ, PhD(chem), 66. *Prof Exp:* NIH fel chem, Harvard Univ, 65-66. *Mem:* Am Chem Soc. *Res:* Synthetic organic chemistry and process development for agricultural and pharmaceutical applications. *Mailing Add:* 216 W Pembrey Dr Wilmington DE 19803-2008

**WATABE, NORIMITSU,** ELECTRON MICROSCOPY, BIOMINERALIZATION. *Current Pos:* from assoc prof to prof, Univ SC, 70-93, dir, Electron Micros Ctr, 70-94,distinguished prof, 93-94, DISTINGUISHED EMER PROF BIOL & MARINE SCI, UNIV SC, 94- *Personal Data:* b Kure City, Japan, Nov 29, 22; m 52, Sakuko Kobayashi; c Shoichi & Sachiko(McAlhany). *Educ:* Tohoku Univ, Japan, MS, 48, DSc, 60. *Honors & Awards:* Elmer Elseworth Award, 52; Humboldt Award, Ger, 76. *Prof Exp:* Res investr biocrystallog pearl cult, Fuji Pearl Res Lab, Japan, 48-52; asst fac fisheries, Mie Prefectural Univ, Japan, 52-55, lectr, 55-59, consult, Fisheries Exp Sta, 53-59; res assoc calcification electron micros, Duke Univ, 57-70. *Concurrent Pos:* Asst, Tohoku Univ, Japan, 48-49; consult, Ford Found Off Latin Am & Caribbean, 68 & SC State Develop Bd, 75-; Russel res award, Univ SC, 80; Nat Inst Dent Res & NSF grants. *Mem:* AAAS; Micros Soc Am; Am Soc Zool; Am Micros Soc; Am Malac Union; fel AAAS. *Res:* Microanatomy; ultrastructural and physiological aspects of mechanism of calcification in invertebrates, algae and fish. *Mailing Add:* 3510 Greenway Dr Columbia SC 29206

**WATADA, ALLEY E,** HORTICULTURE, PLANT PHYSIOLOGY. *Current Pos:* invests leader, USDA, 71-72, proj leader, 72-81, res food technologist, 71-81, CHIEF HORT CROPS QUAL LAB, HORT SCI INST, AGR RES SERV, USDA, 81- *Personal Data:* b Platteville, Colo, July 20, 30; m 56, Yoshimi Hasui; c Pamela & Stuart. *Educ:* Colo State Univ, BS, 52, MS, 53; Univ Calif, Davis, PhD(plant physiol), 65. *Prof Exp:* Lab technician, Univ Calif, Davis, 56-65; from asst prof to assoc prof hort, WVa Univ, 65-71. *Mem:* Fel Am Soc Hort Sci; Am Soc Plant Physiol; Inst Food Technol; Am Inst Biol Sci. *Res:* Postharvest physiology of fruits and vegetables; development of methods for maintaining quality of intact and partially processed fruits and vegetables and determining the mechanisms of regulation of senescence. *Mailing Add:* 3539 Duke St College Park MD 20740. *Fax:* 301-504-5107

**WATANABE, AKIRA,** COMMUNICATIONS SCIENCE. *Current Pos:* ASST PROF, UNIV TOKYO, JAPAN. *Personal Data:* b Vancouver, BC, Sept 17, 35; m 57; c 5. *Educ:* McMaster Univ, BSc, 57; Univ Toronto, MA, 62, PhD(molecular physics), 64. *Prof Exp:* Sci off, 57-69, res scientist, dept commun, Defence Res Telecommun Estab, 69- *Concurrent Pos:* Sci counr, Can Embassy, Tokyo, 76-79. *Mem:* Can Asn Physicists; Optical Soc Am; Inst Elec & Electronics Engrs. *Res:* Optical communications; thin-film waveguides and spectroscopy; laser physics. *Mailing Add:* Suzuka Univ Med Sci & Tech Kishioka Suzuka 510-02 Japan

**WATANABE, DANIEL SEISHI,** COMPUTER SCIENCE. *Current Pos:* assoc dean, Col Natural Sci, 90-92, PROF & CHMN, DEPT INFO & COMPUT SCI, UNIV HAWAII AT MANOA, HONOLULU, 84- *Personal Data:* b Honolulu, Hawaii, Oct 30, 40; div; c David. *Educ:* Harvard Univ, AB, 62, AM, 67, PhD(appl math), 70. *Prof Exp:* Mathematician, Baird-Atomic, Inc, 63-64; asst prof to assoc prof comput sci, Univ Ill, Urbana, 70-83. *Concurrent Pos:* Vis scholar, Tokyo Univ, 79. *Mem:* Sigma Xi; Asn Comput Mach. *Res:* Numerical software; simulation of semiconductor devices. *Mailing Add:* 60 N Beretania St Apt 3402 Honolulu HI 96817-4763. *Fax:* 808-956-3548; *E-Mail:* watanabe@hawaii.edu

**WATANABE, ITARU S,** NEUROPATHOLOGY. *Current Pos:* UNIT DIR, PATH, VET ADMIN MED CTR, 72- *Personal Data:* b Sapporo, Japan, June 20, 33; US citizen; wid; c 3. *Educ:* Keio Univ Sch Med, MD, 58, DMSc, 63. *Prof Exp:* Fel, Sch Med, Ind Univ, 64-69, asst prof, 69-72; assoc prof, Sch Med, Univ Kans, 72-77, prof path, 77. *Mem:* Am Asn Neuropathologists; Soc Neurosci; Int Congress Neuropath; Am Asn Pathologists; AMA. *Res:* Neuropathologic studies of various brain disorders, particularly their ultrastructural aspects. *Mailing Add:* 30 Dundee Circle Belton MO 64012

**WATANABE, KYOICHI A,** ORGANIC & MEDICINAL CHEMISTRY, BIOCHEMISTRY. *Current Pos:* DIR MED CHEM, CODON PHARMACEUT, INC, 96- *Personal Data:* b Amagasaki, Japan, Feb 28, 35; m 62, Kiyoko; c Kanna, Kay, Kenneth, Kim, Kelly & Katharine. *Educ:* Hokkaido Univ, BA, 58, MA, 60, PhD(chem), 63. *Honors & Awards:* Boleslawa Szarecky Medal, 88. *Prof Exp:* Lectr chem, Sophia Univ, Japan, 63; res assoc, Sloan-Kettering Inst, 63-66; res fel, Univ Alta, 66-68; from assoc to assoc mem, Sloan-Kettering Inst, 68-80, mem chem, 80-95. *Concurrent Pos:* Assoc prof, Sloan-Kettering Div, Grad Sch Med Sci, Cornell Univ, 72-80, prof, 81-95, adj prof, 95-; mem, Med Chem A Study Sect, NIH, 81-84. *Mem:* Pharm Soc Japan; Am Chem Soc; Am Asn Cancer Res; Int Asn Heterocyclic Chem; NY Acad Sci; Korean Pharm Soc; AAAS; hon mem Polish Chem Soc. *Res:* Structure, syntheses, reactions and stereochemistry of nitrogen heterocyclics, carbohydrates, nucleosides and antibiotics of potential biological activities; medicinal chemistry; antitumor and antiviral compounds; chemistry of nucleic acids. *Mailing Add:* Codon Pharmaceut Inc 200 Perry Pkwy Gaithersburg MD 20877. *Fax:* 301-208-6997

**WATANABE, MAMORU,** MEDICINE, ENDOCRINOLOGY. *Current Pos:* head, Div Med, Univ Calgary, 74-76, assoc dean educ, 76-80, assoc dean res, 80-81, actg dean, 81, PROF MED, UNIV CALGARY, 73-, DEAN, 82- *Personal Data:* b Vancouver, BC, Mar 15, 33; m 74; c 1. *Educ:* McGill Univ, BSc, 55, MD, CM, 57, PhD, 63; FRCPS(C), 63. *Prof Exp:* Assoc molecular biol, Albert Einstein Col Med, 65-66, asst prof, 66-67; from assoc prof med & biochem to prof med, Univ Alta, 67-73. *Concurrent Pos:* Ayerst fel, Endocrine Soc, 63-64; res fel, Am Col Physicians, 64-67; dir dept med, Foothills Hosp, Calgary, Alta. *Mem:* Am Soc Microbiol; Can Med Asn. *Res:* Secretion rate of aldosterone in normal and abnormal pregnancy; replication of RNA bacteriophages; transport of steroids across cell membranes, using Pseudomonas testosteroni as a model system. *Mailing Add:* Dept Int Med Keio Univ Sch Med 35 Shinanomachi Shinjuku-Ku Tokyo 160 Japan

**WATANABE, MICHIKO,** CELL-CELL ADHESION, CARDIOGENESIS. *Current Pos:* sr res assoc, Dept Genetics, 84-88, ASST PROF, DEPT PEDIAT, SCH MED, CASE WESTERN RES UNIV, 88- *Personal Data:* b Hakodate, Japan, Dec 5, 52; US citizen. *Educ:* Univ Calif, Berkeley, BA, 75; Wesleyan Univ, PhD(develop biol), 81. *Prof Exp:* Res assoc, Dept Biol, Ind Univ, 81-83. *Concurrent Pos:* Assoc lectr, Ohio Col Podiat Med, 83-84; Young anatomist, Am Asn Anatomist, 91-93. *Mem:* Am Soc Cell Biol; Soc Develop Biol; Asn Res Vision & Opthal; Am Heart Asn; Am Asn Anatomist. *Res:* Cell adhesion molecules in embryogenesis; cardiogenesis using immunological reagents and enzymes to purify, localize and probe function in vitro and in vivo. *Mailing Add:* Dept Pediat Div Cardiol Sch Med Case Western Res Univ Rainbow Babies & Childrens Hosp 11100 Euclid Ave Cleveland OH 44106. *Fax:* 216-844-5478

**WATANABE, MYRNA EDELMAN,** HERPETOLOGY, CROCODILIANS. *Current Pos:* PRES, ME WATANABE CONSULT INC, 88- *Personal Data:* b New York, NY, Dec 19, 48; m 84, Peter Brazaitis; c Peter J Brazaitis IV. *Educ:* Barnard Col, AB, 70; NY Univ, MS, 78, PhD(biol), 80. *Prof Exp:* Lectr biol, New York City Community Col, 74-77; instr physiol & biochem, NY Col Podiatric Med, 78-79; asst prof physiol, 79-81; res fel, Nat Prog Adv Study Res, China, 81; asst prof biol, Wagner Col, 82-83; contrib ed, Nature Publ Co, 83-84; assoc, Chemi Serv Assocs Inc, 86-88; pres, ProEx Corp, 87-88. *Concurrent Pos:* Consult, Porton Int Inc, 84-92; adj asst prof animal behav, Marymount Col, 87, Long Island Univ, 91; vis asst prof genetics & physiol, Manhattan Col, 89-91; adj assoc prof biol, Iona Col, 89-91; prin investr, World Wildlife Fund, 90; asst managing ed, Genetic Eng News, 92-93. *Mem:* AAAS; Sigma Xi; Tissue Cult Asn. *Res:* Physiology and behavior of crocodilians; biotechnology and ecology. *Mailing Add:* 51 Landscape Ave Yonkers NY 10705. *Fax:* 914-376-7487; *E-Mail:* myrna.watanabe@execnet.com

**WATANABE, PHILIP GLEN,** TOXICOLOGY, PHARMACOLOGY. *Current Pos:* Assoc scientist, Toxicol Lab, Health & Environ Sci, 74-82, DIR TOXICOL, DOW CHEM CO, 82- *Personal Data:* b Inglewood, Calif, Mar 23, 47. *Educ:* Univ Calif, BS, 69; Utah State Univ, PhD(toxicol), 74; Am Bd Toxicol, dipl, 80. *Honors & Awards:* F R Blood Award, Soc Toxicol, 78 & Achievement Award, 80. *Concurrent Pos:* Vis lectr, Sch Pub Health, Univ Mich, 68-79; toxicol comt, Nat Acad Sci-Nat Res Coun, 78-82. *Mem:* Soc Toxicol; Am Soc Pharmacol & Exp Therapeut; AAAS; Sigma Xi. *Res:* Molecular toxicology; interaction of chemicals with intracellular macromolecules to facilitate the assessment of hazards of chemical exposure. *Mailing Add:* 3425 Lawndale Dr Midland MI 48642. *Fax:* 517-638-9273

**WATANABE, TAKESHI,** IMMUNOLOGY. *Current Pos:* PROF IMMUNOL, MED INST BIOREGULATION, KYUSHU UNIV, 85- *Personal Data:* b Osaka, Japan, July 15, 40; m 69, Tsugiko; c Hiroko, Tomoko & Ayako. *Educ:* Osaka Univ, MD, 66, PhD(immunol), 77. *Prof Exp:* Physician internal med, Osaka Univ Hosp, 67-69; res assoc immunol, Roswell Park Mem Inst, 69-72; asst prof internal med, Sch Med, Osaka Univ, 72-80; prof immunol, Saga Med Sch, Japan, 80-85. *Concurrent Pos:* Researcher immunol, Basel Inst Immunol, 75-77. *Mem:* Am Asn Immunologists. *Res:* Investigation on the allergic and immunological disorders from molecular as well as clinical aspects. *Mailing Add:* Med Inst Bioregulation Kyushu Univ Maidashi 3-1-1 Higashi-ku Fukuoka 812 Japan. *Fax:* 81-92-641-1315

**WATANABE, TOMIYA,** aeronomy, plasma physics, for more information see previous edition

**WATANABE, YOICHI,** RADIATION PHYSICS, RADIATION THERAPY. *Current Pos:* res fel, 94-97, CLIN ASST PHYSICIST, MEM SLOAN-SETTERING CANCER CTR, 97- *Personal Data:* b Miyagi, Japan, June 1, 54; m, Mariko Tsutsumi; c Shin. *Educ:* Univ Tokyo, BS, 78; Univ Tsukuba, MS, 80; Univ Wis-Madison, MS, 82, PhD(nuclear eng), 84. *Honors & Awards:* Nat Res Serv Award, NIH, 95. *Prof Exp:* Assoc develop engr, Univ Calif, 87-89; res engr, Univ Fla, 89-94. *Concurrent Pos:* Vis researcher, Japan Atomic Energy Res Inst, 87. *Mem:* Am Nuclear Soc; Am Asn Physicists Med; Inst Elec & Electronics Engrs; AAAS. *Res:* Physics of radiation interaction with matter, in particular, cellular substances for treatment of cancers; develop better tools for therapy of cancers. *Mailing Add:* Dept Med Phys MSKCC 1275 York Ave New York NY 10021. *E-Mail:* watanaby@mskcc.org

**WATANABE, YOSHIO,** cardiac electrophysiology, electrocardiography, for more information see previous edition

**WATANAKUNAKORN, CHATRCHAI,** INFECTIOUS DISEASES, HOSPITAL EPIDEMIOLOGY. *Current Pos:* DIR INFECTIOUS DIS, ST ELIZABETH HEALTH CTR, 79-, HOSP EPIDEMIOLOGIST, 91-; PROF INTERNAL MED, NORTHERN OHIO UNIVS COL MED, 79- *Personal Data:* b Bangkok, Thailand, Sept 6, 35; US citizen; m 67, Eleanor Good; c Maria I (Poppe) & Paul W. *Educ:* Univ Med Sci, Thailand, MD, 61. *Honors & Awards:* Distinguished Int Physician Award, Am Col Int Physicians, 95. *Prof Exp:* Intern med, Chulalongkorn Hosp, 61-62; intern, St Francis Hosp, Pittsburgh, Pa, 62-63; resident, Cook County Hosp, Chicago, Ill, 63-64; NIH fel clin nutrit, Univ Iowa, 64-65, resident med, 65-66; instr, Univ Cincinnati, 66-79, from asst prof to prof med, 68-79. *Concurrent Pos:* Asst attend physician, Cincinnati Gen Hosp, Ohio, 70-72; attend physician, 73-79; attend physician, Holmes Hosp & Vet Admin Hosp, Cincinnati, 71-79, St Elizabeth Hosp Med Ctr, 79-; consult infectious dis, Drake Mem Hosp & clin microbiol, Vet Admin Hosp, 71-79; consult ed, Am J Med, 77-78; actg dir infectious dis, Univ Cincinnati, 78-79; mem comt rheumatic fever & bacterial endocarditis, AHA, 81-89. *Mem:* Sigma Xi; fel Infectious Dis Soc Am; fel Am Col Chest Physicians; fel Am Col Physicians; Am Soc Microbiol; Soc Healthcare Epidemiol Am. *Res:* Clinical infectious diseases especially in the area of bacteremia and endocarditis; antimicrobial agents especially in combination; staphylococcal infections; streptpcoccal infections. *Mailing Add:* 1044 Belmont Ave Youngstown OH 44501-1790

**WATENPAUGH, KEITH DONALD,** PHYSICAL CHEMISTRY & BIOCHEMISTRY, PROTEIN CRYSTALLOGRAPHY *Current Pos:* sr scientist IV & V, 84-95, DISTINGUISHED SCIENTIST VI, PHARMACIA & UPJOHN, 95- *Personal Data:* b Amarillo, Tex, Sept 3, 39; m 63, Joyce Fischer; c 3. *Educ:* Univ Idaho, BS, 62; Mont State Univ, PhD(chem), 67. *Prof Exp:* Sr fel, Univ Wash, 66-69, res assoc, 69 & 72, from asst prof to assoc prof biochem & molecular struct, 72-87. *Concurrent Pos:* Chair, Struct Biol Synchrotron Users Asn, 89-92 & Indust Macro-Molecular Crystallog Asn, 93-94. *Mem:* Am Crystallog Asn (vpres, 91, pres, 92); AAAS; Protein Soc. *Res:* Structure and mechanisms of electron transport proteins, protein-substrate interactions; computer modelling of molecular structure and interactions; structure-based drug design. *Mailing Add:* Struct Analysis & Med Chem Pharmacia & Upjohn 301 Henrietta St Kalamazoo MI 49001-0199. *E-Mail:* kdwatenp@am.pnu.com

**WATERBURY, LOWELL DAVID,** PHARMACOLOGY. *Current Pos:* staff researcher, 74-80, SR STAFF RESEARCHER, DEPT EXP PHARMACOL, SYNTEX RES, 80- *Personal Data:* b Lansing, Mich, Jan 8, 42. *Educ:* Univ Mich, BS, 64; Univ Vt, PhD(pharmacol), 68. *Prof Exp:* Technician, Univ Mich, 62-64, asst lab instr bot, 62; from instr to asst prof biochem, Inst Lipid Res, Col Med, Baylor Univ, 67-69; asst prof pharmacol, Bowman Gray Sch Med, Wake Forest Univ, 69-74. *Mem:* AAAS; Am Soc Pharmacol & Exp Therapeut; Am Chem Soc; Am Fedn Clin Res; Asn Res Vision & Ophthal. *Res:* Biochemical pharmacology; ocular pharmacology; drugs affecting diabetic retinopathy, cataracts, and ocular inflammation; drugs affecting gastric mucus production and plasma renin activity; determination of mechanism of action of newly synthesized therapeutic agents. *Mailing Add:* Centaur Pharmaceut 484 Oakmead Pkwy Sunnyvale CA 94086

**WATERHOUSE, BARRY D,** NEUROPHYSIOLOGY, NEUROPHARMACOLOGY. *Current Pos:* ASSOC PROF PHYSIOL & BIOPHYS, HAHNEMANN UNIV, PHILADELPHIA, 87- *Personal Data:* b Oct 14, 49; m 73; c 2. *Educ:* Temple Univ, PhD(pharmacol), 78. *Prof Exp:* Asst prof cell biol & anat, Univ Tex Health Sci Ctr, 81-87. *Concurrent Pos:* Klingenstein fel Neurosci. *Mem:* Soc Neurosci; Sigma Xi; Am Soc Pharmacol & Exp Therapeut. *Res:* Neurobiology. *Mailing Add:* Dept Physiol & Biophys Allegheny Univ Health Sci Broad & Vine Sts Philadelphia PA 19102-1192. *Fax:* 215-762-1982

**WATERHOUSE, HOWARD N,** ANIMAL NUTRITION, POULTRY MANAGEMENT. *Current Pos:* CONSULT, POULTRY & ANIMAL NUTRIT, 93- *Personal Data:* b Bethel, Maine, Apr 19, 32; m 60, Doris Carlberg; c Nancy & Carol. *Educ:* Univ Maine, BS, 54; Univ Ill, Urbana, MS, 58, PhD(animal sci), 60. *Prof Exp:* Group leader animal nutrit, Gen Mills, Inc, 60-62, proj leader, 62-67; mgr, Poultry Nutrit Res & Tech Serv, Allied Mills Inc, 67-70; dir nutrit & res, Robin Hood Multifoods Ltd, Can, 70-74; sr poultry scientist, Cent Soya, Inc, Decatur, Ind, 74-78; vpres nutrit, Bell Grain & Milling, 78-90, gen mgr, 90-92. *Mem:* Poultry Sci Asn. *Res:* Amino acid studies with chicks; dog and cat management and nutrition; applied animal husbandry; poultry nutrition; sales and dealer training; egg quality studies. *Mailing Add:* 2837 Sandberg St Riverside CA 92506. *E-Mail:* hnwchick@aol. com

**WATERHOUSE, JOHN P,** histopathology, electron microscopy; deceased, see previous edition for last biography

**WATERHOUSE, JOSEPH STALLARD,** HUMAN ANATOMY, HUMAN PHYSIOLOGY. *Current Pos:* assoc prof biol, 65-72, chmn, Dept Biol Sci, 74-75, PROF BIOL, STATE UNIV NY COL PLATTSBURGH, 72- *Personal Data:* b Toronto, Ont, Apr 28, 29; m 54; c 3. *Educ:* Univ Guelph, BSc, 54; Wash State Univ, MSc, 57, PhD(entom), 62. *Prof Exp:* Aide entom & zool, Wash State Univ, 54-60; asst prof biol, State Univ NY Col Arts & Sci Plattsburgh, 60-64; Ford of Can res fel zool, Carleton Univ, 64-65. *Concurrent Pos:* Pres, United Univ Profs, State Univ NY, 87-90. *Mem:* AAAS; Am Inst Biol Sci; Entom Soc Am; Entom Soc Can; Sigma Xi. *Res:* Biology of the garden symphylan, Scutigerella immaculata; ecology and taxonomy of the carabidae (ground beetles) in upper New York state; incidence of hypertension in upper New York State; entomology. *Mailing Add:* Dept Biol Sci State Univ NY 101 Broad St Plattsburgh NY 12901-2681

**WATERHOUSE, KEITH R,** UROLOGY, SURGERY. *Current Pos:* from asst prof to prof, 61-83, EMER PROF UROL SURG, STATE UNIV NY DOWNSTATE MED CTR, 83- *Personal Data:* b Derby, Eng, May 10, 29; US citizen; m 55, Anne T Milotzky; c Katherine, Vincent, Ursulas, Isabelle & Christopher. *Educ:* Cambridge Univ, BA, 50, MA, 57; Oxford Univ, MB & BChir, 53. *Honors & Awards:* Valentine Medal, NY Acad Med, 92. *Prof Exp:* Instr urol, Kings Co Hosp Ctr, 59-61. *Concurrent Pos:* Consult, Vet Admin Hosp, Brooklyn, NY, St Mary's Hosp, Passaic, NJ & Paterson Gen Hosp, 65-, Samaritan Hosp, Brooklyn, NY, 66- & St Charles Hosp, Port Jefferson, St Francis Hosp, Poughkeepsie, Arden Hill Hosp, Goshen & Brookhaven Mem Hosp, Patchogue, 67- *Mem:* Am Urol Asn; Am Col Surgeons; Am Acad Pediat; Am Fertil Soc; Int Soc Urol; fel Royal Col Surgeons Eng; hon mem Australasian Soc Urol; hon mem Ital Soc Urol; hon mem Panamanian Soc Urol. *Res:* Investigation, diagnosis and treatment of congenital anomalies of the urinary tract in children and the subsequent treatment of these patients when they develop chronic renal failure. *Mailing Add:* PO Box 69 Bonita Springs FL 34133. *Fax:* 941-992-9474

**WATERHOUSE, RICHARD (VALENTINE),** PHYSICS. *Current Pos:* RETIRED. *Personal Data:* b Eng, Feb 28, 24; nat US; div; c 4. *Educ:* Oxford Univ, MA, 49; DSc, 83; Cath Univ, PhD, 59. *Honors & Awards:* Sabine Medal, Acoust Soc Am, 90. *Prof Exp:* Res physicist, Royal Navy Torpedo Exp Estab, Scotland, 44-46, Paint Res Asn, London, 46-49 & Nat Bur Stand, 51-59; prof physics, Am Univ, 61-86, emer prof, 86-88. *Concurrent Pos:* Vis prof, Univ Calif, Berkeley, 69-70 & Univ Delft, Neth, 75-76; consult, US Navy. *Mem:* Fel Acoust Soc Am. *Res:* Waves and vibrations; theoretical physics; acoustics. *Mailing Add:* 2190 Washington St Apt 906 San Francisco CA 94109

**WATERHOUSE, WILLIAM CHARLES,** ALGEBRA, GEOMETRY. *Current Pos:* assoc prof, 75-80, PROF MATH, PA STATE UNIV, UNIVERSITY PARK, 80- *Personal Data:* b Galveston, Tex, Dec 31, 41; m 80, Betty Senk. *Educ:* Harvard Univ, AB, 63, AM, 64, PhD(math), 68. *Honors & Awards:* Ford Award, Math Asn Am, 84. *Prof Exp:* Res assoc math, Off Naval Res & Cornell Univ, 68-69; asst prof, Cornell Univ, 69-75. *Concurrent Pos:* Vis scholar, Harvard Univ, 82. *Mem:* Am Math Soc; Math Asn Am. *Res:* Affine group schemes and descent theory; linear algebra; algebraic number theory; history of mathematics. *Mailing Add:* Dept Math 431 McAllister Bldg Pa State Univ University Park PA 16802-6401. *E-Mail:* wcw@math.psu.edu

**WATERLAND, LARRY R,** HAZARDOUS WASTE INCINERATION. *Current Pos:* Staff engr, Acurex Corp, 75-78, sect leader, 78-79, prog mgr, 75-79, DEPT MGR, ACUREX CORP, 79- *Personal Data:* b St Louis, Mo, Aug 11, 48; m 70; c 2. *Educ:* Calif Inst Technol, BS, 70; Stanford Univ, MS, 72, PhD(chem eng), 75. *Concurrent Pos:* Mem adv panel to State Calif on hazardous waste incinerator permitting. *Mem:* Am Inst Chem Engrs; Air Pollution Control Asn; Combustion Inst. *Res:* Hazardous waste treatment via incineration or other thermal destruction processes; evaluation and control of combustion source air pollutants emissions. *Mailing Add:* 2060 Crist Dr Los Altos CA 94024-7044

**WATERLOW, JOHN C,** HUMAN NUTRITION. *Current Pos:* prof, 70-82, EMER PROF HUMAN NUTRIT, LONDON SCH, 82- *Personal Data:* b London, Eng, June 13, 16. *Educ:* Univ Cambridge, MD, 48. *Honors & Awards:* Bristol Myers Award, 84. *Prof Exp:* Mem, Sci Staff Res Coun, 48-54; dir, Brit Med Res Coun, Trop Metab Res Unit, Univ WI, Jamaica, 54-70. *Mem:* Fel assoc mem Nat Acad Sci; PanAm Health Orgn; Brit Nutrit Soc; Physiol Soc; fel Royal Soc London. *Mailing Add:* 15 Hillgate St London W8 England

**WATERMAN, ALAN T(OWER), JR,** ELECTRICAL ENGINEERING, REMOTE PROBING OF ATMOSPHERE. *Current Pos:* res assoc, 52-57, from assoc prof to prof, 58-83, EMER PROF ELEC ENG, STANFORD UNIV, 83- *Personal Data:* b Northampton, Mass, July 8, 18; m 46; c Linda (Schrader), Donna, Dane & Bruce. *Educ:* Princeton Univ, BA, 39; Calif Inst Technol, BS, 40; Harvard Univ, MA, 49, PhD(eng sci, appl physics), 52. *Prof Exp:* Meteorologist, Am Airlines, 40-41; instr, Univ Minn, 41-42; res assoc,

Calif Inst Technol, 42-45; res scientist, Columbia Univ, 45; chief meteorologist, Univ Tex, 45-46; asst, Harvard Univ, 46-52. *Concurrent Pos:* Consult, Weapons Systs Eval Group, US Dept Defense, 56-61, Nat Security Agency, 58-68, Stanford Res Inst, 58-, Inst Sci & Technol, Univ Mich, 58-61, Missile Systs Div, Lockheed Aircraft Corp, 58-59, Sylvania Elec Prods Co, Inc, 58-59 & Norair Res Coun, 63-68; chmn comn II, Int Sci Radio Union, 61-64; secy, US Nat Comt, 64-67, vchmn, 67-69, chmn, 69-72; ed, Radio Sci, 87-90. *Mem:* Am Meteorol Soc; fel Inst Elec & Electronics Engrs; Am Geophys Union. *Res:* Radio wave and optical propagation; physics of the atmosphere. *Mailing Add:* Star Lab Stanford Univ Durand 231 Stanford CA 94305-4055. *Fax:* 650-723-9251; *E-Mail:* waterman@star.stanford.edu

**WATERMAN, DANIEL,** MATHEMATICS. *Current Pos:* prof, 69-96, chmn, 88-94, EMER PROF MATH, SYRACUSE UNIV, 96- *Personal Data:* b New York, NY, Oct 24, 27; m 60, Mudite Upesleja; c Erica, Susan & Scott. *Educ:* Brooklyn Col, BA, 47; Johns Hopkins Univ, MA, 48; Univ Chicago, PhD, 54. *Prof Exp:* Res assoc, Cowles Comn Res in Econ, 51-52; Fulbright fel, Univ Vienna, 52-53; from instr to asst prof math, Purdue Univ, 53-59; asst prof, Univ Wis-Milwaukee, 59-61; prof, Wayne State Univ, 61-69. *Mem:* Am Math Soc; Math Asn Am. *Res:* Fourier analysis; methods of real analysis applied to Fourier series; generalized bounded variation; summability of series. *Mailing Add:* 116 Donridge Dr Dewitt NY 13214. *E-Mail:* fourier@earthlink.net

**WATERMAN, FRANK MELVIN,** MEDICAL PHYSICS. *Current Pos:* PROF, DEPT RADIATION, ONCOL & NUCLEAR MED, THOMAS JEFFERSON UNIV MED COL, 79- *Personal Data:* b Delhi, NY, Nov 3, 38; m 61, Jeannette; c Katherine, David, Natasha & Karen. *Educ:* Hartwick Col, BA, 60; Clarkson Univ, MS, 69, PhD(physics), 73. *Prof Exp:* Res assoc nuclear physics, Kent State Univ, 72-75; res assoc, Dept Radiol, Univ Chicago, 75-79. *Mem:* Radiation Res Soc; Am Asn Physicists Med; NAm Hyperthermia Soc. *Res:* Thermometry for clinical hyperthermia, response of human tumor blood flow to hyperthermia, heating dynamics and hyperthermia equipment development. *Mailing Add:* Dept Radiation Oncol Thomas Jefferson Univ Hosp 111 S 11th St Bodeine Ctr Rm G321 Philadelphia PA 19107. *Fax:* 215-955-5331

**WATERMAN, MICHAEL ROBERTS,** MOLECULAR BIOLOGY, PROTEIN CHEMISTRY. *Current Pos:* PROF & CHMN BIOCHEM, VANDERBILT UNIV SCH MED, 92- *Personal Data:* b Tacoma, Wash, Nov 23, 39; m 66, MaryAnne DeShula; c Peter A & Amanda L. *Educ:* Willamette Univ, BA, 61; Univ Ore, PhD(biochem), 69. *Prof Exp:* Fel biochem, Johnson Res Found, Sch Med, Univ Pa, 68-70; from asst prof to prof biochem, Health Sci Ctr, Univ Tex, 82-92. *Mem:* Am Chem Soc; Am Soc Biochem & Molecular Biol; Endocrine Soc; AAAS. *Res:* Synthesis of cytochrome P-450; regulation of steroidogenesis in the adrenal cortex; cytochrome P-450 structure and function relationship. *Mailing Add:* Biochem Dept 607 LH Vanderbilt Univ Sch Med Nashville TN 37232-0146. *Fax:* 615-322-4349

**WATERMAN, MICHAEL S,** MATHEMATICS, STATISTICS. *Current Pos:* PROF, UNIV SOUTHERN CALIF, 82- *Personal Data:* b Coquille, Ore, June 28, 42; div; c 1. *Educ:* Ore State Univ, BS, 64, MS, 66; Mich State Univ, MA, 68, PhD(probability, statist), 69. *Prof Exp:* Teaching asst math, Ore State Univ, 64-66; from asst prof to assoc prof, Idaho State Univ, 69-75, NSF res grant, 71-73; staff mem, Los Alamos Sci Lab, 75-81. *Concurrent Pos:* Vis prof, Univ Hawaii, 79-80 & Med Sch, Univ Calif, San Francisco, 82. *Mem:* Am Statist Asn; fel AAAS; Math Asn Am; fel Inst Math Statist; Soc Math Biol. *Res:* Ergodic theory; probabilistic and computational number theory; mathematical biology; combinations and finite mathematics; biological science. *Mailing Add:* Univ Southern Calif 1042 W 36th Pl Los Angeles CA 90089-0001

**WATERMAN, PETER LEWIS,** FUCHSIAN & KLEINIAN GROUPS, RIEMANN SURFACES. *Current Pos:* asst prof, 84-90, ASSOC PROF MATH, NORTHERN ILL UNIV, 90- *Personal Data:* b Bedford, Eng, Dec 28, 55; m 93, Carol J Feltz; c James Austin. *Educ:* Univ Southampton, BSc, 77; Univ Aberdeen, PhD(math), 83. *Prof Exp:* Vis asst prof math, Univ Md, 80-82; Lawton lectr math, Temple Univ, 82-84. *Concurrent Pos:* Vis prof, Inst Haules Etudes Sci, France, 91-92. *Mem:* London Math Soc; Am Math Soc. *Res:* Discrete groups of mobius transformations. *Mailing Add:* Dept Math Northern Ill Univ De Kalb IL 60115-2888. *E-Mail:* waterman@math.niu.edu

**WATERMAN, TALBOT H(OWE),** COMPARATIVE PHYSIOLOGY. *Current Pos:* instr biol, 46-47, from asst prof to prof zool, 47-85, EMER PROF, SR RES ASSOC, YALE UNIV, 85- *Personal Data:* b East Orange, NJ, July 3, 14. *Educ:* Harvard Univ, AB, 36, MA, 38, PhD(zool), 43; Yale Univ, MA Privatim, 58. *Honors & Awards:* Excellence in Res Award, Crustacean Soc, 89. *Prof Exp:* Jr fel, Soc of Fels, Harvard Univ, 38-40, res assoc, Psychoacoust Lab, Off Sci Res & Develop, 40-43; staff mem, Radiation Lab, Mass Inst Technol, 43-45; sci consult, Off Sci Res & Develop, Off Field Serv, USN & USAAF, 45; secy comt res, Sigma Xi, 46. *Concurrent Pos:* Exec fel, Trumbull Col, 46-56; instr invert zool, Marine Biol Lab, Woods Hole, 47-52, mem corp, 48-; mem, Am Inst Biol Sci Adv Comt Hydrobiol, Off Naval Res, 59-65; secy corp, Bermuda Biol Sta Res, 61-61, trustee, 62-75 & 76-80, hon trustee, 80-; assoc ed, J Morphol, 51-54, J Exp Zool, 71-75; Guggenheim fel, 62-63; Sigma Xi nat lectr, 64-65; vis prof, Sch Med, Keio Univ, Japan, 68, Tokyo Women's Med Col, 71; chmn, Div Comp Physiol & Biochem, Am Soc Zoologists, 70-71; vis prof, Japan Soc Prom Sci, 74, vis prof Sophia Univ, Japan, 77-78 & 80; vis lectr & investr, Woods Hole Oceanog Inst, 76, 79, 81 & 84; distinguished vis univ prof, Tex Tech Univ, 78; lectr, Star Island Conf, 90. *Mem:* Fel AAAS; Am Physiol Soc. *Res:* Visual physiology and spatial orientation; deepsea plankton and vertical migrations;

compound eye fine structure and information processing; photoreceptor membrane turnover in compound eyes; polarized light behavior in the sea; animal navigation; comparative physiology; deepsea angler fishes. *Mailing Add:* Dept Biol 802 KBT Yale Univ PO Box 208103 New Haven CT 06520

**WATERS, CORY ANN,** RECEPTOR BIOLOGY, CYTOKINES & GROWTH FACTORS. *Current Pos:* dir cell biol & immunol, 84-97, DIR RES & TECHNOL ASSESSMENT, SERAGEN INC, 97- *Educ:* Brandeis Univ, BA, 69; Harvard Univ, PhD(cell biol), 75. *Honors & Awards:* Triumphs Through Technol Award, Leukemia Soc Am, 94. *Prof Exp:* Postdoctoral fel, Med Res Coun Can, 75-78; asst prof immunol, Med Sch, Univ Alta, 79-84. *Concurrent Pos:* Prin investr, Small Business Innovation Res, NIH, 88-89; co-prin investr, Nat Cancer Inst, NIH, 95- *Mem:* AAAS; Am Asn Immunologists; NY Acad Sci. *Res:* Characterization of cellular and molecular mechanisms by which the immune system learns self-non-self discrimination; design and development of novel biological drugs to achieve selective elimination of mammalian cells involved in disease processes. *Mailing Add:* 12 Clark Rd Bedford MA 01730-1505

**WATERS, DEAN ALLISON,** ENGINEERING, MATERIALS SCIENCE. *Current Pos:* div dir, 88-91, PROG DIR, OAK RIDGE NAT LAB, 92- *Personal Data:* b Jersey City, NJ, May 2, 36; c 3. *Educ:* Yale Univ, BE, 57, BS, 58; NC State Univ, MS, 60. *Honors & Awards:* E O Lawrence Award, Dept of Energy, 78. *Prof Exp:* Dept head, Union Carbide Corp 67-65, prog mgr, 75-77, dep div dir, Nuclear Div, 77-80, div dir, 81-91. *Mem:* Nat Soc Prof Engrs; Am Soc Eng Mgt; Sigma Xi. *Res:* Materials, applied mechanics, stress analysis, vibration, machine dynamics, and systems engineering; separation sciences. *Mailing Add:* 132 Newport Rd Oak Ridge TN 37830-8138

**WATERS, IRVING WADE,** PHARMACOLOGY. *Current Pos:* From asst prof to assoc prof, 66-74, PROF PHARMACOL, UNIV MISS, 74- *Personal Data:* b Baldwyn, Miss, June 19, 31; m 54; c 2. *Educ:* Delta State Col, BS, 58; Auburn Univ, MS, 60; Univ Fla, PhD(pharmacol), 63. *Mem:* Am Soc Pharmacol & Exp Therapeut; Sigma Xi. *Res:* Drug metabolism; toxicology. *Mailing Add:* Dept Pharm Univ Miss Sch Pharmacol University MS 38677-9999

**WATERS, JAMES AUGUSTUS,** ORGANIC MEDICINAL CHEMISTY. *Current Pos:* res chemist, 60-89, PHARMACIST, NAT INST ARTHRITIS, METAB & DIGESTIVE DIS, 90- *Personal Data:* b Postville, Iowa, June 23, 31; m 57; c Jim, Joe, Phil & Anne. *Educ:* Univ Iowa, BS, 53, PhD(pharmaceut chem), 59; Purdue Univ, 59-60. *Prof Exp:* Res fel org chem, Univ Mich, 59-60. *Mem:* Am Chem Soc; Sigma Xi; fel Am Found Pharmaceut Educ. *Res:* Structure elucidation of natural products; steroid biosynthesis; medicinal chemistry; photochemistry; synthesis nicotinic acetylcholine receptor agonists. *Mailing Add:* 5420 Bedfordshire Ave Harrisburg NC 28075

**WATERS, JAMES FREDERICK,** VERTEBRATE ANATOMY, NATURAL HISTORY. *Current Pos:* From asst prof to assoc prof, 66-75, PROF ZOOL, HUMBOLDT STATE UNIV, 75- *Personal Data:* b Oak Park, Ill, Mar 17, 38; m 65, Virginia Sill. *Educ:* Stanford Univ, BA, 59; Univ Wash, PhD(zool), 69. *Concurrent Pos:* Free-lance ed, reviewer, sci translr, Ger to Eng. *Mem:* Soc Study Evolution; Soc Vert Paleont; Am Soc Zoologists; Western Soc Naturalists. *Res:* Functional locomotor anatomy of lizards and snakes. *Mailing Add:* Dept Biol Sci Humboldt State Univ Arcata CA 95521-8299. *E-Mail:* jfw1@axe.humboldt.edu

**WATERS, JOE WILLIAM,** REMOTE SENSING OF THE ATMOSPHERE, STRATOSPHERIC OZONE RESEARCH. *Current Pos:* mem tech staff, 73-80, res scientist, 80-85, SR RES SCIENTIST, CALTECH JET PROPULSION LAB, 85- *Personal Data:* b Clarksville, Tenn, Jan 12, 44. *Educ:* Mass Inst Technol, BS & MS, 67, PhD(elec eng), 71. *Honors & Awards:* Except Sci Achievement Medal, NASA, 85 & 93. *Prof Exp:* Res assoc, Mass Inst Technol, 71-73. *Res:* Development, application and interpretation of microwave remote sensing techniques for studies of earth's atmosphere, especially at millimeter and submillimeter wavelengths. *Mailing Add:* Jet Propulsion Lab 183-701 Pasadena CA 91011

**WATERS, JOHN ALBERT,** PHYSICAL ORGANIC CHEMISTRY, CATALYSIS. *Current Pos:* res specialist, 75-78, RES ASSOC CHEM, MERICHEM CO, 78- *Personal Data:* b Norwich, Eng, Nov 7, 35; c 4. *Educ:* Univ London, BS, 57; Leicester Univ, PhD(org chem), 60. *Prof Exp:* Sr res chemist, Monsanto, 63-75. *Mem:* Am Chem Soc; fel Am Inst Chemists; Catalyst Soc. *Res:* Organometallics; organic reactions. *Mailing Add:* Merichem Co 1503 Central Ave Houston TX 77012-2743

**WATERS, JOSEPH HEMENWAY,** VERTEBRATE ZOOLOGY. *Personal Data:* b Brockton, Mass, Dec 23, 30. *Educ:* Univ Mich, BS, 54, MS, 55; Univ Conn, PhD(zool), 60. *Prof Exp:* Instr biol, Mass State Col Bridgewater, 59-61, Duke Univ, 62-63, Univ RI, 63-64 & Roanoke Col, 64-65; asst prof biol, Villanova Univ, 65-85. *Mem:* Fel AAAS; Am Soc Mammal; Am Soc Ichthyologists & Herpetologists; Sigma Xi. *Res:* Ecology and systematics of vertebrates in eastern North America. *Mailing Add:* 65 Bonney Hill Lane Hanson MA 02341

**WATERS, KENNETH LEE,** pharmacy, medicinal chemistry; deceased, see previous edition for last biography

**WATERS, LARRY CHARLES,** BIOCHEMISTRY, MOLECULAR BIOLOGY & ANALYTICAL CHEMISTRY. *Current Pos:* Am Cancer Soc fel biochem res, 65-67, staff biochemist, Biol Div, 67-90, RES STAFF, CHEM & ANALYTICAL SCI DIV, OAK RIDGE NAT LAB, 91- *Personal Data:* b Glenville, Ga, July 1, 39; m 60, Yvonne Mullis; c Laurie. *Educ:* Valdosta State Col, BS, 61; Univ Ga, MS, 64, PhD(biochem), 65. *Concurrent Pos:* Assoc prof, Univ Tenn, Knoxville. *Mem:* Am Soc Biochem & Molecular Biol. *Res:* Gene regulation, environmental monitoring, analytical methods development. *Mailing Add:* Chem & Analytical Sci Div Oak Ridge Nat Lab PO Box 2008 Oak Ridge TN 37831-6120. *Fax:* 423-576-7956, 574-1274

**WATERS, MICHAEL DEE,** GENETIC TOXICOLOGY. *Current Pos:* unit chief cellular physiol, Cellular Biol Sect, Environ Protection Agency, 71-72, sect chief cellular physiol, Pathobiol Res Br, 72-75, chief, Cellular Biochem Sect, Biomed Res Br, 75-76, chief, Biochem Br, 76-79, coordr genetic toxicol prog, 78-79, dir, Genetic Toxicol Div, 79-92, assoc lab dir, Health Effects Res Lab, 92-95, ASST DIR, NAT HEALTH ENVIRON EFFECTS RES LAB, ENVIRON PROTECTION AGENCY, 95- *Personal Data:* b Charlotte, NC, Apr 17, 42; m 64, 90; c 3. *Educ:* Davidson Col, BS, 64; Univ NC, Chapel Hill, PhD(biochem), 69. *Honors & Awards:* Bronze Medal, Environ Protection Agency, 80 & 87, Sci & Technol Achievement Award, 83 & 85; Alexander Hollaender Award, Environ Mutagen Soc, 96. *Prof Exp:* Lab chief biochem, Biophys Lab, Edgewood Arsenal, Md, 69-71. *Concurrent Pos:* Clin instr, George Washington Univ, 71-72; adj prof, Univ NC, Chapel Hill, 80- & Duke Univ, 92- *Mem:* NY Acad Sci; Am Chem Soc; Tissue Cult Asn; Sigma Xi; Environ Mutagen Soc (pres, 91-92); Soc Risk Analysis. *Res:* Microbial, mammalian cell, organ culture and whole animal systems for studies of genetic, biochemical and physiological effects of environmental pollutants. *Mailing Add:* Nat Health & Environ Effects Res Lab Environ Protection Agency Research Triangle Park NC 27711. *Fax:* 919-541-1440; *E-Mail:* waters@herl45.herl.epa.gov

**WATERS, NORMAN DALE,** ENTOMOLOGY. *Current Pos:* assoc res prof, 70-81, ENTOMOLOGIST, EXP STA, UNIV IDAHO, 57-, EMER RES PROF ENTOMOL, 81- *Personal Data:* b Twin Falls, Idaho, May 1, 22; m 54, Donna M McKnight; c William M & Marie D (McLaughlin). *Educ:* Univ Calif, Berkeley, BS, 49, PhD, 55. *Prof Exp:* Mem staff for parasite introd, India, Pakistan, Nepal & Afghanistan, USDA, 49-51; entomologist, Cashewnut Improv Comn, India, 52-53; pest control supvr citrus, Limonera Co, Calif, 55-57. *Mem:* Entom Soc Am; Int Orgn Biol Control; Sigma Xi. *Res:* Biological control; legume forage insects; pollinating insects. *Mailing Add:* 29410 Pearl Rd R-E Ctr Univ Idaho Parma ID 83660

**WATERS, RICHARD C(ABOT),** AUTOMATED TOOLS. *Current Pos:* SR RES SCIENTIST, MITSUBISHI ELEC RES LABS, 91- *Personal Data:* b Framingham, Mass, Apr 8, 50; m 87. *Educ:* Brown Univ, BS, 72; Harvard Univ, MS, 73; Mass Inst Technol, PhD(comput sci), 78. *Prof Exp:* Res scientist, Mass Inst Technol, 78-82, prin res scientist, 82-91. *Mem:* Sr mem Inst Elec & Electronics Engrs; Asn Comput Mach; Am Asn Artificial Intel. *Res:* Automated tools for the support of the software process. *Mailing Add:* Mitsubishi Elec Res Labs 201 Broadway Cambridge MA 02139

**WATERS, ROBERT CHARLES,** ENGINEERING MANAGEMENT, ENGINEERING ECONOMICS. *Current Pos:* chmn dept, 84-89, PROF ENG ADMIN, GEORGE WASHINGTON UNIV, 79-, CHMN DEPT, 97- *Personal Data:* b Long Beach, Calif, Apr 27, 30; m, Dagmar G Bach; c 4. *Educ:* Univ Calif, Los Angeles, BS, 56, MBA, 63; Univ Southern Calif, DBA(bus econ), 68. *Prof Exp:* Trainee, mfg mgt prog, Gen Elec Co, 56-58, supvr, instrumentation shop, jet engine dept, 58-59; syst analyst admin, TRW Systs Group, 59-61, cost engr, syst lab, 61-63, mkt planning mgr, 63-68; sr res analyst consult, Resource Mgt Corp, 68-69; vpres consult, EMSCO Eng & Mgt Sci Corp, 69-72; assoc prof eng mgt, Univ Mo, Rolla, 72-79. *Concurrent Pos:* Staff specialist, US Water Resources Coun, 76-78; prin investr, Maritime Protection Pract & Proposals, US Dept Transp, 83-85; vis prof, Anderson Grad Sch Mgt, Univ Calif, Los Angeles, 88 & Webb Inst, 96-97. *Mem:* Am Soc Eng Educ; Am Soc Eng Mgt (treas, 80-84); Sigma Xi; AAAS; Inst Mgt Sci; Soc Naval Architects & Marine Engrs. *Res:* Economics and management of transportation, particularly maritime; management of technological innovation; impact of technology on society and vice versa; water resources planning. *Mailing Add:* Dept Eng Mgt George Washington Univ 2029 G St NW Washington DC 20006-4211. *Fax:* 202-994-4606; *E-Mail:* rwaters@seas.gwu.edu

**WATERS, RODNEY LEWIS,** LASERS. *Current Pos:* PRES, FLOROD CORP, 74- *Personal Data:* b Long Beach, Calif, July 13, 36; m 58; c 3. *Educ:* Univ Calif, Los Angeles, BA, 63; Pepperdine Univ, MBA, 79. *Prof Exp:* Res engr, NAm Rockwell, 63-65; prod mgr, Korad Dept, Union Carbide Corp, 65-63; mkt mgr, Quantrad Corp, 73-74. *Concurrent Pos:* Lectr, Univ Calif, Los Angeles, 79-87. *Mem:* Semiconductor Equip & Mat Inst; Int Soc Hybrid Microelectronics. *Res:* Developed first Q-switched YAG laser resistor trimmer; laser for semiconductor photomask repair; laser cutter for very large scale integrated failure analysis; sealed excimer; commercial laser chemical liquid deposition. *Mailing Add:* Florod Corp 17360 S Gramercy Pl Gardena CA 90427-5212

**WATERS, ROLLAND MAYDEN,** ORGANIC CHEMISTRY. *Current Pos:* RES CHEMIST PHEROMONES, USDA, 63- *Personal Data:* b Tucson, Ariz, Apr 7, 26; m 59; c 3. *Educ:* Univ Ark, BS, 48; Yale Univ, PhD(org chem), 54. *Prof Exp:* Sr res chemist gen org chem, Dow Chem Co, 53-63. *Concurrent Pos:* Lectr chem, Univ Md-Univ Col, 72- *Mem:* Am Chem Soc; AAAS. *Res:* Isolation, structure elucidation, and synthesis of chemicals affecting the behavior of insects; the goal is alternative methods of controlling insects to reduce our use of pesticides. *Mailing Add:* 20442 Meadow Pond Pl Gaithersburg MD 20879-1130

**WATERS, THOMAS FRANK,** AQUATIC ECOLOGY, FISHERIES. *Current Pos:* from asst prof to prof, 58-91, EMER PROF FISHERY BIOL, UNIV MINN, ST PAUL, 91- *Personal Data:* b Hastings, Mich, May 17, 26; m 53, Carol Yonker; c Daniel F, Elizabeth L & Benton E. *Educ:* Mich State Univ, BS, 52, MS, 53, PhD(fishery biol), 56. *Honors & Awards:* Excellence in Benthic Sci Award, NAm Benthological Soc (pres, 75). *Prof Exp:* Supvr, Pigeon River Trout Res Sta, Mich Dept Conserv, 56-57. *Mem:* Am Fisheries Soc; Ecol Soc Am; Am Inst Fishery Res Biol; NAm Benthological Soc (pres, 75). *Res:* Limnology; ecology of aquatic invertebrates and stream fish populations. *Mailing Add:* Dept Fisheries & Wildlife Univ Minn St Paul MN 55108

**WATERS, WILLIAM E,** FOREST ENTOMOLOGY. *Current Pos:* dean, Col Natural Resources, 75-77, prof, 77-86, EMER PROF FORESTRY & ENTOM, UNIV CALIF, BERKELEY, 86- *Personal Data:* b Springfield, Mass, July 2, 22; m 43, 76; c 4. *Educ:* State Univ NY Col Forestry, Syracuse, BS, 48; Duke Univ, MF, 49; Yale Univ, PhD, 58. *Honors & Awards:* Distinguished Statist Ecologist Award, Int Asn Ecol, 90. *Prof Exp:* Entomologist, Bur Entom & Plant Quarantine, USDA, 49-53, entomologist, Forest Serv, 53-59, chief div forest insect res, 59-63, div forest insect & dis res, 63-65, asst dir insects & dis, 65-66, chief forest insect & dis lab & prin ecologist, Northeastern Forest Exp Sta, Conn, 66-68, chief forest insect res, Div Forest Insect & Dis Res, 68-73, chief scientist, Pac Southwest Forest & Range Exp Sta, 73-75. *Concurrent Pos:* Instr, Quinnipiac Col, 61-64; lectr, Yale Univ, 64-68; mem pop dynamics working party & chmn impact of destructive agents proj group, Int Union Forest Res Orgn; chmn working party on forest insects & dis, Food & Agr Orgn-NAm Forestry Comn; leader, Pine-Beetle IPM Proj, NSF/Environ Protection Agency, 74-84; assoc dir, Calif Agr Res Sta, Univ Calif, Berkeley, 75-77; chmn, statist ecol sect, Int Asn Ecol, 85-; prin investr, US-Korea Coop Res Prog, 87-90. *Mem:* Entom Soc Am; Soc Am Foresters; Sigma Xi; Int Asn Ecol. *Res:* Forest insect ecology; population dynamics; biometrics; insect behavior; forest pest management. *Mailing Add:* Col Natural Resources 4401 Dwinelle Hall Univ Calif Berkeley CA 94720

**WATERS, WILLIAM F,** PSYCHOLOGY & PSYCHOPHYSIOLOGY, SLEEP DISORDERS. *Current Pos:* dir clin training, 79-89, PROF, DEPT PSYCHOL, LA STATE UNIV, 79-, PROF, PENNINGTON BIOMED RES CTR, LA STATE UNIV, 92- *Personal Data:* b Dayton, Ohio, Apr 25, 43; m 78, Harriet Cohen; c Janice, Jocelyn (Whitesides) & Jason. *Educ:* Tulane Univ, AB, 64; Case Western Res Univ, MS, 66, PhD(psychol), 69, Am Bd Prof Psychol, dipl, 73. *Prof Exp:* Assoc prof med psychol, Dept Psychiat, Univ Mo, Columbia, 68-79, assoc prof psychol, Dept Psychol, 70-79. *Concurrent Pos:* Dir, Psychol Serv, Mid-Mo Ment Health Ctr, 68-74; coordr, Ochsner Clin Baton Rouge Sleep Dis Prog, 88-; coordr, Sleep Dis Ctr, Baton Rouge Gen Med Ctr, 97- *Mem:* Fel Am Psychol Asn; fel Am Sleep Dis Asn; fel Am Psychol Soc. *Res:* Etiology and treatment of insomnia; sleep deprivation and attention; cognitive performance; psychophysiology of selective attention, emotion, habituation; psychophysiological disorders. *Mailing Add:* Dept Psychol Audubon Hall La State Univ Baton Rouge LA 70803. *Fax:* 504-388-4125; *E-Mail:* wwaters@unix1.sncc.lsu.edu

**WATERS, WILLIE ESTEL,** HORTICULTURE. *Current Pos:* asst veg crops, Univ Fla, 58-60, from asst ornamental horticulturist to assoc ornamental horticulturist & head Agr Res Ctr, Apopka, Fla, 68-70, HORTICULTURIST & DIR GULF COAST RES & EDUC CTR, UNIV FLA, 70- *Personal Data:* b Smith Town, Ky, Sept 19, 31; m 52; c 3. *Educ:* Univ Ky, BS, 54, MS, 58; Univ Fla, PhD(veg crops), 60. *Honors & Awards:* Alex Laurie Award, Am Soc Hort Sci, 68. *Prof Exp:* Asst co agr agent, Ky, 54; asst soils, Univ Ky, 56-58. *Mem:* Fel Am Soc Hort Sci. *Res:* Soil and plant nutrition; weed control and physiology of ornamental crops. *Mailing Add:* Gulf Coast Res & Educ Ctr Univ Fla 5007 60th St E Bradenton FL 34203

**WATERSON, JOHN R,** HUMAN GENETICS, PEDIATRICS. *Current Pos:* Inst, 79, ASST PROF PEDIAT, UNIV MICH, 80-; ASSOC PROF PEDIAT & MICROBIOL & IMMUNOL, NORTHEAST UNIV COL MED. *Personal Data:* b Decatur, Ill, May 11, 44; c 4. *Educ:* Univ Mich, BS, 66, MD, 75; Yale Univ, PhD(biophys), 71. *Mem:* Am Soc Human Genetics; Am Acad Pediat. *Res:* Human gene structure and chromosomal organization. *Mailing Add:* Children's Hosp Med Ctr One Perkins Sq Akron OH 44302-1062

**WATERSTRAT, RICHARD MILTON,** ALLOY PHASE EQUILIBRIA, MARTENSITIC TRANSFORMATIONS. *Current Pos:* GUEST SCIENTIST, NAT INST STAND & TECHNOL, 93- *Personal Data:* b Cincinnati, Ohio, Oct 4, 28; m 63, Shirley M. *Educ:* Univ Ill, BS, 61; Univ Geneva, Switz, DSc, 78. *Prof Exp:* Chief res scientist, Am Dent Asn, 61-92. *Concurrent Pos:* Prin investr, Am Dent Asn, 64-92; mem, Comt Alloy Phases, Am Inst Mining, Metall & Petrol Engrs, 69-; vis scientist, Univ Geneva, Switz, 74-75. *Mem:* Mat Res Soc; Am Inst Mining, Metall & Petrol Engrs; fel Am Soc Metals Int. *Res:* Determination of alloy phase diagrams; development of superconducting materials; development of dental materials; biomedical alloys research. *Mailing Add:* Nat Inst Stand & Technol Gaithersburg MD 20899

**WATERWORTH, HOWARD E,** PLANT VIROLOGY. *Current Pos:* Res plant pathologist, USDA, 64-80, res virologist & chief, Germplasm Resources Lab, Res Ctr, 80-82, adminr, 82-89, LEAD SCIENTIST, AGR RES SERV, USDA, BELTSVILLE, 89- *Personal Data:* b Randolph, Wis, Sept 3, 36; m 66, Pamela Dick; c Mary E, Allison R, Rebeccah A & Sarah L. *Educ:* Univ Wis, BS, 58, PhD(plant path), 62. *Mem:* Am Soc Agron; Am Phytopath Soc; Am Soc Hort Sci; Coun Agr Sci & Technol. *Res:* Testing of new stone fruits, grasses, tropical crops and woody ornamentals for the presence of viruses; identification of new viruses; develop methods to detect viruses; author of 80 scientific research publications. *Mailing Add:* Agr Res Serv USDA Bldg 465 Entomology Rd Beltsville MD 20705. *Fax:* 301-504-6737; *E-Mail:* pgqohw@ars-grin.gov

**WATKIN, DONALD M,** NUTRITION, GERONTOLOGY. *Current Pos:* MGR, OCCUP HEALTH DIV, OFF AVIATION MED, FED AVIATION ADMIN, DEPT TRANSP, 81-; RES PROF, SCH MED & HEALTH SCI, GEORGE WASHINGTON UNIV, 81- *Educ:* Harvard Univ, MD, 46. *Res:* Internal medicine. *Mailing Add:* Dept Transp FAA Off Aviation Med 800 Independence Ave SW Washington DC 20591. *Fax:* 202-267-5399

**WATKINS, ALLEN HARRISON,** TECHNICAL MANAGEMENT. *Current Pos:* CHIEF, MAPPING DIV, US GEOL EARTH SCI CTR, 91- *Personal Data:* b Charlottesville, Va, Apr 25, 38; m 62, 83; c 4. *Educ:* Va Polytech Inst, BS, 61. *Honors & Awards:* Pecora Award. *Prof Exp:* Prog mgt space syst, Manned Spacecraft Ctr, NASA, 62-70, prog mgt earth resources, 70-73; dir, Earth Resources Observ Syst Data Ctr, Dept Interior, 73-91. *Mem:* Am Soc Photogram; Am Inst Aeronaut & Astronaut; Int Acad Astronaut. *Mailing Add:* Corp VP Remote Sensing Systs SAIC 1710 Goodridge Dr MS 1-4-1 McLean VA 22102

**WATKINS, ANN E,** STATISTICS EDUCATION, MATHEMATICS EDITING. *Current Pos:* PROF MATH, CALIF STATE UNIV, NORTHRIDGE, 90- *Personal Data:* b Los Angeles, Calif, Jan 10, 49; m 73, William; c 2. *Educ:* Calif State Univ, Northridge, BA, 70, MS, 72; Univ Calif, Los Angeles, PhD(educ), 77. *Concurrent Pos:* Second vpres, Math Asn Am, 87-88, gov, 95-; ed, Col Math J, 89-94; assoc ed, Am Math Monthly, 96- *Mem:* Math Asn Am; Am Statist Asn; Nat Coun Teachers Math. *Res:* Author, editor and workshop leader for projects to improve the teaching of statistics in high schools and colleges, including quantitative literacy, activity-based statistics and core-plus mathematics. *Mailing Add:* Math Dept Calif State Univ Northridge CA 91330-8313. *E-Mail:* ann.watkins@csun.edu

**WATKINS, BRENTON JOHN,** APPLICATIONS OF RADAR TO ATMOSPHERE SCIENCE. *Current Pos:* sr res asst, 72-76, asst prof physics, 80-85, ASSOC PROF PHYSICS, GEOPHYS INST, UNIV ALASKA, 85-, ASSOC PROF GEOPHYS, 80- *Personal Data:* b Adelaide, Australia, Aug 5, 46; US citizen; c 1. *Educ:* Univ Adelaide, BSc Hons, 69; La Trobe Univ, MSc, 72; Univ Alaska, PhD(geophys), 76. *Prof Exp:* Physicist, Dept Sci, Govt Australia, 69-72; tech officer, La Trobe Univ, 77; staff scientist, Lincoln Lab, Mass Inst Technol, 78-80. *Concurrent Pos:* Prin investr, NSF grants, 81-83, 84-86 & 87-89 & NASA, 84-86; co-prin investr, Air Force Off Sci Res Grant, 85-86. *Mem:* Australian Inst Physics; Am Meterol Soc; Am Geophys Union. *Res:* Development of numerical computer simulations of the earth's ionosphere; use of incoherent scatter radar at high latitudes to study the ionosphere; development of radar techniques to study the lower atmosphere using turbulence-scatter; development of hardware and software for radar systems; real-time computer software and hardware. *Mailing Add:* 4072 Teal Ave Fairbanks AK 99709

**WATKINS, CHARLES B,** FLUID MECHANICS, MECHANICAL DESIGN. *Current Pos:* from asst prof to assoc prof, 73-79, PROF MECH ENG, HOWARD UNIV, 79-, CHMN DEPT, 73-; DEAN, SCH ENG, CITY COL, CITY UNIV NEW YORK, 86- *Personal Data:* b Petersburg, Va, Nov 20, 42; m 64, Judith Griffin; c Michael & Stephen. *Educ:* Howard Univ, BSME, 64; Univ NMex, MS, 66, PhD(mech eng), 70. *Honors & Awards:* Ralph R Teetor Award, Soc Automotive Engrs, 80. *Prof Exp:* Staff mem, Sandia Labs, 64-71. *Concurrent Pos:* consult, US Army, US Sandia Labs, 67-; Mem, Eng Chem & Energetics Adv Panel, NSF, 75-78; mem, Selection Panel Nat Res Coun Post Doctoral Fel Prog, 80, Eng Deans Coun, Am Soc Eng Educ, 93-; bd eng educ, Am Soc Mech Engrs, 84-87; mem, Mech, Struct & Mat Eng Adv Bd, NSF, 88-89. *Mem:* Assoc fel Am Inst Aeronaut & Astronaut; fel Am Soc Mech Engrs; Soc Automotive Engrs; Sigma Xi. *Res:* Heat transfer; fluid mechanics; gas bearing dynamics; mechanical design; truck wheels; product liability; author or co-author of 61 publications. *Mailing Add:* Sch Eng City Col Convent Ave 140 St New York NY 10031

**WATKINS, CHARLES H(ENRY),** CHEMICAL ENGINEERING, PETROLEUM ENGINEERING. *Current Pos:* RETIRED. *Personal Data:* b Henshaw, Ky, Mar 21, 13; m 40, Myrtle Vevang; c Charles B, James A, Cheryl (Tanaka) & Marilyn (Spieth). *Educ:* Univ Louisville, BS, 35, MS, 36; Purdue Univ, PhD(chem eng), 39. *Prof Exp:* Res engr, Standard Oil Develop Co, NJ, 39-46; div coordr, Universal Oil Prod Co, 46-60, div coordr eng res & develop, 60-77, consult eng res & develop, Universal Oil Prod Process Div, 77-83. *Mem:* Am Chem Soc; Am Inst Chem Engrs. *Res:* Olefin production; aromatics; polymerization of hydrocarbons; alkyllation of isoparaffines with ethylene, propylene and butenes; hydrogenation; inorganic reactions in organic solvents; hydrofining; hydrocracking; published 36 articles and granted 46 US patents. *Mailing Add:* 8033 SW 103rd Lane Ocala FL 34481

**WATKINS, CHARLES LEE,** CHEMISTRY. *Current Pos:* asst prof, 70-74, ASSOC PROF CHEM, UNIV ALA, BIRMINGHAM, 74- *Personal Data:* b Fairfield, Ala, Oct 27, 42. *Educ:* Univ Ala, Tuscaloosa, BS, 64; Univ Fla, MS, 66, PhD(chem), 68. *Prof Exp:* Res assoc, Univ NC, Chapel Hill, 69-70. *Mem:* Am Chem Soc; Sigma Xi. *Mailing Add:* Dept Chem Univ Ala Univ Sta Birmingham AL 35294-1240

**WATKINS, CLYDE ANDREW,** RESEARCH ADMINISTRATION. *Current Pos:* HEALTH SCIENTIST ADMINR, NIH, 87-, DEP DIR DIV RES. *Personal Data:* b McKees Rocks, PA, Dec 1, 46; m 84; c 2. *Educ:* Duquesne Univ, BS, 69; Pa State Univ, PhD(physiol), 77. *Prof Exp:* Res assoc physiol, M S Hershey Med Ctr, 77-79, asst prof anesthesia & physil, 79-82; asst prof physiol, 82-85, assoc prof physiol & pharmacol, Med Col Ga, 85-87. *Mem:* Am Physiol Soc; Am Thoracic Soc; Am Heart Asn; AAAS. *Res:* Metabolic response of the lung and vasculature to injury with emphasis on membrane processes and protein turnover; molecular basis of anesthesia. *Mailing Add:* 6403 McCahill Dr Laurel MD 20707

**WATKINS, DARRELL DWIGHT, JR,** ORGANOMETALLIC CHEMISTRY. *Current Pos:* SR RES CHEMIST, MONSANTO CO, 76- *Personal Data:* b Woodbine, Iowa, Mar 7, 43; m 64; c 2. *Educ:* Univ Nebr, Omaha, BA, 68; Univ Nebr, Lincoln, PhD(chem), 73. *Prof Exp:* Asst instr chem, Univ Nebr, Omaha, 68-70; res assoc, Ohio State Univ, 73-76. *Mem:* Am Chem Soc. *Res:* Synthesis of new and novel organometallic compounds and the use of those compounds in homogeneous catalysis. *Mailing Add:* 12440 Glengate Dr Maryland Heights MO 63043-2576

**WATKINS, DEAN ALLEN,** ELECTRICAL ENGINEERING. *Current Pos:* pres, 57-67, chief exec officer, 67-79, CHMN BD, WATKINS-JOHNSON CO, 67- *Personal Data:* b Omaha, Nebr, Oct 23, 22; m 44; c 3. *Educ:* Iowa State Col, BS, 44; Calif Inst Technol, MS, 47; Stanford Univ, PhD(elec eng), 51. *Prof Exp:* Engr, Collins Radio Co, Iowa, 47-48; staff mem, Los Alamos Sci Lab, 48-49; head, Microwave Tube Sect, Res & Develop Labs, Hughes Aircraft Co, 51-53; from assoc prof to prof elec eng, Stanford Univ, 53-64, dir, Electron Devices Lab, 55-64. *Concurrent Pos:* Lectr, Stanford Univ, 64-69. *Mem:* Nat Acad Eng; Am Phys Soc; fel Inst Elec & Electronics Engrs. *Res:* Microwave devices and systems. *Mailing Add:* Watkins-Johnson Co 3333 Hillview Ave Palo Alto CA 94304. *Fax:* 650-813-2403

**WATKINS, DON WAYNE,** PHYSIOLOGY. *Current Pos:* asst prof, 70-75, ASSOC PROF PHYSIOL, MED SCH, GEORGE WASHINGTON UNIV, 75-, INTERIM CHAIR PHYSIOL, 89- *Personal Data:* b Louisville, Ky, June 9, 40; m 66; c 3. *Educ:* Univ Louisville, BChE, 63; Univ Wis-Madison, PhD(physiol), 68. *Prof Exp:* Lectr physiol, Med Sch, Makerere Univ, Uganda, 68-70. *Mem:* Am Physiol Soc. *Res:* Membrane transport, physiology, epithelia; kidney salt and water; frog skin; trace element and mineral metabolism. *Mailing Add:* Dept Physiol George Washington Univ Med Sch 2300 Eye St NW Washington DC 20037-2803. *Fax:* 202-994-3553; *E-Mail:* donwtkns@gwuvm.gwu.edu

**WATKINS, DUDLEY T,** ANATOMY. *Current Pos:* Fel anat, 66-67, asst prof, 67-72, assoc prof, 72-80, PROF ANAT, HEALTH CTR, UNIV CONN, 80- *Personal Data:* b Youngstown, Ohio, May 2, 38; m 60; c 3. *Educ:* Oberlin Col, AB, 60; Western Res Univ, MD, 66, PhD(anat), 67. *Mem:* AAAS; Am Diabetes Asn; Am Asn Anatomists; Sigma Xi. *Res:* Mechanism of action of alloxan in the production of diabetes; mechanism of insulin secretion. *Mailing Add:* Dept Anat Univ Conn Sch Med Farmington Ave Farmington CT 06032

**WATKINS, G(ORDON) LEONARD,** POSITRON EMITTING RADIOPHARMACEUTICALS, ELCOSANOIDS. *Current Pos:* CHIEF PET RADIOCHEM, UNIV IOWA HOSPS & CLINS, 89-, ASSOC RADIOL, 89- *Personal Data:* b Mawgan, Cornwall, UK, Jan 16, 41; m 70, Denise A Harold; c Tristan M & Owan C. *Educ:* Univ London, BSc, 67; Univ Southern Calif, PhD(pharmaceut chem), 83. *Prof Exp:* Res chemist, May & Baker Res Inst, UK, 67-74; res assoc, Sch Pharm, Univ Southern Calif, 74-81, assoc dir, Prostaglandin Res Lab, 81-85; sr res fel, Univ Mich Med Sch, 86-89. *Concurrent Pos:* Consult, Louis Pasteur Res Found, 75-78, Res Health Sci Corp, 78-86. *Mem:* Am Chem Soc; Soc Nuclear Med; Int Union Pure & Appl Chem; fel Am Inst Chemists; Int Isotope Soc; Sigma Xi. *Res:* Design, synthesis, development and production of positron-emitting radio pharmaceuticals for use in studying oncologic, neurologic, psychiatric and cardiac disease states; emphasis on low to zero radioactive emissions in a hospital environment. *Mailing Add:* Univ Iowa Hosps & Clins P E T Imaging Ctr Iowa City IA 52242. *Fax:* 319-356-2220

**WATKINS, GEORGE DANIELS,** PHYSICS. *Current Pos:* Sherman Fairchild Prof, 75-95, EMER PROF PHYSICS, LEHIGH UNIV, 95- *Personal Data:* b Evanston, Ill, Apr 28, 24; m 49, Carolyn L Nevin; c Lois R, Paul B & Ann (Romaine). *Educ:* Randolph-Macon Col, BS, 43; Harvard Univ, AM, 47, PhD(physics), 52. *Hon Degrees:* DSc, Randolph-Macon Col, 76. *Honors & Awards:* Oliver E Buckley Prize Solid State Physics, 78; Alexander von Humboldt Sr US Scientist Award, 83-84. *Prof Exp:* Physicist, Res & Develop Ctr, Gen Elec Co, 52-75. *Concurrent Pos:* Adj prof, Rensselaer Polytech Inst, 62-65; NSF fel, Oxford Univ, 66-67; adj prof, State Univ NY, Albany, 70-71. *Mem:* Nat Acad Sci; fel Am Phys Soc; fel AAAS. *Res:* Nuclear and electron spin resonance studies; solid state physics; radiation effects and point defects in solids. *Mailing Add:* Dept Physics Lehigh Univ 16 Memorial Dr E Bethlehem PA 18015. *Fax:* 610-758-4561; *E-Mail:* gdw0@lehigh.edu

**WATKINS, IVAN WARREN,** PHYSICS. *Current Pos:* from asst prof to prof physics, 63-74, PROF GEOG & EARTH SCI, ST CLOUD STATE UNIV, 74- *Personal Data:* b Minneapolis, Kans, Jan 14, 34; m 55; c 4. *Educ:* Univ Kans, BS, 55, MS, 57; Tex A&M Univ, PhD, 68. *Prof Exp:* Instr physics, Ft Hays Kans State Col, 57-62. *Mem:* Am Asn Physics Teachers. *Res:* Theoretical molecular spectroscopy; student attitudes about sciences and how the attitudes correlate with success in science courses. *Mailing Add:* Dept Earth Sci St Cloud State Univ St Cloud MN 56301-4498

**WATKINS, JACKIE LLOYD,** GEOLOGY. *Current Pos:* Assoc prof, 58-72, PROF GEOL, MIDWEST UNIV, 72-, CHMN DEPT, 77- *Personal Data:* b Melvin, Tex, Jan 16, 32; m 55; c 4. *Educ:* Southern Methodist Univ, BS, 52, MS, 54; Univ Mich, PhD(geol), 58. *Concurrent Pos:* Chmn bd, Watkins Mineral Corp. *Mem:* AAAS; Paleont Soc; Soc Econ Paleont & Mineral; Geol Soc Am; Nat Asn Geol Teachers; Sigma Xi. *Res:* Invertebrate paleontology; tetracorals and tabulate corals. *Mailing Add:* Dept Sci Midwestern State Univ 3410 Taft Blvd Wichita Falls TX 76308-2095

**WATKINS, JAMES DAVID,** NUCLEAR ENERGY. *Current Pos:* SECY, DEPT ENERGY, WASHINGTON, 89- *Personal Data:* b Alhambra, Calif, Mar 7, 27; m 50, Sheila Jo McKinney; c Katherine Marie, Laura Jo, Charles Lancaster, Susan Elizabeth, James David & Edward Francis. *Educ:* US Naval Acad, BS, 49; Naval Postgrad Sch, MS, 58. *Hon Degrees:* LHD, Marymount Col, 82 & New York Med Col, 88; DSc, Dowling Col, 83, Univ Ala, 91; LLD, Cath Univ, 85. *Honors & Awards:* Chairman's Award, Am Asn Eng Socs, 91. *Prof Exp:* Chmn, Presidential Comn HIV Epidemic, 87-88. *Mailing Add:* 2021 Indian Circle St Leonard MD 20685

**WATKINS, JEFFREY CLIFTON,** NEUROSCIENCE. *Current Pos:* sr res fel physiol & pharamacol, 73-83, hon sr res fel pharmacol, 83-89, HON PROF PHARMACOL, UNIV BRISTOL, 89- *Personal Data:* b Perth, Australia, Dec 20, 29; m 73, Beatrice J Thacher; c Timothy D & Katherine H. *Educ:* Univ Western Australia, BS, 49, MS, 54; Univ Combridge, PhD, 54. *Honors & Awards:* Bristol-Myers Squibb Award, 95. *Prof Exp:* Res fel chem, Univ Cambridge, 54-55; Yale Univ, 55-57; res fel physiol, Australian Nat Univ, 58-65; vis res scientist, Agr Res Coun, Inst Animal Physiol, 63-64, sci officer, 65-67; sci staff mem, Neuropsychiat Unit, Med Res Coun, 68-73. *Concurrent Pos:* Consult, Sandoz Pharm, Switz, 83-94; consult, Tocris Neuramin Ltd, 85-94, dir, 92-94; consult & dir, Tocris-Cookson Ltd, 94- *Mem:* Fel Royal Soc London; Int Brain Res Orgn; Am Soc Neurosci; Brit Physiol Soc; Brit Pharmacol Soc; Acad Europ. *Mailing Add:* Pharmacol Dept Univ Bristol Sch Med Sci Bristol BS8 ITD England

**WATKINS, JOEL SMITH, JR,** GEOPHYSICS, SEISMOLOGY. *Current Pos:* PROF OCEANOG, TEX A&M UNIV, 85-, COOK PROF GEOSCI, 86-, HEAD, DEPT GEOPHYS, 88- *Personal Data:* b Poteau, Okla, May 27, 32; m 56, 71; c 2. *Educ:* Univ NC, AB, 53; Univ Tex, PhD(geol), 61. *Honors & Awards:* Except Sci Achievement Medal, NASA, 73. *Prof Exp:* Geophysicist, Regional Geophys Br, US Geol Surv, 61-64, Astrogeol Br, 64-66; res assoc geophys, Mass Inst Technol, 66-67; from assoc prof to prof, Univ NC, Chapel Hill, 67-73; prof geophys, Univ Tex Marine Sci Inst, 73-77; sr res assoc, Gulf Res & Develop Co, Houston, 77-79, mgr, Geol Interpreters Dept, Gulf Sci & Tech Co, Pittsburgh, 79-81, mgr geol, Cent Exp Group Int, Gulf Oil E&P Co, Houston, 81-82, expl mgr, Eastern US Frontier, 82-83, vpres, Expl Res, Gulf Res & Develop Co, 83-85. *Concurrent Pos:* Co-investr, Apollo Active Seismic Exp, 65-72, Apollo Lunar Seismic Profiling Exp, 71-73; mem adv comt, Int Phase Ocean Drilling, 74-; co-chief, Deep Sea Drilling Proj, 79. *Mem:* Am Geophys Union; Soc Explor Geophysicists; Geol Soc Am; Am Asn Petrol Geol. *Res:* Marine geophysics; explosion seismology. *Mailing Add:* Dept Geophys Tex A&M Univ College Station TX 77843-3115

**WATKINS, JULIAN F, II,** ENTOMOLOGY. *Current Pos:* asst prof, Baylor Univ, 64-68, assoc prof, 68-79, actg chmn, 79-81, vchmn, 81-84, PROF BIOL, BAYLOR UNIV, 79- *Personal Data:* b Marvell, Ark, Mar 18, 36; m 54, Alma J McCoy; c 2. *Educ:* Univ Ark, BSA, 56; Kans State Univ, MS, 62, PhD(entom), 64. *Prof Exp:* Asst co agent, Ark Agr Exten Serv, 56-60. *Res:* Taxonomy and behavior of army ants. *Mailing Add:* Dept Biol Baylor Univ PO Box 97388 Waco TX 76706-9989

**WATKINS, KAY ORVILLE,** INORGANIC CHEMISTRY, PHYSICAL CHEMISTRY. *Current Pos:* From asst prof to assoc prof, 61-70, PROF CHEM, ADAMS STATE COL, 70-, CHMN, DIV SCI & MATH, 77- *Personal Data:* b Nunn, Colo, Apr 28, 32; m 61; c 3. *Educ:* Adams State Col, BA, 55; Vanderbilt Univ, PhD(inorg chem), 61. *Concurrent Pos:* NSF acad year exten grant, 63-65 & res grant, 65-68; NSF high sch lectr, 66-67 & fac develop fel, 78; vis scientist, Brookhaven Nat Lab, 68-69 & Argonne Nat Lab, 73; vis prof, Univ Utah, 81 & Univ Hawaii, 87. *Mem:* Am Chem Soc. *Res:* Equilibria and kinetic studies of inorganic systems in solution. *Mailing Add:* Adams State Col Alamosa CO 81102

**WATKINS, KENNETH WALTER,** PHYSICAL CHEMISTRY. *Current Pos:* ASST PROF CHEM, COLO STATE UNIV, 66- *Personal Data:* b Philadelphia, Pa, Apr 22, 39; m 62, 84; c 2. *Educ:* Kans State Univ, BS, 61, PhD(chem), 65. *Prof Exp:* Fel chem, Univ Wash, 65-66. *Concurrent Pos:* Vis asst prof chem, Univ Wis, 79-80. *Mem:* Am Chem Soc; AAAS. *Res:* Chemical education. *Mailing Add:* Dept Chem Colo State Univ Ft Collins CO 80523-0002

**WATKINS, LINDA ROTHBLUM,** NEUROANATOMY, NEUROPHYSIOLOGY. *Current Pos:* LECTR NEUROSCI, DEPT PHYSIOL, MED COL VA, 81- *Personal Data:* b Norfolk, Va, June 29, 54; m 76. *Educ:* Va Polytech Inst & State Univ, BS, 76; Med Col Va, PhD(physiol), 80. *Concurrent Pos:* Fel, Dept Physiol, Med Col Va, 81- *Mem:* Int Asn Study Pain. *Res:* Behavioral, neuroanatomical and neuropharmacological investigations of endogennous opiate and non-opiate pain inhibitory systems which are activated by brain stimulation, morphine or environmental stimuli. *Mailing Add:* Dept Psychol Univ Colo Box 345 Boulder CO 80309-0345

**WATKINS, MARK E,** MATHEMATICS, GRAPH THEORY. *Current Pos:* assoc prof, 68-76, PROF MATH, SYRACUSE UNIV, 76- *Personal Data:* b New York, NY, Apr 13, 37; m 90, Benda D Silverman; c Sarah A (Fitts), Rebecca (Kent) & Michaela S. *Educ:* Amherst Col, AB, 59; Yale Univ, MA, 61, PhD(math), 64. *Prof Exp:* Instr math, Univ NC, Chapel Hill, 63-64, asst prof, 64-68. *Concurrent Pos:* Vis assoc prof, Univ Waterloo, 67-68 & 80; vis prof, Vienna Tech Univ, 73-74 & Univ Paris-Orsay, 86; Ger Acad Exchange Serv grants, West Berlin, 80 & 89. *Mem:* Am Math Soc. *Res:* Problems related to vertex-connectivity in graphs; imbedding of graphs; automorphism groups of graphs and systems. *Mailing Add:* Dept Math Syracuse Univ Syracuse NY 13244-1150. *Fax:* 315-443-1475

**WATKINS, MAURICE,** METALLURGICAL ENGINEERING. *Current Pos:* res assoc, 73-85, GROUP LEADER, MAT RES, EXXON PROD RES CO, 85- *Personal Data:* b East Chicago, Ind, Aug 8, 46; m 76, Joyce Gooden. *Educ:* Ill Inst Technol, BS, 68, PhD(metall eng), 73. *Prof Exp:* Engr eng mat, Res & Develop Labs, Continental Can Co, 68-69. *Concurrent Pos:* Vis lectr, Black Exec Exchange Prog, Urban League, 76-; indust adv & prog coordr for Jets Club, Houston Independent Sch Dist, 78-; Exxon rep, Nat Asn Corrosion Engrs & Am Petrol Inst. *Mem:* Am Soc Metals; Nat Asn Corrosion Engrs. *Res:* Welding, corrosion, stress corrosion cracking, hydrogen embrittlement and fatigue of materials used in the manufacture of equipment for oil and gas exploration and production. *Mailing Add:* 5623 Bent Bough Houston TX 77088

**WATKINS, NANCY CHAPMAN,** PHYSICS, POLYMER SCIENCE. *Current Pos:* STAFF ENGR, IBM CORP, 80- *Personal Data:* b Bowling Green, Ky, Mar 19, 39; m 62; c 1. *Educ:* Univ Ky, BS, 61; Rensselaer Polytech Inst, PhD(chem eng), 67. *Prof Exp:* Sr res scientist fiber struct, Am Enka Corp, 67-80. *Mem:* Am Chem Soc. *Res:* Thermal analysis, scanning electron microscopy, x-ray diffraction and computer applications to fiber structural studies; cross-linking technique applied to thermal studies. *Mailing Add:* One Warwick Lane Frankfort KY 40601-3859

**WATKINS, PAUL ALLAN,** BIOCHEMISTRY. *Current Pos:* asst prof, 84-91, ASSOC PROF NEUROL, SCH MED, JOHNS HOPKINS UNIV, 91-, JOINT APPOINTMENT BIOL CHEM, 92- *Personal Data:* b Baltimore, Md, Oct 12, 49; m 90, Karen L Frayer. *Educ:* Johns Hopkins Univ, BA, 71, MD, 78, PhD(biochem), 79. *Prof Exp:* Res assoc, Nat Heart, Lung & Blood Inst, NIH, 78-82, med staff fel, 82-84. *Mem:* Am Soc Biochem & Molecular Biol; Am Fedn Clin Res. *Res:* Regulation of fatty acid metabolism in normal and pathological states; metabolic processes of peroxisomes; peroxisomal diseases. *Mailing Add:* Kennedy Krieger Inst Johns Hopkins Univ Sch Med 707 N Broadway Baltimore MD 21205-1832. *Fax:* 410-550-9839

**WATKINS, ROBERT ARNOLD,** ELECTROOPTICS, MILITARY SYSTEMS. *Current Pos:* TECH DIR, R & R ADVENTURES, 95- *Personal Data:* b Boston, Mass, Aug 3, 26; m 83, Rachel A Spencer; c David J & Sandra J. *Educ:* Brown Univ, ScB, 47; Ohio State Univ, MS, 48, PhD(physics), 53. *Honors & Awards:* Centennial Medal, Inst Elec & Electronics Engrs. *Prof Exp:* Instr physics, Univ WVa, 48-49; engr, Zenith Radio Corp, 52-54; sr engr, Raytheon Co, Goleta, 54-57, sect mgr, 57-60, dept mgr, 60-63, prin engr, 63-80, dept mgr, 80-89, consult engr, 89-95. *Mem:* Inst Elec & Electronics Engrs; Optical Soc Am; Am Inst Aeronaut & Astronaut. *Res:* Optical systems design with associated electronic and mechanical configurations; laser effects on materials; combined radio frequency and optical systems; digital based radio frequency systems. *Mailing Add:* 844 Vereda del Ciervo Goleta CA 93117-5304

**WATKINS, SALLIE ANN,** SCIENCE EDUCATION. *Current Pos:* PRES, HOPE CONSULT, 89- *Personal Data:* b Jacksonville, Fla, June 27, 22. *Educ:* Notre Dame Col, Ohio, BS, 45; Cath Univ, MS, 54, PhD(physics), 58. *Prof Exp:* Instr chem & physics, Notre Dame Acad, Ohio, 45-49, Elyria Dist Cath High Sch, Ohio, 49-50; instr physics, Notre Dame Col, Ohio, 50-53, prof, 57-66; teaching asst, Cath Univ, 55-56; prof physics, Univ Southern Colo, 66-88. *Concurrent Pos:* NSF res grant biophys, 60-63; Oak Ridge Asn Univs res partic fel, Savannah River Lab, 66-68; mcm exec bd, Am Asn Physics Teachers, 83-86; sr educ fel, Am Inst Physics, Washington, DC, 87-88. *Mem:* Am Phys Soc; Am Asn Physics Teachers; AAAS; Sigma Xi. *Res:* Nuclear reactor physics; ultrasonics and biophysics; history and philosophy of science; science education. *Mailing Add:* 1081 S Lynx Dr Pueblo West CO 81007-5032. *Fax:* 719-547-4401; *E-Mail:* saw@uscolo.edu

**WATKINS, SPENCER HUNT,** ORGANIC CHEMISTRY. *Current Pos:* RETIRED. *Personal Data:* b Mayfield, Ky, Sept 15, 24; m 46; c 3. *Educ:* Univ Ill, BS, 47; Univ Wis, PhD(chem), 50. *Prof Exp:* Res chemist, Hercules, Inc, 50-55, res supvr, 55-57, tech rep, 57-60, asst sales mgr, 60-63, mgr tech serv, 63-65, mgr mkt develop, 65-74, dir develop, Pine & Paper Chem Dept, 74-78, dir technol, 78-88. *Mem:* Am Chem Soc; Tech Asn Pulp & Paper Indust; Com Develop Asn; Am Asn Textile Chem & Colorists. *Res:* Paper chemicals, rosin chemistry; urea-formaldehyde resins. *Mailing Add:* 125 Wildwood Lane Naples FL 34105

**WATKINS, STEVEN F,** STRUCTURAL CHEMISTRY, CRYSTALLOGRAPHY. *Current Pos:* asst prof, 68-73, ASSOC PROF CHEM, LA STATE UNIV, BATON ROUGE, 73- *Personal Data:* b Amarillo, Tex, May 14, 40; div; c Bryn & Dan. *Educ:* Pomona Col, BA, 62; Univ Wis, PhD(phys chem), 67. *Honors & Awards:* Coates Award, Am Inst Chem Engrs. *Prof Exp:* Res fel, Bristol Univ, 67-68. *Concurrent Pos:* Vis prof, Univ Houston, 66-67; vis scientist, Brookhaven Nat Lab, 72; chmn, Orgn Prophet Using Scientist, 85; consult, Dow Chem Co, 86-88 & Ethyl Corp, 88-

*Mem:* Am Chem Soc; Am Crystallog Asn; Sigma Xi. *Res:* Molecular structure of organometallic, inorganic and organic biological molecules in the solid state by means of x-ray and neutron crystallography. *Mailing Add:* Dept Chem La State Univ Baton Rouge LA 70803. *Fax:* 504-388-3458; *E-Mail:* steve. watkins@chemgate.chem.lsu.edu

**WATKINS, TERRY ANDERSON,** STATISTICS. *Current Pos:* ASSOC PROF MATH STATIST, UNIV NEW ORLEANS, 77- *Personal Data:* b Brady, Tex, June 29, 38. *Educ:* WTex State Univ, BS, 61; Ill Inst Technol, MS, 64; Tex Tech Univ, PhD(math statist), 72. *Prof Exp:* Instr math, WTex State Univ, 64-65, asst prof, Angelo State Univ, 66-68, 71-72; instr, Tex Tech Univ, 70-71, asst prof, 72-77. *Mem:* Am Statist Asn. *Res:* Estimation; jackknifing procedures. *Mailing Add:* Dept Math Univ New Orleans 2000 Lakeshore Dr New Orleans LA 70148-0001

**WATKINS, TOM R,** LIPID PEROXIDATION, ANTITOXIDANTS. *Current Pos:* LAB DIR, KENNETH L JORDAN HEART FUND, 88- *Personal Data:* b San Jose, Calif, Jan 21, 47. *Educ:* Univ Calif, Berkeley, BA, 70, PhD(nutrit), 75. *Prof Exp:* Asst prof, Univ Del, 76-82; assoc prof, City Univ NY, 83-86; chief, Metab Dis Lab, Dept Pediat, NY Univ Med Sch, 87-88. *Concurrent Pos:* Fel, Univ Calif, Berkeley, 70-74, Harvard Univ, 74-76. *Mem:* Int Lecithin & Phospholipid Soc (pres, 92-93). *Res:* Study of link between diet and disease and the role of lipids, proteins and starches, with emphasis on rancidity and peroxidation and the role of vitamins, minerals, and other natural substances in preventing such diseases. *Mailing Add:* 48 Plymouth St Montclair NJ 07042-2625. *Fax:* 973-746-2918

**WATKINS, W DAVID,** ANESTHESIOLOGY, PHARMACOLOGY. *Current Pos:* PROF & CHMN DEPT ANESTHESIOL, DUKE UNIV MED CTR, 83- *Educ:* Univ Mich, PhD(toxicol); Univ Colo, MD, 75. *Mailing Add:* Montefiore Univ Hosp 3459 Fifth Ave Pittsburgh PA 15213. *Fax:* 412-648-6695

**WATKINS, WILLIAM,** MATHEMATICS, STATISTICS. *Current Pos:* PROF MATH, CALIF STATE UNIV, NORTHRIDGE, 69- *Personal Data:* b Los Angeles, Calif, July 7, 42; c 2. *Educ:* Univ Calif, Santa Barbara, BA, 64, MA, 68, PhD(math), 69. *Concurrent Pos:* Ed, Linear & Multilinear Algebra. *Mem:* Math Asn Am; Soc Indust & Appl Math; Am Math Soc. *Res:* Linear and multilinear algebra. *Mailing Add:* Dept Math Calif State Univ Northridge CA 91330-8313

**WATLING, LES,** TAXONOMY OF CRUSTACEA, MARINE BENTHIC ECOLOGY. *Current Pos:* asst prof oceanog, Univ Maine, 76-80, actg chmn, dept oceanog & zool, 80-81, assoc prof oceanog & zool, 80-89, actg dir, Darling Marine Ctr, 85-90, PROF OCEANOG, UNIV MAINE, 90- *Personal Data:* b Calgary, Alta, Oct 13, 45; m 92, Alison Rieser. *Educ:* Univ Calgary, BSc, 65; Univ Pac, MS, 68; Univ Del, PhD(marine studies), 74. *Prof Exp:* Res biologist, Univ Del, 74-76. *Concurrent Pos:* Assoc ed, J Crustacean Biol, 80-81; mem gov bd, Crustacean Soc, 80-84; sr postdoctoral fel, Smithsonian, 90. *Mem:* Soc Syst Zool; Crustacean Soc (pres, 94-); Palaeont Asn; Ecol Soc Am; Am Soc Limnologists & Oceanogr. *Res:* Ecology of marine benthos, particularly of boreal and polar seas; taxonomy of amphipoda and cumacea from Antarctica to tropics; author of 60 articles & editor of 3 books. *Mailing Add:* Ira C Darling Ctr Univ Maine Walpole ME 04573. *Fax:* 207-563-3119

**WATLINGTON, CHARLES OSCAR,** MEDICINE, PHYSIOLOGY. *Current Pos:* from instr to asst prof, 62-69, assoc prof, 69-76, PROF MED, MED COL VA, VA COMMONWEALTH UNIV, 76- *Personal Data:* b Midlothian, Va, Apr 9, 32; m 55; c 2. *Educ:* Va Polytech Inst, BS, 54; Med Col Va, Va Commonwealth Univ, MD, 58, PhD(physiol), 68. *Prof Exp:* Intern med, Univ Calif, San Francisco, 58-59, asst resident, 60-62. *Concurrent Pos:* Fel endocrinol, Univ Calif, San Francisco. *Mem:* Am Physiol Soc; Am Fedn Clin Res; Endocrine Soc; Am Diabetes Asn; Am Soc Nephrology. *Res:* Regulation of ion transport; sodium and calcium homeostasis; cellular mechanism of action of hormones. *Mailing Add:* Dept Med Endominol 1707 Park Ave Va Commonwealth Univ Sch Med Richmond VA 23298-1900. *Fax:* 804-225-4977

**WATNE, ALVIN LLOYD,** SURGERY. *Current Pos:* RETIRED. *Personal Data:* b Shabbona, Ill, Jan 13, 27; m 66; c 4. *Educ:* Univ Ill, BS, 50, MD, 52, MS, 56. *Prof Exp:* Intern, Indianapolis Gen Hosp, Ind, 52-53; res asst surg, Univ Ill, 53-54; resident, Res & Educ Hosp, Univ Ill, 54-58; assoc cancer res surgeon, Roswell Park Mem Inst, 58-59, assoc chief cancer res surgeon, 59-62; from assoc prof to prof surg, WVa Univ, 62-73, cancer coordr, 62-73, actg chmn surg, 73-75, chmn dept, 75-86; prof & chmn, Col Med, Univ Ill, Peoria, 86-91. *Mem:* Am Asn Cancer Res; Am Col Surgeons; Soc Univ Surgeons; NY Acad Sci; Sigma Xi. *Res:* Cancer metastases, including dissemination of tumor cells via the blood and lymph and their lodgement and growth; etiology and prevention of polyposis and coli and colon cancer. *Mailing Add:* 1653 Mooregate Ct 2128 Penny Lane Marietta GA 30362

**WATNICK, ARTHUR SAUL,** ENDOCRINOLOGY. *Current Pos:* from asst chemist to assoc chemist, Schering Corp, 56-62, from scientist to sr scientist, 62-70, assoc dir, Dept Allergy & Inflammation, 81-85, ASSOC DIR, BIOL RES, SCHERING CORP, 70-, MGR DEPT PHYSIOL, 77, SECT LEADER, 85- *Personal Data:* b Brooklyn, NY, Feb 4, 30; m 57; c 2. *Educ:* Brooklyn Col, BS, 53, MA, 56; NY Univ, PhD(physiol), 63. *Prof Exp:* Biochemist, Sloan-Kettering Inst, 53-54; Beth-El Hosp, Brooklyn, NY, 54-56. *Concurrent Pos:* Lectr endocrinol, Fairleigh Dickenson Univ, 66- & Rutgers

Univ, 71-; lectr physiol anat, Bloomfield Col, 85; adj prof immunol, Fairleigh Dickenson Univ, 88- *Mem:* AAAS; Soc Exp Biol & Med; Am Chem Soc; Endocrine Soc; NY Acad Sci; Reticuloendothelial Soc. *Res:* Reproductive physiology; immunology. *Mailing Add:* 27 Harding Dr South Orange NJ 07079. *Fax:* 973-429-3706

**WATRACH, ADOLF MICHAEL,** VETERINARY PATHOLOGY. *Current Pos:* from instr to prof, 51-85, EMER PROF VET PATH, COL VET MED, UNIV ILL, URBANA, 85- *Personal Data:* b Poland, Jan 7, 18; nat US; m 55. *Educ:* Royal (Dick) Vet Col, Scotland, MRCVS, 48; Glasgow Univ, PhD(path), 58. *Prof Exp:* Asst vet path, Vet Sch, Glasgow Univ, 49-51. *Mem:* AAAS; Electron Micros Soc Am; Am Col Vet Path; Vet Med Asn; Int Acad Path. *Res:* Ultrastructural pathology; virus-cell relationship; viral oncogenesis; mammary tumor biology; cell pathobiology. *Mailing Add:* 645 Cosmos Way Prescott AZ 86303

**WATREL, WARREN GEORGE,** MICROBIOLOGY, BIOCHEMISTRY. *Current Pos:* VPRES, GEORGE WARREN ASST, 84- *Personal Data:* b Brooklyn, NY, Jan 5, 35; m 60; c 3. *Educ:* Syracuse Univ, BS, 57, MS, 58. *Honors & Awards:* Mkt Award, Am Chem Soc; Award, Res & Develop Soc Cosmet Chem. *Prof Exp:* Asst to dir of NSF, Syracuse Univ, 57, instr, 57-58; pharmaceut sales & mkt staff, Lederle Labs, Am Cyanamid Co, 60-62; biochem specialist, M&T Chem, Am Can Co, 62-64; sales mgr, Pharmacia Fine Chem, Inc, 64-65; dir mkt & gen mgr, 65-72; vpres, Vineland, Vista Labs, Inc, Ideal & Nickolson Inst, Damon Corp, 72-74; vpres, Pharmachem Corp, 74-75; exec vpres, Newton Industs Inc, 76-79; vpres, Seton Co, 79-84 & Secol Inc & Selomas Inc, 79-84. *Concurrent Pos:* Am Cyanamid Co & NSF grants, 57-58. *Mem:* AAAS; Am Chem Soc; Am Mkt Asn; Am Soc Microbiol; NY Acad Sci. *Res:* Application research and development of products biologically active for use in commercial products; research and development of products to be used in gel filtration chromatography; development, manufacture and sale of veterinarian, pharmacy, human, cosmetics industrial chemicals and medical electonic instruments. *Mailing Add:* 506 Collins Ave Hasbrouck Heights NJ 07604

**WATROUS, JAMES JOSEPH,** PHYSIOLOGY. *Current Pos:* asst prof, 72-80, ASSOC PROF BIOL, ST JOSEPH'S UNIV, 80-, CHMN DEPT, 77- *Personal Data:* b Cleveland, Ohio, July 20, 42; m 70; c 2. *Educ:* Univ Dayton, BSEd, 65, MS, 69; Georgetown Univ, PhD(biol), 72. *Prof Exp:* Teacher sec sch, Ohio, 64-67; teaching asst biol, Univ Dayton, 67-69 & Georgetown Univ, 69-72. *Mem:* Am Phys Soc; NY Acad Sci; AAAS; Sigma Xi; Am Soc Zoologists. *Res:* Transport of materials across biological membranes; nerve muscle physiology. *Mailing Add:* Dept Biol St Joseph's Univ Philadelphia PA 19131

**WATSCHKE, THOMAS LEE,** AGRONOMY, HORTICULTURE. *Current Pos:* assoc prof agron, 70-80, PROF TURFGRASS SCI, PA STATE UNIV, UNIVERSITY PARK, 80- *Personal Data:* b Charles City, Iowa, Apr 12, 44; m 65. *Educ:* Iowa State Univ, BS, 67; Va Polytech Inst & State Univ, MS, 69, PhD(agron), 71. *Mem:* Am Soc Agron; Crop Sci Soc Am; Int Turfgrass Soc. *Res:* Turfgrass physiology; weed control and growth regulation. *Mailing Add:* Pa State Univ 116 ASI Bldg University Park PA 16802

**WATSON, ALAN KEMBALL,** WEED SCIENCE, BIOLOGICAL CONTROL. *Current Pos:* From asst prof to assoc prof, 75-86, PROF, MACDONALD COL, MCGILL UNIV, 86- *Personal Data:* b Vernon, BC, Sept 1, 48; m 71; c 3. *Educ:* Univ BC, BSc, 70, MSc, 72; Univ Sask, PhD(weed sci), 75. *Honors & Awards:* Medal Agron Distinction, Order Agronomists Que, 85. *Concurrent Pos:* Dir, Biopesticides Res Lab, McGill Univ, 87- *Mem:* Weed Sci Soc Am; Soc Nematologists; Can Phytopath Soc. *Res:* Biology and control of weeds with emphasis on biological control utilizing plant pathogens. *Mailing Add:* Dept Plant Sci McDonald Col 21111 Lakeshore Rd Ste-Anne-de-Bellevue PQ H9X 1C0 Can

**WATSON, ANDREW JOHN,** WEED SCIENCE. *Current Pos:* RETIRED. *Personal Data:* b Mich, Aug 1, 21; m 50, 68, Valarie A Gale. *Educ:* Mich State Univ, PhD(soil sci), 49. *Prof Exp:* agronomist, Dow Chem Co, 49-86. *Mem:* Weed Sci Soc Am. *Res:* Herbicide development. *Mailing Add:* 5509 Siebert St Midland MI 48640

**WATSON, ANDREW SAMUEL,** PSYCHIATRY. *Current Pos:* from asst prof psychiat & asst prof law to assoc prof psychiat & assoc prof law, 59-66, PROF PSYCHIAT, MED SCH, UNIV MICH, ANN ARBOR & PROF LAW, LAW SCH, 66- *Personal Data:* b Highland Park, Mich, May 2, 20; m 67; c 2. *Educ:* Univ Mich, BS, 42; Temple Univ, MD, 50, MS, 51. *Honors & Awards:* Issac Ray Award, Am Psychiat Asn, 78. *Prof Exp:* From instr to asst prof psychiat, Med Sch, Univ Pa, 45-59, assoc prof, Law Sch, 55-59. *Concurrent Pos:* Lectr social work, Sch Social Work, Bryn Mawr Col, 55-59; psychiat consult, Mich Dept Corrections, 59-; comnr, Mich Law Enforcement Criminal Justice Comn, 68-72; mem, Adv Comt Divorce, Nat Conf Comnr Uniform State Laws, 69-70; mem, Surgeon's Gen Sci Adv Comn TV & Social Behav, 69-72. *Mem:* Group Advan Psychiat; Am Col Psychiatrists. *Res:* Family treatment; professionalizing process of lawyers; applications of psychiatric concepts to law. *Mailing Add:* 555 E William 21-D Ann Arbor MI 48104-2427

**WATSON, ANNETTA PAULE,** TERRESTRIAL ECOLOGY, ENTOMOLOGY. *Current Pos:* guest scientist, 77, RES STAFF, HEALTH SCI RES DIV, OAK RIDGE NAT LAB, MARTIN MARIETTA ENERGY SYSTS, 77- *Personal Data:* b Pleasure Ridge Park, Ky, May 2, 48; m 75, R

J Luxmoore. *Educ:* Purdue Univ, West Lafayette, BS, 70; Univ Ky, PhD(entom), 76. *Prof Exp:* Consult res, Oak Ridge Nat Lab, Union Carbide Corp, 75-76; vis scientist, Div Entom, Commonwealth Sci & Indust Res Orgn, Australia, 76. *Concurrent Pos:* Mem, comt health effects mustard gas, Nat Acad Sci, 91-93, subcomt mil field drinking water qual, 93- *Mem:* Nat Asn Environ Prof; AAAS; Sigma Xi. *Res:* Acute and long term toxicity of chemical warfare agents and their breakdown products; assessment of energy technologies on human systems, human ecology, insect ecology, and entomology; litter decomposition. *Mailing Add:* 295 Solomon Hollow Rd Harriman TN 37748. *Fax:* 423-576-7651

**WATSON, BARRY,** BIOPHYSICAL CHEMISTRY. *Current Pos:* RES DIR, ANATRACE INC, 85- *Personal Data:* b Middlesbrough, Eng, Dec 2, 40. *Educ:* Univ Bradford, BSc, 65, PhD(phys chem), 68. *Prof Exp:* Scientist, Unilever Res Ltd, 66-68; Off Saline Water fel, Mellon Inst Sci, 69-72; res chemist, Owens-Ill Inc, 72-85. *Mem:* Royal Soc Chem; Am Chem Soc; Soc Electroanalytical Chem. *Res:* Thermodynamics of aqueous solutions; electrochemistry; biomedical research; electroanalytical chemistry. *Mailing Add:* Anatrace Inc 434 W Dussel Dr Maumee OH 43537

**WATSON, CHARLES S,** PSYCHOACOUSTICS. *Current Pos:* AT DEPT SPEECH & HEARING SCI, UNIV IND. *Personal Data:* b Chicago, Ill, Aug 16, 32; c 4. *Educ:* Ind Univ, AB, 58, PhD(psychol), 63. *Prof Exp:* Teaching assoc psychol, Ind Univ, 59-61; asst prof, Univ Tex, 62-65; from assoc prof to prof, Wash Univ, 67-76; sr res assoc, Cent Inst Deaf, St Louis, 66-76; dir res, Boys Town Inst Commun Dis Children, 76-; prof human commun, Med Sch, Creighton Univ, 76- *Concurrent Pos:* Ed assoc, Perception & Psychophys, 68-73; mem, Comt Hearing & Bioacoust, Nat Res Coun-Nat Acad Sci, 70-, chmn, 81-83; assoc ed, J Acoust Soc Am, 73-78; mem, NSF Rev Panel Sensory Physiol & Perception, 78- *Mem:* Fel Acoust Soc Am; fel Am Psychol Asn; AAAS; Sigma Xi; Asn Res Otolaryngol. *Res:* Hearing and deafness; perception of complex sounds; psychophysical methods; learning, memory and selective attention in auditory perception. *Mailing Add:* Dept Speech & Hearing Sci Ind Univ Bloomington IN 47405

**WATSON, CLARENCE ELLIS, JR,** PLANT BREEDING, EXPERIMENTAL STATISTICS. *Current Pos:* from asst prof to prof agron, 76-97, PROF EXP STATIST, MISS STATE UNIV, 89- *Personal Data:* b Stillwater, Okla, Apr 13, 51; m 72; c 2. *Educ:* NMex State Univ, BS, 72, MS, 74; Ore State Univ, PhD(crop sci), 76. *Prof Exp:* Res asst, NMex State Univ, 73-74; res asst, Ore State Univ, 74-76. *Mem:* Am Soc Agron; Crop Sci Soc Am. *Res:* Forage grass breeding with particular emphasis on host-plant resistance and stress tolerance; quantitative genetics; sweet corn breeding for pest and stress tolerance. *Mailing Add:* Dept Exp Statist Box 9653 Mississippi State MS 39762-9653. *Fax:* 601-325-7779; *E-Mail:* cew1@ra.msstate.edu

**WATSON, CLAYTON WILBUR,** NUCLEAR ENGINEERING. *Current Pos:* RETIRED. *Personal Data:* b Neosho, Mo, Feb 24, 33; m 55; c 3. *Educ:* Wash Univ, BS, 54; Iowa State Univ, MS, 55, PhD(nuclear eng), 60. *Prof Exp:* Engr, Westinghouse Atomic Power, 55-57; res assoc, Rocketdyne, 60-62; asst prof nuclear eng, Univ Fla, 62-63; mem staff, Los Alamos Sci Lab, Univ Calif, 63-94. *Mem:* Am Nuclear Soc. *Res:* Monte Carlo analysis; nuclear reactor physics and applications; radiation environmental analysis; nuclear applications in space; advanced space systems; nuclear weapons; advanced-technology assessment; systems analysis and evaluation; technology development planning. *Mailing Add:* 133 Barranca Rd Los Alamos NM 87544

**WATSON, DAVID ALAN,** molecular basis of bacterial pathogenesis, molecular mechanisms of antibiotic resistance among bacteria, for more information see previous edition

**WATSON, DAVID GOULDING,** PEDIATRICS. *Current Pos:* From asst prof to prof, 59-93, EMER PROF PEDIAT, MED CTR, UNIV MISS, 93- *Personal Data:* b Toronto, Ont, May 7, 29; nat US; m 61, Aileen Fors; c Carmen, Patrice, Eric, Joanna & Andrew. *Educ:* Univ Toronto, MD, 52. *Concurrent Pos:* NIH spec fel, Univ Fla, 72-73. *Mem:* Am Acad Pediat; Am Col Cardiol; Royal Col Physicians Can. *Res:* Pediatric cardiology. *Mailing Add:* Dept Pediat Univ Miss Med Ctr 2500 N State St Jackson MS 39216-4505

**WATSON, DAVID LIVINGSTON,** entomology, for more information see previous edition

**WATSON, DEBORAH KAY,** QUANTUM MECHANICS. *Current Pos:* PROF PHYSICS, UNIV OKLA, 81- *Personal Data:* b Mt Vernon, Ohio, Nov 27, 50; m 79, John B Frick; c Michael, David & Mark. *Educ:* Allegheny Col, BS, 72; Harvard Univ, PhD(phys chem), 77. *Prof Exp:* NSF postdoctoral fel, Calif Inst Technol, 77-79, postdoctoral asst, 79-80; staff scientist, Aerospace Corp, 80-81. *Concurrent Pos:* NSF vis prof, Harvard Univ, 87-88. *Mem:* Am Phys Soc. *Res:* Fundamental quantum mechanical questions for simple atomic systems using dimensional scaling methods; diamagnetic hydrogen, the hydride ion and the underlying dynamical group of the helium atom. *Mailing Add:* Dept Physics & Astron Univ Okla Norman OK 73019. *E-Mail:* watson@phyast.nhn.ou.edu

**WATSON, DENNIS RONALD,** CHEMISTRY. *Current Pos:* From asst prof to assoc prof, 70-81, PROF CHEM, LA COL, 81-, CHMN DEPT, 70- *Personal Data:* b Overton, Tex, Dec 7, 41; m 70; c 1. *Educ:* Howard Payne Col, BA, 64; Univ Colo, Boulder, MS, 67, PhD(chem), 70. *Mem:* Am Chem Soc. *Res:* Air and water pollution topics that can be performed by senior level students dealing with local problems and conditions. *Mailing Add:* Dept Chem La Col Pineville LA 71359-0001

**WATSON, DENNIS WALLACE,** MICROBIOLOGY, IMMUNOLOGY. *Current Pos:* from assoc prof to prof bact, Univ Minn, 49-64, Regents prof, 80, prof & head dept, 64-84, REGENTS EMER PROF MICROBIOL, MED SCH, UNIV MINN, MINNEAPOLIS, 84- *Personal Data:* b Morpeth, Ont, Apr 29, 14; nat US; m 41, Alice May Whittier; c Catherine & William. *Educ:* Univ Toronto, BSA, 34; Dalhousie Univ, MSc, 37; Univ Wis, PhD(bact), 41. *Hon Degrees:* DSc, Univ Wis-Madison, 81. *Prof Exp:* Asst, Biol Bd Can, NS, 35-37, sci asst, 37-38; asst bact, Univ Wis, 38-41, Alumni Res Found fel, 41-42, res assoc, 42; vis investr, Rockefeller Inst, 42; vis instr, Connaught Labs, Toronto, 42-44; asst prof bact, Univ Wis, 46-49. *Concurrent Pos:* Med consult, Fed Security Agency, Washington, DC, 44; assoc mem comn immunization, Armed Forces Epidemiol Bd, 46-59; vis prof, Med Sch, Univ Wash, 50; mem allergy & immunol study sect, NIH, 54-58, mem bd sci counr, Div Biol Stand, 57-59, mem allergy & immunol training grant comt, Nat Inst Allergy & Infectious Dis, 58-60 & 64-66, chmn, 66, mem nat adv coun, 67-71; USPHS spec res fel, WGer, 60-61; mem ad hoc comt med microbiol, Div Med Sci, Nat Acad Sci, vis investr, Osaka Univ, Japan, 71; vis instr, WHO Immunol Course, High Inst Pub Health, Alexandria, Egypt, 81. *Mem:* AAAS; Am Chem Soc; Am Soc Microbiol (vpres, 67-68, pres, 68-69); Soc Exp Biol & Med (pres, 75-76); Infectious Dis Soc Am; Am Asn Immunologists. *Res:* Host-parasite relationships; chemistry and immunology of microbial toxins; pathogenesis of group A streptococci; mechanisms of nonspecific resistance to infection. *Mailing Add:* Med Sch Dept Microbiol Univ Minn Box 196 Mayo Minneapolis MN 55455

**WATSON, DONALD PICKETT,** horticulture; deceased, see previous edition for last biography

**WATSON, DUANE CRAIG,** ANALYTICAL CHEMISTRY. *Current Pos:* RETIRED. *Personal Data:* b Enid, Okla, Dec 8, 30; m 51; c 3. *Educ:* Eastern NMex Univ, BA, 51, BS, 56, MS, 57. *Prof Exp:* Res chemist, El Paso Natural Gas Prod, Tex, 57-63; prof res chemist, Philip Morris Inc, 63-74, sr scientist, 74-90, sec leader, 90- *Concurrent Pos:* Lectr, Univ Tex, El Paso, 61-63. *Res:* Smoke chemistry; trace analyses; pollution; process instrumentation; gas chromatography. *Mailing Add:* 101 Sunnybrook Rd Fairfield VA 24435

**WATSON, EDNA SUE,** immunology, for more information see previous edition

**WATSON, EDWARD BRUCE,** GEOCHEMISTRY. *Current Pos:* chmn, Dept Earth & Environ Scis, 90-95, PROF, RENSSELAER POLYTECH INST, 77-, INST PROF SCI, 95- *Educ:* Univ NH, BA, 72; Mass Inst Technol, PhD(geochem), 76. *Honors & Awards:* F W Clarke Medal, Geochem Soc, 83. *Prof Exp:* Postdoctoral fel, Carnegie Inst, 76-77. *Concurrent Pos:* Vis res fel, Macquarie Univ, Australia, 81; presidential young investr, 84-89; vis scientist, Max-Planck Inst Chem, Mainz, 84; assoc ed, Geochimica et Cosmochimica Acta, 85-88; counr, Geochem Soc, 91-94; ed, Petrol & Geochem, 88-96, Chem Geol, 91-95; vis comt, McGill, 91, Carnegie Inst, 92, Brown, 93, Harvard, 94-97. *Mem:* Nat Acad Sci; Geochem Soc; fel Am Geophys Union; fel Mineral Soc Am (vpres, 97); fel Geol Soc Am; fel Am Acad Arts & Sci. *Mailing Add:* Dept Earth & Environ Sci Rensselaer Polytech Inst Troy NY 12180

**WATSON, EVELYN E,** INTERNAL DOSIMETRY, MATHEMATICAL MODELING. *Current Pos:* res assoc, Med Div, Radiopharmaceut Internal Dose Info Ctr, Oak Ridge Assoc Univs, 71-77, scientist, 77-81, prog mgr, Manpower Educ, Res & Training Div, 81-89, PROG DIR, RADIOPHARMACEUT INTERNAL DOSE INFO CTR, MED SCI DIV, OAK RIDGE ASSOC UNIVS, 89- *Personal Data:* b Corbin, Ky, Dec 15, 28; m 53, Earl G; c Nancy (Donsbach) & Philip A. *Educ:* Univ Ky, BA, 49. *Honors & Awards:* Spec Award, Excellence Technol Transfer, Fed Lab Consortium, 85; Lifetime Sci Achievement Award, Women in Sci, 93, ET Chapter, Health Physics Soc, 95. *Concurrent Pos:* Mem, Med Internal Radiation Dose Comt, 80-, vchmn, 92-94, chmn, 94-; Task Group Nat Coun Radiation Protection & Measurements Sci Comt 57 on Placental Transfer, 85-; prog dir, Radiation Internal Dose Info Ctr, Med Sci Div, Oak Ridge Inst Sci & Educ, 92-94. *Mem:* Soc Nuclear Med; Health Physics Soc; Sigma Xi; Europ Nuclear Med Asn. *Res:* Calculation of radiation dose to normal persons and to patients with various diseases; improve estimation of dose; disseminate information to the nuclear medicine community. *Mailing Add:* 104 New Bedford Lane Oak Ridge TN 37830. *Fax:* 423-576-8673; *E-Mail:* watsonee@aol.com

**WATSON, FLETCHER GUARD,** SCIENCE EDUCATION. *Current Pos:* from asst prof to assoc prof sci educ, Harvard Univ, 46-57, prof educ, 57-66, Henry Lee Shattuck prof, 66-78, EMER PROF EDUC, HARVARD UNIV, 78- *Personal Data:* b Baltimore, Md, Apr 27, 12; m 35, Alice Hodson; c 4. *Educ:* Pomona Col, AB, 33; Harvard Univ, MA, 35, PhD(astron), 38. *Honors & Awards:* Distinguished Serv Citation, Nat Sci Teachers Asn, 72. *Prof Exp:* Instr & asst astron, Harvard Univ, 33-38, exec secy & res assoc, 38-41; instr, Radcliffe Col, 41; tech aide, Nat Defense Res Corp Radiation Lab, Mass Inst Technol, 42-43. *Concurrent Pos:* Ford Found fel, Europe, 64-65; co-dir, Harvard Proj Physics, 64-; prof educ, NY Univ, 78-81. *Mem:* AAAS; Nat Sci Teachers Asn; Am Asn Physics Teachers; Nat Asn Res Sci Teaching; Asn Educ Teachers in Sci (pres, 63-64); AAAS; Sigma Xi. *Res:* Development and evaluation of new high school physics course; studies of development of science teachers and influence of various teacher-types on pupils. *Mailing Add:* 24 Hastings Rd Belmont MA 02178-2329

**WATSON, FRANK YANDLE,** PATHOLOGY. *Current Pos:* assoc pathologist, 61-72, DIR LABS, MOUNTAINSIDE HOSP, NJ, 72-; CLIN ASST PROF PATH, COL MED, STATE UNIV NY DOWNSTATE MED CTR, 61- *Personal Data:* b Charlotte, NC, May 18, 25; m 49; c 4. *Educ:* Univ Md, MD, 49; Am Bd Path, dipl, 58. *Prof Exp:* Res physician path, Charlotte Mem Hosp, NC, 52-56; from instr to asst prof path, Col Med, State Univ NY Downstate Med Ctr, 56-61. *Concurrent Pos:* Surg pathologist, Inst Path, Kings Co Med Ctr, NY, 56-61. *Mem:* Fel Col Am Pathologists; fel Am Soc Clin Pathologists; AMA; Asn Am Med Cols. *Res:* General and surgical pathology. *Mailing Add:* 27 Appleton Pl Glen Ridge NJ 07028

**WATSON, GARY HUNTER,** REPRODUCTIVE ENDOCRINOLOGY, STEROID HORMONE ACTION. *Current Pos:* res scientist endocrinol, Col Osteop Med & Surg, 85-87, asst prof biochem & endocrinol, 87-91, ASSOC PROF BIOCHEM, COL OSTEOP MED, OKLA STATE UNIV, 91- *Personal Data:* b Lewisburg, Tenn, June 28, 51; m 81, Marsha Robertson; c Sara & Carrie. *Educ:* Univ SC, BS, 74; Med Col Ga, PhD(endocrinol), 82. *Prof Exp:* Postdoctoral fel, Tex Tech Health Sci Ctr, 82-85. *Concurrent Pos:* Actg dir res, Col Osteop Med & Surg, Okla State Univ, 85-87, dir res, Col Osteop Med, 87-; adj prof, Col Vet Med, Dept Physiol, Okla State Univ, 88; prin investr, Okla Ctr Advan Sci & Technol Asn, 89. *Mem:* AAAS; NY Acad Sci; Sigma Xi; Endocrine Soc. *Res:* Mechanism of steroid hormone action as it relates to reproduction, cancers of reproductive systems, and adipose accretion and metabolism; steroid control of gene expression. *Mailing Add:* Col Osteop Med Okla State Univ 1111 W 17th St Tulsa OK 74107

**WATSON, GEOFFREY STUART,** MATHEMATICAL STATISTICS. *Current Pos:* chmn dept, 70-79, prof, 70-92, EMER PROF STATIST, PRINCETON UNIV, 92- *Personal Data:* b Bendigo, Australia, Dec 3, 21; m 53, Shirley E Jennings; c Michael, Catharine, Rebecca & Madeleine. *Educ:* Univ Melbourne, BA, 42; NC State Col, PhD, 52. *Hon Degrees:* DSc, Univ Melbourne, 67. *Honors & Awards:* US Polar Medal, NIH. *Prof Exp:* Res officer, Commonwealth Sci & Indust Res Orgn, Australia, 43; tutor math, Trinity Col, Univ Melbourne, 44-47; res officer appl econ, Cambridge Univ, 49-51; sr lectr statist, Univ Melbourne, 51-54; sr fel, Australian Nat Univ, 55-58; res assoc math, Princeton Univ, 58-59; assoc prof, Univ Toronto, 59-62; prof statist & chmn dept, Johns Hopkins Univ, 62-68; on leave to inst genetics, Univ Pavia, 68-69. *Concurrent Pos:* Guggenheim fel, 76-77; dir biostatics, Theradex Inc; Carnegie Fulbright fel. *Mem:* Fel AAAS; fel Inst Math Statist; fel Am Statist Asn; fel Royal Statist Soc; fel Int Statist Inst; Am Geophys Union. *Res:* Application of mathematics, especially probability theory, stochastic processes and statistics, to science; statistical methods in geophysics. *Mailing Add:* Dept Math Fine Hall Princeton Univ Princeton NJ 08544-1000

**WATSON, GEORGE E, III,** ZOOLOGY, ORNITHOLOGY. *Current Pos:* CONSULT, NAT GEOGRAPHIC SOC, TIME LIFE & OTHERS. *Personal Data:* b New York, NY, Aug 13, 31; m 66, Louisa C Johnson; c Elisabeth C & George E IV. *Educ:* Yale Univ, BA, 53, MS, 61, PhD(biol), 64. *Prof Exp:* From asst cur to cur ornith, Nat Mus Natural Hist, Smithsonian Inst, 62-67, chmn, Dept Vert Zool, 67-72, cur vert zool, 72-85; assoc pathobiol, Sch Pub Health & Hyg, Johns Hopkins Univ, 70-85. *Concurrent Pos:* Mem, Seabird Comt, 66-90, Nomenclature Comt, 78-90, Int Ornith Cong & Comt Res & Explor, Nat Geog Soc, 75- *Mem:* Fel AAAS; fel Am Ornith Union (secy, 73-77, vpres, 84-85); Brit Ornith Union; corresp mem Ger Ornith Soc; Sigma Xi; Cooper Ornith Soc. *Res:* Marine ornithology, especially Antarctica; systematics of birds of Palearctic and Oriental realms. *Mailing Add:* 4323 Cathedral Ave NW Washington DC 20016. *Fax:* 202-362-1945; *E-Mail:* gewatson3d@aol.com

**WATSON, HAL, JR,** ENGINEERING MECHANICS. *Current Pos:* from asst prof to assoc prof solid mech, 67-76, ASSOC PROF CIVIL & MECH ENG, INST TECHNOL, SOUTHERN METHODIST UNIV, 77- *Personal Data:* b Jacksonville, Tex, Dec 27, 39; m 63; c 2. *Educ:* Columbia Univ, BA, 62; Univ Tex, Austin, MS, 65, PhD(eng mech), 67. *Prof Exp:* Res engr, Eng Mech Res Lab, Univ Tex, Austin, 64-67. *Concurrent Pos:* NSF study grant, 68-69; Dept Defense-Off Naval Res consult grant, Dept Statist, Southern Methodist Univ. *Mem:* Am Soc Mech Engrs; Soc Exp Stress Analysis; Am Inst Aeronaut & Astronaut; Am Soc Eng Educ; Sigma Xi. *Res:* Acoustics; wave propagation in solids; dynamic properties of materials in high pressure and high temperature environments. *Mailing Add:* Southern Methodist Univ PO Box 750335 Dallas TX 75275-0335

**WATSON, HUGH ALEXANDER,** PHYSICS. *Current Pos:* RETIRED. *Personal Data:* b Ottawa, Ont, Oct 8, 26; US citizen; m 58, Edith Kennedy; c Norah & Gail. *Educ:* Univ Toronto, BS, 48; McGill Univ, MS, 49; Mass Inst Technol, PhD(physics), 52. *Prof Exp:* Mem staff div indust coop, Mass Inst Technol, 51-52; mem tech staff, AT&T Bell Labs, 52-60, dept head, Electron Device Develop, 60-88. *Mem:* Sr mem, Inst Elec & Electronics Engrs. *Res:* Electron lithography, x-ray lithography, integrated circuit development, optoelectronics development. *Mailing Add:* 388 W Woodland Awe Woodland CA 95695-6607

**WATSON, J(AMES) KENNETH,** APPLICATIONS OF MAGNETISM, POWER ELECTRONICS. *Current Pos:* assoc prof, 66-79, PROF ELEC ENG, UNIV FLA, 79- *Personal Data:* b Ada, Okla, Sept 23, 29; m 58, Betty Herr; c Richard, William & Nancy. *Educ:* Univ Okla, BS, 51; Mass Inst Technol, SM, 55; Rice Univ, PhD, 66. *Prof Exp:* Observer, Seismic Eng Co, 51-52; teaching asst elec eng, Mass Inst Technol, 52-54; electronics engr, Gen Electronic Labs, Inc, 54-56; proj engr, Systron-Donner Co, 56-58; asst prof elec eng & proj engr, OSAGE Comput Lab, Univ Okla, 58-63, consult dept prev med & pub health, Med Ctr, 61-63; chief engr, Rice Comput Proj, Rice Univ, 63-66. *Concurrent Pos:* Vis res physicist, Magnetism & Metall Div, US Naval Ord Lab, Md, 72-73; vis prof elec eng, Calif Inst Technol, 80-81; lectr & consult, E J Bloom Assocs, 85-86. *Mem:* Sr mem Inst Elec & Electronics Engrs. *Res:* Characterization and modeling of magnetic materials for device and circuit applications; ferrite transformers; power electronics. *Mailing Add:* 1401 NW 30th St Gainesville FL 32605. *Fax:* 904-392-8671; *E-Mail:* kwats@admin.ee.ufl.edu

**WATSON, JACK ELLSWORTH,** genetics, human genetics, for more information see previous edition

**WATSON, JACK SAMUEL,** CHEMICAL ENGINEERING. *Current Pos:* DEVELOP ENGR, CHEM TECHNOL DIV, OAK RIDGE NAT LAB, 58- *Personal Data:* b Oliver Springs, Tenn, Oct 18, 35; m 60; c 2. *Educ:* Univ Tenn, BS, 58, MS, 62, PhD(chem eng), 67. *Mem:* Am Inst Chem Engrs. *Res:* Mass transfer; ion exchange; solvent extraction; fluid mechanics; heat transfer. *Mailing Add:* 349 Sevenoaks Dr Knoxville TN 37922-3402

**WATSON, JACK THROCK,** ANALYTICAL CHEMISTY. *Current Pos:* PROF BIOCHEM & CHEM, MICH STATE UNIV, 80- *Personal Data:* b Casey, Iowa, May 2, 39; m 66; c 2. *Educ:* Iowa State Univ, BS, 61; Mass Inst Technol, PhD(anal chem), 65. *Prof Exp:* Res chemist, US Air Force Sch Aerospace Med, 65-68; asst prof, Sch Med, Vanderbilt Univ, 69-72, assoc prof pharmacol, 73-79. *Concurrent Pos:* Fel, Univ Strasbourg, 68-69. *Mem:* Am Soc Mass Spectrometry; Am Chem Soc; Sigma Xi. *Res:* Gas chromatography in separation and mass spectrometry in elucidation of structure of biologically significant molecules; prostaglandins; biogenic amines; selective detection of drugs with gas chromatography-mass spectrometry computer systems; biochemical applications of gas chromatography. *Mailing Add:* Biochem Bldg Mich State Univ East Lansing MI 48824

**WATSON, JAMES DEWEY,** HUMAN GENOME RESEARCH. *Current Pos:* dir, 68-94, PRES, COLD SPRING HARBOR LAB, 94- *Personal Data:* b Chicago, Ill, Apr 6, 28; c 2. *Educ:* Univ Chicago, BS, 47; Ind Univ, PhD(zool), 50. *Hon Degrees:* Numerous hon degrees from US & foreign univs, 61- *Honors & Awards:* Nobel Prize in Med, 62; Albert Lasker Prize, Am Pub Health Asn, 60; Eli Lilly Award, 60; John J Carty Gold Medal, Nat Acad Sci, 71; Presidential Medal of Freedom, 77; Kaul Found Award, 92; Copley Medal, Royal Soc, 93; Nat Biotechnol Venture Award, 93; Charles A Dana Award, 94; Lomonosov Medal, Russ Acad Sci, 95; Nat Medal Sci, 97. *Prof Exp:* Res staff mem, Univ Copenhagen, 50-51, Cavendish Lab, Cambridge Univ, 51-52 & 55-56; sr res fel biol, Calif Inst Technol, 53-55; from asst prof to prof, Harvard Univ, 56-76. *Concurrent Pos:* From assoc dir to dir, Nat Ctr Human Genome Res, NIH, 88-92; Newton-Abraham vis prof, Oxford Univ, 94. *Mem:* Nat Acad Sci; Am Asn Cancer Res; AAAS; Am Acad Arts & Sci; Am Philos Soc; fel NY Acad Sci; Am Philos Soc; hon fel Inst Biol London; Nat Acad Sci Ukraine; Russ Acad Sci; Royal Soc London; Danish Acad Arts & Sci; Soc Biol Chemists; Am Soc Biol Chemists. *Res:* Zoology; biology; human genome. *Mailing Add:* Cold Spring Harbor Lab PO Box 100 Cold Spring Harbor NY 11724-0100. *Fax:* 516-367-8480

**WATSON, JAMES E, JR,** HEALTH PHYSICS, RADIATION PROTECTION. *Current Pos:* PROF HEALTH PHYSICS & DIR RADIOL HYG PROG, UNIV NC, 74- *Personal Data:* b Red Springs, NC, Jan 10, 38. *Educ:* NC State Univ, BS, 60, MS, 62; Univ NC, PhD(environ sci & eng), 70. *Prof Exp:* Nuclear engr, US Army Ballistic Res Labs, 62-67; health physics, Oak Ridge Nat Lab, 67; br chief health physics, Tenn Valley Authority, 70-74. *Concurrent Pos:* Mem, Task Force Low-Level Radioactive Waste Mgt, US Dept Energy, 80-81; chmn, NC Radiation Protection Comn, 82-83 & Radiol Health Sect, Am Pub Health Asn, 85; nat lectr, Sigma Xi, 91-92; mem, Nat Acad Sci Comt, 92-93. *Mem:* Fel Health Physics Soc (pres), 85); Am Pub Health Asn; Sigma Xi. *Res:* Radiological assessments of natural sources of radiation, nuclear power generation and low-level radioactive waste management; environmental and occupational radiation surveillance. *Mailing Add:* Dept Environ Sci & Eng Univ NC Chapel Hill NC 27599-7400. *Fax:* 919-966-7911; *E-Mail:* james_watson@unc.edu

**WATSON, JAMES FREDERIC,** METALLURGY, CERAMICS. *Current Pos:* RETIRED. *Personal Data:* b Port Huron, Mich, Aug 26, 31; m 52; c 3. *Educ:* Univ Mich, BS, 53, MS, 56, PhD(metall eng), 58. *Prof Exp:* Metallurgist, Magnesium Div, Dow Chem Co, Mich, 53 & Ballistic Res Lab, Aberdeen Proving Ground, Md, 54-55; staff scientist, Convair-Astronaut Div, Gen Dynamics Corp, 58-62; asst chmn metall, Gulf Gen Atomic, 62-68, mgr, Mat & Processes Lab, 68-70, assoc dir, Res & Develop Div, 70-71, dept mgr mat sci, 71-95. *Concurrent Pos:* Lectr, Univ Calif, Los Angeles, 59-60, 61-62; mem mat adv bd, comt eval mat, Nat Acad Sci, 60-61. *Mem:* Am Soc Metals; Brit Inst Metals. *Res:* High temperature materials for nuclear reactors; materials and processes for components of steam power plants; properties of materials for missiles and spacecraft at cryogenic temperatures. *Mailing Add:* 4961 Quincy St San Diego CA 92109

**WATSON, JAMES KAY GRAHAM,** THEORETICAL SPECTROSCOPY, SYMMETRY. *Current Pos:* sr res officer astrophys, 82-87, PRIN RES OFFICER, NAT RES COUN CAN, 87- *Personal Data:* b Denny, Scotland, Apr 20, 36; m 81, Carolyn M L Kerr. *Educ:* Univ Glasgow, UK, BSc, 58, PhD(chem), 62. *Honors & Awards:* Earle K Plyler Prize, Am Phys Soc, 86; Ioannes Marcus Marci Medal, Czech & Slovak Spectros Soc, 96. *Prof Exp:* Lectr chem physics, Univ Reading, UK, 66-71; vis assoc prof physics, Ohio State Univ, 71-75; sr res fel chem, Univ Southampton, UK, 75-82. *Concurrent Pos:* Vis scientist astrophys, Nat Res Coun Can, 79-80. *Mem:* Fel Royal Soc London; fel Royal Soc Can; fel Am Phys Soc. *Res:* Interpretation of molecular spectra, from laboratory or astronomical sources; development of appropriate quantum and symmetry theory; results give information on molecular structures and forces, and on environment where molecules are formed. *Mailing Add:* 183 Stanley Ave Ottawa ON K1M 1P2 Can. *Fax:* 613-991-2648; *E-Mail:* james.watson@nrc.ca

**WATSON, JAMES RAY, JR,** PLANT TAXONOMY. *Current Pos:* from asst prof to assoc prof bot, 63-78, PROF BIOL SCI, MISS STATE UNIV, 78- *Personal Data:* b Anniston, Ala, Dec 6, 35; m 60; c Laura, Gregory & Jennifer. *Educ:* Auburn Univ, BS, 57, MS, 60; Iowa State Univ, PhD(bot), 63. *Prof Exp:* Res asst agron, Auburn Univ, 58-60. *Concurrent Pos:* NSF fel, 64-65. *Mem:* Sigma Xi; Natural Areas Asn. *Res:* Woody flora of Mississippi. *Mailing Add:* Dept Biol Sci Miss State Univ PO Drawer GY Mississippi State MS 39762-5759

**WATSON, JERRY M,** accelerator development & linear accelerators, free-electron lasers, for more information see previous edition

**WATSON, JOHN ALFRED,** BIOCHEMISTRY. *Current Pos:* asst prof, 69-76, assoc dean admis med, 73-80, PROF BIOCHEM, UNIV CALIF, SAN FRANCISCO, 80- *Personal Data:* b Chicago, Ill, May 21, 40; m 60; c 4. *Educ:* Ill Inst Technol, BS, 64; Univ Ill, Chicago, USPHS fel & PhD(biochem), 67. *Prof Exp:* USPHS fel biochem, Brandeis Univ, 67-69. *Concurrent Pos:* From asst dean, to assoc dean student affairs, 69-73; estab investr, Am Heart Asn, 80- *Mem:* Am Oil Chem Soc; Am Soc Biol Chemists; Sigma Xi; Tissue Cult Asn; Nat Inst Sci. *Res:* Regulation of sterol and non-sterol isopentenoid synthesis in isolated cultured vertebrate and invertebrate cells. *Mailing Add:* Dept Biochem Univ Calif 513 Parnassus San Francisco CA 94143-0001. *Fax:* 415-476-0961

**WATSON, JOHN H L,** ELECTRON MICROSCOPY. *Current Pos:* RETIRED. *Personal Data:* b May 27, 16; m 41, Frances E Cook; c Linda A L (Ackert), John H L III & David C L. *Educ:* McMaster Univ, Hamilton, Ont, BA(math & physics), 39; Univ Toronto, MA, 40, PhD(physics), 43. *Hon Degrees:* LHD, Univ Windsor, 92. *Honors & Awards:* Spec Recognition, Micros Soc Am. *Prof Exp:* Asst demonstr physics, Univ Toronto, 39-40, res asst physics, 40-41; studentship & fel, Nat Res Coun Can, 41-43; Lectr physics, Univ BC, 43-45; physicist, Shawinigan Chem Co, 45-47; chmn dept physics, Edsel B Ford Inst Med Res, Henry Ford Hosp, Detroit, 47-81. *Concurrent Pos:* Placement officer, Micros Soc Am. *Mem:* Micros Soc Am (pres, 57); hon mem Micros Soc Can; emer mem Am Soc Cell Biol; Sigma Xi. *Mailing Add:* 652 Hupp Cross Bloomfield MI 48301

**WATSON, JOHN LESLIE,** COMPUTER APPLICATIONS IN MINERAL PROCESSING, TREATMENT OF MINERAL INDUSTRY WASTE. *Current Pos:* PROF & CHMN METALL ENG, UNIV MO, ROLLA, 81- *Personal Data:* b Scunthorpe, Eng, Apr 22, 45; US citizen; m 66, Ann Layland; c Louise A & Layland J. *Educ:* Univ Nottingham, UK, BS, 66; Univ Bristol, UK, PhD(mech eng), 71. *Prof Exp:* Shift supvr, Imp Smelting Corp, UK, 66-68; lectr, WA Sch Mines, Australia, 71-75; sr lectr, Univ Otago, NZ, 75-81. *Mem:* Am Inst Mech Engrs; Soc Mining Engrs; Minerals, Metals & Mat Soc; Soc Mining, Metall & Explor. *Res:* Recovery of metals from mineral and metal industry wastes; treatment of ore wastes by mineral separation processes; computer applications in the minerals industry. *Mailing Add:* Dept Metall Eng McNutt Hall Univ Mo Rolla MO 65401. *Fax:* 573-341-6934; *E-Mail:* jwatson@umr.edu

**WATSON, JOHN THOMAS,** CARDIOVASCULAR PHYSIOLOGY, BIOMEDICAL ENGINEERING. *Current Pos:* HEAD, BIOENG RES GROUP, NAT HEART, LUNG & BLOOD INST, 76- *Personal Data:* b Indianapolis, Ind, Jan 9, 40; m 86, Diane; c Laura, Linda, Skip, Lisa, Stuart & Julie. *Educ:* Univ Cincinnati, BSME, 62; Southern Methodist Univ, MSME, 66; Univ Tex Southwestern Med Sch, PhD(physiol), 72. *Honors & Awards:* Spec Recognition Award, Pub Health Serv; Dir Award, NIH; Laufmann-Greatbatch Award, Asn Advan Med Instrumentation. *Prof Exp:* Systs engr, Ling-Temco Vought, Inc, 62-66; teaching asst physiol, Univ Tex Health Sci Str, Dallas, 66-69, adj instr, 69-71, instr thoracic & cardiovasc surg & physiol, 71-74, asst prof surg & physiol, 74-76, asst prof, Grad Sch Biomed Sci, 73-80. *Mem:* Am Heart Asn; Am Soc Artificial Internal Organs; Am Soc Mech Engrs; Int Soc Artificial Organs; fel Am Inst Med & Biol Eng. *Res:* Circulatory assistance, ischemic heart disease. *Mailing Add:* Nat Heart Lung & Blood Inst Bioeng Res Group Bethesda MD 20892. *Fax:* 301-480-1336

**WATSON, JOSEPH ALEXANDER,** radiobiology, microbiology, for more information see previous edition

**WATSON, KENNETH,** GEOPHYSICS. *Current Pos:* Geophysicist, 63-76, chief, Br Petrophys & Remote Sensing, 76-79, RES GEOPHYSICIST, US GEOL SURV, 80- *Personal Data:* b Montreal, Que, July 25, 35; US citizen; m 59; c 2. *Educ:* Univ Toronto, BA, 57; Calif Inst Technol, MS, 59,

PhD(geophys), 64. *Concurrent Pos:* Lectr, Northern Ariz Univ, 66-67; prin investr, NASA, 77-81; assoc ed, J Geophys Res, 68-70 & Geophys, 83- *Mem:* AAAS; Soc Explor Geophysicists; Am Geophys Union; Sigma Xi. *Res:* Planetary science; behavior of volatiles on the lunar surface; infrared emission and visible light reflection; terrestrial remote sensing investigations; thermal modeling; analysis of satellite thermal infrared data; remote sensing for mineral exploration. *Mailing Add:* 2519 Xenon Ct Lakewood CO 80228

**WATSON, KENNETH FREDRICK,** BIOCHEMISTRY, MOLECULAR VIROLOGY. *Current Pos:* vpres acad affairs, 85-87, prof biochem, 89-96, ASST PRES, NORTHWEST NAZARENE COL, 89-, DIR INSTNL RES & PLANNING, 94- *Personal Data:* b Pasco, Wash, Feb 17, 42; m 64, Janice P Wilson; c Heidi M & Julie M. *Educ:* Northwest Nazarene Col, AB, 64; Ore State Univ, PhD(biochem), 69. *Prof Exp:* Res assoc molecular virol, Inst Cancer Res, Columbia Univ, 69-71, instr, Col Physicians & Surgeons, 71-72; res assoc virol, Robert Koch Inst, 72-73; from asst prof to assoc prof biochem, Univ Mont, 73-81, prof biochem, 81-83; dir molecular virol, Abbott Labs, 83-85. *Concurrent Pos:* Fel, Nat Cancer Inst, 69-71; res fel, Int Agency Res Cancer, 72-73; fac res award, Am Cancer Soc, 76-81. *Mem:* AAAS; Sigma Xi. *Res:* Replication of viral nucleic acids; mechanism of RNA tumor virus replication and virus-induced cell transformation; characterization of reverse transcriptase and its use in gene synthesis; role of protein phosphorylation in virus life cycle. *Mailing Add:* Asst Pres Northwest Nazarene Col Nampa ID 83686. *E-Mail:* kfwatson@exodus.nnc.edu

**WATSON, KENNETH MARSHALL,** PHYSICS. *Current Pos:* dir, Marine Phys Lab, Scripps Inst Oceanog, 81-93, prof, 81-93, EMER PROF OCEANOG, UNIV CALIF, SAN DIEGO, 93- *Personal Data:* b Des Moines, Iowa, Sept 7, 21; m 46; c 2. *Educ:* Iowa State Col, BS, 43; Univ Iowa, PhD(physics), 48. *Hon Degrees:* DSc, Indiana Univ, 76. *Prof Exp:* Lab instr, Iowa State Col, 42-43; radio engr, US Naval Res Lab, Washington, DC, 43-46; instr physics, Univ Iowa, 48 & Princeton Univ, 48; AEC fel, Inst Advan Study & Radiation Lab, Univ Calif, 48-50; asst prof physics, Ind Univ, 51-53; assoc prof, Univ Wis, 53-59; prof physics, Univ Calif, Berkeley, 59-81. *Concurrent Pos:* Consult, Inc, Mitre Corp & Sci Appl, Inc. *Mem:* Nat Acad Sci; Am Geophys Union; Am Phys Soc. *Res:* Statistical mechanics; physical oceanography. *Mailing Add:* Scripps Inst Oceanog Univ Calif Mail Code 0213 La Jolla CA 92093-0213. *Fax:* 619-553-0764

**WATSON, MARSHALL TREDWAY,** PHYSICAL CHEMISTRY, FIBER SCIENCE. *Current Pos:* RETIRED. *Personal Data:* b Blacksburg, Va, Dec 27, 22; m 52, Betty L Kilgore; c Elizabeth (Rapisarda) & Marshall T Jr. *Educ:* Va Polytech Inst, BS, 43; Princeton Univ, MA, 48, PhD(phys chem), 49. *Prof Exp:* Asst, Princeton Univ, 46-48; from res chemist to sr res chemist, Eastman Kodak Co, 49-63, res assoc, 63-68, head, Fibers Res Div, 68-76, dir, Fibers Res Div, Eastman Chem Div, 76-86. *Mem:* Am Chem Soc; Am Asn Textile Technol. *Res:* Mechanism of protein denaturation; mechanical and rheological properties of polymers; processing of polymers into fibers; structure and properties of fibers. *Mailing Add:* 1700 Longview St Kingsport TN 37660

**WATSON, MARTHA F,** MATHEMATICS. *Current Pos:* Assoc prof, 62-74, PROF MATH, WESTERN KY UNIV, 74- *Personal Data:* b Janesville, Wis, Feb 2, 35. *Educ:* Murray State Col, AB, 56; Univ Ky, MA, 58, PhD(math), 62. *Mem:* Am Math Soc; Math Asn Am. *Res:* Complex analysis. *Mailing Add:* 203 Marksfield Circle Apt 3 Louisville KY 40222

**WATSON, MAURICE E,** SLUDGE ANALYSIS, WATER ANALYSIS. *Current Pos:* LAB HEAD, OHIO STATE UNIV, 76- *Educ:* Univ Nebraska, BSc, 63, MSc, 67; Univ Guelph, PhD, 72. *Prof Exp:* Lab dir, North Carolina State Univ, 72-76. *Mem:* Am Soc Agron; Soil Sci Soc Am. *Res:* Plant tissue analysis. *Mailing Add:* Ohio State Univ Res-Extension Analytical Lab Wooster OH 44691

**WATSON, MAXINE AMANDA,** PLANT POPULATION BIOLOGY. *Current Pos:* asst prof, 80-84, ASSOC PROF POP BIOL, IND UNIV, 84- *Personal Data:* b New Rochelle, NY, May 8, 47. *Educ:* Cornell Univ, BS, 68; Yale Univ, MDH, 70, PhD(pop biol), 74. *Prof Exp:* Asst prof, Univ Utah, 75-80. *Mem:* Soc Study Evolution; Ecol Soc Am; Bot Soc Am; Am Bryological & Lichenological Soc; Aquatic Plant Mgt Soc. *Res:* Regulation of population structure in clonal plants using demographic, morphological and physiological approaches; investigation of patterns of resource allocation in plants designed to identify relevant currencies. *Mailing Add:* Dept Biol Ind Univ Bloomington IN 47405

**WATSON, MICHAEL DOUGLAS,** PROGRAM EVALUATION. *Current Pos:* CONSULT, 91- *Personal Data:* b St Thomas, Ont, July 27, 36; m 59; c 3. *Educ:* Univ Western Ont, BSc, 57, MS, 59, PhD(physics), 61. *Prof Exp:* Asst res officer, Herzberg Inst Astrophys, 61-67, assoc res officer, 67-77, sr res officer, 77-81; dir asst, Can Ctr Space Sci, Nat Res Coun Can, 81-82, chief, Prof Eval Off, 82-86, mgr, Indust Develop Off, 81-89, proj mgr, Admin Serv & Prop Mgt, 90-91. *Res:* Shock-tube excitation of powdered solids; plasma jet diagnostics; optical studies of aurora; observational studies of infrasonic waves from meteors. *Mailing Add:* 660 Sandra Ave Ottawa ON K1G 2Z8 Can. *Fax:* 613-731-9241; *E-Mail:* ag451@freenet.carleton.ca

**WATSON, MILTON C,** AGRICULTURE. *Prof Exp:* Fel Award, Agr Inst Can, 94. *Mailing Add:* 118 Eagel St Del High ON N4B 1S5 Can

**WATSON, NATHAN DEE,** HEAT TRANSFER, DYNAMICS. *Current Pos:* RETIRED. *Personal Data:* b Westfield, NC, Oct 14, 35; m 57; c 1. *Educ:* NC State Univ, BS, 62, PhD, 77; Polytech Inst, MS, 68. *Prof Exp:* Supvr aerospace engr, Langley Res Ctr, NASA, 62-90. *Res:* Thermal design and analysis of hypersonic aircraft and spacecraft; development of mathematical analysis techniques to predict the rigid and flexible body responses of large aerospace aircraft. *Mailing Add:* 110 Claxton Creek Rd Seaford VA 23696

**WATSON, P(ERCY) KEITH,** ELECTRICAL ENGINEERING, PHYSICS. *Current Pos:* STAFF MEM, XEROX CORP, 63- *Personal Data:* b Staffordshire, Eng, Dec 22, 27; m 53; c 4. *Educ:* Univ Birmingham, BSc, 48, PhD(elec eng), 52. *Prof Exp:* Engr, English Elec Co, 53-54; fel, Nat Res Coun Can, 54-56; physicist res lab, Gen Elec Co, 56-62; engr, English Elec Co, 62-63. *Mem:* Sigma Xi. *Res:* Dielectrics and electrostatics; electrical conduction and breakdown in liquids, solids and gases; electrophotography; electrical insulation. *Mailing Add:* Xerox Corp 800 Phillips Rd 0114-23D Webster NY 14580

**WATSON, PHILIP DONALD,** MAMMALIAN CARDIOVASCULAR PHYSIOLOGY, CAPILLARY PERMEABILITY. *Current Pos:* asst prof, 77-80, assoc prof, 80-87, PROF PHYSIOL, UNIV SC, 87- *Personal Data:* b Leeds, Eng, Oct 20, 41; m 65; c 2. *Educ:* Univ Leeds, BSc, 64; Univ Southern Calif, MS, 71, PhD(biomed eng), 75. *Prof Exp:* Res engr, Western Gear Corp, Calif, 66-69; fel physiol, Univ Calif, Davis, 75-77. *Concurrent Pos:* NIH fel, 72-75, 75-77; Pharmacia travel award, Microcirculatory Soc, 81; mem coun Microcirculatory Soc, 84-86. *Mem:* Microcirculatory Soc; Am Physiol Soc. *Res:* Solute and water movement between blood and tissue. *Mailing Add:* Dept Physiol Univ SC Med Sch Columbia SC 29208. *Fax:* 803-781-1523; *E-Mail:* pwatson@univscvm

**WATSON, RAND LEWIS,** CHEMICAL PHYSICS. *Current Pos:* from asst prof to assoc prof, Tex A&M Univ, 69-77, from asst dean to assoc dean sci, 80-85, assoc head chem, 85-86, PROF CHEM, TEX A&M UNIV, 77- *Personal Data:* b Denver, Colo, Aug 29, 40; m 62, Doris Wohlfarth; c Camillie & Mark. *Educ:* Colo Sch Mines, BS, 62; Univ Calif, Berkeley, PhD(nuclear chem), 66. *Prof Exp:* Res assoc, Lawrence Radiation Lab, Univ Calif, 66-67. *Concurrent Pos:* Vis prof, Univ Calif, Berkeley, 78-79; vis scientist, Oak Ridge Nat Lab, 90. *Mem:* Fel Am Phys Soc; Am Chem Soc; Sigma Xi. *Res:* Fast electron rearrangement following multiple ionization in heavy-ion-collisions; excited state distributions in fast ions penetrating solids and gases; x-ray spectroscopy of few-electron ions; molecular dissociation induced by fast ion collisions. *Mailing Add:* Cyclotron Inst Tex A&M Univ College Station TX 77843. *Fax:* 409-845-1899; *E-Mail:* watson@comp.tamu.edu

**WATSON, RAYMOND COKE, JR,** DEFENSE SCIENCES, ELECTRO-OPTICS. *Current Pos:* PRES & PROF ENG & MATH, SOUTHEASTERN INST TECHNOL, HUNTSVILLE, ALA, 76-; CHIEF ENGR & CHIEF SCIENTIST, TELEDYNE BROWN ENG, HUNTSVILLE, ALA, 91- *Personal Data:* b Anniston, Ala, Aug 31, 26; m 48, Charlotte Bagley; c Lee, Cole, Anne & Joseph. *Educ:* Jacksonville State Univ, BS; Univ Ala, MSE; Univ Fla, MS; Calif Coast Univ, MBA, PhD(eng sci). *Honors & Awards:* NASA Pub Serv Award for Contrib to Saturn-Apollo Prog, 69. *Prof Exp:* Chief engr, Dixie Serv Co, 48-54; head dept physics & eng, Jacksonville State Univ, 54-60; vpres, eng & res, Teledyne Brown Eng, 60-70; dir, continuing educ, eng & math, Univ Ala, Huntsville, 70-76. *Concurrent Pos:* NSF sci fac fel, 58-60; Adj assoc prof, Univ Ala, Huntsville, 61-70; consult, var defense industs, 70- *Mem:* Inst Elec & Electronics Engrs; Am Inst Aeronaut & Astronaut; Inst Mgt Sci; Optical Soc Am; Int Soc Optical Engrs; Inst Indust Engrs; Opers Res Soc Am. *Res:* Defense systems, space systems & electro-optics; sensor technologies; space based defense; information technology. *Mailing Add:* Teledyne Brown Eng Cummings Research Park Huntsville AL 35807-7007. *Fax:* 205-726-3434; *E-Mail:* ray.watson@pobox.tbe.com

**WATSON, RICHARD ALLAN,** PHILOSOPHY OF HISTORICAL SCIENCES. *Current Pos:* from asst prof to assoc prof, 64-74, PROF PHILOS, WASHINGTON UNIV, 74-, SR RES ASSOC EARTH & PLANETARY SCI, 77- *Personal Data:* b New Market, Iowa, Feb 23, 31; m 55, Patty J Andersen; c Anna. *Educ:* Univ Iowa, BA, 53, MA, 57, PhD(philos), 61; Univ Minn, MS, 59. *Prof Exp:* Instr philos, Univ Mich, 61-64. *Concurrent Pos:* Aerial photog, USAF, 53-55; geologist, Univ Chicago Orient Inst, 59-60, 68 & 70; consult, US Nuclear Regulatory Comn, 76. *Mem:* AAAS; Cave Res Found (pres 65-67); Philos Sci Asn; Am Philos Asn; hon mem Nat Speleological Soc. *Res:* Landslide geomorphology in New Mexico and Iran; paleoclimatology in New Mexico, Kentucky, Iran and Turkey; Karst geomorphology in Kentucky; theoretical articles in geology, anthropology, and archeology; glacial geomorphology in the Yukon; Pleistocene geomorphology. *Mailing Add:* Dept Philos Washington Univ St Louis MO 63130. *Fax:* 314-935-7349; *E-Mail:* c34815rw@wuvmd.wustl.edu

**WATSON, RICHARD E,** PROPERTIES OF METALS. *Current Pos:* SR RES PHYSICIST, BROOKHAVEN NAT LAB, 65- *Personal Data:* b New York, NY, Sept 30, 31; m 58; c 4. *Educ:* Amherst Col, BA, 53; Mass Inst Technol, PhD(physics), 59. *Honors & Awards:* Hume-Rothery Award, Metall Soc of Am Inst Mining, Metall & Petrol Engrs, 85. *Prof Exp:* Res asst, Mass Inst Technol, 59-60; mem staff, Avco Res & Develop, Wilmington, Mass, 60-61; NSF fel, Atomic Energy Res Estab, Harwell, Eng, 61-62 & Univ Uppsala, Sweden, 62; mem staff, Bell Labs, 63-65. *Concurrent Pos:* Consult, Nat Bur Stand, 65-83; Nordic Inst Theoret Atomic Physics vis prof, Univ Gothenburg, Sweden, 70, Univ Lund, Sweden & Univ Aarhus, Denmark, 75; mem, Nat Acad Panel on Nat Need for Synchrotron Radiation Facil, 76. *Mem:* Fel Am Phys Soc; Mat Res Soc; Metall Soc of Am Inst Mining, Metall & Petrol Engrs. *Res:* Electronic properties of metals and alloys. *Mailing Add:* Physics Dept Brookhaven Nat Lab Upton NY 11973

**WATSON, RICHARD ELVIS,** PHYSICS. *Current Pos:* PROF PHYSICS, SOUTHERN ILL UNIV, CARBONDALE, 58-, CHMN DEPT, 76- *Personal Data:* b Carterville, Ill, Apr 9, 12; m 36; c 2. *Educ:* Southern Ill Norm Univ, BEd, 32; Univ Ill, AM, 35, PhD(physics), 38. *Prof Exp:* Instr physics, Eastern Ill Teachers Col, 38-39; sci ed, Coop Test Serv, NY, 39-40; asst prof physics, Southern Ill Teachers Col, 40-42; res technologist, Elec Div, Leeds & Northrup Co, 46-58. *Mem:* Am Phys Teachers; Inst Elec & Electronics Engrs. *Res:* Scattering of neutrons by light nuclei; scattering of fast electrons by Coulomb field; electrometer amplifiers and recorders; automatic electrical controllers; economic loading of power systems; modelling human visual response. *Mailing Add:* 517 N Almond Carbondale IL 62901

**WATSON, RICHARD WHITE, JR,** CLINICAL LABORATORY MANAGEMENT. *Current Pos:* LAB DIR QASPEC, NAT HEALTH LABS, INC, CRANFORD, NJ, 71- *Personal Data:* b Indiana, Pa, Apr 13, 33; m 58, Alda J Franklin; c Gregory, Lawrence & Gail. *Educ:* Cornell Univ, BS, 59; Rutgers Univ, MS, 61, PhD(bact), 64. *Prof Exp:* Sr lab technician, Rutgers Univ, 61-62; res microbiologist, Anheuser-Busch, Inc, 64-67 & Esso Res & Eng Co, 67-71. *Mem:* Am Soc Microbiol; Am Asn Clin Chem. *Res:* Analytical biochemistry. *Mailing Add:* 16 Walnut St New Providence NJ 07974

**WATSON, ROBERT BARDEN,** physics, lasers; deceased, see previous edition for last biography

**WATSON, ROBERT FLETCHER,** medicine; deceased, see previous edition for last biography

**WATSON, ROBERT FRANCIS,** CHEMISTRY, SCIENCE EDUCATION. *Current Pos:* from asst prog dir to assoc prog dir, Undergrad Educ in Sci, NSF, 68-73, prog mgr, Off Exp Proj & Progs, 73-75, prog dir, Undergrad Instrnl Improvement Progs, 75-78, dep dir, Div Sci Educ Mat Res, 78-81, opers res analysis, 81-83, head, Off Col Sci Instrumentation, 84-87, DIR, DIV UNDERGRAD SCI, ENG & MATH EDUC, NSF, 87-; LIAISON TO COMMUNITY COL, NSF, 93- *Personal Data:* b Knoxville, Tenn, Nov 20, 36; m 58, Janice Moser; c Sara, Margo & Anne. *Educ:* Col Wooster, AB, 58; Univ Tenn, Knoxville, PhD(chem), 63. *Prof Exp:* From asst prof to assoc prof chem, Memphis State Univ, 63-68. *Concurrent Pos:* Res assoc, Oak Ridge Nat Lab, 65; Nat Acad Sci res assoc, Naval Stores Lab, USDA, Fla, 67-68; res anal, US Off Mgt & Budget, 81-83, pres, Sci Adv Off, 83. *Mem:* Am Chem Soc; AAAS. *Res:* Chemistry of indanes; nonclassical ions; physical properties of sulfoxides; federal programs for support of science education and scientific research; federal science policy, administration and budget analysis; science education policy. *Mailing Add:* Div Undergrad Educ NSF Arlington VA 22230

**WATSON, ROBERT LEE,** EPIDEMIOLOGY, PUBLIC HEALTH. *Current Pos:* instr med, Univ Miss, 64-67, asst prof epidemiol, 67-70, asst prof med & prev med, 70-71, assoc prof prev med, 71-78, chief div epidemiol & biostatist, 77, PROF PREV MED, MED CTR, UNIV MISS, 78- *Personal Data:* b Scribner, Nebr, Dec 17, 31; m 53; c 4. *Educ:* Iowa State Univ, DVM, 55; Univ Minn, MPH, 63, PhD, 73. *Prof Exp:* Jr asst vet, Ga State Dept Health, USPHS, 55-57, asst vet, Md State Dept Health, 57, vet epidemiologist, 57-60, sr asst vet, Univ Minn, 60-61, vet epidemiologist, Miss State Bd Health, 61-63; trainee epidemiol, Sch Pub Health, Univ Minn, 63-64. *Concurrent Pos:* Trainee epidemiol, Sch Pub Health, Univ Minn, 64-67; co-investr, NIH grants, 66-73, 77-82, contract, 71-76, 85-; mem, Coun Epidemiol, Am Heart Asn. *Mem:* Soc Epidemiol Res; Asn Teachers Prev Med. *Res:* Health and health care statistics; socio-cultural-economic factors related to blood pressure levels; toxemia of pregnancy; cardiovascular disease. *Mailing Add:* Dept Prev Med Univ Miss Med Ctr 2500 N State St Jackson MS 39216-4505

**WATSON, ROBERT LEE,** ENTOMOLOGY. *Current Pos:* asst prof, 67-71 & chmn dept, ASSOC PROF BIOL, UNIV ARK, LITTLE ROCK, 71- *Personal Data:* b Plainview, Ark, Nov 8, 34; m 65; c 3. *Educ:* Univ Ark, Fayetteville, BS, 56, MS, 63; Auburn Univ, PhD(entom), 68. *Prof Exp:* Instr zool, Auburn Univ, 66-67. *Mem:* Entom Soc Am; Am Inst Biol Sci. *Res:* Taxonomy and ecology of Tabanidae aquatic ecology. *Mailing Add:* Dept Biol Univ Ark Little Rock AR 72204

**WATSON, ROBERT LOWRIE,** PROCESS INSTRUMENTATION. *Current Pos:* res assoc, Res Labs, 81-91, develop assoc, Filter Prod Div, 91-93, TECH ASSOC, ACETATE TOW DIV, EASTMAN CHEM CO, 93- *Personal Data:* b Morristown, Tenn, June 15, 46; m 73, Margaret E O'Neill; c 3. *Educ:* ETenn State Univ, BS, 68, MS, 70. *Prof Exp:* Physicist, Tenn Eastman Co, 69-75, sr physicist, 75-79, res assoc, 79-81. *Mem:* Instrument Soc Am; Optical Soc Am. *Res:* Design of instruments for measuring parameters of chemical streams, plastics, and man-made fibers in laboratory and plant floor environments, primarily using optical sensing techniques. *Mailing Add:* Eastman Chem Co PO Box 511 Kingsport TN 37662

**WATSON, ROBERT TANNER,** PHYSICS. *Current Pos:* RETIRED. *Personal Data:* b Columbus, Ohio, Sept 25, 22; m 44, Jean Mehlig; c Melinda J, Parke T, John M, Todd P & Kate A. *Educ:* DePauw Univ, BA, 43; Mass Inst Technol, PhD, 51. *Prof Exp:* Mem Photo Prod Dept, E I duPont de Nemours & Co Inc, 51-55; staff mem, Electron Tube Div, RCA, 55-59; vpres & gen mgr, Indust Labs Div, Int Tel & Tel Corp, 62-63, pres, 63-68, dep tech dir, Aerospace & Defense Group, 68-71; gen phys scientist, OT & Nat Telecommun Info Admin, Dept Com, 71-90; process studies prog dir, Sci Div,

Mission to Planet Earth, NASA, Washington, 90- *Concurrent Pos:* Mem, Gov's Air Pollution Control Bd, 66-70; trustee, Ind Educ Servs Found, 68-71. *Mem:* Optical Soc Am; Inst Elec & Electronics Engrs; Sigma Xi; Am Inst Mgt. *Res:* X-ray diffraction; radioactive scattering; solid state energy levels; electron emission; magnetic and photography media; electro-optical, laser and telecommunication systems. *Mailing Add:* 1770 Lang Dr Crofton MD 21114-2145

**WATSON, RONALD ROSS,** IMMUNOLOGY, NUTRITION. *Current Pos:* from res assoc prof to res prof, Dept Family & Community Med, Med Sch, 82-88, DIR, ALCOHOL RES CTR, NAT INST ALCOHOL ABUSE & ALCOHOLISM, UNIV ARIZ, 88- *Personal Data:* b Tyler, Tex, Dec 9, 42; m 66; c 4. *Educ:* Brigham Young Univ, BS, 66; Mich State Univ, PhD(biochem), 71. *Prof Exp:* Res fel immunol & microbiol, Sch Pub Health, Harvard Univ, 71-73; asst prof microbiol, Med Ctr, Univ Miss, 73-74; asst prof microbiol & immunol, Sch Med, Ind Univ, Indianapolis, 74-78; assoc prof immunol & nutrit, Purdue Univ, W Lafayette, 78-82. *Concurrent Pos:* Collabr & vis scientist, Int Ctr Med Res, Cali, Colombia, 73-80; res adv, NIH Fel Training Prog Sexually Transmitted Dis, Ind Univ, 74-76; vis prof immunol, Brigham Young Univ, 77 & nutrit, Wash State Univ, 79; vis nutritionist & immunologist, Egyptian Nutrit Inst, Cairo, Egypt, 79 & 80. *Mem:* Am Asn Immunologists; Am Soc Microbiol; Am Inst Nutrit; Sigma Xi; AAAS. *Res:* Alcohol, cocaine, and immunity; effect of nutritional supplements on immune systems and cancer resistance in mice and humans; vitamins, immunomodulation and cancer prevention; drugs of abuse as cofactors in immunomodulation in murine acquired immune deficiency syndrome. *Mailing Add:* Dept Family & Community Med Univ Ariz Col Med Health Sci Ctr 501 N Campbell Ave Tucson AZ 85724-0001

**WATSON, STANLEY ARTHUR,** AGRICULTURAL AND FOOD CHEMISTRY, CROP TECHNOLOGY. *Current Pos:* CONSULT, 86- *Personal Data:* b Los Angeles, Calif, Aug 30, 15; m 42, Hazel E Boyd; c 4. *Educ:* Pomona Col, AB, 39; Univ Ill, AM, 42, PhD(agron), 49. *Prof Exp:* Asst bot, Univ Ill, 38-42, agron, 46-48; from jr chemist to asst chemist Northern Regional Res Lab, Bur Agr & Indust Chem, USDA, 42-46; sect leader, Res Dept, CPC Int, Inc, 48-68, asst dir, Explor Res Dept, 68-75, res scientist, Agron & Milling Dept, 75-78; coordr north-cent regional proj grain qual, Ohio Agr Res & Develop Ctr, Ohio State Univ, 78-86. *Mem:* Am Chem Soc; Am Asn Cereal Chem; Sigma Xi. *Res:* Composition, structure, agronomics and processing of cereal grains; industrial corn wet milled process and products. *Mailing Add:* 4134 Shelby Circle TH74 Wooster OH 44691

**WATSON, STANLEY J, JR,** PSYCHIATRY. *Current Pos:* from asst prof & asst res scientist to assoc prof & assoc res scientist, 78-87, dir, Exp Clin Endocrine Lab, 83-87, PROF & RES SCIENTIST, DEPT PSYCHIAT & MENT HEALTH RES INST, UNIV MICH, 87- *Educ:* Univ Southern Miss, BS, 65; Univ Iowa, PhD(clin psychol), 70; Tulane Med Sch, MD, 74. *Honors & Awards:* Grass Found Lectr, Univ Pittsburgh, 84; Robert J & Clair Pasarow Found Award for Neuropsychiat Res, 94. *Prof Exp:* Intern, Pac Presby Med Ctr, 74; psychiat intern & resident, Dept Psychiat & Behav Sci, Stanford Univ Sch Med, 74-77, res resident, 77-78. *Concurrent Pos:* Giannini fel bio med res, Bank of Am, 77; teacher, Neurosci Psychiatrists, Univ Mich, 80-, assoc dir, Ment Health Res Inst, 84-, assoc chair res, Dept Psychiat, 93-, co-dir, 95-; McAlphin grantee, Nat Ment Health Asn, 80; Pfizer vis prof psychiat, Sinai Med Ctr, NY, 84 & Johns Hopkins Univ Med Ctr, 94; vis prof, Univ Hawaii, 85; Pfizer travelling fel, Clin Res Inst, Montreal, 85; consult, Neurex, Menlo Park, Calif, 86-, Neurocrine Biscis, Calif, 92-, MHCRC Study Suicidal Behav, Univ Pittsburgh, 93- *Mem:* Inst Med-Nat Acad Sci; AMA; AAAS; fel Am Col Neuropsychopharmacol; Sigma Xi; Am Psychiat Asn; Int Soc Neurochem; Int Narcotic Res Asn; Soc Biol Psychiat; Soc Neurosci; Endocrine Soc; Col Int Neuro-Psychopharmacologicum; Histochem Soc. *Res:* Melatonin and pineal extracts; similarities in neurotransmitter modulation of electrical and morphine analgesia; opiate peptides. *Mailing Add:* Ment Health Res Inst Univ Mich 205 Zina Pitcher Pl Ann Arbor MI 48109

**WATSON, STANLEY W,** bacteriology; deceased, see previous edition for last biography

**WATSON, THEO FRANKLIN,** ENTOMOLOGY, ECOLOGY. *Current Pos:* assoc prof, 66-70, PROF & ENTOMOLOGIST, AGR EXP STA, UNIV ARIZ, 70- *Personal Data:* b Plainview, Ark, July 2, 31; m 60; c 4. *Educ:* Univ Ark, BS, 53, MS, 58; Univ Calif, Berkeley, PhD(entom), 62. *Prof Exp:* From asst prof to assoc prof entom, Auburn Univ, 62-66. *Mem:* Entom Soc Am. *Res:* Agricultural entomology and ecology; ecology of cotton insects and the integrated approach to pest control in cotton. *Mailing Add:* 2328 E Greenlee Rd Tucson AZ 85719

**WATSON, VANCE H,** AGRONOMY. *Current Pos:* from asst prof to assoc prof, 66-77, PROF AGRON, MISS STATE UNIV, 77- *Personal Data:* b Kennett, Mo, Nov 25, 42; m 64; c 2. *Educ:* Southeast Mo State Univ, BS, 64; Univ Mo, Columbia, MS, 66; Miss State Univ, PhD(agron), 69. *Prof Exp:* Soil conservationist, Soil Conserv Serv, USDA, 63-64; res asst agron, Univ Mo, Columbia, 64-66. *Mem:* Am Soc Agron; Crop Sci Soc Am; Am Forage & Grassland Coun. *Res:* Forage crop ecology and management. *Mailing Add:* 1436 Pinecrest Rd Starkville MS 39759

**WATSON, VELVIN RICHARD,** GAS DYNAMICS, NUMERICAL ANALYSIS. *Current Pos:* RES SCIENTIST GAS DYNAMICS & NUMERICAL ANALYSIS, AMES RES CTR, NASA, 61- *Personal Data:* b Streator, Ill, June 2, 32; m 58; c 3. *Educ:* Univ Calif, Berkeley, BS, 59, MS,

61; Stanford Univ, PhD(plasma physics), 69. *Concurrent Pos:* Instr, San Jose State Univ, 74-79. *Mem:* Am Inst Aeronaut & Astronaut; Asn Comput Mach; Inst Elec & Electronics Engrs. *Res:* Improving our understanding of plasma dynamics and gas dynamics by utilizing numerical analysis and computer simulations. *Mailing Add:* NASA Ames Res Ctr Mail Stop 258-2 Moffett Field CA 94035

**WATSON, WILLIAM CRAWFORD,** INTERNAL MEDICINE, GASTROENTEROLOGY. *Current Pos:* from assoc prof to prof, 69-93, EMER PROF MED, UNIV WESTERN ONT, 93- *Personal Data:* b Glasgow, Scotland, Dec 20, 27; m 54; c 4. *Educ:* Glasgow Univ, MB, ChB, 50, MD, 60, PhD(med), 64; FRCPS(G), 66; FRCP & FACP, 78. *Prof Exp:* Resident surg, Ballochmyle Hosp, 50-51; resident med, Glasgow Royal Infirmary, 53, sr house officer, 53-54, sr house officer cardiol, 54-55, sr registr med, 55-60, lectr, 61-66, consult, 67-69; prof, Univ EAfrica, 66-67. *Concurrent Pos:* EAfrican Med Res Coun fel, Nairobi, Kenyatta Nat Hosp, 66-67; dir gastroenterol, Victoria Hosp, 69-88, chief staff, 84-90. *Mem:* Brit Soc Gastroenterol; Can Asn Gastroenterol (past pres); Can Soc Clin Invest; Am Gastroenterol Asn. *Res:* Biophysical and biochemical aspects of intestinal structure and function; esophageal dysmotizity. *Mailing Add:* Fac Med Univ Western Ont London ON N6A 4G5 Can

**WATSON, WILLIAM DOUGLAS,** ASTROPHYSICS. *Current Pos:* from asst prof to assoc prof physics & astron, 72-77, PROF PHYSICS & ASTRON, UNIV ILL, URBANA, 77- *Personal Data:* b Memphis, Tenn, Jan 12, 42; m 69. *Educ:* Mass Inst Technol, BS, 64, PhD(physics), 68. *Prof Exp:* Res assoc, Mass Inst Technol, 68-70; res assoc, Cornell Univ, 70-72. *Concurrent Pos:* A P Sloan Res fel, 74. *Mem:* Am Astron Soc; Am Phys Soc; Int Astron Union. *Res:* Theoretical astrophysics; theory of the interstellar medium; atomic and molecular processes. *Mailing Add:* Dept Physics Loomis Lab Univ Ill 1110 W Green St Urbana IL 61801. *Fax:* 217-333-9819

**WATSON, WILLIAM HAROLD, JR,** STRUCTURAL CHEMISTRY, NATURAL PRODUCTS CHEMISTRY. *Current Pos:* From asst prof to assoc prof, 57-64, PROF CHEM, TEX CHRISTIAN UNIV, 64-, DIR FASTBIOS LAB, 72-, CHMN, 81- *Personal Data:* b Tex, Sept 2, 31; m 56; c 2. *Educ:* Rice Univ, BA, 53, PhD(chem), 58. *Concurrent Pos:* Vis prof, Inst Technol, Monterrey, 75-; guest prof, Univ Bonn & Heidelberg, 79. *Mem:* Am Soc Pharmacog; Am Chem Soc; Am Phys Soc; NAm Phytochem Soc; Royal Soc Chem; Sigma Xi. *Res:* Structure of biologically active molecules; phytochemical investigations of Central and South America plants; structure and reactivity of molecule exhibiting deformed pi-election system. *Mailing Add:* Tex Christian Univ Box 298860 Ft Worth TX 76129-0001

**WATSON, WILLIAM MARTIN, JR,** COATINGS POLYMERS, ORGANIZATIONAL DEVELOPMENT & PROCESS MANAGEMENT. *Current Pos:* NEW PROD PROCESS MGR. *Personal Data:* b Annapolis, Md, May 10, 46; m 73, Margaret A Babcock; c Elizabeth & Julia. *Educ:* Ga Inst Technol, BS, 68; Univ Ill, MS, 72, PhD(phys chem), 73. *Prof Exp:* Group leader, Rohm & Haas Co, 73-87; res qual consult, 88-95. *Mem:* AAAS; Am Chem Soc. *Res:* Keeper of the new product process. *Mailing Add:* 1519 Hilltown Pike Hilltown PA 18927. *E-Mail:* wmwatson@rohmhaas.com

**WATSON, WYNNFIELD YOUNG,** ENTOMOLOGY, INVERTEBRATE ZOOLOGY. *Current Pos:* chmn dept biol, 74-80, PROF ZOOL, WILFRID LAURIER UNIV, 80- *Personal Data:* b Toronto, Ont, Feb 5, 24; m 50; c 3. *Educ:* Univ Toronto, BA, 50, PhD(entom), 55. *Prof Exp:* Res officer, Fed Dept Forestry, 50-61; from assoc prof to prof zool, Laurentian Univ, 61-74, chmn dept biol, 67-71, dir grad studies, 69-74. *Concurrent Pos:* Nat Res Coun Can grants, 65-67. *Mem:* Entom Soc Can; Coleopterists Soc. *Res:* Systematics of Coccinellidae; carabidae of eastern North America. *Mailing Add:* Dept Biol Wilfrid Laurier Univ 75 University Ave W Waterloo ON N2L 3C5 Can

**WATT, BOB EVERETT,** HIGH ENERGY LASER DEVELOPMENT. *Current Pos:* PRES & CONSULT, WATTLAB, 77- *Personal Data:* b Tulsa, Okla, July 20, 17; m 46; c 3. *Educ:* Rice Univ, BA, 39, MA, 40, PhD, 46. *Prof Exp:* Staff mem radar develop, Radiation Lab, Mass Inst Technol, 41-45; staff mem well logging, Geophys Res Lab, Texaco, 46-47; staff mem nuclear physics & laser res, Los Alamos Nat Lab, 47-51, group leader, 51-62, polarized nuclear reactions, 62-70, laser fusion res, 70-77. *Mem:* Fel Am Phys Soc; AAAS; Sigma Xi. *Res:* Nuclear reactions of light elements; energy spectrum of fission neutrons; particle scattering from and nuclear reactions with polarized helium (mass no 3); high speed electronic instrumentation; nuclear reactions involving neutrons and gamma rays. *Mailing Add:* 1447 45th St Los Alamos NM 87544

**WATT, DANIEL FRANK,** METALLURGY, MECHANICAL PROPERTIES OF POLYMERS. *Current Pos:* assoc prof, 79-81, PROF ENG MAT, UNIV WINSOR, 81- *Personal Data:* b High River, Alta, Feb 9, 38; m 72. *Educ:* Univ Alta, BSc, 61; McMaster Univ, PhD(metall), 68. *Prof Exp:* Sr scientist, Dept Mines & Tech Surv, Ont, Can, 61-63; Nat Res Coun fel, Cavendish Lab, Eng, 67-69; asst prof eng mat, Univ Windsor, 69-76; gen mgr, Curtis-Hoover Industs, Houston, 77-78. *Concurrent Pos:* Consult, Dominion Foundries & Steel Ltd, Ont, Can, 71. *Mem:* Am Soc Metals; Am Inst Mining, Metall & Petrol Engrs; Soc Plastics Engrs. *Res:* Metal fatigue; mechanical metallurgy. *Mailing Add:* Dept Mech Eng Mat Group Univ Windsor Windsor ON N9B 3P4 Can

**WATT, DAVID MILNE, JR,** SURFACE CHEMISTRY, ENGINEERING MANAGEMENT. *Current Pos:* mgr prog develop, Energy Res Ctr, 85, MGR PROG DEVELOP, SCH ENG, MINES DEVELOP OFF & CTR INNOVATION & BUS DEVELOP, UNIV NDAK, 87-, ASSOC PROF ENG MGT, 90- *Personal Data:* b Cincinnati, Ohio, July 7, 42; m 67; c 2. *Educ:* Princeton Univ, BSE, 64; Univ Calif, Berkeley, PhD(chem eng), 69. *Prof Exp:* Asst prof chem eng, Cornell Univ, 69-71; prod develop chemist, Procter & Gamble Co, Cincinnati, 71-77; proj leader, Cloriox Tech Ctr, 77-84; sr sect head, res & develop, Exxon Enterprises, Epidemic Div, San Jose, Calif, 84-85. *Concurrent Pos:* Petrol Res Fund initiation grant, Cornell Univ, 69-71, NSF starter grant, 70-71; training adminr, Elec Power Res Inst, Palo Alto, Calif, 85; mgt training consult, 85- *Mem:* Am Chem Soc; Am Soc Training & Develop. *Res:* Chemical engineering; formulation of household cleaning products. *Mailing Add:* The Principia 13201 Clayton Rd St Louis MO 63131-1022

**WATT, DEAN DAY,** BIOCHEMISTRY. *Current Pos:* PROF BIOCHEM, SCH MED, CREIGHTON UNIV, 69- *Personal Data:* b McCammon, Idaho, Sept 21, 17; m 46; c 5. *Educ:* Univ Idaho, BS, 42; Iowa State Col, PhD(bact physiol), 49. *Prof Exp:* Res chemist, Westvaco Chlorine Prod, Inc, 42-44; instr bact, Iowa State Col, 47-49; asst microbiologist, Agr Exp Sta, Purdue Univ, 49-53; assoc prof biochem, Tulane Univ, La, 53-60; assoc prof zool, Ariz State Univ, 60-63; mem staff, Midwest Res Inst, Mo, 63-69. *Concurrent Pos:* Sr res biochemist & head dept physiol sci, Southeast La Hosp, Mandeville, La, 53-60. *Mem:* AAAS; Int Soc Toxinology; Sigma Xi. *Res:* Metabolism of bacteria; pigments of fungi; biochemistry of mental disease; chemistry of animal venoms. *Mailing Add:* 618 S 130 St Omaha NE 68154-2910

**WATT, EDWARD WILLIAM,** RESEARCH PHYSIOLOGY OF EXERCISE-ISOLATED HEART REFUSION STUDIES, INTRODUCTION OF PREVENTIVE MEDICINE WELLNESS TO HOSPITAL BASED FACILITIES. *Current Pos:* dir, Dept Cardiovasc Rehab, 81-93, SR CONSULT CARDIOVASC SERVS, SCHUMPERT MED CTR, 93- *Personal Data:* b Farnham, Surrey, Eng, Sept 25, 37; nat US; c John M & David M. *Educ:* Southampton Univ, UK, DEd, 64; Northwestern State Col, BS, 66; Univ Tenn, MS, 67; Univ Mich, PhD, 70. *Prof Exp:* NIH fel human biol, Pa State Univ, 71-72; res assoc, Dept Physiol, Sch Med, Emory Univ, 74-78; co-dir, Prev Cardiol Clin, 74-80, Ga Baptist Hosp, 76-80. *Concurrent Pos:* Fel, Coun Circulation, Am Heart Asn. *Mem:* Am Physiol Soc; NY Acad Sci; fel Am Col Cardiol; Am Heart Asn. *Res:* Effects of exercise training and detraining on lipid metabolism; effects of exercise training of cardiovascular dynamics, also production of circulatory platelet aggregates in coronary patients and oxygen transport mechanisms in post cardiac rehabilitation. *Mailing Add:* Schumpert Med Ctr Dept Cardiol One St Mary Pl PO Box 21976 Shreveport LA 71120-1976

**WATT, HAME MAMADOV,** WATER RESOURCES. *Current Pos:* PROF ENVIRON SCI, UNIV DC, 79- *Personal Data:* b Senegal, Africa, Aug 30, 43; c 2. *Educ:* Univ Grenoble, France, MS, 70; DSc, 72. *Prof Exp:* Instr math, Lycee Voiron, France, 69-70; res asst fluid mech, Univ Grenoble, France, 70-72; teacher math, Sidewell Friends, 73-74; asst prof phys sc, Wash Tech Inst, 74-76; sr res energy, Planning Res Corp, 76-79. *Concurrent Pos:* Dir & prof, DC Water Res Ctr, 79- *Mem:* Soil Conserv Serv; Int Solar Energy Soc; Am Water Works Asn. *Res:* Water resources; energy and environmental projects. *Mailing Add:* Univ DC 4200 Connecticut Ave MB5004 Washington DC 20008

**WATT, JAMES PETER,** GEOPHYSICS, APPLIED PHYSICS. *Current Pos:* CHAIR, PHYSICS DEPT, PHILLIPS ANDOVER ACAD, 88- *Personal Data:* b Truro, NS, Sept 22, 49. *Educ:* Dalhousie Univ, BSc, 71, MSc, 72; Harvard Univ, PhD(appl physics), 78. *Prof Exp:* Vis res fel, Coop Inst Res Environ Sci, Univ Colo, 78-79; res fel, Seismol Lab, Calif Inst Technol, 79-81; asst prof geol, Rensselaer Polytech Inst, 81-88. *Mem:* Am Geophys Union; Can Geophys Union; Soc Explor Geophysicists; AAAS; Sigma Xi. *Res:* Mechanical properties of rocks and minerals. *Mailing Add:* Phillips Acad Andover MA 01810. *E-Mail:* pwatt@andover.edu

**WATT, JOSEPH T(EE), JR,** ELECTRICAL ENGINEERING. *Current Pos:* from asst prof to assoc prof, 65-83, dir eng co-op educ, 84-92, PROF ELEC ENG, LAMAR UNIV, 84- *Personal Data:* b Honolulu, Hawaii, July 16, 33; m 71, Sharon McIntyre; c Kara L & Chad E. *Educ:* Rice Univ, BA, 54, BS, 55; Univ Tex, MS, 63, PhD(elec eng), 65. *Prof Exp:* Eng trainee, Gen Elec Co, 55-56, engr adv eng prog, 57-59, analyst comput sci & info retrieval, 59-60; res asst elec eng, Univ Tex, 61-65. *Mem:* Inst Elec & Electronics Engrs; Am Soc Eng Educ. *Res:* Automatic control theory including system identification and adjustment of adaptive systems; digital systems; operations research; microcomputers. *Mailing Add:* Dept Elec Eng Lamar Univ Box 10029 Beaumont TX 77710. *Fax:* 409-880-8121

**WATT, KENNETH EDMUND FERGUSON,** ECOLOGY. *Current Pos:* assoc prof zool, 63-64, prof, 65-93, EMER PROF ZOOL, UNIV CALIF, DAVIS, 93- *Personal Data:* b Toronto, Ont, July 13, 29; m 55; c 2. *Educ:* Univ Toronto, BA, 51; Univ Chicago, PhD(zool), 54. *Hon Degrees:* LLD, Simon Fraser Univ, 70. *Honors & Awards:* Entom Soc Can Gold Medal, 69. *Prof Exp:* Biometrician, Ont Dept Lands & Forests, 54-57; sr biometrician, Statist Res & Serv, Res Br, Can Dept Agr, 57-61; head statist res & serv, Can Dept Forestry, 61-63. *Concurrent Pos:* Consult, Sci Secretariat, Can Privy Coun, 66; sr fel, East-West Ctr, Honolulu, 75. *Mem:* Ecol Soc Am; Soc Gen Systs Res; Soc Comput Simulation; Japanese Soc Pop Ecol. *Res:* Theoretical, experimental and field ecology of fish and insects; biomathematics; applied statistics; computer simulation studies for evaluating resource management strategies; epidemiology; regional and global modelling and simulation. *Mailing Add:* Evolution Ecol Univ Calif Davis CA 95616-5224

**WATT, LYNN A(LEXANDER) K(EELING),** ELECTRICAL ENGINEERING. *Current Pos:* prof, Univ Waterloo, 66-90, dean grad studies, 72-83, actg dean res, 88-89, ADJ PROF, DEPT ELEC & COMPUT ENG, UNIV WATERLOO; COORDR, ONT CTR EXCELLENCE, 87- *Personal Data:* b Winnipeg, Man, Oct 25, 24; m 48, Pauline Ecnarson; c 4. *Educ:* Univ Man, BSc, 47; Univ Chicago, SM, 51; Univ Minn, PhD(elec eng), 59. *Hon Degrees:* DEng, Carleton Univ, 89. *Prof Exp:* Lectr physics, Univ Man, 48-49, 51-52; asst res off, Atomic Energy Can, Ltd, 52-55; from asst prof to prof elec eng, Univ Wash, 59-66. *Concurrent Pos:* Chmn, Ont Coun Grad Studies, 76-78, exec vchmn, 83-86. *Mem:* Am Phys Soc; Inst Elec & Electronics Engrs; Can Asn Grad Schs (pres, 77-78); Can Asn Physicists; Sigma Xi; Can Soc Study Higher Educ. *Res:* Diffusion in III-IV compounds; imperfections in semiconductors; physical properties of semiconductor devices. *Mailing Add:* 193 Mohawk Ave Waterloo ON N2L 2T4 Can. *Fax:* 519-725-9971

**WATT, ROBERT DOUGLAS,** EXPERIMENTAL HIGH ENERGY PHYSICS, PHYSICS ENGINEERING. *Current Pos:* RETIRED. *Personal Data:* b Santa Paula, Calif, July 7, 19; m 46; c 2. *Educ:* Univ Calif, BS, 42. *Prof Exp:* Physicist, Lawrence Radiation Lab, Univ Calif, 46-67; group leader, Stanford Linear Accelerator Ctr, Stanford Univ, 67-86. *Concurrent Pos:* Consult, Argonne Nat Lab & Lawrence Radiation Lab. *Mem:* Am Phys Soc. *Res:* Particle accelerator development and operation; development and use of liquid hydrogen bubble chambers for detection of high energy particles of nuclear physics; research to prove existence of magnetic monopoles. *Mailing Add:* 11117 Palos Verde Dr Cupertino CA 95014. *Fax:* 408-252-4684

**WATT, WARD B,** BIOCHEMICAL POPULATION GENETICS. *Current Pos:* From asst prof to assoc prof, 69-85, PROF BIOL, STANFORD UNIV, 85- *Personal Data:* b Washington, DC, Oct 21, 40; m 79; c 2. *Educ:* Yale Univ, BA, 62, MS, 64, PhD(biol), 67. *Concurrent Pos:* Mem bd trustees, Rocky Mountain Biol Lab, 71-75, 77-90 & vpres, 82-86, pres, 87-88; mem adv panel syst biol, NSF, 73-75; res assoc entom, Calif Acad Sci, 91- *Mem:* Am Soc Naturalists; Genetics Soc Am; Soc Study Evolution; fel AAAS; Arctic Inst NAm. *Res:* Study of adaptive mechanisms and microevolutionary processes in natural insect populations from perspectives of biochemistry, physiology, genetics and ecology. *Mailing Add:* Dept Biol Sci Stanford Univ Stanford CA 94305-5020

**WATT, WILLIAM JOSEPH,** INORGANIC CHEMISTRY. *Current Pos:* dean col, Washington & Lee Univ, 65-84, from asst prof to prof, 65-94, dept head, 86-91, EMER PROF CHEM & DEAN COL, WASHINGTON & LEE UNIV, 94- *Personal Data:* b Carbondale, Ill, Dec 15, 25; m 56, Helen Gravatt; c John, Phyllis & William Jr. *Educ:* Univ Ill, BS, 49; Cornell Univ, MS, 51, PhD, 56. *Prof Exp:* Asst prof chem, Davidson Col, 51-53. *Mem:* Am Chem Soc. *Res:* Magnesium fluoride gels; inorganic polymers; boron compounds; molten salts. *Mailing Add:* Washington & Lee Univ Dept Chem Lexington VA 24450

**WATT, WILLIAM RUSSELL,** POLYMER CHEMISTRY, COATINGS. *Current Pos:* RETIRED. *Personal Data:* b Camden, NJ, June 28, 20; m 46, Jean Elfreth; c Wendy, Timothy & Bruce. *Educ:* Univ Pa, BA, 49; Univ Del, MS, 52, PhD(chem), 55. *Prof Exp:* Instr gen chem, Philadelphia Col Textiles & Sci, 49-51; instr, Univ Del, 52-54; res chemist, Am Viscose Corp, 54-60; sr res chemist, Avisun Corp, 60-64; sr res assoc polymer chem, Am Can Co, 64-74, res fel, 77-83; chief chemist, Norland Prod Co, 83-86; consult, Union Carbide & Occidental Chem Co, 86-87. *Mem:* Am Chem Soc. *Res:* Photochemistry; organic coatings; ultraviolet curable coatings; cellulose derivatives; stereospecific polymerization; catalysis. *Mailing Add:* 662 Cascade Dr S Mt Laurel NJ 08054

**WATT, WILLIAM STEWART,** PHYSICAL CHEMISTRY, SPECTROSCOPY. *Current Pos:* gen mgr, Wash Opers, 79-80, vpres prog develop, 80-90, SR VPRES & DIR PROGS, W J SCHAFER ASSOC, 91- *Personal Data:* b Perth, Scotland, Feb 25, 37; US citizen; m 88, Adele Bailly; c 3. *Educ:* Univ St Andrews, Scotland, BSc, 59; Univ Leeds, PhD(phys chem), 62. *Honors & Awards:* J B Cohen Res Prize, 62. *Prof Exp:* Cornell Postdoc Fel, Cornell Univ, 62-64; res chemist, Cornell Aeronaut Lab, Buffalo, NY, 64-71; head chem laser sect, Naval Res Lab, 71-73, dep head laser physics br, 73-76, head laser physics br, Optical Sci Div, 76-79. *Concurrent Pos:* Assoc ed, Inst Elec & Electronics Engrs J Quantum Electronics, 78-81. *Mem:* Am Phys Soc; Combustion Inst; Sigma Xi; Inst Elec & Electronics Engrs. *Res:* Laser physics and development; laser-induced chemistry; energy transfer and reaction rate measurements; optical diagnostics. *Mailing Add:* 6721 Pine Creek Ct McLean VA 22101-5519

**WATTENBERG, ALBERT,** PHYSICS, HISTORY OF PHYSICS. *Current Pos:* RETIRED. *Personal Data:* b New York, NY, Apr 13, 17; m 92, Alice Wyers; c Beth, Jill & Nina. *Educ:* City Col New York, BS, 38; Columbia Univ, MA, 39; Univ Chicago, PhD(physics), 47. *Honors & Awards:* "Nuclear Pioneer" Award, Soc Nuclear Med, 77; Bronze Medal, Am Nuclear Soc, 77. *Prof Exp:* Spectroscopist, Schenley Prod, Inc, NY, 39-41; asst, Off Sci Res & Develop, Columbia Univ, 41-42; group leader, Metall Lab, Univ Chicago, 42-46; sr physicist & group leader, Argonne Nat Lab, 47-50; vis asst prof, Univ Ill, 50-51; res physicist, Nuclear Sci Lab & lectr, Mass Inst Technol, 51-58; res prof physics, Univ Ill, Urbana, 59-86. *Concurrent Pos:* Actg dir nuclear physics div, Argonne Nat Lab, 49-50; NSF fel, Univ Rome, 62-63; vis prof, Stanford Univ, 73 & 80-81. *Mem:* Am Phys Soc; Sigma Xi; AAAS; Hist Sci Soc. *Res:* Spectroscopy; nuclear chain reactors; photoneutron techniques; photonuclear reactions; elementary particle physics, decay of mesons, history of physics. *Mailing Add:* Dept Physics Univ Ill Urbana IL 61801. *Fax:* 217-333-4990

**WATTENBERG, FRANKLIN ARVEY,** MATHEMATICS. *Current Pos:* PROF, WEBER STATE UNIV, 93- *Personal Data:* b New York, NY, May 16, 43; m 93, Margo Mankus; c Martin & Alina. *Educ:* Wayne State Univ, BS, 64; Univ Wis-Madison, MS, 65, PhD(math). 68. *Prof Exp:* Benjamin Peirce asst prof math, Harvard Univ, 68-71; from asst prof to prof math, Univ Mass, Amherst, 71-93. *Concurrent Pos:* Vis prof, Carroll Col, Mont, Mont State Univ, 97- *Mem:* Am Math Soc; Math Asn Am. *Res:* Differential topology; nonstandard analysis; algebraic topology; probability; mathematical economics. *Mailing Add:* Math Dept Montana State Univ Bozeman MT 59717

**WATTENBERG, LEE WOLFF,** PATHOLOGY. *Current Pos:* From instr to assoc prof, 56-66, Hill prof, 59-66, PROF PATH, MED SCH, UNIV MINN, MINNEAPOLIS, 66- *Personal Data:* b New York, NY, Dec 22, 21; m 45; c 6. *Educ:* City Col New York, BS, 41; Univ Minn, Minneapolis, BM, 49, MD, 50; Am Bd Path, dipl, 56. *Concurrent Pos:* Lederle med fac award, 57-59. *Mem:* Histochem Soc (vpres, 66); Soc Exp Biol & Med; Am Soc Exp Path; Am Asn Pathologists & Bacteriologists; Am Asn Cancer Res. *Res:* Histochemistry; cancer research; experimental pathology. *Mailing Add:* Dept Lab Med Univ Minn Sch Med Minneapolis MN 55455

**WATTERS, CHRISTOPHER DEFFNER,** CELL BIOLOGY. *Current Pos:* from asst prof to assoc prof, Middlebury Col, 73-78, chmn dept, 76-82, chmn, Div Nat Sci, 82-85, chmn dept, 88-91, PROF BIOL, MIDDLEBURY COL, 78- *Personal Data:* b Ironton, Ohio, Dec 7, 39; m 67; c 3. *Educ:* Univ Notre Dame, BS, 61; Princeton Univ, MA, 64, PhD(biol), 66. *Prof Exp:* Instr biol, Princeton Univ, 64-66; res assoc cell biol prog, Univ Minn, St Paul, 66-68. *Concurrent Pos:* Vis scientist, Physiol Lab, Cambridge Univ, 73-74, Hannah Res Inst, 87-88, Ion Channel Res Group, Univ Vt, 93-94; vis assoc prof, Dartmouth Col, 75; vis prof, Med Sch, Univ Colo, 80-81; Irene Heinz & John LaPorte prof premed sci, 82-; mem comt examiners, grad record examiners bid, 88-94, chair, 92-94. *Mem:* Am Soc Cell Biologists; Biochem Soc Gt Brit; Sigma Xi. *Res:* Lactation calcium transport; structural and functional organization of cell membranes; cellular aspects of development. *Mailing Add:* Dept Biol Middlebury Col Middlebury VT 05753. *Fax:* 802-388-0739; *E-Mail:* watters@m.oo.middlebury.edu

**WATTERS, EDWARD C(HARLES), JR,** MATHEMATICS, ELECTRONICS. *Current Pos:* fel engr, Westinghouse Elec Corp, Baltimore, 57, supv engr, 57-58, adv engr, 58-59 & weapon control dept, 59-61, consult engr, Surface Div, 61-70, consult engr, Electronic Systs Div, 70-84, CONSULT ENGR, DEFENSE OPERS DIV, WESTINGHOUSE ELEC CORP, BALTIMORE, 84- *Personal Data:* b Monroe, Mich, Feb 16, 23; m 46; c 3. *Educ:* Univ Notre Dame, BSEE, 43, MS, 46; Univ Md, PhD, 54. *Prof Exp:* Asst prof math, US Naval Acad, 46-55; sr engr, Bendix Aviation Corp, 55-57. *Res:* Radar; weapon systems; signal processing. *Mailing Add:* 133 Spa View Ave Annapolis MD 21401-3542

**WATTERS, GARY Z,** FLUID MECHANICS, HYDRODYNAMICS. *Current Pos:* dean eng, comput sci & technol, 80-, PROF, COL CIVIL ENG, CALIF STATE UNIV, CHICO. *Personal Data:* b Gilson, Ill, Oct 11, 35; m 57; c 3. *Educ:* Chico State Col, BS, 57; Stanford Univ, MS, 58, PhD(civil eng), 63. *Prof Exp:* From instr to asst prof civil eng, Chico State Col, 58-61; from asst prof to assoc prof civil eng, Utah State Univ, 63-77, prof, 77-80, asst dean, 72-74, assoc dean, 74-76. *Concurrent Pos:* Am Soc Eng Educ/Ford Found resident in eng pract, 71. *Mem:* Am Soc Civil Engrs; Am Soc Eng Educ; Nat Soc Prof Engrs. *Res:* Hydraulic transients; finite element methods in fluid mechanics; economic design of irrigation systems. *Mailing Add:* Col Civil Eng Calif State Univ Chico CA 95929-1000

**WATTERS, GORDON VALENTINE,** NEUROLOGY, PEDIATRICS. *Current Pos:* PROF NEUROL & PEDIAT, MONTREAL CHILDREN'S HOSP, MCGILL UNIV, 69- *Personal Data:* b Winnipeg, Man, Apr 8, 28; m 57; c 3. *Educ:* Univ Minn, Minneapolis, BA, 51; Univ Man, MD, 57. *Prof Exp:* Asst prof neurol, Winnipeg Children's Hosp, Univ Man, 63-65; asst prof, Children's Med Ctr, Harvard Univ, 65-69. *Mem:* Am Acad Neurol; Can Neurol Soc. *Res:* Degenerative disease of nervous system; cerebrospinal fluid dynamics. *Mailing Add:* Montreal Children's Hosp 2300 Tupper St Suite A501 Montreal PQ H3H 1P3 Can

**WATTERS, KENNETH LYNN,** INORGANIC CHEMISTRY, MATERIALS CHEMISTRY. *Current Pos:* from asst prof to assoc prof, 70-88, PROF CHEM, UNIV WIS-MILWAUKEE, 88-, PROVOST & VCHANCELLOR ACAD AFFAIRS, 90- *Personal Data:* b Iowa City, Iowa, Jan 21, 39; m 91, Marica Delair; c Mathew, Geoffrey & Robert. *Educ:* Univ Ill, Urbana, BS, 62; Brown Univ, PhD(chem), 70. *Prof Exp:* Res assoc chem, State Univ NY Buffalo, 69-70. *Mem:* Am Chem Soc; AAAS. *Res:* Spectroscopic studies of transition metal complexes; Raman, resonance Raman, and infrared spectroscopies; studies of catalytic properties of transition metal complexes and metal cluster compounds; studies of thin film deposits. *Mailing Add:* Dept Chem Univ Wis Milwaukee WI 53201

**WATTERS, ROBERT JAMES,** GEOLOGICAL ENGINEERING, ENGINEERING GEOLOGY. *Current Pos:* from asst prof to assoc prof, 78-87, PROF GEOL ENG, MACKAY SCH MINES, UNIV NEV, 87- *Personal Data:* b Glasgow, Scotland, July 22, 46. *Educ:* Univ Strathclyde, BS, 69; Univ London, MS, 70, PhD(eng geol), 72. *Prof Exp:* Resident eng geologist, Sir Alexander Gibb & Partners Consult Engrs, London, 72-74; proj geol engr, Dames & Moore Consult Engrs, Los Angeles, 74-77. *Mem:* Int Soc Rock Mech; Inst Civil Engrs; Brit Geotech Soc; Geol Soc London; Asn Eng Geologists. *Res:* Rock mechanics applied to the design of surface and underground excavations; geotechnical documentation and analysis of soil and rock masses; site investigation techniques; ground improvement and instrumentation. *Mailing Add:* Mackay Sch Mines Univ Nev Reno NV 89557

**WATTERS, ROBERT LISLE,** RADIOCHEMISTRY, HEALTH PHYSICS. *Current Pos:* ENVIRON RADIOACTIVITY SPECIALIST, DIV BIOMED & ENVIRON RES, US DEPT ENERGY, 72-, GROUP LEADER LAND & FRESHWATER RES, 73-, PHYS SCIENTIST, 79- *Personal Data:* b Everett, Wash, June 25, 25; m 48; c 2. *Educ:* Univ Wash, BS, 50, PhD(chem), 63; Harvard Univ, MS, 59; Am Bd Health Physics, dipl, 66; recert, 81. *Prof Exp:* Engr asst, Hanford Atomic Prod Oper, Gen Elec Co, Wash, 50-52, supvr bioassay lab, 52-56, supvr radiation monitoring, 56-58; engr, Boeing Co, 59-60; res specialist radiol hazard eval, Atomic Int Div, NAm Aviation, Inc, Calif, 63-65; assoc prof radiochem, Colo State Univ, 65-72. *Concurrent Pos:* Lectr, Mobile Radioisotope Lab, Oak Ridge Inst Nuclear Studies, 66- *Mem:* AAAS; Health Physics Soc. *Res:* Translocation of plutonium and americium in the body; environmental behavior of polonium; environmental behavior of actinides. *Mailing Add:* PO Box 20048 Poolesville MD 20837

**WATTERS, THOMAS ROBERT,** TECTONICS, PLANETARY GEOLOGY. *Current Pos:* res geologist, Ctr Earth & Planetary Studies, 81-89, actg chmn, 89-92, SUPVRY GEOLOGIST, CTR EARTH & PLANETARY STUDIES, NAT AIR & SPACE MUS, SMITHSONIAN INST, 89-, CHMN, 92- *Personal Data:* b West Chester, Pa, Feb 1, 55; m 83, Nancy R Tracey; c James T, Samantha E & Adam T. *Educ:* WChester Univ, BS, 77; Bryn Mawr Col, MA, 79; George Washington Univ, PhD(geol), 85. *Prof Exp:* Res fel, Am Mus Natural Hist, 78-80; res asst, Dept Terrestrial Magnetism, Carnegie Inst Washington, 80-81. *Concurrent Pos:* Grantee, NASA, 83- *Mem:* AAAS; Geol Soc Am; Am Geophys Union. *Res:* Terrestrial and planetary tectonics and tectonophysics; morphological and structural comparisons of tectonic features on the terrestrial planets and analogous features on Earth; geologic mapping of Mars. *Mailing Add:* Smithsonian Inst Ctr Earth & Planetary Studies Nat Air & Space Mus MS 315 Washington DC 20560. *Fax:* 202-786-2566; *E-Mail:* twatters@ceps.nasm.edu

**WATTERSON, ARTHUR C, JR,** ORGANIC CHEMISTRY, POLYMER CHEMISTRY. *Current Pos:* PROF CHEM, LOWELL TECHNOL INST, 65- *Personal Data:* b Ellwood City, Pa, Apr 19, 38. *Educ:* Geneva Col, BS, 60; Brown Univ, PhD(org chem), 65. *Prof Exp:* Res assoc chem, Johns Hopkins Univ, 64-65. *Mem:* Am Chem Soc; Royal Soc Chem. *Res:* Polymer stereochemistry; nuclear magnetic resonance of macromolecules; synthesis of natural products; decomposition of n-nitroso amides; deamination reactions; nitrogen heterocycles. *Mailing Add:* Dept Chem Univ Mass Lowell MA 01854

**WATTERSON, D MARTIN,** MOLECULAR BIOLOGY. *Current Pos:* Assoc prof, 81-85, PROF PHARMACOL, VANDERBILT UNIV SCH MED, 86- *Personal Data:* b Pensacola, Fla, Sept 9, 46. *Educ:* Emory Col, BS, 69; Emory Univ, PhD(biochem), 75. *Concurrent Pos:* Investr, Howard Hughes Med Inst, 81- *Mem:* Am Soc Biol Chemists; Am Soc Cell Biol; Am Chem Soc; Biophys Soc; AAAS; Am Soc Plant Physiol. *Res:* Molecular mechanism of calcium action. *Mailing Add:* Northwestern Univ Mol Phar 303 E Chicago Ave S215 Chicago IL 60611-3008. *Fax:* 615-322-7192

**WATTERSON, JON CRAIG,** PLANT PATHOLOGY. *Current Pos:* HEAD PATH DEPT, PETOSEED CO INC, 72- *Personal Data:* b Kalamazoo, Mich, Nov 25, 44; m 67; c 2. *Educ:* Carleton Col, BA, 66; Univ Wis, MS, 71. *Prof Exp:* Res asst veg path, Univ Wis, 66-71, res assoc cranberry path, 71-72. *Mem:* Am Phytopath Soc. *Res:* Genetics of disease resistance in vegetable crops; breeding for disease resistance in vegetable crops. *Mailing Add:* Mas Rouzel Chemin Des Canaux Nimes 30900 France

**WATTERSON, KENNETH FRANKLIN,** LITHOGRAPHY. *Current Pos:* SR SCIENTIST PHOTOCHEM, PRINTING PROD DIV, HOECHST CELANESE CORP, 78- *Personal Data:* b London, Eng, July 16, 29; m 68; c 2. *Educ:* Univ London, BSc, 52, PhD(chem), 59. *Prof Exp:* Lect demonstr chem, Birkbeck Col, Univ London, 52-58, res asst, Imp Col, 58-60; res assoc, Cornell Univ, 60-62; sr res chemist, Pennsalt Chem Corp, 62-66; engr, Homer Res Labs, Bethlehem Steel Corp, 66-77. *Res:* Metal-gas reactions; surface analysis; ion microprobe spectrometry; auger spectroscopy; corrosion; photochemistry light-sensitive coatings; lithography. *Mailing Add:* RR 1 Hellertown PA 18055

**WATTERSTON, KENNETH GORDON,** FOREST SOILS, ENVIRONMENTAL MANAGEMENT. *Current Pos:* from asst prof to assoc prof forest soils, 65-75, PROF FOREST SOILS, STEPHEN F AUSTIN STATE UNIV, 75-, ASST DEAN, 87- *Personal Data:* b Rockville Centre, NY, Apr 9, 34; m 61; c 2. *Educ:* State Univ NY Col Forestry, Syracuse, BS, 59, MS, 62; Univ Wis, PhD(soils), 66. *Prof Exp:* Res asst forest soils, State Univ NY Col Forestry, Syracuse, 59-61; res asst soils, Univ Wis, 61-65. *Concurrent Pos:* Chmn, Forest Soils Div, Soil Sci Soc Am, 80-81, bd dirs, 81-82. *Mem:* Soil Sci Soc Am; Ecol Soc Am; Soc Am Foresters. *Res:* Forest soil-site relationships; forest soil classification; soil pollution and reclamation. *Mailing Add:* 2407 Twinoaks Dr Nacogdoches TX 75961

**WATTHEY, JEFFREY WILLIAM HERBERT,** ORGANIC CHEMISTRY, MEDICINAL CHEMISTRY. *Current Pos:* sr staff scientist, 64-83, mgr chem res opers, Pharmaceut Div, 84-89, MGR THERAPEUT AREA DATABASE SUPPORT, CIBA-GEIGY, SUMMIT, NJ, 90- *Personal Data:* b London, Eng, Dec 6, 37; m 61; c 3. *Educ:* Imp Col, Univ London, BSc, 59; St Catherine's Col, Oxford, DPhil(org chem), 62. *Prof Exp:* Res fel, Dept Chem, Univ Calif, Los Angeles, 62-63. *Mem:* Am Chem Soc. *Res:* Organic synthesis; synthesis of biologically active substances, with emphasis on antihypertensive and central nervous system agents. *Mailing Add:* 20211 Red Buckeye Ct Germantown MD 20876

**WATTON, ARTHUR,** SOLID STATE PHYSICS, NUCLEAR MAGNETIC RESONANCE. *Current Pos:* asst prof, 75-81, ASSOC PROF PHYSICS, UNIV VICTORIA, 81- *Personal Data:* b Dudley, Eng, Feb 12, 43. *Educ:* Univ London, BSc, 65; McMaster Univ, PhD(physics), 71; Univ Chicago, SM, 75. *Prof Exp:* Fel physics, Univ Waterloo, 71-74. *Concurrent Pos:* Nat Res Coun Can Grant, 75- *Mem:* Can Asn Physicists. *Res:* NMR studies of molecular motions in the solid state; solid-solid phase transitions; low temperature rotational quantum effects of molecules. *Mailing Add:* Dept Physics Univ Victoria Box 1700 Victoria BC V8W 2Y2 Can

**WATTS, CHARLES D,** HEALTH ADMINISTRATION. *Current Pos:* RETIRED. *Personal Data:* b Atlanta, Ga, Sept 21, 17; c 4. *Educ:* Morehouse Col, BS, 39; Howard Univ Col Med, MD, 43; Am Bd Surg, dipl, 50. *Hon Degrees:* DSc, Duke Univ, 91. *Prof Exp:* Intern, Freedmen's Hosp, Washington, DC, 43-44; instr surg, Dept Sur, Howard Univ, 44-45, dir, Cancer Teaching Proj, Howard Univ & Freedmen's Hosp, 49; dir student health servs, NC Cent Univ, 52-59; vpres & med dir, NC Mutual Life Ins Co, 60-70, sr vpres & med dir, 70-89; pvt pract primary care, 88- *Concurrent Pos:* Mem, Adv Comt Health, NC Comn Civil Rights, 65; clin instr surg, Duke Med Ctr, 69; chmn bd, Health Systs Agency 76-79; attend surg, Watts Hosp, 68-76, Durham Co Gen Hosp, 76-87; Coun Inst Med, NSF, 80-83; founder, developer & dir, Lincoln Community Health Ctr, 70-71; pvt pract surg, 50-; bd trustees, Harvard Univ, 89-97 & NC Sch Sci & Math, 89-97. *Mem:* Inst Med-Nat Acad Sci; fel Am Col Surgeons. *Res:* Medicine and human relations. *Mailing Add:* 829 Lawson St Durham NC 27701

**WATTS, CHARLES EDWARD,** MATHEMATICS. *Current Pos:* from asst prof to prof, 61-93, chmn dept, 76-78, EMER PROF MATH, UNIV ROCHESTER, 93- *Personal Data:* b Mo, Mar 21, 28; m 57; c 2. *Educ:* Drury Col, MusB, 50; Univ Calif, MA, 56, PhD, 57. *Prof Exp:* Instr math, Univ Chicago, 57-69, NSF fel, 60-61. *Mem:* Math Asn Am. *Res:* Algebraic topology; homological algebra. *Mailing Add:* Dept Math Univ Rochester Rochester NY 14627-0001. *E-Mail:* chwa@math.rochester.edu

**WATTS, DANIEL JAY,** CHEMISTRY, BOTANY. *Current Pos:* dir corp liaison, NJ Inst Technol, 83-85, dir opers, 85-88, dep exec dir, Hazardous Substance Mgt Res Ctr, 88-92, DEP EXEC DIR, CTR ENVIRON ENG & SCI, NJ INST TECHNOL, 92-, EXEC DIR, EMISSION REDUCTION RES CTR, 92- *Personal Data:* b East Cleveland, Ohio, Oct 19, 43; m 73, Karen Bush; c Edward J & Amber E. *Educ:* Ohio State Univ, BSc, 65; Ind Univ, Bloomington, AM, 68, PhD(org chem), 69. *Prof Exp:* Res investr org chem, E R Squibb & Sons, Inc, 69-77; res assoc org chem, Am Can Co, 77-81, sr res assoc org chem, 81-83. *Mem:* AAAS; Am Chem Soc; Water Environ Fedn; Bot Soc Am; Royal Chem Soc London; Am Inst Biol Sci. *Res:* Antibiotics; anti-infective agents; organic synthesis; chemotaxonomy; natural products; resource recovery; environmental sciences; pollution prevention; clean manufacturing. *Mailing Add:* Ctr Environ Eng & Sci NJ Inst Technol Newark NJ 07102. *Fax:* 973-642-7170; *E-Mail:* watts@admin.njit.edu

**WATTS, DANIEL THOMAS,** pharmacology; deceased, see previous edition for last biography

**WATTS, DENNIS RANDOLPH,** PHYSICAL OCEANOGRAPHY. *Current Pos:* asst prof, 74-80, assoc prof phys oceanog, 80-88, PROF PHYS OCEANOG, SCH OCEANOG, UNIV RI, 88- *Personal Data:* b Riverside, Calif, Dec 7, 43. *Educ:* Univ Calif, Riverside, BA, 66; Cornell Univ, PhD(physics), 73. *Prof Exp:* Postdoctoral phys oceanog, Yale Univ, 72-74. *Mem:* AAAS; Am Geophys Union; Sigma Xi; Oceanog Soc. *Res:* Descriptive and dynamical study of ocean currents, their fluctuations such as eddies, and other processes controlling the oceanic thermocline. *Mailing Add:* Sch Oceanog Univ RI Kingston RI 02881

**WATTS, DONALD GEORGE,** APPLIED STATISTICS. *Current Pos:* PROF STATIST, QUEEN'S UNIV, ONT, 70- *Personal Data:* b Winnipeg, Man, Dec 4, 33; m 58; c 2. *Educ:* Univ BC, BASc, 56, MASc, 58; Univ London, PhD(elec eng), 62. *Honors & Awards:* Heaviside Premium Award, Brit Inst Elec Engrs, 61. *Prof Exp:* Systs analyst, DeHavilland Aircraft Co, Can, 62-64; vis asst prof math, Univ Wis-Madison, 64-65, assoc prof statist, 65-70. *Concurrent Pos:* Res fel, Rohm & Haas Co, Spring House, Pa, 84-85. *Mem:* Fel Am Statist Asn; Int Statist Inst; Royal Statist Soc; Statist Soc Can. *Res:* Time series analysis, control and applications of statistics in many disciplines; nonlinear estimation; teaching methods. *Mailing Add:* Dept Math & Statist Queen's Univ Kingston ON K7L 3N6 Can

**WATTS, EXUM DEVER,** ORGANIC CHEMISTRY. *Current Pos:* RETIRED. *Personal Data:* b Nashville, Tenn, Mar 19, 26; m 48; c 3. *Educ:* George Peabody Col, BS & MA, 48; Vanderbilt Univ, PhD, 54. *Prof Exp:* Instr chem, Florence State Col, 48-49; asst prof, Harding Col, 52-54; from asst prof to assoc prof, Mid Tenn State Univ, 54-60, prof chem, 60-91, prof physics, 77-91. *Mem:* AAAS; Am Chem Soc; Nat Sci Teachers Asn. *Res:* Organic mercurials; ultraviolet spectra; interpretation of organic spectra. *Mailing Add:* 1503 Sherrill Blvd Murfreesboro TN 37130

**WATTS, JEFFREY LYNN,** VETERINARY MICROBIOLOGY. *Current Pos:* res microbiologist, 90-92, SR RES MICROBIOLOGIST, UPJOHN CO, 92- *Personal Data:* b Homer, La, May 5, 55; m 74, Vickie L Crowell; c Eric M & Danielle A. *Educ:* La Tech Univ, Ruston, BS, 78 & MS, 83. *Prof Exp:* Microbiologist, Bienville Gen Hosp, 75-78; res assoc, Hill Farm Res Sta, 78-83, instr, 83-88, asst prof, 88-90. *Concurrent Pos:* Chairholder, Nat Comt Clin Lab Stand subcomt vet antimicrobiol susceptibility testing, 93- *Mem:*

Asn Vet Microbiologists (pres, 90-91); Nat Reg Microbiologists; Am Soc Microbiol; Am Dairy Sci Asn. *Res:* Epidemiology of microorganisms responsible for bovine mastitis, development of identification methods for mastitis pathogens based upon current species descriptions; virulence factors associated with mastitis pathogens; antimicrobiology susceptibility trends of veterinary pathogens; identification of veterinary pathogens. *Mailing Add:* Animal Health Discovery Res 7923-190-NR Upjohn Co Kalamazoo MI 49001. *Fax:* 616-384-2347

**WATTS, JOHN ALBERT, JR,** CELLULAR PHYSIOLOGY, PHARMACOLOGY. *Current Pos:* from asst prof to assoc prof, 79-90, PROF PHYSIOL, UNIV NC, CHARLOTTE, 90- *Personal Data:* b Brooklyn, NY, Nov 30, 49. *Educ:* Drew Univ, BA, 71; Univ Md, PhD(zool), 77. *Prof Exp:* Teaching asst marine biol, Drew Univ, 69; teaching asst physiol, Univ Md, 71-77; fel physiol, M S Hershey Med Ctr, 77-79. *Concurrent Pos:* Instr seashore life, Children's Sch Sci, 71. *Mem:* Am Physiol Soc; AAAS; Int Soc Heart Res; Sigma Xi. *Res:* Possible roles of calcium and changes in mitochondrial function in the causes of cell death from myocardial ischemic injury; factors limiting reperfusion of heart tissue. *Mailing Add:* Carolina Med Ctr PO Box 32861 Charlotte NC 28223-2861. *Fax:* 704-547-3128

**WATTS, MALCOLM S M,** INTERNAL MEDICINE. *Current Pos:* From asst clin prof to assoc clin prof med, Univ Calif, San Francisco, 53-71, coordr cardiovasc bd, 52-56, actg dir cardiovasc res inst, 56-57, asst dean, 56-66, spec asst to chancellor, 63-71, dir extended progs med educ, 74-85, prof, 71-90, assoc dean, 66-90, EMER CLIN PROF MED, SCH MED, UNIV CALIF, SAN FRANCISCO, 90- *Personal Data:* b New York, NY, Apr 30, 15; m 47; c Pauline, Elizabeth, Malcolm & James. *Educ:* Harvard Univ, AB, 37, MD, 41. *Honors & Awards:* John T McGovern Award, Am Med Writers Asn, 86. *Concurrent Pos:* Ed, Calif Med, 68-73, Western J Med, 74-90 & J Continuing Educ Health Prof, 88-91; proj dir, Calif Area Health Educ Ctr Syst, 79-90; vpres, Hospice San Francisco, 79-85; dir, Extended Progs Med Educ, Univ Calif, San Francisco, 74-85. *Mem:* Nat Inst Med; AAAS; fel Am Col Physicians; master Am Col Physicians. *Res:* Private practice of internal medicine; examination of the role of the physician in modern society; medical education; health professions education. *Mailing Add:* 270 Sea Cliff Ave San Francisco CA 94121

**WATTS, PLATO HILTON, JR,** CLINICAL CHEMISTRY, PHYSICAL CHEMISTRY. *Current Pos:* DIR ALLERGY, ROCHE BIOMED, 88- *Personal Data:* b Florence, SC, May 30, 41; m 75; c 1. *Educ:* Furman Univ, BS, 65; Univ Md, PhD(chem), 70. *Prof Exp:* Res assoc & fel biophys, Sch Med, Univ Md, 70-71; asst prof chem, 72; res assoc mat sci, Ctr Mat Res, 71-72; teacher chem, Char-Meck Sch, 72-75; assoc dir clin chem, Diag Labs, 75-80; house officer, St Louis Childrens Hosp, 85-87. fel pediat, 87-88. *Mem:* AAAS; Sigma Xi; Am Chem Soc; Am Asn Clin Chemists. *Res:* Application of analytical and radioimmunologic techniques to problems in clinical chemistry. *Mailing Add:* 1312 Dogwood Dr Gibsonville NC 27249

**WATTS, SHERRILL GLENN,** PHYSICAL CHEMISTRY. *Current Pos:* actg acad dean, 83-84, ASSOC PROF & CHAIR DEPT MATH & SCI, S GA COL, 82- *Personal Data:* b Meridian, Miss, July 15, 37; m 61; c 2. *Educ:* Miss Southern Col, BA, 59, MS, 61; Emory Univ, PhD(phys chem), 65. *Prof Exp:* Res assoc chem, Emory Univ, 65-67; asst prof, Agnes Scott Col, 67-68; assoc prof math & chem, Atlanta Baptist Col, 68-71, chem, Morehouse Col, 73-74; asst to dean sci & libr studies, Ga Inst Technol, 73-76, asst dean, 76-82. *Concurrent Pos:* Prin investr, NSF Women in Sci Careers Proj, 80-83. *Mem:* Sigma Xi; AAAS; Am Asn Higher Educ; Am Chem Soc. *Res:* Nuclear magnetic resonance coupling in small molecules. *Mailing Add:* Dept Sci & Math S Ga Col Douglas GA 31533

**WATTS, TERENCE LESLIE,** PHYSICS. *Current Pos:* assoc prof, 70-85, PROF PHYSICS, RUTGERS UNIV, NEW BRUNSWICK, 86- *Personal Data:* b Leicester, Eng, May 5, 35; m 62, Ann Chalmers; c 2. *Educ:* Univ London, BSc, 57; Yale Univ, PhD(physics), 63. *Prof Exp:* Res asst nuclear physics, Yale Univ, 63; res assoc particle physics, Duke Univ, 63-64; mem res staff, Lab Nuclear Sci, Mass Inst Technol, 64-65, asst prof physics, 65-70. *Mem:* Am Phys Soc; NY Acad Sci. *Res:* Experimental particle physics; phenomenology; computing in particle physics; triggering and data acquisition. *Mailing Add:* Dept Physics Rutgers Univ New Brunswick NJ 08903. *Fax:* 732-932-4343; *E-Mail:* watts@ruthep.rutgers.edu

**WATTSON, ROBERT K(EAN), JR,** MECHANICAL ENGINEERING. *Current Pos:* assoc chmn aeronaut eng & mech eng, 87-93, EMER PROF AEROSPACE ENG, TRI-STATE UNIV, 93- *Personal Data:* b Kansas City, Mo, Oct 18, 22; wid; c Robert K III, Keith H, Elsie A (Vezey), Vincent A, Meredith S (Lowry) & Bruce C. *Educ:* Okla Agr & Mech Col, BS, 46; Mass Inst Technol, SM, 48. *Prof Exp:* Under eng aide, US Engrs, Mo, 41-42; instr mech eng, Okla Agr & Mech Col, 46-47; asst aeronaut eng, Mass Inst Technol, 47-48; assoc prof mech eng, NDak Agr Col, 48-53; proj engr res dept, Cessna Aircraft Co, 53-56; assoc prof aeronaut eng, Univ Wichita, 56, chief engr & head eng res dept, 57-60; mgr short take-off & landing aerodyn, Boeing Co, Wichita Div, 60-61, mgr vertical take-off & landing aerodyn, 61-63; chief aerodyn, Lear Jet Industs, Inc, 63-64, chief tech staff, 64, chief res & develop, Aircraft Div, 64-67; design specialist adv design-com, Beech Aircraft Corp, 67-70; assoc chmn dept aeronaut eng, Tri-State Col, 70-78; staff tech specialist, Gates Lear-Jet Corp, 78-84; chmn dept mech eng technol, Oregon Inst Technol, 85-87. *Mem:* Soc Automotive Engrs; assoc fel Am Inst Aeronaut & Astronaut; Sigma Xi. *Res:* Vertical/short takeoff and landing aerodynamics; preliminary aerodynamic design. *Mailing Add:* 5004 W Robinson Wichita KS 67212

**WATWOOD, VERNON BELL, JR,** STRUCTURAL ENGINEERING. *Current Pos:* assoc prof, Mich Technol Univ, 73-80, prof civil eng & chmn dept, 80-91, dean eng, 91-93, PROF CIVIL ENG, MICH TECHNOL UNIV, 93- *Personal Data:* b Opelika, Ala, Sept 24, 35; m 58, Patricia Gent; c James, Yvonne & Teresa. *Educ:* Auburn Univ, BCE, 57; Cornell Univ, MS, 61; Univ Wash, PhD(eng), 66. *Prof Exp:* Asst prof civil eng, Miss State Univ, 61-62; engr, Boeing Co, Wash, 62-64; sr res engr, Esso Prod Res Co, Tex, 66-67; eng assoc, Pac Northwest Labs, Battelle Mem Inst, 67-70; lab mgr, Res Labs, Franklin Inst, Pa, 70-73. *Concurrent Pos:* Lectr, Grad Res Ctr, Wash, 69-70; consult, mining indust, 73-; ed, J Struct Eng, 92-94. *Mem:* Fel Am Soc Civil Engrs. *Res:* Finite element methods in stress analysis and dynamic response of structures; mathematical modeling and design of large surface mining and materials handling equipment such as draglines, shovels, conveyors and bucket-wheels. *Mailing Add:* Dept Civil Eng Mich Technol Univ Houghton MI 49931. *Fax:* 906-487-2943; *E-Mail:* vbwatwoo@mtu.edu

**WATZKE, ROBERT COIT,** OPHTHALMOLOGY. *Current Pos:* AT DEPT BIOL, ORE HEALTH SCI UNIV, PORTLAND. *Personal Data:* b Madison, Wis, Dec 19, 22; m 56; c 2. *Educ:* Univ Wis, BS, 50, MD, 52; Am Bd Ophthal, dipl, 57. *Prof Exp:* Intern, Med Ctr, Ind Univ, 52-53; resident, Univ Wis, 56; res asst ophthal, Harvard Med Sch, 56-57; from asst prof to assoc prof, Col Med, Univ Iowa, 66-73, prof ophthal, 73- *Mem:* Fel Am Acad Ophthal. *Res:* Clinical ophthalmology; retinal detachment and the vitreous humor of the eye. *Mailing Add:* Dept Ophthal Casey Eye Inst OHSU 3375 SW Terwilliger Blvd Portland OR 97201-4197

**WATZMAN, NATHAN,** PSYCHOPHARMACOLOGY, PHYSIOLOGY. *Current Pos:* RETIRED. *Personal Data:* b Powhattan Point, Ohio, Feb 15, 26; m 59; c 3. *Educ:* Univ Pittsburgh, BS, 47 & 55; MS, 57, PhD, 61. *Hon Degrees:* DSc, NY Col Podiatric Med, 77. *Prof Exp:* Asst prof pharmacol, Sch Pharm, Northeast La State Col, 59-63; res assoc prof, Sch Pharm, Univ Pittsburgh, 63-68; health sci adminr, Div Res Grants, NIH, 68-69, Bur Health Manpower Educ, 69-74; assoc dir regional progs, Div Assoc Health Professions, Health Resource Admin, 74-78, chief spec progs, 78-81; exec secy, Div Res Grants, NIH, 81-84, chief clin sci rev sect, 84-93. *Mem:* Am Soc Pharmacol & Exp Therapeut. *Res:* Drug interaction with stress and other environmental modifications of behavior. *Mailing Add:* 12015 Devilwood Dr Potomac MD 20854-3414

**WAUCHOPE, ROBERT DONALD,** PESTICIDE ENVIRONMENTAL CHEMISTRY, PESTICIDE SAFETY. *Current Pos:* RES CHEMIST, SOUTHERN WEED SCI LAB, SCI & EDUC ADMIN-AGR RES, USDA, 72- *Personal Data:* b Atlanta, Ga, Aug 31, 42; m 78, Mary; c Lora, Matt, Glen, Neal, Nancy & Carol. *Educ:* Univ NC, Chapel Hill, BS, 65; NC State Univ, MS, 68, PhD(phys chem), 70. *Prof Exp:* Agr chemist, Ore State Univ, 70-72. *Concurrent Pos:* Int Union Pure & Appl Chem; Coun Agr Sci & Tech. *Mem:* Am Chem Soc; Sigma Xi; AAAS; Weed Sci Soc Am. *Res:* Behavior and data of pesticides in soil and water; arsenical pesticides, food residues; nonpoint pollution of water by pesticides; environmental computer simulation modelling. *Mailing Add:* USDA Res Serv PO Box 748 Tifton CA 31793. *Fax:* 912-386-7225; *E-Mail:* don@tifton.cpes.peachnet.edu

**WAUD, BARBARA E,** ANESTHESIOLOGY. *Current Pos:* prof anesthesiol, 76-77, PROF PHARMACOL & ANESTHESIOL, UNIV MASS MED SCH, 77- *Personal Data:* b Kitchener, Ont, May 18, 31; US citizen; m 56; c 3. *Educ:* Univ Western Ont, MD, 56, cert, Am Bd Anesthesiol, 66. *Prof Exp:* Instr anesthesia, Sch Med, Boston Univ, 64-66; instr, Harvard Med Sch, 66-71, asst prof, 71-76. *Mem:* Am Soc Anesthesiologists; Asn Univ Anesthetists; AMA. *Res:* Mechanism of action and kinetics of drugs acting at the neuromuscular junction. *Mailing Add:* Dept Anesthesiol Med Sch Univ Mass 55 Lake Ave N Worcester MA 01655-0001

**WAUD, DOUGLAS RUSSELL,** PHARMACOLOGY. *Current Pos:* PROF PHARMACOL, MED SCH, UNIV MASS, 74- *Personal Data:* b London, Ont, Oct 21, 32; m 56; c 3. *Educ:* Univ Western Ont, MD, 56; Oxford Univ, DPhil(pharmacol), 64. *Prof Exp:* Intern, St Joseph's Hosp, London, Ont, 56-57; instr pharmacol, Harvard Med Sch, 59-60; demonstr, Oxford Univ, 61-63; from assoc to assoc prof, Harvard Med Sch, 63-74. *Concurrent Pos:* USPHS career develop award, 66- *Mem:* AAAS. *Res:* Mechanisms of drug action at molecular level; autonomic and cardiovascular pharmacology; neuromuscular junction physiology and pharmacology; anesthetic agents; uptake and distribution of drugs. *Mailing Add:* Dept Pharmacol Univ Mass Med Sch 55 Lake Ave N Worcester MA 01655-0002

**WAUGH, DOUGLAS OLIVER WILLIAM,** MEDICAL EDUCATION, PATHOLOGY. *Current Pos:* RETIRED. *Personal Data:* b Hove, Eng, Mar 21, 18; m 46, Sheila L Duff. *Educ:* McGill Univ, MD, CM, 42, MSc, 48, PhD(path), 50; Royal Col Physicians & Surgeons Can, cert path, 54; FRCP, 64. *Hon Degrees:* LLD, Dalhousie Univ, 92. *Honors & Awards:* Queen Elizabeth II Jubilee Medal, 77. *Prof Exp:* Demonstr & asst surg pathologist, Path Inst, McGill Univ, 46-47, assoc prof path, 51-57, Miranda Fraser assoc prof comp path, 57; assoc prof path, Univ & asst pathologist, Hosp, Univ Alta, 50-51; from assoc prof to prof, Queen's Univ, Can, 58-64; prof & head dept, Dalhousie Univ, 64-70; prof path & dean fac med, Queen's Univ, Ont, 70-75; exec dir, Asn Can Med Cols, 75-83. *Concurrent Pos:* Asst prov pathologist, Alta, 50-51; mem cancer diag clin, Alta Dept Health, 50-51; mem comt consults, Can Tumor Registry, 55-62; med mem adv comt tumor registry, Nat Cancer Inst, 56-62, dir inst, 65, pres, 74-76; dir labs, Hotel Dieu Hosp, Kingston, 58-64; chmn, Can Cytol Coun, 64-65; adj prof path, Univ Ottawa, 76-83; med journalist, editorialist & essayist, 83-; mem, Bd Accreditation, Can Assoc Univ Sch Nursing, 84-92. *Mem:* Am Soc Exp Pathologists; Am Asn Pathologists & Bacteriologists; Can Asn Pathologists; Int Acad Pathologists; sr mem Can Med Asn; Can Authors Asn (vpres, 92-). *Res:* Renal diseases; hypertension; lesions of experimental hypersensitivity; pathology of renal disease. *Mailing Add:* 183 Marlborough Ave Ottawa ON K1N 8G3 Can

**WAUGH, JOHN DAVID,** SOLID MECHANICS. *Current Pos:* assoc dean, Col Eng, Univ SC, 68-78, dean, 78-87, vprovost, 87-89, PROF ENG, UNIV SC, 58- *Personal Data:* b Charleston, WVa, Sept 20, 32; m 83, Sylvia Hill; c Debra, Donna & John David Jr. *Educ:* Univ SC, BS, 54; Yale Univ, MS, 62. *Honors & Awards:* Litman Award. *Prof Exp:* Stress Analyst Missiles Div, Bendix Corp, 56-58. *Concurrent Pos:* Bd dirs, Assoc Media-based Continuing Eng Educ, 76-, Engrs Deans Coun, 83-88, Nat Inst Eng Mgt, 88- *Mem:* Fel Am Soc Eng Educ; Am Soc Civil Engrs; Nat Soc Prof Engrs (vpres, 94-). *Mailing Add:* Univ SC Col Eng Columbia SC 29208. *Fax:* 803-777-0670

**WAUGH, JOHN LODOVICK THOMSON,** physical inorganic chemistry; deceased, see previous edition for last biography

**WAUGH, JOHN STEWART,** MAGNETIC RESONANCE. *Current Pos:* From instr to prof, Mass Inst Technol, 53-73, A A Noyes prof, 73-88, inst prof, 89-96, EMER INST PROF CHEM, MASS INST TECHNOL, 96- *Personal Data:* b Willimantic, Conn, Apr 25, 29; m 83, Susan Walsh; c Alice & Frederick. *Educ:* Dartmouth Col, AB, 49; Calif Inst Technol, PhD(chem, physics), 53. *Hon Degrees:* ScD, Dartmouth Col, 89. *Honors & Awards:* Robert A Welch Found Lectr, Univ Tex, 69; Irving Langmuir Award, Am Chem Soc, 76; Humboldt-Preis, 72; Falk-Plaut Lectr, Columbia Univ; Reilly Lectr, Univ Notre Dame, 78; Lucy Pickett Lectr, Mt Holyoke Col, 78; Pittsburgh Award in Spectros, 78; McElvain Lectr, Univ Wis, 81; G N Lewis Mem Lectr, Univ Calif, Berkeley, 82; Wolf Prize in Chem, 83-84; Pauling Medal, 84; Dreyfus Lectr, Dartmouth Col, 84; Kistiakowsky Lectr, Harvard Univ, 85; McDowell Lectr, BC, 88; Baker Lectr, Cornell Univ, 90; Richards Medal, 92. *Concurrent Pos:* Sloan res fel, 58-62; assoc, Retina Found, 61-70; vis scientist, USSR Acad Sci, Moscow, 62 & 75; Guggenheim fel & res assoc physics, Univ Calif, Berkeley, 63-64, mem, Sci & Educ Adv Comt, 81-87; consult, Lawrence Radiation Lab, Univ Calif, 64-75; ed, Advan Magnetic Resonance, 65-88; mem, Chem Rev Panel, Argonne Nat Lab, 70-74, chmn, 73-74; vis prof & Humboldt fel, Max Planck Inst Med Res, 72; adv comt mem, Nat Magnet Lab, 76-80, Stanford Magnetic Resonance Lab, 76-, Magnetic Resonance Ctr, Univ SC, 78-82 & Lawrence Berkeley Lab, 80-87; mem, Fel Adv Panel, Alfred P Sloan Found, 77-; mem sci & educ adv comt, Univ Calif, 81-; adv prof, East China Normal Univ, Shanghai, 84; chmn, Div Chem Phys, Am Phys Soc, 84; Joliot-Curie prof, Ecolesuperieure Physics & Chem, Paris, 85; Fairchild scholar, Calif Inst Technol, 89. *Mem:* Nat Acad Sci; fel Am Acad Arts & Sci; Am Phys Soc; AAAS; Int Soc Magnetic Resonance. *Res:* Magnetic resonance; theory and applications to chemistry. *Mailing Add:* Conant Rd Lincoln MA 01773-3909. *E-Mail:* waugh@wccf.mit.edu

**WAUGH, MARGARET H,** cardiovascular & gastro-intestinal pharmacology, for more information see previous edition

**WAUGH, WILLIAM HOWARD,** PHYSIOLOGY, INTERNAL MEDICINE. *Current Pos:* dir clin sci, 71-76, PROF MED & PHYSIOL, SCH MED, ECAROLINA UNIV, 71- *Personal Data:* b New York, NY, May 13, 25; m 52, Eileen Garrigan; c Mark H, Kathleen C & William P. *Educ:* Tufts Col, MD, 48. *Honors & Awards:* Founder's Award, Am Heart Asn, 82. *Prof Exp:* Intern internal med, Long Island Col Hosp, 48-49, asst resident, 50-51; asst resident med, Univ Md Hosp, 51-52; cardiovasc trainee, Med Col Ga, 54-55, asst res prof physiol, 55-60, USPHS sr res fel, 59-60, assoc med, 57-60; from assoc prof to prof med, Col Med, Univ Ky, 60-71, head renal div, 60-68, Ky Heart Asn chair cardiovasc res, 63-71. *Concurrent Pos:* Estab investr, Ga Heart Asn, Med Col Ga, 58, physician in charge hemodialysis sect, 59-60; chmn, Policy Rev Comt Human Res, ECarolina Univ, 72-90. *Mem:* Microcirculatory Soc; Am Soc Nephrology; Am Physiol Soc; Am Heart Asn; fel Am Col Physicians; AAAS. *Res:* Hemodynamics; circulatory and renal physiology; nephrology; adjuvant therapy in acute lung edema; antisickling agents in sickle cell hemoglobinopathy; kidney blood flow regulation; smooth muscle tone and vasoprotection. *Mailing Add:* ECarolina Univ Sch Med Greenville NC 27858-4354. *Fax:* 919-816-3460

**WAUQUIER, ALBERT,** SLEEP RESEARCH, NEUROPHARMACOLOGY OF EPILEPSY. *Current Pos:* PROF NEUROL, TEX TECH UNIV HEALTH SCI CTR, 94-, DIR, SLEEP CTR, 94- *Personal Data:* b Menen, Belg, Feb 17, 40; m 63, Annie J Rooryck; c Ingc. *Educ:* Univ Ghent, Belg, BS, 68, MS, 70; Univ Nijmegen, Neth, PhD(pharmacol/psychol), 76. *Prof Exp:* Staff researcher, Janssen Pharmaceutica, 70-86, dir neuropsychopharmacol, 87-90; prof neurol, Med Col Ohio, 91-94, prof psychiat, 92-94. *Concurrent Pos:* Sci adv, Epilepsy Ctr, Kempenhaeghe, 79-; adj prof anesthesiol & pharmacol, Univ Louisville, 85-; adj prof anesthesiol, Univ Utah, 85-; prof, Univ Leiden, Neth, 89-90; consult, Epilepsy Br, NIH, 93- *Mem:* Dutch Soc Clin Neurophysiol; Europ Sleep Res Soc; Am Soc Sleep Res; Am Sleep Disorders Asn; NY Acad Sci; Int Brain Res Orgn. *Res:* Electroencephalographic dynamics of sleep in humans from wake to sleep and through sleep using newly developed quantitative analysis; neuropharmacology of sleep; neurotransmitters; neuropharmacological research on epilepsy; kindling seizure model. *Mailing Add:* Dept Neurol Tex Tech Univ Health Sci Ctr 3601 Fourth St Lubbock TX 79430-0002. *Fax:* 419-536-2460

**WAVE, HERBERT EDWIN,** ENTOMOLOGY, PLANT PATHOLOGY. *Current Pos:* RETIRED. *Personal Data:* b Portsmouth, NH, Oct 13, 23; m 47; c 1. *Educ:* Univ Maine, BS, 52; Rutgers Univ, MS, 60, PhD(entom), 61. *Prof Exp:* Entomologist, USDA, 52-58; res asst entom, Rutgers Univ, 58-61; entomologist, USDA, 61-62; asst prof entom, Univ Mass, 62-67; assoc prof plant & soil sci, Univ Maine, 67-86. *Concurrent Pos:* Emer ext edur, Fruit Specialist. *Mem:* Sigma Xi. *Res:* Biology and ecology of potato infesting species of aphids; extension pest control for tree and small fruits; orchard herbicides and growth regulators. *Mailing Add:* PO Box 448 East Winthrop ME 04343-0448

**WAVERING, ALBERT,** MECHANICAL ENGINEERING. *Current Pos:* GROUP LEADER, NAT INST STAND & TECHNOL, 85- *Personal Data:* b June 20, 61. *Educ:* Univ Ill, MS, 85. *Res:* Robotics and machine tools. *Mailing Add:* Nat Inst Stand & Technol Rte 270 Bldg 220 Gaithersburg MD 20899

**WAVRIK, JOHN J,** COMPUTER ALGEBRA. *Current Pos:* ASSOC PROF MATH, UNIV CALIF, SAN DIEGO, 69- *Personal Data:* b New York, NY, Mar 17, 41; m 61, Mary Fischer; c Diane & Jayin. *Educ:* Johns Hopkins Univ, AB, 61, MA, 64; Stanford Univ, PhD(math), 66. *Prof Exp:* Joseph Fells Ritt instr math, Columbia Univ, 66-69. *Mem:* Am Math Soc; Math Asn Am. *Res:* Algebraic geometry; computers in pure mathematics. *Mailing Add:* Dept Math 0112 Univ Calif San Diego 9500 Gilman Dr La Jolla CA 92093-0001. *E-Mail:* jjwavrik@ucsd.edu

**WAWERSIK, WOLFGANG R,** ROCK MECHANICS. *Current Pos:* mem tech staff, Sandia Nat Labs, 74-83, distinguished mem tech staff, 83-86, supvr, Geomech Div, 86-92, MGR, SANDIA NAT LABS, 92- *Personal Data:* b Frankenholz, Ger, Apr 23, 36; US citizen; m 65, Carol J; c Stefan & Matthew. *Educ:* Tech Hochsch Aachen, Ger, Dipl-Ing, 61, Univ Minn, MS, 63, PhD(mineral eng/rock mech), 68. *Prof Exp:* Res assoc, Dept Earth & Planetary Sci, Mass Inst Technol, 68-69; from asst prof to assoc prof mech eng, Dept Mech & Indust Eng, Univ Utah, 69-74. *Concurrent Pos:* Vis scientist, Fed Inst Geosci & Natural Resources, Hannover, Ger, 80. *Mem:* Am Inst Mining, Metall & Petrol Engrs; Am Geophys Union; Sigma Xi; Int Soc Rock Mech. *Res:* Experimental rock mechanics. *Mailing Add:* 410 Live Oak Loop NE Albuquerque NM 87122. *Fax:* 505-844-7354; *E-Mail:* wrwawer@sandia.gov

**WAWNER, FRANKLIN EDWARD, JR,** MATERIALS SCIENCE, COMPOSITES. *Current Pos:* res prof, 71-97, EMER PROF, COMPOSITE MAT, DEPT MAT SCI, UNIV VA, 97- *Personal Data:* b Petersburg, Va, Dec 12, 33; m 53, Frances Cuddihy; c Scott, Mark & Susan. *Educ:* Randolph-Macon Col, BS, 59; Univ Va, MS, 68, PhD(mat sci), 71. *Prof Exp:* Physicist, Army Eng Res & Develop Lab, 59-61; sr physicist, Texaco Exp Inc, 61-66. *Concurrent Pos:* Consult, Textron Spec Mat, Lowell, Mass, 69- & various other corps. *Mem:* Metall Soc; Am Ceramic Soc; Am Soc Metal. *Res:* Composite materials; chemical vapor deposition; characterization of mechanical properties; fracture; structure; microstructure. *Mailing Add:* Dept Mat Sci Thornton Hall Univ Va Charlottesville VA 22903. *Fax:* 804-982-5660; *E-Mail:* few@virginia.edu

**WAWSZKIEWICZ, EDWARD JOHN,** MICROBIOLOGY, BIOCHEMISTRY. *Current Pos:* ASSOC PROF MICROBIOL, UNIV ILL MED CTR, 70- *Personal Data:* b North Smithfield, RI, Feb 10, 33. *Educ:* Harvard Univ, AB, 54; Univ Calif, Berkeley, PhD, 61. *Prof Exp:* Asst microbiol, Hopkins Marine Sta, Stanford Univ, 54-55; res asst microbiol, Univ Calif, Berkeley, 55-61; USPHS fel, Max Planck Inst Cell Chem, Ger, 61-63; resident res assoc, Argonne Nat Lab, 64-66; asst mem, Inst Biomed Res, 66-70. *Mem:* AAAS; Am Soc Microbiol; fel Am Inst Chemists; Am Inst Biol Sci; Am Chem Soc. *Res:* Metabolism of thiobacilli; erythritol metabolism by propionibacteria; propionate metabolism; erythromycin biosynthesis; mouse salmonellosis, iron metabolism; pacifarins; enology. *Mailing Add:* Dept Microbiol Univ Ill Chicago Col Med 901 S Walcott Ave Chicago IL 60612-7340

**WAX, HARRY,** biochemistry; deceased, see previous edition for last biography

**WAX, JOAN,** CLINICAL INVESTIGATION, PHARMACOLOGY. *Current Pos:* RETIRED. *Personal Data:* b Detroit, Mich, Sept 14, 21. *Educ:* Wayne State Univ, BA, 43; Univ NC, MS, 47. *Prof Exp:* From res asst to res pharmacologist, Parke, Davis & Co, 47-76, sr scientist & clin pharmacologist, 77-80, clin scientist, Parke-Davis Pharmaceut Res Div, Warner-Lambert Co, 80-86. *Mem:* AAAS; Am Soc Pharmacol & Exp Therapeut; Am Chem Soc; Sigma Xi. *Res:* Analgetic and anti-inflammatory agents; narcotic antagonists; drug-induced gastrointestinal ulcerogenesis; clinical investigation regarding drugs in arthritis, dysmenorrhea. *Mailing Add:* 301 N Roadrunner Pkwy Apt 607 Las Cruces NM 88011-9054

**WAX, ROBERT LEROY,** SPACE PHYSICS. *Current Pos:* consult physicist, 73-78, SR STAFF SYST ENGR, DEFENSE & SPACE SYSTS GROUP, TRW INC, 78- *Personal Data:* b Des Moines, Iowa, July 7, 38. *Educ:* Calif Inst Technol, BS, 60; Univ Ill, Urbana, MS, 61; Univ Calif, Berkeley, PhD(physics), 65. *Prof Exp:* Mem tech staff, TRW Systs Group, 66-71; physicist, Space Environ Lab, Nat Oceanic & Atmospheric Admin, 71-73. *Mem:* Am Geophys Union. *Mailing Add:* 201 S Poinsettia Ave Manhattan Beach CA 90266

**WAXDAL, M J,** FLOW CYTOMETRY, CLINICAL TRIALS. *Current Pos:* CHIEF EXEC OFFICER, FAST SYSTS, INC, 86- *Personal Data:* b San Francisco, Calif, Dec 8, 37; div; c Peter & Michael. *Educ:* Univ Wash, BS, 60, PhD(biochem), 65. *Prof Exp:* Res assoc, Rockefeller Univ, 65-69, asst prof, 69-72; sr staff fel, Nat Inst Allergy & Infectious Diseases, 72-74, sr investr, 74-86. *Concurrent Pos:* Fel, Japanese Asn Prom Sci, 81. *Mem:* NY Acad Sci; Am Soc Biochem & Molecular Biol; Am Chem Soc; Int Soc Analytical Cytometry; Clin Cytometry Soc; AAAS. *Res:* Applications of flow cytometry to medical and biological investigations; provide laboratory support for clinical trials; quality assurance programs for high complexity clinical testing. *Mailing Add:* 8-5 Metropolitan Ct Gaithersburg MD 20878-4022. *Fax:* 301-977-7023

**WAXLER, GLENN LEE,** VETERINARY PATHOLOGY. *Current Pos:* from instr to assoc prof vet path, 57-66, prof, 66-90, EMER PROF PATH, MICH STATE UNIV, 90- *Personal Data:* b Olney, Ill, Feb 24, 25; m 46, Gwendolyn L McKinley; c Susan M (Stahl) & Karol K (Mikula). *Educ:* Univ Ill, BS, 51, DVM, 53; Mich State Univ, MS, 59, PhD(vet path), 61. *Prof Exp:* Pvt pract, 53-57. *Mem:* Am Vet Med Asn; Am Col Vet Path; Asn Gnotobiotics. *Res:* Germ-free research; enteric disease of swine; histopathology of diseases of domestic animals. *Mailing Add:* 1889 Creek Landing Haslett MI 48840-9765

**WAXMAN, ALAN DAVID,** NUCLEAR MEDICINE. *Current Pos:* asst prof, 68-70, ASSOC PROF RADIOL, SCH MED, UNIV SOUTHERN CALIF, 70-; DIR NUCLEAR MED, CEDARS-SINAI MED CTR, 77- *Personal Data:* b New York, NY, Mar 9, 38; m 61; c 3. *Educ:* Univ Southern Calif, BA, 58, MD, 63. *Prof Exp:* Intern med, Los Angeles County Gen Hosp, 63-64; resident med, Los Angeles Vet Admin Hosp, 64-65; res assoc metab, Metab Serv, Cancer Inst, NIH, 65-67. *Concurrent Pos:* Staff physician radiol, Los Angeles Co-Univ Southern Calif Med Ctr, 78- *Mem:* Soc Nuclear Med; Am Fedn Clin Res; AMA; fel Am Col Physicians; Am Col Nuclear Physicians. *Res:* Applications of nuclear medicine technology in the detection and evaluation of disease processes, primarily in oncology and hepatic disease. *Mailing Add:* 8700 Beverly Blvd Los Angeles CA 90048-1804

**WAXMAN, DAVID,** INTERNAL MEDICINE, CARDIOLOGY. *Current Pos:* Instr internal med, Med Ctr, Univ Kans, 61-64, asst prof, 64-69, asst dean, 70-71, assoc dean, 71-72, dean, 72-74, vchancellor students, 74-76, vchancellor, 76-77, dep exec vchancellor, 77, EXEC VCHANCELLOR, MED CTR, UNIV KANS, 77- *Personal Data:* b Albany, NY, Feb 7, 18; m 50; c 6. *Educ:* Syracuse Univ, BS, 42; Syracuse Col Med, MD, 50. *Concurrent Pos:* Consult, Vet Admin Hosp, 61- & Muson Army Hosp, 79-; assoc prof internal med, Med Ctr, Univ Kans, 69-77, dir med outpatient serv, 70-74 & prof internal med, 77-; major gen mobilization & augmentee to surgeon gen, USAF, 70-78, nat consult educ to surgeon gen, 80- *Mem:* AMA; Am Soc Internal Med; fel Am Col Physicians; Sigma Xi. *Res:* Non-invasive methods and techniques for the evaluation and assessment of cardiac disfunction; drug inhibition of fatty acid mobilization and catecholamine-induced metabolic changes in humans. *Mailing Add:* Kans Univ Med Ctr 3901 Rainbow Blvd Kansas City KS 66160-0001

**WAXMAN, HERBERT SUMNER,** medicine, hematology, for more information see previous edition

**WAXMAN, LLOYD H,** PROTEASES, PROTEIN CHEMISTRY. *Current Pos:* SR RES ASSOC, SCH MED, HARVARD UNIV, 81- *Educ:* Harvard Univ, PhD(biochem), 75. *Mailing Add:* Dept Biochem Merck Res Labs WP26-431 West Point PA 19486. *Fax:* 215-661-6913

**WAXMAN, RONALD,** DIGITAL SYSTEM SPECIFICATION & ANALYSIS, COMPUTER HARDWARE DESCRIPTION LANGUAGES. *Current Pos:* PRIN SCIENTIST, UNIV VA, 87- *Personal Data:* b Newark, NJ, Nov 28, 33; m 55; c 3. *Educ:* NJ Inst Technol, BS, 55; Syracuse Univ, MS, 63. *Prof Exp:* Mem eng staff, Int Bus Mach, 55-87. *Concurrent Pos:* Chair, Design Automation Stand Subcomt, Inst Elec & Electronics Engrs Comput Soc, 83-88, Tech Comt, 88-90, lectr, 86-88, mem bd gov, 89-93; mem adv bd, Spec Interest Group Design Automation, Asn Comput Mach, 88- *Mem:* Fel Inst Elec & Electronics Engrs; Inst Elec & Electronics Engrs Comput Soc; Asn Comput Mach. *Res:* Methods of designing digital systems; application of hardware description languages to the design process; system specification and design. *Mailing Add:* 2369 Paddock Lane Reston VA 22091-2607

**WAXMAN, SAMUEL,** HEMATOLOGY, ONCOLOGY. *Current Pos:* CLIN PROF MED, MT SINAI SCH MED, 83-; HEAD, CANCER CHEMOTHER FOUND LAB, 72- *Educ:* State Univ NY Downstate Med Ctr, MD, 63. *Res:* Differentiation therapy. *Mailing Add:* Med Dept Mt Sinai Sch Med New York NY 10029. *Fax:* 212-996-5787

**WAXMAN, SIDNEY,** ORNAMENTAL HORTICULTURE. *Current Pos:* RETIRED. *Personal Data:* b Providence, RI, Nov 13, 23; m 48; c 3. *Educ:* Univ RI, BS, 51; Cornell Univ, MS, 54, PhD(ornamental hort), 57. *Honors & Awards:* Merit Award, Int Plant Propagator's Soc. *Prof Exp:* Prof Ornamental Hort, Univ Conn. *Mem:* Am Soc Hort Sci; hon mem Int Plant Propagators Soc; Am Conifer Soc. *Res:* Photoperiodism; plant propagation; seed and bud dormancy; development of dwarf forms of conifers their introduction and propagation. *Mailing Add:* 51 Cod Fish Falls Rd Mansfield CT 06268

**WAXMAN, STEPHEN GEORGE,** MOLECULAR & CELLULAR NEUROSCIENCE, ION CHANNEL BIOLOGY. *Current Pos:* PROF NEUROL & CHMN DEPT, SCH MED, YALE UNIV & NEUROLOGIST-IN-CHIEF, YALE-NEW HAVEN HOSP, 86-, DIR, NEUROSCI RES CTR, VET ADMIN MED CTR, WEST HAVEN, 86- *Personal Data:* b Newark, NJ, Aug 17, 45; m 68; c 2. *Educ:* Harvard Univ, AB, 67; Albert Einstein Col Med, PhD(neurosci), 70, MD, 72. *Hon Degrees:* MA, Yale Univ, 86. *Honors & Awards:* First Ann Trgyve Tuve Mem Award, Inst Advan Educ Sci, NIH, 75; Nat Inst Neurol & Stroke Res Career Develop Award, 75; Dana Alliance on Brain Initiatives, 93. *Prof Exp:* Res asst biophys, McLean Hosp, Harvard Med Sch, 65-67, clin fel neurol, 72-75, from asst prof to assoc prof, 75-78; res fel neurosci, Albert Einstein Col Med, 70-72; prof neurol & assoc chmn, Stanford Med Sch & chief, neurol, Vet Admin Hosp, Palo Alto, 81-86. *Concurrent Pos:* Epilepsy Found Chauveau

fel, Med Res Coun Cerebral Functions Res Group, Univ Col London, 69; res fel neurosci, Mass Inst Technol, 74-75, from vis asst prof to vis assoc prof biol, 75-78; mem, Comt Decade Brain, Am Acad Neurol & Bd Sci Counselors, Nat Inst Neurol Dis &Stroke, 90-, Bd Biobehav Sci, Inst Med, 91-; estab investr, Nat Mult Sclerosis Soc, 87; fel, Stroke Coun, Am Heart Asn, 92-, US Nat Comt, Int Brain Res Orgn, 92- *Mem:* Inst Med-Nat Acad Sci; Am Acad Neurol; Asn Res Nerv & Ment Dis (pres, 92); Soc Neurosci; Asn Univ Prof Neurol; Am Neurol Asn; fel Royal Soc Med. *Res:* Molecular and cellular organization of the nervous system, with emphasis on understanding recovery of function after injury to the nervous system. *Mailing Add:* Dept Neurol LCI 707 Yale Med Sch PO Box 3333 New Haven CT 06510. *Fax:* 203-785-5694

**WAY, E LEONG,** PHARMACOLOGY, TOXICOLOGY. *Current Pos:* from asst prof to prof pharmacol & toxicol, Med Ctr, Univ Calif, San Francisco, 49-87, vchmn dept, 57-67, chmn dept, 73-78, EMER PROF PHARMACOL & TOXICOL, MED CTR, UNIV CALIF, SAN FRANCISCO, 87- *Personal Data:* b Watsonville, Calif, July 10, 16; m 44, Madeline Li; c Eric & Linette. *Educ:* Univ Calif, BS, 38, MS, 40, PhD(pharmaceut chem), 42. *Honors & Awards:* Am Pharmaceut Found Award, 62; Ebert Prize Cert, Am Pharmaceut Asn, 62; Kauffman lectr, Ohio State Univ, 66; Forbes lectr, Va Commonwealth Univ, 78; Cultural Citation & Gold Medal, Ministry Educ, Repub China, 78; Nathan B Eddy Mem Award, Col Probs Drug Dependence, 79; Sterling-Sullivan lectr, Morehouse Sch Med, Martin Luther King Univ, 82; Pfizer lectr, Univ Miss, 82; Paul K Smith lectr, George Wash Univ, 83; Torald Sollman Award, Am Soc Pharmacol & Exp Therapeut, 93. *Prof Exp:* Asst pharmacol, Univ Calif, 42; pharmaceut chemist, Merck & Co, Inc, NJ, 42-43; from instr to asst prof pharmacol, Med Sch, George Washington Univ, 43-48. *Concurrent Pos:* USPHS spec res fel, Univ Bern, 55-56; China Med Bd res fel, Univ Hong Kong, 62-63; consult, Attorney Gen, Calif, 59-60 & Dept Corrections, Calif, 64-70; mem, Comt Probs Drug Safety, Nat Acad Sci-Nat Res Coun, 65-71 & Comt Probs Drug Dependence, 68-74, 77- & chmn bd, 78-82; mem, Comt on Abuse of Depressant & Stimulant Drugs, HEW, 66-68, mem, Pharmacol Study Sect, 66-70, chmn, 68-70, mem, Comt on Narcotic Addiction & Drug Abuse Rev, 70-74, chmn, 71-74; mem, Sci Adv Comt Drugs, Bur Narcotics & Dangerous Drugs, 68-74; mem, Alcohol & Drug Dependence Serv Adv Group & Merit Rev Bd, Vet Admin, 71-76; mem, Controlled Substances Adv Comt, Food & Drug Admin, 74-78; Sullivan-Sterling distinguished vis prof, Morehouse Sch Med, 81-82; hon prof pharmacol & neurosci, Guangzhou Med Col, 86; vis prof neuropsychopharmacol, Gunma Univ Med Sch, Japan, 89-90; sr staff fel, Nat Inst Drug Abuse, 90; bd dirs, Li Found, 70-, pres, 85-; mem, Nat Adv Coun, Am Bur Med Advan China, 81-; secy, Int Narcotic Res Conf, 83-87, treas, 87- *Mem:* Fel AAAS; Am Soc Pharmacol & Exp Therapeut (pres, 76-77); Am Pharmaceut Asn; fel Am Col Neuropsychopharmacol; Fed Am Soc Exp Biol (pres, 77-78). *Res:* Drug metabolism; pharmacology analgetics, and endophins; drug tolerance and physical dependence mechanisms; approximately 400 publications including several books. *Mailing Add:* Dept Pharmacol Univ Calif San Francisco CA 94143-0450

**WAY, FREDERICK, III,** COMPUTER SCIENCE. *Current Pos:* from assoc prof to prof, 56-88, from assoc dir to dir Jennings Comput Ctr, 56-88, EMER PROF COMPUT ENG & SCI, CASE WESTERN RES UNIV, 88- *Personal Data:* b Sewickley, Pa, Jan 4, 25; m 48, Nellie Shaffer; c Jay F & Robert S. *Educ:* Univ Pittsburgh, BS, 50. *Prof Exp:* Physicist, Babcock & Wilcox Co, 51-54, anal eng, Res Lab, 54-56. *Concurrent Pos:* Consult, Thompson Ramo Wooldridge Co, 59 & Bailey Meter Co, 60- *Mem:* Soc Indust & Appl Math; Asn Comput Mach; Math Asn Am; Sigma Xi. *Res:* Investigation and implementation of automatic programming methods for digital computers. *Mailing Add:* 1258 Castleton Rd Cleveland Heights OH 44121-1524. *E-Mail:* fxw3@po.cwru.edu

**WAY, GEORGE H,** ENGINEERING. *Current Pos:* RETIRED. *Personal Data:* b Wheeling, WVa, May 30, 30; m 53; c 1. *Educ:* Princeton Univ, BSE, 52. *Prof Exp:* Staff mem, Pa Railroad Co, 54-66; res engr, Planning Dept, Chessie Syst, 66-73; asst to vpres, Asn Am Railroads, 73-83, sr asst vpres, 83-85, vpres, Res & Test Dept, 85-92. *Concurrent Pos:* Fel, Permanent Way Inst, 71. *Mem:* Am Railroad Eng Asn. *Res:* Concrete cross tie design and performance; development of automated railway track geometry and assessment techniques; design and evaluation of epoxy glued insulating rail joints; railway track design, construction and maintenance. *Mailing Add:* 1015 St George Barber Rd Davidsonville MD 21035

**WAY, JAMES LEONG,** PHARMACOLOGY, TOXICOLOGY. *Current Pos:* SHELTON PROF PHARMACOL & TOXICOL, DEPT PHARMACOL & TOXICOL, TEX A&M UNIV, 82- *Personal Data:* b Watsonville, Calif, Mar 21, 26; m 92, Diana; c Lori, Jan & Lani. *Educ:* Univ Calif, Berkeley, BA, 51; George Washington Univ, PhD(pharmacol), 55. *Prof Exp:* NIH Nat Cancer Inst fel pharmacol, Univ Wis, 55-57, sr fel, 57-58, from instr to asst prof pharmacol, 59-62; assoc prof, Marquette Med Sch, 62-67; prof pharmacol, Wash State Univ, 67-82. *Concurrent Pos:* USPHS career develop award, 58-62, spec res fel, 73-75; mem, Fed Task Group Toxicol Eval Pesticide Mammalian Species, Environ Protection Agency, 73-75; vis scientist, Div Molecular Pharmacol, Nat Inst Med Res, London, 75-77; mem, Toxicol Study Sect, NIH, 74-78, Toxicol Data Bank Rev Comt, 74-82; pres, Western Pharmacol Soc, 76; mem sci adv bd, Nat Ctr Toxicol Res, 79-82; mem exec bd, Nat Ctr Toxicol Res, 80-82, Environ Health Sci Comt Study Sect, NIH, 85-89; vis prof, NSF, 81-82; Joseph H Shelton endowed chair toxicol, Tex A&M Univ, 82; distinguished scholar, Nat Acad Sci, 85-87; Rockefeller res scholar, Rockefeller Found, 87; assoc ed, Ann Rev Pharmacol & Toxicol, 89-94; pres, Int Soc Carrier Cells, 93- *Mem:* AAAS; Am Chem Soc; Am Soc Pharmacol & Exp Therapeut (secy & treas, 89); Soc Toxicol; Int Soc Resealed Erythuocytes (pres, 96). *Res:* Drug metabolism and anticholinesterase alkylphosphate antagonists; cyanide, nitrite alkylphosphate and hydrogen sulfide, carbon monoxide, poisoning & treatment; molecular and marine pharmacology; environmental toxicology; drug carrier cells. *Mailing Add:* Dept Med Pharmacol & Toxicol Med Sci Bldg Tex A&M Univ College Station TX 77843-1114. *Fax:* 409-845-0699; *E-Mail:* jlway@tamu.edu

**WAY, JON LEONG,** PEDIATRIC DENTISTRY, PUBLIC HEALTH LEAD DENTIST. *Current Pos:* INSTR PEDIAT DENT, UNIV WASH, 93- *Personal Data:* b Madison, Wis, Feb 15, 61. *Educ:* Wash State Univ, BS, 83; Univ Wash, DDS, 87; Univ Calif, Los Angeles, MS, 93. *Prof Exp:* Res technician, Sch Pharm, Wash State Univ, 78-83; lead dentist, Seattle-King Co Dept Pub Health, 88-91. *Concurrent Pos:* Instr pediat dent, Sch Dent, Univ Wash, 90; tribal pediat dent, 93- *Mem:* Am Asn Pediat Dent. *Res:* Cyanide toxicity and its antagonism; selective toxic of squoxin; bond strengths of light cured glass ionomers. *Mailing Add:* 6527 Sunnyside Ave N Seattle WA 98103

**WAY, KATHARINE,** physics; deceased, see previous edition for last biography

**WAY, KERMIT R,** PHYSICAL CHEMISTRY, ATOMIC PHYSICS. *Current Pos:* COMPUT, US GOVT, 91- *Personal Data:* b Detriot, Mich, Sept 21, 39; m 77; c 1. *Educ:* Luther Col, BA, 61; Mich State Univ, MSc, 65; Univ Iowa, PhD(phys chem), 76. *Prof Exp:* Res chemist, Chrysler Corp Detroit, Mich, 61-62; instr, Concordia Col Minn, 64-65; lectr, Waterloo Lutheran Univ, Ont, Can, 65-69; asst prof, Drake Univ Iowa, 75-76; res assoc, Mass Inst Technol, 76-78; asst prof, Augustana, SDak, 79-84; sr proj engr, Bendix Field Corp, Columbia, MD, 84-91. *Concurrent Pos:* Vis asst prof, Carthage Col, Wis, 78-79. *Mem:* Am Phys Soc; Am Chem Soc; Soc Photo-Optical Instrumentation Engrs. *Res:* Optical recording and developmental optical recording systems technical advisors for development from optical recording system. *Mailing Add:* 6100 Fox Point Rd Fredericksburg VA 22407-8330

**WAY, LAWRENCE WELLESLEY,** SURGERY. *Current Pos:* Clin instr, 67-69, from asst prof to assoc prof, 69-75, PROF SURG, SCH MED, UNIV CALIF, SAN FRANCISCO, 75-, VCHMN DEPT, 72-; CHIEF SURG SERV, VET ADMIN HOSP, SAN FRANCISCO, 72- *Personal Data:* b St Louis, Mo, Nov 15, 33; m 71; c 2. *Educ:* Cornell Univ, AB, 55; Univ Buffalo, MD, 59. *Concurrent Pos:* Fel gastrointestinal physiol, Univ Calif, San Francisco, 67-68 & Vet Admin Ctr, Univ Calif, Los Angeles, 68-69; mem, Surg & Bioengineering Study Sect, NIH, 81-85. *Mem:* Am Col Surg; Am Gastroenterol Asn; Am Surg Asn; Soc Surg Alimentary Tract; Soc Univ Surgeons. *Res:* Gastrointestinal secretion; bile formation. *Mailing Add:* Dept Surg Univ Calif 680-A San Francisco CA 94143

**WAY, WALTER,** ANESTHESIOLOGY, PHARMACOLOGY. *Current Pos:* from instr to asst prof anesthesia, 61-63, from asst prof to assoc prof, 63-74, PROF ANESTHESIA & PHARMACOL, MED CTR, UNIV CALIF, SAN FRANCISCO, 74- *Personal Data:* b Rochester, NY, June 27, 31; m 55; c 3. *Educ:* Univ Buffalo, BS, 53; State Univ NY, MD, 57; Univ Calif, MS, 62. *Prof Exp:* USPHS trainee pharmacol, 60-61. *Mem:* Am Soc Pharmacol & Exp Therapeut; Asn Univ Anesthetists. *Res:* Opioid clinical pharmacology. *Mailing Add:* Box 191 Ross CA 94957. *Fax:* 415-476-7378

**WAYE, JOHN STEWART,** MOLECULAR GENETICS OF HUMAN DISEASE, DNA DIAGNOSIS. *Current Pos:* ASST PROF PATH, MCMASTER UNIV, 90-; CO-DIR, PROV HEMOGLOBINOPATHY DNA DIAG LAB, MCMASTER UNIV MED CTR, 90- *Personal Data:* m 83, Jane Richardson; c Andrew W & Stacey M. *Educ:* Univ Guelph, BSc, 81; McMaster Univ, MSc, 84; Univ Toronto, PhD(med genetics), 87. *Prof Exp:* Res scientist molecular genetics, Cent Forensic Lab, Royal Can Mounted Police, 88-90. *Concurrent Pos:* Consult, Royal Can Mounted Police, 90-91; Ctr Forensic Sci, Toronto, 90- *Mem:* Am Soc Human Genetics; Am Acad Forensic Sci. *Res:* Genetic determinants of the clinical severity of B-thalassemia and other globin gene disorders; forensic identity testing using highly polymorphic DNA markers. *Mailing Add:* McMaster Univ Med Ctr Rm 2N33 1200 Main St W Hamilton ON L8N 3Z5 Can. *Fax:* 905-577-0198

**WAYGOOD, EDWARD BRUCE,** BIOCHEMISTRY, MICROBIOLOGY. *Current Pos:* ASST PROF BIOCHEM, UNIV SASK, 77- *Personal Data:* b Macclesfield, Eng, Dec 15, 45; Can citizen; m 73; c 2. *Educ:* Univ Man, BSc, 68, MSc, 69; Univ Toronto, PhD(med biol), 73. *Prof Exp:* Fel biol, Johns Hopkins Univ, 74-77. *Concurrent Pos:* Med Res Coun Can grant, 74-76 & 76-78. *Res:* Microbial physiology; microbial transport; metabolic regulation; bacterial sugar-phosphotransference system. *Mailing Add:* Dept Biochem Health Sci Bldg Univ Sask 107 Wiggins Rd Rm A3 Saskatoon SK S7N 0W0 Can

**WAYGOOD, ERNEST ROY,** PLANT PHYSIOLOGY, BIOCHEMISTRY. *Current Pos:* prof, 54-79, EMER PROF BOT, UNIV MAN, 79- *Personal Data:* b Bramhall, Eng, Oct 26, 18; m 50; c 1. *Educ:* Ont Agr Col, BSc, 41; Univ Toronto, MSc, 47, PhD, 49. *Prof Exp:* Assoc prof plant physiol, McGill Univ, 49-54. *Mem:* Can Soc Plant Physiol (pres, 59-60); fel Inst Can; fel Royal Soc Can; Am Soc Plant Physiol; Sigma Xi. *Res:* Enzyme mechanisms in respiration and photosynthesis; physiology of host parasite relationships. *Mailing Add:* 802-1245 Quayside Dr New Westminster BC V3M 6J6 Can

**WAYLAND, BRADFORD B,** INORGANIC CHEMISTRY. *Current Pos:* From asst prof to assoc prof, 64-75, PROF CHEM, UNIV PA, 75- *Personal Data:* b Lakewood, Ohio, Dec 14, 39. *Educ:* Western Res Univ, AB, 61; Univ Ill, PhD(inorg chem), 64. *Mem:* Am Chem Soc; Royal Soc Chem. *Res:* Transition metal ion complexes; molecular complexes; thermodynamics; magnetic resonance; metalloporphyrin species; metal ions in biological systems; surface complexes; metal site catalysis. *Mailing Add:* Dept Chem Univ Pa Philadelphia PA 19104-6382

**WAYLAND, J(AMES) HAROLD,** MICROCIRCULATION, INTRAVITAL MICROSCOPY. *Current Pos:* from assoc prof to prof appl mech, 49-63, prof, 63-79, EMER PROF ENG SCI, CALIF INST TECHNOL, 79- *Personal Data:* b Boise, Idaho, July 2, 09; m 33, Virginia Kartzke; c Ann M Peters, Elizabeth Wayl & Barbr. *Educ:* Univ Idaho, BS, 31; Calif Inst Technol, MS, 35, PhD(physics), 37. *Hon Degrees:* DSc, Univ Idaho, 77. *Honors & Awards:* Ehrenmitglied Ges, Mikrozircultation, 80; Eugene M Landis Award, Microcirculatory Soc, 81; Malpighi Prize, Europ Soc Microcirculation, 88. *Prof Exp:* Asst math, Calif Inst Technol, 31-34; instr, Univ Idaho, 34-35; asst prof physics, Univ Redlands, 38-45; physicist, US Naval Ord Test Sta, Calif, 45-48. *Concurrent Pos:* Fel, Calif Inst Technol, 38-41, war res fel, 44-45; contract employee, US Naval Ord Lab, 41-42 & 11th Naval Dist, US Dept Navy, 42-44; Guggenheim fel, Univ Strasbourg, 53-54; vis prof, Shinshu Univ Midsch, 73, Univ Limburg, Holland, 79 & Univ Tsukuba, Japan, 87; mem, Int Comn Microcirculation & Capillary Exchange, Int Union Physiol Sci, 78-84; Alexander von Humboldt sr scientist, 81; distinguished vis prof, Univ Del, 85. *Mem:* Microcirculation Soc; Am Soc Eng Educ; Am Soc Enol; Am Phys Soc; Int Soc Biorheology; Am Physiol Soc; AAAS; hon mem Europ Soc Microcirculation. *Res:* Biological engineering science; hemorheology; intravital microscopy; biophysics and bioengineering of the peripheral circulation. *Mailing Add:* 900 E Harrison Ave Apt B-21 Pomona CA 91767. *Fax:* 626-449-5163; *E-Mail:* wayland@alumni.caltech.edu

**WAYLAND, JAMES ROBERT, JR,** ASTROPHYSICS & GEOPHYSICS, AGRICULTURAL PHYSICS. *Current Pos:* mem, 74-90, SR MEM TECH STAFF, SANDIA NAT LABS, 90- *Personal Data:* b Plainview, Tex, May 3, 37; m 61; c Sarah & Jennifer. *Educ:* Univ South, BS, 59; Univ Ariz, PhD(physics), 67. *Honors & Awards:* IR-100 Award. *Prof Exp:* Res assoc astrophys, Univ Md, 67-70; asst prof astrophys & agr physics, Tex A&M Univ, 70-74. *Concurrent Pos:* Prog coordr, Res & Develop NQA-1, Am Soc Mech Engrs. *Mem:* Am Phys Soc; Am Soc Qual Control. *Res:* Cosmic ray physics; environmental impact of energy generating systems; health physics; petroleum engineering. *Mailing Add:* Sandia Nat Labs PO Box 5800 M/S 1367 Albuquerque NM 87185. *Fax:* 505-844-1390

**WAYLAND, ROSSER LEE, JR,** TEXTILE CHEMISTRY. *Current Pos:* RETIRED. *Personal Data:* b Charlottesville, Va, Dec 30, 30; m 53, Margaret Buck; c Rosser L III, Robert J & Richard A. *Educ:* Univ Va, BS, 49, MS, 50, PhD(chem), 52. *Honors & Awards:* Olney Medal, Am Asn Textile Chemists & Colorists, 75. *Prof Exp:* Res chemist, Dan River, Inc, 51-54, group leader, Res Div, 54-60, asst dir res, 60-74, mgr, Chem Prod Dept, 74-78, vpres, 78-79, tech dir, Chem Prod Div, 79-90; tech dir, Hickson Danchem Corp, 90-93, vpres, 93-96. *Concurrent Pos:* Consult, A L Philpott Mfg Ctr, 96-; sr chemist, Larchmont Technol LC, 96- *Mem:* Am Asn Textile Chemists & Colorists; Am Chem Soc. *Res:* Organic synthesis; thermosetting textile resins. *Mailing Add:* 319 W Main St Danville VA 24541-2804. *Fax:* 804-792-3674; *E-Mail:* lwayland@gamewood.net

**WAYLAND, RUSSELL GIBSON,** MINING & PETROLEUM GEOLOGY, ENGINEERING. *Current Pos:* CONSULT ENERGY MINERALS, 80- *Personal Data:* b Treadwell, Alaska, Jan 23, 13; m 43, 65, Virginia Phillis; c Nancy & Paul R. *Educ:* Univ Wash, BS, 34; Univ Minn, MS, 35, PhD(econ geol), 39; Harvard Univ, AM, 37. *Honors & Awards:* Distinguished Serv Award, Dept Interior, 68. *Prof Exp:* Geologist & engr, Homestake Mining Co, SDak, 30-39; geologist, US Geol Surv, 39-42; minerals specialist, Army-Navy Munitions Bd, 42-45; mining indust control officer, Off Mil Govt, Ger, 45-48; US chmn, Combined Coal Control Group, Allied High Comn, Ger, 48-52; staff engr, Off Dir, US Geol Surv, 52-58, regional geologist, Conserv Div, Los Angeles, 58-66, asst chief, Conserv Div, DC, 66-67, chief, Conserv Div, Reston, Va, 67-78, res, Off Dir, 78-80. *Concurrent Pos:* Res asst, Univ Minn, 34-36, instr, 37-39; geologist & engr, Alaska Juneau Gold Mining Co, 37; Wash rep, Am Inst Prof Geologists, Wash, 82-88; comnr, Va Oil & Gas Conserv Comn, 82-90. *Mem:* Fel Mineral Soc Am; Am Inst Mining, Metall & Petrol Engrs; Geol Soc Am; Soc Econ Geologists; Am Inst Prof Geologists; Asn Eng Geologists; fel AAAS; Sigma Xi; Cosmos Club. *Res:* Industrial minerals; coal, petroleum and gold; mineral land appraisal. *Mailing Add:* 4660 N 35th St Arlington VA 22207-4462

**WAYMAN, C(LARENCE) MARVIN,** METALLURGY. *Current Pos:* From asst prof to assoc prof, 57-64, PROF METALL, UNIV ILL, URBANA, 64- *Personal Data:* b Wheeling, WVa, Aug 12, 30; m 56; c 2. *Educ:* Purdue Univ, BS, 52, MS, 55; Lehigh Univ, PhD(metall), 57. *Honors & Awards:* Zay Jeffries Award, Am Soc Metals, 77; Matthewson Gold Medal, Am Inst Mining & Metall Engrs, 78. *Concurrent Pos:* Guggenheim fel, 69; overseas fel, Churchill Col, Cambridge Univ, 69. *Mem:* Fel Am Soc Metals; fel Am Inst Mining & Metall Engrs; fel Inst Metallurgists Gt Brit; Japan Inst Metals; Mat Res Soc. *Res:* Solid state phase transformations; growth and properties of thin films; transmission electron microscopy; shape memory alloys. *Mailing Add:* 2204 Pond St Urbana IL 61801

**WAYMAN, MICHAEL LASH,** METALLURGY. *Current Pos:* from asst prof to assoc prof, 69-77, PROF METALL, UNIV ALTA, 78- *Personal Data:* b Kingston, Ont, Feb 1, 43; m 65; c 2. *Educ:* Univ BC, BASc, 64; McMaster Univ, MSc, 66; Cambridge Univ, PhD(metall), 68. *Prof Exp:* Res assoc metall, Univ Toronto, 68-69. *Mem:* Am Soc Metals; Can Inst Mining & Metall. *Res:* Effects of environment on structure and on mechanical properties of metals and alloys. *Mailing Add:* Dept Chem & Mat Eng Univ Alta Edmonton AB T6G 2G6 Can

**WAYMAN, MORRIS,** ORGANIC & WOOD CHEMISTRY, BIOTECHNOLOGY. *Current Pos:* ADJ PROF CHEM ENG, UNIV ALTA, 93- *Personal Data:* b Toronto, Can, Mar 19, 15; m 37, Sara; c Michael L & Thomas E. *Educ:* Univ Toronto, BA, 36, MA, 37, PhD(chem), 41. *Prof Exp:* Asst chem, Univ Toronto, 36-40; res chemist, Dye & Chem Co, Can, 41-43 & Can Int Paper Co, 43-48; mem staff, Indust Cellulose Res Ltd, 48-52; tech dir, Columbia Cellulose Co, Ltd, 52-59; res dir, Sandwell & Co, Ltd, 59-63; prof chem eng & appl chem, Univ Toronto, 63-93, prof forestry, 73-93. *Concurrent Pos:* Assoc ed, Process Biochem, 91- *Mem:* Fel AAAS; Am Chem Soc; Tech Asn Pulp & Paper Indust; Can Soc Microbiologists; fel Royal Soc Can; fel Chem Inst Can. *Res:* Chemistry of wood; lignin; pulp and paper; cellulose to alcohol conversion; conversion of municipal solid waste (garbage) to fuels and chemicals; feasibility analysis; author of books. *Mailing Add:* 3243 1-G San Amadeo Laguna Hills CA 92653. *Fax:* 403-492-2881

**WAYMAN, OLIVER,** ANIMAL PHYSIOLOGY, ANIMAL NUTRITION. *Current Pos:* Asst animal husbandman, Univ Hawaii, 51-52, assoc animal scientist, 52-57, chmn dept animal sci, 54-60, animal scientist, 57-80, EMER ANIMAL SCIENTIST, UNIV HAWAII, 80- *Personal Data:* b Logan, Utah, Jan 8, 16; m 53, Rosalie McLeod; c Mary ann (Schwartz), James (McLeod), Carole Ellen (Larsen), David Andrew & Amy Elizabeth. *Educ:* Utah State Agr Col, BS, 47; Cornell Univ, PhD, 51. *Concurrent Pos:* Res assoc psychoenergetic lab, Univ Mo, 60-61; Rockefeller Found grant, Colombian Land & Cattle Inst, 69; USDA Coop State Res Serv grant, Honolulu, 71-74; Dept Planning & Econ Develop grant, Hawaii, 75-77. *Mem:* Am Soc Animal Sci; Soc Study Reproduction. *Res:* Influence of tropical environment upon growth, development and reproduction of cattle; improvement of feeding value of tropical by-products and forage; use of the whole pineapple plant as ruminant feed. *Mailing Add:* 2749 Peter St Honolulu HI 96816

**WAYMIRE, EDWARD CHARLES,** APPLIED PROBABILITY, SPATIAL STOCHASTIC PROCESSES. *Current Pos:* PROF MATH & STATIST, ORE STATE UNIV, 81- *Personal Data:* b Alton, Ill, Apr 16, 49; m 78, Linda J Feitner. *Educ:* Southern Ill Univ, BS, 71; Univ Ariz, MS, 72, PhD(math), 76. *Prof Exp:* Asst prof math, Clarkson Univ, 76-78, Univ Miss, 78-81. *Concurrent Pos:* Mem, Precipitation Comt, Am Geophys Union, 82-88; vis prof math, Utah State Univ, 85-86; fac fel, NASA Goddard Space Flight Ctr, 86; assoc ed, J Am Geophys Union, 88-92. *Mem:* Am Geophys Union; Am Math Soc; Inst Math Statist; Math Asn Am; Soc Indust & Appl Math. *Res:* Applications of probability theory to problems in the geosciences; prediction of flows from ungauged river networks; spatial/temporal variability of rainfall and climate dynamics. *Mailing Add:* Math Dept Ore State Univ Corvallis OR 97331-4605. *E-Mail:* waymire@math.orst.edu

**WAYMIRE, JACK CALVIN,** NEUROBIOLOGY, NEUROCHEMISTRY. *Current Pos:* chmn dept, 84-88, assoc prof, 78-91, PROF NEUROBIOL, MED SCH, UNIV TEX, HOUSTON, 91-, DIR, NEUROSCI PROG, 92- *Personal Data:* b Dayton, Ohio, Jan 10, 41; div; c Kellie S. *Educ:* Earlham Col, BA, 63; Ohio State Univ, PhD(physiol), 69. *Prof Exp:* Res assoc, Med Ctr, Univ Colo, 69-73; asst prof neurochem, Univ Calif, Irvine, 73-78. *Concurrent Pos:* Prin investr, Nat Inst Neurol & Commun Dis & Stroke, 74- & Nat Inst Aging, 76-78. *Mem:* Soc Neurosci; Sigma Xi. *Res:* Cellular basis for regulation of monoamine synthesis, secretion and plasticity; aging of the nervous system. *Mailing Add:* Dept Neurobiol & Anat Univ Tex 6431 Fannin St Houston TX 77030-1501. *Fax:* 713-792-5795; *E-Mail:* jwaymire@nba19.med.uth.tme.edu

**WAYMOUTH, CHARITY,** cell biology, biochemistry, for more information see previous edition

**WAYMOUTH, JOHN FRANCIS,** APPLIED PHYSICS. *Current Pos:* INDEPENDENT CONSULT, 88- *Personal Data:* b Ingenio Barahona, Dominican Repub, May 24, 26; m 49; c 4. *Educ:* Univ of the South, BS, 47; Mass Inst Technol, PhD(physics), 50. *Honors & Awards:* W Elenbaas Award, Eindhoven Tech Univ, Dutch Phys Soc & N V Philips Co, 73; IES Medal, Illum Eng Soc NAm, 91. *Prof Exp:* Lab asst, Univ of the South, 43-44 & 46-47; asst, Mass Inst Technol, 49-50; sr engr, Sylvania Elec Prod Inc Div, Gen Tel & Electronics Corp, 50-58, sect head, 58-65, mgr physics lab, 65-69, dir res Sylvania Lighting Prod Group, 69-88. *Concurrent Pos:* Consult, Magnet Lab, Mass Inst Technol, 58-65; mem, US Govt Adv Comt, Tech Electron Prod Radiation Safety Standards Comt, 77-79 & Adv Comt Physics, NSF, 81-83. *Mem:* Am Phys Soc; Illum Eng Soc. *Res:* Oxide cathodes; electroluminescent phosphors; gaseous electronics. *Mailing Add:* 16 Bennett Rd Marblehead MA 01945

**WAYMOUTH, ROBERT MEBANE,** CHEMISTRY. *Current Pos:* asst prof, 88-94, ASSOC PROF, CHEM DEPT, STANFORD UNIV, 94- *Personal Data:* b Warner Robins, Ga, May 20, 60. *Educ:* Washington & Lee Univ, BA & BS, 82; Calif Inst Technol, PhD, 87. *Honors & Awards:* Young Investr Award, NSF, 92, Alan T Waterman Award, 96; Arthur C Cope Scholar Award, Am Chem Soc, 95. *Prof Exp:* Res fel, Inst Polymer Sci, Tech Sch, Zurich, Switz, 87-88. *Concurrent Pos:* Bing fel, Stanford Univ, 94. *Mailing Add:* Dept Chem Stanford Univ Stanford CA 94305-5080. *Fax:* 650-725-0259; *E-Mail:* waymouth@leland.stanford.edu

**WAYNANT, RONALD WILLIAM,** ELECTRO-OPTICS, FIBER OPTICS. *Current Pos:* SR OPTICAL ENGR, FOOD & DRUG ADMIN, 86- *Personal Data:* b Gettysburg, Pa, Oct 4, 40. *Educ:* Johns Hopkins Univ, BES, 62; Cath Univ, MSEE, 66, PhD(elec eng), 71. *Prof Exp:* Asst engr, laser res & develop, Westinghouse Corp, 62-69; res elec engr, short wave length laser, Naval Res Lab, 69-86. *Concurrent Pos:* Adj prof, elec eng & fac quantum electronics, Cath Univ; ed-in-chief, Circuits & Devices Mag, 86- *Mem:* Fel Inst Elec & Electronics Engrs; fel Optical Soc Am; Soc Photo-Optical Instrumentation Eng. *Res:* Medical fiber optics; laser surgery including angioplasty and ophthalmology; laser interaction with tissue; non-linear interaction; optical imaging. *Mailing Add:* 13101 Claxton Dr Laurel MD 20708-1805

**WAYNE, BURTON HOWARD,** ELECTRICAL ENGINEERING. *Current Pos:* assoc prof, 64-71, PROF ENG ANALYSIS & DESIGN & CHMN DEPT, UNIV NC, CHARLOTTE, 71- *Personal Data:* b Acton, Mass, Nov 18, 24; m 47; c 3. *Educ:* Mich State Univ, BS, 51, MS, 54, PhD(elec eng), 60. *Prof Exp:* Instr elec eng, Mich State Univ, 55-64. *Mem:* Inst Elec & Electronics Engrs; Am Soc Eng Educ; Nat Soc Prof Engrs. *Res:* Circuit theory. *Mailing Add:* Dept Elec Eng Univ NC University Sta Charlotte NC 28223-0002

**WAYNE, CLARENCE EUGENE,** DYNAMICAL SYSTEMS, STATISTICAL MECHANICS. *Current Pos:* asst prof, 83-86, ASSOC PROF MATH, PA STATE UNIV, 86- *Personal Data:* b Moundsville, WVa, June 5, 56. *Educ:* Univ Va, BS, 78; Harvard Univ, AM, 79, PhD(physics), 82. *Prof Exp:* Postdoctoral fel, Inst Math & Appln, Univ Minn, 82-83. *Concurrent Pos:* Res instr, Univ Va, 83-84. *Mem:* Am Phys Soc; Am Math Soc. *Res:* Dynamical systems, particularly hamiltonian systems with many degrees of freedom; classical statistical mechanics. *Mailing Add:* Dept Math Pa State Univ 414 McAlister Bldg University Park PA 16802-6401

**WAYNE, GEORGE JEROME,** psychiatry, psychoanalysis; deceased, see previous edition for last biography

**WAYNE, JENNIFER SUSAN,** TEACHING & INVESTIGATING BIOMECHANICS BOTH FROM FUNDAMENTAL ASPECTS & FROM MORE ADVANCED SPECIALTIES, NORMAL & REPAIRED RECONSTRUCTED MECHANICAL CHARACTERISTICS OF MUSCULOSKELETAL TISSUES. *Current Pos:* ASST PROF, VA COMMONWEALTH UNIV, 91- *Personal Data:* b Brooklyn, NY, June 22, 61; m 84, Forrest E Sloan; c Stephanie A. *Educ:* Va Polytech Inst & State Univ, BS, 83; Tulane Univ, MS, 84; Univ Calif, San Diego, PhD(bioeng), 90. *Mem:* Am Soc Mech Engrs; Orthop Res Soc; Am Soc Biomech; Biomed Eng Soc. *Res:* Analyze the normal mechanical characteristics of components of the musculoskeletal system, particularly joints, cartilage, ligaments. *Mailing Add:* Orthop Res Lab Va Commonwealth Univ MCV Box 980694 Richmond VA 23298-0694. *Fax:* 804-828-4454; *E-Mail:* jwayne@gems.vcu.edu

**WAYNE, LAWRENCE GERSHON,** MICROBIOLOGY, MYCROBACTERIA. *Current Pos:* ASSOC CLIN PROF MED, UNIV CALIF, IRVINE-CALIF COL MED, 70-; CHIEF TUBERC RES LAB, VET ADMIN HOSP, LONG BEACH, 71- *Personal Data:* b Los Angeles, Calif, Mar 11, 26; m 48, 62, 92; c Mark, Paul, Sharon & Samantha. *Educ:* Univ Calif, Los Angeles, BS, 49, MA, 50, PhD(microbiol), 52. *Honors & Awards:* Bergey Award, 88; JR Porter Award, 91. *Prof Exp:* Chief bact res lab, Vet Admin Hosp, San Fernando, Calif, 52-71. *Concurrent Pos:* Mem, Infectious Dis Res Prog Comt, Vet Admin, 61-64, Pulmonary Dis Res Prog Comt, 64; mem, Lab Comt, Vet Admin-Armed Forces Coop Study Chemother Tuberc, 61-66; consult, Calif Dept Pub Health, 63-69; mem mycobacterium taxon subcomt, Int Asn Microbiol Socs, 66-, chmn, 76-; mem bact & mycol study sect, Nat Inst Allergy & Infectious Dis, 71-74; mem judicial comn, Int Comt Syst Bact 73-86, chmn 78-96. *Mem:* Fel Am Acad Microbiol; Am Soc Microbiol. *Res:* Natural history and diagnostic techniques of tuberculosis and fungus diseases; physiology and classification of mycobacteria. *Mailing Add:* Tuberc Res Lab Dept Vet Affairs Hosp 5901 E Seventh St Long Beach CA 90822

**WAYNE, LOWELL GRANT,** AIR POLLUTION, ENVIRONMENTAL HEALTH. *Current Pos:* RETIRED. *Personal Data:* b Washington, DC, Nov 27, 18; m 42, Martha L Dolson; c Garth L & Randall R. *Educ:* Univ Calif, Berkeley, BS, 37; Calif Inst Technol, PhD(inorg chem), 49; Am Bd Indust Hyg, dipl. *Prof Exp:* Fel petrol refining, Mellon Inst, 49-52; sr phys chemist, Stanford Res Inst, 53-54; indust health engr, Univ Calif, Los Angeles, 54-56; res photochemist, Air Pollution Control Dist, Los Angeles, 56-62; res analyst, Allan Hancock Found, Univ Southern Calif, 62-69, res assoc comput sci, 63-65, res assoc biol sci, 65-69, sector head, Air Pollution Control Inst, 65-72, res assoc, Sch Pub Admin, 69-72; vpres & dir res, PAC Environ Serv Inc, 72-85, sr scientist, 85-90; sr scientist, Valley Res Corp, 87-90. *Concurrent Pos:* Prof consult, Comt Motor Vehicles Emissions, Nat Acad Sci-Nat Res Coun, 71-73. *Mem:* Fel AAAS; fel Am Inst Chemists; Am Chem Soc; Air & Waste Mgt Asn; Am Indust Hyg Asn; Sigma Xi. *Res:* Kinetics and photochemistry of gas phase reactions, especially chemical reactions in polluted urban atmospheres; oxides of nitrogen; air quality modelling; air quality evaluation; atmospheric chemistry. *Mailing Add:* 285 Bayside Rd Arcata CA 95521-6463

**WAYNE, WILLIAM JOHN,** GEOMORPHOLOGY, QUATERNARY STRATIGRAPHY. *Current Pos:* from assoc prof to prof, 68-92, EMER PROF GEOL, UNIV NEBR, LINCOLN, 92- *Personal Data:* b Cass Co, Mich, Apr 23, 22; m 46, Naomi Liebl; c Nancy, John & Annette. *Educ:* Ind Univ, AB, 43, MA, 50, PhD(geol), 52. *Prof Exp:* Head glacial geologist, State Geol Surv, Ind, 52-68. *Concurrent Pos:* Vis prof, Univ Wis, 66-67; res, Inst Arg de Nivologia y Glaciologia, 80; NSF grants, Int Progs, 80, 82-84, Nat Geog Soc res grant, 87-88; Fulbright lectr, Arg, 87; Fulbright res award, Arg, 93-94. *Mem:* Int Asn Eng Geologists; Geol Soc Am; Asn Geol Arg; Ger Quaternary Asn; Am Quaternary Asn; Am Inst Prof Geologists; Asn Eng Geologists. *Res:* Quaternary stratigraphy and paleontology; geomorphology; environmental geology; geomorphology and Pleistocene stratigraphy in Indiana and Nebraska; alpine geomorphology in Nevada and Argentina. *Mailing Add:* City Campus Lincoln NE 68588-0340. *Fax:* 402-472-4917

**WAYNER, MATTHEW JOHN,** NEUROSCIENCE, PSYCHOPHARMACOLOGY. *Current Pos:* DIR, DIV LIFE SCI, UNIV TEX, 83- *Personal Data:* b Clifton, NJ, Sept 7, 27; c 3. *Educ:* Dartmouth Col, AB, 49; Tufts Univ, MS, 50; Univ Ill, PhD(psychol), 53. *Prof Exp:* From asst prof to prof psychol, Brain Res Lab, Syracuse Univ, 53-82. *Concurrent Pos:* Ed-in-chief, Physiol & Behav, Pharmacol, Biochem & Behav, Brain Res Bull & Neurosci Biobehav Rev. *Mem:* Am Psychol Asn; Am Physiol Soc; Int Brain Res Orgn; Soc Neurosci; Am Col Neuropsychopharmacol. *Res:* Hypothalamic mechanisms and ingestive behavior; neural mechanisms of ingestive behavior and drug action. *Mailing Add:* Div Life Sci Univ Tex 6900 N Loop 1604 W San Antonio TX 78249-1130. *Fax:* 210-691-4510; *E-Mail:* Bitnet: editoff@utsavm1

**WAYNER, PETER C, JR,** CHEMICAL ENGINEERING. *Current Pos:* from asst prof to assoc prof, 65-75, PROF CHEM ENG, RENSSELAER POLYTECH INST, 75- *Personal Data:* b Taunton, Mass, Aug 18, 34; m 63, Donna Shpikula; c Peter III, Taras & Elizabeth. *Educ:* Rensselaer Polytech Inst, BSChE, 56; Mass Inst Technol, SM, 60; Northwestern Univ, PhD(chem eng), 63. *Prof Exp:* Res engr, United Aircraft Res Labs, Conn, 63-65. *Concurrent Pos:* Consult heat transfer & fluid mech; chmn, Heat Transfer & Energy Conversion Div, Am Inst Chem Engrs, 85. *Mem:* Fel Am Inst Chem Engrs; Am Chem Soc; Am Soc Mech Engrs; fel Am Inst Chem Eng. *Res:* Use of interfacial phenomena to control transport phenomena; heat and mass transfer; fluid mechanics; boiling. *Mailing Add:* Dept Chem Eng Rensselaer Polytech Inst Troy NY 12180-3590. *Fax:* 518-276-4030; *E-Mail:* wayner@ipi.edu

**WAYRYNEN, ROBERT ELLIS,** GENERAL CHEMISTRY. *Current Pos:* RETIRED. *Personal Data:* b Lake Norden, SDak, Oct 24, 24; m 46, Edna Larsen; c Peggy & Kathy. *Educ:* SDak State Col, BS, 48; Univ Utah, PhD(chem), 53. *Prof Exp:* From chemist to sr chemist, Photo Prod Dept, E I Du Pont de Nemours & Co, Inc, 52-62, res supvr, 62-65, tech serv group supvr, 65-66, field sales mgr, 66-69, tech mgr photo prod dept, 69-85. *Mem:* Soc Imaging Sci & Technol. *Res:* Photosynthesis; photography; photographic chemistry. *Mailing Add:* 1138 Webster Dr Webster Farm Wilmington DE 19803

**WAZIRI, RAFIQ,** NEUROBIOLOGY, PSYCHIATRY. *Current Pos:* ASSOC PROF PSYCHIAT, COL MED, UNIV IOWA, 72- *Personal Data:* b Afghanistan, Dec 11, 33; US citizen; m 67; c 3. *Educ:* Am Univ, Beirut, BS, 56, MD, 60. *Prof Exp:* Res fel neurophysiol, Med Sch, Harvard Univ, 64-66; asst prof psychiat, Col Med, Univ Iowa, 66-68; asst prof physiol & assoc prof psychiat, Col Med, Univ Tenn, 70-72. *Mem:* Soc Neurosci; Sigma Xi; Soc Biol Psychiat; Am Psychiat Asn; AMA. *Res:* Alcohol effects on neural tissues; neurochemistry of psychotic illness of schizophrenia. *Mailing Add:* Univ Iowa Col Med 200 Hawkins Dr Iowa City IA 52246

**WAZZAN, A R FRANK,** NUCLEAR ENGINEERING, FLUID MECHANICS. *Current Pos:* From asst prof to assoc prof eng, 63-69, PROF ENG & APPL SCI, UNIV CALIF, LOS ANGELES, 74-, DEAN, SCH ENG, 87- *Personal Data:* b Lattakia, Syria, Oct 17, 35; US citizen; m 59; c 3. *Educ:* Univ Calif, Berkeley, BS, 59, MS, 61, PhD(eng sci), 63. *Concurrent Pos:* Guggenheim fel, Copenhagen, 66; consult, McDonnell Douglas Corp, 62-71, Lawrence Radiation Lab, 65-67, Westinghouse Elec Corp, 74-76, NAm Aviation, 75-78, Honeywell, 76-78 & Rand Corp, 75-; reviewer heat & mass transfer, thermodyn & quantum mech, fluid mech & nuclear eng, Appl Mech Rev, 71-; vis scholar with EDF, Paris & Off Comnr Atomic Energy, Saclay, France, 73 & 79. *Mem:* Fel Am Nuclear Soc; Am Inst Aeronaut & Astronaut. *Res:* Modeling of fuel elements for fast breeder reactor; stability and transition of laminar flows; thermodynamics of solids and of dense gases; thermal hydraulics of pressurized water reactors. *Mailing Add:* Sch Eng & Appl Sci Univ Calif Los Angeles Box 951600 7400 Boelter Hall Los Angeles CA 90095-1600

**WEAD, WILLIAM BADERTSCHER,** MICROCIRCULATION, VASCULAR SMOOTH MUSCLE CELL CONTRACTION. *Current Pos:* asst prof, 69-81, basic sci coordr nursing & allied health, 75-80, ASSOC PROF PHYSIOL, SCH MED, UNIV LOUISVILLE, 81-, VCHMN, DEPT PHYSIOL & BIOPHYS, 85- *Personal Data:* b Columbus, Ohio, Mar 11, 40; m 62; c 3. *Educ:* Wabash Col, BA, 62; Ohio State Univ, MS, 67, PhD(physiol), 69. *Prof Exp:* Res & teaching asst physiol, Ohio State Univ, 63-69. *Concurrent Pos:* Prin investr, Am Heart Asn & Am Lung Asn; fel pulmonary pathophysiol, Health Sci Ctr, Univ Tex, Dallas, 82. *Mem:* Am Heart Asn; Am Physiol Soc; Int Union Physiol Sci; Europ Microcirculatory Soc. *Res:* Isolated vascular smooth muscle cell control. *Mailing Add:* Dept Physiol & Biophys Univ Louisville Sch Med Health Sci Ctr A-1115 Louisville KY 40292-0001. *Fax:* 502-588-6239; *E-Mail:* wbweadoll@ulkyvm.louisville.edu

**WEAKLIEM, HERBERT ALFRED, JR,** PHYSICAL CHEMISTRY. *Current Pos:* CONSULT, 90- *Personal Data:* b Newark, NJ, Mar 24, 26; m 55; c 4. *Educ:* Rutgers Univ, BSc, 53; Cornell Univ, PhD(phys chem), 58. *Prof Exp:* mem tech staff, RCA Labs, 58-84; sr scientist, Chronar Corp, 84-90. *Concurrent Pos:* Vis prof physics, Univ Calif, Los Angeles, 72-73. *Mem:* Am Chem Soc; Am Phys Soc; Sigma Xi; Optical Soc. *Res:* Solid state and molecular spectroscopy; plasma chemistry; optics. *Mailing Add:* 132 King George Rd Pennington NJ 08534-2318

**WEAKS, THOMAS ELTON,** PLANT PHYSIOLOGY. *Current Pos:* from asst prof to assoc prof bot, 71-82, PROF BIOL SCI, MARSHALL UNIV, 82- *Personal Data:* b Cumberland City, Tenn, Sept 12, 34; m 59; c 2. *Educ:* Austin Peay State Univ, BS, 56; George Peabody Col, MA, 60; Univ Tenn, Knoxville,

PhD(bot), 71. *Prof Exp:* High sch instr, Fla, 58-65; instr biol, Brevard Jr Col, 66-67. *Concurrent Pos:* Sigma Xi res grant, 74; instnl res grant, Marshall Univ, 75; consult, US Army CEngr. *Mem:* Am Soc Plant Physiologists; Sigma Xi; Scand Soc Plant Physiologists. *Res:* Inhibitory action of canavanine in higher plants; phytotoxin effects on fungus diseases of legumes; allelopathic interference as factor affecting periphyton communities. *Mailing Add:* Dept Biol Sci Marshall Univ 400 Hal Greer Blvd Huntington WV 25755-0001

**WEAR, JAMES OTTO,** PHYSICAL CHEMISTRY, CLINICAL ENGINEERING & HOSPITAL SAFETY. *Current Pos:* res chemist, Southern Res Support Ctr, Vet Admin, 65-66, dir opers, 66-68, actg chief, 67-68, chief cent res instrument prog, 66-85, DIR EDUC & TRAINING CTR ENG & CONSTRUCT MGT, VET ADMIN HOSP, LITTLE ROCK, 72-; PROF BIOMED INSTRUMENTATION TECHNOL & CHMN DEPT, COL HEALTH RELATED PROF, UNIV ARK, LITTLE ROCK, 72- *Personal Data:* b Francis, Okla, Oct 25, 37; m 59, Judy Curtis; c Eric Otto & Kay (Adams). *Educ:* Univ Ark, BS, 59, MS, 60, PhD(phys chem), 62. *Prof Exp:* Staff mem, Sandia Corp, 61-65. *Concurrent Pos:* Abstractor, Chem Abstr Servs, 62-65; prof, Philander Smith Col, 66-85; asst prof, Grad Inst Technol, Univ Ark, 66-69, from asst prof to assoc prof, Med Sch, 68-76; chmn, Cert Hosp Safety Exam Comt, 88-90; mem, Cert Bd Examr Biomed Equip Technol, 73-78; mem, Clin Eng Bd Exam, 82-87; pres, Ark Sci Assocs, 69-73; chmn, Ark Sci & Technol Coun, 73-75. *Mem:* AAAS; Am Chem Soc; Asn Advan Med Instrumentation; fel Am Soc Hosp Engrs; fel Am Inst Chemists. *Res:* Hospital safety; electrochemistry; radiochemistry; science education; research support and management; hospital instrumentation maintenance; health and social planning and program evaluation. *Mailing Add:* 5104 Randolph Rd North Little Rock AR 72116. *Fax:* 501-688-1673

**WEAR, ROBERT LEE,** ORGANIC POLYMER CHEMISTRY. *Current Pos:* Sr res chemist, 49-55, group supvr, 55-61, res specialist, 62-67, SR RES SPECIALIST, MINN MINING & MFG CO, 67- *Personal Data:* b Princeville, Ill, Feb 28, 24; m 46; c 2. *Educ:* Univ Ill, BS, 46; Univ Nebr, MS, 48, PhD(chem), 50. *Mem:* Am Chem Soc. *Res:* Condensation polymers. *Mailing Add:* 93 Kraft Rd West St Paul MN 55118-3813

**WEARDEN, STANLEY,** STATISTICS. *Current Pos:* dir, Div Statist, WVa Univ, 66-69, chmn, Dept Statist & Comput Sci, 69-73, prof statist, 66-93, dean, Grad Sch, 72-93, EMER PROF, WVA UNIV, 93- *Personal Data:* b Goliad, Tex, Oct 1, 26; m 51; c 5. *Educ:* St Louis Univ, BS, 50; Univ Houston, MS, 51; Cornell Univ, PhD, 57. *Prof Exp:* Asst biol, Univ Houston, 50-51, instr, 51-53; asst animal husb, Cornell Univ, 53-57; asst prof math, Kans State Univ, 57-59, from assoc prof to prof statist, 59-66. *Concurrent Pos:* Hon res fel, Birmingham Univ, 63-64; USPHS spec fel, 63-64. *Mem:* Am Statist Asn; Am Soc Animal Sci; Biomet Soc. *Res:* Statistical methods in study of quantitative inheritance; low temperature biology; statistics in agricultural research and genetics. *Mailing Add:* 1452 Dogwood Ave Morgantown WV 26506

**WEARE, BRYAN C,** CLIMATE DYNAMICS, ATMOSPHERIC SCIENCE. *Current Pos:* asst prof, 76-82, ASSOC PROF ATMOSPHERIC SCI, UNIV CALIF, DAVIS, 82- *Personal Data:* b York, Maine, Aug 22, 47. *Educ:* Bates Col, BS, 69; State Univ NY, Buffalo, PhD(biophys sci), 74. *Prof Exp:* Res assoc, dept meteorol, Mass Inst Technol, 74-76. *Concurrent Pos:* Vis prof, Meteorol Inst, Univ Munich, 83-84. *Mem:* Am Meteorol Soc; Royal Meteorol Soc. *Res:* Interaction of oceans and atmosphere of tropical regions. *Mailing Add:* 2924 Avila Bay Pl Davis CA 95616

**WEARE, JOHN H,** CHEMISTRY. *Current Pos:* asst prof, 69-80, ASSOC PROF PHYS CHEM, UNIV CALIF, SAN DIEGO, 80- *Personal Data:* b Boston, Mass, Mar 8, 40; m 63; c 1. *Educ:* Harvey Mudd Col, BS, 62; Johns Hopkins Univ, PhD(chem), 67. *Prof Exp:* NSF grant, Air Force Off Sci Res, 68-69. *Res:* Theoretical chemistry, particularly molecular and atomic structure and interactions and the study of irreversible processes. *Mailing Add:* Dept Chem Univ Calif San Diego 9500 Gilman Dr La Jolla CA 92093-0601

**WEARLY, WILLIAM L,** MINING ENGINEERING. *Current Pos:* RETIRED. *Personal Data:* b Warren, Ind, Dec 5, 15. *Educ:* Purdue Univ, BSEE, 37. *Hon Degrees:* Dr Eng, Purdue Univ, 59. *Prof Exp:* Engr, Joy Mfg Co, Pittsburgh, Pa, 37-42, vpres sales, 42-55, pres & chief exec officer, 55-62; vpres & dir, Ingersoll Rand, 62-67, chmn & chief exec officer, 67-80. *Concurrent Pos:* Dir, Am-SAfrican Co & Med Care Int. *Mem:* Nat Acad Eng; Am Inst Elec Eng; Am Soc Mining Engrs; sr mem Inst Elec & Electronics Engrs. *Mailing Add:* One Milbank Unit 2F Greenwich CT 06830

**WEART, HARRY W(ALDRON),** PHYSICAL METALLURGY. *Current Pos:* prof metall eng & chmn dept, 64-88, prof, 89-, EMER PROF, METALL ENG, UNIV MO, ROLLA. *Personal Data:* b Seneca Falls, NY, July 10, 27; m 53; c 3. *Educ:* Rensselaer Polytech Inst, BMetE, 51; Univ Wis, MS, 52, PhD(metall), 57. *Prof Exp:* Instr foundry metall, Univ Wis, 53-56; res engr metal physics, Res Lab, Westinghouse Elec Corp, 56-60; asst prof phys metall, Cornell Univ, 60-64. *Concurrent Pos:* Am Coun Educ intern acad admin, Univ Calif, Berkeley, 70-71; vis foreign lectr, Inst Appl Physics, Univ Tsukuba, Japan, 89. *Mem:* Am Soc Eng Educ; Am Soc Metals Int; Am Inst Mining, Metall & Petrol Engrs; Mat Res Soc. *Res:* Phase transformations; diffusion, especially surface diffusion; crystal growth; amorphization in layered structures. *Mailing Add:* Dept Ceramic Eng Univ Mo Rolla MO 65409-0330

**WEART, RICHARD CLAUDE,** stratigraphy, paleontology, for more information see previous edition

**WEART, SPENCER RICHARD,** PHYSICS HISTORY. *Current Pos:* DIR CTR HIST PHYSICS, AM INST PHYSICS, 74- *Personal Data:* b Detroit, Mich, Mar 8, 42; m 71, Carole Ege; c Kimi & Gen. *Educ:* Cornell Univ, BA, 63; Univ Colo, PhD(physics & astrophys), 68. *Prof Exp:* Teaching & res asst physics, Joint Inst Lab Astrophys, Univ Colo, 63-68; res asst astron, Hawaii Inst Astrophys, Univ Hawaii, 66-67; fel solar physics, Mt Wilson & Palomar Observ, 68-71; res assoc hist, Univ Calif, Berkeley, 71-74. *Concurrent Pos:* Teaching asst, Calif Inst Technol, 69-70; res apprenticeship, Inst Int Studies, 72-73; vis prof, Princeton, 90. *Mem:* Am Astron Soc; Hist Sci Soc (treas, 83-87); Soc Social Studies Sci; Am Geophys Union. *Res:* Solar chromosphere and climatology; origins of sunspots; space telescopes; history of geophysics, solid state and nuclear physics, French science, and modern astrophysics. *Mailing Add:* Am Inst Physics Ctr Hist Physics One Physics Ellipse College Park MD 20740. *Fax:* 301-209-0882; *E-Mail:* sweart@aip.org

**WEART, WENDELL D,** RADIOACTIVE WASTE MANAGEMENT GEOTECHNICAL. *Current Pos:* geophysicist, Sandia Corp, 59-69, supvr, Underground Physics Div, 69-75, dept mgr, Nuclear Waste Systs, 75-91, WIPP PROJ MGR & SR SCIENTIST, SANDIA LABS, 91- *Personal Data:* b Brandon, Iowa, Sept 24, 32; m 54, 81, Leanne; c 3. *Educ:* Cornell Col, BA, 53; Univ Wis, PhD(geophys), 61. *Prof Exp:* Geophysicist, Ballistics Res Lab, 56-59. *Mem:* AAAS; Am Geophys Union. *Res:* Earth physics relating to underground explosion; nuclear waste disposal in geologic media, particular emphasis on salt. *Mailing Add:* 5500 Edwards Dr NE Albuquerque NM 87111

**WEARY, MARLYS E,** PYROGENS, ENDOTOXINS. *Current Pos:* PRIN, MERIT CONSULT SERV, 90- *Personal Data:* b Chicago, Ill, Mar 13, 39. *Educ:* Valparaiso Univ, BA, 60; Univ Ill, MS, 62; Lake Forest Sch Mgt, MBA, 81. *Prof Exp:* Pharmacologist, Baxter Travenol Labs, Inc, 62-66, supvr biol control, 66-81, mgr Microbiol Tech Serv, 81-82, pyrogen technol, 82-86, microbiol/pyrogen technol, 86-89, sr res scientist, Baxter Healthcare Corp, Inc, 89-90. *Concurrent Pos:* Lectr, Ctr Prof Advan, Sch Pharm, Univ Ill; USP Expert Adv Panel Microbiol & Process Validation, 95- *Mem:* NY Acad Sci; Parenteral Drug Asn; Int Endotoxin Soc. *Res:* Biologic control and pyrogen testing; limulus lysate research; endotoxin research; depyrogenation. *Mailing Add:* Merit Consult Serv 15 S Pine St No 404 Mt Prospect IL 60056

**WEARY, PEYTON EDWIN,** DERMATOLOGY. *Current Pos:* from asst resident to resident, 58-61, from instr to assoc prof, 61-70, PROF DERMAT, SCH MED, UNIV VA, 70-, VCHMN DEPT, 75- *Personal Data:* b Evanston, Ill, Jan 10, 30; m 52, Janet G; c 3. *Educ:* Univ Va, MD, 55. *Honors & Awards:* Gold Medal, Am Acad Dermat, 90. *Prof Exp:* Intern, Univ Hosps Cleveland, 55-56. *Concurrent Pos:* Chmn, Coun Nat Prog Dermat, 72-75. *Mem:* Am Dermat Asn; Am Acad Dermat (pres, 93-); Soc Invest Dermat. *Res:* Exploration of the keratinolytic abilities of various dermatophyte fungal organisms and investigation of ecology of certain lipophilic yeast organisms on the skin surface. *Mailing Add:* Dept Dermat Univ Va Hosp Primary Care Ctr Bldg Charlottesville VA 22908. *Fax:* 804-924-5936

**WEAST, CLAIR ALEXANDER,** FOOD CHEMISTRY. *Current Pos:* FREE LANCE CONSULT, 78- *Personal Data:* b Modesto, Calif, Oct 13, 13; m 40; c 2. *Educ:* Univ Calif, BS, 37, MS, 39, PhD(agr chem), 42. *Prof Exp:* Asst, Univ Calif, 37-42; chemist, USDA, 42-44; chief chemist, Pac Can Co, 44-46; res dir, Tillie Lewis Foods, Inc, 46-78. *Res:* Food products; chlorophyllase. *Mailing Add:* J 16127 S Cottage Manteca CA 95336

**WEATHERBEE, CARL,** ORGANIC CHEMISTRY. *Current Pos:* RETIRED. *Personal Data:* b Michigan City, Ind, Nov 21, 16; m 50; c 5. *Educ:* Hanover Col, AB, 40; Univ Ill, AM, 46; Univ Utah, PhD(chem), 50. *Prof Exp:* Asst chem, Univ Ill, 46; instr, Reed Col, 50; asst prof, Univ Hawaii, 50-51; prof chem & chmn dept, Millikin Univ, 52-82, emer prof, 82. *Concurrent Pos:* Researcher, Univ Utah, 59-60, NDak State Univ, 69-70. *Mem:* Am Chem Soc; Am Inst Chemists; Sigma Xi. *Res:* Mannich bases; nitrogen mustards. *Mailing Add:* 1360 W Macon St Decatur IL 62522-2704

**WEATHERBEE, JAMES A,** MICROTUBULES, GROWTH FACTORS. *Current Pos:* sr staff scientist, 85-89, DIR, RES DEVELOP, R & D SYSTS, 89- *Personal Data:* b Chicago, Ill, Jan 22, 43; c 2. *Educ:* Ill Inst Technol, PhD(biol), 72. *Concurrent Pos:* From adj instr to adj asst prof, Rutgers Med Sch, Univ Med & Dent NJ, 81-85. *Mem:* Am Soc Cell Biol. *Res:* Biochemistry and biological effects of growth factor. *Mailing Add:* R & D Systs 614 McKinley Pl NE Minneapolis MN 55413-2690. *Fax:* 612-379-6580

**WEATHERBY, GERALD DUNCAN,** BIOCHEMISTRY. *Current Pos:* chmn dept chem, 81, assoc prof, 81-82, PROF CHEM, OKLAHOMA CITY UNIV, 83- *Personal Data:* b Neodesha, Kans, Mar 13, 40; m 68; c 2. *Educ:* Univ Kans, BS, 62 & 63, PhD(biochem), 69. *Prof Exp:* Teacher high sch, Kans, 63-65; asst prof chem, Lake Superior State Col, 69-77, assoc prof, 77-81. *Res:* Mechanism of riboflavin catalyzed carbon-carbon bond oxidations; extrapolation of these model system studies to elucidate mechanisms of flavoenzyme catalysis. *Mailing Add:* Dept Chem Okla City Univ 2501 N Blackwelder Oklahoma City OK 73106-1402

**WEATHERFORD, THOMAS WALLER, III,** PERIODONTOLOGY. *Current Pos:* Intern pedodontics, Sch Dent, 61-62, instr dent, 62-69, from asst prof to assoc prof periodont, 69-77, PROF PERIODONT, SCH DENT, UNIV ALA, 77-, DIR POSTDOCTORAL EDUC, 70-, ASST PROF COMP MED, SCH MED & SR SCIENTIST, INST DENT RES, 77- *Personal Data:* b Uriah, Ala, Mar 12, 30; m 57; c 2. *Educ:* Auburn Univ, DVM, 54; Univ Ala, Birmingham, DMD, 61, MSD, 69; Am Bd Periodont, dipl, 76. *Concurrent Pos:* NIH trainee, 61-62; staff dentist, Birmingham Vet Admin Hosp, 62-65, resident periodont, 66-68, res assoc, 68-70; resident periodont, Sch Dent, Univ Ala, 66-68; consult, Dept Animal Serv, Univ Ala, 67-69; investr, Inst Dent Res, 70-; mem, Am Asn Dent Schs; consult, Birmingham Vet Admin Hosp, Tuskegee Vet Admin Hosp, Children's Hosp & Eye Found Hosp, Birmingham. *Mem:* AAAS; Am Dent Asn; Int Asn Dent Res; Am Acad Periodont; Am Asn Lab Animal Sci; Sigma Xi. *Res:* Animal models in periodontal research; dental plaque control; histochemistry of the periodontium. *Mailing Add:* Sch Dent SDB412E Univ Sta Birmingham AL 35294-0007

**WEATHERFORD, W(ILLIAM) D(EWEY), JR,** CHEMICAL ENGINEERING, COMBUSTION. *Current Pos:* CONSULT, CHEM ENGR, 85- *Personal Data:* b Orange, Tex, Nov 20, 23; m 45, Barbara Wallace; c William Dewey III & Gerry Lynn. *Educ:* Univ Tex, BS, 44; Univ Pittsburgh, MS, 49, PhD(chem eng), 54. *Prof Exp:* Tutor chem eng, Univ Tex, 44-45; asst process engr, Neches Butane Products Co, 45-47; jr fel, Mellon Inst, 47-54, fel, 54-58; sr res engr, Southwest Res Inst, 58-60, sect mgr, 60-68, staff engr, 68-71, sect mgr, 71-83, inst engr, 83-85. *Concurrent Pos:* Consult, Appl Physics Lab, Johns Hopkins Univ, 54-56; mem FAA-Safer Tech Group, Post-crash fire hazard reduction & Nat Res Coun, assessment mat submarine hull insulation. *Mem:* Combustion Inst; Am Inst Chem Engrs; Sigma Xi. *Res:* Principles and applications of fluid flammability, combustion and fire safety; mechanisms of fretting wear; diffusional processes; fire-resistant fuels; thermophysical properties of alkali metals; properties and physical chemistry of invert microemulsion. *Mailing Add:* 219 Anne Lewis Dr San Antonio TX 78216-6606

**WEATHERLEY, ALAN HAROLD,** FISH & POLLUTION BIOLOGY. *Current Pos:* prof zool, Life Sci Div, Scarborough Col, 75-93, EMER PROF, UNIV TORONTO, 93- *Personal Data:* b Sydney, Australia, Mar 28, 28. *Educ:* Univ Sydney, BSc, 49; Univ Tasmania, MSc, 59; Univ Glasgow, PhD(zool), 61. *Honors & Awards:* Publ Award, Wildlife Soc, 72; Hilary Jolly Award, Australian Soc Limnol, 74. *Prof Exp:* Res fel physiol, Univ Sydney, 49-51; res scientist fishery biol, Commonwealth Sci & Indust Res Orgn, 51-57; asst lectr zool, Univ Glasgow, 58-59, acting lectr, 59-60; lectr zool, Australian Nat Univ, 60-62, sr lectr, 62-71, reader, 71-72; prof fisheries biol, Inst Biol & Geol, Univ Troms, 74-75. *Concurrent Pos:* Vis fel, Leverhulme Trust, 70. *Mem:* Can Soc Zool; Am Fisheries Soc; Australian Soc Limnol (pres 65-66); fel Int Acad Fishery Scientists. *Res:* Studies on freshwater fish in fields of ecology, distribution, taxonomy, physiology, especially thermal tolerance and somatic growth, conservation and heavy metal pollution. *Mailing Add:* Codys RR No 1 Queens Cty Cambridge-Narrows NB E0E 1E0 Can

**WEATHERLY, GEORGES LLOYD,** OCEANOGRAPHY. *Current Pos:* from asst prof to assoc prof, 73-78, PROF OCEANOG, FLA STATE UNIV, 78- *Personal Data:* b 1942; m 94, Tamara Alagoua; c 2. *Educ:* Univ Va, BS, 64; Harvard Univ, MA, 66, MEng, 67; Nova Univ, PhD(phys oceanog), 71. *Prof Exp:* Fel, Nova Univ, 71-72; exchange scientist, Inst Oceanog, USSR Acad Sci, 72-73. *Mem:* Am Geophys Union; AAAS. *Res:* Near bottom currents and deep circulation in the ocean; ocean's bottom boundary layer; suspended sediment transport dynamics in the oceans; turbulent processes in the ocean. *Mailing Add:* Dept Oceanog Fla State Univ Tallahassee FL 32306

**WEATHERLY, NORMAN F,** MEDICAL PARASITOLOGY. *Current Pos:* NIH trainee parasitol, Sch Pub Health, 62-63, from asst prof to prof, 63-89, EMER PROF PARASITOL, UNIV NC, CHAPEL HILL, 89- *Personal Data:* b Elkton, Ore, June 22, 32; m 52; c 6. *Educ:* Ore State Univ, BS, 53, MS, 60; Kans State Univ, PhD(parasitol), 62. *Concurrent Pos:* Consult, Nat Inst Gen Med Sci, 76-80; adj prof, Dept Microbiol, Duke Univ, 81- *Mem:* Am Soc Parasitol; Am Soc Trop Med & Hyg; Am Micros Soc. *Res:* General immunobiology of helminth parasites; cell mediated responses of hosts to helminth parasites. *Mailing Add:* 101 Hunter Pl Carrboro NC 27510

**WEATHERRED, JACKIE G,** PHYSIOLOGY. *Current Pos:* RETIRED. *Personal Data:* b Pampa, Tex, Mar 14, 34; m 60; c 3. *Educ:* Univ Tex, DDS, 59, PhD(physiol), 65. *Prof Exp:* Dent consult, Tex Inst Rehab & Res, 60-62; instr physiol & res assoc oral path, Med Col Va, 62-63; from asst prof to assoc prof physiol, Dent Sch, Univ Md, Baltimore, 63-69; prof, Oral Biol, Sch Dent, Med Col Ga, 69-90, coordr physiol & dir grad progs, 90-93. *Concurrent Pos:* Mem test construction comt, Coun Nat Bd Dent Examr; basic sci consult, Coun Dent Educ; Am Col Dent fel, 71; mem oral biol & med study sect, NIH, 76-80; chmn coun of fac, Am Asn Dent Sch, 78-79; vpres fac, Am Asn Dent Sch, 79-82. *Mem:* AAAS; Int Asn Dent Res; NY Acad Sci. *Res:* Plasma kinins and oral physiology; circulation in dental pulp; predisposing factors in experimental carcinoma of the hamster cheek pouch; membrane transport in oral epithelium. *Mailing Add:* 206 Buckhead Ct Augusta GA 30907

**WEATHERS, DWIGHT RONALD,** ORAL PATHOLOGY. *Current Pos:* From asst prof to prof oral path, 67-92, PROF DERMAT & PATH, SCH DENT, EMORY UNIV, 88-, VCHMN, DEPT PATH, SCH MED, 93- *Personal Data:* b Milledgeville, Ga, Aug 14, 38; m 75, Jean Adams; c Margo, Karen (Carbonara), Ken & Jason M. *Educ:* Emory Univ, DDS, 62, MSD, 66. *Concurrent Pos:* Dean, Emory Sch Dent, 85-92; pres, Am Bd Oral Path, 87-88. *Mem:* Am Acad Oral Path (pres, 92-93); Am Dent Asn; fel Am Col Dentists; fel Int Col Dentists. *Res:* Herpes simplex virus; neoplasia of oral cavity; vesiculo-bullous disease of oral cavity. *Mailing Add:* Emory Univ 1364 Clifton Rd NE Rm C175 Atlanta GA 30322

**WEATHERS, LEWIS GLEN,** PLANT PATHOLOGY. *Current Pos:* vchmn dept plant path, 71-73, chmn dept, 73-77, PROF PLANT PATH & PLANT PATHOLOGIST, UNIV CALIF, RIVERSIDE, 53-, ASSOC DEAN, COL NATURAL & AGR SCI, 77- *Personal Data:* b Sunset, Utah, July 5, 25; m 46; c 4. *Educ:* Utah State Col, BS, 49, MS, 51; Univ Wis, PhD(phytopath), 53. *Prof Exp:* Asst bot, Utah State Univ, 49-51; asst plant path, Univ Wis, 51-53. *Concurrent Pos:* Guggenheim fel, 61-62; Rockefeller fel, 63; NATO fel, 73. *Mem:* Am Phytopath Soc; Int Orgn Citrus Virol; Sigma Xi. *Res:* Citrus and virus diseases; scion and rootstock uncongenialities in citrus; effect of environmental factors on virus diseases; interactions of unrelated viruses in mixed infections. *Mailing Add:* 3023 Central Ave Riverside CA 92506

**WEATHERS, WESLEY WAYNE,** ENVIRONMENTAL PHYSIOLOGY. *Current Pos:* asst prof, 75-76, assoc prof, 76-, PROF AVIAN SCI, AGRIC & ENVIR SCI, UNIV CALIF, DAVIS. *Personal Data:* b Homer, Ill, Sept 28, 42. *Educ:* San Diego State Col, BS, 64; Univ Calif, Los Angeles, MA, 67, PhD(zool), 69. *Prof Exp:* USPHS cardiovasc scholar, Sch Med, Univ Calif, Los Angeles, 69-70; from asst prof to assoc prof physiol, Rutgers Univ, New Brunswick, 70-75. *Mem:* Am Physiol Soc; Am Soc Zoologists; Sigma Xi; Cooper Ornith Soc; Am Ornith Union. *Res:* Comparative physiology of temperature regulation and vertebrate ecological energetics. *Mailing Add:* Dept Avian Sci Univ Calif Davis CA 95616

**WEATHERSBY, AUGUSTUS BURNS,** MEDICAL ENTOMOLOGY, PARASITOLOGY. *Current Pos:* prof, 62-82, EMER PROF ENTOM, UNIV GA, 82- *Personal Data:* b Pinola, Miss, May 19, 13; m 45; c 2. *Educ:* La State Univ, AB, 38, MS, 40, PhD(entom), 54. *Prof Exp:* Asst dist entomologist, State Dept Agr, La, 40-42; entomologist-parasitologist, Naval Med Res Inst, 42-62. *Mem:* AAAS; Entom Soc Am; Am Soc Parasitol; Am Soc Trop Med & Hyg; Am Mosquito Control Asn; fel Royal Soc Trop Med & Hyg. *Res:* Medical entomology; innate immunity of mosquitoes to malaria; malaria survey, control and parasitology; drug action and immunity in malaria; life cycles of malaria; exoerythrocytic stages, tissue culture, and time-lapse cinephotomicrography; cryobiology. *Mailing Add:* 210 Bishop Dr Athens GA 30606

**WEATHERSPOON, CHARLES PHILLIP,** SILVICULTURE, TREE SEEDLING PHYSIOLOGY. *Current Pos:* forester silvicult, Kaibab Nat Forest, 73-76, forester timber inventory, Southwestern Region, 76-78, RES FORESTER SILVICULT & TREE SEEDLING PHYSIOL RES, PAC SOUTHWEST FOREST & RANGE EXP STA, US FOREST SERV, 78- *Personal Data:* b Tucson, Ariz, Dec 1, 42; m 64; c 2. *Educ:* Univ Ariz, BS, 64; Duke Univ, PhD(plant physiol), 68. *Prof Exp:* Res botanist remote sensing, US Army Eng Topog Labs, 70-73. *Concurrent Pos:* Consult, Nat Acad Sci, Comt Effects Herbicides, Vietnam, 72-73. *Mem:* Soc Am Foresters; Am Soc Plant Physiol; Sigma Xi. *Res:* Establishment and growth of forest stands in relation to their environment; effects of cultural treatment, especially prescribed fire, on this environment; assessment of physiological condition of tree seedlings. *Mailing Add:* 6857 Granada Dr Redding CA 96002-9732

**WEAVER, ALBERT BRUCE,** PHYSICS, ACADEMIC ADMINISTRATION. *Current Pos:* prof, Univ Ariz, 58-85, head, Physics Dept, 58-70, assoc dean, Col Lib Arts, 61-70, provost acad affairs, 70-72, exec vpres, 72-83, EMER PROF PHYSICS, UNIV ARIZ, 85- *Personal Data:* b Mont, May 27, 17; m 45; c 3. *Educ:* Univ Mont, AB, 40; Univ Idaho, MS, 41; Univ Chicago, PhD(physics), 52. *Prof Exp:* Physicist, US Naval Ord Lab, 42-45; res assoc physics, Univ Chicago, 52-53 & Univ Wash, 53-54; from asst prof to assoc prof physics, Univ Colo, 54-58, chmn dept, 56-58. *Mem:* Fel AAAS; fel Am Phys Soc; NY Acad Sci. *Res:* Cosmic rays; high energy physics. *Mailing Add:* 5726 E Holmes St Tucson AZ 85711

**WEAVER, ALFRED CHARLES,** COMPUTER SCIENCE. *Current Pos:* PROF COMPUT SCI, UNIV VA, 77- *Personal Data:* b Johnson City, Tenn, July 18, 49; m 80, Debra Hilliard; c Jessica. *Educ:* Univ Tenn, BS, 71; Univ Ill, MS, 73, PhD(comput sci), 76. *Honors & Awards:* Hornfeck Award, Inst Elec & Electronics Engrs. *Prof Exp:* Vis asst prof, Univ Ill, 76-77. *Concurrent Pos:* Consult, Gen Elec, Lockheed, NASA, Johnson Controls & Johnson & Johnson, 72- *Mem:* Asn Comput Mach; fel Inst Elec & Electronics Engrs; Sigma Xi. *Res:* Design, analysis, implementation, and performance measurement of computer networks and their communications protocols; electronic commerce software systems for the internet; telemedicine. *Mailing Add:* Thornton Hall Univ Va Charlottesville VA 22901. *Fax:* 804-982-2214; *E-Mail:* weaver@virginia.edu

**WEAVER, ALLEN DALE,** PHYSICS. *Current Pos:* RETIRED. *Personal Data:* b Galesburg, Ill, Nov 15, 11; wid; c 2. *Educ:* Knox Col, BS, 33; Univ Mich, MS, 47; NY Univ, PhD(sci educ), 54. *Prof Exp:* High sch teacher, Ill, 35-37; jr high sch teacher, 37-40; instr physics, phys sci & math, Md State Teachers Col, Salisbury, 47-55; assoc prof phys sci, Northern Ill Univ, 55-60, prof physics, 60-81. *Mem:* Nat Sci Teachers Asn; Nat Asn Res Sci Teaching. *Res:* Science education. *Mailing Add:* 591 Garden Rd De Kalb IL 60115

**WEAVER, ANDREW ALBERT,** entomology, for more information see previous edition

**WEAVER, CHARLES EDWARD,** CLAY MINERALOGY, SEDIMENTOLOGY. *Current Pos:* assoc prof, 63-65, dir, Sch Geophys Sci, 70-81, PROF MINERAL, GA INST TECHNOL, 65- *Personal Data:* b Lock Haven, Pa, Jan 27, 25; m 46, Janice B Hartland; c Alaine, Patrice & Allison. *Educ:* Pa State Univ, BS, 48, MS, 50, PhD(mineral), 52. *Honors & Awards:* Mineral Soc Am Award, 58; Sigma Xi Res Award, 72; Distinguished Mem Clay Minerals Soc, 85; Pioneer Clay Sci Award, 91. *Prof Exp:* Res assoc mineral, Pa State Univ, 52; res assoc mineral, Shell Res & Develop Co, 52-55, res scientist, 55-59; res group leader mineral, Continental Oil Co, 59-63. *Mem:* Clay Minerals Soc (vpres, 66, pres, 67); Mineral Soc Am; Geochem Soc; Geol Soc Am; Soc Econ Paleontologists & Mineralogists. *Res:* Clay mineralogy and petrology; geochemistry of sediments; clay-water chemistry; radioactive dating of sediments; geothermometry of shales; diagenesis-metamorphism; salt mineralogy; envionmental geochemistry, biogeochemistry. *Mailing Add:* 3276 Craggy Pt Atlanta GA 30339. *Fax:* 404-853-0232

**WEAVER, CHARLES HADLEY,** ELECTRICAL ENGINEERING. *Current Pos:* RETIRED. *Personal Data:* b Tenn, Jan 27, 20; m 44; c 4. *Educ:* Univ Tenn, BS, 43, MS, 48; Univ Wis, PhD(elec eng), 56. *Prof Exp:* Engr & supvr, Tenn Eastman Corp, 43-46; from instr to prof elec eng, Univ Tenn, 46-59; Westinghouse prof, Auburn Univ, 59-63, head prof, 63-65; dean eng, Univ Tenn, Knoxville, 65-68, chancellor, 68-71, vpres continuing educ, 71-81, dean, Space Inst, 75-81, prof elec eng, 82-89. *Concurrent Pos:* Consult, Sverdrup & Parcel, Inc, 53-54 & Oak Ridge Nat Lab, 55-64. *Mem:* Inst Elec & Electronics Engrs; Am Soc Eng Educ. *Mailing Add:* 832 Chateugay Rd Knoxville TN 37923

**WEAVER, CHRISTOPHER SCOT,** OPTICAL VIDEODISC, TELECOMMUNICATIONS. *Current Pos:* PRES, MEDIA TECHNOL ASSOCS, LTD, 82- *Personal Data:* b New York, NY, Feb 6, 51. *Educ:* Hobart Col, AB, 73; Wesleyan Univ, MA & MS, 76, CAS, 77. *Honors & Awards:* NSF/Navy Award. *Prof Exp:* Assoc dir news, Nat Broadcasting Co, 77-78; mgr technol res, Am Broadcasting Co, 78-80; vpres sci & technol, Nat Cable TV Asn, 80-81; vpres res & develop, VML Labs, 81-83. *Concurrent Pos:* Asst prof aerodyn, Norwich Univ, 78; telecommun ed, Video Mag, 80-81; res fel, Mass Inst Technol, 80-82, vis scholar, 82-; US Nat Comt rep, Int Union Radio Sci, 81; tech adv, subcomt commun, US Cong, 81-83 & Off Technol Assessment, 83-85. *Mem:* Inst Elec & Electronics Engrs; Soc Info Display; Soc Motion Picture & TV Engrs. *Res:* Participatory and interactive videodisc systems; computer graphics; idiosyncratic computer systems; optical data storage; man-machine interface. *Mailing Add:* c/o Media Technol 1370 Piccard Dr Suite 120 Rockville MD 20850

**WEAVER, CONNIE MARIE,** NUTRITION. *Current Pos:* PROF FOODS & NUTRIT, PURDUE UNIV, 78- *Personal Data:* b LaGrande, Ore, Oct 29, 50; m 71; c 3. *Educ:* Ore State Univ, BS, 72, MS, 74; Fla State Univ, PhD(foods & nutrit), 78. *Concurrent Pos:* Res fel, Kraft Inc. *Mem:* Sigma Xi; Inst Food Technol; Am Chem Soc; Am Inst Nutrit. *Res:* Mineral bioavailability. *Mailing Add:* Dept Foods & Nutrit Purdue Univ West Lafayette IN 47907. *Fax:* 765-494-0674

**WEAVER, DAVID DAWSON,** MEDICINE, HUMAN GENETICS. *Current Pos:* asst prof, 76-81, assoc prof, dept med genetics, 81-86, PROF, SCH MED, IND UNIV, 86-, DIR CLIN SERV, 76- *Personal Data:* b Twin Falls, Idaho, Feb 12, 39; m 67, Pamela Kae; c Mark David & Kurt E. *Educ:* Albertson Col, Idaho, BS, 61; Univ Ore, MS & MD, 66. *Prof Exp:* Intern med gen rotation, Milwaukee County Gen Hosp, Wis, 66-67; biogeneticist, Arctic Health Res Ctr, 67-70, pediat residency, Med Sch, Univ Ore, 70-72; USPHS fel human genetics, Med Sch, Univ Wash, 72-74; March of Dimes fel, Genetics & Metab Dis, Dept Pediat, Univ Ore Health Sci Ctr, Portland, 74-76. *Concurrent Pos:* Lectr genetics & cell biol, Univ Alaska, 68-70. *Mem:* Am Soc Human Genetics; Sigma Xi; Teratology Soc. *Res:* Dysmorphology; birth defects; prenatal diagnosis; microcephaly; syndromes. *Mailing Add:* Dept Med & Molecular Genetics Ind Univ Sch Med 975 W Walnut St Indianapolis IN 46202-5251. *Fax:* 317-274-2387; *E-Mail:* dweaver@medgen.iupui.edu

**WEAVER, DAVID LEO,** THEORETICAL PHYSICS. *Current Pos:* from asst prof to assoc prof, 64-77, PROF PHYSICS, TUFTS UNIV, 77- *Personal Data:* b Albany, NY, Apr 18, 37; m 66. *Educ:* Rensselaer Polytech Inst, BS, 58; Iowa State Univ, PhD(physics), 63. *Prof Exp:* Res assoc physics, Iowa State Univ, 63-64. *Concurrent Pos:* NATO fel physics, Europ Orgn Nuclear Res, Switz, 65-66; Nat Nuclear Energy Comt fel, Frascati Nat Lab, Italy, 68-69. *Mem:* Am Phys Soc. *Res:* Theoretical elementary particle physics; mathematical physics; molecular biophysics. *Mailing Add:* Dept Physics Tufts Univ Medford MA 02155

**WEAVER, DONALD K(ESSLER), JR,** ELECTRICAL ENGINEERING. *Current Pos:* assoc prof elec eng & dir electronics lab, 56-64, dir eng exp sta, 64-69, PROF ELEC ENG, MONT STATE UNIV, 64- *Personal Data:* b Great Falls, Mont, July 18, 24; m 48; c 2. *Educ:* Stanford Univ, BS, 48, MS, 49, EE, 50, PhD(elec eng), 59. *Prof Exp:* Asst, Stanford Univ, 48-50; sr res engr, Stanford Res Inst, 50-56. *Mem:* Am Soc Eng Educ; Inst Elec & Electronics Engrs. *Res:* Network theory; communication theory. *Mailing Add:* 2404 Spring Creek Dr Bozeman MT 59715

**WEAVER, EDWIN SNELL,** PHYSICAL CHEMISTRY. *Current Pos:* from asst prof to assoc prof, 58-71, chmn dept, 72-78, PROF CHEM, MT HOLYOKE COL, 71- *Personal Data:* b Hartford, Conn, Jan 30, 33; m 55; c 5. *Educ:* Yale Univ, BS, 54; Cornell Univ, PhD(chem), 59. *Prof Exp:* Asst chem, Cornell Univ, 55-57. *Concurrent Pos:* NSF sci fac fel & vis prof, Univ Calif, San Diego, 64-65; vis prof, Univ Conn, 71-72; vis fel, Yale Univ, 78-79; NSF Sci Fac fel, 78-79. *Mem:* AAAS; Am Chem Soc. *Res:* Physical chemistry of polymers and proteins; neutron activation analysis. *Mailing Add:* 115 Woodbridge St South Hadley MA 01075-1128

**WEAVER, ELLEN CLEMINSHAW,** PLANT PHYSIOLOGY, REMOTE SENSING OF OCEAN COLOR. *Current Pos:* CONSULT, 92- *Personal Data:* b Oberlin, Ohio, Feb 18, 25; m 44, Harry E; c Lynne W (Board) & Thomas Scott. *Educ:* Western Res Univ, AB, 45; Stanford Univ, MA, 52; Univ Calif, PhD(genetics), 59. *Prof Exp:* Staff mem, Carnegie Inst Dept Plant Biol, 61-62; res assoc, Biophys Lab, Stanford Univ, 62-67; resident res assoc, Ames Res Ctr, NASA, 67-69; dir off sponsored res, San Jose State Univ, 74-77, assoc prof, 69-77, interium exec vpres, 78-79, prof biol sci, 78-92. *Concurrent Pos:* Sr res assoc, Nat Acad Sci/Nat Res Coun, 67-69; Vis prof, Univ Hawaii, 85; pres scholar, San Jose State Univ, 96. *Mem:* Fel AAAS; Am Soc Plant Physiol; Fel Asn Women Sci. *Res:* Mechanisms of photosynthesis, using wild type and mutant strains of algae; light-induced electron transport as monitored by means of electron paramagnetic resonance spectroscopy; evolution of photosynthesis; remote sensing of chlorophyll in oceans. *Mailing Add:* 987 Westridge Rd Portola Valley CA 94028. *Fax:* 650-851-0641; *E-Mail:* weaver@biomail.sjsu.edu

**WEAVER, GEORGE THOMAS,** forest ecology, silviculture, for more information see previous edition

**WEAVER, HAROLD FRANCIS,** ASTRONOMY. *Current Pos:* physicist, Radiation Lab, Univ Calif, 44-45, from asst astronr to assoc astronr, Lick Observ, 45-51, assoc prof, 51-56, dir radio astron lab, 58-72, PROF ASTRON, UNIV CALIF, BERKELEY, 56- *Personal Data:* b San Jose, Calif, Sept 25, 17; m 39; c 3. *Educ:* Univ Calif, AB, 40, PhD(astron), 42. *Prof Exp:* Nat Res Coun fel, Yerkes Observ, Chicago & McDonald Observ, 42-43; tech aide, Nat Defense Res Comt, DC, 43-44. *Concurrent Pos:* Mem, USAAF-Nat Geog Soc eclipse exped, Brazil, 47. *Mem:* Int Astron Union; Am Astron Soc; Sigma Xi. *Res:* Spectroscopy of peculiar stars; star clusters; galactic structure; radio astronomy. *Mailing Add:* 655 Campbell Hall Univ Calif Berkeley CA 94720

**WEAVER, HARRY EDWARD, JR,** EXPERIMENTAL PHYSICS. *Current Pos:* ED CONSULT, ENCYCL APPL PHYSICS, 88- *Personal Data:* b Philadelphia, Pa, Feb 1, 23; m 44; c Lynne W (Board) & Thomas S. *Educ:* Case Inst Technol, BS, 43, MS, 48; Stanford Univ, PhD(physics), 52. *Honors & Awards:* Albert F Sperry Award, Instrument Soc Am, 92. *Prof Exp:* Physicist, Manhattan Proj, Tenn, 44-46; instr physics, Case Inst Technol, 46-48; asst, Stanford Univ, 48-52 & Physics Inst, Zurich, 52-54; physicist, Varian Assocs, Calif, 54-69, Hewlett-Packard Co, 69-88 & Sets, Inc, Mililani, Hawaii, 88-90. *Concurrent Pos:* Vis lectr, Univ Zurich, 59-61. *Mem:* Am Phys Soc; Sigma Xi; NY Acad Sci. *Res:* Nuclear magnetic and electron resonance, especially in solids; cryogenic engineering and application of high field superconductive materials in high field solenoids for high resolution nuclear magnetic resonance; trajectory analysis of ions in electric fields produced by quadrupole structures of finite length and with imperfections as applied to the design of mass spectrometers; x-ray photoelectron spectroscopy; super critical fluid, especially carbon dioxide; Raman spectroscopy of simple molecules & solvents effects of ultraviolet spectra of chromophores. *Mailing Add:* 987 Westridge Dr Portola Valley CA 94028

**WEAVER, HARRY TALMADGE,** SOLID STATE PHYSICS. *Current Pos:* mem staff physics, 68-78, supvr, 78-91, MGR, SANDIA LABS, 91- *Personal Data:* b Brewton, Ala, Dec 15, 38; m 59; c 3. *Educ:* Auburn Univ, BS, 60, MS, 61, PhD(physics), 69. *Prof Exp:* Mem staff eng, Humble Oil & Refining Co, 62-63. *Mem:* Am Phys Soc; Inst Elec & Electronics Engrs; AAAS. *Res:* Design and development of III-V semiconductor devices and optoelectronic components. *Mailing Add:* Sandia Labs PO Box 5800 MS 1077 Albuquerque NM 87185-1077

**WEAVER, HENRY D, JR,** PHYSICAL CHEMISTRY. *Current Pos:* RETIRED. *Personal Data:* b Harrisonburg, Va, May 5, 28; m 52; c 4. *Educ:* George Washington Univ, BS, 50; Univ Del, MS & PhD(phys chem), 53. *Prof Exp:* Assoc prof chem, Eastern Mennonite Col, 51-57; assoc prof, Goshen Col, 57-71, actg dean, 70-72, prof chem, 71-79, provost, 72-79; dep dir educ abroad, Univ Calif, Santa Barbara, 79-91, adj lectr chem, 80-91. *Concurrent Pos:* Tech adv, Lima, Peru, 64-65; Fulbright lectr, Tribhuvan Univ, Nepal, 69-70. *Mem:* AAAS; Am Chem Soc; Am Sci Affil (pres, 62). *Res:* Heterogenous kinetics; metal; acid systems; kinetics of complex ion formation. *Mailing Add:* 4985 Old Oak Pl Santa Barbara CA 93111

**WEAVER, JAMES B, JR,** GENETICS, AGRONOMY. *Current Pos:* CONSULT, 87- *Personal Data:* b Hartwell, Ga, Jan 28, 26; m 49, Betty Dove; c James B III. *Educ:* Univ Ga, BSA, 50, NC State Univ, MS, 52, PhD(genetics, agron), 55. *Honors & Awards:* Cotton Genetics Award. *Prof Exp:* Asst co agt, Univ Ga, 52-53, asst prof agron, 55-58; dir cotton res, DeKalb Agr Res Inc, 58-63; dir cotton res, Cotton Hybrid Res, Inc, 63-65; supt grounds & agronomist, Univ Ga, 65-67, from asst prof to prof agron, 67-87. *Mem:* Am Soc Agron; Crop Sci Soc Am; Entom Soc Am. *Res:* Basic research on cotton improvement; utilization of hybrid vigor in cotton; insect resistance. *Mailing Add:* 155 Hardin Dr Athens GA 30605-1519

**WEAVER, JAMES COWLES,** BIOPHYSICS, MEDICAL PHYSICS. *Current Pos:* Fel physics, Res Lab Electronics, Mass Inst Technol, 69-72, res assoc, 72-74, staff physicist, 74-78, LECTR PHYSICS, MASS INST TECHNOL, 74-, RES ASSOC BIOPHYS, DEPT NUTRIT & FOOD SCI, 78- *Personal Data:* b Faribault, Minn, Sept 8, 40; m 66; c 2. *Educ:* Carleton Col, BS, 62; Yale Univ, MS, 63, PhD(physics), 69. *Concurrent Pos:* Lectr med physics, Harvard-Mass Inst Technol, Div Health Sci & Technol, 78-86, assoc dir, Biomed Eng Ctr, 85-, prin res scientist, 86- *Mem:* Am Phys Soc; Am Chem Soc; Bioelectrochem Soc; AAAS; Sigma Xi; Int Soc Analytical Cytol; Bioelectromagnetics Soc. *Res:* Biophysics and medical physics; electromagnetic field effects on cells and tissue, particularly electroporation; rapid methods of cell analysis; biosensors. *Mailing Add:* Biomed Eng Ctr Mass Inst Technol 20A-128 Cambridge MA 02139

**WEAVER, JOHN HERBERT,** SOLID STATE PHYSICS. *Current Pos:* dir, grad studies mat sci, 83-92, Amundson prof, 94, PROF, DEPT CHEM ENG & MAT SCI, UNIV MINN, 82- *Personal Data:* b Cincinnati, Ohio, Sept 16, 46; m 83, Mary J Arttus; c Toni Marie & Jeremy John. *Educ:* Univ Mo, BS, 67, MS, 69; Iowa State Univ, PhD(physics), 73. *Honors & Awards:* GJ Lapeyre Award Synchrotron Radiation Res, 82; Alexander Von Humboldt Sr Res Award, 95. *Prof Exp:* Fel physics, Mat Res Ctr, Univ Mo-Rolla, 73; res assoc Synchrotron Radiation Ctr, Univ Wis-Madison, 74-75, asst scientist, 75-77, assoc scientist, 77-82, adj prof, Mat Sci Prog, 81-82; fac assoc, Argonne Nat Lab, 82-87. *Concurrent Pos:* Assoc, Ames Lab, US Dept Energy, 75-85; lectr, Int Ctr Condensed Matter Physics, Univ Brasilia, 93; univ prof, Inst Mat Res, Tohoku Univ, Japan, 94; vis scientist, Fritz-Haber Inst, Max-Planck Res Soc, Berlin, 95; prof, Royal Soc Kan Tong Po, Univ Hong Kong, 95- *Mem:* Fel Am Phys Soc; Am Vacuum Soc (pres-elect, pres, past-pres, 94-99); Mat Res Soc. *Res:* Electronic interactions; morphologies of interfaces and interface formation; ordered and disordered solids; surface and interface phenomena; clusters; fullerene-based systems; nanostructural materials. *Mailing Add:* Dept Chem Eng & Mat Sci Univ Minn 151 Amundson Hall Minneapolis MN 55455. *Fax:* 612-625-6043; *E-Mail:* weave001@maroon.tc.umn.edu

**WEAVER, JOHN TREVOR,** GEOPHYSICS. *Current Pos:* from asst prof to assoc prof, 66-72, PROF PHYSICS, UNIV VICTORIA, 72-, JT APPOINTMENT, SCH EARTH & OCEAN SCI, 91-, DEAN SCI, 93- *Personal Data:* b Birmingham, Eng, Nov 5, 32; m 60, Ludmilla Krawchenko; c Andrew, Anthony & Alexandra. *Educ:* Bristol Univ, BSc, 53; Univ Sask, MSc, 55, PhD(physics), 59. *Prof Exp:* From instr to asst prof math, Univ Sask, 58-61; leader appl math group, Defense Res Estab Pac, BC, 61-66. *Concurrent Pos:* Lectr math, Univ Victoria, 62-64; Nat Sci Eng Res Coun Can res grants, 66-; travel fel, Univ Cambridge, 72-73; actg chmn physics, Univ Victoria, 78-79, chmn, 80-88, actg dean sci, 88-89; vis fel, Univ Edinburgh, 79-80; sci collabr, Cantonal Observ, Neuchatel, Switz, 84; Nat Sci Eng Res Coun Can & Roy Soc Bilateral Exchange, Univ Edinburgh, 89 & Swiss NSF Bilateral Exchange Cantonal Observ, Neuchatel, 90; BC Asia Pac Univ scholars award, 91; vis fel, Res Sch Earth Sci, Australian Nat Univ, 96-; vis fel, St Edmund's Col, Cambridge, UK, 97. *Mem:* Am Geophys Union; Can Asn Physicists; fel Royal Astron Soc; Can Geophys Union; Europ Geophys Soc. *Res:* Electromagnetic induction in the earth; electromagnetic theory; geomagnetic variations. *Mailing Add:* Off Dean Sci Univ Victoria Victoria BC V8W 3P4 Can. *Fax:* 250-721-7059; *E-Mail:* weaver@uvphys.phys.uvic.ca

**WEAVER, KEITH ERIC,** PLASMID BIOLOGY, DNA REPLICATION & STABLE INHERITANCE OF GENETIC ELEMENTS. *Current Pos:* ASST PROF MICROBIOL, UNIV SDAK, 89- *Personal Data:* b Berwick, Pa, Nov 16, 58; m 80, Elizabeth Miller; c Dariel & Sara B. *Educ:* Pa State Univ, BS, 80; Univ Tex, PhD(microbiol), 85. *Prof Exp:* Fel, Univ Mich, 85-89. *Mem:* Sigma Xi; Am Soc Microbiol. *Res:* Determining the molecular mechanisms controlling the replication and stable inheritance of the pheromone - inducible conjugative Enterococcus faecalis. *Mailing Add:* 220 Linden Ave Vermillion SD 57069-3206. *E-Mail:* kweaver@charlie.usd.edu

**WEAVER, KENNETH NEWCOMER,** GEOLOGY. *Current Pos:* CONSULT GEOLOGIST, 92- *Personal Data:* b Lancaster, Pa, Jan 16, 27; m 50, Mary Elizabeth Hoover; c Wendy E & Matthew O. *Educ:* Franklin & Marshall Col, BS, 50; Johns Hopkins Univ, MA, 52, PhD(geol), 54. *Honors & Awards:* John Wesley Powell Award, 94. *Prof Exp:* Geologist, Medusa Portland Cement Co, 56-61, mgr geol & quarry dept, 61-63; dir, Md Geol Surv, 62-92. *Concurrent Pos:* Governor's rep, Interstate Oil Compact Comn, 64-92 & Interstate Mining Compact, 74-92, Chmn, 77; chmn, Md Land Reclamation Comt, 68-76 & 79-92, State Mapping Comt, 76-92, Comt Abandoned Mined Lands Res Priorities, Nat Res Coun, 87, GEOREF Adv Comt, Am Geol Inst, 91-94; mem, Md Mining Coun, 73-88, chmn, 77-88; mem, Mid-Atlantic Gov Coastal Resources Coun, 74-79, Subcomt Mgt Major Underground Projs, US Nat Comt Tunneling Technol, Nat Res Coun, 77-79, Comt Surface Mining & Reclamation, 78-80, Comt Disposal Excess Spoil, 80-81, Comt Geol Mapping, 83- & Comt Water Res, 89-94; mem Md-Del Joint Boundary Comn, 74-92, Outer Continental Shelf Policy Comt, 74-79 & 85-92, Md Comn Artistic Property, 86-92 & Delamarva Comt, Nat Water Qual Assessment Prog, US Geol Surv; mem, Groundwater Interagency Taskforce, Sci & Technol Comts, US House Rep, 78-79; liaison mem, Bd Earth Sci, 83-88; secy/treas NET Serv Geol Soc Am, 86-; mem-at-large, Am Geol Inst Ex Comt, 89-90. *Mem:* Fel AAAS; fel Geol Soc Am; Am Inst Mining, Metall & Petrol Eng; Am Inst Prof Geologists; Asn Am State Geol (vpres, 71, pres, 73). *Res:* Geology of industrial minerals; environmental and structural geology; research administration. *Mailing Add:* 14002 Jarrettsville Pike Phoenix MD 21131-1409. *E-Mail:* kweaver438@aol.com

**WEAVER, L(ELLAND) A(USTIN) C(HARLES),** ELECTRICAL ENGINEERING. *Current Pos:* DIR, STRATEGIC PLANNING, SOFTWARE ENG INST, 91- *Personal Data:* b Winnipeg, Man, Sept 29, 37; US citizen; m 58, 73, Kathryn E Maksinchuk; c Julie D, Cheryl A & Sean W. *Educ:* Univ Toronto, BASc, 60; Univ Ill, MS, 62, PhD(elec eng), 66; Univ Pittsburgh, MBA, 76. *Prof Exp:* Instr elec eng, Univ Ill, 62-66; sr engr, Optical Physics Dept, Westinghouse Res Labs, 66-74, mgr gas laser res, 74-77, prog mgr excimer laser technol, 77-79, asst to dir power systs res & develop, 79-82, dir int res & develop, 82-85, managing dir, Advan Prod Tech, Europe, Westinghouse Elec, 85-87, dir, indust & com res & develop, 87-91. *Mem:* Sr mem Inst Elec & Electronics Engrs; Am Phys Soc; Sigma Xi. *Res:* Gaseous and quantum electronics; gas lasers; research planning; technology assessment; robotics; environmental tech; software systems. *Mailing Add:* 216 Harwick Dr Pittsburgh PA 15235. *E-Mail:* law@sei.cmu.edu

**WEAVER, LAWRENCE CLAYTON,** PHARMACOLOGY. *Current Pos:* prof pharmacol & dean, 66-84, emer dean, 89-94, INTERIM DEAN, COL PHARM, UNIV MINN, 94- *Personal Data:* b Bloomfield, Iowa, Jan 23, 24; m 49; c 4. *Educ:* Drake Univ, BS, 49; Univ Utah, PhD(pharmacol), 53. *Hon Degrees:* DSc, Drake Univ, 92, Union Univ, 93. *Honors & Awards:* Am Pharmaceut Asn Found Res Achievement Award, 63; Remington Hon Gold Medal, Am Pharmaceut Asn, 89; Distinguished Serv Award, Bd Dirs, Am Asn Col Pharm, 89. *Prof Exp:* Asst pharmacol, Univ Utah, 49-53; pharmacologist, Res Dept, Pitman-Moore Co, 53-58, dir pharmacol labs, 59-60, assoc dir pharmacol res, 60-61, head biomed res, Pitman-Moore Div, Dow Chem Co, 61-64, asst dir res & develop labs, 64-65, asst to gen mgr, 65-66; vpres-prof rel, Pharmaceut Mfrs Asn, 84-89; exec dir, Comn Drugs Rare Dis. *Mem:* Am Soc Pharmacol; Soc Exp Biol & Med; Am Pharmaceut Asn; Am Pub Health Asn; Acad Pharmaceut Sci. *Res:* Combinations and assay of anticonvulsant drugs; pharmacology of cardiovascular and central nervous system drugs; social and administrative pharmacy; health care delivery systems; discovery, development and distribution of orphan products. *Mailing Add:* Larry Weaver Assoc 7110 Riverview Terr DE Fridley MN 55432-3045. *Fax:* 612-624-6891

**WEAVER, LEO JAMES,** ORGANIC CHEMISTRY. *Current Pos:* RETIRED. *Personal Data:* b Springfield, Mo, Apr 18, 24; m 49. *Educ:* Drury Col, BS, 49; Univ Mich, MS, 50. *Honors & Awards:* Monsanto du Bois Res Award, 54. *Prof Exp:* Res chemist, Org Chems Div, Monsanto Chem Co, 50-54, res chemist, Inorg Chem Div, 54-56, res group leader detergents & surfactants, 56-60, asst dir res, 60-62, dir prod sales, 62-64, dir com develop, 64-65, dir res & develop, 65-69, pres, Monsanto Enviro-Chem Systs, Inc, 69-72; exec vpres, Calgon Corp, 72-86. *Concurrent Pos:* Mem, Indust Res Inst. *Mem:* AAAS; Am Mgt Asn; Am Chem Soc; NY Acad Sci. *Res:* Alkylation reactions of aromatics and olefins; sulfonation and sulfation of organics; detergents and surfactants. *Mailing Add:* 1005 Tall Trees Dr Upper St Clair PA 15241

**WEAVER, LYNN E(DWARD),** ELECTRICAL ENGINEERING, NUCLEAR ENGINEERING. *Current Pos:* PRES, FLA INST TECHNOL, MELBOURNE, 87- *Personal Data:* b St Louis, Mo, Jan 12, 30; m 83; c 5. *Educ:* Univ Mo, BSEE, 51; Southern Methodist Univ, MSEE, 55; Purdue Univ, PhD(elec eng), 58. *Prof Exp:* Develop engr, McDonnell Aircraft Corp, 52-53; aerophys engr, Convair Corp, 53-55; instr elec eng, Purdue Univ, 55-58; assoc prof, Univ Ariz, 58-59, prof nuclear eng & head dept, 59-69; assoc dean, Univ Okla, 69-70; exec asst to pres & dir off environ studies, Argonne Univs Asn, 70-72; dir, Sch Nuclear Eng & Health Physics, Ga Inst Technol, 72-82; dean eng & distinguished prof, Auburn Univ, 82-87. *Concurrent Pos:* Mem, Govt Comt Atomic Energy, Ariz, 62-64; comnr, Ariz AEC, 64-69; mem adv comt space power & propulsion, NASA, 70-75; exec ed, Ann Nuclear Energy, 78-; chmn coord comt energy, Am Asn Eng Soc, 81-82; chmn pub affairs coun, Am Asn Eng Soc, Washington DC, 84-87. *Mem:* Am Soc Eng Educ; fel Am Nuclear Soc; Inst Elec & Electronics Engrs; Sigma Xi. *Res:* Nuclear reactor dynamics and control. *Mailing Add:* Fla Inst Technol 150 W University Blvd Melbourne FL 32901-6974

**WEAVER, LYNNE C,** PHYSIOLOGY OF THE AUTONOMIC NERVOUS SYSTEM. *Current Pos:* STAFF, JOHN P ROBARTS RES INST, DEPT STROKE & AGING, 87- *Personal Data:* b June 14, 1945. *Educ:* Mich State Univ, DVM, 68, PhD(pharmacol), 75. *Honors & Awards:* Res Career Develop Award, NIH. *Prof Exp:* Prof physiol, Mich State Univ, 84-86. *Mem:* Soc Neurosci; Am Physiol Soc. *Res:* Sympathetic reflexes affecting kidney and splanchic circulation; organization of discrete patterns of sympathetic discharge. *Mailing Add:* John P Robarts Res Inst 100 Perth Dr PO Box 5015 London ON N6A 5K8 Can. *Fax:* 519-663-3789

**WEAVER, MICHAEL JOHN,** CHEMISTRY, ELECTROCHEMISTRY. *Current Pos:* assoc prof, 82-85, PROF, DEPT CHEM, PURDUE UNIV, 85- *Personal Data:* b London, Eng, Mar 30, 47. *Educ:* London Univ, BSc, 68, PhD(chem) & DIC, 72. *Honors & Awards:* David C Grahame Award, Electrochem Soc, 89; Carl Wagner Mem Award, 97; Faraday Electrochem Medal, Royal Soc Chem, 95. *Prof Exp:* Res fel chem, Calif Inst Technol, 72-75; from asst prof to assoc prof chem, Mich State Univ, 75-82. *Concurrent Pos:* Vis scientist, IBM Res Lab, 81-82; Alfred P Sloan Found fel, 82-87; Alexander von Humboldt fel, 86; vis prof, Calif Inst Technol, 87; chmn, Gordon Res Conf Electrochem, 90; Humboldt sr scientist, Fritz-Haber Inst, Berlin, Ger, 91-92. *Mem:* Am Chem Soc; Electrochem Soc; Am Vacuum Soc; Int Soc Electrochem. *Res:* Surface electrochemistry, electron transfer and catalytic processes; electrochemical, gas-phase and ultrahigh vacuum surface science, including surface Raman and infrared spectroscopies, scanning tunneling microscopy, electrochemical and gas-phase heterogeneous catalysis; double-layer structure and electrode kinetics. *Mailing Add:* Dept Chem Purdue Univ Lafayette IN 47907-1393. *Fax:* 705-494-0239; *E-Mail:* weaver@chem.purdue.edu

**WEAVER, MILO WESLEY,** MATHEMATICS. *Current Pos:* from instr to assoc prof, 45-77, EMER ASSOC PROF MATH, UNIV TEX, AUSTIN, 77- *Personal Data:* b Lufkin, Tex, Feb 16, 13; m 34, Jessie A McGirk; c Billy, Gary, Mike, Shirley (Davis) & Sharon (Garrison). *Educ:* Univ Tex, BA, 35, MA, 50, PhD, 56. *Prof Exp:* Pub sch teacher, Tex, 34-45. *Concurrent Pos:* NSF res fel, 58-59. *Mem:* Am Math Soc; Math Asn Am. *Rcs:* Theory of semigroups; mappings on a finite set; associative algebras; fermats last theorem. *Mailing Add:* 1051 Lonesome Trail Driftwood TX 78619

**WEAVER, MORRIS EUGENE,** ANATOMY, ZOOLOGY. *Current Pos:* RETIRED. *Personal Data:* b Morrison, Okla, June 10, 29; m 50, Helen Holbrook; c Ona L, Eric J, Joy D & Mark E. *Educ:* York Col, Nebr, BS, 51; Univ Omaha, BS, 53; Ore State Univ, MA, 56, PhD(zool), 59. *Prof Exp:* From instr to prof anat, Dent Sch, Ore Health Sci Univ, 58-89. *Concurrent Pos:* Nat Inst Dent Res fel, Inst Animal Physiol, Eng, 66-67; vis reader, Med Sch, Univ Ibadan, 72-73; NATO fel, Med Sch, Bristol, Eng, 79-80; prof anat, Med Sch, Ross Univ, 93. *Mem:* Am Asn Anatomists; Int Asn Dent Res; Sigma Xi. *Res:* Cell biology and mitosis; dental research using swine as experimental animals; microcirculation and temperature regulation; tooth eruption; embryology of the head and face. *Mailing Add:* 6354 SW Garden Home Rd Portland OR 97201

**WEAVER, NEVIN,** INSECT PHYSIOLOGY, BEE BEHAVIOR. *Current Pos:* RETIRED. *Personal Data:* b Navasota, Tex, Jan 4, 20; m 62; c 2. *Educ:* Southwestern Univ, AB, 41; Tex A&M Univ, MS, 43; Tex A&M Univ, PhD(entom), 53. *Prof Exp:* Asst biol, Southwestern Univ, 38-41; asst, Tex A&M Univ, 41-43; beekeeper, 46-48; asst entom, Tex A&M Univ, 48-51; from instr to assoc prof, 51-65; chmn dept biol, Univ Mass, Boston, 65-68 & 74-76, chmn campus planning, 69-70, prof biol, 65-87, emer prof, 88- *Concurrent Pos:* Secy, Am comt, Bee Res Asn, 58; fel biol, Harvard Univ, 59-60; assoc ed, J Apicult Res, 82-87. *Mem:* AAAS; Int Bee Res Asn; Animal Behav Soc. *Res:* Honeybee and stingless bee dimorphism, development, physiology, biochemistry, especially lipids, pheromones and behavior; the roles of pheromonal and behavioral signals in the interactions of queen and worker honeybees. *Mailing Add:* Main Barnstable MA 02630

**WEAVER, OLIVER LAURENCE,** MATHEMATICAL PHYSICS, ATOMIC PHYSICS. *Current Pos:* from asst prof to assoc prof, 70-84, PROF PHYSICS, KANS STATE UNIV, 84- *Personal Data:* b Birmingham, Ala, Feb 6, 43; m 89, Gabrielle Thompson; c Christopher Bailey, James, Amanda & Nathaniel Thompson-Weaver. *Educ:* Calif Inst Technol, BS, 65; Duke Univ, PhD(physics), 70. *Prof Exp:* Instr & res assoc, Duke Univ, 69-70. *Concurrent Pos:* Vis prof, Univ Kassel, 88-89. *Mem:* Sigma Xi; Am Phys Soc. *Res:* Atomic and nuclear scattering theory. *Mailing Add:* Dept Physics Kans State Univ Manhattan KS 66506. *E-Mail:* lweaver@ksuvm.bitnet

**WEAVER, PAUL FRANKLIN,** ELECTRICAL ENGINEERING. *Current Pos:* assoc prof, 65-72, chmn, 76-79, PROF ELEC ENG, UNIV HAWAII, 72- *Personal Data:* b Allentown, Pa, Feb 11, 26; m 64, Carol Kellner; c Juliana M, Alisa R & Malia E. *Educ:* Cornell Univ, BEng, 46, MS, 52, PhD(elec eng), 59. *Prof Exp:* Mem tech staff, Bell Tel Labs, 47-52; asst prof elec eng, Cornell Univ, 59-65. *Concurrent Pos:* Staff mem, Space Environ Lab, Nat Oceanic & Atmospheric Admin, Boulder, Colo, 71-72; fac fel & consult, GTE Labs, 78-84; vis prof, Naval Res Labs, Washington, DC, 88-89 & 90. *Mem:* Inst Elec & Electronics Engrs; Am Soc Eng Educ. *Res:* Radio wave propagation; ionospheric physics; microwave circuit design; superconductor circuits. *Mailing Add:* Dept Elec Eng Univ Hawaii 2540 Dole St Honolulu HI 96822

**WEAVER, R(OBERT) E(DGAR) C(OLEMAN),** TECHNICAL MANAGEMENT. *Current Pos:* VPRES & TECH DIR, INT MATEX TERMINALS, 86- *Personal Data:* b New Orleans, La, Mar 30, 32; m 65, Karen C Coci; c Robert C & Peter W. *Educ:* Tulane Univ, BS, 53, MS, 55; Princeton Univ, MA, 57, PhD(chem eng), 58. *Prof Exp:* Process design engr, Ethyl Corp, 58-60; from asst prof to assoc prof chem eng, Tulane Univ, 60-66, prof & chmn dept, 66-81; prof chem, Metall & Polymer Eng & Dean, Col Eng, Univ Tenn, 81-84. *Concurrent Pos:* Consult, Ethyl Corp, 60-65, Humble Oil & Refining Co, 65-73; NATO fel, Ger & Norway, 70; Fulbright prof, Ecuador, 71; exec aide to secy, Dept Natural Resources, State of La, 74-84; assoc dir, Gulf S Res Inst, 84-86. *Mem:* Am Inst Chem Engrs; Soc Petrol Engrs. *Res:* Automatic control; process design, dynamics and simulation; biomedical engineering; applied economimcs; resource management; environmental engineering. *Mailing Add:* 321 Saint Charles Ave New Orleans LA 70130. *Fax:* 504-525-7633

**WEAVER, RALPH SHERMAN,** MATHEMATICAL MODELING OF BIOPHYSICAL & BIOMEDICAL CONCERNS, ENVIRONMENTALLY SUSTAINABLE DEVELOPMENT. *Current Pos:* RETIRED. *Personal Data:* b Doaktown, NB, Nov 7, 35. *Educ:* Univ NB, BSc, 56; McGill Univ, MSc, 59, PhD(nuclear physics), 62. *Prof Exp:* Demonstr, McGill Univ, 56-61, res asst, 61-62; sci officer, Defense Res Bd, 62-73, group head, 73-75; asst dep minister, Alta Environ Ctr, Alta Dept Environ, 89-93, exec dir, 75-94. *Concurrent Pos:* Dir, Can Asn Physicists, 66-68, & Inst Res Pub Policy, 81-91; mem, Fac Grad Studies, York Univ, 66-69; vpres, Fifth Int Conf Indoor Air Qual, 90- *Mem:* Can Asn Physicists; Sigma Xi; Can Res Mgt Asn. *Res:* Heat, vapor and diffusion modeling; underwater life support systems and decompression models; biomedical and physiological systems; disposal of hazardous wastes; air pollution; environmental impacts. *Mailing Add:* 2648 Saddle Ridge Dr Westbank BC V4T 2K7 Can

**WEAVER, RICHARD WAYNE,** SOIL MICROBIOLOGY, WATER & ENVIRONMENTAL QUALITY. *Current Pos:* Assoc prof, 70-76, PROF SOIL MICROBIOL, TEX A&M UNIV, 82- *Personal Data:* b Twin Falls, Idaho, June 25, 44; m 64, Patricia Kay Follett; c David, Amy, & Stacy. *Educ:* Utah State Univ, BS, 66; Iowa State Univ, PhD(soil microbiol), 70. *Concurrent Pos:* Fulbright Distinguished lectr, 86; mem sci bd dirs, Am Type Culture Collection, 96- *Mem:* Fel Soil Sci Soc Am; fel Am Soc Agron; Am Soc Microbiol; fcl Crop Sci Soc Am. *Res:* Soil nitrogen; microbial ecology; nitrogen fixation; waste disposal; bioremediation oil spills. *Mailing Add:* Dept Soil & Crop Sci Tex A&M Univ College Station TX 77843

**WEAVER, ROBERT F,** BIOCHEMISTRY, MOLECULAR BIOLOGY. *Current Pos:* from asst prof to assoc prof, 71-81, chmn dept, 84-95, PROF BIOCHEM, UNIV KANS, 81-, ASSOC DEAN, COL LIB ARTS & SCI, 95- *Personal Data:* b Topeka, Kans, July 18, 42; m 65, Elizabeth Stout; c Virginia & Stephanie. *Educ:* Col Wooster, BA, 64; Duke Univ, PhD(biochem), 69. *Prof Exp:* NIH fel, Univ Calif, San Francisco, 69-71. *Concurrent Pos:* Res grants, NIH, 72-90, Am Cancer Soc, 75-77, 81-82 & 85-88 & NSF, 92-95; Am Cancer Soc res scholar, Univ Zurich, Switz, 78-79 & NERC Inst Virol, Oxford, UK, 89-90. *Mem:* Am Soc Biochem & Molecular Biol; Am Soc Virol; AAAS. *Res:* Structure and function of eucaryotic RNA polymerases; transcription control; molecular biology of baculoviruses. *Mailing Add:* Dept Biochem Univ Kans Lawrence KS 66044-2106. *Fax:* 785-864-5331; *E-Mail:* rob@clasmain.clas.ukans.edu

**WEAVER, ROBERT HINCHMAN,** BIOCHEMISTRY. *Current Pos:* from assoc prof to prof, 61-90, EMER PROF CHEM, UNIV WIS, STEVENS POINT, 90- *Personal Data:* b Buckhannon, WVa, Dec 2, 31; m 58; c 1. *Educ:* WVa Wesleyan Col, BS, 53; Univ Md, MS, 55, PhD(biochem), 57. *Prof Exp:* Fel, Enzyme Inst, Univ Wis, 57-61. *Mem:* AAAS; Am Chem Soc. *Res:* Amine and carbohydrate metabolism; enzyme chemistry. *Mailing Add:* Dept Chem Univ Wis Stevens Point WI 54481

**WEAVER, ROBERT MICHAEL,** CLAY MINERALOGY, SOIL SCIENCE. *Current Pos:* MEM STAFF, CLAY DIV, J M HUBER CORP, 78- *Personal Data:* b Goshen, Ind, June 23, 42; m 75; c 2. *Educ:* Berea Col, BA, 64; Mich State Univ, MS, 66; Univ Wis-Madison, PhD(soil sci), 70. *Prof Exp:* Asst prof soil sci, Cornell Univ, 71-78. *Mem:* Soil Sci Soc Am; Clay Minerals Soc. *Res:* Genesis of clay minerals; clay mineralogy of tropical soils. *Mailing Add:* 4306 Nandina Ct Evans GA 30809

**WEAVER, ROBERT PAUL,** astrophysics, physics, for more information see previous edition

**WEAVER, W DOUGLAS,** PREHOSPITAL CARDIAC CARE, CARDIAC TECHNOLOGY. *Current Pos:* asst prof, 79-85, ASSOC PROF CARDIOL, UNIV WASH, 85- *Personal Data:* b Ft Fairfield, Maine, Mar 14, 45. *Educ:* Univ Maine, BA, 67; Tufts Univ Sch Med, MD, 71. *Concurrent Pos:* Prin investr, Myocardial Infraction Triage & Intervention Trial, 87-; mem, Coun Clin Cardiol, Am Heart Asn, 84- *Mem:* Am Heart Asn; fel Am Col Cardiol. *Res:* Epidemiology of sudden death; prehospital emergency cardiac care; thrombolytic therapy shelves; development and testing of automatic external defibrinators. *Mailing Add:* Div Cordiol RG-22 Univ Wash 1959 NE Pacific St Seattle WA 98195

**WEAVER, WARREN ELDRED,** PHARMACEUTICAL CHEMISTRY & PHARMACY, ADMINISTRATION & ETHICS. *Current Pos:* assoc prof chem & pharmaceut chem, Med Col Va, 50-54, from actg chmn to chmn dept, 50-56, dean, Sch Pharm, 56-81, PROF CHEM & PHARMACEUT CHEM, MED COL VA, 54-, EMER DEAN, SCH PHARM, 81- *Personal Data:* b Sparrows Point, Md, June 5, 21; m 45, 69, Esther Schiesser; c Glenn, Karen, Janet & Julie. *Educ:* Univ Md, BS, 42, PhD(pharmaceut chem), 47. *Prof Exp:* Asst pharm, Univ Md, 42, asst antigas prep, Off Sci Res & Develop, 42-44; asst insecticides, 44-45; chemist, US Naval Res Lab, 45-50. *Concurrent Pos:* Mem pharm rev comt, NIH, 68-72; mem bd dirs, Am Found Pharm Educ, 69-73; mem, Secretary's Comn to rev Report of President's Task Force on Prescription Drugs, 70; mem, Am Coun Pharmaceut Educ, 74-80. *Mem:* AAAS; Am Chem Soc; Am Pharmaceut Asn; Am Inst Hist Pharm; Am Asn Cols Pharm (vpres, 67-68, pres, 68-69). *Res:* Synthetic peptides; insecticides; correlation of structure with fungicidal activity. *Mailing Add:* 403 Horsepen Rd Richmond VA 23229

**WEAVER, WILLIAM BRUCE,** ATOMIC & MOLECULAR PHYSICS, PLASMA PHYSICS. *Current Pos:* pres, 86-92, RES ASTRONOMER, MONTEREY INST RES ASTRON, 72-, DIR RES, 92-; SR PRIN STAFF, BDM, INC, 72- *Personal Data:* b Catskill, NY, Sept 1, 46; c 2. *Educ:* Univ Ariz, BS, 68; Case Inst Technol, MS, 71; Case Western Res Univ, PhD(astrophys), 72. *Concurrent Pos:* trainee, NSF & Case Western Res Univ, 68-72. *Mem:* Am Astron Soc; Royal Astron Soc; Astron Soc Pac; Int Astron Union. *Res:* Automatic spectral classification; statistics and astrophysics of star formation; spectrophotometry of peculiar stars; design & construction of astronomical instrumentation including spectrophotometers and solid state detectors; neurol networks and expert systems. *Mailing Add:* Monterey Inst Res Astron 200 Eighth St Marina CA 93933. *Fax:* 408-375-3406; *E-Mail:* mira@nps.navy.mil, bu@mira.eng

**WEAVER, WILLIAM JUDSON,** PATHOPHYSIOLOGY. *Current Pos:* ASSOC PROF BIOL, LINFIELD COL, PORTLAND, ORE, 83- *Personal Data:* b Twin Falls, Idaho, May 7, 36; m 65, Kathleen Milne; c Margaret & Mary. *Educ:* Col Idaho, BS, 58; Univ Ore, MS, 65, PhD(exp path), 71. *Prof Exp:* Res assoc surg, Ore Health Sci Univ, 71-83. *Mem:* AAAS; NY Acad Sci. *Res:* Pathophysiology. *Mailing Add:* 24 Del Prado Lake Oswego OR 97035-1312

**WEAVER, WILLIAM MICHAEL,** ORGANIC CHEMISTRY. *Current Pos:* from instr to assoc prof, 58-70, PROF ORG CHEM, JOHN CARROLL UNIV, 70- *Personal Data:* b Lima, Ohio, Feb 18, 31; m 66, Therese Consolo; c William J. *Educ:* Johns Carroll Univ, BS, 53; Purdue Univ, MS, , 56, PhD, 58. *Prof Exp:* Asst org chem, Purdue Univ, 53-58. *Mem:* Am Chem Soc. *Res:* Aliphatic nitrocompound; kinetics; reactions in aprotic solvents. *Mailing Add:* 22279 Douglas Rd Cleveland OH 44122-2038

**WEBB, ALAN WENDELL,** HIGH PRESSURE MATERIALS SCIENCE. *Current Pos:* RES CHEMIST, US NAVAL RES LAB, 68- *Personal Data:* b Enid, Okla, Sept 20, 39; m 61, Suellen Stone; c Laura, Lisa, Andrew & Rebecca. *Educ:* Brigham Young Univ, BS, 63, PhD(phys chem), 69. *Concurrent Pos:* Nat Acad Sci-Nat Res Coun resident res associateship, 68-70. *Mem:* Am Chem Soc; Am Soc Home Inspectors; Am Phys Soc. *Res:* High pressure and high temperature (HPHT) synthesis of inorganic compounds; effects of HPHT on potential superconductors; use of syncrotron radiation for high pressure structural studies. *Mailing Add:* 300 Brockton Rd US Naval Res Lab Oxen Hill MD 20745

**WEBB, ALBERT DINSMOOR,** ENOLOGY. *Current Pos:* From asst prof to prof enol, Univ Calif, 48-60, from asst chemist to chemist, Exp Sta, 48-82, prof enol, Col Agr, 60-82, chmn, Dept Viticult & Enol, 73-81, EMER PROF & CHEMIST EXP STA, UNIV CALIF, DAVIS, 82- *Personal Data:* b Victorville, Calif, Oct 10, 17; m 43, 87, June Moore; c Robert D & Bradford C. *Educ:* Univ Calif, BS, 39, PhD(chem), 48. *Hon Degrees:* Dr, Univ Bordeaux, 82. *Honors & Awards:* Merit Award, Am Soc Enologists, 84; Leon D Adams Award, 87. *Concurrent Pos:* Fulbright res scholar, Australia, 58, Alko Res Labs, Helsinki, Finland, 69; NATO scholar, Bordeaux, 62; vis res prof, Univ Stellenbosch, SAfrica, 70; asst ed, Am J Enol, 71-76, ed, 76-81; scholar res sta, Siebeldingen, WGer, 81; mem coun & bd dirs, Wine Indust Tech Sem, 76-; pres, ADW Enological, 82- *Mem:* Am Chem Soc; Am Soc Enologists (vpres, 72-74, pres, 74-75). *Res:* Isolation and identification of trace aroma and pigment materials in grapes and wines; most aspects of winemaking and some of grape growing; author of 150 technical research papers. *Mailing Add:* 27326 Willowbank Rd Davis CA 95616-5056

**WEBB, ALFREDA JOHNSON,** veterinary medicine; deceased, see previous edition for last biography

**WEBB, ALLEN NYSTROM,** PHYSICAL CHEMISTRY. *Current Pos:* RETIRED. *Personal Data:* b Wichita, Kans, Dec 14, 21; m 43, Georgine H Creo; c Marc C, Todd C & Charis I (Forney). *Educ:* Kans State Univ, BS, 43; Univ Calif, Berkeley, PhD(phys chem), 49. *Prof Exp:* Jr chemist, Boston Consol Gas Co, 43; res chemist, Stand Oil Co, Ind, 44-46; res asst chem, Univ Calif, 46-49; from res chemist to sr res chemist, Texaco Inc, 49-66, res assoc, 66-80. *Concurrent Pos:* Chmn, Gordon Res Conf Catalysis, 70; mem adv bd, Petrol Res Fund, 70-72. *Mem:* Am Chem Soc. *Res:* Catalysis; chemisorption; molecular spectra; fuel cells; exchange reactions; kinetics; hydrodesulfurization. *Mailing Add:* 5901 Cedar Cliff Dr Austin TX 78759-5140. *E-Mail:* awebb@bga.com

**WEBB, ANDREW CLIVE,** DEVELOPMENTAL BIOLOGY. *Current Pos:* Fel biol, Purdue Univ, West Lafayette, 73-75, asst prof, 75-81, ASSOC PROF BIOL SCI, WELLESLEY COL, 81- *Personal Data:* b Bishop's Stortford, Eng, Feb 17, 47; m 80; c 1. *Educ:* Southampton Univ, BSc, 69, PhD(biol), 73. *Concurrent Pos:* Prin investr, NIH, 80-82. *Mem:* Brit Soc Develop Biol; AAAS; Sigma Xi. *Res:* Ultrastructure and biochemistry of amphibian oogenesis with special reference to the organization and expression of the mitochondrial genome. *Mailing Add:* Dept Biol Wellesley Col Sci Ctr Wellesley MA 02181

**WEBB, BILL D,** RICE GRAIN COMPOSITION & FUNCTIONAL PROPERTIES. *Current Pos:* RETIRED. *Personal Data:* b Ralls, Tex, June 13, 28; m 54, Gladys Schram; c Douglas, Dennis, & Diane. *Educ:* Tex A&M Univ, BS, 56, MS, 59, PhD(biochem & nutrit), 61. *Prof Exp:* Res chemist, Agr Res Serv, USDA, 61-90, res leader, Rice Unit, 90-96. *Concurrent Pos:* Collabr & rice grain qual consult, Agr Res Serv, USDA. *Mem:* Am Asn Cereal Chem; Inst Food Technologists; Sigma Xi. *Res:* Physicochemical properties of the rice grain and their relation to rice milling, cooking, processing and nutritive quality. *Mailing Add:* 106 Lone Star Dr Georgetown TX 78628. *Fax:* 409-752-5720

**WEBB, BURLEIGH C,** AGRONOMY, PLANT PHYSIOLOGY. *Current Pos:* PROF AGRON, NC A&T STATE UNIV, 59-, DEAN SCH AGR, 65- *Personal Data:* b Greensboro, NC, Jan 9, 23; m 49; c 3. *Educ:* Agr & Tech Col, NC, BS, 43; Univ Ill, MS, 47; Mich State Univ, PhD, 52. *Prof Exp:* Instr agron, Tuskegee Inst, 47-49; asst prof, Ala Agr & Mech Col, 51-52; assoc prof, Tuskegee Inst, 52-59. *Mem:* AAAS; Am Soc Agron; Sigma Xi. *Res:* Plant physiology and ecology of forage crop plants; role of growth regulators in developmental and growth phenomena in crop plants. *Mailing Add:* 137 N Dudley St Greensboro NC 27401

**WEBB, BYRON H,** DAIRY INDUSTRY. *Current Pos:* RETIRED. *Personal Data:* b New York, NY, May 2, 03; m 32; c 4. *Educ:* Univ Calif, BS, 25; George Washington Univ, MS, 28; Cornell Univ, PhD(dairy indust), 31. *Honors & Awards:* Borden Award, Am Dairy Sci Asn, 43. *Prof Exp:* Jr dairy mfg specialist, Bur Dairy Indust, USDA, 26-29, from assoc specialist to sr specialist, 30-48, prin dairy technologist, 48-51; sr scientist, Nat Dairy Res Labs, Inc, 51-53, asst dir res, 53-54, dir, 54-60, chief dairy prods lab, Eastern Utilization Res & Develop Div, Agr Res Serv, USDA, DC, 50-72. *Concurrent Pos:* Consult, dairy & food technol, 72-88. *Mem:* AAAS; Am Chem Soc; Am Dairy Sci Asn; Inst Food Technologists. *Res:* Methods of improvement of dairy products; development of new products, by-products from milk. *Mailing Add:* 5426 Burkittsville Rd Burkettsville MD 21718-9309

**WEBB, BYRON KENNETH**, AGRICULTURAL ENGINEERING. *Current Pos:* From asst prof to assoc prof agr eng, Clemson Univ, 55-72, head dept, 77-84, assoc dean & dir, 84-87, PROF AGR ENG, CLEMSON UNIV, 72-, DEAN & DIR, 87- *Personal Data:* b Cross Anchor, SC, Feb 2, 34; m 61; c 1. *Educ:* Clemson Univ, BS, 55, MS, 62; NC State Univ, PhD(agr eng), 66. *Mem:* Am Soc Agr Engrs; Am Soc Eng Educ; Sigma Xi. *Res:* Fruit and vegetable mechanization. *Mailing Add:* 217 Hunter Ave Clemson SC 29631-2204

**WEBB, CAROL F**, IMMUNOGLOBULIN GENES, TRANSCRIPTION. *Current Pos:* ASST MEM, OKLA MED RES FOUND, 90-; ADJ ASST PROF, UNIV OKLA, HEALTH SCI CTR, 91- *Personal Data:* b Casper, Wyo, Nov 28, 57; m, Mark A Wolfe; c Emily. *Educ:* Washington Univ, St Louis, AB, 79; Univ Ala, Birmingham, PhD(microbiol), 85. *Prof Exp:* Fel, Children's Hosp, Harvard Univ, 85-86, Univ Tex Southwestern Med Ctr, 86-90. *Mem:* Fedn Am Socs Exp Biol; Am Asn Immunologists; Am Soc Microbiol. *Res:* Transcription-related events and proteins involved in murine heavy chain immunoglobulin expression; Bcell differentiation and gene expression in general. *Mailing Add:* Dept Immunobiol Okla Med Res Found 825 NE 13th St Oklahoma City OK 73104-5097. *Fax:* 405-271-8568

**WEBB, CHARLES ALAN**, TECHNICAL & BUSINESS, MANAGEMENT. *Current Pos:* Chemist, E I DuPont de Nemours & Co, Inc, Textile Fibers Dept, 69-70, res chemist, 75-78, mkt rep, Polymer Prod Dept, 78-80, res supvr, 80-82, tech mfg supt, 82-85, sr planning consult, 85-86, venture mgr, Packaging Prod Div, 86-88, bus mgr, packaging prod, 89-93, BUS MGR, CORP PROCESS DEVELOP & SMALL LOTS MFG, E I DUPONT DE NEMOURS & CO, INC, 94- *Personal Data:* b Charlottesville, Va, July 23, 47; m 74, Mary J Adams; c Christine E. *Educ:* Lehigh Univ, BA, 69; Univ Miami, PhD(phys chem), 75. *Res:* Electrochemical corrosion of copper in chloride and amino acid solutions; spunbonded nonwoven polymer technology; stabilization, polyethylene and Surlyn product development; polypropylene stabilization; vinyl acetate and polyvinyl alcohol technology. *Mailing Add:* E I DuPont de Nemours & Co Inc PO Box 80249 Wilmington DE 19880-0249

**WEBB, CYNTHIA ANN GLINERT**, development biology, cell biology, for more information see previous edition

**WEBB, DAVID RITCHIE, JR**, PROTEIN PURIFICATION & ANALYSIS, ANALYSIS OF CYTOKINE-MEDIATED REGULATION OF CELL FUNCTION. *Current Pos:* DISTINGUISHED SCIENTIST, SYNTEX RES, 87-, DIR, INST IMMUNOL & BIOL SCI, 90- *Personal Data:* b Taft, Calif, Nov 10, 44; m 66; c 2. *Educ:* Calif State Col, Fullerton, BA, 66, MA, 68; Rutgers State Univ, Phd(microbiol), 71. *Prof Exp:* Dernham fel immunol, Univ Calif, San Francisco, 71-73; asst mem, Roche Inst Molecular Biol, 73-79, assoc mem, 79-87. *Concurrent Pos:* Adj prof biochem, City Univ New York, 76-79; adj assoc prof, Dept Zool, Rutgers Univ, 78-87 & Dept Human Genetics, Columbia Univ, 80-87; mem adv comt, Physiol, Cell & Molecular Biol, NSF, 80-82; affil, Cancer Biol Prog, Stanford Univ, 89-; mem, merit rev bd oncol, Vets Health Admin, 91-92, chmn, 93- *Mem:* Am Asn Immunologists; Sigma Xi; Am Soc Microbiol; NY Acad Sci; AAAS. *Res:* Molecular basis of lymphocyte activation; regulation of immunity at the cellular and molecular level; development of immune modulating drugs. *Mailing Add:* Capus Pharmaceut 777 Old Saw Mill Rd Tarrytown NY 10591-6705. *Fax:* 650-354-7846; *E-Mail:* syntex/g=webb@mhs.att.mail.com

**WEBB, DAVID THOMAS**, PHOTOMORPHOGENESIS, PLANT TISSUE CULTURE. *Current Pos:* RES SCIENTIST, BC RES CORP, 88- *Personal Data:* b Darby, Pa, Aug 2, 45; m 75. *Educ:* West Chester State Col, BA, 67; Univ Mont, PhD(bot), 78. *Prof Exp:* Asst prof biol, Simmons Col, 78-80; asst prof bot, Univ PR, 80-84; asst prof biol, Queens Univ, Ont, 84-87. *Concurrent Pos:* Proj leader, Agrogen Biotech, 88. *Mem:* Bot Soc Am; Can Bot Asn; Can Soc Plant Physiologists. *Res:* Effects of light on cycad root growth and nodulation; cycad-Nostoc cymbiosis in virto; clonal propagation of economically important gymnosperms. *Mailing Add:* Dept Bot Univ Hawaii Manoa 3190 Marle Way Honolulu HI 96822-2270

**WEBB, DENIS CONRAD**, MICROWAVE ENGINEERING, MAGNETICS. *Current Pos:* supvr electron eng acoust, 72-87, SUPVR ELECTRON ENG, MICROWAVE TECH, NAVAL RES LAB, 87- *Personal Data:* b Skowheghan, Maine, May 12, 38; m 73, Barbara Sollner; c Lisa. *Educ:* Univ Mich, BSE, 60, MS, 61; Stanford Univ, PhD(appl physics), 71. *Prof Exp:* From assoc to sr engr electromagnetics, Westinghouse Defense & Space Ctr, 61-66; engr magnetics, Phys Electron Lab, 71-72. *Mem:* Inst Elec & Electronics Engrs; Sigma Xi. *Res:* Magnetoelastic propagation in highly magnetostrictive materials; excitation and propagation of magnetostatic surface waves; microwave superconductivity. *Mailing Add:* Naval Res Lab Code 6850 Washington DC 20375-0001. *Fax:* 202-767-0455

**WEBB, DONALD WAYNE**, ENTOMOLOGY. *Current Pos:* from asst taxonomist to assoc taxonomist, 66-82, TAXONOMIST, ILL NATURAL HIST SURV, 82- *Personal Data:* b Brandon, Man, July 12, 39; m 61; c 2. *Educ:* Univ Man, BSc, 61, MSc, 63; Univ Ill, PhD, 81. *Prof Exp:* Lectr, St Paul's Col, Man, 62-63. *Concurrent Pos:* Assoc prof agr entom, Univ Ill, 81- *Res:* Aquatic insect ecology and the taxonomy of mature and immature stages of the Chironomidae; systematics of mecoptera and diptera. *Mailing Add:* Univ Ill 295 Natural Resources Champaign IL 61820

**WEBB, FRED, JR**, GEOLOGY. *Current Pos:* from asst prof to assoc prof, 68-73, chmn dept, 72-94, PROF GEOL, APPALACHIAN STATE UNIV, 73- *Personal Data:* b Hinton, WVa, Feb 23, 35; m 56, Barbara A Haynes; c Jennie L & Ann H. *Educ:* Duke Univ, AB, 57; Va Polytech Inst, MS, 59, PhD(struct geol), 65. *Prof Exp:* Asst geol, Va Polytech Inst, 59-60, instr, Eng Exp Sta, 61-63, instr, Inst, 63-66, resident dir, Summer Field Sta, 65; assoc prof geol, Catawba Col, 66-68. *Concurrent Pos:* Vis prof, Va Polytech Inst & State Univ, 71-84; exchange prof geol, Northeast Univ, Shenyang, People's Repub China, 82-83 & 94, hon prof, 85- *Mem:* Nat Asn Geol Teachers; Soc Econ Paleontologists & Mineralogists; Geol Soc Am. *Res:* Stratigraphy and tectonics of southern Appalachians; Ordovician paleotopography; stratigraphy and regional geology of northeastern China; Ordovician/Carboniferous unconformity in northeast China; environments of deposition of Proterozoic rocks in Liaoning Province, China. *Mailing Add:* Dept Geol Appalachian State Univ Boone NC 28608. *Fax:* 704-262-2127; *E-Mail:* webbfj@appstate.edu

**WEBB, GEORGE DAYTON**, ION TRANSPORT, HYPERTENSION. *Current Pos:* asst prof, 66-69, ASSOC PROF PHYSIOL, UNIV VT, 69- *Personal Data:* b Oak Park, Ill, June 22, 34; m 57, Norma Beach; c Gordon, Valerie & Forrest. *Educ:* Oberlin Col, AB, 56; Yale Univ, MAT, 57; Univ Colo, PhD(physiol), 62. *Prof Exp:* High sch teacher, DC, 57-58. *Concurrent Pos:* Vis fel biochem, Univ Copenhagen, 62-63; vis fel neurol & biochem, Columbia Univ, 63-66; vis prof, Univ PR, 74, Nat Univ Singapore, 93. *Mem:* Am Physiol Soc; Am Soc Hypertension; Soc Gen Physiol; Biophys Soc; fel Am Col Nutrit. *Res:* Sodium and potassium transport through cell membranes, especially in relation to essential hypertension; effects of exercise and aging. *Mailing Add:* Dept Molecular Physiol & Biophys Given Med Bldg Univ Vt Burlington VT 05405. *Fax:* 802-656-0747; *E-Mail:* webb@northpole.med.uvm.edu

**WEBB, GEORGE N**, CLINICAL ENGINEERING, ELECTRICAL SAFETY ENGINEERING. *Current Pos:* RETIRED. *Personal Data:* b Fredericktown, Ohio, Mar 24, 20; m 46; c 2. *Educ:* Univ Toledo, BE, 47; NC State Col, MS, 52. *Prof Exp:* Instr elec eng, Univ Toledo, 47-49; instr NC State Col, 49-51, res engr, 51-52; electronics engr, Sch Med, Johns Hopkins Univ, 52-57, asst, 57-61, instr, 61-64, asst prof biomed eng, 64-, clin engr, Hosp, 71- *Concurrent Pos:* Secy gen, Int Fedn Med Electronics & Biol Engrs, 67-71, mem conf planning & policies comt, 69-; chmn const comt, Alliance for Engrs in Med & Biol, 69-; mem instrumentation group, Int Soc Comn Heart Dis Resources, 70-; partic, appl physiol & bioeng study sect, NIH, 72-76. *Mem:* AAAS; Inst Elec & Electronics Engrs; Asn Advan Med Instrumentation; Int Fedn Med Electronics & Biol Engrs; Biomed Eng Soc; Sigma Xi. *Res:* Instruments for data acquisition; processing and display for intensive care; electro-cardiogram, cardiac pressure, respiratory function; methodology for assuring quality of performance and safe operation of patient related electrical equipment; codes and standards for electrical safety. *Mailing Add:* 13801 York Rd Apt G12 Cockeysville MD 21030-1807

**WEBB, GEORGE RANDOLPH**, ENGINEERING SCIENCE, STABILITY. *Current Pos:* assoc prof physics, 73-76, PROF PHYSICS, CHRISTOPHER NEWPORT COL, 76- *Personal Data:* b Norfolk, Va, Feb 25, 38; m 59, Jane Carter; c Lewis W III, G Randolph Jr, Wade L R & Charlotte. *Educ:* Mass Inst Technol, BS, 59; Va Polytech Inst, PhD(eng mech), 64. *Prof Exp:* From asst prof to assoc prof mech eng, Tulane Univ, 64-73. *Concurrent Pos:* NSF vis scientist, Univ Va, 71-72, NSF pub serv resident, Smithfield Times, 77-78. *Mem:* Soc Naval Archit & Marine Eng; Soc Natural Philos; Am Soc Mech Engrs; Am Soc Eng Educ; Sigma Xi. *Res:* Theories of stability; bifurcation theory and catastrophe theory applications. *Mailing Add:* Dean Col Bus, Sci & Technol Christopher Newport Univ 50 Shoe Lane Newport News VA 23606-2949. *Fax:* 757-594-7919; *E-Mail:* gwebb@pcs.cnu.edu

**WEBB, GLENN FRANCIS**, MATHEMATICAL ANALYSIS. *Current Pos:* From asst prof to assoc prof, 68-79, PROF MATH, VANDERBILT UNIV, 79-, CHAIR, MATH DEPT, 87- *Personal Data:* b Cleveland, Ohio, Sept 30, 42; m 73; c 2. *Educ:* Ga Inst Technol, BS, 65; Emory Univ, MS, 66, PhD(math), 68. *Concurrent Pos:* Vis assoc prof math, Univ Ky, 73; Ital Nat Coun Res fel, Univ Rome, 74; vis prof math, Univ Padova, 80 & Univ Graz, 81. *Mem:* Am Math Soc; Math Asn Am. *Res:* Differential equations and functional analysis and mathematical biolgy. *Mailing Add:* Dept Math Vanderbilt Univ 1326 Stevenson Ctr Nashville TN 37240-0001

**WEBB, GLENN R**, MALACOLOGY. *Current Pos:* prof, 63-84, EMER PROF BIOL, KUTZTOWN STATE COL, 84- *Personal Data:* b Chicago, Ill, May 22, 18; m 53; c 1. *Educ:* Univ Ill, BS, 48, MS, 49; Univ Okla, PhD, 60. *Prof Exp:* Res asst, Univ Ill, 48-49; instr biol, Henderson State Teachers Col, 56-57; fishery res biologist, US Fish & Wildlife Surv, Ft Worth, Tex, 58-59; instr, Coastal Carolina Jr Col, 59-60 & SC, Florence & Conway Branches, 60-62; asst prof, High Point Col, 62-63. *Mem:* Am Malacol Union. *Res:* Pulmonate land snails life histories with special regard to sexology as a clue to phylogeny; snail autoecology; Polygyridae-Helicoidea; inter-species hybridization. *Mailing Add:* 1668 Hwy 544 Conway SC 29526-8451

**WEBB, HAROLD DONIVAN**, electrical engineering, applied physics; deceased, see previous edition for last biography

**WEBB, HELEN MARGUERITE**, invertebrate physiology, for more information see previous edition

**WEBB, J(OHN) WARREN,** FOREST, WETLAND & ANIMAL ECOLOGY, ENVIRONMENTAL POLICY IMPACT ANALYSIS & REVIEW. *Current Pos:* RES STAFF, OAK RIDGE NAT LAB, 78- *Personal Data:* b Austin, Tex, Apr 4, 45; div; c Jason, Kerrigan & Laura. *Educ:* Univ Tex, Austin, BA, 67; Rhodes Univ, Grahamstown, SAfrica, PhD(insect ecol), 75. *Prof Exp:* Natural sci chmn, Mary Holmes Jr Col, West Point, Miss, 69-71; lectr entomol, Rhodes Univ, SAfrica, 74-75; res assoc ecol & forest entomol, Univ Ga, Athens, 75-78. *Concurrent Pos:* Prin investr, Elec Power Res Inst, 80-82; consult forest mitigation, CEngr, Tenn Tombigbee Proj, 83, environ trends; c Elizbeth, Deborah & David. *Educ:* Northeast La State Col, BS, 61; Univ Ark-Fayetteville, MS, 64; Tex A&M Univ, PhD(physics), 69. *Prof Exp:* Instr physics, Cent State Col, Okla, 62-65. *Concurrent Pos:* Res partic, Savannah River Lab, Aiken, SC, 70. *Mem:* Am Asn Physics Teachers; Am Asn Univ Prof. *Res:* Three particle scattering problem. *Mailing Add:* Div Math & Sci Univ Ark Box 3598 Monticello AR 71655

**WEBB, JOHN DAY,** POLYMER DEGRADATION, PHOTOVOLTAIC MATERIALS DEVICE & CHARACTERIZATION. *Current Pos:* SR CHEMIST, NAT RENEWABLE ENERGY LAB, 78-; MGR, FOURIER TRANSFORM INFRARED SPECTROS LAB, 90-, SPEAKER & CONSULT, 96- *Personal Data:* b Washington, DC, Nov 30, 49. *Educ:* Univ Colo, Denver, BA, 73; Univ Colo, Boulder, BS, 77; Univ Denver, MS, 82. *Prof Exp:* Chemist, Protex Industs, Inc, 73-75; teaching asst chem, Univ Colo, 75-77; process engr, Shell Chem Co, 77-78. *Concurrent Pos:* Scholar, NATO Advan Inst Polymer Photochem, San Mineato, Italy, 85- *Mem:* Am Chem Soc. *Res:* Fourier transform infrared spectroscopy of semiconductors, polymers, and surfaces, also Fourier transform-Raman and Fourier transform-photoluminescence spectroscopy. *Mailing Add:* Nat Renewable Energy Lab 1617 Cole Blvd Golden CO 80401. *Fax:* 303-384-6604; *E-Mail:* john_webb@nrel.gov

**WEBB, JOHN RAYMOND,** agronomy; deceased, see previous edition for last biography

**WEBB, JULIAN PIERCE,** OPTICAL METROLOGY, LASER PHYSICS. *Current Pos:* Res scientist, Kodak Res Labs, Eastman Kodak Co, 68-71 & 73-92, prin investr, Kodak Apparatus Div, 71-73, res scientist, 92-96, SR STAFF/SR RES SCIENTIST, SENSITIZED GOODS PLATFORM, EASTMAN KODAK CO, 96- *Personal Data:* b Rochester, NY, Sept 29, 35; m 64, Elizabeth Lyon; c Sarah E & Allen P. *Educ:* Harvard Col, AB, 57; Stanford Univ, MS, 66, PhD(physics), 68. *Mem:* Am Phys Soc; Optical Soc Am; Coun Optical Radiation Measurements. *Res:* Optical metrology, optical calibration and quality control for a major optical testing laboratory; develop significant new control procedures and writing calibration and instrument control codes; dye laser research; x-ray photoconductors. *Mailing Add:* 4 Brookwood Rd Pittsford NY 14534-1808. *E-Mail:* pwebb@kodak.com

**WEBB, JAMES L A,** ORGANIC CHEMISTRY. *Current Pos:* RETIRED. *Personal Data:* b Webb, Miss, Nov 17, 17; m 46, Jeanne DeHoff; c Mary Jo (Locker), James L A & Jeanne (Mosekey). *Educ:* Washington & Lee Univ, BS, 39; Johns Hopkins Univ, PhD(org chem), 43. *Prof Exp:* Jr instr chem, Johns Hopkins Univ, 39-43, instr, 43-45; from asst prof to prof, Southwestern at Memphis, 45-59; prof chem, Goucher Col, 59-83, chmn dept, 65-83. *Concurrent Pos:* Res chemist, Chapman Chem Co, 51-59. *Mem:* Am Chem Soc. *Res:* Organic heterocyclic compounds; theory and antidotes for heavy metal poisoning; disubstituted pyridines; bipyrryls and pyrrole pigments; asphalt additives. *Mailing Add:* Island on Lake Travis 3404 American Dr No 1206 Lago Vista TX 78645

**WEBB, JAMES R,** ELECTRICAL ENGINEERING, COMPUTER SCIENCES. *Current Pos:* VPRES ENG, DATA RAY CORP, 77- *Personal Data:* b Lafayette, Ind, Sept 18, 45; m 74; c 3. *Educ:* Univ Colo, BS, 69. *Prof Exp:* Technician, Colo Inst Inc, 61-69; group leader, ESSA-NOAA, McMurdo Sta, 69-71; electronic engr, Colo Instr Inc, 71-72; pres, Commodore Eng Corp, 72-73; dir engr prod develop, Commodore Bus Mach, 73-74; staff engr new prod, Data Pathing Inc, 74-76; staff engr space telescope, Ball Brothers Res Corp, 76-77. *Mem:* Inst Elec & Electronics Engrs. *Res:* Patents relative to keyboards and calculators. *Mailing Add:* Display Labs Inc 2540 Frontier Ave Suite 109 Boulder CO 80301

**WEBB, JAMES RAYMOND,** QUASAR VARIABILITY, MULTIFREQUENCY SPECTRA. *Current Pos:* ASST PROF PHYSICS, FLA INT UNIV, 90- *Personal Data:* b Anderson, Ind, Aug 5, 54; m 83. *Educ:* Ball State Univ, BS, 81; Univ Fla, MA, 84, PhD(astron), 88. *Prof Exp:* Asst prof physics, Stephen F Austin State Univ, 88-89; resident astronr, Comput Sci Corp, 89-90. *Mem:* Am Astron Soc; Nat Space Soc. *Res:* Variations of quasars in all frequency ranges, radio through x-ray; optical variations; energetics of quasar outbursts; continuum models of quasars. *Mailing Add:* Dept Physics Fla Int Univ Miami FL 33199-0400

**WEBB, JERRY GLEN,** THEORETICAL PHYSICS. *Current Pos:* assoc prof, 69-75, head, Dept Phys Sci, 78-80, PROF PHYSICS, UNIV ARK, MONTICELLO, 75- *Personal Data:* b Rosefield, La, Feb 17, 38; m 61, Rose Zuber; c Elizbeth, Deborah & David. *Educ:* Northeast La State Col, BS, 61; Univ Ark-Fayetteville, MS, 64; Tex A&M Univ, PhD(physics), 69. *Prof Exp:* Instr physics, Cent State Col, Okla, 62-65. *Concurrent Pos:* Res partic, Savannah River Lab, Aiken, SC, 70. *Mem:* Am Asn Physics Teachers; Am Asn Univ Prof. *Res:* Three particle scattering problem. *Mailing Add:* Div Math & Sci Univ Ark Box 3598 Monticello AR 71655

**WEBB, KENNETH EMERSON, JR,** ANIMAL NUTRITION. *Current Pos:* From asst prof to assoc prof, 69-82, PROF RUMINANT NUTRIT, VA POLYTECH INST & STATE UNIV, 82- *Personal Data:* b Hamilton, Ohio, Feb 26, 43; c 2. *Educ:* Ohio Univ, BS, 65; Univ Ky, MS, 67, PhD(animal sci), 69. *Mem:* Am Soc Animal Sci; Am Inst Nutrit; Animal Nutrit Res Coun; Agr Res Inst. *Res:* Ruminant nutrition, protein, amino acids and gastrointestinal physiology. *Mailing Add:* 3020 Animal Sci 0306 Va Polytech Inst Blacksburg VA 24061-0306. *Fax:* 540-231-3010; *E-Mail:* Bitnet: ruminan@vtvm2

**WEBB, KENNETH L,** MARINE BIOLOGY, BIOLOGICAL OCEANOGRAPHY. *Current Pos:* from asst prof to prof, 65-87, CHANCELLOR PROF MARINE SCI, COL WILLIAM & MARY, 87- *Personal Data:* b Old Fort, Ohio, July 18, 30; m 73, Susan R Stevick. *Educ:* Antioch Col, BA, 53; Ohio State Univ, MSc, 54, PhD(plant physiol), 59. *Prof Exp:* Res assoc, Marine Inst, Univ Ga, 60-65; assoc marine scientist, Va Inst Marine Sci, 65-79, sr marine scientist, 79-83. *Concurrent Pos:* Vis assoc prof, Ohio State Univ, 65 & Dept Oceanog, Univ Hawaii, 72-73; mem, Adv Comt Ocean Sci, NSF, 78-81. *Mem:* Fel AAAS; Am Soc Limnol & Oceanog; Estuarine Res Fedn; Phycol Soc Am; Sigma Xi. *Res:* Intedisciplinary investigations related to energy flow and nutrient cycling in marine environments including estuaries, salt marshes, seagrass systems, and coral reefs; physiology of marine organisms; image analysis. *Mailing Add:* Sch Marine Sci Col William & Mary Gloucester Point VA 23062. *Fax:* 804-684-7293; *E-Mail:* webb@vims.edu

**WEBB, LELAND FREDERICK,** MATHEMATICS EDUCATION. *Current Pos:* from asst prof to assoc prof, 71-78, chmn dept, 82-85 & 90-96, PROF MATH & MATH EDUC, CALIF STATE UNIV, BAKERSFIELD, 78- *Personal Data:* b Hollywood, Calif, July 27, 41; m 63, Janie R Yoder; c Robert L & Tamara L. *Educ:* Univ Calif, Santa Barbara, BA, 63; Calif State Polytech Univ, San Luis Obispo, MA, 68; Univ Tex, Austin, PhD(math & educ), 71. *Prof Exp:* Lectr math & educ, Calif State Polytech Univ, San Luis Obispo, 67-68; curric writer math, Southwest Educ Develop Lab, 70; teaching asst math, Univ Tex, Austin, 71; res assoc math, Res & Develop Ctr Teacher Educ, Austin, 71. *Concurrent Pos:* Consult, Educ Develop Ctr, Newton, Mass, 71-76, Greenfield Sch Dist, Bakersfield, 73-87 & Maricopa Sch Dist, Calif, 74-75; NSF sec sch math & sci grant, 73-75 & 74-75; sabbatical leave, Agder Reg Col, Kristiansand, Norway, 80; consult, Bishop Union Elem Sch Dist, 80-; vis lectr, NSF Inst, Tokyo, Japan, 75. *Mem:* Sigma Xi; Nat Coun Teachers Math; Nat Coun Supervisors Math; Sch Sci & Math Asn. *Res:* Learning in science and mathematics education; author of kindergarten through eighth grade mathematics textbook series. *Mailing Add:* Dept Math Calif State Univ Bakersfield CA 93311. *Fax:* 805-664-2039

**WEBB, MARY ALICE,** PLANT CELL BIOLOGY, IMMUNOCYTOCHEMISTRY. *Current Pos:* ASST PROF PLANT ANAT & CELL BIOL, PURDUE UNIV, 89- *Personal Data:* b Austin, Tex, Jan 16, 51. *Educ:* Univ Tex, Austin, BA, 75, Univ Tex, Arlington, MA, 80; Univ Wis-Madison, PhD(plant cell biol), 88. *Mem:* AAAS; Am Soc Plant Physiologists; Bot Soc Am; Micros Soc Am; Sigma Xi. *Res:* Calcification in plants; nitrogen-fixing symbioses in plants; light and electron microscopy; immunological approaches. *Mailing Add:* Bot & Plant Path Dept Purdue Univ West Lafayette IN 47907

**WEBB, MAURICE BARNETT,** PHYSICS. *Current Pos:* assoc prof, 61-65, PROF PHYSICS, UNIV WIS-MADISON, 65- *Personal Data:* b Neenah, Wis, May 14, 26; m 56; c 2. *Educ:* Univ Wis, BS, 50, MS, 52, PhD, 56. *Prof Exp:* Proj Lincoln, Mass Inst Technol, 52-53; res lab, Gen Elec Co, 56-61. *Mem:* Am Phys Soc. *Res:* Solid state physics; x-ray scattering; surface physics; low energy electron diffraction. *Mailing Add:* 1805 Baker Ave Madison WI 53705. *Fax:* 608-265-2334

**WEBB, NEIL BROYLES,** BIOCHEMISTRY, MICROBIOLOGY. *Current Pos:* PRES, WEBB FOODLAB, INC, 72- *Personal Data:* b Junta, WVa, May 19, 30; m 53; c 5. *Educ:* WVa Univ, BS, 53; Univ Ill, MS, 57; Univ Mo, PhD(food sci), 59. *Prof Exp:* Asst prof food sci, Mich State Univ, 59-62; dir food tech, Eckert Packing Co, Ohio, 62-66; assoc prof food sci, NC State Univ, 66-77. *Mem:* Inst Food Technol; Am Meat Sci Asn; Am Chem Soc. *Res:* Food processing systems; product development; nutritional quality foods. *Mailing Add:* 4019 Glen Laurel Dr Raleigh NC 27612

**WEBB, NORVAL ELLSWORTH, JR,** PHARMACY, PHARMACEUTICAL CHEMISTRY. *Current Pos:* RETIRED. *Personal Data:* b Indianapolis, Ind, Oct 17, 27; m 50; c 3. *Educ:* Purdue Univ, BS, 50, MS, 52, PhD(pharm), 56. *Prof Exp:* Asst pharm, Purdue Univ, 50-52; from instr to assoc prof, SDak State Col, 52-62; chemist, Pharmaceut Res & Develop Dept, Merrell-Dow Pharmaceut Div, Dow Chem Co, Inc, 80-90. *Mem:* Am Pharmaceut Asn; Acad Pharmaceut Sci. *Res:* Interaction of pharmaceutical dose forms with packaging materials; dose form development. *Mailing Add:* 605 Branchhill Loveland Rd Loveland OH 45140

**WEBB, PAUL,** BIOMECHANICS, PHYSIOLOGICAL ECOLOGY. *Current Pos:* from asst prof to assoc prof, 72-80, PROF NATURAL RESOURCES, SCH NATURAL RESOURCES, UNIV MICH, 80- *Personal Data:* b Hemel Hempstead, Eng, Dec 23, 45; m 70; c 2. *Educ:* Univ Bristol, BSc, 67, PhD(zool), 71. *Prof Exp:* Nat Res Coun fel, Pac Biol Sta, 70-72. *Concurrent Pos:* NSF grants, 75-83; consult, Calif Inst Tech & Detroit Edison. *Mem:* AAAS; Am Fisheries Soc; Am Soc Zool; Can Soc Zool; Soc Exp Biol. *Res:* Functional morphology, biomechanics and behavior of animals, particularly fish; whole animal bioenergetics and energetic correlates of environmental adaptation, including responses to manmade stress. *Mailing Add:* 1121 Natural Sci Biol Univ Mich 830 N University Ave Ann Arbor MI 48109-1048

**WEBB, PAUL,** THERMAL PHYSIOLOGY, HUMAN CALORIMETRY. *Current Pos:* CONSULT, 83- *Personal Data:* b Cleveland, Ohio, Dec 2, 23; m 48, Eileen Whalen; c Shaun & Paula. *Educ:* Va, BA, 43, MD, 46; Seattle, Wash, MS, 52. *Prof Exp:* Intern, Mont Gen Hosp, Can, 46-47, asst res med, 47-48; post surgeon, Arctic Training Ctr, US Army, Alaska, 49-50; res assoc, Seattle, Wash, 50-51; asst prof physiol, Okla, 52-54; res physiologist & med officer, Med Lab, USAF, 54-57, chief, Environ Sect, 57-58; prin assoc, Webb Assocs, 58-83; assoc prof prev med, Ohio State Univ, 70-75. *Concurrent Pos:* Med C, US Army, 43-50; pres & chmn, Environ, Inc, 59-66; foreign res scientist, INSERM, Paris, 83; vis prof, Univ Limburg, Neth, 86, Univ Wis, 88 & Univ Uppsala, 89; clin prof, Community Health, 80- *Mem:* Fel AAAS; Am Soc Clin Nutrit; Human Factors Soc; Physiol Soc; fel Aerospace Med Asn; Undersea Med Soc (pres, 81). *Res:* Environmental physiology; human thermal tolerance; protective clothing; artificial atmospheres; respiratory heat loss; hygrometry; heat regulation; human energy and nutrition; human calorimetry. *Mailing Add:* 370 Orton Rd Yellow Springs OH 45387

**WEBB, PAUL,** PHYSICS, OPTOELECTRONICS. *Current Pos:* STAFF MEM, EG&G OPTOELECTRONICS CAN. *Honors & Awards:* Outstanding Achievement in Indust & Appl Physics Award, Can Asn Physicists, 91. *Prof Exp:* Staff mem, Gen Elec Can. *Mailing Add:* EG&G Optoelectronics 22001 Dumberry Rd Vaudreuil PQ J7V 8P7 Can

**WEBB, PETER NOEL,** GEOLOGY, MICROPALEONTOLOGY. *Current Pos:* PROF MICROPALEONT & CHMN DEPT, OHIO STATE UNIV, 80- *Personal Data:* b Wellington, NZ, Dec 14, 36; m 78; c 2. *Educ:* Victoria Univ Wellington, BSc, 59, MSc, 60; State Univ Utrecht, PhD(geol), 66. *Honors & Awards:* Hamilton Prize, Royal Soc NZ, 60; Cotton Prize, Victoria Univ Wellington, 60; Medal, US Polar Serv, 79. *Prof Exp:* Micropaleontologist, NZ Geol Surv, 60-73; prof micropaleont & chmn dept, Northern Ill Univ, 73-80. *Concurrent Pos:* Vis micropaleontologist, Hebrew Univ Jerusalem, 67 & Fed Geol Surv, Hanover, Ger, 69; secy, Nat Comt Geol, NZ, 70-73; Late Cenozoic Working Group, Sci Comt Antarctic Res, 72-77, convenor, Ice Shelf Drilling Group, 73-78; ad hoc comt, Antarctic Geol, Nat Acad Sci. *Mem:* Soc Econ Paleontologists & Mineralogists; Geol Soc New Zealand; Geol Soc Am; Paleont Soc; Antarctican Soc; Am Geophys Union. *Res:* Cretaceous, Tertiary and recent Foraminifera from Southern Hemisphere, particularly New Zealand, Antarctica, South America and intervening areas, with special emphasis on biostratigraphy, population compositions and climate relationship. *Mailing Add:* Dept Geol Ohio State Univ 125 S Oval Mal Columbus OH 43210-1308

**WEBB, PHILIP GILBERT,** INDUSTRIAL ORGANIC CHEMISTRY. *Current Pos:* plant tech mgr, Chemetron Corp, BASF Corp, 74-76, plant mgr, 76-79, technol serv mgr pigments, 79-91, MGR GROUP TECHNOL, BASF CORP, 91- *Personal Data:* b Norwich, NY, Oct 17, 43; m 68, Cynthia Pickering; c Stephen, Jeffrey & Sherry. *Educ:* Hamilton Col, AB, 65; Univ Rochester, PhD(org chem), 70. *Prof Exp:* Res chemist org pigments, Pigments Div, Am Cyanamid Co, 69-74. *Mem:* Am Chem Soc; Water Pollution Control Fedn. *Res:* New and improved organic pigments; dispersability and lightfastness of organic compounds in inks, paints and plastics. *Mailing Add:* 1 N Brookwood Dr Montclair NJ 07042

**WEBB, R CLINTON,** CARDIOVASCULAR PHYSIOLOGY, HYPERTENSION. *Current Pos:* res scientist, 79-80, asst prof, 80-83, ASSOC PROF PHYSIOL, UNIV MICH, 83- *Personal Data:* b Evansville, Ind, Dec, 31, 48; m 71; c 2. *Educ:* Southern Ill Univ, BA, 71, MS, 73; Univ Iowa, PhD(anat), 76. *Honors & Awards:* C & F Demuth Award, Int Soc Hypertension, 82. *Prof Exp:* Fel physiol, Univ Mich, 76-78, fel pharmacol, Univ Instelling Antwerpen, 78-79. *Concurrent Pos:* Mem, Coun High Blood Pressure Res, Soc Exp Biol & Med. *Mem:* Am Physiol Soc; Soc Exp Biol Med. *Res:* Physiology of vascular smooth muscle, with particular emphasis placed on: vascular reactivity in hypertension and diabetes, cellular and subcellular mechanisms of contraction and relaxation and adrenerqic neurotransmission in vascular smooth muscle. *Mailing Add:* 7813 Med Sci II 0622 Ann Arbor MI 48109-0622. *Fax:* 313-936-8813

**WEBB, RALPH L,** MECHANICAL ENGINEERING, HEAT TRANSFER. *Current Pos:* assoc prof, 77-80, PROF MECH ENG, PA STATE UNIV, 80- *Personal Data:* b Parker, Kans, Feb 22, 34; m 61, Sylvia Apple; c 2. *Educ:* Kans State Univ, BS, 57; Rensselaer Polytech Inst, MS, 62; Univ Minn, PhD(mech eng), 69. *Honors & Awards:* Thermotank Gold Medal, Heat Transfer Design Refrig Indust, Inst Refrig Hall, 87; Heat Transfer Mem Award, Am Soc Mech Engrs, 87. *Prof Exp:* Instr mech eng, Kans State Univ, 57; exp engr, Knolls Atomic Power Lab, 60-62; mgr heat transfer res dept, Trane Co, 63-77. *Concurrent Pos:* Assoc tech ed, J Heat Transfer, 73-76; tech ed, Heat Transfer Eng, 77- & J Heat Recovery Systs, 82-; ed-in-chief, J Enhanced Heat Transfer, 83- *Mem:* Fel Am Soc Mech Engrs; Am Inst Chem Engrs; Am Soc Heating & Refrig Engrs. *Res:* Applied research on enhanced heat transfer, including convection, two-phase flow, boiling and condensation; design of heat exchangers; author of one book. *Mailing Add:* Dept Mech Eng 207 Reber Bldg Pa State Univ University Park PA 16802-1009. *Fax:* 814-863-4848

**WEBB, RICHARD A,** MACROSCOPIC QUANTUM TUNNELING, AHARONOU-BOHM EFFECTS & PHYSICS OF INSULATORS. *Current Pos:* ALFORD S WARD CHAIRED PROF SEMICONDUCTOR PHYSICS, CTR SUPERCONDUCTIVITY RES, DEPT PHYSICS, UNIV MD, 93- *Personal Data:* b Los Angeles, Calif, Sept 10, 46; c 2. *Educ:* Univ Calif, Berkeley, BA, 68; Univ Calif, San Diego, MS, 70, PhD, 73. *Honors & Awards:* Simon Mem Prize, 89; Oliver E Buckley Prize, 92. *Prof Exp:* Res assoc, Univ Calif, San Diego, 73-75; from asst to assoc res physicist, Argonne Nat Lab, 75-78; res staff mem & mgr, T J Watson Res Ctr, IBM, 78-93. *Mem:* Nat Acad Sci; fel Am Phys Soc. *Res:* Macroscopic quantum tunneling in Josephson junctions at low temperatures; investigations of the Aharonov-Bohm effect and universal periodic conductance fluctuations in very small semiconducting and normal metal rings; measurement and temperature, magnetic field, and Fermi Energy dependencies of the conduction process of very small Si MOSFET devices in both insulating and metallic regimes. *Mailing Add:* Ctr Superconductivity Res Dept Physics Univ Md College Park MD 20742. *Fax:* 301-405-3779; *E-Mail:* rawebb@squid.umd.edu

**WEBB, RICHARD C(LARENCE),** ELECTRICAL ENGINEERING. *Current Pos:* RETIRED. *Personal Data:* b Omaha, Nebr, Sept 2, 15; m 41, Virginia I Rolston; c James R. *Educ:* Univ Denver, BS, 37; Purdue Univ, MS, 44, PhD(elec eng), 51. *Hon Degrees:* DSc, Univ Denver, 96. *Prof Exp:* Traffic trainee, Mountain States Tel & Tel Co, 37-39; instr elec eng, Purdue Univ, 39-45; res engr labs, Radio Corp Am, 45-50 & 52; prof elec eng, Iowa State Univ, 50 & Univ Denver & sect head, Denver Res Inst, 52-56; pres, Colo Res Corp, 56-61; pres & tech dir, Colo Instruments, Inc, 61-73; pres, Webb Eng Co, 73-96 & Data Ray Corp, 79-85. *Concurrent Pos:* Consult, electronic eng; vis lectr elec eng, Univ Colo. *Mem:* Fel Inst Elec & Electronics Engrs; Sigma Xi; Soc Motion Pictures & TV Engrs. *Res:* Communication and information theory; electro-mechanical and electrooptical instruments; television; digital data systems. *Mailing Add:* PO Box 3078 Estes Park CO 80517-3078. *E-Mail:* webbco@aol.com

**WEBB, RICHARD LANSING,** POLYMER CHEMISTRY. *Current Pos:* RETIRED. *Personal Data:* b Mountain Lakes, NJ, July 28, 23; m 49; c 3. *Educ:* Mass Inst Technol, BS, 48; Columbia Univ, MA, 49. *Prof Exp:* Jr chemist, Cent Labs, Gen Foods Corp, NJ, 48 & 49-50; res chemist, Cent Res Div, Am Cyanamid Co, 50-60, sr res chemist, 60-69, group leader, Lederle Labs Div, NY, 69-76, sr res chemist, Chem Res Div, Conn, 76-89. *Mem:* Am Chem Soc. *Res:* Reactions of acrylonitrile and derivatives; hydrogen cyanide polymerization; x-ray induced addition reactions of olefins including polymerization; synthesis of polymers for biological applications; photosensitive polymers. *Mailing Add:* 85 Hilltop Pl New London NH 03257

**WEBB, ROBERT CARROLL,** HIGH ENERGY PHYSICS, COLLIDING BEAMS EXPERIMENTS. *Current Pos:* assoc prof, Tex A&M Univ, 80-87, assoc dean, Col Sci, 92, interim dept head physics, 93-94, PROF PHYSICS, TEX A&M UNIV, 87- *Personal Data:* b Petersburg, Va, Mar 6, 47; c Robert Jr, Suzanne & Nicole. *Educ:* Univ Pa, BA, 68; Princeton Univ, MA, 70, PhD(physics), 72. *Prof Exp:* Adj asst prof physics, Univ Calif, Los Angeles, 72-74; res assoc, Princeton Univ, 75-76, asst prof, 76-80. *Concurrent Pos:* Prin investr, US Dept Energy, 81- & Robert A Welch Found, 83-86. *Mem:* Am Phys Soc; Inst Elec & Electronics Engrs. *Res:* Experiments in high energy particle physics; charge conjugation symmetry in proton-antiproton collisions; production of new particle states in high energy hadron collisions; searches for super heavy GUT magnetic monopoles in cosmic rays; the study of high energy proton-antiproton collisions. *Mailing Add:* Physics Dept Tex A&M Univ College Station TX 77843-4242. *Fax:* 409-845-2590; *E-Mail:* webb@phys.tamu.edu

**WEBB, ROBERT G,** VERTEBRATE ZOOLOGY. *Current Pos:* PROF BIOL, UNIV TEX, EL PASO, 62- *Personal Data:* b Long Beach, Calif, Feb 18, 27; m 86, Pat Peden; c Chris. *Educ:* Univ Okla, BS, 50, MS, 52; Univ Kans, PhD(zool), 60. *Prof Exp:* Instr biol, WTex State Univ, 57-58. *Mem:* Am Soc Ichthyol & Herpet; Soc Study Amphibians & Reptiles (pres, 80); Herpetologists League. *Res:* Systematics, zoogeography and evolution of amphibians and reptiles, especially in the southwestern United States and northern Mexico; trionychid turtles worldwide. *Mailing Add:* Biol Sci Univ Tex El Paso TX 79968-0001

**WEBB, ROBERT HOWARD,** MEDICAL PHYSICS, BIOENGINEERING & BIOMEDICAL ENGINEERING. *Current Pos:* scientist, 78-86, SR SCIENTIST, SCHAPENS EYE RES INST RETINA FOUND, 86-; SR SCIENTIST, WELLONAW LABS, MGH LASER CTR, 93- *Personal Data:* b Burlington, Vt, Oct 17, 34; m 53, 81; c 2. *Educ:* Harvard Univ, AB, 55; Rutgers Univ, PhD(physics), 59. *Honors & Awards:* IR-100, 81. *Prof Exp:* Res assoc physics, Stanford Univ, 59-63; asst prof, Tufts Univ, 63-69; sr staff scientist, Block Eng Inc, 69-78. *Mem:* Asn Res Vision & Ophthal; Am Asn Physics Teachers; Optic Soc Am; Inst Elec & Electronics Engrs. *Res:* Medical diagnostic instrumentation; flow cytometry, scanning microscopy optics; chemical and solid state physics; electron and nuclear spin resonance; low temperatures. *Mailing Add:* MGH Laser Ctr 50 Blossom St Boston MA 02114. *Fax:* 617-726-4103; *E-Mail:* webb@helix.mgh.harvard.edu

**WEBB, ROBERT LEE,** ORGANIC CHEMISTRY. *Current Pos:* PRES, R L WEBB & ASSOCS INC. *Personal Data:* b Topeka, Kans, Nov 19, 26; m 52; c 2. *Educ:* Washburn Univ, BS, 49. *Honors & Awards:* Pioneer Terpene Chem Award, Am Chem Soc. *Prof Exp:* Anal chemist, I H Milling Co, 49-50; res chemist, Org Chem Dept, Glidden Co, 50-56, mgr res lab, 56-59, prod mgr, 59-61, asst tech dir, 61-62, vpres, Terpene Res Inst, 62-64; asst mgr aromatic chem develop, Union Camp Corp, 64-65, supt mfg tech serv terpenes, 65-68, gen mgr terpene & aromatic chem, 68-75, sr vpres & gen mgr, chem group, 75-87. *Mem:* Am Chem Soc. *Res:* Terpene and resin chemistry; synthesis and manufacture of flavor and perfumery chemicals from terpenes; composition and reconstitution of essential oils. *Mailing Add:* PO Box 2219 Orange Park FL 32067-2219. *Fax:* 904-278-0768

**WEBB, ROBERT MACHARDY,** physical geography; deceased, see previous edition for last biography

**WEBB, RODNEY A,** INVERTEBRATE PHYSIOLOGY, NEUROENDOCRINOLOGY. *Current Pos:* res assoc zool, 75-77, asst prof, 77-81, ASSOC PROF BIOL, YORK UNIV, 81- *Personal Data:* b Eng, July 23, 46; Can citizen; m 70. *Educ:* Univ London, BSc, 68; Univ Toronto, PhD(zool), 72. *Prof Exp:* Demonstr zool, Univ Toronto, 68-72; Nat Res Coun Can fel parasitol, Inst Parasitol, MacDonald Col, McGill Univ, 72-74; asst prof zool, Univ NB, 74-75. *Mem:* Can Soc Zoologists; Am Soc Parasitologists. *Res:* Fine structure, physiology and biochemistry of parasitic helminths; neurobiology and neuroendocrinology of annelids and helminths; endocrine control of spermatogenesis in leeches. *Mailing Add:* Dept Biol York Univ 4700 Keele St North York ON M3J 1P3 Can

**WEBB, ROGER P(AUL),** ELECTRICAL ENGINEERING. *Current Pos:* from asst prof to assoc prof, 63-77, ASSOC DIR & GA POWER PROF ELEC ENG, GA INST TECHNOL, 78- *Personal Data:* b Cedar City, Utah, Dec 28, 36; m 57. *Educ:* Univ Utah, BSEE, 57; Univ Southern Calif, MSEE, 59; Ga Inst Technol, PhD(elec eng), 64. *Prof Exp:* Engr, Douglas Aircraft Corp, 57-59; proj engr, Sperry Phoenix Co, 59-60. *Concurrent Pos:* Consult, Lockheed-Ga Co, 66- *Mem:* Inst Elec & Electronics Engrs. *Res:* Automatic control systems. *Mailing Add:* Sch Elec Eng Ga Inst Technol Atlanta GA 30332-0001

**WEBB, RYLAND EDWIN,** NUTRITIONAL BIOCHEMISTRY. *Current Pos:* from asst prof to assoc prof biochem & nutrit, 63-73, head dept, 73-82, PROF HUMAN NUTRIT & FOODS, VA POLYTECH INST & STATE UNIV, 73- *Personal Data:* b Dondi, Angola, Africa, Jan 24, 32; US citizen; m 58, Wanda Compton; c Stanley D, Linda D & Susan D. *Educ:* Univ Ill, BS, 54, PhD(nutrit), 61. *Prof Exp:* Res scientist, Lederle Labs, Am Cyanamid Co, 61-63. *Mem:* Am Inst Nutrit; Am Dietetic Asn. *Res:* Nutrition and toxicant interactions; applied international nutrition programs. *Mailing Add:* Human Nutrit & Foods Va Polytech Inst & State Univ Blacksburg VA 24061-0430. *Fax:* 540-231-3916

**WEBB, SAWNEY DAVID,** PALEONTOLOGY, ZOOLOGY. *Current Pos:* from asst cur mus & asst prof zool to assoc cur & assoc prof, 64-70, PROF GEOL & ZOOL & CUR FOSSIL VERT, FLA STATE MUS, UNIV FLA, 70- *Personal Data:* b Los Angeles, Calif, Oct 31, 36; m 58; c 2. *Educ:* Cornell Univ, BA, 58; Univ Calif, Berkeley, MA, 61, PhD(paleont), 64. *Prof Exp:* Instr paleont, Univ Calif, Berkeley, 63-64. *Concurrent Pos:* NSF grants; Guggenheim fel, 73-74; vis prof, Yale Univ, 76; ed, Paleobiology, 75-78, Soc Vert Paleont News Bulletin, 79-82 & Quaternary Res, 82-86; pres, Soc Vert Paleont, 78-79; chmn, US Nat Comn 1st Quaternary Asn, 82-86; bd mem, Simroe Found. *Mem:* Soc Vert Paleont (pres, 79-); Soc Study Evolution; Am Soc Mammal; Int Quaternary Asn; Sigma Xi. *Res:* Fossil mammals, evolution, paleoecology and functional morphology. *Mailing Add:* Fla State Museum Univ Fla Gainesville FL 32611

**WEBB, THEODORE STRATTON, JR,** APPLIED PHYSICS, AEROSPACE ENGINEERING. *Current Pos:* Dir aerospace tech dept, Gen Dynamics, 69-74, vpres res & eng, 74-80, vpres F-16 prog, 80-89, consult, 89-90, VPRES A-12 PROG, GEN DYNAMICS, 91- *Personal Data:* b Oklahoma City, Okla, Mar 4, 30; m 52; c 2. *Educ:* Univ Okla, BS, 51; Calif Inst Technol, PhD(physics), 55. *Concurrent Pos:* Adj prof physics, Tex Christian Univ, 55-71. *Mem:* Am Phys Soc; AAAS. *Res:* Management of research and development; aircraft design and development; propulsion systems; nuclear shielding and reactor theory; low energy particle physics. *Mailing Add:* 4901 Westridge Ave Ft Worth TX 76116

**WEBB, THOMAS EVAN,** BIOCHEMISTRY, CANCER RESEARCH. *Current Pos:* assoc prof physiol, 70-74, PROF MED BIOCHEM, COL MED, OHIO STATE UNIV, 74- *Personal Data:* b Edmonton, Alta, Mar 4, 32; m 61, Ellen A Armstrong; c Linda C (Treglia) & Sharon L. *Educ:* Univ Alta, BSc, 55, MSc, 57; Univ Toronto, PhD(biochem), 61. *Prof Exp:* Nat Res Coun Can fels, Nat Res Coun, Ont, 61-63 & Univ Wis-Madison, 63-65; asst prof biochem, Med Sch, Univ Man, 65-66; asst prof, Cancer Res Unit, McGill Univ, 66-70, actg dir, 69-70. *Concurrent Pos:* Prin investr, NIH grants, contracts. *Mem:* AAAS; Am Asn Cancer Res; Am Soc Biol Sci; Fedn Am Socs Exp Biol. *Res:* The biochemistry of cancer, development of cancer-detection and carcinogens-detection tests and development of anti-carcinogens and chemopreventive agents. *Mailing Add:* Dept Med Biochem 333 Hamilton Hall Ohio State Univ 1645 Neil Ave Columbus OH 43210-1239. *Fax:* 614-292-4118

**WEBB, THOMPSON, III,** PALEOCLIMATOLOGY, PALEOECOLOGY. *Current Pos:* asst res prof, 72-75, assoc prof, 75-84, PROF GEOL SCI, BROWN UNIV, 84- *Personal Data:* b Los Angeles, Calif, Jan 13, 44; m 69, Joan Moscovitch; c Rosanna V & Sarah M. *Educ:* Swarthmore Col, BA, 66; Univ Wis-Madison, PhD(meteorol), 71. *Prof Exp:* Res assoc, Univ Mich, Ann Arbor, 70-71, asst res paleoecologist, Great Lakes Res Div, 71-72. *Concurrent Pos:* Vis fel, Clare Hall & Bot Sch, Cambridge Univ, Eng, 77-78, Cires, Univ Colo, Boulder, 88-89; ed, Rev Palaeobot & Palynology, 80-, J Veg Sci, 90-, Quaternary Sci Revs, 82-, Ecol & Ecol Monographs, 85-88, J Quaternary Sci, 85-, J Climate, 88-95; prin investr, Coop Holocene Mapping Proj, 77-95, Tempo, 95-; pres, Subcomn Holecene NAm & Greenland, Int Union Quaternary Res, 82-91; acad adv, Ctr for the First Americans, Orono, Maine, 84-; Bullard fel, Harvard Univ, 95-96. *Mem:* Fel AAAS; Am Meteorol Soc; Am Quaternary Asn; Sigma Xi; Ecol Soc Am. *Res:* Compile global paleoecological data sets for use in testing earth-system models; use of multivariate statistical techniques for calibrating quaternary pollen data in vegetational and climatic terms; production of paleoclimatic and paleovegetation maps. *Mailing Add:* Dept Geol Sci Box 1846 Brown Univ Providence RI 02912-1846. *Fax:* 401-863-2058; *E-Mail:* thompson__webb__111@brown.edu

**WEBB, WATT WETMORE,** CONDENSED MATTER PHYSICS. *Current Pos:* assoc prof eng physics, 61-65, dir, 83-88, PROF APPL PHYSICS, CORNELL UNIV, 65- *Personal Data:* b Kansas City, Mo, Aug 27, 27; m 50; c 3. *Educ:* Mass Inst Technol, ScB, 47, ScD(metall), 55. *Honors & Awards:* Biol Physics Prize, Am Phys Soc, 91. *Prof Exp:* Res engr, Union Carbide Metals Co, 47-52, res scientist, 55-59, coordr fundamental res, 59-60, asst dir res, 61. *Concurrent Pos:* Consult; mem var adv panels, Nat Res Coun, NSF, 58-; John Simon Guggenheim Found fel, 74-75; assoc ed, Phys Rev Lett, 75-; exec comt, Div Biol Physics, Am Phys Soc, 75-78, chmn, 89-90; mem, Publ Comt, Biophys J; chmn, Long Range Planning Comt, Cornell Res Found, 85-88; NIH Fogarty int scholar, 88-; dir, Develop Resource for Biophys Imaging Optoelectronics, NIH. *Mem:* Nat Acad Sci; Nat Acad Eng; Biophys Soc; Am Soc Cell Biol; Inst Soc Photo Optical Engrs; Fel Am Phys Soc; fel AAAS. *Res:* Critical and collective phenomena; fluctuations; superconductivity; membrane and cellular biophysics; biophysical processes; biophysical instrumentation; chemical kinetics; fluid dynamics. *Mailing Add:* Sch Appl & Eng Physics 212 Clark Hall Cornell Univ Ithaca NY 14853-2501

**WEBB, WATTS RANKIN,** SURGERY. *Current Pos:* PROF SURG & CHMN DEPT, SCH MED, TULANE UNIV, 77- *Personal Data:* b Columbia, Ky, Sept 8, 22; m 44; c 4. *Educ:* Univ Miss, BA, 42; Johns Hopkins Univ, MD, 45; Am Bd Surg, dipl, 52; Am Bd Thoracic Surg, dipl, 53. *Prof Exp:* Chief surgeon, Miss State Sanatorium, 52-63; prof surg & chmn, Div Thoracic & Cardiovasc Surg, Univ Tex Southwest Med Sch Dallas, 64-70; prof surg & chmn dept, State Univ NY Upstate Med Ctr, 70-77. *Concurrent Pos:* Prof, Sch Med, Univ Miss, 55-63. *Mem:* Fel Am Col Surgeons; Am Asn Thoracic Surgeons; fel Am Col Chest Physicians; Am Col Cardiol; Am Soc Artificial Internal Organs; Am Surg Asn; Soc Univ Surgeons; Soc Thoracic Surgeons. *Res:* Shock; cardiac-pulmonary transplantation; organ preservation; hypothermia; myocardial physiology. *Mailing Add:* Tulane Med Ctr 1111 Med Ctr Blvd Ste N 504 Marrero LA 70072

**WEBB, WILLIAM ALBERT,** MATHEMATICS. *Current Pos:* from asst prof to assoc prof math, 69-82, PROF MATH, WASH STATE UNIV, 82- *Personal Data:* b Paterson, NJ, Mar 10, 44; m 66; c 2. *Educ:* Mich State Univ, BS, 65; Pa State Univ, University Park, PhD(math), 68. *Prof Exp:* Res instr math, Pa State Univ, 68-69. *Mem:* Am Math Soc; Math Asn Am. *Res:* Analytic and combinatorial number theory; number theoretic questions concerning polynomial rings over finite fields; combinatorics and graph theory; cryptology. *Mailing Add:* Dept Math Wash State Univ Pullman WA 99164-3113

**WEBB, WILLIAM GATEWOOD,** MEDICINAL CHEMISTRY. *Current Pos:* res assoc, Res Div, Sterling-Winthrop Res Inst, 55-57, Patent Div, 57-61, PATENT AGENT, STERLING RES GROUP, 61- *Personal Data:* b Charleston, SC, July 17, 25; m 52; c 3. *Educ:* Univ of South, BS, 50; Univ Rochester, PhD(org chem), 54. *Prof Exp:* Res chemist, Columbia-Southern Chem Corp, WVa, 54-55. *Mem:* Am Chem Soc; NY Acad Sci. *Res:* Synthetic organic chemistry. *Mailing Add:* 4 Timberledge Rd East Greenbush NY 12061-2712

**WEBB, WILLIAM LOGAN,** psychiatry; deceased, see previous edition for last biography

**WEBB, WILLIAM PAUL,** ORGANIC CHEMISTRY. *Current Pos:* RETIRED. *Personal Data:* b Bismarck, NDak, Dec 30, 22; m 47; c 4. *Educ:* Univ Notre Dame, BS, 44 & 47; Univ Minn, PhD(org chem), 51. *Prof Exp:* Sr res assoc, Chevron Res Co, Standard Oil Co Calif, San Francisco, 51-86. *Mem:* Am Chem Soc. *Res:* Petrochemicals; patent liaison. *Mailing Add:* 16 Chestnut Ave San Rafael CA 94901

**WEBB, WILLIS KEITH,** REGULATORY VETERINARY MEDICINE. *Current Pos:* RETIRED. *Personal Data:* b McCoy, Va, Apr 21, 28; m 50; c 5. *Educ:* Tex A&M Univ, DVM, 57. *Prof Exp:* Vet livestock inspector, Animal Dis Eradication Div, USDA, 57; vet, US Food & Drug Admin, 57-62; res assoc, Mead Johnson & Co, Ind, 62-70; vet med officer, USDA, 70-91. *Res:* Regulatory veterinary medicine; eradication of disease from domestic animals; animal welfare; interstate movement of livestock. *Mailing Add:* 2732 Sugargrove Rd Christiansburg VA 24073

**WEBB, WILLIS LEE,** METEOROLOGY. *Current Pos:* MEM STAFF, SCHELLENGER RES LAB, UNIV TEX, EL PASO, 80- *Personal Data:* b Nevada, Tex, July 9, 23; m 42; c 1. *Educ:* Southern Methodist Univ, BS, 52; Univ Okla, MS, 70; Colo State Univ, PhD, 72. *Prof Exp:* Meteorol observer, US Weather Bur, 42-43, meteorologist, 46-52, physicist, 52-55; meteorologist & chief scientist, Atmospheric Sci Lab, US Army Electronics Command, 55-80. *Concurrent Pos:* Mem upper atmosphere rocket res comt, Space Sci Bd, Nat Acad Sci, 59-65; chmn meteorol rocket network comt, Inter-Range Instrumentation Group, 60-; consult, Cath Univ, 60-61; adj prof physics, Univ Tex, El Paso, 63-; mem air blast subcomt, Inter-Oceanic Canal Studies Group, 64-71; Army adv, Nat Comt Clear Air Turbulence, 65-66. *Mem:* Am Meteorol Soc; Am Geophys Union; Am Inst Aeronaut & Astronaut; Am Phys Soc. *Res:* Synoptic exploration of the 25-100 kilometer region with small rocket vehicles to determine the circulation, thermal and composition structure; development of meteorological satellite techniques for mesoscale applications such as severe storm, air pollution, and combat on a global basis. *Mailing Add:* 4929 Blue Ridge Circle El Paso TX 79904

**WEBBER, CHARLES LEWIS, JR,** MEDICAL & RESPIRATORY PHYSIOLOGY, NONLINEAR DYNAMICS. *Current Pos:* from asst prof to assoc prof, 75-95, PROF PHYSIOL, LOYOLA UNIV, CHICAGO, 95- *Personal Data:* b Bay Shore, NY, July 26, 47; m 70, Constance Folkers; c Kevin & Stephanie. *Educ:* Taylor Univ, AB, 69; Loyola Univ, Chicago, PhD(physiol), 74. *Prof Exp:* Fel physiol, Max Planck Inst Physiol & Clin Res, Bad Nauheim, 73-75. *Concurrent Pos:* Sect leader prog proj grant, Nat Heart, Lung & Blood Inst, 75-80; prin investr, NIH res grant. *Mem:* Am Physiol Soc; Soc Neurosci; Am Sci Affil. *Res:* Central nervous system regulation of cardiopulmonary mechanisms; structure function correlations in the central nervous system; application of nonlinear dynamics to physiological systems and rhythms; computational biology and bioinformatics; recurrence quantification analysis. *Mailing Add:* Dept Physiol Stritch Sch Med Loyola Univ Chicago 2160 S First Ave Maywood IL 60153. *Fax:* 708-216-6308; *E-Mail:* cwebber@luc.edu

**WEBBER, DONALD SALYER,** REMOTE SENSING. *Current Pos:* RETIRED. *Personal Data:* b Los Angeles, Calif, Jan 15, 17; m 51, Mary Boodakian; c Donald A & Zachary M. *Educ:* Univ Calif, Los Angeles, BA, 38, MA, 41, PhD(physics), 54; Calif Inst Technol, MS, 42. *Prof Exp:* Assoc physics, Univ Calif, Los Angeles, 49-54, instr, 54-55; mem tech staff, Ramo-Wooldridge Div, Thompson Ramo Wooldridge, Inc, 55-60, mem sr staff, 60-61, assoc mgr photo equip dept, 61; mgr solar physics prog, Calif Div, Lockheed Aircraft Corp, 61-63, mgr astron sci lab, 64-65; sr staff engr, TRW Systs Group, 65-80. *Concurrent Pos:* Consult physicist, 80-; prin invest, Study Correlation Guid Ref Mats, 66, Lab Measurements Satellite Optical Signatures, 72, Measurements of Atmospheric Pollutants, 75. *Mem:* Am Phys Soc; Optical Soc Am; Sigma Xi. *Res:* Infrared spectroscopy of crystals; photo-optical instrumentation; solar physics; remote sensing. *Mailing Add:* 3551 Knobhill Dr Sherman Oaks CA 91423-4408

**WEBBER, EDGAR ERNEST,** BOTANY, PLANT MORPHOLOGY. *Current Pos:* from asst prof to assoc prof, 67-74, PROF BIOL, KEUKA COL, 74- *Personal Data:* b Worcester, Mass, Sept 11, 32; m 58, Judith Nobbs; c Jeffrey & Laura. *Educ:* Univ Mass, BS, 55, PhD(bot), 67; Cornell Univ, MS, 61. *Prof Exp:* Instr bot, Wellesley Col, 61-62; asst prof, Pa State Univ, Behrend Campus, 65-67. *Concurrent Pos:* NSF grant, 65, Am Philos Soc grant, 68, Pa State fac grant, 65-67, Keuka Col fac grants, 87-88 & 92; teaching/res, Marine Sci Inst, Nahant, Mass, 68-80. *Mem:* Phycol Soc Am; Int Phycol Soc; Brit Phycol Soc. *Res:* Ecology and systematics of benthic salt marsh algae; culture and life history studies; morphology; 28 published papers in marine botany. *Mailing Add:* Dept Biol Keuka Col Keuka Park NY 14478

**WEBBER, GAYLE MILTON,** ORGANIC CHEMISTRY. *Current Pos:* Sr res asst, 58-74, RES INVESTR, G D SEARLE & CO, 74- *Personal Data:* b Sioux City, Iowa, Aug 30, 31; m 60; c 3. *Educ:* Morningside Col, BS, 53; Univ Iowa, MS, 58. *Mem:* Am Chem Soc. *Res:* Steroids; peptides and amino acids. *Mailing Add:* 2026 Harrison St Evanston IL 60201-2222

**WEBBER, GEORGE ROGER,** GEOLOGY. *Current Pos:* RETIRED. *Personal Data:* b Toronto, Ont, Nov 2, 26; m 54, Joan Hill. *Educ:* Queen's Univ, Can, BSc, 49; McMaster Univ, MSc, 52; Mass Inst Technol, PhD(geol), 55. *Prof Exp:* Res assoc, McGill Univ, 55-59, from asst prof to assoc prof geol, 59-88. *Mailing Add:* 66 13th St Roxboro PQ H8Y 1L7 Can

**WEBBER, HERBERT H,** BIOLOGY. *Current Pos:* asst prof biol, 72-74, ASSOC PROF MARINE RESOURCES, HUXLEY COL ENVIRON STUDIES, WESTERN WASH UNIV, 74- *Personal Data:* b Vancouver, BC, Oct 15, 41; m 63. *Educ:* Univ BC, BSc, 63, PhD(zool), 66. *Prof Exp:* NATO fel, Can for Study at Hopkins Marine Sta Stanford, 66-68; asst prof biol, Wake Forest Univ, 68-72. *Mem:* AAAS. *Res:* Invertebrate physiology; reproductive physiology of Gastropoda Mollusca. *Mailing Add:* Dept Environ Sci Huxley Col Western Wash Univ MS 9079 Bellingham WA 98225-5996

**WEBBER, J ALAN,** MEDICAL REGULATORY AFFAIRS. *Current Pos:* Sr org chem, 66-70, from res scientist to sr res, 70-88, REGULATORY SCIENTIST, LILLY CORP CTR, 88- *Personal Data:* b Chicago, Ill, Aug 14, 40; div; c Michael A. *Educ:* Univ Colo, BA, 62; Stanford Univ, PhD(org chem), 66. *Mem:* Am Chem Soc. *Res:* Structural modification and synthesis of natural products and complex organic molecules; medicinal chemistry of agents with antibiotic activity. *Mailing Add:* Dept MC 676 Lilly Corp Ctr Indianapolis IN 46285

**WEBBER, JOHN CLINTON,** RADIO ASTRONOMY, COMPUTER CONTROL. *Current Pos:* DIV VPRES, INTERFEROMETRICS INC, 88- *Personal Data:* b Shreveport, La, Apr 2, 43; m 64; c 2. *Educ:* Calif Inst Technol, BS, 64, PhD(astron), 70. *Prof Exp:* Res assoc astron, Univ Ill, Urbana-Champaign, 69-71, asst prof, 71-77, sr scientist, 77-80; res staff, 80-83, asst dir astron, Haystack Observ, Mass Inst Technol, 83-88. *Mem:* Am Astron Soc; Int Astron Union; Int Union Radio Sci,. *Res:* Radio astronomy research; quasars and very-long-baseline interferometry; equipment development; computer control of radio telescopes and data acquisition systems; recorder system for very-long-baseline array; satellite tracking. *Mailing Add:* 3360 Brookside Dr Charlottesville VA 22901

**WEBBER, LARRY STANFORD,** BIOMETRICS, BIOSTATISTICS. *Current Pos:* PROF & CHAIR BIOSTATIST & EPIDEMIOL, TULANE SCH PUB HEALTH & TROP MED, 91- *Personal Data:* b New Orleans, La, Apr 1, 45; m 67, Rhoda Binder; c David H & Howard A. *Educ:* La State Univ, BS, 67; Yale Univ, MPhil, 70, PhD(epidemiol & pub health), 73. *Prof Exp:* Nat Acad Sci statistician, Atomic Bomb Casualty Comn, 72-74; from asst prof to prof, Med Ctr, La State Univ, 74-91. *Mem:* Am Statist Asn; Biomet Soc; Am Heart Asn; Am Pub Health Asn; Sigma Xi. *Res:* Design, implementation and analysis of an ongoing longitudinal research study of cardiovascular risk factor variables in an entire community; development of health promotion model for school children. *Mailing Add:* Dept Biostatist & Epidemiol Tulane Univ Sch Pub Health & Trop Med 1501 Canal St New Orleans LA 70112-2699. *Fax:* 504-584-1706; *E-Mail:* lwebber@mailhost.tcs.tulane.edu

**WEBBER, MARION GEORGE,** pharmaceutical chemistry; deceased, see previous edition for last biography

**WEBBER, MILO M,** RADIOLOGY, NUCLEAR MEDICINE. *Current Pos:* Intern surg serv, Univ Calif, Los Angeles, 55-56, resident radiol, 56-57 & 59-60, instr, 60-61, lectr, 61-62, from asst prof to assoc prof, 62-74, PROF RADIOL SCI, SCH MED, UNIV CALIF, LOS ANGELES, 74- *Personal Data:* b Los Angeles, Calif, Sept 27, 30; m 55; c Sonja (Ericson) & Linda (Jelloian). *Educ:* Univ Calif, Los Angeles, BA, 52, MD, 55; Am Bd Radiol, dipl, 61; Am Bd Nuclear Med, dipl, 72. *Concurrent Pos:* Consult, Queen of Angels Hosp, Los Angeles, 65-77; res radiologist, Lab Nuclear Med & Radiation Biol, Sch Med, Univ Calif, Los Angeles, 65-78. *Mem:* Am Col Radiol; AMA; Soc Nuclear Med; Radiol Soc NAm. *Res:* Development and refinement of organ radioisotope scanning procedures, including development of white blood cell scanning and thrombosis localization techniques; application of telecommunications to the practice of radiology and nuclear medicine. *Mailing Add:* Radiol Sci BL428 CHS 172 115 Univ Calif Los Angeles CA 90095-1721

**WEBBER, PATRICK JOHN,** ECOLOGY, BIOLOGY. *Current Pos:* DIR, KELLOG BIOL STA & PROF FORESTRY, MICH STATE UNIV, 90- *Personal Data:* b Bedfordshire, UK, Feb 24, 38; m 63. *Educ:* Univ Reading, BSc, 60; Queen's Univ, Ont, MSc, 63, PhD, 71. *Prof Exp:* Asst prof biol, York Univ, 66-69; from asst prof to prof biol, Univ Colo, Boulder, 69-89, mem fac, Inst Arctic & Alpine Res, 69-89. *Concurrent Pos:* Dir ecol prog, NSF, Washington DC, 87-89. *Mem:* AAAS; Ecol Soc Am; Arctic Inst NAm; Can Bot Asn. *Res:* Primary productivity, phenology and phytosociology of terrestrial communities; long-term ecological research; landscape ecology. *Mailing Add:* Dept Forestry Mich State Univ 166 Plant Biol East Lansing MI 48824-1312

**WEBBER, RICHARD HARRY,** ANATOMY. *Current Pos:* from assoc prof to prof, 61-89, EMER PROF ANAT, SCH MED, STATE UNIV NY, BUFFALO, 89- *Personal Data:* b Camillus, NY, Jan 2, 24; m 46; c 7. *Educ:* St Benedict's Col, BS, 48; Univ Notre Dame, MS, 49; St Louis Univ, PhD(anat), 54. *Prof Exp:* Instr biol, St Benedict's Col, 48; instr, Niagara Univ, 49-51; asst anat, Sch Med, St Louis Univ, 51-54; asst prof, Sch Med, Creighton Univ, 54-59; assoc prof, Sch Med, Temple Univ, 59-61. *Concurrent Pos:* Lederle med fac scholar, 56-59; from chmn elect to chmn, Sect Anat Sci, Am Asn Dent Schs, 71-73; mem, Am Benedictine Acad; fel, Human Biol Coun; vis prof, Anat Inst, Univ Heidelberg, 82-83, 85-87, 90 & 91-92, guest prof, 84 & 87. *Mem:* Am Asn Anatomists; Sigma Xi; Cajal Club. *Res:* Peripheral autonomic nervous system. *Mailing Add:* 2947 Sunset Dr Grand Island NY 14072

**WEBBER, RICHARD LYLE,** PHYSIOLOGICAL OPTICS, DENTISTRY. *Current Pos:* PROF, DEPTS DENT & RADIOL, BOWMAN GRAY SCH MED, WINSTON-SALEM, NC, 90- *Personal Data:* b Akron, Ohio, Nov 2, 35; m 91, Katherine S Eggert; c Robert L, Lauren M (Hottinger), Katherine E (Perryman) & Alexandra H (Perryman). *Educ:* Albion Col, AB, 58; Univ Mich, Ann Arbor, DDS, 63; Univ Calif, Berkeley, PhD(physiol optics), 71. *Honors & Awards:* Commendation Medal, USPHS. *Prof Exp:* Intern dent, USPHS Hosp, Seattle, Wash, 63-64, clin investr, Mat & Technol Br, Dent Health Ctr, Div Dent Health, USPHS, 64-68, lectr, Univ Calif, Berkeley, 70-71; clin investr, Nat Inst Dent Res, NIH, 71-72, chief, Clin Invests & Res Servs Br, 73-75, Clin Invests Br & Methodology Sect, 75-80, Diag Systs Br & Diag Methodology Sect, 80-83 & Diag Systs Br, 83-88; chmn, Dept Diag Sci, Sch Dent, Univ Ala, Birmingham, 88-90. *Mem:* Fel AAAS; Int Soc Optical Eng; Int Asn Dent Res; Am Acad Oral & Maxillofacial Radiol; Sigma Xi; Int Asn Dento-Maxillo-Facial Radiol; fel Am Inst Med & Biol Eng. *Res:* Image processing and the study of factors influencing diagnostic systems. *Mailing Add:* Bowman Gray Sch Med Dept Dent Medical Center Blvd Winston-Salem NC 27157-1093. *Fax:* 910-716-4204; *E-Mail:* webber@relito.medeng.wfu.edu

**WEBBER, STANLEY EUGENE,** ELECTRICAL ENGINEERING. *Current Pos:* RETIRED. *Personal Data:* b Boston, Mass, June 8, 19; c 4. *Educ:* Mass Inst Technol, BS, 41, MS, 42. *Prof Exp:* Res assoc, Gen Elec Co, 42-57, mgr eng, 57-64; mgr eng, Litton Industs, Inc, 64-67, mgr linear beam dept, Electron Tube Div, 67-76, vpres, 72-76, vpres, 76-84. *Mem:* Fel Inst Elec & Electronics Engrs. *Res:* Design and manufacture of ultra high frequency vacuum tubes. *Mailing Add:* 960 Industrial Rd San Carlos CA 94070

**WEBBER, STEPHEN EDWARD,** PHYSICAL CHEMISTRY, POLYMER SPECTROSCOPY. *Current Pos:* from asst prof to assoc prof, 66-82, PROF CHEM, UNIV TEX, AUSTIN, 83- *Personal Data:* b Springfield, Mo, Sept 19, 40; m 62, Josephine Kanevsky; c Stephanie, David & Michael. *Educ:* Wash Univ, AB, 62; Univ Chicago, PhD(chem), 65. *Prof Exp:* NSF fel, Univ Col, Univ London, 65-66. *Concurrent Pos:* Vis prof, Fed Polytech Lausanne, Switz, 83, Univ Paris, Orsey, 85. *Mem:* Am Chem Soc; Sigma Xi. *Res:* Energy transfer in polymers; polymer photochemistry. *Mailing Add:* Dept Chem Univ Tex Austin TX 78712. *Fax:* 512-471-8696; *E-Mail:* cmsew@utxdp.dp.utexas.edu

**WEBBER, WILLIAM A,** HISTOLOGY, PHYSIOLOGY. *Current Pos:* from asst prof to assoc prof anat, Univ BC, 61-69, assoc dean med, 71-77, dean, 77-90, PROF ANAT, UNIV BC, 69-, ASSOC VPRES ACAD, 90- *Personal Data:* b Nfld, Can, Apr 8, 34; m 58; c 3. *Educ:* Univ BC, MD, 58. *Prof Exp:* Intern, Vancouver Gen Hosp, 58-59; fel physiol, Med Col, Cornell Univ, 59-61. *Mem:* Am Asn Anatomists; Can Asn Anatomists. *Res:* Renal physiology; kidney structure. *Mailing Add:* Dept Anat Univ BC Vancouver BC V6T 1Z3 Can. *Fax:* 604-822-2316; *E-Mail:* webber@unixg.ubc.ca

**WEBBER, WILLIAM R,** PHYSICS, ASTROPHYSICS. *Current Pos:* PROF ASTRON, NMEX STATE UNIV, 89- *Personal Data:* b Bedford, Iowa, June 9, 29; m 61; c 1. *Educ:* Coe Col, BS, 51; Univ Iowa, MS, 54, PhD(physics), 57. *Prof Exp:* Asst prof physics, Univ Md, 58-59; NSF fel, Imp Col, Univ London, 59-61; from asst prof to assoc prof, Univ Minn, Minneapolis, 61-69; prof physics & dir, Space Sci Ctr, Univ NH, 69-89. *Concurrent Pos:* Co-ed, J Geophys Res, Am Geophys Union, 61-; mem, Fields & Particles Subcomt, NASA, 63-66; consult, Boeing Aircraft Co & NAm Aviation, Inc, 63-; vis prof, Univ Adelaide, 68-69 & Danish Space Res Ctr, 71; NSF fel, Univ Tasmanes, 76 & von Humboldt, Max Planck Inst Physics & Astrophys, Garching, 85-86. *Mem:* Am Phys Soc; Am Geophys Union; Am Astron Soc. *Res:* Charge composition and energy spectrum of cosmic rays; motion of charged particles in the earths magnetic field; solar-terrestrial relationships; particle detectors; x-ray and gamma ray astronomy. *Mailing Add:* 4074 Shadow Run Ave Las Cruces NM 88011

**WEBBINK, RONALD FREDERICK,** ASTROPHYSICS. *Current Pos:* Res assoc astron, Univ Ill, 75-77, res asst prof, 77-78, from asst prof to assoc prof, 78-85, PROF ASTRON, UNIV ILL, 85-, DEPT CHAIR, 89- *Personal Data:* b Hutchinson, Kans, Sept 21, 45; m 70; c 2. *Educ:* Mass Inst Technol, BS, 67; Univ Cambridge, PhD(astron), 75. *Concurrent Pos:* Vis fel, Joint Inst Lab Astrophys, Boulder, Colo, 84-85. *Mem:* Am Astron Soc; Royal Astron Soc; Astron Soc Pac; Int Astron Union. *Res:* Structure and evolution of close binary stars; mass and angular momentum loss from stars; stellar interiors; cataclysmic variable stars; globular star clusters. *Mailing Add:* Astron Dept Univ Ill 103 Astron Bldg 1002 W Green St Urbana IL 61801

**WEBBON, BRUCE WARREN,** BIOENGINEERING, MECHANICAL ENGINEERING. *Current Pos:* BR CHIEF, EXTRAVEHICULAR BR, AMES RES CTR, NASA, 86- *Personal Data:* b Bridgeport, Conn, June 7, 45; div; c 2. *Educ:* Ga Inst Technol, BSME, 68; Univ Fla, MSME, 69; Univ Mo, PhD(mech eng), 78. *Prof Exp:* Turbine aerodyn engr jet engines, Pratt & Whitney Aircraft Co, 67-68; res asst mech eng, Univ Fla, 68-69; sr thermodyn engr life support syst, LTV Aerospace Corp, 69-72; res assoc mech eng, Univ Mo, 72-75; res scientist life sci, Ames Res Ctr, NASA, 75-81; prog dir, Bioinstrumentation Technol, SRI Int, 81-86. *Mem:* Am Inst Aeronaut & Astronaut; AAAS; Aerospace Med Asn. *Res:* Zero gravity fluid mechanics and phase change processes; human thermoregulation; life support systems; physiological instrumentation. *Mailing Add:* 1380 Stage Rd Pescadero CA 94060-0792

**WEBER, ALFONS,** PHYSICS. *Current Pos:* physicist, Nat Bur Stand, 77-80, chief, Molecular Physics Div, 80-96, SR SCIENTIST, NAT INST STAND & TECHNOL, 96- *Personal Data:* b Dortmund, Ger, Oct 8, 27; nat US; m 55, Jeannine K Niebergall; c Karl, Louise & Paul. *Educ:* Ill Inst Technol, BS, 51, MS, 53, PhD(physics), 56. *Prof Exp:* Asst physics, Ill Inst Technol, 51-53, instr, 53-56; fel, Nat Res Coun Can, 56-57; from asst prof to prof physics, Fordham Univ, 57-81, chmn dept, 64-69. *Mem:* Fel Am Phys Soc; AAAS; Optical Soc Am; Coblentz Soc. *Res:* High resolution Raman and infrared spectroscopy; molecular mechanics; optics. *Mailing Add:* Optical Technol Div 844 Rm B208 Bldg 221 Nat Inst Stand & Technol Gaithersburg MD 20899. *Fax:* 301-975-3038; *E-Mail:* aweber@tiber.nist.gov

**WEBER, ALFRED HERMAN,** nuclear & space physics, biophysics; deceased, see previous edition for last biography

**WEBER, ALLEN HOWARD,** ATMOSPHERIC DIFFUSION, MICROMETEOROLOGY. *Current Pos:* FEL METEOROLOGIST, SAVANNAH RIVER LAB, 87- *Personal Data:* b Lorenzo, Idaho, May 15, 38; m 59; c 3. *Educ:* Brigham Young Univ, BS, 60; Univ Ariz, MS, 62; Univ Utah, PhD(meteorol), 66. *Prof Exp:* Asst prof meteorol, Univ Okla, 66-68 & meteorol & environ health, 68-69; consult, Nat Severe Storms Lab, 69; from asst prof to assoc prof meteorol, NC State Univ, 69-77. *Concurrent Pos:* NSF grant, Univ Okla, 68-69; res meteorologist, Environ Protection Agency, Nat Environ Res Ctr, 70-72; Environ Protection Agency grant, NC State Univ & NC Water Resources Res Inst, 72-77 & turbulence & diffusion res, Savannah River Lab, 77- *Mem:* Am Meteorol Soc; Am Nuclear Soc. *Res:* Atmospheric turbulence; physical meteorology. *Mailing Add:* Nonproliferation Technol Sect Savannah River Tech Ctr Aiken SC 29808

**WEBER, ALLEN THOMAS,** MICROBIOLOGY. *Current Pos:* Asst prof, 70-73, ASSOC PROF BIOL, UNIV NEBR, OMAHA, 73- *Personal Data:* b Long Prairie, Minn, Sept 7, 43; m 69; c 2. *Educ:* Univ Mich, Ann Arbor, BS, 65; Univ Wis-Madison, MS, 67, PhD(bact), 70. *Mem:* AAAS; Am Soc Microbiol; Sigma Xi. *Res:* Morphogenesis and development of microorganisms; cellular slime molds; microbial genetics. *Mailing Add:* Dept Biol Univ Nebr 60th & Dodge St Omaha NE 68182

**WEBER, ALVIN FRANCIS,** CYTOLOGY. *Current Pos:* from asst prof to assoc prof, 49-55, head dept, 65-73, PROF VET ANAT, UNIV MINN, ST PAUL, 55- *Personal Data:* b Hartford, Wis, Mar 13, 18; m 45; c 3. *Educ:* Iowa State Col, DVM, 44; Univ Wis, BA, 46, MS, 48, PhD(vet sci), 49. *Prof Exp:* Instr vet sci, Univ Wis, 44-49. *Concurrent Pos:* USPHS spec fel, Univ Giessen, 59; NIH fel, Univ Bern, 72. *Mem:* Am Asn Anat; Sigma Xi. *Res:* Bovine uterine histology, histological and cytochemical changes of the adrenal gland and structure of secretory components of the udder; electron microscopic studies of the hematopoietic organs of domestic animals. *Mailing Add:* Dept Vet Anat 239A Vet Sci Univ Minn St Paul MN 55108

**WEBER, ANNEMARIE,** PHYSIOLOGY, BIOCHEMISTRY. *Current Pos:* PROF BIOCHEM, UNIV PA, 72- *Personal Data:* b Rostock, Ger, Sept 11, 23; US citizen. *Educ:* Univ Tubingen, MD, 50. *Prof Exp:* Res asst physiol, Univ Tubingen, 50-51; res fel biophys, Univ Col, London & physiol, Univ Md, 51; Rockefeller fel phys chem, Harvard Med Sch, 52; res fel physiol, Univ Tubingen, 53-54; res assoc neurol, Columbia Univ, 54-59; asst mem physiol, Inst Muscle Dis, New York, 59-63, assoc mem, 63-65; prof biochem, St Louis Univ, 65-72. *Mem:* Am Physiol Soc; Soc Gen Physiol; Biophys Soc; Am Soc Biol Chemists; Sigma Xi. *Res:* Regulation of muscular activity. *Mailing Add:* Dept Biochem & Biophys Univ Pa Rear 36th & Pine Philadelphia PA 19104

**WEBER, ARTHUR L,** BIOCHEMISTRY, ORGANIC CHEMISTRY. *Current Pos:* RES ASSOC, NASA, AMES RES CTR, MOFFITT FIELD, CALIF, 93- *Personal Data:* b June 7, 43; m 74. *Educ:* Univ Miami, PhD(biochem), 73. *Prof Exp:* Postdoctoral, Univ Ala, Birmingham, 73-75, Univ Calif, Berkeley, 75-76 & Salk Inst, 76-79; res assoc, Salk Inst Biog Studies, 79-93. *Mem:* Am Chem Soc; Fedn Am Socs Exp Biol; Int Soc Study Origin of Life. *Res:* Study of the chemical origin of life. *Mailing Add:* NASA Ames Res Ctr MS-239-4 Moffett Field CA 94035-1000

**WEBER, ARTHUR PHINEAS,** CONTINUOUS CHEMICAL REACTOR DESIGN, MIXING. *Current Pos:* OWNER CONSULT, ARTHUR PHINEAS WEBER ENGRS, 51- *Personal Data:* b Brooklyn, NY, Mar 10, 20; m 42, Jean B Abelman; c S Geoffrey & Diane L (Lichtman). *Educ:* City Col NY, BS, 41; Oak Ridge Inst Reactor Technol, 47. *Prof Exp:* Design engr, Hendrick Mfg Co, 41-42; exec engr, Chemurgy Design Corp, 42-44; dir process develop & design, Kellex Corp, 44-49; tech dir, Int Eng Inc, 49-55. *Concurrent Pos:* Instr chem eng, City Col, New York, 43-44; assoc prof nuclear eng, NY Univ, 51-54; prof chem eng, Polytech Univ, Brooklyn, 55-67; consult, Nat Res Coun; regist prof engr, NY, Ohio, Pa. *Mem:* Fel AAAS; Am Inst Chem Engrs; Am Chem Soc; Nat Soc Prof Engrs; Am Soc Safety Engrs; NY Acad Sci. *Res:* Continuous chemical reactor design; mixing; nuclear physics design; drying systems; process equipment optimization; engineering parameters of insurance liability. *Mailing Add:* 1334 Surrey Lane Rockville Centre NY 11570

**WEBER, BARBARA C,** ENTOMOLOGY. *Current Pos:* proj leader, USDA, 83-86, legis asst, 87-88, staff asst, 88-91, RES ENTOMOLOGIST, FOREST SERV, USDA, 75-, ACTG DIR, 91- *Personal Data:* b Prairie du Chien, Wis, Nov 15, 47; c 1. *Educ:* Viterbo Col, BA, 69; Univ Minn, St Paul, MS, 71; Southern Ill Univ Carbondale, PhD, 82. *Honors & Awards:* Am Black Walnut Res Award, 83. *Prof Exp:* Conserv forest pest specialist entom, Minn Dept Natural Resources, 73-74; entomologist Dutch elm dis, Minn Dept Agr, 74-75. *Concurrent Pos:* Ed, Walnut Coun Bull, 81-85; cong fel, Am Polit Sci Asn, 86-87. *Mem:* Entom Soc Am; Soc Am Foresters; Sigma Xi. *Res:* Insect pests of black walnut; disease transmission by insects; taxonomy of scolytid insects; silvicultural management of black walnut to control insect problems. *Mailing Add:* USDA Forest Serv PO Box 96090 Washington DC 20090-6090

**WEBER, BRUCE HOWARD,** BIOCHEMISTRY. *Current Pos:* asst prof, 70-72, assoc prof, 72-76, PROF CHEM, CALIF STATE UNIV, FULLERTON, 76- *Personal Data:* b Cleveland, Ohio, June 8, 41. *Educ:* San Diego State Univ, BS, 63; Univ Calif, San Diego, PhD(chem), 68. *Prof Exp:* Am Cancer Soc fel, Molecular Biol Inst, Univ Calif, Los Angeles, 68-70. *Concurrent Pos:* NIH res fel, 75; res scientist, Div Neurosci, City of Hope Nat Med Ctr, 75-77. *Mem:* AAAS; Am Chem Soc; Brit Soc Hist Sci; Am Soc Biol Chemists; Sigma Xi. *Res:* Structure, function, and evolution of proteins; history of biochemistry. *Mailing Add:* Dept Chem Calif State Univ Fullerton CA 92634. *Fax:* 714-449-5316

**WEBER, CARL JOSEPH,** RADIATION CROSSLINKED POLYMER SYSTEMS, FLUOROPOLYMERS. *Current Pos:* res chemist, Polymer Mat Develop, Raychem Corp, 85-87, develop group leader, 87-90, eng mgr, Thermofit Div, 90-91, MFG MGR, RAYCHEM CORP, 92- *Personal Data:* b Evanston, Ill, Nov 7, 54; m 77, Judith D Malmin; c Elizabeth A, Matthew J & Samuel P. *Educ:* Univ Calif, Santa Barbara, BS, 76; Univ Mass, MS, 80, PhD(chem), 81. *Prof Exp:* Develop engr electron mat develop, Thick Film Systs, Subsid Ferro Corp, 76-78; fel inorg & polymer chem, Univ Mass, Amherst, 81; res chemist process res, US Borax Res Corp, Div US Borax Chem Corp, 81-85. *Mem:* Am Chem Soc; AAAS; Sigma Xi. *Mailing Add:* 220-W Floresta Way Portola Valley CA 94028. *Fax:* 650-361-5882

**WEBER, CHARLES L,** COMMUNICATION SYSTEMS, RADAR SYSTEMS. *Current Pos:* from asst prof to assoc prof, 64-79, PROF ELEC ENG, UNIV SOUTHERN CALIF, LOS ANGELES, 79- *Personal Data:* b Dayton, Ohio, Dec 2, 37. *Educ:* Univ Dayton, BSEE, 58; Univ Southern Calif, MSEE, 60; Univ Calif, Los Angeles, PhD, 64. *Prof Exp:* Mem tech staff, Hughes Aircraft Co, Calif, 58-62. *Concurrent Pos:* Consult. *Mem:* Inst Elec & Electronics Engrs. *Res:* Blind equalization; spread spectrum systems. *Mailing Add:* Dept Elec Eng Univ Southern Calif PHE 404 0272 Los Angeles CA 90089-0002

**WEBER, CHARLES WALTER,** BIOCHEMISTRY, NUTRITION. *Current Pos:* from asst prof to assoc prof, 66-73, PROF NUTRIT BIOCHEM, UNIV ARIZ, 73- *Personal Data:* b Harold, SDak, Nov 30, 31; m 61, Marylou A Weber; c Matthew & Scott. *Educ:* Colo State Univ, BS, 56, MS, 58; Univ Ariz, PhD(biochem, nutrit), 66. *Prof Exp:* Res chemist, Univ Colo, 60-63. *Mem:* Inst Food Technologists; Poultry Sci Asn; Am Soc Clin Nutrit; NY Acad Sci; Am Inst Nutrit; Am Asn Cereal Chem. *Res:* Interaction between trace elements and fiber; evaluation of desert plants for nutritional quality. *Mailing Add:* Dept Nutrit Sci Rm 309 Shantz Bldg Univ Ariz Tucson AZ 85721. *Fax:* 520-621-9446

**WEBER, CHARLES WILLIAM,** ANALYTICAL CHEMISTRY, ENVIRONMENTAL MONITORING. *Current Pos:* RETIRED. *Personal Data:* b Streator, Ill, Dec 28, 22; m 48, Phyllis Starkey; c Kathy, Paul & Andrew. *Educ:* Northwestern Univ, BS, 49; Ind Univ, PhD(anal chem), 53. *Prof Exp:* Anal chemist, Martin Marietta Energy Systs, Inc, 53-58, Sect Anal Develop, 58-62, dept head chem anal, Oak Ridge Gaseous Diffusion Plant, 62-77, environ analysis five-plant coordr, 77-94. *Mem:* AAAS; Sigma Xi; fel Am Inst Chem; Am Chem Soc; NY Acad Sci; Am Soc Testing & Mat. *Res:* Instrument development; gas analysis; automation; laboratory management; process control. *Mailing Add:* 1021 W Outer Dr Oak Ridge TN 37830

**WEBER, CLIFFORD E,** ADVANCED NUCLEAR REACTORS, NUCLEAR ELEMENT. *Current Pos:* int specialist, 78-89, DEP DIR, ADVAN REACTOR PROGS, DEPT ENERGY, 89- *Personal Data:* b Fresno, Calif, May 20, 18; m 44; c 2. *Educ:* Univ Calif, Berkeley, BS, 41; Johns Hopkins Univ, PhD(chem), 44. *Prof Exp:* Group leader, Manhattan Proj, Johns Hopkins Univ, 42-46; sect head, Knolls Atomic Power Lab, Gen Elec Co, 46-61; dir, Atomics Int, 61-62, proj mgr, 62-68; br chief, AEC, 68-75 & Energy Res & Develop Admin, 75-77. *Mem:* Fel Am Soc Metals. *Res:* Nuclear fuels and materials; nuclear fuel development; fluorins and fluorocarbons; sodium corrosion; fast reactor development; nuclear reactor technology; author of numerous technical publications; awarded one patent. *Mailing Add:* 15317 Carrolton Rd Rockville MD 20853

**WEBER, DARRELL J,** BIOCHEMISTRY, PLANT PATHOLOGY. *Current Pos:* assoc prof, 69-73, PROF BOT, BRIGHAM YOUNG UNIV, 73- *Personal Data:* b Thornton, Idaho, Nov 16, 33; m 62, Carolyn Foremaster; c Bradley, Becky, Brian, Todd, Kelly, Jason & Trent. *Educ:* Univ Idaho, BS, 58, MS, 59; Univ Calif, PhD(plant path), 63. *Honors & Awards:* Maeser Award, 74; Fulbright Scholar SAfrica, 95. *Prof Exp:* Res asst agr chem, Univ Idaho, 57-59; res asst plant path, Univ Calif, 59-63; res assoc biochem, Univ Wis, 63-65; asst prof, Univ Houston, 65-69. *Concurrent Pos:* Fels, Univ Wis, 63-65; consult, NASA, 66-67; grants, USDA, 66-68, NASA, 67-68, NIH, 68-71 & NSF, 71-78; fel biochem, Mich State Univ, 75-76, NSF, 79-76 & 84-88, USDA, 80-81 & 88-90, Nat Park Serv, 90-93. *Mem:* NAm Mushroom Soc; Am Phytopath Soc; Am Bot Soc; New Crops Soc; Am Mycol Soc. *Res:* Phytochemistry; mode of action of fungicides; metabolism of fungal spores; biochemistry of host-parasite complexes; salt tolerance of plants; toxic compounds in plants. *Mailing Add:* Dept Bot 285 Widtsoe Brigham Young Univ Provo UT 84602. *Fax:* 801-378-7499

**WEBER, DAVID ALEXANDER,** MEDICAL PHYSICS, NUCLEAR MEDICINE. *Current Pos:* PROF RADIOL, STATE UNIV NY, STONY BROOK, 88-; HEAD, NUCLEAR MED RES GROUP, GROUP LEADER & SR SCIENTIST, BROOKHAVEN NAT LAB, 87- *Personal Data:* b Lockport, NY, Mar 6, 39; m 61; c Sarah & David Jr. *Educ:* St Lawrence Univ, BS, 60; Univ Rochester, PhD(radiation biol & biophys), 71. *Prof Exp:* Teaching asst physics, Univ Buffalo, 60-61; asst attend physicist, Mem Sloan-Kettering Cancer Ctr, 61-68; AEC grad lab fel radiation biol & biophys, Univ Rochester, 68-70, asst prof radiol, 70-75, asst prof radiation biol & biophys, 70-80, assoc prof radiol, 75-87, assoc prof radiation biol & biophys, Sch Med & Dent, 80-87. *Concurrent Pos:* Clin fac, Sch Health Related Prof, Rochester Inst Technol, 76-86; vis scientist, Lund Univ Hosp, Sweden, 78-79; Fogart Sr Int fel, 78-79; tech assistance expert, Int Atomic Energy Agency, 85, 88. *Mem:* Soc Nuclear Med; Am Asn Physicists Med; Health Physics Soc; fel Am Col Nuclear Physicians; Sigma Xi. *Res:* Development of tracer procedures for the study of bone, brain, heart and lungs; metabolic and functional radionuclide studies to investigate physiological processes and mechanisms of disease; development of single photon emission computed tomography (SPECT) technology, planar imaging techniques and methods of computer assisted image processing. *Mailing Add:* 37 Dartmouth Rd Shoreham NY 11786. *Fax:* 516-282-5311; *E-Mail:* weber@bnlcl1.bnl.gov

**WEBER, DAVID FREDERICK,** CYTOGENETICS. *Current Pos:* From asst prof to assoc prof, 67-78, PROF GENETICS, ILL STATE UNIV, 78- *Personal Data:* b North Terre Haute, Ind, Nov 18, 39; m 63; c 2. *Educ:* Purdue Univ, BS, 61; Ind Univ, MS, 63; PhD(genetics), 67. *Concurrent Pos:* Contract, 70-83 & USDA, 86- *Mem:* AAAS; Sigma Xi; Genetics Soc Am. *Res:* Analysis of meiosis in monosomics; cytological behavior of univalents; effects of a monosomic chromosome on recombination; study of the frequency and types of spontaneous chromosome abberations arising in monosomics; determination of effects of monosomy on lipid content in Zea mays; screening for ultrastructural differences in monosomics; determination of free amino acid profiles in monosomics; analysis of restriction fragment length polymorphisms with monosomics; identification and mapping of duplicate RFLP loci in maize. *Mailing Add:* Dept Biol Sci 4120 Ill State Univ Normal IL 61790-4120

**WEBER, DEANE FAY,** SOIL MICROBIOLOGY. *Current Pos:* RETIRED. *Personal Data:* b Aberdeen, SDak, May 17, 25; m 50; c 3. *Educ:* Jamestown Col, BS, 50; Kans State Univ, MS, 52, PhD, 59. *Prof Exp:* Biochemist & bacteriologist, Quain & Ramstad Clin, Bismarck, NDak, 52-55; asst vet bact, pathogenic bact & virol, Kans State Univ, 57-58; soil scientist, Soil & Water Conserv Br, Agr Res Serv, USDA, 58-64 & IRI Res Inst, Campinas, Brazil, 64-66, microbiologist soybean invests, Crops Res Div, USDA, 67-72, microbiologist, Cell Cult & Nitrogen Fixation Lab, 72-82, Nitrogen Fixation & Soybean Genetics Lab, 82-89. *Mem:* AAAS. *Res:* Legume microbiology; nitrogen fixation. *Mailing Add:* 14972 Belle Ami Dr Laurel MD 20707

**WEBER, DENNIS JOSEPH,** DRUG METABOLISM, PHARMACOKINETICS. *Current Pos:* RETIRED. *Personal Data:* b Kalamazoo, Mich, Mar 30, 34; m 96, Ruth L Lucas; c 6. *Educ:* Western Mich Univ, BS, 58, MA, 62; Univ Fla, PhD(pharm), 67. *Prof Exp:* Res asst phys & analytical chem, Upjohn Co, 58-62; mgr analytical chem, Syntex Labs, Calif, 67-70; res scientist phys & anal chem, Upjohn Co, 70-79, res scientist drug metab res, 79-91; instr chem, Western Mich Univ, 91-94. *Mem:* Am Pharmaceut Asn; Acad Pharmaceut Sci; Royal Soc Chem; Am Chem Soc; Am Asn Pharmaceut Scientists. *Res:* Kinetics of hydrolysis of drugs; correlation of spectra and structure of hydrazones; structure and stability constants of metal complexes of thiouracils; partition chromatography of steroids; high pressure liquid chromatography; pharmacokinetics. *Mailing Add:* 901 Jenks Kalamazoo MI 49006. *E-Mail:* 73170.1676@compuserve.com, dweber1061@aol.com

**WEBER, EDWARD JOSEPH,** AURORAL PHYSICS, SPACE PHYSICS. *Current Pos:* res physicist ionospheric physics, Geophys Lab, 74-90, GEOPHYS DIR, GPIA, PHILLIPS LAB, HANSCOM AFB, USAF, MASS, 90- *Personal Data:* b Troy, NY, July 17, 48. *Educ:* Union Col, BS, 70; Boston Col, PhD(physics), 75. *Honors & Awards:* Marcus O'Day Award, USAF, 85, 90. *Prof Exp:* Res asst physics, Boston Col, 70-74. *Mem:* Am Geophys Union; Sigma Xi; Int Union Radio Sci. *Res:* Auroral dynamics; ionospheric structure and dynamics; optical detection of aurora and airglow; magnetospheric dynamics inferred from the aurora. *Mailing Add:* 61 Brooks Ave Newton MA 02160-1535

**WEBER, EICKE RICHARD,** SEMICONDUCTOR MATERIALS. *Current Pos:* asst prof mat sci, 83-87, ASSOC PROF MAT SCI, UNIV CALIF, BERKELEY, 87- *Personal Data:* b Munnerstadt, WGer, Oct 28, 49; m 85. *Educ:* Univ Cologne, WGer, BS, 70; MS, 73, PhD(physics), 76, DrS(physics), 83. *Honors & Awards:* Prince distinguished lectr, Ariz State Univ, 83. *Prof Exp:* Sci asst solid state physics, Tech Univ Aachen, WGer, 73-76, Univ Cologne, WGer, 76-82. *Concurrent Pos:* Int fel solid state physics, State Univ NY, Albany, 79-80; res assoc solid state physics, Univ Lund, Sweden, 82-83; assoc fac, Lawrence Berkeley Lab, 84-; consult, semiconductor indust co, 83- *Mem:* Am Physical Soc; Ger Physical Soc; Mat Res Soc; Electrochem Soc; Metall Soc. *Res:* Investigations of lattice defects in semiconductors, microscopic identification, electronic properties; influence on the device performance; specific topics include transition metal gettering in silicon, deep level defects in semiconductors, metals GaAs contacts, heteroepitoxial growth of semiconductors; microwave asorption of semiconductors. *Mailing Add:* Mat Sci & Mineral Eng Dept Univ Calif Hearst Mining Bldg Berkeley CA 94720

**WEBER, ERNST,** electrical engineering; deceased, see previous edition for last biography

**WEBER, ERWIN WILBUR,** ELECTRICAL ENGINEERING. *Current Pos:* Res engr, Ill Inst Technol, 60-61, from instr to asst prof, 61-70, res engr, Res Inst, 66-76, ASSOC PROF ELEC ENG, ILL INST TECHNOL, 70-, DIR, DAN F ADAL RICE CAMPUS, 76- *Personal Data:* b Chicago, Ill, Oct 8, 31. *Educ:* Ill Inst Technol, BS, 58, MS, 59, PhD(network theory), 64. *Concurrent Pos:* Assoc engr, Armour Res Found, 62-63. *Mem:* AAAS; Inst Elec & Electronics Engrs; Sigma Xi. *Res:* Network theory; electrical network synthesis; computer aided circuit design. *Mailing Add:* 32 Crooked Creek Dr Yorkville IL 60560

**WEBER, EVELYN JOYCE,** LIPID BIOCHEMISTRY. *Current Pos:* prof, 82-87, EMER PROF PLANT BIOCHEM, UNIV ILL, URBANA, 87- *Personal Data:* b Tower Hill, Ill, Nov 9, 28. *Educ:* Univ Ill, BS, 53; Iowa State Univ, PhD(biochem), 61. *Prof Exp:* Asst biochem, Iowa State Univ, 56-61; res assoc, Univ Ill, 61-65, from asst prof to prof plant biochem, 65-82; res chemist, USDA, 65-87. *Concurrent Pos:* Consult & ed, Univ Ill, Urbana, 87- *Mem:* Am Chem Soc; fel Am Inst Chem; Am Oil Chem Soc. *Res:* Identification and characterization of complex lipids; metabolism of fatty acids and lipids in corn and other plants; metabolism of vitamin E, carotenoids and other natural antioxidants. *Mailing Add:* 808 E Mumford Dr Urbana IL 61801-6325

**WEBER, FAUSTIN N,** ORTHODONTICS. *Current Pos:* From asst prof to assoc Univ Tenn Ctr Health Sci, Memphis, 36-51, chmn dept, 36-78, prof, 78-82, EMER PROF ORTHOD, UNIV TENN CTR HEALTH SCI, MEMPHIS, 81- *Personal Data:* b Toledo, Ohio, Nov 5, 11; m 37; c 4. *Educ:* Univ Mich, DDS, 34, MS, 36; Am Bd Orthod, dipl. *Hon Degrees:* FACD, FICD. *Honors & Awards:* Albert H Ketcham Award, 80; Distinguished Serv Scroll, Am Asn Orthod, 82. *Concurrent Pos:* Consult. *Mem:* Am Asn Orthod; Am Cleft Palate Asn; AAAS; fel Am Col Dent; fel Int Col Dent; Int Dent Fedn; Int Asn Dent Res; Am Asn Dent Res; NY Acad Sci; Am Asn Dent Schs; Am Dent Asn; So Asn Orthod. *Res:* Child growth and development. *Mailing Add:* 279 Ridgefield Rd Memphis TN 38111

**WEBER, FLORENCE ROBINSON,** GEOLOGY. *Current Pos:* geologist, Alaska Br, 49-54, DC, 54-57, GEOLOGIST, ALASKA BR, US GEOL SURV, 57-; DISTINGUISHED LECTR GEOL, UNIV ALASKA, FAIRBANKS, 59- *Personal Data:* b Milwaukee, Wis, Aug 26, 21; m 59. *Educ:* Univ Chicago, BS, 43, MS, 48. *Hon Degrees:* DSc, Univ Alaska, 87. *Prof Exp:* Lab instr & librn, Univ Chicago, 42-43, librn, 47; subsurface geologist, Shell Oil Co, Tex, 43-47 & State Geol Surv, Mo, 47. *Concurrent Pos:* Arctic Inst NAm grant, 56. *Mem:* AAAS; Geol Soc Am; Am Asn Petrol Geol; Arctic Inst NAm; Sigma Xi. *Res:* Stratigraphy; structure; geomorphology; glaciology; petrology; paleontology; petroleum geology. *Mailing Add:* PO Box 80745 Fairbanks AK 99708-0745

**WEBER, FRANK E,** FOOD SCIENCE. *Current Pos:* RETIRED. *Personal Data:* b Chicago, Ill, Feb 1, 35; m 57; c 3. *Educ:* Ill Inst Technol, BS, 57; Univ Ill, MS, 63, PhD(food sci), 64. *Prof Exp:* Res scientist-leader, Chem Sect, R T French Co, 64-71, mgr prod develop, 71-73, mgr tech res, 73-76; tech dir, Reckitt & Colman NAm Inc, 76-80, dir res & develop, 81-94; mgr new prod res, Miller Brewing Co, 81-94. *Mem:* Am Chem Soc; Inst Food Technologists; Am Asn Cereal Chemists; Sigma Xi. *Res:* Product development; quality control; natural and artificial flavorings; isolation and analysis of flavor substances; food analysis methodology product development; industrial waste treatment; brewing technology. *Mailing Add:* 12163 Badger Ellison Bay WI 54210

**WEBER, FRANK L,** CERAMICS ENGINEERING, ANALYTICAL CHEMISTRY. *Current Pos:* RETIRED. *Personal Data:* b St Louis, Mo, Feb 14, 24; m 47, 77; c 7. *Educ:* Mo Sch Mines & Metall, BA. *Prof Exp:* Chemist, Johnston Foil Mfg Co, 46-49; analyst, Am Brake Shoe Co, 49-57; chemist, Walsh Refractories Co, 57-68; qual control supvr, Div Combine Eng, C E Refractories Co, 68-72; process engr, Findlay Refractories Co, 72-88. *Mem:* Am Ceramic Soc. *Res:* Ceramics engineering. *Mailing Add:* 1891 W Chestnut St Washington PA 15301

**WEBER, FREDERICK, JR,** MICROBIOLOGY, PUBLIC HEALTH. *Current Pos:* RETIRED. *Personal Data:* b Hilgen, Ger, Feb 14, 23; nat US; m 46; c 3. *Educ:* Univ RI, BS, 48; Pa State Univ, MS, 50; Mich State Univ, PhD, 56. *Prof Exp:* Instr, Wartburg Col, 50-51 & Wayne State Univ, 51-53; mem res staff, Swift & Co, 56-59; mem res staff, Joseph E Seagram & Sons, Inc, 59-85. *Mem:* Am Soc Microbiol. *Res:* Psychiophiles in dairy products; flavor development by microorganisms in foods; aerobic digestion of wastes; alcoholic fermentations. *Mailing Add:* 9927 Silverwood Lane V Sta Louisville KY 40272

**WEBER, GEORGE,** ONCOLOGY, PHARMACOLOGY. *Current Pos:* assoc prof biochem & microbiol, 59-60, assoc prof pharmacol, 60-61, PROF PHARMACOL, SCH MED, IND UNIV, INDIANAPOLIS, 61-, DIR LAB EXP ONCOL, 74-, DISTINGUISHED PROF & DIR ONCOL & DISTINGUISHED PROF PHARMACOL & TOXICOL, 90- *Personal Data:* b Budapest, Hungary, Mar 29, 22; nat US; m 58; c 3. *Educ:* Queen's Univ, Ont, BA, 50, MD, 52. *Hon Degrees:* Dr Med & Surg, Univ Chieti, Italy; Dr Med, Med Univ, Budapest, Hungary & Univ Leipzig, Ger; DSc, Tokushima Univ, Japan. *Honors & Awards:* Alecce Award, Cancer Res, Rome, Italy, 71; G H A Clowes Award, Am Asn Cancer Res, 82; G F Gallanti Prize, Int Soc Clin Chemists, 84; J H Wilkinson Award, Int Soc Clin Enzym, 87. *Prof Exp:* Nat Cancer Inst Can fel, Univ BC, 52-53; Cancer Res Soc sr fel, Montreal Cancer Inst, 53-58, head, Dept Path Chem, 56-59. *Concurrent Pos:* Ed, Adv in Enzyme Regulation, 62-; Oxford Biochem Soc lectr, 69; assoc ed, Cancer Res, 70-; rapporteur, Int Cancer Cong, Tex, 70; mem, Sci Adv Comt, Pharmacol B Study Sect, USPHS, 70-74 & 84-86, chmn, Exp Therapeut Study Sect, Nat Cancer Inst, 76-78; mem, Tiberine Acad, 71-; mem, Sci Adv, Damon Runyon Mem Fund, 71-75; mem, Adv Comt Instnl Grants, Am Cancer Soc, 72-76; Aaron Brown lectureship, Case Western Res Univ, 77; mem, US Nat Organizing Comt & Prog Comt, 13th Int Cancer Cong, 79-82 & Int Adv Comt, 14th Int Cancer Cong, 83-86; outstanding invest award, Nat Cancer Inst, 86-93. *Mem:* Am Soc Pharmacol & Exp Therapeut; hon mem All-Union Biochem Soc, USSR Nat Acad Sci; Am Asn Cancer Res; hon mem Hungarian Cancer Soc. *Res:* Oncology; biochemical pharmacology; regulation of enzymes and metabolism; neoplasia; chemotherapy; liver, kidney and colon tumors of different growth rates; hormone action; leukemia treatment. *Mailing Add:* Lab Exp Oncol Ind Univ Sch Med Indianapolis IN 46202-5200

**WEBER, GEORGE RUSSELL,** BACTERIOLOGY. *Current Pos:* RETIRED. *Personal Data:* b Novinger, Mo, Dec 29, 11; m 47; c 2. *Educ:* Univ Mo, BS, 35; Iowa State Col, PhD(sanit & food bact), 40. *Hon Degrees:* DSc, Int Univ Found Malta, 86. *Honors & Awards:* Bronze Medal, Albert Einstein Int Acad Found, 87. *Prof Exp:* Asst chemist, Exp Sta, Univ Mo, 35-36; instr, Iowa State Col, 40-42; bacteriologist, USPHS, 46; sr asst scientist, 47-49, scientist, 49-53, chief sanitizing agents unit, 51-53; proj leader, US Indust Chem Co, Nat Distillers & Chem Corp, 53-73, sr res microbiologist, Res Div, 73-75, res assoc, 75-76. *Concurrent Pos:* Asst, Iowa State Col, 36-40; lectr, Eve Col, Univ Cincinnati, 69-70. *Mem:* AAAS; Am Soc Microbiol; fel Am Pub Health Asn; NY Acad Sci; fel Royal Soc Health; Sigma Xi; fel Int Biog Asn. *Res:* Sanitary and food bacteriology; germicidal efficiency of hypochlorites, chloramines and quaternary ammonium compounds; antibiotics; fermentations; yeast hybridization; ruminant and chinchilla nutrition; biological metal corrosion. *Mailing Add:* 1525 Burney Lane Cincinnati OH 45230

**WEBER, GREGORIO,** BIOCHEMISTRY, BIOPHYSICS. *Current Pos:* prof biochem, 62-86, prof, Ctr Advan Studies, 71-86, EMER PROF BIOCHEM, UNIV ILL, URBANA, 86- *Personal Data:* b Buenos Aires, Arg, July 4, 16; US citizen; m 47; c 3. *Educ:* Univ Buenos Aires, MD, 43; Cambridge Univ, PhD(biochem), 47. *Honors & Awards:* First Nat Lectr, Biophys Soc, 69; NATO Lectr, Europe, 75; Rumford Prize, 80; Repligen Award, Chem Biol Processes, Am Chem Soc, 86. *Prof Exp:* Beit mem fel biochem, Cambridge Univ, 48-52; lectr biochem, Sheffield Univ, 53-56, sr lectr, 56-60, reader biophys, 60-62. *Concurrent Pos:* Vis lectr, Univ Ill, 59 & Stanford Univ, 61 & 79; vis prof, Brandeis Univ, 60, Univ Wash, 64, Harvard Univ, 70 & Univ Calif, Los Angeles, 77; ed, J Biol Chem, Am Soc Biol Chemists, 68; Guggeheim Found fel, 70; coun mem, Am Biophys Soc, 70-73; vis res lectr, Nat Comn Sci & Technol Res, Univ Buenos Aires, 81 & hon prof, 87- *Mem:* Nat Acad Sci; Am Soc Biol Chemists; Am Chem Soc; fel Am Acad Arts & Sci; Am Biophys Soc. *Res:* Physical chemistry of proteins; fluorescence methods; excited states. *Mailing Add:* 419 Roger Adams Lab 600 S Matthews Ave Urbana IL 61801

**WEBER, HANS JOSEF,** OPERATIONS MANAGEMENT, PROGRAM DEVELOPMENT. *Current Pos:* PRES & PROPRIETOR, WEBER TECHNOL APPLNS, 92-; PRES, IMAGE NET, 93- *Personal Data:* b Aachen, WGer, Mar 5, 42; m 68, Mary Mannino. *Educ:* Gonzaga Univ, BS, 64; San Diego State Univ, MA, 68. *Prof Exp:* Corp vpres, IRT Corp, 82-86; sr vpres, Sci Applns Int Corp, 86-92. *Concurrent Pos:* Fulbright scholar. *Mem:* Am Nuclear Soc; Am Soc Non Destructive Testing; Am Defense Preparedness Asn; Int Soc Optical Eng; Nat Air Transp Asn. *Res:* Development of non-destructive assay instrumentation for special nuclear materials; development of explosive detection systems for letter bombs; development of non-destructive evaluation systems for aviation and space applications. *Mailing Add:* 7916 Laurelridge Rd San Diego CA 92120. *Fax:* 619-286-9467; *E-Mail:* nansweber@earthlink.net

**WEBER, HANS JURGEN,** THEORETICAL NUCLEAR PHYSICS. *Current Pos:* asst prof, 68-71, assoc prof, 71-76, PROF THEORET NUCLEAR PHYSICS, UNIV VA, 77- *Personal Data:* b Berlin, Ger, May 3, 39; m 66, Edith Enzian; c Christian H. *Educ:* Univ Frankfurt, BS, 60, MS, 61, PhD(theoret physics), 65. *Prof Exp:* Res assoc theoret nuclear physics, Duke Univ, 66-67. *Concurrent Pos:* Sesquicentennial assoc, Max Planck Inst, Mainz & Univ Frankfurt, 72-73, Orsay, 79, Lyon, 78. *Mem:* Am Phys Soc; AAAS; Sigma Xi; Am Asn Physics Teachers. *Res:* Medium energy physics; photonuclear physics; group theory; quark models and quantum chromodynamics. *Mailing Add:* Dept Physics Univ Va Charlottesville VA 22901. *Fax:* 804-924-4576; *E-Mail:* hjw@theory.phys.virginia.edu

**WEBER, HARRY A,** INDUSTRIAL MANAGEMENT, ELECTRICAL ENGINEERING. *Current Pos:* chief, Prog Sect, US Atomic Energy Comn, 50-54, chief, Opers Br, 54, dir, Develop & Prod Div, 54-56, dir, Non-Nuclear Div, 56-57, dir, Plant Opers, 57-60, dir weapons prod, 60-69, WEAPONS PROG MGR, US DEPT ENERGY, 69- *Personal Data:* b Indianapolis, Ind, July 13, 21; m 49, Janet Baker; c Stephen V, Gary A & Karen D. *Educ:* Purdue Univ, BSEE, 42. *Prof Exp:* Dept mgr, Delco-Remy Div, Gen Motors Corp, 43-44; proj engr, US Naval Ord Plant, 46-50. *Concurrent Pos:* Gen partner, Big Bend Co, Colo & NMex. *Mem:* Nat Soc Prof Engrs; Inst Elec & Electronics Engrs. *Res:* Technical administration. *Mailing Add:* 7133 Kiowa Ave NE Albuquerque NM 87110

**WEBER, HARRY P(ITT),** ELECTRICAL ENGINEERING, PHYSICS. *Personal Data:* b Pittsburgh, Pa, June 20, 31; m 52, Marilyn Sharp; c David, Lisa & William. *Educ:* Univ Pittsburgh, BSEE, 58, MSEE, 61, DSc(elec eng), 64. *Prof Exp:* Res asst, Mellon Inst Indust Res, 56-59; asst prof elec eng, Univ Pittsburgh, 59-64; sr syst analyst, RCA Missile Test Proj, Patrick AFB, 64-65; head dept elec eng, 66-71, dean eng & sci, 71-79, dean eng & sci, 71-79, dean Grad Sch, 68-82, assoc vpres acad affairs, Fla Inst Technol, 80-82; pres, Hawthorne Col, 82-86; mgr, Tech Analysis, GE Missile Test Proj, Raytheon, Patrick AFB, Fla, 86-88, mgr oper analysis, Comput Sci Raytheon, 88-93, mgr eval & analysis comput sci, 93-96. *Concurrent Pos:* Consult, Radio Corp Am Missile Test Proj, Patrick AFB, 66-68. *Mem:* Sigma Xi; Inst Elec & Electronics Engrs. *Res:* Missile test range, instrumentation and tracking, space test range concepts. *Mailing Add:* 310 Greenway Ave Satellite Beach FL 32937

**WEBER, HEATHER R(OSS) WILSON,** BIOCHEMISTRY. *Current Pos:* res assoc biochem, Univ Southern Calif, 73-74, NIH cancer training grant, 74-76, NIH fel biochem, 76-79, res scientist, 79-84, RES ASST PROF, MOLECULAR BIOL SECT BIOL DEPT, UNIV SOUTHERN CALIF, 85- *Personal Data:* b Passaic, NJ, Mar 7, 43; m 63; c 4. *Educ:* Boston Univ, BA, 65; Univ Southern Calif, PhD(cellular & molecular biol), 74. *Prof Exp:* Res asst hemat, Peter Bent Brigham Hosp, 65-67; res asst biochem, Harvard Med Sch, 67-68. *Mem:* AAAS; Am Chem Soc; Am Soc Biochem & Molecular Biol; Sigma Xi; Am Soc Cell Biol. *Res:* Transcriptional regulation of eucaryotic gene expression; mechanism of hormonal effects on cyclic nucleotide metabolism; membrane bound enzymes. *Mailing Add:* 3341 Country Club Dr Los Angeles CA 90019-3535. *Fax:* 213-740-8631

**WEBER, HELMUT E(RNST),** SHOCK WAVE ENGINES & TURBINES, FLUID DYNAMICS & THERMODYNAMICS. *Current Pos:* adj prof, 62-68, prof, asst dean & dir, Grad Sch, 68-84, EMER PROF MECH ENG, PA STATE UNIV, 84-; PRES & CONSULT, FLOW ENERGY ENG, 84- *Personal Data:* b Burkhardtsdorf, Ger, Oct 16, 24; US citizen; m 48, Elizabeth M Heiden; c Daniel G, Gary H, Constance E (Santroch) & Raymond F. *Educ:* Mass Inst Technol, SB & SM, 51, ScD(mech eng), 55. *Prof Exp:* Instr mech eng, Mass Inst Technol, 52-55; engr, EI du Pont de Nemours & Co, 51-52,

Shell Develop Co, 55-56; thermodyn specialist, Gen Elec Co, 56-58, mgr thermodyn, 58-60, mgr aerothermodyn, 60-67; mgr papermaking, Scott Paper Co, 67-68; pres & vpres, Gen Power Corp, 69-84. *Concurrent Pos:* Adj prof mech eng, Univ Calif, Berkeley, 58-60; consult, 68- *Mem:* Am Soc Mech Engrs. *Res:* Shock wave engines; turbine type engines; cycle analysis; fluid dynamics; ejector nozzles for jet propulsion and electric arc heaters. *Mailing Add:* 5433 Drover Dr San Diego CA 92115

**WEBER, J K RICHARD,** HIGH TEMPERATURE MATERIALS. *Current Pos:* DIR & PRINCIPLE SCI, CRI, 93- *Personal Data:* b London, UK, May 29, 57; m 89, Mary J Doxas. *Educ:* Sir John Cass Col, London, BS, 83; Imperial Col, London, PhD(metall) & DIC, 86; Inst Metals, CEng, 90. *Prof Exp:* Res consult corrosion, Int Nickel Co, 83-86; res assoc chem, Univ Toledo, Ohio, 86-88; prin scientist res & develop, Intersonics Corp, 88-93. *Mem:* Inst Metals; Am Ceramic Soc; Metall Soc; Mat Res Soc; Am Soc Metall Int. *Res:* Containerless processing; high temperature materials; chemical kinetics and corrosion; ceramics and glass processing research, development and design; oxide fibers processing. *Mailing Add:* Containeless Res Inc 910 University Pl Evanston IL 60201-3149. *Fax:* 847-467-2679; *E-Mail:* weber_r@nwu.edu

**WEBER, JAMES ALAN,** BOTANY-PHYTOPATHOLOGY, ECOLOGY. *Current Pos:* Asst, 73-78, ASST RES SCIENTIST, UNIV MICH, 78- *Personal Data:* b Santa Monica, Calif, Mar 16, 44; m 70. *Educ:* Univ Calif, Berkeley, AB, 66; Univ Mich, AM, 67, PhD(bot), 73. *Concurrent Pos:* Co-ed, Mich Botanist, 84- *Mem:* Sigma Xi; Am Soc Plant Physiologists; Bot Soc Am; Ecol Soc Am; Am Inst Biol Sci; AAAS. *Res:* The interaction of physiological processes with environmental factors; photosynthesis and growth. *Mailing Add:* 2160 NW Beechwood Pl Corvallis OR 97330-1001

**WEBER, JAMES EDWARD,** CORNEA, CONTACT LENSES. *Current Pos:* MEM CLIN STAFF, VISTAKON, 87- *Personal Data:* b Chicago, Ill, Nov 16, 57. *Educ:* Southern Ill Univ, Carbondale, BA, 80, MS, 83, PhD(physiol), 87; New England Col Optom, Boston, OD, 89. *Prof Exp:* Teaching asst anat, Southern Ill Univ, Carbondale, 81-87; consult. *Mem:* Fel Am Acad Optom; Sigma Xi; Am Asn Anatomists; Am Soc Cell Biol; AAAS; Am Optom Asn. *Res:* Ocular response to contact lens wear; contact lens/tear film interactions. *Mailing Add:* Vistakon PO Box 10157 Jacksonville FL 32247. *Fax:* 904-443-1783; *E-Mail:* jweber@visus.jnj.com

**WEBER, JAMES H(AROLD),** CHEMICAL ENGINEERING. *Current Pos:* from instr to prof chem eng, Univ Nebr, Lincoln, 48-64, chmn dept, 58-71, regents prof chem eng, 64-84, EMER PROF, UNIV NEBR, LINCOLN, 84- *Personal Data:* b Pittsburgh, Pa, Nov 21, 19; m 43; c 3. *Educ:* Univ Pittsburgh, BS, 41, MS, 47, PhD(chem eng), 48. *Prof Exp:* Asst, Univ Pittsburgh, 46-48. *Concurrent Pos:* Consult, Phillips Petrol Co, 52-79, Natural Gas Processors Asn, 59 & 64 & C F Braun & Co, 65. *Mem:* Am Chem Soc; Am Inst Chem Engrs; Soc Hist Technol. *Res:* Non-adiabatic absorption of ammonia in a wetted wall tower; applied thermodynamics; distillation; absorption; kinetics. *Mailing Add:* 2670 Leisure World Mesa AZ 85206

**WEBER, JAMES HAROLD,** ENVIRONMENTAL CHEMISTRY. *Current Pos:* Asst prof, 63-70, assoc prof, 70-77, PROF CHEM, UNIV NH, 77- *Personal Data:* b Madison, Wis, July 21, 36. *Educ:* Marquette Univ, BS, 59; Ohio State Univ, PhD(chem), 63. *Mem:* Am Chem Soc. *Res:* Chemistry of estuaries; environmental organometallic chemistry; biogeochemistry of tin and mercury. *Mailing Add:* Parsons Hall Univ NH Durham NH 03824. *Fax:* 603-862-4278

**WEBER, JAMES R,** ANALYSIS OF OIL RESERVES. *Current Pos:* PRES, CORAL PROD CORP, 86- *Personal Data:* b May 16, 45. *Educ:* St Louis Univ, BS, 67; Colo Sch Mines, MS, 71. *Prof Exp:* Geol engr, Gulf Oil Corp, 68-72; geol engr, Pennzoil Co, Tex, 72-74; consult, oil industry, 74-86. *Res:* Geological & engineering analysis of the reserves & potential reserves of the Morrow Formation in southwestern Colorado. *Mailing Add:* Coral Prod Corp 1600 South St Ste 1810 Denver CO 80202

**WEBER, JANET CROSBY,** COMPUTER SCIENCE, SOFTWARE SYSTEMS. *Current Pos:* RETIRED. *Personal Data:* b Chicago, Ill, June 1, 23; m 49; c 3. *Educ:* Iowa State Univ, BS, 45; Univ Ill, Urbana, PhD(chem), 48. *Prof Exp:* Asst prof vet res, Mont State Univ, 48-50; res assoc, Med Ctr, Ind Univ, Indianapolis, 60-63, from instr to assoc profopthal, 63-91. *Mem:* Mended Hearts Asn Women Sci; Sigma Xi. *Res:* Computer methods in clinical and research studies; development of computer programs for statistical analysis; microcomputers for research; application of statistics and computers to ophthalmic research. *Mailing Add:* 4125 Flamingo East Dr Indianapolis IN 46226

**WEBER, JEAN ROBERT,** GEOPHYSICS. *Current Pos:* RES SCIENTIST, DOM OBSERV, DEPT ENERGY, MINES & RESOURCES, CAN, 60- *Personal Data:* b Thun, Switz, Apr 28, 25; Can citizen; m 54; c 3. *Educ:* Swiss Fed Inst Technol, Prof Eng, 52; Univ Alta, PhD(physics), 60. *Prof Exp:* Res engr, PTT Res Labs, Berne, Switz, 51-53; lectr, Univ Alta, 57-58; geophysicist-in-chg, Oper Hazen, Int Geophys Year, 58-59. *Concurrent Pos:* Mem Arctic Inst NAm Baffin Island Exped, 53 & Univ Toronto, Salmon Glacier Exped, 56; leader, Dom Observ NPole Exped, 67. *Mem:* Am Geophys Union; Soc Explor Geophys; fel Arctic Inst NAm; Glaciol Soc. *Res:* Communications electronics; dosimetry of beta radiation and biological effects on allium cepa roots; regional gravity interpretations; continental margins; upper mantle, Arctic Ocean; application of geophysics to glaciology. *Mailing Add:* Geo Surv Can-Geophys Dept One Observatory Crescent Ottawa ON K1A 0L2 Can

**WEBER, JEROME BERNARD,** SOIL CHEMISTRY, WEED SCIENCE. *Current Pos:* Assoc prof soil pesticide chem, 62-71, PROF SOIL PESTICIDE CHEM & WEED SCI, NC STATE UNIV, 71- *Personal Data:* b Claremont, Minn, Sept 19, 33; m 56, Mary Traxler; c Mark, Joel, Paul & Nancy. *Educ:* Univ Minn, BS, 57, MS, 59, PhD(soil chem), 63. *Honors & Awards:* Sigma Xi Res Award; Res Award, Weed Sci Soc Am; Wright lectr, Purdue Univ, 80. *Concurrent Pos:* NSF lectr, Clemson Univ, 79; consult, WHO, Venezuela, 80, Univ SAfrica, 82; Int Asn Develop & Mgt Existing & New Towns, Arg, 89, Univ SAfrica, 90; mem, Coun Agr Sci & Technol. *Mem:* Fel AAAS; Am Soc Agron; fel Weed Sci Soc Am; Am Chem Soc; Clay Minerals Soc; Soil Sci Soc Am. *Res:* Chemistry of soil, fate and biological availability of applied organic compounds, especially herbicides; effects of pesticides on environmental quality; weed ecology studies; behavior of gases in soil; behavior of toxic organics in waters and soils. *Mailing Add:* 7701 Ligon Mill Rd Wake Forest NC 27587-8891. *Fax:* 919-515-5315

**WEBER, JOHN DONALD,** PHARMACEUTICAL CHEMISTRY. *Current Pos:* RES CHEMIST, FOOD & DRUG ADMIN, 79- *Personal Data:* b Lagon, La, Nov 1, 34; m 62; c 2. *Educ:* Xavier Univ La, BS, 57; Univ Notre Dame, MS, 61; Georgetown Univ, PhD(org chem), 72. *Prof Exp:* Instr chem, Southern Univ New Orleans, 62-63; anal chemist, Food & Drug Admin, 63-68, res chem, 68-78; mem staff org synthesis, USDA, 78-79. *Mem:* Am Chem Soc; Sigma Xi; Asn Off Analytical Chemists; NY Acad Sci. *Res:* Pharmaceutical analyses; chromatography, nuclear magnetic resonance fluorimetric techniques; optical purity of drugs; stereochemistry and chemical kinetics; problems of relationships between stereoisomerism and physiological activity. *Mailing Add:* 7204 Seventh St NW Washington DC 20012

**WEBER, JOHN R,** PLANT PHYSIOLOGY. *Current Pos:* RETIRED. *Personal Data:* b Ft Madison, Iowa, Mar 18, 24; m 48; c 2. *Educ:* Univ Iowa, AB, 48, MS, 49. *Prof Exp:* Prin lab technician, Citrus Exp Sta, Univ Calif, 52-56; plant physiologist, FMC Corp, 56-67, mem spec projs egg handling systs, 67-76, int mgr, Citrus Mach Div, 76-82. *Res:* Post-harvest physiology of fruits and vegetables. *Mailing Add:* 2102 Oak Crest Dr Riverside CA 92506

**WEBER, JOHN W,** STRUCTURAL MECHANICS, THERMOELASTICITY. *Current Pos:* RETIRED. *Personal Data:* b Apr 16, 35; c 1. *Educ:* Pa State Univ, BS, 52, MS, 56; Univ Colo, PhD(struct mech), 67. *Prof Exp:* Instr eng mech, Pa State Univ, 56-58; asst prof eng mech, Mich Technol Univ, 60-63; teaching assoc civil eng, Univ Colo, 63-66; from asst prof to assoc prof, Wash State Univ, 66-84; prof & chmn, Tex A&M Univ, Kingsville, 84-96. *Mem:* Am Soc Elec Engrs; Am Soc Civil Engrs; NW Sci Asn. *Res:* Engineering: structural mechanics, engineering mechanics, thermoelasticity; biology: taxonomy of Larus gulls. *Mailing Add:* Dept Civil Eng Tex A&M Univ 700 University Blvd Kingsville TX 78363-8203

**WEBER, JOSEPH,** PHYSICS. *Current Pos:* Prof elec eng, 48-60, prof physics, 61-89, SR RES SCIENTIST, UNIV MD, COLLEGE PARK, 90- *Personal Data:* b Paterson, NJ, May 17, 19; m 42, 72, Virginia L Trimble; c Jonathan, Paul, James & David. *Educ:* US Naval Acad, BS, 40; Cath Univ Am, PhD(physics), 51. *Honors & Awards:* First Prize, Gravity Res Found, 59; Sigma Xi Award, 70; Boris Pregel Prize, NY Acad Sci, 73. *Concurrent Pos:* Vis prof, Univ Calif, Irvine; Nat Res Coun & Guggenheim fels, 55-56; fel, Inst Advan Study, 55-56, 62-63 & 69-70 & Lorentz Inst Theoret Physics, State Univ Leiden, 56. *Mem:* Fel Am Phys Soc; fel Inst Elec & Electronics Engrs. *Res:* General relativity; microwave spectroscopy; irreversibility; scattering; weak interactions; quantum electronics. *Mailing Add:* Dept Physics Univ Md College Park MD 20742. *Fax:* 301-314-9525; *E-Mail:* jwll6@umail.umd.edu

**WEBER, JOSEPH M,** VIROLOGY, MOLECULAR BIOLOGY. *Current Pos:* asst prof to assoc prof, 70-80, dept head, 88-95, PROF MICROBIOL, UNIV SHERBROOKE, 80- *Personal Data:* b Budapest, Hungary, Oct 10, 39; Can citizen; m 64, 73, Cowan; c Heidi & Julia. *Educ:* Univ BC, BSc, 64, MSc, 66; McMaster Univ, PhD(virol), 69. *Prof Exp:* Nat Cancer Inst res assoc virol, Ohio State Univ, 69-70. *Concurrent Pos:* Lectr, Ohio State Univ, 69-70; Med Res Coun Can scholar, 71-76; Nat Cancer Inst Can scholar, 76-80, res assoc, 80-85, Terry Fox cancer res scientist, 85-89. *Mem:* Am Asn Cancer Res; Am Soc Virol. *Res:* Adenovirus encoded endopeptidase and its role in virous infection, using protein engineering of enzyme and substrate, substrae phages and phage dislpay libraries; adenovirus-lymphocyte interactions. *Mailing Add:* Dept Microbiol 3001-12 Ave N Sherbrooke PQ J1H 5N4 Can. *Fax:* 819-564-5392; *E-Mail:* jweber@courrier.usherb.ca

**WEBER, JOSEPH T,** NEUROANATOMY, NEURODEVELOPMENT. *Current Pos:* asst prof, 80-83, assoc prof, 83-86, PROF NEUROANAT, MED SCH, TULANE UNIV, 86- *Personal Data:* b Brooklyn, NY, Jan 1, 38; m 77; c 1. *Educ:* Univ Calif, Berkeley, AB, 73; Univ Wis, PhD(anat), 78. *Prof Exp:* Fel neuroanat, Med Sch, Univ Wis, 78-80. *Concurrent Pos:* Ad hoc reviewer, NSF, 81-; prin investr, NIH, 81- *Mem:* Soc Neurosci; Am Asn Anatomists; AAAS; Sigma Xi. *Res:* Anatomical studies of extrageniculate visual pathways; mechanisms involved in the control of head and eye movements; development of visual centers. *Mailing Add:* Tulane Univ Sch Med 1430 Tulane Ave New Orleans LA 70112

**WEBER, JULIUS,** CYTOLOGY, PHOTOGRAPHY. *Current Pos:* HEAD DEPT PHOTOG RES, BETH ISRAEL HOSP, 49-; EMER RES ASSOC, EINSTEIN SCH MED, 84- *Personal Data:* b Brooklyn, NY, Apr 8, 14; m 47, Mary Siegel; c Robert, Lenora, Margaret & Nancy. *Hon Degrees:* DSc, Jersey City State Col, 74. *Prof Exp:* Asst, Brooklyn Jewish Hosp, NY, 33-35; chief histol technician, Kingston Ave Hosp Infectious Dis, 35-36 & Israel Zion Hosp, Brooklyn, 36-39; head dept med photog, Columbia-Presby Med Ctr, NY, 39-49. *Concurrent Pos:* Mem training div, Inst Inter-Am Affairs, US Dept State, 46; consult, Western Union Tel Co, 46-48, Chem Corps, US Army, 47-50, Ansco Div, Gen Aniline & Film Corp, 47-48, Nat Film Bd Can, 51, US Naval Hosp, St Albans, NY, 51-52, St Francis Hosp, NY, 59, Perkin-Elmer Corp, 60 & Ehrenreich Photo-Optical Industs, Inc, 63; lectr, Sch Med, Univ Calif, Los Angeles, 48; guest lectr, Col Physicians & Surgeons, Columbia Univ, 50, Sch Eng, 60; dir med photog, William Douglas McAdams, Inc, 52-59; head dept med photog, Hosp Joint Dis, 53-73; res assoc, Waldemar Med Res Found, 55-; lectr, Grad Sch Pub Admin, NY Univ, 55-57; head dept med photog, Misericordia Hosp, 56-; med photographer, Knickerbocker Hosp, 58-63; assoc, Dept Mineral, Am Mus Natural Hist, 60; ed, Image Dynamics Sci & Med, 69-71; dir, Wildcliff Natural Sci Ctr, 69-74; res assoc, Dept Mineral, Royal Ont Mus, Toronto, 71-; res assoc, Dept Med, Einstein Sch Med, 76-84. *Mem:* Soc Photog Sci & Eng; assoc Photog Soc Am; fel Biol Photog Asn; fel Royal Micros Soc; fel Royal Photog Soc Gt Brit. *Res:* Photographic instrumentation for endoscopy, micromineralogy; time lapse photomicrography and cinematography; ultraviolet, infrared and interference photomicrography and photomacrography; neurocytology and neuropathology photoimpregnation techniques. *Mailing Add:* 1040 Cove Rd Mamaroneck NY 10543

**WEBER, KARL T,** INTERNAL MEDICINE, CARDIOLOGY. *Current Pos:* DIR, DIV CARDIOL & CARDIOVASC INST, DEPT MED, MICHAEL REESE HOSP, UNIV CHICAGO, 83- *Educ:* Temple Univ, MD, 68. *Mailing Add:* Cardiol Div Univ Mo MA432 Med Sci Bldg Columbia MO 65212-0001. *Fax:* 573-884-4691; *E-Mail:* medparky@mizzou1.missouri.edu

**WEBER, KENNETH C,** PULMONARY BIOLOGY. *Current Pos:* from asst prof to prof physiol, 68-82, PROF PHARMACOL & TOXICOL, WVA UNIV, 82- *Personal Data:* b Cold Spring, Minn, June 30, 37; m 57, Bertha Williams; c Charles, Gerald, Terry & Patrica. *Educ:* Univ Minn, BSEE, 63, PhD(physiol), 68. *Prof Exp:* USPHS trainee physiol, Univ Minn, 62-68. *Concurrent Pos:* Chief physiol sect, 68-85, chief, Lab Invest Br, Appalachian Lab Occup Respiratory Dis, Nat Inst Occup Safety & Health, 85-; chmn, Gordon Res Conf Non-Ventilatory Lung Function, 75. *Mem:* AAAS; Am Physiol Soc; Am Thoracic Soc; Am Heart Asn (vpres, 81-82); Am Lung Asn. *Res:* Respiration physiology; non-ventilatory lung function; lung metabolism; inhalation toxicology; occupational respiratory disease. *Mailing Add:* Nat Inst Occup Safety & Health ALOSH Bldg 1095 Willowdale Rd Rm 4009 Morgantown WV 26505. *Fax:* 304-285-6126; *E-Mail:* kcwi@cdc.gov

**WEBER, LAVERN J,** PHARMACOLOGY, ACADEMIC ADMINISTRATION. *Current Pos:* assoc prof pharmacol & toxicol, Ore State Univ, 69-75, asst dean, Grad Sch, 74-77, dir, Marine & Freshwater Biomcd Ctr, 78-81, PROF PHARMACOL, TOXICOL & FISHERIES, SCH PHARM, ORE STATE UNIV, 75-, DIR, MARINE SCI CTR, 77- *Personal Data:* b Isabel, SDak, June 7, 33; m 59, 92, Pat Lewis; c Timothy, Peter, Pamela & Elizabeth. *Educ:* Pac Lutheran Univ, BA, 58; Univ Wash, MS, 62, PhD(pharmacol), 64. *Prof Exp:* From instr to asst prof pharmacol, Sch Med, Univ Wash, 64-69. *Concurrent Pos:* Dir, Hatfield Marine Sci Ctr, Ore State Univ, 77-; supt, Coastal Ore Marine Exp Sta, 88- *Mem:* Am Soc Pharmacol & Exp Therapeut; Soc Toxicol; Soc Exp Biol & Med; Sigma Xi; Am Asn Lab Animal Sci. *Res:* Marine sciences; biochemistry of autonomic nervous system; comparative pharmacology, physiology and toxicology; comparative pharmacology of the autonomic nervous system; liver toxicology; comparative neuromuscular pharmacology. *Mailing Add:* Ore State Univ Marine Sci Ctr Newport OR 97365

**WEBER, LEON,** SURFACE CHEMISTRY, PHYSICAL CHEMISTRY. *Current Pos:* SCIENTIST SURFACE CHEM, SCM CHEMICALS, INC, 67- *Personal Data:* b Detroit, Mich, Feb 4, 31; m 52; c 3. *Educ:* Wayne State Univ, BS, 52, MS, 54; Carnegie-Mellon Univ, MS & PhD(phys chem), 67. *Prof Exp:* Chemist, Wayne County Rd, Comn, 51-54; res chemist, Shell Develop Co, 54-56; scientist nuclear chem, Westinghouse Atomic Power Co, 56-57; sr res chemist, Gulf Res & Develop Co, 57-67. *Mem:* AAAS; Am Chem Soc; Sigma Xi. *Res:* Colloid and surface chemistry of pigments; gas-solid sorption phenomena; reaction kinetics by thermal analysis. *Mailing Add:* 8246 Streamwood Dr Baltimore MD 21208-2135

**WEBER, LESTER GEORGE,** CHEMICAL & POLYMER ENGINEERING, TECHNICAL MANAGEMENT. *Current Pos:* RETIRED. *Personal Data:* b St Louis, Mo, July 23, 24; m 49, Ruth E Duell; c Anne K, Kay L, Alan P, Donald M & Sue E. *Educ:* Purdue Univ, BS, 49; Wash Univ, MS, 54. *Prof Exp:* Analyst, Uranium Div, Mallinckrodt Chem Works, Mo, 49-50, engr pilot plant, 50-51, supvr metal pilot plant, 51-54, asst mgr plant design liaison group, Uranium Div, 54-57, tech supt mfg dept, 57-58, supvr prod tech dept, 58-60, asst mgr, 60-62, asst mgr develop dept, 62-63; res engr, Yerkes Res & Develop Lab, E I DuPont de Nemours & Co Inc, NY, 63-65, res engr, Circleville Res & Develop Lab, Ohio, 65-66, staff engr, 66, res supvr, 66-69, tech supt cellophane, Clinton Film Plant, 69-73, customer serv mgr, Plastic Prod & Resins Dept, Packaging Films Div, BIVAC Meat Packaging Systs, 73-76, staff engr, Polymer Prod Dept, Mfg Div, Washington Works, 76-77, sr tech assoc, 78-89. *Mem:* Am Inst Chem Engrs; Am Soc Plastics Engrs. *Res:* Process developments in recovery and recycling uranium slag and solvent and waste polyimide film. *Mailing Add:* 2030 Mackenzie Dr Columbus OH 43220

**WEBER, MARK,** vibration-rotation theory of molecules, inrared spectroscopy, for more information see previous edition

**WEBER, MARVIN JOHN,** LASERS, SPECTROSCOPY. *Current Pos:* physicist & group leader, 73-87, assoc div leader, 87-93, PARTIC GUEST, LAWRENCE LIVERMORE NAT LAB, 93-; PARTIC GUEST, LAWRENCE BERKELEY LAB, 93- *Personal Data:* b Fresno, Calif, Feb 26, 32; m 87, Shirley A Glen; c Ann H & Eve K. *Educ:* Univ Calif, Berkeley, AB, 54, MA, 56, PhD(physics), 59. *Honors & Awards:* IR-100 Award, 79; George W Morey Award, Am Ceramics Soc, 83. *Prof Exp:* Asst physics, Univ Calif, 54-59; prin res scientist & mgr solid state lasers, Res Div, Raytheon Co, 59-73. *Concurrent Pos:* Vis res assoc, Stanford Univ, 66; consult, Div Mat Res, NSF, 73-76; ed-in-chief, Handbk Series Laser Sci & Technol, CRC, 78-; transfer assignment, US Dept Energy, 84-85; guest worker, Nat Bur Stand, 84-85; assoc ed, J Luminescence, 85-; tech consult, US Dept Energy, 86-87 & Battelle Pac NW Lab, 88-; regional ed, J Non-Crystalline Solids, 88-; spokesman, Nat Labs Synchrotron Radiation Facil, Univ Calif, 88-; consult prof, Stanford Univ, 90-92. *Mem:* Fel Am Phys Soc; fel Optical Soc Am; fel Am Ceramics Soc; Am Asn Crystal Growth; Mat Res Soc; Sigma Xi. *Res:* Optical spectroscopy of solids; luminescence materials; lasers; solid state physics; materials science. *Mailing Add:* Berkeley Lab MS50A-4119 Berkeley CA 94720. *E-Mail:* mjw@llnl.gov

**WEBER, MICHAEL JOSEPH,** VIROLOGY, CELL BIOLOGY. *Current Pos:* AT DEPT MICROBIOL, SCH MED, UNIV VA, CHARLOTTESVILLE. *Personal Data:* b New York, NY, Aug 23, 42; m 67. *Educ:* Haverford Col, BSc, 63; Univ Calif, San Diego, PhD(biol), 68. *Prof Exp:* Am Cancer Soc Dernham jr fel, Univ Calif, Berkeley, 68-70; asst prof microbiol, Univ Ill, Urbana, 70-75, assoc prof, 75- *Concurrent Pos:* NIH res career develop award, 75. *Mem:* Am Soc Microbiol; Tissue Cult Asn; Soc Gen Physiologists; Am Soc Biol Chemists. *Res:* Control of growth of animal cells and malignant transformation; tumor virus-induced cell surface changes. *Mailing Add:* Dept Microbiol Univ Va Sch Med Box 441 Charlottesville VA 22908-0001. *Fax:* 804-924-0689

**WEBER, MORTON M,** MICROBIOLOGY, BIOCHEMISTRY. *Current Pos:* from asst prof to prof, 59-92, chmn dept, 64-87, EMER CHMN, DEPT MICROBIOL, ST LOUIS UNIV, SCH MED, 87-, EMER PROF, 92- *Personal Data:* b New York, NY, May 26, 22; m 55, Phyllis L; c Stephen A & Ethan L. *Educ:* City Col Ny, BS, 49; Johns Hopkins Univ, ScD(microbiol), 53. *Prof Exp:* Instr zool & parasitol, St Francis Col, 49; instr med microbiol, Johns Hopkins Univ, 51-55; instr bact & immunol, Harvard Med Sch, 56-59. *Concurrent Pos:* Am Cancer Soc fel, McCollum-Pratt Inst, Johns Hopkins Univ, 53-56; mem, Microbiol Chem Study Sect, NIH, 69-73; vis sci, Microbiol Unit, Dept Biochem, Oxford Univ & Linacre Col, 70-; mem, John's Hopkins Univ Soc Scholars, 86. *Mem:* Fel AAAS; Am Soc Biol Chemists & Molecular Biologists; Am Soc Microbiol; Am Acad Microbiol; NY Acad Sci; fel Infectious Dis Soc Am; Soc Gen Microbiol UK; Sigma Xi. *Res:* Physiology and biochemistry of microorganisms; pathways and mechanisms of electron transport; mode of action of antibiotics and other antimicrobial agents; biochemical regulatory mechanisms. *Mailing Add:* Dept Microbiol Sch Med St Louis Univ 1402 S Grand St Louis MO 63104. *Fax:* 314-773-3403; *E-Mail:* webermm@sluvca.slu.edu

**WEBER, NEAL ALBERT,** ENTOMOLOGY, ECOLOGY. *Current Pos:* from assoc prof to prof, 47-74, EMER PROF ZOOL, SWARTHMORE COL, 74- *Personal Data:* b Towner, NDak, Dec 14, 08; m 40; c 3. *Educ:* Univ NDak, AB, 30, MS, 32; Harvard Univ, AM, 33, PhD(zool), 35. *Hon Degrees:* ScD, Univ NDak, 58. *Honors & Awards:* John F Lewis Prize, Am Philos Soc, 73. *Prof Exp:* Assoc prof biol, Univ NDak, 36-43 & anat, Sch Med, 43-47. *Concurrent Pos:* Mem expeds, WI, 33-36, Trinidad, 34-36, Orinoco Delta, 35, Brit Guiana, 35-36, Barro Colo Island, CZ & Colombia, 38, Anglo-Egyptian Sudan, Uganda & Kenya, 39; biologist, Am Mus Natural Hist Exped, CAfrica, 48, Middle East, 50-52, Trop Am, 54- & Europ Mus, 57; consult, Arctic Res Lab, Alaska, 48-50; mem dept zool, Col Arts & Sci Univ Baghdad, Iraq, 50-52; vis prof, Univ Wis, 55-56; mem panel biol & med sci, Comt Polar Res, Nat Acad Sci, 58-60, panel fels, 64-66; mem & US del spec comt Antarctic res, Int Coun Sci Unions, Australia, 59; sci attache, Am Embassy, US Dept State, Buenos Aires, Arg, 60-62; mem, Latin Am Colloquium, Arg, 65 & Brazil, 68; consult, Venezuelan Univs, 72; adj prof biol sci, Fla State Univ, Tallahassee, 74- *Mem:* AAAS; fel Entom Soc Am; Ecol Soc Am; Mycol Soc Am; Am Soc Zool. *Res:* Tropical ecology; fungus-growing ants and their fungi; zoogeography. *Mailing Add:* 1805 Aaron Rd Tallahassee FL 32303

**WEBER, NORMAN,** THERMAL SCIENCES. *Current Pos:* supvr thermal & hydraul anal, 74-81, ASST HEAD, NUCLEAR SAFEGUARDS & LICENSING DIV, SARGENT & LUNDY ENGRS, 81-, ASSOC, 85- *Personal Data:* b San Luis Obispo, Calif, Nov 25, 34; m 71; c 6. *Educ:* Calif State Polytech Univ, BS, 57; Univ Southern Calif, MS, 67; Mont State Univ, PhD(mech eng), 71. *Prof Exp:* From res engr to sr res engr heat transfer res, Rocketdyne, Div Rockwell Int, 57-68; res asst, Mont State Univ, 68-71; sr develop engr II nuclear safety prog mgr, Westinghouse Hanford Co, 71-74. *Mem:* Am Nuclear Soc; Am Soc Mech Engrs; AAAS; NY Acad Sci; Am Solar Energy Soc. *Res:* Natural and forced convection heat transfer. *Mailing Add:* 3426 Butler Walk Naperville IL 60564-8210

**WEBER, PAUL VAN VRANKEN,** plant pathology, for more information see previous edition

**WEBER, PETER B,** BIOCHEMISTRY. *Current Pos:* from asst prof to assoc prof, 68-84, PROF BIOCHEM, ALBANY MED COL, 84- *Personal Data:* b Berlin, Ger, July 31, 34; c 1. *Educ:* Univ Cologne, DNatSc(biol, chem), 61. *Prof Exp:* NIH grants, Univ Ill, Chicago, 64-65; NSF grants, State Univ NY Buffalo, 65-68. *Mem:* Fedn Am Socs Exp Biol; Soc Complex Carbohydrates; Sigma Xi; NY Acad Sci. *Res:* Biochemistry of membrane glycoproteins and bacterial polysaccharides. *Mailing Add:* Dept Biochem Albany Med Col New Scotland Ave Albany NY 12208-3412

**WEBER, RICHARD GERALD,** ENTOMOLOGY. *Current Pos:* INSTR INSECT STRUCT, INSECT PHOTOGRAPHY, NATURAL HIST INSECTS, DEPT ENTOM & APPL SCI, UNIV DEL, 77- *Personal Data:* b Newport News, Va, Dec 20, 39. *Educ:* Eastern Mennonite Col, BS(biol) & BA(foreign lang), 69; Univ Del, MS, 71; Kans State Univ, PhD(entom), 75. *Prof Exp:* Instr insect morphol, insect taxonomy, gen entomology, Kans State Univ, 75-77. *Mem:* Am Entom Soc; Am Mosquito Control Asn; Entom Soc Am; Biol Photographic Asn. *Res:* Insect morphology in relation to behavior; mosquito oviposition behavior; photographic and electronics applications for entomological research. *Mailing Add:* 1203 Media Rd Oxford PA 19363-2028

**WEBER, RICHARD RAND,** RADIO ASTRONOMY, INSTRUMENTATION. *Current Pos:* RES SCIENTIST RADIO ASTRON, GODDARD SPACE FLIGHT CTR, NASA, 64- *Personal Data:* b Columbia, Pa, July 28, 38; m 65; c 3. *Educ:* Franklin & Marshall Col, AB, 60; Univ Md, MS, 68. *Prof Exp:* Teacher physics & math, Wilson High Sch, West Lawn, Pa, 60-61. *Mem:* Am Astron Soc; Am Geophys Union; Int Union Radio Sci. *Res:* Microwave studies of cosmic background radiation; low frequency; studies of galactic, solar, planetary radio emissions; radio experiments on spacecraft. *Mailing Add:* 10715 Moosberger Ct Columbia MD 21044

**WEBER, ROBERT EMIL,** POLYMER CHEMISTRY. *Current Pos:* Res chemist, Res & Develop Ctr, Kimberly-Clark Corp, Wis, 58-66, sr res scientist, 66-68, mgr prod develop lab, Munising Div, Mich, 68-71, group leader, Advan Develop Lab, Res & Eng Ctr, Neenah, 71-75, dir res & develop, Munising Paper Div, 75-82, SR RES FEL, KIMBERLY-CLARK CORP, 82- *Personal Data:* b Oshkosh, Wis, Dec 17, 30; m 53, Jeanne M Friess; c Thomas, Kathy & James. *Educ:* Univ Wis-Oshkosh, BS, 53; Univ Iowa, PhD, 59. *Mem:* Am Chem Soc. *Res:* Physical properties of polymers solutions; physical-chemical properties of fiber-elastomer composites. *Mailing Add:* Kimberly-Clark Corp 1400 Holcomb Bridge Rd Roswell GA 30076-9703

**WEBER, ROBERT HARRISON,** GEOLOGY. *Current Pos:* RETIRED. *Personal Data:* b Wauseon, Ohio, Feb 8, 19; m 41; c 2. *Educ:* Ohio State Univ, BSc, 41; Univ Ariz, PhD(geol), 50. *Prof Exp:* Geologist, Shell Oil Co, 41-42; econ geologist, NMex Bur Mines & Minerals Resources, 50-66, sr geologist, 66-85. *Concurrent Pos:* Fac assoc, NMex Inst Mining & Technol, 65- *Mem:* Fel AAAS; fel Geol Soc Am; Soc Econ Geol; Soc Am Archaeol; Am Quaternary Asn. *Res:* Mineral deposits; petrography and petrology of volcanic rocks; Quaternary stratigraphy and geomorphology of the Southwest; meteoritics; early man in the New World. *Mailing Add:* 1502 Evergreen Dr Socorro NM 87801

**WEBER, STEPHEN VANCE,** NUMERICAL SIMULATION, INERTIAL FUSION. *Current Pos:* RES SCIENTIST & PHYSICIST, LAWRENCE LIVERMORE NAT LAB, 82- *Personal Data:* b Wooster, Ohio, Oct 31, 51; m 80, Marie Christensen; c Erik & Kristina. *Educ:* Princeton Univ, AB, 73, Univ Calif, MA, 74, PhD, 78. *Honors & Awards:* Excellence in Plasma Physics Award, Am Phys Soc, 95. *Prof Exp:* Res fel, Calif Inst Technol, 78-80; asst prof, Dartmouth Col, 80-82. *Mem:* Am Astron Soc; Am Phys Soc. *Res:* Investigations of Rayleigh-Taylor instability and implosions in internal confinement fusion; contributed articles to professional journals. *Mailing Add:* Lawrence Livermore Nat Lab MS L477 PO Box 808 Livermore CA 94550

**WEBER, THOMAS,** FORESTRY. *Current Pos:* DEP CHIEF MGT & STRATEGIC PLANNING, NATURAL RESOURCES CONSERV PROGS, 96- *Educ:* Northern Ariz Univ, MSF, 72; Stanford Univ, MSM, 89. *Mailing Add:* Natural Resources Conserv Progs 1400 Independence Ave SW 51105 Washington DC 20250

**WEBER, THOMAS BYRNES,** BIOCHEMISTRY. *Current Pos:* AT SCI PAC CREATIVE RES, 90- *Personal Data:* b Oklahoma City, Okla, Sept 1, 25; m 58; c 4. *Educ:* Okla State Univ, BS, 48; La State Univ, PhD(biochem), 54. *Prof Exp:* Res scientist, Animal Dis Res Ctr, Agr Res Ctr, USDA, 54-57; head biochem dept, US Navy Dent Res Inst, 57-59; head atmospheric & gas anal, USAF Sch Aerospace Med, 59-62; head adv Res Med Develop, Beckman Instruments, Inc, 62-67; pres, Biosci Planning Inc, 67-69; pres, Weber Dent Prod, Generics Int, 74-77, pres, 74-86. *Concurrent Pos:* Life sci consult to indust, 58-62; consult, Life Sci & Instrumentation, US Govt, 63-; mem bd dirs, Metab Dynamic Found, 64- *Mem:* AAAS; Am Chem Soc. *Res:* Life support systems; multiphasic screening methods; biochemical and physiological instrumentation; monitoring in closed ecological systems; body fluid analysis; automation of testing tools; handling of ethical pharmaceuticals; heat transfer; high temperature combustion and incineration. *Mailing Add:* 3936 Caminito Silvela San Diego CA 92122-4370

**WEBER, THOMAS W(ILLIAM),** CHEMICAL ENGINEERING. *Current Pos:* from asst prof to assoc prof, State Univ NY, 63-83, assoc chmn dept, 80-82, chmn dept, 82-89, PROF CHEM ENG, STATE UNIV NY, BUFFALO, 83- *Personal Data:* b Orange, NJ, July 15, 30; m 66, Marianne S Hartmann; c Anne L & William A. *Educ:* Cornell Univ, BChE, 53, PhD(chem eng), 63; Newark Col Eng, MS, 58. *Honors & Awards:* ASEE Award, AT&T Found, 87-88. *Prof Exp:* Engr, Esso Res & Eng, Linden, NJ, 55-58; instr chem engr, Cornell Univ, 61-62. *Concurrent Pos:* NSF grant, 66-68. *Mem:* Fel Am Inst Chem Engrs; fel Am Soc Eng Educ; Sigma Xi. *Res:* Dynamics and control of chemical engineering equipment and processes. *Mailing Add:* Dept Chem Eng Furnas Hall State Univ NY Amherst NY 14260. *Fax:* 716-645-3822; *E-Mail:* twweber@eng.buffalo.edu

**WEBER, WALDEMAR CARL,** MATHEMATICS. *Current Pos:* Asst prof, 68-72, asst chair, Dept Math & Statist, 77-87, ASSOC PROF MATH, BOWLING GREEN STATE UNIV, 72 - *Personal Data:* b Chicago, Ill, May 4, 37; m 69. *Educ:* US Naval Acad, BSc, 59; Univ Ill, Urbana, MSc, 64, PhD, 68. *Mem:* Am Math Soc; Math Asn Am. *Res:* Geometry; applied mathematics. *Mailing Add:* Dept Math & Statist Bowling Green State Univ Bowling Green OH 43403-0001

**WEBER, WALLACE RUDOLPH,** SYSTEMATIC BOTANY. *Current Pos:* from asst prof to assoc prof, 67-79, PROF BIOL, SOUTHWEST MO STATE UNIV, 79- *Personal Data:* b Murphysboro, Ill, Aug 1, 34; m 60, Erma Roethe; c Renee (Karre) & Amy. *Educ:* Southern Ill Univ, BA, 56, MS, 59; Ohio State Univ, PhD(bot), 68. *Prof Exp:* Instr biol, Otterbein Col, 59-62; teaching assoc bot, Ohio State Univ, 63-67. *Mem:* Bot Soc Am; Am Soc Plant Taxon; Int Asn Plant Taxon; Sigma Xi; Nat Asn Biol Teachers. *Res:* Floristics of Missouri Ozarks; biosystematic studies. *Mailing Add:* Dept Biol Southwest Mo State Univ Springfield MO 65802. *Fax:* 417-836-6934; *E-Mail:* wrn5744@nic.smsu.edu

**WEBER, WALTER J, JR,** ENVIRONMENTAL & WATER RESOURCES ENGINEERING. *Current Pos:* from asst prof to prof civil & water resources eng, Univ Mich, Ann Arbor, 63 & 87, dir, Univ Prog Water Resources, 68-92, Earnest Boyce distinguished prof eng, 87-94, DIR, GREAT LAKE & MID-ATLANTIC HAZARDOUS SUBSTANCE RES CTR, UNIV MICH, ANN ARBOR, 88-, GORDON MASKEW FAIR & EARNEST BOYCE DISTINGUISHED UNIV PROF, 94- *Personal Data:* b Pittsburgh, Pa, June 16, 34; c 4. *Educ:* Brown Univ, ScB, 56; Rutgers Univ, ScM, 59; Harvard Univ, AM, 61, PhD(water resources eng), 62; Am Acad Environ Engrs, dipl, 75. *Honors & Awards:* Faraday Lectr, Univ Mich, 70; James R Rumsey Mem Award, Mich Water Control Asn, 75; Nalco Res Award, Asn Environ Eng Prof, 79; Willard F Shephard Award, Mich Water Pollution Control Asn, 80; Rudolph Herning Medal, Am Soc Civil Engrs, 80; Simon W Freese Award, 84, G Brooks Ernest Award, 85; F J Zimmerman Award, Am Chem Soc, 82; Thomas R Camp Award, Boston Soc Civil Engrs, 82; Eng Sci Res Award, Asn Environ Eng Prof, 84; Thomas R Camp Medal, Water Pollution Control Fedn, 88, Gordon M Fair Medal, 90. *Prof Exp:* Engr, Caterpillar Tractor Co, 56-57; instr civil eng, Rutgers Univ, 57-59; fel water resources eng, Harvard Univ, 62-63. *Concurrent Pos:* Engr, Soil Conserv Serv, 57-59; vis scholar, Univ Calif, Berkeley & Univ Melbourne, 71. *Mem:* Nat Acad Eng; AAAS; Am Chem Soc; Am Inst Chem Engrs; Am Soc Civil Engrs; Water Pollution Control Fedn; Sigma Xi; Am Water Works Asn; Asn Environ Eng Professors; Int Asn Water Pollution Res & Control. *Res:* Water quality and pollution control; water and wastewater treatment; water resources systems design, modeling and water basin management. *Mailing Add:* Dept Civil & Environ Eng Univ Mich 181 Water Resources Eng Bldg 1-A Ann Arbor MI 48109-2125. *Fax:* 313-763-2275

**WEBER, WENDELL W,** PHARMACOLOGY, PHARMACOGENETICS. *Current Pos:* PROF PHARMACOL, UNIV MICH, ANN ARBOR, 74- *Personal Data:* b Maplewood, Mo, Sept 2, 25; m 52; c 2. *Educ:* Cent Methodist Col, BA, 45; Northwestern Univ, PhD(phys chem), 50; Univ Chicago, MD, 59. *Prof Exp:* Asst prof chem, Univ Tenn, 49-51; opers res analyst, Off of Chief Chem Officer, Dept Army, Washington, DC, 51-55; from resident to chief resident pediat, Univ Calif, San Francisco, 60-62; NIH spec fel human genetics, Univ Col, Univ London, 62-63; from instr to prof pharmacol, Sch Med, NY Univ, 63-74. *Concurrent Pos:* NIH spec fel biochem, Sch Med, NY Univ, 63-65; Health Res Coun NY career scientist award, 65-70 & 70-; mem pharmacol-toxicol comt, Nat Inst Gen Med Sci, 69-73. *Mem:* Am Chem Soc; Am Soc Pharmacol & Exp Therapeut; Am Soc Human Genetics; fel NY Acad Sci. *Res:* Physical chemistry; human genetics; biochemical genetics and pharmacogenetics; drug metabolism and toxicity. *Mailing Add:* Dept Pharmacol Univ Mich 13011 Med Sci Res Bldg III Ann Arbor MI 48109-0626. *Fax:* 313-763-4450

**WEBER, WILFRIED T,** PATHOLOGY, IMMUNOLOGY. *Current Pos:* CONSULT, 89- *Personal Data:* b Rosenheim, Ger, Feb 10, 36; US citizen; m 60; c 2. *Educ:* Cornell Univ, BS, 59, DVM, 61; Univ Pa, PhD(path), 66. *Honors & Awards:* Lindback Award, 75. *Prof Exp:* From asst prof to prof, 66-75, prof path & chmn Dept Pathobiol, Sch Vet Med, Univ Pa, 78-89. *Concurrent Pos:* NIH res grants, 67-83; USDA grants, 83- *Mem:* Am Vet Med Asn; Reticuloendothelial Soc; Am Asn Pathologists; Am Asn Immunologists. *Res:* Hematology; immunopathology; cancer research; tissue culture of lymphoid cells and macrophages. *Mailing Add:* Dept Pathobiol Univ Pa Sch Vet Med 3800 Spruce St Philadelphia PA 19104-6008. *Fax:* 215-898-9923

**WEBER, WILLES HENRY,** CONDENSED MATTER RAMEN SPECTROSCOPY, FIBER OPTIC SENSORS. *Current Pos:* Sr res scientist, Ford Motor Co, 68-71, prin res scientist assoc, 71-77, staff scientist, 77-92, PRIN RES SCIENTIST, RES STAFF, FORD MOTOR CO, 92- *Personal Data:* b Reno, Nev, Sept 22, 42; m 65, Kathleen Barker; c Michael. *Educ:* Calif Inst Technol, BS, 64; Univ Wis, MS, 65, PhD(physics), 68. *Concurrent Pos:* Assoc ed, Optics Lett, Optical Soc Am, 77-80; adj assoc prof physics, Univ Mich, Ann Arbor, 77-88; topical ed, J Optical Soc Am, 80-86; pres, Ann Arbor Chap, Optical Soc Am, 85-86; ed-in-chief, J Optical Soc Am, 87-88; vis prof physics, Univ Mich, Ann Arbor, 88-89, adj prof physics, 90-; vis fel, Joint Inst Lab Astrophysics, Univ Colo, Boulder, 97. *Mem:* Fel Am Phys Soc; fel Optical Soc Am; Sigma Xi. *Res:* Atomic and molecular physics; semiconductor physics, injection phenomena, instabilities, lasers, luminescence; plasma effects in metals and semiconductors; infrared laser spectroscopy; optical effects at surfaces; Raman spectroscopy of solids; over 100 publications in refered scientific journals. *Mailing Add:* 2947 Hickory Lane Ann Arbor MI 48104. *Fax:* 313-594-6863

**WEBER, WILLIAM ALFRED,** BOTANY, LICHENOLOGY. *Current Pos:* From asst prof to assoc prof, 46-82, EMER PROF NATURAL HIST & CUR HERBARIUM, UNIV COLO, BOULDER, 82- *Personal Data:* b New York, NY, Nov 16, 18; m 40, Selma R Herrmann; c Linna, Heather & Erica. *Educ:* Iowa State Col, BS, 40; State Col Wash, MS, 42, PhD(bot), 46. *Concurrent Pos:* Cur, Lichen Herbarium, Am Bryol & Lichenological Soc, 54-70. *Mem:* AAAS; Bot Soc Am; Am Bryol & Lichenological Soc; Am Soc Plant Taxon; Int Asn Plant Taxon; Lichenological Soc London; fel Linnean Soc London. *Res:* Lichen and bryophyte flora of Colorado, Galapagos Islands and Australasia; boreal and arctic elements in the Rocky Mountain flora; vascular flora of Rocky Mountains/Altai. *Mailing Add:* 1905 Bluff St Boulder CO 80304

**WEBER, WILLIAM J,** RADIATION EFFECTS, ADVANCED CERAMICS. *Current Pos:* STAFF SCIENTIST, PAC NORTHWEST DIV, BATTELLE, 77- *Personal Data:* b Watertown, Wis, July 19, 49; div. *Educ:* Univ Wis-Oshkosh, BS, 71; Univ Wis-Madison, MS, 72, PhD(nuclear energy), 77. *Concurrent Pos:* Vis scientist, Europ Inst Transuranium Elements, Karlsruhe, Ger, 83; lectr, Tri-cities Univ Ctr, 88; prog mgr, special assignment, US Dept Energy, 88-93. *Mem:* Am Ceramic Soc; Mat Res Soc; Sigma Xi. *Res:* Materials science research on radiation effects in materials; defect/property relationships; advanced ceramic processing and properties; electrical transport in ceramics; materials characterization, especially x-ray diffraction and electron microscopy techniques. *Mailing Add:* PO Box 999 MS K2-44 Richland WA 99352. *E-Mail:* wj_weber@pnl.gov

**WEBER, WILLIAM MARK,** QUATERNARY GEOLOGY. *Current Pos:* PRES, WEBER & ASSOC, INC, 77-; GEOLOGIST, CTR DISEASE CONTROL, AGENCY TOXIC SUBSTANCES, 89- *Personal Data:* b Great Bend, Kans, Nov 24, 41; m 64; c 2. *Educ:* Colo Col, BS, 63; Mont State Univ, MS, 65; Univ Wash, PhD(geol), 71. *Prof Exp:* Lab technician, Lincoln DeVore Testing Lab, 59-63, consult geologist, 65-67; instr geol, Colo Col, 67-68; asst prof, Minot State Col, 70-74; mem staff, Dept Geol, Univ Mont, 74-77; geologist, Lewis & Clark Nat Forest, 77-89. *Concurrent Pos:* Instr, Univ Colo, Cragmoor Campus, 66-68; co-dir exp col, Minot State Col, 71-72, NSF grant, 71-72. *Mem:* Geol Soc Am; Asn Prof Geol Scientists. *Mailing Add:* Agency Toxic Substances & Dis Registry 1600 Clifton Rd E56 Atlanta GA 30333

**WEBER, WILLIAM PALMER,** SYNTHETIC INORGANIC & ORGANOMETALLIC CHEMISTRY. *Current Pos:* from asst prof to assoc prof, 68-78, PROF CHEM, UNIV SOUTHERN CALIF, LOS ANGELES, 78- *Personal Data:* b Washington, DC, Nov 7, 40; m 63, Heather; c Edward, Robert, Justin & Nathaniel. *Educ:* Univ Chicago, BS, 63; Harvard Univ, MS, 65, PhD(chem), 68. *Prof Exp:* Res chemist, Dow Chem, 67-68. *Concurrent Pos:* Chair, Univ Admis Comt, Univ Southern Calif, 80-84, pres, Fac Senate, 85-86 & chair, Dept Chem, 86-89, assoc dir, Loker Hydrocarbon Res Inst. *Mem:* Am Chem Soc. *Res:* Organosilicon polymer synthesis; ruthenium catalyzed polymer synthesis. *Mailing Add:* Loker Hydrocarbon Res Inst Univ Southern Calif Los Angeles CA 90089-1661. *Fax:* 213-740-6678; *E-Mail:* wpweber@bcf.usc.edu

**WEBERG, BERTON CHARLES,** ORGANIC CHEMISTRY. *Current Pos:* RETIRED. *Personal Data:* b St Paul, Minn, Dec 23, 30; m 58; c 4. *Educ:* Hamline Univ, BS, 54; Univ Colo, PhD(org chem), 58. *Prof Exp:* Sr res chemist, Abrasives Lab, Minn Mining & Mfg Co, 58-64; prof chem, Mankato State Univ, 64-95. *Mem:* Am Chem Soc. *Res:* Chemistry of hindered ketones and vinyl ethers; polymer chemistry. *Mailing Add:* 1116 Adams St Mankato MN 56001-4250

**WEBERS, GERALD F,** PALEONTOLOGY. *Current Pos:* PROF GEOL, MACALESTER COL, 66- *Personal Data:* b Racine, Wis, Apr 14, 32; m 58; c 2. *Educ:* Lawrence Univ, BS, 54; Univ Minn, MS, 61, PhD(geol), 64. *Prof Exp:* Res assoc geol, Univ Minn, 64-66. *Mem:* Geol Soc Am; Paleont Soc. *Res:* Evolution, taxonomy and paleoecology of Paleozoic invertebrate fossil faunas, especially trilobites, primitive mollusks and conodonts; antarctic geology. *Mailing Add:* 1757 Albert St N St Paul MN 55113-6210

**WEBERS, VINCENT JOSEPH,** ORGANIC CHEMISTRY. *Current Pos:* chemist, Cent Res Dept, E I du Pont de Nemours & Co, Inc, 49-53, res chemist, Photo Prod Dept, 53-65, res assoc, 65-66 & Org Chem Dept, 66-67, res supvr, Photo Prod Dept, 67-73, res assoc, 73-76, res fel, 76-85, CONSULT, E I DU PONT DE NEMOURS & CO, INC, 85- *Personal Data:* b Racine, Wis, Apr 28, 22; m 49, Anita Croucher; c 6. *Educ:* Univ Wis, BS, 43; Univ Minn, PhD(org chem), 49. *Honors & Awards:* V F Payne Award, Am Chem Soc, 65. *Prof Exp:* Lab asst, Univ Minn, 43-45; chemist, Wyeth Inst Appl Biochem, 46; lab asst, Univ Minn, 47. *Mem:* Am Chem Soc; Sigma Xi; Soc Imaging Sci & Technol. *Res:* Polymer chemistry; lithography; photochemistry; photopolymerization; sensitometry; photosensitive systems; metal coating and plating. *Mailing Add:* 2322 Wynnwood Rd Wilmington DE 19810-2735

**WEBERT, HENRY S,** BOTANY, PLANT PHYSIOLOGY. *Current Pos:* from asst prof to assoc prof, 64-70, PROF BIOL, NICHOLLS STATE UNIV, 70- *Personal Data:* b New Orleans, La, Jan 21, 29; m 70; c 3. *Educ:* Loyola Univ, Ill, BS, 51, MEd, 53; La State Univ, MS, 62, PhD(bot), 65. *Prof Exp:* Teacher high sch, Ill, 54-59; partic biol, NSF Acad Year Inst, Brown Univ, 59-60; res asst bot, La State Univ, 60-64. *Mailing Add:* 207 Garden Dr Thibodaux LA 70301

**WEBRE, NEIL WHITNEY,** computer science, applied physics, for more information see previous edition

**WEBSTER, ALEXANDER JAMES,** AGROLOGY. *Current Pos:* PRES, EXP CONSULT LTD, 84-; DIR INT PROJ, O&T AGDEVCO, 85- *Personal Data:* b St Walburg, Sask, Sept 5, 25; m 49, Margaret Jean Robinson; c Craig R, Stuart B & Brenda L. *Educ:* Univ Sask, BSA, 49; Colo State Univ, MEd, 53. *Honors & Awards:* Fel Award, Agr Inst Can, 91. *Prof Exp:* Agr rep, Sask Dept Agr, 49-55; asst dir, Agr Exten, Regina-Sask, 55-65, dir animal indust, 65-67, dir prod & mkt, 67-72, asst dep, 72-78, actg dep, 79, dep, Dept Rural Affairs, 79-82; chmn, Land Bank Comn, 82-83; mgr, Sask Farm Purchase Prog, 83-84, exec dir land admin, 84-85. *Concurrent Pos:* Leader, Red Meat Trade Mission, 71; head four-man agr mission to China, 80. *Mem:* Can Inst Agrologists. *Mailing Add:* 3910 Hill Ave Regina SK S4S 0X5 Can

**WEBSTER, ALLEN E,** PROCESS CONTROL SYSTEMS, INSTRUMENTATION. *Current Pos:* RETIRED. *Personal Data:* b Minneapolis, Minn, Oct 9, 38; m 60, Lynn Northway; c Kari & Brian. *Educ:* Univ Minn, BSME, 60. *Prof Exp:* Proj engr, DuPont, 60-64, tech engr, 64-67, res design engr, 67-74, sr res design engr, 74-81, res engr, 81-83, sr res engr, 83-86, sr tech engr, 86-96. *Concurrent Pos:* Consult, Process Control & Eng. *Mem:* Instrument Soc Am; Indust Comput Soc. *Res:* Substrates for floppy disks; film processing procedures and equipment; microwave drying; film coating and treating; film handling and slitting; batch processing with PLCs and tristate matrix programming; DCS systems configuration; equipment and process design and installation. *Mailing Add:* 5309 Chickadee Circle Orient OH 43146. *E-Mail:* awebster@freenet.columbus.oh.us

**WEBSTER, BARBARA DONAHUE,** PLANT MORPHOGENESIS. *Current Pos:* instr agron, Univ Calif, 58-72, res morphologist & lectr agron & range sci, 72-79, prof & assoc dean biol sci, 79-81, assoc dean grad studies & res, 81-89, ASSOC VCHANCELLOR RES, DEPT AGRON & RANGE SCI, UNIV CALIF, DAVIS, 89- *Personal Data:* b Winthrop, Mass, May 19, 29; m 56; c 1. *Educ:* Univ Mass, BS, 50; Smith Col, MA, 52; Harvard Univ, PhD, 54. *Prof Exp:* Instr plant sci, Vassar Col, 52-54; instr biol, Tufts Univ, 57-58. *Concurrent Pos:* Res investr, Brookhaven Nat Lab, 52-53 & 55; NSF fel, Purdue Univ, 58-60; mgt fel, Univ Calif, Davis, 80; vis prof, Univ Nairobi, Kenya, 83; vis scholar, Univ Tex, Austin, Nat Acad Sci & NSF, 87. *Mem:* Bot Soc Am (pres elect, 82, pres, 83); Am Soc Plant Physiol; fel Am Sci Hort Sci; fel AAAS. *Res:* Plant growth regulators and abscission; morphology and physiology of plant growth; reproductive biology and pollination mechanisms. *Mailing Add:* Dept Agron & Range Sci Univ Calif Davis CA 95616-5224

**WEBSTER, BURNICE HOYLE,** thoracic diseases; deceased, see previous edition for last biography

**WEBSTER, CARL DAVID,** APPLIED DIET FORMULATIONS FOR FINFISH & CRUSTACEANS, ALTERNATIVE PROTEIN SOURCES FOR USE IN AQUACULTURE DIETS. *Current Pos:* Co-investr, 89-92, PRIN INVESTR, KY STATE UNIV, 92- *Personal Data:* b Huntsville, Ala, June 28, 60; m 94, Nancy C Deutsch; c NancyAnn C. *Educ:* Drew Univ, BA, 82; Southern Ill Univ, MS, 84; Auburn Univ, PhD(fisheries & allied aquacult), 89. *Concurrent Pos:* Ed, J Appl Aquacult. *Mem:* World Aquacult Soc; Am Fisheries Soc; Am Oil Chemists Soc; Am Soc Animal Sci; Am Inst Nutrit. *Res:* Evaluate inclusion of various alternative feedstuffs in prepared diets, determine physiological nutrient requirements, develop economical and nutritious diets for larval, juvenile and adult finfish and crustaceans which are currently, or are prospective, aquaculture species. *Mailing Add:* Aquacult Res Ctr Ky State Univ Frankfort KY 40601. *Fax:* 502-564-9118; *E-Mail:* cwebster@dcr.net

**WEBSTER, CLYDE LEROY, JR,** INORGANIC CHEMISTRY, GEOCHEMISTRY. *Current Pos:* SR RES SCIENTIST, GEOSCI RES INST, LOMA LINDA UNIV, 83- *Personal Data:* b Colorado Springs, Colo, Nov 15, 44; m 65; c 2. *Educ:* Walla Walla Col, BSc, 68; Colo State Univ, PhD(chem), 72. *Prof Exp:* Consult chem, Accu-Labs Res Inc, 73-74; asst mgr chem, Instrument Anal Div, Com Testing & Eng, 74-75; asst prof chem, Loma Linda Univ, 75-78; assoc chmn dept, 77-80; assoc prof chem & chmn dept, Walla Walla Col, 80-83. *Concurrent Pos:* Consult, Geosci Res Inst, 75- *Mem:* Am Chem Soc. *Res:* Ore body genesis and processes of fossilization as related to the great deluge theory. *Mailing Add:* 5183 Sierra Vista Riverside CA 92505-2531

**WEBSTER, CURTIS CLEVELAND,** MATHEMATICS, NUCLEAR ENGINEERING. *Current Pos:* develop engr, Develop Dept Opers Div, 62-70, COMPUT APPLNS SPECIALIST, MATH DIV, OAK RIDGE NAT LAB, 70- *Personal Data:* b Roxbury, Vt, Sept 22, 22; m 47; c 5. *Educ:* Univ Vt, AB, 47; Mo Sch Mines, MS, 50. *Prof Exp:* Lab asst physics, Case Inst Technol, 47-48; instr, Mo Sch Mines, 48-50; scientist, Oak Ridge Nat Lab, 50-56; sr scientist, Radiation & Nucleonics Lab, Mat Eng Dept, Westinghouse Elec Corp, 56-58, sr scientist, Atomic Power Dept, 58-59, proj engr, Testing Reactor, 59-60, hazards eval engr, 60-62. *Mem:* AAAS. *Res:* Neutron radiation effects; reactor fuel element development; reactor power measurement by activation of oxygen in coolant; heat transfer problems in water cooled reactor; safety problems in nuclear reactors; reactor physics; application of computers to science and engineering. *Mailing Add:* 122 N Western Ave Oak Ridge TN 37830

**WEBSTER, D(ONALD) S(TEELE),** CHEMICAL ENGINEERING. *Current Pos:* RETIRED. *Personal Data:* b Wellsboro, Pa, Nov 27, 17; m 56; c 4. *Educ:* Pa State Univ, BS, 40. *Prof Exp:* Jr engr, Eng Serv Div, E I du Pont de Nemours & Co, 40-42, engr, US Army contract, Metall Lab, Chicago, 42-43, engr, Clinton Lab, Tenn, 43-44, engr, Hanford Eng Works, Wash, 44-45, engr, Eng Serv Div, Titanium Plant, Del, 45-46, engr, Eng Res Lab,

Exp Sta, 46-52, res supvr, Savannah River Lab, SC, 54-56, sr res supvr, 56-62, res mgr chem eng, 62-69; assoc dir, Chem Eng Div, Argonne Nat Lab, 69-76, dep dir, 76-82. *Mem:* Am Inst Chem Engrs; Am Chem Soc; AAAS. *Res:* Fluid dynamics; solvent extraction methods; radiochemical processing; fluidized-bed combustion. *Mailing Add:* 4271 Vaucluse Rd Aiken SC 29801

**WEBSTER, DALE ARROY,** BIOCHEMISTRY. *Current Pos:* from asst prof to assoc prof, 68-78, PROF BIOL, ILL INST TECHNOL, 78- *Personal Data:* b St Clair, Mich, Jan 11, 38; m 59, Jean M Lyons; c Mark. *Educ:* Univ Mich, BS, 60; Univ Calif, Berkeley, PhD(biochem), 65. *Prof Exp:* Res fel med, Mass Gen Hosp & Harvard Med Sch, 65-68. *Concurrent Pos:* Vis prof biol, Osaka Univ, Japan, 74-75; guest prof biol, Konstanz Univ, Ger, 79; vis prof, Dept Pub Health, Kyoto Univ, Japan, 83-84. *Mem:* Am Soc Microbiol; Am Soc Biochem & Molecular Biol. *Res:* The structure, function and regulation of biosynthesis of heme proteins in bacterial respiration and terminal electron transport; sodium ion pumping during terminal respiration; bacterial hemoglobin; microbial coal desulfurization. *Mailing Add:* Dept Biol Ill Inst Technol Chicago IL 60616

**WEBSTER, DAVID DYER,** MEDICINE, NEUROLOGY. *Current Pos:* PROF NEUROL, MED SCH, UNIV MINN, MINNEAPOLIS, 57- *Personal Data:* b Grand Rapids, Minn, May 27, 18; m 46; c 2. *Educ:* Univ Minn, BS, 42, MD, 51; Am Bd Psychiat & Neurol, dipl, 60. *Concurrent Pos:* Staff neurologist & dir neurophysiol lab, Minneapolis Vet Hosp, 55-, chief neurol serv, 76- *Mem:* AAAS; AMA; Am Acad Neurol. *Res:* Movement disorders; medical electronics. *Mailing Add:* Dept Neurol 6845 Pillsbury Ave Minneapolis MN 55423

**WEBSTER, DAVID HENRY,** HORTICULTURE. *Current Pos:* RETIRED. *Personal Data:* b Berwick, NS, Oct 29, 34; m 60, Alsion Gray; c Janet. *Educ:* Acadia Univ, BSc, 54, MSc, 55; Univ Calif, Davis, PhD(plant physiol), 65. *Prof Exp:* Res scientist, Can Dept Agr, 65-95. *Res:* Fruit tree physiology; nutrition; soil physical properties; nitrate dishcharge from land. *Mailing Add:* 16 Overlook Rd Kentville NS B4N 2P4 Can

**WEBSTER, DENNIS BURTON,** INDUSTRIAL ENGINEERING. *Current Pos:* PROF INDUST ENG, LA STATE UNIV, 95- *Personal Data:* b Covington, Va, Dec 14, 42. *Educ:* WVa Univ, BSIE, 65, MSIE, 66; Purdue Univ, Lafayette, PhD(indust eng), 69. *Prof Exp:* Field studies analyst, Am Viscose Div, FMC Corp, 64; indust engr, 66; from asst prof to prof indust eng, Auburn Univ, 70-94. *Concurrent Pos:* Mem, Col Indust Coun Mat Handling Educ. *Mem:* Am Inst Indust Engrs. *Res:* Materials flow models; simulation models and simulation optimization; scheduling and production control. *Mailing Add:* CEBA Dept Indust & Mfg Syst Eng La State Univ Baton Rouge LA 70803

**WEBSTER, DOUGLAS B,** OTORHINOLARYNGOLOGY. *Current Pos:* PROF OTORHINOLARYNGOL & ANAT, LA STATE UNIV MED CTR, NEW ORLEANS, 73-, CLIN PROF AUDIOL & SPEECH PATH, SCH ALLIED HEALTH, 74- *Personal Data:* b Fond du Lac, Wis, Jan 14, 34; m 55; c 2. *Educ:* Oberlin Col, AB, 56; Cornell Univ, PhD(zool), 60. *Prof Exp:* Fel psychobiology, Calif Inst Technol, 60-62; from asst prof to prof biol, NY Univ, 62-73, actg chmn dept, 67-68. *Concurrent Pos:* NIH grants, NY Univ, 63-65, NY Univ & La State Univ Med Ctr, 65-75 & La State Univ Med Ctr, 73-91. *Mem:* AAAS; Am Asn Anatomists; Soc Neurosci; Am Soc Zoologists (secy, 69-75); Sigma Xi. *Res:* Morphology, behavior and physiology of hearing in vertebrates. *Mailing Add:* Med Ctr La State Univ 2020 Gravier St Suite A New Orleans LA 70112

**WEBSTER, EDWARD WILLIAM,** RADIOLOGICAL PHYSICS. *Current Pos:* radiation safety officer, Mass Gen Hosp, 62-80, prof radiol, Div Health Sci & Technol, Harvard-Mass Inst Technol, 78-86, PHYSICIST, MASS GEN HOSP, 53-, DIR, RADIOL SCI DIV, 70-, PROF RADIOL PHYSICS, HARVARD MED SCH, 75- *Personal Data:* b London, Eng, Apr 12, 22; nat US; m 50, 61, Dorothea Wood; c John S, Peter W, D Anne, Edward R, Mark V & Susan V. *Educ:* Univ London, BSc, 43, PhD(elec eng), 46. *Hon Degrees:* AM, Harvard Univ, 90. *Honors & Awards:* Garland lectr, Calif Radiol Soc, 80; William Coolidge Medal, Am Asn Physicists Med, 83; Landauer lectr, Health Physics Soc, 84; Gold Medal, Am Col Radiol, 91; Taylor lectr, Nat Coun Radiation Protection, 92. *Prof Exp:* Res engr, Eng Elec Co, UK, 45-49; guest researcher, Mass Inst Technol, 49-50, radiation physicist, 50-51; lectr elec eng & nuclear energy, Queen Mary Col, Univ London, 52-53. *Concurrent Pos:* London Co Coun Blair traveling fel, Mass Inst Technol, 49-50; from asst to asst prof, Harvard Med Sch, 53-67, assoc clin prof physics in radiol, 67-69, assoc prof radiol, 69-75; invited examr physics, Am Bd Radiol chmn, Physics Credentials Comt, 66-76; consult, USPHS, 61-63 & WHO, 65 & 67; mem, Comt Radiol, Nat Acad Sci, 62-68; consult, Children's Hosp Med Ctr, Boston, 62-88; mem, Nat Coun Radiation Protection & Measurements, 65-89, bd dirs, 81-88, hon mem, 89-; USPHS spec fel, 65-66; secy-gen, Second Int Conf Med Physics, 69; mem, Radiol Health Study Sect, Dept HEW, 69-72, Radiol Training Grant Comt, NIH, 69-73 & Adv Comt Med Uses Isotopes, US Nuclear Regulatory Comn, 71-93, Adv Comt Environ Hazards, Dept Vet Affairs, 85-95; lectr med radiation physics, Sch Pub Health, Harvard Univ, 71-86, consult, Mass Eye & Ear Infirmary, 57- & Int Atomic Energy Agency, 60-64; mem, Comt Biol Effects Ionizing Radiation, Nat Acad Sci, 77-80 & US Nat Comt, Int Union Pure & Appl Biophys, 71-74, Oversight Comt Radioepidemiologic Tables, 83-84, Comt Ionizing Radiation Dosimetry, 85-86; mem, US deleg, UN Sci Comt Effects Atomic Radiation, 87-, pres, Adv Comt Human Radiation Exp, 94-95; consult, Radiation Effects Res Found, Hiroshima, Japan, 88; Sigma Xi Nat lectr, Health Physics, 88-89. *Mem:* Fel Am Asn Physicists Med (pres, 63-64); Radiol Soc NAm (vpres, 77-78); fel Am Col Radiol; fel Health Physics Soc; Soc Nuclear Med;

Radiation Res Soc. *Res:* Radiological physics; application of radiation, radioisotopes and electronic methods to medical diagnosis and therapy; radiation protection and risk assessment; radiation dosimetry. *Mailing Add:* 23 Forest Hill Rd Wayland MA 01778-3204. *Fax:* 617-726-5123

**WEBSTER, ELEANOR RUDD,** ORGANIC CHEMISTRY, HISTORY OF SCIENCE. *Current Pos:* from instr to prof, Wellesley Col, 52-85, dean of freshmen & sophomores, 56-60, chmn dept chem, 64-67, & 79-81, dir inst chem, 64-72, dir continuing educ, 69-70, EMER PROF CHEM, WELLESLEY COL, 85- *Personal Data:* b Cleveland, Ohio, Oct 11, 20. *Educ:* Wellesley Col, AB, 42; Mt Holyoke Col, MA, 44; Radcliffe Col, MA, 50, PhD(chem), 52. *Prof Exp:* Asst chem, Mt Holyoke Col, 42-44; chemist synthetic org res, Eastman Kodak Co, 44-47. *Concurrent Pos:* Fulbright grant, Belg, 51-52; NSF sci fac fel, Univ Chicago, Oak Ridge, Univ Calif, Berkeley, 60-61, Univ East Anglia, 81-82; vis prof, New Hall, Cambridge Univ, 68 & Univ East Anglia, 81-82. *Mem:* Am Chem Soc; Hist Sci Soc. *Res:* Physical organic chemistry; dissemination of science, the public's understanding since 1850; nineteenth century physical science. *Mailing Add:* 162 Western Ave Sherborn MA 01770

**WEBSTER, EMILIA,** OPTICAL COMMUNICATIONS, OPTICS. *Current Pos:* mem tech staff electro-optics, 80-81, MEM TECH STAFF ADVAN SPACE COMMUN, AEROSPACE CORP, 81- *Personal Data:* b Arad, Romania, Oct, 27, 50; US citizen. *Educ:* Univ Calif, Los Angeles, BS, 74, MS, 78, PhD(physics), 80. *Prof Exp:* Teaching assoc physics, Univ Calif, Los Angeles, 74-79. *Mem:* Am Phys Soc; Optical Soc Am; Inst Elec & Electronics Engrs; Soc Photo-Optical Instrumentation Engrs; Soc Photog Scientists & Engrs. *Res:* Laser communications; lasers; optics; communications theory. *Mailing Add:* 1137 Lake St Venice CA 90291

**WEBSTER, FERRIS,** PHYSICAL OCEANOGRAPHY. *Current Pos:* PROF PHYS OCEANOG, UNIV DEL, 83- *Personal Data:* b St Boniface, Man, Aug 7, 34. *Educ:* Univ Alta, BSc, 56, MSc, 57; Mass Inst Technol, PhD(geophys), 61. *Prof Exp:* Res asst phys oceanog, Woods Hole Oceanog Inst, 59-62, res assoc, 62-63, asst scientist, 63-65, assoc scientist, 65-70, chmn dept phys oceanog, 71-73, sr scientist, 70-78, assoc dir, 73-78; asst adminr res & develop, Nat Oceanic & Atmospheric Admin, 78-82; sr fel, Nat Acad Sci, 82-83. *Concurrent Pos:* Asst prof, Mass Inst Technol, 66-68. *Mem:* AAAS; Am Geophys Union; Am Meteorol Soc. *Res:* Ocean currents; the influence of the ocean on climate variability; management of oceanic data, emphasizing needs of World Climate Research Program; time-series analysis. *Mailing Add:* Col Marine Studies Univ Del Newark DE 19717-0001

**WEBSTER, FRANCIS X,** ISOLATION IDENTIFICATION & SYNTHESIS OF PHEROMONES. *Current Pos:* Fel, 86-87, ASSOC PROF, COL ENVIRON SCI & FORESTRY, STATE UNIV NY, Syracuse, 87- *Personal Data:* b Niagara Falls, NY, Apr 18, 56; m, Kathryn G Thresh; c Conor, Kathryn & Caroline. *Educ:* State Univ NY, BS, 79, PhD(chem), 86. *Honors & Awards:* Bronze Medal Award, Int Soc Chem Ecol, 95. *Mem:* Int Soc Chem Ecol (treas); Am Chem Soc. *Res:* Isolation, identification and synthesis of insect and mammalian pheromones with an emphasis on the practical synthesis of insect pheromones and the application of pheromones to pest control. *Mailing Add:* Dept Chem Col Environ Sci & Forestry State Univ NY Syracuse NY 13210. *Fax:* 315-470-6856; *E-Mail:* fwebster@mailbox.syr.edu

**WEBSTER, GARY DEAN,** GEOLOGY, PALEONTOLOGY. *Current Pos:* from asst prof to assoc prof, 68-77, chmn dept, 80-85, PROF GEOL, WASH STATE UNIV, 77- *Personal Data:* b Hutchinson, Kans, Feb 15, 34; m 64; c 2. *Educ:* Univ Okla, BS, 56; Univ Kans, MS, 59; Univ Calif, Los Angeles, PhD(geol), 66. *Prof Exp:* Geologist, Amerada Petrol Corp, 56-57; geologist, Belco Petrol Corp, 60; geologist, Shell Oil Co, 63; lectr phys geol, Calif Lutheran Col, 63-64; mus scientist, Univ Calif, Los Angeles, 64-65; asst prof geol & paleont, San Diego State Col, 65-68. *Concurrent Pos:* Mem, Am Geol Inst, Int Field Inst, Spain, 71. *Mem:* AAAS; Soc Econ Paleont & Mineral; Paleont Soc; fel Geol Soc Am; Brit Palaeont Asn; Am Inst Prof Geol. *Res:* Late Paleozoic paleontology and stratigraphy, especially crinoids and conodonts; stratigraphy sedimentation. *Mailing Add:* Dept Geol Wash State Univ Pullman WA 99164-2812. *Fax:* 509-335-7816

**WEBSTER, GEORGE CALVIN,** BIOCHEMISTRY, GERONTOLOGY. *Current Pos:* RETIRED. *Personal Data:* b South Haven, Mich, July 17, 24; m 60, Sandra L Whitman; c Jeffrey C & Kimberley A. *Educ:* Western Mich Univ, BS, 48; Univ Minn, MS, 49, PhD(biol), 52. *Prof Exp:* Res fel, Calif Inst Technol, 52-55; from assoc prof to prof biochem, Ohio State Univ, 55-61; vis prof enzyme chem, Univ Wis, 61-65; chief chemist, Aerospace Serv Div, Cape Kennedy, Fla, 65-70; prof biol sci & head dept, Fla Inst Technol, 70-86, assoc dean, Col Sci & Eng, 85-86. *Concurrent Pos:* USPHS spec res fel, 61-63; Am Heart Asn estab investr, 63-65. *Mem:* AAAS; Am Soc Biol Chemists; Sigma Xi; Am Soc Cell Biol. *Res:* Molecular biology of aging; control of gene expression. *Mailing Add:* 530 Majorca Ct Satellite Beach FL 32937-3266. *E-Mail:* webstergc@aol.com

**WEBSTER, GORDON RITCHIE,** SOIL CHEMISTRY. *Current Pos:* from assoc prof to prof, 60-87, EMER PROF SOIL SCI, UNIV ALTA, 87- *Personal Data:* b Kindersley, Sask, Jan 7, 22; m 50; c 2. *Educ:* Univ BC, BSA, 49, MSA, 51; Univ Ore, PhD(soils), 58. *Prof Exp:* Res officer soil sci, Can Dept Agr, 49-60. *Mem:* Can Soc Soil Sci; Int Soc Soil Sci. *Res:* Reclamation of solonetzic soils; reclamation of salt spills. *Mailing Add:* 11817 76th Ave Edmonton AB T6G 0L1 Can

**WEBSTER, GRADY LINDER,** PLANT TAXONOMY. *Current Pos:* EMER PROF BOT, UNIV CALIF, DAVIS, 66- *Personal Data:* b Ada, Okla, Apr 14, 27; m 56; c 1. *Educ:* Univ Tex, BA, 47, MA, 49; Univ Mich, PhD(bot), 54. *Honors & Awards:* Engler Award, Int Asn Plant Taxon, 96. *Prof Exp:* Lectr trop bot, Harvard Univ, 53, NSF fel biol, 53-55, instr bot, 55-58; from asst prof to assoc prof biol sci, Purdue Univ, 58-66; dir, J M Tucker Herbarium, 87-93. *Concurrent Pos:* Guggenheim fel bot, State Univ Utrecht, 64-65; prog dir systematic biol, NSF, 81-82; regional coordr & taxon ed, Flora N Am. *Mem:* Am Soc Plant Taxon (pres, 82); Soc Study Evolution; Bot Soc Am (pres, 93-94); Asn Trop Biol; Int Asn Plant Taxon; Sigma Xi; Linnaean Soc London. *Res:* Evolution and systematics of vascular plants, especially Euphorbiaceae; vegetational and floristic plant geography especially Andean cloud forest; pollination ecology. *Mailing Add:* Sect Plant Biol Univ Calif Davis CA 95616

**WEBSTER, HAROLD FRANK,** PHYSICS. *Current Pos:* RETIRED. *Personal Data:* b Buffalo, NY, June 25, 19; m 51, Helen Voorhis; c Sue H, Kenneth H & Jean P. *Educ:* Univ Buffalo, BA, 41, MA, 44; Cornell Univ, PhD(physics), 53. *Honors & Awards:* Baker Award, Inst Elec & Electronics Eng, 58. *Prof Exp:* Mem staff, Radiation Lab, Mass Inst Technol, 43-45; asst, Cornell Univ, 45-51; physicist, Res Lab, Gen Elec Co, 51-86. *Concurrent Pos:* US deleg gen assembly, Int Sci Radio Union, 60; mem adv comt, Physics Today, 77-80. *Mem:* Am Phys Soc; Inst Elec & Electronics Eng. *Res:* Thermionic emission from single crystal surfaces; metal surface wetting; electron beam dynamics; cesium plasma; energy conversion; ultraviolet sensors; microelectronics; wave guide component development. *Mailing Add:* 77 St Stephens Lane W Schenectady NY 12302

**WEBSTER, HARRIS DUANE,** veterinary pathology; deceased, see previous edition for last biography

**WEBSTER, HENRY DEFOREST,** NEUROLOGY, NEUROPATHOLOGY. *Current Pos:* Assoc chief, Lab Neuropath & Neuronat, 75-84, chief, Lab Exp Neuropath, 84-97, EMER SCIENTIST, NIH, 97- *Personal Data:* b New York, NY, Apr 22, 27; m 51, Marion Havas; c Christopher W, Henry D II, Sally A, David L & Steven C. *Educ:* Amherst Col, BA, 48; Harvard Med Sch, MD, 52; Am Bd Psychiat & Neurol, dipl & cert neurol, 59. *Honors & Awards:* Humboldt Award, Fed Rep Ger, 85; Weil Award, Am Asn Neuropathologists, 60; Sci Award, Peripheral Nerve Asn, 94. *Prof Exp:* Intern & asst resident med, Harvard Serv, Boston City Hosp, 52-54; asst resident & resident neurol, Mass Gen Hosp, 54-56, res fel neuropath, 56-58; asst instr & assoc neurol, Harvard Med Sch, 58-66, asst prof neuropath, 66; assoc prof neurol, Sch Med, Univ Miami, 66-69, prof, 69. *Concurrent Pos:* Prin investr, Nat Inst Neurol Dis & Stroke grants, 62-69, partic neuroanat vis scientist prog, 64-65; assoc neurologist & asst neuropathologist, Mass Gen Hosp, 63-66. *Mem:* Am Asn Neuropath (vpres, 76-77, pres, 78-79); Am Soc Cell Biol; Am Acad Neurol; Am Neurol Asn; Sigma Xi; Int Soc Neuropath (vpres, 80-84, pres, 86-90); hon mem Japanese Soc Neuropath. *Res:* Experimental neuropathology utilizing electron microscopy, immunocytochemistry, and in situ hybridization, especially the formation and breakdown of myelin. *Mailing Add:* 4515 Willard Ave Bethesda MD 20815-3622. *Fax:* 301-402-1030

**WEBSTER, JACKSON DAN,** PARASITOLOGY, ORNITHOLOGY. *Current Pos:* assoc prof, 49-53, prof, 53-84, EMER PROF BIOL, HANOVER COL, 84- *Personal Data:* b Tacoma, Wash, Feb 26, 19; m 44; c 3. *Educ:* Whitworth Col, Wash, BSc, 39; Cornell Univ, MSc, 41; Rice Inst, PhD(parasitol), 47. *Prof Exp:* Field researcher ornith, Alaska, 40 & 46; asst prof biol, Jamestown Col, 47-49. *Concurrent Pos:* Field researcher ornith, 50-88. *Mem:* Soc Parasitol; Wilson Ornith Soc; Cooper Ornith Soc; Am Ornith Union. *Res:* Septematics, distribution and populations of birds; systematics of tapeworms. *Mailing Add:* Dept Biol Hanover Col Hanover IN 47243

**WEBSTER, JACKSON ROSS,** STREAM ECOLOGY. *Current Pos:* From asst prof to assoc prof, 75-87, PROF BIOL, VA POLYTECH INST & STATE UNIV, 87- *Personal Data:* b Brigham City, Utah, May 3, 45; m 68, Sandra Bonsett; c Robert & David. *Educ:* Wabash Col, BA, 67; Univ Ga, PhD(ecol, zool), 75. *Concurrent Pos:* Vis scientist, Oak Ridge Nat Lab, 81-82. *Mem:* Ecol Soc Am; Am Soc Limnol & Oceanog; NAm Benthological Soc; Int Asn Theoret & Appl Limnol; Am Soc Naturalists. *Res:* Nutrient and energy dynamics in stream ecosystems; ecosystem modeling; effects of watershed disturbance on streams. *Mailing Add:* Dept Biol Va Polytech Inst & State Univ Blacksburg VA 24061. *E-Mail:* jwebster@vt.edu

**WEBSTER, JAMES ALBERT,** ORGANIC CHEMISTRY. *Current Pos:* RETIRED. *Personal Data:* b Mineola, NY, June 2, 28; m 51, Jean Dutch; c 4. *Educ:* Col Wooster, BA, 51; Univ Pittsburgh, MS, 56. *Prof Exp:* Res chemist, Res & Eng Div, Monsanto Chem Co, 56-61, res chemist, Monsanto Res Corp, 61-66, sr res chemist, 66-71, sr group leader, 71-75, sr res specialist, 75-85; vis scientist, Wright Patterson AFB; vpres, DayChem Labs, 87-89. *Mem:* Am Chem Soc. *Res:* Polymer synthesis; fluorine chemistry. *Mailing Add:* 7611 Eagle Creek Dr Dayton OH 45459-3411

**WEBSTER, JAMES ALLAN,** ENTOMOLOGY. *Current Pos:* Res entomologist, 68-93, LAB DIR, AGR RES SERV, USDA, 93- *Personal Data:* b Lincoln, Nebr, May 1, 39; m 67, Arletta Visser; c Jennifer J & Bradley J. *Educ:* Univ Ky, BS, 61, MS, 64; Kans State Univ, PhD(entom), 68. *Honors & Awards:* Recognition in Entomol Award, Entomol Soc Am, 96. *Concurrent Pos:* From adj asst prof to adj assoc prof, Dept Entom, Mich State Univ, 68-81; adj assoc prof, Dept Entom, Okla State Univ, 81-89, adj prof, 89- *Mem:* Entom Soc Am; Am Soc Agron. *Res:* Insect resistance in grain and forage crops. *Mailing Add:* 1301 N Western Rd Stillwater OK 74075-2714

**WEBSTER, JAMES RANDOLPH, JR,** PULMONARY PHYSIOLOGY. *Current Pos:* From asst prof to assoc prof, 67-77, PROF MED, MED SCH, NORTHWESTERN UNIV, CHICAGO, 77- *Personal Data:* b Chicago, Ill, Aug 25, 31; m 54; c 3. *Educ:* Northwestern Univ, Chicago, BS, 53, MS & MD, 56. *Concurrent Pos:* USPHS fel pulmonary physiol, Med Sch, Northwestern Univ, Chicago, 62-64; assoc dir inhalation ther, Chicago Wesley Mem Hosp, 65-66, dir pulmonary function lab, 66-; chief med, Northwestern Mem Hosp, 72- *Mem:* Am Thoracic Soc; Am Fedn Clin Res; Am Col Physicians. *Res:* Diseases of the chest. *Mailing Add:* 250 E Superior Chicago IL 60611-2914

**WEBSTER, JOHN GOODWIN,** MEDICAL INSTRUMENTATION, ELECTRODES. *Current Pos:* from asst prof to assoc prof, 67-73, PROF ELEC & COMPUT ENG, UNIV WIS-MADISON, 73- *Personal Data:* b Plainfield, NJ, May 27, 32; m 54, Nancy Egan; c Paul, Robin, Mark & Lark. *Educ:* Cornell Univ, BEE, 53; Univ Rochester, MSEE, 65, PhD(elec eng), 67. *Honors & Awards:* Donald P Eckman Educ Award, Instrument Soc Am, 74; Western Electric Fund Award, Am Soc Eng Educ, 78; Theo C Pilkington Outstanding Educator Award, Am Soc Eng Educ, 94; Laufman-Greatbatch Prize, Asn Adran Med Instrumentation, 96. *Prof Exp:* Res engr, NAm Aviation, Inc, 54-55; head instrumentation, Boeing Airplane Co, 55-59; head telemetry, Radiation, Inc, 59-61; staff engr, Mitre Corp, 61-62, Int Bus Mach Corp, 62-63; res assoc elec eng, Univ Rochester, 67. *Concurrent Pos:* NSF res grant, 68-70 & 84-93; NIH res career develop award, 71-76; NASA res grant, 72-73; NIH res grant, 76-83, 88-91 & 96-99; dir, Biomed Eng Ctr, 76-80; assoc ed, Trans Biomed Eng, Inst Elec & Electronics Engrs, 78-85; mem, NIH Surg Bioeng Study Sect, 86-90. *Mem:* Fel Inst Elec & Electronics Engrs; fel Instrument Soc Am; fel Am Inst Med & Biol Eng. *Res:* Medical devices and instrumentation; electrodes for monitoring and stimulation; biopotential amplifiers radio frequency cardiac ablation and measurement of vigilance interference; electrosurgical units; pulse oximeters; cardiac pacemakers. *Mailing Add:* Dept Elec & Comput Eng Univ Wis 1415 Eng Dr Madison WI 53706. *Fax:* 608-265-4623; *E-Mail:* webster@engr.wisc.edu

**WEBSTER, JOHN H,** RADIOTHERAPY. *Current Pos:* PROF, DEPT RADIOL, ONCOL CTR, UNIV PITTSBURGH, 80- *Personal Data:* b Belleville, Ont, Dec 17, 28; m 53; c 3. *Educ:* Queen's Univ, Ont, MD, 55. *Prof Exp:* Sr cancer res radiologist, Roswell Park Mem Inst, 59-62, assoc cancer res radiologist, 62-63, assoc chief cancer res radiologist, 63-64, chief cancer res radiologist, 64-74; prof therapeut radiol & chmn dept, McGill Univ, 74-80. *Concurrent Pos:* USPHS grants; therapeut radiologist-in-chief, Montreal Gen Hosp, Royal Victoria Hosp, Montreal Children's Hosp & Jewish Gen Hosp, 74-79; sr consult radiotherapist, Montreal Neurol Hosp, 74-79; consult radiotherapist, Presby Univ Hosp & Mazec Womens Hosp, 79- *Mem:* Am Col Radiol; Am Soc Therapeut Radiol; Can Med Asn; Soc Chmn Acad Radiation Oncol Progs; Can Asn Radiologists. *Res:* Experimental radiotherapy and allied fields; oncologically related research; cancer patient care systems. *Mailing Add:* Joint Radiol & Oncol Ctr Magee Women's Hosp Div Forbes Ave & Halket St Pittsburgh PA 15213

**WEBSTER, JOHN ROBERT,** food science, for more information see previous edition

**WEBSTER, JOHN THOMAS,** STATISTICS. *Current Pos:* assoc prof, 62-76, PROF STATIST, SOUTHERN METHODIST UNIV, 76- *Personal Data:* b Fond du Lac, Wis, Sept 12, 27; m 55; c 3. *Educ:* Ripon Col, BA, 51; Purdue Univ, MS, 55; NC State Col, PhD(statist), 60. *Prof Exp:* Statistician, Westinghouse Elec Corp, 55-57; asst prof statist, Bucknell Univ, 60-62. *Mem:* Am Statist Asn; Biomet Soc; Am Soc Qual Control. *Res:* Design and analysis of experiments. *Mailing Add:* 1225 Glen Cove Dr Richardson TX 75080-3965

**WEBSTER, KARL SMITH,** MECHANICAL ENGINEERING, ENGINEERING MECHANICS. *Current Pos:* Dept Interior consult, River Syst as Reactor Proj, Univ Water Resources, Univ Maine, Orono, 67-69, asst to vpres acad affairs, Univ, 70-72, assoc prof mech eng, 65-77, assoc prof, 77-80, prof mech eng technol, 80-89, EMER PROF MECH ENG TECHNOL, SCH ENG TECHNOL, COL ENG & TECHNOL, UNIV MAINE, ORONO, 89- *Personal Data:* b Orleans, Vt, Aug 18, 24; m 53, Jean Gardyne; c Susan (Jackson) & Anne (Emerson). *Educ:* Univ Vt, BSME, 49; Pa State Univ, MS, 58. *Prof Exp:* Test engr, Gen Elec Co, NY, 49-50, appln eng, Mass, 50-52; chief engr, W J Nolan Co, 52-53; develop engr, Fels Gear Shaper Co, 53-54; res asst mech eng, Pa State Univ, 54, instr, 54-58; asst prof, Univ NH, 58-62, assoc prof mech design technol, Tech Inst, 62-65. *Concurrent Pos:* Sabbatical mfg engr, resources & equip develop, GE, Burlington, Vt, 86-87. *Mem:* Am Soc Eng Educ. *Res:* Internal combustion engine projects; industrial and manufacturing engineering. *Mailing Add:* Jones Point Rd Brooksville ME 04617

**WEBSTER, LARRY DALE,** MECHANICS, MATERIALS SCIENCE. *Current Pos:* RETIRED. *Personal Data:* b Westfall, Kans, Feb 8, 39; m 63; c 1. *Educ:* Colo Sch Mines, MetE, 61; Cornell Univ, PhD(mat sci), 65. *Prof Exp:* Chmn sci dept, Lamar Community Col, 65-67; res scientist weapons effects, Kaman Sci Corp, 67-73; sr engr reactor technol, Bettis Atomic Power Lab, Pa, 73-77; res scientist acoust devices, Kaman Sci Corp, 77-90. *Res:* Finite element analyses of coupled structural and electromagnetic fields; model development for piezoelectric devices and for magnetically driven flyer plates associated with impact test facilities. *Mailing Add:* 2523 Mirror Lake Ct Colorado Springs CO 80919

**WEBSTER, LEE ALAN,** TRANSPORTATION & TRAFFIC ENGINEERING. *Current Pos:* PROF & COORDR ENG SCI, GREENFIELD COMMUNITY COL, 79- *Personal Data:* b Mt Holly, NJ, June 30, 41; m 64; c 2. *Educ:* Univ Del, BCE, 63; Univ Ill, Urbana, MSc, 65, PhD(traffic eng), 68. *Prof Exp:* Asst prof civil eng, Univ Mass, Amherst, 68-76; transp engr, Curran Assocs, 76-79. *Mem:* Am Soc Civil Engrs; Am Soc Eng Educ. *Res:* Transportation and traffic engineering education; transportation planning; computer applications to engineering and education. *Mailing Add:* Dept Natural Sci Greenfield Community Col One College Dr Greenfield MA 01301

**WEBSTER, LESLIE T, JR,** BIOCHEMISTRY. *Current Pos:* J H Hord prof & chmn dept, Sch Med, Case Western Res Univ, 76-91, dir, med scientist training prog, 79-92, co-dir, 92-96, EMER J H HORD PROF PHARMACOL SCH MED, CASE WESTERN RES UNIV, 92- *Personal Data:* b New York, NY, Mar 31, 26; m 55, Alice H Holland; c Katharine W, Susan H, Leslie T III & Romi A. *Educ:* Amherst Col, BA, 47; Harvard Med Sch, MD, 48; Am Bd Internal Med, dipl, 57. *Hon Degrees:* ScD, Amherst Col, 81. *Prof Exp:* Demonstr med, Sch Med, Case Western Res Univ, 55-57, instr, 57-60, from sr instr to asst prof biochem, 58-66, asst prof med, 60-70, from asst prof to assoc prof pharmacol, 66-70; prof pharmacol & chmn dept, Med & Dent Schs, Northwestern Univ, Chicago, 70-76. *Concurrent Pos:* Nat Vitamin Found Wilder fel, 56-59; sr investr, USPHS, 59-61, res career develop award, 61-69; mem gastroenterol & nutrit training grants comt, Nat Inst Arthritis & Metab Dis, 65-69; consult, NIH, 71-, WHO, 77-83 & Rockefeller Found, 78-86; Macy fac scholar, 80-81; mem, Cellular & Molecular Basis Dis Rev Comt, Nat Inst Gen Med Sci, 84-88. *Mem:* Am Col Physicians; emer mem Am Soc Clin Invest; emer mem Am Soc Biol Chemists; emer mem Am Soc Pharmacol & Exp Therapeut; emer mem Asn Med Sch Pharmacol. *Res:* Drug metabolism; enzymology; pharmacoparasitology. *Mailing Add:* Univ Hosp Cleveland Div Pediat Clin Pharmacol & Critical Care Rainbow Babies & Childrens Hosp 2074 Abington Rd Cleveland OH 44106. *Fax:* 216-844-5122

**WEBSTER, MERRITT SAMUEL,** mathematics; deceased, see previous edition for last biography

**WEBSTER, ORRIN JOHN,** AGRONOMY. *Current Pos:* ADJ PROF AGRON, UNIV ARIZ, 74- *Personal Data:* b Arkansas City, Kans, June 26, 13; m 36, LeVenia Hile; c Dean G, Thomas F & Jean M. *Educ:* Univ Nebr, BSc, 34, MSc, 40; Univ Minn, PhD(plant breeding & genetics), 50. *Prof Exp:* Agronomist, Soil Conserv Serv, USDA, 35-36, Dryland Agr Div, 36-43 & Cereal Corps Res Br, Agr Res Serv, 43-63, dir-coordr major cereal proj, Orgn For African Unity, 63-71, proj leader corn, sorghum & millet res, Fed Exp Sta, PR, 71-74. *Concurrent Pos:* Adv corn & sorghum breeding, Govt Nigeria, Liberia, Sudan & Africa, 51; secy sorghum res comt, USDA, 53-67; mem comt preserv indigenous strains sorghum, Nat Acad Sci, 61- *Mem:* Am Soc Agron. *Res:* Plant breeding of sorghum; genetics and cytogenetics of sorghum. *Mailing Add:* 5649 E Seventh St Tucson AZ 85711-3260

**WEBSTER, OWEN WRIGHT,** POLYMER CHEMISTRY. *Current Pos:* RETIRED. *Personal Data:* b Devils Lake, NDak, Mar 25, 29; m 53, Lillian Brostek; c Ellen, Anne, John, James & Mary. *Educ:* Univ NDak, BS, 51; Pa State Univ, PhD(chem), 55. *Hon Degrees:* DSc, Univ NDak, 86. *Honors & Awards:* Appl Polymer Sci Award, Am Chem Soc, 93; Du Pont Lavoisier Award, 96. *Prof Exp:* Res chemist, E I DuPont de Nemours & Co, Inc, 55-74, group leader, 74-79, res leader & fel, 84-95. *Mem:* Am Chem Soc; Sigma Xi; AAAS; Am Inst Chemists. *Res:* Synthetic organic chemistry; adamantanes; cyanocarbons; hydrogen cyanide; polymers; group transfer polymerization. *Mailing Add:* 2106 Navaro Rd Wilmington DE 19803. *Fax:* 302-695-9799

**WEBSTER, PAUL DANIEL, III,** MEDICINE, GASTROENTEROLOGY. *Current Pos:* assoc prof, 68-71, PROF MED, MED COL GA, 71-, CHMN DEPT, 77- *Personal Data:* b Mt Airy, NC, Apr 26, 30; m 57; c 2. *Educ:* Univ Richmond, BS, 52; Bowman Gray Sch Med, MD, 56. *Prof Exp:* Fel med, Univ Minn, 60-63; fel gastroenterol, Sch Med, Duke Univ, 63-66, asst prof med, Med Ctr, 67-68. *Concurrent Pos:* USPHS fel, 65-66; chief med serv, Vet Admin Hosp, Augusta, Ga, 73. *Mem:* Am Gastroenterol Asn; Am Physiol Soc; Am Col Gastroenterol; Am Inst Nutrit; Am Soc Clin Invest. *Res:* Hormonal control of pancreatic protein synthesis; pancreatic structure and function; cancer of pancreas. *Mailing Add:* Dept Med & Gastroenterol Med Col Ga 1120 15th St Augusta GA 30912-3120

**WEBSTER, PETER JOHN,** METEOROLOGY, CLIMATOLOGY. *Current Pos:* PROF ASTROPHYS & OCEANIC SCI, UNIV COLO, 92- *Personal Data:* b Stockport, UK, May 30, 42; c 2. *Educ:* Mass Inst Technol, PhD(meteorol), 71. *Honors & Awards:* Wilson Res Award, 89; Jule G Charney Award, 90; Humboldt Award, 90. *Prof Exp:* Asst prof, Univ Wash, Seattle, 72-77; prin res scientist, Commonwealth Sci & Indust Res Orgn, Aspendale Victoria, Australia, 77-83; prof meteorol, Dept Meteorol, Pa State Univ, 83-92. *Concurrent Pos:* Tata prof res, Indian Inst Sci, Bangalore, India, 82; George Haltiner prof res, Dept Naval Postgrad, Monterey, Calif, 83; chief ed, J Atmospheric Sci, Am Meteorol Soc, 83-86; consult, NASA Goddard Lab Atmospheres, Nat Geog Soc, 83-86. *Mem:* Fel Am Meteorol Soc. *Res:* Dynamics of low frequencies flow with particular emphasis on the evolution of monsoons and equatorial waves. *Mailing Add:* Dept Astrophys & Oceanic Sci Univ Colo Box 391 PAOS Boulder CO 80309-0391

**WEBSTER, PORTER GRIGSBY,** MATHEMATICS. *Current Pos:* PROF MATH, UNIV SOUTHERN MISS, 61- *Personal Data:* b Wheatley, Ky, Nov 25, 29; m 61. *Educ:* Georgetown Col, BA, 51; Auburn Univ, MS, 56, PhD(math), 61. *Mem:* Am Math Soc; Math Asn Am. *Mailing Add:* Southern Sta Box 8226 Univ Southern Miss Hattiesburg MS 39406

**WEBSTER, ROBERT EDWARD,** MOLECULAR BIOLOGY, MOLECULAR GENETICS. *Current Pos:* assoc prof, 71-76, PROF BIOCHEM, MED CTR, DUKE UNIV, 76- *Personal Data:* b New Haven, Conn, May 31, 38; m 60, Sererlee Selden; c Jonathan, Malcolm & Alexander. *Educ:* Amherst Col, BA, 59; Duke Univ, PhD(microbiol), 65. *Prof Exp:* NSF fel genetics, Rockefeller Univ, 65-66, asst prof, 66-71. *Mem:* AAAS; Am Soc Cell Biol; Am Soc Biol Chemists; Am Soc Microbiol; Am Soc Virol. *Res:* Phage genetics and morphogenesis; membrane structure and synthesis. *Mailing Add:* Dept Biochem Med Ctr Duke Univ Durham NC 27710-0001

**WEBSTER, ROBERT G,** VIROLOGY, IMMUNOLOGY. *Current Pos:* ASSOC PROF, 68-74, CLIN PROF MICROBIOL, UNIV TENN CTR HEALTH SCI MEMPHIS, 74-; MEM, LABS VIROL & IMMUNOL, ST JUDE CHILDERN'S RES HOSP, 69- *Personal Data:* b Balclutha, NZ, July 5, 32; Australian citizen; c 3. *Educ:* Otago Univ, BS, 55, MS, 57; Australian Nat Univ, PhD(microbiol), 62. *Prof Exp:* Virologist, NZ Dept Agr, 58-59; Fulbright scholar, Dept Epidemiol, Sch Pub Health, Univ Mich, Ann Arbor, 62-63; res fel microbiol, John Curtin Med Sch, Australian Nat Univ, 64-66, fel, 66-67; assoc mem, Lab Immunol, St Jude Children's Res Hosp, 68-69. *Concurrent Pos:* Coordr, US-USSR Joint Comt Health Coop, Ecol of Human Influenza & Animal Influenza Rels to Human Infection, 74- *Mem:* Am Soc Microbiol; Am Asn Immunologists. *Res:* Structure and immunology of influenza viruses. *Mailing Add:* 295 Richbriar Memphis TN 38120

**WEBSTER, ROBERT K,** PHYTOPATHOLOGY. *Current Pos:* from asst prof to assoc prof, 66-75, PROF PLANT PATH, UNIV CALIF, DAVIS, 75- *Personal Data:* b Solomonville, Ariz, Jan 15, 38; m 59; c 3. *Educ:* Utah State Univ, BS, 61; Univ Calif, Davis, PhD(plant path), 66. *Prof Exp:* Res assoc plant path, NC State Univ, 66. *Mem:* Mycol Soc Am; Am Phytopathological Soc; Am Soc Naturalists. *Res:* Genetics of plant pathogenic fungi; field crop diseases. *Mailing Add:* Dept Plant Path Univ Calif Davis CA 95616-5224

**WEBSTER, RONALD LEWIS,** COMPUTER-AIDED ENGINEERING & INTEGRATED PRODUCT DEVELOPMENT, ENGINEERING MECHANICS METHODS DEVELOPMENT. *Current Pos:* SR STAFF ENGR, PROPULSION GROUP, THIOKOL CORP, 77- *Personal Data:* b Salt Lake City, Utah, Aug 23, 36; m 60, Linda Hall; c Mark, Adeena, David, Ronna Lin, Ann, John, Paul, Scott, Brent, Lori, Brian, Adam & Chelsea. *Educ:* Utah State Univ, BS, 65; Brigham Young Univ, MS, 69; Cornell Univ, PhD(civil eng-struct), 76. *Prof Exp:* Sci programmer, Boeing Aircraft Co, 65-66; engr, Wasatch Div, Thiokol Chem Corp, 66-67, Lockheed Propulsion Co, 67-68, Electronic Syst Div, Gen Elec Co, 69-77. *Concurrent Pos:* Consult struct mech & ocean eng, 76- *Mem:* Assoc fel Am Inst Aeronaut & Astronaut; Am Soc Mech Engrs. *Res:* Consulting on computer aided engineering and engineering analysis methods; developed and support a major computer code for simulation of general underwater cable structures and their nonlinear responses in moorings, towing and suspension systems. *Mailing Add:* 720 Eliason Ave Brigham City UT 84302-0707. *E-Mail:* webstrl@thiokol.com

**WEBSTER, TERRY R,** BOTANY, PLANT MORPHOLOGY. *Current Pos:* Asst prof bot, 65-71, ASSOC PROF BIOL, UNIV CONN, 71- *Personal Data:* b Hamilton, Ohio, Feb 10, 38; m 64; c 1. *Educ:* Miami Univ, BA, 60; Univ Sask, MA, 62, PhD(bot), 65. *Mem:* Am Fern Soc (secy, 73-76); 73-78); Soc Am. *Res:* Morphology of the genus Selaginella. *Mailing Add:* Dept Ecol Univ Conn U-42 75 N Eagleville Storrs Mansfield CT 06269-0002

**WEBSTER, THOMAS G,** PSYCHIATRY, ACADEMIC ADMINISTRATION. *Current Pos:* prof psychiat & behav sci & chmn dept, George Washington Univ, 72-75, prof child develop & health, 75-80, prof, 75-86, EMER PROF PSYCHIAT & CHILD HEALTH & DEVELOP, GEORGE WASHINGTON UNIV, 86- *Personal Data:* b Topeka, Kans, Jan 23, 24; m 48, Mary T Dooly; c Warnie, Guy & David. *Educ:* Ft Hays Kans State Col, AB, 46; Wayne State Univ, MD, 49. *Prof Exp:* Commonwealth fel, Col Ment Health, Mass Inst Technol, 54-56; NIMH career teacher grant, Harvard Med Sch, 56-58, instr psychiat, 59-63; training specialist, Psychiat Training Br, NIMH, 63-66, chief, Continuing Educ Br, 66-72. *Concurrent Pos:* Dir, Presch Retard Children's Prog Greater Boston, 58-62; vis prof phychiat, Harvard Med Sch, 80-82. *Mem:* AAAS; Am Psychiat Asn; Am Col Psychiat; Am Acad Child Psychiat; Group Advan Psychiat; AMA. *Res:* Psychiatric education; child development; psychopathology; health policy, international; program evaluation in fields of manpower and training. *Mailing Add:* 2112 F St NW Suite No 700 Washington DC 20037-2715

**WEBSTER, WILLIAM DAVID,** ENDANGERED SPECIES, VERTEBRATE ECOLOGY. *Current Pos:* Coordr environ studies prog, 89-94, PROF & CUR MAMMALS, UNIV NC, WILMINGTON, 83- *Personal Data:* b Charlotte, NC, Aug 24, 54; m 84, Penelope Pittenger; c Michael D & Benjamin W. *Educ:* Univ NC, Wilmington, BS, 76; Mich State Univ, MS, 78; Tex Tech Univ, PhD(zool), 83. *Concurrent Pos:* Adj prof, Dept Earth, Atmospheric & Marine Sci, NC State Univ, 89-; mem, Marine Mammal Stranding Network. *Mem:* Am Soc Mammalogists; Soc Syst Biol; World Conserv Union; Sigma Xi. *Res:* Endangered species, especially sea turtles and mammals. *Mailing Add:* Dept Biol Sci Univ NC Wilmington NC 28403-3297. *Fax:* 910-350-7276

**WEBSTER, WILLIAM JOHN, JR,** PLANETARY SCIENCES. *Current Pos:* resident res assoc, Nat Acad Sci-Nat Res Coun,Solar Physics Lab, Goddard Space Flight Ctr, 70-71, staff scientist, Meteorol & Earth Sci Lab, 71-74, staff scientist, Geol & Geomagnetism Br, Lab Terrestrial Physics, 74-91, STAFF SCIENTIST, COMPUT SUPPORT OFF, LAB TERRESTRIAL PHYSICS, GODDARD SPACE FLIGHT CTR, 91-

*Personal Data:* b New York, NY, May 3, 43; m 80, Mary A Cor; c John L. *Educ:* Univ Rochester, BS, 65; Case Western Res Univ, PhD(astron), 70. *Honors & Awards:* Pub Serv Award, NASA, 79, Group Achievement Award, 90. *Prof Exp:* Res assoc astron, Nat Radio Astron Observ, Va, 68-70. *Mem:* Am Astron Soc; Am Inst Aeronaut & Astronaut. *Res:* Radio interferometry; gaseous nebulae; microwave observation of earth; planetary radio astronomy; asteroids; comets; space texbers; geomagenetism. *Mailing Add:* 8908 Hickory Hill Ave Lanham MD 20706. *Fax:* 301-286-1757; *E-Mail:* webster@godzilla.gsfc.nasa.gov

**WEBSTER, WILLIAM MERLE,** PHYSICS. *Current Pos:* RETIRED. *Personal Data:* b Warsaw, NY, June 13, 25; m 47; c 2. *Educ:* Union Col, NY, BS, 45; Princeton Univ, PhD(elec eng), 54. *Honors & Awards:* Fredrik Philips Award, Inst Elec & Electronics Engrs, 80. *Prof Exp:* Res engr, RCA Labs, RCA Corp, 46-54, mgr adv develop, RCA Semiconductor & Mat Div, 54-59, dir, Electronic Res Lab, 59-66, staff vpres mat & devices res, 66-68, vpres labs, 68-85, vpres & sr tech adv, 85. *Mem:* Nat Acad Eng; fel Inst Elec & Electronics Engrs. *Res:* Solid state and gaseous electronics; electron physics. *Mailing Add:* Couble Bay Governor's Harbor Eleuthera Bahamas

**WEBSTER, WILLIAM PHILLIP,** DENTISTRY. *Current Pos:* RETIRED. *Personal Data:* b Mt Airy, NC, Apr 26, 30; m 52; c 4. *Educ:* Univ NC, Chapel Hill, BS, 56, DDS, 59, MS, 68. *Prof Exp:* Instr prosthodont, Univ NC, Chapel Hill, 59-61, asst prof periodont & oral path, 61-65, asst prof periodont, oral path & path, 65-67, trainee, 67-68, assoc prof path, 69-71, assoc prof dent ecol, 69-73, prof path & dent ecol, Schs Med & Dent, 72-90; chief, Div Oral Med, Hosp Dent Serv, DC Mem Hosp, 68-90. *Concurrent Pos:* Res assoc, Sch Med, Univ NC, Chapel Hill, 59-65; mem med adv comt, Vet Admin Hosp, Fayetteville, NC & sci adv comt, World Fedn Hemophilia. *Mem:* Am Acad Forensic Sci; Am Dent Asn; Am Soc Exp Path; NY Acad Sci; Int Soc Thrombosis & Haemostasis. *Res:* Transplantation; biology; blood coagulation; pathology; oral medicine; oral oncology; hematology. *Mailing Add:* 4025 NE 18th St Ocala FL 34470

**WECHSLER, MARTIN T,** MATHEMATICS. *Current Pos:* from instr to prof, Wayne State Univ, 56-75, chmn dept, 68-75, assoc dean, Col Liberal Arts, 75-83, PROF MATH, WAYNE STATE UNIV, 83- *Personal Data:* b New York, NY, July 27, 21; m 53; c 3. *Educ:* Queen's Col, NY, BS, 42; Univ Mich, MA, 46, PhD(math), 52. *Prof Exp:* Physicist, Nat Bur Standards, 42-45; instr math, Wayne State Univ, 51-52 & Princeton Univ, 52-53; from instr to asst prof, Wash State Univ, 53-56. *Mem:* Am Math Soc. *Res:* Topology; groups of homeomorphisms. *Mailing Add:* 20431 Brentwood St Livonia MI 48152

**WECHSLER, MONROE S(TANLEY),** MATERIALS SCIENCE, SOLID STATE PHYSICS. *Current Pos:* chmn, Dept Metall, Iowa State Univ, 70-75, chief, Metall Div, Ames Lab, USAEC, 70-75, sr metallurgist, Ames Lab, US Dept Energy, 70-75, prof, Dept Mat Sci & Eng, 70-90, prof nuclear eng, 90-93, EMER PROF NUCLEAR ENG, IOWA STATE UNIV, 93-; ADJ PROF, NC STATE UNIV, RALEIGH, 94- *Personal Data:* b New York, NY, May 1, 23; m 50; c 3. *Educ:* City Col New York, BS, 44; Columbia Univ, MA, 50, PhD(physics), 53. *Prof Exp:* Elec engr, USN Air Magnetics Lab, 47-48; mem sci staff, Columbia Univ, 51-54; physicist, Oak Ridge Nat Lab, 54-69; prof metall, Univ Tenn, 65-69. *Concurrent Pos:* Ed, Nuclear Eng Mat Handbk, 77. *Mem:* Fel Am Phys Soc; Am Inst Mining, Metall & Petrol Engrs; Am Soc Metals; Am Nuclear Soc; Am Soc Eng Educ; Sigma Xi. *Res:* Irradiation effects on metals; materials for nuclear reactors; phase transformations; shape-memory alloy heat engines. *Mailing Add:* 106 Hunter Hill Pl Chapel Hill NC 27514-9128

**WECHSLER, STEVEN LEWIS,** MOLECULAR GENETICS, VIROLOGY. *Current Pos:* RES, CEDARS SINAI MED CTR RES INST, 87- *Personal Data:* b Bronx, NY, May 30, 48; m 74; c 1. *Educ:* City Col NY, BS, 70; Univ NC, Chapel Hill, PhD(molecular genetics), 75. *Prof Exp:* Res fel measles virus, Dept Microbiol, Harvard Med Sch, 75-87. *Mem:* Am Soc Microbiol. *Res:* Molecular genetics of measles virus and its relationship to persistent infections and chronic diseases such as subacute sclerosing panencephalites and multiple sclerosis. *Mailing Add:* Cedars Sinai Med Ctr Res Inst Ophthal Res D5069 8700 Beverly Blvd Los Angeles CA 90048

**WECHTER, MARGARET ANN,** ANALYTICAL CHEMISTRY, RADIOCHEMISTRY. *Current Pos:* ASSOC PROF CHEM, SOUTHEASTERN MASS UNIV, 73, MEM FAC, DEPT CHEM, SOUTHEASTERN MASS UNIV, 80- *Personal Data:* b Chicago, Ill, Sept 30, 35. *Educ:* Mundelein Col, BS, 62; Iowa State Univ, PhD(anal chem), 67. *Prof Exp:* Fel chem, Purdue Univ, 67-68, asst prof chem, Calumet Campus, 69-73. *Concurrent Pos:* Mem staff, Ames Lab, Iowa State Univ, 70-80. *Mem:* Am Chem Soc; Sigma Xi. *Res:* Development, analytical applications and electrochemistry of the tungsten bronze electrodes; activation analysis. *Mailing Add:* Dept Chem Univ Mass North Dartmouth MA 02747

**WECHTER, WILLIAM JULIUS,** PHARMACOLOGIC MAINTENANCE OF SKELETAL BONE. *Current Pos:* RES PROF MED, SCH MED, LOMA LINDA UNIV, 88-, DIR, LAB CHEM ENDOCRINOL, 91- *Personal Data:* b Louisville, Ky, Feb 13, 32; m 52, 82, Kathryn E Edwards; c Laurie J, Diane J & Julie L. *Educ:* Univ Ill, AB, 53, MS, 54; Univ Calif, Los Angeles, PhD, 57. *Honors & Awards:* Upjohn Prize Award, 75; W Heinlein Hall Lectureship, 78. *Prof Exp:* Asst chem, Univ Ill, 54; asst org chem, Univ Calif, Los Angeles, 55-56; res assoc, Dept Chem, Upjohn Co, 57-68, res head, 68-79, res mgr hypersensitivity dis, 79-84; dir res & develop planning, Boehringer Ingelheim Bd, 84; dir, Clin & Pharmaceut Res, Boots Pharmaceut, Inc, 85-88. *Concurrent Pos:* Vis scholar, Depts Chem & Med Microbiol, Stanford Univ,

67-68; vchmn, Gordon Conf Med Chem, 72, chmn, 73; adj prof biochem, Kalamazoo Col, 74-84; vis lectr path, Harvard Med Sch, 77-78; adj prof pharmacol & therapeut, La State Univ Med Ctr, Shreveport, 85-88. *Mem:* AAAS; Am Soc Clin Pharm & Therapeut; Am Chem Soc; Am Soc Nephrology; Am Asn Immunologists; Am Col Rheumatology; fel Am Col Clin Pharmacol; Royal Soc Med. *Res:* Isolation, structure and synthesis of hormones of mineral metabolism; chiral drugs; pharmacological maintenance of skeletal bone; cancer treatment colon, prostate and breast; clinical pharmacology, inflammation. *Mailing Add:* Loma Linda Univ Med Ctr Loma Linda CA 92350. *Fax:* 909-796-0290; *E-Mail:* wechter@pcinternet.com

**WECK, FRIEDRICH JOSEF,** organic chemistry, physical chemistry; deceased, see previous edition for last biography

**WECKER, LYNN,** NEUROPHARMACOLOGY, ACETYLCHOLINE METABOLISM. *Current Pos:* PROF PHARMACOL, COL MED, UNIV SFLA, 90-, CHAIR, 91- *Personal Data:* b New York, NY, Sept 27, 47. *Educ:* State Univ NY, BS, 69; Univ Fla, PhD(pharmacol), 72. *Prof Exp:* Postdoctoral fel, Vanderbilt Univ Sch Med, 73-74, instr pharmacol, 74-75, asst prof, 76-78; asst prof med chem & pharm, Col Pharm, Northeastern Univ, 75-76; from asst prof to prof pharmacol, La State Univ Med Ctr, 78-90. *Concurrent Pos:* Mem coun, Am Soc Neurochem. *Mem:* AAAS; Am Inst Nutrit; Am Soc Pharmacol & Exp Therapeut; NY Acad Sci; Sigma Xi; Int Soc Neurochem. *Res:* Regulation of the synthesis and release of acetylcholine by brain and the enhancement of these regulatory processes by pharmacological and nutritional manipulations; neurochemical effects of chronic nicotine administration and plasticity of neuronal nicotinic and GABAergic receptors; neurochemical changes in the aged brain. *Mailing Add:* Pharmocol Univ Fla 12901 Bruce B Downs Blvd MDC9 Tampa FL 33612

**WECKER, STANLEY C,** VERTEBRATE ECOLOGY, APPLIED ECOLOGY. *Current Pos:* RETIRED. *Personal Data:* b New York, NY, Apr 29, 33; m 64. *Educ:* City Col New York, BS, 55; Univ Mich, MS, 57, PhD(zool), 62. *Honors & Awards:* Award, Am Soc Mammal, 61. *Prof Exp:* Asst prof biol, Hofstra Univ, 62-63; from instr to prof biol, City Col New York, 63-92, dir, Energy Ecol Environ Prog, 76-92. *Concurrent Pos:* Res grants, Sigma Xi, 63 & NSF, 64-68; US Dept HEW Off Educ grant & staff ecologist, Environ Educ Proj, North Westchester-Putnam Coop Educ Serv, NY, 71-72; spec consult, NY State Educ Dept, 72; mem, Environ Defense Fund, NASA, 75-77. *Mem:* Fel AAAS; Am Inst Biol Sci; Ecol Soc Am; Am Soc Mammal; NY Acad Sci; Sigma Xi. *Res:* Behavioral ecology of deer mice, especially habitat orientation; application of satellite data to coastal zone management. *Mailing Add:* 76 Poillon Dr Chappaqua NY 10514

**WECKESSER, LOUIS BENJAMIN,** HEAT TRANSFER, MECHANICAL ENGINEERING. *Current Pos:* RETIRED. *Personal Data:* b Baltimore, MD, Feb 22, 28; m 49; c 3. *Educ:* Univ MD, BS, 52, MS, 56. *Prof Exp:* group supvr, Eng Appl Physics Lab, Johns Hopkins Univ, 52-92. *Mem:* Am Inst Aeronaut & Astronaut. *Res:* Tactical missile thermal design; thermal insulation development; missile radome design and test. *Mailing Add:* 10126 Century Dr Ellicott City MD 21042

**WECKLER, GENE PETER,** ELECTRICAL ENGINEERING. *Current Pos:* DIR ENG, RETICON CORP, 71- *Personal Data:* b San Francisco, Calif, July 3, 32; m 56; c 4. *Educ:* Utah State Univ, BS, 58; San Jose State Col, MS, 64; Stanford Univ, DEng, 68. *Prof Exp:* Jr engr, Convair Astronaut, 58-59; elec engr, Shockley Transistor Corp. 59-62; develop engr, Opto-Electronic Devices, Inc, 62-63; mem tech staff, Fairchild Semiconductor Div, 63-71. *Mem:* Inst Elec & Electronics Engrs; Int Soc Optical Eng. *Res:* Development of silicon p-n junction photodetectors, especially integrated arrays for image sensing; development and application of solid state devices for signal processing. *Mailing Add:* Optoelectronics Eg&G 2175 Mission College Blvd Santa Clara CA 95054

**WECKOWICZ, THADDEUS EUGENE,** PSYCHIATRY. *Current Pos:* RETIRED. *Personal Data:* b Iskorst, USSR, Oct 10, 18; Can citizen; m 66. *Educ:* Univ Edinburgh, MB & ChB, 45; Univ Leeds, DPM, 52; Univ Sask, PhD(psychol), 62. *Prof Exp:* Registr psychiat, Univ Leeds, 53-54, sr registr, Bolton Group Hosps, Eng, 54-55; sr resident, Hosp, Univ Sask, 55-56; res psychiatrist, Weyburn Ment Hosp, Sask, 56-59; res assoc psychiat & sessional lectr psychol, Univ Alta, 62, from asst prof to assoc prof, 62-74, prof psychiat & psychol, 74-84, mem staff, Ctr Advan Study Theoret Psychol, 66-84, emer prof, 84- *Concurrent Pos:* Fel, Hosp, Univ Sask, 55-56. *Mem:* Can Psychiat Asn. *Res:* Psychological and biological aspects of schizophrenia; psychotropic drug research, particularly hallucinogenic drugs; psychopharmacology; multivariate study of depression; studies of learned helplessness retardation in depression. *Mailing Add:* 11406 72nd Ave Edmonton AB T6G 2B7 Can

**WECKSUNG, GEORGE WILLIAM,** COMPUTER IMAGE PROCESSING, APPLIED MATHEMATICS. *Current Pos:* STAFF MEM, COMPUT IMAGE PROCESSING, LOS ALAMOS NAT LAB, 74- *Personal Data:* b Muscatine, Iowa, Oct 31, 31; m 61; c 3. *Educ:* Univ Iowa, BA, 58; Calif State Univ, Long Beach, MA, 63. *Prof Exp:* Comput engr inertial navig, Autonetics, 61-64; sci specialist digital signal processing EG&G, Inc, Las Vegas, 64-69; res engr inertial navig, Teledyne Systs Co, 69-70; sci specialist comput image processing EG&G, Inc, Los Alamos, 70-74. *Mem:* Soc Photo-optical Instrumentation Engrs. *Res:* Remote sensing; computer image processing; stereo imagery and photogrammetry; digital holography; computed tomography. *Mailing Add:* 161 El Corto St Los Alamos NM 87544

**WECKWERTH, VERNON ERVIN,** EXECUTIVE EDUCATION, HEALTHCARE ADMINISTRATION. *Current Pos:* from lectr to assoc prof, 60-68, PROF, HEALTH CARE MGT & POLICY, COORDR CONTINUING HOSP EDUC & PROF FAMILY PRACT, MED SCH, UNIV MINN, MINNEAPOLIS, 68- *Personal Data:* b Herman, Minn, Apr 29, 31; m 55, Joanne Christenson; c Vicki, Marsha, Debra, Amy & Mark. *Educ:* Univ Minn, BS, 54, MS, 56, PhD(biostatist), 63. *Prof Exp:* Teaching asst biostatist, Univ Minn, 54-56, instr, 56-58; head res & statist, Am Hosp Asn, 58-60. *Concurrent Pos:* Assoc dir, Hosp Res & Educ Trust, 58-60; mem adv comt to Nat Ctr for Health Servs Res & Develop, 69- *Mem:* Am Statist Asn; Biomet Soc; Am Hosp Asn; Am Pub Health Asn; Sigma Xi. *Res:* Continuing education of health care workers including professionals; health care delivery systems research; teaching research and statistics in health care. *Mailing Add:* 1666 Coffman St Apt 334 St Paul MN 55108-1340. *Fax:* 612-626-1186; *E-Mail:* weckw001@maroon.tc.umn.edu

**WEDBERG, STANLEY EDWARD,** MICROBIOLOGY. *Current Pos:* from instr to assoc prof bact, Univ Conn, 41-59, head dept, 55-66, prof, 59-69, fac coordr educ TV, 67-69, prof biol, 68-69, EMER PROF BIOL, UNIV CONN, 69- *Personal Data:* b Bridgeport, Conn, Aug 28, 13; m 41, Mary B Stewart; c Karen E (Miller) & Robin C (Brown). *Educ:* Univ Conn, BS, 37; Yale Univ, PhD(bact), 40. *Prof Exp:* Instr immunol, Sch Med, Yale Univ, 40-41. *Concurrent Pos:* Consult bacteriologist, Windham Community Mem Hosp, Conn, 46-57; biologist, Southwestern Col, Calif, 69-80; lectr, San Diego Paramedic Prog, 79- & San Diego Health Dept; mem, Conn Clean Water Task Force, vchmn, Conn Clean Air Task Force, Conn adv comt, Foods, Drugs, Cosmetics & Devices; co-producer & performer, Survival, 68-69; prof microbiol, Southwestern Col. *Mem:* AAAS; Sigma Xi; Am Soc Microbiol; Am Acad Microbiol. *Res:* Microbial thermogenesis; bacterial capsule staining; antihistamines on antibody production of rabbits; germicidal gases; author of three microbiology texts. *Mailing Add:* 3361 Ullman St Point Loma San Diego CA 92106

**WEDDELL, DAVID S(TOVER),** CHEMICAL ENGINEERING. *Current Pos:* RETIRED. *Personal Data:* b Philadelphia, Pa, Mar 8, 17; m 43; c 4. *Educ:* Pa State Col, BS, 38; Mass Inst Technol, ScD(chem eng), 41. *Prof Exp:* Chem engr, Monsanto Co, Ala, 41-44, 45-47, develop dir, Wash, 49-50, develop dept, Mo, 50-52, asst dir, 53-54, Europ tech rep, 54-60, asst dir develop, Overseas Div, 60-62, dir, 63-64, dir proj eval, 65-82, financial analyst, int div, 83-86. *Concurrent Pos:* Mem Nat Defense Res Comt, Ohio, 44-45, Mo, 47-48. *Mem:* Am Inst Chem Engrs. *Res:* Turbulent mixing in flames and its reproduction in liquid models; process design; application of phosphate chemicals; commercial chemical development; investment analysis and planning; international operations. *Mailing Add:* 21 Fair Oaks St Louis MO 63124

**WEDDELL, GEORGE G(RAY),** CHEMICAL ENGINEERING. *Current Pos:* RETIRED. *Personal Data:* b Baltimore, Md, Jan 30, 23; m 56, Mary Ann Anderson. *Educ:* Pa State Univ, BS, 44. *Prof Exp:* Asst, SAM Labs, Columbia Univ, 44-45; asst, Carbide & Carbon Chem Co, NY, 45-46, chem engr, Tenn, 46-47; fel, Mellon Inst, 47-52; vpres, Geotic Industs, Inc, 52-53, pres, 54-55; asst mgr, O Hommel Co, 55-56; fel engr, Bettis Atomic Power Lab, Westinghouse Elec Corp, 56-66, supvr, 66-71, mgr, 71-89. *Mem:* Am Chem Soc; Am Nuclear Soc. *Res:* Utilization of fine particles; manufacture and application of perlite; radioactive waste disposal; thermal and hydraulic nuclear engineering; nuclear fuel cycle. *Mailing Add:* 349 Dale Rd Bethel Park PA 15102

**WEDDELL, JAMES BLOUNT,** SPACE PHYSICS. *Current Pos:* RETIRED. *Personal Data:* b Evanston, Ill, Apr 29, 27; m 60, Beatrice. *Educ:* Drew Univ, AB, 49; Northwestern Univ, MS, 51, PhD(physics), 53. *Prof Exp:* Asst physics, Northwestern Univ, 49-53; res engr, Westinghouse Elec Corp, 53-57; sr scientist, Martin-Marietta Co, 57-62; supvr, Rockwell Int Corp, 62-80, mgr, 80-85, chief scientist, 85-87, proj mgr, 87-90. *Mem:* Sigma Xi. *Res:* Space shuttle payload and cargo integration; solar physics; magnetosphere; nuclear reactions; radiation shielding; solar-electric propulsion systems. *Mailing Add:* 26427 S Flame Tree Dr Sun Lakes AZ 85248-9261

**WEDDING, BRENT (M),** EXPERIMENTAL PHYSICS. *Current Pos:* res supvr, 75-76, SR PHYSICIST, CORNING GLASS WORKS, 67-, DEVELOP ASSOC PHYSICS, 76-, MGR PHYS PROPERTIES RES, 79- *Personal Data:* b Walnut, Ill, May 3, 36; m 69; c 2. *Educ:* Hamilton Col, AB, 58; Univ Ill, Urbana, MS, 61, PhD(physics), 67. *Prof Exp:* Lectr physics, Southern Ill Univ, Carbondale, 62-63. *Mem:* Am Phys Soc; Optical Soc Am; Am Ceramic Soc; Sigma Xi. *Res:* Optical glass development. *Mailing Add:* Corning Glass Works Corning NY 14830

**WEDDING, RANDOLPH TOWNSEND,** biochemistry, enzymology; deceased, see previous edition for last biography

**WEDDLETON, RICHARD FRANCIS,** POLYMER CHEMISTRY. *Current Pos:* sr engr, 77-80, asst to Gen Mgr, 80-82, ADV ENG, WESTINGHOUSE ELEC CORP, 82- *Personal Data:* b Boston, Mass, Oct 10, 39; m 62; c 3. *Educ:* Mass Inst Technol, BS, 61; Ind Univ, Bloomington, MS, 63, PhD(org chem), 65. *Prof Exp:* Chemist, Mat & Processes Lab, Gen Elec Co, 65-73; mgr insulation eng, Nat Elec Coil Div, McGraw-Edison Co, 73-77. *Mem:* Am Chem Soc; Inst Elec & Electronics Eng. *Res:* Project management, development and testing of insulation system for use in electrical rotating machinery. *Mailing Add:* Westinghouse Elec Corp Mc 303 The Quadrangle 4400 Alafaya Trail Orlando FL 32826-2399

**WEDEEN, RICHARD P,** NEPHROLOGY, ENVIRONMENTAL HEALTH. *Current Pos:* Prof prev med & dir, Div Occup & Environ Med, 76-78, clin prof interdisciplinary med, Grad Sch Health Related Prof, 90, PROF MED, UNIV MED & DENT NJ, 76-; ASSOC CHIEF STAFF RES & DEVELOP, VET ADMIN MED CTR, 78- *Personal Data:* b New York, NY, Jan 19, 34; m 57, Roberta Rubier; c Timothy D. *Educ:* NY Univ, MD, 59. *Prof Exp:* Lectr, Harvard Med Sch, 68-69; vis prof med, Univ Antwerp, Belg, 85; contrib ed, Arch Environ Health; asst ed, Mt Sinai J Med; actg chief staff, Vet Admin Med Ctr, 88. *Mem:* Emer mem Am Soc Clin Invest; fel Am Col Physicians; Harvey Soc; Am Physiol Soc; Am Soc Nephrology. *Res:* The role of lead as a cause of renal disease in the occupational setting and as a cause of hypertension and gout with renal disfunction; animal research demonstrating pathogenic mechanisms of interstitial nephritis including crystal nephropathy; occupational renal diseases; history of occupational medicine; author of one book; co-editor of one book and author of over 150 scientific papers. *Mailing Add:* Vet Admin Med Ctr East Orange NJ 07019

**WEDEGAERTNER, DONALD K,** ORGANIC CHEMISTRY. *Current Pos:* from asst prof to assoc prof, 63-71, chmn dept chem, 74-80, PROF ORG CHEM, UNIV PAC, 71- *Personal Data:* b Kingsburg, Calif, Sept 9, 36; m 58; c 2. *Educ:* Univ Calif, Berkeley, BS, 58; Univ Ill, Urbana, PhD(org chem), 62. *Prof Exp:* Res asst org chem, Iowa State Univ, 62-63. *Concurrent Pos:* Res asst org chem, Univ Rochester, 69-70, vis prof, 78-79; vis prof, Univ Utah, 83-84. *Mem:* Am Chem Soc. *Res:* Reaction mechanisms. *Mailing Add:* Dept Chem Univ Pac Stockton CA 95211

**WEDEKIND, GILBERT LEROY,** FLUID & THERMAL SCIENCES. *Current Pos:* from asst prof to assoc prof, 66-77, PROF ENG, OAKLAND UNIV, 77-; PRES, FTS ENG & CONSULT, INC, 73- *Personal Data:* b Zion, Ill, Feb 28, 33; m 53, June L Zoehler; c Ty E (Wedekind) & Rene L (Otto). *Educ:* Univ Ill, BS, 59, MS, 61, PhD(mech eng), 65. *Prof Exp:* Res assoc mech eng, Univ Ill, 65-66. *Concurrent Pos:* NSF eng res grants, 67-69, 72-74, 80-82, 84-86 & 95-; consult, Propulsion Systs Lab, US Army Tank-Automotive Command, 67-70, Climate Control Opers, Ford Motor Co, 71-73 & Mfg Develop, Gen Motors Tech Ctr, 73-80, Chrysler Tech Ctr, Chrysler Corp, 96- *Mem:* Am Soc Mech Engrs; Am Soc Eng Educ; Sigma Xi. *Res:* Thermal modeling of spacecraft; experimental and theoretical study of transient two-phase evaporating and condensing flow phenomena; thermal management, electonic cooling, modeling components, processes and systems which utilize fluid and thermal phenomena for their operation. *Mailing Add:* Sch Eng & Comput Sci Oakland Univ Rochester MI 48309

**WEDEL, ARNOLD MARION,** MATHEMATICS. *Current Pos:* PROF MATH, BETHEL COL, KANS, 51- *Personal Data:* b Lawrence, Kans, Jan 31, 28; m 54; c 3. *Educ:* Bethel Col, Kans, AB, 47; Univ Kans, MA, 48; Iowa State Col, PhD(math), 51. *Mem:* Math Asn Am; Am Math Soc. *Res:* Hypergeometric series and volterra transforms. *Mailing Add:* Dept Math Bethel Col North Newton KS 67117

**WEDEMEYER, GARY ALVIN,** FISHERIES, BIOCHEMISTRY. *Current Pos:* BIOCHEMIST, FISH PHYSIOL, NAT FISHERIES RES CTR, US DEPT INTERIOR, 65- *Personal Data:* b Fromberg, Mont, Oct 15, 35; m 57; c 2. *Educ:* Univ Wash, BS, 57, MS, 63, PhD(fisheries), 65. *Concurrent Pos:* Affil prof, Col Fisheries, Univ Wash, 65- *Mem:* Am Inst Fishery Res Biol; Am Fisheries Soc. *Res:* Biochemistry and physiology of fishes; pollution, disease, aquaculture; tolerance of fish and fish populations to environmental stress. *Mailing Add:* 10619 Sand Point Way NE Seattle WA 98125

**WEDEPOHL, LEONHARD M,** ELECTRICAL ENGINEERING, ELECTRICAL POWER SYSTEMS. *Current Pos:* dean appl sci, 79-85, PROF ELEC ENG, UNIV BC, VANCOUVER, 85- *Personal Data:* b Pretoria, SAfrica, Jan 26, 33; m, Sylvia A St Jean; c Martin & Graham. *Educ:* Rand Univ, BSc, 53; Univ Manchester, PhD, 57. *Honors & Awards:* Award Bison, Govt Manitoba. *Prof Exp:* Planning engr, Escom, SAfrica, 57-61; mgr, L M Ericson, 61-62; sect leader, Reyrolle, Eng, 62-64; prof & head dept, Manchester Univ, 64-74; dean eng, Univ Man, 74-79. *Concurrent Pos:* Mem, Sci Res Coun, London, 68-74; dir, Man Hydro, Winnipeg, 75-79, BC Hydro, Vancouver, 80-84; BC Sci Coun, 81-84; vpres, Quantic Labs, Winnipeg, 86; consult, Horizon Robotics, 86, Cepel, Rio De Janeiro; head, Protection Develop Reyrolle, Rolls-Royce Indust Power Group, 95-96. *Mem:* Fel Inst Elec Engrs. *Res:* Applied science; electrical engineering; power system protection; power system performance; high frequency; performance fo transmission systems. *Mailing Add:* Dept Elec Eng Univ BC 2324 Main Mall Vancouver BC V6T 1Z4 Can. *Fax:* 604-822-5949; *E-Mail:* wedepohl@direct.ca

**WEDGWOOD, RALPH JOSIAH PATRICK,** PEDIATRICS, RHEUMATOLOGY. *Current Pos:* assoc prof, 62-63, chmn dept, 62-72, prof, 63-91, EMER PROF PEDIAT, SCH MED, UNIV WASH, 91- *Personal Data:* b Eng, May 25, 24; nat US; m 43, Virginia L Hunt; c Josiah, Jeffrey & John. *Educ:* Harvard Med Sch, MD, 47; Am Bd Pediat, dipl, 55. *Prof Exp:* Res fel pediat, Harvard Med Sch, 49-51; sr instr pediat & biochem, Western Reserve Univ, 53-57, asst prof pediat & prev med, Sch Med, 57-62. *Concurrent Pos:* Markle scholar, 60-65, vis scholar, St John's Col, Cambridge U; spec consult & mem gen clin res ctr comt, NIH, 62-66, mem nat adv res resources Coun, 66-70; mem sci adv comn, Nat Found, 69-; mem sci adv bd, St Jude's Children's Res Hosp, Memphis, 70-76. *Mem:* Am Asn Immunologists; Am Rheumatism Asn; Heberden Soc; Am Pediat Soc; Infectious Dis Soc Am. *Res:* Immunobiology; natural resistance factors; infectious and rheumatic diseases in children; general pediatrics. *Mailing Add:* 3717 41st Ave NE Seattle WA 98102-5436. *Fax:* 206-543-3184; *E-Mail:* wedgwood@u.washington.edu

**WEDIN, WALTER F,** AGRONOMY. *Current Pos:* from assoc prof to prof, 61-90, dir, World Food Inst, 73-77, EMER PROF AGRON, IOWA STATE UNIV, 91- *Personal Data:* b Frederic, Wis, Nov 28, 25; m 55; c 2. *Educ:* Univ Wis, BS, 50, MS, 51, PhD(agron, soils), 53. *Prof Exp:* Wis Alumni Res Found assistantship agron, Univ Wis, 50-53, proj assoc hort, 53, asst prof, 53-57; res agronomist, Forage & Range Res Br, Crops Res Div, Agr Res Serv, USDA, Minn, 57-61. *Concurrent Pos:* Asst prof, Inst Agr, Univ Minn, 59-61; consult, US Agency Int Develop-Iowa State Univ, Uruguay, 64; consult, Coop States Res Serv, USDA, 64, 70, 72 & 74, prin agronomist, 68; adj prof. Dept Agron & Plant Genetics, Univ Minn, 91- *Mem:* AAAS; fel Am Soc Agron; Crop Sci Soc Am; Am Soc Animal Sci; Am Forage & Grassland Coun (pres, 85); Coun Agr Sci & Technol; Soil & Water Conserv Soc; Nature Conserv. *Res:* Evaluation of forage crops, especially utilization as pasture, hay or silage; techniques involved in measurement of forage nutritive value; animal intake and digestibility; grassland development, international. *Mailing Add:* 6901 W 84th St No 360 Minneapolis MN 55438

**WEDLER, FREDERICK CHARLES OLIVER, JR,** biochemistry; deceased, see previous edition for last biography

**WEDLICK, HAROLD LEE,** HEALTH PHYSICS, ENVIRONMENTAL HEALTH. *Current Pos:* SR PRIN ENG, WESTINGHOUSE HANFORD CO, 86- *Personal Data:* b Detroit, Mich, Feb 26, 36; m 59; c 2. *Educ:* Wayne State Univ, BS, 61, MS, 63; Am Bd Health Physics, cert, 74. *Prof Exp:* Chemist, City Detroit Health Dept, Mich, 61-63; res assoc environ health, Univ Mich, 64-66; assoc prof radiol sci, Lowell Technol Inst, 66-75; res assoc, Occup & Environ Safety Dept, Pac Northwest Labs, Battelle Mem Inst, 75-80; owner & dir, Wedlick's Educ Develop Systs Safety, 80-86. *Mem:* Health Physics Soc; Conf Radiol Health; Am Nuclear Soc. *Res:* Transfer mechanisms and measurements of radionuclides in the environment. *Mailing Add:* 2102 S Buntin Kennewick WA 99337

**WEDLOCK, BRUCE D(ANIELS),** SOLID STATE PHYSICS. *Current Pos:* RETIRED. *Personal Data:* b Providence, RI, Mar 20, 34; div, 96; c Karen (Danielson) & Walter Cole. *Educ:* Mass Inst Technol, SB & SM, 58, ScD(elec eng), 62. *Prof Exp:* From instr to assoc prof elec eng, Mass Inst Technol, 60-71; staff scientist, Block Eng, Inc, Mass, 71-72; dir, Lowell Inst Sch, 73-96. *Concurrent Pos:* Ford Found fel, 62-64. *Mem:* Fel Inst Elec & Electronics Engrs; Am Soc Eng Educ. *Res:* Physical electronics of solid state devices; development of two-year technical school curricula in emerging technologies. *Mailing Add:* Mass Inst Technol Rm 38-473 Cambridge MA 02139. *E-Mail:* wedlock@mit.edu

**WEDMAN, ELWOOD EDWARD,** veterinary microbiology; deceased, see previous edition for last biography

**WEE, WILLIAM GO,** INTELLIGENT SYSTEMS. *Current Pos:* assoc prof, 71-77, PROF ELEC & COMPUT ENG, UNIV CINCINNATI, 77- *Personal Data:* b Iloilo City, Philippines, Sept 9, 37; m 67, Elizabeth Lin; c Larry & Anthony. *Educ:* Mapua Inst Technol, BSEE, 62; Purdue Univ, Lafayette, MS, 65, PhD(elec eng), 67. *Prof Exp:* Prin res engr, Honeywell Systs & Res Ctr, 67-71. *Mem:* Sr mem Inst Elec & Electronics Engrs. *Res:* Theory and application of pattern recognition; adaptive and learning systems; artificial neural networks; computer vision; artificial intelligence. *Mailing Add:* Elec & Comput Eng Dept Univ Cincinnati Hall Location 30 Cincinnati OH 45221. *Fax:* 513-556-7326; *E-Mail:* wwee@uceng.uc.edu

**WEED, GRANT B(ARG),** CERAMICS ENGINEERING, METALLURGY. *Personal Data:* b Salt Lake City, Utah, Aug 19, 35; m 64; c 4. *Educ:* Univ Utah, BS, 61, PhD(ceramic eng), 67. *Prof Exp:* Source engr, Hercules Powder Co, Utah, 60-61; res chemist, Exp Sta, E I du Pont de Nemours & Co, 66-72; res engr, Cent Res Labs, NL Industs, 72-73; supvr mat equip develop, Tech Dept, Magnesium Div, 73-80; At Magnesium Div, AMAX Speciality Metals Corp, 80-86; sr mech eng, Ford, Bakum, Davis, Inc, 86-94. *Mem:* Am Ceramic Soc; Nat Inst Ceramic Engrs. *Res:* High temperature ceramics and ceramic-metal composites; refractories for molten salt containment. *Mailing Add:* 1011 E Millbrook Way Bountiful UT 84010

**WEED, H(OMER) C(LYDE),** PHYSICAL CHEMISTRY. *Current Pos:* chemist, Inorg Mat Div, Lawrence Livermore Nat Lab, Univ Calif, 57-76, chemist, Earth Sci Div, 76-91, lab assoc, 92, PARTIC GUEST, LAWRENCE LIVERMORE NAT LAB, UNIV CALIF, 93- *Personal Data:* b Sun City, Kans, Mar 30, 20; m 58, Emily Davis. *Educ:* Univ Ariz, BS, 42; Ohio State Univ, MS, 48, PhD(chem), 57. *Prof Exp:* Assoc develop chemist, Tenn Eastman Corp, 42-46. *Mem:* Fel AAAS; Am Chem Soc; Am Geophys Union. *Res:* High temperature chemistry; high pressure mechanical properties of solids and powders; radionuclide transport in earth materials; rheology of silicate melts; infrared spectroscopy on silicates; kinetics of uranium dioxide dissolution. *Mailing Add:* 805 Los Alamos Ave Livermore CA 94550. *Fax:* 510-423-1057; *E-Mail:* weed1@llnl.gov

**WEED, HERMAN ROSCOE,** ELECTRICAL ENGINEERING, BIOMEDICAL ENGINEERING. *Current Pos:* from instr to assoc prof, 46-59, PROF ELEC ENG, OHIO STATE UNIV, 59-, DIR, BIOMED ENG CTR, 71-, PROF PREV MED, 78- *Personal Data:* b Union City, Pa, Aug 5, 22; m 46; c 3. *Educ:* Pa State Col, BS, 45; Ohio State Univ, MS, 48. *Honors & Awards:* Outstanding Biomed Engr Year, Am Soc Eng Educ, 87. *Prof Exp:* Instr elec eng, Pa State Col, 43-46. *Concurrent Pos:* Mem staff, Westinghouse Elec Corp, 49; mem staff, Res Found, Ohio State Univ, 48-50, mem staff, Exp Sta, 52-53, consult, 51-; mem staff & consult, Robbins & Myers Co, 53-78; US deleg, Am Control Coun, Int Fedn Automatic Control Cong, Russia, 60, London, 66, chmn systs comt, Am Automatic Control Coun; consult, Solid-State Controls, Inc, 61-65 & Am Inst Biol Sci, 77-80; vis prof, Univ Cairo Egypt, Univ Karlsruhe, WGer, 79; hon prof, Zhejiang Med Univ, Hangzhou, People's Repub China, 86; dir, Biomed Eng, Proj Hope Worldwide, 79- *Mem:* Inst Elec & Electronics Engrs; Am Soc Eng Educ; Asn Advan Med Instrumentation. *Res:* Automatic control; bioelectrical instrumentation; electronics; systems; non-invasive diagnosis; ultrasound; physiological systems; biomedical-clinical engineering education; functional muscle stimulation for handicapped; real time visual information for visually handicapped. *Mailing Add:* Elec Eng Dept Ohio State Univ 2015 Neil Ave Columbus OH 43210-1272. *Fax:* 614-292-7596

**WEED, JOHN CONANT,** OBSTETRICS & GYNECOLOGY. *Current Pos:* RETIRED. *Personal Data:* b Lake Charles, La, July 7, 12; m 39; c 4. *Educ:* Tulane Univ, BS, 33, MD, 36, MS, 40; Am Bd Obstet & Gynec, dipl, 46. *Prof Exp:* Instr anat, Sch Med, Tulane Univ, 39-41, from assoc clin prof to clin prof, 53-83, emer prof obstet & gynec, 83- *Concurrent Pos:* Mem staff, Ochsner Clin, 45-; chmn dept obstet & gynec, Ochsner Found Hosp, 63-73; bd trustees, Alton Ochsner Med Found. *Mem:* AMA; Am Fertil Soc (pres, 73-74); Am Col Obstet & Gynec; Am Col Surgeons; Soc Reproductive Surg; Soc Gynec Surg. *Res:* Infertility; investigation of auto-immune factors in cases of moderate to severe endometriosis has revealed C'3 (complement) deposition in uterine endometrium, searching for antibody and serologic proof. *Mailing Add:* 109 Stella St Metairie LA 70005-4541

**WEED, LAWRENCE LEONARD,** COMPUTER SCIENCE, MEDICINE. *Current Pos:* prof commun med, 69-82, EMER PROF, UNIV VT, COL MED, 82-; PRES, PKC CORP, 84- *Personal Data:* b Troy, NY, Dec 26, 23; m 52; c 5. *Educ:* Hamilton Col, BA, 45, Col Physicians & Surgeons, MD, 47. *Prof Exp:* Asst prof med & pharmacol, Yale Univ, Sch Med, 54-56; dir, Med Educ, Eastern Maine Gen Hosp, Bangor, 56-60; asst prof microbiol, Case Western Res Univ, 61-64, assoc prof, 64-69. *Concurrent Pos:* Prof med & dir, Outpatient Clin, Cleveland Metrop Gen Hosp, 64-69; dir, Promis Lab, 69-81, chief scientist, Promis Info Systs, Inc, 81-82. *Mem:* Am Col Physicians; Am Soc Microbiol. *Res:* Problem oriented medical information system. *Mailing Add:* 120 Irish Settlement Rd Cambridge VT 05489

**WEED, STERLING BARG,** SOIL CHEMISTRY. *Current Pos:* from asst prof to prof, 56-92, EMER PROF SOILS, NC STATE UNIV, 92- *Personal Data:* b Salt Lake City, Utah, Mar 25, 26; m 49; c 2. *Educ:* Brigham Young Univ, AB, 51; NC State Col, MS, 53, PhD(soils), 55. *Prof Exp:* Asst prof soils, Cornell Univ, 55-56. *Mem:* Soil Sci Soc Am; Clay Minerals Soc; Int Soc Soil Sci; Int Clay Minerals Soc. *Res:* Clay mineralogy; clay-organic interactions. *Mailing Add:* 5036 New Castle Rd Raleigh NC 27606

**WEEDEN, ROBERT BARTON,** ZOOLOGY. *Current Pos:* prof wildlife mgt, 68-74, head, Dept Biol & Wildlife, 86-88, PROF RESOURCE MGT, UNIV ALASKA; RES BIOLOGIST, ALASKA DEPT FISH & GAME, 59- *Personal Data:* b Fall River, Mass, Jan 8, 33; m 59; c 3. *Educ:* Univ Mass, BSc, 53; Univ Maine, MSc, 55; Univ BC, PhD(zool), 59. *Prof Exp:* Asst, Univ Maine, 53-55; asst, Univ BC, 55-58; instr zool, Wash State Univ, 58-59. *Concurrent Pos:* Dir, Policy Develop, Off of Gov, Alaska, 75-76. *Mem:* Arctic Inst NAm; Cooper Ornith Soc; Wildlife Soc; Am Ornith Union. *Res:* Avian ecology, particularly of Tetraonidae and alpine-arctic environments; resource policy and land use. *Mailing Add:* 1446 Grenac Rd Fairbanks AK 99709

**WEEDMAN, DANIEL WILSON,** OBSERVATIONAL ASTRONOMY, TELESCOPE DESIGN. *Current Pos:* PROF ASTRON, PA STATE UNIV, 78- *Personal Data:* b Nashville, Tenn, Oct 19, 42; m 68, Suzanne Dallas; c Diana & Sylvia. *Educ:* Vanderbilt Univ, BA, 64; Univ Wis, PhD(astron), 67. *Prof Exp:* Fac assoc astron, Univ Tex, 67-69; asst prof, 69-70; asst prof, Vanderbilt Univ, 70-73, assoc prof, 75-78; assoc prof, Univ Minn, 74-75. *Concurrent Pos:* Exchange scientist, Nat Acad Sci, USSR, 70 & 78; mem bd dirs, Asn Univ Res Astron, Inc, 78-81; counr, Am Astron Soc, 80-83; vis sr scientist, NASA HQ, 90-92, dir, Astrophys Div, 93-95. *Mem:* Am Astron Soc; Int Astron Union. *Res:* Observational research in extragalactic astronomy, primarily galactic nuclei, quasars, and starburst galaxies using optical, ultraviolet, radio and infrared techniques; astrophysics management. *Mailing Add:* Astron Dept 525 Davey Lab Pa State Univ University Park PA 16802-6305

**WEEDON, ALAN CHARLES,** ORGANIC PHOTOCHEMISTRY. *Current Pos:* Res assoc, 77-80, from asst prof to assoc prof, 80-91, PROF CHEM, UNIV WESTERN ONT, 91-, DEAN GRAD STUDIES, 96- *Personal Data:* b Oxford, Eng, Mar 29, 51. *Educ:* London Univ, BSc, 73, PhD(chem) & DIC, 76; ARCS, 73. *Honors & Awards:* Merck Frosst Award, Can Inst Chem, 91. *Concurrent Pos:* Mem, Photochem Unit, Univ Western Ont, 80-, actg dir, 82, dir, 85-91. *Mem:* Can Inst Chem; Am Chem Soc. *Res:* Organic photochemistry and synthetic organic chemistry; applications of photochemistry to organic synthesis; mechanistic photochemistry; light induced-electron transfer. *Mailing Add:* Fac Grad Studies Univ Western Ont London ON N6A 5B7 Can. *Fax:* 519-661-3730; *E-Mail:* grad.dean@uwo.ca

**WEEDON, GENE CLYDE,** POLYMER CHEMISTRY. *Current Pos:* res chemist, 66-71, res mgr, 71-90, DIR RES & DEVELOP, FIBERS DIVISIONS CO, ALLIED SIGNAL CORP, 90- *Personal Data:* b Washington, DC, June 11, 36; m 61, Diane; c Mary B, Michael & Paul. *Educ:* Va Polytech Inst & State Univ, BS, 59. *Prof Exp:* Res chemist, Esso Res & Eng Co, 60-66. *Mem:* Am Chem Soc; Res Soc Am; Soc Plastics Engrs; Sigma Xi; Am Inst Chem. *Res:* Development of modified polymers and processes for applications in films, fibers, and moldings area; commercialization of high strength polyethylene fiber. *Mailing Add:* 4919 Waycrest Terr Richmond VA 23234-4794

**WEEGE, RANDALL JAMES,** GEOLOGY. *Current Pos:* RETIRED. *Personal Data:* b May 14, 26; US citizen; m 51; c 3. *Educ:* Univ Wis-Madison, BS, 51, MS, 55. *Prof Exp:* Geologist, Anaconda Co, 55-56; geologist-engr, Uranium Div, Calumet & Hecla, Inc, 56-60, resident geologist, Calumet Div, 60-61, asst chief geologist, 61-65, dir geol, 65-68; dir geol, Universal Oil Prod Co, 68-74, dir explor, 74, dir mineral develop, Mineral Sci Div, 74-81, dir mineral exp, 82- *Concurrent Pos:* Mineral consult, Parsons-Jurden Corp, 66-, Consol Papers Inc, Coleman Eng Co Nord Inc. *Mem:* Soc Econ Geologists; Am Inst Mining, Metall & Petrol Eng; fel Geol Soc Am; Soc Geol Appl Mineral Deposits. *Res:* Mineral exploration techniques and methods. *Mailing Add:* HC 2 Box 783 No 783 Florence WI 54121

**WEEKES, TREVOR CECIL,** GAMMA RAY ASTRONOMY, ASTROPHYSICS. *Current Pos:* fel astrophys, Smithsonian Inst, 66-67, astrophysicist, 67-92, resident dir, Mt Hopkins Observ, 69-76, SR ASTROPHYSICIST, SMITHSONIAN INST, 92- *Personal Data:* b Dublin, Ireland, May 21, 40; m 64, Ann Owens; c Karina, Fiona & Lara. *Educ:* Nat Univ Dublin, BSc, 62, PhD(physics), 66; Nat Univ Ireland, DSc, 78. *Honors & Awards:* Bruno Rossi Prize, Am Astron Soc, 97. *Prof Exp:* Lectr III physics, Univ Col, Dublin, 64-66. *Concurrent Pos:* Consult, Atomic Energy Res Estab, Harwell, 64-66; res assoc, Harvard Col Observ, 67- & Steward Observ, Univ Ariz, 76-; vis prof, Dublin Inst Advan Studies, 71 & Univ Ariz, 72 & 74; vis prof, Royal Greenwich Observ, 80; assoc ed, Phys Rev Lett. *Mem:* AAAS; Am Astron Soc; Royal Astron Soc; Am Phys Soc. *Res:* Gamma ray astronomy; cosmic ray physics; meteor detection; atmospheric Cerenkov and fluorescence radiation; transient astronomy; extragalactic astronomy. *Mailing Add:* 1132 W Calle San Jose Sahuarita AZ 85629-9736. *Fax:* 520-670-5713; *E-Mail:* weekes@cfa.harvard.edu

**WEEKMAN, VERN W(ILLIAM), JR,** REACTION ENGINEERING, CATALYSIS. *Current Pos:* Chem engr, Mobil Oil Corp, 54-55, res chem engr, Res Dept, 57-60, fel, 60-63, sr res chem engr, 63-65, eng assoc, 66-67, mgr, Systs Res, 67-76, mgr, Spec Proc, 76-77, mgr, Catalyst Res, 77-79, mgr, Proc Res & Develop, 79-80, pres, Mobil Solar Energy Corp, 80-85, MGR, CENT RES LAB, MOBIL OIL CORP, 85- *Personal Data:* b Jamestown, NY, June 28, 31; m 55, Barbara Palm; c David E & Vern W III. *Educ:* Purdue Univ, BS, 53, PhD(chem eng), 63; Univ Mich, MS, 54. *Honors & Awards:* Wilhelm Award, Am Inst Chem Engrs, 82. *Concurrent Pos:* Ed, Indust & Eng Chem Ann Rev, Am Chem Soc, 71-75; inst lectr, Am Inst Chem Engrs, 79; dir, Am Inst Chem Engrs, 89-92; Coun Chem Res, 93- *Mem:* Nat Acad Eng; Am Inst Chem Engrs; Am Chem Soc; Sigma Xi. *Res:* Chemical reaction kinetics; diffusion and heat transfer in catalysis; process dynamics and control; solar photovoltaics. *Mailing Add:* 2 Canal Run E Washington Crossing PA 18977. *Fax:* 609-737-4722

**WEEKS, CHARLES MERRITT,** BIOPHYSICS. *Current Pos:* SR RES SCIENTIST, X-RAY CRYSTALLOG, MED FOUND BUFFALO, 70- *Personal Data:* b Buffalo, NY, Mar 23, 44; m 75; c 2. *Educ:* Cornell Univ, BS, 66; State Univ NY Buffalo, PhD(biophys), 70. *Mem:* Am Crystallog Asn; Sigma Xi. *Res:* Direct methods of phase determination in x-ray crystallography; crystal structures of steroids and related biological materials; protein crystallography. *Mailing Add:* Hauptman Woodward Med Res Inst 73 High St Buffalo NY 14203-1196

**WEEKS, DAVID LEE,** EXPERIMENTAL STATISTICS. *Current Pos:* Asst math, 54-57, from asst to assoc prof statist, 57-66, PROF STATIST, OKLA STATE UNIV, 66- *Personal Data:* b Boone, Iowa, June 24, 30; m 57; c 4. *Educ:* Okla State Univ, BS, 52, MS, 57, PhD(statist), 59. *Concurrent Pos:* Consult, Phillips Petrol Co, 61-91, Air Force Armament Lab, 69-73 & ASI Systs Int, Inc, 78-91; NSF fac fel, Cornell Univ, 67-68; statist consult, RCA, Albuquerque, 73 & Decisions & Designs, 84; vis prof NMex State Univ, 76-77 & 83-84. *Mem:* Am Statist Asn; Biomet Soc; Sigma Xi. *Res:* Design and analysis of experiments; linear models. *Mailing Add:* 71 University Circle Stillwater OK 74074

**WEEKS, DONALD PAUL,** PLANT GENETIC ENGINEERING, ALGAL MOLECULAR BIOLOGY. *Current Pos:* dir, Ctr Biotechnol, 89-97, PROF BIOCHEM & BIOL SCIS, UNIV NEBR, LINCOLN, 89-, SR CONSULT, CTR BIOTECHNOL, 97- *Personal Data:* b Terre Haute, Ind, Feb 15, 41; m 64, Rita A Stableton; c Emily, John, Derek & Drew. *Educ:* Purdue Univ, BSA, 63; Univ Ill, PhD(agron), 67. *Prof Exp:* Res assoc molecular biol, Inst Cancer Res, 67-68, NIH fel, 68-70, res assoc, 70-74, asst mem, 74-78, assoc mem, 78-82; prin scientist, Zoecon Res Inst, Sandoz Agro, Palo Alto, Calif, 82-89. *Concurrent Pos:* Mem, Molecular Biol & Genetics Grad Groups, Univ Pa, 76-82, Nat Agr Biotechnol Coun; consult outside contracts, 85- *Mem:* AAAS; Am Soc Plant Physiol; Am Soc Cell Biol; Int Soc Plant Molecular Biol; Am Soc Microbiol; Am Chem Soc. *Res:* Protein synthesis; gene regulation; plant cell transformation; genetic eng plants. *Mailing Add:* Ctr Biotechnol N300 Beadle Ctr Lincoln NE 68588-0665. *Fax:* 402-472-7842; *E-Mail:* btec001@unlvm.unl.edu

**WEEKS, GEORGE ELIOT,** AEROSPACE ENGINEERING. *Current Pos:* RETIRED. *Personal Data:* b Montgomery, Ala, July 10, 39; m 62; c 2. *Educ:* Univ Ala, BS, 60, MS, 61; Va Polytech Inst, PhD(mech), 66. *Prof Exp:* Stress analyst aircraft, Hayes Int, 61; asst prof aerospace eng, Miss State Univ, 61-63; aerospace technologist, NASA Langley Field, 63-67; from asst prof to prof, aerospace eng, 67-97. *Concurrent Pos:* Consult, US Army Missile Command, Hayes Int Corp, Remtech, Inc, Norton Co. *Mem:* Am Inst Aeronaut & Astronaut. *Res:* Composite materials; structural dynamics; stress analysis; numerical mathematics. *Mailing Add:* Univ Ala Box 870280 Tuscaloosa AL 35487-0280

**WEEKS, GERALD,** BIOCHEMISTRY, MOLECULAR BIOLOGY. *Current Pos:* from asst prof to assoc prof, 71-84, PROF MICROBIOL, UNIV BC, 84- *Personal Data:* b Birmingham, Eng, Feb 5, 41. *Educ:* Birmingham Univ, BSc, 62, PhD(biochem), 66, DSc, 93. *Prof Exp:* Res assoc biochem, Duke Univ Med Ctr, 66-69; res fel, Leicester Univ, 69-71. *Mem:* Am Soc Microbiol; Can Biochem Soc; Am Soc Cell Biol. *Res:* Molecular basis of cell-cell interaction during the differentiation of the cellular slime mould, Dictyostelium discoideum. *Mailing Add:* Dept Microbiol Univ BC No 300-6174 University Blvd Vancouver BC V6T 1Z3 Can

**WEEKS, GREGORY PAUL,** TEXTILE CHEMISTRY, INSTRUMENTATION. *Personal Data:* b Seattle, Wash, July 16, 47. *Educ:* Univ Wash, BS, 69; Univ Ill, Urbana, PhD(phys chem), 74. *Res:* Development of instrumentation for on-line automated analysis of polymer solutions used in synthetic textile fiber manufacture; synthetic textile technology generally, with emphasis on infrared engineering technology for instrumentation. *Mailing Add:* 108 Cameron Dr Hockessin DE 19707-9684

**WEEKS, HARMON PATRICK, JR,** WILDLIFE ECOLOGY. *Current Pos:* asst prof, 74-79, assoc prof, 79-96, PROF WILDLIFE MGT, PURDUE UNIV, WEST LAFAYETTE, 96- *Personal Data:* b Orangeburg, SC, Oct 4, 44; m 65, 90, Sally Spurgeon; c Donna S & Christie L. *Educ:* Univ Ga, BSF, 67, MS, 69; Purdue Univ, PhD(wildlife ecol), 74. *Prof Exp:* Lectr wildlife ecol, Yale Univ, 73-74. *Mem:* Wildlife Soc; Am Soc Mammalogists; Am Ornithologists Union; Soc Conserv Biol. *Res:* Effects of fragmentation and silvicultural practices on wildlife populations; adaptations of homeothermic vertebrates to sodium deficiencies; avian breeding biology. *Mailing Add:* Dept Forestry & Nat Resources Purdue Univ West Lafayette IN 47907-1159. *Fax:* 765-496-1344; *E-Mail:* hpw@forest1.fnr.purdue.edu

**WEEKS, JAMES ROBERT,** PHARMACOLOGY. *Current Pos:* RETIRED. *Personal Data:* b Des Moines, Iowa, Aug 13, 20; m 43, Mary E McMaster; c James Jr, Diane & Linda. *Educ:* Univ Nebr, BSc, 41, MS, 46; Univ Mich, PhD(pharmacol), 52. *Prof Exp:* From instr pharm to prof pharmacol, 50-57; res assoc, Upjohn Co, 57-84. *Mem:* AAAS; Am Soc Pharmacol & Exp Therapeut; Soc Exp Biol & Med; Sigma Xi. *Res:* Cardiovascular pharmacology; hypertension; prostaglandins; experimental addiction. *Mailing Add:* 1417 Sheridan Dr Kalamazoo MI 49001-4429. *Fax:* 616-345-8229

**WEEKS, JOHN DAVID,** CHEMICAL PHYSICS, MATERIALS PHYSICS. *Current Pos:* prof, 90-95, DISTINGUISHED UNIV PROF, INST PHYS SCI & TECHNOL & DEPT CHEM, UNIV MD, 95- *Personal Data:* b Birmingham, Ala, Oct 11, 43; m 88, Kaja Parming; c Aili. *Educ:* Harvard Col, BA, 65; Univ Chicago, PhD(chem physics), 69. *Honors & Awards:* Joel Henry Hildebrand Award, Am Chem Soc, 90. *Prof Exp:* Res fel chem, Univ Calif, San Diego, 69-71; res fel physics, Cambridge Univ, 72; mem tech staff mat physics, Bell Tell Labs 73-90. *Mem:* Fel Am Phys Soc; Am Chem Soc; AAAS. *Res:* Statistical physics; theory of crystal growth; pattern formation. *Mailing Add:* Inst Phys Sci & Technol Univ Md College Park MD 20742. *E-Mail:* jdw@ipst.umd.edu

**WEEKS, JOHN R(ANDEL), IV,** METALLURGY. *Current Pos:* RETIRED. *Personal Data:* b Orange, NJ, Oct 30, 27; m 51, Barbara Brewster; c Ann & John. *Educ:* Colo Sch Mines, EMet, 49; Univ Utah, MS, 50, PhD(metall), 53. *Prof Exp:* Asst metall eng, Univ Utah, 49-52; assoc metallurgist, Brookhaven Nat Lab, 53-59, metallurgist, 59-72, leader, corrosion sci group, 74-83, sr metallurgist & head mat technol div, 83-87, sr consult, 87-96. *Concurrent Pos:* Adj assoc prof, State Univ NY, Stony Brook, 62-63; consult, Aerojet-Gen Corp, 65-71 & US Nuclear Regulatory Comn, 75-88. *Mem:* Fel Am; Am Inst Mining, Metall & Petrol Engrs; Am Nuclear Soc; Nat Asn Corrosion Engrs. *Res:* Corrosion in aqueous solutions; liquid metal corrosion; reactor metallurgy; corrosion and stress corrosion cracking of nuclear reactor materials. *Mailing Add:* 25 Acorn Lane Stony Brook NY 11790-2127

**WEEKS, L(ORAINE) H(UBERT),** ELECTRICAL ENGINEERING. *Current Pos:* RETIRED. *Personal Data:* b Mt Lake Park, Md, Feb 27, 18; m 41; c 2. *Educ:* Univ Md, BS, 40. *Prof Exp:* Elec engr, Copper Wire Eng Asn, DC & Mo, 40-43; elec engr, Frank Horton & Co, Mo, 46-48; dist design engr, Monongahela Power Co, WVa, 48-50, planning engr, 50-63, mgr planning eng, 63-68; mgr syst transmission planning, Allegheny Power Serv Corp, 68-69, mgr spec planning studies, 70-73, exec dir, 73-83. *Concurrent Pos:* Elec engr consult, 83-84. *Mem:* Inst Elec & Electronics Engrs; Nat Soc Prof Engrs. *Res:* Electric utility planning of generation and transmission facilities. *Mailing Add:* 3035 McClellan Dr Greensburg PA 15601

**WEEKS, LEO,** genetics; deceased, see previous edition for last biography

**WEEKS, LESLIE VERNON,** SOIL PHYSICS. *Current Pos:* RETIRED. *Personal Data:* b Lazear, Colo, July 24, 18; m 44, Marjorie Alling; c William V & Bruce G. *Educ:* Univ Calif, Berkeley, BS, 52; Univ Calif, Riverside, PhD(soil sci), 66. *Prof Exp:* Sr lab technician, Univ Calif, Riverside, 51-56, prin lab technician, 56-70, staff res assoc soil sci, 70-78, lectr soil sci, 75-78. *Res:* Water movement in liquid and vapor phases due to water potential and thermal gradients in unsaturated soils; use of computers in water movement studies under transient flow conditions. *Mailing Add:* 5496 Jurupa Ave Riverside CA 92504

**WEEKS, MAURICE HAROLD,** TOXICOLOGY. *Current Pos:* RETIRED. *Personal Data:* b Germantown, NY, Nov 9, 21; m 48; c 2. *Educ:* Union Col, BS, 49, MS, 50. *Prof Exp:* Collab path, Forest Prod Lab, US Forest Serv, Wis, 49; chemist, Hanford Works, Gen Elec Co, 50-55; pharmacologist, Directorate Med Res, Army Chem Ctr, 55-66; pharmacologist, US Army Environ Hyg Agency, Aberdeen Proving Ground, 66- *Mem:* AAAS; Sci Res Soc Am; Am Indust Hyg Asn; Soc Toxicol. *Res:* Animal metabolism studies of administered chemicals; toxicology and hazard evaluation of inhaled aerosols and vapors. *Mailing Add:* 27 Idlewild Bel Air MD 21014

**WEEKS, PAUL MARTIN,** SURGERY. *Current Pos:* CHIEF DIV PLASTIC SURG, DEPT SURG, SCH MED, WASH UNIV, 71- *Personal Data:* b Clinton, NC, June 11, 32; m 57; c 6. *Educ:* Duke Univ, AB, 54; Univ NC, MD, 58. *Prof Exp:* From instr to prof surg, Med Ctr, Univ Ky, 64-70. *Mem:* Am Col Surgeons; Soc Univ Surgeons; Am Chem Soc; Plastic Surg Res Coun. *Res:* Interrelationships of collagen and mucopolysaccharides in determining tissue compliance; effects of environment in cell synthesis, particularly regarding mucopolysaccharide or collagen synthesis; effects of irradiation on collagen and mucopolysaccharide synthesis. *Mailing Add:* Wash Univ Sch Med One Barnes Hosp Plaza Suite 17424 St Louis MO 63110-1094

**WEEKS, RICHARD W(ILLIAM),** ELECTRICAL ENGINEERING. *Current Pos:* assoc prof elec eng, Nat Resources Res Inst, 65-71, ASSOC PROF ELEC ENG, UNIV WYO, 71- *Personal Data:* b Los Angeles, Calif, Mar 21, 22; m 47; c 1. *Educ:* Calif Inst Technol, BS, 52; Stanford Univ, MS, 58. *Prof Exp:* Assoc engr, Res Lab, Int Bus Mach Corp, 52-55; lectr elec eng, San Jose State Col, 55-56, assoc prof, 58-60; develop engr, Pick Labs, 56-58; asst prof elec eng, Mont State Univ, 60-63; supv bioeng lab, Presby Med Ctr, 63-65. *Concurrent Pos:* Consult various indust concerns. *Mem:* Am Soc Eng Educ; Inst Elec & Electronics Engrs. *Res:* Applications of bioengineering to wildlife management and domestic livestock husbandry; general electronic instrumentation and telemetry. *Mailing Add:* 13743 S Janas Pky Lockport IL 60441-9496

**WEEKS, RICHARD WILLIAM,** AQUEOUS CORROSION, NUCLEAR FUELS. *Current Pos:* Asst mech engr, Argonne Nat Lab, 68-71, group leader fatigue & fracture, 71-73, assoc div dir, Mat Sci Div, 73-86, div dir, Mat & Comp Tech Div, 86-93, GEN MGR, ENERGY & INDUST TECHNOL, ARGONNE NAT LAB, 93- *Personal Data:* b Borger, Tex, April 12, 42; m 68; c 2. *Educ:* Swarthmore Col, BS, 64; Calif Inst Technol, MS, 65; Univ Ill, PhD(theoret & appl mech), 68; Univ Chicago, MBA, 82. *Concurrent Pos:* Consult, Elec Power Res Inst, 76-80; assoc ed, J Nuclear Eng & Des, 76-; sr mech engr, Argonne Nat Lab, 79-; lectr, Short Course, Northwestern Univ, 80-87. *Mem:* Sigma Xi. *Res:* Aqueous stress corrosion cracking in light water reactor systems; high temperature mechanical properties including creep-fatigue interactions; computer modelling of nuclear fuel element performance; materials science engineering; superconductivity technology; technology transfer. *Mailing Add:* 13743 Janas Pkwy Lockport IL 60441

**WEEKS, ROBERT A,** SOLID STATE PHYSICS, PROPERTIES OF AMORPHOUS SOLIDS. *Current Pos:* PRIN INVESTR, REDOX EQUILIBRIA IN OPTICAL WAVEGUIDE MAT, VANDERBILT UNIV, 81-, RES PROF, DEPT MECH & MAT ENG, 84- *Personal Data:* b Birmingham, Ala, Aug 23, 24; m 48, Jane Sutherland; c Kevin D, Robin D, Loren (Hammond) & Kerry A. *Educ:* Birmingham-Southern Col, BS, 48; Univ Tenn, MS, 51; Brown Univ, PhD(physics), 66. *Prof Exp:* Physicist, Solid State Div, Oak Ridge Nat Lab, 51-84, prin investr, lunar mat, 68-74, prin investr, Libyan desert glass, 68-81. *Concurrent Pos:* Distinguished vis prof, Am Univ Cairo, 68, 70-71; res fel, Univ Reading, 71; consult, Dept Phys Sci & Mat Eng, Am Univ Cairo, 71-; assoc ed, J Geophys Res, 68-74, Fulbright short term lectr, 80, invite prof, Fed Polytech Sch Lausannne, 81; consult, Kuwait Inst Sci Res, Technol Develop Coop, 76-, Spectran Corp, 82-, Ga Inst Tech, 83-, Gen Elec Corp, 84-85 & UT Corp, 84-; adj prof, Univ Pa, 77- & Vanderbilt Univ, 79-; co-div, Libyan Desert Grass Geol Exped, 81; co-chmn, First Int Conf Effects of Modes of Formation on Struct of Glasses, 84, co-ed proc, 85, prin investr, New Mat by Ion Implantation, NSF grant, 86-89, co-prin investr, Radiation Effects on Low Thermat Expansion Mat, NRL grant & Free Electron Laser Effects on Mat, SDI grant, co-chmn, 2nd Int Conf Effects of Modes of Formation on Struct of Glasses, 87, co-ed proc, 88, ed, J Non-Crystalline Solids, 88-, co-chmn, Int Conf Editing Refereed Sci, 92. *Mem:* AAAS; Am Phys Soc; Sci Res Soc Am; Am Ceramic Soc. *Res:* Optical and magnetic properties of intrinsic and extrinsic defects of crystalline and glassy solids; effects of photon and particle irradiation upon the properties of diamagnetic non-conducting solids; magnetic properties of extraterrestrial solids; transport in solids; ion implantation effects on solids. *Mailing Add:* Dept Mech & Mat Eng Vanderbilt Univ PO Box 1678 Nashville TN 37235

**WEEKS, ROBERT JOE,** MYCOLOGY, MEDICAL MICROBIOLOGY. *Current Pos:* CONSULT ENVIRON MYCOL, 85- *Personal Data:* b Quapaw, Okla, Feb 19, 29; m 48; c 3. *Educ:* Southwest Mo State Col, BS, 61. *Hon Degrees:* ScD, Mo State Col, 71. *Prof Exp:* Mycologist, Kans City Field Sta, Commun Dis Ctr, Bur Labs, USPHS, 62-64, microbiologist, 64-67, chief soil ecol unit, Mycoses Sect, Kansas City Labs, Ecol Invests Prog, Ctr Dis Control, 67-74, microbiologist, microbiol sect, Proficiency Testing Br, 74-79; microbiologist, Mycotic Dis Div, Ctr Infectious Dis, Ctr Dis Control, Atlanta, Ga, 79-85. *Mem:* Mycol Soc Am. *Res:* Relationship of the pathogenic fungi to their soil environment; ecology, epidemiology and control of animal-human pathogenic fungi. *Mailing Add:* 720 S Scott Circle Republic MO 65738. *E-Mail:* rweeks@mail.orion.org

**WEEKS, STEPHAN JOHN,** ANALYTICAL SPECTROMETRY. *Current Pos:* CHEMIST, AMES LAB, 84- *Personal Data:* b Minneapolis, Minn, Apr 13, 50; m 77; c 3. *Educ:* St Olaf Col, BA, 72; Univ Fla, PhD(chem), 77. *Prof Exp:* Res chemist lasers spectros, Nat Bur Stand, 77-79, res chemist, tribology, 79-84. *Concurrent Pos:* Res assoc, Nat Res Coun fel, 77-79. *Mem:* Am Chem Soc; Soc Appl Spectros. *Res:* Trace molecular analysis; method development; laser spectrometry; trace atomic analysis; computer data analysis. *Mailing Add:* Spec Technologies Lab 5520 Ekwill St Suite B Santa Barbara CA 93111. *Fax:* 515-294-7953

**WEEKS, STEPHEN CHARLES,** EVOLUTION OF LIFE HISTORIES, EVOLUTION OF SEXUAL REPRODUCTION. *Current Pos:* TEMP ASST RES ECOLOGIST, SAVANNAH RIVER ECOL LAB, 92- *Personal Data:* b Harbor City, Calif, Dec 14, 60; m 90, Claudia Weil. *Educ:* Univ Calif, Santa Barbara, BA, 83, Riverside, MA, 86; Rutgers Univ, PhD(ecol), 91. *Prof Exp:* Teaching asst biol, Univ Calif, Riverside, 83-86; excellence fel, Rutgers Univ, 86-90, teaching asst genetics, 90-91; fel, NIH, 91. *Concurrent Pos:* Res asst, Univ Calif, Riverside, 84-86. *Mem:* Soc Study Evolution; Am Soc Naturalists; Ecol Soc Am; Am Soc Ichthyologists & Herpetologists; Crustacean Soc. *Res:* Evolution of sexual reproduction using clonal and sexual aquatic organisms; evolution of life-history strategies using livebearing fish. *Mailing Add:* Dept Biol Univ Akron SC 44325. *Fax:* 330-972-8445; *E-Mail:* weeks@srel.edu

**WEEKS, STEPHEN P,** SILICON MATERIALS DEVELOPMENT, ELECTRONIC CERAMICS. *Current Pos:* DIR PLANNING & CONTROL, BP AM RES, 91- *Personal Data:* b Wilmington, Del, July 3, 49; m 73; c 2. *Educ:* Univ Del, BS, 71; Col William & Mary, MS, 73; Univ Pa, PhD(solid state physics), 77. *Prof Exp:* Felt, AT&T Bell Labs, 77-78, mem tech staff, 79-84, distinguished tech staff, 84-85; res mgr, Stand Oil Ohio, 85-87; res coordr, Brit Petrol, London, 87-90. *Mem:* Am Phys Soc. *Res:* Integrated circuit process technology development; electronic/optical materials research. *Mailing Add:* 3149 Van Aken Blvd Cleveland OH 44120

**WEEKS, THOMAS F,** PLANT PHYSIOLOGY. *Current Pos:* assoc prof, 71-80, PROF BIOL, UNIV WIS-LA CROSSE, 80- *Personal Data:* b Wheeling, WVa, Apr 12, 35; m 55; c 2. *Educ:* WLiberty State Col, AB, 63; Purdue Univ, MS, 67, PhD(develop bot), 70. *Prof Exp:* Mem staff sec educ, Ohio Co Bd Educ, WVa, 63-64; guest lectr biol, Purdue Univ, 70-71. *Mem:* AAAS; Bot Soc Am; Am Soc Plant Physiol. *Res:* Plant growth regulators; control mechanisms in plants. *Mailing Add:* Dept Biol Univ Wis La Crosse 1725 State St La Crosse WI 54601-3742

**WEEKS, THOMAS JOSEPH, JR,** CATALYSIS. *Current Pos:* group leader, Ashland Chem Corp, 78-80, res mgr, 80-83, com develop mgr, 83-86, dept head, Res & Develop, 87-93, DIR, PROD INFO-ENVIRON HEALTH & SAFETY, ASHLAND CHEM CORP, 93- *Personal Data:* b Tarrytown, NY, Aug 31, 41; m 67; c 2. *Educ:* Colgate Univ, BA, 63; Univ Colo, PhD(chem), 67. *Prof Exp:* Res chemist, Res & Eng Ctr, Johns-Manville Corp, Manville, NJ, 66-68; sr res chemist, Union Carbide Corp, Tarrytown, NY, 70-72, proj chemist, 72-73, sr staff chemist, 73-75, supvr, 75-78. *Mem:* Am Chem Soc; AAAS. *Res:* Waste management and safety-research and development building administration; synthesis, testing and manufacturing of heterogeneous catalysts; management of environmental, Health and Toxicology programs. *Mailing Add:* Ashland Chem Co PO Box 2219 Columbus OH 43216-2219

**WEEKS, WILFORD FRANK,** sea ice geophysics; deceased, see previous edition for last biography

**WEEKS, WILLIAM THOMAS,** ENGINEERING PHYSICS. *Current Pos:* RETIRED. *Personal Data:* b Portchester, NY, Mar 28, 32; m 54, Ann Armstrong; c Linda & James. *Educ:* Williams Col, BA, 54; Univ Mich, MS, 56, PhD(physics), 60. *Prof Exp:* Assoc physicist, Data Systs Div, IBM Corp, 60-61, staff physicist, Systs Develop Div, 61-64, adv physicist, Components Div, 64-68, sr engr, 68-84, sr tech staff mem, Gen Technol Div, 84-93. *Mem:* Sigma Xi. *Res:* Scientific computation and numerical analysis as applied to design of electronic digital computers. *Mailing Add:* Innsbruck Blvd Hopewell Junction NY 12533. *E-Mail:* weekswt@aol.com

**WEEMS, CHARLES WILLIAM,** REPRODUCTIVE ENDOCRINOLOGY, GROWTH PHYSIOLOGY. *Current Pos:* PROF & CHMN, DEPT ANIMAL SCI, UNIV HAWAII, MANOA, 83- *Personal Data:* b Greeneville, Tenn, Mar 1, 41; m 87, Yoshie Suzuyli; c Nathan, Garrett & Kristin. *Educ:* ETenn State Univ, BS, 64, MA, 66; WVa Univ, PhD(endocrinol), 75. *Prof Exp:* Capt chem corps, US Army Biol Labs, Ft Detrick, Md, 66-68; instr, Fairmont State Col, WVa, 68-71, from asst prof to assoc prof biol & physiol, 71-76; from assoc prof to prof agr & endocrinol, Ariz State Univ, 76-83. *Concurrent Pos:* Prin investr, UpJohn Co, Inc, 76-; adhoc reviewer reproduction & growth, USDA, 85-, biotechnol peer panel reviewer growth, 85-; prog dir, USDA Biotech Grants, 87; endocrinol ed, Prostaglandins, 91- *Mem:* NY Acad Sci; Soc Study Reproduction; Endocrine Soc; Am Soc Animal Sci; Sigma Xi; Soc Study Fertil. *Res:* Mechanisms regulating ovarian, corpus luteum, and uterine function; embryonic signals regulating pregnancy and conception; uterine capacity; survival of embryos; mechanisms of action and regulation of hormone receptors. *Mailing Add:* Dept Animal Sci Univ Hawaii 1800 East-West Rd Honolulu HI 96822. *Fax:* 808-956-4883

**WEEMS, HOWARD VINCENT, JR,** ENTOMOLOGY. *Current Pos:* TAXON ENTOMOLOGIST, DIV PLANT INDUST, FLA DEPT ARG & CONSUMER SERV, 53-, PROF ENTOM, UNIV FLA, 73- *Personal Data:* b Rome, Ga, Apr 11, 22; m 50; c 4. *Educ:* Emory Univ, BA, 46; Univ Fla, MS, 48; Ohio State Univ, PhD(entom), 53. *Prof Exp:* Asst entom, Univ Fla, 46-47, assoc prof entom, 66-73; instr biol, Univ Miss, 48-49; res asst, Ohio Biol Surv, Ohio State Univ, 49-53. *Concurrent Pos:* Head Cur, Fla State Collection Arthropods, 54-; assoc arthropods, Fla State Mus Natural Hist, 59-; ed, Arthropods of Fla & Neighboring Land Areas, Fla State Collection Arthropods, Fla Dept Agr & Consumer Serv, 65-; assoc ed, Fla Entomologist; courtesy assoc prof entom, Fla A&M Univ, 77-; dir, Ctr Syst Entom Inc. *Mem:* Fel AAAS; Asn Trop Biol; Entom Soc Am; assoc Ecol Soc Am; Soc Syst Zool; Am Forestry Asn; Asn Syst Collections; Sigma Xi; Smithsonian Natural Hist Asn; Brazilian Entom Soc; Lepidopterists Soc. *Res:* Taxonomy and ecology of syrphid flies; identifications of Florida arthropods. *Mailing Add:* PO Box 2309 Hawthorne FL 32640-0760

**WEEMS, MALCOLM LEE BRUCE,** PHYSICS. *Current Pos:* instr, E Cent State Univ, 72-75, dir, Sci Lab Prog Blind, 74-80, asst prof physics, 75-79, assoc prof, 79-82, chmn, Dept Physics, 82-89, intern dean, Sch Math & Sci, 90-91, PROF PHYSICS, E CENT STATE UNIV, 82-, CHMN, DEPT PHYS & ENVIRON SCI, 89-, DEAN, MATH & SCI DIV, 91- *Personal Data:* b Nashville, Kans, Dec 8, 45; m 72; c 1. *Educ:* Kans State Teachers Col, BSE, 67, MS, 69; Okla State Univ, PhD(physics), 72. *Prof Exp:* Lectr physics, Kans State Teachers Col, 68-69. *Mem:* Am Inst Physics; Am Asn Physics Teachers. *Res:* Stellar atmospheres; educational innovation. *Mailing Add:* Sch Phys Sci E Cent Univ Ada OK 74820-6899

**WEEMS, ROBERT EDWIN,** GEOLOGY. *Current Pos:* RES GEOLOGIST, US GEOL SURV, 78- *Personal Data:* b Richmond, Va, Jan 22, 47; m 83; c 3. *Educ:* Randolph-Macon Col, BS, 68; Va Polytech Inst & State Univ, MS, 75; George Washington Univ, PhD(geol), 78. *Prof Exp:* Instr, George Mason Univ, 76-79. *Concurrent Pos:* Consult, Dahlgren Naval Res Lab, 77-79. *Mem:* Am Asn Ichthyologists & Herpetologists. *Res:* Vertebrate paleontology; stratigraphy and paleoseismicity of the Maryland, Virginia, West Virginia, North Carolina and South Carolina region from the Precambrian to present; Atlantic coastal plain stratigraphy; Newark supergroup statigraphy. *Mailing Add:* 3003 Jonquilla Ct Herndon VA 20171-2290

**WEEMS, WILLIAM ARTHUR,** NEUROPHYSIOLOGY, GASTROINTESTINAL MOTILITY. *Current Pos:* asst prof, 76-82, ASSOC PROF PHYSIOL, MED SCH, UNIV TEX, HOUSTON, 82- *Personal Data:* b Carlsbad, NMex, July 3, 44; m 65; c 2. *Educ:* Baylor Univ, BS, 67, MS, 70; Univ Ill, PhD(physiol), 73. *Prof Exp:* Res fel, Mayo Found, 73-76. *Mem:* Sigma Xi; Soc Neurosci; Am Physiol Soc; Asn Comput Mach. *Res:* Information processing in sympathetic prevertebral ganglia and neural control of gastrointestinal motility. *Mailing Add:* Dept Physiol & Cell Biol Univ Tex Med Sch PO Box 20708 Houston TX 77225-0708. *Fax:* 713-792-5417; *E-Mail:* wweems@oac.hsc.uth.tmc.edu

**WEERS, JEFFRY GREG,** COLLOID & INTERFACE SCIENCE, FLUOROCARBON BLOOD SUBSTITUTES. *Current Pos:* res fel, 91-92, DIR ADV PROD RES, ALLIANCE PHARMACEUT CORP, 93- *Personal Data:* b Jamestown, NDak, Nov 10, 58; m 88, Janice G Briones; c Alena N, Emma A & Audrey E. *Educ:* Univ Puget Sound, BS, 80; Univ Calif, Davis, PhD(chem), 85. *Prof Exp:* Scientist II, Clorox Tech Ctr, 85-88, sr scientist, 88-90. *Concurrent Pos:* Sect ed, Current Opinion Colloid Interface Sci. *Mem:* Am Chem Soc; Int Soc Artificial Cells Blood Substitutes & Immobilization Biotechnol. *Res:* Spectroscopy and rheological characterization of colloidal microstructures and biopolymers; biomedical applications of fluorocarbons; drug delivery; mixed surfactants; emulsion technology. *Mailing Add:* 12191 Salix Way San Diego CA 92129. *Fax:* 619-558-3625; *E-Mail:* jgw@allp.com

**WEERSINK, ALFONS JOHN,** PRODUCTION ECONOMICS, RESOURCE ECONOMICS. *Current Pos:* Asst prof, 89-91, ASSOC PROF PROD ECON & RESOURCE ECON, DEPT AGR ECON & BUS, UNIV GUELPH, 91- *Personal Data:* b St Marys, Ont, Aug 5, 59; m 82, Maureen Muller; c Erin, Kristen, Marc & Bryan. *Educ:* Univ Guelph, BSc, 82; Mont State Univ, MS, 84; Cornell Univ, PhD(agr econ), 89. *Concurrent Pos:* Co-ed, Can J Agr Econ, 91-96; assoc ed, Am J Agr Econ, 97- *Mem:* Can Agr Econ & Farm Mgt Soc; Am Agr Econ Asn; Am Econ Asn. *Res:* Examination of the impacts of government policies, including environmental regulations, and new technology on the optimal decision of agricultural producers and the structure of agriculture. *Mailing Add:* Dept Agr Econ & Bus Univ Guelph Guelph ON N1G 2W1 Can. *Fax:* 519-767-1510; *E-Mail:* aweersin@uoguelph.ca

**WEERTMAN, JOHANNES,** MATERIAL SCIENCE, GLACIOLOGY FRACTURE. *Current Pos:* from assoc prof to prof, 59-68, dept chair, 64-68, PROF GEOPHYS, 63-, WALTER P MURPHY PROF MAT SCI, NORTHWESTERN UNIV, EVANSTON, 68- *Personal Data:* b Fairfield, Ala, May 11, 25; m 50, Julia Randall; c Bruce R & Julia A. *Educ:* Carnegie Inst Technol, BS, 48, DSc(physics), 51. *Honors & Awards:* Horton Award, Sect Hydrol, Am Geophys Union, 62; Mathewson Gold Medal, Am Inst Mining, Metall & Petrol Eng, 77; Seligman Crystal Award, Int Glaciol Soc, 83; Acta Metallurgica Gold Medal, 80. *Prof Exp:* Fulbright fel, Ecole Normal Superieure, Paris, 51-52; solid state physicist, US Naval Res Lab, 52-58, sci liaison officer, US Off Naval Res US Embassy, Eng Lab, 58-59. *Concurrent Pos:* Consult, US Army Cold Regions Res & Eng Lab, 60-75, US Naval Res Lab, 60-67, Bain Lab, US Steel Co, 60-62 & Oak Ridge Nat Lab, 63-68; vis prof, Calif Inst Technol, 64; consult, Los Alamos Sci Lab, 67-; Guggenheim fel, 70-71; vis prof, Scott Polar Res Inst, Cambridge Univ, 71-72, Swiss Fed Reactor Res Inst, 86. *Mem:* Nat Acad Eng; AAAS; fel Geol Soc Am; fel Am Phys Soc; fel Am Soc Metals; fel Am Geophys Union; fel Metals Minerals & Mat Soc; fel Am Acad Mechs. *Res:* Creep of crystals; dislocation theory; internal friction; theory of glacier movement; metal physics; glaciology; geophysics; fatigue; fracture. *Mailing Add:* Dept Mat Sci & Eng Northwestern Univ Evanston IL 60208. *Fax:* 847-467-6573

**WEERTMAN, JULIA RANDALL,** SOLID STATE PHYSICS. *Current Pos:* vis asst prof, Northwestern Univ, 72-73, from asst prof to prof, 73-88, dept chmn, 87-92, WALTER P MURPHY PROF MAT SCI, NORTHWESTERN UNIV, EVANSTON, 88- *Personal Data:* b Muskegon, Mich, Feb 10, 26; m 50, Johannes; c Bruce & Julia. *Educ:* Carnegie Inst Technol, BS, 46, MS, 47, DSc(physics), 51. *Honors & Awards:* Creativity Res Award, NSF, 81 & 86; Achievement Award, Soc Women Eng, 91; Leadership Award Minerals, Metals & Mat Soc. *Prof Exp:* Rotary Int fel, Ecole Normale Superieure, Univ Paris, 51-52; physicist, US Naval Res Lab, 52-58. *Concurrent Pos:* Guest prof, Confederated Tech Univ, Zurich, 86; Guggenheim fel, 86-87. *Mem:* Nat Acad Eng; Am Inst Phys; fel Am Soc Metals Int; Am Soc Testing & Mat; Mat Res Soc; Am Phys Soc; fel Minerals Metals & Mat Soc. *Res:* Dislocation theory; high temperature fatigue; small angle neutron scattering; nanocrystalline material. *Mailing Add:* Dept Mat Sci & Eng Northwestern Univ Evanston IL 60208. *Fax:* 847-467-6573; *E-Mail:* jrweertman@nwu.edu

**WEESE, JOHN AUGUSTUS,** MECHANICAL ENGINEERING, ENGINEERING MECHANICS. *Current Pos:* head, Eng Technol Dept, 86-97, PROF MECH ENG & ENG ACCREDITATION COORDR, TEX A&M UNIV, 86- *Personal Data:* b Topeka, Kans, July 24, 33; m 55, Betty Kay Dietrich; c Carol A & Katherine L. *Educ:* Kans State Univ, BS, 55; Cornell Univ, MS, 58, PhD, 59. *Honors & Awards:* Ben C Sparks Medal, Am Soc Mech Engrs, 94; Frederick J Berger Award, Am Soc Eng Educ, 97. *Prof Exp:* Asst prof, USAF Acad, 60-62; from assoc prof to prof mech eng, Univ Denver, 63-74, chmn mech sci & environ eng, 68-70, dean eng, 70-74; dean eng, Old Dominion Univ, 74-73; dir mech eng & appl mech, NSF, 83-85, dir mech struct & mat eng, 85-86. *Concurrent Pos:* Struct dynamics engr, Boeing Co, Wichita, 59-60, res specialist, 62-63; res engr, Martin-Marietta Corp, 63; chmn, Eng Res Coun, Am Soc Eng Educ, 88-90; mem bd dirs, Accreditation Bd Eng & Technol. *Mem:* Fel Am Soc Eng Educ; fel Am Soc Mech Engrs; Am Inst Aeronaut & Astronaut; Soc Exp Mech; Nat Soc Prof Engrs. *Res:* Three-dimensional solid mechanics; structural dynamics; vibrations engineering; engineering technology education and accreditations. *Mailing Add:* 2802 Barwick Circle Bryan TX 77802-2101. *Fax:* 409-845-3081; *E-Mail:* j-weese@tamu.edu

**WEESE, RICHARD HENRY,** ORGANIC POLYMER CHEMISTRY. *Current Pos:* From scientist chem to sr scientist chem, 67-78, RES SECT MGR, RES LABS, ROHM & HAAS CO, BRISTOL, 78- *Personal Data:* b Hyer, WVa, Dec 13, 38; m 68. *Educ:* WVa State Col, BS, 64; Bucknell Univ, MS, 67. *Mem:* Soc Plastic Engrs. *Res:* Synthesis and application of organic polymers, including additives or modifiers. *Mailing Add:* 123 Glenwood Dr Washington Crossing PA 18977

**WEETALL, HOWARD H,** IMMUNOCHEMISTRY, ENZYMOLOGY. *Current Pos:* res biologist, 91-92, group leader biosensor technol, 92-97, RES BIOLOGIST, NAT INST STAND & TECHNOL, 97- *Personal Data:* b Chicago, Ill, Nov 17, 36; m 62, Billie; c Laurel & Marla. *Educ:* Univ Calif, Los Angeles, BA, 59, MA, 61. *Honors & Awards:* DIFCO Award, Am Pub Health Asn, 78. *Prof Exp:* Scientist, Jet Propulsion Lab, Calif Inst Technol, 61-65; sr res biologist, Space Gen Corp, 65-66; immunochemist, Bionetics Res Corp, 66-67; res biochemist, Corning Glass Works, 67-71, res assoc, 71-73, sr res assoc biochem, 73-78, mgr biosci res, 78-84, mgr biomed res, 78-91. *Concurrent Pos:* Res fel, Corning Glass Works, 84-90. *Mem:* AAAS; Am Chem Soc; Am Soc Microbiol; NY Acad Sci; Am Soc Biol Chemists; Am Asn Immunol. *Res:* Immobilized biologically active molecules, including antigens, antibodies and enzymes and the characteristics of such materials; stabilization of proteins in sol-gel glasses, development of biosensors using electrochemical methods; wave techniques; eranescent; studies of analogs of bacteriorhodopsin. *Mailing Add:* Nat Inst Stand & Technol Gaithersburg MA 20899. *E-Mail:* howard.weetall@nist.gov

**WEETE, JOHN DONALD,** FUNGAL PHYSIOLOGY, FUNGAL BIOCHEMISTRY. *Current Pos:* from asst prof to prof, 72-86, ALUMNI PROF BOT & MICROBIOL, AUBURN UNIV, 86- *Personal Data:* b Dallas, Tex, June 14, 42; c 1. *Educ:* Stephen F Austin State Univ, BS, 65, MS, 68; Univ Houston, PhD(biol), 70. *Honors & Awards:* Res Award, Am Phytopath Soc, 68; William Howard Smith Fac Res Award, Auburn Univ, 80; Int Sci Exchange Award, Can, 87. *Prof Exp:* Fel, Baylor Col Med, 69-70; vis scientist, Lunar Sci Inst, 70-71; staff scientist, 71-72, NASA prin investr lunar sample anal, 72. *Concurrent Pos:* Vis prof, Univ Zurich, 80; invited prof, Univ Paul Sabatier, Toulouse, France; assoc ed, Can J Microbiol; assoc dean, Col Sci & Math, Auburn Univ, dir, Nuclear Sci Ctr. *Mem:* Am Phytopath Soc; Am Soc Microbiologists; Sigma Xi; fel Am Acad Microbiol; Mycol Soc Am; Am Oil Chemists Soc; AAAS. *Res:* Fungus physiology and biochemistry; lipid composition, function and metabolism of fungi; role of sterols in membranes; mode of action of antifungal sterol biosynthesis inhibitors; herbicide metabolism; lipases. *Mailing Add:* Bot Ctr Auburn Univ Auburn AL 36849-3501. *Fax:* 334-844-6917; *E-Mail:* weetejd@mail.auburn.edu

**WEETMAN, DAVID G,** ORGANIC CHEMISTRY. *Current Pos:* RES CHEMIST, TEXACO RES LAB, TEXACO, INC, 68- *Personal Data:* b Poughkeepsie, NY, Feb 20, 38; m 65; c 2. *Educ:* Pa State Univ, BS, 59; Univ Minn, PhD(org chem), 68. *Mem:* Am Chem Soc. *Res:* Synthesis and reactions of dihalocyclopropanes derived from 2- and 3- methyl substituted 4-ethoxy-2H-1-benzothiopyrans. *Mailing Add:* 12 Prentiss Dr Hopewell Junction NY 12533-6015

**WEETMAN, GORDON FREDERICK,** FORESTRY. *Current Pos:* prof silvicult, Fac Forestry, Univ NB, Fredericton, 72-78, PROF SILVICULT, FAC FORESTRY, UNIV BC, VANCOUVER, 78- *Personal Data:* b York, Eng, Apr 24, 33; Can citizen; c 3. *Educ:* Univ Toronto, BScF, 55; Yale Univ, MS, 58, PhD(forestry), 62. *Honors & Awards:* Can Forest Serv Achievement Award, 92. *Prof Exp:* Res forester, Pulp & Paper Res Inst Can, 55-72. *Concurrent Pos:* Ed, Forestry Chronicle, Can Inst Forestry, 67-71; dir, Silvicult Inst BC. *Mem:* Can Inst Forestry (pres, 73-74); Sigma Xi. *Res:* Blockage of the nitrogen cycle by raw humus accumulations in boreal forests; nitrogen fertilization; nutrient losses in logging; silviculture; Canadian forestry problems. *Mailing Add:* Fac Forestry Univ BC Vancouver BC V6T 1W5 Can

**WEFEL, JOHN PAUL,** PHYSICS, ASTROPHYSICS. *Current Pos:* ASST PROF PHYSICS, LA STATE UNIV, 82- *Personal Data:* b Cleveland, Ohio, Apr 28, 44; m 67; c 2. *Educ:* Valparaiso Univ, BS, 66; Wash Univ, MA, 68, PhD(physics), 71. *Prof Exp:* Nat Acad Sci-Nat Res Coun resident res assoc astrophys, Naval Res Lab, 71-73, res physicist, 73-75; Robert R McCormick fel, Enrico Fermi Inst, Univ Chicago, 75-77, sr res assoc, 77-82. *Mem:* AAAS; Am Phys Soc; Sigma Xi. *Res:* Cosmic ray astrophysics; utilized both passive and electronic detectors to measure element and isotopic abundances; studied nuclear fragmentation reactions of importance in cosmic ray propagation calculations; nucleosynthesis studies; instrument development. *Mailing Add:* 689 Castle Kirk Dr Baton Rouge LA 70808-6016

**WEFERS, KARL,** CRYSTALLOGRAPHY, SURFACE CHEMISTRY. *Current Pos:* RETIRED. *Personal Data:* b Bonn, Ger, Aug 4, 28; m 57, Ursula Harms; c 2. *Educ:* Univ Bonn, Dr rer nat, 58. *Prof Exp:* Group leader crystallog & struct chem, Vereinigte Aluminum Werke, Bonn, Ger, 58-66; sci assoc, Alcoa Res Labs, Alcoa Tech Ctr, 67-80, fel, Alcoa Labs, 80-93. *Mem:* Sigma Xi; Adhesion Soc. *Res:* Physical chemistry and structural chemistry of extractive metallurgy of aluminum; surface chemistry of aluminum; adhesion; surface finishing. *Mailing Add:* 528 Joyce Ave Apollo PA 15613-8706

**WEG, JOHN GERARD,** PULMONARY DISEASES. *Current Pos:* assoc prof internal med, 71-74, physician in charge Pulmonary & Crit Care Med Div, 71-85, PROF INTERNAL MED, MED SCH, UNIV MICH, 74- *Personal Data:* b New York, NY, Feb 16, 34; m 56; c 6. *Educ:* Col Holy Cross, AB, 55; New York Med Col, MD, 59. *Prof Exp:* Actg chief pulmonary, Wilford Hall, USAF Hosp, Lackland AFB, 63-64, chief pulmonary & inhalation ther sect, 64-66, pulmonary & infectious dis, 66-67; asst prof internal med, Baylor Col Med, 67-71, assoc prof, 71. *Concurrent Pos:* Clin dir pulmonary & internal med, Jefferson Davis Hosp, 67-71; consult, Area Consult Surgeon Gen, Methodist Hosp, Houston, Tex & Med Adv Comt, Assoc Degree Prog Health Sci, South Tex Jr Col, 68-71; Vet Admin Hosp, Ann Arbor, Mich, 72- & Wayne Count Gen Hosp, 73-84; NIH Rev Panel & Study Sect. *Mem:* Am Col Chest Physicians (pres 80-81); Am Col Physicians; Am Thoracic Soc (secy & treas 74-76); Am Bd Internal Med; Am Fedn Clin Res. *Res:* Correlation of clinical, physiologic, biochemical-immunologic, and pathologic mechanisms of pulmonary disease; acute respiratory failure; pulmonary emboli; diffuse interstitial disease; sarcoidosis; occupational and environmental medicine. *Mailing Add:* Univ Mich Hosp 1500 E Medical Center Dr BI-H-245 Box 0026 Ann Arbor MI 48109-0026

**WEG, RUTH B(ASS),** GERONTOLOGY. *Current Pos:* Res assoc, Dept Biochem, Univ Southern Calif, 58-59, Dept Biol & Physiol, 60-70, biochemist, 62-64, biologist in residence, Air Plollution Control Inst, 66, assoc prof biol, Univ & assoc dir educ & training, 68-74, assoc prof biol & geront, 75-84, PROF BIOL & GERONT, UNIV SOUTHERN CALIF, 84-, RES ASSOC, GERONT RES INST, ETHEL PERCY ANDRUS GERONT CTR, 85- *Personal Data:* b New York, NY, Oct 12, 20; c 3. *Educ:* Hunter Col, BA, 40; Univ Southern Calif, MS, 54, PhD(zool), 58. *Honors & Awards:* Dr George C Griffiths Mem Award, 77. *Concurrent Pos:* Consult, Rossmoor-Cortese Inst Study Retirement & Aging, Univ Southern Calif, 67, mem teaching fac, summer inst study geront, 68-, pre-med adv, Univ, 70-, dean student affairs, Leonard Davis Sch Geront, 74-76; head Res Group wellness, 86. *Mem:* AAAS; Am Inst Biol Sci; Fedn Am Socs Exp Biol; Geront Soc; Am Soc Aging; Asn Geront Higher Educ. *Res:* Normal pathological aging; nutrition and age, health and wellness in the later years; sexuality and sex roles in mid-life and later years; mid-life men and women; education for gerontology; sex differences in morbidity, mortality and longevity. *Mailing Add:* Univ Park Campus Ger 228 Univ Southern Calif Los Angeles CA 90089-0191

**WEGE, WILLIAM RICHARD,** radiology, for more information see previous edition

**WEGENER, PETER PAUL,** FLUID PHYSICS, GAS DYNAMICS. *Current Pos:* prof appl sci, Yale Univ, 60-72, chmn dept, 66-71, Harold Hodgkinson prof, 72-87, HAROLD HODGKINSON EMER PROF ENG & APPL SCI, YALE UNIV, 87- *Personal Data:* b Berlin, Ger, Aug 29, 17; nat US; m 61, Annette Schleier Macher. *Educ:* Univ Berlin, Dr rer nat(physics, geophys), 43; Yale Univ, MA, 60. *Hon Degrees:* Dr Ing Eh, Univ Karlsruhe, 79. *Honors & Awards:* Sr Am Scientist Humboldt Award, 79. *Prof Exp:* Mem & head, Basic Res Group Wind Tunnels, Ger, 43-45; head Res Group Hypersonic Wind Tunnel Design & Res, US Naval Ord Lab, 46-53; chief, Fluid Mech Sect, Jet Propulsion Lab, Calif Inst Technol, 53-60. *Concurrent Pos:* Consult; fel, Inst Advan Studies Berlin, 86. *Mem:* Fel Am Phys Soc. *Res:* Gas dynamics; fluid dynamics; chemical physics related to flow problems such as chemical kinetics and condensation. *Mailing Add:* 29 Montogomery Pkwy Branford CT 06405-5825

**WEGENER, WARNER SMITH,** MICROBIOLOGY, BIOCHEMISTRY. *Current Pos:* asst prof, 68-72, ASSOC PROF MICROBIOL, SCH MED, IND UNIV, INDIANAPOLIS, 72- *Personal Data:* b Cincinnati, Ohio, June 23, 35; m 58; c 3. *Educ:* Univ Cincinnati, BS, 57, PhD(microbiol), 64. *Prof Exp:* Asst mem, Res Labs, Albert Einstein Med Ctr, 64-68. *Concurrent Pos:* NIH fel, 65-66. *Mem:* Am Soc Microbiol. *Res:* Intermediary metabolism and cellular regulatory processes; biochemical basis of microbial pathogenicity. *Mailing Add:* Dept Microbiol Ind Univ Sch Med 1120 South Dr Indianapolis IN 46202-5135

**WEGGEL, JOHN RICHARD,** COASTAL ENGINEERING, HYDROLOGY & HYDRAULICS ENGINEERING. *Current Pos:* assoc prof, 83-88, head, Dept Civil & Archit Eng, 88-91, PROF, DREXEL UNIV, 88- *Personal Data:* b Philadelphia, Pa, Nov 29, 41; m 64, Martha Eyer; c David, Craig & Robert. *Educ:* Drexel Inst Technol, BS, 64; Univ Ill, MS, 66, PhD(civil eng), 68. *Honors & Awards:* Moffatt & Nichol Harbor & Coastal Eng Award, Am Soc Civil Eng, 93. *Prof Exp:* Asst prof, Univ Ill, Urbana, 68-71; hydraul engr, Coastal Eng Res Ctr, 71-73, spec asst to dir, 73-76, chief eval br, 76-83. *Concurrent Pos:* Mem steering comt, Deep Draft Harbor Study, NAtlantic Div, CEngr, US Army, 72-; mem, PIANC Waves Comn, 73-76; prof lectr, George Washington Univ, 74-83; consult, US Army CEngr & var munic; Marine Bd Comt Beach Nourishment, Nat Res Coun. *Mem:* Am Soc Civil Engrs; Am Geophys Union; Am Shore & Beach Preserv Asn; Sigma Xi. *Res:* Coastal engineering; civil engineering; coastal processes and ocean engineering; development of design criteria for coastal works and littoral processes. *Mailing Add:* 627 Rodman Ave Jenkintown PA 19046

**WEGGEL, ROBERT JOHN,** GENERATION OF INTENSE MAGNETIC FIELDS. *Current Pos:* Res staff, 61-97, ASST HEAD, MAGNET TECHNOL DIV, FRANCIS BITTER NAT MAGNET LAB, MASS INST TECHNOL, 97- *Personal Data:* b Cleveland, Ohio, Mar 16, 43; m 80, Diane Avery. *Educ:* Mass Inst Technol, BS, 64; Harvard Univ, BS, 66. *Concurrent Pos:* Consult magnet design, var cos & individuals, 66- *Mem:* Sigma Xi. *Res:* Designer of intense continuous field electromagnets employing water-cooled solenoids separately or in combination with superconducting coils (hybrid magnets), or long-duration pulse coils precooled with liquid nitrogen. *Mailing Add:* 54 Scotland Rd Rm NW 14-2124 Reading MA 01867. *E-Mail:* bob__weggel@men.com

**WEGMAN, DAVID HOWE,** OCCUPATIONAL DISEASE EPIDEMIOLOGY. *Current Pos:* PROF & CHAIR, DEPT WORK ENVIRON, COL ENG, UNIV MASS, LOWELL, 87-, ADJ PROF, MED SCH, DEPT FAMILY & COMMUNITY MED. *Personal Data:* b Baltimore, Md, Mar 13, 40; m 69, Peggy Nelson; c Jesse H & Marya N. *Educ:* Swarthmore Col, BA, 62; Harvard Med Sch, MD, 66; Harvard Sch Pub Health, MS, 72. *Honors & Awards:* Alfred L Frechette Award, Mass Pub Health Asn, 79; Harriet L Hardy Award, New Eng Col Occup & Environ Med. *Prof Exp:* Med intern, Cleveland Metrop Gen Hosp, 66-67; med epidemiologist, Nat Commun Dis Ctr, USPHS, 67-69; dir, indust health, Urban Planning Aid, Inc, 69-71; occup hyg physician, Div Occup Hyg, Commonwealth Mass, 72-78; from asst prof to assoc prof occup health, Harvard Sch Pub Health, 72-83; assoc physician, Brigham & Women's Hosp, 82-83; prof & dir environ & occup health sci, Univ Calif, Los Angeles, 83-87. *Concurrent Pos:* Mem, Task Group Surveillance, Nat Inst Occup Safety & Health, 76-77, Study Sect, 80-83, Sci Comt Epidemiol, Int Comn Occup Health, 82-, Task Force III, Nat Inst Environ Health Sci, 84, Bd Sci Counr, Nat Inst Occup Health & Safety, 88-91; contrib ed, Am J Indust Med, 78-; vis prof, Swed Nat Bd Occup Safety & Health, 84; mem, Bd Sci Counr, Nat Inst Occup Health & Safety, 88-91; secy & chmn, Sci Comt, Int Comn Occup Health, 90-; IOM Comt Health Consequences Persian Gulf War, 94-; chair, Comt Health & Safety Impications Child Labor, Inst Occup Med; adj prof, Harvard Sch Pub Health; bd dirs, Int Comn Occup Health. *Mem:* Fel Am Col Epidemiol; fel Am Col Prev Med; Am Pub Health Asn; Int Comn Occup Health; Soc Occup & Environ Health; Soc Epidemiol Res; Am Occup & Environ Med Asn; Int Epidemiol Asn. *Res:* Epidemiologic study of occupational cancer and occupational respiratory disease; the development of occupational disease and hazard surveillance strategies; the evaluation of effectiveness of public health policy and regulations. *Mailing Add:* Dept Work Environ Univ Mass Lowell MA 01854. *Fax:* 978-452-5711; *E-Mail:* wegmand@woods.uml.edu

**WEGMAN, EDWARD JOSEPH,** MATHEMATICAL STATISTICS, COMPUTATIONAL STATISTICS. *Current Pos:* DUNN PROF, GEORGE MASON UNIV, 86-, DIR, CTR COMPUTATIONAL STATIST, 86-, CO-DIR, INST COMPUTATIONAL SCI, 90-, CHAIR, DEPT APPL & ENG STATIST, 92- *Personal Data:* b Terre Haute, Ind, July 4, 43; m 67, Barbara J Bordeaux; c Lisa A (Jarvis) & Katherine E. *Educ:* St Louis Univ, BS, 65; Univ Iowa, MS, 67, PhD(statist), 68. *Honors & Awards:* Meritorious Civilian Serv Medal, USN, 82. *Prof Exp:* From asst prof to assoc prof statist, Univ NC, 68-78; dir statist & probability prog, 78-82, head, Math Sci Div, Off Naval Res, 82-86. *Concurrent Pos:* Res assoc, NSF, 68-72 & Off Naval Res, 72-74; consult, Naval Coastal Syst Lab, 72-74, NC State Utilities Comn, 74, Gov James Hunt NC, 75, NC Dept Pub Instr, 76-77, US Off Mgt & Budget, 80-81; prin investr, Air Force Off Sci Res, 74-78, Off Naval Res, 86-91, Army Res Off, 86-91, NSF, 87-91; sr fac fel, NSF, 76-77. *Mem:* Fel Inst Math Statist; fel Am Statist Asn; fel Royal Statist Soc; sr mem Inst Elec & Electronics Engrs; Soc Indust Appl Math; fel AAAS. *Res:* Statistical inference under order restrictions; time series analysis; function estimation; computational statistics; parallel computing. *Mailing Add:* Ctr Comput Statist St 11-157 George Mason Univ Fairfax VA 22030

**WEGMAN, MYRON EZRA,** PUBLIC HEALTH, PEDIATRICS. *Current Pos:* dean, Sch Pub Health, 60-74, prof pub health & prof pediat, 60-78, EMER DEAN, SCH PUB HEALTH, MED SCH, UNIV MICH, ANN ARBOR, 74-, JOHN G SEARLE EMER PROF PUB HEALTH & EMER PROF PEDIAT & COMMUN DIS, 78- *Personal Data:* b Brooklyn, NY, July 23, 08; m 36, Isabel Howe; c Judith W (Hirst), David H, Jane W (Dunatchik) & Elizabeth G (Petersen). *Educ:* City Col City Univ New York, BA, 28; Yale Univ, MD, 32; Johns Hopkins Univ, MPH, 38. *Honors & Awards:* Grulee Award, Am Acad Pediat, 58; Townsend Harris Medal, City Col New York, 61; Bronfman Prize, 67; Walter P Reuther Award, United Automobile Workers, 74; Sedgwick Medal, Am Pub Health Asn, 74; Spes Hominum Award, Nat Sanit Found, 88. *Prof Exp:* From asst to instr pediat, Sch Med, Yale Univ, 32-36; pediat consult, State Dept Health, Md, 36-41; asst prof child hyg, Sch Trop Med, Univ PR, 41-42; dir training & res, Dept Health, New York, 42-46, dir, Sch Health Serv, 43-46; prof pediat & head dept, Sch Med, La State Univ, 46-52; dir div educ & training, Pan Am Sanit Bur, WHO, 52-56, secy gen, Pan Am Health Orgn, 57-60. *Concurrent Pos:* From intern to resident, New Haven Hosp, Conn, 32-36; lectr, Maternal & Child Health, Johns Hopkins Univ, 39-46; asst prof, Col Physicians & Surgeons, Columbia Univ, 41-44, Med Col, Cornell Univ, 42-46; pediatrician-in-chief, Charity Hosp, New Orleans, 46-52, pres, Vis Staff, 50-51; consult, Children's Hosp, Washington, DC, 53-60; spec lectr, Sch Med, George Washington Univ, 53-60; chmn exec bd, Am Pub Health Asn, 65-70, pres, 72; pres, Comprehensive Health Planning Coun, SE Mich, 68-74; WHO vis prof, Univ Malaya, 74; mem, Soc of Scholars, Johns Hopkins Univ, 75; John G Searle prof pub health, Univ Mich, 75-78; chmn comt pediat hospitalization rates, Nat Res Coun, 75-77; adv, Kellogg Nat Fel Prog; external examr, Nat Univ Singapore, 83. *Mem:* Fel AAAS; Am Pub Health Asn (pres, 72); Am Pediat Soc; Soc Exp Biol & Med; fel AMA; Soc Pediat Res; Asn Sch Pub Health (pres, 63-66); Am Asn World Health (pres, 82-84); Pan Am Health & Educ Found (pres, 84-85); Physicians Soc Responsibility. *Res:* Infant mortality; prepaid health care; international health organization; vital statistics in quality assessment. *Mailing Add:* Sch Pub Health Univ Mich Ann Arbor MI 48109-2029. *Fax:* 313-764-4338; *E-Mail:* wegman@umich.edu

**WEGMAN, STEVEN M,** ELECTROMAGNETISM, ENERGY AUDITS. *Current Pos:* STAFF ENGR, SDAK PUB UTILITIES COMN, 91- *Personal Data:* b Sioux Falls, SDak, Apr 29, 53; m 78, Donna R Endahl; c Rachel & Adriane. *Educ:* SDak State Univ, BS, 77. *Prof Exp:* Proj engr, SDak Energy Off, 78-82; dir, Govt Off Energy Policy, 82-90. *Concurrent Pos:* Consult, SDak Renewable Energy Asn, 79-, Western Area Power Admin, 80-, SDak Cement Plant, 85- & Govt Off Energy Policy, 90-; lectr, SDak State Univ, 80- *Mem:* Am Soc Heating Refrig & Air Conditioning Engrs. *Res:* Energy use in residential, commercial and institutional buildings. *Mailing Add:* SDak Pub Utilities Comn 125 S Madison Pierre SD 57501. *Fax:* 605-773-3809; *E-Mail:* stevew@puc.state.sd.us

**WEGMANN, THOMAS GEORGE,** GENETICS, IMMUNOLOGY. *Current Pos:* assoc prof immunol, 74-76, prin investr, Med Res Coun Immunobiol Unit, 76-86, PROF IMMUNOL, UNIV ALTA, 76- *Personal Data:* b Milwaukee, Wis, Sept 29, 41; m 65; c 1. *Educ:* Univ Wis, BA, 63, PhD(med genetics), 68. *Prof Exp:* From asst prof to assoc prof biol, Harvard Biol Labs, 69-74. *Concurrent Pos:* Bd dirs, Janus Biomed Inc. *Mem:* Am Asn Immunologists; Can Soc Immunol. *Res:* Reproductive immunology, diagnostics and bone marrow transplantation. *Mailing Add:* Dept Immunol Univ Atla Edmonton AB T6G 2E2 Can. *Fax:* 403-492-0368; *E-Mail:* twegmann@gpa.sru.ualberta.ca

**WEGNER, DENNIS L,** MICROBIOLOGY, SEROLOGY. *Current Pos:* CONSULT CLIN MICROBIOLOGIST, LAB CONTROL LTD, 80- *Personal Data:* b Mar 18, 44; div; c 2. *Educ:* Hope Col, BA, 66; Univ Wis, PhD(med microbiol), 73. *Prof Exp:* Clin microbiologist, Dept Path, Mercy Hosp, Des Moines, 76-78, Iowa Methodist Med Ctr, Des Moines, 78-80. *Concurrent Pos:* Inst microbiol & infectious dis, Indian Hills Community Col, 79-87. *Mem:* Am Soc Microbiol; Europ Soc Clin Microbiol & Infectious Dis. *Res:* Microbiology and serology. *Mailing Add:* 217 W Golf Ave Ottumwa IA 52501-1345. *Fax:* 515-682-8976

**WEGNER, GARY ALAN,** PHYSICS & ASTRONOMY. *Current Pos:* from asst prof to assoc prof, 82-88, MARGARET ANNE & EDWARD LEEDE DISTINGUISHED PROF PHYSICS & ASTRON, DARTMOUTH COL 88-; DIR, MICH-DARTMOUTH-MASS INST TECHNOL OBSERV, 91- *Personal Data:* b Seattle, Wash, Dec 26, 44; m 66, Cynthia K Goodfellow; c Josef, Kurt, Christian, Peter-Jurgen & Emma. *Educ:* Univ Ariz, BS, 67; Univ Wash, PhD, 71. *Prof Exp:* Fulbright fel, Mt Stromlo Observ, Canberra, 71-72; dept demonstr astrophys, Oxford Univ, 72-75; sr sci res officer, SAfrican Astron Observ, Cape Town, 75-78; Annie J Cannon fel, Univ Del, 78-79; asst prof, Pa State Univ, 79-82. *Concurrent Pos:* Vis Astronr, Cornell Univ, 92; Keeley fel, Wadham Col, Oxford, 92-93; vis fel astrophys, Oxford Univ, 92-93; res prize, Alexander von Humboldt Found, 93. *Mem:* Am Astron Soc; Int Astron Union. *Res:* White dwarfs; large-scale structure of the universe. *Mailing Add:* Dept Physics & Astron Dartmouth Col Wilder Lab Hanover NH 03755

**WEGNER, GENE H,** FERMENTATION TECHNOLOGY, SINGLE CELL PROTEIN. *Current Pos:* RETIRED. *Personal Data:* b Madison, Wis, Aug 30, 30; m 53; c 4. *Educ:* Univ Wis, BS, 53, MS, 57, PhD(bact, biochem), 62. *Prof Exp:* Asst bact, Univ Wis, 55-57; microbiologist, Eli Lilly & Co, 57-59; asst bact, Univ Wis, 59-60, dept fel, 60-61; sr res microbiologist, Phillips Petrol Co, 62-80, biotechnol sect supvr, 80-84; vpres, res & develop, Provesta Corp, 84-87; mgr fermentation prod res & develop, Phillips Petrol Co, 88-92. *Mem:* Am Soc Microbiol; Am Chem Soc; Soc Indust Microbiol. *Res:* Hydrocarbon microbiology; fatty acid metabolism; microbial lipids; single cell protein; continuous culture; pilot plant development; biopolymcrs; biotechnology; rDNA fermentations and product isolation; yeast and food fermentations; bioremediation. *Mailing Add:* PO Box 210 Ketchum OK 74349-0210

**WEGNER, HARVEY E,** relativistic nuclear physics, low energy accelerator construction; deceased, see previous edition for last biography

**WEGNER, KARL HEINRICH,** medicine, pathology, for more information see previous edition

**WEGNER, MARCUS IMMANUEL,** BIOCHEMISTRY, NUTRITION. *Current Pos:* CONSULT FOOD SCI & NUTRIT, 80- *Personal Data:* b South Haven, Mich, Mar 3, 15; m 41; c 4. *Educ:* St Norbert Col, BS, 36; Univ Wis, PhD(nutrit biochem), 41. *Prof Exp:* Asst chemist, Exp Sta, Agr & Mech Col, Univ Tex, 41-43; asst nutritionist, Exp Sta, NDak Col, 43-44; res chemist, Mead Johnson & Co, Ind, 44-48; asst res dir, Res Div, Oscar Mayer & Co, 48-51; nutritionist, Pet Milk Co, 51-59, sect leader new prod develop, 59-60, group mgr, 60-61; res dir, Ward Foods, Inc, 61-64; asst res dir, Best Foods Div, Corn Prod Co, 64-69; br chief & diet appraisal, Consumer & Food Economics Div, Agr Res Serv, USDA, 69-71, asst dir, Eastern Regional Res Lab, 71-80. *Mem:* Am Asn Cereal Chem; Am Chem Soc; Inst Food Technol; Sigma Xi. *Res:* Chemistry and nutrition of protein hydrolysates; bakery products; food and diet appraisal; new and wider uses for American farm commodities; meats and dairy products; convenience frozen foods; new product development. *Mailing Add:* 401 Woodley Rd Santa Barbara CA 93108

**WEGNER, PATRICK ANDREW,** ORGANOMETALLIC CHEMISTRY. *Current Pos:* from asst prof to assoc prof, 69-74, PROF CHEM, CALIF STATE UNIV, FULLERTON, 75-, CHMN DEPT, 78- *Personal Data:* b South Bend, Ind, Nov 14, 40. *Educ:* Northwestern Univ, Evanston, BA, 62; Univ Calif, Riverside, PhD(chem), 66. *Prof Exp:* Res chemist, E I du Pont de Nemours & Co, Inc, 66-68; vis prof chem, Harvey Mudd Col, 68-69. *Concurrent Pos:* Grants, Petrol Res Corp, Calif State Univ, Fullerton, 68-72, 74-78, Res Corp, 70-72, NASA, 72-74; Alexander von Humboldt fel, 77-78. *Mem:* Am Chem Soc. *Res:* Boron hydride chemistry; transition metal organometallic chemistry. *Mailing Add:* Dept Chem Calif State Univ Fullerton CA 92634

**WEGNER, PETER,** COMPUTER SCIENCE. *Current Pos:* assoc prof comput sci, 69-, PROF, BROWN UNIV, 75- *Personal Data:* b Aug 20, 32; US citizen; m 56; c 4. *Educ:* Univ London, BSC, 53, PhD(comput sci), 68; Pa State Univ, MA, 59. *Prof Exp:* Res assoc, Comput Ctr, Mass Inst Technol, 59-60; asst dir statist lab, Harvard Univ, 60-61; lectr comput sci, London Sch Econ, 61-64; asst prof, Pa State Univ, 64-66; assoc prof, Cornell Univ, 66-69. *Concurrent Pos:* Ed-in-chief, Asn Comput Mach Press Bks. *Mem:* Asn Comput Mach; Math Asn Am. *Res:* Programming language theory and implementation; computer science education; semantics of programming languages; software engineering. *Mailing Add:* Dept Comput Sci Brown Univ Brown Sta Box 1910 Providence RI 02912

**WEGNER, ROBERT CARL,** GEOPHYSICS, GEOLOGY. *Current Pos:* geophys interpreter, Exxon Co USA, 69-70, res specialist, 74-80, supvr geophys, Exxon Prod Res Co, 80-86, SUPVR, EXXON CO, INT, 86- *Personal Data:* b New York, NY, Jan 7, 44; m 69; c 2. *Educ:* Queen's Col, NY, BA, 67; Lehigh Univ, MS, 72; Rice Univ, PhD(geophys), 78. *Prof Exp:* Vis lectr geol, Am Geol Inst, 68. *Concurrent Pos:* Cities Serv fel, 70; adj prof, Rice Univ, 81-82; chmn, Continuing Educ Comt, Soc Explor Geophysicists, 86. *Mem:* Am Geophys Union; Soc Explor Geophysicists; Sigma Xi; AAAS. *Res:* Geophysical research in reflection seismology applied to the exploration of oil and gas reservoirs. *Mailing Add:* Exxon Prod Res PO Box 2189 Houston TX 77252-2189

**WEGNER, THEODORE H,** CHEMICAL ENGINEERING. *Current Pos:* chem engr, 72-84, proj leader, 84-90, ASST DIR, USDA FOREST SERV, 90- *Personal Data:* b Milwaukee, Wis, Sept 18, 45; c Theodore & Gretchen. *Educ:* Univ Wis, BS, 67; Univ Ill, MS, 69, PhD(chem eng), 72. *Prof Exp:* Res asst, Univ Ill, 67-72; res engr, E I Dupont de Nemours, 72-77. *Mem:* Tech Asn Pulp & Paper Indust; Am Chem Soc; Am Inst Chem Engrs; Mat Res Soc; Sigma Xi. *Res:* High yield mechanical pulping, wastepaper recycling, wet press dewatering of fiber webs, dewatering of pulp fiber suspensions. *Mailing Add:* 7314 Branford Lane W Madison WI 53717-1004

**WEGNER, THOMAS NORMAN,** ANIMAL PHYSIOLOGY, BIOCHEMISTRY. *Current Pos:* Asst animal pathologist, 64-66, asst prof dairy sci, 67-76, LECTR & RES ASSOC ANIMAL SCI, AGR EXP STA, UNIV ARIZ, 76- *Personal Data:* b Cleveland, Ohio, July 8, 32; m 62; c 1. *Educ:* Mich State Univ, BS, 54; Colo State Univ, MS, 56; Univ Calif, Davis, PhD(animal physiol), 64. *Mem:* Am Dairy Sci Asn. *Res:* Carbohydrate metabolism in ruminant animals; pathogenesis of coccidioidomycosis, biochemistry of the immune responses; physiology of abnormal milk production and heat stress on dairy cows. *Mailing Add:* 3701 N Camino de Oeste Tucson AZ 85745

**WEGST, WALTER F, JR,** RADIOLOGICAL HEALTH. *Current Pos:* CONSULT, 88- *Personal Data:* b Philadelphia, Pa, Dec 26, 34; div; c 2. *Educ:* Univ Mich, BSE, 56, MSE, 57, PhD(environ health), 63; Am Bd Health Phys, Dipl, 66; Bd Cert Safety Prof, Cert. *Prof Exp:* Reactor health physicist, Phoenix Mem Lab, Univ Mich, 57-58, lab health physicist, 58-59, lab supvr, 59-60; inst health physicist, Calif Inst Technol, 63-68, safety mgr, 68-71, mgr security, 71-73, mgr safety, 71-79; dir res & occup safety, Univ Calif, Los Angeles, 79-88. *Concurrent Pos:* Consult, City of Hope Nat Med Ctr, Atomics Int Div Rockwell Int, 74-, Southern Calif Edison, Genetech & Training Resources Div, Nuclear Support Serv; mgr environ safety & health,

Raytheon Serv Nev, Las Vegas, 90-95. *Mem:* Health Phys Soc; Am Indust Hyg Asn; Sigma Xi; AAAS; Am Health Physics Soc; Am Conf Govt Indust Hygienists. *Res:* Radiobiological studies on mammalian cells; secondary electron production by charged particle passage through matter; university health physics problems. *Mailing Add:* 8390 Las Lunas Way Las Vegas NV 89129-1820

**WEGWEISER, ARTHUR E,** MARINE GEOLOGY, MICROPALEONTOLOGY. *Current Pos:* chmn, Dept Earth Sci, 69-75, PROF GEOL, EDINBORO UNIV PA, 65-, DIR MARINE SCI CONSORTIUM, 68- *Personal Data:* b New York, NY, Feb 20, 34; m, Marilyn Kressel; c 2. *Educ:* Brooklyn Col, BA, 55; Hofstra Univ, MS, 58; Wash Univ, St Louis, PhD(geol), 66. *Prof Exp:* Sci teacher, Island Trees High Sch, 58-61. *Concurrent Pos:* Adj lectr, Hofstra Univ, 58-61; fel, Woods Hole Oceanog Inst & Washington Univ, St Louis, Mo. *Mem:* Soc Econ Paleont & Mineral; Sigma Xi; Nat Asn Geol Teachers. *Res:* Micropaleontology-ecology of recent Foraminifera; environments of deposition. *Mailing Add:* Geol Sci Edinboro Univ Pa 219 Meadville St Edinboro PA 16444-0001

**WEHAUSEN, JOHN VROOMAN,** WATER WAVE THEORY, SHIP HYDRODYNAMICS. *Current Pos:* assoc res mathematician, Inst Eng Res, Univ Calif, Berkeley, 56-57, res mathematician, Dept Naval Archit, 57-58, assoc prof, 58-59, PROF ENG SCI, UNIV CALIF, BERKELEY, 59- *Personal Data:* b Duluth, Minn, Sept 23, 13; m 38, Mary K Wertime; c Sarah, Peter, Julia & John. *Educ:* Univ Mich, BS, 34, MS, 35, PhD(math), 38. *Hon Degrees:* Dr Joseph Fourier Univ, Grenoble, 93. *Honors & Awards:* Davidson Medal, Soc Naval Archit Marine Eng, 84. *Prof Exp:* Instr math, Brown Univ, 37-38, Columbia Univ, 38-40 & Univ Mo, 40-44; consult opers res group, Off Field Serv, Off Sci Res & Develop, USN, 44-46, mathematician, David Taylor Model Basin, 46-49, actg head mech br, Off Naval Res, 49-50, exec ed, Math Rev, 50-56. *Concurrent Pos:* Lectr, Univ Md, 45-50; vis prof, Univ Hamburg, 60-61, Flinders Univ SAustralia, 67, Univ Nantes, France, 73 & 84, Univ Grenoble, 79, Technion, 82, Univ Tel Aviv, 82 & Chalmers Univ, Sweden, 82; ed, Ann Rev Fluid Mech, 70-85. *Mem:* Nat Acad Eng; fel Soc Naval Archit & Marine Eng; Math Asn Am; Am Math Soc; fel AAAS. *Res:* Fluid mechanics, especially theory of water waves and hydrodynamics of ships and other floating bodies. *Mailing Add:* Dept Naval Archit & Offshore Eng Univ Calif Berkeley CA 94720. *Fax:* 510-642-6128; *E-Mail:* wehausen@garnet.berkeley.edu

**WEHE, ROBERT L(OUIS),** MECHANICAL ENGINEERING. *Current Pos:* RETIRED. *Personal Data:* b Topeka, Kans, Apr 14, 21; m 42; c 5. *Educ:* Univ Kans, BS, 48; Univ Ill, MS, 51. *Prof Exp:* Instr mech eng, Univ Ill, 48-51; asst prof, Cornell Univ, 51-57, assoc prof, 57-90. *Concurrent Pos:* Consult, Corning Glass Works, 55-59, proj engr, 57-58; consult, Lycoming Div, Avco, Inc, 56; NSF fac fel, Univ Ill, 59-60. *Mem:* Am Soc Mech Engrs; Am Soc Eng Educ. *Res:* Hydrodynamic lubrication; design of automatic machinery. *Mailing Add:* 409 Campbell Dr Ithaca NY 14850

**WEHINGER, PETER AUGUSTUS,** ASTRONOMY, OBSTERVATIONAL. *Current Pos:* RES PROF, DEPT PHYSICS & ASTRON, ARIZ STATE UNIV, 81- *Personal Data:* b Goshen, NY, Feb 18, 38; m 67. *Educ:* Union Col, NY, BS, 60; Ind Univ, MA, 62; Case Western Res Univ, PhD(astron), 66. *Honors & Awards:* Sigma Xi Prize, 60. *Prof Exp:* Res asst astron, Ind Univ, 60-62; NASA fel, Warner & Swasey Observ, Case Western Res Univ, 63-65; from instr to asst prof, Univ Mich, 65-70; assoc prof, Univ Kans, 70-72; vis assoc prof, Tel-Aviv Univ, Israel, 72-75; prin res fel, Royal Greenwich Observ, Eng, 75-78; vis sr scientist, Max Planck Inst Astron, Heidelberg, Ger, 78-80. *Concurrent Pos:* Sr res assoc, Ohio State Univ, 78-79; vis astron, Royal Greenwich Observ, Eng, 83; NASA fel, 63-65; Smithsonian fel, Wise Observ, 72-75; prin res fel, UK Sci Res Coun, 75-78; sr fel, Max Planck-Gesellschaft, 78-80; vis res fel, Stromlo & Siding Spring Observ, Australian Nat Univ, 86, 87, 89 & 90; ed, Halley Hotline, Electronic Bull Bd, Int Halley Watch, 85-87, Electronic Newslett on Comets, 89-90; discipline spec spectros Int Halley Watch, NASA, Jet Propulsion Lab, 82-90; dir, Ariz Space Consortium, Ariz State Univ, 90-; astronr, Steward Observ, Univ Ariz, 93- *Mem:* Am Astron Soc; Royal Astron Soc; Int Astron Union; Sigma Xi; Planetary Soc. *Res:* Astronomical instrumentation; molecular spectroscopy; digital archiving of cometary spectra; cometary spectroscopy; spectroscopy and imaging of active galaxies, quasars and quasar host galaxies; Jupiter-Io sodium cloud. *Mailing Add:* 2135 E Loma Vista Dr Tempe AZ 85282. *Fax:* 602-965-7954; *E-Mail:* peter@quasar.la.asu.edu

**WEHLAU, AMELIA W,** ASTRONOMY. *Current Pos:* Lectr, 65-71, from asst to assoc prof, 71-95, EMER PROF ASTRON, UNIV WESTERN ONT, 95- *Personal Data:* b Berkeley, Calif, Feb 5, 30; m 50, William H; c Ruth, Jeanne, David & Alice. *Educ:* Univ Calif, Berkeley, AB, 49, PhD(astron), 53. *Concurrent Pos:* Mem, Can Comt, Int Astron Union, 67-70. *Mem:* Am Astron Soc; Astron Soc Pac; Can Astron Soc; Int Astron Union; fel Royal Astron Soc. *Res:* Variable stars in globular clusters and related stellar systems. *Mailing Add:* Dept Astron Univ Western Ont London ON N6A 3K7 Can. *Fax:* 519-661-2009; *E-Mail:* afwehlau@uwo.ca

**WEHLAU, WILLIAM HENRY,** astronomy; deceased, see previous edition for last biography

**WEHLE, LOUIS BRANDEIS, JR,** AERONAUTICAL ENGINEERING. *Current Pos:* Stress analyst, Grumman Aerospace Corp, 41-48, head, Struct Methods Group, 48-56, head, Nuclear Sect, 56-59, staff engr, 61-72, CHIEF SCIENTIST, GRUMMAN AEROSPACE CORP, BETHPAGE, 72- *Personal Data:* b Washington, DC, Dec 28, 18; m 46; c 4. *Educ:* Harvard Univ, BS, 40. *Mem:* Am Phys Soc; Am Inst Aeronaut & Astronaut. *Res:* Stress analysis; structural mechanics. *Mailing Add:* 28 Camel Hollow Rd Huntington NY 11743

**WEHMANN, ALAN AHLERS,** PARTICLE PHYSICS. *Current Pos:* physicist I, Meson Lab Sect, Fermi Accelerator Lab, 69-80, scientist I, Magnet Test Facil, 80-82, Tevatron I Antiproton Source Sect, 83-85, SCIENTIST I, RES DIV, FERMI ACCELERATOR LAB, 85- *Personal Data:* b New York, NY, Dec 28, 40; m 68; c 2. *Educ:* Rensselaer Polytech Inst, BS, 62; Harvard Univ, MA, 63, PhD(physics), 68. *Prof Exp:* Res assoc physics, Univ Rochester, 67-69. *Concurrent Pos:* Vis scientist, Inst Physics, Univ Mex, 83. *Mem:* Am Phys Soc. *Res:* Experimental high energy particle physics. *Mailing Add:* Fermilab MS 119 PO Box 500 Batavia IL 60510

**WEHMEIER, HELGE H,** ORGANIC CHEMISTRY. *Current Pos:* PRES & CHIEF EXEC OFFICER, BAYER CORP, 91- *Personal Data:* b Goettingen, Ger, 1943; c 2. *Prof Exp:* Mkt synthetic fibers US & Can, Mobay, 69; mkt mgr, Leverkusen, Ger, 74-78; gen mgr, UK, 78-80, mgr, Org Chem Div, 81-84; head, Indust Photog Div, Agfa-Gevaert AG Subs, 84-89, pres & chief exec officer, 89-91. *Mem:* Chem Mfr Asn. *Mailing Add:* Bayer Corp 100 Bayer Rd Pittsburgh PA 15205-9741

**WEHNER, ALFRED PETER,** TOXICOLOGY, INHALATION TOXICOLOGY. *Current Pos:* PRES, BIOMED & ENVIRON CONSULT CORP, 89- *Personal Data:* b Wiesbaden, Ger, Oct 23, 26; US citizen; m 55, Ingeborg H Miller; c Alfred P Jr, Patricia, Jackie D & Peter H. *Educ:* Johannes Gutenberg Univ, Can Med, 49, DMD, 51, ScD, 53; Acad Toxicol Sci, dipl, 88. *Prof Exp:* Pvt pract, WGer, 51-53; dr dent, Guggenheim Dent Clin, 53-54; dr med dent, 7100th Hosp, USAF, Europe, 54-56; res asst microbiol, Field Res Lab, Mobil Oil Co, Tex, 57-62; sr res scientist biomed res, Biomet Instrument Corp, 62-64; dir & pres, Electro-Aerosol Inst, Inc, 64-67; prof biol & chmn, Dept Sci, Univ Plano, 66-67; res assoc inhalation toxicol, Battelle Pac Northwest Labs, 67-77, mgr environ & indust toxicol, 78-80, task leader indust toxicol, 80-89. *Concurrent Pos:* Fel clin pedodontia, Guggenheim Dent Clin, 53-54; consult, Vet Admin Hosp, McKinney, Tex, 63-65; exec bd, Int Soc Aerosols Med, 70-80; US rep, Int Soc Biometeorol, 72-80; bd dirs, Am Inst Biomed Climatol, 73-90, pres, 84-90, proj dir & prin investr res projs exceeding $15 million; ed, Medicef, Biol Interaction of Inhaled Mineral Fibers & Cigarette Smoke; ed-in-chief, Bull Am Inst Biomed Climat, 88-90; mem, subcomt D221101, Am Soc Testing & Mat. *Mem:* Int Soc Biometeorol; Int Soc Aerosols Med; Sigma Xi; Int Soc Aerobiol. *Res:* Inhalation toxicology; biological effects of electro-aerosols and air ions; bioclimatology; investigation of biological effects of various air pollutants in animal models; author of more than 120 science papers and contributions to science books. *Mailing Add:* 312 Saint St Richland WA 99352. *Fax:* 509-375-5693

**WEHNER, DONALD C,** WATER POLLUTION, ENVIRONMENTAL SCIENCES. *Current Pos:* RETIRED. *Personal Data:* b Middletown, NY, Apr 1, 29; m 50, Marjorie B; c 3. *Educ:* Univ Bridgeport, BA, 51. *Prof Exp:* Biologist, Lederle Div, 51-54 & 56-58, res biologist, Indust Chem Div, 58-69, asst to dept head, Water Treating Chem Dept, 69-70, microbiologist-field engr, 70-74, dist sales mgr, 74-75, tech specialist, Paper Chems Dept, Am Cyanamid Co, 75-91. *Concurrent Pos:* Mem subcomt biol anal of waters for sub-surface injection, Am Petrol Inst, 59-64. *Mem:* Soc Indust Microbiol (treas, 66-68, vpres, 69-70, pres, 71-72); Am Inst Biol Sci; Water Pollution Control Fedn; Tech Asn Pulp & Paper Indust. *Res:* Research and development of industrial algicides, bactericides and fungicides. *Mailing Add:* 4059 Westmoreland Dr S Mobile AL 36609

**WEHNER, GOTTFRIED KARL,** physics; deceased, see previous edition for last biography

**WEHNER, JEANNE M,** SEIZURES, RECEPTOR PLASTICITY. *Current Pos:* ASST PROF PHARM & MOLECULAR GENETICS, INST BEHAV GENETICS, UNIV COLO. *Educ:* Univ Minn, PhD(biochem). *Mailing Add:* Inst Behav Genetics Univ Colo PO Box 447 Boulder CO 80309-0001. *Fax:* 303-492-8063; *E-Mail:* wehne@lbg.colorado.edu

**WEHNER, PHILIP,** INDUSTRIAL ORGANIC CHEMISTRY. *Current Pos:* RETIRED. *Personal Data:* b Chicago, Ill, July 21, 17; m 43, G; c 2. *Educ:* Univ Chicago, PhD(org chem), 43. *Prof Exp:* Res chemist, Gen Aniline & Film Corp, Pa, 43-46; assoc chemist, Argonne Nat Lab, 46-52; chemist, Ciba States Ltd, 52-55; chemist, Toms River-Cincinnati Chem Corp, 55-60, mgr res & develop, 60-64, vpres, 64-68, pres, 68-73; vpres prod & tech develop, Ciba-Geigy Corp, 73-78, vpres tech affairs, Dyestuffs & Chem Div, 78-79. *Mem:* Am Chem Soc; Am Asn Textile Chem & Colorists. *Mailing Add:* 3404 Old Onslow Rd Greensboro NC 27407-7824

**WEHR, ALLAN GORDON,** CHEMICAL ENGINEERING, MATERIALS ENGINEERING. *Current Pos:* RETIRED. *Personal Data:* b Brooklyn, NY, July 31, 31; m 51; c 2. *Educ:* Mo Sch Mines, BS, 58; Univ Mo, PhD(metall eng), 62. *Prof Exp:* Res engr, P R Mallory Co, 59-60; assoc prof metall eng, Miss State Univ, 61-62, prof mat eng & head dept, 62-73, prof chem eng, 73-91. *Mem:* Am Soc Metals; Am Soc Eng Educ; Am Inst Chem Engrs. *Res:* Fracture; magnetohydrodynamics; mechanical behavior of materials; nitrogen oxide generation and control; uses of microwave and radio requency energy. *Mailing Add:* 106 Winsor Rd Starkville MS 39759

**WEHR, CARL TIMOTHY,** BIOCHEMISTRY, GENETICS. *Current Pos:* MGR, CAPILLARY ELECTROPHORESIS APPLNS LAB, BIO-RAD LABS, 89- *Personal Data:* b San Francisco, Calif, Feb 15, 43; m 66, Carol Meyer; c 2. *Educ:* Whitman Col, BA, 65; Ore State Univ, PhD(microbial physiol), 69. *Prof Exp:* Fel microbiol, Dept Bact, Univ Calif, Davis, 69-71; res biologist molecular biol, Virus Lab, Univ Calif, Berkeley, 71-75; dir res chem,

Agr Sci Labs, 75-78; sr chemist biochem, Varian Instruments, 78-80, mgr, High Performance Liquid Chromatography Lab, 80-89. *Concurrent Pos:* Jane Coffin Childs Mem Fund Med Res fel, 69-71; instr, Univ Calif Exten, 89- *Res:* Development of instrumentation and analytical methods for biomedical research and biotechnology. *Mailing Add:* Analytical Systs Div Bio-Rad Labs 2000 Alfred Nobel Dr Hercules CA 94547. *E-Mail:* twehr@bio.rad

**WEHR, HERBERT MICHAEL,** FOOD SCIENCE, MICROBIOLOGY. *Current Pos:* DIR DAIRY PROD STAND, NAT MILK PROD FEDN, 97- *Personal Data:* b San Francisco, Calif, Feb 15, 43; m 67; c 1. *Educ:* Univ Calif, Berkeley, BS, 66; Ore State Univ, MS, 68, PhD(biochem), 72. *Honors & Awards:* Distinguished Serv Award, Gov Mgt Award, 85, 89. *Prof Exp:* Supvr microbiol & food chem, Ore Dept Agr, 71-73, asst adminr, 73-77, adminr lab serv, 78-92, adminr, Export Serv Ctr, 90-92; dir int trade stand, Tac Inc/ Norigen Sci Inc, Washington DC, 92-97. *Concurrent Pos:* Mem, Conf on Interstate Milk Shipments, Nat Lab Comn, 77-; chmn, Ore Comt Synthetic Chem Environ, 77-; adminr, Pesticide Analysis & Response Ctr, 85-; mem, Nat Dairy Coun, Dairy Res Found Sci Adv Comt, 85-88, Nat Comt, Microbiol Criteria Foods, 88-90; mem bd dirs, Asn Off Analytical Chemists, 87-, pres, 90-91. *Mem:* Inst Food Technologists; Asn Off Anal Chemists; Int Asn Milk, Food & Environ Sanitarians; Am Chem Soc; Coun Agr Sci & Technol. *Res:* Food microbiology; food biochemistry; methods development in food chemistry and microbiology. *Mailing Add:* Nat Milk Prod Fedn 1840 Wilson Blvd Arlington VA 22201. *Fax:* 703-841-9328

**WEHR, THOMAS A,** BIOLOGICAL PSYCHIATRY. *Current Pos:* Clin assoc, Sect Psychiat, Lab Clin Sci, Intramural Res Prog, NIMH, 73-75, res med officer, 75-76, psychiatrist, 76, chief, Clin Res Unit, 77-84, CHIEF, CLIN PSYCHOBIOL BR, INTRAMURAL RES PROG, NIMH, 82- *Personal Data:* b Louisville, Ky, Oct 15, 41; m 63; c 1. *Educ:* Yale Univ, BA, 65; Univ Louisville, MD, 69; Am Bd Psychiat & Neurol, 83. *Honors & Awards:* Anna-Monika Found Award, 81, 91. *Concurrent Pos:* USPHS, 73-75, 76-; instr, Washington Sch Psychiat, DC, 76-78; pvt pract psychiat, Bethesda, Md, 77-; vis prof, Univ Naples Med Sch, Italy, 84; adj prof, Dept Biol Sci, Univ Md, 86- *Mem:* Am Psychiat Asn; Am Col Neuropsychopharmacol; Soc Biol Psychiat; Sleep Res Soc; Soc Res Biol Rhythms; Soc Light Treatment & Biol Rhythms. *Res:* Psychobiology; patents; investigate role of sleep and circadian and seasonal rhythms in pathogenesis of recurrent mood disorders. *Mailing Add:* Clin Psychobiol Br NIH NIMH Bldg 10 Rm 4S239 10 Center Dr MSC 1390 Bethesda MD 20892-1390

**WEHRBEIN, WILLIAM MEAD,** RADIATIVE TRANSFER. *Current Pos:* asst prof, 81-85, ASSOC PROF PHYSICS, NEBR WESLEYAN UNIV, 81- *Personal Data:* b Omaha, Nebr, Sept 12, 48. *Educ:* Nebr Wesleyan Univ, BS, 70; Univ Colo, PhD(astro-geophysics), 77. *Prof Exp:* Res assoc postdoctoral, Atmospheric Sci, Univ Wash, 77-81. *Concurrent Pos:* Chair, Physics Dept, Nebr Wesleyan Univ, 85- *Mem:* Am Asn Physics Teachers; AAAS; Am Meteorol Soc; Union Concerned Scientists. *Res:* Planetary atmospheres, especially IR radiative transfer. *Mailing Add:* Dept Physics & Astron Nebr Wesleyan Univ 5000 St Paul Ave Lincoln NE 68504-2760

**WEHRENBERG, JOHN P,** MINERALOGY. *Current Pos:* From asst prof to assoc prof, 55-66, PROF GEOL, UNIV MONT, 66- *Personal Data:* b Springfield, Ill, Aug 10, 27; m 66. *Educ:* Univ Mo, BS, 50; Univ Ill, MS, 52, PhD, 56. *Concurrent Pos:* Vis scientist, FBI Acad, Va. *Mem:* Mineral Soc Am; Geochem Soc; Am Crystallog Asn. *Res:* Forensic mineralogy; crystallography; infrared spectra of minerals. *Mailing Add:* 3828 Lincoln Rd Missoula MT 59802

**WEHRING, BERNARD WILLIAM,** RADIATION PHYSICS, NEUTRON PHYSICS. *Current Pos:* PROF MECH ENG, UNIV TEX, AUSTIN, 89-, DIR, NUCLER ENG TEACHING LAB, 89- *Personal Data:* b Monroe, Mich, Aug 3, 37; m 59, Margaret Robinson; c Mary A, James, Susan & Barbara. *Educ:* Univ Mich, BSE(physics) & BSE(math), 59; Univ Ill, MS, 61, PhD(nuclear eng), 66. *Prof Exp:* From asst prof to prof nuclear eng, Univ Ill, Urbana, 66-84; prof nuclear eng, NC State Univ, 84-89, dir, Nuclear Reactor Prog, 84-89. *Concurrent Pos:* Consult, Construct Eng Res Lab, Champaign, Ill, 70-71, Los Alamos Sci Lab & Argonne Nat Lab, 77-79; sabbatical, Van de Graaff Lab, Oak Ridge Nat Lab, 73-74; mem, Cross Sect Eval Working Group, Fission Prod, Brookhaven Nat Lab, 75- *Mem:* Fel Am Nuclear Soc; Am Soc Eng Educ; Am Phys Soc; Inst Elec & Electronics Engrs; Sigma Xi. *Res:* Fission physics; interaction of radiation with matter; radiation detection; neutron spectroscopy and dosimetry; neutron physics. *Mailing Add:* Nuclear Eng Teaching Lab Pickle Res Campus Austin TX 78712. *Fax:* 512-471-4589; *E-Mail:* wehring@uts.cc.utexas.edu

**WEHRLE, PAUL F,** PEDIATRICS, MICROBIOLOGY. *Current Pos:* prof, 61-71, Hastings Prof pediat, 71-, EMER PROF, UNIV SOUTHERN CALIF; EMER PROF, UNIV CALIF, IRVINE. *Personal Data:* b Ithaca, NY, Dec 18, 21; m 44; c 4. *Educ:* Univ Ariz, BS, 47; Tulane Univ, MD, 47. *Honors & Awards:* Medal of Merit, Int Pediat Asn. *Prof Exp:* Clin instr pediat, Col Med, Univ Ill, 50-51; res assoc epidemiol & microbiol, Grad Sch Pub Health, Univ Pittsburgh, 51-53; res assoc, Poliomyelitis Lab, Johns Hopkins Univ, 53-55; from asst prof to assoc prof pediat, Col Med, State Univ NY Upstate Med Ctr, 55-61, actg chmn, Dept Microbiol, 59-61. *Concurrent Pos:* Asst med supt, Chicago Munic Contagious Dis Hosp, Ill, 50-51; head physician contagious dis serv, Los Angeles Co-Univ Southern Calif Med Ctr, 61-63, chief physician, Children's Div, 63- *Mem:* Am Acad Pediat; Soc Pediat Res; Am Soc Microbiol; Am Pub Health Asn; Am Asn Immunologists. *Res:* Viral infections in man, especially enteroviruses; antibiotic action; epidemiology of infectious diseases. *Mailing Add:* 233 Esplanade San Clemente CA 92672

**WEHRLI, PIUS ANTON,** CHEMISTRY. *Current Pos:* Sr chemist, Hoffmann-La Roche Inc, 67-69, res fel, 69-70, res group chief, 70-73, res sect chief, 73-78, dir, Kilo Lab & Process Res, Chem Res Dept, 78-85, ASST VPRES & DIR TECH & PROD DEVELOP, HOFFMANN-LA ROCHE INC, 85- *Personal Data:* b Bazenheid, Switz, July 27, 33; m 62; c 1. *Educ:* Swiss Fed Inst Technol, Dipl Chem Eng, 64, PhD(chem), 67. *Mem:* Am Chem Soc; Swiss Chem Soc; Soc Ger Chem. *Res:* Development in synthetic organic chemistry. *Mailing Add:* Hoffmann-La Roche Inc Kingsland Rd Nutley NJ 07110-1199

**WEHRLY, THOMAS EDWARD,** STOCHASTIC MODELLING, NONPARAMETRIC FUNCTION ESTIMATION. *Current Pos:* From asst prof to assoc prof, 76-88, PROF, DEPT STATIST, TEX A&M UNIV, 88- *Personal Data:* b Richmond, Ind, Nov 5, 47; m 76; c 2. *Educ:* Univ Mich, BS, 69; Univ Wis-Madison, MA, 70, PhD(statist), 76. *Concurrent Pos:* Vis res fel, Australian Nat Univ, 90. *Mem:* Am Statist Asn; Biometrics Soc; Inst Math Statist; Royal Statist Soc. *Res:* Stochastic modelling for biological systems and statistical inference for these stochastic models; nonparametric function estimation. *Mailing Add:* Dept Statist Tex A&M Univ College Station TX 77843-0100

**WEHRMANN, RALPH F(REDERICK),** ELECTROCHEMISTRY. *Current Pos:* SPECIALIST EXTEN FAC, UNIV MO, 73- *Personal Data:* b Williamstown, Mo, June 24, 18. *Educ:* Culver-Stockton Col, BA, 39; St Louis Univ, MS, 41, PhD(inorg chem), 43. *Prof Exp:* Group leader, Manhattan Proj, 43-47; asst res dir, Fansteel Co, 48-61; res scientist, LTV Corp, 62-67; res dir, Poco Graphite Div, Unocal Co, 68-72. *Mem:* Am Chem Soc; fel Am Inst Chemists; Am Ceramic Soc. *Res:* Coatings for uranium and thorium; isolation and purification of radioactive elements; preparation of and applications for refractory metals, alloys and compounds; refractory oxidation-resistant materials; preparation and properties of synthetic graphite; high temperature chemistry. *Mailing Add:* 212 S Kingshighway St Charles MO 63301-1637

**WEHRMEISTER, HERBERT LOUIS,** CHEMISTRY. *Current Pos:* RETIRED. *Personal Data:* b Chicago, Ill, Nov 8, 20; m 53; c 3. *Educ:* Ill Inst Technol, BS, 44; Northwestern Univ, MS, 46, PhD(chem), 48. *Prof Exp:* Lab asst, Portland Cement Asn, Ill, 38-40; control chemist, W H Barber Co, 40-44; res chemist, Miner Labs, 44-46; res chemist, Com Solvents Corp, 49-77, IMC Corp, 77-86. *Mem:* Sigma Xi; Am Chem Soc. *Res:* Organic chemistry; derivatives of sulfenic acids; syntheses in the thiazole series; nitoparaffin and hydroxylamine derivatives; zearalenone and derivatives. *Mailing Add:* 2711 Deming St Terre Haute IN 47803-2813

**WEHRY, EARL L, JR,** ANALYTICAL CHEMISTRY, SPECTROSCOPY. *Current Pos:* from asst prof to assoc prof, 70-77, PROF CHEM, UNIV TENN, KNOXVILLE, 77- *Personal Data:* b Reading, Pa, Feb 13, 41. *Educ:* Juniata Col, BS, 62; Purdue Univ, PhD(chem), 65. *Honors & Awards:* Meggers Award, Soc Appl Spectros, 82. *Prof Exp:* Instr chem, Ind Univ, 65-66, asst prof, 66-70. *Mem:* AAAS; Soc Appl Spectros; Am Chem Soc; Optical Soc Am. *Res:* Fluorescence and phosphorescence; photochemistry; laser spectroscopy. *Mailing Add:* Dept Chem Univ Tenn Knoxville TN 37916. *Fax:* 423-974-3454

**WEI, CHING-YEU,** MATERIALS SCIENCE ENGINEERING. *Current Pos:* Staff res scientist, 77-89, MGR, GEN ELEC CORP RES & DEVELOP, 89- *Personal Data:* b Tainan, Taiwan, Dec 17, 48; US citizen; c 3. *Educ:* Nat Taiwan Univ, BS, 70; Cornell Univ, PhD(mat sci), 77. *Mem:* Sr mem Inst Elec & Electronics Engrs. *Res:* Amorphous-silicon devices; radiation-hardened micron and submicron CMOS process as well as various infrared detector technologies; manager of a medical imager development program. *Mailing Add:* Gen Elec Corp Res & Develop 1 River Rd Schenectady NY 12309

**WEI, CHUNG-CHEN,** ORGANIC CHEMISTRY, PHOTOCHEMISTRY. *Current Pos:* SR CHEMIST, HOFFMANN-LA ROCHE INC, 74- *Personal Data:* b Taiwan, Apr 9, 40; m 65; c 1. *Educ:* Nat Taiwan Univ, BS, 63; Colo State Univ, PhD(org chem), 69. *Prof Exp:* Fel org chem, Johns Hopkins Univ, 69-71; res assoc bio-org chem, Yale Univ, 71-73; assoc chemist, Midwest Res Inst, 73. *Mem:* Am Chem Soc. *Res:* Synthesis of heterocyclic compounds and natural products; organic photochemistry. *Mailing Add:* Chem Res Dept Hoffmann-La Roche Inc 340 Kingsland St Bldg 76/11 Nutley NJ 07110-1199

**WEI, DAVID TAI-YU,** SUPER-MIRROR FOR LASER SCIENCE, OPTICAL COMMUNICATION. *Current Pos:* PRES, WEI & ASSOCS, 94- *Personal Data:* b Shanghai, China, June 26, 32; US citizen; m 63, Auna Lo; c Alexander. *Educ:* Okla State Univ, BS, 56; Ind Univ, MS, 58; Univ Mass, PhD(physics & astron), 69. *Prof Exp:* Develop physicist, Sarkes Tarzian Inc, 58-60; eng specialist, Westinghouse Res & Develop Ctr, 60-64; mem tech staff, GTE Labs, 69-72; phys scientist, Rand Corp, 72-74; eng specialist & prin investr mirror res, Litton, Guid & Control Div, 74-76, mem tech staff, 76; prin engr, Xerox Corp, 76-85, consult engr, 86-92, staff engr, 92-95. *Mem:* Am Phys Soc; Optical Soc Am; Soc Photo-Instrumentation Engrs; Am Vacuum Soc; Inst Elec & Electronics Engrs; Photonic Soc Chinese-Americans (treas, 96-98). *Res:* Photonic, microelectronic and ionic technologies; achievement having strong impact to science and technology, national and worldwide, is the invention of super-mirror for laser, geological photonic and astronomical sciences. *Mailing Add:* 3715 Malibu Vista Dr Malibu CA 90265-5606. *Fax:* 310-454-3501

**WEI, DIANA YUN DEE (FAN)**, MATHEMATICS. *Current Pos:* RETIRED. *Personal Data:* b Che-Kiang, China, June 8, 30; m 62, Benjamin M; c 1. *Educ:* Taiwan Norm Univ, BS & BEd, 53; Univ Nebr, MS, 60; McGill Univ, PhD(math), 67. *Honors & Awards:* Commemorative Gold Medal Honor, Am Biog Inst, 87. *Prof Exp:* Lectr math, Taipei Inst Technol, Taiwan, 53-58; teaching asst, Univ Nebr, 58-60 & Univ Wash, 60-62; lectr, McGill Univ, 62-65; asst prof, Marianopolis Col, 65-68 & Sir George Williams Univ, 68-72; prof, Sch Comn Baldwin-Cartier, 72-75; prof math, Norfolk State Univ, 75-96. *Concurrent Pos:* Nat Res Coun Can grant award, 69, 70, 71. *Mem:* Am Math Soc; Can Math Cong. *Res:* Groups, rings and modules; homology; category; linear algebra; author of 2 publications. *Mailing Add:* 1152 Janaf Pl Norfolk VA 23502

**WEI, EDWARD T**, PHARMACOLOGY, TOXICOLOGY. *Current Pos:* from asst prof to assoc prof, 70-80, PROF TOXICOL, UNIV CALIF, SCH PUB HEALTH, BERKELEY, 80- *Personal Data:* b Shanghai, China, Dec 6, 44; m 66; c 2. *Educ:* Univ Calif, Berkeley, AB, 65; Univ Calif, San Francisco, PhD(pharmacol), 69. *Honors & Awards:* Merit Award, Nat Inst Drug Abuse, 87. *Prof Exp:* Nat Inst Arthritis & Metab Dis fel, Stanford Univ, 69-70. *Concurrent Pos:* Nat Inst Drug Abuse fel, 70-81; Nat Inst Environ Health Sci fel, 74-76; assoc prof toxicol, Dept Pharmacol, Univ Calif, San Francisco, 75-80, prof, 80-; sr Int Fogarty Fel, 84-85. *Mem:* AAAS; Soc Toxicol; Am Soc Pharmacol & Exp Therapeut. *Res:* Anti-inflammatory peptides; toxic chemicals and their mechanisms of action; biological mechanisms of morphine dependence. *Mailing Add:* Univ Calif Berkeley Sch Pub Health Berkeley CA 94720-0001. *Fax:* 510-642-5815

**WEI, ENOCH PING**, CEREBRAL MICROCIRCULATION, PERIPHERAL CIRCULATION. *Current Pos:* Fel, Med Col Va, 71-73, res assoc med, 73-85, res asst prof med, 85-92, DIR RES, MED COL VA, 81-, RES ASSOC PROF MED, 92- *Personal Data:* b Shanghai, China, July 19, 42; US citizen; m 68, Darien Liang; c Sonya & Micah. *Educ:* Univ NC, Chapel Hill, BA, 67, PhD(physiol), 72. *Mem:* Am Physiol Soc; Int Soc Cerebral Blood Flow & Metab; Am Fedn Clin Res; Microcirculatory Soc; Am Heart Asn. *Res:* Regulatory mechanisms of the cerebral circulation in association with high blood pressure, brain injury, ischemia/reperfusion, and seizure. *Mailing Add:* Med Col Va PO Box 980282 Richmond VA 23298-0282. *Fax:* 804-786-8700

**WEI, GUANG-JONG JASON**, PHYSICAL BIOCHEMISTRY. *Current Pos:* res specialist, 77-80, SCIENTIST, UNIV MINN, ST PAUL, 80- *Personal Data:* b Fu-Chou, China, Mar 14, 46; m 71. *Educ:* Cheng Kung Univ, Taiwan, BS, 68; Univ Ill, Urbana, PhD(phys chem), 74. *Prof Exp:* Res assoc, 74-75, NIH fel phys biochem, Mich State Univ, 75-77. *Mem:* Am Chem Soc. *Res:* Physical chemistry of macromolecules; dynamic light scattering. *Mailing Add:* ECOLAB 840 Sibley Hwy St Paul MN 55118-1700

**WEI, JAMES**, CHEMICAL ENGINEERING. *Current Pos:* head, 77-88, Warren K Lewis prof, 77-91, SR LECTR & EMER PROF, DEPT CHEM ENG, MASS INST TECHNOL, 77-91; DEAN ENG & APPL SCI, POMEROY & BETTY PERRY SMITH PROF & PROF CHEM ENG, PRINCETON UNIV, 91- *Personal Data:* b Macao, China, Aug 14, 30; nat US; m 56; c 4. *Educ:* Ga Inst Technol, BChE, 52; Mass Inst Technol, MS, 54, ScD(chem eng), 55. *Honors & Awards:* Petrol Chem Award, Am Chem Soc, 66; Prof Progress Award, Am Inst Chem Engrs, 70; William H Walker Award, 80, Warren K Lewis Award, 85, Founders Award, 90; First Jack A Gerster Lectr, Univ Del, 71; Peter C Reilly Lectr, Univ Notre Dame, 73; First Richard H Wilhelm Lectr, Princeton Univ, 74; Phillips Lectr, Okla State Univ, 79; M Van Winkle Lectr, Univ Tex, Austin, 83; Stanley Katz Lectr, City Univ NY, 84; BASF Renowned Scientist Lectr, Wayne State Univ, 85; Distinguished Achievement Award, Chinese Inst Engrs, 86; Victor Marquez Award, Inter-Am Confed Chem Eng, 88; Harry G Fair Mem Lectr, Univ Okla, 89. *Prof Exp:* Res assoc, Socony Mobil Oil Co, Inc, 55-65, sr res assoc, Mobil Oil Corp, 65-68, sr scientist, Mobil Res & Develop Corp, 68-69, mgr anal, LRAS Group, Mobil Oil Corp, NY, 69-70; Allan P Colburn prof chem eng, Univ Del, 71-77. *Concurrent Pos:* Vis prof, Princeton Univ, 62-63 & Calif Inst Technol, 65; consult, Mobil Oil Corp, 71-, Batelle Mem Inst, 71-73, Minn Mining & Mfg Co, 73-77, Milliken, 81-84; consult ed, Chem Eng Ser, McGraw-Hill; vis prof, Princeton Univ, 62-63 & Calif Inst Technol, 65; mem, Sci Adv Bd, Environ Protection Agency, 76-79; Fairchild scholar, Calif Inst Technol, 77; chief ed, Adv Chem Eng, 80-; dir, Textile Res Inst, Princeton, NJ, 93- *Mem:* Nat Acad Eng; Am Chem Soc; Am Inst Chem Engrs (vpres, 87, pres, 88); Am Acad Arts & Sci; AAAS; Am Asn Univ Profs; Sigma Xi. *Res:* Catalysis and kinetics; chemical reactors; applied mathematics; structure of chemical processing industries. *Mailing Add:* Sch Eng & Appl Sci Rm C23 Eng Quad Princeton Univ Princeton NJ 08544-5263. *Fax:* 609-258-6744

**WEI, L(ING) Y(UN)**, SOLID STATE PHYSICS, ELECTRICAL ENGINEERING. *Current Pos:* RETIRED. *Personal Data:* b Hangyang, China, May 23, 20; Can citizen; m 44; c 4. *Educ:* Northwestern Col Eng, China, BS, 42; Univ Ill, MS, 49, PhD(solid state physics), 58. *Prof Exp:* Engr, Directorate Gen Telecommun, China & Formosa, 42-56; asst prof elec eng, Univ Wash, 58-60; assoc prof elec eng, Univ Waterloo, 60-63, prof, 63-91, adj prof, 91. *Mem:* AAAS; Biophys Soc; Inst Elec & Electronics Engrs. *Res:* Semiconductor materials; physics of thin films and physical mechanisms of nerve conduction. *Mailing Add:* Waterloo Univ University Ave Waterloo ON N2L 3X8 Can

**WEI, LEE-JEN**, BIOSTATISTICS. *Current Pos:* PROF STATIST, HARVARD, 91- *Personal Data:* b China, Apr 2, 48; c 1. *Educ:* Fu Jen Univ, Taiwan, BS, 70; Univ Wis, Madison, PhD(statist), 75. *Prof Exp:* Asst prof statist, Univ SC, 75-79, assoc prof, 79-80; cancer expert, Nat Cancer Inst, 80-81; prof statist, George Washington Univ, 81-91. *Concurrent Pos:* Comt mem, Nat Res Coun, 82- *Mem:* Am Statist Asn. *Mailing Add:* Dept Biostatist Harvard Sch Pub Health 677 Huntington Ave Boston MA 02115

**WEI, LESTER YEEHOW**, ANALYTICAL CHEMISTRY. *Current Pos:* CONSULT, 91- *Personal Data:* b Foochow, China, Sept 4, 44; US citizen; m 72; c 2. *Educ:* Cheng Kung Univ, BSE, 67; ETex State Univ, MS, 70, EdD(chem), 74. *Prof Exp:* Res assoc chem, Emory Univ 74-76 & Ill Geol Surv, 76-77; res chemist, Ill Natural Hist Surv, 77-91. *Concurrent Pos:* Sr scientist, Sandoz Agro Inc, 92-97. *Mem:* Am Chem Soc. *Res:* Chemistry and analysis of pesticides; gas chromatography; mass spectroscopy; high performance liquid chromatography; methods development; plant and insect metabolism studies. *Mailing Add:* 110 W McHenry Urbana IL 61801

**WEI, LUN-SHIN**, FOOD SCIENCE. *Current Pos:* Asst agron, Univ Ill, 55-57, sci analyst, 57-59, res assoc food sci, 59-64, asoc prof, 64-76, PROF FOOD SCI, UNIV ILL, URBANA, 76- *Personal Data:* b Hou-long, Formosa, Jan 14, 29; m 56; c 4. *Educ:* Taiwan Prov Col Agr, BS, 51; Univ Ill, MS, 55, PhD, 58. *Honors & Awards:* Educ & Res Award, Land of Lincoln Soybean Asn, 73. *Mem:* AAAS; Am Chem Soc; Inst Food Technologists. *Res:* Foods and plant materials analysis; food processing and preservation; product development; food utilization of soybeans. *Mailing Add:* 309 E McHenry St Urbana IL 61801-6672

**WEI, PAX SAMUEL PIN**, PHYSICAL CHEMISTRY. *Current Pos:* res scientist, Boeing Sci Res Labs, 69-71, RES SCIENTIST, BOEING AEROSPACE CO, 72- *Personal Data:* b Chungking, China, Nov 11, 38; US citizen; m 64, Amy J Hsu; c Pamela, Oliver & Regina. *Educ:* Nat Taiwan Univ, BS, 60; Univ Ill, Urbana, MS, 63; Calif Inst Technol, PhD(chem), 68. *Prof Exp:* Mem tech staff, Bell Tel Labs, NJ, 67-69. *Mem:* Am Chem Soc; Am Phys Soc. *Res:* Atomic and molecular spectroscopy; surface science; electron diffraction; laser effects. *Mailing Add:* 6612-129th Pl SE Bellevue WA 98006-4041

**WEI, PETER HSING-LIEN**, MEDICINAL CHEMISTRY. *Current Pos:* RETIRED. *Personal Data:* b Shantung, China, Feb 11, 22; m 48; c 4. *Educ:* St John's Univ, China, BS, 48; Columbia Univ, MA, 53; Univ Pa, PhD, 69. *Prof Exp:* Res chemist, Norwich Pharmacal Col, 52-60; res chemist, Wyeth Labs, Inc, 60-69, sr res chemist, 69-77, group leader, 77-87. *Mem:* Am Chem Soc. *Res:* Pharmaceuticals; synthesis of heterocyclic compounds of biological interest; synthetic approach to studies of chemical compounds as anticancer, antinflammatory and antiallergic agents acting through the immune system of animals and humans. *Mailing Add:* 322 Paoli Pointe Dr Paoli PA 19301

**WEI, ROBERT**, BIOCHEMISTRY, IMMUNOLOGY. *Current Pos:* ASSOC PROF BIOCHEM, CLEVELAND STATE UNIV, 78- *Personal Data:* b Apr 16, 39; US citizen; m 76; c 2. *Educ:* George Washington Univ, BA, 62, PhD(biochem), 72; Georgetown Univ, MS, 69. *Prof Exp:* Prin res chemist clin chem, Wash Ref Lab Inc, 74-75; sr res scientist clin chem, Electro-Nucleonics, Inc, 75-76, sr res scientist immunol, 76-78. *Mem:* Am Bd Clin Chem; Am Asn Immunol. *Res:* Oxygen radical mediated tissue damage. *Mailing Add:* Dept Chem Cleveland State Univ 1983 E 24th St Cleveland OH 44115-2403

**WEI, ROBERT PEH-YING**, APPLIED MECHANICS, MATERIALS SCIENCE. *Current Pos:* assoc prof, 66-70, PROF MECH, LEHIGH UNIV, 70- *Personal Data:* b Nanking, China, Sept 16, 31; m 54; c 2. *Educ:* Princeton Univ, BSE, 53, MSE, 54, PhD(mech eng), 60. *Prof Exp:* Instr mech eng, Princeton Univ, 54-57, res asst aeronaut eng, 58-59; assoc technologist, fracture mech, Appl Res Lab, US Steel Corp, 59-61, technologist, 61-62, sr res engr, 62-64, assoc res consult, 64-66. *Mem:* Am Soc Testing & Mat; Sigma Xi. *Res:* Fracture mechanics; mechanics and metallurgical aspects of fatigue crack growth and stress corrosion cracking; experimental stress analysis. *Mailing Add:* Dept Mech Eng & Mech Lehigh Univ Bethlehem PA 18015

**WEI, SUSANNA**, COMPUTER GRAPHICS, SCIENTIFIC VISUALIZATIONS. *Current Pos:* ASSOC PROF COMPUT SCI, ST JOSEPHS UNIV, 92- *Personal Data:* b Taiwan, Aug 23, 46; US citizen; m 71, William W S; c Stephen, Stanley & Jessica. *Educ:* Univ Wis-Madison, BA, 74, MS, 76; Univ Pa, MSE, 84, PhD(comput & info sci), 90. *Prof Exp:* Sr analyst, Ford Aerospace & Commun Corp, 77-83; asst prof comput sci, Towson State Univ, 90-92. *Concurrent Pos:* Vis researcher, Univ Pa, 90-, US Army Chem Res Develop & Eng Ctr, 91 & 92. *Mem:* Inst Elec & Electronics Engrs Comput Soc; Asn Comput Mach; Sigma Xi. *Res:* Computer graphics, human figure modeling and strength data display; scientific visualization. *Mailing Add:* 5600 City Ave Philadelphia PA 19131-1395. *Fax:* 215-473-0001; *E-Mail:* swei@sju.edu

**WEI, WEI-ZEN**, TUMOR IMMUNOLOGY, VIRAL IMMUNOLOGY. *Current Pos:* res assoc, 80-81, instr, 81-82, CLIN INSTR, DEPT PATH, OHIO STATE UNIV, 83-; ASSOC MEM, MICH CANCER FOUND, 91- *Personal Data:* b Tainan, Taiwan, May 1, 51; US citizen; m 73, Kuang-Chung; c John & Benjamin. *Educ:* Nat Taiwan Univ, BS, 73; State Univ NY, MS, 75; Brown Univ, PhD(biol), 78. *Prof Exp:* Fel, Dept Path, Health Ctr, Univ Conn, 78-79. *Concurrent Pos:* Scientist, Dept Immunol, Mich Cancer Found, 83-86, asst mem, 86-91; adj prof cancer biol, Dept Pharmacol, Wayne State Univ, 90-; mem, Exp Immunol Study Sect, Nat Cancer Inst, 92- *Mem:* Am Asn Immunologists; Am Asn Cancer Res. *Res:* Cellular and humoral immune reactivities during mammary neoplastic progressions; immunomodulation to prevent tumorigenesis from preneoplastic lesions; retroviral superantigen activity. *Mailing Add:* Dept Immunol Mich Cancer Found 110 E Warren Ave Detroit MI 48201-1379. *Fax:* 313-831-7518

**WEI, WILLIAM WU-SHYONG,** STATISTICS, MATHEMATICS. *Current Pos:* From asst prof to assoc prof, Temple Univ, 74-85, dir bus statist, 77-82, chmn dept, 82-87, PROF STATIST, TEMPLE UNIV, 86- *Personal Data:* b Shin-Chu, Taiwan, June 2, 40; m 71, Susanna Fan-Chiang; c Stephen, Stanley & Jessica. *Educ:* Nat Taiwan Univ, BA, 66; Univ Ore, BA, 69; Univ Wis-Madison, PhD(statist), 74. *Concurrent Pos:* Assoc ed, J Forecasting, 85- & J Appl Statist Sci, 92- *Mem:* Am Statist Asn; Inst Math Statist; Int Statist Inst; Royal Statist Soc. *Res:* Time series analysis, forecasting, statistical modelling and applications. *Mailing Add:* Dept Statist Temple Univ Philadelphia PA 19122-2595. *Fax:* 215-204-1501; *E-Mail:* v1000e@vh.temple.edu

**WEI, YEN,** MATERIALS CHEMISTRY, CHEMICAL EDUCATION. *Current Pos:* asst prof chem, 87-91, ASSOC PROF CHEM, DEPT CHEM, DREXEL UNIV, 91- *Personal Data:* b Linchuan, Jiangxi Prov, China, Sept 1, 57; m 86, Jane Cai; c Elizabeth & Robert. *Educ:* Peking Univ, Beijing, China, BS, 79, MS, 81; City Col New York, MA, 84; City Univ New York, PhD(chem), 86. *Prof Exp:* Assoc polymer sci, Dept Mat Sci & Eng, Mass Inst Technol, 86-87. *Concurrent Pos:* Chmn, Polymer Group, Am Chem Soc, Philadelphia Sect, 87-; Drexel res scholar award, Drexel Univ, 88; DuPont young fac award, DuPont Co, 91; chmn, Polymer Group, Am Chem Soc, Philadelphia Sect, 87- *Mem:* Am Chem Soc; Sigma Xi; AAAS. *Res:* Polymer chemistry; electrically conductive polymers; mechanistic studies of polymerizations; nonlinear optical materials; polymer network and composites; solid state organic chemistry; high temperature superconductors biomedical applications of polymers. *Mailing Add:* Dept Chem Drexel Univ Philadelphia PA 19104-2875. *Fax:* 215-895-1265; *E-Mail:* weiyen@duvm.ocs.drexel.edu

**WEIBEL, ARMELLA,** MATHEMATICS, SCIENCE EDUCATION. *Current Pos:* from instr to asst prof, 52-53, ASSOC PROF MATH, ALVERNO COL, 56- *Personal Data:* b Ewing, Nebr, Feb 7, 20. *Educ:* Alverno Col, BSE, 46; Univ Wis, MS, 52. *Prof Exp:* Teacher, St Clara Sch, Ill, 38-48; teacher, Frankenstein High Sch, Mo, 48-50. *Concurrent Pos:* Dir, Alverno Ctr, NSF Minn Math & Sci Teaching Proj, 63-70. *Mem:* Nat Coun Teachers Math. *Res:* Math education. *Mailing Add:* 3333 S 39th St Milwaukee WI 53215

**WEIBEL, CHARLES ALEXANDER,** ALGEBRAIC K-THEORY, HOMOLOGICAL ALGEBRA. *Current Pos:* from asst prof to prof, 80-89, PROF MATH, RUTGERS UNIV, 89- *Personal Data:* b Terre Haute, Ind, Oct 28, 50; m 86, Laurel VanLeer; c Chad & Aubrey. *Educ:* Univ Mich, BS(physics) & BA(math), 72; Univ Chicago, SM, 73, PhD(math), 77. *Prof Exp:* Opers res analyst, Stand Oil, Ind, 70-76; mem, Inst Advan Study, 77-78, 85-86; asst prof math, Univ Pa, 78-80. *Concurrent Pos:* Ed, J Pure & Appl Algebra, 83-; managing ed, 89-; vis prof, Univ Paris VII, 92, Univ Strasbourg, 93. *Mem:* Am Math Soc. *Res:* Algebraic K-theory: computational methods, structural relationships and applications to other research areas, primarily algebra and topology. *Mailing Add:* Dept Math Rutgers Univ New Brunswick NJ 08903. *Fax:* 732-445-5350; *E-Mail:* weibel@math.rutgers.edu

**WEIBEL, DALE ELDON,** agronomy; deceased, see previous edition for last biography

**WEIBELL, FRED JOHN,** BIOMEDICAL ENGINEERING, COMPUTER SCIENCES. *Current Pos:* RETIRED. *Personal Data:* b Murray, Utah, Oct 18, 27; m 49, Carol Finch; c Mark, Carol Lee, Marci & John. *Educ:* Univ Utah, BS, 53; Univ Calif, Los Angeles, MS, 69, PhD(eng), 77. *Prof Exp:* Staff mem eng, Sandia Corp, 53-57, sect supvr, 57-62; chief biomed eng sect, Vet Admin Western Res Support Ctr, 62-67, asst chief biomed eng & comput sci, 67-72, chief, Vet Admin Biomed Eng & Comput Ctr, 72-93. *Mem:* Biomed Eng Soc (secy-treas, 69-). *Res:* Electrical safety in the hospital; management information systems covering all medical research in Veterans Administration; medical instrumentation. *Mailing Add:* 18914 Kinzie St Northridge CA 91324

**WEI-BERK, CAROLINE,** physical properties of polymers, polymer composites, for more information see previous edition

**WEIBLEN, PAUL WILLARD,** GEOLOGY, PETROLOGY. *Current Pos:* Asst prof, 65-71, assoc prof, 71-80, PROF GEOL, UNIV MINN, MINNEAPOLIS, 80- *Personal Data:* b Miller, SDak, Feb 15, 27; m 67, Katharine C Busch; c George & Ann. *Educ:* Wartburg Col, BA, 50; Univ Minn, MA, 52, MS & PhD(geol), 65. *Mem:* Electron Probe Analysis Soc Am; Sigma Xi; Am Geophys Union. *Res:* Petrology, especially the study of gabbroic rocks and associated mineralization; lunar petrology; Precambrian geology; application of electron probe analysis to problems in mineralogy, geochemistry and petrology. *Mailing Add:* 1519 Brook Ave SE Minneapolis MN 55414

**WEIBRECHT, WALTER EUGENE,** INORGANIC CHEMISTRY. *Current Pos:* asst prof, 66-77, ASSOC PROF CHEM, UNIV MASS, BOSTON, 77- *Personal Data:* b New York, NY, June 25, 37. *Educ:* Franklin & Marshall Col, BS, 59; Cornell Univ, PhD(chem), 64. *Prof Exp:* Am Oil fel chem, Harvard Univ, 63-64; asst prof, Mich State Univ, 64-66. *Mem:* AAAS; Am Chem Soc; The Chem Soc. *Res:* Studies involving borazine as a Lewis acid; B-hydroxyborazines; synthesis; silicon-nitrogen bond cleavage in symmetrically and unsymmetrically alkoxylated silazanes; silicon, germanium and tin transamination equilibria. *Mailing Add:* Dept Chem Univ Mass 100 Morrissey Blvd Boston MA 02125-3386

**WEIBUST, ROBERT SMITH,** GENETICS, EVOLUTION. *Current Pos:* from asst prof to assoc prof, 70-81, PROF BIOL, MOORHEAD STATE UNIV, 81- *Personal Data:* b Newport, RI, May 6, 42. *Educ:* Colby Col, AB, 64; Univ Maine, Orono, MS, 66, PhD(zool), 70. *Prof Exp:* Nat Cancer Inst fel, Jackson Lab, 64-65, Nat Inst Gen Med Sci fel, Jackson Lab & Univ Maine, Orono, 68-70, fel, Jackson Lab, 70. *Mem:* AAAS; Am Genetic Asn; Sigma Xi; Genetics Soc Am. *Res:* Mammalian genetics. *Mailing Add:* Dept Biol Moorhead State Univ 1104 Seventh Ave S Moorhead MN 56563

**WEICHEL, HUGO,** LASERS. *Current Pos:* CHIEF SCIENTIST, NICHOLS RES CORP, 89- *Personal Data:* b Selz, Ukraine, July 23, 37; US citizen; m 61, Barbara J Baer; c Christine A & Barbara E. *Educ:* Portland State Univ, BS, 60; USAF Inst Technol, MS, 65; Univ Ariz, PhD, 72. *Prof Exp:* USAF, 60-89, res physicist, nuclear rocket propulsion, Edwards AFB, Calif, 61-63, student arc plasmas, Aeronaut Res Lab, Ohio, 64-65, proj officer laser res, Air Force Weapons Lab, NMex, 65-69, assoc prof & dep dept head physics, USAF Inst Technol, 72-78, aeronaut engr, 78-83, dir physics, Air Force Off Sci Res, 83-87, dep dir, Defense Nuclear Agency, 87-89. *Mem:* Am Phys Soc; fel Int Soc Optical Eng. *Res:* Lasers; optics; laser repair; plasmas; laser radar; optical and infrared sensors. *Mailing Add:* 4533 Gilbertson Rd Fairfax VA 22032

**WEICHENTHAL, BURTON ARTHUR,** ANIMAL NUTRITION. *Current Pos:* ASSOC DIR, PANHANDLE RES & EXTEN CTR, UNIV NEBR, 81-, BEEF SPECIALIST, 87- *Personal Data:* b Stanton, Nebr, Nov 7, 37; m 60; c 1. *Educ:* Univ Nebr, BS, 59; SDak State Univ, MS, 62; Colo State Univ, PhD(nutrit), 67. *Prof Exp:* Beef cattle exten specialist, Univ Ill, Urbana, 67-81. *Mem:* Am Soc Animal Sci; Coun Agr Sci & Technol; Am Registry Prof Animal Scientists. *Res:* Ruminant nutrition. *Mailing Add:* Panhandle Res & Exten Ctr Univ Nebr Lincoln 4502 Ave I Scottsbluff NE 69361. *Fax:* 308-632-1365

**WEICHERT, DIETER HORST,** SEISMOLOGY. *Current Pos:* res scientist, Earth Physics Br, Geol Surv Can, Dept Energy, Mines & Resources, 65-78, res scientist, Pac Geosci Ctr, 78-96, actg dir, 78-96, 88-90, head, Pac Geosci Ctr, 96-97, EMER SCIENTIST, GEOL SURV CAN, DEPT ENERGY, MINES & RESOURCES, 97- *Personal Data:* b Breslau, Ger, May 2, 32; Can citizen; m 62; c 2. *Educ:* Univ BC, BASc, 61, PhD(geophys), 65; McMaster Univ, MSc, 63. *Prof Exp:* Res asst geophys, Univ BC, 60-61, elec eng, Nat Res Coun Can, 61 & geophys, Univ Toronto, 63. *Concurrent Pos:* Vis scientist, Geophys Inst, Univ Karlsruhe, 70, UK Atomic Energy Authority, 71, Inst, Frankfurt Univ, 71 & Fed Rep Ger Seismol Ctr, Graefenberg, 76. *Mem:* Seismol Soc Am; Am Geophys Union; Can Geophys Union. *Res:* Geophysics. *Mailing Add:* 9860 W Saanich Rd PO Box 6000 Sidney BC V8L 4B2 Can. *Fax:* 250-363-6565; *E-Mail:* weichert@pgc.emr.ca

**WEICHLEIN, RUSSELL GEORGE,** microbiology; deceased, see previous edition for last biography

**WEICHMAN, BARRY MICHAEL,** anti-inflammatory drugs, pulmonary pharmacology, for more information see previous edition

**WEICHMAN, FRANK LUDWIG,** EXPERIMENTAL CONDENSED MATTER PHYSICS, PHYSICS EDUCATION. *Current Pos:* From asst prof to prof, 58-94, EMER PROF PHYSICS, UNIV ALTA, 94- *Personal Data:* b Liegnitz, Ger, Sept 23, 30; Can citizen; m 58; c 2. *Educ:* Brooklyn Col, BS, 53; Northwestern Univ, PhD(physics), 59. *Concurrent Pos:* Mem fac, Univ Strasbourg, 65-66; vis prof, Technion, Haifa, Israel, 73-74; sr indust fel, Bell Northern Res Ltd, Ottawa, 81-82. *Mem:* Can Asn Physicists; Am Phys Soc; Solar Energy Soc Can. *Res:* Optical and electrical properties of gallium arsenide with emphasis on the role of defect structures on photoconductivity, luminescence and electroluminescence; solar energy as applied to photovoltaics and greenhouses; creation of real life elementary physics problems for teachers. *Mailing Add:* Dept Phys Univ Alta Edmonton AB T6G 2J1 Can

**WEICHMAN, PETER BERNARD,** PHASE TRANSITION & CRITICAL PHENOMENA, LOW TEMPERATURE PHYSICS. *Current Pos:* Res fel, 86-89, ASST PROF PHYSICS, CALIF INST TECHNOL, 89- *Personal Data:* b Edmonton, Alta, Mar 6, 59; US citizen; m 89; c 1. *Educ:* Univ Alta, BSc, 81; Cornell Univ, MS, 84 PhD(physics), 86. *Mem:* Am Phys Soc. *Res:* Phase transitions and critical phenomena, especially in quantum mechanical systems, including super-fluidity of helium in porous media and thin film conductors; turbulence in fluids and ocean surface waves. *Mailing Add:* 429 Northcliff Rd Pasadena CA 91107

**WEICHSEL, MORTON E, JR,** PEDIATRICS, NEUROLOGY. *Current Pos:* assoc prof, 74-80, PROF PEDIAT & NEUROL, HARBOR GEN HOSP & SCH MED, UNIV CALIF, LOS ANGELES, 80-, PROF PEDIAT, KING/DREW MED CTR, 89-; CHIEF PROF SERV, CALIF CHILDRENS SERV, LOS ANGELES CO, 93- *Personal Data:* b Pueblo, Colo, June 17, 33. *Educ:* Univ Colo, Boulder, BA, 55; Univ Buffalo, MD, 62; Am Bd Pediat, dipl & cert; Am Bd Psychiat & Neurol, dipl & cert child neurol. *Prof Exp:* Intern pediat, Buffalo Children's Hosp, NY, 63; resident, Med Ctr, Stanford Univ, 63-65, fel pediat neurol, 65-67; fel, Med Ctr, Univ Colo, 67-68; clin instr pediat, Med Ctr, Stanford Univ, 68-69, fel develop neurochem, 69-71; asst prof human develop & med, Col Human Med, Mich State Univ, 71-74. *Mem:* Soc Neurosci; Am Acad Neurol; Soc Pediat Res; Child Neurol Soc; Am Fedn Clin Res; Am Acad Pediat. *Res:* Developmental neurochemistry. *Mailing Add:* Calif Childrens Serv 19720 W Arrow Way Covina CA 91724

**WEICHSEL, PAUL M,** MATHEMATICS, GRAPH THEORY. *Current Pos:* from asst prof to assoc prof, 66-75, PROF MATH, UNIV ILL, URBANA, 75-, ASSOC CHAIR MATH DEPT, 93- *Personal Data:* b New York, NY, July 22, 31; m 55, 84, Linda Holm; c Joel, Rae (Spooner), Jeremy, Johanna & Joshua. *Educ:* City Col New York, BS, 53; NY Univ, MS, 54; Calif Inst Technol, PhD(math), 60. *Prof Exp:* From instr to asst prof math, Univ Ill, Urbana, 60-65; NATO fel, Math Inst, Oxford, Eng, 61-62; res fel, Inst Advan Studies, Australian Nat Univ, 65-66. *Concurrent Pos:* Part time consult, Argonne Nat Lab, 63-64; vis prof, Hebrew Univ, Jerusalem, 70-71, Univ Tel Aviv, Israel, 71-72, Weizmann Inst Sci, Rehorot, Israel, 88-89; math coordr, Nat Coord Ctr Curric Develop, Dept Technol & Soc, Col Eng, State Univ NY, Stony Brook, 76-78. *Mem:* Am Math Soc; Math Asn Am. *Res:* Algebra; theory of graphs; theory of finite groups; use of techniques from linear algebra and group theory to study graphs, especially those with many symmetries and those with a high degree of regularity. *Mailing Add:* Dept Math Univ Ill 1409 W Green St Urbana IL 61801. *Fax:* 217-333-9576; *E-Mail:* weichsel@math. uiuc.edu

**WEICHSELBAUM, RALPH R,** ONCOLOGY. *Current Pos:* PROF & CHMN, DEPT RADIATION & CELLULAR ONCOL, PRITZKER SCH MED, UNIV CHICAGO, 84-; HEAD, MICHAEL REESE/UNIV CHICAGO CTR RADIATION THER, 84- *Educ:* Univ Wis, BS, 67; Univ Ill, Chicago, MD, 71. *Prof Exp:* Intern, Alameda Co Hosp, Oakland, Calif, 71-72; resident radiation ther, Harvard Med Sch, 72-75, assoc prof, Harvard Med Ctr, 80-84, assoc prof, Dept Cancer Biol, Sch Pub Health, 83-84. *Concurrent Pos:* Harold H Hines Jr prof & chmn, Univ Chicago, 90. *Mem:* Inst Med-Nat Acad Sci. *Res:* Radiation and cellular oncology. *Mailing Add:* 2031 N Sedgwick Rd Chicago IL 60614-4716

**WEICK, CHARLES FREDERICK,** INORGANIC CHEMISTRY. *Current Pos:* Assoc prof, 58-80, PROF CHEM, UNION COL, NY, 80- *Personal Data:* b Buffalo, NY, Jan 19, 31; m 2. *Educ:* Mt Union Col, BS, 53; Univ Rochester, PhD, 59. *Concurrent Pos:* Fel, Univ Kent, Canterbury, Eng, 71-72. *Mem:* Am Chem Soc. *Res:* Coordination chemistry; radiochemistry. *Mailing Add:* 1338 McClellan St Union Col Schenectady NY 12309-5610

**WEICK, RICHARD FRED,** NEUROENDOCRINOLOGY, REPRODUCTION. *Current Pos:* PROF PHYSIOL, UNIV WESTERN ONT, 73- *Personal Data:* b 1934; m 57, Jean Church; c Carrie & Joel. *Educ:* Tex A&M, BS, BA, 56; Stanford Univ, PhD(physiol), 70. *Prof Exp:* Res scientist, NASA, 59-66. *Concurrent Pos:* Vis fel, Corpus Christi Col, Cambridge, UK, 89-90. *Mem:* Soc Study Reprod; Int Soc Neuroendocrinol; Am Physiol Soc; Can Physiol Soc; Soc Neurosci. *Res:* Neuroendocrine regulation of gonadotropin secretion and the reproductive cycle. *Mailing Add:* Dept Physiol Univ Western Ont London ON N6A 5C1 Can. *Fax:* 519-661-3827

**WEIDANZ, WILLIAM P,** IMMUNOLOGY, MEDICAL MICROBIOLOGY. *Current Pos:* from asst prof to assoc prof, 66-77, PROF MICROBIOL, HAHNEMANN MED COL, 77- *Personal Data:* b Jackson Heights, NY, Jan 30, 35; m 60; c 6. *Educ:* Rutgers Univ, BS, 56; Univ RI, MS, 58; Tulane Univ, PhD(microbiol), 61. *Prof Exp:* NIH fel, 61-64; asst prof immunol & pathogenic bact, La State Univ, 64-66. *Concurrent Pos:* NIH res grant, 64-67 & 75-78; fac res coun fel, La State Univ, 65; Eleanor Roosevelt Int Cancer fel, Fibiger-Laboratoriet, Copenhagen, Denmark, 75-76. *Mcm:* Am Asn Immunologists; Am Soc Microbiol. *Res:* immunity to malaria. *Mailing Add:* Dept Med Microbiol & Immunol Univ Wis Med Sch 1300 University Ave 439 SMI Madison WI 53706. *Fax:* 608-262-8418

**WEIDE, DAVID L,** REGIONAL GEOLOGY, GEOMORPHOLOGY. *Current Pos:* asst prof, 73-78, dept chmn, 80-81, ASSOC PROF, DEPT GEOSCI, UNIV NEV, LAS VEGAS, 78- *Personal Data:* b Jan 9, 36. *Educ:* Univ Calif, AB, 58, MA, 68, PhD(geomorphol), 74. *Prof Exp:* Geologist, Calif Well Logging Co, 58-59; geologist, US Army, 59-61; assoc res geologist, Douglas Aircraft Co, 61-64; mus scientist, Dept Geol, Univ Calif, Los Angeles, 64-73; staff geologist, Archaeol Surv Off, 64-73. *Res:* Geology applied to archaeology, air photo interpretation and related remote sensing; budget and personnel management; mineralogy and petrology; scientific editing; geologic cartography. *Mailing Add:* Dept Geosci Univ Nev 4505 Maryland Pkwy Las Vegas NV 85202-4822

**WEIDEN, MATHIAS HERMAN JOSEPH,** INSECT TOXICOLOGY. *Current Pos:* RETIRED. *Personal Data:* b Narrowsburg, NY, Nov 3, 23; m 54; c 4. *Educ:* Manhattan Col, BS, 46; Cornell Univ, PhD(entom), 54. *Prof Exp:* Chemist, Lederle Labs, Am Cyanamid Co, 46-47; asst entom, Cornell Univ, 47-48 & 51-52, asst prof insecticide chem, 54-59; entomologist, Union Carbide Agr Prod Co, 59-66, res scientist, Explor Insecticide Res, 66-86; scientist, Discovery Res, Rhone-Poulenc Ag Co, 87-90. *Concurrent Pos:* Exclusive consult, 90- *Mem:* Entom Soc Am; Am Chem Soc. *Res:* Action of insecticides and detoxication mechanisms in insects; insecticide research and development. *Mailing Add:* 525 North St Chapel Hill NC 27514-3729

**WEIDENBAUM, SHERMAN S,** CHEMICAL ENGINEERING. *Current Pos:* prof, 68-70, proj mgr & dir, 70-77, PROF PHYS SCI, USCG ACAD, 77- *Personal Data:* b New York, July 8, 25; m 48; c 3. *Educ:* Columbia Univ, BS, 47, MS, 48, PhD(chem eng), 53. *Prof Exp:* Asst chem eng, Columbia Univ, 48-49; sr chem engr, Corning Glass Works, 52-56, sr melting engr, 56-58, res chem engr, 58-66, managing dir UN Proj, Israel Ceramic & Silicate Inst, Haifa, 62-65, proj engr, Corning Glass Works, 65-66, mgr tech serv, Latin Am Area, Corning Glass Int, 66-68. *Mem:* Electrochem Soc; Am Soc Qual Control; Am Chem Soc; Am Inst Chem Engrs; Sigma Xi. *Res:* Solids mixing and processing; paste mixing; pelletizing; applications to glass batch preparation; glass melting; theoretical and practical aspects of solids mixing; industrial statistics; international technical assistance. *Mailing Add:* 17 Fifth Ave Waterford CT 06385

**WEIDENBENNER, CLEMENT,** VARIETY DEVELOPMENT, PRODUCTION SYSTEMS ENHANCEMENT. *Current Pos:* SOYBEAN BREEDER, IMC AGRIBUS-SEED RES, 92- *Personal Data:* b Belleville, Ill, Dec 6, 56. *Educ:* Western Ill Univ, BS, 77; Univ Nebr, Lincoln, MS, 81, PhD(agron), 89. *Prof Exp:* Res technologist, Univ Nebr, Lincoln, 80-89; soybean breeder, Callahan Enterprises, Inc, 89-92. *Mem:* Am Soc Agron; Crop Sci Soc Am; Sigma Xi. *Res:* Increase and secure yield and quality of soybean; varietal improvement through breeding; agronomic research to optimize production. *Mailing Add:* 273 Yankeetown St Mt Sterling OH 43143

**WEIDENSAUL, T CRAIG,** PLANT PATHOLOGY, FORESTRY. *Current Pos:* from asst prof to assoc prof, 70-79, PROF PLANT PATH & FORESTRY, OHIO STATE UNIV, 79- & DIR LAB ENVIRON STUDIES, OHIO AGR RES & DEVELOP CTR, 70- *Personal Data:* b Reedsville, Pa, Apr 4, 39; m 65; c 3. *Educ:* Gettysburg Col, BA, 62; Duke Univ, MF, 63; Pa State Univ, PhD(plant path), 69. *Honors & Awards:* Gov Award, Nat Wildlife Fedn. *Prof Exp:* Plant pathologist, USDA Forest Serv, 63-66; res asst, Pa State Univ, 66-69, fel scholar, 69-70. *Concurrent Pos:* Consult forester & plant pathologist; fel, Indust Applns Ctr, NASA; asst dir, Sch Natural Resources, Ohio State Univ, 90- *Mem:* Soil Sci Soc Am; Am Phytopath Soc; Soc Am Foresters; Am Soc Agron; Sigma Xi. *Res:* Epidemiology of fusarium canker of sugar maple; precipitation quality and effects on terrestrial ecosystems; effects of gaseous and metallic air pollutants on plants and plant disease. *Mailing Add:* 6550 Fredericksburg Rd Wooster OH 44691

**WEIDENSCHILLING, STUART JOHN,** PLANETARY SCIENCE, ASTRONOMY. *Current Pos:* res scientist, 78-, SR SCIENTIST, PLANETARY SCI INST, SCI APPLN, INC. *Personal Data:* b Montclair, NJ, Sept 22, 46; m 73, Susan Olsen; c Anna, Erika & Christa. *Educ:* Mass Inst Technol, BS, 68, MS, 69, PhD(earth & planetary sci), 76. *Prof Exp:* Fel, Dept Terrestrial Magnetism, Carnegie Inst, 76-78. *Mem:* Fel Am Geophys Union; Am Astron Soc; Int Astron Union. *Res:* Origin and evolution of the solar system. *Mailing Add:* 5622 E North Wilshire Dr Tucson AZ 85711. *Fax:* 520-622-8060; *E-Mail:* sjw@psi.edu

**WEIDHAAS, DONALD E,** MEDICAL ENTOMOLOGY. *Current Pos:* RETIRED. *Personal Data:* b Northampton Mass, Feb 12, 28; m 53, Helen Mills; c Katherine A (Carlew) & James A. *Educ:* Univ Mass, BS, 51; Cornell Univ, NY, PhD(entom), 55. *Prof Exp:* Med entomologist, Sci & Educ Admin-Agr Res, USDA, 56-62, asst chief, 62-67, actg chief, 67, dir insects affecting man & animals res lab, 67-84. *Concurrent Pos:* Consult, 85- *Mem:* Am Mosquito Control Asn. *Res:* Chemical and alternative methods of control, resistance studies, physiology, toxicology and biology of insects affecting man or of medical importance; integrated control; dynamics and modelling. *Mailing Add:* 1330 NW 25th Terr Gainesville FL 32605-5117

**WEIDHAAS, JOHN AUGUST, JR,** HORTICULTURE, FORESTRY. *Current Pos:* assoc prof, 67-90, EMER ASSOC PROF ENTOM & EXTEN SPECIALIST, VA POLYTECH INST & STATE UNIV, 90- *Personal Data:* b Northampton, Mass, Oct 13, 25; m 48, 75, Joan M Gaskin; c Martha G (Wile), Lynn D (Hare), Ellen D, Gary A, Jeffrey J, Gail (Robert), Lesley (Michie) & Peter Croot. *Educ:* Univ Mass, BS, 49, MS, 52, PhD(entom), 59. *Honors & Awards:* Award Merit, Int Soc Arboncult, 91. *Prof Exp:* Instr entom, Univ Mass, 51 & 53-59; from asst prof to assoc prof, Cornell Univ, 59-67. *Concurrent Pos:* Collabr, Agr Res Serv, USDA; consult, Elm Res Inst. *Mem:* Entom Soc Am; Entom Soc Can; Int Soc Arboricult; hon mem Soc Munic Arborists; Arboricultural Res & Educ Acad. *Res:* Forest, shade tree, ornamental and beneficial insects; Acarina. *Mailing Add:* 1100 Highland Circle Blacksburg VA 24060-5619

**WEIDIE, ALFRED EDWARD,** GEOLOGY. *Current Pos:* From asst prof to prof, 61-94, chmn, Dept Earth Sci, 67-73, EMER PROF GEOL, UNIV NEW ORLEANS, 94- *Personal Data:* b New Orleans, La, July 31, 31; m 60; c 3. *Educ:* Vanderbilt Univ, BA, 53; La State Univ, MS, 58, PhD(geol), 61. *Res:* Structural geology and physical stratigraphy. *Mailing Add:* Dept Geol & Geophys Univ New Orleans 2000 Lakeshore Dr New Orleans LA 70148. *Fax:* 504-286-7396

**WEIDIG, CHARLES F,** MARKETING, PHARMACEUTICALS INTERMEDIATES. *Current Pos:* sr res chemist, 76-85, PROD MGR, ETHYL CORP, 85- *Personal Data:* b Houston, Tex, Oct 24, 45; m 67; c 2. *Educ:* Tex Christian Univ, BS, 69, PhD(chem), 74; Sam Houston State Univ, MA, 71. *Prof Exp:* Anal chemist, Indust Labs, Ft Worth, 66-69; res fel, Edsel B Ford Inst Med Res, 74-76. *Mem:* Am Chem Soc; Sigma Xi. *Res:* Rapid reaction kinetics and mechanisms of enzyme-catalyzed reactions; synthesis, kinetics and mechanism of hydrolysis of nitrogen base adducts of substituted boranes; transition metal chemistry; homogeneous and heterogeneous catalysis; lubricant additives; fuel additives; polymer synthesis; epoxy and polyurethane chemistry; pharmaceutical chemistry; pesticides; antioxidants. *Mailing Add:* 12348 Schlayer Ave Baton Rouge LA 70816

**WEIDLER, DONALD JOHN,** INTERNAL MEDICINE, CLINICAL PHARMACOLOGY. *Current Pos:* ASSOC PROF & CHIEF DIV CLIN PHARMACOL, SCH MED, UNIV MIAMI, 79- *Personal Data:* b Fredericksburg, Iowa, Sept 26, 33; m 58; c 2. *Educ:* Wartburg Col, BA, 59; Univ Iowa, MS, 62, MD, 65, PhD(physiol, biophys), 69. *Prof Exp:* Intern internal med, Boston City Hosp, 65-66; instr physiol & biophys, Univ Iowa, 66-69; from asst prof & mem grad fac to assoc prof physiol & biophys, Univ Nebr Med Ctr, 69-72; resident internal med, Sch Med, Univ Mich, 72-74, instr pharmacol, 73-77, asst prof internal med, 74-79. *Concurrent Pos:* NIH fel, Univ Iowa, 66-69. *Mem:* Am Physiol Soc; Am Col Physicians; Am Soc Clin Pharmacol & Therapeut; Am Soc Internal Med; Am Col Clin Pharmacol; Sigma Xi. *Res:* Clinicial pharmacology; clinical pharmacodynamics; clinical pharmacokinetics. *Mailing Add:* 3652 Chamblee Dunwoody Rd Chamblee GA 30341

**WEIDLICH, JOHN EDWARD, JR,** mathematics, for more information see previous edition

**WEIDLINGER, PAUL,** CIVIL ENGINEERING, ENGINEERING MECHANICS. *Current Pos:* PRES, WEILINGER ASSOCS, 47-, CONSULT ENG, 48- *Personal Data:* b Budapest, Hungary, Dec 22, 37. *Educ:* Swiss Polytech Inst, MS, 37. *Honors & Awards:* J James Croes Award, 63, Ernest E Howad Award, 85, Brown Medal, 87. *Concurrent Pos:* Vis lectr civil eng, Harvard Univ, 46-, Mass Inst Technol, 64- *Mem:* Nat Acad Eng; Am Inst Aeronaut & Astronaut; NY Acad Sci; Am Soc Civil Engrs. *Mailing Add:* Weidlinger Assocs 375 Hudson St New York NY 10014

**WEIDMAN, PATRICK DAN,** FLUID MECHANICS. *Current Pos:* ASSOC PROF, DEPT MECH ENG, UNIV COLO, 81- *Personal Data:* b Santa Clara, Calif, Nov 18, 41. *Educ:* Calif State Polytech Col, BS, 63; Calif Inst Technol, MS, 64; Univ Southern Calif, PhD(aerospace eng), 73. *Prof Exp:* Fel, Univ Southern Calif, 73-75, res assoc & lectr, 75-81. *Mem:* AAAS; Am Phys Soc; Am Geophys Union; Sigma Xi; Soc Indust & Appl Math. *Res:* Wave theory, stability of fluid flow porus; fluid mechanics; wave propagation theory; stokes flow; porus media flow fluid stability; low-gravity fluid mechanics. *Mailing Add:* Dept Mech Eng, Univ Colo Campus Box 427 Boulder CO 80309-0427

**WEIDMAN, ROBERT MCMASTER,** GEOLOGY. *Current Pos:* from instr to assoc prof, 53-68, dir, Geol Field Sta, 78-86, PROF GEOL, UNIV MONT, 68- *Personal Data:* b Missoula, Mont, Mar 20, 23; m 51; c 4. *Educ:* Calif Inst Technol, BS, 44; Univ Ind, MA, 49; Univ Calif, PhD, 59. *Prof Exp:* Geologist, Stand Oil Co, Calif, 44-47 & State Geol Surv, Ind, 48; instr, Fresno State Col, 49-50. *Mem:* Geol Soc Am; Am Asn Petrol Geologists. *Res:* Geologic remote sensing. *Mailing Add:* 409 King St Missoula MT 59801-8607

**WEIDMAN, ROBERT STUART,** BAND THEORY, SURFACE PHYSICS. *Current Pos:* ASST PROF PHYSICS, MICH TECHNOL UNIV, 80- *Personal Data:* b Philadelphia, Pa, Feb 17, 54. *Educ:* Univ Del, BS, 76; Univ Ill, PhD(physics), 80. *Prof Exp:* Res assoc, Univ Ill, 80. *Mem:* Am Phys Soc; Sigma Xi. *Res:* Band theory and optical properties of semiconductors and insulators; electronic structure of point defects and impurities; theory of heterogeneous catalysis. *Mailing Add:* Dept Phys Mich Tech Univ Houghton MI 49931

**WEIDMAN, SCOTT THOMAS,** RESEARCH & DEVELOPMENT PERFORMANCE ASSESSMENT. *Current Pos:* DIR, TECH ASSESSMENT BD, ARMY RES LAB, 96- *Personal Data:* b Burlington, NJ, Jan 27, 55; m 92. *Educ:* Northwestern Univ, BS & BA, 77; Univ Va, MS, 81, PhD(appl math), 85. *Prof Exp:* Tech mkt specialist, Gen Elec Corp, 77-78; actuarial trainee, Gen Accident Ins, 78-79; postdoctoral mathematician, Exxon Res & Eng Co, 85-86; mem tech staff, MRJ, Inc, 86-89; sr staff officer math sci, Nat Res Coun, 89-92, sr staff officer chem sci, 92-95. *Mem:* Soc Indust & Appl Math; Inst Elec & Electronics Engrs; Sigma Xi. *Res:* Identification of mathematical and chemical science research frontiers; radioactive waste remediation policy. *Mailing Add:* Nat Res Coun Rm HA-476P 2101 Constitution Ave Washington DC 20418

**WEIDMANN, SILVIO,** CARDIAC CELLULAR ELECTROPHYSIOLOGY. *Current Pos:* Assoc prof, 58-68, chmn, 68-86, EMER PROF PHYSIOL, UNIV BERN, 86- *Personal Data:* b Konolfinger Berne, Switz, Apr 7, 21; m 47, Ruth Brandenberger; c Marcus, Bernhard & Simon. *Educ:* Univ Bern, MD, 47. *Hon Degrees:* Dr hc, Univ Paris, Sud, 76; Med Dr hc, Uppsala, 77; DSc hc, Leicester, 82. *Concurrent Pos:* Vis prof, Downstate Med Ctr, State Univ, NY, Brooklyn, NY, 54-55 & Univ PR, 76-77; rector, Univ Bern, 74-75. *Mem:* Hon mem Am Physiol Soc; hon mem UK Physiol Soc; hon mem Iceland Physiol Soc. *Res:* Cardiac electrophysiology using intracellular microelectrodes, ionic fluxes in heart, cell-to-cell coupling in heart. *Mailing Add:* Physiol Inst Univ Bern Buehlplatz Five Bern CH-3012 Switzerland. *Fax:* 41-31-631-4611

**WEIDNER, BRUCE VAN SCOYOC,** CHEMISTRY. *Current Pos:* RETIRED. *Personal Data:* b Pottstown, Pa, Oct 29, 08; m 34; c 2. *Educ:* Pa State Col, BS, 31, MS, 32, PhD(inorg chem), 35. *Prof Exp:* Asst chem, Pa State Col, 32-35, instr arts & sci, Hazleton Undergrad Ctr, 35-37; instr, Univ Alaska, 37-39, asst prof chem, 39-42; asst prof chem, Middlebury Col, 42-46; assoc prof, Utah State Agr Col, 46-47; from assoc prof to prof chem, Miami Univ, 47-79. *Concurrent Pos:* Dir, NSF Summer Sec-Sci Insts Teachers, 60-73; first sem, Miami, 85-86. *Mem:* Am Chem Soc; Soc Appl Spectros; AAAS; Sigma Xi. *Res:* Quantitative and inorganic chemistry (air pollution). *Mailing Add:* 308 University Ave Oxford OH 45056-1354

**WEIDNER, DONALD J,** GEOPHYSICS. *Current Pos:* From asst prof to assoc prof, 72-82, PROF GEOPHYS, STATE UNIV NY, STONY BROOK, 82-, DIR, MINERAL PHYSICS INST, 88-, DIR, CTR HIGH PRESSURE RES, 91- *Personal Data:* b Dayton, Ohio, Apr 26, 45; m 68, Deborah M Ray; c Raymond V & Jennifer L. *Educ:* Harvard Univ, AB, 67; Mass Inst Technol, PhD(geophys), 72. *Honors & Awards:* James B Macelwane Award, Am Geophys Union, 81. *Mem:* Fel Am Geophys Union. *Res:* Large volume high pressure studies with synchrotron radiation; determining the equation of state of earth materials; phase stability fields of minerals. *Mailing Add:* Dept Earth & Space Sci Ctr High Pressure Res State Univ NY Stony Brook NY 11794

**WEIDNER, EARL,** ZOOLOGY. *Current Pos:* from asst prof to assoc prof, 72-86, PROF, DEPT ZOOL & PHYSIOL, LA STATE UNIV, 86- *Personal Data:* b Burke, SDak, Nov 13, 35. *Educ:* Univ SDak, BS, 58, MS, 60; Tulane Univ, PhD(biol), 69. *Prof Exp:* Postdoctoral, Rockefeller Univ, 69-72. *Mem:* Am Soc Cell Biol; Soc Protozool; Invert Path Soc. *Res:* Interactions of intracellular parasites with host cells; interface of host-parasite interaction; microsporidian invasions into host cells. *Mailing Add:* Dept Zool La State Univ Baton Rouge LA 70803-1725

**WEIDNER, MICHAEL GEORGE, JR,** SURGERY. *Current Pos:* PROF SURG, MED UNIV SC, 68- *Personal Data:* b Birmingham, Ala, July 18, 22; m 60; c 1. *Educ:* Vanderbilt Univ, BA, 44, MD, 46; Am Bd Surg, dipl, 56. *Prof Exp:* Instr surg, Sch Med, Vanderbilt Univ, 53-57; from sr instr to asst prof, Sch Med, Western Reserve Univ, 57-62; assoc prof, Med Univ SC, 62-68, asst dean student affairs, 70-72, assoc dean student affairs & proj dir, Area Health Educ Ctr, 72-76, assoc dean, 76-83; chief of staff, Vet Admin Hosp, 76-83. *Concurrent Pos:* Res fel, Vanderbilt Univ, 54-57; chief surg serv, Vet Admin Hosp, Charleston, SC, 66-72. *Mem:* AAAS; Am Col Surgeons; Soc Univ Surgeons; Soc Exp Biol & Med; NY Acad Sci. *Res:* Hemorrhagic shock; animal and human gastrointestinal physiology, especially ulcer disease. *Mailing Add:* 668 Herbert Creek Dr Charleston SC 29412

**WEIDNER, RICHARD TILGHMAN,** PHYSICS, MAGNETIC RESONANCE. *Current Pos:* from instr to prof physics, Rutgers Univ, 47-88, asst dean, Col Arts & Sci, 66-70, assoc dean, Rutgers Col, 70-77 & actg dean, 77-78, EMER PROF PHYSICS, RUTGERS UNIV, NEW BRUNSWICK, 88- *Personal Data:* b Allentown, Pa, Mar 31, 21; wid; c Christopher, Allegra & Timothy. *Educ:* Muhlenberg Col, BS, 43; Yale Univ, MS, 43, PhD(physics), 48. *Prof Exp:* Physicist, US Naval Res Lab, 44-46; lab asst & instr physics, Yale Univ, 43-44, asst, 46-47. *Mem:* Fel Am Phys Soc; Sigma Xi. *Res:* Electron spin resonance; texts in elementary physics; general physics. *Mailing Add:* 1426-E Calypso Ave Bethlehem PA 18018

**WEIDNER, TERRY MOHR,** PLANT PHYSIOLOGY. *Current Pos:* From asst prof to assoc prof, 64-74, PROF BOT, EASTERN ILL UNIV, 74-, CHMN DEPT, 76- *Personal Data:* b Allentown, Pa, May 31, 37; m 62; c 3. *Educ:* West Chester State Col, BSEd, 59; Ohio State Univ, MS, 61, PhD(bot), 64. *Mem:* Am Inst Biol Sci; Am Soc Plant Physiol; Sigma Xi. *Res:* Carbohydrate translocation in higher plants; active ion uptake by roots of higher plants; sulfur dioxide effects on mosses. *Mailing Add:* VPAA Off Eastern Ill Univ Charleston IL 61920

**WEIDNER, VICTOR RAY,** OPTICAL PHYSICS. *Current Pos:* RETIRED. *Personal Data:* b Clarion, Pa, Jan 4, 32; m 67. *Educ:* Clarion State Col, BS, 60. *Honors & Awards:* Bronze Metal Award, US Dept Com. *Prof Exp:* Physicist, Nat Bur Stand, 60-87. *Mem:* Optical Soc Am. *Res:* Infrared spectrophotometry; development of research spectrophotometers and spectrophotometric standards. *Mailing Add:* 24401 Hipsley Mill Rd Gaithersburg MD 20882

**WEIDNER, WILLIAM JEFFREY,** PHYSIOLOGY, EXPERIMENTAL BIOLOGY. *Current Pos:* ASST PROF PHYSIOL, UNIV CALIF, DAVIS, 75- *Personal Data:* b Michigan City, Ind, Jan 21, 47; m 71. *Educ:* Mich State Univ, BA, 68, MS, 71, PhD(physiol), 73. *Prof Exp:* Res assoc physiol, Mich State Univ, 73-74; fel, Univ Calif, San Francisco, 74-75. *Mem:* AAAS; Am Physiol Soc; Sigma Xi; Aerospace Med Asn. *Res:* Cardiopulmonary physiology; acceleration biology; history of science. *Mailing Add:* Sec Neurobiol Physiol & Behavior Univ Calif Davis CA 95616

**WEIER, RICHARD MATHIAS,** MEDICINAL CHEMISTRY. *Current Pos:* res investr, 69-77, from res scientist I to res scientist II, 77-92, SR RES SCIENTIST I, GD SEARLE, 92- *Personal Data:* b Streator, Ill, July 18, 40; m 69, Marilyn Doyle; c 2. *Educ:* Loras Col, BS, 62; Wayne State Univ, PhD(org chem), 67. *Prof Exp:* Res chemist, Ash-Stevens, Inc, 66-67; res chemist, Res & Develop Div, Kraftco Corp, 68-69. *Mem:* AAAS; Am Chem Soc. *Res:* Synthesis of steroids and natural products; aldosterone blockade; diuretics; prostaglandin synthesis; gastric antisecretory agents; carbohydrate synthesis; design and synthesis of inhibitors of platelet-activating factor and cyclooxygenase-2. *Mailing Add:* Searle Res & Develop G D Searle & Co 4901 Searle Pkwy Skokie IL 60077

**WEIFFENBACH, CONRAD VENABLE,** NUCLEAR PHYSICS. *Current Pos:* MEM FAC, PHYSICS DEPT, UNIV MAINE, 80- *Personal Data:* b Oak Park, Ill, Aug 25, 42. *Educ:* Univ Mich, BS, 64, PhD(physics), 70. *Prof Exp:* Res fel, Foster Radiation Lab, McGill Univ, 71-74; vol physics, US Peace Corp, King Mongkut Inst Technol, Bangkok, 76-78; asst prof physics, Kean Col NJ, 78-80. *Res:* Experimental nuclear structure physics. *Mailing Add:* 166 Rodney Ct Madison WI 53715

WEIGAND, WILLIAM ADAM, CHEMICAL ENGINEERING, BIOCHEMICAL ENGINEERING. *Current Pos:* PROF CHEM ENG, UNIV MD, COLLEGE PARK, 88- *Personal Data:* b Chicago, Ill, Oct 26, 38; m 63, Gazella Polinski; c Corinne, Odette & Christye. *Educ:* Ill Inst Technol, BS, 62, MS, 63, PhD(chem eng), 68. *Prof Exp:* Engr res, Esso Res Labs, 63-64; asst prof, Purdue Univ, 67-72, assoc prof chem eng, 72-79; prog dir, NSF, 76-77, 79-83 & 95-96; prof chem eng, Ill Inst of Tech, 83-88. *Concurrent Pos:* Prog dir, NSF, 76-77. *Mem:* Am Inst Chem Eng; Am Chem Soc; Sigma Xi. *Res:* Growth kinetics; dynamic modeling; optimal fermentor type and operation; automatic control of bioreactors; bioremediation of toxic chemicals. *Mailing Add:* Dept Chem Eng Univ Md College Park MD 20742. *Fax:* 301-314-9126; *E-Mail:* weigand@eng.umd.edu

WEIGEL, PAUL H(ENRY), CELL SURFACE RECEPTORS, GLYCOPROTEINS. *Current Pos:* from asst prof to assoc prof, Univ Tex Med Br, Galveston, 78-87, vchmn, 90-93, actg chmn, 92-93, PROF BIOCHEM & CELL BIOL, UNIV TEX MED BR, GALVESTON, 87- *Personal Data:* b New York, NY, Aug 11, 46; m 92, Janet Oka; c Dana, Kelly, Erick & Thomas. *Educ:* Cornell Univ, BA, 68; Johns Hopkins Univ Sch Med, MA, 69, PhD(biochem), 75. *Prof Exp:* Nat Cancer Inst postdoctoral fel, Biol Dept, Johns Hopkins Univ, 75-78. *Concurrent Pos:* Consult, TelTech Inc; Pathobiochem Study Sect, NIH 85-87; prin investr NIH grants. *Mem:* Am Chem Soc; Am Soc Cell Biol; Am Soc Biochem & Molecular Biol; AAAS; NY Acad Sci. *Res:* Receptor mediated endocytosis; cell surface receptors for extracellular matrix molecules; cell recognition and responses to external complex carbohydrate molecules; metabolism of asialoglycoproteins and hyaluronic acid; the role of hyaluronic acid in wound healing; hyaluronic acid synthesis. *Mailing Add:* Dept Biochem & Molecular Biol Okla Univ Health Sci Ctr BMSB 853 PO Box 26901 Oklahoma City OK 73190. *Fax:* 409-772-2034

WEIGEL, ROBERT DAVID, VERTEBRATE ZOOLOGY. *Current Pos:* RETIRED. *Personal Data:* b Buffalo, NY, Dec 31, 23. *Educ:* Univ Buffalo, BA, 49, MA, 55; Univ Fla, PhD(zool). 58. *Prof Exp:* Instr gen biol, Univ Fla, 57; asst prof biol, Howard Col, 58-59; from assoc prof to prof biol, Ill State Univ, 64-83. *Mem:* Sigma Xi. *Res:* Avian paleontology; ornithology; osteology. *Mailing Add:* PO Box 427 Normal IL 61761-0427

WEIGEL, RUSSELL C(ORNELIUS), JR, PLANT TISSUE CULTURE. *Current Pos:* ASSOC PROF, DEPT BIOL SCI, FLA INST TECHNOL, 86- *Personal Data:* b Teaneck, NJ, Dec 10, 40. *Educ:* Univ Del, BA, 62; George Washington Univ, BS, 63; Univ Md, College Park, MS, 68, PhD(plant physiol), 70. *Prof Exp:* Agr res investr, E I du Pont de Nemours & Co, Inc, 64-65; teaching asst bot & plant physiol, Univ Md, 65-69; res biologist, Plant Res Lab, E I du Pont de Nemours & Co, Inc, 69-80, sr res biologist, Biochem Dept, 80-82; adj assoc prof, Dept Bot, Univ Tenn, 82-86. *Mem:* Am Soc Plant Physiol; Sigma Xi; AAAS; Int Asn Plant Tissue Cult; Tissue Cult Asn. *Res:* Various aspects of plant tissue culture; regeneration; mutant selection; micropropagation. *Mailing Add:* Fla Inst Technol Melbourne FL 32901-6988

WEIGENSBERG, BERNARD IRVING, EXPERIMENTAL PATHOLOGY. *Current Pos:* SCIENTIST/PROF, DIV CARDIOVASC SURG, McGILL UNIV & ROYAL VICTORIA HOSP, 91- *Personal Data:* b Montreal, Que, Feb 6, 26; m 50, Audrey Helfield; c 3. *Educ:* McGill Univ, BSc, 49, MSc, 51, PhD(biochem), 53. *Prof Exp:* Res asst biochem, McGill Univ, 49-54, res assoc path chem, 54-62, asst prof, 62-74, assoc prof exp path, 74-91. *Concurrent Pos:* Res assoc, Can Heart Found, 58-66. *Mem:* Fel Am Soc Study Arteriosclerosis; Am Soc Exp Path; Can Atherosclerosis Soc. *Res:* Atherosclerosis from cholesterol and lipoproteins; atherosclerosis from white mural non-occlusive thrombisis; myointimal thickenings from injury; lipid and connective tissue metabolism; pathobiology of aneurysms. *Mailing Add:* 2650 Bedford Rd Montreal PQ H3S 1G1 Can

WEIGHT, FORREST F, NEHROPHYSIOLOGY, NEURPHARMACOLOGY. *Current Pos:* chief, Lab Preclin Studies & Sect Electrophysiol, 78-91, CHIEF, LAB MOLECULAR & CELLULAR NEUROBIOL, NAT INST ALCOHOL ABUSE & ALCOHOLISM, NIH, 91- *Personal Data:* b Waynesboro, Pa, Apr 17, 36. *Educ:* Princeton Univ, BA, 58; Columbia Univ, Col Physicians & Surgeons, MD, 62. *Honors & Awards:* Outstanding Performance Medal, USPHS, 90, Meritorious Serv Medal, 92. *Prof Exp:* Intern med, Univ NC Hosp, 62-63; resident, Mary Imogene Bassett Hosp, 63-64; vis scientist, Univ Goteborg, Sweden, 68-69; chief, Sect Synaptic Pharmacol, NIMH, 69-78. *Concurrent Pos:* Vis fel, Swed Med Res Coun, 68-69; Heritage vis lectr, 89. *Mem:* Am Physiol Soc; Am Soc Pharmacol & Exp Therapeut; Soc Neurosci; Int Brain Res Orgn; Res Soc Alcoholism; Int Soc Biomed Res Alcoholism. *Res:* Cellular mechanisms of communication and information processing in the nervous system; mechanisms of synaptic transmission; mechanisms controlling nerve cell excitability; identification of neurotransmitters; molecular basis of membrane permeability changes; cellular and molecular mechanisms of drug actions. *Mailing Add:* Lab Molecular & Cellular Neurobiol Nat Inst Alcohol Abuse & Alcoholism NIH Bethesda MD 20892

WEIGL, PETER DOUGLAS, ECOLOGY, ANIMAL BEHAVIOR. *Current Pos:* Asst prof, 68-74, assoc prof, 74-80, PROF BIOL, WAKE FOREST UNIV, 80- *Personal Data:* b New York, NY, Nov 9, 39; m 68. *Educ:* Williams Col, AB, 62; Duke Univ, PhD(vert ecol), 69. *Mem:* AAAS; Am Soc Zoologists; Am Soc Mammal; Ecol Soc Am; Soc Study Evolution; Sigma Xi. *Res:* Vertebrate zoology; evolution; energetics of behavior; species interactions, functional morphology. *Mailing Add:* Dept Biol Wake Forest Univ 2240 Reynolds Rd Winston-Salem NC 27106-5193

WEIGLE, JACK LEROY, PLANT BREEDING. *Current Pos:* RETIRED. *Personal Data:* b Montpelier, Ohio, Sept 5, 25; m 54; c 4. *Educ:* Purdue Univ, BS, 50, MS, 54; Mich State Univ, PhD, 56. *Prof Exp:* Asst prof hort, Colo State Univ, 56-61; from asst prof to assoc prof, Iowa State Univ, 61-73, prof hort, 73-90. *Mem:* Am Soc Hort Sci; Am Genetic Asn. *Res:* Genetic, cytogenetic and physiological investigations and development of new cultivars of ornamental plants. *Mailing Add:* 48 Cottage St Fredonia NY 14063

WEIGLE, ROBERT EDWARD, APPLIED MECHANICS, APPLIED MATHEMATICS. *Current Pos:* DIR, PHYS SCI LAB, NMEX STATE UNIV, 88- *Personal Data:* b Shiloh, Pa, Apr 27, 27; m 49, Mona J Long; c Geoffrey R. *Educ:* Rensselaer Polytech Inst, BCE, 51, MS, 57, PhD, 59. *Honors & Awards:* Crozier Prize, 85; Presidential Citations, 65, 78 & 82. *Prof Exp:* Eng consult, 52-54; construct supt, Long Serv Co, Inc, 54-55; assoc res scientist, Dept Mech, Rensselaer Polytech Inst, 55-59; res dir, Res Lab, US Army, 59-62, tech dir, Benet Weapons Lab, 62-69, dir lab, Watervliet Arsenal, 69-77, chief scientist, Benet Weapons Lab, 70-77, tech dir, Armament Res & Develop Command, 77-82, dir, Army Res Off, 82-88. *Concurrent Pos:* Consult high pressure technol comt, Nat Res Coun, 60-61; Army mem gun tube technol comt, Mat Adv Bd, 67-69; mem, Adv Panel Weapons & Mat, NATO, 60-67, consult, Adv Group Aeronaut Res & Develop-Struct & Mat Panel, 71; mem, Dept Defense Forum Phys & Eng Sci; mem, Army Res Coun, 68-70, US Army Mat Command Tech Adv Bd, 77-84, actg dep Res & Tech, 83, chmn, reorganization study panel, 84, Dept Defense Comt Res, 82-88; mem, Army Sci Bd, 90- *Mem:* Nat Soc Prof Eng; Soc Exp Mech; AAAS; Am Defense Preparedness Asn; Am Acad Mech; Am Soc Mech Engrs; Sigma Xi. *Res:* Fatigue and fracture behavior of high strength alloy steels as applied to high performance, large caliber weapons and related equipment; mechanical behavior of hi-performance composite materials. *Mailing Add:* 607 Upper Sondley Asheville NC 28805. *Fax:* 505-522-9434

WEIGLE, WILLIAM O, IMMUNOLOGY, CELL BIOLOGY. *Current Pos:* assoc mem, Scripps Clin & Res Found, 61-63, mem dept, 63-82, chmn, Dept Immunopathol, 78-82, vchmn dept, 82-85, MEM, DEPT IMMUNOL, SCRIPPS CLIN & RES FOUND, 82-, HEAD, DIV CELLULAR IMMUNOL, 84-, CHMN DEPT, 85- *Personal Data:* b Monaca, Pa, Apr, 28, 27; div; c 2. *Educ:* Univ Pittsburgh, BS, 50, MS, 51, PhD(bact), 56. *Honors & Awards:* Parke-Davis Award, Am Soc Exp Path, 67. *Prof Exp:* Res technician, Dept Path, Sch Med, Univ Pittsburgh, 51-52, res assoc, 55-58, asst res prof, 58-59, asst prof immunochem, 59-61. *Concurrent Pos:* USPHS fel, 56-59, sr res fel, 59-61, career res award, 62-; adj assoc prof, Univ Calif, San Diego, 61-67, adj prof biol, 67- *Mem:* Am Soc Microbiol; Am Asn Immunologists; Am Soc Exp Path; Am Acad Allergy; NY Acad Sci. *Res:* Mechanisms involved in immunity and diseases of hypersensitivity; immunochemistry; immunopathology. *Mailing Add:* Dept Immunol IMM9 Scripps Res Inst 10666 N Torrey Pines Rd La Jolla CA 92037-1092. *Fax:* 619-554-6705

WEIGMAN, BERNARD J, ENGINEERING PHYSICS, COMPUTER SCIENCE. *Current Pos:* From instr to assoc prof physics, Loyola Col, 58-67, chmn, Dept Math, 60-64 & chmn, Dept Physics & Eng, 64-73, PROF PHYSICS, LOYOLA COL, MD, 67- *Personal Data:* b Baltimore, Md, Nov 18, 32; m 60; c 4. *Educ:* Loyola Col, Md, BS, 54; Univ Notre Dame, PhD(physics), 59. *Concurrent Pos:* Consult, Martin Co, 59-61 & Westinghouse Corp, 74-, dir, Master Eng Sci Digital Systs. *Mem:* Am Asn Physics Teachers; Asn Comput Mach. *Res:* Optical and electrical properties of thin films; behavior of an aerosol system; thermoelectric, photoelectric and field emission of electrons; properties of molecules; small computer systems; real time data collection. *Mailing Add:* Dept Eng Sci Loyola Col 4501 N Charles St Baltimore MD 21210-2601. *Fax:* 410-617-2157; *E-Mail:* bjw@loyola.edu

WEIGMANN, HANS-DIETRICH H, TEXTILE CHEMISTRY. *Current Pos:* fel, Textile Res Inst, Princeton, 61-63, sr scientist, 63-67, assoc dir chem res, 67-70, ASSOC DIR RES, TEXTILE RES INST, PRINCETON, 70- *Personal Data:* b Rostock, Ger, Jan 12, 30; m, Christa; c Stefanie & Jessica. *Educ:* Univ Hamburg, Ger, Vordiplom, 54; dipl org chem, 58; Tech Sch, Aachen, Ger, Dr rer nat, 60. *Honors & Awards:* Olney Medal, Am Asn Textile Chemists & Colorists, 90. *Prof Exp:* Scientist, Ger Wool Res Inst, 60-61. *Concurrent Pos:* Chmn, Gordon Res Conf Fiber Sci, 75; mem, Div Cellulose, Wood & Fiber Chem & Div Org Coatings & Plastics Chem, Am Chem Soc. *Mem:* Am Chem Soc; Am Asn Textile Chemists & Colorists. *Res:* Applied dyeing theory. *Mailing Add:* Textile Res Inst PO Box 625 Princeton NJ 08540

WEIHAUPT, JOHN GEORGE, ASTROGEOLOGY, NATURAL SCIENCE. *Current Pos:* VCHANCELLOR, ACAD AFFAIRS, & PROF GEOL, UNIV COLO, DENVER, 82- *Personal Data:* b La Crosse, Wis, Mar 5, 30; m 61, Audrey Reis. *Educ:* Univ Wis, BS, 52, MS, 53 & 71, PhD(geomorphol), 73. *Honors & Awards:* Mountain in Victoria Land, Antarctica, named in honor, Mt Weihaupt, 66. *Prof Exp:* Teaching asst geol, Univ Wis, 52-53, res asst, 53-54; explor geologist, Anaconda Co, 56-57; seismologist, United Geophys Corp, 57-58; geophysicist, Arctic Inst NAm & NSF, 58-63; chmn, Dept Phys & Biol Sci, US Armed Forces Inst, Madison, 63-73; asst dean, Grad Sch Sci, Ind Univ-Purdue Univ, 73-78; prof geol, vpres Univ Res Found, dean grad studies, San Jose State Univ, 78-82. *Concurrent Pos:* Explor geologist, Am Smelting & Ref Co, 53; codiscoverer, USARP Range, Antarctica, 59-60; lectr, Univ Wis-Madison, 63-73; hon mem, Exped Polaire Francais; mem, Man/Environ Commun Ctr, Community Coun Pub TV & Int Coun Corresp Educ; sci consult, McGraw-Hill Book Co, 65, geol consult, 68-; sci consult, Holt, Rinehart & Winston, Inc, 65-; ed & consult, John Wiley & Sons, 68; vpres, Univ Res Found, San Jose State Univ; liaison rep, AAAS; prof geol, assoc dean acad affairs, Ind Univ, Ind, 73-78. *Mem:* AAAS; Am Geophys Union; fel Geol Soc Am; fel Explorers Club; Int Soc Study Time. *Res:* Polar studies; astrogeology; gravity; impact phenomena; ancient explorations and maps; discoverer of the Wilkes Land Anomaly, Victoria Land, Antartica; author of seven books and 50 research articles. *Mailing Add:* Univ Colo PO Box 173346 Denver CO 80217-3364. *Fax:* 303-556-6197; *E-Mail:* jweihaup@carbon.cudenver.edu

**WEIHER, JAMES F,** CATALYSIS. *Current Pos:* CONSULT, 86- *Personal Data:* b Waverly, Iowa, Mar 30, 33; m 75, Carolyn Smith. *Educ:* Carleton Col, BA, 55; Iowa State Univ, PhD(phys chem), 61. *Prof Exp:* Res chemist, Los Alamos Sci Lab, 55; res chemist, Study Group Radiochem, Max Planck Inst, Mainz, Ger, 55-57; res asst, Inst Atomic Res, Iowa State Univ, 57-61; fel, E I Du Pont de Nemours & Co, Inc, 61-62, Cent Res Dept, 62-86. *Concurrent Pos:* Fulbright fel, JohannesGuttenberg Univ, 55-57. *Res:* Nuclear chemistry and radiochemistry; kinetics; molecular structure; solid state; Mossbauer effect; magnetic susceptibility; catalysis; lab automation and control. *Mailing Add:* 8 Pinecrest Dr Wilmington DE 19810-1414. *E-Mail:* weiher@udel.edu

**WEIHING, JOHN LAWSON,** PLANT PATHOLOGY. *Current Pos:* RETIRED. *Personal Data:* b Rocky Ford, Colo, Feb 26, 21; m 48; c 4. *Educ:* Colo Agr & Mech Col, BS, 42; Univ Nebr, MS, 49, PhD(bot), 54. *Prof Exp:* Assoc plant path, Agr Exten, Univ Nebr; Lincoln, 49-50, exten plant pathologist, 50-64, dir, Panhandle Sta, 71-84, prof plant path, 60-85. *Concurrent Pos:* Mem Univ Nebr group, Agency Inst Develop, 64- *Mem:* Bot Soc Am; Am Phytopath Soc; AAAS; Am Inst Biol Sci. *Res:* Epidemiology of plant diseases. *Mailing Add:* 1605 Holly Dr Gering NE 69341

**WEIHING, ROBERT RALPH,** BIOCHEMISTRY, CELL BIOLOGY. *Current Pos:* RESIDENT PATH, UNIV MD, 89- *Personal Data:* b Ft Collins, Colo, Jan 14, 38. *Educ:* Rice Univ, BA, 59; Johns Hopkins Univ, PhD(biochem), 65, MD, 67. *Prof Exp:* Staff assoc, NIH, 68-71; staff scientist, Worcester Found Exp Biol, 71-77, sr scientist cell biol, 77-85; res prof biol, Clark Univ, 85-88. *Concurrent Pos:* Am Cancer Soc res scholar, 77-80. *Mem:* Am Soc Cell Biol; Am Soc Biochem & Molecular Biol. *Res:* Molecular basis of movement in non-muscle cells. *Mailing Add:* 600 S Curson Ave Apt 505 Los Angeles CA 90036-5800

**WEIHS, DANIEL,** AEROSPACE ENGINEERING. *Current Pos:* Dean fac aerospace eng, 87-88, dir, S Neaman Inst Advan Studies Sci & Technol, 90-95, DEAN, GRAD SCH, TECHNION ISRAEL INST TECHNOL, HAIFA, ISRAEL, PROF, FAC AEROSPACE ENG. *Personal Data:* b Kweilin, China, Oct 29, 42; m 67, Nira; c 3. *Educ:* Technion Israel Inst Technol, BSc, 64; MSc, 68, DSc(aeronaut eng), 71. *Concurrent Pos:* Bd dirs, Bet Shemesh Engines, 82-84, Israel Aircraft Indust, 87-91 & Israel Oceanog & Limnol Corp; chmn, Sci Space Prog Comt, 87-89; mem, Israel Space Agency Exec Nat Space Infrastruct Comt & Nat Comt Space Res; bd govs, Ben Gurion Univ. *Mem:* Foreign assoc Nat Acad Eng. *Res:* Aerodynamics; biological fluid dynamics; aerospace engineering management; policy research. *Mailing Add:* Grad Sch Technion-Israel Inst Technol Technion City Haifa 32000 Israel. *Fax:* 972-4-8221600; *E-Mail:* dweihs@tx.technion.ac.il

**WEIJER, JAN,** GENETICS. *Current Pos:* RETIRED. *Personal Data:* b Heerenveen, Neth, Jan 28, 24; m 52. *Educ:* Univ Groningen, BSc, 51, MSc, 52, DSc, 54. *Prof Exp:* Asst genetics, Univ Groningen, 46-52 & exp embryol, 51-52; geneticist, Firestone Bot Res Inst, 52-54, Can, 55-57; prof hort, Univ Alta, 57-59, chmn, Dept Genetics, 67-69, prof genetics, 60-80. *Concurrent Pos:* Lectr, Neth, 59; consult, US AEC, 67; mem coun, Int Orgn Pure & Appl Biophys. *Mem:* AAAS; Radiation Res Soc; Am Genetic Assn; Genetics Soc Am; NY Acad Sci. *Res:* Microbial genetics and cytology, especially fine structure of the gene; biochemical genetics and mutation; biological assessment of radiation damage in humans. *Mailing Add:* 10939 82nd Ave Suite 201 Edmonton AB T6G 0S7 Can

**WEIK, MARTIN H, JR,** PHYSICS, ELECTRICAL ENGINEERING. *Current Pos:* SYSTS ANALYST, DYNAMIC SYSTS, INC, 81- *Personal Data:* b New York, NY, Oct 5, 22; m 43; c 6. *Educ:* City Col New York, BS, 49; Columbia Univ, MS, 51; George Washington Univ, DSc, 79. *Honors & Awards:* Meritorious Civilian Serv Award, US Army. *Prof Exp:* Asst eng, Columbia Univ, 49-52; designer electronic digital comput, Ballistic Res Labs, Aberdeen Proving Ground, Md, 53-64; chief res & eng systs br & off chief res & develop, US Army Res Off, 64-69, chief data mgt div, 69-73; eng systs analyst, US Mil Commun Electronics Bd, Defense Commun Agency, 73-79. *Concurrent Pos:* Chief US deleg, Int Orgn Standardization Tech Comt 97, subcomt 1 vocabulary, 61-; chmn, Am Nat Standards Inst Tech Comt X3K5 Vocabulary. *Mem:* AAAS; Inst Elec & Electronics Engrs; Asn Advan Med Instrumentation. *Res:* Logical design of electronic digital computers; design and development of technical information systems; information processing and computer language and vocabulary development; fiber optics. *Mailing Add:* Hwy 606 Gladstone VA 24553

**WEIKEL, JOHN HENRY, JR,** TOXICOLOGY. *Current Pos:* RETIRED. *Personal Data:* b Palmerton, Pa, June 14, 29. *Educ:* Trinity Col, Conn, BS, 51; Univ Rochester, PhD(pharmacol), 54. *Prof Exp:* Res assoc, AEC Proj, Univ Rochester, 51-54; pharmacologist, Div Pharmacol, Food & Drug Admin, 54-56; sr pharmacologist, Mead Johnson & Co, 56-58, group leader, 58-59, sect leader, 59-61, asst dept dir, Res Ctr, 61-62, dir, Chem Pharmacol & Safety Eval, 62-68, dir path & toxicol, 68-89. *Mem:* Am Chem Soc; Soc Exp Biol & Med; Am Soc Pharmacol & Exp Therapeut; Soc Toxicol; NY Acad Sci. *Res:* Inorganic metabolism; drug metabolism; toxicology. *Mailing Add:* 3201 Johnson Rd Mt Vernon IN 47620-9570

**WEIL, ANDRE,** MATHEMATICS. *Current Pos:* EMER PROF MATH, INST ADVAN STUDY, 76- *Educ:* Univ Paris, Doctorate, 28. *Honors & Awards:* Kyoto Prize in Basic Sci, 94. *Mem:* Nat Acad Sci. *Res:* Branches of number theory and algebraic geometry; created theorem of mathematical conjecture, called the Riemann hypothesis; Weil conjectures; unification of arithmetic, algebra, geometry and topology; researching the history of mathematics including editing the works of Jacques Bernoulli and Pierre de Fermat. *Mailing Add:* Sch Math Inst Advan Study Princeton NJ 08540

**WEIL, ANDREW THOMAS,** MEDICINE, ETHNOPHARMACOLOGY. *Current Pos:* LECTR, UNIV ARIZ, COL MED, 83-, DIR, PROG INTEGRATIVE MED, 96- *Personal Data:* b Philadelphia, Pa, June 8, 42; m 90, Sabine Kremp; c Diana D. *Educ:* Harvard Col, AB, 64; Harvard Med Sch, MD, 68. *Honors & Awards:* Norman E Zinberg Award for Achievement in Med, 90. *Prof Exp:* Inst Current World Affairs fel, 71-75; res assoc ethnopharmacol, Harvard Bot Mus, 71-84. *Concurrent Pos:* Pres, Ctr Integrataive Med, 93- *Mem:* Sigma Xi. *Res:* Ethnopharmacology, especially native uses of psychoactive and medicinal plants; drug abuse; herbal medicine; alternative and holistic medicine; altered states of consciousness; mind body interactions. *Mailing Add:* Div Social Perspectives Med Ariz Health Sci Ctr Col Med Tucson AZ 85724. *Fax:* 520-797-8974

**WEIL, BENJAMIN HENRY,** CHEMICAL ENGINEERING, COMMUNICATIONS. *Current Pos:* RETIRED. *Personal Data:* b St Joseph, Mo, July 8, 16; m 44; c Lewis, Jeanne (Nimmo) & Carolyn (Arndt). *Educ:* Univ Mo, Columbia, BS, 39; Univ Wis-Madison, MS, 40. *Honors & Awards:* Patterson-Crane Award, Am Chem Soc, 77, Herman Skolnik Award, 81; Miles Conrad lectr, Nat Fedn Abstracting & Indexing Serv, 78. *Prof Exp:* Head, Info Sect & chem mkt researcher, Chem Div, Gulf Res & Develop Co, 40-45; mgr, Info Serv Div, Eng Exp Sta, Ga Inst Technol, 45-50; mgr info serv, Ethyl Corp Res Labs, 50-57; head, Tech Info Sect, Exxon Res & Eng Co, 57-72, sr staff adv & monographs ed, 72-82; info consult, 82-90. *Concurrent Pos:* Trustee, Eng Index Inc, 64-79, dir, 65-68 & vpres, 65-67; creator, Copyright Clearance Ctr, Asn Am Publ, 77, vpres, 77-80; mem bd, Int Coun Sci Unions, 77-88, US Nat Rep Abstr Bd, Nat Acad Sci-Nat Res Coun, 78-81. *Mem:* Am Chem Soc; Nat Fedn Abstr & Info Serv (secy, 68-69 & 72-73, treas, 71-72, pres, 75-76); Info Indust Asn; Spec Libr Asn. *Res:* Information-center management and design; information systems; copyright-compliance operations; internal-reporting operations and systems; technical writing, editing and publishing. *Mailing Add:* 4 Wells Lane Warren NJ 07059-5311

**WEIL, CARROL S,** BIOMETRICS-BIOSTATISTICS. *Current Pos:* CONSULT, CARROL S WEIL, INC, 83- *Personal Data:* b St Joseph, Mo, Dec 16, 17; m 40; c 2. *Educ:* Univ Mo, BA, 39, MA, 40. *Honors & Awards:* Herbert E Stokinger Lectr & Award, Am Conf Govt Indust Hygienists, 84; George H Scott Award, Toxicol Forum, 84; Merit Award, Soc Toxicol, 85. *Prof Exp:* Bacteriologist, Anchor Serum Co, Mo, 41-42; res assoc & toxicologist, Carnegie-Mellon Univ, 42-43; unit head, Manhattan Div, Univ Rochester, 43-45; fel, Carnegie-Mellon Univ, 45-52, chief toxicologist & fel, Carnegie-Mellon Res Inst, 52-80; corp fel, Bushy Run Res Ctr, Union Carbide Corp, 80-82. *Concurrent Pos:* Ambassador Toxicol, Soc Toxicol, 89. *Mem:* Am Chem Soc; Am Indust Hyg Asn; Biomet Soc; distinguished fel Soc Toxicol (secy, 63-67, pres, 68-69). *Res:* Chemical hygiene and toxicology; biometrics. *Mailing Add:* 4326 McCaslin St Pittsburgh PA 15217-2831

**WEIL, CLIFFORD EDWARD,** REAL ANALYSIS. *Current Pos:* from asst prof to assoc prof, 66-78, PROF MATH, MICH STATE UNIV, 78- *Personal Data:* b East Chicago, Ind, Nov 19, 37; m 60; c 3. *Educ:* Wabash Col, BA, 59; Purdue Univ, MS, 61, PhD(math), 63. *Prof Exp:* Instr math, Princeton Univ, 63-64 & Univ Chicago, 64-66. *Concurrent Pos:* Vis prof math, Philipps-Univ, WGer, 73-74. *Mem:* Am Math Soc; Math Asn Am. *Res:* Functions of a real variable. *Mailing Add:* Dept Math A231 Mich State Univ East Lansing MI 48824-1027

**WEIL, EDWARD DAVID,** ORGANIC CHEMISTRY, POLYMER CHEMISTRY. *Current Pos:* CONSULT, INTERTECH SERV, 86-; RES PROF, POLYTECH UNIV, BROOKLYN, NY, 88- *Personal Data:* b Philadelphia, Pa, June 13, 28; m 52; c David & Claudia. *Educ:* Univ Pa, BS, 50; Univ Ill, MS, 51, PhD(org chem), 53; Pace Univ, MBA, 82. *Honors & Awards:* IR-100 Award, Indust Res Inst, 74. *Prof Exp:* Res & develop chemist, Hooker Electrochem Co, 53-56, supvr agr chem res, Hooker Chem Corp, 56-65; supvr org res, Stauffer Chem Co, Dobbs Ferry, 65-69, sr res assoc, 69-76, sr scientist, 76-86. *Mem:* Am Chem Soc; Sigma Xi; Soc Plastics Engrs. *Res:* Vinyl polymers; organic sulfur; chlorine derivatives; pesticides; organic phosphorus; rubber chemicals; flame retardants; textile chemicals; polymer additives; research planning; specialty chemicals and polymers. *Mailing Add:* 200 E 57th St Apt 5L New York NY 10022. *Fax:* 718-260-3136; *E-Mail:* ewail@poly.edu

**WEIL, FRANCIS ALPHONSE,** ENVIRONMENT & ENERGY CONSERVATION, RADIO-ACTIVE MATERIALS. *Current Pos:* dean sci & eng, 80-90, PROF PHYSICS, UNIV MONCTON, 68- *Personal Data:* b Selestat, France, Nov 5, 38; Can citizen; m 96, Anne Albert; c Olivier & Sarah-Nadine. *Educ:* Univ Strasbourg, BSc, 58; Univ Paris, DiplEng, 61; Dalhousie Univ, MSc, 62, PhD(physics), 68. *Honors & Awards:* Prix Schlumberger Award, 89. *Prof Exp:* Teaching asst math, Univ Paris at the Sorbonne, France, 60-61; res asst physics, Saclay Nuclear Res Ctr, France, 66-67. *Concurrent Pos:* Fel, Killam Found, 68; Nat Res Coun grant, Univ Moncton, 69-70, Univ Res Coun, 70-72; Fisheries & Oceans, Can, grant, 89, 90-91; dir, Sci Peace. *Mem:* Can Asn Physicists; Fr-Can Asn Advan Sci; Am Asn Physics Teachers. *Res:* Quantum field theory; energy conservation (environment). *Mailing Add:* Dept Physics Univ Moncton Moncton NB E1A 3E9 Can. *Fax:* 506-858-4541; *E-Mail:* weilf@umoncton.ca

**WEIL, HERSCHEL,** ELECTROMAGNETIC SCATTERING. *Current Pos:* res assoc, Univ Mich, 52-53, assoc res engr, 53-55, res engr, 55-60, lectr, 58-60, assoc prof elec eng, 60-67, prof, 67-87, EMER PROF ELEC ENG & COMPUT SCI, UNIV MICH, ANN ARBOR, 87- *Personal Data:* b Rochester, NY, July 26, 21; m 43; c 2. *Educ:* Univ Rochester, BS, 43; Brown Univ, ScM, 45, PhD(appl math), 48. *Prof Exp:* Optical engr, Bausch & Lomb Optical Co, 43-44; asst appl math, Brown Univ, 46-47, res assoc, 47-48; engr, Gen Elec Co, 48-52. *Concurrent Pos:* Vis assoc prof, Univ Paris-Orsay, 64-65; sr vis fel, Nuffield Radio Astron Labs, Univ Manchester, 75; sr fel, Nat Ctr Atmospheric Res, 77-78. *Mem:* Inst Elec & Electronics Engrs; Optical Soc Am. *Res:* Electromagnetic theory and applications to engineering and atmospheric optics. *Mailing Add:* 1301 Beal St Ann Arbor MI 48109

**WEIL, JESSE LEO,** NUCLEAR PHYSICS & SPECTROSCOPY NEUTRON SCATTERING. *Current Pos:* from asst to assoc prof, 63-73, PROF NUCLEAR PHYSICS, UNIV KY, 73- *Personal Data:* b Ann Arbor, Mich, Dec 9, 31; div; c Janna G & Alexandra A. *Educ:* Calif Inst Technol, BS, 52; Columbia Univ, PhD(physics), 59. *Prof Exp:* Res asst nuclear physics, Columbia Univ, 54-58; res assoc, Rice Univ, 59-60 & 61-63 & Univ Hamburg, 60-61. *Concurrent Pos:* Res assoc, Rutherford High Energy Lab, 71-72. *Mem:* Am Asn Univ Prof; Am Phys Soc; Sigma Xi. *Res:* Nuclear reactions; scattering of nucleons and nuclei; nuclear energy level studies; nuclear energy level density; nuclear spectroscopy. *Mailing Add:* Dept Physics & Astron Univ Ky Lexington KY 40506. *Fax:* 606-323-2648; *E-Mail:* weil@ukcc.uky.edu

**WEIL, JOHN A,** CHEMICAL PHYSICS. *Current Pos:* prof, 71-96, EMER PROF CHEM, UNIV SASK, 96- *Personal Data:* b Hamburg, Ger, Mar 15, 29; nat US; m 47, Andrea L Moellenhoff; c 2. *Educ:* Univ Chicago, MS, 50, PhD(chem), 55; Univ Sask, DSc, 85. *Honors & Awards:* Erskine lectr, Univ Canterbury, 87. *Prof Exp:* Res chemist, Inst Study Metals, Univ Chicago, 49-52, Inst Nuclear Studies, 53-54; Corning fel chem, Princeton Univ, 55-56, instr phys chem, 56-59; from assoc scientist to sr scientist, Argonne Nat Lab, Ill, 59-71. *Concurrent Pos:* Fulbright scholar physics, Univ Canterbury, NZ, 67; vis prof, Univ Chicago, 80; vis prof, Lehigh Univ, 87; vis prof chem, Univ Ill, Urbana, 93; vis prof, Clarendon Lab, Univ Oxford, 94; vis fel, Royal Soc, 94; distinguished researcher, Univ Sask, 96. *Mem:* Fel Chem Inst Can; Am Phys Soc; Brit Int Physics & Phys Soc; Int Soc Magnetic Res; Int Electron Paramagnetic Resonance Spectros Soc. *Res:* Paramagnetic resonance; quantum chemistry; electronic structure of inorganic complexes; defect structure of silicates and other solids; organic free radicals. *Mailing Add:* Dept Chem Univ Sask 110 Science Pl Saskatoon SK S7N 5C9 Can

**WEIL, JOHN VICTOR,** INTERNAL MEDICINE. *Current Pos:* asst prof, 68-72, ASSOC PROF MED, MED CTR, UNIV COLO, DENVER, 72- *Personal Data:* b Detroit, Mich, May 10, 35; m 64; c 1. *Educ:* Yale Univ, BS, 57, MD, 61. *Prof Exp:* Intern path, Sch Med, Yale Univ, 61-62, intern med, 62-63, asst resident, 63-64 & 67-68. *Concurrent Pos:* NIH res fel cardiol, Univ Colo, Denver, 66-67. *Res:* Physiological responses to hypoxia; peripheral circulation, erythropoiesis, ventilation, oxygen transport. *Mailing Add:* Dept Med CVP Res Lab Univ Colo Health Sci Ctr 4200 E Ninth Ave Box B-133 Denver CO 80262-0001. *Fax:* 303-270-5969

**WEIL, JON DAVID,** HUMAN GENETICS, GENETIC COUNSELING. *Current Pos:* res geneticist, 77-86, asst adj prof, 86-93, ADJ ASSOC PROF PEDIAT, UNIV CALIF, SAN FRANCISCO, 93-; DIR, PROG GENETIC COUNSELING, UNIV CALIF, BERKELEY, 89- *Personal Data:* b Evansville, Ind, Mar 24, 37; m 85, Zita Dominguez; c 2. *Educ:* Swarthmore Col, BA, 58; Univ Calif, Davis, PhD(genetics), 63, Wright Inst, PhD(clin psychol), 84. *Prof Exp:* NSF fel molecular biol, Univ Ore, 63-65; NIH fel, Harvard Univ, 65-67; from asst prof to assoc prof molecular biol, Vanderbilt Univ, 67-77. *Concurrent Pos:* Postdoctoral fel psychol, Dept Pediat, Univ Calif, San Francisco, 84-86; lectr, Calif Sch Prof Psychol, 77, 86-88. *Mem:* Am Soc Human Genetics; AAAS; Am Psychol Asn; Nat Soc Genetic Coun. *Res:* Activities; pathogenic mechanisms of human aneuploidy; psychological consequences of genetic diseases. *Mailing Add:* 2015 Mira Vista Dr El Cerrito CA 94530. *Fax:* 510-643-8771; *E-Mail:* weilj@violet.berkeley.edu

**WEIL, MARVIN LEE,** PEDIATRICS, CHILD NEUROLOGY. *Current Pos:* from asst prof to prof, 68-89, EMER PROF PEDIAT & NEUROL, SCH MED, UNIV CALIF, LOS ANGELES, 89- *Personal Data:* b Gainesville, Fla, Sept 28, 24; m 54, Joyce Zimmerman; c Daniel I, Clifford F & Meredith. *Educ:* Univ Fla, BS, 43; Johns Hopkins Univ, MD, 46; Am Bd Pediat, dipl; Am Bd Psychiat & Neurol, dipl. *Prof Exp:* Intern pediat, Duke Univ, 46-47, asst resident, 47-48; asst chief, Neurotrop Virus Sect, Div Virus & Rickettsial Dis, Army Med Dept Res & Grad Sch, 48-50; researcher, Cincinnati Children's Hosp, 50-52; clin instr, Univ Cincinnati, 52-53; clin asst prof, Univ Miami Sch Med, 54-65; spec fel pediat neurol, Nat Inst Neurol Dis & Blindness, Johns Hopkins Univ, 65-66, Nat Inst Neurol Dis & Blindness, Univ Calif, Los Angeles, 66-68. *Concurrent Pos:* Pvt pract pediat, Miami, Fla, 53-65; mem, Accident Prev Comt, Am Acad Pediat, 64-67 & Bd Dirs, Child Neurol Soc, 80-82; Fogarty Int Ctr, sr int fel, Dept Virol, Karolinska Inst, Stockholm, Sweden, NIH, 76-77; acad visitor, Dept Biochem, Univ Oxford, UK, 89- *Mem:* Child Neurol Soc; Am Pediat Soc; fel Am Asn Immunologists; fel Am Acad Pediat; fel Am Acad Neurol; Int Child Neurol Soc. *Res:* Etiology, immunology and biochemistry of infections and inflammation of the nervous system; effects of intracranial hypertension on brain metabolism; pathogenesis of demyelination. *Mailing Add:* 82 Thames St Oxford 0X1 1SU England. *Fax:* 44-865-794617; *E-Mail:* 106150.3367@compuserve.com

**WEIL, MAX HARRY,** CARDIOVASCULAR DISEASES. *Current Pos:* DISTINGUISHED PROF MED & PHYSIOL & CHMN, CHICAGO MED SCH, 82-, CHIEF, DIV CARDIOL, 83- *Personal Data:* b Baden, Switz, Feb 9, 27; nat US; m 55; c 2. *Educ:* Univ Mich, AB, 48; State Univ NY Downstate Med Ctr, MD, 52; Univ Minn, PhD(med), 57; Am Bd Internal Med, dipl, 62. *Prof Exp:* Intern internal med, Cincinnati Gen Hosp, Ohio, 52-53; resident, Univ Hosps, Univ Minn, 53-55; asst clin prof, Sch Med, Univ Southern Calif, 57-59, from asst prof to assoc prof, 59-71, dir, Ctr Critically Ill, 68-80, prof med, 71-81, prof biomed eng, 72-81; dir, Inst Critical Care Med, Los Angeles, 76-82. *Concurrent Pos:* Vis prof, Univ Pittsburgh; chief cardiol, City of Hope Med Ctr, Duarte, Calif, 57-59, consult, 59-63; attend physician, Los Angeles County Gen Hosp, 58-71, sr atten cardiologist, Children's Div, 58-65; consult physician, Cedars-Sinai Med Ctr, 65-81, hon physician, 81-; chmn, Dept Med, Univ Health Sci, Chicago Med Sch, 82-; past mem comt shock, Nat Acad Sci-Nat Res Coun; fel coun circulation & coun thrombosis, Am Heart Asn; pres, Int Critical Care Med, Inc, 75- *Mem:* Fel Am Col Cardiol; fel Am Col Physicians; Am Physiol Soc; Am Soc Pharmacol & Exp Therapeut; Inst Elec & Electronics Engrs. *Res:* Clinical cardiology and cardiorespiratory physiology; critical care medicine; studies on circulatory shock and cardiopulmonary resuscitation both experimental and clinical; biomedical instrumentation and automation; applications of computer techniques to bedside medicine. *Mailing Add:* Inst Critical Care Med 1695 N Sunrise Way Palm Springs CA 92262-5309

**WEIL, MICHAEL RAY,** COMPARATIVE ENDOCRINOLOGY. *Current Pos:* ASST PROF BIOL, UNIV WIS-EAU CLAIRE, 79- *Personal Data:* b Buffalo, NY, Feb 10, 51; m 84. *Educ:* Univ Mich, BA, 72; St Louis Univ, MS, 76, PhD(biol), 80. *Mem:* Soc Study Amphibians & Reptiles; Herpetologists League; Am Soc Ichthyologists & Herpetologists; Sigma Xi; Am Soc Zoologists; Soc Study Evolution. *Res:* Comparative vertebrate endocrinology; seasonal cycles of reptilian and amphibian reproductive hormones; hormone binding proteins in the blood; developmental endocrinology. *Mailing Add:* Dept Biol Univ Wis PO Box 4004 Eau Claire WI 54702-4004

**WEIL, RAOUL BLOCH,** AMORPHOUS SILICON, II-VI SEMICONDUCTOR FERROELECTRICS. *Current Pos:* from assoc prof to prof, 71-96, EMER PROF PHYSICS, ISRAEL INST TECHNOL, 96- *Personal Data:* b La Paz, Bolivia; US citizen; m 56, Marguerite Narychkine; c Thierry E & K David. *Educ:* Univ San Andres, Bachiller, 45; Univ Ill, Urbana, BSEE, 49; Univ Calif, Riverside, MA, 63, PhD(physics), 66. *Prof Exp:* Trainee, Allis Chalmers Mfg Co, 49-51; consult engr, Bolivian Com Corp, 51-53, head, Tech Dept, 53-55; prof elec eng, Univ San Andres, 56-60; res asst cosmic ray physics, Univ Chicago, 60-61; solid state physics, Univ Calif, 61-65; res physicist, Monsanto Co, 65-67, proj leader, 67-69; assoc prof elec eng, Wash Univ, 69-71. *Concurrent Pos:* Res assoc, Cosmic Physics Lab, Chacaltaya, 57-60; secy, Bolivian Nat Comt for the Int Geophys, 57-60; vis assoc prof, Univ Ill, Urbana, 77-78; vis prof, Univ Louis Pasteur, Strasbourg, France, 85 & Solar Energy Res Inst, Golden, Colo, 86; mem Israel rep, Thins Films Div, Int Union Vacuum Sci Tech & Appl Physics Comt, Europ Phys Soc, 86; mem Israel rep, Applied Physics Comt, Europ Phys Soc, 86. *Mem:* Am Phys Soc; Inst Elec & Electronics Engrs; Israel Laser & Electrooptics Soc (secy, 73-75, pres, 76-77); Israel Phys Soc (secy, 76-77); Sigma Xi; Israel Vacuum Soc. *Res:* Solar cells; optical properties of semiconductors in the infrared; lasers; superionic conductors; amorphous silicon, ferroelectricity. *Mailing Add:* Physics Dept Technion Israel Inst Technol Haifa 32000 Israel. *Fax:* 972-4-8235107; *E-Mail:* phrg4rw@physics.technion.ac.il

**WEIL, RAYMOND R,** SOIL FERTILITY, CROPPING SYSTEMS. *Current Pos:* from asst prof to assoc prof, 79-91, PROF SOIL SCI, DEPT NATURAL RESOURCE SCI, UNIV MD, 91- *Personal Data:* b Detroit, Mich, May 27, 48; m 68, 83, Patricia L Driggers; c Benjamin S & Joshua J. *Educ:* Mich State Univ, BS, 70; Purdue Univ, MS, 72; Va Polytech Inst & State Univ, PhD(soil ecol), 77. *Prof Exp:* Agron Vol, US Peace Corp, Ethiopia, 70-71; farm mgr, Nat Share Croppers Fund, 72-73; instr agron, Va Polytech Inst & State Univ, 75-77; lectr soil sci, Univ Malawi, 77-79. *Concurrent Pos:* Soils consult, Govt Sri Lanka, 81, Accokeek Found, 85-92, World Bank, 92 & 96, Govt Tanzania, 93-94; fac mem, USDA Grad Sch, 83; J. Fulbright fel, 85 & 94; res grants, USAID, 83-85 & 88-92, US Dept Interior, 83, 86 & 90, USDA, 91-; assoc ed, J African Policy Studies, 92-96; Am J Alt Agr, 92-97. *Mem:* Am Soc Agron; Soil Sci Soc Am; Soil Conserv Soc Am; Int Soil Sci Soc; Inst African Affairs; Inst Alt Agr. *Res:* Plant use and cycling of nutrients; multiple cropping systems; impacts on soil and water environmental quality; organic wastes applied to land and indigenous nutrients in African countries. *Mailing Add:* Dept Natural Resource Sci Univ Md College Park MD 20742. *Fax:* 301-405-1314; *E-Mail:* rw17@umail.umd.edu

**WEIL, ROLF,** METALLURGY, ELECTROCHEMISTRY. *Current Pos:* from asst prof to prof mat sci & eng, 56-91, EMER PROF MAT SCI & ENG STEVENS INST TECHNOL, 91- *Personal Data:* b Neunkirchen, Ger, Aug 5, 26; nat US. *Educ:* Carnegie Inst Technol, BS, 46, MS, 49; Pa State Univ, PhD(metall), 51. *Hon Degrees:* ME, Stevens Inst Technol, 67. *Honors & Awards:* Sci Achievement Award, Am Electroplaters Soc; Res Award, Electrodeposition Div, Electrochem Soc. *Prof Exp:* Metallurgist, Duquesne Smelting Corp, 46-48; grad asst, Pa State Univ, 49-51; assoc metallurgist, Argonne Nat Lab, 51-54. *Mem:* Fel Electrochem Soc; Am Inst Mining, Metall & Petrol Engrs; Am Electroplaters & Surface Finishers Soc; fel Brit Inst Metal Finishing. *Res:* Structure and properties of electrodeposited metals; electron microscopy; metal strengthening mechanisms; corrosion. *Mailing Add:* Dept Mat Sci & Eng Castle Point Sta Hoboken NJ 07030. *Fax:* 201-216-8306

**WEIL, THOMAS ANDRE,** PEDROCHEMICAL PROCESS & PRODUCT DEVELOPMENT. *Current Pos:* res chemist, Amoco Chem Corp, 74-77, res supvr, 77-82, dir explor res, 82-87, mgr, New Prod Res & Develop, 87-94, RES MGR, AMOCO CHEM CORP, 94- *Personal Data:* b Ft Riley, Kans, June 27, 44; m 70, Barbara Quattrone; c 2. *Educ:* State Univ NY Col Oswego, BA, 66; Univ Cincinnati, PhD(chem), 70. *Hon Degrees:* DSc, State Univ NY, 94. *Prof Exp:* Nat Res Coun fel, US Bur Mines, Pa, 70-71; asst prof chem, Trenton State Col, 71-72; NIH fel, Univ Chicago, 72-74. *Concurrent Pos:* NSF exchange fel, US-USSR Sci & Technol, 74. *Mem:* Am Chem Soc. *Res:* Catalysis; heterogeneous and homogeneous catalysis; transition metal complexes; metals in organic synthesis; mechanisms of metal catalyzed reactions; energy related research; petrochemical process and product research. *Mailing Add:* Amoco Chem Corp Box 400 Naperville IL 60560-0400. *Fax:* 630-951-7963; *E-Mail:* taweil@amoco.com

**WEIL, THOMAS P,** HOSPITAL ADMINISTRATION, PUBLIC HEALTH. *Current Pos:* PRES, BEDFORD HEALTH ASSOCS, INC, 75- *Personal Data:* b Mt Vernon, NY, Oct 2, 32; m 65, Janet Whalen. *Educ:* Union Col, NY, AB, 54; Yale Univ, MPH, 58; Univ Mich, PhD(med care orgn), 65. *Prof Exp:* S S Goldwater fel hosp admin, Mt Sinai Hosp, New York, 57-58; assoc consult, John G Steinle & Assocs, Mgt Consults, 58-61; asst prof, Sch Pub Health, Univ Calif, Los Angeles, 62-65; assoc dir & consult, Touro Infirmary, New Orleans, 64-66; prof grad studies health serv mgr & dir, Schs Med, Bus & Pub Admin, Univ Mo, Columbia, 66-71; vpres & prin, E D Rosenfeld Assocs, Inc, New York, 71-75. *Concurrent Pos:* Consult to numerous hosps, planning agencies & med ctrs; vis prof & W K Kellogg Found grant, Univ NSW, 69. *Mem:* Fel Am Pub Health Asn; Am Hosp Asn; Am Col Health Care Adminr; Am Asn Hosp Consult. *Res:* Management, organization and financing of health services, especially hospital and physician care. *Mailing Add:* 1400 Town Mountain Rd Asheville NC 28804. *Fax:* 704-253-3820

**WEIL, WILLIAM B, JR,** PEDIATRICS. *Current Pos:* chmn dept, 68-79, prof, 68-94, EMER PROF PEDIAT HUMAN DEVELOP, MICH STATE UNIV, 94- *Personal Data:* b Minneapolis, Minn, Dec 3, 24; m 49; c Susan (Bates) & Constance (Brisselte). *Educ:* Univ Minn, BA, 45, BS, 46, MB, 47, MD, 48. *Prof Exp:* USPHS & univ res fels, Harvard Univ, 51-52; assoc prof, Col Med, Univ Fla, 63-65, E I du Pont prof for handicapped children, 65-68. *Mem:* AAAS; Soc Pediat Res (secy-treas, 62-69, pres, 69-70); Am Pediat Soc; Am Acad Pediat; NY Acad Sci. *Res:* Renal disease; diabetes; nutrition. *Mailing Add:* Mich State Univ Life Sci Bldg Rm B240 East Lansing MI 48824-1317. *Fax:* 517-353-8464

**WEILER, EDWARD JOHN,** ASTRONOMY. *Current Pos:* CHIEF ULTRA VIOLET, VISIBLE ASTRO PHYSICS BRANCH, NASA, 90- *Personal Data:* b Chicago, Ill, Jan 15, 49. *Educ:* Northwestern Univ, BA, 71, MS, 73, PhD(astron), 76. *Prof Exp:* Res assoc astron, Avionics Lab, Northwestern Univ, 73-74; res assoc, Princeton Univ-Nasa Goddard Space Flight Ctr, 76-90. *Mem:* AAAS. *Res:* Chromospheric activity in late-type binary stars and the evolution of galaxies. *Mailing Add:* Astrophys Div NASA HQ Code SZ 300 E St SW Washington DC 20546

**WEILER, ERNEST DIETER,** ORGANIC CHEMISTRY. *Current Pos:* chemist, Rohm & Haas Co, 67-73, chemist animal health res, 73-74, proj leader animal health res, 74-75, proj leader process res, 75-77, dept mgr, plastics intermediates, 77-82, dir plastics, Europ Labs, 82-85, dir toxicol, 85-86, DIR, PROD INTEGRITY, ROHM & HAAS CO, 86- *Personal Data:* b Neuwied, Ger, June 30, 39; US citizen; m 67. *Educ:* Univ Minn, BChem, 62; Univ Nebr, PhD(org chem), 66; Temple Univ, MBA, 74. *Prof Exp:* Fel, Univ Basel, 66-67. *Mem:* Am Chem Soc; Sigma Xi. *Mailing Add:* 913 Chesterfield Dr Lower Gwynedd PA 19002

**WEILER, JOHN HENRY, JR,** PLANT TAXONOMY. *Current Pos:* PROF PLANT SCI, CALIF STATE UNIV, FRESNO, 62- *Personal Data:* b Lincoln, Nebr, July 8, 25; m 58; c 2. *Educ:* Univ Nebr, BSc, 58; Univ Calif, Berkeley, PhD(taxon), 62. *Mem:* Am Soc Plant Taxon; Bot Soc Am; Int Asn Plant Taxon. *Res:* Biosystematics; floristics of central California. *Mailing Add:* 1146 W Rialto Ave Fresno CA 93705

**WEILER, KURT WALTER,** RADIO INTERFEROMETRY, OPTICAL INTERFEROMETRY. *Current Pos:* RADIO ASTRONOMER, NAVAL RES LAB, WASHINGTON, DC, 85- *Personal Data:* b Phoenix, Ariz, Mar 16, 43; m 79, Geertje Stoelwinder; c Corinn, Anil & Sanna. *Educ:* Univ Ariz, BS, 64; Calif Inst Technol, PhD(physics), 70. *Prof Exp:* Sr sci officer, Neth Found Radio Astron, 70-74; sci collabr, Lab Radio Astron, Bologna, Italy, 75-76; res assoc, Max Planck Inst Radio Astron, 76-79; prog dir, NSF, Washington, DC, 79-85. *Concurrent Pos:* Consult, Max Planck Inst Radio Astron, Bonn, Ger, 76; proj dir, Optical Interferometry Proj, US Naval Observ, Naval Res Lab, 89-91. *Mem:* Am Astron Soc; Int Astron Union; Royal Astron Sci; Int Union Radio Sci. *Res:* Radio emission from supernovae and supernova remnants. *Mailing Add:* Naval Res Lab Code 7214 Washington DC 20375-5320. *Fax:* 202-404-8894

**WEILER, LAWRENCE STANLEY,** ORGANIC CHEMISTRY. *Current Pos:* From asst prof to assoc prof, 68-80, PROF CHEM, UNIV BC, 80- *Personal Data:* b Middleton, NS, July 11, 42; m 64, Agnes McCallum; c Catherine, Nancy Lynn & Patricia. *Educ:* Univ Toronto, BSc, 64; Harvard Univ, PhD(org chem), 68. *Honors & Awards:* Merck, Sharpe & Dohme Award, Chem Inst Can. *Mem:* Am Chem Soc; Chem Inst Can; Royal Soc Chem; Swiss Chem Soc; Can Soc Chem. *Res:* Synthesis and study of novel organic compounds; synthesis of natural products. *Mailing Add:* Dept Chem 2036 Main Mall Univ BC Vancouver BC V6T 1Z1 Can. *Fax:* 604-822-2847; *E-Mail:* lsw@chem.ubc.ca

**WEILER, MARGARET HORTON,** PHYSICS. *Current Pos:* STAFF ENGR, LORAL INFRARED & IMAGING SYSTS, 88- *Personal Data:* b Sewickley, Pa, Apr 30, 41; m 62, William; c Christopher & Theodore. *Educ:* Radcliffe Col, AB, 62; Univ Maine, MS, 64; Mass Inst Technol, PhD(physics), 77. *Prof Exp:* Instr physics, Univ Maine, 64-65; comput programmer linguistics, Harvard Computation Ctr, 65; res staff mem, Francis Bitter Nat Magnet Lab, Mass Inst Technol, 65-74, asst prof physics, 77-83; sr scientist, Res Div, Raytheon Co, 83-88. *Mem:* AAAS; Am Phys Soc; Int Elec & Electronics Engrs. *Res:* Semiconductor device physics. *Mailing Add:* Loral Infrared & Imaging Systs 2 Forbes Rd Lexington MA 02173

**WEILER, ROLAND R,** GEOCHEMISTRY. *Current Pos:* RETIRED. *Personal Data:* b Estonia, Feb 23, 36; Can citizen; m 65; c 3. *Educ:* Univ Toronto, BA, 59, MA, 60; Dalhousie Univ, PhD(oceanog), 65. *Prof Exp:* Res scientist, Bedford Inst Oceanog, Can Dept Energy, Mines & Resources, 64-67 & Can Ctr Inland Waters, 67-80; coordr spec studies & res, Ontario Ministry Environ, 80-94. *Mem:* AAAS; Am Soc Limnol & Oceanog; Int Asn Gt Lakes Res. *Res:* Chemical limnology and geochemistry of sediments. *Mailing Add:* 37 Mercer St Dundas ON L9H 2N8 Can

**WEILER, THOMAS JOSEPH,** ELEMENTARY PARTICLE PHYSICS. *Current Pos:* AT DEPT PHYS & ASTRON, VANDERBILT UNIV. *Personal Data:* b St Louis, Mo, May 5, 49. *Educ:* Stanford Univ, BS, 71; Univ Wis, PhD(physics), 76. *Prof Exp:* Sr res asst, Univ Liverpool, 76-78; res assoc theoret physics, Northeastern Univ, 78-81; asst res physicist II, Univ Calif, San Diego, 81- *Concurrent Pos:* Vis theoret physics, Ctr Europ Nuclear Res, Rutherford Lab, 77, Aspen Ctr, 80, 81. *Mem:* Sigma Xi; Am Phys Soc. *Res:* Work towards the description of the ultimate subunits of matter and the forces by which they interact and combine; implications of particle physics for cosmology. *Mailing Add:* Dept Physics & Astron Vanderbilt Univ Box 1807 Sta B Nashville TN 37235. *Fax:* 615-343-7263

**WEILER, WILLIAM ALEXANDER,** BACTERIOLOGY, MICROBIAL ECOLOGY. *Current Pos:* asst prof, 69-74, assoc prof, 74-80, PROF BOT, EASTERN ILL UNIV, 80- *Personal Data:* b Milwaukee, Wis, Nov 8, 41; m 63; c 3. *Educ:* Dartmouth Col, AB, 63; Purdue Univ, PhD(microbiol), 69. *Prof Exp:* Instr microbiol, Purdue Univ, 66-69. *Mem:* Am Soc Microbiol. *Res:* Herbicide effects on soil microflora; petroleum degradation in soil and water ecosystems. *Mailing Add:* Dept Bot Eastern Ill Univ 600 Lincoln Ave Charleston IL 61920-3011

**WEILL, CAROL EDWIN,** organic chemistry; deceased, see previous edition for last biography

**WEILL, DANIEL FRANCIS,** PETROLOGY, GEOCHEMISTRY. *Current Pos:* PROG DIR, NSF, 85- *Personal Data:* b Paris, France, Nov 29, 31; US citizen; m 57, Margaret A Mateus; c Katherine A, Paul A & Michele C. *Educ:* Cornell Univ, AB, 56; Univ Ill, MS, 58; Univ Calif, Berkeley, PhD(geol), 62. *Prof Exp:* Res assoc geochem, Univ Calif, Berkeley, 62-63; asst prof gcol, Univ Calif, San Diego, 63-66; from assoc prof to prof geol, Univ Ore, 66-85, dir, Ctr Volcanology, 69-70, assoc dean arts & sci, 76-78 & 81-83, prog mgr, Dept Energy (basic energy sci), 83-85. *Concurrent Pos:* Grants, NSF, 65-66, 66-68, & 79, NASA, 68-78, 71-78 & 79-81 & Am Chem Soc, 70-72; Fulbright-Hays sr res fel, UK, 72-73. *Mem:* Mineral Soc Am; Royal Soc Chem; Am Geophys Union. *Res:* Physical chemistry of geological systems; silicate liquid density, viscosity; diffusion; lunar sample analysis; redox equilibria in silicate melts; experimental trace element distribution; thermodynamic properties of mineral and liquid silicate systems; science administration. *Mailing Add:* Div Earth Sci NSF 4201 Wilson Blvd Arlington VA 22230. *Fax:* 703-306-0382; *E-Mail:* dweill@nsf.gov

**WEILL, GEORGES GUSTAVE,** MATHEMATICAL ANALYSIS, APPLIED MATHEMATICS. *Current Pos:* PROF, POLYTECH UNIV NY, 66- *Personal Data:* b Strasbourg, France, Apr 9, 26. *Educ:* Univ Paris, DSc(physics), 55; Univ Calif, Los Angeles, PhD(math), 60. *Prof Exp:* Rcs scientist, Gen Radio Co, France, 52-56; res fel, Calif Inst Tech, 56-59; res fel math, Harvard Univ, 60-62; lectr & res fel, Yale Univ, 62-64; asst prof, Yeshiva Univ, 64-65. *Concurrent Pos:* Consult, Electro-Optical Systs, Inc, 59-60 & Raytheon Co, 61-62. *Mem:* Am Math Soc; sr mem Inst Elec & Electronics Engrs; Math Soc France. *Res:* Complex analysis; Riemann surfaces; diffraction theory; antennas; theoretical and applied electromagnetics. *Mailing Add:* Dept Math Polytech Univ NY 333 Jay St Brooklyn NY 11201

**WEILL, HANS,** MEDICINE, PHYSIOLOGY. *Current Pos:* From instr to prof med, 62-85, dir, Ctr Bioenvironmental Res, 90-93, SCHLIEDER PROF PULMONARY MED, TULANE UNIV MED SCH, 85-, DIR, SURG BASIC RES PROG, 92- *Personal Data:* b Berlin, Ger, Aug 31, 33; US citizen; c 3. *Educ:* Tulane Univ, BA, 55, MD, 58; Am Bd Internal Med, dipl & Am Bd Pulmonary Dis, dipl, 65. *Concurrent Pos:* Attend staff, Vet Admin Hosp, New Orleans, 63-85; consult, USPHS Hosp, 64-76; dir, Specialized Ctr Res & consult, Task Force Environ Lung Dis, Nat Heart, Lung & Blood Inst, 72-, mem, Pulmonary Dis Adv Comt, 81, chmn, 82; mem, Pulmonary Dis Bd, Am Bd Internal Med, 80-86; mem, Nat Heart Lung & Blood Adv Coun, NIH, 86-90; bd gov, Am Bd Internal Med, 85-88. *Mem:* Am Thoracic Soc (pres, 76-77); fel Am Col Chest Physicians; fel Am Col Physicians; Am Fedn Clin Res; fel Royal Soc Med. *Res:* Occupational respiratory diseases; environmental health sciences. *Mailing Add:* Tulane Med Ctr Hosp & Clin 1415 Tulane Ave New Orleans LA 70112-2605. *Fax:* 504-588-5035; *E-Mail:* weill@mailhost.tcs.tulane.edu

**WEIMANN, LUDWIG JAN,** PHYSICAL CHEMISTRY, PHOTOCHEMISTRY. *Current Pos:* TECH DIR RES & DEVELOP, BERTEK, INC, 80- *Personal Data:* b Lipnica, Ger, May 24, 41; m 72; c 2. *Educ:* Univ Poznan, MS, 63, PhD(photochem), 70. *Prof Exp:* Instr photochem & radiochem, Univ Poznan, 63-70; fel theoret chem, Kans Univ, 70-72; fel vision chem, Univ Mo, Kansas City, 72-73, instr phys & gen chem, 73-75, vis asst prof phys chem, 75-76; res & develop dir polymer photochem, K C Coatings Inc, 76-80. *Mem:* Am Chem Soc; Soc Mfg Eng. *Res:* Radical and cationic photopolymerization; application in ink making area; kinetics of photopolymerization and physicochemical properties of ultraviolet-cured films; kinetics of drug transport through membranes. *Mailing Add:* Jonergin/Bertek Inc 110 Lake St St Albans VT 05478-2237

**WEIMAR, VIRGINIA LEE,** PHYSIOLOGY. *Current Pos:* RETIRED. *Personal Data:* b Condon, Ore, Oct 23, 22. *Educ:* Ore State Col, MS, 47; Univ Pa, PhD(physiol), 51. *Prof Exp:* Physiologist, USN, 51; res assoc biochem, Wills Eye Hosp, Philadelphia, Pa, 52-54; researcher ophthal, Col Physicians & Surgeons, Columbia Univ, 55-58, res assoc, 58-59, asst prof, 59-61; res assoc, Med Sch, Ore Health Sci Univ, Portland, 61-63, asst prof, 63-68, assoc prof ophthal, 68-78. *Concurrent Pos:* Nat Cancer Inst, Univ Pa, 54-55; NIH travel award; deleg, Int Cong Ophthal, Belg, 58 & Jerusalem Conf Prev of Blindness, 71. *Mem:* Harvey Soc; Am Physiol Soc; Asn Res Vision & Ophthal; Soc Gen Physiol; Am Soc Cell Biol. *Res:* Biochemistry and physiology of trauma; wound healing; inflammation; corneal wound healing; cellular ultramicrochemistry; biomathematics. *Mailing Add:* 305 SE 84th Ave Portland OR 97216

**WEIMBERG, RALPH,** PHYSIOLOGY, PLANT BACTERIOLOGY. *Current Pos:* RETIRED. *Personal Data:* b San Diego, Calif, Dec 22, 24; m 52; c 2. *Educ:* Univ Calif, AB, 49, MA, 51, PhD(bact), 55. *Prof Exp:* Fel, Biol Div, Oak Ridge Nat Labs, 55-56; instr microbiol, Sch Med, Western Res Univ, 56-58; biochemist, Northern Utilization Res & Develop Div, 58-65, biochemist, US Salinity Lab, 65-, Agr Res Serv, US Dept Agr. *Concurrent Pos:* Vis assoc prof, Univ Calif, Davis, 64; vis res scientist, Bot Dept, Hebrew Univ, Jerusalem, 77 & 81. *Mem:* AAAS; Am Soc Microbiol; Am Soc Plant Physiol; Am Soc Biol Chemists; NY Acad Sci. *Res:* Plant physiology and metabolism; properties and location of enzymes; biochemistry. *Mailing Add:* 5444 Quince St Riverside CA 92506-3357

**WEIMER, DAVID,** GAS DYNAMICS. *Current Pos:* ASSOC PROF PHYSICS, OHIO NORTHERN UNIV, 69- *Personal Data:* b Marion, Ind, Oct 13, 19; m 44; c 4. *Educ:* Ohio State Univ, BS, 41, MS, 46. *Prof Exp:* Res asst physics, Princeton Univ, 41-45; prof, Am Col SIndia, 46-47; res assoc, Princeton Univ, 47-52; res engr, Armour Res Found, Ill, 52-55 & Am Mach & Foundry Co, 55-56; sr staff scientist physics, Lockheed Corp, Calif, 56-58, 60-64; asst prof, Ohio Northern Univ, 64-68; staff scientist, Martin-Marietta Corp, Colo, 68-69. *Concurrent Pos:* Sr staff engr, Martin-Marietta Corp, Colo, 72-73. *Mem:* Am Phys Soc. *Res:* Gas physics and shock wave phenomena; dissociation and ionization of gas at high temperatures; radiation of excited species in planetary atmospheres. *Mailing Add:* PO Box 234 Ada OH 45810-0234

**WEIMER, F(RANK) CARLIN,** ELECTRICAL ENGINEERING. *Current Pos:* Asst, 39-41, from instr to prof, 41-83, EMER PROF ELEC ENG, OHIO STATE UNIV, 83- *Personal Data:* b Dayton, Ohio, July 27, 17; m 44, Lillian Van Harlingen; c Ann, Richard & Philip. *Educ:* Univ Ohio, BS, 38; Ohio State Univ, MSc, 39, PhD(elec eng), 43. *Honors & Awards:* Centennial Medal, Inst Elec & Electronics Engrs, 84. *Concurrent Pos:* Consult, Battelle Mem Inst, 57-85. *Mem:* AAAS; Am Soc Eng Educ; Nat Soc Prof Engrs; Inst Elec & Electronics Engrs; Sigma Xi. *Res:* Servomechanisms; magnetic fields in machinery; permeance analysis; automatic control; signal processing. *Mailing Add:* Dept Elec Eng Ohio State Univ 2015 Neil Ave Columbus OH 43210-1272. *Fax:* 614-292-7596

**WEIMER, JOHN THOMAS,** biology, toxicology, for more information see previous edition

**WEIMER, KATHERINE E,** PHYSICS EDUCATION. *Current Pos:* RETIRED. *Personal Data:* b NJ. *Educ:* Ohio State Univ, PhD(physics), 42. *Prof Exp:* Tech staff, Princeton Univ, 55-84. *Mem:* Am Phys Soc; Sigma Xi. *Mailing Add:* 112 Random Princeton NJ 08540-4146

**WEIMER, PAUL KESSLER,** PHYSICS. *Current Pos:* CONSULT, 81- *Personal Data:* b Wabash, Ind, Nov 5, 14; m 42, Katherine Mounce; c Katherine L (Lasslob), Barbara J (Blackwell) & Patricia W (Hess). *Educ:* Manchester Col, AB, 36; Univ Kans, AM, 38; Ohio State Univ, PhD(physics), 42. *Hon Degrees:* DSc, Manchester Col, 68. *Honors & Awards:* Award, TV Broadcasters Asn, 46; Zworykin Prize, Inst Elec & Electronics Engrs, 59, Morris Liebmann Mem Prize, 66; Albert Rose Award, Inst Graphic Commun, 87. *Prof Exp:* Asst, Univ Kans, 36-37; prof physics, Tabor Col, 37-39; asst, Ohio State Univ, 39-42; res engr, RCA Labs, 42-64, fel tech staff, 64-81. *Mem:* Nat Acad Eng; fel Inst Elec & Electronics Engrs; Ger Photog Soc. *Res:* Nuclear physics; electron optics; photoconductivity; secondary emission; semiconductor devices; television camera tubes and solid state image sensors. *Mailing Add:* 112 Random Rd Princeton NJ 08540

**WEIMER, ROBERT FREDRICK,** CHEMICAL ENGINEERING. *Current Pos:* tech mgr process technol, 82-85, CHIEF ENGR, AIR PROD & CHEM INC, 85- *Personal Data:* b Wheeling, WVa, Jan 16, 40. *Educ:* Mass Inst Technol, SB, 61; Univ Calif, Berkeley, PhD(chem eng), 65. *Prof Exp:* Staff

engr, Air Prod & Chem Inc, 67-73, process mgr, 73-76, develop mgr, 76-78, dir develop, Corp Res & Develop Dept, 78-81; chief engr, Int Coal Refining Co, 81-82. *Mem:* AAAS; Am Inst Chem Engrs; Am Chem Soc. *Res:* Internal consultant on design of chemical process equipment with emphasis on heat and mass tranfer and gas separations. *Mailing Add:* Air Prod & Chem Inc 7201 Hamilton Blvd Allentown PA 18195

**WEIMER, ROBERT J,** GEOLOGY. *Current Pos:* from asst prof to assoc prof, Colo Sch Mines, 57-72, head dept, 64-69, Getty prof geol eng, 78-83, PROF GEOL, COLO SCH MINES, 72-, EMER PROF GEOL ENG, 83- *Personal Data:* b Glendo, Wyo, Sept 4, 26; m 48; c 3. *Educ:* Univ Wyo, BA, 48, MA, 49; Stanford Univ, PhD, 53. *Honors & Awards:* Sidney Powers Medal, 84; Medal, Colo Sch Medal. *Prof Exp:* Dist geologist, Union Oil Co Calif, Mont, 53-54; consult res geologist, 54-57. *Concurrent Pos:* Consult, petrol indust, 54-; exchange prof, Univ Colo, 60; Fulbright lectr, Univ Adelaide, 67; vis prof, Univ Calgary, 70; mem res assoc comt, Nat Acad Sci, 70-73; mem, Inst Technol, Bandung, Indonesia, 75. *Mem:* AAAS; Geol Soc Am; hon mem Am Asn Petrol Geol; hon mem Soc Econ Paleont & Mineral (secy-treas, 66-68, vpres, 71, pres, 72). *Res:* Stratigraphic research in the application of modern sedimentation studies to the geologic record; regional framework of sedimentation in the Cretaceous, Jurassic and Pennsylvanian rock systems; tectonics and sedimentation; geologic history of the Rocky Mountain region; stratigraphic record of global sea level changes. *Mailing Add:* 25853 Mt Vernon Rd Rte 3 Golden CO 80401-9699

**WEIN, ALAN JEROME,** UROLOGY. *Current Pos:* asst instr surg, Sch Med, Univ Pa, 67-68, fel, Harrison Dept Surg Res Urol, 68-69, asst instr urol, 69-71, from instr to assoc prof, 71-83, PROF UROL, SCH MED, UNIV PA, 83- *Personal Data:* b Newark, NJ, Dec 15, 41. *Educ:* Princeton Univ, AB, 62; Univ Pa, MD, 66; Am Bd Urol, dipl. *Prof Exp:* Intern mixed surg, Hosp Univ Pa, Philadelphia, 66-67, resident surg, 67-68. *Concurrent Pos:* Resident urol, Univ Pa, 69-72, asst chief, 74-79, dir, Urodyn Eval Ctr, 74-, coordr progs urol oncol, 76-, chmn, Div Urol, 81- & chief urol, 81-; chief urol, Vet Admin Hosp, Philadelphia, 74-82, attend urologist, 82-; asst surgeon, Childrens Hosp, Philadelphia, 77-; numerous res grants, 74-; assoc surgeon, Pa Hosp Philadelphia, 77-; attending urologist, Grad Hosp, Philadelphia, 80-; asst ed, J Urol, 80-89, Neurol & Urodyn, 82-; mem, Coun Urol, Nat Kidney Found; chmn, Bladder Health Coun, Am Found Urol Dis, 90-; consult, Coun Incontinence, Ctrs Dis Control, 90- *Mem:* Fel Am Col Surgeons; AAAS; AMA; Am Acad Clin Neurophysiol; Am Surg Asn; Am Asn Genito-Urinary Surgeons; Am Fertil Soc; Am Inst Ultrasound Med; Am Soc Pharmacol & Exp Therapeut; Am Soc Androl; Am Soc Clin Oncol; Am Urol Asn; Asn Acad Surg; Can Urol Asn; Clin Soc Genito-Urinary Surgeons; Royal Soc Med; Soc Sex Ther & Res; Soc Pelvic Surgeons; Soc Urol Oncol. *Res:* Neuro-urology; voiding function and dysfunction. *Mailing Add:* Hosp Univ Pa 3400 Spruce St-5-1 Rhoads Philadelphia PA 19104

**WEIN, ROSS WALLACE,** PLANT & FIRE ECOLOGY, ARCTIC STUDIES. *Current Pos:* dir northern studies, Boreal Inst, 87-90, PROF FORESTRY, UNIV ALTA, EDMONTON, 87- *Personal Data:* b Exeter, Ont, Oct 29, 40; m 67, Eleanor Schmidt; c Laurie P & Daniel E. *Educ:* Univ Guelph, BSA, 65, MSc, 66; Utah State Univ, PhD(ecol), 70. *Prof Exp:* Can Nat Res Coun fel, Univ Alta, 69-71, vis asst prof plant ecol, 71-72; from asst prof to prof plant ecol, Univ NB, 72-78, dir, Fire Sci Ctr, Fredericton, 78-87. *Concurrent Pos:* Adj prof bot, Can Circumpolar Inst. *Mem:* Ecol Soc Am; Can Bot Asn. *Res:* Plant production and nutrient cycling following wildfire; plant community dynamics; boreal and arctic ecology of the circumpolar North; climate change. *Mailing Add:* Renewable Resources Univ Alta Edmonton AB T6G 2H1 Can. *Fax:* 403-492-4323

**WEINACHT, RICHARD JAY,** MATHEMATICS. *Current Pos:* from asst prof to assoc prof, 63-74, PROF MATH, UNIV DEL, 74- *Personal Data:* b Union City, NJ, Dec 10, 31; m 55; c 6. *Educ:* Univ Notre Dame, BS, 53; Columbia Univ, MS, 55; Univ Md, PhD(math), 62. *Prof Exp:* NSF fel math, Courant Inst Math Sci, NY Univ, 62-63. *Concurrent Pos:* Vis assoc prof, Rensselaer Polytech Inst, 69-70; Fulbright fel & vis prof, Darmstadt Tech Univ, 76-77; Ger Acad Exchange Serv vis scientist, Univ Cologne, 80; vis prof, Univ Rome, 84. *Mem:* Am Math Soc; Soc Indust & Appl Math. *Res:* Partial differential equations; singular perturbations. *Mailing Add:* Dept Math Sci Univ Del 501 Ewing Hall Newark DE 19711

**WEINBACH, EUGENE CLAYTON,** BIOCHEMISTRY. *Current Pos:* RETIRED. *Personal Data:* b Pine Island, NY, Nov 5, 19; m 38; c 2. *Educ:* Univ Md, BS, 42, PhD(org med chem), 47. *Prof Exp:* Res chemist, US Naval Res Lab, Washington, DC, 47; USPHS & Nat Cancer Inst fel, Sch Med, Johns Hopkins Univ, 47-48, instr physiol chm, 48-50; res chemist, NIH, 50-93, head, Sect Physiol & Biochem, Lab Parasitic Dis, Nat Inst Allergy & Infectious Dis, 69-93. *Concurrent Pos:* Guest worker, Wenner-Gren Inst, Stockholm, Sweden, 60-62. *Mem:* Am Chem Soc; Am Soc Biol Chemists; Sigma Xi. *Res:* Biochemical mechanisms of drug action; intermediary metabolism of parasites and their hosts; biological oxidations and phosphorylations; biochemistry of mitochondria. *Mailing Add:* 3303 Pendleton Dr Silver Spring MD 20902-2426

**WEINBAUM, CARL MARTIN,** MATHEMATICS. *Current Pos:* SOFTWARE ENGR, UMECORP, 88- *Personal Data:* b Manchester, Eng, Jan 16, 37; US citizen; m 63, 91; c 4. *Educ:* Queens Col, NY, BS, 58; Harvard Univ, AM, 60; NY Univ, PhD(math), 63. *Prof Exp:* Asst prof math, Univ Calif, Los Angeles, 63-68; assoc prof, Univ Hawaii, 68-70 & Hawaii Loa Col, 70-77; fac mem, Woodmere Acad, 77-78; mem tech staff, Network Anal Corp, 78-79; programmer/analyst, Royal Ins Co, 80-84; software engr, Grumman Aerospace Corp, 84-88. *Mem:* Am Math Soc. *Res:* Infinite groups, particularly word problems and small cancellation and knot groups. *Mailing Add:* 246 Miller Ave Mill Valley CA 94941-2829

**WEINBAUM, GEORGE,** PULMONARY RESEARCH, INFLAMMATORY DISEASES. *Current Pos:* res assoc prof, 82-88, RES PROF, DEPT MED, UNIV PA, 88-; RES PROF MICROBIOL, HEALTH SCI CTR, TEMPLE UNIV, 73- *Personal Data:* b Brooklyn, NY, July 27, 32; m 63, Carol Rosenblatt; c Eve, Cindy, Laura & Elliot. *Educ:* Univ Pa, AB, 53; Pa State Univ, MS, 55, PhD(biochem), 57. *Prof Exp:* Chief biochem labs, Geisinger Med Ctr, 57-61; asst mem, Res Labs, Albert Einstein Med Ctr, 61-66, assoc mem, 66-71, bioscientist, Dept Pulmonary Dis, 71-82. *Concurrent Pos:* Fulbright res fel, Tokyo, 59-61; NIH res career develop award, 69-74; chief, Res Div, Dept Med, Grad Hosp, 82- *Mem:* Am Soc Biochem & Molecular Biol; Am Soc Invest Path; Am Soc Microbiol; Am Chem Soc; Sigma Xi; Am Thoracic Soc. *Res:* Membrane structure, synthesis and function; etiology of emphysema and pulmonary fibrosis; action of proteinases on cell membranes; regulation of neutrophil function during inflammation. *Mailing Add:* 6532 N 12th St Melrose Park PA 19126-3640

**WEINBAUM, SHELDON,** FLUID PHYSICS, CHEMICAL ENGINEERING. *Current Pos:* from asst prof to prof mech eng, 67-80, Herbert G Kayser chair prof eng, 80-86, DISTINGUISHED PROF MECH ENG, CITY COL NEW YORK, 86- *Personal Data:* b Brooklyn, NY, July 26, 37; m 62, Alexandra T Wolkowicz; c Alys & Daniel. *Educ:* Rensselaer Polytech Inst, BAE, 59; Harvard Univ, SM, 60, PhD(eng), 63. *Honors & Awards:* Pub Serv Award, Fund for the City of New York, 88; Melville Medal, 96. *Prof Exp:* Mem res staff, Sperry Rand Res Ctr, 63-64; prin scientist, Avco Everett Res Lab, 64; theoret aerodynamicist, Gen Elec Space Sci Lab, 64-67, prin scientist, 67. *Concurrent Pos:* Consult, Avco Everett Res Lab, 60-61, Wilmer Eye Inst, Sch Med, Johns Hopkins Univ, 67-70, Gen Elec Co, 68-69 & Boeing Sci Res Labs, 68-70; vis prof, Physiol Flow Studies Unit Imp Col Sci Tech, London, 73-74; sr fel Sci Res Coun, Gt Brit, 74; Russell Springer vis prof mech eng, Univ Calif, Berkeley, 79; vis prof mech eng, Mass Inst Technol, 80-81; creativity grant award, NSF, 85; Gordon McKay Prize fel, Harvard Univ, 59; NSF fel, 60; dir, City Col Consortial Ctr Biomed Eng. *Mem:* Nat Acad Eng; fel Am Soc Mech Engrs; fel Am Phys Soc; fel Am Inst Med Biol Eng; sr mem Biomed Eng Soc. *Res:* Fluid mechanics; biofluid mechanics; bioheat transfer; biophysics; two phase flow; low Reynolds number flow; high speed gas dynamics; interacting boundary layers and wakes; heat transfer; mechanics. *Mailing Add:* Dept Mech Eng 140th St & Convent Ave New York NY 10031. *Fax:* 212-650-8010

**WEINBERG, ALVIN MARTIN,** NUCLEAR PHYSICS. *Current Pos:* dir, 75-85, DISTINGUISHED FEL, INST ENERGY ANALYSIS, 85- *Personal Data:* b Chicago, Ill, Apr 20, 15; m 40, 74; c 2. *Educ:* Univ Chicago, AB, 35, MS, 36, PhD(physics), 39. *Hon Degrees:* LLD, Univ Chattanooga, 63, Alfred Univ & Denison Col, 67; ScD, Univ of the Pac, 66, Worcester Polytech Inst, 71, Univ Rochester & Butler Univ, 73, Wake Forest Univ, 74 & Univ Louisville, 78; EngD, Stevens Inst Technol, 73. *Honors & Awards:* Atoms for Peace Award, 60; Lawrence Mem Award, US AEC, 69; Heinrich Hertz Prize, Univ Karlsruhe, 75; Award, NY Acad Sci; Enrico Fermi Award, 80; Harvey Prize, Technion, 82. *Prof Exp:* Asst math biophys, Univ Chicago, 39-41, physicist, Metall Lab, 41-45; physicist, Clinton Labs, Tenn, 45-48; dir, Physics Div, Oak Ridge Nat Lab, 48-49, res dir, 49-55, dir, 55-74; dir, Off Energy Res & Develop, Fed Energy Admin, 74. *Concurrent Pos:* Mem sci adv bd, USAF, 56-59; mem, President's Sci Adv Comt, 60-62; Regents' lectr, Univ Calif, 66 & 78; distinguished fel, Inst Energy Anal, 85- *Mem:* Nat Acad Sci; Nat Acad Eng; Am Philos Soc; fel Am Nuclear Soc (pres, 59-60); Royal Neth Acad Sci; Am Acad Arts & Sci. *Res:* Nuclear energy; mathematical theory of nerve function; science policy; energy analysis. *Mailing Add:* 111 Moylan Lane Oak Ridge TN 37830

**WEINBERG, BARBARA LEE HUBERMAN,** MOLECULAR BIOLOGY. *Current Pos:* CONSULT, TECHNOL CTR, SILICON VALLEY, 90- *Personal Data:* b New York, NY, Nov 28, 34; m 57, Daniel; c Kenneth, Linda (Roselaar) & Sanford. *Educ:* City Col New York, BS, 55; Yale Univ, MS, 58; Duke Univ, PhD(biochem), 64. *Prof Exp:* Asst prof org chem & microbiol, Marymount Col, 79-80; fel endocrine res, Res Inst Hosp Joint Dis, 80-81; fel biochem, NY Med Col, 81-84; consult, 84-86. *Mem:* AAAS; Sigma Xi. *Res:* Recombinant plasmids have been constructed to study synthesis and regulation of expression of genes for initiation factor-3 and other synthetases; analysis of molecular mechanisms at level of transcriptional or translational control. *Mailing Add:* 1844 Schooldale Dr San Jose CA 95124-1136

**WEINBERG, BERND,** SPEECH PATHOLOGY. *Current Pos:* dir, 87-96, ASSOC INSTNL RELS, RES CORP TECHNOL, 96- *Personal Data:* b Chicago, Ill, Jan 30, 40. *Educ:* State Univ NY, BS, 61; Ind Univ, MA, 63, PhD, 65. *Prof Exp:* Prof otolaryngol, Sch Med & prof speech path, Sch Dent, Ind Univ, 64-66; res fel speech sci, Nat Inst Dent Res, 66-68; dir speech res lab, Med Ctr, Ind Univ, Indianapolis, 68-74; prof & dept head, audiol & speech sci, Purdue Univ, West Lafayette, 74-87. *Mem:* Acoust Soc Am; Am Speech & Hearing Asn. *Res:* Speech acoustics; speech physiology; speech restretion follow laryngectomy. *Mailing Add:* Res Corp Technol 101 N Wilmot Suite 600 Tucson AZ 85711. *Fax:* 520-748-0075

**WEINBERG, CRISPIN BERNARD,** VASCULAR APPROACHES TO TUMOR THERAPY, TISSUE ENGINEERING. *Current Pos:* FOUNDER, ANGIO-ONCOL SCI INC, 94- *Personal Data:* b Minneapolis, Minn, Jan 13, 51; m 80, Deborah A Levey; c 3. *Educ:* Univ Chicago, SB & SM, 73; Harvard Univ, PhD(neurobiol), 80. *Prof Exp:* Teaching fel neurobiol, Harvard Univ, 73-76; res fel, Mass Inst Technol, 81-84; dir BVE res, Organogenesis Inc, 85-90, dir, Graft Artery Prog, 91-92, Biotechnol consult, 93. *Mem:* Am Soc Cell Biol; AAAS. *Res:* Developing cancer therapies combining anti-tumor vasculature and anti-angionesis stragegies; previously developed a biological vascular graft based on principle of guided tissue regeneration. *Mailing Add:* 25 Beals St Brookline MA 02146. *E-Mail:* cbweinberg@delphi.com

**WEINBERG, DANIEL I,** COMPUTER ENGINEERING, ELECTROMAGNETIC FIELD HAZARDS. *Current Pos:* CONSULT, 90- *Personal Data:* b New York, NY, July 11, 28; m 57, Barbara Huberman; c Kenneth, Sanford & Linda (Roselaar). *Educ:* Clarkson Univ, BEE, 48; Duke Univ, MS, 62, PhD(physiol), 69. *Prof Exp:* Engr, Fairchild Engine & Airplane Corp, 48-51; sr engr, Atomic Prod Div, Gen Elec Co, 51-57; assoc, Astra, Inc, Conn & NC, 57-59, mgr med eng, 59-64; staff engr, Adv Systs Develop Div, IBM Corp, 64-70, adv systs engr, Data Processing Div, 70-75 & Gen Systs Div, 75-78, adv systs anal, 78-80, sr engr internal telecommun, 81-86, sr engr & scientist, Santa Teresa Lab, 87-90. *Concurrent Pos:* Consult, 57-64; res assoc, Med Ctr, Duke Univ, 60-64; assoc, Col Physicians & Surgeons, Columbia Univ, 65-69; adv lab safety, Bd Educ, Scarsdale, NY, 81-84; Tech Mus Innovation, 90- *Mem:* Inst Elec & Electronics Engrs. *Res:* Application of engineering to solution of biological research and medical problems; computers in medicine and instrumentation; electrical safety in medicine; cardiac electrophysiology; physiological monitoring; instrumentation and measurement; control of nonionizing electromagnetic fields from industrial facilities; communications systems; biological effects of electromagnetic fields. *Mailing Add:* 1844 Schooldale Dr San Jose CA 95124-1136. *E-Mail:* danw@svpal.org

**WEINBERG, DAVID S,** PATHOLOGY. *Current Pos:* ASSOC PROF PATH, BRIGHAM & WOMENS HOSP, 82- *Personal Data:* b Philadelphia, Pa, Feb 5, 49. *Educ:* Temple Univ, BS, 71; NY Univ Med Sch, MS, 75, PhD(immunol), 77, MD, 77. *Mem:* Am Soc Clin Path; Am Immunol Soc; Int Immunol Soc. *Res:* Pathology. *Mailing Add:* Dept Path Brigham & Womens Hosp 75 Francis St Boston MA 02115

**WEINBERG, DAVID SAMUEL,** ORGANIC ANALYTICAL CHEMISTRY. *Current Pos:* SECT MGR, SOUTHERN RES INST, ALA, 83- *Personal Data:* b St Louis, Mo, Feb 15, 38; m 61; c 2. *Educ:* Univ Ariz, BS, 60, PhD(phys org chem), 65. *Prof Exp:* Res assoc, Stanford Univ, 64-65; res chemist, Phillips Petrol Co, Okla, 65-71; group leader, Owens-Ill Co, Ohio, 71-79; sect mgr, Sverdrup Technol, Inc, Tenn, 79-83. *Mem:* Am Chem Soc. *Res:* Structure and mechanism in organic chemistry; trace organic analysis. *Mailing Add:* 600 Belle Terre Circle Birmingham AL 35226-2420

**WEINBERG, ELLIOT CARL,** MATHEMATICS. *Current Pos:* From instr to asst prof, 60-66, ASSOC PROF MATH, UNIV ILL, URBANA, 66-, DIR UNDERGRAD STUDIES IN MATH, 88- *Personal Data:* b Chicago, Ill, Aug 17, 32; m 62, 79, Rosalind; c Leah, Audrey, Avital & Maayan. *Educ:* Purdue Univ, BA, 56, MS, 58, PhD(math), 61. *Mem:* Am Math Soc; Math Asn Am. *Res:* Ordered algebraic structures. *Mailing Add:* Dept Math Univ Ill 1409 W Green St Urbana IL 61801. *E-Mail:* weinberg@math.uiuc.edu

**WEINBERG, ELLIOT HILLEL,** SOLID STATE PHYSICS. *Current Pos:* RETIRED. *Personal Data:* b Duluth, Minn, Dec 28, 24; m 47; c 2. *Educ:* Univ Mich, BS & MS, 47; Univ Iowa, PhD(physics), 53. *Prof Exp:* Asst, Univ Mich, 42-43, res assoc, 47-48, from instr to assoc prof physics, 49-58; res physicist, Mass Inst Technol, 48-49; prof & chmn dept, NDak State Univ, 58-62; chief scientist, San Francisco Br, 62-67, dir div phys sci, 67-71, liaison scientist, London, 65-66, dir res Off Naval Res, 71-79; dir, Navy Ctr Int Sci & Technol, Naval Grad Sch, Monterey, Calif, 83-90. *Concurrent Pos:* Mem, Col Physics Comn Rev, 62. *Mem:* AAAS; Am Phys Soc; Am Soc Eng Educ; Am Asn Physics Teachers. *Res:* Solid state physics; meteorology; atmospheric and underwater optics; laser physics and applications; foreign science and technology. *Mailing Add:* 167 Littlefield Rd Monterey CA 93940. *E-Mail:* ellweinb@redshift.com

**WEINBERG, ERIC S,** DEVELOPMENTAL BIOLOGY, NEURAL DEVELOPMENT. *Current Pos:* assoc prof, 79-96, chair, Grad Group Molecular Biol, 87-91, PROF DEPT BIOL, UNIV PA, 96- *Personal Data:* b New York, NY, May 15, 42; c Tanya. *Educ:* Univ Rochester, BA, 63; Rockefeller Univ, PhD(develop biol), 69. *Prof Exp:* Helen Hay Whitney Found res fel, Univ Palermo, Italy, 69-70, Lab Molecular Embryol, Naples, 70-71, Univ Edinburgh, 71-72; asst prof, Dept Biol, Johns Hopkins Univ, 72-79. *Concurrent Pos:* Mem, Molecular Biol Study Sect, NIH, 83-87, Biol Sci 1 Study Sect, 96-; vis scientist, Max-Planck-Inst Develop Biol, 91. *Mem:* Am Soc Develop Biol. *Res:* Anterior grain formation, neural specification, inner ear development, heart development and sometogenesis, all using the zebrafish as a model system. *Mailing Add:* Dept Biol Univ Pa Philadelphia PA 19104. *Fax:* 215-898-8780; *E-Mail:* eweinber@sas.upenn.edu

**WEINBERG, ERICK JAMES,** QUANTUM FIELD THEORY. *Current Pos:* from asst prof to assoc prof, 75-87, PROF PHYSICS, COLUMBIA UNIV, 87- *Personal Data:* b Ossining, NY, Aug 29, 47; m 72; c 2. *Educ:* Manhattan Col, BS, 68; Harvard Univ, MA, 69, PhD(physics), 73. *Prof Exp:* Mem, Inst Advan Study, 73-75. *Concurrent Pos:* Alfred P Sloan Found fel, 78-80. *Mem:* Am Phys Soc. *Res:* Theoretical elementary particle physics and quantum field theory, including the study of the very early universe. *Mailing Add:* Physics Dept Columbia Univ New York NY 10027. *Fax:* 212-932-3169

**WEINBERG, EUGENE DAVID,** MEDICAL MICROBIOLOGY. *Current Pos:* from instr to assoc prof, 50-61, assoc dean res & grad develop, 77-79, PROF MICROBIOL & MED SCI, IND UNIV, BLOOMINGTON, 61- *Personal Data:* b Chicago, Ill, Mar 4, 22; m 49; c 4. *Educ:* Univ Chicago, BS, 42, MS, 48, PhD(microbiol), 50. *Prof Exp:* Asst instr microbiol, Univ Chicago, 47-50. *Mem:* AAAS; Am Soc Microbiol; fel Am Acad Microbiol. *Res:* Roles of trace metals and of metal-binding agents in microbial physiology and in chemotherapy; nutritional immunity; antimicrobial compounds; environmental control of secondary metabolism. *Mailing Add:* Med Sci Prog Ind Univ Myers Hall Bloomington IN 47405-4401

**WEINBERG, FRED,** MATERIALS SCIENCE ENGINEERING. *Current Pos:* prof, 67-90, EMER PROF METALL, UNIV BC, 90- *Personal Data:* b Poland, Apr 3, 25; nat Can; m 56; c 1. *Educ:* Univ Toronto, BASc, 47, MA, 48, PhD(metall), 51. *Honors & Awards:* Robert Woolson Hunt Award, Am Inst Mech Engrs, 80; Alcan Award, Can Inst Mining & Metall, 80. *Prof Exp:* Res scientist, Phys Metall Div, Mines Br, Can Dept Energy, Mines & Resources, 51-67, head, Metal Physics Sect, 61-67. *Concurrent Pos:* Vis prof, Cavendish Lab, Cambridge Univ, 62-63 & Hebrew Univ, Jerusalem, 75-76; head, Dept Metall Eng, Univ BC, 80. *Mem:* Fel Am Inst Mining, Metall & Petrol Eng; fel Metall Soc; fel Can Inst Metall; Royal Soc Can. *Res:* Metal physics; deformation and solidification of metals. *Mailing Add:* Dept Metal & Mat Eng Rm 309 Univ BC 6350 Stores Rd Vancouver BC V6T 1Z4 Can

**WEINBERG, I JACK,** COMPUTER SCIENCE, APPLIED MATHEMATICS. *Current Pos:* PROF, UNIV LOWELL, 80- *Personal Data:* b New York, NY, May 25, 35; m 58; c 2. *Educ:* Yeshiva Univ, BA, 56; Mass Inst Technol, SM, 58, PhD(math), 61. *Prof Exp:* Mgr math, Avco Corp, 61-70; assoc prof math, Lowell Technol Inst, 70-73, prof, 73-80. *Concurrent Pos:* Instr, Northeastern Grad Sch Arts & Sci, 64-69. *Mem:* Am Math Soc; Soc Indust & Appl Math; Asn Comput Mach; Math Asn Am. *Res:* Numerical analysis; differential equations; theory of elasticity. *Mailing Add:* 84 Rawson Rd Brookline MA 02146-4508

**WEINBERG, IRVING,** physics, for more information see previous edition

**WEINBERG, JERRY L,** astrophysics, atmospheric physics, for more information see previous edition

**WEINBERG, LOUIS,** NETWORK THEORY, APPLIED MATHEMATICS. *Current Pos:* PROF, DEPT MATH & COMPUT SCI, GRAD SCH, CITY UNIV NY. *Personal Data:* b July 15, 19; m 51, Isabella Goldin; c Amy, Mark & Paul. *Educ:* Brooklyn Col, AB, 41; Harvard Univ, SM, 47; Mass Inst Technol, ScD(elec eng), 51. *Prof Exp:* Instr elec eng, Mass Inst Technol, 47-51; res physicist & head commun & networks res sect, Hughes Aircraft Co, 51-61; vpres info processing, Conductron Corp, 61-64; vis prof elec eng, Univ Mich, 64-65; prof elec eng, City Col NY, 65-90. *Concurrent Pos:* Lectr, Univ Calif, Los Angeles, 52-54; vis assoc prof, Univ Southern Calif, 55-56; vis prof, Calif Inst Technol, 58-59; vchmn comn VI, Int Union Radio Sci, 60; NSF grant, City Col NY, 66-68, Res Found grant, 70-72; consult, Gen Elec Co & IBM, T J Watson Res Ctr; vis prof math eng, Univ Tokyo, 79; res fel, Japan Soc Prom Sci, 79. *Mem:* Fel AAAS; Am Soc Eng Educ; fel Inst Elec & Electronics Engrs; fel NY Acad Sci. *Res:* Network analysis; synthesis of lumped networks and lumped-distributed networks; graphs and matroids; games, computers, and switching networks; fault detection and test pattern generation. *Mailing Add:* 11 Woodland St Tenafly NJ 07670-2309. *E-Mail:* pymgc@cunyvm.cuny.edu

**WEINBERG, MARC STEVEN,** AERONAUTICAL ENGINEERING, INERTIAL INSTRUMENTS. *Current Pos:* STAFF ENGR INERTIAL GUID, CHARLES STARK DRAPER LAB, 75-, GROUP LEADER, 87- *Personal Data:* b Boston, Mass, Aug 9, 48; m 71, Judith Omansky; c Hannah & Eli. *Educ:* Mass Inst Technol, BS & MS, 71, ME, 73, PhD(mech eng), 74. *Prof Exp:* Res asst ground transp, Mech Eng Dept, Mass Inst Technol, 71-74; mil officer gas turbine engines, Aeronaut Syst Div, USAF, 74-75. *Concurrent Pos:* Nat Sci Fel, 71-73; Norway Sci fel, 84. *Mem:* Am Soc Mech Engrs; Am Inst Aeronaut & Astronaut. *Res:* Inertial navigation gyroscopes and accelerometers; applied control and estimation; microfabrication; micromachining. *Mailing Add:* Charles Stark Draper Lab Inc 555 Tech Sq MS 37 Cambridge MA 02139. *E-Mail:* mweinberg@draper.com

**WEINBERG, MYRON SIMON,** TOXICOLOGY, RESEARCH ADMINISTRATION. *Current Pos:* PRES, WEINBERG CONSULT GROUP INC, 83- *Personal Data:* b New York, NY, July 18, 30; m 54; c 3. *Educ:* NY Univ, BA, 50; Fordham Univ, BS, 54; Univ Md, MS, 56, PhD(med chem, pharmacol), 58. *Prof Exp:* Res assoc med, Sinai Hosp, Baltimore, 56-58; chemist, Ortho Res Found, NJ, 58-59; chief chemist, Norwalk Hosp, Conn, 59-65; assoc dir biol opers, Food & Drug Res Labs, NY, 65-67; dir biol sci lab, Foster D Snell, Inc, 67-68, exec vpres, 69-70, pres, 70-73; vpres, Church & Dwight Co, Inc, 73-77; sr vpres, Booz, Allen & Hamilton, Inc, 77-83. *Concurrent Pos:* Prof, Med Sch, Georgetown Univ, lectr, City Col New York & Fairfield Univ. *Mem:* Fel Royal Soc; fel Royal Soc Health; Am Soc Clin Pharmacol & Chemother; Am Chem Soc; AAAS; fel Am Inst Chem; fel Am Inst Chem Eng. *Res:* Human and animal testing of chemicals; pharmaceuticals; cosmetics; governmental liaison and regulatory advice; research management; regulatory administration and compliance; biology; new uses for chemicals; new business opportunities; litigation strategy; legal and regulatory strategy. *Mailing Add:* Box 19125 Washington DC 20036-9125

**WEINBERG, PHILIP,** COMMUNICATIONS, ELECTRICAL ENGINEERING. *Current Pos:* prof & head dept, Bradley Univ, 56-77, dean Col Commun & Fine Arts, 78-86, dean, Col Eng & Technol, 86-89, EMER PROF ENG & TECHNOL, BRADLEY UNIV, 89- *Personal Data:* b New York, NY, Dec 13, 25; m 47, Jaffe; c Frederic M, Susan G & Andrea L. *Educ:* Univ Denver, BSEE, 50; Stanford Univ, MSEE, 51. *Hon Degrees:* LHD, Bradley Univ, 71. *Prof Exp:* Instr elec eng, Univ NMex, 52; asst prof, Univ Utah, 53-56. *Concurrent Pos:* Pres, Ill Valley Pub Telecommun Corp, 69-; dir, West Cent Ill Educ Telecommun Corp, 77-85. *Res:* Urban telecommunications; information utilities. *Mailing Add:* Global Commun Ctr Bradley Univ Peoria IL 61625

**WEINBERG, ROBERT A,** MOLECULAR BIOLOGY. *Current Pos:* res assoc, 72-73, from asst prof to assoc prof, Dept Biol & Ctr Cancer Res, 73-82, PROF BIOL, MASS INST TECHNOL, CAMBRIDGE, 82-; MEM, WHITEHEAD INST BIOMED RES, CAMBRIDGE, MASS, 82- *Personal Data:* b Pittsburgh, Pa, Nov 11, 42; m 76; c 2. *Educ:* Mass Inst Technol, BS, 64, PhD(biol), 69. *Hon Degrees:* DSc, Northwestern Univ, 84, State Univ NY, Stony Brook, 88; ScD, City Univ New York, 89. *Honors & Awards:* Millard Schult Lectr, Mass Gen Hosp, 82, Warren Triennial Prize, 83; Robert Koch Found Medal, Bonn, Ger, 83; Hammer Cancer Found Award & US Steel Found Award, Nat Acad Sci, 84; Howard Taylor Ricketts Award, Univ Chicago Med Ctr, 84; Brown-Hazen Award, NY State Dept Health, 84; Antonio Feltrinelli Prize, Nat Acad Lincei, Rome, 84; Bristol-Myer Award for Distinguished Achievement in Cancer Res, 84; Katherine Berkann Judd Award, Mem Sloan-Kettering Cancer Ctr, 86; Sloan Prize, Gen Motors Cancer Res Found, 87; Lucy Wortham James Award, Soc Surg Oncol, 89; Res Recognition Award, Samuel Roberts Noble Found, 90; Nat Medal of Sci, 97. *Prof Exp:* Instr biol, Stillman Col, Ala, 65-66; fel, Weizmann Inst, 69-70 & Salk Inst, 70-72. *Concurrent Pos:* Fel, Helen Hay Whitney Found, 70; res scholar award, Am Cancer Soc, 74-77; Rita Allen Found scholar, 76-80; chmn, Sci Panel Oncogen Res, Inst Med-Nat Acad Sci, 84, Med Consumers Adv Comt, Mass Inst Technol, 88- & Comt Biol Warfare, Fedn Am Scientist, 89-; Am Cancer Soc res prof, Whitehead Inst Biomed Res & Mass Inst Technol, 85-; distinguished basic scientist award, Milken Family Med Found, 90; Lila Gruber cancer res award, Am Acad Dermat, 90; mem adv bd, Nat Coun, Fedn Am Scientists, Inst Molecular Path, Austria, Comt Responsible Conduct Res, US Inst Med & Weizmann Inst, Israel. *Mem:* Nat Acad Sci; fel AAAS; fel Am Acad Arts & Sci. *Res:* Gene transfer, allowing the detection and isolation of a series of genes from human tumor cells, each of which is capable of inducing the normal cell to undergo conversion to a tumor cell; determine how oncogenes and tumor suppressor genes fit together in the complex circuitry that controls cell growth. *Mailing Add:* Whitehead Inst Biomed Res Rm 367 9 Cambridge Ctr Cambridge MA 02142

**WEINBERG, ROBERT P,** THERMAL PHYSIOLOGY. *Current Pos:* RES PHYSIOLOGIST, US NAVAL MED RES INST, 83- *Personal Data:* b Gary, Ind, Feb 12, 55; m 85; c 1. *Educ:* Purdue Univ, BS, 77; Ind Univ, PhD(physiol), 82. *Mem:* Sigma Xi; NY Acad Sci; Am Physiol Soc; Inst Elec & Electronics Engrs. *Res:* Thermal protection in cold environments; diving. *Mailing Add:* US Naval Med Res Inst 8901 Wisconsin Ave Code 5212 Bethesda MD 20889. *Fax:* 301-295-0782

**WEINBERG, ROGER,** BIOSTATISTICS. *Current Pos:* PROF BIOMET, MED CTR, LA STATE UNIV, NEW ORLEANS, 72- *Personal Data:* b New York, NY, Jan 1, 31. *Educ:* Univ Tex, PhD(genetics), 54; Univ Mich, Ann Arbor, PhD(comput sci), 70. *Prof Exp:* USPHS fel microbiol, Calif Inst Technol, 57-58; from instr to asst prof bact, Univ Pittsburgh, 58-65; USPHS spec fel biostatist, Univ Mich, Ann Arbor, 65-68, res assoc logic of comput, 68-70; assoc prof comput sci, Kans State Univ, 70-72. *Mem:* Biometric Soc; Asn Comput Mach. *Res:* Computer applications to medicine. *Mailing Add:* Dept Biomet La State Univ Med Ctr 1542 Tulane Ave New Orleans LA 70112-2825

**WEINBERG, SIDNEY B,** pathology; deceased, see previous edition for last biography

**WEINBERG, STEVEN,** THEORETICAL PHYSICS. *Current Pos:* JOSEY PROF SCI, UNIV TEX, AUSTIN, 82- *Personal Data:* b New York, NY, May 3, 33; m 54; c 1. *Educ:* Cornell Univ, AB, 54; Princeton Univ, PhD(physics), 57. *Hon Degrees:* DSc, Knox Col & Univ Chicago, 78, Univ Rochester & Yale Univ, 79, City Univ New York, 80, Clark Univ, 82 & Dartmouth Col, 84, Univ Salamanca, 92, Univ Barcelona, 96; DLitt, Wash Col, 85; Dr, Weizmann Inst, 85 & Columbia Univ, 90. *Honors & Awards:* Nobel Prize in Physics, 79; Nat Medal Sci, 91; Morris Loeb Lectr, Harvard Univ, 66; J R Oppenheimer Prize, 73; Am Inst Physics-US Steel Found Sci Writing Award, 77; Richtmeyer Lectr, Am Asn Physics Teachers, 74; Scott Lectr, Cavendish Lab, Cambridge Univ, 75; Dannie Heineman Prize, 77; Silliman Lectr, Yale Univ, 77; Elliot Cresson Medal, Franklin Inst, 79; Madison Medal, Princeton Univ, 91; Lauritsen Lectr, Calif Inst Technol, 79; Shalit Lectr, Weizmann Inst, 79; Henry Lectr, Princeton Univ, 79; Schild Lectr, Univ Tex, 79; Bampton Lectr, Columbia Univ, 83; Hilldale Lectr, Univ Wis, 85; Klein Lectr, Univ Stockholm, 89. *Prof Exp:* Instr physics, Columbia Univ, 57-59; res assoc, Lawrence Radiation Lab, Univ Calif, Berkeley, 59-60, from asst prof to prof physics, 60-69; prof, Mass Inst Technol, 69-73; Higgins prof physics, Harvard Univ, 73-83. *Concurrent Pos:* Consult, Inst Defense Anal, 60-73; Sloan Found fel, 61-65; vis prof, Mass Inst Technol, 67-69; consult, US Arms Control & Disarmament Agency, 71-73; counr, Am Phys Soc, 72-75; consult, Stanford Res Inst, 73-; sr scientist, Smithsonian Astrophys Observ, 73-; mem, Bd Overseers Superconducting Supercollider, 83-86; Morris Loeb Lectr, Harvard Univ, 83-; sr consult, Smithsonian Astrophys Observ, 83-; dir, Jerusalem Sch Theoret Physics, 83-; vis prof, Harvard, 83-; coun scholar, Libr Cong, 82-85; mem, Sci Bk Comt, Sloan Found, 85; mem, Supercollider Site Eval Comt, Nat Acad Sci-Nat Acad Eng, 87, Supercollider Sci Policy Comt, 89-92; pres, Philos Soc Tex, 92; bd govs, Headliner's Found, 94. *Mem:* Nat Acad Sci; Am Acad Arts & Sci; Am Phys Soc; Int Astron Union; Royal Soc London; Am Philos Soc. *Res:* Elementary particles; field theory; cosmology. *Mailing Add:* Dept Physics Univ Tex Austin TX 78712-1081. *Fax:* 512-471-4888; *E-Mail:* weinberg@physics.utexas.edu

**WEINBERG, WENDY C,** PATHOLOGY. *Current Pos:* SR STAFF FEL PATH, NIH, 91- *Personal Data:* b Chicago, Ill. *Educ:* Univ Ill, BS, 78; Northwestern Univ, PhD(path), 87. *Prof Exp:* Fel path, Nat Cancer Inst, 87-91. *Mem:* Am Soc Cancer Res; Am Soc Cell Biol; AAAS. *Res:* Pathology. *Mailing Add:* Nat Cancer Inst Bldg 37 Rm 3B25 NIH Bethesda MD 20895-4255

**WEINBERG, WILLIAM HENRY,** CHEMICAL ENGINEERING, CHEMICAL PHYSICS. *Current Pos:* PROF CHEM ENG & CHEM, UNIV CALIF, SANTA BARBARA, 89- *Personal Data:* b Columbia, SC, Dec 5, 44; m 89, Ann E Muir. *Educ:* Univ SC, BS, 66; Univ Calif, Berkeley, PhD(chem eng), 71. *Honors & Awards:* Wayne B Nottingham Prize, Am Phys Soc, 72; Victor K Lamer Award, Am Chem Soc, 72, Kendall Award, 91; A P Colburn Award, Am Inst Chem Engrs, 81; Alexander von Humboldt Sr US Scientist Award, 82. *Prof Exp:* NATO fel phys chem, Cambridge Univ, 71-72; from asst prof to assoc prof chem eng, Calif Inst Technol, 72-74, prof chem eng & chem physics, 77-89, Chevron distinguished prof, 81-86. *Concurrent Pos:* Prin investr, US-USSR Exchange Prog Chem Catalysis, 74-80; Alfred P Sloan Found fel, 76; Camille & Henry Dreyfus Found teacher-scholar, 76; vis prof chem, Harvard Univ, 80; vis prof, Univ Pittsburgh, 87-88, Oxford Univ, 91; ed, Appl Surf Sci, Surface Sci Reports, Langmuir, Surface Sci. *Mem:* Nat Acad Eng; Am Chem Soc; Am Inst Chem Engrs; fel Am Vacuum Soc; fel Am Phys Soc; AAAS. *Res:* Physics and chemistry of solids and solid surfaces; gas-surface interactions; chemical adsorption and heterogeneously catalyzed surface reactions; semiconductor surface chemistry and physics. *Mailing Add:* Dept Chem Eng Univ Calif Santa Barbara CA 91306. *Fax:* 805-893-4731; *E-Mail:* chari@engineering.ucsb.edu

**WEINBERGER, CHARLES BRIAN,** CHEMICAL ENGINEERING. *Current Pos:* from asst prof to assoc prof, 72-92, actg dept head, 81-82, DEPT HEAD, DREXEL UNIV, 88-, PROF CHEM ENG, 92- *Personal Data:* b Macon, Ga, Jan 31, 41; m 76; c 2. *Educ:* Univ Calif, Berkeley, BS, 63; Univ Mich, Ann Arbor, MSE, 64, PhD(chem eng), 70. *Prof Exp:* Engr, Shell Develop Co, 64-66; res engr, Eng Tech Lab, E I du Pont de Nemours & Co, Inc, 70-72. *Mem:* Am Inst Chem Engrs; Soc Rheology; Sigma Xi. *Res:* Extension flow of non-Newtonian fluids; polymer processing; fluid mechanics. *Mailing Add:* Dept Chem Eng Drexel Univ Philadelphia PA 19104

**WEINBERGER, DANIEL R,** BRAIN DISORDER RESEARCH. *Current Pos:* res ward dir, Adult Psychiat Br, Intramural Res Prog, NIMH, 77-78, staff psychiatrist, 77-81, head, Clin Neuropsychiat & Neurobehav Unit, St Elizabeths Hosp, 81-82, chief, Sect Clin Neuropsychiat & Neurobehav, Neuropsychiat Br, 83-86, CHIEF, CLIN BRAIN DIS BR, INTRAMURAL RES PROG, NEUROSCI CTR, ST ELIZABETHS, WASHINGTON, DC, 86- *Personal Data:* b New York, NY, May 24, 47; c 1. *Educ:* Johns Hopkins Univ, BA, 69; Univ Pa, MD, 73; Am Bd Psychiat & Neurol, cert psychiat, 78, cert neurol, 84. *Honors & Awards:* Morton Prince Award, Am Psychopath Asn, 84; Judith B Silver Award, Nat Alliance Ment Ill, 85; Joel Elkes Int Award, Am Col Neuropsychopharmacol, 89; Leber Award, Nat Alliance Res Schizophrenia & Depressions. *Prof Exp:* Grad fel med, Univ Calif, Los Angeles Sch Med, 73-74; clin fel psychiat, Harvard Med Sch, 74-77. *Concurrent Pos:* Gen med prac, Bridgewater Med Ctr, Mass, 74-76; emergency rm physician, Cardinal Cushing Gen Hosp, Mass, 74-77; asst clin prof psychiat, George Washington Univ, 78-81; dir, Movement Dis, Dementia Clin & Nat Inst Neurol & Commun Dis & Stroke, NIH, 83-86, Behav Neurol Serv, St Elizabeths Hosp, 83-88. *Mem:* AMA; Am Psychiat Asn; AAAS; Am Acad Neurol; Soc Neurosci; Am Neuropsychiat Asn. *Res:* Neurology; psychiatry. *Mailing Add:* 5415 Connecticut Ave W Washington DC 20015-2765

**WEINBERGER, DOREEN ANNE,** OPTICAL PHYSICS, NONLINEAR OPTICS. *Current Pos:* ASSOC PROF PHYSICS, SMITH COL, 91- *Personal Data:* b Bethlehem, Pa, Jan 27, 54. *Educ:* Mt Holyoke Col, BA, 75; Univ Ariz, MS, 80, PhD(optical sci), 84. *Honors & Awards:* Presidential Young Investr Award, NSF, 86. *Prof Exp:* Sr tech aide solid state physics, Bell Tel Labs, 74; res student solar physics, Kitt Peak Nat Observ, 75; res asst physics, Mass Inst Technol, 75-78; res asst optical sci, Univ Ariz, 78-84; asst prof elec eng & comput sci, Univ Mich, 84-91. *Concurrent Pos:* Trainee physics, Gen Motors Labs, 78; assoc fac instr, Pima Community Col, Tucson, Ariz, 80-81. *Mem:* Optical Soc Am; Sigma Xi; Asn Women Sci; AAAS; Am Phys Soc. *Res:* Nonlinearities in optical fibers; second harmonic generation; nonlinear pulse propagation; physics of optical nonlinearities of semiconductors and heterostructures; optical waveguides; optical tests of quantum mechanics. *Mailing Add:* Dept Phys Smith Col Northampton MA 01063-0001

**WEINBERGER, EDWARD BERTRAM,** computer science; deceased, see previous edition for last biography

**WEINBERGER, HANS FELIX,** APPLIED MATHEMATICS. *Current Pos:* assoc prof, Univ Minn, 60-61, head, Sch Math, 67-69, dir, Inst Math & Appln, 81-87, PROF MATH, UNIV MINN, MINNEAPOLIS, 61- *Personal Data:* b Vienna, Austria, Sept 27, 28; nat US; m 57, Laura Larrick; c 3. *Educ:* Carnegie Inst Technol, BS & MS, 48, ScD, 50. *Prof Exp:* Fel, Inst Fluid Dynamics & Appl Math, Univ Md, 50-51, res assoc, 51-53, from asst res prof to assoc res prof, 53-60. *Concurrent Pos:* Vis mem, Courant Inst Math Sci, NY Univ, 66-67; vis prof, Univ Ariz, 70-71 & Stanford Univ, 72-73. *Mem:* Am Math Soc; Soc Natural Philos; Soc Indust & Appl Math. *Res:* Approximation of eigenvalues, quadratic functionals and solutions of partial differential equations. *Mailing Add:* Dept Math Vincent Hall 206 Church St SE Minneapolis MN 55455. *Fax:* 612-626-2017; *E-Mail:* hfw@math.umn.edu

**WEINBERGER, LEON WALTER,** SANITARY ENGINEERING. *Current Pos:* PRES, LEON W WEINBERGER & ASSOC, LTD & ENVIRON QUAL SYSTS INC, 71- *Personal Data:* b New York, NY, Aug 28, 23; m 50; c 3. *Educ:* Cooper Union, BCE, 43; Mass Inst Technol, MS, 47, ScD, 49. *Prof Exp:* Eng draftsman, NAm Aviation, Inc, 43; asst, Mass Inst Technol, 47-48, res assoc, 48-49; from asst prof to assoc prof civil & sanit eng, Case Inst Technol, 49-62; chief, Basic & Appl Sci Br, Div Water Supply & Pollution Control, USPHS, 63-66; asst comnr res & develop, Fed Water Pollution Control Admin, 66-68; vpres environ control mgt, Zurn Industs Inc, 68-70. *Concurrent Pos:* Nat Found Fels consult engr, 49-62; chmn, Am Sci Team, Am-Ger Coop Exchange Water Pollution; US rep, Comt Water Pollution, Orgn Econ Coop & Develop; mem, Expert Adv Panel Environ Health; WHO; mem comts water & pollution, Nat Acad Sci; US rep, Int Oceanog Comt; mem, Comt Water Resources Res; prof, Nat Grad Univ & univ seminar assoc, Columbia Univ, 68-; mem adv bd, Dept Natural Resources, State Md, 74-77. *Mem:* Fel Am Soc Civil Engrs; Water Pollution Control Fedn; Am Water Works Asn; Am Acad Environ Engrs. *Res:* Water supply and treatment; waste water treatment; water pollution control. *Mailing Add:* 14 Coolfont Rd Berkeley Springs WV 25411-3601

**WEINBERGER, LESTER,** OPTICAL COMPUTING, OPTICAL SENSORS. *Current Pos:* SR SCIENTIST, ADVAN CONCEPT & PLANS OFF, US ARMY RES LAB, ADELPHI, MD, 87- *Personal Data:* b Feb 21, 23; US citizen; div; c Jeffrey. *Educ:* Rutgers Univ, BS, 44; Stevens Inst Technol, MS, 52; Univ Pa, PhD(org chem), 59. *Prof Exp:* Fel biophys, Columbia Univ, 62-63; sect chief, color electronic imaging systs, Xerox Corp, 63-69; res dir, SCM Corp, 69-72; res assoc polymers, Sch Eng, Columbia Univ, 72-73; mgr explor res, Polychrome Corp, 73-80; head, Counterfeit Deterence Br, Dept Treas, Bur Engraving & Printing, 80-87. *Mem:* Am Chem Soc; Soc Photog Scientists & Engrs; AAAS; Sigma Xi; Inst Elec & Electronics Engrs; Inventors Soc Am. *Res:* Laser imaging systems; novel organic photoconductors, both monomeric and polymeric; invention and development of organic/inorganic optical switching devices-diodes and optical gates; awarded 30 patents. *Mailing Add:* 11920 Frost Valley Way Potomac MD 20854. *E-Mail:* lwein@arl.mil

**WEINBERGER, MILES,** PEDIATRICS, RESPIRATORY DISEASE. *Current Pos:* Assoc prof pediat & pharmacol, 75-80, PROF PEDIAT, UNIV IOWA, 80-, DIR, PEDIAT ALLERGY & PULMONARY DIV & DIR, CYSTIC FIBROSIS CTR, 75- *Personal Data:* b McKeesport, Pa, June 28, 38; m 93, Leslie Kramer; c David, Marc, Sharon & Kendra. *Educ:* Univ Pittsburgh, MD, 65. *Mem:* Fel Am Acad Allergy; fel Am Acad Pediat; fel Soc Pediat Res; Am Thoracic Soc; fel Am Col Allergy. *Res:* Pharmacotherapy of asthma; clinical pharmacology of antiasthmatic drugs; pediatric allergy; pulmonology. *Mailing Add:* Dept Pediat Univ Iowa Hosp Iowa City IA 52242

**WEINBERGER, MYRON HILMAR,** INTERNAL MEDICINE, HYPERTENSION. *Current Pos:* from asst prof to assoc prof, 69-76, PROF MED, SCH MED, IND UNIV, 76- *Personal Data:* b Cincinnati, Ohio, Sept 21, 37; m 60, Myrna M Rosenberg; c 3. *Educ:* Ind Univ, AB, 59, MD, 63. *Honors & Awards:* Robert Tigerstedt Award, Am Soc Hypertension. *Prof Exp:* Intern internal med, Sch Med, Ind Univ, 63-64, resident, 64-66; res fel endocrinol, Sch Med, Stanford Univ, 66-69. *Concurrent Pos:* Investr, Specialized Ctr Res Hypertension, Ind Univ, 70-75, prin investr-dir, 75-; mem prog comt, Coun High Blood Pressure Res, 78. *Mem:* Am Heart Asn; Am Fedn Clin Res; Endocrine Soc; Am Soc Hypertension; Int Soc Hypertension. *Res:* Blood pressure control; salt and water metabolism, hormones; circulation; kidney; adrenal; high blood pressure. *Mailing Add:* Ind Univ Sch Med 541 Clinical Dr Rm 423 Indianapolis IN 46202-5111. *Fax:* 317-278-0673; *E-Mail:* mweinbe@indyvax.iupui.edu

**WEINBERGER, NORMAN MALCOLM,** PSYCHOBIOLOGY, NEUROPHYSIOLOGY. *Current Pos:* from asst prof to assoc prof, 65-74, chmn, 75-78, PROF PSYCHOBIOL, UNIV CALIF, IRVINE, 74- *Personal Data:* b Cleveland, Ohio, Aug 10, 35; m 54; c 7. *Educ:* Western Reserve Univ, AB, 57, MS, 59, PhD(psychol), 61. *Prof Exp:* Res physiological, Univ Calif, Los Angeles, 64. *Concurrent Pos:* Consult ed, Physiol Psychol; assoc ed, Exp Neurol; found mem, Ctr Neurobiol Learning & Memory. *Mem:* AAAS; Soc Neurosci; Int Brain Res Orgn; NY Acad Sci. *Res:* Neurobiological bases of learning and attention. *Mailing Add:* Dept Psychobiol Univ Calif Irvine CA 92717-0001

**WEINBERGER, PETER JAY,** MATHEMATICS, COMPUTER SCIENCE. *Current Pos:* mem staff comput sci res, 76-83, dept head, Comput Sci Res, 83-90, DIR, SOFTWARE & SYSTS RES LAB, BELL LABS, 90- *Personal Data:* b New York, NY, Aug 6, 42. *Educ:* Swarthmore Col, BA, 64; Univ Calif, Berkeley, PhD(math), 69. *Prof Exp:* Mem tech staff, Bellcomm Inc, 69-70; asst prof math, Univ Mich, Ann Arbor, 70-76. *Mem:* Am Math Soc; Asn Comput Mach; Math Asn Am; Sigma Xi. *Res:* Number theory; operating systems and compilers; data bases and distributed computing. *Mailing Add:* 22 Clinton Ave 295 N Maple Ave Rm 6329H2 Maplewood NJ 07040

**WEINBERGER, STEVEN ELLIOTT,** PULMONARY DISEASE. *Current Pos:* from instr to assoc prof, 78-95, PROF MED, HARVARD UNIV SCH MED, 95-; CHIEF, PULMONARY UNIT, BETH ISRAEL HOSP, BOSTON, 92- *Personal Data:* b Philadelphia, Pa, Jan 28, 49; m 70; c 2. *Educ:* Princeton Univ, AB, 69; Harvard Univ, MD, 73. *Prof Exp:* Clin assoc, Pulmonary Br, Nat Heart, Lung & Blood Inst, NIH, 75-78; clin dir, Pulmonary Unit, Beth Israel Hosp, Boston, 86-92. *Concurrent Pos:* Assoc chmn educ, Harvard Univ Sch Med, 92- *Mem:* Am Col Physicians; Am Thoracic Soc; Am Col Chest Physicians. *Res:* Pulmonary disease, sarcoidosis. *Mailing Add:* Pulmonary Unit Beth Israel Hosp 330 Brookline Ave Boston MA 02215

**WEINBLATT, ANITA,** IMMUNOLOGY. *Current Pos:* SCI RES ADMIN IMMUNOL, NIH, 87- *Personal Data:* b Boston, Mass. *Educ:* Mt Wachusett Commun Col, BS, 64; Tufts Univ, PhD(physiol), 77. *Prof Exp:* Res immunologist, Am Type Culture Collection Inst, 80-87. *Mem:* Am Asn Immunologists; Sigma Xi. *Res:* Immunology. *Mailing Add:* DRG IMS NIH 6701 Rockledge Dr MSC 7812 Bethesda MD 20892-7812

**WEINBRANDT, RICHARD M,** PETROLEUM ENGINEERING. *Current Pos:* CONSULT, ENHANCED OIL RECOVERY, 81- *Personal Data:* b Lexington, Nebr, July 20, 44; m 67, 87; c 3. *Educ:* Univ Calif, Berkeley, BS, 67, MS, 68; Stanford Univ, PhD(petrol eng), 72. *Prof Exp:* Res engr, Chevron Oil Field Res, 68-69 & Union Oil Co, 71-76; mgr eng, Aminoil, 76-81. *Concurrent Pos:* Teaching asst, Univ Calif, Berkeley, 68 & Stanford Univ, 71; consult, Alcoa, Aminoil, Dow Chem, Gary Energy, PQ Energy Serv Sci Software, Westinghouse, Bichel & Brewer, Pan Can Petrol, Wiser Oil, Exxon Petro Ecuador, Intevep, PEMEX, Polish Oil & Gas, OXY, FINA Stauffer, Egyptian Gen Petrol & Anshutz. *Mem:* Am Inst Mining, Metall & Petrol Engrs; Soc Petrol Engrs. *Res:* Improved oil recovery methods; reservoir simulation; fluid flow in porous media. *Mailing Add:* Enhanced Oil Recovery Consult Skyline RanchBox 20 Jackson WY 83001

**WEINDLING, JOACHIM I(GNACE),** OPTIMIZATION, ENGINEERING ECONOMY. *Current Pos:* chmn, Dept Opers Res & Syst Analysis, 73-74, dir, Opers Res Prog, 70-92, PROF SYSTS ENG, POLYTECH UNIV, NY, 69-,. *Personal Data:* b Antwerp, Belg, Feb 18, 27; US citizen; m 54, Evelyn Marder; c Marsha (Pottash), Steven, & Elissa. *Educ:* City Col NY, BME, 48; Columbia Univ, MS, 49, PhD(opers res), 67. *Prof Exp:* Lectr mech eng, City Col NY, 48-51; chief engr, Korfund Dynamics, Inc, 51-59; vpres eng, Vibration Mountings & Controls, Inc, 59-61; assoc prof mech eng, Drexel Inst, 61-67; prof eng, PMC Cols, 67-69. *Concurrent Pos:* Lectr, City Col NY, 51-61; adj assoc prof, NY Univ, 58-61; indust consult, 61- *Mem:* Am Soc Mech Engrs; Opers Res Soc Am; Am Soc Eng Educ; Am Inst Indust Engrs; Sigma Xi. *Res:* Markov chains; reliability; computer-aided optimum designs; shock and vibration controls; mathematical programming; optimal radiation therapy planning. *Mailing Add:* 204 Fairfield Dr Wallingford PA 19086-6814

**WEINDRUCH, RICHARD,** GERIATRICS, NUTRITION. *Current Pos:* from asst prof to assoc prof, 90-96, ASSOC DIR, INST AGING, UNIV WIS, MADISON, 90-, MEM, CLIN CANCER CTR, 91-, PROF, DEPT MED, 96- *Personal Data:* b Mar 18, 50; m 83, Robin Steinhardt. *Educ:* Univ Ill, Urbana, BS, 72, MS, 73; Univ Calif, Los Angeles, PhD(exp path), 78. *Honors & Awards:* Bio-Serv Award, Am Inst Nutrit, 88. *Prof Exp:* Fel gerontology, Univ Calif, Los Angeles, 78-80, adj asst prof, Dept Path, 80-86, adj assoc prof, 86-87; health scientist adminr, Nat Inst Aging, NIH, Bethesda, 87-90. *Concurrent Pos:* Chmn, Geriatrics & Rehab Study Sect, NIH, 94- *Mem:* Fel Gerontological Soc Am; Oxygen Soc. *Res:* Investigates the retardation of aging and diseases by caloric restriction in rodents and non human primates; studying the possibility that reduced oxidative stress is causally involved. *Mailing Add:* Vet Admin Hosp GRECC 11G 2500 Overlook Terr Madison WI 53705. *Fax:* 608-262-7648; *E-Mail:* rhweindr@facstaff.wisc.edu

**WEINER, ANDREW MARC,** ELECTRICAL ENGINEERING. *Current Pos:* PROF ELEC ENG, PURDUE UNIV, 92- *Personal Data:* b Boston, Mass, July 25, 58; m 89, Brenda Joyce Garland. *Educ:* Mass Inst Technol, SB, 79, SM, 81, ScD, 84. *Honors & Awards:* Adolph Lomb Award, Optical Soc Am, 90. *Prof Exp:* Mem tech staff, Bellcore, 84-89, dist mgr, 89-92. *Concurrent Pos:* Assoc ed, J Quantum Electronics, Inst Elec & Electronics Engrs, 88-94, Photonics Tech Lett, 94-95. *Mem:* Fel Optical Soc Am; fel Inst Elec & Electronics Engrs. *Res:* Techniques for manipulating the shapes of ultrashort laser pulses; ultrafast nonlinear optics. *Mailing Add:* Sch Elec Eng Purdue Univ West Lafayette IN 47907-1285

**WEINER, BRIAN LEWIS,** MATHEMATICAL STRUCTURE OF REDUCED DENSITY MATRICES, COHERENT STATES. *Current Pos:* asst prof, 86-90, ASSOC PROF, DEPT PHYSICS, PA STATE UNIV, 90- *Personal Data:* b London, Eng, June 21, 45; m 80, Ulla Mansikka; c Emily J. *Educ:* Univ Leicester, BSc, 66, PhD(math & chem), 70. *Prof Exp:* Inst math, Leicester Col Art & Technol, 69-70; fel, Dept Math, Queens Univ, Ont, Can, 70-73; Royal Soc fel, Quantum Chem Group, Uppsala Univ, Sweden, 73-75, res asst, 75-80, res asst math, Dept Quantum Chem, 79-80; vis assoc prof, Quantum Theory Proj, Univ Fla, 80-81, Dept Comput Sci, 84-85, Dept Math, 85-86. *Concurrent Pos:* Vis assoc prof, Dept Chem, Univ Fla, Gainsville, 80-86. *Mem:* Am Phys Soc; Am Math Soc. *Res:* Theoretical development of quantum mechanical methods for the description of processes involving atomic, molecular and condensed matter systems, especially the use of lie group methods; quantum chemical calculations of reactions on surfaces; molecular spectra and percursor reactions in the formation of soot; group theoretic structure of Quantum mechanics. *Mailing Add:* 1036 Crabapple Dr State Col PA 16801. *E-Mail:* bqw@psu.edu

**WEINER, CHARLES,** HISTORY OF PHYSICS, HISTORY OF BIOLOGY. *Current Pos:* Dir proj hist of recent physics in US, Am Inst Physics, 64-65, dir, Ctr for Hist of Physics, 65-74, PROF HIST SCI & TECHNOL, MASS INST TECHNOL, 74-, DIR, ORAL HIST PROG, 75- *Personal Data:* b Brooklyn, NY, Aug 11, 31; div; c 1. *Educ:* Case Inst Technol, BS, 60, MA, 63, PhD(hist of sci), 65. *Concurrent Pos:* NSF grants, 65-79 & 81; mem adv comt, Nat Union Catalog of Manuscript Collections, Libr of Cong, 65-71; vis lectr, Polytech Inst Brooklyn, 66; proj dir comt hist of contemp physics, Joint Am Inst Physics-Am Acad Arts & Sci, 66-74; Guggenheim fel, Niels Bohr Inst, Copenhagen, Denmark, 70-71. *Mem:* Fel AAAS; Hist Sci Soc; Soc Hist Technol; Am Hist Asn; Orgn Am Historians. *Res:* History of twentieth century science; social impact of science and technology; development of the physical sciences in the United States; history of genetic engineering and of university-industry relations; ethical issues in science and engineering. *Mailing Add:* Dept Technol & Human Affairs Mass Inst Technol 77 Mass Ave Cambridge MA 02139-4307

**WEINER, DANIEL LEE,** PHARMACOKINETICS, NONLINEAR MODELING. *Current Pos:* VPRES STATIST OPERS, QUINTILES, INC, 94- *Personal Data:* b Dayton, Ky, Apr 13, 50; m 91, Gail Knowlton; c Brian & Michael. *Educ:* Univ Ky, BS, 72, MS, 73, PhD(statist), 76. *Prof Exp:* Head, biostatist, Merrell Dow Pharmaceut, Div Dow Chem Co, 82-85; exec vpres, Statist Consult Inc, 85-88; vpres, Res Data Mgt, Syntex Res, 88-93. *Concurrent Pos:* Adj assist prof, Dept Environ Health, Div Epidemiol & Biostat, Col Med, Univ Cincinnati, 79-81, adj assoc prof, 82-87, adj assoc prof pharmacokinetics, 85-93. *Mem:* Am Statist Asn; Biomet Soc. *Res:* Bioavailability, pharmacokinetic and pharmacodynamic modeling; application of statistics to the evaluation of drugs. *Mailing Add:* Quintiles Inc PO Box 13979 Research Triangle Park NC 27709-3979. *Fax:* 919-941-6258

**WEINER, EUGENE ROBERT,** PHYSICAL CHEMISTRY. *Current Pos:* from asst prof to assoc prof, 65-84, PROF CHEM, UNIV DENVER, 84- *Personal Data:* b Pittsburgh, Pa, Sept 16, 28; m 52, 81; c 4. *Educ:* Ohio Univ, BS, 50; Univ Ill, MS, 57; Johns Hopkins Univ, PhD(chem), 63. *Prof Exp:* Sect chief appl physics sect, Interior Ballistics Lab, Aberdeen Proving Grounds, Md, 50-55; instr, McCoy Col, 62-63; sr scientist, Johnston Labs, Inc, 63-65. *Concurrent Pos:* Consult, US Geol Surv, 70- *Mem:* Am Chem Soc; Am Phys Soc. *Res:* Atomic and molecular collisions; photochemistry at liquid-solid interface; gas phase ion-molecule reactions, free radical reactions, gas kinetics and energetics; laser Raman spectroscopy. *Mailing Add:* 1484 S Eudora St Denver CO 80222-3528

**WEINER, HENRY,** BIOCHEMISTRY, MOLECULAR BIOLOGY. *Current Pos:* from asst prof to assoc prof, 66-76, PROF BIOCHEM, PURDUE UNIV, LAFAYETTE, 76- *Personal Data:* b Cleveland, Ohio, May 18, 37; m 60, Esther R Blankfeld; c Suzanna & Alexander. *Educ:* Case Inst Technol, BS, 59; Purdue Univ, PhD(org chem), 63. *Prof Exp:* Res assoc biol, Brookhaven Nat Lab, 63-65; NIH res fel biochem, Karolinska Inst, Sweden, 65-66. *Concurrent Pos:* Adj biochem dept, Ind Univ Sch Med, Indianapolis; sr scientist, Nat Inst Alchohol Abuse & Alcoholism, 83-93. *Mem:* Res Soc Alcoholism; Am Soc Biol Chem; Am Asn Univ Prof; Int Soc Biomed Res Alcoholism. *Res:* Enzymology; protein chemistry; enzyme precursors; acetaldehyde metabolism; protein import into mitochondria structure of signal peptides. *Mailing Add:* Dept Biochem Purdue Univ West Lafayette IN 47907-1153. *Fax:* 765-494-7897; *E-Mail:* weiner@aclcb.purdue.edu

**WEINER, HERBERT,** PSYCHIATRY, NEUROLOGY. *Current Pos:* from instr to assoc prof, 55-66, PROF PSYCHIAT, ALBERT EINSTEIN COL MED, 66-, PROF NEUROSCI, 74-; PROF PSYCHIAT, UNIV CALIF, LOS ANGELES, 82- *Personal Data:* b Vienna, Austria, Feb 6, 21; nat US; m 53, Dora Bierer; c Tim, Richard & Anthony. *Educ:* Harvard Univ, AB, 43; Columbia Univ, MD, 46. *Hon Degrees:* Dr, Tech Univ, Munich, 88. *Honors & Awards:* Spec Presidential Commendation from Am Psychiat Asn, 87. *Prof Exp:* Exchange fel neurol, 50; USPHS fel psychiat, 52-53; instr psychiat, Sch Med & Dent, Univ Rochester, 53-54; guest lectr, Wash Sch Psychiat, 54-55. *Concurrent Pos:* Asst vis psychiatrist & chief adult psychiat in-patient serv, Bronx Munic Hosp Ctr, 55-56, asst vis physician, 56-61, assoc vis psychiatrist, 56-; consult, Home Care Dept, Montefiore Hosp, 55-59; USPHS fel ment health, 56-58 & res career develop award, 62-65; Stern fel, 59-62; mem bd trustees, Scarborough Country Day Sch, 62-; mem ment health study sect, Div Res Grants, NIH, 62-, chmn, 66-67; attend psychiatrist & dir educ prog, Div Psychiat, Montefiore Hosp & Med Ctr, New York, 65-69, chmn dept psychiat, 69-; fel, Ctr Advan Study Behav Sci, Stanford Univ; ed-in-chief, Psychosom Med, 72-82; hon sr Fulbright fel, 89; Alexander von Humboldt prize, 89. *Mem:* AAAS; Am Acad Neurol; Am Psychosom Soc (pres, 71-72); Asn Res Nerv & Dis (pres, 79-80); Psychiat Res Soc; Acad Behav Med Res (pres, 83-84); Int Col Psychosom Med (pres, 87-89). *Res:* Neurophysiology; psychophysiology; experimental model of gastric erosions; anorexia nervosa. *Mailing Add:* Neuropsychiat Inst UCLA Health Sci Ctr Los Angeles CA 90024-1759

**WEINER, HOWARD JACOB,** PROBABILITY. *Current Pos:* from asst prof to assoc prof, 65-72, vchmn dept, 76-80, PROF MATH, UNIV CALIF, DAVIS, 72- *Personal Data:* b Chicago, Ill, Aug 26, 37; m 71. *Educ:* Ill Inst Technol, BSEE, 58; Univ Chicago, MS, 60; Stanford Univ, PhD(statist), 64. *Prof Exp:* Actg asst prof statist, Univ Calif, Berkeley, 64; asst prof, Stanford Univ, 64-65. *Concurrent Pos:* Vis assoc prof statist, Stanford Univ, 76, vis res assoc, 77 & 78. *Mem:* Math Asn Am. *Res:* Age dependent branching processes; sequential random packing. *Mailing Add:* PO Box 72030 Davis CA 95617

**WEINER, IRWIN M,** PHARMACOLOGY. *Current Pos:* assoc prof, 66-68, PROF PHARMACOL, STATE UNIV NY UPSTATE MED CTR, 68-, DEAN, COL MED, 87-, VPRES MED & BIOMED EDUC, 87- *Personal Data:* b New York, NY, Nov 5, 30; c 2. *Educ:* Syracuse Univ, AB, 52; State Univ NY, MD, 56. *Prof Exp:* Fel pharmacol, Sch Med, Johns Hopkins Univ, 56-58, from instr to asst prof pharmacol & exp therapeut, 58-66. *Concurrent Pos:* Fel pharmacol & exp therapeut, Sch Med, Johns Hopkins Univ, 58-60; vis prof molecular biol, Albert Einstein Col Med, 64-65; USPHS res career develop award, 64-69; mem study sect pharmacol & exp therapeut, NIH, 65-69; ed, J Pharmacol & Exp Therapeut, 65-72; consult, Sterling Winthrop Res Inst, 68-82. *Mem:* AAAS; Am Soc Pharmacol & Exp Therapeut; NY Acad Sci. *Res:* Pharmacology of diuretics and uricosuric agents; renal excretion of drugs; intestinal absorption of bile salts; bacterial cell wall biosynthesis. *Mailing Add:* State Univ NY Health Sci Ctr Brooklyn 450 Clarkson Ave Brooklyn NY 11203-2098

**WEINER, JACOB,** PLANT ECOLOGY, BOTANY. *Current Pos:* Asst prof, 78-84, ASSOC PROF BIOL, SWARTHMORE COL, 84- *Personal Data:* b Brooklyn, NY, Dec 24, 47. *Educ:* Antioch Col, BA, 70; Univ Mich, MS, 74; Univ Ore, PhD(biol), 78. *Concurrent Pos:* Trainee syst biol, NIH, 77-78; vis scholar, Harvard Univ, 81; vis scientist, Univ Col NWales, 81-82, Imp Col, Silwood Park, 89-90 & Univ Basel, 90; Smithsonian postdoctoral fel, 84. *Mem:* Brit Ecol Soc; Ecol Soc Am; Bot Soc Am; Sigma Xi. *Res:* Plant population biology. *Mailing Add:* Dept Biol Swarthmore Col 500 College Ave Swarthmore PA 19081-1390

**WEINER, JEROME HARRIS,** APPLIED MATHEMATICS. *Current Pos:* L HERBERT BALLOU UNIV PROF ENG & PHYSICS, BROWN UNIV, 68- *Personal Data:* b New York, NY, Apr 5, 23; m 50; c 2. *Educ:* Cooper Union, BME, 43; Columbia Univ, AM, 47, PhD(math), 52. *Prof Exp:* Asst tech dir, Heat & Mass Flow Analyzer Lab, Columbia Univ, 51-57, asst prof civil eng & eng mech, 52-56, prof mech eng, 56-68. *Mem:* Am Math Soc; Am Phys Soc. *Res:* Thermal stresses; crystal defects. *Mailing Add:* 24 Taber Ave Providence RI 02906-4113

**WEINER, JOEL HIRSCH,** MICROBIOLOGY, MOLECULAR BIOLOGY. *Current Pos:* from asst prof to assoc prof, 76-84, PROF BIOCHEM, UNIV ALTA, 84-, ASSOC DEAN RES, FAC MED, 93- *Personal Data:* b Montreal, Que, Dec 23, 46; m 71, Linda Van Duyne; c Philip & Isaac. *Educ:* McGill Univ, BSc, 68; Cornell Univ, PhD(biochem), 72. *Prof Exp:* Fel biochem, Stanford Univ, 72-76. *Concurrent Pos:* Med Res Coun scholar, Univ Alta, 76-81; regional dir, Med Res Coun, 93-96; chair, Asn Can Med Cols Res Comt; vpres, Can Soc Biochem & Molecular Biol & Cell Biol; assoc dean res, Fac Med Oral Health Scis. *Mem:* Am Soc Biol Chemists; Am Soc Microbiol; Can Biochem Soc; AAAS; Sigma Xi. *Res:* Investigation of membrane bioenergetics using molecular biological and biochemical approaches with emphasis on bacterial anaerobic electron transport chain proteins; study of membrane protein structure and function using biochemical and biophysical techniques. *Mailing Add:* Dept Biochem Univ Alta Edmonton AB T6G 2H7 Can. *E-Mail:* jdel.weimer@ualscrta.ca

**WEINER, JOHN,** CHEMICAL PHYSICS. *Current Pos:* assoc prof, 78-83, PROF CHEM, UNIV MD, 83- *Personal Data:* b Malvern, NY, Apr 14, 43; wid; c 2. *Educ:* Pa State Univ, BS, 64; Univ Chicago, PhD(chem), 70. *Prof Exp:* Fel & lectr chem, Yale Univ, 70-73; asst prof chem, Dartmouth Col, 73-78. *Concurrent Pos:* Vis fel, Univ Paris, 77-78. *Mem:* Am Chem Soc; Am Phys Soc; AAAS; Sigma Xi; Optical Soc Am. *Res:* Reactive and inelastic collision processes in ion-molecule systems; internal state excitation leading to chemiluminescence phenomena; laser-induced excitation; ionization and reactive collisions in crossed-beam studies; optical/collisional interactions. *Mailing Add:* Dept Chem Univ Md College Park MD 20742-0001. *Fax:* 301-314-9935

**WEINER, LAWRENCE MYRON,** MICROBIOLOGY, IMMUNOLOGY. *Current Pos:* From instr to assoc prof, Wayne State Univ, 51-65, chmn dept & assoc dean, 70-72, dep dean, 72-79, dean, 79-81, PROF MICROBIOL & PATH, SCH MED, WAYNE STATE UNIV, 65- *Personal Data:* b Milwaukee, Wis, May 21, 23; m 44; c 2. *Educ:* Univ Wis, BA, 47, MS, 48, PhD(med microbiol), 51. *Concurrent Pos:* Pres, Mich State Bd Examr Basic Sci, 62-68. *Mem:* Am Soc Microbiol; Soc Exp Biol & Med. *Res:* Immunology of infectious diseases; hypersensitivity to chemical agents; clinical microbiology. *Mailing Add:* 540 E Canfield Ave Detroit MI 48201-1928

**WEINER, LESLIE PHILIP,** NEUROLOGY-MULTIPLE SCLEROSIS, IMMUNOLOGY. *Current Pos:* PROF NEUROL & MICROBIOL, UNIV SOUTHERN CALIF MED SCH, 75-, CHMN NEUROL, 79- RICHARD ANGUS GRANT SR CHMN NEUROL, 87- *Personal Data:* b Brooklyn, NY, Mar 17, 36; m 59, Judith Marilyn Hoffman; c Patrice, Allison, Matthew & Jonathan. *Educ:* Wilkes Col, BA, 57; Univ Cincinnati, MD, 61. *Prof Exp:* Fel med, Sch Med, Johns Hopkins Univ, 67-69; NIH lab fel, 69-70; from asst prof to assoc prof, Sch Med, Johns Hopkins Univ, 69-75. *Concurrent Pos:* Vis prof, FLEN Neurol Inst Buenos Aires, Arg, 96; consult, Nat Inst Neurol Dis & Stroke. *Mem:* Am Acad Neurol; AAAS; Am Soc Microbiol; Am Asn Neuropathologists; Asn Univ Profs Neurol; Am Neurol Asn. *Res:* Inflammatory responses in the brain; multiple sclerosis including gene therapy, T cell vaccines and characterizing chronic multiple sclerosis; inflammation and Alzheimer's disease. *Mailing Add:* 1510 San Pablo St Suite 646 Los Angeles CA 90033-4606. *Fax:* 213-342-5794

**WEINER, LOUIS I,** textile engineering; deceased, see previous edition for last biography

**WEINER, LOUIS MAX,** ALGEBRA, MATHEMATICS GENERAL. *Current Pos:* RETIRED. *Personal Data:* b Chicago, Ill, Nov 11, 26; m 57, June Belmont; c Howard, Joel & Todd. *Educ:* Univ Chicago, SB, 47, SM, 48, PhD(math), 51. *Prof Exp:* Asst, Univ Chicago, 48; personnel examr, Chicago Civil Serv Comn, 51-52; asst prof math, DePaul Univ, 52-58; res engr, Mech Res Div, Am Mach & Foundry Co, 58-62, supvr, Anal Sect, Gen Am Res Div, 62-64; assoc prof, Northeastern Ill Univ, 64-68, chmn dept, 68-74, prof math, 64-93. *Concurrent Pos:* Instr, Amundsen Br, Chicago City Jr Col, Oakton Community Col, 77-92; assoc ed, Math Mag, 68-72. *Mem:* Am Math Soc; Math Asn Am; Sigma Xi. *Res:* Algebra; linear algebras; operations research; slide rule type computers. *Mailing Add:* 3144 Greenleaf Wilmette IL 60091-2008

**WEINER, MATEI,** MEDICAL MYCOLOGY, ANTIBIOTIC SUSCEPTIBILITY STUDIES. *Current Pos:* SUPVR, MICROBIOL DEPT, METHODIST HOSP BROOKLYN, 70- *Personal Data:* b Bucharest, Romania, Aug 21, 33; US citizen; m 66; c 2. *Educ:* Univ Bucharest, Romania, Zoo Nic Engr, 57; Wagner Col, Staten Island, MS, 70. *Prof Exp:* Inspector & technologist, Dept Health, City Bucharest, Romania, 58-66; asst supvr & technologist, Maimonides Med Ctr, Brooklyn, 67-70. *Concurrent Pos:* Sr lectr, Sch Med Technol, Methodist Hosp Brooklyn, 71-; clin instr, Health Sci Ctr, State Univ NY, 80-; clin assoc, Tech Col, City Univ New York, 80-82. *Mem:* Am Soc Microbiol. *Res:* Senior or contributing author of 24 publications in clinical microbiology and medical research. *Mailing Add:* NY Methodist Hosp 506 Sixth St Brooklyn NY 11215

**WEINER, MURRAY,** MEDICINE. *Current Pos:* CLIN PROF MED, UNIV CINCINNATI, 72-, DIR CLIN PHARMACOL, 81- *Personal Data:* b New York, NY, Apr 18, 19; m 51; c 1. *Educ:* City Col New York, BS, 39; NY Univ, MS & MD, 43. *Prof Exp:* From instr to asst prof med, Col Med, NY Univ, 54-72; vpres & dir biol res, Geigy Res Labs, NY, 67-72; vpres res & sci affairs, Merrell-Nat Labs, 72-81. *Concurrent Pos:* Asst vis physician & consult, Bellevue Hosp, NY, 49-72, Univ Hosp, 53-72, Long Island Jewish Hosp, 54-57 & North Shore Hosp, NY, 55-72; assoc vis physician, Willard Parker Hosp, NY, 52-57 & Goldwater Mem Hosp, NY, 56-72; vis staff, Cincinnati Gen Hosp & Christian Holmes Hosp, Ohio, 72- *Mem:* Soc Exp Biol & Med; Am Physiol Soc; AMA; Am Heart Asn. *Res:* Clotting mechanism; anticoagulant and anti-inflammatory drugs; drug disposition. *Mailing Add:* Univ Cincinnati Med Ctr 234 Goodman St Logan Hall Cincinnati OH 45267-0539. *Fax:* 513-558-8581, 558-2979

**WEINER, MYRON,** PHARMACOLOGY. *Current Pos:* ASSOC PROF PHARMACOL, SCH PHARM, UNIV MD, 77- *Personal Data:* b Baltimore, Md, May 27, 43; m 87; c 2. *Educ:* Univ Md, Baltimore City, BS, 66, PhD(pharmacol), 72. *Prof Exp:* Instr pharmacol, Sch Nursing, Univ Md, Baltimore City, 67-68; instr anat & physiol, Sch Nursing, St Agnes Hosp, 68-70; instr, Catonsville Community Col, Md, 70-71; asst prof pharmacol, Sch Pharm, Univ Southern Calif, 71-77. *Concurrent Pos:* Nat Inst Aging grant, 84-85, basic res support grant, 86-88; Nat Cancer Inst grant, 73-76. *Mem:* AAAS; NY Acad Sci; Am Col Clin Pharmacol; Am Pharmaceut Asn; Am Asn Cols Pharm. *Res:* Alteration of drug biotransformation caused by cyclic nucleotides; mechanisms of altered hepatic and extrahepatic drug metabolism (oxidative and conjugative) caused by cancer, diabetes, and aging. *Mailing Add:* 4528 Stonecrest Dr Ellicott City MD 21043-6000

**WEINER, NORMAN,** PHARMACOLOGY. *Current Pos:* chmn dept, 67-77, interim dean, 83-84, PROF PHARMACOL, MED CTR, UNIV COLO, DENVER, 67- *Personal Data:* b Rochester, NY, July 13, 28; m 55; c Steven, David, Jeffrey, Gareth & Eric. *Educ:* Univ Mich, BS, 49; Harvard Med Sch, MD, 53. *Honors & Awards:* Res Career Develop Award, USPHS, 63; Kaiser Permanente Award, 74, 81; Otto Krayer Award, Am Soc Pharmacol & Exp Therapeut; Julius Axelrod Medal, FIDIA Res Found, 93. *Prof Exp:* Intern, Harvard Med Serv, Boston City Hosp, 53-54, instr pharmacol, Harvard Med Sch, 56-58, assoc, 58-61, asst prof, 61-67. *Concurrent Pos:* Dir neuropharmacol lab, Mass Ment Health Ctr, 64-67; div vpres pharmaceut discovery, Abbott Labs, 85-87. *Mem:* AAAS; Am Soc Pharmacol & Exp Therapeut; Am Soc Neurochem; Am Col Neuropsychopharmacol; Asn Med Sch Pharmacologists. *Res:* Metabolism of biologically active amines; regulation of synthesis of neurotransmitters; synthesis, storage and release of tissue amines; effect of drugs on energy metabolism of brain; ionization of drugs, drug distribution and relation to biological activity. *Mailing Add:* Dept Pharmacol C-236 Univ Colo Health Sci Ctr 4200 E Ninth Ave Denver CO 80262. *Fax:* 303-315-7097; *E-Mail:* norman.weiner@uchsc.edu

**WEINER, RICHARD,** PHYSIOLOGY. *Current Pos:* from instr to asst prof, 66-72, ASSOC PROF PHYSIOL, NEW YORK MED COL, 73- *Personal Data:* b Brooklyn, NY, Aug 21, 36; m 60; c 2. *Educ:* Long Island Univ, BS, 58; NY Univ, PhD(physiol), 65. *Prof Exp:* USPHS fel microcirc, NY Univ Med Ctr, 65, asst res scientist, 66. *Mem:* AAAS; Am Physiol Soc; Microcircuitry Soc. *Res:* Regulation of vascular smooth muscle. *Mailing Add:* 14 Horse Chestnut Rd Briarcliff Manor NY 10510

**WEINER, RICHARD D,** PSYCHIATRY. *Current Pos:* Med res assoc psychiat, Durham Vet Admin Med Ctr, 77-79, res assoc, 77-79, asst prof, 79-83, staff physician, 80-90, ASSOC PROF, DUKE UNIV MED CTR, 84-; CHIEF, PSYCHIAT SERV, DURHAM VET ADMIN MED CTR, 93- *Personal Data:* b Brooklyn, NY, Nov 25, 45; m 68; c 2. *Educ:* Mass Inst Technol, BS, 67; Univ Pa, MSE, 69; Duke Univ, PhD(physiol), 73 & MD, 73. *Concurrent Pos:* Chmn, Task Force on Electroconvulsive Ther, Am Psychiat Asn, 78. *Mem:* Am Psychiat Asn; Soc Biol Psychiat; Am EEG Soc; Col Int Neuro-Psychopharmacol. *Res:* Beneficial and adverse effects of electroconvulsive and neurophysiologic correlates of the mind. *Mailing Add:* Duke Univ Med Ctr PO Box 3309 Durham NC 27710

**WEINER, RICHARD IRA,** NEUROENDOCRINOLOGY. *Current Pos:* assoc prof, 74-80, PROF OBSTET & GYNEC & PHYSIOL, SCH MED, UNIV CALIF, SAN FRANCISC0, 80- *Personal Data:* b New York, NY, Nov 6, 40. *Educ:* Pa State Univ, BS, 63, MS, 65; Univ Calif, San Francisco, PhD(endocrinol), 69. *Prof Exp:* Fel, Brain Res Inst, Univ Calif, Los Angeles, 69-71; asst prof physiol, Univ Tenn Med Units, 71-72; asst prof anat, Sch Med, Univ Southern Calif, 72-74. *Concurrent Pos:* Mem & chmn, Biochem Endocrinol Study Sect, NIH; chmn, Grad Prog Endocrinol, Univ Calif, San Francisco. *Mem:* Endocrine Soc; Int Neuroendocrine Soc; Soc Neurosci; Am Physiol Soc. *Res:* Mechanisms of action of hypothalamic hormones in the neuroendocrine regulation of prolactin. *Mailing Add:* Dept Obstet & Gynec Univ Calif Sch Med 513 Parnassus Ave San Francisco CA 94122-2722. *Fax:* 415-753-3271

**WEINER, ROBERT ALLEN,** REACTOR MATERIALS, FUEL PIN MODELLING. *Current Pos:* sr scientist, Advan Reactors Div, 75-84, sr engr, Nuclear Fuels Div, 84-86, PRIN ENGR, NUCLEAR FUELS DIV, WESTINGHOUSE ELEC CO, 86- *Personal Data:* b New York, NY, Apr 3, 40; m 61; c 2. *Educ:* Columbia Univ, AB, 61; Harvard Univ, AM, 62, PhD(physics), 67. *Prof Exp:* Asst res physicist, Univ Calif, San Diego, 67-69; asst prof physics, Carnegie-Mellon Univ, 69-75. *Mem:* Am Nuclear Soc; AAAS; Am Phys Soc. *Res:* Irradiation damage mechanisms in metals and alloys; fast breeder reactor fuel; cladding model development; nuclear fuel rod performance. *Mailing Add:* 1433 Denniston Ave Pittsburgh PA 15217

**WEINER, RONALD MARTIN,** MICROBIOLOGY, MOLECULAR BIOLOGY. *Current Pos:* asst prof to assoc prof, 70-87, PROF MICROBIOL & CTR MARINE BIOTECH, UNIV MD, COL PARK, 87- *Personal Data:* b Brooklyn, NY, May 7, 42; m 64; c Keri, Tamra & Arin. *Educ:* Brooklyn Col, BS, 64; LI Univ, MS, 67; Iowa State Univ, PhD(microbiol), 70. *Honors & Awards:* Fulbright Award, 90. *Prof Exp:* Bacteriologist, Greenpoint, Coney Island Hosps, NY, 64-66; teaching asst, Iowa State Univ, 67-68, instr, 69-70. *Mem:* Soc Indust Microbiol; Am Soc Microbiol; Am Inst Biol Sci; fel Am Acad Microbiol. *Res:* Morphogenesis of Hyphomonas; mechanisms of procaryote-invertebrate symbiosis: settlement, exopolysaccharide films; molecular approaches to the study of microbial ecology; biofouling; bioremediation. *Mailing Add:* Dept Microbiol Univ Md College Park MD 20742. *Fax:* 301-314-9489; *E-Mail:* rw19@umail.umd.edu

**WEINER, STEPHEN DOUGLAS,** APPLIED PHYSICS. *Current Pos:* Mem staff, 65-73, assoc group leader, 73-, GROUP LEADER, LINCOLN LAB, MASS INST TECHNOL. *Personal Data:* b Philadelphia, Pa, Jan 1, 41; m 61; c 2. *Educ:* Mass Inst Technol, BS, 61, PhD(physics), 65. *Res:* Missile defense research; reentry physics; electromagnetic scattering and propagation; operations research. *Mailing Add:* Lincoln Lab Mass Inst Technol 244 Wood St Lexington MA 02173

**WEINER, STEVEN ALLAN,** PHYSICAL ORGANIC CHEMISTRY. *Current Pos:* staff scientist, Ford Motor Co, 68-74, proj mgr, Res Staff, 74-77, prin staff engr, 77-90, MGR PROCESS DEVELOP, FORD MOTOR CO, 90- *Personal Data:* b New York, NY, June 6, 42; m 71; c 1. *Educ:* Columbia Univ, AB, 63; Iowa State Univ, PhD(org chem), 67. *Honors & Awards:* Leibmann Mem Award, Am Chem Soc, 59. *Prof Exp:* Res assoc, Calif Inst Technol, 67-68. *Concurrent Pos:* Lectr, Univ Mich-Dearborn, 70-71. *Mem:* Opers Res Soc Am; Am Chem Soc; AAAS; Sigma Xi. *Res:* Photochemistry; free radical kinetics; combustion products and reactions; sodium-sulfur battery; energy storage and conversion; metal casting and heat treating; energy management; process modeling and control; manufacturing process development. *Mailing Add:* Ford Motor Co 24500 Glendale Ave Detroit MI 48239

**WEINFELD, HERBERT,** BIOCHEMISTRY. *Current Pos:* RETIRED. *Personal Data:* b New York, NY, Feb 7, 21; m 46, Norma Zukerman; c 1. *Educ:* City Col New York, BS, 42; Univ Mich, MS, 48, PhD(biochem), 52. *Prof Exp:* Asst biochem, Univ Mich, 47-49, res fel, Sloan-Kettering Inst, 51-54; instr, Inst Indust Med, NY Univ-Bellevue Med Ctr, 54-55; assoc cancer res scientist, 55-65, prin cancer res scientist, Dept Med, Roswell Park Mem Inst, 65-80. *Concurrent Pos:* Res prof biochem and chmn dept, Roswell Park Grad Div, State Univ NY, Buffalo, 71-80. *Mem:* Sigma Xi; Am Chem Soc; Am Soc Biochem & Molecular Biol. *Res:* Metabolism of nucleosides, nucleotides and nucleic acids; cellular agents controlling mitotic events. *Mailing Add:* 51 Brookville Dr Tonawanda NY 14150-7165

**WEINGARTEN, DONALD HENRY,** THEORETICAL PHYSICS. *Current Pos:* RES STAFF MEM, T J WATSON RES CTR, IBM, 83- *Personal Data:* b Boston, Mass, Feb 16, 45; m 71; c 2. *Educ:* Columbia Col, AB, 65; Columbia Univ, PhD(physics), 70. *Honors & Awards:* Rahman Prize for Comput Physics, 97. *Prof Exp:* Res assoc theoret particle physics, Fermi Nat Accelerator Lab, 69-71; res fel, Niels Bohr Inst, Univ Copenhagen, 71-73; res assoc, Lab Theoret Physics, Univ Paris XI, 73-74; res assoc, Univ Rochester, 74-76; from asst prof to assoc prof, Ind Univ, 76-83, prof physics, 83-84. *Mem:* Fel Am Phys Soc. *Res:* Theoretical particle physics; mathematical physics. *Mailing Add:* IBM TJ Watson Res Ctr PO Box 218 Yorktown Heights NY 10598. *Fax:* 914-945-4506

**WEINGARTEN, NORMAN C,** FLIGHT SIMULATION, FLYING QUALITIES. *Current Pos:* Intern, Calspan Corp, 68, res engr, 69-83, prin engr, 84-90, PROG MGR, CALSPAN CORP, 88-, SECT HEAD, 90- *Personal Data:* b Buffalo, NY, Jan 11, 47; m 69, Carole Wolkind; c Eric & Michael. *Educ:* State Univ NY, Buffalo, BS, 68. *Concurrent Pos:* Mem, Am Inst Aeronaut & Astronaut Flight Simulation Tech Comt, 85-88, Flight Mechs Comt, 96-99. *Mem:* Sr mem, Am Inst Aeronaut & Astronaut; Sigma Xi. *Res:* Flight simulation directed towards development of flight control systems and aircraft flying qualities, stability and control. *Mailing Add:* Calspan Corp 150 N Airport Dr Buffalo NY 14225. *Fax:* 716-631-6990; *E-Mail:* weingarten@calspan.com

**WEINGARTEN, VICTOR I,** ENGINEERING MECHANICS, CIVIL ENGINEERING. *Current Pos:* from assoc prof to prof, 64-96, chmn dept, 73-82, EMER PROF CIVIL ENG, UNIV SOUTHERN CALIF, 96- *Personal Data:* b New York, NY, Jan 18, 31; m 54; c 2. *Educ:* City Col NY, BME, 52; NY Univ, MSME, 54; Univ Calif, Los Angeles, PhD(eng mech), 64. *Prof Exp:* Stress analyst, Northrop Corp, 56-59; mem tech staff eng mech, TRW Systs, Inc, 59-61; mem tech staff eng mech, Aerospace Corp, 61-64. *Concurrent Pos:* Consult, Aerojet-Gen Corp, 64-65, Northrop Norair, 64-71

& Hughes Aircraft Co, 67-83. *Mem:* Am Soc Mech Engrs; Am Soc Civil Engrs. *Res:* Buckling of nuclear containment vessels; elastic stability and free vibrations of plates and shells; fluid-structure interaction problem; application of visco-elastic finite element techniques to biomechanics problems. *Mailing Add:* 3653 Malibu Dr Malibu CA 90265

**WEINGARTNER, DAVID PETER,** PHYTOPATHOLOGY, PLANT NEMATOLOGY. *Current Pos:* asst prof & asst plant pathologist, 69-75, ASSOC PROF & ASSOC PLANT PATHOLOGIST, AGR RES & EDUC CTR, INST FOOD & AGR, UNIV FLA, 75- *Personal Data:* b Escanaba, Mich, Mar 13, 39; m 64; c 2. *Educ:* Univ Mich, BS, 62; Mich State Univ, PhD(plant path), 69. *Prof Exp:* Teacher high sch, Inkster, Mich, 62-64. *Concurrent Pos:* Res award, Fla Fruit & Veg Asn, 75. *Mem:* Soc Nematol; Am Phytopath Soc; Potato Asn Am. *Res:* Nematode and disease control in vegetables; nematode population dynamics; epidemiology; disease forecasting; pest management; potato corky ringspot; early blight; bacterial wilt. *Mailing Add:* 1506 San Rafael Way St Augustine FL 32084

**WEINGARTNER, HERBERT,** PSYCHOBIOLOGY, PSYCHOPHARMACOLOGY. *Current Pos:* CHIEF, COGNITION SECT, NAT INST AGING, 91- *Personal Data:* b Karlsruhe, Ger, Apr 4, 35; US citizen; m 67; c 2. *Educ:* City Univ NY, BS, 56; Johns Hopkins Univ, MA, 62, PhD(exp psychol), 66. *Prof Exp:* Teacher math & sci, Bd Educ, New York City, 56-58; clin psychologist & lectr, Sheppard & Enoch Pratt Hosp, 61-63; from instr to asst prof psychol & assoc dir med psychol, Sch Med, Johns Hopkins Univ, 64-70; from assoc prof to prof psychol, Univ Md, 70-77; res psychologist, NIMH, 77-78, actg chief psychol, Lab Psychol & Psychopath, 78-81, chief, Unit on Cofrutive Studies, 82-86; chair, Dept Psychol, George Washington Univ, 87-90. *Concurrent Pos:* Vis scientist psychol, NIMH, 74-75 & 76-77; Gilman fel, Johns Hopkins Univ; NIH res fel; mem, Huntington's Comn, 77-78; chief, Cognitive Neurosci Sect, Nat Inst Alcohol Abuse & Alcoholism. *Mem:* Am Psychol Asn; Sigma Xi; Am Psychol Soc. *Res:* Biology of learning and memory; cognitive psychology; mood disturbance; state dependent learning; impairments on memory. *Mailing Add:* 11213 Debra Dr Potomac MD 20854

**WEINGARTNER, KARL ERNST,** UTILIZATION OF SOY BEANS. *Current Pos:* SCIENTIST, SOYBEAN UTILIZATION SPECIALIST, GRAIN LEGUME IMPROV PROG, INT INST TROP AGR, 85- *Educ:* Univ Ill, PhD(food sci). *Mailing Add:* 210 W Vermont Ave Urbana IL 61801. *Fax:* 217-333-5838

**WEINGEIST, THOMAS ALAN,** ANATOMY, OPHTHALMOLOGY. *Current Pos:* From asst prof to assoc prof, 76-83, PROF, DEPT OPHTHAL, UNIV IOWA, 83-, HEAD DEPT 86- *Personal Data:* b Jan 28, 40; m, Catherine M; c Aaron, Rachel, Robbie & David. *Educ:* Earlham Col, BA, 63; Columbia Univ, PhD(cell biol), 69, Univ Iowa, MD, 72. *Honors & Awards:* Honor Award, Am Acad Ophthal, 79, Sr Honor Award, 89. *Concurrent Pos:* Dir vitreoretinal serv, Univ Iowa, 84-86 & 92-; chief ophthal serv, Vet Admin Med Ctr, Iowa City, 80-85, consult ophthal serv, Des Moines, 87- *Mem:* Am Acad Ophthal; Asn Univ Profs Opthal. *Res:* Principle investigator for collaborative ocular melanoma study; vitreoretinal diseases. *Mailing Add:* Dept Ophthal Univ Iowa Hospitals & Clinics 200 Hawkins Dr Iowa City IA 52242-1091. *Fax:* 319-353-6030; *E-Mail:* thomas_weingeist@uiowa.edu

**WEINGOLD, ALLAN BYRNE,** OBSTETRICS & GYNECOLOGY. *Current Pos:* PROF OBSTET & GYNEC & CHMN DEPT, SCH MED, GEORGE WASHINGTON UNIV, 73- *Personal Data:* b New York, NY, Sept 2, 30; m 52; c 4. *Educ:* Oberlin Col, BA, 51; New York Med Col, MD, 55; Am Bd Obstet & Gynec, dipl, 64. *Prof Exp:* From asst prof to prof obstet & gynec, NY Med Col, 70-73, asst chmn dept, 71-73. *Concurrent Pos:* Am Cancer Soc fel gynec malignancy, 60-61; training dir, USPHS grant, 66-68; chief obstet & gynec, Metrop Hosp, NY, 67-70; consult, NIH Cancer Ctr, Walter Reed Army Med Ctr, Columbia Hosp for Women & Fairfax Hosp; mem sub-spec bd, Maternal Fetal Med, 76- *Mem:* Fel Am Col Obstet & Gynec; Am Gynec Soc; Soc Perinatal Obstetricians; Perinatal Res Soc; fel Am Col Surgeons. *Res:* Studies on monitoring of the fetal environment by endocrine, biochemical and biophysical indices. *Mailing Add:* Dept Obstet & Gynec George Washington Univ Off VPres Med Affairs 2300 Eye St NW Washington DC 20037-2396

**WEINHOLD, ALBERT RAYMOND,** PLANT PATHOLOGY. *Current Pos:* Res asst, Univ Calif, Davis, 55-57, from instr to assoc prof, 59-72, from jr plant pathologist to assoc plant pathologist, 59-72, chmn dept, Berkeley, 76-84, actg dean, Col Nat Resources, 84-86, prof, 72-92, EMER PROF PLANT PATH & PLANT PATHOLOGIST, EXP STA, UNIV CALIF, BERKELEY, 93- *Personal Data:* b Evans, Colo, Feb 14, 31; m 52, Connie Seastrand; c Albert R & Kathryn B. *Educ:* Colo State Univ, BS, 53, MS, 55; Univ Calif Davis, PhD(plantpath), 58. *Concurrent Pos:* Sr ed, Phytopath, 70-73, ed-in-chief, 73-75. *Mem:* Fel AAAS; fel Am Phytopath Soc (pres, 87-88). *Res:* Disease and pathogen physiology; soil-borne pathogens; root diseases; potato diseases. *Mailing Add:* 145 Mulford Hall Plant Path Univ Calif Berkeley CA 94720-3114

**WEINHOLD, PAUL ALLEN,** BIOCHEMISTRY. *Current Pos:* From asst prof to assoc prof, 72-84, PROF BIOCHEM, MED SCH, UNIV MICH, ANN ARBOR, 84- *Personal Data:* b Evans, Colo, Sept 23, 35; m 56, Yvonne Livingston; c Julie, Lisa, Scott & Michael. *Educ:* Colo State Univ, BS, 57; Univ Wis, PhD(biochem), 61. *Concurrent Pos:* USPHS res fel biochem, Harvard Med Sch, 63-65; res career scientist, Vet Affairs, Med Res; biochemist, Vet Affairs Hosp, 65-77, supv res biochemist, 77-90, res career scientist, 90- *Mem:* AAAS; Am Soc Biol Chemists; Am Chem Soc. *Res:* Biochemistry of development, phospholipid metabolism and control mechanisms in metabolism. *Mailing Add:* Dept Biochem Vet Admin Med Ctr Ann Arbor MI 48105

**WEINHOUSE, SIDNEY,** BIOCHEMISTRY, CANCER. *Current Pos:* SR SCIENTIST, LANKENAU MED RES CTR, 87- *Personal Data:* b Chicago, Ill, May 21, 09; c 3. *Educ:* Univ Chicago, BS, 33, PhD(chem), 36; Dr Med & Surg, Unoiv Chieti, Italy, 79. *Hon Degrees:* DSc, Med Col Pa, 72, Temple Univ, 76, Jefferson Med Col, 85. *Honors & Awards:* Philadelphia Sect Award, Am Chem Soc, 66; G H A Clowes Award, Am Asn Cancer Res, 72; Papanicolaou Award, 76; Lucy Wortham James Award, Soc Surg Oncol, 79; Nat Award, Am Cancer Soc; Achievement Award, Am Cancer Soc, 87. *Prof Exp:* Coman fel org chem, Univ Chicago, 41-44; head biochem res, Houdry Process Corp, Pa, 44-47; biochem res dir, Res Inst, Temple Univ, 47-50, prof chem & biol, chmn, Div Biochem, Inst Cancer Res & head, Dept Metab Chem, Lankenau Hosp Res Inst, 50-57, dir, Fels Res Inst, 63-74, prof, 57-79, emer prof biochem, Sch Med, 80-87. *Concurrent Pos:* Mem biochem study sect, NIH, 53-58 & nat adv coun, Nat Cancer Inst, Dept HEW, 58-62; assoc dir, Fels Res Inst, 61-63; chmn comt biol chem, Div Chem & Chem Technol, Nat Acad Sci-Nat Res Coun, 62-64; mem sci adv comt, Damon Runyon Mem Fund, 52-60 & Environ Health Sci Adv Comt, 68-72. *Mem:* Nat Acad Sci; Am Soc Biol Chemists; Am Soc Biol Chem & Molecular Biol; Soc Exp Biol & Med; Am Chem Soc; Am Cancer Soc; fel NY Acad Sci; hon mem Japanese Asn Cancer Res. *Res:* Carbohydrate and fatty acid metabolism in normal and neoplastic cells; dietary and hormonal regulation of enzymes of carbohydrate and fatty acid metabolism in liver tumors; effects of hormones on gluconeogenesis; comparative studies on control of respiration and glycolysis in liver and liver tumors. *Mailing Add:* Lakenau Med Res Ctr 100 Lancaster Ave Wynnewood PA 19096

**WEINIG, SHELDON,** METALLURGY. *Current Pos:* RETIRED. *Personal Data:* b New York, NY, Jan 15, 28; div; c 3. *Educ:* NY Univ, BME, 51; Columbia Univ, MS, 53, DEngSc, 55. *Hon Degrees:* LLD, St Thomas Aquinas Col. *Honors & Awards:* Semmy Award, Semiconductor Equipment & Mat Inst, 80. *Prof Exp:* Pres, chmn & chief exec officer, Mat Res Corp, 57-90, chmn bd, 90-95. *Concurrent Pos:* Mem adv comt, US Dept Com, 76-78; dir, Semiconductor Equip & Mat Inst, 76-; mem adv comt, Polytech Univ NY, 77-; mem, US-Japan Coop Sci Comt. *Mem:* Nat Acad Sci; AAAS; Am Inst Mining, Metall & Petrol Engrs; Am Soc Metals; Am Phys Soc. *Res:* Electronic materials. *Mailing Add:* 25 Sutton Pl New York NY 10022

**WEININGER, STEPHEN JOEL,** ORGANIC CHEMISTRY. *Current Pos:* from asst prof to assoc prof, 65-77, PROF CHEM, WORCESTER POLYTECH INST, 77- *Personal Data:* b New York, NY, Mar 28, 37; m 61, Jennifer Barkham; c Elliot, J Daniel & David. *Educ:* Brooklyn Col, BA, 57; Univ Pa, PhD(org chem), 64. *Prof Exp:* Sr demonstr phys chem, Univ Durham, 64-65. *Concurrent Pos:* Vis prof, Colo State Univ, 76-78; consult, Natick Res & Develop Command, US Army, 79-90; Danforth assoc, 79-85; Mellon fel, Prog Sci Tech & Sci, Mass Inst Technol, 87. *Mem:* Am Chem Soc; Soc Lit & Sci; Hist Sci Soc; Soc Hist Chem Alchem. *Res:* Chemistry of hot intermediates; organic synthesis; laser photochemistry; photoelectron transfer; intramolecular energy transfer; historical relations of chemistry and physics; role of language in science. *Mailing Add:* Dept Chem Worcester Polytech Inst Worcester MA 01609-2280. *E-Mail:* stevejw@wpi.edu

**WEINKAM, ROBERT JOSEPH,** MEDICINAL CHEMISTRY, ANALYTICAL CHEMISTRY. *Current Pos:* DIR ANALYTICAL SCI, SONOFI RES, MALVERN, PA, 91- *Personal Data:* b Cincinnati, Ohio, Dec 27, 42; m, Mona Kwan; c 4. *Educ:* Xavier Univ, Ohio, BS, 64; Duquesne Univ, PhD(chem), 68. *Prof Exp:* Fel, Syra Res Inst Calif, 68-69; fel, Sch Med, Univ Calif, San Francisco, 69-70, asst prof pharmaceut chem, 71-80, asst prof neurosurg, 78-80; assoc prof med chem, Purdue Univ, West Lafayette, 80-84; dir, Allurgen, Irvine, Calif, 84-91. *Concurrent Pos:* Res Career Develop award, 75-80. *Mem:* Am Chem Soc; Am Soc Mass Spectros. *Res:* Biomedical application of mass spectrometry; drug metabolism; pharmaceutical research and development. *Mailing Add:* Sanofi Res Great Valley Rd Malvern PA 19355

**WEINLAND, STUART LOUIS,** CERAMICS PROCESSING. *Current Pos:* SR SCI ASSOC, LAWRENCE LIVERMORE NAT LAB, 76- *Personal Data:* b Dayton, Ohio, Sept 25, 40. *Educ:* Alfred Univ, BS, 62; Miss State Univ, MS, 65. *Prof Exp:* Assoc ceramic engr, Babcock & Wilcox Co, 62-63; scientist, Lockheed Missiles & Space Co, 65-67; sr engr, Martin Marietta Corp, 68-70. *Mem:* Am Ceramic Soc. *Res:* Ceramic materials and fabrication processes, including ceramic-metal composites, cements and fibrous insulation. *Mailing Add:* PO Box 808 L-369 Livermore CA 94551

**WEINMAN, JAMES A,** METEOROLOGY. *Current Pos:* SR SCIENTIST, GODDARD SPACE FLIGHT CTR, NASA, GREENBELT, MD. *Honors & Awards:* Losey Atmospheric Sci Award, Am Inst Aeronaut & Astronaut, 95. *Mailing Add:* Goddard Space Flight Crt NASA Greenbelt Rd Greenbelt MD 20771

**WEINMANN, CLARENCE JACOB,** PARASITOLOGY. *Current Pos:* from asst prof to assoc prof, 62-75, PROF ENTOM & PARASITOL, UNIV CALIF, BERKELEY, 75- *Personal Data:* b Oakland, Calif, May 27, 25; m 57; c 2. *Educ:* Univ Calif, BS, 50, PhD(parasitol), 58. *Prof Exp:* Instr microbiol, Col Med, Univ Fla, 58-60; res fel biol, Rice Univ, 60-62. *Concurrent Pos:* Fel trop med & parasitol, Univ Cent Am, 59. *Mem:* AAAS; Am Soc Parasitol; Entom Soc Am; Am Soc Trop Med & Hyg; Wildlife Dis Asn. *Res:* Immunity in helminth infections; arthropod-borne helminthiases. *Mailing Add:* 1303 Grizzly Peak Blvd Berkeley CA 94708

**WEINREB, EVA LURIE,** BIOLOGICAL STRUCTURE, CELL BIOLOGY. *Current Pos:* assoc prof, 73-80, PROF BIOL, COMMUNITY COL PHILADELPHIA, 80- *Personal Data:* b New York, NY; m 50. *Educ:* NY Univ, BA, 48; Univ Wis, MA, 49, PhD(zool), 55. *Prof Exp:* Asst zool, Univ Wis, 49 & 51-55; res assoc path, Sch Med, Marquette Univ, 55-56; dir basic sci, St Mary's Hosp, Sch Nursing, Milwaukee, 56-57; head animal res, Kolmer Res Ctr, 57-58; asst prof biol, Milwaukee-Downer Col, 59-60; fel cell biol & res assoc anat, Med Col, Cornell Univ, 61-63; asst prof biol, Washington Square Col, NY Univ, 63-69; cell biologist & sr res scientist, Biomed Sect, Geometric Data Corp, 71-72. *Concurrent Pos:* Consult, Volu-Sol Med Industs, Inc, 72-73, Trial Advocacy Found Pa. *Mem:* AAAS; Am Asn Anatomists; Am Soc Cell Biol; Am Soc Zool; Am Soc Allied Health Prof. *Res:* Comparative histology; hematology; pathology; electron microscopy; anatomy. *Mailing Add:* 328 Overhill Rd Wayne PA 19087

**WEINREB, MICHAEL PHILIP,** ATMOSPHERIC PHYSICS, REMOTE SENSING. *Current Pos:* PHYSICIST, NAT ENVIRON SATELLITE, DATA & INFO SERV, NAT OCEANIC & ATMOSPHERIC ADMIN, 70- *Personal Data:* b Lakewood, NJ, Feb 2, 39; m 66, Alice Kogan; c Jenya & Elizabeth. *Educ:* Univ Pa, BA, 60; Brandeis Univ, PhD(physics), 66. *Honors & Awards:* Bronze Medal, US Dept Commerce, 95. *Prof Exp:* Instr physics, Brandeis Univ, 64-65; physicist, Electronics Res Ctr, NASA, Mass, 65-70. *Concurrent Pos:* Adj prof math, Am Univ, 84-85. *Mem:* Am Meteorol Soc; Optical Soc Am; Am Geophys Union. *Res:* Radiative transfer theory; atomic and molecular physics; remote sensing of atmospheric temperature and constituent profiles. *Mailing Add:* Nat Environ Satellite Data & Info Serv Nat Oceanic & Atmospheric Admin Washington DC 20233. *Fax:* 301-763-8108; *E-Mail:* mweinreb@nesdis.noaa.gov

**WEINREB, ROBERT NEAL,** GLAUCOMA, GLAUCOMA SURGERY. *Current Pos:* PROF & VCHMN, DEPT OPHTHAL, UNIV CALIF, SAN DIEGO, 84- *Personal Data:* b New York, NY, Nov 23, 49. *Educ:* Mass Inst Technol, BS, 71; Harvard Med Sch, MD, 75. *Honors & Awards:* Alcon Prize, Alcon Res Inst, 83 & 92; Hon Award, Am Acad Ophthal, 86; Senior Hon Award, Am Acad Ophthal, 96. *Mem:* Asn Res Vision & Ophthal; Am Acad Ophthal; Am Glaucoma Soc; Int Soc Eye Res; Found Eye Res. *Res:* Glaucoma diagnosis, treatment and pathogenesis; optic nerve in health and disease. *Mailing Add:* Glaucoma Ctr Res Labs Univ Calif San Diego La Jolla CA 92093-0946

**WEINREB, SANDER,** RADIO ASTRONOMY, MICROWAVE ENGINEERING. *Current Pos:* MGR, MILLIMETER WAVE DESIGN & TEST, MARTIN MARIETTA LABS, 88- *Personal Data:* b New York, NY, Dec 9, 36; m 57, Marjorie J Quint; c Glenn & Ellen. *Educ:* Mass Inst Technol, BSEE, 58, PhD(elec eng), 63. *Prof Exp:* Staff mem, Lincoln Lab, Mass Inst Technol, 63-65; head electronics div, Nat Radio Astron Observ, 65-77, scientist, 77-84, asst dir electronics, 85-88. *Concurrent Pos:* Foreign adv, Neth Found Radio Astron, 72-77; adv, Nat Astron & Ionospheric Observ, 72-78. *Mem:* Sigma Xi; fel Inst Elec & Electronics Engrs. *Res:* Low noise receivers; millimeter wave devices. *Mailing Add:* Martin Marietta Labs 1450 S Rolling Rd Baltimore MD 21227

**WEINREB, STEVEN MARTIN,** ORGANIC CHEMISTRY. *Current Pos:* from assoc prof to prof, 78-87, MARKER PROF CHEM, PA STATE UNIV, 87- *Personal Data:* b Brooklyn, NY, May 10, 41; m 65; c 2. *Educ:* Cornell Univ, AB, 63; Univ Rochester, PhD(chem), 67. *Prof Exp:* NIH fel, Columbia Univ, 66-67; NIH fel, Mass Inst Technol, 67-68, res assoc, 68-70; from asst prof to assoc prof chem, Fordham Univ, 70-78. *Concurrent Pos:* Res fel, Alfred P Sloan Found, 75-79; res career develop award, NIH, 75-80; Guggenheim fel, 83-84. *Mem:* Am Chem Soc. *Res:* Synthesis of natural products; heterocyclic chemistry. *Mailing Add:* Dept Chem Pa State Univ University Park PA 16802. *Fax:* 814-865-3314; *E-Mail:* smw@chem.psu.edu

**WEINREICH, GABRIEL,** PHYSICS. *Current Pos:* vis assoc prof, Univ Mich, 60, assoc prof, 60-64, col prof, 74-76, prof, 64-95, EMER PROF PHYSICS, UNIV MICH, ANN ARBOR, 95- *Personal Data:* b Vilna, Poland, Feb 12, 28; nat US; m 51, 71, Gerane S Benamou; c Cathcrinc, Marc, Daniel, Rebecca & Natalie. *Educ:* Columbia Univ, AB, 48, MA, 49, PhD(physics), 54. *Honors & Awards:* Int Medal, French Acoust Soc; Klopsteg Award, Am Asn Physics Teacher. *Prof Exp:* Asst physics, Columbia Univ, 49-51; mem tech staff, Bell Tel Labs, 53-60. *Concurrent Pos:* Assoc ed, J Acoust Soc Am, 87-90. *Mem:* Fel Acoust Soc Am. *Res:* Atomic spectra; solid state theory; electron-phonon interactions; nonlinear optics; thermodynamics; electron-atom scattering; musical acoustics; atomic beam kinetics. *Mailing Add:* Randall Lab Physics Univ Mich Ann Arbor MI 48109-1120. *Fax:* 313-763-9694; *E-Mail:* weinreic@umich.edu

**WEINRICH, ALAN JEFFREY,** industrial hygiene, occupational health & safety, for more information see previous edition

**WEINRICH, JAMES D,** SEXOLOGY, GENDER TRANSPOSITIONS. *Current Pos:* proj mgr, Neurobehav Effects AIDS, HIV Neurobehav Res Ctr, 87-89, ctr mgr & data mgr, 89-91, sr investr, Sexology Proj, 91-93, PRIN INVESTR, SEXOLOGY PROJ, HIV NEUROBEHAV RES CTR, 93-; ASST ADJ PROF PSYCHIAT, UNIV CALIF, SAN DIEGO, 91- *Personal Data:* b Cleveland, Ohio, July 2, 50. *Educ:* Princeton Univ, AB, 72; Harvard Univ, PhD(biol), 76. *Honors & Awards:* Hugo Beigel Award, Soc Sci Study of Sex, 87. *Prof Exp:* Teaching asst evolution, Harvard Univ, 76-77; jr fel, Soc Fels, 77-80; NIH training grant fel med psychol, Psychohormonal Res Unit, Sch Med, Johns Hopkins Univ, 80-81; instr psychiat, 81-83; res fel, Sch Med, Boston Univ, 82-83, asst res prof psychiat, family studies, 83-87, assoc dir,

Family Studies Lab, 85-87; asst res psychobiologist, Sch Med, Univ Calif, San Diego, 87-91. *Concurrent Pos:* Bd mem, Found Sci Study Sexuality, 87- *Mem:* Int Acad Sex Res; Soc Sci Study Sex. *Res:* The development, evolution and expression of human sex roles, sexual orientation, transvestism, and transsexualism health and disease, especially AIDS; the relationship of lovemaps to safe and unsafe sex. *Mailing Add:* HIV Neurobehav Res Ctr 2760 Fifth Ave No 200 San Diego CA 92103. *E-Mail:* Internet Home Page: http://math.ucsd.edu/nweinrich

**WEINRICH, MARCEL,** PHYSICS. *Current Pos:* chmn dept, 69-73, PROF PHYSICS, JERSEY CITY STATE COL, 69- *Personal Data:* b Jendiesow, Poland, July 23, 27; nat US; div; c 1. *Educ:* Bethany Col, WVa, BS, 46; Univ WVa, MS, 48; Columbia Univ, PhD, 57. *Prof Exp:* Instr physics, Univ WVa, 47-49; physicist, Res & Develop Ctr, Gen Elec Co, 57-69. *Concurrent Pos:* Coordr gen studies review, Jersey City State Col, co-chmn, Pres Task Force for the 1980's. *Mem:* Fel AAAS; Am Inst Physics; Am Asn Physics Teachers (pres, 72-74); Am Phys Soc; NY Acad Sci. *Res:* Meson and plasma physics; breakdown of parity conservation in meson decays; controlled fusion reactors. *Mailing Add:* Dept Physics Jersey City State Col 2039 Kennedy Blvd Jersey City NJ 07305

**WEINRYB, IRA,** BIOCHEMISTRY, PHARMACOLOGY. *Current Pos:* DIR CLIN RES & DEVELOP, WYETH-AYERST RES, 88- *Personal Data:* b New York, NY, Nov 20, 40; m 67, Lucia C Ciervo; c Rachel & Rose M. *Educ:* Columbia Univ, BS, 61; Yale Univ, MEng, 62, MS, 65, PhD(molecular biophys), 67. *Prof Exp:* Nat Acad Sci-Nat Res Coun resident res assoc, Lab Phys Biochem, Naval Med Res Inst, Nat Naval Med Ctr, 67-69; from res investr to sr res investr, Dept Biochem Pharmacol, Squibb Inst Med Res, 69-73, head biochem sect, 73-75; dir biochem & drug disposition, USV Pharmaceut Corp, 75-81; assoc dir dir biol res, Revlon Health Care, 81-84, div dir chem res & develop, 84-86; dir preclin develop, Rorer Cent Res, 86-88. *Concurrent Pos:* Chmn, Biochem Pharmacol Discussion Group, 75-81; mem finance comt, Int Soc Study Xenobiotics, 92- *Mem:* Am Soc Biochem Molecular Biol; fel NY Acad Sci; Am Soc Clin Pharmacol Therapeut; Int Soc Study Xenobiotics. *Res:* Drug discovery and development, drug design, biochemical pharmacology, immunopharmacology, molecular bases of disease; spectroscopy of biological molecules; biochemical pharmacology; mechanism of drug action; clinical pharmacology. *Mailing Add:* Wyeth-Ayerst Res 145 King of Prussia Rd Radnor PA 19087

**WEINSCHEL, BRUNO OSCAR,** MICROWAVE ENGINEERING, ELECTROMAGNETISM. *Current Pos:* PRES & CHIEF ENGR, WEINSCHEL RES FOUND, 87-, CHIEF ENGR, WEINSCHEL ASN, 88- *Personal Data:* b Stuttgart, Ger, May 26, 19; US citizen; m, Shirley K Carpenter; c Dana, Lisa, Karen, Stephie, Ian & Benj. *Educ:* Technische Hochschule, Stuttgart, BA, 38; Technische Hochschule, Munich, Dr Ing, 66. *Hon Degrees:* DSc, Capitol Inst Tech, 84. *Honors & Awards:* William A Wildhack Award, Nat Conf Stand Lab, 85; Richard M Emberson Award, Inst Elec & Electronics Engrs, 92. *Prof Exp:* Regist prof engr, MD, DC & sr engr, Western Elec, 43-44; chief engr, Indust Instruments Co, 44-48; group leader & res scientist, Nat Bur Stand, 49-52; chief engr & pres, Weinschel Eng Co, Inc, 52-86. *Concurrent Pos:* Consult, Weinschel Eng, 87-88. *Mem:* Fel Inst Elec & Electronics Engrs (pres, 86). *Res:* Design of microwave precision measurements and calibration standards; microwave passive devices; inventor and co-inventor with 20 patents; author over 50 publications. *Mailing Add:* Weinschel Res Found PO Box 2092 Gaithersburg MD 20886

**WEINSHANK, DONALD JEROME,** COMPUTER SCIENCE EDUCATION. *Current Pos:* From instr to prof natural sci, 67-81, prof comput sci & natural sci, 81-87, PROF COMPUT SCI, UNIV COL, MICH STATE UNIV, 87- *Personal Data:* b Chicago, Ill, Apr 29, 37; m 59, Annette Barshefsky; c Joshua & Joel. *Educ:* Northwestern Univ, BA, 58; Univ Wis-Madison, MS, 61, PhD(biochem), 69. *Mem:* Asn Comput Mach; Am Chem Soc. *Res:* Computer science education; computer assisted instruction; concordances to works of Charles Darwin. *Mailing Add:* Comput Sci Dept A-732 Wells Hall Mich State Univ East Lansing MI 48824. *Fax:* 517-432-1061; *E-Mail:* weinshan@cps.msu.edu, Internet Home Page: http://www.cps.msu.edu/-weinshan/

**WEINSHILBOUM, RICHARD MERLE,** PHARMACOLOGY, INTERNAL MEDICINE. *Current Pos:* consult asst prof pharmacol & internal med, Mayo Found, 72-75, chief, Clin Pharmacol Unit, 74-90, assoc prof pharmacol, 76-79, internal med, 77-79, prof pharmacol & internal med & William L McKnight-3M prof neurosci, 79-84, dir res, 84-89, CHMN, DEPT PHARMACOL, MAYO FOUND, 89-, DIR EDUC, 92- *Personal Data:* b Eldorado, Kans, Mar 31, 40; m 65; c 2. *Educ:* Univ Kans, BA, 62, MD, 67. *Honors & Awards:* Rawls-Palmer Award, Am Soc Clin Pharmacol Therapeut, 79. *Prof Exp:* Intern internal med, Mass Gen Hosp, 67-68, asst resident, 68-69; res assoc pharmacol, Lab Clin Sci, NIMH, 69-71; sr resident internal med, Mass Gen Hosp, 71-72. *Concurrent Pos:* Consult, Mayo Clin, 72-; Pharmaceut Mfg Asn Fedn fac develop award, 73-75; estab investr, Am Heart Asn, 76-81; Burroughs-Wellcome scholar clin pharmacol, 81-86. *Mem:* Am Soc Pharmacol & Exp Therapeut; Am Soc Clin Pharmacol & Therapeut; Am Fedn Clin Res; Am Soc Neurochem; Soc Neurosci. *Res:* Molecular pharmacogenetics; pharmacogenetics; biochemical genetics and clinical pharmacology. *Mailing Add:* Dept Pharmacol Mayo Clinic Rochester MN 55901

**WEINSIER, ROLAND LOUIS,** CLINICAL NUTRITION. *Current Pos:* PROF NUTRIT & DIR CLIN DIV, MED CTR, UNIV ALA, BIRMINGHAM, 75- *Educ:* Harvard Univ, MD & PhD(pub health), 73. *Mailing Add:* Dept Nutrit Sci Univ Ala Med Ctr UAB Sta PO Box 188 Birmingham AL 35294-3360. *Fax:* 205-934-7049

**WEINSTEIN, ALAN DAVID,** GEOMETRY. *Current Pos:* from asst prof to assoc prof, 69-76, PROF MATH, UNIV CALIF, BERKELEY, 76- *Personal Data:* b New York, NY, June 17, 43; m 67; c 1. *Educ:* Mass Inst Technol, BS, 64; Univ Calif, Berkeley, MA, 66, PhD(math), 67. *Prof Exp:* Vis fel, Inst Advan Sci Studies, France, 67; C L E Moore instr math, Mass Inst Technol, 67-68; NATO fel, Math Inst, Univ Bonn, 68-69. *Concurrent Pos:* Sloan fel, 71-73; vis prof, Rice Univ, 78-79. *Mem:* Am Math Soc; Math Asn Am. *Res:* Symplectic manifolds; fourier integral operators; Hamiltonian dynamical systems; riemannian geometry. *Mailing Add:* Dept Math Univ Calif 2120 Oxford St Berkeley CA 94720-3840

**WEINSTEIN, ALAN IRA,** METEOROLOGY, OCEANOGRAPHY. *Current Pos:* dir res, Naval Environ Prediction Res Facil, Off Naval Res, 77-84, dir, Ocean Sci Div, 84-88, dir Ocean & Atmospheric Physics Div, 88-94, ASSOC INTEGRATION, OFF NAVAL RES, 94- *Personal Data:* b New York, NY, Apr 7, 40; m 66; c 2. *Educ:* City Col New York, BS, 61; Pa State Univ, MS, 63, PhD(meteorol), 68. *Prof Exp:* Res meteorologist, Meteorol Res Inc, 63-66; res asst meteorol, Pa State Univ, 66-68; res scientist, Meteorol Res Inc, Cohu Electronics Inc, 69-71; res physicist, 71-74, br chief stratiform cloud physics, Air Force Geophys Labs, 74-77. *Mem:* Am Meteorol Soc; Royal Meteorol Soc; Sigma Xi; AAAS; Am Geophys Union; Oceanog Soc. *Res:* Marine meteorology; atmospheric physics; physical oceanography. *Mailing Add:* Off Naval Res PSC 802 Box 39 FPO AE 09499-0700

**WEINSTEIN, ALAN JAY,** COLLIDER DETECTOR DESIGN. *Current Pos:* ASST PROF PHYSICS, CALIF INST TECHNOL, 88- *Personal Data:* b Brooklyn, NY, Dec 22, 57; m 91. *Educ:* Harvard Univ, BA, 78, PhD(physics), 83. *Prof Exp:* Asst res physicist high energy physics, dept physics, Harvard Univ, 83-84; asst res physicist high energy physics, Univ Calif, Santa Cruz, 84-88. *Concurrent Pos:* SSC Fel, Superconducting Supercollider Lab, 91- *Mem:* Am Phys Soc. *Res:* High energy e plus e minus collisions; decays of clepton, charmed and bottom mesons; design of high energy physics collider; tracking detectors. *Mailing Add:* Caltech 256-48 Pasadena CA 91125. *Fax:* 626-795-3951

**WEINSTEIN, ALVIN SEYMOUR,** MECHANICAL ENGINEERING & LAW, PREVENTIVE LAWYERING FOR CORPORATIONS IN RISK REDUCTION. *Current Pos:* PRES, WEINSTEIN ASSOCS, 93- *Personal Data:* b Lynn, Mass, June 12, 28; m 52, 88, Anne Richmond; c Ruth, Sonora & Marc. *Educ:* Univ Mich, BS, 51; Carnegie Inst Technol, MS, 53, PhD(mech eng), 55; Franklin Pierce Law Ctr, JD, 83. *Honors & Awards:* Melville Medal, Am Soc Mech Engrs, 72; Western Elec Teaching Award, Am Soc Eng Educ, 73. *Prof Exp:* prof mech eng & pub policy, Carnegie-Mellon Univ, 55-85; adj prof law, Franklin Pierce Law Ctr & legal-tech consult, 85-93. *Concurrent Pos:* Res award, Am Soc Test & Mat, 65; pres, TEC Consults. *Mem:* Am Soc Mech Engrs; Am Soc Testing & Mat. *Res:* Materials forming; technical aspects of products liability litigation; methodology for developing product safety standards; product safety analysis. *Mailing Add:* Weinstein & Assoc 23 Union St Brunswick ME 04011

**WEINSTEIN, ARTHUR,** RHEUMATOID ARTHRITIS & SYSTEMIC LUPUS ERYTHEMATOSUS, LYME DISEASE & SCLERODERMA. *Current Pos:* PROF MED & HEAD, DIV RHEUMATIC DIS & IMMUNOL, NY MED COL, 85- *Personal Data:* b 1944; m 86, Ellen Spin; c Stephanie R, Alyssa D & Michelle S. *Educ:* Univ Toronto, MD, 67. *Prof Exp:* Asst prof med, Univ Toronto, 75-76; assoc prof, Univ Conn, Sch Med, 76-85. *Concurrent Pos:* Chief rheumatology, Westchester Med Ctr; dir, Diag Immunol Lab, NY Med Col, Dir, Rheumatology Training Prog; NIH res grant, Chronic lyme dis, 94-; mem, Educ Coun, Am Col Rheumatology, 96-; *Mem:* Can Rheumatol Soc; fel Am Col Physicians; fel Am Col Rheumatology; Am Asn Immunologists; Am Fedn Clin Res; AAAS; fel Royal Col Physician Can. *Res:* Therapeutic studies in rheumatoid arthritis; laboratory studies in systemic lupus erythematosis and Lyme disease; pathogenesis and treatment of chronic lyme disease; treatment studies in scleroderma. *Mailing Add:* Div Rheumatic Dis & Immunol Munger Pavillion G73 New York Med Col Valhalla NY 10595. *E-Mail:* arthur_weinstein@nymc.edu

**WEINSTEIN, ARTHUR HOWARD,** ORGANIC POLYMER CHEMISTRY, RUBBER CHEMISTRY. *Current Pos:* RETIRED. *Personal Data:* b Brooklyn, NY, Jan 20, 24; wid; c Daniel L & Diane R. *Educ:* Queens Col, NY, BS, 44; Ohio State Univ, MS, 48, PhD(org chem), 50. *Prof Exp:* Asst path chemist, Bellevue Hosp, New York, 46; anal chemist, Dept Purchase, New York, 50; sr res chemist, chem res & develop div, Goodyear Tire & Rubber Co, 51-87. *Concurrent Pos:* Chmn prof activ comt, Akron Div, Am Chem Soc, 52. *Mem:* Am Chem Soc. *Res:* Aminocellulose derivatives; synthesis of aromatic sulfur compounds; emulsion polydienes with terminal or internal functionality; polymerization modifiers; castable pre-elastomers; polydiene elastomers self-resistant to oxidation or to combustion; chemically-resistant saturated nitrilated elastomers; urethane-cured polydienes; inventor/co-inventor of 15 US patents. *Mailing Add:* 2400 Cambridge Dr Hudson OH 44236

**WEINSTEIN, BERNARD ALLEN,** SOLID STATE PHYSICS. *Current Pos:* PROF, DEPT PHYSICS & ASTRON, STATE UNIV NY, BUFFALO, 87- *Personal Data:* b Bridgeport, Conn, Nov 15, 46; m 70; c 2. *Educ:* Univ Rochester, BS, 68; Brown Univ, PhD(physics), 74. *Prof Exp:* Max Planck Inst Solid State Res fel, Stuttgart, 71-73; res assoc solid state mat, Nat Bur Stand, 73-75; asst prof physics, Purdue Univ, West Lafayette, 75-78; res scientist, Xerox Corp, 78-87. *Concurrent Pos:* Alfred P Sloan res fel, 75-77. *Mem:* Am Phys Soc; Fedn Am Scientists. *Res:* Optical properties of semiconductors, with specific work in Raman scattering, visible and infrared spectroscopy and ultra-high pressure research. *Mailing Add:* Dept Physics State Univ NY 239 Fronczak Hall Buffalo NY 14260

**WEINSTEIN, BERTHOLD WERNER,** GENERAL PHYSICS, MATHEMATICS. *Current Pos:* RES PHYSICIST, GROUP & DIV LEADER, LAWRENCE LIVERMORE NAT LAB, UNIV CALIF, 74- *Personal Data:* b New York, NY, Oct 11, 47; m 70; c 2. *Educ:* Brigham Young Univ, BS, 71; Univ Ill, Urbana, MS, 73, PhD(physics), 75. *Mem:* Am Phys Soc; AAAS. *Res:* Inertial fusion target fabrication and measurement; liquid metal ion beam sources; computer simulation and analysis of high energy physics experiments; electrohydrodynamics, particularly ion spraying; high energy physics; nuclear weapons. *Mailing Add:* Lawrence Livermore Nat Lab Div L-389 PO Box 808 Livermore CA 94551. *Fax:* 510-422-4563

**WEINSTEIN, CONSTANCE DE COURCY,** BIOCHEMISTRY. *Current Pos:* health sci adminr, NIH, 75-81, exec secy, div res grants, 81-86, dep chief cardiac dis br, 86-89, CHIEF CARDIAC DIS BR, NAT HEART, LUNG & BLOOD INST, NIH, 89- *Personal Data:* b London, Eng, Aug 31, 24; US citizen; m 59; c 3. *Educ:* Univ London, BSc, 48, PhD(biochem), 53. *Prof Exp:* Res biochemist, Hosp Sick Children, London, 53-54; res fel biochem, Jefferson Med Col, Philadelphia, 55-56; sr instr biochem, Med Sch, Western Reserve Univ, Cleveland, 56-61; res scientist cancer, City of Hope, Duarte, Calif, 70-74. *Mem:* Am Heart Asn; Int Soc Heart Res. *Mailing Add:* Cardiac Dis Br Nat Heart Lung & Blood Inst 9000 Rockville Pike Fed Bldg Rm 3C06 Bethesda MD 20892

**WEINSTEIN, CURT DAVID,** COMMUNICATIONS EFFECTIVENESS, MEASUREMENT SCIENCE. *Current Pos:* PRES, PHARMACEUT & COSMETIC EVAL, NEURO COMMUN RES LABS INC, 87- *Personal Data:* b New York, NY, May 11, 51. *Educ:* Clarkson Col Technol, BA, 73; Univ Mich, MA, 75. *Prof Exp:* Res assoc, Neuro Commun Res Labs Inc, 75-78, vpres, 78-84; dir, Adam Info, 85-87. *Concurrent Pos:* Proprieter, Weinstein's Market Res & Analysis, 84- *Res:* Perception, communications-effects, cosmetic-skin, measurement science, biodetection, electrophysiological applications of neuropsychology. *Mailing Add:* 36 Mill Plain Rd Suite 412 Danbury CT 06811

**WEINSTEIN, DAVID ALAN,** NUTRIENT CYCLING, COMPUTER MODELING. *Current Pos:* RES ASSOC, ECOSYST RES CTR, ENVIRON PROTECTION AGENCY CTR EXCELLENCE, CORNELL UNIV, 81-, BOYCE THOMPSON INST FOREST ECOLOGIST/ENVIRON BIOLOGIST, 81- *Personal Data:* b New York City, NY, Mar 26, 51. *Educ:* Darmouth Col, BA, 73; Univ NH, MS, 76; Univ Tenn, PhD(ecol), 82. *Prof Exp:* Grad res fel, Environ Sci Div, Oak Ridge Nat Lab, 77-81. *Concurrent Pos:* Vis Libra prof ecol, Univ Maine. *Mem:* Ecol Soc Am; Sigma Xi. *Res:* Mechanisms of response of ecosystems to perturbations through the analysis of nutrient cycling patterns by computer simulation techniques. *Mailing Add:* 123 Boyces Thompson Inst Ithaca NY 14853

**WEINSTEIN, DAVID E,** MOLECULAR BIOLOGY. *Current Pos:* FEL BIOCHEM, SALK INST, 92- *Personal Data:* b Newark, NJ, Dec 16. *Res:* Molecular biology. *Mailing Add:* Albert Einstein Col Med 1300 Morris Park Ave Bronx NY 10461

**WEINSTEIN, HAREL,** BIOPHYSICAL CHEMISTRY. *Current Pos:* from asst prof to assoc prof, 74-79, PROF PHARMACOL, MT SINAI SCH MED, 79-, PROF PHYSIOL & BIOPHYS & CHMN DEPT, 85- *Personal Data:* b June 5, 45; US citizen; m 67, Barbara Manski; c Ellhav. *Educ:* Israel Inst Technol, BSc, 66, MSc, 68, DSc(quantum chem), 71. *Honors & Awards:* Int Soc Quantum Biol Award, 87; Parke-Davis Distinguished Lectr, 88; Res Scientist Award, Nat Inst Drug Abuse, NIH, 95. *Prof Exp:* Asst chem, Israel Inst Technol, 66-68, sr res asst, 68-71, lectr, 71-73; res assoc, Johns Hopkins Univ, 73-74. *Concurrent Pos:* Consult res assoc biochem, Tel-Aviv Univ, 73-78; vis scientist genetics, Med Ctr, Stanford Univ, 74-75; mem ed & adv bd, Molecular Pharmacol, 77-; Irma T Hirschl Trust res career scientist, 78-82; Alcohol, Drug Abuse & Ment Health Admin res grant, 79-83 & 84-90; consult, Merck Sharp & Dohme, 79-81, Pfizer, 92 & Burroughs-Welcome, 92-93; consult, US Environ Protection Agy, 83-; NSF res grants, 83-86; bd sci adv, NIH-NCI; adv panel, NIH-DRR, 85-; coop agreement grant, US Environ Protection Agency, 84- *Mem:* Biophys Soc; Am Soc Pharmacol Exp Therapeut; Am Chem Soc; Int Soc Quantum Biol (pres, 85-); Am Physiol Soc; NY Acad Sci. *Res:* Development and application of theoretical methods to study molecular structure, reactivity and interactions of biological systems; molecular recognition in hormone and drug action and energy transfer and storage in proteins; receptor theory and molecular mechanisms of neurotransmission and enzyme activity; structure and function of calcium binding protein; protein DNA interactions and regulation of gene expression. *Mailing Add:* Dept Physiol & Biophys Mt Sinai Sch Med Box 1218 New York NY 10029-6574. *E-Mail:* hawms@inka.mssm.edu

**WEINSTEIN, HERBERT,** FLUIDIZATION, CHEMICAL REACTOR ENGINEERING. *Current Pos:* prof, 77-87, HERBERT G KAYSER PROF CHEM ENG, CITY UNIV NEW YORK, 87- *Personal Data:* b Brooklyn, NY, Mar 10, 33; m 57, Judith Cooper; c Michael H, Edward M & Ellen R. *Educ:* City Col New York, BEChE, 55; Purdue Univ, MSChE, 57; Case Inst Technol, PhD(eng), 63. *Prof Exp:* Staff mem, Los Alamos Sci Lab, 56-58; res engr, Lewis Lab, NASA, 59-63; asst prof chem eng, Ill Inst Technol, 63-66, assoc prof, 66-72, prof, 72-77. *Concurrent Pos:* Vis res assoc, Michael Reese Hosp & Med Ctr, 65-77; vis prof mech eng, Technion Israel Inst Technol, 72-73, biomed eng, Rush Med Col, 73-76; Lady Davis prof mech eng, Technion Israel Inst Technol, 85. *Mem:* Am Inst Chem Engrs; Sigma Xi. *Res:* Chemical reactor engineering: fluidization, tracer methods, heat and mass transfer in catalysts; fluid mechanics; biomedical engineering: tracer methods in the circulation and glucose sensors. *Mailing Add:* Dept Chem Eng City Univ New York 138th St & Convent New York NY 10031. *Fax:* 212-650-6660; *E-Mail:* hweinst@che-mail.engr.ccny.cuny.edu

**WEINSTEIN, HOWARD,** NEUROCHEMISTRY, CELL PHYSIOLOGY. *Current Pos:* STAFF SCIENTIST, NAT INST NEUROL DIS & STROKE, 74- *Personal Data:* b New York, NY, Nov 9, 27. *Educ:* Cornell Univ, BA, 49; State Univ Iowa, PhD(zool), 56. *Prof Exp:* Instr zool & physiol, Wis State Univ-Stevens Point, 56-57; USPHS fel neuroendocrinol, Case Western Reserve Univ, 58-61; res scientist, City of Hope Med Ctr, Duarte, Calif, 61-74. *Concurrent Pos:* USPHS grants, 68- *Mem:* Soc Neurosci; Am Soc Neurochem; Int Soc Neurochem; Am Soc Zoologists. *Res:* Membrane transport processes in central nervous system. *Mailing Add:* 14012 Eagle Ct Rockville MD 20853

**WEINSTEIN, HYMAN GABRIEL,** biochemistry, nutrition, for more information see previous edition

**WEINSTEIN, I BERNARD,** MEDICINE. *Current Pos:* from asst prof to assoc prof med, 61-73, dir, Div Environ Sci, Sch Pub Health, 77-90, PROF, COLUMBIA UNIV, 73-, FRODE JENSEN PROF MED, GENETICS & DEVELOP & PUB HEALTH, 96-; EMER DIR, HERBERT IRVING COMPREHENSIVE CANCER CTR, COLUMBIA PRESBY MED CTR, 96- *Personal Data:* b Madison, Wis, Sept 9, 30; m 52; c 3. *Educ:* Univ Wis, BS, 52, MD, 55. *Hon Degrees:* DSc, Univ Wis, 92. *Honors & Awards:* Meltzer Medal, 64; Louise Weissberger Lectr, Univ Rochester, 81; Mary Ann Swetland Lectr, Case Western Res Univ, 83; Daniel Laszlo Mem Lectr, Montefiore Med Ctr, 83; Samuel Kuna Distinguished Lectr, Rutgers Univ, 85; Clowes Award, Am Asn Cancer Res, 87; Ester Langer Lectr, Univ Chicago, 89; Harris Mem Lectr, Mass Inst Technol, 89; Silvio O Conte Award, Environ Health Inst, 90. *Prof Exp:* Intern & med resident, Montefiore Hosp, NY, 55-57; clin assoc metab servs, Nat Cancer Inst, Bethesda, 57-59; Nat Cancer Inst spec res fel bact & immunol, Harvard Med Sch & Mass Inst Technol, 59-61. *Concurrent Pos:* Assoc vis physician, Francis Delafield Hosp, 61-66; career scientist, Health Res Coun, City of New York, 61-72; from asst attend physician to assoc attend physician, Presby Hosp, 67-81, attend physician, 81-; Europ Molecular Biol Orgn travel fel, 70-71; adv, Lung Cancer Segment, Carcinogenesis Prog, Nat Cancer Inst, 71-74 & Chem & Molecular Biol Segment, 73-76; mem, Interdisciplinary Commun Prog, Smithsonian Inst, 71-74, Pharmacol B Study Sect, NIH, 71-75 & numerous sci & adv comts, Nat Cancer Inst & Am Cancer Soc, 76-88; adv, Roswell Park Mem Inst, Buffalo, NY, Brookhaven Nat Lab, Div Cancer Cause & Prevention, Nat Cancer Inst, Coun on Anal & Projs, Am Cancer Soc, Int Agency for Res on Cancer, WHO, Lyon, France; assoc ed, Cancer Res, 73-76 & 86-, J Environ Path & Toxicol, 77-84 & J Cellular Physiol, 82-89; coun deleg, AAAS, 85-88; Nakasone vis prof, Tokyo, 87; Gen Motors Cancer Res Found vis prof, Int Agency Res Cancer, Lyon, 88. *Mem:* Inst Med-Nat Acad Sci; Am Soc Microbiol; Int Soc Quantum Biol; Am Asn Cancer Res; fel AAAS (pres, 90-91); Am Soc Clin Invest; NY Acad Sci; Royal Acad Med; Am Asn Physicians; fel Am Acad Arts & Sci. *Res:* Oncology; cellular and molecular aspects of carcinogenesis; environmental carcinogenesis; control of gene expression. *Mailing Add:* Col Physicians & Surgeons Columbia Univ 701 W 168th St Rm 1509 New York NY 10032

**WEINSTEIN, IRA,** ENDOCRINOLOGY, BIOCHEMICAL PHARMACOLOGY. *Current Pos:* PROF, UNIV TENN CTR HEALTH SCI, MEMPHIS, 81- *Personal Data:* b Oak Park, Ill, Jan 30, 28; m 54; c 3. *Educ:* Roosevelt Univ, BS, 49; Univ Ill, MS, 52; George Washington Univ, PhD(microbiol), 60. *Prof Exp:* From instr to asst prof pharmacol, Vanderbilt Univ, 60-69; assoc prof, Sch Med, Univ Fla, 69-75; assoc prof pharmacol, Sch Med, Univ Mo-Columbia, 75-80, prof, 80-81. *Concurrent Pos:* Fel pharmacol, Med Sch, Vanderbilt Univ, 60-63; USPHS fels, 60-64; Olson Mem Fund fel, 65-66; vis lectr, Hebrew Univ Israel, 65-66; Am Heart Asn advan res fel, 65-67; fel coun on arteriosclerosis, Am Heart Asn. *Mem:* Sigma Xi; Am Soc Microbiol; Am Soc Pharmacol & Exp Therapeut. *Res:* Bacterial physiology, endocrines and drug effects upon lipid metabolism. *Mailing Add:* Univ Tenn Memphis Health Sci Ctr 874 Union Ave Memphis TN 38163-0001

**WEINSTEIN, IRAM J,** SENSOR SYSTEMS ANALYSIS, SIGNAL PROCESSING. *Current Pos:* sr scientist, 89-92, VPRES & CHIEF ENG, TECH RES GROUP, SCI APPLN INT CORP, 93- *Personal Data:* b Brooklyn, NY, Oct 17, 36; m 70, Marilyn Mausee; c David, Karen, Katherine & Sarah. *Educ:* Rensselaer Polytech Inst, BS, 56; Northeastern Univ, MSEE, 61; Stanford Univ, PhD(elec eng), 67. *Prof Exp:* Sr engr, Raytheon Corp, 56-60; sr res engr, Stanford Res Inst, 60-68, dir syst eval, 68-72, dir, Ctr Analysis Pub Serv, 72-76; chief scientist & vpres measurement syst, Systs Planning Corp, 78-89. *Concurrent Pos:* Lectr, Stanford Univ, 67-69. *Mem:* Inst Elec & Electronics Engrs. *Res:* Analysis and evaluation of large scale systems; radar systems engineering; signal processing. *Mailing Add:* Sci Appln Int Corp 4001 N Fairfax Dr Suite 500 Arlington VA 22203. *Fax:* 703-522-6108; *E-Mail:* iramw@try1.salc.com

**WEINSTEIN, IRWIN M,** HEMATOLOGY, INTERNAL MEDICINE. *Current Pos:* vis assoc prof, 55-56, assoc clin prof, 57-70, CLIN PROF MED, UNIV CALIF, LOS ANGELES, 70-; PVT PRACT HEMAT-MED ONCOL & INTERNAL MED, 59- *Personal Data:* b Denver, Colo, Mar 5, 26; m 51, Judith Braun; c James & David. *Educ:* Univ Colo, Denver, MD, 49; Am Bd Internal Med, dipl, 56, Am Bd Hematol, dipl, 72. *Honors & Awards:* Israel Cancer Res Fund Founders Award, 87. *Prof Exp:* Instr med, Univ Chicago, 53-54, asst prof, 54-55. *Concurrent Pos:* Chief hemat, Vet Admin Ctr, Wadsworth Hq, Los Angeles, 56-59; chief, Hemat Sect, Dept Med, Cedars-Sinai Med Ctr, Los Angeles, 60-72; dir hemat training prog, 60-72; gov-elect, Southern Calif Region I, Am Col Physicians, 88-89, gov, 89-93. *Mem:* Inst Med-Nat Acad Sci; Am Soc Hemat; fel Am Col Physicians; Am Fedn Clin Res; AAAS; AMA; Am Soc Clin Oncol; Am Soc Internal Med; Asn Am Med Col; NY Acad Sci. *Res:* Mechanisms of anemia; radioactive chromium and iron for studying red cell production and distruction. *Mailing Add:* 8635 W Third St No 1165N Los Angeles CA 90048

**WEINSTEIN, JEREMY SAUL,** OPERATIONS RESEARCH, COMPUTER SCIENCE. *Current Pos:* Res engr, Whirlpool Corp, Benton Harbor, Mich, 70-72, mgr bus planning, Laundry Group, 72-76, mgr prod scheduling & mis, 76-79, mgr indust eng & mis, Marion Div, 79-82, dir, Mfg Eng, Findlay Div, 82-88, group dir, Mfg Serv, 88-89, VPRES, OPERS & PLANNING, WHIRLPOOL CORP, BENTON HARBOR, MICH, 89- *Personal Data:* b Brooklyn, NY, Apr 9, 44; m 67; c 3. *Educ:* City Col New York, BE, 66; Purdue Univ, Lafayette, MSIE, 68, PhD(indust eng), 71. *Concurrent Pos:* Instr, Benton Harbor Exten, Mich State Univ, 70-71. *Mem:* Inst Mgt Sci; Inst Indust Engrs. *Mailing Add:* Whirlpool Corp 2000 N State Rte 63 Mail Drop 4500 Benton Harbor MI 49022

**WEINSTEIN, LEONARD HARLAN,** PLANT PHYSIOLOGY, ENVIRONMENTAL BIOLOGY. *Current Pos:* dir, Ecosysts Res Ctr, 89-90, ADJ PROF NAT RESOURCES, CORNELL UNIV, 79- *Personal Data:* b Springfield, Mass, Apr 11, 26; m 50, Sylvia Sherman; c Beth R & David H (deceased). *Educ:* Pa State Univ, BS, 49; Univ Mass, MS, 50; Rutgers Univ, PhD(plant physiol), 53. *Prof Exp:* Fel soils, Rutgers Univ, 53-54; from assoc plant physiologist to plant physiologist, 55-63, prog dir plant chem, 63-69; prog dir environ biol, Boyce Thompson Inst Plant Res, 69-91. *Concurrent Pos:* Mem bd dirs, Boyce Thompson Inst Plant Res, 73-96, trustee, 78-96; mem & dir, Boyce Thompson Southwestern Arboretum, Sci Adv Comn, Environ Sci Div, Oak Ridge Nat Lab, 85-87, Ecosysts Res Ctr Adv Comn, 85-91, Environ Protection Agency, Sci Adv Bd Environ Effects, Transp & Rate, 87-90, Off Technol & Assessment, Adv Panel Oxidants, 87-88, Nat Asn State Univ & Land Grant Cols, Environ Comn, 87-93. *Mem:* AAAS; Am Soc Plant Physiol. *Res:* Air pollution; plant nutrition; plant senescence; environmental biology; effects of atmospheric pollutants on plant growth, development, productivity and quality; plant toxicology; phytoremediation. *Mailing Add:* Boyce Thompson Inst Plant Res at Cornell Tower Rd Ithaca NY 14853. *Fax:* 607-254-1242

**WEINSTEIN, LEONARD MURREY,** FLOW VISUALIZATION, TURBULENT FLOWS. *Current Pos:* aerospace engr, 62-84, group leader, 84-91, SR RES SCIENTIST, LANGLEY RES CTR, NASA, 91- *Personal Data:* b Louisville, Ky, Aug 7, 40; m 67, Runell E Alford; c Sandra L (Raven). *Educ:* Fla State Univ, BSc, 62; George Washington Univ, MSc, 72, SCD, 81. *Honors & Awards:* IR-100 Award, Res & Develop Mag, 87. *Mem:* Assoc fel Am Inst Aeronaut & Astronaut. *Res:* Experimental fluid mechanics; use of several flow visualization and measurement techniques to improve understanding of underlying physics of complex flows. *Mailing Add:* 18 Langley Blvd MS 493 Hampton VA 23681-0001. *Fax:* 757-864-8315; *E-Mail:* l.m.weinstein@larc.nasa.gov

**WEINSTEIN, LOUIS,** INTERNAL MEDICINE, INFECTIOUS DISEASES. *Current Pos:* physician, 75-83, SR CONSULT MED, BRIGHAM & WOMEN'S HOSP, BOSTON, 83-; EMER PROF MED, MED SCH, TUFTS UNIV, BOSTON, 85- *Personal Data:* b Bridgeport, Conn, Feb 26, 09; m 34. *Educ:* Yale Univ, BS, 28, MS, 30, PhD(bact), 31; Boston Univ, MD, 43. *Hon Degrees:* ScD, Boston Univ, 73. *Honors & Awards:* Finland Award & Bristol Award, Am Soc Infectious Dis; Medal lectr, Am Col Chest Physicians. *Prof Exp:* Instr bact, Med Sch, Yale Univ, 37-39; res assoc immunol, Sch Med, Boston Univ, 39-44, asst med, 43-44, from instr to assoc prof, 44-57; lectr pediat, Med Sch, Tufts Univ, 50-57, prof med, 57-75; chief infectious dis serv, Vet Admin Hosp, West Roxbury, Mass, 75-78. *Concurrent Pos:* Asst, Harvard Med Sch, 45-46, instr, 46-49, lectr, 49-75, vis prof med, 75-83, lectr med, 83-; chief infectious dis serv, Mass Mem Hosp, 47-57 & New Eng Ctr Hosp & Boston Floating Hosp, 57-75; assoc physician, Med Serv, Mass Gen Hosp, 58-75, mem, bd consult, 75-83, hon physician, 83-; assoc physician in chief, New Eng Med Ctr Hosps, 62-71; mem, bact & mycol study sect, Nat Inst Allergy & Infectious Dis, NIH, 62-66; assoc ed, J Infectious Dis, 68-79; chmn, Infectious Dis Bd, Am Bd, Internal Med, 71-76; mem, Int Adv Comt, Kuvin Ctr Study Infectious & Trop Dis, Jerusalem, Israel, 75-; ed-in-chief, Infectious Dis Pract, 77- *Mem:* Am Acad Arts & Sci; AAAS; AMA; Am Soc Microbiol; Am Soc Infectious Dis; Am Soc Clin Invest; Am Fedn Clin Res; Asn Am Physicians; Sigma Xi. *Res:* Chemotherapy of infection; host factors in infectious disease. *Mailing Add:* 75 Francis St Boston MA 02115-6195

**WEINSTEIN, MARK JOEL,** BLOOD COAGULATION PROTEIN. *Current Pos:* ACTG LAB CHIEF, LAB HEMOSTASIS, CTR BIOL EVAL & RES, FOOD & DRUG ADMIN, 93-, DIR, DIV HEMAT, 96- *Personal Data:* b Syracuse, NY, Mar 2, 45; m 69; c 1. *Educ:* State Univ NY, Binghamton, BA, 66; Univ Calif, San Diego, PhD(chem), 71. *Prof Exp:* NIH postdoctoral fel, Univ Wash, 72-74; res chemist, Boston Vet Admin Med Ctr, 74-83; asst prof biochem, Sch Med, Boston Univ, 76-84, assoc prof, 84-93; spec sci staff, Boston City Hosp, 84-93. *Concurrent Pos:* Prin investr, 78-92 & 86-89. *Mem:* Am Soc Hemat; Am Soc Biol Chemists. *Res:* Development and production of national standards for coagulation factors; antihemophilic factor, thrombin and von Willebrand factor; regulation of blood and blood products. *Mailing Add:* Div Hemat Ctr Biol Eval & Res Food & Drug Admin 1401 Rockville Pike Rockville MD 20814. *Fax:* 301-402-2780; *E-Mail:* weinstein@a1.cber.fda.gov

**WEINSTEIN, MARVIN,** THEORETICAL HIGH ENERGY PHYSICS. *Personal Data:* b Bronx, NY, June 7, 42; m 67; c 1. *Educ:* Columbia Univ, BS, 63, MS, 64, PhD(physics), 67. *Prof Exp:* Physics mem, Inst Advan Study, 67-69; vis asst prof physics, Yeshiva Univ, 69-70 & NY Univ, 70-72; sr res assoc physics, Stanford Linear Accelerator Ctr, Stanford Univ, 72-80. *Mem:* Sigma Xi; Am Chem Soc. *Res:* Current algebra; gauge theories of strong, weak and electromagnetic interactions; non-perturbatic methods in quantum field theory. *Mailing Add:* 24 Maddaket Southwyck Village Scotch Plains NJ 07076-3136

**WEINSTEIN, MARVIN STANLEY,** UNDERWATER ACOUSTICS, NUCLEAR DETONATION EFFECTS. *Current Pos:* RETIRED. *Personal Data:* b New York, NY, May 24, 27; m 52, Dorothy Goldstein; c Joseph & Judith (Balthazar). *Educ:* St Louis Univ, BS, 48; Univ Md, MS, 51, PhD, 56. *Prof Exp:* Asst, Univ Md, 48-49; physicist, US Naval Ord Lab, 49-59; vpres, Underwater Systs Inc, 59-62, pres, 62-74, chmn bd, 75-87; dir, Mandex Corp, 84-89. *Mem:* Acoust Soc Am. *Res:* Underwater acoustics; propagation at long and short range in deep and shallow water, noise, sinusoidal and explosive signals; ultrasonics; ultrasonic modeling; electronics; detection and identification of underwater nuclear or other explosive devices; sonar systems and anti-submarine warfare. *Mailing Add:* 14305 Northwyn Dr Silver Spring MD 20904

**WEINSTEIN, NORMAN J(ACOB),** POLLUTION CONTROL SYSTEMS, HAZARDOUS WASTE MANAGEMENT. *Current Pos:* INDEPENDENT CONSULT, 96- *Personal Data:* b Rochester, NY, Dec 31, 29; m 57, Ann Keiles; c Maury, Aaron & Kenneth. *Educ:* Syracuse Univ, BChE, 51, MChE, 53; Ore State Univ, PhD(chem eng), 56. *Prof Exp:* Chem engr, Esso Res & Eng Co, 56-61, sr engr, 61-66, eng assoc, 66; eng & develop asst dir, Princeton Chem Res Inc, 66-67, eng & develop dir, 67-69; pres, Recon Environ Corp, 69-96. *Concurrent Pos:* Adj prof, Newark Col Eng, 63-66; chief tech adv, Indian Pollution Control Res Inst, 84-87. *Mem:* Am Chem Soc; fel Am Inst Chem Engrs; Am Soc Testing & Mat; NY Acad Sci; Am Acad Environ Engrs; Asn Consult Chemists & Chem Engrs. *Res:* Air and water pollution control; petroleum, petrochemical and metallurgical processes; catalysis; fluidized solids; hydrocarbon and coal gasification; economic evaluation; liquid and solid waste disposal and recycling. *Mailing Add:* 1005 Canal Rd Princeton NJ 08540-9801

**WEINSTEIN, PAUL P,** DEVELOPMENTAL BIOLOGY. *Current Pos:* chmn dept, 69-75, prof, 69-90, EMER PROF BIOL, UNIV NOTRE DAME, 90- *Personal Data:* b Brooklyn, NY, Dec 9, 19; m 54, Rachel Hazan; c Amy & Michael. *Educ:* Brooklyn Col, AB, 41; Johns Hopkins Univ, ScD, 49. *Honors & Awards:* Ashford Award, Am Soc Trop Med & Hyg, 57; Hon Ann Lectr & Award, Japan Soc Parasitologists, 89. *Prof Exp:* Jr parasitologist, USPHS, St Bd Health, Fla, 42-44; sr asst sanitarian, Ctr Dis Control, NIH, 44-46, from scientist to scientist dir & chief, Lab Parasitic Dis, 49-68. *Concurrent Pos:* Vis scientist, Nat Inst Med Res, Eng, 62-63; mem, Parasitic Dis Panel, US-Japan Coop Med Sci Prog, 65-69, chmn, 69-73; mem, comt int ctr med res & training, NIH, 70-73; mem adv sci bd, Gorgas Mem Inst Trop Prev Med, 72-88; mem, Nat Adv Comt, Primate Res Ctr, Univ Calif, Davis, 73-77; consult, Walter Reed Army Inst Res, US Army, 77-79; mem, microbiol & infectious dis adv comt, NIH, 78-81; vis prof, Juntendo Univ Sch Med, Tokyo, Japan, 89. *Mem:* Fel AAAS; Am Soc Trop Med & Hyg (pres, 85); Am Soc Parasitol (pres, 72). *Res:* Cultivation and physiology of parasitic helminths; host-parasite relationships; cobalamins and parasite development. *Mailing Add:* Dept Biol Univ Notre Dame Notre Dame IN 46556

**WEINSTEIN, ROBERT,** VASCULAR CELL BIOLOGY, HEMOSTASIS & THROMBOSIS. *Current Pos:* CHIEF, DIV CLIN RES, VASCULAR LAB, SAINT ELIZABETH HOSP, BOSTON, 85-, DIR, TRANSFUSION SERV, 85- *Personal Data:* b Brooklyn, NY, Aug 10, 49; m 83; c 2. *Educ:* Brandeis Univ, AB, 71; NY Univ, MD, 75. *Concurrent Pos:* Investr biomed res, St Elizabeth Hosp, 85-; assoc prof med, Tufts Med Sch. *Mem:* AAAS; Am Soc Cell Biol; Am Soc Hemat; Am Fedn Clin Res; Am Asn Blood Banks; NY Acad Sci; Am Soc Apheresis. *Res:* Erykrocyte-endorelial interaction and the pathogenesis of vascular disease in sickle cell anemia. *Mailing Add:* St Elizabeth's Med Ctr 736 Cambridge St MMR 1TS Boston MA 02135-2997

**WEINSTEIN, RONALD S,** EXPERIMENTAL PATHOLOGY, ELECTRON MICROSCOPY. *Current Pos:* PROF PATH & CHMN DEPT, RUSH MED COL, 75- *Personal Data:* b Schenectady, NY, Nov 20, 38; m 64; c 2. *Educ:* Union Col, NY, BS, 60; Tufts Univ, MD, 65; Am Bd Path, dipl. *Prof Exp:* Res asst electron micros, Mass Gen Hosp, 62-63; instr path, Sch Med, Tufts Univ, 67-69, assoc prof, 72-75. *Concurrent Pos:* From intern to resident path, Mass Gen Hosp, 65-70, head, Mixter Lab Electron Micros, 66-70; teaching fel, Harvard Med Sch, 65-70; investr toxicol, Aerospace Med Res Lab, Wright-Patterson AFB, 70-72; chmn dept, Rush-Presbyterian-St Lukes Med Ctr. *Mem:* Soc Develop Biol; NY Acad Sci; Am Asn Anatomists; Soc Toxicol; Am Asn Path. *Res:* Development and application of high resolution electron microscopy techniques to the study of biological membrane ultrastructure; comparative and functional studies on normal and neoplastic cell membranes; environmental toxicology. *Mailing Add:* Dept Pathol Univ Ariz Health Sci Ctr 1501 N Campbell Ave Rm 5205 Tucson AZ 85724-0001. *Fax:* 520-626-1027

**WEINSTEIN, ROY,** ACCELERATOR EXPERIMENTS, TRAPPED FIELD SUPERCONDUCTING PERMANENT MAGNETS. *Current Pos:* prof & dean natural sci, 82-88, PROF DEPT PHYSICS & DIR, INST BEAM PARTICLE DYNAMICS, UNIV HOUSTON, 88- *Personal Data:* b New York, NY, Apr 21, 27; m 96, Gail; c Lee & Sara. *Educ:* Mass Inst Technol, BS, 51, PhD(physics), 54. *Hon Degrees:* Lycoming Col, ScD, 81. *Honors & Awards:* Nat Triennial Scholar, Phi Kappa Phi, 82-85; Founders Award, Int Cong Superconductivity. *Prof Exp:* From instr to asst prof physics, Brandeis Univ, 54-56; asst prof physics, Mass Inst Technol, 56-59; from assoc prof to prof physics, Northeastern Univ, 61-74, prof & chmn, 74-82. *Concurrent Pos:* Ed, McGraw Hill, 59-64; NSF fel, Bohr Inst, 59-60, Harvard Univ, 69-70 & Guggenheim fel, Stanford Univ, 68-69,; prin investr, NSF res at Univs, 61-; consult, Camb Electron Accel (Harvard Univ), Stanford Univ Lin Accel & several co, 66-; vis scholar, 66-67. *Mem:* Fel Am Phys Soc; Mat Res Soc. *Res:* Particle physics; neutrino astrophysics; nuclear physics; atomic physics; superconducting permanent magnets; bulk superconductivity; exotic pinning centers. *Mailing Add:* Inst Beam Particle Dynamics Rm 632 SR 1 Univ Houston Houston TX 77204-5506. *E-Mail:* weinstein@uh.edu

**WEINSTEIN, SAM,** ORTHODONTICS. *Current Pos:* RETIRED. *Personal Data:* b Omaha, Nebr, May 24, 16; m 46, Helen Davidson; c David & Laurie. *Educ:* Creighton Univ, DDS, 41; Northwestern Univ, MSD, 48; Am Bd Orthod, dipl. *Honors & Awards:* Louise Ada Jarabak Mem Int Orthod Teachers & Res Award, 83. *Prof Exp:* From asst prof to prof orthod, Col Dent, Univ Nebr, 54-71; chmn dept, 55-71; prof orthod, Univ Conn, 71-83, emer prof orthod, 83-97. *Concurrent Pos:* Vis prof, Northwestern Univ, 57-71; mem dent study sect, NIH, 69-73; consult, Coun Dent Educ, Am Dent Asn, 69-76; examr, Coun on Educ, Can Dent Asn, 74-77. *Mem:* Fel AAAS; Sigma Xi; Int Asn Dent Res; Int Soc Cranio-Facial Biol. *Res:* Theoretical mechanics application to soft tissue forces and tooth movement; cleft palate embryology; growth. *Mailing Add:* 23 Mallard Dr Avon CT 06001

**WEINSTEIN, STANLEY EDWIN,** MATHEMATICS, COMPUTER SCIENCE. *Current Pos:* PROF & CHMN, DEPT MATH & COMPUT SCI, OLD DOMINION UNIV, 75- *Personal Data:* b New York, NY, Apr 26, 42; m 64. *Educ:* Hunter Col, BA, 62; Mich State Univ, MS, 64, PhD(math), 67. *Prof Exp:* Teaching asst math, Mich State Univ, 62-67; from asst to assoc prof math, Univ Utah, 67-75. *Concurrent Pos:* USAF Off Sci Res grant, Univ Utah, 72-73; vis assoc prof, Dept Math, Ariz State Univ, 72-73. *Mem:* Soc Indust & Appl Math; Asn Comput Mach; Am Math Soc. *Res:* Approximation theory; numerical analysis; solution of nonlinear equations. *Mailing Add:* Dept Math & Statist Old Dominion Univ 5215 Hampton Blvd Norfolk VA 23529-0077

**WEINSTEIN, STEPHEN B,** MULTIMEDIA COMMUNICATIONS & TERMINALS, DISTRIBUTED SYSTEMS. *Current Pos:* FEL, NEC COMMUNS & COGNITION RES LAB, NEC AM, 94- *Personal Data:* b New York, NY, Nov 25, 38; m 35, Judith Benham; c Brant & Anna. *Educ:* Mass Inst Technol, SB, 60; Univ Mich, MS, 62; Univ Calif, PhD(elec eng), 66. *Prof Exp:* Mem tech staff, Bell Telephone, 68-79; vpres technol strategy, Am Express, 79-84; dept head, Multimedia Commun & Systs Integration Res, Bell Commn Res, 84-93. *Concurrent Pos:* Lectr, Data Commun, Polytech Col Brooklyn, 81, Princeton Univ, 86-87. *Mem:* Fel Inst Elec & Electronics Engrs; Inst Elec & Electronics Engrs Commun Soc (pres, 96-97). *Res:* Multimedia communications; network software. *Mailing Add:* NEC C & C Res Lab 4 Independence Way Princeton NJ 08540

**WEINSTEIN, STEPHEN HENRY,** DRUG METABOLISM. *Current Pos:* sect head, Squibb Inst Med Res, 80-85, sr group leader, 85- 88, asst dept dir, 88-89, EXEC DIR, METAB & PHARMACOKINETICS DEPT, BRISTOL-MYERS SQUIBB INST PHARMACEUT RES, 89- *Personal Data:* b Bronx, NY, Apr 14, 37; m 66; c 1. *Educ:* Queens Col, NY, BS, 58; Adelphi Col, MS, 61; Adelphi Univ, PhD(biochem), 67. *Prof Exp:* Scientist, Warner-Lambert Res Inst, 67-68; sr biochemist, 68-73, group leader, Endo Labs, Inc, 73-77; sr res biochemist, E I du Pont de Nemours & Co, Inc, 77-80. *Mem:* Am Soc Pharmacol & Exp Therapeut; Int Soc Study Xenobiotics; Am Asn Pharmaceut Scientists. *Res:* Metabolism and function of phosphatides; mechanisms of membrane transport; pharmacokinetics; drug metabolism; biochemical pharmacology. *Mailing Add:* Bristol-Myers Squibb PO Box 4500 Princeton NJ 08543-4500. *Fax:* 609-252-6802

**WEINSTEIN, TILLA,** MATHEMATICS, GEOMETRY. *Current Pos:* prof math, Douglass Col, 70-73, chmn dept, 78-80, PROF MATH, RUTGERS UNIV, 80- *Personal Data:* b New York, NY, Sept 29, 34; m 91, Kive; c David Klotz & Daniel Kael. *Educ:* NY Univ, BA, 55, MS, 56, PhD(math), 59. *Prof Exp:* NSF fel, 58-59; instr math, Univ Calif, Los Angeles, 59-60, lectr, 60-61, from asst prof to assoc prof, 61-69; assoc prof, Boston Col, 69-70. *Concurrent Pos:* Vis mem, Courant Inst Math Sci, NY Univ, 64-65, 77, 91, Mass Inst Technol, 68-69, Inst Advan Study, 74, 95, Univ Md, 83-84, City Univ New York, 87-88. *Mem:* Math Asn Am; Am Math Soc; Asn Women Math. *Res:* Differential geometry of surfaces within semi-Riemannian manifolds; indefinite metric geometry on surfaces; Lorentz surfaces (the indefinite metric analogs of Riemann surfaces); harmonically immersed surfaces. *Mailing Add:* Dept Math Rutgers Univ New Brunswick NJ 08903. *Fax:* 732-445-5530; *E-Mail:* tilla@math.rutgers.edu

**WEINSTOCK, ALFRED,** CELL BIOLOGY, PERIODONTOLOGY. *Current Pos:* assoc prof, 70-76, chmn sect periodont, 71-74, CLIN PROF DENT & ANAT, SCH DENT & SCH MED, CTR HEALTH SCI, UNIV CALIF, LOS ANGELES, 77-, MEM, DENT RES INST, 73- *Personal Data:* b Toronto, Ont, May 3, 39; div; c 2. *Educ:* Univ Toronto, DDS, 62; McGill Univ, PhD(anat), 69. *Honors & Awards:* Res Award, Can Dent Asn, 71. *Prof Exp:* Res fel dent med, Forsyth Dent Ctr, Boston, 62-63; Nat Res Coun Can res fel periodont, Sch Dent Med, Harvard Univ, 63-66; Nat Res Coun Can res fel anat sci, Sch Med, McGill Univ, 66-67, from lectr to asst prof, 67-70. *Concurrent Pos:* Nat Res Coun Can res scholar, Sch Med, McGill Univ, 67-69, Med Res Coun Can res scholar, 69-70; NIH res grant, Univ Calif, Los Angeles, 71-79; consult, Vet Admin Hosp, Brentwood & Sepulveda, Calif, 72-; mem staff, Univ Calif, Los Angeles Med Ctr Hosp, Cedars-Sinai Med Ctr, 76-; chmn, Div Dent, Cedars-Sinai Med Ctr, 82-86. *Mem:* AAAS; Am Acad Periodont; Am Asn Anatomists; Am Dent Asn; Sigma Xi; Am Soc Cell Biol. *Res:* Structural and functional aspects of secretory cells involved in the elaboration of collagen, enamel and other glycoproteins, mainly in mineralizing tissues; histology; experimental pathology; periodontal disease. *Mailing Add:* 9201 W Sunset Blvd West Hollywood CA 90069

**WEINSTOCK, BARNET MORDECAI,** SEVERAL COMPLEX VARIABLES, FUNCTIONAL ANALYSIS. *Current Pos:* assoc prof, Univ NC, 77-80, actg chmn, 80-81, chmn dept, 81-85, PROF MATH, UNIV NC, CHARLOTTE, 80- *Personal Data:* b Brooklyn, NY, Oct 10, 40; m 66; c 2. *Educ:* Columbia Univ, BA, 62; Mass Inst Technol, PhD(math), 66. *Prof Exp:* From instr to asst prof math, Brown Univ, 66-73; assoc prof math, Univ Ky, 73-77. *Mem:* Am Math Soc; Math Asn Am. *Res:* Functional analysis; several complex variables. *Mailing Add:* Dept Math Univ NC Charlotte NC 28223-0001

**WEINSTOCK, GEORGE MATTHEW,** MOLECULAR GENETICS, GENETIC ENGINEERING. *Current Pos:* assoc prof, 84-90, PROF, UNIV TEX MED SCH, 90- *Personal Data:* b Chicago, Ill, Feb 6, 49; m 74, Erica Sodergren; c Beth. *Educ:* Univ Mich, BS, 70; Mass Inst Techn PhD(microbiol), 77. *Prof Exp:* Jane Coffin Childs fel, Stanford Univ Med Sch, 77-79, Bank Am-Gianini fel, 79-80; scientist & sect head, Frederick Cancer Res Facil, 80-84; adj prof, Univ Md, Baltimore Co, 81-84. *Concurrent Pos:* Instr, Cold Spring Harbor Lab, 86-90; lectr, Internat Ctr Genetic Eng Biotech, 90-93; fel, Stanford Univ Med Sch, 93-94. *Mem:* Genetics Soc Am; Am Soc Biochem & Molecular Biol; AAAS; Am Soc Microbiol; fel Am Acad Microbiol. *Res:* Analysis of structure and expression of bacterial genes, particularly those important to virulence; genomic sequencing and structure analysis; vaccine development; heterologous expression of foreign genes in bacteria. *Mailing Add:* Biochem Dept Tex Med Sch 6431 Fannin St Houston TX 77030-1501. *Fax:* 713-794-4150; *E-Mail:* georgew@utmmg.med.uth.tmc.edu

**WEINSTOCK, HAROLD,** SQUID MAGNETOMETRY, THERMAL ELECTRICAL & MAGNETIC MEASUREMENTS IN SOLIDS. *Current Pos:* PROG MGR, AIR FORCE OFF SCI RES, 86- *Personal Data:* b Philadelphia, Pa, Dec 25, 34; m 61, Linda A Paul; c Steven G & Allen N. *Educ:* Temple Univ, BA, 56; Cornell Univ, PhD(helium three), 62. *Hon Degrees:* Dr, INSA de Lyon, 97. *Prof Exp:* From res asst to res assoc physics, Cornell Univ, 56-62; asst prof, Mich State Univ, 62-65; assoc prof physics, Ill Inst Technol, 65-73, prof, 73-86, dir, Educ Technol Ctr, 79-85, Technol & Continuing Educ, 85-86. *Concurrent Pos:* Vis staff mem, Sandia Nat Lab, 69 & 71 & Los Alamos Nat Lab, 72-86; vis prof, Cath Univ Leuven, 70 & Cath Univ Nijmegen, 72-73 & INSA Lyon, 93 & 95; consult, Tech Adv Serv for Atty, 74- & Air Force Off Sci Res, 85-86; dir, NATO Advan Study Inst, 76, 85, 88, 90, 92, 95 & 97; contract employee, Naval Res Lab, 82-83; vis distinguished Welch prof, Univ Houston, 97-98. *Mem:* Fel Am Phys Soc; AAAS. *Res:* Thermal, electrical and magnetic properties of solids; radiation damage in solids; superconductivity; computer use in science education; nondestructive evaluation; superconductive magnetometry. *Mailing Add:* Air Force Off Sci Res-NE 110 Duncan Ave Suite B115 Bolling AFB Washington DC 20332-0001. *E-Mail:* harol.weinstock@afosr.af.mil

**WEINSTOCK, IRWIN MORTON,** BIOCHEMISTRY, SCIENCE ADMINISTRATION. *Current Pos:* CLIN DIR, RES TEST LABS INC, 80- *Personal Data:* b New York, NY, July 17, 25; m 56; c 3. *Educ:* Univ Okla, BS, 47; Univ Ill, MS, 48, PhD(chem), 51. *Prof Exp:* Res assoc biochem, Dept Psychiat, Med Col, Cornell Univ, 51-57; res assoc, New York Med Col, 57-59; from asst mem to assoc mem, Inst Muscle Dis, 64-74; dir spec neurol lab, Nassau County Med Ctr, 74-80. *Concurrent Pos:* Lectr, Hunter Col, 53-54 & Columbia Univ, 68-75; adj assoc prof med, Health Sci Ctr, State Univ NY, Stony Brook, 76-80. *Mem:* AAAS; Harvey Soc. *Res:* Intermediary metabolism and enzymology of muscle wasting conditions. *Mailing Add:* Res Test Labs Inc 255 Great Neck Rd Great Neck NY 11021

**WEINSTOCK, JEROME,** PLASMA PHYSICS, FLUID MECHANICS. *Current Pos:* SR SCIENTIST, NAT OCEANIC & ATMOSPHERIC ADMIN, 65- *Personal Data:* b Brooklyn, NY, Sept 12, 33; m 55; c 3. *Educ:* Cooper Union, BChE, 55; Cornell Univ, PhD(phys chem), 59. *Prof Exp:* Sr scientist, Nat Bur Standards, 59-65. *Concurrent Pos:* Nat Res Coun-Nat Acad Sci res fel, 59-62; Emil Schweingerg scholarship. *Mem:* Am Phys Soc; Am Geophys Union. *Res:* Statistical mechanics; turbulence theory; transport theory; fluctuation theory; molecular collision theory; basic research in turbulence theory, atmospheric waves, and plasma physics; statistical physics. *Mailing Add:* Nat Oceanic & Atmospheric Admin 325 Broadway Boulder CO 80303

**WEINSTOCK, JOEL VINCENT,** GASTROENTEROLOGY, INTERNAL MEDICINE. *Current Pos:* DIR, DIV GASTROENTEROL, UNIV IOWA, 86- *Educ:* Wayne State Univ, MD, 73. *Mailing Add:* Univ Iowa Div & Gastro Dept Med Iowa City IA 52240. *Fax:* 319-353-6399

**WEINSTOCK, JOSEPH,** MEDICINAL CHEMISTRY, COMBINATORIAL CHEMISTRY. *Current Pos:* sr chemist, Smith Kline & French Labs, 56-62, group leader, 62-67, sr investr, 67-76, asst dir chem, 78-87, fel, 87-90, sr fel, 90-94, DIR, SMITHKLINE BEECHAM PHARMACEUT, 94- *Personal Data:* b New York, NY, Jan 30, 28; wid; c David, Daniel, Sarah J (Paikowsky), Rachel A, Jonathan, Michael, Joshua, Rebecca L (Sky), Nathaniel & Jeremiah. *Educ:* Rutgers Univ, BS, 49; Univ Rochester, PhD(chem), 52. *Prof Exp:* Res assoc chem, Northwestern Univ, 52-54, instr, 54-56. *Mem:* AAAS; Am Chem Soc; NY Acad Sci. *Res:* Medicinal and synthetic organic chemistry; organic reaction mechanisms; pteridines; diuretic, anti-inflammatory, antihypertensive agents; drug metabolism and identification of metabolites; dopamine agonists; benzazepines; angiotensin antagonists, peptidomimetics; combinatorial chemistry. *Mailing Add:* Med Chem UW2430 Res & Develop SmithKline Beecham Pharmaceut PO Box 1539 King of Prussia PA 19406-0939. *Fax:* 610-270-6609; *E-Mail:* joseph__weinstock@sbphrd.com

**WEINSTOCK, MANUEL,** MECHANICAL ENGINEERING, AERONAUTICAL ENGINEERING. *Current Pos:* RETIRED. *Personal Data:* b Philadelphia, Pa, Apr 15, 27; m 54; c 3. *Educ:* Drexel Inst, BS, 47; Univ Pa, MS, 50. *Prof Exp:* Struct designer, Widdicombe Eng Co, Pa, 47-50; stress analyst, Piasecki Helicopter Corp, 50-51; aeronaut engr, Naval Air Develop Ctr, 51-54; mech engr, Frankford Arsenal, US Army, 54-57 & 58-62, supvry ord engr, 57-58, supvry mech engr, Mech Eng Propellant Actuated Devices Dept, 62-74, supvr ind eng, 74-77, supvr mech engr artil & tank metal parts, 77-90. *Mem:* Am Soc Mech Engrs; Sigma Xi. *Res:* Interior ballistics; digital and analog simulation of the performance of propellant actuated devices and complete systems used for emergency escape from military aircraft. *Mailing Add:* 1016 City Ave Wynnewood PA 19096

**WEINSTOCK, ROBERT,** MATHEMATICAL PHYSICS, SEVENTEENTH CENTURY MECHANICS. *Current Pos:* vis assoc prof math, 59-60, from assoc prof to prof, 60-83, EMER PROF PHYSICS, OBERLIN COL, 83- *Personal Data:* b Philadelphia, Pa, Feb 2, 19; m 50, Elizabeth W Brownell; c Frank M & Robert B. *Educ:* Univ Pa, AB, 40; Stanford Univ, PhD, 43. *Prof Exp:* Instr physics, Stanford Univ, 43-44, math, 46-50, actg asst prof, 50-54; res assoc radar countermeasures, Radio Res Lab, Harvard Univ, 44-45; from asst prof to assoc prof math, Univ Notre Dame, 54-59. *Concurrent Pos:* NSF fel, Oxford Univ, 65-66. *Mem:* Fel AAAS; Am Phys Soc; Am Asn Physics Teachers. *Res:* Mathematical physics; Newton's Principia. *Mailing Add:* Dept Physics Oberlin Col Oberlin OH 44074

**WEINSTOCK, W,** RADAR & DEFENSE SYSTEM DESIGN. *Current Pos:* RETIRED. *Personal Data:* b Philadelphia, Pa, Aug 18, 25. *Educ:* Univ Pa, BSEE, 46, MSEE, 54, PhD(elec eng), 64. *Prof Exp:* Design engr radar design, Philco, 46-49; prin scientist, missile & surface radar div, RCA, 49-87. *Concurrent Pos:* Consult, 87- *Mem:* Fel Inst Elec & Electronics Engrs. *Mailing Add:* Six Beryl Rd Cheltenham PA 19012

**WEINSWIG, MELVIN H,** PHARMACEUTICAL CHEMISTRY. *Current Pos:* assoc dean, 71-76, PROF PHARM & CHMN EXTEN SERV PHARM, SCH PHARM, UNIV WIS-MADISON, 69- *Personal Data:* b Lynn, Mass, Feb 2, 35; m 60; c 3. *Educ:* Mass Col Pharm, BS, 55, MS, 57; Univ Ill, PhD(pharmaceut chem), 61. *Honors & Awards:* Award of Merit Continuing Educ, Am Asn Cols Pharm. *Prof Exp:* From asst prof to assoc prof pharmaceut chem, Butler Univ, 61-69. *Concurrent Pos:* Consult, Continuing Co, Educ Health Prof. *Mem:* Am Chem Soc; Am Pharmaceut Asn; Am Asn Cols Pharm. *Res:* Novel analytical approach to combination pharmaceutical products; drug abuse education and research. *Mailing Add:* 5206 Tolman Terr Madison WI 53711. *Fax:* 608-262-2431

**WEINTRAUB, BRUCE DALE,** ENDOCRINOLOGY, INTERNAL MEDICINE. *Current Pos:* SR INVESTR ENDOCRINOL, NAT INST ARTHRITIS, METAB & DIGESTIVE DIS, 72- *Personal Data:* b Buffalo, NY, Sept 19, 40; m 68; c 1. *Educ:* Princeton Univ, AB, 62; Harvard Med Sch, MD, 66. *Prof Exp:* Intern med, Peter Bent Brigham Hosp, Boston, Mass, 66-67, resident, 67-68; clin assoc endocrinol, Nat Inst Arthritis & Metab Dis, 68-71; instr med, Harvard Med Sch, 71-72. *Concurrent Pos:* Clin & res fel, Nat Inst Arthritis & Metab Dis, 68-71; USPHS res grant & asst med, Mass Gen Hosp, Boston, 71-72. *Mem:* Am Fedn Clin Res; Endocrine Soc. *Res:* Structure and properties of hormones secreted by tumors; applications of affinity chromatography to endocrinology; subunits of glycoprotein hormones. *Mailing Add:* Nat Inst Arthritis Bldg 10 Rm 8N 316 Bethesda MD 20892-0001

**WEINTRAUB, HAROLD M,** gene expression, cellular regulation; deceased, see previous edition for last biography

**WEINTRAUB, HERBERT D,** ANESTHESIOLOGY, MEDICAL EDUCATION. *Current Pos:* assoc prof, George Washington Univ, 71-74, dir med educ, Dept Anesthesia, Med Ctr, 71-78, dir operating rm, 76-90, interim chmn, 91, PROF ANESTHESIOL, GEORGE WASHINGTON UNIV, 74-, ASSOC CHMN, DEPT ANESTHESIA, MED CTR, 79-,. *Personal Data:* b New York, NY, Feb 17, 30; m 63; c 3. *Educ:* NY Univ, BA, 50; Oxford Univ, MA, 58, BM, BCh, 59. *Prof Exp:* Intern rotating, Strong Mem Hosp, Univ Rochester, 59-61; resident anesthesiol, Columbia Presby Hosp & Med Ctr, New York, 61-63, NIH res fel, 63-64; asst prof, Med Sch, Univ Pa, 64-69; asst prof, Med Sch, Univ Chicago, 69-71. *Concurrent Pos:* Mem sr staff, Hosp Univ Pa, 64-69; assoc dir, Dept Anesthesiol, Michael Reese Hosp, Chicago, 69-71. *Mem:* Am Asn Univ Anesthetists; Am Soc Anesthesiol; Int Anesthesia Res Soc; Soc Neurosurg Anesthetists & Neurol Supportive Care; Soc Cardiovasc Anesthesiologists. *Res:* Anesthesia for cardio-thoracic surgery; educational methods as applied to anesthesiology. *Mailing Add:* Dept Anesthesiol George Washington Univ Med Sch 2300 1st St NW Washington DC 20037-2337

**WEINTRAUB, HERSCHEL JONATHAN R,** MOLECULAR GRAPHICS, DRUG DESIGN. *Current Pos:* ASST DIR, MED CHEM, R W JOHNSON PRI, 93- *Personal Data:* b Cincinnati, Ohio, Aug 19, 48; m 81. *Educ:* Case Inst Technol, BS, 70; Case Western Res Univ, MS, 73, PhD(macromolecular sci), 75. *Prof Exp:* Res assoc, Dept Med Chem, Purdue Univ, 75-76, dir comput based educ, Sch Pharm, 76-77, asst prof med chem, 77-82; sr phys chemist, Lilly Res Labs, Eli Lilly & Co, 82-83; sr chemist, Abbott Lab, Chicago, Ill, 83-86; head, Theoret Chem Dept, Marion Merrell Dow Res Inst, 86-93. *Concurrent Pos:* Nat Libr Med fel, Dept Comput Sci, Univ Ill, Urbana, 78; Consult, var pharmaceut & chem co, 78-; prin investr, NIH grants, dept med chem, Purdue Univ, 79-81; adj prof med chem, 82-; adj prof med chem, Univ Cincinnati, 86-93. *Mem:* Am Chem Soc; Inst Elec & Electronics Engrs; Biophys Soc; Int Soc Quantum Biol. *Res:* Drug design, with emphasis on solution conformational properties of drugs; modeling drug-receptor interactions; development of drug design software systems. *Mailing Add:* Helios Pharms 9800 Bluegrass Pkwy Louisville KY 40299

**WEINTRAUB, JOEL D,** ANIMAL BEHAVIOR, ENVIRONMENTAL SCIENCES. *Current Pos:* From asst prof to assoc prof, 68-77, dir environ studies, 72-75, & 85, PROF ZOOL, CALIF STATE UNIV, FULLERTON, 77- *Personal Data:* b New York, NY, May 2, 42; m 68; c Anita L & Jody S. *Educ:* City Col New York, BS, 63; Univ Calif, Riverside, PhD(zool), 68. *Concurrent Pos:* Environ consult. *Mem:* Am Soc Ichthyol & Herpet; Sigma Xi; Ecol Soc Am; Herpetologists League; Soc Conserv Biol. *Res:* Ecology of birds, amphibians and reptiles; homing and orientation of vertebrates; urban ecology; vertebrate food habits. *Mailing Add:* Dept Biol Sci Calif State Univ Fullerton CA 92834. *E-Mail:* jweintraub@ccuax.fullerton.edu

**WEINTRAUB, JOSEPH,** SOFTWARE DEVELOPMENT. *Current Pos:* DIR ADVAN TECHNOL, THINKING SOFTWARE INC, 87- *Personal Data:* b New York, NY, May 15, 54; m, Valerie; c Sharon & Anna. *Educ:* City Univ NY, BA, 68; Harvard Univ, PhD, 72. *Honors & Awards:* Loebner Prize, Cambridge Ctr Behav Studies, 92. *Prof Exp:* Programmer, Great Am Ins Co, 68-72; Time Inc, 72-73; systs develop mgr, Abraham & Straus, 73-80; proj mgr & lectr, Pace Univ, 80-81; staff mem, Interpub Group Cos, 81-87. *Mem:* Am Asn Artificial Intel. *Res:* Computing. *Mailing Add:* Thinking Software 46-16 65th Pl Flushing NY 11377

**WEINTRAUB, LEONARD,** ORGANIC CHEMISTRY, PHARMACEUTICAL CHEMISTRY. *Current Pos:* CONSULT, 85- *Personal Data:* b New York, NY, Apr 21, 26; m 50, Estelle Lang; c Gail & Ellen. *Educ:* City Col New York, BS, 48; Polytech Inst Brooklyn, MS, 54, PhD(org chem), 68. *Prof Exp:* Org chemist, Francis Delafield Hosp, NY, 50-54; org chemist, Bristol Myers Co, 54-62, group leader, 62-68, dept head org chem, 68-69, dir chem res, 69-85. *Concurrent Pos:* Adj prof chem, NJ Inst Technol, 68-69. *Mem:* AAAS; Am Chem Soc; Royal Soc Chem; NY Acad Sci; Am Pharmaceut Asn. *Res:* Heterocyclic chemistry; molecular complexes in organic chemistry; salicylate chemistry; synthetic methods; pharmaceutical and cosmetic analysis. *Mailing Add:* 88 Greenwood Dr Millburn NJ 07041-1428. *Fax:* 973-467-9064; *E-Mail:* lenwgin@aol.com

**WEINTRAUB, LESTER,** ORGANIC POLYMER CHEMISTRY. *Current Pos:* group leader polymer res, 71-73, TECH MGR POLYMERS & CONSULT SPECIALTY POLYVINYL CHLORIDE POLYMERS, PANTASOTE CO, INC, 85-; SR RES CHEM, PERMEABLE TECHNOL, INC, 86- *Personal Data:* b New York, NY, Feb 1, 24; m 50, Harriet M Weintraub; c Beverly C (Srolovitz) & Mitchel K. *Educ:* City Col New York, BS, 46; Fordham Univ, MS, 49; NY Univ, PhD(org chem), 54. *Prof Exp:* Sr chemist, Atomic Energy Comn Proj, Columbia Univ, 53-55, group leader, 55-58; group leader, Adv Res Proj Agency Proj, NY Univ, 58-59; sr chemist, Cent Res Labs, Air Reduction Co, Inc, NJ, 59-71. *Mem:* Am Chem Soc; Am Inst Chem; Soc Plastics Eng. *Res:* Organic polymer synthesis and structure determination; polyvinyl chloride technology. *Mailing Add:* Ten Pardee Ct Mt Laurel NJ 08054-3044

**WEINTRAUB, LEWIS ROBERT,** HEMATOLOGY. *Current Pos:* assoc prof, 72-77, PROF MED, SCH MED, BOSTON UNIV, 77- *Personal Data:* b New York, NY, Aug 15, 34; m 67; c 2. *Educ:* Dartmouth Col, AB, 55; Harvard Med Sch, MD, 58. *Prof Exp:* Intern med, Hosp, Univ Pa, 58-59; asst resident res in med, Hosp, Univ Mich, 59-61; fel hemat, Mt Sinai Hosp, New York, 61-62; res hematologist, Walter Reed Army Inst Res, 62-65; from asst prof to assoc prof med, Sch Med, Tufts Univ, 65-72. *Concurrent Pos:* Asst chief hemat, Walter Reed Gen Hosp, 62-65; asst hematologist & asst physician, New Eng Med Ctr Hosps, 65-72; assoc vis physician, Boston Univ Hosp, 72-, chief & physician, hemat sect, 77-; NIH res career develop award, 66. *Mem:* AAAS; AMA; Am Soc Hemat; NY Acad Med. *Res:* Clinical hematology and research in field of iron metabolism; chemotherapy trials for hematologic malignancies. *Mailing Add:* Boston Univ Med Ctr 75 E Newton Boston MA 02118-2347. *Fax:* 617-638-7065

**WEINTRAUB, MARVIN,** PLANT VIROLOGY. *Current Pos:* RETIRED. *Personal Data:* b Radom, Poland, Oct 17, 24; nat Can; m 48, Rita Enushevsky; c Laura, Mark, Lisa & John. *Educ:* Univ Toronto, BA, 47, PhD(bot), 50. *Honors & Awards:* Queen's Silver Jubilee Medal, 77. *Prof Exp:* Demonstr bot, Univ Toronto, 45-50; prin res scientist & head virus chem & physiol sect, Res Br, Can Dept Agr, 50-71, dir, Res Sta, Agr Can, 71-90. *Concurrent Pos:* Hon prof, Univ BC, 71- *Mem:* AAAS; Am Phytopath Soc; Can Phytopath Soc; fel NY Acad Sci; Int Soc Plant Morphol. *Res:* Metabolism and cytology of virus-infected plants; fine structure and electron microscopy; virus inhibitors; movement in plants. *Mailing Add:* 6785 Laurel St Vancouver BC V6P 3T4 Can

**WEINTRAUB, PHILIP MARVIN,** ORGANIC CHEMISTRY. *Current Pos:* SCIENTIST, MARION MERRELL DOW RES INST, 70- *Personal Data:* b Cleveland, Ohio, Feb 22, 39; m 83; c 3. *Educ:* Ohio State Univ, BSc, 60, MSc, 63, PhD(chem), 64. *Prof Exp:* Res chemist, Pioneering Res Lab, Textile Fibers Dept, E I du Pont de Nemours & Co, Inc, 64-66; sr chemist, Hess & Clark, 66-70. *Mem:* Am Chem Soc; NY Acad Sci; Int Soc Heterocyclic Chem. *Res:* Steroids; heterocycles; strained ring polycyclic systems; mechanism based enzyme inhibitors. *Mailing Add:* Hoechst Marion Roussel 2110 E Galbraith Rd Cincinnati OH 45215

**WEINTRAUB, ROBERT LOUIS,** plant & cell physiology; deceased, see previous edition for last biography

**WEINZIMMER, FRED,** NUCLEAR ENGINEERING, MECHANICAL ENGINEERING. *Current Pos:* RETIRED. *Personal Data:* b New York, NY, May 29, 25; m 47; c 2. *Educ:* Clarkson Col Technol, BME, 50; Polytech Inst Brooklyn, MME, 55. *Prof Exp:* Draftsman diesel design, US Dept Navy, NY, 43; engr, Am Gas & Elec Co, 50-51; asst proj engr, R R Popham, 51-52; engr, Ebasco Serv, Inc, 52-54; systs engr, Bettis Plant, Westinghouse Elec Corp, 54-55, lead systs engr, 55-56; systs tech supvr, Atomic Power Equip Dept, Gen Elec Co, 56-57, lead systs engr, 57-62, specialist, Vallecitos Exp Superheat Reactor Prog & Design, 62-65, prin engr, ECPL Proj, 65-66, mgr proj analysis, 67, proj mgr, Shoreham Proj, 67-71, proj mgr, Nine Mile Pt Unit 2, 71-74, proj mgr, Nuclear Energy Div, Somerset 1 & 2 Proj, 74-76, proj mgr, BWRSD-High Flow Hydraul Facil, 76-78, proj mgr, NPD-Clinton 1 & 2 Proj, 78-81; dir proj eng, GPU Nuclear Corp, 81-82, dir spec projs, 82-84, mgr spec projs, Oyster Creek NGS, GPU nuclear, 84-89. *Res:* Major nuclear power plant operation, design, layout and construction for utility application. *Mailing Add:* 780 Nantucket Circle Lake Worth FL 33467

**WEINZWEIG, AVRUM ISRAEL,** MATHEMATICS. *Current Pos:* PROF MATH, STATIST & COMPUT SCI, UNIV ILL, CHICAGO, 65- *Personal Data:* b Toronto, Ont, Apr 22, 26; m 53, 63, Lila Perlis; c Ari, Meira, Lauren, Michael & Carmi. *Educ:* Univ Toronto, BASc, 50; Harvard Univ, AM, 53, PhD(math), 57. *Prof Exp:* Asst chief geophysicist, Weiss Geophys Corp, 50-52; instr math, Univ Calif, Berkeley, 57-59, actg asst prof, 59-60; asst prof, Northwestern Univ, 60-65. *Concurrent Pos:* Consult, Solomon Schechter Day Schs, Ill, 64-80 & Second Int Study Math, 76-; dir, Inst Learning & Teaching Math, 84-; Math Adv Comt, Ill Off Educ, 84-86; pres, Int Comn for Study & Improv of Teaching of Math, 88-; consult, Sabin Magnet Sch, 88-; dir, Math Prep Elem Sch Teachers Proj. *Mem:* Am Math Soc; Math Asn Am; Nat Coun Teachers Math; Math Asn Am; Asn Teachers Math; Nat Coun Supvr Math. *Res:* Algebraic topology, particularly fiber spaces; category theory; learning theory; learning and acquisition of mathematical concepts; mathematics education. *Mailing Add:* 9711 Kildare Ave Univ Ill Box 4348 Skokie IL 60076. *Fax:* 312-996-1491; *E-Mail:* izzie@jackos.math.uic.edu

**WEIPERT, EUGENE ALLEN,** INDUSTRIAL ORGANIC CHEMISTRY. *Current Pos:* RETIRED. *Personal Data:* b Monroe, Mich, Nov 17, 31; m 60, Helen Riley; c Brad, Paul, Thomas, Daniel, Timothy, Eve, Michael & Martha. *Educ:* Univ Detroit, BS, 52, MS, 54; Iowa State Univ, PhD(org chem), 57. *Prof Exp:* Res supvr, Wyandotte Chem Corp, Mich, 58-72; tech mgr, Southern Sizing Co, 72-82; lab mgr, Mazer Chem Co, 82-87, dir res & develop, PPG, 88-91; dir, Dr Gene, Inc, 91-96. *Res:* Alkylene oxides, amines; organometallics; organic reaction mechanisms; surfactants. *Mailing Add:* 211 68th St Kenosha WI 53143

**WEIR, ALEXANDER, JR,** CHEMICAL ENGINEERING. *Current Pos:* CONSULT, 88- *Personal Data:* b Crossett, Ark, Dec 19, 22; m 46; c 3. *Educ:* Univ Ark, BSChE, 43; Polytech Inst Brooklyn, MChE, 46; Univ Mich, PhD, 54. *Prof Exp:* Chem engr, Stanford Res Labs, Am Cyanamid Co, Conn, 43-47; from asst to proj supvr, Aircraft Propulsion Lab, Univ Mich, 48-57, lectr chem & metall eng, 54-56, asst prof, 56-58; from consult to asst mgr, Atlas Prog Off, Space Tech Labs, Ramo-Wooldridge Corp, 56-60; corp sr sci & tech adv res & develop mgt, Northrop Corp, 60-67, dir plans & progs, Corp Labs, 67-70; prin scientist air qual, Southern Calif Edison Co, 70-76, mgr, chem systs res & develop, 76-84, environ res, 84-85, chief scientist, 85-88. *Mem:* AAAS; Am Geophys Union; Am Chem Soc; Combustion Inst; Am Inst Chem Engrs. *Res:* Effects of beta radiation on combustion; spectroscopic investigation of flames, temperatures and compositions behind detonation waves; flow through sonic orifices; location of Mach discs in supersonic jets; development of sulfur dioxide and nitrogen oxide removal systems for electric generating stations; fluegas desulferization; coal gasification (cool water project); solar central thermal power (solar one); solar salt ponds. *Mailing Add:* Billow Vista Dr Playa Del Rey CA 90293-7807

**WEIR, BRUCE SPENCER,** POPULATION GENETICS, QUANTITATIVE GENETICS. *Current Pos:* from assoc prof to prof, 76-92, WILLIAM N REYNOLDS PROF STATIST & GENETICS, NC STATE UNIV, 92- *Personal Data:* b Christchurch, NZ, Dec 31, 43; m 71, Elizabeth Swainson; c Claudia & Henry. *Educ:* Univ Canterbury, NZ, BSc Hons, 65; NC State Univ, PhD(statist), 68. *Prof Exp:* Sr lectr statist, Massey Univ, 70-75, reader, 76. *Concurrent Pos:* Assoc ed, Genetics, 77-, Theoret Pop Biol, 79-87, & 93-, Biomet, 84-89, J Heredity, 90-, Am J Human Genetics, 93-; Guggenheim fel, 83; ed, Theoret Pop Biol, 95- *Mem:* Am Statist Asn; Biomet Soc; Am Soc Human Genetics; Genetics Soc Am; Soc Study Evolution; Am Acad Forensic Sci. *Res:* Development of statistical methodology for the analysis of genetic data; development of population genetics theory; statistical mean of interpreting DNA profiles for human identification. *Mailing Add:* Dept Statist NC State Univ Box 8203 Raleigh NC 27695-8203. *Fax:* 919-515-7315; *E-Mail:* weir@stat.nscu.edu

**WEIR, BRYCE KEITH ALEXANDER,** NEUROLOGY. *Current Pos:* MAURICE GOLDBLATT PROF SURG & NEUROL, UNIV CHICAGO, 92-, DIR, BRAIN RES INST, 93- *Personal Data:* b Edinburgh, Scotland, Apr 29, 36; m 76, Mary Lou Lauber; c Leanora, Glyncora & Brocke. *Educ:* McGill Univ, BSc, 58, MD, CM, 60, MSc, 63; Am Bd Neurol Surg, dipl. *Honors & Awards:* White Lectr, Harvard Univ; Gainey Lectr, Mayo Clin; Grass Gold Medal, Soc Neurol Surgeons, 92. *Prof Exp:* Intern, Montreal Gen Hosp, 60-61; resident neurosurg, Neurol Inst, Montreal, 62-64 & 65-66, NY Neurol Inst, 64-65; neurosurgeon, Univ Alta, Edmonton, 67-92, dir, Div Neurosurg, 82-86, Walter Anderson prof & chmn dept, 86-92; surgeon-in-chief, Univ Alta Hosps, 86-92. *Concurrent Pos:* Mem, Neurol A Study Sect, NIH, 91-93; vis prof numerous univs. *Mem:* Inst Med-Nat Acad Sci; fel Am Col Surgeons; fel Royal Col Surgeons Can; hon mem Royal Col Surgeons Edinburgh; Am Surg Asn; Am Acad Neurol Surgeons; Soc Neurol Surgeons. *Res:* Understanding of cerebral vasospasm; surgical management of intracranial aneurysms; contributed over 250 articles to medical journals. *Mailing Add:* 4950 S Chicago Beach Dr Chicago IL 60615-3207

**WEIR, EDWARD EARL, II,** CHEMISTRY, COMPUTER SOFTWARE. *Current Pos:* VPRES & TECH DIR, ANALYTICAL DATA PROCESSING, 82- *Personal Data:* b St Petersburg, Fla, Mar 9, 45; m 86, Masako Doi. *Educ:* Ga Inst Technol, BS, 67; Fla State Univ, PhD(chem), 72. *Prof Exp:* Res assoc biochem, Fla State Univ, 67-72; res assoc oncol, Univ Ala, 72-73, instr biochem, 73-74; res assoc oncol, Johns Hopkins Hosp, 74-77; anal lab mgr & qual assurance coordr, Hittman Assocs, 77-82. *Concurrent Pos:* Fels, NIH, 72-74; Am Cancer Soc, 74-76 & USPHS, 76-77. *Res:* Quality assurance coordinator as well as laboratory manager for organic and inorganic analytical laboratories dealing in coal, synthetic fuels, water and other media; computer programs dealing with data reduction, data base (particularly quality assurance), cost analysis and purchasing; biochemical ecology and pesticide fate and effects. *Mailing Add:* 602 St Johnsbury Rd Baltimore MD 21228-4046

**WEIR, EDWARD KENNETH,** PULMONARY VASCULAR RESEARCH, CLINICAL CARDIOLOGY. *Current Pos:* assoc prof, 78-85, PROF MED, MED SCH, UNIV MINN, 85- *Personal Data:* b Jan 7, 43; m 71, Elizabeth V Pearman; c Fergus G & Conor K. *Educ:* Univ Oxford, UK, BA, 64, MA, BM, Bch, 67, DM, 76; Royal Col Phys, MRCP, 71; Am Bd Internal Med, dipl, 80,81. *Concurrent Pos:* Fulbright fel, 73-75; staff physician med, Vet Admin Med Ctr, Minn, 78; dir, Grover Conf, 84-94; sr Int Fogarty fel, 93. *Mem:* Am Physiol Soc; Am Col Cardiol; Am Col Chest Physicians; Am Soc Exp Biol & Med; Am Thoracic Soc; Am Fedn Clin Res. *Res:* Pulmonary vascular reactivity and the mechanisms involved in hypoxic pulmonary vasoconstriction; sulfhydryl redox status in cell division and hypertrophy. *Mailing Add:* 1262 Hunter Dr Wayzata MN 55391

**WEIR, JAMES HENRY, III,** MEDICAL RESEARCH. *Current Pos:* From med res assoc to dir, Med Serv, 63-75, DIR, MED RES, WARNER-LAMBERT CO, 75-, VPRES REGULATORY & MED AFFAIRS, 81- *Personal Data:* b East Orange, NJ, Sept 25, 32; m 58; c 3. *Educ:* Princeton Univ, AB, 54; Columbia Univ, MD, 58. *Concurrent Pos:* Macy teaching fel obstet-gynec, Col Physicians & Surgeons, Columbia Univ, 62-63. *Mem:* Am Fertil Soc; Am Fedn Clin Res; Sigma Xi. *Res:* Clinical investigation of new drugs and instrumentation devices; administration of government regulatory affairs and medical affairs. *Mailing Add:* 454 Haworth Ave Haworth NJ 07641

**WEIR, JAMES ROBERT, JR,** METALLURGICAL ENGINEERING. *Current Pos:* CONSULT, 94- *Personal Data:* b Middletown, Ohio, Dec 29, 32; m 52, 81; c James, David, Todd, Patrick & Scott. *Educ:* Univ Cincinnati, BS, 55; Univ Tenn, MS, 61. *Honors & Awards:* E O Lawrence Award, AEC, 73. *Prof Exp:* Metallurgist, Oak Ridge Nat Lab, 55-57, group leader metall, 60-66, asst sect chief, 67-70, sect chief, 70-73, DIR, 73-84 assoc dir, Metals & Ceramics Div, 84-94,. *Concurrent Pos:* Mem bd trustees, Am Soc Metals, 77-80. *Mem:* Fel Am Soc Metals; fel AAAS. *Res:* High-temperature properties of metals; fatigue; radiation damage in metals, fuel element design. *Mailing Add:* 10513 Sandpiper Lane Knoxville TN 37922

**WEIR, JOHN ARNOLD,** GENETICS. *Current Pos:* from asst prof to prof, 50-84, EMER PROF GENETICS, UNIV KANS, 84- *Personal Data:* b Saskatoon, Sask, Apr 5, 16; nat US; m 46, Ruth R Ward; c M Ann & Arnold W. *Educ:* Univ Sask, BSA, 37; Iowa State Col, MS, 42, PhD(genetics), 48. *Prof Exp:* Asst animal breeding, Dom Exp Sta, Alta, 37-40; instr, Univ Sask, 42, assoc prof animal husb, 48-50. *Concurrent Pos:* Consult, Animal Resources Adv Comt, USPHS, 64-67; USPHS spec fel & hon res assoc hist sci, Harvard Univ, 66-67. *Mem:* Genetics Soc Am; Am Genetic Asn; Sigma Xi. *Res:* Mammalian genetics; sex ratio and behavior of mice; history of genetics; history of aeronautics; history of agriculture. *Mailing Add:* 1319 Spencer Dr Lawrence KS 66044

**WEIR, MELANIE LYNN,** RECEPTORS, MEMBRANE TRAFFICKING. *Current Pos:* POSTDOCTORAL FEL, DEPT CELL BIOL, HOSP SICK CHILDREN, CAN, 96- *Personal Data:* b London, Eng, July 5, 66; Can citizen. *Educ:* Queen's Univ, Can, BSc, 88, PhD(biochem), 94. *Prof Exp:* Postdoctoral fel, London Regional Cancer Ctr, Can, 94-96. *Res:* Protein machinery involved in vesicle secretory pathway of cells. *Mailing Add:* Dept Cell Biol Rm 5009B McMaster Bldg Hosp Sick Children 555 University Ave Toronto ON M5G 1X8 Can

**WEIR, MICHAEL ROSS,** OTITIS MEDIA, PEDIATRIC NEPHROLOGY. *Current Pos:* SR STAFF, DEPT PEDIAT, SCOTT & WHITE HOSP & CLIN, TEMPLE, TEX, 93- *Personal Data:* B Austin, Tex, Dec 30, 42; m 64; c 3. *Educ:* Harvard Univ, BA, 65; Univ Tex, Galveston, MD, 69. *Prof Exp:* Internship residency pediat, Letterman Army Med Ctr, 69-72; chief pediat, Vicenza Army Hosp, Italy, 72-76; staff pediatrician, William Beaumont Army Med Ctr, 76-78, chief outpatient serv, 78-82, asst chief pediat, 82-84, chief Dept Clin Invest, 84-87; chief pediat, Madigan Army Med Ctr, 87-91, dep comdr clin serv, 91-92, dir med educ, 92-93. *Mem:* Am Acad Pediat; AMA. *Res:* Otitis media; pediatric nephrology; fluid and electrolyte abnormalities; toxicology. *Mailing Add:* 2516 Canyon Creek Dr Temple TX 76502-3105

**WEIR, ROBERT JAMES, JR,** TOXICOLOGY. *Current Pos:* CONSULT & PRES, ROBERT WEIR & ASSOC, 82- *Personal Data:* b Washington, DC, Nov 26, 24; m 47, Ruth Grove; c Shannon, Robert III & Dana. *Educ:* Univ Md, College Park, BS, 48, MS, 50, PhD, 55. *Prof Exp:* Asst physiol, Univ Md, 48-51; res assoc toxicol, Hazleton Labs, Va, 51-56, head agr chem dept, 56-58, res applns specialist, 58-62, dir, Hazleton Labs, SA, Lausanne, Switz, 62-65, vpres, Inst Indust & Biol Res, Cologne, Ger, 63-66, vpres mkt, Hazleton Labs, Va, 67-69; vpres, Litton Bionetics, Inc, 69-82. *Mem:* Am Chem Soc (secy-treas, Agr & Food Div, 67-68); Soc Toxicol. *Res:* Toxicology; biochemistry; pharmacology; safety evaluation of drug, cosmetic, food chemical and pesticide development. *Mailing Add:* 1606 Simmons Ct McLean VA 22101-5154

**WEIR, RONALD DOUGLAS,** THERMODYNAMICS & MATERIAL PROPERTIES. *Current Pos:* Nat Res Coun Can fel, Royal Mil Col Can, 66-68, from asst prof to assoc prof, 68-81, head, Dept Chem & Chem Eng, 90-95, PROF ENG, ROYAL MIL COL CAN, 76-, PROF CHEM ENG, 81-, DEAN GRAD STUDIES & RES, 95- *Personal Data:* b St John, NB, Jan 10, 41; m 63; c 2. *Educ:* Univ NB, BSc, 63; Univ London, DIC & PhD, 66. *Concurrent Pos:* Sr vis inorg chem, Oxford Univ, 78-79; vis prof chem, Univ Mich, 85-90; adj prof, Queen's Univ, 86-; mem, Thermodyn Comt, Int Union Pure & Appl Chem, 89-, secy, 94-; ed, J Chem Thermodyn, 93- *Mem:* Fel Chem Inst Can; Can Soc Chem Engrs; fel Royal Soc Chem; Am Soc Eng Educ; Int Union Pure & Appl Chem. *Res:* Thermodynamic properties and orientational disorder in solids; low temperature calorimetry; dielectrics; equations of state and intermolecular forces. *Mailing Add:* Dept Chem & Chem Eng Royal Mil Col Can Kingston ON K7K 5L0 Can. *Fax:* 613-542-9489; *E-Mail:* weirr@rmc.ca

**WEIR, WILLIAM CARL,** RESEARCH ADMINISTRATION. *Current Pos:* RETIRED. *Personal Data:* b Lakeview, Ore, Aug 24, 19; m 46; c 2. *Educ:* Ore State Col, BS, 40; Univ Wis, MS, 41, PhD(animal husb, biochem), 48. *Prof Exp:* Asst, Univ Wis, 45-46, instr, 47; assoc prof animal sci, Ore State Col, 48; from asst prof to prof, Univ Calif, Davis, 48-73, dean students, 58-65, prof nutrit & chmn dept, 73-81, assoc prog dir, Small Ruminant Prog, 81-88, assoc dean, int progs, 85-90. *Concurrent Pos:* Fulbright res grant, Univ Western Australia, 65-66; mem comt sheep nutrit, Nat Acad Sci-Nat Res Coun; vis scientist & Univ Calif rep, Univ Chile-Univ Calif Coop Prog, Santiago, Chile, 70-72. *Mem:* Am Soc Animal Sci. *Res:* Sheep nutrition; sheep and goat management. *Mailing Add:* 887 Linden Lane Davis CA 95616

**WEIR, WILLIAM DAVID,** PHYSICAL CHEMISTRY. *Current Pos:* PRES, TRELLIS TECHNOL, 86- *Personal Data:* b Oakland, Calif, Mar 15, 41; c Wendy & William S. *Educ:* Occidental Col, AB, 62; Princeton Univ, AM, 63, PhD(chem), 65. *Prof Exp:* Instr chem, Harvard Univ, 65-68; from asst prof to assoc prof chem, Reed Col, 68-86. *Concurrent Pos:* Consult, indust & govt. *Mem:* Am Med Informatics Asn; Health Info Mgt Syst Soc; Asn Comput Machinery; Inst Elec & Electronics Engrs. *Res:* Architecture, design and implementation of complex, mission-critical computer applications; intelligent systems, embedding extensive knowledge resources; search strategies; massive parallel computatons; theoretical protein dynamics; computer graphics and interactive modelling applications in chemistry. *Mailing Add:* 104 Hilltop Dr Los Gatos CA 95030

**WEIR, WILLIAM THOMAS,** SYSTEMS ENGINEERING, OPERATIONS RESEARCH. *Current Pos:* PRIN STAFF ENGR, PUB SERV ELEC & GAS, 91- *Personal Data:* b Wildwood, NJ, Dec 23, 31; m 54, Sarah McGowan; c William Thomas, Blair Stephen, Timothy Andrew & James Christopher. *Educ:* Drexel Univ, BSEE, 54, MS, 58; Univ Pa, PhD(systms eng, opers res), 72. *Prof Exp:* Component engr elec eng, RCA Corp, 54-56; mgr syst eng, Gen Elec Co, 56-73; pres & chmn bd dir, Eval Assoc, Inc, 73-91. *Concurrent Pos:* Adj prof physics, Drexel Univ, 58-, adj prof eng mgt, 63-; mem, US Sci Deleg, Peoples Repub China, 79. *Mem:* Fel Inst Elec & Electronics Engrs (treas, past vpres); Oper Res Soc Am; Inst Elec & Electronics Engrs Reliability Soc (pres, 93 & 94). *Res:* Reliability. *Mailing Add:* 513 19th St PO Box 506 Ocean City NJ 08226-0506

**WEIRICH, GUNTER FRIEDRICH,** INSECT ENDOCRINOLOGY. *Current Pos:* RETIRED. *Personal Data:* b Eisenach, Ger, Feb 17, 34; US citizen; div. *Educ:* Univ Munich, PhD(zool), 63. *Prof Exp:* Res assoc endocrinol, Philipps Univ, Marburg, Ger, 64-65 & 66-70; res fel insect physiol, Biol Div, Oak Ridge Nat Lab, 65-66; sr scientist biol chem, Zoecon Corp, 70-73; res assoc biol chem, Tex A&M Univ, 73-77; res entomologist biol chem, Beltsville Agr Res Ctr, USDA, 77-97. *Mem:* AAAS. *Res:* Metabolism of insect hormones. *Mailing Add:* 7919 Mandan Rd No 103 Greenbelt MD 20770-2828

**WEIRICH, WALTER EDWARD,** VETERINARY SURGERY. *Current Pos:* from asst prof to assoc prof cardiol & surg, Purdue Univ, 71-75, actg head, Dept Cardiol & Surg, 75-76, head, Dept Small Animal Clin, Sch Vet Med, 76-87, PROF CARDIOL & SURG, PURDUE UNIV, WEST LAFAYETTE, 78- *Personal Data:* b Saginaw, Mich, Nov 20, 38; m 60; c 2. *Educ:* Mich State Univ, BS, 61, DVM, 63; Univ Wis, MS, 70, PhD(vet sci, cardiol), 71; Am Col Vet Surgeon, dipl, 78. *Prof Exp:* Officer in chg, Vet Corps, US Army, 63-65; pract vet, Madison Vet Clin, 65-68; NIH fel cardiol, Univ Wis-Madison, 68-71. *Concurrent Pos:* Mem cardiol comt, Am Animal Hosp Assoc, 73-; reviewer, J Am Vet Med Asn. *Mem:* Am Vet Med Asn; Am Acad Vet Cardiol (pres elect); Am Asn Vet Med Cols; Sigma Xi; Am Asn Vet Clin. *Res:* Hypothermia for cardiac arrest surgery; myocardial infarctions and vascular surgery in the canine. *Mailing Add:* Vet Clin Sch Vet Med Purdue Univ West Lafayette IN 47907

**WEIS, ARTHUR EDWARD,** EVOLUTION, PLANT-ANIMAL INTERACTION. *Current Pos:* ASSOC PROF BIOL, DEPT ECOL & EVOLUTION, UNIV CALIF, 89- *Personal Data:* b Aurora, Ill, July 31, 51; m, Audrey Kapelinski; c Adam & Alexander. *Educ:* De Paul Univ, BA, 74; Univ Ill, PhD(entom), 81. *Prof Exp:* Asst prof biol sci, Northern Ill Univ, 84-89. *Concurrent Pos:* Vis ecologist, Fermi Nat Accelerator Lab, 86- *Mem:* Bot Soc Am; Brit Ecol Am; Ecol Soc Am; Entom Soc Am; Europ Soc

Evolutionary Biol; Soc Study Evolution. *Res:* Ecological and genetic factors in the evolution of plant-insect interactions; gall-inducing insects. *Mailing Add:* Dept Ecol & Evolution Univ Calif Irvine CA 92717-0001. *Fax:* 714-725-2181; *E-Mail:* aeweis@uci.edu

**WEIS, JERRY SAMUEL,** BIOLOGY. *Current Pos:* asst prof, 66-71, asst dir, 69-73, ASSOC PROF BIOL, KANS STATE UNIV, 72-, ASSOC DIR, DIV BIOL, 75- *Personal Data:* b Salina, Kans, Dec 23, 35; m 61; c 3. *Educ:* Kans Wesleyan Univ, AB, 58; Univ Kans, MA, 60, PhD(bot), 64. *Prof Exp:* Asst prof biol, Univ Minn, 64-65; NIH fel biol, Yale Univ, 65-66. *Mem:* AAAS; Inst Soc Ethics & Life Sci; Am Asn Higher Educ. *Res:* Bioethics. *Mailing Add:* Div Biol Kans State Univ 7232 Ackert Hall Manhattan KS 66506-4901

**WEIS, JUDITH SHULMAN,** AQUATIC BIOLOGY, ECOLOGY. *Current Pos:* from asst prof to assoc prof, 67-76, assoc dean, 85-86, PROF ZOOL, RUTGERS UNIV, NEWARK, 76- *Personal Data:* b New York, NY, May 29, 41; m 62, Peddrick; c Jennifer & Eric. *Educ:* Cornell Univ, BA, 62; NY Univ, MA, 64, PhD(biol), 67. *Prof Exp:* Lectr biol, Hunter Col, 64-67. *Concurrent Pos:* Rutgers Res Coun grant, 67-76, NJ sea grant, Nat Oceanic & Atmospheric Admin, 77-; AAAS Cong Sci fel, 83-84; consult, Environ Protection Agency, 84-, NOAA, NJ Dept Environ Protection; mem bd, Am Inst Biol Sci, 87-89, 90-92 & Soc Environ Toxicol & Chem, 90-93; prog dir, NSF, 88-90; marine bd, Nat Res Coun, 91-94. *Mem:* Am Soc Zoologists; Am Inst Biol Sci; Estuarine Res Fedn; Soc Environ Toxicol & Chem; AAAS; Am Fisheries Soc; Asn Women Sci; fel AAAS. *Res:* Marine biology; effects of pollutants on aquatic animals; ecology. *Mailing Add:* Dept Biol Sci Rutgers Univ Newark NJ 07102. *Fax:* 973-648-5518; *E-Mail:* jweis@andromeda. rutgers.edu

**WEIS, LEONARD WALTER,** GEOLOGY. *Current Pos:* ASST PROF GEOL, UNIV WIS CTR-FOX VALLEY, 65- *Personal Data:* b New York, NY, June 23, 23; m 55; c 2. *Educ:* Harvard Univ, SB, 43; Mass Inst Technol, SM, 47; Univ Wis, PhD(geol), 65. *Prof Exp:* Res observer, Blue Hill Meteorol Observ, 43; asst meteorol, Mass Inst Technol, 44-47; instr geol & geog, Univ RI, 47-49; asst prof geol & actg chmn dept, Coe Col, 53-54; asst prof, Lawrence Univ, 55-65. *Mem:* Am Meteorol Soc; Geol Soc Am; Am Geophys Union; Geochem Soc; NY Acad Sci; Sigma Xi. *Res:* Igneous and metamorphic petrology; glacial geology, including petrography of sediments; paleoclimatology; meteorological instruments and observations. *Mailing Add:* 120 N Green Bay Rd Appleton WI 54911-5625

**WEIS, PAUL LESTER,** GEOLOGY. *Current Pos:* RETIRED. *Personal Data:* b Chicago, Ill, June 22, 22; m 45, 69, Alice E French; c Mary J (Henger) & Sally A (Seim). *Educ:* Univ Wis, BS, 47, PhD(geol), 52. *Prof Exp:* Geologist, US Geol Surv, 50-51 & 53-81; asst prof geol, Univ Va, 51-53. *Concurrent Pos:* Consult geologist, 81- *Mem:* Fel Geol Soc Am. *Res:* Mineral resources; aerial geology of northwestern United States; geochemistry of stable carbon isotopes; metallic mineral deposits in sedimentary rocks; creation "science" and its impact on science education in public schools. *Mailing Add:* S 5106 Sunward Dr Spokane WA 99223

**WEIS, PEDDRICK,** TOXICOLOGY, EMBRYOLOGY. *Current Pos:* from asst prof to assoc prof, 67-78, PROF ANAT, NJ MED SCII & GRAD SCII BIOMED SCI, UNIV MED & DENT NJ, 78- *Personal Data:* b South Paris, Maine, June 4, 38; m 62, Judith Shulman; c 2. *Educ:* NY Univ, DDS, 63. *Prof Exp:* NSF res fel, 63-64; instr anat, Col Dent, NY Univ, 64-67. *Concurrent Pos:* Nat Acad Sci/Nat Res Coun sr res fel, US Environ Protection Agency, 92. *Mem:* AAAS; Soc Environ Toxicol Chem. *Res:* Ultrastructural and biochemical effects of environmental pollutants, especially heavy metals; effects of pollutants on development and behavior of aquatic organisms. *Mailing Add:* Dept Anat NJ Med Sch Univ Med & Dent NJ Newark NJ 07103. *Fax:* 973-982-7489; *E-Mail:* weis@umdnj.edu

**WEIS, ROBERT E(DWARD),** CHEMICAL ENGINEERING. *Current Pos:* RETIRED. *Personal Data:* b Ark, May 11, 18; m 48; c 4. *Educ:* Univ Cincinnati, MS, 41. *Prof Exp:* Asst chem eng, Univ Cincinnati, 40-41; asst chem engr, Phillips Petrol Co, 41-42, assoc chem engr, 42-43, master chem engr, 43-44, sr chem engr, 44-48, pilot plant mgr, 48-51, asst supt, Philtex Exp Sta, 51, supt, 51-53, mgr, Bartlesville Develop Pilot Plant, 53-60, asst to mgr, Process Develop Div, 60-61, systs eng adminr, 61-63, mgr, Process Optimization Br, 63-68; dir, Process Optimization Dept, Appl Automation, Inc, 68-77; res & develop proj coordr, Phillips Petrol Co, Bartlesville, 77-82, facilities, planning, res & develop proj coord, 82-84. *Mem:* AAAS; Am Chem Soc; Am Inst Chem Engrs. *Res:* Process optimization; development and application of digital computer systems with on-line instrumentation and control to test, model, evaluate, and optimize operations and profitability of complex petroleum and chemical processes. *Mailing Add:* Box 553 Bartlesville OK 74005-0553

**WEISBACH, JERRY ARNOLD,** ORGANIC CHEMISTRY, MEDICINAL CHEMISTRY. *Current Pos:* PRES, PARKE DAVIS PHARMACEUT RES DIV, WARNER LAMBERT CORP, 79-, VPRES, 81- *Personal Data:* b New York, NY, Dec 23, 33; m 58; c 3. *Educ:* Brooklyn Col, BS, 55; Harvard Univ, MA, 56, PhD(chem), 59. *Prof Exp:* Sr med chemist, Smith Kline & French Labs, 60-65, group leader, 65-67, assoc dir chem, 67-71, assoc dir res, US Pharmaceut Prod, 71-75, dep dir res, 75-77, vpres res, 77-79. *Mem:* AAAS; Am Chem Soc; Acad Pharmaceut Sci; NY Acad Sci; Am Soc Microbiol. *Res:* Structure, isolation and synthesis of natural products, particularly antibiotics, alkaloids and lipids; organic biochemistry and synthetic medicinal chemistry. *Mailing Add:* 1351 Glendaloch Circle Ann Arbor MI 48104-2830

**WEISBART, MELVIN,** COMPARATIVE ENDOCRINOLOGY, COMPARATIVE PHYSIOLOGY. *Current Pos:* head dept, 89-92, PROF, DEPT BIOL, UNIV REGINA, 89- *Personal Data:* b Toronto, Ont, Dec 28, 38; m 63, Marilyn Greenwood; c Cindy E, Michael J & Caren J. *Educ:* Univ Toronto, BSc, 61, MA, 63; Univ BC, PhD(physiol), 67. *Prof Exp:* Nat Res Coun Can fel, Fisheries Res Bd Can, 68-69; asst prof biol, Wayne State Univ, 69-76; from asst prof to prof biol, St Francis Xavier Univ, 76-89, chmn, Dept Biol, 83-89. *Concurrent Pos:* Fac res award, Wayne State Univ, 70; res assoc, Univ Wash, 76-78. *Mem:* Fel AAAS; Soc Integrative & Comp Biol; Can Soc Zoologists (pres, 83-89); Am Physiol Soc; Soc Protection Old Fishes. *Res:* Fish physiology and endocrinology; evolution of corticosteroids; role of corticosteroids in salmonid adaptation to marine environment; steroid receptors in salmonid egg maturation; role of cortisol in human amnion. *Mailing Add:* Dept Biol Univ Regina 3737 Wascana Pkwy Regina SK S4S 0A2 Can. *Fax:* 306-585-4894; *E-Mail:* weisbart@meena.cc.uregina.ca

**WEISBECKER, HENRY B,** ELECTRICAL ENGINEERING. *Current Pos:* INDEPENDENT ENG CONSULT, 72- *Personal Data:* b Kassel, Ger, July 20, 25; US citizen; m 72, Barbara Schilling; c Miriam & Henry. *Educ:* Pratt Inst, BEE, 45; NY Univ, MEE, 48; Munich Tech Univ, Dr Ing(elec eng), 57. *Prof Exp:* Sr engr, A B Dumont Labs, 50-51, W L Maxson Corp, 52-54 & Simmons Aerocessories, 54-58; dir res elec eng, Manson Labs, Conn, 58-59 & Loral Inc, 60; sr prin engr, Litton Industs, 60-66; assoc prof elec eng, NJ Inst Technol, 66-72. *Concurrent Pos:* Independent consult engr, 72- *Mem:* Sr mem Inst Elec & Electronics Engrs. *Res:* Transistors; servos; infrared techniques; communications; author of textbooks and numerous articles. *Mailing Add:* PO Box 613 North Bergen NJ 07047

**WEISBERG, HERBERT,** MEDICINE, GASTROENTEROLOGY. *Current Pos:* PVT PRACT. *Personal Data:* b New York, NY, June 30, 31; m 76, Sally J Rulfs; c Robin, Jonathan & Ariel. *Educ:* City Col New York, BS, 53; Univ Lausanne, MD, 58. *Prof Exp:* From instr to asst prof med, NY Med Col-Flower & Fifth Ave Hosp, 64-71, assoc prof anat & med, 71-76; preceptor family med, Univ Calif, Davis, 77-79; assoc prof med, Univ Wash, Seattle, 86- *Concurrent Pos:* USPHS trainee gastroenterol, NY Med Col-Flower & Fifth Ave Hosp, 62-64, USPHS spec fel electron micros, 66-68; vis prof, Sch Med, NY Univ, 71. *Mem:* Am Gastroenterol Asn. *Res:* Intracellular pathway of absorption for nutrients in the intestine, especially vitamin B-12. *Mailing Add:* Group Health Coop Cent Hosp & Specialty Ctr 200 15th Ave E Seattle WA 98112. *Fax:* 206-326-2379

**WEISBERG, JOSEPH SIMPSON,** OCEANOGRAPHY, METEOROLOGY. *Current Pos:* chmn dept geosci, 73-83, PROF GEOSCI, JERSEY CITY STATE COL, 60-, DEAN, SCH ARTS & SCI, 83- *Personal Data:* b Jersey City, NJ, June 7, 37; m 64; c 2. *Educ:* Jersey City State Col, BA, 60; Montclair State Col, MA, 64; Columbia Univ, EdD(earth sci educ), 69. *Honors & Awards:* Award Merit, US Environ Protection Agency, 78. *Prof Exp:* Teacher pub schs, NJ, 60-64. *Concurrent Pos:* Sci consult, US Off Educ, 68-69; adv, NJ Dept Environ Protection, 75- *Mem:* AAAS; Geol Soc Am; Am Meteorol Soc; Nat Asn Geol Teachers; Nat Sci Teachers Asn. *Res:* Use of visual aids in science teaching; inquiry and learning; environmental aspects of the geosciences; author of various works on oceanography and meteorology; use of microcomputers in education. *Mailing Add:* Dean Arts & Sci Jersey City State Col 2039 Kennedy Mem Blvd Jersey City NJ 07305-1527

**WEISBERG, ROBERT H,** PHYSICAL OCEANOGRAPHY, OCEAN CIRCULATION. *Current Pos:* assoc prof, 84-85 & 87-88, PROF, DEPT MARINE SCI, UNIV SFLA, 88- *Personal Data:* b Brooklyn, NY, May 20, 47; m 69, Cynthia; c Seth & Ari. *Educ:* Cornell Univ, BS, 69; Univ RI, MS, 72, PhD(phys oceanog), 75. *Prof Exp:* Res asst, Grad Sch Oceanog, Univ RI, 69-74, res assoc phys oceanog, 74-76; asst prof, Dept Geosci, NC State Univ, 76-81, assoc prof, Dept Marine, Earth & Atmospheric Sci, 81-86. *Mem:* Am Geophys Union; Am Meteorol Soc; Oceanog Soc. *Res:* Equatorial, coastal, and estuarine circulation dynamics. *Mailing Add:* Dept Marine Sci Univ SFla 140 Seventh Ave S St Petersburg FL 33701

**WEISBERG, SANFORD,** APPLIED STATISTICS. *Current Pos:* PROF APPL STATIST, UNIV MINN, ST PAUL, 72- *Personal Data:* US citizen; c 1. *Educ:* Univ Calif, AB, 69; Harvard Univ, AM, 70, PhD(statist), 73. *Honors & Awards:* Youden Prize, 89. *Mem:* Fel Am Statist Asn; Inst Math Statist; Biomet Soc; Royal Statist Soc; Int Statist Inst. *Res:* Data analysis and methods; linear models; statistical computing; graphical methods. *Mailing Add:* Dept Appl Statist 270 Vincent Hall Univ Minn 206 Church St SE St Paul MN 55108-6042. *E-Mail:* sandy@umn.edu

**WEISBERG, STEPHEN BARRY,** POPULATION BIOLOGY, ICHTHYOLOGY. *Current Pos:* EXEC DIR, SOUTHERN CALIF COASTAL WATER RES PROJ AUTHORITY, 96- *Personal Data:* b New York, NY, Apr 19, 54; m 84, Gayle Hopper; c Sara & Becca. *Educ:* Univ Mich, BGS, 74; Univ Del, PhD(biol), 81. *Honors & Awards:* Polgar Award. *Prof Exp:* Res asst nutrient dynamics, Univ Del, 77-80; instr ecol & wildlife biol, West Chester State Col, 80-81; mgr monitoring & field opers, Versar, 81-96. *Concurrent Pos:* Adj assoc prof, Univ Md, 86- *Mem:* Ecol Soc Am; Am Soc Zoologists; Am Fisheries Soc; Estuarine Res Fedn. *Res:* Population dynamics and feeding ecology of fish; impacts of fish feeding on population dynamics of prey species; biological monitoring programs; benthic ecology. *Mailing Add:* Southern Calif Coastal Water Res Proj 7171 Fenwick Lane Westminster CA 92683. *Fax:* 714-894-9699; *E-Mail:* stevew@sccwrp.org

**WEISBERGER, WILLIAM I,** THEORETICAL HIGH ENERGY PHYSICS. *Current Pos:* PROF PHYSICS, STATE UNIV NY, STONY BROOK, 70- *Personal Data:* b New York, NY, Dec 20, 37; m 61, Dian Boukstein; c Sharon, Michael & David. *Educ:* Amherst Col, BA, 59; Mass Inst Technol, PhD(physics), 64. *Prof Exp:* Res assoc physics, Stanford Linear Accelerator Ctr, 64-66; asst prof, Princeton Univ, 66-70. *Concurrent Pos:* Sloan Found fel, 67-69; vis scientist, Weizmann Inst Sci, 68-69 & 74-75; Guggenheim fel, 74-75; vis prof, Univ Wash, 78-79. *Mem:* Fel Am Phys Soc; AAAS. *Mailing Add:* Inst Theoret Physics State Univ NY Stony Brook East Stony Brook NY 11794-3840. *Fax:* 516-632-7954; *E-Mail:* weisberg@max. physics.sunysb.edu

**WEISBRODT, NORMAN WILLIAM,** PHYSIOLOGY, PHARMACOLOGY. *Current Pos:* from instr to asst prof physiol, 71-75, ASSOC PROF PHYSIOL & PHARMACOL, UNIV TEX MED SCH HOUSTON, 75- *Personal Data:* b Cleves, Ohio, June 30, 42; m 65; c 3. *Educ:* Univ Cincinnati, BS, 65; Univ Mich, Ann Arbor, PhD(pharmacol), 70. *Prof Exp:* USPHS res fel, Univ Iowa, 70-71. *Concurrent Pos:* Fel, Univ Iowa, 70-71; assoc prof, Univ Tex Grad Sch Biomed Sci, 71-; res scientist develop, Nat Inst Drug Abuse, 76-81; assoc ed, Am J Physiol, 77-80. *Mem:* Am Asn Clin Res; Am Physiol Soc; Soc Exp Biol & Med; Am Gastroenterol Asn. *Res:* Smooth muscle physiology and pharmacology; gastrointestinal motility. *Mailing Add:* Dept Physiol & Pharmacol Univ Tex Med Sch PO Box 20708 Houston TX 77225-0708. *E-Mail:* weisbrod@girch1med.uth.tmc.edu

**WEISBROT, DAVID R,** POPULATION GENETICS. *Current Pos:* assoc prof, 72-78, PROF BIOL, WILLIAM PATERSON COL, NJ, 78- *Personal Data:* b Brooklyn, NY, Dec 29, 31; m 60; c 3. *Educ:* Brooklyn Col, BS, 53, MA, 58; Columbia Univ, PhD(zool), 63. *Prof Exp:* Substitute instr biol, Brooklyn Col, 56-58; res asst genetics, Univ Conn, 58-59 & Long Island Biol Asn, 59-60; instr biol, City Col New York, 60-62; fel genetics, Univ Calif, Berkeley, 63-64; asst prof biol, Tufts Univ, 64-69; assoc prof, State Univ NY Binghamton, 69-72. *Concurrent Pos:* Adj assoc prof, Columbia Univ, 76-81. *Mem:* AAAS; Genetics Soc Am; Am Genetic Asn; Sigma Xi. *Res:* Genotypic interactions among competing strains of Drosophila; relationship of genetic and morphological differences among sibling species; cytogenetics. *Mailing Add:* Dept Biol William Paterson Col Wayne NJ 07470

**WEISBROTH, STEVEN H,** LABORATORY ANIMAL MEDICINE, COMPARATIVE PATHOLOGY. *Current Pos:* PRES, ANIMAL MED LABS, INC, 70- *Personal Data:* b New York, NY, Sept 16, 34; m 58; c 3. *Educ:* Cornell Univ, BS, 58; Wash State Univ, MS, 60, DVM, 64; Am Col Lab Animal Med, dipl. *Honors & Awards:* Res Award, Am Asn Lab Animal Sci, 72. *Prof Exp:* NIH fel, Lab Animals med, NY Univ Med Ctr, 64-66; asst prof path & dir animal facil, Rockerfeller Univ, 66-69; asst prof path & dir, Dept Lab Animal Med, State Univ NY, Stony Brook, 69-70, assoc prof path & dir, Div Lab Animal Resources, 70-78. *Concurrent Pos:* NIH fel, Lab Animals Med, Rockefeller Univ, 69-; mem coun, Am Asn Accreditation Lab Animal Care, 75-79. *Mem:* Am Vet Med Asn; Am Asn Lab Animal Sci; Am Soc Exp Path. *Res:* Spontaneous diseases in laboratory animals. *Mailing Add:* 10800 S Glen Rd Potomac MD 20854

**WEISBURGER, ELIZABETH KREISER,** CHEMICAL CARCINOGENESIS, TOXICOLOGY. *Current Pos:* CONSULT, 89- *Personal Data:* b Greenlane, Pa, Apr 9, 24; div; c William, Diane & Andrew. *Educ:* Lebanon Valley Col, BS, 44; Univ Cincinnati, PhD(org chem), 47. *Hon Degrees:* DSc, Univ Cincinnati, 81; DSc, Lebanon Valley, 89. *Honors & Awards:* Hillebrand Prize & Garvan Medal, Am Chem Soc, 81; Stokinger Award, Am Conf Goven Indust Hygienists, 96. *Prof Exp:* Res assoc, Univ Cincinnati, 47-49; res fel, Nat Cancer Inst, 49-51, res org chemist, Biochem Lab, 51-61, carcinogen screening sect, 61-72, chief, Carcinogen Metab & Toxicol Br, 73-78, chief, Lab Carcinogen Metab, 78-81, asst dir chem carcinogen, Div Cancer Etiology, 81-89. *Concurrent Pos:* Asst chief ed, J Nat Cancer Inst, 71-87; mem, Chem Substances Comt, Am Conf Govt Indust Hygenists, 78- *Mem:* AAAS; Am Asn Cancer Res; Am Chem Soc; Royal Soc Chem; Soc Toxicol; Am Soc Biol Chem & Molecular Biol. *Res:* Metabolism of chemical carcinogens, carcinogen testing, chemical carcinogenesis and toxicology. *Mailing Add:* 5309 McKinley St Bethesda MD 20814-1413

**WEISBURGER, JOHN HANS,** NUTRITION, ENVIRONMENTAL HEALTH. *Current Pos:* RES PROF PATH, NY MED COL, 74-; PRES, WEISBURGER ASSOCS, NORTH WHITE PLAINS, NY, 87-; SR MEM, AM HEALTH FOUND, VALHALLA, NY, 87- *Personal Data:* b Stuttgart, Ger, Sept, 15, 21; nat US; m 78, Helga Preschel; c William R, Diane S & Andrew J. *Educ:* Univ Cincinnati, AB, 47, MS, 48, PhD(org chem & cancer res), 49. *Hon Degrees:* MD, Umea Univ, 80. *Honors & Awards:* Merit Award, Soc Toxicol, 81, Ambassador Award, 90; Distinguished Serv Award, Am Soc Prev Oncol, 90; Meyer & Anna Prentis Award, Mich Cancer Ctr. *Prof Exp:* Fel, Nat Cancer Inst, 49-50, head, Phys-Org Chem Unit, Lab Biochem, 50-61, head, Carcinogen Screening Sect, 61-72, dir, Bioassay Segment, 71-72; vpres res, Am Health Found & dir, Naylor Dana Inst Dis Prev, Valhalla, NY, 72-87. *Concurrent Pos:* Assoc ed, J Nat Cancer Inst, 60-62; Cancer Res, 69-80, Arch Toxicol, 77-87, J Am Col Toxicol, 82-, Prev Med, 89-; mem, Working Groups Monographs Series, Int Agency Res Cancer; mem, HEW, Food & Drug Admin, USDA, Pub Health Serv, Interdept Tech Panel on Carcinogens, 62-71; chmn, Approach 1-3, Nat Cancer Prog Strategic Plan, 71-74; chmn, subcomt positive controls, Nat Acad Sci, Nat Res Coun conf on Carcinogen Testing of New Drugs, 73; mem, USDA Expert Panel Nitrites & Nitrosamines, 73-77; chmn, Workshop Colorectal Cancer, Int Union Against Cancer, Geneva, 75; mem, Nat Cancer Inst Clearinghouse Environ Carcinogens, 76-78; mem, Orgn Comt, Princess Takamatsu Cancer Res Found, Seventh Int Symp, 76; co-chmn, Orgn Comt, US-Japan Coorp Workshop GI Tract Cancer, 79; chmn, Symp Large Bowel Cancer, Organ

Gastroenterol Seventh Cong, 82; chmn, Int Union Against Cancer Natural Carcinogens Human Cancer Develop, 82; mem, Panel Irritants & Vesicants Comn Life Sci, Nat Res Coun-Nat Acad Sci, 83; co-chmn, Prof Educ Comt Westchester Div, Am Cancer Soc, 83-89 & 85-88; coun, Europ Asn Cancer Res, 85-89; chmn, Sci Rev Panel, NJ State Comn Cancer Res, 88-90; co-chmn, Workshop Health Effects Tea, 91; res fel, Japanese Found Prom Cancer Res, Nat Cancer Ctr Res Inst, Tokyo, 92; lectr, 2nd Conf Int Fedn Socs Toxicologic Path; chmn, Int Conf Health Effects Tomatoes Lycopore, NY, 97; invited lectr numerous nat & int conf. *Mem:* Am Asn Cancer Res; hon mem Japan Cancer Res Asn; Am Soc Pharmacol & Exp Therapeut; Soc Exp Biol & Med; Soc Toxicol; Am Chem Soc; Am Gastroenterol Asn; fel NY Acad Sci; Sigma Xi; hon mem Am Soc Prev Oncol; Biochem Soc. *Res:* Etiology of cancer, mechanisms of carcinogenesis; bioassay and metabolism of carcinogens and drugs; host factors in cancer induction and development; nutrition, endocrinology, immunology, cancers of the endocrine, digestive and excretory organs; preventive medicine; preventive oncology; published about 500 papers, book chapters and books. *Mailing Add:* Am Health Found Naylor Dana Inst Dis Prev Valhalla NY 10595-1599. *Fax:* 914-592-6317; *E-Mail:* john__weisburger@nymc.edu

**WEISE, CHARLES MARTIN,** POPULATION ECOLOGY, ORNITHOLOGY. *Current Pos:* from asst prof to assoc prof, 55-66, chmn dept, 61-63, 78-84, PROF BIOL SCI, UNIV WIS-MILWAUKEE, 66-, CHMN DEPT, 89- *Personal Data:* b Bridgeville, Pa, July 8, 26; m 51; c 5. *Educ:* Ohio Univ, BS, 50; Univ Ill, MS, 51, PhD(zool), 56. *Prof Exp:* Asst prof biol, Fisk Univ, 53-56. *Mem:* AAAS; Cooper Ornith Soc; Wilson Ornith Soc; Am Soc Zoologists; Am Ornith Union; Sigma Xi. *Res:* Annual physiological and reproductive cycles in birds; field ornithology; behavioral ecology and population ecology. *Mailing Add:* Dept Biol Sci Univ Wis PO Box 413 Milwaukee WI 53201

**WEISE, JURGEN KARL,** POLYMER CHEMISTRY, ORGANIC CHEMISTRY. *Current Pos:* TECH RES DIR, DENTSPLY, GER, 86- *Personal Data:* b Nov 7, 37; US citizen; m 64; c 3. *Educ:* Univ Bonn, BS, 60; Polytech Inst Brooklyn, PhD(polymer chem), 66. *Prof Exp:* Ger Res Asn fel chem, Univ Mainz, 66-67; res chemist, Cent Res Dept, E I du Pont de Nemours & Co, 67-71, res chemist, Elastomer Chem Dept, 71-77; mgr res lab, Bostik Tech Ctr, Europe 77-82; mgr profit ctr, Schill & Seilacher, Hamburg, Europe, 83-84. *Mem:* Am Chem Soc. *Res:* Reactions of polymers; polymer structures and their effects on properties; ring-opening polymerization; fluoro-polymers; specialty elastomers; adhesives and sealants development. *Mailing Add:* AM Hohen Berg 30 61250 Usingen Germany

**WEISEL, GEORGE FERDINAND, JR,** ZOOLOGY. *Current Pos:* RETIRED. *Personal Data:* b Missoula, Mont, Mar 21, 15; m 50; c 2. *Educ:* Univ Mont, BS, 41, MA, 42; Univ Calif, Los Angeles, PhD(zool), 49. *Prof Exp:* Asst zool, Univ Mont, 41-42, Univ Mich, 42-43 & Scripps Inst Oceanog, Univ Calif, San Diego, 47-48; from instr to assoc prof comp anat & gen zool, Univ Mont, 47-69, prof comp anat & ichthyol, 69-90. *Mem:* Am Soc Ichthyol & Herpet; Am Soc Zoologists; Sigma Xi. *Res:* Anatomy, histology, sex organs, life histories, osteology and endocrinology of fish. *Mailing Add:* 615 Pattee Canyon Dr Missoula MT 59803-1618

**WEISEL, JOHN WINFIELD,** STRUCTURAL BIOLOGY, BLOOD COAGULATION. *Current Pos:* asst prof, 81-88, ASSOC PROF CELL & DEVELOP BIOL, SCH MED, UNIV PA, 88- *Personal Data:* b Abington, Pa, Sept 3, 46; m 70, Johannah Fine; c 6. *Educ:* Swarthmore Col, BS, 68; Brandeis Univ, PhD(biophys), 74. *Prof Exp:* Jane Coffin Childs fel, Rosenstiel Ctr, Brandeis Univ, 74-76, fel, Med Found, 76-78, sr res assoc, 79-81. *Concurrent Pos:* Estab investr, Am Heart Asn, 80-85; prin investr, NIH & Am Heart Asn grants; mem, Coun Thrombosis, Am Heart Asn. *Mem:* Biophys Soc; Am Heart Asn; Micros Soc Am; AAAS; Fedn Am Socs Exp Biol; Inst Elec & Electronics Engrs. *Res:* Using methods of structural biology including electron microscopy and computer image processing to analyze molecular mechanisms in blood clotting and fibrinoysis. *Mailing Add:* Dept Cell & Develop Biol Univ Pa Sch Med Philadelphia PA 19104-6058

**WEISENBERG, RICHARD CHARLES,** CELL BIOLOGY. *Current Pos:* asst prof, 71-73, ASSOC PROF BIOL, TEMPLE UNIV, 73- *Personal Data:* b Columbus, Ohio, Apr 2, 41. *Educ:* Univ Calif, Santa Barbara, BA, 63; Univ Chicago, PhD(biophys), 68. *Prof Exp:* USDA trainee, Brandeis Univ, 68-70. *Concurrent Pos:* Investr, Marine Biol Lab, Woods Hole, 71- *Mem:* Am Soc Cell Biol. *Res:* Cell division and motility; biochemistry of microtubules. *Mailing Add:* Dept Biol Temple Univ Philadelphia PA 19122. *Fax:* 215-787-6646

**WEISENBORN, FRANK L,** ORGANIC CHEMISTRY, INFORMATION SCIENCE. *Current Pos:* RETIRED. *Personal Data:* b Portland, Ore, Feb 26, 25; div; c Alan L, Eric J, Lynn A & Robert E. *Educ:* Reed Col, BA, 45; Univ Wash, PhD(chem), 49. *Prof Exp:* AEC fel, Harvard Univ, 49-50, USPHS fel, 50-51; sr res chemist, Riker Labs, Inc, 51-53; res assoc, Univ Calif, Los Angeles, 53; sr res chemist, E R Squibb & Sons Inc, 53-59, from res assoc to sr res assoc, 59-63, dir org chem, 63-81, dir sci info, Squibb Inst Med Res, 81-91. *Concurrent Pos:* Chmn, Gordon Res Conf Natural Prod, 75-76. *Mem:* Am Chem Soc; Royal Soc Chem. *Res:* Structure and synthesis of antibiotics, steroids and alkaloids; natural and synthetic hypotensive agents; computer assisted molecular modeling; information science. *Mailing Add:* 65045 Hopper Rd Bend OR 97701-8986

**WEISER, CONRAD JOHN,** PLANT STRESS PHYSIOLOGY, RETHINKING SCHOLARSHIP. *Current Pos:* prof hort & dept head, 73-91, dean, Col Agr Sci, 91-94, EMER PROF & DEAN, ORE STATE UNIV, 94- *Personal Data:* b Middlebury, Vt, June 20, 35; M 72, Adrienne Paulson; c Russell, Rachael & Andrea. *Educ:* NDak State Univ, BS, 57; Ore State Univ, PhD(hort), 60. *Honors & Awards:* Alex Laurie Award, Am Soc Hort Sci, 66, J H Gourley Award, 73. *Prof Exp:* Asst prof, Hort Dept, Univ Minn, 61-63, assoc prof, 63-66, prof, 66-73. *Concurrent Pos:* Chair, Nat Agr Sci Team, 80-, Temperature Stress in Plants, Gordon Conf, 89; mem, adv coun, NSF, Int Div, 81-84, bd agr, Nat Acad Sci, Nat Res Coun, 86-92, Nat Arboretum Adv Coun, 88-99, Coun, AAAS, 92-94; co-chair, Ore State Univ Long-Range Planning Comn, 86-87. *Mem:* Fel Am Soc Hort Sci (vpres, 79-80, pres-elect, 79-80, pres, 80-81); Am Soc Plant Physiol; Soc Cryobiol; fel AAAS; Coun Agr Sci Tech. *Res:* Crop stress physiology, plant freezing injury and physiological responses which permit plants to acclimate in response to environmental stimuli. *Mailing Add:* Dean's Off Dept Agr Ore State Univ Corvallis OR 97331-1801

**WEISER, DAN,** MATHEMATICS. *Current Pos:* LECTR POLIT SCI, UNIV TEX, DALLAS, 93- *Personal Data:* b St Louis, Mo, July 10, 33; m 54, Louette Kestenberg; c Alan (deceased), Martin, David & Michael. *Educ:* Rice Univ, BA, 54, MA, 56, PhD(math), 58. *Prof Exp:* Asst math, Rice Univ, 57-58; sr res mathematician, Field Res Lab, Mobil Res & Develop Co, 58-77, statistician, Mobil Explor & Prod Serv, Inc, 77-93. *Mem:* Soc Indust & Appl Math. *Res:* Applied mathematics and political science. *Mailing Add:* 3851 Rugged Circle Dallas TX 75224

**WEISER, KURT,** PHYSICS. *Current Pos:* PROF DEPT ELEC ENG & DIR, SOLID STATE INST, TECHNION, 73- *Personal Data:* b Vienna, Austria, Dec 24, 24; US citizen; m 57; c 3. *Educ:* Harvard Univ, BA, 49; Cornell Univ, PhD(phys chem), 54. *Prof Exp:* Mem tech staff, RCA, 54-58 & T J Watson Ctr, IBM Corp, 58-73. *Mem:* Fel Am Phys Soc. *Res:* Solid state physics with emphasis on semiconductors. *Mailing Add:* Dept Elec Eng Technion Haifa Israel

**WEISER, ROBERT B(RUCE),** CHEMICAL ENGINEERING, ORGANIC CHEMISTRY. *Current Pos:* CONSULT, 90- *Personal Data:* b Ashley, Ohio, July 19, 27; m 53, 72, Marion Harris; c Bruce, Mark, Jeffrey, Douglas & Laura. *Educ:* Ohio State Univ, BS & MS, 51, PhD, 54. *Prof Exp:* Res engr, Exp Sta, Polychem Dept, E I Du Pont de Nemours & Co, Inc, Del, 54-58, Res & Develop Lab, Wash Works, 58-90. *Concurrent Pos:* Lectr, Marietta Col, 61-65. *Mem:* Am Inst Chem Engrs. *Res:* Reaction kinetics; diffusional operations; fluid mechanics. *Mailing Add:* One Fox Hill Dr Parkersburg WV 26101

**WEISER, RUSSEL SHIVELY,** BACTERIOLOGY, IMMUNOLOGY. *Current Pos:* Assoc bact & path, Univ Wash, 34-36, from instr to assoc prof & actg exec officer, 36-45, assoc prof microbiol, 45-49, prof, 49-77, EMER PROF IMMUNOL, SCHS MED & DENT, UNIV WASH, 77- *Personal Data:* b Grimes, Iowa, Sept 28, 06; m 31; c 1. *Educ:* NDak Col, BS, 30, MS, 31; Univ Wash, PhD(bact), 34. *Concurrent Pos:* Mem leprosy res panel, US-Japan Coop Med Sci Prog. *Mem:* Am Asn Immunologists; Reticuloendothelial Soc; Brit Soc Immunol; Transplantation Soc. *Res:* Immunology of syphilis; immunology of cancer; immunologic tissue injury; macrophages; cell-mediated immunity. *Mailing Add:* Dept Immunol Univ Wash Sch Med Seattle WA 98195-0001

**WEISFELD, LEWIS BERNARD,** PLASTICS PRODUCTS LIABILITY. *Current Pos:* CONSULT CHEMIST, WEISFELD & ASSOCS, 79- *Personal Data:* b Philadelphia, Pa, July 2, 29; m 66, Ruth L Heiman. *Educ:* Univ Pa, BA, 52; Univ Del, MS, 53, PhD(phys-org chem), 56. *Prof Exp:* Res engr, Silicone Prod Dept, Gen Elec Co, 56-58; sr res scientist, US Rubber Co, 58-63; dir labs, Advan Div, Cincinnati Milacron Chems, 63-74, vpres & sci dir, 74-75, dir res, Cincinnati Milacron Inc, 75-79; dir res & develop, Plastics Div, Container Corp Am, 79. *Concurrent Pos:* Comnr, Nat Cert Comn Chem & Chem Eng, 83-89. *Mem:* Am Chem Soc; fel Soc Plastics Engrs; NY Acad Sci; AAAS; Am Soc Testing & Mat; Asn Consult Chemists & Chem Engrs (pres, 82-84). *Res:* Government regulatory developments related to plastics industry. *Mailing Add:* One Franklin Town Blvd Suite 1204 Philadelphia PA 19103-1246. *E-Mail:* 76674.1441@compuserve.com, lweisfeld@aol.com

**WEISFELDT, MYRON LEE,** CARDIOLOGY, CARDIOPULMONARY RESUSCITATION. *Current Pos:* SAMUEL BARD PROF MED & CHAIR, COL PHYSICIANS & SURGEONS, COLUMBIA UNIV, 91-; DIR MED SERV, PRESBY HOSP, NY, 91-; HEAD, CARDIOVASC CTR, COLUMBIA-PRESBYTERIAN MED CTR, 91- *Personal Data:* b Milwaukee, Wis, Apr 25, 40; m 63, Linda Zaremski; c Ellyn, Lisa & Sara. *Educ:* Johns Hopkins Univ, BA, 62, MD, 65. *Honors & Awards:* Award of Merit, Am Heart Asn, 92. *Prof Exp:* Intern & asst resident med, Columbia Presby Med Ctr, 65-67; clin assoc, NIH, 67-69; sr asst resident, Mass Gen Hosp, 69-70, fel cardiol, 70-72; from asst prof to prof, Johns Hopkins Univ, 72-91, Robert Levy prof, 79-91. *Concurrent Pos:* Guest investr, Nat Inst Aging, Nat Inst Child Health & Human Develop, 72-77; dir, Ischemic Heart Dis Spec Ctr Res, Nat Heart, Lung & Blood Inst, 77-91. *Mem:* Inst Med-Nat Acad Sci; Am Soc Clin Invest; Am Asn Physicians; Am Heart Asn (pres, 89-90); fel Am Col Cardiol; Asn Univ Professors; Am Soc Clin Res; Gerintol Soc; Am Physiol Soc; fel AAAS; fel Am Col Physicians; Am Heart Asn (pres, 89-90); Int Soc Heart Res; NY Acad Sci. *Res:* Hemodynamics and left ventricular function, particularly using magnetic resonance imaging and spectroscopy; cardiopulmonary resuscitation hemodynamics and age associated changes in the cardiovascular system. *Mailing Add:* Dept Med Columbia Presby Med Ctr 630 W 168th St New York NY 10032. *Fax:* 212-305-8466

**WEISGERBER, DAVID WENDELIN,** CHEMICAL INFORMATION, CHEMICAL DATABASES. *Current Pos:* assoc indexer, Chem Abstracts Serv, 69-71, group leader compound name data base, 71-72, sr indexer, 72-73, asst to ed, 73-77, mgr chem substance handling, 77-79, dir ed opers, 79-82, ED, CHEM ABSTRACTS SERV, 82- *Personal Data:* b Delphos, Ohio, May 20, 38; m 65, Carole A Friemoth; c Jason & Erik. *Educ:* Bowling Green State Univ, BS, 60; Univ Ill, PhD(org chem), 65. *Prof Exp:* Chemist res, E I du Pont de Nemours & Co, Inc, 64-69. *Mem:* Am Chem Soc; NY Acad Sci; Am Soc Info Sci. *Res:* Synthetic organic chemistry; chemical nomenclature; scientific information storage and retrieval. *Mailing Add:* 6178 Middlebury Dr E Worthington OH 43085. *Fax:* 614-447-3713; *E-Mail:* dweisgerb@cas.org

**WEISGERBER, GEORGE AUSTIN,** PETROLEUM CHEMISTRY. *Current Pos:* from res chemist to sr chemist, Esso Res & Eng Co, 51-60, from res assoc to sr res assoc, 60-74, SR RES ASSOC, EXXON RES & ENG CO, 74- *Personal Data:* b Philadelphia, Pa, Dec 31, 18; m 47; c 2. *Educ:* Philadelphia Col Pharm, BSc, 40; Univ Del, MSc, 50, PhD(org chem), 51. *Prof Exp:* Res chemist, Johnson & Johnson, NJ, 40-48. *Mem:* Am Chem Soc; Tech Asn Pulp & Paper Indust; Am Soc Testing & Mat. *Res:* Petroleum product research; additives, burner fuels, industrial and motor lubricants; wax; asphalt. *Mailing Add:* 208 Oak Lane Cranford NJ 07016-2042

**WEISGRABER, KARL HEINRICH,** ORGANIC CHEMISTRY, BIOCHEMISTRY. *Personal Data:* b Norwich, Conn, July 13, 41; m 64; c 2. *Educ:* Univ Conn, BA, 64, PhD(org chem), 69. *Prof Exp:* Staff fel, Nat Inst Arthritis & Metab Dis, 69-70 & Nat Res Coun Res Assoc, USDA, Calif, 70-71; prin scientist, Meloy Labs, Va, 71-72; sr staff fel, Nat Heart & Lung Inst, 72-81. *Mem:* Am Chem Soc; The Chem Soc; NY Acad Sci. *Res:* Experimental atherosclerosis; study of serum lipoproteins; mechanism of transport of serum constituents across aortic endothelium. *Mailing Add:* Gladstone Inst Cardiovasc Dis PO Box 419100 San Francisco CA 94141-9100. *Fax:* 415-285-5632

**WEISHEIT, JON CARLETON,** ATOMIC PHYSICS, ASTROPHYSICS. *Current Pos:* PROF SPACE PHYSICS & ASTRON, RICE UNIV, 88-, CHMN, 92- *Personal Data:* b Mt Vernon, Wash, Oct 10, 44; m 65, Janet Lucas; c 2. *Educ:* Univ Tex, El Paso, BS, 66; Rice Univ, MS, 69, PhD(physics), 70. *Prof Exp:* Res fel astron, Harvard Univ, 70-72, lectr astron, 71-72; physicist, Lawrence Livermore Nat Lab, Univ Calif, 72-79, group leader atomic physics, 78-79; res physicist, Plasma Physics Lab, Princeton Univ, 79-81, lectr astron, 80-81; staff scientist, Lawrence Livermore Nat Lab, 81-87. *Mem:* Fel Am Phys Soc; Am Astron Soc; Int Astron Union; Sigma Xi. *Res:* Atomic processes in laboratory and cosmic plasmas; extragalactic astronomy. *Mailing Add:* Space Physics& Astron Dept MS 108 Rice Univ Houston TX 77005-1892

**WEISLEDER, DAVID,** ORGANIC CHEMISTRY, NUCLEAR MAGNETIC RESONANCE. *Current Pos:* RES CHEMIST, NAT CTR AGR UTILIZATION RES, AGR RES, USDA, 66- *Personal Data:* b New York, NY, Sept 30, 39; m, Laura Garfinkel; c Aaron, Ruth, Daniel & Sarah. *Educ:* City Col New York, BS, 61; Univ Cincinnati, PhD(chem), 66. *Mem:* Am Chem Soc. *Res:* Nuclear magnetic resonance spectroscopy of natural products and their derivatives or analogs. *Mailing Add:* Nat Ctr Agr Utilization Res USDA Agr Res Serv 1815 N University St Peoria IL 61604-3902

**WEISLER, LEONARD,** ORGANIC CHEMISTRY. *Current Pos:* RETIRED. *Personal Data:* b Rochester, NY, Sept 9, 12; m 42; c 4. *Educ:* Univ Rochester, BS, 34, MS, 36, PhD(org chem), 39. *Prof Exp:* Asst, Univ Rochester, 35-38; anal chemist, Distillation Prod, Inc, 42-53; org res & develop chemist, Paper Serv Div, Eastman Kodak Co, 53-78. *Concurrent Pos:* Sr lectr chem, Univ Rochester, 54-84; adj prof chem, Monroe Community Col, Rochester, NY, 79-84. *Mem:* Am Chem Soc. *Res:* Alkylation of nitro compounds; chemistry and biochemistry of vitamin E; synthesis of vitamin A; fats, oils and hydrocarbons; metallurgy; photographic chemistry. *Mailing Add:* Six Eastland Ave Rochester NY 14618

**WEISLOW, OWEN STUART,** VIROLOGY, IMMUNOLOGY. *Current Pos:* scientist III, 76-80, SR SCIENTIST IMMUNOL, FREDERICK CANCER RES CTR, LITTON BIONETICS INC, 80- *Personal Data:* b Cleveland, Ohio, Mar 11, 38. *Educ:* Del Valley Col Sci & Agr, BS, 65; Thomas Jefferson Univ, MS, 68, PhD(microbiol), 70. *Prof Exp:* Fel immunol, Albert Einstein Med Ctr, Philadelphia, 70-71; fel immunol & virol, Thomas Jefferson Univ, 71-73, instr, 73-74; assoc found scientist immunol, Southwest Found Res & Educ, 74-76. *Mem:* Am Soc Microbiol; AAAS; Am Asn Immunologists. *Res:* Immunobiology of oncogenic viruses; tumor immunology; regulation of cell proliferation. *Mailing Add:* SRA Technol Inc 4 Research Ct Rockville MD 20850

**WEISMAN, GARY ANDREW,** RECEPTOR BIOCHEMISTRY, MOLECULAR BIOLOGY. *Current Pos:* asst prof, 85-92, ASSOC PROF BIOCHEM, UNIV MO, COLUMBIA, 92- *Personal Data:* b Brooklyn, NY, June 18, 51; m 79, Sandra Hille; c Laura, Pamela & Veronica. *Educ:* Polytech Inst NY, BS, 73; Univ Nebr, Lincoln, PhD(chem & biochem), 82. *Prof Exp:* Res assoc, Cornell Uiv, 80-85. *Concurrent Pos:* Prin investr, USDA Agr Exp Sta, 86-, NIH, 88-93. *Mem:* Am Soc Biochem & Molecular Biol; Am Chem Soc; AAAS; Am Heart Asn; NY Acad Sci. *Res:* Biochemistry and molecular biology of P2 purinergic receptors for nucleotides and the role they play in cardiovascular, epithelial and transformed cell functions. *Mailing Add:* Univ Mo Dept Biochem M121 Med Sci Bldg Columbia MO 65212. *Fax:* 573-884-4597; *E-Mail:* bchemgaw@mizzou1.missouri.edu

**WEISMAN, GARY RAYMOND,** ORGANIC CHEMISTRY, PHYSICAL CHEMISTRY. *Current Pos:* ASST PROF ORG CHEM, UNIV NH, 77- *Personal Data:* b Cincinnati, Ohio, Apr 17, 49; m 71; c 2. *Educ:* Univ Ky, BS, 71; Univ Wis, PhD(org chem), 76. *Prof Exp:* Res chemist org chem, Univ Calif, Los Angeles, 76-77. *Concurrent Pos:* Prin investr, Petrol Res Found grant, 78-81 & res corp grant, 79- *Mem:* Am Chem Soc; Sigma Xi. *Res:* Organic host guest chemistry; conformational analysis; applications of nuclear magnetic resonance; structure and chemistry of radical ions; organic electrochemistry and electron spin resonance in mechanistic investigations. *Mailing Add:* Dept Chem Parsons Hall Univ NH Durham NH 03824

**WEISMAN, HARVEY,** HISTOLOGY, NEUROPHARMACOLOGY. *Current Pos:* Lectr zool, 58-65, asst prof, 65-72, ASSOC PROF PHARMACOL, UNIV MAN, 82-, PROF, ASSOC HEAD, DIR GRAD STUDIES FAC MED, 82- *Personal Data:* b Winnipeg, Man, Feb 25, 27; m 57; c 2. *Educ:* Univ Man, BSc, 53, MSc, 55, PhD(histol), 69. *Mem:* Can Asn Anatomists; Pharmacol Soc Can. *Res:* Histological, cytological and biochemical reorganization of the central nervous system in mammals as a result of psychopharmacological drugs; histopathology of primary and secondary cardiomyopathics; pathological effects of maternal smoking on fetal growth and health. *Mailing Add:* Dept Pharmacol & Therapeut Univ Man Fac Med 753 McDermot Ave Winnipeg MB R3E 0W3 Can

**WEISMAN, JOEL,** CHEMICAL ENGINEERING, NUCLEAR ENGINEERING. *Current Pos:* from asst prof to prof, 68-96, dir, Nuclear Energy Prog, 76-86, EMER PROF NUCLEAR ENG, UNIV CINCINNATI, 96- *Personal Data:* b New York, NY, July 15, 28; m 55, Bernice Newman; c Jay (deceased). *Educ:* City Col New York, BChE, 48; Columbia Univ, MS, 49; Univ Pittsburgh, PhD, 68. *Prof Exp:* Chem engr, Etched Prod Corp, NY, 50-51; assoc chem engr, Brookhaven Nat Lab, 51-54; from engr to sr engr, Atomic Power Dept, Westinghouse Elec Corp, 54-57, supvry engr, 58-59; sr engr, Nuclear Develop Corp Am, NY, 59-60; fel engr, Westinghouse Elec Corp, Pa, 60-66, mgr thermal & hydraul anal, Atomic Power Dept, 67-68. *Concurrent Pos:* Consult nuclear power indust, 69- *Mem:* Fel Am Nuclear Soc; Am Inst Chem Engrs; Sigma Xi. *Res:* Nuclear power reactor technology; experimental heat transfer and fluid flow; design of large scale experiments; system optimization. *Mailing Add:* Dept Mech Indust & Nuclear Eng Univ Cincinnati Cincinnati OH 45221

**WEISMAN, LOIS SUE,** CELL BIOLOGY, YEAST GENETICS. *Current Pos:* ASST PROF, DEPT BIOCHEM, UNIV IOWA, 93- *Personal Data:* b Newark, NJ, Oct 9, 52; m 79, Robert E Cohen; c 2. *Educ:* Douglas Col Rutgers Univ, AB, 74; Univ Calif, PhD(biochem), 82. *Prof Exp:* Fel, Univ Calif, Berkeley, 82-85, Univ Calif, Los Angeles, 86-89, res assoc, 90-93. *Mem:* AAAS; Am Chem Soc; Genetic Soc Am; Am Soc Cell Biol. *Res:* Organelle partitioning like chromosome segregation is essential for cell division; studies are being performed to visualize organelle inheritance and to elucidate the biochemical basis of this process. *Mailing Add:* Dept Biochem Univ Iowa Iowa City IA 52242. *Fax:* 319-335-9570; *E-Mail:* lois-weisman@uiowa.edu

**WEISMAN, R(OBERT) BRUCE,** MOLECULAR PHOTOPHYSICS AND PHOTOCHEMISTRY. *Current Pos:* from asst prof to assoc prof, 79-93, PROF CHEM, RICE UNIV, 93- *Personal Data:* b Baltimore, Md, Nov 23, 50; m 86, Kathleen Beckingham; c Caroline. *Educ:* Johns Hopkins Univ, BA, 71; Univ Chicago, PhD(chem), 77. *Honors & Awards:* Res fel, Alfred P Sloan Found, 85. *Prof Exp:* Fel, Univ Pa, 77-79. *Mem:* Am Phys Soc; AAAS; Sigma Xi; Am Chem Soc; Electrochem Soc. *Res:* Use of time-resolved laser spectroscopies to study molecular photophysics and photochemistry. *Mailing Add:* Dept Chem MS 60 Rice Univ 6100 S Main St Houston TX 77005. *Fax:* 713-285-5155; *E-Mail:* weisman@rice.edu

**WEISMAN, ROBERT A,** BIOCHEMISTRY. *Current Pos:* chmn dept biochem, Wright State Univ, 87-89, dir, biomed sci PhD prog, 71-86, assoc dir, Magnetic Res Lab, 85-93, PROF BIOCHEM, SCH MED & COL SCI & MATH, WRIGHT STATE UNIV, 77-, ASSOC DEAN, COL SCI & MATH, 93-, ASSOC DEAN, SCH MED, 94- *Personal Data:* b Kingston, NY, Dec 16, 36. *Educ:* Union Univ, NY, BS, 58; Mass Inst Technol, PhD(biochem), 63. *Prof Exp:* Staff fel biochem, Sect Cellular Physiol, Lab Biochem, Nat Heart Inst, 63-66; asst prof biochem, Med Col Pa, 66-68; from asst prof to assoc prof, Univ Tex Health Sci Ctr San Angonio, 68-74, prof biochem, 74-77. *Mem:* Am Soc Biol Chemists. *Res:* Magnetic resonance; position emission tomography. *Mailing Add:* Wright State Univ 134 Oelman Hall Dayton OH 45435

**WEISMAN, RUSSELL,** MEDICINE, HEMATOLOGY. *Current Pos:* Res fel med, Case Western Res Univ, 52-54, instr, 54-55, sr instr clin med & path, 55-57, from asst prof to prof, 57-92, EMER PROF MED, CASE WESTERN RES UNIV, 92- *Personal Data:* b Cleveland, Ohio, Jan 20, 22; m 72, June Douglas; c 4. *Educ:* Western Res Univ, AB, 44, MD, 46. *Mem:* AAAS; Am Soc Hemat; Am Fedn Clin Res; Sigma Xi; Am Asn Blood Banks; Cent Soc Clin Res. *Res:* Hemolytic anemia; immunohematology; relation of the spleen and blood destruction. *Mailing Add:* 11100 Euclid Ave Cleveland OH 44106

**WEISMANN, THEODORE JAMES,** PHYSICAL CHEMISTRY. *Current Pos:* PROF CHEM, DEQUESNE UNIV, 96- *Personal Data:* b Pittsburgh, Pa, Apr 21, 30. *Educ:* Duquesne Univ, BS, 52, MS, 54, PhD(phys chem), 56. *Prof Exp:* res dir, Gulf Res & Develop Co, 56-96. *Mem:* Am Chem Soc; Geochem Soc; Am Phys Soc; Am Soc Mass Spectrometry; AAAS; Sigma Xi. *Res:* Boron chemistry; mass spectrometry; organic and isotopic geochemistry; marine geochemistry; molecular structure of organic radicals; magnetic susceptibilities; geochronometry. *Mailing Add:* Dept Chem Duquesne Univ Pittsburgh PA 15282-1503

**WEISMILLER, RICHARD A,** AGRONOMY. *Current Pos:* PROF, SOIL & WATER RESOURCES, UNIV MD, 83- *Personal Data:* b Elwood, Ind, Feb 23, 42; m 66; c 2. *Educ:* Purdue Univ, BS, 64, MS, 66; Mich State Univ, PhD(soil chem, clay mineral), 69. *Prof Exp:* Spec scientist soil stabilization, USAF Weapons Lab, 69-73; res agronomist remote sensing, Purdue Univ, West Lafayette, 73- 83. *Mem:* Am Soc Agron; Soil Sci Soc Am; Clay Minerals Soc; Soil & Water Conserv Soc; Sigma Xi. *Res:* Relation of spectral reflectance of soils to their physicochemical properties; application of remote sensing to soils mapping, land use inventories and change detection as related to land use; BMP's for nonpoint source pollution control. *Mailing Add:* Dept Agron Univ Md College Park MD 20742-0001

**WEISS, ALAN,** LARGE DEVIATIONS. *Current Pos:* MEM TECH STAFF, AT&T BELL LABS, 81- *Personal Data:* b Cleveland, Ohio, Dec 5, 55; m 78; c 2. *Educ:* Case Western Reserve Univ, BS(math) & BS(physics), 76; NY Univ, MA, 79, PhD(math), 81. *Concurrent Pos:* Vis lectr, Systs Res Ctr, Univ Md, 86. *Mem:* Oper Res Soc Am. *Res:* Applications of the theory of large deviations to computer and communication systems; efficiency of certain algorithms for parallel computation. *Mailing Add:* AT&T Bell Labs Rm 2C-118 600 Mountain Ave Murray Hill NJ 07974-2010

**WEISS, ALVIN H(ARVEY),** CHEMICAL ENGINEERING, CATALYSIS. *Current Pos:* assoc prof, 66-68, PROF CHEM ENG, WORCESTER POLYTECH INST, 68- *Personal Data:* b Philadelphia, Pa, Apr 28, 28; c 2. *Educ:* Univ Pa, BS, 49, PhD(phys chem), 65; Newark Col Eng, MS, 55. *Prof Exp:* Chem engr, Fiber Chem Co, 49-51, US Army Chem Ctr, Edgewood Proving Ground, 51-53, Colgate Palmolive Co, 53-55 & Houdry Process Corp, 55-63; res assoc interdisciplinary res, Inst Coop Res, Univ Pa, 63-65, res investr, 65-66. *Concurrent Pos:* Lectr, Univ Pa, 64-66. *Mem:* AAAS; fel Am Inst Chem Engrs; Am Chem Soc; Catalysis Soc (secy, 68-); Ger Soc Chem Apparatus. *Res:* Petroleum and petrochemical processing; hydrodealkylation; hydrodechlorination; dehydrogenation; kinetics and mechanisms of complex reactions; catalysis. *Mailing Add:* 26 Oakland Ave Shrewsbury MA 01545-2146

**WEISS, ANDREW W,** ATOMIC PHYSICS, THEORETICAL PHYSICS. *Current Pos:* PHYSICIST, NAT BUR STANDARDS, 61- *Personal Data:* b Streator, Ill, Mar 13, 30; m 61; c 3. *Educ:* Univ Detroit, BS, 52, MS, 54; Univ Chicago, PhD(atomic physics), 61. *Honors & Awards:* Dept Com Silver Medal; Fel, Am Phys Soc. *Mem:* Am Phys Soc. *Res:* Application of electronic computers to the determination of the electronic structure and properties of atoms and simple molecules. *Mailing Add:* Div 842 Nat Inst Stand & Technol Gaithersburg MD 20899. *Fax:* 301-975-3038

**WEISS, ARTHUR JACOBS,** INTERNAL MEDICINE. *Current Pos:* Instr, 57-62, ASST PROF MED, JEFFERSON MED COL, 62- *Personal Data:* b Philadelphia, Pa, Apr 11, 25; m 52; c 3. *Educ:* Pa State Col, BS, 45; Univ Pa, MD, 50. *Concurrent Pos:* Am Heart Asn advan res fel, 57- *Mem:* Am Asn Cancer Res; Am Soc Hemat; Am Soc Pharmacol & Exp Therapeut; Am Col Physicians; Am Soc Clin Oncol. *Res:* Long-term storage of various tissues; hematology; malignant diseases; oncology. *Mailing Add:* 1015 Chestnut No 412 Philadelphia PA 19107-4304

**WEISS, BENJAMIN,** BIOCHEMISTRY, ORGANIC CHEMISTRY. *Current Pos:* PROF NEUROPSYCHOPHARMACOL, DEPT PHARMACOL, PA MED COL. *Personal Data:* b Newark, NJ, Nov 16, 22; m 47; c 6. *Educ:* Univ Iowa, BS, 44; Univ Ill, PhD(biochem), 49. *Prof Exp:* Asst inorg chem, Univ Ill, 47-49; res biochemist, Harper Hosp, 49-53; res assoc, Columbia Univ, 53-65, asst prof brain metab, Col Physicians & Surgeons & mem staff, NY State Psychiat Inst, 53-76; res scientist, Inst Neurochem, Ward's Island, NY, 76- *Mem:* Am Chem Soc; Am Soc Biol Chemists. *Res:* Chemistry and biochemistry of long chain bases; synthesis of long chain base antimetabolites; lipid metabolism; chemical modification of enzymes; isolation of natural products. *Mailing Add:* Dept Pharmacol EPPI Allegheny Univ Health Sci 3200 Henry Ave 3200 Henry Ave Philadelphia PA 19129-1137

**WEISS, BERNARD,** NEUROTOXICOLOGY. *Current Pos:* assoc prof radiation biol & biophys & brain res, Univ Rochester, 65-67, prof radiation biol & biophys, psychol & brain res, Sch Med & Dent, 67-79, prof toxicol, Environ Health Sci Ctr, 79-93, PROF ENVIRON MED, UNIV ROCHESTER, 93- *Personal Data:* b New York, NY, May 27, 25; m 78, Susan Edelman; c Wendy & Thomas. *Educ:* NY Univ, BA, 49; Univ Rochester, PhD(psychol), 53. *Honors & Awards:* Stockinger Award, Am Conf Govt Indust Hygienists, 90. *Prof Exp:* Res assoc psychol, Univ Rochester, 53-54; exp & physiol psychologist, Sch Aviation Med, USAF, 54-56; instr med, Sch Med, Johns Hopkins Univ, 56-65, from instr to asst prof pharmacol, 59-65. *Concurrent Pos:* Mem behav pharmacol comt, NIMH, 65-67; mem comt biol effects of atmospheric pollutants, Nat Acad Sci-Nat Res Coun, 71-74, Sci Adv Bd, Environ Protection Agency, 83-; partic, US-USSR Environ Health Exchange Prog, 73-79; mem comt, Environ Protection Agency, 81-, Toxicol Study Sect, NIH, 81-85 & complex mixtures, Nat Acad Sci-Nat Res Coun, 85-88, Comt Neurotoxicol & Risk Assessment, 88- *Mem:* ΛΛAS; Am Soc Pharmacol & Exp Therapeut; Am Psychol Asn; Behav Pharmacol Soc (pres, 61-64); Soc Toxicol. *Res:* Chemical influences on behavior, particularly neurotoxic agents such as heavy metals, solvents, pesticides. *Mailing Add:* Dept Environ Med Univ Rochester Sch Med & Dent Rochester NY 14642. *Fax:* 716-256-2591; *E-Mail:* weiss@enumed.rochester.edu

**WEISS, BERNARD,** DNA REPAIR. *Current Pos:* PROF, DEPT PATH, UNIV MICH, 89- *Personal Data:* b New York, NY, July 17, 36; m 66; c 1. *Educ:* Columbia Univ, AB, 56; Col Physicians & Surgeons, Columbia Univ, MD, 60. *Prof Exp:* Fel biochem, Harvard Med Sch, 65-67; from asst prof to assoc prof microbiol, Sch Med, Johns Hopkins Univ, 67-80, prof molecular biol & genetics, 80-89. *Mem:* Am Soc Microbiol; Am Soc Biol Chemists. *Res:* Enzymatic repair of DNA in bacteria; microbial genetics. *Mailing Add:* Med Sch Dept Path Univ Mich 1301 Catherine Rd Ann Arbor MI 48109-0602

**WEISS, C DENNIS,** computer science, engineering, for more information see previous edition

**WEISS, CHARLES, JR,** SCIENCE POLICY, ENVIRONMENT. *Current Pos:* PRES, GLOBAL TECHNOL MGT, INC, 90-, PROF LECTR, NITZE SCH ADVAN INT STUDIES, JOHNS HOPKINS UNIV, 94- *Personal Data:* b San Francisco, Calif, Dec 20, 37; m 69, Edith Brown; c Jed A & Tamara G. *Educ:* Harvard Univ, AB, 59, PhD(chem physics, biochem), 65. *Prof Exp:* Teaching fel, Harvard Univ, 62-64; NIH fel biophys, Lab Chem Biodyn, Lawrence Radiation Lab, Univ Calif, 67-69; biophysicist, IBM Watson Lab, Columbia Univ, 69-71; sci & technol adv, Int Bank Reconstruct & Develop, 71-86; adj prof, Univ Pa, 86-90; chmn, Int Technol Develop & Finance, Inc, 86-89; vis lectr, Woodrow Wilson Sch, Princeton Univ, 89-94. *Concurrent Pos:* Mem corp bd, Vols Tech Assistance, Nat Climate Adv Bd, Coun Foreign Rels & World Acad Arts & Sci; exec officer, Fund Biol Explor & Conserv, 95- *Mem:* AAAS; Am Phys Soc; Am Chem Soc; Soc Int Develop. *Res:* Science and technology in developing countries and former communist; environmental policy and institutions in developing countries; role of development assistance organizations in technological research and technology transfer; history of the Marshall Plan. *Mailing Add:* 6309 Crathie Lane Bethesda MD 20816. *Fax:* 301-229-4628; *E-Mail:* charles@weiss.csgi.com

**WEISS, CHARLES FREDERICK,** PEDIATRICS, PHARMACOLOGY. *Current Pos:* MED EXEC DIR, SUNLAND CTR, ORLANDO, 84-; CLIN ASSOC PROF, DEPT PEDIAT, UNIV S FLA, 92- *Personal Data:* b Cohoctah, Mich, Apr 2, 21; m 47; c 3. *Educ:* Univ Mich, BA, 42; Vanderbilt Univ, MD, 49; Am Bd Pediat, dipl, 60. *Honors & Awards:* President's Award, Am Acad Pediat, 84, Outstanding Serv Award, 86. *Prof Exp:* Pvt pract, 54-58; med coordr clin invest in pediat & virus res, Parke, Davis & Co, Mich, 58-69; from instr to assoc prof pharm & pharmacol & assoc prof pediat, Col Med, Univ Fla, 69-73; chief staff, Hope Haven Children's Hosp, 73-77; coordr prof affairs & consult pediat to surgeon gen, USAF, 77-84; vpres med affairs & chmn, Bd Sci Adv Himedics, 85-89; dir planning & develop & consult pediat pharmacol, Dakle, Inc, 85-89. *Concurrent Pos:* Staff physician, Children's Hosp, Mich, 54-69 & Receiving Hosp, Detroit; clin asst prof pediat & commun dis, Univ Hosp, Univ Mich, Ann Arbor; med consult to dir, Div Ment Retardation, State Fla, 69-; med dir & vpres, Fla Special Olympics, 76; consult & qual assurance, Dept Health & Rehab Serv, State Fla, 84- *Mem:* Am Soc Clin Pharmacol & Therapeut; AMA; fel Am Acad Pediat; Am Fedn Clin Res. *Res:* Virus and infectious diseases; pediatric clinical pharmacology; author of many publications. *Mailing Add:* PO Box 31576 Sarasota FL 34242-1688

**WEISS, CHARLES MANUEL,** AQUATIC BIOLOGY. *Current Pos:* assoc prof sanit sci, 56-62, dep head, Dept Environ Sci & Eng, 67-77, PROF ENVIRON BIOL, SCH PUB HEALTH, UNIV NC, CHAPEL HILL, 62- *Personal Data:* b Scranton, Pa, Dec 7, 18; m 42. *Educ:* Rutgers Univ, BS, 39; Johns Hopkins Univ, PhD(biol), 50. *Prof Exp:* Asst bacteriologist, Woods Hole Oceanog Inst, 40-42, res assoc & biologist in-chg, Miami Beach Sta, 42-46, res assoc marine biol, 46-47; chemist-biologist, Baltimore Harbor Proj, Dept Sanit Eng, Johns Hopkins Univ, 47-50; basin biologist, Div Water Pollution Control, USPHS, 50-52; biologist, Sanit Chem Br, Med Labs, Army Chem Ctr, Edgewood, Md, 52-56. *Concurrent Pos:* Consult, Pan Am Health Orgn; Bigelow fel, Woods Hole Oceanog Inst. *Mem:* Fel AAAS; Am Chem Soc; Soc Int Limnol; Am Soc Microbiol; fel Am Pub Health Asn; fel NY Acad Sci. *Res:* Response of aquatic biota to environmental stress; water quality criteria and indices; limnology of lakes and impoundments; stream pollution. *Mailing Add:* 155 N Hamilton Rd Chapel Hill NC 27514

**WEISS, DANIEL LEIGH,** PATHOLOGY, MEDICAL SCIENCE. *Current Pos:* CONSULT MED SYSTS, RES, CARE & EDUC, 87- *Personal Data:* b Long Branch, NJ, July 27, 23; m 51, Mary Caudill; c Peter C, Leah W, & Harry M. *Educ:* Columbia Univ, AB, 43, MD, 46. *Honors & Awards:* Sunderman Clin Scientist Award, Asn Clin Scientists. *Prof Exp:* Med Corps, US Army Lt to Capt Virus & Rickettsial Dis, Walter Reed Army Med Ctr & 6th Army Med Labs, 48-50; res asst path & exp med, Beth Israel Hosp, 50-51; res asst path, Mt Sinai Hosp, NY, 49-50 & 51-53; dir inst path & lab med, DC Gen Hosp, 53-63; prof path, Col Med, Univ Ky, 63-77; exec secy, div med sci, Nat Res Coun, Nat Acad Sci, 77-82; dep dir, Affil Educ Progs Serv, Off Acad Affairs, Dept Med & Surg, Vet Admin, 83-87. *Concurrent Pos:* Clin prof, Georgetown Univ, 53-63, George Washington Univ, 53-63 & 79- & Howard Univ, 59-63; consult, NIH, 56-73, Booz-Allen Hamilton, Titan Corp, Oak Ridge Assoc Univs 87- & Indian Health Serv, USPHS, Santa Fe 92-; US liason rep, Comt Genetic Experimentation, WHO, 78-82; mem biomech adv comn, US Dept Transp, 79-81 & Health Servs Comn, Am Red Cross, 80; rep, Nat Res Coun, Interagency Comn, Handicapped Res, 80-81 & Comn Nat Standards, Medicolegal Invest Death, Nat Inst Justice, US Dept Justice, 80-82; Vet Admin rep, Educ & Pub Info Task Force, Pub Working Group for Health, Nat Disaster Med Serv, Exec Off Pres, 83-87; mem, Comt Interagency Radiation Res & Policy Coord, Off Sci & Technol Policy, Exec Off of Pres, 87-90; vis prof, Univ Kans, Ind Univ, Univ Copenhagen, Univ Oslo, Edinburgh Univ, Cambridge Univ. *Mem:* Am Soc Clin Path; Am Asn Path; Col Am Path; Am Soc Exp Path; Asn Clin Sci; Am Asn Hist Med. *Res:*

Experimental virus infection; primary and secondary vasculitis; pathology of infection and immunity; skeletal pathology; paleopathology; science administration; radiation pathobiology; environmental pathobiology; medical education; History of Medicine; Leprosy. *Mailing Add:* 5903 Mount Eagle Dr No 418 Alexandria VA 22303. *E-Mail:* dlmweiss@aol.com

**WEISS, DAVID STEVEN,** PHOTOCONDUCTIVITY, PHOTOCHEMISTRY. *Current Pos:* RES ASSOC, EASTMAN KODAK CO, 78- *Personal Data:* b Newark, NJ, Mar 3, 44; m 97, Ludmila S Belave. *Educ:* Lehigh Univ, BS, 65; Columbia Univ, PhD(chem), 69. *Prof Exp:* NIH fel, Iowa State Univ, 69-72; asst prof chem, Univ Mich, Ann Arbor, 72-78. *Mem:* Inter-Am Photochem Soc; Am Chem Soc; Sigma Xi; Soc Imaging Sci & Technol. *Res:* Photoreceptors for electrophotographic technologies. *Mailing Add:* 67 Eastwood Trail Rochester NY 14622. *E-Mail:* dweiss@kodak.com

**WEISS, DAVID WALTER,** MICROBIOLOGY, IMMUNOLOGY. *Current Pos:* PROF IMMUNOL & CHMN, LAUTENBERG CTR GEN RES & TUMOR IMMUNOL, HADASSAH MED SCH, HEBREW UNIV, JERUSALEM, 68- *Personal Data:* b Vienna, Austria, July 6, 27; nat US; m 51, Judith T Weintrob; c Hille J, Joshuah M & Jeremy M. *Educ:* Brooklyn Col, BA, 49; Rutgers Univ, PhD(microbiol), 52; Oxford Univ, DPhil, Med, 57. *Hon Degrees:* DSc, Brooklyn Col, City Univ, NY, 83. *Honors & Awards:* Ungerman-Lubin Cancer Res Award, 77; Frank Sinatra Award, Pan Am Cancer Cytol Soc, 73; Prentis Prize & Medal, 83. *Prof Exp:* Asst, Rockefeller Inst 52-55; dir med res coun tuberc unit, Oxford Univ, 56-57; from asst prof to prof bact & immunol, Univ Calif, Berkeley, 57-67, res immunologist, Cancer Res Genetics Lab, 62-67. *Concurrent Pos:* Merck sr fel, Nat Acad Sci, 55-57; Am Cancer Soc scholar, 62-63; res prof, Miller Inst Basic Res Sci, 66-67; Herbert Abeles scholar, 74; vis prof neoplastics dis, Mt Sinai Med Sch, NY, 77-78; mem, Midwinter Conf Immunologists. *Mem:* Am Asn Cancer Res; Transplantation Soc; Am Asn Immunologists; NY Acad Sci; Path Soc Gt Brit & Ireland. *Res:* Pathogenesis and host-parasite relationships; development of nonliving vaccines; relationship of specific and nonspecific immunogenic activities of microorganisms; tumor immunology; mechanisms of immunological activation; oncogenic viruses; antibody formation; endotoxins; psychoneuroimmunology. *Mailing Add:* Dept Immunol Hadassah Med Sch Hebrew Univ PO Box 1172 Jerusalem 91010 Israel. *Fax:* 972-2-424653

**WEISS, DENNIS,** MICROPALEONTOLOGY, ENVIRONMENTAL GEOLOGY. *Current Pos:* Lectr geol, 64-71, asst prof, 71-80, ASSOC PROF EARTH & PLANETARY SCI, CITY COL NEW YORK, 80-, CHMN DEPT, 78- *Personal Data:* b New York, NY, July 2, 40; m 65; c 3. *Educ:* City Col New York, BS, 63; NY Univ, MS, 67, PhD(geol), 71. *Mem:* AAAS; Geol Soc Am; Soc Econ Paleontologists & Mineralogists; Am Asn Stratig Palynologists; Nat Asn Geol Teachers. *Res:* Quaternary paleo-environments. *Mailing Add:* Dept Earth Sci City Univ NY City Col 160 Convent Ave New York NY 10031-9101

**WEISS, DOUGLAS EUGENE,** ORGANIC POLYMER CHEMISTRY, RADIATION CHEMISTRY & PROCESSING OF POLYMERS. *Current Pos:* res specialist, 3M Co, 78-81, prod develop supvr, 81-85, mat res mgr, 85-88, TECH MGR, CORP RES PROCESS TECHNOL LAB, 3M CO, 88- *Personal Data:* b Aurora, Ill, July 28, 45. *Educ:* Univ Kans, BS, 68; Univ Nebr, PhD(org chem), 72. *Prof Exp:* Sr res assoc polymers, Univ E Anglia, 72-73; res assoc org chem, Univ Nebr, 73-74; chemist, Elastomer Chem Dept, E I du Pont de Nemours & Co, Inc, 74-78. *Mem:* Am Chem Soc; Sigma Xi. *Res:* Heat-shrinkable technology; radiation processing; olefinic polymers; radiation-grafting; primers; hot melt and pressure sensitive adhesives; optical properties of polymers; elastomers; polyurethanes; C-13 nuclear magnetic reanance. *Mailing Add:* 400 Natchez Ave N Golden Valley MN 55422-5206

**WEISS, EARLE BURTON,** PULMONARY MEDICINE & PHYSIOLOGY. *Current Pos:* assoc prof, 71-77, PROF MED, MED SCH, UNIV MASS, 77-; SR PULMONARY SCIENTIST, DEPT ANESTHESIA RES, BRIGHAM & WOMEN'S HOSP, 88- *Personal Data:* b Waltham, Mass, Nov 23, 32; m 63, Ruth V Lithwick; c Ilana J & Joshua N. *Educ:* Northeastern Univ, BS, 55; Mass Inst Technol, MS, 57; Albert Einstein Col Med, MD, 61; Am Bd Internal Med, dipl, 69. *Honors & Awards:* Chadwick Medal, 90. *Prof Exp:* Nat Heart Inst fel, Tufts Lung Sta, Boston City Hosp, 64-66; from instr to assoc prof, Sch Med, Tufts Univ, 66-77; dir, Dept Respiratory Dis, St Vincent Hosp, 71-89. *Concurrent Pos:* Assoc, Tufts Lung Sta, Boston City Hosp, 66-71, physician chg, Pulmonary Function & Physiol Sect, Hosp, 66-71 & Cent Arterial Blood Gas Lab, 67-71, assisting physician, Tufts Med Serv, 67-70, assoc dir, 69-70, dir respiratory intensive care unit, 70-71; consult physiol, Norfolk Co Sanatorium, Mass, 66-69; mem toxicol info prog, Nat Libr Med, 70-; tuberc consult, Mass Dept Pub Health, 72-; lectr med, Med Sch, Tufts Univ, 78; assoc affil prof life sci, Worcester Polytech Inst, 76-; vis prof, Fac Med, Harvard Med Sch, Boston, 89-97. *Mem:* AAAS; Am Thoracic Soc; fel Am Col Physicians; fel Am Col Chest Physicians; Am Soc Internal Med. *Res:* Mechanisms of airway hyperactivity and toxic oxygen radicals and intracellular calcium. *Mailing Add:* Brigham & Women's Hosp Dept Anesthesia Res Boston MA 02115. *Fax:* 617-732-6927; *E-Mail:* eweiss@bics.bwh.harvard.edu

**WEISS, EMILIO,** MEDICAL MICROBIOLOGY. *Current Pos:* RETIRED. *Personal Data:* b Pakrac, Yugoslavia, Oct 4, 18; nat US; m 43, Hilda Damick; c Natalie A (Holzwarth) & Elizabeth R. *Educ:* Univ Kans, AB, 41; Univ Chicago, MS, 42, PhD(bact), 48. *Prof Exp:* Asst histol, parasitol & bact, Univ Chicago, 42 47-48; res assoc, 48-50; instr bact, Loyola Univ, Ill, 47-48; asst prof, Ind Univ, 50-53; chief virol br, Chem Corps Biol Lab, US Dept Army,

Ft Detrick, Md, 53-54; res prof prev med & biometrics, Uniformed Serv Univ Health Sci, 77-84; asst head virol div, Naval Med Res Inst, 54-63, dep dir microbiol dept, 63-72, dir, 72-74, chmn microbiol dept, 74-80, chair sci, 80-86. *Concurrent Pos:* Vis scientist, Naval Med Res Inst, 86- *Mem:* Am Soc Microbiol; Soc Exp Biol & Med; Am Asn Immunologists; Am Acad Microbiol; Am Soc Rickettsiol (pres, 80-82). *Res:* Microbiol physiology and pathogenesis; rickettsiae, chlamydiae and other bacterial pathogens. *Mailing Add:* 3612 Raymond St Chevy Chase MD 20815-4152

**WEISS, FRED TOBY,** ANALYTICAL CHEMISTRY, ENVIRONMENTAL CHEMISTRY. *Current Pos:* RETIRED. *Personal Data:* b Oakland, Calif, July 24, 16; m 40; c 3. *Educ:* Univ Calif, Los Angeles, BS, 38; Harvard Univ, MS, 40, PhD(chem), 41. *Prof Exp:* Res chemist, Shell Oil Co, Ill, 41-43, group leader fuels res, 43-46, res chemist, Shell Develop Co, Calif, 46-52, res supvr, 52-72, staff res chemist, Bellaire Res Ctr, Tex, 72-75, sr staff res chemist, Bellaire Res Ctr, Shell Develop Co, Tex, 75-81, sr staff environ scientist, Shell Oil Co, 81-83; environ consult, 83-90. *Concurrent Pos:* Mem adv comt, NSF-Res Appl to Nat Needs Study of Petrol Indust in Del Estuary, 74-77; mem outer continental shelf adv bd, US Dept Interior, 79-90; pres, Bd Trustees, Judah Magnes Mus Western Jewish Studies, Berkeley, Calif, 95-; trustee, Desert Res Inst Found, Reno, Nev, 96- *Mem:* AAAS; Am Chem Soc. *Res:* Characterization and analysis of organic structures; analytical methods for process control; combined use of chemical and physical methods for analysis of organic compounds; environmental analysis; development of analytical methods for studying fate and effects of petroleum in marine environments; surveys of impacts of offshore petroleum operations in the environment. *Mailing Add:* Three Indian Gulch Piedmont CA 94611

**WEISS, GARY BRUCE,** ONCOLOGY, HEMATOLOGY. *Current Pos:* from asst prof to assoc prof int med, human biol chem & genetics, 77-84, CLIN ASSOC PROF, UNIV TEX MED BR GALVESTON, 84- *Personal Data:* b New York, NY, Oct 5, 44; div; c 1. *Educ:* NY Univ, BA, 65, MD, 71, PhD(biochem), 72. *Prof Exp:* Intern med, Sch Med, Univ Calif, San Francisco, 71-72, resident, 72-73; res assoc hemat, Nat Heart & Lung Inst, Bethesda, Md, 73-76; fel hemat, Univ Wash, 76-77. *Mem:* Am Fedn Clin Res; Asn Comput Mach; Am Soc Hemat; Am Soc Biol Chemists; Am Statist Asn. *Res:* Medical ethics in clinical oncology. *Mailing Add:* 400 Med Ctr Blvd Suite 111 Univ Tex Med Br Webster TX 77598-4223. *Fax:* 281-332-8429

**WEISS, GEORGE B,** PHARMACOLOGY. *Current Pos:* EXEC DIR, M HURLEY & ASSOC INC, 92- *Personal Data:* b Plainfield, NJ, Apr 29, 35; wid; c William & Debra. *Educ:* Princeton Univ, AB, 57; Vanderbilt Univ, PhD(pharmacol), 62. *Prof Exp:* USPHS res fels pharmacol, Vanderbilt Univ, 62 & Univ Pa, 62-64; from asst prof to assoc prof pharmacol, Med Col Va, 64-70; from assoc prof to prof pharmacol, Univ Tex Health Ctr, Dallas, 70-82; sr res fel, Ciba-Geigy Corp, 82-88, dist res fel, 89-92. *Mem:* Biophys Soc; Am Soc Pharmacol & Exp Therapeut; Am Physiol Soc. *Res:* Cellular pharmacology; actions of drugs on membrane permeability to ions; excitation-contraction coupling and calcium ion in smooth (especially vascular) and striated muscle; actions of calcium antagonists, especially calcium channel blockers. *Mailing Add:* M Hurley & Assoc Inc 1 Main St Chatham NJ 07928

**WEISS, GEORGE HERBERT,** APPLIED MATHEMATICS, APPLIED PROBABILITY. *Current Pos:* study grant, 64-67, CHIEF PHYS SCI LAB, DIV COMPUT RES & TECHNOL, NIH, 67- *Personal Data:* b New York, NY, Feb 19, 30; m 61, Delia Orgel; c Miriam J, Alan K & Daniel J. *Educ:* Columbia Univ, AB, 51; Univ Md, MA, 53, PhD, 58. *Prof Exp:* Physicist, US Naval Ord Lab, 51-54; math asst, Ballistic Res Lab, Aberdeen Proving Ground, US Army, 54-56; asst math, Inst Fluid Dynamics & Appl Math, Univ Md, 56-58, res assoc, 59-60, res asst prof, 60-63; Weizmann fel, Weizmann Inst Sci, 58-59; NIH study grant, Rockefeller Inst, 63-64. *Concurrent Pos:* Physicist, US Naval Ord Lab, 56-61; consult, Gen Motors Corp, 60-64; IBM Corp, 64; Fulbright sr fel, Imp Col, Univ London, 68-69; assoc ed, Transp Res, 73- & Cancer Res, 82-; Chemometrics & Intel Lab Systs, 86- *Mem:* Opers Res Soc Am; Soc Indust & Appl Math. *Res:* Applied optics; statistical mechanics; biometry; biochemical separation techniques, stochastic processes. *Mailing Add:* 1105 N Belgrade Rd Silver Spring MD 20902. *Fax:* 301-402-4544

**WEISS, GERALD S,** INORGANIC CHEMISTRY. *Current Pos:* assoc prof, 67-69, PROF CHEM, MILLERSVILLE STATE COL, 69-, CHMN DEPT, 75- *Personal Data:* b Boyertown, Pa, July 26, 34; m 58; c 3. *Educ:* Drexel Inst, BS, 57; Univ Pa, PhD(inorg chem, anal chem), 65. *Prof Exp:* Res chemist, Rohm & Haas Co, 57-59; instr chem, Drexel Inst, 59-65, asst prof, 65-67. *Mem:* Am Chem Soc. *Res:* Synthesis of volatile hydrides of group IV elements; infrared spectroscopic analysis of small molecules; heavy metal complex ion synthesis and spectroscopic analysis. *Mailing Add:* Dept Chem Millersville Univ Millersville PA 17551-0302

**WEISS, GERSON,** REPRODUCTIVE ENDOCRINOLOGY. *Current Pos:* PROF & CHMN DEPT OBSTET & GYNEC, NJ MED SCH, 85- *Personal Data:* b New York, NY, Aug 1, 39; m 59, Linda M Gordon; c Jonathan, David, Michele & Andrew. *Educ:* NY Univ, BA, 60, MD, 64; Am Bd Obstet & Gynec, dipl, 71, cert reproductive endocrinol, 74, 81, 93. *Honors & Awards:* Perdue-Frederick Award for Med Res. *Prof Exp:* From instr to prof obstet & gynec, Sch Med, NY Univ, 69-85, dir, Div Reproduction & Endocrinol, Med Ctr, 80-85. *Concurrent Pos:* Fel reproductive endocrinol, Sch Med, Univ Pittsburgh, 71-73; John Polachek Found Med Res grant, 75; Nat Inst Child Health & Human Develop res grant, 75; United Cerebral Palsy res grant, 77-81; prin investr, Mellon Found; res grants, NIH; dir, Am Bd Obstet & Gynec. *Mem:* Soc Gynec Invest; Endocrine Soc; Am Fertil Soc; Soc

Study Reproduction; NY Acad Med; NY Acad Sci. *Res:* Control and function of the pregnancy and postpartum corpus luteum; relaxing physiology; control of pituitary gonadotropin secretion. *Mailing Add:* Dept Obstet-Gynec NJ Med Sch 185 S Orange Ave Newark NJ 07103

**WEISS, GUIDO LEOPOLD,** MATHEMATICS, HARMONIC ANALYSIS & WAVELETS. *Current Pos:* chmn dept, 67-70, prof, 66-84, ELINOR ANHEUSER PROF MATH, WASHINGTON UNIV, 84- *Personal Data:* b Trieste, Italy, Dec 29, 28; nat US; m, Barbara I Gibgot; c Paul E & Michael E. *Educ:* Univ Chicago, PhB, 49, MS, 51, PhD, 56. *Hon Degrees:* Dr, Beijing Normal Univ, 85, Univ Barcelon, 94, Univ Milano, 94. *Honors & Awards:* Chauvenet Prize, Math Asn Am, 67. *Prof Exp:* From instr to assoc prof math, DePaul Univ, 55-60. *Concurrent Pos:* Hon prof, Math Dept, Beijing Normal Univ, 85; Elinor Anheuser prof math. *Mem:* Am Math Soc; Math Asn Am; AAAS. *Res:* Harmonic analysis; complex and real variables; classical and abstract harmonic analysis; theory of interpolation of operators; complex variables and the theory of wavelets. *Mailing Add:* Dept Math Washington Univ St Louis MO 63130. *E-Mail:* guido@math.wustl.edu

**WEISS, HAROLD GILBERT,** INORGANIC CHEMISTRY, PHYSICAL CHEMISTRY. *Current Pos:* PRES, WEST COAST TECH SERV, INC, 66- *Personal Data:* b Perth Amboy, NJ, Feb 6, 23; m 44; c 2. *Educ:* Univ Calif, Los Angeles, BS, 48. *Prof Exp:* Res chemist, US Naval Ord Test Sta, 48-52; supvr catalysis res, Olin Mathieson Chem Corp, 52-59; lab mgr, Nat Eng Sci Co, 59-61; dir chem, Dynamic Sci Corp, 61-66. *Mem:* Am Chem Soc; Am Inst Chemists; Inst Environ Sci. *Res:* Boron hydrides; organoboranes; surface chemistry and catalysis; analytical chemistry; mass and infrared spectrometry; high vacuum technology; combustion-fire research; environmental control; analytical instrumentation. *Mailing Add:* 4016 Montego Dr Huntington Beach CA 92649-2494

**WEISS, HAROLD SAMUEL,** CARDIOPULMONARY, CANCER. *Current Pos:* from assoc prof to prof, 62-91, EMER PROF PHYSIOL, COL MED, OHIO STATE UNIV, 91- *Personal Data:* b New York, NY, Sept 10, 22; m 49, Ann Socolow; c Ronald, Karen, Pamela & Seymour. *Educ:* Rutgers Univ, BSc, 47, MSc, 49, PhD(physiol), 50. *Prof Exp:* From instr to assoc prof avian physiol, Rutgers Univ, 50-62. *Concurrent Pos:* Meteorol, Air Traffic Control, USAF, 43-46, Res & Develop, Aviation Physiol, 51-54. *Mem:* Am Physiol Soc; Poultry Sci Asn; Soc Exp Biol & Med; Aerospace Med Asn; Undersea Med Soc; AAAS. *Res:* Cardiopulmonary; blood pressure; atherosclerosis; lung mechanics; environmental physiology; acceleration; temperature control; gaseous environment and respiratory disease; environment and cancer; colitis. *Mailing Add:* 302 Hamilton Hall Ohio State Univ Col Med 1645 Neil Ave Columbus OH 43210

**WEISS, HARRY JOSEPH,** APPLIED MECHANICS, APPLIED MATHEMATICS. *Current Pos:* RETIRED. *Personal Data:* b Pittsburgh, Pa, Feb 15, 23; m 47; c 3. *Educ:* Carnegie Mellon Univ, BS, 47, MS, 49, DSc(appl math), 51. *Prof Exp:* Instr math, Carnegie-Mellon Univ, 49-51; asst prof appl math, Brown Univ, 51-53; from asst prof to prof math, Iowa State Univ, 54-64, prof eng mech & head dept, 64-86, prof eng mech, 86-89. *Concurrent Pos:* Vis scientist, Nat Bur Stand, 61; consult, Gen Dynamics Astronaut, 62-66; vis prof overseas progs, Boston Univ & Univ Med, 89-91. *Mem:* Soc Eng Sci (vpres, 77-79); Am Soc Mech Engrs; Sigma Xi; Am Soc Eng Educ. *Res:* Integral transforms; partial differential equations; boundary value problems; elasticity. *Mailing Add:* 2529 Northwood Dr Ames IA 50010

**WEISS, HARVEY JEROME,** INTERNAL MEDICINE, HEMATOLOGY. *Current Pos:* assoc clin prof, 69-71, assoc prof, 72-74, PROF MED, COL PHYSICIANS & SURGEONS, COLUMBIA UNIV, 75- *Personal Data:* b New York, NY, June 30, 29; m 57, Thirell M Lipsey; c Deborah & Adrienne (Frechter). *Educ:* Harvard Univ, AB, 51, MD, 55. *Honors & Awards:* Distinguished Career Award, Int Soc Thrombasis & Haemostasis, 95. *Prof Exp:* Intern, Bellevue Hosp, Columbia Univ, 55-56; resident med, Manhattan Vet Admin Hosp, NY, 56-58; Dazian fel hemat, Mt Sinai Hosp, NY, 58-59; instr, Sch Med, NY Univ, 62-64; asst attend hematologist, Mt Sinai Hosp, 65-69. *Concurrent Pos:* Consult, Walter Reed Army Med Ctr, 65-70; asst prof med, Mt Sinai Sch Med, 66-69; dir, Div Hemat, Roosevelt Hosp, NY, 69-; mem hemat speciality comt, Am Bd Internal Med, 81-87; vis scientist, Inst Cellular Path, France. *Mem:* Soc Exp Biol & Med; Am Physiol Soc; Am Soc Clin Invest; Am Soc Hemat; Am Am Physicians. *Res:* Hematology; blood coagulation; disorders of hemostasis; platelet physiology; numerous contributions to the field of hemostasis and thrombosis, including the effects of drugs on platelets, original reports on the pathogenesis of platelet disorders, the physiologic role of von Willebrand factor, and rheological aspects of thrombosis. *Mailing Add:* Dept Med St Luke's Roosevelt Hosp Ctr 1000 Tenth Ave New York NY 10019. *Fax:* 212-523-6677

**WEISS, HARVEY RICHARD,** PHYSIOLOGY, PHARMACOLOGY. *Current Pos:* from asst prof to assoc prof, 71-82, PROF PHYSIOL, RUTGERS MED SCH, UNIV MED & DENT NJ, 82- *Personal Data:* b New York, NY, May 13, 43; m 66; c 2. *Educ:* City Col New York, BS, 65; Duke Univ, PhD(physiol), 69. *Prof Exp:* Warner-Lambert joint fel pharmacol, Warner-Lambert Res Inst & Col Physicians & Surgeons, Columbia Univ, 69-71. *Mem:* AAAS; Am Physiol Soc. *Res:* Physiologic and pharmacologic control of oxygen transport to tissue; coronary circulation; regional cerebral and myocardial oxygen consumption. *Mailing Add:* Dept Physiol & Biophys Univ Med & Dent NJ Robert Wood Johnson Med Sch 675 Hoes Lane Piscataway NJ 08854

**WEISS, HERBERT KLEMM,** SYSTEMS DESIGN & SYSTEMS SCIENCE. *Current Pos:* RETIRED. *Personal Data:* b Lawrence, Mass, June 22, 17; m 45; c 2. *Educ:* Mass Inst Technol, BS, 37, MS, 38. *Prof Exp:* Mech engr, Coast Artillery Bd, Va, 38-42, Anti-aircraft Artillery Bd, NC, 42-44 & Army Ground Forces Bd, Tex, 44-46; chief, Weapons Effect Br & dep chief, Terminal Ballistics Lab, Aberdeen Proving Ground, US Dept Army, Md, 46-50, chief, Weapon Systs Lab, 50-53; chief, Weapon Systs Anal Dept, Northrop Aircraft Corp, 53-58; mgr, Adv Systs Develop, Aeronutronic Div, Ford Motor Co, 58-60, mgr, Mil Systs Planning, 60-62; dir, Systs Anal & Eval, Aerospace Corp, 62-65; sr scientist, Litton Industs, 65-80, scientist, Data Systs Div, 80-82. *Concurrent Pos:* Mem tech adv panel ord, Off Asst Secy Defense Res & Develop, 54-64; consult, Weapons Systs Eval Group, Off Asst Secy Defense, 55-56; lectr, Univ Calif, Los Angeles, 57-58; consult, Sci Adv Bd, USAF, 58-59, mem, 59-63; summer mem study group, Nat Acad Sci-USAF, 58 & Proj Endicott, Opers Eval Group, USN, 60; consult, Opers Eval Group, USN, 60-62; mem, US Army Sci Adv Panel, 65-76; consult, Pres Sci Adv Comt 66-72. *Mem:* AAAS; Opers Res Soc Am (vpres, 58-59); assoc fel Am Inst Aeronaut & Astronaut; sr mem Inst Elec & Electronics Engrs. *Res:* Fire control; servo-mechanisms; computing devices; weapon systems research and development; operations research; systems analysis; ballistics; management sciences. *Mailing Add:* PO Box 2668 Palos Verdes Peninsula CA 90274

**WEISS, HERBERT V,** CHEMISTRY. *Current Pos:* ADJ PROF, SAN DIEGO STATE UNIV, 88- *Personal Data:* b Brooklyn, NY, Nov 16, 21; m 55; c 2. *Educ:* NY Univ, BA, 42, MS, 49; Univ Cincinnati, PhD(biochem), 52. *Prof Exp:* Toxicologist, Chief Med Exam Lab, NY, 47-49; fel physiol, Sch Med, Univ Rochester, 52-53; instr indust med, Post-grad Med Sch, NY Univ, 53-56; supvry radiochemist, US Naval Radiol Defense Lab, San Francisco, 56-69; res chemist, Naval Oceans Systs Ctr, 69-88. *Mem:* AAAS; Am Chem Soc. *Res:* Nuclear chemistry; analytical chemistry; industrial hygiene and toxicology; environmental chemistry. *Mailing Add:* 6536 Ridge Manor Ave San Diego CA 92120

**WEISS, IRA PAUL,** NEUROSCIENCES. *Current Pos:* res psychologists neurosci, Childrens Hosp Nat Med Ctr, 72-80, vchmn, Dept Psychol, 75-76, co-dir, Evoked Response Lab, 78-91, DIR, EVOKED RESPONSE LAB, CHILDRENS NAT MED CTR, 92- *Personal Data:* b New York, NY, Feb 27, 42; m 67, Susan Diamondstein; c Elaine R & Joanna G. *Educ:* City Col New York, BS, 65; Syracuse Univ, PhD(physiol, psychol), 69. *Prof Exp:* Instr psychol, Onondaga Community Col, 68; NIH fel neurophysiol, Callier Hearing & Speech Ctr, Dallas, Tex, 69-70, NIH spec fel neurophysiol & consult res design, 70-72. *Concurrent Pos:* Asst prof lectr, Sch Med, George Washington Univ, 72-80, assoc prof lectr, 80-81, assoc prof, 82- *Mem:* Am Psychol Soc; Soc Neurosci; Am Soc Neurophysiol Monitoring; AAAS. *Res:* Relationships of brainstem and cortical sensory evoked potentials to developments, neurological and sensory disorders and to behavior. *Mailing Add:* Evoked Response Lab Childrens Hosp Nat Med Ctr 111 Michigan Ave MW Washington DC 20010. *Fax:* 202-884-3461; *E-Mail:* iraweiss@gwis2. circ.gwu.edu or iweiss@cnmc.org

**WEISS, IRMA TUCK,** BIOCHEMISTRY, ORGANIC CHEMISTRY. *Current Pos:* Asst instr chem, Washington Sq Col, NY Univ, 40-42, from instr to assoc prof biochem, Col Dent, 43-76, prof, 76-80, EMER PROF BIOCHEM, COL DENT, NY UNIV, 80- *Personal Data:* b New York, NY, Aug 5, 13; m 38; c 2. *Educ:* NY Univ, BS, 33, MS, 36, PhD, 42. *Mem:* Sigma Xi (secy, Sci Res Soc Am, 59-60, treas, 60-61, vpres, 61-62, pres, 62-63); Am Chem Soc. *Res:* Organic synthesis; application of biochemistry in clinical dentistry; electrophoresis studies of salivary proteins. *Mailing Add:* 401 First Ave Apt 19D New York NY 10010-4007

**WEISS, IRVING,** MATHEMATICAL STATISTICS. *Current Pos:* RETIRED. *Personal Data:* b New York, Apr 10, 19; m 44; c 3. *Educ:* Univ Mich, BS, 41; Columbia Univ, MA, 48; Stanford Univ, PhD(statist), 55. *Prof Exp:* Res asst statist, Stanford Univ, 51-55; instr math, Lehigh Univ, 55-56; tech staff statistician, Bell Tel Labs, 56-59 & Mitre Corp, 59-62; assoc prof math, Univ Colo, Boulder, 62-90. *Concurrent Pos:* Consult, State Dept Employ, Colo, 63, Beech Aircraft Corp, 63-64, Dept Biol, Univ Rochester, 64-65, Nat Ctr Atmospheric Res, 64-72 & 75, Behav Res & Eval Corp, 73-74 & US Environ Protection Agency, 75. *Mem:* Inst Math Statist; Am Statist Asn. *Res:* Probability; applied probability theory; statistical inference; stochastic processes; control charts; tolerance intervals. *Mailing Add:* 1635 Mariposa Ave Boulder CO 80302

**WEISS, JAMES ALLYN,** ORGANIC CHEMISTRY. *Current Pos:* ASST PROF CHEM, PA STATE UNIV, WORTHINGTON SCRANTON CAMPUS, 70- *Personal Data:* b W Bend, Wis, Apr 16, 43; m 71; c 2. *Educ:* Univ Wis-Madison, AB, 65; Pa State Univ, Univ Park, PhD(chem), 71. *Mem:* AAAS; Am Chem Soc; Sigma Xi; Am Chem Soc. *Res:* Organic synthesis; isolation and structural elucidation of natural products; stereochemistry of organic molecules. *Mailing Add:* Chem Dept Pa State Univ 120 Ridge View Dr Dunmore PA 18512

**WEISS, JAMES MOSES AARON,** PSYCHIATRY. *Current Pos:* assoc prof & founding chmn dept, Univ Mo, 60-61, prof psychiat & chmn dept, 61-91, prof community med, 71-91, EMER PROF, SCH MED, UNIV MO, COLUMBIA, 91- *Personal Data:* b St Paul, Minn, Oct 22, 21; m 46; c 2. *Educ:* Univ Minn, AB, 41, BS, 47, MB, 49, MD, 50; Yale Univ, MPH, 51; Am Bd Psychiat & Neurol, dipl, 57. *Honors & Awards:* Distinguished Serv Commendation, Nat Coun Community Ment Health Centers, 82, 83, & 86; Kohler Distinguished Lectr, St Louis Univ, 88; Distinguished Serv Award, Vet Admin, 91. *Prof Exp:* Asst psychol, Col St Thomas, 41-42; intern med,

USPHS Hosp, Seattle, 49-50; from instr to asst prof psychiat, Sch Med, Wash Univ, 54-60. *Concurrent Pos:* Res & clin fel psychiat, Sch Med, Yale Univ, 51-53; dir training, Malcolm Bliss Ment Health Ctr, City of St Louis, 54-60, dir, Psychiat Clin, 54-59, dir, Div Community Psychiat Serv, 58-59; vis psychiatrist, St Louis City Hosps, Barnes & Affil Hosps & Wash Univ Clins, 54-60; fac fel, Inter-Univ Coun Inst Soial Geront, Univ Conn, 58; consult to state, fed & nat agencies & orgn, 60-; vis prof, Inst Criminol, Cambridge Univ, 68-69; chancellor's emissary, Univ Mo, Columbia, 79-81; sr res fel, NSF & Am Coun Educ, 84; vis prof, All India Inst Med Sci & Univ Malaya, 84. *Mem:* Fel Royal Col Psychiatrists; fel Am Psychiat Asn; fel Am Pub Health Asn; fel Royal Soc Med; fel Am Col Psychiatrists; fel Am Col Prev Med. *Res:* Social psychiatry and gerontology; psychiatric problems of aging; suicide; homicide; antisocial behavior. *Mailing Add:* 4300 Richmond Rd Columbia MO 65201

**WEISS, JAMES OWEN,** ORGANIC CHEMISTRY, POLYMER CHEMISTRY. *Current Pos:* chem develop mgr, 73-78, qual control dir, 78-81, FILAMENT PROD DIR, HOECHST FIBERS INDUSTS, 81- *Personal Data:* b Memphis, Tenn, Sept 25, 31; m 55; c 3. *Educ:* Duke Univ, BS, 52; Univ Va, MS, 54, PhD(org chem), 57. *Prof Exp:* Res chemist, Shell Oil Co, 57-58 & E I du Pont de Nemours & Co, 58-61; res chemist, Chemstrand Res Ctr, 61-66; res mgr fiber develop, Beaunit Fibers, 66-68; group leader fiber develop, Celanese Fibers Co, 68-72. *Mem:* Am Chem Soc. *Res:* Polyester fiber research and development; nylon, high temperature resistant fiber, spandex fiber, polypropylene fiber and vinyl polymer and fiber research and development. *Mailing Add:* 310 Continental Dr Greenville SC 29615-3418

**WEISS, JAY M,** PSYCHOPHYSIOLOGY. *Current Pos:* PROF, PSYCHIAT DEPT, GEORGIA MENTAL HEALTH INST, 92- *Personal Data:* b Jersey City, NJ, Mar 20, 41; m 63; c 2. *Educ:* Lafayette Col, BA, 62; Yale Univ, PhD(psychol), 67. *Prof Exp:* USPHS fel & guest investr, Rockefeller Univ, 67-68, from asst prof to assoc prof physiol, 69-85; prof, Psychiat Dept, Duke Univ, 85-92. *Concurrent Pos:* MacArthur fel. *Res:* Psychological factors influencing physiological effects of stress; psychosomatic disorders; motivation. *Mailing Add:* Georgia Mental Health Inst 1256 Barcliff Rd 5th fl Atlanta GA 30306

**WEISS, JEFFREY MARTIN,** REMOTE SENSING, COMPUTATIONAL ELECTROMAGNETICS. *Current Pos:* sr res physicist, 85-86, ASST DIR, APPL ELECTROMAGNETICS & OPTICS LAB, SRI INT, MENLO PARK, CALIF, 87- *Personal Data:* b Philadelphia, Pa, July 1, 44; m 67, Carol Levine; c Erika Lea & Theodore Eliot. *Educ:* Princeton Univ, AB, 66; Harvard Univ, MA, 67, PhD(physics), 72. *Prof Exp:* Vis scientist, Europ Orgn Nuclear Res, Geneva, Switz, 72-74; res assoc, Nevis Labs, Columbia Univ, 74-76; res assoc physics, Stanford Linear Accelerator Ctr, Stanford Univ, 76-81; physicist, Argonne Nat Lab, 81-85. *Concurrent Pos:* NSF fel, Europ Orgn Nuclear Res, 72-73; consult electromagnetics, 78-85; secy-treas, Stanford Linear Accelerator Ctr-Lawrence Berkely Lab Users Orgn, 84-85. *Mem:* Am Phys Soc; Inst Elec & Electronics Engrs Antennas & Propagation Soc; Geosci & Remote Sensing Soc; Appl Computational Electromagnetics Soc; Am Geophys Union. *Res:* Geophysical phenomenology in remote sensing; electromagnetics; finite-difference time-domain calculations of electromagnetic field propagation; surface gravity wave nearshore propagation; advanced signal processing techniques. *Mailing Add:* SRI Int 333 Ravenswood Ave Menlo Park CA 94025. *Fax:* 650-859-6259; *E-Mail:* weiss@unix.sri.com

**WEISS, JERALD AUBREY,** MICROWAVE PHYSICS. *Current Pos:* from asst prof to assoc prof, 62-66, PROF PHYSICS, WORCESTER POLYTECH INST, 66- *Personal Data:* b Cleveland, Ohio, June 9, 22; m 49; c 2. *Educ:* Ohio State Univ, PhD(physics), 53. *Prof Exp:* Instr math, Univ Wyo, 49-51; mem tech staff magnetic mat, Bell Tel Labs, Inc, 53-61; vpres, Hyletronics Corp, Mass, 61-62. *Concurrent Pos:* Consult, US Army Natick Res & Develop Ctr, 75 & Lincoln Lab, Mass Inst Technol, 62- *Mem:* Am Phys Soc; sr mem Inst Elec & Electronics Engrs; AAAS; Sigma Xi. *Res:* Theory of atomic and molecular structure; magnetic materials and electromagnetic interactions, theory and applications; magnetic resonance spectroscopy and microwave applications. *Mailing Add:* 30 Wayland Hills Rd Wayland MA 01778-3830

**WEISS, JEROME,** PHYSICAL CHEMISTRY. *Current Pos:* ASST PROF CHEM, SUFFOLK COUNTY COMMUNITY COL, 73- *Personal Data:* b Brooklyn, NY, Aug 27, 22; m 43; c 2. *Educ:* Cornell Univ, BA, 48; Ind Univ, PhD(phys chem), 51. *Prof Exp:* Asst chem, Ind Univ, 48-50, instr, Exten, 50; chemist, Brookhaven Nat Lab, 51-73. *Concurrent Pos:* Lectr, Hofstra Col, 55; Dewar res fel, Univ Edinburgh, 57; consult, Am Soc Testing & Mat & Brookhaven Nat Lab, 85; teacher, Smithtown High Sch, 75-77 & Northport High Sch, 78-86. *Mem:* AAAS; Radiation Res Soc; Royal Soc Chem; NY Acad Sci; fel Am Inst Chemists. *Res:* Organic radiation chemistry; chemical dosimetry; health physics; membrane transport. *Mailing Add:* 17 Locust Ave Stony Brook NY 11790

**WEISS, JOAN WYZKOSKI,** NUMERICAL ANALYSIS, TECHNOLOGY IN MATHEMATICS EDUCATION. *Current Pos:* ASSOC PROF MATH, FAIRFIELD UNIV, 85- *Personal Data:* b Pittsburgh, Pa, Feb 14, 49; m 89, Marshall Stuart; c Robert Marshall. *Educ:* Carnegie Mellon Univ, BS, 71; Univ Del, MS, 75; Idaho State Univ, DA(math), 79. *Prof Exp:* Asst prof math, Bradley Univ, 79-85. *Concurrent Pos:* Am Soc Eng Educ fel, NASA-Johnson Space Ctr, 83 & 84, Naval Ship Res, 85; Air Force Off Sci Res fel, Kirkland AFB, 87. *Mem:* Math Asn Am; Am Math Soc; Soc Indust & Appl Math; Nat Coun Teachers Math; Am Asn Univ Profs. *Res:* Use of technology, especially a graphing calculator, to enhance the learning of mathematics, especially calculus. *Mailing Add:* Dept Math & Comput Sci Fairfield Univ Fairfield CT 06430. *Fax:* 203-254-4126; *E-Mail:* weiss@fair1.fairfield.edu

**WEISS, JONAS,** PRODUCT SAFETY & REGULATORY COMPLIANCE, PRODUCT REGISTRATIONS. *Current Pos:* group leader polymer applns, 74-80, sr staff scientist, 80-84, DIR PROD SAFETY & REGULATORY AFFAIRS, CIBA-GEIGY CORP, 84- *Personal Data:* b New York, NY, Feb 17, 34; m 59; c 3. *Educ:* City Col New York, BS, 55; NY Univ, PhD(phys chem), 62. *Prof Exp:* Chemist, Esso Res & Eng Co, 62-64; supvr org & polymer chem, Am Standard Co, 64-70; group leader polymer chem, Nat Patent Develop Corp, 70-74. *Mem:* Am Chem Soc; Soc Plastics Indust. *Res:* Polymers and plastics for composites, coatings, sealants, adhesives and binders; permeability and rate of release of polymers; polymers and plastics for building materials; foam insulation; indicators and controls; semi-permeable membranes; ion-exchange polymers. *Mailing Add:* CIBA Specialty Chem Corp 281 Fields Lane Brewster NY 10509. *Fax:* 914-785-3476; *E-Mail:* jonas.weiss@usbw.mhs.ciba.com

**WEISS, JOSEPH FRANCIS,** BIOCHEMISTRY, RADIOBIOLOGY. *Current Pos:* res chemist biochem & radiobiol, Armed Forces Radiobiol Res Inst, 74-76, chief, Physiol Chem Div, 78-86, chief, Radioprotection Div, 86-91, chief, Res Requirements Div, 91-92, SUPVR RES CHEMIST, ARMED FORCES RADIOBIOL RES INST, 92- *Personal Data:* b Taylor, Pa, Jan 26, 40; m 68, Elvira deCastro; c Joseph & Michael. *Educ:* Univ Scranton, BS, 61; Ohio State Univ, MS, 63, PhD(physiol chem). 66. *Prof Exp:* NIH fel neurochem, Inst Pharmacol, Univ Milan, Italy, 66-68; instr neurosurg in biochem cancer, Med Ctr, NY Univ, 68-72, asst prof exp neurosurg, 72-74. *Concurrent Pos:* Vis prof, Univ Cagliari, Italy, 88, Univ Pisa, Italy, 90-92. *Mem:* Am Chem Soc; Europ Radiation Biol; Am Asn Cancer Res; Am Soc Clin Oncol; Radiation Res Soc. *Res:* Biochemical markers of cancer and radiation injury; glycoproteins, lipids, trace metals; radiobiology; immunopharmacology; neurochemistry; carcinogenesis; radio protection. *Mailing Add:* EH-63 230CC US Dept Energy 19901 Germantown Rd Germantown MD 20874-1290. *Fax:* 301-295-1032; *E-Mail:* weiss@vax.afrri.usuhs.mil

**WEISS, JOSEPH JACOB,** RHEUMATOLOGY. *Current Pos:* Asst dir, Rheum Sect, 72, ATTEND PHYSICIAN, WAYNE COUNTY GEN HOSP, 71-; ASST PROF INTERNAL MED, MED SCH, UNIV MICH, 72- *Personal Data:* b Detroit, Mich, Mar 22, 34; m 68; c 2. *Educ:* Univ Mich, BA, 55, MD, 61. *Concurrent Pos:* Rheumatol consult, Vet Admin Hosp, Ann Arbor, Mich, 75- *Mem:* Fel Am Col Physicians; Am Soc Clin Res; Am Fedn Clin Res. *Res:* Investigation of the etiology of frozen shoulder; use of arthrography to delineate the cause and assist the diagnosis of shoulder pain and immobility. *Mailing Add:* SAMC 18829 Farmington Rd Livonia MI 48152-3262

**WEISS, KARL H,** PHYSICAL CHEMISTRY. *Current Pos:* from asst prof to prof, Northeastern Univ, 61-91, chmn dept, 69-79, vprovost, res & grad studies, 79-83, vpres res & vprovost, 83-88, vpres acad develop, 88-91, interim vpres coop educ, 90-91, EMER PROF CHEM, NORTHEASTERN UNIV, 91- *Personal Data:* b Hamburg, Ger, June 21, 26; nat US; m 48, Madeleine Witsenhausen; c Carol Anne & Alan Edwin. *Educ:* Columbia Univ, BS, 51; NY Univ, PhD(chem), 57. *Hon Degrees:* DSc, Northeastern Univ, 93. *Prof Exp:* Res chemist, Color Res Corp, 47-50, tech adminr, 50-54; instr chem, NY Univ, 56-59, asst prof, 59-61. *Concurrent Pos:* NSF sr fel, Quantum Chem Group, Univ Uppsala, 68-69; Fulbright-Hayes scholar, 77-78; vis prof, Univ Konstanz, WGer, 77-78; dir, Mass Technol Park Corp, 82-, vchmn bd, 87-92 & 95-, chmn bd, 92-95; tour lectr, Am Chem Soc, 73-75, adv bd coop educ, 79-85, chmn Task Force Implement Report Chem Educ, 86-89; northeast regional lectr, Sigma Xi, 73-75. *Mem:* Am Chem Soc; NY Acad Sci; Royal Soc Chem; fel Am Inst Chem; Am Soc Photobiol; AAAS. *Res:* Photochemistry of complex molecules; laser photochemistry; quantum chemistry; charge transfer interaction. *Mailing Add:* Northeastern Univ 15 Tanglewood Rd Needham MA 02194. *E-Mail:* weiss@sprynet.com

**WEISS, KENNETH MONRAD,** GENETIC EPIDEMIOLOGY, BIOLOGICAL ANTHROPOLOGY. *Current Pos:* PROF GENETICS & HEAD DEPT ANTHROP, PA STATE UNIV, UNIVERSITY PARK, 85- *Personal Data:* b Cleveland, Ohio, Nov 29, 41; m 81; c 3. *Educ:* Oberlin Col, BA, 63; Univ Mich, MA, 69, PhD(biol anthrop), 72. *Honors & Awards:* Juan Comas Award, Am Asn Phys Anthropologists, 72; Leigh Lectr, Univ Utah, 85. *Prof Exp:* Res assoc human genetics, Med Sch, Univ Mich, 72-73; prof demog & pop genetics, Univ Tex Grad Sch Biomed Sci, Houston, 73-85. *Concurrent Pos:* Prof, Univ Tex Sch Pub Health, Houston, 74- *Mem:* AAAS; Am Asn Phys Anthropologists; Soc Epidemiol Res; Sigma Xi; Am Asn Human Genetics. *Res:* Demographic evolution of human populations; demographic genetic epidemiology of degenerative diseases; human evolution and biological anthropology. *Mailing Add:* Dept Anthrop Pa State Univ 409 Carpenter University Park PA 16802

**WEISS, KLAUDIUSZ ROBERT,** NEUROBIOLOGY. *Current Pos:* PROF PHYSIOL & BIOPHYS, MT SINAI SCH MED, 90- *Personal Data:* b Le Mans, France, June 7, 44. *Educ:* Univ Warsaw, MA, 67; State Univ NY Stony Brook, PhD(psychol), 73. *Prof Exp:* Fel, Col Physicians & Surgeons, Columbia Univ, 73-76, asst prof, Dept Anat & Psychiat, Columbia Univ Col Physicians & Surgeons, 77-; sr res scientist, NY State Psychiat Inst, 76-90. *Mem:* Soc Neurosci; Am Soc Zool. *Res:* Analysis of the neural basis of behavioral plasticity. *Mailing Add:* Dept Physiol-City Univ NY Mt Sinai Sch Med One Gustave Levy Plaza New York NY 10029-6504

**WEISS, LAWRENCE H(EISLER),** PRODUCT DEVELOPMENT, PROCESS DESIGN & DEVELOPMENT. *Current Pos:* CONSULT, 93- *Personal Data:* b Chicago, Ill, May 14, 38; m 62, Ida Yvette Lerner; c Mark & Rachel. *Educ:* Ill Inst Technol, BS, 59; Univ Calif, Berkeley, MS, 62; Johns

Hopkins Univ, PhD(chem eng), 68. *Prof Exp:* Assoc develop engr, United Tech Ctr Div, United Aircraft Corp, 61-63; res scientist, Res & Develop Div, Union Camp Corp, NJ, 67-72; chem systs res specialist, Consol Edison Co NY, Inc, 72-75; sr technologist, Chem Systs Inc, 75-77, mgr eng proj, 77-82; managing partner, Energy Technol Assoc, 82-86; mgr, Process Indust Com Develop, Airco Indust Gases, 86-87; mgr, Bus Develop, Princeton Combustion Res Labs, 87-88; sr consult, Pa Consult Group, 89-93. *Concurrent Pos:* Mem, Interagency Flue Gas Desulfurization Task Force, US Environ Protection Agency; mem, Clean Fuels Task Force, Elec Power Res Inst; mem, Fossil Fuel & Advan Generation Cmt, Empire State Elec Energy Res Corp; Proj Adv Am Gas Asn, Dept Energy Joint Coal Gasification Demonstration Prog. *Mem:* Am Inst Chem Engrs; Am Chem Soc; Inst Elec & Electronics Engrs. *Res:* Chemical and biochemical process research and development; low volume manufacturing; product development; bioabsorbable materials; process design. *Mailing Add:* 301 State Rd Princeton NJ 08540. *Fax:* 609-921-8067; *E-Mail:* maraly@juno.com

**WEISS, LEON,** CELL BIOLOGY, IMMUNOLOGY. *Current Pos:* PROF CELL BIOL & CHMN DEPT ANIMAL BIOL, SCH VET MED, UNIV PA, 76- *Personal Data:* b Brooklyn, NY, Oct 4, 25; m 49; c 6. *Educ:* Long Island Col Med, MD, 48. *Prof Exp:* Intern med, Maimonides Hosp, Brooklyn, NY, 48-49, asst resident, 49-50; instr med, Col Med, State Univ NY Downstate Med Ctr, 52-53; lectr, Grad Sch, Univ Md, 54-55; assoc anat, Harvard Med Sch, 55-57, from asst prof to prof anat, 57-76, Sch Med, Johns Hopkins Univ. *Concurrent Pos:* USPHS res fel anat, Harvard Med Sch, 50-52; mem med mission to establish hemat lab, Nat Defense Med Ctr, Formosa, 55. *Mem:* Electron Micros Soc Am; Histochem Soc; Am Asn Anatomists; Tissue Cult Asn. *Res:* Microscopic anatomy; electron microscopy; histochemistry; tissue culture; connective tissues; reticuloendothelial system; histophysiology of the lympho-hematopoietic system; molecular biology. *Mailing Add:* Dept Animal Biol Univ Pa Sch Vet Med 3800 Spruce St Philadelphia PA 19104-6046

**WEISS, LEONARD,** APPLIED MATHEMATICS, ENGINEERING. *Current Pos:* MINORITY STAFF DIR, US SENATE COMT GOVT AFFAIRS, 87- *Personal Data:* b Brooklyn, NY, Mar 14, 34; m 58; c 2. *Educ:* City Col New York, BEE, 56; Columbia Univ, MSEE, 59; Johns Hopkins Univ, PhD(elec eng), 62. *Hon Degrees:* MA, Brown Univ, 66. *Prof Exp:* Lectr elec eng, City Col New York, 56-59; staff scientist, Res Inst Adv Studies, 62-64; from asst prof to assoc prof appl math & eng, Brown Univ, 64-68; prof elec eng, Inst Fluid Dynamics & Appl Math, Univ Md, College Park, 68-78; staff dir, Subcomt Energy, Nuclear Proliferation & Fed Serv, US Senate, 77-86. *Concurrent Pos:* Alfred P Sloan res fel, 66-68; res mathematician, Naval Res Lab, Washington, DC, 70-77; legis asst to Sen John Glenn, 76-77; Cong sci fel, Inst Elec & Electronics Engrs, 76-77. *Mem:* AAAS; Am Math Soc; Soc Indust & Appl Math; Math Asn Am; Inst Elec & Electronics Engrs. *Res:* System theory; control theory; signal theory; analysis and structure of dynamical systems described by differential equations; nuclear proliferation. *Mailing Add:* Minority Staff Dir US Senate Comt Govt Affair 340 Dirksen Senate Bldg Rm 326 Washington DC 20510

**WEISS, LEONARD,** PATHOLOGY, CELL BIOLOGY. *Current Pos:* res prof biophys, 65-74, res prof dermat, 74-91, EMER PROF EXP PATH, SCH MED STATE UNIV NY, BUFFALO, 91- *Personal Data:* b London, Eng, June 15, 28; m 51, Maureen A Jones; c Gregory, Simon & Emma. *Educ:* Cambridge Univ, BA, 50, MA, MB, BChir, 53, MD, 58, PhD(biol), 63, ScD, 71, FRC, Path, FCAP. *Prof Exp:* House physician, Westminster Hosp, Univ London, 54-55, resident pathologist, res assoc & registr morbid anat, Med Sch, 55-58; mem sci staff, Med Res Coun, Nat Inst Med Res, London, 58-60 & Strangeways Res Lab, Cambridge Univ, 60-64; dir cancer res & chief cancer res clinician, Dept Exp Path, Roswell Park Mem Inst, 64-93. *Mem:* Fel AAAS; Path Soc Gt Brit & Ireland; fel Royal Col Path; fel Brit Inst Biol; fel Col Am Pathologists. *Res:* Metastasis; biophysics of cell contact phenomena. *Mailing Add:* 60 Willowbrook Dr Williamsville NY 14221-6930. *Fax:* 716-633-0220

**WEISS, LIONEL EDWARD,** geology, for more information see previous edition

**WEISS, LIONEL IRA,** MATHEMATICAL STATISTICS. *Current Pos:* assoc prof, 57-61, PROF OPERS RES, CORNELL UNIV, 61- *Personal Data:* b New York, NY, Sept 5, 23; m 46; c 3. *Educ:* Columbia Univ, BA, 43, MA, 45, PhD(math statist), 53. *Prof Exp:* From asst prof to assoc prof statist, Univ Va, 49-56; assoc prof math, Univ Ore, 56-57. *Concurrent Pos:* Mem, Nat Res Coun, 66-69. *Mem:* Inst Math Statist; NY Acad Sci; Sigma Xi. *Res:* Statistical decision theory; asymptotic statistical theory. *Mailing Add:* Oper Res Dept 200 ETC Bldg Cornell Univ Ithaca NY 14853

**WEISS, MALCOLM PICKETT,** GEOLOGY. *Current Pos:* ADJ PROF, UNIV CALIF, SANTA BARBARA, 94- *Personal Data:* b Washington, DC, June 28, 21; wid; c Rolfe C, Malcolm A, Kathleen C & Carolyn J. *Educ:* Univ Minn, PhD(geol), 53. *Prof Exp:* From instr to assoc prof geol, Ohio State Univ, 52-67; chmn dept, Northern Ill Univ, 67-72, prof, 67-88, emer prof, 88-94. *Mem:* Geol Soc Am; Soc Econ Paleontologists & Mineralogists; Am Asn Petrol Geologists; AAAS. *Res:* Stratigraphy; sedimentary petrography; carbonate petrology; history of geology. *Mailing Add:* Dept Geol Sci Univ Calif Santa Barbara CA 93106. *Fax:* 815-753-1445

**WEISS, MARK LAWRENCE,** PRIMATOLOGY, PHYSICAL ANTHROPOLOGY. *Current Pos:* From asst prof to assoc prof, 69-87, CHMN, DEPT ANTHROP, WAYNE STATE UNIV, 83-, PROF, 87- *Personal Data:* b Brooklyn, NY, Nov 1, 45; m 93, Linda Smith; c 2. *Educ:*

State Univ NY Binghamton, BA, 66; Univ Calif, Berkeley, MA, 68, PhD(anthrop), 69. *Concurrent Pos:* Adj prof anat, Sch Med, Wayne State Univ, 69-; fel, William Beaumont Hosp, 74; res assoc genetics, Leicester Univ, UK, 82-83; on leave, NSF, 90-91 & 96. *Mem:* AAAS; Am Anthrop Asn; Am Asn Phys Anthropologists; Brit Soc Study Human Biol; Am Asn Anthrop Genetics. *Res:* Biochemical and DNA polymorphisms; primate genetics; primate microevolution. *Mailing Add:* Dept Anthrop Wayne State Univ Detroit MI 48202. *Fax:* 313-577-5958

**WEISS, MARTIN,** GEOLOGY. *Current Pos:* RETIRED. *Personal Data:* b New York, NY, Jan 21, 19; m 49; c 3. *Educ:* City Col New York, BS, 48; Univ Mich, MS, 51, PhD(geol), 54. *Prof Exp:* Asst geol, Mus Paleont, Univ Mich, 51-53; geologist, US Geol Surv, 53-63; oceanogr, Nat Oceanog Data Ctr, 63-72, marine geologist, Nat Geophys & Solar Terrestrial Data Ctr, Nat Oceanic & Atmospheric Admin, 68-75; mem staff, US Geol Surv, Reston, 75-86. *Mem:* Geol Soc Am; Am Geophys Union; Marine Technol Soc. *Res:* Geological oceanography; military geology; Paleozoic ostracoda; review of environmental impact statements. *Mailing Add:* 3710 Prado Pl FAirfax VA 22031

**WEISS, MARTIN JOSEPH,** ORGANIC CHEMISTRY. *Current Pos:* res chemist, Pharmaceut Res Dept, Calco Chem Div, Am Cyanamid Co, 50-54, group leader, 54-75, dept head, 75-83, ASSOC DIR PHARMACEUT RES, LEDERLE LABS, AM CYANAMID CO, 83- *Personal Data:* b New York, NY, May 4, 23; m 51; c 3. *Educ:* NY Univ, AB, 44; Duke Univ, PhD(chem), 49. *Prof Exp:* Asst, Duke Univ, 44-47; res fel org chem, Hickrill Chem Res Found, 49-50. *Concurrent Pos:* Asst, Comt Med Res, Off Sci Res & Develop, Duke Univ, 44-45. *Mem:* Am Chem Soc. *Res:* Synthetic medicinal chemistry in prostaglandins, antibiotics, steroids, nucleosides and carbohydrates, indoles and other heterocyclics; chemotherapy; anti-arthritic, anti-allergy, anti-atherosclerotic and hypoglycemic agents. *Mailing Add:* 1600 Parker Ave Apt 20F Ft Lee NJ 07024

**WEISS, MARVIN,** PHARMACEUTICAL CHEMISTRY, SCIENCE ADMINISTRATION. *Current Pos:* RETIRED. *Personal Data:* b New York, NY, Feb 6, 14; m 40; c Kenneth, Janet & Phyllis. *Educ:* Brooklyn Col, BS, 37; Univ Ill, MS, 38. *Prof Exp:* Dir, develop & control labs, Am Pharmaceut Co, 41-57; dir, anal lab, Berkeley Chem Corp, 57-66; group leader, corp control & anal, Millmaster Onyx Corp, 66, dir, anal lab, Berkeley Chem Corp, 66-78, corp tech dir, 66-78, tech dir, AGross & Co, 78-83. *Concurrent Pos:* Group consult, Mantrose-Hauser Div, US Printing Ink Div, Onyx Div & Carboquimica SA Div, 65-83. *Mem:* Am Chem Soc; Am Oil Chemists Soc. *Res:* Urethanes; nitrogen heterocycles; multiple condensations; acetic acid-ammonium acetate reactions with carbonyl compounds; crossed Cannizzaro syntheses; urea reactions; radiation curable inks and coatings; fatty acids and fatty acid derivates; shellac and shellac derivatives. *Mailing Add:* 227 Elkwood Ave New Providence NJ 07974-1816

**WEISS, MAX LESLIE,** MATHEMATICS. *Current Pos:* from asst prof to prof, 64-91, EMER PROF MATH, UNIV CALIF, SANTA BARBARA, 91- *Personal Data:* b Salt Lake City, Utah, Aug 12, 33; m 71, Karen; c Karen, Karl, Frieda, Ellen & Dan. *Educ:* Yale Univ, BA, 55; Cornell Univ, MS, 58; Univ Wash, PhD(math), 62. *Prof Exp:* Instr math, Reed Col, 58-60 & Univ Wash, 62-63; NSF fel, Inst Advan Study, 63-64. *Concurrent Pos:* Assoc provost, Col Creative Studies, 71-77, 83-84, actg provost, 84-86, provost, 86-89, assoc provost, 89-90. *Res:* Function algebras and complex variables. *Mailing Add:* 363 C Cannon Green Dr Goleta CA 93117

**WEISS, MAX TIBOR,** PHYSICS. *Current Pos:* RETIRED. *Personal Data:* b Hungary, Dec 29, 22; nat US; m 53; c 4. *Educ:* Mass Inst Technol, MS, 47, PhD(physics), 51. *Honors & Awards:* Centennial Medal, Inst Elec & Electronics Engrs, 84, Frederick Philips Award, 93. *Prof Exp:* Engr, Radio Corp Am, 43-44 & US Naval Ord Lab, 45-46; res assoc, Milrowave Spectros Lab, Mass Inst Technol, 46-50; mem tech staff, Bell Tel Labs, Inc, 50-59; assoc dept mgr, Appl Physics Dept, Hughes Aircraft Corp, 59-61; dir, Electronics Lab, Aerospace Corp, 61-63, gen mgr, Labs Div, 63-67, asst mgr eng opers, TRW Systs, 67-68; gen mgr, Electronics & Optics Div, Aerospace Corp, 68-78, vpres & gen mgr lab opers, 78-81, vpres eng group, 81-86; vpres, Tech & Electronics Syst Group, Northrop Grumman Corp, 86-91, vpres & gen mgr, Electronics Syst Div, 91-94, corp vpres & dept gen mgr, Electronics Systs & Integration, 94-96, corp vpres. *Concurrent Pos:* Lectr, City Col New York, 53. *Mem:* Nat Acad Eng; fel Inst Elec & Electronics Engrs; fel Am Phys Soc; AAAS. *Res:* Microwaves; magnetics; quantum electronics; communications; microelectronics. *Mailing Add:* 2185 Guthrie Dr Los Angeles CA 90034

**WEISS, MICHAEL DAVID,** MATHEMATICAL ECONOMICS, BEHAVIOR UNDER UNCERTAINTY. *Current Pos:* math statistician, 76-85, AGR ECONOMIST, ECON RES SERV, USDA, 85- *Personal Data:* b Chicago, Ill, Nov 12, 42. *Educ:* Brandeis Univ, BA, 64; Brown Univ, PhD(math), 70; Univ Md, MA, 84. *Prof Exp:* Asst prof math, Wayne State Univ, 69-74; analyst, Ketron Inc, 74-76. *Concurrent Pos:* Intergovt personnel act fel, US Dept Agr, 78; vis lectr, Soc Indust & Appl Math, 92-, pres, Wash-Baltimore sect, Soc Indust & Appl Math, 92- *Mem:* Am Agr Econ Asn; Am Math Soc; Soc Indust & Appl Math. *Res:* Economic theory of behavior under uncertainty; mathematical economics; probability and statistics; ergodic theory; theory of fuzzy sets; mathematical applications in agriculture. *Mailing Add:* 7797 Heatherton Lane Potomac MD 20854-3264. *Fax:* 202-219-0477; *E-Mail:* mdweiss@econ.ag.gov

**WEISS, MICHAEL JOHN,** PEST MANAGEMENT. *Current Pos:* ASST PROF ENTOM, NDAK STATE UNIV, 85- *Personal Data:* b St Paul, Minn, June 13, 55. *Educ:* Purdue Univ, BS, 77; Ohio State Univ, MS, 79; Univ Nebr, PhD(entom), 83. *Prof Exp:* Asst prof res, Mont State Univ, 83-85. *Mem:* Sigma Xi; Entom Soc Am. *Res:* Applied insect ecology; agroecosystem research. *Mailing Add:* Dept Entom NDak State Univ Main Campus PO Box 5346 Fargo ND 58105-5346

**WEISS, MICHAEL STEPHEN,** SPEECH & HEARING SCIENCES, SPEECH PATHOLOGY. *Current Pos:* assoc prof dept speech path & audiol, 78-84, PROF DEPT COMMUN DIS, WEST CHESTER UNIV, 84- *Personal Data:* b Queens Co, NY, Mar 20, 43; m 65; c 2. *Educ:* Long Island Univ, BA, 64; Purdue Univ, MS, 68, PhD(speech sci), 70. *Prof Exp:* Coordr res, Cleveland Hearing & Speech Ctr & sr res assoc speech sci, Case Western Res Univ, 70-71; asst prof speech, Howard Univ, 71-72; instr laryngol & otol & sci dir, Info Ctr Hearing, Speech & Dis Human Commun, Sch Med, Johns Hopkins Univ, 72-76; coordr continuing educ media, Boys Town Inst Commun Dis Children, 76-78. *Concurrent Pos:* Lectr, Gallaudet Col, 74-76; assoc prof otolaryngol, Creighton Univ, 76-78. *Mem:* Am Speech & Hearing Asn; Acoust Soc Am; NY Acad Sci. *Res:* Speech science; physiological and acoustical events which underlie speech production and perception. *Mailing Add:* Dept Commun Dis West Chester Univ 700 S High St West Chester PA 19383-0002

**WEISS, MITCHELL JOSEPH,** INVERTEBRATE ZOOLOGY. *Current Pos:* asst prof biol, 74-81, vis asst prof, 81-82, GUEST INVESTR, RUTGERS UNIV, NEW BRUNSWICK, 82- *Personal Data:* b Chicago, Ill, Nov 12, 42. *Educ:* Brown Univ, ScB, 64; Univ Mich, PhD(zool), 70; Rutgers Univ, MLS, 88. *Prof Exp:* Instr zool, Univ Iowa, 73-74. *Concurrent Pos:* NIH res fel, Univ Wash, 70-73; prin investr NSF res grant, 76-78; consult, Oriel Corp, 83. *Mem:* Am Soc Info Sci; Am Micros Soc; Int Asn Meiobenthologists. *Res:* Functional and comparative anatomy and development of insect brain centers at microscopic and ultrastructural levels; biology of phylum Gastrotricha; current emphasis on sexuality, life cycles and systematics of freshwater gastrotrichs. *Mailing Add:* 51-B Phelps Ave New Brunswick NJ 08901

**WEISS, NOEL SCOTT,** EPIDEMIOLOGY, BIOSTATISTICS. *Current Pos:* from asst prof to assoc prof, 73-79, chmn dept, 84-93, PROF, DEPT EPIDEMIOL, SCH PUB HEALTH & COMMUNITY MED, UNIV WASH, SEATTLE, 79- *Personal Data:* b Chicago, Ill, Mar 10, 43. *Educ:* Stanford Univ, AB, 65, MD, 67; Harvard Univ, MPH, 69, DrPH, 71. *Prof Exp:* Epidemiologist, Nat Ctr Health Statist, 71-73. *Concurrent Pos:* Asst mem, Fred Hutchinson Cancer Res Ctr, Seattle, Wash, 74-76, assoc mem, 76-82, mem, 82-; Nat Cancer Inst res grants, 75-; assoc ed, Cancer Epidemiol & Prev, 87-90; chair, Adv Comt Occup Studies Sect, Environ Epidemiol Br & mem, Bd Sci counselors, Div Cancer Etiology, Nat Cancer Inst, NIH; mem, Adv Comt Study Intermediate Outcome Breast Cancer, Ctr Health Studies, Group Health Coop, 88-90, Cancer Epidemiol Pac Basin, Hawaii, 89 & Workshop Etiology Mult Myeloma, Nat Cancer Inst, 90. *Mem:* Nat Acad Sci. *Res:* Endocrinologic determinants of disease; author of 160 technical publications. *Mailing Add:* Dept Epidemiol Box 357236 Univ Wash Seattle WA 98195. *E-Mail:* nweiss@u.wa.edu

**WEISS, NORMAN JAY,** MATHEMATICAL ANALYSIS. *Current Pos:* asst prof, 71-72, ASSOC PROF MATH, QUEENS COL, NY, 73- *Personal Data:* b Brooklyn, NY, May 28, 42; m 65; c 2. *Educ:* Harvard Univ, BA, 63; Princeton Univ, PhD, 66. *Prof Exp:* Instr math, Princeton Univ, 66-68; asst prof, Columbia Univ, 68-71. *Mem:* Am Math Soc. *Res:* Real and Fourier analysis. *Mailing Add:* Dept Math Queens Col 65-30 Kissena Blvd Flushing NY 11367-0904

**WEISS, PAUL STORCH,** SURFACE CHEMISTRY, SURFACE PHYSICS. *Current Pos:* asst prof, 89-95, ASSOC PROF CHEM, PA STATE UNIV, 95- *Personal Data:* b Ithaca, NY, Oct 10, 59; m 82, Kendall L Munk; c Walter P, Lucien E & Maxwell K. *Educ:* Mass Inst Technol, SB & SM, 80; Univ Calif, Berkeley, PhD(phys chem), 86. *Honors & Awards:* Nobel Laureate Signature Award, Am Chem Soc, 96. *Prof Exp:* Mem tech staff, AT&T Bell Labs, 86-88. *Concurrent Pos:* Vis scientist, Almaden Res Ctr, IBM Corp, 88-89; NSF presidential young investr, 91; Alfred P Sloan Found fel, 95; John Simon Guggenheim Mem Found fel, 97. *Mem:* Am Chem Soc; Am Phys Soc; Sigma Xi; Am Vacuum Soc; Mats Res Soc. *Res:* Analytical and physical chemistry; surface chemistry and physics; low temperature scanning tunneling microscopy; solid state chemistry; novel techniques for imaging, spectroscopy and detection; single molecule separations and detection. *Mailing Add:* Dept Chem 152 Davey Lab Pa State Univ University Park PA 16802. *Fax:* 814-863-8081; *E-Mail:* stm@psu.edu

**WEISS, PHILIP,** ORGANIC CHEMISTRY. *Current Pos:* ADJ PROF, DEPT CHEM, OAKLAND UNIV, 80- *Personal Data:* b New York, NY, June 12, 16; m 43; c 2. *Educ:* NY Univ, BS, 39, MSc, 41, PhD(org chem), 48. *Honors & Awards:* Exner Medal, 69. *Prof Exp:* Res chemist, Lederle Labs, Am Cyanamid Co, 41-46; sr res chemist, Wallace & Tiernan Prod, Inc, 46-52; sr proj chemist, Colgate-Palmolive Co, 52-57; sr res scientist, Electrochem Dept, Res Labs, Gen Motors Corp, 57-58, asst head electrochem & polymers dept, 58-59, head, Polymers Dept, Res Labs, 59-81. *Concurrent Pos:* Instr, Cooper 49-51; ed, J Appl Polymer Sci; mem, Comt Crit & Strategic Mat, Nat Mat Adv Bd, Adv Bd, Col Eng, Univ Detroit & Adv Bd, Polymer Prog, Col Eng, Princeton Univ; US rep, Plastics & High Polymers Sect, Int Union Pure & Appl Chem; proj mgr, Paint Res Inst. *Mem:* Am Chem Soc; Soc Plastics Engrs. *Res:* Polymer synthesis, research and development in plastics, rubber, adhesives and surface coatings; graft and block copolymers; mechanisms of finish failure; adhesion and cohesion; mechanical behavior of polymers; polymer flammability, aging, waste disposal and processing; electrically conducting polymers. *Mailing Add:* 520 S Cranbrook Cross Rd Bloomfield Hills MI 48301-3433

**WEISS, RAINER,** PHYSICS. *Current Pos:* from asst prof to assoc prof, 64-73, PROF PHYSICS, MASS INST TECHNOL, 73- *Personal Data:* b Berlin, Ger, Sept 29, 32; US citizen; m 59; c 2. *Educ:* Mass Inst Technol, BS, 55, PhD(physics), 62. *Honors & Awards:* Achievement Award, NASA, 84, Group Achievement Award, 90. *Prof Exp:* Asst prof physics, Tufts Univ, 60-62; res assoc, Princeton Univ, 62-64. *Concurrent Pos:* Phys sci comt, NASA, 70-74, Mgt Opers Working Group, Shuttle Astron, 73-76, Airborne Astron, 73-86, chmn, Panel Exp Relativity & Gravitation, 74-76, SSSC comt, 79-82, Infrared Detector Panel 78, Space & Earth Sci Adv Comt, 82; chmn subcomt gravitational physics, NSF, 78, coordr panel interferometric observ for gravitational waves, 86; mem, Nat Acad Space Sci Bd, 83-86; mem, Panel Joint Inst Lab Astrophys, Bd Assessment of NBS Progs, Nat Acad Sci, 85- *Mem:* AAAS; Am Phys Soc; Am Astron Soc. *Res:* Experimental atomic physics, atomic clocks, laser physics; experimental gravitation; millimeter and sub-millimeter astronomy; cosmic background measurements. *Mailing Add:* Dept Physics Mass Inst Technol 77 Massachusetts Ave Cambridge MA 02139

**WEISS, RICHARD GERALD,** PHOTOCHEMISTRY, PHYSICAL ORGANIC CHEMISTRY. *Current Pos:* from asst prof to assoc prof, 70-85, PROF CHEM, GEORGETOWN UNIV UNIV, 86- *Personal Data:* b Akron, Ohio, Nov 13, 42. *Educ:* Brown Univ, ScB, 65; Univ Conn, MS, 67, PhD(chem), 69. *Prof Exp:* NIH res fel chem, Calif Inst Technol, 69-71; vis prof, Inst Chem, Univ Sao Paulo, 71-74. *Concurrent Pos:* Nat Acad Sci overseas fel, 71-74; vis scientist, Max Planck Inst Radiation Chem, 81-82; vis prof, Nat Superior Sch Chem, Strasbourg, 82 & Univ Bordeaux, 82; consult, World Bank, 83-; vis prof, Indian Inst Sci, Bangalore, India, 89-90. *Mem:* Am Chem Soc; InterAm Photochem Soc; Europ Photochem Asn; Am Asn Univ Professors. *Res:* Mechanisms and rates of organic and photochemical reactions; steric effects in electronic energy transfer and in decay of excited states; mechanistic studies in ordered media. *Mailing Add:* Dept Chemistry Georgetown Univ Washington DC 20057-0002

**WEISS, RICHARD JEROME,** PHYSICS, SCIENTIFIC POPULARIZATION. *Current Pos:* RETIRED. *Personal Data:* b New York, NY, Dec 14, 23; m 59, Daphne Watson; c Randi, Catharine & Christopher. *Educ:* City Col New York, BS, 44; Univ Calif, MA, 47; NY Univ, PhD(physics), 50. *Honors & Awards:* Rockefeller Pub Serv Award, 56. *Prof Exp:* Physicist, US Army Mat Res Ctr, 50-80; prof, Univ Surrey, England, 81-85 & Kings Col, London, 80-90. *Concurrent Pos:* Vis fel, Cavendish Labs, Cambridge Univ, 56-57; lectr, Mass Inst Technol, 59; Secy Army fel, Imp Col, Univ London, 62-63; chmn, Comn Electron Distributions, Int Union Crystallog, 72-75; ed, Int J Optical Sensors, 85-90; contrib ed, Lasers & Optronics, 90- & O/E Reports, 93- *Mem:* Am Phys Soc; Am Crystallog Soc. *Res:* Solid state, neutron and x-ray physics; electron structure of solids, materials; lasers; optoelectronics. *Mailing Add:* 4 Lawson St Avon MA 02322

**WEISS, RICHARD LOUIS,** BIOCHEMISTRY, GENETICS. *Current Pos:* from asst prof to assoc prof, 74-85, PROF BIOCHEM, UNIV CALIF, LOS ANGELES, 85- *Personal Data:* b Evanston, Ill, June 24, 44; m 84, Marjorie A McPeak. *Educ:* Univ Mich, BS, 66; Univ Wash, PhD(biochem), 71. *Prof Exp:* USPHS fel, Univ Mich, 71-72; Am Cancer Soc fel, 72-73. *Concurrent Pos:* USPHS fel, Stanford Univ, 90-91. *Mem:* Am Chem Soc; Am Soc Microbiol; Genetics Soc Am; Am Soc Biochem & Molecular Biol. *Res:* Regulation of amino acid metabolism in eucaryotic microorganisms. *Mailing Add:* Biochem Univ Claif 405 Hilgard Ave Los Angeles CA 90095-1569. *Fax:* 310-206-4038; *E-Mail:* rlw@chem.ucla.edu

**WEISS, RICHARD RONALD,** MECHANICAL ENGINEERING, ROCKET PROPULSION. *Current Pos:* RETIRED. *Personal Data:* b Detroit, Mich, Nov 11, 34; m 57, Sally Anita Sparkman; c Mark, Kevin, Todd & Scott. *Educ:* Univ Mich, BS, 57; Univ Southern Calif, MSME, 64; Purdue Univ, PhD(mech eng), 70. *Honors & Awards:* Wyld Propulsion Award, Am Inst Aeronaut & Astronaut, 94. *Prof Exp:* Develop engr, Jupiter Missile Rocket Engine, Rocketdyne, 57-58; unit chief & test comdr, THOR Missile test prog, Air Force Rocket Propulsion Lab, 58-61, various tech positions, 61-65, various eng mgt positions, 65-74, chief scientist, 74-89, 1st dir, Strategic Defense Initiative Tech Off, 85-87, dir, Astronaut Lab, 89-90, chief scientist & dir, 90-91, dir propulsion, Phillips Lab Oper Location, 91-93; dep dir space launch systs & technol, Off Under Secy of Def, Strategic & Space Systs, Missiles & Space Systs, 93-94. *Concurrent Pos:* US Rep, Agard Propulsion & Energetics Panel, Paris, 87-; mem, Nat Res Coun Aeronaut & Space Eng Bd, Advan Space Tech Panel, Washington, 92-94; tech panel chmn, Space Launch Modernization Plan, 94. *Mem:* Fel Am Inst Aeronaut & Astronaut. *Res:* Rocket propulsion developments for most of the nations space and missile systems, including Apollo Space Shuttle, Titan, Atlas, Peace Keeper, Minuteman, Strategic Defense Initiative. *Mailing Add:* 5912 Walnut Way Palmdale CA 93551-2812

**WEISS, ROBERT ALAN,** POLYMER SCIENCE. *Current Pos:* ASSOC PROF, DEPT CHEM ENG, UNIV CONN, 81- *Personal Data:* b Cleveland, Ohio, Oct 29, 50. *Educ:* Northwestern Univ, BS, 72; Univ Mass, PhD(chem eng), 76. *Prof Exp:* Res engr, Exxon Chem Co, 75-77; staff engr, Exxon Res & Eng Co, 77-81. *Concurrent Pos:* Vis prof, Stevens Inst Tech, 80; chmn, Eng Property Struct Div, Am Chem Soc, 83-86 & Plastics Anal Div, 85-86. *Mem:* Soc Plastics Engrs; Am Chem Soc; Soc Rheol; NAm Thermal Anal Soc. *Res:* Polymer structure; property relationships; ionomers; composite materials. *Mailing Add:* Inst Mat Sci Conn Univ 97 N Eagleville Rd Storrs CT 06269-3136

**WEISS, ROBERT JEROME,** PSYCHIATRY, PUBLIC HEALTH. *Current Pos:* prof psychiat & social med, Col Physicians & Surgeons, Columbia Univ, 75-86, dir community health systs, 75-86, Delemar prof pub health pract & dean, 80-86, EMER DEAN, SCH PUB HEALTH, COLUMBIA UNIV, 86-, EMER DELEMAR PROF, 86-, EMER PROF SOCIAL MED & PSYCHIAT, 86- *Personal Data:* b West New York, NJ, Dec 9, 17; m 45, Minnie Moore; c Scott, J Woodrow & Elizabeth. *Educ:* George Washington Univ, AB, 47; Columbia Univ, MD, 51. *Hon Degrees:* MA, Dartmouth Col, 64. *Honors & Awards:* Bi-Centennial Medal, Columbia Univ Col Physicians & Surgeons, 67. *Prof Exp:* Intern, Columbia Div, Bellevue Hosp, 51, asst resident med, 53; resident psychiat, Columbia Psychoanal Clin, 54-59; chief, Mary Hitchcock Mem Hosp, Hanover, NH, 59-70; vis prof, Ctr Community Health & Med Care, Harvard Med Sch, 70-75, assoc dir, 70-75, assoc dean health care progs, 71-75. *Concurrent Pos:* NIMH career teacher trainee, Columbia Univ, 56-58; resident, NY State Psychiat Inst & Presby Hosp, NY, 57; asst attend, Vanderbilt Clin, 57-58 & Presby Hosp, 58-59; assoc, Col Physicians & Surgeons, Columbia Univ, 57-59; consult, NH Div Ment Health, 59-70, Vet Admin Hosp, White River Junction, Vt, 60-70 & Bur Health Manpower Educ, 72-; prof psychiat & chmn dept, Dartmouth Med Sch, 59-70; chmn adv comn, NH Dept Health & Welfare, 61; coordr panel, NIMH, 65-67, chmn subcomt psychiat, 67-68; psychiatrist, Beth Israel Hosp, 70-75; attend, Presby Hosp, NY, 75-; consult, Nat Ctr Health Serv Res, 75- & NIMH, 77-; vis scholar, Univ Calif, 86-87; vis prof, Community Med, Univ NMex Med Sch, 87-; vis prof psychiat, Harvard Univ, 89- *Mem:* AAAS; fel Am Psychiat Asn; Am Asn Med Cols; Am Acad Psychoanal; NY Acad Sci. *Res:* Epidemiology; health care; preventive psychiatry; community medicine. *Mailing Add:* PO Box 579 Orono ME 04473-0579. *Fax:* 207-866-4437

**WEISS, ROBERT JOHN,** MATHEMATICS. *Current Pos:* assoc prof & head dept, 68-74, PROF MATH, MARY BALDWIN COL, 74- *Personal Data:* b Pomona, Calif, Apr 9, 37; m 64; c 2. *Educ:* La Verne Col, BA, 58; Univ Calif, Los Angeles, MA & PhD(math), 62. *Prof Exp:* Assoc prof math, Bridgewater Col, 62-68. *Mem:* Am Math Soc; Math Asn Am; Sigma Xi. *Res:* Algebraic topology. *Mailing Add:* 411 Rainbow Dr Staunton VA 24401-2139

**WEISS, ROBERT MARTIN,** UROLOGY, PHARMACOLOGY. *Current Pos:* instr surg-urol, Sch Med, Yale Univ, 67-68, asst prof urol, 68-71, assoc prof surg-urol, 71-76, PROF SURG-UROL, SCH MED, YALE UNIV, 76-, PROF & CHIEF UROL, 88- *Personal Data:* b New York, NY; m 73, Ilana Shemer; c Erik D & Dana A. *Educ:* Franklin & Marshall Col, BS, 57; State Univ NY Downstate Med Ctr, MD, 60. *Hon Degrees:* MA, Yale Univ, 76. *Honors & Awards:* Lifetime Achievement Award, Urodynamics Soc. *Prof Exp:* Intern med, Second (Cornell) Med Div, Bellevue Hosp, NY, 60-61; resident gen surg, Beth Israel Hosp, NY, 61-62; resident urol, Columbia-Presby Med Ctr, 63-64; fel, Col Physicians & Surgeons, Columbia Univ, 64-65; resident, Columbia-Presby Med Ctr, 65-67. *Concurrent Pos:* Res assoc pharmacol, Col Physicians & Surgeons, Columbia Univ, 67-75, adj assoc prof, 75-77, adj prof, 77-; attend, Yale-New Haven Hosp, 67-; consult, West Haven Vet Admin Hosp, 67- & Waterbury Hosp, 76-; mem obstruction & neuromuscular dis comt, Nat Inst Arthritis, Metab & Digestive Dis, 74-75; fel, Timothy Dwight Col, Yale Univ, 74-; asst ed, J Urol, 75-82; mem adv panel, US Pharmacopeia & Nat Formulary, 76-81, 86-91 & 95-; assoc sect ed, J Urol, 86- *Mem:* Am Physiol Soc; Soc Gen Physiologists; Am Acad Pediat; Am Col Surgeons; Am Urol Asn. *Res:* Studies of signal transduction in urinary tract smooth muscle and the role of nitric oxide in urinary tract infections and interstitial cystitis. *Mailing Add:* Urol Sect Sch Med Yale Univ 333 Cedar St New Haven CT 06510

**WEISS, ROGER HARVEY,** ANALYTICAL CHEMISTRY. *Current Pos:* from asst prof to prof, 59-89, EMER PROF CHEM, HUMBOLDT STATE UNIV, 89- *Personal Data:* b New York, NY, July 13, 26; m 53; c 2. *Educ:* Col Holy Cross, BNaval Sci, 46; Cornell Univ, AB, 50; Ga Inst Technol, PhD(chem), 68. *Prof Exp:* Instr chem, Univ Toledo, 54-57. *Concurrent Pos:* Fulbright lectr, Univ Sind, Pakistan, 73-74. *Mem:* Am Chem Soc. *Res:* Titrimetry with solid titrants; trace analysis; chelation; absorption spectrophotometry; photometric titrations. *Mailing Add:* 5118 Jacoby Creek Rd Bayside CA 95527

**WEISS, ROLAND GEORGE,** INDUSTRIAL ENGINEERING. *Current Pos:* CHIEF ENGR, CTA INC, ROCKVILLE, MD, 88- *Personal Data:* b Milwaukee, Wis, July 11, 49. *Educ:* Univ Wis-Milwaukee, BS, 72; Northwestern Univ, MS, 75, PhD(indust eng), 76. *Prof Exp:* Oper res analyst technol policy, Exp Technol Incentives Prog, Ctr Field Methods, Nat Bur Standards, 76-79; systs engr, Bell Labs, 79-83. *Concurrent Pos:* Prof rels vchmn, Col Pub Progs & Processes, Inst Mgt Sci, 77-81. *Mem:* AAAS; Am Inst Indust Engrs; Am Psychol Asn; Inst Elec & Electronics Engrs; Inst Mgt Sci. *Res:* Development of methodology for analyzing complex, unstructured problems, including systems analysis, decision and architectural design and administrative experimentation; systems engineering of large, advanced systems with hardware, software, organizational market components. *Mailing Add:* 7375 Executive Pl Seabrook MD 20706

**WEISS, RONALD,** FOOD SCIENCE. *Current Pos:* RES PROG MGR, FOOD RES INST, UNIV WIS-MADISON, 95- *Personal Data:* b Chicago, Ill, Jan 29, 37; m 67; c 3. *Educ:* Ariz State Univ, BS, 58, MS, 59; Mich State Univ, PhD(chem), 64, MBA, 67. *Prof Exp:* Res chemist, Miles Labs, Inc, 64-67, proj coordr, 67-69, mgr prod develop, 69-73, dir growth & develop, 73-75, dir planning, 75-80; pres, Rhone Poulenc, 80-95. *Mem:* Am Chem Soc; Inst Food Technologists; Soft Drink Technologists Asn; Sigma Xi. *Mailing Add:* Food Res Inst Univ Wis 1925 Willow Dr Madison WI 53706

**WEISS, ROY E,** ENDOCRINOLOGY. *Current Pos:* Instr, 86-90, ASST PROF MED, UNIV CHICAGO MED CTR, 90- *Personal Data:* b Philadelphia, Pa, Oct 14, 53. *Educ:* Duke Univ, BA, 75; Univ Sarasota, PhD(cell biol), 78; Tel Aviv Univ, MD, 85. *Concurrent Pos:* Clin investr award, NIH. *Mem:* Am Thyroid Asn; Endocrinol Soc; Am Asn Fed Res; Am Med Asn. *Res:* Endocrinology. *Mailing Add:* Dept Internal Med Univ Chicago Med Ctr MC 3090 5841 S Maryland Ave Chicago IL 60637

**WEISS, SAMUEL BERNARD,** BIOCHEMISTRY. *Current Pos:* asst prof, 58-63, PROF BIOCHEM, UNIV CHICAGO, 63- *Personal Data:* b New York, NY, May 18, 26; m 61; c 2. *Educ:* City Col New York, BS, 48; Univ Southern Calif, PhD(biochem), 54. *Honors & Awards:* Theobold Smith Award, AAAS, 61; Am Chem Soc Award Enzyme Chem, 66. *Prof Exp:* Res assoc biochem, Mass Gen Hosp, Boston, 56-57; asst prof, Rockefeller Inst, 57-58. *Concurrent Pos:* Am Heart Asn fel biochem, Univ Chicago, 54-56; Guggenheim fel, Salk Inst, 70-71; res assoc, Argonne Cancer Res Hosp, 58-, assoc dir, 67-74. *Mem:* Am Soc Biol Chemists; Am Acad Arts & Sci. *Res:* Enzymology of reactions in the synthesis of lipids, proteins and nucleic acids; viral transfer RNAs; mechanism of action of polycyclic aromatic hydrocarbons. *Mailing Add:* Dept Biochem Univ Chicago Pritzker Sch Med 920 E 58th St Chicago IL 60637-1432

**WEISS, SCOTT T,** RESPIRATORY EPIDEMIOLOGY, GENETIC EPIDEMIOLOGY. *Current Pos:* From instr to prof, 72-95, PROF MED, HARVARD MED SCH, 95- *Personal Data:* b New York, NY, Apr 16, 46; m 68, Deborah Jackson; c Benjamin & Matthew. *Educ:* Haverford Col, BA, 68; Case Western Res Univ, MD, 72; Harvard Univ, MS, 77. *Concurrent Pos:* Vis prof, Univ Groningen, Neth, 86-; consult, Nat Heart, Lung & Blood Inst, NIH, 86-; chair, Environ & Occup Health Assembly, Am Thoracic Soc, 93-95. *Mem:* Am Thoracic Soc; Am Col Physicians; Soc Epidemiol Res; Am Col Chest Physicians; Am Soc Human Genetics. *Res:* Investigated the health effects of passive smoking, airway reactivity in children and adults, allergen exposure, asthma genetics and asthma health policy; Respiratory epidemiology particularly the obstructive airway diseases, asthma and chronic obstructive pulmonary diseases. *Mailing Add:* Channing Lab 181 Longwood Ave Boston MA 02115. *Fax:* 617-525-2274; *E-Mail:* scott.weiss@channing. harvard.edu

**WEISS, SIDNEY,** BIOCHEMISTRY. *Current Pos:* RETIRED. *Personal Data:* b New York, NY, Dec 16, 20; m 44; c 3. *Educ:* Queens Col, NY, BS, 42; Fordham Univ, MS, 46, PhD(biochem), 49; Rutgers Univ, MS, 66. *Prof Exp:* Res chemist, Food Res Labs, Inc, NY, 42-46; res assoc biochem, Inst Cancer Res, Philadelphia, Pa, 49-58; sr res chemist, Colgate-Palmolive Co, 58-59, sect head, 59- 63, mgr biol res, 63-74, assoc dir res, 74-79, dir basic res, 79- 85. *Mem:* Am Chem Soc; Am Soc Biol Chem; Am Asn Dent Res; Am Statist Asn. *Res:* Biological oxidations; enzymatic reactions and microbiological transformations. *Mailing Add:* 76 Juniper Dr Levittown PA 19056-2731

**WEISS, SOL,** MATHEMATICS. *Current Pos:* from asst prof to assoc prof math, 64-78, EMER PROF MATH SCI, WEST CHESTER UNIV, 78- *Personal Data:* b Austria, Apr 19, 13; US citizen; m 40, Evelyn Hochman; c Eric & Carl. *Educ:* Brooklyn Col, BS, 34; Columbia Univ, MA, 36. *Prof Exp:* Teacher, Philadelphia Pub Sch Syst, Pa, chmn dept math, 50-64. *Concurrent Pos:* Consult, Wilmington Sch Dist, Del, 64; Philadelphia Pub Sch Syst, 64-65 & 67-, Cecil County Pub Schs, Md, 66, Upward Bound Prog, Franklin & Marshall Col, 67 & Lehigh Univ Social Restoration Prog, Pa State Prisons, 73-74; trustee, West Chester Univ; lectr, Chinese Univ, 86. *Mem:* Math Asn Am. *Res:* Mathematics education for the low achiever; author of book for parents on how to help their children with math and books on methods of teaching mathematics. *Mailing Add:* 102 Crosshill Rd Wynnewood PA 19096-3508

**WEISS, STANLEY,** METALLURGY. *Current Pos:* EMER PROF, MAT ENG, UNIV WIS-MILWAUKEE, 68- *Personal Data:* b New York, NY, Apr 9, 29; m 60; c 3. *Educ:* Polytech Inst Brooklyn, BMetE, 51; Mass Inst Technol, SM, 55, ScD(metall), 64. *Prof Exp:* Engr, Gen Elec Co, 51-54; corp engr, Alco Prod, 55-56; mgr eng, Gen Elec Co, Ohio, 56-61; res assoc metall, Mass Inst Technol, 64-68. *Concurrent Pos:* Consult, Gen Elec Co, 61-, Stand Thomson Corp, 63-68, Walter Kidde-Fenwal Div, 64-68 & Cryogenics Technol, 65-; corp consult, Snap-On Tools Corp, 71- *Mem:* Am Welding Soc; Am Soc Mech Engrs; Am Soc Metals; Am Soc Testing Mat; Sigma Xi. *Res:* Brazing mechanisms; residual stresses in welding; failure analysis; forged powder metals; joining of forged powder metals; corrosion of prosthetic devices. *Mailing Add:* Weiss & Burck Limited 744 N Fourth St Milwaukee WI 53203-2106

**WEISS, STANLEY H,** MEDICAL ONCOLOGY, CLINICAL EPIDEMIOLOGY. *Current Pos:* asst prof, 87-92, ASSOC PROF, DEPT PREV MED & COMMUNITY HEALTH, UNIV MED & DENT NJ, 93-, CHIEF, DIV AIDS & RETROVIRAL EPIDEMIOL, 88-, DIR, DIV INFECTIOUS DIS EPIDEMIOL, 89- *Personal Data:* b Brooklyn, NY, Jan 28, 54; m 81, Robin Joanna Kase; c Madeline J & Jeremy M. *Educ:* Yale Univ, BA, 74; Harvard Univ, MD, 78. *Honors & Awards:* Barge Math Prize, 71; Am Soc Clin Oncol Award, 85; Bausch & Lomb Medal, 70. *Prof Exp:* Res assoc immunol, Robert B Brigham Hosp, 75; dir path diagnosis regist, Peter B Brigham Hosp, 76-78; intern med, Montefiore Hosp & Med Ctr, 78-79, resident, 79-81, asst attend physician, 81-82; clin assoc oncol, Nat Cancer Inst, 82-87, med staff fel epidemiol, 83-87. *Concurrent Pos:* Res assoc epidemiol, Ctr Dis Control, 80; adj asst prof, Dept Prev Med & Biomet, Uniformed Serv Univ Health Sci, NIH, 86-; special consult, WHO, Special Prog Res, Develop & Res Training in Human Reproduction, 87, mem, NIH

Study Sect, 88; assoc att med, Univ Med & Dent, NJ, Univ Hosp, 89-, dir, Div Infectious Dis Epidemiol, 89-, acquired immune deficiency syndrome fac, Acad Med, NJ, 89-, exec sci comt, NJ, Community Res Initiative, 89-; mem, Physicians Adv Comm, NJ Dept Health, 90-, sci adv comm, clin dir Network, Comm Prog Clinic Res Acquired Immune Deficiency Syndrome, 90-, Army Breast Cancer Study, sect, 94; chair, Sixth Int Conf Human Retrovirology, 93; guest expert, Blood Prod Adv Comt, Food & Drug Admin, 96. *Mem:* Am Soc Clin Oncol; fel Am Col Physicians; Am Soc Microbiol; fel Infectious Dis Soc Am; Am Fedn Clin Res; Am Pub Health Asn. *Res:* Epidemiology of the acquired immunodeficiency syndrome and other retroviral associated illnesses; mathematical modeling and decision theory applied to the pathogenesis of neoplasms and chronic diseases; critical evaluation of diagnostic and therapeutic modalities; author of over 85 articles and over 100 scientific abstracts; epidemiology of breast cancer; infectious diseases; laboratory diagnostics. *Mailing Add:* 42 Ridge Dr Livingston NJ 07039-3716. *Fax:* 973-982-6556; *E-Mail:* weiss@umdnj.edu

**WEISS, STEPHEN FREDRICK,** COMPUTER SCIENCE. *Current Pos:* From asst prof to assoc prof, 70-84, PROF COMPUT SCI, UNIV NC, CHAPEL HILL, 84- *Personal Data:* b Berkeley, Calif, Mar 6, 44; m 68, Iris Roshfeld; c Jeremy & Daniel. *Educ:* Carnegie-Mellon Univ, BS, 66; Cornell Univ, MS, 69, PhD(comput sci), 70. *Concurrent Pos:* Consult, Environ Protection Agency, 75-78, Res Triangle Inst & Lipids Res Clinics. *Mem:* Asn Comput Mach; Asn Computational Ling. *Res:* Natural language analysis; information retrieval; computer science education. *Mailing Add:* Dept Comput Sci Univ NC Chapel Hill NC 27599-3175. *Fax:* 919-962-1799; *E-Mail:* weiss@cs.unc.edu

**WEISS, THEODORE JOEL,** lipid chemistry; deceased, see previous edition for last biography

**WEISS, THOMAS E,** MEDICINE. *Current Pos:* RETIRED. *Personal Data:* b New Orleans, La, June 15, 16; m 50; c 2. *Educ:* Tulane Univ, MD, 40. *Prof Exp:* From instr to assoc prof med, Sch Med, Tulane Univ, 47-64, prof clin med, 64-84, emer prof med, 64- *Concurrent Pos:* Mem staff, Ochsner Clin; trustee, Alton Ochsner Med Found, chmn, vol support comt, 84- *Mem:* Am Rheumatism Asn (past pres). *Res:* Rheumatic diseases; gout, clinical observations and correlating clinical finds with test and treatments; studies of radioisotope joint scanning in patients with arthritis. *Mailing Add:* Alton Ochsner Med Found 1514 Jefferson Hwy New Orleans LA 70121-2483

**WEISS, VOLKER,** METALLURGY. *Current Pos:* res assoc metall, 54-57, from asst prof to assoc prof, 57-65, PROF MAT SCI, L C SMITH COL ENG, SYRACUSE UNIV, 65-, PROF ENG & PHYSICS, 86- *Personal Data:* b Rottenmann, Austria, Sept 2, 30; nat US; m 57; c 2. *Educ:* Vienna Tech Univ, dipl, 53; Syracuse Univ, MS, 55, PhD(solid state sci & technol), 57. *Honors & Awards:* Minor Award, NASA, 68. *Prof Exp:* Asst, Neth Steel Factory, 52. *Concurrent Pos:* Indust consult, US & Ger, 56-; sr sci fel, NATO, 67-68; assoc chem metall, L C Smith Col Eng, Syracuse Univ, 65-72, chmn solid state sci & technol prog, 60-67, assoc dean sponsored progs, 72-78, vpres res & grad affairs, 77-86; chmn, Dept Mech, Aerospace & Mfg Eng, 92-; Fulbright Professorship, 93. *Mem:* Fel Am Soc Metals; Am Soc Testing & Mat; Am Inst Mining, Metall & Petrol Engrs; Brit Inst Metals; Ger Metall Soc. *Res:* Metal physics; fracture mechanics; fatigue; residual stresses; solid state reactions; superplasticity; x-ray diffraction; application of Ai to materials science. *Mailing Add:* 449 Link Hall Syracuse Univ Syracuse NY 13244-0001

**WEISS, WILLIAM,** BIOSTATISTICS. *Current Pos:* PVT CONSULT STATIST, 84- *Personal Data:* b New York, NY, June 12, 23; m 56; c 4. *Educ:* George Washington Univ, BA, 48. *Prof Exp:* Chief statistician, US Food & Drug Admin, 52-62; asst chief perinatal res br, Nat Inst Neurol & Commun Dis & Stroke, NIH, 62-66, chief, Off Biomet & Field Studies, 66-84. *Mem:* Biomet Soc; fel Am Statist Asn; Drug Info Asn; fel AAAS. *Res:* Biostatistical applications in neurology; design and analysis of clinical trials in multiple sclerosis. *Mailing Add:* 609 Jerry Lane NW Vienna VA 22180

**WEISS, WILLIAM,** PULMONARY DISEASES, EPIDEMIOLOGY. *Current Pos:* from assoc prof to prof med, Hahnemann Med Col, 66-84, dir div occup med, 75-84, EMER PROF MED, HAHNEMANN UNIV, 84- *Personal Data:* b Philadelphia, Pa, July 30, 19; wid; c Winifred, Seth & Deborah. *Educ:* Univ Pa, BA, 40, MD, 44. *Honors & Awards:* Merit in Authorship Awards, Am Occup Med Asn, 74 & 85; Ann Sci Award, Am Cancer Soc, 79. *Prof Exp:* Mem staff, Sch Med & Grad Sch Med, Univ Pa & Med Col Pa, 45-66. *Concurrent Pos:* Chief tuberc, Harbor Gen Hosp, Torrance, Calif, 49-50; clin dir, Pulmonary Dis Serv, Philadelphia Gen Hosp, 50-74; chest consult, Norristown State Hosp, Pa, 51-60; dir, Philadelphia Pulmonary Neoplasm Res Proj, 57-67; Int Agency Res Cancer travel fel, London Mass Radiography Units, 69; ed, Philadelphia Med, 76- *Mem:* AMA; Am Thoracic Soc; fel Am Col Physicians. *Res:* Pulmonary disease, particularly lung cancer; epidemiology and etiology; smoking related diseases of respiratory tract; asbestos-related disease. *Mailing Add:* 3912 Netherfield Rd Philadelphia PA 19129

**WEISSBACH, ARTHUR,** VIROLOGY. *Personal Data:* b New York, NY, Aug 27, 27; m 58, Joyce Olhoeft; c Lyle & Claudia. *Educ:* City Col New York, BS, 47; Columbia Univ, PhD(biochem), 53. *Prof Exp:* Nat Found Infantile Paralysis fel, NIH, 53-55; asst prof biochem, Albany Med Col, Union Univ, NY, 55-56; biochemist, NIH, 56-68; head plant cell biol, Roche Inst Molecular Biol, 68-82, assoc dir, 83-89; exec ed, Analytical Biochem, 88-96. *Concurrent Pos:* Prof lectr, Georgetown Univ, 57-58; NSF fel, 59-60; prof lectr, George Washington Univ, 61-66; adj prof, Dept Human Genetics & Develop,

Columbia Univ, 69-80, Univ Med & Dent, NJ, 81-88; adj mem, Roche Inst Molecular Biol, 89-95. *Mem:* Am Soc Biochem & Molecular Biol; Int Soc Plant Molecular Biol. *Res:* Biochemistry of plant and animal nucleic acids; DNA methylation. *Mailing Add:* PO Box 168 Sanibel FL 33957. *Fax:* 941-395-1868

**WEISSBACH, HERBERT,** GENE EXPRESSION, MOLECULAR BIOLOGY. *Current Pos:* DISTINGUISHED RES PROF, DEPT BIOL SCI, FLA ATLANTIC UNIV, BOCA RATON, 97-, HEAD, CTR MOLECULAR BIOL & BIOTECHNOL, 97- *Personal Data:* b New York, NY, Mar 16, 32; m 53; c 4. *Educ:* City Univ NY, BS, 53; George Washington Univ, MS, 55, PhD, 57. *Honors & Awards:* Enzyme Award, Am Chem Soc, 70. *Prof Exp:* Chemist, Nat Heart Inst, 53-68; lectr, George Washington Univ, 64-69; head, Sect Enzymes & Metab & actg chief, Lab Clin Biochem, NIH, 68-69; assoc dir, Dept Biochem, Roche Inst Molecular Biol, 69-83, dir, 83-96. *Concurrent Pos:* NSF travel grant, Int Cong Biol Chem Socs, Moscow, 61; ed, J Pharmacol & Exp Therapeut, 67-72, Int J Neuropharmacol, 69-76 & J Biol Chem, 72-77; adj prof, Dept Human Genetics, Columbia Univ, 69-85, Univ Med & Dent NJ, 81-93, Health Sci Ctr, State Univ NY, 89-; vis lectr, Princeton Univ, 84-85. *Mem:* Nat Acad Sci; AAAS; Am Soc Biol Chemists; Am Chem Soc; Am Soc Microbiol; Am Soc Pharmacol & Exp Therapeut; Geront Soc Am; Am Soc Biochem & Molecular Biol (treas, 97); NY Acad Sci. *Res:* Protein synthesis; gene expression; mechanism of enzyme and coenzyme action. *Mailing Add:* Dept Biol Sci Fla Atlantic Univ 777 Glades Rd Boca Raton FL 33431

**WEISSBERG, ALFRED,** MATHEMATICS, SCIENCE ADMINISTRATION. *Current Pos:* Sci & Technol Commun Off, 70-80, SCI ADMIN, NAT INST NEUROL COMMUN DIS & STROKE, NIH, 80- *Personal Data:* b Boston, Mass, Jan 29, 28; wid; c 3. *Educ:* Northeastern Univ, BS, 52; Univ NH, MS, 54. *Prof Exp:* Prin mathematician, Battelle Mem Inst, 53-60; math statistician, US Food & Drug Admin, 60-64; supvry opers res analyst, Nat Bur Standards, 64-67; head file orgn & statist, Toxicol Info Prog, Nat Libr Med, 67-70. *Mem:* AAAS; Am Soc Info Sci; Am Statist Asn. *Res:* Mathematical statistics; information system design and operation; application of computer systems to information retrieval. *Mailing Add:* 1024 Noyes Dr Silver Spring MD 20910

**WEISSBURG, MARC JOEL,** OLFACTORY-MEDIATED BEHAVIOR OF MARINE ORGANISMS, NEUROPHYSIOLOGICAL, MECHANISMS OF BEHAVIOR. *Current Pos:* instr, NIH FEL & ASST PROF BIOL & ECOL, GA STATE UNIV, 92- *Personal Data:* b Los Angeles, Calif, Sept 16, 60. *Educ:* Univ Calif, BA, 83; State Univ NY, Stony Brook, PhD (Ecol & evolution), 90. *Prof Exp:* Instr pop & theoret ecol, Barnard Col, 88; NSF researcher, Univ Ala, 90-91, Univ SC, 91-92. *Concurrent Pos:* Co-prin investr, NSF, 92-; NIH fel, NIMH, 92- *Mem:* Animal Behav Soc; Asn Chemoreception Sci; Ecol Soc Am. *Res:* Behavioral and physiological aspects of olfactory-mediated processes, including methods of coding spatial and temporal aspects of chemical signals in moving fluids, orientation mechanism and predator-prey relationships involving chemosensation. *Mailing Add:* Sch Biol Ga Inst Technol Atlanta GA 30332-0230. *E-Mail:* biomjw@bwl.gsu.edu

**WEISSE, ALLEN B,** CARDIOLOGY, MEDICINE. *Current Pos:* from instr to assoc prof, 65-74, PROF MED, NJ MED SCH, UNIV MED & DENT NJ, 74- *Personal Data:* b New York, NY, Dec 6, 29; m 67, Laura Van Raalte; c Danielle & Charles. *Educ:* NY Univ, BA, 50; State Univ NY, MD, 58; Am Bd Internal Med, dipl, 65, cert cardiovasc dis, 67. *Prof Exp:* Res fel cardiol, Sch Med, Univ Utah, 61-63; instr med, Sch Med, Seton Hall Univ, 63-65. *Mem:* Am Fedn Clin Res; Am Physiol Soc; Am Heart Asn; fel Am Col Physicians; fel Am Col Cardiol. *Res:* Cardiovascular physiology and disease; medical history. *Mailing Add:* NJ Med Sch Univ Med & Dent NJ 185 S Orange Ave Newark NJ 07103

**WEISSENBERGER, STEIN,** DECISION ANALYSIS. *Current Pos:* group leader & dep div leader, 76-82, DIV LEADER, LAWRENCE LIVERMORE LAB, UNIV CALIF, 82- *Personal Data:* b San Francisco, Calif, July 30, 37; m 59; c 2. *Educ:* Mass Inst Technol, BS & MS, 60; Stanford Univ, PhD(aeronaut & astronaut sci), 65. *Prof Exp:* Dynamics engr, Lockheed Missiles & Space Co, 62-65; from asst prof to assoc prof mech eng, Univ Santa Clara, 65-76. *Concurrent Pos:* Sr res assoc, Nat Res Coun, NASA-Ames Res Ctr, 73-75. *Mem:* Am Soc Mech Engrs; Inst Elec & Electronics Engrs; Opers Res Soc Am. *Res:* Control and decision theory; control systems. *Mailing Add:* Lawrence Livermore Nat Lab PO Box 808 Livermore CA 94551

**WEISSENBURGER, DON WILLIAM,** MAGNETODYNAMICS, MAGNETOSTATICS. *Current Pos:* STAFF ENGR, GRUMAN SPACE ELECTRONIC DIV 93-; CONSULT 93- *Personal Data:* b New Brunswick, NJ, May 22, 47. *Educ:* Colo Col, BS, 69. *Prof Exp:* Mem eng & sci staff, Plasma Physics Lab, Princeton Univ, 75- *Res:* Design and analysis of magnetic fields, eddy currents and related phenomena associated with controlled fusion research. *Mailing Add:* Gruman Space Syst 4 Independence Way Princeton NJ 08540

**WEISSENBURGER, JASON T,** NOISE CONTROL, VIBRATIONS. *Current Pos:* PRES & FOUNDER, ENG DYNAMICS INT, 70- *Personal Data:* b Wheeling, WVa, Dec 11, 32; m 92, Beverly J Gordon; c Dale E. *Educ:* Washington Univ, St Louis, BSME, 55, MS, 59, DSc(appl mech), 66. *Prof Exp:* Tech specialist struct dynamics, McDonnell Aircraft Corp, 59-69. *Concurrent Pos:* Adj prof & lectr appl mech, Washington Univ, St Louis, 55-70; adj prof, Univ Mo, Rolla & Cent Mo State Univ. *Mem:* Nat Coun Acoust Consults (pres, 88-90); Acoust Soc Am; Am Soc Mech Engrs; Inst Noise Control Eng; Nat Soc Prof Engrs. *Res:* Eigenvalue mathematics; auditorium acoustics. *Mailing Add:* 219 Orrick Lane St Louis MO 63122-4438. *Fax:* 314-991-2099

**WEISSER, EUGENE P,** CHEMICAL ENGINEERING. *Current Pos:* mgr res eng, Arco Polymers, Inc, Atlantic Richfield Co, Philadelphia, 77-81, MGR, PILOT PLANT SERV, ARCO CHEM CO, PHILADELPHIA, 81- *Personal Data:* b Pittsburgh, Pa, Feb 12, 22; m 48; c 5. *Educ:* Univ Pittsburgh, BS, 49. *Prof Exp:* Res asst chem eng, Mellon Inst, 49-51; jr chem engr, Res Dept, Koppers Co, Inc, Monroeville, Pa, 51-55, chem engr, 55-60, sr chem engr, 60-61, group mgr res eng, 61-67, sr res group mgr, 67-77. *Mem:* Am Inst Chem Engrs. *Res:* The design, construction and operation of pilot plants, particularly concerning polymers. *Mailing Add:* 5031 Impala Dr Pittsburgh PA 15239

**WEISSGERBER, RUDOLPH E,** medicine; deceased, see previous edition for last biography

**WEISSKOPF, BERNARD,** PEDIATRICS, PSYCHIATRY. *Current Pos:* assoc prof, 66-72, PROF PEDIAT, SCH MED, UNIV LOUISVILLE, 72-, ASSOC PSYCHIAT, ASSOC OBSTET & GYNEC & DIR CHILD EVAL CTR, 66- *Personal Data:* b Berlin, Ger, Dec 11, 29; US citizen; m 65; c 2. *Educ:* Syracuse Univ, BA, 51; State Univ Leiden, MD, 55; Am Bd Pediat, dipl, 65. *Prof Exp:* Physician, State Univ Leiden, 58; intern, Meadowbrook Hosp, Hempstead, NY, 58-59, resident pediat, 59-60; asst chief pediat, USAF Hosp, Maxwell AFB, 60-62; fel pediat & child psychiat, Hosp & Sch Med, Johns Hopkins Univ, 62-64; asst prof pediat, Univ Ill Col Med, 64-66. *Concurrent Pos:* Clin coordr, Ill State Pediat Inst, 64-66. *Mem:* Fel Am Acad Pediat; Am Asn Ment Deficiency; Am Soc Human Genetics. *Res:* Behavioral aspects of pediatrics, especially learning disorders and mental retardation genetics. *Mailing Add:* Univ Louisville Sch Med Child Eval Ctr 224 E Broadway Suite 500 Louisville KY 40202-1739

**WEISSKOPF, MARTIN CHARLES,** X-RAY ASTRONOMY, ASTROPHYSICS. *Current Pos:* SR X-RAY ASTRON ASTROPHYS & AXAF PROJ SCI, 77-, CHIEF, X-RAY ASTRON BR, 84- *Personal Data:* b Omaha, Nebr, Apr 21, 42; m 88; c 2. *Educ:* Oberlin Col, AB, 64; Brandeis Univ, PhD(physics), 69. *Prof Exp:* Res assoc physics, Brandeis Univ, 68-69; res assoc, Columbia Univ, 69-71, lectr, 70-71, asst prof, 71-77. *Concurrent Pos:* Co-investr, High Energy Astron Observ-2, NASA, 72- & Columbia Exp NASA's OSO-8, 75-77; guest-investr, NASA's High Energy Astrophys Observ-1, 78- *Mem:* Am Phys Soc; Am Astron Soc. *Res:* X-ray astronomy and high energy astrophysics. *Mailing Add:* Code ES-01 Marshall Space Flight Ctr Bldg 4481 Huntsville AL 35812

**WEISSKOPF, VICTOR FREDERICK,** PHYSICS. *Current Pos:* prof, 46-74, EMER INST PROF PHYSICS, MASS INST TECHNOL, 74- *Personal Data:* b Vienna, Austria, Sept 19, 08; nat US; m 34; c 2. *Educ:* Univ Gottingen, PhD(physics), 31. *Hon Degrees:* 25 from various US & foreign univs, 61-70. *Honors & Awards:* Planck Medal, 56; Prix Mondial Cino Del Duca, 72; Nat Medal Sci, 80; Fermi Prize, 89; Pub Serv Medal, Nat Acad Sci; Gian Carlo Wick Medal, 92. *Prof Exp:* Res assoc, Univ Berlin, 31-32; Rockefeller Found fel, Univs Copenhagen & Cambridge, 32-33; res assoc, Swiss Fed Inst Technol, 33-36 & Univ Copenhagen, 36-37; from instr to asst prof physics, Univ Rochester, 37-43; dep div leader, Los Alamos Sci Lab, 43-46. *Concurrent Pos:* Dir gen, Europ Ctr Nuclear Res, 61-65. *Mem:* Nat Acad Sci; fel Am Phys Soc (vpres, 59, pres, 60); Fedn Am Sci; corresp mem Fr, Austrian, Danish, Span, Scottish, Ital, Pontif, Soviet & Bavarian Acad Sci; Am Acad Arts & Sci (pres, 77-80). *Res:* Quantum mechanics; electron theory; theory of nuclear phenomena; particle physics. *Mailing Add:* 20 Bartlett Terr Newton MA 02159-2314

**WEISSLER, ARNOLD M,** CARDIOLOGY, INTERNAL MEDICINE. *Current Pos:* PROF MED, MAYO MED SCH, CONSULT CARDIOVASC DIS, MAYO CLIN. *Personal Data:* b Brooklyn, NY, May 13, 27; m, Sandra L Carter; c 4. *Educ:* NY Univ, BA, 48; State Univ NY Downstate Med Ctr, MD, 53. *Prof Exp:* Trainee internal med, Maimonides Hosp, 53-54 & Duke Hosp, 54-60, assoc med, Duke Hosp, 59-60; asst prof, Med Br, Univ Tex, Galveston, 60-61; from asst prof to prof, Ohio State Univ, 61-71, dir, Div Cardiol, 63-71; prof med & chmn dept, Wayne State Univ, 71-81; prof & chmn, Dept Med, Rose Med Ctr, Univ Colo, 81-89. *Concurrent Pos:* Am Heart Asn res fel, Duke Hosp, Durham, NC, 55-57; chief, Dept Med, Harper-Grace Hosps, 71-81; mem cardiovasc bd, Am Bd Internal Med, chmn, 75-77; fel, Coun Clin Cardiol, Am Heart Asn, 78, chmn, 78-80. *Mem:* Fel Am Col Physicians; Am Clin & Climat Asn; fel Am Col Cardiol; Am Soc Clin Invest; Am Soc Pharmacol & Exp Therapeut; Asn Am Physicians. *Res:* Cardiovascular physiology; congestive heart failure; noninvasive techniques in cardiology; myocardial metabolism. *Mailing Add:* 1051 Foxcroft Circle SW Rochester MN 55902

**WEISSLER, GERHARD LUDWIG,** physics; deceased, see previous edition for last biography

**WEISSMAN, ALBERT,** PSYCHOPHARMACOLOGY. *Current Pos:* sr res psychologist, Pfizer Res Labs, 58-61, mgr psychopharmacol, 61-72, ASST DIR PHARMACOL, PFIZER INC, 72- *Personal Data:* b New York, NY, Aug 1, 33; m 57; c 5. *Educ:* NY Univ, BA, 54; Columbia Univ, MA, 55, PhD, 58. *Prof Exp:* Instr psychol, Columbia Univ, 57. *Mem:* Am Soc Pharmacol & Exp Therapeut. *Res:* Catecholamines and indolylalkylamines; learning and memory; addiction. *Mailing Add:* Asst Dir Pharmacol Pfizer Inc Eastern Pt Rd Groton CT 06340-5196

**WEISSMAN, CHARLES,** CRITICAL CARE MEDICINE, INTERNAL MEDICINE. *Current Pos:* assoc prof, Clin Anesthesiol & Clin Med, 89-93, PROF ANESTHESIOL & MED, COL PHYSICIANS & SURGEONS, COLUMBIA UNIV, 93-; ATTEND ANESTHESIOLOGIST & PHYSICIAN, PRESBY HOSP, 93- *Personal Data:* b New York, NY, April, 24, 51. *Educ:* Yeshiva Univ, BA, 72; Downstate Med Ctr, State Univ NY, MD, 76. *Prof Exp:* Asst prof anesthesiol & med, Col Physicians & Surgeons, Columbia Univ, 83-89. *Concurrent Pos:* Co-dir, Surg-Anesthesiol Intensive Care Unit & med dir, Respiratory Care Serv, Presby Hosp, asst attend physician anesthesiol & med, 93, attend anesthesiologist & physician, 93-, assoc attend physician anesthesiol,. *Mem:* Asn Univ Anesthesiologists; Soc Critical Care Med. *Res:* The metabolic and respiratory aspects of critically ill patients; the respiratory patterns of postoperative patients; anesthesiology. *Mailing Add:* Columbia Univ 622 W 168th St New York NY 10032-2575. *Fax:* 212-305-3204

**WEISSMAN, DAVID E(VERETT),** ELECTRICAL ENGINEERING. *Current Pos:* from asst prof to assoc prof, 68-82, PROF ENG, HOFSTRA UNIV, 82- *Personal Data:* b New York, NY, Sept 18, 37; m 61; c 4. *Educ:* NY Univ, BA & BEE, 60, MEE, 61; Stanford Univ, PhD(elec eng), 68. *Honors & Awards:* Centennial Medal, Inst Elec & Electronics Engrs, 84. *Prof Exp:* Asst elec eng, NY Univ, 60-61; elec engr, Dorne & Margolin, Inc, 61-63; res engr, Stanford Res Inst, 63-68. *Concurrent Pos:* Ed-in-chief, Inst Elec & Electronics Engrs J Oceanic Eng, 79-82. *Mem:* AAAS; Inst Elec & Electronics Engrs; Int Sci Radio Union; Am Geophys Union. *Res:* Development of radar remote sensing techniques for ocean surface observation from aircraft and satellites and other random media probing; demonstrated the usefulness of dual frequency radars to the measurement of ocean wave heights and directional spectrum; radar remote sensing. *Mailing Add:* Dept Eng Hofstra Univ 1000 Fulton Ave Hempstead NY 11550-1090

**WEISSMAN, IRVING L,** BIOLOGICAL SCIENCES. *Current Pos:* NIH fel, Dept Radiol, Stanford Univ, 65-67, res assoc, 67-68, from asst prof to assoc prof, Dept Path, 69-81, PROF PATH, SCH MED, STANFORD UNIV, 81-, PROF DEVELOP BIOL, 89- *Personal Data:* b Great Falls, Mont, Oct 21, 39; m 61; c 4. *Educ:* Mont State Col, BS, 60; Stanford Univ, MD, 65. *Hon Degrees:* DSc, Mont State Univ, 92. *Honors & Awards:* James McGinnis Mem lectr, Duke Univ, 82; George Feigen Mem lectr, Stanford Univ, 86; Albert Coons Mem lectr, Harvard Univ, 87; James Stahlman lectr, Vanderbilt Univ, 87; R E Smith lectr, Univ Tex Syst Cancer Ctr, 88; Chauncey D Leake lectr, Univ Calif, 89; Pasarow Award, 89; Harvey lectr, Rockefeller Univ, 89; Rose Litman lectr, 90. *Concurrent Pos:* Sr Dernham fel, Calif Div, Am Cancer Soc, 69-73, fac res award, Nat Am Cancer Soc, 74-78; Josiah Macy Found scholar, 74-75; mem, Immunobiol Study Sect, NIH, 76-80, outstanding investr award, 86; mem, Sci Rev Bd, Howard Hughes Med Inst, 86-; mem, Steering & Res Panels on AIDS, Nat Acad Sci-Nat Inst Med, 86-; mem, Sci Adv Comt, Irvington House Inst, 87-; Karel & Avice Beekhuis prof cancer biol, 87; Fifth Ann vis prof cancer biol, Univ Tex Health Sci Ctr, 87; distinguished lectr, Western Soc Clin Invest, 90. *Mem:* Nat Acad Sci; fel AAAS; Am Acad Arts & Sci; Am Asn Immunologists; Am Asn Univ Pathologists; Am Asn Pathologists; Am Soc Microbiol; Am Asn Cancer Res; Int Immunol. *Res:* Lymphocyte differentiation; molecular biology of lymphocyte surface receptors; viral oncogenesis; cellular immunology. *Mailing Add:* Dept Path B257 Beckman Ctr Sch Med Stanford Univ Stanford CA 94305-5428. *Fax:* 650-723-4034

**WEISSMAN, MICHAEL BENJAMIN,** FLUCTUATION SPECTROSCOPY, ONE-F NOISE. *Current Pos:* Asst prof physics, 78-83, assoc prof, 83-89, PROF PHYSICS, UNIV ILL, URBANA, 89- *Personal Data:* b St Louis, Mo, Aug 28, 49; m 81, Ellen Fireman; c Daniel & Jonathan. *Educ:* Harvard Univ, AB, 70; Univ Calif, San Diego, MS, 72, PhD(physics), 76. *Prof Exp:* Res fel chem, Harvard Univ, 76-78. *Concurrent Pos:* NSF fel, 77-78. *Mem:* Fel Am Phys Soc. *Res:* Fluctuation spectroscopy; origins of 1/f noise; mesoscopic probes of disordered states, glasses and spin-glasses. *Mailing Add:* Dept Physics Univ Ill 1110 W Green St Urbana IL 61801. *Fax:* 217-333-9819; *E-Mail:* mbw@uiuc.edu

**WEISSMAN, MICHAEL HERBERT,** PEDIATRICS, BIOMEDICAL ENGINEERING. *Current Pos:* CLIN ASST PROF PEDIAT, ALBERT EINSTEIN COL MED, YESHIVA UNIV, 82-; PEDIATRICIAN, MT KISCO MED GROUP, 80-; CHIEF PEDIATS, NORTHERN WESTCHESTER HOSP CTR, 93- *Personal Data:* b New York, NY, Jan 15, 42; m 67; c 5. *Educ:* Cooper Union, BME, 63; Northwestern Univ, Evanston, MS, 65, PhD(civil eng), 67; Wash Univ, MD, 76. *Honors & Awards:* George F Gill Prize Pediat, Wash Univ, 76. *Prof Exp:* Res asst, Northwestern Univ, Evanston, 65-67; asst prof bioeng, Carnegie-Mellon Univ, 67-71, assoc prof bioeng & chem eng, 71-73; pediat resident, Bronx Munic Hosp Ctr, 76-79, pediat chief resident, 79-80. *Concurrent Pos:* NIH grant, Carnegie-Mellon Univ, 69-74; fel, NASA-ASEE, 71- *Mem:* Sigma Xi; AMA; Am Acad Pediat. *Res:* Artificial internal organs; biological transport processes; physiological systems analysis; fluid mechanics; physiological simulation; general pediatrics. *Mailing Add:* Dept Pediat Mt Kisco Med Group Mt Kisco NY 10549. *Fax:* 914-242-1391; *E-Mail:* mikew@cloda.net

**WEISSMAN, MYRNA MILGRAM (KLERMAN),** EPIDEMIOLOGY, PSYCHIATRY. *Current Pos:* CHIEF, DIV CLIN GENETIC EPIDEMIOL, NY STATE PSYCHIAT INST, 87-; PROF EPIDEMIOL & PSYCHIAT, COL PHYSICIANS & SURGEONS, COLUMBIA UNIV, 87- *Personal Data:* b Boston, Mass, Apr 17, 35; c 4. *Educ:* Brandeis Univ, BA; Univ Pa, MSW; Yale Univ, PhD(chronic dis epidemiol), 74. *Honors & Awards:* Found Fund Prize, Res Psychiat, Am Psychiat Asn, 78; Rema Lapouse Ment Health Epidemiol Award, Am Pub Health Asn, 85; Anna Monika Found Award, 86; Maudsley Bequest Lectr, Royal Col Psychiat, London & Cambridge Univ,

Eng; Outstanding Res in Affective Dis Award, Nat Depressive & Manic Depressive Asn, 89; Res Award, Am Suicide Found, 90; Ann Pollock Lederer Found Res Award study depression in young adults, 91; Sr Investr Award, Nat Alliance Res on Schizophrenia & Depression, 91; Rhoda & Bernard Sarnat Int Prize Ment Health, 94; Zubin Award, 96; Res Prize, Am Psychopath Asn, 96. *Prof Exp:* From asst prof to prof psychiat & epidemiol, Yale Univ Sch Med, 74-87. *Concurrent Pos:* Consult, Psychopharmacol Res Br, NIMH, 73-76, Clin Res Br, 77 & Nat Inst Drug Abuse, 77; mem, White House Task Force Epidemiol of Ment Health, 77-78, Nat Adv Comt, NIMH, 78 & Res Study Sect, Nat Inst Alcohol Abuse & Alcoholism, 75-80; consult planning epidemiol res, Alcohol, Drug Abuse & Ment Health Admin, 78; consult, Dept HEW, 79, Inst Med-Nat Acad Sci & White House Off Sci & Technol Policy, 80, Soc Sci Res Coun & NIMH, 81, Nat Health Res & Develop Prog, Health & Welfare Can, 81-83, NIMH & WHO, 83; vis sr scholar, Inst Med, Nat Acad Sci & Ment Health Sect, 79-80; vpres, Am Coun Affective Dis, Inc, NY, 83; mem, adv bd, Ctr Alcohol Studies, Rutgers Univ, NJ, 86-90, Nat Depressive & Manic Depressive Asn, 86-; mem, Task Force Res, Am Psychiat Asn, 88-89; mem, Extramural Sci Adv Bd, NIMH, 88-92; mem, comt, Epidemiol & Vet Follow-Up Studies, Inst Med, Nat Acad Sci, 89-; mem, Depression Panel of Coun on Sci Affairs, AMA, 90; mem, Sci Adv Comt, Panic Dis Prev & Pub Educ Prog, NIMH, 90-92; mem, bd dirs, Am Sucide Found, & NY State Res Found Ment Hyg, 90; consult, numerous orgns and insts; Method to Extend Res in Time, Sci Coun, NIMH, 90- *Mem:* Inst Med-Nat Acad Sci; AAAS; Soc Epidemiol Res; Am Pub Health Asn; Int Epidemiol Asn; Am Psychopath Asn; fel Am Col Neuropsychopharmacol; fel Am Psychiat Asn; Am Suicide Found, Inst of Med. *Res:* Effectiveness of pharmacotherapy and psychotherapy in the treatment of depression; cross national epidemiology; genetics of panic disorders; studies of children at high risk for psychiatric disorders. *Mailing Add:* Col Physicians & Surgeons Columbia Univ 722 W 168th St Unit 14 New York NY 10032. *Fax:* 212-568-3534; *E-Mail:* weissman@child.cpmc.columbia.edu

**WEISSMAN, NORMAN,** CLINICAL CHEMISTRY, TOXICOLOGY. *Current Pos:* asst dir, Chem Dept, 70-74, sr res scientist, Res Dept, 74-80, RES ASSOC, BIO-SCI LABS, 80- *Personal Data:* b New York, NY, Sept 12, 14; m 37; c 3. *Educ:* City Col New York, BS, 35; Columbia Univ, PhD(biochem), 41. *Prof Exp:* Res fel dent med, Harvard Sch Dent Med, 41-43, instr, 43-46; lectr, Johns Hopkins Univ, 46-47, asst prof physiol chem & prev med, Sch Med, 47-51; assoc prof med, Col Med, State Univ NY Downstate Med Ctr, 51-56; assoc prof path & biochem, Col Med, Univ Utah, 56-70. *Concurrent Pos:* Chemist, Maimonides Hosp, NY, 51-56 & Univ Hosp, Univ Utah, 57-65; consult, Vet Admin Hosp, Salt Lake City, Utah, 60-70. *Mem:* Am Soc Biol Chemists; Am Asn Clin Chemists; Am Acad Forensic Sci; Harvey Soc; Sigma Xi. *Res:* Amino acid metabolism; bacterial chemistry; histochemistry; copper and connective tissue; toxicology methods. *Mailing Add:* 16901 Mooncrest Dr Encino CA 91436-3510

**WEISSMAN, PAUL MORTON,** organometallic chemistry, bioinorganic chemistry, for more information see previous edition

**WEISSMAN, PAUL ROBERT,** COMETS & SOLAR SYSTEM ORIGIN, PLANETARY SCIENCES. *Current Pos:* Sr scientist, Jet Propulsion Lab, Calif Inst Technol, 74-80, res scientist, 80-95, dep proj scientist, Comet Rendezous Mission, 87-92, SR RES SCIENTIST, JET PROPULSION LAB, CALIF INST TECHNOL, 95-, PROJ SCIENTIST, CHAMPOLLION MISSION, 96- *Personal Data:* b Brooklyn, NY, Sept 28, 47. *Educ:* Cornell Univ, AB, 69; Univ Mass, MS, 71; Univ Calif, Los Angeles, MS, 73, PhD(planetary physics), 78. *Honors & Awards:* Asteroid named in honor, 86. *Concurrent Pos:* Vis mem, Inst Advan Study, 85; Harlow Shapley Vis Lectr, 82-; dir, San Gabriel Space Sci Inst, 83- *Mem:* Am Astron Soc; Sigma Xi; AAAS; Int Astron Union; Am Geophys Union. *Res:* Physical and dynamical studies of small bodies in the solar system: comets, meteors and asteroids; theories of origin and implications for formation of the solar system; design of spacecraft and trajectories for solar system exploration; celestial mechanics; planetary sciences. *Mailing Add:* Jet Propulsion Lab Mail Stop 183 601 4800 Oak Grove Dr Pasadena CA 91109. *E-Mail:* pweissman@issac.jpl.nasa.gov

**WEISSMAN, ROBERT HENRY,** SOLID STATE ELECTRONIC DEVICES. *Current Pos:* Mem tech staff res & develop light-emitting diode devices, Hewlett Packard Co, 70-73, proj mgr res & develop mat & processes, 73-80, res & develop sect mgr, 80-84, TECHNOL RES & DEVELOP MGR, HEWLETT PACKARD CO, 84- *Personal Data:* b Chicago, Ill, July 4, 42; m 87, Diane Chimicz; c Emily. *Educ:* Univ Mich, BS, 64; Stanford Univ, MS, 65, PhD(elec eng), 70. *Mem:* Electrochem Soc; Int Soc Hybrid Microelectronics; Optical Soc Am. *Res:* Materials and process technology; solid state device physics; optoelectronic devices; optical fiber technology. *Mailing Add:* 3436 Shady Spring Lane Mountain View CA 94040-4543. *Fax:* 408-435-6335

**WEISSMAN, SAMUEL ISAAC,** SPECTROSCOPY, MAGNETIC RESONANCE. *Current Pos:* from asst prof to assoc prof, 46-55, prof, 55-80, EMER PROF CHEM, WASH UNIV, 80- *Personal Data:* b South Bend, Ind, June 25, 12; m 43; c 2. *Educ:* Univ Chicago, BS, 33, PhD(phys chem), 38. *Hon Degrees:* Univ Siena, Italy, 86; Wash Univ, 88. *Prof Exp:* Fel, Univ Chicago, 39-41; Nat Res Coun fel, Univ Calif, 41-42; res chemist, Manhattan Proj, Calif, 42-43 & NMex, 43-46. *Mem:* Nat Acad Sci; Am Chem Soc. *Res:* Chemical spectroscopy; fluorescence; electrical conductivity; paramagnetic resonance. *Mailing Add:* Dept Chem Wash Univ St Louis MO 63130

**WEISSMAN, SHERMAN MORTON,** PHYSIOLOGY, BIOCHEMISTRY. *Current Pos:* from assoc prof to prof med, molecular biophys & biochem, 67-72, prof, 72-87, STERLING PROF HUMAN GENETICS MED, MOLECULAR BIOPHYS & BIOCHEM, SCH MED, YALE UNIV, 91- *Personal Data:* b Chicago, Ill, Nov 22, 30; m 59; c 4. *Educ:* Northwestern Univ, BS, 50; Univ Chicago, MS, 51; Harvard Univ, MD, 55. *Prof Exp:* Intern, Boston City Hosp, 55-56; clin assoc metab serv, Gen Med Br, Nat Cancer Inst, NIH, 56-58; asst resident med, Ill Educ & Res Hosp, Chicago, 58-59; spec res fel, Dept Biochem, Univ Glasgow, Scotland, Nat Cancer Inst, 59-60; sr investr metab serv, Nat Cancer Inst, NIH, 60-67. *Concurrent Pos:* Mem, Virol & Cell Biol Study Sect, Am Cancer Soc, 72-74, co-chmn, 74-75, chmn, 76; mem, Ad Hoc Comt Synthetic Nucleic Acids, Nat Res Coun Assembly Life Sci, 74, Bd Sci Counselors, Nat Cancer Inst, 75-79, chmn, 77-79, mem, Cancer Spec Progs Adv Comt, 79-83; assoc dir, Comprehensive Cancer Ctr, Yale Univ, 75-81; assoc ed, Cancer Res, 80-81. *Mem:* Nat Acad Sci; Am Soc Biol Chemists; Am Soc Clin Invest; Asn Am Physicians; Brit Biochem Soc; fel AAAS; Am Physiol Soc; Am Soc Hemat; Am Soc Human Genetics. *Res:* Nucleic acid metabolism; molecular genetics; author of over 170 technical journal articles. *Mailing Add:* Dept Human Genetics Yale Univ Sch Med 295 Congress Ave - 366 BCMM New Haven CT 06510

**WEISSMAN, SUZANNE HEISLER,** ANALYTICAL CHEMISTRY, TOTAL QUALITY MANAGEMENT. *Current Pos:* mem tech staff, 80-86, supvr, 86-90, MGR, SANDIA NAT LABS, 90- *Personal Data:* b The Dalles, Ore, June 20, 49; m 76, Steven J; c 1. *Educ:* Ore State Univ, BS, 71; Univ Ill, MS, 73, PhD(chem), 75. *Prof Exp:* Vis lectr chem, Univ Ill, 75, vis asst prof, 76; chemist, Lovelace Biomed & Environ Res Inst, Inc. 76-80. *Mem:* Am Chem Soc; Soc Appl Spectros; Am Soc Qual Control. *Res:* Total quality management; environmental safety and health; determination of trace elements, ultratrace analyses; inductively coupled plasma-atomic emission spectroscopy. *Mailing Add:* Sandia Labs MS0724 PO Box 5800 Albuquerque NM 87185-0724. *Fax:* 505-844-6753; *E-Mail:* shweiss@sandia.gov

**WEISSMAN, WILLIAM,** surface chemistry, for more information see previous edition

**WEISSMANN, BERNARD,** BIOCHEMISTRY, ENZYMOLOGY. *Current Pos:* from asst prof to prof, 58-81, EMER PROF BIOL CHEM, UNIV ILL COL MED, 81- *Personal Data:* b New York, NY, Dec 2, 17; m 41, 61, Lenore Bernstein; c David, Karen, Arnold & Daniel. *Educ:* City Col New York, BS, 38; Univ Mich, MS, 39, PhD, 51. *Prof Exp:* Res assoc, Col Physicians & Surgeons, Columbia Univ, 50-53 & Mt Sinai Hosp, NY, 53-57. *Concurrent Pos:* Res chemist, Nat Inst Arthritis, Metab & Digestive Dis, NIH, 79-80. *Mem:* Am Soc Biol Chem; Am Chem Soc. *Res:* Enzymology and structure of acid mucopolysaccharide catabolism; synthetic carbohydrate chemistry; enzymes of catabolism of acid mucopolysaccharides and derived oligosaccharides; synthetic carbohydrate chemistry. *Mailing Add:* 1124 Dobson St Evanston IL 60202-3819. *E-Mail:* bwe400@nwu.edu

**WEISSMANN, GERALD,** CELL BIOLOGY, INTERNAL MEDICINE. *Current Pos:* from instr to assoc prof, 59-70, PROF MED, SCH MED, NY UNIV, 70-, DIR DIV RHEUMATOLOGY, 74- *Personal Data:* b Vienna, Austria, Aug 7, 30; US citizen; m 53; c Lisa B & Andrew. *Educ:* Columbia Univ, BA, 50; NY Univ, MD, 54; Am Bd Internal Med, dipl, 63. *Honors & Awards:* Alessandro Robecchi Prize for Rheumatology, 72; Marine Biol Lab Prize, 74 & 79, Centennial Award, 88; Lila Gruber Award, 79; Distinguished Investr Award, Am Col Rheumatology, 92. *Prof Exp:* Res fel biochem, Arthritis & Rheumatism Found, 58-59. *Concurrent Pos:* USPHS spec res fel, Strangeways Res Lab, Cambridge Univ, 60-61; sr investr, Arthritis & Rheumatism Found, 61-65; career investr, Health Res Coun, NY, 66-70; consult, US Food & Drug Admin & Nat Heart & Lung Inst, NIH; investr & instr physiol, Marine Biol Lab, Woods Hole, Mass, 70-, trustee, 85 & 89; Guggenheim fel, Ctr Immunol & Physiol, Paris, 73-74; ed-in-chief, Inflammation, Advan Inflammation Res. *Mem:* Am Soc Cell Biol; Am Soc Clin Invest; Am Rheumatism Asn (pres, 81-82); Harvey Soc (pres, 80-81); Asn Am Physicians; Am Soc Biol Chem & Molecular Biol; fel AAAS. *Res:* Study of lysosomes as they relate to cell injury; physiology and pharmacology of lysosomes and of artificial lipid structures; neutrophil activation; prostaglandins; leukotrienes; liposomes. *Mailing Add:* Dept Med NY Univ Sch Med 550 First Ave New York NY 10016-6401. *Fax:* 212-263-8804

**WEISSMANN, GERD FRIEDRICH HORST,** MATERIALS & SOIL SCIENCE. *Current Pos:* PRES, DAMPING MEASUREMENT SYSTS, 81- *Personal Data:* b Leipzig, Ger, Nov 26, 23; US citizen; m 54; c 3. *Educ:* Tech Univ, Berlin, Dipl Ing, 50, Dr Ing, 70; Pa State Univ, MS, 53. *Prof Exp:* supvr mech mat, Bell Tel Labs, 53-81. *Mem:* Am Soc Civil Engrs; Am Soc Testing & Mat; Soc Exp Stress Analysis. *Res:* Materials research; classification of metals; soil dynamics; foundation engineering; experimental mechanics. *Mailing Add:* 36 Circle Rd Florham Park NJ 07932

**WEISSMANN, SIGMUND,** CRYSTALLOGRAPHY. *Current Pos:* Res specialist x-ray diffraction, Col Eng, 49-87, prof mat sci & dir, Mat Res Lab, 63-87, EMER PROF MAT SCI, RUTGERS UNIV, NEW BRUNSWICK, 87- *Personal Data:* b Vienna, Austria, July 1, 17; nat US; m 45, Ilse G Barth; c Lyme & Karen. *Educ:* Polytech Inst Brooklyn, PhD(chem), 52. *Honors & Awards:* Howe Medal, Am Soc Metals, 62; NSF Res Creativity Award, 83. *Concurrent Pos:* Consult, Lawrence Livermore Lab & Univ Calif, Savannah River Lab, US Steel Corp, Monroeville, Pa; ed, Metals & Alloys, Joint Comt Powder Diffraction Stand, Int Ctr Diffraction Data; nat lectr, Sigma Xi, 62; Lady Davis vis prof, Hebrew Univ, Jerusalem, 80; fel, Int Ctr Diffraction Data. *Mem:* Am Crystallog Asn; Am Inst Mining, Metall & Petrol Engrs; Am Soc Metals; Am Soc Testing & Mat; NY Acad Sci. *Res:* X-ray crystallography; crystal imperfections of metals and alloys; irradiation of solids; recrystallization; recovery deformation; creep and fatigue of metals and alloys; displacive phase transformation; fracture, stress-corrosion. *Mailing Add:* 112 Clarendon Ct Metuchen NJ 08840-1507

**WEIST, WILLIAM GODFREY, JR,** geology, hydrology, for more information see previous edition

**WEISTROP, DONNA ETTA,** EXTRAGALACTIC ASTRONOMY. *Current Pos:* ASSOC PROF ASTRON, UNIV NEV, LAS VEGAS, 90- *Personal Data:* b New York, NY, June 10, 44; m 79, David B Shaffer. *Educ:* Wellesley Col, BA, 65; Calif Inst Technol, PhD(astron), 71. *Prof Exp:* Vis lectr astron, Tel Aviv Univ, 71-73; univ fel, Ohio State Univ, 73-74; asst astronr, Kitt Peak Nat Observ, 74-77; res fel, Univ Ariz, 77-78; astrophysicist, Goddard Space Flight Ctr, NASA, 78-85; sr scientist, Appl Res Corp, 85-90. *Concurrent Pos:* Vis scientist, Lunar & Planetary Lab, Univ Ariz, 78-80. *Mem:* Am Astron Soc; Int Astron Union; AAAS; Astron Soc Pac. *Res:* Nature of galaxies in voids, space astronomy; development of and applications for electronic detectors; QSO's and BL lac objects; identification of faint radio sources; characteristics of emission line galaxies. *Mailing Add:* Physics Dept Univ Nev Las Vegas NV 89154-4002

**WEISZ, JUDITH,** REPRODUCTIVE PHYSIOLOGY, NEUROENDOCRINOLOGY. *Current Pos:* PROF, DIV REPRODUCTIVE BIOL, DEPT OBSTET & GYNEC, MILTON S HERSHEY MED CTR, PA STATE UNIV, 76-, HEAD DIV, 75-, SR MEM, GRAD SCH FAC, UNIV, 73- *Personal Data:* b Budapest, Hungary, Aug 6, 26; Brit citizen. *Educ:* Newnham Col, Eng, BA, 48, MB, BCh, 51. *Prof Exp:* Clin training, London Hosp, Eng, 48-51; intern, Hadassah Med Sch, Hebrew Univ, Jerusalem, 52-54; second asst internal med, Tel Hashomer Govt & Mil Hosp, Israel, 54-56; registr internal med, London Hosp, Eng, 56-57; first asst internal med, Tel Hashomer Govt & Mil Hosp, Israel, 57-59; res fel endocrinol, Mt Sinai Hosp, New York, 60-62; fel, Training Prog Steroid Biochem, Worcester Found Exp Biol, Mass, 62-63; staff scientist, Training Prog Reproductive Physiol, 63-70, assoc dir, Training Prog Physiol Reproduction, 68-72, sr scientist, Worcester Found Exp Biol, 70-72. *Concurrent Pos:* Chmn, pub bd enquiry, Depo-provera, Food & Drug Admin, 82-85. *Mem:* Brit Med Asn; Endocrine Soc; Int Soc Neuroendocrinol; Soc Study Reproduction. *Res:* Neuroendocrine regulation of reproductive function; steroid biochemistry. *Mailing Add:* Dept Obstet & Gynec Penn State Univ Col Med PO Box 850 Hershey PA 17033-0850

**WEISZ, PAUL B,** EMBRYOLOGY. *Current Pos:* from instr to assoc prof, 47-57, PROF BIOL, BROWN UNIV, 57- *Personal Data:* b Vienna, Austria, Nov 3, 21; nat US; m 45; c 3. *Educ:* McGill Univ, BSc, 43, MSc, 44, PhD(zool), 46. *Prof Exp:* Demonstr zool, McGill Univ, 43-46, lectr, 46-47; lectr biol, Sr George Williams Col, 43-44, lectr, 44-47. *Concurrent Pos:* Mem, Ed Policies Comn & Comn Undergrad Educ Biol Sci. *Mem:* Soc Develop Biol; Am Soc Zool; Nat Asn Biol Teachers; Nat Sci Teachers Asn; Am Chem Soc. *Res:* Embryology and development of amphibians and crustaceans; morphogenesis; cytochemistry and nuclear functions in Protozoa; comparative embryology; science writing. *Mailing Add:* 135 Freeman Pkwy Providence RI 02906

**WEISZ, PAUL BURG,** CHEMICAL ENGINEERING, CATALYSIS BIOMEDICAL ENGINEERING. *Current Pos:* distinguished prof, 84-, EMER DISTINGUISHED PROF CHEM & BIOENG, UNIV PA, 84- *Personal Data:* b Pilsen, Czech, July 2, 19; m 43, Rhoda A M Burg; c P Randall & Ingrid B. *Educ:* Auburn Univ, BSc, 40; Swiss Fed Inst Technol, ScD, 66. *Hon Degrees:* ScD, Swiss Fed Inst Technol, 80. *Honors & Awards:* Murphee Award, Am Chem Soc, 72, Chem Contemp Technol Probs Award, 86 & Carothers Award, 87; Leo Friend Award, Am Chem Soc, 77; Wilhelm Award, Am Inst Chem Eng, 78; Lavoisier Medal, Soc Chem France, 83; Perkin Medal, Soc Chem Indust, 85; Pioneer Award, Am Inst Chemists, 74; DGKM Kolleg Award, 88; Nat Medal Technol, 92. *Prof Exp:* Asst, Univ Berlin, 38-39 & Bartol Res Found, Pa, 40-46; res assoc, Mobil Res & Develop Corp, 46-61, sr scientist, 61-67, mgr process res, 67-69, mgr, Cent Res Lab, 69-82, sr scientist & sci adv, 82-84. *Concurrent Pos:* Instr, Swarthmore Col, 42-43; vis prof, Princeton Univ, 74-76; agent, US Patent Off; chmn policy bd, Ctr Catalysis Sci & Technol, Univ Del, 77-81; mem, Energy Res Adv Bd, 85-90; consult, res & develop strategy, catalysis & biomed, 84- *Mem:* Nat Acad Eng; Am Chem Soc; Fel Am Phys Soc; fel Am Inst Chemists; Am Inst Chem Engrs. *Res:* Diffusion phenomena; petroleum processes; energy technology; basic and interdisciplinary phenomena in the sciences; angiogenesis; cell proliferation; biochemical pharmacology. *Mailing Add:* Bioeng Dept Univ Pa Philadelphia PA 19104-6392

**WEISZ, ROBERT STEPHEN,** INORGANIC CHEMISTRY. *Current Pos:* RETIRED. *Personal Data:* b New York, NY, May 24, 18; m 56, Noel Yao; c John, Catherine & Madeline. *Educ:* Cornell Univ, AB, 39, PhD(chem), 42. *Prof Exp:* Res fel, Westinghouse Elec & Mfg Co, 42, res engr, 42-46; res engr, Thomas A Edison, Inc, 46-49 & RCA Labs, 49-56; res dir, Telemeter Memories, Inc, 56-60, Ampex Comput Prod Co, 60-61 & Electronics Memories, Inc, 61-69; indust consult, 69-77. *Mem:* Am Chem Soc. *Res:* Reactions in solids; ceramics; electrical properties of inorganic compounds; magnetic materials. *Mailing Add:* 2109 Mt Calvary Rd Santa Barbara CA 93105

**WEISZ, ZVI S,** PHYSICS. *Current Pos:* chmn dept physics, 78-87, PROF PHYSICS, UNIV PR, 69- *Educ:* Hebrew Univ, PhD(physics), 62. *Concurrent Pos:* affil with Univ PR, 64- *Res:* Electrical and optical properties of thin films; hydrogenated amorphous silicon-germanium alloys; two dimensional electron systems; surface analysis. *Mailing Add:* Physics Dept Univ PR PO Box 23343 Rio Piedras PR 00931

**WEISZ-CARRINGTON, PAUL,** PATHOLOGY, IMMUNOLOGY. *Current Pos:* DIR LABS, PATH & IMMUNOL, SHREVEPORT VET MED CTR, 80- *Educ:* Nat Univ, Mex, MD, 71. *Prof Exp:* Prof path, MCV Va Commonwealth Univ. *Concurrent Pos:* Dir path & lab mech, McGuire Vet Admin Med Ctr, Richmond, Va. *Mem:* Am Asn Immunol; Am Asn Blood Banks; Am Asn Clin Pathologists; Col Am Pathologists; Am Asn Path. *Res:* Anatomic pathology; lymphoytes; immunoglobulin A. *Mailing Add:* Dept Path Chief Lab Med McGuire VA Med Ctr 1201 Broad Rock Rd Richmond VA 23249

**WEITH, HERBERT LEE,** NUCLEIC ACID CHEMISTRY, CHEMICAL SYNTHESIS. *Current Pos:* ASSOC PROF BIOCHEM, PURDUE UNIV, 76- *Educ:* Purdue Univ, PhD(biochem), 69. *Res:* Physical chemistry. *Mailing Add:* Dept Biochem Purdue Univ West Lafayette IN 47907-1968. *Fax:* 765-494-7877

**WEITKAMP, LOWELL R,** BIOCHEMICAL GENETICS. *Current Pos:* from asst prof to assoc prof, 69-78, PROF GEN, SCH MED, UNIV ROCHESTER, 78- *Personal Data:* b Lincoln, Nebr, June 13, 36; m 73; c 1. *Educ:* Reed Col, BA, 58; Univ Rochester, MD, 63; Univ Mich, MS, 66. *Honors & Awards:* Clarke Inst Award. *Prof Exp:* Internship, Univ Wis Hosp, Madison, 63-64; fel, Univ Mich, 64-66, res assoc, 66-69. *Concurrent Pos:* NIH res career develop award, 71-76; vis prof, Univ Inst Med Genetics, Univ Copenhagen, 73; vis fel, Dept Human Biol, John Curtin Sch Med Res, Australian Nat Univ, 75-76; NIMH res scientist develop award, 76-81; fel, Dept Clin Immunol, Univ Western Australia, 91-92. *Mem:* Am Genetic Asn; Am Soc Human Genetics; Int Soc Animal Genetics. *Res:* Biochemical genetic markers in susceptibility to nonmendelian familial diseases and decreased reproductive performance. *Mailing Add:* Div Genetics Univ Rochester 601 Elmwood Ave Rochester NY 14642-0001. *Fax:* 716-473-1482

**WEITKAMP, WILLIAM GEORGE,** NUCLEAR PHYSICS. *Current Pos:* sr res assoc, 68-73, res assoc prof, 73-78, RES PROF PHYSICS, UNIV WASH, 78-, TECH DIR, NUCLEAR PHYSICS LAB, 68- *Personal Data:* b Fremont, Nebr, June 22, 34; m 56; c 3. *Educ:* St Olaf Col, BA, 56; Univ Wis, MS, 61, PhD(physics), 65. *Prof Exp:* Res asst physics, Univ Wis, 59-64; res asst prof, Univ Wash, Seattle, 64-67; asst prof, Univ Pittsburgh, 67-68. *Concurrent Pos:* Acad guest, Fed Polytech, Zurich, Switz, 74-75. *Mem:* Am Phys Soc. *Res:* Polarization phenomena in reactions involving light nuclei; time reversal invarience in nuclear reactions; isobaric analog states in heavy nuclei; nuclear instrumentation. *Mailing Add:* 2019 Elouisast Seattle WA 98112

**WEITLAUF, HARRY,** REPRODUCTIVE PHYSIOLOGY. *Current Pos:* HEAD DEPT ANAT, TEX TECH UNIV HEALTH SCI CTR. *Personal Data:* b Seattle, Wash, July 8, 37; m 64. *Educ:* Univ Wash, BS, 59, MD, 63. *Prof Exp:* Fel reproductive physiol, Med Ctr, Univ Kans, 66-68, from asst prof to assoc prof anat, 68-74; assoc prof, Univ Ore Med Ctr, 74-80, prof, 80- *Mem:* Am Asn Anat; Soc Study Reproduction. *Res:* Blastocyst metabolism during the preimplantation phase of development. *Mailing Add:* Dept Cell Biol & Anat Tex Tech Univ Health Sci Ctr 3601 Fourth St Lubbock TX 79430-0001

**WEITSMAN, ALLEN WILLIAM,** MATHEMATICS. *Current Pos:* From asst prof to assoc prof, 68-74, PROF MATH, PURDUE UNIV, LAFAYETTE, 74- *Personal Data:* b Greenbelt, Md, July 11, 40; div; c 4. *Educ:* Syracuse Univ, BS, 62, MS, 64, PhD(math), 68. *Concurrent Pos:* NSF grants, 69-81; Sloan Found grant, 72. *Res:* Classical function theory. *Mailing Add:* 906 Sunrise Ave Lafayette IN 47904

**WEITZ, DAVID A,** COMPLEX FLUIDS, SOFT CONDENSED MATTER PHYSICS. *Current Pos:* PROF PHYSICS, DEPT PHYSICS & ASTRON, UNIV PA, 95- *Personal Data:* b Ottawa, Ont, Oct 3, 51. *Educ:* Univ Waterloo, BSc, 73; Harvard Univ, AM, 75, PhD(physics), 78. *Prof Exp:* Res physicist, Exxon Res & Eng, 78-95. *Mem:* Fel Am Phys Soc; Optical Soc Am; Am Chem Soc. *Res:* Structure and properties of soft materials such as colloids, emulsions, liquid crystals and biomaterials. *Mailing Add:* Dept Phys & Astron Univ Pa Philadelphia PA 19104-6396. *Fax:* 215-898-2010; *E-Mail:* weitz@ dept.physics.upenn.edu

**WEITZ, ERIC,** CHEMICAL PHYSICS, PHYSICAL CHEMISTRY. *Current Pos:* from asst prof to assoc prof, 74-84, PROF CHEM, NORTHWESTERN UNIV, EVANSTON, 84- *Personal Data:* b New York, NY, Sept 18, 47; m, Elizabeth W Burrell; c 2. *Educ:* Mass Inst Technol, BS, 68; Columbia Univ, PhD(chem), 72. *Prof Exp:* Res assoc chem, Univ Calif, Berkeley, 72-74. *Concurrent Pos:* Alfred P Sloan fel; vis fel, Joint Inst Lab Astrophys, 83-84. *Mem:* Fel Am Phys Soc; Am Chem Soc. *Res:* Vibrational energy transfer in small molecules and the relation of internal energy to chemical reactivity; applications to laser-induced chemistry; studies of matrix isolated molecules; laser induced surface processes; transient spectroscopy. *Mailing Add:* Dept Chem Northwestern Univ Evanston IL 60208

**WEITZ, JOHN HILLS,** ECONOMIC GEOLOGY. *Current Pos:* RETIRED. *Personal Data:* b Cleveland, Ohio, Sept 20, 16; m 45, Anne Moore; c Susan, Margaret & John Jr. *Educ:* Wesleyan Univ, BA, 38; Lehigh Univ, MS, 40; Pa State Univ, PhD(geol), 54. *Prof Exp:* Asst, Johns Hopkins Univ, 40-42; from jr mineral economist to mineral economist, US Bur Mines, Washington, DC, 42-46; coop geologist, State Geol Surv, Pa, 46-52; asst prof geol, Lehigh Univ, 47-52; geologist & secy, Independent Explosives Co, 52-61, pres, 61-88. *Mem:* AAAS; Geol Soc Am; Mineral Soc Am; Am Inst Mining, Metall & Petrol Engrs. *Res:* Economic geology; clay minerals. *Mailing Add:* 12 Chippenham Ct Rocky River OH 44116

**WEITZ, JOSEPH LEONARD,** GEOLOGY. *Current Pos:* from assoc prof to prof, 62-83, EMER PROF GEOL, COLO STATE UNIV, 83- *Personal Data:* b Cleveland, Ohio, June 2, 22; m 49, Jean Corthell; c Sally A, Leonard Corthell & Phoebe J. *Educ:* Wesleyan Univ, BA, 44; Yale Univ, MS, 46, PhD(geol), 54. *Prof Exp:* Geologist, Fuels Br, US Geol Surv, 48-55 & Independent Explosives Co, Pa, 55-58; asst prof geol, Wesleyan Univ, 58-60 & Colo State Univ, 60-61; assoc prof, Hanover Col, 61-62. *Concurrent Pos:* Geologist, US Geol Surv, 66-88; dir, Earth Sci Curric Proj, Colo, 67-69; mem, Coun Educ Geol Sci, 67-72; ed, J Geol Educ, 71-74. *Mem:* Geol Soc Am; Am Asn Petrol Geologists; Sigma Xi; Nat Asn Geol Teachers. *Res:* Geology of mineral fuels; Mesozoic stratigraphy; structural geology; geologic compilation. *Mailing Add:* 1301 Stoney Hill Dr Ft Collins CO 80525-1297

**WEITZMAN, STANLEY HOWARD,** ICHTHYOLOGY. *Current Pos:* assoc cur, 63-67, CUR, DIV FISHES, DEPT VERT ZOOL, SMITHSONIAN INST, 67- *Personal Data:* b Mill Valley, Calif, Mar 16, 27; m 48; c 2. *Educ:* Univ Calif, AB, 51, AM, 53; Stanford Univ, PhD(biol), 60. *Honors & Awards:* Robert H Gibbs Jr Mem Award, Am Soc Ichthyologists & Herpetologists. *Prof Exp:* Sr lab technician, Univ Calif, 50-56; instr anat, Sch Med, Stanford Univ, 57-62. *Mem:* Am Soc Ichthyologists & Herpetologists; Am Fisheries Soc; Soc Syst Zool; Soc Study Evolution. *Res:* Evolution, systematics and morphology of fishes, especially South American freshwater fishes. *Mailing Add:* Div Fishes Nhb Stop Smithsonian Inst Washington DC 20560-0001. *Fax:* 202-357-2986

**WEITZNER, HAROLD,** APPLIED MATHEMATICS, PLASMA PHYSICS. *Current Pos:* assoc res scientist, NY Univ, 59-60, res scientist, 60-62, from asst prof to assoc prof, 62-69, PROF MATH, COURANT INST MATH SCI, NY UNIV, 69-, DIR, MAGNETOFLUID DYNAMICS DIV, 87-, CHAIR, DEPT MATH, 88- *Personal Data:* b Boston, Mass, May 19, 33; m 62; c 2. *Educ:* Univ Calif, AB, 54; Harvard Univ, AM, 55, PhD(physics), 58. *Prof Exp:* Consult, Los Alamos Nat Lab, Univ Calif, 62-, Lawrence Livermore Lab, Livermore, 77-81 & Oak Ridge Nat Lab, 78-; Magnetic Fusion Energy Adv Comt, 87-90. *Mem:* Fel Am Phys Soc. *Res:* Wave propagation problems in magnetohydrodynamics; kinetic theory and plasma oscillation problems; magnetohydrodynamic equilibrium; stability theory. *Mailing Add:* Courant Inst Math Sci NY Univ 251 Mercer St New York NY 10012-1185. *Fax:* 212-995-4121

**WEITZNER, STANLEY,** pathology, for more information see previous edition

**WEJKSNORA, PETER JAMES,** GENE EXPRESSION, SOMATIC CELL HYBRIDS. *Current Pos:* asst prof genetics, 81-87, ASSOC PROF BIOL SCI, DEPT BIOL SCI, UNIV WIS, MILWAUKEE, 87- *Personal Data:* b New York, NY, Jan 12, 50; c 1. *Educ:* Brooklyn Col, BS, 72; Brandeis Univ, PhD(biol), 77. *Prof Exp:* Fel, Albert Einstein Col Med, 77-81. *Mem:* Am Soc Cell Biol; Am Soc Microbiol; Am Soc Biol Chem. *Res:* Molecular biology; control of eukaryotic gene expression particularly ribosomal RNA and protein genes; gene control in somatic cell hybrids. *Mailing Add:* Dept Biol Sci Univ Wis PO Box 413 Milwaukee WI 53201-3102. *Fax:* 414-229-3926; *E-Mail:* pjw@csd4.csd.uwm.edu

**WEKELL, MARLEEN MARIE,** FOOD MICROBIOLOGY, BIOCHEMISTRY. *Current Pos:* DIR SEAFOOD PROD RES CTR, US FOOD & DRUG ADMIN, BOTHELL, WASH, 82- *Personal Data:* b Spokane, Wash, Sept 26, 42; m 64, John C; c Wendy A (Alfaro). *Educ:* Seattle Univ, BS, 64; Univ Wash, MS, 72, PhD(environ microbiol, 75. *Prof Exp:* Teaching asst Dept Chem, Seattle Univ, 61-65; res technician biochem, Sch Med, Univ Wash, 65-70, teaching asst marine biochem, Sch Fisheries, 70-72, res asst environ microbiol, Dept Food Sci, 72-75; res chemist environ biochem, Nat Marine Fisheries Serv, Seattle, Wash, 75-77; asst prof, Dept Nutrit Sci, Univ Wash, 77-82. *Concurrent Pos:* Traineeship, US Environ Protection Agency, 70-72; W F Thompson, scholar, Univ Wash, 72; chmn Local Sect, Inst Food Technologist, 82-83; adj res prof, Dept Chem, Seattle Univ, 86-; adj res assoc prof, Dept Food Sci, Univ Wash, 86-92; adj res prof, Sch Fisheries, 92-; gen refcrcc seafood, Asn Official Analytical Chemists, Int Asn Milk, Food & Environ Sanitarians, 87; gen referee seafood, Asn Official Anal Chemists. *Mem:* AAAS; Am Soc Microbiol; Am Chem Soc; Am Anthrop Asn. *Res:* Environmental and food microbiology; food chemistry; marine biotoxins (PSP, domoic acid, brevetoxins, ciguatera); development of microbial and chemical indicators of seafood quality; application molecular biological techniques for detection of microbial pathogens in seafoods. *Mailing Add:* 21431 NE Sixth St Redmond WA 98053-3906. *Fax:* 425-483-4996

**WEKEZER, JERZY WLADYSLAW,** FINITE ELEMENT ANALYSIS & APPLICATIONS, STRUCTURES. *Current Pos:* PROF & DEPT CHAIR, DEPT CIVIL ENG, FLA A&M UNIV/FLA STATE UNIV COL ENG, 94- *Personal Data:* b Czestochowa, Poland, June 27, 46; US citizen; m 83, Henryka Debska; c Michal & Joanna. *Educ:* Gdansk Tech Unv, Poland, BS & MS, 69, PhD(struct mech), 74. *Prof Exp:* Asst prof civil eng dept, Gdansk Tech Univ, Poland, 74-81; vis asst prof surv & dynamics, Civil Eng Dept, Univ Southern Calif, Los Angeles, 82-85; from assoc prof to prof, Sch Eng, Univ Alaska, Anchorage, 85-94; dept head, 90-94. *Concurrent Pos:* Lectr struct anal structs dept, Univ Basrah, Iraq, 76-80 & 82; res hwy engr, Fed Hwy Admin, 91-94. *Mem:* Am Soc Civil Engrs. *Res:* Numerical and finite element methods applied to structures and especially thin-walled beams; statics, dynamics, stability and non-linear analysis of structures; engineering applications; finite element modeling of highway safety structures. *Mailing Add:* Fla State Univ Col Eng 2525 Pottsdamer Rd Tallahassee FL 32310

**WEKSLER, BABETTE BARBASH,** HEMATOLOGY, INTERNAL MEDICINE. *Current Pos:* asst prof, 70-75, assoc prof, 75-80, PROF MED, MED COL, CORNELL UNIV, 81- *Personal Data:* b New York, NY, Jan 18, 37; m 58; c 2. *Educ:* Swarthmore Col, BA, 58; Columbia Univ, MD, 63. *Prof Exp:* Intern med, Bronx Munic Hosp, 63-64; resident, Georgetown Univ Hosp, 65-67; USPHS fel microbiol, Wright Fleming Inst St Mary's Hosp Med Sch, London, 67-68; Am Cancer Soc Clin fel hemat, NY Hosp Cornell Med Ctr, 68-69. *Concurrent Pos:* Assoc attend physician, NY Hosp Cornell Med Ctr, 75-80, attend physician, 81- *Mem:* Fel NY Acad Sci (gov, 78-80); Am Fedn Clin Res; Am Soc Hemat; Am Physiol Soc; Am Soc Clin Invest; Am Asn Physicians. *Res:* Platelet physiology and biochemistry; inflammation and hemostasis; prostaglandins; vascular wall biology. *Mailing Add:* Dept Med Cornell Univ Med Col 1300 York Ave Rm C-606 New York NY 10021. *E-Mail:* babette@med.cornell.edu

**WEKSLER, MARC EDWARD,** MEDICINE, IMMUNOLOGY. *Current Pos:* From asst prof to assoc prof, 70-78, WRIGHT PROF MED, MED COL, CORNELL UNIV, 78-, DIR, DIV GERIAT & GERONT, 78- *Personal Data:* b New York, NY, Apr 16, 37; m 58; c 2. *Educ:* Swarthmore Col, BA, 58; Columbia Univ, MD, 62. *Honors & Awards:* Merit Award, NIH, 90. *Concurrent Pos:* USPHS fel, Transplantation Unit, St Mary's Hosp, London, Eng, 67-68 & spec fel, NY Hosp, 68-70; asst attend physician, NY Hosp, 70-75, assoc attend physician, 75-78, attend physician, 78 & dir geront & geriat; adj physician, Mem Hosp, NY; law lectr, Cornell Univ, 80; consult, World Health Org, Pontifical Acad Sci, Nat Res Coun; pres, Am Fedn Aging Res. *Mem:* Am Soc Clin Invest; fel Am Col Physicians; Am Asn Immunologists; Geront Soc; Am Asn Physicians. *Res:* Gerontology and cellular immunology. *Mailing Add:* Dept Med Cornell Univ Med Col 1300 York Ave New York NY 10021-4896

**WEKSTEIN, DAVID ROBERT,** PHYSIOLOGY, GERONTOLOGY. *Current Pos:* From instr to assoc prof, 62-76, PROF PHYSIOL, COL MED, UNIV KY, 78-, ASSOC DIR, SANDERS BROWN CTR, AGING, 79- *Personal Data:* b Boston, Mass, Feb 26, 37; m 58, Merle Barbara Weiner; c Lauren J, Karen G, Debra S & Jeffrey B. *Educ:* Boston Univ, AB, 57, MA, 58; Univ Rochester, PhD(physiol), 62. *Mem:* AAAS; Soc Exp Biol & Med; Geront Soc; Am Soc Zoologists; Am Physiol Soc; Am Geriatric Soc. *Res:* Developmental physiology; physiology of temperature regulation; biology of aging; circadian rhythms; Alzheimer's disease. *Mailing Add:* Dept Physiol & Biophys Univ Ky Col Med Lexington KY 40536-0230

**WELBER, IRWIN,** TELECOMMUNICATIONS, NATIONAL SECURITY RESEARCH & DEVELOPMENT. *Current Pos:* RETIRED. *Personal Data:* b New York, NY, Mar 3, 24; m 46; c 3. *Educ:* Union Col, BS, 48; Rennselaer Polytech Inst, MS, 50. *Prof Exp:* Staff mem transmission systs, Bell Tel Labs, 50-65, dir microwave transmission, 65-71, from assoc exec dir to exec dir transmission syst, 71-81, vpres transmission systs, AT&T Bell Labs, 81-85; sr exec vpres, Nat Lab, Sandia Corp, 85-86, pres, 86-89. *Mem:* Nat Acad Eng; AAAS; NY Acad Sci; fel Inst Elec & Electronics Engrs; Sigma Xi. *Res:* Telecommunications systems including first active communication satellite-Telstar; research and activity in submarine cable systems and microwave radio. *Mailing Add:* 1604 La Tuna Pl SE Albuquerque NM 87123. *Fax:* 505-323-5450; *E-Mail:* irwin@lobo.net

**WELBOURNE, TOMAS C,** PHYSIOLOGY. *Current Pos:* Assoc prof, 69-77, PROF PHYSIOL, LA STATE UNIV MED CTR, 77- *Personal Data:* b Milwaukee, Wis, Nov 30, 42. *Educ:* Cornell Univ, BS, 64; Univ Tenn, PhD(physiol), 68. *Mem:* Am Physiol Soc; Am Soc Cell Biol. *Res:* Physiology. *Mailing Add:* Dept Physiol & Biophys La State Univ Med Ctr PO Box 33932 Shreveport LA 71130-3932

**WELBY, CHARLES WILLIAM,** HYDROGEOLOGY, STRATIGRAPHY. *Current Pos:* from assoc prof to prof, 65-91, EMER PROF GEOL, NC STATE UNIV, 91- *Personal Data:* b Bakersfield, Calif, Oct 9, 26; m 48, Eleanor Morse; c Mary L & Nancy S. *Educ:* Univ Calif, BS, 48, MS, 49; Mass Inst Technol, PhD(geol), 52. *Prof Exp:* Geologist, Calif Co, 52-54; asst prof geol, Middlebury Col, 54-58, Trinity Col, Conn, 58-61 & Rennselaer Polytech Inst, 61-62; assoc prof geol & chmn dept, Southern Miss Univ, 62-65. *Concurrent Pos:* Consult groundwater, environ geol, remote sensing, shoreline erosion. *Mem:* Am Asn Petrol Geologists; fel Geol Soc Am; Soc Econ Paleont & Mineral; Asn Eng Geologists; Nat Water Well Asn; Sigma Xi. *Res:* Occurrence and management of ground water; structure and stratigraphy; ground water pollution; environmental geology; engineering geology; ground water and land use planning. *Mailing Add:* Dept Marine Earth Atmospheric Sci NC State Univ PO Box 8208 Raleigh NC 27695-8208

**WELCH, AARON WADDINGTON,** BOTANY. *Current Pos:* RETIRED. *Personal Data:* b Georgetown, Md, July 25, 16; m 41; c 3. *Educ:* Univ Md, BS, 37; Iowa State Col, PhD(plant path), 42. *Prof Exp:* Mgr, Southeastern Exp Sta, Iowa, 40-42; assoc pathologist, Div Forage Crops, USDA, 45-47; plant pathologist, Exp Sta, E I Du Pont de Nemours & Co, Inc, 47-60, mgr res & develop farm, Clayton, 60-73, dir res & develop farm, Clayton, 73-88. *Mem:* Am Phytopath Soc. *Res:* Plant pathology; helminthology; herbicides. *Mailing Add:* 5922 Carmel Lane Raleigh NC 27609

**WELCH, ARNOLD D(EMERRITT),** pharmacology, chemotherapy, for more information see previous edition

**WELCH, ASHLEY JAMES,** ELECTRICAL & BIOMEDICAL ENGINEERING. *Current Pos:* prof elec eng & biomed engr, 75-86, MARRON E FORSMAN PROF ELEC & COMPUTER ENG & BIOMED ENG, UNIV TEX, AUSTIN, 86- *Personal Data:* b Ft Worth, Tex, May 3, 33; m 52; c 3. *Educ:* Tex Tech Col, BS, 55; Southern Methodist Univ, MS, 59; Rice Univ, PhD(elec eng), 64. *Prof Exp:* Aerophys engr, Gen Dynamics, Ft Worth, 57-60; instr elec eng, Rice Univ, 60-64. *Mem:* Fel Inst Elec & Electronics Engrs; Am Soc Laser Surg & Med. *Res:* Laser-tissue interaction; application of lasers in medicine. *Mailing Add:* Dept Elec Eng Univ Tex Austin TX 78712-1104

**WELCH, CLARK MOORE,** CELLULOSE CHEMISTRY, COTTON TEXTILE CHEMISTRY. *Current Pos:* res chemist, 56-66, res leader, 66-82, RES CHEMIST, SOUTHERN REGIONAL RES CTR, 82- *Personal Data:* b Mountain Grove, Mo, Mar 3, 25; m 66; c 3. *Educ:* Univ Tenn, BS, 46, MS, 47, PhD(chem), 52. *Honors & Awards:* Fed Inventors Award, US Dept Com, 85; Award Merit, Am Asn Textile Chemists & Colorists, 85; Outstanding Scientist, Southern Regional Res Ctr, USDA, 87, Agr Res Serv Technol Transfer Award, 92. *Prof Exp:* Res chemist, Monsanto Chem Co, 47-48; fel, Univ Tenn, 52; asst prof, La State Univ, 52-56. *Mem:* Am Chem Soc; Am Asn Textile Chemists & Colorists; AAAS; Sigma Xi. *Res:* Polycarboxylic acids as formaldehyde-free durable press reagents for cotton fabrics; development of glyoxal glycol coreactants as formaldehyde-free crosslinking agents for cotton; metal complexes of hydrogen peroxide as durable antibacterial agents for cotton textiles; high speed esterification of cellulose. *Mailing Add:* 5704 Ruth St Metairie LA 70003

**WELCH, CLAUDE ALTON,** ZOOLOGY. *Current Pos:* prof, 69-73, chmn dept, 69-77, O T WALTER PROF BIOL, MACALESTER COL, 73- *Personal Data:* b Flint, Mich, Oct 24, 21; m 49; c 2. *Educ:* Mich State Univ, BS, 48, PhD(zool), 57. *Prof Exp:* From instr to prof natural sci, Mich State Univ, 53-69. *Concurrent Pos:* Supvr blue version writing team, Biol Sci Curric Study, 61; consult, Adaptation Comt, Japan, 63-65 & Turkey, 65. *Mem:* AAAS; Nat Asn Biol Teachers (pres, 72); Nat Sci Teachers Asn. *Res:* Cell physiology. *Mailing Add:* 148 El Viento Green Valley AZ 85614-2222

**WELCH, CLETUS NORMAN,** PHYSICAL INORGANIC CHEMISTRY. *Current Pos:* Res assoc, 66-81, sr res assoc, 81-86, SCIENTIST, PPG INDUSTS, INC, 86- *Personal Data:* b Convoy, Ohio, Feb 2, 37; m 60; c 2. *Educ:* Bowling Green State Univ, BS, 61; Ohio State Univ, MS, 64, PhD(chem), 66. *Mem:* Am Chem Soc; Soc Vac Coaters. *Res:* Halogen and halogen-oxygen chemistry; synthesis of electrocatalysts; electrode processes; electrochemical cell design and materials of construction; electroless, electrolytic and vapor deposition of metallic coatings; photochronics, electrochromics, thin films. *Mailing Add:* 3317 Hermar Dr Murrysville PA 15668-1602

**WELCH, DAVID O(TIS),** MATERIALS SCIENCE, SOLID STATE PHYSICS. *Current Pos:* from assoc physicist to physicist, Physics Dept, Brookhaven Nat Lab, 72-77, Mat Sci Div, 77-90, from asst head to head, Mat Sci Div, Dept Appl Sci, 82-92, dept head, 92-96, SR MAT SCIENTIST, SR PHYSICIST, BROOKHAVEN NAT LAB, 90-, DIV HEAD, 96- *Personal Data:* b Richmond, Va, Mar 9, 38; m 78, Sharon Doyle; c Wendy & Alison. *Educ:* Univ Tenn, BS, 60; Mass Inst Technol, SM, 62; Univ Pa, PhD(metall), 64. *Prof Exp:* Res assoc metal physics, Res Inst Advan Studies, Martin Co, 62; NATO res fel, Solid State Physics Div, Atomic Energy Res Estab, Harwell, Eng, 64-65; asst prof metal phys, Solid State & Mat Prog, Princeton Univ, 66-72, res fel, 72. *Concurrent Pos:* Consult, Metals & Ceramics Div, Oak Ridge Nat Lab, 66-68; consult & vis scientist, Mat Sci Div, Argonne Nat Lab, 68; vis prof, Univ Sao Paulo, 70, Univ Campinas, 88; vis scientist, KFA Julich, 74; adj prof mat sci, State Univ NY, Stony Brook, 80-; mem solid state sci panel, Nat Res Coun, 80-84. *Mem:* AAAS; Am Phys Soc; Sigma Xi; Mats Res Soc; Metals Minerals & Mat Soc. *Res:* Theory of materials, especially the thermal, cohesive, superconducting, and magnetic properies of metals and ceramics. *Mailing Add:* Bldg 480 Brookhaven Nat Lab PO Box 5000 Upton NY 11973-5000. *Fax:* 516-344-4071; *E-Mail:* welch@sun2.bnl.gov

**WELCH, DAVID WARREN,** FISHERIES OCEANOGRAPHY & CLIMATE CHANGE. *Current Pos:* Fel, 84-86, res scientist, 86-90, PROG HEAD, HIGH SEAS SALMON RES, DEPT FISHERIES & OCEANS, GOVT CAN, 90- *Personal Data:* b Montreal, Que, Nov 10, 55; m 80, Masako Takada; c Mariko, Kenji & Erika. *Educ:* Univ Toronto, BSc, 77; Dalhousie Univ, PhD(oceang), 85. *Concurrent Pos:* Can mem, Salmon Subcomt, Int NPac Fisheries Comn, 88-92, Sub Arctic Gyre Working Group, NPac Marine Sci Orgn, 93-, NPac Anadromous Fish Comn, 93; chmn, Tech Working Group, Faser River Task Force, Integrated Salmon Prod & Mgt Plan, 93- *Res:* Developed and led a substantial international research effort to study the factors determining the oceanic productivity of salmon; develop and apply new operations research techniques to improve fisheries management. *Mailing Add:* Pac Biol Sta Nanaimo BC V9R 5K6 Can

**WELCH, DEAN EARL,** ORGANIC CHEMISTRY. *Current Pos:* RETIRED. *Personal Data:* b Aledo, Ill, Aug 5, 37; m 58; c 6. *Educ:* Monmouth Col, BA, 59; Mass Inst Technol, PhD(org chem), 63. *Prof Exp:* Chemist, Escambia Chem Corp, 63-64; assoc scientist, Salsbury Labs, 64-66, scientist, 66-68, qual assurance dir, 68-69, chem res dir, 69-71, res dir, 71-72, vpres res, 72-84, vpres opers, 84-94. *Mem:* Am Chem Soc. *Res:* Organic synthesis; research and development administration. *Mailing Add:* 910 Charwood Dr Lexington KY 40515-5007

**WELCH, FRANK JOSEPH,** ORGANIC CHEMISTRY. *Current Pos:* RETIRED. *Personal Data:* b Fresno, Calif, Aug 5, 29; m 54; c 5. *Educ:* Fresno State Univ, BS, 51; Stanford Univ, PhD(org chem), 54. *Prof Exp:* Res chemist polymers, Union Carbide Chem Co, 54-62, group leader latex polymerization, Res & Develop Dept, Union Carbide Corp, 62-71; dir res, Avery Label Div, Avery Int, 71-88, sr res assoc, Avery Dennison Corp, 88-96. *Mem:* Tech Asn Pulp & Paper Indust; Am Chem Soc; Tech Asn Graphic Arts. *Res:* Ionic and free radical polymerization kinetics; organo-metallic and organophosphorus chemistry; latex polymerization; coatings and printing inks; adhesives. *Mailing Add:* 9339 Amelga Dr Whittier CA 90603-1001

**WELCH, GARTH LARRY,** ACADEMIC ADMINISTRATION, INORGANIC CHEMISTRY. *Current Pos:* RETIRED. *Personal Data:* b Brigham City, Utah, Feb 14, 37; m 60; c 6. *Educ:* Univ Utah, BS, 59, PhD(inorg chem), 63. *Prof Exp:* Fel, Univ Calif, Los Angeles, 62-64; from asst prof to prof chem, Weber State Univ, 64-97, dean, Sch Natural Sci, 74-83, exec dir bus affairs, 83-89, assoc vpres phys fac, 90-92. *Concurrent Pos:* Vis prof, Brigham Young Univ, 80. *Mem:* Am Chem Soc; Sigma Xi. *Res:* Kinetics of complex ions; reversion rates of polymers. *Mailing Add:* 3910 N 800 W Ogden UT 84414

**WELCH, GARY ALAN,** ASTRONOMY. *Current Pos:* asst prof, 74-78, ASSOC PROF ASTRON, SAINT MARY'S UNIV, HALIFAX, 78- *Personal Data:* b Santa Monica, Calif, June 19, 42. *Educ:* Harvey Mudd Col, BSc, 64; Univ Wash, MSc, 67, PhD(astron), 69. *Prof Exp:* Postdoctoral res assoc, Van Vleck Observ, Wesleyan Univ, 69-72, Mich State Univ, 72-73; asst prof astron, Wheaton Col, 73-74. *Concurrent Pos:* Hon fel astron, Univ Wis, Madison, 80-81. *Mem:* Int Astron Union; Am Astron Soc; Can Astron Soc; Royal Astron Soc Can; Astron Soc Pac. *Res:* Structure stellar content and evolution of ES0 galaxies; photometric studies of peculiar early-type galaxies; digital imaging techniques and processing of digital data in astronomy. *Mailing Add:* Dept Astron Saint Mary's Univ Robie St Halifax NS B3H 3C3 Can

**WELCH, GARY WILLIAM,** ANESTHESIOLOGY, CRITICAL CARE MEDICINE. *Current Pos:* DEAN, HEALTH SCI, TEX TECH UNIV, 94- *Personal Data:* b Buffalo, NY, Jan 4, 43; m 72; c 5. *Educ:* Univ Va, BA,64, MD, 70, PhD(anat), 70, JD, 87. *Prof Exp:* Chief anesthesiol sect, US Army Inst Surg Res, 74-76; asst prof, Univ Mass Med Ctr, 77-79, dir, Surg Intensive Care Unit, 78-82, vchmn, Dept Anesthesiol, 80-81, actg chmn, 81-82, assoc prof, Anesthesiol & Surg, 79-94, chmn, Dept Anethesiol & assoc dir, Surg Intensive Care Unit, 82-94. *Mem:* Soc Critical Care Med; Am Shock Soc; Am Burn Asn; Am Soc Anesthesiologists. *Res:* High frequency; high pressure; jet ventilation; metabolic changes following major surgery; use of epidural narcotics for pain relief; fluid therapy for treatment of shock; genetic analysis malignant hyperthermia. *Mailing Add:* Univ Mass Med Ctr Anes 55 N Lake Ave Worcester MA 01655-0001

**WELCH, GEORGE BURNS,** AGRICULTURAL ENGINEERING. *Current Pos:* RETIRED. *Personal Data:* b Soso, Miss, Nov 23, 20; m 54; c 1. *Educ:* Miss State Univ, BS, 47; Tex Agr & Mech Col, MS, 50; Okla State Univ, PhD(eng), 65. *Prof Exp:* Instr agr, Jones County Jr Col, 47-48; instr agr eng, Miss State Univ, 48-49, assoc agr engr, Miss Agr Exp Sta, 51-62, assoc prof agr eng, 52-62; res asst, Okla State Univ, 62-65; prof agr eng & agr engr, Miss State Univ, 65-80, prof agr & biol eng, 80-91. *Concurrent Pos:* Miss State Univ-US Agency Int Develop seed processing engr, Brazil, 70-72. *Mem:* Am Soc Agr Engrs. *Res:* Design of agricultural machinery and agricultural buildings; design of seed processing and storage facilities for tropical countries. *Mailing Add:* 301 Colonial Circle Starkville MS 39759

**WELCH, GEORGE RICKEY,** THEORETICAL BIOCHEMISTRY, BIOPHYSICAL CHEMISTRY. *Current Pos:* ASST PROF BIOL SCI, UNIV NEW ORLEANS, 78- *Personal Data:* b Rockwood, Tenn, May 29, 47; m 67; c 2. *Educ:* Univ Tenn, BS, 70, PhD(biochem), 75. *Prof Exp:* Res fel theoret biophys, Univ Libre Bruxelles, 75-77; res scientist biochem, Univ Tex Med Sch, 77-78. *Concurrent Pos:* Res fel, Solvay Int Inst Physics & Chem, 75-77. *Mem:* AAAS; Am Phys Soc; Biophys Soc. *Res:* Enzymology and metabolic regulation; theoretical biophysical chemistry; modeling of biochemical processes; bioenergetics. *Mailing Add:* Dept Biol Sci Univ New Orleans 2000 Lakeshore Dr New Orleans LA 70148-0001

**WELCH, GORDON E,** MICROBIOLOGY. *Current Pos:* assoc prof, 67-73, PROF BIOL, ANGELO STATE UNIV, 73-, DEAN COL SCI, 77- *Personal Data:* b Sabinal, Tex, Aug 20, 33; m 57; c 3. *Educ:* Southwest Tex State Univ, BS, 60, MA, 62; Tex A&M Univ, PhD(microbiol), 66. *Prof Exp:* Chmn dept biol & chem, Southwest Tex Jr Col, 60-62; assoc prof biol, San Antonio Col, 66-67. *Concurrent Pos:* Consult, Bexar Co Hosp Dist, San Antonio, Tex, 66. *Mem:* AAAS; Am Soc Microbiol; Am Inst Biol Sci. *Res:* Virology, particularly myxoviruses, their nature, properties and pathogenicity. *Mailing Add:* Dean Sci Angelo State Univ San Angelo TX 76909-0001

**WELCH, GRAEME P,** BIOPHYSICS. *Current Pos:* RETIRED. *Personal Data:* b Los Angeles, Calif, Nov 25, 17; m 45, Florence Clarkson; c 4. *Educ:* Univ Calif, Los Angeles, AB, 40; Univ Calif, Berkeley, MA, 50, PhD(biophys), 57. *Prof Exp:* Assoc physicist, Div War Res, Univ Calif, 41-45, physicist, Donner Lab, 48-59; engr biophys, Saclay Nuclear Res Ctr, France, 59-61; biophysicist, Donner Lab, Berkeley Radiation Lab, Univ Calif, Berkeley, 61-80. *Mem:* Radiation Res Soc. *Res:* Biological effects of radiation; physics and dosimetry of heavy-particle radiations. *Mailing Add:* 1020 Oxford St Berkeley CA 94707

**WELCH, H(OMER) WILLIAM,** ELECTRONIC & ELECTRICAL ENGINEERING. *Current Pos:* asst dean, Col Eng Sci, Ariz State Univ, 68-80, PROF, 67-, DIR, PROG SOC, VALUES & TECHNOL, 79-, EMER PROF ENG, ARIZ STATE UNIV, 87- *Personal Data:* b Beardstown, Ill, Oct 21, 20; m 42; c 2. *Educ:* DePauw Univ, BA, 42; Univ Mich, MS, 49, PhD, 52. *Prof Exp:* Asst physics & electronics, Univ Wis, 42-43; res assoc, Radio Res Lab, Harvard Univ, 43-45; instr physics, Purdue Univ, 45-46; res physicist, Eng Res Inst, Univ Mich, 46-50, proj leader, Electronic Defense Group, 51-53, from assoc prof to prof elec eng, 53-57; dir res & develop, Motorola Mil Electronics Div, 57-62, gen mgr control syst div, 62-66, asst to chief tech off, 66-67. *Concurrent Pos:* Mem adv groups, US Dept Defense. *Mem:* Fel Inst Elec & Electronics Engrs; Am Soc Eng Educ; Soc Hist Technol; fel AAAS. *Res:* Microwave tubes and solid state devices; communications systems; integrated microelectronics; remote monitoring and control systems; social impacts of technology. *Mailing Add:* 5206 E Osborn Rd Phoenix AZ 85018

**WELCH, HUGH GORDON,** EXERCISE PHYSIOLOGY, RESPIRATORY PHYSIOLOGY. *Current Pos:* assoc prof, 68-76, PROF PHYSIOL, UNIV TENN, KNOXVILLE, 76- *Personal Data:* b Memphis, Tenn, Oct 30, 37; m 59; c 2. *Educ:* Lambuth Col, BA, 59; Univ Fla, PhD(physiol), 66. *Prof Exp:* Asst prof, Univ Mich, Ann Arbor, 66-68. *Concurrent Pos:* Guest scientist, Univ Copenhagen, Denmark, 74-75. *Mem:* Am Physiol Soc; Am Col Sports Med. *Res:* Physiology of exercise-in particular in the study of those factors that limit human work capacity in health and in certain disease states. *Mailing Add:* Dept Zool Univ Tenn 2173 Tudor Mountain Rd Gatlinburg TN 37738-9803

**WELCH, J PHILIP,** HUMAN GENETICS. *Current Pos:* from asst prof to assoc prof, 67-68, PROF PEDIAT, ATLANTIC RES CTR, DALHOUSIE UNIV, 86-; DIR, CATOGENETICS DIV, IWK-GRACE HEALTH CTR. *Personal Data:* b Macclesfield, Eng, June 18, 33; m 58, Elvira Gonnella; c Jonathan, Jeremy, Andrew & Alison. *Educ:* Univ Edinburgh, MB & ChB, 58; Johns Hopkins Univ, PhD, 69. *Prof Exp:* Fel med, Johns Hopkins Hosp, 63-67. *Concurrent Pos:* Consult, IWK-Grace Health Ctr, Queen Elizabeth II Health Sci Ctr, Queen Elizabeth Hosp, Charlottetown PEI, St John Reg Hosp, Sr John N B, Reg Hosp, Bathway, NB. *Mem:* Am Soc Human Genetics; Am Fedn Clin Res; Am Asn Advan Aging Res; Can Genetics Soc; Soc Study Social Biol; Can fel Col Med Genetics. *Res:* Biochemical, behavioral and cytogenetic aspect of mental abilities and aberrations; cancer genetics; adult onset genetic disorder. *Mailing Add:* Atlantic Res Ctr WK-Grace Health Ctr Box 3070 Halifax NS B3S 3G9 Can. *Fax:* 902-428-8709

**WELCH, JAMES ALEXANDER,** ANIMAL PHYSIOLOGY, PHYSIOLOGY OF REPRODUCTION IN DOMESTIC ANIMALS. *Current Pos:* From asst prof to assoc prof animal husb, Univ WVa, 52-60, actg chmn dept animal sci, 62, prof & animal scientist, 60-87, EMER PROF ANIMAL SCI, UNIV WVA, 88- *Personal Data:* b Versailles, Ky, May 25, 24; m 51, Doris N Cromley; c Thomas D & Paul D. *Educ:* Univ Ky, BS, 47; Univ Ill, PhD(animal sci), 52. *Concurrent Pos:* Chief party, WVa Univ-AID contract team, Uganda & lectr, Vet Training Inst, Entebbe, 63-66. *Mem:* Fel AAAS. *Res:* Estrus control in cattle; non-protein nitrogen utilization by ruminants. *Mailing Add:* 1370 Headlee Ave Morgantown WV 26505

**WELCH, JAMES EDWARD,** GENETICS, PLANT BREEDING. *Current Pos:* from asst to assoc olericulturist, 47-79, EMER ASSOC OLERICULTURIST, EXP STA, UNIV CALIF, DAVIS, 79- *Personal Data:* b San Rafael, Calif, July 19, 11; m 37, Doris Culbertson; c Nancy J, James R & Wendee A (Smith). *Educ:* Univ Calif, BS, 34, MS, 35; Cornell Univ, PhD(genetics), 42. *Honors & Awards:* Western Res Man of Yr Award, Pac Seedmens Asn, 65. *Prof Exp:* Trainee agron, Soil Conserv Serv, USDA, 35, jr agr aide, 35-36, agr aide, 36; jr olericulturist, Exp Sta, Univ Hawaii, 36-38, asst olericulturist, 38-39; asst, Maize Genetics Coop, Cornell Univ, 40-42; asst horticulturist, Exp Sta, La State Univ, 42-43; assoc horticulturist, Regional Veg Breeding Lab, USDA, SC, 43-47. *Concurrent Pos:* Lectr veg crops, Col Agr, Univ Calif, Davis, 49-59 & 76-79; collabr, Plant Sci Res Div, USDA, 58-74. *Mem:* Fel AAAS; Am Inst Biol Sci; Am Soc Hort Sci; Am Genetic Asn. *Res:* Plant morphological characters associated with earworm resistance in maize; genetic linkage in autotetraploid maize; genetics of male sterility in the carrot; breeding improved varieties of vegetable crops, especially sweet corn, lima beans, carrots, celery, tomatoes and lettuce. *Mailing Add:* 739 A St Davis CA 95616-3604

**WELCH, JAMES GRAHAM,** ANIMAL NUTRITION. *Current Pos:* assoc prof, 67-70, PROF ANIMAL SCI, UNIV VT, 70- *Personal Data:* b Ithaca, NY, Aug 16, 32; m 56; c 4. *Educ:* Cornell Univ, BS, 55; Univ Wis, MS, 57, PhD(biochem, animal husb), 59. *Prof Exp:* Asst, Univ Wis, 55-59; asst prof animal husb, Rutgers Univ, 59-63, assoc prof nutrit, 63-67. *Mem:* Am Soc Animal Sci; Am Dairy Sci Asn; Am Inst Nutrit. *Res:* Ruminant nutrition. *Mailing Add:* Dept Animal Sci Univ Vt Burlington VT 05405

**WELCH, JAMES LEE,** HEALTH SCIENCES. *Current Pos:* CHMN & ASSOC PROF MED TECHNOL HEALTH SCI, CALIF STATE UNIV, DOMINGUEZ HILLS, 75- *Personal Data:* b Medford, Ore, June 23, 46. *Educ:* SOre State Col, BS, 68; Loma Linda Univ, BS, 69, MPH, 72, DHSC, 74. *Prof Exp:* Chief technologist med technol, Park Ave Hosp, 69-70; supvr lab, Hollywood Presby Hosp, 70-72, Temple Hosp, 72- *Concurrent Pos:* Mem, Am Bd Bioanal, 75-; consult exten allied health, Univ Calif, Riverside, 74- *Mem:* AAAS; Am Soc Clin Pathologists; Am Pub Health Asn. *Mailing Add:* Dept Clin Studies Calif State Univ 1000 E Victoria Dominguez Hills Carson CA 90747

**WELCH, JANE MARIE,** NUCLEAR WASTE FORMS. *Current Pos:* SCIENTIST & ENVIRON MGR, EG&G IDAHO, INC, 80- *Personal Data:* b Springfield, Mass, May 16, 50; m 77. *Educ:* Univ Mass, BS, 72; Pa State Univ, MS, 74, PhD(geochem & mineral), 78. *Mem:* Am Ceramic Soc; Mat Res Soc. *Res:* Phase equilibria of silicate and titanate systems; development and characterization of nuclear waste forms. *Mailing Add:* 895 Mirage Ct Idaho Falls ID 83402

**WELCH, JASPER ARTHUR, JR,** OPERATIONS RESEARCH. *Current Pos:* PRIV CONSULT RES & DEVELOP, 83- *Personal Data:* b Baton Rouge, La, Jan 5, 31; m 53, 85, Jane A Alford; c Jasper III, Carroll (Pawlikowski) & Brent. *Educ:* La State Univ, BS, 52; Univ Calif, Berkeley, MA, 54, PhD(physics), 58. *Prof Exp:* Group leader, Lawrence Livermore Lab, 53-57, Weapons Lab, 57-62; sr staff, Rand Corp, 62-64; asst to comdr systs command, USAF, 64-65, tech dir, WCoast Study Facil, 65-68, chief analyst studies & anal, 69-71, asst dir defense res & eng, Off Secy Defense, 71-73, sr asst, Secy Defense Atomic Energy, 73-74, asst, Strategic Initiatives Hq, 74-75, asst chief staff studies & anal, 75-79, coordn, Defense Pol, Nat Security Coun, 79-81, spec asst chief staff, Hq, 81, asst dep chief staff, 81-83. *Concurrent Pos:* Mem, NASA Adv Comt Fluid Mech, 64-66; consult, President's Sci Adv Comt, 62-65, Defense Sci Bd, 68-, NATO Adv Group Aerospace, Res & Develop, 71-80; mem adv coun, NASA, 84-88. *Mem:* Nat Acad Eng; Am Geophys Union; Coun Foreign Rel; Am Phys Soc. *Res:* Aerospace system requirements, design and program management. *Mailing Add:* 2129 Foothills Rd Santa Fe NM 87505

**WELCH, JOHN F, JR,** SCIENCE ADMINISTRATION. *Current Pos:* Var mgt positions, Gen Elec Co, 60-68, gen mgr, Plastics Bus Dept, 68-72, vpres, 72-79, vchmn, 79-81, CHMN & CHIEF EXEC OFFICER, GEN ELEC CO, 81- *Personal Data:* b Salem, Mass, Nov 11, 35. *Educ:* Univ Mass, BS, 57; Univ Ill, MS, 58, PhD(chem eng), 60. *Concurrent Pos:* Chmn, Bus Coun; mem, Bus Roundtable. *Mem:* Nat Acad Eng. *Mailing Add:* Gen Elec Co 3135 Easton Turnpike Fairfield CT 06431. *Fax:* 203-373-2884

**WELCH, LIN,** SPEECH PATHOLOGY. *Current Pos:* PROF SPEECH PATH & AUDIOL, CENT MO STATE UNIV, 56-, CHMN, 68- *Personal Data:* b Tahoka, Tex, Dec 9, 27; m 50; c 3. *Educ:* WTex State Univ, BS, 48; Baylor Univ, MA, 49; Univ Mo, PhD(speech path), 60. *Prof Exp:* Instr speech, Blue Mountain Col, 52-53; instr, Univ Mo, 53-56. *Concurrent Pos:* Chmn, Continuing Educ Comt, Am Speech & Hearing Asn, 72-73; mem, Educ & Standards Bd, Am Speech & Hearing, 80-82; mem, Adv Comn Commun Dis, Mo Bd Med & Healing Arts. *Mem:* Fel Am Speech & Hearing Asn. *Res:* Cleft palate; stuttering. *Mailing Add:* Dept Speech Path & Audiol Cent Mo State Univ Warrensburg MO 64093

**WELCH, LLOYD RICHARD,** MATHEMATICS, COMBINATORICS. *Current Pos:* assoc prof elec eng, 65-68, PROF ELEC ENG, UNIV SOUTHERN CALIF, 68- *Personal Data:* b Detroit, Mich, Sept 28, 27; m 53, Irene A Main; c Pamela I (Towery), Melinda Ann & Diana L (Worthington). *Educ:* Univ Ill, BS, 51; Calif Inst Technol, PhD(math), 58. *Prof Exp:* Sr res engr, Jet Propulsion Lab, Calif Inst Technol, 57-59; staff mathematician, Inst Defense Analysis, 59-65. *Mem:* Nat Acad Eng; Math Asn Am; Soc Indust & Appl Math; Am Math Soc; fel Inst Elec & Electronics Engrs. *Res:* Communication theory; combinatorics; probability theory. *Mailing Add:* Dept Elec Eng Univ Southern Calif Bldg 500A Los Angeles CA 90089-2565. *E-Mail:* welch@irving.usc.edu

**WELCH, LYNNE BRODIE,** RURAL RESEARCH, MULTIDISCIPLINARY EDUCATION OF HEALTH PROFESSIONS STUDENTS. *Current Pos:* DEAN, SCH NURSING, MARSHALL UNIV, 91- *Personal Data:* b Norwalk, Conn, Oct 19, 41. *Educ:* Univ Conn, BSN, 63; Cath Univ Am, MSN, 68; Columbia Univ, EdD(nursing educ admin), 79. *Prof Exp:* Instr, Sch Nursing, Stanford Hosp, 64-65, Children's Hosp, DC, 65-66; instr & asst prof med surg nursing, Western Conn State Univ, 70-79; chairperson community & med surg nursing, Pace Univ, 79-82; dean & prof nursing, Southern Conn State Univ, 82-86; dean & prof nursing & allied health, Univ Tex, El Paso, 86-89; statewide nursing coordr, Area Health Educ Ctr, Med Univ SC, 89-91. *Res:* Multidisciplinary research in diabetes related to standards of care and patients attitudes and beliefs in an Appalachian population. *Mailing Add:* 3200 Orchard Dr Huntington WV 25701

**WELCH, MELVIN BRUCE,** INORGANIC CHEMISTRY, POLYMER CHEMISTRY. *Current Pos:* Res chemist, Phillips Petrol Co, 74-80, sr res chemist, 80-86, sect supvr, 86-92, RES ASSOC, PHILLIPS PETROL CO, 93- *Personal Data:* b Hood River, Ore, Feb 24, 45; m 67; c 3. *Educ:* Linfield Col, BA, 67; Univ Utah, PhD(inorg chem), 74. *Mem:* Am Chem Soc. *Res:* Olefin polymerization and organometallic chemistry. *Mailing Add:* 4750 Lewis Dr Bartlesville OK 74006-6932

**WELCH, MICHAEL JOHN,** RADIOCHEMISTRY, NUCLEAR MEDICINE. *Current Pos:* from asst prof to assoc prof, 67-74, PROF RADIATION CHEM IN RADIOL, MALLINCKRODT INST RADIOL, WASHINGTON UNIV, 74-, PROF, DEPT CHEM, 78-, DIR, DIV RADIOL SCI, 90-, PROF MOLECULAR BIOL & PHARMACOL, SCH MED, 93- *Personal Data:* b Stoke-on-Trent, Eng, June 28, 39; div; c Colin & Lesley. *Educ:* Cambridge Univ, BA, 61, MA, 64; Univ London, PhD(radiochem), 65. *Honors & Awards:* Paul C Aebersold Award, Soc Nuclear Med, 80, Berson-Yalow Award, 88 & 90, de Hevesy Nuclear Pioneer Award, 92; St Louis Award, Am Chem Soc, 88, Nat Award Nuclear Chem, 90, Midwest Award, 91. *Prof Exp:* Res assoc chem, Brookhaven Nat Lab, 65-67. *Mem:* Royal Soc Chem; Am Chem Soc; Soc Nuclear Med (pres, 84-85); Radiation Res Soc. *Res:* Hot atom chemistry; isotopes in medicine. *Mailing Add:* 1 Spoede Lane St Louis MO 63141-7763. *Fax:* 314-362-8399; *E-Mail:* welch@mirlink.wush.edu

**WELCH, PETER D,** MATHEMATICAL STATISTICS. *Current Pos:* RETIRED. *Personal Data:* b Detroit, Mich, May 19, 28; m 74; c 2. *Educ:* Univ Wis, MS, 51; NMex State Univ, MS, 56; Columbia Univ, PhD(math statist), 63. *Prof Exp:* Assoc mathematician, Phys Lab, NMex State Univ, 51-56; res staff mem probability & statist, IBM Res Ctr, 56-93. *Concurrent Pos:* Adj prof, Columbia Univ, 64-65, 74-75, 84-90. *Mem:* Opers Res Soc. *Res:* Queueing theory; time series analysis; signal processing. *Mailing Add:* 85 Croton Ave Mt Kisco NY 10549

**WELCH, RAYMOND LEE,** ORGANIC CHEMISTRY, ORGANIC COATINGS. *Current Pos:* DIR TECH SERV, MAGNOX INC, 86- *Personal Data:* b Emporia, Kans, Nov 2, 43; m 64; c 2. *Educ:* Kans State Teachers Col, BA, 65; Iowa State Univ, PhD(org chem), 69. *Prof Exp:* Group leader, Hercules Res Ctr, Wilmington, 69-86. *Mem:* Am Chem Soc. *Res:* Product development; organic coatings; magnetic recording. *Mailing Add:* 7467 Bluffview Dr Radford VA 24141-8957

**WELCH, RICHARD MARTIN,** BIOCHEMICAL PHARMACOLOGY. *Current Pos:* RETIRED. *Personal Data:* b Brooklyn, NY, Nov 4, 33; m 54; c 3. *Educ:* St John's Univ, NY, BS, 57; Jefferson Med Col, MS, 60, PhD(pharmacol), 62. *Prof Exp:* Asst prof pharmacol, Jefferson Med Col, 62-63; group leader med biochem, Burroughs Wellcome Res Labs, 65-94, sr pharmacologist, 77-94, prin scientist & asst, dir pharmacokinetic & drug metab. *Concurrent Pos:* Fel, Albert Einstein Col Med, 63-65. *Mem:* Am Soc Pharmacol & Exp Therapeut; Soc Toxicol. *Res:* Pharmacodynamics; absorption, distribution and metabolism of drugs. *Mailing Add:* 8808 Katharina Ct Raleigh NC 27613

**WELCH, ROBIN IVOR,** EARTH SCIENCE, ECOLOGY. *Current Pos:* RETIRED. *Personal Data:* b Douglas, Ariz, Mar 13, 30; m 68; c 4. *Educ:* Univ Calif, Berkeley, BS, 55, MS, 56, PhD(wildland resource sci), 71. *Prof Exp:* Sr eng photo interpretation res, Mark Systs, Inc, 63-66; sr eng syst anal res, Stanford Res Inst, 66-70; res eng remote sensing res & teaching, Earth Satellite Corp, 70-75; assoc res scientist & vis assoc prof, Tex A&M Univ, 75-77; prog mgr & dir training remote sensing res Airview Specialists Corp contract, Ames Res Ctr, NASA, Humboldt State Univ, 77-81; pres & founder aerial photo res, Airview Specialists Corp, 54-; opers res specialist & syts eng, Lockheed Missles & Space Co, 81-92. *Concurrent Pos:* Consult, State Alaska Dept Econ Develop, 69-72, NASA Johnson Space Ctr, 75-77, Cent Intel Agency, 73-75, Greek Govt, 72-73 & Argentine Govt, 70-71. *Mem:* Am Soc Photogram; Am Forestry Asn. *Res:* Remote sensing of earth agriculture and water resources; data analysis by interactive man and machine systems of remote sensing data; teaching methods and curriculum development in remote sensing applications. *Mailing Add:* 3419 Churin Dr Mountain View CA 94040

**WELCH, RONALD MAURICE,** ATMOSPHERIC PHYSICS & METEOROLOGY, SATELLITE REMOTE SENSING. *Current Pos:* CHAIR, DEPT ATMOS SCI, UNIV HUNTSVILLE, 97- *Personal Data:* b Chicago, Ill, Dec 30, 43; div; c Mathew & Joshua. *Educ:* Calif State Univ, Long Beach, BS, 65, MA, 67; Univ Utah, PhD(physics), 71, PhD(meteorol), 76. *Prof Exp:* Engr-scientist, Missile & Space Systs Div, Douglas Aircraft Co, Calif, 66; res assoc geophys, Univ Utah, 71-72, res assoc physics, 72, teaching assoc, 72-73, assoc instr, Meteorol Dept, 73-74, res assoc, 74-76; res assoc, Dept Atmospheric Sci, Colo State Univ, 76-78; mem staff, Meteorol Inst, Univ Mainz, Ger, 78-81; assoc prof meteorol, Old Dom Univ, 81-82; sr scientist, SDak Sch Mines Technol, 82-90, prof, dept meteorol, 90-97. *Concurrent Pos:* Vis scientist, Inst Meterol, Univ Mainz, 78-81; Naval Oceanog & Atmospheric Res Lab, Univ Calif, Monterey, 89-90; adj prof, Colo State Univ, 87-; Am Soc Environ Educ fac fel, NASA, Langley, 83, 84 & 88; mem sci adv panel, Earth Observing Syst Data & Info Syst; dir, Ctr Robotics, Artificial Intel & Remote Sensing & head remote sensing, SDak Sch Mines & Technol; EOS CERES and ASTER Team comt member; co-chmn NASA Langley EOS DAAC Advisory Panel; Am Meteor Soc Radiation Comm and AMS, Artificial Intelligence Appl to Environ Sci; team member on int sci proj, IASI, SCARAB,.POLDER and OCTS; SAIC/TRW Steering Commt NPOESS, Lockhead Martin Sci Comt NPOESSS Polar-Orbiting. *Mem:* AAAS; Am Phys Soc; Am Geophys Union; Sigma Xi; Am Meteorol Soc; Inst Elec & Electronics Engrs. *Res:* Radiative transfer in planetary atmospheres; climatology; electronic properties of materials, remote sensing; artificial intelligence; satellite remote sensing of cloud and aerosol properties, fire, smoke and ecosystems; Global Climate change and spread of infectious diseases; 3-D modeling of cloud fields, artificial intelligence. *Mailing Add:* Dept Atmospheric Sci SDak Sch Mines Technol Rapid City SD 57701. *Fax:* 605-394-6061; *E-Mail:* welch@cloud.ius.sdsmt.edu

**WELCH, ROSS MAYNARD,** PLANT NUTRITION, PLANT PHYSIOLOGY. *Current Pos:* assoc prof, 81-87, PROF PLANT NUTRIT, CORNELL UNIV, 87-; PLANT PHYSIOLOGIST, AGR RES SERV, US PLANT, SOIL & NUTRIT LAB, USDA, 72- *Personal Data:* b Lancaster, Calif, May 8, 43; m 65, Jill S Varley; c Renell C & Brent R. *Educ:* Calif State Polytech Univ, San Luis Obispo, BS, 66; Univ Calif, Davis, MS, 69, PhD(soil sci), 71. *Honors & Awards:* Res Award, Am Soc Agron, 92. *Prof Exp:* Res assoc plant mineral nutrit, Dept Agron & US Plant, Soil & Nutrit Lab, Agr Res Serv, USDA, 71-72, from asst prof to assoc prof, 74-87. *Concurrent Pos:* Prof, Cornell Univ, 74-; vis prof, Sch Environ & Life Sci, Murdoch Univ, WAustralia, 80-81; distinguished vis lectr, Univ Adelaide, SAustralia, 91. *Mem:* NY Acad Sci; Sigma Xi; Am Soc Plant Physiol; fel Am Soc Agron; Soc Environ Geochem & Health; fel Soil Sci Soc Am; Crop Sci Soc Am. *Res:* Plant mineral nutrition; ion transport by whole plants, plant tissues and cells; trace element physiology and biochemistry; physiological form and bioavailability of mineral elements in plants to animals and humans; micronutrient fuctions inplants; food systems for improved health holistic food-based systems for sustainable nutrition. *Mailing Add:* US Plant Soil & Nutrit Lab Cornell Univ Tower Rd Ithaca NY 14853-2901. *Fax:* 607-255-2459; *E-Mail:* rmw1@cornell.edu

**WELCH, ROY ALLEN,** GEOGRAPHY, PHOTOGRAMMETRY. *Current Pos:* assoc prof geog, 71-77, prof geog, 77-80, RES PROF, DEPT GEOG, UNIV GA, 80- *Personal Data:* b Waukesha, Wis, Nov 14, 39; m 67. *Educ:* Carroll Col, BS, 61; Univ Okla, MA, 65; Univ Glasgow, PhD(geog, photogram), 68. *Honors & Awards:* III Talbert Abrams, Am Soc Photogram, 71, Presidential Citation, 75. *Prof Exp:* Photo-analyst geog, US Govt, 62-64; mgr earth sci dept, Itek Corp, 68-69; Nat Acad Sci-Nat Res Counc res assoc, US Geol Surv, 69-71. *Concurrent Pos:* Consult, AID, 72; mem working group image qual & optical transfer function-modulation transfer function, Comn I, Int Soc Photogram, 72-76; mem remote sensing comt, Asn Am Geogrs, 73-75; remote sensing specialist, US Geol Surv, 73-, dir, Ctr Remote Sensing & Mapping Sci, 84- *Mem:* Am Soc Photogram; Brit Photogram Soc; Asn Am Geogrs; Brit Cartog Soc; Sigma Xi; Inst Elec & Electronics Engrs. *Res:* Analyses of the quality and applications of aircraft and satellite imagery for geographic tasks, with particular reference to land use mapping and cartography. *Mailing Add:* 4745 Barnett Shoals Rd Athens GA 30605-4731

**WELCH, STEPHEN MELWOOD,** AGROMETEROLOGY, SYSTEMS SCIENCE. *Current Pos:* From asst prof to prof entom, Kans State Univ, 78-84, tech develop coordr, 85-86, exten computer systs coordr, 87-89, PROF AGRON, KANS STATE UNIV, 90- *Personal Data:* b San Diego, Calif, July 1, 49; m 73; c 2. *Educ:* Mich State Univ, BS, 71, PhD(zool), 77. *Honors & Awards:* Pres Award, Asn Agr Comput Co, 90. *Concurrent Pos:* Mem bd dir, Asn Agr Comput Co, 89-90; interim dir comput & asst to vprovost acad sci, Kans State Univ, 92-93. *Mem:* Am Soc Agron; Asn Comput Mach; Am Soc Agr Engrs; Asn Agr Comput Co; Am Math Asn; Am Soc Photogram & Remote Sensing. *Res:* Application of computers and systems science to agriculture. *Mailing Add:* Dept Agron Kans State Univ Manhattan KS 66506-7001

**WELCH, STEVEN CHARLES,** CHEMISTRY. *Current Pos:* PROF & CHAIR, CALIF STATE UNIV, SAN MARCOS, 90- *Personal Data:* b Inglewood, Calif, Feb 18, 40; m 86; c Pamela D & Melody R. *Educ:* Univ Calif, Los Angeles, BS, 64; Univ Southern Calif, PhD(chem), 68. *Prof Exp:* NIH fel, Calif Inst Technol, 68-70; from asst prof to prof chem & pharm, Univ Houston, 70-90. *Concurrent Pos:* Nat Inst Gen Med Sci grant, Univ Houston, 71-77, Welch Found grant, 72-90; Nat Cancer Inst contract, 77-80, Nat Cancer Inst grant, 87-90. *Mem:* Am Chem Soc. *Res:* Synthetic organic chemistry; synthesis of terpene natural products and development of new synthetic methods and reagents. *Mailing Add:* Dept Chem Calif State Univ San Marcos CA 92096. *E-Mail:* steve_welch@csusm.edu

**WELCH, WALTER RAYNES,** MARINE BIOLOGY. *Current Pos:* RETIRED. *Personal Data:* b Rumford, Maine, Oct 25, 20; m 44; c 3. *Educ:* Univ Maine, BS, 47, MS, 50. *Honors & Awards:* Unit Citation, Nat Oceanic & Atmospheric Admin, 73. *Prof Exp:* Fisheries res biologist, Clam Prog, US Nat Marine Fisheries Serv, 49-58, prog leader, 58-64, proj leader lobster prog, 64-67, prog leader, 67-71, asst lab dir, 71-73, consult div water resources mgt & marine adv serv, 71-73; marine resource scientist & proj leader, Maine Dept Marine Resources, 73-78, div chief, 78-81, asst res dir, 81-85. *Concurrent Pos:* Pvt consult molluscan & environ probs, 78-86. *Res:* Molluscan and crustacean ecology; environmental measurement and interpretation. *Mailing Add:* Six Factory Cove Rd Boothbay Harbor ME 04538

**WELCH, WAYNE WILLARD,** EDUCATIONAL PSYCHOLOGY, PROGRAM EVALUATION. *Current Pos:* from asst prof to assoc prof, 69-74, asst dean, 70-74, PROF EDUC PSYCHOL, UNIV MINN, 74- *Personal Data:* b Clinton, Iowa, May 20, 34; m 51; c 3. *Educ:* Univ Wis, La Crosse, BS, 56; Univ Pa, MS, 60; Purdue Univ, MS, 63; Univ Wis, PhD(sci educ), 66. *Honors & Awards:* Fulbright lect, Weizemann Inst Sci, Israel, 79. *Prof Exp:* Res assoc, Harvard Univ, 65-69. *Concurrent Pos:* Prin investr eval teacher educ proj, NSF, 71-77, nat assessment educ progress, 80-84, prog officer, 72-73; vis prof, Univ Wash, 76-77; mem comt sci indicators, Nat Res Coun, 83-87; vis scholar, Western Australia Inst Technol, 84; Fulbright Res Scholar, Univ Waikato, NZ, 85; head Off Studies & Prog Assessment, NSF, 88-89, expert consult; consult, Proj 2061, AAAS & Scope, Sequence & Coordination, Nat Sci Teachers Asn. *Mem:* Nat Asn Res Sci Teaching (pres, 73-74); fel AAAS; Am Educ Res Asn; Nat Sci Teachers Asn. *Res:* Improvement of science education; program evaluation assessment of science learning; program evaluation assessment of science learning. *Mailing Add:* 210 Burton Hall Univ Minn Minneapolis MN 55455

**WELCH, WILLARD MCKOWAN, JR,** ORGANIC CHEMISTRY. *Current Pos:* RES CHEMIST, MED RES LABS, PFIZER, INC, 70- *Personal Data:* b Frankfort, Ky, Mar 1, 44; m 66; c 2. *Educ:* Mass Inst Technol, BS, 65; Rice Univ, PhD(org chem), 69. *Res:* Synthetic organic chemistry; central nervous system drugs; heterocyclic chemistry. *Mailing Add:* Pfizer Inc Med Res Labs Groton CT 06340-5196

**WELCH, WILLIAM HENRY, JR,** BIOCHEMISTRY. *Current Pos:* asst prof, 70-76, ASSOC PROF BIOCHEM, UNIV NEV, RENO, 76- *Personal Data:* b Los Angeles, Calif, Dec 13, 40; m 65; c 4. *Educ:* Univ Calif, Berkeley, BA, 63; Univ Kans, PhD(biochem), 69. *Prof Exp:* NIH fel, Brandeis Univ, 69-70. *Mem:* Sigma Xi; AAAS; Am Chem Soc. *Res:* Enzymology; molecular basis of adaptation to temperature stress; mechanisms by which metal ions alter enzyme action and protein conformation. *Mailing Add:* Dept Biochem Univ Nev Mail Stop 330 Reno NV 89557

**WELCH, WILLIAM JOHN,** RADIO ASTRONOMY. *Current Pos:* From asst prof to prof elec eng, 60-72, PROF ELEC ENG & ASTRON & DIR RADIO ASTRON LAB, UNIV CALIF, BERKELEY, 72- *Personal Data:* b Chester, Pa, Jan 17, 34; m 55; c Eric, Leslie & Jeanette. *Educ:* Stanford Univ, BS, 55; Univ Calif, Berkeley, PhD(eng sci), 60. *Hon Degrees:* Dr, Univ Bordeaux I, 79. *Concurrent Pos:* Mem, NSF Astron Adv Panel, 73-76; trustee at large, Assoc Univ Inc, 74-81; mem, Arecibu Adv Bd, 77-80; chmn, Comn J Radio Astron, Int Sci Radio Union, 87-90. *Mem:* Fel Am Astron Soc; Inst Elec & Electronics Engrs; Int Sci Radio Union; AAAS; Int Astron Union. *Res:* Radio astronomical studies of the planets, interstellar medium and extragalactic radio sources; instrumentation for radio astronomy at millimeter wave lengths. *Mailing Add:* 2727 Shasta Rd Berkeley CA 94708-1923. *E-Mail:* welch@bkyast

**WELCH, ZARA D,** ORGANIC CHEMISTRY. *Current Pos:* res fel chem, Purdue Univ, 42-49, from instr to assoc prof, 49-83, admin asst to head, 49-68, asst to head dept, 68-83, EMER PROF CHEM, PURDUE UNIV, 83- *Personal Data:* b North Manchester, Ind, June 28, 15. *Educ:* Manchester Col, AB, 37; Purdue Univ, MS, 39, PhD(org chem), 42. *Prof Exp:* Asst, Purdue Univ, 37-41; res chemist, Va Smelting Co, 42. *Concurrent Pos:* Off Sci Res & Develop fel, 42-43. *Mem:* Am Chem Soc; fel AAAS. *Res:* Dehydrohalogenation; halogenation; fluorine chemistry; recovery of uranium. *Mailing Add:* 1051 Cumberland Ave West Lafayette IN 47906

**WELCHER, RICHARD PARKE,** CHEMISTRY. *Current Pos:* RETIRED. *Personal Data:* b Hartford, Conn, July 21, 19; m 50, Alice Dessert; c Peter J, Joan W (Tougas), Patricia W (Tougas), Andrew A & Barbara W (Cooper). *Educ:* Trinity Col, Conn, AB, 41; Mass Inst Technol, BS, 43, PhD(org chem), 47. *Prof Exp:* Control supvr anal dept, Tenn Eastman Corp, Tenn, 44-45; sr res chemist, Am Cyanamid Co, Stamford, 47-81. *Mem:* Am Chem Soc; Sigma Xi. *Res:* Heterocyclic compounds; organophosphorus, nitrogen and sulfur chemistry; nitriles, amides, polyamines, cyanogen, s-triazines, dicyandiamide; biocides, ion and electron exchange resins; surfactants; mining chemicals; chemistry of cationic polymers. *Mailing Add:* 16 Watch Tower Lane Old Greenwich CT 06870-1109

**WELDEN, ARTHUR LUNA,** MYCOLOGY. *Current Pos:* from instr to prof bot, Tulane Univ, 55-79, chmn, Dept Biol, 85-90, Ida Richardson Prof, 80-93, EMER IDA RICHARDSON PROF BOT, TULANE UNIV, 94- *Personal Data:* b Birmingham, Ala, Jan 27, 27; m 50, France M Colvin; c Charles W & Arthur F. *Educ:* Birmingham-Southern Col, AB, 50; Univ Tenn, MS, 51; Univ Iowa, PhD(bot), 54. *Honors & Awards:* Socio Honorario, Soc Mycol Mex. *Prof Exp:* Asst prof biol, Milliken Univ, 54-55. *Concurrent Pos:* Am Philos Soc grant, 57; prin investr, NSF, 69-73. *Mem:* Mycol Soc Am; Sigma Xi; Int Asn Plant Taxon; Asn Trop Biol; fel AAAS. *Res:* Myxomycetes; tropical fungi; Thelephoraceae. *Mailing Add:* Dept Ecol/Evolution & Org Biol Tulane Univ New Orleans LA 70118. *Fax:* 504-862-8706; *E-Mail:* awelden@mailhost.tcs.tulane.edu

**WELDES, HELMUT H,** TECHNICAL MANAGEMENT, CHEMISTRY. *Current Pos:* PRES, PERMETHYL CORP, 85- *Personal Data:* b Munich, Fed Repub Ger, July 4, 28; US citizen. *Educ:* Univ Karlsruhe, Fed Repub Ger, BS, 51, MS, 54; Univ Aachen, Fed Repub Ger, PhD(chem), 56. *Prof Exp:* Res assoc, Max Planck Inst Coal Res, 54-57; res & develop group leader, P Q Corp, 57-64, res mgr, 64-66, dir res & develop, 66-72, vpres, P Q Int, Inc, 72-78; res dir in Egypt, Nat Acad Sci, 78-81; owner, Tech Transfer Int, 81-85. *Concurrent Pos:* Partner, R D Systs, 81- *Mem:* Am Chem Soc; Am Inst Chem Engrs; Am Inst Chemists; Ger Chem Soc. *Res:* Small ring and multi-ring organic compounds; organometallics; soluble silicates; finally divided silica; aliphatic and olefinic hydrocarbon oligomers; detergents and cleaners; silicones and related compounds. *Mailing Add:* 2912 Wesley Ave Ocean City NJ 08226

**WELDON, EDWARD J, JR,** INFORMATION SCIENCE. *Current Pos:* assoc prof, 66-71, PROF ELEC ENG, UNIV HAWAII, 71- *Personal Data:* b New York, NY, Apr 8, 38; m 65; c 3. *Educ:* Manhattan Col, BSEE, 58; Univ Fla, MSEE, 60, PhD(elec eng), 63. *Prof Exp:* Engr, Bell Tel Labs, 63-66. *Concurrent Pos:* Pres, Adtech, Inc. *Mem:* AAAS; Inst Elec & Electronics Engrs. *Res:* Information theory; coding error control. *Mailing Add:* Dept Elec Eng Univ Hawaii Manoa 2444 Dole St Honolulu HI 96822

**WELDON, HENRY ARTHUR,** ELEMENTARY PARTICLE PHYSICS. *Current Pos:* from asst prof to assoc prof, 86-96, PROF PHYSICS, WVA UNIV, 96- *Personal Data:* b Atlanta, Ga, July 11, 47; m 69. *Educ:* Mass Inst Technol, SB, 69, PhD(physics), 74. *Prof Exp:* Res assoc, Stanford Linear Accelerator Ctr, 74-76; res assoc physics, Univ Pa, 76-79, asst prof, 79-86. *Mem:* Am Phys Soc. *Res:* High temperature quantum field theory; quark-gluon plasma; ultrarelativistic heavy ion collisions; CP violation. *Mailing Add:* Dept Physics WVa Univ Morgantown WV 26506. *Fax:* 304-293-5769

**WELDON, VIRGINIA V,** PEDIATRIC ENDOCRINOLOGY, MEDICAL ADMINISTRATION. *Current Pos:* vpres sci affairs, 89, vpres pub policy, 89-93, SR VPRES PUB POLICY, MONSANTO CO, 93- *Personal Data:* b Toronto, Ont, Sept 8, 35; US citizen; div; c 2. *Educ:* Smith Col, AB, 57; State Univ NY, Buffalo, MD, 62. *Hon Degrees:* LHD, Rush Univ, 85. *Prof Exp:* Intern, resident & fel, Sch Med, Johns Hopkins Univ & Hosp, 62-67, instr pediat, Univ, 67-68; from instr to prof pediat, Sch Med, Wash Univ, 68-89, asst dir, Clin Res Ctr, 72-78, co-dir, Div Pediat Endocrinol & Metab, 73-77, asst vchancellor med affairs, 75-81, assoc vchancellor, 81-83, vpres Med Ctr, 81-89, dep vchancellor med affairs, 83-89. *Concurrent Pos:* Consult, Adv

Comt Endocrinol & Metab, Food & Drug Admin, 73-76; co-dir, Div Metab & Endocrinol, St Louis Children's Hosp, 73-77; mem, State of Mo Health Manpower Planning Task Force, 76-; mem, Gen Clin Res Ctr Adv Comt, NIH, 76-80, Nat Adv Res Resources Coun, 80-84; comnr, St Louis Zool Park & vpres comn, 83-; chmn, Asn Am Med Cols, 85-86; bd dirs, Southwest Bell Corp, 85-91, G D Searle & Co & Nutrasweet Co; adv dir, Monsanto Bd Dirs, mem adv comts, Monsanto Agr Co & Monsanto Chem Co. *Mem:* Inst Med-Nat Acad Sci; fel AAAS; Sigma Xi; Endocrine Soc; Soc Pediat Res; Am Pediat Soc; Asn Am Med Cols; fel Am Acad Pediat. *Res:* Aldosterone secretion in children; disorders of growth and growth hormone secretion in children. *Mailing Add:* Monsanto Co 800 N Lindberg Blvd Dept D1A St Louis MO 63167

**WELDON, WILLIAM FORREST,** ELECTROMAGNETIC LAUNCH, ELECTROMECHANICS. *Current Pos:* res engr, Univ Tex, Austin, 73-77, tech dir, 77-85, dir, Ctr Electromech, 85-93, PROF ELEC & MECH ENG, UNIV TEX, AUSTIN, 86-, JOSEY CENTENNIAL PROF ENERGY RESOURCES, 92- *Personal Data:* b San Marcos, Tex, Jan 12, 45; US citizen; m 68, Morey McGonigle; c 2. *Educ:* Trinity Univ, Tex, BS, 67; Univ Tex, Austin, MS, 70. *Honors & Awards:* Peter Mark Medal, 86. *Prof Exp:* Engr, Cameron Iron Works, 67-68; proj engr, Glastron Boat Co, 70-71; chief proj engr, Nalle Plastics Co, 71-73. *Concurrent Pos:* Mem, Nat Dept Defense Adv Panel Electromagnetics Tech, 78-83 & Nat Res Coun Comt Mobile Elec Power, 87- & Naval Res Adv Comm, 91-, vchair, 95-97. *Mem:* Inst Elec & Electronics Engrs; fel Am Soc Mech Engrs; Nat Soc Prof Engrs. *Res:* Development of rotating electrical machines for pulsed power applications; industrial applications of pulsed power; development of electromagnetic launch technology. *Mailing Add:* Dept Mech Eng Univ Tex Austin G2200 Austin TX 78712

**WELFORD, NORMAN TRAVISS,** MEDICAL DEVICE REGULATION, LEGAL TESTIMONY. *Current Pos:* RETIRED. *Personal Data:* b London, Eng, Feb 5, 21; nat US; m 44; c 3. *Educ:* Cambridge Univ, BA, 41, MA & MB, BCh, 45. *Prof Exp:* Intern & resident, Addenbrooks Hosp, Cambridge, Eng, 45-46; res assoc biophys, Univ Western Ont, 55-56; assoc prof psychophysiol, Antioch Col & res assoc psychophysiol-neurophysiol, Fels Res Inst, 55-66; dir biomed eng & fac assoc psychiat, Univ Tex Med Br, Galveston, 66-78; med officer, Ctr for Devices & Radiol Health, Food & Drug Admin, 78-87. *Concurrent Pos:* USPHS res fel, Univ Western Ont, 55-56. *Mem:* Inst Elec & Electronics Engrs; Sigma Xi; Asn Advan Med Instrumentation. *Res:* Automation of data gathering and handling and stimulus presentation; psychophysiology of human sensory-motor performance and fetal heart rate behavior. *Mailing Add:* 19 Lakeshore Dr NE Albuquerque NM 87112-4254

**WELGE, HENRY JOHN,** FLUID DYNAMICS. *Current Pos:* CONSULT PETROL PRODS, 72- *Personal Data:* b St Louis, Mo, Aug 15, 07; m 40, 87, Myrtle LaLonde; c Henry John Jr & Mary Joan. *Educ:* Univ Ill, BSc, 29; Calif Inst Technol, MSc, 32, PhD(phys chem), 36. *Honors & Awards:* Anthony Incas Gold Medal, Soc Petrol Engrs. *Prof Exp:* Anal chemist, Richfield Oil Co, Calif, 29-31; res chemist, Tex Co, 37; from instr to asst prof chem, Agr & Mech Col, Tex, 37-44; sr res chemist, Exxon Prod Res Co, Houston, Tex, 44-72. *Mem:* Am Inst Mining, Metall & Petrol Eng; Soc Petrol Engrs. *Res:* Photochemistry; reaction kinetics and equilibria and diffusion; capillarity in petroleum production; single phase and multiphase fluid flow in porous media. *Mailing Add:* 286 St Josephs Long Beach CA 90803

**WELHAN, JOHN ANDREW,** ISOTOPE GEOCHEMISTRY, GEOTHERMAL CHEMISTRY. *Current Pos:* Staff res assoc III, 74-81, FEL RES GEOLOGIST VI, SCRIPPS INST OCEANOG, 81- *Personal Data:* b Winnipeg, Man, Aug 24, 50; m 78; c 2. *Educ:* Univ Man, BSc, 72; Univ Waterloo, MSc, 74; Univ Calif, San Diego, PhD(geol sci), 81. *Concurrent Pos:* Consult, Geothermal Div, Union Oil Co & Harding-Lawson Assocs, 80. *Mem:* Am Geophys Union. *Res:* Origins and geochemical significance of hydrothermal methane in mid-ocean ridges and continental geothermal systems; carbon hydrogen and nitrogen isotopic anomalies in hydro-thermal gases and correlations with gas and helium isotope compositions. *Mailing Add:* Dept Geol Idaho State 921 S Eighth Ave Pocatello ID 83209-0001

**WELIKY, IRVING,** CLINICAL PHARMACOLOGY, PHARMACOKINETICS. *Current Pos:* CONSULT CLIN PHARMACOL, 90- *Personal Data:* b Mt Vernon, NY, Aug 29, 24; m 51, Virginia Spicer; c Joan (Conaway), Lora (Griffin), James & David. *Educ:* Ill Wesleyan Univ, BS, 48; Columbia Univ, PhD(biochem), 58. *Prof Exp:* Res asst, Sloan-Kettering Inst Cancer Res, 49-52; res fel, Mass Gen Hosp, 57-60, asst biochemist, 60-62; asst prof biochem, Sch Med, Univ Pittsburgh, 62-68; sr res investr, Squibb Inst Med Res, 68-69, res group leader drug metab, 69-73, asst clin pharmacol dir, 73-76, assoc clin pharmacol dir, 76-77; assoc dir clin pharmacol, Wallace Labs, 77-79, dir clin pharmacol, 79-89. *Concurrent Pos:* Res fel biol chem, Harvard Med Sch, 57-60, res assoc, 60-62; asst prof obstet & gynec & mem grad fac, Univ Pittsburgh, 62-68. *Mem:* Am Soc Clin Pharmacol & Therapeut. *Res:* Intermediary metabolism and biosynthesis of nucleic acids, porphyrins and steroid hormones; clinical pharmacology; pharmacokinetics; drug metabolism. *Mailing Add:* 851 Black Canyon Dr Estes Park CO 80527

**WELIKY, NORMAN,** SEPARATION TECHNIQUES, BIOMOLECULAR PROCESSES. *Current Pos:* CONSULT, 85- *Personal Data:* b New York, NY, Nov 1, 19; m 55, Berta Gandelman; c Karen & Michael. *Educ:* City Col New York, BChE, 39; Polytech Inst Brooklyn, PhD(chem), 57. *Prof Exp:* Chemist, Mineral Pigments Corp, 46-47 & Reichhold Chem, Inc, 50-52; Nuclear Magnetic Resonance res fel chem, Harvard Univ, 56-57; res fel hemoglobins, Dept Chem & Chem Eng, Calif Inst Technol, 57-59, group supvr molecular struct & synthesis, Jet Propulsion Lab, 59-65; mem tech staff,

Biosci Dept, TRW Systs, 66-67, asst mgr biosci & electrochem dept, 68-71, sr scientist, 71-75; res scientist div allergy & immunol, dept pediat, Los Angeles County Harbor-Univ Calif Los Angeles Med Ctr, 76-81; asst res scientist, Dept Cytol & Cytogenetics, City of Hope Nat Med Ctr, 83-85. *Concurrent Pos:* Consult, separation techniques, immunochemistry. *Mem:* Fel AAAS; Am Chem Soc; Sigma Xi. *Res:* Physical chemistry; enzyme chemistry; specific insoluble adsorbents; biological specificity; immunology-allergy; environmental quality criteria; cancer; autoimmune disease, phagocytosis; autoimmune disease in mouse model; phagocytics in macrophages, endocytic and exocytic steps. *Mailing Add:* 1072 Ridge Crest St Monterey Park CA 91754

**WELKER, EVERETT LINUS,** mathmatical statistics; deceased, see previous edition for last biography

**WELKER, GEORGE W,** PARASITOLOGY, BACTERIOLOGY. *Current Pos:* RETIRED. *Personal Data:* b Cumberland City, Tenn, July 4, 23; m 50; c 3. *Educ:* Mid Tenn State Univ, BS, 44; George Peabody Col, MA, 50; Ohio State Univ, PhD, 62. *Prof Exp:* Teacher high sch, Ohio, 46-49; asst biol, George Peabody Col, 49-50; from asst prof to assoc prof, Ball State Univ, 50-65, prof biol, 65-86, chmn, Biol Dept 80-86. *Concurrent Pos:* Danforth teacher study grant, 57-58. *Mem:* AAAS; Am Sci Affil; Sigma Xi. *Res:* Helminth parasites and microbial physiology. *Mailing Add:* 1732 N Colson Dr Muncie IN 47304

**WELKER, J(OHN) REED,** CHEMICAL ENGINEERING. *Current Pos:* PROF ENG, UNIV ARK, 83- *Personal Data:* b Rexburg, Idaho, Dec 1, 36; m 58; c 3. *Educ:* Univ Idaho, BS, 59, MS, 61; Univ Okla, PhD(chem eng), 65. *Prof Exp:* Instr, Univ Idaho, 60-61; group leader, Oil Recovery Corp, 62-63; res engr, Res Inst, Univ Okla, 65-70; vpres, Univ Engrs, Inc, 70-77; pres, Appl Technol Corp, 77-83. *Mem:* Am Inst Chem Engrs; Am Chem Soc; Am Gas Asn. *Res:* Fire research; fire safety; atmospheric dispersion; liquefied natural gas plant safety; fire extinguishment and control. *Mailing Add:* Chem Eng Dept Univ Ark Fayetteville AR 72701

**WELKER, NEIL ERNEST,** BIOCHEMISTRY. *Current Pos:* from asst prof to assoc prof biol sci, 64-74, PROF BIOCHEM, MOLECULAR & CELL BIOL, NORTHWESTERN UNIV, 74- *Personal Data:* b Batavia, NY, Apr 21, 32; m 76; c 6. *Educ:* Univ Buffalo, BA, 58; Western Reserve Univ, PhD(microbiol), 63. *Prof Exp:* Fel, Univ Ill, Urbana, 63-64. *Mem:* AAAS; Am Soc Microbiol; Brit Soc Gen Microbiol; Am Soc Biol Chemists. *Mailing Add:* Dept Biochem Molecular Biol Northwestern Univ Evanston IL 60208-3500. *Fax:* 847-467-1380

**WELKER, WALLACE I,** NEUROPHYSIOLOGY, NEUROANATOMY. *Current Pos:* NIH fel neurophysiol, Univ Wis-Madison, 54-56, Sister Kenny Found Scholar, 57-62, NIH career develop fel, 62-67, prof, 67-90, EMER PROF NEUROPHYSIOL, MED SCH, UNIV WIS-MADISON, 90- *Personal Data:* b Batavia, NY, Dec 17, 26; m, Carol L Dizack; c Mara, Nila & Jeremy. *Educ:* Univ Chicago, PhD(psychol), 54. *Prof Exp:* Asst, Yerkes Labs Primate Biol, 52-54. *Mem:* Am Asn Anatomists; Soc Neurosci. *Res:* Comparative neurobiology; neurophysiology and neuroanatomy; analysis of somato sensory circuits of mammalian brain; analysis of Brain of Florida manatee; assembly of largest existing comparative mammalian brain collection. *Mailing Add:* Dept Neurophysiol Univ Wis 1300 University Ave Madison WI 53706-1510. *Fax:* 608-265-3500; *E-Mail:* welker@neurophys.wisc.edu

**WELKER, WILLIAM V, JR,** WEED SCIENCE, HORTICULTURE. *Current Pos:* RETIRED. *Personal Data:* b Milwaukee, Wis, Nov 12, 28; m 51; c 4. *Educ:* Univ Wis, BS, 52, PhD(hort, plant physiol), 62. *Prof Exp:* Res horticulturist, Sci & Educ Admin-Agr Res, USDA, 59-; res prof soils & crops, Rutgers Univ, New Brunswick, 59-80; weed scientist, USDA-Agr Res Serv, Appalachin Fruit Res Sta, 80-91. *Mem:* Weed Sci Soc Am; Am Soc Hort Sci. *Res:* Chemical control of weeds in horticultural crops; influence of long term use of herbicides upon crops; fate of herbicides in soil. *Mailing Add:* 282 Tuscawilla Hills Charles Town WV 25414

**WELKIE, GEORGE WILLIAM,** VIROLOGY, PLANT PHYSIOLOGY. *Current Pos:* Asst prof, 57-62, ASSOC PROF BOT & PLANT PATH, UTAH STATE UNIV, 62- *Personal Data:* b Hazleton, Pa, Apr 11, 32; m 57; c 2. *Educ:* Pa State Univ, BS, 52, MS, 54; Univ Wis, PhD(plant path), 57. *Concurrent Pos:* NSF fel virol, Rothamsted Exp Sta, Eng. *Mem:* Am Phytopath Soc; Sigma Xi. *Res:* Virus infection and synthesis; effect of virus infection on host metabolism; mineral nutrition of plants with relation to metabolism. *Mailing Add:* Dept Biol Utah State Univ Logan UT 84322-0001

**WELKOWITZ, WALTER,** ELECTRICAL ENGINEERING. *Current Pos:* RETIRED. *Personal Data:* b Brooklyn, NY, Aug 3, 26; m 51, Joan Horowitz; c David, Lawrence & Julie. *Educ:* Cooper Union, BS, 48; Univ Ill, MS, 49, PhD, 54. *Honors & Awards:* Centennial Medal, Inst Elec & Electronics Engrs, 84; Career Achievement Award, Inst Elec & Electronics Engrs, 91 & Eng Med Biol Soc, 91. *Prof Exp:* Res assoc elec eng, Bioacoust Lab, Univ Ill, 48-54; lectr acoust, Grad Sch Eng, Columbia Univ, 54-55; gen mgr, Gulton Industs, Inc, 55-64; prof elec eng, Rutgers Univ, New Brunswick, 64-86, chmn dept, 72-86, prof biomed eng, 86-91, chmn dept, 86-91. *Concurrent Pos:* Adj prof, Robert Wood Johnson Med Sch, Col Med & Dent, NJ, 72- *Mem:* Fel Inst Elec & Electronics Engrs; Am Soc Artificial Inter; Soc Math Biol; NY Acad Sci; fel Int Asn Med & Biol Eng. *Res:* Biomedical engineering; instrumentation; cardiovascular and respiratory modeling. *Mailing Add:* Dept Biomed Eng Rutgers Univ PO Box 909 Piscataway NJ 08854. *Fax:* 413-637-0416; *E-Mail:* wwelkowitz@aol.com

**WELLAND, GRANT VINCENT,** MATHEMATICS. *Current Pos:* from asst prof to assoc prof, 66-77, PROF MATH & COORDR PROBS & STATIST, UNIV MO, ST LOUIS, 77- *Personal Data:* b Toronto, Ont, June 25, 40; m 66. *Educ:* Purdue Univ, BS, 63, MS, 65, PhD(math), 66. *Prof Exp:* Teaching asst math, Purdue Univ, 63-65. *Concurrent Pos:* Dir, NSF undergrad res prog, 67-68; NSF res grant, 68-70; vis prof, Univ Madrid, 70. *Mem:* AAAS; Am Math Soc. *Res:* Harmonic analysis and differentiation. *Mailing Add:* Dept Math Univ Mo 8001 Nat Bridge Rd St Louis MO 63121-4499

**WELLAND, ROBERT ROY,** MATHEMATICS. *Current Pos:* asst prof, 63-74, ASSOC PROF MATH, NORTHWESTERN UNIV, EVANSTON, 74- *Personal Data:* b Toronto, Ont, Jan 31, 33; m 57; c 3. *Educ:* Univ Okla, BS, 56, MA, 57; Purdue Univ, PhD, 60. *Prof Exp:* Instr math, Univ Okla, 56-57; NSF asst, Purdue Univ, 57-58, from instr to asst prof, 58-60; asst prof, Ohio State Univ, 60-63. *Concurrent Pos:* Vis instr, Univ Chicago, 61. *Mem:* Am Math Soc. *Res:* Functional analysis; special spaces; nonlinear analysis. *Mailing Add:* Dept Math Northwestern Univ 2033 Sheridan Rd Evanston IL 60208

**WELLDON, PAUL BURKE,** POLYMER CHEMISTRY, RESEARCH ADMINISTRATION. *Current Pos:* RETIRED. *Personal Data:* b Nashua, NH, May 10, 16; m 41, Marjorie Veazie; c Douglas B & Paula J. *Educ:* Dartmouth Col, AB, 37, AM, 39; Univ Ill, PhD(org chem), 42. *Prof Exp:* Instr chem, Dartmouth Col, 37-39; res chemist, Hercules Inc, 42-51, mgr, Cellulose Prod Res Div, 52-60, tech asst to dir res, 60-62, mgr, Appln Res Div, 62-65, mgr, Personnel Div, Res Ctr, 67-79. *Mem:* Am Chem Soc. *Res:* Chlorination of organic compounds; chemistry of cellulose derivatives; polyolefins; polymer applications; organic chemistry. *Mailing Add:* Harbor Lights HC344 Islesboro ME 04848

**WELLE, STEPHEN LEO,** ENERGY METABOLISM, NOREPINEPHRINE METABOLISM. *Current Pos:* ASST PROF MED, SCH MED & DENT, UNIV ROCHESTER, 78- *Educ:* Northern Ill Univ, PhD(bio-psychol), 78. *Mailing Add:* Endocrinol Metab Unit Med & Physiol Monroe Community Hosp 435 E Henrietta Rd Rochester NY 14620-4684. *Fax:* 716-274-7391

**WELLENREITER, RODGER HENRY,** POULTRY NUTRITION. *Current Pos:* Sr scientist, 70-80, RES SCIENTIST POULTRY NUTRIT, LILLY RES LABS, ELI LILLY & CO, 80- *Personal Data:* b Bloomington, Ill, Oct 23, 42; m 63; c 2. *Educ:* Ill State Univ, BS, 64; Mich State Univ, MS, 67, PhD(animal husb), 70. *Concurrent Pos:* Sigma Xi res award, 70. *Mem:* Poultry Sci Asn; World Poultry Sci Asn; Sigma Xi. *Res:* Means of improving the efficiency of conversion of animal feedstuffs into products for human consumption. *Mailing Add:* Eli Lilly Co Animal Sci Develop 2001 W Main St Greenfield IN 46140

**WELLER, CHARLES STAGG, JR,** OCEAN SCIENCE, SPACE SCIENCE. *Current Pos:* SR RES SCIENTIST, DAVID TAYLOR RES CTR, 86- *Personal Data:* b Nashville, Tenn, Dec 28, 40; m 66; c 2. *Educ:* Mass Inst Technol, BS, 62; Univ Pittsburgh, PhD(physics), 67. *Prof Exp:* Res physicist, Naval Res Lab, 67-86, sect head, 74-86. *Mem:* Am Phys Soc; Am Geophys Union; Am Astron Soc; Int Astron Union. *Res:* Space science; upper atmospheric studies; interplanetary medium; ultraviolet optics; ocean sciences; electromagnetic signatures; radar. *Mailing Add:* Code 7200 David Taylor Model Basin Naval Surface Warfare Ctr 9500 MacArthur Blvd West Bethesda MD 20817-5700

**WELLER, DAVID LLOYD,** BIOCHEMISTRY, MOLECULAR BIOLOGY. *Current Pos:* asst prof agr biochem, Univ Vt, 67-71, chmn biol sci prog, 71-75, chmn cell biol, 72-75, asst dean, Col Agr & assoc dir, Agr Exp Sta, 75-77, assoc prof, 71-77, PROF BIOCHEM & MICROBIOL, UNIV VT, 77- *Personal Data:* b Munfordville, Ky, Sept 28, 38; m 68; c 1. *Educ:* Rochester Inst Technol, BS, 62; Iowa State Univ, PhD(bio-chem), 66. *Prof Exp:* Res fel molecular biol, Children's Cancer Res Found, Boston, Mass, 66-67. *Mem:* Am Chem Soc; Biophys Soc; NY Acad Sci; Am Inst Chem; Soc Protozoologists. *Res:* Ribosomes and RNAases of Entamoeba; isoelectric focusing of proteins. *Mailing Add:* 38 Main St Vergennes VT 05491-1156

**WELLER, EDWARD F(RANK), JR,** ELECTRONICS ENGINEERING, SEMICONDUCTOR DEVICES. *Current Pos:* RETIRED. *Personal Data:* b Baltimore, Md, Nov 30, 19; m 43, Mary E Rourke; c Edward, Stephen & Geoffrey. *Educ:* Univ Cincinnati, EE, 43. *Prof Exp:* Res engr instrumentation, Gen Motors Res Labs, 46-52, asst head, Physics Dept, 52-62, head, Electronics & Instrumentation Dept, 62-74, head, Electronics Dept, 74-82. *Mem:* Fel Inst Elec & Electronics Engrs; Sigma Xi. *Res:* Ferroelectricity; automotive instrumentation, semiconductor technology. *Mailing Add:* 14230 Boliver Dr Sun City AZ 85351

**WELLER, GLENN PETER,** MATHEMATICS. *Current Pos:* ASST PROF, KENNEDY-KING COL, 75- *Personal Data:* b New Orleans, La, Dec 7, 43; m 69; c 2. *Educ:* Tulane Univ, BA, 64; Univ Chicago, SM, 65, PhD(math), 68. *Prof Exp:* Asst prof math, Roosevelt Univ, 68-69 & Univ Ill, Chicago Circle, 69-75. *Mem:* Math Asn Am. *Res:* Geometric topology. *Mailing Add:* Dept Comput Info Systs Harold Washington Col 30 E Lake St Chicago IL 60601-2420

**WELLER, GUNTER ERNST,** POLAR METEOROLOGY. *Current Pos:* from asst prof to assoc prof geophys, Univ Alaska, 68-73, prof geophys, Geophys Inst, 73-97, assoc dir planning, 78-83, dep dir, 84-97, DIR, CTR GLOBAL CHANGE & ARCTIC SYST RES, UNIV ALASKA, 90-, DIR COOP INST ARCTIC RES, 94-, EMER PROF, 97- *Personal Data:* b Haifa, June 14, 34; m 63, Sigrid Beilharz; c Yvette, Kara & Britta. *Educ:* Univ Melbourne, BSc, 62, MSc, 65, PhD(meteorol), 67. *Honors & Awards:* Polar Medal, Commonwealth of Australia, 69; Antarctic Serv Medal, US Govt, 74. *Prof Exp:* Meteorologist, Commonwealth Bur Meteorol, 60-61; glaciologist, Australian Nat Antarctic Res Exped, 62-66; NSF res fel, Univ Melbourne, 67. *Concurrent Pos:* Prog mgr polar meteorol, Off Polar Progs, NSF, 72-74; US rep, Working Group Meteorol, Sci Comt Antarctic Res, 74-; proj mgr, Arctic Proj Off, Outer Continental Shelf, Nat Oceanic & Atmospheric Admin, 75-81; mem, Polar Res Bd, Nat Acad Sci, 75-79, chmn, 85-90; pres, Int Comn Polar Meteorol, Int Union Geol & Geophys, 80-83; mem, Climate Res Comt, Nat Acad Sci, 81-84; chair, Polar Meteorol, Am Meteorol Soc, 81-83; dir, NASA-Univ Alaska, SAR Facil, 86-93, Nat Oceanic & Atmospheric Admin Panel on Climate & Global Change, 87-90, Ctr Global Change & Arctic Syst Res, 90-, Boarden Global Change, Nat Res Coun, 91- *Mem:* Am Meteorol Soc; Am Geophys Union; fel Arctic Inst NAm; Int Glaciol Soc; AAAS; Oceanog Soc. *Res:* Polar meteorology and climatology; micrometeorology; glacio-meteorology; problems of resource recovery and remote sensing in polar regions. *Mailing Add:* Geophys Inst Univ Alaska Fairbanks AK 99775-7320. *Fax:* 907-474-7290; *E-Mail:* gunter@gino.alaska.gi.edu

**WELLER, HENRY RICHARD,** EXPERIMENTAL NUCLEAR PHYSICS. *Current Pos:* PROF PHYSICS, DUKE UNIV, 80- *Personal Data:* b East Rutherford, NJ, Mar 15, 41; m 64; c Kira, Emily & Aaron. *Educ:* Fairleigh Dickinson Univ, BS, 62; Duke Univ, PhD(nuclear physics), 68. *Prof Exp:* Fel physics, Univ Fla, 67-68, from asst prof to prof, 68-80. *Concurrent Pos:* Georg Simon Ohms vis prof, Univ Cologne, Ger, 95. *Mem:* Fel Am Phys Soc. *Res:* Experimental nuclear structure studies, especially capture reactions involving polarized and unpolarized projectiles; studies of D-state effects in A; study of capture reactions with polarized beams below 80 keV-relevant to nuclear astrophysics; developing a polarized monoenergetic gamma-ray beam using backscattered free-election laser light. *Mailing Add:* Dept Physics TUNL Box 90308 Duke Univ Durham NC 27708-0308. *Fax:* 919-660-2634; *E-Mail:* weller@tunl.duke.edu

**WELLER, LAWRENCE ALLENBY,** ELECTROMAGNETIC PULSE, AIRCRAFT ELECTRONICS. *Current Pos:* INSTR MATH, BUTLER CO COMMUNITY COL, 91- *Personal Data:* b New York, NY, July 3, 27; m 57, Doris Rothman; c Robert J & Steven J. *Educ:* City Col New York, BS, 49; Univ Toronto, MA, 52; Ohio State Univ, PhD(physics), 73. *Prof Exp:* Physicist, Warner & Swasey Res Corp, 53-56, Foster Wheller Corp, 56-68; sr res physicist, Monsanto Co, 58-71; res asst & fel, Dept Physics, Ohio State Univ, 71-74; engr, Cincinnati Electronics Corp, 74-75; physicist, Kornylak Corp, 75-76; sr scientist, Pedco Environ Inc, 76-77; eng technician, Nat Inst Occup Safety & Health, 77-80; specialist engr, Boeing Co, 80-89; instr math, Kans Newman Col, 90-95. *Concurrent Pos:* Res assoc, Dept Physics, Ohio State Univ, 74-80; consult, Dept Psychiat, Med Sch, Univ Kans, 90-91; consult, Rose & Assoc, 95- *Mem:* Am Phys Soc; Am Nuclear Soc; Inst Elec & Electronics Engrs. *Res:* Infrared spectra of molecules; lasers; materials handling machinery; isotope separation; nuclear engineering; protective equipment for workers; electromagnetic pulse effects on electrical and electronic systems; radar. *Mailing Add:* 8612 Chalet Dr Wichita KS 67207

**WELLER, LOWELL ERNEST,** ORGANIC CHEMISTRY, BIOCHEMISTRY. *Current Pos:* from assoc prof to prof, 57-89, head dept, 57-89, EMER PROF CHEM, UNIV EVANSVILLE, 89- *Personal Data:* b Continental, Ohio, Apr 17, 23; m 44, Eloise Leone Barrick; c Ronald Alan & Donald Ernest. *Educ:* Bowling Green State Univ, BS, 48; Mich State Univ, MS, 51, PhD(chem), 56. *Prof Exp:* Asst chem, Bowling Green State Univ, 46-48; from instr to asst prof biochem, Mich State Univ, 48-57. *Concurrent Pos:* NSF, AEC & Energy Res & Develop Admin grants. *Mem:* AAAS; Am Chem Soc; Royal Soc Chem; Sigma Xi. *Res:* Organic synthesis, reaction mechanisms and structure determination especially by spectroscopic methods. *Mailing Add:* 1617 Bayard Park Dr Evansville IN 47714-2027

**WELLER, MILTON WEBSTER,** ECOLOGY, FISH & WILDLIFE SCIENCES. *Current Pos:* Kleberg chair prof wildlife, 82-94, EMER PROF WILDLIFE ECOL, TEX A&M UNIV, 94- *Personal Data:* b St Louis, Mo, May 23, 29; m 47, Doris Leach; c 1. *Educ:* Univ Mo, AB, 51, MA, 54, PhD(zool), 56. *Honors & Awards:* Lifetime Achivement Award, Soc Wetland Scientists, 96. *Prof Exp:* Instr zool, Univ Mo, 56-57; from asst prof to prof, Iowa State Univ, 57-74, chmn fisheries & wildlife sect, 67-74; prof & head, Dept Entom, Fisheries & Wildlife, Univ Minn, St Paul, 74-82. *Concurrent Pos:* NSF res grants, 64-65, 70-74 & 76-77, Dept Interior res grants, 76-81, 86-94, Corps Engrs, 92-94. *Mem:* Fel AAAS; Ecol Soc Am; Cooper Ornith Soc; Wildlife Soc; fel Am Ornith Union; Soc Wetland Scientists. *Res:* Wetland and waterbird ecology, including habitat restoration and evaluation. *Mailing Add:* 4302 Ocean Dr Corpus Christi TX 78412

**WELLER, PAUL FRANKLIN,** PHYSICAL CHEMISTRY. *Current Pos:* RETIRED. *Personal Data:* b Kankakee, Ill, Aug 30, 35; m 58, Gail Seibert; c Mark & David. *Educ:* Univ Ill, BS, 57; Cornell Univ, PhD(chem), 62. *Prof Exp:* Res scientist, T J Watson Res Ctr, Int Bus Mach Corp, 61-65; from asst prof to prof chem, State Univ NY Col Fredonia, 65-75, chmn dept, 74-75; prof chem & dean arts & sci, Western Ill Univ, 75-79; acad vpres, Calif Polytech Univ, Pomona, 79-85; pres, Framingham State Col, 85-97. *Mem:* Am Asn Higher Educ; Am Chem Soc; Sigma Xi. *Res:* Wide band gap semiconductors; defect oxides; solid state materials characterization; crystal growth. *Mailing Add:* 2025 Misty Sunrise Trail Sarasota FL 34240. *Fax:* 508-626-4592

**WELLER, PETER FAHEY,** MEDICINE, PARASITOLOGY. *Current Pos:* from asst prof to assoc prof, 77-96, PROF MED, HARVARD MED SCH, 96- *Personal Data:* b Boston, Mass, May 5, 40; m 79, Anne Nicholson; c Susan R & Nathaniel N. *Educ:* Harvard Univ, AB, 68, MD, 72. *Honors & Awards:* Bailey Ashford Award, Am Soc Trop Med & Hyg, 92. *Concurrent Pos:* Co-chief infectious dis & chief allergy & inflammation, Beth Israel Deaconess Med Ctr. *Mem:* Am Soc Trop Med & Hyg (secy-treas, 92-); Am Asn Immunologists; fel Am Asn Alllergy Immunol; fel Infectious Dis Soc Am; fel Am Col Physicians. *Res:* Immunoparasitology and host defense, asthma, allergic diseases and eosinophilia. *Mailing Add:* Beth Israel Hosp Infectious Dis DA617 330 Brookline Ave Boston MA 02215-5491. *Fax:* 617-277-6061

**WELLER, RICHARD IRWIN,** PHYSICS, ACADEMIC ADMINISTRATION. *Current Pos:* CONSULT, 81- *Personal Data:* b Newark, NJ, Mar 3, 21; m 53, Juanita Mustain; c Rosalyn E & Mark D. *Educ:* City Col New York, BEE, 44; Union Col, BS, 48; Fordham Univ, MS, 50, PhD(physics), 53. *Prof Exp:* Elec engr, NAm Phillips Co, 44, Guy F Atkinson Co, 44-45, NAm Phillips Co, 45-46, Crow, Lewis & Wick, 47, Edward E Ashley, 48, Allied Processes Co, 50, V L Falotico & Assocs, 50-51 & Singmaster & Breyer, 51; instr physics, Brooklyn Col, 52-53; asst prof, State Univ, NY Maritime Col, 53-54; med physicist, Brookhaven Nat Lab, 54-57; prof physics, Franklin & Marshall Col, 57-70, chmn dept, 57-61; prof physics & dean, Sch Sci & Math, Edinboro State Col, 70-81. *Concurrent Pos:* Instr, Manhattan Col, 49-50, Fordham Univ, 50-52, Newark Col Eng, 52-53, Broward Community Col, 81-83, Brevard Community Col, 83-84 & Fla Inst Technol, 84-85; consult, Brookhaven Nat Lab, Fairchild Camera & Instrument Corp & Nuclear Sci & Eng Corp; mem Nat Res Coun subcomt, Nat Acad Sci. *Mem:* AAAS; Am Asn Univ Prof; Inst Elec & Electronics Engrs; Sigma Xi; Am Soc Eng Educ; Health Physics Soc; Am Asn Physics Teachers; Am Physics Soc. *Res:* Atmospheric electricity; radioactivity; radioisotopes dosimetry and instrumentation; biophysics. *Mailing Add:* 750 N Atlantic Ave-PH-1 Cocoa Beach FL 32931-3154. *E-Mail:* weller@iv.net

**WELLER, ROBERT ANDREW,** OCEANOGRAPHY. *Current Pos:* scholar, Woods Hole Oceanog Inst, 79-80, from asst scientist to assoc scientist, 80-88, assoc scientist with tenure, 88-92, SR SCIENTIST, WOODS HOLE OCEANOG INST, 92-, HENRY BRYANT BIGELOW CHAIR, 93- *Personal Data:* b Boston, Mass, July 27, 50; m 72, Kathleen J; c Stephen & Benjamin. *Educ:* Harvard Univ, BA, 72; Univ Calif, San Diego, PhD(oceanog), 78. *Honors & Awards:* James B Macelwane Award, Am Geophys Union, 86. *Prof Exp:* Res asst, Harvard Univ, 70-72; Res asst, Scripps Inst Oceanog, 72-78, res oceanographer, Woods Hole Oceanog Inst, 78-79. *Mem:* AAAS; fel Am Geophys Union; Am Meteorol Soc; Oceanog Soc. *Res:* Experimental work in observing and understanding the response of the upper ocean to atmospheric forcing. *Mailing Add:* Clark Lab Woods Hole Oceanog Inst Woods Hole MA 02543. *Fax:* 508-457-2181; *E-Mail:* rweller@whoi.edu

**WELLER, S(OL) W(ILLIAM),** PHYSICAL CHEMISTRY, CHEMICAL ENGINEERING. *Current Pos:* actg chmn dept chem eng, State Univ NY, 68-69, 72-73 & 76-77, prof chem eng, 65-89, C C Furnas Mem prof, 83-89, EMER PROF CHEM ENG, STATE UNIV NY, BUFFALO, AMHERST, 89- *Personal Data:* b Detroit, Mich, July 27, 18; m 43; c 4. *Educ:* Wayne State Univ, BS, 38; Univ Chicago, PhD(chem), 41. *Honors & Awards:* H H Storch Award, 81; E V Murphree Award, 82; J F Schoellkopf Medal, 84; Dean's Award, 91. *Prof Exp:* Fel, NY Univ, 41; res assoc, Nat Defense Res Comt, Chicago, 41-43; proj leader, Gen Foods Corp, 43-44; res scientist, Manhattan Proj, Columbia Univ, 44-45; phys chemist, US Bur Mines, Pa, 45-47, asst chief, Coal Hydrogenation Sect, 47-50; chief, Fundamental Res Sect, Houdry Process Corp, 50-58; mgr, Propulsion Dept Aeronutronic Div, Ford Motor Co, 58-60, mem sr staff, 60, mgr chem & mat, 60-63, dir, Chem Lab, 63-65; vis fel, Oxford Univ, 89. *Concurrent Pos:* Civilian, AEC, 44; vis prof, Univ Calif, Berkeley, 67; UN tech expert, Israel, 71-72; sr Fulbright lectr, Univ Madrid, 75, Istanbul Tech Univ, 81. *Mem:* AAAS; Am Chem Soc; Am Inst Chem Engrs. *Res:* Catalysis; kinetics and mechanisms of catalytic reactions; synthetic liquid fuels. *Mailing Add:* Dept Chem Eng State Univ NY at Buffalo Amherst NY 14260

**WELLER, THOMAS HUCKLE,** TROPICAL MEDICINE, INFECTIOUS DISEASES. *Current Pos:* instr comp path & trop med, Harvard Univ, 48-49, from asst prof to assoc prof trop pub health, 49-54, head dept, 54-81, Strong prof, 54-85, dir, Ctr Prev Infectious Dis, 66-81, EMER PROF TROP PUB HEALTH, SCH PUB HEALTH, HARVARD UNIV, 85- *Personal Data:* b Ann Arbor, Mich, June 15, 15; m 45; c 4. *Educ:* Univ Mich, AB, 36, MS, 37; Harvard Med Sch, MD, 40. *Hon Degrees:* LLD, Univ Mich, 56; ScD, Gustavus Adolphus Col, 75; LHD, Lowell Univ, 77; ScD, Univ Mass, 85. *Honors & Awards:* Nobel Prize Physiol & Med, 54; Mead Johnson Award, Am Acad Pediat, 53; Kimble Methodol Award, 54; Ledlie Prize, 63; Weinstein Award, 73; Bristol Award, Infectious Dis Soc Am, 80. *Prof Exp:* Res fel comp path & trop med, Harvard Med Sch, 40, teaching fel bact, 40-41, Milton fel pediat, 47-48; USPHS fel, 48. *Concurrent Pos:* Intern, Children's Hosp, 41-42, asst res, 46, asst dir res, Div Infectious Dis, Children's Med Ctr, 49-56, assoc physician, 49-55; area consult, US Vet Admin, 49-64; consult & mem trop med & parasitol study sect, USPHS, 53-55; dir, Comn Parasitic Dis, Armed Forces Epidemiol Br, 53-59, mem, 59-72. *Mem:* Nat Acad Sci; Am Soc Trop Med & Hyg (pres, 64); Asn Am Physicians; hon mem Royal Soc Trop Med & Hyg, 87. *Res:* In vitro cultivation of viruses, especially poliomyelitis, mumps and Coxsackie viruses; etiology of epidemic pleurodynia, varicella and Herpes zoster; cytomegalic inclusion and Rubella; helminth infections, especially schistosomiasis and enterobiasis. *Mailing Add:* 56 Winding River Rd Needham MA 02192

**WELLERSON, RALPH, JR,** MICROBIOLOGY. *Current Pos:* Sr scientist, 54-62, RES FEL MICROBIOL, DIV MICROBIOL, ORTHO RES FOUND, ORTHO PHARMACEUT CORP, RARITAN, NJ, 62- *Personal Data:* b New York, NY, Dec 12, 24; m 51; c 2. *Educ:* Hobart Col, BS, 49; Rutgers Univ, MS, 51; Purdue Univ, PhD(bact), 54. *Mem:* Am Soc Microbiol. *Res:* Metabolism and nutrition of microorganisms; microbial fermentations; chemotherapy of Trichomonas vaginalis; immunological control of fertility. *Mailing Add:* 14 Oxbow Lane Basking Ridge NJ 07920

**WELLES, HARRY LESLIE,** pharmaceutics, for more information see previous edition

**WELLES, SAMUEL PAUL,** vertebrate paleontology, for more information see previous edition

**WELLING, DANIEL J,** THEORETICAL PHYSICS, BIOPHYSICS. *Current Pos:* vis assoc prof path, 72-73, assoc prof path & physiol, 73-80, RES PROF PATH & PHYSIOL, MED CTR, UNIV KANS, 80- *Personal Data:* b Kansas City, Mo, May 1, 37; c 3. *Educ:* Rockhurst Col, BS, 58; St Louis Univ, PhD(physics), 63. *Prof Exp:* Asst prof physics, Southern Ill Univ, 64; AEC fel theoret physics, Argonne Nat Lab, 64-66; asst prof & assoc scientist, Univ Wis-Milwaukee, 66-72. *Concurrent Pos:* Assoc scientist, McDonnell Aircraft Corp, 63; res scientist, VA Med Ctr, Kans City, Mo. *Mem:* Am Phys Soc; Am Soc Nephrology. *Res:* Medical physics; mathematical modeling of transport in the nephron. *Mailing Add:* 9535 Birch St Shawnee Mission KS 66207

**WELLING, LARRY WAYNE,** RENAL PHYSIOLOGY, PATHOLOGY. *Current Pos:* STAFF PATHOLOGIST, VET ADMIN MED CTR, KANSAS CITY, MO, 72- *Educ:* Univ Kans, PhD(physiol), 72. *Mailing Add:* Lab Serv 151 Vet Admin Med Ctr 4801 Linwood Blvd Kansas City MO 64128-2226

**WELLING, PETER GEOFFREY,** PHARMACOKINETICS, DRUG METABOLISM. *Current Pos:* DEPT HEAD, PHARMACOKINETICS, INST RES, FRANCE, 96- *Personal Data:* b London, Eng, June 23, 32; US & UK citizen; m 88, Josephine Kwong; c Luisa A, Caroline Y, Graham C, Christine A & Stephen J. *Educ:* Univ Sydney, BPharm, 64, MSc, 63, PhD(drug metab), 68. *Hon Degrees:* DSc, Univ Sydney, 80. *Prof Exp:* Proj leader drug metab, Pfizer Ltd, UK, 70-71; from asst prof to prof pharmaceut, Univ Wis, 72-84; dir, Park-Davis Pharmaceut Res Div, Warner-Lambert Co, 84-87, vpres, Dept Pharmaconkinetics & Drug Metab, 87-96. *Concurrent Pos:* Hon consult clin pharmacol, Queen Elizabeth Hosp, Birmingham Cent Dist, 78-79; sr lectr clin pharmacol, Sch Med, Univ Birmingham, 78-79; assoc mem, Wis Clin Cancer Ctr, 79-84; mem, Pharmacol Study Sect, NIH, 82-87; vis fel, Western Australian Inst Technol, Wash, 83; ed, Antimicrobial Agents & Chem, 84 88. *Mem:* Fel Am Asn Pharmaceut Scientists, Am Soc Microbiol; Brit Soc Antimicrobial Chemother; Brit Pharmacol Soc; Am Pharmaceut Asn. *Res:* Drug pharmacokinetics and drug metabolism; drug absorption and concentration-effect relationship; author or co-author of numerous scientific publications. *Mailing Add:* Inst Res Jeureinale 3-9 Rue De La Loge BP Fresnes Cedex 100 94265 France. *Fax:* 313-996-5115

**WELLINGTON, GEORGE HARVEY,** ANIMAL SCIENCE. *Current Pos:* from asst prof to prof, 47-77, EMER PROF ANIMAL SCI, CORNELL UNIV, 78- *Personal Data:* b Springport, Mich, Sept 19, 15; m 39, Gladys Brown; c Earl C, Mary (Daly) & Ann (Marguet). *Educ:* Mich State Univ, BS, 37, Kans State Univ, MS, 40. *Honors & Awards:* Signal Serv Award, Am Meat Sci Asn, 66. *Prof Exp:* Asst, Kans State Univ, 38-40; agr exten agent, Mich, 45-46. *Concurrent Pos:* Ford Found consult livestock in Syria, 62; vis prof, Univ Aleppo, Syria, 65-66; consult, Fed Univ Minas Gerias, Brazil, 78, Govt Botswana, 79, Govt Malawi, 82, Va State Univ, 84, & Govt Bangladesh, 85- *Mem:* Am Soc Animal Sci; Am Meat Sci Asn. *Res:* Meat animal growth development and composition; meat quality factors and processing. *Mailing Add:* 18 Strawberru Hill Rd Ithaca NY 14850

**WELLINGTON, JOHN SESSIONS,** PATHOLOGY. *Current Pos:* PROF PATH & ASSOC DEAN, JOHN A BURNS SCH MED, UNIV HAWAII, HONOLULU, 77- *Personal Data:* b Glendale, Calif, Sept 28, 21; m 44; c 2. *Educ:* Univ Calif, Berkeley, AB, 42; Univ Calif, San Francisco, MD, 45. *Prof Exp:* Instr path, Sch Med, Univ Calif, 53-55, lectr, 55-56; vis asst prof, Univ Indonesia, 56-58; assoc prof path, Sch Med, Univ Calif, San Francisco, 58-69, prof, 69-77, assoc dean, 65-77. *Mem:* Fel Col Am Path; Am Soc Exp Path; Int Acad Path. *Res:* Leukemia; injury and repair in hematopoietic tissue. *Mailing Add:* PO Box 663 Kenwood CA 95452-0663

**WELLMAN, ANGELA MYRA,** MICROBIAL PHYSIOLOGY. *Current Pos:* Nat Res Coun Can fel, Univ Western Ont, 59-61, instr, 61-62, lectr, 62-64, asst prof, 64-68, assoc prof bot, 68-82, from asst dean to assoc dean sci, 74-82, EMER PROF, UNIV WESTERN ONT, 96- *Personal Data:* b Sudbury, Suffolk, Eng, June 13, 35; m 59, William John Willman. *Educ:* Bristol Univ, BSc, 56, PhD(mycol), 61. *Prof Exp:* Demonstr bot, Bristol Univ, 56-59. *Mailing Add:* 488 Spring St Port Stanley ON N5L 1G6 Can

**WELLMAN, DENNIS LEE,** SYSTEMS ENGINEERING, ATMOSPHERIC RESEARCH PLATFORMS. *Current Pos:* ELECTRONICS ENGR, NAT OCEANIC & ATMOSPHERIC ADMIN, 72- *Personal Data:* b Freeport, Ill, Mar 18, 42; m 68, Kathleen G Markwell; c Jennifer L & Timothy Sean. *Educ:* Univ Colo, BS, 71. *Prof Exp:* Electronics engr aerospace, Ball Bros Res Corp, 72. *Mem:* Am Geophys Union. *Res:* Physical and chemical characteristics of natural and man-made aerosols; chemical reactions of pollutant gases; air quality, acid precipitation and deposition, pollutant transport; alterations of precipitation distribution and amount. *Mailing Add:* NOAA/ERL/ARL/SRRB 325 Broadway Boulder CO 80303-3328. *Fax:* 303-497-6546; *E-Mail:* dwellman@srrb.noaa.gov

**WELLMAN, HENRY NELSON,** INTERNAL MEDICINE. *Current Pos:* PROF MED & RADIOL, SCH MED, IND UNIV, 71- *Personal Data:* b Kansas City, Kans, Nov 10, 33; m 57; c 6. *Educ:* Rockhurst Col, BS, 56; Sch Med, St Louis Univ, MD, 60. *Prof Exp:* Intern med, St Louis Univ Hosps, 60-61, postgrad radiol biol & med, 61; resident med, Univ Cincinnati, 63-65, fel, 65-66, asst prof med & radiol, Sch Med, 66-69, assoc prof, 69-71. *Concurrent Pos:* Asst attend physician, Cincinnati Gen Hosp, 67-70; chief nuclear med sect, Pop Studies Prog, Dept Health, Educ & Welfare, 69-71; sr scientist award, Alexander Von Humboldt Found, 79-80; US tech advisor, Int Electrotech Comt, 77-81; dir nuclear med, Sch Med, Ind Univ, 72- & staff radiol med, Univ Med Ctr, 71-; consult, Bur Drugs, Div Oncol & Radiopharm, 75- & WHO, 77- *Mem:* AMA; fel Am Col Physicians; fel Am Col Radiol; fel Am Col Nuclear Physicians (secy, 85-87); Soc Nuclear Med. *Res:* Development of newer diagnostic uses of radiolabelled substances, especially in pulmonary, skeletal cerebral and neoplastic processes for clinical nuclear medicine. *Mailing Add:* Dept Rediol Div Nuclear Med Ind Univ 550 N Univ Blvd UH 0663 Indianapolis IN 46202-5250

**WELLMAN, RUSSEL ELMER,** XEROGRAPHY, THERMOGRAPHY. *Current Pos:* RETIRED. *Personal Data:* b New Berlin, NY, July 16, 22; m 48, Elisabeth Galle; c 2. *Educ:* Howard Col, BA, 50; Univ Rochester, PhD(phys chem), 55. *Prof Exp:* Res chemist, Callery Chem Co, 55, group leader appl chem, 56-60; sr chemist, Inorg & Phys Chem Sect, Southern Res Inst, 60-66; unit mgr polymer technol, Xerox Corp, Rochester, NY, 66-67, scientist, 67-76; consult, 76-77; sr chemist, Pitney Bowes, Danbury & Trumbull, Conn, 78-95. *Mem:* Am Chem Soc; NY Acad Sci; Am Inst Chem; Soc Photog Sci & Eng; Am Soc Testing & Mat; AAAS. *Res:* Viscometry; physical chemistry of polymers; adhesion of polymers; microencapsulation; materials for non-impact printing processes. *Mailing Add:* 206 Grasslands Rd Southbury CT 06488

**WELLMAN, SUSAN ELIZABETH,** NUCLEIC ACID STRUCTURE. *Current Pos:* res asst, Dept Biochem, Univ Miss Med Ctr, 83-86, res assoc, 86-87, fel, 87-90, ASST PROF, DEPT PHARMACOL, UNIV MISS MED CTR, 90- *Personal Data:* b Morganton, NC, Sept 16, 55; m 80, Donald B Sittman. *Educ:* Univ NC, Chapel Hill, BS, 76; Fla State Univ, PhD(chem), 86. *Prof Exp:* Lab technologist, Dept Zool, Univ NC, Chapel Hill, 77-79; lab technician, Dept Biol, Fla State Univ, 79-80, grad teaching asst, Dept Chem, 80-81, grad res asst, 81-82. *Mem:* Am Soc Cell Biol; Am Soc Pharmacol & Exp Therapeut; Biophys Soc. *Res:* Interactions between the H1 histones and DNA; focus on quantitation of the binding affinity and determination of DNA sequence preference of the H1 histones; comparison of these characteristics for each of the H1 variants. *Mailing Add:* Dept Pharmacol & Toxicol Univ Miss Med Ctr 2500 N State St Jackson MS 39216-4505. *Fax:* 601-984-1637; *E-Mail:* wellman@fiona.umsmed.edu

**WELLMAN, WILLIAM EDWARD,** ORGANIC CHEMISTRY. *Current Pos:* RETIRED. *Personal Data:* b Ft Wayne, Ind, Oct 22, 32; m 66; c 2. *Educ:* Col Wooster, BA, 54; Ohio State Univ, PhD(org chem), 60. *Prof Exp:* Chemist, Esso Res & Eng Co, 60-63, proj leader, 64-69, res assoc, 68-73, sect head, 69-73, mgr oxygen solvents & lower alcohols, Solvents Technol Div, 73-80, mgr technol develop & appln, Exxon Chem Co, 80-87. *Res:* Petrochemicals, solvents and fiber intermediates; process development. *Mailing Add:* Exxon Chem Co 1900 E Linden Linden NJ 07036

**WELLNER, DANIEL,** BIOCHEMISTRY. *Current Pos:* asst prof, 67-69, ASSOC PROF BIOCHEM, MED COL, CORNELL UNIV, 69- *Personal Data:* b Antwerp, Belg, June 9, 34; US citizen; m 62, Vaira Pamiljans; c Philip A. *Educ:* Harvard Col, AB, 56; Tufts Univ, PhD(biochem), 61. *Prof Exp:* Instr biochem, Sch Med, Tufts Univ, 62-63, sr instr, 63-65, asst prof, 65-67. *Concurrent Pos:* NATO fel biochem, Weizmann Inst Sci, 61-62; Lederle med fac award, 64-67; ad hoc mem, Pathobiol Chem Study Sect, NIH, 79, mem, Med Biochem Study Sect, 81-85. *Mem:* Sigma Xi; Am Chem Soc; NY Acad Sci; Harvey Soc; Am Soc Biochem & Molecular Biol. *Res:* Ribonuclease; amino acid oxidases; flavoproteins; mechanism of enzyme action; biochemistry of cancer; inborn errors of metabolism. *Mailing Add:* Cornell Univ Med Col 1300 York Ave New York NY 10021. *Fax:* 212-746-8875; *E-Mail:* dwelln@med.cornell.edu

**WELLNER, MARCEL,** FRACTALS IN GAUGE FIELDS, NUMERICAL SOLUTIONS OF FIELD EQUATIONS. *Current Pos:* from asst prof to prof, 64-95, EMER PROF PHYSICS, SYRACUSE UNIV, 95-; RES PROF, STATE UNIV NY HEALTH SCI CTR, SYRACUSE, 95- *Personal Data:* b Antwerp, Belg, Feb 8, 30; US citizen; m 61, Magdeleine Misselyn; c Pierre & Lucie. *Educ:* Mass Inst Technol, BS, 52; Princeton Univ, PhD(physics), 58. *Prof Exp:* Instr physics, Princeton Univ, 56-58 & Brandeis Univ, 58-59; mem, Inst Advan Study, 59-60; res assoc physics, Univ Ind, 60-63; NSF fel, Atomic Energy Res Estab, Eng, 63-64. *Concurrent Pos:* Physicist, Cavendish Lab, Cambridge Univ, Eng, 68-69; vis scientist, Inst Advan Studies, Dublin, Ireland, 80. *Mem:* Am Phys Soc. *Res:* Quantum field theory and mathematical methods; studying the formation of fractals in classical Yang-Mills systems; waves in reaction-diffusion media. *Mailing Add:* Dept Physics Syracuse Univ Syracuse NY 13244-1130. *Fax:* 315-464-8014

**WELLNER, VAIRA PAMILJANS,** BIOCHEMISTRY. *Current Pos:* res assoc biochem, Col Med, 72-87, res assoc, Dept Surg, Burn Ctr, 87-93, RES ASSOC, CORNELL UNIV MED COL, 93- *Personal Data:* b Aluksne, Latvia, Jan 28, 36; US citizen; m 62; c 1. *Educ:* Boston Univ, AB, 58; Tufts Univ, PhD(biochem), 64. *Prof Exp:* Res assoc biochem, Sch Med, Tufts Univ, 66-67. *Concurrent Pos:* Res fel biochem, Sch Med, Tufts Univ, 63-66 & Col Med, Cornell Univ, 67-72. *Mem:* Am Chem Soc; Sigma Xi; Am Soc Biochem & Molecular Biol; AAAS; Am Burn Asn. *Res:* Mechanisms of enzyme action; amino acid metabolism. *Mailing Add:* Cornell Univ Med Col 1300 York Ave New York NY 10021

**WELLONS, JESSE DAVIS, III,** WOOD TECHNOLOGY, POLYMER SCIENCE. *Current Pos:* MGR RES & DEVELOP, CHEM DIV, GA PAC CORP, 81- *Personal Data:* b Roanoke, Va, Apr 4, 38; m 58; c 4. *Educ:* Duke Univ, BS, 60, MF, 63, PhD(wood technol, polymer sci), 66. *Prof Exp:* Res chemist, Res Triangle Inst, NC, 62-65, res assoc wood chem, Iowa State Univ, 65-66, from asst prof to assoc prof, 66-70; assoc prof forest prod chem, Ore State Univ, 70-77, prof, 77-81. *Mem:* Forest Prod Res Soc; Soc Wood Sci & Technol; Am Chem Soc. *Res:* Wood adhesives; tannin adhesives; plywood processing; use of plastics to modify properties of wood; sorption and diffusion of monomers in wood. *Mailing Add:* PO Box 740075 Atlanta GA 30374-0075

**WELLS, ADONIRAM JUDSON,** PHYSICAL CHEMISTRY. *Current Pos:* CONSULT, AM LUNG ASN, 81- *Personal Data:* b Chicago, Ill, Apr 1, 17; m 37, 94, Anne Jessup; c 6. *Educ:* Harvard Univ, SB, 38, AM, 40, PhD(phys chem), 41. *Prof Exp:* Res chemist, Ammonia Dept, E I du Pont de Nemours & Co, Del, 41-46, res supvr, 46-48, mgt asst, 48-50, mgr film develop, 50-53, dir, Yerkes Res Lab, NY, 53-55, asst res dir, Film Dept, Del, 55-59, res dir, Electrochem Dept, 59-69, dir, Indust Prod Div, 69-77, dir, Specialty Prods Div, Fabrics & Finishes Dept, 77-80. *Mem:* Am Chem Soc; Soc Epidemiol Res; Am Pub Health Asn. *Res:* Infrared and Raman spectroscopy; thermodynamics; process and market development; polymer chemistry; high temperatures; epidemiology of passive smoking. *Mailing Add:* 5 Ingleton Circle Kennett Square PA 19348

**WELLS, ALAN HILARY,** MEDICAL SCIENCES. *Current Pos:* POSTDOCTORAL, BROWN UNIV, 81- *Personal Data:* b New York, NY, Dec 15, 58. *Educ:* Brown Univ, AB, 79; Karolonska Inst, Dr Meds, 82. *Honors & Awards:* Int Cancer Res Technol Transfer Award, Union Int Against Cancer, Geneva, 80. *Prof Exp:* Assoc prof, Okayama Univ Med Sch, Japan, 83-84; postdoctoral fel, Univ Calif, San Francisco, 84-86. *Mem:* AAAS; Ny Acad Sci. *Res:* Contributed articles to professional journals. *Mailing Add:* Hooper Found Univ Calif HSW 1501 San Francisco CA 94143

**WELLS, BENJAMIN B, JR,** MATHEMATICAL ANALYSIS. *Current Pos:* assoc prof, 71-76, PROF MATH, UNIV HAWAII, 76- *Personal Data:* b Rochester, Minn, May 31, 41; m 67. *Educ:* Univ Mich, BS, 61, MS, 62; Univ Calif, Berkeley, PhD(math), 67. *Prof Exp:* From instr to asst prof math, Univ Ore, 67-70; Fulbright lectr, Univ Santiago, Chile, 70-71. *Mem:* Am Math Soc. *Res:* Measure theory; harmonic analysis. *Mailing Add:* 2500 Wisconsin Ave NW 842 Washington DC 20007

**WELLS, BOBBY R,** SOIL CHEMISTRY, SOIL FERTILITY. *Current Pos:* asst soils, 59-60, from asst prof to prof, 66-93, UNIV PROF AGRON, RICE EXP STA, UNIV ARK, FAYETTEVILLE, 93- *Personal Data:* b Wickliffe, Ky, July 30, 34; m 60, Marcia R Willetts; c Teresa L. *Educ:* Murray State Univ, BS, 59; Univ Ark, MS, 61; Univ Mo, PhD(soil chem), 64. *Prof Exp:* Asst county agent, Univ Mo, 60-61, asst soils, 61-64; asst prof agr, Murray State Univ, 64-66. *Concurrent Pos:* Interim dept head, agron, Univ Ark, 93- *Mem:* Fel Am Soc Agron; Soil Sci Soc Am; Sigma Xi. *Res:* Investigations into soil-plant relationships for rice and wheat. *Mailing Add:* Agron 115 Pl Sci Univ Ark Fayetteville AR 72701. *Fax:* 501-575-7465

**WELLS, CHARLES EDMON,** PSYCHIATRY, NEUROLOGY. *Current Pos:* assoc prof neurol, 61-75, psychiat, 68-72, PROF NEUROL, SCH MED, VANDERBILT UNIV, 75-, PROF PSYCHIAT & VCHMN DEPT, 72- *Personal Data:* b Dothan, Ala, May 19, 29; m 62; c 3. *Educ:* Emory Univ, AB, 48, MD, 53. *Prof Exp:* From intern to asst resident med, NY Hosp, 53-54; clin assoc neurol, NIH, 54-56; resident, NY Hosp, 57-58. *Concurrent Pos:* NIH fel neurol, NY Hosp-Cornell Med Ctr, 58-59; mem coun aging, Am Psychiat Asn, 82- *Mem:* Am Psychiat Asn; Am Col Psychiat; Am Neurol Asn; Asn Res Nerv & Ment Dis. *Res:* Dementia; neuropsychiatry; use of literature in teaching of psychiatry. *Mailing Add:* Psychiat Cons PC 310 25th Ave N Suite 309 Nashville TN 37203-1515

**WELLS, CHARLES FREDERICK,** CATEGORY THEORY, PROGRAMMING LANGUAGE MODEL THEORY. *Current Pos:* From asst prof to assoc prof, 65-80, PROF MATH, CASE WESTERN RES UNIV, 80- *Personal Data:* b Atlanta, Ga, May 4, 37; m 62; c 2. *Educ:* Oberlin Col, AB, 62; Duke Univ, PhD(math), 65. *Concurrent Pos:* Prin investr, NSF grants, 65-67 & 87-89; guest, Math Res Inst, Swiss Fed Inst Technol, Zurich, 75-76 & 83 & Oxford Univ Comput Lab, 90. *Mem:* Math Asn Am; Am Math Soc; Asn Comput Mach. *Res:* Category theory, theoretical computer science. *Mailing Add:* Dept Math Case Western Res Univ 10900 Euclid Ave Cleveland OH 44106-7058. *E-Mail:* cfw2@po.cwru.edu

**WELLS, CHARLES HENRY,** PHYSIOLOGY. *Current Pos:* WITH CRITIKON CORP, 80- *Personal Data:* b Chicago, Ill, Dec 6, 31; m 56; c 2. *Educ:* Randolph-Macon Col, BA, 54; Mich State Univ, MS, 60, PhD(physiol), 63. *Prof Exp:* Instr physiol, Univ Tex Med Br, 62-64; asst prof, Med Col SC, 64-67; asst prof, Univ Tex Med Br, Galveston, 67-73, assoc prof physiol, 73-80. *Concurrent Pos:* Consult, USAF, 69-; chief, Physiol Div, Shriners Burns Inst. *Mem:* Fedn Am Socs Exp Biol; Undersea Med Soc; Am Physiol Soc; Am Burn Asn; Int Soc Burn Injury. *Res:* Blood rheology, microcirculation in stress; thermal injury; decompression sickness; computer aided instructional systems development. *Mailing Add:* Johnson & Johnson PO Box 31800 Tampa FL 33631

**WELLS, CHARLES VAN,** botany; deceased, see previous edition for last biography

**WELLS, DANIEL R,** ASTRONOMY, ASTRO-PHYSICS. *Current Pos:* assoc prof, 64-67, PROF PHYSICS, UNIV MIAMI, 67- *Personal Data:* b New York, NY, May 2, 21; m 43, Mary O'Connell; c Donna M & Christina M. *Educ:* Cornell Univ, BME, 42; NY Univ, MS, 55; Stevens Inst Technol, PhD(physics), 63. *Prof Exp:* Res assoc plasma physics, Princeton Univ, 55-64. *Concurrent Pos:* Res assoc, Stevens Inst Technol, 61-64; assoc prof, Seton Hall, 62-64; res grants, AEC & Air Force Off Sci Res, 64-74. *Mem:* Am Phys Soc. *Res:* Controlled thermonuclear research; solar system formation and structure; unified theory of physical forces. *Mailing Add:* 6950 SW 62nd St Miami FL 33143

**WELLS, DARRELL GIBSON,** PLANT BREEDING, PLANT PATHOLOGY. *Current Pos:* prof wheat breeding, 62-83, EMER PROF WHEAT BREEDING, SDAK STATE UNIV, 85- *Personal Data:* b Pierre, SDak, Feb 21, 17; m 46; c Howard, Alan & David. *Educ:* SDak State Col, BS, 41; State Col Wash, MS, 43; Univ Wis, PhD, 49. *Prof Exp:* Asst agronomist, State Col Wash, 43-45; asst, Univ Wis, 45-49; from assoc prof to prof agron, Miss State Univ, 49-62. *Concurrent Pos:* Mem tech asst mission, Western Region, Nigeria, Int Develop Serv, 58-60. *Res:* Small grain genetics and breeding; cowpea and lima bean breeding. *Mailing Add:* Rte 4 Box 233 Brookings SD 57006

**WELLS, DARTHON VERNON,** ORGANIC CHEMISTRY. *Current Pos:* RETIRED. *Personal Data:* b Saline Co, Ark, Oct 11, 29; m 50; c 2. *Educ:* Univ Northern Ala, BS, 54; Univ Miss, MS, 57; Univ SC, PhD(chem), 60. *Prof Exp:* Res assoc chem, Brown Univ, 59-61; from asst prof to prof, La State Univ, Alexandria, 61-97. *Mem:* Am Chem Soc. *Res:* Chemistry of organic peroxide decomposition; nucleophilic displacement of phosphorus; carbanion rearrangement reactions. *Mailing Add:* Dept Chem La State Univ Alexandria LA 71302

**WELLS, DAVID ERNEST,** GEODESY, OCEAN MAPPING. *Current Pos:* PROF HYDROGRAPHY GEOD, UNIV NB, 80- *Personal Data:* b Montreal, Que, June 29, 39; m 64; c 3. *Educ:* Mt Allison Univ, BSc, 61; Univ BC, BASc, 63, MASc, 66; Univ NB, PhD(geod), 74. *Prof Exp:* Res scientist, Dept Fisheries & Oceans, Bedford Inst Oceanog, 74-80. *Concurrent Pos:* Nat deleg, Int Asn Geod, 86-88; pres, Can GPS Assocs, 86-; mem, Nat Marine Coun Can, 88- & Int Adv Bd, Int Hydrographic Orgn & Int Cong Surv, 90- *Mem:* Am Geophys Union; Am Cong Surv & Mapping; Hydrographic Soc; Int Asn Geod. *Res:* Ocean mapping data cleaning, interpretation and management software tool development; kinematic applications of the global positioning system. *Mailing Add:* Dept Survey Sci Univ NB PO Box 4400 Fredericton NB E3B 5A3 Can

**WELLS, EDDIE N,** PLANETOLOGY, REMOTE SENSING. *Current Pos:* OPERS ASTROM, COMPUT SCI CORP, SPACE TELESCOPE SCI INST, BALTIMORE, MD, 82- *Personal Data:* b Mar 13, 40; US citizen. *Educ:* Murray State Univ, BS, 62; Univ Pittsburgh, PhD(earth & planets), 77. *Prof Exp:* Res assoc, Lab Planetary Studies, Cornell Univ, 77-79; res assoc, Univ Pittsburgh, 79-81, res asst prof geol & planetary sci, 81-82. *Mem:* Am Geophys Union; Am Astron Soc. *Res:* Remote sensing of the earth; astronomical observations of planets, satellites and asteroids; laboratory studies of optical properties of rocks, minerals, glasses, and ices. *Mailing Add:* 2527 Steele Rd No B Baltimore MD 21209

**WELLS, EDWARD JOSEPH,** PHYSICAL CHEMISTRY. *Current Pos:* asst prof chem, Simon Fraser Univ, 65-67, actg chmn dept, 75-76, chmn dept, 76-79, ASSOC PROF CHEM, SIMON FRASER UNIV, 67-, ASSOC MEM PHYSICS DEPT, 69- *Personal Data:* b Sydney, Australia, Oct 10, 36; m 62; c 2. *Educ:* Univ Sydney, BSc, 58, MSc, 60; Oxford Univ, DPhil(magnetic resonance), 62. *Prof Exp:* Gowrie travelling scholar, 59-61; fel magnetic resonance, Univ BC, 61-63; instr phys chem, 63-64; res assoc magnetic resonance, Univ Ill, Urbana, 64-65. *Concurrent Pos:* With Australian Nat Serv, 55-58. *Mem:* Fel Chem Inst Can; fel Royal Soc Chem; Am Inst Physics; fel Royal Soc Arts; Can Asn Physicists; Sigma Xi. *Res:* Chemical and biological applications of nuclear magnetic resonance. *Mailing Add:* Dept Chem Simon Fraser Univ Burnaby BC V5A 1S6 Can

**WELLS, ELIZABETH FORTSON,** PLANT TAXONOMY, FLAVONOID CHEMOTAXONOMY. *Current Pos:* ASST PROF BOT, GEORGE WASHINGTON UNIV, 79- *Personal Data:* b Shreveport, La, March 4, 43. *Educ:* Agnes Scott Col, Decataur, Ga, BA, 65; Univ NC, Chapel Hill, MA, 70, PhD (bot), 77. *Prof Exp:* Instr biol, Univ Richmond, 70-72; fel, Univ BC, 77-79. *Mem:* Am Soc Plant Taxonomists; Bot Soc Am; Int Asn Plant Taxon; Asn Southeastern Biologists; Am Inst Biol Sci; Sigma Xi. *Res:* Revising the genus Heuchera (Saxifragaceae) using breeding studies, flavonoid analysis and morphometrics; flavonoids in Leucanthemum (Asterceae). *Mailing Add:* Dept Biol George Washington Univ Washington DC 20052-0001

**WELLS, FRANK EDWARD,** RAPID ANALYTICAL METHODOLOGY. *Current Pos:* RETIRED. *Personal Data:* b Granby, Mo, Mar 29, 25; m 47; c 2. *Educ:* Southwest Mo State Univ, BS, 51; Purdue Univ, MS, 58, PhD(bact), 61. *Prof Exp:* Med technologist, Vets Admin Hosp, Springfield, 51-53; lab dir, Henningsen Foods Inc, 53-56; instr food prods technol, Purdue Univ, 56-61; tech dir, Monarck Egg Corp, 61; sr microbiologist, Midwest Res Inst, 61-65, prin microbiologist, 65-90. *Mem:* Soc Invert Path; Wildlife Dis Asn. *Res:* Control agents for food spoilage; microbial insect control agents; disease monitoring of laboratory animals; biodegradation of xenobiotics in soil; detection of aerosolized biological agents; industrial fermentations; enzyme immobilization. *Mailing Add:* 3200 NE 64th Terr Kansas City MO 64119

**WELLS, FREDERICK JOSEPH,** SEISMOLOGY. *Current Pos:* Res geophysicist, Marathon Oil Co, 72-75, advan res geophysicist, Denver Res Ctr, 75-77, sr geophysicist, 77-80, MGR GEOPHYS PROJ, MARATHON INT OIL CO, 80- *Personal Data:* b Dayton, Ohio, Nov 13, 44. *Educ:* Univ Dayton, BS, 66; Brown Univ, ScM, 68, PhD(seismol), 72. *Mem:* Soc Explor Geophysicists; Am Asn Petrol Geologists. *Mailing Add:* 18303 Cransley Dr Houston TX 77084

**WELLS, GARLAND RAY,** FORESTRY, ECONOMICS. *Current Pos:* asst prof, 65-75, ASSOC PROF FORESTRY, UNIV TENN, KNOXVILLE, 75- *Personal Data:* b El Dorado, Ark, Oct 10, 36; m 56; c 1. *Educ:* La Polytech Inst, BS, 58; NC State Univ, MF, 61; Duke Univ, DF, 68. *Prof Exp:* From instr to asst prof forestry, La Polytech Inst, 62-65. *Mem:* Soc Am Foresters; Am Econ Asn. *Res:* Land ownership research especially the practice of forestry by private, non-industrial forest owners. *Mailing Add:* Dept Forestry Univ Tenn 1345 Circle Park Knoxville TN 37996-0001

**WELLS, GARY NEIL,** PLANT PHYSIOLOGY, BIOCHEMISTRY. *Current Pos:* from asst prof to assoc prof, 73-83, assoc head, 85-86, PROF BIOL, FLA INST TECHNOL, 83-, HEAD DEPT BIOL, 86- *Personal Data:* b Springfield, Ill, Nov 19, 41; m 65; c 2. *Educ:* Western Ill Univ, BA, 65, MS, 67; Univ Ill, PhD(plant biochem), 71. *Prof Exp:* Chem eng tech chem, Ill State Dept, 61-63; res assoc molecular biol, Univ Okla, 71-73. *Concurrent Pos:* NIH fel, Univ Okla, 72-73. *Mem:* AAAS; Am Soc Plant Physiol; Am Soc Photo Biol. *Res:* Molecular biology of development; regulatory mechanisms operating at the level of transcription and translation and their role in plant growth and development. *Mailing Add:* Dept Biol Sci Fla Inst Technol Melbourne FL 32901

**WELLS, GORDON LEE,** MARINE PHYTOPLANKTON ECOLOGY, TECHNOLOGY IN SCIENCE EDUCATION. *Current Pos:* assoc prof nat sci, 76-84, chmn, Div Natural & Appl Sci, 86-94, ASSOC PROF NATURAL SCI, OHIO VALLEY COL, 86- *Personal Data:* b Dallas, Tex, Dec 2, 48; m 70, Carolyn Kerns; c Elizabeth Ann & Phillip Wayne. *Educ:* Marshall Univ, BS, 71; Fla State Univ, MS, 75. *Prof Exp:* instr math, Barboursville High Sch, 71-72; teaching asst biol & microbiol, Fla State Univ, 72-73, res asst biol & oceanog, 73-75; inst math & sci, Fla Keys Community Col, 75-76. *Concurrent Pos:* Res asst, Univ Mich, 84-85, Thomas A & Elizabeth Mann Diamond fel, Sch Educ Merit fel, 85, instr, Dept Prof Develop, 95-96. *Mem:* Am Soc Limnol & Oceanog; Nat Sci Teachers Asn; Human Anat & Physiol Soc. *Res:* Environmental affects on marine phytoplankton; use of computers in teaching science with consideration given to learning styles and microcomputer based labs. *Mailing Add:* 4805 Eighth Ave Vienna WV 26105. *E-Mail:* wells@access.mountain.net

**WELLS, HARRINGTON,** POPULATION ECOLOGY, POPULATION GENETICS. *Current Pos:* Asst prof, 80-85, ASSOC PROF BIOL, UNIV TULSA, 86- *Personal Data:* b Columbia, Mo, June 20, 52; m 74, 88, 92, Laurisa R Mills; c 3. *Educ:* Occidental Col, BA, 74; Univ Calif, Santa Barbara, PhD(biol), 79. *Concurrent Pos:* Co-dir & co-prin investr, Tulsa Teacher Enhancement, NSF grant, 85-92; vis assoc prof, Dept Entom, G B Pant Univ, Pantnagar, India, 90-91 & 94; dir & prin investr, Okla Statewide Teacher Sci Lit, 91-96. *Mem:* AAAS; Am Soc Zoologists. *Res:* Population biology based reproduction kinetics; factors altering population growth at low densities and resulting kinetic models for conservation biology; foraging ecology of nectivores; potential evolutionary and agricultural implications of alternate foraging behaviors. *Mailing Add:* Dept Biol Sci Univ Tulsa 600 S College Tulsa OK 74104-3126

**WELLS, HENRY BRADLEY,** BIOSTATISTICS. *Current Pos:* from instr to assoc prof biostatist, 58-69, prof, 69-80, EMER PROF BIOSTATIST, SCH PUB HEALTH, UNIV NC, CHAPEL HILL, 81-; PROF BIOSTATIST, BOWMAN GRAY SCH MED, WAKE FOREST UNIV, 81- *Personal Data:* b Ridgeland, SC; m 47; c 4. *Educ:* Emory Univ, BA, 50; Univ NC, MSPH, 53, PhD(biostatist), 59. *Prof Exp:* Chief statistician, Ga State Dept Pub Health, 50-55; statistician, NC State Bd Health, 56-58, consult, 58-64. *Mem:* Fel Am Statist Asn; Biomet Soc; fel Am Pub Health Asn; Int Statist Inst; Int Asn Surv Statisticians; AAAS. *Res:* Design of clinical trials, survivorship analysis; survey methods in demographic research; evaluation of health programs. *Mailing Add:* 21416 Twiggs Lane Mooresville NC 28115

**WELLS, HERBERT,** PHARMACOLOGY, ORTHODONTICS. *Current Pos:* PROF PHARMACOL, HENRY M GOLDMAN SCH GRAD DENT, BOSTON UNIV, 68-, ASST DEAN, PREDOCTORAL PROG, 80- *Personal Data:* b New Haven, Conn, July 27, 30; m 59; c 3. *Educ:* Yale Univ, BA, 52; Harvard Univ, DMD, 56. *Honors & Awards:* Lord-Chaim Res Award, 60; Oral Sci Prize, Int Asn Dent Res, 64. *Prof Exp:* Res assoc orthod, Sch Dent Med, Harvard Univ, 59-60, assoc pharmacol, 60-63, asst prof dent & dir, Dent Clin, 63-68. *Concurrent Pos:* Res fel orthod & pharmacol, Sch Dent Med, Harvard Univ, 56-59; mem, Panel Drugs Dent, Nat Res Coun, 66- & Dent Study Sect, NIH, 74- *Mem:* Am Soc Pharmacol & Exp Therapeut; Int Asn Dent Res; Sigma Xi. *Res:* Growth and secretion of exocrine and endocrine glands; salivary glands; parathyroid glands; experimental teratology; cleft palate formation. *Mailing Add:* Oral Pharmacol Lab 214 Highland St Milton MA 02186-4431

**WELLS, HERBERT ARTHUR,** MECHANICAL ENGINEERING. *Current Pos:* Mem tech staff, 47-56, SUPVR, BELL TEL LABS, INC, 56- *Personal Data:* b Jersey City, NJ, Aug 4, 21; m 46; c 3. *Educ:* Cooper Union, BME, 47; Newark Col Eng, MSME, 52. *Mem:* Am Soc Mech Engrs; Nat Soc Prof Engrs. *Res:* Ship design and cable laying methods; hardening of structures to resist nuclear blast effects; antenna structural design for arctic and other applications. *Mailing Add:* 772 Norman Pl Westfield NJ 07090-3466

**WELLS, HOMER DOUGLAS,** PLANT PATHOLOGY. *Current Pos:* RETIRED. *Personal Data:* b Blaine, Ky, Nov 11, 23; m 42; c 1. *Educ:* Univ Ky, BS, 48, MS, 49; NC State Col, PhD(plant path), 54. *Honors & Awards:* Cert Merit, USDA, 86. *Prof Exp:* Tech asst agron agr exp sta, Univ Ky, 48-49, asst, 49-50; asst plant path, NC State Col, 50-52; asst agronomist, Ga Coastal Plain Exp Sta, USDA, 52-53, pathologist forage crops, 53-88. *Mem:* Am Phytopath Soc; Sigma Xi; AAAS. *Res:* Turf and forage crop disease problems. *Mailing Add:* 1535 Old Tusculum Rd Springfield GA 31329-4114

**WELLS, IBERT CLIFTON,** BIOCHEMISTRY OF DISEASE. *Current Pos:* chmn dept, Creighton Univ, 61-76, prof biochem, Sch Med, 61-92, prof med, 76-92, DEPT BIOMED, CREIGHTON UNIV, 92- *Personal Data:* b Fayette, Mo, Apr 12, 21; m 48, Katherine Joe Ann Haerle; c Mary J, Kevin C, Bruce A, Gary V, Mary L & Mary K. *Educ:* Cent Methodist Col, AB, 42; St Louis Univ, PhD(biochem), 48. *Honors & Awards:* Com Solvents Corp Award, 52. *Prof Exp:* From instr to assoc prof biochem, Col Med, State Univ NY Upstate Med Ctr, 50-61. *Concurrent Pos:* Nat Res Coun fel, Calif Inst Technol, 48-50. *Mem:* Am Soc Biol Chemists; Soc Exp Biol & Med. *Res:* Cholesterol metabolism; choline and one-carbon metabolism; biochemistry of disease. *Mailing Add:* Dept Biomed Creighton Univ Sch of Med Calif at 24th St Omaha NE 68178-0001. *Fax:* 402-280-2690

**WELLS, JACK NULK,** MEDICINAL CHEMISTRY, PHARMACOLOGY. *Current Pos:* vis scholar, Vanderbilt Univ, 72-73, asst prof physiol, 73-75, asst prof pharmacol, 75-77, FROM ASSOC PROF TO PROF PHARMACOL, SCH MED, VANDERBILT UNIV, 77- *Personal Data:* b McLouth, Kans, May 17, 37; m 60; c 2. *Educ:* Park Col, BA, 59; Univ Mich, MS, 62, PhD(med chem), 63. *Prof Exp:* From asst prof to assoc prof med chem, Purdue Univ, 63-67. *Concurrent Pos:* Fel, Ohio State Univ, 63. *Mem:* AAAS; Am Soc Pharmacol & Exp Therapeut; Am Chem Soc; Sigma Xi. *Res:* Phosphodiesterase; smooth muscle physiology and airchemistry. *Mailing Add:* 3604 Saratoga Dr Nashville TN 37205-2540. *Fax:* 615-343-6532

**WELLS, JACQUELINE GAYE,** ALGEBRA. *Current Pos:* RETIRED. *Personal Data:* b Pittsburgh, Pa, May 17, 31; m 51; c 2. *Educ:* Univ Pittsburgh, BS, 52, MS, 64, PhD(math), 72. *Prof Exp:* Asst prof math, Pa State Univ, McKeesport, 64-91. *Mailing Add:* 4255 Gulf Dr No 123 Holmes Beach FL 34217

**WELLS, JAMES HOWARD,** MATHEMATICS. *Current Pos:* assoc prof, 62-69, PROF MATH, UNIV KY, 69- *Personal Data:* b Howe, Tex, June 20, 32; m 53; c 2. *Educ:* Tex Tech Col, BS, 52, MS, 54; Univ Tex, PhD(math), 58. *Prof Exp:* Instr math, Univ Tex, 57-58; from instr to asst prof, Univ NC, 58-59; vis asst prof, Univ Calif, Berkeley, 60-61. *Mem:* Am Math Soc; Math Asn Am. *Res:* Analysis. *Mailing Add:* 933 Patterson Tower Lexington KY 40506-0001

**WELLS, JAMES RAY,** PLANT TAXONOMY, PLANT ECOLOGY. *Current Pos:* BOTANIST, CRANBROOK INST SCI, 66- *Personal Data:* b Delaware, Ohio, May 28, 32; m 58, Janris McManus; c 2. *Educ:* Univ Tenn, BS, 54, MS, 56; Ohio State Univ, PhD(bot), 63. *Prof Exp:* Asst prof biol, E Carolina Univ, 63-64 & Old Dominion Univ, 64-66. *Concurrent Pos:* Vis prof, Stephen F Austin State Col, 64; NSF grant, 67-69; adj prof biol, Oakland Univ, 69- & Wayne State Univ, 73-; chmn, Mich Natural Areas Coun, 70-72; pres, Mich Bot Club, 81-83. *Mem:* Bot Soc Am; Am Soc Nat; Sigma Xi. *Res:* Plant ecology; botany of Michigan Islands; cultivation of Michigan rare plants for research. *Mailing Add:* 127 Stoneybrook Lane Pontiac MI 48304

**WELLS, JAMES ROBERT,** CHEMISTRY, STRATEGIC PLANNING. *Current Pos:* Chemist, Plastics Dept, Exp Sta, E I du Pont de Nemours & Co, Inc, 67-70, sr res chemist, Sabine River Works, Plastics Prod & Resins Dept, 76-77, res mgr, Feedstocks Res & Develop Div, Cent Res & Develop Dept, 77-79, prin consult, Corp Plans Dept, Wilmington, 79-81, PRIN CONSULT, CENT RES & DEVELOP DEPT, I E DU PONT DE NUMOURS & CO, INC, 81- *Personal Data:* b Moundsville, WVa, Apr 5, 40; m 81; c 2. *Educ:* Wheeling Col, BS, 62; Univ Pittsburgh, PhD(chem), 67. *Mem:* Am Chem Soc. *Mailing Add:* 24 Drake Rd Chesapeake City MD 21915-1709

**WELLS, JANE FRANCES,** ALGEBRA. *Current Pos:* div chair, 78-79, actg div chair, 93-94, UNIV PROF, GOV STATE UNIV, 74- *Personal Data:* b Davenport, Iowa, Feb 24, 44; m 81, Burt Ferrini; c Katherine. *Educ:* Marycrest Col, BA, 66; Univ Iowa, MS, 67, PhD(math), 70, Univ Il, MS, 90. *Prof Exp:* Asst prof math, Purdue Univ, Ft Wayne, 70-74. *Concurrent Pos:*

Vis appointment, US Environ Protection Agency, 80-81. *Mem:* Math Asn Am; Asn Women Math; Asn Comput Mach; Inst Elec & Electronics Engrs Comput Soc. *Res:* Information retrieval, data base systems, programming languages. *Mailing Add:* Div Sci Gov State Univ University Park IL 60466. *Fax:* 708-534-7895; *E-Mail:* j-wells@uxa.ecn.bgu.edu

**WELLS, JOHN CALHOUN, JR,** EXPERIMENTAL NUCLEAR PHYSICS. *Current Pos:* from asst prof to assoc prof, 70-80, PROF PHYSICS, TENN TECHNOL UNIV, 80- *Personal Data:* b Tampa, Fla, May 12, 41; m 63, Marilee W Mays; c Sarah K & John B. *Educ:* Fla State Univ, BS, 61; Johns Hopkins Univ, PhD(physics), 68. *Prof Exp:* assoc & res physicist, Nat Acad Sci-Nat Res Coun, US Naval Ord Lab, Md, 68-70. *Concurrent Pos:* Consult, Physics Div, Oak Ridge Nat Lab, 71-76; adj res scientist, Physics Div, Oak Ridge Nat Lab, 76- *Mem:* Am Phys Soc; Sigma Xi; Am Asn Univ Prof; Am Asn Physics Teachers. *Res:* Nuclear structure studies; gamma-ray spectroscopy; lifetimes of high-spin nuclear states; heavy-ion reactions. *Mailing Add:* Dept Physics Tenn Technol Univ Cookeville TN 38505. *E-Mail:* jcw2429@tntech.edu

**WELLS, JOHN MORGAN, JR,** DIVING PHYSIOLOGY, HYPERBARIC. *Current Pos:* sci coordr marine biol, Manned Undersea Sci & Technol Off, 72-79, dir, diving prog, 79-91, DIR, EXP DIVING UNIT, NAT OCEANIC & ATMOSPHERIC ADMIN, 91- *Personal Data:* b Hopewell, Va, Apr 12, 40. *Educ:* Randolph-Macon Col, BS, 62; Univ Calif, San Diego, PhD(marine biol), 69. *Prof Exp:* Res physiologist, Wrightsville Marine Bio-Med Lab, NC, 69-72; asst prof physiol, Sch Med, Univ NC, 70-72. *Concurrent Pos:* Guest Scientist, Naval Med Res Inst, 84-85. *Mem:* Undersea & Hyperbaric Med Soc; Am Acad of Underwater Sci; Nat Asn Diver Med Tech. *Res:* Blood function at high hydrostatic and inert gas pressures; physiological symbiosis between algae and invertebrates; community metabolism of marine benthic communities; protection of divers in polluted waters. *Mailing Add:* PO Box 696 North VA 23128. *Fax:* 757-878-3511

**WELLS, JOSEPH,** NEUROANATOMY, NEUROBIOLOGY. *Current Pos:* assoc prof anat, 68-91, PROF ANAT & NEUROBIOL, COL MED, UNIV VT, 91- *Personal Data:* b Boston, Mass, Oct 6, 34; m 56; c 5. *Educ:* Univ RI, BS, 56; Duke Univ, PhD(anat), 59. *Prof Exp:* Instr anat, Duke Univ, 59-61 & Yale Univ, 61-63; asst prof, Sch Med, Univ Md, Baltimore, 63-68. *Concurrent Pos:* NIH fel, 59-61; NIH res grant, 64-67, 83-; Lederle Med Fac Award, Univ Md, 68, Sandoz Found fel neurosci, 78-80. *Mem:* Am Asn Anatomists; Soc Neurosci. *Res:* Neuroanatomy using silver stains; systems neurobiology using electron microscopy; neuronal plasticity of somatosensory system; neural transplantation. *Mailing Add:* Dept Anat Univ Vt Sch Med Burlington VT 05405. *Fax:* 802-656-8704; *E-Mail:* jxwells@moose.uvm.edu

**WELLS, JOSEPH S,** PHYSICS. *Current Pos:* Proj leader microwave noise, Electronics Calibration Ctr, Nat Bur Stand, 59-62, physicist, Radio & Microwave Mat Sect, 62-67, res physicist, Quantum Electronics Div, 67-73, RES PHYSICIST, TIME & FREQUENCY DIV, NAT BUR STAND, 74- *Personal Data:* b Meade, Kans, Mar 19, 30; m 56; c 4. *Educ:* Kans State Univ, BS, 56, MS, 58; Univ Colo, PhD(physics), 64. *Honors & Awards:* Gold Medal, Dept Com, 74. *Concurrent Pos:* Res assoc, Physics Dept, Univ Colo, 64-66, lectr, 66-73, adj prof, 73-79. *Mem:* Am Phys Soc; Sci Res Soc Am. *Res:* Paramagnetic and antiferromagnetic resonance; microwave measurements; infrared frequency synthesis; laser stabilization and frequency measurements; tunable lasers and spectroscopy; infrared frequency standards and molecular spectroscopy. *Mailing Add:* 2385 Kohler Dr Boulder CO 80303

**WELLS, KENNETH,** MYCOLOGY. *Current Pos:* Instr & jr botanist, Univ Calif, Davis, 57-58, from asst prof & asst botanist to assoc prof & assoc botanist, 59-72, prof, 72-91, chmn, Dept Bot & Agr Bot, 78-82, EMER PROF BOT & BOTANIST, UNIV CALIF, DAVIS, 91- *Personal Data:* b Portsmouth, Ohio, July 24, 27; m 54, Ellinor Kirschner; c 2. *Educ:* Univ Ky, BS, 50; Univ Iowa, MS & PhD(bot), 57. *Prof Exp:* Asst bot, Univ Iowa, 54-57. *Concurrent Pos:* Fulbright res fel, Inst Bot, Sao Paulo, Brazil, 63-64; Nat Acad Sci exchange scientist, Romania, 71-72; Fulbright grant, Univ Tubingen, Ger, 83-84. *Mem:* Mycol Soc Am; Brit Mycol Soc. *Res:* Taxonomy of the saprobic Heterobasidiomycetes; compatibility and mating tests as a guide to speciation; ultrastructure of the fungi, especially as related to systematics. *Mailing Add:* Sect Plant Biol Univ Calif Davis CA 95616. *Fax:* 530-752-5410

**WELLS, KENNETH B,** MENTAL HEALTH, QUALITY OF CARE. *Current Pos:* PROF PSYCHIAT & BEHAV SCI, SCH MED, UNIV CALIF, LOS ANGELES. *Personal Data:* b Pasadena, Calif, 1948. *Educ:* Univ Calif, San Francisco, MD, 74. *Mem:* Inst Med-Nat Acad Sci. *Res:* Depression. *Mailing Add:* Dept Psychiat & Behav Sci 88-201 NPI Univ Calif MC 175919 Los Angeles CA 90024

**WELLS, KENNETH LINCOLN,** SOIL SCIENCE, AGRONOMY. *Current Pos:* from asst prof to assoc prof agron, prof, 69-77, EXTEN PROF AGRON, UNIV KY, 77- *Personal Data:* b Lone Mountain, Tenn, May 28, 35; m 60. *Educ:* Univ Tenn, BS, 57, MS, 59; Iowa State Univ, PhD(soil sci), 63. *Prof Exp:* Res assoc soils, Iowa State Univ, 59-63; agriculturist, Tenn Valley Authority, 63-65, agronomist, 65-69. *Mem:* Am Soc Agron; Soil Sci Soc Am. *Res:* Soil fertility, crop production, genesis and classification. *Mailing Add:* Dept Agron Univ Ky 500 Limestone St Lexington KY 40506-0001

**WELLS, KENTWOOD DAVID,** HERPETOLOGY, ANIMAL BEHAVIOR. *Current Pos:* From asst prof to assoc prof, 73-89, PROF BIOL, UNIV CONN, 89- *Personal Data:* b Alexandria, Va, Mar 23, 48; m 88, Marta Martinez; c Camila M. *Educ:* Duke Univ, AB, 70; Cornell Univ, PhD(vert zool), 76. *Concurrent Pos:* Fel, Smithsonian Trop Res Inst, 75-76. *Mem:* Am Soc Ichythol & Herpet; Soc Study Amphibians & Reptiles; Ecol Soc Am; Animal Behav Soc; Int Soc Behav Ecol; Hist Sci Soc. *Res:* Social behavior, mating systems and behavioral ecology of vertebrates, especially amphibians; history of science, especially evolutionary biology and early behavioral studies. *Mailing Add:* Dept Ecol Evolution Biol Univ Conn U-43 Storrs CT 06269-3043

**WELLS, LARRY GENE,** AGRICULTURAL ENGINEERING. *Current Pos:* From asst prof to assoc prof, 74-86, PROF AGR ENG, UNIV KY, 86- *Personal Data:* b Covington, Ky, July 28, 47; m 71; c 2. *Educ:* Univ Ky, BS, 69, MS, 71; NC State Univ, PhD(biol, agr eng & math), 75. *Concurrent Pos:* Prin investr, NSF Res Initiation Grant, 76-78, Philip Morris Res Grant, 82-88, Coop State Res Serv, 87-88; investr, Sci & Educ Admin Grant, 78-80. *Mem:* Am Soc Agr Eng; Int Soc Terrain Vehicle Systs. *Res:* Design and development of agricultural machinery; simulation of machinery systems; dynamic soil - machinery interactions; limiting vehicular soil compaction in surface mine reclamation. *Mailing Add:* Dept Agr Eng Univ Ky Lexington KY 40506-0001

**WELLS, MARION ROBERT,** MOLECULAR BIOLOGY. *Current Pos:* assoc prof, 64-77, PROF BIOL, MID TENN STATE UNIV, 77-, ASSOC DEAN, GRAD COL. *Personal Data:* b Jackson, Miss, Feb 9; m 59, Tommie Butts; c Cindy, Beth, Amy & Robert. *Educ:* Memphis State Univ, BS, 60, MA, 63; Miss State Univ, PhD(zool), 71. *Prof Exp:* Instr biol, Troy State Col, 63-64. *Mem:* Sigma Xi; Am Physiol Soc. *Res:* Binding of insecticides to cell particulate. *Mailing Add:* Dept Biol Mid Tenn State Univ Box 252 Murfreesboro TN 37132. *E-Mail:* mrwells@mtsu.edu

**WELLS, MICHAEL ARTHUR,** BIOCHEMISTRY. *Current Pos:* from asst prof to prof, 67-86, HEAD BIOCHEM, UNIV ARIZ, 86- *Personal Data:* b Los Angeles, Calif, Nov 8, 38; m 58; c 3. *Educ:* Univ Southern Calif, BA, 61; Univ Ky, PhD(biochem), 65. *Prof Exp:* Am Cancer Soc fel biochem, Univ Wash, 65-67. *Concurrent Pos:* Macy fac scholar, Josiah Macy Found, 75-76. *Mem:* AAAS; Am Chem Soc; Am Soc Biol Chemists. *Res:* Lipid and lipoprotein metabolism in insects. *Mailing Add:* Dept Biochem Biosci W Univ Ariz Tucson AZ 85721-0002. *Fax:* 520-621-9288; *E-Mail:* wells@biosci.arizona.edu

**WELLS, MICHAEL BYRON,** OPTICAL PHYSICS, RADIATION PHYSICS. *Current Pos:* CONSULT, WELL CONSULTS INC, 85- *Personal Data:* b Kansas City, Mo, July 3, 22; m 48; c 4. *Educ:* Univ Mo, Kansas City, BA, 48, MA, 50. *Prof Exp:* Instr, Univ Mo, Kansas City, 50-56; proj nuclear engr, Gen Dynamics, Ft Worth, Tex, 56-63; vpres, Radiation Res Assocs, Inc, 63-89. *Concurrent Pos:* Instr, Tex Christian Univ, 58-63. *Mem:* Am Nuclear Soc; Optical Soc Am. *Res:* Nuclear radiation transport calculations; radiation shielding; atmospheric optics; ultraviolet, visible and infrared radiation transport in planetary atmospheres; nuclear engineering. *Mailing Add:* Well Consults Inc 3812 Glenmont Dr Ft Worth TX 76133

**WELLS, MILTON ERNEST,** ANIMAL BREEDING. *Current Pos:* SELF EMPLOYED. *Personal Data:* b Calera, Okla, Nov 28, 32; m 55; c 2. *Educ:* Okla State Univ, BS, 55, MS, 59, PhD(animal breeding), 62. *Prof Exp:* Asst prof animal sci, Imp Ethiopian Col Agr, 61-65; asst prof dairy sci, Okla State Univ, 65-74, assoc prof, 74-77, prof animal sci, 77-80. *Mem:* Am Soc Animal Sci; Am Dairy Sci Asn. *Res:* Reproductive physiology; vibriosis; international animal agriculture; acrosome of sperm cells. *Mailing Add:* Rte 1 Box 645 Stillwater OK 74075

**WELLS, OTHO SYLVESTER,** HORTICULTURE. *Current Pos:* Asst prof, 66-71, ASSOC PROF PLANT SCI, UNIV NH, 71-, EXTEN HORTICULTURIST, VEG, 74- *Personal Data:* b Burgaw, NC, Sept 15, 38; m 68; c 2. *Educ:* NC State Univ, BS, 61; Mich State Univ, MS, 63; Rutgers Univ, PhD(hort), 66. *Mem:* Am Soc Hort Sci. *Res:* Crop production under environmentally controlled conditions. *Mailing Add:* Dept Plant Biol Univ NH 125 Technology Dr Durham NH 03824-4724

**WELLS, OUIDA CAROLYN,** zoology, for more information see previous edition

**WELLS, PATRICK HARRINGTON,** BEE LANGUAGE CONTROVERSY. *Current Pos:* from asst prof to prof, 57-90, EMER PROF BIOL, OCCIDENTAL COL, 90- *Personal Data:* b Palo Alto, Calif, June 19, 26; m 51, Pearl Pernich; c Harrington, Patricia & John. *Educ:* Univ Calif, AB, 48; Stanford Univ, PhD(biol), 51. *Prof Exp:* Asst prof zool, Univ Mo, 51-57. *Concurrent Pos:* Res assoc, Univ Calif, 67-72; ed, Southern Calif Acad Sci Bull, 72-75; ecol consult, 90- *Mem:* Fel AAAS; Bee Res Asn; Am Soc Zool; Lepidop Soc; Sigma Xi; Hist Sci Soc. *Res:* Foraging behavior and recruitment in honey bees; pollination biology; natural history; population biology, ecology and physiology of butterflies and other arthropods. *Mailing Add:* Dept Biol Occidental Col Los Angeles CA 90041

**WELLS, PATRICK ROLAND,** PHARMACOLOGY. *Current Pos:* prof pharmacol & dean, 70-90, EMER DEAN, SCH PHARM, TEX SOUTHERN UNIV, 90- *Personal Data:* b Liberty, Tex, Apr 1, 31. *Educ:* Tex Southern Univ, BS, 57; Univ Nebr, MS, 59, PhD(pharmaceut sci), 61. *Prof Exp:* Asst prof pharmacol, Fordham Univ, 61-63; from asst prof to assoc prof & actg chmn dept, Univ Nebr, 63-70. *Mem:* Nat Pharmaceut Asn; Sigma Xi; Am Pharmaceut Asn. *Res:* Cardiovascular screening of plant tissue culture. *Mailing Add:* St Francis Assisi 5102 Dabnay Houston TX 77026

**WELLS, PHILIP VINCENT,** BOTANY. *Current Pos:* from asst prof to assoc prof bot, 62-71, PROF BOT & SYST ECOL, UNIV KANS, 71- *Personal Data:* b Brooklyn, NY, Apr 24, 28; m 59; c 4. *Educ:* Brooklyn Col, BA, 51; Univ Wis, MS, 56; Duke Univ, PhD(bot), 59. *Prof Exp:* Asst, Univ Wis, 54-55 & Duke Univ, 55-58; instr bot, Univ Calif, Santa Barbara, 58-59 & Calif Polytech Col, 59-60; res assoc biol, NMex Highlands Univ, 60-62. *Concurrent Pos:* Actg dir, Bot Garden & vis assoc prof, Univ Calif, Berkeley, 66-67. *Mem:* AAAS; Soc Study Evolution; Bot Soc Am; Ecol Soc Am. *Res:* Pleistocene paleobotany; systematics, ecology and evolution in Arctostaphylos; vegetation of North America; physiological ecology. *Mailing Add:* Dept Biol Sci Univ Kans Lawrence KS 66045-0001

**WELLS, PHILLIP RICHARD,** FOOD SCIENCE, DAIRY SCIENCE. *Current Pos:* sect leader, New Prod Develop, Corn Prod Co, 66-72, asst to dir res, 72-75, asst dir tech serv, 75-78, asst to dir nutrit, 78-79, NUTRIT RES ASSOC, BEST FOODS, CPC INT, 79- *Personal Data:* b Northampton, Mass, May 23, 36; m 62, Adele Reytar; c 3. *Educ:* Univ Mass, BS, 57; Pa State Univ, MS, 59; Rutgers Univ, PhD(dairy sci), 62. *Prof Exp:* Proj leader, Food Prod Develop, Colgate Palmolive Co, 62-66. *Mem:* Nutrit Today Soc; Inst Food Technol. *Res:* Dried and concentrated dairy products; snack products; stabilizers and emulsifiers; protein based foods; dried eggs; research management; food laws; advertising and labeling. *Mailing Add:* Best Foods Tech Ctr CPC Int 150 Pierce St Call Box 6710 Somerset NJ 08873-6710

**WELLS, RALPH GORDON,** MATERIALS SCIENCE, CRYSTALLOGRAPHY. *Current Pos:* RETIRED. *Personal Data:* b Newark, Ohio, Sept 24, 15; m 42, Ruth Ruffner. *Educ:* Muskingum Col, BA, 39; Ohio State Univ, MSc, 47; Univ Mich, PhD(mineral), 51. *Prof Exp:* Res metallurgist, US Steel Corp, 47-51, supvry technologist, 51-55; assoc res engr, Univ Mich, 56-59; sr res scientist, Res Ctr, Crucible Inc, 59-80. *Concurrent Pos:* Res assoc earth Sci, Carnegie Mus Natural Hist, 76- *Mem:* Am Phys Soc; sr mem Inst Elec & Electronics Engrs; Am Inst Mining Metall & Petrol Eng; Sigma Xi. *Res:* Application of tools and techniques of mineralogy and crystallography to metallurgy and ceramics. *Mailing Add:* 5253 Sherwood Dr Pittsburgh PA 15236-1838

**WELLS, RAYMOND O'NEIL, JR,** MATHEMATICS. *Current Pos:* from asst prof to assoc prof, 65-74, chmn dept, 76-79, PROF MATH, RICE UNIV, 74-, PROF & CHMN, DEPT EDUC, 94- *Personal Data:* b Dallas, Tex, June 12, 40; m 63, Rena Schwarze; c 2. *Educ:* Rice Univ, BS, 62; NY Univ, MS, 64, PhD(math), 65. *Concurrent Pos:* Vis asst prof, Brandeis Univ, 67-68; Fulbright grant, 68; mem, Inst Advan Study, 70-71 & 79-80; mem, Regional Conf Bd Math Sci, 74-77; Guggenheim fel, John Simon Guggenheim Mem Found, 74-75; US sr scientist award, Alexander von Humboldt Found, 74-75; vis prof math, Univ Gottingen, 74-75; mem, Coun Am Math Soc, 79-, US Nat Comt Math, 84-87 & US Comn Math Instr; Ulam vis prof, Univ Colo, 83-84; Nat Acad Sci exchange vis, Bulgaria, 84; mem, US Comn Math Inst, 85-91; dir, Sch Math Proj, Rice Univ, 87- Computational Math Lab, 90- *Mem:* Am Math Soc; Math Asn Am; fel AAAS; Asn Mem Inst Advan Study. *Res:* Analytic continuation and approximation theory in variables; algebraic geometry; mathematical physics; several complex variables, algebreic geometry, mathematical physics, applied mathematics and mathematics education. *Mailing Add:* Dept Math Rice Univ Houston TX 77251. *Fax:* 713-285-5437; *E-Mail:* wells@rice.edu

**WELLS, ROBERT DALE,** BIOCHEMISTRY, MOLECULAR BIOLOGY. *Current Pos:* prof & head, Dept Biochem, 90-92, found dir, Inst Biosci & Technol, 90-94, DIR, CTR GENOME RES & PROF, DEPT BIOCHEM & BIOPHYSICS, TEX A&M UNIV, 90- *Personal Data:* b Uniontown, Pa, Oct 2, 38; m 60; c 2. *Educ:* Ohio Wesleyan Univ, BS, 60; Univ Pittsburgh, PhD(biochem), 64. *Prof Exp:* NIH fel, Univ Pittsburgh, 64; NIH fel, Enzyme Inst, Univ Wis-Madison, 64-66; from asst prof to prof biochem, Univ Ala, Birmingham, 66-81, chmn dept, 82-90. *Concurrent Pos:* Mem, Regional Coun, Am Inst Biol Sci, 66-68; Guggenheim Award, 76-77; ed, J Biol Chem, 77- *Mem:* AAAS; Am Chem Soc; Am Soc Biol Chem; Sigma Xi; Am Soc Microbiol. *Res:* DNA physical chemistry, synthesis and replication; DNA structure; triplet repeats and human hereditary neurological diseases. *Mailing Add:* Inst Biosci & Technol 2121 Holcombe Blvd Houston TX 77030-3303. *Fax:* 713-677-7689; *E-Mail:* rwells@ibt.tamu.edu

**WELLS, RONALD ALLEN,** ARCHAEOASTRONOMY, EGYPTOLOGY. *Current Pos:* Assoc res astronr I, Space Sci Lab, Univ Calif, Berkeley, 67-69, II, 69-71 & III, 71-72 & res assoc, 73-79, res assoc, Dept Near Eastern Studies, 81-91, MICROCOMPUT SPECIALIST, DEPT PLANT BIOL, PLANT GENE EXPRESSION CTR, UNIV CALIF, BERKELEY, 89-; NOVELL ONE, 96- *Personal Data:* b Norton, Va, Sept 12, 42; div; c 2. *Educ:* Univ Calif, Berkeley, AB, 64; Univ London, dipl, 66, PhD(astron), 67. *Concurrent Pos:* Proj dir, NASA grant, 71-72; prin investr, Nat Endowment Humanities grant, 83-84; sr fel, Binat Fulbright Comn, Cairo, 83-84; lectr physics & astron, The Crowden Sch, Berkeley, 84-87; publ asst, Freeman-Cooper & Co, San Francisco, 85-86; sr fel, Binat Fulbright Comn, Hamburg, WGer, 87-88; prin investr, Michela Schiff Giorgini Found grant, 87. *Mem:* Fel Royal Astron Soc; Am Astron Soc; Am Res Ctr Egypt. *Res:* Origins and applications of astronomy in ancient Egypt from hieroglyphic texts, inscriptions, precise temple orientations and stellar-lunar rise and set positions; chronology and calendars of ancient Egypt. *Mailing Add:* Dept Plant Biol 111 Koshland Hall Univ Calif Berkeley CA 94720

**WELLS, RUSSELL FREDERICK,** EXERCISE PHYSIOLOGY, SPORTS MEDICINE. *Current Pos:* asst prof, 71-74, assoc dean col, 81-83, ASSOC PROF BIOL, ST LAWRENCE UNIV, 74- *Personal Data:* b Brooklyn, NY, Oct 24, 37; div; c Dayna B (Bradley) & Leslie B (O'Malley). *Educ:* Lafayette Col, BA, 59; Springfield Col, MS, 62; Univ NC, Chapel Hill, MA, 66; Purdue Univ, PhD(biol educ), 70. *Prof Exp:* Teacher & coach pvt sch, NC, 62-65; NSF acad year fel zool, Univ NC, Chapel Hill, 65-66; asst prof biol, Montclair State Col, 66-68; asst prof biol sci, Purdue Univ, 70-71. *Concurrent Pos:* Adj prof, San Diego State Univ, 78-79; vis assoc res physiologist, Univ Calif, San Diego, 78-79; vis physiologist, Australian Inst Sport, Canberra, 80-87; vis fel, Fac Sci, Australian Nat Univ, 86-87; adj prof, San Diego State Univ, 93-94. *Mem:* Am Col Sports Med; Am Alliance Health, Phys Educ, Recreation & Dance. *Res:* Physiology of exercise as it pertains to adult fitness and intercollegiate athletes. *Mailing Add:* Dept Biol St Lawrence Univ Canton NY 13617-1455. *Fax:* 315-379-5804; *E-Mail:* rwel@music.stlawru.edu

**WELLS, SAMUEL ALONZO, JR,** GENERAL SURGERY. *Current Pos:* BIXBY PROF SURG & CHMN DEPT, SCH MED, WASH UNIV, ST LOUIS, MO, 81- *Personal Data:* b Cuthbert, Ga, Mar 16, 36; m 64; c Barbara Atwood. *Educ:* Emory Univ, Atlanta, Ga, MD, 61. *Honors & Awards:* Ernst Jung-Preisfur Medizin Award, Fed Rep Ger, 95; Joseph H Burchenal Clin Res Award, Am Asn Clin Res, 96. *Prof Exp:* Intern & resident internal med, Johns Hopkins Hosp, Baltimore, Md, 61-63; guest investr, Dept Tumor Biol, Karolinska Inst, Stockholm, Sweden, 63-64; clin assoc, Surg Br, Pub Health Serv, Nat Cancer Inst, NIH, Bethesda, Md, 64-66; asst resident & resident surg, Duke Univ, Durham, NC, 66-70; sr investr, Surg Br, Nat Cancer Inst, NIH, 70-72; from assoc prof to prof, Duke Univ Med Ctr, 72-81. *Concurrent Pos:* Mem, Treatment Comt, Breast Cancer Task Force, Nat Cancer Inst, NIH, 74-77, chmn, 77-78, bd sci counrs, Div Cancer Treatment, Nat Cancer Inst, 82-86, chmn, 84-86; ed-in-chief, World J Surg, 83-86; pres, Gen Motors Cancer Res Found, 96- *Mem:* Inst Med; Am Surg Asn (pres, 95-96); Am Col Surgeons; Soc Surg Oncol (pres, 93-94); Int Surg Soc; Endocrine Soc; Am Col Surgeons; Soc Clin Surg (treas, 80-84); Soc Clin Surg (pres, 88-90). *Res:* Cancer; endocrinology. *Mailing Add:* Dept Surg Sch Med Wash Univ 660 S Euclid Ave Box 8109 St Louis MO 63110. *Fax:* 314-454-1898; *E-Mail:* wells@am.wudosz.wustl.edu

**WELLS, STEPHEN GENE,** GEOMORPHOLOGY OF ARID-SEMIARID LANDS, QUATERNARY GEOLOGY & LANDSCAPE EVOLUTION. *Current Pos:* PROF GEOMORPHOL, DEPT EARTH SCI, UNIV CALIF, RIVERSIDE, 91- *Personal Data:* b Linton, Ind, Mar 4, 49; m 74, Bethany J Grover; c Christopher & Caitlin. *Educ:* Ind Univ, BS, 71, Univ Cincinnati, MS, 73, PhD(geol), 76. *Honors & Awards:* Gladys Cole Mem Res Award, Geol Soc Am, 91. *Prof Exp:* From asst prof to prof geol/geomorphol, Dept Geol, Univ NMex, 76-91, asst chair, 86-89, chair, 89-91. *Concurrent Pos:* Fac res assoc, USAF Weapons Lab, Kirtland AFB, 77; fac appointment geologist, Western Minerals Br, US Geol Surv, 82-85; panel mem, Geol Soc Am, Quaternary Geol & Geomorphology Div, 83-85; vis lectr, Dept Geog, Univ Liverpool, 84; prin investr, NSF grants, 86-; pres, Neotec Inc, 88-; pres lectr, Univ NMex, 88-90; vis affil, Earth & Environ Sci Div, Los Alamos Nat Labs, NMex, 89; chair, Res Grants Comt, Geol Soc Am, 92, chmn, Quatarnary Geol & Geomorphol Div, 93. *Mem:* Fel Geol Soc Am; Am Geophys Union; Int Asn Sedimentologists; Cave Res Found; Sigma Xi. *Res:* Geomorphology, quaternary geology, and environmental geology with an emphasis on surficial processes of dry (arid-semiarid) lands and quaternary stratigraphy and landscape evolution within the southwestern United States; geomorphology and stratigraphy of alluvial fans and eolian landforms in arid and humid environments; arroyo/valley-floor processes and watershed management with emphasis on the variations in geomorphic processes related to changes in land management practices, vegetation conditions, and climate; reconstructions and semi-quantitative models of geomorphic and hydrologic responses to late quaternary climatic changes in the Mojave Desert of southern California; quantitative assessments of differential uplift rates related to complex plate tectonic geometries of Central America and Spain; tectonic geomorphology of the eastern Mojave Desert Block and northern Rio Grande Rift in New Mexico; volcanic geomorphology/hazards in southwestern United States and quantifying the periodicity and character of small basaltic volcanic eruptions related to the proposed radioactive waste repository in southern Nevada; research problems are applied to practical problems of hazardous waste siting, reclamation, and land management problems. *Mailing Add:* Dept Earth Sci Univ Calif 900 Univ Ave Riverside CA 92521-0101. *Fax:* 909-787-4324; *E-Mail:* wells@ucrac1.ucr.edu

**WELLS, TIMOTHY R,** LIFE SCIENCE. *Current Pos:* Actg dir, Import Opers Br, Off Regional Opers & Invests, Baltimore Dist, actg dep regional food & drug dir, Pac Region, actg dir, Div Prod Surveillance, Off Compliance & Surveillance, actg dep dir, actg dir, Div Enforcement II, chief, Prod Eval Br II, CHIEF OBSTET/GYNEC & GASTROENTEROL, UROL BR, DIV ENFORCEMENT II, OFF COMPLIANCE, CTR DEVICES & RADIOL HEALTH, FOOD & DRUG ADMIN. *Educ:* Univ Wis, BS, 75. *Mem:* Regulatory Affairs Prof Soc. *Mailing Add:* Div Enforcement II Off Compliance Ctr Devices & Radiol Health Food & Drug Admin 2094 Gaither Rd Rockville MD 20850

**WELLS, WARREN F,** BIOCHEMISTRY. *Current Pos:* from instr to assoc prof, 59-91, dir student serv, 77-91, EMER ASSOC PROF BIOCHEM, MED & DENT SCHS, NORTHWESTERN UNIV, CHICAGO, 91- *Personal Data:* b Des Moines, Iowa, May 16, 26; m 50, Rosemary Siplen; c

Wendy R, Jeffrey J & Jerrold P. *Educ:* Univ Northern Iowa, BA, 50, MA, 55; Univ Ill, PhD(biochem), 59. *Prof Exp:* Instr sci, Clear Lake High Sch, Iowa, 50-52; instr chem, Undergrad Div, Univ Ill, 53-54, res asst biochem, Col Med, 54-59. *Concurrent Pos:* Consult, Col Am Path, 62-64 & Vet Admin Hosp, 64-74; biochemist, Vet Admin Hosp, 63-65; lectr, Dept Ment Health, State of Ill, 67-69. *Mem:* Sigma Xi. *Mailing Add:* 1129 Cherry St Deerfield IL 60015-2705

**WELLS, WILLARD H,** FIBEROPTIC COMMUNICATIONS, CRYPTOLOGY. *Current Pos:* PVT CONSULT, 96- *Personal Data:* b Austin, Tex, Feb 23, 31; m 93, Judith Strupp; c Steven S & Wendy E. *Educ:* Univ Tex, BS, 52; Calif Inst Technol, PhD(physics), 59. *Prof Exp:* Scientist, Jet Propulsion Lab, Calif Inst Technol, 59-62, res group supvr, 62-67; chief scientist, Tetra Tech, Inc, Honeywell, 67-96. *Res:* Quantum electronics and mechanics; applied mathematics; spacecraft mechanics and space communications; underwater optical systems; optical communications, especially fiber optics; radiactive transfer; coherent fiberoptics and interferometry; cryptology; applied math. *Mailing Add:* 3385 Tulane Ct No 212 San Diego CA 92122

**WELLS, WILLIAM LOCHRIDGE,** FLUE GAS DESULFURIZATION, FORENSIC CHEMISTRY. *Current Pos:* CONSULT ENGR, ENERGY & ENVIRON AFFAIRS, 91-; FORENSIC SCI CONSULT & EXPERT WITNESS, 92- *Personal Data:* b Mayfield, Ky, Oct 12, 39. *Educ:* Univ Ky, BSChE, 62; Univ Ill, Urbana, MS, 64, PhD(chem), 67; Univ SC, MSChE, 74; Univ Tenn, MBA, 82. *Prof Exp:* Asst, Univ Ill, 62-67; asst prof, Murray State Univ, 67-69; NSF grant & res assoc, Wayne State Univ, 69-71; asst prof, Southwest Baptist Col, 71-72; res asst chem eng, Univ SC, 72-73; prof, Midlands Tech Col, 73-75; chem engr, Tenn Valley Authority, 75-77, projs mgr air res, 77-80, prog mgr gaseous emission control, 80-83; dir, Ctr Res Sulfur Coal, 83-91. *Concurrent Pos:* Consult, var pvt & pub orgs, 83-; vis prof chem, Murray State Univ, 92-93 & 95. *Mem:* Am Chem Soc; Royal Soc Chem; Am Inst Chem Engrs. *Res:* Comparative economic evaluations; coal cleaning; coal conversion; flue gas desulfurization; blood alcohol measurement; forensic expert witness testimony. *Mailing Add:* Symsonia Rd PO Box 407 Mayfield KY 42066

**WELLS, WILLIAM RAYMOND,** AEROSPACE ENGINEERING, APPLIED MATHEMATICS. *Current Pos:* DEAN COL ENG, UNIV NEV, LAS VEGAS, 84- *Personal Data:* b Winder, Ga, Nov 28, 36; m 56; c 3. *Educ:* Ga Inst Technol, BS, 59; Va Polytech Inst, MS, 61, PhD(aerospace eng), 68; Harvard Univ, MA, 64. *Prof Exp:* Aerospace technologist, Langley Res Ctr, NASA, 59-68; from asst prof to prof aerospace eng, Univ Cincinnati, 68-77; prof eng & chmn dept, Wright State Univ, 77-84. *Concurrent Pos:* NASA grant, Langley Res Ctr, 70-; consult, Flight Dynamics Lab, USAF, 72- *Mem:* Assoc fel Am Inst Aeronaut & Astronaut; Am Soc Eng Educ; Am Acad Mech; Am Asn Univ Prof; Sigma Xi. *Res:* Systems identification, flight mechanics and control theory. *Mailing Add:* 3561 Gallup Ct Las Vegas NV 89121-5901

**WELLS, WILLIAM WOOD,** BIOCHEMISTRY. *Current Pos:* PROF BIOCHEM, MICH STATE UNIV, 66- *Personal Data:* b Traverse City, Mich, June 8, 27; m 50; c 4. *Educ:* Univ Mich, BS, 49, MS, 51; Univ Wis, PhD, 55. *Prof Exp:* Res assoc, Upjohn Co, 51-52; asst biochem, Univ Wis, 52-55; from instr to assoc prof, Univ Pittsburgh, 55-66. *Concurrent Pos:* Mem, Metab Study Sect, NIH, 66-70. *Mem:* Am Chem Soc; Am Soc Biol Chem; Am Soc Neurochem; Int Soc Neurochem; Am Inst Nutrit. *Res:* Sterol structure and metabolism; relationship of sterol metabolism to experimental atherosclerosis; galactose metabolism and mental retardation; brain energy metabolism; metabolic regulations of lysosomes; microtubule associated enzymes; myoinositol and polyphosphoinositide metabolism; thioltransferase function. *Mailing Add:* Dept Biochem 413 Biochem Bldg Mich State Univ East Lansing MI 48824-1319

**WELLSO, STANLEY GORDON,** CEREAL INSECTS & BUPRESTIDAE. *Current Pos:* RETIRED. *Personal Data:* b Oshkosh, Wis, Feb 13, 35; m 57; c 2. *Educ:* Univ Wis, BS, 57; Tex A&M Univ, MS, 62, PhD(entom), 66. *Prof Exp:* Asst prof entom, Colo State Univ, 65-67; entomologist, Agr Res Serv, Sci & Educ Admin-Fed Res, USDA, Mich State Univ, 67-73, res leader entom & small grains, 73-85, adj prof entom, 77-86; res entomolgoist & adj assoc prof, Purdue Univ, 86-91. *Mem:* AAAS; Entom Soc Am; Sigma Xi; Coleopterists Soc. *Res:* Diapause induction and termination in insects; influence of photoperiod on insect's growth and development; rearing insects on artificial diets; host plant resistance of cereal insects; taxonomy and ecology of buprestids; small grain insects; insect behavior and feeding during oviposition; buprestid taxonomy; sugar depletion and cold hardiness of wheat affected by Hessian fly larval feeding; Hessian fly diapause; systematics of buprestids in the Chrysobthris femorata complex from North America and Actenodes especially from Central America. *Mailing Add:* 511 Wailupe Crescent Bastrop TX 78602

**WELMERS, EVERETT THOMAS,** MATHEMATICS, URBAN PLANNING. *Current Pos:* RETIRED. *Personal Data:* b Orange City, Iowa, Oct 27, 12; wid; c Thomas & Marina. *Educ:* Hope Col, AB, 32; Univ Mich, PhD(math), 37. *Hon Degrees:* ScD, Hope Col, 66. *Prof Exp:* From instr to asst prof math, Mich State Col, 37-44; flight res engr, Bell Aircraft Corp, 44, flutter engr, 44-46, group leader dynamic analysis, 46-49, chief dynamics, 49-57, dir, L D Bell Res Ctr, 57-60, asst to pres, Corp, 58-60; group dir satellite systs, Aerospace Corp, 60-63, asst for tech oper, Manned Systs Div, 64-67, asst to gen mgr, El Segundo Tech Opers, 67-68, asst to pres, 68-77, aerospace historian, 78-80; dean, Col Eng, Northrop Univ, 80-82. *Concurrent Pos:* Prof, Millard Fillmore Col, 45-59; mem, Air Training Command Adv Bd,

57-68; on leave to Inst Defense Anal & Adv Res Proj Agency, 59-60; comnr, Community Redevelop Agency, City Los Angeles, 68-83. *Mem:* Am Math Soc; Math Asn Am; Am Inst Aeronaut & Astronaut; Inst Elec & Electronics Engrs; Opers Res Soc Am. *Res:* Integration theory; jet propulsion; flutter; applied mathematics; aircraft and helicopter dynamics; operations analysis; computers; system analysis; satellites; history of science; engineering education. *Mailing Add:* 1626 Old Oak Rd Los Angeles CA 90049-2506

**WELNA, CECILIA,** MATHEMATICS. *Current Pos:* from asst prof to prof, Univ Hartford, 56-68, prof math & chmn dept, 68-82, dean, Col Educ, Nursing & Health Professions, 82-91; EMER PROF, DEPT MATHS, PHYSICS & COMPUT SCI, UNIV HARTFORD, 91- *Personal Data:* b New Britain, Conn. *Educ:* St Joseph Col, Conn, BS, 49; Univ Conn, MA, 52, PhD(ed), 60. *Prof Exp:* Instr, Mt St Joseph Acad, 49-50; asst instr math, Univ Conn, 50-55; instr, Univ Mass, 55-56. *Mem:* Math Asn Am; Sigma Xi; Nat Coun Teachers Math. *Mailing Add:* 31 Clover Hill Pl Kensington CT 06037

**WELPLY, JOSEPH KEVIN,** BIOCHEMISTRY. *Current Pos:* sr res chemist, 86-87, res specialist, 87-89, SR RES SPECIALIST, MONSANTO CO, 89- *Personal Data:* b New York, NY, Jan 2, 53; m 84; c 2. *Educ:* Univ Calif, Santa Barbara, BA, 75, Los Angeles, PhD(biochem), 81. *Prof Exp:* Fel biochem, Johns Hopkins Sch Med, 81-83, M D Anderson Hosp & Tumor Inst, 83-85, Oxford Univ, 85-86. *Concurrent Pos:* Assoc ed, Glycobiol, 91. *Mem:* AAAS. *Res:* Role of cell surface carbohydrate-recognizing proteins in cell adhesion, particularly as adhesion relates to inflammation; development of agents which prevent cell-adhesion and result in anti-inflammatory therapeutics. *Mailing Add:* Monsanto 700 Chesterfield Village St Louis MO 63198

**WELSCH, CLIFFORD WILLIAM, JR,** PHYSIOLOGICAL CHEMISTRY, ONCOLOGY. *Current Pos:* RETIRED. *Personal Data:* b St Louis, Mo, Sept 10, 35; m 58, Margaret Goodrich; c Jeffrey, David & Richard. *Educ:* Univ Mo, BS, 57, MS, 62, PhD(physiol chem), 65. *Prof Exp:* Instr physiol chem, Univ Mo, 63-65; asst prof natural sci, Mich State Univ 65-66, from asst prof to prof anat, 68-88, prof pharm/toxicol, Col Human Med, 88- *Concurrent Pos:* Nat Cancer Inst res fel oncol, Mich State Univ, 66-68; NIH career develop award, 71-76; assoc ed, Cancer Res, 78-90. *Mem:* AAAS; Am Asn Cancer Res; Soc Exp Biol & Med; Am Physiol Soc. *Res:* Investigations in mammary gland carcinogenesis. *Mailing Add:* 11408 Forest Hill Rd DeWitt MI 48820

**WELSCH, FEDERICO,** MOLECULAR BIOLOGY, MEDICINE. *Current Pos:* ASSOC DIR, INT AFFAIRS, NAT CANCER INST, 88- *Personal Data:* b Sevilla, Spain, Dec 26, 33; US citizen; m 59; c 4. *Educ:* Univ Barcelona, BA, 50; Univ Valencia. MD, 55, DMedSci, 57; Ctr Res & Advan Study, Mex, MS, 65; Dartmouth Col, PhD(molecular biol), 68. *Prof Exp:* Intern internal med, Univ Hamburg, 54-55; from instr to asst prof physiol chem, Univ Valencia, 55-57; prof physiol, Univ Guadalajara, 58-60; prof biochem, Univ Chihuahua, 60-63; instr, Ctr Advan Res & Study, Mex, 63-65; asst prof, Dartmouth Med Sch, 68-70; assoc dir, Worcester Found Exp Biol, 70-74; assoc res prof biochem, Med Sch, Univ Mass, 70-88. *Concurrent Pos:* USPHS & Am Heart Asn grants; hon collabr, Span Res Coun, 58; sr Fulbright scholar, Peru, 75; pub policy scholar, Off Dir, NIH, 77; mem IV prog, health syst mgt, Bus Sch, Harvard Univ, 75; govt affairs liaison, Asn Independent Res Insts; budget analyst, Deleg Basic Biomed Res, 78- *Mem:* AAAS; Am Chem Soc; Asn Am Med Cols; Asn Independent Res Insts (pres, 83-85). *Res:* Molecular biology and medicine. *Mailing Add:* 9208 Villa Dr Bethesda MD 20817

**WELSCH, FRANK,** PRENATAL TOXICOLOGY, TERATOGENESIS & REPRODUCTIVE TOXICOLOGY. *Current Pos:* staff scientist, 82-93, SR SCIENTIST, NON-CANCER PROG, DEPT EXP PATH & TOXICOL, CHEM INDUST INST TOXICOL, 93- *Personal Data:* b Berlin, Ger, Apr 14, 41; m 92, Brigitte Philipp; c Derek. *Educ:* Free Univ, Berlin, DVM, 65; Am Bd Toxicol, dipl, 81. *Prof Exp:* From instr pharmacol to prof pharmacol & toxicol, Mich State Univ, East Lansing, 71-82. *Concurrent Pos:* Prin investr, Extramural Prog, NIH, Nat Inst Child Health & Human Develop, 72-80, Nat Found March Dimes, 75-78 & Nat Inst Environ Health Sci, 80-82; res fel award, Alexander von Humboldt Found, 77-78; mem, Sci Rev Panel Health Res, Environ Protection Agency, 86-92, Reproduction & Develop Toxicol Prog Rev Subcomt, Bd Sci Coun, Nat Toxicol Prog, 87-92, Rev Comt Health Effects, Elec Power Res Inst, 87-91. *Mem:* Am Soc Pharmacol & Exp Therapeut; Soc Toxicol; Teratol Soc; Ger Soc Pharmacol & Toxicol; Europ Teratol Soc. *Res:* Effects of chemicals on structural, biochemical and functional development of mammalian species; mechanisms of teratogenesis; placenta function. *Mailing Add:* Chem Indust Inst Toxicol PO Box 12137 Res Triangle Park NC 27709. *Fax:* 919-558-1300; *E-Mail:* welsch@ciit.org

**WELSCH, GERHARD EGON,** MATERIALS SCIENCE & ENGINEERING, TITANIUM & REFRACTORY METALS PROCESSING. *Current Pos:* PROF, CASE WESTERN RES UNIV, 79- *Personal Data:* b Saarland, Ger, Sept 19, 44; m 73, Martha Fishel; c Eric J, Bettina A, Camilla J & Hannah M. *Educ:* Aachen Tech Univ, Dipl Ing, 68; Case Western Reserve Univ, MS, 70, PhD(mat sci), 74. *Prof Exp:* Res scientist aircraft mat, Deutsche Forschungs, Versuchsanstalt for Luft, Raumfahrt, Cologne, Ger, 74-76; sr res engr refractory metals, Gen Elec Co, 76-79. *Mem:* Am Soc Metals; Metall Soc-Am Inst Mining Engrs; Mat Res Soc. *Res:* Refractory metals and titanium alloys; heat treatment and processing of metals; electron microscopy; ion implantation into metal surfaces; metallurgy of high temperature materials; synthesis of materials with internal microstructural fences. *Mailing Add:* 2514 Edgehill Rd Cleveland Heights OH 44106. *Fax:* 216-932-6730

**WELSCH, ROY ELMER,** STATISTICS. *Current Pos:* Asst prof opers res, 69-73, assoc prof, 73-79, PROF MGT SCI & STATIST, SLOAN SCH MGT, MASS INST TECHNOL, 79- *Personal Data:* b Kansas City, Mo, July 31, 43. *Educ:* Princeton Univ, AB, 65; Stanford Univ, MS, 66, PhD(math), 69. *Concurrent Pos:* Assoc ed, J Am Statist Asn. *Mem:* Fel Am Statist Asn; Inst Math Statist. *Res:* Data analysis; robust statistics; multiple comparisons; graphics. *Mailing Add:* Dept Mgt & Statist Rm E53-383 Mass Inst Technol 77 Massachusetts Ave Cambridge MA 02139-4307

**WELSH, BARBARA LATHROP,** MARINE ECOLOGY. *Current Pos:* asst prof biol sci, 73, ASSOC PROF MARINE SCI & BIOL SCI, UNIV CONN, 73- *Personal Data:* b New London, Conn; c 5. *Educ:* Mt Holyoke Col, BA, 57; Univ Md, MS, 70; Univ RI, PhD(oceanog), 73. *Prof Exp:* Instr zool, Univ Md, 68-69; sr ecologist marine systs, Vast, Inc, 72-73. *Concurrent Pos:* Appointment, comt hazardous mat, Nat Res Coun, Nat Acad Sci, 73-76; consult, Normandean Assocs, 75- & Environ Qual Bd, Commonwealth PR, 76-77. *Mem:* Estuarine Res Fedn (pres, 81-83); Am Geophys Union; Sigma Xi. *Res:* Ecology of marine coastal systems, particularly detrital based systems with tidal interaction. *Mailing Add:* Dept Marine Sci Univ Conn U-6 438 Whitney Storrs Manfield CT 06269-0002

**WELSH, DAVID ALBERT,** ORGANIC CHEMISTRY, POLYMER CHEMISTRY. *Current Pos:* SR RES SCIENTIST, RES DEPT, ARCO/POLYMERS INC, 74- *Personal Data:* b Pittsburgh, Pa, Oct 25, 42; m 64; c 3. *Educ:* Carnegie Mellon Univ, BS, 64, MS, 68, PhD(org chem), 69. *Prof Exp:* Res chemist, Kippers Co Res Labs, 68-69, Edgewood Arsenal, 69-71 & Koppers Co Res Labs, 71-74. *Mem:* Am Chem Soc; Sigma Xi. *Res:* Free radical polymerization and copolymerization; polymer properties; organic synthesis. *Mailing Add:* 1042 Harvard Rd Monroeville PA 15146

**WELSH, DAVID EDWARD,** INTERCONNECTION ENGINEERING, FIBER OPTICS INTERCONNECTION TECHNOLOGY. *Current Pos:* VPRES ENG, NOMA APPLIANCE & ELECTRONICS, 96- *Personal Data:* b Chicago, Ill, July 20, 42; m 85; c Juliana. *Educ:* Calif Coast Univ, BS, 76, MS, 88. *Prof Exp:* Proj engr IC sockets, Scanbe Div Zero Mfg, 69-73; prog mgr keyswitches, Hi-Tek, 75-76; mgr eng serv elec connectors, Malco, A Microdot Co, 76-82, mgr res & develop fiber optics, 82-87; sr prod engr elec connectors, ITT, 73-75, mgr new prod develop, 87-96. *Concurrent Pos:* Chmn, US Chess Fedn Comput Chess Comt, 82-90. *Mem:* AAAS; Inst Elec & Electronics Engrs; Int Inst Connector & Interconnection Technol. *Res:* Interconnection technology; fiber optics; computer simulation of optical interconnections, wargaming; author of various publications. *Mailing Add:* 1 Bridle Path Tillsonburg ON N4G 5L9 Can. *Fax:* 519-842-9404

**WELSH, JAMES FRANCIS,** ZOOLOGY. *Current Pos:* asst prof anat & physiol, 59-67, assoc prof physiol, 67-70, PROF ZOOL, HUMBOLDT STATE UNIV, 70- *Personal Data:* b Pittsburgh, Pa, June 21, 30; m 55; c 5. *Educ:* State Univ NY, BA, 53; Univ Calif, Los Angeles, PhD, 59. *Prof Exp:* Instr biol, St Mary's Col, 57-58; instr zool & human anat, Univ Calif, Los Angeles, 58-59. *Mem:* AAAS; Am Soc Parasitol; Wildlife Dis Asn; Genetics Soc Am. *Res:* Immunological research on Hymenolepis nana; enzyme systems of trematodes. *Mailing Add:* Dept Biol Humboldt State Univ 1 Harps St Arcata CA 95521-8299

**WELSH, JAMES P,** THERMAL SYSTEMS MANAGEMENT. *Current Pos:* PRES, THERMAL TECH LAB, BUFFALO, NY, 71- *Personal Data:* b Buffalo, NY. *Educ:* Carnegie Tech, Pittsburg, BS, 38. *Mem:* Fel Inst Elec & Electronics Engrs. *Res:* Light weight magnetic and thermal design of lightweight power systems. *Mailing Add:* Thermal Tech Lab 422 Niagara Falls Blvd Buffalo NY 14223

**WELSH, JAMES RALPH,** PLANT BREEDING, PLANT GENETICS. *Current Pos:* DIR NATURAL RESOURCES, RES CTR, 90- *Personal Data:* b Langdon, NDak, Sept 4, 33; m 52; c 4. *Educ:* NDak State Univ, BS, 56; Mont State Univ, PhD(plant genetics), 63. *Prof Exp:* Exten agt agron, NDak Exten Serv, 56-60; from asst prof to assoc prof, Mont State Univ, 63-68; assoc prof, Colo State Univ, 68-72, prof agron, 72-80; dean agr & dir, Agr Exp Sta, Mont State Univ, 80-90. *Mem:* Fel Am Soc Agron; Crop Sci Soc Am; Sigma Xi. *Res:* Wheat breeding and genetics; drought tolerance in winter wheat; high yielding cultivars. *Mailing Add:* USDA ARS NPA 1201 Oakridge Dr Suite 150 Ft Collins CO 80525

**WELSH, JOHN ELLIOTT, SR,** GEOLOGY. *Current Pos:* RETIRED. *Personal Data:* b Berea, Ky, Nov 4, 27; m 65; c John, Howard & Jennifer. *Educ:* Berea Col, AB, 50; Univ Wyo, MA, 51; Univ Utah, PhD(geol), 59. *Prof Exp:* Jr geologist, Magnolia Petrol Corp, 51; geologist, Shell Oil Co, 53-56; asst prof geol, Western State Col Colo, 56-61 & Colo State Univ, 61-62; res geologist, Kennecott Explor Inc, Salt Lake City, 70-79; consult geologist, 79-95. *Concurrent Pos:* Consult geologist, 56-70. *Mem:* Am Asn Petrol Geol. *Res:* Structural and stratigraphic analyses of mining districts; stratigraphy and structure of the overthrust belt and the basin and range province in the western United States; nonmetallic geology. *Mailing Add:* 4780 Bonair St Salt Lake City UT 84117

**WELSH, LAWRENCE B,** SOLID STATE PHYSICS. *Current Pos:* group leader mat sci, 74-81, RES SCI, UOP, INC, 81- *Personal Data:* b Santa Barbara, Calif, Oct 21, 39; m 61; c 2. *Educ:* Pomona Col, BA, 61; Univ Calif, Berkeley, PhD(physics), 66. *Prof Exp:* Fel physics, Univ Pa, 66-68; asst prof, Northwestern Univ, Evanston, 68-74. *Concurrent Pos:* Vis asst prof physics, Northwestern Univ, 74-75. *Mem:* Am Phys Soc; AAAS. *Res:* Ceramics; thin film depositions; fuel cell technology; nuclear magnetic resonance in metals; zeolites; catalysts. *Mailing Add:* 2203 Lincolnwood Dr Evanston IL 60201-2019

**WELSH, MICHAEL JAMES,** MEMBRANE PHYSIOLOGY, EPITHELIAL TRANSPORT. *Current Pos:* assoc prof, 81-, PROF MED, DEPT INTERNAL MED, UNIV IOWA. *Educ:* Univ Iowa, MD, 74. *Mem:* Inst Med-Nat Acad Sci. *Res:* Airway smooth muscle. *Mailing Add:* Howard Hughes Med Inst Dept Med Physiol & Biophysiol Univ Iowa Col Med 500 EMRB Iowa City IA 52242-0001. *Fax:* 319-335-7623

**WELSH, ROBERT EDWARD,** PHYSICS. *Current Pos:* assoc prof physics, Col William & Mary, 63-68, asst dir, Space Radiation Effects Lab, 67-72, chair, Dept Physics, 88-91, PROF PHYSICS, COL WILLIAM & MARY, 68-, CHANCELLOR PROF, 93- *Personal Data:* b Pittsburgh, Pa, Oct 1, 32; m 56, 88, Karen Rose; c Patrick, Richard, Edward & Maia. *Educ:* Georgetown Univ, BS, 54; Pa State Univ, PhD(physics), 60. *Prof Exp:* Res physicist, Carnegie Inst Technol, 60-63, asst dir nuclear res ctr, 62-63. *Concurrent Pos:* Consult, Langley Res Ctr, NASA, 64-66 & Los Alamos Sci Lab 77-80; guest scientist, Argonne Nat Lab & Brookhaven Nat Lab, 71-; res physicist, Rutherford Lab, Eng, 72-73; sci assoc, Europ Ctr Nuclear Res, Geneva, Switz, 83, 84; physicist, Oxford Univ & Rutherford Lab, Eng, 94-95. *Mem:* Fel Am Phys Soc; Am Asn Univ Professors. *Res:* Experimental nuclear and particle physics; muon physics; exotic atoms studies with muons, pions, kaons, and sigma hyperons; antiproton-proton atomic systems; rare decay searches with neutral K mesons. *Mailing Add:* Dept Physics Col William & Mary Williamsburg VA 23187-8795. *Fax:* 757-221-3540

**WELSH, RONALD,** PATHOLOGY. *Current Pos:* from asst prof to assoc prof, 57-63, PROF PATH, SCH MED, LA STATE UNIV, NEW ORLEANS, 63- *Personal Data:* b Houston, Tex, Oct 13, 26; m 50; c 3. *Educ:* Univ Tex, BA, 47, MD, 50; Am Bd Path, dipl, 55. *Honors & Awards:* Am Cancer Soc Award, 81. *Prof Exp:* Asst prof path, Univ Tex Med Br, Galveston, 55-57. *Concurrent Pos:* Pathologist, Univ Tex Med Br Hosps, Galveston, 55-57; sr vis pathologist, Charity Hosp, New Orleans, 57-, sect dir surg path; path consult, Vet Admin Hosp, New Orleans, Children's Hosp New Orleans. *Mem:* AMA; Am Soc Clin Path; Col Am Path; Int Acad Path. *Res:* Thyroid disease; electron microscopy, particularly of basic activities of inflammatory cells; oncology; surgical pathology. *Mailing Add:* Dept Path La State Univ Med Ctr 1901 Perdido St New Orleans LA 70112

**WELSH, SUSAN,** food & nutrient consumption patterns, for more information see previous edition

**WELSH, THOMAS LAURENCE,** food science, pharmaceutical chemistry, for more information see previous edition

**WELSH, WILLIAM JAMES,** THEORETICAL & PHYSICAL CHEMISTRY. *Current Pos:* ASST PROF DEPT CHEM & PHYSICS, EDGECLIFF COL, 78- *Personal Data:* b Philadelphia, Pa, Dec 24, 47. *Educ:* St Joseph Col, BS, 69; Univ Pa, PhD(theoret phys chem), 75. *Prof Exp:* Instr chem, Univ Pa, 69-74; chemist, Procter & Gamble Co, 75-78; asst prof, Univ Cincinnati, 80-85. *Concurrent Pos:* Fel theoret polymer chem, Univ Cincinnati, 78-; extramural assoc, NIH, 86. *Mem:* Am Chem Soc; Am Phys Soc. *Res:* Configuration, dependent properties and conformational energies of long chain molecules; statistical mechanics; intermolecular forces; theory of liquids; physical adsorption; structure-property relationships of anticancer drugs and other bioactive materials; molecular computer graphics. *Mailing Add:* Chem Dept Univ Mo 8001 Natural Bridge Rd St Louis MO 63121-4401

**WELSHIMER, HERBERT JEFFERSON,** BACTERIOLOGY. *Current Pos:* from asst prof to prof bact, 49-85, EMER PROF MICROBIOL & IMMUNOL, MED COL VA, VA COMMONWEALTH UNIV, 85- *Personal Data:* b West Mansfield, Ohio, Feb 23, 20; m 46; c 3. *Educ:* Ohio State Univ, BSc, 43, PhD(bact), 47. *Prof Exp:* Asst med bact, Ohio State Univ, 44-46; instr bact, Ind Univ, 47-49. *Concurrent Pos:* USPHS fel, Ohio State Univ, 47; attend bacteriologist, Johnston-Willis Hosp, 54-80; chmn subcomt listeria & related organisms, Int Comt Syst Bact, 74-82. *Mem:* AAAS; Am Soc Microbiol; fel Am Acad Microbiol; NY Acad Sci. *Res:* Clinical bacteriology; immunology; lysozyme; bacteriophage; bacterial cytology; listeriosis. *Mailing Add:* 1403 Brandermill Woods Trail Apt 208 Midlothian VA 23112

**WELSHONS, WILLIAM JOHN,** GENETICS. *Current Pos:* RETIRED. *Personal Data:* b Pitcairn, Pa, July 18, 22; m 49; c 4. *Educ:* Univ Calif, BA, 49, MA, 52, PhD(zool), 54. *Prof Exp:* Res assoc, Biol Div, Oak Ridge Nat Lab, 54-55, mem staff, 55-65; head dept, Iowa State Univ, 65-75, prof genetics, 65- *Concurrent Pos:* NSF sr fel, Santiago, Chile, 63-64; mem adv comt, Chem Rev Bd, State Iowa, 70-71. *Mem:* Genetics Soc Am; Am Inst Biol Sci; Sigma Xi. *Res:* Gene structure recombination and cytogenetic analysis in Drosophila; mammalian sex determination and cytogenetics. *Mailing Add:* 2729 Northwood Dr Ames IA 50010

**WELSTEAD, WILLIAM JOHN, JR,** ORGANIC CHEMISTRY, PHARMACEUTICAL & ANALYTICAL CHEMISTRY. *Current Pos:* res chemist, Whitehall-Robins, 64-72, assoc dir chem res, 72-73, dir chem res, 73-90, assoc dir QAGMP, 90-92, dir analytical res & develop, 92-96, ASST VPRES ANALYTICAL DEVELOP, WHITEHALL-ROBINS, 96- *Personal Data:* b Newport News, Va, July 17, 35; m 57; c 3. *Educ:* Univ Richmond, BS, 57; Univ Va, PhD(chem), 62. *Prof Exp:* Org chemist, Army Chem Ctr, Md, 62; NSF grant, Iowa State Univ, 63. *Mem:* AAAS; Am Chem Soc; Sigma Xi; Am Asn Pharmaceut Scientists. *Res:* Synthetic organic and medicinal chemistry; heterocyclics; pharmaceutical chemistry. *Mailing Add:* 10471 Jordan Pkwy Hopewell VA 23860-3271. *Fax:* 804-257-2998; *E-Mail:* welstew@md.ahp.com

**WELSTED, JOHN EDWARD,** PHYSICAL GEOGRAPHY. *Current Pos:* from asst prof to assoc prof, 65-78, PROF GEOG, BRANDON UNIV, 78- *Personal Data:* b Norwich, Eng, Dec 6, 35; div; c 2. *Educ:* Bristol Univ, BSc, 58, cert educ, 61, PhD(geog), 71; McGill Univ, MSc, 60. *Honors & Awards:* Autometric Award, Am Soc Photogram, 80; Prairie Div Award, Can Asn Georg, 96. *Prof Exp:* Asst master geog, Maidenhead Grammar Sch, Eng, 61-62; teacher, Oromocto High Sch, NB, 62-64; demonstr geog, Bristol Univ, 64-65. *Mem:* Can Asn Geog; Can Water Resources Asn. *Res:* Rate of meander migration on rivers in southwest Manitoba; flooding by the rivers of southwest Manitoba; legal implications of shifting river channels in Southwest Manitoba; water resources of Manitoba. *Mailing Add:* Dept Geog Brandon Univ Brandon MB R7A 6A9 Can. *Fax:* 204-728-7346; *E-Mail:* welsted@brandonu.ca

**WELT, ISAAC DAVIDSON,** INFORMATION SCIENCE, DOCUMENTATION. *Current Pos:* RETIRED. *Personal Data:* b Montreal, Que, May 13, 22; nat US; m 45; c 3. *Educ:* McGill Univ, BSc, 44, MSc, 45; Yale Univ, PhD(physiol chem), 49. *Honors & Awards:* Info Sci & Technol Coun Award. *Prof Exp:* Instr chem, Sir George Williams Col, 46; lab asst anat, Yale Univ, 46-47, asst, Nutrit Lab, 47-48; instr chem, New Haven YMCA Jr Col, Conn, 48-49; asst, Div Physiol & Nutrit, Pub Health Res Inst New York, Inc, 49-51; asst prof biochem, Col Med, Baylor Univ, 51-53; res assoc pharmacol, Chem-Biol Coord Ctr, Nat Res Coun, Washington, DC, 53-55, dir cardiovasc lit proj, Div Med Sci, Nat Acad Sci-Nat Res Coun, 55-61; assoc dir & chief, Wash Br, Inst Advan Med Commun, 61-64; prog dir sci & tech info systs, Comput Sci Info Syst, AM Univ, 64-67; prof info sci, Ctr Technol & Admin, 64-87, prof, 92. *Concurrent Pos:* Asst dir radioisotope unit, Vet Admin Hosp, Tex, 51-53; prof lectr chem, Am Univ, 56-61. *Mem:* AAAS; Am Soc Info Sci. *Res:* Endocrine influences and isotopes in intermediary; metabolism; nutrition; medical and biological literature research; chemical-biological correlations; research administration; education in information science and documentation; information storage and retrieval systems; computers and society. *Mailing Add:* 117 N Edgewood St Arlington VA 22201

**WELT, MARTIN A,** RADIATION PRESERVATION OF FOOD, INTERACTION OF IONIZING RADIATION WITH MATTER. *Current Pos:* FOUNDER & CHMN, ALPHA OMEGA TECHNOL, INC, 86- *Personal Data:* b Brooklyn, NY, Oct 7, 32; m 62, Ruth Braunstein; c Andrew, Bruce & Jodi. *Educ:* Clarkson Col, BChE, 54; Iowa State Univ, MS, 55; Mass Inst Technol, SM, 57; NC State Univ, PhD(physics), 64. *Honors & Awards:* Golden Knight Award, Clarkson Univ. *Prof Exp:* Reactor physicist, US AEC, Washington, DC, 57-58; supvr energy conversion sect, Chance Vought Corp, 59-61; pres, Int Sci Corp, NC, 61-67; asst prof & dir, Nuclear Reactor Proj, NC State Univ, 63-67; vpres res, Gamma Process Co, 67-68; founder, chmn, chief exec officer, pres, Radiation Technol, Inc, 68-86. *Concurrent Pos:* Mem, Ames Lab, US AEC, 54-55; aeronaut res scientist, Lewis Lab, Nat Adv Comt Aeronaut, 56 & Union Carbide Co, Tenn, 56-66; lectr, George Washington Univ, 58; adj prof, Southern Methodist Univ, 60-62; dir, Adv Res Assocs, 62-63; mem, Working Comt, Proj Starfire, Southern Interstates Nuclear Bd, 64-65; dir, Nuclear Reactor Proj, NC State Univ, 64-66, asst prof, 64-67. *Mem:* AAAS; Am Nuclear Soc; Am Chem Soc; Am Phys Soc; Inst Food Technologists; NY Acad Sci. *Res:* Radiation preservation of food; radioisotope and radiation physics; plasma oscillations; radiation processing; design and analysis of nuclear facilities; hazards evaluation; thermoelectric energy conversion; nuclear research administration; radiation preservation of fresh poultry, fresh port, spices, herbs, vegitables, seasonings and dried powdery enzymes; drafted international standard for food production. *Mailing Add:* Alpha Omega Technol Inc 14 Ridgedale Ave Cedar Knolls NJ 07927-1106. *Fax:* 201-292-4999; *E-Mail:* wstr24@prodigy.com

**WELTER, ALPHONSE NICHOLAS,** ANATOMY, HYDROBIOLOGY. *Current Pos:* RES SPECIALIST, 3M CO, 67- *Personal Data:* b Dudelange, Luxembourg, Apr 8, 25; US citizen; m 54; c 5. *Educ:* Loras Col, AB, 52; Univ Ill, MS, 57, PhD(physiol), 59. *Prof Exp:* Instr physiol, Sch Med, Marquette Univ, 59-62; res physiologist, Lederle Div, Am Cyanamid Co, 62-67. *Concurrent Pos:* USPHS fel, 59-61; Nat Heart Inst res fel, 61-62; grants, Wis Heart Asn, 60-61 & Am Heart Asn, 60-62. *Mem:* AAAS; assoc mem Am Physiol Soc; NY Acad Sci; Soc Environ Toxicol & Chem. *Res:* Cardiovascular physiology and pharmacology, specifically pulmonary circulation; respiratory and renal physiology. *Mailing Add:* 7181 Courtly Rd Woodbury MN 55125-1659

**WELTER, C JOSEPH,** MICROBIOLOGY, IMMUNOLOGY. *Current Pos:* PRES, AMBICO, INC, 74- *Personal Data:* b Tiffin, Ohio, June 11, 32; m 55; c 3. *Educ:* King's Col, BS, 54; Univ Notre Dame, MS, 56; Mich State Univ, PhD, 59. *Prof Exp:* Asst zool, Univ Notre Dame, 54-56; asst parasitol, Mich State Univ, 56-59; dir res, Diamond Labs, Inc, 59-69, vpres res, 69-74. *Mem:* AAAS; Am Soc Parasitol; US Animal Health Asn; Am Soc Trop Med & Hyg; Am Soc Microbiol. *Res:* Protozoology; parasitology; virology. *Mailing Add:* 3906 SW 28 Pl Des Moines IA 50321

**WELTER, DAVE ALLEN,** CYTOGENETICS, CHROMOSOME STRUCTURE. *Current Pos:* instr, 70-72, asst prof, 72-79, ASSOC PROF ANAT, MED COL GA, 79- *Personal Data:* b Lorain, Ohio, Aug 7, 36; m 64; c 2. *Educ:* Univ Ga, BS, 61; Med Col Ga, MS, 62, PhD(anat), 70. *Prof Exp:* Dir cytogenetics lab, Gracewood Hosp, 62-69. *Concurrent Pos:* Cytogenetic consult, Ft Gordon Hosp, 65 & Gracewood Hosp, Ga, 69- *Res:* Birth defects; neuroanatomy; gross anatomy; embryology. *Mailing Add:* Anat Med Col Ga Sch Med 1120 15th St Augusta GA 30901-3181. *Fax:* 706-721-6839

**WELTMAN, ARTHUR,** PHYSIOLOGY. *Current Pos:* PROF HUMAN SERV & MED, UNIV VA, 84- *Personal Data:* b New York, NY, June 13, 50. *Educ:* Queens Col, BS, 72; Univ Mich, MS, 74, PhD(physiol), 76. *Prof Exp:* Assoc prof exercise Physiol, Univ Colo, 80-84. *Mem:* Am Sports Med. *Res:* Physiology. *Mailing Add:* Human Servs Univ Va 147 Ruffner Hall Charlottesville VA 22903-2495

**WELTMAN, CLARENCE A,** physical chemistry, organic chemistry; deceased, see previous edition for last biography

**WELTMAN, JOEL KENNETH,** IMMUNOLOGY, BIOCHEMISTRY. *Current Pos:* asst prof, 66-70, ASSOC PROF MED, BROWN UNIV, 70 - *Personal Data:* b New York, NY, May 22, 33; m 56; c 2. *Educ:* State Univ NY, MD, 58; Univ Colo, PhD(microbiol), 63. *Hon Degrees:* MA, Brown Univ, 72. *Prof Exp:* Intern, Ind Univ, 58-59; instr microbiol, Univ Colo, 63. *Mem:* Clin Immunol Soc; Am Soc Biol Chemists; Am Acad Allergy Immunol. *Res:* Targeted immunotherapy. *Mailing Add:* Dept Med Brown Univ 300 Hanover St Fall River MA 02720

**WELTNER, WILLIAM, JR,** PHYSICAL CHEMISTRY. *Current Pos:* PROF CHEM, UNIV FLA, 66- *Personal Data:* b Baltimore, Md, Dec 8, 22; m 47; c 3. *Educ:* Johns Hopkins Univ, BE, 43; Univ Calif, PhD(chem), 50. *Prof Exp:* Res asst, Hercules Powder Co, Del, 43-44 & Manhattan Proj, Columbia Univ, 44-46; fel, Univ Minn, 50; instr chem, Johns Hopkins Univ, 50-54; fel, Harvard Univ, 54-56; res chemist, Union Carbide Res Inst, Tarrytown, NY, 56-66. *Concurrent Pos:* Mem opers res group, US Army Chem Ctr, 51-52; consult, Nat Bur Stand, 54. *Mem:* Am Chem Soc; Am Phys Soc. *Res:* Quantum and high temperature chemistry; molecular spectroscopy and structure; electron-spin resonance. *Mailing Add:* Dept Chem Univ Fla Gainesville FL 32611-7200. *Fax:* 352-392-0872; *E-Mail:* Weltner@pine.circa.ufl.edu

**WELTON, ANN FRANCES,** MOLECULAR PHARMACOLOGY. *Current Pos:* asst vpres & sr dir pharmacol, Hoffmann-LaRoche, Inc, 90-91, assoc vpres & group dir pharmacol, 91-92, assoc vpres & group dir bronchopulmonary dis, 92-93, VPRES BRONCHOPULMONARY, HOFFMANN-LA ROCHE, INC, NUTLEY, NJ, 94-, VPRES PRECLIN DEVELOP, 94- *Personal Data:* b Evanston, Ill, Oct 6, 47; M 86, Mehdi Nafissi. *Educ:* Lake Forest Col, BA, 69; Mich State Univ, PhD(biochem), 74. *Prof Exp:* Asst biochem dept, Mich State Univ, 69-74; fel lab nutrit & endocrinol, Nat Inst Health, 74-77; sr scientist pharmacol, Hoffmann-La Roche, NC, Nutley, NJ, 77-79, res group chief, 80-82, sect head, Dept Pharmacol II, 82-83, asst dir, 83-85, dir Allergy & Inflammation Res, Dept Pharmacol & Chemother, 85-88, sr dir Allergy & Inflammation Res, Dept Pharmacol & Chemother, 88-90, sr dir pharmacol, 89-90. *Concurrent Pos:* NSF fel, 69-79; NATO travel award, 74; NIH fel, Nat Res Serv Award, 74-77; adj asst prof, Dept Biochem, Univ Med & Dent NJ, 83-88, adj assoc prof, 88-92. *Mem:* AAAS; Biophys Soc; NY Acad Sci; Am Soc Pharm & Exp Therapeuts; Am Women Sci; Sigma Xi. *Res:* Membrane biochemistry; development of antiallergy agents; immunology; therapeutics for pulmonary and allergic diseases; arachidonic acid metabolism; preclinical development (drug metabolism, toxicology and pathology, parmaceutical research and development, substance supply). *Mailing Add:* 37 Maple Dr North Caldwell NJ 07006. *Fax:* 973-235-8897; *E-Mail:* annwelton@roche.com

**WELTON, THEODORE ALLEN,** THEORETICAL PHYSICS. *Current Pos:* RETIRED. *Personal Data:* b Saratoga Springs, NY, July 4, 18; m 43; c 4. *Educ:* Mass Inst Technol, BS, 39; Univ Ill, PhD(physics), 43. *Prof Exp:* Instr physics, Univ Ill, 43-44; jr scientist theoret physics, Los Alamos Sci Lab, 44-45; res assoc, Mass Inst Technol, 46-48; asst prof, Univ Pa, 48-50; prin physicist, Oak Ridge Nat Lab, 50-59, sr physicist, 59-82; Ford Found adj prof physics, Univ Tenn, 63-82. *Mem:* Fel AAAS; fel Am Phys Soc; Electron Micros Soc Am. *Res:* Quantum theory of fields; theoretical nuclear physics; quantum theory of irreversible processes; theory of nuclear reactors and shielding; theory of particle accelerators; theory of lasers; theory of electron microscopy. *Mailing Add:* 17 Rivers Ct Oak Ridge TN 37830

**WELTON, WILLIAM ARCH,** DERMATOLOGY. *Current Pos:* CHMN DIV DERMAT, SCH MED, WVA UNIV, 61- *Personal Data:* b Fairmont, WVa, June 21, 28; m 56; c 2. *Educ:* Harvard Univ, AB, 50; Univ Md, MD, 54. *Concurrent Pos:* Osborne fel dermal path, 59-60. *Mem:* Am Acad Dermat. *Res:* Skin pathology. *Mailing Add:* WVa Univ Med Ctr Morgantown WV 26505

**WELTY, JAMES RICHARD,** MECHANICAL ENGINEERING, CHEMICAL ENGINEERING. *Current Pos:* instr mech eng, Ore State Univ, 58-61, from asst prof to prof, 62-96, head dept, 70-96, EMER PROF MECH ENG, ORE STATE UNIV, 96- *Personal Data:* b Garden City, Kans, Oct 23, 33; m 53; c 5. *Educ:* Ore State Univ, BS, 54, MS, 59, PhD(chem eng), 62. *Prof Exp:* Test engr, Pratt & Whitney Aircraft, 54. *Concurrent Pos:* Res engr, US Bur Mines, Ore, 62-64; mem tech staff, Bell Tel Labs, Pa, 64; vis prof, Thayer Sch Eng, Dartmouth Col, 67; res grants, US Environ Protection Agency, 68-71, US AEC, US Dept Energy & NSF, 69- *Mem:* Am Soc Mech Engrs. *Res:* Heat transfer; natural convection in liquid metals; non-Newtonian fluids in natural and forced flows; numerical modeling of thermal plumes; fluidized bed heat transfer. *Mailing Add:* Dept Mech Eng 204 Rogers Hall Ore State Univ Corvallis OR 97331-6001

**WELTY, JOSEPH D,** pharmacology, physiology, for more information see previous edition

**WELTY, RONALD EARLE,** AGRICULTURE, PLANT PATHOLOGY. *Current Pos:* RES PLANT PATHOLOGIST, AGR RES SERV, USDA, 66-; PROF PLANT PATH, ORE STATE UNIV, 82- *Personal Data:* b Winona, Minn, Dec 7, 34; m 62, Terrie Johnston; c Beth C & Kurt R. *Educ:* Winona State Univ, BS, 56; Univ Minn, MS, 61, PhD(plant path), 65. *Prof Exp:* Teacher high sch, Minn, 56-57 & 58-59; res asst plant path, Univ Minn, 59-61 & 62-65; instr bot & plant path, La State Univ, 62; res assoc, 65-66, from asst prof to prof plant path, NC State Univ, 66-82. *Mem:* Sigma Xi; Mycol Soc Am; Am Phytopath Soc; Am Forage & Grassland Coun. *Res:* Diseases of forage crops grown for seed and seedborne plant pathogens; general phytopathology; fungus diseases. *Mailing Add:* 3632 NW Wisteria Pl Corvallis OR 97330. *Fax:* 541-750-8750

**WEMMER, DAVID EARL,** MAGNETIC RESONANCE. *Current Pos:* from asst prof to assoc prof, 85-92, PROF CHEM, UNIV CALIF, BERKELEY, 92- *Personal Data:* b Sacramento, Calif, Aug 27, 51; m 75; c 3. *Educ:* Univ Calif, Davis, BS, 73, Berkeley, PhD(chem), 79. *Prof Exp:* Fel physics, Univ Dortmund, Fed Repub Ger, 78-79; res assoc biophys, Stanford Magnetic Resonance Lab, Stanford Univ, 79-82; res asst prof, Univ Wash, 82-85. *Mem:* Am Chem Soc; Sigma Xi; Protein Soc. *Res:* Applications of magnetic resonance in biophysics; problems of molecular structure and dynamics. *Mailing Add:* Dept Chem Univ Calif Berkeley CA 94720-1460. *E-Mail:* dewemmer@lbl.gov

**WEMPE, LAWRENCE KYRAN,** POLYMER SYNTHESIS, DIELECTRIC MATERIALS. *Current Pos:* RES & DEV, MGR ADVANCED DEV, ELF, 90- *Personal Data:* b Hutchinson, Kans, Oct 3, 41; m 65; c 1. *Educ:* Rockhurst Col, BA, 63; Univ Kans, PhD(org chem), 68. *Prof Exp:* Lab asst water treatment chem, Deady Chem Co, Kans, 62-63; sr chemist, Rohm & Haas Co, 68-77; sr prin res chemist, Air Prod & Chem, Inc, 77-83; from supvr to group supvr, Pennwalt Corp, 83-90. *Concurrent Pos:* Instr, Montgomery County Community Col, Blue Bell, Pa, 73-76. *Res:* Polymer chemistry, polymer synthesis and polymer structure/property relationships; organic synthesis; dielectric materials; polymers for drug delivery; free radical polymerization, emulsion polymerization and polymerization mechanisms; textile and paper chemistry; coatings and composites; polymer crosslinking mechanisms; electrical properties of polymers. *Mailing Add:* ELF-ATO Chem North America Inc PO Box 61536 King of Prussia PA 19406-0936

**WEMPLE, STUART H(ARRY),** SOLID STATE PHYSICS, ELECTRICAL ENGINEERING. *Current Pos:* Mem tech staff, 54-85, DEPT HEAD, BELLABS, 85- *Personal Data:* b Rockford, Ill, July 27, 30; m 67; c 3. *Educ:* Northwestern Univ, BS, 53; Calif Inst Technol, MS, 54; Mass Inst Technol, PhD(elec eng), 63. *Mem:* Am Phys Soc; Inst Elec & Electronics Engrs; Sigma Xi. *Res:* Transport and optical properties of wide band gap semiconductors, including the effects of phase transition; gallium arsenide field-effect transistors and integrated circuits. *Mailing Add:* 222 Evans Ave Reading PA 19610-2326

**WEMPNER, GERALD ARTHUR,** MECHANICAL ENGINEERING. *Current Pos:* prof, 73-93, EMER PROF ENG MECH, GA INST TECHNOL, 93- *Personal Data:* b Waupun, Wis, Nov 11, 28; m 52; c 2. *Educ:* Univ Wis, BS, 52, MS, 53; Univ Ill, PhD(eng mech), 57. *Prof Exp:* From instr to asst prof mech, Univ Ill, 53-59; assoc prof mech & civil eng, Univ Ariz, 59-62; vis prof struct mech, Univ Calif, Berkeley, 62-63; NSF fel eng mech, Stanford Univ, 63-64; prof, Univ Ala, Huntsville, 64-73. *Concurrent Pos:* Humboldt sr fel, Ruhr Univ, Ger, 73-74; Gillam fel, Univ Calgary, Alta, 83. *Mem:* Fel Am Soc Mech Engrs; fel Am Soc Civil Engrs; fel Am Acad Mech. *Res:* Contributions to theory and approximation of solids and shells with particular theories and methods for finite deformations and related nonlinear problems. *Mailing Add:* 3397 Hidden Acres Dr Doraville GA 30340

**WEMYSS, COURTNEY TITUS, JR,** ZOOLOGY. *Current Pos:* RETIRED. *Personal Data:* b Arlington, NJ, Dec 30, 22; m 51; c 3. *Educ:* Swarthmore Col, AB, 47; Rutgers Univ, PhD, 51. *Prof Exp:* Asst zool, Rutgers Univ, 47-51; res fel bact & immunol, Harvard Med Sch, 51-52; asst prof biol, Loyola Univ, 53-54; instr physiol, NY Med Col, 54-60; from assoc prof to prof biol, Hofstra Univ, 60-89. *Concurrent Pos:* Guest investr, Rockefeller Inst, 60- *Mem:* NY Acad Sci. *Res:* Invertebrate immunity; comparative serology; tissue specificity. *Mailing Add:* 62 Oldfield Rd Huntington NY 11743

**WEN, CHI-PANG,** OCCUPATIONAL MEDICINE, PREVENTIVE MEDICINE. *Current Pos:* CLIN PROF, UNIV TEX SCH PUB HEALTH & UNIV TEX MED SCH, HOUSTON, 79-; PHYSICIAN ADV, CHEVRON CORP, 85- *Personal Data:* b Taipei, Taiwan, Oct 23, 40; US citizen; c Christopher & Fred. *Educ:* Nat Taiwan Univ, MD, 66; Harvard Univ, MPH, 69, DrPH, 72. *Prof Exp:* Med dir, Develop Health Maintenance Orgn, 76; clin epidemiologist, Gult Corp, 76-78, dir clin epidemiol, 78-83, med dir, 83-85. *Res:* Long term co-host study on health effects among oil refinery workers; methodological issues of occupational epidemiology. *Mailing Add:* PO Box 2100 Houston TX 77252-2100

**WEN, RICHARD YUTZE,** ORGANIC POLYMER CHEMISTRY. *Current Pos:* sr chemist, 69-74, res specialist, Cent Res Labs, 74-78, RES SPECIALIST, MAGNETIC TAPE DIV, 3M CO, 78- *Personal Data:* b Shanghai, China, Mar 17, 30; m 62; c 2. *Educ:* Wesleyan Univ, BA, 51; Univ Mich, MS, 53; Ind Univ, PhD(org chem), 62. *Prof Exp:* Chemist, Nalco Chem Co, 53-56; res chemist, Dow Chem Co, Mich, 62-69. *Mem:* AAAS; Am Chem Soc. *Res:* Coating technology. *Mailing Add:* 1900 Fredeen Ct New Brighton MN 55112-2412

**WEN, SHIH-LIANG,** KORTEWEG-DEVRIES EQUATIONS. *Current Pos:* from asst prof to assoc prof, 68-81, PROF, OHIO UNIV, 81-, CHMN, 85- *Personal Data:* b China; US citizen; c Dennis, Andy & Jue. *Educ:* Nat Taiwan Univ, BS, 56; Univ Utah, MS, 61; Purdue Univ, MS, 65, PhD(math), 68. *Prof Exp:* Assoc res engr, Boeing Co, Seattle, Wash, 61-63; teaching asst, Purdue Univ, 63-68. *Concurrent Pos:* Res analyst, Appl Math Res Lab, USAF, Wright-Patterson, 72; vis res scientist, Courant Inst Math Sci, NY Univ, 78-79; hon prof, Jiangxi Univ, Jiangxi, China, 85- & Lanzhou Univ, Lanzhou, China, 88- *Mem:* Am Math Soc; Math Asn Am; Soc Indust & Appl Math. *Res:* Asymptotic evaluation of multiple fourier integrals; water wave problems; eigenvalue problems in fluid mechanics; boundary layer dynamics; classical toroidal plasma; two-dimensional Korteweg-deVries equations. *Mailing Add:* Math Dept Ohio Univ 321 Morton Hall Athens OH 45701-2979

**WEN, SUNG-FENG,** MEDICINE. *Current Pos:* asst prof med, Univ Wis-Madison, 70-74, assoc prof, 74-79, Rennebohm Prof, 75-80, PROF MED, UNIV WIS-MADISON, 79- *Personal Data:* b Hsinchu, Taiwan, Mar 3, 33; US citizen; m 66; c 2. *Educ:* Nat Taiwan Univ, MB, 58. *Prof Exp:* Intern med, Univ Louisville, 62-63; resident, Chicago Med Sch, 63-64; res fel nephrol, Univ Wis-Madison, 64-66, instr, 66-67; res fel renal physiol, McGill Univ, 67-70. *Concurrent Pos:* Mem, Coun Kidney Cardiovasc Dis, Am Heart Asn. *Mem:* Am Fedn Clin Res; Am Soc Nephrol; Int Soc Nephrol; Nat Kidney Found. *Res:* Renal physiology and pathophysiology, especially related to renal transport of sodium, potassium, phosphate and glucose under normal and abnormal conditions using micropuncture techniques; hemodynamic alterations and diabetic nephropathy. *Mailing Add:* Dept Med 523 Clin Sci Ctr Univ Wis 600 Highland Ave Madison WI 53792-0001

**WEN, WEN-YANG,** PHYSICAL CHEMISTRY. *Current Pos:* from asst prof to assoc prof, 62-73, PROF CHEM, CLARK UNIV, 73- *Personal Data:* b Hsin-tsu, Taiwan, Mar 7, 31; m 59, Sue Liu; c Lilian & Alvin. *Educ:* Nat Taiwan Univ, BS, 53; Univ Pittsburgh, PhD(chem), 57. *Prof Exp:* Res assoc, Univ Pittsburgh, 57-58; res fel, Northwestern Univ, 58-60; asst prof chem, DePaul Univ, 60-62. *Concurrent Pos:* Humboldt scholar, Univ Karlsruhe, 70-71 & 73, Univ Goettingen, 76 & Morgantown Energy Technol Ctr, Dept Energy, 78-79; vis prof, Kyoto Univ & Toyama Med & Pharmaceut Univ, Japan, 91. *Mem:* Am Chem Soc; AAAS; Sigma Xi. *Res:* Structure of water; thermodynamic properties of large ions in solutions; tetraalkylammonium salts and hydrophobic bonds; nuclear magnetic resonance; alkali metal catalysis on coal gasification; thermal and catalytic cracking of coal tar; polymer-gas interaction by NMR. *Mailing Add:* Dept Chem Clark Univ Worcester MA 01610. *E-Mail:* wwen@vax.clarku.edu

**WENCEL-DRAKE, JUNE D,** PHARMACOLOGY, HEMATOLOGY. *Current Pos:* ASSOC PROF HEMAT, UNIV ILL, CHICAGO, 90- *Educ:* Univ Mich, BS, 74; Univ Ill, PhD(path), 81. *Prof Exp:* Res prof pharmacol, Univ Chicago, 85-90. *Mem:* Am Physiol Soc; Am Asn Hemat. *Res:* Pharmacology; hematology. *Mailing Add:* Med Lab Sci MC 518 Univ Ill 808 S Wood St Chicago IL 60612-0001

**WENCLAWIAK, BERND WILHELM,** SUPERCRITICAL FLUIDS. *Current Pos:* ASSOC PROF ANALYTICAL CHEM, UNIV TOLEDO, 85- *Personal Data:* b Du-Hamborn, WGer, Aug 11, 51; m 76; c 4. *Educ:* Westphalian Wilhelms Univ, Munster, dipl chem, 75, PhD(chem), 78. *Prof Exp:* Sci asst anal chem, Westphalian Wilhelms Univ, Munster, 78-84; res assoc, Univ Colo, Boulder, 82 & 84-85. *Concurrent Pos:* Consult, Ger Prod Testing Found, 79-80. *Mem:* Soc Ger Chemists; Am Chem Soc; Am Asn Mass Spectros. *Res:* Analytical and environmental chemistry; chromatography; mass spectrometry; metal-containing compounds, such as metal chelates; reactions of antitumor drugs of the cisplatinum type with DNA. *Mailing Add:* Universitat GH Siegen Analy Ch I Postfach 57072 Siegen Germany

**WEND, DAVID VAN VRANKEN,** MATHEMATICS. *Current Pos:* RETIRED. *Personal Data:* b Poughkeepsie, NY, Oct 18, 23; m 53; c 3. *Educ:* Univ Wis, BS, 45, MA, 46, PhD(math), 55. *Prof Exp:* Instr math, Reed Col, 49-51 & Iowa State Univ, 52-55; from asst prof to assoc prof, Univ Utah, 55-66; from assoc prof to prof math, Mont State Univ, 66-91. *Mem:* Math Asn Am. *Res:* Functions of a complex variable; differential equations. *Mailing Add:* 402 N Mill St North Manchester IN 46962-1831

**WENDE, CHARLES DAVID,** SPACE PHYSICS. *Current Pos:* astrophysicist, NASA, 69-81, sci data systs mgr, HST Proj, Goddard Space Flight Ctr, 81-91, PROG MGR, OFF MISSION PLANET EARTH, NASA HQ, 91- *Personal Data:* b Wilmington, Del, Dec 4, 41; m 65, Carolee Metcalfe; c Christian W. *Educ:* Mass Inst Technol, BS, 63; Univ Iowa, MS, 66, PhD(physics), 68. *Prof Exp:* Res assoc space physics, Univ Iowa, 68-69. *Mem:* AAAS; Am Geophys Union; Int Union Radio Sci; Sigma Xi. *Res:* Plan future technology development; oversee implementation of portions of earth observing system; application of interactive computing to modeling experiment hardware and to data reduction and analysis. *Mailing Add:* 8700 Nightingale Dr Seabrook MD 20706. *E-Mail:* cwende@hq.nasa.gov

**WENDEL, CARLTON TYRUS,** SCIENCE EDUCATION. *Current Pos:* From instr to assoc prof, 67-89, chmn dept, 80-89, PROF CHEM & CHAIR, TEX WOMAN'S UNIV, 89- *Personal Data:* b Fredericksburg, Tex, Oct 6, 39; m 63, Jeannine Spitzer; c Melissa & Dierdre. *Educ:* Tex Lutheran Col, BS, 62; Tex Tech Col, MS, 65, PhD(chem), 67. *Mem:* Am Chem Soc; Sigma Xi. *Res:* Measurement of conceptual skills development. *Mailing Add:* Box 425859 Tex Woman's Univ Denton TX 76204. *E-Mail:* d__wendel@twu.edu

**WENDEL, JAMES G,** PROBABILITY THEORY. *Current Pos:* from asst prof to prof math, 55-87, assoc chmn dept, 68-70, 73-77 & 79-84, EMER PROF MATH, UNIV MICH, ANN ARBOR, 87- *Personal Data:* b Portland, Ore, Apr, 18, 22; m 44, June Herzog; c 6. *Educ:* Reed Col, BA, 43; Calif Inst Technol, PhD(math), 48. *Prof Exp:* Asst Nat Defense Res Comt, Calif Inst Technol, 42-45, instr, 45-48; instr math, Yale Univ, 48-51; assoc mathematician, Rand Corp, 51-52; from asst prof to assoc prof math, La State Univ, 52-55. *Concurrent Pos:* Vis prof, Aarhus Univ, 62-64, Univ London, 70-71, Univ WAustralia, 78, Calif Inst Technol, 79, Weizmann Inst, 85 & Univ Hawaii, 86. *Mem:* Am Math Soc; Math Asn Am. *Res:* Probability theory. *Mailing Add:* 437 Ferne Ave Palo Alto CA 94306-4621. *Fax:* 650-494-2532; *E-Mail:* jwendel@isdmnl.wr.usgs.gov

**WENDEL, JONATHAN F,** MOLECULAR EVOLUTION, PLANT SYSTEMATICS. *Current Pos:* from asst prof to assoc prof, 86-96, PROF BOT, IOWA STATE UNIV, 96- *Personal Data:* b Baton Rouge, La, Nov 30, 54; m 79, Kathleen J Foster; c Benjamin, Mara & Joseph. *Educ:* Univ Mich, BS, 76; Univ NC, PhD(bot), 83. *Prof Exp:* Geneticist, Agr Res Serv, USDA, 83-86. *Mem:* Am Soc Plant Taxonomists; Bot Soc Am; Soc Study Evolution; Soc Syst Biol; Am Genetic Asn. *Res:* Molecular tools are used to address issues of plant systematics, genome evolution and speciation processes, especially polyploidy. *Mailing Add:* Dept Bot Iowa State Univ Ames IA 50011. *Fax:* 515-294-1337; *E-Mail:* jfw@iastate.edu

**WENDEL, OTTO THEODORE, JR,** NEUROPHARMACOLOGY, CARDIOVASCULAR PHARMACOLOGY. *Current Pos:* asst dean med educ, 86-90, DEAN, ALLIED HEALTH PROFESSIONS, WESTERN UNIV, 90- CHANCELLOR, 95- *Personal Data:* b Philadelphia, Pa, Mar 21, 48; m 89, Janet Canole; c Laura & Sarah. *Educ:* St Andrews Col, BA, 69; Wake Forest Univ, MS, 73, PhD(pharmacol), 74. *Honors & Awards:* A T Still Award Excellence in Teaching, 83. *Prof Exp:* Instr neuropharmacol, Dept Neurol, Bowman Gray Sch Med, 74-76, instr pharmacol, 76-78, asst prof, 78-79; asst prof pharmacol, Kirksville Col Osteop Med, 79-86. *Concurrent Pos:* Assoc community med, Bowman Gray Sch Med, 74-79. *Mem:* Sigma Xi; Soc Neurosci; Am Soc Pharmacol & Exp Therapeut; Western Pharmacol Soc. *Res:* The relationship between endogenous opioid activity and the genesis and or maintenance of hypertension. *Mailing Add:* Western Univ Health Sci 1400 W Third St Chico CA 95928. *Fax:* 530-898-7038

**WENDEL, SAMUEL REECE,** BIOINORGANIC CHEMISTRY, ORGANOMETALLIC CHEMISTRY. *Current Pos:* Chemist, 66-69, SR PROJ CHEMIST ORGANOSILICON CHEM, DOW CORNING CORP, 73- *Personal Data:* b Charleston, Ill, Sept 1, 44; m 67; c 3. *Educ:* Univ Ill, Urbana, BS, 66; Univ Mont, PhD(org chem), 73. *Mem:* AAAS; Am Chem Soc. *Res:* Design and synthesis of bioactive organosilicon compounds; silicone biomaterials. *Mailing Add:* Eli Lilly & Co Lilly Corp Ctr Indianapolis IN 46285-3317

**WENDELKEN, JOHN FRANKLIN,** SURFACE & SOLID STATE PHYSICS. *Current Pos:* PHYSICIST SURFACE PHYSICS, OAK RIDGE NAT LAB, 74- *Personal Data:* b Lexington, Ky, Nov 12, 45; m 68; c 2. *Educ:* Univ Ill, BS, 68, MS, 70, PhD(physics), 75. *Mem:* Am Phys Soc; Am Vacuum Soc; Am Chem Soc. *Res:* Geometric, electronic and vibrational properties of clean and absorbate covered single crystal surfaces. *Mailing Add:* Solid State Div MS 6024 Bldg 3025 Oak Ridge Nat Lab PO Box 2008 Oak Ridge TN 37831. *Fax:* 423-874-4143

**WENDER, IRVING,** FUEL SCIENCE, ORGANOMETALLIC CHEMISTRY & CATALYSIS. *Current Pos:* RES PROF, DEPT CHEM/ PETROL ENG, UNIV PITTSBURGH, 81- *Personal Data:* b New York, NY, June 19, 15; m 42; c 3. *Educ:* City Col New York, BS, 36; Columbia Univ, MA, 45; Univ Pittsburgh, PhD(chem), 50. *Honors & Awards:* Bituminous Coal Res Award, 56, 60; H H Storch Award, 64; Pittsburgh Award, Am Chem Soc, 68; K K Kelley Award, 69; Career Serv Award, Nat Civil Serv League, 76; Award Petrol Chem, Am Chem Soc, 82; H H Lowry Award, Dept Energy, 88. *Prof Exp:* Chemist & res assoc, Manhattan Proj, Univ Chicago, 44-46; org chemist, Pittsburgh Coal Res Ctr, US Bur Mines, 46-53; chief chem sect, 53-71, res dir, Pittsburgh Energy Res Ctr, Energy Res & Develop Admin, 71-75, dir, 75-77, dir, Pittsburgh Energy Technol Ctr, Dept Energy, 77-78, spec adv to asst dir fossil energy, 78-79, dir, Off Advan Res & Technol, Off Fossil Energy, 79-81. *Concurrent Pos:* Lectr, Univ Pittsburgh, 63-69, adj prof, 69-78, 82- *Mem:* Am Chem Soc; Am Inst Chem Eng; AAAS. *Res:* Chemistry of carbon monoxide, metal carbonyls, coal conversion; catalysis; reactions at high pressures; synthetic fuels from coal; carbon monoxide chemistry. *Mailing Add:* 1261 Denniston Ave Pittsburgh PA 15217-1328

**WENDER, PAUL ANTHONY,** PHOTOCHEMISTRY, BIOLOGICAL ACTIVITY. *Current Pos:* PROF, STANFORD UNIV, 81-, BERGSTROM PROF, 93- *Educ:* Wilkes Col, BS, 69; Yale Univ, PhD, 73. *Hon Degrees:* PhD, Wilkes Univ, 93. *Honors & Awards:* Guenther Award, Am Chem Soc; ICI Am Chem Award, Stuart Pharmaceut; NIH Merit Award; Pfizer Res Award. *Prof Exp:* From asst prof to assoc prof, Harvard Univ, 74-81. *Concurrent Pos:* Consult, Eli Lilly & Co, 80- & Donelanco; lectr, Am Chem Soc; ed, Synthesis; Alexander von Humboldt Award. *Mem:* Am Chem Soc; AAAS. *Res:* Organic synthesis; organic photochemistry; computer modelling; tumor promotion; organometallic chemistry; medicinal chemistry. *Mailing Add:* Dept Chem Stanford Univ Stanford CA 94305

**WENDER, PAUL H,** PSYCHIATRY, CHILD PSYCHIATRY. *Current Pos:* PROF PSYCHIAT, COL MED, UNIV UTAH, 73- *Personal Data:* b New York, NY, May 12, 34; m 70; c 3. *Educ:* Harvard Univ, AB, 55; Columbia Univ, MD, 59. *Honors & Awards:* Hofheimer Award, Am Psychiat Asn, 74. *Prof Exp:* Intern, Barnes Hosp, St Louis, 59-60; resident adult psychiat, Mass Ment Health Ctr, 60-62; resident, St Elizabeth's Hosp, 62-63; resident child psychiat, Johns Hopkins Univ, 64-67, asst prof pediat & psychiat, 67-73. *Concurrent Pos:* NIMH fel, NIH, Bethesda, Md, 64-66, res psychiatrist, 67-73. *Mem:* Am Psychiat Asn; Am Acad Child Psychiat; Psychiat Res Soc. *Res:* Genetics and schizophrenia; minimal brain dysfunction in children. *Mailing Add:* Univ Utah Col Med Psyc Salt Lake City UT 84132

**WENDER, SIMON HAROLD,** BIOCHEMISTRY. *Current Pos:* RETIRED. *Personal Data:* b Dalton, Ga, Sept 4, 13; m 42, Ruth Wisenberg; c Joe, Barbara & Sheryl. *Educ:* Emory Univ, AB, 34, MS, 35; Univ Minn, PhD(agr biochem), 38. *Honors & Awards:* Okla Chemist Award, 83. *Prof Exp:* Res assoc, Med Sch, Emory Univ, 38-39; assoc chemist, Exp Sta, Agr & Mech Col, Tex, 39-41; from instr to asst prof chem, Univ Ky, 41-46; from assoc prof to prof biochem, Univ Okla, 46-53, res prof, 53-83, George L Cross emer prof, 83-93. *Concurrent Pos:* Former mem bd dirs, Oak Ridge Assoc Univs; chmn coun, Oak Ridge Inst Nuclear Studies, Okla, rep to coun, 52-64 & 71-80; vis res assoc, Argonne Nat Lab, 54-64; vis prof, Univ Wis, 66 & Univ Calif, Davis, 73. *Mem:* Fel AAAS; Am Chem Soc; Am Soc Biol Chem; Soc Exp Biol & Med; Am Soc Plant Physiol; Phytochem Soc NAm. *Res:* Chromatography; plant phenolics and plant and animal oxidoreductases. *Mailing Add:* Univ Okla 2614 Meadowbrook Dr Norman OK 73072-6928

**WENDLAND, WAYNE MARCEL,** METEOROLOGY, PALEOCLIMATOLOGY. *Current Pos:* RETIRED. *Personal Data:* b Beaver Dam, Wis, Aug 9, 34; m 56; c 4. *Educ:* Lawrence Col, BA, 56; Univ Wis-Madison, MS, 65, PhD(meteorol), 72. *Prof Exp:* Weather forecaster, USAF, 56-64; proj supvr meteorol, Univ Wis-Madison, 66-70, instr climat, 70, asst prof geog & meteorol. 70-76; assoc prof geog, Univ Ill, Urbana, 76-80; head, Climat Sect, Ill State Water Surv, 80-84, prin scientist & state climatologist, 84-96. *Concurrent Pos:* Adj prof geog, Univ Ill, Urbana. *Mem:* Am Meteorol Soc; Am Quaternary Asn; Am Asn State Climatologists. *Res:* Past climatic circulation patterns; climatic episodes of the Holocene; climatic reconstructions from tree rings; climatic variability. *Mailing Add:* 1901 Crescent Dr Champaign IL 61821. *E-Mail:* wayne@uiuc.edu

**WENDLAND, WOLFGANG LEOPOLD,** MATHEMATICS, MECHANICAL ENGINEERING. *Current Pos:* PROF, UNIV STUTTGART. *Personal Data:* b Poznan, Poland, Sept 20, 36; Ger citizen; m 64, Gisela Born; c David & Katrin. *Educ:* Tech Univ, Berlin, BS(mech eng), 58, BS(math), 58, dipl ing, 61, Dr Ing, 65, Habilitation, 69. *Prof Exp:* Sci collabr, Tech Univ Berlin, 61-63, sci asst, 63-64; sci asst, Dept Numerical Math, Hahn Meitner Inst, Berlin, 64-69, prof, 69-70; prof, Tech Univ Darmstadt, 70-86. *Concurrent Pos:* Vis unidel chair prof, Univ Del, 73-74; chmn, Math Dept, Tech Univ Darmstadt, 74-75; Fulbright Stipendium, Univ Del, 77 & 89; vis prof, Ore State Univ, 77-, Univ Md, 81, Univ Del, 81, Univ Concepcion, Chile, 81, 89, 90, 95 & 96, Australian Nat Univ, Canberra, 85, 89, 90, 95 & 96, Australian Univ, NSW, 97. *Mem:* Am Math Soc; Ger Asn Appl Math Mech; Soc Appl Math Mech; Int Soc Interaction Mech Math; Int Soc Comp Mech Eng; Int Asn Boundary Element Methods. *Res:* Applied mathematics; partial differential equations; integral equations; mathematical physics. *Mailing Add:* Univ Stuttgart Pfaffenwaldring 57 70569 Stuttgart Germany. *Fax:* 49-771685-5599; *E-Mail:* wendland@mathematik. uni-stuttgart.de

**WENDLANDT, WESLEY W,** INORGANIC CHEMISTRY, ANALYTICAL CHEMISTRY. *Current Pos:* chmn dept, 66-72, PROF CHEM, UNIV HOUSTON, 66- *Personal Data:* b Galesville, Wis, Nov 20, 27. *Educ:* Wis State Col, River Falls, BS, 50; Univ Iowa, MS, 52, PhD(chem), 54. *Honors & Awards:* Mettler Award, 70. *Prof Exp:* From asst prof to prof chem, Tex Tech Col, 54-66. *Concurrent Pos:* Vis prof, NMex Highlands Univ, 61; ed-in-chief, Thermochimica Acta. *Mem:* AAAS; Am Chem Soc; The Chem Soc; NAm Thermal Anal Soc; Int Contedn Thermal Anal. *Res:* Coordination compounds; metal chelates; thermogravimetry; differential thermal analysis; solid state chemistry; reflectance spectroscopy. *Mailing Add:* 7818 Sands Point Dr Houston TX 77036

**WENDLER, GERD DIERK,** METEOROLOGY. *Current Pos:* asst geophysicist, 66-67, asst prof meteorol, 67-70, ASSOC PROF METEOROL, GEOPHYS INST, UNIV ALASKA, FAIRBANKS, 70- *Personal Data:* b Hamburg, WGer, June 16, 39; m 69; c 2. *Educ:* Innsbruck Univ, PhD(meteorol), 64. *Prof Exp:* Data process asst meteorol, Inst Meteorol, Innsbruck Univ, 60-64, res asst, 65-66. *Concurrent Pos:* NSF grant, McCall Glacier, Geophys Inst, Univ Alaska, Fairbanks, 69-, Sea grant Arctic Ocean, 71- & NASA satellite grant cent Alaska, 72- *Mem:* Am Meteorol Soc; Am Geophys Union; Glaciol Soc; Arctic Inst NAm; Ger Soc Polar Res. *Res:* Meteorology in the arctic, especially of Alaska. *Mailing Add:* Dept Physics Univ Alaska PO Box 755900 Fairbanks AK 99775-5920

**WENDRICKS, ROLAND N,** PHYSICAL CHEMISTRY, PLASTICS ENGINEERING. *Current Pos:* RETIRED. *Personal Data:* b Casco, Wis, July 26, 30; m 52, Laverne Lardo; c Wayne, Julie, Lauri & Lisa. *Educ:* St Norbert Col, BS, 52; Northwestern Univ, MS, 61. *Prof Exp:* Group supvr blow molding process, Am Can Co, 52-67; supvr blow molding plastics res & develop, 67-70, mgr plastics equip eng, 70-88. *Concurrent Pos:* Chmn, SPE-Blow Molding Div, 82; consult plastics processing, 94-97. *Mem:* Soc Plastics Eng. *Res:* Processing of thermoplastic polymers. *Mailing Add:* E831 County Line Rd Luxemburg WI 54217

**WENDROFF, BURTON,** MATHEMATICS. *Current Pos:* GROUP LEADER & STAFF MEM, LOS ALAMOS SCI LAB, 73- *Personal Data:* b New York, NY, Mar 10, 30. *Educ:* NY Univ, BA, 51, PhD(math), 58; Mass Inst Technol, SM, 52. *Prof Exp:* Staff mem, Los Alamos Sci Lab, 52-66; from assoc prof to prof math, Univ Denver, 66-74. *Mem:* Am Math Soc; Soc Indust & Appl Math. *Res:* Applied mathematics; numerical analysis. *Mailing Add:* Los Alamos Nat Lab MS 8284 Los Alamos NM 87544

**WENDT, ARNOLD,** MATHEMATICS. *Current Pos:* PROF MATH, WESTERN ILL UNIV, 52- *Personal Data:* b Red Bud, Ill, Jan 14, 22; m 43; c 1. *Educ:* Univ Wis, PhD(math), 52. *Mem:* AAAS; Am Math Soc; Math Asn Am. *Res:* Analysis and applied mathematics. *Mailing Add:* 406 S Lafayette St Macomb IL 61455-2948

**WENDT, CHARLES WILLIAM,** SOIL PHYSICS, SOIL-PLANT-WATER RELATIONS. *Current Pos:* res asst soil physics, Tex A&M Univ, 63-65, res assoc, 65-66, from asst prof to prof, 66-91, EMER PROF SOIL PHYSICS, TEX A&M UNIV, 91- *Personal Data:* b Plainview, Tex, July 12, 31; m 55, Clara A Diller; c Charles D, John W, Eric D (deceased), Elaine A & Cynthia L. *Educ:* Tex A&M Univ, BS, 51, PhD(soil physics), 66; Tex Tech Col, MS, 57. *Honors & Awards:* Outstanding Res Scientist, High Plains Res Found, 82. *Prof Exp:* Res asst agron, Tex Tech Col, 53-55, from instr to asst prof, 57-63. *Concurrent Pos:* Consult cotton prod, Ministry Agr, Repub Sudan, Dryland Agr, Cong US, Technol & Assement Off, Int Irrigation Asn, proj eval, Environ Protection Agency, Nat Water Resources Coun, Nat Res Coun, Southeast Consortium, Int Develop. *Mem:* AAAS; Am Soc Agron; Soil Sci Soc Am; Am Soc Plant Physiol; Brit Plant Growth Regulator Group; Plant Growth Regulation Soc Am. *Res:* Efficient utilization of rainfall and limited irrigation water through plant modification (breeding, growth regulators, antitranspirants) and soil modification (irrigation, furrow, diking, and evaporation suppressants), in US; semi-arid agriculture in Africa. *Mailing Add:* Tex Agr Exp Sta Tex A&M Univ Agr Res & Exten Ctr Rte 3 Lubbock TX 79401. *Fax:* 806-746-6528, 795-4744; *E-Mail:* absent@aol.com

**WENDT, JOST O L,** CHEMICAL ENGINEERING, COMBUSTION. *Current Pos:* from asst prof to assoc prof, 72-79, PROF CHEM ENG, UNIV ARIZ, 79- *Personal Data:* b Berlin, Ger, July 2, 41; m 61, Marianne S Mersch; c Rolf & Karen. *Educ:* Glasgow Univ, BSc, 63; Johns Hopkins Univ, MSE, 66, PhD(chem eng), 68. *Honors & Awards:* Environ Sci & Technol Achievement Award, US Environ Protection Agency, 88. *Prof Exp:* Instr thermodyn, Johns Hopkins Univ, 66-67; engr, Emeryville Res Ctr, Shell Develop Co, Calif, 68-72. *Concurrent Pos:* Consult combustion appln, Nat Acad Sci/Nat Acad Engrs; Nat Acad Sci/Nat Acad Eng sr vis scientist, Environ Protection Agency, 84-85; prin investr, res grants on combustion; mem, Coalition Responsible Waste Incineration. *Mem:* Am Inst Chem Engrs; Combustion Inst; Int Flame Res Found. *Res:* Combustion generated air pollution; pollution aspects of burner design; coal combustion; kinetics; combustion science; hazardous waste incineration. *Mailing Add:* Dept Chem Eng Univ Ariz Tucson AZ 85721. *E-Mail:* wendt@bigdog.engr.arizona.edu

**WENDT, RICHARD P,** physical chemistry, transport processes; deceased, see previous edition for last biography

**WENDT, ROBERT CHARLES,** SURFACE & POLYMER CHEMISTRY. *Current Pos:* Res chemist, Yerkes Lab, Film Dept, E I Du Pont de Nemours & Co, Inc, 55-64, staff scientist, Exp Sta Lab, Film Dept, 69-75, sr res chemist, 76-81, RES ASSOC, EXP STA LAB, POLYMER PRODS DEPT, E I DU PONT DE NEMOURS & CO, INC, 81- *Personal Data:* b Aurora, Ill, July 5, 29; m 53; c 4. *Educ:* NCent Col, Ill, BA, 51; Univ Ill, PhD(phys chem), 55. *Mem:* Am Chem Soc; Am Vacuum Soc; Elec Micros Soc Am. *Res:* Diffusion phenomena; polymer physical properties; adhesion; polymer surface chemistry and physics; electron spectroscopy. *Mailing Add:* 3316 Coachman Rd Wilmington DE 19803-1943

**WENDT, ROBERT L(OUIS),** ENGINEERING. *Current Pos:* RETIRED. *Personal Data:* b Chicago, Ill, July 10, 20; m 46, Ruth Munro. *Educ:* Harvard Univ, AB, 40. *Prof Exp:* Eng, Sperry Gyroscope Co, 40-52, mgr eng, 52-57, mgr sales & subcontracts, 57-62, mgr B-58 bomb navig syst prog, 62-63, dir prog control, 63-64, mgr, Polaris/Poseidon, 64-69, group mgr ship & mil systs, 69-71, vpres & gen mgr, Systs Mgt, 71-75, vpres & gen mgr, Gyroscope, 75-80, pres, Sperry Div, Sperry Corp, 80-84, vpres exec develop, 84-85. *Mem:* Sr mem Inst Elec & Electronics Engrs; Am Soc Naval Engrs. *Res:* Management of major programs, especially development and production of complex electronic systems. *Mailing Add:* One Hillcrest Lane Woodbury NY 11797

**WENDT, ROBERT LEO,** hypertension, cardiac diseases, for more information see previous edition

**WENDT, THEODORE MIL,** microbiology, chemistry, for more information see previous edition

**WENESER, JOSEPH,** THEORETICAL PHYSICS. *Current Pos:* RETIRED. *Personal Data:* b New York, NY, Nov 23, 22; m 56. *Educ:* City Col, BS, 42; Columbia Univ, MA, 48, PhD(physics), 52. *Prof Exp:* Asst physics, Manhattan Proj, Columbia Univ, 42-46; assoc physicist, Brookhaven Nat Lab, 52-55; asst prof, Univ Ill, 55-57; chmn Dept Physics, Brookhaven Nat Lab, 70-75, sr physicist, 57-96. *Mem:* Fel Am Phys Soc; fel AAAS. *Res:* Theoretical nuclear physics. *Mailing Add:* Dept Physics Bldg 510A Brookhaven Nat Lab Upton NY 11973. *Fax:* 516-282-2918

**WENG, LIH-JYH,** ELECTRICAL ENGINEERING, COMPUTER SCIENCE. *Current Pos:* consult engr, Digital Equip Corp, 78-81, sr consult, 81-94, FEL, QUANTUM CORP, 94- *Personal Data:* b Fukien, China, Dec 3, 37; m, Liman Zhu; c Peter & Christina. *Educ:* Cheng Kung Univ, Taiwan, BS, 59; Northeastern Univ, MSEE, 63, PhD(elec eng), 66. *Prof Exp:* Res engr, Adcom, Inc, 65-66; sr res assoc coding theory, Northeastern Univ, 66-67; from asst prof to assoc prof elec eng, 67-73; sr eng specialist, CNR, Inc, 73-78. *Concurrent Pos:* NSF initiation grant, 68-69; consult, Honeywell Info Systs Inc, Mass, 70-71; lectr, Northeastern Univ, 73-82. *Mem:* Inst Elec & Electronics Engrs. *Res:* Algebraic coding theory; digital communications; mass storage techniques in computers; error-control; communication theory; cryptology. *Mailing Add:* Quantum Corp SHR 1-3/E29 333 South St Shrewsbury MA 01545-4112

**WENG, TUNG HSIANG,** ELECTRICAL ENGINEERING. *Current Pos:* from asst prof to assoc prof, 69-83, PROF ELEC ENG, OAKLAND UNIV, 83- *Personal Data:* b Fukien, China, Jan 16, 33; m 61; c 3. *Educ:* Nat Taiwan Univ, BS, 56; Univ Iowa, MS, 59; Univ Mo, Columbia, PhD(elec eng), 67. *Prof Exp:* Design engr, Oak Mfg Co, 60-61; proj engr, Sula Elec Co, 61-63 & Simpson Elec Co, 63-64; asst prof elec eng, Univ Mo, Columbia, 67-69. *Mem:* Inst Elec & Electronics Engrs; Sigma Xi. *Res:* Solid state properties and devices. *Mailing Add:* Sch Eng Oakland Univ Rochester MI 48309-4402

**WENG, (FRANK) TZONG-RUEY,** MEDICINE, PEDIATRICS. *Current Pos:* STAFF MEM, CHILDREN'S HOSP DETROIT. *Personal Data:* b Jakarta, Indonesia, Jan 5, 34; US citizen; m 72. *Educ:* Nat Taiwan Univ, MD, 60. *Prof Exp:* Asst prof pediat, Sch Med, NY Univ, 70-75; assoc prof pediat, Sch Med, Wayne State Univ, 75-80; mem staff, Children's Hosp Pittsburgh, 80- *Mem:* Fel Am Acad Pediat; fel Am Col Chest Physicians; Am Thoracic Soc. *Res:* Pulmonary diseases in children. *Mailing Add:* 2326 Benton Ave Kalamazoo MI 49008

**WENG, WU TSUNG,** ELECTROMAGNETISM, ENGINEERING PHYSICS. *Current Pos:* accelerator physicist, Accelerator Dept, 77-83, mgr, Booster Proj, AGS Dept, 87-90, ACCELERATOR DIV HEAD, AGS DEPT, BROOKHAVEN NAT LAB, 90- *Personal Data:* b Taiwan, China, Aug 11, 44; m 67; c 2. *Educ:* Nat Taiwan Univ, BS, 66; Nat Tsing Hua Univ, MS, 68; State Univ NY, Stony Brook, PhD(physics), 74. *Prof Exp:* Accelerator physicist, Stanford Linear Accelerator Ctr, 83-87. *Concurrent Pos:* Chmn, Accelerator Sci & Technol Comt, Nuclear & Plasma Sci Soc, Inst Elec & Electronics Engrs. *Mem:* Am Phys Soc; Inst Elec & Electronics Engrs. *Res:* Accelerator physics; non-linear dynamits; beam control and feedback. *Mailing Add:* Bldg 911B Ags Dept Brookhaven Nat Lab Mt Sinai NY 11766

**WENGER, CHRISTIAN BRUCE,** THERMOREGULATION, CIRCULATION & HEAT ILLNESS. *Current Pos:* RES PHARMACOLOGIST, THERMAL PHYSIOL & MED DIV, US ARMY RES INST, ENVIRON MED, 84- *Personal Data:* b Philadelphia, Pa, July 24, 42; m 93, Lynn L Lameka. *Educ:* Col Wooster, AB, 64; Yale Univ, MD, 70, PhD(environ physiol), 73. *Prof Exp:* Instr physics, Col Wooster, 67-68; vis asst fel, John B Pierce Found Lab, 74-75, asst fel, 75-82, assoc fel physiol, 82-84, vis assoc fel, 84-86. *Concurrent Pos:* Guest referee ed, Am Physiol Soc, 73-; fel, Dept Epidemiol & Pub Health, Yale Univ, 74-76, asst prof, 76-, sr res assoc & lectr, 82-83, res scientist & lectr, 83-84; res assoc physiol, Sch Pub Health, Harvard Univ, 85-89. *Mem:* Am Physiol Soc; Sigma Xi. *Res:* Thermoregulatory physiology; circulatory effects of heat and cold stress and exercise; heat acclimatization; heat and cold disorders. *Mailing Add:* Military Performance Div US Army Res Inst Environ Med Kans St Natick MA 01760-5007. *Fax:* 508-233-5298; *E-Mail:* bwenger@natick_ccmail.army.mil

**WENGER, FRANZ,** PHYSICAL CHEMISTRY. *Current Pos:* GROUP V PRES-IN-CHG RES & DEVELOP & ENG, ENGELHARD INDUSTS DIV, ENGELHARD MINERALS & CHEM CORP, NEWARK, 69- *Personal Data:* b Bern, Switz, Nov 28, 25; nat US; m 55. *Educ:* Univ Bern, Lic phil nat, 53, PhD(chem), 54. *Prof Exp:* Chemist, Lonza, Inc, Switz, 55; fel photochem, Nat Res Coun Can, 55-57; fel polymer sci, Mellon Inst, 58-63; sr staff assoc, Cent Res Lab, Celanese Corp, NJ, 63-66; mgr spec prod res, Polaroid Corp, Mass, 66-69. *Mem:* Am Chem Soc. *Res:* Reaction kinetics; structure-properties relationship of polymeric materials; photographic technology; process research and development. *Mailing Add:* 363 Cherry Hill Rd Mountainside NJ 07092

**WENGER, GALEN ROSENBERGER,** OPERANT BEHAVIOR, BEHAVIORAL PHARMACOLOGY & TOXICOLOGY. *Current Pos:* from asst prof to assoc prof, 78-86, PROF PHARMACOL, UNIV ARK MED SCI, LITTLE ROCK, 86-, DIR, DIV PHARMACOL, 91- *Personal Data:* b Sellersville, Pa, May 16, 46; m 72, Carolyn Liechty; c Alyssa & Aaron. *Educ:* Goshen Col, Ind, BA, 68; WVa Univ, PhD(pharmacol), 71. *Prof Exp:* Fel, Univ Col Med Ctr, 72-73; fel, Harvard Med Sch, 73-75, instr pharmacol, 75-78. *Concurrent Pos:* Ad hoc consult, Nat Inst Environ Health Sci; consult, Nat Ctr Toxicol Res, 83-89; prin investr, res grant, Nat Inst Drug Abuse, 83-; toxicol study sect mem, NIH, 90-94. *Mem:* Am Soc Pharmacol & Exp Therapeut; Soc Toxicol; Behav Pharmacol Soc; Behav Toxicol Soc. *Res:* Behavioral effects of drugs of abuse affecting the central nervous system; behavioral effects of toxic agents; toxicology; experimental psychology; pharmacology. *Mailing Add:* Dept Pharmacol Slot 611 Univ Ark Med Sci 4301 W Markham Little Rock AR 72205

**WENGER, JAY D,** INFECTIOUS DISEASES. *Current Pos:* MED OFFICER, CHILDREN'S VACCINE INITIATIVE & EXPANDED PROG IMMUNIZATION, WHO, 96- *Personal Data:* b Camden, NJ, Feb 24, 55; m 82, Patricia Daley; c Rachel, Kristen & Jon. *Educ:* Wheaton Col, BS, 77; Temple Univ, MD, 81; Am Bd Internal Med, cert, 84, cert infectious dis, 86. *Prof Exp:* Intern & resident internal med, Univ Hosps Cleveland, Case Western Res Univ, 81-84, fel geog med & infectious dis, 84-87; epidemic intel serv officer, Meningitis & Spec Pathogens Br, Ctr Dis Control, 87-89, med epidemiologist, 89-90, actg chief, 91-93, chief, Childhood & Respiratory Dis Br, Div Bact & Mycotic Dis, Nat Ctr Infectious Dis, Ctr Dis Control & Prev, 93-96. *Mem:* Infectious Dis Soc Am; Am Soc Microbiol. *Res:* Epidemiology of bacterial infections; impact and efficacy of new bacterial vaccines. *Mailing Add:* WHO 22 Ave Appia CH-1211 Geneva 27 Switzerland. *E-Mail:* wengerj@who.ch

**WENGER, JOHN C,** MEASURE THEORY. *Current Pos:* PROF MATH, CITY COL CHICAGO, 68- *Personal Data:* b Manhattan, NY, Jan 13, 41; m 63, Sally Caplan; c Susan & Karen. *Educ:* Univ Mich, BS, 63; Univ Chicago, SM, 66; Ill Inst Technol, PhD(math), 79. *Concurrent Pos:* Grievance chmn, Cook Co Col Teachers Union, 86- *Mem:* Math Asn Am; Am Math Soc; Nat Coun Teachers Math. *Res:* Generalizations of the Riesz-Markov representation theorem in both topological and more abstract settings. *Mailing Add:* 198 Bloom Highland Park IL 60035-1439

**WENGER, LOWELL EDWARD,** PHYSICS. *Current Pos:* asst prof, 76-81, assoc prof, 81-85, PROF PHYSICS, WAYNE STATE UNIV, 85-, ASSOC DEAN, COL SCI, 96- *Personal Data:* b Middlebury, Ind, Nov 17, 48; m 76; c 2. *Educ:* Purdue Univ, BS, 71, MS, 73, PhD(physics), 75. *Prof Exp:* Res assoc physics, Purdue Univ, 75-76. *Concurrent Pos:* Grants, Cottrell Res Corp, 77-79 & Wayne State Fac Res Award, 77-78, 84-85; fel, Alfred P Sloan Res Found, 78-82, Fulbright Res, 82-83; career develop chmn, Wayne State, 84-85. *Mem:* Am Phys Soc; Sigma Xi; Mat Res Soc. *Res:* Study of magnetic properties of magnetic alloys; heat capacity and magnetic susceptibilities of solids at very low temperatures; characterization of high-temperature superconducting oxides. *Mailing Add:* Dept Physics Wayne State Univ Detroit MI 48202. *Fax:* 313-577-3932; *E-Mail:* wenger@hal.physics.wayne.edu

**WENGER, NANETTE KASS,** MEDICINE, CARDIOLOGY. *Current Pos:* instr med, Emory Univ, 59-62, assoc, 62-64, from asst prof to assoc prof, 64-71, PROF MED, SCH MED, EMORY UNIV, 71-; DIR, CARDIAC CLIN, GRADY MEM HOSP, ATLANTA, 60- *Personal Data:* b New York, NY, Sept 3, 30. *Educ:* Hunter Col, BA, 51; Harvard Med Sch, 54. *Honors & Awards:* Myrtle Wreath Award, 67. *Prof Exp:* Intern, Mt Sinai Hosp, New York, 54-55, resident med, 55-56, chief resident cardiol, 56-57; sr asst resident med, Grady Mem Hosp, Atlanta, 58. *Concurrent Pos:* Fel cardiol, Sch Med, Grady Mem Hosp, Emory Univ, 58-59; fel, Coun Clin Cardiol, Am Heart Asn, 70; dir, Proj Cardiac Eval & Med & Voc Rehab, 66-; mem, Rehab Comt, Inter-Soc Comn Heart Disease Resources, 69-75; mem, Nat Thrombosis Adv Comt, 71-74 & Heart Panel, Heart, Lung & Blood Vessel Dis Act, 72; consult, Int Div Social & Rehab Serv, Dept Health, Educ & Welfare, 70- & J Chest, 70-; chmn, Prog Comt, Am Heart Asn, 75-76; mem, Clin Trials Comn, Nat Heart, Lung & Blood Inst, 78-81; assoc ed, J Behav Med, 77; ed, J Cardiol, 82-; consult ed, J Cardiovasc & Pulmonary Med, 83- *Mem:* AMA; fel Am Col Cardiol; Am Heart Asn (past vpres); Am Fedn Clin Res; Am Thoracic Asn (vpres, 75-). *Res:* Urokinase pulmonary embolism trial; ischemic heart disease in young adults; clinical evaluation of myocardial infarction patients; evaluation of patient education programs; author of over 500 scientific books. *Mailing Add:* Med Cardiovasc Emory Univ Sch Med 1440 Clifton Rd NE Atlanta GA 30307-1053

**WENGER, RONALD HAROLD,** MATHEMATICS. *Current Pos:* ASSOC PROF MATH, UNIV DEL, 65-, ASST TO PROVOST FOR ACAD PLANNING, 69- *Personal Data:* b Dayton, Ohio, Nov 30, 37; m 63. *Educ:* Miami Univ, Ohio, AB, 59; Mich State Univ, MS, 61, PhD(math), 65. *Concurrent Pos:* Assoc dean, Col Arts & Sci, Univ Del, 68-69, 72-; Am Coun Educ fel acad admin, 70-71. *Mem:* Am Math Soc; Math Asn Am. *Res:* Semigroup rings. *Mailing Add:* 20 Winslow Rd Newark DE 19711

**WENGER, SHARON LOUISE,** CYTOGENETICS. *Current Pos:* asst prof, 80-89, ASSOC PROF PEDIAT, UNIV PITTSBURGH, 89- *Personal Data:* b Washington, DC, Sept 25, 49; m 76, George E Fromlak Jr; c Nicholas E, Holly L & Andrea L. *Educ:* Thiel Col, BA, 71; Univ Pittsburgh, MS, 73, PhD(human genetics), 76. *Prof Exp:* Fel, Children's Hosp Pittsburgh, 77-80. *Mem:* Am Soc Human Genetics; Am Col Med Genetics. *Res:* Utilization of cytogenetic techniques to study genetic syndromes and diseases, including sister chromatid exchange, fragile site expression, late DNA synthesis, special banding procedures and in situ hybridization. *Mailing Add:* Children's Hosp Pittsburgh 3705 Fifth Ave at Desoto St Pittsburgh PA 15213

**WENGER, THOMAS LEE,** MEDICINE. *Current Pos:* SR CLIN RES SCIENTIST, BURROUGHS WELLCOME CO, 78-, DIR, PROF SER DIV, MED. *Personal Data:* b New York, NY, Feb 20, 45; c 2. *Educ:* Princeton Univ, AB, 66; Boston Univ, MD, 71. *Prof Exp:* House officer, Harlem Hosp Med Ctr, 71-75; res assoc, Columbia Presby Med Ctr, 74-75; cardiol fel, Duke Univ Med Ctr, 75-78. *Concurrent Pos:* Adj assoc prof med, Duke Univ Med Ctr, 78- *Mem:* Am Heart Asn; fel Am Col Cardiol; AAAS. *Res:* Cardiovascular electrophysiology and pharmacology. *Mailing Add:* 1114 Watt St Durham NC 27701

**WENGERD, SHERMAN ALEXANDER,** civil engineering, geographical exploration; deceased, see previous edition for last biography

**WENIG, HAROLD G(EORGE),** MECHANICAL ENGINEERING, ELECTROMAGNETISM. *Current Pos:* PRES, WRIGHT INDUSTS, INC, 59- *Personal Data:* b New York, NY, Sept 24, 24; m 49, Shirley Tedlis; c 2. *Educ:* City Col New York, BME, 45; Yale Univ, ME, 48; NY Univ, ScD(mech eng), 52. *Honors & Awards:* I B Laskowitz Gold Medal, NY Acad Sci, 68. *Prof Exp:* Stress analyst, Otis Elevator Co, 45; mech designer, H K Ferguson Co, 47; mech engr, Sanderson & Porter Co, 48-49; dir eng projs, Bulova Res & Develop Labs, Inc, 51-58; consult engr, 58-59. *Concurrent Pos:* Dir, Krystinel Corp. *Mem:* AAAS; fel NY Acad Sci; Tech Asn Pulp & Paper Indust; Inst Elec & Electronics Engrs; Soc Photog Scientists & Engrs; Am Phys Soc; Am Soc Mech Engrs; Nat Soc Prof Engrs. *Res:* Aerothermodynamics; dynamics of rigid bodies in extreme force fields; hydrology; research and development management; magnetism and magnetic materials. *Mailing Add:* 375-08E S End Ave New York NY 10280

**WENIS, EDWARD,** CHEMICAL ENGINEERING. *Current Pos:* RETIRED. *Personal Data:* b Linden, NJ, May 21, 19; m 42; c 2. *Educ:* Newark Col Eng, BS, 40; Stevens Inst Technol, MS, 42. *Prof Exp:* Salesman, Sun Oil Co, 38-39; chemist & co supvr Dutch elm disease, USDA, Pa, 39-42; org chemist, Hoffman-LaRoche Inc, 42-66, mgr, Thin Layer Chromatogram Labs & Res Serv, 67-79. *Mem:* Am Chem Soc; fel Am Inst Chemists. *Res:* Synthesis of new drugs; development of riboflavin, lyxoflavin, folic acid and khellin; antituberculosis, hypoglycemic agents and psychoenergizers. *Mailing Add:* 104 Hillcrest Ave Leonia NJ 07605-1531

**WENK, EDWARD, JR,** SCIENCE POLICY, CIVIL ENGINEERING. *Current Pos:* prof, 70-96, dir, Prog Social Mgt Technol, 73-96, EMER PROF ENG & PUB AFFAIRS, UNIV WASH, 90- *Personal Data:* b Baltimore, Md, Jan 24, 20; m 41, Carolyn Lyford; c Lawrence S, Robin A & Jerry A. *Educ:* Johns Hopkins Univ, BE, 40, DEng, 50; Harvard Univ, MSc, 47. *Hon Degrees:* DSc, Univ RI, 68; LHD, Johns Hopkins Univ, 90. *Prof Exp:* Ship struct designer, Boston Navy Shipyard, Mass, 41-42; supvr, Turret Test Sect, David Taylor Model Basin, US Naval Dept, 42-45, supt, Struct Dynamics Sect, 45-48, head, Submarine Struct Br, 48-50, chief, Struct Div, 50-56; chmn, Dept Eng Mech, Southwest Res Inst, 56-59; sr specialist sci & technol, Legis Reference Serv, Libr Cong, 59-61; tech asst to Pres Kennedy's Sci Adv, White House, 61-62; tech asst to dir, Off Sci & Technol & exec secy, Fed Coun Sci & Technol, 62-64, chief, Sci Policy Res Div & spec adv to librn, Libr Cong, 64-66; exec secy, Nat Coun Marine Resources & Eng Develop, Exec Off of Pres, 66-70. *Concurrent Pos:* Lectr, Univ Md, 52 & 54-56, Seattle Univ, 84; mem, Pressure Vessel Res Comt & chmn, Design Div, Welding Res Coun, 53-59; consult comt undersea warfare, Nat Acad Sci, 57-58, mem panel naval vehicles, 60-71; chmn comt pub eng policy, Nat Acad Eng, 69-75; vis scholar, Woodrow Wilson Int Ctr Scholars, 70-71; Ford Found fel, 70-72; mem, Nat Adv Comt Oceans & Atmosphere, 71-72; mem bd dirs, URS Syst Corp, 71-88; vchmn, US Cong Technol Assessment Adv Coun, 74-79; consult to White House, US Cong, Nat Oceanic & Atmospheric Admin & UN Secretariat, UK, Sweden, Australia & Philippines, States of Alaska & Wash; regents lectr, Univ Calif, 89; mem, Alaska Comn Wreck Exxon Valdez, 89-90. *Mem:* Nat Acad Eng; Nat Acad Pub Admin; Am Soc Civil Engrs; Soc Exp Stress Anal (pres, 57-58); fel Am Soc Mech Engrs; Sigma Xi; Int Asn Impact Assessment (pres, 82-83); fel AAAS; Marine Tech Soc; Am Soc Pub Admin. *Res:* Applied mechanics; strength of ships and deep-diving submarines; experimental stress analysis; thin shell structures; ocean engineering; marine affairs; technology assessment; science policy research; public administration; futures; decision theory; technology-intensive public policy; technology as social process; principles for social management of technology; technological literacy, techno-ethics; education reform; corporate culture. *Mailing Add:* Univ Wash 121 More Hall Box 352700 Seattle WA 98195

**WENK, EUGENE J,** HORMONE RECEPTORS, OCULAR TISSUE. *Current Pos:* From instr to asst prof, 72-79, assoc prof anat, 79-96, PROF CELL BIOL & ANAT, NY MED COL, 96- *Personal Data:* b New York, NY, Oct 21, 27; m 54, Elizabeth Gould; c Karen, Laura & Marsha (decreased). *Educ:* Columbia Univ, AB, 50, AM, 51; NY Med Col, PhD(anat), 72. *Mem:* NY Acad Sci; Am Asn Clin Anatomists. *Res:* Ultrastructure and function of ocular tissue. *Mailing Add:* Dept Cell Biol & Anat NY Med Col Valhalla NY 10595. *Fax:* 914-993-4653; *E-Mail:* wenk@nymc.edu

**WENK, HANS-RUDOLF,** TEXTURE ANALYSIS, ELECTRON MICROSCOPY. *Current Pos:* From asst prof to assoc prof geol, 67-73, PROF GEOL & GEOPHYS, UNIV CALIF, BERKELEY, 73- *Personal Data:* b Zurich, Switz, Oct 25, 41; m 70, Julia Wehausen. *Educ:* Univ Basel, BA, 63; Univ Zurich, PhD(crystallog), 65. *Honors & Awards:* Humboldt Sr US Scientist Award, 87; B Matthias Award, 92. *Concurrent Pos:* Affil, LANL-CMS, 84- *Mem:* Mineral Soc Am; Am Geophys Union. *Res:* Structural geology of metamorphic belts; texture analysis of deformed rocks, ceramics and metals; electron microscopy and x-ray diffraction of rockforming minerals. *Mailing Add:* Dept Geol & Geophys Univ Calif 497 McCone Hall Berkeley CA 94720. *Fax:* 510-643-9980; *E-Mail:* wenk@seismo.berkeley.edu

**WENK, MARTIN LESTER,** CELL BIOLOGY. *Current Pos:* PRIN INVESTR & HEAD DEPT, MICROBIOL ASSOCS, INC, BETHESDA, 85- *Educ:* Columbia Univ, PhD(cell biol), 71. *Res:* In vivo experimental carcinogenesis. *Mailing Add:* Div Mammalian Toxicol Microbiol Assoc Inc 9900 Blackwell Rd Rockville MD 20850. *Fax:* 301-654-6916

**WENKERT, ERNEST,** ORGANIC CHEMISTRY. *Current Pos:* PROF CHEM, UNIV CALIF, SAN DIEGO, 80- *Personal Data:* b Vienna, Austria, Oct 16, 25; nat US; m 48; c 4. *Educ:* Univ Wash, BS, 45, MS, 47; Harvard Univ, PhD(chem), 51. *Hon Degrees:* Dr, Univ Paris-Sud, 78. *Honors &*

*Awards:* Ernest Guenther Award, Am Chem Soc. *Prof Exp:* Instr chem, Lower Columbia Jr Col, 47-48; from asst prof to prof org chem, Iowa State Univ, 51-61; prof, Ind Univ, Bloomington, 61-69, Herman T Briscoe prof, 69-73; E D Butcher prof chem, Rice Univ, 73-80, chmn dept, 76-80. *Concurrent Pos:* Lectr & vis prof, var US & foreign orgn & acad insts, 51-; actg head dept org chem, Weizmann Inst, 64-65; Guggenheim fel, 65-66; mem NIH med chem B study sect, 71-72, chmn, 72-75; chmn, Gordon Conf Steroids & Other Natural Prod, 64 & 65; mem, NIH med chem B fel rev comn, 67-70; mem, Comt Direction, Inst Chem Substances Naturelles, France, 74-77; mem, Oak Ridge Nat Lab Chem Div Adv Comn, 75-; chief tech adv, UNESCO, 78. *Mem:* Am Chem Soc; Royal Soc Chem; corresp mem Acad Brazileira Ciencias; Swiss Chem Soc. *Mailing Add:* Chem Dept 0506 Univ Calif San Diego La Jolla CA 92093

**WENNBERG, JOHN E,** EPIDEMIOLOGY, PUBLIC POLICY. *Current Pos:* assoc prof, 79, PROF EPIDEMIOL, DEPT COMMUNITY & FAMILY MED, DARTMOUTH MED SCH, HANOVER, NH, 80-, DIR, CTR EVAL CLIN SCI, 89- *Personal Data:* b June 2, 34. *Educ:* Stanford Univ, BA, 56; McGill Med Sch, MD, 61; Johns Hopkins Univ, MPH, 66. *Prof Exp:* Intern med, DC Gen Hosp, 61-62; assoc med resident, Johns Hopkins Hosp, Baltimore, Md, 62-63, fel, Renal Dis & Pharmacol, 63-65; resident chronic dis, Baltimore City Hosp, Md, 66-67; dir, Northern New Eng Regional Med Prog, Burlington, Vt, 67-71; interim dir, Coop Health Info Ctr, Vt, 72-73; sr assoc, Harvard Ctr Community Health & Med Care, Harvard Med Sch, Boston, Mass, 73-75, asst prof, Dept Prev & Social Med, 73-78. *Concurrent Pos:* Asst prof, Dept Med, Univ Vt, Burlington, 67-72; mem, Comt Health Data Systs, Inst Med, 73-74, Comt Study Resources Clin Invest, 88-, Health Sci Policy Bd, 89-; mem, Coun Res & Develop, Am Hosp Asn, 73-75; mem, Ctr Analytical Health Pract, Harvard Sch Pub Health, 75-78; mem bd dirs, Am Med Rev Res Ctr, 85-, Collab Ctr Small Area Analysis, Univ Copenhagen, 86-88; mem, Physicians Adv Group, New York Health & Hosps Corp, 88-; Peggy Thomson Prof Eval Clin Sci, 94; Johns Hopkins Soc Scholars, 97. *Mem:* 051681ed-Nat Acad Sci. *Mailing Add:* Dartmouth Med 7251 Strasenburgh Hanover NH 03755-3863

**WENNER, ADRIAN MANLEY,** ZOOLOGY. *Current Pos:* from asst prof biol sci to assoc prof biol, 60-73, PROF NATURAL HIST, UNIV CALIF, SANTA BARBARA, 73- *Personal Data:* b Roseau, Minn, May 24, 28; m 57; c 2. *Educ:* Gustavus Adolphus Col, BS, 51; Chico State Col, MA, 55; Univ Mich, MS, 58, PhD(zool), 61. *Prof Exp:* Prin elem sch, Ore, 54-55; teacher high sch, Calif, 55-56; fel zool, Univ Mich, 56-60. *Concurrent Pos:* Consult, Teledyne, Inc, 62-64 & Autonetics Div, NAm Aviation, Inc, 64-65. *Mem:* AAAS; Am Soc Zoologists; Sigma Xi; Am Soc Naturalists; Crustacean Soc. *Res:* Problems of growth and egg production in marine crustaceans as they occur in nature; natural history of marine crustacea; animal communication. *Mailing Add:* Biol Sci Dept Natural Hist Univ Calif Santa Barbara CA 93106

**WENNER, BRUCE RICHARD,** TOPOLOGY. *Current Pos:* from asst prof to assoc prof, 68-76, PROF MATH, UNIV MO, KANSAS CITY, 76-, MATH DEPT CHMN, 92- *Personal Data:* b Lancaster, Pa, Apr 25, 38; m 65, Frances Clark; c Kathleen, Brian & Thomas. *Educ:* Col Wooster, BA, 60; Duke Univ, PhD(math), 64. *Prof Exp:* Asst prof math, Univ Vt, 64-68. *Concurrent Pos:* NASA res grant, 65-66. *Mem:* Am Math Soc; Math Asn Am. *Res:* Dimension theory with regard to topological dimension functions, especially metrizable spaces. *Mailing Add:* Dept Math Univ Mo Kansas City MO 64110

**WENNER, CHARLES EARL,** BIOCHEMISTRY. *Current Pos:* sr scientist, 56-61, assoc scientist, 61-65, ASSOC CHIEF SCIENTIST, DEPT EXP BIOL, ROSWELL PARK MEM INST; RES PROF BIOCHEM, GRAD SCH, STATE UNIV NY, BUFFALO, 70-, CHMN, DEPT BIOCHEM, ROSWELL PARK DIV, 80- *Personal Data:* b Lattimer, Pa, May 2, 24; m 48; c 4. *Educ:* Temple Univ, BA, PhD(chem), 53. *Prof Exp:* Res fel, Lankenau Hosp Res Inst & Inst Cancer Res, 50-54, res assoc, 54-55. *Concurrent Pos:* Runyon fel, Inst Cancer Res, 52-54; from asst prof to assoc prof biochem, Grad Sch, State Univ NY Buffalo, 58-70; Johnson Res Found vis res prof, Univ Pa, 65-66. *Mem:* Am Chem Soc; Am Asn Cancer Res; Biophys Soc; Fedn Am Soc Exp Biol. *Res:* Energy control mechanisms; transforming growth factors and signal transduction mechanisms; mechanism of action of cocarcinogens; membrane transport and cell proliferation. *Mailing Add:* Dept Biochem Roswell Park Cancer Inst Elm & Carlton Sts Buffalo NY 14263-0001. *Fax:* 716-845-3545; *E-Mail:* v20272xd@ubvms.bitnet

**WENNER, DAVID BRUCE,** GEOCHEMISTRY, GEOLOGY. *Current Pos:* Vis asst prof, 71, asst prof, 71-80, ASSOC PROF GEOL, UNIV GA, 80- *Personal Data:* b Flint, Mich, May 28, 41; m 68, 83, Helen Briggs; c Morgan & Evan. *Educ:* Univ Cincinnati, BS, 63; Calif Inst Technol, MS, 66, PhD(geochem), 71. *Mem:* Geol Soc Am; Am Geophys Union. *Res:* Stable isotope geochemistry with applications to petrology, hydrology and archaeology. *Mailing Add:* Dept Geol Univ Ga 210 Field Dr Athens GA 30602

**WENNER, HERBERT ALLAN,** MEDICINE. *Current Pos:* distinguished prof pediat, 69-81, clin prof, 70-88, EMER PROF, UNIV MO, KANSAS CITY, 88- *Personal Data:* b Drums, Pa, Nov 14, 12; m 42; c 4. *Educ:* Bucknell Univ, BSc, 33; Univ Rochester, MD, 39; Am Bd Microbiol, dipl, 62; Am Bd Pediat, 49. *Honors & Awards:* Presidential & Distinguished Serv Awards, Nat Found Infantile Paralysis; Cert Serv Award, Panel Picornaviruses, NIH. *Prof Exp:* Instr prev med, Sch Med, Yale Univ, 44-46; from asst prof to assoc prof pediat & bact, Univ Kans, 46-51, res prof pediat, 51-69. *Concurrent Pos:* Babbott fel, Sch Med, Yale Univ, 41-42; Nat Res Coun fel, Yale Univ & Johns Hopkins Univ, 43-44; NIH res career award,

62-69; assoc physician, Dept Internal Med, New Haven Hosp, Conn, 44-46; consult, Mo State Bd Health & Nat Commun Dis Ctr; mem, Echovirus Subcomt, Picornavirus Study Group, NIH; clin prof pediat, Univ Kans Med Ctr, Kansas City, 73- *Mem:* Fel AAAS; fel Am Acad Pediat; fel Am Pub Health Asn; Soc Pediat Res; Am Pediat Soc. *Res:* Etiology, pathogenesis and epidemiology of infectious diseases. *Mailing Add:* 9711 Johnson Ave Shawnee Mission KS 66203

**WENNERBERG, A(LLAN) L(ORENS),** ELECTRONICS ENGINEERING. *Current Pos:* res engr, Whirlpool Corp, 57-65, mgr electronics res, 65-67, dir electronics res, 67-69, DIR RES, WHIRLPOOL CORP, 69- *Personal Data:* b Chicago, Ill, Jan 20, 32; m 53; c 2. *Educ:* Ind Inst Technol, BSEE, 56; Univ Notre Dame, MSEE, 61. *Prof Exp:* Res engr, Sylvania Microwave Res Lab, 56-57. *Mem:* Inst Elec & Electronics Engrs; Sci Res Soc Am; Sigma Xi. *Res:* Precision control systems involving digital techniques implemented with microcircuitry. *Mailing Add:* 2804 Sunnydale Ave St Joseph MI 49085-2426

**WENNERSTROM, ARTHUR J(OHN),** AXIAL COMPRESSORS, TURBO MACHINERY. *Current Pos:* RETIRED. *Personal Data:* b New York, NY, Jan 11, 35; m 90, Vicki L Merrick. *Educ:* Duke Univ, BS, 56; Mass Inst Technol, MS, 58; Swiss Fed Inst Technol, DScTech(compressor aerodyn), 65. *Honors & Awards:* Airbreathing Propulsion Award, Am Inst Aeronaut & Astronaut, 79; Cliff Garrett Turbomachinery Award, Soc Automotive Engrs, 86; R Tom Sawyer Award, Am Soc Mech Engrs, 93. *Prof Exp:* Sr engr, Aircraft Armaments, Inc, 58-59; res engr, Sulzer Bros, Ltd, Switz, 60-62; proj engr, Northern Res & Eng Corp, 65-67; group leader, Air Force Aerospace Res Labs, 67-75, chief compressor res, Aerospace Propulsion Lab, 75-91; dir, Adv Group Aerospace Res & Develop, NATO, 91-94. *Concurrent Pos:* US coordr, Propulsion & Energetics Panel, Adv Group Aerospace Res & Develop, NATO, 77-85; chmn, Gas Turbine Div, Am Soc Mech Engrs, 80-81; consult UNESCO, Nat Aeronaut Lab, India, 81; ed, Am Soc Mech Engrs J Eng Gas Turbines & Power, 83-88, Am Soc Mech Engrs J Turbomachinery, 86-88; consult, 94-; hon prof, Beijing Univ Aeronaut & Astronaut, 94, Inst Eng Thermophys, Chinese Acad Sci, 94. *Mem:* Fel Am Soc Mech Engrs; fel Am Inst Aeronaut & Astronaut. *Res:* Gas turbines; aerodynamics of transonic and supersonic axial compressors; experimental aerodynamics; aerodynamic instrumentation and measurement techniques. *Mailing Add:* 5 Sosegado Lane Hot Springs Village AZ 71909-7744. *Fax:* 501-922-4221; *E-Mail:* wennco@ipa.net

**WENNERSTROM, DAVID E,** MICROBIAL PHYSIOLOGY, MICROBIAL PATHOGENESIS. *Current Pos:* ASST PROF MICROBIAL PHYSIOL, DEPT MICROBIOL & IMMUNOL, UNIV ARK MED SCI, 76- *Personal Data:* b Glendale, Calif, June 19, 45; m 73; c 2. *Educ:* Univ Ark, BS, 68, MS, 70; Univ Tenn, PhD(microbiol), 73. *Prof Exp:* Fel lipid biochem, Hormel Inst, Univ Minn, 73-76. *Concurrent Pos:* Prin invest, Inst Allergy & Infectious Dis, NIH, Univ Ark Med Sci, 80-83. *Mem:* Am Soc Microbiol; AAAS; Sigma Xi. *Res:* Pathogenesis of group B streptococci in lung tissue is studied using mice which have been shown to be an appropriate model of early-onset group B streptococcal disease of the human newborn. *Mailing Add:* Dept Microbiol & Immunol Univ Ark Med Sci 4301 W Markham Little Rock AR 72205-7101

**WENNOGLE, LAWRENCE,** MOLECULAR BIOLOGY, BIOCHEMISTRY. *Personal Data:* b Cambridge, Mass, Dec 15, 49. *Educ:* Ithaca Col, BA, 71; Univ Colo, MS, 74, PhD(biochem), 77. *Prof Exp:* Fel biochem, Univ Colo, 77-80; researcher biochem, Lotterly Labs, 80-83. *Mem:* NY Acad Sci; Am Soc Biochem & Molecular Biol; AAAS. *Res:* Molecular biology; biochemistry. *Mailing Add:* Ciba-Geigy Corp 556 Morris Ave Summit NJ 07901-1398

**WENRICH, KAREN JANE,** GEOLOGY, ECONOMIC GEOLOGY. *Current Pos:* GEOLOGIST, US GEOL SURV, 74- *Personal Data:* b Lebanon, Pa, Apr 9, 47; m 69, 83, Miles L Silberman. *Educ:* Pa State Univ, BS, 69, MS, 71, PhD(geol), 75. *Prof Exp:* Geologist, Molybdenum Corp Am, 69; instr geol, Bucknell Univ, 73-74. *Concurrent Pos:* US Geol Surv adv, Energy Res & Develop Admin Nat Uranium Resource Eval Prog, 75-78. *Mem:* Geol Soc Am; Sigma Xi; Am Geophys Union; Asn Explor Geochemists; Friends Mineral (vpres, 92-93, pres, 94-). *Res:* Uranium exploration, specifically the use of uranium in water, stream sediments, soils and modern decaying plant materials as a tool for exploration; trace element geochemistry in volcanic rocks; mineralization breccia pipes; ore deposition in karst environments; author of 140 professional publications. *Mailing Add:* 635 Devinney St Golden CO 80401

**WENSCH, GLEN W(ILLIAM),** PHYSICAL METALLURGY. *Current Pos:* RETIRED. *Personal Data:* b Chicago, Ill, Nov 15, 17; m 42; c 2. *Educ:* Univ Ill, BS, 46, MS, 47, PhD(metall eng), 49. *Prof Exp:* Staff metall engr, Los Alamos Sci Lab, 49-51; sr res metallurgist, Fansteel Metall Co, 51-52; chief reactor mat br, Savannah River Proj, US AEC, 52-54; sr metall engr, Vitro Corp, 54-55; chief, Liquid Metals Projs Br, US AEC, 55-70, dir reactor develop, 70-76, exec asst to asst adminr, Energy Res & Develop Admin, 76-78; consult engr, 78-85. *Concurrent Pos:* Chief, Fast Reactor Team, Europe, 55, 57, 59, 60 & 63; pres, Int Plutonium Conf, France, 60; mem & leader, Power Reactor Deleg, USSR, 64 & 70; US mem, Int Working Group Fast Reactors, Int Atomic Energy Agency; pres, Glen W Wensch Corp; consult, Argonne Nat Lab, Dept Energy, 89- *Mem:* AAAS; fel Am Soc Metals; Am Nuclear Soc; fel NY Acad Sci; fel Am Inst Chemists. *Res:* Plutonium; sodium components and technology; fast breeder reactors. *Mailing Add:* 413 S Rising Rd Champaign IL 61821-9708

**WENT, HANS ADRIAAN,** PHYSIOLOGY. *Current Pos:* From instr to asst prof, 59-69, ASSOC PROF ZOOL, WASH STATE UNIV, 69- *Personal Data:* b Bogor, Indonesia, Dec 3, 29; nat US; m 51; c 2. *Educ:* Univ Calif, AB, 51, MA, 53, PhD(zool), 58. *Mem:* Am Soc Zool; Sigma Xi. *Res:* Cell division, especially molecular origin of mitotic apparatus; cell physiology. *Mailing Add:* 1915 NE Valley Rd Pullman WA 99163-4220

**WENTE, HENRY CHRISTIAN,** MATHEMATICS. *Current Pos:* from asst prof to prof, 71-89, DISTINGUISHED PROF MATH, UNIV TOLEDO, 89- *Personal Data:* b New York, NY, Aug 18, 36. *Educ:* Harvard Univ, BA, 58, MA, 59, PhD(math), 66. *Prof Exp:* From instr to asst prof, Tufts Univ, 63-70, lectr, 70-71. *Mem:* AAAS; Am Math Soc; Sigma Xi. *Res:* Existence theorems in the calculus of variations, especially those arising from two-dimensional parametric surfaces immersed in Euclidean space; surfaces minimizing area subject to a volume constraint; integrable solutions for constant mean curvature surfaces; mathematics of soap films and liquid drops. *Mailing Add:* Dept Math Univ Toledo 2801 W Bancroft St Toledo OH 43606. *E-Mail:* hwente@math.utoledo.edu

**WENTLAND, MARK PHILIP,** MEDICINAL CHEMISTRY, ORGANIC CHEMISTRY. *Current Pos:* adj prof, 71-94, PROF CHEM, RENSSELAER POLYTECH INST, 94- *Personal Data:* b New Britain, Conn, Jan 22, 45; m 70, Clara Kennedy; c Rebecca & Matthew. *Educ:* Cent Conn State Univ, BS, 66; Rice Univ, PhD(chem), 70. *Prof Exp:* Res investr, Sterling Winthrop Inc, 70-81, sr res investr, 81-84, prin res investr, 84-87, res leader, 87-89, asst res dir, 89-94, Sterling Winthrop fel, 94. *Concurrent Pos:* Adj prof, Albany Med Col, 97- *Mem:* Am Chem Soc; Sigma Xi; Am Asn Cancer Res. *Res:* The design and synthesis of potentially useful medicinal agents. *Mailing Add:* Dept Chem Rensselaer Polytech Inst Troy NY 12180. *E-Mail:* wentmp@rpi.edu

**WENTLAND, STEPHEN HENRY,** BIOCHEMISTRY, ORGANIC CHEMISTRY. *Current Pos:* PROF CHEM, HOUSTON BAPTIST UNIV, 77-, CHMN DEPT, 83- *Personal Data:* b New Britain, Conn, May 1, 40; m 65; c 2. *Educ:* Rensselaer Polytech Inst, BS, 62; Yale Univ, MS, 64, PhD(chem), 68. *Prof Exp:* NIH fel chem, Ind Univ, Bloomington, 68-70; sr org chemist, Smith Kline & French, Inc, 70-72; res assoc biochemist, Univ Colo Med Ctr, Denver, 72-74, instr med, 74-77. *Concurrent Pos:* Dir, Great er Houston Sect, Am Chem Soc, 95- *Mem:* Am Chem Soc. *Res:* Molecular modeling of biochemical and organic chemical systems; writing computer programs and texts for organic chemistry and biochemistry technical report writing. *Mailing Add:* Dept Chem Houston Baptist Univ Houston TX 77074-3204. *Fax:* 281-649-3489; *E-Mail:* wentsh@hbu.edu

**WENTORF, ROBERT H, JR,** CHEMICAL ENGINEERING. *Current Pos:* DISTINGUISHED RES PROF, DEPT CHEM ENG, RPI, TROY, NY, 88- *Personal Data:* b Wis, May 28, 26; m 93, Frances C Gillespie; c 3. *Educ:* Univ Wis, BSChE, 48, PhD(chem), 52. *Hon Degrees:* DSc, Univ Wis, 81. *Honors & Awards:* Ipatieff Prize, 65; New Mat Prize, Am Phys Soc, 77; E M Merchant Medal, Am Soc Mech Engrs, 93. *Prof Exp:* Asst chem, Univ Wis, 46; res assoc chem, Corp Res & Develop Ctr, Gen Elec Co, 52-88. *Concurrent Pos:* Brittingham vis prof, Univ Wis, 66-67. *Mem:* Nat Acad Eng; Am Chem Soc; Sigma Xi; Am Inst Chem Engrs. *Res:* High pressure chemistry and physics, diamond synthesis, cubic BN, energy systems, solar energy utilization and semiconductor processing. *Mailing Add:* RR 3 Box 154A Greenwich NY 12834-9803

**WENTWORTH, BERNARD C,** AVIAN PHYSIOLOGY. *Current Pos:* assoc prof, 69-73, PROF POULTRY SCI, UNIV WIS-MADISON, 73- *Personal Data:* b Freedom, Maine, Feb 16, 35; m 60; c 4. *Educ:* Univ Maine, Orono, BS, 57; Univ Mass, MS, 60, PhD(avian physiol), 63. *Prof Exp:* Physiologist, US Dept Interior, 63-69. *Mem:* AAAS; Poultry Sci Asn; Soc Study Reproduction; Endocrine Soc. *Res:* Basic physiology of birds and comparative endocrinology of animals as related to applied benefits to biomedicine and agriculture; primodial germ cell differentiation. *Mailing Add:* Dept Poultry Sci 260 Animal Sci Bldg Univ Wis 1675 Observatory Dr Madison WI 53706-1205

**WENTWORTH, CARL M, JR,** TECTONICS, ENVIRONMENTAL GEOLOGY. *Current Pos:* GEOLOGIST, US GEOL SURV, 63- *Personal Data:* b New York, NY, Feb 8, 36; m 68; c 2. *Educ:* Dartmouth Col, AB, 58; Stanford Univ, MS, 60, PhD(geol), 67. *Mem:* Geol Soc Am; AAAS. *Res:* Neotectonics; major geologic hazards of United States; active faults and movement histories; landslides and slope stability; engineering character of geologic materials; geology of California Coast Ranges. *Mailing Add:* 280 Dedaiera Dr Portola Valley CA 94028

**WENTWORTH, GARY,** ESTER & POLYESTER CHEMISTRY, STRUCTURE-PROPERTY RELATIONSHIPS. *Current Pos:* TECH DIR, C P HALL CO, 94- *Personal Data:* b Orange, Mass, Aug 3, 39. *Educ:* Rensselaer Polytech Inst, BS, 61; Ga Inst Technol, PhD(org chem), 66. *Prof Exp:* Res chemist, Union Carbide Corp, 66-68; sr res chemist, Monsanto Develop Ctr, 68-73, res specialist, 73-76, res group leader, Mosanto Polymers & Resins Co, 76-82; dir polymer technol, Sherwin-Williams Co, 82-86, dir res, 86-94. *Concurrent Pos:* Adj prof polymer sci, Roosevelt Univ, 89- *Mem:* Am Chem Soc; Am Soc Testing & Mat. *Res:* Ester and polyester chemistry: products, processes, analytical and quality control methods; mechanisms of plasticizer action in elastomers and thermoplastics; design of oligomers for high solids coatings. *Mailing Add:* C P Hall Co 5851 W 73rd St Bedford Park IL 60499

**WENTWORTH, RUPERT A D,** INORGANIC CHEMISTRY. *Current Pos:* from asst prof to assoc prof, 65-74, PROF CHEM, COL ARTS & SCI, GRAD SCH, IND UNIV, BLOOMINGTON, 74- *Personal Data:* b Hattiesburg, Miss, Nov 5, 34; m 56, 72; c 3. *Educ:* Fordham Univ, BS, 55; Mich State Univ, PhD(inorg chem), 63. *Prof Exp:* Fel with Prof T S Piper, Univ Ill, 63-65. *Mem:* Am Chem Soc. *Res:* The chemistry of simple molybdenum complexes with substrates for molybdoenzymes. *Mailing Add:* 4450 N Benton Ct Bloomington IN 47408

**WENTWORTH, STANLEY EARL,** ORGANIC POLYMER CHEMISTRY, ADHESION SCIENCE. *Current Pos:* RETIRED. *Personal Data:* b Natick, Mass, July 13, 40; m 67, Blanche Oczkowski; c Thomas & David. *Educ:* Northeastern Univ, BS, 63, PhD(org chem), 67. *Prof Exp:* Res chemist, Army Natick Labs, 67-68 & Emerging Mat Div, Army Mat Tech Lab, 70-95. *Concurrent Pos:* Army liaison rep on several nat mat adv bd study comts; consult. *Mem:* Adhesion Soc. *Res:* Organic synthesis in the areas of organofluorine compounds, diazoalkanes and monomers for high temperature resins; thermal analysis of organic materials; synthesis of polyphenylquinoxalines and polyurethanes; studies of adhesives and adhesive bonding; synthesis of semiconductive polymers; composite materials technology; studies in adhesion science. *Mailing Add:* 270 Concord Rd Bedford MA 01730. *Fax:* 617-923-5046

**WENTWORTH, THOMAS RALPH,** PLANT ECOLOGY. *Current Pos:* From asst prof to assoc prof, 76-89, PROF BOT, NC STATE UNIV, 89- *Personal Data:* b Boston, Mass, Sept 4, 48; m 92, Linda E Rudd. *Educ:* Dartmouth Col, AB, 70; Cornell Univ, PhD(plant ecol), 76. *Mem:* Ecol Soc Am; Brit Ecol Soc; Sigma Xi; Torrey Bot Club; Int Asn Veg Sci. *Res:* Plant community ecology. *Mailing Add:* Dept Bot Box 7612 NC State Univ Raleigh NC 27695-7612. *Fax:* 919-515-3436; *E-Mail:* tom___wentworth@ncsu.edu

**WENTWORTH, WAYNE,** ANALYTICAL CHEMISTRY, PHYSICAL CHEMISTRY. *Current Pos:* from asst prof to assoc prof, 59-68, PROF CHEM, UNIV HOUSTON, 68- *Personal Data:* b Rochester, Minn, May 29, 30; m 54; c 4. *Educ:* St Olaf Col, BA, 52; Fla State Univ, PhD(chem), 57. *Prof Exp:* Res mathematician, Radio Corp Am, 56-59. *Mem:* Am Chem Soc. *Res:* Electron attachment to molecules; molecular complexes; molecular spectroscopy; chromatographic detector development. *Mailing Add:* Dept Chem Univ Houston Cullen Blvd Houston TX 77004

**WENTZ, WILLIAM BUDD,** OBSTETRICS & GYNECOLOGY, ONCOLOGY. *Current Pos:* assoc prof obstet & gynec, 66-71, PROF REPRODUCTIVE BIOL, SCH MED, CASE WESTERN RESERVE UNIV, 71- *Personal Data:* b Philadelphia, Pa, Aug 9, 24; m 45; c 3. *Educ:* Univ Pa, BA, 51, MA, 53; Western Reserve Univ, MD, 58; Am Bd Obstet & Gynec, dipl, 66. *Prof Exp:* Prin investr physiol, US Naval Aviation Med Acceleration Lab, 53-54; intern med, Lankenau Hosp, Philadelphia, Pa, 48-49, prin investr gynec & oncol, 59-63; asst prof obstet & gynec, Hahnemann Med Col, 63-66. *Concurrent Pos:* Am Cancer Soc grants, Lankenau Hosp, Philadelphia, 59-63; Nat Cancer Inst grants, 64- *Mem:* Am Col Obstet & Gynec; Soc Gynec Oncol; Am Soc Cytol. *Res:* Experimental gynecological pathology; carcinogenesis; cancer research treatment of malignant and premalignant disease. *Mailing Add:* Dept Reproductive Biol Case Western Reserve Univ 10900 Euclid Ave Cleveland OH 44106

**WENTZ, WILLIAM HENRY, (JR),** AERONAUTICAL ENGINEERING, MECHANICAL ENGINEERING. *Current Pos:* from asst prof to prof aeronaut eng, 63-83, DISTINGUISHED PROF, WICHITA STATE UNIV, 83-, EXEC DIR, INST AVIATION RES, 88- *Personal Data:* b Wichita, Kans, Dec 18, 33; m 55; c 2. *Educ:* Univ Wichita, BS, 55, MS, 61; Univ Kans, PhD(eng mech), 69. *Honors & Awards:* Teetor Award, Soc Automotive Engrs, 73; Gen Aviation Award, Am Inst Aeronaut & Astronaut, 81. *Prof Exp:* Instr mech eng, Univ Wichita, 57-58; res engr, Boeing Co, 58-63. *Concurrent Pos:* NSF sci fac fel, 67-68; prin investr NASA res grants, Wichita State Univ, 70- *Mem:* Assoc fel Am Inst Aeronaut & Astronaut; Am Soc Eng Educ; Soc Automotive Engrs. *Res:* Aerodynamics of wings and bodies; low speed delta wing vortex flows; trailing vortices and wake turbulence; computer analysis of airfoil sections; airfoil, flap and control surface design; separated flows; wind tunnel testing techniques and instrumentation; wind turbine blade and control system design. *Mailing Add:* 2263 N Bluff St Wichita KS 67220

**WENTZEL, DONAT GOTTHARD,** ASTROPHYSICS. *Current Pos:* from assoc prof to prof, 67-94, EMER PROF ASTRON, UNIV MD, COLLEGE PARK, 94- *Personal Data:* b Zurich, Switz, June 25, 34; US citizen; m 59; c 1. *Educ:* Univ Chicago, BA, 54, BS, 55, MS, 56, PhD(physics), 60. *Prof Exp:* From instr to assoc prof astron, Univ Mich, 60-66. *Concurrent Pos:* Alfred P Sloan res fel, 62-66; vis lectr, Princeton Univ, 64; vis prof, Tata Inst Fundamental Res, Bombay, 73; acad guest, Fed Inst Technol, Zurich, 78; President Comn on Teaching Astron, Int Astron Union, 79-82; prog dir, NSF, 86-88; secy, Int Astron Union, Schs Young Astronomers, 91- *Mem:* Fel AAAS; Am Astron Soc; Int Astron Union; Sigma Xi. *Res:* Effects of magnetic fields on fluid dynamics and charged particles on the sun and in interplanetary and interstellar space; astronomy education. *Mailing Add:* 5800 Nicholson Lane Apt L03 Rockville MD 20852-2962

**WENTZELL, PETER DALE,** CHEMOMETRICS. *Current Pos:* ASST PROF CHEM, DALHOUSIE UNIV, 89- *Personal Data:* b Moncton, NB, Mar 3, 60. *Educ:* Dalhousie Univ, BSc, 82, Mich State Univ, PhD(analytical chem), 87. *Honors & Awards:* Tomas Hirschfeld Award, Fedn Analytical Chem & Spectros Soc, 87. *Prof Exp:* Res assoc, Univ BC, 88-89. *Mem:* Can Soc Chem;

Am Chem Soc. *Res:* Statistics as applied to the extraction of information from chemical measurements and includes optimization, signal processing, pattern recognition and calibration. *Mailing Add:* Dept Chem Dalhousie Univ Halifax NS B3H 4J3 Can. *Fax:* 902-494-1310; *E-Mail:* wentzell@ac.dal.ca

**WENZEL, ALEXANDER B,** MECHANICAL ENGINEERING, ENGINEERING PHYSICS. *Current Pos:* sr engr ballistics & explosives, SW Res Inst, 68-71, group leader, 71-73, mgr, 73-77, dir ballistics & explosives, 77-81, dir, Dept Energetic Systs, 81-88, DIR, DEPT FIRE TECHNOL, SW RES INST, 88- *Personal Data:* b Mexico City, Mex, Aug 12, 36; US citizen; m 60, Consuelo; c 3. *Educ:* NMex Mil Inst, BS, 56; NMex State Univ, MS, 59; St Mary's Univ, MBA, 72. *Prof Exp:* Instr physics & math, NMex State Univ, 56-57; Univ Md, 57-60 & Univ Del, 60-62; head terminal ballistics, Lab Ballistics & Explosives, Gen Motors Defense Labs, 62-66; mgr mat dynamics, Lab Ballistics & Shock Physics, Cleveland Army Tank-Auto Comn, 66-68. *Concurrent Pos:* Sci adv, Phys Sci Lab, NMex, 56-57; Capt, US Army Ballistics Res Labs, 59, 62; mem Int Conf Building Off; consult, NATO. *Mem:* Am Defense Preparedness Asn; Instrument Soc Am; Am Inst Aeronaut & Astronaut; Nat Fire Protect Asn; Am Soc Testing & Mat; Am Soc Mech Engrs; Am Soc Chem Engrs. *Res:* Explosive and ballistic technology; impulsive loading of structures; vulnerability and survivability analyses; hazards and safety analysis; response of materials to high strains and pressures; weapons effects; penetration mechanics; shaped charge technology; fire dynamics, materials and structure response to fires; combustion and explosion phenomena; combustion toxicology; director and manager of various technical departments and laboratories. *Mailing Add:* 3211 Hitching Post San Antonio TX 78217. *Fax:* 210-522-3377

**WENZEL, BERNICE MARTHA,** NEUROBEHAVIOR, AVIAN OLFACTION. *Current Pos:* from asst prof to assoc prof physiol, Univ Calif, Los Angeles, 59-69, vchmn dept, 71-73, prof physiol, 69-89, prof psychiat, 71-89, asst dean, 74-89, EMER PROF, SCH MED, UNIV CALIF, LOS ANGELES, 89- *Personal Data:* b Bridgeport, Conn, June 22, 21; m 52, Wendell E Jeffrey. *Educ:* Beaver Col, AB, 42; Columbia Univ, AM, 43, PhD(psychol), 48. *Prof Exp:* Instr psychol, Newcomb Col, Tulane Univ, 45-46; from instr to asst prof, Barnard Col, Columbia Univ, 46-55. *Concurrent Pos:* Fel, Ment Health Training Prog, Sch Med, Univ Calif, Los Angeles, 57-59. *Mem:* Am Physiol Soc; Int Brain Res Orgn; Soc Neurosci; fel Am Psychol Asn; Asn Chemoreception Sci. *Res:* Behavioral physiology; olfaction; ethology and evolution of chemoreception, especially olfaction in birds. *Mailing Add:* 3334 Scadlock Lane Sherman Oaks CA 91403. *E-Mail:* bwenzel@ucla.edu

**WENZEL, BRUCE ERICKSON,** PHYSICAL & ANALYTICAL CHEMISTRY, ENVIRONMENTAL SCIENCES. *Current Pos:* SR ANALYTICAL CHEMIST, CHEM WASTE MGT, 89- *Personal Data:* b New Orleans, La, Jan 14, 38; m 64; c 3. *Educ:* Tulane Univ, BS, 59; Mich State Univ, PhD(chem), 69. *Prof Exp:* Instrument analyst chem, Univ Mich, 61-63; proj chemist, Stand Oil Co, 68-70, analytical chemist, 70-76; group leader anal, Ashland Petrol Co, 76-80; Lago Oil & Transp, 80-82; sr chemist, Henkel Corp, 83-86; chem lab mgr, Minn Dept Health, 86-87; environ group leader, Fed Cartridge Co, 88-89. *Concurrent Pos:* Indust adv comt, dept chem, Marshall Univ, 77-80; adv comt, Mat Anal Dept, Inst Mining & Minerals Res, Ky Ctr Energy Res, 78-80. *Mem:* Sigma Xi; Am Chem Soc. *Res:* Sulfur specific detectors in gas chromatography; gas chromatographic analysis of petroleum, shale oil and coal liquifaction products; general analysis of petroleum, shale oil and coal liquifaction fractions; environmental analysis; hazardous waste remediation; quality assurance; quality control laboratory; analysis of hazardous waste. *Mailing Add:* 7250 W College Dr Palos Heights IL 60463

**WENZEL, FREDERICK J,** BIOCHEMISTRY, BIOLOGY. *Current Pos:* dir labs, Marshfield Clin, 53-65, secy found, 58-64, exec dir, Marshfield Med Found, 65-76, EXEC DIR, MARSHFIELD CLIN, 76- *Personal Data:* b Marshfield, Wis, Aug 5, 30; m 52; c 6. *Educ:* Univ Wis-Stevens Point, BS, 56; Univ Chicago, MBA, 79. *Prof Exp:* Res asst, St Joseph's Hosp, Marshfield, 50-53. *Mem:* Am Pub Health Asn; NY Acad Sci; Am Fedn Clin Res. *Res:* Hypersensitivity phenomenon in the lung, such as farmer's lung and maple bark disease; health services; natural history of pulmonary thromboembolism, especially diagnosis and treatment and studies of the fibrinolytic process in this disease. *Mailing Add:* 4521 Winnequah Rd Monona WI 53716

**WENZEL, HARRY G, JR,** CIVIL ENGINEERING. *Current Pos:* from asst prof to assoc prof, 64-84, PROF CIVIL ENG & ASST DEAN, UNIV ILL, URBANA, 84- *Personal Data:* b Pittsburgh, Pa, Sept 4, 37; m 63; c 1. *Educ:* Carnegie Inst Technol, BS, 59, MS, 61, PhD(civil eng), 64. *Honors & Awards:* Walter L Huber Res Prize, Am Soc Civil Engrs, 77. *Prof Exp:* Instr civil eng, Carnegie Inst Technol, 62-64. *Mem:* Am Soc Civil Engrs; Am Geophys Union; Am Soc Eng Educ. *Res:* Hydrology; hydraulic engineering; urban water resources. *Mailing Add:* 803 E Buckthorn Circle Mahomet IL 61853

**WENZEL, JAMES GOTTLIEB,** OCEAN ENGINEERING, OCEAN MINING & THERMOENERGY. *Current Pos:* PRES & CHMN, MARINE DEVELOP ASSOCS, INC, 84- *Personal Data:* b Springfield, Minn, Oct 16, 26; m 50; c 4. *Educ:* Univ Minn, BAeroEng, 48, MS, 50. *Hon Degrees:* PhD, Calif Lutheran Col, 85. *Prof Exp:* Aerodyn engr, Convair, San Diego, 48-55, proj mgr anti-submarine warfare & ocean systs, 56-57, asst to vpres eng, 58-59; asst to sr vpres eng, Gen Dynamics, San Diego, 59-61; mgr govt planning, USN, 61-62; mgr cruise missiles systs, Lockheed Missles & Space Craft Co, Inc, 62-63, mgr ocean systs, 63-70, asst gen mgr, Res & Develop Div & dir ocean systs, 70-72, vpres ocean systs, 72-84. *Concurrent Pos:* Instr, Univ Minn, 49-50; lectr eng, Univ Calif, Los Angeles, 50-57, lectr ocean syst develop planning, 66, lectr deep submergence systs develop, 68; vpres, Lockheed Petrol Systs Ltd, Vancouver, BC, 70-75; pres & chmn, Maine Develop Asn Inc, 84, pres, Maine Develop Asn, Sci & Tech Inc, 85; chmn, Ore Resource Expos, 86- *Mem:* Nat Acad Eng; fel & assoc mem Am Inst Aeronaut & Astronaut; assoc mem Royal Aeronaut Soc; Soc Naval Architects & Marine Engrs; Marine Tech Soc. *Res:* Pioneer in development of Deep Quest research submarine system, 8,000 feet, deep submergence rescue system, 5,000 feet, deep submergence search vehicle, 20,000 feet, offshore petroleum system and deep ocean mining system. *Mailing Add:* PO Box 3409 Saratoga CA 95070. *Fax:* 408-741-1506; *E-Mail:* jgwenmda001@aol.com

**WENZEL, JOHN THOMPSON,** PLASTICS RECYCLING. *Current Pos:* PROF CERAMICS ENG, RUTGERS UNIV, 87-, DIR, CTR PLASTICS RECYCLING RES, 89- *Personal Data:* b Philadelphia, Pa, June 23, 46; m 71; c 2. *Educ:* Stanford Univ, BS, 67; Univ Chicago, MS, 70, PhD(chem), 75. *Honors & Awards:* IR-100 Award, Indust Res Inst, 79. *Prof Exp:* Chemist, Nat Bur Standards, 76-81; engr, St Gobain Res, 81-83; dir res, Co St Gobain, 83-87. *Concurrent Pos:* Vis scientist, Danish AEC, 71-74; SRC res fel physics, Univ Kent & AERE Harwell, UK, 74-76; sci coun, Centre Nat Res Sci, 85-87; course dir glass technol, Ctr Prof Advan, 89- *Mem:* Am Chem Soc; Am Phys Soc; Fel Am Ceramic Soc; Inst Elec & Electronics Engrs. *Res:* Technical, economic and social aspects of plastics recycling, including collection schemes, sorting systems, resin recovery, plastics reprocessing and end-use market studies. *Mailing Add:* Dept Ceramics Rutgers Univ PO Box 909 Piscataway NJ 08855. *Fax:* 732-932-3258

**WENZEL, LEONARD A(NDREW),** CHEMICAL ENGINEERING. *Current Pos:* from asst prof to assoc prof, 51-61, chmn dept, 62-84, PROF CHEM ENG, LEHIGH UNIV, 61-; CHIEF SCI, ARENCIBIA TECH, 87- *Personal Data:* b Palo Alto, Calif, Jan 21, 23; m 44; c 4. *Educ:* Pa State Col, BS, 43; Univ Mich, MS, 48, PhD(chem eng), 49. *Honors & Awards:* Hillman Award, Lehigh Univ, 84, Stabler Award, 87. *Prof Exp:* Develop engr, Colgate-Palmolive-Peet Co, 49-51. *Concurrent Pos:* Mem exec comt, Cryogenic Eng Conf, 64-67; lectr, Univ Ala, Huntsville, 64- & Esso Res & Eng Co, 65-66; expert chem eng & proj coord, Proj COL-5, UNESCO, Bucaramanga, Colombia, 69-70; consult, Air Prod & Chem, Pearsall Chem Co & United Aircraft Corp; vis sr engr, Exxon Chem Co, 84-85. *Mem:* Am Chem Soc; Am Inst Chem Engrs; Am Soc Eng Educ. *Res:* Low temperature processing; heat transfer; thermodynamics; fluidization. *Mailing Add:* Dept Chem Eng Lehigh Univ Bethlehem PA 18105

**WENZEL, RICHARD LOUIS,** PUBLIC HEALTH ADMINISTRATION, PREVENTIVE MEDICINE. *Current Pos:* HEALTH COMNR, TOLEDO & LUCAS COUNTY HEALTH DEPTS, 70- *Personal Data:* b Marietta, Ohio, Sept 4, 21; wid; c 3. *Educ:* Marietta Col, AB, 43; Ohio State Univ, MD, 46; Univ Mich, MPH, 47; Am Bd Prev Med, cert pub health, 63. *Prof Exp:* Intern, Jersey City Med Ctr, 46-47; resident obstet & gynec, St Ann's Maternity Hosp, Columbus, Ohio, 47; chief commun dis & dep health off, Columbus Dept Health, 53-58; health officer, Marietta & Washington County, 58-60; assoc prof pub health admin, Sch Pub Health, Univ Mich, Ann Arbor, 60-70. *Concurrent Pos:* Asst prof, Col Med, Ohio State Univ, 54-57; consult, Div Health Mobilization, USPHS, 61-72, Div Indian Health, 64-67 & Bur Med Serv, 66-67; mem, Emergency Health Preparedness Adv Comt, 67-72; consult, Nat Comn Community Health Serv, 64-66; assoc clin prof, Dept Med, Med Col Ohio, 72-; adj prof pub health admin, Sch Pub Health, Univ Mich, Ann Arbor, 70-73; mem, courtesy med staff, Toledo Hosp, 83- *Mem:* Fel Am Pub Health Asn; fel Am Col Prev Med; US Conf City Health Offs. *Res:* Survey, assessment, and evaluation of community health services. *Mailing Add:* Toledo Health Dept 635 N Erie St Toledo OH 43624-1317

**WENZEL, ROBERT GALE,** PHYSICS, OPTICS. *Current Pos:* RETIRED. *Personal Data:* b Terra Bella, Calif, June 23, 32; m 73; c 2. *Educ:* Univ Calif, Berkeley, BA, 59; Univ NMex, MS, 66, PhD(physics), 79. *Prof Exp:* Staff mem physics, Los Alamos Nat Lab, 59-92. *Concurrent Pos:* Int Atomic Energy Agency vis scientist, Inst Atomic Energy, Sao Paulo, Brazil, 66-67; sr vis fel, UK Sci Res Coun, Heviot-Watt Univ, 81. *Mem:* Optical Soc Am. *Res:* Tunable lasers, nonlinear optics and picosecond optical devices. *Mailing Add:* Rte 22 Box 33W Santa Fe NM 87505

**WENZEL, RUPERT LEON,** ZOOLOGY. *Current Pos:* asst cur, Field Mus Natural Hist, 40-50, cur, 51-80, chmn, Dept Zool, 70-77, EMER CUR INSECTS, FIELD MUS NATURAL HIST, 81- *Personal Data:* b Owen, Wis, Oct 16, 15; m 40; c Judith (Andersen), Rupert Jr & Stephen. *Educ:* Cent YMCA Col, AB, 38, Univ Chicago, PhD(zool), 62. *Honors & Awards:* Order of Vasco Nunez de Balboa, Panama, 67. *Prof Exp:* Asst zool, Cent YMCA Col, 36-38; res asst, Univ Chicago, 37-40. *Concurrent Pos:* Lectr, Roosevelt Col, 46-47 & Univ Chicago, 62-80; res assoc biol, Northwestern Univ, 59-80, vis prof, 63. *Mem:* Entom Soc Am; Soc Study Evolution; Coleopterists Soc. *Res:* Taxonomy of streblid and nycteribiid batflies and histerid beetles; zoogeography; evolution of ectoparasites of terrestrial vertebrates. *Mailing Add:* 1025 Randolph St No 314 Oak Park IL 60302

**WENZEL, WILLIAM ALFRED,** ELEMENTARY PARTICLE PHYSICS. *Current Pos:* res physicist, 53-91, assoc dir physics, 70-73, EMER ASSOC DIR PHYSICS, LAWRENCE BERKELEY LAB, UNIV CALIF, 91- *Personal Data:* b Cincinnati, Ohio, Apr 30, 24; m 55, Carol Lotz; c Anne & Stuart. *Educ:* Williams Col, AB, 44; Calif Inst Technol, MS, 48, PhD(physics), 52. *Prof Exp:* Res fel physics, Calif Inst Technol, 52-53. *Mem:* Fel Am Phys Soc; AAAS; Sigma Xi. *Res:* Experimentation in elementary particle physics; study of weak and electromagnetic interactions and of hadron phenomena at high transverse momenta; development of electronic instrumentation and accelerator facilities. *Mailing Add:* Bldg 50 Rm 137 Lawrence Berkeley Lab Univ Calif Berkeley CA 94720. *Fax:* 510-486-7115; *E-Mail:* wenzel@lbl.gov

**WENZINGER, GEORGE ROBERT,** CHEMISTRY. *Current Pos:* asst prof, 63-76, ASSOC PROF ORG CHEM, UNIV SFLA, 76- *Personal Data:* b Newport News, Va, July 24, 33. *Educ:* Washington Univ, AB, 55; Univ Rochester, PhD(chem), 60. *Prof Exp:* NSF fel, Yale Univ, 62-63. *Mem:* AAAS; Am Chem Soc. *Res:* Conjugate elimination reactions; synthesis. *Mailing Add:* Dept Chem Univ SFla Tampa FL 33620

**WENZL, JAMES E,** PEDIATRIC NEPHROLOGY. *Current Pos:* Asst prof, 67-71, assoc prof, 71-75, PROF PEDIAT, UNIV OKLA HEALTH SCI CTR, OKLAHOMA CITY, 75- *Personal Data:* b Greenleaf, Kans, Mar 24, 35; c 4. *Educ:* Creighton Univ, MD, 59; Univ Minn, Minneapolis, MS, 63. *Concurrent Pos:* Chief pediat, Nephrology Serv, Okla Children's Mem Hosp, Olkahoma City, 73-; interim chmn pediatrics, Health Sci Ctr, Univ Okla, Oklahoma City, 76-77, vchmn, 77-; J Pediat Prof, Eastern Va Med Sch, Norfolk & Med Col Va, Richmond, 76; vis prof, Hosp Nat DeNinos, Sch Med, Univ Costa Rica, San Jose, 77; assoc ed, Contemporary Dialysis, 81- *Mem:* Am Soc Nephrology; Am Soc Pediat Nephrology; Int Soc Nephrology; AMA. *Mailing Add:* PO Box 26901 Pd Oklahoma City OK 73190

**WEPFER, WILLIAM J,** MECHANICAL ENGINEERING, HEAT TRANSFER. *Current Pos:* from asst prof to assoc prof, 80-92, PROF MECH ENG, GEORGE W WOODRUFF SCH MECH ENG, GA TECH, 92-, ASSOC DIR GRAD STUDIES, 89- *Personal Data:* b Milwaukee, Wis, Dec 17, 52; m 79, Lynne Mickey; c Kathryn C. *Educ:* Marquette Univ, BSE, 74; Stanford Univ, MS, 76; Univ Wis-Madison, PhD(mech eng), 79. *Honors & Awards:* Teetor Award, Soc Automotive Engrs, 85; Delos-Fluke Award, Am Soc Eng Educ, 88; E K Campbell Award, Am Soc Heating Refrig & Air Conditioning Engrs, 89; Minorities in Eng Award, Am Soc Eng Educ, 95. *Concurrent Pos:* Dow Young fac award, Am Soc Eng Educ, 86, AT&T Found Award, 88. *Mem:* Am Soc Mech Engrs; Am Soc Heating Refrig & Air Conditioning Engrs; Instrument Soc Am; Am Soc Eng Educ; Sigma Xi; Soc Automotive Engrs. *Res:* Thermal systems analysis; thermal performance of solid-vapor heat pump systems; heat transfer analysis of engine cooling systems; vapor-compression heat pumps hvac systems; heat and mass transfer studies of textile drying processes; analysis of high temperature solid-oxide fuel cell systems. *Mailing Add:* 2995 Randolph Rd NE Atlanta GA 30345. *Fax:* 404-894-8336; *E-Mail:* bill.wepfer@me.gatech.edu

**WEPPELMAN, ROGER MICHAEL,** BIOCHEMISTRY, ENDOCRINOLOGY. *Current Pos:* mgr, regulatory affairs, Animal Sci Div, 89-91, REGULATORY COMPLIANCE OFFICER, MONSANTO, 91. *Personal Data:* b Pittsburgh, Pa, Nov 4, 44; m 71, Marsha L Beers. *Educ:* Univ Pittsburgh, BS, 65, PhD(microbiol), 70. *Prof Exp:* Instr microbiol, Univ Pittsburgh, 70-71; Am Cancer Soc fel biochem, Univ Calif, Berkeley, 71-73; sr res biochemist, Dept Basic Animal Sci Res, Merck & Co, 73-77, res fel, 77-80, sr res fel, 80-84, mgr, Microbiol & Agr Res Div, Merck, Sharp & Dohme Res Labs, 84-87, assoc dir, Regulatory Affairs Animal Health, 87-89. *Concurrent Pos:* Assoc mem, Grad Fac, Rutgers Univ, 82-89. *Mem:* Sigma Xi; Am Chem Soc. *Res:* Endocrinology of avian growth and reproduction; genetics of drug resistance of parasitic protozoa; registration of animal health and agricultural products; regulatory compliance. *Mailing Add:* 10 Saddle Creek Ct Chesterfield MO 63005

**WERBACH, MELVYN ROY,** MEDICINE. *Current Pos:* asst clin prof, Dept Anesthesiol, 80-94, ASST CLIN PROF, DEPT PSYCHIAT, SCH MED, UNIV CALIF, LOS ANGELES, 78- *Personal Data:* b New York, NY, Nov 11, 40; m 67, Gail Leibsohn; c Kevin & Adam. *Educ:* Columbia Col, BA, 62; Tufts Univ Sch Med, MD, 66. *Honors & Awards:* Clarke lect, Am Col Advan Med, 89; Book of the Year Award, Int J Alternative & Complementary Med, London, 92. *Prof Exp:* Consult, div clin neurol, City of Hope Nat Med Ctr, 72-75; dir psychol serv, Pain Control Unit, Univ Calif, Los Angeles Hosp & Clins, 75-80. *Concurrent Pos:* Chmn, dept ment health, Ross-Loos Med Co, Cigna Health Plans, 71-75, dir, Biofeedback Med Clin, 72-96. *Mem:* Am Col Nutrit. *Res:* Nutritional medicine; writer; scientific literature. *Mailing Add:* 4751 Viviana Dr Tarzana CA 91356

**WERBEL, LESLIE MORTON,** ORGANIC CHEMISTRY, MEDICINAL CHEMISTRY. *Current Pos:* CONSULT DRUG DISCOVERY & DEVELOP, 91- *Personal Data:* b New York, NY, Mar 31, 31; m 58, Phyllis Isaacson; c Cheryl, Debra & Aaron. *Educ:* Queens Col, NY, BS, 51; Columbia Univ, AM, 52; Univ Ill, PhD(chem), 57. *Prof Exp:* Res chemist, Parke Davis Pharmaceut Res Div, Warner Lambert Co, 57-67, sr res chemist, 67-75, sr scientist, 75-76, sr res assoc, 76-77, dir chem prod contract res, Parke-Davis & Co, 77-80, dir chem contract res, 80-82, dir cancer chem synthesis, 82-89, sr res fel, 89-91. *Concurrent Pos:* Lectr, Col Pharm, Univ Mich, 67, adj prof, 71-91. *Mem:* Am Chem Soc; Am Asn Cancer Res. *Res:* Medicinal chemistry; chemotherapy of parasitic infections; cancer chemotherapy; relation of intermediary metabolism of host and invading organism to drug action; novel heterocyclic ring systems. *Mailing Add:* 1570 Covington Dr Ann Arbor MI 48103

**WERBELOW, LAWRENCE GLEN,** NUCLEAR MAGNETIC RESONANCE SPECTROSCOPY, QUANTUM THEORY ANGULAR MOMENTUM. *Current Pos:* PROF CHEM, NMEX INST MINING TECHNOL, 80- *Personal Data:* b Ross, Calif, Dec 19, 47. *Educ:* Humboldt State Univ, BS, 70; Univ BC, PhD(chem physics), 74; Univ Provence, DSc, 79. *Concurrent Pos:* Consult, Los Alamos Nat Labs, 80- *Res:* Studies of the creation and dissipation of relaxation induced multispine order; the isolation and identification of ultra fine interactions in magnetic resonance; product operator formalisms; line shape analysis of multiquantum coherance. *Mailing Add:* 907 Michigan Ave Socorro NM 87801. *Fax:* 505-835-5626; *E-Mail:* werbelow@.titan.nmt.edu

**WERBER, FRANK XAVIER,** ORGANIC CHEMISTRY, POLYMER CHEMISTRY. *Current Pos:* NAT PROG STAFF, DEPT AGR, AGR RES SERV, BELTSVILLE, MD, 84- *Personal Data:* b Vienna, Austria, Apr 8, 24; nat US; m 50; c 2. *Educ:* Queens Col, NY, BS, 44; Univ Ill, MS, 47, PhD(chem), 49. *Prof Exp:* Asst, Queens Col, NY, 46; res chemist, Org Res Dept, Res Ctr, B F Goodrich Co, 49-55, sr res chemist, 55-56; dir polymer res, Res Div, W R Grace & Co, 57-63, vpres, res, 63-67; vpres res & develop, J P Stevens & Co, Inc, 67-84. *Concurrent Pos:* Chmn bd, Textile Res Inst, 73-75; mem bd, Indust Res Inst, 76-82, 83-86; chmn, Sect Indust Sci, AAAS, 92-93. *Mem:* Fel AAAS; Am Chem Soc; NY Acad Sci; Am Asn Textile Technol; Am Asn Textile Chemists & Colorists; Textile Res Inst. *Res:* Industrial organic chemistry; modification of polymers; adhesives; condensation polymers; textile chemistry, technology, machinery and engineering. *Mailing Add:* 63 Dennison Rd Essex CT 06426. *Fax:* 301-504-5467

**WERBIN, HAROLD,** BIOLOGICAL CHEMISTRY, CANCER. *Current Pos:* ADJ PROF, DEPT CELL BIOL & NEUROSCI, SOUTHWESTERN MED CTR, UNIV TEX, 89- *Personal Data:* b New York, NY, Oct 2, 22; m 77, Francine Burrows. *Educ:* Brooklyn Col, BS, 44; Polytech Inst Brooklyn, MS, 47, PhD(chem), 50. *Prof Exp:* Asst, Brooklyn Jewish Hosp, 44-46; res assoc, Polytech Inst Brooklyn, 47-48; dir labs, Hillside Hosp, 50-53; res assoc biochem, Argonne Cancer Res Hosp, Chicago, 53-56; res biochemist dept physiol & soils & plant nutrit, Univ Calif, Berkeley, 57-66; from assoc prof to prof Biol, Univ Tex, Dallas, 66-89. *Concurrent Pos:* AEC contract, 67-, Energy Res & Develop Admin contract, 75-76; NSF grant, 67-71 & 78-80; Robert A Welch Found grant, 71-82 & Meadows Found grant, 84-86; NIH sr res fel, Dept Cell Biol, Univ Tex Health Sci Ctr, 82-83; NIH grant, subcontractor, 85-88. *Mem:* Am Soc Biol Chem. *Res:* Regulation of telomerase in cancer progression. *Mailing Add:* Dept Cellular Biol & Neurosci Univ Tex Southwestern Med Ctr 5323 Harry Hines Blvd Dallas TX 75235-9039. *Fax:* 214-648-8694

**WERBLIN, FRANK SIMON,** BIOENGINEERING. *Current Pos:* From asst prof to assoc prof, 70-75, PROF ELEC ENG, UNIV CALIF, BERKELEY, 75- *Personal Data:* b New York, NY, Jan 24, 37; c 1. *Educ:* Mass Inst Technol, BS, 58, MS, 62; Johns Hopkins Univ, PhD(bioeng), 68. *Concurrent Pos:* Guggenheim fel, 74; Miller prof, Miller Found, 76. *Res:* Neurophysiological and biochemical basis for function of the vertebrate retina; mechanisms of light transduction, contrast detection, gain control studied in terms of molecular events in photoreceptors, ionic events at synapses, membrane events in neurons. *Mailing Add:* 22175 Highway 1 Marshall CA 94940

**WERBOS, PAUL JOHN,** NEURAL NETWORKS, QUANTUM FOUNDATIONS. *Current Pos:* PROG DIR NEUROENG, NSF, 88- *Personal Data:* b Darby, Pa, Sept 9, 47; m 79, Lily Fountain; c Elizabeth, Alexander & Maia. *Educ:* Harvard Univ, BA, 67, SM, 69, PhD(appl math), 74; London Sch Econ, MSc, 68. *Prof Exp:* Res assoc, Mass Inst Technol, 73-75; asst prof, Univ Md, 75-79; analyst/forecaster, US Dept Energy, 79-89. *Mem:* Int Neural Network Soc (secy, 90, pres, 91-92). *Res:* Developed back propagation new and used in about 70% of artificial neural net applications; intelligent control designs and tests of neuroscience implications. *Mailing Add:* 8411 48th Ave College Park MD 20740. *Fax:* 703-306-0305; *E-Mail:* pwerbos@nsf.gov

**WERDEGAR, DAVID,** COMMUNITY HEALTH. *Current Pos:* from asst prof to assoc prof, Fresno, 65-75, PROF FAMILY & COMMUNITY MED & ASSOC DEAN, DEPT FAMILY & COMMUNITY MED, SCH MED, UNIV CALIF, SAN FRANCISCO, 75-; DIR, SAN FRANCISCO DEPT HEALTH, 85- *Personal Data:* b New York, NY, Sept 16, 30; m 61; c 2. *Educ:* Cornell Univ, AB, 51, MA, 52; NY Med Col, MD, 56; Univ Calif, Berkeley, MPH, 70. *Prof Exp:* Consult, Calif State Dept Pub Health, 64-65. *Concurrent Pos:* NIMH spec fel, Univ Calif, San Francisco, 63-64, Dept Health, Educ & Welfare Div Chronic Dis fel, 64-67; co-dir, Regional Med Prog Cardiovasc Dis Prev Northwest Calif, 67-70; planning officer, Regional Med Prog, Calif; med dir, Univ Calif Home Care Serv, 65- *Mem:* Fel AAAS; Am Pub Health Asn; Asn Teachers Prev Med; Am Fedn Clin Res; Am Col Physicians. *Res:* Family medicine; health policy; social aspects of health care; organization of health care services; evaluation of quality of health care. *Mailing Add:* Off State Wide Health Planning & Develop 1600 Ninth St Rm 433 Sacramento CA 95814

**WERDEL, JUDITH ANN,** INFORMATION SCIENCE, SCIENCE POLICY. *Current Pos:* RETIRED. *Personal Data:* b Lackawanna, NY, June 22, 37. *Educ:* State Univ NY, Buffalo, BA, 58; Mt Holyoke Col, MA, 59. *Prof Exp:* Sci info specialist, Shell Develop Co, Calif, 59-63; prof asst info sci, Off Doc, 63-70, prof assoc, Bd Int Orgn & Progs & Bd Sci & Technol for Int Develop, 70-74, staff officer, Comt Int Sci & Tech Info Progs, 74-81, prof assoc, Bd Sci & Technol, Int Develop, Comn Int Rels, Nat Acad Sci, 81-83; proj adminr, Develop Info Res & Ref Serv, USAID, 83-86; independent consult, 86-96. *Concurrent Pos:* Secy bd dirs, Doc Abstr, Inc, 66-68. *Mem:* Am Soc Info Sci. *Res:* National and international policies and programs for the development of scientific and technical information systems; technical assistance in scientific and technical information systems; promotion and development of the field of information science and technology. *Mailing Add:* 1817 Corcoran St NW Washington DC 20009

**WERDER, ALVAR ARVID,** MICROBIOLOGY. *Current Pos:* RETIRED. *Personal Data:* b Sweden, Mar 12, 17; nat US; m 44; c 2. *Educ:* Univ Minn, BA, 45, MS, 47, PhD, 49. *Prof Exp:* From instr to asst prof bact, Univ Minn, 49-52; from assoc prof to prof microbiol, Sch Med, Univ Kans, 52-84, chmn dept, 61-82. *Mem:* Am Soc Microbiol; Am Asn Pathologists. *Res:* Oncogenic viruses; studies on germfree animals. *Mailing Add:* 3311 W 74th Terr Shawnee Mission KS 66208

**WERGEDAL, JON E,** BIOCHEMISTRY. *Current Pos:* AT DEPT BIOCHEM, LOMA LINDA UNIV, CALIF. *Personal Data:* b Eau Claire, Wis, Feb 19, 36. *Educ:* St Olaf Col, BA, 58; Univ Wis, MS, 60, PhD(biochem), 63. *Prof Exp:* biochemist, Vet Admin Hosp, Seattle, 62- *Concurrent Pos:* Res instr med, Sch Med, Univ Wash, 63-71, res asst prof, 71-76. *Mem:* AAAS. *Res:* Bone metabolism. *Mailing Add:* 1355 Parker Ct Redlands CA 92373

**WERGIN, WILLIAM PETER,** CYTOLOGY, ELECTRON MICROSCOPY. *Current Pos:* Res cytologist plant path, USDA, 70-72, res cytologist weed sci, 72-74, res cytologist nematol & proj leader animal reproduction, Agr Res Serv, 74-79, res leader, Plant Stress Lab, 79-88, RES LEADER, ELECTRON MICROS LAB, USDA, 88- *Personal Data:* b Manitowoc, Wis, Apr 20, 42; m 62, Mary E Guse; c W Peter & Anne M. *Educ:* Univ Wis-Madison, BS, 64, PhD(bot), 70. *Honors & Awards:* Diamond Award, Bot Soc Am, 75. *Concurrent Pos:* Prin investr, Agr Competitive Grants Prog, 78 & co-prin investr, US-Israel Agr Res & Develop Fund, 79. *Mem:* Am Soc Cell Biol; Bot Soc Am; Micros Soc Am; Am Soc Plant Physiologists; Soc Nematologists; AAAS; Sigma Xi; fel Royal Micros Soc. *Res:* Current transmission and scanning electron microscopic examinations include host-parasite interactions between higher plants and nematodes and effects of environmental stress on crop plants; environmental stress effects caused by air pollutants, mineral deficiencies or toxicities and temperature, water and light extremes in plants; develops techniques relating to low temperature scanning electron microscopy. *Mailing Add:* Beltsville Agr Res Ctr-E Agr Res Serv USDA Beltsville MD 20705. *Fax:* 301-504-8923; *E-Mail:* wwergin @ ggpl.arsusda.gov

**WERKEMA, GEORGE JAN,** PHYSICAL CHEMISTRY, HEALTH PHYSICS. *Current Pos:* chief, Health Protection Br, 81-83, CHIEF, NUCLEAR MGT BR, US DEPT ENERGY, ALBUQUERQUE, 83- *Personal Data:* b Vancouver, Wash, Nov 24, 36; m 69; c 2. *Educ:* Calvin Col, BS, 58; Univ Colo, PhD(chem), 65. *Prof Exp:* From res chemist to sr res chemist, Dow Chem Co, 63-72, res mgr, Rocky Flats Div, 72-75; health physicist, US Energy Res & Develop Admin, 75-81. *Mem:* Am Chem Soc; Sigma Xi. *Res:* X-ray crystallography; computer programming; instrument development; health physics; environmental control and monitoring; industrial hygiene. *Mailing Add:* 1109 Calif SE Albuquerque NM 87108

**WERKHEISER, ARTHUR H, JR,** LASERS. *Current Pos:* assoc prof, Physics Dept, 70-89, MGR, LASER APPLICATIONS RES LAB, SR RES SCIENTIST, CTR APPL OPTICS, UNIV ALA, HUNTSVILLE, 89- *Personal Data:* b Easton, Pa, May 2, 35; m 62; c 2. *Educ:* Lafayette Col, BS, 57; Univ Tenn, MS, 59, PhD(physics), 65. *Prof Exp:* Instr physics, Univ Tenn, 64; physicist, Res & Develop Directorate, 65-75, br chief, Modeling & Anal Div, Army High Energy Lasers Res & Eng Directorate, 75-82, actg div chief, Concepts & Prog Mgt, Directed Energy Directorate, US Army Missile Command, Redstone Arsenal, 82-88. *Mem:* Am Phys Soc. *Res:* Isomer shifts of solid solutions, conduction electron polarization, Mossbauer effect physics, mathematical modeling of high energy laser systems; laser propagation; high power laser processing of materials. *Mailing Add:* 1602 Drake Ave SE Huntsville AL 35802-1055

**WERKING, ROBERT JUNIOR,** SCIENCE EDUCATION. *Current Pos:* Asst prof physics, Ind Wesleyan Univ, 65-69, asst prof sci educ, 71-73, chmn div natural sci & math, 73-92, PROF SCI EDUC, IND WESLEYAN UNIV, 92- *Personal Data:* b Richmond, Ind, Jan 21, 30; m 51; c 2. *Educ:* Hillsdale Col, BS, 61; Syracuse Univ, MS, 65; Ind Univ, Bloomington, EdD(sci educ), 71. *Mem:* Am Asn Physics Teachers; fel Am Sci Affil. *Res:* Science instruction; instructional objectives; teaching effectiveness; instructional methods. *Mailing Add:* 4562 S Star Dr Marion IN 46953

**WERKMAN, JOYCE,** CHEMISTRY, INSTRUMENTATION. *Current Pos:* PRES & OWNER, INSTRUMENTS RES & IND, 65- *Personal Data:* b Ill, 1940. *Res:* Development of instruments to detect toxic gases, and for research and plant operations; design and manufacture of safety products for laboratory sciences and instruments for automatizing tedious laboratory tasks; design and manufacture of other devices that facilitate laboratory work in fields of chemistry and biochemistry. *Mailing Add:* 108 Franklin Ave Cheltenham PA 19012

**WERKMAN, SIDNEY LEE,** MEDICINE. *Current Pos:* PVT CONSULT, WASHINGTON, DC, 89- *Personal Data:* b Washington, DC, May 3, 27; c 1. *Educ:* Williams Col, AB, 48; Cornell Univ, MD, 52. *Prof Exp:* Assoc prof psychiat, Med Sch, George Washington Univ, 61-69; assoc prof psychiat, Univ Colo Med Ctr, Denver, 69-72, prof, 72-89. *Concurrent Pos:* Commonwealth Fund fel, Florence, Italy, 63-64; res consult, USPHS, 60-68; assoc dir, Joint Comn Ment Health Children, 67-68; consult, NIMH, 74- *Mem:* AAAS; Am Psychiat Asn; Am Acad Child Psychiat; Am Orthopsychiat Asn; Group Advan Psychiat. *Res:* Psychological factors in nutrition and development; brain dysfunction in children; attitude studies; psychological adjustment of Americans overseas. *Mailing Add:* 3636 16th St NW Suite AG-29 Washington DC 20010-1146

**WERLING, LINDA L,** SIGMA RECEPTORS, REGULATION OF CATECHOLAMINE RELEASE. *Current Pos:* asst prof, 89-96, ASSOC PROF PHARMACOL, MED CTR, GEORGE WASHINGTON UNIV, 96- *Personal Data:* b Henderson, Ky, Aug 24, 54. *Educ:* Duke Univ, PhD(pharmacol), 83. *Prof Exp:* Postdoctoral fel, Uniformed Serv Univ, 83-85, res instr, 85-87, res asst prof, 87-89. *Mem:* Soc Neurosci; Am Socc Pharmacol & Exp Therapeut. *Res:* Regulation of catecholamine release by sigma receptor ligands and the second messenger systems underlying that regulation. *Mailing Add:* Dept Pharmacol Med Ctr George Washington Univ 2300 Eye St NW Washington DC 20037

**WERMAN, ROBERT,** NEUROPHYSIOLOGY. *Current Pos:* PROF NEUROPHYSIOL, HEBREW UNIV, JERUSALEM, 69- *Personal Data:* b Brooklyn, NY, May 2, 29; m 54; c Michael, Aaron, Rachel & Ariel. *Educ:* NY Univ, AB, 48, MD, 52. *Prof Exp:* Intern, Montefiore Hosp, New York, 52-53; resident neurol, Mt Sinai Hosp, 53-54 & 56-58; asst prof, Col Physicians & Surgeons, Columbia Univ, 60-61; prof psychiat, Sch Med, Ind Univ, Indianapolis, 61-69, prof anat & physiol, Ind Univ Bloomington, 64-69. *Concurrent Pos:* Nat Inst Neurol Dis & Blindness trainee neurophysiol, Columbia Univ, 58-60; vis scientist, Cambridge Univ, 60-61. *Mem:* AAAS; Soc Gen Physiologists; Am Physiol Soc. *Res:* Electrophysiology; neuromuscular junction; membrane properties and ionic movements; synaptic physiology; spinal cord; death of neurons; Ca2. *Mailing Add:* Dept Neurobiol Hebrew Univ Jerusalem Jerusalem 91904 Israel. *Fax:* 972-2-623-2081; *E-Mail:* rwerman @ vms.huji.ac.il

**WERMUND, EDMUND GERALD, JR,** GEOLOGY. *Current Pos:* res scientist, 71-73, assoc dir, 73-88, RES SCIENTIST, BUR ECON GEOL, UNIV TEX, AUSTIN, 88- *Personal Data:* b Arlington, NJ, Apr 15, 26; wid; c H Dirk & Edmund G III. *Educ:* Franklin & Marshall Col, BS, 48; La State Univ, PhD(geol), 61. *Prof Exp:* Instr geol, La State Univ, 52-57; sr res technologist, Field Res Lab, Mobil Oil Corp, 57-68, res assoc, Mobil Res & Develop Corp, 68-70; tech mgr, Remote Sensing, Inc, 70-71. *Mem:* AAAS; Am Asn Petrol Geologists; fel Geol Soc Am; Am Soc Photogram; Sigma Xi; Asn Geoscientists Int Develop. *Res:* Petroleum geology, environmental geology; regional geology. *Mailing Add:* Box X Bur Econ Geol Univ Tex Austin TX 78713-7508. *Fax:* 512-471-0140; *E-Mail:* wermundgebegv.beg. utexas.edu

**WERMUS, GERALD R,** BIOCHEMISTRY, CLINICAL CHEMISTRY. *Current Pos:* res chemist, E I Du Pont de Nemours & Co, Inc, 61-72, res supvr, 72-74, res mgr, 74-78, tech serv mgr, Instrument Prod Div, 78-81, mgr, new methods, 81-83, proj mgr, 84-86, PROD MGR, MED PROD DEPT, CLIN SYSTS DIV, E I DU PONT DE NEOOURS & CO, INC, 87- *Personal Data:* b St Paul, Minn, May 8, 38; m 65; c 2. *Prof Exp:* Formulation chemist, Econ Lab, Inc, 60-61. *Concurrent Pos:* Mem, Nat Comt Clin Lab Standards. *Mem:* Am Asn Clin Chem; Am Chem Soc. *Res:* Development of clinical laboratory methodology; bacterial metabolism; lipid peroxidation; laboratory administration; product management; project management. *Mailing Add:* 114 Venus Dr Newark DE 19711

**WERMUTH, JEROME FRANCIS,** DEVELOPMENTAL BIOLOGY. *Current Pos:* asst prof, 69-78, asst dean, 84-86, ASSOC PROF BIOL, PURDUE UNIV, CALUMET CAMPUS, 78-, EXEC ASST TO CHANCELLOR, 87- *Personal Data:* b Madison, Wis, Oct 19, 36; m 64, Alice Riney; c Sarah, Mary, Alison, Anneliese & Leah. *Educ:* Univ Wis-Madison, BS, 57, MS, 60; Ind Univ, PhD(zool), 68. *Prof Exp:* Instr biol, Rockhurst Col, 61-64; asst prof, St Joseph's Col, Ind, 65-66; res assoc, Univ Notre Dame, 68-69. *Concurrent Pos:* Vis asst prof & Nat Cancer Inst spec res fel life sci, Ind State Univ, Terre Haute, 72-73; vis asst prof zool, Ind Univ, Bloomington, 75-76. *Res:* Effects of x-irradiation on the developmental physiology of colonial marine cnidarians. *Mailing Add:* Exec Asst to Chancellor Purdue Univ Calumet Hammond IN 46323. *Fax:* 219-989-2581; *E-Mail:* wermuth @ calumet.purdue.edu

**WERNAU, WILLIAM CHARLES,** STREPTOMYCES FERMENTATION, ANTIBIOTICS BIOTRANSFORMATION. *Current Pos:* Res scientist, Pfizer, Inc, 72-76, sr res scientist, 76-77, proj leader, 77-81, mgr, 81-82, asst dir, 82-87, DIR BIOPROCESS RES, PFIZER, INC, 87- *Personal Data:* b Flushing, NY, Jan 22, 47; m 68; c 4. *Educ:* Cooper Union, BS, 68; Univ Calif, Berkeley, PhD(chem eng), 72. *Mem:* Am Soc Microbiol; Am Chem Soc. *Res:* Pilot plant scale-up, fermentor design, fermentation and recovery process development; mass transfer in aerobic systems; antibiotics, anticoccidials, antiparasitics and streptomyces genetics; biotransformation; genetherapy; vaccines; cell culture. *Mailing Add:* 27 Quinley Way Waterford CT 06385. *Fax:* 860-441-4119; *E-Mail:* wernaw @ pfizer.com

**WERNER, ARNOLD,** PSYCHOSOMATIC MEDICINE, MEDICAL EDUCATION. *Current Pos:* from asst prof to assoc prof, 69-78, PROF PSYCHIAT, MICH STATE UNIV, 78- *Personal Data:* b Brooklyn, NY, June 8, 38. *Educ:* Brooklyn Col, BS, 59; Univ Rochester, MD, 63. *Prof Exp:* Instr psychiat, Sch Med, Univ Rochester, 66-67; Temple Univ, 67-69. *Mem:* Fel Am Psychiat Asn; Am Psychosom Soc. *Res:* Adaptation to cancer; medical education; health concerns of normal people. *Mailing Add:* A228 E Fee Hall Dept Psychiat Mich State Univ East Lansing MI 48824-1316. *Fax:* 517-432-2893; *E-Mail:* werner @ msu.edu

**WERNER, EARL EDWARD,** ECOLOGY, ZOOLOGY. *Current Pos:* PROF BIOL, UNIV MICH, 86- *Personal Data:* b Aliquippa, Pa, July 11, 44; m 71. *Educ:* Columbia Univ, AB, 66; Mich State Univ, PhD(ecol), 72. *Honors & Awards:* Mercer Award, Ecol Soc Am, 78. *Prof Exp:* Asst prof, Univ Iowa, 72-73; assoc prof zool, Mich State Univ, Kellogg Biol Sta, 78-84. *Mem:* AAAS; Ecol Soc Am; Brit Ecol Soc; Int Soc Theoret & Appl Limnol; Am Soc Naturalists. *Res:* Community ecology; population biology; competition; foraging strategies. *Mailing Add:* Dept Biol 1121 Nat Sci Bldg Univ Mich 830 N University Ave Ann Arbor MI 48109-1048

**WERNER, ERVIN ROBERT, JR,** ORGANIC CHEMISTRY. *Current Pos:* res chemist, 60-69, staff chemist, 69-72, RES ASSOC, E I DU PONT DE NEMOURS & CO, INC, 72- *Personal Data:* b Philadelphia, Pa, May 2, 32; m 53, Lorraine L Montieth; c Robert J, Mark K, Debra K, Renee L & Andrea L. *Educ:* Haverford Col, BS, 54; Univ Md, MS, 58; Univ Pa, PhD(org chem),

60. *Prof Exp:* Chemist, Rohm & Haas Co, 57-60. *Mem:* Am Chem Soc; Fedn Soc Paint Technol. *Res:* Organic synthesis; flame retardant polyesters; organophosphorus chemistry; water solution polymers; aqueous wire enamels; emulsion systems and house paints; interior emulsion paints; automotive clear finishes; automotive waterborne basecoats. *Mailing Add:* 9 Sovergin Lane Ormond Beach FL 32176

**WERNER, F(RED) E(UGENE),** PHYSICAL METALLURGY, MAGNETIC MATERIALS. *Current Pos:* CONSULT, 88- *Personal Data:* b Mansfield, Ohio, Sept 22, 27; m 51; c 3. *Educ:* Mass Inst Technol, SB, 50, ScD(metall), 55. *Prof Exp:* Instr metall, Mass Inst Technol, 50-53, asst, 53-55; res engr, Res Labs, Westinghouse Elec Corp, 55-60, sect mgr alloy studies, 60-62, mgr, Metall Dept, 62-68, mat consult, 69, mgr, Magnetics Dept, 70-82, mgr patents & libr, 82-88. *Concurrent Pos:* Gen chem, Magnetism Conf, 83; chmn, Magnetism adv comt, 84; treas, MMM & Intermag conf. *Mem:* Soc Metals; Inst Mining, Metall & Petrol Engrs; Inst Elec & Electronics Engrs; fel Am Soc Metals. *Res:* Metallic alloys; application of metals and alloys to practical uses; metals processing, research and development in physical and mechanical metallurgy; metals joining; soft and permanent magnetic materials. *Mailing Add:* 5825 Fifth Ave No 111A Pittsburgh PA 15232-2720. *E-Mail:* fewrnr@aol.com

**WERNER, FLOYD GERALD,** ENTOMOLOGY. *Current Pos:* from asst prof to prof, 54-89, EMER PROF ENTOM, UNIV ARIZ, 89- *Personal Data:* b Ottawa, Ill, June 1, 21; m 52; c 3. *Educ:* Harvard Univ, SB, 43, PhD(biol), 50. *Prof Exp:* From asst prof to assoc prof zool, Univ Vt, 50-54. *Mem:* AAAS; Entom Soc Am; Coleopterists Soc. *Res:* Taxonomy of Coleoptera, Meloidae and Anthicidae. *Mailing Add:* 3216 N Jackson Ave Tucson AZ 85719

**WERNER, FRANK D(AVID),** AERONAUTICAL ENGINEERING. *Current Pos:* PRES & DIR, ORIGIN INC, 68- & TECH LINE CORP, 90- *Personal Data:* b Junction City, Kans, Mar 14, 22; m 46, Alice Martel; c JoAnn (Blomberg), F David & Robert J. *Educ:* Kans State Col, BS, 43; Univ Minn, MS, 48, PhD(aeronaut eng), 55. *Prof Exp:* Jr physicist, Appl Physics Lab, Johns Hopkins Univ, 43-47; res assoc, Rosemount Aeronaut Lab, Univ Minn, 47-56; pres & dir, Rosemount, Inc, 56-68; pres, Park Energy Co, 76-82. *Concurrent Pos:* Consult, 48-57. *Mem:* Am Phys Soc; Instrument Soc Am; Sigma Xi. *Res:* Instrumentation, particularly temperature and pressure measurement; platinum resistance thermometry and measurement of air data parameters for airplane flights; solar heat collectors. *Mailing Add:* PO Box SR9 Jackson WY 83001

**WERNER, GERHARD,** PHARMACOLOGY, PSYCHIATRY. *Current Pos:* chmn dept, Univ Pittsburgh, 65-75, dean, Sch Med, 74-78, prof psychiat, 78-89, FS Cheever distinguished prof, 80-81, PROF PHARMACOL, SCH MED, UNIV PITTSBURGH, 65-, PROF PSYCHOL, 70-, EMER PROF PSYCHIAT, 89- *Personal Data:* b Vienna, Austria, Sept 28, 21; m 58; c 2. *Educ:* Univ Vienna, MD, 45. *Honors & Awards:* Humboldt Prize, 84. *Prof Exp:* From instr to asst prof pharmacol, Univ Vienna, 43-52; prof, Univ Calcutta, 52-54 & Med Sch, Univ Sao Paulo, 55-57; assoc prof, Med Col, Cornell Univ, 57-61 & Med Sch, Johns Hopkins Univ, 61-65. *Concurrent Pos:* Mem adv bd, Indian Coun Med Res, 52-54; mem, Pharmacol Study Sect, NIH, 65-69, mem, Chem-Biol Info Handling Prog, 68-71; NSF consult, 69-71; pres, Medcoup, Inc, 90-; contractor, Motorola, 95- *Mem:* Asn Computer Mach; Int Brain Res Orgn; Asn Res Nerv & Ment Dis; Sigma Xi; Am Asn Artificial Intel; Am Psychiat Asn. *Res:* Neuropharmacology; psychoanalysis; neurophysiology; computer applications; expert systems for medical diagnosis; artificial intelligence. *Mailing Add:* 4723 Cat Mountain Dr Austin TX 78731

**WERNER, HARRY EMIL,** geology, for more information see previous edition

**WERNER, JOHN ELLIS,** METALLURGY, CHEMICAL ENGINEERING. *Current Pos:* PRES & CHIEF EXEC OFFICER, BEN FRANKLIN TECHNOL CTR CENT/NORTHERN PA, INC, 89- *Personal Data:* b Erie, Pa, Oct 25, 32; m 57; c 4. *Educ:* Pa State Univ, BS, 54, MS, 60. *Prof Exp:* Metall engr, Lackawanna Plant, Bethlehem Steel Corp, 54-58, res engr, Res Dept, 60-65, supvr steelmaking processes, Steelmaking Sect, 65-66, asst sect mgr, 66-69, sect mgr phys metall, Homer Res Labs, 69-74, asst div mgr prod res, 74-76, asst div mgr primary processes, 76-78, div mgr raw mat & chem processes, Res Dept, 78-82, dir res, 82-84, dir technol transfer & ventures, diversified group, Bethlehem Steel Corp, 84-88. *Mem:* Am Inst Mining, Metall & Petrol Engrs; Am Soc Metals. *Res:* Steelmaking processes; microstructural control to enhance properties; research management; technical forecasting. *Mailing Add:* Ben Franklin Tech Ctr CNT & NPa 115 Technol Ctr University Park PA 16802-7000

**WERNER, JOHN KIRWIN,** HERPETOLOGY, PARASITOLOGY. *Current Pos:* PART-TIME PROF BIOL, KALISH KOOTENIA COMMUNITY COL, 93-, ENVIRONMENTAL FIELD CONSULT, 93- *Personal Data:* b Conrad, Mont, Sept 14, 41; m 67; c 2. *Educ:* Carroll Col, Mont, BA, 63; Univ Notre Dame, PhD(biol), 68. *Prof Exp:* Chief dept med zool, 406th Med Lab, US Med Command, Japan, 68-71; asst prof biol, Northern Mich Univ, 71-75, head dept, 75-78, assoc prof biol, 79-93. *Concurrent Pos:* Assoc investr, US Army Res & Develop Protocol, 68-71; US Forest Serv grants amphibian ecol, 71-75; scientist, Int Ctr Med Res, Cali, Colombia, 78-81. *Mem:* Herpetologists League; Am Soc Parasitologists; Am Soc Ichthyologists & Herpetologists. *Res:* Ecology and reproduction of amphibians and reptiles; blood parasites of lower vertebrates. *Mailing Add:* 4163 Canyon Mill Rd Ronan MT 59864

**WERNER, LINCOLN HARVEY,** ORGANIC CHEMISTRY. *Current Pos:* RETIRED. *Personal Data:* b New York, NY, Feb 19, 18; m 44; c 2. *Educ:* Swiss Fed Inst Technol, dipl, 41, DrTechSci, 44. *Prof Exp:* Asst, Swiss Fed Inst Technol, 44-46; res chemist, Ciba-Geigy Ltd, Basel, Switz, 46-47, res chemist, Ciba Pharmaceut Prods, Inc, NJ, 47-68, mgr chem res admin, Ciba Pharmaceut Co, 68-84. *Mem:* Am Chem Soc. *Res:* Pharmaceuticals; cardiovascular drugs; diuretics. *Mailing Add:* 94 Larned Rd Summit NJ 07901-3405

**WERNER, MARIO,** LABORATORY MEDICINE. *Current Pos:* PROF LAB MED, GEORGE WASHINGTON UNIV, 72- *Personal Data:* b Zurich, Switz, Aug 21, 31; US citizen; m 68, Elsbeth Nievergelt; c Conrad J. *Educ:* Univ Zurich, MD, 56, DrMed, 60. *Honors & Awards:* CCE Commissioners Medal, Am Soc Clin Path. *Prof Exp:* Asst physician, Kantonsspital St Gallen, Switz, 57-58 & Univ Basel, 58-61; NIH res fel metab, Swiss Acad Med Sci, 61-62; NIH res fel physiol, Rockefeller Univ, 62-64; head physician, Med Sch Essen, WGer, 64-66; asst prof lab med, Univ Calif, San Francisco, 67-70; assoc prof med path, Wash Univ, 70-72. *Concurrent Pos:* Consult, Univ Tex M D Anderson Hosp & Tumor Inst, 70-80 & Nat Heart & Lung Inst, 73-83; chmn health care delivery comt, Bi-State Regional Med Prog, 71-72; trustee, Found Interdisciplinary Biocharacterizations Pop, 71-75; mem, Path A Study Sect, NIH, 75-80 & Clin Chem Device Classification Panel, Food & Drug Admin, 77-79; dir, Am Bd Clin Chem, 79-85; chmn, Nat Coun Health Lab Serv, 87-89. *Mem:* Am Soc Clin Path; Col Am Path; Acad Clin Lab Physicians & Sci; Am Asn Clin Chem; Am Fedn Clin Res; Nat Acad Clin Biochem; Int Soc Clin Enzym (pres, 86-90); hon mem Ital Soc Lab Med; corresp mem Ger Soc Lab Med; hon mem Polish Acad Arts & Sci. *Res:* Laboratory data processing and diagnostic discrimination by computer; blood protein and lipoprotein metabolism. *Mailing Add:* Div Lab Med George Washington Univ Med Ctr Washington DC 20037. *Fax:* 202-994-5522

**WERNER, MICHAEL WOLOCK,** ASTROPHYSICS, INFRARED ASTRONOMY. *Current Pos:* SR RES SCIENTIST, JET PROPULSION LAB, 90- *Personal Data:* b Chicago, Ill, Oct 9, 42; m 67, Edwenna Rosser; c Erica & Alexander. *Educ:* Haverford Col, BA, 63; Cornell Univ, PhD(astron), 68. *Prof Exp:* Res physicist, US Naval Res Lab, 63-64; vis fel, Inst Theoret Astron, Cambridge, Eng, 68-69; lectr physics, Univ Calif, Berkeley, 69-72; asst prof, Calif Inst Technol, 72-79, staff assoc, Hale Observ, 72-79; res scientist, Ames Res Ctr, NASA, 79-90. *Concurrent Pos:* Alfred P Sloan fel, 72; Proj scientist, Space Infrared Telescope Facil, 84-; lectr physics, Calif Inst Technol, 92-; vis prof astron, Univ Calif, Los Angeles, 92. *Mem:* AAAS; Am Astron Soc. *Res:* Observational infrared astronomy; astrophysics of the interstellar medium; development of telescopes and systems for infrared space astronomy. *Mailing Add:* Jet Propulsion Lab MS126-304 Pasadena CA 91109. *Fax:* 818-393-4426; *E-Mail:* mww@ipac.caltech.edu

**WERNER, MILTON HENRY,** STRUCTURAL BIOLOGY, NUCLEAR MAGNETIC RESONANCE SPECTROSCOPY. *Current Pos:* ASST PROF & HEAD LAB, ROCKEFELLER UNIV, 96- *Personal Data:* b Los Angeles, Calif; m 90, Dawn Renae Fossey. *Educ:* Univ Southern Calif, BS, 84; Univ Calif, Berkeley, PhD(chem), 91. *Prof Exp:* Intramural fel, NIH, 91-96. *Concurrent Pos:* Kimmel cancer scholar, 97. *Mem:* AAAS; Am Chem Soc; Am Asn Biochemists & Molecular Biologists. *Res:* Structure/function analysis of transcriptional enhancers and other macromolecular interactions in gene regulation; molecular bases for human clinical disorders in sex determination. *Mailing Add:* Molecular Biophysics Lab Rockefeller Univ 1230 York Ave Box 42 New York NY 10021. *Fax:* 212-327-7222; *E-Mail:* mwerner@portugal.rockefeller.edu

**WERNER, PATRICIA ANN SNYDER,** ECOLOGY, BOTANY & ZOOLOGY. *Current Pos:* prof & chmn wildlife ecol & conserv, 92-96, PROF & DIR, CTR BIOL CONSERV, UNIV FLA, 94- *Personal Data:* b Flint, Mich, July 7, 41; m 71, 91, David L Wigston; c Alexa J (Dobinson). *Educ:* Mich State Univ, MS, 68, PhD(plant ecol), 72. *Prof Exp:* Res assoc ecol, Univ Iowa, 72-73; from asst prof to prof bot & zool, Mich State Univ, 81-86; dir, Trop Ecosyst Res Ctr, Commonwealth Sci & Indust Res Orgn, Australia, 85-90; dir, Div Environ Biol, NSF, Washington, DC, 90-92. *Concurrent Pos:* Prin investr grants, NSF, 73-86, USDA, 82-86; vis prof, Univ Otago, Dunedin, NZ, 81, Harvard Univ, 82 & Australian Nat Univ, 82. *Mem:* Ecol Soc Am; Brit Ecol Soc; Int Soc Plant Pop Biol (secy-treas, 77-85, pres, 85-); fel AAAS. *Res:* Plant population ecology; life histories and competition; biogeography; community ecology; savannas; Australia. *Mailing Add:* Dept Wildlife Univ Fla PO Box 110430 Gainesville FL 32611. *Fax:* 352-392-6984; *E-Mail:* pawe@gnv.ifas.ufl.edu

**WERNER, RAYMOND EDMUND,** ORGANIC CHEMISTRY. *Current Pos:* RETIRED. *Personal Data:* b Cincinnati, Ohio, Apr 18, 19; m 41; c 2. *Educ:* Univ Cincinnati, ChE, 41, MS, 43, ScD(org chem), 45; Xavier Univ, Ohio, MBA, 69. *Prof Exp:* Res chemist, Interchem Corp, Ohio, 45-46; develop chemist, Sterling Drug, Inc, 46-55, dir develop, 55-75, vpres res & develop, Tech Ctr, Hilton Davis Div, 75-80. *Mem:* Am Chem Soc; Sigma Xi. *Res:* Administration of research and development in areas of fine organics, dyes, pharmaceuticals, pigments and graphic arts materials. *Mailing Add:* 9400 Southgate Dr Cincinnati OH 45241-3341

**WERNER, RICHARD ALLEN,** INSECT ECOLOGY. *Current Pos:* CONSULT, 96- *Personal Data:* b Reading, Pa, Feb 20, 36; m 73, Patricia Thomas. *Educ:* Pa State Univ, BS, 58 & 60; Univ Md, MS, 66; NC State Univ, PhD(entom), 71. *Prof Exp:* Forester, US Forest Serv, USDA, 57-59, res entomologist, Forestry Sci Lab, NC, 60-74, res entomologist, Inst Northern Forestry, 74-84, prog leader, 85-91; prin res assoc, Inst Arctic Biol, 82-96. *Concurrent Pos:* NIH/NSF res grant, Univ Md, 64-65; affil prof forestry,

Univ Alaska, 76-96. *Mem:* Soc Am Foresters; Entom Soc Can; Entom Soc Am; Soc Chem Ecol. *Res:* Aggregation behavior of bark beetles to semiochemicals; host susceptibility to bark beetles in white spruce ecosystems; insect pest management; spruce bark beetles. *Mailing Add:* Entom Serv 2038 Alston Rd Fairbanks AK 99709-5307. *E-Mail:* pwerner@polarnet.com

**WERNER, ROBERT GEORGE,** ZOOLOGY. *Current Pos:* assoc prof, 70-76, PROF ZOOL, COL ENVIRON SCI & FORESTRY, STATE UNIV NY, 76-; CO-DIR, GREAT LAKES RES CONSORTIUM, 86- *Personal Data:* b Plymouth, Ind, Mar 6, 36; m 58; c 2. *Educ:* Purdue Univ, BS, 58; Univ Calif, Los Angeles, MA, 63; Ind Univ, PhD(zool), 66. *Prof Exp:* Asst prof zool, State Univ NY Col Forestry, Syracuse, 66-69; asst prof fisheries, Cornell Univ, 69-70. *Concurrent Pos:* Vis scientist, Scottish Marine Biol Asn, 78; pres, Early Life Hist Sect, Am Fisheries Soc; Fulbright fel, 88. *Mem:* Am Fisheries Soc; Am Soc Limnol & Oceanog; Ecol Soc Am. *Res:* Ecology of larval freshwater fish. *Mailing Add:* Dept Environ & Forest Biol Col Environ Sci & Forestry State Univ NY Syracuse NY 13210-2723

**WERNER, RUDOLF,** CHEMISTRY. *Current Pos:* assoc prof, 70-77, PROF BIOCHEM, SCH MED, UNIV MIAMI, 77- *Personal Data:* b Königsberg, Ger, Dec 17, 34; m 61; c 2. *Educ:* Univ Freiburg, Dipl(chem), 60, Dr rer nat(chem), 63. *Prof Exp:* Res asst, Inst Macromolecular Chem, Univ Freiburg, 61-65; res assoc, Carnegie Inst Genetics Res Unit, 65-67; sr staff investr, Cold Spring Harbor Lab Quant Biol, 68-70. *Concurrent Pos:* Estab investr, Am Heart Asn, 69-74. *Mem:* AAAS; Am Soc Biol Chemists. *Res:* Molecular biology; DNA replication. *Mailing Add:* Dept Biochem R629 Univ Miami PO Box 016129 Miami FL 33101-6129. *E-Mail:* rwerner@miasun.med.miami.edu

**WERNER, SAMUEL ALFRED,** SOLID STATE PHYSICS, FUNDAMENTAL NEUTRON PHYSICS. *Current Pos:* chmn dept physics & astron, 81-83, PROF PHYSICS, UNIV MO, COLUMBIA, 75-, MILLSAP DISTINGUISHED PROF PHYSICS, 85-, CUR PROF 93- *Personal Data:* b Elgin, Ill, Jan 5, 37; m 61, Laura Reed; c Catherine L (Canterbury). *Educ:* Dartmouth Col, AB, 59, MS, 61; Univ Mich, Ann Arbor, PhD(nuclear eng), 65. *Prof Exp:* Instr solid state physics & mat, Thayer Sch Eng, Dartmouth Col, 60-61; staff scientist, Physics Dept, Sci Lab, Ford Motor Co, 64-70, sr scientist, 70-75. *Concurrent Pos:* Vis scientist, Argonne, Oak Ridge & Brookhaven Nat Labs, 64-, Aktiebolaget Atomenergi, Sweden, 70 & Inst Laue-Langevin, France, 77-; consult, Argonne Nat Lab, 68-; adj assoc prof, Univ Mich, 69-74; fel Swed Res Coun, 70; mem neutron scattering adv comt, Oak Ridge Nat Lab, 81-; mem panel access current status facil & res neutron scattering, Nat Acad Sci, 83-84; vis scientist, Nat Bur Stand, 83-84. *Mem:* AAAS; fel Am Phys Soc; Sigma Xi; NY Acad Sci; Neutron Scattering Soc Am (pres). *Res:* Neutron scattering; magnetism; phase transitions; fundamental neutron physics; neutron interferometry; charge density and spin density waves. *Mailing Add:* Dept Physics Univ Mo Columbia MO 65211. *Fax:* 573-882-4195; *E-Mail:* werner@nopt.physics.missouri.edu

**WERNER, SANFORD BENSON,** PREVENTIVE MEDICINE, INFECTIOUS DISEASE EPIDEMIOLOGY. *Current Pos:* MED EPIDEMIOLOGIST, DIV COMMUN DIS CONTROL, CHIEF DIS INVESTS SECT, CALIF DEPT HEALTH SERV, 70- *Personal Data:* b Newark, NJ, Jan 5, 39; m 68, Carolyn Morrill; c Zoe & Max. *Educ:* Rutgers Univ, BA, 60; Wash Univ, MD, 64; Univ Calif, MPH, 70. *Honors & Awards:* Langmuir Prize, Ctrs Dis Control & Prev, 69. *Prof Exp:* Intern internal med, Vanderbilt Univ Hosp, Nashville, Tenn, 64-65; med epidemiologist, Epidemic Intel Serv, Ctr Dis Control, Ga, 65-67; resident internal med, Univ Wash Hosps, Seattle, 67-69; internist, Alaska Clin, Anchorage, 69. *Concurrent Pos:* Resident prev med, Sch Pub Health, Univ Calif, Berkeley, 70-71, lectr infectious dis epidemiol, Sch Pub Health, 70-; WHO fel, communicable dis Asia; consult, Nat Acad Sci, 84-85. *Mem:* Fel Am Col Prev Med; fel Am Col Epidemiol. *Res:* Epidemiology of botulism, typhoid, salmonellosis and other enteric diseases. *Mailing Add:* Chief Dis Invests Sect Calif Dept Health Serv 2151 Berkeley Way Berkeley CA 94704. *Fax:* 510-540-2570; *E-Mail:* bwerner@hwi.calnet.gov

**WERNER, THOMAS CLYDE,** FLUORESCENCE, CYCLODEXTRYNS. *Current Pos:* from asst prof to assoc prof, 71-85, dept chmn, 85-91, PROF CHEM, UNION COL, NY, 85- *Personal Data:* b York, Pa, June 19, 42; m 65, Mary Beaver; c Jeffrey & Jonathan. *Educ:* Juniata Col, BS, 64; Mass Inst Technol, PhD(analytical chem), 69. *Prof Exp:* Fel chem, Harvard Med Sch & Mass Gen Hosp, Boston, 69-70; fel med sch, Tufts Univ, 70-71. *Mem:* Am Chem Soc; Sigma Xi. *Res:* Application of luminescence spectroscopy to the study of guest/cyclodextrim chemistry. *Mailing Add:* Dept Chem Union Col Schenectady NY 12308. *Fax:* 518-388-6789; *E-Mail:* wernert@gar.union.edu

**WERNER, THOMAS R,** SOLID STATE PHYSICS. *Current Pos:* PRIN RES SCIENTIST, HONEYWELL INC, 84- *Personal Data:* b Milwaukee, Wis, July 19, 49. *Educ:* Marquette Univ, BS, 71; Northwestern Univ, PhD(physics), 83. *Mem:* Am Phys Soc; Sigma Xi. *Mailing Add:* 3660 Technology Dr MN65-2500 Minneapolis MN 55418-1096

**WERNER, WILLIAM ERNEST, JR,** ECOLOGY. *Current Pos:* PROF BIOL, BLACKBURN COL, 54- *Personal Data:* b Mt Marion, NY, June 30, 25; m 47; c 2. *Educ:* State Univ NY, BA, 50, MA, 51; Cornell Univ, PhD(mammal), 54. *Prof Exp:* Instr biol, State Univ NY Col Teachers, Albany, 51-52. *Concurrent Pos:* Nat Heart Inst fel, Marine Inst, Miami, 63-64. *Mem:* AAAS; Am Soc Mammalogists; Am Soc Ichthyologists & Herpetologists; Ecol Soc Am; Sigma Xi. *Res:* Ecology of mammals, reptiles, amphibians and marine invertebrates. *Mailing Add:* 333 E Cherry St Carlinville IL 62626

**WERNICK, JACK H(ARRY),** PHYSICAL METALLURGY, SOLID STATE CHEMISTRY. *Current Pos:* PRIN ED, ELSEVIER-NORTH HOLLAND, 90- *Personal Data:* b St Paul, Minn, May 19, 23; m 47, Charlotte Greenholtz; c Phyllis R (Lauer) & Rosanne P (Wernick). *Educ:* Univ Minn, BS, 47, MS, 48; Pa State Univ, PhD(metall chem), 54. *Prof Exp:* Metallurgist, Manhattan Proj, Los Alamos Sci Lab, Calif, 44-46; instr metall, Pa State Univ, 49-54; mem tech staff, Bell Commun Res, 54-64, head, Physical Metall Res Dept, 64-73, head, Solid State Chem Res Dept, 73-81, head device Mat Res Dept, Bell Labs, 81-83, mgr mat sci res, 84-92. *Mem:* Nat Acad Eng; fel Am Soc Metals; fel Am Inst Mining, Metall & Petrol Engrs; fel Am Phys Soc; fel NY Acad Sci; Electrochem Soc; AAAS. *Res:* Constitution and physical chemistry of materials, particularly thermodynamic, magnetic and semiconducting properties. *Mailing Add:* 21 Haran Circle Millburn NJ 07974

**WERNICK, ROBERT J,** MATHEMATICS. *Current Pos:* ASSOC PROF MATH, STATE UNIV NY, OSWEGO, 69- *Personal Data:* b New York, NY, June 19, 28; m 54; c 3. *Educ:* Univ Mich, Ann Arbor, BSE, 49; Stevens Inst Technol, MS, 52; Rensselaer Polytech Inst, PhD(math), 69. *Prof Exp:* Res engr, Stevens Inst Technol, 51-53; tech asst, Panel Hydrodyn Submerged Bodies, Comt Undersea Warfare, Nat Res Coun, Washington, DC, 54; mathematician, Gen Eng Labs, Gen Elec Co, NY, 59-62 & Mech Technol, Inc, 62-64; asst prof math, State Univ NY, Albany, 64-68. *Concurrent Pos:* Consult, Advan Technol Labs, Gen Elec Co, NY, 63-66 & Mech Technol, Inc, 65; referee, J Appl Mech, 69- *Mem:* Am Math Soc; Soc Indust & Appl Math; Math Asn Am. *Res:* Numerical analysis; game theory applied to determining the spectra of linear operators. *Mailing Add:* 4500 Ulloa St San Francisco CA 94116-2033

**WERNICK, WILLIAM,** mathematics, for more information see previous edition

**WERNSMAN, EARL ALLEN,** CROP BREEDING. *Current Pos:* from asst prof to assoc prof, 64-72, PROF GENETICS, NC STATE UNIV, 72- *Personal Data:* b Vernon, Ill, Nov 4, 35; m 59; c 1. *Educ:* Univ Ill, Urbana, BS, 58, MS, 60; Purdue Univ, PhD(genetics), 63. *Prof Exp:* Res assoc genetics, Iowa State Univ, 63-64. *Mem:* Fel Am Soc Agron; Am Genetic Asn; Genetics Soc Can; AAAS; Sigma Xi; Crop Sci Soc Am. *Res:* Genetics of Nicotiana and alkaloid production; physiology of cytoplasmic male-sterility in Nicotiana; interspecific hybridization in Nicotiana, tissue and anther culture. *Mailing Add:* Crop Sci NC State Univ Raleigh NC 27695-0001

**WERNTZ, CARL W,** THEORETICAL NUCLEAR PHYSICS, ASTROPHYSICS. *Current Pos:* assoc prof, 62-70, chmn dept, 75-78, PROF PHYSICS, CATH UNIV AM, 70- *Personal Data:* b Washington, DC, Aug 7, 31; m 58; c 2. *Educ:* George Washington Univ, BS, 53; Univ Minn, MS, 55, PhD(physics), 60. *Prof Exp:* Res assoc physics, Univ Wis, 60-62. *Mem:* Am Phys Soc; Am Asn Physics Teachers; Sigma Xi. *Res:* Theory of interaction of pions with nuclei; study of solar nuclear reactions; three body problem. *Mailing Add:* Dept Physics Cath Univ Washington DC 20064-0001

**WERNTZ, JAMES HERBERT, JR,** EDUCATIONAL ADMINISTRATION, PHYSICS. *Current Pos:* VCHANCELLOR ACAD AFFAIRS & PROF PHYSICS, UNIV NC, CHARLOTTE, 81- *Personal Data:* b Wilmington, Del, Sept 3, 28; m 55; c 4. *Educ:* Oberlin Col, BA, 50; Univ Wis, MS, 52, PhD(physics), 57. *Honors & Awards:* Distinguished Serv Citation, Am Asn Physics Teachers, 68. *Prof Exp:* From asst prof to prof physics, Univ Minn, Minneapolis, 56-81, dir, Ctr Educ Develop, 67-81 & Univ Col, 78-81. *Mem:* Fel AAAS; Am Asn Higher Educ; Am Phys Soc; Am Asn Physics Teachers; Sigma Xi. *Res:* Physics of very low temperatures, especially liquid helium phenomena; science education. *Mailing Add:* UNCC Sta Univ NC Charlotte NC 28223

**WERNY, FRANK,** NATURAL PRODUCTS CHEMISTRY, TEXTILE TECHNOLOGY. *Current Pos:* PRIN CONSULT & OWNER, C&F CONSULT, 93- *Personal Data:* b Ger, June 6, 36; US citizen; m, Dorothy C Corswirt; c Mark, Scott, Chris, Todd & Tim. *Educ:* Univ Puget Sound, BS, 58; Univ Hawaii, PhD(org chem), 63. *Prof Exp:* Ford Found fel, Free Univ Berlin, 62-63; res chemist, Carothers Res Lab, E I du Pont de Nemours & Co Inc, 63-67, sr res chemist, Textile Res Lab, 67-72, Christina Labs, 72-76, Chestnut Run Textile Res Lab, 76-85, res assoc, 85-93. *Mem:* Am Chem Soc; Am Soc Testing & Mat; Fiber Soc. *Res:* Polyamide polymers and fibers; flammability of polymers and textiles; irradiation grafting and melt blending of polymers; polymer rheology; carpet yarns and carpets; nonwoven fabric research and development; fiber light scattering, carpet luster; nylon, polypropylene and polyester extrusion. *Mailing Add:* 334 Old Bailey Lane West Chester PA 19382-8437. *Fax:* 610-399-9068; *E-Mail:* fwerny@chesco.com

**WERSHAW, ROBERT LAWRENCE,** HYDROLOGY, GEOCHEMISTRY. *Current Pos:* HYDROLOGIST, US GEOL SURV, 63- *Personal Data:* b Norwalk, Conn, Sept 17, 35; m 63; c 2. *Educ:* Tex Western Col, BS, 57; Calif Inst Technol, MS, 59; Univ Tex, PhD(geol), 63. *Mem:* Geochem Soc; Am Chem Soc. *Res:* Geochemistry of naturally occurring polyelectrolytes and their interaction with water pollutants. *Mailing Add:* 1566 Winona Ct Denver CO 80204-1143

**WERSTIUK, NICK HENRY,** ORGANIC CHEMISTRY, PHYSICAL CHEMISTRY. *Current Pos:* From asst prof to assoc prof, 67-78, PROF CHEM, MCMASTER UNIV, 78- *Personal Data:* b Dec 31, 39; Can citizen. *Educ:* Univ Alta, BSc, 62; Johns Hopkins Univ, MA, 63, PhD(chem), 66.

*Mem:* Chem Inst Can; Am Chem Soc. *Res:* Base-catalyzed H-D exchange and rearrangement of polycyclic betones and other carbon acids; synthesis of hydrogen-isotope labelled organic compounds; photoelectron spectroscopy of transients. *Mailing Add:* Dept Chem McMaster Univ 1280 Main St W Hamilton ON L8S 4L8 Can

**WERT, CHARLES ALLEN,** FUEL TECHNOLOGY & PETROLEUM ENGINEERING. *Current Pos:* from assoc prof to prof mining & metall eng, 50-56, head dept, 66-86, RACHEFF PROF MAT ENG, UNIV ILL, 86- *Personal Data:* b Battle Creek, Iowa, Dec 31, 19; wid; c 2. *Educ:* Morningside Col, BA, 41; Univ Iowa, MS, 43, PhD(physics), 48. *Honors & Awards:* Alexander von Humboldt Found sr scientist award, WGer, 81, 87; Albert Easton White Award, Am Soc Mat, 89. *Prof Exp:* Mem staff radiation lab, Mass Inst Technol, 43-45; asst, Univ Iowa, 46-48; instr, Inst Study Metals, Univ Chicago, 48-50. *Mem:* Fel Am Phys Soc; fel Am Soc Mat; fel AAAS; Sigma Xi; fel Am Soc Eng Educ. *Res:* Internal friction of metals; diffusion in solids; electron microscopy of solids; alloying behavior of metals with carbon, nitrogen, oxygen and carbon; chemistry and physical structure of coal. *Mailing Add:* 201 Metall Mining Bldg Univ Ill 1304 W Green St Urbana IL 61801

**WERT, JAMES J,** ENGINEERING, MATERIALS SCIENCE. *Current Pos:* from asst prof to prof metall eng, Vanderbilt Univ, 61-72, dir mat sci & eng div, 67-69, chmn dept mat sci & eng, 69-72, chmn mat, mech & struct div, 72-76, chmn dept mech eng & mat sci, 76-82, GEORGE A SLOAN PROF METALL, VANDERBILT UNIV, 72- *Personal Data:* b Barron County, Wis, Jan 9, 33; m 58, Jane A Thornton; c Thaddeus T & Melissa J. *Educ:* Univ Wis, BS, 57, MS, 58, PhD(metall eng), 61. *Honors & Awards:* Fulbright lectr, Middle East, 82. *Prof Exp:* Asst engr, Bettis Atomic Power Lab, 58-59; res scientist, A O Smith Corp, 61. *Concurrent Pos:* Westinghouse fel, Carnegie Inst Technol; consult, Nat Acad Sci; vis prof, Cambridge Univ, 74-75; Fulbright lectr, Middle East, 82. *Mem:* Fel Am Soc Metals; Am Soc Testing & Mat; Am Inst Mining, Metall & Petrol Engrs; Am Welding Soc; fel Am Soc Mech Engrs; Am Asn Univ Professors. *Res:* X-ray diffraction studies of the effects of deformation on superlattice structures; kinetics of antiphase domain growth; residual stresses in metals, friction and wear; fracture, fatigue and failure analysis. *Mailing Add:* 2510 Ridgewood Dr Nashville TN 37215-4518

**WERT, JONATHAN MAXWELL, JR,** MANAGEMENT CONSULTANT, NUCLEAR INDUSTRY. *Current Pos:* PRES, MGT DIAGNOSTICS INC, MGT CONSULTS, 83- *Personal Data:* b Port Royal, Pa, Nov 8, 39; m 83, Monica K Manbeck; c Jonathan III, Kimberly D, Jon A, Justin T & Amanda E. *Educ:* Austin Peay State Univ, BS, 66, MS, 68; Univ Ala, PhD(educ admin), 74. *Honors & Awards:* Am Motors Conserv Award, 76. *Prof Exp:* Chief naturalist, Pa Dept Environ Resources, 68-69; Bays Mountain Park, 69-71; chief naturalist; supvr environ educ sect, Tenn Valley Authority, 71-75; consult energy conserv, Environ Ctr, Univ Tenn, Knoxville, 75-77; sr prof assoc, Energy Exten Serv, Pa State Univ, 77-81; chief, Div Energy Prog Develop, Pa Dept Community Affairs, 81-83. *Mem:* Inst Mgmt Consult; US Energy Asn. *Res:* Development of methodologies for carrying out comprehensive environmental planning, including technological assessment, cost-benefit analysis and environmental impact assessment; energy conservation; systems planning; development of numerous models and survey instruments for assing organization and management effectiveness, organization culture and climate including safety culture; behavioral scientist; organization culture assessment; workprocess improvement; total quality management; status tracking system; stragetic planning; organization design/right sizing; performance measures; environmental impact assessment. *Mailing Add:* PO Box 240 Port Royal PA 17082-0240. *Fax:* 717-436-8938

**WERTH, GLENN CONRAD,** GEOPHYSICS. *Current Pos:* RETIRED. *Personal Data:* b Denver, Colo, July 21, 26; m 50; c 3. *Educ:* Univ Colo, BS, 49; Univ Calif, Los Angeles, MS, 50, PhD(physics, acoust), 53. *Prof Exp:* Physicist, Arthur D Little, Inc, 53-54 & Calif Res Corp, 54-59; physicist, Lawrence LIvermore Lab, Univ Calif, 59-66, assoc dir, 66-81; dir new prog develop, Woodward Clyde Consults, 81-90. *Mem:* Seismol Soc; Am Nuclear Soc; Am Geophys Union; Corporate Planning Asn. *Res:* Seismology; geophysical exploration for oil; use of nuclear explosives in industry and commerce; development of alternate energy supplies; analysis of energy issues and role for research and development; corporate planning. *Mailing Add:* 11473 Ghirardelli Ct Rancho Cordova CA 95670

**WERTH, JEAN MARIE,** MICROBIAL PHYSIOLOGY. *Current Pos:* Asst prof, 72-77, assoc prof, 77-82, PROF BIOL, WILLIAM PATERSON COL, 82- *Personal Data:* b Rochester, NY, Jan 21, 43. *Educ:* Nazareth Col Rochester, BS, 64; Syracuse Univ, MS, 69, PhD(molecular biol), 73. *Concurrent Pos:* Vis scientist, Roche Inst Molecular Biol, 80-81. *Mem:* AAAS; Am Soc Microbiol; Sigma Xi; NY Acad Sci. *Res:* Gene expression in mormoniella vitripennis during various developmental stages. *Mailing Add:* 24 Reality Dr Kinnelon NJ 07405-3133

**WERTH, RICHARD GEORGE,** organic chemistry; deceased, see previous edition for last biography

**WERTH, ROBERT JOSEPH,** ZOOLOGY. *Current Pos:* Asst prof, 69-76, ASSOC PROF BIOL, PURDUE UNIV, CALUMET CAMPUS, 76- *Personal Data:* b Hays, Kans, Apr 4, 40; c 1. *Educ:* St Benedict's Col, Kans, BS, 61; Univ Mo, Kansas City, MS, 65; Univ Colo, Boulder, PhD(zool), 69. *Mem:* AAAS; Am Soc Ichthyologists & Herpetologists. *Res:* Reptilian ccology and physiology; correlation of environmental requirement with physiological adaptation. *Mailing Add:* Dept Biol Purdue Univ Calumet 2233 171st St Hammond IN 46323-2051

**WERTHAMER, N RICHARD,** PHYSICS. *Current Pos:* MGT CONSULT, CHELSEA TECHNOLS, 93- *Personal Data:* b Milwaukee, Wis, Feb 9, 35; div; c Leslie. *Educ:* Harvard Col, BA, 56; Univ Calif, PhD(physics), 61. *Prof Exp:* Res assoc, Univ Calif, San Diego, 61-62; mem tech staff, Bell Labs, 62-75; mem, Corp Planning Staff, AT&T, 75-76; chmn, NY State Energy Res & Develop Authority, 76-78; sr adv, Sci & Technol Dept, Exxon Corp, 78-83; dir, Becton Dickinson & Co, 83-90; exec officer, Am Phys Soc, 90-93. *Mem:* Fel Am Phys Soc; fel AAAS. *Mailing Add:* Chelsea Technols 43 W 16th St Suite 7-D New York NY 10011

**WERTHEIM, ARTHUR ROBERT,** medicine; deceased, see previous edition for last biography

**WERTHEIM, GUNTHER KLAUS,** SURFACE SCIENCE & PHOTOEMISSION. *Current Pos:* CHIEF SCIENTIST, WOODLAND CONSULT, 96- *Personal Data:* b Berlin, Ger, Feb 26, 27; nat US; m 56, Lee Hilles; c Elisabeth (Fraebel), Frederick & Charles G. *Educ:* Stevens Inst Technol, ME, 51; Harvard Univ, AM, 52, PhD(physics), 55. *Honors & Awards:* Humboldt Sr Scientist Award, 86. *Prof Exp:* Assoc phys oceanog, Woods Hole Oceanog Inst, 54; mem tech staff, Bell Tel Labs, Inc, 55-62, head, Crystal Physics Res Dept, 62-84, distinguished mem tech staff, 84-96. *Concurrent Pos:* Adj prof, Stevens Inst Technol, 66-68; mem 'vis comts physics, Harvard Univ, 69-75 & Bartol Res Found, 72-87. *Mem:* Am Phys Soc; Sigma Xi; NY Acad Sci. *Res:* X-ray photo-electron spectroscopy; Mossbauer effect; angular correlations; magnetism; semiconductors; synchrotron radiation. *Mailing Add:* 175 Woodland Ave Convent Station NJ 07961. *E-Mail:* gkw@physics.att.com

**WERTHEIM, ROBERT HALLEY,** NUCLEAR PHYSICS. *Current Pos:* CONSULT, 88- *Personal Data:* b Carlsbad, NMex, Nov 9, 22; m 46, Barbara Selig; c Joseph H & David A. *Educ:* US Naval Acad, BS, 45; Mass Inst Technol, SM, 54. *Honors & Awards:* William S Parsons Award, 71; Gold Medal, Am Soc Naval Engrs, 73. *Prof Exp:* Staff officer, Armed Forces Spec Weapons Proj, USN, 48-49, spec asst nuclear applns, Spec Projs Off, 56, head re-entry body sect, 56-61, weapons develop dept, Naval Ord Test Sta, 61-62, mem staff, Dir of Defense Res & Eng, 62-65, head missile br, Spec Projs Off, 65-67, dep tech dir, 67-68, tech dir, 68-77, dir, Spec Projs Off, 77-80; sr vpres sci & eng, Lockheed Corp, 81-88. *Concurrent Pos:* Consult, Off Secy Defense, Inst Def Anal & Ctr Naval Analysis; mem, Comt Int Security & Arms Control, Nat Acad Sci; mem, Nat Security Adv Group, Los Alamos Nat Lab, Charles Stark Draper Lab Corp, Sci Adv Group, US Strategic Command, Lawrence Livermore Nat Lab, Univ Calif; mem, Lab Opers Bd, Dept Energy; Nat Security Panel, Univ Calif Pres Coun. *Mem:* Nat Acad Eng; Sigma Xi; Am Soc Naval Engrs; fel Am Inst Aeronaut & Astronaut. *Res:* Weapons systems research, development and testing, especially ballistic missiles and nuclear applications. *Mailing Add:* 177705 Devereux Rd San Diego CA 92128

**WERTHEIMER, ALAN LEE,** OPTICAL ENGINEERING, MICROPROCESSORS. *Current Pos:* SR SCIENTIST OPTICS RES, LEEDS & NORTHRUP CO, 74- *Personal Data:* b Cleveland, Ohio, Dec 22, 46; m 69; c 2. *Educ:* Univ Rochester, BS, 68, PhD(optics), 74. *Prof Exp:* Optical syst & lens design, Itek Corp, 68-69. *Mem:* Optical Soc Am; Soc Photo-Optical Instrumentation Eng. *Res:* Light scattering to analyze particle size distributions in air and liquid media; engineering and project management of optically based, microprocessor controlled measuring and recording instruments; optical processing of photographic images; fiber optics communications. *Mailing Add:* 9 Kalleston Dr Pittsford NY 14534

**WERTHEIMER, ALBERT I,** PUBLIC HEALTH ADMINISTRATION. *Current Pos:* DIR, OUTCOMES RES & MGT, 83- *Personal Data:* b Buffalo, NY, Sept 14, 42; m 65; c 2. *Educ:* Univ Buffalo, BS, 65; State Univ NY, Buffalo, MBA, 67; Purdue Univ, PhD(med sociol, pharm), 69. *Prof Exp:* Asst prof pharm, Sch Pharm, State Univ NY, Buffalo, 69-71; asst prof mkt, Sch Mgt, 70-71; researcher med care, Social Security Admin, Dept HEW, 72 & USPHS, 72-73; prof pharm admin & dir grad prog, Univ Minn, Minneapolis, 73-83. *Concurrent Pos:* WHO fel, 75. *Mem:* Am Pub Health Asn; Am Pharmaceut Asn; Am Sociol Asn; AMA. *Res:* Drug use process; drug ecology studies. *Mailing Add:* Dept Outcomes Res & Mgt 770 Sumney Town Pike West Point PA 19486-0004

**WERTHEIMER, MICHAEL ROBERT,** SOLID STATE PHYSICS, MATERIALS SCIENCE ENGINEERING. *Current Pos:* PROF ENG PHYSICS, ECOLE POLYTECH, MONTREAL, 73- *Personal Data:* b Capetown, SAfrica, Jan 22, 40; Can citizen; m 73, Marielle Audet; c Eve & Sophie. *Educ:* Univ Toronto, BASc, 62, MA, 63; Univ Grenoble, Dr es Sc, 67. *Prof Exp:* Process engr thermodyn, Can Liquid Air Ltd, 63-64, res engr cryog, 67-72. *Concurrent Pos:* Pres, Polyplasma Inc, 82-; Killam res fel, Can Coun, 90-92. *Mem:* Fel Inst Elec & Electronics Engrs; Elec Insulation Soc; Am Phys Soc; Can Asn Physicists. *Res:* Electrical insulation; dielectrics; polymers; plasma chemistry; materials science; surface science; engineering physics. *Mailing Add:* Dept Eng Physics Ecole Polytech PO Box 6079 Sta Centre Ville Montreal PQ H3C 3A7 Can. *Fax:* 514-340-3218

**WERTMAN, LOUIS,** BIOMEDICAL ENGINEERING. *Current Pos:* Assoc prof, New York City Community Col, 51-65, adminr electromech, 66-85, vpres eng pharm, 85-93, PROF MECH TECHNOL, NEW YORK CITY COMMUNITY COL, 65-; DIR SCI PROD, OHGARIC STERLIZATION TECHNOL, 93- *Personal Data:* b New York, NY, Oct 2, 25; m 50; c 3. *Educ:* City Col New York, BME, 50. *Concurrent Pos:* Consult engr, 60-85. *Mem:* AAAS; Am Soc Eng Educ; Soc Mfg Engrs; Nat Soc Prof Engrs. *Res:*

Automated biomedical engineering utilizing electromechanical components and systems; educational research in new program development; computer control of medical devices for pharmaceutical industry. *Mailing Add:* 18616 Aberdeen Rd Jamaica NY 11432. *Fax:* 516-231-9124

**WERTMAN, WILLIAM THOMAS,** PETROLEUM ENGINEERING, CHEMICAL ENGINEERING. *Current Pos:* RETIRED. *Personal Data:* b Franklin, Pa, Dec 25, 20; m 42, Virginia Graham; c William T, James M & Mark G. *Educ:* Grove City Col, BS, 42. *Prof Exp:* Chem engr, Joseph E Seagram & Sons, Inc, Md, 42-45 & Bradford Labs, Inc, Pa, 46-48; chem engr, Petrol & Natural Gas Div, US Bur Mines, Pa, 48-54, proj leader, Morgantown Petrol Res Lab, WVa, 54-63, proj cooodr, 63-65, actg chief lab, 65-66, chief lab, 66-70, dep res dir, Morgantown Energy Res Ctr, 70-75, sr staff specialist, Morgantown Energy Technol Ctr, US Dept Energy, 75-81; sr petrol engr, Sci Applns Inc, Morgantown, WVa, 81-82. *Concurrent Pos:* Consult eng, 82- *Mem:* Am Chem Soc; Soc Petrol Engrs; Am Petrol Inst; Am Gas Asn. *Res:* Petroleum and natural gas production; reservoir engineering and rock analysis; subsurface formation temperatures; fluid flow through porous media; water analysis and treatment; coal chemistry and gasification research. *Mailing Add:* 1264 Colonial Dr Morgantown WV 26505

**WERTZ, DAVID LEE,** INORGANIC CHEMISTRY, PHYSICAL CHEMISTRY. *Current Pos:* From asst prof to assoc prof, 66-74, PROF CHEM, UNIV SOUTHERN MISS, 74- *Personal Data:* b Hammond, Ind, Feb 3, 40; m 61; c 2. *Educ:* Ark State Univ, BS, 62; Univ Ark, PhD(chem), 66. *Mem:* Am Chem Soc. *Res:* X-ray diffraction and spectral studies of solute-solvent interactions in concentrated solutions; x-ray diffraction studies of liquid structure. *Mailing Add:* Univ Southern Miss Box 5043 Southern Sta Hattiesburg MS 39406-5043

**WERTZ, DENNIS WILLIAM,** PHYSICAL CHEMISTRY. *Current Pos:* asst prof, 69-74, ASSOC PROF CHEM, NC STATE UNIV, 74- *Personal Data:* b Reading, Pa, Mar 21, 42; m 62; c 2. *Educ:* Univ Md, BS, 64; Univ SC, PhD(chem), 68. *Prof Exp:* Res assoc spectros, Mass Inst Technol, 68-69. *Mem:* AAAS. *Res:* Resonance Raman and electronic absorption spectroscopy of metal dimines and their reduction properties; localization of the redox electron. *Mailing Add:* Dept Chem NC State Univ Box 8204 Raleigh NC 27695-0001

**WERTZ, DOROTHY C,** ETHICAL, LEGAL & SOCIAL ISSUES IN HUMAN GENETICS, CROSS-CULTURAL PERSPECTIVES ON MEDICAL ETHICS. *Current Pos:* SR SCIENTIST SOC SCI, ETHICS & LAW, EUNICE KENNEDY SHRIVER CTR MENT RETARDATION, INC, 91-; RES PROF PUB HEALTH, BOSTON UNIV SCH PUB HEALTH, 84- *Personal Data:* b Buffalo, NY, May 18, 37; m 67, Richard W. *Educ:* Radcliffe Col, AB, 58, AM, 61; Harvard Univ, PhD, 69. *Honors & Awards:* Silver Gavel Award, Am Bar Asn, 91. *Prof Exp:* Instr relig, Bryn Mawr Col, 63-65; instr soc sci, Kingsborough Community Col, 65-66, Univ Lowell, 71-72; asst prof sociol, Boston Col, 66-68, RI Col, 68-69, Bridgewater State Col, 69-71; assoc prof sociol, Univ Bridgeport, 72-73, Univ New Haven, 73-74, Suffolk Univ, 75-81; fel, Nat Endowment Humanities, 74-75, Boston Univ Sch Pub Health, 81-84. *Concurrent Pos:* Consult ethics, Sci Council Can, 87-89, Royal Comn New Reproductive Technol Can, 91-93; prin investr, 37 Nation Surv Ethics & Genetics, Shriver Ctr, 91-; consult sci theatre, Mus Sci, Boston, 92-; mem, Social Issues Comt, Am Soc Human Genetics, 92-; consult ethics, Inst Med, Nat Acad Sci, 92. *Mem:* Human Genome Orgn; Am Soc Human Genetics; Am Pub Health Asn; Nat Soc Genetic Coun; Am Sociol Asn; Soc Study Soc Probs. *Res:* National and international surveys of ethical and social issues in human genetics, including patients and providers in 37 nations; privacy and disclosure, indications for prenatal diagnosis, sex selection, genetic screening and counseling. *Mailing Add:* Shriver Ctr 200 Trapelo Rd Waltham MA 02254. *Fax:* 781-642-0292; *E-Mail:* dwertz@shriver.org

**WERTZ, GAIL T WILLIAMS,** VIROLOGY, MOLECULAR BIOLOGY. *Current Pos:* PROF MICROBIOL, UNIV ALA MED SCH, 87- *Personal Data:* b Washington, DC, Oct 31, 43; m 66, 87. *Educ:* Col William & Mary, BS, 66; Univ Pittsburgh, PhD(microbiol), 70. *Prof Exp:* NIH fel, Med Sch, Univ Mich, Ann Arbor, 70-71, sr res assoc virol, 71-73; from asst prof to assoc prof, Bact & Immunol, Univ NC Med Sch, 73-83, prof microbiol, 83-87. *Concurrent Pos:* NSF & NIH res grants; vis prof, Univ Wis, 83-84; consult, WHO Vaccine Prog, 83-91; ASM Div lectr, Am Soc Microbiol, 87, found lectr, 91. *Mem:* AAAS; Am Soc Microbiol; Am Soc Virol; Sigma Xi. *Res:* Virus-host interactions; viral replication; mechanism of viral nucleic acid synthesis and replication; effect of virus on host macromolecular synthesis and host response to infection-interference phenomenon. *Mailing Add:* Dept Microbiol Univ Ala Sch Med 1717 Seventh Ave S Birmingham AL 35294-0001

**WERTZ, HARVEY J,** ELECTRICAL ENGINEERING, APPLIED MATHEMATICS. *Current Pos:* consult, Aerospace Corp, 64-65, 68-69, mem tech staff, 66-68, 69-73, head, Orbital Systs Prog Dept, 73-79, PRIN DIR COMPUT SYSTS SUBDIV, AEROSPACE CORP, 79- *Personal Data:* b Muskogee, Okla, May 1, 36. *Educ:* Univ Kans, BSEE, 58, MSEE, 59; Univ Wis, PhD(elec eng), 62. *Prof Exp:* Instr elec eng, Univ Kans, 58-59; from asst prof to assoc prof, Univ Wis-Madison, 62-69. *Concurrent Pos:* Asst prof, Math Res Ctr, US Army. *Mem:* Soc Indust & Appl Math; Asn Comput Mach; Inst Elec & Electronics Engrs. *Res:* Application of analytical and computer-oriented mathematics to the analysis and synthesis of physical systems; coordinated development of algorithms and custom hardware to achieve highly efficient processing, specification and development of computer software. *Mailing Add:* 1004 Centinela Ave Santa Monica CA 90403

**WERTZ, JAMES RICHARD,** THEORETICAL ASTROPHYSICS, ASTRONAUTICS. *Current Pos:* PRES, MICROCOSM, INC, TORRANCE, CALIF, 84- *Personal Data:* b Kingman, Ariz, Feb 20, 44; m 67, Alice Valerie; c Laura (Koerner), Cheryl & Julie. *Educ:* Mass Inst Technol, SB, 66; Univ Tex, Austin, PhD(physics), 70. *Prof Exp:* Asst prof physics & astron, Moorhead State Col, 70-73, NSF inst grant, 71-73; sr analyst, Comput Sci Corp, 73-78; dir spacecraft eng, Western Union Space Comt, TRW, 78-80, sr systs engr, TRW, 80-84. *Concurrent Pos:* Mem, Task Group Educ Astron, Am Astron Soc, 74- *Mem:* AAAS; Brit Interplanetary Soc; Am Phys Soc; Am Astron Soc; Am Inst Aeronaut & Astronaut; Sigma Xi. *Res:* Spacecraft attitude determination, interstellar travel and navigation; hierarchical cosmology low-cost rocket development; autonomous navigation; astronautics book development. *Mailing Add:* 2377 Crenshaw Blvd # 350 Torrance CA 90501. *Fax:* 310-320-0252; *E-Mail:* jwertz@smad.com

**WERTZ, JOHN EDWARD,** CHEMISTRY. *Current Pos:* instr mech eng, 45-47, from asst prof to prof phys chem, 48-74, PROF CHEM, UNIV MINN, MINNEAPOLIS, 74- *Personal Data:* b Denver, Colo, Dec 4, 16; m 43; c 3. *Educ:* Univ Denver, BS, 37, MS, 38; Univ Chicago, PhD(chem), 48. *Prof Exp:* Asst prof chem, Augustana Col, 41-44; instr physics, Gustavus Adolphus Col, 44-45. *Concurrent Pos:* Fulbright res scholar & Guggenheim fel, Clarendon Lab, Oxford Univ, 57-58. *Mem:* Fel Am Phys Soc; Brit Inst Physics; Am Chem Soc; The Chem Soc. *Res:* Fluorescence of crystals; surface energy of solids; adsorption of vapors on solids; magnetic susceptibility of adsorbed layers; nuclear and paramagnetic resonance; structure and electronic properties of defects in solids; infrared detectors. *Mailing Add:* 700 Arbogast St St Paul MN 55126-4123

**WERTZ, PHILIP WESLEY,** DERMATOLOGY, ORAL PATHOLOGY. *Current Pos:* assoc prof, 90-93, PROF ORAL PATH, DOWS INST DENT RES, 93- *Personal Data:* b Lykens, Pa, Oct 25, 49; m 73, Nancy M Halverson; c Henry T & Jocelyn M. *Educ:* Rutgers Univ, AB, 71; Univ Wis-Madison, PhD(biochem), 76. *Prof Exp:* Fel, McArdle Lab Cancer Res, 76-79, res assoc, 79-81; asst scientist, Univ Iowa Col Med, 84-90. *Mem:* Soc Investigative Dermat; Am Oil Chemists Soc; Am Soc Biochem & Molecular Biol; Am Asn Dent Res. *Res:* Investigation of the structure, composition and metabolism of epithelial lipids and attempting to define relationships between molecular structure and function of lipids in normal and diseased skin and oral mucosa. *Mailing Add:* Dows Inst Dent Res Univ Iowa Col Dent Iowa City IA 52242. *Fax:* 319-335-8295

**WERTZ, RONALD DUANE,** INDUSTRIAL & MANUFACTURING ENGINEERING. *Current Pos:* DIR, PRODUCTIVITY LAB, BALL CORP, 61- *Personal Data:* b Loveland, Colo, Jan 29, 29; m 51; c 5. *Educ:* Univ Colo, BS, 52. *Prof Exp:* Mem tech staff, Hughes Aircraft Corp, 52-55; sect engr, Lockheed Missiles & Space Div, 55-61. *Mem:* Inst Elec & Electronics Engrs; Soc Mfg Engrs; Am Soc Nondestructive Testing. *Res:* Specialized instruments and equipment to improve manufacturing productivity; electro-optics; ultrasonics; computer science; electronics; mechanisms; robotics; machine design. *Mailing Add:* 2005 Vassar Dr Boulder CO 80303

**WESCHLER, CHARLES JOHN,** INDOOR AIR CHEMISTRY. *Current Pos:* mem tech staff chem, Bell Labs, 75-84, mem tech staff chem, Bell Communs Res, 84-87, DISTINGUISHED MEM PROF STAFF ENVIRON SCI & TECHNOL RES GROUP, BELLCORE, 87-, PROG MGR, ADVANCED ENVIRON STRATEGIES, 95- *Personal Data:* b Youngstown, Ohio, Jan 29, 48; m 71, Louise Blumenauer. *Educ:* Boston Col, BS, 69; Univ Chicago, MS, 72, PhD(chem), 74. *Prof Exp:* Fel phys inorg chem, Northwestern Univ, 74-75. *Concurrent Pos:* Lab grad partic, Argonne Nat Lab, 72-73; mem Nat Acad Sci comt, Advan Assessing Human Exposure Airborne Pollutants, 87-90 & Rev Struct & Performance Health Effects Inst; vis scientist, Lawrence Berkeley Lab, 91-92. *Mem:* AAAS; Am Chem Soc; Am Geophys Union; Am Soc Testing & Mat; Air & Waste Mgt Asn; Int Soc Indoor Air Qual & Climate. *Res:* Indoor aerosols; indoor ozone, nitrogen oxides, volatile organic compounds; chemistry occurring within indoor environments; factors influencing concentrations of indoor airborne pollutants; organic constituents of airborne particles. *Mailing Add:* Bell Commun Res 331 Newman Springs Rd Red Bank NJ 07701-7040. *Fax:* 732-758-2804; *E-Mail:* lamar@cc.bellcore.com

**WESCOTT, EUGENE MICHAEL,** SPACE PHYSICS, EXPLORATION GEOPHYSICS. *Current Pos:* sr res asst, 58-64, from asst prof to assoc prof, 64-74, PROF RES GEOPHYS, GEOPHYS INST, UNIV ALASKA, 74- *Personal Data:* b Hampton, Iowa, Feb 15, 32; div; c 3. *Educ:* Univ Calif, Los Angeles, AB, 55; Univ Alaska, MS, 60, PhD(geophys), 64. *Prof Exp:* Geophysicist, Geophys Res & Develop Br, US AEC, 55-58. *Concurrent Pos:* Nat Acad Sci resident res assoc, NASA-Goddard Space Flight Ctr, 66-69; vis prof inst geophys & planetary physics, Univ Calif, Los Angeles, 76-77. *Mem:* Am Geophys Union; Int Asn Geomagnetism & Aeronomy; Soc Explor Geophys; Geothermal Resources Coun. *Res:* Electric and magnetic fields of the upper atmosphere and of magnetospheric plasmas; auroral mechanisms; geothermal resources exploration research. *Mailing Add:* 342 Beggars Roost Run Fairbanks AK 99709

**WESCOTT, LYLE DUMOND, JR,** ORGANIC CHEMISTRY, POLYMER CHEMISTRY. *Current Pos:* from asst prof to assoc prof, 68-77, head dept, 74-83, PROF CHEM, CHRISTIAN BROS COL, 77- *Personal Data:* b Hackensack, NJ, Jan 27, 37; m 85; c 2. *Educ:* Ga Inst Technol, BS, 59; Pa State Univ, PhD(chem), 63. *Prof Exp:* Res fel, Pa State Univ, 63-64; res chemist, Baytown Labs, Esso Res & Eng Co, Tex, 64-68. *Mem:* Am Chem Soc; Royal Soc Chem. *Res:* Low temperature reactions of vapor species of refractory materials; stabilization of polymeric materials; flame and smoke suppressants for polymeric materials adhesives. *Mailing Add:* Christian Brothers Univ 650 E Pkwy S Memphis TN 38104

**WESCOTT, RICHARD BRESLICH,** VETERINARY PARASITOLOGY. *Current Pos:* PROF VET PATH, WASH STATE UNIV, 71- *Personal Data:* b Chicago, Ill, July 8, 32; m 54; c 3. *Educ:* Univ Wis, BS, 54, MS, 64, PhD(vet med), 65; Univ Minn, DVM, 58; Am Col Lab Animal Med, dipl, 67. *Prof Exp:* USPHS fel parasitol, Univ Wis, 62-65; assoc prof vet microbiol, Sch Vet Med, Univ Mo, Columbia, 65-71. *Concurrent Pos:* Actg chmn dept vet path, Wash State Univ, 75-77. *Mem:* Am Vet Med Asn; Sigma Xi. *Res:* Laboratory animal medicine; nematode-virus interactions in gnotobiotic host animals. *Mailing Add:* 4420 E 51st Lane Spokane WA 99223

**WESCOTT, ROGER WILLIAMS,** ANTHROPOLOGY & LINGUISTICS. *Current Pos:* prof & chmn, 66-91, EMER PROF ANTHROP & LING, DREW UNIV, 91- *Personal Data:* b Philadelphia, Pa, Apr 28, 25; m 64, Hilja J Brigadier; c Walter & Wayne. *Educ:* Princeton Univ, BA, 45, MA, 47, PhD, 48; Oxford Univ, MLitt, 53. *Honors & Awards:* Korzybski lectr, Inst Gen Semantics, 76. *Prof Exp:* Asst prof hist & human rels, Boston Univ & Mass Inst Technol, 53-57; assoc prof eng & soc sci & dir African lang prog, Mich State Univ, 57-62; prof anthrop & hist, Southern Conn State Col, 62-66. *Concurrent Pos:* Ford fel, 55-56; foreign lang consult, US Off Educ, 61; pres, Sch Living, 62-65; exec dir, Inst Explor Educ, 63-66; presidential prof, Colo Sch Mines, 80-81; forensic linguist, NJ State Courts, 82-83. *Mem:* Fel Am Anthrop Asn; fel AAAS; fel African Studies Asn; Int Soc Comp Study Civilizations (pres, 92-); Ling Asn Can & US (pres, 76-77); Int Ling Asn. *Res:* Linguistics; history; reconstruction of prehistoric languages, mainly Proto-Indo-European and Proto-Nostratic. *Mailing Add:* 16A Heritage Crest Southbury CT 06488-1370

**WESCOTT, WILLIAM B,** ORAL PATHOLOGY. *Current Pos:* CLIN PROF ORAL & MAXILLOFACIAL PATH, SCH DENT, UNIV CALIF, SAN FRANCISCO, 85- *Personal Data:* b Pendleton, Ore, Nov 10, 22; m 89, Gloria Greer; c Diane & Douglas. *Educ:* Univ Ore, DMD, 51, MS, 62. *Prof Exp:* Pvt practr gen dent, Ore, 53-59; asst gen path, Med Sch, Univ Ore, 59-60; from asst prof to assoc prof path, 62-69, prof path & assoc dean admin affairs, 69-72; co-dir res & educ training prog, Oral Dis Res Lab, Vet Admin Hosp, Houston, 72-75; chief dent serv, Vet Admin Hosp, Durham, NC, 75-78; co-dir, Southeastern Regional Med Educ Ctr, Birmingham, 78-79; prof oral diag, oral med & oral path, Sch Dent, Univ Calif, Los Angeles, 79-85. *Concurrent Pos:* Dir oral tumor registry, Dent Sch, Univ Ore, 53-54, clin assoc oral & dent med, Med Sch & sr clin investr, 67-69; Am Cancer Soc fel, 59-61; USPHS fel, 61-63; prof path, Univ Tex Dent Br, Houston, 72-75 & Duke Univ Med Sch, 76-78; prof dent, Univ NC, 75-78; prof oral diag radiol path, Dent Sch, Loma Linda Univ, 79-85; dir, Dent Educ Ctr, Los Angeles, 79-85; consult, US Nabal Regional Dent Ctr, 82-; chief dent serv, Vet Admin Med Ctr, San Francisco, 85-94; prof, Golden Gate Univ, 86-; consult, Northern Calif Syst Clin & Vet Admin Med Ctrs, Fresno, Palo Alto, San Francisco & Martinez. *Mem:* Am Dent Asn; Int Asn Dent Res; fel Am Acad Oral Path; Int Asn Microbiol; fel Am Col Dent; Asn Mil Surgeons US. *Res:* Correlation of clinical and histopathologic findings; fluorescent antibody technic; foreign body reaction; bacteriologic and fungal changes under bizarre atmospheres and increased pressures; immunology; salivary glands (xerostomia); oral manifestations of human innumodeficiency virus infection. *Mailing Add:* 437 Justeson Rd Gridley CA 95948-9434. *E-Mail:* globil@manznet.com

**WESELOH, D V (CHIP),** ORNITHOLOGY, WILDLIFE TOXICOLOGY. *Current Pos:* WILDLIFE BIOLOGIST, CAN WILDLIFE SERV, 78- *Personal Data:* b Hutchinson, Minn, Aug 7, 45; Can citizen; m, Linda McKeane; c Sean, Derek, Liam & Kier. *Educ:* Gustavus Adolphus Col, BA, 67; Mich Tech Univ, MS, 69; Univ Calgary, PhD(avian ecol), 77. *Prof Exp:* Cur ornith, Prov Mus Alta, 75-77. *Concurrent Pos:* Dir, Colonial Waterbird Soc, 82-85; pres, Ont Field Ornithologists, 83-86. *Mem:* Am Ornithologists Union; Wilson Ornith Soc; Colonial Waterbird Soc; Cooper Ornith Soc; Asn Field Ornithologists. *Res:* Monitoring contaminant levels and their effects in fish-eating birds on the Great Lakes, such as deformities, population size and productivity in gulls, cormorants and terns. *Mailing Add:* Can Wildlife Serv PO Box 5050 Burlington ON L7R 4A6 Can. *Fax:* 905-336-6434

**WESELOH, RONALD MACK,** ENTOMOLOGY. *Current Pos:* Asst agr scientist, 70-75, assoc agr scientist, 75-81, AGR SCIENTIST, CONN AGR EXP STA, 81- *Personal Data:* b Los Angeles, Calif, June 30, 44; m 74, Eleanor l Helgert. *Educ:* Brigham Young Univ, BS, 66; Univ Calif, Riverside, PhD(entom), 70. *Mem:* Entom Soc Am; Entom Soc Can; Sigma Xi; Int Orgn Biol Control; Ecol Soc Am. *Res:* Control of insect pests by means of parasites and predators; insect behavior and ecology. *Mailing Add:* Conn Agr Exp Sta PO Box 1106 123 Huntington St New Haven CT 06504. *Fax:* 203-789-7232; *E-Mail:* caesent@yalevm.edu

**WESELY, MARVIN LARRY,** MICROMETEOROLOGY. *Current Pos:* asst meteorologist, Argonne Nat Lab, 73-76, sect head, Atmospheric Physics Sect, Radiol & Environ Res Div, 81-83, prog mgr, Atmospheric Physics Prog, Environ Res Div, 83-87, meteorologist, 76-93, SECT HEAD, ATMOSPHERIC RES SECT, ARGONNE NAT LAB, 87-, SR METEOROLOGIST, 93- *Personal Data:* b Cedar Bluffs, Nebr, May 5, 44; m 68, Meridel Berola; c Jennifer & Pamela. *Educ:* Univ Nebr, Lincoln, BS, 65; Univ Wis-Madison, MS, 68, PhD(soil sci), 70. *Prof Exp:* Physicist, US Army Ballistic Res Labs, 70-73. *Mem:* Am Meteorol Soc; Am Soc Agron; Am Geophys Union; Royal Meteorol Soc; AAAS. *Res:* Studies of turbulent transfer of heat, momentum and pollutants in the lower atmosphere; remote sensing of turbulence with ground-based systems; atmospheric boundary layer physics. *Mailing Add:* Argonne Nat Lab Bldg 203 ER Argonne IL 60439. *Fax:* 630-252-5498; *E-Mail:* mlwesely@anl.gov

**WESEMAEL, FRANCOIS,** PHYSICS. *Current Pos:* PROF PHYSICS, UNIV MONTREAL. *Honors & Awards:* Rutherford Medal, Royal Soc Can, 92. *Mailing Add:* Univ Montreal PO Box 6128 St A Montreal PQ H3C 3J7 Can

**WESENBERG, CLARENCE L,** ELECTRONICS ENGINEERING. *Current Pos:* SR RELIABILITY ENGR, 3M CO, 67- *Personal Data:* b Bradley, SDak, May 15, 20; m 42; c 6. *Educ:* SDak State Univ, BS, 43. *Prof Exp:* Radial-physics surveyor, Argonne Nat Lab, 44-46, electronics designer, 46-53; electronics engr, Stromberg-Carlson Co, 53-58, reliability engr, Gen Dynamics/Electronics, 58-62; prof reliability engr, Honeywell, Inc, 62-67. *Mem:* Inst Elec & Electronics Engrs. *Res:* Metrology engineering involving calibration and measurements via mechanical and electromechanical instruments; maintaining accurate parameter measurement control for all magnetic tape parameters affecting performance and usage. *Mailing Add:* 8617 W River Rd N Minneapolis MN 55444

**WESENBERG, DARRELL,** AGRONOMY, GENETICS. *Current Pos:* RES AGRONOMIST, RES & EXTEN CTR, AGR RES SERV, USDA, 68- *Personal Data:* b Madison, Wis, Dec 6, 39; m 68, Janice M Peterson; c 3. *Educ:* Univ Wis-Madison, BS, 62, MS, 65, PhD(agron), 68. *Prof Exp:* Res asst, Univ Wis-Madison, 62-68. *Mem:* Crops Sci Soc Am; Am Soc Agron; AAAS; Am Genetic Asn; Sigma Xi. *Res:* Plant breeding and plant genetics in cereal crops. *Mailing Add:* USDA-ARS Nat Small Grains Germplasm Res Facil PO Box 307 Aberdeen ID 83210. *Fax:* 208-397-4165; *E-Mail:* dwesenb@uidaho.edu

**WESER, DON BENTON,** ORGANIC CHEMISTRY. *Current Pos:* PROF & CHAIR CHEM, FROSTBURG STATE UNIV, 77- *Personal Data:* b Wellsburg, WVa, Feb 7, 42; m 65; c Alice, Katherine & Martha. *Educ:* Bethany Col, BS, 64; WVa Univ, MS, 66; Ga Inst Technol, PhD(org chem), 71. *Prof Exp:* Asst prof chem, Clemson Univ, Sumter, 66-67 & 71-73; assoc prof, Univ SC, Sumter, 73-77. *Concurrent Pos:* Consult, Fibred Co, Lavale & med prof, 87; prof, Goucher Col, 88-90. *Mem:* Sigma Xi; Am Chem Soc. *Res:* Synthesis of certain alkaloids and precursors to such compounds; reaction mechanisms for nucleophilic substitution reactions. *Mailing Add:* Dept Chem Frostburg State Univ Frostburg MD 21532. *Fax:* 301-687-7966; *E-Mail:* weser@antoine.fsu.umd.edu

**WESER, ELLIOT,** MEDICINE, GASTROENTEROLOGY. *Current Pos:* CHIEF MED SERV, AUDIE L MURPHY VET ADMIN HOSP, SAN ANTONIO, 76- *Personal Data:* b New York, NY, Jan 12, 32; m 55; c 1. *Educ:* Columbia Univ, AB, 53, MD, 57; Am Bd Internal Med, dipl, 64; Am Bd Nutrit, cert, 71. *Prof Exp:* Med intern & asst resident, Sch Med & King County Hosp, Univ Wash, 57-59; sr resident med, Bronx Munic Hosp Ctr, Albert Einstein Col of Med, 59-60; clin assoc gastroenterol, Nat Inst Arthritis & Metab Dis, 61-63; from instr to asst prof med, Med Col, Cornell Univ, 63-67; prof physiol & med, Univ Tex Med Sch, San Antonio, 67-76, dep chmn dept, 69-76, head sect gastroenterol, 67-76. *Concurrent Pos:* Res fel med, New York Hosp-Cornell Med Ctr, 60-61; New York Res Coun career scientist award, 63-67; asst attend physician, New York Hosp, 64-67; asst vis physician, Bellevue Hosp, 64-67; attend physician, Bexar County Hosps, 67- *Mem:* AAAS; fel Am Col Physicians; Am Fedn Clin Res; Am Gastroenterol Asn; AMA. *Mailing Add:* Audie L Murphy Vet Admin Hosp 7400 Merton Minter Blvd San Antonio TX 78284-0001. *Fax:* 512-567-4654

**WESLER, OSCAR,** MATHEMATICS, STATISTICS. *Current Pos:* PROF STATIST & MATH, NC STATE UNIV, 64- *Personal Data:* b Brooklyn, NY, July 12, 21. *Educ:* City Col New York, BS, 42; NY Univ, MS, 43; Stanford Univ, PhD(math statist), 55. *Prof Exp:* Asst math, NY Univ, 42-43; asst & instr, Princeton Univ, 43-46; res assoc math statist, Stanford Univ, 52-55, actg asst prof statist, 55-56; from asst prof to assoc prof math, Univ Mich, 56-64. *Concurrent Pos:* Consult inst sci & technnol, Univ Mich, 56-64; vis assoc prof, Stanford Univ, 60, vis prof, 62-63, 73, 74 & 78; NSF nat lectr, 63-; prof on-site studies prog, Int Bus Mach Corp, 66-; vis scholar, Univ Calif, Berkeley, 72-73. *Mem:* Am Math Soc; Inst Math Statist. *Res:* Probability and statistics; stochastic processes; statistical decision theory; functional analysis. *Mailing Add:* Dept Statist NC State Univ PO Box 8203 Raleigh NC 27695-8203

**WESLEY, DEAN E,** SOIL FERTILITY. *Current Pos:* from asst prof to assoc prof agron, 66-74, assoc prof, 74-80, PROF AGR, WESTERN ILL UNIV, 80- *Personal Data:* b Flint, Mich, Feb 26, 37; m 59; c 4. *Educ:* Mich State Univ, BS, 61; SDak State Univ, PhD(soil fertil), 65. *Prof Exp:* Exten soil specialist & asst SCI & Educ Admin-Agr Res, Univ Nebr, 65-66. *Mem:* Am Soc Agron; Soil Sci Soc Am; Soil Conserv Soc Am. *Res:* Plant nutrition; nutrients such as phosphorus, zinc, iron and sulfur. *Mailing Add:* 8 Indian Trail Rd Macomb IL 61455

**WESLEY, ROBERT COOK,** DENTISTRY. *Current Pos:* asst prof prosthodont, Univ Ky, 67-72, actg dir, Gen Pract Residency Dent, 80, dir, 78-90, assoc prof family pract & dir, Div Oral Health, Dept Family Pract, Col Med, 75-78, ASSOC PROF PROSTHODONT, COL DENT, UNIV KY, 72- *Personal Data:* b Jamestown, Ky, Aug 19, 26; m 53; c 2. *Educ:* Berea Col, AB, 50; Univ Louisville, DMD, 54. *Prof Exp:* Pvt practr, 54-67. *Concurrent Pos:* Consult, Vet Admin Hosp, Lexington, Ky, 72; ed, Southeastern Acad Newslett, 73-81; assoc ed, J Prosthetic Dent, 73-81. *Mem:* Int Asn Dent Res; Am Dent Asn; Fed Prosthetic Organs (secy, 84-, pres, 89); Am Prosthodont Soc. *Res:* Complete dentures especially related to geriatric patients. *Mailing Add:* 3367 Keithshire Way Lexington KY 40503

**WESLEY, ROY LEWIS,** food science; deceased, see previous edition for last biography

**WESLEY, WALTER GLEN,** THEORETICAL PHYSICS. *Current Pos:* From asst prof to assoc prof physics, 66-75, PROF PHYSICS, MOORHEAD STATE UNIV, 75- *Personal Data:* b Ft Worth, Tex, Oct 12, 38; m 68, Beverly Guthmiller; c Leanne, Debie, Vadnais, Randy, Vadnais & Michael Vodnais. *Educ:* Tex Christian Univ, BA, 61; Univ NC, PhD(physics), 70. *Mem:* Royal Astron Soc Can; Am Asn Physics Teachers; Am Phys Soc. *Res:* Gravitational theory and quantum gravitation; interaction of science and society; history of astronomy and physics: 17-19th century cognitive science. *Mailing Add:* Dept Physics Moorhead State Univ Moorhead MN 56563-0001

**WESNER, JOHN WILLIAM,** ENGINGEERING & CONSUMER PRODUCT DESIGN, QUALITY MANAGEMENT. *Current Pos:* supvr, IS Res & Develop, 83-86, TECH MGR, BCS, LUCENT TECHNOLOGIES, 87- *Personal Data:* b Newark, NJ, July 14, 36; m 65, Monica A Fischer; c Katrin & Francis. *Educ:* Carnegie Inst Technol, BS, 58; Calif Inst Technol, MS, 59; Carnegie-Mellon Univ, PhD(mech eng), 68. *Honors & Awards:* Robert E Abbott Award, Am Soc Mech Engrs. *Prof Exp:* Sr engr, Atomic Power Div, Westinghouse Elec Corp, 64-68; from mem tech staff to supvr, Bell Tel Lab, 68-82. *Concurrent Pos:* Chairperson, Design Educ Comt, Am Soc Mech Engrs, 83-87, chairperson, Design for Manufacturability Comt, 87-89, chair, Design Eng Div, 91-92; assoc ed, Mfg Rev, 88-96, adv ed, Res Eng Design, 89-95; chair, Technols Execs Conf, Am Soc Mech Engrs, 93-96, vpres systs & design, 96-; consult ed eng improv, Addison Wesley Pub, 93-*Mem:* Fel Am Soc Mech Engrs; Sigma Xi. *Res:* Physical design (mechanical design and development) of small business telecommunications systems; engineering process management and improvement; improving how engineering design is carried out. *Mailing Add:* 63 Glendale Dr Freehold NJ 07728-1357. *E-Mail:* jwesnet@lucent.com

**WESOLOWSKI, DAVID JUDE,** AQUEOUS SPECIATION, MINERAL SOLUBILITIES. *Current Pos:* Eugene P Wigner fel, Oak Ridge Nat Lab, 83-85, res staff mem, 85-89, geochem group leader, 89-96, SR RES STAFF, CHEM & ANALYTICAL SCI DIV, OAK RIDGE NAT LAB, 95- *Personal Data:* b Canonsburg, Pa, May 12, 54; m 75, Mary Ann Ruffing; c James John, Anne Marie, Steven David & Peter Michael. *Educ:* Univ Pittsburgh, BS, 76; Pa State Univ, PhD(geochem & mineral), 84. *Honors & Awards:* Lockheed Martin Tech Achievement Award, 96. *Prof Exp:* Explor geologist, US Steel Corp, 76-77. *Concurrent Pos:* Adj prof, Univ Tenn, Knoxville, 90- & Univ Nebr Lincoln, 97-; assoc ed, Geochimica Et Cosmuchimica Acta, 92-; consult, Elec Power Res Inst, 94-95; ed, Geochem News, 95-; co-organizer, Fifth Int Symp Hydrothermal Reactions, 97. *Mem:* AAAS; Am Geophys Union; Geochem Soc (secy, 95-); Geol Soc Am; Int Asn Geochem & Cosmochem. *Res:* High temperature ph-measurement cells to study the dissociation constants of inorganic and organic acids and bases; hydrolysis and complexation of metal ions; kinetics of organic acid decomposition; surface charge properties of minerals and mineral solubility; light stable isotope partitioning in hydrothermal systems. *Mailing Add:* Oak Ridge Nat Lab PO Box 2008 Oak Ridge TN 37831-6110. *Fax:* 423-574-4961; *E-Mail:* dqw@ornl.gov

**WESOLOWSKI, WAYNE EDWARD,** PHYSICAL & ENVIRONMENTAL CHEMISTRY. *Current Pos:* ASSOC PROF, ILL BENEDICTINE COL, 74-*Personal Data:* b Cicero, Ill, July 25, 45; m 68; c 2. *Educ:* St Procopius Col, BS, 67; Univ Ariz, PhD(chem), 71. *Prof Exp:* Res scientist, Freeman Lab, Inc, 71-73; vpres, Chicago Sci, Inc, 73-74. *Concurrent Pos:* Fel, Res Corp, 74-75. *Mem:* Am Chem Soc; Air Pollution Control Asn. *Res:* Paramagnetic behavior of transition metals in anisotropic ligand fields; isokinetic particulate sampling of stationary environmental pollution sources. *Mailing Add:* Dept Chem Benedictine Col Lisle IL 60532-0900

**WESS, JULIUS,** MATHEMATICAL PHYSICS. *Current Pos:* DIR, WERNER-HEISENBERG INST, MAX PLANCK INST PHYSICS. *Personal Data:* b 1934. *Honors & Awards:* Eugene P Wigner Award, Am Nuclear Soc, 92; Walter Thirring Int Prize, 97. *Mailing Add:* Max Planck Inst Physics Fohringer Ring 6 Postfach 401212 80805 Munich Germany

**WESSEL, FRANK J,** PHYSICS OF ULTRA HIGH ENERGY DENSITY, PULSED POWER ELECTRONICS. *Current Pos:* RES PHYSICIST, UNIV CALIF, IRVINE, 86- *Educ:* Calif State Univ, BA, 75; Univ Calif, MA, 77, PhD(physics), 80. *Prof Exp:* Scientist, Hughes Res Labs, 80-83; sr scientist, Western Res, 83-84, Jaycor, 84-86. *Mem:* Am Phys Soc; Am Geophys Soc. *Mailing Add:* Dept Physics Univ Calif Irvine CA 92697

**WESSEL, GUNTER KURT,** ASTRONOMY. *Current Pos:* RETIRED. *Personal Data:* b Berlin, Ger, Mar 29, 20; US citizen; m 53; c 3. *Educ:* Tech Hochsch, Berlin, BS, 40; Univ Gottingen, dipl, 47, PhD(physics), 48. *Prof Exp:* Physicist, Lorenz Radio AG, Berlin, 43-45; fel, Nat Res Coun Can, 51-53; consult physics, Gen Elec Co, Syracuse NY, 53-61; prof physics, Syracuse Univ, 61-86. *Res:* Atomic physics; spectroscopy; masers; lasers; magnetic resonance. *Mailing Add:* Four Jamar Dr Fayetteville NY 13066

**WESSEL, HANS U,** CARDIOLOGY, PHYSIOLOGY. *Current Pos:* RETIRED. *Personal Data:* b Duisburg, Ger, Apr 18, 27; US citizen; m 55; c 5. *Educ:* Univ Freiburg, MD, 53. *Prof Exp:* Instr med, Northwestern Univ, Chicago, 60-63, assoc, 63-65, asst prof pediat, 65-67, asst prof pediat, 67-71, assoc prof eng sci, 73-76, prof pediat, Med Sch, 76-97, prof eng sci, 76-97. *Concurrent Pos:* NIH cardiovasc res trainee, Med Sch, Northwestern Univ, Chicago, 61-63; Am Heart Asn estab investr, 65-70, fel coun circulation, 65- *Mem:* AAAS; assoc fel Am Col Cardiol; assoc mem Inst Elec & Electronics Engrs; sr mem Instrument Soc Am; Biomed Eng Soc. *Res:* Bioengineering; effect of pulmonary vascular disease on pulmonary gas exchange; instrumentation; indicator dilution techniques; thermal velocity probes; patient monitoring system; exercise physiology in children. *Mailing Add:* 63 Mulberry Rd Deerfield IL 60015

**WESSEL, JOHN EMMIT,** CHEMICAL PHYSICS, REMOTE SENSING. *Current Pos:* mem tech staff, 74-78, res scientist, 78-80, SR SCIENTIST, CHEM & PHYSICS LAB, AEROSPACE CORP, 80- *Personal Data:* b Los Angeles, Calif, Mar 8, 42. *Educ:* Univ Calif, Los Angeles, BS, 65; Univ Chicago, PhD(chem), 70. *Honors & Awards:* Aerospace Corp Pres Award. *Prof Exp:* Fel chem, Univ Pa, 69-72, instr, 72-74. *Concurrent Pos:* Prin investr, Dept Energy & Aerospace Corp Sponsored Prog. *Mem:* Am Phys Soc; Sigma Xi; AAAS; Am Chem Soc. *Res:* Laser spectroscopy applied to molecular detection, laser and microwave remote sensing. *Mailing Add:* 919 Duncan Ave Manhattan Beach CA 90266-6625

**WESSEL, WILLIAM ROY,** GLOBAL WEATHER FORECASTING, PLANETARY ATMOSPHERE MODELING. *Current Pos:* SCI CONSULT, W ROY WESSEL & ASSOCS, 87- *Personal Data:* b Louisville, Ky, Nov 20, 37. *Educ:* Univ Notre Dame, BS, 59; Univ Mich, MS, 61, PhD(physics), 65. *Prof Exp:* Fel, Univ Chicago, 64-66; res scientist, Argonne Nat Lab, 66-72; res assoc, Fla State Univ, 72-74; vis scientist, Nat Ctr Atmospheric Res, 74-79; sr consult, Control Data Corp, 79-87. *Mem:* Soc Indust & Appl Math; Am Math Soc. *Res:* Construction and adaptation of fluid dynamic models in the form of computer programs; development of numerical algorithms and writing of scientific software. *Mailing Add:* 3545 Arthur Ct No 3 Boulder CO 80304

**WESSELLS, NORMAN KEITH,** DEVELOPMENTAL BIOLOGY. *Current Pos:* from asst prof to prof biol sci, Stanford Univ, 62-88, chmn dept, 72-78, actg dir, Hopkins Marine Sta, 72-76, assoc dean humanities & sci, 77-81, dean humanities & sci, 81-88, EMER PROF BIOL SCI, STANFORD UNIV, 88-; PROF BIOL, UNIV ORE, 88- *Personal Data:* b Jersey City, NJ, May 11, 32; m, Catherine Briggs; c Elizabeth, Colin, Philip, Stephen & Christopher. *Educ:* Yale Univ, BS, 54, PhD(zool), 60. *Honors & Awards:* Herman Beerman Award, Soc Investigative Dermat, 71. *Prof Exp:* Am Cancer Soc fel, 60-62. *Concurrent Pos:* Am Cancer Soc scholar cancer res, Dept Biochem, Univ Wash, 68-69; Guggenheim Found fel, 75-76; chmn, Yale Coun Comt Biol Sci; vpres acad affairs & provost, Univ Ore, 88-94. *Mem:* Am Soc Zoologists; Soc Develop Biol (pres, 78). *Res:* Embryonic induction; cytodifferentiation; chemistry, ultrastructure of skin, pancreas development; development of nerve cells, axons. *Mailing Add:* 28015 Stonehenge Lane Eugene OR 97402

**WESSELS, BRUCE WARREN,** MATERIALS SCIENCE, ELECTRONIC MATERIALS. *Current Pos:* from asst prof to assoc prof, 77-83, prof elec eng & comput sci, 89, PROF MAT SCI, NORTHWESTERN UNIV, 84- *Personal Data:* b New York, NY, Oct 18, 46; m 68, Tiedemann; c David & Kirston. *Educ:* Univ Pa, BS, 68; Mass Inst Technol, PhD(mat sci), 73. *Prof Exp:* Mem tech staff, Gen Elec Res Ctr, 72-77. *Concurrent Pos:* Prin investr, NSF grant, DOE grant; consult, NSF, ARO, Raychem; chmn, Elec Mat Comn, Metall Soc; mem ed bd, J Electronic Mats, 90; bd dir & div dir, Minerals, Metals & Mat Soc; vis scientist, Argonne Nat Lab, 78. *Mem:* Electrochem Soc; Mat Res Soc; Minerals, Metals & Mat Soc (vpres, 95, pres, 96); fel Am Soc Metall. *Res:* Semiconductor physics; defects in semiconductors; thin films; electronic and photonic property measurements; electro-optic materials and devices. *Mailing Add:* Dept Mat Sci & Dept Elec & Comput Eng Northwestern Univ Evanston IL 60208. *Fax:* 847-491-7820

**WESSELSKI, CLARENCE J,** AEROSPACE ENGINEERING. *Current Pos:* AEROSPACE TECHNICIAN, LOCKHEED ENG, HOUSTON. *Honors & Awards:* Engr Year Award, Am Inst Aeronaut & Astronaut, 90. *Mailing Add:* Aerospace Technician Lockheed Eng MS B14 Houston TX 77058

**WESSINGER, WILLIAM DAVID,** BEHAVIORAL PHARMACOLOGY, PSYCHOPHARMACOLOGY. *Current Pos:* res assoc pharmacol, 83-85, from instr to asst prof, 85-92, ASSOC PROF PHARMACOL & TOXICOL, UNIV ARK MED SCI, 92- *Personal Data:* b Honolulu, Hawaii, Nov 8, 51; m 88, Laura L Fike; c Eliza, Kathleen & Marinna. *Educ:* Rutgers Univ, BS, 73; Med Col Va, PhD(pharmacol & toxicol), 83. *Prof Exp:* Res asst environ sci, Rutgers Univ, 71-73; teaching asst oceanog, Univ Mass, Amherst, 73-74. *Concurrent Pos:* Consult drug testing, Fed Aviation Admin, 90-92. *Mem:* Am Soc Pharmacol & Exp Therapeut; Soc Stimulus Properties Drugs; Int Study Group Investigating Drugs as Reinforcers; Soc Neurosci; Behav Pharmacol Soc; Behav Toxicol Soc; Col Probs Drug Dependence. *Res:* Behavioral pharmacology of narcotics, phencyclidine and other psychoactive drugs; discriminative stimulus properties of drugs, tolerance, dependence and drug interactions; drugs of abuse. *Mailing Add:* Dept Pharmacol & Toxicol Univ Ark Med Sci Slot 611 Little Rock AR 72205. *Fax:* 501-686-5521; *E-Mail:* wdwessinger@life.uams.edu

**WESSLER, MAX ALDEN,** THERMODYNAMICS, COMBUSTION. *Current Pos:* from asst prof to assoc prof, 56-71, chmn dept, 74-96, PROF MECH ENG, BRADLEY UNIV, 71-,. *Personal Data:* b Jacksonville, Ill, Jan 16, 31; m 53, Ardith Mehrings; c Kirk, Peter & Tamara. *Educ:* Bradley Univ, BSME, 52; Univ Southern Calif, MSME, 54; Purdue Univ, PhD, 66. *Prof Exp:* Mech engr, Guided Missiles Labs, Hughes Aircraft Co, Calif, 52-54; first lieutenant, USAF, 54-56. *Concurrent Pos:* Mem tech staff, Electron Dynamics Dept, Hughes Res Labs, 60-62; mem bd dirs, Soc Automotive Engrs, 76-78; mem bd dirs, Accreditation Bd Eng & Technol, 77-83 & Eng Accreditation Comt, 84-88; chmn, Mech Eng Div, Am Soc Eng Educ, 86-87. *Mem:* Soc Automotive Engrs; Am Soc Eng Educ; Am Soc Mech Engrs. *Res:* Thermodynamics and combustion; fluid mechanics. *Mailing Add:* Dept Mech Eng Bradley Univ 1501 W Bradley Ave Peoria IL 61625-0002. *Fax:* 309-677-3453; *E-Mail:* max@bradley.bradley.edu

**WESSLER, STANFORD,** MEDICINE. *Current Pos:* PROF MED & ASSOC DEAN POST-GRAD, MED SCH, NY UNIV, 74- *Personal Data:* b New York, NY, Apr 20, 17; m 42; c 3. *Educ:* Harvard Univ, BA, 38; NY Univ, MD, 42; Am Bd Internal Med, dipl. *Honors & Awards:* James F Mitchell Award, Heart & Vascular Res, 72; Award of Merit, Am Heart Asn, 78. *Prof Exp:* Asst med, Harvard Med Sch, 49-51, instr, 51-54, assoc, 54-57, asst prof & tutor, 57-64; prof med, Sch Med, Wash Univ, 64-74, John E & Adeline Simon prof, 66-74. *Concurrent Pos:* Res fel med, Harvard Med Sch, 46-49; Nat Heart Inst trainee, 49-51; Am Heart Asn estab investr, 54-59; James F Mitchell Award heart & vascular res, 72-; asst, Beth Israel Hosp, Boston, 46-49, assoc, 49-56, physician, Vasc Clin, 54-64, assoc vis physician, 57-58, vis physician, 59-64, head, Anticoagulation Clin, 60-64, dir, Clin Res Ctr Thrombosis & Atherosclerosis, Harvard Med Sch, 61-64, assoc dir, 64-; mem, Comt Thrombosis & Hemorrhage, Nat Res Coun, 60-64, Inst Med, 86-88; physician-in-chief, Jewish Hosp, St Louis & assoc physician, Barnes Hosp, 64-75; mem, Med Adv Bd, Coun Circulation, Am Heart Asn, 64- & Coun Stroke, 67-76, vchmn, Coun Thrombosis, 71-74, chmn, 74-76, chmn, Publ Comt, 72-77, vpres coun, 74-76; vchmn heart training comt, Nat Heart Inst, 65-67 & mem, Thrombosis Adv Comt, 67-71; chmn, Subgroup Thromboembolism, Inter-Soc Comn Heart Dis Resources, 69-72; dir, Nat Heart & Lung Inst Thrombosis Ctr, Wash Univ Sch Med, 71-74; mem, Comn Stroke, Nat Inst Neurol Dis & Stroke, 72-74; attend physician, NY Univ Med Ctr, Univ Hosp, New York, 74- & Bellevue Hosp Ctr, 74- *Mem:* Am Fedn Clin; Am Soc Hemat; Int Soc Internal Med; Am Soc Clin Invest; fel Am Col Physicians; Am Physiol Soc; Asn Am Physicians. *Res:* Blood coagulation; peripheral vascular disease. *Mailing Add:* Dept Med NY Univ Sch Med 60 Rye Rd Rye NY 10580

**WESSLER, SUSAN R,** TRANSPOSABLE ELEMENTS IN PLANTS, GENE REGULATION IN MAIZE. *Current Pos:* from asst prof to assoc prof, 83-89, PROF BOT, UNIV GA, 89-, DIR, CTR PLANT CELLULAR & MOLECULAR BIOL, 91-, PROF GENETICS, 93-, RES PROF, 94- *Personal Data:* b New York, NY, Sept 26, 53; m 79, Mark A Schell; c Nicole & Rebecca. *Educ:* State Univ NY, Stony Brook, BS, 74; Cornell Univ, PhD(biochem), 80. *Prof Exp:* Am Cancer Soc Fel, Dept Embryol, Carnegie Inst, 80-83. *Concurrent Pos:* Mem, Comt Plant Scis & Nat Plant Genetics, Resources Bd, Nat Res Coun, 90-91; prin investr, NIH, NSF, Dept Energy, McKnight Found & Rockefeller Found, 83-; mem, Genetics Study Sect, NIH. *Mem:* Genetics Soc; Am Soc Plant Physiol; AAAS. *Res:* Isolation of active transposable elements from maize and an assessment of their mechanism of transposition and their role in genome evolution; natural variation of a family of regulatory genes to understand mechanisms of post transcriptional gene regulation and how such mechanisms may have evolved. *Mailing Add:* Genetics Dept Univ Ga Athens GA 30602. *Fax:* 706-542-3910; *E-Mail:* sue@dogwood.botany.uga.edu

**WESSLING, RITCHIE A,** PHYSICAL CHEMISTRY, POLYMER SCIENCE. *Current Pos:* chemist, Polymer Res Lab, Dow Chem Co, 62, assoc scientist, polymer sci group, 68-78, res scientist, Cent Res, Phys Res Lab, 78-80, AG Prod Dept, 80-82, res scientist, 82-87, SR RES SCIENTIST, CENT RES, DOW CHEM CO, 87- *Personal Data:* b Iowa, Sept 15, 32; m 61; c 5. *Educ:* Mich State Univ, BS, 57, MS, 59; Univ Pa, PhD(phys chem), 62. *Prof Exp:* Chemist, Wyandotte Chem Co, 59. *Mem:* Am Chem Soc; AAAS; Am Inst Chemists. *Res:* Relationship between physical properties of polymeric materials and their chemical structure; membranes. *Mailing Add:* 867 Calabasas Rd Watsonville CA 95076

**WESSON, JAMES ROBERT,** MATHEMATICS. *Current Pos:* RETIRED. *Personal Data:* b Jackson Gap, Ala, Nov 1, 21; m 43; c 4. *Educ:* Birmingham-Southern Col, BS, 49; Vanderbilt Univ, MA, 49, PhD(math), 53. *Prof Exp:* Instr math, Univ Tenn, 49-50; from asst prof to assoc prof, Birmingham-Southern Col, 51-57; from asst prof to assoc prof, Vanderbilt Univ, 57-66, assoc dean, prof math, 61-90. *Concurrent Pos:* Dir undergrad studies, Vanderbilt Univ, 70-77. *Mem:* Math Asn Am. *Res:* Projective planes; abstract algebra; numerical solutions of differential equations. *Mailing Add:* 612 Spring House Ct Brentwood TN 37027

**WESSON, LAURENCE GODDARD, JR,** physiology, internal medicine, for more information see previous edition

**WESSON, PAUL STEPHEN,** COSMOLOGY, SOLAR SYSTEM. *Current Pos:* assoc prof, 84-88, PROF PHYSICS, UNIV WATERLOO, CAN, 88- *Personal Data:* b Nottingham, Eng, Sept 11, 49; Can citizen; c Amanda, Emily & Jasper. *Educ:* Univ London, BSc, 71; Univ Cambridge, MSc, 72, PhD(astron), 79. *Prof Exp:* Asst prof physics, Univ Alta, Can, 80-84. *Concurrent Pos:* Vis prof space sci, Univ Calif, Berkeley, 90-95 & Gravity Group, Stanford Univ, 90-97. *Mem:* Int Astron Union; Royal Astron Soc; Am Astron Asn; Can Inst Theoret Astrophys. *Res:* Cosmology; solutions of general relativity; clusters of galaxies; fundamental constants of physics; the solar system and its origin; formation and rotation of earth. *Mailing Add:* Dept Physics Univ Waterloo Waterloo ON N2L 3G1 Can. *Fax:* 519-746-8115; *E-Mail:* wesson@watsci.uwaterloo.ca

**WESSON, ROBERT LAUGHLIN,** SEISMOLOGY, TECTONOPHYSICS. *Current Pos:* Res assoc, US Geol Surv, 70-72, chief, Off Earthquake Studies, 78-80, asst dir res, 80-81, asst dir res progs, 81-82, GEOPHYSICIST, US GEOL SURV, 72- *Personal Data:* b San Francisco, Calif, Feb 26, 44; m 66; c 2. *Educ:* Mass Inst Technol, SB, 66; Stanford Univ, MS, 68, PhD(geophys), 70. *Concurrent Pos:* US chmn, US-USSR Working Group Earthquake Prediction, 78-82. *Mem:* Am Geophys Union; Seismol Soc Am; Geol Soc Am; Earthquake Engr Res Inst; AAAS. *Res:* Earthquake prediction; seismology; tectonophysics. *Mailing Add:* US Geol Surv PO Box 25046 Denver CO 80225

**WEST, A(RNOLD) SUMNER,** CHEMICAL ENGINEERING, CHEMICAL PRODUCT SAFETY & REGULATIONS. *Current Pos:* OWNER & PRIN, A S WEST ASSOCS, 87- *Personal Data:* b Philadelphia, Pa, Jan 12, 22; m 46, Beverly Lehman; c 2. *Educ:* Univ Pa, BS, 43; Pa State Univ, MS, 46. *Honors & Awards:* Founders Award, Am Inst Chem Engrs, 79, T J Hamilton Mem Award, 82 & F J Van Antwerpen Award, 83. *Prof Exp:* Asst, Pa State Univ, 43-46; process engr, Rohm & Haas Co, 46-52, process group leader, 52-62, semi-works supt & head res comput lab, 62-72, mgr petrol chem res, 72-77, sr tech specialist govt & regulatory affairs, 78-87. *Concurrent Pos:* Pres, United Eng Trustees, Inc, 86-87; vchmn, Chem Heritage Found, 84-92. *Mem:* Am Chem Soc; Nat Soc Prof Engrs; Am Inst Chem Engrs (pres, 77); Soc Automotive Engrs; Water Environ Fedn. *Mailing Add:* A S West Assocs 3896 Sidney Rd Huntingdon Valley PA 19006-2347

**WEST, ANITA,** TECHNOLOGY TRANSFER, SCIENCE POLICY. *Current Pos:* PVT CONSULT, 91- *Personal Data:* b New York, NY, Oct 21, 30; m 55, David L; c David & Laurie. *Educ:* Univ Denver, BA, 60, MS, 62, PhD(math educ), 69. *Prof Exp:* Eng, Martin Marietta, 60-63; systs analyst, IBM, 63-64; res math, Denver Res Inst, 64-88, div head, 78-88, chief oper officer, 86-88; prin scientist, Appl Res Assocs, 88-90; sr dir, McRel, 88-91. *Concurrent Pos:* Instr, civil eng, Univ Denver, 64-68; instr math, Arapahoe Community Col, 70-74; Gov Sci & Adv Coun, Colo, 81-85. *Mem:* Sigma Xi; NY Acad Sci; AAAS. *Res:* Plan, direct and publish policy studies and evaluations in the fields of education and training technology; distance learning; technology transfer with cost-benefit analysis and ethics studies. *Mailing Add:* 3235 S St Paul St Denver CO 80210

**WEST, ANN H,** GENETICS. *Current Pos:* ASST PROF, DEPT CHEM & BIOCHEM, UNIV OKLA, 96- *Personal Data:* b Hong Kong, Feb 14, 61; Brit citizen. *Educ:* Wesleyan Univ, BA, 83; Yale Univ, PhD(genetics), 91. *Prof Exp:* Postdoctoral fel, Univ Med & Dent NJ, 91-96. *Mem:* AAAS; Am Crystallog Asn. *Res:* Two-component signal transduction pathways; protein phosphorylation. *Mailing Add:* Dept Chem & Biochem Univ Okla 620 Parrington Oval Rm 208 Norman OK 73019. *Fax:* 405-325-6111; *E-Mail:* awest@chemdept.chem.ou.edu

**WEST, ARTHUR JAMES, II,** parasitology, marine biology, for more information see previous edition

**WEST, BOB,** TOXICOLOGY. *Current Pos:* PRES, BOB WEST ASSOCS, INC, STAMFORD, CONN, 75-; PRIN, FOOD, DRUG, CHEM SERV, FAIRFAX, VA. *Personal Data:* b Ellenville, NY, Mar 7, 31; m 57, 82, Jacqueline Cutler; c Lauren, Elizabeth A & Sharon L. *Educ:* Union Univ, BS, 52; Purdue Univ, MS, 54, PhD, 56. *Prof Exp:* Vpres, Rosner-Hixson Labs, Chicago, 60-68; dir, sci & regulatory affairs, Vick Chem Co, Mt Vernon, NY, 68-75. *Mem:* Am Soc Pharmacol & Exp Therapeut; Soc Toxicol; Acad Pharmaceut Sci; Drugs Info Asn (past pres); Am Col Clin Pharmacol. *Res:* Pharmaceuticals; chemicals, biotechnology and devices; clinical pharmacology and safety evaluation. *Mailing Add:* Food Drug Chem Serv 3771 Center Way Fairfax VA 22033. *Fax:* 703-255-6434

**WEST, BRUCE DAVID,** BIOCHEMISTRY. *Current Pos:* RETIRED. *Personal Data:* b Madison, Wis, July 10, 35; m 57; c 2. *Educ:* Univ Wis, BS, 57, MS, 61, PhD(biochem), 62. *Prof Exp:* Fel biochem, Univ Wis, 62-63; asst prof chem, Univ NMex, 63-69; asst prof, Eastern Mich Univ, 69-74, assoc prof chem, 74-90. *Mem:* Am Chem Soc; The Chem Soc. *Res:* Coumarin anticoagulants; structure-activity relationship, synthesis, biodegradation. *Mailing Add:* 10684 Liss Rd Willis MI 48191

**WEST, BRUCE JOSEPH,** NONLINEAR DYNAMICS SYSTEMS THEORY, QUANTUM MANIFESTATIONS OF CHAOS. *Current Pos:* chair, 89-93, PROF PHYSICS, UNIV NTEX, 89- *Personal Data:* b Buffalo, NY, Oct 15, 41; m 68, Sharon S Sparacio; c Jason B & Damien J. *Educ:* State Univ NY, Buffalo, BA, 65; Univ Rochester, MA, 67, PhD(physics), 70. *Honors & Awards:* Decker Award, 93. *Prof Exp:* Res assoc low energy theory, Physics Dept, Univ Rochester, 70-71, fel, Inst Fundamental Studies, 71-72; staff scientist, Phys Dynamics Inc, 72-79; res scientist, La Jolla Inst, 79-89, assoc dir, Ctr Studies Nonlinear Dynamics, 80-85, dir, Div Appl Nonlinear Probs, 83-89. *Concurrent Pos:* Consult, Phys Dynamics, 79-90, NASA, 84-85 & John P & Catherine T MacArthur Found, 84-85; res assoc, Physics Dept, Univ Calif, San Diego, 83-86, vis res physicist, Inst Nonlinear Sci, 86-89; mem, Automation & Robotics Panel, NASA, 84-85; sr lectr, Scripps Inst Oceanog, 87; mem, Nonlinear Ocean Waves Panel, Off Naval Res, 90; fel, Am Phys Soc, 92; Decker scholar, Univ NTex, 94-; vchair, Biol Physics Div, Am Phys Soc, 97. *Mem:* Fel Am Phys Soc; Am Geophys Union; AAAS; NY Acad Sci; Soc Indust & Appl Math; Soc Math Biol. *Res:* Application of dynamic systems theory to biomedical time series, to quantum phenomena and the foundations of statistical mechanics. *Mailing Add:* Univ NTex Dept Physics PO Box 5368 Denton TX 76203. *Fax:* 817-565-2515; *E-Mail:* west@soliton.phys.unt.edu

**WEST, CHARLES ALLEN,** PLANT BIOCHEMISTRY. *Current Pos:* Instr chem, Univ Calif, Los Angeles, 52 & 55, from asst prof to prof, 56-93, vchmn dept, 70-75, chmn dept, 81-84, actg dean phys sci, 88, EMER PROF CHEM, UNIV CALIF, LOS ANGELES, 93- *Personal Data:* b Greencastle, Ind, Nov 4, 27; m 52, Carol Venerable; c 2. *Educ:* DePauw Univ, AB, 49; Univ Ill, PhD(chem), 52. *Hon Degrees:* DSc, DePauw Univ, 81. *Concurrent Pos:* Guggenheim fel, 61-62. *Mem:* Am Chem Soc; Am Soc Biol Chemists; Am Soc Plant Physiol. *Res:* Chemistry and biosynthesis of natural products of physiological importance, including gibberellins and other plant growth regulators; metabolic regulation; molecular basis of plant disease resistance. *Mailing Add:* Dept Chem & Biochem Univ Calif 405 Hilgard Ave Los Angeles CA 90095-1569. *Fax:* 310-206-4038

**WEST, CHARLES DAVID,** ANALYTICAL CHEMISTRY. *Current Pos:* from asst prof to assoc prof, 67-80, chmn dept, 80-83, PROF CHEM, OCCIDENTAL COL, 80- *Personal Data:* b Riverside, Calif, July 25, 37; m 63; c 3. *Educ:* Pomona Col, BA, 59; Mass Inst Technol, PhD(analytical chem), 64. *Prof Exp:* From res chemist to sr res chemist, Beckman Instruments, Inc, 64-67. *Concurrent Pos:* Sci adv, US Food & Drug Admin. *Mem:* AAAS; Am Chem Soc; Soc Appl Spectros. *Res:* Emission spectroscopy; flame photometry; atomic absorption instrument design; atomic and molecular fluorescence instrumentation. *Mailing Add:* Dept Chem Occidental Col 1600 Campus Rd Los Angeles CA 90041-3397. *Fax:* 213-259-2958; *E-Mail:* west@oxy.edu

**WEST, CHARLES DONALD,** BIOCHEMISTRY. *Current Pos:* from asst res prof to assoc res prof biochem, 57-71, assoc prof med, 65-69, PROF MED, MED CTR, UNIV UTAH, 69-, PROF BIOCHEM, 71-, CO-DIR, CLIN RES CTR, 66- *Personal Data:* b Ogden, Utah, Oct 25, 20; m 46; c 4. *Educ:* Univ Utah, BA, 41, MD, 44, PhD, 50. *Prof Exp:* Instr med, Med Col, Cornell Univ, 50-54, res assoc, Sloan-Kettering Div, 52-53, asst prof, 53-57. *Concurrent Pos:* From asst to assoc, Sloan-Kettering Inst Cancer Res. 50-57; asst dir prof serv res & assoc chief staff, Vet Admin Hosp, Salt Lake City, 57-65. *Mem:* AAAS; Endocrine Soc; Asn Cancer Res; Fedn Clin. *Res:* Harvey Soc. Res: Endocrinology. *Mailing Add:* 50 N Medical Dr Salt Lake City UT 84132-1001

**WEST, CHARLES HUTCHISON KEESOR,** PHYSIOLOGY, NEUROPHYSIOLOGY. *Current Pos:* at DEPT PSYCHIAT, UNIV ILL. *Personal Data:* b Wheeling, WVa, Aug 9, 48; m 72; c 2. *Educ:* Ohio Univ, BS, 70, MS, 72; Mich State Univ, PhD(physiol), 77. *Prof Exp:* Res asst zool, Ohio Univ, 71, teaching asst, 71-72; res asst physiol, Mich State Univ, 72-77; fel neurophysiol, Univ Wis, 77-80; res scientist, Ga Ment Health Inst, 80-; asst prof, Dept Psychiat, Emory Univ, 80- *Mem:* AAAS; Am Soc Zool; Soc Neurosci. *Res:* Basic motivation and attention controlling brain mechanisms and their relationship to mental illness; electrophysiology and intracranial self-stimulation paradigm with various physiological, pharmacological and behavioral manipulations. *Mailing Add:* Dept Educ Psychiat Univ Ill 1310 S Sixth St Champaign IL 61820-6925

**WEST, CHARLES PATRICK,** FORAGE PHYSIOLOGY & QUALITY. *Current Pos:* asst prof, 84-90, ASSOC PROF, UNIV ARK, 90- *Personal Data:* b Minneapolis, Minn, June 13, 52. *Educ:* Univ Minn, BS, 74, MS, 78; Iowa State Univ, PhD(agron), 81. *Prof Exp:* Res fel, Ministry Agr & Fisheries, NZ, 82-84. *Concurrent Pos:* Bd dirs, Crop Sci Soc Am. *Mem:* Am Soc Agron; Am Forage & Grassland Coun; Crop Sci Soc Am. *Res:* Physiological and pest interactions in endophyte-infected grasses. *Mailing Add:* Univ Ark Fayetteville Altheimer Lab 224 Fayetteville AR 72703-6804

**WEST, CHRISTOPHER DRANE,** neuroanatomy, for more information see previous edition

**WEST, CLARK DARWIN,** IMMUNOLOGY, NEPHROLOGY. *Current Pos:* from asst prof to prof, 51-89, EMER PROF PEDIAT, COL MED, UNIV CINCINNATI, 89- *Personal Data:* b Jamestown, NY, July 4, 18; m 44, Ruthann Asbury; c Charles M, John C & Lucy F. *Educ:* Col Wooster, AB, 40; Univ Mich, MD, 43. *Honors & Awards:* Henry L Barnett Award, Am Acad Pediat, 95; John P Peters Award, Am Soc Nephrology, 96. *Prof Exp:* Intern surg, Univ Mich Hosp, 43-44, resident pediat, 44-46. *Concurrent Pos:* Children's Hosp Res Found scholar, 48-49, fel, 53-89; Nat Res Coun sr fel pediat, Children's Hosp Res Found, 49-50 & Cardiopulmonary Lab, Bellevue Hosp, New York, 50-51; res assoc, Children's Hosp Res Found, 51-53, assoc dir, 63-89, supv biochemist, Hosp, 51-65, attend pediatrician, 51-89; attend pediatrician, Cincinnati Gen Hosp, 53-89; mem, Gen Clin Res Ctr Comt, Div Res Facilities & resources, NIH, 65-69; mem, Urol & Renal Dis Training Comt, Nat Inst Arthritis, Metab & Digestive Dis, 72-73. *Mem:* Am Physiol Soc; Soc Pediat Res (secy-treas, 58-62, pres, 63-64); Am Soc Nephrology; Am Asn Immunologists; Am Pediat Soc. *Res:* Abnormalities of the immune system related to the pathogenesis of glomerulonephritis. *Mailing Add:* Children's Hosp Res Found Elland Ave & Bethesda Cincinnati OH 45229-2899

**WEST, COLIN DOUGLAS,** CLASSICAL PHYSICS. *Current Pos:* res assoc planning, Oak Ridge Nat Lab, 77-80, mgr, Systs Technol Group, 81-85, dir, Advan Neutron Sci Proj, 86-95, PROG OFF DIR, ADVAN NEUTRON SCI PROJ, OAK RIDGE NAT LAB, 95- *Personal Data:* b Rochdale, Eng, June 21, 41; m 65; c 1. *Educ:* Univ Liverpool, BSc, 61, MSc, 64, PhD(physics), 65. *Honors & Awards:* Jointly Awarded Sci, Educ & Mgt Premium, Inst Elec Engrs, London, 75. *Prof Exp:* Res fel, Res Lab, Harwell, 65-68; sci officer, UK Atomic Energy Authority, 68-73; vis scientist, Oak Ridge Nat Lab, 73-74; proj mgr physics, UK Atomic Energy Res Lab, 74-77. *Concurrent Pos:* Nuclear physics res fel, Univ Liverpool, 63-65. *Res:* Application of long range planning techniques to laboratory and research organizations; small scale heat engines for irrigation and other applications; irradiation engineering. *Mailing Add:* 242 Joel Rd Oliver Springs TN 37840

**WEST, DAVID ARMSTRONG,** GENETICS. *Current Pos:* asst prof, 62-68, ASSOC PROF ZOOL, VA POLYTECH INST & STATE UNIV, 68- *Personal Data:* b Beirut, Lebanon, Apr 9, 33; US citizen; m 58, Lindsay Butte; c Peter, Roger & Susan. *Educ:* Cornell Univ, BA, 55, PhD(vert zool), 59. *Prof Exp:* Asst prof zool, Cornell Univ, 59-60; NATO fel, 60-61; USPHS fel, 61-62. *Concurrent Pos:* Sci Res Coun sr vis fel, 66; ed, Va J Sci, 74-76. *Mem:* Lepidopterist Soc; Lepidoptera Res Found; Soc Study Evolution; Am Soc Naturalists. *Res:* Ecological genetics; genetics of natural populations of butterflies; polymorphisms. *Mailing Add:* Dept Biol Va Polytech Inst & State Univ Blacksburg VA 24061-0406. *E-Mail:* bach@vtvm1.cc.vt.edu

**WEST, DAVID B,** CELL BIOLOGY. *Current Pos:* ASSOC PROF OBESITY, PENNINGTON BIOMED RES CTR, LA STATE UNIV, 91- *Personal Data:* b Pittsburgh, Pa, Mar 23, 53. *Educ:* Univ Wash, BS, 77, PhD(physiol), 84. *Prof Exp:* Asst prof physiol, Eastern Va Med Sch, 88-91. *Mem:* Am Inst Nutrit; Am Physiol Soc; Am Neurosci Soc; NAm Obesity Soc. *Res:* Physiology, metabolism and genetics of obesity. *Mailing Add:* Dept Obesity Diabetes & Metab Pennington Biomed Res Ctr La State Univ 6400 Perkins Rd Baton Rouge LA 70808-4124

**WEST, DENNIS R,** CROP BREEDING, QUANTITATIVE GENETICS. *Current Pos:* asst prof, 79-84, ASSOC PROF PLANT & SOIL SCI, UNIV TENN, 84- *Personal Data:* b Kennett, Mo, Nov 22, 46; m 69; c 1. *Educ:* Miss State Univ, BS, 69, MS, 75; Univ Nebr, PhD(agron), 78. *Prof Exp:* Res assoc, NC State Univ, 78-79. *Mem:* Am Soc Agron; Crop Sci Soc Am; AAAS; Coun Agr Sci & Technol. *Res:* Basic and applied research in plant breeding and genetics; quantitative genetics; maize breeding; host plant resistance; development of maize germplasm. *Mailing Add:* 6748 Greenbrook Dr Knoxville TN 37931

**WEST, DONALD K,** ASTROPHYSICS. *Current Pos:* ASTROPHYSICIST, GODDARD SPACE FLIGHT CTR, NASA, 64-, IUE OBSERV DIR, 78- *Personal Data:* b Providence, RI, May 14, 29; m 57; c 3. *Educ:* Univ RI, BS, 57; Rutgers Univ, MS, 60; Univ Wis, PhD(astron), 64. *Mem:* Am Astron Soc. *Res:* Physics of emission line stars; astronomical observations from space telescopes. *Mailing Add:* Code 684 Goddard Space Flight Ctr Greenbelt MD 20771

**WEST, DONALD MARKHAM,** ANALYTICAL CHEMISTRY. *Current Pos:* from asst prof to assoc prof, 56-65, PROF CHEM, SAN JOSE STATE UNIV, 65- *Personal Data:* b Pasadena, Calif, Apr 22, 25; m 48. *Educ:* Stanford Univ, BS, 49, PhD(chem), 58. *Prof Exp:* Actg instr chem, Stanford Univ, 54-55. *Mem:* Am Chem Soc; Sigma Xi; AAAS; Am Asn Univ Profs. *Res:* Analysis of organic compounds; co-author of 2 books. *Mailing Add:* Dept Chem San Jose State Univ 125 S Seventh St San Jose CA 95192-0101

**WEST, DOUGLAS BRENT,** GRAPH THEORY, OPTIMIZATION. *Current Pos:* from asst prof to assoc prof, dept math, 82-91, from asst prof to assoc prof res, Coord Sci Lab, 82-91, PROF DEPT MATH & RES PROF, COORDR SCI LAB, UNIV, ILL, 91- *Personal Data:* b Queens, NY, Nov 14, 53; m 86. *Educ:* Princeton Univ, AB, 74; Mass Inst Technol, PhD(math), 78. *Prof Exp:* Vis lectr & res asst, Dept Comput Sci, Stanford Univ, 78-79; asst prof, Dept Math, Princeton Univ, 79-82. *Concurrent Pos:* Co-prin investr, Off Naval Res res grant, 85-91; prin investr, NSF res grant, 85-87 & NSA res grant, 90-96; assoc ed, Am Math Monthly, 86-; mem res staff, IDA/CCR, Univ Calif, Berkeley, 87-88, vis assoc prof, comp sci, 89-90; assoc ed, Soc Indust Appl Math Discrete Math Newsletter, 91-, vchair activity group, Discrete Math, 97- *Mem:* Math Asn Am; Soc Indust & Appl Math. *Res:* Graph theory; partially ordered sets; extremal, structural and algorithmic questions discrete mathematics. *Mailing Add:* Dept Math Univ Ill 1409 W Green St Urbana IL 61801. *Fax:* 217-333-9576; *E-Mail:* west@math.uiuc.edu

**WEST, DOUGLAS XAVIER,** METAL COMPLEXES, COORDINATION CHEMISTRY. *Current Pos:* chmn dept, 75-86, prof, 86-93, DISTINGUISHED PROF INORG CHEM, ILL STATE UNIV, 93- *Personal Data:* b Tacoma, Wash, June 11, 37; m 64; c 2. *Educ:* Whitman Col, AB, 59; Wash State Univ, PhD(chem), 64. *Prof Exp:* Instr chem, Upsala Col, 64-65; from asst prof to prof, Cent Mich Univ, 65-75, dir univ honors progs, 70-72. *Concurrent Pos:* Vis prof, Univ Leicester, 72, 74 & 81 , Wash State Univ, 80, Univ Poona, 90; Indo Am fel, 90. *Mem:* Am Chem Soc; Sigma Xi. *Res:* Transition metal complexes of n-oxides, thiosemicarbazones and thioureas; electron spin resonance and other forms of spectroscopy. *Mailing Add:* Dept Chem Ill State Univ Normal IL 61790-4160. *Fax:* 309-438-5538; *E-Mail:* oxwest@rs6000.cmp.ILstu.edu

**WEST, ERIC NEIL,** STATISTICS, COMPUTER SCIENCE. *Current Pos:* assoc prof statist & comput sci, 72-73, ASSOC PROF QUANT METHODS, SIR GEORGE WILLIAMS CAMPUS, CONCORDIA UNIV, 73-; at DEPT BUS ADMIN, UNIV WINDSOR, CAN. *Personal Data:* b Montreal, Que, Mar 28, 41; m 65; c 2. *Educ:* Royal Mil Col Can, BSc, 63; Iowa State Univ, MS, 67, PhD(statist), 70. *Prof Exp:* Res assoc statist & comput, Iowa State Univ, 67-70; asst prof comput sci, Univ Alta, 70-72. *Concurrent Pos:* Consult, Pro Data Serv, 70-; pvt consult, 70- *Mem:* Am Statist Asn; Inst Math Statist; Sigma Xi. *Res:* Statistical inference; computation systems analysis; business decision making; forecasting. *Mailing Add:* Dean Bus Admin Univ Windsor Windsor ON N9B 3P4 Can

**WEST, FELICIA EMMINGER,** SCIENCE EDUCATION. *Current Pos:* RETIRED. *Personal Data:* b Chicora, Pa, Sept 14, 26; m 48; c 2. *Educ:* J B Stetson Univ, BS, 48; Univ Fla, MEd, 65; EdD(sci educ, geol), 71. *Prof Exp:* Teacher high sch, Fla, 60-64; instr physics & earth sci, Miami Dade Jr Col, 65-66; instr earth sci & phys sci, St Johns River Jr Col, 66-67; teacher & student gen sci, Lab Sch, Univ Fla, 67-69, teacher & asst prof gen sci & earth sci, 69-72; staff assoc, AAAS, 72-75; chmn, Div Natural Sci, Math & Phys Educ, Fla Jr Col, S Campus, 75-94. *Concurrent Pos:* Coord ed, Fla Asn Sci Teachers J, 75-; mem bd dirs, Fedn Unified Sci Educ. *Res:* Development of unified science curriculum materials for use at community college level; development of field guides to specific sites in Florida for use by secondary and community college instructors. *Mailing Add:* 424-E Oceanwood Dr Neptune Beach FL 32266

**WEST, GARY R,** PUBLIC HEALTH & EPIDEMIOLOGY. *Current Pos:* chief, Prog Opers Br, Div Stand/HIV Prev, Ctr Dis Control, 93-95, asst dep dir HIV, Nat Ctr Prev Servs, 87-93, dep dir, 95-96, ACTG DIR, DIV HIV PREV INTERVENTION, RES & SUPPORT, CTR DIS CONTROL, 96- *Personal Data:* b Seattle, Wash, Oct 23, 46. *Educ:* Western Wash State Univ, BA, 70; Calif State Univ, MPA, 86. *Prof Exp:* Pub health adv, Utah, SC, Pa, Okla & Chicago, Ill, 71-87; sr adv refugee health, SEAsia, 79-81; mem, Small Pox Eradication Prog, 85. *Mem:* Am Pub Health Asn. *Mailing Add:* HPIRS Ctr Dis Control MSC D21 Atlanta GA 30333. *Fax:* 404-639-0910

**WEST, GEORGE CURTISS,** PHYSIOLOGICAL ECOLOGY, ORNITHOLOGY. *Current Pos:* RETIRED. *Personal Data:* b Newton, Mass, May 13, 31; c 4. *Educ:* Middlebury Col, BA, 53; Univ Ill, Urbana, MS, 56, PhD(physiol ecol), 58. *Prof Exp:* Fel, Div Biosci, Nat Res Coun Can, 59-60; asst prof zool, Univ RI, 60-63; from asst prof to prof zoophysiol, Inst Arctic Biol, Univ Alaska, 63-83, actg dean, Col Biol Sci & Renewable Resources, 74-75, actg dir, Div Life Sci & Inst Arctic Biol, 74-77, dir Biomed Ctr, 72-80, prof zoophysiol, 80-83. *Concurrent Pos:* Alexander von Humboldt Found fel, Aschoff Div, Max Planck Inst Physiol of Behav, 71-72; mem US-USSR bilateral exchange working group protection northern ecosyst, 75- *Mem:* Am Ornith Union; Am Physiol Soc; Ecol Soc Am; Wildlife Soc; Wilson Ornith Soc. *Res:* Bioenergetics and temperature regulation of birds; migration, fat deposition, food habits of birds; fatty acid analysis of plant and animal lipids. *Mailing Add:* 909 S Clara Vista Circle Green Valley AZ 85614

**WEST, GORDON FOX,** GEOPHYSICS. *Current Pos:* lectr geophys, 58-66, assoc prof, 66-72, PROF PHYSICS, UNIV TORONTO, 72- *Personal Data:* b Toronto, Ont, Apr 21, 33. *Educ:* Univ Toronto, BASc, 55, MA, 57, PhD(geophys), 60. *Prof Exp:* Geophysicist, Dom Gulf Co, 55-56. *Mem:* Soc Explor Geophysicists; Am Geophys Union; Geol Asn Can; Can Asn Physicists. *Res:* Electromagnetic geophysical methods; geophysical studies of precambrian shields. *Mailing Add:* Dept Physics McClellan Phys Labs Univ Toronto 60 St George St Toronto ON M5S 1A7 Can

**WEST, HARRY IRWIN, JR,** SPACE PHYSICS, NUCLEAR PHYSICS. *Current Pos:* RETIRED. *Personal Data:* b Foley, Ala, Dec 3, 25; m 56; c 4. *Educ:* Auburn Univ, BS, 46, MS, 47; Stanford Univ, PhD(physics), 55. *Prof Exp:* Physicist, Lawrence Livermore Nat Lab, Univ Calif, 55-93. *Mem:* Fel Am Phys Soc; Am Geophys Union. *Res:* Nuclear spectroscopy and measurements of charged particles in the earth's radiation belts. *Mailing Add:* 1126 Tulane Ct Livermore CA 94550

**WEST, HERSCHEL J,** HIGH VOLTAGE PHENOMENA. *Current Pos:* ELEC ENGR, DIV LABS, BONNEVILLE POWER ADMIN, 66- *Personal Data:* b Portsmouth, Va, Nov 13, 37; m 63, Dee A Knudson; c Kevin L & Kimberly N. *Educ:* Brigham Young Univ, BS, 63; Kinsington Univ, MS, 80; Donsbach Univ, PhD(nutrit), 82. *Prof Exp:* Eng officer, USN, 63-66, Proj Supvr, Team Leader, Sect Head. *Concurrent Pos:* Consult unexplained elec flashovers, 75-, res consult new human growth factor, 82- *Mem:* Inst Elec & Electronics Engrs. *Res:* High voltage phenomena; unexplained outages; electrophoresis. *Mailing Add:* 3801 Edgewood Dr Vancouver WA 98661

**WEST, JAMES E,** ACOUSTICAL ENGINEERING. *Current Pos:* MEM TECH STAFF, DEPT ACOUST & AUDIO COMMUN, AT&T BELL LABS. *Honors & Awards:* Silver Medal, Acoust Soc Am, 95. *Mailing Add:* Dept Acoust & Audio Commun AT&T Bell Labs 600 Mountain Ave Murray Hill NJ 07974

**WEST, JAMES EDWARD,** MATHEMATICS. *Current Pos:* from asst prof to assoc prof, 69-76, PROF MATH, CORNELL UNIV, 76- *Personal Data:* b Grinnell, Iowa, May 1, 44; m 65; c 2. *Educ:* La State Univ, BS, 64, PhD(math), 67. *Prof Exp:* Asst prof math, Univ Ky, 68-69. *Concurrent Pos:* Mem, Inst Advan Study, 67-68, 77-78 & 84-85, Math Sci Res Inst, 85; vis prof, La State Univ, 72, Univ KY, 80; lectr, Stefan Bunach Inst, Warsaw, 74; exchange scientist, Nat Acad Sci, USSR & Poland, 78; NSF res grant, 70-92; invited address, Int Cong Math, 78. *Mem:* Am Math Soc; NY Acad Sci; AAAS. *Res:* Topology of infinite-dimensional spaces and manifolds; geometric and point-set topology. *Mailing Add:* Dept Math White Hall Cornell Univ Ithaca NY 14853-7901

**WEST, JERRY LEE,** FISH BIOLOGY, ZOOLOGY. *Current Pos:* From asst prof to assoc prof, 67-90, actg head dept biol, 74-77 & 88-89, PROF BIOL, WESTERN CAROLINA UNIV, 90- *Personal Data:* b North Wilkesboro, NC, Nov 1, 40; m 65; c 2. *Educ:* Appalachian State Univ, BS, 62; NC State Univ, MS, 65, PhD(zool), 68. *Mem:* Am Fisheries Soc; Am Inst Fishery Res Biologists. *Res:* Ecology of fishes in Southern Appalachian streams. *Mailing Add:* Dept Biol Western Carolina Univ Cullowhee NC 28723

**WEST, JOHN B(ERNARD),** CHEMICAL ENGINEERING, NUCLEAR ENGINEERING. *Current Pos:* RETIRED. *Personal Data:* b Elliott, Iowa, Feb 23, 25; m 47, Helen J Walker; c John, Richard, Patricia & Carol. *Educ:* Iowa State Univ, BS, 48, PhD, 54. *Prof Exp:* Jr engr, Gen Elec Co, NY, 48-50; from asst prof to prof, Sch Chem Eng, Okla State Univ, 54-76; mgr, Black Fox Sta Proj, Pub Serv Co Okla, 81-83, mgr, Black Fox Sta Eng, 76-81, dir fuels, 83-89; fuels consult, 89-90. *Concurrent Pos:* Consult, 90- *Mem:* Am Inst Chem Engrs. *Res:* Fossil fuel price and availability forecasting; project management. *Mailing Add:* 7901 S Yukon Tulsa OK 74132-2644. *E-Mail:* 105003.1501@compuserve.com

**WEST, JOHN B,** PHYSIOLOGY, MEDICINE. *Current Pos:* PROF MED & PHYSIOL, UNIV CALIF, SAN DIEGO, 69- *Personal Data:* b Adelaide, Australia, Dec 27, 28; US citizen. *Educ:* Univ Adelaide, BS & MB, 51, MD, 58, DSc, 80; Univ London, PhD(appl physiol), 60. *Hon Degrees:* Dr, Univ Barcelona, 87. *Honors & Awards:* Ernst Jung Prize Med, 77; George C Griffith lectr, Am Heart Asn, 78, Dickinson W Richards lectr, 80; I S Ravdin lectr, Am Col Sur, 82; Telford Mem lectr, Manchester Univ, UK, 83; Harry G Armstrong lectr, Aerospace Med Asn, 84; J Burns Amberson lectr, Am Thoracic Soc, 84; Suzanne Kronheim lectr, Undersea Med Soc, 84; Orr Reynolds Prize, Am Physiol Soc, 87. *Prof Exp:* Res assoc respiratory physiol, Royal Postgrad Med Sch, London, 54-60; physiologist, Himalayan Sci & Mountaineering Exped, 60-61; asst prof physiol, Univ Buffalo, 61-62; lectr med, Royal Postgrad Sch, London, 63-68. *Concurrent Pos:* Mem, Cardiovasc Study Sect, NIH, 71-75, chmn, 73-75; chmn fac, Univ Calif, San Diego Sch Md, 72-73; mem physiol comt, Nat Bd Med Examrs, 73-76, life sci adv comt, NASA, 85-86, comt space biol & med, Nat Acad Sci, 86- & Int Union Physiol Sci, 84-87. *Mem:* Am Physiol Soc; Am Soc Clin Invest; Am Thoracic Soc; Brit Physiol Soc; Royal Col Physicians London; Am Soc Gravitation & Space Biol; Asn Am Physicians; Asn Chmn Dept Physiol; Fleischner Soc (pres, 85); Royal Geog Soc; Royal Soc Med; Russ Acad Sci; Int Soc Mountain Med. *Res:* Respiratory function in health and disease including pulmonary gas exchange, pulmonary circulation, high altitude physiology and medicine, space physiology and medicine, and bioengineering aspects of the lung. *Mailing Add:* Dept Med Univ Calif San Diego La Jolla CA 92093-0623. *Fax:* 619-534-4812

**WEST, JOHN M(AURICE),** FERMENTATION, BIOCHEMICAL ENGINEERING. *Current Pos:* RETIRED. *Personal Data:* b Long Branch, NJ, June 10, 27; m 51, Margarida Pyles; c Paul D & Laura L. *Educ:* Columbia Univ, BA, 50, BS, 51, MS, 54. *Prof Exp:* Res chem engr, E R Squibb Div, Olin Mathieson Chem Corp, 53-60; prod mgr enzymes, Nopco Chem Co, 60-63; group leader, Hoffmann-La Roche, Inc, 63-77, dir fermentation process develop, 77-80, dir biotechnol, 80-85; mgr biotechnol, John Brown Engrs & Constructors, Stamford, Conn, 85-86; sr proj mgr, Am Cyanamid Agr Res & Develop, Princeton, NJ, 86-94. *Concurrent Pos:* Bioprocess consult. *Mem:* Am Soc Microbiol; Am Inst Chem Engrs; Am Chem Soc. *Res:* Fermentation process development and engineering; continuous sterilization and automatic foam control; automatic chemical analysis and control; pH control; deeptank and semi-solid fermentations; isolation recovery, purification of fermentation and natural products; biotechnology process evaluations; process design, project management; plant trouble shooting and manufacturing cost reduction; cell culture; technology assessment and technology transfer. *Mailing Add:* 57 Union St Apt 72 Montclair NJ 07042. *Fax:* 973-746-6098; *E-Mail:* guida__johnwest@worldnet.att.net

**WEST, JOHN M,** NUCLEAR ENGINEERING. *Current Pos:* RETIRED. *Personal Data:* b Stillwell, Okla, Jan 18, 20; m 45, Navlion F Farmer; c J Cornel & L Clark. *Educ:* Northeastern Okla State Univ, BS, 35; Univ Iowa, MS, 41. *Honors & Awards:* Charter A Coffin, Gen Elec Corp, 49; Walter H Zinn, Am Nuclear Soc, 82. *Prof Exp:* Assoc dir, Reactor Eng Div, Argonne Nat Lab, 49-57; exec vpres, Gen Nuclear Eng Corp, 57-65; sr vpres, Combustion Eng Inc, 65-85. *Concurrent Pos:* Consult. *Mem:* Nat Acad Eng; Am Nuclear Soc. *Res:* Radiation shielding, radiochemistry, reactor physics, nuclear safety. *Mailing Add:* 1608 SE 40th Terr Cape Coral FL 33904

**WEST, JOHN WYATT,** POULTRY NUTRITION. *Current Pos:* ASSOC DEAN, SCH AGR, CALIF POLYTECH STATE UNIV, SAN LUIS OBISPO, 68- *Personal Data:* b Decaturville, Tenn, Oct 18, 23; m 47; c 3. *Educ:* Univ Tenn, BSA, 47, MS, 48; Purdue Univ, PhD(poultry nutrit), 51. *Prof Exp:* Asst dir feeds res, Security Mills, Inc, Tenn, 51; from assoc prof to prof poultry husb, Miss State Univ, 52-56; prof poultry sci & head dept, Okla State Univ, 56-68. *Mem:* Poultry Sci Asn. *Res:* Arsenic compounds and vitamin-amino acid interrelationships in poultry nutrition; nutritional value of cottonseed meal in broiler and turkey rations; antibiotic-protein interrelationships in broiler rations. *Mailing Add:* Dept Animal Sci 215 Highland Dr San Luis Obispo CA 93405

**WEST, KEITH P,** ZOOLOGY, RADIATION BIOLOGY. *Current Pos:* RETIRED. *Personal Data:* b Simla, Colo, Aug 20, 20; m 46; c 3. *Educ:* Chico State Col, AB, 42; Stanford Univ, MA, 48. *Prof Exp:* Instr biol & chem, Vallejo Col, 47-48; from instr to prof biol sci, Drexel Univ, 48-86. *Concurrent Pos:* Asst dean, Col Eng & Sci, Drexel Univ, 67-68, actg head, Dept Biol Sci, 71-72, & 83; consult. *Mem:* AAAS; Health Physics Soc. *Res:* Biological effects of radiation; sanitary quality control of food products. *Mailing Add:* 2803 Dogwood Lane Broomall PA 19008

**WEST, KENNETH CALVIN,** ANALYTICAL CHEMISTRY. *Current Pos:* Asst prof, 67-75, ASSOC PROF CHEM, ST LAWRENCE UNIV, 75- *Personal Data:* b Broken Bow, Nebr, Apr 1, 35; m 60; c 3. *Educ:* Wheaton Col, Ill, BS, 56; Ind Univ, PhD(analytical chem), 67. *Mem:* Am Chem Soc. *Res:* Instrumentation. *Mailing Add:* Dept Chem St Lawrence Univ Canton NY 13617-9673

**WEST, KEVIN JAMES,** COMPLEX FORMATION. *Current Pos:* ASST PROF ANALYTICAL CHEM, UNIV WIS-WHITEWATER, 89- *Personal Data:* b Urbana, Ill, July 22, 58; m 81; c 1. *Educ:* Ripon Col, BA, 80; Univ Iowa, PhD(chem), 86. *Prof Exp:* Instr analytical chem, Ind Univ-Purdue Univ, Ft Wayne, 84-86, asst prof, 86-89. *Mem:* Am Chem Soc; Sigma Xi. *Res:* Ultraviolet-visible spectrophotometry of metal-ligand complexes for the determination of metal ion concentration; adaptation and development of instrumental measurements to undergraduate education; Use of computers as teaching aids in general and analytical chemistry. *Mailing Add:* 1868 Haymarket Rd Waukesha WI 53186

**WEST, LOUIS JOLYON,** PSYCHIATRY, NEUROLOGY. *Current Pos:* PROF PSYCHIAT & CHMN DEPT, SCH MED, UNIV CALIF, LOS ANGELES, 69-, MED DIR, NEUROPSYCHIAT INST, 69-, PSYCHIATRIST IN CHIEF, UNIV CALIF HOSPS & CLINS, 69- *Personal Data:* b New York, NY, Oct 6, 24; m 44; c 3. *Educ:* Univ Minn, BS, 46, MB, 48, MD, 49; Am Bd Psychiat & Neurol, dipl, 54. *Prof Exp:* Intern med, Univ Hosps, Univ Minn, 48-49; asst psychiat, Med Col, Cornell Univ, 49-52; prof psychiat & head dept psychiat, neurol & behav sci, Sch Med, Univ Okla, 54-69. *Concurrent Pos:* Resident, Payne Whitney Clin, New York Hosp, 49-52; res coordr, Okla Alcoholism Asn & chief behav sci, Okla Med Res Found, 56-69; consult, Oklahoma City Vet Admin Hosp, 56-69, USAF Hosp, Tinker AFB, Okla, 56-66,USAF Aero-Space Med Ctr, 61-66 & Peace Corps, 62-63; nat consult, Surgeon Gen, USAF, 57-62, mem adv coun, Behav Sci Div, Air Force Off Sci Res, 56-58; mem prof adv coun, Nat Asn Ment Health, 59-64; consult, US Info Agency, 60-61; mem exec coun adv comt behav res, Nat Acad Sci-Nat Res Coun, 61-63; mem nat adv comt psychiat, neurol & psychol, Spec Med Adv Group, US Vet Admin; mem, Nat Adv Ment Health Coun, NIMH, 65-69, White House Conf Civil Rights, 66 & Nat Adv Comt Alcoholism, Dept HEW; consult ed, Med Aspects Human Sexuality, 67-; mem bd dir, Kittay Found, 72-; mem residency rev comt psychiat & neurol, AMA, 73-; mem adv panel res & develop, US Army, 74- *Mem:* Fel Am Col Neuropsychopharmacol; fel Am Col Psychiat; fel Am Psychiat Asn; Pavlovian Soc NAm (pres, 74-75); Soc Biol Psychiat. *Res:* Experimental psychopathology, especially relating to disturbances of perception and altered states of consciousness; psychophysiological correlates in clinical practice; alcohol and drug abuse; life-threatening behavior; interaction of biological, psychological and sociocultural factors in personality development and function. *Mailing Add:* Neuropsychiat Inst Univ Calif 760 Westwood Plaza Los Angeles CA 90024-1759

**WEST, MARTIN LUTHER,** RADIATION CHEMISTRY, RADIATION PHYSICS & THERMAL PHYSICS. *Current Pos:* DIR TECH SERV, AM FURNACE, 84- *Personal Data:* b Waco, Tex, Dec 25, 36; m 68; c David Carson & Christyl Ann. *Educ:* Univ Tex, BS, 60, MA, 62, PhD(physics), 67. *Prof Exp:* Sr res scientist physics, Pac Northwest Lab Battelle Northwest, 67-84. *Mem:* AAAS; Radiation Res Soc. *Res:* Reaction mechanisms and fast kinetic measurements for charged particle impact; pulsed radioluminescence and UV spectroscopy instrumentation. *Mailing Add:* 1628 Davison Ave Richland WA 99352. *E-Mail:* jaguar7@aol.com

**WEST, MICHAEL ALLAN,** SURGICAL CRITICAL CARE, SURGICAL INFECTIOUS DISEASE. *Current Pos:* clin asst prof, 89-94, ASSOC PROF SURG & DIR SURG CRITICAL CARE, HENNEPIN CO MED CTR, UNIV MINN, 94- *Personal Data:* b Newport, RI, Apr 12, 54; m 78, Susan Koscielnjak; c Kristine, Andrew & Kathryn. *Educ:* Univ Wis, BS, 76; Loyola-Stritch Sch Med, MD, 80; Univ Minn, PhD(surg), 88. *Prof Exp:* Asst prof surg, Washington Univ, 88-89. *Concurrent Pos:* Prin investr, NIH First Award, Regulation of Macrophage Function in Sepsis, Nat Inst Gen Med Sci, 90- *Mem:* Asn Acad Surg; Surg Infection Soc; Am Col Surgeons; Soc Univ Surgeons; Am Asn Surg Trauma; Cent Surg Soc. *Res:* Examination of factors regulating macrophage mediator production in response to endotoxin; effect of multiple inflammatory stimuli on autocrine regulation; investigating wuetuer dysregulation of macrophage function is in important in surgical sepsis and macrophage function. *Mailing Add:* Dept Surg Hennepin Co Med Ctr 701 Park Ave Minneapolis MN 55415-1623. *Fax:* 612-904-4297

**WEST, MIKE HAROLD,** ANALYTICAL CHEMISTRY. *Current Pos:* STAFF MEM, LOS ALAMOS NAT LAB, 86- *Personal Data:* b Lewiston, Idaho, Feb 29, 48; m 73, Sandra L; c Tasheba & Michael. *Educ:* Western Wash State Col, BA, 70; Wash State Univ, PhD(chem), 76. *Prof Exp:* Res assoc, Univ New Orleans, 75-76; asst prof chem, Tougaloo Col, 76-77; res assoc, Tex A&M Univ, 77-78; sr chemist, Coors Spectro Chem Lab, Coors Porcelain Co, 78-81; sr chemist, energy systs group, Rockwell Hanford Opers, 81-86. *Mem:* Am Chem Soc; Soc Appl Spectros. *Res:* Use of molten salts for the processing of actinide elements; mechanisms for the purification and recovery of actinides with molten salt systems. *Mailing Add:* 8704 Dover Ct Westminster CO 80005-1552

**WEST, NEIL ELLIOTT,** ECOLOGY. *Current Pos:* From asst prof to assoc prof plant ecol, Dept Range Sci & Ecol Ctr, 64-75, PROF RANGE LAND RESOURCES, UTAH STATE UNIV, 75- *Personal Data:* b Portland, Ore, Dec 17, 37; m 63, Alexa Aho; c Alisa. *Educ:* Ore State Univ, BS, 60, PhD(plant ecol), 64. *Honors & Awards:* W R Chapline Res Award, Soc Range Mgt, 91. *Concurrent Pos:* Forest ecologist, Ore Forest Res Lab, Ore State Univ, 63; NSF fel & vis prof, Inst Ecol, Univ Ga, 70-71; Mellon vis lectr, Yale Sch Forestry & Environ Studies, 78-79; vis scholar, Adelaide Univ, 85; vis prof, Hebrew Univ, 86; consult, Nat Park Serv, Occidental Petrol, Argonne Nat Lab & Environ Protection Agency. *Mem:* Int Asn Ecol; Ecol Soc Am; Brit Ecol Soc; Int Asn Veg Sci; Int Asn Landscape Ecol; fel AAAS. *Res:* Plant ecology theory and its application to wildland resource management, particularly desertification, synecology and soil-vegetation relationships; systems ecology; community structure succession, productivity, in arid, semi-arid, and woodland ecosystems; monitoring of rangeland health. *Mailing Add:* Dept Range-Land Resources Utah State Univ Logan UT 84322-5230. *Fax:* 435-750-3796

**WEST, NORMAN REED,** NEUROBIOLOGY, PSYCHOPHARMACOLOGY. *Current Pos:* ASST PROF PATH & ANAT, STATE UNIV NY, HEALTH SCI CTR, SYRACUSE, NY, 77- *Personal Data:* b Oak Park, Ill, Aug 13, 43; m 68, Karin L Ziesemer; c Jefferson, Alys & Wendy. *Educ:* Judson Col, BA, 67; Thomas Jefferson Univ, PhD(pharmacol), 74. *Concurrent Pos:* PMAF fel, Dept Anat & Neurobiol, Sch Med, Washington Univ, Mo, 73-75, NIH fel, 75-77; pres res award, Psychopharmacol Prog, Am Soc Pharmacol & Exp Therapeut; researcher, LENP, Nat Inst Neurol Dis & Stroke, NIH, 92-94. *Mem:* Soc Neurosci; Am Asn Anat; Soc Exp Neuropath; Electron Microsc Soc Am; Int Brain Res Orgn; Int Soc Stereology. *Res:* Neurobiology of cryogenic lesions in the central nervous system; tissue culture modelling of neuropathologic lesions in human tissue; response of neurons to endogenous and exogenous agents in vivo and in tissue culture. *Mailing Add:* Dept Path State Univ NY Health Sci Ctr 766 Irving Ave Syracuse NY 13210. *Fax:* 315-464-7130; *E-Mail:* west@vax.cs.nscsyr.edu

**WEST, PHILIP WILLIAM,** ENVIRONMENTAL SCIENCES. *Current Pos:* from instr to prof, 40-53, Boyd prof, 53-80, EMER BOYD PROF CHEM, LA STATE UNIV, BATON ROUGE, 80-; CHMN & DIR, WEST-PAINE LABS, BATON ROUGE, 80- *Personal Data:* b Crookston, Minn, Apr 12, 13; m 35, 64, Foymae Stinson; c Dorothy A (Faldwell), Linda K (Gueho) & Patty S (Esltrott). *Educ:* Univ NDak, BS & MS, 35, 36; Univ Iowa, PhD(chem), 39. *Hon Degrees:* DSc, Univ NDak, 58. *Honors & Awards:* Southwest Award, Am Chem Soc, 54; Coates Award, 67; Fisher Award, 74 & Creative Advan Environ Sci & Technol Award, Am Chem Soc, 81. *Prof Exp:* Asst chemist, State Geol Surv, NDak, 35-36; asst sanit chem, Univ Iowa, 36-37; asst chemist, State Dept Health, Iowa, 37-40; res chemist & microchemist, Econ Lab, Inc, Minn, 40. *Concurrent Pos:* Smith lectr, Okla State Univ, 55; consult, Ethyl Corp, A D Little Co & USPHS; consult, Kem-Tech Labs, Inc & chmn bd, 66-73; ed, Analytica Chimica Acta, 58-77; co-ed, Sci Total Environ, 73-77; mem working party 1, Sci Comt Probs Environ, 71-74; adj prof, Environ Protection Agency; mem chem panel, NSF; pres comt new reactions, Int Union Pure & Appl Chem & pres anal chem div, 66-70, mem sect toxicol & indust hyg, 71-73; mem study sect, USPHS, 60-65; vis prof, Rand Afrikaans Univ, SAfrica, 80, Univ Colo, 63; mem, tech adv comt La Air Pollution Control Comm, 79-85; mem, Gov Task Force Environ Health, 83-85. *Mem:* Am Chem Soc; hon mem Brit Soc Anal Chem; hon mem Austrian Asn Microchem & Anal Chem; hon men Japanese Soc Anal Chem. *Res:* Water treatment and analysis; polarized light microscopy; spot tests; organic reagents; complex ions; analysis of petroleum; polarography; chromatography; high frequency titrations; inorganic extractions; catalyzed and induced reactions; air pollution; industrial hygiene; personal monitors. *Mailing Add:* 605 Nelson Dr Baton Rouge LA 70808-5067

**WEST, RICHARD LOWELL,** ORNITHOLOGY, ORGANIC CHEMISTRY. *Current Pos:* RES ASSOC ORNITH, DEL MUS NATURAL HIST, 87- *Personal Data:* b Quincy, Fla, Mar 20, 34; m 56; c 4. *Educ:* Univ of the South, BS, 55; Univ Rochester, PhD(chem), 61; Univ Del, MBA, 73. *Prof Exp:* Sr chemist, Atlas Chem Ind, Inc, 59-66; res chemist, ICI Am Inc, 66-70, res supvr chem, 70-74, mgr chem & polymer res, 75-79, mgr herbicides & PGR chem, 79-81, asst dir corp res, 81-83, mgr anal chem & info sci, 84-86, asst dir res, 86-87. *Concurrent Pos:* dir, Del Breeding Bird Atlas Proj, 83-87; ornithologist, 87-; ed, Am Birds, 89- *Mem:* Am Ornithol Union. *Res:* Research management; organic synthesis; industrial chemical development; avian population studies. *Mailing Add:* 2808 Rabbit Hill Rd Tallahassee FL 32312-3137

**WEST, ROBERT A,** PLANETARY ATMOSPHERES, RADIATIVE TRANSFER. *Current Pos:* mem tech staff, Jet Propulsion Labs, Calif Inst Technol, 84-89, outer planets group leader, 89-90, planetary atmospheres group supvr, 90-95, RES SCIENTIST, JET PROPULSION LAB, CALIF INST TECHNOL, 95- *Personal Data:* b Valparaiso, Ind, June 14, 51; m 79, Karen Reinhard; c Laura B. *Educ:* Calif Inst Technol, BS, 73; Univ Ariz, PhD(planetary sci), 77. *Honors & Awards:* Group Achievement Awards, Hubble Space Telescope, Galileo, Voyager, Pioneer & Solar Mesosphere Explorer, NASA. *Prof Exp:* Res assoc, Univ Colo, Boulder, 78-84, lectr astron, 79-84. *Concurrent Pos:* Co-invest, Voyager Photopolarimeter Exp, 80-90, Galileo Ultraviolet Spectrometer Exp, 87-, Cassini Imaging Team, 90-, Cassini Ultraviolet Spectrometer Exp, 90-, Cassini Huygens DISR Exp, 90- *Mem:* Am Astron Soc; Am Geophys Union; Int Astron Union. *Res:* Radiative transfer in planetary atmospheres including observation and interpretation of multiply-scattered light observed by spacecraft and ground-based instruments. *Mailing Add:* MS 169-237 JPL 4800 Oak Grove Dr Pasadena CA 91109. *Fax:* 818-393-4619; *E-Mail:* raw@west.jpl.nasa.gov

**WEST, ROBERT C,** ORGANOSILICON CHEMISTRY. *Current Pos:* from asst prof to assoc prof, 56-63, PROF CHEM, UNIV WIS, 63- *Personal Data:* b Glen Ridge, NJ, Mar 18, 28; c David R & Arthur S. *Educ:* Cornell Univ, BA, 50; Harvard Univ, AM, 52, PhD(chem), 54. *Hon Degrees:* DSc, Tech Univ Iosi, Romania, 95. *Honors & Awards:* F S Kipping Award, Am Chem Soc, 75; Chem Pioneer Award, Am Inst Chemists, 88; Wacker Silicon Prize, Wacker Corp, 89; Humboldt Sr Scientist Award, Alexander von Humboldt Found, 90. *Prof Exp:* Asst prof, Lehigh Univ, 54-56. *Concurrent Pos:* Co-ed, Advan Organometallic Chem, 63-; vis prof, Univ Wurzburg, 68, Tohoku Univ, 76, Hebrew Univ Jerusalem, 79, Chinese Acad Sci, Lanzhou, 84, Univ Giesson, 84, Gunma Univ, 87, Univ Estadual de Campinas, Brazil, 89 & 93, Technion, Haifa, Israel, 90, Tech Univ Munich, 90 & 92 & Ben Gurion Univ, Israel, 93; chair, Div Chem Educ, Am Chem Soc, 74-75; adj prof, Southern Ore State Col, 84-; consult, E I DuPont de Nemours Co, 90- *Mem:* Am Chem Soc; Royal Chem Soc; Electrochem Soc; fel AAAS. *Res:* Synthesis and reactions of multiply-bonded silicon compounds, polysilane polymers and silylenes; structural and chemical bonding studies of organosilicon compounds; synthesis and structure of aromatic oxocarbons and of derivatives of carbon 60, buckminsterfullerene. *Mailing Add:* 305 Nautilus Dr Madison WI 53705. *Fax:* 608-262-6143; *E-Mail:* west@chem.wisc.edu

**WEST, ROBERT ELMER,** EXPLORATION GEOPHYSICS. *Current Pos:* CONSULT GEOPHYSICIST, 85- *Personal Data:* b Blackfoot, Idaho, Apr 2, 38; div; c Alane M, Mark R & Matthew B. *Educ:* Univ Idaho, BS, 61; Univ Ariz, MS, 70, PhD(geosci), 72. *Prof Exp:* Physicist, Phillips Petrol Co, 61-62, 65; res assoc geophys, Univ Ariz, 68-69, 71-72; geophysicist, Humble Oil & Refining Co, 72-74 & Mining Geophys Surv, 74-85. *Mem:* Soc Explor Geophysicists. *Res:* Application of gravity, magnetic and electrical methods to exploration for ore deposits and ground water. *Mailing Add:* 2821 N Fontana Tucson AZ 85705

**WEST, ROBERT MACLELLAN,** VERTEBRATE PALEONTOLOGY. *Current Pos:* CHIEF EXEC OFFICER, INFORMAL SCI, INC, 93- *Personal Data:* b Appleton, Wis, Sept 1, 42; m 65, Jean Sydow; c Christopher M. *Educ:* Lawrence Col, BA, 63; Univ Chicago, SM, 64, PhD(evolutionary biol), 68. *Honors & Awards:* Guyot Award, Nat Geog Soc, 81. *Prof Exp:* Res assoc geol & geophys sci, Princeton Univ, 68-69; asst prof biol, Adelphi Univ, 69-74; cur geol, Milwaukee Pub Mus, 74-83; dir, Carnegie Mus Natural Hist, 83-87; dir, Cranbrook Inst Sci, 87-91; vpres, Cranbrook Educ Community, 87-91; prin, RMW Sci Action, 92-95. *Concurrent Pos:* Adj assoc prof, Dept Geol Sci, Univ Wis-Milwaukee, 74-83; adj prof, Dept Earth & Planetary Sci, Univ Pittsburgh, 83-; hon cur, Milwaukee Pub Mus, 84; adj prof, Dept Biol Sci & Anthrop & Sociol, Oakland Univ, 87, 88-91; Indo-US Subcomt Educ & Cult, 90-96. *Mem:* Geol Soc Am; Am Asn Mus; Soc Vert Paleont; Paleontol Soc. *Res:* Asiatic mammalian evolution; paleontologic aspects of plate tectonics; evolution of early tertiary mammals and mammalian communities; biostratigraphy of tertiary deposits of intermontane basins in North America. *Mailing Add:* Informal Sci Inc PO Box 42328 Washington DC 20015. *Fax:* 202-362-3596

**WEST, RONALD E(MMETT),** CHEMICAL ENGINEERING. *Current Pos:* From asst prof to assoc prof, 57-74, prof, 74-95, EMER PROF CHEM ENG, UNIV COLO, BOULDER, 95- *Personal Data:* b Rosebush, Mich, Sept 7, 33; m 55; c 3. *Educ:* Univ Mich, BSE, 54, MSE, 55, PhD(chem eng), 58. *Mem:* Am Inst Chem Engrs. *Mailing Add:* 4774 McKinley Dr Boulder CO 80303

**WEST, RONALD ROBERT,** PALEOBIOLOGY, PALEOECOLOGY. *Current Pos:* from asst prof to assoc prof paleobiol, 69-79, ancillary prof, Biol Div, 74-79, PROF PALEOBIOL, DEPT GEOL, KANS STATE UNIV, 79- *Personal Data:* b Centralia, Ill, Nov 14, 35; m 58, 78, 82; c 2. *Educ:* Univ Mo, Rolla, BS, 58; Univ Kans, MS, 62; Univ Okla, PhD(paleoecol geol), 70- *Honors & Awards:* Geol Soc Am Award, 72. *Prof Exp:* Stratigrapher, Shell Oil Co, Okla, 56, micropaleontologist, La, 58-59; invert paleontologist, Kans Geol Surv, 60, geologist, 61; paleobiologist & paleoecologist, Humble Oil & Refining Co, Tex & Okla, 61-67; instr geol, Univ Okla, 67-68. *Concurrent Pos:* Am Chem Soc-Petrol Res Fund grant paleobiol; mem adv coun, Friends of Woodrow Wilson Nat Fel Found; consult res lab, Amoco Prod Co, Okla, 74-; NSF grant, Nat Mus Natural Hist, 77-78; vis prof, Oxford, Univ Kans, 80; geologist, Tell Qargen, Syria, 84; fel Woodrow Wilson, 59-61; ACS-PRF grant, chaetetids reefs, 85-87; collabr, Dept Paleobiol, Sovi Hisonia Inst, 78-; corresp mem subcommission conb strat found, Int Geophys Union, 81-; tech ed, Paleontol Soc, 85- *Mem:* Int Palcont Asn; Paleont Soc; Soc Econ Mineralogists & Paleontologists; Paleont Asn; Geol Soc Am; Sigma Xi. *Res:* Paleoecology and paleobiology of upper paleozoic invertebrates; structure and dynamics of benthic fossil communities; carbonate sedimentation (reefs); recent marine invertebrate ecology; organism substrate relationships and functional morphology of marine invertebrates especially cocalline sponges (chaetetids) and chaetetids taxonomy and biology. *Mailing Add:* Geol Dept Kans State Univ Thompson Hall Rm 108 Manhattan KS 66506-3201

**WEST, ROSE GAYLE,** PHYSICAL CHEMISTRY. *Current Pos:* Asst prof chem, 68-73, actg chmn dept, 72-74, ASSOC PROF CHEM, WILLIAM CAREY COL, 73-, CHMN DEPT, 74- *Personal Data:* b Pascagoula, Miss, Oct 31, 43; m 62; c 1. *Educ:* Univ Southern Miss, BA, 65, PhD(phys chem), 69. *Mem:* Am Chem Soc. *Res:* Thermo chemistry, heats of combustion and resonance energies of aromatic hydrocarbons and 5- and 6-membered aromatic nitrogen heterocyclic compounds; special projects for undergraduate physical chemistry laboratories. *Mailing Add:* 1126 Old Hwy 24 No 104 Sumrall MS 39482-9236

**WEST, SHERLIE HILL,** PLANT PHYSIOLOGY, AGRONOMY & SEED SCIENCE. *Current Pos:* from asst agronomist to assoc agronomist, Univ Fla, 58-70, asst dean res, Inst Food & Agr Sci, 72-79, AGRONOMIST, UNIV FLA, 70-, PROF SEED TECHNOL, 79- *Personal Data:* b Pall Mall, Tenn, Feb 18, 27; m 49; c 1. *Educ:* Tenn Polytech Univ, BS, 49; Univ Ky, MS, 54; Univ Ill, PhD(agron, bot), 58. *Honors & Awards:* Seed Sci Award, Crops Sci Soc Am, 95. *Prof Exp:* Asst agronomist, Univ Ky, 54-55; res agronomist, USDA, 58-60; plant physiologist and location coordr, USDA, 83-97. *Concurrent Pos:* Consult, AID Progs, 59-64; plant physiologist, USDA, 60-72; collabr & prof agron, Agr Res Serv, USDA. *Mem:* Am Chem Soc; Am Soc Plant Physiol; fel Am Soc Agron; fel Crop Sci Soc Am; fel AAAS. *Res:* Nucleic acid metabolism and growth due to environmental factors; mechanism of hormone action; drought and cold tolerance; genetic criteria of selection of superior plants; cool temperature effects on carbohydrate metabolism; mechanisms of cool temperature dormancy in tropical grasses; seed quality, deterioration and dormancy; seed science. *Mailing Add:* Dept Agron Bldg 661 Univ Fla Gainesville FL 32611

**WEST, TERRY RONALD,** ENGINEERING GEOLOGY, CIVIL ENGINEERING. *Current Pos:* from instr to assoc prof eng geol, 61-96, PROF ENG GEOL, PURDUE UNIV, WEST LAFAYETTE, 96- *Personal Data:* b St Louis, Mo, Aug 15, 36; m 57; c 2. *Educ:* Wash Univ, AB & BSGE, 59, MA, 62; Purdue Univ, Lafayette, MSCE, 64, PhD(eng geol), 66. *Prof Exp:* Teaching asst geol, Wash Univ, 59-61; staff engr, H M Reitz Consult Engr, Mo, 61. *Concurrent Pos:* Consult, ATEC Assoc Inc, 69-80; team leader eng soils group, lab appl remote sensing, 69-77; consult, 80- *Mem:* Geol Soc Am; Am Soc Civil Engrs; Asn Eng Geol; Am Soc Testing & Mat. *Res:* Evaluation of geological materials for engineering uses; remote sensing of earth materials; subsurface geology and ground water. *Mailing Add:* Dept Earth & Atmospheric Sci Purdue Univ West Lafayette IN 47907. *Fax:* 765-496-1210

**WEST, THEODORE CLINTON,** PHARMACOLOGY. *Current Pos:* RETIRED. *Personal Data:* b Central, SC, May 17, 19; m 42, Juliann Orton; c David H, Donald O & Lynne A. *Educ:* Univ Wash, BS, 48, MS, 49, PhD(pharmacol), 52. *Prof Exp:* From instr to prof pharmacol, Univ Wash, 49-68, asst chmn dept, 63-68, asst dean planning, 66-68; prof med educ & pharmacol & dir off med educ, Univ Calif, Davis, 68-77, prof med sch pharmacol, 78-86. *Mem:* Am Soc Pharmacol & Exp Therapeut; Sigma Xi. *Res:* Pharmacology of cardiac and smooth muscle; medical education. *Mailing Add:* 8807 72nd St SE Snohomish WA 98290-5877

**WEST, THOMAS PATRICK,** GENE EXPRESSION, MICROBIAL PHYSIOLOGY. *Current Pos:* assoc prof, 88-93, PROF CHEM, SDAK STATE UNIV, 93- *Personal Data:* b Peabody, Mass, Dec 9, 53. *Educ:* Purdue Univ, BS, 74; Tex A&M Univ, MS, 76, PhD(biochem), 80. *Prof Exp:* Res assoc microbiol, Mich State Univ, 80-81 & Univ Ariz Health Sci Ctr, 81-82; NIH postdoctoral chem, Boston Col, 82-83; asst prof biol, Univ Southern Miss, 83-87. *Concurrent Pos:* Prin investr, NIH grant, 88-90 & USDA grant, 94-97. *Mem:* Am Chem Soc; AAAS; Am Soc Microbiol; Sigma Xi; Genetics Soc Am; Soc Exp Biol & Med; Soc Indust Microbiol. *Res:* Study of pyrimidine biosynthesis and utilization by pseudomonads, fungal synthesis of biopolymers, and amylolytic enzymes. *Mailing Add:* Sta Biochem SDak State Univ Box 2170 Brookings SD 57007. *Fax:* 605-688-6295

**WEST, WALTER SCOTT,** ECONOMIC GEOLOGY, GEOCHEMISTRY. *Current Pos:* eng aide & cartographer, Alaskan Geol Br, US Geol Surv, 42-46, geologist, 46-54, secy geol names comt, Geol Div, 54-67, CHIEF, WIS LEAD-ZINC PROJ, EASTERN MINERAL RESOURCES BR, GEOL DIV, US GEOL SURV, 66- *Personal Data:* b Fayette, Wis, Mar 12, 12; m 40; c 3. *Educ:* Cornell Col, AB, 34; Univ Wis-Platteville, BE, 35; Univ Tenn, MS, 37. *Prof Exp:* Prin & basketball coach, High Sch, Mo, 37-38; instr geol, Univ NC, 39-42. *Concurrent Pos:* Dir, Citizens Nat Bank, Darlington, Wis, 68- *Mem:* Am Inst Mining, Metall & Petrol Eng; Arctic Inst NAm; Soc Econ Geologists. *Res:* Radioactive mineral and bse metaldeposits, pumice and riprap in Alaska; trace element and lead isotope studies; mineralogy and genesis of lead and zinc deposits in Wisconsin and Tennessee; geologic and geochemical mapping and topical studies in Upper Mississippi Valley zinc-lead district, Wisconsin, Illinois, Iowa and Minnesota; stratigraphy. *Mailing Add:* 601 E Louisa St Darlington WI 53530

**WEST, WARWICK REED, JR,** INVERTEBRATE ZOOLOGY. *Current Pos:* from asst prof to prof, 52-88, chmn dept, 65-85, EMER PROF BIOL, UNIV RICHMOND, 88- *Personal Data:* b Evington, Va, Feb 9, 22; m 46, Alyce Johnson; c W Reed III, Leila (Morris) & Jane (Sawyer). *Educ:* Lynchburg Col, BS, 43; Univ Va, PhD(biol), 52. *Prof Exp:* Instr biol, Lynchburg Col, 46-49. *Mem:* Sigma Xi. *Res:* Milipede anatomy. *Mailing Add:* 6806 Lakewood Dr Richmond VA 23229-6931

**WEST, WILLIAM LIONEL,** ZOOLOGY, PHARMACOLOGY. *Current Pos:* from instr to assoc prof pharmacol, 56-73, PROF PHARMACOL & RADIOL & CHMN, DEPT PHARMACOL, COL MED, HOWARD UNIV, 73- *Personal Data:* b Charlotte, NC, Nov 30, 23; m 72. *Educ:* J C Smith Univ, BS, 47; Univ Iowa, PhD, 55. *Prof Exp:* Asst zool, Univ Iowa, 49-55, res assoc radiation, Col Med, 55-56. *Mem:* Am Soc Zool; Am Soc Pharmacol & Exp Therapeut; Am Physiol Soc; Am Nuclear Soc; NY Acad Sci; Sigma Xi. *Res:* Biochemical and endocrine pharmacology; cellular physiology. *Mailing Add:* Dept Pharmacol Howard Univ Washington DC 20059-0001. *Fax:* 202-806-4453

**WEST, WILLIAM T,** histology, anatomy, for more information see previous edition

**WESTALL, FREDERICK CHARLES,** BIOCHEMISTRY. *Current Pos:* PRES, INST DIS RES, 84-; PROF, ORE INST SCI & MED, 93- *Personal Data:* b Pasadena, Calif, Nov 6, 43; m 68, Janet Robertson; c Andrew, Amy, Abby & Adrienne. *Educ:* Univ Calif, Los Angeles, BS, 64; San Diego State Col, MS, 66; Univ Calif, San Diego, PhD(chem), 70. *Prof Exp:* Multiple Sclerosis Soc res fel biochem, Salk Inst, 70-72, res assoc, 72-73, from asst res prof to assoc res prof, 73-84; prof, Calif Polytech, Pomona, 89-93. *Concurrent Pos:* Adj prof, Harvey Mudd Col, 87-89. *Mem:* Soc Neurosci; Am Chem Soc. *Res:* Biochemistry of neurological diseases; solid phase peptide synthesis; aging; immunological effects of adjuvants; biochemistry of neurotransmitters. *Mailing Add:* Ore Inst Sci & Med 2251 Dick George Rd Cave Junction OR 97523

**WESTAWAY, KENNETH C,** PHYSICAL ORGANIC CHEMISTRY, KINETIC ISOTOPE EFFECTS. *Current Pos:* Asst prof chem, Laurentian Univ, 68-75, chmn dept, 74-76, assoc prof, 75-82, PROF CHEM, LAURENTIAN UNIV, 82- *Personal Data:* b Hamilton, Ont, Aug 14, 38; m 62, Margaret Beale; c Bruce, Michelle, Ian. *Educ:* McMaster Univ, BSc, 62, PhD(phys org chem), 68. *Concurrent Pos:* Vis prof, Univ Wis-Madison, 76-77, Univ Sask, 85-86, Uppsala Univ, Sweden, 91, 92 & 93. *Mem:* Fel Chem Inst Can; Am Chem Soc; Int Isotope Soc. *Res:* Mechanisms of organic reactions; nucleophilic substitution reactions and elimination reactions; kinetic isotope effects; solvent effects and substituent effects on transition state structure; acid mists and gaseous pollutants in dieselized underground mines; identification and analysis of organic compounds. *Mailing Add:* Dept Chem Laurentian Univ Sudbury ON P3E 2C6 Can. *Fax:* 705-675-4844; *E-Mail:* kwestawa@laurentian.nickel.ca

**WESTBERG, KARL ROGERS,** CHEMISTRY, PHYSICS. *Current Pos:* MEM TECH STAFF, AEROSPACE CORP, 68- *Personal Data:* b Norwalk, Conn, Dec 17, 39; m 71, Carole Shirley; c Melissa, Brent & Gavin. *Educ:* Bowdoin Col, BA, 61; Brown Univ, PhD(chem), 69. *Prof Exp:* Engr, Perkin-Elmer Corp, 61. *Concurrent Pos:* Vis res fel, Univ Birmingham, Eng, 85. *Mem:* Am Phys Soc. *Res:* Chemical kinetics; spacecraft contamination; aerospace sciences; air-pollution chemistry. *Mailing Add:* Aerospace Corp PO Box 92957 Los Angeles CA 90009

**WESTBROOK, DAVID REX,** APPLIED MATHEMATICS. *Current Pos:* asst prof, 66-71, ASSOC PROF MATH, UNIV CALGARY, 71- *Personal Data:* b London, Eng, May 12, 37; m 60, 74; c 4. *Educ:* Univ London, BSc, 58, PhD, 61. *Prof Exp:* Lectr math, Univ Singapore, 61-64; sr lectr, Univ Melbourne, 64; lectr, Univ Nottingham, 64-65; vis mem, NY Univ, 65-66. *Concurrent Pos:* Nat Res Coun Can res grant, 67-68. *Mem:* Soc Indust & Appl Math; Inst Math & Appl UK; Can Appl Math Soc. *Res:* Applications of applied maths to industrial problems; numerical methods for PDE. *Mailing Add:* Dept Math Univ Calgary 2500 University Dr NW Calgary AB T2N 1N4 Can

**WESTBROOK, EDWIN MONROE,** PROTEIN CRYSTALLOGRAPHY, STRUCTURAL BIOLOGY. *Current Pos:* asst scientist, 83-87, scientist biophys, 87-90, DIR, STRUCT BIOL CTR, ARGONNE NAT LAB, 90- *Personal Data:* b San Juan, PR, June 30, 48; m 74; c 4. *Educ:* Univ Calif, Berkeley, AB, 69; Stanford Univ, MS, 71; Univ Chicago, MD & PhD(biophys), 81. *Prof Exp:* Teaching fel biochem, Univ Calif, Los Angeles, 81-83. *Concurrent Pos:* Asst prof biochem & molecular biol, Univ Chicago, 83-88; assoc prof biochem, molecular biol & cell biol, Northwestern Univ, 88- *Mem:* Am Crystallog Asn. *Res:* Application of protein crystallographic methods to the study of biological macromolecules; steroid-protein interaction; enzyme kinetics; antimicrobial proteins; microbial toxins. *Mailing Add:* Div Biol & Med Res Argonne Nat Lab 9700 S Cass Ave Argonne IL 60439

**WESTBROOK, J(ACK) H(ALL),** PHYSICAL METALLURGY, CERAMICS. *Current Pos:* PRES & PRIN CONSULT, BROOKLINE TECHNOL, 91- *Personal Data:* b Troy, NY, Aug 19, 24; wid; c 5. *Educ:* Rensselaer Polytech Inst, BMetE, 44, MMetE, 47; Mass Inst Technol, ScD(metall), 49. *Honors & Awards:* Turner Award, Electrochem Soc, 57; Templin Award, Am Soc Testing & Mat, 59; Geisler Award, Am Soc Metals, 59; Campbell Mem lectr, 76; Am Inst Mining, Metall & Petrol Engrs Award, 63; Am Ceramic Soc Award, 67; Hofmann Prize, Lead Develop Asn, 71; Jeffries Mem lectr, Am Soc Metals, 79. *Prof Exp:* Asst metall, Rensselaer Polytech Inst, 44, 46-47 & Mass Inst Technol, 47-49; res assoc, Res & Develop Ctr, Gen Elec Co, 49-71, mgr eng mat & processes info oper, 71-74, mgr, Mat Info Serv, Corp Res & Develop, 74-81, mgr spec projs, 81-85; pres & prin consult, Sci Tech Knowledge Systs, 85-91. *Concurrent Pos:* Adj assoc prof, Rensselaer Polytech Inst, 57-59; mem subcomts, Nat Mat Adv Bd, Nat Acad Sci, 59-63, 68, 75-77 & 79-82; chmn, Gordon Conf Solid State Studies in Ceramics, 60; Nat Acad Sci US-USSR exchange fel, 71; consult, USAF, US Army, Nat Sci Fedn, NASA & Advan Res Proj Agency, Dept Defense; chmn, Mat Info Comn, Fedn Mat, 74-; mem, Mat Adv Panel, Off Technol Assessment, US Cong, 75-77. *Mem:* Nat Acad Eng; Am Inst Mining, Metall & Petrol Engrs; fel Am Ceramic Soc; Electrochem Soc; fel AAAS; Sigma Xi; fel Am Inst Chemists; fel Am Soc Metals. *Res:* Intermetallic compounds; mechanical properties of refractory materials; hardness measurement techniques; grain boundaries; materials information; research and development planning; technological forecasting and assessment; history of metallurgy. *Mailing Add:* 5 Brookline Rd Ballston Spa NY 12020. *Fax:* 518-885-8840

**WESTBY, CARL A,** MICROBIAL PHYSIOLOGY. *Current Pos:* assoc prof, 73-80, PROF MICROBIOL, SDAK STATE UNIV, 80- *Personal Data:* b Los Angeles, Calif, Feb 8, 36; m 58; c 6. *Educ:* Univ Calif, Riverside, AB, 58; Univ Calif, Davis, PhD(bact), 64. *Prof Exp:* Fel bact physiol, Sch Med, Univ Pa, 64-67; asst prof bact, Utah State Univ, 67-73. *Concurrent Pos:* Med prod consult, Med Prod Div, 3M Co, 74- *Mem:* Am Soc Microbiol; Sigma Xi. *Res:* Bacterial physiology, genetics, and gene engineering. *Mailing Add:* Dept Microbiol SDak State Univ PO Box 2207B Brookings SD 57007-0001

**WESTCOTT, KEITH R,** PROTEIN CHEMISTRY. *Current Pos:* SCIENTIST, AMGEN, INC, 86- *Personal Data:* b Salt Lake City, Utah, Sept 30, 52. *Educ:* Univ Calif, Berkeley, AB, 74; Univ Ill, Urbana-Champaign, MS, 78, PhD(biochem), 80. *Prof Exp:* Res assoc, Dept Biochem, Duke Univ Med Ctr, 80-83; researcher, Dept Biol Chem, Univ Calif, Los Angeles, 83-85; scientist, Alpha Therapeut Corp, 85-86. *Mem:* Am Soc Biochem & Molecular Biol; Am Chem Soc; AAAS; Protein Soc; Sigma Xi; NY Acad Sci. *Res:* Development of protein purification methods for human therapeutics; growth factor and cytokine isolation; protein folding. *Mailing Add:* Amgen Inc Amgen Ctr 14-2D Thousand Oaks CA 91320-1789. *Fax:* 805-499-7464

**WESTDAL, PAUL HAROLD,** ENTOMOLOGY, VIROLOGY. *Current Pos:* RETIRED. *Personal Data:* b Wynyard, Sask, Nov 5, 21; m 47, Mae Gillis; c Laureen (Goodridge), Carol (McGeough), & Neil P. *Educ:* Univ Man, BSc, 47, MSc, 50, PhD(entom), 69. *Prof Exp:* Res entomologist, Agr Can, 46-74, sr res entomologist econ entom, 75-82; consult, Westdal Agri Consults, 82-95. *Concurrent Pos:* Adj prof, Univ Man, 71-82; ed, The Man Entomologist, 77-81. *Mem:* Entom Soc Can; Sigma Xi. *Res:* Biology and control of insect pests of sunflowers and canola. *Mailing Add:* 40 Garnet Bay Winnipeg MB R3T 0L6 Can

**WEST-EBERHARD, MARY J,** ENTOMOLOGY. *Current Pos:* assoc, 73-75, ENTOMOLOGIST, DEPT ENTOM, SMITHSONIAN TROP RES INST, 75- *Personal Data:* b Pontiac, Mich, Aug 20, 41; m 67; c Jessica R, Anna C & Andrew W. *Educ:* Univ Mich, BA, 63, MS, 64, PhD(zool), 67. *Prof Exp:* Teaching fel, Dept Zool, Univ Mich, 63-65; fel biol, Harvard Univ, 67-69. *Concurrent Pos:* Milton fel, Harvard Univ, 68-69; staff mem, Dept Biol, Univ Valle, Cali, Colombia, 72-78; distinguished vis scientist, Mus Zool, Univ Mich, 82; mem, Int Comt, Int Union Study Social Insects; mem bd dirs, Orgn Trop Studies, 85-87; mem adv comt, Monteverde Conserv League Comt Human Rights, Nat Acad Sci, 90- *Mem:* Nat Acad Sci; Am Soc Naturalists; Sigma Xi; Int Union Study Social Insects; Soc Study Evolution (vpres II, 87-88, pres, 92); Int Soc Hist, Philos & Social Studies Biol. *Res:* Author and co-author of over 50 publications. *Mailing Add:* Escvela de Biologia Univ de Costa Rica San Jose Costa Rica. *Fax:* 506-28-0001

**WESTENBARGER, GENE ARLAN,** PHYSICAL CHEMISTRY. *Current Pos:* asst prof, 63-67, ASSOC PROF PHYS CHEM, OHIO UNIV, 67- *Personal Data:* b Lancaster, Ohio, July 25, 35; m 58; c 4. *Educ:* Ohio Univ, BS, 57; Univ Calif, Berkeley, PhD(phys chem), 63. *Prof Exp:* Chemist, Battelle Mem Inst, 57; res & develop coordr, Qm Food & Container Inst, 58-59. *Mem:* Am Phys Soc; Am Chem Soc. *Res:* Thermodynamic and magnetic studies at low temperature. *Mailing Add:* Dept Chem Ohio Univ Athens OH 45701

**WESTENBERG, ARTHUR AYER,** CHEMICAL PHYSICS. *Current Pos:* RETIRED. *Personal Data:* b Menomonie, Wis, Mar 1, 22; m 45; c 1. *Educ:* Carleton Col, AB, 43; Harvard Univ, AM, 48, PhD(chem), 50. *Honors & Awards:* Hillebrand Award, Am Chem Soc, 66; Silver Medal, Combustion Inst, 66. *Prof Exp:* Chemist, Mayo Clin, 50; asst prof chem, Lafayette Col, 50-52; sr staff mem, Appl Physics Lab, Johns Hopkins Univ, 52-58, prin staff mem, 58-77, supvr chem physics res, 63-77. *Concurrent Pos:* Consult, Proj Squid, Off Naval Res, 60-65; mem adv comt, Army Res Off, 66-71; mem, Comt Assess Environ Effects of Supersonic Transport, US Dept Com, 71. *Res:* Chemical kinetics; high temperature gas properties; combustion; air pollution chemistry; electron spin resonance spectroscopy. *Mailing Add:* PO Box 295 Manchester VT 05254

**WESTENFELDER, CHRISTOF,** NEPHROLOGY, PHYSIOLOGY. *Current Pos:* fac biomed eng, Ctr Artificial Hearts Devices, 85, PROF MED, SCH MED, UNIV UTAH, 83-; CHIEF NEPHROLOGY, VET ADMIN MED CTR, SALT LAKE CITY, 83-; DIR, TRANSPLANT & ACUTE CARE UNIT, 84- *Personal Data:* b Stuttgart, WGer, July 1, 42. *Educ:* Univ Munich, BS, 68; Univ Kiel-Lubek, WGer, MD, 69. *Prof Exp:* Intern, Rittbegkrankenhaus, WBerlin, 69-70 & Cook Co & Suburban Hosps, Chicago, 70-71; resident internal med, Abraham Lincoln Sch Med, Univ, 71-73, fel nephrology, 73-75, asst prof, 75-81; dir hemodialysis, Univ Ill Hosp, 75-80 & Vet Admin Med Ctr, W Side Hosp, 81-82. *Concurrent Pos:* Vis prof, Univ Chicago, 79-82, Univ Freiburg, Fed Repub Ger, 80, Univ Vienna, Austria, 81, Univ Calif, San Francisco, 82, Cleveland Clin, 84-85, Univ Winnipeg, Can, 85, Univ BC, Vancouver, 85. *Mem:* Am Physiol Soc; Am Soc Renal Biochem & Metab; fel Am Col Physicians; Am Fedn Clin Res; Nat Kidney Found; AMA; Am Soc Nephrology; Int Soc Nephrology; Am Soc Artificial Internal Organs; Am Heart Asn; Ger Med Asn; AAAS. *Res:* Atrial natriuretic factor release in animals with artificial hearts; acute renal failure, bioenergetics; contratility of glomeruli; renal converting enzyme, enzymology. *Mailing Add:* Sec Nephrology Salt Lake City Vet Admin Med Ctr 500 Foothill Blvd Salt Lake City UT 84148-0001. *Fax:* 801-584-1251; *E-Mail:* chriwest@cc.utah.edu

**WESTENSKOW, DWAYNE R,** ANESTHESIOLOGY. *Current Pos:* res instr, Dept Anesthesiol, Univ Utah, 75-78, from asst prof to assoc prof, 79-88, res instr, Dept Surg, 78-85, res asst prof, 79-88, res assoc prof, Dept Bioeng, 82-89, PROF, DEPT ANESTHESIOL, UNIV UTAH, 88-, RES PROF, DEPT BIOENG, 89- *Personal Data:* b LaGrande, Ore, Apr 16, 47; m; c 5. *Educ:* Brigham Young Univ, BS, 72; Univ Utah, ME, 75, PhD(bioeng), 76. *Honors & Awards:* Career Achievement Award, Asn Advan Med Instrumentation, 79 & Award for Excellence in Commun, 85. *Prof Exp:* Bioengr, Pulmonary Functions Lab, LDS Hosp, Salt Lake City, Utah, 73; proj engr, Health Sci Res Div, Sandoz, Inc, 75-76. *Concurrent Pos:* Consult, var corp, foreign & US, 76-; grants, foreign & US, corp & educ, 77-91; mem bd dirs, Instrumentation Res Labs, 77-80, subcomt, Equip Monitoring & Eng Technol, Am Soc Anesthesiologists, 85, 90 & 91; mem, Int Adv Comt, Comput in Anesthesia, 82-; sect ed, J Annals Biomed Eng, 82-85, field ed, Anesthesia & Analgesia, 82-, Inst Elec & Electronics Engrs, 81-, consult ed, J Crit Care, 85- *Mem:* Asn Univ Anesthetists; sr mem Biomed Eng Soc; Asn Advan Med Instrumentation; sr mem Inst Elec & Electronics Engrs; Int Anesthesia Res Soc; Am Soc Anesthesiologists; Crit Care Soc. *Res:* Development continuous oxygen consumption measuring system and computer control of intravenous fluid infusion rate; computerization of anesthesia monitoring; control of mechanical ventilation; over 100 technical papers published; granted 13 patents. *Mailing Add:* Dept Anesthesiol Univ Utah 50 N Medical Dr Salt Lake City UT 84132-0001

**WESTER, DERIN C,** pediatric audiology, for more information see previous edition

**WESTER, RONALD CLARENCE,** PERCUTANEOUS ABSORPTION, PHARMACOKINETICS. *Current Pos:* ADJ PHARM, SCH PHARM & RES DERMATOLOGIST, SCH MED, UNIV CALIF, SAN FRANCISCO, 81- *Personal Data:* b Gardner, Mass, Aug 26, 40; m 67; c 2. *Educ:* Clark Univ, AB, 62; Univ Ill, Urbana, MS, 69, PhD(physiol), 70. *Prof Exp:* Res asst metab, Univ Rochester Sch Med, 64-66, res asst, Worcester Fedn Exp Biol, 62-64; res investr, G D Searle & Co, 72-76, res scientist drug metab, 76-81. *Concurrent Pos:* Fel, Univ Ill, 66-70, Cornell Univ, 70-72; vis scientist, Ore Regional Primate Ctr, 72. *Mem:* Am Soc Clin Pharmacol & Therapeut; Am Asn Pharmaceut Scientists; Controlled Release Soc. *Res:* Bioavailability and drug metabolism in experimental animals and man; percutaneous absorption in experimental animals and man; clinical dermatology and pharmaceutical sciences. *Mailing Add:* 8 Locksley Ave San Francisco CA 94122

**WESTERBERG, ARTHUR WILLIAM,** CHEMICAL ENGINEERING. *Current Pos:* dir, Design Res Ctr, Carnegie-Mellon Univ, 78-80, dept head, 80-83, dir, Eng Design Res Ctr, 86-89, PROF CHEM ENG, CARNEGIE-MELLON UNIV, 76-, SWEARINGEN PROF CHEM ENG, 82-, UNIV PROF, 92- *Personal Data:* b St Paul, Minn, Oct 9, 38; m 63, Barbara A Dyson; c Kenneth & Karl. *Educ:* Univ Minn, Minneapolis, BSc, 60; Princeton Univ, MSc, 61; Univ London, PhD(chem eng) & Imp Col, dipl, 64. *Honors & Awards:* Comput Syst Technol Div Award, Am Inst Chem Engrs, 83, William H Walker Award, 87; Chem Eng Div Award, Am Soc Eng Educ, 81; Murphree Award, Am Chem Soc, 97. *Prof Exp:* Sr analyst software eng, Control Data Corp, 65-67; from asst prof to prof chem eng, Univ Fla, 67-76. *Concurrent Pos:* Lectr, Chem Eng Div, Am Soc Eng Educ, 81; inst lectr, Am Inst Chem Engrs, 89. *Mem:* Nat Acad Eng; Am Inst Chem Engrs. *Res:* Developing computer software systems to aid in process analysis, optimization and information modeling; process synthesis; expert systems in process design. *Mailing Add:* Dept Chem Eng Carnegie-Mellon Univ Pittsburgh PA 15213. *Fax:* 412-268-7139; *E-Mail:* a.westerberg@cmu.edu

**WESTERDAHL, CAROLYN ANN LOVEJOY,** SURFACE SCIENCE, ENERGETIC MATERIALS. *Current Pos:* CHEMIST, PICATINNY ARSENAL, 67- *Personal Data:* b Oklahoma City, Okla, Apr 16, 35; m 61. *Educ:* Univ Chicago, BA, 55, BS, 57; Univ Calif, Berkeley, PhD(chem), 61. *Mem:* Sigma Xi; Am Chem Soc. *Res:* Surface studies. *Mailing Add:* 7 Commanche Trail Denville NJ 07834-1113

**WESTERDAHL, RAYMOND P,** PHYSICAL CHEMISTRY, POLLUTION CONTROL. *Current Pos:* res chemist, Feltman Res Lab, Picatinny Arsenal, 67-77, CHEM ENGR, US ARMY ARMAMENT RES & DEVELOP CTR, 77- *Personal Data:* b Chicago, Ill, Mar 22, 29; m 61. *Educ:* Univ Ill, BS, 51; Univ Chicago, MS, 59, PhD(phys chem), 62. *Prof Exp:* Res chemist, Esso Res & Eng Co, Stand Oil Co, NJ, 62-67. *Mem:* AAAS; fel Am Inst Chemists; Am Chem Soc; Soc Appl Spectros. *Res:* Mechanisms of pyrotechnic reactions; Raman spectroscopy; chemiluminescent reactions; reactions in fused salts; analysis and control of air and water pollutants. *Mailing Add:* 7 Comanche Trail Denville NJ 07834

**WESTERFELD, WILFRED WIEDEY,** MOLYBDENUM XANTHINE OXIDAZE, CARBOLIGASE REACTIONS. *Current Pos:* RETIRED. *Personal Data:* b St Charles, Mo, Dec 13, 13; m 38; c 5. *Educ:* Mo Univ, BS, 34; St Louis Univ, PhD(biochem), 38. *Hon Degrees:* DSc, State Univ NY, 89. *Honors & Awards:* Am Chem Soc, 68. *Prof Exp:* Assoc prof biochem, Harvard Med Sch, 40-45; prof biochem, Upstate Med Ctr, State Univ NY, 45-79. *Mailing Add:* 7607 Hunt Lane Fayetteville NY 13066-2514

**WESTERHOF, NICOLAAS,** ANIMAL PHYSIOLOGY. *Current Pos:* researcher physiol, 69-72, lectr, 72-80, PROF PHYSIOL, FREE UNIV AMSTERDAM, 80- *Personal Data:* b DeBilt, Utrecht, May 4, 37; m 61; c 2. *Educ:* Univ Utrecht, Neth, BS, 57, MS, 62; Univ Pa, PhD(biomed eng), 68. *Prof Exp:* Res assoc physics, Univ Utrecht, 60-64; res assoc physiol, Georgetown Univ, Washington, DC, 64-66; res assoc biomed eng, Univ Pa, Philadelphia, 66-69. *Mem:* Biomed Eng Soc; Inst Elec & Electronics Engrs. *Res:* Cardiovascular physiology, especially hemodynamics; cardiac pump function and coronary pressure-flow relations. *Mailing Add:* Lab Physiol Free Univ Amsterdam Van der Boechorst Str 7 1081 BT Amsterdam Netherlands. *Fax:* 31 20 661 3369; *E-Mail:* hsara@11v50znico

**WESTERHOUT, GART,** RADIOASTRONOMY, ASTROMETRY. *Current Pos:* RETIRED. *Personal Data:* b The Hague, Neth, June 15, 27; m 56, Judith M Monaghan; c Magda C, Gert T, Brigit M & Julian C. *Educ:* Leiden Univ, Neth, Drs, 54, PhD(astron), 58. *Honors & Awards:* Alexander von Humboldt Award, Ger, 73. *Prof Exp:* Res asst astron, Univ Observ, State Univ Leiden, Neth, 52-54, sci officer, 54-59, chief sci officer, 59-62; dir, Astron Prog, Univ Md, College Park, 62-73, chmn, Div Math, Physics & Eng Sci, 72-73, prof astron, 62-77; sci dir, US Naval Observ, 77-93. *Concurrent Pos:* NATO fel, 59; mem user's comt, Nat Radio Astron Observ, 65-78; mem, NSF Dicke Panel Radio Astron Facil, 67-69; vchmn, Div Phys Sci, Nat Res Coun, 69-73, mem, Comt Radio Frequencies, 72-82; trustee-at-large, Assoc Univs Inc, 71-74; mem US nat comt, Int Astron Union, 71-74; mem US nat comt, Int Sci Radio Union, 72-78, pres Int, Comn Radio-Astron, 75-78; Humboldt Found Award, Ger, 73-74; mem, Inter-Union Comn for Allocation of Frequencies, 75-82; mem vis comn, Max Planck Inst Radion Astron, Bonn, Ger, 76-81; mem vis comn, Haystack Observ, Mass Inst Technol, 76-81 & chmn, 79-81; mem, Arecibo Adv Bd, Cornell Univ, 77-80 & chmn, 79; mem, Sci Coun, Stellar Data Ctr, Strasbourg, Fr, 78-84, chmn, 81; coun, Am Astron Soc, 78-80; chmn, Working Group on Astrometry, Astron Survey Cons, Nat Acad Sci, 79-81; chmn, Working Group Astron Data, Int Astron Union, 85-91. *Mem:* Am Astron Soc (vpres, 85-87); Royal Astron Soc; Int Astron Union; Int Sci Radio Union; Sigma Xi. *Res:* Radio astronomy; 21-centimeter line research; fundamental astronomy; galactic structure; optical and radio astrometry; very long baseline interferometry, optical interferometry; data distribution. *Mailing Add:* 811 W 38th St Baltimore MD 21211-2203

**WESTERMAN, ARTHUR B(AER),** METALLURGY. *Current Pos:* RETIRED. *Personal Data:* b Pittsburgh, Pa, June 29, 19; m 42; c 3. *Educ:* Carnegie Inst Technol, BS, 39. *Prof Exp:* Asst metallurgist, Crucible Steel Co Am, Pa, 39-42; res metallurgist, Metals Res Lab, Carnegie Inst Technol, 42-43; res engr, Battelle Develop Corp, 43-50, asst div chief, 50-58, proj coordr, 58-62, asst res mgr, 62-75, coordr large proj, 75-80, mem staff, Battelle Mem Inst, 80-90. *Mem:* Am Soc Metals; AAAS. *Res:* Scientific and technical information. *Mailing Add:* 71 N Merkle Rd Columbus OH 43209

**WESTERMAN, DAVID SCOTT,** TECTONIC GEOLOGY. *Current Pos:* asst prof, 82-83, ASSOC PROF GEOL, NORWICH UNIV, 83- *Personal Data:* b Ann Arbor, Mich, July 12, 46; m 68, 84; c 2. *Educ:* Allegheny Col, BS, 69; Lehigh Univ, MS, 71, PhD(geol), 72. *Prof Exp:* Asst prof earth sci, Northeastern Univ, 72-78; vis asst prof, Univ Southern Maine, 78-79; asst prof geol, Univ Maine, Orono, 80; asst prof, Colloy Col, 80-82. *Concurrent Pos:* Field geologist bedrock mapping, Maine Geol Surv, 75-83 & Vt Geol Surv, 83-; co-ed, Geol Sci Maine, 78-; vis asst prof geol, Unity Col, 82. *Mem:* Geol Soc Am; Sigma Xi; Planetary Soc. *Res:* Reconstruction of ancient global-scale tectonic events which are recorded in Central Vermont and Eastern Maine; resolution of ancient stress fields in Maine. *Mailing Add:* Dept Earth Sci Norwich Univ 65 S Main St Northfield VT 05663-1004

**WESTERMAN, EDWIN J(AMES),** METALLURGICAL ENGINEERING, METALLURGY. *Current Pos:* metallurgist, Dept Metall Res, Kaiser Aluminum, Spokane, Wash, 61-69, head, Alloy Metall Sect, 70-73, mgr, Alloy & Properties Res Dept, 73-79, mgr, Reduction Res Dept, 80-83, TECH MGR, CTR TECHNOL, KAISER ALUMINUM & CHEM CORP, PLEASANTON, CALIF, 69-, MGR CAN STOCK RES PROG, 84- *Personal Data:* b USA, Jan 18, 35; m 59, 81; c 8. *Educ:* Mont Sch Mineral Sci & Technol, BS, 56; Rensselaer Polytech Inst, PhD(metall), 59. *Prof Exp:* Metallurgist, Res Lab, Gen Elec Co, 59-61. *Mem:* Am Soc Metals; Am Inst Mining, Metall & Petrol Engrs. *Res:* Powder metallurgy; aluminum alloy development; x-ray diffraction; electron and ion microprobes; nondestructive testing of metals; can stock metallurgy and technology. *Mailing Add:* 164 Woodview Circle San Ramon CA 94583

**WESTERMAN, HOWARD ROBERT,** SYSTEMS ENGINEERING. *Current Pos:* mem tech staff, 54-66, dept head syst eng, 66-94, CONSULT, AT&T BELL LABS, 94- *Personal Data:* b Jersey City, NJ, Feb 17, 26; m 50; c 2. *Educ:* St Peter's Col, BS, 48; Univ Chicago, SM, 49; Columbia Univ, PhD(chem physics), 52. *Prof Exp:* Analyst oper res, Off Chief Naval Oper, 52-54. *Concurrent Pos:* Allied Chem Co fel, Columbia Univ, 52-53. *Mem:* Sigma Xi. *Res:* Quantum mechanics; operations research; orbital mechanics. *Mailing Add:* 37 Cheshire Sq Little Silver NJ 07739

**WESTERMAN, IRA JOHN,** ORGANIC CHEMISTRY, POLYMER CHEMISTRY. *Current Pos:* SR RES CHEMIST POLYMER CHEM, PHILLIPS PETROL CO, 80- *Personal Data:* b Louisville, Ky, Oct 10, 45; m 79. *Educ:* Univ Ky, BS, 67; Duke Univ, MS, 69, PhD(org chem), 73. *Prof Exp:* Res fel, Univ Ariz, 73-74; sr res chemist polymer chem, B F Goodrich Chem Div, 74-80. *Mem:* Am Chem Soc; Soc Plastics Engrs. *Res:* Polyelectrolytes; water-soluble polymers; heterocyclic chemistry; polar cycloadditions; oil recovery chemicals. *Mailing Add:* 299 Pheasant Run Wadsworth OH 44281-2347

**WESTERMAN, MAXWELL P,** HEMATOLOGY. *Current Pos:* PROF MED HEMAT, CHICAGO MED SCH, 68- *Educ:* Allegheny Col, AB, 43; Univ Louisville, MD, 50. *Prof Exp:* Res asst prof med, Med Sch, Univ Pittsburgh, 58-68. *Res:* Sickle red cell membrane lipids; sickle cell disease. *Mailing Add:* Hemat-Mt Sinai Hosp 15th & California Ave Chicago IL 60608

**WESTERMAN, PHILIP WILLIAM,** NUCLEAR MAGNETIC RESONANCE SPECTROSCOPY, MEMBRANE BIOPHYSICS. *Current Pos:* from asst prof to assoc prof, 76-88, PROF BIOCHEM, NORTHEASTERN OHIO UNIVS COL MED, 88-, ACTG CHMN BIOCHEM, 97- *Personal Data:* b Brisbane, Queensland, Australia, June 16, 45; m 70, Janice M Carson; c Natasha A & Karen L. *Educ:* Univ Sydney, BSc, 67, PhD(org chem), 71. *Prof Exp:* Fel, Case Western Res Univ, 71-73; res fel, Australia Nat Univ, 74-75, Calif Inst Technol, 75-76. *Concurrent Pos:* Prin investr, NIH, 80-86, co-prin investr, 84; mem, Liquid Crystal Inst, Kent State Univ, 80-, adj prof chem, 82-, grad fac mem, Sch Biomed Sci, 81-; vis prof, Sch Physics, Univ NSW, 85, 87 & 90, Dept Chem, Univ Calabria, Italy, 87, 90, 93 & 96; prin investr, Am Heart Asn, 92-96; consult, Diamond-Shamrock & Sohio. *Mem:* Am Soc Biochem & Molecular Biol; Biophys Soc; Am Chem Soc; Int Liquid Crystal Soc; Int Soc Magnetic Resonance; Sigma Xi. *Res:* Physical properties of model and biological membranes; molecular mechanisms of general anesthesia; physical properties of lipid dispersions in upper gastrointestinal tract. *Mailing Add:* 343 Burr Oak Dr Kent OH 44240. *Fax:* 440-325-2524; *E-Mail:* pww@riker.neoucom.edu

**WESTERMAN, RICHARD EARL,** METALLURGY. *Current Pos:* res assoc corrosion res, Pac Northwest Lab, Battelle Mem Inst, 64-66, mgr, 66-69, res assoc, Metall Sect, 69-80, TECH LEADER ENVIRON MECH PROPERTIES, PAC NORTHWEST LAB, BATTELLE MEM INST, 80- *Personal Data:* b Great Falls, Mont, Jan 18, 35; m 58; c 4. *Educ:* Mont Col Mineral Sci & Technol, BS, 56; Rensselaer Polytech Inst, PhD(metall), 60. *Prof Exp:* Engr, Hanford Labs, Gen Elec Co, 56-62, sr scientist, 62-64. *Concurrent Pos:* Lectr, Richland Joint Ctr Grad Study. *Mem:* Am Soc Metals. *Res:* Kinetics of high temperature oxidation and evaporation of superalloys; diffusion and solubility of hydrogen in iron, zirconium and titanium alloys; gas-metal reactions; aqueous corrosion; thermodynamics; powder metallurgy; dental implant development; nuclear waste disposal. *Mailing Add:* 1804 Marshall Ave Richland WA 99352

**WESTERMAN, WILLIAM JOSEPH, II,** MECHANICAL ENGINEERING, PHYSICS. *Current Pos:* PRES, COGSDILL TOOL PROD CORP, 80- *Personal Data:* b St Louis, Mo, June 27, 37; m 63; c 3. *Educ:* Vanderbilt Univ, BSME, 59, MS, 61; Washington Univ, DSc, 64. *Prof Exp:* Lectr elec eng, Washington Univ, 60-63; res scientist mech eng, Martin Co, 64-67; mgr, Special Eng Prog, McDonnell Douglas, 67-74; gen mgr res & develop, Chamberlain Mfg Co, 74-80. *Concurrent Pos:* Adj assoc prof, Univ Fla, 64-73; fel, NSF, 62-63. *Mem:* Am Soc Mech Eng; Soc Mfg Engr; Soc Automotive Engrs; Cutting Tool Mfrs Am (dir, 84-85). *Res:* Fluidics; automatic controls; fluid systems contamination; metal cutting; burnishing; reaming. *Mailing Add:* 207 East Springs Rd Columbia SC 29223

**WESTERMANN, D T,** SOIL SCIENCE, SOIL CHEMISTRY. *Current Pos:* SOIL SCIENTIST, SNAKE RIVER CONSERV RES CTR, SCI & EDUC ADMIN-AGR RES, 68-; LAB DIR & RES LEADER, NW IRRIG & SOILS RES LAB, USDA. *Personal Data:* b July 4, 41; US citizen; c 3. *Educ:* Colo State Univ, BS, 63; Ore State Univ, MS, 65, PhD, 68. *Concurrent Pos:* Affil prof, Univ Idaho, 71- & Utah State Univ, 87- *Mem:* Sigma Xi. *Res:* Plant nutrition. *Mailing Add:* 3793 N 3600 E USDA-ARS Kimberly ID 83341

**WESTERMANN, FRED ERNST,** METALLURGICAL & MATERIALS ENGINEERING. *Current Pos:* fac metall eng, 48-91, EMER PROF, COL ENG, UNIV CINCINNATI, 91- *Personal Data:* b Cincinnati, Ohio, Mar 14, 21; m 49, Margie Kopp; c Kathy, Paul & Ann. *Educ:* Univ Cincinnati, ChE, 43, MS, 47, PhD(metall eng), 57. *Prof Exp:* Jr engr develop elastomers, Inland Mfg Div Gen Motors Corp, 43-44. *Concurrent Pos:* Consult, Gen Elec Aircraft Nuclear Propulsion, 57-61; Metcut Res Assoc, Inc, 65-74 & Delhi Foundry Sand Co, 75-78; co investr grant, NSF, 73-76, mem, Mat Adv Team Educ Modules Mat Sci & Eng, 76-80, Fusite Div, Emerson Elec, 77-89; consult metall eng; consult, legal cases, 91- *Mem:* Fel Am Soc Metals Int; Am Soc Eng Educ; Am Foundrymen's Soc; Sigma Xi; Am Soc Eng Educ. *Res:* Powder metallurgy; powder characterization, compaction and sintering; foundry engineering; molding materials; cast iron structure property relationships; welding metallurgy. *Mailing Add:* 9575 Millbrook Dr Cincinnati OH 45231-2641

**WESTERMANN, GERD ERNST GEROLD,** GEOLOGY. *Current Pos:* from lectr to assoc prof, 57-69, PROF GEOL, MCMASTER UNIV, 69- *Personal Data:* b Berlin, Ger, May 11, 27; m 56; c 3. *Educ:* Brunswick Tech Univ, BSc, 50; Univ Tubingen, MSc & PhD(geol, paleont), 53. *Prof Exp:* Paleontologist, Geol Surv Ger, 53-57. *Concurrent Pos:* Consult, 58-62; mem, Leader Int Geol Correl Prog. *Mem:* Paleont Res Inst; Am Paleont Soc; Soc Econ Paleont & Mineral; UK Palaeont Asn; Int Paleont Asn (secy-gen, 74-82); Can Geol Asn. *Res:* Mesozoic Mollusca, especially Jurassic Ammonoidea and Triassic Pectinacea; functional morphology of cephalopods; taxonomy; intercontinental biochronology and biogeography. *Mailing Add:* Dept Geol McMaster Univ 1280 Main St W Hamilton ON L8S 4M1 Can

**WESTERN, ARTHUR BOYD,** OPTICS, SOLID STATE PHYSICS. *Current Pos:* PROF PHYSICS & APPL OPTICS, ROSE-HULMAN INST TECHNOL, 86-, DEPT HEAD, 91- *Personal Data:* b Detroit, Mich, Feb 29, 44; m 66, Jonnee Givens; c Douglas, Sara & Teresa. *Educ:* Rollins Col, BS, 65; Mont State Univ, MS, 72, PhD(physics), 76. *Prof Exp:* Asst prof physics, Mont Col Mineral Sci & Technol, 76-81, head, Dept Physics & Geophys Eng, 78-86, assoc prof physics, 81-86. *Mem:* Am Asn Physics Teachers; Int Soc Optical Eng. *Res:* Holographic interferometry, phase transitions, ultrasonic measurements, dielectric measurements, refractory ceramics, robotics; design of high-interaction magnetohydrodynamics generators. *Mailing Add:* Dept Physics & Appl Optics Rose-Hulman Inst Technol 5500 Wabash Ave Terre Haute IN 47803. *Fax:* 812-877-3198; *E-Mail:* arthur.western@rose-hulman.edu

**WESTERN, DONALD WARD,** MATHEMATICS. *Current Pos:* from assoc prof to prof math, Franklin & Marshall Col, 48-74, chmn, Dept Math & Astron, 52-72, Charles A Dana prof, 74-80, EMER PROF MATH, FRANKLIN & MARSHALL COL, 80- *Personal Data:* b Poland, NY, May 7, 15; m 43; c 5. *Educ:* Denison Univ, BA, 37; Mich State Col, MA, 39; Brown Univ, PhD(math), 46. *Prof Exp:* Instr math, Mich State Col, 37-39. *Concurrent Pos:* NSF fac fel, 60. *Mem:* Am Math Soc; Math Asn Am. *Res:* Inequalities in the complex plane. *Mailing Add:* 38 Girard Ave Lancaster PA 17603-4537

**WESTERVELT, CLINTON ALBERT, JR,** INVERTEBRATE ZOOLOGY, PARASITOLOGY. *Current Pos:* From asst prof to assoc prof, 65-82, PROF BIOL, CHAPMAN COL, 82- *Personal Data:* b Portland, Ore, June 15, 36; m 65. *Educ:* Lewis & Clark Col, BA, 58; Univ Ariz, MS, 61, PhD(zool), 66. *Mem:* Am Soc Parasitologists. *Res:* Biology and systematics of rhabdocoel turbellarians. *Mailing Add:* Dept Biol Chapman Col 333 N Glassell St Orange CA 92666-1011

**WESTERVELT, FRANKLIN HERBERT,** ENGINEERING, COMPUTER SCIENCE. *Current Pos:* prof eng & comput sci & dir comput serv ctr, 71-83, PROF ENG & COMPUT SCI, WAYNE STATE UNIV, 83-; EXEC VPRES RES, ST SYSTS DEVELOP INC, 83- *Personal Data:* b Benton Harbor, Mich, Mar 26, 30; m 48; c 2. *Educ:* Univ Mich, Ann Arbor, BSE(mech eng) & BSE(math), 52, MSE, 53, PhD(mech eng), 61. *Prof Exp:* Instr eng graphics, Univ Mich, Ann Arbor, 53-56, res assoc, Comput Ctr, 61-66, assoc dir ctr, 66-71, from asst prof to prof mech eng, 61-71. *Concurrent Pos:* Proj dir conversational use of comput, Advan Res Projs Agency-US Dept Defense, 65-70; trustee, Argonne Univ Asn, 71-75, 81-82. *Mem:* Asn Comput Mach; Nat Soc Prof Engrs. *Res:* Computing systems; very large databases; interactive computing; systems architecture; micro-programming; information management systems; parallel distributed processors. *Mailing Add:* Dept Elec & Comp Eng Wayne State Univ 3100 W Eng Detroit MI 48202-4095. *Fax:* 313-577-1101; *E-Mail:* westervelt@eng.wayne.edu

**WESTERVELT, FREDERIC BALLARD, JR,** NEPHROLOGY. *Current Pos:* HEAD, RENAL DIV, DEPT MED, UNIV VA, 64-, DIR, DEPT RENAL SERV, 65-, PROF MED, 78- *Personal Data:* b Washington, DC, June 11, 31; m; c 2. *Educ:* Univ Va, MD, 55. *Mem:* Am Col Physicians; Am Soc Artificial Internal Organs. *Res:* Hermodialysis; uremia. *Mailing Add:* Jefferson Nephrol Ltd 925 E Jefferson St Charlottesville VA 22902-5355

**WESTERVELT, PETER JOCELYN,** THEORETICAL PHYSICS. *Current Pos:* from asst prof to prof, 51-90, EMER PROF PHYSICS, BROWN UNIV, 90- *Personal Data:* b Albany, NY, Dec 16, 19; m, Alice Brown; c Dirck E & Abby B. *Educ:* Mass Inst Technol, BS, 47, MS, 49, PhD(physics), 51. *Honors & Awards:* Recipient Rayleish Medal, Inst Acoust, UK, 85- *Prof Exp:* Mem staff, Radiation Lab, Mass Inst Technol, 40-41 & Underwater Sound Lab, 41-45, asst physics, 46-47, res assoc, 48-50. *Concurrent Pos:* Consult to asst attache for res, USN, Am Embassy, London, 51-52, Bolt, Beranek & Newman, Inc & Appl Res Labs, Univ Tex, Austin, 71-81, mem, Subcomt Aircraft Noise, NASA, 54-59; mem, Comt Hearing & Bio-acoust, Armed Forces-Nat Res Coun, 57-83, mem exec coun, 60-61, chmn, 67-68 & 80-83; mem, Sonic Boom Comt, Nat Acad Sci, 68-71. *Mem:* Fel Acoust Soc Am; fel Am Phys Soc. *Res:* Physical effects of high amplitude sound waves; air acoustics; underwater sound; general relativity. *Mailing Add:* Dept Physics Brown Univ Providence RI 02912. *Fax:* 401-751-3425

**WESTFAHL, PAMELA KAY,** REPRODUCTIVE PHYSIOLOGY. *Current Pos:* ASST PROF, BASIC SCIENTIST DEPT, CALIF COL PODIAT MED, 88- *Personal Data:* b Miami, Okla. *Educ:* Wash State Univ, BS, 74; Univ Okla, PhD(physiol), 80. *Prof Exp:* Fel, Ore Regional Primate Res Ctr, 80-83; asst prof, Dept Zool, Miami Univ, 83-88. *Mem:* Soc Study Reproduction; Endocrine Soc; Am Physiol Soc. *Res:* Factors involved in regulation of the corpus luteum during the menstrual or estrous cycle and pregnancy; feedback relationships of gonadal hormones on hypothalamic-pituitary function. *Mailing Add:* 6165 SW Valley Ave Beaverton OR 97008

**WESTFALL, DAVID PATRICK,** PHARMACOLOGY. *Current Pos:* PROF & CHMN PHARMACOL, SCH MED, UNIV NEV, 82- *Personal Data:* b Harrisburg, WVa, June 9, 42; m 65, Shirley Spencer; c Timothy D & Alison (Spencer). *Educ:* Brown Univ, BA, 64; WVa Univ, MS, 66, PhD(pharmacol), 68. *Prof Exp:* Demonstr pharmacol, Oxford Univ, 68-70; from asst prof to prof pharmacol, Med Sch, WVa Univ, 70-82. *Concurrent Pos:* J H Burn fel pharmacol, Oxford Univ, 68-70. *Mem:* AAAS; Am Soc Pharmacol & Exp Therapeut; Soc Neurosci. *Res:* Pharmacology and physiology of smooth and cardiac muscle; factors governing the sensitivity of muscle to drugs; co-transmitters in autonomic nerves; regulation of release of neurotransmitters. *Mailing Add:* Dept Pharmacol Sch Med Univ Nev Reno NV 89557-0001

**WESTFALL, DWAYNE GENE,** ENVIRONMENTAL SOIL SCIENCE, AGRONOMY. *Current Pos:* PROF AGRON, COLO STATE UNIV, 78- *Personal Data:* b Aberdeen, Idaho, Nov 21, 38; m 61; c 3. *Educ:* Univ Idaho, BS, 61; Wash State Univ, PhD(soils), 68. *Honors & Awards:* Agron Achievement Award, Am Soc Agron; Appl Res Award, Soil Sci Soc Am. *Prof Exp:* Res asst soils, Wash State Univ, 66-67; from asst prof to assoc prof soil chem, Tex A&M Univ, 67-74; sr plant nutritionist, Great Western Sugar Co, Agr Res Ctr, Longmont, 74-78. *Concurrent Pos:* Mem staff soil fertil, Colo State Univ Water Mgt Res Prog, Lahore, Pakistan, 78-80, Int Develop. *Mem:* Sigma Xi; fel Am Soc Agron; fel Soil Sci Soc Am; Int Soil & Sci Soc. *Res:* Fertility of sugarbeets, small grains and other agranomic crops; nitrogen efficiency and utilization; research and training programs in developing countries; dryland crop production systems; water quality. *Mailing Add:* Dept Soil Sci Colo State Univ Ft Collins CO 80523-0001

**WESTFALL, HELEN NAOMI,** BACTERIAL PHYSIOLOGY, PATHOGENICITY. *Current Pos:* RETIRED. *Personal Data:* b Grafton, WVa, June 23, 33; m 52; c 3. *Educ:* Old Dominion Univ, BS, 71, MS, 74; WVa Univ, PhD(med microbiol), 80. *Prof Exp:* Res asst, Old Dominion Univ, 71-72, asst, Gen Biol & Life Sci Labs, 73-74; sci instr, Portsmouth Cath High Sch, 74-75; instr biol, Alderson-Broaddus Col, 75-77; Benedum fel, WVa Univ, 77-80; nat res coun assoc, Naval Med Res Inst, 80-82, res microbiologist, 82-85; from asst prof to assoc prof, SDak State Univ, 85-93. *Mem:* Am Soc Microbiol; Sigma Xi; Am Women Sci. *Res:* Characterization of chemotaxis by Campylobacter species; isolation, purification and characterization of nitrate reductase from species of campylobacter; expression of Leptospira antigens by Escherichia coli, potential for use as diagnostic reagents or vaccines. *Mailing Add:* HCR 67 Box 66 Fremont MO 63941

**WESTFALL, JANE ANNE,** NEUROCYTOLOGY, CELL ULTRASTRUCTURE. *Current Pos:* asst prof anat, 67-70, assoc prof physiol sci & dir, Ultrastruct Res Lab, 70-76, PROF ANAT & PHYSIOL, KANS STATE UNIV, 76- *Personal Data:* b Berkeley, Calif, June 21, 28. *Educ:* Col Pac, AB, 50; Mills Col, MA, 52; Univ Calif, Berkeley, PhD(zool), 65. *Prof Exp:* Res asst zool, Univ NC, 52-53 & Univ Calif, Berkeley, 55-56; lab technician cancer res, Univ Calif, Berkeley, 57-58, lab technician zool, 58-65, asst res zoologist, 65-67. *Concurrent Pos:* Vis prof molecular, cellular & develop biol, Univ Colo, Boulder, 74-75. *Mem:* Micros Soc Am; Am Soc Cell Biol; Am Soc Zoologists; Soc Neurosci; Am Asn Anat; fel AAAS. *Res:*

Electron microscopy of sensory receptor cells, synapses and neuromuscular junctions in simple nervous systems; ultrastructure of lung tissues with stress and respiratory disease. *Mailing Add:* Dept Anat & Physiol Kans State Univ 1600 Dennison Manhattan KS 66506-5602. *Fax:* 785-532-4557; *E-Mail:* westfall@vet.ksu.edu

**WESTFALL, MINTER JACKSON, JR,** BIOLOGY. *Current Pos:* RETIRED. *Personal Data:* b Orlando, Fla, Jan 28, 16; m 45; c 3. *Educ:* Rollins Col, BS, 41; Cornell Univ, PhD(nature study), 47. *Prof Exp:* Wildlife technician, Ala Coop Wildlife Res Unit, 37; asst dir mus, Rollins Col, 37-40; from asst to sr asst biol, Cornell Univ, 42-47; from asst prof to prof zool & entom, Univ Fla, 47-95. *Concurrent Pos:* US dep game warden, 36-70; Howell fel, Highlands Biol Sta, NC, 53. *Mem:* Entom Soc Am. *Res:* Wildlife management of mourning dove; bird migration and movement; taxonomy, ecology, zoogeography, life histories of the Odonata. *Mailing Add:* 2235 Jess Jewell Pkwy 600A Hamilton Pl Gainesville GA 30507

**WESTFALL, RICHARD MERRILL,** EXTRATERRESTRIAL RESOURCE DEVELOPMENT, SUPERCONDUCTIVITY POWER SUPPLY DESIGN. *Current Pos:* FOUNDER & RES DIR, CEL SYSTS CORP, DENVER, 82-, GALACTIC MINING INDUSTS INC, DENVER, 88- *Personal Data:* b Denver, Colo, Dec 17, 56. *Prof Exp:* Res asst, Nat Oceanic & Atmospheric Admin, Boulder, Colo, 78-79; chemist photovoltaic res, Solar Energy Res Inst, Golden, Colo, 79-80; res dir, Galactic Prod Inc, Denver, 80-82; assoc engr process chem & optoelectronic device fabrication, Tex Med Instruments, 86-87. *Concurrent Pos:* Founder, Galactic Educ Develop Inst, 89- *Res:* Solid-state physics device fabrication; optoelectronic device experience; spacecraft propulsion system design; ultra-high power to weight ratio superconducting power supply design; orbital metallurgical satellite design; author of one publication; granted three patents. *Mailing Add:* 370 17th St Denver CO 80202

**WESTFALL, THOMAS CREED,** PHARMACOLOGY. *Current Pos:* MEM FAC, DEPT PHARMACOL, SCH MED, ST LOUIS UNIV, 80- *Personal Data:* b Latrobe, Pa, Oct 31, 37; m 61; c 1. *Educ:* WVa Univ, AB, 59, MS, 61, PhD(pharmacol), 62. *Prof Exp:* From instr to asst prof pharmacol, WVa Univ, 62-65; from asst prof to assoc prof pharmacol, 65-69, Sch Med, Univ Va, prof, 69-80. *Concurrent Pos:* Nat Heart Inst fel physiol, Karolinska Inst, Sweden, 63-64; dir grad studies, Dept Pharmacol, Sch Med, Univ Va, 68-; IUPHAR int fel, 74; vis fac scholar, Group Biochem Neuropharmacol, Lab Molecular Biol, Col France, Paris, 74-75. *Mem:* AAAS; Am Soc Pharmacol & Exp Therapeut; Soc Exp Biol & Med; Soc Neurosci; Am Heart Asn. *Res:* Autonomic, cardiovascular, biochemical and neuropharmacology; influence of drugs on the syntheses, uptake, storage, metabolism and receptor interaction of biogenic amines, particularly catecholamines; cardiovascular and autonomic actions of nicotine; neurotransmitter physiology and pharmacology. *Mailing Add:* Dept Pharmacol & Physiol Sci St Louis Univ Sch Med 1402 S Grand Blvd St Louis MO 63104

**WESTFIELD, JAMES D,** ENVIRONMENTAL ENGINEERING, TECHNOLOGY ASSESSMENT. *Current Pos:* VPRES, INT RESOURCES GROUP, WASHINGTON, DC, 83- *Personal Data:* b Nov 21, 37; US citizen; m 61; c 4. *Educ:* Univ Nev, Reno, BS, 61; Univ Mich, Ann Arbor, MPH, 64, PhD(environ sci), 66. *Prof Exp:* Chemist, Nev State Health Dept, 61-62; consult engr sanit eng, industs, 62-66; asst prof civil eng, Ga Inst Technol, 66-68; sr sanit engr & off mgr, Eng Sci Inc, Calif, 68-72; dir, Environ Eng Group, Tetra Tech Inc, 72-73; vpres, Develop Sci Inc, Sagamore, 73-83. *Concurrent Pos:* Dir, Solid Waste Training Prog, Ga Inst Technol; consult, Agua Tech Inc & prin, Eco Sci Labs, 67-68; Ford Found residency in eng pract grant, 68-69. *Mem:* Am Soc Civil Engrs; Am Chem Soc; Sigma Xi. *Res:* Energy systems design; chemical and physical water and wastewater treatment; resource management; technology assessment. *Mailing Add:* 2315 Stryker Ave Vienna VA 22181-3123

**WESTGARD, JAMES BLAKE,** ELEMENTARY PARTICLE PHYSICS. *Current Pos:* asst prof, 66-73, assoc prof, 66-80, PROF PHYSICS, IND STATE UNIV, TERRE HAUTE, 80- *Personal Data:* b Billings, Mont, Feb 12, 35; m 66; c 3. *Educ:* Reed Col, BA, 57; Syracuse Univ, PhD(physics), 63. *Prof Exp:* Res fel physics, Carnegie Inst Technol, 63-66. *Concurrent Pos:* Vis prof, Dartmouth Col, 83. *Mem:* Am Phys Soc; AAAS. *Res:* Particle physics; biomathematics; computer applications; electromagnetism. *Mailing Add:* 8 W Lawrin Blvd Terre Haute IN 47803

**WESTHAUS, PAUL ANTHONY,** ATOMIC PHYSICS, MOLECULAR PHYSICS. *Current Pos:* ASSOC PROF PHYSICS, OKLA STATE UNIV, 68- *Personal Data:* b St Louis, Mo, Dec 10, 38. *Educ:* St Louis Univ, BS, 61; Washington Univ, PhD(physics), 66. *Prof Exp:* Proj assoc, Theoret Chem Inst, Univ Wis, 66-67. *Concurrent Pos:* Res staff scientist, Yale Univ, 69; NIH career develop award, 72-77. *Mem:* Am Phys Soc; Sigma Xi. *Res:* Atomic structure and radiative transitions; electronic structure of molecules and intermolecular forces; quantum biology; many-electron problem. *Mailing Add:* 618 S Willis St Stillwater OK 74074

**WESTHEAD, EDWARD WILLIAM, JR,** BIOCHEMISTRY. *Current Pos:* assoc prof & actg head dept, 66-71, PROF BIOCHEM, UNIV MASS, AMHERST, 71- *Personal Data:* b Philadelphia, Pa, June 19, 30; c 2. *Educ:* Haverford Col, BA, 51, MA, 52; Polytech Inst Brooklyn, PhD(polymer & phys chem), 55. *Prof Exp:* Am Scand Found res fel, Biochem Inst, Univ Uppsala, 55-56, NSF res fel, 56-57; res assoc physiol chem, Univ Minn, 58-60; asst prof biochem, Dartmouth Med Sch, 61-66. *Concurrent Pos:* NIH career develop award, 61-66; NIH spec fel, Oxford Univ, 72-73. *Mem:* Am Chem

Soc; Am Soc Biol Chemists. *Res:* Enzyme mechanisms and control; biochemistry of catecholamine secretion. *Mailing Add:* Dept Biochem Univ Mass Amherst MA 01003-0001. *Fax:* 413-545-3291; *E-Mail:* westheap@biochem.u.mass.edu

**WESTHEIMER, FRANK HENRY,** ORGANIC CHEMISTRY, ENZYMOLOGY. *Current Pos:* prof, Harvard Univ, 54-60, chmn dept, 59-62, Loeb prof, 60-82, sr prof, 82-83, EMER LOEB PROF CHEM, HARVARD UNIV, 83- *Personal Data:* b Baltimore, Md, Jan 15, 12; m 37; c 2. *Educ:* Dartmouth Col, AB, 32; Harvard Univ, MA, 33, PhD(chem), 35. *Hon Degrees:* DSc, Dartmouth Col, 61, Univ Chicago, 73, Univ Cincinnati, 76, Tufts Univ, 78, Univ NC & Bard Col, 83, Weizmann Inst, 87 & Univ Ill, Chicago, 88. *Honors & Awards:* Willard Gibbs Medal, 70; James Flack Norris Award, Am Chem Soc, 70; Theodore William Richards Medal, 76; Richard Kokes Award, Nat Acad Sci, 80; Chas Frederick Chandler Award, 80; Lewis C Rosenstiel Award, 81; Robert A Welch Award, 82; Arthur C Cope Award, 82; Nichols Medal, 82; Ingold Medal, 83; Nat Medal of Sci, 86; Paracelsus Medal, 88; Priestley Medal, 88. *Prof Exp:* Nat Res Coun fel chem, Columbia Univ, 35-36; res assoc org chem, Univ Chicago, 36-37; from instr to asst prof chem, 37-44; res supvr, Explosives Res Lab, Nat Defense Res Comt, Pa, 44-45; from assoc prof to prof chem, Univ Chicago, 46-54. *Concurrent Pos:* Vis prof chem, Harvard Univ, 53-54; chmn, Comt Surv Chem, Nat Acad Sci, 64-65, mem coun, 72-75 & 76-79; mem, President's Sci Adv Comt, 67-70; vis prof, Univ Calif, Los Angeles, 55, Berkeley, 58, Boston Univ, 84, Ohio State Univ, 85, Univ Calif, San Diego, 86 & 88; mem coun, Am Philos Soc, 81-84. *Mem:* Nat Acad Sci; Am Philos Soc; Am Chem Soc; fel Am Acad Arts & Sci (secy, 85-90); foreign mem Royal Soc London. *Res:* Electrostatic effects in organic chemistry; mechanism of nitration; chemical and biochemical oxidation; molecular mechanics; enzymic and chemical decarboxylation; phosphate esters; photoaffinity labeling. *Mailing Add:* Converse Lab Harvard Univ Cambridge MA 02138

**WESTHEIMER, GERALD,** PHYSIOLOGICAL OPTICS, VISION SCIENCE. *Current Pos:* assoc prof physiol optics & optom, Univ Calif, Berkeley, 60-63, prof physiol optics, 63-68, chmn, Physiol Optics Group, 64-67, prof physiol, 68-89, head, Div Neurobiol, 87-92, prof neurobiol, 89-94, PROF GRAD SCH, UNIV CALIF, BERKELEY, 94- *Personal Data:* b Berlin, Ger, May 13, 24. *Educ:* Univ Sydney, BSc, 47; Ohio State Univ, PhD(physics), 53. *Hon Degrees:* DSc, Univ NSW, Australia, 88; ScD, State Univ NY, 90. *Honors & Awards:* Tillyer Medal, Optical Soc Am, 78; Proctor Medal, Asn Res Vision & Ophthal, 79; von Sallman Prize, Columbia Univ, 86; Prentice Medal, Am Acad Optom, 86; Bicentennial Medal, Australia Optom Asn, 88; Sackler lectr, Tel Aviv Univ, 89; Hebb lectr, McGill Univ, 91-; Ferrier lectr, Royal Soc London, 92. *Prof Exp:* Optometrist, Australia, 45-51; assoc optom, Ohio State Univ, 51-52; prof, Univ Houston, 53-54; from asst prof to assoc prof physiol optics, 54-60. *Concurrent Pos:* Mem, Nat Acad Sci-Nat Res Coun Comt Vision, 57-72, mem exec coun, 69-72; vis researcher, Physiol Lab, Cambridge Univ, 58-59; mem, Visual Sci Study Sect, NIH, 66-70, mem, Vision Res Training Comt, Nat Eye Inst, 70-74; ed, Vision Res, 72-79 & 85-89, chmn, 86-91; assoc ed, Invest Ophthal, 73-74, Exp Brain Res, 73-89, Optics Lett, 77-79, J Optical Soc Am, 80-82, Human Neurobiol, 81-87, Spatial Visions, 85 & Ophthal & Physiol Optics, 85, J Physiol, 87-94; mem commun sci cluster, President's Biomed Res Panel, 75, 94; chmn, Visual Sci B Study Sect, NIH, 77-79; mem, Bd Sci Counrs, Nat Eye Inst, NIH, 80-84, chmn, 81-83; ed, Proc Royal Soc London, B, 90-96; adj prof, Rockefeller Univ, 92- *Mem:* Fel AAAS; Sigma Xi; fel Optical Soc Am; Soc Neurosci; Brit Physiol Soc; Int Brain Res Orgn; fel Royal Soc London; fel Nat Vision Res Inst Australia; Am Acad Arts & Sci. *Res:* Biophysics and physiology of visual system; neurophysiology. *Mailing Add:* Dept Molecular & Cell Biol Univ Calif Div Neurobiol Berkeley CA 94720-3200. *Fax:* 510-643-6791; *E-Mail:* gwest@violet.berkeley.edu

**WESTHOFF, DENNIS CHARLES,** FOOD MICROBIOLOGY. *Current Pos:* From asst prof to assoc prof, 70-79, PROF DAIRY SCI, UNIV MD, COLLEGE PARK, 79-, CHMN, DEPT ANIMAL SCI, 85- *Personal Data:* b Jersey City, NJ, Nov 20, 42; m 63, 78; c 2. *Educ:* Univ Ga, BSA, 66; NC State Univ, MS, 68, PhD(food sci), 71. *Concurrent Pos:* Sci adv, Food & Drug Admin, 76- *Mem:* Am Soc Microbiol; Am Dairy Sci Asn. *Res:* Bioprocessing of foods; food safety. *Mailing Add:* Dept Animal Sci Univ Md College Park MD 20742-0001

**WESTINE, PETER SVEN,** PENETRATION MECHANICS, ARMOR. *Current Pos:* RETIRED. *Personal Data:* b Boston, Mass, Apr 8, 40; m 62, Patricia Myers; c Karen (Emmons) & Sven E. *Educ:* Swarthmore Col, Pa, BS, 62; Cornell Univ, MCE, 64. *Prof Exp:* Res engr, Southwest Res Inst, 64-71, sr engr, 71-79, staff engr, 79-87; tech consult, Alcoa Tech Ctr, 87-92. *Res:* The effects of explosion (ground shock, air blast, fragments, and thermal fireballs) on shelters, buildings, people, aircraft and vehicles; aircraft and vehicle armors; KE and CE threats with passive and reactive systems including metals, composites, ceramics, explosives, etc. *Mailing Add:* 603 Jefferson Dr Apollo PA 15613. *E-Mail:* pwestine@aol.com

**WESTING, ARTHUR H,** ECOLOGY, CONSERVATION. *Current Pos:* CONSULT, 90- *Personal Data:* b New York, NY, July 18, 28; m 56, Carol Eck; c Jeanne K (Svensson) & Stephen H. *Educ:* Columbia Univ, AB, 50; Yale Univ, MF, 54, PhD, 59. *Hon Degrees:* DSc, Windham Col, 73. *Honors & Awards:* NY Acad Sci Award, 83; Bulgarian Protection of Nature Medal, 84; Global 500 Award, UN, 90. *Prof Exp:* Res forester, US Forest Serv, 54-55; asst prof forestry, Purdue Univ, 59-64; assoc prof tree physiol, Univ Mass, 64-65; assoc prof biol, Middlebury Col, 65-66; assoc prof bot, Windham Col, 66-71, chmn, Dept Biol, 66-74, prof bot, 71-76; sr res fel, Stockholm Int Peace Res Inst, 76-78 & 83-87; prof ecol & dean, Sch Natural Sci, Hampshire Col, 78-83; sr res fel, Int Peace Res Inst, Oslo, 88-90. *Concurrent Pos:* Fel forest biol, NC State Col, 60; Bullard fel, Harvard Univ, 63-64, res fel, 70; fel bot, Univ Mass, 66; trustee, Vt Wild Land Found, 66-75, Vt Acad Arts & Sci, 67-71 & 91- & Rachel Carson Coun, 79-87, World Coun Biosphere, 88-; fel nuclear sci, St Augustine's Col, 68; vis scholar, Stockholm Int Peace Inst, 75 & 81, Europ Univ Ctr Peace Studies, 89- *Mem:* Fel AAAS; Fauna & Flora Protection Soc; fel Scientists' Inst Pub Info; fel Int Soc Naturalists; Sigma Xi; Int Primate Protection League. *Res:* Forest ecology; environmental effects of war; environmental security. *Mailing Add:* Fred Houghton Rd Putney VT 05346. *Fax:* 802-387-4001

**WESTKAEMPER, JOHN C(ONRAD),** AERONAUTICAL ENGINEERING, MECHANICAL ENGINEERING. *Current Pos:* spec instr, Appl Res Lab, 57-60, asst prof aerospace eng, 60-67, ASSOC PROF AEROSPACE ENG, UNIV TEX, AUSTIN, 67-, RES ENGR, APPL RES LAB, 60- *Personal Data:* b San Antonio, Tex, Dec 5, 23; m 47; c 2. *Educ:* Univ Tex, BS, 47, MS, 59, PhD, 67. *Prof Exp:* Aerodynamicist, Consol Vultee Aircraft Corp, 47-50; from sr engr to asst proj engr, Sverdrup & Parcel, Inc, 50-52; sr res engr, Convair Div, Gen Dynamics Corp, 52-55; res engr, Defense Res Lab, Univ Tex, 55-60; res engr, Res Br, Engine Test Facil, ARO, Inc, 60. *Mem:* Am Inst Aeronaut & Astronaut; Sigma Xi; Am Soc Eng Educ. *Res:* Fluid mechanics and heat transfer, including testing and test facility design. *Mailing Add:* 3402 Foothills Terr Austin TX 78731

**WESTLAKE, DONALD G(ILBERT),** METALLURGY. *Current Pos:* RETIRED. *Personal Data:* b Aurora, Ill, July 9, 28; m 50, Helen Gum; c 1. *Educ:* Northern Ill Univ, BS, 50; Iowa State Univ, PhD(metall), 59. *Prof Exp:* Teacher high sch, Ill, 50-51; jr chemist, Argonne Nat Lab, 51-52; asst, Iowa State Univ, 54-59; asst metallurgist, Mat Sci Div, Argonne Nat Lab, 59-64, assoc metallurgist, 64-72, metallurgist, 72-81, sr metallurgist, 81-84. *Mem:* Fedn Am Scientists. *Res:* Metal-hydrogen alloys; structure and properties of metal hydrides; reaction rates and diffusion; hydrogen embrittlement of metals; interstitial occupancy in hydrides of intermetallic compounds; deformation twinning. *Mailing Add:* 611 Plamondon Ct Wheaton IL 60187-6305

**WESTLAKE, DONALD WILLIAM SPECK,** MICROBIOLOGY. *Current Pos:* from assoc prof to prof, 66-94, chmn dept, 69-89, EMER PROF MICROBIOL, UNIV ALTA, 94- *Personal Data:* b Woodstock, Ont, Feb 27, 31; m 54; c 2. *Educ:* Univ BC, BS, 53, MS, 55; Univ Wis, PhD, 58. *Honors & Awards:* Can Soc of Microbiol Award, 86. *Prof Exp:* From asst res officer to assoc res officer, Nat Res Coun Can, 58-66. *Mem:* Can Soc Microbiol; Chem Inst Can; Can Soc Biochem; Brit Soc Gen Microbiol. *Res:* Microbial biochemistry; environmental microbiology; metabolic pathways; fermentations. *Mailing Add:* 3375 Anchorage Ave Victoria BC V9C 1X4 Can

**WESTLAKE, ROBERT ELMER, SR,** INTERNAL MEDICINE, CARDIOLOGY. *Current Pos:* EMER CLIN PROF, STATE UNIV NY UPSTATE MED CTR, 81- *Personal Data:* b Jersey City, NJ, Oct 2, 18; m 44, Agnes V Kumpf; c Robert E Jr, Barbara E (Walker) & Richard L. *Educ:* Princeton Univ, AB, 40; Columbia Univ, MD, 43. *Prof Exp:* From instr to asst prof med, Col Med, State Univ NY Upstate Med Ctr, 49-52, from clin asst prof to clin prof, 52-67; dir, Prof Serv, Community-Gen Hosp, 67-81. *Concurrent Pos:* Mem, Adv Comt Heart, Cancer & Stroke, Surgeon Gen, 66-67; mem, Adv Coun, US Dept Defense, 69-74; electrocardiographer, Syracuse Med Ctr. *Mem:* Fel Am Col Physicians; Am Soc Internal Med (pres, 65-66); fel Am Soc Informatics; fel Am Col Physicians. *Res:* Electrocardiography; Wolfe-Parkinson-White syndrome, including its inheritance and relation to outflow tract hypertrophy. *Mailing Add:* 5056 SE Bent Wood Dr Stuart FL 34997-1603. *E-Mail:* westarz@juno.com

**WESTLAND, ALAN DUANE,** INORGANIC CHEMISTRY. *Current Pos:* RETIRED. *Personal Data:* b Toledo, Ohio, Dec 29, 29; m 56. *Educ:* Univ Toronto, BA, 53, MA, 54, PhD(chem), 56. *Prof Exp:* Fel, Univ Muenster, 56-58; from asst prof to assoc prof, Univ Ottawa, 58-69, prof inorg chem, 69-92. *Mem:* Am Chem Soc; Chem Inst Can; Royal Soc Chem. *Res:* Analytical and physical inorganic chemistry of the transition elements. *Mailing Add:* 43 Chdelamine Chelsea ON J0X 1N0 Can

**WESTLAND, ROGER D(EAN),** PHARMACEUTICAL CHEMISTRY, ORGANIC CHEMISTRY. *Current Pos:* from assoc res chemist to sr res chemist, Parke-Davis Pharmaceut Res, 59-71, res scientist, 71-73, mgr, 73-85, DIR CHEM-BIOL INFO, PARKE-DAVIS PHARMACEUT RES, 85- *Personal Data:* b Winnebago Co, Iowa, June 26, 28; m 56; c 2. *Educ:* St Olaf Col, AB, 50; Univ Kans, MS, 52; Univ Mich, PhD(chem), 59. *Prof Exp:* Asst res chemist, Parke, Davis & Co, 52-55; asst, Univ Mich, 57-58. *Mem:* Am Chem Soc; Sigma Xi. *Res:* Medicinal chemistry and information science. *Mailing Add:* 2137 Medford Rd Apt 16 Ann Arbor MI 48104-4936

**WESTLER, WILLIAM MILO,** PHYSICAL BIOCHEMISTRY. *Current Pos:* OPER DIR, NAT MAGNETIC RESONANCE FACIL, UNIV WIS, MADISON, 88- *Personal Data:* b Grove City, Pa, Dec 28, 50; m 80. *Educ:* Grove City Col, BS, 72; John Carroll Univ, MS, 74; Purdue Univ, PhD(chem), 80. *Prof Exp:* Oper dir, Biochem Magnetic Resonance Lab, Purdue Univ, 79-88. *Mem:* Am Chem Soc; Sigma Xi. *Res:* One dimensional and two dimensional nuclear magnetic resonance spectroscopic techniques applied to the investigation of the structural and the dynamic properties of biological macromolecules. *Mailing Add:* Dept Biochem 110 Univ Wis Biochem Bldg 420 Henry Mall Madison WI 53706-1502

**WESTLEY, JOHN LEONARD,** ENZYMOLOGY, SULFUR BIOCHEMISTRY. *Current Pos:* from instr to assoc prof, 56-64, PROF BIOCHEM, UNIV CHICAGO, 64- *Personal Data:* b Wilsonville, Nebr, Aug 29, 27; m 56; c 3. *Educ:* Univ Chicago, PhB, 48, PhD(biochem), 54. *Prof Exp:* NSF fel biochem, Calif Inst Technol, 54-55, res fel, 55-56. *Concurrent Pos:* USPHS res career develop award, 62-72. *Mem:* Am Soc Biol Chemists. *Res:* Mechanisms of enzyme action; sulfur metabolism; kinetic analysis; enzyme regulation; cyanide detoxication. *Mailing Add:* Dept Biochem Univ Chicago 920 E 58th St Chicago IL 60637-1432. *Fax:* 773-702-0439

**WESTLEY, JOHN WILLIAM,** organic chemistry, biochemistry, for more information see previous edition

**WESTMACOTT, KENNETH HARRY,** PHYSICAL METALLURGY, MATERIALS SCIENCE. *Current Pos:* SR SCIENTIST, LAWRENCE BERKELEY LAB, 76- *Personal Data:* b Wantage, Eng, Nov 22, 29; m 64, Judith Quinones-Amezquita; c Michael & Paul. *Educ:* Univ Birmingham, PhD(phys metall, mat sci), 69. *Prof Exp:* Exp officer metall, Atomic Energy Res Estab, Eng, 51-62; res assoc mat sci, Stanford Univ, 63; res physicist metal physics, Michelson Lab, US Naval Weapons Ctr, 64-76. *Concurrent Pos:* Managing dir, Nat Ctr Elec Micros, Lawrence Berkeley Lab, 85-91; vis prof, Ecole Des Mines, Paris, 85, Sophia Antipolis, 91 & Univ Seville, Spain, 91; Joliet-Curie chair, Paris, 92. *Mem:* Assoc Brit Inst Metall; Am Inst Mining, Metall & Petrol Engrs; Electron Micros Soc Am. *Res:* Structure of metals; crystal lattice defects; mechanical properties; relation of microstructure to properties; quench and irradiation damage; dislocation theory; transmission electron microscopy; phase transformations; thin film epifaxy. *Mailing Add:* 78 Greenfield Dr Moraga CA 94556. *Fax:* 510-486-5888; *E-Mail:* microst@lbl.gov

**WESTMAN, JACK CONRAD,** CHILD PSYCHIATRY. *Current Pos:* coordr, Diag & Treat Unit, Ctr Ment Retardation & Human Develop, 66-74, dir, Child Psychiat Div, Univ Hosp, 65-78, PROF PSYCHIAT, MED SCH, UNIV WIS-MADISON, 65- *Personal Data:* b Cadillac, Mich, Oct 28, 27; m 53; c 3. *Educ:* Univ Mich, BS, 49, MD, 52, MS, 59. *Prof Exp:* Intern, Duke Univ Hosp, 52-53; resident psychiat, Univ Mich, 56-57; from instr to assoc prof, Med Sch, Univ Mich, 58-65. *Concurrent Pos:* Fel child psychiat, Univ Mich, 57-59; lectr, Sch Social Work, Univ Mich, 59-64; mem sr staff, Children's Psychiat Hosp, Ann Arbor, Mich, 59-65, dir, Outpatient Serv, 61-62, dir, Outpatient & Day Care Serv, 62-65. *Mem:* Fel Am Orthopsychiat Asn; Asn Am Med Cols; fel Am Acad Child Psychiat; Am Asn Ment Deficiency; Soc Prof Child Psychiatrists; Sigma Xi. *Res:* Efficacy of medication of hyperkinesis; psychiatric aspects of learning disabilities and mental retardation; the role of child psychiatry in divorce; predicting later adjustment from nursery school behavior; individual differences in children; child advocacy. *Mailing Add:* 1234 Dartmouth Rd Madison WI 53705

**WESTMANN, RUSSELL A,** CIVIL ENGINEERING, APPLIED MECHANICS. *Current Pos:* from asst prof to assoc prof mech & struct, Univ Calif, Los Angeles, 66-73, actg chmn dept, Sch Eng & Appl Sci, 69-70, assoc dean, 76-81, prof mech & struct, Sch Eng & Appl Sci, 73-, EMER PROF, UNIV CALIF, LOS ANGELES. *Personal Data:* b Fresno, Calif, May 20, 36; m 58; c 2. *Educ:* Univ Calif, Berkeley, BS, 59, MS, 60, PhD(civil eng), 62. *Prof Exp:* Actg asst prof civil eng, Univ Calif, Berkeley, 62; NSF fel math, 62-63; res fel aeronaut, Calif Inst Technol, 63-65, asst prof civil eng, 65-66. *Concurrent Pos:* Mem, Transp Res Bd, Nat Res Coun, 65-75; sr vis fel, Sci Res Coun, Eng, 74. *Mem:* Am Soc Civil Engrs. *Res:* Solid mechanics; engineering mathematics; fracture mechanics. *Mailing Add:* Dept Mech Eng Univ Calif 48-21 Eng IV Bldg Los Angeles CA 90024

**WESTMEYER, PAUL,** SCIENCE EDUCATION. *Current Pos:* PROF EDUC, UNIV TEX, SAN ANTONIO, 73- *Personal Data:* b Dillsboro, Ind, Dec 9, 25; m 47, June Van Skyock; c Jean, Joseph, Crystal, Kenneth, Paula & Matthew. *Educ:* Ball State Univ, BS, 49, MS, 53; Univ Ill, EdD, 60. *Prof Exp:* Pub sch teacher, Ind, 49-54; instr chem & sci, Univ Ill High Sch, 54-61; from asst prof to assoc prof sci educ, Univ Ill, 60-63; assoc prof, Univ Tex, 63-66; prof, Fla State Univ, 66-73. *Concurrent Pos:* Instr, Exten, Purdue Univ, 51-54; consult, Chicago Sch Bd, Ill, 54; proj assoc, Earlham Col, 59-62; partic, Int Seminar Chem, Dublin, Ireland, 60; consult, CBA Insts, 61-63; NSF in-serv grant, 64-65, coop col-sch sci grants, 64-66, summer inst grants & in-serv grants, 67-73 & 81-82; vis scientist, Uniformed Servs Univ Health Scis, 87-90. *Mem:* AAAS; Am Chem Soc; Nat Asn Res Sci Teaching; Nat Sci Teachers Asn; Asn Educ Teachers Sci (pres, 71-72). *Res:* Course development and evaluation; computer-assisted-instruction in chemistry; development of laboratory materials, tests and instructional procedures in chemistry; better utilization of staff in science teaching; computer programs for teaching statistics; higher education; technology assisted instruction in health sciences. *Mailing Add:* 6900 Loop 1604 W San Antonio TX 78249. *Fax:* 210-458-4510

**WESTMORE, JOHN BRIAN,** MASS SPECTROMETRY. *Current Pos:* asst prof, 63-69, assoc prof, 69-76, PROF CHEM, UNIV MAN, 76- *Personal Data:* b Welling, Eng, Apr 23, 37; m 61, Patricia B Salveson; c David B & Michael S. *Educ:* Univ London, BSc, 58, PhD(phys chem), 61. *Prof Exp:* Fel chem, Nat Res Coun Can, 61-63. *Mem:* Chem Inst Can; Chem Soc; Am Soc Mass Spectrometry; Can Soc Mass Spectrometry. *Res:* Ionization and dissociation of molecules; chromatography and mass spectrometry of metal chelates, nucleosides, nucleotides and steroids; analytical chemistry; studies of metal chelation; peptides and proteins. *Mailing Add:* Dept Chem Univ Man Winnipeg MB R3T 2N2 Can. *Fax:* 204-275-0905; *E-Mail:* westmor@cc.umanitoba.ca

**WESTMORELAND, BARBARA FENN,** ELECTROENCEPHALOGRAPHY, NEUROSCIENCE. *Current Pos:* from asst prof to assoc prof, 73-85, PROF NEUROL, MAYO MED SCH, 85- *Personal Data:* b New York, NY, July 22, 40. *Educ:* Mary Washington Col, BS, 61; Univ Va, MD, 65. *Honors & Awards:* Colgate Darden Award, Mary Washington Col, 61. *Prof Exp:* Intern, Vanderbilt Univ, 65-66; resident neurol, Univ Va, 66-70; fel, EEG, Mayo Clin, 70-71. *Concurrent Pos:* Consult, EEG, Mayo Clin, 71-; epilepsy adv comt, NIH, 81-85; prog dir, Div Clin Neurophysiol, Mayo Med Sch, 87-; mem, Clin Neurophysiol Sect, Am Bd Psychiat & Neurol, 91-; treas & chair educ, Sect Clin Neurophysiol, Am Acad Neurol, 96- *Mem:* Am Epilepsy Soc (treas, 78-80, pres, 87-88); Am EEG Soc (secy, 85-87, pres, 87-88); Cent EEG Asn (secy & treas, 76-78, pres, 79-80); Sigma Xi (pres, Mayo Chap, 87-88); NIH; Am Acad Neurol. *Res:* Clinical electroencephalography as it relates to various types of EEG patterns and the EEG findings in various disease entities as in epilepsy, metabolic derangements, and coma; clinical neurophysiology. *Mailing Add:* Mayo Clin Rochester MN 55901

**WESTMORELAND, DAVID GRAY,** ANALYTICAL & PHYSICAL CHEMISTRY. *Current Pos:* Sr scientist chem, 73-83, RES FEL, ROHM & HAAS CO, 83- *Personal Data:* b Mooresville, NC, Aug 5, 46; m 80; c 2. *Educ:* Univ NC, Chapel Hill, BS, 68; Stanford Univ, PhD(chem), 73. *Mem:* Am Chem Soc; Am Soc Mass Spectrometry; AAAS. *Res:* Structure determination of unknown compounds; trace analysis for organic compounds. *Mailing Add:* Rohm & Haas Co 727 Norristown Rd Spring House PA 19477-0904

**WESTMORELAND, PHILLIP R,** COMBUSTION KINETICS, GAS KINETICS. *Current Pos:* asst prof, 86-92, ASSOC PROF, CHEM ENG DEPT, UNIV MASS, AMHERST, 92- *Personal Data:* b Asheboro, NC, Mar 20, 51; m 79, Kathleen J Beach; c Nathaniel P & Ariel K. *Educ:* NC State Univ, BS, 73; La State Univ, MS, 74; Mass Inst Technol, PhD(chem eng), 86. *Prof Exp:* Res engr, Chem Technol Div, Oak Ridge Nat Lab, 74-79; consult, Oak Ridge Nat Lab, 80, Mass Inst Technol, 86-89. *Concurrent Pos:* NSF presidential young investr, 90; chem engr, Nat Inst Stand & Technol, guest researcher, 93- *Mem:* Am Inst Chem Engrs; Am Chem Soc; Mat Res Soc; Combustion Inst; Electrochem Soc. *Res:* Quantum theories of elementary-reaction Kinetics; experiments and modeling of chemical reactions in microelectronics fabrication (particularly plasma-enhanced CVD), flame combustion, pyrolysis and steam cracking of hydrocarbons; materials synthesis. *Mailing Add:* Dept Chem Eng Univ Mass 159 Goessmann Lab PO Box 33110 Amherst MA 01003-3110. *Fax:* 413-545-1647; *E-Mail:* westm@ecs.umass.edu

**WESTMORELAND, WINFRED WILLIAM,** DENTISTRY. *Current Pos:* RETIRED. *Personal Data:* b Santa Maria, Calif, Feb 7, 19; m 42; c 3. *Educ:* Col Physicians & Surgeons San Francisco, DDS, 42; Univ Calif, MPH, 57; Am Bd Dent Pub Health, dipl. *Prof Exp:* Extern oral surg, San Francisco Hosp, 46-47; clin instr oper dent, Col Physicians & Surgeons, Univ of Pac, 49-53, asst clin prof prosthetic dent & lectr dent mat, 53-58, lectr pub health dent, 58-69, asst clin prof dent pub health, 66-69; sr dent consult, Calif Dept Health, Oakland, 67-81; dent health prog consult, 81-84. *Concurrent Pos:* Pub health dent officer, Calif State Dept Health, 55-67; consult, Resident Training Prog, US Army, Ft Ord, Calif, 67-72; pvt practr. *Mem:* Am Dent Asn; Am Pub Health Asn; Int Asn Dent Res. *Res:* Epidemiology of dental caries; periodontal disease; cleft lip and palate; radiation exposure; dental fluorosis; dental health administration and education. *Mailing Add:* 18815 Eighmy Rd Cottonwood CA 96022

**WESTNEAT, DAVID FRENCH,** ANALYTICAL CHEMISTRY. *Current Pos:* chmn dept, 68-72, assoc prof, 65-77, PROF CHEM, WITTENBERG UNIV, 77- *Personal Data:* b Oradell, NJ, June 18, 29; m 58; c 3. *Educ:* Allegheny Col, BS, 50; Univ Pittsburgh, PhD(chem), 56. *Prof Exp:* Res chemist, E I du Pont de Nemours & Co, 56-60; asst prof chem, Akron Univ, 60-65. *Concurrent Pos:* Vis prof, Sci & Soc Prog, Cornell Univ, 72-73; vis scientist, Univ Hyg Lab, Univ Iowa, 80-81. *Mem:* AAAS; Sigma Xi. *Res:* Instrumental analysis, especially absorption spectroscopy and gas chromatography. *Mailing Add:* 611 W South College St Yellow Springs OH 45387-1426

**WESTNEAT, DAVID FRENCH, JR,** BEHAVIORAL ECOLOGY, ORNITHOLOGY. *Current Pos:* asst prof, 90-95, ASSOC PROF BIOL & DIR, CTR ECOL, EVOLUTION & BEHAV, UNIV KY, LEXINGTON, 95- *Personal Data:* b Wilmington, Del, June 16, 59; m 85; c 1. *Educ:* Carleton Col, BA, 81; Univ NC, PhD(zool), 86. *Honors & Awards:* Young Investr Award, Am Soc Naturalists, 89. *Prof Exp:* Vis lectr behav, Univ NC, Chapel Hill, 87; NSF fel res, Cornell Univ, Ithaca, NY, 87-89, res assoc, 89-90. *Concurrent Pos:* Prin investr, Cornell Univ/Univ Ky, 89- *Mem:* Sigma Xi; Am Ornithologists Union; Animal Behav Soc; Int Soc Behav Ecol; Am Soc Naturalists; Cooper Ornith Soc. *Res:* Ecological causes and evolutionary consequences of animal social behavior; use of genetic techniques to analyze the outcome of alternative mating behavior in birds and to study the costs and benefits of parental behavior. *Mailing Add:* 101 Morgan Bldg Univ Ky Lexington KY 40506-0225. *E-Mail:* westneat@ceeb.uky.edu

**WESTOFF, CHARLES F,** POPULATION RESEARCH. *Current Pos:* PROF DEMOG & SOCIOL, PRINCETON UNIV, 62- *Honors & Awards:* Taeuber Award; Award, Pop Asn Am. *Mem:* Inst Med-Nat Acad Sci; Am Acad Arts & Sci; Pop Asn Am (past pres). *Mailing Add:* Princeton Univ Pop Res Off 21 Prospect Ave Princeton NJ 08544

**WESTON, ARTHUR WALTER,** PHARMACEUTICAL LICENSING. *Current Pos:* PRES, ARTHUR W WESTON & ASSOCS, 79- *Personal Data:* b Smiths Falls, Ont, Can, Feb 13, 14; nat US; m 40, Dawn Thompson; c Roger, Randall & Cynthia. *Educ:* Queen's Univ, Ont, BA, 34, MA, 35; Northwestern Univ, PhD(org chem), 38. *Prof Exp:* Asst chem, Northwestern Univ, 35-37, postdoctoral fel, 38-40; from res chemist to asst head org res, Abbott Labs, 40-54, asst to dir develop, 54-55, asst dir, 55-57, dir res, 57-59, dir res & develop, 59-61, dir co, 59-69, vpres res & develop, 61-68, vpres sci affairs, 68-78, vpres & dir, San-Abbott, 76-79, vpres corp licensing, 78-79, consult, 79-85. *Concurrent Pos:* Mem, War Manpower Comn, Off Sci Res & Develop, 42-45; mem ad hoc comt chem agts, Dept Defense, 61-65; mem, Indust Res Inst, bd dirs, 70-73; mem, indust Panel Sci & Technol, NSF, 74-79. *Mem:* Am Chem Soc; Sigma Xi. *Res:* Organic medicinals; antibiotics; plant processes. *Mailing Add:* 349 E Hilldale Pl Lake Forest IL 60045-3031

**WESTON, CHARLES ALVIN,** ENVIRONMENTAL ANALYSIS, HIGH RESOLUTION MASS SPECTROSCOPY. *Current Pos:* TECH DIR, ENVIRON TESTING CORP, 90- *Personal Data:* b Skowhegan, Maine, Jan 28, 36; m 62, Norma Bressler. *Educ:* Bowdoin Col, BA, 58; Rutgers Univ, PhD(org chem), 67. *Prof Exp:* Res chemist, Am Cyanamid, 66-71; mass spectrometrist, Rutgers Univ, 72-77; mgr fragrance technol, Norda Inc, 77-82. *Mem:* Am Chem Soc; AAAS. *Res:* Developed new methods for analysis of environmental samples by gas chromatograph/mass spectrometry; data systems enhancements and method development. *Mailing Add:* ETC Corp 10 Herman Thau Rd Annandale NJ 08801

**WESTON, CHARLES RICHARD,** DEVELOPMENTAL BIOLOGY, MICROBIAL ECOLOGY. *Current Pos:* lectr, 68-69, ASSOC PROF BIOL, CALIF STATE UNIV, NORTHRIDGE, 70- *Personal Data:* b South Gate, Calif, Apr 24, 33; m 53; c 4. *Educ:* Univ Calif, Santa Barbara, BA, 57; Princeton Univ, PhD(biol), 65. *Prof Exp:* Res scientist, E R Squibb Inst Med Res, 60-61; res assoc & asst prof, Univ Rochester, 62-66; Nat Acad Sci-Nat Res Coun resident res assoc, Jet Propulsion Lab, Calif Inst Technol, 66-68. *Mem:* AAAS; Bot Soc Am; Am Soc Microbiol. *Res:* Morphogenesis of fungal mycelium; development of instrumentation for remote life detection; interactions and distribution of soil microorganisms. *Mailing Add:* Dept Biol Calif State Univ 18111 Nordhoff St Northridge CA 91330-0001

**WESTON, GARY STEVEN,** ASTROPHYSICS. *Current Pos:* ASST PROF ASTROPHYS & NUCLEAR PHYSICS, CALIF STATE UNIV, HAYWARD, 88- *Personal Data:* b Detroit, Mich, Sept 3, 57; m 88, Joanie Char; c Brian. *Educ:* Wayne State Univ, BS, 79; Univ Calif, Los Angeles, MS, 81, PhD(physics), 84. *Prof Exp:* Mem tech staff, AT&T Bell Labs, 84-86; mgr, AT&T Int, 86-87. *Mem:* Am Physics Soc; Am Astron Soc; Am Asn Physics Teachers; Astron Soc Can. *Res:* Analyze data on gamma ray bursts in astrophysics; proton-nucleus scattering experiments. *Mailing Add:* Physics Dept Calif State Univ Hayward CA 94542

**WESTON, HENRY GRIGGS, JR,** ECOLOGY, VERTEBRATE ZOOLOGY. *Current Pos:* RETIRED. *Personal Data:* b Hemet, Calif, Apr 7, 22; m 47; c 3. *Educ:* San Diego State Col, BA, 43; Univ Calif, Berkeley, MA, 47; Iowa State Col, PhD(zool), 50. *Prof Exp:* Asst prof biol, Grinnell Col, 50-55; prof biol, San Jose State Univ, 55-87. *Mem:* Wildlife Soc; Cooper Ornith Soc; Am Ornith Union; Am Soc Mammal. *Res:* Birds of California; bird-banding; field ecology. *Mailing Add:* PO Box 2596 Kings Beach CA 96143

**WESTON, JAMES A,** DEVELOPMENTAL BIOLOGY, CELL BIOLOGY. *Current Pos:* assoc prof, 70-74, PROF BIOL, UNIV ORE, 74- *Personal Data:* b Washington, DC, June 20, 36; m 58; c 2. *Educ:* Cornell Univ, AB, 58; Yale Univ, PhD(biol), 62. *Prof Exp:* USPHS fel zool, Univ Col, London, 62-64; from asst prof to assoc prof biol, Case Western Res Univ, 64-70. *Concurrent Pos:* Mem med adv bds, Nat Neurofibromatosis Found, Inc & Familial Dysautonomia Found, Inc. *Mem:* Fel AAAS; Soc Develop Biol (secy, 73-76); Int Soc Develop Biol; Am Soc Cell Biol. *Res:* Cellular control of morphogenetic movements in vertebrate development; regulation of cellular phenotypic expression of neural crest cells in vivo and in vitro; properties of cell surfaces in normal and transformed states. *Mailing Add:* Biol Univ Ore Eugene OR 97403. *Fax:* 541-346-4548; *E-Mail:* Bitnet: weston@uoneuro.uoregon.edu

**WESTON, JOHN COLBY,** histology, embryology, for more information see previous edition

**WESTON, KENNETH CLAYTON,** COMPUTER AIDED ENGINEERING. *Current Pos:* assoc prof mech & aerospace eng, 68-80, prof, 80-95, EMER PROF MECH ENG, UNIV TULSA, 95- *Personal Data:* b Buffalo, NY, Jan 8, 32; m 63, Ruth Deason; c Patricia, June & Marla. *Educ:* Cornell Univ, BME, 55; Rice Univ, MS, 65, PhD(mech eng), 69. *Honors & Awards:* Teetor Award, Soc Automotive Engrs, 78; Robert W Cox Award, Am Soc Mech Engrs. *Prof Exp:* Res scientist aerodyn & thermodyn, Lewis Res Ctr, NASA, Ohio, 55-58, res engr, Space Task Group, Va, 58-60, sect head aerothermodyn, Manned Spacecraft Ctr, Tex, 60-68. *Concurrent Pos:* Vis prof, US Mil Acad, 85-86 & 93-94. *Mem:* Am Soc Eng Educ; Am Inst Aeronaut & Astronaut; Am Soc Mech Engrs; Soc Automotive Engrs. *Res:* Thermodynamics; fluid mechanics; energy conversion; computer aided design and graphics; gas turbines; engineering software tools; stationary and transportation power plant studies. *Mailing Add:* Dept Mech Eng Univ Tulsa 600 S College Ave Tulsa OK 74104

**WESTON, KENNETH W,** ALGEBRA. *Current Pos:* assoc prof, 71-89, PROF, UNIV WIS, PARKSIDE, 89- *Personal Data:* b Milwaukee, Wis, Feb 1, 29; m 66; c 2. *Educ:* Univ Wis, BS, 53, MS, 55, PhD(math), 63. *Prof Exp:* Instr math, Univ Wis, Milwaukee, 61-63; asst prof, Univ Notre Dame, 63-69; assoc prof, Marquette Univ, 69-71. *Mem:* Am Math Soc; Math Asn Am. *Res:* Groups satisfying Engel condition and connections between ring and group theory; model theory. *Mailing Add:* 5470 S Overlook Dr New Berlin WI 83117

**WESTON, RALPH E, JR,** CHEMICAL KINETICS, PHOTOCHEMISTRY. *Current Pos:* from assoc chemist to chemist, Brookhaven Nat Lab, 51-65, dep dept chmn, 82-89, sr chemist, 65-94, CONSULT, BROOKHAVEN NAT LAB, 94- *Personal Data:* b San Francisco, Calif, Nov 9, 23; m 51, Virginia L Priest; c Judith, Joan & Barbara. *Educ:* Univ Calif, BS, 46; Stanford Univ, PhD(chem), 50. *Prof Exp:* Asst, Harvard Univ, 49-51. *Concurrent Pos:* Vis scientist, Saclay Nuclear Res Ctr, France, 60-61; vis lectr, Univ Calif, Berkeley, 68-69; lectr, Columbia Univ, 71-72; mem, Comt Chem Kinetics, Nat Res Coun, 75-77, Army Basic Res Comt, 75-81, adv bd, Off Chem & Chem Technol, 80-81. *Mem:* Am Chem Soc; Sigma Xi. *Res:* Kinetics and dynamics of gas phase reactions; photochemistry; using lasers; molecular energy transfer. *Mailing Add:* Chem Dept Brookhaven Nat Lab Upton NY 11973. Fax: 516-282-5815; E-Mail: weston@bnl.gov

**WESTON, RAYMOND E,** CARDIOVASCULAR DISEASE, NUTRITION. *Current Pos:* Assoc clin prof med, 78-93, EMER PROF MED, UNIV CALIF, LOS ANGELES, 93-, EMER SR ATTEND PHYSICIAN, CEDAR SINAI MED CTR, LOS ANGELES, 93- *Personal Data:* b July 15, 17. *Educ:* Univ Chicago, MD & PhD(physiol), 41. *Mem:* Am Bd Int Med; Am Fedn Clin Res; Am Physiol Soc; Am Soc Clin Invest; Soc Exp Biol & Med. *Res:* Salt and water metabolism and congestive heart failure. *Mailing Add:* 803 N Roxbury Dr Beverly Hills CA 90210

**WESTON, ROY FRANCIS,** ENVIRONMENTAL ENGINEERING. *Current Pos:* PRES & CHMN BD, ROY F WESTON, INC, ENVIRON CONSULTS, 55-, EMER CHMN, 91- *Personal Data:* b Reedsburg, Wis, June 25, 11; m 34; c 2. *Educ:* Univ Wis, BCE, 33; NY Univ, MCE, 39; Environ Eng Intersoc, dipl. *Hon Degrees:* DEng, Drexel Univ, 81. *Honors & Awards:* Indust Wastes Medal, Water Pollution Control Fedn, 50, Arthur Sidney Bedell Award, 59; Gordon Maskew Fair Award, Am Acad Environ Engrs, 77. *Prof Exp:* Jr hwy engr, Wis Hwy Dept, 34-36; dist engr, Wis Dept Health, 36-37; sanit eng res fel, NY Univ, 37-39; sanit engr, Atlantic Refining Co, Philadelphia, 39-55. *Concurrent Pos:* Mem vis comt, Dept Civil & Urban Eng, Univ Pa & Ctr Marine & Environ Studies, Lehigh Univ; mem, US Environ Control Seminar, Neth & Eastern Europe, 72; pres, Am Acad Environ Engrs, 73-74; mem, Comt Environ, US Chamber Com, 75; mem, Indust & Prof Adv Comt, Pa State Univ, 75. *Mem:* Nat Acad Engr; fel Am Soc Civil Engrs, Am Pub Health Asn; Am Chem Soc; Am Inst Chem Engrs. *Res:* Environmental control. *Mailing Add:* Roy F Weston Inc 1 Weston Way West Chester PA 19380-1499. Fax: 610-701-3186

**WESTON, VAUGHAN HATHERLEY,** APPLIED MATHEMATICS, THEORETICAL PHYSICS. *Current Pos:* PROF MATH, PURDUE UNIV, WEST LAFAYETTE, 69- *Personal Data:* b Parry Sound, Ont, May 1, 31; m 54; c 4. *Educ:* Univ Toronto, BA, 53, MA, 54, PhD, 56. *Prof Exp:* Lectr math, Univ Toronto, 57-58; res assoc, Radiation Lab, Univ Mich, 58-59, from assoc res mathematician to res mathematician, 59-69. *Mem:* Am Math Soc; Soc Indust & Appl Math; Am Phys Soc. *Res:* Electromagnetic theory; diffraction; plasmas; inverse scattering. *Mailing Add:* 2222 Carberry Dr West Lafayette IN 47906

**WESTON, WILLIAM LEE,** PEDIATRIC DERMATOLOGY, CUTANEOUS IMMUNOLOGY. *Current Pos:* resident dermat, Univ Colo, 70-72, fel immunol, 72-73, from asst prof to assoc prof, 73-79, CHMN, DEPT DERMAT, UNIV COLO, 76-, PROF DERMAT & PEDIAT, 79- *Personal Data:* b Grand Rapids, Minn, Aug 13, 38; m 64, Janet Atkinson; c Elizabeth C & William K. *Educ:* Whitman Col, AB, 60; Univ SDak, BMS, 63; Univ Colo, MD, 65. *Prof Exp:* Resident pediat, Univ Colo, 65-67; resident pediat, Univ Calif, San Francisco, 67-68; med officer, Mead, Md, 68-70. *Mem:* Soc Pediat Dermat (secy/treas, 76-80, pres, 83-84); Am Acad Dermat; Soc Invest Dermat; Am Acad Pediat; Am Fedn Clin Res. *Res:* Skin diseases in children, especially birthmarks. *Mailing Add:* Univ Colo Sch Med 4200 E Ninth Ave Denver CO 80220-3706

**WESTOVER, JAMES DONALD,** ORGANIC CHEMISTRY. *Current Pos:* from asst prof to assoc prof, 70-82, PROF CHEM, CALIF POLYTECH STATE UNIV, 82- *Personal Data:* b Clarkdale, Ariz, Sept 22, 34; m 59; c 4. *Educ:* Ariz State Univ, BS, 50, MS, 62; Brigham Young Univ, PhD(chem), 66. *Prof Exp:* Res chemist, Dacron Res Lab, E I du Pont de Nemours & Co, Inc, NC, 65-70. *Res:* Synthetic organic chemistry in area of nitrogen heterocyclic compounds; polyester fibers. *Mailing Add:* 141 Del Norte Way San Luis Obispo CA 93405-1507

**WESTOVER, LEMOYNE BYRON,** ANALYTICAL CHEMISTRY. *Current Pos:* RETIRED. *Personal Data:* b Curwensville, Pa, Aug 12, 28; m 52; c 3. *Educ:* Dickinson Col, BS, 50; Pa State Univ, MS, 52. *Prof Exp:* Chemist analytical chem, Hercules, 52-54; US Army, 54-56; chemist analytical chem, Dow Chem Co, 56-69, group leader mass spectros, 59-70, res mgr analytical chem, 70-89. *Mem:* Am Chem Soc; Sigma Xi. *Res:* Mass spectrometry; liquid chromatography; gas chromatography; infrared spectroscopy. *Mailing Add:* 138 Mt Everest Ct Clayton CA 94517

**WESTOVER, THOMAS A(RCHIE),** ELECTRICAL ENGINEERING. *Current Pos:* RETIRED. *Personal Data:* b Westover, Pa, June 1, 09; m 40; c 3. *Educ:* Carnegie Inst Technol, BSc, 36; Stevens Inst Technol, MSc, 45. *Prof Exp:* Tester & inspector, Allis Chalmers Mfg Co, Pa, 36-40; tester, Pub Serv Elec & Gas Co, NJ, 40-42; sr engr, Fairchild Camera & Instrument Corp, 42-46, proj engr, 46-47; staff engr, Servo Corp Am, 47-54, engr in chg control systs, Eng Dept, 54-61; asst chief electronics engr, Missile Systs Div, Repub Aviation Corp, 61-63; asst chief engr, Electronic Prod Div, Fairchild Hiller Corp, 63-65; eng mgr, RR Prods Div, Servo Corp Am, 65-70, sr consult engr, Advan Eng Dept, 70-72. *Concurrent Pos:* Instr, State Univ NY Agr & Tech Inst, Long Island, 50-60. *Mem:* Sr mem Inst Elec & Electronics Engrs. *Res:* Servomechanisms; electricity and magnetism; instruments and equipment; electronic and infrared systems; meteorological measurement systems. *Mailing Add:* 22 Parkway Noyack Dr Sag Harbor NY 11963

**WESTPFAHL, DAVID JOHN,** ASTROPHYSICS. *Current Pos:* ASST PROF ASTROPHYS, NMEX INST MINING & TECHNOL, 89- *Personal Data:* b Scranton, Pa, Aug 19, 53. *Educ:* Dartmouth Col, AB, 75; Mont State Univ, MS, 78 & PhD(physics), 85; Yale Univ, MS, 79. *Prof Exp:* Instr physics, Mont State Univ, 85-86; res assoc astrophys, Dominion Astrophys Observ, 86-88; asst scientist, Nat Radio Astron Observ, 88-89. *Concurrent Pos:* Fel, Kahlmeyer Found, 89, dir, 90-; dir & prin investr, Joint Observ Cometary Res, 90-; collaborating scientist, Nat Radio Astron Observ, 90- *Mem:* Am Astron Soc. *Res:* Internal kinematics and dynamics of disk galaxies; evolution of gas in spiral galaxies. *Mailing Add:* 692 Bluebird Lane NE Albuquerque NM 87122

**WESTPHAL, HEINER,** MAMMALIAN GENE RESEARCH. *Current Pos:* CHIEF, LAB MAMMALIAN GENES & DEVELOP, NAT INST CHILD HEALTH & HUMAN DEVELOP, NIH, 72- *Personal Data:* b Seesen, Ger, Feb 13, 35; m; c 2. *Educ:* Med Sch, Bonn, MD, 62, Venia legendi, Ulm, 75. *Honors & Awards:* Gerhard-Domagk Prize. *Prof Exp:* Mem staff, Inst Biochem, Freiburg, Ger, 62-65, Inst Hyg & Microbiol, 65-66, Salk Inst Biol Sci, San Diego, Calif, 67-70 & Cold Spring Harbor Lab, NY, 72- *Concurrent Pos:* Assoc ed, Molecular Biol & Med; adv bd mem, Experientia; instr, FAES Grad Sch, NIH. *Mem:* Soc Develop Biol. *Res:* Enzyme biochemistry and regulation in yeast; induction of cell DNA synthesis during lytic infection of monkey cells with SV40; integration of SV40 DNA in transformed cells; mammalian gene regulation. *Mailing Add:* 5104 Wickett Terr Bethesda MD 20814

**WESTPHAL, JAMES ADOLPH,** PLANETARY SCIENCES. *Current Pos:* PROF PLANETARY SCI, CALIF INST TECHNOL, 78- *Personal Data:* b Dubuque, Iowa, June 13, 30; m 67; c 1. *Educ:* Univ Tulsa, BS, 53. *Prof Exp:* Sr res fel, Calif Inst Technol, 66-71, assoc prof planetary sci, 71-77 *Concurrent Pos:* Prin investr, wide field/planetary camera, space telescope. *Mem:* Am Astron Soc. *Res:* Infrared astronomy; infrared atmospheric properties; planetary astronomy; astronomical instrumentation; space astronomy. *Mailing Add:* MS 150-21 Planetary Sci Calif Inst Technol Pasadena CA 91125

**WESTPHAL, KLAUS WILHEM,** PALEONTOLOGY. *Current Pos:* DIR, GEOL MUS, UNIV WIS-MADISON, 69-, INSTR PALEONT, 77- *Personal Data:* b Berlin, Ger, Mar 20, 39; m 69, Margaret E Wagner; c Barbara, Marianne & Christine. *Educ:* Eberhard-Karls Univ, Ger, BS, 60, MS, 64, PhD(paleont), 69. *Concurrent Pos:* Leader expeds fossil vert, 77-94. *Res:* Geology and paleontology. *Mailing Add:* Geol Mus Univ Wis 1215 W Dayton St Madison WI 53706. Fax: 608-262-0693; E-Mail: kwwestph@facstaff.wisc.edu

**WESTPHAL, MILTON C, JR,** PEDIATRICS, GASTROENTEROLOGY. *Current Pos:* RETIRED. *Personal Data:* b Philadelphia, Pa, June 2, 26; m 78; c 6. *Educ:* Yale Univ, BS, 47; Univ Pa, MD, 51; Am Bd Pediat, dipl, 57. *Prof Exp:* Intern, Univ Pa Hosp, 51-52; resident, Children's Hosp Philadelphia, 54-56; from asst instr to instr pediat, Sch Med, Univ Pa, 55-61; from asst prof to assoc prof, State Univ NY, Buffalo, 61-67; chmn dept, Col Med, Med Univ SC, 67-76, prof pediat, 67-, chief, Sect Gastroenterol, 76-90. *Concurrent Pos:* Chief resident, Children's Hosp Philadelphia, 56-57; from asst physician to assoc physician, 57-61, mem, Res Dept, 57-61; asst pediatrician to outpatients, Pa Hosp, 57-58, hosp, 58-59, assoc pediatrician, 59-61; asst attend, Children's Hosp Buffalo, 61-64, assoc attend, 64-; dir, Buffalo Poison Control Ctr, 61-67; proj dir & chmn, Comt Prin Investrs, Collab Study Cerebral Palsy, Ment Retardation & Other Neurol & Sensory Dis Infancy & Childhood, 63-64; asst dean admis, Univ SC, 86- *Mem:* Am Pediat Soc. *Res:* Gastroenterology; ion transport across intestinal muscosain in cystic fibrosis. *Mailing Add:* 171 Ashley Ave Charleston SC 29425-0001

**WESTPHAL, WARREN HENRY,** ENERGY MINERAL DEVELOPMENT. *Current Pos:* RETIRED. *Personal Data:* b Easton, Pa, Feb 19, 25; m 46; c 3. *Educ:* Columbia Univ, AB, 47. *Honors & Awards:* Founder Award, Energy Minerals Div, Am Asn Petrol Geologists. *Prof Exp:* Jr mining engr, NJ Zinc Co, NJ, 47-48, geologist, 48-49, res geologist, Pa, 49-50, geophysicist, Colo, 50-55; sr geologist, Tidewater Assoc Oil Co, NMex, 55; chief geophysicist, Utah Construct & Mining Co, 56-59; sr geophysicist, Stanford Res Inst, 59-66, chmn, Earth Sci Dept, 66-69; vpres mining, Intercontinental Energy Corp, 69-79; pres, Westphal Assocs Inc, 79-89. *Mem:* AAAS; Am Inst Prof Geologists; Am Asn Petrol Geologists; Am Inst Mining, Metall & Petrol Engrs; Soc Economic Geologists. *Res:* Earthquake seismology; uranium geology; in-situ mining; underground coal gasification; geochemistry of gold deposition. *Mailing Add:* 2020 S Monroe St Apt 125 Denver CO 80210-3766

**WESTRUM, EDGAR FRANCIS, JR,** PHYSICAL CHEMISTRY, THERMODYNAMICS. *Current Pos:* from asst prof to prof, 46-89, EMER PROF PHYS CHEM, UNIV MICH, ANN ARBOR, 89- *Personal Data:* b Albert Lea, Minn, Mar 16, 19; m 43, Florence E Barr; c Ronald M, Michael L, James S & Margaret K. *Educ:* Univ Minn, BChem, 40; Univ Calif, PhD(phys chem), 44. *Honors & Awards:* Hugh Huffman Award, F D Rossini lectr, Bausch & Lomb Hon Sci Award, Distinguished Fac Achievement Award. *Prof Exp:* Res chemist, Metall Lab, Univ Chicago, 44-46 & Radiation Lab, Univ Calif, 46. *Concurrent Pos:* Chmn, Comt Data for Sci & Technol, Nat Acad Sci, 73; chmn, Comn & Phys Chem Div, Int Union Pure & Appl Chem, 73-77; ed, J Chem Thermodyn, 68-79 & Bull Thermodyn & Thermochem, 55-75; secy gen, Comt on Data for Sci & Technol, 74-81, ed-in-chief, 82- *Mem:* Fel AAAS; fel Am Inst Chemists; Am Chem Soc; Royal Soc Chem; fel Am Phys Soc. *Res:* Thermodynamics, actinide, lanthanide, and transition compounds; thermochemistry; cryogenic calorimetry; molecular dynamics plastic crystals; thermophysics of phase ordering, Schottky, transitions, thermophysics of vitreous state; phonon dispersion and heat capacity. *Mailing Add:* Dept Chem Univ Mich Ann Arbor MI 48109-1055. *Fax:* 313-647-4865

**WESTRUM, LESNICK EDWARD,** NEUROSURGERY, BIOLOGICAL STRUCTURE. *Current Pos:* res asst prof, 66-67, asst prof, 67-77, ASSOC PROF SURG & BIOL STRUCT, SCH MED, UNIV WASH, 77- *Personal Data:* b Tacoma, Wash, Oct 19, 34. *Educ:* Wash State Univ, BS, 58; Univ Wash, MD, 63; Univ London, PhD(anat), 66. *Prof Exp:* NIH fel, Univ London, 63-66, hon res asst anat, Univ Col, 64-66. *Mem:* AAAS; Am Asn Anatomists; Soc Neurosci. *Res:* Studies of synapses in normal and experimental conditions; emphasis on trigeminal and limbic systems. *Mailing Add:* Dept Neurol Surg & Biol Struct Univ Wash Sch Med Box 356470 Seattle WA 98195-6470

**WESTWATER, EDGEWORTH RUPERT,** ATMOSPHERIC PHYSICS. *Current Pos:* physicist atmospheric physics, 70-84, SUPV PHYSICIST, NAT OCEANIC & ATMOSPHERIC ADMIN, 84- *Personal Data:* b Denver, Colo, Oct 29, 37; div; c 3. *Educ:* Western State Col Colo, BA, 59; Colo Univ, MS, 62, PhD(physics), 70. *Prof Exp:* Chemist cement chem, Ideal Cement Co, 59-60; physicist atmospheric physics, Nat Bur Stand, 60-65 & Environ Sci Serv Admin, 65-70. *Concurrent Pos:* Mem ad hoc working group inversion methods, Radiation Comn, Int Asn Meteorol & Atmospheric Physics, 66-; Comt on Radio Frequencies, Nat Acad Sci; mem, Comn F, URSI. *Mem:* Am Meteorol Soc; Optical Soc Am; Soc Indust & Appl Math; Math Asn Am; Inst Elec & Electronics Engrs. *Res:* Remote sensing of the atmosphere; radiative transfer in the atmosphere; mathematics of ill-posed problems. *Mailing Add:* 7732 Jade Ct Boulder CO 80303. *Fax:* 303-497-6978; *E-Mail:* ewestwater@wpl.erl.gov

**WESTWATER, J(AMES) W(ILLIAM),** CHEMICAL ENGINEERING, HEAT TRANSFER. *Current Pos:* From asst prof to prof, 48-88, head dept, 62-80, EMER PROF CHEM ENG, UNIV ILL, 88- *Personal Data:* b Danville, Ill, Nov 24, 19; m 42, Elizabeth Keener; c Barbara, Judith, David & Beverly. *Educ:* Univ Ill, BS, 41; Univ Del, MChE, 43, PhD(chem eng), 48. *Honors & Awards:* Reilly Lectr, Notre Dame Univ, 58; William H Walker Award, Am Inst Chem Engrs, 66; Max Jakob Award, Am Soc Mech Engrs, 72; Vincent Bendix Award, Am Soc Eng Educ, 74; Donald L Katz Lectr, Univ Mich, 78. *Concurrent Pos:* Lectr, Am Inst Chem Engrs, 64. *Mem:* Nat Acad Eng; Am Chem Soc; Am Soc Eng Educ; fel Am Inst Chem Engrs; Am Soc Mech Engrs. *Res:* Heat transfer; phase changes; boiling; condensation. *Mailing Add:* Dept Chem Eng Univ Ill Urbana IL 61801

**WESTWICK, ROY,** MATHEMATICS. *Current Pos:* from asst prof to assoc prof, 62-70, PROF MATH, UNIV BC, 70- *Personal Data:* b Vancouver, BC, May 23, 33; m 59; c 3. *Educ:* Univ BC, BA, 56, MA, 57, PhD(math), 60. *Prof Exp:* Nat Res Coun Can overseas fel, math, Univ Col, London, 60-62. *Concurrent Pos:* Can Coun sr fel, 67-68. *Mem:* Can Math Soc. *Res:* Linear and multilinear algebra. *Mailing Add:* Dept Math Univ BC 121-1984 Mathematics Rd Vancouver BC V6T 1Z2 Can

**WESTWOOD, ALBERT RONALD CLIFTON,** RESEARCH MANAGEMENT, MATERIALS SCIENCE. *Current Pos:* RETIRED. *Personal Data:* b Birmingham, Eng, June 9, 32; nat US; m 56, Jeannie; c 2. *Educ:* Univ Birmingham, BSc, 53, PhD(phys metall), 56, DSc(mat sci), 68; Coun Eng Inst, UK, CEng, 78. *Honors & Awards:* Beilby Gold Medal & Prize, Royal Inst Chem, Soc Chem Indust & Inst Metals UK, 70; Tewksbury Lectr, Univ Melbourne, Australia, 74; Burgess Lectr, Am Soc Metals, 84; Campbell Mem Lectr, Am Soc Metals Int, 87; Henry Krumb Lectr, Metall Soc & Soc Mining Engrs, 88; Leadership Award, Minerals, Metals & Mat Soc, 92; Wenk Lectr, Johns Hopkins Univ, 95; J Herbert Holloman Award, 96. *Prof Exp:* Tech officer, Res Dept, Imp Chem Industs, Eng, 56-58; scientist, Res Inst Advan Studies, Martin Marietta Labs, Baltimore, Md, 58-61, sr scientist, 61-64, assoc dir & head, Mat Sci Dept, 64-69, dep dir, 69-74, dir, 74-84, corp dir res & develop, Martin Marietta Corp, Bethesda, Md, 84-87, vpres res & develop, 87-90, vpres sci, 90, vpres, Res & Technol, 90-93; vpres res & explor technol, Sandia Nat Labs, Albuquerque, NM, 93-96. *Concurrent Pos:* Lectr, Chance Tech Col, Eng, 54 & Handsworth Tech Col, 54-56; fel, Johns Hopkins Univ, 65-; guest mem comt, Acad Sci, USSR, 69, 76, 78, 81, 86 & 89; mem adv comt, Inorg Mat Div, Nat Bur Stand, 72-75; mem adv bd, J Mat Sci, UK, 74-, Colloids & Surfaces, 79-83 & Mech & Physics Surfaces, 79-; bd dirs, Metall Soc, Inc, 80-83, financial officer, 85-; mem, Rev Comt, Mat Sci Div, Argonne Nat Labs, 76-82; mem, Mat Res Adv Comn, NSF, 80-84; mem, Nat mat Adv Comn, Nat Res Coun, 80-85 & Comn Eng & Tech Studies, 85-88, chmn, 92; mem, Md Humanities Coun, 84-90, chmn, 88-89; bd dir, Martin Marietta Energy Systs, Inc, 84-93; bd dirs, US Advan Ceramics Asn, 85-88; chmn, Sect P Indust Sci, AAAS, 89-90; distinguished lectr, Am Soc Mech Engrs, 89-91

& Am Soc Mat Int & Minerals, Metals & Mat Soc, 95; trustee, Am Inst Mining, Metall & Petrol Engrs, 90-92; mem, Vis Comt, Nat Inst Stand & Technol, 90-96; chmn, Comt Global Aspects Intellectual Property Rights Sci & Technol, 91-92; chmn, Pub Info Comt, Nat Acad Eng, 95-96; bd dirs, US Civilian Res Develop Found, 95- *Mem:* Nat Acad Eng; fel Am Soc Metals Int; fel Brit Inst Physics; fel AAAS; foreign assoc Royal Swed Acad Eng Sci; Indust Res Inst (pres, 89-90); fel Minerals, Metals & Mat Soc (pres, 90-91); foreign mem Russ Acad; foreign mem Royal Acad Eng. *Res:* Research and development management theory; mechanical behavior, chemomechanical effects, surface and environmental effects; metals, ceramics, semiconductors. *Mailing Add:* 1413 Pinnacle View NE Albuquerque NM 87112. *Fax:* 505-293-6616; *E-Mail:* arwestwood@aol.com

**WESTWOOD, MELVIN (NEIL),** POMOLOGY, PLANT PHYSIOLOGY. *Current Pos:* assoc prof, Ore State Univ, prof, 67-80, res dir, Nat Clonal Germplasm Repository, 80-82, nat tech adv clonal germplasm, 82-86, EMER PROF HORT, ORE STATE UNIV, 86- *Personal Data:* b Hiawatha, Utah, Mar 25, 23; m 46, Wanda Shields; c Rose, Nancy, Robert & Kathryn. *Educ:* Utah State Univ, BS, 53; Wash State Univ, PhD(pomol, plant physiol), 56. *Honors & Awards:* Gourley Award, Am Soc Hort Sci, 58 & 77 & Stark Award, 69 & 77; Paul Howe Shepard Award, Am Pomol Soc, 68-82, Wilder Medal Award, 81; Outstanding Res Award, Am Soc Hort, 86. *Prof Exp:* Asst field botanist, Utah State Univ, 51-52, supt, Hort Res Field Sta, 52-53; asst, Wash State Univ, 53-55; from asst res horticulturist to res horticulturist, USDA, 55-60. *Mem:* AAAS; fel Am Soc Hort Sci (pres, 74-75); Am Soc Plant Physiologists; Am Pomol Soc. *Res:* Deciduous fruit tree and rootstock physiology; growth dynamics; plant hormones; chemical thinning; high density orchard systems. *Mailing Add:* 2130 NW Elmwood Pl Corvallis OR 97330

**WESTWOOD, WILLIAM DICKSON,** PHYSICS. *Current Pos:* CONSULT THIN FILMS, 97- *Personal Data:* b Kirkcaldy, Scotland, Jan 4, 37; Can citizen; m 61, Eveline Cook; c Karen. *Educ:* Univ Aberdeen, BSc, 59, PhD(physics), 62, DSc, 86. *Prof Exp:* Scientist, Northern Elec Co Ltd, 62-65; lectr physics, Flinders Univ, Australia, 66-69; scientist, Northern Elec Co Ltd, 69-70; mgr thin film physics, Bell-Northern Res Ltd, 71-79, mgr mat & device res, 79-96. *Mem:* Fel Brit Inst Physics; Can Asn Physicists; Am Vacuum Soc (secy, 85-96); Sigma Xi. *Res:* Thin film physics; sputtering; spectroscopy of gas discharges; integrated optics; surface analysis; optical recording devices; optoelectronic devices; gallium-arsenide devices communication systems. *Mailing Add:* 7 Mohawk Crescent Nepean ON K2H 7G7 Can. *E-Mail:* westwood@istar.ca

**WESWIG, PAUL HENRY,** ANIMAL NUTRITION. *Current Pos:* from asst prof to prof biochem, 41-79, asst chemist, Exp Sta, 41-42, EMER PROF BIOCHEM, COL ANIMAL SCI, ORE STATE UNIV, 79- *Personal Data:* b St Paul, Minn, July 13, 13; m 40, Dorothy Johnson; c John & Charles. *Educ:* St Olaf Col, BA, 35; Univ Minn, MS, 39, PhD(biochem), 41. *Prof Exp:* Instr chem, St Olaf Col, 36-37; asst biochem, Univ Minn, 38-41. *Concurrent Pos:* Nutrit Surv, Ethiopia, 58, Malaya, 62, Paraguay, 65, 72, Sri Lanka, 79. *Mem:* Am Chem Soc; Am Inst Nutrit; Am Dairy Sci Asn; Am Soc Animal Sci. *Res:* Trace mineral metabolism in ruminants and laboratory animals including requirement, interrelationship, toxicity, tissue enzyme activity and element concentration including selenium, copper and heavy metals. *Mailing Add:* 2112 NW Polk St Corvallis OR 97330-5603

**WETEGROVE, ROBERT LLOYD,** MICROBIOLOGY, INDUSTRIAL WATER TREATMENT. *Current Pos:* Res scientist microbiol, Nalco Chem Co, 78-81, res group leader waste treat chem, 81-82, cooling water chem, 82-84, mkt develop mgr, 84-87, res develop mgr biotechnol, 87-89, CORP RES ASSOC, NALCO CHEM CO, 89- *Personal Data:* b San Diego, Calif, Jan 25, 48; m 71. *Educ:* Univ Tex, Austin, BA, 70, MA, 72; Univ Tex (microbiol), 78; Ill Inst Technol, MBA, 88. *Concurrent Pos:* Indust adv bd, Ctr Microbiol Ecol, Mich State Univ; mem, Res & Develop Coun, Am Mgt Asn. *Mem:* Am Soc Microbiol; Soc Indust Microbiol; Sigma Xi. *Res:* Biotechnology relating to industrial water treatment. *Mailing Add:* One Nalco Ctr Nalco Chem Co Naperville IL 60563. *Fax:* 630-305-2895; *E-Mail:* rwetegrove@nalco.com

**WETHERALD, RICHARD TRYON,** GENERAL CIRCULATION MODELING, MATH & COMPUTER ANALYSIS. *Current Pos:* RES ASSOC CLIMATE RES, GEOPHYS FLUID DYNAMICS LAB, NAT OCEANIC & ATMOSPHERIC ADMIN, 64- *Personal Data:* b Plainfield, NJ, Mar 28, 36; m 63; c 3. *Educ:* Univ Mich, BS, 62, MS, 63. *Prof Exp:* Assoc engr comput develop, Westinghouse Elec, 63-64. *Concurrent Pos:* Investr, Dept Energy, 87-, Prog Climate Model Diag & Intercomparison, 90-; contribr, Intergovt Panel Climate Change, 89- *Res:* Climate research; climate sensitivity; greenhouse warming; changes in solar insulation; cloud feedback; oxygen-induced changes of temperature, hydrology and clouds. *Mailing Add:* 78 Taylor Terr Hopewell NJ 08525

**WETHERALL, NEAL T,** RESEARCH ADMINISTRATION. *Current Pos:* SCI DIR, VIROMED LABS INC, 91- *Res:* Research administration. *Mailing Add:* Viromed Labs Inc 61001 Blue Circle Dr Minneapolis MN 55343-9108

**WETHERELL, DONALD FRANCIS,** PLANT PHYSIOLOGY. *Current Pos:* RETIRED. *Personal Data:* b Manchester, Conn, Nov 25, 27; m 49; c 4. *Educ:* Univ Conn, BA, 51; Univ Md, MS, 53, PhD(plant physiol), 56. *Prof Exp:* Res assoc & lectr plant physiol, Univ Md, 56-58; from asst prof to assoc prof plant physiol, Univ Conn, 58-67, actg chmn, Dept Bot, 61-64, chmn, Regulatory Biol Sect, 67-68, prof plant physiol, 67-89. *Concurrent Pos:* Guggenheim fel, 65-66. *Mem:* Am Soc Plant Physiologists; Int Asn Plant Tissue Cult. *Res:* Regulatory mechanisms of growth and development in plants. *Mailing Add:* 33 Summit Rd Storrs Mansfield CT 06268-1421

**WETHERELL, HERBERT,** PHARMACOLOGY, TOXICOLOGY. *Current Pos:* RETIRED. *Personal Data:* b Chicago, Ill, Jan 25, 27; m 62, Theresa Urzendowski; c Julie. *Educ:* Yale Univ, BS, 49, PhD(pharmacol), 54. *Prof Exp:* Asst prof physiol & pharmacol, Med Col, Univ Nebr, 53-61; toxicologist, Wayne Co Med Examr Off, 62-72; toxicologist, Crime Lab, Mich Dept Pub Health, 72-77; toxicologist, Crime Lab, Mich State Police, 77-92. *Mem:* Am Chem Soc; Am Acad Forensic Sci; Royal Soc Chem London; Sigma Xi. *Res:* Relationship between chemical structure and pharmacologic activity; toxicology and drug metabolism; chlorophyll chemistry; infrared spectrophotometry. *Mailing Add:* 15906 Burdette Omaha NE 68116

**WETHERHOLD, ROBERT CAMPBELL,** COMPOSITE MATERIALS. *Current Pos:* asst prof, 83-89, ASSOC PROF MECH & MAT, STATE UNIV NY, BUFFALO, 89- *Personal Data:* b Wilmington, Del, Nov 19, 51. *Educ:* Univ Del, BME & BA, 74, MMAE, 76, PhD(mech eng), 83. *Prof Exp:* Engr, E I du Pont Co, 76-78, spec engr, 80-81; res assoc, Ctr Composite Mat, Univ Del, 78-80. *Concurrent Pos:* Am Soc Eng Educ/NASA-Lewis fac fel, 85 & 86; Air Force Off Sci Res fac fel, Wright-Patterson AFB, 87 & 88; vis scientist, Air Force Mat Lab, Wright-Patterson AFB, 89 & Rockwell Int Sci Ctr, 90. *Mem:* Am Soc Mech Engrs; assoc fel Am Inst Aeronaut & Astronaut; Am Ceramic Soc; Am Soc Composite. *Res:* All aspects of composite materials, from their fabrication through their end use; durability issues such as fracture of composites; smart materials and structures. *Mailing Add:* Dept Mech & Aerospace Eng State Univ NY Buffalo NY 14260-4400. *Fax:* 716-645-2593 Ext 2241; *E-Mail:* mecrcw@acsu.buffalo.edu

**WETHERILL, GEORGE WEST,** PLANETARY SCIENCE. *Current Pos:* dir, Dept Terrestrial Magnetism, 75-91, STAFF MEM, CARNEGIE INST WASHINGTON, 91- *Personal Data:* b Philadelphia, Pa, Aug 12, 25; wid; c Rachel, George & Sarah. *Educ:* Univ Chicago, PhB, 48, SB, 49, MS, 51, PhD(physics), 53. *Honors & Awards:* Leonard Medal, Meteoritical Soc, 81; Gilbert Award, Geol Soc Am, 84; Kuiper Prize, Am Astron Soc, 86; H H Hess Medal, Am Geophys Union, 91; Nat Medal of Sci, 97. *Prof Exp:* Mem staff, Carnegie Inst, Wash Dept Terrestrial Magnetism, 53-60; prof geophys & geol, Univ Calif, Los Angeles, 60-75, chmn, Dept Planetary & Space Sci, 68-72. *Concurrent Pos:* Vis prof, Calif Inst Technol, 59; assoc ed, Ann Rev Earth & Planetary Sci, 71-80, ed, 81-96. *Mem:* Nat Acad Sci; fel Am Acad Arts & Sci; fel Am Geophys Union; Meteoritical Soc (vpres, 72-74 & 80-82, pres, 82-84); Geochem Soc (vpres, 73-74, pres, 74-75); Int Astron Union; Int Asn Geochem & Cosmochem (pres, 77-80); Int Soc Study Origin Life; Am Astron Soc. *Res:* Planetology; geochronology; meteorites; origin and evolution of solar system; lunar history; Precambrian geology; kinetics of human lead metabolism; habitability of planetary systems. *Mailing Add:* Dept Terrestrial Magnetism Carnegie Inst 5241 Broad Br Rd Washington DC 20015. *Fax:* 202-364-8276; *E-Mail:* wetherill@cros.ciw.edu

**WETHERINGTON, RONALD K,** BIOLOGICAL ANTHROPOLOGY. *Current Pos:* PROF ANTHROP, SOUTHERN METHODIST UNIV, 64- *Personal Data:* b St Petersburg, Fla, Nov 27, 35; m 72; c 5. *Educ:* Tex Tech Univ, BA, 58; Univ Mich, MA, 60, PhD(anthrop), 64. *Mem:* Sigma Xi; Soc Med Anthrop; AAAS; Am Asn Phys Anthrop. *Res:* Skeletal growth and development in man; human ecology and evolutionary theory; adaptive aspects of human demography. *Mailing Add:* Dept Anthrop Southern Methodist Univ PO Box 750001 Dallas TX 75275-0001

**WETHERN, JAMES DOUGLAS,** CHEMICAL ENGINEERING. *Current Pos:* RETIRED. *Personal Data:* b Minneapolis, Minn, July 12, 26; m 48; c 4. *Educ:* Univ Wis, BS, 47; Inst Paper Chem, MS, 49, PhD(paper chem eng), 52. *Prof Exp:* Sr engr, Crown Zellerbach Corp, 51-53, chief, Pulping Sect, 53-55 & Paper Sect, 55-56, coordr appl res, 56-59; tech dir, Pulp & Paperboard Div, Riegel Paper Co, 59, mgr, Mfg Serv, 59-65, vpres & res mgr, La Opers, 65-68, vpres mfg, Paper Div, 68-72; vpres mgr, Brunswick & Paper Co, GA Pac, 72-80, pres, 80-82, mgr planning & develop, 82-90. *Mem:* Fel Tech Asn Pulp & Paper Indust; Am Mgt Asn; Can Pulp & Paper Asn. *Res:* Pulp and paper. *Mailing Add:* 218 Devonwood Dr St Simons Island GA 31522

**WETHINGTON, JOHN A(BNER), JR,** NUCLEAR ENGINEERING, NUCLEAR CHEMISTRY. *Current Pos:* from asst prof to assoc prof chem eng, 53-60, prof, 60-85, EMER PROF NUCLEAR ENG, UNIV FLA, 85- *Personal Data:* b Tallahassee, Fla, Apr 18, 21; m 43; c 1. *Educ:* Emory Univ, AB, 42, MS, 43; Northwestern Univ, Evanston, PhD(chem & physics), 50. *Honors & Awards:* Award, Am Soc Eng Educ, 57. *Prof Exp:* Vis res asst chem, Princeton Univ, 43-44; scientist, Fercleve Corp, Tenn, 44-45; assoc scientist, Oak Ridge Nat Lab, 45-46, sr scientist, 49-53. *Concurrent Pos:* US deleg, Geneva Atomic Energy Conf, Switz, 58; consult, PR Nuclear Ctr, 61-63; vis scientist, Oak Ridge Nat Lab, 58, 79-80 & Lawrence Livermore Lab, 71-72; tech adv, Fla Power & Light, 89-91. *Mem:* AAAS; Am Chem Soc; Am Nuclear Soc. *Res:* Surface physics; exchange reactions; use of nuclear explosions; processing of nuclear reactor fuel; isotope separation; effect of ionizing radiation on fluorocarbons; radioactive waste disposal; technologically enhanced natural radiation. *Mailing Add:* Univ Fla 202 Nuclear Sci Ctr Gainesville FL 32611

**WETLAUFER, DONALD BURTON,** PROTEIN BIOCHEMISTRY. *Current Pos:* chmn dept, 75-85, Du Pont prof, 75-96, EMER PROF CHEM, UNIV DEL, 96- *Personal Data:* b New Berlin, NY, Apr 4, 25; m 50, Lucille Croce; c Lise & Eric. *Educ:* Univ Wis, BS, 46, PhD(biochem), 54. *Prof Exp:* Jr chemist, Argonne Nat Lab, 44 & 46-47; res chemist, Bjorksten Res Labs, Inc, 48-50; asst anal chem, Univ Wis, 44-46, asst biochem, 50-52, res assoc enzymol, Inst Enzyme Res, 54; res assoc, Children's Cancer Res Found & Dept Biol Chem, Harvard Med Sch, 58-61; asst prof biochem, Sch Med, Ind Univ, Indianapolis, 61-62; from assoc prof to prof biochem, Med Sch, Univ Minn, Minneapolis, 62-75. *Concurrent Pos:* Nat Found Infantile Paralysis fel protein chem, Carlsberg Lab, Denmark, 55-56; Am Heart Asn fel, Biol Labs, Harvard Univ, 56-58; tutor, Harvard Univ, 58-61; prin investr, USPHS, 61-85; res career develop award, USPHS, 61-66; consult, Nat Inst Gen Med Sci, 64-; vis investr, Max Planck Inst Ernahrungsphysiologie, 74-78; consult, 80-84, NSF, prin investr, 80-89. *Mem:* Am Chem Soc; Am Soc Biochem & Molecular Biol; Protein Soc; fel Am Inst Chemists; AAAS. *Res:* Chemical and physical basis of structure, stability and reactivity of proteins; acquisition of three-dimensional structure of macromolecules; high performance protein separation and purification. *Mailing Add:* Dept Chem & Biochem Univ Del Newark DE 19716. *Fax:* 302-831-6335

**WETMORE, CLIFFORD MAJOR,** LICHENOLOGY. *Current Pos:* from asst prof to assoc prof, 70-84, PROF BOT, UNIV MINN, ST PAUL, 84- *Personal Data:* b Akron, Ohio, June 18, 34; m 59, Ruth E Small; c Cynthia J & Lawrence A. *Educ:* Mich State Univ, BS, 56, MS, 59, PhD(bot), 65. *Prof Exp:* From instr to assoc prof biol, Wartburg Col, 64-70. *Concurrent Pos:* NSF res grants, 66-68 & 71-73, fel, 70; nat park serv contracts, 82-; cur cryptograms, Univ Minn, 70- *Mem:* Am Bryol & Lichenological Soc; Int Asn Plant Taxonomists; Brit Lichen Soc; Sigma Xi. *Res:* Lichens of the Black Hills, South Dakota, and Minnesota; desert lichens; lichen genera; distributions of lichens; herbarium computer techniques; lichens and air pollution; monographic studies of caloplaca. *Mailing Add:* Dept Plant Biol Univ Minn St Paul MN 55108. *Fax:* 612-625-1738; *E-Mail:* wetmore@vz.cis.umn.edu

**WETMORE, DAVID EUGENE,** COMPUTER LITERACY. *Current Pos:* PROF CHEM & COMPUT SCI, BREVARD COL, 85- *Personal Data:* b Stella, Nebr, Dec 18, 35; m 59; c 2. *Educ:* Park Col, BA, 58; Univ Kans, MA, 62; Tex A&M Univ, PhD(org chem), 65. *Prof Exp:* Res chemist, Sun Oil Co, 65-67; from asst prof to assoc prof chem, St Andrew Presby Col, 67-81, chmn, Chem Prog, 68-77, chmn, sci div, 77-81, prof chem & comput sci, 82-84. *Mem:* Asn Comput Mach. *Res:* Computer education. *Mailing Add:* Dept Comput Sci Brevard Col Brevard NC 28712-3497. *E-Mail:* dew@brevard.edu

**WETMORE, STANLEY IRWIN, JR,** ORGANIC CHEMISTRY. *Current Pos:* from instr to assoc prof, Va Mil Inst, 64-69, head, Dept Chem, 83-89, PROF CHEM, VA MIL INST, 79-, DIR RES LABS, 85- *Personal Data:* b Queens, NY, June 1, 39; m 61; c 2. *Educ:* Rensselaer Polytech Inst, BS, 60, MS, 62; State Univ NY, Buffalo, PhD(org chem), 73. *Prof Exp:* Chemist, Mobil Oil Corp, 62-63. *Concurrent Pos:* NSF sci fac fel, 70-71. *Mem:* Am Chem Soc; Sigma Xi. *Res:* Synthesis and properties of unique carbenes; photochemistry of small ring heterocyclic compounds; development of ethanol as farm fuel. *Mailing Add:* Dept Chem Va Mil Inst Lexington VA 24450

**WETMUR, JAMES GERARD,** BIOPHYSICAL CHEMISTRY. *Current Pos:* assoc prof, 74-82, PROF MICROBIOL, MT SINAI SCH MED, CITY UNIV NEW YORK, 82- *Personal Data:* b New Castle, Pa, July 1, 41; m 65; c 3. *Educ:* Calif Univ, BS, 63; Calif Inst Technol, PhD(chem), 67. *Prof Exp:* Asst prof chem & biochem, Univ Ill, Urbana, 69-74. *Concurrent Pos:* Vpres, NY Acad Sci, 86-89. *Mem:* Am Chem Soc; Am Soc Biol & Molecular Biol; Am Soc Microbiol; Sigma Xi; NY Acad Sci. *Res:* Kinetics of renaturation of DNA; DNA-protein interactions; molecular biology - gene expression. *Mailing Add:* 994 Post Rd Scarsdale NY 10583

**WETS, ROGER J B,** MATHEMATICS. *Current Pos:* PROF MATH, UNIV KY, 71- *Personal Data:* b Uccle, Belg, Feb 20, 37; m 61; c 2. *Educ:* Free Univ Brussels, BA, 59; Univ Calif, Berkeley, PhD(appl math), 64. *Prof Exp:* Staff mem, Boeing Sci Res Lab, Wash, 64-70; prof math, Univ Chicago, 70-71. *Concurrent Pos:* Vis lectr, Univ Wash, 66, Univ Calif, Berkeley, 67 & Inst Info & Automation Res, Paris, 69; vis res, Math Ctr, Montreal, 70; Guggenheim fel, 81-82. *Mem:* Am Math Soc; Soc Indust & Appl Math. *Res:* Mathematical programming; stochastic optimization. *Mailing Add:* 2121 Pinehurst Ct El Cerrito CA 94530-1879

**WETSTONE, HOWARD J,** MEDICINE, HOSPITAL ADMINISTRATION. *Current Pos:* asst resident, Conn Health Syst 53-54, resident, 54-55, dir, Liver Enzyme Lab, 58-60, dir, Biochem Res Lab, 60-63, dir, Med Res, 63-66, asst dir, Dept Med, 66-70, dir, Outpatient Dept, 70-72, sr physician internal med, 70-88, dir, Ambulatory Serv, 72-83, vpres med affairs, 83-92, MED DIR, MEDSPAN, CONN HEALTH SYST, 88- *Personal Data:* b Hartford, Conn, Apr 27, 26; m 47, Roan Horowitz; c 4. *Educ:* Wesleyan Univ, BA, 47; Tufts Univ, MD, 51. *Prof Exp:* Intern med, New Eng Ctr Hosp, 51-52, jr asst resident, 52-53. *Concurrent Pos:* Assoc prof med & community med & health care, Med Sch, Univ Conn, 71- *Mem:* Sigma Xi; Am Col Physicians. *Res:* Pharmacogenetics; hypertension; enzymology; community health systems; primary care; managed care. *Mailing Add:* 77 Kenwood Circle Bloomfield CT 06002-3435

**WETTACH, WILLIAM,** CHEMICAL ENGINEERING. *Current Pos:* RETIRED. *Personal Data:* b Pittsburgh, Pa, Mar 13, 10; m 40, Alice Savers; c Thomas, Donald & William. *Educ:* Princeton Univ, BS, 32, ChE, 33; Univ Pittsburgh, PhD(chem eng), 41. *Prof Exp:* Vpres, W W Lawrence & Co, 33-35 & Wettach Paint & Chem Co, 35-38; chemist, Peerless Paint & Chem Co, 38-40; managing dir, Indust Paint Co, 40-53, pres, 53-69; vpres & tech dir, Sterling Div, Reichhold Chem Inc, 69-80. *Concurrent Pos:* Vpres, Sterling Varnish Co, 41-69, Mercury Varnish & Sterling Varnish Can, 67-75. *Mem:* AAAS; Am Chem Soc; Am Inst Chem Engrs; fel Am Inst Chem; Sigma Xi. *Res:* Development of water soluble alkyd resins; formulation of industrial coatings for metallic substances. *Mailing Add:* 659 Grove St Sewickley PA 15143-1234

**WETTACK, F SHELDON,** PHYSICAL CHEMISTRY. *Current Pos:* from asst prof to assoc prof, 67-72, PROF CHEM, HOPE COL, 72-, DEAN NATURAL SCI, 74- *Personal Data:* b Coffeyville, Kans, Dec 5, 38; m 56; c 4. *Educ:* San Jose State Col, AB, 60, MA, 62; Univ Tex, Austin, PhD(chem), 68. *Prof Exp:* High sch teacher, Calif, 61-64. *Concurrent Pos:* Camille & Henry Dreyfus Found Teacher-Scholar Award, 70-75. *Mem:* Am Chem Soc. *Res:* Photochemistry; energy transfer; fluorescence spectroscopy. *Mailing Add:* Harvey Mudd Col 301 E 12th Claremont CA 91711

**WETTE, REIMUT,** BIOSTATISTICS, BIOMATHEMATICS. *Current Pos:* RETIRED. *Personal Data:* b Mannheim, Ger, May 12, 27; US citizen; m 51; c 5. *Educ:* Univ Heidelberg, MS, 52, DSc(natural sci), 55. *Prof Exp:* Sci asst biomet, Zool Inst, Univ Heidelberg, 52-61; asst biometrician, Univ Tex, 61-64, assoc prof biomath, M D Anderson Hosp & Tumor Inst, 64-66, mem grad fac, 65-66; from prof to emer prof biostatist, Wash Univ, 66-91. *Mem:* Am Statist Asn; Biomet Soc; Inst Math Statist. *Res:* Mathematical approaches to basic science and medical aspects of neoplasia; application and problem-oriented development of mathematical-statistical methodology in biomedical research; methods of mathematical-genetical epidemiology. *Mailing Add:* 5390 Pershing Apt 405 St Louis MO 63112

**WETTEMANN, ROBERT PAUL,** REPRODUCTIVE PHYSIOLOGY. *Current Pos:* From asst prof to prof animal sci, 72-80, REGENTS PROF, OKLA STATE UNIV, 84- *Personal Data:* b New Haven, Conn, Nov 12, 44; m 68; c 3. *Educ:* Univ Conn, BS, 66; Mich State Univ, MS, 68, PhD(dairy), 72. *Honors & Awards:* Richard Hoyt Award, Am Dairy Sci Asn, 71. *Concurrent Pos:* Vis prof, Univ Fla, 80-81. *Mem:* Am Soc Animal Sci; Am Dairy Sci Asn; Soc Study Fertil; Soc Study Reproduction. *Res:* Influence of the environment on endocrine and reproductive function in animals. *Mailing Add:* Animal Sci Bldg Okla State Univ Stillwater OK 74078-0001

**WETTERHAHN, KAREN E,** INORGANIC BIOCHEMISTRY, PHYSICAL BIOCHEMISTRY. *Current Pos:* from asst prof to assoc prof chem, 76-86, asst prof, Biochem Prog, 78-82, PROF, DEPT CHEM, DARTMOUTH COL, 86-, ASSOC DEAN, FAC SCI, 90- *Personal Data:* b Plattsburgh, NY, Oct 16, 48. *Educ:* St Lawrence Univ, BS, 70; Columbia Univ, PhD(chem), 75. *Prof Exp:* Chemist formulations, Mearl Corp, 70-71; res fel chem, Columbia Univ, 71-75; fel biochem, Inst Cancer Res, 75-76. *Concurrent Pos:* Alfred P Sloan fel, 81-85. *Mem:* AAAS; Am Chem Soc; Am Asn Cancer Res. *Res:* Mechanisms of chemical carcinogenesis; metabolism and nucleic acid interactions of carcinogens; inorganic (metal) carcinogenesis; structure-function relationships of modified nucleic acids. *Mailing Add:* Chem Sci Dartmouth Col 6128 Burke Lab Hanover NH 03755-3564

**WETTSTEIN, FELIX O,** MOLECULAR BIOLOGY. *Current Pos:* assoc prof, 67-74, PROF MOLECULAR BIOL, MED MICROBIOL & IMMUNOL, UNIV CALIF, LOS ANGELES, 74-, VCHMN DEPT, 77- *Personal Data:* b Uerikon, Switz, Jan 1, 32; m 60; c 3. *Educ:* Swiss Fed Inst Technol, BS, 56, PhD(agr chem), 60. *Prof Exp:* Fel, Univ Pittsburgh, 60-64; asst res biochemist, Univ Calif, Berkeley, 64-67. *Mem:* AAAS; Am Soc Microbiol. *Res:* Regulation of RNA and protein biosynthesis in differentiating and transformed animal cells; viral carcinogenesis. *Mailing Add:* Dept Microbiol & Immunol Univ Calif Sch Med 10833 Le Conte Ave Los Angeles CA 90024-1300

**WETTSTEIN, JOSEPH G,** neuropharmacology, psychopharmacology, for more information see previous edition

**WETTSTEIN, PETER J,** IMMUNOGENETICS, TRANSPLANTATION. *Current Pos:* CONSULT, DEPT SURG, MAYO CLIN, 91- *Educ:* Univ NC, Chapel, Hill, PhD(genetics), 77. *Prof Exp:* Assoc prof, Wistar Inst, Philadelphia, 83-88; sr scientist, McLaughlin Res Inst, 88-91. *Mailing Add:* Dept Surg & Immunol Mayo Found 200 First St SW Rochester MN 55905-0001. *Fax:* 507-284-3757

**WETZEL, ALBERT JOHN,** MISSILE & SPACE TECHNOLOGY, AIRCRAFT FLIGHT TESTING. *Current Pos:* RETIRED. *Personal Data:* b New Orleans, La, Dec 29, 17; m 46, Helen E Zurad; c Albert Jr, Elizabeth, Joan & E Russell. *Educ:* Tulane Univ, BEng, 39; Johns Hopkins Univ, MS, 50. *Prof Exp:* Exp test pilot, USAF, 43-45, tech asst to secy defense, US Dept Defense, 50-55, comdr, 40th Bombardment Wing-Jet, USAF Strategic Air Command, 55-56, prog dir, Space & Missile Div, 56-62, dir, Strategic Prog, 62-65; from dir res & sponsored progs to dir univ develop, Tulane Univ, 65-76, vpres alumni & univ affairs, 76-80, sr adv to pres, 80-81, asst to pres, 81-94. *Concurrent Pos:* Adj prof mgt & eng mgt, 65-; mem, Rocket & Space Panel, President's Sci Adv Comt, 65-71; bd dirs, Gulf S Res Inst & Inst Defense Analysis; deleg, Nat Conf Advan Res. *Mem:* Fel Am Inst Aeronaut & Astronaut; AAAS; Sigma Xi; Regist Prof Engrs. *Res:* Space and missile technology; aircraft flight testing; missile guidance systems. *Mailing Add:* 7 Richmond Pl New Orleans LA 70115-5019

**WETZEL, ALLAN BROOKE,** NEUROPSYCHOLOGY. *Current Pos:* instr surg, 70-74, ASST PROF SURG & OTO-MAXILLOFACIAL SURG, MED SCH, NORTHWESTERN UNIV, CHICAGO, 74- *Personal Data:* b Dayton, Ohio, May 29, 33; m 59; c 3. *Educ:* Univ Ky, BS, 54; Ohio State Univ, MA, 63, PhD(psychol), 65. *Prof Exp:* Trainee biosci, Stanford Univ, 65-67; trainee neurophysiol, Univ Wis-Madison, 67-69, Nat Inst Neurol Dis & Stroke spec fel, 68-69. *Concurrent Pos:* Res investr neuropsychol, Neurosurg Res Lab, Northwestern Mem Hosp, 70-74. *Mem:* AAAS; Am Psychol Asn; Soc Neurosci; Sigma Xi. *Res:* Brain function; neurophysiology; neuroendocrinology. *Mailing Add:* 5222 N Sawyer Ave Chicago IL 60625-4716

**WETZEL, GAYLE DELMONTE,** CELLULAR IMMUNOLOGY, IMMUNOCHEMISTRY. *Current Pos:* PRIN SCIENTIST, MILES BIOTECHNOL, INC, 91- *Personal Data:* m, Esther Spirgi; c Benjamin D, Sabine F & Niels J. *Educ:* Univ Tex, Dallas, PhD(microbiol), 80. *Prof Exp:* Assoc res biologist II, Univ Calif, San Diego, 80-85; lab head & chief, Basel Inst Immunol, 85-89; sr staff fel, Nat Inst Dent Res, 90-91. *Mem:* Am Asn Immunologists; Int Soc Immunol; Soc Analytical Cytology; Leukocyte Biol Soc. *Res:* Influence of interleukins and cellular subsets on lymphocyte activation and responses. *Mailing Add:* Miles Biotechnol Inc PO Box 1986 Berkeley CA 94701. *Fax:* 510-420-5478

**WETZEL, JOHN EDWIN,** MATHEMATICS. *Current Pos:* From instr to asst prof, 61-68, assoc prof, 68-87, PROF MATH, UNIV ILL, URBANA-CHAMPAIGN, 87- *Personal Data:* b Hammond, Ind, Mar 6, 32; m 62, Rebecca Sprunger. *Educ:* Purdue Univ, Lafayette, BS, 54; Stanford Univ, PhD(math), 64. *Mem:* Am Math Soc; Math Asn Am. *Res:* Classical and combinatorial geometry. *Mailing Add:* Dept Math Univ Ill Urbana-Champaign 1409 W Green St Urbana IL 61801. *E-Mail:* j-wetzel@uiuc.edu

**WETZEL, KARL JOSEPH,** EXPERIMENTAL NUCLEAR PHYSICS. *Current Pos:* from asst prof to assoc prof, 72-81, PROF PHYSICS & DEAN, GRAD SCH, UNIV PORTLAND, 81- *Personal Data:* b Waynesboro, Va, May 29, 37; m 68; c Sebastian & Christopher. *Educ:* Georgetown Univ, BS, 59; Yale Univ, MS, 60, PhD(physics), 65. *Honors & Awards:* Culligan Award, Univ Portland, 85. *Prof Exp:* NSF fel, Inst Tech Nuclear Physics, Darmstadt, Ger, 65-66; Ger Govt guest res fel, 66-67; fel, Argonne Nat Lab, 67-69. *Concurrent Pos:* Vis assoc prof neurol, Health Sci Ctr, Univ Ore, 76-77, chmn phys & life sci, 80-86; NSF fac fel, 76-77; dean, Grad Sch, 87- *Mem:* Am Phys Soc; Am Asn Univ Profs. *Res:* Neutron capture gamma rays; electron and photon scattering; photonuclear processes; electroneurological measurements; pionic atoms. *Mailing Add:* c/o Grad Sch Univ Portland 5000 N Willamette Blvd Portland OR 97203

**WETZEL, NICHOLAS,** NEUROSURGERY. *Current Pos:* Clin asst, Med Sch, Northwestern Univ, Chicago, 52-54, instr, 54-55, assoc, 55-57, asst prof, 57-63, EMER PROF SURG, MED SCH, NORTHWESTERN UNIV, CHICAGO, 63- *Personal Data:* b Jacksonville, Fla, July 17, 20; m 45; c 6. *Educ:* Princeton Univ, AB, 42; Northwestern Univ, MD, 46, MS, 50, PhD, 58. *Mem:* AAAS; Am Asn Neurol Surg; AMA; Am Col Surgeons. *Res:* Human stereotaxic surgery for movement disorders; intractable pain; human olfactory system. *Mailing Add:* 1625 Judson Ave Evanston IL 60201

**WETZEL, ROBERT GEORGE,** LIMNOLOGY. *Current Pos:* BISHOP PROF BIOL, UNIV ALA, 90- *Personal Data:* b Ann Arbor, Mich, Aug 10, 36; m 59, Carol A Andree; c Paul R, Pamela J, Timothy M & Kristina M. *Educ:* Univ Mich, BSc, 58, MSc, 59; Univ Calif, Davis, PhD(limnol), 62. *Hon Degrees:* PhD, Univ Uppsala, Sweden, 83. *Honors & Awards:* Baldi Mem Award, 89; Naumann-Thienemann Medal, 92; G E Hutchinson Medal, 92; Burnum Award, 94. *Prof Exp:* Tech asst, Univ Mich, 58-59; res technician, US Fish & Wildlife Serv, Mich, 59; res & tech asst, Univ Calif, 59-62; res assoc, Ind Univ, 62-65; from asst prof to prof bot, Mich State Univ, 65-86, adj prof zool, 79-86; prof biol & res scientist, Univ Mich, 86-90. *Concurrent Pos:* Res fel, Aquatic Res Unit, Ind Dept Natural Resources, 63-64; NSF res fel, 63-65 & 67-69, travel award, Int Asn Limnol Cong, 65 & 68; partic, AEC contract, 65-; co-ed, Commun, 68- & Archiv fuer Hydrobiologie, 81-; Off Water Resources Res res fel, 69-71; int consult, Int Biol Prog, Int Coun Sci Unions, 69-; numerous NSF grants, 64-94; mem bd dirs, Am Soc Limnol & Oceanog, 68-71 & Ecol Soc Am, 70-72; US rep, Aquatic Ecol Comn, Int Asn Ecol, 68-; external examr, var schs & univs, 70-94; adv, Aqua Fennica, Water Asn Finland & Finnish Limnol Soc, 90-, Aquatic Plant Mgt Res, Univ Fla, 75, Ecol Sci Improv, Ark, 79, Elec Power Res Inst, 80-90, Environ Protection Agency, 82 & other insts. *Mem:* Fel AAAS; Am Inst Biol Sci; Am Soc Limnol & Oceanog (vpres, 79-80, pres, 80-81); Ecol Soc Am; Int Asn Theoret & Appl Limnol (gen secy & treas, 68-); Sigma Xi; Aquatic Plant Mgt Soc; Freshwater Biol Asn UK; Int Asn Ecol; Int Asn Great Lakes Res; Royal Danish Acad Sci; Am Acad Sci Arts. *Res:* Biological productivity of California, Indiana and Michigan lakes; physiological ecology of algae and aquatic macrophytes; author of 14 books and over 340 scientific publications. *Mailing Add:* Dept Biol Univ Ala Tuscaloosa AL 35487-0206

**WETZEL, ROLAND H(ERMAN),** CHEMICAL ENGINEERING. *Current Pos:* RETIRED. *Personal Data:* b Wis, Apr 29, 23; m 45; c 2. *Educ:* Univ Wis, BS, 45, PhD(chem eng), 51. *Prof Exp:* Asst chem eng, Univ Wis, 46-50; res engr process develop, E I du Pont de Nemours & Co, Inc, 51-53, res supvr, 54-66, res mgr, 67-69, asst lab dir, Pigments Dept, 69-73, tech supt, 73-75, eng assoc, 76-77. *Mem:* Sigma Xi. *Res:* Unit operations; process development. *Mailing Add:* RD 4 Box 253 Landenberg PA 19350

**WETZEL, RONALD BURNELL,** PROTEIN CHEMISTRY, PROTEIN ENGINEERING. *Current Pos:* RES FEL, MACROMOLECULAR SCI DEPT, SMITHKLINE BEECHAM, 89- *Personal Data:* b Hanover, Pa, May 26, 46; m 76; c 2. *Educ:* Drexel Univ, BS, 69; Univ Calif, Berkeley, PhD(org chem), 73. *Prof Exp:* Fel, Max Planck Inst Exp Med, 73-75 & Dept Molecular Biophys & Biochem, Yale Univ, 75-78; sr scientist, Dept Protein Biochem, Genentech Inc, 78-82, sr scientist, Biomolecular Chem Dept, 82-89. *Concurrent Pos:* Adj assoc prof, Dept Chem, Univ Calif, Santa Cruz, 85-89; ed, Protein Eng, 86- *Mem:* Am Chem Soc; AAAS; Peptide Soc. *Res:* Protein structure/function relationships studied by chemical and molecular biological approaches; medical applications of protein engineering; roles of disulfide bonds in globular proteins. *Mailing Add:* 1732 Hamilton Dr Phoenixville PA 19460

**WETZSTEIN, H(ANNS) J(UERGEN),** ELECTRICAL ENGINEERING. *Current Pos:* RETIRED. *Personal Data:* b Wuppertal-E, Ger, June, 1920; nat US; m 54, Inge J Goldstein; c Barbara & Linda Wetzstein. *Educ:* Univ Cape Town, BSc, 47; Harvard Univ, MS, 49, DSc(elec eng), 52. *Prof Exp:* Dir res, Sci Specialties Corp, 53-55; sr eng scientist, Missile Electronics & Controls Dept, RCA, 55-61; mem staff, Inst Naval Studies, Inst Defence Analysis, 61-65; sr mem staff, Arthur D Little, Inc, Mass, 65-67; sr eng scientist, Aerospace Syst Div, RCA Corp, 67-71; prin elec engr, Optical Syst Div, ITEK Corp, Lexington, 71-77; sr staff engr, W J Schafer Assocs Inc, 77-83; consult, Itek Optical Systs, 86-88. *Concurrent Pos:* Vis lectr laser appln, Univ Auckland, NZ, 91. *Mem:* Inst Elec & Electronics Engrs, London. *Res:* Servomechanism; system analysis; transistor measurements; analog-digital conversion and computers; passive detection physics and techniques; submarine and antisubmarine warfare; laser systems; active optics; military detection systems. *Mailing Add:* 33 Bayfield Rd Wayland MA 01778-4205

**WEWERKA, EUGENE MICHAEL,** PHYSICAL ORGANIC CHEMISTRY. *Current Pos:* STAFF MEM, LOS ALAMOS SCI LAB, 65- *Personal Data:* b St Paul, Minn, Nov 7, 38; m 59; c 4. *Educ:* Univ Minn, BA, 62, PhD(org chem), 65. *Concurrent Pos:* Adj prof, Univ NMex, 72- *Mem:* Fel Am Inst Chemists; Am Chem Soc. *Res:* Chemical kinetics; mechanism studies; polymer characterization; analytical methods; physical chemistry of polymers; chemistry of coal and oil shale conversion processes; fossil fuels environmental studies; environmental chemistry. *Mailing Add:* PO Box 1202 Los Alamos NM 87544

**WEXELL, DALE RICHARD,** GLASS & CERAMICS, MICROWAVE PROCESSING. *Current Pos:* SR RES ASSOC, CORNING INC, 93- *Personal Data:* b Corning, NY, Apr 10, 43; m 78, Kathleen Swistak; c Heather & Christopher. *Educ:* Fordham Univ, BS, 64; Georgetown Univ, MS, 69, PhD(inorg chem), 71. *Prof Exp:* Instr chem, Georgetown Univ, 64-70; fel, Corning Glass Works, 71-72, res scientist glass chem, 72-80, res assoc, 81-92. *Concurrent Pos:* Mem bd educ, Corning, 76-96; mem, Nat Mat Res Coun, 81-84; lectr, Elmira Col; mem, State Univ NY Genesco Col Coun, 88-96; chmn bd dirs, Corning Sci & Discovery Ctr Inc; fel, Royal Inst Chem. *Mem:* AAAS; Am Chem Soc; Royal Soc Chem; Am Ceramic Soc; Sigma Xi. *Res:* Aqueous silicates; heteropoly electrolytes; high-temperature materials; surface chemistry of glass; inorganic coatings technology; opal glasses; microwave processing; photochromism; electrical, magnetic and optical behavior in glass and ceramics; fiber reinforced composites; batteries. *Mailing Add:* Corning Inc SP-FR-5-1 Corning NY 14831. *Fax:* 607-974-3675; *E-Mail:* wexell_dr@corning.com

**WEXLER, ARTHUR SAMUEL,** analytical chemistry; deceased, see previous edition for last biography

**WEXLER, BERNARD CARL,** EXPERIMENTAL MEDICINE. *Current Pos:* from asst prof to assoc prof exp path, 55-71, exp med, 71-75, PROF EXP MED & PATH, COL MED, UNIV CINCINNATI, 75- *Personal Data:* b Boston, Mass, May 1, 23; m 46; c 3. *Educ:* Univ Ore, BS, 47; Univ Calif, MA, 48; Stanford Univ, PhD(anat, biochem), 52. *Prof Exp:* Asst anat, Sch Med, Stanford Univ, 49-52; mem res staff, Baxter Labs, 52-55; res assoc, May Inst Med Res, 55-61; asst dir, 61-64; dir, 64-81. *Concurrent Pos:* Am Heart Asn advan res fel, 60-62; Nat Heart Inst res career develop award, 62-72; lectr, Dominican Col, 50-52; res assoc, Stanford Res Inst, 51-52; mem, Coun Arteriosclerosis & Coun Basic Sci, Am Heart Asn, 62-, Coun Stroke & Coun High Blood Pressure Res; mem, Coun Arteriosclerosis & Ischemic Heart Dis, Int Soc Cardiol; mem med staff, Jewish Hosp, Cincinnati. *Mem:* Am Soc Physiologists; AAAS; Am Diabetes Asn; Asn Am Med Cols; Endocrine Soc. *Res:* Pituitary-adrenal physiology; experimental pathology. *Mailing Add:* 7640 De Mar Rd Cincinnati OH 45243

**WEXLER, BERNARD LESTER,** QUANTUM ELECTRONICS. *Current Pos:* RES PHYSICIST, LASER PHYSICS BR, OPTICAL SCI DIV, NAVAL RES LAB, 73- *Personal Data:* b Newton, Mass, Apr 20, 45; m 68; c 2. *Educ:* Yale Col, BS, 66, MS, 68, PhD(quantum electronics), 73. *Res:* Infrared laser, particularly 16 micron laser; gas lasers and related areas in atomic and molecular physics; excimer laser development; phase conjugation; nonlinear optics. *Mailing Add:* 5314 Second St Arlington VA 22203-1212

**WEXLER, JONATHAN DAVID,** COMPUTER SCIENCE. *Current Pos:* RETIRED. *Personal Data:* b Phoenix, Ariz, Dec 12, 37. *Educ:* Ariz State Univ, BS, 59; Univ Wis-Madison, MS, 65, PhD(comput sci), 70. *Prof Exp:* Asst mathematician, Ill Inst Technol Res Inst, 61-64; asst prof, Comput Sci Dept, State Univ NY, Buffalo, 70-75; software eng specialist, Western Develop Labs, Ford Aerospace & Commun Corp, Palo Alto, 76-79; software develop engr, BTI Comput Systs, Sunnyvale, Calif, 79-82; pres, Starflower Technol Inc, 82-83; sr software engr, MedaSonics Inc, 84-85; mem tech staff, DocuGraphix Inc, Cupertino, Calif, 85-86; staff engr, Lockheed Missles & Space Co, Sunnyvale, Calif, 87-91. *Mem:* Asn Comput Mach. *Res:* Data structure representations of knowledge; software engineering methodologies; artificial intelligence; knowledge-based remote diagnostic systems for computers; microcomputer-based merged text-graphics systems; expert systems for computer software debugging. *Mailing Add:* 986 Starflower Ct Sunnyvale CA 94086-8623

**WEXLER, NANCY SABIN,** CLINICAL NEUROPSYCHOLOGY. *Current Pos:* prof neuropsychol, 85-92, PROF CLIN NEUROPSYCHOL, COL PHYSICIANS & SURGEONS, COLUMBIA UNIV, 92-, HIGGINS PROF NEUROPSYCHOL, DEPTS NEUROL & PSYCHIAT. *Personal Data:* b Washington, DC, July 19, 45. *Educ:* Radcliffe Col, AB, 67; Univ Mich, PhD(clin psychol), 74. *Hon Degrees:* DHL, NY Med Col, 91; DSc, Univ Mich, 91. *Honors & Awards:* Robert J & Claire Pasarow Found Award, 87; Living Legacy Award, Womens Int Soc, 88; Venezuelan Presidential Award, 90; Distinguished Serv Award, Nat Asn Biol Teachers, 93; Nat Med Res Award, Nat Health Coun, 93; Albert Lasker Pub Serv Award, 93. *Prof Exp:* Psychol intern & teaching fel, Univ Mich, 68-74; asst prof psychol, Grad Fac, New Sch Social Res, New York, 74-76; health sci adminr, Comn Dis & Stroke, Nat Inst Neurol, NIH, 78-83. *Concurrent Pos:* Pvt pract psychol, 74-76; pres, Heriditary Dis Found, Santa Monica, Calif, 83-; trustee, Nat Huntingtons Dis Asn, 83-85, Marine Biol Lab, 84-86, Eleanor Roosevelt Inst Cancer Res, 85-91, Found Care & Cure Huntingtons Dis, 88-; mem, Ctr Brain & Behav, Col Physicians & Surgeons, Columbia Univ, 85; chair, Ethical, Legal, Social Issues Working Group Human Genome, NIH/Dept Energy, 89-; fel, Hastings Ctr, 90; co-chair, Ethical, Legal & Social Issues Comt, Human Genome Orgn, 91- *Mem:* Inst Med-Nat Acad Sci; AAAS; Am Psychiat Asn; Am Soc Law & Med; Soc Neurosci; Am Psychol Soc; Am Soc Human Genetics; World Fedn Neurol; Am Neurol Asn. *Mailing Add:* Dept Neuropsychol Col Physicians & Surgeons Columbia Univ 630 W 168th St New York NY 10032-3702

**WEY, ALBERT CHIN-TANG,** ACOUSTIC MICROSCOPY, ELECTRO-OPTICS. *Current Pos:* RES DIR ACOUST MICROS, SONOSCAN, INC, 88- *Personal Data:* b Kaohsiung, Taiwan, July 28, 55; US citizen; m 92, Shu-Ju Ko. *Educ:* Nat Chiao-Tung Univ, Taiwan, BS, 77; State Univ NY, Stony Brook, MS, 80, PhD(elec eng), 86; Univ Chicago, MBA, 94. *Honors & Awards:* IR-100 Award, Res & Develop Mag, 86-87. *Prof Exp:* Lectr commun, Chinese Army Commun & Elec Sch, 77-79; res engr lasers, Quantronix Corp, 80-84; res assoc magneto-optics, US Naval Res Lab, 84-86; sr engr electro-optics, Amphenol Fiber Optic Prod, Allied-Signal Inc, 86-88. *Concurrent Pos:* Dir, Chinese Inst Engrs, USA, 80-83. *Mem:* Inst Elec & Electronics Engrs Ultrasonics Soc; Soc Mfg Engrs; Am Soc Nondestructive Testing; Am Ceramic Soc; Am Soc Metals Int; Soc Photo-Optical Instrumentation Engrs. *Res:* Acoustic microscopy technologies and their applications in nondestructive testing and evaluation of microelectronic components and structural materials, such as ceramics, metals, polymers, and other advanced composite materials; author of 60 publications. *Mailing Add:* 129 Rumsey Pl Westmont IL 60559

**WEY, JONG-SHINN,** CHEMICAL ENGINEERING. *Current Pos:* sr res chemist, Eastman Kodak, 73-78, res assoc, 78-84, lab head, 84-91, SR LAB HEAD, RES LABS, EASTMAN KODAK, 91- *Personal Data:* b Taiwan, Oct 26, 44; m 66, Hseh-Yi Su; c Johnny & Nancy. *Educ:* Nat Taiwan Univ, BS, 67; Clarkson Col Technol, MS, 70, PhD(chem eng), 73. *Honors & Awards:* J Award, Photog Sci & Eng, 80. *Prof Exp:* Res asst chem eng, Clarkson Col Technol, 68-73. *Concurrent Pos:* Nat Crystallization Comt, Am Inst Chem Eng, 77. *Mem:* Am Inst Chem Eng; fel Soc Photog Sci & Eng. *Res:* Crystallization; precipitation; nucleation; growth, size-distribution control; solid liquid separation; photographic emulsion. *Mailing Add:* Res Labs Eastman Kodak Co Rochester NY 14650. *Fax:* 716-722-3862; *E-Mail:* jwey@kodak.com

**WEYAND, JOHN DAVID,** CERAMIC ENGINEERING, GEOLOGICAL ENGINEERING. *Current Pos:* STAFF ENGR CERAMICS, ALUMINUM CO AM, 73- *Personal Data:* b Faulkton, SDak, Aug 13, 39; m 63; c 5. *Educ:* SDak Sch Mines & Technol, BS, 61; Univ Mo, Rolla, MS, 64, PhD(ceramic eng), 71. *Prof Exp:* Jr geologist field geol, Shell Oil Co, 61; ceramic engr, 3M Co, 62-66 & Battelle Mem Inst, 66-68; supvr refractories, Interpace Corp, 71-73. *Mem:* Am Ceramic Soc; Nat Inst Ceramic Eng, Am Soc Testing & Mat. *Res:* Boride, nitride and oxide ceramic development for placement in chloride and fluoride electroylsis cells as corrosion resistant refractories or electrodes; development refractories, substrate, infrared and light transmitting ceramics and glass elements; mechanical property determination of advanced ceramics. *Mailing Add:* 1044 W 350 S Logan UT 84321-6294

**WEYBREW, JOSEPH ARTHUR,** PLANT CHEMISTRY. *Current Pos:* assoc res prof animal nutrit, NC State Univ, 46-49, assoc res prof agron, 49-51, res prof, 51-56, res prof chem, 56-60, actg head chem res, 57-60, WILLIAM NEALS REYNOLDS DISTINGUISHED PROF AGR, NC STATE UNIV, 57- *Personal Data:* b Wamego, Kans, July 13, 15; m 42; c 2. *Educ:* Kans State Col, BS, 38, MS, 39; Univ Wis, PhD(plant physiol), 42. *Prof Exp:* Res dir, W J Small Co, 42; asst nutritionist, Exp Sta, Kans State Col, 42-43; chief chemist, Indust Hyg Div, State Bd Health, Kans, 43. *Concurrent Pos:* Res prof field crops, 60-76. *Mem:* AAAS; Am Chem Soc. *Res:* Tobacco biochemistry, especially fluecuring and quality evaluation; tobacco biogenetics. *Mailing Add:* 112 Pineland Circle Raleigh NC 27606

**WEYENBERG, DONALD RICHARD,** ORGANOSILICON CHEMISTRY, SILICONE MATERIALS. *Current Pos:* Chemist, Chem Labs, Dow Corning Corp, 51-65, res mgr chem, 65-68, dir, Corp Develop, 68-70, silicone res, 70-71, mgr, Resins & Chem Bus, 71-74, New Venture Bus, 74-77, dir res, 77-79, VPRES RES & DEVELOP, DOW CORNING CORP, 79- *Personal Data:* b Gelvil, Nebr, July 11, 30; m 55; c 2. *Educ:* Univ Nebr, BS, 51; Pa State Univ, PhD(chem), 58. *Honors & Awards:* Award, Am Chem Soc, 83. *Mem:* Am Chem Soc; NY Acad Sci; Am Ceramic Soc; Soc Chem Indust Brit; Sigma Xi; AAAS. *Res:* Research and development management in organosilicon chemistry, siloxane polymers and the application of silicone materials. *Mailing Add:* 4601 Arbor Dr Midland MI 48640-2644

**WEYH, JOHN ARTHUR,** ANALYTICAL CHEMISTRY, INORGANIC CHEMISTRY. *Current Pos:* from asst prof to assoc prof chem, 68-78, PROF CHEM, WESTERN WASH UNIV, 78- *Personal Data:* b Havre, Mont, Sept 9, 42; m 62; c 4. *Educ:* Col Great Falls, BA, 64; Wash State Univ, MS, 66,

PhD(chem), 68. *Prof Exp:* Instr chem, Wash State Univ, 66-67. *Mem:* Am Chem Soc. *Res:* Synthesis, characterization and kinetic studies on coordination compounds. *Mailing Add:* Dept Chem Western Wash Univ M/S 9058 Bellingham WA 98225-5996

**WEYHENMEYER, JAMES ALAN,** NEUROIMMUNOLOGY, DEVELOPMENTAL NEUROSCIENCE. *Current Pos:* from asst prof to assoc prof, 79-96, PROF CELL & STRUCT BIOL & PATH, COL MED, UNIV ILL, 96- *Personal Data:* b Hazelton, Pa, Feb 12, 51; m 73; c James Jonathan. *Educ:* Knox Col, BA, 73; Ind Univ, PhD(cell biol), 77. *Honors & Awards:* Heart Torch Award, Am Heart Asn. *Prof Exp:* Assoc instr anat, Sch Med, Ind Univ, 73-77; fel, Col Med, Univ Iowa, 77-79. *Concurrent Pos:* Mem, Univ Ill Biotechnol Ctr. *Mem:* Soc Neurosci; AAAS; Am Chem Soc; Am Soc Cell Biol. *Res:* Cell and molecular biology of cytokines (growth factors) and their receptors in the mammalian central nervous system; cell and molecular characterization of angiotensin binding proteins in the central nervous system and their relationship to the neuronal development and differentiation. *Mailing Add:* Dept Cell Struct Biol Univ Ill Urbana IL 61801. *Fax:* 217-244-1648; *E-Mail:* weyhen@ux1.cso.uiuc.edu

**WEYHMANN, WALTER VICTOR,** SOLID STATE PHYSICS, LOW TEMPERATURE PHYSICS. *Current Pos:* from asst prof to assoc prof, 64-75, PROF PHYSICS & HEAD, SCH PHYSICS & ASTRON, UNIV MINN, MINNEAPOLIS, 75- *Personal Data:* b Roanoke, Va, Nov 27, 35; m 57; c 1. *Educ:* Duke Univ, BS, 57; Harvard Univ, AM, 58, PhD(physics), 63. *Prof Exp:* Res fel physics, Harvard Univ, 63-64. *Mem:* Am Phys Soc. *Res:* Nuclear magnetic resonance measurement of sublattice magnetizations; weak magnetic phenomena and nuclear ordering at very low temperatures; production of very low temperatures. *Mailing Add:* 198 Windsor Ct St Paul MN 55112

**WEYL, PETER K,** ENVIRONMENTAL MANAGEMENT. *Current Pos:* RETIRED. *Personal Data:* b Ger, May 6, 24; nat US; m 47, Muriel Reisman; c Ruth, Stephen & Lisa. *Educ:* Univ Chicago, ScM, 51, PhD(physics), 53. *Prof Exp:* Lectr physics, Roosevelt Col, 51-53; asst prof, Brazilian Ctr Phys Res, 53-54; physicist, Explor & Prod Res Labs, Shell Develop Co, 54-59, sr physicist, 59-63; prof oceanog, Ore State Univ, 63-66; prof oceanog, State Univ NY, Stony Brook, 66-93, emer prof, 94- *Concurrent Pos:* Lectr, Univ Houston, 55-62; vis prof, Hebrew Univ, Jerusalem, 72 & Univ Concepcion, Chile, 79. *Mem:* AAAS; Am Geophys Union. *Res:* Chemical and physical oceanography; ocean-climate interaction; environmental stability; coastal zone management. *Mailing Add:* 90 Christian Ave Stony Brook NY 11790

**WEYLAND, JACK ARNOLD,** PHYSICS, SCIENCE COMMUNICATIONS. *Current Pos:* FAC, DEPT PHYSICS, RICKS COL. *Personal Data:* b Butte, Mont, June 12, 40; m 65; c 5. *Educ:* Mont State Univ, BS, 62, PhD(solid state physics), 69. *Prof Exp:* Asst prof physics, SDak Sch Mines & Technol, 68-77, prof, 78- *Concurrent Pos:* Grants, US Dept Transp, 69-72 & Res Corp, 70-77. *Mem:* AAAS; Am Phys Soc; Am Asn Physics Teachers. *Res:* High pressure diffusion and magnetic susceptibility studies; adhesion of ice to concrete surfaces; science errors in the movies. *Mailing Add:* Dept Physics Ricks Col Rexburg ID 83440

**WEYLER, MICHAEL E,** FAILURE ANALYSIS, FORENSIC ENGINEERING. *Current Pos:* consult engr, Houston, 90-93, BR MGR, CH&A CORP, WASHINGTON, 93- *Personal Data:* b Boston, Mass, 1940; m 62; c 3. *Educ:* Tufts Univ, BSME, 62; Univ Mich, Ann Arbor, MSE, 63, PhD(mech eng), 69. *Prof Exp:* Asst prof, Univ Mich, Dearborn, 63-69; construct officer, US Navy, 70-71, ocean engr, 71-78, pub works officer, Antarctica, 78-80; instr mech eng, US Naval Acad, Annapolis, 80-82; sr res specialist, Exxon Prod Res, Houston, 82-86; dir facil progs, US Naval Reserve, 86-90. *Concurrent Pos:* Capt, Civil Eng Corps, US Naval Reserve. *Mem:* Nat Soc Prof Engrs. *Res:* Application of field experience in engineering and construction to the analysis of failure in mechanical systems; specializes in analysis of failures due to extreme environmental conditions, such as arctic and offshore conditions. *Mailing Add:* 113226 Memory Lane Fairfax VA 22033

**WEYMANN, RAY J,** ASTRONOMY, SPECTROSCOPY. *Current Pos:* dir, 86-88, STAFF, OBSERV CARNEGIE INST WASHINGTON, 88- *Personal Data:* b Los Angeles, Calif, Dec 2, 34; m 56; c 3. *Educ:* Calif Inst Technol, BS, 56; Princeton Univ, PhD(astron), 59. *Prof Exp:* Res fel astron, Calif Inst Technol, 59-61; from asst prof to prof astron, Univ Ariz, 61-86, head, Dept Astron & dir, 70-75, astron, Steward Observ, 70-86. *Mem:* Nat Acad Sci; Am Astron Soc. *Res:* Theoretical astrophysics; stellar spectroscopy. *Mailing Add:* Observ Carnegie Inst Washington 813 Santa Barbara St Pasadena CA 91101

**WEYMOUTH, JOHN WALTER,** ARCHAEOMETRY, GEOPHYSICS. *Current Pos:* from asst prof to prof, 58-89, EMER PROF PHYSICS, UNIV NEBR, LINCOLN, 89- *Personal Data:* b Palo Alto, Calif, Jan 14, 22; m 66, Laura Hyland; c 3. *Educ:* Univ Calif, AB, 43, MA, 50, PhD(physics), 51. *Prof Exp:* Instr physics, Vassar Col, 52-54; from asst prof to assoc prof, Clarkson Col Technol, 54-58. *Mem:* Am Phys Soc; Soc Am Archaeol; Soc Hist Archaeol; Soc Archaeol Sci (vpres, 81-82, pres 82-83). *Res:* Physical methods in archaeology; geophysical surveying of archaeological sites. *Mailing Add:* Dept Physics Univ Nebr Lincoln NE 68588-0111

**WEYMOUTH, PATRICIA PERKINS,** NATURAL SCIENCE, HISTORY OF SCIENCE. *Current Pos:* from asst to assoc prof, 69-75, prof natural sci, 75-86, EMER PROF, MICH STATE UNIV, 86- *Personal Data:* b Birmingham, Mich, Dec 31, 18; div; c 3. *Educ:* Russell Sage Col, AB, 40; Univ Cincinnati, PhD(biochem), 44. *Prof Exp:* Asst biochem, Armored Med Res Lab, Ft Knox, 44-46; res assoc med physics, Univ Calif, 46-49; res assoc radio, Stanford-Lane Hosp, San Francisco, 49-52, Vassar Col, 52-54 & Clarkson Col Technol, 54-58; res assoc biochem & nutrit, Univ Nebr, 58-67. *Concurrent Pos:* Dir, Kedzie Lects, for high sch sci students, 88. *Mem:* Fel AAAS; NY Acad Sci; Sigma Xi. *Res:* Bacteriological and cancer biochemistry; nucleic acid and enzyme studies; interpenetrance of science and other disciplines. *Mailing Add:* 4544 Van Atta Rd Okemos MI 48864

**WEYMOUTH, RICHARD J,** ANATOMY, ENDOCRINOLOGY. *Current Pos:* RETIRED. *Personal Data:* b Brewer, Maine, July 19, 28; c 1. *Educ:* Univ Maine, BS, 50; Univ Mich, MS & PhD, 55; Marquette Univ, MD, 63. *Prof Exp:* Instr anat, Miami Univ, 55-59; asst prof, Sch Med, Marquette Univ, 59-61; intern, Univ Mich Hosps, 63-64; from assoc prof to prof anat, Med Col Va, 64-75; chmn dept, Sch Med, Univ SC, 75-84, prof anat, 75-93, assoc dean student affairs & admis, 76-82, assoc dean acad affairs, 82-93. *Concurrent Pos:* Lectr med, Med Col Va, 64-75; Fulbright scholar, Ankara, Turkey, 85-86. *Mem:* Am Asn Anatomists; Sigma Xi; Transplantation Soc. *Res:* Electron microscopy, endocrine glands and kidney. *Mailing Add:* 2205 Bee Ridge Rd Columbia SC 29223

**WEYNA, PHILIP LEO,** ORGANIC CHEMISTRY, POLYMER CHEMISTRY. *Current Pos:* CONSULT, 82- *Personal Data:* b Chicago, Ill, May 11, 32; m 54; c 4. *Educ:* Loyola Univ, Ill, BS, 54; Univ Wis, PhD(org chem), 58. *Prof Exp:* Res chemist, Morton Chem Co, 58-64, supvr polymer res, 64-66, dir, 66-73, mgr, Chem Specialties Bus Group, 73-76, dir com develop, 76-82. *Mem:* Am Chem Soc; Tech Asn Pulp & Paper Indust. *Res:* Polymeric coatings and adhesives. *Mailing Add:* 6604 Rhode Island Trail Crystal Lake IL 60012-3118

**WEYNAND, EDMUND E,** MECHANICAL ENGINEERING, AERODYNAMICS. *Current Pos:* assoc prof, 56-62, PROF MECH ENG, SOUTHERN METHODIST UNIV, 62- *Personal Data:* b San Antonio, Tex, Nov 21, 20; m 50; c 4. *Educ:* Univ Tex, BS, 49; Mass Inst Technol, SM, 50, MechE, 51, ScD(mech eng), 53. *Prof Exp:* Asst eng & draftsman, San Antonio Air Depot, 42; asst, Proj Squid, Mass Inst Technol, 52-53; sr & proj propulsion engr, Convair Div, Gen Dynamics Corp, Tex, 53-56. *Concurrent Pos:* Consult, Convair Div, Gen Dynamics Corp, 57-59 & Ling-Tempco-Vought, Vought Aeronaut. *Mem:* Am Inst Aeronaut & Astronaut; Am Soc Eng Educ; Sigma Xi. *Res:* Internal aerodynamics; nozzles; jet mixing; base drag; inlets; wind tunnel testing; ejectors; optical instrumentation; thermodynamics; heat transfer; fluid mechanics. *Mailing Add:* 4195 Lively Lane Dallas TX 75220

**WEYTER, FREDERICK WILLIAM,** BIOCHEMICAL GENETICS. *Current Pos:* From instr to asst prof, 62-73, ASSOC PROF BIOL, COLGATE UNIV, 73- *Personal Data:* b Philadelphia, Pa, Oct 7, 34; m 65; c 2. *Educ:* Univ Pa, AB, 56; Amherst Col, MA, 58; Univ Ill, PhD(biochem), 62. *Concurrent Pos:* Fulbright lectr, Afghanistan, 65-66. *Mem:* Am Chem Soc. *Res:* Drug metabolism in microorganisms; regulation of arginine biosynthesis in E coli. *Mailing Add:* Biol Colgate Univ 13 Oak Dr Hamilton NY 13346-1338

**WEZEMAN, FREDERICK H,** CELL & MOLECULAR BIOLOGY OF BONE, CONNECTIVE TISSUE STRUCTURE & FUNCTION. *Current Pos:* assoc prof, 80-85, PROF ANAT, LOYOLA UNIV SCH MED, 85-, PROF ORTHOP SURG, 94- *Personal Data:* b Oak Park, Ill, Sept 14, 42; m 71, Jill Phillips; c Frederick III & Bethany. *Educ:* Hope Col, Holland, Mich, BA, 64; Univ Ill Col Med, MS, 67, PhD(anat & cell biol), 69. *Prof Exp:* NIH fel, Rush-Presby St Luke's Med Ctr, Chicago, 69-71; asst prof anat, Univ Ill Col Med, 71-73; assoc anatomist med staff & dir grad med educ, Michael Reese Med Ctr, Chicago, 73-80. *Concurrent Pos:* Co-prin investr, NIH Div Res Grants, 69-71; assoc ed, Anat Rec, 77-; prin investr, Arthritis Found Ill, 78-81, Am Cancer Soc, 85-87, Cancer Fedn, 88-; prof & chmn biol, Loyola Univ, 86-93. *Mem:* Am Asn Anatomists; Am Soc Bone & Mineral Res; Am Soc Cell Biol; Orthop Res Soc. *Res:* Investigations of bone cells, metabolic diseases of bone and interrelationships of tumor cells and tumor cell products with bone. *Mailing Add:* 35 73rd Ct Tinley Park IL 60477

**WHALEN, CAROL KUPERS,** PSYCHOLOGY. *Current Pos:* asst res psychologist, Univ Calif, Irvine, 70-71, asst prof social ecol, 70-73, assoc prof psychiat & human behav, 74-79, assoc prof soc ecol, 73-79, actg dir, Prog Social Ecol, 85-86, PROF PSYCHIAT & HUMAN BEHAV & SOCIAL ECOL, UNIV CALIF, IRVINE, 79- *Educ:* Stanford Univ, BS, 63; Univ Calif, Los Angeles, MA, 65 & PhD(clin develop psychol), 67. *Prof Exp:* Res asst, Stanford Univ, 61-63; intern, Psychol Clin, Univ Calif, Los Angeles, 64-65, Long Beach Vet Admin Hosp & Fernald Sch, Univ Calif, Los Angeles, 65-66, Fairview State Hosp & S Coast Child Guid Clin, 66-67; res specialist & co-prin investr, Therap Pyramids Proj, Fairview State Hosp, 67-70. *Concurrent Pos:* Res asst, Stanford Univ, 61-63; teaching asst, 62; ed consult, J Appl Behav Anal, J Appl Develop Psychol, J Child Psychol & Psychiat, J Consult & Clin Psychol & J Personality & Social Psychol; USPHS predoc fel, Univ Calif, Los Angeles, 64-67; res consult, Educ Assessment Ctr Handicapped Children, 70-71; Nat Regist Health Serv Providees Psychol; Panel Deinstitutionalized Children & Youth, NAS, 78-81; Res Review Panel, NIMH, 80-84; Comt Child Develop Res & Pub Policy, NAS, 82-87; Data & Safety Monitoring Comt, Dictary Intervention Study Children, Nat Heart, Lung & Blood Inst, 87- *Mem:* Fel Am Psychol Asn. *Res:* Author of over 25 publications. *Mailing Add:* Social Ecol Univ Calif Irvine CA 92717-0001

**WHALEN, JAMES JOSEPH,** ELECTROMAGNETIC COMPATIBILITY, MICROWAVES. *Current Pos:* from asst prof to assoc prof, 70-81, PROF ELEC ENG, STATE UNIV NY, BUFFALO, 81-, CHMN, DEPT ELEC & COMPUT ENG, 95- *Personal Data:* b Meriden, Conn, Feb 16, 35; m 59, Barbara A Jakiel; c Elizabeth, Catherine & Thomas. *Educ:* Cornell Univ, BEE, 58; Johns Hopkins Univ, MSE, 62, PhD(elec eng), 69. *Prof Exp:* Res staff asst, Carlyle Barton Lab, Johns Hopkins Univ, 62-69, assoc res scientist, 69-70; res scientist, Nat Oceanic & Atmospheric Admin, 70. *Concurrent Pos:* Consult, McDonnell Douglas Corp, St Louis, Mo, 76-78, Southeast Ctr Elec Eng Educ, 77-79 & 82-94, Universal Energy Systs, 79-82 & Digital Equip Corp, 84-85, NE Consortium Eng Educ, 94- *Mem:* Inst Elec & Electronics Engrs; Am Soc Eng Educ. *Res:* Semiconductor devices; microwave overstressing and damage analysis of gallium arsenide metal-semiconductor field-effect transistors and integrated circuits; electronic circuit analysis program applications; electromagnetic compatibility, RFI effects in integrated circuits; microwaves; millimeter waves; prediction, measurement and suppression of electromagnetic interference in microelectronic circuits; determination of the microwave electrical overstress properties of gallium arsenide metalized semiconductor field-effect microwave transistors; measurements. *Mailing Add:* Dept Elec & Comput Eng State Univ NY Buffalo 215 B Bonner Hall Buffalo NY 14260. *Fax:* 716-645-5964; *E-Mail:* jjw@acsu.buffalo.edu

**WHALEN, JAMES WILLIAM,** SURFACE CHEMISTRY. *Current Pos:* chmn, Dept Chem, Univ Tex, El Paso, 68-72, prof, 68-89, dean, Col Sci, 72-75, EMER PROF CHEM, UNIV TEX, EL PASO, 89- *Personal Data:* b Enid, Okla, Mar 16, 23; m 46; c 2. *Educ:* Univ Okla, BS, 46, MS, 47, PhD(chem), 51. *Prof Exp:* Res assoc, Mobil Oil Corp, 50-68. *Concurrent Pos:* Vis prof, Univ Heidelberg, 84, Univ Regensburg, 84; consult, Ballard Res Inc, Vancouver, BC, 76-86; vis sr scientist, Ballard Res, 86; lectr, Tex Univ Consortium/Inst Technol Malaysia, Shah Alam, Malaysi, 87-88. *Mem:* Am Chem Soc; Int Asn Colloid & Interface Scientists. *Res:* Surface phenomena; adsorption; calorimetry. *Mailing Add:* 1109 Madeline Dr El Paso TX 79902-2409

**WHALEN, JOSEPH WILSON,** BIOCHEMISTRY, MICROBIOLOGY. *Current Pos:* RETIRED. *Personal Data:* b Battle Creek, Mich, May 27, 23; m 54, Alice M Speltz; c Joseph W Jr & Ann E. *Educ:* Mich State Univ, BS, 49, MS, 51, PhD(microbiol), 55. *Prof Exp:* Bacteriologist, Arthur S Kimball Sanatorium, Battle Creek, 48-50, lab dir, 54-55; bacteriologist, Calhoun Co Health Dept, Mich, 50-52; bacteriologist, Biol Labs, Pitman-Moore Co, 55-56, head, Bact Dept, 56-64, mgr, Bact & Immunochem Depts, 64-71; asst to dir, Biol Labs, Dow Chem Co, 72-73, res specialist, 73-76, sr res specialist, 76-90; res scientist, Whalen Enterprises, 90- *Concurrent Pos:* Res fel, Am Tuberc Asn, 52-54; tech adv, LIFE Labs, Quito, Ecuador, 64-73; consult, Mich Dept Health, 88-, Cal Tech, Midland Mich. *Mem:* Sigma Xi; Am Soc Microbiol; AAAS. *Res:* Bacteriological and immunochemical investigations in tuberculosis; bacterins and vaccines; antimicrobial agents; antibiotics; chemotherapy; microbial genetics; environmental microbiology. *Mailing Add:* 6014 Sturgeon Creek Pkwy Midland MI 48640. *Fax:* 517-496-0212

**WHALEN, THOMAS EARL,** PSYCHOLOGY. *Current Pos:* chair, Educ Psychol Dept, 87-89 & 95-96, assoc dean, Sch Educ, 87-89, PROF, CALIF STATE UNIV, HAYWARD, 70- *Personal Data:* b Toledo, Ohio, June 26, 38; m 60, Carolyn Margaret Lapham; c Jennifer Susan & Holly Elizabeth. *Educ:* Univ Calif, Los Angeles, BA, 60; San Diego State Univ, MA, 67; Univ Conn, PhD, 70. *Prof Exp:* Sec teacher, San Diego City Schs, 64-68; res assoc, Southwest Regional Lab, 69. *Concurrent Pos:* Res consult, Eval Assocs, San Francisco Bay Area Schs 71-88, Lawrence Livermore Nat Lab, 82-83; US Off Educ fel, Univ Conn, 68-70; postdoctoral scholar, Am Educ Res Asn, Univ Iowa, 72. *Mem:* Am Educ Res Asn; Am Psychol Asn. *Res:* Author of numerous articles. *Mailing Add:* 325 Conway Dr Danville CA 94526-5511

**WHALEN, THOMAS J(OHN),** physical metallurgy, ceramics, for more information see previous edition

**WHALEN, WILLIAM JAMES,** PHYSIOLOGY. *Current Pos:* CONSULT, 80- *Personal Data:* b Ft Dodge, Iowa, July 9, 15; m 46, Ruth Kort Kamp; c Ilona, Robert & Lee. *Educ:* Stanford Univ, BA, 48, MA, 49, PhD(physiol), 51. *Prof Exp:* Asst physiol, Stanford Univ, 48-49, res assoc, 49-51, instr, 50-51; from instr to asst prof, Univ Calif, Los Angeles, 51-60; assoc prof, Col Med, Univ Iowa, 60-67; dir res, St Vincent Charity Hosp, 67-; prof, Case Western Res Univ, 67-80. *Concurrent Pos:* Fulbright scholar, 58-59; adj prof, Case Western Res Univ, 67-80, emer prof, 80- *Mem:* AAAS; Microcirc Soc; Am Physiol Soc; Cardiac Muscle Soc (pres, 66-68); NY Acad Sci. *Res:* Cardiovascular research; cardiac function in isolated preparations; respiratory control mechanisms; autonomic pharmacology; tissue oxygen tension and cell metabolism; chemoreceptors. *Mailing Add:* 2805 Bellamah Dr Santa Fe NM 87505

**WHALEY, HOWARD ARNOLD,** organic chemistry, for more information see previous edition

**WHALEY, JULIAN WENDELL,** PLANT PATHOLOGY, PLANT SCIENCE. *Current Pos:* prof, 70-92, EMER PROF PLANT PATH, CALIF STATE UNIV, FRESNO, 92-; CONSULT, WHALEY & ASSOC FORENSIC PLANT PATHOLOGISTS. *Personal Data:* b Parkersburg, WVa, Aug 12, 37; m 61, 70, Jeanine Fortner; c Julie, Jay, Jill & Jennifer. *Educ:* W Liberty State Col, BS, 59; WVa Univ, MS, 61; Univ Ariz, PhD(plant path), 64. *Prof Exp:* Sr plant pathologist, Eli Lilly & Co, 64-70. *Mem:* Am Phytopath Soc; Coun Agr Sci & Technol. *Res:* Plant protection; pesticides; soil fungi; grape diseases; forensic plant path. *Mailing Add:* 1545 E Calimyrna Ave Fresno CA 93710

**WHALEY, KATHARINE BIRGITTA,** CHEMICAL DYNAMICS, CONDENSED PHASE CHEMISTRY. *Current Pos:* ASSOC PROF CHEM, UNIV CALIF, BERKELEY, 86- *Personal Data:* b Barnehurst, Eng, 1956. *Educ:* Oxford Univ, BA, 78, MA, 80; Univ Chicago, MSc, 81, PhD(chem), 84. *Honors & Awards:* Bergman Award, 86. *Prof Exp:* Goldmeir fel, Hebrew Univ Jerusalem, 84-85; fel, Tel Aviv Univ, 85-86. *Concurrent Pos:* A P Sloan fel, 91-93. *Mem:* Am Chem Soc; Am Phys Soc; Royal Soc Chem. *Res:* Chemical dynamics of interacting quantum systems; description of clusters and development of techniques for study of strongly correlated finite systems. *Mailing Add:* Dept Chem Univ Calif Berkeley CA 94720

**WHALEY, PETER WALTER,** GEOLOGY. *Current Pos:* From asst prof to assoc prof, 68-77, PROF GEOL, MURRAY STATE UNIV, 77- *Personal Data:* b Baltimore, Md, June 27, 37; m 60; c 3. *Educ:* Ohio Wesleyan Univ, BA, 59; Univ Ky, MS, 64; La State Univ, PhD(geol), 69. *Mem:* Soc Econ Paleontologists & Mineralogists; Geol Soc Am; Sigma Xi. *Res:* Modern depositional environments; carboniferous system of the Eastern United States. *Mailing Add:* 802 Guthrie Dr Murray KY 42071-3047

**WHALEY, ROSS SAMUEL,** FOREST ECONOMICS, NATURAL RESOURCE & ENVIRONMENTAL POLICY. *Current Pos:* PRES, COL ENVIRON SCI & FORESTRY, STATE UNIV NY, 84- *Personal Data:* b Detroit, Mich, Nov 7, 37; m 58; c 3. *Educ:* Univ Mich, BS, 59, PhD(natural resource econ), 69; Colo State Univ, MS, 61. *Prof Exp:* Instr forestry, Colo State Univ, 60-61 & assoc dean, Col Forestry & Natural Resources, 70-73; res forester, Southern Forest Exp Sta, US Forest Serv, 61-63; asst prof natural resource econ, Utah State Univ, 65-67, prof forest sci & head dept, 67-69; head, Dept Landscape Archit & Regional Planning, Univ Mass, 73-76, dean, Col Food & Natural Resources, 76-78; dir forest econ, Forest Serv, USDA, 78-84. *Concurrent Pos:* Consult, Intermountain Forest & Range Exp Sta, USDA Forest Serv, 66-67, Rocky Mountain Forest & Range Exp Sta, 67, Pub Land Law Rev Comn, 70, Wallace, McHarg, Roberts & Todd, Joe Meheen Eng & Geddes, Brecher, Qualls, Cunningham, Architects, UN, Gov Interstate Task Force on Northern Forest Lands. *Mem:* Soc Am Foresters; Sigma Xi. *Res:* Application of economic theory to problems of natural resources policy and regional planning. *Mailing Add:* Pres State Univ NY Col Environ Sci & Forestry 1 Forestry Dr Syracuse NY 13210-2723

**WHALEY, THOMAS PATRICK,** APPLIED SOLAR THERMAL ENERGY. *Current Pos:* assoc dir solar energy, 76-81, SR ADV, INST GAS TECHNOL, 81- *Personal Data:* b Atchison, Kans, Jan 13, 23; m 46, 69; c 2. *Educ:* St Benedicts Col, BS, 42; Univ Kans, PhD(chem), 50. *Prof Exp:* Proj leader, Res Lab, Ethyl Corp, 50-55, res supvr, Develop Lab, 55-58, sr res assoc, 58-62; mgr inorg & phys chem, Int Minerals & Chem Corp, 62-69, dir, Anal & Tech Serv, 69-74, tech dir, Slpi Metals Corp, 74-76. *Concurrent Pos:* Consult, Dearborn Chem Co, 74; instr, Oakton Community Col, 74; pres, Consanal Corp, 74-; ed, Chem Bull, 76-81. *Mem:* Am Chem Soc. *Res:* Alkali metals; organometallics; inorganic compounds of alkali and alkaline earth metals; refractory metals; metal plating; inorganic phosphates; non-ferrous metals; precious metals; solar energy; fossil fuels; solar production of chemicals; energy planning and systems analysis. *Mailing Add:* 11022 Camden Circle Sun City AZ 85351

**WHALEY, THOMAS WILLIAMS,** ORGANIC CHEMISTRY. *Current Pos:* MEM STAFF CHEM, LOS ALAMOS SCI LAB, UNIV CALIF, 71- *Personal Data:* b Albuquerque, NMex, June 13, 42. *Educ:* Univ NMex, BS, 67, MS, 69, PhD(chem), 71. *Concurrent Pos:* Adj asst prof chem, Univ NMex, Los Alamos Grad Ctr, 73-; ed, J Labelled Compounds & Radiopharmaceut, 74- *Mem:* Am Chem Soc; Sigma Xi; AAAS. *Res:* Organic synthesis with stable isotopes. *Mailing Add:* 1003 Bishop's Lodge Rd PO Box 1663 Santa Fe NM 87501

**WHALEY, WILSON MONROE,** TEXTILE CHEMISTRY. *Current Pos:* RETIRED. *Personal Data:* b Baltimore, Md, July 21, 20; m 56; c 3. *Educ:* Univ Md, BS, 42, MS, 44, PhD(chem), 47. *Prof Exp:* Org chemist, Naval Res Lab, 44-47; fel chem, Univ Ill, 47-49; asst prof, Univ Tenn, 49-53; asst dir res labs, Pabst Brewing Co, 53-55; sect head chem, Res Ctr, Gen Foods Corp, 55-59; asst tech dir, Midwest Div, Arthur D Little, Inc, 59-62; mgr indust develop, IIT Res Inst, 62-65, mgr org chem, 63-65; dir res & planning, Burlington Industs, Inc, 65-71; pres, Whaley Assocs, NY, 71-75; prof textile chem & head dept, NC State Univ, 75-85. *Concurrent Pos:* Consult, Oak Ridge Nat Lab, 51-55; adj assoc prof, Cornell Univ, 74-75. *Mem:* Am Chem Soc; Am Inst Chemists. *Res:* Synthesis and chemistry of dyes; heterocyclic and organophosphorus compounds; polymer syntheses; textile fibers, finishes and processes; plastics, resins and composite structures; textile chemicals, polymers and processes; mutagenicity and carcinogenicity of dyes and intermediates. *Mailing Add:* PO Box 1009 St Michaels MD 21663-1009

**WHALIN, EDWIN ANSIL, JR,** PHYSICS. *Current Pos:* assoc prof, 66-70, PROF PHYSICS, EASTERN ILL UNIV, 70- *Personal Data:* b Barlow, Ky, Mar 6, 24; m 48; c 4. *Educ:* Univ Ill, BS, 45, MS, 47, PhD(physics), 54. *Prof Exp:* From asst prof to prof physics, Univ NDak, 54-66. *Mem:* Am Phys Soc; Sigma Xi. *Res:* Nuclear physics. *Mailing Add:* 9 Heather Dr Charleston IL 61920-3845

**WHALIN, ROBERT W,** OCEANOGRAPHY. *Current Pos:* DIR WATERWAYS, ARMY WATERWAYS EXP STA, 92- *Personal Data:* b Nov 1, 37. *Educ:* Tex A&M Univ, PhD(phys oceanog), 71. *Mailing Add:* Waterways Exp Station/CEWES 3909 Halls Ferry Rd Vicksburg MS 39180

**WHALING, WARD,** ATOMIC PHYSICS. *Current Pos:* Fel, 49-52, from asst prof to assoc prof, 52-62, PROF PHYSICS, CALIF INST TECHNOL, 62- *Personal Data:* b Dallas, Tex, Sept 29, 23. *Educ:* Rice Inst, BA, 44, MA, 47, PhD(physics), 49. *Mem:* Am Phys Soc. *Res:* Penetration of charged particles through matter; atomic spectroscopy. *Mailing Add:* 106-38 Kellogg Radiation Lab Calif Inst Technol Pasadena CA 91125

**WHAN, GLENN A(LAN),** chemical & nuclear engineering, for more information see previous edition

**WHANG, ROBERT,** INTERNAL MEDICINE, NEPHROLOGY. *Current Pos:* PROF MED & VHEAD DEPT MED, COL MED, UNIV OKLA, OKLAHOMA CITY, 78-; CHIEF, MED SERV, VET ADMIN HOSP, 78- *Personal Data:* b Honolulu, Hawaii, Mar 7, 28; m 56; c 4. *Educ:* St Louis Univ, BS, 52, MD, 56; Am Bd Internal Med, dipl, 65, 74, cert nephrol, 72; Am Bd Nutrit, cert, 81. *Prof Exp:* Intern med, Johns Hopkins Univ Hosp, 56-57; asst resident, Baltimore City Hosps, 57-59, resident, 59-60; from instr to assoc prof med, Sch Med, Univ NMex, 63-71; prof, Sch Med, Univ Conn, 71-73; assoc dean, Vet Admin Hosp Affairs, 72-73; prof med, Sch Med, Ind Univ, Indianapolis, 73-78. *Concurrent Pos:* Life Ins Med res fel, Univ NC, 60-62, USPHS trainee renal dis, 62-63; chief metab, Vet Admin Hosp, Albuquerque, 66-71; chief staff, Vet Admin Hosp, Newington, Conn, 71-73 & Indianapolis, Ind, 73-78. *Mem:* Fel Am Col Physicians; Am Fedn Clin Res; Int Soc Nephrology; Am Soc Nephrology; Am Col Nutrit. *Res:* Magnesium deficiency, interrelationship of magnesium and potassium, electrolyte changes in uremia. *Mailing Add:* Va Med Regional Off Ctr 300 Ala Moana Blvd Honolulu HI 96850

**WHANG, SUKOO JACK,** MEDICAL MICROBIOLOGY, IMMUNOLOGY. *Current Pos:* CHIEF, MICROBIOL & IMMUNOL DIV, CLIN LAB, WHITE MEM MED CTR, LOS ANGELES, 77-, PATHOLOGIST, 77- *Personal Data:* b Seoul, Korea, Feb 3, 34; US citizen; m 63; c 3. *Educ:* Univ Calif, Los Angeles, MS, 60, PhD(med microbiol, immunol), 63, MD, 72; Am Bd Med Microbiol, dipl, 75; Am Bd Path, dipl, 77. *Prof Exp:* Asst prof microbiol, Calif State Polytech Univ, 63-64; chief, Microbiol & Serol Dept, Providence Hosp, Southfield, Mich, 64-65; chief, Microbiol & Immunol Dept, Ref Lab, Div Abbott Labs, Calif, 65-69. *Concurrent Pos:* Chief, Microbiol & Immunol Div, Clin Lab, White Mem Med Ctr, 69-70. *Mem:* NY Acad Sci; Am Soc Microbiol; Sigma Xi; fel Am Col Physicians; fel Am Soc Clin Pathologists; Am Med Asn; Col Am Pathologists. *Res:* Clinical microbiology, pathology and serology; syphilis serology; diagnostic tests for the detection of inborn errors of metabolism; fluorescent antibody testing. *Mailing Add:* 1325 Via Del Rey South Pasadena CA 91030

**WHANG, SUNG H,** INTERMETALLIC MATERIALS, SUPERCONDUCTING OXIDES PROCESSING. *Current Pos:* assoc prof, 85-91, PROF METALL & MAT SCI, POLYTECH UNIV, 91- *Personal Data:* b Suh-Byuck, SKorea, Feb 17, 36; US citizen; m 30; c 4. *Educ:* Seoul Nat Univ, BS, 62; Columbia Univ, MS, 75, DEngsci, 78. *Prof Exp:* Lectr metall eng, Seoul Nat Univ, 69-72; staff scientist, Northeastern Univ, 79-81, sr scientist mat sci, 81-85. *Concurrent Pos:* Mem, Bd Rev Met Trans A, 89-; ed, Conf Proc on Superconducting Mat, TMS, 89- & vchmn, 90- *Mem:* Am Soc Metals; Mat Res Soc; Sigma Xi; Metall Soc; NY Acad Sci; Am Inst Mech Engrs. *Res:* Processing of high Jc superconducting oxide materials; deformation and properties of titanium aluminides for high temperature applications; composite materials processing for structural damping applications; rapid solidification processing. *Mailing Add:* 6 Metrotech Ctr Polytech Univ Brooklyn NY 11201

**WHANG, YUN CHOW,** SPACE SCIENCE, FLUID MECHANICS. *Current Pos:* from asst prof to assoc prof space sci, 62-67, chmn dept, 71-84, PROF MECH ENG, CATH UNIV AM, 67- *Personal Data:* b Foochow, China, Dec 13, 33; m 59, Yeong-Ping Chu; c Ruth, Joyce & Kenneth. *Educ:* Taiwan Col Eng, BS, 54; Univ Minn, Minneapolis, PhD(fluid mech), 61. *Prof Exp:* Asst prof acrospace eng, Univ Fla, 61-62. *Concurrent Pos:* NASA grant, 69-, NSF grant, 71-, USAF Off Sci Res grant, 86-89. *Mem:* Am Geophys Union. *Res:* Solar wind; solar wind interaction with the earth, the moon and other planets; slow shocks; the outer heliosphere; solar wind interation with interstellar medium. *Mailing Add:* Dept Mech Eng Cath Univ Am Washington DC 20064

**WHANGBO, MYUNG HWAN,** SOLID STATE CHEMISTRY. *Current Pos:* from asst prof to assoc prof, 78-87, PROF CHEM, NC STATE UNIV, 87- *Personal Data:* b Korea, Oct 21, 45; US citizen; m 71, Jin-Ok Lee; c Jennifer & Albert. *Educ:* Seoul Univ, BSc, 68, MSc, 70; Queens Univ, PhD(chem), 74. *Honors & Awards:* Sigma Xi Res Award, 81. *Prof Exp:* Fel, Queens Univ, 75-76; assoc chem, Cornell Univ, 76-77. *Concurrent Pos:* Camille & Henry Dreyfus teacher-scholar, 80-85; vis prof, Bell Labs, Murray Hill, 81, Univ de Nantes, 84, Argonne Nat Lab, 85, 86 & Univ Paris-Sud, 87, 89-93, Mat Res Ctr, Albert-Ludwigs Univ, 94-96; Alexander von Humboldt Sr US Scientist res award, 94. *Mem:* Am Chem Soc; Sigma Xi. *Res:* Molecular orbital interpretation of structures and reactivities of organic and inorganic systems; structure property relationships of crystalline materials; theoretical chemistry. *Mailing Add:* Dept Chem NC State Univ Raleigh NC 27695-8204. *Fax:* 919-515-7832; *E-Mail:* whangbo@chvzmw.chem.ncsu.edu

**WHANGER, PHILIP DANIEL,** NUTRITIONAL BIOCHEMISTRY. *Current Pos:* from asst prof to assoc prof, 66-78, PROF NUTRIT & BIOCHEM, ORE STATE UNIV, 78- *Personal Data:* b Lewisburg, WVa, Aug 30, 36; m 64; c 2. *Educ:* Berry Col, BS, 59; WVa Univ, MS, 61; NC State Univ, PhD(nutrit), 65. *Prof Exp:* Res assoc biochem, Mich State Univ, 65-66. *Concurrent Pos:* NIH res fel, Mich State Univ, 66-67, res grants selenium & myopathies, Ore State Univ, 68-; NIH spec fel, 72; assoc staff, Harvard Med Sch, 72-73; vis scientist, Gen Acad Exchange Serv, Univ Tubingen, 86; NSF Int fel, 80-81; vis scientist, Commonwealth Sci & Indust Res Orgn, Wembley, Western Australia & Acad Prev Med, Beijing, China, 88. *Mem:* Am Inst Nutrit; Am Soc Animal Sci; Int Bioinorg Scientists; Soc Environ Geochem & Health. *Res:* Altered metabolic pathways under selenium deficiency; relationships of vitamin E and selenium in myopathies; biochemical properties of selenium and cadmium metallo-proteins; metabolic pathways for incorporation of selenium into proteins; selenium and glutathione peroxidise in human blood fractions; selenium deficiencies in primates; selenium intake on human blood and urine fractions. *Mailing Add:* Dept Agr Chem ALS1007 Ore State Univ Corvallis OR 97331. *Fax:* 541-737-0497; *E-Mail:* whangerp@ard.bcc.orst.edu

**WHARRY, STEPHEN MARK,** COMPUTER PROGRAMMING, CRUDE OIL ANALYSES. *Current Pos:* Res chemist, 81-87, SR RES CHEMIST, PHILLIPS PETROL, 87- *Personal Data:* b Dalheart, Tex, Oct 23, 55. *Educ:* Iowa State Univ, BS, 77; Northwestern Univ, MS, 79, PhD(phys org chem), 81. *Mem:* Am Chem Soc; Sigma Xi; Soc Appl Spectros; AAAS. *Res:* Applications of nuclear magnetic resonance spectroscopy to petroleum fractions and engineering plastics; method development and automation. *Mailing Add:* 4842 Clearview Circle Bartlesville OK 74006-5501

**WHARTON, CHARLES BENJAMIN,** PLASMA PHYSICS, MICROWAVE TECHNOLOGY. *Current Pos:* dir, Lab Plasma Studies, 72-73, prof, 67-92, EMER PROF PLASMA PHYSICS, CORNELL UNIV, 92- *Personal Data:* b Gold Hill, Ore, Mar 29, 26; m 53, Gloria J Dorris; c Carl G, Kristi A & Mark T. *Educ:* Univ Calif, Berkeley, BSEE, 50, MS, 52. *Honors & Awards:* Alexander von Humboldt sr scientist award, 73; Socio Onorario, Univ Milan, Italy, 79. *Prof Exp:* Proj engr, Lawrence Radiation Lab, Univ Calif, 50-62; staff mem exp physics, Gen Atomic Div, Gen Dynamics Corp, Calif, 62-67. *Concurrent Pos:* Tech advisor, UN Conf on Peaceful Uses of Atomic Energy, Geneva, Switz, 58; sci engr, Max Planck Inst Physics & Astrophys, Ger, 59-60; consult, Aerojet-Gen Nucleonics Div, Gen Tire & Rubber Co, 60-62, US Naval Res Lab, Washington, DC, 70-, Lawrence Livermore Lab, 75-77, Power Conversion Technol, Inc, 79-81, Occidental Res Corp, 79-82, Sandia Nat Lab, Albuquerque, NMex, 82-86 & Los Alamos Nat Lab, NMex, 83-84; controlled fusion res mem, Eval Panel on Quantum Electronics & Plasma Physics, Nat Res Coun, 70-73; vis scientist, Max Planck Inst Plasma Physics, Munich, Ger, 73-74; dir courses, Int Sch Plasma Physics, Varenna, Italy, 78, 82, 86, 88 & 91; vis prof, Univ Calif, Irvine, 79-80 & Occidental Res Corp, 80-81; US participating scientist, Joint Prog Plasma Physics, Cornell Univ & Physical Res Lab, Ahmedabad, India, 81-84. *Mem:* Fel Am Phys Soc; fel Inst Elec & Electronics Engrs; Nuclear & Plasma Sci Soc (vpres, 75). *Res:* Plasma diagnostic techniques; waves in plasmas; plasma instabilities; microwave technology; electronic circuitry; nonlinear waves; relativistic electron beams; plasma heating; controlled fusion research; intense ion beams; 525 material processing with plasma. *Mailing Add:* 303 N Sunset Dr Ithaca NY 14850. *Fax:* 607-255-3004; *E-Mail:* wharton@lps.cornell.edu

**WHARTON, DAVID CARRIE,** BIOCHEMISTRY. *Current Pos:* PROF & CHMN BIOL, NORTHEASTERN UNIV, BOSTON, 81- *Personal Data:* b Avoca, Pa, Nov 3, 30; m 61; c 3. *Educ:* Pa State Univ, BS, 52, MS, 54, PhD(plant biochem), 56. *Prof Exp:* Asst plant biochem, Pa State Univ, 52-56; fel enzyme chem, Enzyme Inst, Univ Wis, 59-61, asst prof biochem, 62-64 & Sch Med, Univ Va, 64-66; res scientist, E I du Pont de Nemours & Co, 61-62; asst prof biochem, Sch Med, Univ Va, 64-66; from asst prof to assoc prof, Cornell Univ, 66-73; prof biochem, Univ Tex Health Sci Ctr, San Antonio, 73-81. *Mem:* Am Soc Biol Chemists; Am Chem Soc; Brit Soc Gen Microbiol; Am Soc Microbiol. *Res:* Electron transport; metalloenzymes. *Mailing Add:* Dept Biol Northeastern Univ 414 Mugar Boston MA 02115

**WHARTON, H(ARRY) WHITNEY,** ANALYTICAL CHEMISTRY. *Current Pos:* RETIRED. *Personal Data:* b Watertown, NY, May 4, 31; m 55, Bonnie B Brenholdt; c Lisa M & Paul W. *Educ:* Iowa State Univ, BS, 53, MS, 58, PhD(anal chem), 60. *Prof Exp:* Res chemist, Rath Packing Co, 56; asst anal chem, Iowa State Univ, 56-60; res chemist, Procter & Gamble Co, 60-61, group leader anal chem, 61-64, group leader, Soap Prod Div, 65, sect head anal chem, Food Prod Div, 65-70, sect head new prod res, 70-74, sect head foods anal, Food Prod Div, 74-93. *Concurrent Pos:* Docent, Cincinnati Mus Nat Hist & Sci. *Res:* Micro methods of analysis involving spectrophotometry, microdiffusion, spectrophotometric and nonaqueous titrations, polarography and inorganic oxidation-reduction reactions; managing the development of analytical methods for food products. *Mailing Add:* 3204 Compton Rd Cincinnati OH 45251

**WHARTON, JAMES HENRY,** PHYSICAL CHEMISTRY. *Current Pos:* Asst prof, La State Univ, Baton Rouge, 62-63 & 65-69, assoc dean, Col Chem & Physics, 69-71, assoc prof, 69-80, DEAN, GEN COL, LA STATE UNIV, BATON ROUGE, 71-, PROF CHEM, 80-, CHANCELLOR. *Personal Data:* b Mangum, Okla, July 23, 37; m 56; c 2. *Educ:* Northeast La Univ, BS, 59; La State Univ, PhD(phys chem), 62. *Concurrent Pos:* Consult, Univ Tex, San Antonio, 70-71. *Mem:* Am Chem Soc. *Res:* Molecular spectroscopy; electron spin resonance. *Mailing Add:* Dept Chem La State Univ Baton Rouge LA 70803-0001

**WHARTON, LENNARD,** PHYSICAL CHEMISTRY. *Current Pos:* VPRES & DIR CHEM ENG, PACKER ENG, 87- *Personal Data:* b Boston, Mass, Dec 10, 33; m 57; c 3. *Educ:* Mass Inst Technol, BS, 55; Univ Cambridge, MA, 57; Harvard Univ, PhD(chem), 63. *Prof Exp:* From asst prof to assoc prof, Univ Chicago, 63-78, prof chem, 78; vpres eng & technol, Worthington Group, McGraw Edison Co, 78-87; fac, Dept Chem, Univ Chicago, Ill, 87. *Concurrent Pos:* Alfred P Sloan res fel, 64-66; res assoc prof, Univ Chicago, 78-83; consult, Northrop Electronics Div, 77-78; vpres technol, Studebaker Worthington Corp, 78- *Mem:* Am Phys Soc; sr mem Inst Elec & Electronics Engrs; Am Inst Chem Engrs; AAAS; Am Soc Mech Engrs. *Res:* Molecular beams and structure; spectroscopy; chemical kinetics; experimental physical chemistry; scattering phenomena; surface sciences; solar energy conversion; electrical power transmission and distribution. *Mailing Add:* 10 Park Pl Short Hills NJ 07078

**WHARTON, PETER STANLEY,** ORGANIC CHEMISTRY. *Current Pos:* PROF CHEM, WESLEYAN UNIV, 68- *Personal Data:* b Oxford, Eng, May 9, 31; m 55; c 4. *Educ:* Cambridge Univ, BA, 52, MA, 57; Yale Univ, MS, 57, PhD, 59. *Honors & Awards:* Frederick Gardner Cottrell Award, 61. *Prof Exp:* Fel, Columbia Univ, 58-60; from instr to prof org chem, Univ Wis-Madison, 60-68. *Mem:* Am Chem Soc; Chem Soc. *Res:* Synthetic and mechanistic alicyclic chemistry. *Mailing Add:* Dept Chem Wesleyan Univ Middletown CT 06457-3262

**WHARTON, RUSSELL PERRY,** ELECTRICAL ENGINEERING, ELECTROMAGNETICS. *Current Pos:* PRES & CHIEF EXEC OFFICER, WHARTON ASSOC, INC, 93- *Personal Data:* b Memphis, Tenn, Sept 11, 41; m 63, Carroll; c Colleen & Andrew. *Educ:* Ga Inst Technol, BEE, 63, MSEE, 66, PhD(elec eng), 70. *Prof Exp:* Elec engr, Gen Dynamics, Pomona, 63-64; instr, Ga Inst Technol, 64-70; sr mgr, Schlumberger, 70-86; vpres & dir, London Off, PCA, 86-93. *Concurrent Pos:* Consult, Sperry Microwave Electronics Co, 68-70 & Univ Houston, 80-; co-founder, Drug/Alcohol Abuse Halfway House, Houston, 79-; presented papers & lectures, NAm, SAm, Europe, Mid East & Far East. *Mem:* Sr mem Inst Elec & Electronics Engrs; Am Phys Soc; Soc Explor Geophys; Sigma Xi; Am Soc Qual Control. *Res:* Investigation into biological effects of low frequency electromagnetic field radiation; development of business management methods in engineering organizations; research and development instrumentation in geophysics. *Mailing Add:* 1407 Briar Bayou Dr Houston TX 77077. *Fax:* 281-496-9312; *E-Mail:* k4dxs@worldnet.att.net

**WHARTON, WALTER WASHINGTON,** physical chemistry; deceased, see previous edition for last biography

**WHARTON, WILLIAM RAYMOND,** EXPERIMENTAL NUCLEAR PHYSICS, ASTRONOMY. *Current Pos:* asst prof, 84-89, sci dir coordr, 86-89, PROF PHYSICS, WHEATON COL SCI STA, 89-, CHAIR PHYSICS, GEOL DEPT, 91- *Personal Data:* b Knoxville, Tenn, Mar 30, 43; m 67, Gwen Shumway; c Ken, Paul & Michelle. *Educ:* Stanford Univ, BS, 65; Univ Wash, PhD(nuclear physics), 72. *Prof Exp:* Res assoc exp nuclear physics, Argonne Nat Lab, 72-74 & Rutgers Univ, 74-75; from asst prof to assoc prof physics, Carnegie-Mellon Univ, 75-84. *Concurrent Pos:* Dir, Wheaton Col Sci Sta, 90 & 93. *Mem:* Am Phys Soc; Am Asn Physics Teachers; AAAS; Am Sci Asn; Union Concerned Scientists. *Res:* Experimental medium energy nuclear physics involving the study of nuclei or nucleons interacting with pions, kaons and antiprotons. *Mailing Add:* 633 W Hawthorne Blvd Wheaton IL 60187. *Fax:* 630-752-5996; *E-Mail:* bwhatson@david.wheaton.edu

**WHATLEY, ALFRED T,** PHYSICAL CHEMISTRY. *Current Pos:* RETIRED. *Personal Data:* b Denver, Colo, Apr 20, 22; m 94, Mary Siekman; c Christine (Hodgson), Trudy (Havener), Barney II & Kathrin (Gunnels). *Educ:* Princeton Univ, AB, 48, AM, 50, PhD(chem), 52. *Prof Exp:* Chemist, Hanford Works, Gen Elec Co, 52-55, eng consult, Aircraft Nuclear Propulsion, 55-57, physicist, Vallecitos Atomic Lab, 57-61; staff engr, Martin Co, 61-62; sr sci specialist, EG&G, 62-70; exec dir, Western Interstate Nuclear Bd, Lakewood, Colo, 70-76. *Concurrent Pos:* Mem, Colo Air Pollution Control Comn, chmn, 78- *Mem:* Am Nuclear Soc; Sigma Xi. *Res:* Nuclear science. *Mailing Add:* PO Box 540 Breckenridge CO 80424-0540. *E-Mail:* whatley@cobrado.net

**WHATLEY, BOOKER TILLMAN,** HORTICULTURE, PLANT PHYSIOLOGY. *Current Pos:* PRES, WHATLEY FARMS, INC, 81- *Personal Data:* b Alexandria, Ala, Nov 5, 15; m 43. *Educ:* Ala Agr & Mech Col, BS, 41; Rutgers Univ, PhD, 57. *Prof Exp:* Agr exten agent, Butler Co, Ala, 46-47; prin high sch, Ala, 47-50; tech oper officer, Chofu Hydroponic Farm, Japan, 50-54; assoc prof & head, Dept Hort, Southern Univ, 57-60; adv hort, US Opers Mission, Ministry Agr, Ghana, 60-62; prof hort, Southern Univ, 62-68; prof plant & soil sci, Tuskegee Inst, 68-81. *Mem:* AAAS; Am Soc Hort Sci; Am Soc Plant Physiol; Sigma Xi. *Res:* The effect of budding methods, wrapping materials and hormones on Myristica fragrans and its vegetative propagation. *Mailing Add:* 7 S Haardt Dr Montgomery AL 36105

**WHATMORE, GEORGE BERNARD,** MEDICINE, CLINICAL NEUROPHYSIOLOGY. *Current Pos:* PVT PRACT PHYSICIAN INTERNAL MED & CLIN NEUROPHYSIOL, 51-; PRIN INVESTR NEUROPHYSIOL FUNCTIONAL DIS, PAC NORTHWEST RES FOUND, SEATTLE, 66- *Personal Data:* b Seattle, Wash, Aug 31, 17; m 42, Frances Beatty; c Pamela F, David B & Nancy J. *Educ:* Univ Wash, BS, 40, MS, 41; Univ Chicago, PhD(neurophysiol), 46, MD, 48. *Prof Exp:* Intern & resident med, King Co Hosp, Seattle, 48-50; resident physician clin neurophysiol, Lab Clin Physiol, Chicago, 50-51. *Concurrent Pos:* Univ fel physiol, Univ Chicago, 42-43, Rawson fel, 43-44, Sheldon fel, 45-46, teaching asst, 42-45. *Mem:* AAAS; Behav Ther & Res Soc; Acad Psychosom Med; Asn Appl Psychophysiol & Biofeedback; Sigma Xi; Int Stress & Tension Control

Asn. *Res:* Investigation of the neurophysiologic mechanisms and pathways involved in conditioning and learning; investigation of the neurophysiology and treatment of functional disorders. *Mailing Add:* 10524 SE 27th St Bellevue WA 98004-7231

**WHAYNE, TOM FRENCH,** medicine, for more information see previous edition

**WHEALTON, JOHN HOBSON,** PLASMA PHYSICS. *Current Pos:* MEM STAFF, THERMONUCLEAR DIV, OAK RIDGE NAT LABS, 75- *Personal Data:* b Brooklyn, NY, Apr 27, 43; m 72. *Educ:* Univ Lowell, BS, 66; Univ Del, MS, 68, PhD(physics), 71. *Prof Exp:* Res assoc Div Eng, Brown Univ, 71-72, res assoc, Dept Chem, 72-73; res assoc, Joint Inst Lab Astrophys, Univ Colo, Nat Bur Stand, 73-75. *Mem:* Fel Am Phys Soc; Inst Elec & Electronics Engrs; Am Nuclear Soc. *Res:* Analysis of drift tube swarm experiments; kinetic theory of diffusion and mobility in collision-dominated weakly ionized gases in presence of strong fields; space charge ion extraction optics; R F accelerator modeling; 3-dimensional analysis of Maxwell equations. *Mailing Add:* 185 Outer Dr Oak Ridge TN 37830

**WHEASLER, ROBERT,** AERONAUTICAL ENGINEERING, AERODYNAMICS. *Current Pos:* prof, 84-90, EMER PROF AERONAUT & MECH ENG, UNIV WYO, 90- *Personal Data:* b Indianapolis, Ind, Dec 26, 24; m 46; c Ray S III & Christy A (Davis). *Educ:* Purdue Univ, BS, 53, MS, 54, Univ Okla, PhD(eng sci), 64. *Prof Exp:* Res engr, Boeing Airplane Co, 54-55; res engr, Aircraft Gas Turbine Div, Gen Elec Co, 55; instr aeronaut eng, Purdue Univ, 55-58. *Concurrent Pos:* Instr, Univ Okla, 60; vis prof, US Naval Acad, 82-83; brig gen, USAF, 46-84. *Mem:* Sigma Xi; Air Force Hist Found; Air Force Asn. *Res:* Thermodynamics; heat transfer; aircraft and missile propulsion; gas dynamics; propulsion. *Mailing Add:* 1162 N 19th St Laramie WY 82070

**WHEAT, JOHN DAVID,** ANIMAL GENETICS. *Current Pos:* RETIRED. *Personal Data:* b Ranger, Tex, July 12, 21; m 50; c 3. *Educ:* Agr & Mech Col, Tex, BS, 42, MS, 51; Iowa State Col, PhD(animal breeding, genetics), 54. *Prof Exp:* From asst prof to prof animal sci, Kans State Univ, 54-88. *Concurrent Pos:* Beef cattle breeding adv, Ministry Animal & Forest Resources, US Agency Int Develop-Kans State Univ Contract Team, Northern Nigeria, 66-68; mem fac, Ahmadu Bello Univ, Nigeria, 66-68; livestock breeding consult, Taiwan, 72 & 75, Costa Rica, 80 & 81 & Nigeria, 84. *Mem:* Am Soc Animal Sci; Am Genetic Asn. *Res:* Population genetics; muscling selection research in swine. *Mailing Add:* 3501 Dickens Ave Manhattan KS 66502

**WHEAT, JOSEPH ALLEN,** chemistry; deceased, see previous edition for last biography

**WHEAT, ROBERT WAYNE,** MICROBIOLOGY, BIOCHEMISTRY. *Current Pos:* instr biochem, Duke Univ, 56-58, assoc, 58-60, assoc prof microbiol, 66-74, ASST PROF BIOCHEM, SCH MED, DUKE UNIV, 60-, PROF MICROBIOL, 74- *Personal Data:* b Springfield, Mo, Nov 10, 26; m 48; c 3. *Educ:* Washington Univ, PhD(microbiol), 55. *Prof Exp:* USPHS fel biochem, NIH, Md, 55-56. *Concurrent Pos:* Sabbatical vis prof Freilurg, Breisgan, WGer, Max Planck Inst Immunobiol, 65; NIH consult, 69-72, 85-89; vis scientist, Rocky Mountain Lab, Nat Inst Allergy & Infectious Dis, NIH, 78-79. *Mem:* Am Chem Soc; Am Soc Biol Chem; Am Soc Microbiol. *Res:* Biochemistry of microorganisms, amino sugars and polysaccharides; cell surface antigens. *Mailing Add:* Dept Microbiol Duke Univ 2720 Montgomery St Durham NC 27705

**WHEATLAND, DAVID ALAN,** INORGANIC CHEMISTRY. *Current Pos:* RETIRED. *Personal Data:* b Boston, Mass, Aug 27, 40; m 65; c 1. *Educ:* Brown Univ, ScB, 63; Univ Md, PhD(inorg chem), 67. *Prof Exp:* Asst prof chem, Bowdoin Col, 67-73; res chemist, S D Warren Res Lab, 73-92. *Concurrent Pos:* Petrol Res Fund grant, 68-70. *Res:* Reprographic research and development. *Mailing Add:* 20 Stornoway Rd Cumberland Foreside ME 04110

**WHEATLEY, W(ILLIAM) A(RTHUR),** ELECTRONICS. *Current Pos:* COMMUN CONSULT, HARVEY J KRASNER ASSOCS INC, 72- *Personal Data:* b Deming, NMex, Nov 9, 23; m 45; c 4. *Educ:* Univ Mich, BS, 47, MS, 48. *Prof Exp:* Res assoc electronics, Willow Run Res Ctr, Univ Mich, 48-50, res engr res admin, 50-55; vpres, Strand Eng Co, 55-60; vpres, Electronic Assistance Corp, 60-64; mgt consult, 64-68; mkt mgr, United Telecontrol Electronics, 68-70; gen mgr, Wave Energy Systs, Inc, Newtown, Pa, 70-72. *Mem:* Inst Elec & Electronics Engrs. *Res:* Analog computers; complex military system design; electronic equipment prototype design; field test; research administration; engineering management; management consulting. *Mailing Add:* 25 Bamm Hollow Rd Middleton NJ 07748

**WHEATON, BURDETTE CARL,** ALGEBRA. *Current Pos:* asst prof, 65-72, PROF MATH, MANKATO STATE UNIV, 72- *Personal Data:* b Mankato, Minn, July 3, 38; m 68, Margaret A Ehlbeck; c Timothy, Michael & Julie A. *Educ:* Mankato State Col, BS, 59; Univ Iowa, MS, 61, PhD(math), 65. *Prof Exp:* Instr math, Univ Iowa, 59-63; asst prof, Western Ill Univ, 63-65. *Mem:* Am Math Soc; Math Asn Am; Sigma Xi; Nat Coun Teachers Math. *Res:* Abstract algebra, particularly group theory and group representations. *Mailing Add:* 326 Floral Ave Mankato MN 56001. *Fax:* 507-389-6376

**WHEATON, ELMER PAUL,** ENGINEERING, OCEANOGRAPHY. *Current Pos:* DIR, MARINE DEVELOP ASSOCS, INC, 85- *Personal Data:* b Elyria, Ohio, Aug 15, 09; m 33, Martha Davis; c Sara & Mark. *Educ:* Pomona Col, BA, 33. *Honors & Awards:* Robert M Thompson Award for outstanding civilian leadership, Navy League US, 71; Aerospaces Contrib to Soc Award, Am Inst Aeronaut & Astronaut, 78. *Prof Exp:* Sound technician, Columbia Motion Picture Studios, 33; riveter & assembler, Douglas Aircraft Co, 34-36, res engr, 36-40, asst chief res sect, 40-43 & Eng Labs, 43, spec asst to vpres eng, 43-44, on loan to radiation lab, Mass Inst Technol, 44, on loan to Rand Corp, 45, mgr, Appl Physics Lab, 45, chief dynamics & sound control, Missile Projs, 45-55, chief missiles engr, 55-58, dir, Missiles & Space Systs, 58, vpres eng, 58-60, vpres eng technol, 60-61, vpres eng & corp vpres, 61, dir, Astropower, Inc, 61; asst to pres, Lockheed Missiles & Space Co, Lockheed Aircraft Corp, 62, vpres & gen mgr, Space Prog Div, 62-63, vpres & gen mgr, Res & Develop Div, 63-74, vpres, Corp, 62-74, pres, Lockheed Petrol Serv Ltd, 72-74. *Concurrent Pos:* Lectr, Guggenheim Aeronaut Lab, Calif Inst Technol, 41-54; mem spec indust comt missiles for res & develop, Off Secy USAF, 54; consult, Adv Panel Aeronaut Res & Eng, Off Dir Defense, 57-59; mem, Comt Ocean Eng, Nat Acad Eng, 67-; consult & mem, Panel Ocean Eng, Nat Coun Marine Resources & Eng Develop, 68-69; mem, Calif State Marine Res Comt, 72-78, marine bd, Nat Acad Sci-Nat Acad Eng, adv panel, Int Decade Ocean Explor, NSF, 70-71 & Sea Grant Coord Coun, Univ Calif, 70-; consult, 74- *Mem:* Nat Acad Eng; fel Am Inst Aeronaut & Astronaut; fel Am Astronaut Soc; fel Marine Technol Soc; AAAS. *Res:* Acoustics; electronics; aeronautical and systems engineering; flutter and vibration; missile and space systems engineering; aerospace management; ocean systems engineering and management; research and development management. *Mailing Add:* 501 Portola Rd PO Box 8087 Portola Valley CA 94028-7603. *E-Mail:* EWHEA215@AOL

**WHEATON, GREGORY ALAN,** organic chemistry, for more information see previous edition

**WHEATON, JONATHAN EDWARD,** NEUROENDOCRINOLOGY. *Current Pos:* asst prof, 75-80, ASSOC PROF PHYSIOL, UNIV MINN, ST PAUL, 80- *Personal Data:* b Fullerton, Calif, Jan 22, 47; m 67; c 2. *Educ:* Univ Calif, Davis, BS, 69; Ore State Univ, MS, 70, PhD(animal physiol), 73. *Prof Exp:* Fel neuroendocrinol, Southwestern Med Sch, 73-75. *Mem:* Am Soc Animal Sci; Sigma Xi; Soc Study Reprod. *Res:* Control and effects of neurohormones; reproductive endocrinology. *Mailing Add:* Dept Animal Sci 122 Peters Hall Univ Minn 1404 Gortner Ave St Paul MN 55108-6160

**WHEATON, ROBERT MILLER,** INDUSTRIAL CHEMISTRY. *Current Pos:* RETIRED. *Personal Data:* b Danbury, Ohio, Oct 11, 19; m 43, 67; c 5. *Educ:* Oberlin Col, AB, 41. *Prof Exp:* Chemist, Celotex Corp, 41; chemist & process specialist, Trojan Powder Co, 42-43, head process specialists, 44-45; chemist, Dow Chem Co, 46-49, group leader res, 50-55, div leader, 56-71, assoc scientist, Western Div Res, 72-82. *Concurrent Pos:* Chmn, Gordon Res Conf Ion Exchange, 63. *Mem:* Am Chem Soc; Sigma Xi. *Res:* Synthesis, applications and properties of ion exchange resins. *Mailing Add:* 156 Warwick Dr Walnut Creek CA 94598-3223

**WHEATON, THOMAS ADAIR,** PLANT PHYSIOLOGY, HORTICULTURE. *Current Pos:* Asst horticulturist, 63-70, assoc prof hort & assoc horticulturist, 70-79, PROF & HORTICULTURIST, INST FOOD & AGR SCI, AGR RES & EDUC CTR, UNIV FLA, LAKE ALFRED, 79- *Personal Data:* b Orlando, Fla, Apr 5, 36; m 61; c 2. *Educ:* Univ Fla, BS, 58, MS, 60; Univ Calif, Davis, PhD(plant physiol), 63. *Mem:* Am Soc Plant Physiol; Am Soc Hort Sci; Sigma Xi. *Res:* Chilling injury in plants; nitrogen metabolism and growth regulation in citrus. *Mailing Add:* Univ Fla Agr Res & Educ Ctr 700 Experimental Station Rd Lake Alfred FL 33850

**WHEBY, MUNSEY S,** INTERNAL MEDICINE. *Current Pos:* assoc prof, 66-72, PROF MED, SCH MED, UNIV VA, 72-, CHAIR, DEPT MED, 96- *Personal Data:* b Roanoke, Va, Nov 19, 30; m 55; c 3. *Educ:* Roanoke Col, BS, 51; Univ Va, MD, 55. *Prof Exp:* Asst chief hemat, Walter Reed Army Inst Res & Walter Reed Gen Hosp, 59-61, chief gastroenterol, Walter Reed Army Inst Res, 61-62, chief, Med Div, US Army Trop Res Med Lab, 62-65; assoc prof med, Rutgers Med Sch, 65-66. *Concurrent Pos:* Gov, Am Col Physicians, 95- *Mem:* Am Fedn Clin Res; AMA; Am Soc Hemat; Am Col Cardiovasc Asn. *Res:* Gastrointestinal absorption of iron; folic acid and B-12 metabolism. *Mailing Add:* Dept Med Univ Va Sch Med Charlottesville VA 22908-0001. *Fax:* 804-982-3583; *E-Mail:* msw4x@virginia.edu

**WHEEDEN, RICHARD LEE,** MATHEMATICS. *Current Pos:* from asst prof to assoc prof, 67-74, PROF MATH, RUTGERS UNIV, NEW BRUNSWICK, 74- *Personal Data:* b Baltimore, Md, Nov 29, 40; m 62, Sharon Lee McGlasson; c Michael David & Catherine Abigail. *Educ:* Johns Hopkins Univ, AB, 61; Univ Chicago, MS, 62, PhD(math), 65. *Prof Exp:* Instr math, Univ Chicago, 65-66; mem, Inst Adv Study, 66-67. *Concurrent Pos:* NSF fel, 66-67; NSF grants, 67- *Mem:* Am Math Soc. *Res:* Harmonic analysis. *Mailing Add:* Dept Math Rutgers Univ New Brunswick NJ 08903

**WHEELER, ALFRED GEORGE, JR,** ENTOMOLOGY. *Current Pos:* ENTOMOLOGIST, BUR PLANT INDUST, PA DEPT AGR, 71- *Personal Data:* b Nebraska City, Nebr, Apr 11, 44. *Educ:* Grinnell Col, BA, 66; Cornell Univ, PhD(insect ecol), 71. *Honors & Awards:* Distinguished Achievement Award Regulatory Entom, Entom Soc Am, 86, Distinguished Serv Award, Eastern Br, 94. *Concurrent Pos:* Consult, Dames & Moore, 73-74; from adj asst prof to adj assoc prof, Pa State Univ, 73-88, prof, 88-; ed, Regulatory Hort, 75-, Melsheimer Entom Ser, 78-83; vis fel, Cornell Univ, 86, 87 & 88;

res assoc, Mohonk Preserve, NY, 90-; consult, Off Technol Assessment, US Cong, 91. *Mem:* Entom Soc Am. *Res:* Life history studies of Hemiptera-Heteroptera, especially Miridae; biology of insects affecting ornamental plants; study of insect-plant associations. *Mailing Add:* Pa Dept Agr Bur Plant Indust 2301 N Cameron St Harrisburg PA 17110-9408. *Fax:* 717-783-3275

**WHEELER, ALFRED PORTIUS,** PHYSIOLOGY, CELL BIOLOGY. *Current Pos:* asst prof, 76-81, ASSOC PROF ZOOL, CLEMSON UNIV, 82- *Personal Data:* b Brooklyn, NY, Sept 16, 47; m 69; c 4. *Educ:* Butler Univ, BS, 69; Duke Univ, PhD(zool), 75. *Prof Exp:* Instr, Duke Univ, 74-76. *Concurrent Pos:* Vis prof, Duke Univ, 77- *Mem:* Sigma Xi; Am Soc Zoologists. *Res:* Physiology of biomineralization, especially in molluscs; physiology and subcellular localization of carbonic anhydrase; matrix function in biomineralization; the biology and industrial applications of mineralization inhibitors. *Mailing Add:* Dept Biol Sci Clemson Univ 201 Sikes Hall Clemson SC 29632-0001

**WHEELER, ALLAN GORDON,** PHARMACOLOGY, PHYSIOLOGY. *Current Pos:* RETIRED. *Personal Data:* b Gary, Ind, July 12, 23; m 49; c 4. *Educ:* Valparaiso Univ, BA, 48; Univ Wis, MA, 50. *Prof Exp:* Asst pharmacol & anesthesiol, Univ Wis, 50-54; assoc pharmacologist, Res Ctr, Mead Johnson & Co, Ind, 54-58, sr pharmacologist, 54-59, group leader toxicol, 59-68; supvr indust toxicol, ICI US, Inc, 68-89, toxicol coordr, Bio-Med Res Lab, 88-89. *Mem:* Am Indust Hyg Asn; Drug Info Asn; Environ Mutagen Soc; Sigma Xi; Am Asn Lab Animal Sci. *Res:* Anesthesiology; toxicology. *Mailing Add:* 7 Brandywine Blvd Edgewood Hills Wilmington DE 19809

**WHEELER, BERNICE MARION,** ZOOLOGY. *Current Pos:* RETIRED. *Personal Data:* b Winsted, Conn, June 30, 15. *Educ:* Conn Col, AB, 37; Smith Col, MA, 39; Yale Univ, PhD(zool), 48. *Prof Exp:* Asst zool, Smith Col, 37-39; instr, Westbrook Jr Col, 39-42; asst, Yale Univ, 42-47; from instr to emer prof zool, Conn Col, 47-80. *Concurrent Pos:* Ford Found fel, 54-55. *Mem:* Sigma Xi. *Res:* Genetics; ecology; evolution. *Mailing Add:* 35 W Main St Niantic CT 06357-2329

**WHEELER, BRUCE CHRISTOPHER,** INSTRUMENTATION, SIGNAL PROCESSING. *Current Pos:* ASSOC PROF ELEC & COMPUT ENG, BECKMAN INST, UNIV ILL, URBANA-CHAMPAIGN, 88-, ASSOC HEAD UNDERGRAD AFFAIRS, 95- *Personal Data:* b Schenectady, NY, Dec 7, 48; m 77, Gayle M Quinn; c Jean & Julie. *Educ:* Mass Inst Technol, SB, 71; Cornell Univ, MS, 77, PhD(elec eng), 81. *Prof Exp:* Vis asst prof elec eng, Univ Ill, Urbana-Champaign, 80-82, asst prof, 82-88. *Concurrent Pos:* Chair, bioeng fac, Univ Ill, Urbana-Champaign, 89-90, Neurosci Prog, 90-93. *Mem:* Inst Elec & Electronics Engrs; Soc Neurosci; Am Soc Eng Educ. *Res:* Instrumentation for neuroscience; microelectrode array fabrication; neural signal processing; neural network and pattern recognition; image processing; biomedical engineering. *Mailing Add:* Beckman Inst Univ Ill 405 N Mathews Ave Urbana IL 61801. *Fax:* 217-244-5180

**WHEELER, C HERBERT,** ARCHITECTURAL ENGINEERING. *Current Pos:* prof archit eng, 64-80, EMER PROF ARCHIT ENG, PA STATE UNIV, 80- *Personal Data:* b Merchantville, NJ, June 6, 15; m 40, Cicely Pointer; c Pamela, Janet & Betsy. *Educ:* Univ Pa, BArch 37; Mass Inst Technol, MArch, 40. *Prof Exp:* Archit designer, Austin Co, 38-41; from archit to chief archit, JG White Eng Co, 41-55; mgr eng, Stran Steel Corp, 55-58; mgr, Environ Systs, Curtiss-Wright Corp, Quehanna Pa, 58-64. *Mem:* Emer fel Am Inst Architects; emer mem Am Soc Eng Educ. *Mailing Add:* 638 Franklin St State College PA 16803-3459

**WHEELER, CHARLES H(ORATIO), III,** MATHEMATICAL STATISTICS. *Current Pos:* RETIRED. *Personal Data:* b Wheeling, WVa, Oct 30, 04; m 40, Elizabeth Darracot; c Charles H IV, Anne (Stratton) & William. *Educ:* Washington & Jefferson Col, BS, 26; Johns Hopkins Univ, PhD(math), 33. *Prof Exp:* Asst prof, Univ Richmond, 28-29, assoc prof, 29-41, prof, 41-75, secy & treas, 42-75. *Concurrent Pos:* Pres & treas, Univ Richmond Bd Publ, 33-75; secy/treas, E R Petterson Educ Found, 63-93. *Mem:* Sigma Xi. *Res:* Saving funds for educational purposes. *Mailing Add:* Univ Richmond Richmond VA 23226

**WHEELER, CLAYTON EUGENE, JR,** DERMATOLOGY. *Current Pos:* chmn dept, 72-87, chief div, 62-72, PROF DERMAT, SCH MED, UNIV NC, CHAPEL HILL, 62- *Personal Data:* b Viroqua, Wis, June 30, 17; m 52; c 3. *Educ:* Univ Wis, BA, 38, MD, 41; Am Bd Dermat, dipl, 51. *Honors & Awards:* Rothman Award, 79. *Prof Exp:* Resident & instr internal med, Med Sch, Univ Mich, 42-44, resident & instr dermat, 49-51; from asst prof to prof, Sch Med, Univ Va, 51-62. *Concurrent Pos:* Res fel endocrinol & metab, Univ Mich, 47-48; chmn, Residency Rev Comt Dermat; rep, Am Bd Med Specialties; pres, Am Bd Dermat, 77-78. *Mem:* Soc Invest Dermat (pres, 73-74); AMA; Am Acad Dermat (pres, 84-85); Asn Prof Dermat (pres, 75-76); Am Dermat Asn (pres, 82-83). *Res:* Viral diseases of skin, especially Herpes simplex. *Mailing Add:* Dept Dermat 3100 Thurston Bowles Bldg S CB 7287 Univ NC Chapel Hill NC 27599

**WHEELER, DARRELL DEANE,** MEMBRANE PHYSIOLOGY, TRANSPORT. *Current Pos:* from asst prof to prof, 68-95, EMER PROF PHYSIOL, MED UNIV SC, 95- *Personal Data:* b West Liberty, Ky, Feb 24, 39; m 63, Priscilla Rose; c Melissa & Brian. *Educ:* Transylvania Col, AB, 62; Univ Ky, PhD(physiol), 67. *Concurrent Pos:* NIH fel physiol & biophys, Univ Ky, 67-68; instr, Transylvania Univ, 68; NIH res grants prin investr, 69-72, 75-86 & 90-93. *Mem:* Am Physiol Soc; AAAS. *Res:* Cell physiology; membrane transport in the nervous system. *Mailing Add:* Dept Physiol Med Univ SC Charleston SC 29425. *Fax:* 803-792-4423

**WHEELER, DAVID M,** ANESTHESIOLOGY. *Current Pos:* ANESTHESIOLOGIST, GREATER LAUREL BELTSVILLE HOSP, 91. *Personal Data:* b Philadephia, Pa, Aug 13, 53. *Res:* Anesthesiology. *Mailing Add:* Laurel Regional Hosp 7300 Van Dusen Rd Laurel MD 20707

**WHEELER, DESMOND MICHAEL SHERLOCK,** organic chemistry, for more information see previous edition

**WHEELER, DIANA ESTHER,** PHYSIOLOGICAL BASIS OF CASTE, SOCIAL INSECT BIOLOGY. *Current Pos:* asst prof, 87-93, ASSOC PROF, DEPT ENTOM, UNIV ARIZ, 93- *Personal Data:* b New Haven, Conn, Aug 4, 50; m, Donald R Davis. *Educ:* Duke Univ, BS, 72, PhD(zool), 82; Univ Del, MS, 77. *Prof Exp:* Fel, Smithsonian Inst, 82-83; res fel, Harvard Univ, 83-85; asst prof, Univ Southwestern La, 86-87. *Concurrent Pos:* Assoc ed, J Morphology, 91-; mem, Ed Comt, Ann Rev Entom, 94- *Mem:* Int Union Study Social Insects; AAAS; Sigma Xi; Soc Study Evolution; Entom Soc Am. *Res:* Analysis of mechanisms that produce caste differences in ants, including how worker forms become different, how females produce and fail to produce eggs and how queens store sperm. *Mailing Add:* Dept Entom Univ Ariz Tucson AZ 85721

**WHEELER, DONALD ALSOP,** HUMAN GENETICS, EVOLUTION. *Current Pos:* RETIRED. *Personal Data:* b Philadelphia, Pa, Aug 16, 31; m 53, Dorothy Grezeszak; c Jean L (Christiansen), David A, Michael M & John D. *Educ:* Mich State Univ, BS, 53, MS, 56; Cornell Univ, PhD(plant breeding), 61. *Prof Exp:* Instr biol, Delta Col, 61-65, head dept, 63-65; assoc prof biol, Edinboro Univ Pa, 65-73, asst head dept biol, 71-73, prof biol, 73-97. *Concurrent Pos:* Vis assoc, Calif Inst Technol, 92. *Mem:* Sigma Xi; AAAS. *Mailing Add:* 5471 Sherrod Hill Rd Edinboro PA 16412-1864

**WHEELER, DONALD BINGHAM, JR,** PHYSICS. *Current Pos:* asst prof, 47-57, ASSOC PROF PHYSICS, LEHIGH UNIV, 57- *Personal Data:* b Cleveland, Ohio, May 24, 17. *Educ:* Lehigh Univ, BS, 38; Calif Inst Technol, PhD(physics), 47. *Prof Exp:* Instr physics, Occidental Col, 41-42. *Mem:* Am Phys Soc. *Res:* Electric dipole moment determinations; microwave propagation; dispersion and absorption of electromagnetic waves in fatty acids. *Mailing Add:* 1806 Main St Bethlehem PA 18018

**WHEELER, ED R,** TOPOLOGY. *Current Pos:* HEAD, DEPT MATH & COMPUT SCI, ARMSTRONG STATE COL, 87- *Personal Data:* m, Claire Mosteller; c Aaron & Jodi. *Educ:* Samford Univ, BA, 69; Univ Va, PhD, 73. *Prof Exp:* Instr, Lynchburg Col, 69-70; teaching asst, Univ Va, 70-73; assoc prof, Northern Ky Univ, 73-80; head math sci, Meredith Col, 80-87. *Mem:* Math Asn Am; Am Math Soc. *Res:* Introductory college mathematics. *Mailing Add:* Dept Math & Comput Sci Armstrong St Col Savannah GA 31419. *Fax:* 912-921-2083; *E-Mail:* erw@pirates.armstrong.edu

**WHEELER, EDWARD NORWOOD,** ORGANIC CHEMISTRY. *Current Pos:* RETIRED. *Personal Data:* b Yancey, Tex, Oct 11, 27; m 50, Luella Brossette; c Gordon A, Sterling R, Darrell S, Charlotte (Wolfe) & Murray H. *Educ:* Tex Col Arts & Indust, BS, 47, BSCE, 49; Univ Tex, MA, 51, PhD(org chem), 53. *Prof Exp:* Res chemist, Celanese Chem Co, 53-55, group leader, 55-62, sect head, 62-67, dir chem res, 67-69, dir res, Tech Ctr, 69-72, dir develop, 72-74, dir planning, 74-75, dir res, develop & planning, 75-76, vpres res, develop & planning, 76-79, vpres res & develop, 79-83. *Concurrent Pos:* Consult petrochem process litigation. *Mem:* Am Chem Soc. *Res:* Acrylic acid; vinyl monomers; propiolactone reactions; palladium-olefin reactions; liquid phase oxidation of carbonyl compounds and olefins; process development and synthesis of petrochemicals. *Mailing Add:* 9238 Moss Haven Dallas TX 75231-1412

**WHEELER, EDWARD STUBBS,** RESEARCH ADMINISTRATION. *Current Pos:* INDEPENDENT MGT CONSULT, 86- *Personal Data:* b Philadelphia, Pa, June 3, 27; m 52, Joan M Petersen; c Joan, Edward, Paul & Anne. *Educ:* Haverford Col, AB, 48; Cornell Univ, PhD(chem), 52. *Prof Exp:* Asst chem, Cornell Univ, 48-51; assoc chemist org chem res, Atlantic Ref Co, 52-53, supv chemist, 53-59; mgr, Adhesives Div, Amchem Prods, Inc, 59-62; mgr thermosetting polymer develop, Insulating Mat Dept, Gen Elec Co, 63-66, mgr-engr, Insulator Dept, 66-71, consult, Corp Exec Staff, 71-75; vpres technol, Lapp Insulator Co, 75-85, vpres & gen mgr, Organic Insulators Div, 85-86. *Concurrent Pos:* Mem bd dirs, Am Nat Metric Coun, 74-75. *Mem:* Fel AAAS; Am Chem Soc; Inst Elec & Electronics Engrs; Sigma Xi. *Res:* Insulators; polymers; electrical insulation; synthetic organic chemistry; engineering standards; metric conversion. *Mailing Add:* 33 Longate Rd Clinton CT 06413-1343

**WHEELER, FRANK CARLISLE,** PHARMACEUTICAL CHEMISTRY. *Current Pos:* RETIRED. *Personal Data:* b Millinocket, Maine, Jan 26, 17; m 46, Jeanette Woodlock; c 2. *Educ:* Mass Col Pharm, BS, 40, MS, 42; Purdue Univ, PhD(pharmaceut chem), 49. *Prof Exp:* Analytical chemist, Burroughs Wellcome & Co, 42-43; pharmaceut chemist, Eli Lilly & Co, 49-58, chief, Ampoule Pilot Plant, 58-65, head, 65-66, dir, Parenteral Opers Div, 66-75, dir, Qual Control & Tech Serv, 75-79. *Mem:* Am Chem Soc; Am Pharmaceut Asn; Pharmaceut Mfrs Asn; Parenteral Drug Asn. *Res:* Pharmaceutical development; manufacture and control of chiefly parenteral products. *Mailing Add:* 23 Southern Pine Trail Ormond Beach FL 32174-5988

**WHEELER, GEORGE LAWRENCE,** PHYSICAL CHEMISTRY, BIOCHEMISTRY. *Current Pos:* from asst prof to prof, 77-85, J F BUCKMAN PROF CHEM, UNIV NEW HAVEN, 85- *Personal Data:* b Rockville Center, NY, June 16, 44; m 68; c 2. *Educ:* Cath Univ Am, AB, 67; Univ Md, PhD(phys chem), 73. *Prof Exp:* Res assoc phys chem, Yale Univ, 73-75, NIH fel, Med Sch, 75-77. *Concurrent Pos:* NSF/Inst Sci Equip Prog grant, Univ New Haven, 77-80; staff mem, Life Sci Div, Los Alamos Nat Lab, 81-83. *Mem:* Am Chem Soc; Am Crystallog Asn; NY Acad Sci. *Res:* Biochemistry of light activated enzymes in the retina; intermolecular interactions in molecular crystals; oscillating chemical reactions. *Mailing Add:* Chem Dept Univ New Haven 300 Orange Ave West Haven CT 06516-1916

**WHEELER, GILBERT VERNON,** CHEMISTRY, SPECTROSCOPY. *Current Pos:* RETIRED. *Personal Data:* b Sour Lake, Tex, July 5, 22; m 42, Glorene Batchelor; c David (deceased) & Margaret. *Educ:* Millikin Univ, BS, 44; Univ Ill, MS, 47. *Honors & Awards:* Distinguished Serv Award, Soc Appl Spectros, 85. *Prof Exp:* Instr physics, Millikin Univ, 43-44; physicist, Res & Develop Dept, Phillips Petrol Co, 48-51, physicist, Atomic Energy Div, 52-53, reactor engr, 51-52, supvr, Spectrochem Lab, 53-63, supvr, Spectros Sect, 63-65; supvr, Spectros Sect, Allied Chem Corp, 65-78; staff scientist, Exxon Nuclear Idaho, 78-81. *Concurrent Pos:* Int del, Soc Appl Spectros, 75, 77 & 79. *Mem:* Soc Appl Spectros (pres, 73). *Res:* Graphite furnaces; inductive coupled plasmas and sputter sources for spectroscopy; isotopic and isotope dilution mass spectrometry. *Mailing Add:* Rte 1 Box 235 A Salmon ID 83467

**WHEELER, GLYNN PEARCE,** BIOCHEMISTRY. *Current Pos:* RETIRED. *Personal Data:* b Milan, Tenn, Oct 13, 19; m 43, Annie F Lester; c William H & Anne P. *Educ:* Vanderbilt Univ, AB, 41; Univ Akron, MS, 47; Vanderbilt Univ, PhD(org chem), 50. *Prof Exp:* Anal chemist, Tenn Coal, Iron & RR Co, Ala, 41; shift supvr, Ala Ord Works, 42; res chemist, B F Goodrich Co, Ohio, 42-46; chemist, Southern Res Inst, 46-48, biochemist, 50-56, head, Intermediary Metab Sect, 56-66, head, Cancer Biochem Div, 66-85. *Mem:* AAAS; Am Chem Soc; Am Asn Cancer Res; Am Soc Biol & Molecular Chem. *Res:* Cancer biochemistry; chemotherapy of cancer; nucleic acids. *Mailing Add:* PO Box 59388 Birmingham AL 35259

**WHEELER, GRANT N,** cell biology, for more information see previous edition

**WHEELER, HAROLD A(LDEN),** radio engineering; deceased, see previous edition for last biography

**WHEELER, HARRY ERNEST,** PHYTOPATHOLOGY. *Current Pos:* PROF PLANT PATH, UNIV KY, 67- *Personal Data:* b West Charleston, Vt, Jan 25, 19; m 44. *Educ:* Univ Vt, BS, 41; La State Univ, MS, 47, PhD(bot), 49. *Prof Exp:* Lab asst bot & bact, Univ Vt, 39-41; asst bot & plant path, La State Univ, 46-49, from asst prof to prof bot & plant path, 49-67. *Concurrent Pos:* Vis investr & res partic, Biol Div, Oak Ridge Nat Lab, 49-50; Guggenheim fel, Biol Labs, Harvard Univ, 58. *Mem:* AAAS; Bot Soc Am; Am Phytopath Soc; Mycol Soc Am. *Res:* Genetics and cytology of fungi; host relations of plant pathogens; electron microscopy. *Mailing Add:* 3293 Bellefonte Dr Lexington KY 40502

**WHEELER, HENRY ORSON,** MEDICINE. *Current Pos:* RETIRED. *Personal Data:* b Los Angeles, Calif, Apr 7, 24; m 47; c 2. *Educ:* Harvard Med Sch, MD, 51. *Prof Exp:* Assoc prof med, Col Physicians & Surgeons, Columbia Univ, 62-68; prof med, Sch Med, Univ Calif, San Diego, 68-86. *Mem:* Fedn Am Socs Exp Biol; AAAS; Am Soc Clin Invest; Am Physiol Soc. *Res:* Hepatic physiology; bile formation; gallbladder; ion transport. *Mailing Add:* 1594 Crespo Dr La Jolla CA 92037

**WHEELER, JAMES DONLAN,** BIOCHEMISTRY, EXERCISE PHYSIOLOGY. *Current Pos:* from instr to assoc prof, 56-74, head dept, 67-74, PROF CHEM, ROCKHURST COL, 74- *Personal Data:* b St Louis, Mo, July 19, 23. *Educ:* St Louis Univ, AB, 47, PhL, 48, MS, 52, STL, 56; Univ Mo, Kansas City, PhD(pharmaceut chem), 65. *Prof Exp:* Instr chem, St Louis Univ High Sch, 50-51. *Mem:* AAAS; Am Chem Soc; Nat Sci Teachers Asn. *Res:* Biochemistry and physiology of the effects of training and exercise; learning theory as applied to freshman chemistry students. *Mailing Add:* Rockhurst Col 1100 Rockhurst Rd Kansas City MO 64110-2561. *E-Mail:* wheeler@vax1.rockhurst.edu

**WHEELER, JAMES ENGLISH,** PATHOLOGY. *Current Pos:* assoc, 70-72, from asst prof to assoc prof, 72-86, PROF PATH & OBSTET & GYNEC, SCH MED, UNIV PA, 86- *Personal Data:* b Durham, NC, May 5, 38; m 66, Jenette Harvey; c John M, Robert T & Elizabeth Z. *Educ:* Harvard Univ, AB, 58; Johns Hopkins Univ, MD, 62. *Prof Exp:* Intern med, Johns Hopkins Univ, 62-63, resident path, 63-66; resident path, State Univ NY Upstate Med Ctr, 69-70. *Concurrent Pos:* USPHS cancer control sr clin trainee, Mem Hosp Cancer & Allied Dis, New York, 66-67. *Mem:* Fel US-Can Acad Path; AAAS; Int Soc Gynec Pathologists; A P Stout Soc Surg Path. *Res:* Surgical and gynecological pathology. *Mailing Add:* Dept Path Hosp Univ Pa Philadelphia PA 19104

**WHEELER, JAMES WILLIAM, JR,** ORGANIC CHEMISTRY. *Current Pos:* from asst prof to assoc prof, 64-71, NIH spec fel, 71-72, PROF CHEM, HOWARD UNIV, 71- *Personal Data:* b Clarksburg, WVa, Oct 2, 34; m 57; c 1. *Educ:* Antioch Col, BS, 57; Stanford Univ, MS, 59, PhD(chem), 62. *Prof*

*Exp:* NSF fel chem, Cornell Univ, 63-64, NIH trainee, 64. *Mem:* AAAS; Am Chem Soc; Am Soc Mass Spectros. *Res:* Chemistry of arthropod and mammalian pheromones, small ring compounds and monoterpenes. *Mailing Add:* Chem Dept Howard Univ Washington DC 20059-9998

**WHEELER, JEANETTE NORRIS,** ENTOMOLOGY. *Current Pos:* RES ASSOC, FLA DEPT AGR, 86- *Personal Data:* b Newton, Iowa, May 21, 18; m 41; c Ralph A. *Educ:* Univ NDak, BA, 39, MS, 56, PhD, 62. *Prof Exp:* From instr biol to asst prof, Univ NDak, 46-65, res assoc, 65-67; res assoc, Desert Res Inst, Univ Nev Syst, Reno, 67-85. *Concurrent Pos:* Res assoc entom, Natural Hist Mus, Los Angeles Co, 76- *Mem:* Entom Soc Am; Sigma Xi. *Res:* Taxonomy and morphology of the ant larvae; desert ants; Western ants. *Mailing Add:* 3338 NE 58th Ave Silver Springs FL 34488

**WHEELER, JOE DARR,** chemical engineering, thermodynamics; deceased, see previous edition for last biography

**WHEELER, JOHN ARCHIBALD,** THEORETICAL PHYSICS. *Current Pos:* dir, Ctr Theoret Physics, Univ Tex, Austin, 76-86, Ashbel Smith prof, 79-86, Roland Blumberg prof, 81-86, EMER PROF PHYSICS, UNIV TEX, AUSTIN, 86-; EMER PROF PHYSICS, PRINCETON UNIV, 76- *Personal Data:* b Jacksonville, Fla, July 9, 11; m 35, Janette Hegner; c Isabel L (Ufford), James E & Alison C (Lahnston). *Educ:* Johns Hopkins Univ, PhD(physics), 33. *Hon Degrees:* ScD, Western Res Univ, 58, Univ NC, 59, Univ Pa, 68, Middlebury Col, 69, Yeshiva Univ, 73, Yale Univ, 74, Univ Md, 77, Gusbarus Adolphus Univ, 81, Cath Univ Am, 82, Univ Newcastle upon Tyme, 83, Princeton Univ, 86, Univ Conn, 89; PhD, Univ Uppsala, 75; LLD, Johns Hopkins Univ, 77; LittD, Drexel Univ, 87. *Honors & Awards:* Morrison Prize, NY Acad Sci, 46; Einstein Prize, Strauss Found, 65; Enrico Fermi Award, AEC, 68; Franklin Medal, Franklin Inst, 69; Nat Medal Sci, 71; J Robert Oppenheimer Mem Prize, 84; Wolf Prize in Physics, 97. *Prof Exp:* Nat Res Coun fel, NY Univ & Copenhagen Univ, 33-35; from asst prof to assoc prof physics, Univ NC, 35-38; asst prof, Princeton Univ, 38-42, physicist, Atomic Energy Proj, 39-42; physicist, Metall Lab, Univ Chicago, 42-43, E I du Pont de Nemours & Co, Del, 43-44; Hanford Eng Works, Wash, 44-45 & Los Alamos Sci Lab, 50-53; from assoc prof to prof, Princeton Univ, 45-66, Joseph Henry prof, 66-76. *Concurrent Pos:* US rep, Cosmic Ray Comn, Int Union Pure & Appl Physics, Poland, 47, vpres, Union, 51-54; Guggenheim fel, Univ Paris & Copenhagen Univ, 49-50; dir, proj Matterhorn, Princeton Univ, 51-53; Lorentz prof, Univ Leiden, 56; mem adv comt, Oak Ridge Nat Lab, 57-67; sci adv, US Senate Del, Conf NATO Parliamentarians, France, 57; adv, Joint Cong Comt Atomic Energy; chmn proj 137, forerunner present proj Jason, Dept Defense Advan, Res Proj Agency, 58; consult, AEC; trustee, Battelle Mem Inst, 59-89; Fulbright prof, Kyoto Univ, 62; chmn, Joint Comt on Hist Theoret Physics in 20th Century, Am Phys Soc-Am Philos Soc, 62-; vis fel, Clare Col, Cambridge Univ, 64; mem, US Gen Adv Comt Arms Control & Disarmament, 69-76; Battelle Mem prof, Univ Wash, 75; II Rabi vis prof, Columbia Univ, 83. *Mem:* Nat Acad Sci; fel Am Phys Soc (pres, 66); Am Philos Soc (vpres, 71-73); Am Math Soc; Am Acad Arts & Sci; Int Astron Union; Danish Royal Acad Sci; NY Acad Sci; Int Acad Philos Sci (vpres, 87-90); fel AAAS. *Res:* Atomic and nuclear physics; scattering theory; fission; nuclear chain reactors; direct electromagnetic interaction between particles; mathematics of semiclassical analysis of physical processes; mu-meson; relativity; space-time and geometrodynamics. *Mailing Add:* Dept Physics Princeton Univ Princeton NJ 08544-0708

**WHEELER, JOHN C,** THEORETICAL CHEMISTRY, CHEMICAL PHYSICS. *Current Pos:* from asst prof to assoc prof 69-81, PROF CHEM, UNIV CALIF, SAN DIEGO, 81- *Personal Data:* b Urbana, Ill, Mar 26, 41; m, Jacqueline Hanson; c Robert. *Educ:* Oberlin Col, BA, 63; Cornell Univ, PhD(theoret chem), 68. *Prof Exp:* NSF fel chem, Harvard Univ, 67-69. *Concurrent Pos:* Alfred P Sloan Found fel, 72-76; John Simon Guggenheim fel, 83-84. *Mem:* Sigma Xi; fel Am Phys Soc; Am Chem Soc; fel AAAS. *Res:* Statistical mechanics and thermodynamics of single and multi component systems, phase transitions and critical phenomena; rigorous bounds in statistical mechanics and thermodynamics; equilibrium polymerization, polymer solutions, micellar solutions and microemulsions; reconstruction of densities from modified moments; surface properties of solids from modified moments. *Mailing Add:* Dept Chem & Biochem 0340 Univ Calif La Jolla CA 92093-0340. *E-Mail:* jwheeler@ucsd.edu

**WHEELER, JOHN CRAIG,** THEORETICAL ASTROPHYSICS. *Current Pos:* from assoc prof to prof, 74-85, dept chmn, 86-90, SAMUEL T & FERN YANAGISAWA REGENTS PROF ASTRON, UNIV TEX, AUSTIN, 85- *Personal Data:* b Glendale, Calif, Apr 5, 43; m 66; c 2. *Educ:* Mass Inst Technol, BS, 65; Univ Colo, PhD(physics), 69. *Honors & Awards:* Fulbright Travel Award, Italy, 91. *Prof Exp:* Res fel, Calif Inst Technol, 69-71; asst prof astron, Harvard Univ, 71-74. *Mem:* Am Astron Soc; Sigma Xi; Int Astron Union. *Res:* High energy and relativistic astrophysics; supernova hydrodynamics; black hole physics; active nuclei of galaxies; compact objects in binary systems. *Mailing Add:* Dept Astron Univ Tex Austin TX 78712

**WHEELER, JOHN OLIVER,** GEOLOGY. *Current Pos:* tech officer, Geol Surv Can, 52-55, geologist, 56-67, head, Cordilleran & Pac Margins Sect, 67-70, chief, Regional & Econ Geol Div, 70-73, dep dir, 73-79, res scientist, 79-90, EMER RES SCIENTIST, GEOL SURV CAN, 90- *Personal Data:* b Mussoorie, India, Dec 19, 24; m 52, Nora Jean Hughes; c Kathleen & Jennifer. *Educ:* Univ BC, BASc, 47; Columbia Univ, PhD(geol), 56. *Honors & Awards:* Queen's Silver Jubilee Medal, 77; Logan Medal, Geol Asn Can, 83. *Prof Exp:* Asst geol, Columbia Univ, 49-51. *Concurrent Pos:* Vis prof, Univ Toronto, 72; gen ed, Geol Can, Decade NAm Geol, Geol Soc Am, 81- *Mem:* Fel Royal Soc Can; fel Geol Soc Am; Geol Asn Can (pres, 70-71); Can

Inst Mining & Metall; Can Geosci Coun (pres, 81). *Res:* Geological mapping in Central and Southern Yukon and Southeastern British Columbia; glacial geology in Southern Yukon; tectonics and structure of southern part of Western Canadian cordillera; recent glacier fluctuations of Selkirk Mountains; geological maps of Canadian cordillera and Canada. *Mailing Add:* Geol Surv Can Pac 101-605 Robson St Vancouver BC V6B 5J3 Can

**WHEELER, KEITH WILSON,** INFORMATION SCIENCE. *Current Pos:* RETIRED. *Personal Data:* b Iowa City, Iowa, Jan 9, 18; m 40; c 2. *Educ:* Knox Col, AB, 38; Purdue Univ, MS, 40, PhD(org chem), 44. *Prof Exp:* Asst, Purdue Univ, 39-43; res chemist, William S Merrell Co, Ohio, 43-56, head, Records Off, 57-64, head, Sci Info Dept, 64-71; sr prin investr, Tech Info Serv Dept, Mead Johnson Res Ctr, 71-80, sr res assoc, Planning Dept, 80-83. *Mem:* Fel AAAS; fel Am Inst Chemists; Sigma Xi; Am Chem Soc; Drug Info Asn. *Res:* Documentation. *Mailing Add:* 115 Wilson Point Dr Hot Springs AR 71913

**WHEELER, KENNETH THEODORE, JR,** BIOPHYSICS, RADIATION BIOLOGY. *Current Pos:* PROF RADIOL & DIR, EXP RADIATION ONCOL, BOWMAN GRAY SCH MED, WAKE FOREST UNIV, 86- *Personal Data:* b Dover, NH, Sept 11, 40; m 80; c Ginger & Trey. *Educ:* Harvard Univ, BA, 62; Wesleyan Univ, MAT, 63; Univ Kans, PhD(radiation biophys), 70. *Hon Degrees:* MA, Brown Univ, 83. *Prof Exp:* Asst radiation biologist, Colo State Univ, 70-72, asst prof radiation biol, 72; from asst prof to assoc prof neurol surg & radiol, Med Sch, Univ Calif, San Francisco, 72-76; assoc prof radiation oncol, Univ Rochester, 76-81; prof radiation med, RI Hosp, Brown Univ, 81-83; prof & sr scientist, Radiation Biophys, Univ Kans, 83-86. *Mem:* Radiation Res Soc; Biophys Soc; Am Asn Cancer Res; Sigma Xi; Int Soc Anal Cytol; Am Soc Ther Radiol Oncol. *Res:* In vivo DNA damage and repair in normal nondividing tissue and tumor tissue; radiation-inducted DNA damage as a detector of hypoxic cells; influence of the hydration layer on induction of DNA damage. *Mailing Add:* Dept Radiation Oncol Bowman Gray Sch Wake Forest Univ Med Ctr Blvd Winston-Salem NC 27157. *Fax:* 910-716-5972

**WHEELER, LEWIS TURNER,** MECHANICS. *Current Pos:* From asst prof to assoc prof, 68-76, PROF MECH ENG & MATH, UNIV HOUSTON, 76- *Personal Data:* b Houston, Tex, Sept 28, 40; m, Cecile A Mendel; c Michael & David. *Educ:* Univ Houston, BS, 63, MS, 64; Calif Inst Technol, PhD, 69. *Concurrent Pos:* NSF grants, 69-71, 72-74 & 74-76; assoc ed, J Applied Mech, 84-91, tech ed, 93- *Mem:* Fel Am Soc Mech Engrs; Soc Indust & Appl Math; Soc Natural Philos; fel Am Acad Mech. *Res:* Mathematical theory of elasticity; wave propagation in solids; forest history. *Mailing Add:* Cullen Col Eng 4800 Calhoun Rd Houston TX 77204-4792. *Fax:* 409-845-6049; *E-Mail:* lwheeler@uh.edu

**WHEELER, MARSHALL RALPH,** ZOOLOGY, GENETICS. *Current Pos:* From instr to prof, 47-77, EMER PROF ZOOL, UNIV TEX, AUSTIN, 77- *Personal Data:* b Carlinville, Ill, Apr 7, 17; m 44, 66; c 3. *Educ:* Baylor Univ, BA, 39; Univ Tex, PhD(genetics), 47. *Concurrent Pos:* Gosney fel, Calif Inst Technol, 49-50. *Mem:* Genetics Soc Am; Am Soc Nat; Soc Study Evolution; Soc Syst Zool; Entom Soc Am. *Res:* Speciation and taxonomy in Drosophila; biology of acalyptrate Diptera; insect cytogenetics. *Mailing Add:* Dept Zool Univ Tex Austin TX 78712-1064

**WHEELER, MARY FANETT,** NUMERICAL ANALYSIS. *Current Pos:* from programmer to instr, 65-73, from asst prof to assoc prof, 73-81, PROF MATH SCI, RICE UNIV, 81- *Personal Data:* b Cuero, Tex, Dec 21, 38; m 63; c 1. *Educ:* Univ Tex, BA, 60, MA, 63, PhD(math), 71. *Prof Exp:* Programmer math, Univ Tex Comput Ctr, 61-65. *Concurrent Pos:* Noah Harding prof, Rice Univ. *Mem:* Am Math Soc; Soc Indust & Appl Math. *Res:* Numerical solution of partial and ordinary differential equations; parallel computation; flow in porous media. *Mailing Add:* Univ Tex TICAM 2-400 Taylor Hall Austin TX 78712

**WHEELER, MICHAEL HUGH,** BIOCHEMISTRY, BIOLOGY. *Current Pos:* RES CHEMIST, NAT COTTON PATH RES LAB, AGR RES SERV, USDA, 72- *Personal Data:* b Rolla, Mo, Nov 13, 40; m 69; c 2. *Educ:* Tex A&M Univ, BS, 65, MS, 70. *Prof Exp:* Microbiologist, Wadley Inst Molecular Biol, 71-72. *Mem:* Am Soc Microbiol; Am Phytopath Soc. *Res:* Biochemical and utrastructural aspects of fungal physiology and morphogenesis; melanogenesis; cell wall composition; nuclear behavior and host-plant, fungal-parasite interactions. *Mailing Add:* 1003 Timm Dr College Station TX 77840

**WHEELER, NED BRENT,** ELECTRO-OPTICS, INTERFEROMETER DESIGN & MEASUREMENTS. *Current Pos:* ENGR, PHILLIPS LAB, HANSCOM AFB, 68- *Personal Data:* b Ogden, Utah, May 4, 36; m 56; c 4. *Educ:* Utah State Univ, BS, 64, MS, 65. *Prof Exp:* Instr elec eng, Weber State Univ, 65-67; engr, Stewart Radiance Lab, 67-68. *Concurrent Pos:* Lectr elec eng, Univ Lowell, 67- *Res:* Development of hardware, techniques and procedures for training astronauts for operating payloads in orbit; infrared radiation measuring sensors and equipment for upper atmosphere measurements; radiometer and photometer design and measurements; author of 20 papers and publications. *Mailing Add:* 19 Porter Rd Chelmsford MA 01824

**WHEELER, NICHOLAS ALLAN,** MATHEMATICAL PHYSICS. *Current Pos:* asst prof, 63-65, assoc prof, 65-77, PROF PHYSICS, REED COL, 77- *Personal Data:* b The Dalles, Ore, May 24, 33; m 62; c 2. *Educ:* Reed Col, BA, 55; Brandeis Univ, PhD(physics), 60. *Prof Exp:* NSF fel, State Univ Utrecht & Europ Orgn Nuclear Res, 60-62; res assoc physics, Brandeis Univ, 62-63. *Res:* Structure and interconnections among physical theories, especially classical and quantum dynamics, classical field theories, statistical mechanics and thermodynamics. *Mailing Add:* Dept Physics Reed Col 3203 SE Woodstock Blvd Portland OR 97202-8199

**WHEELER, ORVILLE EUGENE,** STRUCTURAL MECHANICS, COMPUTER APPLICATIONS. *Current Pos:* dean, 78-87, HERF PROF STRUCT MECH, MEMPHIS STATE UNIV, 87- *Personal Data:* b Memphis, Tenn, Dec 31, 32; m 56; c 1. *Educ:* Vanderbilt Univ, BE, 54; Univ Mo, MSCE, 56; Tex A&M Univ, PhD(civil eng), 66. *Prof Exp:* Stress analyst, Chance Vought Aircraft, 59-60 & Hayes Aircraft Brown Eng, 60-62; sect chief, Marshall Space Flight Ctr, NASA, 62-66; design specialist, Gen Dynamics, 66-72; chief struct engr, Bucyrus Erie Co, 72-78. *Concurrent Pos:* Vis prof, Univ Tex, 67-70, Southern Methodist Univ, 67-72; consult, Wheeler Engrs Inc, 79- *Mem:* Am Soc Civil Engrs; Am Soc Testing Mat; Am Inst Steel Construct; Inst Elec & Electronics Engrs Comput Soc; NY Acad Sci; Asn Comput Mach. *Res:* Structural mechanics particularly computer applications, fracture mechanics, design methodology and fatigue; software engineering and database systems. *Mailing Add:* PO Box 241396 Memphis TN 38124

**WHEELER, RALPH JOHN,** ANALYTICAL CHEMISTRY. *Current Pos:* toxicologist, 86-89, pres, 89-92, VPRES ADMIN, TPS, INC, 92- *Personal Data:* b Devine, Tex, Sept 14, 29; m 57, JoAnn Tobias; c Cyndie (Mitchell). *Educ:* Trinity Univ, San Antonio, Tex, BS, 63. *Prof Exp:* Res chemist, Southwest Res Inst, 63-68; analytical chemist, Gulf South Res Inst, 68-73, mgr analytical chem, 73-74, assoc dir, Life Sci Div, 74-83, dir mkt, Intox Labs, 83-85. *Mem:* Soc Toxicol. *Res:* Carcinogenesis bioassay of pesticides and other environmental chemicals; development of new chromatographic instrumentation and methodology for the analysis of airborne polynuclear arenes; pharmaceutical and chemical safety evaluations through animal research. *Mailing Add:* 4315 Joyce Lane Mt Vernon IN 47620-9624

**WHEELER, RICHARD HUNTING,** FOREST HYDROLOGY, WATERSHED MANAGEMENT. *Current Pos:* CONSULT HYDROLOGIST. *Personal Data:* b Brooklyn, NY, Jan 30, 31; m 54; c 3. *Educ:* Univ Maine, Orono, BS, 53; Colo State Univ, MF, 69. *Prof Exp:* Forester, Savannah River Proj, US Forest Serv-AEC, SC, 57-59; forester, Ouachita Nat Forest, US Forest Serv, 59-62, forester & staff consult water resources, Roosevelt Nat Forest, 62-64 & Arapaho Nat Forest, 64-66, hydrologist & staff consult, Northern Region, Div Soil, Air & Water Mgt, 66-74; forest hydrologist & consult, Food & Agr Orgn UN, Mae Sa Watershed Proj, Chiang Mai, Thailand, 74-77; hydrologist & staff consult, Northern Region, USDA Forest Serv, Missoula, Mont, 77-79; hydrologist & staff consult, Mt Hood Nat Forest, 79-86. *Concurrent Pos:* Consult to UN Environ Prog, Asia & Pac Region, Bangkok, Thailand, 76; fac affil, Sch Forestry, Univ Mont, 78-79. *Mem:* Soc Am Foresters. *Res:* Wildlife water quality and water resource management; general forest management; wetlands; biogeochemical prospecting in forested and non-forested terrain. *Mailing Add:* 5013 SE 22nd St Gresham OR 97080-9125

**WHEELER, ROBERT FRANCIS,** FUNCTIONAL ANALYSIS, GENERAL TOPOLOGY. *Current Pos:* from asst prof to prof, 72-91, PRESIDENTIAL PROF MATH, NORTHERN ILL UNIV, 91- *Personal Data:* b Austin, Tex, Nov 3, 43. *Educ:* Rice Univ, BS, 65; Univ Mo, Columbia, MA, 68, PhD(math), 70. *Prof Exp:* Vis asst prof math, La State Univ, 71-72. *Concurrent Pos:* Math res grants, NSF, 77-78 & 80-81. *Mem:* Am Math Soc; Sigma Xi. *Res:* Measures on topological spaces; the strict topology on spaces of continuous functions; Banach space theory. *Mailing Add:* 18 Golfview Pl DeKalb IL 60115-1855. *E-Mail:* wheeler@math.niu.edu

**WHEELER, ROBERT LEE,** INTEGRAL EQUATIONS, VISCOELASTICITY. *Current Pos:* assoc prof, 80-83, PROF MATH, VA POLYTECH INST & STATE UNIV, 83- *Personal Data:* b Minneapolis, Minn, Jan 17, 44; m 67, Barbara Petersen; c Elliott, Catherine & Brian. *Educ:* Univ Minn, BS, 66; Univ Wis-Madison, MA, 69, PhD(math), 71. *Prof Exp:* From asst prof to assoc prof math, Univ Mo, Columbia, 71-80. *Concurrent Pos:* Vis asst prof math, Iowa State Univ, 74-75. *Mem:* Am Math Soc; Soc Indust & Appl Math; Math Asn Am; Inst Elec & Electronics Engrs. *Res:* Volterra integral equations; integro-partial differential equations; dynamics of viscoelastic structures. *Mailing Add:* Dept Math Va Polytech Inst & State Univ Blacksburg VA 24061-0123. *Fax:* 540-231-5960; *E-Mail:* wheeler@math.vt.edu

**WHEELER, RURIC E,** MATHEMATICAL STATISTICS, NUMBER THEORY & MATHEMATICS EDUCATION. *Current Pos:* from assoc prof to prof math, Samford Univ, 53-65, head, Dept Math & Eng, 55-65, chmn, Div Natural Sci, 65-67, asst to acad dean, 67-68, dean, Howard Col Arts & Sci, 68-70, vpres acad affairs, 70-87, univ prof math, 87-94, RES PROF MATH, SAMFORD UNIV, 94- *Personal Data:* b Clarkson, Ky, Nov 30, 23; div; c 2. *Educ:* Western Ky Univ, AB, 47; Univ Ky, MS, 48, PhD(math, statist), 52. *Honors & Awards:* Humboldt Award, Fed Repub Ger, 86. *Prof Exp:* Instr math & statist, Univ Ky, 48-52; asst prof statist, Fla State Univ, 52-53. *Concurrent Pos:* Consult, Dynamics Dept, Hayes Int Corp, 56-67; trustee, Mid-South Technol Inst, 58-67; dir, NSF vis sci prog, 63-67 & Coop Prog, 65-67; trustee, Gorgas Found, 68-; mem, Am Conf Acad Deans; chmn, Southeastern Sect, Math Asn Am; pres, Am Educ Asn Southern Conf Acad Deans, 80. *Mem:* Am Math Soc; Math Asn Am; Am Asn Higher Educ; Am

Asn Univ Adminr (vpres, 74-76, pres, 76-77). *Res:* Statistical distributions; stochastic processes; mathematics education; author of fifteen college textbooks, two translated into Spanish and one into Chinese. *Mailing Add:* Dept Math Samford Univ Birmingham AL 35229-0001

**WHEELER, RUSSELL LEONARD,** earthquake hazards, tectonics, for more information see previous edition

**WHEELER, SAMUEL CRANE, JR,** astronomy; deceased, see previous edition for last biography

**WHEELER, THOMAS JAY,** MEMBRANE TRANSPORT, METABOLIC REGULATION. *Current Pos:* asst prof, 81-90, ASSOC PROF BIOCHEM, UNIV LOUISVILLE, SCH MED, 90- *Personal Data:* b Schenectady, NY, Apr 12, 51; m 73, Valerie Ives; c Jay & Eric. *Educ:* Mass Inst Technol, BS(chem) & BS(life sci), 73; Brandeis Univ, PhD(biochem), 79. *Prof Exp:* Fel, Cornell Univ, 78-81. *Concurrent Pos:* Vis prof, Univ Med Dent, NJ, R W Johnson Med Sch, 93-94. *Mem:* Am Soc Biochem & Molecular Biol; AAAS; Sigma Xi; Nat Ctr Sci Educ. *Res:* Research on kinetics and regulation of glucose transport; reconstitution of transport proteins in liposomes. *Mailing Add:* Dept Biochem Univ Louisville Sch Med Louisville KY 40292. *Fax:* 502-852-6222; *E-Mail:* tjwhee01@ulkyvm.louisville.edu

**WHEELER, THOMAS NEIL,** PESTICIDES, SYNTHETIC ORGANIC CHEMISTRY. *Current Pos:* res chemist, 75-80, RES SCIENTIST/GROUP LEADER, UNION CARBIDE CORP, 80- *Personal Data:* b Ocala, Fla, Feb 6, 43; m 67. *Educ:* Univ Fla, BS, 64; Cornell Univ, PhD(org chem), 69. *Prof Exp:* From asst prof to assoc prof chem, Fla Technol Univ, 69-75. *Concurrent Pos:* Petrol res fund type B grant, Fla Technol Univ, 70-72. *Mem:* Am Chem Soc. *Res:* Exploratory synthesis of pesticides. *Mailing Add:* 8605 Woodlawn Dr Raleigh NC 27612-2673

**WHEELER, WILLIAM CRAWFORD,** agricultural engineering; deceased, see previous edition for last biography

**WHEELER, WILLIAM HOLLIS,** MATHEMATICAL LOGIC. *Current Pos:* Asst prof, 72-80, ASSOC PROF MATH, IND UNIV, BLOOMINGTON, 80- *Personal Data:* b Akron, Ohio, Feb 10, 46. *Educ:* Vanderbilt Univ, BA, 68; Yale Univ, PhD(math), 72. *Concurrent Pos:* Vis lectr math, Bedford Col, Univ London, 73-74. *Mem:* Am Math Soc; Asn Symbolic Logic. *Res:* Model theory; metamathematics of algebra; applications of logic to algebra. *Mailing Add:* Dept Math Ind Univ Bloomington IN 47405-4301

**WHEELER, WILLIAM JOE,** MEDICINAL CHEMISTRY. *Current Pos:* sr pharmaceut chemist, 70-80, res scientist, 80-93, SR RES SCIENTIST, ELI LILLY & CO, 93- *Personal Data:* b Flora, Ind, Oct 14, 40; m 62; c 2. *Educ:* Purdue Univ, BS, 62; Butler Univ, MS, 66; Purdue Univ, PhD(med chem), 70. *Prof Exp:* Teacher math & sci, Northwestern Sch Corp, Ind, 62-63; anal chemist, Allison Div, Gen Motors Corp, Ind, 63-65; org chemist, Eli Lilly & Co, 65-67; asst, Purdue Univ, Lafayette, 67-68, fel, 68-70. *Mem:* Am Chem Soc; Am Soc Microbiol; Sigma Xi; Int Isotope Soc. *Res:* Synthesis of both stable and radioactive isotopically labeled compounds for drug metabolism studies; new methodology for isotopic labeling. *Mailing Add:* 12030 Emerald BLF Indianapolis IN 46236-8970. *Fax:* 317-276-9159; *E-Mail:* b__wheeler@lilly.com

**WHEELER, WILLIS BOLY,** BEHAVIOR & FATE OF PESTICIDES, ANALYSIS OF PESTICIDES. *Current Pos:* from asst prof to assoc prof, 66-78, chmn, Food Sci & Human Nutrit Dept, 88-91, PROF PESTICIDES, UNIV FLA, 78- *Personal Data:* b Oakland, Calif, June 13, 38; m 64, Heijia Lee; c Patricia & Christopher. *Educ:* George Washington Univ, BS, 61, MS, 63; Pa State Univ, PhD(biochem), 66. *Prof Exp:* Res asst cancer, George Washington Univ, 61-63; instr chem pesticides, Pa State Univ, 64-66. *Concurrent Pos:* Prin environ toxicologist, IPA, USDA-CSRS. *Mem:* AAAS; Am Chem Soc; Sigma Xi. *Res:* Disappearance of chemical from plant and plant environment; behavior of pesticides in soil ecosystems; movement through soils; registration of minor-use pesticides; metabolism; residue detection methodology; bound residues; benefits of pesticides. *Mailing Add:* 4801 Hampden Lane No 702 Bethesda MD 20814

**WHEELESS, LEON LUM, JR,** ANALYTICAL CYTOLOGY. *Current Pos:* assoc prof, Univ Rochester, 71-81, prof elec eng, 81-92, PROF PATH & LAB MED, MED CTR, UNIV ROCHESTER, 81-, DIR, ANALYTICAL CYTOL UNIT, DEPT PATH, 75-, PROF UROL, 87-, PROF ONCOL, 96- *Personal Data:* b Jackson, Miss, Nov 6, 35; m 57, Waldine Jones; c Susan, Diane & Linda. *Educ:* Mass Inst Technol, SB, 58; Univ Rochester, MS, 62, PhD(elec eng), 65. *Honors & Awards:* Inst Elec & Electronics Engrs Centennial Medal, 84. *Prof Exp:* Sect head, Electronics Dept, Bausch & Lomb, Inc, 58-61, tech specialist, Biophys Dept, 61-65, res scientist, Cent Res Lab, 65-68, sr res scientist, Biomed Res Dept, Ana Systs Div, 68-69, dir biomed res, 69-71. *Mem:* Inst Elec & Electronics Engrs; Am Soc Cytol; Int Soc Anal Cytol; Am Urol Asn. *Res:* Biomedical instrumentation; systems for automatic recognition of abnormal cells; automated cytopathology instrumentation; pattern recognition; image and flow cytometry; bladder cancer. *Mailing Add:* Dept Path Univ Rochester Med Ctr Rochester NY 14642. *Fax:* 716-273-1027; *E-Mail:* wheeless@acu.pathology.rochester.edu

**WHEELIS, MARK LEWIS,** MICROBIOLOGY, GENETICS. *Current Pos:* asst prof, 70-76, ASSOC PROF BACT, COL LETT & SCI, UNIV CALIF, DAVIS, 76- *Personal Data:* b Chelsea, Mass, Jan 8, 44; m 65; c 2. *Educ:* Univ Calif, Berkeley, AB, 65, MA, 67, PhD(bact), 69. *Prof Exp:* Lab technician bact, Univ Calif, Berkeley, 65-66; res assoc, Univ Ill, Urbana-Champaign, 69-70. *Concurrent Pos:* USPHS res grant, Univ Calif, Davis, 72-73. *Mem:* Am Soc Microbiol; Genetics Soc Am; Brit Soc Gen Microbiol; Am Soc Biol Chemists. *Res:* Bacterial metabolism; dissimilation of aromatic acids. *Mailing Add:* Dept Microbiol Univ Calif Davis CA 95616-5200

**WHEELOCK, EARLE FREDERICK,** ONCOLOGY. *Current Pos:* PROF PATH, HAHNEMANN MED COL, 81- *Personal Data:* b New York, NY, Feb 19, 27; m 55; c 3. *Educ:* Mass Inst Technol, BS, 50; Columbia Univ, MD, 55; Rockefeller Inst, PhD(biol), 61. *Prof Exp:* Intern med, Clins, Univ Chicago, 55-56; resident, Strong Mem Hosp, Rochester, NY, 56-57; fel biol & virol, Rockefeller Inst, 57-61; from asst prof to assoc prof prev med, Western Res Univ, Sch Med, 61-71; prof microbiol, Jefferson Med Col, 71-81. *Concurrent Pos:* USPHS res career develop award, 66-71. *Mem:* Am Soc Clin Invest; Am Asn Immunol; Soc Exp Biol & Med; Am Soc Microbiol; Am Asn Cancer Res. *Res:* Animal virology; mechanism of host resistance to viral infections; role of leucocytes and interferon in human viral infections; effect of nontumor viruses on virus-induced leukemia in mice; suppression of leukemia viral infections; tumor dormant states in animals and man. *Mailing Add:* Dept Path Allegheny Univ 3300 Henry Ave Philadelphia PA 19129

**WHEELOCK, KENNETH STEVEN,** PETROLEUM & INORGANIC CHEMISTRY, POLYMER CHEMISTRY PLASTICS. *Current Pos:* PATENT AGENT, GEN ELEC PLASTICS, PITTSFIELD, MASS, 93- *Personal Data:* b Kansas City, Mo, Sept 18, 43; m 72, Mary C Percy; c Michael Steven & Celeste Marie. *Educ:* Univ Mo, Kansas City, BS, 65; Tulane Univ, PhD(chem), 70. *Honors & Awards:* Award, Am Chem Soc, 65. *Prof Exp:* Chemist, Exxon Res & Develop Labs, 69-72, res chemist, 72-77, staff chemist, 77-83, sr staff chemist, 83-87; assoc prof physics, La State Univ, 87; sr patent chemist, Phillips Petrol, Bartleville, Okla, 87-89, sr res chemist, 89-91. *Concurrent Pos:* Consult, Dept Chem, Tulane Univ, 70- *Mem:* Am Chem Soc; AAAS; NY Acad Sci; Sigma Xi; fel Am Inst Chemists; Licensing Exec Soc; Asn Univ Technol Mgrs. *Res:* Theoretical aspects of transition metal chemistry and catalysis; low valent complexes of transition metals with unsaturated ligands; quantum chemistry of catalysis; theory of finely divided metals; perovskite catalysts, fluid catalytic cracking, silicone chemistry and plastics. *Mailing Add:* Gen Elec Plastics 1 Plastics Ave Pittsfield MA 01201. *Fax:* 413-448-7601; *E-Mail:* steve.wheelock@gep.ge.com

**WHEELOCK, THOMAS DAVID,** CHEMICAL ENGINEERING. *Current Pos:* from instr to prof, 57-94, UNIV PROF CHEM ENG, IOWA STATE UNIV, 94- *Personal Data:* b Chihuahua, Mex, May 15, 25; m 52, Edra Smith; c David & Ann. *Educ:* Iowa State Univ, BS, 49, PhD(chem eng), 58. *Prof Exp:* Sales engr, Chem Equip Co Calif, 49-51; chem engr, Westvaco Chlor-Alkali Div, Food Mach & Chem Corp, 51-54. *Concurrent Pos:* Masua hon lectr, 80-81. *Mem:* Am Chem Soc; Am Soc Eng Educ; Soc Mining Engrs; Sigma Xi; fel Am Inst Chem Engrs. *Res:* Process thermodynamics and kinetics; fluidized bed reactors; coal and other mineral utilization processes. *Mailing Add:* Dept Chem Eng Iowa State Univ Ames IA 50011. *Fax:* 515-294-2689; *E-Mail:* ikedson@iastate.edu

**WHEELON, ALBERT DEWELL,** THEORETICAL PHYSICS. *Current Pos:* RETIRED. *Personal Data:* b Moline, Ill, Jan 18, 29; m 84, Cicely Evans; c 2. *Educ:* Stanford Univ, BS, 49; Mass Inst Technol, PhD(theoret physics), 52. *Honors & Awards:* US Distinguished Intel Medal, 66; von Karmen Award, Am Inst Aeronaut & Astronaut, 86, Goddard Astronaut Award, 97; Baker Medal, 93; R V Jones Medal, 94. *Prof Exp:* Asst, Res Lab Electronics, Mass Inst Technol, 51-52; sr mem tech staff, Ramo-Wooldridge Corp, 53-62; dep dir sci & technol, Cent Intel Agency, 62-66; vpres eng, Hughes Aircraft Co, 66-70, sr vpres & pres Space & Commun Group, 70-86, chmn, bd dirs & chief exec officer, 86-88. *Concurrent Pos:* Defense Sci Bd, 68-77; mem, Pres Comn Space Shuttle Challenger Accident, 86-; vis prof, Mass Inst Technol, 89; trustee, Calif Inst Technol, Rand Corp. *Mem:* Nat Acad Eng; Am Phys Soc; fel Inst Elec & Electronics Engrs; fel Am Inst Aeronaut & Astronaut. *Res:* Meson theory; turbulence theory; analysis of ballistic missile and space systems; electromagnetic propagation; author of numerous publications. *Mailing Add:* 181 Sheffield Dr Montecito CA 93108

**WHEELWRIGHT, EARL J,** NUCLEAR CHEMISTRY. *Current Pos:* res assoc, 65-77, SR STAFF SCIENTIST, PAC NW NAT LAB, BATTELLE MEM INST, 77- *Personal Data:* b Rexburg, Idaho, Mar 26, 28; m 47, Rayola V Howell; c Dean A, Carolyn, Ross W, Scott E, Paul D & Marie. *Educ:* Brigham Young Univ, BS, 50; Iowa State Univ, PhD, 55. *Honors & Awards:* Glenn T Seaborg Actinide Separations Award, 93. *Prof Exp:* Chemist, Hanford Atomic Prod Oper, Gen Elec Co, 55-60, sr scientist, 60-64. *Mem:* Fel Am Nuclear Soc. *Res:* Separation chemistry, solvent extraction, ion exchange and chelation chemistry as applied to lanthanides, actinides and fission products; design and operation of hot cell process equipment for pilot-plant-scale demonstration of separation/purification processes. *Mailing Add:* 1416 Sunset Richland WA 99352

**WHEELWRIGHT, NATHANIEL T,** ECOLOGY. *Current Pos:* ASSOC PROF ECOL, ORNITH & BEHAV ETHOLOGY, DEPT BIOL, BOWDOIN COL, 86- *Personal Data:* b Pittsfield, Mass, Feb 25, 52. *Educ:* Yale Univ, BS, 75; Univ Wash, Seattle, PhD(zool), 82. *Prof Exp:* Carr postdoctoral fel, Univ Fla, 82-84; vis asst prof ecol, Cornell Univ, 84-86. *Concurrent Pos:* Fulbright scholar, Cent Am, 89-90 & Univ Botswana, 94-95; Coun, Asn Field Ornithologists, 91-94. *Mailing Add:* Dept Biol Bowdoin Col Brunswick ME 04111. *Fax:* 207-725-3405

**WHELAN, CHRISTOPHER JOHN,** PLANT ANIMAL INTERACTIONS, AVIAN ECOLOGY. *Current Pos:* EMILY RODGERS DAVIS CHAIR ECOL, MORTON ARBORETUM, 89- *Personal Data:* b La Crosse, Wis, Nov 3, 58; m 92, Anna Chorobik; c Cara Alexa. *Educ:* Univ Wis, BS, 82; Dartmouth Col, PhD(biol sci), 87. *Prof Exp:* Res assoc, Univ Ill, 87-88. *Concurrent Pos:* Prin invest, Am Mus Nat Hist, 83 & 91, US Forest Serv, 84, Joyce Found, 90, Chevron USA, Inc, 90 & 91, Monsanto Corp, 91; adj asst prof biol, Univ Ill, 91-, vis asst prof, 93; consult, Fermilab. *Mem:* Am Ornithol Union; Ecol Soc Am; Cooper Ornithol Soc; AAAS; Soc Conserv Biol; Nat Areas Asn. *Res:* Plant animal interactions; various ways plants influence the behavioral ecology of passerine birds; examined the ecological and evolutionary consequences of bird behavior on plant life histories. *Mailing Add:* Morton Arboretum Lisle IL 60532. *Fax:* 630-712-2433; *E-Mail:* chrwhelen@aol.com

**WHELAN, DAVID ARTHUR,** ELECTROMAGNETIC RADIATION, LASER PHYSICS PHENOMENA. *Current Pos:* actg dir, Sensor Technol Off, 95-96, DIR, TACTICAL OFF, DEFENSE ADVAN RES PROJS AGENCY, 96- *Educ:* Univ Calif, BA, 77, MS, 78, PhD(physics), 83. *Prof Exp:* Eng specialist, B2 Div, Northrop Corp, 83-85; res physicist, Lawrence Livermore Nat Lab, 85-88 & 94-95; prog mgr, Radar Systs Group, Hughes, 88-94. *Mem:* Am Phys Soc; Inst Elec & Electronics Engrs; Am Inst Aeronaut & Astronaut. *Res:* Patentee in antenna and low observable technology; scientific x-ray imaging instruments; ultra fast pulse generators. *Mailing Add:* ARPA 3701 N Fairfax Dr Arlington VA 22203-1714

**WHELAN, ELIZABETH M,** EPIDEMIOLOGY, PUBLIC HEALTH. *Current Pos:* exec dir, 80-89, PRES, AM COUN SCI & HEALTH, 89- *Personal Data:* b New York, NY, Dec 4, 43; m 71, Stephen T; c Christine. *Educ:* Conn Col, BA, 65; Yale Univ, MPH, 67; Harvard Univ, MS, 68, ScD, 71. *Honors & Awards:* Early Career Award, Am Pub Health Asn, 82; Walter C Alvarez Award, Am Med Writers Asn, 86; Homer Calver Award, Am Pub Health Asn, Environ Div, 92; Epic Award, Am Inst Chemists, 96. *Prof Exp:* Res consult, Pop Coun, Tech Assistance Div, NY, 72-76; res assoc, Harvard Sch Pub Health, 75-80. *Concurrent Pos:* Commentator, Cable News Network, 80-81. *Mem:* Am Pub Health Asn; Nutrit Today Soc; Am Inst Nutrit; Am Med Writers Asn; Pop Asn Am; Am Cancer Soc. *Res:* Epidemiology, public health, demography and biostatistics; author or coauthor of over 100 publications. *Mailing Add:* Am Coun Sci & Health 1995 Broadway 2nd Floor New York NY 10023. *Fax:* 212-362-4919

**WHELAN, JAMES ARTHUR,** ECONOMIC GEOLOGY. *Current Pos:* PROF GEOL & GEOPHYS SCI, UNIV UTAH, 71- *Personal Data:* b Steele Co, Minn, Sept 25, 28; m 50; c 3. *Educ:* Univ Minn, BMinE, 49, MS, 56, PhD, 59. *Prof Exp:* Instr mining eng, Univ Minn, 57-59; from asst prof to prof mineral, Univ Utah, 59-68, prof mining & geol eng, 68-69; dep off in chg construct, US Navy, Marianas, 69-71. *Mem:* Geol Soc Am. *Res:* Geochemistry; mineralogy. *Mailing Add:* 2312 Sunnyside Ave Salt Lake City UT 84108

**WHELAN, JEAN KING,** ORGANIC GEOCHEMISTRY. *Current Pos:* res assoc, 75-78, res specialist, 78-83, SR RES SPECIALIST, WOODS HOLE OCEANOL INST, 83- *Personal Data:* b Reno, Nev, Nov 12, 39; wid. *Educ:* Univ Calif, Davis, BS, 61; Mass Inst Technol, PhD(org chem), 65. *Prof Exp:* NIH fel chem, Brandeis Univ, 65-67; from asst prof to assoc prof, Fairleigh Dickinson Univ, 67-75. *Concurrent Pos:* Shipboard org chemist, Deep Sea Drilling Proj; mgt counr, Global Basins Res Network. *Mem:* Am Asn Petrol Geologists; Geol Soc Am; AAAS; Am Chem Soc; Sigma Xi. *Res:* Using organic geochemistry to quantitate subsurface processes; petroleum genesis and migration; gas generation and migralion; development of new organic geochemical methods. *Mailing Add:* Dept Chem Fye Bldg Woods Hole Oceanog Inst Woods Hole MA 02543. *Fax:* 508-457-2164; *E-Mail:* jwhelan@whoi.edu

**WHELAN, JOHN MICHAEL,** POLYMER CHEMISTRY. *Current Pos:* RETIRED. *Personal Data:* b Lyndhurst, NJ, Sept 12, 21; m 43, Helen C Keckeisen; c Kathleen, Dennis & Kerry. *Educ:* Stevens Inst Technol, ME, 41, MS, 43; Polytech Inst Brooklyn, PhD(org chem), 59. *Prof Exp:* Res chemist, Union Carbide Corp, 41-53, group leader, 53-55, sect head, 55-63, asst dir res & develop, 63-72, res assoc, 72-83. *Mem:* Am Chem Soc. *Res:* Synthetic polymers; organometallic polymerization catalysts. *Mailing Add:* 38 Colony Ct Murray Hill NJ 07974

**WHELAN, THOMAS, III,** MARINE GEOCHEMISTRY. *Current Pos:* PRES, CARBON SYSTS, INC, 79- & WHELAN & ASSOC INC. *Personal Data:* b Houston, Tex, Dec 21, 44; m 68; c 1. *Educ:* Austin Col, BA, 66; Univ Tex, Austin, MA, 68; Tex A&M Univ, PhD(chem oceanog), 71. *Prof Exp:* Asst prof marine sci, Coastal Studies Inst, La State Univ, Baton Rouge, 71-75, assoc prof marine sci, 75-79. *Mem:* Geochem Soc; AAAS; Am Asn Plant Physiologists; Sigma Xi. *Res:* Organic geochemistry of marine environments; geochemistry of natural gases; effects of oil in coastal environment. *Mailing Add:* On Site Analytical PO Box 720478 Houston TX 77272-0478

**WHELAN, WILLIAM JOSEPH,** BIOCHEMISTRY. *Current Pos:* prof & chmn dept, 67-91, PROF BIOCHEM & MOLECULAR BIOL, SCH MED, UNIV MIAMI, 91- *Personal Data:* b Salford, UK, Nov 14, 24; wid. *Educ:* Univ Birmingham, BSc, 45, PhD, 48, DSc(org chem), 55. *Honors & Awards:* Carl Lucas Alsberg Lectr, 67; Ciba Medal & Lectr, 69; Diplome d'Honneur, Fedn Europ Biochem Socs, 74; Saare Medal, Asn Cereal Res, 79. *Prof Exp:* Sr lectr, Univ Col NWales, 48-55; sr mem, Lister Inst Prev Med, London, Eng, 56-64; prof biochem, Royal Free Hosp Sch Med, Univ London, 64-67.

*Concurrent Pos:* Secy-gen, Fedn Europ Biochem Socs, 65-67 & Pan-Am Asn Biochem Socs, 69-72; mem, Physiol Chem Study Sect, NIH, 71-75, chmn, 73-75; gen-secy, Int Union Biochem, 73-83; ed-in-chief, Trends Biochem Sci, 76-78; chmn, Comt Genetic Exp, 77-81; mem exec bd, Int Coun Sci Unions, 78-80; ed-in-chief, J Bio Essays, 84-89; pres, Portland Press Inc, 94- *Mem:* Brit Biochem Soc; Am Soc Biol Chem; Am Chem Soc; Sigma Xi; Am Soc Cell Biol; fel AAAS; fel Royal Soc London; hon mem Royal Col Physicians London. *Res:* Glycogen and starch, structure and metabolism. *Mailing Add:* Dept Biochem & Molecular Biol 7823 Univ Miami Sch Med PO Box 016129 Miami FL 33101-6129. *Fax:* 305-324-5665; *E-Mail:* wwhelan@mednet.med. miami.edu

**WHELAN, WILLIAM PAUL, JR,** ORGANIC POLYMER CHEMISTRY. *Current Pos:* RETIRED. *Personal Data:* b Brooklyn, NY, Sept 22, 23; wid; c 3. *Educ:* Holy Cross Col, AB, 43, MS, 47; Columbia Univ, PhD(chem), 52. *Prof Exp:* Res scientist, Uniroyal Inc, World Hq, Middlebury, 52-66, sr res scientist, Corp Res & Develop, 66-85. *Mem:* Am Chem Soc; Sigma Xi. *Res:* Flame and smoke inhibition in polymers; rocket motor insulators; rubber and plastic product formulation; cellular products; polyurethane synthesis; vinyl polymerization; blowing agents; ablatives; organic synthesis; reaction mechanisms; solvolysis theory; crystallization kinetics; photopolymers; low profile additives. *Mailing Add:* 27 Orchard Lane Woodbury CT 06798

**WHELLY, SANDRA MARIE,** BIOCHEMISTRY. *Current Pos:* res asst prof, 77-81, ASST PROF BIOCHEM, TEX TECH UNIV HEALTH SCI CTR, 81- *Personal Data:* b Fall River, Mass, Aug 8, 45. *Educ:* Salve Regina Col, BA, 68; Univ Nebr, PhD(biochem), 73. *Prof Exp:* Res asst chem, Salve Regina Col, 67-68; res asst microbiol, Peter Bent Brigham Hosp, 68-69; NIH trainee biochem, Eppley Inst, Col Med, Univ Nebr, 69-72, grad res asst, 72- 73; fel, Temple Univ, Sch Med, 74-76, res assoc 76-77. *Concurrent Pos:* Res assoc grant, Am Cancer Soc, 74-75; NIH res grant, Child Health & Develop, 81-84 & 85-89. *Res:* Transcriptional and translational control mechanisms of cellular proliferation; biochemistry of hormone action. *Mailing Add:* Dept Cell Biol & Biochem Health Sci Ctr Tex Tech Univ Lubbock TX 79430

**WHELPDALE, DOUGLAS MURRAY,** BIOGEOCHEMICAL CYCLING, ENVIRONMENTAL MONITORING. *Current Pos:* Res scientist, 70-85, SR RES SCIENTIST, ENVIRON CAN, ATMOSPHERIC ENVIRON SERV, 85-; PROF, UNIV TORONTO, 85- *Personal Data:* b Toronto, Ont, Oct 21, 42; m 66; c 2. *Educ:* Univ Toronto, BSc, 64, MSc, 67, PhD(physics), 70. *Concurrent Pos:* NATO vis fel, Joham Wolfgang Goethe Univ, 73; vis sr scientist, Norweg Int Air Res, 81. *Mem:* Fel Royal Soc Can. *Res:* Investigation of large-scale transport and deposition of pollutants; sulfur and nitrogen global environmental air monitoring; acid rain research and monitoring. *Mailing Add:* 4905 Dufferin St Downsview ON M3H 5T4 Can. *Fax:* 416-739-4288

**WHELTON, ANDREW,** MEDICINE. *Current Pos:* ASSOC PROF MED, SCH MED, JOHNS HOPKINS UNIV, 76- *Personal Data:* b Cork, Ireland, Oct 6, 40; m 74; c 2. *Educ:* Nat Univ Ireland, MB & MD, 63, FCP, 75, FACP, 83. *Prof Exp:* Mem staff, Renal Metal Unit, Walter Reed Army Inst Res, 67-68. *Concurrent Pos:* Consult renal dis, USPHS Hosp, Baltimore, 71-, surgeon gen, USAF, Washington, DC, 71- & Union Mem Hosp, 73-; consult med, Dept Obstet & Gynec, Johns Hopkins Univ, 75- *Mem:* Int Soc Nephrology; AMA; Am Soc Nephrology; Am Fedn Clin Res; fel Am Col Clin Pharmacol (pres elect); fel Am Col Physicians. *Res:* Drug metabolism in renal failure; drug nephrotoxicity; acute renal failure. *Mailing Add:* Med Nephrol Div Johns Hopkins Univ Sch Med 720 Rutland Ave Baltimore MD 21205-2109

**WHELTON, BARTLETT DAVID,** MEDICINAL CHEMISTRY, INTERMEDIARY METABOLISM. *Current Pos:* from asst prof to assoc prof, 74-85, PROF MED CHEM, EASTERN WASH UNIV, 85- *Personal Data:* b San Francisco, Calif, Dec 2, 41. *Educ:* Univ San Francisco, BS, 63; Univ Wash, PhD(med chem), 69. *Prof Exp:* Fel med chem, Univ Alta, 69-71; asst prof med chem, Univ of the Pac, 71-74. *Concurrent Pos:* Fac res fel, Argonne Nat Lab, 82-83. *Mem:* Am Chem Soc; Sigma Xi. *Res:* Synthesis of antineoplastic agents; heavy metal toxicology; owl distribution and behavior. *Mailing Add:* Dept Chem & Biochem MS 74 Eastern Wash Univ 526 Fifth St Cheney WA 99004-2431

**WHEREAT, ARTHUR FINCH,** CARDIOVASCULAR DISEASES. *Current Pos:* assoc in biochem, 56-60, asst prof med, 60-68, ASSOC PROF MED, SCH MED, UNIV PA, 68-; CHIEF OF STAFF, VET ADMIN HOSP, PHILADELPHIA, 76- *Personal Data:* b New York, NY, June 30, 27; m 53; c 3. *Educ:* Williams Col, BA, 47; Univ Pa, MD, 51. *Prof Exp:* Intern & med resident internal med, Hosp Univ Pa, 51-54, fel cardiol, 54-56. *Concurrent Pos:* Mem, Coun Arteriosclerosis, Am Heart Asn, 64 & Coun Clin Cardiol, 69. *Mem:* Fel Am Col Physicians; fel Am Col Cardiol; Am Soc Biol Chemists; Am Physiol Soc; Am Heart Asn. *Res:* Biochemical changes in arterial wall associated with atherogenesis; biochemical changes in heart muscle during hypoxia and ischemia. *Mailing Add:* Univ Pa Hosp 3400 Spruce St Philadelphia PA 19104-4219

**WHERRETT, JOHN ROSS,** NEUROLOGY, NEUROCHEMISTRY. *Current Pos:* RETIRED. *Personal Data:* b Regina, Sask, Nov 28, 30; m 58; Doreen Johnson; c Christopher & Brian. *Educ:* Queen's Univ, MDCM, 55; Royal Col Physicians & Surgeons, FRCP, 63; Univ London, PhD(biochem), 66. *Prof Exp:* Clin teacher, Univ Toronto, 63-65, assoc, 65-68, from asst prof to prof & dir, Neurol Prog Med, 68-89, actg dir, Inst Med Sci, 91- *Concurrent Pos:* Travelling fel, R S McLaughlin Found, 58-60; res fel, Am Col Physicians, 63-66; scholar acad med, Markle Found, 63-68; staff physician, Toronto Gen Hosp, 63-; mem & chmn, Grant Comt Neurosci, Med Res Coun Can, 67-72; consult neurol, Clarke Inst Psychiat, Univ Toronto, 69-75; mem, Inst Med Sci, Univ Toronto, 69-; mem & chmn, Comt Fel Review, Ont Ministry Health, 71-77; mem, Bd & Med Res Comt, Ont Heart Found, 77-82; mem bd & chmn adv bd, Parkinson Found Can, 84- *Mem:* Am Acad Neurol; Am Neurol Asn; Am Soc Neurochem; Can Neurol Soc (pres, 78-79); Can Soc Clin Invest. *Res:* Investigation of the structure and metabolism of glycosphingolipids and phospholipids and of the disturbances occurring in inherited degenerative and in inflammatory diseases of the nervous system. *Mailing Add:* Toronto Hosp 200 Elizabeth St Toronto ON M5G 2C4 Can. *E-Mail:* j.wherrett@utoronto.ca

**WHETSEL, KERMIT BAZIL,** MOLECULAR SPECTROSCOPY, COLOR MEASUREMENT. *Current Pos:* RETIRED. *Personal Data:* b Tenn, Dec 9, 23; m 49; c 4. *Educ:* ETenn State Univ, BS, 43; Univ Tenn, MS, 47, PhD(chem), 50. *Prof Exp:* From chemist to sr chemist, Tenn Eastman Co Div, Eastman Kodak Co, 50-66, develop assoc, 66-73, sr develop assoc 73-81, develop fel, 81-86. *Concurrent Pos:* Nat Acad Sci-Nat Res Coun resident res assoc, US Naval Res Lab, 60-61. *Mem:* Am Chem Soc; Soc Appl Spectros; Coblentz Soc; fel Am Soc Testing & Mat; Sigma Xi; Am Inst Chemists. *Res:* Instrumental analysis of organic compounds; correlation of absorption spectra with structure; solvent effects on infrared spectra; spectroscopic study of hydrogen bonded complexes. *Mailing Add:* 1501 Dobyns Dr Kingsport TN 37664-2263

**WHETTEN, JOHN T,** GEOLOGY, OCEANOGRAPHY. *Current Pos:* asst div leader, Los Alamos Nat Lab, 80-81, dep div leader, 81-84, div leader, Earth & Space Sci Div, 84-86, ASSOC DIR, ENERGY & RES APPLN, LOS ALAMOS NAT LAB, 86- *Personal Data:* b Willimantic, Conn, Mar 16, 35; m 60; c 3. *Educ:* Princeton Univ, AB, 57; Univ Calif, Berkeley, MA, 59; Princeton Univ, PhD(geol), 62. *Prof Exp:* Fulbright fel, Australia & NZ, 62-63; res instr oceanog, Univ Wash, 63-64, res asst prof, 64-65, from asst prof to prof geol, 65-80, assoc dean, Grad Sch, 68-69, chmn dept, 69-74; geologist, US Geol Surv, Seattle, 75-80. *Mem:* AAAS; Geol Soc Am; Soc Econ Paleontologists & Mineralogists. *Res:* Sedimentology; sedimentary petrology; marine geology. *Mailing Add:* 154 Piedra Loop Los Alamos NM 87544

**WHETTEN, NATHAN REY,** PHYSICS. *Current Pos:* TECH DIR, AM VACUUM SOC, 92- *Personal Data:* b Provo, Utah, Aug 11, 28; m 53; Virginia Wheting; c Timothy J, Nathan L & Kathryn A. *Educ:* Yale Univ, BS, 49, MS, 50, PhD(physics), 53. *Prof Exp:* Physicist, Res Lab, Gen Elec Co, 53-92. *Concurrent Pos:* Vis lectr, Union Col, 64-65, adj prof, 67- *Mem:* Am Phys Soc; hon life mem Am Vacuum Soc (pres-elect, 75, pres, 76, treas, 84-). *Res:* Cosmic rays; secondary electron emission; surface physics; high vacuum; mass spectrometry; electron physics; medical physics. *Mailing Add:* 159 Eastside Dr Ballston Lake NY 12019

**WHETTEN, ROBERT LLOYD,** ATOMIC & MOLECULAR CLUSTERS. *Current Pos:* PROF PHYSICS, GEORGIA INST TECHNOL, 93- *Personal Data:* b Mesa, Ariz, Oct 15, 59. *Educ:* Weber State Col, BA, 80; Cornell Univ, MS, 82, PhD(phys chem), 84. *Prof Exp:* Res fel, NSF, 81-84 & Exxon Res & Eng Co, 84-85; asst prof chem & biochem, Univ Calif, Los Angeles, 85-93. *Mem:* Am Chem Soc; Am Phys Soc. *Res:* Investigation of metal-atom and other clusters by laser and radiofrequency spectroscopy and chemical kinetics; spectroscopy of molecular excited states; quantum and semiclassical theory of molecular states; molecular interactions with electromagnetic fields. *Mailing Add:* Sch Physics Georgia Inst Technol Atlanta GA 30332-0430

**WHICKER, DONALD,** STRUCTURAL ANALYSIS. *Current Pos:* Assoc sr res engr, 73-79, sr res engr, 79-80, STAFF RES ENGR, GEN MOTORS RES LABS, 80- *Personal Data:* b Noblesville, Ind, Nov 23, 44. *Educ:* Purdue Univ, BS, 67, MS, 68, PhD(eng), 73. *Mem:* Am Soc Mech Engrs; Soc Automotive Engrs. *Res:* Lubrication; tire traction; tire rolling resistance; development and application of analytical techniques for engine structural analysis and design. *Mailing Add:* 5232 Babbit Dr Troy MI 48098

**WHICKER, FLOYD WARD,** radiation biology, ecology, for more information see previous edition

**WHICKER, LAWRENCE R,** MICROWAVE PHYSICS, ELECTROMAGNETISM. *Current Pos:* MGR, GAAS PROGS, WESTINGHOUSE ELEC CO, BALTIMORE, MD. *Personal Data:* b Bristol, Va, Oct 3, 34; m 58; c 2. *Educ:* Univ Tenn, BS, 57, MS, 58; Purdue Univ, PhD(elec eng), 64. *Prof Exp:* Teaching asst, Univ Tenn, 58; sr engr, Microwave Electronics Div, Sperry Rand Corp, 58-61; fel engr, Surface Div, Westinghouse Elec Corp, 64-65, assoc dir appl physics, 65-66, mgr, Microwave Physics Group, Aerospace Div, 66-68, adv engr, Microwave & Antenna Group, 68-69; head, Microwave Tech Br, Electronics Div, Val Res Lab, 69- *Concurrent Pos:* Lectr, Univ Md, 64-; vpres res & develop, I-Tel, Inc, 67-68. *Mem:* Fel Inst Elec & Electronics Engrs. *Res:* Millimeter-coupled mode techniques; microwave filters; electromagnetic propagation studies; microwave solid state techniques, including microwave latching phasers, acoustics and integrated circuits. *Mailing Add:* 1218 Balfour Dr Arnold MD 21012

**WHIDBY, JERRY FRANK,** ANALYTICAL CHEMISTRY, PHYSICAL CHEMISTRY. *Current Pos:* res assoc analytical chem, Philip Morris Inc, 72-75, res chemist, 75-80, sr scientist, 80-81, MGR RES & DEVELOP, PHILIP MORRIS INC, 81- *Personal Data:* b Baltimore, Md, Oct 29, 43; m

67; c 3. *Educ:* NGa Col, BS, 65; Univ Ga, PhD(analytical chem), 70. *Prof Exp:* Res chemist, Gen Elec Co, Mo, 71-72. *Mem:* Am Chem Soc. *Res:* Proton exchange kinetics; environmental research-sensors; kinetics of filter action. *Mailing Add:* Philip Morris USA Res Ctr PO Box 26583 Richmond VA 23261-6583

**WHIDDEN, STANLEY JOHN,** DIVING PHYSIOLOGY & MEDICINE, FORENSIC MEDICINE. *Current Pos:* CONSULT, US ARMY CTR HEALTH PROM & PREV MED, ABERDEEN, MD, 93- *Personal Data:* b Bayshore, NY, Oct 10, 47; m 87, Jan Venable. *Educ:* Southeastern La Univ, Hammond, BS, 71, MS, 73; Auburn Univ, PhD(physiol), 79; Univ Autonoma de Ciudad Juarez, Mex, MD, 84. *Prof Exp:* Res fel shock physiol, La State Univ Med Ctr, 80-82; chief researcher diving med, Baromed Res Inst, JESMC, 84-86; fac fel aerospace med, HNC, SAM, USAF, Brooks AFB, Tex, 86-87 & SBRI, Johnson Space Ctr, NASA, Tex, 87-88; major, Army Res Civil Affairs, Oper Just Cause, Panama, 89-90 & Desert Shield/Storm, Saudi Arabia, 90-91; asst dir sci forensic med, Nat Inst Justice, US Dept Justice, 89-93. *Concurrent Pos:* Lectr, Physiol Dept, Univ Wis, Madison, 78-79; vis asst prof biol sci, Univ New Orleans, La, 79-80; NIH shock & trauma fel grant, 80, USPHS cardiovasc training grant, 80 & shock & trauma training grant, 81; asst prof physiol, La State Univ Med Ctr, 85- & asst prof, Nat Defense Univ, Washington, DC, 88-; dir, Technol Assessment Prog, Nat Inst Justice, 88- *Mem:* AAAS; Am Chem Soc; Am Physiol Soc; Shock Soc; Soc Neurosci; Undersea & Hyperbaric Med Soc; Aerospace Physiol Soc; Am Vet Physiol & Pharmacol Soc; NY Acad Sci; Aerospace Med Asn; Am Burn Soc. *Res:* Underlining preventive medical requirements during complex disasters with resources and help from the US government and non-government agencies. *Mailing Add:* PO Box 1252 Temple Hills MD 20757-1252. *Fax:* 410-612-7010; *E-Mail:* swhidden@aehai.apgea.army.mil

**WHIFFEN, JAMES DOUGLASS,** SURGERY, BIOENGINEERING. *Current Pos:* resident, Univ Wis-Madison, 56-57 & 59-62, from instr to assoc prof, 62-71, actg chmn dept, 72-74, PROF SURG, MED SCH, UNIV WIS-MADISON, 71-, ASST DEAN MED SCH, 75- *Personal Data:* b New York, NY, Jan 16, 31; m 60; c 1. *Educ:* Univ Wis, BS, 52, MD, 55; Am Bd Surg, dipl, 63. *Prof Exp:* Intern, Ohio State Univ, 55-56. *Concurrent Pos:* Nat Heart Inst res fel, 62-64; res career develop award, 65-75; Markle scholar, 66- *Mem:* Am Col Surg; Am Soc Artificial Internal Organs; Am Soc Test & Mat. *Res:* Cardiovascular prostheses; cardiopulmonary support devices; biomaterials. *Mailing Add:* Univ Hosp Med Sch 600 Highland Ave Madison WI 53792-0001

**WHIGAN, DAISY B,** ANALYTICAL CHEMISTRY, PHARMACEUTICAL CHEMISTRY. *Current Pos:* RES PROJ LEADER, BRISTOL-MYERS SQUIBB PHARM RES INST, 90- *Personal Data:* b Nueva Vizcaya, Philippines, Oct 5, 47; US citizen. *Educ:* Adamson Univ, Philippines, BS, 66; Univ Hawaii, MS, 69. *Prof Exp:* Sr res investr, Squibb Inst Med Res, 69-90. *Mem:* Am Chem Soc; NY Acad Sci; AAAS. *Res:* Analytical method development for pharmaceuticals in bulk formulations and body fluids; supervision of atomic spectroscopy laboratory research involving inductively coupled plasma atomic emission spectroscopy, graphite furnace and flame atomic absorption; robotics/automation. *Mailing Add:* Bristol-Myers Squibb PO Box 191 New Brunswick NJ 08903

**WHIGHAM, DAVID KEITH,** AGRONOMY. *Current Pos:* from asst prof to assoc prof, 77-82, PROF AGRON, IOWA STATE UNIV, 82- *Personal Data:* b Blanchard, Iowa, Aug 15, 38; m 64, Myrna Schnegelberger; c Scott, Leah & Anya. *Educ:* Iowa State Univ, BS, 66, MS, 69, PhD(crop prod), 71. *Prof Exp:* Instr agron, Iowa State Univ, 68-71; agronomist, USDA, 71-73; asst prof agron, Univ Ill, Urbana, 73-77. *Concurrent Pos:* Dir, Int Affairs & leader agron exten, Iowa State Univ; cert prof, Agron Crops & Soils, Am Reg. *Mem:* Fel Am Soc Agron; fel Crop Sci Soc Am. *Res:* Crop production of economic crops; cropping systems research; soybean management research; precision agriculture. *Mailing Add:* Dept Agron Iowa State Univ Ames IA 50011-1010. *E-Mail:* soy@instate.edu

**WHIKEHART, DAVID RALPH,** PLASMA MEMBRANES, TRANSPORT ENZYMES. *Current Pos:* from asst prof to assoc prof, 78-90, PROF, SCH OPTOM, UNIV ALA, BIRMINGHAM, 90- *Personal Data:* b Pittsburgh, Pa, Aug 21, 39; m 69; c 2. *Educ:* WVa Univ, PhD(biochem), 69. *Prof Exp:* Res assoc, Harvard Med Sch, 71-72; asst biochemist, McLean Hosp, Belmont, Mass, 71-72; spec fel, Nat Eye Inst, 72-74; sr staff fel ophthalmic biochem, 74-78. *Concurrent Pos:* Res fel neurochem, Harvard Med Sch, 69-71, fel neurochem, McLean Hosp, Belmont, Mass, 69-71; asst prof, Dept Biochem, Sch Med, Univ Ala, Birmingham, 79- 82, assoc prof, 82-90. *Mem:* Asn Res Vision & Ophthal. *Res:* Metabolism and transport in the cornea; biochemistry of alkali burned corneas; biochemistry of corneal tissue cultures; ocular diabetes. *Mailing Add:* 1137 Mountain Oaks Dr Birmingham AL 35226

**WHILLANS, IAN MORLEY,** GLACIOLOGY, GEOPHYSICS. *Current Pos:* ASST PROF GEOL, OHIO STATE UNIV, 90- *Personal Data:* b Toronto, Ont, Feb 25, 44; m 87, Baird; c Andrew & Claire. *Educ:* Univ Bristol, BSc, 66; Ohio State Univ, PhD(geol), 75. *Prof Exp:* Vis scientist glaciol, Geophys Isotope Lab, Univ Copenhagen, 75-76, Lab de Glaciologie, France, 83 & Norweg Polon Inst, 90; res assoc, Inst Polar Studies, 76-77. *Mem:* Int Glaciol Soc; Am Geophys Union. *Res:* Dynamics of polar ice sheets; mechanics of quaternary ice sheets; inversion of strain rates for force budget; use of precision gas. *Mailing Add:* 2633 Westmont Blvd Columbus OH 43221. *Fax:* 614-292-4697; *E-Mail:* whillanst@osu.edu

**WHINNERY, JAMES ELLIOTT,** FIGHTER AVIATION MEDICINE, ACCELERATION PHYSIOLOGY. *Current Pos:* CHIEF AEROSPACE MED SCIENTIST, NAVAL AIR DEVELOP CTR, 86- *Personal Data:* b Amarillo, Tex, May 1, 46; m 85, Angela M Geraci; c Chance T. *Educ:* WTex State Univ, BS, 68; Tex Christian Univ, PhD(phys chem) & MAT, 72; Univ Tex, Galveston, MD, 75; Air War Col, dipl, 76. *Honors & Awards:* Arnold D Tuttle Award, Aerospace Med Asn, 79 & 86. *Prof Exp:* Flight surgeon, USAF Sch Aerospace Med, 75-80, chief, Biodyn, 83-85; dir, Cardiovasc & Renal Med, Merck Sharp & Dohme Res Labs, 80-83. *Concurrent Pos:* Flight surgeon, Tex Air Nat Guard, 75-80, clin comdr, 83-85; sr flight surgeon, Pa Air Nat Guard, 80-83 & Ala Air Nat Guard, 85-86; spec res fel, Air Power Res Inst, Air War Col, 85-86; adv air surgeon, Nat Guard Bur, 86-90 & 91-93; asst command surgeon, USAF, Europe & Air Force Surgeon, Opers Desert Shield-Desert Storm, 90-91. *Mem:* Fel Am Col Cardiol; fel Aerospace Med Asn; fel Am Inst Chemists; Sigma Xi; Am Chem Soc. *Res:* Expert fighter aviation medicine; acceleration cardiovascular; neurophysiology; acceleration induced loss of consciousness. *Mailing Add:* 3520 Sleepy Hollow Amarillo TX 79121. *Fax:* 215-441-3758

**WHINNERY, JOHN R(OY),** OPTICS. *Current Pos:* from lectr to prof, Univ Calif, Berkeley, 46-87, head dept, 56-59, dean, Col Eng, 59-63, EMER PROF ELEC ENG, UNIV CALIF, BERKELEY, 87- *Personal Data:* b Read, Colo, July 26, 16; m 44, Patricia Barry; c Carol, Catherine & Barbara. *Educ:* Univ Calif, BS, 37, PhD(elec eng), 48. *Honors & Awards:* Educ Medal, Inst Elec & Electronics Engrs, 67, Medal Honor, 85; Lamme Award, Am Soc Eng Educ, 75; Founders Award, Nat Acad Eng, 86; Nat Medal of Sci, 92; Hall of Fame Medal, Am Soc Eng Educ, 93, Centennial Medal, 93. *Prof Exp:* From test engr to res assoc, Gen Elec Co, NY, 37-46. *Concurrent Pos:* Head microwave tube res, Hughes Aircraft Co, 51-52, Guggenheim fel, 59; vis mem tech staff, Bell Tel Labs, 63-64; mem, Sci & Technol Comt Manned Space Flight, NASA, 64-70; mem, Standing Comt Controlled Thermonuclear Res, AEC, 70-; mem, President's Comt Nat Medal Sci, 70-72 & 79-81. *Mem:* Nat Acad Sci; Nat Acad Eng; Am Phys Soc; fel Inst Elec & Electronics Engrs; fel Optical Soc Am; fel Am Acad Arts & Sci; fel AAAS. *Res:* Microwave and quantum electronics, including microwave electron devices, wave guiding systems, optical guiding systems and lasers for communication purposes. *Mailing Add:* Dept Elec Eng & Comput Sci Univ Calif Berkeley CA 94720-1770. *E-Mail:* whinnery@cs.berkeley.edu

**WHIPKEY, KENNETH LEE,** mathematics, statistics, for more information see previous edition

**WHIPP, BRIAN JAMES,** RESPIRATORY PHYSIOLOGY. *Current Pos:* PROF PHYSIOL & MED, HARBOR-UNIV CALIF LOS ANGELES MED CTR, 70- *Personal Data:* b Tredegar, Wales, Mar 3, 37. *Educ:* Stanford Univ, PhD(physiol), 67; Loughborough Univ, Eng, DSc, 82. *Mem:* Am Physiol Soc; Am Thoracic Soc; Am Col Sports Med; Physiol Soc. *Mailing Add:* Dept Physiol Cranmer Terr Tooting St Georges Hosp Med Sch London SW17 0RE England. *Fax:* 81 784 7093

**WHIPP, SHANNON CARL,** VETERINARY PHYSIOLOGY, VETERINARY MICROBIOLOGY. *Current Pos:* RETIRED. *Personal Data:* b Jacksonville, Fla, May 3, 31; m 56; c 5. *Educ:* Univ Minn, BS, 57, DVM, 59, PhD(physiol), 65. *Prof Exp:* Field vet, Minn Livestock Bd, 59-60; instr physiol, Univ Minn, 60-65; res vet, Nat Animal Dis Ctr, Agr Res Serv, USDA, 65-77, res leader, 77-80, chief, Physiopath Div, 80-94. *Concurrent Pos:* NIH fel, 62-65. *Mem:* Am Soc Vet Physiol & Pharmacol; Am Vet Med Asn; Comp Gastroenterol Soc; Conf Res Workers Animal Dis; NY Acad Sci; Sigma Xi. *Res:* Mechanisms of diarrhea; secretory diarrhea; enteric colibacillosis. *Mailing Add:* RR 3 Box 7 Leon IA 50144

**WHIPPEY, PATRICK WILLIAM,** PHYSICS EDUCATION. *Current Pos:* lectr, 66-67, asst prof, 67-72, ASSOC PROF PHYSICS, UNIV WESTERN ONT, 72- *Personal Data:* b Reading, UK, Feb 18, 40; m; c 3. *Educ:* Univ Reading, BSc, 62, PhD(physics), 66. *Prof Exp:* Asst lectr physics, Univ Reading, 65-66. *Mem:* Am Asn Physics Teachers. *Mailing Add:* Dept Physics & Astron Univ Western Ont London ON N6A 3K7 Can. *Fax:* 519-661-2033; *E-Mail:* whippey@uwo.ca

**WHIPPLE, CHRISTOPHER GEORGE,** RISK ANALYSIS, RADIOACTIVE WASTE MANAGEMENT. *Current Pos:* VPRES, ICF KAISER ENVIRON & ENERGY GROUP, 90- *Personal Data:* b Columbus, Ohio, Feb 17, 49; m 70, Francine Machtinger; c Matthew & Allison. *Educ:* Purdue Univ, BS, 70; Calif Inst Technol, MS, 71, PhD(eng sci), 74. *Honors & Awards:* Outstanding Serv Award, Soc Risk Analysis, 90. *Prof Exp:* Mem tech staff, Elec Power Res Inst, 74-90. *Concurrent Pos:* Lectr mech eng, Stanford Univ, 78-79; course dir, Chautauqua-Type Short Course, Col Teachers, NSF-AAAS, 78-81, Adv Study Inst Technol Risk Assessment, NATO, 81; mem Adv Comt, NSF Proj Risk Assessment, 78, 81-82, 85; mem, Comt Health & Ecol Effects Synfuel Industs, Nat Acad Sci, 82-83 & Bd Radioactive Waste Mgt, 85-95, chmn, 92-; mem, Comt Nuclear Safety Res, 85-86, Risk Perception & Commun, 88-90, Waste Isolation Pilot Plant, 89-, Radioactive Waste Mgt with USSR, 90, Tech Basis for Yucca Mountain Stand, 92-95. *Mem:* Soc Risk Analysis (pres, 82-83); AAAS; Sigma Xi; Nat Asn Environ Prof. *Res:* Analysis and management of technological risks; risk communication; radioactive waste management. *Mailing Add:* ICF Kaiser 1800 Harrison St Oakland CA 94612. *Fax:* 510-419-5355; *E-Mail:* cwhipple@icfkaiser.com

**WHIPPLE, EARL BENNETT,** PHYSICAL CHEMISTRY. *Current Pos:* RETIRED. *Personal Data:* b Thomson, Ga, Apr 9, 30; m 90, Helena Brakel; c 4. *Educ:* Emory Univ, BS, 51, PhD(phys chem), 59. *Prof Exp:* Chemist, Va-Carolina Chem Corp, Va, 52-53; res scientist chem, Union Carbide Res Inst, 59-66, group leader chem, 66-70, mgr res, Cent Sci Lab, Tarrytown Tech Ctr, Union Carbide Corp, 70-74; res adv cent res, Pfizer, Inc, 74-95. *Concurrent Pos:* Adj prof, Rockefeller Univ, 69-74. *Mem:* NY Acad Sci; Am Chem Soc; AAAS; Int Soc Magnetic Resonance. *Res:* Chemical applications of nuclear and electron spin resonance; structure and electronic properties of molecules. *Mailing Add:* 7 Forest Hills Dr Madison CT 06443

**WHIPPLE, FRED LAWRENCE,** ASTRONOMY, SPACE PHYSICS. *Current Pos:* Mem staff, Observ, Harvard Univ, 31-77, instr, Univ, 32-38, lectr, 38-45, from assoc prof to prof, 45-70, chmn dept, 49-56, Phillips prof, 70-77, EMER PHILLIPS PROF ASTRON, HARVARD UNIV, 77- *Personal Data:* b Red Oak, Iowa, Nov 5, 06; m 46, Babette S Vilmont; c 3. *Educ:* Univ Calif, Los Angeles, AB, 27; Univ Calif, Berkeley, PhD(astron), 31; Harvard Univ, MA, 45. *Hon Degrees:* DSc, Am Int Col, 48, Temple Univ, 61 & Univ Ariz, 79; DLitt, Northeastern Univ, 61. *Honors & Awards:* Lowell Lectr, Lowell Technol Inst, 47; Donohue Medal; Smith Medal, Nat Acad Sci, 49; Am Astronaut Soc Award, 61; Space Pioneers Medallion, 68; Leonard Medal, Meteoritical Soc, 70; Kepler Medal, AAAS, 71; Henry Medal, Smithsonian Inst, 73; Gold Medal, Royal Arts Soc, Eng, 83; Bruce Gold Medal, Astron Soc Pac, 86. *Concurrent Pos:* mem, Vpres & Pres Comns, Int Astron Union, 32-, voting rep, 52 & 55; deleg, Inter-Am Astrophys Cong, Mex, 42; res assoc, Radio Res Lab, Off Sci Res & Develop, 42-45; leader, Harvard Proj Upper Atmospheric & Meteor Res, Bur Ord, US Navy, 46-51, Air Res & Develop Command, USAF, 48-62, Off Naval Res, 51-57, Off Ord Res, US Army, 53-57, dir, Harvard Radio Meteor Proj, Nat Bur Stand, 57-61, NSF, 60-63 & NASA, 63-; mem subcomt, Nat Adv Comt Aeronaut, 46-52; mem, Panel Upper Atmosphere, US Res & Develop Bd, 47-52; mem, Comn 3, US Nat Comt, Int Sci Radio Union, 49-61; mem, Adv Pael Astron, NSF, 52-55, chmn, 54-55, mem, Div Comt Math & Phys Sci, 64-; mem, Sci Adv Bd, USAF, 53-62, assoc adv, 63-67, mem, Geophys & Space Tech Panels; mem, Working Group Satellite Tracking & Comput & chief investr, Proj Optical Tracking Artificial Earth Satellites, Int Geophys Yr, 55-58, mem, Tech Panel Earth Satellite Prog & Tech Panel Rocketry, 55-59; dir, Astrophys Observ, Smithsonian Inst, 55-73, sr scientist, 73-77; dir, Optical Satellite Tracking Proj & proj dir, Orbiting Astron Observ, NASA, 58-72, mem, Space Sci Working Group Orbiting Astron Observ, 59-69, consult, Aeronomy Subcomt, 61-63, dir, Meteorite Photog & Recovery Prog, 62-73, mem, Working Group Geod Satellite Prog, 63- & mem, Comet & Astroid Sci Adv Comt, 71-72, chmn, 73-74; mem, Comts Meteorol & Atmospheric Sci, Nat Acad Sci-Nat Res Coun, 58-, space sci bd, 58- & Subcomt Potential Contamination & Interference Space Exp, 63-; mem, Joint Bio-Astronaut Comt, Armed Forces-Nat Res Coun, 59-61; spec consult, Comt Sci & Astronaut, US House Rep, 60-73; mem, Working Groups Geod Satellites & Tracking, Telemetry & Dynamics, Comt Space Res, 60-, chmn, Sci Coun Geol Uses Artificial Satellites, 65-; chmn, Gordon Res Conf Chem & Physics Space, 63; trustee-at-large, Univ Corp Atmospheric Res, Colo, 64-68 & mem, Comt Nat Ctr Atmospheric Res Staff-Univ rels, 65-68. *Mem:* Nat Acad Sci; fel Am Astron Soc (vpres, 48-50); fel Am Astronaut Soc (vpres, 62-64); fel Am Geophys Union; fel Am Inst Aeronaut & Astronaut; Am Acad Arts & Sci; Am Philos Soc; Sigma Xi; AAAS; Am Meteorol Soc. *Res:* Photometry; comet discoveries and theory; colors of external galaxies; novae; meteor orbits; earth's upper atmosphere. *Mailing Add:* Smithsonian Astrophys Observ 60 Garden St Cambridge MA 02138. *Fax:* 617-495-7356

**WHIPPLE, GERALD HOWARD,** MEDICINE. *Current Pos:* PROF CARDIOL MED & DIR, DIV CARDIOL, UNIV NEV, RENO, 78- *Personal Data:* b Calif, Feb 6, 23; m 47; c 5. *Educ:* Harvard Univ, SB, 43; Univ Calif, MD, 46; Am Bd Internal Med, dipl, 60. *Prof Exp:* Instr, Sch Med, Boston Univ, 56-57, assoc, 57-60, from asst prof to assoc prof, 60-68; from assoc prof to prof med, Col Med, Univ Calif, Irvine, 71-78, chief, Cardiol Div, 74-78. *Concurrent Pos:* Res fel med, Harvard Univ, 53-56; vol asst med, Congenital Heart Clin, Children's Med Ctr, Boston, 54-56; physician in chg, EKG Lab, Univ Hosp, Boston Univ, 56-58, physician, Cardiac Care Univ, 65-68, assoc vis physician, 56-68, assoc mem, Evans Mem Res Found, 56-68, sect head clin cardiol res; consult cardiol, Congenital Heart Clin, Boston City Hosp, 58-59; res consult, Providence Vet Admin Hosp, RI, 60-68; res assoc, Mass Inst Technol, 63-66; fel, Coun Clin Cardiol, Am Heart Asn; heart coordr area VIII, Regional Med Prog Cancer, Heart & Stroke, 68-; physician & dir, Intensive Cardiac Care Unit, Orange Co Med Ctr, 69-70; chief, Med Serv, Vet Admin Hosp, Long Beach, 70-74 & Reno, 81- *Mem:* Fel Am Col Physicians; fel Am Col Cardiol. *Res:* Academic cardiology; cardiology; cardiac arrhythmias; epidemiologic evaluation of acute ischemic heart disease and sudden death. *Mailing Add:* PO Box 1190 Verdi NV 89439

**WHIPPLE, ROYSON NEWTON,** FOOD TECHNOLOGY. *Current Pos:* RETIRED. *Personal Data:* b Buffalo, NY, May 28, 12; m 59, Martha Stevens; c Sharon L & Enid D. *Educ:* Univ Mich, BS, 35; Cornell Univ, MS, 39. *Prof Exp:* Instr high sch, NY, 35-45; prof & head, Div Food Technol, State Univ NY Agr & Tech Col, Morrisville, 45-57, pres, 57-78. *Mem:* Inst Food Technologists. *Res:* Background needs for food technologists engaged in fruit and vegetable processing. *Mailing Add:* 330 Bahama Dr Indialantic FL 32903-3006

**WHIRLOW, DONALD KENT,** FLUID DYNAMICS, AERODYNAMICS. *Current Pos:* Sr engr, 66-71, mgr fluid dynamics, 71-76, ADV ENGR, FLUID DYNAMICS RES, WESTINGHOUSE SCI & TECHNOL CTR, 76- *Personal Data:* b Pittsburgh, Pa, May 2, 38; m 62; c 3. *Educ:* Carnegie Inst Technol, BS, 60, MS, 61, PhD(mech eng), 64. *Mem:* Am Soc Mech Engrs; Sigma Xi. *Res:* Fluid dynamics and heat transfer; turbomachinery; acoustic flowmetering; transformers; transonic flow; unsteady aerodynamics; two-phase steam flow; finite element analysis. *Mailing Add:* 4040 W Benden Dr Murrysville PA 15668

**WHISLER, FRANK DUANE,** SOIL PHYSICS. *Current Pos:* PROF AGRON & AGRONOMIST, MISS STATE UNIV, 73- *Personal Data:* b Burton, WVa, Nov 20, 34; m 56; c 4. *Educ:* Univ WVa, BS, 57, MS, 58; Univ Ill, PhD(soil physics), 64. *Honors & Awards:* Award, Soil Sci Soc Am, 63. *Prof Exp:* Soil scientist, Agr Res Serv, USDA, Ill, 58-69, soil scientist, Water Conserv Lab, 69-73. *Mem:* Am Soc Agron; Soil Sci Soc Am; Sigma Xi. *Res:* Water movement into and through soils or other porous material from both a theoretical and experimental point of view. *Mailing Add:* PO Box 5248 Mississippi State MS 39762

**WHISLER, HOWARD CLINTON,** BOTANY, MICROBIOLOGY. *Current Pos:* from asst prof to assoc prof, 63-73, PROF BOT, UNIV WASH, 73- *Personal Data:* b Oakland, Calif, Feb 4, 31; m 53; c 2. *Educ:* Univ Calif, Berkeley, BSc, 54, PhD(bot), 61. *Prof Exp:* NATO fel, Univ Montpellier, 60-61; asst prof bot, McGill Univ, 61-63. *Concurrent Pos:* NSF fel, Univ Geneva, 68-69. *Mem:* Mycol Soc Am; Soc Invert Path. *Res:* Development of the aquatic phycomycetes; insect microbiology. *Mailing Add:* Bot KB-15 Univ Wash 3900 Seventh Ave NE Seattle WA 98195-0001

**WHISLER, KENNETH EUGENE,** robotics & automation using computers & bar codes, for more information see previous edition

**WHISLER, WALTER WILLIAM,** BIOCHEMISTRY, NEUROSURGERY. *Current Pos:* PROF BIOCHEM & NEUROSURG & CHMN, DEPT NEUROSURG, RUSH MED COL, 70- *Personal Data:* b Davenport, Iowa, Feb 9, 34; m 59; c 2. *Educ:* Augustana Col, AB, 55; Univ Ill, MD, 59, PhD(biochem), 69; Am Bd Neurol Surg, dipl, 67. *Prof Exp:* USPHS fel, 64-65. *Concurrent Pos:* Attend neurosurgeon & chmn, Dept Neurosurg, Presby-St Luke's Hosp, 70-; clin assoc prof, Univ Ill Col Med, 70- *Mem:* AMA; Am Asn Neurol Surg; Cong Neurol Surg; Int Soc Res Stereoencephalotomy. *Res:* Mechanisms of catecholomine oxidation; metabolism of the psychotomimetic amines; biochemistry of brain tumors. *Mailing Add:* 1725 W Harrison Suite 1117 Chicago IL 60612

**WHISNANT, JACK PAGE,** MEDICINE, NEUROLOGY. *Current Pos:* From instr to assoc prof, 56-69, PROF NEUROL, MAYO MED SCH, UNIV MINN, 69-, CHMN DEPT, 71- *Personal Data:* b Little Rock, Ark, Oct 26, 24; m 44; c 3. *Educ:* Univ Ark, BS, 48, MD, 51. *Concurrent Pos:* Consult, Mayo Clin, 55-, head, Sect Neurol, 63-71. *Mem:* Am Acad Neurol; Am Neurol Asn; Sigma Xi. *Res:* Clinical neurology, especially vascular diseases of the nervous system. *Mailing Add:* Health Sci Res Mayo Clin 200 SW First St Rochester MN 55905-0001

**WHISONANT, ROBERT CLYDE,** STRATIGRAPHY, SEDIMENTOLOGY. *Current Pos:* from asst prof to assoc prof, 71-81, PROF GEOL, RADFORD UNIV, 81- *Personal Data:* b Columbia, SC, Apr 20, 41; m 63, Brenda Lark; c Dell R & Robert D. *Educ:* Clemson Univ, BS, 63; Fla State Univ, MS, 65, PhD(geol), 67. *Honors & Awards:* Neil Miner Award, Nat Asn Geol Teachers, 93. *Prof Exp:* Petrol geologist, Humble Oil & Ref Co, 67-71. *Concurrent Pos:* Consult, Humble Oil & Refining Co, 72 & Nat Geog Soc, 81; grantee, Geol Soc Am, 72, Petrol Res Fund, Am Chem Soc, 83-85 & Jeffres Mem Trust, 83-85, 86 & 89-91; mem, Va Oil & Gas Conserv Bd, 82-90; mem, Nat Asn Geol Teachers; mem, Va Bd Geol, 93-; chair, SE Sect Geol Soc Am, Comt Exam & Asn Bds Geol. *Mem:* Geol Soc Am; Am Asn Petrol Geol; Soc Econ Paleontologists & Mineralogists; Sigma Xi; Asn Eng Geologists. *Res:* Paleozoic rocks of the southern Appalachians, specifically, sedimentary petrography and paleocurrent features; paleoenvironmental determinations; stratigraphic analysis; slope stability analysis in valley and ridge of western Virginia; erosion and sediment control; geology and the civil war; engineering geology. *Mailing Add:* Dept Geol Radford Univ Radford VA 24142

**WHISSELL-BUECHY, DOROTHY Y E,** human genetics, for more information see previous edition

**WHISTLER, ROY LESTER,** CARBOHYDRATES. *Current Pos:* prof, Purdue Univ, West Lafayette, 46-75, asst dept head, 48-60, chmn, Inst Agr Utilization Res, 61-78, Hillenbrand distinguished prof, 75-82, ADJ PROF, WHISTLER CTR CARBOHYDRATE RES, PURDUE UNIV, WEST LAFAYETTE, 82- *Personal Data:* b Morgantown, WVa, Mar 21, 12; m 35; c 1. *Educ:* Heidelberg Col, BS, 34; Ohio State Univ, MS, 35; Iowa State Univ, PhD, 38. *Hon Degrees:* DSc, Heidelberg Univ, 53; DLitt, St Thomas Inst Advan Study, 82; DAgr, Purdue Univ, 85. *Honors & Awards:* Hudson Award, Am Chem Soc, 60; Payen Award, 67; Annual Res Award, Japanese Tech Soc Starch, 67; Alsberg Schoch Award, Am Asn Cereal Chem, 70, Osborn Medal, 74; Ger Saare Medal, 74; Spencer Award, 75; Hendricks Award, USDA, 91. *Prof Exp:* Instr chem, Iowa State Col, 35-38; fel, Nat Bur Stand, 38-40; head, Starch Struct Sect, USDA, 40-45 & Northern Regional Res Lab, Bur Agr Chem & Eng, 45-46. *Concurrent Pos:* Vis lectr, Univ Witwatersrand, 61 & 85, Cape Town, 65, NZ & Australia, 67 & 74, Czech Acad Sci & Hungarian Acad Sci, 68, Taiwan, 70 & France & Poland, 75; Far East, Vladivostok Acad Sci lectr to USSR, 76; Nat Res Coun lectr, Brazil, 77; Welsh Found lectr, Tex, 77; guest lectr, Repub SAfrica, 77 & 85; guest, Polish Acad Sci, 78 & 85, People's Repub China, 84, 85. *Mem:* AAAS (pres, 73); Am Chem Soc; Am Soc Biochemists; Am Asn Cereal Chem (pres, 72-73); Am Inst Chemists (pres, 80-81); Int Carbohydrate Orgn (pres, 60); hon mem Arg Chem Soc; Sigma Xi. *Res:* Chemistry and biochemistry of carbohydrates, both fundamental and practical; simple sugars; polysaccharides; carbohydrates in industry; basic and industrial medicine and foods. *Mailing Add:* Dept Biochem Purdue Univ Biochem Bldg West Lafayette IN 47907-1968

**WHITACRE, CAROLINE C,** NEUROIMMUNOLOGY, AUTOIMMUNE DISEASE. *Current Pos:* Asst prof med, 81-86, from asst prof to assoc prof, 86-92, PROF & INTERIM CHAIR MED MICROBIOL & IMMUNOL, OHIO STATE UNIV, 92- *Personal Data:* b Cincinnati, Ohio, Nov 4, 49; m 75, Michael Para; c Alexander. *Educ:* Ohio State Univ, BA, 71, PhD(med microbiol), 75. *Mem:* AAAS; Am Soc Microbiol; Am Asn Immunologists. *Res:* Immunology of multiple sclerosis; animal models of autoimmune disease; oral tolerance in therapy of autoimmune disease; immunologic dysfunction in Acquired Immune Dificiency Disorder; genetic mechanisms in autoimmunity; stress effects on autoimmunity. *Mailing Add:* Dept Med Microbiol & Immunol 2078 Graves Hall Ohio State Univ 333 W Tenth Ave Columbus OH 43210-1239. *Fax:* 614-292-9805

**WHITACRE, DAVID MARTIN,** ENVIRONMENTAL SCIENCES. *Current Pos:* vpres res, 86, head agr res, Switz, 86-87, VPRES, DEVELOP CROP, NOVARTIS PROTECTION CORP, 87- *Personal Data:* b Mariemont, Ohio, Dec 4, 43; m 66; c 2. *Educ:* Wilmington Col, Ohio, AB, 65; Ohio State Univ, MSc, 66; Univ Ariz, PhD(entom, zool), 69; Am Bd Toxicol, dipl, 82. *Prof Exp:* Asst prof biol, Univ PR, Mayaguez, 69-71; State Ariz res grant entom, Univ Ariz, 71-72; proj mgr entom toxicol, Velsicol Chem Corp, 72-73; dir environ res, 73-76, dir environ sci & toxicol, 76-85. *Concurrent Pos:* Fel, Univ Ky, 72. *Mem:* Entom Soc Am; Am Chem Soc. *Res:* Metabolism of pesticides in plants and animals. *Mailing Add:* Novartis Protection Corp 410 Swing Rd Greensboro NC 27409

**WHITACRE, GALE R(OBERT),** MECHANICAL ENGINEERING. *Current Pos:* Res mech engr, Battelle Mem Inst, 57-65, sr mech engr, 65-71, fel, 71-77, PRIN RESEARCHER, BATTELLE MEM INST, 77- *Personal Data:* b Salem, Ohio, June 23, 33; m 57; c 3. *Educ:* Univ Cincinnati, BS, 56; Purdue Univ, MS, 58. *Mem:* Am Soc Mech Engrs. *Res:* Heat transfer; boundary layer flow; ablation; re-entry thermal analysis. *Mailing Add:* 3042 Midgard St Columbus OH 43202

**WHITAKER, ELLIS HOBART,** PLANT PHYSIOLOGY. *Current Pos:* from assoc prof to prof, 64-76, EMER PROF BIOL, SOUTHEASTERN MASS UNIV, 76- *Personal Data:* b Salem, Mass, Dec 2, 08; m 35, 66; c 2. *Educ:* Worcester Polytech Inst, BS, 30; Cornell Univ, MS, 36, PhD(plant physiol), 49. *Prof Exp:* Engr, Gilbert & Barker Mfg, Mass, 30-31; teacher, Monson Acad, 33-35 & Westover Sch, Conn, 36-39; asst gen bot, Cornell Univ, 40-41; instr phys sci & gen biol, State Univ NY Col Oneonta, 41-48; asst prof chem, 48-54, assoc prof biol, 54-64. *Concurrent Pos:* Consult, W W Norton Co, 79-80. *Mem:* Fel AAAS. *Res:* General biology; enzymes in insectivorous plants. *Mailing Add:* 32 Prospect St Dartmouth MA 02748

**WHITAKER, EWEN A,** HISTORY OF SELENOGRAPHY, PLANETARY SCIENCES. *Current Pos:* RETIRED. *Personal Data:* b London, Eng, June 22, 22; m 46, Beryl J Horswell; c Malcolm John, Graham David & Eiona (Whitaker-Andrews). *Educ:* Brit Inst Mech Eng, cert, 42. *Honors & Awards:* Walter Goodacre Prize & Gold Medal, Brit Astron Asn, 82. *Prof Exp:* Lab asst chem anal & phys testing, Siemens Bros & Co Ltd, 40-41, lab asst spectrochem analysis, 41-49; sci asst, Royal Greenwich Observ, 49-53, from asst exp officer to exp officer, 53-58; res assoc, Yerkes Observ, Univ Chicago, 58-60; res fel, Lunar & Planetary Lab, Univ Ariz, 60-82, assoc res scientist, 82-87. *Concurrent Pos:* Co-experimenter, Ranger moonshots, 62-66; mem, TV Exp Team, Surv Spacecraft, 64-68; mem, Site Selection Team, Orbiter 5, 67-68; mem, Apollo Orbital Sci Photo Team, 69-73; lectr, Lunar & Planetary Lab, Univ Ariz, 83-87. *Mem:* Int Astron Union; Am Astron Soc; fel Royal Astron Soc. *Res:* Study of moon, particularly of surface features and properties by earthbased telescopic observations and research and spacecraft; history of selenography; standardization of lunar nomenclature. *Mailing Add:* 4332 E Sixth St Tucson AZ 85711

**WHITAKER, JAMES E,** DERMATOLOGY. *Current Pos:* ASST CANCER RES SCIENTIST DERMAT, ROSWELL PARK CANCER INST, 90- *Res:* Dermatology. *Mailing Add:* Dept Dermat Roswell Park Cancer Inst Elm & Carlton Sts Buffalo NY 14263-0001

**WHITAKER, JOHN O, JR,** VERTEBRATE ECOLOGY, MAMMALOGY. *Current Pos:* From asst prof to assoc prof, 62-70, PROF LIFE SCI, IND STATE UNIV, TERRE HAUTE, 70- *Personal Data:* b Oneonta, NY, Apr 22, 35; m 57; c John, Royce L Bagg; c John, Lynne & William. *Educ:* Cornell Univ, BS, 57, PhD(vert zool), 62. *Mem:* Fel AAAS; Am Soc Mammal; Ecol Soc Am; Entom Soc Am. *Res:* Studies of food habits, ectoparasites, habitats and interrelations of species of small mammals, expecially bats, rodents and insectivores. *Mailing Add:* Dept Life Sci Ind State Univ Terre Haute IN 47809. *E-Mail:* lswhitak@scifac.indstate.edu

**WHITAKER, JOHN ROBERT,** FOOD SCIENCE & TECHNOLOGY, AGRICULTURAL & FOOD CHEMISTRY. *Current Pos:* from instr to assoc prof, Univ Calif, Davis, 56-67, assoc dean, Col Agr & Environ Sci, 75-83, 86-90, prof & chair, Dept Biochem & Biophys, 84-85, prof & biochemist food sci & technol, 67-92, assoc dean affairs, Col Agr & Environ Sci, 86-90, EMER PROF, UNIV CALIF, DAVIS, 93- *Personal Data:* b Lubbock, Tex, Sept 13, 29; m 52, Gwen Crow; c Dianne, Pamela, Brenda & Judy. *Educ:* Berea Col, AB, 51; Ohio State Univ, PhD(agr biochem), 54. *Honors & Awards:* William V Cruess Award, Inst Food Technologists, 73; spec fel, NIH, 72-73; Fulbright-Hays Award, 85; Agr & Food Chem Res Award, Am Chem Soc, 85; Agr & Food Chem Distinguished Serv Award, 89, Agr & Food Chem Fel Award, 90. *Prof Exp:* Lab asst chem, Berea Col, 50-51; asst agr biochem, Ohio State Univ, 51-52, asst instr, 53-54, fel, 54. *Concurrent Pos:* Enzyme Group Med Res Lab, US Army, Army Chem Ctr, Md, 54-56; NIH spec fel,

Northwestern Univ, 63-64; vis prof, Nat Univ, Mexico City, 68, Vet Col, Norway, 72, Univ Bristol, Eng, 72-73, Norweg Food Res Inst, 79, Nat Polytech Inst, Mex, 80, Univ Campinas, Brazil, 80, Metrop Univ Mex, 80, People's Repub China, 85, 87; Fulbright fel, Univ Sao Paulo, Brazil, 85. *Mem:* Am Chem Soc; Am Soc Biol Chemists; Am Soc Plant Physiologists; fel Inst Food Technologists. *Res:* Relationship between structure and function in enzymes; chemical and enzymatic modification of food proteins; naturally occurring enzyme inhibitors; over 210 publications on enzymes and enzyme inhibitors important to food science, including much work on beans, and on chemical and enzymatic modification of protein. *Mailing Add:* Dept Food Sci & Technol Univ Calif Davis CA 95616-5224. *Fax:* 530-752-4759; *E-Mail:* jrwhitaker@ucdavis.edu

**WHITAKER, JOHN SCOTT,** HIGH ENERGY PHYSICS. *Current Pos:* assoc prof, 85-91, PROF PHYSICS, BOSTON UNIV, 91- *Personal Data:* b Oroville, Calif, Nov 10, 48; m 83; c 2. *Educ:* Univ Calif, Berkeley, BA, 70, PhD(physics), 76. *Prof Exp:* Asst, Lawrence Berkeley Lab, 76; sci assoc, Europ Ctr Nuclear Res, 77-78; from asst prof to assoc prof physics, Mass Inst Technol, 78-85. *Mem:* Am Phys Soc; Am Asn Physics Teachers; Am Asn Univ Profs. *Res:* High energy particle physics. *Mailing Add:* Dept Physics Boston Univ 590 Commonwealth Ave Boston MA 02215. *E-Mail:* scott@buphyc.bu.edu

**WHITAKER, MACK LEE,** MATHEMATICS. *Current Pos:* RETIRED. *Personal Data:* b Forest City, NC, Dec 2, 31; m 56; c 2. *Educ:* Appalachian State Teachers Col, BS, 53, MA, 56; Fla State Univ, EdD, 61. *Prof Exp:* Teacher, Piedmont High Sch, 56-58; from assoc prof to prof math, Radford Col, 60-68, chmn dept, 62-66; assoc prof math educ, Auburn Univ, 68-69; prof math, Radford Univ, 69-96. *Mem:* Math Asn Am. *Res:* Mathematics education; abstract algebra; foundations of mathematics. *Mailing Add:* HC 67 Box 405 Floyd VA 24091

**WHITAKER, R BLAKE,** IMMUNOLOGY. *Current Pos:* PRES IMMUNOL, IMMUNET, 85- *Personal Data:* b Beverly, Mass, Aug 8, 52. *Educ:* Bates Col, BS, 74; Yale Univ, PhD(immunol), 80. *Prof Exp:* Prof biol, Bates Col, 80-85. *Mem:* Sigma Xi; AAAS; Am Asn Immunol. *Mailing Add:* Lewiston Auburn Col 54 Westminster St Lewiston ME 04240

**WHITAKER, ROBERT DALLAS,** INORGANIC CHEMISTRY. *Current Pos:* RETIRED. *Personal Data:* b Tampa, Fla, Mar 5, 33; m 60; c 3. *Educ:* Univ Washington & Lee, BS, 55; Univ Fla, PhD(inorg chem), 59. *Prof Exp:* Asst prof chem, Washington & Lee Univ, 59-62; from asst prof to prof, Univ SFla, Tampa, 62-92. *Mem:* Am Chem Soc. *Res:* Molecular addition compounds. *Mailing Add:* 836 Bayside Dr Tampa FL 33609

**WHITAKER, SIDNEY HOPKINS,** GEOLOGY, HYDROGEOLOGY. *Current Pos:* SCI ADV, ATOMIC ENERGY CAN LTD, 81- *Personal Data:* b Spring Valley, Ill, Apr 7, 40; c Joel F. *Educ:* Oberlin Col, BA, 62; Univ Ill, PhD(geol), 65. *Prof Exp:* Fel, Sask Res Coun, 65-67, asst res officer, 67-71, assoc res officer geol, 71-75, sr res scientist geol, 75-77; pres, Silverspoon Res & Consult Ltd, 77-81. *Concurrent Pos:* Mem, Geosci Working Group, Can Adv Comt Remote Sensing, Can Ctr Remote Sensing, 75-81; mem, Coord Group Geol Disposal, Nuclear Energy Agency, Orgn Econ Cooperation & Develop, 82-85 & tech subgroup, Stripa Proj, 87-92. *Mem:* Glaciol Soc; Geol Asn Can; Geol Soc Am; Sigma Xi. *Res:* Review Canadian geoscience programs for deep disposal of radioactive waste; techniques of groundwater exploration; hydrogeology; field geology; mapping; subsurface exploration and stratigraphy; lignite exploration. *Mailing Add:* PO Box 46 River Hills Manitoba MB R0E 1T0 Can

**WHITAKER, THOMAS BURTON,** AGRICULTURAL ENGINEERING. *Current Pos:* From asst prof to assoc prof, 67-76, PROF BIOL & AGR ENG, NC STATE UNIV, 76-, AGR ENGR, AGR RES SERV, USDA, 67- *Personal Data:* b Asheville, NC, May 16, 39; m 60; c 3. *Educ:* NC State Univ, BS, 62, MS, 64; Ohio State Univ, PhD(agr eng), 67. *Honors & Awards:* Bailey Award, Am Peanut Res & Educ Asn, 76; Golden Peanut Res Award, Nat Peanut Coun, 80. *Mem:* Am Soc Agr Engrs; Am Peanut Res & Educ Soc; Sigma Xi; Asn Off Analytical Chemists. *Res:* Quality control of agricultural commodities with main emphasis concerning the detection, control, and elimination of mycotoxins in food products. *Mailing Add:* Dept Biol & Agr Eng 124 Weaver Labs PO Box 7625 Raleigh NC 27695

**WHITAKER, THOMAS WALLACE,** genetics, for more information see previous edition

**WHITAKER, WILLIAM ARMSTRONG,** COMPUTER SCIENCE, NATURAL SCIENCE. *Current Pos:* RETIRED. *Personal Data:* b Little Rock, Ark, Jan 10, 36; m 57; c 2. *Educ:* Tulane Univ, BS, 55, MS, 56; Univ Chicago, PhD(physics), 63. *Prof Exp:* Asst physics, Tulane Univ, 54-56; prof off res & develop, USAF, 57-68, chief, High Altitude Group, Weapons Lab, 68-70, chief scientist, 70-72, mil asst res, Off Dir Defense Res & Eng, 73-75, spec asst to dir, Defense Advan Res Proj Agency, 75-80, tech dir for digital applns, Air Force Armament Develop Lab, Elgin AFB, 80-87. *Mem:* Am Phys Soc; Am Astron Soc; Am Geophys Union; Am Meteorol Soc; Inst Elec & Electronics Engrs. *Res:* Direction of advanced research, defense software management, common high order computer programming languages. *Mailing Add:* PO Box 3036 McLean VA 22103

**WHITAKER-AZMITIA, PATRICIA MACK,** NEUROPHARMACOLOGY, DEVELOPMENTAL PHARMACOLOGY. *Current Pos:* asst prof, 83-90, ASSOC PROF PSYCHIAT, STATE UNIV NY, STONY BROOK, 90- *Personal Data:* b Winnipeg, Man, Jan 24, 53; m 83; c 2. *Educ:* Univ Man, BSc, 75; Univ Toronto, MSc, 76, PhD(pharmacol), 79. *Prof Exp:* Vis scientist biol psychiat, Clin Res Centre, Harrow, UK, 79-80; asst prof psychiat, Univ Toronto, 81-83. *Concurrent Pos:* Adj assoc prof, Dept Biol, NY Univ, 83-; assoc prof, Dept Psychol, State Univ NY, Stony Brook, 90-; chmn, Biomed Sect, NY Acad Sci, 91-92. *Mem:* Soc Neurosci; Int Soc Develop Neurosci; NY Acad Sci; Int Brain Res Orgn. *Res:* Developmental pharmacology; function and pharmacology of serotonin receptors; pharmacology of astroglial cells; role of neurotransmitters in brain development. *Mailing Add:* Dept Psychiat State Univ NY Stony Brook NY 11794-8101

**WHITBY, OWEN,** STATISTICS, ACTUARIAL METHODS. *Current Pos:* vpres, 84-88, sr vpres, 88-90, EXEC VPRES, ATRIUM CORP, 90- *Personal Data:* b Luton, Eng, Feb 24, 42; Can & UK citizen; m 70. *Educ:* McMaster Univ, BSc Hons, 64; Stanford Univ, MS, 66, PhD(statist), 72. *Prof Exp:* From asst prof to assoc prof statist, Teachers Col, Columbia Univ, 71-78; consult, 78-79; from actuarial assoc to secy, Swiss Re Holding, 79-80; secy, North Am Reins Corp, 80-84, asst vpres, 84-87, vpres, 87-89. *Mem:* AAAS; Am Statist Asn; Asn Comput Mach; Biomet Soc; Inst Math Statist; Soc Actuaries; Int Actuarial Asn. *Res:* Biostatistics; mathematical statistics; actuarial methods. *Mailing Add:* 106 Morningside Dr New York NY 10027-6026

**WHITCOMB, CARL ERWIN,** HORTICULTURE, PLANT ECOLOGY. *Current Pos:* PRES, LACEBARK INC, 86- *Personal Data:* b Independence, Kans, Oct 26, 39; m 63; LaJean Carpenter; c Andrew & Benjamin. *Educ:* Kans State Univ, BSA, 64; Iowa State Univ, MS, 66, PhD(hort, plant ecol), 69. *Honors & Awards:* Chadwick Award, Am Asn Nurserymen; Porter Henegar Award, Southern Nurserymens Asn, Wight Award. *Prof Exp:* Asst prof ornamental hort, Univ Fla, 67-72; prof hort, Okla State Univ, 72-86. *Concurrent Pos:* Expert witness, consult & lectr. *Mem:* Am Soc Hort Sci; fel Int Plant Propagators Soc; Am Soc Agron; Soc Am Foresters; Weed Sci Soc; Am Ecol Soc Am. *Res:* Plant interactions in man-made or man-managed landscapes; production, establishment and maintenance of landscape plants; plant growth and development; author of 4 books; inventor of containers that stimulate root branching and accelerate plant growth and ease of harvest and transplanting; agronomy, horticulture, nursery production, landscape management; holder of 17 US patents. *Mailing Add:* Lacebark Inc PO Box 2383 Stillwater OK 74076. *Fax:* 405-377-0131

**WHITCOMB, DONALD LEROY,** analytical chemistry, for more information see previous edition

**WHITCOMB, JAMES HALL,** SEISMOLOGY, GEOPHYSICS. *Current Pos:* PROG DIR GEOPHYS, NSF, 89- *Personal Data:* b Sterling, Colo, Dec 10, 40. *Educ:* Colo Sch Mines, GP Eng, 62; Ore State Univ, MS, 64; Calif Inst Technol, PhD(geophys), 73. *Prof Exp:* Sr res fel, Calif Inst Technol, 73-79; assoc prof, Univ Colo, 79-85; pres, Boulder Systs Inc, 86-88. *Mem:* Am Geophys Union; Seismog Soc Am; Soc Explor Geophys; AAAS. *Res:* Tectonics of earthquakes; core and mantle structures. *Mailing Add:* NSF Earth Sci Div 4201 Wilson Blvd No 785 Arlington VA 22230

**WHITCOMB, RICHARD T,** ENGINEERING ADMINISTRATION. *Current Pos:* RETIRED. *Personal Data:* b Evanston, Ill, Feb 21, 21. *Educ:* Worcester Polytech Inst, BS, 43. *Hon Degrees:* DSc, Old Dominion Univ, 85. *Honors & Awards:* Sci Achievement Medal, NASA, 59; Sylvanus Albert Reed Award, Am Inst Aeronaut & Astronaut, 69; Nat Medal of Sci, Pres US, 73; Wright Bros Mem Trophy, Nat Aeronaut Asn, 74; Meritorious Serv Aviation Award, Nat Bus Aircraft Asn, 78. *Prof Exp:* Assoc, Transonic Aerodyn Br, Langley Res Ctr, NASA, 43-58, head br, 58-80, distinguished res assoc, 80-90. *Concurrent Pos:* Consult, 80- *Mem:* Nat Acad Eng; fel Am Inst Aeronaut & Astronaut. *Res:* Author of various publications. *Mailing Add:* 46 Lakeshore Dr Apt 1B Hampton VA 23666

**WHITCOMB, STANLEY ERNEST,** GRAVITATIONAL WAVE ASTRONOMY, PRECISION OPTICAL MEASUREMENTS. *Current Pos:* dep dir, 91-95, res & develop group leader, 95, DETECTOR GROUP LEADER, LIGO PROJ, CALIF INST TECHNOL, 96- *Personal Data:* b Denver, Colo, Jan 23, 51; m 77, Laurie Silberman. *Educ:* Calif Inst Technol, BS, 73; Univ Chicago, PhD(physics), 80. *Prof Exp:* Nat Needs fel, Univ Chicago, 80; asst prof physics, Calif Inst Technol, 80-85; res engr, Electronics Div, Northrop Corp, 85-89; sr systs specialist, Loral Electro-Optical Systs, 89-91. *Mem:* Optical Soc Am; Am Phys Soc. *Res:* Development of ultra-high precision optical interferometers for gravitational wave detection, gravitational wave astrophysics, precision optical measurements. *Mailing Add:* Calif Inst Technol MS 51-33 Pasadena CA 91125. *Fax:* 626-304-9834

**WHITCOMB, WALTER HENRY,** INTERNAL MEDICINE, NUCLEAR MEDICINE. *Current Pos:* from asst prof to assoc prof, 62-79, PROF MED, SCH MED, UNIV OKLA, 79-; DIR, VET ADMIN MED CTR, 81- *Personal Data:* b Enid, Okla, Jan 26, 28; m 46; c 3. *Educ:* Univ Okla, BA, 50, MD, 53; Am Bd Nuclear Med, dipl, 72. *Prof Exp:* Clin asst, Sch Med & chief res med, Med Ctr, Univ Okla, 56-57, chief, Exp Med Group, Radiobiol Lab, Univ Tex-USAF, 58-60; investr & instr radiobiol, Bionucleonics Dept, USAF Sch Aerospace Med, 60-62. *Concurrent Pos:* Res fel hemat, Univ Okla, 57-58; clin investr, Southwest Cancer Chemother Study Group, Vet Admin Hosp, 62-66, chief, Radioisotopes Serv & Hemat Sect, 62-70, assoc chief staff res & educ, 63-67; from asst prof to assoc prof radiol, Sch Med, Univ Okla, 64-79, asst

dean vet affairs, 70-79; chief staff, Vet Admin Hosp, 70-79; mgt support staff, Dept Med & Surg, Vet Admin Cent Off, 79-81. *Mem:* Am Col Physicians; Cent Soc Clin Res; Am Soc Hemat. *Res:* Biological effects of radiation; control of erythropoiesis; physiology of erythropoietin and erythropoietin inhibitor factors; operations research. *Mailing Add:* Vet Admin Hosp 921 NE 13th St Oklahoma City OK 73104-5028

**WHITCOMB, WILLARD HALL,** TROPICAL ENTOMOLOGY. *Current Pos:* prof, 67-84, EMER PROF ENTOM, UNIV FLA, 84- *Personal Data:* b Manchester, NH, July 2, 15; m 43, Dorothy Goodwin. *Educ:* Bates Col, BS, 38; Agr & Mech Col, Tex, MS, 42; Cornell Univ, PhD(entom), 47. *Prof Exp:* Entomologist, Ministry Agr, Venezuela, 47-52 & Shell Co, Venezuela, 52-56; prof entom, Univ Ark, 56-67; pres, Fito Technica Floridana Corp, 84-93. *Mem:* Entom Soc Am; Int Orgn Biol Control; Int Palm Soc. *Res:* Biological control of arthropods; ecology and population dynamics; pest management; tropical entomology; cotton pests; Formicidae and Araneida in natural biological control; tropical entomology pheromone use; habitat management for biological control. *Mailing Add:* 4013 NW 39th Way Gainesville FL 32606

**WHITE, ADDISON HUGHSON,** SCIENCE ADMINISTRATION. *Current Pos:* RETIRED. *Personal Data:* b Clovis, Calif, Oct 13, 09; m 34; c 1. *Educ:* Occidental Col, AB, 30. *Prof Exp:* Mem staff, Bell Tel Labs, 30-53, dir chem physics res, 53-58, exec dir res phys sci, 58-67. *Concurrent Pos:* Dir semiconductor res, Bell Tel Labs, 54-58. *Mem:* Am Phys Soc. *Res:* Dielectric properties of solids; electron diffraction of thin films; thermionic emission. *Mailing Add:* 47 Woodland Ave Summit NJ 07901

**WHITE, ALAN DAVID,** GAS LASERS, LENS DESIGN. *Current Pos:* CONSULT, A D WHITE ASSOCS INC, 84- *Personal Data:* b Rahway, NJ, July 6, 23; m 52, Elizabeth Jones; c Alice, Jeffrey & Gregory. *Educ:* Rutgers Univ, BA, 49; Syracuse Univ, MSc, 51. *Honors & Awards:* David Sarnoff Award, Inst Elec & Electronics Engrs, 84. *Prof Exp:* Mem tech staff, Fed Telecommun Labs, 51-52, Bell Tel Labs, 53-83. *Mem:* Optical Soc Am; fel Inst Elec & Electronics Engrs. *Res:* X-ray projection lithography lens design; gas tubes; hene gas lasers; photoelectric tubes; photolithographic lens design. *Mailing Add:* 127 Hillside Ave Berkeley Heights NJ 07922. *E-Mail:* adwhite@worldnet.att.net

**WHITE, ALAN WAYNE,** BIOLOGICALLY ACTIVE MOLECULES. *Current Pos:* from res chemist to sr res chemist, 81-88, PRIN RES CHEMIST, EASTMAN CHEM DIV, EASTMAN KODAK CO, 89- *Personal Data:* b Kingsport, Tenn, Feb 18, 54; m 75; c 3. *Educ:* Univ Tenn, BS, 76; Harvard Univ, PhD(chem), 81. *Prof Exp:* Teaching fel org chem, Harvard Univ, 76-78, res asst, 78-81. *Mem:* Am Chem Soc; Sigma Xi; Drug Info Asn. *Res:* Design and synthesis of novel organic compounds and polymers. *Mailing Add:* 228 Montsweag Ct Kingsport TN 37664-5715

**WHITE, ALAN WHITCOMB,** PHYTOPLANKTON ECOLOGY & PHYSIOLOGY. *Current Pos:* MARINE RESOURCES MGT SPECIALIST, NAT MARINE FISHERIES SERV, WOODS HOLE, MASS, 90- *Personal Data:* b Norwood, Mass, Mar 15, 45; m 71; c 3. *Educ:* Col William & Mary, BS, 66; Harvard Univ, MA, 69, PhD(biol), 72. *Prof Exp:* Fel, Dept Microbiol & Chem, Hadassah Med Sch, Jerusalem, 72-73; res scientist, Can Dept Fisheries & Oceans, 73-86; marine sci adv, Sea Grant Prog, Woods Hole Oceanog Inst, 86-90. *Concurrent Pos:* Asst ed, J Fisheries Res Bd, Can, 78; vis scientist, Nansei Regional Fisheries Res Lab, Hiroshima, Japan, 82-83; leader, Nat Coord Ctr Harmful Algae Blooms; chmn, Third Int Conf Toxic Dinoflagellates, 85. *Mem:* Phycol Soc Am; Am Soc Limnol & Oceanog. *Res:* Ecology, physiology and toxicology of toxic dinoflagellate blooms and red tides; the fate of dinoflagellate toxins in the marine food web; consequences of toxins for fisheries resources. *Mailing Add:* Mass Maritime Acad Buzzards Bay MA 02543-1097

**WHITE, ALBERT CORNELIUS,** ENTOMOLOGY. *Current Pos:* INDEPENDENT CONSULT, 78- *Personal Data:* b Clearwater, Fla, July 17, 27; m 49; c 3. *Educ:* Clemson Col, BS, 51; Univ Wis, MS, 53. *Prof Exp:* res entomologist, Ortho Div, Chevron Chem Co, 53-69, int res specialist, 69-76. *Concurrent Pos:* Entomologist, WFla Arthropod Res Lab, 77-78; pres, Fla Entom Soc. *Mem:* Entom Soc Am; Mex Entom Soc. *Res:* Contract research and development on all pesticides, citrus production and pest control consultation; investigations of pesticide damage and environmental studies. *Mailing Add:* 817 W Fairbanks Ave Orlando FL 32804

**WHITE, ALBERT GEORGE, JR,** MATHEMATICS. *Current Pos:* assoc prof, 69-77, PROF MATH, ST BONAVENTURE UNIV, 77-, CHMN DEPT, 70- *Personal Data:* b Centralia, Ill, July 16, 40; m 67; c 4. *Educ:* Southern Ill Univ, Edwardsville, BA, 62; Univ Mo, Columbia, MA, 64; St Louis Univ, PhD(math), 68. *Prof Exp:* Asst prof math, Ill State Univ, 67-69. *Mem:* Am Math Soc; Math Asn Am. *Mailing Add:* Dept Math St Bonaventure Univ St Bonaventure NY 14778

**WHITE, ALBERT M,** CLINICAL PHARMACY. *Current Pos:* from instr to assoc prof, 56-72, PROF PHARM, ALBANY COL PHARM, 72-, ASSOC DEAN, 74- *Personal Data:* b Derby, Conn, June 12, 26; m 55, Carolyn; c Michael, Timothy, Megan, Brian, Patrick & Daniel. *Educ:* Univ Conn, BS, 48, MS, 52. *Hon Degrees:* DSc, Union Univ, 90. *Honors & Awards:* Lederle Award. *Prof Exp:* Asst chem & pharm, Univ Conn, 50-52. *Concurrent Pos:* Clin assoc prof admin med, State Univ NY Upstate Med Ctr; assoc clin prof, Albany Vet Admin Hosp; consult, Whitney M Young Health Ctr & Villa

Mary Immaculate Nursing Home & NY Dept Health, Parsons Family Care Ctr; state dir, Am Bd Dipl in Pharm; consult, Parsons Family Care Ctr; vis prof, Thailand Col Pharm. *Mem:* Am Pharmaceut Asn; Am Soc Hosp Pharmacists; Am Soc Consult Pharmacists; Am Asn Cols Pharm; Pres Pharm Leadership Soc; Am Soc Health Syst Pharm. *Res:* Delivery of clinical pharmaceutical services to institutionalized and health center patients; practice of clinical pharmacy by community pharmacists; evaluation of practice experience programs; development of pharmaceutical care practice programs. *Mailing Add:* 3 Nina Dr Albany NY 12205. *Fax:* 518-445-7202

**WHITE, ALICE ELIZABETH,** SOLID STATE PHYSICS, TECHNICAL MANAGEMENT. *Current Pos:* Mem tech staff, 82-88, DEPT HEAD, AT&T BELL LABS, 88- *Personal Data:* b Glen Ridge, NJ, Apr 5, 54; m 90, Donald P Monroe; c Ellen E Monroe & Janet C Monroe. *Educ:* Middlebury Col, BA, 76; Harvard Univ, MA, 78, PhD(physics), 82. *Honors & Awards:* Maria Goeppert-Mayer Award, Am Phys Soc, 91. *Concurrent Pos:* Consult, Lincoln Labs, Mass Inst Technol, 79-82. *Mem:* Am Phys Soc; Mat Res Soc; Optical Soc Am. *Res:* High dose ion implantation for compound formation; defects in superconductors; silicon optical bench waveguides. *Mailing Add:* Lucent Technol Bell Labs Rm 1D-339 PO Box 636 Murray Hill NJ 07974-0636. *Fax:* 908-582-2783

**WHITE, ALVIN MURRAY,** MATHEMATICS, SCIENCE EDUCATION. *Current Pos:* assoc prof, 62-80, PROF MATH, HARVEY MUDD COL, 80- *Personal Data:* b New York, NY, June 21, 25; m 46, Myra Goldstein; c Louis & Michael. *Educ:* Columbia Univ, AB, 49; Univ Calif, Los Angeles, MA, 51; Stanford Univ, PhD, 61. *Prof Exp:* Asst prof math, Univ Santa Clara, 54-61; mem, Math Res Ctr, US Army, Wis, 61-62. *Concurrent Pos:* Fac fel, Danforth Found, 75-76; vis scientist, Div Study & Res in Educ, Mass Inst Technol, 76; mem, Blue Ribbon Comt on Writing Stand, Calif Comn Post Sec Educ, 80; initiator & proj dir, New Interdisciplinary Holistic Approaches to Teaching/ Learning, Fund Improv Post Sec Educ, 77-81; ed, Humanistic Math Network Newslet. *Mem:* Am Math Soc; Math Asn Am; Fedn Am Scientists; AAAS; Am Asn Univ Profs; Sigma Xi. *Res:* Function theoretical aspects of partial differential equations; quasiconformal mapping; nature of scientific creativity; nurture of scientific creativity; interdisciplinary teaching; science education. *Mailing Add:* Dept Math Harvey Mudd Col 301 E 12th St Claremont CA 91711-5990

**WHITE, ANDREW MICHAEL,** ICHTHYOLOGY, LIMNOLOGY. *Current Pos:* PROF BIOL, JOHN CARROLL UNIV, 70-; PRES, ENVIRON RESOURCE ASSOCS, 77- *Personal Data:* b Elyria, Ohio, Mar 17, 42; div; c Pamela & Jennifer. *Educ:* Ohio State Univ, BS, 66, PhD(zool), 73. *Prof Exp:* Res assoc parasitol, US Dept Interior Dis Invest Lab, 63-64; teaching assoc zool, Ohio State Univ, 65-70; trustee ecol, Cleveland Environ Res, 73-77. *Concurrent Pos:* Res dir grant, USEPA Study Lake Erie Fisheries, 72-75; assoc cur fishes, Cleveland Mus Natural Hist, 75-; mem, Endangered Species Comt, Ohio Biol Surv, 76-; consult, Nat Comn Water Qual, 76-77; res dir grant, Fish Degradation NE Ohio Streams, Ohio Dept Natural Resources, 72-82, sea lamprey grant, US Fish & Wildlife Serv, 83-, endangered species grant, 85-; pres, Ohio Acad Sic, 87. *Mem:* Am Asn Parasitol; Am Fisheries Soc; Am Asn Limnol Oceanog; Int Asn Great Lakes Res. *Res:* Freshwater fisheries research, especially concerned with the Great Lakes ecosystem; major emphasis of ecology of non-game species in relation to spawning, growth, zoogeography, subspeciation and niche utilization. *Mailing Add:* Dept Biol John Carroll Univ 20700 N Park Blvd Cleveland OH 44118-4520

**WHITE, ANDREW WILSON, JR,** SOIL CONSERVATION, SOIL FERTILITY. *Current Pos:* CONSULT, 86- *Personal Data:* b Thomaston, Ga, Aug 1, 27; m 50; c 2. *Educ:* Univ Ga, BS, 49, MS, 58, PhD, 69. *Prof Exp:* Soil scientist, Soil & Water Conserv Res Div, USDA, 51-61, res soil scientist, Southern Piedmont Conserv Res Ctr, 61-75, soil scientist, Southeastern Fruit & Nut Tree Lab, Sci & Educ Admin-Agr Res, 75-86. *Mailing Add:* 180 High Shoals Rd Watkinsville GA 30677

**WHITE, ARLYNN QUINTON, JR,** BENTHIC MARINE ORGANISMS, WATER QUALITY. *Current Pos:* From asst prof to assoc prof, 76-88, prof & chair biol & marine sci, 88-94, CHAIR, DIV SCI & MATH, JACKSONVILLE UNIV, 94- *Personal Data:* b Norfolk, Va, Jan 17, 46; m 83, Susan H; c A Quinton III, Stephanie & Garrett. *Educ:* NC Wesleyan Col, BS, 68; Univ Va, MS, 72; Univ SC, PhD(biol), 76. *Concurrent Pos:* Consult, A Quinton White & Assoc, 76-; assoc dir, Environ Ctr, 78- & Charter Marine Sci Ctr, 80- *Mem:* Nat Marine Educr Asn (treas, 86-90); Estuarine Res Fedn; Sigma Xi; AAAS; Am Inst Biol Sci. *Res:* Marine science ecology of St Johns River; behavior and physiology of benthic marine organism; water quality-pollution impacts on marine organisms; estuarines and artificial reefs; marine science-pollution and ecology of St Johns River; manatees. *Mailing Add:* Dept Biol & Marine Sci Jacksonville Univ Jacksonville FL 32211. *Fax:* 352-745-7573; *E-Mail:* qwhite@junix.ju.edu

**WHITE, ARNOLD ALLEN,** BIOCHEMISTRY. *Current Pos:* from asst prof to assoc prof, 56-77, PROF BIOCHEM, UNIV MO, COLUMBIA, 77-, INVESTR, DALTON RES CTR, 66- *Personal Data:* b New York, NY, Oct 13, 23; m 53; c 5. *Educ:* Univ Iowa, AB, 47, MS, 49; Georgetown Univ, PhD(biochem), 54. *Prof Exp:* From instr to asst prof biochem, Georgetown Univ, 52-56. *Mem:* AAAS; Am Soc Biol Chemists; Sigma Xi. *Res:* Signal translation mechanisms; cyclic nucleotide research. *Mailing Add:* 4755 N Camino Gaccia Tucson AZ 85718-6813. *Fax:* 573-884-4232

**WHITE, ARTHUR C,** INTERNAL MEDICINE, INFECTIOUS DISEASES. *Current Pos:* RETIRED. *Personal Data:* b Williamsburg, Ky, Aug 1, 25; m 49; c 3. *Educ:* Univ Ky, BS; Harvard Univ, MD, 52. *Prof Exp:* Instr med, Vanderbilt Univ, 53-58; from instr to asst prof, Univ Louisville, 58-63; assoc prof, Med Col Ga, 63-67; prof med, Sch Med, Ind Univ, Indianapolis, 67-96. *Concurrent Pos:* Consult, Vet Admin Hosps, Louisville, Ky, 59-63 & Augusta, Ga, 63-67; Drug Efficacy Study, Nat Acad Sci, 66. *Mem:* Am Soc Microbiol; Am Fedn Clin Res; Am Col Physicians; Infectious Dis Soc Am. *Res:* Staphylococcal epidemiology and immunology; immunoglobulins and their activity; immunology of gram negative infections; histamine release. *Mailing Add:* 6363 Glencoe Dr Indianapolis IN 46260

**WHITE, ARTHUR THOMAS, II,** MATHEMATICS. *Current Pos:* from asst prof to assoc prof, 69-79, PROF MATH, WESTERN MICH UNIV, 79- *Personal Data:* b Orange, NJ, Oct 7, 39; m 61, Elizabeth Siber; c Toby Andrew & Terrence Adam. *Educ:* Oberlin Col, AB, 61; Mich State Univ, MS, 66, PhD(math), 69. *Prof Exp:* Actuarial trainee, Home Life Ins Co, 61-62. *Concurrent Pos:* Commun electronics officer, USAF, 62-65; asst & fel, Mich State Univ, 65-69; NSF grant, 73-74; vis prof, Royal Holloway Col, Univ London, 77-78; managing ed, J Graph Theory, 78-80; vis lectr, Clemson Univ, 79; vis fel, Wolfson Col, Oxford Univ & sr vis, Math Inst, 84-85 & 91-92; fac teaching fel, Western Mich Univ, 85-86; Clarke Benedict Williams lectureship math, Kalamazoo Col, 88; vis lectr, Math Asn Am, 93-96. *Mem:* Am Math Soc; London Math Soc; Math Asn Am; Sigma Xi; Nat Coun Teachers Math. *Res:* Topological graph theory; imbedding of graphs; genus of graphs and of groups; block designs; symmetrical maps; change ringing; random topological graph theory; enumerative topological graph theory; genus of geometries. *Mailing Add:* Dept Math Western Mich Univ Kalamazoo MI 49008. *Fax:* 616-387-4530; *E-Mail:* white@umich.edu

**WHITE, AUGUSTUS AARON, III,** ORTHOPEDIC SURGERY, BIOMEDICAL ENGINEERING. *Current Pos:* PROF ORTHOP SURG, HARVARD MED SCH, 78- *Personal Data:* b Memphis, Tenn, June 4, 36; m 74; c 3. *Educ:* Brown Univ, BA, 57; Stanford Univ, MD, 61; Karolinska Inst, Stockholm, Sweden, Dr Med Sci, 69. *Hon Degrees:* LHD, Univ New Haven, Conn. *Honors & Awards:* Eastern Orthop Asn Award, Outstanding Spine Res, 80. *Prof Exp:* Intern, Univ Hosp, Ann Arbor, Mich, 61-62; from instr to assoc prof orthop surg, Sch Med, Yale Univ, 65-78, dir biomech res, Sect Orthop Surg, 73-78; orthop surgeon-in-chief, Beth Israel Hosp, 78-91. *Concurrent Pos:* Chief resident orthop surg, Vet Admin Hosp, W Haven, Conn, 66; attend orthop surgeon, Yale-New Haven Hosp, 69-78; consult, Vet Admin Hosp, W Haven & Hill Health Ctr, New Haven, 69-78; mem, Bioeng Res Comt, Int Coun Sports & Phys Educ, 74; Am Brit Can traveling fel award, Am Orthop Asn, 75; mem adv coun, Nat Arthritis, Metab & Digestive Dis, 79-82; bd fel, Brown Univ, 81-92, emer fel, 92. *Mem:* Orthop Res Soc; Cervical Spine Res Soc (pres, 88); Int Soc Study Lumbar Spine; Am Acad Orthop Surgeons; Nat Med Asn. *Res:* Mechanical studies on the entire human spine designed to provide knowledge and technology applicable to clinical problems; development of an engineering system which will accelerate fracture healing. *Mailing Add:* Beth Israel Deaconess Med Ctr 330 Brookline Ave Boston MA 02215

**WHITE, BENJAMIN STEVEN,** STOCHASTIC PROCESSES, WAVE PROPAGATION. *Current Pos:* sr staff mathematician, 81-84, head, Appl Math Group, 86-89, RES ASSOC, EXXON RES & ENG CO, 85- *Personal Data:* b Boston, Mass, Sept 29, 45; m 66, Helen K Frazer; c Adam Frazer & Ethan Abraham. *Educ:* Mass Inst Technol, SB, 67; Univ Ariz, MA, 68; New York Univ, PhD(math), 74. *Prof Exp:* Vis mem, Courant Inst, New York Univ, 74-75; instr appl math, Calif Inst Technol, 75-78; mem tech staff, Jet Propulsion Lab, 78-81. *Concurrent Pos:* Instr, Math Dept, New York Univ, 71-72; vpres, Perceptive Systs Inc, Pasadena, Calif, 81. *Mem:* Soc Indust & Appl Math; Am Math Soc; AAAS. *Res:* Applications of stochastic processes; wave propagation; wave propagation in random media. *Mailing Add:* Exxon Res & Eng Co Rte 22 E Annandale NJ 08801. *Fax:* 908-730-3232; *E-Mail:* bswhite@erenj.com

**WHITE, BERNARD HENRY,** PHYSICAL CHEMISTRY, CHEMICAL ENGINEERING. *Current Pos:* Res scientist, Exxon Co, USA, 76-78, sr scientist, 78-81, sect head, Exxon Res & Eng Co, 81-86, PRECIOUS METALS CATALYSTS, EXXON CO, USA, 86- *Personal Data:* b Chicago, Ill, Oct 15, 47; m 68, Joan Fierst; c Simma, Miriam & Chaim. *Educ:* Univ Cincinnati, BS, 69; Univ Wash, MS, 71; Univ Houston, PhD(phys chem), 76. *Concurrent Pos:* Robert A Welch res fel, Dept Chem, Univ Houston, 73-76. *Mem:* Am Chem Soc; Am Phys Soc. *Res:* Synthetic fuels, both liquids and gases, derived from coal and shale; chemistry of coal liquefaction and gasification; process designs for coal and shale; oil refining processes; reforming and hydrocracking. *Mailing Add:* Exxon Co USA PO Box 4552 Houston TX 77210. *Fax:* 713-656-7211

**WHITE, BERNARD J,** BIOCHEMISTRY. *Current Pos:* asst prof, 68-74, ASSOC PROF BIOCHEM, IOWA STATE UNIV, 74- *Personal Data:* b Portland, Ore, Jan 8, 37; m 63; c 5. *Educ:* Univ Portland, BS, 58; Univ Ore, MA, 61, PhD(biochem), 63. *Prof Exp:* Asst prof chem, Loras Col, 63-68. *Concurrent Pos:* Vis prof, Univ Md, 76-77. *Mem:* AAAS; Am Chem Soc. *Res:* Protein structure; biochemical evolution; enzymology. *Mailing Add:* 4210 Molec Biol Iowa State Univ Ames IA 50011-0001. *Fax:* 515-294-0453; *E-Mail:* b.white@molebioliastateedu

**WHITE, BLANCHE BABETTE,** chemistry; deceased, see previous edition for last biography

**WHITE, BRIAN,** CARBONATE SEDIMENTOLOGY. *Current Pos:* from instr to asst prof, 68-73, assoc prof & chmn dept, 73-82, PROF GEOL, SMITH COL, 82- *Personal Data:* b Brigg, Eng, Feb 19, 36; m 62; c 2. *Educ:* Univ Wales, BSc, 63, PhD(geol), 66. *Prof Exp:* Fel, Dalhousie Univ, 66-68. *Mem:* Soc Econ Paleontologists & Mineralogists; Geol Soc Am; Sigma Xi; Int Asn Sedimentologists. *Res:* Stratigraphy, sedimentary petrology and micropaleobotany of precambrian sedimentary rocks; onaternary carbonates; fossil coral reefs. *Mailing Add:* Dept Geol Smith Col Northampton MA 01063

**WHITE, BRUCE LANGTON,** PHYSICS. *Current Pos:* RETIRED. *Personal Data:* b Wellington, NZ, Mar 2, 31; m 54; c 2. *Educ:* New Zealand, BSc, 52; Univ London, DIC & PhD, 56. *Prof Exp:* Res fel physics, Univ BC, 56-59, res assoc, 59-60, from asst prof to assoc prof, 60-70, prof, 70- *Mem:* Am Phys Soc. *Res:* Experimental low energy nuclear physics; experimental cosmology and gravitation; Mossbauer effect. *Mailing Add:* Dept Physics Univ BC Univ Campus 6224 Agr Rd Vancouver BC V6T 1Z1 Can

**WHITE, CALVIN LAMONT,** INTERGRANULAR FRACTURE & SEGREGATION, WELDING & JOINING. *Current Pos:* PROF METALL ENG, MICH TECHNOL UNIV, 86-, CHAIR, DEPT METALL & MAT ENG, 96- *Personal Data:* b Chico, Calif, Nov 14, 47; m 68, Elsie J Mertens; c Calvin F. *Educ:* Univ Calif, Davis, BS, 69; Univ Minn, MS, 71; Mich Technol Univ, PhD(metall eng), 74. *Honors & Awards:* Mat Sci Res Award, US Dept Energy, 84. *Prof Exp:* Res staff, Oak Ridge Nat Lab, 74-86. *Concurrent Pos:* Adj prof mech eng & mat sci, Vanderbilt Univ, 77-86; vis prof metall & mat eng, Fed Univ, Rio de Janeiro, 83; adj assoc prof mat sci eng, Univ Tenn, 85-88; vchair, Mat Sci Div, Am Soc Metals Int, 86-88; bd dirs, Metals Minerals & Mats Soc, 88-91; vis distinguished prof mat eng, Univ Ala, Birmingham, 89. *Mem:* Metals Minerals & Mats Soc; Am Soc Metals Int. *Res:* Trace element segregation to interfaces and the effects of segregation on the performance of engineering materials. *Mailing Add:* 604 E Seventh Ave Houghton MI 49931

**WHITE, CHARLES A, JR,** OBSTETRICS & GYNECOLOGY. *Current Pos:* RETIRED. *Personal Data:* b San Diego, Calif, Aug 1, 22; m 60, Suza Alikadi; c Craig Charles, Scott Michael & Jennifer Helen. *Educ:* Colo Agr & Mech Col, DVM, 45; Univ Utah, MD, 55; Am Bd Obstet & Gynec, dipl, 64. *Prof Exp:* Pvt pract vet med, 45-51; intern, Salt Lake Co Gen Hosp, 55-56; resident obstet & gynec, Dee Mem Hosp, Ogden, Utah, 56-57; resident, Univ Hosp, Univ Iowa, 59-61, assoc, Col Med, 61-62, from asst prof to prof, 62-74; prof obstet & gynec & chmn dept, WVa Univ, 74-80; prof obstet & gynec & head dept, Sch Med, La State Univ, 80-92. *Concurrent Pos:* Examr, Am Bd Obstet & Gynec, 71-94. *Mem:* Am Gynec & Obstet Soc; Am Col Obstet & Gynec; Soc Gynec Surgeons; Obstet & Gynec Travel Club; Am Col Surgeons; Am Gynec Club; Central Asn Obstet/Gynec; Asn Profs Obstet/Gynec. *Mailing Add:* 33 Chateau Du Jardin Dr Kenner LA 70065-2014

**WHITE, CHARLES HENRY,** DAIRY MICROBIOLOGY. *Current Pos:* PROF & E W CUSTER CHAIR DAIRY SCI, MISS STATE UNIV, 85- *Personal Data:* b Birmingham, Ala, Mar 15, 43; m 65; c 1. *Educ:* Miss State Univ, BS, 65, MS, 69; Univ Mo, PhD(dairy microbiol), 71. *Prof Exp:* Sr food scientist, Archer Daniels Midland Co, 71-72; asst prof dairy microbiol, Univ Ga, 72-76; dir qual assurance, Dean Foods Co, 76-80; prof dairy sci, La State Univ, 80-85. *Concurrent Pos:* Dairy consult; partic, Comt Revise Stand Methods Exam Dairy Prod, 74- *Mem:* Am Dairy Sci Asn; Inst Food Technol; Int Asn Milk & Food Sanitarians; Nat Environ Health Asn; Cult Dairy Prod Inst. *Res:* Psychrotrophic bacteria and relationship with shelf-life of dairy products, including measurement of proteolytic activity of raw milk as well as determination of heat-stable protease from the psychrotrophs; diacetyl reductases. *Mailing Add:* Dept Food Sci & Technol Miss State Univ PO Box NH Mississippi State MS 39762-9999

**WHITE, CHARLES RAYMOND,** OPERATIONS RESEARCH, INDUSTRIAL ENGINEERING. *Current Pos:* RETIRED. *Personal Data:* b Wabash, Ind, Dec 23, 33; c 1. *Educ:* Purdue Univ, BSME, 55, MSIE, 57, PhD(opers res), 63. *Prof Exp:* Opers res analyst, Armour & Co, 63-66; assoc prof, Indust Eng, Auburn Univ, 66-94. *Mem:* Inst Mgt Sci; Am Inst Indust Engrs; Sigma Xi. *Res:* Maintenance engineering and energy conservation. *Mailing Add:* 200 Bibb Ave Auburn AL 36830

**WHITE, CHARLEY MONROE,** ecology, wildlife biology, for more information see previous edition

**WHITE, CHRISTOPHER CLARKE,** MATHEMATICS. *Current Pos:* ASSOC PROF MATH, CASTLETON STATE COL, 70-, CHMN DEPT, 74- *Personal Data:* b Haverhill, Mass, June 24, 37. *Educ:* Bowdoin Col, AB, 59; Miami Univ, MA, 63; Univ Ore, PhD(math), 67. *Prof Exp:* Asst prof math, Univ NH, 67-70. *Mem:* Sigma Xi. *Res:* Banach algebras; harmonic analysis. *Mailing Add:* PO Box 1554 Castleton VT 05735-1554

**WHITE, CLARK WOODY,** PHYSICS. *Current Pos:* MEM RES STAFF PHYSICS, OAK RIDGE NAT LAB, 75- *Personal Data:* b Rome, Ga, May 4, 40; m 70; c 2. *Educ:* Mass Inst Technol, BS, 62; Duke Univ, PhD(physics), 67. *Honors & Awards:* IR-100 Award, 83; Woody Award, Mat Res Soc, 84. *Prof Exp:* Mem tech staff physics, Bell Labs, 67-75. *Mem:* Mat Res Soc (pres, 84); fel Am Phys Soc. *Res:* Solid state physics; ion-solid collisions; surface physics; ion implantation; laser annealing. *Mailing Add:* Solid State Div Oak Ridge Nat Lab Bldg 3137 MS-6057 Oak Ridge TN 38731. *Fax:* 423-576-8135

**WHITE, CLAYTON M,** VERTEBRATE ZOOLOGY, ECOLOGY. *Current Pos:* from asst prof to assoc prof, 70-78, PROF ZOOL, BRIGHAM YOUNG UNIV, 78- *Personal Data:* b Afton, Wyo, Apr 19, 36; m 59; c 5. *Educ:* Univ Utah, AB, 61, PhD(zool), 68. *Honors & Awards:* Francis B Roberts Award, 68. *Prof Exp:* Instr zool & cur birds, Univ Kans, 65-66; instr zool & res fel, Cornell Univ, 68-70. *Concurrent Pos:* Consult, Columbus Labs, Battelle Mem Inst, 72-, Bechtel Group, 80-; NAm coordr, Int Coun Bird Preservation, 81; mem adv comt, Div Polar Progs, NSF, 82- *Mem:* AAAS; Am Ornith Union; Soc Syst Zool; Cooper Ornith Union; Wilson Ornith Soc. *Res:* Avian evolution and systematics; ecology of raptorial birds; impact of environmental pollution in avian populations. *Mailing Add:* 1146 S 300 W Orem UT 84058

**WHITE, COLIN,** BIOMETRY. *Current Pos:* from asst prof to assoc prof, 53-62, PROF PUB HEALTH, SCH MED, YALE UNIV, 62- *Personal Data:* b Australia, Aug 25, 13; m 43; c 2. *Educ:* Univ Sydney, BSc, 35, MSc, 36, MB & BS, 40. *Prof Exp:* Intern, Sydney Hosp, Australia, 41; lectr physiol, Univ Sydney, 42; med officer, Australian Inst Anat, 43-46; lectr physiol, Univ Birmingham, 46-48; asst prof, Univ Pa, 48-50; lectr physiol, Univ Birmingham, 50-53. *Mem:* Am Statist Asn; Biomet Soc; Royal Statist Soc; fel Int Statist Inst; Sigma Xi. *Res:* Epidemiology of chronic diseases; vital statistics. *Mailing Add:* Div Animal Prod CSIRO Private Bag Wembley WA 6014 06517 Australia 6014. *Fax:* 61-9-387-8991

**WHITE, DAVID,** PHYSICAL CHEMISTRY, CRYOGENICS. *Current Pos:* dir, Lab Res Struct Matter, 81-87, chmn, Chem Dept, 66-79, PROF CHEM, UNIV PA, 79- *Personal Data:* b Russia, Jan 14, 25; nat US; m 45, Birdye Ruckenstern; c Sharon, Jacqueline & Edward. *Educ:* McGill Univ, BSc, 44; Univ Toronto, PhD(chem), 47. *Prof Exp:* Asst, Univ Toronto, 44-46; fel, Ohio State Univ, 47-48, lectr, 48-50, asst dir, Cryogenic Lab, 50-53; asst prof chem, Syracuse Univ, 53-54; from asst prof to prof, Ohio State Univ, 54-63. *Concurrent Pos:* Vis prof, Technion & Weizmann Insts, Israel, 63-64; Fulbright fel & vis prof, Univ Kyoto & Univ Tokyo, Japan, 65; Nat Ctr Sci Res fel & vis prof, Inst Appl Quantum Mech, France, 74-75; fel, Inst Dynamics Molecular Interactions, 78-94. *Mem:* Am Chem Soc; Sigma Xi; Am Phys Soc. *Res:* Low temperature thermodynamics and solid state nuclear magnetic resonance; molecular structure from Nuclear Magnetic Resonance studies; matrix isolated spectroscopy; optical coherence and relaxation studies of solids at low temperatures; catalysis, structures and dynamics of adsorption complexes. *Mailing Add:* Dept Chem Univ Pa Philadelphia PA 19104. *Fax:* 215-573-2112; *E-Mail:* dwhite@a.chem.upenn.edu

**WHITE, DAVID,** MICROBIOLOGY. *Current Pos:* asst prof, 67-74, ASSOC PROF MICROBIOL, IND UNIV, BLOOMINGTON, 74-, ASSOC PROF GEOL, 80- *Personal Data:* b Boston, Mass, Apr 26, 36; m 59; c 3. *Educ:* Brandeis Univ, AB, 58, PhD(biol), 65. *Prof Exp:* Res scientist, Exobiol Div, Ames Res Ctr, NASA, 63-65; res assoc microbial physiol, Med Sch, Univ Minn, 65-67. *Concurrent Pos:* Res grants, Am Cancer Soc, 68-70, NSF, 68-70, 70-72. *Mem:* Am Soc Microbiol. *Res:* Microbial physiology; microbial development; myxobacteria. *Mailing Add:* Dept Biol Ind Univ Bloomington IN 47405

**WHITE, DAVID ARCHER,** GEOLOGY. *Current Pos:* PVT CONSULT, 86- *Personal Data:* b Philadelphia, Pa, Jan 22, 27; m 52, Hester Wolfe; c Jonathan, Daniel & Jennifer. *Educ:* Dartmouth Col, BA, 50; Univ Minn, MS, 51, PhD(geol), 54. *Prof Exp:* Sr res adv, Exxon Prod Res Co, 54-86. *Mem:* Geol Soc Am; Am Asn Petrol Geol; Soc Independent Prof Earth Scientists. *Res:* Geology of the Mesabi range, Minnesota; geochemistry; stratigraphy; hydrocarbon assessment; risk analysis. *Mailing Add:* 8114 W Court Austin TX 78759

**WHITE, DAVID CALVIN,** ELECTRICAL POWER TECHNOLOGY. *Current Pos:* from asst prof to prof, Mass Inst Technol, 52-62, Ford prof, 62-92, dir, Energy Lab, 72-89, dep dir, 90-92, EMER FORD PROF, MASS INST TECHNOL, 92- *Personal Data:* b Sunnyside, Wash, Feb 18, 22; m 49, 66, Margot Fuller; c Julie A (deceased) & Constance A. *Educ:* Stanford Univ, BS, 46, MS, 47, PhD, 49. *Honors & Awards:* Westinghouse Award, Am Soc Eng Educ, 61. *Prof Exp:* Elec engr, Kaiser Co Inc, 42-45; assoc prof elec eng, Univ Fla, 49-52. *Concurrent Pos:* Lectr, Univ London, 61; vis prof & consult, Purdue Univ, 64-68; sr adv & vis prof, Birla Inst Technol & Sci, Pilani, India, 68-70; coun mem, Univ Benin, Nigeria, 70-72; trustee, Lowell Technol Inst, 72-74; mem adv coun, Elec Power Inst, 80-87, chmn, 84-86; mem, Res Coord Panel, Gas Res Inst, 80-87, chmn, 84-86; mem corp, Woods Hole Oceanog Inst, 77-83. *Mem:* Nat Acad Eng; fel Am Acad Arts & Sci; Am Soc Eng Educ; fel Inst Elec & Electronics Engrs. *Res:* Energy supply and demand analysis; energy conversion devices and systems; research and development planning. *Mailing Add:* Mass Inst Technol Energy Lab 1 Amherst St Bldg E40 AC3-455 Cambridge MA 02139-4307

**WHITE, DAVID CLEAVELAND,** TOXICOLOGY, ANALYTICAL CHEMISTRY. *Current Pos:* PROF MICROBIOL & ECOL, UNIV TENN, 86-, DIR, INST APPL MICROBIOL, 86-, DISTINGUISHED SCIENTIST, OAK RIDGE NAT LAB, 86- *Personal Data:* b Moline, Ill, May 18, 29; m 56, Sandra Shoults; c Winifred, Christopher & Andrew. *Educ:* Dartmouth Col, AB, 51; Tufts Univ, MD, 55; Rockefeller Univ, PhD(biochem), 62. *Honors & Awards:* P R Edwards Award, Am Soc Microbiol, 81; Sci & Tech Achievement Award, US Environ Protection Agency, 87; Proctor & Gamble Prize, Appl & Environ Microbiol, Am Soc Microbiol, 93; Athalie Richardson Irvine Clark Prize, Nat Water Res Inst, 95. *Prof Exp:* Intern, Univ Hosp, Univ Pa, 55-56, instr physiol, 56-58, res assoc med, 58; from asst prof to prof biochem, Univ Ky, 62-72; prof biol & assoc dir, Prog Med Sci, Fla State Univ, 72-86. *Concurrent Pos:* Prof community health & family med, Med Sch, Univ Fla, Gainesville, 75-86; adj prof, Interdept Toxicol Prog, Med Ctr, Univ Ark,

Little Rock & Nat Ctr Toxicol Res, Jefferson, 81-; vis prof, Am Soc Microbiol. *Mem:* Am Soc Biol Chem; Am Soc Limnol & Oceanog; Soc Toxicol; Am Soc Microbiol; Am Soc Moss Spectromists; Am Chem Soc. *Res:* Microbial ecology of microbially influenced corrosion; toxicant biodegradation; groundwater bioremediation; application of analytical chemistry to microbiol system; indoor air bioconamination; drinking water microbiology; microbiol biofilm ecology. *Mailing Add:* 11104 Poplar Ridge 10515 Research Dr Suite 300 Knoxville TN 37932-2575. *Fax:* 423-974-8027; *E-Mail:* pa112238@utkumi

**WHITE, DAVID EVANS,** FOREST ECONOMICS. *Current Pos:* from asst prof to assoc prof, 64-71, dir, Div Forestry, 66-76, PROF FOREST ECON & POLICY, WVA UNIV, 71- *Personal Data:* b Syracuse, NY, Dec 13, 32; m 52; c 4. *Educ:* State Univ NY Col Forestry, Syracuse Univ, BS, 59, MS, 60, PhD(econ), 65. *Prof Exp:* Forester, Crown-Zellerbach Corp, 60-61; instr forest econ, State Univ NY Col Forestry, Syracuse Univ, 61-64. *Mem:* Fel Soc Am Foresters. *Res:* Forest resources policy and administration; multi-disciplinary studies in environmental decision-making; natural resources economics; land use planning. *Mailing Add:* Rte 2 Unit 6 Box 15 Terra Alta WV 26764

**WHITE, DAVID GOVER,** INORGANIC CHEMISTRY. *Current Pos:* From asst prof to assoc prof, 53-62, PROF CHEM, GEORGE WASHINGTON UNIV, 62- *Personal Data:* b Woodbury, NJ, Sept 21, 27; m 59. *Educ:* Cornell Univ, BChE, 50; Harvard Univ, PhD(chem), 54. *Concurrent Pos:* NSF fel, 60. *Mem:* Am Chem Soc; Royal Soc Chem. *Res:* Organometallic chemistry; boron-nitrogen compounds; metal complexes. *Mailing Add:* Dept Chem George Washington Univ Washington DC 20052-0001

**WHITE, DAVID HYWEL,** EXPERIMENTAL PARTICLE PHYSICS. *Current Pos:* group leader nuclear & particle physics res, 86-94, STAFF SCIENTIST, LOS ALAMOS NAT LAB, 94- *Personal Data:* b Cardiff, Wales, June 4, 31; m 54, Frances Shearman; c Richard & Christopher. *Educ:* Univ Wales, BSc, 53; Univ Birmingham, PhD(physics), 56. *Prof Exp:* Res fel physics, Univ Birmingham, 56-58, asst lectr, 58-59; res assoc, Univ Pa, 59-61, asst prof, 61-64; from assoc prof to prof physics, Cornell Univ, 64-78; sr physicist, Brookhaven Nat Lab, 78-86. *Mem:* Am Phys Soc. *Res:* Experimental particle physics; weak interactions; neutrino physics. *Mailing Add:* P-11 H846 Los Alamos Nat Lab Los Alamos NM 36830. *Fax:* 505-665-7920; *E-Mail:* white@lanl.gov

**WHITE, DAVID SANFORD,** LIMNOLOGY, AQUATIC ENTOMOLOGY. *Current Pos:* res scientist limnol, 77-80, ASSOC RES LIMNOLOGIST, GREAT LAKES RES DIV & ASST PROF NATURAL RESOURCES, UNIV MICH, 80- *Personal Data:* b Ashburnham, Mass, Sept 16, 45; m 66; c 1. *Educ:* DePauw Univ, AB & MS, 70; Univ Louisville, PhD (biol), 74. *Prof Exp:* Res biol ecol, Univ Okla, Biol Sta, 74-77. *Concurrent Pos:* Vis scientist, Ill Natural Hist Surv, 77. *Mem:* Entom Soc Am; Am Entom Soc; Ecol Soc Am; Sigma Xi. *Res:* Benthic ecology, the distribution and abundance of aquatic invertebrates in relation to sediment and water quality; ecology and systematics of riffle beetles. *Mailing Add:* RR 7 Box 788 Murray KY 42071-9061

**WHITE, DEAN KINCAID,** DENTAL PATHOLOGY. *Current Pos:* PROF ORAL PATH & CHMN DEPT, COL DENT, UNIV KY, 77- *Personal Data:* b Tulsa, Okla, Aug 27, 44; m 67; c 1. *Educ:* Univ Okla, BS, 66; Univ Mo, Kansas City, DDS, 70; Ind Univ, MSD, 72; Am Bd Oral Path, dipl, 75. *Prof Exp:* Asst prof path, Sch Dent, Temple Univ, 72-77. *Concurrent Pos:* Consult, Vet Admin. *Mem:* Am Dent Asn; Am Acad Oral Path. *Res:* Clinical research in oral neoplasia. *Mailing Add:* Dept Oral Path Univ Ky Col Dent Lexington KY 40536

**WHITE, DONALD BENJAMIN,** ORNAMENTAL HORTICULTURE, GENETICS. *Current Pos:* from asst prof to assoc prof, 61-69, PROF HORT, UNIV MINN, ST PAUL, 69-, PROF LANDSCAPE ARCHIT, 74- *Personal Data:* b Framingham, Mass, Feb 15, 30; m 53; c 6. *Educ:* Univ Mass, BS, 56; Iowa State Univ, PhD(hort genetics, breeding), 61. *Prof Exp:* Res assoc hort, Iowa State Univ, 56-59, res asst, 59-61. *Mem:* Am Soc Hort Sci; Am Soc Agron; Soil Sci Soc Am. *Res:* Physiology of cold acclimation and dwarfing of woody plants; breeding and genetics of grasses; physiology of chemical growth regulation of monocots. *Mailing Add:* Dept Hort Sci Univ Minn St Paul 1970 Folwell Ave St Paul MN 55108-6007

**WHITE, DONALD EDWARD,** GEOLOGY. *Current Pos:* geologist, 39-63, res geologist, 63-92, EMER SCIENTIST, US GEOL SURV, 92- *Personal Data:* b Dinuba, Calif, May 7, 14; m 41, Helen B Severance; c Margaret (Matlin), Eleanor (Cannan) & Catherine. *Educ:* Stanford Univ, AB, 36; Princeton Univ, PhD(econ geol, petrol), 39. *Honors & Awards:* Geothermal Pioneer Award, Geothermal Resources Coun; Penrose Medal, Geol Soc Am, 84, Soc Econ Geol, 92. *Prof Exp:* Assoc geologist, Geol Surv Nfld, Can, 37-38. *Concurrent Pos:* Asst chief, Mineral Deposits Br, US Geol Surv, DC, 58-60. *Mem:* Nat Acad Sci; fel Geol Soc Am; fel Soc Econ Geologists (pres, 82); fel Mineral Soc Am; Geochem Soc; Int Asn Geochem. *Res:* Origin and geochemistry of thermal and mineral springs, their precipitation minerals and their relations to volcanism and ore deposits; geothermal energy; origin and nature of ore-forming fluids; origin and characteristics of geysers; isotope geology of waters and associated rock alteration; abnormal geothermal gradients conductive and convective. *Mailing Add:* 501 Portola Rd No 8029 Portola Valley CA 94028

**WHITE, DONALD GLENN,** BREEDING FOR DISEASE RESISTANCE IN CORN. *Current Pos:* PROF PLANT PATH, UNIV ILL, URBANA, 74- *Personal Data:* b Charleston, WVa, Mar 16, 46; m 68, Sharon C Eastwood; c Lisa M & Brian R. *Educ:* Marshall Univ, BA, 68, MS, 70; Ohio State Univ, PhD(plant path), 73. *Prof Exp:* Lectr plant path, Ohio State Univ, 73-74. *Mem:* Am Phytopath Soc; Crop Sci Soc Am; Am Soc Agron. *Res:* Fungal diseases of field crops; stalk rot, ear rot, storage molds of corn; mycotoxins. *Mailing Add:* Dept Plant Path Univ Ill N 425 Turner Urbana IL 61801

**WHITE, DONALD HARVEY,** NUCLEAR SPECTROSCOPY. *Current Pos:* prof physics, 71-95, EMER PROF PHYSICS, WESTERN ORE STATE COL, 95- *Personal Data:* b Berkeley, Calif, Apr 30, 31; m 53, Beverly Jones; c Jeri, Brett, Holly, Scott & Erin. *Educ:* Univ Calif, Berkeley, AB, 53; Cornell Univ, PhD(physics), 60. *Prof Exp:* Asst, Cornell Univ, 53-57, DuPont scholar, 58-59; res physicist, Lawrence Livermore Lab, Univ Calif, 60-71. *Concurrent Pos:* Lectr, Univ Calif, Berkeley, 70; consult, Lawrence Livermore Lab, 71-82; vis res physicist, Inst Laue-Langevin, Grenoble, France, 77-78, 84-85 & 91-92; fel, Minna-Heineman, 77-78; pres, Ore Acad Sci, 79-80. *Mem:* Am Phys Soc; Am Asn Physics Teachers. *Res:* Neutron capture gamma-ray and conversion electron spectroscopy of trans-uranium nucleides; nuclear models. *Mailing Add:* Div Natural Sci & Math Western Ore State Col Monmouth OR 97361. *E-Mail:* whited@fsa.wosc.osshe.edu

**WHITE, DONALD HENRY,** ENVIRONMENTAL CONTAMINANTS ON WILDLIFE & THEIR HABITATS. *Current Pos:* Zoologist, US Fish & Wildlife Serv, Patuxent Wildlife Res Ctr, Laurel, Md, 74-76, res zoologist, Gulf Coast Fields Sta, Victoria, Tex, 76-83, RES ZOOLOGIST & GROUP LEADER, US FISH & WILDLIFE SERV, PATUXENT WILDLIFE RES CTR, SOUTHEAST RES STA, ATHENS, GA, 83-; ADJ ASSOC PROF, SCH FOREST RESOURCES, UNIV GA, ATHENS, 83- *Personal Data:* b West Monroe, La, May 9, 40. *Educ:* Northeast La Univ, BS, 70, MS, 71; Univ Ark, PhD(zool), 75. *Mem:* Am Ornithologists Union; Asn Field Ornithologists; Nat Wildlife Fedn. *Res:* Study the effects of environmental contaminants on wildlife and their habitats, primarily birds in aquatic habitats. *Mailing Add:* Biol Resources USGS Warnell Sch Forest Res Univ Ga Athens GA 30602-2152

**WHITE, DONALD ROBERTSON,** OPTICAL PHYSICS, SHOCK WAVES. *Current Pos:* RETIRED. *Personal Data:* b Schenectady, NY, Sept 27, 24; m 47, 96, Nancy Delong; c Glenn H, Paul R, Robert D & Walker A. *Educ:* Union Col, BS, 48; Princeton Univ, MA, 50, PhD(physics), 51. *Prof Exp:* Res asst physics, Princeton Univ, 51-52; physicist, Gen Elec Co, 52-68, mgr, Optical Physics Br, 68-79, tech adminr, Corp Res & Develop Ctr, 79-85. *Concurrent Pos:* Coffin fel, 48; adj prof, Rensselaer Polytech Inst, 60-65. *Mem:* Fel Am Phys Soc; Combustion Inst. *Res:* Shock tubes and shock wave phenomena; gaseous detonation; optically pumped lasers. *Mailing Add:* 16 Garnsey Rd Rexford NY 12148

**WHITE, DWAIN MONTGOMERY,** ORGANIC CHEMISTRY, POLYMER CHEMISTRY. *Current Pos:* RES CHEMIST, RES & DEVELOP CTR, GEN ELEC CO, 56- *Personal Data:* b Minneapolis, Minn, Feb 16, 31; m 56; c 4. *Educ:* Univ Wis, BS, 53; Mass Inst Tech, PhD (chem), 56. *Concurrent Pos:* Coolidge fel, 88. *Mem:* Am Chem Soc; Sigma Xi. *Res:* Organic synthesis and structure determination; oxidative coupling reactions; heterocyclics; synthesis and reactions of polyphenylene oxides. *Mailing Add:* 2334 St Joseph Dr Schenectady NY 12301-2214

**WHITE, EDMUND W(ILLIAM),** CHEMICAL ENGINEERING, FUELS CHEMISTRY & STABILITY. *Current Pos:* RETIRED. *Personal Data:* b Philadelphia, Pa, July 8, 20; m 48, K Nathalie Cadwallader; c Christine, William, Thomas & James. *Educ:* Columbia Univ, AB, 40, BS, 41, ChE, 42; Lehigh Univ, PhD(chem eng), 52; Am Univ, cert opers res, 71. *Honors & Awards:* Award of Merit, Am Soc Testing & Mat, 92; Com D02 Award for Achievement, Am Soc Testing & Mat, 93. *Prof Exp:* Chem engr, Westvaco Chlorine Prods Corp, 42-44; design engr, C L Mantell, 46-47; tech staff engr, Diamond Alkali Co, 47-49; asst chem eng & res asst heat transfer, Inst Res, Lehigh Univ, 49-50 & teach asst, 50-51; pilot plant engr & proj leader, Cities Serv Res & Develop Co, NJ, 51-56, staff engr, NY, 56-60, staff engr & budget officer, Cities Serv Athabasca, Inc, 60-65; oper res analyst, Naval Supply Systs Command, 65-66, fuel res engr, David Taylor Res Ctr, Annapolis Lab, 66-95. *Concurrent Pos:* Instr indust stoichoimetry, Drexel Univ, 56; chmn, Petrol Prods & Lubricants, 88-91; chmn, Am Soc Testing & Mat Com D02, 88-93 chair, 94- *Mem:* Am Chem Soc; Am Inst Chem Engrs; Sigma Xi; Am Soc Testing & Mat; Int Asn Stability & Handling Liquid Fuels. *Res:* Fuels storage and stability; ship fuels and fuel systems; fuel purification; liquid-solid and liquid-liquid separations; filters and filter/separators; synfuels properties and composition; fuels at low temperatures. *Mailing Add:* 908 Crest Park Dr Silver Spring MD 20903-1307

**WHITE, EDWARD,** IMMUNOLOGY, ENDODONTICS. *Current Pos:* chmn dept, 72-77, PROF ENDODONTICS, COL DENT MED, MED UNIV SC, 72- *Personal Data:* b Florence, SC, Nov 23, 33; m 55; c 5. *Educ:* Emory Univ, DDS, 58; Med Univ SC, MS, 66; Univ Calif, Los Angeles, PhD(microbiol, immunol), 69. *Prof Exp:* Asst prof microbiol & immunol, Sch Dent, Univ Southern Calif, 69-72. *Mem:* Transplantation Soc; Am Soc Microbiol. *Res:* Immunology of transplantation; etiology of dental pulpal disease. *Mailing Add:* 505 W Cheves St Florence SC 29501-4449

**WHITE, EDWARD AUSTIN,** BIOCHEMISTRY, NUTRITION. *Current Pos:* chief, Chem Gen Lab, Japan, 47-50, adv med sci, 50-57, RUSS/GER TRANSLR, US DEPT ARMY, WASHINGTON, DC, 57- *Personal Data:* b Brooklyn, NY, Nov 28, 15; m 48; c 2. *Educ:* Fordham Univ, BS, 37, MS, 40, PhD(biochem), 46. *Prof Exp:* Instr anal chem, Fordham Univ, 37-40; anal res chemist, Calco Chem Co, NJ, 40-42 & Winthrop Chem Co, NY & DC, 42-43; prof biochem, Col Mt St Vincent, 43-46; actg head, Dept Chem, Inst Appl Arts & Sci, NY, 46-47. *Mem:* Fel AAAS; Am Chem Soc; fel Am Inst Chem. *Res:* Nutrition in animals; analytical methods; pharmaceuticals; scientific translation. *Mailing Add:* 5307 Sangamore Rd Bethesda MD 20816

**WHITE, EDWARD JOHN,** ELECTRICAL ENGINEERING. *Current Pos:* ASSOC DEAN & RES PROF ELEC ENG, VANDERBILT UNIV, 87- *Personal Data:* b Haverhill, Iowa, Jan 26, 32; m 59, Ellen L LaVoy; c Andrew, Mary, Renee, Curtis & Brook S. *Educ:* Iowa State Univ, BS, 58; Univ Va, MEE, 62, DSc(elec eng), 66. *Prof Exp:* Electronic engr, US Govt, 58-59; instr, Univ Va, 59-65, lectr, 65-66, asst prof elec eng, 66-69, assoc prof, 69-86, asst to dean, Sch Eng & Appl Sci, 74-77, actg asst dean, 76-77, asst dean, 77-79, asst chmn, Dept Elec Eng, 80-86. *Mem:* Inst Elec & Electronics Engrs; Am Soc Eng Educ; Sigma Xi. *Res:* Computer graphics; computer aided circuit design. *Mailing Add:* 510 Clematis Dr Nashville TN 37215-3151. *Fax:* 615-343-8006; *E-Mail:* ejw@vuse.vanderbilt.edu

**WHITE, EDWARD LEWIS,** neuroanatomy, for more information see previous edition

**WHITE, EDWIN HENRY,** FORESTRY, SOIL SCIENCE. *Current Pos:* PROF FOREST RESOURCES, COL ENVIRON SCI & FORESTRY, SCH FORESTRY, STATE UNIV NY, SYRACUSE, 80-, DEAN RES, 92- *Personal Data:* b Gouverneur, NY, Dec 22, 37; m 61; c 3. *Educ:* Col Forestry, State Univ NY, Syracuse Univ, BS, 62, MS, 64; Auburn Univ, PhD(soils), 69. *Prof Exp:* Technician forest soils, Col Forestry, State Univ NY, Syracuse Univ, 61-62; instr forestry, Auburn Univ, 64-65, res asst, 65-68; fel forestry & soils, Univ Fla, 68-69; res soil scientist, US Forest Serv, Miss, 69-70; asst prof forestry, Univ Ky, 70-74; assoc prof forest resources, Univ Minn, 74-78, prof, 78-80. *Mem:* Soil Sci Soc Am; Soil Conserv Soc Am; fel Soc Am Foresters. *Res:* Forest soils and silviculture; soil-site-species relationships; tree planting research; acidic deposition. *Mailing Add:* Fac Forestry State Univ NY Col Environ Sci & Forestry 1 Forestry Dr Syracuse NY 13210-2778

**WHITE, ELIZABETH LLOYD,** experimental embryology, molecular biology; deceased, see previous edition for last biography

**WHITE, ELIZABETH LOCZI,** MATERIALS SCIENCE ENGINEERING. *Current Pos:* res assoc, 75-83, SR RES ASSOC, STORMWATER MODELING & ENG PROBS CARBONATE ROCKS, PA STATE UNIV, 83- *Personal Data:* b McKees Rocks, Pa, Mar 9, 36; m 59; c 2. *Educ:* Univ Pittsburgh, BS, 58; Pa State Univ, MS, 69, PhD(civil eng), 75. *Prof Exp:* Civil engr II highway design, Pa Dept Transp, 57, civil engr IV bridge design, 58-59. *Concurrent Pos:* Anna Rose Hawkes fel Award, Am Asn Univ Women, 74-75; consult, Hydrol Invest. *Mem:* Am Asn Univ Women; Grad Women Sci; Nat Soc Prof Engrs. *Res:* Surface water hydrology; sediment transport, soil properties and flood frequency statistics; chemistry and properties of high temperature cements; geothermal wells and nuclear waste disposal; engineering problems in carbonate rock terrains; computer application to civil engineering; kinetic modeling of cement and cementitious materials; storm water management. *Mailing Add:* Dept Civil Eng 212 Sackett Bldg University Park PA 16802

**WHITE, EMIL HENRY,** ORGANIC CHEMISTRY. *Current Pos:* from asst prof to prof org chem, 57-80, D MEAD JOHNSON PROF CHEM, JOHNS HOPKINS UNIV, 80- *Personal Data:* b Akron, Ohio, Aug 17, 26. *Educ:* Univ Akron, BS, 47; Purdue Univ, MS, 48, PhD(chem), 50. *Prof Exp:* Fel, Univ Chicago, 50-51 & Harvard Univ, 51-52; instr org chem, Yale Univ, 52-56. *Concurrent Pos:* Guggenheim fel, 58-59; NIH sr fel, 65-66 & 72-73. *Mem:* AAAS; Am Chem Soc. *Res:* Mechanism of reaction in organic chemistry; active site mapping of enzymes; chemiluminescence and bioluminescence; deamination reactions. *Mailing Add:* Dept Chem Johns Hopkins Univ Baltimore MD 21218-2680

**WHITE, EUGENE L,** computer programmer, for more information see previous edition

**WHITE, EUGENE WILBERT,** INSTRUMENTATION, MINERALOGY. *Current Pos:* CONSULT. *Personal Data:* b Indiana, Pa, Jan 23, 33; m 52; c 3. *Educ:* Pa State Univ, BS, 55, MS, 58, PhD(solid state tech), 65. *Prof Exp:* Res asst mineral, Pa State Univ, 55-59; head, X-ray Diffraction Applns Lab, Picker X-ray Co, Ohio, 59-61; design engr, Tem-Pres Res, Inc, Pa, 61; res asst electron microprobe, Pa State Univ, 62-65, from asst prof to prof solid state sci, Mat Res Lab, 65-97. *Mem:* Am Crystallog Asn; Sigma Xi. *Res:* Electron microprobe research; x-ray spectroscopy. *Mailing Add:* RD 1 Box 182 Rossiter PA 15772

**WHITE, FRANK M,** MECHANICAL ENGINEERING. *Current Pos:* PROF MECH & OCEAN ENG, UNIV RI, 67- *Educ:* Ga Inst Technol, BME, 54, PhD(mech eng), 59; Mass Inst Technol, SM, 56. *Honors & Awards:* Westinghouse Award, Am Soc Eng Educ, 70; Lewis F Moody Award, Am Soc Mech Engrs,73, Fluids Eng Award, 91. *Prof Exp:* Staff mem, Aerospace Eng Dept, Ga Inst Technol. *Concurrent Pos:* Assoc ed, J Fluids Eng, 74-77, tech ed, 79-90. *Mem:* Fel Am Soc Mech Engrs; Am Inst Aeronaut & Astronaut; Sigma Xi. *Res:* Viscous fluid flow; fluid mechanics; heat and mass transfer. *Mailing Add:* Dept Mech & Ocean Eng Univ RI Kingston RI 02881

**WHITE, FRANKLIN ESTABROOK,** INSTRUMENTATION. *Current Pos:* RETIRED. *Personal Data:* b Denver, Colo, Mar 26, 22; m 44; c 2. *Educ:* Univ Denver, BS, 48, MA, 51; Univ Mich, MS, 55. *Prof Exp:* Res assoc atmospheric infrared studies, Univ Denver, 49-51; infrared instrumentation, Univ Mich, 51-55; teacher, Univ Denver, 59-62, res physicist, 55-83, sr res physicist, 83. *Concurrent Pos:* Consult, Air Force Opers Anal Off, 56-71. *Mem:* Am Phys Soc; Sigma Xi. *Res:* Atmospheric infrared absorption; balloon and rocket instrumentation; radio propagation and telemetry; operations analysis; electronics. *Mailing Add:* 2499 S Colorado Blvd Apt 2499 Denver CO 80222-5930

**WHITE, FRANKLIN HENRY,** VETERINARY MICROBIOLOGY. *Current Pos:* from asst bacteriologist to assoc bacteriologist, Univ Fla, 55-67, assoc prof bact, 61-67, prof bact & bacteriologist, 67-85, EMER PROF BACT, UNIV FLA, 85- *Personal Data:* b Alton, Ill, Feb 11, 19; m 47; c 2. *Educ:* Shurtleff Col, BS, 42; Univ Ill, MS, 48, PhD(bact), 55; Am Bd Med Microbiol, cert pub health & med lab microbiol, 74. *Prof Exp:* Bacteriologist, State Dept Pub Health, Ill, 46-49; instr bact, Col Vet Med, Univ Ill, 49-55. *Mem:* Am Soc Microbiol; Conf Res Workers Animal Dis; Wildlife Dis Asn; US Animal Health Asn. *Res:* Pathogenic microbiology and immunology; leptospirosis; vibriosis; wildlife diseases; epizootiology. *Mailing Add:* 3525 NW 12th Ave Gainesville FL 32605

**WHITE, FRED NEWTON,** CARDIOVASCULAR PHYSIOLOGY, COMPARATIVE PHYSIOLOGY. *Current Pos:* PROF PHYSIOL & DIR, PHYSIOL RES LAB, SCRIPPS INST OCEANOG, UNIV CALIF, SAN DIEGO, 76- *Personal Data:* b Yelgar, La, June 17, 27; m 51. *Educ:* Univ Houston, BS, 50, MS, 51; Univ Ill, PhD(zool), 55. *Prof Exp:* Asst prof biol, Univ Houston, 55-57; asst prof exp med, Southwestern Med Sch, Univ Tex, 58-59 & 62-63; assoc prof physiol, Am Univ Beirut, 59-62; prof physiol, Sch Med, Univ Calif, Los Angeles, 63-76. *Concurrent Pos:* Am Physiol Soc cardiovasc training fels, 57 & 58. *Mem:* Am Physiol Soc; Fedn Am Socs Exp Biol; Soc Exp Biol & Med. *Res:* Control of renin secretion; peripheral circulation; comparative aspects of vertebrate circulation; environmental physiology. *Mailing Add:* PO Box 633 Fredericksburg TX 78624

**WHITE, FREDERICK ANDREW,** MASS SPECTROMETRY. *Current Pos:* CONSULT, NASA, 75- *Personal Data:* b Detroit, Mich, Mar 11, 18; m 42; c 3. *Educ:* Wayne State Univ, BS, 40; Univ Mich, MS, 41; Univ Wis, PhD, 59. *Prof Exp:* Res asst physics, Manhattan Proj, Univ Rochester, 43-46; res assoc, Gen Elec Co, 47-62; prof nuclear eng & eng sci, Rensselaer Polytech Inst, 62-81. *Concurrent Pos:* Sci adv, Rochester Gas & Elec, 80-; adj prof physics, State Univ NY, Albany, 81-88. *Mem:* Acoust Soc Am; Am Chem Soc; Am Phys Soc; Am Soc Mass Spectrometry; Inst Elec & Electronics Engrs; Optical Soc Am. *Res:* Application of isotopic abundance measurements in the physical sciences; acoustics; mass spectrometry; industrial research. *Mailing Add:* 2456 Hilltop Rd Schenectady NY 12309

**WHITE, FREDERICK HOWARD, JR,** PROTEIN CHEMISTRY, CIRCULAR DICHROISM. *Current Pos:* RETIRED. *Personal Data:* b Washington, DC, Jan 19, 26. *Educ:* Univ Va, BS, 49; Univ Md, 52; Univ Wis, PhD(biochem), 57. *Prof Exp:* Asst chem, Univ Md, 51-52; chemist, Nat Heart Inst, 52-53; asst biochem, Univ Wis, 53-56; chemist, Lab Biochem, Nat Heart, Lung & Blood Inst, 56-75 & Lab Cell Biol, 75-83. *Concurrent Pos:* Vis fel, Australian Nat Univ, Canberra, 84-87; courtesy res scientist, Fla State Univ, 87- *Mem:* Am Soc Biol Chem; Radiation Res Soc. *Res:* Chemistry of sulfur in proteins; protein conformation; radiolysis of proteins; lysozyme, milk proteins. *Mailing Add:* Chem Dept Fla State Univ Tallahassee FL 32306-1607

**WHITE, FREDRIC PAUL,** BIOCHEMISTRY, NEUROSCIENCES. *Current Pos:* asst prof, 74-77, ASSOC PROF BIOCHEM, MEM UNIV NFLD, 78- *Personal Data:* b New York, NY, July 24, 42; m 64; c 1. *Educ:* Purdue Univ, BChE, 64; Ind Univ, PhD(biol chem), 71. *Prof Exp:* Chem engr, E I du Pont de Nemours & Co, Inc, 64-66; biochem trainee, NIH, 67-71; res scientist neurochem, Med Sch, Univ Colo, 72-73; vis asst prof neurophys, Ind State Univ, 73-74. *Concurrent Pos:* Vis scientist, Med Res Coun, 81-82. *Mem:* Am Soc Neurochem; Soc Neurosci. *Res:* Cellular physiology of cerebral endothelial cells and pericytes; synthesis of the stress protein traumin by cells in response to trauma. *Mailing Add:* 310 SW Skyline Dr Pullman WA 99163

**WHITE, GEORGE CHARLES, JR,** physics; deceased, see previous edition for last biography

**WHITE, GEORGE MATTHEWS,** communication science, for more information see previous edition

**WHITE, GEORGE MICHAEL,** COMPUTER SCIENCE. *Current Pos:* ASST PROF COMPUT SCI, UNIV OTTAWA, 70- *Personal Data:* b Toronto, Ont, June 14, 39; m 64; c 3. *Educ:* Univ Toronto, BASc, 61; Univ Alta, MSc, 65; Univ Calgary, PhD, 68. *Prof Exp:* Systs engr, CAE Electronics, 61-62; Irish Govt fel, Univ Col, Dublin, 68-70. *Mem:* Asn Comput Mach; Can Info Processing Soc. *Mailing Add:* 28 Elmdale Ave Ottawa ON K1M 1A2 Can

**WHITE, GEORGE NICHOLS, JR,** APPLIED MATHEMATICS. *Current Pos:* RETIRED. *Personal Data:* b Concord, Mass, July 1, 19; m 48; c 3. *Educ:* Harvard Univ, BS, 41; Brown Univ, MS, 48, PhD(appl math), 50. *Prof Exp:* Trainee, Phys Test Lab, T Mason Co, 41-42; technician radar, US Civil Serv, 42-45; technician electronics, Oceanog Inst, Woods Hole, 45-46; res assoc appl math, Brown Univ, 48-50; mem staff appl math, Los Alamos Nat Lab, 50-85. *Concurrent Pos:* Prof, Univ NMex, 57-60. *Mem:* Am Math Soc; Soc Indust Appl Math. *Res:* Mathematics theory of plasticity; hydrodynamics; elasticity. *Mailing Add:* 119 Tunyo Los Alamos NM 87544-2423

**WHITE, GEORGE ROWLAND,** HIGH TECHNOLOGY, IMAGING SYSTEMS. *Current Pos:* from div mgr to chief scientist, Xerox Corp, 64-67, eng dept mgr, 67-68, div vpres, 68-72, staff vpres, 72-73, vpres prod planning, 74-76, vpres advan develop, 77-79, VPRES RES & DEVELOP & ENG, XEROX CORP, 79- *Personal Data:* b Niagara Falls, NY, Feb 22, 29; m 57. *Educ:* Wesleyan Univ, BA, 50; Iowa State Univ, PhD(physics), 55; Univ Calif, Los Angeles, MS, 67. *Prof Exp:* From engr to dept mgr, Sperry Gyroscope Co, 55-64. *Concurrent Pos:* Carroll-Ford Found vis prof bus admin, Grad Sch Bus Admin, Harvard Univ, 76-77; chmn, Human Relations Comn, Monroe Co, 77-79; chmn planning bd, Polytech Inst NY, Inst Imaging Sci, 79- *Mem:* Optical Soc Am; Am Phys Soc; Inst Elec & Electronics Engrs; Indust Res Inst. *Res:* Management of technological innovation; development of xerographic and electronic imaging systems; lasers; microwave tubes; particle physics. *Mailing Add:* Gateway Towers 12C Pittsburgh PA 15222

**WHITE, GERALD M(ILTON),** COMPUTER SCIENCE. *Current Pos:* RETIRED. *Personal Data:* b Detroit, Mich, Dec 6, 29; m 56; c Charles, Andrew, Judith & Abigale. *Educ:* Univ Mich, BS, 51; Harvard Univ, MS, 53, PhD(appl physics), 58. *Prof Exp:* Res assoc, Res Lab, Gen Elec Co, 57-64, mgr comput oper, Res & Develop Ctr, 64-69, res assoc info systs, 69-77, info systs engr, 77-94. *Mem:* Inst Elec & Electronics Engrs; Sigma Xi. *Res:* Information processing; computer systems and languages; information systems; applied databases. *Mailing Add:* 1274 Hawthorne Rd Schenectady NY 12309-4609

**WHITE, GIFFORD,** PHYSICS. *Current Pos:* CHMN BD, WHITE PROPERTIES, INC, 84- *Personal Data:* b San Saba, Tex, Feb 17, 12; m 35; c 2. *Educ:* Univ Tex, BA & MA, 39. *Honors & Awards:* Cert of Appreciation, US War Dept, 45. *Prof Exp:* Geophysicist, Humble Oil & Refining Co, 34-38; res engr, Sperry Gyroscope Co, 41-47; vpres, Statham Instruments, Inc, 47-52; pres, White Instruments, Inc, 53-79, chmn bd, 79-84. *Mem:* Am Phys Soc; Soc Explor Geophys; fel Inst Elec & Electronics Engrs. *Res:* Instrumentation for physical measurements; circuit theory. *Mailing Add:* 1034 Liberty Park Dr Austin TX 78746

**WHITE, GILBERT FOWLER,** WATER RESOURCES, NATURAL HAZARDS. *Current Pos:* prof, 70-78, EMER DISTINGUISHED PROF GEOG & EMER DIR, INST BEHAV SCI, UNIV COLO, 78- *Personal Data:* b Chicago, Ill, Nov 26, 11; wid; c William, Mary & Frances. *Educ:* Univ Chicago, SB, 32, SM, 34, PhD(geog), 42. *Honors & Awards:* Daly Medal, Am Geog Soc, 71; Eben Award, Am Water Resources Asn, 72; Environ Award, Nat Acad Sci, 80; Sasakawa Prize, UN, 85; Tyler Prize, 87; Laureat d'Honneur, Int Geog Union, 88; Caulfield Prize, Am Water Resources Asn, 89; Volvo Prize, 95. *Prof Exp:* Geogr, Miss Valley Comt, Pub Work Admin, 34-35, Nat Resources Planning Bd, 35-40, Bur Budget, 40-42; vol, Am Friends Serv Comt, 42-46; pres, Haverford Col, 46-55; prof geog, Univ Chicago, 56-69; dir, Natural Hazards Info Ctr, 76-84 & 91-93. *Concurrent Pos:* VChmn, Pres Water Resources Policy Comn, 50-51; vis prof, Univ Oxford, 62-63; chmn, Bur Budget Task Force Fed Flood Policy, 65-66; chmn bd, Resources Future, 74-79; chmn, Comn Natural Resources, Nat Res Coun, 77-80, pres, Sci Comt Problems Environ, 76-82; exec ed, Environment, 83-93; chmn, Comt Sustainable Water Supplies Middle East, 95- *Mem:* Nat Acad Sci; Asn Am Geographers (pres, 61-62); Am Geophys Union; hon mem Am Planning Asn; Russ Acad Sci; Royal Geog Soc. *Res:* Natural resources management; environmental policy; natural hazards. *Mailing Add:* Inst Behav Sci Campus Box 482 Univ Colo Boulder CO 80309. *Fax:* 303-492-2151

**WHITE, GLENN E,** REGULATION OF MUSCLE GENE EXPRESSION. *Current Pos:* ASST PROF MED RES, DUKE UNIV, 89- *Personal Data:* b Sasebo-Shu, Nagusaki-Ken, Japan, Aug 21, 57. *Educ:* Harvard Univ, PhD(anat & cell biol), 83. *Prof Exp:* Res fel med, Beth Israel Hosp, Boston, 83-85; res fel cardiol, Children's Hosp Med Ctr, 85-89. *Mem:* Am Soc Cell Biol; NY Acad Sci. *Mailing Add:* Ashland Univ Kettering Bldg Grant St Ashland OH 44805. *Fax:* 919-684-3687; *E-Mail:* Bitnet: glennwhite@ cellbiodukeedu

**WHITE, HAROLD BANCROFT, III,** VITAMIN METABOLISM, PROTEIN STRUCTURE & FUNCTION. *Current Pos:* from asst prof to assoc prof, 71-83, PROF CHEM, UNIV DEL, 83- *Personal Data:* b Hartford, Conn, Feb 26, 43; m 66, Jean Spicer; c Anna L, Laura F & Rachel E. *Educ:* Pa State Univ, BS, 65; Brandeis Univ, PhD(biochem), 70. *Prof Exp:* Res fel chem, Harvard Univ, 70-71. *Concurrent Pos:* Vis res scientist genetics, Univ Calif, Davis, 77-78; Res career develop award, NIH, 77-81; vis scientist, AFRC-Poultry Res Ctr, Edinburgh, Scotland, 84-85. *Mem:* AAAS; Am Soc Biochem & Molecular Biol; Am Entom Soc; Soc Study Evolution; Am Inst Nutrit. *Res:* Vitamin and coenzyme metabolism; biotin; riboflavin; vitamin binding proteins; egg yolk deposition; molecular evolution; problem-based learning in science education; odonata; entomology; science education. *Mailing Add:* Dept Chem & Biochem Univ Del Newark DE 19716. *Fax:* 302-831-6335; *E-Mail:* halwhite@udel.edu

**WHITE, HAROLD BIRTS, JR,** BIOCHEMISTRY. *Current Pos:* FAC, DEPT BIOCHEM, UNIV DEL. *Personal Data:* b Little Rock, Ark, Mar 13, 29; m 58; c 2. *Educ:* Columbia Univ, AB, 51, MA, 53, PhD(physiol), 57. *Prof Exp:* Fel, Purdue Univ, 57-59, asst prof biochem, 59-61; from asst prof to assoc prof, Sch Med, Univ Miss, 61-68, prof biochem, 68- *Concurrent Pos:* Vis scientist, Univ Milan, 68-69. *Mem:* Am Chem Soc; Am Soc Biol Chem; Sigma Xi. *Res:* Brain lipid modification; poxvirus influence on lipid metabolism. *Mailing Add:* Dept Biochem Univ Del Newark DE 19716-2522

**WHITE, HAROLD D(OUGLAS),** AGRICULTURAL ENGINEERING. *Current Pos:* from assoc prof to prof, 45-74, EMER PROF AGR ENG, UNIV GA, 74- *Personal Data:* b Sugar Valley, Ga, Aug 29, 10; m 35; c 2. *Educ:* Univ Ga, BS, 34; Iowa State Col, MS, 38. *Prof Exp:* Agr engr, Abraham Baldwin Agr Col, 34-37; asst, Exp Sta, Univ Iowa, 37; instr agr eng, Iowa State Col, 38-41; asst agr engr, Univ Ga, 41-43; spec supvr, State Dept Educ, Ga, 43-45. *Concurrent Pos:* Pres, Prof Engrs & Assocs P C, 76- *Mem:* Sigma Xi; fel Am Soc Agr Engrs; Nat Soc Prof Engrs; Poultry Sci Asn. *Res:* Food and feed processing facilities and equipment; materials handling; dairy and poultry engineering. *Mailing Add:* 561 University Dr Athens GA 30605

**WHITE, HAROLD J,** pathology, for more information see previous edition

**WHITE, HAROLD KEITH,** ORGANIC CHEMISTRY, BIOCHEMISTRY. *Current Pos:* from assoc prof to prof, 55-88, EMER PROF CHEM, HANOVER COL, 88- *Personal Data:* b Straughn, Ind, July 11, 23; m 47; c 3. *Educ:* Butler Univ, BS, 47; Purdue Univ, MS, 50; Ind Univ, PhD(org chem), 54. *Prof Exp:* Asst chemist, State Chem Off Ind, 47-49; res chemist, Mead Johnson & Co, 53-55. *Mem:* Am Chem Soc. *Res:* Stereochemistry; synthesis of polycyclics; medicinal chemistry. *Mailing Add:* 257 Garritt St Hanover IN 47243-9680

**WHITE, HAROLD MCCOY,** ORGANIC CHEMISTRY. *Current Pos:* from asst prof to assoc prof, 64-71, PROF CHEM, SOUTHWESTERN STATE COL, 71- *Personal Data:* b Camden, SC, Feb 1, 32; m 55; c 3. *Educ:* Clemson Univ, BS, 54, PhD(org chem), 62. *Prof Exp:* Chemist, SC Agr Res Sta, 54-55; fel ozone chem, Univ Tex, 62-64. *Concurrent Pos:* Welch Found fel, 63-64. *Mem:* Am Chem Soc; Sigma Xi. *Res:* Reactions of ozone with organic compounds; mechanism of the ozonation of hydrocarbons and reactions of ozone in basic media. *Mailing Add:* Dept Chem Southwestern Okla State Univ 100 University Cir Weatherford OK 73096

**WHITE, HARRIS HERMAN,** BIOLOGICAL OCEANOGRAPHY. *Current Pos:* ECOLOGIST, NAT OCEANIC SERV, NAT OCEANIC & ATMOSPHERIC ADMIN, 80- *Personal Data:* b Ft Worth, Tex, June 24, 49; m 73; c 5. *Educ:* Univ Wash, BS(oceanog) & BS(zool), 71; Univ RI, PhD (oceanog), 76. *Prof Exp:* Asst prof oceanog, Old Dominion Univ, 76-79. *Res:* Marine pollution. *Mailing Add:* N/ORCA-22 1305 E West Hwy Rm 10536 Silver Spring MD 20910

**WHITE, HARRY JOSEPH,** ORGANIC CHEMISTRY. *Current Pos:* RETIRED. *Personal Data:* b Philadelphia, Pa, Feb 19, 31; m 56; c 4. *Educ:* LaSalle Col, BA, 54; Univ Notre Dame, PhD(org chem), 58. *Prof Exp:* Res chemist, Rohm & Haas Co, 58-67, coordr PhD recruiting, 67-68, asst mgr manpower & employment, 68-72, mgr recruiting & placement, 72-85, res personnel dir, 85-88, dir univ rel, 88- *Mem:* Am Chem Soc. *Res:* Technical recruiting, placement and manpower planning; petroleum additives; polymer chemistry. *Mailing Add:* 1574 Campus Dr Maple Glen PA 19002-3309

**WHITE, HELEN LYNG,** biochemistry, enzymology; deceased, see previous edition for last biography

**WHITE, HENRY W,** PHYSICS. *Current Pos:* ASSOC PROF PHYSICS, UNIV MO, COLUMBIA, 69- *Personal Data:* b Blytheville, Ark, Dec 20, 41; m 62; c 2. *Educ:* Pepperdine Col, BA, 63; Univ Calif, Riverside, MS, 65, PhD(physics), 69. *Mem:* Am Phys Soc; Am Asn Physics Teachers. *Res:* Low temperature thermal properties; inelastic electron tunneling spectroscopy. *Mailing Add:* Dept Physics Univ Mo Columbia MO 65211. *Fax:* 573-882-4195

**WHITE, HERMAN BRENNER, JR,** PARTICLE PHYSICS. *Current Pos:* STAFF PHYSICIST PARTICLE PHYSICS, FERMI NAT ACCELERATOR LAB, 78- *Personal Data:* b Tuskegee, Ala, Sept 28, 48. *Educ:* Earlham Col, BA, 70; Mich State Univ, MS, 74; Fla State Univ, PhD, 91. *Prof Exp:* Resident res assoc nuclear physics, Argonne Nat Lab, 71; Alfred P Sloan Found fel accelerator & particle physics, Europ Lab Particle Physics, Geneva, Switz, 72; staff physicist particle physics, Univs Res Asn, Fermi Nat Accelerator Lab, 74-76; teaching fel physics, Yale Univ, 76-78. *Concurrent Pos:* Jr res assoc, Brookhaven Nat Lab; res & develop corridor fel, Physics, N Cent Col, Ill, 94- *Mem:* Am Inst Physics. *Res:* Study of high energy hadrons production and neutrino production; hadronic constituent scattering; charge, parity and time coordinates symmetry. *Mailing Add:* Res Div MS-231 Fermilab PO Box 500 Batavia IL 60510. *E-Mail:* hwhite@fnal.gov

**WHITE, HORACE FREDERICK,** PHYSICAL CHEMISTRY. *Current Pos:* from asst prof to assoc prof, 65-75, actg chmn dept, 66-68, PROF CHEM, PORTLAND STATE UNIV, 75- *Personal Data:* b Fresno, Calif, Apr 25, 25; m 52; c 3. *Educ:* Fresno State Col, AB, 47; Ore State Col, MS, 50; Brown Univ, PhD(phys chem), 53. *Prof Exp:* Fel, Univ Minn, 52-54; spectroscopist, Res Dept, M W Kellogg Co Div, Pullman, Inc, 54-56, instrumental methods supvr, 56-57; spectroscopist, Res Dept, Union Carbide Chem Co, 57-65. *Mem:* Am Chem Soc; Sigma Xi. *Res:* Molecular structure using infrared spectroscopy and nuclear magnetic resonance spectrometry techniques; mass spectrometry; x-ray crystallography for structural determinations. *Mailing Add:* Portland State Univ PO Box 751 Portland OR 97207-0751

**WHITE, HOWARD DWAINE,** BIOCHEMISTRY. *Current Pos:* ASST PROF BIOCHEM, UNIV ARIZ, 78- *Personal Data:* b Des Moines, Iowa, Oct 24, 46. *Educ:* Univ Colo, BA, 69; Brandeis Univ, PhD(biochem), 73. *Prof Exp:* Fel biophys, Med Res Coun, London, 73-76; mem sci staff, 76-78. *Mem:* Biophys Soc; Brit Biophys Soc. *Res:* The mechanism by which ATP hydrolysis is coupled to the production of mechanical work in muscle and other contractile systems. *Mailing Add:* E Va Med Sch 700 Olney Rd Norfolk VA 23501. *Fax:* 757-623-4864; *E-Mail:* Bitnet: white@eumsums

**WHITE, HOWARD JULIAN, JR,** SCIENCE ADMINISTRATION. *Current Pos:* asst chief, Phys Chem Div, 64-66, PROG MGR, OFF STAND REFERENCE DATA, NAT BUR STAND, 66-, GUEST SCIENTIST, 88- *Personal Data:* b Batavia, NY, Nov 20, 20; m 49, Elizabeth S Wangler; c Matthew P & Michael H. *Educ:* Princeton Univ, AB, 42, PhD(chem), 47; Univ Wis, MS, 44. *Prof Exp:* Asst chem, Univ Wis, 42-44; from res chemist to assoc dir res, Textile Res Inst, NJ, 47-57, dir, 57-60; sr phys chemist, Stanford Res Inst, 60-61; spec asst res to Asst Secy Navy, Res & Develop, 61-64. *Mem:* AAAS; Am Chem Soc; Fiber Soc; hon fel, Int Asn Properties Water & Stream; Am Soc Mech Engrs. *Res:* Surface chemistry; solutions, swelling, adsorption and dyeing of fibers; reference data on thermodynamics and transport properties and colloid and surface properties. *Mailing Add:* 8028 Park Overlook Dr Bethesda MD 20817

**WHITE, IRVIN LINWOOD,** energy research & development, for more information see previous edition

**WHITE, J COURTLAND,** PHARMACOLOGY. *Current Pos:* PVT PRACT, 93- *Personal Data:* b Philadelphia, Pa, May 25, 48; m. *Educ:* Univ Va, PhD(biochem), 73. *Prof Exp:* Assoc prof biochem, Bowman Gray Sch Med, Wake Forest Univ, 80-93. *Mem:* Am Asn Cancer Res; Am Soc Biol Chem; AAAS. *Res:* Biochemical pharmacology of anticancer agents, especially for leukemia. *Mailing Add:* Biltmore Sq Mall Suite 772-A Asheville NC 28806

**WHITE, JACK LEE,** MATERIALS SCIENCE, CARBON & GRAPHITE. *Current Pos:* RES SCIENTIST, UNIV CALIF, SAN DIEGO, 88- *Personal Data:* b Los Angeles, Calif, Oct 29, 25; m 50; c 1. *Educ:* Calif Inst Technol, BS, 49; Carnegie Inst Technol, BS, 50; Imp Col Univ London, dipl, 55; Univ Calif, PhD(metall), 55. *Honors & Awards:* Graffin lectr, 84; Skakel Award, Am Carbon Soc, 87. *Prof Exp:* Res engr, Univ Calif, 55; Nat Acad Sci res assoc, US Naval Res Lab, 55-57; mem staff, Gen Atomic, 58-67; res off, Petten Ctr, Europ AEC, 67-69; vis scientist, Gulf Gen Atomic, 69-70; assoc prof mat sci, Univ Calif, Davis, 71-72; staff scientist, Aerospace Corp, 73-88. *Concurrent Pos:* Consult, Gulf Gen Atomic, Europe AEC, 70-73; chair, Am Carbon Soc. *Mem:* AAAS; Am Chem Soc; Am Ceramic Soc; Am Inst Mining, Metall & Petrol Eng; Brit Inst Metals; Am Carbon Soc. *Res:* Carbonaceous and graphitic materials; high-temperature materials; high-temperature physical chemistry; carbon fiber. *Mailing Add:* 690 Rimini Rd Del Mar CA 92014

**WHITE, JAMES CARL,** ANALYTICAL CHEMISTRY. *Current Pos:* RETIRED. *Personal Data:* b Ft Wayne, Ind, Mar 1, 22; m 46, Mary Frechtling; c Andrew, James, Teresa (Dillard) & Thomas. *Educ:* Ind Univ, BS, 43; Ohio State Univ, MS, 48, PhD(chem), 50. *Prof Exp:* Chemist, Joslyn Mfg Co, 46; asst, Ohio State Univ, 46-50; asst div dir, Oak Ridge Nat Lab, 50-67, from assoc dir to dir, Anal Chem Div, 67-76; gen plant serv mgr, Martin Marietta Energy Systs, Inc, 76-86. *Mem:* AAAS; Am Chem Soc; Int Union Pure & Appl Chem; Fedn Anal Chem & Spectros. *Res:* Research administration; molten salts; separations; reference materials. *Mailing Add:* 5425 Shenandoah Trail Knoxville TN 37909

**WHITE, JAMES CARRICK,** FOOD MICROBIOLOGY, CLIMATE CHANGE. *Current Pos:* RETIRED. *Personal Data:* b Scobey, Mont, Oct 29, 16; m 41, Ruth Babcock; c James C Jr, Waldo G & Deborah A. *Educ:* Cornell Univ, PhD(bact), 44. *Prof Exp:* Dir res, Borden Cheese Co, 44-46; assoc prof dairy indust, Cornell Univ, 46-51, prof dairy indust, 51-, prof food sci, 77-80, asst dean hotel admin, 79-82, prof hotel admin, 72- *Concurrent Pos:* Sci adv, Ctr Environ Info. *Mem:* Inst Food Technol; Int Asn Milk, Food & Environ Sanitarians. *Res:* Food poisoning; waste technology; food sanitation; acid rain; climate change. *Mailing Add:* Statler Hall Cornell Univ No W209 Ithaca NY 14851

**WHITE, JAMES DAVID,** ORGANIC CHEMISTRY. *Current Pos:* assoc prof, 71-76, PROF CHEM, ORE STATE UNIV, 76- *Personal Data:* b Bristol, Eng, June 14, 35; m 60; c 2. *Educ:* Cambridge Univ, BA, 59; Univ BC, MSc, 61; Mass Inst Technol, PhD(org chem), 65. *Prof Exp:* From instr to asst prof chem, Harvard Univ, 65-71. *Concurrent Pos:* Consult med chem, NIH; assoc ed, J Am Chem Soc; Guggenheim fel, 88. *Mem:* Am Chem Soc; Royal Soc Chem; Swiss Chem Soc. *Res:* Organic synthesis and photochemistry; chemistry of natural products; heterocyclic compounds. *Mailing Add:* Dept Chem Ore State Univ Corvallis OR 97331-4003

**WHITE, JAMES DONALD,** PLANT PATHOLOGY. *Current Pos:* asst prof, 65-70, PROF BOT, LA TECH UNIV, 70-, PROF BACT, 77- *Personal Data:* b Hodge, La, July 7, 36; m 57; c 2. *Educ:* La Polytech Inst, BS, 59; La State Univ, MS, 61, PhD(plant path), 63. *Prof Exp:* Asst prof bot, Southeastern La Col, 63-65. *Mem:* Am Phytopath Soc. *Res:* Pathological histology and studies of Tabasco pepper plants infected with tobacco etch virus. *Mailing Add:* Dept Bot La Tech Univ Ruston LA 71272-0001

**WHITE, JAMES EDWARD,** ACOUSTICS. *Current Pos:* Charles Henry Green prof explor geophys, 76-88, EMER PROF, COLO SCH MINES, 87- *Personal Data:* b Cherokee, Tex, May 10, 18; m 41, Courtenay Brumby; c Rebecca W (Vanderslice), Peter M, Margaret M (Jamieson) & Courtenay W (Forte). *Educ:* Univ Tex, BS, 40, MA, 46; Mass Inst Technol, PhD(physics), 49. *Honors & Awards:* Maurice Ewing Medal, 86; Halliburton Award, 87; Kapitsa Gold Medal, Russ Acad, 96. *Prof Exp:* Physicist, Underwater Sound Lab, Mass Inst Technol, 41-45; Defense Res Lab, Univ Tex, 45-46, Mobil Oil Co, 49-55; Marathon Oil Co, 55-69 & Globe Universal Sci, Inc, 69-72; mem fac, Colo Sch Mines, 72-73; L A Nelson prof geol sci, Univ Tex, El Paso, 73-76. *Concurrent Pos:* Nat Acad Sci exchange scientist, USSR & Yugoslavia, 73-74; mem, Space Appl Bd, Nat Acad Eng, 73-78; Esso vis prof, Univ Sydney, Australia, 75; vis prof, Mass Inst Technol, 82, Univ Tex Austin, 85, Macquarie Univ, Sydney, NSW, 88. *Mem:* Nat Acad Eng; fel Acoust Soc Am; Europ Asn Explor Geophys; hon mem Soc Explor Geophys; Am Geophys Union. *Res:* Seismic prospecting; waves in solids; engineering geophysics; earthquake dynamics. *Mailing Add:* Dept Geophys Colo Sch Mines Golden CO 80401. *E-Mail:* jewhite@dix.mines.colorado.edu

**WHITE, JAMES EDWIN,** BIOLOGY, ECOLOGY. *Current Pos:* from instr to assoc prof, 62-74, PROF BIOL, KEUKA COL, 74-, CHMN DEPT, 69- *Personal Data:* b Pittsburgh, Pa, June 4, 35; m 60, Cynthia Will; c Wendy A & Amy L. *Educ:* Dartmouth Col, AB, 57; Rutgers Univ, PhD(zool), 61. *Prof Exp:* Asst prof biol, Parsons Col, 61-62. *Concurrent Pos:* Consult, NY State Scholar Exam, 64-65; actg acad dean, Keuka Col, 77-78. *Mem:* AAAS; Am Soc Mammal; Ecol Soc Am. *Res:* Mammal population ecology; animal behavior; small mammal parasites. *Mailing Add:* Div Natural Sci & Math Keuka Col Keuka Park NY 14478

**WHITE, JAMES GEORGE,** HEMATOLOGY, PEDIATRICS. *Current Pos:* REGENTS PROF HEMAT-PEDIAT, DEPTS LAB MED, PATH & PEDIAT, SCH MED, UNIV MINN, 84-, ASSOC DEAN RES. *Personal Data:* b Aug 28, 29; m 55, Mary Simonet; c Catherine, Gregory (deceased), Thomas, James & Michael. *Educ:* Univ Minn, MD, 55. *Honors & Awards:* Gane Nugent Cochems Prize, 64; Mead Johnson Award, 73; H P Smith Award, 78; Edward Kowalski Award, 81; Distinguished Career Award, Int Soc Thrombosis & Haemostasis, 87. *Mem:* Int Soc Thrombosis & Haemostasis; Am Soc Hemat; Am Soc Pediat Res; Am Soc Clin Invest; Asn Am Physicians; Am Heart Asn. *Res:* Platelets and other blood cells; hematosis; thrombosis; occlusive vascular disease. *Mailing Add:* Depts Lab Med Path & Pediat Sch Med Univ Minn Mayo Bldg PO Box 490 Minneapolis MN 55455. *E-Mail:* white003@maroon.tc.umu.edu

**WHITE, JAMES L(INDSAY),** POLYMER PROCESSING. *Current Pos:* dir, Polymer Eng Ctr, 83-88, HEAD, DEPT POLYMER ENG, UNIV AKRON, 83-, DIR, INST POLYMER ENG, 88- *Personal Data:* b Brooklyn, NY, Jan 3, 38; wid. *Educ:* Polytech Inst Brooklyn, BChE, 59; Univ Del, MChE, 62, PhD(chem eng), 65. *Honors & Awards:* Bingham Medal, Soc Rheology, 81, Yoko Sho Award, Japan, 84; Int Res Award, Soc Plastics Engrs, 92. *Prof Exp:* Res engr, Res Ctr, US Rubber Co, NJ, 63-66, Mich, 66-67; from assoc prof to prof eng, Univ Tenn, Knoxville, 67-70, alumni distinguished serv prof, 74-83, prof-in-chg polymer eng, 76-83. *Concurrent Pos:* Ed, J Polymer Eng, 81-87 & Americas: Int Polymer Process, 87-89; ed-in-chief, Int Polymer Process, 89- *Mem:* Polymer Processing Soc (pres, 85-87); Soc Rheology; Soc Plastics Engrs; Soc Rheology Japan; Am Chem Soc. *Res:* Rheology of polymer systems; extrusion especially twin screw extrasion; characterization of structure and orientation in solid polymers in polymer processing; filled polymer systems and rubber technology. *Mailing Add:* Polymer Eng Ctr Univ Akron Akron OH 44325-0001

**WHITE, JAMES PATRICK,** MICROBIAL PHYSIOLOGY. *Current Pos:* From asst prof to assoc prof microbiol, 70-77, PROF BIOL, ST BONAVENTURE UNIV, 77- *Personal Data:* b Indianapolis, Ind, Sept 13, 39; m 62; c 4. *Educ:* Marian Col, Ind, BS, 62; Univ Ark, MS, 65, PhD(microbiol), 67. *Mem:* AAAS; Am Soc Microbiol; Mycol Soc Am; Sigma Xi. *Res:* Physiology and nutrition of pigment formation in Helminthosporium species; effects of trace elements in nitrogen metabolism of microorganisms. *Mailing Add:* Dept Biol St Bonaventure Univ Gen Del St Bonaventure NY 14788-9999

**WHITE, JAMES RUSHTON,** BIOCHEMISTRY. *Current Pos:* from asst prof to prof, 62-85, EMER PROF BIOCHEM, SCH MED, UNIV NC, CHAPEL HILL, 85- *Personal Data:* b Ft Benning, Ga, July 28, 23; m 55; c 2. *Educ:* Stanford Univ, BS, 48, PhD(chem), 53. *Prof Exp:* Res chemist, Pioneering Res Lab, E I Du Pont de Nemours & Co Inc, 53-59; res assoc biochem, Univ Pa, 59-62. *Concurrent Pos:* NSF fel, 60-62. *Mem:* AAAS. *Res:* Macromolecular metabolism in bacteria; antibacterial action of antibiotics and other inhibitors; complexes of nucleic acids with low molecular weight ligands. *Mailing Add:* 210 Ridgecrest Dr Chapel Hill NC 27514-2101

**WHITE, JAMES RUSSELL,** physical chemistry; deceased, see previous edition for last biography

**WHITE, JAMES VICTOR,** ACOUSTICS, DYNAMICS. *Current Pos:* MEM TECH STAFF, ANALYTICAL SCI CORP, 80- *Personal Data:* b Hammond, Ind, May 20, 41; m 66. *Educ:* Northwestern Univ, Evanston, BS, 64; Harvard Univ, SM, 65, PhD(acoust), 70. *Prof Exp:* Engr, Jensen Mfg Co, 63-64; asst prof mech eng, Stevens Inst Technol, 70-74; staff scientist, Sound Reproduction Dept, CBS Tech Ctr, 74-80. *Concurrent Pos:* Fel, Harvard Univ, 70. *Mem:* Inst Elec & Electronics Engrs; Am Soc Mech Engrs; Acoust Soc Am; Audio Eng Soc. *Res:* Stylus-groove interaction in phonographs; noise control; modeling and identification of dynamic systems. *Mailing Add:* TASC 55 Walkers Brook Dr Reading MA 01867-3297. *Fax:* 781-942-7100; *E-Mail:* jvwhite@tasc.com

**WHITE, JAMES WILSON,** PHYSICS. *Current Pos:* RETIRED. *Personal Data:* b Salisbury, NC, May 29, 14; m 42; c 3. *Educ:* Davidson Col, BS, 34; Univ NC, MS, 36, PhD(physics), 38. *Hon Degrees:* DSc, King Col, 65. *Prof Exp:* Instr physics, Emory Jr Col, 38-39; prof, King Col, 39-42; instr, Univ Tenn, 42-44; res physicist, Fulton Sylphon Co, 44-45; from asst prof to prof physics, Univ Tenn, Knoxville, 45-84. *Mem:* Am Phys Soc; Am Asn Physics Teachers. *Res:* Instrumentation. *Mailing Add:* 3611 Montlake Dr Knoxville TN 37920

**WHITE, JANE VICKNAIR,** NUTRITION. *Current Pos:* From asst prof to assoc prof, 75-93, PROF NUTRIT, DEPT FAMILY PRACT MED, UNIV TENN, KNOXVILLE, 93- *Personal Data:* b Houma, La, Feb 10, 47; m 68; c 2. *Educ:* St Mary's Dominican Col, BS, 68; Univ Tenn, Knoxville, PhD(nutrit), 75. *Concurrent Pos:* Clin nutrit consult, Vet Admin Cent Off, Washington, DC, 79-85; mem, Tech Rev Comt, Nutrit Screening Initiative, 89- *Mem:* Am Dietetic Asn; Soc Teachers Family Med. *Res:* Nutrition education in family practice residency programs; nutrition screening and assessment of vulnerable population groups, i.e., elderly. *Mailing Add:* 1924 Alcoa Hwy-U67 Knoxville TN 37920

**WHITE, JERRY EUGENE,** organic chemistry, for more information see previous edition

**WHITE, JESSE EDMUND,** HISTORY OF CHEMISTRY. *Current Pos:* from asst prof to assoc prof, 59-71, prof, 71-96, EMER PROF CHEM, SOUTHERN ILL UNIV, EDWARDSVILLE, 96- *Personal Data:* b Indianapolis, Ind, June 9, 27; m 50, Betty Evans; c Janet R, James E & Douglas G. *Educ:* Va Mil Inst, BS, 49; Ind Univ, PhD(chem), 58. *Prof Exp:* Asst prof chem, Lafayette Col, 55-59. *Mem:* Am Chem Soc; Hist Sci Soc; Asn Univ Professors. *Res:* History of chemistry, especially 18th century. *Mailing Add:* 1128 State St Alton IL 62002

**WHITE, JESSE STEVEN,** PARASITOLOGY. *Current Pos:* Asst prof, Delta State Univ, 46-59, head, Div Sci, 59-70, prof, 59-80, EMER PROF BIOL, DELTA STATE UNIV, 80- *Personal Data:* b Cleveland, Miss, May 9, 17. *Educ:* Delta State Col, BS, 40; Miss State Col, MS, 49; Univ Ala, PhD, 59. *Concurrent Pos:* NSF fel, 58-59. *Mem:* Sigma Xi. *Res:* Medical entomology. *Mailing Add:* 118 W Sunflower St Cleveland MS 38732

**WHITE, JOE LLOYD,** SOIL MINERALOGY, SOIL CHEMISTRY. *Current Pos:* From asst prof to prof, 47-88, EMER PROF AGRON, PURDUE UNIV, WEST LAFAYETTE, 88- *Personal Data:* b Pierce, Okla, Nov 8, 21; m 45, Wanita I Robertson; c Lerrill, Darla, Ronna, Bren & Janeil. *Educ:* Okla State Univ, BS, 44, MS, 45; Univ Wis, PhD(soil chem), 47. *Honors & Awards:* Charles Medal, Charles Univ, Prague, 61; Soil Sci Award, Am Soc Agron, 69; Sr US Scientist Award, Alexander von Humboldt Found, 80; Pioneer Clay Sci, Clay Mineral Soc, 94. *Concurrent Pos:* Rockefeller fel natural sci, Nat Res Coun, 53-54; NSF sr fel, Louvain, 65-66; Soil Sci Soc Am Rep, Earth Sci Div, Nat Res Coun, 70-73; Fulbright res scholar, Athens, 72-73; Guggenheim fel, Versailles, 72-73; consult, William H Rorer Co, Pa, 78-; Alexander von Humboldt Found fel, Munich Tech Univ, 80-81. *Mem:* Fel AAAS; Am Chem Soc; fel Am Soc Agron; fel Mineral Soc Am; Clay Minerals Soc (treas, 69-72); fel Royal Soc Chem. *Res:* Weathering of micaceous minerals; pesticide-soil colloid interactions; application of infrared spectroscopy to study of aluminosilicates; structure and properties of aluminum hydroxide gels and aluminum chlorohydrates; clay-drug interactions; aluminum vaccine adjuvants. *Mailing Add:* 2505 Roselawn Ave West Lafayette IN 47904

**WHITE, JOE WADE,** PHYSICAL ORGANIC CHEMISTRY. *Current Pos:* Sr chemist, 3M Co, 67-71, res specialist chem, Indust Tape Lab, 71-72, res supvr, Indust Specialties Lab, 72-73, res mgr, 73-78, lab mgr, Struct Prod Dept, 78-81, tech dir, Decorative Prod Div, 81-87, TECH DIR, INDUST SPECIALITIES DIV, 3M CO, 87- *Personal Data:* b Dill City, Okla, Aug 22, 40; m 62; c 2. *Educ:* Okla State Univ, BS, 63; Univ Ariz, PhD(chem), 67. *Mem:* Am Chem Soc; Soc Plastics Eng. *Res:* Kinetics and rheology of gelling polymerizations. *Mailing Add:* Indust Specialties Lab 3M Co Bldg 230-3N-02 St Paul MN 55144-1000

**WHITE, JOHN ANDERSON,** VERTEBRATE ZOOLOGY, PALEONTOLOGY. *Current Pos:* RETIRED. *Personal Data:* b Bahia, Brazil, Oct 18, 19; m 76; c 1. *Educ:* William Jewell Col, AB, 42; Univ Kans, PhD(zool), 53. *Prof Exp:* Instr biol, William Jewell Col, 46-47 & Univ Ill, 53-55; prof, Calif State Col Long Beach, 55-66; cur vert paleont, Idaho Mus Natural Hist & prof biol, Idaho State Univ, 66-85; res assoc, Dept Geo Sci, Univ Ariz, 85- *Mem:* Fel AAAS; Am Soc Mammal; Soc Syst Zool; Soc Vert Paleont; Paleont Soc. *Res:* Systematics, evolution and ecology of late Tertiary and Quaternary rodents and logomorphs. *Mailing Add:* 4831 N Via Entrada Tucson AZ 85718

**WHITE, JOHN ARNOLD,** THERMODYNAMIC FLUCTUATIONS & PHASE TRANSITIONS, RENORMALIZATION GROUP THEORY OF FLUIDS. *Current Pos:* assoc prof, 66-68, PROF PHYSICS, AM UNIV, 68- *Personal Data:* b Chicago, Ill, Jan 30, 33; m 64, Rebecca Cotten; c Lauren, Thomas & Julia. *Educ:* Oberlin Col, BA, 54; Yale Univ, MS, 55, PhD(physics), 59. *Honors & Awards:* Boyden Premium, Franklin Inst, 80. *Prof Exp:* Instr physics, Yale Univ, 58-59; instr, Harvard Univ, 59-62; res assoc, Yale Univ, 62-63; physicist, Nat Bur Stand, 63-64; res assoc physics, Univ Md, 65-66. *Concurrent Pos:* Consult, Nat Bur Stand, 66-72 & 81; NSF grants, Am Univ, 66, 67, 69 & 71; vis scientist, Mass Inst Technol, 72, Nat Bur Stand, 81 & 86; res contracts, Off Naval Res, 73 & 74; fel, Am Soc Eng Educ, Naval Res Lab, 85; Dept Energy, Off Basic Energy Sci res grants, 86, 88, 90. *Mem:* AAAS; Sigma Xi; fel Am Phys Soc. *Res:* Atomic beams; magnetism of rare earth ions in solids; lasers; spontaneous emission in external fields; speed of light; unified time-length standardization; relativity; laser light scattering; critical point phenomena; theory of thermodynamic fluctuations and phase transitions in fluids. *Mailing Add:* Dept Physics Am Univ Washington DC 20016-8058. *Fax:* 301-885-2723

**WHITE, JOHN AUSTIN, JR,** MATERIAL HANDLING, FACILITIES PLANNING. *Current Pos:* from assoc prof to prof, 75-84, REGENTS PROF INDUST & SYSTS ENG, GA INST TECHNOL, 84-, EUGENE C GWALTNEY PROF MFG, 88-, DEAN ENG, 91- *Personal Data:* b Portland, Ark, Dec 5, 39; m 63, Mary Elizabeth Quarles; c Kimberly Elizabeth (Brakmann) & John A III. *Educ:* Univ Ark, Fayetteville, BS, 61; Va Polytech Inst, MS, 66; Ohio State Univ, PhD(indust eng), 69. *Hon Degrees:* DEng, Cath Univ Leuven, 85; DSc, George Washington Univ, 91. *Honors & Awards:* Outstanding Indust Eng Award, Inst Indust Engrs, 80, Albert G Holzman Distinguished Educ Award, 88, David F Baker Distinguished Res Award, 90, Frank & Lillian Gilbreth Indust Eng Award, 94; Reed-Apple Award, Mat Handling Educ Found, 85; Kenneth Andrew Roe Award, Am Asn Eng Socs, 89; Donald E Marlowe Award, Am Soc Eng Educ, 94; Rodney D Chipp Mem Award, Soc Women Engrs, 94. *Prof Exp:* Indust engr, Tenn Eastman Co, 61-63; instr indust eng, Va Polytech Inst, 63-66; teaching assoc, Ohio State Univ, 66-69; from asst prof to assoc prof indust eng & opers res, Va Polytech Inst & State Univ, 70-74; actg dep dir, NSF, 90-91. *Concurrent Pos:* Mem bd dir, Mat Handling Educ Found, 77-81, 88-90; dir, Mat Handling Res Ctr, Ga Inst Technol, 82-87; exec consult, Coopers & Lybrand, 84-; mem Mfg Studies Bd, Nat Res Coun, 86-89; sr ed, Inst Indust Engrs Trans, 84-88; chmn bd dirs, Am Asn Eng Studies, 86; mem, Coun Logistics Mgt, Warehouse Educ & Res Coun; asst dir eng, NSF, 88-90; mem, bd dir, CAPS Logistics Inc, 89-, Russel Corp, 92-, Eastman Chem Co, 94- & Motorola Inc, 95- *Mem:* Nat Acad Eng; Opers Res Soc Am; Am Soc Eng Educ; fel Am Inst Indust Engrs (pres, 83-84); Int Mat Mgt Soc; Nat Soc Prof Engrs; Soc Mfg Engrs. *Res:* Development of design algorithms for facilities layout, material handling and warehousing systems; author and co-author of numerous publications, books and handbooks. *Mailing Add:* Col Eng Ga Inst Technol Atlanta GA 30332

**WHITE, JOHN DAVID,** PATHOGENESIS, INFECTIOUS DISEASES. *Current Pos:* RETIRED. *Personal Data:* b Newark, NJ, Feb 14, 28; m 51; c 1. *Educ:* Univ Buffalo, BA, 48, MA, 50; Vanderbilt Univ, PhD(bact), 53. *Prof Exp:* Asst bact, Univ Buffalo, 48-50; asst bot, Vanderbilt Univ, 50-53; res bacteriologist, US Army Hosp, Camp Kilmer, 54-55; bacteriologist, Armed Forces Inst Path, 55-56; bacteriologist, Path Div, US Dept Army, Ft Detrick, 56-59, chief, Clin Path Br, 59-68, actg chief, Path Div, 68-71; microbiologist, Path Div, US Army Med Res Inst Infectious Dis, 71-92. *Mem:* Sigma Xi; Am Asn Pathologists; NY Acad Sci; Electron Micros Soc Am. *Res:* Immunology; fluorescent antibody methods; electron microscopy. *Mailing Add:* 5707 Old National Pike Frederick MD 21702-3663

**WHITE, JOHN FRANCIS,** GEOLOGY, GROUND WATER. *Current Pos:* CONSULT, 80- *Personal Data:* b New Orleans, La, Feb 9, 21; m 50, 74, Patricia Palmer; c David, Paul, Mark, John III & Corey. *Educ:* Univ Calif, BS, 47, PhD, 55. *Prof Exp:* Geologist, Mining Co Guatemala, 47-48, Consol Coppermines Corp, 48-51; consult, Hydrothermal Res Proj, Antioch Univ, 55-59; from asst prof to assoc prof, 55-71, prof geol, 71-85, emer prof, 85- *Concurrent Pos:* Vis assoc, Calif Inst Technol, 62. *Res:* Economic geology; geomorphology; petrology; ground water in competent rocks. *Mailing Add:* Dept Geol Antioch Col 795 Livermore St Yellow Springs OH 45387

**WHITE, JOHN FRANCIS,** CELL PHYSIOLOGY, BIOPHYSICS. *Current Pos:* asst prof, 73-80, ASSOC PROF PHYSIOL, EMORY UNIV, 80- *Personal Data:* b Indianapolis, Ind, July 21, 44; c 3. *Educ:* Marian Col, BS, 66; Ind Univ, PhD(physiol), 70. *Concurrent Pos:* NSF training fel, Univ Rochester, 71-72; NIH fel, Univ BC, 72-73; res career develop award, NIH. *Mem:* Biophys Soc; Am Physiol Soc. *Res:* Mechanisms and regulation of intestinal transport of ions and solutes by absorptive cells; intracellular ionic activities and compartmentalization of ions. *Mailing Add:* Dept Physiol Emory Univ 1364 Clifton Rd NE Atlanta GA 30322

**WHITE, JOHN FRANCIS,** FOOD & DAIRY SCIENCE. *Current Pos:* RETIRED. *Personal Data:* b Madison, Wis, Dec 2, 29; div; c 1. *Educ:* Univ Wis, BS, 51; Harvard Bus Sch, AMP, 74. *Prof Exp:* Food scientist, Kraft Inc, 54-66, div res coordr, 66-68, tech asst, 68-74, vpres & dir res & develop, 74-85, gen mgr spec projs, Retail Venture Div, 85-87. *Mem:* AAAS; Inst Food Technol; Am Chem Soc. *Mailing Add:* 1439 Pebble Creek Dr Glenview IL 60025

**WHITE, JOHN FRANCIS,** CHEMISTRY, CATALYSIS. *Current Pos:* MGR PROCESS RES, ARCO CHEM RES & DEVELOP, 81- *Personal Data:* b Boston, Mass, Oct 31, 45; m 70; c 1. *Educ:* Amherst Col, BA, 67; Mass Inst Technol, PhD(inorg chem), 72. *Prof Exp:* Group leader res & develop, Emery Industs, 72-76; sr res chemist res & develop, Halcon Res & Develop, 76-78; mgr new ventures res, Oxirane Int, 78-81. *Mem:* Am Chem Soc; Sigma Xi. *Res:* Petrochemical process development; homogeous and heterogeneous catalysis; aroma chemical process development. *Mailing Add:* 33 Knob Hill Rd Summit NJ 07901-3024

**WHITE, JOHN GRAHAM,** SCIENCE RESEARCH. *Current Pos:* PROF DIR INTEGRATED MICROS RESOURCE, UNIV WIS-MADISON, 93- *Personal Data:* b Prestatyn, Wales, Aug, 9, 43; m 80, 94, Claudia Cummins; c Phoebe, Ben, Amelia & Ruth. *Educ:* Brunel Univ, London, BTech, 69; Cambridge Univ, Eng, PhD, 74. *Honors & Awards:* Queen's Award Technol, 91; Mullard Award, Royal Soc, 94. *Prof Exp:* Technician, Med Res Coun, London, 64-69, scientist, 69-93. *Concurrent Pos:* Consult, Bio-Rad, Herculese, Calif, 88- *Res:* Granted two patents for confocal microscopy. *Mailing Add:* Univ Wis 2710 Sommers Ave Madison WI 53704

**WHITE, JOHN GREVILLE,** CHEMISTRY. *Current Pos:* prof, 66-86, EMER PROF CHEM, FORDHAM UNIV, 87- *Personal Data:* b Saltcoats, Scotland, Mar 27, 22; nat US; m 53, Julia Adams; c Susan A, David G & Ian S. *Educ:* Glasgow Univ, BSc, 44, PhD(chem), 47. *Prof Exp:* Asst chem, Glasgow Univ, 45-47; from instr to asst prof, Princeton Univ, 47-55; mem tech staff, RCA, 56-66. *Mem:* Am Crystallog Asn. *Res:* X-ray crystal structure analysis; complex organic structures; accurate small organic structures; inorganic structures. *Mailing Add:* 323 E Beckwith Ave Missoula MT 59801

**WHITE, JOHN JOSEPH, III,** MECHANICAL ENGINEERING, BALLISTIC SCIENCE. *Current Pos:* TECH CONSULT, WOODLAN TOOL & MACH CO, 91- *Personal Data:* b Arlington, Mass, Apr 24, 39; m 68, Marian P Wagner; c John J IV & Edmund T. *Educ:* Col William & Mary, BS, 60; Univ NC, PhD(physics), 65; State Ohio, PE, 76. *Honors & Awards:* Order of the Engr, Sigma Xi. *Prof Exp:* Res assoc physics, Univ NC, 65; capt, US Army (ME), Aberdeen PG, Md, 65-67; asst prof, Univ Ga, 67-73; sr engr, BDM Corp, 73-74; res scientist, Battelle Mem Inst, 74-78, prin res scientist, 78-81, group leader, Columbus Div, 81-91. *Concurrent Pos:* Dir, Ga State Sci Fair, 73; mem, Landing Vehicle Assault Design Review Panel, 76; mem, Pub Rels Comt, Nat Soc Prof Engrs, 78; mem, Physics Res Eval Group, Air Force Off Sci Res, 78-91; pres, Wolfpack TC, 78-; vpres, Ohio USATF, 82-95; ed, Midwestern Epigraphic J, 94- *Mem:* Am Phys Soc; Am Soc Mech Engrs; Am Defense Preparedness Asn; Midwestern Epigraphic Soc. *Res:* Applied mechanics; impact phenomena; explosion containment; assessment of advanced defense technology; optical properties of silver halides, high resolution specific heat measurements in antiferromagnets; superconductivity in quenched alloys; methods of data analysis; military and space vehicle design; analysis of ancient history and linguistics. *Mailing Add:* 4865 Arthur Pl Columbus OH 43220-3102. *Fax:* 614-459-2547

**WHITE, JOHN MARVIN,** GENETICS, ANIMAL BREEDING. *Current Pos:* From asst prof to prof dairy sci, 67-78, HEAD, DEPT DAIRY SCI, VA POLYTECH INST & STATE UNIV, 78- *Personal Data:* b Martin, Tenn, June 9, 37; m 56; c 2. *Educ:* Univ Tenn, BS, 59; Pa State Univ, MS, 64; NC State Univ, PhD(animal breeding), 67. *Mem:* Biomet Soc; Am Dairy Sci Asn; Am Soc Animal Sci; Sigma Xi. *Res:* Quantitative genetics; measurement of response to single and multiple trait selection and correlated responses in mice and dairy cattle. *Mailing Add:* Dept Dairy Sci Va Polytech Inst PO Box 0315 Blacksburg VA 24063-0001

**WHITE, JOHN MICHAEL,** CHEMICAL PHYSICS. *Current Pos:* From asst prof to prof, 66-85, NORMAN HACKERMAN PROF CHEM, UNIV TEX, AUSTIN, 85- *Personal Data:* b Danville, Ill, Nov 26, 38; m 60; c 3. *Educ:* Harding Col, BS, 60; Univ Ill, MS, 62, PhD(chem), 66. *Concurrent Pos:* Vis staff mem, Los Alamos Sci Lab. *Mem:* Am Chem Soc; Am Phys Soc. *Res:* Surface chemistry. *Mailing Add:* Dept Chem & Biochem Univ Tex Austin TX 78712-1104

**WHITE, JOHN R,** IMMUNOLOGY. *Current Pos:* SR SCIENTIST BIOCHEM, SMITHKLINE BEECHAM LABS, 87- *Personal Data:* b London, Eng, Nov 27, 55. *Educ:* Univ Col London, BS, 78, PhD(chem & biochem), 81. *Prof Exp:* Fel biochem, Johns Hopkins Univ, 81-84, assoc prof biochem, 84-87. *Mem:* Am Asn Immunol; NY Acad Sci; Immunol Res Asn. *Res:* Immunology. *Mailing Add:* SmithKline Beecham Labs L101 709 Swedeland Rd UW 2101 King of Prussia PA 19406

**WHITE, JOHN THOMAS,** MATHEMATICS. *Current Pos:* assoc prof, 65-87, chmn dept 79-87, PROF MATH, TEX TECH UNIV, 87- *Personal Data:* b El Paso, Tex, Aug 23, 31; m 58; c 3. *Educ:* Univ Tex, BA, 52, MA, 53, PhD(math), 62. *Prof Exp:* Spec instr math, Univ Tex, 59-62; asst prof, Univ Kans, 62-65. *Concurrent Pos:* Fel, Tex Ctr Res, 66-; assoc dir, Comt Undergrad Prog Math, Univ Calif, Berkeley, 70-71. *Mem:* Math Asn Am; Am Math Soc; Soc Indust & Appl Math; Sigma Xi. *Res:* Distribution theory and transform analysis; integral transform theory. *Mailing Add:* Tex Tech Univ Lubbock TX 79409-1042

**WHITE, JOHN W,** GREENHOUSE STRUCTURES, ENERGY CONSERVATION. *Current Pos:* From asst prof to assoc prof, 64-75, PROF FLORICULT & ASSOC DIR, UNIV OFF INDUST RES & INNOVATION, PA STATE UNIV, UNIVERSITY PARK, 75- *Personal Data:* b Ardmore, Okla, Aug 9, 33; m 58; c 3. *Educ:* Okla State Univ, BS, 55; Colo State Univ, MS, 57; Pa State Univ, PhD(hort), 64. *Honors & Awards:* Garland Award, Am Carnation Soc; Alex Laurie Award Educ & Res; Int Award, Dow Corning. *Concurrent Pos:* Rev ed, J Am Soc Hort Sci, 71-; consult, Gulf Res Corp, Fafard Peat Co, Lombardo Assocs, Gen Mills Corp, Gov's Waste Heat Energy Coun, Wellsley Col, St Mary's Col, Gen Elec, Dow Corning. *Mem:* Fel Am Soc Hort Sci; Soil Sci Soc Am; Int Solar Energy Soc; Soc Am Floricult. *Res:* Physical and chemical properties of soil; experimental designs and glazings for greenhouse structures; effects of the environment on plant growth; energy conservation for greenhouses; passive solar heating systems; water quality management and waste water treatment. *Mailing Add:* 208 W Hamilton Ave Apt 168 State College PA 16801

**WHITE, JUNE BROUSSARD,** INORGANIC CHEMISTRY, ANALYTICAL CHEMISTRY. *Current Pos:* RETIRED. *Personal Data:* b Elizabeth, La, Aug 27, 24; div; c 2. *Educ:* La Polytech Univ, BS, 44; Univ Southwestern La, BS, 59, MS, 61; La State Univ, Baton Rouge, PhD(inorg chem), 70. *Prof Exp:* Analytical chemist, Cities Serv Refining Corp, La, 44-45; chemist, Esso Lab, Stand Oil Co, NJ, La, 45-48; teacher, Parish Sch Bd, La, 53-59; asst prof chem, Univ Southwestern La, 61-66; NSF res partic, La State Univ, Baton Rouge, 64 & 66, instr, 66-68; chmn, Div Natural Sci, Union Univ, Tenn, 69-71, prof chem & physics & chmn dept, 68-82. *Mem:* Am Chem Soc. *Res:* Transition metal complexes which have d-2 electronic system; electron spin resonance; electronic transitions; magnetic properties. *Mailing Add:* 115 Crawford St Lafayette LA 70506-6205

**WHITE, KERR LACHLAN,** EPIDEMIOLOGY, INTERNAL MEDICINE. *Current Pos:* RETIRED. *Personal Data:* b Winnipeg, Man, Jan 23, 17; nat US; m 43, Isabel Pennefather; c Susan & Margot. *Educ:* McGill Univ, BA, 40, MD & CM, 49; Am Bd Internal Med, dipl, 57. *Hon Degrees:* Dr Med, Univ Leuven, 78; DSc, McMaster Univ, 83. *Honors & Awards:* Distinguished Career Award, Asn Health Serv Res, 87; Robert J Glaser Award, Soc Gen Internal Med, 90. *Prof Exp:* Personnel asst, RCA Victor Co, Can, 41-42; intern & resident med, Mary Hitchcock Mem Hosp, Hanover, NH, 49-52; from asst prof to assoc prof med & prev med, Sch Med, Univ NC, 53-62; prof epidemiol & community med & chmn dept, Col Med, Univ Vt, 62-64; chmn dept, Sch Hyg & Pub Health, Johns Hopkins Univ, 64-72, prof health care orgn, 64-76; dir, Inst Health Care Studies, United Hosp Fund, 77-78; dep dir health sci, Rockefeller Found, NY, 78-84. *Concurrent Pos:* Hosmer fel med & psychiat, Royal Victoria Hosp, McGill Univ, 52-53; Commonwealth Fund advan fel, Med Res Coun Gt Brit & Sch Hyg & Trop Med, Univ London, 59-60; consult, Nat Ctr Health Statist & Health Resources Admin, HEW, 66-78; chmn, US Nat Comn Vital & Health Statist, 75-80; mem, Expert Panel Orgn Med Care, WHO, 67-83; mem bd dirs, Found Child Develop, NY, 69-80; trustee, Case Western Res Univ, 74-78; mem, Health Adv Panel, Off Technol Assessment, US Cong, 75-82; consult, China, Australia, Switz, NZ & Sask, Can govt; mem adv comt, Population Health, Can Inst Advan Res. *Mem:* Inst Med-Nat Acad Sci; fel Am Col Prev Med; fel Am Pub Health Asn; fel Am Col Physicians; hon mem Int Epidemiol Asn. *Res:* Medical education, health services research and epidemiology. *Mailing Add:* 2401 Old Ivy Rd No 1410 Charlottesville VA 22903-4858

**WHITE, KEVIN JOSEPH,** MOLECULAR PHYSICS, COMBUSTION PHYSICS. *Current Pos:* PHYSICIST, BALLISTIC RES LABS, 65- *Personal Data:* b Queens, NY, Aug 28, 36; m 66, Jane Carroll; c Hilary, Brian & Alison. *Educ:* Georgetown Univ, BS, 58; Duke Univ, PhD(physics), 65. *Prof Exp:* Physicist, Naval Ord Lab, 58; res assoc physics, Duke Univ, 65. *Mem:* Am Phys Soc. *Res:* Millimeter wave microwave spectroscopy; Stark effect in rotational spectra; electron spin resonance; radiation damage in oxidizers; radical formation by atom addition and abstraction reactions; supersonic molecular beams for studying high pressure chemical reactions; combustion of propellants. *Mailing Add:* 406 Fowler Ct Joppa MD 21085. *E-Mail:* kwhite@arl.mil

**WHITE, LARRY DALE,** RANGE ECOSYSTEM MANAGEMENT. *Current Pos:* PROF & RANGE EXTEN SPECIALIST, TEX A&M UNIV, 78- *Personal Data:* b Sayre, Okla, Nov 24, 40; m 64; c 2. *Educ:* Northern Ariz Univ, BS, 63; Univ Ariz, MS, 65, PhD(range ecol), 68. *Honors & Awards:* Outstanding Achievement Award, Soc Range Mgt, 91. *Prof Exp:* Asst forester, US Forest Serv, 63; range adv, Near East Found, Kenya Govt, 67-69; from asst prof to assoc prof range ecosyst mgt, Univ Fla, 70-78. *Mem:* Soc Range Mgt. *Res:* Educational programs for national, state and county range needs; total range planning; grazing systems; use of prescribed fire; producer training and demonstration; brush control; range seeding; livestock-wildlife habitat relationships; range ecosystem environmental issues; manipulation of range ecosystems; range watershed. *Mailing Add:* Dept Rangeland Ecol & Mgt Tex A&M Univ College Station TX 77843-0100. *Fax:* 409-845-6430

**WHITE, LAWRENCE KEITH,** INTEGRATED CIRCUIT PROCESSING, PHYSICAL CHEMISTRY. *Current Pos:* SR MEM TECH STAFF ADVAN SILICON TECHNOL, DAVID SARNOFF RES CTR, SUBSID OF SRI INT, 78- *Personal Data:* b Lafayette, Ind, Sept 16, 48; m 77; c 3. *Educ:* Earlham Col, AB, 70; Univ Ill, Urbana, PhD(phys chem), 75. *Prof Exp:* Res assoc bio-inorg chem, Univ NH, 75-76; res scientist pulp & paper chem, Union Camp Corp, 77-78. *Mem:* Am Chem Soc; Sigma Xi; Electrochem Soc. *Res:* Solid state science and technology; integrated circuit processing; magnetic resonance; metalloproteins; transition metal chemistry; resist technology; lithography. *Mailing Add:* David Sarnoff Res Ctr RCA Labs Princeton NJ 08543

**WHITE, LAWRENCE S,** PHYSICS. *Current Pos:* RETIRED. *Personal Data:* b Chelsea, Mass, Mar 9, 23; m 46; c 2. *Educ:* Mass Inst Technol, BS, 47. *Prof Exp:* Physicist, Res Lab, Titanium Div, Nat Lead Co, South Amboy, 48-62, sr technologist, 62-70; assoc physicist, Hoffman-La Roche Inc, Nutley, 70-73, sr scientist, 74-80, group leader & mgr, 80-85. *Mem:* Am Chem Soc; AAAS; Acad Pharmaceut Sci; Sigma Xi. *Res:* Physical properties and colorimetry of titania pigments; electron microscopy and diffraction; light scattering; surface properties of pharmaceutical solids; scanning electron microscopy. *Mailing Add:* 3 Sturbridge Dr PO Box 142 South Orleans MA 02662-0142

**WHITE, LEE JAMES,** COMPUTER SCIENCE, ELECTRICAL ENGINEERING. *Current Pos:* PROF COMPUT SCI, CASE WESTERN RES UNIV, 88- *Personal Data:* b Saginaw, Mich, Apr 9, 39; m 65; c 2. *Educ:* Univ Cincinnati, BSEE, 62; Univ Mich, MSEE, 63, PhD(elec eng), 67. *Prof Exp:* Coop engr, Dow Chem Co, 57-61; asst prof eng, Wright State Univ,

67-68; from asst prof to assoc prof, comput & info sci, Ohio State Univ, 68-77, prof, 77-80, chmn dept, 80-88; mem fac, Dept Comput Sci, Univ Alta, Can. *Concurrent Pos:* Consult, Rockwell Int, 73-74 & Monsanto Res Corp, 77- *Mem:* Inst Elec & Electronics Engrs; Asn Comput Mach. *Res:* Analysis of algorithms and software analysis and testing; pattern recognition, automatic document classification, combinational computing and graph theory. *Mailing Add:* Dept Comput Eng Case Western Res Univ 10900 Euclid Ave Crawford Hall 511 Cleveland OH 44106

**WHITE, LENDELL AARON,** MICROBIOLOGY. *Current Pos:* RETIRED. *Personal Data:* b Sabetha, Kans, Nov 10, 26; m 48, June R; c Charles L & Peggy Ann. *Educ:* Univ Kans, BA, 51, MA, 55. *Prof Exp:* Bacteriologist, State Pub Health Lab, Kans, 51-53; asst, Virol Lab, Univ Kans, 53-54; bacteriologist, Spec Res Unit, Lab Br, Ctr Dis Control, USPHS, 55-57, Virus Diag Unit, 57-59, Encephalitis Sect, Tech Br, 59-60, Venereal Dis Res Lab, 60-63, Viral Reagents Unit, 63-85, supvry res microbiologist, 71-89. *Mem:* AAAS; Am Soc Microbiol; Sigma Xi. *Res:* Virology; isolation, identification, typing and determination of antigenic relationships of viruses with established strains; serologic and antigenic relationships among the arthropod-borne encephalitides; infectivity and fluorescent antibody studies with Neisseria gonorrhoeae; production of viral reagents; immunization procedures for reference antisera; inactivation procedures for use with viral antigens; stability of viral cultures and reagents; susceptibility of cell cultures to viral infection, large volume suspension culture. *Mailing Add:* 2534 Wilson Woods Dr Decatur GA 30033

**WHITE, LEROY ALBERT,** PHYSICAL CHEMISTRY. *Current Pos:* RETIRED. *Personal Data:* b New York, NY, June 24, 29; m 58; c 2. *Educ:* Mass Inst Technol, BS, 50; Columbia Univ, MS, 51. *Prof Exp:* Res chemist, Monsanto Chem Co, 51-55; proj mgr, Springborn Lab Consults, Hazardville, 55-94. *Mem:* Am Chem Soc. *Res:* Organic synthesis; vinyl polymerization; nylon and epoxy reactions; general polymer development; coatings; membrane technology; photodegradable plastics; adhesives. *Mailing Add:* 24 Tampa St West Haven CT 06516

**WHITE, LOWELL ELMOND, JR,** NEUROSURGERY, MEDICAL EDUCATION. *Current Pos:* chmn dept, 72-80, PROF NEUROSCI, UNIV S ALA, 72- *Personal Data:* b Tacoma, Wash, Jan 16, 28; m 47; c 3. *Educ:* Univ Wash, BS, 51, MD, 53. *Prof Exp:* Asst neurosurg, Sch Med, Univ Wash, 54-57, from instr to assoc prof, 57-70, assoc dean, 65-68; prof neurol surg & chief div, Univ Fla, 70-72. *Concurrent Pos:* Guggenheim Found fel, Univ Oslo, 57-58; consult, Div Res Resources & chmn, Nat Adv Comt Animal Resources, NIH, 65-69; consult, USPHS, 65-, grants admin adv comt, HEW, 66-70. *Mem:* Am Asn Neuropath; Am Asn Anat; Am Asn Neurol Surg; AMA; Asn Am Med Cols; Sigma Xi. *Res:* Neuroanatomy and neurological surgery. *Mailing Add:* 5750 Huffman Dr N Mobile AL 36693

**WHITE, MALCOLM LUNT,** PHYSICAL CHEMISTRY. *Current Pos:* RETIRED. *Personal Data:* b Schenectady, NY, Aug 16, 27; m 51; c 3. *Educ:* Colgate Univ, BA, 49; Northwestern Univ, PhD(chem), 53. *Prof Exp:* Investr geochem, NJ Zinc Co, 53-59; res chemist, Am Cyanamid Co, 59-61; mem tech staff, Bell Tel Labs, 61-82; res scientist, Lehigh Univ, 83-88. *Mem:* Am Chem Soc; Sigma Xi; Nat Asn Corrosion Engrs. *Res:* Nucleation; geochemistry; physical chemistry of colloid systems; surface chemistry; materials for electron device technology; coating and encapsulation of solid state devices; integrated circuit processing development; organic coatings for corrosion control. *Mailing Add:* 1830 Wilson Ave Bethlehem PA 18018-2132

**WHITE, MARJORIE A,** NURSING, SOCIOLOGY. *Current Pos:* asst prof & prof co-dir, Family Nurse Practr Prog, 74-76, PROF & DIR, CTR NURSING RES, STATE UNIV NY, BUFFALO, 95- *Personal Data:* b South Bend, Ind. *Educ:* Univ Minn, BS, 52; Univ Rochester, MS, 60; Case Western Res Univ, MA, 72, PhD(sociol), 76. *Prof Exp:* Asst dir nursing serv, Mt Sinai Hosp, Minneapolis, 53; asst nursing instr, Genesee Hosp Sch Nursing, Rochester, 53-54; instr & obstet supvr, Mem Hosp, South Bend Sch Nursing Ind, 54-55; instr maternity nursing, Akron City Hosp Sch Nursing, Ind, 57-59; nursing assoc, Rochester Reg Hosp Coun, 60; instr & asst dir nursing educ, Children's Hosp Akron, 60-63, curric consult, 65-67; instr, Nursing of Children, Univ Mich Sch Nursing, 63-65; asst prof & coordr, Univ Adron Col Nursing, 67-69; assoc prof & proj dir, Univ Wis-Madison Sch Nursing, 76-80; from assoc prof to prof, Univ Fla, Gainesville, 80-95. *Concurrent Pos:* Grantee, HEW, 77-82, Univ Wis-Madison, 81, Univ Fla, 81, 83-84, 86-87, 91-92 & 94, Ministry of Health & Univ Iceland, 87, Iceland Thors mem Fund & Am Scandinavian Found, 88, 89-91, Med Bd Denmark, 89-91, Fla League Nursing, 89-91, Helsingborg Health Care District, 91-93, Univ AKureyri, Iceland, 90-95 & Finnish Fulbright Found, 94-95; Fulbright sr scholar, Finland, 94-95. *Mem:* Fel Am Acad Nursing; Sigma Xi; Am Nurses Asn; Am Sociol Asn; Int Soc Univ Nurses. *Res:* Family and community nursing; health care systems; family and medical sociology; social exchange theory; families and bureaucracy; research methods issues; pediatric nursing research; nursing theory. *Mailing Add:* Sch Nursing State Univ NY 916 Kimball Tower Buffalo NY 14214. *Fax:* 716-829-2021

**WHITE, MARK GILMORE,** CHEMICAL ENGINEERING. *Current Pos:* from asst prof to assoc prof, 77-94, assoc dir, 88-94, DIR, FOCUSED RES PROG SURFACE SCI & CATALYSIS, 90-, PROF CHEM, 94- *Personal Data:* b Galveston, Tex, Jan 15, 49; m 85, Kathy McDaniel; c Alyson. *Educ:* Univ Tex, Austin, BSChE, 71; Purdue Univ, MSChE, 73; Rice Univ, PhD(chem eng), 78. *Prof Exp:* Res engr, Amoco Oil Co, 73-74. *Mem:* Am Inst Chem Eng; Sigma Xi; Am Chem Soc. *Res:* Heterogeneous catalysis, kinetics and reactor design; research with the elucidation of reaction mechanisms over catalysts by a study of the kinetics; characterization of the catalysts and the use of isotopic compounds; synthesis of novel amorphous and crystalline materials using the designed dispersion approach. *Mailing Add:* Sch Chem Eng Ga Inst Technol Atlanta GA 30332. *Fax:* 404-894-2866

**WHITE, MARVIN HART,** SOLID STATE ELECTRONICS & PHYSICS. *Current Pos:* SHERMAN FAIRCHILD PROF SOLID STATE STUDIES, ELEC & COMPUT ENG DEPT, LEHIGH UNIV, 81- *Personal Data:* b Bronx, NY, Sept 6, 37; m 65; c 1. *Educ:* Univ Mich, Ann Arbor, BSE(physics) & BSE(math), 60, MS, 61; Ohio State Univ, PhD(elec eng), 69. *Honors & Awards:* Electron Device Nat lectr, Inst Elec & Electronics Engrs, 82. *Prof Exp:* Adv engr, Advan Technol Labs, Westinghouse Elec Corp, 61-81. *Concurrent Pos:* Fulbright res vis prof, Cath Univ, Louvain-la-Nueve, Belg, 70-79; ed, Electron Device Nat Newslett, 73-76. *Mem:* Fel Inst Elec & Electronics Engrs; Sigma Xi. *Res:* Solid state electron devices and systems; semiconductor surfaces; integrated circuits; solid state electron device modeling and characterization. *Mailing Add:* CSEE/EE Sherman Fairchild Lab Bldg 161 Lehigh Univ Bethlehem PA 18015

**WHITE, MARY ANNE,** SOLID STATE CHEMISTRY, THERMAL PROPERTIES OF SOLIDS & MATERIALS SCIENCE. *Current Pos:* from asst prof to assoc prof, 83-92, PROF CHEM & PHYSICS, DALHOUSIE UNIV, 92-, KILLAM RES PROF MAT SCI, 96- *Personal Data:* b London, Ont, Dec 28, 53; m 77, Robert L; c David & Alice. *Educ:* Univ Western Ont, BSc, 75; McMaster Univ, PhD(chem), 80. *Honors & Awards:* Stig Sunner Mem Award, Calorimetry Conf, 94; Noranda Award, Can Soc Chem, 96. *Prof Exp:* Fel chem, Natural Sci & Eng Res Coun, Oxford Univ, 79-81; res fel, Natural Sci & Eng Res Coun, Univ Waterloo, 81-83. *Concurrent Pos:* Jr res fel, St Hilda's Col, Oxford Univ, 79-81; comt mem, Natural Sci & Eng Res Coun, Can, 84; mem bd dirs, Calorimetry Conf, 84-86, Discovery Centre, 87-93; nat coordr, Nat Chem Week, 93-94; chair, Gordon Res Conf Order/Disorder Solids, 94. *Mem:* Chem Inst Can; Can Asn Physicists; Am Inst Physics; Mat Res Soc. *Res:* Measurement of thermal properties of solids; investigation of polymorphism, especially in disordered solids and in inclusion compounds; thermal properties of materials; heat storage materials; investigations of dynamically disordered solids; melting pheromena in binary systems. *Mailing Add:* Chem Dept Dalhousie Univ Halifax NS B3H 4J3 Can. *Fax:* 902-494-1310; *E-Mail:* mary.anne.white@dal.ca

**WHITE, MAURICE LEOPOLD,** MICROBIOLOGY. *Current Pos:* instr, 63-73, LECTR MED MICROBIOL & IMMUNOL, SCH MED, UNIV CALIF, LOS ANGELES, 73-; CHIEF, MICROBIOL UNIT, LAB SERV, VET AFFAIRS MED CTR, WEST LOS ANGELES, 85- *Personal Data:* b New York, NY, Sept 30, 28; m 51, Mae Drizeck; c Marlisse & Micah. *Educ:* Univ Calif, Los Angeles, BA, 51, PhD, 57; Am Bd Med Microbiol, dipl, 66. *Prof Exp:* Chief, Dept Bact, Cedars of Lebanon Hosp, Los Angeles, Calif, 57-63. *Mem:* Am Soc Microbiol. *Res:* Staphylococcal phosphatase; nutrition and bacteriophage studies of Bordetella pertussis; taxonomy of Brucellaceae and Enterobacteriaceae; clinical microbiology. *Mailing Add:* Path & Lab Med Serv 113 Vet Affairs Med Ctr 11301 Wilshire Blvd West Los Angeles CA 90073. *Fax:* 310-268-4721

**WHITE, MERIT P(ENNIMAN),** engineering mechanics; deceased, see previous edition for last biography

**WHITE, MICHAEL GEORGE,** IONIZATION DYNAMICS, ELECTRON SPECTROSCOPY. *Current Pos:* from asst chemist to assoc chemist, 80-84, CHEMIST, BROOKHAVEN NAT LAB, 84- *Personal Data:* b Oakpark, Ill, May 29, 53; m 75; c 1. *Educ:* Univ Pittsburgh, BS, 74; Univ Calif, Berkeley, PhD(chem), 79. *Prof Exp:* Res fel, Dept Chem, Univ BC, Vancouver, 79-80. *Mem:* Am Phys Soc. *Res:* Photoelectron studies of the photoionization dynamics of free molecules; non-radiative decay of super-excited neutral states lying in the ionization continuum; spectroscopy and ionization dynamics of optically prepared excited states via multiphoton ionization. *Mailing Add:* Chem Dept Brookhaven Nat Lab Upton NY 11973

**WHITE, MORENO J,** POLYMER MATRIX COMPOSITES, AEROSPACE ENGINEERING. *Current Pos:* sr engr, 82-88, TECH DIR, AEROSPACE SCI, SPARTA, INC, 88- *Personal Data:* b Evergreen, Ala, Dec 19, 48; m 78; c 2. *Educ:* Univ Ala, BS, 72; Calif State Univ, MS, 75. *Honors & Awards:* Technol Transfer Award, Am Defense Preparedness Asn & Strategic Defense Initiation Orgn, 89; Composite Systs Award, Dupont-Am Soc Metals, 93; Award of Excellence, Composites Inst, 97. *Prof Exp:* Jr engr, McDonnel Douglas Astronaut Corp, 72-73; staff engr, Rockwell Int, 73-75; eng assoc, P D A Eng, 75-76; staff eng, Sci Applications, Inc, 76-80; sr engr, Gen Res Corp, 80-82. *Mem:* Am Soc Mech Engrs; Am Soc Metals; Am Defense Preparedness Asn. *Res:* Advanced materials research and development; structural analysis; advanced composites design; bioengineering; hypervelocity projects design and analysis. *Mailing Add:* Sparta Inc 10540 Heater Ct San Diego CA 92121

**WHITE, MYRON EDWARD,** MATHEMATICS, COMPUTER SCIENCE. *Current Pos:* From instr to assoc prof, 53-73, dir sci training progs, 63-73, PROF MATH, STEVENS INST TECHNOL, 73-, DIR, MOVE AHEAD PROG, 74- *Personal Data:* b Boston, Mass, May 1, 20; m 48; c 4. *Educ:* Wesleyan Univ, AB, 41; Columbia Univ, AM, 50, PhD(math), 62. *Hon Degrees:* MEng, Stevens Inst Technol, 83. *Concurrent Pos:* Teacher, NSF Math Insts; adv bd, math, sci & comp sci, NJ Dept Higher Educ; consult, US Agency Int Develop, India. *Mem:* Am Math Soc; Math Asn Am. *Res:* Computer programming languages. *Mailing Add:* 1363 Sussea Rd Teaneck NJ 07666-2806

**WHITE, NATHANIEL MILLER,** ASTRONOMY. *Current Pos:* Res assoc astron, 69-71, astronr, 72-78, SR ASTRONR, LOWELL OBSERV, 78- *Personal Data:* b Providence, RI, Feb 28, 41; m 67; c 3. *Educ:* Earlham Col, AB, 64; Ohio State Univ MSc, 67, PhD(astron), 71; Northern Ariz Univ,

BScE, 84. *Concurrent Pos:* Prin investr, NSF, 72-90; fac astron, Yavapai Community Col, 77-78; elected coun mem & vice-mayor, City Flagstaff, 88-92. *Mem:* Am Astron Soc; Int Astron Union; Inst Elec & Electronics Engrs; Sigma Xi; Soc Photo-Optical Instrumentation Engrs. *Res:* Basic data on the atmospheres of cool stars; lunar occultation observations; absolute flux measurements of stars; instrumentation; telescope design and control. *Mailing Add:* Lowell Observ Mars Hill Rd-1400 W Flagstaff AZ 86001

**WHITE, NICHOLAS R,** ION BEAM PHYSICS, SEMICONDUCTOR MANUFACTURING EQUIPMENT DESIGN. *Current Pos:* VPRES TECHNOL, DIAMOND SEMICONDUCTOR GROUP INC, 91- *Personal Data:* b London, UK, June 14, 52. *Educ:* Univ Oxford, UK, BA, 73, MA & DPhil(physics), 81. *Prof Exp:* Prin scientist, Eaton Corp, 84-86; sr physicist, Ionex/HEI, 86-88; dir technol appl mat, Implant Div, 88-90. *Mem:* Sr mem Inst Elec & Electronics Engrs; Am Phys Soc. *Res:* Physics, generation, transport and control of heavy ion beams at the highest continuous beam perveances; design of commercial manufacturing equipment based on this technology mainly for semiconductor applications. *Mailing Add:* 21 Friend Ct Wenham MA 01984

**WHITE, NILES C,** CHEMICAL ENGINEERING. *Current Pos:* tech adv, Prop Div, 80-90, CONSULT, ATLANTIC RES CORP, 90- *Personal Data:* b Saragossa, Ala, Feb 14, 22; m 52, Doris Vann; c Richard & Carol (Propes). *Educ:* Univ Ala, BS, 50. *Honors & Awards:* Res & Develop Achievement Award, Dept Army, 61. *Prof Exp:* Chem engr, US Naval Ord Sta, 50-51 & Redstone Arsenal, 51-56; supv chemist, Army Rocket & Guided Missile Agency, US Army Missile Command, 56-62, supv res chemist, 62-64, chief, Solid Propellant Chem Br, 64-80. *Mem:* AAAS; Am Chem Soc; Am Inst Chem Engrs; Am Inst Aeronaut & Astronaut. *Res:* Rocket propulsion; propellants; combustion; polymer crystallinity; physical properties of elastomers. *Mailing Add:* 823 Watts Dr Huntsville AL 35801-2057

**WHITE, NOEL DAVID GEORGE,** STORED PRODUCTS, ECOSYSTEM ANALYSIS. *Current Pos:* RES SCIENTIST, AGR CAN RES STA, 81-, PROJ LEADER, 89-, SECT HEAD, 91- *Personal Data:* b Simcoe, Ont, Dec 16, 51; m 73, Sandra Linton; c Ryan & Andrew. *Educ:* Univ Guelph, BScAgr, 74, MSc, 76; Univ Man, PhD(entom), 79. *Prof Exp:* Res assoc, Dept Agr Eng, Univ Man, 79-81. *Concurrent Pos:* Adj prof, Dept Agr Eng, Univ Man, 87-, Dept Entom, 91- *Mem:* Entom Soc Am; Agr Inst Can; Sigma Xi. *Res:* Improved basis to manage stored cereals, oil seeds and their products with minimal quality loss from insects, mites and molds, using a multi-disciplinary ecosystem approach. *Mailing Add:* Agr Can Res Sta 195 Dafoe Rd Winnipeg MB R3T 2M9 Can. *Fax:* 204-983-4604

**WHITE, NORMAN EDWARD,** PHYSICAL CHEMISTRY. *Current Pos:* RETIRED. *Personal Data:* b Springfield, Ohio, Jan 20, 17; m 54, Myrle C Wagner; c Elizabeth C. *Educ:* Wittenberg Univ, AB, 38; Univ Pa, MS, 41, PhD(phys chem), 54. *Prof Exp:* From instr to prof chem, Drexel Univ, 47-65; prof chem, Bloomsburg Univ, 65-85, chmn dept, 65-71. *Mem:* Am Chem Soc. *Res:* Hydrogen bond association; molecular weights in solution by freezing point depression method. *Mailing Add:* 6 Kent Rd Bloomsburg PA 17815-8553

**WHITE, PAUL A,** MATHEMATICS. *Current Pos:* RETIRED. *Personal Data:* b Hollywood, Calif, Aug 21, 15; m 39; c 4. *Educ:* Univ Calif, Los Angeles, AB, 37, MA, 39; Univ Va, PhD(math), 42. *Prof Exp:* Asst math, Univ Calif, Los Angeles, 37-39; instr, Univ Va, 39-42; asst prof, La State Univ, 42-46; from asst prof to prof, Univ Southern Calif, 46-95. *Concurrent Pos:* Asst prof, Tulane Univ, 44; mathematician, Ballistics Res Lab, Aberdeen Proving Ground, 45; vis prof, Univ Innsbruck, 60-61; writer & lectr, African Ed Proj, 66-68; NSF lectr, India, 67; writer, UNESCO Arab Math Proj, 69-70; writer & adv bd mem, Sec Sch Math Curric Improv Study, 70-72; mem adv bd, Sch Math Study Group, 70-72. *Mem:* Am Math Soc. *Res:* Topology; R-regular convergence spaces. *Mailing Add:* 1019 W 52nd Los Angeles CA 90037

**WHITE, PAUL C,** PHYSICS. *Current Pos:* mem staff, Ctr Nat Security Studies, Los Alamos Nat Labs, 75-80, group leader, Thermonuclear Appln Group, 80-83, assoc div leader, Appl Theoret Phys Div, 83-85, dep dir, 85-88, actg dir, 88-89, div leader, Appl Theoret Phys Div, Ctr Nat Security Studies, 89-92, prog mgr spec studies, 92-97, PROG MGR, LOS ALAMOS NAT LABS, 97- *Personal Data:* b Boston, Mass, Oct 2, 41; m 64; c Mark & Nathan. *Educ:* Harpur Col, BA, 63; State Univ NY, Binghamton, MA, 66; Univ Tex, Austin, PhD(physics), 70. *Prof Exp:* From asst to assoc prof physics, St Edward's Univ, 69-75, chmn, Div Physics & Biol Sci, 72-74. *Mem:* AAAS; Am Asn Physics Teachers; Int Inst Strategic Studies. *Res:* General relativistic astrophysics; inhomogeneous cosmologies; relativistic transport theory; radiation biophysics; radiation transport; national security policy and arms control technology. *Mailing Add:* Los Alamos Nat Lab PO Box 1663 MS-K760 Los Alamos NM 87545. *E-Mail:* 76012.3313@compuserve.com

**WHITE, PAUL MALCOLM,** HIGH EFFICIENCY POWER AMPLIFIER DESIGN, DEVICE MODELING. *Current Pos:* sr engr, Raytheon Co, 80-85, prin engr, 85-86, PRIN STAFF ENGR, RAYTHEON MICROELECTRONICS, 89- *Personal Data:* b Bexley Heath, UK, Dec 29, 42; US citizen; m 74, Evelyn M Richards; c Robert D & Emma J. *Educ:* Univ Nottingham, UK, BSc, 64, PhD(physics), 68. *Prof Exp:* Prin scientist, Plessey Res Ltd, UK, 68-74, sr prin scientist, 74-78, chief engr, 79-80. *Concurrent Pos:* Eng leader, Microwave Semiconductor Corp, 86-88. *Mem:* Sr mem Inst Elec & Electronics Engrs. *Res:* Design of high power, high efficiency monolithic microwave integrated circuit amplifiers; harmonic terminations. *Mailing Add:* 8 Revolutionary Rd Acton MA 01720

**WHITE, PETER,** HEMATOLOGY. *Current Pos:* ASSOC DEAN & PROF MED, MED COL OHIO, 85- *Personal Data:* b Philadelphia, Pa, June 12, 30; m 53, Polly Myers; c Katharine, Peter, Jennifer & Jeffrey. *Educ:* Yale Univ, BA, 51; Univ Pa, MD, 55. *Prof Exp:* From assoc to asst prof med, Sch Med, Univ Pa, 63-69, assoc dir, Clin Res Ctr, 67-69; assoc prof, Med Col Ohio, 69-72, dep chmn, Dept Med, 69-75, prof & chief, Div Hemat, 72-77; dir & prof, Presby Univ Pa Med Ctr, 77-85. *Concurrent Pos:* USPHS res fel hemat, Sch Med, Univ Pa, 63-65; mem, Res in Nursing in Patient Care Rev Comt, Bur Health Prof Educ & Manpower Training, NIH, 70-75; mem, Coun Thrombosis, Am Heart Asn; chief-of-staff, Med Col Hosp, Toledo, Ohio, 90-92; pres, Assoc Physicians MCO, Inc, 96- *Mem:* Am Col Physicians; AAAS; Am Soc Hemat; Am Fedn Clin Res; Int Soc Haemostasis and Thrombosis; Am Geriat Soc. *Res:* Hemoglobin metabolism; platelet metabolism; Alzheimer's disease; cancer in the elderly. *Mailing Add:* Dept Med Med Col Ohio PO Box 10008 Caller Sender 10008 Toledo OH 43699. *Fax:* 419-382-0354; *E-Mail:* pwhite@vortex.mco.edu

**WHITE, PHILIP CLEAVER,** RESEARCH ADMINISTRATION, CHEMISTRY & FOSSIL FUEL TECHNOLOGY. *Current Pos:* RETIRED. *Personal Data:* b Chicago, Ill, May 10, 13; m 39; c 3. *Educ:* Univ Chicago, BS, 35, PhD(org chem), 38. *Prof Exp:* Res chemist, Stand Oil Co, Ind, 38-45, group leader, 45, chief chemist, 46-50, div dir, 50-51, mgr res, 56-58, gen mgr res & develop, 58-60, gen mgr res, Amoco Res Ctr, 69-75; mgr res & develop, Pan Am Refining Corp, 51-56, gen mgr res & develop, Am Oil Co, 61-65, vpres res & develop, 66-69; gen mgr res, Amoco Res Ctr, Stand Oil Co, Ind, 69-75; asst adminr, ERDA, US Govt, 75-77; sr tech adv, Dept Energy, 77-78; pres & owner, Energy Consults Inc, 79-88. *Concurrent Pos:* Pres, Indust Res Inst, 71-72, pres, Coord Res Coun, 73-75; consult, 78-79. *Mem:* Am Chem Soc; fel Am Inst Chem Engrs. *Res:* Petroleum products, processes and analysis; research administration. *Mailing Add:* 1812 Kalorama Sq Washington DC 20008

**WHITE, RALPH E,** ELECTROCHEMICAL SYSTEMS, MATHEMATICAL MODELLING. *Current Pos:* PROF CHEM ENG & CHMN DEPT, UNIV SC, 93- *Personal Data:* b Clovis, NMex, Nov 6, 42; m 81, Marjorie Nicholson; c David Stewart, Robert Edward, Priscilla Anne, Lillian Leigh & Samuel Joseph. *Educ:* Univ SC, BS, 71; Univ Calif, Berkeley, MS, 73, PhD(chem eng), 77. *Honors & Awards:* Halliburton Educ Found Award Excellence, 87; Battery Div Res Award, Electro Chem Soc, 91, Electrodeposition Div Res Award, 92. *Prof Exp:* From asst prof to prof chem eng, Tex A&M Univ, 77-92, assoc head dept, 90-92. *Concurrent Pos:* Prin investr, Tex A&M Univ, 77-; consult, Dow Chem, 79-93, Exxon Corp, 81-82, Gen Motors Corp, 84-87, Allied Corp, 85-86 & WR Grace & Co, 88-89; chmn, STex Sect, Electrochem Soc, 86-87, Div Ed Indust Electrolytic, 87-90, chmn, Indust Electrolytic Div, 88-90, mem bd dirs, 88-; distinguished scientist, Westinghouse Savannah River Co, 93- *Mem:* Electrochem Soc (treas, 90-); Am Inst Chem Engrs; Int Soc Electrochemists; Am Electroplaters & Surface Finishers Soc; Nat Asn Corrosion Engrs; Soc Indust & Appl Math. *Res:* Electrochemical systems; mathematical modelling; fuel cells; plating; corrosion; batteries. *Mailing Add:* Dept Chem Eng Univ SC Columbia SC 29208. *Fax:* 803-777-8265; *E-Mail:* rew.sun.che.sc.edu

**WHITE, RALPH LAWRENCE, JR,** SYNTHETIC ORGANIC CHEMISTRY. *Current Pos:* sr res chemist, 69-80, RES ASSOC, NORWICH-EATON PHARMACEUT, 80- *Personal Data:* b Troy, NC, June 19, 41; m 68. *Educ:* Univ NC, Chapel Hill, BS, 63; Ind Univ, Bloomington, PhD(org chem), 67. *Prof Exp:* Fel, 67-68; instr med chem, Sch Pharm, Univ NC, Chapel Hill, 68-69. *Mem:* Am Chem Soc. *Res:* Chemistry and synthesis of thiophene compounds; synthesis of potential biologically active compounds. *Mailing Add:* 2 Hillview Dr Norwich NY 13815-1007

**WHITE, RANDY D,** ANIMAL TOXICOLOGY & NUTRITION, BIOMEDICAL-BIOVETERINARY RESEARCH. *Current Pos:* mgr toxicol, 89-94, TECH DIR TOXICOL, BAXTER HEALTH CARE CORP, 94- *Personal Data:* b Brigham City, Utah, Aug 23, 48; m 79, Melanie Greenway; c Elizabeth, Joseph, Gentry, Alese, & Tyler. *Educ:* Brigham Young Univ, BS, 72, MS, 78; Ore State Univ, PhD(animal nutrit & toxicol), 82. *Prof Exp:* Biol sci asst, Letterman Army Inst Res, 73-76; res asst prof, Utah State Univ, 82-86; mgr animal toxicol, Utah Biomed Test Lab, 86-89, mgr toxicol & assoc dir, 89. *Concurrent Pos:* Consult, 82-; adj asst prof, Utah State Univ, 86-90; auxilary fac/clin instr, Univ Utah, 89-91. *Mem:* Soc Toxicol; Am Col Toxicol; Am Asn Lab Animal Sci; Soc of Biomat. *Res:* regulatory toxicology and product risk assessment. *Mailing Add:* Baxter Healthcare Corp Rte 120 & Wilson Rd WG2-1S Round Lake IL 60073-0490. *Fax:* 847-270-5471; *E-Mail:* whiter@baxter.com

**WHITE, RAY HENRY,** NEURAL NETWORKS. *Current Pos:* asst prof physics, Univ San Diego, 68-70, chmn dept, 70-72 & 84-85, chmn, Dept Sci & Math, 72-75 & 76-78, assoc prof, 70-81, PROF PHYSICS & COMPUT SCI, UNIV SAN DIEGO, 81- *Personal Data:* b Lakewood, Ohio, Apr 28, 36; m 62, Christine K Tan; c Kenneth, Karen & Peter. *Educ:* Calif Inst Technol, BS, 57; Univ Calif, Berkeley, PhD(physics), 64. *Prof Exp:* Res asst physics, Univ Calif, 58-63; lectr, Univ Singapore, 63-67; asst prof, Calif State Polytech Col, 67-68. *Concurrent Pos:* Vis fel, Univ Singapore, 75-76; vis scholar, Univ Calif, San Diego, 82-83, 89-90. *Mem:* Int Neural Network Soc. *Res:* Learning algorithms in neural networks; superconductivity; physics of music. *Mailing Add:* Dept Physics Univ San Diego 5998 Alcala Park San Diego CA 92110. *E-Mail:* white@teetot.acusd.edu

**WHITE, RAYMOND E,** ASTRONOMY. *Current Pos:* From instr to prof astron, Steward Observ, Univ Ariz, 64-95, asst dir, 72-74, res assoc & lectr, 74-81, assoc prof & assoc astronr, 81-93, UNIV DISTINGUISHED PROF & ASTRONOMER, STEWARD OBSERV, UNIV ARIZ, 95- *Personal Data:* b Freeport, Ill, May 6, 33; m 56, Ruby E Fisk; c Raymond E III, Kathleen M (Wade) & Kevin D. *Educ:* Univ Ill, Urbana, BS, 55, PhD(astron), 67. *Honors & Awards:* Harlow Shapley lectr, Am Astron Soc, 78. *Concurrent Pos:* Sr vis scholar, Inst Astron, Cambridge Univ, Eng, 80; fac fel, Univ Ariz, 88-; Fulbright scholar, Dublin Inst Advan Study, 96-97; vis lectr, Dept Physics, Trinity Col, Dublin, 96-97. *Mem:* AAAS; Am Astron Soc; Royal Astron Soc; Int Astron Union; Sigma Xi; Am Asn Physics Teachers. *Res:* Observational astronomy; structure of the Milky Way Galaxy, particularly with respect to the identification and distribution of Population II stellar component; archaeo-astronomy, especially of Inca culture in Peru. *Mailing Add:* Steward Observ Univ Ariz Tucson AZ 85721. *Fax:* 520-621-1532; *E-Mail:* rwhite@as.arizona.edu

**WHITE, RAYMOND GENE,** LABORATORY ANIMAL MEDICINE, BOVINE PRODUCTION MEDICINE. *Current Pos:* coordr, Reg Off Vet Med, 82-85, dir, Inst Animal Care Prog, 85-93, DIR, RES COMPLIANCE SERV, UNIV NEBR, 93- *Personal Data:* b Elana, WVa, Oct 10, 30; m 52, Donna Wilmoth; c Keith A & Janice L (Richert). *Educ:* Okla State Univ, BS, 58, DVM, 60; Univ Nebr, MS, 71. *Prof Exp:* Pvt vet pract, 60-64; res vet, Chemagro Corp, 64-69; res vet, Univ Nebr, 69-76, dir, N Platte Sta, 76-80; assoc dean, Col Vet Med, Miss State Univ, 80-82. *Concurrent Pos:* Consult, Vet Med Mgt. *Mem:* Am Vet Med Asn; Am Asn Exten Vet; Am Asn Bovine Practitioners; Am Asn Lab Animal Sci; Am Soc Animal Sci; fel Am Acad Vet Pharmacol & Therapeut. *Res:* Initiating and supervising field research activities involving animal health products, pesticides and anthelmintics; author or co-author of over 50 scientific and non-scientific publications; co-owner of one patent. *Mailing Add:* 1320 Twin Ridge Rd Lincoln NE 68510-5063. *Fax:* 402-472-9323; *E-Mail:* rw61821@navix.net

**WHITE, RAYMOND L,** HUMAN GENETICS. *Current Pos:* assoc prof cellular, viral & molecular biol, Univ Utah, 80-84, investr, Howard Hughes Med Inst, 80-, co-chair, Human Genetics Dept, Sch Med, 84-, prof cellular, viral & molecular biol, 85-, prof human genetics, 85-, PROF & CHMN, DEPT ONCOL SCI & EXEC DIR, HUNTSMAN CANCER INST, UNIV UTAH, 94- *Educ:* Univ Ore, BS, 65; Mass Inst Technol, PhD(microbiol), 71. *Honors & Awards:* Sword of Hope Award, Am Cancer Soc, 95. *Prof Exp:* Assoc prof, Microbiol Dept, Univ Mass Sch Med, 78-80. *Concurrent Pos:* Distinguished prof human genetics & biol, 93. *Mem:* Nat Acad Sci; Am Soc Human Genetics. *Res:* Development of a new technology for mapping and ultimately identifying human genes causing disease; discovery of fundamental genes and genetic mechanisms important in the inherited and cellular pathways to cancer. *Mailing Add:* Univ Utah Eccles Inst Human Genetics Bldg 533 Suite 7410 Salt Lake City UT 84132. *Fax:* 801-585-3833; *E-Mail:* ram.white@genetics.utah.edu

**WHITE, RAYMOND PETRIE, JR,** ANATOMY, ORAL SURGERY. *Current Pos:* dean, Sch Dent, 74-81, assoc dean, Sch Med, 81-93, PROF ORAL & MAXILLOFACIAL SURG, UNIV SC, 74-, DALTON L MICHAEL PROF, 93- *Personal Data:* b New York, NY, Feb 13, 37; m 61, Betty; c Karen & Michael. *Educ:* Med Col Va, DDS, 62, PhD(anat), 67; Am Bd Oral Surg, dipl, 74. *Prof Exp:* Intern oral surg, Med Col Va, 64-65; from asst resident to resident, 65-67; from asst prof to assoc prof, Col Dent, Univ Ky, 67-71, chmn dept, 69-71; asst dean admin affairs & prof oral surg, Va Commonwealth Univ, 71-74. *Concurrent Pos:* Mem adv comt, Am Bd Oral Surg, 74-77, Fayetteville Vet Admin Hosp, NC, 74-96; assoc chief staff, NC Mem Hosp, 81-93. *Mem:* Inst Med-Nat Acad Sci; Int Asn Dent Res; Am Asn Oral & Maxillofacial Surg. *Res:* Correction facial deformity with surgery-orthodontic therapy; dental health policy and health care delivery. *Mailing Add:* Dept Oral Maxillofacial Surg Univ NC Sch Dent Chapel Hill NC 27599-7450. *Fax:* 919-966-6019; *E-Mail:* rwhite.deutce@mhs.unc.edu

**WHITE, RICHARD ALAN,** DEVELOPMENTAL ANATOMY, MORPHOLOGY. *Current Pos:* from asst prof to assoc prof, 63-73, chmn dept, 76-85, PROF PLANT ANAT, DUKE UNIV, 73-, DEAN ART & SCI & TRINITY COL, 85- *Personal Data:* b Philadelphia, Pa, Oct 25, 35; m 65; c 3. *Educ:* Temple Univ, BS & MEd, 57; Univ Mich, MA, 59, PhD(bot), 62. *Prof Exp:* NSF fel, Univ Manchester, 62-63. *Concurrent Pos:* Treas, Orgn Trop Studies, 85- *Mem:* AAAS; Bot Soc Am; Torrey Bot Club; Am Fern Soc; Int Soc Plant Morphol; Am Phys Soc. *Res:* Comparative morphology of tracheary cells of ferns; developmental studies of fern stellar patterns; comparative and developmental studies of lower vascular plants. *Mailing Add:* Dept Bot Duke Univ Durham NC 27706-8001

**WHITE, RICHARD ALLAN,** ASTROPHYSICS. *Current Pos:* Nat Acad Sci & Nat Res Coun assoc, 80-93, ASTROPHYSICIST, GODDARD SPACE FLIGHT CTR, NASA, 89- *Personal Data:* b Boston, Mass, June 9, 46. *Educ:* Univ Calif, Berkeley, AB, 68; Univ Chicago, MS, 71, PhD(astron), 78. *Prof Exp:* Res asst astron, Univ Chicago, 69-74; res assoc radio astron, Nat Radio Astron Observ, 77-80. *Concurrent Pos:* Assoc scientist, Comput Sci Corp, 83-86, Appl Res Corp, 86-89. *Mem:* Am Astron Soc; Int Astron Union. *Res:* Galaxies; clusters of galaxies; astronomical data. *Mailing Add:* 5000 Battery Lane No 802 Bethesda MD 20814. *Fax:* 301-286-1771; *E-Mail:* richard.a.white.1@gsfc.nasa.gov

**WHITE, RICHARD EARL,** SYSTEMATIC ENTOMOLOGY. *Current Pos:* RETIRED. *Personal Data:* b Akron, Ohio, Aug 23, 33; m 77, Pyn-Ye Kim; c Bonnie & Daniel. *Educ:* Univ Akron, BS, 57; Ohio State Univ, MSc, 59, PhD(entom), 63. *Prof Exp:* Asst prof zool, Union Col, Ky, 64-65; res entomologist, USDA, 65- *Mem:* AAAS; Entom Soc Am; Coleopterists Soc. *Res:* Taxonomy of Coleoptera, especially the families Anobiidae and Chrysomelidae; insect illustrations. *Mailing Add:* Syst Entom Lab c/o US Nat Mus Natural Hist Washington DC 20560

**WHITE, RICHARD EDWARD,** INTERSTELLAR MATTER, OBSERVATIONAL ASTRONOMY. *Current Pos:* asst prof, Smith Col, 74-75 & 76-82, lectr, 75-76, assoc prof, 82-92, PROF ASTRON, SMITH COL, 92- *Personal Data:* b Chicago, Ill, Jan 18, 44; m 70, 88, Angeline F Schrater. *Educ:* St Joseph's Col, BS, 65; Columbia Univ, PhD(astron), 71. *Prof Exp:* Carnegie fel, Hale Observ, 70-72; resident res assoc, Goddard Inst Space Studies, NASA, 72-74. *Concurrent Pos:* Mem, Users Comt, Kitt Peak Nat Observ, 77-79, NASA Proposal Rev Comt, Int Ultraviolent Explorer, 81 & Rev Comt, Dept Physics & Astron, Bowdoin Col, 86; proj dir, NSF Grant Instrnl Sci Equip, 78-80; vis astronr, Smithsonian Inst, Moent Hopkins Observ, 80, F L Whipple Observ, 82-83, Smithsonian Astrophys Observ, 84 & Wyo Infrared Observ, 87-88; assoc chair, Undergrad Prog, Five Col Astron Dept, Clark Sci Ctr, Smith Col, 84-87 & 89-90; prin investr, NASA res grant, 86-87; supply assoc prof, Univ Wyo, 87; asst to pres, Smith Col, 88-89; prin investr, NSF Res Grant, 91-97; adj prof, Univ Wyo, 94-97. *Mem:* Am Astron Soc; Astron Soc Pac; AAAS; Int Astron Union; Sigma Xi. *Res:* Observational investigation of the interstellar medium, primarily at visual and infrared wavelengths, with particular attention to the region near the Pleiades star cluster. *Mailing Add:* 5 Col Astron Dept Clark Sci Ctr Smith Col Northampton MA 01063. *Fax:* 413-585-3786; *E-Mail:* rwhite@smith.edu

**WHITE, RICHARD HAMILTON,** RETINAL CELL BIOLOGY, INSECT VISION. *Current Pos:* vis assoc prof, Univ Mass, Boston, 70-71, assoc prof, 71-77, chair, Dept Biol, 92-95, PROF BIOL, UNIV MASS, BOSTON, 77-, UNIV RES PROF, 96- *Personal Data:* b Rochester, NY, Feb 16, 34. *Educ:* Univ Rochester, BA, 56; Wash Univ, PhD(zool), 61. *Prof Exp:* Asst prof biol sci, Purdue Univ, 62-69; res fel, Harvard Univ, 69-70. *Concurrent Pos:* NIH fel, Univ Va, 69-70; NIH spec fel, Harvard Univ, 69-70. *Mem:* AAAS; Asn Res Vision & Ophthal; Soc Neurosci. *Res:* Structure and turn over of photosensitive membrane; molecular biology of insect visual pigments; behavior dependent on wavelength discrimination. *Mailing Add:* Dept Biol Univ Mass 100 Morrissey Blvd Boston MA 02125-3393. *Fax:* 617-287-6650; *E-Mail:* rwhite@umbsky.cc.umb.edu

**WHITE, RICHARD KENNETH,** ORGANIC RESIDUES, WATER QUALITY. *Current Pos:* NEWMAN PROF NATURAL RESOURCES ENG, CLEMSON UNIV, 85- *Personal Data:* b Mercer, Pa, Mar 20, 30; m 72; c 2. *Educ:* Pa State Col, BS, 52; NY Theol Sem, STB, 59; Pa State Univ, MS, 66; Ohio State Univ, PhD(agr eng), 69. *Honors & Awards:* Gunlogson Countryside Eng Award, Am Soc Agr Engrs, 80. *Prof Exp:* From asst prof to prof agr eng, Ohio State Univ, 70-85. *Mem:* Am Soc Agr Engrs; Soil & Water Conserv Soc; Water Environ Fedn. *Res:* Application and utilization of organic residues (livestock manures, municipal and industrial sludges) on cropland; planning and design of municipal solid waste systems; control of odors from livestock facilities; water resource management including surface and groundwater. *Mailing Add:* Dept Agr Eng Clemson Univ 106 McAdams Hall Clemson SC 29634-0357. *Fax:* 864-656-0338; *E-Mail:* rkwhite@clemson.edu

**WHITE, RICHARD MANNING,** APPLIED PHYSICS, ELECTRICAL ENGINEERING. *Current Pos:* PROF ELEC ENG & COMPUT SCI, UNIV CALIF, BERKELEY, 62- *Personal Data:* b Denver, Colo, Apr 25, 30; div; c 2. *Educ:* Harvard Col, BA, 51; Harvard Univ, AM, 52, PhD(appl physics), 56. *Honors & Awards:* Cleo Brunetti Award, Inst Elec & Electronics Engrs, 86, Achievement Award, 88. *Prof Exp:* Mem tech staff microwave electronics, Gen Elec Microwave Lab, 56-62. *Concurrent Pos:* Fel, John Simon Guggenheim Found, 68-69. *Mem:* Nat Acad Eng; Am Inst Physics; AAAS; fel Inst Elec & Electronics Engrs; Asn Appl Solar Energy. *Res:* Sensors, ultrasonics, chiefly surface and plate acoustic waves; solar energy. *Mailing Add:* Dept Elec Eng & Comput Sci Univ Calif Berkeley CA 94720. *Fax:* 510-643-6637; *E-Mail:* rwhite@eecs.berkeley.edu

**WHITE, RICHARD NORMAN,** STRUCTURAL ENGINEERING. *Current Pos:* from asst prof to assoc prof, Cornell Univ, 61-72, dir, Sch Civil & Environ Eng, 78-84, assoc dean engr, 87-90, PROF STRUCT ENG, CORNELL UNIV, 72-, JAMES A FRIEND FAMILY DISTINGUISHED PROF ENG, 88- *Personal Data:* b Chetek, Wis, Dec 21, 33; m 57, Margaret Howell; c Barbara A & David C. *Educ:* Univ Wis, BS, 56, MS, 57, PhD(plate stability), 61. *Honors & Awards:* Collingwood Prize, Am Soc Civil Engrs, 67; Kelly Award, Am Concrete Inst, 92, Wason Medal, 93, Struct Res Prize, 94. *Prof Exp:* Engr, John A Strand, 58-59; instr struct, Univ Wis, 58-61. *Concurrent Pos:* Consult, Oak Ridge Nat Labs, 66-68; staff assoc, Gen Atomic Div, Gen Dynamics Corp, Calif, 67-68; vis prof, Univ Calif, Berkeley, 74-75; consult, Sandia Nat Lab, 81- *Mem:* Nat Acad Eng; fel Am Concrete Inst (pres, 97-); Am Soc Eng Educ; Nat Soc Prof Engrs; Earthquake Eng Res Inst; Prestressed Concrete Inst; fel Am Soc Civil Engrs. *Res:* Structural engineering and model analysis; behavior of reinforced concrete structures; nuclear power plant structures; earthquake engineering. *Mailing Add:* 54 Sunnyslope Rd Ithaca NY 14850. *Fax:* 607-255-9004; *E-Mail:* rnw3@cornell.edu

**WHITE, RICHARD PAUL,** PHARMACOLOGY. *Current Pos:* from instr to assoc prof, 56-70, PROF PHARMACOL, MED UNITS, UNIV TENN, MEMPHIS, 70- *Personal Data:* b Gary, Ind, May 27, 25; m 47; c 2. *Educ:* Ind State Univ, BS, 47; Univ Kans, MS, 49, PhD(physiol), 54. *Prof Exp:* Instr physiol, Univ Kans, 49-54; psychophysiologist, Galesburg State Res Hosp, Ill, 54-56. *Concurrent Pos:* NIH career develop award, 59-69. *Mem:* Soc Biol Psychiat; Int Col Neuropsychopharmacol; Soc Neurosci; Int Soc Biochem Pharmacol; Sigma Xi. *Res:* Neuropharmacology. *Mailing Add:* Dept Pharmacol Univ Tenn Med Ctr 800 Madison Ave Memphis TN 38163-0001

**WHITE, ROBERT ALLAN,** AERODYNAMICS, HEAT TRANSFER. *Current Pos:* from asst prof to assoc prof, 65-72, PROF MECH ENG, UNIV ILL, URBANA, 72- & DIR, AUTOMOTIVE SYSTS LAB, 79- *Personal Data:* b Chicago, Ill, Dec 16, 34; m 57; c 2. *Educ:* Univ Ill, Urbana, BS, 57, MS, 59, PhD(mech eng), 63. *Honors & Awards:* Ralph R Teetor Award, Soc Automotive Engrs. *Prof Exp:* Instr mech eng, Univ Ill, 59-63; aeronaut engr, Aeronaut Res Inst Sweden, 60-61, sr res scientist, 63-65. *Concurrent Pos:* NATO sr fel & Thord-Gray fel, Aeronaut Res Inst Sweden, 68, consult, 69; mem, AF Studies Bd, 84-90; assoc fel, Am Inst Aeronaut & Astronaut, 86. *Mem:* Sigma Xi. *Res:* Aerodynamics of propulsion systems and vehicle integration; separated flows at subsonic and supersonic mach numbers; dynamics and aerodynamics of automotive systems. *Mailing Add:* 2009 S Cottage Grove Ave Urbana IL 61801-6322

**WHITE, ROBERT ALLEN,** BIOMATHEMATICS, CHEMICAL PHYSICS. *Current Pos:* proj investr, Univ Tex, 75-76, asst prof, 76-81, assoc prof biomath, 81-95, PROF BIOMATH, M D ANDERSON CANCER CTR, UNIV TEX, 95- *Personal Data:* b Las Cruces, NMex, Nov 19, 44; m 71, Sara Lehr; c 2. *Educ:* NMex State Univ, BS, '66; Univ Chicago, PhD (chem physics), 70. *Prof Exp:* Fel chem, Rice Univ, 70-75. *Mem:* AAAS; Radiation Res Soc; Cell Proliferation Soc; Int Soc Anal; Radiation Res Soc. *Res:* Mathematical biology; estimation of cell kinetics parameters; cytometry; genetic sequence analysis. *Mailing Add:* M D Anderson Cancer Ctr Dept Biomath Univ Tex 1515 Holcombe Blvd PO Box 237 Houston TX 77030. *Fax:* 713-792-4362; *E-Mail:* alkn@odin.mdacc.tmc.edu

**WHITE, ROBERT B,** PSYCHIATRY. *Current Pos:* assoc prof, 62-67, PROF PSYCHIAT, MED BR, UNIV TEX, GALVESTON, 67- *Personal Data:* b Ennis, Tex, Jan 5, 21; m 42; c 3. *Educ:* Tex A&M Univ, BS, 41; Univ Tex, MD, 44; Western New Eng Inst Psychoanalysis, cert, 59. *Honors & Awards:* David Rapaport Prize, Western New Eng Inst Psychoanal, 59. *Prof Exp:* From asst psychiatrist to sr psychiatrist, Austen Riggs Ctr, Inc, 51-62. *Concurrent Pos:* Teaching analyst, New Orleans Psychoanal Inst, 62-66; training analyst psychoanal, 66-; consult, Alcoholism Res Proj, Col Med, Baylor Univ, 63-65 & Hedgecroft Hosp, Houston, 63-65; mem, Gen Planning Comt Comprehensive Statewide Ment Health Prog Planning, Tex State Dept Health, Austin, 63-65; mem, Residency Rev Comt Psychiat & Neurol, 71-77; training analyst, Houston-Galveston Psychoanal Sch, 74- *Mem:* AAAS; Am Psychoanal Asn; fel Am Psychiat Asn; fel Am Col Psychiatrists; fel Am Col Psychoanal. *Res:* Psychoanalysis. *Mailing Add:* 1013 Harbor View Dr Galveston TX 77550-3109

**WHITE, ROBERT CARL,** AEROSPACE ENGINEERING, SIGNAL PROCESSING. *Current Pos:* RES SCIENTIST, TERA RES, INC, 97- *Personal Data:* b Tachikawa, Japan, June 15, 58; US citizen. *Educ:* Univ Callif, Santa Barbara, BA & BS, 80; Univ Calif, Davis, MS, 82 PhD(nonlinear dynamics & plasma theory), 87. *Prof Exp:* Physicist, Lawrence Livermore Nat Lab, 80-87 & TRW Space & Technol Group, 87-88; res engr, Palo Alto Res & Develop Labs, Lockheed Martin Missiles & Space, 88-97. *Concurrent Pos:* Consult, Lawrence Livermore Nat Labs, 88-89. *Mem:* Am Phys Soc; Math Asn Am. *Res:* Antenna design; electronic systems analysis; numerical simulations; charged particle beam transport; magnetic fusion energy; free electron laser amplifier design simulations; transport; diffusion and energy conversion studies. *Mailing Add:* 255 S Bayview Ave Apt E Sunnyvale CA 94086. *E-Mail:* rcwhite@tera-research.com

**WHITE, ROBERT E(DWARD),** chemical engineering; deceased, see previous edition for last biography

**WHITE, ROBERT J,** BRAIN SURGERY TRANSPLANTATION. *Current Pos:* from asst prof to assoc prof, 61-66, co-chmn dept, 72-83, PROF NEUROSURG, SCH MED, CASE WESTERN RES UNIV, 66-; DIR, NEUROSURG & BRAIN RES LAB, CLEVELAND METROP GEN HOSP, 61- *Personal Data:* b Duluth, Minn, Jan 21, 26; m 55, Patricia R Murray; c Christopher T, Christopher E, Patricia E, Michael J, Daniel J, Pamela M, James W, Richard P, Marguerite L & Ruth A. *Educ:* Univ Minn, BS, 51; Harvard Univ, MD, 53, PhD(neurosurg physiol), 62. *Hon Degrees:* DSc, John Carroll Univ, 79 & Cleveland State Univ, 80. *Honors & Awards:* L W Freeman Award, Nat Paraplegia Found, 77; Svien lectr, Mayo Clin, 77; Knight of Equestrian, Order of the Holy Sepulchre, Jerusalem. *Prof Exp:* Intern surg, Peter Bent Brigham Hosp, 53-54; resident, Boston Children's Hosp & Peter Bent Brigham Hosp, 54-55; asst to staff, Mayo Clin, 58-59, res assoc neurophysiol, 59-61. *Concurrent Pos:* Fel neurosurg, Mayo Clin, 55-58; assoc neurosurgeon, Univ Hosps & sr attend neurosurgeon, Vet Admin Hosp, 61-; vis prof var univs; consult, Burdenko Neurosurg Inst, Moscow, Polenov Inst, Leningrad, Neurosurg Inst, Kiev & Univs, Rome, Naples, Milan & Palermo; fifteen lectureships, USSR, 61-81 & People's Repub China, 77-81; mem bd dirs, Allen Mem Med Libr & Int Ctr Artificial Organs & Transplantation; Adv Comt Biotechnol Appl Man, Pontifical Acad Sci. *Mem:* Int Soc Transplantation; Am Physiol Soc; Soc Univ Surgeons; Soc Univ Neurosurg (pres, 77); Am Col Surg; Neurosurg Soc Am; Am Asn Neurol Surgeons. *Res:* Special neurosurgical techniques for vascular disease and tumors of the brain utilizing low temperature and extracorporeal perfusion systems; treatment for spinal cord and head injury involving chemotherapy and low temperature; isolation and maintenance of the subhuman primate brain as an isolated organ for brain transplantation; neurochemical and circulatory studies; mind/brain relationship, bioethics and dynamics in health care delivery in the United States and communist countries. *Mailing Add:* Metrohealth Med Ctr 3395 Scranton Rd Metrohealth Med Ctr 2500 Metro Health Dr Cleveland OH 44109-1998. *Fax:* 216-459-5616

**WHITE, ROBERT KELLER,** PSYCHOPHYSIOLOGY, RADIOBIOLOGY. *Current Pos:* chmn dept, 70-71, PROF PSYCHOL, WILLIAM PATERSON COL, 70- *Personal Data:* b Greeneville, Tenn, Mar 3, 30; m 52; c 2. *Educ:* Milligan Col, BA, 52; Univ Tex, PhD(psychol), 62. *Prof Exp:* Res scientist, Radiobiol Lab, Balcones Res Ctr, Univ Tex, 56-61; asst prof psychol, Tex Tech Col, 61-65; proj dir, Armed Forces Radiobiol Res Lab, Defense Atomic Support Agency, 65-67; mem tech staff space res, Bellcomm, Inc, 67-70. *Concurrent Pos:* Lectr, USDA Grad Sch, 65- & Col Gen Studies, George Washington Univ, 66-67. *Mem:* Am Psychol Asn; Simulation Coun; Am Soc Cybernet. *Res:* Effects of whole body irradiation upon the physiology and behavior of various species; in uterine irradiation of rats; gamma neutron pulse irradiation upon the psychophysiology of monkeys. *Mailing Add:* Dept Psychol William Paterson Col NJ 300 Pompton Rd Wayne NJ 07470-2103

**WHITE, ROBERT LEE,** ELECTRICAL ENGINEERING, MAGNETIC MATERIALS. *Current Pos:* dir, Inst Electronics Med, 73-81, chmn, Dept Elec Eng, 81-87, PROF ELEC ENG & MAT SCI, STANFORD UNIV, 63-, DIR, CTR RES INFO STORAGE MATS, 91- *Personal Data:* b Plainfield, NJ, Feb 14, 27; m 52; c Lauren A, Kimberly A, Christopher L & Matthew P. *Educ:* Columbia Univ, BA, 49, MA, 51, PhD(physics), 54. *Prof Exp:* Res physicist, Res Labs, Hughes Aircraft Co, 54-61; head, Magnetics Dept, Labs, Gen Tel & Electronics Corp, 61-63. *Concurrent Pos:* Indust consult, 63-; Guggenheim fel, Oxford Univ, 69-70; vis prof, Tokyo Univ, 75; Guggenheim fel, Swiss Fed Inst Technol, Zurich, 78, Christensen fel, St Catherine's Col, Oxford, 86; spec ltd partner, Mayfield Fund, Mayfield II, 69-80; consult ltd partner, Alpha Partners, 84-; dir Analog Design Tools, 84-88; dir Biostim, Inc, 79-85; consult, IBM, Varian, Novacor, Ampex & Lockheed; William E Ayer prof elec eng, 85-; dir, Exploratorium, 87-89, Ctr Res Info Storage Mat, 90- *Mem:* Fel Am Phys Soc; fel Inst Elec & Electronics Engrs; Japan Asn Prom Sci. *Res:* Microwave spectroscopy; solid state physics, especially magnetics; neurophysiology; neural prostheses, especially auditory; magnetic recording. *Mailing Add:* 450 El Escarpado Stanford CA 94305. *Fax:* 650-725-4034

**WHITE, ROBERT LESTER,** BIOSYNTHESIS OF NATURAL PRODUCTS, ENZYMES OF SECONDARY METABOLISM. *Current Pos:* asst prof, 90-95, ASSOC PROF CHEM, DALHOUSIE UNIV, 95- *Personal Data:* b Halifax, NS, Apr 25, 53; m 77, Mary A Millar; c David & Alice. *Educ:* Dalhousie Univ, BSc Hons, 74; McMaster Univ, PhD(chem), 80. *Prof Exp:* Nat Sci & Eng Res Coun biochem, Univ Oxford, UK, 79-81; Nat Sci & Eng Res Coun res fel, Syntex Inc, Ont, 81-83 & Dalhousie Univ, 83-84; asst prof chem, Acadia Univ, 84-90. *Mem:* Am Chem Soc; fel Chem Inst Can; Royal Soc Chem; Int Soc Amino Acid Res; fel Am Soc Pharmacog. *Res:* Bioorganic chemistry; biosynthesis of amino acids and antibiotics; enzymes of secondary metabolism; analysis of amino acids and aminosugars by high-power liquid chromatography; production of amino acids by fermentation; chemical synthesis of amino acids. *Mailing Add:* Dept Chem Dalhousie Univ Halifax NS B3H 4J3 Can. *E-Mail:* rlwhite@chem1.chem.dal.ca

**WHITE, ROBERT M,** METEOROLOGY. *Current Pos:* SR FEL, UNIV CORP ATMOSPHERIC RES, 95- *Personal Data:* b Boston, Mass, Feb 13, 23; m 48; c 2. *Educ:* Harvard Univ, BA, 44; Mass Inst Technol, MS, 49, PhD, 50. *Hon Degrees:* DSc, Long Island Univ, 76, Rensselaer Polytech Inst, 77 & Univ Wis, 78; ScD, Univ Bridgeport, 84, Univ RI, 86, Clarkson Univ; PhD, John Hopkins Univ, 82, Drexel Univ, 85, Ill Inst, 85, Ill Inst Technol, 94. *Honors & Awards:* Cleveland Abbe Award, Am Meteorol Soc, 69, Fiftieth Anniversary Medal, 70; Matthew Fontaine Maury Award, Smithsonian Inst, 76; Int Conserv Award, Nat Wildlife Fedn, 77; Neptune Award, Am Oceanic Orgn, 77; Spec Award, Marine Technol Soc, 77; Charles E Lindbergh Award; Int Meteorol Orgn Prize, World Meteorol Orgn; Karit Compton Lectr Mass Inst Technol, 95. *Prof Exp:* Asst meteorol, Mass Inst Technol, 48-50; chief, Large Scale Processes Sect, Air Force Cambridge Res Ctr, 52-58 & Meteorol Develop Lab, 58-59; res assoc, Mass Inst Technol, 59; assoc dir res, Travelers Ins Co, 59-60, pres, Travelers Res Ctr, Inc, 60-63; chief, Weather Bur, 63-65 & Environ Sci Serv Admin, 65-70, adminr, Nat Oceanic & Atmospheric Admin, US Dept Com, 71-77; chmn, Climate Res Bd, Nat Acad Sci, 77-79, adminr, Nat Res Coun & exec officer, Nat Acad Sci, 79-80; pres, Univ Corp Atmospheric Res, 80-83; pres, Nat Acad Eng, 83-95. *Concurrent Pos:* US permanent rep, World Meteorol Orgn, 63-78, mem exec comt, 63-78; fed coordr, Meteorol Serv & Supporting Res, 64-70; co-chmn, Dept Com Meteorol Satellite Prog Rev Bd, NASA, 64-73; mem, Pres Comn Marine Sci Eng & Resources, 67-68; mem, Comt Water Resources Res, Fed Coun Sci & Technol, 67-75; chmn, Interagency Comt Marine Sci & Eng, 70-76; chmn fed comt, Meteorol Serv & Supporting Res, 70-77; chmn, Nat Marine Fisheries Adv Comt, 70-77; mem US deleg, UN Conf Human Environ, Stockholm, 71; chief US deleg, Intergovt Oceanog Comn, UNESCO, Paris, 72-73; mem US deleg, Gov Coun, UN Environ Prog, Nairobi, 73-74; US comnr, Int Whaling Comn, London, 73-77; US chmn, US-France Coop Prog Oceanog, 73-77; chief US deleg, Conf Global Environ Monitoring Systs, UN Environ Prog, 74; US chmn, US-USSR Joint Comn Explor World Oceans, 74-77; chmn, Comt Climate Change, White House Domestic Coun, 75, chmn, Comt Weather Modification, 76; mem US deleg, UN Conf Desertification, Nairobi, 77; mem coun, Nat Acad Eng, 77-; chmn, Comt Atmosphere & Oceans, Fed Coord Coun Sci, Eng & Technol, 77; mem, Comt Atmospheric Sci, Nat Res Coun, 78-, mem, Space Appln Bd, 78- & vchmn; mem US deleg, ICSU Gen Assembly, Athens, 78; sr fel, John Heinz IV Ctr Sci, Econs & Environ, 96- *Mem:* Nat Acad Eng (pres, 83-); Am Geophys Union; Am Meteorol Soc; AAAS; Marine Technol Soc (vpres, 75-77); Royal Meteorol Soc. *Res:* Atmospheric and ocean sciences; environmental science. *Mailing Add:* 1200 New York Ave NW Suite 410 Washington DC 20005

**WHITE, ROBERT MARSHALL,** MAGNETIC RECORDING. *Current Pos:* UNIV PROF & HEAD ELEC & COMPUT ENG, CARNEGIE MELLON UNIV, 93- *Personal Data:* b Reading, Pa, Oct 2, 38. *Educ:* Mass Inst Technol, BS, 60; Stanford Univ, PhD(physics), 64. *Honors & Awards:* Von Humboldt Prize, Ger Govt, 80; Distinguished Contrib Pub Serv Award, Inst Elec & Electronics Engrs, 93. *Prof Exp:* Asst prof physics, Stanford Univ, 66-72; prin scientist, Xerox Corp, 72-84; vpres, data storage prod, Control Data Corp, 84-87, vpres & chief tech officer, 87-90; under secy technol, US Dept Com, 90-93. *Concurrent Pos:* Consult prof appl physics, Stanford Univ, 72-92; vchair, Comn Magnetism, Int Union Pure & Appl Physics, 87-90; mem, Nat Comt Semiconductors, 90-93; chair, Panel Pub Affairs, Am Phys Soc, 97; dir, Zilog SGS-Thomson Ontrack Data Int. *Mem:* Nat Acad Eng; fel Am Phys Soc; fel AAAS; fel Inst Elec & Electronics Engrs. *Res:* Phenomena and properties of magnetic materials ranging from discovery of spin wave sidebands to tunneling between magnetic electrodes. *Mailing Add:* Dept Elec & Comput Eng Carnegie Mellon Univ Pittsburgh PA 15213. *Fax:* 412-268-5787; *E-Mail:* white@gauss.ece.cmu.edu

**WHITE, ROBERT STEPHEN,** ASTROPHYSICS, SPACE PHYSICS. *Current Pos:* prof physics, Univ Calif, Riverside & assoc dir, Inst Geophys & Planetary Physics, 67-92, chmn, Dept Physics, 70-73, EMER PROF PHYSICS & RES PHYSICIST, INST GEOPHYS & PLANETARY PHYSICS, UNIV CALIF, RIVERSIDE, 92- *Personal Data:* b Elsworth, Kans, Dec 28, 20; m 42, Freda M Bridgewater; c Nancy L (Shindler), Margaret D (Wimmer), John S & David B. *Educ:* Southwestern Col, Kans, AB, 42; Univ Ill, MS, 43; Univ Calif, PhD(physics), 51. *Hon Degrees:* DSc, Southwestern Col, Kans, 71. *Prof Exp:* Asst physics, Univ Ill, 42-44; asst, Univ Calif, 46-48; physicist, Lawrence Radiation Lab, Univ Calif, 48-61; physicist & head, Particles & Fields Dept, Space Physics Lab, Aerospace Corp, 62-67. *Concurrent Pos:* Lectr, Univ Calif, 53-54 & 57-59; NSF sr fel, 61-62; grantee, NASA, NSF, USAF & Nat Off Social Responsibility. *Mem:* Fel AAAS; fel Am Phys Soc; Am Geophys Union; Am Astron Soc. *Res:* Space physics and astrophysics; gamma ray bursts; gamma-rays from astrophysical sources. *Mailing Add:* 5225 Austin Rd Santa Barbara CA 93111-2905. *Fax:* 805-967-0871; *E-Mail:* swhite@physics.ucsb.edu

**WHITE, RONALD,** COMPUTER SCIENCE, ELECTRONICS. *Current Pos:* PROF COMPUT SCI, JACKSONVILLE STATE UNIV, 87- *Personal Data:* b Talladega, Ala, Feb 10, 43; m 67; c 2. *Educ:* Auburn Univ, BEE, 65, MSEE, 66, PhD(elec eng), 71. *Prof Exp:* Res asst digital res, Auburn Univ, 65- 66; sr engr eng design, Sperry Rand Space Support Div, Sperry Rand Corp, 67-69; res assoc digital res, Auburn Univ, 69-71; engr mgr data process, USAF, Elgin AFB, 71-78. *Res:* Application of mini computers and microprocessors. *Mailing Add:* Dept Comput Sci Jacksonville State Univ Jacksonville AL 36265-1573

**WHITE, RONALD E,** ENZYMOLOGY, DRUG METABOLISM. *Current Pos:* ASSOC DIR DRUG METAB, BRISTOL-MYERS SQUIBB, 87- *Personal Data:* b DeSoto, Mo, Feb 21, 48; m; c 2. *Educ:* Univ Wis, PhD(org chem), 74. *Prof Exp:* From asst prof to assoc prof biochem, Univ Conn, 79-87. *Concurrent Pos:* Mem, Pharmacol Study Sect, NIH, 90- *Mem:* Am Chem Soc; Am Soc Biol Chemists; AAAS. *Res:* Catalytic chemistry of cytochrome P-450; bioorganic chemistry; drug metabolism; biological oxidation mechanisms; predictive models in biology. *Mailing Add:* Dept Metab & Pharmacokinetics Bristol-Myers Squibb PO Box 4000 Princeton NJ 08543-4000. *Fax:* 609-252-6802

**WHITE, RONALD JEROME,** ZOOLOGY, PHYSIOLOGY. *Current Pos:* From asst prof to assoc prof, 69-76, PROF BIOL, EASTERN WASH UNIV, 76- *Personal Data:* b Wibaux, Mont, Oct 31, 36; m 61; c 2. *Educ:* Calif State Polytech Col, BS, 59; Ore State Univ, MS, 61, PhD(physiol), 68. *Concurrent Pos:* Chmn, Dept Biol, Eastern Wash Univ, 80-82. *Mem:* AAAS; Am Soc Zool; Sigma Xi. *Res:* Physiology of reproduction in the pigtail macaque. *Mailing Add:* Dept Biol Eastern Wash Univ Cheney WA 99004

**WHITE, RONALD JOSEPH,** theoretical chemistry, applied mathematics, for more information see previous edition

**WHITE, RONALD PAUL, SR,** SOIL FERTILITY, CROP MANAGEMENT & CROP BREEDING. *Current Pos:* RETIRED. *Personal Data:* b Coral Gables, Fla, Mar 1, 35; m 60; c 4. *Educ:* Mass State Col, Bridgewater, BS, 61; Univ Mass, MS, 63; Mich State Univ, PhD(soil sci), 68. *Prof Exp:* Instr soil sci, Mich State Univ, 65-66; res scientist, Res Sta, Can Dept Agr, 68-96. *Concurrent Pos:* Pvt agr consult corn mgt & breeding, 97- *Mem:* Am Soc Agron; Soil Sci Soc Am; Agr Inst Can; Can Soc Agron. *Res:* Soil fertility requirements and crop management practices of corn and potatoes; agronomy; corn hybrid breeding and evaluation; seed potato production. *Mailing Add:* 28 Selkirk Cresent Charlottetown PE C1A 3R6 Can. *Fax:* 902-566-6821; *E-Mail:* whiter@em.agr.ca

**WHITE, ROSCOE BERYL,** PLASMA PHYSICS. *Current Pos:* RES PHYSICIST, PRINCETON UNIV, 74- *Personal Data:* b Freeport, Ill, Dec 20, 37; m 66; c 1. *Educ:* Univ Minn, BS, 59; Princeton Univ, PhD(physics), 63. *Prof Exp:* Res asst, Princeton Univ, 62, instr, 62-63; res assoc, Univ Minn, 63; US Acad Sci exchange scientist, Lebedev Inst, Moscow, 63-64; vis scientist, Int Ctr Theoret Physics, Italy, 64-66; asst prof physics, Univ Calif, Los Angeles, 66-72; mem, Inst Advan Study, 72-74. *Mem:* Am Phys Soc. *Res:* Theoretical plasma physics. *Mailing Add:* Plasma Physics Lab Princeton Univ PO Box 451 Princeton NJ 08543. *Fax:* 609-243-2662

**WHITE, ROSEANN SPICOLA,** BIOCHEMISTRY, IMMUNO-CHEMISTRY. *Current Pos:* From asst prof to assoc prof, 72-86, PROF MICROBIOL, UNIV CENT FLA, 86- *Personal Data:* b Tampa, Fla, Aug 4, 43; m 65; c 2. *Educ:* Univ Fla, BS, 65; Univ Tex Southwestern Med Sch, Dallas, PhD(biochem), 70. *Concurrent Pos:* Clin chemist, Orange Mem Hosp, 69-72; consult, Plant Fingerprinting for Patent Atty, 78-, allergy & immunol, Found Cent Fla, 80-; chmn, Med Sci Sect, Fla Acad Sci, 85-; lectr path, Residency Prog & Med Technol Prog. *Mem:* AAAS; Am Soc Microbiol; Sigma Xi. *Res:* Control vitamin B-6 biosynthesis; vitamin B-6 regulation of apoenzyme levels; isolation and immuno-chemical analysis of allergens; chemical characterization of H capsulatum antigens; lymphocytes subsets in acquired immune deficiency syndrome and acquired related complex; plant fingerprinting. *Mailing Add:* Dept Biol Sci Univ Cent Fla PO Box 25000 Orlando FL 32816-0001

**WHITE, SAMUEL GRANDFORD, JR,** EDUCATION ADMINISTRATION, ELECTRONICS ENGINEERING. *Current Pos:* VPRES ACAD AFFAIRS & PROF ELEC ENG, ELECTRO-OPTICS, IND INST TECHNOL, 93- *Personal Data:* b Anniston, Ala, Feb 6, 45; m 68, Sandra Kirby; c Samuel G III & Sherri C. *Educ:* Tuskegee Univ, BS, 67, MS, 70; Univ Ill, Urbana, PhD(elec eng), 78. *Prof Exp:* Engr, Westinghouse Elec Corp, 67-68; staff engr, IBM, 70-72; assoc prof & chair elec eng, Digital Electronics & Solid State Electronics, NC A&T State Univ, 82-85; assoc prof elec eng & chair eng, Solid State Electronics, Purdue Univ, Ft Wayne, 85-87; tech dir, Sensor Systs Group, Magnavox Govt, Indust Electronics, 87-90; electro-optics, eng dir educ & training, 90-93. *Concurrent Pos:* Consult, AT&T, 83-85; prog reviewer, NSF, Presidential Young Investigator, 84; reviewer, NSF, Res Initiatives for Minority Insts, 84; prog evaluator, Eng Accreditation Comn, Inst Elec & Electronics Engrs, 90- *Mem:* Sr mem Inst Elec & Electronics Engrs; Am Soc Eng Educ; Nat Tech Asn. *Res:* Flat-panel electronic displays. *Mailing Add:* Sch Eng & Technol Hampton Univ Hampton VA 23668. *Fax:* 219-422-7696

**WHITE, SANDRA L,** PRECLINICAL THERAPEUTICS, TUMOR IMMUNOBIOLOGY. *Current Pos:* ASSOC RES PROF, DEPT MED, DUKE UNIV MED CTR, DURHAM, NC, 96- *Personal Data:* b Columbia, SC, Aug 30, 41; m 84, Kenneth Olden; c Rosalind, Stephen, Kenneth & Heather. *Educ:* Hampton Univ, BA, 63; Univ Mich, MS, 71, PhD(microbiol), 74. *Prof Exp:* Asst prof microbiol, Mem Cancer Center, Howard Univ, Col Med, 74-76, asst prof, 79-85, assoc prof microbiol & oncol, 85-96. *Concurrent Pos:* Health sci consult, Curber Assoc, Washington DC, 75; sci proj adv, Verve Res, Inc, Rockville, MD, 75-76; staff fel, Lab Immunodiagnosis, Nat Cancer Inst, NIH, 76-79; mem, NIH Path B Study Sect, 80-84; Bd Sci Counrs, Div Cancer Biol & Diagnosis, Nat Cancer Inst, NIH, 85-89; Nat Bd Med Examiners, 89-93. *Mem:* Am Soc Cell Biol; Reticuloendothelial Soc; Am Soc Microbiologists; Am Asn Cancer Res; Am Asn Immunol; Women Cancer Res. *Res:* Pre-clinical therapeutics, with a focus on the development of anti-tumor and antimetastatic agents which can be orally administered, are biomodulators of the immune response and/or myeloproliferative. *Mailing Add:* Dept Med Duke Univ Med Ctr PO Box 3410 Durham NC 27710. *Fax:* 919-684-4099; *E-Mail:* white040@mc.duke.edu

**WHITE, SIDNEY EDWARD,** GEOMORPHOLOGY & GLACIAL GEOLOGY, VOLCANOLOGY & ECOLOGY. *Current Pos:* from asst prof to prof, 51-85, EMER PROF GEOL, OHIO STATE UNIV, 85- *Personal Data:* b Manchester, NH, Mar 14, 16; m 46; c 1. *Educ:* Tufts Col, BS, 39; Harvard Univ, MA, 42; Syracuse Univ, PhD(geol), 51. *Prof Exp:* Lab asst, Tufts Col, 37-40, lab instr, 41-42, instr geol, 47-48; lab instr, Harvard Univ, 42; asst instr geol, Syracuse Univ, 48-51. *Concurrent Pos:* Recorder, US Geol Surv, 41-42, geologist, 46-48; ed, Geol Soc Am, Geomorph Div, 62-71; geologist, NSF Projs, Univ Colo, 64-66, assoc prof, 65-66, 72, 73; Univ Colo Men & Women Scholastic Hon award, 65-66. *Mem:* Geol Soc Am; Am Quaternary Asn; Mex Geol Soc. *Res:* Glacial and Pleistocene geology; volcanology; alpine and periglacial mass movement studies. *Mailing Add:* Dept Geol Sci Ohio State Univ Columbus OH 43210. *Fax:* 614-292-7688

**WHITE, SIMON DAVID MANTON,** GRAVITATIONAL DYNAMICS, PHYSICAL COSMOLOGY. *Current Pos:* assoc prof, 84-87, PROF ASTRON, STEWARD OBSERV, UNIV ARIZ, 87- *Personal Data:* b Kent, Eng, Sept 30, 51; m 84. *Educ:* Univ Cambridge, BA, 72; Univ Toronto, MSc, 74 & PhD(astron), 77. *Honors & Awards:* Helen B Warner Prize, Am Astron Soc, 86. *Prof Exp:* Lindemann fel, Astron Dept, Univ Calif Berkeley, 77-78; res fel astron, Churchill Col, 79-80; sr fel astron, Space Sci Lab, Univ Calif, Berkeley, 80-84. *Concurrent Pos:* Vis astronr, Nat Radio Astron Observ, 78; sci attache, Astrophys Inst Paris, 80; presidential young investr, NSF, 84. *Mem:* Am Astron Soc; Royal Astron Soc. *Res:* Structure, dynamics and evolution of galaxies and systems of galaxies, their formation and their relation to the large scale structure of the universe. *Mailing Add:* Inst Astron The Observatories Madingley Rd Cambridge CB3 OHA England. *Fax:* 44-22-3337523

**WHITE, STANLEY A,** DIGITAL SIGNAL PROCESSING, NEURAL NETWORKS & LEARNING SYSTEMS. *Current Pos:* PRES, SIGNAL PROCESSING & CONTROLS ENG CORP, 90- *Personal Data:* b Providence, RI, Sept 25, 31; US citizen; m 56, Edda M Castano-Benitez; c Dianne, Stanley Jr, Paul & John. *Educ:* Purdue Univ, BS, 57, MS, 59, PhD(elec eng), 65. *Honors & Awards:* Centennial Medal, Inst Elec & Electronics Engrs, 84, Tech Achievement Award, 96; Leonardo da Vinci Medal, Soc Hist Technol, 86. *Prof Exp:* Electronics technician, Allison Div, Gen Motors Corp, 56, circuit designer, 57; engr, Radiochem Corp, 58; mem tech staff, Autonetics Navig Systs Div, NAm Rockwell Corp, 59-61, staff to mgr advan technol, 65-67, group scientist, Digital Systs Group, Info Sci Br, 67-70, supvr advan inertial instrument res, Navig & Comput Div, 70, mem,

Tech Staff Prod Eng Group, NAm Rockwell Microelectronic Co, 70-72, group leader, Digital Systs Group, Info Sci Br, Advan Technol Dept, Res & Technol Div, 72-77, mgr digital systs & signal processing, Electronics Res Ctr, 78-82, sr scientist, Autonetics Sensors & Aircraft Systs Div, Rockwell Int, 82-90. *Concurrent Pos:* Mem fac, Purdue Univ, Univ Calif, Los Angeles, Irvine & Davis; lectr, Univ Southern Calif & Univ Nev, Reno; chmn & fac mem, Nat Electronics Conf; adj prof elec eng, Univ Calif, Irvine; vis lectr, Davis & Univ Southern Calif; mem bd dir, Asilomar Conf Corp, 87-; consult, Rockwell Int Corp, 90, Perceptrix, 90, Western Digital, 91, NSF, 90-91 & Interstate Electronics, 92; lectr, Nat Electronics Conf, 68-75, Tech Mkt Soc Am, State Art Sem, Hyman Silver Assoc, Technol Transfer Soc, 80-84; int dir, Eta Kappa Nu Int, 80-82; distinguished lectr, Inst Elec & Electronics Eng, 90-92; consult, Boeing NAm Inc, 97- *Mem:* Fel AAAS; Sigma Xi; fel Inst Elec & Electronics Engrs; fel NY Acad Sci; fel Inst Advan Eng; Am Inst Aeronaut & Astronaut. *Res:* Digital signal processing architectures, algorithms, & devices; neural, fuzzy logic, and learning systems; microelectronics; digital filtering; nonlinear and sampled-data feedback systems engineering; author or coauthor of over 100 publications; recipient of over 50 US patents. *Mailing Add:* 433 E Avenida Cordoba San Clemente CA 92672. *Fax:* 714-493-6129; *E-Mail:* sawhite@aol.com

**WHITE, STEPHEN EDWARD,** POPULATION GEOGRAPHY. *Current Pos:* from asst prof to assoc prof, 75-85, head dept, 79-87 & 94-97, PROF GEOG, KANS STATE UNIV, 85- *Personal Data:* b Frankfort, Ky, Apr 15, 47; m 69, Susan M Clockhorn; c Eric S & Benjamin N. *Educ:* Univ Ky, BS, 69, MA, 72, PhD(geog), 74. *Honors & Awards:* Award Excellence Scholar, Nat Coun Geog Educ, 69, Jour Geog Award, 87. *Prof Exp:* Planner, Dir Planning, Ky Dept Transp, 69; Lt, Mil Intel, US Army, 69-71; planner & sect head, Statewide Transp Systs Planning, 74-75. *Concurrent Pos:* Prin investr, NSF, 78-80, US Dept Interior, 79-81, Gen Serv Found, 83-85 & Ford Found, 88-89, 90-91 & 92-94, Asn Am Geogrs/NASA, 96-89 & DOE/NIGEC, 96-97; fel Appalachian Studies, Mellon Found, 81; secy-treas, Pop Specialty Group, Asn Am Geographers, 82-84, vpres, 84-85, pres, 85-86; hons res lectr, Mid-Am State Univs Asn, 88-89; distinguished lectr, Kans Acad Sci, 91-92; Presidential lectr, Kans State Univ, 92-97. *Mem:* Asn Am Geographers; Nat Coun Geog Educ; Pop Asn Am; Pop Ref Bur. *Res:* Interregional migration research methods; return migration to Appalachia; groundwater depletion in the American High Plains; environmental perception; human response to global environmental change. *Mailing Add:* Dept Geog Dickens Hall Kans State Univ Manhattan KS 66506. *Fax:* 785-532-7310; *E-Mail:* sewhite@ksu.edu

**WHITE, STEPHEN HALLEY,** BIOPHYSICS, PHYSIOLOGY. *Current Pos:* asst prof, Univ Calif, Irvine, 72-75, vchmn dept, 74-75, assoc prof physiol, 75-78, chmn dept, 77-89, PROF PHYSIOL & BIOPHYS, UNIV CALIF, IRVINE, 78- *Personal Data:* b Wewoka, Okla, May 14, 40; m 61, 84, Jackie M Dooley; c Saill, Shell, Storn, Shorr, Skye & Scude. *Educ:* Univ Colo, BA, 63; Univ Wash, MS, 65, PhD(physiol, biophys), 69. *Prof Exp:* Fel, USPHS, Univ Va, 71-72. *Concurrent Pos:* Guest biophysicist, Brookhaven Nat Lab, 77-; mem coun, Biophys Soc, 81-84, prog chmn, 85; assoc chmn, Dept Physiol Coun, 81-84, pres, 86-87; res grants, NSF & NIH. *Mem:* Biophys Soc (secy, 87-95, pres, 96-97); Soc Gen Physiologists (treas, 85-88); Am Physiol Soc; Protein Soc; Am Soc Biochem & Molecular Biol; Am Crystallog Asn. *Res:* Structure of biological membranes and the physical chemistry of lipid bilayer membranes; utilizing x-ray and neutron diffraction and nuclear magnetic resonance; protein folding in membrane environments. *Mailing Add:* Dept Physiol & Biophys Univ Calif Irvine CA 92697-4560. *E-Mail:* shwhite@uci.edu

**WHITE, STUART COSSITT,** DENTAL RADIOLOGY. *Current Pos:* Asst prof, 73-75, assoc prof, 75-80, ASSOC DEAN, UNIV CALIF, LOS ANGELES, 79-, PROF DENT, 80- *Personal Data:* b Pasadena, Calif, July 20, 42; m 68; c 2. *Educ:* Univ Calif, Berkeley, AB, 64; Univ Calif, Los Angeles, DDS, 68; Univ Rochester, PhD(radiation biol), 73. *Honors & Awards:* Edward H Hattan Award, Int Asn Dent Res, 67. *Concurrent Pos:* USPHS trainee, Univ Rochester, 68-73; prin investr NIH grant, 77-80; co-investr, Clin Cancer Educ Prog, Univ Calif, Los Angeles, 76-79; prin investr grant, Am Fund Dent Health, 77-78; consult, Xerox Corp, 77-; fel, Am Acad Dent Radiol, 78-; mem bd dirs, Am Bd Oral & Maxillofacial Radiol, 80- *Mem:* Radiation Res Soc; Am Acad Dent Radiol. *Res:* Radiation dosimetry; radiographic imaging technique; utility of radiographic examinations. *Mailing Add:* Univ Calif Los Angeles Sch Dent 10833 LeConte Ave Rm 53-068 Los Angeles CA 90095

**WHITE, THOMAS DAVID,** NEUROCHEMISTRY, NEUROPHARMACOLOGY. *Current Pos:* From asst prof to assoc prof, 71-82, PROF PHARMACOL, FAC MED, DALHOUSIE UNIV, 82- *Personal Data:* b Sarnia, Ont, Apr 8, 43. *Educ:* Univ Western Ont, BSc, 65, MSc, 67; Bristol Univ, PhD(pharmacol), 70. *Honors & Awards:* Pres Award, Nat Res Coun Can, 88. *Concurrent Pos:* Med Res Coun Can fel, Univ Alta, 70-71. *Mem:* Int Soc Neurochem; Soc Neurosci. *Res:* Physiology and pharmacology of brain synapses; role of extracellular adenosine in CNS disorders. *Mailing Add:* Dept Pharmacol Dalhousie Univ Fac Med Halifax NS B3H 4H7 Can. *Fax:* 902-494-1388; *E-Mail:* tdwhite@ac.dal.ca

**WHITE, THOMAS GAILAND,** plant breeding, for more information see previous edition

**WHITE, THOMAS JAMES,** BIOCHEMISTRY, MICROBIOLOGY. *Current Pos:* sr dir, 89-91, VPRES RES & DEVELOP, ROCHE MOLECULAR SYSTS, 91- *Personal Data:* b Stamford, Conn, Oct 5, 45; m 87, Leslie Scalapino. *Educ:* Johns Hopkins Univ, BA, 67; Univ Calif, Berkeley, PhD(biochem), 76. *Prof Exp:* Fel biochem, G W Hooper Found, Univ Calif, San Francisco, 76-77 & Univ Wis-Madison, 77-78; scientist, Recombinant Molecular Res, Cetus Corp, 78-80, dir, 81-84, vpres res, 84-87, vpres & assoc dir res & develop, 87-88; sabbatical, Univ Calif, Berkeley, 88. *Concurrent Pos:* NIH, fel, 77-78; vis scholar, Univ Calif, Berkeley, 88- *Mem:* Am Soc Microbiol; Soc Study Evolution; Am Inst Biol Sci; Genetics Soc Am; Soc Molecular Biol Evolution; Int Soc Molecular Evolution. *Res:* Molecular evolution. *Mailing Add:* Roche Molecular Systs 1145 Atlantic Ave No 100 Alameda CA 94501

**WHITE, TIMOTHY LEE,** QUANTITATIVE FOREST GENETICS. *Current Pos:* RES FORESTER GENETICS & BIOMET, INT PAPER CO, 79- *Personal Data:* b San Diego, Calif, May 5, 51; m 79; c 1. *Educ:* Univ Calif, Berkeley, BS, 73; NC State Univ, Raleigh, MS, 75; Ore State Univ, PhD(forest genetics), 80. *Mem:* Sigma Xi. *Res:* Population dynamics and genetics of forest ecosystems. *Mailing Add:* Univ Fla 4315 SW 82nd Terr Gainesville FL 32608-4202

**WHITE, TIMOTHY P,** MUSCLE PHYSIOLOGY. *Current Pos:* PROF PHYS ED, UNIV CALIF. *Personal Data:* b Buenos Aires, Arg, July 9, 49. *Educ:* Univ Calif, Berkeley, PhD(phys educ), 77. *Prof Exp:* Assoc prof Kinesiol, Univ Mich, 83- *Concurrent Pos:* Assoc res scientist, Inst Geol, Univ Mich, 86-; bd trustees, Am Col Sports Med, 88- *Mem:* Am Heart Asn; Am Physiol Soc; fel Am Col Sports Med. *Mailing Add:* Col Health & Human Performance Ore State Univ 123 Women's Bldg Corvallis OR 97331-6802

**WHITE, W(ILLIAM) ARTHUR,** MINERALOGY, PETROLOGY. *Current Pos:* Spec asst chem, Ill State Geol Surv, 43-44, res asst, 44-47, asst geologist, 47-48, assoc geologist, 48-54, head, Clay Resources & Clay Mineral Tech Sect, 58-73, geologist, 54-79, EMER GEOLOGIST, ILL STATE GEOL SURV, 79- *Personal Data:* b Sumner, Ill, Dec 9, 16; m 41. *Educ:* Univ Ill, BS, 40, MS, 47, PhD(geol), 55. *Concurrent Pos:* Prof appl clay mineral technol, Fed Univ Rio Grande do sol, Porto Alegre, Brazil, 70; consult, 79-89. *Mem:* Fel AAAS; fel Mineral Soc Am; Am Chem Soc; fel Am Geol Soc; Geochem Soc; Clay Mineral Soc. *Res:* Physical properties of clays as related to soil mechanics; ceramic properties of clays and sediments; clay mineralogy of sediments and the environments in which they were accumulated; the role of clay minerals in environmental geology. *Mailing Add:* 603 Colorado Ave Urbana IL 61801-5923

**WHITE, WARREN D,** ELECTRONICS ENGINEERING, MATHEMATICS. *Current Pos:* RETIRED. *Personal Data:* b Springfield, Mo, July 7, 15; m 40; c 2. *Educ:* Drury Col, BS, 36; Univ Mo, Rolla, BSEE, 38. *Honors & Awards:* Barry Carleton Award, Inst Elec & Electronics Engrs Aerospace & Electronic Systs Soc, 83. *Prof Exp:* Consult radio engr, DC, 39-41; engr in charge, Radio Frequency Div, Columbia Broadcasting Syst, 41-46; eng consult, Airborne Instruments Lab, Cutler-Hammer Inc, 46-65; staff mem, Inst Defense Analysis, 65-67; eng consult, Cutler Hammer Inc, 67-74, tech asst to pres, Airborne Instrument Lab, 74-80. *Concurrent Pos:* Spec res assoc, Radio Res Lab, Harvard Univ, 42-45; consult electronics, 80-86. *Mem:* Fel Inst Elec & Electronics Engrs. *Res:* Radar systems; information theory; antenna and propagation adaptive processes. *Mailing Add:* Laclede Oaks Manor Apt 469 705 S Laclede Station Rd Webster Groves MO 63119

**WHITE, WILLARD WORSTER, III,** MAGNETOHYDRODYNAMICS, PLASMA PHYSICS. *Current Pos:* Res physicist, 72-77, sr scientist & asst atmospheric phenomenology div leader, 74-84, SR SCIENTIST & MHD GROUP LEADER, MISSION RES CORP, 84- *Personal Data:* b Perth Amboy, NJ, July 6, 44; m 72. *Educ:* Univ Del, BS, 66; Rensselaer Polytech Inst, PhD(physics), 70. *Concurrent Pos:* Res assoc, Rensselaer Polytech Inst, 70-72. *Mem:* Am Phys Soc. *Res:* Electromagnetic phenomena in the ionosphere; surface physics of materials; radiation damage in solids; laser propagation phenomena. *Mailing Add:* 29 Arbor Lane Hollis NH 03049

**WHITE, WILLIAM,** medical physics, research administration; deceased, see previous edition for last biography

**WHITE, WILLIAM ALEXANDER,** GEOLOGY, GEOMORPHOLOGY. *Current Pos:* RETIRED. *Personal Data:* b Paterson, NJ, June 15, 06; c 2. *Educ:* Duke Univ, AB, 30; Univ NC, MA, 31, PhD(geol), 38; Mont Sch Mines, MS, 34. *Prof Exp:* Petrogr, Lago Petrol Corp, Venezuela, 38-40; from assoc prof to prof geol, Univ NC, Chapel Hill, 44-78; assoc prof, Univ NC, Chapel Hill, 44-50, prof, 50- *Mem:* Fel Am Geol Soc. *Res:* Geomorphology; glacial geology. *Mailing Add:* 407 Patterson Pl Chapel Hill NC 27516

**WHITE, WILLIAM BLAINE,** GEOCHEMISTRY, MATERIALS SCIENCE. *Current Pos:* res assoc geochem, Pa State Univ, 62-63, from asst prof to assoc prof, 63-72, chmn, Grad Prog Mat, 90-93, PROF GEOCHEM, PA STATE UNIV, 72- *Personal Data:* b Huntingdon, Pa, Jan 5, 34; m 59, Elizabeth Loczi; c Nikki E & William B (deceased). *Educ:* Juniata Col, BS, 54; Pa State Univ, PhD(geochem), 62. *Prof Exp:* Res assoc chem physics, Mellon Inst, 54-58. *Mem:* AAAS; Am Geophys Union; Am Ceramic Soc; Am Mineral Soc; Nat Speleol Soc (exec vpres, 65-67). *Res:* High temperature chemistry; infrared and optical spectroscopy of solids; mineralogy; ground water hydrogeology; solid state chemistry; glass science; infrared, optical and luminescence spectroscopy; geomorphology. *Mailing Add:* 210 Mat Res Lab Pa State Univ University Park PA 16802

**WHITE, WILLIAM CHARLES,** PHYSICS, ASTRONOMY. *Current Pos:* RETIRED. *Personal Data:* b Jacksonville, Fla, May 12, 22; m 52. *Educ:* Ohio Wesleyan Univ, BA, 48; Ohio State Univ, MS, 50. *Prof Exp:* Physicist, Naval Weapons Ctr, 50-73, opers res analyst, 73-78, consult, 78-82. *Concurrent Pos:* Consult, Astrophys Observ, Smithsonian Inst, 59-60, Dearborn Observ, Northwestern Univ, 60-62, Ketron, 79-80 & Mammoth Mt SR area, 81-82; sci observer, Stargazer Balloon Flight, 61; partic, Aerial Photog Eclipse of Quiet Sun, 62, NASA Mobile Launch Exped, 65, Sandia Eclipse Exped, 65 & Oceanog & Geophys Exped, SAm, 67. *Mem:* Am Astron Soc; NY Acad Sci; Sigma Xi. *Res:* Astrophysical research with infrared detectors and balloon-borne observatories; atmospheric physics research with high altitude balloons; ozone as a function of latitude; electronic warfare. *Mailing Add:* PO Box 707 Clinton WA 98236-0707

**WHITE, WILLIAM MICHAEL,** GEOCHEMISTRY. *Current Pos:* PROF GEOL SCI, CORNELL UNIV, ITHACA, NY, 86- *Personal Data:* b Allentown, Pa, Aug 10, 48; m 70; c 4. *Educ:* Univ Calif, Berkeley, BA, 71; Univ RI, PhD(oceanog), 77. *Prof Exp:* Fel geochem, Dept Terrestrial Magnetism, Carnegie Inst, Washington, 77-79; asst res prof, Col Sch Mines, Golden, Col, 79-80; staff mem, Max-Planck Inst Chem, 80-85; assoc prof oceanog, Ore State Univ, Corvallis, 85-86. *Mem:* Am Geophys Union; fel Geochem Soc; fel Europ Asn Geochem. *Res:* Isotope and trace element geochemistry of igneous rocks; composition and chemical evolution of earth's mantle; geochemistry of marine sediments. *Mailing Add:* Dept Geol Sci 2122 Snee Hall Cornell Univ Ithaca NY 14853-0001. *E-Mail:* white@geology. cornell.edu

**WHITE, WILLIAM NORTH,** PHYSICAL ORGANIC CHEMISTRY, KINETICS & MECHANISM. *Current Pos:* prof, 63-76 & 77-95, chmn dept, 63-71 & 75-76, EMER PROF CHEM, UNIV VT, 95- *Personal Data:* b Walton, NY, Sept 16, 25; m 51, Childa Sauter; c Carla & Eric. *Educ:* Cornell Univ, AB, 50; Harvard Univ, MA, 51; PhD(org chem), 53. *Prof Exp:* Nat Res Coun fel, Crellin Labs, Calif Inst Technol, 53-54; from asst prof to assoc prof chem, Ohio State Univ, 54-63; prof & chmn, Dept Chem, Univ Tex, Arlington, 76-77. *Concurrent Pos:* NSF sr fel biol, Brookhaven Nat Labs, 63-64; NSF sr fel chem, Harvard Univ, 65; vis scholar biochem, Brandeis Univ, 74-75. *Mem:* AAAS; Am Chem Soc; Royal Soc Chem. *Res:* Reaction mechanisms; rearrangements; structure reactivity correlations; electrophilic and nucleophilic substitution mechanisms; carbanion and carbonyl group chemistry. *Mailing Add:* Dept Chem Univ Vt Burlington VT 05405-0125. *Fax:* 802-656-8705; *E-Mail:* wnwhite@zoo.uvm.edu

**WHITE, WILLIAM WALLACE,** OPERATIONS RESEARCH, COMPUTER SCIENCE. *Current Pos:* Staff mem mgt sci, Philadelphia Sci Ctr, IBM Corp, 66-74, advan appl adv, Advan Syst Develop Div, 74-75, sr systs analyst, Syst Prod Div, 75-77, RES STAFF MEM, T J WATSON RES CTR, IBM CORP, 77- *Personal Data:* b Cleveland, Ohio, Sept 7, 39; m 64; c 2. *Educ:* Princeton Univ, AB, 61; Univ Calif, Berkeley, MS, 63, PhD(eng sci), 66. *Concurrent Pos:* Adj assoc prof statist, Columbia Univ, 72-74, adj assoc prof math, 74-79. *Mem:* Opers Res Soc Am; Asn Comput Mach; Math Prog Soc; Inst Elec & Electronics Engrs Comput Soc; Comput Measurement Group. *Res:* Computer measurement evaluation; mathematical programming and computer performance; analysis, applied to computer design. *Mailing Add:* IBM Corp PO Box 704 Yorktown Heights NY 10598

**WHITE, WILLIS S, JR,** ELECTRICAL ENGINEERING. *Current Pos:* RETIRED. *Personal Data:* b Dec 17, 26; m; c 3. *Educ:* Va Polytech Inst & State Univ, BS; Mass Inst Technol, MS. *Prof Exp:* Elec engr elec design & syst planning & oper, Am Elec Power Serv Corp, NY, 48-52, asst to pres, 52-54, off mgr, 54-58, asst to oper vpres, 58-61, asst mgr, Lynchburg Dist, Appalachian Power Co, Va, 61-62, mgr, 62-66, asst gen mgr, 66-67, asst vpres, 67-69, vpres, 69, exec vpres & oper head, 69-73, sr exec vpres, NY, 73-75, vchmn, 75-76, chief exec officer, 76-90, chmn bd, 76-92. *Concurrent Pos:* Chmn bd trustees, Greater Columbus Conv Ctr; trustee, Battelle Mem Inst; dir, Bank NY, Riverside Methodist Hosp & Methodist Theol Sch Ohio. *Mem:* Nat Acad Eng; sr mem Inst Elec & Electronics Engrs. *Mailing Add:* 2430 Onandaga Dr Columbus OH 43221

**WHITED, DEAN ALLEN,** GENETICS, AGRONOMY. *Current Pos:* from asst prof to assoc prof, 68-80, chmn, Genetics Inst, 71-89, PROF AGRON, NDAK STATE UNIV, 80-, PROF, DEPT CROP & WEED SCI, 89- *Personal Data:* b Nebraska City, Nebr, Mar 28, 40; m 64; c 2. *Educ:* Univ Nebr, Lincoln, BS, 62, MS, 64; NDak State Univ, PhD(agron), 67. *Prof Exp:* Agency Int Develop grant & res assoc wheat qual, Univ Nebr, Lincoln, 67-68. *Mem:* Am Soc Agron; Am Genetic Asn. *Res:* Genetics; genetic counseling at Muscular Dystrophy Clinic; soybean genetics and soybean production. *Mailing Add:* 201 28th Ave N Fargo ND 58102

**WHITEFIELD, PHILIP DOUGLAS,** SPECTROSCOPY, DISCHARGE-FLOW KINETICS. *Current Pos:* RES ASSOC PROF, UNIV MO, ROLLA, 90- *Personal Data:* b Taunton Somerset, Eng, Apr 10, 53; US citizen; m 83; c 2. *Educ:* Queen Mary Col; Univ London, BSc, 75, PhD(phys chem), 79. *Prof Exp:* Res asst, Air Force Weapons Lab, 79-81; scientist, McDonnell Douglas Res Lab, 81-90. *Concurrent Pos:* Asst prof, Univ Mo, 84-85. *Mem:* Am Chem Soc; Combustion Inst; Am Inst Aeronaut & Astronaut. *Res:* Atmospheric environmental chemistry associated with heterogeneous reaction chemistry on particulate surfaces, in particular reactions in exhaust flumes. *Mailing Add:* Cloud & Aerosol Sci Lab Physics Dept Univ Mo Rolla MO 65401

**WHITEHAIR, CHARLES KENNETH,** nutrition, pathology; deceased, see previous edition for last biography

**WHITEHAIR, LEO A,** VETERINARY MEDICINE, FOOD SCIENCE. *Current Pos:* dir, Lab Animal Sci Prog, Animal Resources Br, Div Res Resources, 87-88, DIR, COMP MED PROG, NAT CTR RES RESOURCES, NIH, 89- *Personal Data:* b Abilene, Kans, June 13, 29; m 58, Gloria; c Kirsten, Robert & Courtney. *Educ:* Kans State Univ, BS & DVM, 53; Univ Wis, MS, 54, PhD(food sci), 62; Am Col Lab Animal Med, dipl, 96. *Honors & Awards:* Helwig-Jennings Award, 81; Commendation Medal, USPHS, 85; Griffin Award, 95. *Prof Exp:* Vet, Off Nutrit Br, Aeromed Lab, Wright-Patterson AFB, Ohio, 54-58; lab vet, Nutrit Br, Food Inst Armed Forces, Ill, 61-62; vet food technologist, Biol Br, Div Biol & Med, US AEC, 62-67; health scientist adminr, NIH, 68-75, dir, Primate Res Ctr Prog, Animal Resources Br, Div Res Resources, 75-85; assoc, Res Admin Am Red Cross Biomed Res & Develop Labs, 85-87. *Concurrent Pos:* Consult adv, Food & Agr Orgn-UN-WHO-Int Atomic Energy Agency Joint Expert Comt Meeting, Rome, 64; tech adv int prog irradiation fruit & fruit juices, Inst Biol & Agr, Seibersdorf Reactor Ctr, Austria, 65; vet off dir, USPHS; bd councillors, Am Col Vet Prev Med, 79-80. *Mem:* Am Vet Med Asn; Am Col Vet Prev Med (secy-treas, 75-78, pres, 84-85); Am Soc Primatologists; Am Asn Vet Nutritionists; Sigma Xi. *Res:* Animal nutrition; wholesomeness and public health safety aspects of irradiated foods; laboratory animal resources; animal models for biomedical research. *Mailing Add:* 707 Wilson Ave Rockville MD 20850-2147. *Fax:* 301-594-9149

**WHITEHEAD, ANDREW BRUCE,** PLANETOLOGY, PHYSICS. *Current Pos:* RETIRED. *Personal Data:* b Quebec, Que, Oct 18, 32; m 62; c 3. *Educ:* Univ NB, BSc, 53; McGill Univ, MSc, 55, PhD(physics), 57. *Prof Exp:* Res fel nuclear physics, Atomic Energy Res Estab, Harwell, Eng, 57-60; res fel nuclear physics, Jet Propulsion Lab, 61-62, res specialist, 63-65, group supvr physics, 65-67, sect mgr physics, 67-69, mgr, Lunar & Planetary Sci Sect, 69-71, asst proj scientist, Mariner 9, 71-73, actg asst mgr, Space Sci Div, 73-75, staff scientist, 75-78; mgr progs, Honeywell Corp, 78-79, mgr, Sensors & Controls Dept, Honeywell Corp Phys Sci Ctr, 80-81, prin staff scientist, Honeywell Sensors & Signal Processing Lab, 82-88. *Mem:* Am Phys Soc. *Res:* Nuclear structure; particle detection; secondary electron emission; atomic stopping; photovoltaics; computer science; sensors; controls. *Mailing Add:* 3045 Lakeshore Ave Maple Plain MN 55359

**WHITEHEAD, ARMAND T,** ENTOMOLOGY. *Current Pos:* Asst prof, 69-78, ASSOC PROF ZOOL, BRIGHAM YOUNG UNIV, 78- *Personal Data:* b Reno, Nev, May 19, 36; m 54; c 5. *Educ:* Brigham Young Univ, BS, 65; Univ Calif, Berkeley, PhD(entom), 69. *Concurrent Pos:* Vis asst prof, Univ Ill, 75-76; vis prof, Univ Alta, 88-89. *Mem:* Entom Soc Am. *Res:* Neurophysiology and morphology of insect sensory receptors. *Mailing Add:* Zool Dept Brigham Young Univ Provo UT 84602-1049

**WHITEHEAD, DANIEL L(EE),** ELECTRICAL ENGINEERING. *Current Pos:* CONSULT HIGH VOLTAGE MEASURING TECHNOL & SAFETY TECHS, 81- *Personal Data:* b Walland, Tenn, Dec 25, 15; m 37; c 3. *Educ:* Univ Tenn, BS, 39; Cornell Univ, MS, 40. *Honors & Awards:* Instrumentation & Measurements Comt Award, Inst Elec & Electronics Engrs, 87. *Prof Exp:* Engr, Cent Sta, Westinghouse Elec Corp, 41-47, supvr analog comput, 47-51, mgr, High Voltage Labs, 51-68, mgr eng labs, 68-81. *Concurrent Pos:* Lectr, Univ Pittsburgh, 44- & Carnegie-Mellon Univ, 57-58; lectr high voltage test tech, Inst Elec & Electronics Engrs, 81- *Mem:* Fel Inst Elec & Electronics Engrs; Am Nat Stand Inst. *Res:* High voltage and high power phenomena and measuring techniques. *Mailing Add:* 4400 Roundtop Rd Export PA 15632

**WHITEHEAD, DONALD REED,** BOTANY, PALEOECOLOGY. *Current Pos:* AT DEPT BIOL, IND UNIV. *Personal Data:* b Quincy, Mass, Sept 14, 32; m 55; c 2. *Educ:* Harvard Univ, AB, 54, AM, 55, PhD(biol), 58. *Prof Exp:* From instr to assoc prof biol, Williams Col, 59-67; assoc prof biol, Ind Univ, Bloomington, 67-74, prof zool, 74-77; res entomologist, Syst Entom Lab, US Nat Mus, USDA, 77- *Concurrent Pos:* Fulbright fel, Geol Surv Denmark, 58-59; res grant, 63; consult, Jersey Prod Res Co, 60; res prof bot mus, Univ Bergen, 63; NSF grants, 63. *Mem:* AAAS; Ecol Soc Am; Am Ornith Union. *Res:* Pleistocene environmental changes in unglaciated regions; pollen morphology. *Mailing Add:* Dept Biol Ind Univ Bloomington IN 47405

**WHITEHEAD, EUGENE IRVING,** PLANT BIOCHEMISTRY. *Current Pos:* Lab asst, Sdak State Univ, 40-42, sta analyst, 42-43, asst agr chemist, 43-46, assoc chemist, 46-60, assoc prof sta biochem, Grad Fac, 60-67, PROF STA BIOCHEM, GRAD FAC, SDAK STATE UNIV, 67- *Personal Data:* b Canton, SDak, Mar 4, 18; m 55; c 2. *Educ:* SDak State Col, BS, 39, MS, 41. *Mem:* Am Soc Plant Physiol; Am Chem Soc. *Res:* Nitrogen metabolism of cereal crops; winter hardiness of cereal plants. *Mailing Add:* HC 55 Box 853 Sturgis SD 57785-9290

**WHITEHEAD, FLOY EUGENIA,** NUTRITION. *Current Pos:* chmn, Dept Home Econ, 55-71, prof, 55-78, EMER PROF HOME ECON, UNIV IOWA, 78- *Personal Data:* b Athens, Ga, Feb 10, 13. *Educ:* Univ Ga, BS, 36, MS, 42; Harvard Univ, DSc, 51; Am Bd Nutrit, dipl, 52. *Honors & Awards:* Roberts Award, Am Dietetic Asn, 56. *Prof Exp:* Teacher, High Schs, Ga, 36-40; asst prof home econ, WGa Col, 40-42; assoc dir health educ, State Dept Pub Health, Ga, 42-43; assoc prof home econ, La State Univ, 44-48 & Miss State Col, 48-49; fel, Sch Pub Health, Harvard Univ, 49-52; dir nutrit, Wheat Flour Inst, Ill, 52-53; dir nutrit educ, Nat Dairy Coun, 53-55. *Concurrent Pos:* Vis lectr, Harvard Univ, 52-54; co-dir nutrit educ res pub schs, Mo, 52-55; pres elect, Nat Coun Adminr Home Econ, 66-67, pres, 67-68; res grant off nutrit, AID, US Dept State. *Mem:* AAAS; Am Pub Health Asn; Am Home Econ Asn; Am Dietetic Asn. *Res:* Dietary surveys; nutrition education; analysis of nutrition education research, 1900-1970. *Mailing Add:* 306 Ferson Ave Iowa City IA 52240

**WHITEHEAD, FRED,** chemistry; deceased, see previous edition for last biography

**WHITEHEAD, GEORGE WILLIAM,** TOPOLOGY. *Current Pos:* from asst prof to prof, 49-85, EMER PROF MATH, MASS INST TECHNOL, 85- *Personal Data:* b Bloomington, Ill, Aug 2, 18; m 44, Kathleen E Butcher. *Educ:* Univ Chicago, SB, 37, SM, 38, PhD(math), 41. *Prof Exp:* Instr math, Univ Tenn, 39, Purdue Univ, 41-45 & Princeton Univ, 45-47; from asst prof to assoc prof, Brown Univ, 47-49. *Concurrent Pos:* Guggenheim fel & Fulbright res scholar, 55-56; vis prof, Princeton Univ, 58-59; NSF sr fel, 65-66; vis res fel, Birkbeck Col, Univ London, 73; vis, Imp Col, Univ London Oxford Univ, 81. *Mem:* Nat Acad Sci; fel Am Acad Arts & Sci; Am Math Soc; Math Asn Am; London Math Soc. *Res:* Algebraic topology, especially homotopy theory. *Mailing Add:* 25 Bellevue Rd Arlington MA 02174-7919

**WHITEHEAD, JAMES RENNIE,** PHYSICS. *Current Pos:* INDEPENDENT CONSULT SCI POLICY, 86- *Personal Data:* b Clitheroe, Eng, Aug 4, 17; m 44, Nesta D James; c Valerie L (deceased) & Michael J Rennie. *Educ:* Univ Manchester, BSc, 39; Cambridge Univ, PhD(physics), 49. *Prof Exp:* Scientist, Telecommun Res Estab, Eng, 39-51; assoc prof physics, McGill Univ, 51-55; dir res, RCA Victor Co, Ltd, 55-65; dep dir sci secretariat, Govt Can, 65-67; prin sci adv, 67-71; asst secy int affairs, Ministry of State for Sci & Technol, 71-73; spec adv, 73-75; sr adv, Int Develop Res Ctr, Govt Can, 75-76; sr vpres, Philip A Lapp Ltd, 76-82 & Lapp Hancock Assocs, 82-86. *Concurrent Pos:* Sr sci officer, Brit Air Comn, Washington, DC, 44-45 & Cambridge Univ, 46-49; consult, Defence Res Bd Can, 52-54; mem, Sci Comt, NATO, 69-75; consult sci policy, Venezuela & Guyana, UNESCO, 70-75; Can deleg, Sci & Technol Policy Comt, Orgn Econ Coop & Develop, vchmn, Comt Sci & Policy, 73-75. *Mem:* Fel Royal Soc Can; sr mem Inst Elec & Electronics Engrs; fel Brit Inst Elec Eng; fel Brit Inst Physics; fel Can Aeronaut & Space Inst. *Res:* Physical electronics; circuits; systems propagation; electron microscopy; friction; science policy. *Mailing Add:* 1368 Chattaway Ave Ottawa ON K1H 7S3 Can. *Fax:* 613-731-1759; *E-Mail:* jrennie@magi.com

**WHITEHEAD, JOHN ANDREWS,** OCEANOGRAPHY, GEOPHYSICS. *Current Pos:* asst scientist, 71-73, assoc scientist, 73-88, SR SCIENTIST, WOODS HOLE OCEANOG INST, 88- *Personal Data:* b Amesbury, Mass, Apr 21, 41; m 64, Linda Dow; c Glen C, Wendilee W (Lino) (deceased) & Amie L. *Educ:* Tufts Univ, BS, 63; Yale Univ, MS, 65, PhD(appl sci), 68. *Prof Exp:* Fel, Inst Geophys & Planetary Physics, Univ Calif, Los Angeles, 68-69, asst res geophysicist, 69-71. *Concurrent Pos:* Mem, Comt Geod, Nat Acad Sci-Nat Res Coun, 76-; sr fel, Nat Ctr Atmospheric Res, 77-78 & fel, John Simon Guggenheim Mem Found, 82; mem, Space & Terrestrial Applns Comt, NASA, 78-81. *Mem:* Fel Am Phys Soc; Am Geophys Union; NY Acad Sci; AAAS; Sigma Xi; Am Meteorol Soc. *Res:* Geophysical fluid dynamics of oceans, atmospheres and planetary interiors. *Mailing Add:* Dept Phys Oceanog Woods Hole Oceanog Inst Woods Hole MA 02543. *Fax:* 508-457-2181; *E-Mail:* jwhitehead@whoi.edu

**WHITEHEAD, KENNETH E,** CHEMICAL ENGINEERING. *Current Pos:* RETIRED. *Personal Data:* b Niagara Falls, Ont, 1928; US citizen; m 57; c 3. *Educ:* Univ Toronto, BASc, 52; Ohio State Univ, MSc, 53. *Prof Exp:* Supvr process eng, Atlantic Richfield Co, 62-69; supvr, Union Oil Co, Calif, 72-75, mgr, Process Eng Res Dept, 75-90. *Concurrent Pos:* Chmn, Subcomt Liquid Wastes, Am Petrol Inst, 76-77. *Mem:* Am Inst Chem Eng. *Res:* Process development and design in petrochemicals and petroleum refining. *Mailing Add:* 566 N Lincoln Ave Fullerton CA 92831

**WHITEHEAD, MARIAN NEDRA,** NUCLEAR PHYSICS, PARTICLE PHYSICS. *Current Pos:* RETIRED. *Personal Data:* b Calif, Sept 5, 22; m 75, Burns Macdonald. *Educ:* Reed Col, AB, 44; Columbia Univ, MS, 45; Univ Calif, PhD(physics), 52. *Prof Exp:* Physicist, US Naval Ord Test Sta, 45-46 & Radiation Lab, Univ Calif, 49-60; Fulbright sr res fel, Inst Physics, Bologna, Italy, 61-62; physicist, Stanford Linear Accelerator Ctr, Stanford Univ, 62-64; from assoc prof to prof physics, Calif State Univ, Hayward, 64-84, chmn dept, 69-75. *Mem:* Fel Am Phys Soc; Am Asn Physics Teachers (treas, 74-78). *Res:* Meson and cosmic physics. *Mailing Add:* 6009 Ocean View Dr Oakland CA 94618. *E-Mail:* nedra@earthlink.net

**WHITEHEAD, MARVIN DELBERT,** PHYTOPATHOLOGY, MYCOLOGY. *Current Pos:* RETIRED. *Personal Data:* b Paoli, Okla, Dec 18, 17; m 40; c 1. *Educ:* Okla State Univ, BS, 39, MS, 46; Univ Wis, PhD(plant path, mycol), 49. *Prof Exp:* Asst agr aide, Soil Conserv Serv, USDA, Okla, 36-38; asst agron, Okla State Univ, 39-40; sr seed analyst, Fed State Seed Lab, Ala, 40-42; asst plant path, Univ Wis, 46-48; asst prof, Tex A&M Univ, 49-55; assoc prof, Univ Mo, 55-60; prof bot, Edinboro State Col, 60-63; prof plant path, Ga Southern Col, 63-68; prof bot & plant path, Ga State Univ, 68-75. *Concurrent Pos:* Consulting plant pathologist, US Army, Ft McPherson, Ga, 74-, Ft Riley, Kans, 75- & Ft Campbell, Ky, 78-; owner & dir, Marvern Plant Health Inc, Atlanta, 78-; ed, Ga J Sci, 74- *Mem:* AAAS; Am Phytopath Soc; Mycol Soc Am; Bot Soc Am; Am Inst Biol Sci. *Res:* Field crop disease pathology; soil borne and seed borne diseases; phytopathological histology and techniques; fungus and smut taxonomy; yield loss from plant disease; disease resistance; antibiotics and fungicides in control of Dutch elm disease, oak wilt, verticillium wilt of maple, decline of oak, and hackberry; developed Phyton 27, Dutch Elm disease control. *Mailing Add:* 3260 College Pl Apt 81 Lemon Grove CA 91945. *Fax:* 619-465-2426

**WHITEHEAD, MICHAEL ANTHONY,** THEORETICAL & QUANTUM CHEMISTRY, NUCLEAR QUADRUPOLE RESONANCE. *Current Pos:* from asst prof to assoc prof, 62-75, PROF CHEM, MCGILL UNIV, 75- *Personal Data:* b London, Eng, June 30, 35; m 77; c Christopher. *Educ:* Univ London, BSc, 56, PhD(phys chem), 60, DSc(theoret & phys chem), 74. *Prof Exp:* Asst lectr chem, Queen Mary Col, Univ London, 58-60; Fulbright scholar, Univ Cincinnati, 60-62, fel, 60-61, asst prof, 61-62. *Concurrent Pos:* Nat Res Coun Can travel fel & vis prof, Cambridge Univ, 71-72; vis prof theoret chem, Oxford Univ, 72-74, Dept Chem & Physics, Univ Geneva, 83-84; vis prof fel, Univ Wales, Aberystwyth, 80; vis prof, Oxford Univ, 90-91. *Mem:* Am Phys Soc; Am Chem Soc; Can Inst Chem; Royal Soc Chem; Sigma Xi; Royal Soc Arts. *Res:* Nuclear quadrupole resonance; electronegativity theory; molecular orbital calculations; beyond Hartree-Fock calculations; surface absorption; chemical absorption; theoretical chemistry; spin density functional theory. *Mailing Add:* Dept Chem McGill Univ 801 Sherbrooke St W Montreal PQ H3A 2K6 Can. *Fax:* 514-398-3797; *E-Mail:* tony@mawchem.mcgill.ca

**WHITEHEAD, ROBERT E,** MECHANICAL ENGINEERING, AERONAUTICAL & ASTRONAUTICAL ENGINEERING. *Current Pos:* dir, Subsonic Transp Div, 92-94, dep assoc adminr aeronaut, 94-95, ASSOC ADMINR, AERONAUT & SPACE TRANSP TECHNOL, NASA, 95- *Educ:* Va Polytech Inst, BS, 67, MS, 69, PhD(eng mech), 71. *Prof Exp:* Res engr, US Navy David Taylor Res Ctr; dir, Mech Div, Off Naval Res, 92. *Mem:* Fel Am Inst Aeronaut & Astronaut. *Mailing Add:* Off Assoc Admnr Aeronaut & Space Transport Technol NASA Washington DC 20546

**WHITEHEAD, WALTER DEXTER, JR,** NUCLEAR PHYSICS, ATOMIC PHYSICS. *Current Pos:* from asst prof to assoc prof, Univ Va, 56-61, chmn dept, 68-69, dean fac arts & sci, 71-72, PROF PHYSICS, UNIV VA, 61-, DIR CTR ADVAN STUDIES, 65-, DEAN, GRAD SCH ARTS & SCI, 69- *Personal Data:* b San Diego, Calif, Nov 30, 22; m 49; c 2. *Educ:* Univ Va, BS, 44, MS, 46, PhD(physics), 49. *Prof Exp:* Asst, Univ Va, 43-45; physicist, Bartol Res Found, 49-53; from asst prof to assoc prof physics, NC State Col, 53-56. *Concurrent Pos:* Vis scientist, Inst Nuclear Physics, 59-60; mem bd admin, Va Inst Marine Sci, 71-78; mem Nat Res Coun eval panel, Ctr Radiation Res, Inst Basic Stand, 71-74. *Mem:* AAAS; fel Am Phys Soc; Am Asn Physics Teachers; Sigma Xi. *Res:* Nuclear spectroscopy; neutron scattering; photonuclear reactions; x-ray interactions. *Mailing Add:* 5762 St George Ave Crozet VA 22932

**WHITEHORN, WILLIAM VICTOR,** PHYSIOLOGY, MEDICINE. *Current Pos:* EMER PROF, UNIFORMED SERV UNIV HEALTH SCI, 88- *Personal Data:* b Detroit, Mich, Oct 3, 15; m 38, Sarah Holland; c David & Gene A. *Educ:* Univ Mich, AB, 36, MD, 39. *Prof Exp:* Asst physiol, Univ Mich, 40-42; res assoc, Ohio State Univ, 42-44; from instr to asst prof physiol & med, 44-47; asst prof physiol, Col Med, Univ Ill, Chicago, 47-50, prof, 54-70; dir, Div Health Sci & spec asst to pres med affairs, Univ Del, 70-74; asst comnr, Prof & Consumer Prog, Food & Drug Admin, 74-80. *Concurrent Pos:* Vis prof physiol, Uniformed Serv Univ Health Sci, 80-87. *Mem:* AAAS; Am Physiol Soc; Soc Exp Biol & Med; Am Heart Asn; Cent Soc Clin Res. *Res:* Cardiac mechanics and function; applied physiology of respiration and circulation. *Mailing Add:* 13612 Sherwood Forest Dr Silver Spring MD 20904-1133

**WHITEHOUSE, BRUCE ALAN,** POLYMER CHEMISTRY, TEXTILE CHEMISTRY. *Current Pos:* tech dir advan mat, 90-93, TECH DIR NYLON, DUPONT, 94- *Personal Data:* b Henderson, Ky, Sept 6, 39; m 61; c 2. *Educ:* Col Charleston, BS, 63; Ga Inst Technol, PhD(phys chem), 67. *Prof Exp:* Res chemist, Plastics Dept, Polyolefins Div, E I Du Pont de Nemours & Co, Inc, Orange Tex, 67-72, res chemist, Textile Fibers Dept, Nylon Tech Div, Chattanooga, Tenn, 72-73, sr res chemist, 73, res supvr, Dacron Res Lab, 73-76, res supvr, Textile Res Lab, 76-78, mgr prod strategy, Indust Fibers Div, 78-79, res mgr, Textile Res Lab, Textile Fibers Dept, 79-83, tech mgr, Tyvek & Spanborded Div, 83-88, lab dir, Pioneering Res Lab, 88-90. *Mem:* Am Chem Soc; Soc Advan Mat & Process Eng. *Res:* Solid state structure and properties; structure and properties of polymers; chromatography; polymer synthesis composites; textile science; technical management. *Mailing Add:* 2208 Kendall St Virginia Beach VA 23451

**WHITEHOUSE, DAVID R(EMPFER),** ELECTRICAL ENGINEERING. *Current Pos:* PRES, WHITEHOUSE ASSOC, 85- *Personal Data:* b Evanston, Ill, Nov 13, 29; m 56, Ruth Walker; c Walker P, Laura L & Sanford D. *Educ:* Northwestern Univ, BS, 52; Mass Inst Technol, SM, 54, DSc, 58. *Prof Exp:* From asst prof to assoc prof elec eng, Mass Inst Technol, 58-65; prin res scientist, Res Div, Raytheon Co, 65-67, mgr, Laser Advan Develop Ctr, 67-85. *Concurrent Pos:* Consult, 59-65 & 85-; chmn bd, Dymed Corp, 87-89; bd dir, Surgilase Inc, 87-91. *Mem:* Am Phys Soc; Inst Elec & Electronics Engrs; Laser Inst Am (pres, 81); Sigma Xi. *Res:* Lasers; laser and plasma physics. *Mailing Add:* 99 South Ave Weston MA 02193. *Fax:* 781-891-0440

**WHITEHOUSE, FRANK, JR,** SCIENCE EDUCATION. *Current Pos:* from instr to assoc prof, 54-95, EMER ASSOC PROF MICROBIOL, UNIV MICH, ANN ARBOR, 95- *Personal Data:* b Ann Arbor, Mich, Nov 20, 24; m 51, Helen A Schimkat; c Lynne, Beth Ann, Frank Scott & Kim Elain. *Educ:* Univ Mich, BA & MD, 53. *Honors & Awards:* Sr Fulbright lectr microbiol, 79-80. *Prof Exp:* Intern, Blodgett Mem Hosp, Grand Rapids, Mich, 53-54. *Concurrent Pos:* Lectr, Ohio State Univ, 59; pre-prof counsr, Univ Mich, 60-; exec dir, Nat Asn Adv Health Professions. *Mem:* Am Soc Microbiol. *Res:* Enzymatic degradation of antibodies; science education and test analysis, chemotherapy. *Mailing Add:* Dept Microbiol & Immunol 6605c Med Sci Bldg II Univ Mich Med Sch Ann Arbor MI 48109-0620. *Fax:* 313-764-3562; *E-Mail:* frwhe@umich.edu

**WHITEHOUSE, GARY E,** COMPUTER APPLICATIONS, SIMULATION & NETWORKS. *Current Pos:* prof indust eng & mgt systs & chmn dept, 78-85, dean eng, 87-93, PROVOST & VPRES ACAD AFFAIRS, UNIV CENT FLA, 93- *Personal Data:* b Trenton, NJ, Aug 13, 38; m 63, Marian Greenhalgit; c Gail & Glenn. *Educ:* Lehigh Univ, BS, 60, MS, 62; Ariz State Univ, PhD(indust eng), 66. *Honors & Awards:* Maynard Award, Inst Indust Engrs; Western Elec Award, Am Soc Eng Educ. *Prof Exp:* Instr indust eng, Lehigh Univ, 62-63 & Ariz State Univ, 63-65; from asst prof to prof, Lehigh Univ, 65-78. *Concurrent Pos:* Consult, Air Prod & Chem Inc, Martin Marietta, USN. *Mem:* Am Inst Indust Engrs; Nat Soc Prof Engrs; Opers Res Soc Am; Am Soc Eng Educ; Sigma Xi. *Res:* Theory and applications of networks; mathematical programming; decision theory; production and inventory control; computer applications to industrial engineering simulation. *Mailing Add:* 435 Boxwood Circle Winter Springs FL 32708-3436. *Fax:* 407-823-5407; *E-Mail:* whitehse@ucf1vm.cc.ucf.edu

**WHITEHOUSE, GERALD D(EAN),** MECHANICAL ENGINEERING. *Current Pos:* from asst prof to assoc prof, 66-77, PROF MECH ENG & CHMN DEPT, LA STATE UNIV, BATON ROUGE, 77- *Personal Data:* b Sapulpa, Okla, May 17, 36; m 58; c 3. *Educ:* Univ Mo-Rolla, BS, 58; Okla State Univ, MS, 64, PhD(mech eng), 67. *Prof Exp:* Vibration engr, Douglas Aircraft Co, 58-59. *Mem:* Acoust Soc Am; Am Soc Mech Engrs. *Res:* Research activity in the mechanical design area, particularly in stress analysis and vibrations. *Mailing Add:* 8126 One Calais Ave Baton Rouge LA 70809

**WHITEHOUSE, RONALD LESLIE S,** ELECTRON MICROSCOPY, MICROBIOLOGY. *Current Pos:* prof assoc food microbiol, 67-68, asst prof med bact & electron micros, 68-74, ASSOC PROF BACT, UNIV ALTA, 74- *Personal Data:* b Birmingham, Eng, Aug 9, 37; Can citizen; div; c 2. *Educ:* Univ Nottingham, BSc, 59; Univ Alta, MSc, 61, PhD(plant physiol, biochem), 65. *Prof Exp:* Nat Res Coun Can overseas fel, Bot Lab, Univ Bergen, 66. *Concurrent Pos:* Sabbatical leaves, Dept Molecular Biol, Pasteur Inst, Paris, 75, 83. *Mem:* Micros Soc Can; NY Acad Sci. *Res:* Electron microscopic methods for biological materials; electron microscopic investigation of chromosomal activity during sporulation in Bacillus Subtilis; development of preparative techniques; bacterial ultrastructure; simonsiella sp; oral microbiology. *Mailing Add:* Dept Med Microbiol & Immunol Univ Alta Fac Med Edmonton AB T6G 2G3 Can

**WHITEHURST, BROOKS M,** CHEMICAL ENGINEERING. *Current Pos:* PRES, BROOKS WHITEHURST ASSOC, INC, 81- *Personal Data:* b Reading, Pa, Apr 9, 30; m 51; c 3. *Educ:* Va Polytech Inst, BS, 51. *Prof Exp:* Sr tech asst, Am Enka Corp, 51-56; sr engr, Ind Chem Div, Mobil Chem Co, 56-63; proj engr, Texaco Exp, Inc, 63-66; process engr, Tex Gulf Sulphur Co, 67-70; supt, Tech Surv, Tex Gulf Inc, 70-75, mgr, Eng Serv, 75-81. *Concurrent Pos:* Chmn, Indust Adv Coun, Elizabeth City State Univ. *Mem:* Am Inst Chem Engrs; fel Am Inst Chem; Int Solar Energy Soc; Nat Soc Prof Engrs; Royal Soc Chem. *Res:* Rayon yarns; phosphate, fertilizer, fluorine and environmental processes in air and water; alternate energy systems (solar, wood, alcohol), peat-oil slurry fuels, industrial products from sweet potatoes, carbohydrates and chemical aluminum polishing; the development of chelates from carbohydrates, and the development of chelated metals for agriculture, and industrial waste treatment. *Mailing Add:* 1983 Hoods Creek Dr New Bern NC 28564

**WHITEHURST, CHARLES A(UGUSTUS),** MECHANICAL ENGINEERING, ENVIRONMENTAL ENGINEERING. *Current Pos:* assoc prof mech & aerospace eng, 63-66, from assoc prof to prof, Div Eng Res, 66-77, PROF COASTAL ENG & ASSOC DEAN RES & GRAD ACTIV, LA STATE UNIV, BATON ROUGE, 77- *Personal Data:* b Cottondale, Fla, June 27, 29; m 56; c 3. *Educ:* La State Univ, BS, 56; Southern Methodist Univ, MS, 59; Tex A&M Univ, PhD(mech eng), 62. *Prof Exp:* Aerodyn engr, Gen Dynamics /Ft Worth, 56, propulsion engr, 56-59; assoc prof, La Polytech Inst, 62-63. *Concurrent Pos:* Dir & prin investr, Heat, Mass & Momentum Transfer Studies at Low Temperatures Proj, NSF, 62-63; lectr, Manned Spacecraft Ctr, Tex, 65-66; prin investr, Flow Losses in Flexible Hose Proj, NASA, 65-66, prin investr, Jet Shock Interactions Proj, 66-67, prog mgr & prin investr sustaining univ grant, 66-, prin investr related multidiscipline res, NASA Ctr, 69-, prin investr remote sensing studies La Delta, 72-; consult, La Joint Legis Comt Environ Qual, 71-72, prog mgr La environ mgt syst, 72; prog mgr & prin investr res, Off Water Resources Res, 72- *Mem:* Am Soc Mech Engrs; Am Soc Eng Educ; Sigma Xi. *Res:* Thermodynamics; fluid mechanics; heat transfer; environmental engineering; water resource management and environmental impact assessments. *Mailing Add:* 1090 Longwood Dr Baton Rouge LA 70806

**WHITEHURST, DARRELL DUAYNE,** ORGANIC CHEMISTRY. *Current Pos:* Res chemist, Mobil Res & Develop Corp, 64-65, sr res chemist, 65-68, group leader catalysis, 68-73, res assoc, 74-75, PRIN INVESTR THREE EPRI CONTRACTS, MOBIL RES & DEVELOP CORP, 75-, GROUP MGR COAL & HEAVY LIQUIDS RES, 80- *Personal Data:* b Vernon, Ill, July 8, 38; m 67; c 2. *Educ:* Bradley Univ, AB, 60; Univ Iowa, MS, 63, PhD(org chem), 64. *Honors & Awards:* Richard A Glen Award & Henry H Storch Award, Am Chem Soc. *Concurrent Pos:* Mem, Comt Task Force Motor Fuel & Photochem Smog, Am Petrol Inst; res assoc, BPRI, 73, prin investr, Fundamental Coal Chem Study, 75; res scientist, 83. *Mem:* Carbon Soc; Am Chem Soc. *Res:* Organic syntheses; acetylene oxidations and coordination compounds of platinum; catalysis by ion exchange resins; catalysis by transition metals and compounds thereof; catalysis by zeolites; homogeneous-heterogeneous catalysts interconversion; metal plating; petrochemicals. *Mailing Add:* 303 Washington Crossing Penn Rd Titusville NJ 08560

**WHITEHURST, ELDRIDGE AUGUSTUS,** CIVIL ENGINEERING. *Current Pos:* RETIRED. *Personal Data:* b Norfolk, Va, May 26, 23; m 69; c 5. *Educ:* Va Mil Inst, BSCE, 47; Purdue Univ, MSCE, 51. *Prof Exp:* Assoc res engr, Portland Cement Asn, 47-49; res asst, Joint Hwy Res Proj, Purdue Univ, 50-51, res engr, 51-52; res engr, Tenn Hwy Res Prog, Univ Tenn, Knoxville, 52-62, dir, 52-72, assoc dir, Eng Exp Sta, 54-72, res prof, 62-72; assoc dir, Transp Res Ctr, Ohio State Univ, 72-80, prof civil eng, 72-, dir, Transplex, 80-88. *Concurrent Pos:* Consult var firms; mem, Hwy Res Bd, Nat Acad Sci-Nat Res Coun. *Mem:* Fel Am Soc Testing & Mat; Am Rd Builders. *Res:* Highway materials; nondestructive testing of concrete, particularly by pulse velocity techniques; slipperiness of pavements, stabilization of pavement base courses; durability of concrete; performance of aggregates; bituminous materials and mixes. *Mailing Add:* 423 Kendall Rd Knoxville TN 37919

**WHITEHURST, GARNETT BROOKS,** BIOCHEMISTRY, ANALYTICAL CHEMISTRY. *Current Pos:* RES DIR RES & DEVELOP, BROOKS WHITEHURST ASSOCS INC, 89- *Personal Data:* b Whitepine, Tenn, Sept 26, 52. *Educ:* NC State Univ, BS, 75; Iowa State Univ, PhD(biochem), 80. *Prof Exp:* Fac teaching, Barton Col, Atlantic Christian, 82-89. *Concurrent Pos:* Adj fac, Webster Univ, Pope AFB, 87-; vis asst prof, ECarolina Univ, 91- *Mem:* Am Chem Soc; AAAS; Asn Comput Mach; Inst Elec & Electronics Engrs Comput Soc; Am Inst Nutrit; Asn Off Analytical Chemists. *Res:* Development of products for chelation of metal ions; development of processes for production of chelating agents. *Mailing Add:* PO Box 3335 New Bern NC 28564-3335

**WHITEHURST, HARRY BERNARD,** PHYSICAL CHEMISTRY. *Current Pos:* from assoc prof to prof, 59-92, EMER PROF CHEM, ARIZ STATE UNIV, 92- *Personal Data:* b Dallas, Tex, Sept 13, 22; m 48; c 2. *Educ:* Rice Inst, BA, 44, MA, 48, PhD(chem), 50. *Prof Exp:* Fel, Univ Minn, 50-51; res chemist, Owens-Corning Fiberglas Corp, 51-59. *Mem:* Fel AAAS; Am Chem Soc; fel Am Inst Chemists; Sigma Xi. *Res:* Radiochemistry; adsorption; surface chemistry of glass; electrical properties of oxides; investigation of ionizing radiation effects in solids and photoexcitation of electrons in solids. *Mailing Add:* 630 E Concorda Dr Tempe AZ 85282-2319

**WHITEHURST, VIRGIL EDWARDS,** PHARMACOLOGY, TOXICOLOGY. *Current Pos:* PHARMACOLOGIST & TOXICOLOGIST, FOOD & DRUG ADMIN, WASHINGTON, DC, 71- *Personal Data:* b Dunkirk, Ind, 1932; m 55, Mary E Scott; c Scott V. *Educ:* Anderson Col, BA, 53; Butler Univ, MS, 62; Ind Univ, PhD(biochem), 68. *Prof Exp:* Asst nutrit fluoride chem & prev dent, Ind Univ, 67-68; assoc prof microbiol & biochem, Howard Univ, 68-73. *Concurrent Pos:* Vis prof, Howard Univ, 73-78, assoc prof; consult, Commun Progress Inc, New Haven, Ct, 75-77, Murtis H Taylor Multi-Serv Ctr, Cleveland, Ohio, 78-80. *Mem:* Sigma Xi; Soc Black Scientists; Soc Toxicol. *Res:* Investigate the cardiotoxic effects of beta adrenergic agonists methylxanthenes when used separately and concurrently; cardiotoxic effects of the concurrent use of steroids and methylxanthines; propanolol as an antidote for throphylline; the role of phospholipids, arachidonic acid in isoproterenol induced sudden death in rats; cardiac toxicity from beta adrengeric drugs in the asthmatic animal rat model; cardiotoxic studies in asthmatic rats with hyperactive arrays; mechanisms involved in development of vasculitis in Sprague-Dawley rats by melhylxanlhines. *Mailing Add:* 5600 Fishers Lane Rockville MD 20857. *Fax:* 301-443-9284

**WHITEKER, MCELWYN D,** ANIMAL SCIENCE. *Current Pos:* LIVESTOCK EXTEN SPECIALIST, UNIV KY, 67-, PROF ANIMAL SCI, 69- *Personal Data:* b Harrison Co, Ky, Aug 4, 29; m 50; c 3. *Educ:* Univ Ky, BS, 51, MS, 52, PhD(nutrit, biochem), 61. *Prof Exp:* From asst prof to assoc prof animal sci, Iowa State Univ, 61-67. *Mem:* Am Soc Animal Sci. *Res:* Nutrition; animal breeding. *Mailing Add:* 317 Melbourne Way Lexington KY 40502

**WHITEKER, ROY ARCHIE,** GENERAL CHEMISTRY, ANALYTICAL CHEMISTRY. *Current Pos:* RETIRED. *Personal Data:* b Long Beach, Calif, Aug 22, 27; m 60, Jean MacLean; c Scott M. *Educ:* Univ Calif, Los Angeles, BS, 50, MS, 52; Calif Inst Technol, PhD(chem), 56. *Prof Exp:* Instr chem, Mass Inst Technol, 55-57; from asst prof to prof, Harvey Mudd Col, 57-74, actg chmn dept, 69-71; dep exec secy, Coun Int Exchange Scholars, 71-72, exec secy, 72-75, dir, 75-76; dean, Univ Pac, 76-89, prof, 76-92. *Concurrent Pos:* NSF sci fac fel, Royal Inst Technol, Sweden, 63-64; vis assoc prof, Univ Calif, Riverside, 67; assoc dir fel off, Nat Res Coun, 67-68; dir summer session, Claremont Grad Sch, 69-70. *Mem:* Am Chem Soc; Sigma Xi. *Res:* Electroanalytical chemistry; complex ions. *Mailing Add:* 3734 Portsmouth Circle N Stockton CA 95219-3843. *Fax:* 209-946-2607; *E-Mail:* rwhiteker@uop.edu

**WHITELAW, R(OBERT) L(ESLIE),** SYSTEMS DESIGN. *Current Pos:* prof, 66-88, EMER PROF MECH & NUCLEAR ENG, VA POLYTECH INST & STATE UNIV, 88- *Personal Data:* b S China, Apr 24, 17; nat US; m 42, Clara L Harper; c John, Richard & Edwin. *Educ:* Univ Toronto, MSc, 40. *Prof Exp:* Liaison officer, Brit Air Comn, DC, 40-43; sr tech officer, Winnipeg Test Sta, Nat Res Coun Can, 43-45; sr designer, A V Roe Can Ltd, 45-46; chief gas turbine res & develop, De Laval Co, NJ, 46-48; staff engr, Res Ctr, Babcock & Wilcox Co, 48-55, proj engr, NS Savannah, 55-60; spec asst to dir res, Allison Div, Gen Motors Corp, 60-66. *Concurrent Pos:* Assoc prof, US Naval Postgrad Sch, 63-64; vis expert, Int Atomic Energy Agency, Cent Atomic Bariloche, Arg, 81; pub policy expert, Heritage Found, 83-97. *Mem:* Am Soc Mech Engrs; Am Nuclear Soc; Am Soc Heating, Refrig & Air-Conditioning Engrs. *Res:* Thermodynamics; power cycles;

cable-suspended transportation systems; geothermal power; underwater vehicles; advanced reactor design; flywheel energy storage; gas turbines and jet propulsion; steam power generation; network analysis. *Mailing Add:* 111 Alleghany St Blacksburg VA 24060. *Fax:* 540-231-9100

**WHITELAW, WILLIAM ALBERT,** RESPIRATION. *Current Pos:* from asst prof to assoc prof, 76-85, PROF MED, UNIV CALGARY, 85- *Personal Data:* b Halifax, NS, Sept 3, 41; m 70; c 2. *Educ:* Univ Toronto, BSc, 64; McGill Univ, MDCM, 68, PhD(physiol), 78. *Prof Exp:* Intern, Montreal Gen Hosp, 68-69; resident med, Royal Victoria Hosp, Montreal, 69-71; res fel cardiol, Que Med Res Ctr, Makerere Univ, 71-72; res fel respiration, Can Med Res Ctr, Dept Physiol, McGill Univ, 72-75; clin fel chest med, McLaughlin Found, Edinburgh, 75-76. *Concurrent Pos:* Med med staff, Foothills Hosp, 76-; assoc ed-in-chief, Fr Rev Respiratory/Illness, 79-; chief, Div Pulmonary Med, Univ Calgary, 81-; mem, Comt Respiration, Can Med Res Ctr, 85-88; mem, Res Grant Rev Comt, Am Thoracic Soc, 85-87. *Mem:* Royal Col Physicians & Surgeons Can; Am Physiol Soc; Can Soc Clin Invest; AAAS; Can Thoracic Soc; Am Thoracic Soc. *Res:* Control of muscles of respiration in man and experimental mammals; mechanics of the diaphragm, dyspnea, breath holding and upper airway receptors. *Mailing Add:* Dept Med Heritage Med Res Bldg Univ Calgary Fac Med 3330 Hospital Dr NW Calgary AB T2N 1N4 Can. *Fax:* 403-270-8928

**WHITELEY, PHYLLIS ELLEN,** CELLULAR IMMUNOLOGY, ANIMAL MODELS. *Current Pos:* SR RES IMMUNOLOGIST AUTOIMMUNITY, MERCK, SHARP & DOHME, 89- *Personal Data:* b Manhasset, NY, Dec 4, 57; m 84; c 3. *Educ:* Washington Univ, St Louis, BA, 79, PhD(pharmacol), 84. *Prof Exp:* Fel immunol, Med Sch, Washington Univ, 84-87, res asst prof path, Jewish Hosp, 87-89. *Mem:* Am Asn Immunologists; Am Asn Women in Sci. *Res:* Development, initiation, and regulation of T lymphocytes in autoimmune diseases; develop therapeutics to inhibit T cell activation in diseases such as diabetes and rheumatoid arthritis. *Mailing Add:* Roche Bio Sci 3401 Hillview Ave MS R7-201 Rahway CA 07065

**WHITELEY, ROGER L,** MECHANICAL METALLURGY. *Current Pos:* Engr, supvr & asst sect mgr, Bethlehem Steel Corp, 53-64, sect mgr mech processing, 64-68, asst mgr forming & finishing res, 68-69, MGR CONTROL SYSTS RES, BETHLEHEM STEEL CORP, 69- *Personal Data:* b Trenton, NJ, Jan 30, 30. *Educ:* Rensselaer Polytech Inst, BS, 52, MS, 53. *Honors & Awards:* Grossman Award, Am Soc Metals, 60. *Mem:* Am Soc Metals; Am Inst Mining & Metall Engrs; Am Iron & Steel Engrs; Am Iron & Steel Inst; Am Inst Physics. *Res:* Sheet steel metallurgy, forming and fabrication of metals, fracture and fatigue; instrumentation and automation of steel processes, rolling and rolling mill analysis, systems analysis. *Mailing Add:* 6246 Woodfern Dr Emmaus PA 18049

**WHITEMAN, ALBERT LEON,** mathematics; deceased, see previous edition for last biography

**WHITEMAN, CHARLES E,** VETERINARY PATHOLOGY. *Current Pos:* RETIRED. *Personal Data:* b Eldred, Ill, Sept 28, 18; m 43; c 3. *Educ:* Kans State Col, DVM, 43; Iowa State Univ, PhD(vet path), 60; Am Col Vet Pathologists, dipl. *Prof Exp:* Assoc prof vet path, Mich State Univ, 60-61; assoc prof vet path, Colo State Univ, 61-71, prof, 71- *Mem:* Am Vet Med Asn; Am Asn Avian Pathologists. *Res:* Placental pathology; respiratory diseases; poultry diseases. *Mailing Add:* 2401 East Ridge Ct Ft Collins CO 80524

**WHITEMAN, ELDON EUGENE,** ZOOLOGY. *Current Pos:* prof biol, Spring Arbor Col, 46-80, chmn, Natural Sci Div, 63-71, dir, Environ Studies, 72-80, EMER PROF BIOL, SPRING ARBOR COL, 80- *Personal Data:* b Tarentum, Pa, May 5, 13; m 39; c 3. *Educ:* Greenville Col, BS, 36; Mich State Univ, MS, 41, PhD(zool), 65. *Prof Exp:* Asst dir, Kellogg Bird Sanctuary, 39-41. *Mem:* Nat Audubon Soc; Nat Wildlife Soc. *Res:* Development of a summer travel course for the college student in the area of environmental studies. *Mailing Add:* 170 Harmony Rd PO Box 136 Spring Arbor MI 49283

**WHITEMAN, JOE V,** ANIMAL BREEDING. *Current Pos:* From asst prof to assoc prof, 52-63, PROF ANIMAL SCI, OKLA STATE UNIV, 63- *Personal Data:* b Walkerville, Ill, July 13, 19; m 45; c 1. *Educ:* NMex State Univ, BS, 43; Okla State Univ, MS, 51, PhD, 52. *Mem:* AAAS; Am Soc Animal Sci; Biomet Soc. *Res:* Genetic and environmental factors governing the growth and development of meat animals. *Mailing Add:* 724 S Ridge Rd Stillwater OK 74074

**WHITEMAN, JOHN DAVID,** COATINGS RESEARCH & DEVELOPMENT. *Current Pos:* Sr res chemist analytical chem, Rohm & Haas Co, 72-75, sr res chemist pharmaceut, 75-76, sr res chemist pioneering coatings, 77-79, res sect mgr indust coatings, 80-84, res mgr Europe polymer, 84-87, res sect mgr pressure sensitive adhesives, 87-89, RES DEPT MGR LEATHER CHEM, ROHM & HAAS CO, 89- *Personal Data:* b Darby, Pa, May 24, 43; m 69; c 2. *Educ:* LaSalle Col, BA, 65; Univ Pa, PhD(phys chem), 71. *Concurrent Pos:* Fel, Dept Chem, Univ Pa, 71-72. *Mem:* Am Phys Soc; Am Chem Soc. *Res:* Energy band structure of molecular crystals; polymer physics; structure activity relationships in agricultural and pharmaceutical chemicals; organic coatings; analytical chemistry; high solids coatings; pressure sensitive adhesives; leather chemicals. *Mailing Add:* 24 Sassafras Dr Churchville PA 18966-1221

**WHITENBERG, DAVID CALVIN,** PLANT PHYSIOLOGY, BIOCHEMISTRY. *Current Pos:* asst prof, 65-67, assoc prof, 67-80, PROF BIOL, SOUTHWEST TEX STATE UNIV, 80- *Personal Data:* b Duffau, Tex, Feb 6, 31; div; c 1. *Educ:* Tex A&M Univ, BS, 57, MS, 59, PhD(plant physiol, biochem), 62. *Prof Exp:* Res plant physiologist, USDA, 61-65. *Mem:* Am Soc Plant Physiologists; Sigma Xi; Sci Res Soc. *Res:* Seed physiology and biochemistry. *Mailing Add:* Dept Biol Southwest Tex State Univ San Marcos TX 78666-4602

**WHITESELL, JAMES JUDD,** ENTOMOLOGY. *Current Pos:* assoc prof entom & zool, Dept Biol, 76-80, assoc prof, 81-84, PROF SCI EDUC & BIOL, SEC EDUC DEPT, VALDOSTA STATE COL, 84- *Personal Data:* b Philadelphia, Pa, Oct 14, 39; m 65; c 1. *Educ:* Dickinson Col, BS, 62; Univ Fla, MEd, 67, MS, 69, PhD(entom), 74. *Prof Exp:* Teacher sci, James S Rickards Jr High Sch, 63-67; res assoc lovebug res, Dept Entom, Univ Fla, 73-74; teacher biol & zool, Snead State Jr Col, Ala, 74-76, chmn, Sci & Math Div, 75-76. *Mem:* Sigma Xi; Entom Soc Am. *Res:* Insect behavioral ecology. *Mailing Add:* Educ Ctr Valdosta State Col Valdosta GA 31698

**WHITESELL, JAMES KELLER,** SYNTHETIC ORGANIC CHEMISTRY, MATERIALS CHEMISTRY. *Current Pos:* from asst prof to assoc prof, 73-87, PROF CHEM, UNIV TEX, AUSTIN, 87- *Personal Data:* b Philadelphia, Pa, Nov 2, 44; m 71, Mary A Fox; c Christopher & Robert. *Educ:* Pa State Univ, BS, 66; Harvard Univ, PhD(chem), 71. *Prof Exp:* Fel chem, Woodward Res Inst, 70-73. *Mem:* Am Chem Soc; AAAS. *Res:* Total synthesis of naturally occurring and theoretically interesting molecules; asymmetric induction; molecular recognition; crystal packing; materials chemistry; nonlinear optics. *Mailing Add:* Dept Chem Univ Tex Austin TX 78712. *Fax:* 512-471-7791; *E-Mail:* whitesell@mail.utexas.edu

**WHITESELL, WILLIAM JAMES,** THEORETICAL PHYSICS. *Current Pos:* from asst prof to assoc prof, 63-81, PROF PHYSICS, ANTIOCH COL, 81- *Personal Data:* b Newnan, Ga, Dec 23, 27; m 60, Corinne Brown; c David, Selwa, Elizabeth, Daniel & Janet. *Educ:* Univ SC, BS, 48; Purdue Univ, MS, 51, PhD(physics), 59. *Prof Exp:* From instr to asst prof physics, Brooklyn Col, 58-63. *Concurrent Pos:* Sr lectr, Victoria Univ, Wellington, 70-72. *Mailing Add:* Dept Physics Antioch Col Yellow Springs OH 45387

**WHITESIDE, BOBBY GENE,** FISHERIES, ICHTHYOLOGY. *Current Pos:* Assoc prof, 67-77, PROF BIOL, SOUTHWEST TEX STATE UNIV, 77- *Personal Data:* b Keota, Okla, June 16, 40; m 64; c 2. *Educ:* Okla State Univ, BS, 62, MS, 64, PhD(fisheries), 67. *Concurrent Pos:* Mem several sci orgn comts & off, 69-97; grantee, Tex Water Develop Bd, 72-73, 74 & 91-92, US Fish & Wildlife Serv, 76, 86-89 & 90-96, Am Fishing Tackle Mfrs Asn & Pro Bass Mag, 77, Tera Corp, 78 & 88, Tex Parks & Wildlife, 87-96, NSF, 88-89, Edwards Underground Water Dist, 91-92, Us Forest Serv, 91, 93 & 94, City of Ft Smith, Ark & Midwest Sci Ctr, 94, Trout Unlimited, 94 & 96, Guadalupe-Blanco River Authority, 95, Nat Biol Serv, 95 & 97; fel, City of New Braun, Tex, 91. *Mem:* Am Fisheries Soc. *Res:* Fisheries management; population dynamics; ecology; numerous papers presented at professional meetings. *Mailing Add:* Dept Biol Southwest Tex State Univ San Marcos TX 78666-4602

**WHITESIDE, CHARLES HUGH,** ANALYTICAL CHEMISTRY, ENVIRONMENTAL SCIENCES. *Current Pos:* PRES, ANA-LAB CORP, 67- *Personal Data:* b Grapevine, Tex, June 25, 32; m 56; c 2. *Educ:* Tex A&M Univ, BS, 53, MS, 58, PhD(biochem), 60. *Prof Exp:* Robert A Welch Found res fel, Dept Biochem & Nutrit, Tex A&M Univ, 60-61; sr scientist, Mead Johnson & Co, 61-64; teacher chem, Kilgore Col, 64-67, chmn dept, 67-71. *Mem:* Am Chem Soc; Am Oil Chemists' Soc; Am Soc Testing Mat. *Res:* Water quality and waste water technology; animal nutrition; solar energy. *Mailing Add:* ANA Lab Corp PO Box 9000 Kilgore TX 75662-9000

**WHITESIDE, EUGENE PERRY,** soil science; deceased, see previous edition for last biography

**WHITESIDE, JACK OLIVER,** PLANT PATHOLOGY. *Current Pos:* assoc plant pathologist, 68-73, prof plant path, 73-90, EMER PROF PLANT PATH, CITRUS EXP STA, 90- *Personal Data:* b Barnstaple, Eng, June 5, 28; m 51; c 2. *Educ:* Univ London, BSc, 48, PhD(plant physiol), 53. *Prof Exp:* Plant physiologist, Ministry Agr, Zimbabwe, Africa, 48-53, from plant pathologist to chief plant pathologist, 53-67. *Mem:* Int Soc Citricult; Am Phytopath Soc. *Res:* Identification and control of plant diseases present in Zimbabwe; behavior and control of fungus diseases of citrus in Florida. *Mailing Add:* Citrus Res & Educ Ctr Univ Fla Lake Alfred FL 33850

**WHITESIDE, JAMES BROOKS,** COMPOSITE MATERIALS, STRUCTURAL MECHANICS. *Current Pos:* Sr engr struct mech, Grumman Aerospace Corp, 68-74, group leader composite structures, 74-79, res lab head appl mech, 79-94, PRIN ENGR, MAT & PROCESSING SCI, NORTHROP GRUMMAN CORP, 94- *Personal Data:* b Tyler, Tex, Jan 5, 42; m 66; c 3. *Educ:* Tulane Univ, BS, 64; Sheffield Univ, PhD(mech eng), 68. *Concurrent Pos:* Mem, Fed Aviation Admin Panel Independent Experts Struct, 81-; prof engr, 73- *Mem:* Soc Advan Mat Processing Eng; assoc fel Am Inst Aeronaut & Astronaut. *Res:* Design allowables and stress analysis of composites; moisture diffusion in polymers; fatigue and fracture; experimental stress analysis; mechanical and environmental behavior of composite materials; materials and processes simulation. *Mailing Add:* A01-26 Northrop Grumman Corp Bethpage NY 11714-3582

**WHITESIDE, MELBOURNE C,** AQUATIC ECOLOGY. *Current Pos:* from asst prof to assoc prof, 72-80, PROF ZOOL, UNIV TENN, KNOXVILLE, 80- *Personal Data:* b Washington, DC, Dec 16, 37; m 61; c 2. *Educ:* Willamette Univ, BA, 62; Ariz State Univ, MS, 64; Ind Univ, Bloomington, PhD(zool), 68. *Prof Exp:* Res fel limnol, Univ Minn, 68-69; asst prof ecol & limnol, Calif State Univ, Fullerton, 69-72. *Mem:* Am Soc Limnol & Oceanog; Ecol Soc Am. *Res:* Paleolimnology; community ecology and population dynamics of aquatic organisms; sampling problems in aquatic environments. *Mailing Add:* Dept Biol Univ Minn Duluth MN 55812-2496

**WHITESIDE, THERESA L,** IMMUNOLOGY, IMMUNOPATHOLOGY. *Current Pos:* from asst prof to assoc prof, 73-89, from assoc dir to dir clin immunopath, 73-88, PROF PATH, MED SCH, UNIV PITTSBURGH, 89-, PROF OTOLARYNG, 93- *Personal Data:* b Katowice, Poland, Mar 10, 39; US citizen; m 61, 83, Thomas H Nimick Jr; c George A III. *Educ:* Columbia Univ, BS, 62, MA, 64, PhD(microbiol), 67; Am Bd Med Lab Immunol, dipl, 79. *Prof Exp:* NIH fel, Sch Med, NY Univ, 67-69, lectr microbiol & assoc res scientist, 69-70; res assoc ophthal, Col Physicians & Surgeons, Columbia Univ, 70-73. *Concurrent Pos:* NIH spec fel ophthal, Col Physicians & Surgeons, Columbia Univ, 72-73; Fogarty Int sr fel, Ludwig Inst, Lausanne, Switz, 84-85; mem & dir, Immunol Monitoring Lab, Pittsburgh Cancer Inst, 85- *Mem:* AAAS; Am Asn Immunologists; Am Asn Pathologists; Am Soc Microbiol; Am Asn Cancer Res; Clin Immunol Soc. *Res:* Immunotherapy of cancer; tumor immunology; tumor infiltrating lymphocytes in human tumors; lymphocyte membrane receptors; clinical immunology; cytokines. *Mailing Add:* PO Box 672 Pittsburgh PA 15230. *Fax:* 412-624-0264

**WHITESIDE, WESLEY C,** botany, for more information see previous edition

**WHITESIDES, GEORGE MCCLELLAND,** ORGANIC CHEMISTRY. *Current Pos:* PROF CHEM, HARVARD UNIV, 82- *Personal Data:* b Louisville, Ky, Aug 3, 39; m 69, Barbara Breastele; c George T & Benjamin H. *Educ:* Harvard Univ, AB, 60; Calif Inst Technol, PhD(chem), 64. *Prof Exp:* From asst prof to assoc prof, Mass Inst Technol, 63-74, prof chem, 74-82. *Mem:* Nat Acad Sci; Am Chem Soc; Am Acad Arts & Sci; fel AAAS. *Res:* Mechanisms and structure; use of enzymes in organic synthesis; applied biochemistry; structure-property relations in organic materials science; heterogeneous catalysis. *Mailing Add:* Chem Dept Harvard Univ Cambridge MA 02138

**WHITESIDES, JOHN LINDSEY, JR,** FLUID MECHANICS, AERONAUTICS. *Current Pos:* Asst res prof mech eng, 68-74, assoc prof, 74-80, PROF ENG & APPL SCI, GEORGE WASHINGTON UNIV, 80-; ASSOC DIR, JOINT INST ADVAN FLIGHT SCI, LANGLEY RES CTR, NASA, 84- *Personal Data:* b San Antonio, Tex, Feb 27, 43; m 94, Andrea M Chavez; c Lisa D & John G. *Educ:* Univ Tex, Austin, BS, 65, PhD(aerospace eng), 68. *Honors & Awards:* Distinguished Pub Serv Medal, NASA, 93; Malina Medal, Int Astronaut Fedn, 95. *Concurrent Pos:* Coordr, George Washington Univ-NASA Prog, Langley Res Ctr, NASA, 68-75; asst dir, George Washington Univ, 75-84. *Mem:* Assoc fel Am Inst Aeronaut & Astronaut; Soc Eng Sci; Am Soc Eng Educ; AAAS. *Res:* Analytical methods in fluid mechanics and aeronautics; graduate engineering education. *Mailing Add:* Langley Res Ctr J1AFS MS 269 NASA Hampton VA 23665

**WHITESITT, JOHN D,** MATH EDUCATION. *Current Pos:* CHAIR, DEPT MATH, SOUTHERN ORE STATE UNIV, 81- *Personal Data:* b Bozeman, Mont, Aug 24, 47. *Educ:* Mont State Univ, BS, 69, MS, 71, DEd, 81. *Mem:* Nat Coun Teachers Math; Math Asn Am. *Res:* Math education. *Mailing Add:* 156 W Nevada St Ashland OR 97520

**WHITESITT, JOHN ELDON,** MATHEMATICS. *Current Pos:* RETIRED. *Personal Data:* b Stevensville, Mont, Jan 15, 22; m 44; c 3. *Educ:* Mont State Univ, AB, 43; Univ Ill, AM, 49, PhD(math), 54. *Prof Exp:* From instr to prof math, Mont State Univ, 46-84, head dept, 61-66. *Mem:* Am Math Soc; Math Asn Am. *Res:* Ring theory; linear algebra; Boolean algebra. *Mailing Add:* 3316 NE Avery Newport OR 97365

**WHITEWAY, STIRLING GIDDINGS,** PHYSICAL CHEMISTRY, INORGANIC CHEMISTRY. *Current Pos:* RETIRED. *Personal Data:* b Stellarton, NS, May 17, 27; m 52, Ruth MacKenzie; c Malcolm S & D Lorne. *Educ:* Dalhousie Univ, BSc, 47, dipl, 48, MSc, 49; McGill Univ, PhD(phys chem), 53. *Prof Exp:* Fel photochem, Pure Chem Div, Atlantic Res Lab, Nat Res Coun Can, 52-53, from asst res officer to prin res officer, 53-83. *Concurrent Pos:* Spec lectr, Dalhousie Univ, 54-55; adj prof, Tech Univ NS, 84- *Mem:* Chem Inst Can; Can Inst Mining & Metall; Sigma Xi. *Res:* Chemistry of high temperature reactions; chemistry of coal; ceramics. *Mailing Add:* 20 Day Ave Dartmouth NS B2W 2V6 Can

**WHITFIELD, CAROL F(AYE),** PHYSIOLOGY, MOLECULAR BIOLOGY. *Current Pos:* from res assoc to asst prof, 68-83, ASSOC PROF PHYSIOL, MILTON S HERSHEY MED CTR, COL MED, PA STATE UNIV, HERSHEY, 83-, DIR, MULTIDISCIPLINE LABS, 88-, CO-DIR, PROB-BASED LEARNING, 92- *Personal Data:* b Altoona, Pa, May 14, 39; div. *Educ:* Juniata Col, BS, 61; Syracuse Univ, MS, 64; George Washington Univ, PhD(physiol), 69. *Prof Exp:* Teaching asst zool, Syracuse Univ, 61-63. *Concurrent Pos:* Mem bd trustees, Juniata Col, 83-86; prin investr, Nat Heart, Lung & Blood Inst, NIH & Am Heart Asn, 77- *Mem:* Biophys Soc; Am Physiol Soc; Am Soc Cell Biol. *Res:* Sickle cell anemia; red cell membrane structure, regulation of carrier-mediated sugar transport in erythrocytes and muscles; research in undergraduate medical education. *Mailing Add:* Dept Physiol Milton S Hershey Med Ctr Pa State Univ PO Box 850 Hershey PA 17033-0850. *Fax:* 717-531-7667; *E-Mail:* cwhitfield@cmp.hmc.psu.edu

**WHITFIELD, CAROLYN DICKSON,** BIOCHEMISTRY. *Current Pos:* FAC, COL MED, HOWARD UNIV, WASHINGTON, DC. *Personal Data:* b Indianapolis, Ind, Aug 21, 41; m 65. *Educ:* Wellesley Col, AB, 63; Univ Chicago, MS, 65; George Washington Univ, PhD(biochem), 69. *Prof Exp:* Wellcome Found fel, Univ Edinburgh, 69-70; Am Cancer Soc fel, Med Sch, Univ Mich, Ann Arbor, 70-72, asst res biol chemist, 72-74, scholar human genetics, 74-76, asst prof, Dept Biol Chem, Med Sch, Univ Mich, Ann Arbor, 76- *Concurrent Pos:* Estab investr, Am Heart Asn, 77-82. *Mem:* Am Soc Biol Chemists. *Res:* Mechanism of action of flavoproteins; isolation and biochemical characterization of Chinese hamster cell mutants in tissue culture; methionine biosynthesis. *Mailing Add:* Dept Biol Chem Col Med Howard Univ Washington DC 20059-0001. *Fax:* 202-667-1686

**WHITFIELD, GARY HUGH,** entomology, for more information see previous edition

**WHITFIELD, GEORGE BUCKMASTER, JR,** BIOCHEMISTRY. *Current Pos:* RETIRED. *Personal Data:* b Newark, NJ, Dec 4, 23; m 44, Joan Root; c Carol, Ann & George III. *Educ:* Cornell Col, BA, 46; Univ Ill, MS, 51, PhD(chem), 53. *Prof Exp:* Jr res scientist, Upjohn Co, 47-51, sr res scientist, 53-59, sect head microbiol, 59-66, mgr, 66-68, infectious dis res mgr, 68-78, coor prod group adminr, Infectious Dis & Cardiovasc Dis, 78-85. *Mem:* Am Chem Soc; Am Soc Microbiol; Sigma Xi. *Res:* Isolation and characterization of new antibiotics and antitumor agents; paper chromatography; microbiological assay; tissue culture; in vitro, in vivo and clinical evaluation of new antibiotics, antifungal and antiparasitic agents. *Mailing Add:* 1706 William Ave Henderson NV 89014-0153

**WHITFIELD, HARVEY JAMES, JR,** MOLECULAR BIOLOGY. *Current Pos:* asst prof, 70-75, ASSOC PROF BIOCHEM, MED SCH, UNIV MICH, 75-; MED STAFF FEL, BIOL PSYCH BR, NIMH. *Personal Data:* b Chicago, Ill, Apr 10, 40; m 65. *Educ:* Univ Ill, Urbana, BS, 61; Univ Ill Col Med, MD, 64. *Prof Exp:* Intern, Res & Educ Hosp, Chicago, 64-65; staff asst molecular biol, NIH, 65-69; USPHS spec fel, Med Res Coun Microbial Genetics Unit, Univ Edinburgh, 69-70. *Concurrent Pos:* USPHS grant, Univ Mich, Ann Arbor, 71- *Mem:* AAAS; Am Soc Biol Chemists; Am Soc Microbiol; Genetics Soc Am. *Res:* Replication and segregation of episomal DNA; microbial genetics. *Mailing Add:* Dept Psychiat & Biochem Univ Ill Rm 325 W 1601 W Taylor St M/C912 Chicago IL 60612-4397. *Fax:* 312-996-4358

**WHITFIELD, JACK D,** aeronautical engineering, gas dynamics; deceased, see previous edition for last biography

**WHITFIELD, JAMES F,** CELL PHYSIOLOGY, CANCER. *Current Pos:* head, Cell Physiol Sect, Radiation Biol Div, Nat Res Coun Can, 65-72, head, Cell Physiol Group, 72-86, head, Cellular Oncol Group, Biol Sci Div, 86-90, head, Cell Systs Sect, Inst Biol Sci, 90-94, head, Tissue Reg Group, 94-97, PROJ MGR OSTEOPOROSIS, NAT RES COUN CAN, 97- *Personal Data:* b Sarnia, Ont, July 1, 31; m 51, Barbara; c 4. *Educ:* McGill Univ, BSc, 51; Univ Western Ont, MSc, 52, PhD(bact, immunol), 55. *Prof Exp:* Res officer bact & viral genetics, Atomic Energy Can Ltd, 55-58, res officer cellular radiobiol, 58-62; sect chief, Europ Joint Res Ctr, Europ AEC, Italy, 62-65. *Mem:* Tissue Cult Asn; Am Soc Cell Biol; NY Acad Sci; AAAS; Am Asn Cancer Res. *Res:* Control of cell proliferation; in vivo and in vitro effects of calcium, hormones, cyclic nucleotides and oncogenes; protein science; parathyroid hormone fragments and treatment for osteoporosis. *Mailing Add:* Inst Biol Sci Nat Res Coun Can Ottawa ON K1A 0R6 Can. *Fax:* 613-941-4475; *E-Mail:* jim.whitfield@nrc.ca

**WHITFIELD, JOHN HOWARD MERVYN,** MATHEMATICS. *Current Pos:* From asst prof to assoc prof, Lakehead Univ, 65-82, chmn dept, 72-75, dean arts & sci, 86-90, PROF MATH, LAKEHEAD UNIV, 82-, VPRES ACAD, 91- *Personal Data:* b Thessalon, Ont, Sept 11, 39; m 60, Diane Huntsman; c Karen, Megan, Brian & Evan. *Educ:* Abilene Christian Col, BA, 61; Tex Christian Univ, MA, 62; Case Inst Technol, PhD(math), 66. *Concurrent Pos:* Vis scholar, Univ Wash, 71-72; vis prof, Univ Waterloo, 78-79, Univ Canadianne France, 93. *Mem:* Am Math Soc; Math Asn Am; Can Math Soc; Sigma Xi. *Res:* Functional analysis; differentiable functions and norms; geometry of Banach spaces. *Mailing Add:* Dept Math Sci Lakehead Univ Thunder Bay ON P7B 5E1 Can. *Fax:* 807-343-8075; *E-Mail:* jwhitfield@deans___row.lakeheadu.ca

**WHITFIELD, RICHARD GEORGE,** PHYSICAL & ANALYTICAL CHEMISTRY. *Current Pos:* SR RES CHEMIST ANALYSIS, OLIN CHEM GROUP, 78- *Personal Data:* b Philadelphia, Pa, Nov 11, 51; m 73; c 1. *Educ:* Glassboro State Col, BA, 73; Mich State Univ, PhD(chem), 77. *Mem:* Am Chem Soc; Sigma Xi. *Res:* Analytical applications of infrared, raman, ultraviolet and visible spectroscopy; instrumental and method development; investigations of the solid state via vibrational spectroscopy; office systems; analytical chemistry as well as materials support. *Mailing Add:* Pharmacia Upjohn 4851-259-175 700 Portage Rd Kalamazoo MI 49001

**WHITFILL, DONALD LEE,** PHYSICAL INORGANIC CHEMISTRY. *Current Pos:* LEADER, RESERVOIR ROCK PROPERTIES, GEOSCI & RESERVOIR RES, 93- *Personal Data:* b Madill, Okla, Mar 13, 39; m 60, Bernice Jacks; c Charles R & Donya L. *Educ:* Southeastern State Col, BS, 61; Univ Okla, PhD(chem), 66. *Honors & Awards:* Distinguished Lectr, Soc Petrol Engrs. *Prof Exp:* Instr chem, Univ Okla, 66-67; res scientist, Plant Foods Res Div, Continental Oil Co, 67-70, res scientist, 70-78, sr res scientist,

78-79; res group leader, Conoco Inc, 79-88, sect mgr, Prod Res Div, 88-93. *Mem:* Soc Petrol Engrs. *Res:* Transition metal chemistry; electrochemistry; drilling fluid and cement technology; drilling and completions; reservoir and enhanced recovery. *Mailing Add:* 1700 Cedar Lane Ponca City OK 74604

**WHITFORD, ALBERT EDWARD,** ASTROPHYSICS. *Current Pos:* astronr & dir, 58-68, astronr & prof, 68-73, EMER PROF ASTRON, LICK OBSERV, UNIV CALIF, SANTA CRUZ, 73- *Personal Data:* b Milton, Wis, Oct 22, 05; m 37; c 3. *Educ:* Milton Col, BA, 26; Univ Wis, MA, 28, PhD(physics), 32. *Prof Exp:* Asst, Washburn Observ, Univ Wis, 32-33; Nat Res Coun fel, Mt Wilson Observ & Calif Inst Technol, 33-35; res assoc astron, Washburn Observ, Univ Wis, 35-38, asst prof astrophys, 38-46, assoc prof astron, 46-48, prof & dir observ, 48-58. *Concurrent Pos:* Mem staff, Radiation Lab, Mass Inst Technol, 41-46; vis astronr, Univ Wis, 96- *Mem:* Nat Acad Sci; Am Astron Soc (vpres, 65-67, pres, 67-70); Am Acad Arts & Sci. *Res:* Photoelectric instrumentation; interstellar absorption; spectrophotometry of stars and galaxies; stellar population of galaxies. *Mailing Add:* 110 S Henry St No 1408 Madison WI 53703

**WHITFORD, GARY M,** TOXICOLOGY, PHYSIOLOGY. *Current Pos:* from asst prof to prof, 72-85, REGENTS PROF ORAL BIOL, MED COL GA, 85- *Personal Data:* b Gouveneur, NY, Mar 9, 37; m 85; c 3. *Educ:* Univ Rochester, BS, 65, MS, 69, PhD(toxicol), 72; Med Col Ga, DMD, 75. *Honors & Awards:* H Trendley Dean Award, 86; Rolex Prize, Europ Orgn Caries Res, 92. *Prof Exp:* Instr oral biol, NJ Dent Sch, 71-72. *Mem:* Sigma Xi; Soc Exp Biol Med; Int Asn Dent Res; Europ Orgn Caries Res; Am Physiol Soc. *Res:* Metabolism, biological effects and toxicology of fluoride. *Mailing Add:* Dept Oral Biol Med Col Ga Augusta GA 30912-1129

**WHITFORD, HOWARD WAYNE,** VETERINARY MICROBIOLOGY. *Current Pos:* bacteriologist, Diag Serv, 74-87, HEAD, DIAG MICROBIOL, TEX VET MED DIAG LAB, 87- *Personal Data:* b Benavides, Tex, Apr 6, 40; m 65, Peggy R Jordan; c Jeffrey S & Darci C. *Educ:* Tex A&M Univ, BS, 63, DVM, 64, PhD(vet microbiol), 76; Am Col Vet Microbiologists, dipl, 73. *Prof Exp:* Vet lab officer res, US Army Med Unit, Frederick, Md, 65-68; vet officer, Rocky Mountain Lab, Nat Inst Allergy & Infectious Dis, USPHS, 68-70; NIH fel vet microbiol, Sch Vet Med, Tex A&M Univ, 70-71, from grad asst to instr, 71-74. *Concurrent Pos:* Mem, Sheep & Goat Comt, US Animal Health Asn, 74-; consult, Stauffer Chem Co, Tex Facil, Houston, 80-82; mem, Mycoplasmosis Comt, Am Asn Vet Lab Diagnosticians, 81-, chmn, 84-90; chmn, Small Ruminant Pract Comt, Tex Vet Med Asn, 84-86 & 88-90, Peer Asst Comt, 87- *Mem:* Am Col Vet Microbiologists; Am Asn Vet Lab Diagnosticians; Am Vet Med Asn; US Animal Health Asn; Am Asn Small Ruminant Practrs. *Res:* Bacteriologic diagnostic techniques; infectious diseases of sheep and goats; pathogenic bacteriology and mycology; epidemiology of anthrax. *Mailing Add:* Drawer 3040 College Station TX 77841. *Fax:* 409-845-1794; *E-Mail:* h-whitford@tamu.edu

**WHITFORD, LARRY ALSTON,** botany; deceased; see previous edition for last biography

**WHITFORD, WALTER GEORGE,** ECOLOGY. *Current Pos:* SR RES ECOLOGIST, US ENVIRON PROTECTION AGENCY, 93- *Personal Data:* b Providence, RI, June 12, 36; m 59, 69; c 3. *Educ:* Univ RI, BA, 61, PhD(zool), 64. *Prof Exp:* From asst prof to prof biol, NMex State Univ, 64-93. *Concurrent Pos:* Ecol consult, Pub Serv Co NMex, 71- & Union Oil Co Calif, 74-; ed, Ecol Soc Am, 75-79, Biol Fertil Soils; prin investr, Journada Long Term Ecol Res Prog, 81-92. *Mem:* Ecol Soc Am; Herpetologists' League. *Res:* Desert ecology; ecology of social insects; soil biology; plant ecology. *Mailing Add:* Jornada Exp Range PO Box 30001 Dept 3JER NMex State Univ Las Cruces NM 88003

**WHITFORD-STARK, JAMES LESLIE,** REMOTE SENSING-PLANETS, VOLCANOLOGY. *Current Pos:* from asst prof to assoc prof, 82-87, chmn teaching, Geol Dept, 87-92, PROF, SUL ROSS STATE UNIV, 93- *Personal Data:* b London, Eng, Sept 28, 48; m 83, Seta Z Choubaralian; c Edward & Amy S. *Educ:* Keele Univ, BA, 71; Univ Lancaster, MS, 75; Brown Univ, PhD(geol), 80. *Prof Exp:* Field geologist res, Radiogeol & Rare Minerals Unit, Inst Geol Sci, London, 69; res asst, Dept Environ Sci, Univ Lancaster, 71-76; vis asst prof teaching, Geol Dept, Univ Mo, Columbia, 80-82. *Concurrent Pos:* Consult, Open Univ, Eng, 75, Volcres, 80-; prin investr, Planetary Geol Prog, NASA, 81, Galilean Satellite Mapping Prog, 82-86; mem, Bd Sci, Chihuahua Desert Res Inst, 87-; dir, NSF China-US Coop Res Proj, 88-90. *Mem:* Fel Geol Soc Am; Am Geophys Union; Int Asn Volcanology & Chem Earth's Interior; fel Geol Soc London. *Res:* Mapping and remote sensing of volcanic materials on all of the terrestrial planets; specializing in the volcanic products on the Moon, Io, and mainland Asia. *Mailing Add:* Geol Dept Sul Ross State Univ Alpine TX 79832. *Fax:* 915-837-8692; *E-Mail:* jlwstark@ sulross-1.sulross.edu

**WHITHAM, GERALD BERESFORD,** FLUID MECHANICS. *Current Pos:* PROF APPL MATH, CALIF INST TECHNOL, 62- *Personal Data:* b Halifax, Eng, Dec 13, 27; m 51; c 3. *Educ:* Univ Manchester, BSc, 48, MSc, 49, PhD, 53. *Honors & Awards:* Wiener Prizer Appl Math, 80. *Prof Exp:* Res assoc, Inst Math Sci, NY Univ, 51-53; lectr math, Univ Manchester, 53-56; assoc prof, Inst Math Sci, NY Univ, 56-59; prof, Mass Inst Technol, 59-62. *Mem:* Fel Am Acad Arts & Sci; fel Royal Soc. *Res:* Fluid dynamics; wave propagation. *Mailing Add:* Dept Appl Math Calif Inst Technol Firestone 217-50 Pasadena CA 91125-0001

**WHITING, ALLEN R,** NONDESTRUCTIVE TESTING. *Current Pos:* asst res engr, Dept Mat Eng, Southwest Res Inst, 62-64, res engr, 64-67, sr res engr, 67-69, mgr appl eng, 69-70, mgr appl eng, Dept Spec Eng Serv, 70-72, asst dir, 72-74, dir, Dept Res & Eng, 74-75, dir, Dept Energy Serv, 75-78, exec dir, Qual Assurance Systs & Eng Div, 78-87, DIR, SYSTS ENG & INTEGRATION, CTR NUCLEAR WASTE REGULATORY ANALYSIS, SOUTHWEST RES INST, 87- *Personal Data:* US citizen. *Educ:* Univ Tex, BS, 61. *Prof Exp:* X-ray lab technician, Univ Tex, 61; spray dept supvr, Aztec Tile Co, 61-62. *Mem:* Am Soc Nondestructive Testing; Am Soc Testing & Mat; Am Soc Mech Engrs. *Res:* Nondestructive testing including X- and gamma-radiography, ultrasonics, magnetic particle and penetrants as they are applied to solve industry problems and also in the research and development area. *Mailing Add:* 48 Dodge Boerne TX 78006

**WHITING, ANNE MARGARET,** vertebrate anatomy, embryology, for more information see previous edition

**WHITING, FRANK M,** NUTRITION, BIOCHEMISTRY. *Current Pos:* res asst, Univ Ariz, 65-71, asst prof & asst animal scientist, 71-76, assoc prof & assoc animal scientist, 76-81, PROF ANIMAL SCI & ANIMAL SCIENTIST, UNIV ARIZ, 81- *Personal Data:* b Tucson, Ariz, Dec 5, 32; m 58; c 2. *Educ:* Univ Ariz, BS, 56, MS, 68, PhD(agr biochem, nutrit), 71. *Prof Exp:* Field man qual control, United Dairymen Ariz, 56-60, res technician pesticide residues, 60-65. *Mem:* Am Dairy Sci Asn; Sigma Xi. *Res:* Pesticide chemistry; ruminant nutrition; lipid metabolism; pesticide residues in feeds and animal products. *Mailing Add:* Dept Animal Sci Univ Ariz Tucson AZ 85721-0001

**WHITING, JOHN DALE, JR,** FORENSIC TOXICOLOGY, DRUG ABUSE DETECTION. *Current Pos:* PRES, TOXICHEM LABS, INC, 85- *Personal Data:* b New Castle, Pa, Mar 23, 47. *Educ:* Westminister Col, BS, 69; Duke Univ, PhD(biochem), 74. *Prof Exp:* Res assoc biol, Princeton Univ, 74-77; res assoc biochem, George Washington Univ, 77-79; res chemist toxicol, Armed Forces Inst Path, 79-85. *Concurrent Pos:* Mem, Subcomt Chromatographic Methods, Nat Comn Clin Lab Studies, 82- *Mem:* AAAS; Am Chem Soc; Am Acad Forensic Sci. *Res:* Isolation and identification of drugs and drug metabolites from tissues using high performance liquid chromatography, gas chromatography, gel chromatography and mass spectrometry and Fourier transform infrared; development of analytical procedures to detect tetrahydrocannabinol and its metabolites and other substances of abuse in biological fluids and tissues. *Mailing Add:* Hewlett Packard Co 2850 Centerville Rd Wilmington DE 19808

**WHITING, PETER JOHN,** HYDROLOGY, WATER RESOURCES. *Current Pos:* ASST PROF GEOL SCI, CASE WESTERN RES UNIV, 91- *Personal Data:* b Washington, DC, Sept 16, 60; m. *Educ:* Carleton Col, BA, 82; Univ Calif, Berkeley, PhD(geol), 90. *Prof Exp:* Geomorphologist, EA Eng, Sci & Technol, 90-91. *Concurrent Pos:* Consult, 90-; vis prof, Univ Genoa, Italy, 90. *Mem:* Geol Soc Am; Am Geophys Union. *Res:* Stream channels - the processes controlling their form; the effect of land use on such channels and their role in transporting water sediment and pollutants. *Mailing Add:* Dept Geol Sci Case Western Res Univ Cleveland OH 44106. *E-Mail:* pjw5@po.cwru.edu

**WHITING, R(OBERT) L(OUIS),** PETROLEUM ENGINEERING. *Current Pos:* assoc prof, 46-50, head dept, 46-76, PROF PETROL ENG, TEX A&M UNIV, 50- *Personal Data:* b San Antonio, Tex, Feb 25, 18; m 44; c 3. *Educ:* Univ Tex, BS, 39, MS, 42. *Honors & Awards:* Mineral Indust Educ Award, Am Inst Mech Engrs, 73. *Prof Exp:* Instr petrol eng, Univ Tex, 39-43; assoc prof, Mo Sch Mines, 45-46. *Concurrent Pos:* Int consult, US Fed Govt, FTC, var petrol co & foreign govts, 46-; dir, Tex Petrol Res Comt, 51-76. *Mem:* Am Inst Mining, Metall & Petrol Engrs; Am Asn Univ Professors; Am Petrol Inst; Am Asn Eng Educ; Sigma Xi. *Res:* Drilling, production, transportation and marketing in petroleum and natural gas. *Mailing Add:* Dept Petrol Eng Tex A&M Univ College Station TX 77843-3116

**WHITING, RICHARD CHARLES,** MODELING FOODBORNE MICROBIAL PATHOGENS, MEAT PRODUCTS & PROCESSING. *Current Pos:* res food technologist, Meat Lab, 77-87, RES FOOD TECHNOLOGIST, MICROBIOL FOOD SAFETY, USDA AGR RES SERV, 87- *Personal Data:* b Madison, Wis, Sept 15, 46; m 76, Joan L Underwood; c Caitlin. *Educ:* Univ Wis-Madison, BS, 68; Univ BC, MS, 70; Ore State Univ, PhD(food sci), 74. *Honors & Awards:* Award Merit for Excellence in Technol Transfer, Fed Lab Consortium, 93. *Prof Exp:* Res fel, Dept Food Sci, Univ BC, Vancouver, 74-77. *Mem:* Inst Food Technologists; Am Meat Sci Asn. *Res:* Develop mathematical models for the growth, death and survival of food borne microbial pathogens with emphasis on meat products; production and microbiology of low-salt meat products. *Mailing Add:* 519 E Moreland Ave Glenside PA 19308. *Fax:* 215-233-6581; *E-Mail:* rwhiting@arserrc.gov

**WHITING, SYLVIA MARGARET ANDERSON,** PSYCHIATRIC MENTAL HEALTH NURSING. *Current Pos:* INTERIM DEPT CHAIR & PROF NURSING, SC STATE UNIV, 92- *Personal Data:* b Lewiston, Maine; m 49, Howard; c Judith, Brenda, Steven & Brian. *Educ:* Med Univ SC, BSN, 72; Tex Women's Univ, MS, 76; Univ SC, PhD(nursing), 92. *Prof Exp:* Clin nurse, Med Univ SC, 68-71, from instr to assoc prof, Col Nursing, 73-82; independent pract, People Helpers, 77-85; instr, Orangeburg-Calhoun Tech Col, 89-92. *Concurrent Pos:* Independent ment health nurse specialist, 85- *Mem:* Am Nurses Asn; Soc Educ & Res Psychiat Nursing; Nat League Nursing; Asn Child & Adolescent Psychiat Nursing. *Res:* Human behavior; dependence, interdependence; effects of college-age mentors on fifth and sixth graders over 5 years. *Mailing Add:* 109 Forest Ridge Ct Goose Creek SC 29445. *Fax:* 803-533-3868; *E-Mail:* smtpswhiting@scsu.edu

**WHITLA, WILLIAM ALEXANDER,** COMPUTER ASSISTED INSTRUCTION. *Current Pos:* asst prof, 67-75, ASSOC PROF CHEM, MT ALLISON UNIV, 75- *Personal Data:* b Galt, Ont, Oct 16, 38; m 64; c 3. *Educ:* McMaster Univ, BSc, 60, PhD(inorg chem), 65. *Prof Exp:* Nat Res Coun overseas fel x-ray crystallog, Oxford Univ, 65-66; teaching fel, Univ BC, 66-67. *Mem:* Chem Inst Can. *Res:* Development of computer programs for chemistry instruction. *Mailing Add:* Dept Chem Mt Allison Univ Sackville NB E0A 3C0 Can. *Fax:* 506-364-2313; *E-Mail:* awhitla@mta.ca

**WHITLATCH, ROBERT BRUCE,** MARINE & POPULATION ECOLOGY. *Current Pos:* asst prof biol, 77-83, assoc prof marine sci, 83-89, PROF, UNIV CONN, 90- *Personal Data:* b Boise, Idaho, July 18, 48. *Educ:* Univ Utah, BS, 70; Univ of the Pac, MS, 72; Univ Chicago, PhD(evolutionary biol), 76. *Prof Exp:* Scholar biol, Woods Hole Oceanog Inst, 76-77. *Concurrent Pos:* Vis scientist, Neth Inst Sea Res, 84-85; sr fel, Nat Res Coun, 85-86. *Mem:* AAAS; Am Inst Biol Sci; Ecol Soc Am; Estuarine Res Fedn. *Res:* Population community ecology of marine benthic systems; role of disturbance agents on community structure; resource partitioning in deposit feeding organisms. *Mailing Add:* Dept Marine Sci Univ Conn U-6 438 Whitney Storrs Mansfield CT 06269-0002

**WHITLEY, JAMES R,** BIOCHEMISTRY, NUTRITION. *Current Pos:* SUPT FISHERIES RES, MO DEPT CONSERV, 62- *Personal Data:* b Jamesport, Mo, Apr 21, 21; m 42. *Educ:* Univ Mo, AB, 42, MS, 47, PhD(agr chem), 52. *Prof Exp:* Pvt herbicide bus, 52-62. *Mem:* Am Fisheries Soc; Weed Sci Soc Am; Water Pollution Control Fedn. *Res:* Ecology of fish and other aquatic organisms. *Mailing Add:* 303 S Glenwood Columbia MO 65203

**WHITLEY, LARRY STEPHEN,** ENVIRONMENTAL BIOLOGY. *Current Pos:* RETIRED. *Personal Data:* b Mattoon, Ill, Jan 30, 37; m 58; c 3. *Educ:* Eastern Ill Univ, BS, 58; Purdue Univ, MS, 60, PhD(ecol), 63. *Prof Exp:* Instr environ biol, Purdue Univ, 63; from asst prof to prof zool, Eastern Ill Univ, 63-94. *Concurrent Pos:* NIH res grants, 65-67; Fed Water Qual Admin grant, Dept Interior, 69-71. *Mem:* AAAS; Ecol Soc Am; Soc Syst Zool. *Res:* Physiology and systematics of tubificid worms; biology of polluted aquatic ecosystems and the tolerance mechanisms of aquatic organisms. *Mailing Add:* 1926 Ashby Dr Charleston IL 61920

**WHITLEY, NANCY O'NEIL,** RADIOLOGY. *Current Pos:* PROF RADIOL, UNIV MD SCH MED, 78- *Personal Data:* b Winston-Salem, NC, Feb 21, 32; m 58; c 2. *Educ:* Bowman Gray Sch Med, MD, 57. *Prof Exp:* Intern, Jefferson Davis Hosp, Houston, Tex, 57-58; cardiovasc trainee, Bowman Gray Sch Med, 59-61; physician, Med Dept, Western Elec Co, 63-66; resident radiol, Bowman Gray Sch Med, 66-69, from instr to assoc prof, 69-78. *Concurrent Pos:* Fel cardiol, Bowman Gray Sch Med, 58-59. *Mem:* Am Roentgenol Ray Soc; AMA; Asn Univ Radiologists; Radiol Soc NAm; Am Col Radiol; fel Am Col Radiol. *Res:* Techniques and procedures of angiography. *Mailing Add:* Univ Md Dept Radiol 22 S Greene St Baltimore MD 21201-1544

**WHITLEY, WILLIAM THURMON,** MATHEMATICS. *Current Pos:* assoc prof, 79-82, PROF, UNIV NEW HAVEN, 79- *Personal Data:* b De Land, Fla, Oct 24, 41; m 68, Wilma Yates; c Andrew. *Educ:* Stetson Univ, BS, 63; Univ NC, Chapel Hill, MA, 66; Va Polytech Inst & State Univ, PhD(math), 69. *Prof Exp:* Instr math, Va Polytech Inst & State Univ, 69-70; assoc prof math, Marshall Univ, 70-79. *Mem:* Am Math Soc; Math Asn Am. *Res:* Deleted products of topological spaces; rings of continuous real-valued functions; collegiate mathematics education. *Mailing Add:* Dept Math Univ New Haven West Haven CT 06516-1999

**WHITLOCK, CHARLES HENRY,** CIVIL & AERONAUTICAL ENGINEERING. *Current Pos:* Aerospace res engr flight mechanics, Langley Res Ctr, NASA, 61-70, head, Syst Dynamics Sect, 70-72, asst head, Marine Analysis Sect, 72-74, head, Data Analysis Sect, 74-76, head, Wave Modeling Group, 74-77, HEAD SPECTRAL SIGNATURE & OPTICAL MODELING GROUP, MARINE ENVIRON, LANGLEY RES CTR, NASA, 76- *Personal Data:* b Richmond, Va, Mar 24, 39; m 62; c 2. *Educ:* Univ Va, BAE, 61, MAE, 65; Col William & Mary, MBA, 70; Old Dominion Univ, PhD(civil eng), 77. *Concurrent Pos:* Instr math, Hampton Inst, 66-67. *Mem:* Am Soc Civil Eng; Am Soc Photogram. *Res:* Remote sensing including optical modeling of spectral signals. *Mailing Add:* 2933 Brook Blvd Quinton VA 23141

**WHITLOCK, DAVID GRAHAM,** NEUROANATOMY, NEUROPHYSIOLOGY. *Current Pos:* PROF ANAT & CHMN DEPT, UNIV COLO MED CTR, DENVER, 67- *Personal Data:* b Portland, Ore, Aug 26, 24; m 48; c 3. *Educ:* Ore State Col, BS, 46; Univ Ore, MD, 49, PhD, 51. *Prof Exp:* Instr anat, Med Sch, Univ Ore, 50-51; asst prof, Univ Calif, Los Angeles, 51-54; from asst prof to prof, State Univ NY Upstate Med Ctr, 55-67, chmn dept, 66-67. *Concurrent Pos:* Fulbright res scholar, Inst Physiol, Pisa, Italy, 51-52; consult, US Sci Exhibit, 61 & Neurol Study Sect, USPHS, 60-64; chmn, Neurol B Study Sect, Nat Inst Neurol Dis & Blindness, 66-67. *Mem:* Am Asn Anatomists; Int Brain Res Orgn. *Res:* Anatomy and physiology of peripheral and central nervous system pathways. *Mailing Add:* Dept Anat B111 Univ Colo Med Sch 4200 E Ninth Ave Denver CO 80262

**WHITLOCK, GAYLORD PURCELL,** AGRICULTURE, BIOCHEMISTRY. *Current Pos:* prog leader family & consumer sci, Agr Exten Serv, Univ Calif, Berkeley, 61-74, agriculturist coop exten & vpres agr sci, 73-74, exten nutritionist, 74-80, EMER EXTEN NUTRITIONIST, UNIV CALIF, BERKELEY, 80- *Personal Data:* b Mt Vernon, Ill, July 7, 17; m 41, Margaret Baumbach; c Margay Jo & Pamela Kay (Nicholson). *Educ:* Southern Ill Univ, BEd, 39; Pa State Col, MS, 41, PhD(agr, biochem), 42. *Prof Exp:* Res asst, Iowa State Col, 43-46, asst prof, 46-47; specialist nutrit serv, Merck & Co, Inc, 47-56; dir health ed, Nat Dairy Coun, 56-61. *Mem:* Am Chem Soc; Soc Nutrit Educ; NY Acad Sci; Sigma Xi. *Res:* Vitamins; human and animal nutrition; foods. *Mailing Add:* 1641 Rockville Rd Suisun CA 94585

**WHITLOCK, JOHN HENDRICK,** veterinary parasitology, parasitology; deceased, see previous edition for last biography

**WHITLOCK, L RONALD,** ANALYTICAL CHEMISTRY, POLYMER CHEMISTRY. *Current Pos:* res assoc, 72-85, lab head, Imaging Mats Res Labs, 86-92, UNIT DIR POLYMER CHARACTERIZATION, ANALYTICAL TECHNOL, EASTMAN KODAK CO, 92- *Personal Data:* b Canton, Pa, July 6, 44; m 68; c 2. *Educ:* Pa State Univ, BS, 66; Univ Mass, PhD(analytical chem), 71. *Prof Exp:* Fel polymer sci, Univ Mass, 70-72. *Mem:* Am Chem Soc; Sigma Xi. *Res:* Development of new methods for chemical analysis of polymers using modern analytical instruments; polymer characterization. *Mailing Add:* 4 Cavan Way Pittsford NY 14534

**WHITLOCK, LAPSLEY CRAIG,** EXPERIMENTAL NUCLEAR PHYSICS, SPECTROSCOPY. *Current Pos:* From asst prof to assoc prof, 69-81, PROF PHYSICS, MISS COL, 81-, HEAD DEPT, 70- *Personal Data:* b Lebanon, Ky, Aug 31, 42; m 62; c 3. *Educ:* Georgetown Col, BS, 64; Vanderbilt Univ, PhD, 69. *Honors & Awards:* Pegram Award, Southeast Sect Am Phys Soc. *Mem:* Am Phys Soc; Am Asn Physics Teachers. *Res:* Gamma ray spectroscopy in decay of radioactive nuclides. *Mailing Add:* Dept Physics Miss Col Clinton MS 39058-4004

**WHITLOCK, RICHARD T,** THEORETICAL PHYSICS. *Current Pos:* ASSOC PROF PHYSICS, UNIV NC, GREENSBORO, 67-, DIR, RESIDENTIAL COL, 77- *Personal Data:* b Columbus, Ohio, July 8, 31; m 60; c 1. *Educ:* Capital Univ, BS, 58; Western Res Univ, MS, 61, PhD(physics), 63. *Prof Exp:* Asst physics, Western Res Univ, 58-60, instr, 62-63; from asst prof to assoc prof, Thiel Col, 63-67. *Mem:* Am Asn Physics Teachers. *Res:* Many-body boson problem with applications to the theory of liquid helium; two-fluid hydrodynamics with applications to the theory of liquid helium; light and sound interactions. *Mailing Add:* 6748 Hickory Hammock Bradenton FL 34207

**WHITLOCK, ROBERT HENRY,** VETERINARY MEDICINE, INFECTIOUS DISEASES. *Current Pos:* chief large animal med, 78-88, prof med, 83-92, ASSOC PROF, UNIV PA VET COL, 93- *Personal Data:* b Canton, Pa, July 28, 41; m 63, Marion E Long; c Christopher, Craig & Karin. *Educ:* Cornell Univ, DVM, 65, PhD(nutrit path), 70. *Hon Degrees:* MA, Univ Pa, 77. *Prof Exp:* Intern vet med, NY State Vet Col, Cornell Univ, 65-67, NIH spec fel, 69-70, asst prof, 70-76; assoc prof vet med, Col Vet Med, Univ Ga, 76-78. *Concurrent Pos:* Mem, Nat Acad Pract Vet Med; chair, Johne's Comt, US Animal Health Asn; mem, Liaison Comt, Pa Vet Med Asn. *Mem:* Comp Gastroenterol Soc; Am Soc Vet Clin Path; Am Vet Med Asn; Am Col Vet Internal Med; Am Asn Bovine Practrs; Nat Acad Practr. *Res:* Pathogenesis of infectious metabolic diseases in domestic animals; paratuberculosis in cattle; botulism in animals. *Mailing Add:* New Boltan Ctr Univ Pa Vet Col Kennett Square PA 19348

**WHITLOW, GRAHAM ANTHONY,** METALLURGY. *Current Pos:* RETIRED. *Personal Data:* b Cardiff, Wales, May 12, 38; m 62; c 2. *Educ:* Univ Manchester, BScTech, 59; Univ Wales, PhD(metall), 62. *Prof Exp:* Sci officer metall, Atomic Weapons Res Estab, UK Atomic Energy Authority, 62-67; fel engr, Advan Reactors Div, Westinghouse Elec Corp, 67-79, fel engr, Metall Sci Dept & Develop Ctr, 79-94. *Mem:* Am Inst Mining, Metall & Petrol Engrs; Metall Soc; Am Inst Mech Engrs; Nat Asn Corrosion Engrs. *Res:* Energy materials development; effects of corrosive environments on high temperature materials; turbine materials development. *Mailing Add:* 4505 Dell Ct Murrysville PA 15668

**WHITLOW, LON WEIDNER,** DAIRY CATTLE NUTRITION & MANAGEMENT. *Current Pos:* from asst prof to assoc prof, 79-89, PROF DAIRY SCI, NC STATE UNIV, RALEIGH, 89- *Personal Data:* b Scottsville, Ky, Aug 26, 50; m 75, Karen Lockwood; c Zackary, Micah & Caleb. *Educ:* Univ Ky, BS, 72; Univ Fla, MS, 74; Univ Wis, PhD(dairy sci), 79. *Prof Exp:* Res asst, Univ Fla, 72-74, asst exten dairyman, 74-75; res asst, Univ Wis, 74-79. *Mem:* Am Dairy Sci Asn; Am Soc Animal Sci. *Res:* The optimum feeding and nutrition of dairy cattle; effects of mycotoxins on dairy cattle health and productivity; dairy cattle nutrition, toxicology, and management. *Mailing Add:* Animal Sci NC State Univ PO Box 7621 Raleigh NC 27695-0001. *Fax:* 919-515-7780; *E-Mail:* lwhitlow@wolf.ces.ncsu.edu

**WHITLOW, MARC DAVID,** PROTEIN ENGINEERING OF ANTIBODIES, CRYSTALLOGRAPHY OF MACROMOLECULES. *Current Pos:* HEAD BIOPHYS, BERLEX BIOSCI, 94- *Personal Data:* b Seattle, Wash, Apr 20, 56; m 90, Reetta Raag; c Nicholai. *Educ:* Univ Wash, BS, 78; Boston Univ, PhD(biochem), 86. *Prof Exp:* Scientist, Genex Corp, 87-89, dir protein eng, 89-91; group leader crystallog, Enzon Inc, 91-92, assoc dir protein eng, 92-94. *Mem:* Am Crystallog Asn. *Res:* Protein engineering of antibodies, particular single-chain Fvs and multivalent Fvs; protein crystallography of xylose isomerase, subtilisin, DHFR, Fabs, single-chain Fvs, protein G and alpha-purothionin; structure based drug design. *Mailing Add:* Berlex Biosci 15049 San Pablo Ave PO Box 4099 Richmond CA 94804. *Fax:* 510-262-7844; *E-Mail:* marc_whitlow@berlex.com

**WHITMAN, ALAN B,** CONTINUUM MECHANICS, MECHANICS. *Current Pos:* res asst biomech, Wayne State Univ, 66-68, asst prof mech, 68-71, assoc prof, 71-79, PROF MECH, WAYNE STATE UNIV, 79- *Personal Data:* b Joliet, Ill, Apr 7, 41. *Educ:* Univ Ill, Urbana, BS, 63; Univ Minn, Minneapolis, MS, 66, PhD(eng mech), 68. *Prof Exp:* Res asst mech, Univ Minn, 63-64; engr, Honeywell, Inc, 64-65; res asst mech, Univ Minn, 65-66. *Concurrent Pos:* NSF initiation grant, Wayne State Univ, 69-70, res grants, 71-73 & 74-77; res fel, Univ Man, 78-79. *Mem:* Soc Eng Sci; Am Acad Mech. *Res:* Theories of rods and shells, stability theory of continuous systems. *Mailing Add:* Dept Mech Eng Wayne State Univ 5050 Anthony Wayne Dr Detroit MI 48202

**WHITMAN, ALAN M,** COHERENCE THEORY. *Current Pos:* PROF & CHMN, DEPT MECH ENG, VILLANOVA UNIV, 88- *Personal Data:* b Philadelphia, Pa, Jan 26, 37; m 78; c 3. *Educ:* Univ Pa, BSME, 58, MSME, 59, PhD(mech eng), 66. *Prof Exp:* Sr res engr, Power Transmission Div, Gen Elec Co, 65-67; asst prof mech eng, Univ Pa, 67-72, assoc prof, 72-80; assoc prof, Tel Aviv Univ, 80-83, prof interdisciplinary studies, Sch Eng, 83-88. *Mem:* Fel Optical Soc Am; Am Soc Mech Engrs. *Res:* Wave propagation in random and layered media; rail vehicle dynamic stability; structural acoustics; fluid-solid interaction. *Mailing Add:* Dept Mech Eng Villanova Univ Villanova PA 19085-1672

**WHITMAN, ANDREW PETER,** NON-RIEMANNIAN GEOMETRY. *Current Pos:* FAC, ARIZ STATE UNIV. *Personal Data:* b Detroit, Mich, Feb 28, 26. *Educ:* Tulane Univ, BS, 45; Cath Univ, MS, 58, PhD(math), 61; Woodstock Col, Md, STL, 64. *Prof Exp:* Instr civil eng, Tulane Univ, 46-51; asst prof math, Loyola Univ, La, 65-66, actg chmn dept, 66-67; from asst prof to assoc prof math, Univ Houston, 67-74; assoc prof, Cath Univ Rio de Janeiro, Brazil, 74-89; sr lectr, Col Holly Cross, 89- *Concurrent Pos:* NSF res grant, 66-68. *Mem:* Am Math Soc; Math Asn Am; Soc Brasileira Math; Sigma Xi. *Res:* Differential topology and geometry; harmonic maps in non-riemannian manifolds. *Mailing Add:* Jesuit Community Vatican Observ 2017 E Lee St Tucson AZ 85719-4340

**WHITMAN, DONALD RAY,** THEORETICAL CHEMISTRY, PHYSICAL CHEMISTRY. *Current Pos:* From asst prof to assoc prof, 57-70, assoc vpres, 72-74, VPRES, CASE WESTERN RES UNIV, 74-, PROF PHYS CHEM, 70- *Personal Data:* b Ft Wayne, Ind, Nov 7, 31; div; c 2. *Educ:* Case Western Res Univ, BS, 53; Yale Univ, PhD(phys chem), 57. *Mem:* Am Phys Soc; AAAS. *Res:* Molecular quantum mechanics. *Mailing Add:* Dept Chem Case Western Res Univ Cleveland OH 44106

**WHITMAN, GERALD MARTIN,** ANTENNAS, WAVE PROPAGATION. *Current Pos:* from asst prof to prof elec eng, NJ Inst Technol, 70-85, asst vpres acad affairs, Grad Studies & Res, 85-87, dir, Ctr Microwave & Lightwave Eng, 85-96, ASSOC CHMN GRAD STUDIES, NJ INST TECHNOL, 96- *Educ:* Queens Col, BS, 63; Columbia Univ, BSEE, 63; Polytech Inst NY, MS, 67, PhD(electroph), 69. *Honors & Awards:* Region I Award, Inst Elec & Electronics Engrs, 87. *Prof Exp:* Fel electroph, Dept Elec Eng, Polytech Inst NY, 69-70. *Concurrent Pos:* Consult, Cecom, US Army Ft Monmouth, 73-, Microwave Res Inst, Polytech Inst, NY, 79, County Newark, 84-85, County Franklin Lakes, 87 & Bellcore, NJ, 88; deleg, NATO Advan Study Inst, Univ East Anglia, Eng, 79; vis prof, Dept Elec Eng, Polytech Inst NY, 80-81. *Mem:* Inst Elec & Electronics Engrs; Sigma Xi. *Res:* Electromagnetics: scattering from periodic surfaces, radiation by integrated dielectric waveguides and antenna devices, transmission and compression of signals in plasma media, scattering in random media using transport theory, microstrip antennas, numerical methods and propagation in buildings; rough surface scattering. *Mailing Add:* Dept Elec & Comput Eng NJ Inst Technol University Heights Newark NJ 07102

**WHITMAN, PATRICK GENE,** DYNAMICS OF LONG PERIOD COMETS, GALACTIC OSCILLATIONS OF COMETS. *Current Pos:* from asst prof to assoc prof, 79-92, HEAD, DEPT PHYSICS, UNIV SOUTHWESTERN LA, 92-, PROF, 94-, DIR, ACADIANA RES LAB, 94- *Personal Data:* div; c Jeremy & Leslie. *Educ:* Lamar Univ, BS, 70, MS, 71; Univ NTex, PhD(theoret physics), 78. *Prof Exp:* Asst prof physics, Benedictine Col, 78. *Mem:* Int Soc Optical Eng. *Res:* Instrumental in demonstrating the major cause of the flux of long period comets is due to the galactic tide and not passing stars; demonstrated the variability in the flux of comets with a period that agrees with the cratering rate of the largest craters. *Mailing Add:* Univ Southwestern La USL Box 44210 Lafayette LA 70504-4210. *Fax:* 318-482-6699; *E-Mail:* pgwhiteman@usl.edu

**WHITMAN, PHILIP MARTIN,** MATHEMATICS. *Current Pos:* prof, 61-86, chmn dept, 61-67, EMER PROF MATH, RI COL, 87- *Personal Data:* b Pittsburgh, Pa, Dec 23, 16. *Educ:* Haverford Col, BS, 37; Harvard Univ, AM, 38, PhD(math), 41. *Prof Exp:* Instr math, Harvard Univ, 38-41 & Univ Pa, 41-44; scientist, Los Alamos Sci Lab, Univ Calif, 44-46; asst prof math, Tufts Col, 46-48; mathematician, Appl Physics Lab, Johns Hopkins Univ, 48-61. *Concurrent Pos:* Consult, Weapons Systs Eval Group, Off Secy Defense, 51-55; Parsons fel, Johns Hopkins Univ, 58-59; consult, Opers Eval Group, Off Chief Naval Opers, 60-61. *Mem:* AAAS; Am Math Soc; Opers Res Soc Am; Math Asn Am; Nat Coun Teachers Math. *Res:* Lattice theory; operations research; authored college algebra and trigonometry texts. *Mailing Add:* 1010 Waltham St D427 Nursing Ctr Lexington MA 02173-8044

**WHITMAN, ROBERT V(AN DUYNE),** EARTHQUAKE ENGINEERING, GEOTECHNICAL ENGINEERING. *Current Pos:* res engr, 51-53, from asst prof to prof, 53-97, EMER PROF CIVIL ENG, MASS INST TECHNOL, 97- *Personal Data:* b Pittsburgh, Pa, Feb 2, 28; m 54; c 2. *Educ:* Swarthmore Col, BS, 48; Mass Inst Technol, SM, 49, ScD(civil eng), 51. *Hon Degrees:* Dr, Swarthmore Col, 90. *Honors & Awards:* Huber Res Prize, Am Soc Civil Engrs, 64; Terzaghi lectr, 81; Terzaghi Award, 87. *Concurrent Pos:* Consult, govt & indust, 54-; engr, Stanford Res Inst, 63-64; mem, Soil Dynamics Panel, Comt Earthquake Eng Res, Nat Acad Eng, 66-68; chmn, Risk Assessment Comt, Appl Technol Coun, 74-77, Panel Local Effects, Int Workshop Strong Motion Instrument Arrays, 78 & Seismic Loads Subcomt, Am Nat Stand Inst, 78-85; vis scholar, Cambridge Univ, Eng, 76-77; mem, Earthquake Eng Res Inst, dir, 78-81 & 84-88; mem, Comt Nat Disasters, Nat Res Coun, 80-83, Comt Seismol, 84-87 & Comt Earthquake Eng, 85-; vis prof & sr fel, Norweg Geotech Inst, Univ Calif, Davis, 84- *Mem:* Nat Acad Eng; Am Soc Civil Engrs; Seismol Soc Am; Int Soc Soil Mech & Found Engrs; Earthquake Eng Res Inst (vpres, 79-81, pres 85-87). *Res:* Soil mechanics, especially dynamic problems; author of various publications. *Mailing Add:* Dept Civil & Environ Eng Rm 374 Mass Inst Technol Cambridge MA 02139

**WHITMAN, ROLLIN LAWRENCE,** ELECTRICAL ENGINEERING, COMPUTER SCIENCE. *Current Pos:* SECT LEADER, SIGNAL PROCESS & RADIOGRAPHIC IMAGE ANALYSIS, LOS ALAMOS NAT LAB, 76- *Personal Data:* b Pittsfield, Mass, Aug 25, 47; m 70; c 4. *Educ:* Univ Wis, BSEE, 70; Univ Colo, MSEE, 74. *Honors & Awards:* Award Excellence, Nuclear Weapons Prog, 86, Res & Develop 100 Award, 88. *Prof Exp:* Engr sci programmer, Martin Marietta Co, 70-76. *Mem:* Inst Elec & Electronics Engrs. *Res:* Computer image processing and signal analysis in laser fusion target inspection, modeling reactor safety coolant problems; two-dimensional digital filtering on both large scale computers and interactive minicomputer systems; 1D and 2D fitting by modeling and incorporation of system modulation transfer function; computed tomography; radiographic deblurring; 2D point spread function estimation of a high energy x-ray source; quantitative radiography edges and density. *Mailing Add:* Los Alamos Nat Lab PO Box 1663 MS P 940 Los Alamos NM 87545

**WHITMAN, ROY MILTON,** PSYCHIATRY. *Current Pos:* assoc prof, Col Med, Univ Cincinnati, 57-67, actg chmn dept, 80-83, chmn dept, 83-89, PROF PSYCHIAT, COL MED, UNIV CINCINNATI, 67- *Personal Data:* b New York, NY, June 16, 25; m 68, Ester Guttman; c Joy, Bruce, Laura, Rebecca & Michael. *Educ:* Ind Univ, BS, 44, MD, 46. *Honors & Awards:* Alexander Prize, Chicago Inst Psychoanal. *Prof Exp:* Intern, Kings Co Hosp, 46-47; resident psychiat, Duke Hosp, 47-48; from instr to asst prof, Univ Chicago, 52-54; from asst prof to assoc prof neurol & psychiat, Med Sch, Northwestern Univ, 54-57, assoc prof, 57. *Concurrent Pos:* USPHS fel, Clins, Univ Chicago, 50-52; chief neurol & psychiat, Vet Admin Res Hosp, Chicago, Ill, 54-57; consult, Vet Admin Hosp, Cincinnati, Ohio, 57-, Ill State Psychiat Inst, 63-68, Cent Clin, Cincinnati, Ohio & Vet Admin Res Hosp, Chicago; clinician, Cincinnati Univ Hosp. *Mem:* Am Psychiat Asn; Am Psychoanal Asn; Int Psychoanal Asn; Sigma Xi. *Res:* Psychophysiology of dreaming; sex research; psychoanalytic methods; techniques in psychoanalysis; psychosomatic medicine; leadership and organizational behavior. *Mailing Add:* 7137 Fair Oaks Dr Cincinnati OH 45237

**WHITMAN, VICTOR,** PEDIATRIC CARDIOLOGY. *Current Pos:* CARDIOLOGIST, MIAMI CHILDREN'S HOSP, FLA, 86- *Educ:* Univ Tex, MD, 64. *Mailing Add:* Dept Pediat Cardiol Miami Children's Hosp 6125 SW 31st St Miami FL 33155-3098

**WHITMARSH, JOHN,** BIOPHYSICS, BIOENERGETICS. *Current Pos:* PROF BIOPHYS & PLANT BIOL, UNIV ILL, 81-; PLANT PHYSIOLOGIST, AGR RES SERV, USDA. *Personal Data:* b San Diego, Calif, Apr 11, 46; m 80, Barbara Koch; c Jason, Magan, Ian, Holden, Amelia & Colin. *Educ:* Harvard Univ, MA, 70, PhD(physics), 75. *Prof Exp:* Fel biophys, Ctr Nuclear Studies, Saclay, France, 74-75; fel biophys, Purdue Univ, 75-79; asst prof, Queens's Univ, Can, 80. *Mem:* Biophys Soc; Am Soc Plant Physiol. *Res:* Investigate the function and regulation of the photosynthetic apparatus of plants and its response to environmental stress. *Mailing Add:* Dept Plant Biol 197 PABL Univ Ill 1201 W Gregory Dr Urbana IL 61801-3838. *Fax:* 217-244-4419

**WHITMER, JEFFREY THOMAS,** CARDIOVASCULAR CLINICAL TRIALS, ONCOLOGY PROMOTIONAL COMPLIANCE. *Current Pos:* from asst dir to assoc dir clin trials, 88-91, dir med develop metab, 91-92, DIR, REGULATORY AFFAIRS/PROMO COMPLIANCE, BRISTOL-MYERS SQUIBB CO, 92- *Personal Data:* b Mar 22, 48; m 75, Kyra M Riegle. *Educ:* Pa State Univ, BS, PhD(physiol), 74, MD, 77. *Honors & Awards:* Physician Scientists Award, Am Heart Asn. *Prof Exp:* Assoc prof pediat, Children's Hosp Med Ctr, 82-88. *Mem:* Am Heart Asn; Am Physiol Soc; Int Soc Heart Res; Cardiac Muscle Soc; Regulatory Affairs Prof Soc; Drug Info Asn. *Res:* Use of the isolated experimental animal heart perfusion technique to study hemodynamics and relate this to intracellular metabolic regulation in health and disease, as well as during the ischemia of cardioplegic arrest in immature and mature hearts. *Mailing Add:* Bristol-Myers Squibb Co PO Box 4500 Princeton NJ 08543-4500. *E-Mail:* jwhitmer@usccmail.bms. com

**WHITMER, JOHN CHARLES,** PHYSICAL CHEMISTRY. *Current Pos:* from asst prof to assoc prof, 69-76, PROF CHEM, WESTERN WASH UNIV, 76- *Personal Data:* b Kingfisher, Okla, Jan 28, 39; m 67, Kathryn Steenson; c Charles & David. *Educ:* Univ Rochester, BS, 60; Univ Mich, MS,

62, PhD(chem), 65. *Prof Exp:* Asst prof chem, Western Wash Univ, 65-66; lectr, Univ EAfrica, 67-69. *Concurrent Pos:* Vis prof, Inst Phys Chem, Univ Trondheim, Norway, 76-77 & Univ York, Eng, 90. *Mem:* AAAS; Am Chem Soc. *Res:* Molecular dynamics and structure. *Mailing Add:* Dept Chem Western Wash Univ Bellingham WA 98225. *E-Mail:* whitmer@chem.wwu.edu

**WHITMER, ROBERT MOREHOUSE,** PHYSICS, ELECTRICAL ENGINEERING. *Current Pos:* CONSULT, 73- *Personal Data:* b Battle Creek, Mich, June 14, 08; m 36, 51; c 2. *Educ:* Univ Mich, BA, 28, MA, 34, PhD(physics), 38. *Prof Exp:* Mem staff, Bell Tel Labs, Inc, 28-32; mem fac, Amherst Col, 32-33; engr, Philco Radio & TV Corp, Pa, 35-36; physicist, Hercules Powder Co, 36; instr physics, Purdue Univ, 37-41; mem staff, Radiation Lab, Mass Inst Technol, 41-46; prof physics, Rensselaer Polytech Inst, 46-56; sr staff physicist, TRW Systs, 56-73. *Concurrent Pos:* Consult, USAF, 52-53; mem, Security Resources Panel, Off Defense Mobilization, 57; mem, Reentry Body Identification Group, Off Secy Defense, 58. *Mem:* AAAS; Am Phys Soc; sr mem Inst Elec & Electronics Engrs. *Res:* Electromagnetics; wave propagation; electromagnetic shielding; military systems and policy studies. *Mailing Add:* 724 Tenth St Manhattan Beach CA 90266-5806

**WHITMIRE, CARRIE ELLA,** BACTERIOLOGY, TOXICOLOGY. *Current Pos:* RETIRED. *Personal Data:* b Electra, Tex, Oct 17, 26. *Educ:* Univ Tex, BA, 46; Univ Kans, MA, 53, PhD(bact), 55. *Prof Exp:* Bacteriologist, Parkland Hosp, Dallas, Tex, 46-47, Vet Admin Hosp, 47-48 & US Army Chem Ctr, Ft Detrick, Md, 48-52; asst virologist, Univ Kans, 52-55; assoc scientist, Ortho Res Found, NJ, 55-61; proj supvr, Merck Sharp & Dohme Biol Div, Pa, 61-64; tech asst, Winthrop Labs, Biol, NY, 64-67; proj dir & viral oncologist, Microbiol Assocs, Inc, 67-75, dir, Dept Exp Oncol, 75-78; toxicologist, Nat Cancer Inst, 79-81; toxicologist, Qual Assurance, GLP Compliance, Toxicol Res Testing Prog Br, Nat Toxicol Prog, Nat Inst Environ Health Sci, 81-87. *Mem:* Am Soc Microbiol; Soc Toxicol. *Res:* Medical human, animal and oncology virology and bacteriology; cancer and toxicology research. *Mailing Add:* Grove Crabtree Valley Apts 6110 Grove Crest Ct No 412 Raleigh NC 27613

**WHITMIRE, KENTON HERBERT,** CLUSTER CHEMISTRY, MAIN GROUP ELEMENT CHEMISTRY. *Current Pos:* from asst prof to assoc prof, 82-94, PROF CHEM, RICE UNIV, 94- *Personal Data:* b Roanoke, Va, July, 20, 55; m 81; c 2. *Educ:* Roanoke Col, BS, 77; Northwestern Univ, MS, 78, PhD, 82. *Prof Exp:* Fel chem, Cambridge Univ, 81-82. *Concurrent Pos:* NATO fel & Alexander von Humboldt res fel; assoc ed, Organometallics, 96- *Mem:* Sigma Xi; Am Chem Soc. *Mailing Add:* Dept Chem Rice Univ 6100 Main St Houston TX 77005-1892. *Fax:* 713-737-5652; *E-Mail:* whitmir@rice.edu

**WHITMORE, BRADLEY CHARLES,** GALACTIC STRUCTURE, GALACTIC DYNAMICS. *Current Pos:* asst astronr, 83-95, PROF, SPACE TELESCOPE SCI INST, 95- *Personal Data:* b Minneapolis, Minn, Jan 14, 53; m 77; c 2. *Educ:* Univ Mich, BS, 75, MS, 77, PhD(astron), 80. *Prof Exp:* Instr, Univ Mich, 80; Carnegie fel astron, Dept Terrestrial Magnetism, Carnegie Inst, Washington, DC, 80-82; asst prof, Ariz State Univ, 82-83. *Mem:* Am Astron Soc; Int Astron Union. *Res:* Structure, dynamics, and evolution of galaxies; comparison of the dynamics of elliptical galaxies with the spheroidal component of spiral galaxies; observations of polar ring galaxies. *Mailing Add:* Space Telescope Sci Inst 3700 San Martin Dr Baltimore MD 21218

**WHITMORE, DONALD HERBERT, JR,** COMPARATIVE PHYSIOLOGY. *Current Pos:* asst prof, 73-79, assoc prof, 79-91, PROF BIOL, UNIV TEX, ARLINGTON, 91- *Personal Data:* b Buffalo, NY, May 6, 44; m 70, Elaine Peters; c Andrew & Laura. *Educ:* Ind Univ, BA, 66; Northwestern Univ, PhD(biol sci), 71. *Prof Exp:* NIH fel insect physiol, Northwestern Univ, 71-73. *Concurrent Pos:* Dir, UTA for Fish Studies; assoc ed, Trans Am Fisheries Soc. *Mem:* Sigma Xi; Am Fisheries Soc; Am Soc Zoologists. *Res:* The role of environmental influences on the physiology and biochemistry of animals, particularly how animals adapt to environmental stress. *Mailing Add:* 2723 Westridge Dr Arlington TX 76012. *Fax:* 817-273-2855; *E-Mail:* whitmore@albert.uta.edu

**WHITMORE, EDWARD HUGH,** geometry; deceased, see previous edition for last biography

**WHITMORE, FRANK CLIFFORD, JR,** SYSTEMATICS OF FOSSIL CETACEA, TERTIARY PALEOGEOGRAPHY. *Current Pos:* geologist, 44-84, EMER SCIENTIST, US GEOL SURV, 84- *Personal Data:* b Cambridge, Mass, Nov 17, 15; m 39, Martha Kremers; c Geoffrey, John, Katherine & Susan. *Educ:* Amherst Col, AB, 38; Pa State Univ, MS, 39; Harvard, AM, 41, PhD, 42. *Honors & Awards:* Medal of Freedom, 46; Meritorious Serv Award, US Dept Interior, 81; Arnold Guyot Mem Award, Nat Geog Soc, 93. *Prof Exp:* Teaching fel, Harvard Univ, 40-42; instr, RI State Col, 42-44. *Concurrent Pos:* Sci consult, US Army, 45-46; chief, Mil Geol Br, 46-59; res geologist, paleontol, 59-84; res assoc, Smithsonian Inst, 67-; vchmn, Comt Res & Explor, Nat Geol Soc, 70-96. *Mem:* Fel Geol Soc Am; fel AAAS; hon mem Soc Vert Paleont; Paleont Soc; Soc Marine Mammal. *Res:* Endocranial anatomy of Oligocene Artiodactyla; Pleistocene mammal faunas of Kentucky and Tertiary mammals of the Atlantic and Gulf Coastal Plain and Panama; whale evolution and biogeography; Daleocene vertebrates of Saudi Arabia. *Mailing Add:* Nat Mus Natural Hist Smithsonian Inst NHB 137 Washington DC 20560. *Fax:* 202-343-8620

**WHITMORE, FRANK WILLIAM,** PLANT PHYSIOLOGY, BIOCHEMISTRY. *Current Pos:* RETIRED. *Personal Data:* b Ponca City, Okla, May 15, 32; m 55, Betty Spear; c Susan & David. *Educ:* Okla State Univ, BS, 54; Univ Mich, MF, 56, PhD(forestry), 64. *Prof Exp:* Res forester, US Forest Serv, 57-61, plant physiologist, 64-65; res assoc forestry, Univ Mich, 65-67; from asst prof to assoc prof, Ohio Agr Res & Develop Ctr, Ohio State Univ, 67-76, prof forestry, 76- *Concurrent Pos:* Agr Biotechnol Res Adv Comt, USDA, 88- *Mem:* AAAS; Soc Am Foresters; Am Soc Plant Physiologists; Int Soc Plant Molecular Biol. *Res:* Lignin biochemistry; tissue culture; conifer embryology. *Mailing Add:* 614 Bowman Dr Salisbury MD 21801. *Fax:* 216-263-3658

**WHITMORE, GORDON FRANCIS,** RADIOBIOLOGY, CANCER. *Current Pos:* RETIRED. *Personal Data:* b Saskatoon, Sask, June 29, 31; m 54; c 2. *Educ:* Univ Sask, BA, 53, MA, 54; Yale Univ, PhD(biophys), 57. *Honors & Awards:* Ernest Berry-Anderson Prize, Royal Soc Edinburgh, 66. *Prof Exp:* From asst prof to prof biophys, Univ Toronto, 60-, head dept, 71-, assoc dead fac med, 74-; physicist, Ont Cancer Inst, 56-, assoc dir, Phys Div, 57-, chmn, Dept Med Biophys, 80- *Concurrent Pos:* Vis prof, Pa State Univ, 63; mem, Nat Cancer Inst Grants Panel, 63- & Nat Res Coun Assoc Comt Radiobiol, 64-; mem, Radiation Study Sect, NIH, 65- *Mem:* Biophys Soc; Radiation Res Soc; Can Soc Cell Biol; Can Asn Physicists; Royal Soc Can. *Res:* Radiation physics; radiobiology of mammalian cells in vitro; action of chemotherapeutic agents; mammalian cell genetics. *Mailing Add:* 78 Roxborough St W Toronto ON M5R 1T8 Can. *Fax:* 416-926-6529

**WHITMORE, HOWARD LLOYD,** VETERINARY MEDICINE. *Current Pos:* MEM FAC, DEPT VET CLIN MED, COL VET MED, UNIV ILL, 80- *Personal Data:* b Dallas, Wis, Dec 3, 35; m 62; c 2. *Educ:* Okla State Univ, BS, 58, DVM, 60; Univ Wis, PhD(vet sci), 73; Am Col Theriogenologists, dipl. *Honors & Awards:* Burr Beach Award, Dept Vet Sci, Univ Wis, 73. *Prof Exp:* Vet pvt pract, 60-69; assoc prof, Col Vet Med, Univ Minn, St Paul, 74-80. *Mem:* Am Vet Med Asn; Sigma Xi. *Res:* Fertility; abortion and pregnancy diagnosis in dairy cattle. *Mailing Add:* 2807 Woodhaven Dr Champaign IL 61821-7528

**WHITMORE, MARY (ELIZABETH) ROWE,** ANATOMY, ZOOLOGY. *Current Pos:* RETIRED. *Personal Data:* b Oakland, Calif, Oct 26, 36; m 61, Stephen C; c Sarah, Michael & Daniel. *Educ:* Univ Calif, Berkeley, BA, 59; Smith Col, MA, 61; Univ Minn, Minneapolis, PhD(anat), 69. *Prof Exp:* Teaching asst zool, Smith Col, 59-61; teaching asst anat, Univ Minn, Minneapolis, 61-66; vis asst prof zool, Univ Okla, 70-71, asst prof, 72-93. *Mem:* AAAS; Am Soc Zool; Electron Micros Soc Am; Sigma Xi. *Res:* Comparative morphology and histology of endocrine glands in the lower vertebrates; biology of cyclostomes. *Mailing Add:* 120 Gabaldon Rte Las Vegas NM 87701

**WHITMORE, RALPH M,** MATHEMATICS, PROBABILITY. *Current Pos:* ADJ PROF MATH, TEMPLE JR COL, 89- *Personal Data:* b Medina, Tex, Oct 22, 17; m 42; c 2. *Educ:* Trinity Univ, BA, 38; Univ Tex, Austin, MA, 41, PhD(math), 64. *Prof Exp:* Instr math, Peacock Acad, 38-39; statistician electronics, City San Antonio, 39-40; instr math statist, Trinity Univ, 40-41; chief instr electronics math, Air Force Tech Sch, 42-44; prof math, physics & comput sci & chmn, Dept Math, Southwestern Univ, 44-89. *Concurrent Pos:* Statistician & consult, Sandia Corp, 53-61; NSF fel, Univ Okla, 64. *Mem:* Math Asn Am; Soc Indust & Appl Math. *Mailing Add:* 3411 Primrose Trail Georgetown TX 78628-2815

**WHITMORE, ROY ALVIN, JR,** FORESTRY. *Current Pos:* PROF FORESTRY, UNIV VT, 58- *Personal Data:* b Baltimore, Md, Aug 14, 28; m 53; c 3. *Educ:* Univ Mich, BSF, 52, MF, 54. *Prof Exp:* Forest economist, Cent States Forest Exp Sta, USDA, 52-58. *Mem:* Soc Am Foresters; Forest Prod Res Soc. *Res:* Forest products utilization and marketing. *Mailing Add:* Dept Forestry Univ Vt Aiken Ctr Burlington VT 05405-0088

**WHITMORE, ROY WALTER,** STATISTICS. *Current Pos:* STATISTICIAN, RES TRIANGLE INST, 80- *Personal Data:* b San Antonio, Tex, Jan 21, 47; m 69; c 2. *Educ:* Tex Tech Univ, BS, 69, MS, 71; Tex A&M Univ, PhD(statist), 78. *Prof Exp:* Instr math, Stephen F Austin State Univ, 69-71; lectr statist, Tex A&M Univ, 77-78; asst prof math, Univ NC, Greensboro, 78-80. *Mem:* Sigma Xi; Am Statist Asn; Biomet Soc. *Res:* Survey research; environmental surveys; health surveys; education surveys. *Mailing Add:* 3040 Cornwallis Rd Research Triangle Park NC 27709-2194

**WHITMORE, STEPHEN CARR,** PHYSICS. *Current Pos:* asst prof, 69-85, ASSOC PROF PHYSICS, UNIV OKLA, 85- *Personal Data:* b Holyoke, Mass, Oct 17, 31; m 61; c 3. *Educ:* Amherst Col, BA, 54; Univ Minn, PhD(liquid helium), 66. *Prof Exp:* Res assoc physics, Univ Mich, 66-69. *Mem:* Am Phys Soc. *Res:* Low temperature physics; liquid helium; superconducters; semiconductors. *Mailing Add:* 120 Gaba Idon Los Vegas NM 87701

**WHITMORE, WILLIAM FRANCIS,** mathematics, oceanography; deceased, see previous edition for last biography

**WHITNEY, ARTHUR EDWIN, JR,** HEAT TRANSFER, THERMODYNAMICS. *Current Pos:* RETIRED. *Personal Data:* b St Louis, Mo, Apr 21, 38. *Educ:* Washington Univ, BSME, 59, MS, 60, DSc(mech eng), 64. *Prof Exp:* Asst prof mech eng, Washington Univ, 64-65; sr group engr,

McDonnell Douglas Corp, 65-92. *Mem:* Am Soc Mech Engrs; Am Inst Aeronaut & Astronaut. *Res:* Heat transfer methods and computer applications applied to aircraft, missiles and spacecraft. *Mailing Add:* 15890 Richborough Rd Chesterfield MO 63017

**WHITNEY, CHARLES ALLEN,** ASTROPHYSICS. *Current Pos:* RETIRED. *Personal Data:* b Milwaukee, Wis, Jan 31, 29; m 51; c 5. *Educ:* Mass Inst Technol, BS, 51; Harvard Univ, AM, 53, PhD(astron), 55. *Prof Exp:* Physicist, Smithsonian Astrophys Observ, 56-95. *Concurrent Pos:* From assoc prof to prof astron, Harvard Univ, 63-95; Guggenheim Found fel, 71. *Mem:* Int Astron Union; Am Astron Soc; Am Acad Arts & Sci. *Res:* History of astronomy; theory of variable stars and associated problems of gas dynamics. *Mailing Add:* 60 Bradford Rd Weston MA 02193

**WHITNEY, CHARLES CANDEE, JR,** PHARMACEUTICAL DEVELOPMENT, DRUG METABOLISM. *Current Pos:* RETIRED. *Personal Data:* b Newfane, Vt, Oct 12, 39; m 86, Alberta; c Charles III & Susan. *Educ:* Northeastern Univ, AB, 62; Middlebury Col, MS, 64; Univ Calif, Davis, PhD(org chem), 68. *Prof Exp:* Res chemist, E I du Pont de Nemours & Co, Inc, 68; asst chief clin chem, 3rd US Army Med Lab, 68-70; sr res biochemist, E I du Pont de Nemours & Co, Wilmington, Del, 70-80, res assoc, 80-82, res supvr, 82-84, res mgr drug metab, 85-88, dir analytical res & develop, Exp Sta, 88-94. *Concurrent Pos:* Pres, Lab Mgt Systs Inc, 94-; consult, Pharmaceut Lab, 94- *Mem:* Am Chem Soc; Sigma Xi; Am Soc Clin Pharm & Therapeut; Am Asn Pharmaceut Scientists. *Res:* Develop regulatory compliant laboratory programs for customers; perform laboratory certification and develop method validation programs; set-up and run metrology programs for laboratories. *Mailing Add:* 235 Steeplechase Circle Wilmington DE 19808. *Fax:* 302-992-9067; *E-Mail:* ccw@lmsi.com

**WHITNEY, CYNTHIA KOLB,** MATHEMATICAL PHYSICS, OPERATIONS RESEARCH. *Current Pos:* VIS PROF, TUFTS UNIV, 87-; STAFF, W J SHAFER ASSOC INC, 87- *Personal Data:* b Cumberland, Md, July 11, 41; m 63, Daniel; c David & Karl. *Educ:* Mass Inst Technol, SB, 63, SM, 65, PhD(physics), 68. *Honors & Awards:* David Rist Prize, Mil Opers Res Soc. *Prof Exp:* Staff physicist, Charles Stark Draper Lab Inc, 67-80, assoc div leader & proj mgr, 80-87. *Concurrent Pos:* Consult, Advan Appln Flight Exp Prog, NASA, 75; assoc ed, Galilean Electrodyn, 93- *Mem:* AAAS; Sigma Xi. *Res:* Statistical description of complex physical systems; decision analysis for complex systems; mathematical formalisms in fundamental physics. *Mailing Add:* Tufts Univ EOTC 4 Colby St Medford MA 02155

**WHITNEY, DANIEL EUGENE,** MECHANICAL ENGINEERING, AUTOMATION & ROBOTICS. *Current Pos:* from asst prof to assoc prof mech eng, 68-74, PRIN RES ASSOC, MASS INST TECHNOL, 93- *Personal Data:* b Chicago, Ill, June 8, 38; m 63, Cynthia Kolb; c David & Karl. *Educ:* Mass Inst Technol, SB, 60 & 61, MS, 65, PhD(mech eng), 68. *Prof Exp:* Sect chief, Charles Stark Draper Lab, 74-93. *Concurrent Pos:* Consult, Charles Stark Draper Lab, 68-74; mem, Automation Res Coun, 71-78; NSF grant, Mass Inst Technol, 72-73 & Charles Stark Draper Lab, 78-80, 79-81, 81-84, 85-87 & 88-91. *Mem:* Sr mem Inst Elec & Electronics Engrs; fel Am Soc Mech Engrs; Robotics Inst Am. *Res:* Application of computers to engineering design and manufacturing; robotics; CAD; automation. *Mailing Add:* 141 Rhinecliff St Arlington MA 02174-7331. *E-Mail:* dwhitney@mit.edu

**WHITNEY, DONALD RANSOM,** STATISTICS, MATHEMATICAL STATISTICS. *Current Pos:* prof math, Ohio State Univ, 48-70, chmn dept, 70-80, prof statist, 70-82, EMER PROF STATIST, OHIO STATE UNIV, 82- *Personal Data:* b Cleveland Heights, Ohio, Nov 27, 15; m 39; c 4. *Educ:* Oberlin Col, BA, 36; Princeton Univ, MA, 39; Ohio State Univ, PhD(math), 48. *Prof Exp:* Instr math, Mary Washington Col, 39-42. *Concurrent Pos:* Consult discrimination cases, Ohio Bell Tel Co, Pub Utilities Comn, Cincinnati Bell Tel Co, NAm Aviation & Goodyear Atomic Corp. *Mem:* Fel AAAS; fel Am Statist Asn; Inst Math Statist; Biomet Soc; Am Math Soc. *Res:* Non-parametric statistics; general statistical methodology. *Mailing Add:* 388 Westview Ave Columbus OH 43214-1428

**WHITNEY, ELLSWORTH DOW,** PHYSICAL CHEMISTRY. *Current Pos:* assoc prof, Univ Fla, 70-75, founding dir, Ctr Res Mining & Mineral Resources, 72-82, affil prof, Dept Nuclear Eng Sci, 76-90, PROF MAT SCI & ENG, UNIV FLA, 75- *Personal Data:* b Buffalo, NY, Sept 17, 28; m 54; c 2. *Educ:* Univ Buffalo, BA, 50; NY Univ, PhD(phys chem), 54. *Prof Exp:* Res chemist, Olin Mathieson Chem Corp, 54-57, chem res proj specialist, 57-59; sr res chemist, Carborundum Co, 59-62, sr res assoc, 62-70. *Concurrent Pos:* Asst prof, Erie Co Technol Inst, 63-68; lectr, Eve Sch, State Univ NY, Buffalo, 66-69; partner, Mat Consult Inc, Gainesville, Fla, 72- *Mem:* Am Ceramic Soc; Am Chem Soc; Am Inst Mining, Metall & Petrol Engrs; Soc Mfg Engrs; Am Asn Univ Prof. *Res:* Crystal growth; kinetics of surface exchange; heterogeneous catalysis; boron and metal hydrides; borohydrides; fluorine oxidizers; high energy propellants; ultrahigh pressure solid state phenomena; phase transformations in solids; ceramic cutting tools and abrasives; solid state reaction kinetics, hard materials; mining and mineral research. *Mailing Add:* PO Box 116400 Univ Fla Gainesville FL 32611

**WHITNEY, ELVIN DALE,** plant pathology, plant breeding; deceased, see previous edition for last biography

**WHITNEY, EUGENE C,** ELECTRICAL ENGINEERING, MOTORS & HYDROGENATORS. *Current Pos:* RETIRED. *Personal Data:* b Columbus, Ohio, Aug 26, 13. *Educ:* Univ Mich, BS, 35. *Honors & Awards:* Tesla Award, Inst Elec & Electronics Engrs, 84. *Prof Exp:* Mgr sychronous condensers & hydrogenerator, Westinghouse Corp, 49-72, consult elec eng, 72-75; independent consult, 75- *Mem:* Nat Acad Eng; Power Eng Soc; Inst Elec & Electronics Engrs. *Res:* Responsible for the design of the world's largest water generators and synchronous motors. *Mailing Add:* 249 Cascade Rd Forest Hills Pittsburgh PA 15221

**WHITNEY, GEORGE STEPHEN,** organic chemistry, biochemistry; deceased, see previous edition for last biography

**WHITNEY, GINA MARIE,** CORROSION, ELECTROCHEMICAL PROCESS. *Current Pos:* ADV ENGR, IBM CORP, 87- *Personal Data:* b Berea, Ohio, Sept 3, 58. *Educ:* Case Western Res Univ, BS, 80; Univ Calif, PhD, 87. *Mem:* Am Inst Chem Engrs; Am Electroplaters & Surface Finishers Soc; Electrochem Soc. *Res:* Electrodeposition and corrosion of magnetic and electronic materials; transport phenomena in electrolytic processes. *Mailing Add:* IBM Corp 5600 Cottle Rd San Jose CA 95193

**WHITNEY, HARVEY STUART,** PHYTOPATHOLOGY, MYCOLOGY. *Current Pos:* RETIRED. *Personal Data:* b Langdon, Alta, Oct 14, 35; m 62; c 2. *Educ:* Univ Sask, BSA, 56, MSc, 58; Univ Calif, Berkeley, PhD(plant path), 63. *Prof Exp:* Res officer seedling dis, Forest Biol Div, Can Dept Agr, 58-61; res scientist, Can Forest Serv, Can Dept Environ, 61-91. *Concurrent Pos:* Can Forest Serv fel, Univ Calif, Berkeley, 70-71, Cornell Univ, Ithaca, 85-86. *Mem:* AAAS; Sigma Xi. *Res:* Mycology phytopathology. *Mailing Add:* 5033 Ayum Rd RR 1 Sooke BC V0S 1N0 Can. *E-Mail:* hwhitney@islandnet.com

**WHITNEY, J(OHN) BARRY, III,** MOLECULAR GENETICS, BIOCHEMICAL GENETICS. *Current Pos:* asst prof, 80-86, ASSOC PROF MOLECULAR GENETICS, MED COL GA, 87- *Personal Data:* b Ft Benning, Ga, Oct 4, 44; m 67, Beverly Bricker; c Suzanne R, Michelle L & John B IV. *Educ:* Univ NC, BS, 66; Univ NC, Chapel Hill, PhD(genetics), 72. *Prof Exp:* NIH fel, Univ Wis, 72-76; res assoc, Jackson Lab, 76-78; expert, NIH, 78-80. *Mem:* Am Soc Human Genetics; Genetics Soc Am; Sigma Xi; AAAS. *Res:* Detection and characterization of genetic mutations and variations that affect protein structure or expression in laboratory animals; silent amino acid substitutions; gene mapping; comparative genetics; inborn errors of metabolism; genetic therapy. *Mailing Add:* Dept Biochem & Molecular Biol Med Col Ga Augusta GA 30912-2100. *Fax:* 706-721-6608; *E-Mail:* barrywh@uscn.cc.uga.edu

**WHITNEY, JAMES ARTHUR,** EDUCATION & ADMINISTRATION, VOLCANOLOGY. *Current Pos:* from asst prof to assoc prof, 72-83, prof geol & head dept, 83-91, ASSOC VPRES ACAD AFFAIRS, UNIV GA, 92- *Personal Data:* b Middlebury, Vt, Apr 19, 46; m 75, Sandra Endrodi; c Nathaniel & Daniel. *Educ:* Mass Inst Technol, SB & MS, 69; Stanford Univ, PhD(geol), 72. *Prof Exp:* Instr geol, Chabot Jr Col, 71-72. *Concurrent Pos:* Woodrow Wilson fel, 68; NSF fel, 68-72; geologist, US Geol Surv, Reston, Va, 79. *Mem:* Fel Mineral Soc Am; fel Geol Soc Am; Am Geophys Union; AAAS; Sigma Xi; Soc Econ Geol. *Res:* Origin, fractionation, volatile components and tectonic significance of granitic magmatism with application to the understanding of tectonic processes, large volume ash-flow tuffs and the generation of ore deposits. *Mailing Add:* 145 Gibbons Way Athens GA 30605-4416. *Fax:* 706-542-0419; *E-Mail:* jwhitney@uga.cc.uga.edu

**WHITNEY, JAMES MARTIN,** MATERIALS SCIENCE ENGINEERING. *Current Pos:* PROF GRAD MAT ENG, UNIV DAYTON, 91- *Personal Data:* b Owosso, Mich, Sept 6, 36; m 63; c 3. *Educ:* Ill Col, BA, 59; Ga Inst Technol, BSTE, 59, MSTE, 61; Ohio State Univ, MS, 64, PhD(eng mech), 68. *Honors & Awards:* Award of Merit, Am Soc Testing & Mat, 83; Distinguished Res Award, Am Soc Composites, 91. *Prof Exp:* Mat engr, Nonmetallic Mat Div, USAF Mat Lab, 61-66, mat res engr, 66-91. *Concurrent Pos:* Air Force liaison rep to ad hoc comt micromech fibrous composites, Mat Adv Bd, 63-64; mem, Struct & Mat Comt, Aerospace Div, Am Soc Mech Engrs. *Mem:* Am Soc Composites; fel Am Soc Mech Engrs; assoc fel Am Inst Aeronaut & Astronaut; Soc Advan Mat & Process Engrs; fel Am Soc Testing & Mat. *Res:* Determination of the mechanical behavior of fibrous composites as a function of constituent properties and geometry, using principles of mechanics and applied mathematics; authored or coauthored over 100 publications including two texts. *Mailing Add:* 4371 Roundtree Dr Dayton OH 45432-1840

**WHITNEY, JODIE DOYLE,** AGRICULTURAL ENGINEERING. *Current Pos:* From asst agr engr to assoc agr engr, 65-79, AGR ENGR, CITRUS RES & EDUC CTR, UNIV FLA, 79- *Personal Data:* b Bosque Co, Tex, Oct 14, 37; m 60; c 2. *Educ:* Tex A&M Univ, BS, 59; Pa State Univ, MS, 62; Okla State Univ, PhD(agr eng), 66. *Mem:* Am Soc Agr Engrs. *Res:* Mechanization of low volume spraying and citrus harvesting; management of close spaced citrus plantings. *Mailing Add:* 1350 Stately Oaks Dr NW Winter Haven FL 33881. *Fax:* 941-956-4631

**WHITNEY, JOEL GAYTON,** ORGANIC CHEMISTRY. *Current Pos:* Sr res chemist, 63-80, res supvr, Biochem Dept, 80-84, RES ADMINR PHARMACEUT, E I DU PONT DE NEMOURS & CO, INC, 84- *Personal Data:* b Cambridge, Mass, Oct 13, 37; m 71. *Educ:* Harvard Univ, AB, 59; Mass Inst Technol, PhD(org chem), 63. *Mem:* Am Chem Soc. *Res:* Amino acid syntheses; medicinal chemistry, especially heterocyclic chemistry; synthesis of central nervous system agents. *Mailing Add:* 111 Marlbrook Way Kennett Square PA 19348-1719

**WHITNEY, JOHN BARRY, JR,** plant physiology; deceased, see previous edition for last biography

**WHITNEY, JOHN GLEN,** microbiology, for more information see previous edition

**WHITNEY, KENNETH DEAN,** BOTANY, PHYTOPATHOLOGY. *Current Pos:* Teaching fel & lect biol, 83-84, asst prof biol, 84-85, NSF RES FEL BIOL, UNIV TEX, ARLINGTON, 85- *Personal Data:* b San Diego, Calif, Oct 14, 52; m 77; c 2. *Educ:* Calif State Univ, Chico, BA, 78, MA, 80; Univ NC, Chapel Hill, PhD(bot), 83. *Concurrent Pos:* Grad fel, Mycol Soc Am, 81; res fel, NSF, 84. *Mem:* AAAS; Bot Soc Am; Mycol Soc Am; Sigma Xi; Soc Protozoologists. *Res:* Morphology, development and ultrastructure of calcium oxalate crystals in fungi; ultrastructure and development of Mycetozoans; biosystematics of Myxomycetes. *Mailing Add:* 3929 Sweetwater Dr Rocklin CA 95677

**WHITNEY, LESTER F(RANK),** FOOD ENGINEERING, MACHINE DESIGN. *Current Pos:* prof, 63-91, EMER PROF FOOD ENG, UNIV MASS, AMHERST, 91- *Personal Data:* b New Bedford, Mass, Mar 21, 28; m 50, Phyllis Burrill; c Marcia, Mark, Scott, Dean, David, John & Steven. *Educ:* Univ Maine, BS, 49; Mich State Univ, MSAE, 51, PhD(agr eng), 64. *Prof Exp:* Design & develop engr, Ariens Co, Wis, 51-53 & Maine Potato Growers, Inc, 53-54; develop engr, Wirthmore Feed Div, Corn Prod, Inc, 54-56, asst chief engr, Mass, 56-59; asst prof agr eng, Univ Mass, 59-62; NSF fel, Mich State Univ, 62-63. *Concurrent Pos:* Consult engr food mach processing. *Mem:* Am Soc Agr Engrs; Int Food Technologists; Sigma Xi. *Res:* Agricultural processes; stress analysis; systems analysis; water resources; forage dehydration; fish processing; shellfish depuration; fish waste byproducts. *Mailing Add:* 48 Jeffery Lane Amherst MA 01002-2532

**WHITNEY, MARION ISABELLE,** GEOLOGY, AERODYNAMIC ASPECTS OF WIND EROSION. *Current Pos:* RETIRED. *Personal Data:* b Austin, Tex, Apr 23, 11. *Educ:* Univ Tex, BA, 30, MA, 31, PhD(geol, paleont), 37. *Prof Exp:* Teacher pub sch, 33-36; asst prof geol, Kans State Teachers Col, 37-42; teacher geol & biol, Kilgore Col, 42-46; asst prof geol, Tex Christian Univ, 46-51 & Sul Ross State Col, 51-52; prof geol & biol, Ark Polytech Col, 52-54; assoc prof geol, Tulane Univ, 54-55; assoc prof, La Tech Inst, 55-60; teacher biol, Texarkana Col, 60-61; from assoc prof to prof biol, Cent Mich Univ, 61-81. *Mem:* Am Asn Petrol Geol; Soc Econ Paleont & Mineral; Geol Soc Am; Sigma Xi. *Res:* Description of the fauna of the Glen Rose formation of Texas; development of new data concerning the method of aerodynamic erosion of rock, dunes and snow. *Mailing Add:* PO Box 277 Shepherd MI 48853-0277

**WHITNEY, NORMAN JOHN,** MYCOLOGY, PLANT PATHOLOGY. *Current Pos:* lectr biol, Univ NB, 65-73, student counr, 66-73, assoc prof, 73-80, PROF BIOL & COUNR STUDENT SERV, UNIV NB, 80- *Personal Data:* b Langdon, Alta, July 24, 25; m 51; c 4. *Educ:* Univ Alta, BSc, 47; Univ Western Ont, MSc, 49; Univ Toronto, PhD(mycol, plant path), 53; McGill Univ, BD, 64. *Prof Exp:* Lectr bot, Univ Toronto, 50-52; plant pathologist, Res Sta, Can Dept Agr, 52-61; lectr bot, McGill Univ, 61-64. *Mem:* AAAS; Can Phytopath Soc. *Res:* Soil-borne diseases of plants; marine mycology; science and religion; spore germination in the phyllosphere. *Mailing Add:* Dept Biol Sci Univ NB Box 4400 Fredericton NB E3B 5A3 Can

**WHITNEY, RICHARD RALPH,** FISHERY BIOLOGY. *Current Pos:* INDEPENDENT SCI ADV BD, NAT MARINE FISH SERV, 96- *Personal Data:* b Salt Lake City, Utah, June 29, 27; m 50, Mary L MacArthur; c Jennifer, William R, Robert P & Gale. *Educ:* Univ Utah, BA, 49, MS, 51; Iowa State Col, PhD(fisheries mgt), 55. *Honors & Awards:* Excellence Award, Western Div Am Fish Soc, 80; Meritorious Serv Award, US Dept Interior, 82. *Prof Exp:* Res biologist, Salton Sea Invest, Univ Calif, 54-57; proj leader, Susquehanna Fishery Study, State Dept Res & Educ, Md, 58-60; chief tuna behav invests, Tuna Resources Lab, US Bur Com Fisheries, 61-67; unit leader, Wash Coop Fishery Res Unit, 67-83; prof fisheries, Univ Wash, 67-94; chmn, Sci Rev Group Bonn Power Admin, 89-94; mem, Independent Sci Rev Group NW Power Plan Coun, 94-95. *Concurrent Pos:* Consult, Conn Yankee Atomic Power Co, 65-74; tech adv & chmn, Fisheries Adv Bd, George H Boldt, Sr Judge US Dist Court, Tacoma, 74-78; mem sci & statist comt, Pac Fishery Mgt Coun, 76-80; coordr & chmn, Mid-Columbia Studies Comt, 80-94; comnr, salmon & steelhead adv comn, 81-84; chmn, Fish Propagation Panel, Northwest Power Planning Coun, 83-84. *Mem:* Fel Am Inst Fishery Res Biol; Am Fisheries Soc; Sigma Xi. *Res:* Aquatic ecology; fisheries. *Mailing Add:* 16500 River Rd Leavenworth WA 98826

**WHITNEY, RICHARD WILBUR,** AGRICULTURAL ENGINEERING. *Current Pos:* instr, 62-69, asst prof, 77-80, ASSOC PROF AGR ENG, OKLA STATE UNIV, 80- *Personal Data:* b Osawatomie, Kans, Nov 1, 38; m 59; c 4. *Educ:* Kans State Univ, BS, 61; Okla State Univ, MS, 67, PhD(agr eng), 72. *Prof Exp:* Instr, Kans State Univ, 61-62; asst prof, La State Univ, Baton Rouge, 72-77. *Concurrent Pos:* Consult, Charles Machine Works, Perry, Okla, 75, Kincaid Equip Co, Haven, Kans, 77-79, US Pollution Control, Oklahoma City, 80, Kahrs, Nelson, Fanning, Hite & Kellogg, 80 & Eagle Aircraft Co, Boise, Idaho, 81. *Mem:* Am Soc Agr Engrs; Sigma Xi. *Res:* Mechanization of food and fiber production of cotton and horticultural crops; low volume pesticide application equipment and delivery techniques for tick control; development of improved production equipment for forage grasses; determination of potential human inhalation exposure to airborne pentachlorophenol within treated structures. *Mailing Add:* Dept Agr Eng Okla State Univ 522 N Washington Stillwater OK 74078-0002

**WHITNEY, ROBERT ARTHUR, JR,** LABORATORY ANIMAL MEDICINE, COMPARATIVE MEDICINE. *Current Pos:* PRES, EARTHSPAN, 94- *Personal Data:* b Oklahoma City, Okla, July 27, 35; m 86, Elizabeth Whitney-Teeple; c Stacy, Tara, Mark & Laura. *Educ:* Okla State Univ, BS, 58, DVM, 59; Ohio State Univ, MS, 65. *Honors & Awards:* Charles River Prize & Animal Welfare Award, Am Vet Med Asn. *Prof Exp:* US Army fel & resident, Lab Animal Med, Ohio State Univ, 63-65, chief, Animal Resources Br, US Army Edgewood Arsenal, 65-70, dir, Lab Animal Training Prog, US Army Vet Corps, 68-70, commanding officer, 4th Med Detachment, Vietnam, 70-71; proj officer, Animal Resources Br, Nat Ctr Res Resources, NIH, 71-72, chief, Vet Resources Br, 72-85, dir, Nat Ctr Res Resources, 85-92, dir, Off Animal Care & Use, 87-92, dep surgeon gen, 92-94. *Concurrent Pos:* Consult, Lab Animal Med, Surgeon Gen Off, US Army, 67-70; exec dir, US Govt Interagency Primate Steering Comt, 80-81; chief vet officer, USPHS, 84-88; chmn, US Govt Interagency Res Animal Comt, 84-92, actg surgeon gen, 93. *Mem:* Am Col Lab Animal Med; Am Vet Med Asn; Am Asn Lab Animal Sci; Am Asn Lab Animal Practitioners; Sigma Xi; Am Vet Epidemiol Soc. *Res:* Diseases of laboratory animals; primatology; environmental monitoring. *Mailing Add:* 314 Second St Steilacoom WA 98388. *Fax:* 253-581-6792; *E-Mail:* 73407.253@compuserve.com

**WHITNEY, ROBERT BYRON,** organic chemistry; deceased, see previous edition for last biography

**WHITNEY, ROBERT C,** SCIENCE EDUCATION, PHYSICS. *Current Pos:* RETIRED. *Personal Data:* b Seattle, Wash, July 20, 19; m 42; c 2. *Educ:* Univ Wash, BS, 47; Cornell Univ, MS, 58, PhD(sci educ, physics), 63. *Prof Exp:* Teacher, Washington High Sch, 47-55, 56-57 & 58-59; assoc dir shell merit fels, Shell Found, Cornell Univ, 59-61, assoc dir, Acad Year Inst, NSF, 61-63; assoc prof phys sci, Calif State Univ, Hayward, 63-66, prof, 66- *Concurrent Pos:* Consult, Murray, Fremont & Palo Alto Sch Dist, Calif, 65-66 & Livermore Sch Dist, 67; NSF fel, Univ Wash, 71-72. *Mem:* AAAS; Am Asn Physics Teachers; Nat Sci Teachers Asn. *Res:* Improvement of high school physics facilities; improvement in the teaching of high school physics and elementary science. *Mailing Add:* 3160 Gilbert Lane Alameda CA 94502

**WHITNEY, ROY DAVIDSON,** FOREST PATHOLOGY. *Current Pos:* RETIRED. *Personal Data:* b Langdon, Alta, Dec 30, 27; m 53; c 4. *Educ:* Univ BC, BSF, 51; Yale Univ, MF, 54; Queen's Univ, Ont, PhD(forest path), 60. *Prof Exp:* Res scientist, Can Forestry Serv, 51- *Mem:* Am Phytopath Soc; Can Phytopath Soc. *Res:* Investigations of root rots of conifers, including identification of causal fungi, symptomatology, infection courts, damage appraisal and spore germination; determination of pathogenic potentials by inoculations. *Mailing Add:* 47 Cumberland Dr NW Calgary AB T2K 1S8 Can

**WHITNEY, ROY P(OWELL),** CHEMICAL ENGINEERING. *Current Pos:* prof chem eng, Inst Paper Chem, 47-79, res assoc & group leader, 47-57, dean, 56-76, vpres, 58-77, asst to pres, 78-79, EMER PROF CHEM ENG, INST PAPER CHEM, 79- *Personal Data:* b Milo, Maine, May 30, 13; m 41, Virginia M Gordon; c Patricia & Donald. *Educ:* Mass Inst Technol, SB, 35, SM, 37, ScD(chem eng), 45; Lawrence Univ, MS, 79. *Honors & Awards:* Colburn Award, Am Inst Chem Engrs, 48; Div Award, Tech Asn Pulp & Paper Indust, 69, Gold Medal, 80; Pro Bono Labore Award, Finnish Paper Engrs Asn, 78. *Prof Exp:* Asst, Mass Inst Technol, 35-36, asst dir sch chem eng practice, Bangor Sta, 36-38, dir, 38-42, asst prof chem eng, Univ, 39-45; dir, Dept Indust Coop, Univ Maine, 45-47, prof chem eng & actg head dept, 46-47. *Concurrent Pos:* Tech adv, Chem Warfare Serv Develop Lab, US Dept Army, 42-45, consult, Chem Corps, 50-52; chmn, Comt Paper Base Mat, Nat Acad Sci-Nat Res Coun, 60-66. *Mem:* Am Chem Soc; Am Soc Eng Educ; fel Tech Asn Pulp & Paper Indust; fel Am Inst Chem Engrs; fel Am Inst Chemists. *Res:* Heat and mass transfer, particularly gas absorption and drying; pulp and paper technology. *Mailing Add:* 1709 S Douglas St Appleton WI 54914

**WHITNEY, THOMAS ALLEN,** organic chemistry; deceased, see previous edition for last biography

**WHITNEY, WENDELL KEITH,** ENTOMOLOGY, AGRICULTURE. *Current Pos:* RETIRED. *Personal Data:* b Miltonvale, Kans, Nov 27, 27; m 45, Charlotte A Edlin; c Judy A (Alink) & Kenneth K. *Educ:* Kans State Univ, BS, 56, MS, 58, PhD(entom), 62. *Prof Exp:* Biol aide, Stored Prod Insect Br, USDA, Kans, 51-56, entomologist, 56-58; instr entom, Kans State Univ, 58-62; entomologist, Bioprod Dept, Dow Chem Co, 62-68; Ford Found entomologist, Int Inst Trop Agr, Nigeria, 68-73; chief entomologist, Plant Prod Res & Develop, Am Cyanamid Co, 74-82, prin scientist, 82-87. *Concurrent Pos:* Res grantee, 58-62; consult, Industs & USDA, 59-62. *Mem:* Entom Soc Am; Nigerian Soc Plant Protection. *Res:* Plant pest control; effects of chemicals on insects. *Mailing Add:* 3005 S Burma Rd Salina KS 67401

**WHITNEY, WILLIAM MERRILL,** PHYSICS, VERY LARGE SCALE INTEGRATION TECHNOLOGY. *Current Pos:* mem tech staff, Jet Propulsion Lab, 63-67, mgr guid & control res sect, 67-70, mgr, Info Systs Res Sect, 70-84, tech leader, Robot Res Prog, 71-78, mgr, Microelectronics Technol Sect, 84-86, sr mem tech staff, 86-87, DIV TECHNOLOGIST, OBSERVATIONAL SYSTS DIV, JET PROPULSION LAB, 87- *Personal Data:* b Coeur d'Alene, Idaho, Dec 5, 29; m 50, 78; c 2. *Educ:* Calif Inst Technol, BS, 51; Mass Inst Technol, PhD(physics), 56. *Honors & Awards:* Except Serv Medal, NASA, 82. *Prof Exp:* From instr to asst prof physics, Mass Inst Technol, 56-63. *Mem:* AAAS; Am Phys Soc. *Res:* Low temperature and semiconductor physics; computer science. *Mailing Add:* 1161 E Howard St Pasadena CA 91104-2551

WHITSEL, BARRY L, NEUROPHYSIOLOGY, NEUROPHARMACOLOGY. *Current Pos:* assoc prof dent res & physiol, 72-80, PROF PHYSIOL, SCH MED, UNIV NC, CHAPEL HILL, 80- *Personal Data:* b Mt Union, Pa, Aug 26, 37; m 60, Ruth A Clegg; c Jessica, Eric & Lee. *Educ:* Gettysburg Col, AB, 59; Univ Pa, MS, 63; Univ Ill, PhD(pharmacol), 65. *Prof Exp:* Res asst psychopharmacol, Wyeth Inst, 59-61; res assoc pharmacol, Sch Med, Univ Pittsburgh, 65-66, from instr to assoc prof, 66-72. *Concurrent Pos:* Res scientist develop award, NIMH, 68-73. *Mem:* Soc Neurosci. *Res:* Experimental and modeling/simulation studies of somatosensory nervous system organization and function; investigation of the neurol mechanisms underlying normal and abnormal somatosensory perception. *Mailing Add:* Dept Physiol Sch Med Univ NC Chapel Hill NC 27599-7545

WHITSELL, JOHN CRAWFORD, II, SURGERY, THORACIC SURGERY. *Current Pos:* Instr surg, Med Col, Cornell Univ, 63-66, asst attend surgeon, New York Hosp, 63-68, from asst prof to assoc prof, 66-70, surg dir, Renal Transplant Unit, 68-75, PROF SURG, MED COL, CORNELL UNIV, 70-, SURG CONSULT RENAL TRANSPLANT UNIT, NEW YORK HOSP-CORNELL MED CTR, 75- *Personal Data:* b St Joseph, Mo, Dec 21, 29; m 65, Rose Marie Schultz. *Educ:* Grinnell Col, AB, 50; Washington Univ, MD, 54; Am Bd Surg, dipl, 62; Am Bd Thoracic Surg, dipl, 64. *Concurrent Pos:* Assoc attend surgeon, New York Hosp, 68-70, attend surgeon, 70- *Mem:* AMA; Am Col Surg; Transplantation Soc; NY Acad Sci; Harvey Soc; Am Soc Transplant Surgeons. *Res:* Renal transplantation. *Mailing Add:* 449 E 68th St New York NY 10021

WHITSETT, CAROLYN F, PATHOLOGY, MEDICINE. *Current Pos:* ASSOC PROF PATH & MED, EMORY UNIV, SCH MED, 77- *Personal Data:* b Portsmouth, Va, Nov 21, 45. *Educ:* Howard Univ, BS, 66, MD, 70. *Prof Exp:* Med internship, 70-71; jr asst resident, Downstate Med Ctr, 71-72; sr asst resident, New York Hosp, 72-73; fel hemat, Montefiore Hosp & Med Ctr, 73-74; fel immunohemat, New York Blood Ctr, 74-75; fel, Med Hemat Div, Mem Hosp, 74-75; asst prof med, Cornell Univ, Med Col, 75-77. *Concurrent Pos:* Res assoc, Tissue Typing Lab, Mem Sloan Kettering Cancer Ctr, 75-77; asst attending physician hemat serv, Mem Hosp, 75-77; asst med dir, Mem Hosp Blood Bank, 76-77; med dir, Emory Univ Hosp Blood Bank & Sch Blood Banking, 77- *Mem:* Am Asn Blood Banks; Am Asn Clin Histocompatibility Testing. *Mailing Add:* Dept CP Emory Univ Hosp Atlanta GA 30322

WHITSETT, JOHNSON MALLORY, II, ANIMAL BEHAVIOR, REPRODUCTIVE PHYSIOLOGY. *Current Pos:* from asst prof to assoc prof, 71-81, PROF ZOOL, NC STATE UNIV, 81- *Personal Data:* b San Antonio, Tex, Jan 26, 41; m 64; c 1. *Educ:* Univ Tex, Austin, BA, 63, PhD(psychol), 70; Univ Tex, Austin, 69-71. *Concurrent Pos:* Res assoc, NC Dept Ment Health, 71-73; mem physiol fac, NC State Univ, 74-; NSF res grant, 78. *Mem:* AAAS; Animal Behav Soc; Am Ornithol Union; Soc Study Reproduction. *Res:* Hormonal and stimulus control of sexual and aggressive behavior in birds and mammals; environmental influence on reproduction; behavioral aspects of sexual development; photoperiodism. *Mailing Add:* 6908 Elmhurst Rd Amarillo TX 79106

WHITSETT, THOMAS L, INTERNAL MEDICINE, CLINICAL PHARMACOLOGY. *Current Pos:* from asst prof med to assoc prof, 70-78, asst prof pharmacol, 70-77, PROF MED, MED CTR, UNIV OKLA, 78-, ASSOC PROF PHARMACOL, 77- *Personal Data:* b Tulsa, Okla, July 14, 36; m 59; c 2. *Educ:* Pasadena Col, BA, 58; Univ Okla, MD, 62. *Prof Exp:* Clin asst, Med Ctr, Univ Okla, 67-68; vis asst prof med, Sch Med, Emory Univ, 69-70. *Concurrent Pos:* Found fac develop award, Pharmaceut Mfr Asn, 71; trainee clin pharmacol, Med Ctr, Univ Okla, 67-68 & Sch Med, Emory Univ, 68-70. *Mem:* Am Heart Asn; Am Fedn Clin Res; Am Soc Pharmacol & Exp Therapeut; Sigma Xi. *Res:* Early phases of new drug investigation, especially cardiovascular and respiratory agents. *Mailing Add:* Dept Med & Cardiol Univ Okla Med Ctr 920 Stanton L Young Blvd Rm 5 Sp300 Oklahoma City OK 73104-5041

WHITSON, PAUL DAVID, BOTANY, PLANT ECOLOGY. *Current Pos:* from asst prof to assoc prof, 72-81, PROF BIOL, UNIV NORTHERN IOWA, 81- *Personal Data:* b Gravette, Ark, Mar 20, 40; m 78, Anita M Hildebrand. *Educ:* Baylor Univ, BS, 62, MS, 65; Univ Okla, PhD(bot), 71. *Prof Exp:* Grad asst biol, Baylor Univ, 63-65; grad asst bot, Univ Okla, 65-71; asst prof biol, Baylor Univ, 70-71. *Concurrent Pos:* Res consult, Nat Park Serv Univ Okla Res Inst, 69-70; Int Biol Prog fel biol, NMex State Univ, 71-72; prin investr desert biomed, Int Biol Prog, 72-75; staff assoc environ biol, NSF, 76-77; exec secy, Fed Comt Ecol Reserves, 76-77; investr endangered species, US Fish & Wildlife Serv, 78-81 & Iowa Dept Natural Resources, 82-86; investr veg chg, US Nat Park Serv, 88-93; mem adv bd, Leopold Ctr Sustainable Agr, 92- *Mem:* Ecol Soc Am; Brit Ecol Soc; Sigma Xi; Cactus & Succulent Soc Am; Am Orchid Soc. *Res:* Structure, dynamics and human influences upon woodland and desert vegetation; phenology and productivity of desert annuals; species biology, Southern Appalachian and Midwestern endangered plants; decide forest and prairie reconstruction; terrestial orchid ecology. *Mailing Add:* Biol Univ Northern Iowa Cedar Falls IA 50614-0421. *Fax:* 319-273-2893

WHITT, DIXIE DAILEY, MICROBIAL ECOLOGY, MICROBIAL PATHOGENESIS. *Current Pos:* res assoc microbiol, 69-87, LECTR MICROBIOL, UNIV ILL COL MED, URBANA, 87- *Personal Data:* b Longmont, Colo, Mar 9, 39; m 63, Gregory S. *Educ:* Colo State Univ, BS, 61, PhD(zool), 65. *Prof Exp:* USPHS fel biochem genetics, Yale Univ, 65-68, lectr & res staff biologist, 68-69. *Mem:* Am Genetics Asn; Int Soc Anaerobic Bacteria; AAAS; Soc Microbiol Ecol & Dis; Am Soc Microbiol; fel Am Acad Microbiol. *Res:* Host-parasite interactions; biochemical genetics of microorganisms; host-parasite relationships as an expression of the host's environmental conditions; host-intestinal microflora interactions; molecular pathogenesis. *Mailing Add:* Dept Microbiol Univ Ill 601 S Goodwin Ave B103 Chem & Life Sci Lab Urbana IL 61801. *Fax:* 217-244-6697; *E-Mail:* d____ whitt1@uiuc.edu

WHITT, GREGORY SIDNEY, MOLECULAR PHYLOGENETICS, MOLECULAR EVOLUTION. *Current Pos:* From asst prof to assoc prof zool, 69-72, prof genetics & develop, 77-87, PROF ECOL, ETHOLOGY & EVOLUTION, UNIV ILL, 87- *Personal Data:* b Detroit, Mich, June 13, 38; m 63, Dixie Dailey. *Educ:* Colo State Univ, BS, 62, MS, 65; Yale Univ, PhD(biol), 70. *Concurrent Pos:* Mem adv bd, Biochem Genetics, 75-; affil, Ctr Aquatic Ecol, Ill Natural Hist Surv, Urbana, 81-; mem ed bd, J Molecular Evolution, 79- *Mem:* Am Genetic Asn; Am Soc Ichthyologists & Herpetologists; fel AAAS; Int Soc Molecular Evolution; Soc Protection Old Fishes; Soc Syst Biologists. *Res:* Biochemical and molecular evolution and systematics of fishes; use of RNA sequences and isozyme gene structure and regulation to investigate the evolution and phylogenetics of genes and organisms. *Mailing Add:* Dept Ecol Ethology & Evolution Univ Ill 505 S Goodwin Ave Urbana IL 61801-3799. *E-Mail:* g-whitt@uiuc.edu

WHITT, MICHAEL A, VIROLOGY, PROTEIN TRANSPORT & TARGETING. *Current Pos:* ASST PROF, DEPT MICROBIOL & IMMUNOL, UNIV TENN CTR HEALTH SCI, 91- *Personal Data:* b Parsons, Kans, Dec 25, 58; m 81, Kerri L; c Cody & Kendall. *Educ:* Univ Kans, BA, 81; Univ Calif, Davis, PhD(microbiol), 87. *Concurrent Pos:* Prin investr, Am Cancer Soc, 93-96, NIH, 97- *Mem:* Am Soc Microbiol; AAAS; Am Soc Virol. *Res:* Mechanisms underlying the assembly of enveloped animal viruses; dissecting the events leading to the infection of mammalian cells with those viruses. *Mailing Add:* 858 Madison Ave Memphis TN 38163. *Fax:* 901-448-8462; *E-Mail:* mwhitt@utmem1.utmem.edu

WHITT, WARD, QUEUEING THEORY, STOCHASTIC PROCESSES. *Current Pos:* MEM TECH STAFF, AT&T LABS, 77- *Personal Data:* b Buffalo, NY, Jan 29, 42; m 83; c 2. *Educ:* Dartmouth Col, AB, 64; Cornell Univ, PhD(opers res), 69. *Prof Exp:* Vis asst prof opers res, Stanford Univ, 68-69; asst prof admin sci, Sch Orgn & Mgt, Yale Univ, 69-73, assoc prof admin sci & statist, 73-77. *Concurrent Pos:* NSF res initiation grant admin sci, Yale Univ, 71-73, jr fac fel, 72-73, res grant, 73-75. *Mem:* Nat Acad Eng; Inst Math Statist; Oper Res Soc Am. *Res:* Probability theory and its applications; mathematical models in the social sciences; queueing theory; stochastic processes. *Mailing Add:* 86 Hill Top Rd Basking Ridge NJ 07920

WHITTAKER, FREDERICK HORACE, PARASITOLOGY. *Current Pos:* from asst prof to assoc prof, 64-72, PROF ZOOL, UNIV LOUISVILLE, 72- *Personal Data:* b Columbus, Ohio, Mar 9, 28; m 52; c 2. *Educ:* Otterbein Col, BA, 51; Univ Ga, MSc, 56; Univ Ill, PhD(zool, parasitol), 63. *Prof Exp:* Instr biol & chem, Spartanburg Jr Col, 57-58; res biologist, Abbott Labs, Ill, 63-64. *Concurrent Pos:* Consult, Abbott Labs, 64-65. *Mem:* Sigma Xi; Am Soc Parasitologists. *Res:* Effects of fermentation liquors on invertebrates; taxonomy and life cycles of trematodes and cestodes; scanning electron microscopy of cestodes and trematodes of sharks, skates and rays; systematics and ecology of helminths of cavefishes. *Mailing Add:* 401 Deerfield Lane Louisville KY 40207

WHITTAKER, J RICHARD, EMBRYOLOGY, EVOLUTION. *Current Pos:* chmn biol, 92-97, PROF BIOL, UNIV NB, FREDERICTON, 92- *Personal Data:* b Cornwall, Ont, Aug 19, 34; div. *Educ:* Queen's Univ, Ont, BA, 58, MSc, 59; Yale Univ, PhD(develop biol), 62. *Honors & Awards:* Marine Biol Lab Award, Woods Hole, 71. *Prof Exp:* Asst prof zool, Univ Calif, Los Angeles, 62-67; assoc prof, Wistar Inst Anat & Biol, 67-81; prof biol & dir, Marine Prog, Boston Univ, 81-85; sr scientist, Marine Biol Lab, 85-92. *Concurrent Pos:* Investr, Woods Hole, 69-, trustee, 78-86, actg dir, Marine Biol Lab, 86-87; assoc prof anat, Sch Med, Univ Pa, 71-81; mem, Alpha Helix Philippine Exped, 79; vis prof, Kewalo Marine Lab, Univ Hawaii, 81; adj prof biol, Boston Univ, 86-92; vis assoc, Calif Inst Technol, 88, 91. *Mem:* Am Soc Zool; Soc Develop Biol; Int Soc Develop Biol; Sigma Xi. *Res:* Localization and segregation of morphogenetic determinants in ascidian embryos; gene regulation in early embryonic development of marine invertebrates; melanocyte differentiation; developmental genetics of Tunicate and chordate evolution. *Mailing Add:* Biol Dept Univ NB Bag Serv 45111 Fredericton NB E3B 6E1 Can. *Fax:* 506-453-3583

WHITTAKER, JAMES VICTOR, MATHEMATICS. *Current Pos:* from instr to assoc prof, 58-69, PROF MATH, UNIV BC, 69- *Personal Data:* b Los Angeles, Calif, Aug 1, 31. *Educ:* Univ Calif, Los Angeles, BA, 53, MA, 54, PhD, 58. *Prof Exp:* Assoc math, Univ Calif, Los Angeles, 57-58. *Mem:* Am Math Soc; Math Asn Am; Can Math Cong; Sigma Xi. *Res:* Geometric topology; probability. *Mailing Add:* 1650 Tasmania Cres Vancouver BC V6T 1W5 Can

WHITTAKER, PAUL, TOXICOLOGY, BIOCHEMISTRY. *Current Pos:* SUPVRY CHEMIST, FOOD & DRUG ADMIN, 86- *Personal Data:* b Spokane, Wash, Jan 10, 43. *Educ:* Utah State Univ, PhD(nutrit), 83. *Mem:* Am Soc Clin Nutrit; Am Inst Nutrit; Sigma Xi; Am Asn Cancer Res. *Res:* Nutrient interactions of trace elements, with a primary interest in iron metabolism, toxicology and bioavailability. *Mailing Add:* 4909 Penny Royal Ct Rockville MD 20853. *Fax:* 301-594-0517; *E-Mail:* pvw@fdacfsan.bitnet

**WHITTAM, JAMES HENRY,** PHYSICAL CHEMISTRY, CHEMICAL ENGINEERING. *Current Pos:* mgr res chem & chem eng, 78-80, DIR HEALTH SCI, SHAKLEE CORP RES LAB, 80- *Personal Data:* b New York, NY, Apr 23, 49. *Educ:* City Col New York, BS, 72, PhD(phys chem), 75; Boston Univ, MBA, 78. *Prof Exp:* Instr chem, City Col New York, 72-75; proj chemist, Gillette Co, 75-78. *Concurrent Pos:* Consult, Gen Foods Corp, 73-74; adv ed, Cosmetic Tech, 78- *Mem:* Am Chem Soc; Soc Cosmetic Chem; Inst Food Technol; Am Oil Chem Soc. *Res:* Surface and colloid science pertaining to the fields of hair and skin cosmetology and food science, nutrition and engineering. *Mailing Add:* Shaklee Corp 444 Market St San Francisco CA 94111-5378. *Fax:* 415-391-2545

**WHITTEMBURY, GUILLERMO,** BIOPHYSICS. *Current Pos:* sr scientist, Venezuelan Inst Sci Res, 67-90, head, Dept Gen Physiol, 67-70, MEM STAFF, VENEZUELAN INST SCI RES, 61-, EMER SR SCIENTIST, 90- *Personal Data:* b Trujillo, Peru, Nov 17, 29; m 62, Dorothy Hauswedell; c Guillermo, Anamaria & Roberto. *Educ:* San Marcos Univ, Lima, BM, 55; Univ Cayetano Heredia, Peru, MD, 65. *Hon Degrees:* Prof, Univ Cagetano Heredia, Lima, 83. *Honors & Awards:* Daniel Carrion Prize, Peru, 65. *Prof Exp:* Instr anat, San Marcos Univ, Lima, 49-50, asst prof med, 55-57, asst prof biophys, 60-62. *Concurrent Pos:* Res fel, Biophys Lab, Harvard Med Sch, 57-60; Rockefeller Found fel, 57-59; Helen Hay Whitney Found fel, 59-60; mem, Int Union Pure & Appl Biophys, 63; vis prof, Yale Univ, 70; dir, Latin Am Ctr Biol, 73-84; fel, Churchill Col, Cambridge, 76-; vis scientist, Max Planck Inst Biophys, Frankfurt, 86. *Mem:* Am Soc Nephrology; Biophys Soc; Peruvian Nephrology Soc; Int Soc Nephrology; Soc Gen Physiologists; Peruvian Acad Med. *Res:* Transport processes across membranes; kidney physiology. *Mailing Add:* Venezuelan Inst Sci Res PO Box 21827 Caracas 1020A Venezuela. *Fax:* 58-2-5041120; *E-Mail:* gwhitt@cbb.ivic.ve

**WHITTEMORE, ALICE S,** BIOMATHEMATICS, BIOSTATISTICS. *Current Pos:* fac mem, Dept Statist, 76-87, PROF HEALTH RES & POLICY, DEPT EPIDEMIOL, STANFORD UNIV, 87- *Personal Data:* b New York, NY, July 5, 36; m 58; c 2. *Educ:* Marymount Manhattan Col, BS, 58; Hunter Col, MA, 64; City Univ New York, PhD(math), 67. *Prof Exp:* From asst prof to assoc prof math, Hunter Col, 67-74; adj assoc prof environ med, Med Ctr, NY Univ, 74-76. *Concurrent Pos:* City Univ New York res grants, 69 & 70; Sloan Found res grant, Soc Indust & Appl Math Inst Math & Soc, 74-76; Rockefeller Found res grant, 76-77. *Mem:* Inst Med-Nat Acad Sci; Soc Indust & Appl Math; Sigma Xi; Am Math Soc; Math Asn Am; AAAS. *Res:* Environmental carcinogenesis; genetic epidemiology of prostate and ovarian cancer. *Mailing Add:* Dept Health Res & Policy Stanford Univ Sch Med HBP Redwood Bldg Stanford CA 94305-5092

**WHITTEMORE, CHARLES ALAN,** ORGANIC CHEMISTRY. *Personal Data:* b Grand Junction, Colo, Dec 14, 35; m 63; c 2. *Educ:* Stanford Univ, BSc, 57; Univ Colo, PhD(org chem), 63. *Prof Exp:* Sr chemist, Cent Res Labs, 3M Co, 63-69; from asst prof to assoc prof chem, Colo Women's Col, 69-77; sr develop chemist, Ga-Pac, 77-82, group leader, 82-87, scientist, 87-93, res scientist, 93. *Mem:* Am Chem Soc; Forest Res Soc. *Res:* Organic reaction mechanisms; phenolic resins; organic synthesis; wood adhesives. *Mailing Add:* 3145 Hurleywood Way Albany OR 97321-9651

**WHITTEMORE, DONALD OSGOOD,** GEOCHEMISTRY, HYDROGEOLOGY. *Current Pos:* assoc scientist, 78-95, SR SCIENTIST, KANS GEOL SURV, 95-, CHIEF GEOHYDROL SECT, 95- *Personal Data:* b Pittsburgh, Pa, May 4, 44; m 71, Andrea Yaswinski; c Luke, Paul & Mark. *Educ:* Univ NH, BS, 66; Pa State Univ, University Park, PhD(geochem), 73. *Prof Exp:* Asst prof geol, Kans State Univ, 72-78. *Concurrent Pos:* Courtesy assoc prof geol, Univ Kans. *Mem:* Nat Ground Water Asn; Soil Sci Soc Am; Int Asn Geochem Cosmochem; Am Geophys Union. *Res:* Geochemical identification of saltwater pollution sources in water resources; factors controlling spatial and temporal variations in groundwater quality; geochemistry of oilfield brines; geochemistry of regional aquifer systems. *Mailing Add:* Kans Geol Surv Univ Kans Lawrence KS 66047. *Fax:* 785-864-5317

**WHITTEMORE, O(SGOOD) J(AMES),** CERAMIC ENGINEERING. *Current Pos:* from assoc prof to prof, 64-87, EMER PROF CERAMIC ENG, UNIV WASH, 87- *Personal Data:* b Clear Lake, Iowa, Jan 24, 19; m 41, Barbara Greenwood; c Donald, Bonnie & Corin. *Educ:* Iowa State Univ, BS, 40, CerE, 50; Univ Wash, Seattle, MS, 41. *Honors & Awards:* Admiral Earle Award, Worcester Eng Soc, 49; Trinks Indust Heating Award, 55; Azevedo Prize, Brazil, 79 & 82. *Prof Exp:* Fel refractories, Mellon Inst, 41-44; group leader, Manhattan Proj, Mass Inst Technol, 44-46; sr engr, Norton Co, 46-56, chief ceramic engr, 56-59, res assoc explor res, 59-64. *Concurrent Pos:* Mem ad hoc comt, Mat Adv Bd, 56 & 58; NASA ceramic mat res grant, 64-78; vis prof, Univ BC, Can, 74-75 & 90; prof, Univ Fed de Sao Carlos, Brazil, 76; NSF sintering grant, 79-85; dir, Wash Mining & Mineral Resources Res Inst, 82-87. *Mem:* Nat Inst Ceramic Engrs; fel Am Ceramic Soc (vpres, 75-76); Brit Ceramic Soc; fel Inst Ceramics; Int Inst Sci Sintering. *Res:* Refractories; processing; minerals. *Mailing Add:* 10015 Lakeshore Blvd NE Seattle WA 98125. *Fax:* 206-517-5537; *E-Mail:* whit75@u.washington.edu

**WHITTEMORE, RUTH,** PEDIATRICS, CARDIOLOGY. *Current Pos:* CLIN PROF PEDIAT, SCH MED, YALE UNIV, 66- *Personal Data:* b Cambridge, Mass, June 11, 17. *Educ:* Mt Holyoke Col, BA, 38; Johns Hopkins Univ, MD, 42; Am Bd Pediat, dipl, 53, cert pediat cardiol, 61. *Hon Degrees:* DSc, Mt Holyoke Col, 83. *Honors & Awards:* First Award for Res, Soc Perinatal Obstetricians, 85; Founders Award, Dept Pediat Cardiol, Am Acad Ped, 96. *Prof Exp:* Intern & resident pediat, New Haven Hosp, 42-44; resident, Johns Hopkins Hosp, 44-45, asst physician, Harriet Lane Cardiac Clin, 45-47; physician, Div Crippled Children, 47-59; dir, New Haven Rheumatic Fever & Cardiac Prog, State Dept Health, Conn, 47-60, sr pediatrician, New Haven Pediat Cardiac Res Prog, 59-66, pediat cardiologist & dir, 66-83. *Concurrent Pos:* From asst clin prof to assoc clin prof, Sch Med, Yale Univ, 47-66; vchmn, Am Heart Dis Youth, Am Heart Asn, 56-60, chmn, Comt Congenital Heart Dis, 56-60; chmn, Task Force Heart Dis & Youth, Conn Heart Asn, 75-77. *Mem:* Fel Am Acad Pediat; fel Am Col Cardiol; NY Acad Sci; Sigma Xi; Am Pediat Soc. *Res:* Rheumatic fever; etiology and genetics of congenital heart defects; diagnostic services and care of the pediatric cardiac patient; pregnancy in the congenital cardiac, growth and development of offspring; hyperlipemia; thirty year follow-up of blood pressure in childhood; incidence of cogenital heart defect in the 827 offspring of 53 affected parents. *Mailing Add:* Dept Pediat Box 208064 Yale Univ Sch Med New Haven CT 06520-8064. *Fax:* 203-737-2786; *E-Mail:* ewmfl@aol.com

**WHITTEMORE, WILLIAM LESLIE,** NUCLEAR PHYSICS & ENGINEERING, OTHER MEDICAL & HEALTH SCIENCES. *Current Pos:* physicist, Gen Atomic Div, Gen Dynamics Corp, 57-67, staff physicist, Triga Reactors Facil, 67-90, SR SCI ADV, GEN ATOMIC CO, 78- *Personal Data:* b Skowhegan, Maine, Sept 25, 24; m 50, Alice Peterson. *Educ:* Colby Col, AB, 45; Harvard Univ, MA, 47, PhD(physics), 49. *Prof Exp:* Assoc scientist, Brookhaven Nat Lab, 48-50, physicist, 50-56. *Concurrent Pos:* Vis lectr, Harvard Univ, 50-51; sci consult, Korean Atomic Energy Res Inst, 60-, Indonesian Atomic Agency, 65 & NSF, 70 & 75. *Mem:* Am Phys Soc; fel Am Nuclear Soc; Archaeol Inst Am; Sigma Xi. *Res:* Utilization of research reactors; neutron research; neutron radiography, isotopes for nuclear medicine; boron neutron capture therapy, design and construction. *Mailing Add:* Gen Atomics PO Box 85608 San Diego CA 92138. *Fax:* 619-457-8786

**WHITTEN, BARBARA L,** ATOMIC & MOLECULAR PHYSICS, GENDER & SCIENCE. *Current Pos:* assoc prof physics, 87-95, PROF PHYSICS, COLO COL, 95- *Personal Data:* b Minneapolis, Minn, Sept 26, 46; m 82, William L Morgan; c Penelope A & Jacob L. *Educ:* Carleton Col, BA, 68; Univ Rochester, MA, 71, PhD(physics), 77. *Prof Exp:* Instr, Western Col, Miami Univ, 74-76, asst prof interdisciplinary studies, 76-80; res assoc, Physics Dept, Rice Univ, 80-81; physicist, Lawrence Livermore Nat Lab, 81-87. *Mem:* Sigma Xi; Am Phys Soc; Am Asn Physics Teachers; Am Women Sci. *Res:* Physics of soft x-ray lasers; theoretical and computational studies of atomic and molecular processes in plasmas. *Mailing Add:* Physics Dept Colo Col Colorado Springs CO 80903. *E-Mail:* bwhitten@cc.colorado.edu

**WHITTEN, BERTWELL KNEELAND,** ENVIRONMENTAL PHYSIOLOGY, COMPARATIVE PHYSIOLOGY. *Current Pos:* assoc prof, 72-74, dept head, 81-86, PROF BIOL SCI, MICH TECHNOL UNIV, 74-, DEAN RES & GRAD SCH, 86- *Personal Data:* b Boston, Mass, Apr 1, 41; m 62; c 3. *Educ:* Middlebury Col, AB, 62; Purdue Univ, MS, 64, PhD(environ physiol), 66. *Prof Exp:* Res physiologist, US Army Med Res & Nutrit Lab, Fitzsimons Gen Hosp, 66-68, res physiologist, Res Inst Environ Med, Army Natick Labs, 68-72. *Concurrent Pos:* Dir, Biosource Res Inst, Mich Technol Univ. *Mem:* AAAS; Am Soc Zoologists; Am Physiol Soc. *Res:* Cardiovascular adaptations to hypoxia; exercise physiology. *Mailing Add:* Vp res Student Serv Mich Technol Univ 1400 Townsend Dr Houghton MI 49931-1200. *Fax:* 906-487-3167

**WHITTEN, CHARLES A, JR,** NUCLEAR PHYSICS, INTERMEDIATE ENERGY PHYSICS. *Current Pos:* asst prof nuclear physics, 68-74, assoc prof, 74-80, PROF PHYSICS, UNIV CALIF, LOS ANGELES, 80- *Personal Data:* b Harrisburg, Pa, Jan 20, 40; m 65, Joan Emann; c Charles A III. *Educ:* Yale Univ, BS, 61; Princeton Univ, MA, 63, PhD(physics), 66. *Prof Exp:* Res physicist, A W Wright Nuclear Struct Lab, Yale Univ, 65-68. *Concurrent Pos:* Vis scientist, Ctr Nuclear Studies, Saclay, France, 80-81 & 86-87. *Mem:* Am Phys Soc; Sigma Xi. *Res:* Nuclear structure studies with intermediate energy probes; nucleon-nucleon scattering at intermediate energies; use of polarized beams and targets to study structures in nuclear and elementary particle physics; spin physics. *Mailing Add:* Dept Physics & Astron Univ Hilgarden Los Angeles CA 90095-1547. *E-Mail:* whitten@microp.physics.ucla.edu

**WHITTEN, DAVID G,** BIOPHYSICAL & PHYSICAL ORGANIC CHEMISTRY. *Current Pos:* C E KENNETH MEES PROF CHEM, UNIV ROCHESTER, 83-, CHMN, DEPT CHEM, 88-, DIR, CTR PHOTOINDUCED CHARGE TRANSFER, 89- *Personal Data:* b Washington, DC, Jan 25, 38; m 60; c 2. *Educ:* Johns Hopkins Univ, BA, 59, MA, 61, PhD(org chem), 63. *Prof Exp:* Sr scientist, Jet Propulsion Lab, Calif Inst Technol, 63-65, NIH fel chem, Inst, 65-66; from asst prof to prof chem, Univ NC, Chapel Hill, 66-80, M A Smith prof, 80-83. *Concurrent Pos:* Consult, Sci Data Systs, Inc, 66, Tenn Eastman Co, 66-79, Polaroid Corp, 81-83, Eastman Kodak, 84- & L D Caulh, 83-; Alfred P Sloan Found fel, 70-; Alexander von Humboldt fel, Max Planck Inst Biophys Chem, 72-73; Alexander von Humboldt sr scientist award, 74-75; fel, Japan Soc Prom Sci; Humboldt award, 83. *Mem:* Am Chem Soc; Royal Soc Chem; Am Soc Photobiol; Interam Photochem Soc (pres, 83-86). *Res:* Photobiology; photochemistry in microheterogeneous media; solid state and interfacial chemistry; electron transfer photochemistry; porphyrins and organometallic compounds. *Mailing Add:* Chem Univ Rochester 500 Joseph C Wilson Rochester NY 14627-9000

**WHITTEN, ELMER HAMMOND,** MEDICAL PHYSIOLOGY. *Current Pos:* from asst prof med physiol to assoc prof physiol & pharmacol, Univ Health Sci, 70-72, prof physiol, 79, assoc dean acad affairs, 72-88, chmn, Dept Physiol, 71-88, PRES, UNIV HEALTH SCI, 88-; PRES, UNIV TOWERS INC, 88- *Personal Data:* b Stoughton, Mass, Feb 18, 27; m 50; c 2. *Educ:*

Northeastern Univ, BS, 52; Mass State Col, Bridgewater, MEd, 67; Colo State Univ, PhD(physiol), 70. *Prof Exp:* Med serv rep drug sales, Pitman-Moore Co, Dow Chem Co, 54-56; admin asst sales, Metals & Controls, Inc, 56-58; head, Customer Serv, Tex Instruments Inc, 58-66; instr human physiol, Colo State Univ, 70. *Concurrent Pos:* Pres, Lakeside Hosp Asn, 88-; bd gov, AACOM, 88- *Mem:* NY Acad Sci; Sigma Xi. *Res:* Neonatal enteritis; transport phenomena across the intestinal wall during stages in the progress of enteritis as it affects electrolytes and water. *Mailing Add:* 10001 Rosehill Rd Lenexa KS 66215

**WHITTEN, ERIC HAROLD TIMOTHY,** GEOLOGY. *Current Pos:* RETIRED. *Personal Data:* b Ilford, Eng, July 26, 27; m 53, 76, Mary Cleopha Staciva; c Catherine, Peter, Jennifer, Adam & Joshua. *Educ:* Univ London, BSc, 48, PhD(geol), 52, DSc(geol), 68. *Honors & Awards:* William Krumbein Medal, Int Asn Math, Geol, 88. *Prof Exp:* Managerial chief clerk, Rex Thomas, Ltd, 43-45; lectr geol, Queen Mary Col, Univ London, 48-58; vpres acad affairs & prof geol, Mich Tech Univ, Houghton, 81-90; provost, 88-90; Ctr Environ Resources, Univ Exetes, UK, 90-93. *Concurrent Pos:* Vis assoc prof, Univ Calif, Berkeley, 57 & 60, Univ Calif, Santa Barbara, 59 & Univ Colo, 61 & 63; Daniel Pidgeon Fund grantee, Geol Soc Land, 54. *Mem:* Fel Geol Soc Am; fel Geol Soc London; Brit Geol Asn; Int Asn Math Geol (pres, 80-84). *Res:* Structural geology and petrology of granitic and deformed rocks; application of statistical analysis to quantitative geology problems. *Mailing Add:* Lower Bonehill Farm Widecomb-in-the-Moor near Newton Abbot Devon TQ13 7TD England

**WHITTEN, JERRY LYNN,** THEORETICAL CHEMISTRY & EDUCATIONAL ADMINISTRATION. *Current Pos:* PROF CHEM & DEAN PHYS & MATH SCI, NC STATE UNIV, 89- *Personal Data:* b Bartow, Fla, Aug 13, 37; m 80, Adela Chrzeszeyzk; c Jerrard & Christina. *Educ:* Ga Inst Technol, BS, 60, PhD(chem), 64. *Honors & Awards:* Alexander von Humboldt, Sr Scientist Award, 79. *Prof Exp:* Res assoc chem, Princeton Univ, 63-65, instr, 65; asst prof, Mich State Univ, 65-67; from asst prof to prof chem, State Univ NY, Stony Brook, 67-89, chmn dept, 85-89. *Concurrent Pos:* Res grants, Petrol Res Fund, 66-67, 74-76 & 77-81 & NSF, 67-72; Dept Energy res grants, 77-93; Alfred P Sloan fel, 69-71; vis prof, Univ Bonn & Wuppertal, 79 & Swiss Fed Inst Technol, Zurich, 84; Alfred P Sloan fel, 69-71; mem bd dirs, Burroughs Wellcome Fund, 93- *Mem:* Am Phys Soc; Am Chem Soc; Sigma Xi; NY Acad Sci. *Res:* Theoretical studies of molecular structure and bonding; ab initio many-electron theory; theory of excited electronic states, metallic surfaces and chemisorption. *Mailing Add:* Phys & Math Sci NC State Univ Box 8201 Raleigh NC 27695

**WHITTEN, KENNETH WAYNE,** INORGANIC CHEMISTRY, CHEMICAL EDUCATION. *Current Pos:* asst prof & coord gen chem, 67-70, assoc prof, 70-83, PROF CHEM & COORDR GEN CHEM, UNIV GA, 84- *Personal Data:* b Collinsville, Ala, Feb 4, 32; m 58, Betty J Jones; c Kenneth A & Mary K. *Educ:* Berry Col, AB, 53; Univ Miss, MS, 58; Univ Ill, PhD(inorg chem), 65. *Prof Exp:* Instr chem, Univ Miss, 55-56; asst prof, Berry Col, 56-58; instr, Univ Southwestern La, 58-59; asst prof, Miss State Col Women, 59-60 & Univ Ala, 63-66. *Mem:* Am Chem Soc. *Res:* Synthesis in fused salt media; chemical education; theories of testing. *Mailing Add:* Dept Chem Univ Ga 1180 E Broad St Athens GA 30601-3040

**WHITTEN, MAURICE MASON,** HISTORY OF SCIENCE & TECHNOLOGY. *Current Pos:* prof, 78-83, EMER PROF CHEM, UNIV SOUTHERN MAINE, 83- *Personal Data:* b Providence, RI, Oct 1, 23; m 83, Doris R Meserve; c 7. *Educ:* Colby Col, AB, 45; Columbia Univ, MA, 49; Ohio State Univ, PhD, 71. *Honors & Awards:* Elizabeth Thompson Award, Am Acad Arts & Sci, 54. *Prof Exp:* Sci teacher, Wilton Acad, 45-48 & Lewiston Maine High Sch, 48-55; instr phys sci, Gorham State Teachers Col, 55-59; TV sci teacher, State Dept Educ, Maine, 59-60; from asst prof to prof phys sci & chem, Univ Maine, Portland-Gorham, 61-77. *Concurrent Pos:* Lectr, Cent Maine Gen Hosp, Lewiston, 52-53. *Mem:* AAAS; Am Chem Soc; Nat Sci Teachers Asn; Hist Sci Soc. *Res:* Science education; history of the gunpowder mills of Maine. *Mailing Add:* 11 Lincoln St Gorham ME 04038-1703

**WHITTEN, ROBERT CRAIG, JR,** AERONOMY. *Current Pos:* RETIRED. *Personal Data:* b Bristol, Va, Dec 6, 26; m 53, Sally Marie Kriz; c 2. *Educ:* US Merchant Marine Acad, BS, 47; Univ Buffalo, BA, 55; Duke Univ, MA, 58, PhD(theoret physics), 59; San Jose State Univ, MS, 71. *Honors & Awards:* NASA Group Achievement Award, 80 & 81. *Prof Exp:* Asst, Duke Univ, 55-57, instr, 57-58, asst, 58-59; from physicist to sr physicist, Stanford Res Inst, 59-67; res scientist, NASA-Ames Res Ctr, 67-89. *Concurrent Pos:* Lectr, Stanford Univ, 61-62 & 64-66, Univ Santa Clara, 64 & 69 & San Jose State Univ, 72, 79 & 84; consult sci, eng & tech doc. *Mem:* Am Geophys Union; assoc fel Am Inst Aeronaut & Astronaut. *Res:* Structure, chemistry and dynamics of planetary atmospheres and ionospheres; chemistry and meteorology of the stratosphere; the quantum mechanical three body problem. *Mailing Add:* 1117 Yorkshire Dr Cupertino CA 95014

**WHITTENBERGER, JAMES LAVERRE,** AIR POLLUTION HEALTH EFFECTS, OCCUPATIONAL HEALTH. *Current Pos:* RETIRED. *Personal Data:* b Dahina, Ill, Feb 12, 14; m 43; c 3. *Prof Exp:* Internship, Cincinnati Gen Hosp, 38-39; res fel surg, Univ Chicago, 39-40; res fel med, Harvard Univ, 40-42, from assoc prof to prof physiol, 46-82; res fel physiol, NY Univ, 43; prof & dir environ med, Univ Calif, Irvine, Los Angeles, 82-88. *Concurrent Pos:* Dept head physiol, Sch Pub Health, Harvard Univ, 48-80; James Stevens Simmons prof pub health, 58-82, dir, Kresge Ctr Environ Health, 58-82, assoc dean, 66-78; sci adv bd, US Environ Protection Agency, 73-81; dir, Occup Health Ctr, Univ Calif, Irvine & Los Angeles, 82-88; chair,

Dept Commun & Environ Med, Col Med, Univ Calif Irvine, 82-88; chair, Bd Sci Counselors, US Dept Hosp Health Serv, Nat Inst Occup Safety & Health, 84- *Res:* Air pollution health effects. *Mailing Add:* Imov Calif Irvine N Campus FRF Rm 8 Irvine CA 92717-1825. *Fax:* 714-725-2070

**WHITTIER, ANGUS CHARLES,** PHYSICS. *Current Pos:* RETIRED. *Personal Data:* b Ottawa, Ont, Oct 17, 21; m 48, Dorothy C Wein; c Sue, Rob, Maggie & John. *Educ:* Royal Mil Col, Kingston, Ont, BSc, 41; Queen's Univ, Ont, BSc, 48; McGill Univ, MSc & PhD(physics), 52. *Prof Exp:* Asst res officer, Atomic Energy Can, Ltd, 52-55; supv physicist, Atomic Power Dept, Can Gen Elec, 55-67, mgr reactor analysis, 67-70; supt, Shielding & Comput Br Power Projs, 70-75, mgr, Shielding & Reactor Physics, Eng Co, 77-84, mgr physics, Atomic Energy Can Ltd, Candu Opers, Sheridan Park, 85-86. *Mem:* Am Nuclear Soc; Can Nuclear Soc. *Res:* Nuclear physics, particularly reactor physics. *Mailing Add:* 2493 Vineland Rd Mississauga ON L5K 2A3 Can

**WHITTIER, DEAN PAGE,** PLANT MORPHOLOGY. *Current Pos:* from asst prof to assoc prof, 65-77, chmn, Dept Gen Biol, 75-78, PROF BIOL, VANDERBILT UNIV, 77- *Personal Data:* b Worcester, Mass, July 2, 35; m 58; c 2. *Educ:* Univ Mass, BS, 57; Harvard Univ, AM, 59, PhD(biol), 61. *Prof Exp:* Asst prof bot, Va Polytech Inst, 61-64; NIH fel biol, Harvard Univ, 64-65. *Mem:* Bot Soc Am; Am Fern Soc (treas, 74 & 75, vpres, 80 & 81, pres, 82 & 83); Int Soc Plant Morphologists; Int Asn Pteridologists (treas, 93-97). *Res:* Morphogenesis; apomixis in lower vascular plants. *Mailing Add:* Dept Biol Vanderbilt Univ Nashville TN 37235

**WHITTIER, HENRY O,** BOTANY, BRYOLOGY. *Current Pos:* PROF BIOL, UNIV CENT FLA, 79-, DIR ARBORETUM, 86- *Personal Data:* b Schenectady, NY, Sept 1, 37; m 59; c 1. *Educ:* Miami Univ, BS, 59, MA, 61; Columbia Univ, PhD(biol), 68. *Prof Exp:* Res asst bot, Miami Univ Schooner Col Rebel Exped to SPac, 60; instr, Univ Hawaii, 62-64; res asst bryol, NY Bot Garden, 64-68; from asst prof to prof biol sci, Fla Technol Univ, 68-79. *Mem:* Am Bryol & Lichenological Soc; Am Inst Biol Sci; Sigma Xi. *Res:* Plant systematics, tropical botany, taxonomy, ethnobotany, ecology and biogeography, especially Pacific islands Bryophyta; conservation biology. *Mailing Add:* Dept Biol Fla Tech Univ PO Box 162368 Orlando FL 32816-2368

**WHITTIER, JAMES S(PENCER),** SPACE LAUNCH ENGINEERING. *Current Pos:* Mem tech staff, Aerospace Corp, 61-65, sect mgr, 65-67, dept head, 67-87, spec assignment, Off Secy Defense, 87-89, prin engr, 90-93, DISTINGUISHED ENGR SPACE LAUNCH OPERS, AEROSPACE CORP, 93- *Personal Data:* b Farmington, Minn, June 19, 35; m 61, Virginia Soennichsen; c Laura. *Educ:* Univ Minn, BS, 57, MS, 58, PhD(mech, mat), 61. *Concurrent Pos:* Sr res fel, Appl Phys Dept, Cornell Univ, 74-75; chmn, Plasmadynamics & Lasers Tech Comt, Am Inst Aeronaut & Astronaut, 83-85. *Mem:* Optical Soc Am; Am Inst Aeronaut & Astronaut; Soc Exp Mech. *Res:* Space launch systems; chemical lasers; laser effects; remote sensing of motions; stress wave propagation. *Mailing Add:* 2101 Via Estudillo Palos Verdes Peninsula CA 90274

**WHITTINGHAM, M(ICHAEL) STANLEY,** SOLID STATE CHEMISTRY. *Current Pos:* PROF CHEM & DIR, INST MAT RES, STATE UNIV NY, BINGHAMTON, 88- *Personal Data:* b Nottingham, Eng, Dec 22, 41; nat US; m 69; c 2. *Educ:* Oxford Univ, BA, 64, MA, 67, DPhil(chem), 68. *Prof Exp:* Res assoc mat sci, Stanford Univ, 68-72; mem sci staff, Exxon Res & Eng Co, 72-75, head, Chem Physics Group, 75-78, dir, Solid State & Catalytic Sci Lab, Corp Res Labs, 78-80, mgr chem eng, Technol Div, 80-84; dir phys sci, Schlumberger, 84-88. *Concurrent Pos:* Demonstr, Dept Inorg Chem, Oxford Univ, 65-67; prin ed, J Solid State Ionics & assoc ed, Chem Mat. *Mem:* Am Chem Soc; Electrochem Soc; Am Phys Soc; Mat Res Soc; Am Inst Chem Engrs. *Res:* Chemical properties of highly non-stoichiometric materials; fast ion transport in solids; electrochemical control of the properties of materials; solid state electrochemistry; high energy-density batteries; synthetic fuels technology. *Mailing Add:* Chem Dept State Univ NY Mat Res Ctr Binghamton NY 13902-6000. *Fax:* 607-777-4623

**WHITTINGHILL, MAURICE,** GENETICS. *Current Pos:* from assoc prof to prof, 52-74, vis prof, 74, EMER PROF ZOOL, UNIV NC, CHAPEL HILL, 74- *Personal Data:* b St Joseph, Mo, May 15, 09; m 32, 55, Martha M Speaks; c Diana W (Steele) & Warren C (deceased). *Educ:* Dartmouth Col, AB, 31; Univ Mich, PhD(zool), 37. *Prof Exp:* Instr, Dartmouth Col, 31-33; asst, Univ Mich, 35; Nat Res Coun fel biol sci, Calif Inst Technol, 36-37; fel biol, Bennington Col, 37-42. *Concurrent Pos:* Prof, Univ Mich, 46; sr biologist, Oak Ridge Nat Lab, 49; Wachtmeister vis prof biol, Va Mil Inst, 76; vis prof biol, Univ NC, Wilmington, 77; T E Powell Jr prof biol, Elon Col, 79-81. *Mem:* Genetics Soc Am; Am Soc Zool; Am Soc Nat; Am Soc Human Genetics; Am Genetic Asn (vpres, 72, pres, 73); Biomet Soc. *Res:* Genetics of Drosophila; irradiation and temperature effects; mutation and crossing over; spondylitis. *Mailing Add:* 1905 S Lake Shore Dr Chapel Hill NC 27514

**WHITTINGTON, BERNARD W,** ENGINEERING, ELECTRICAL FORENSIC ENGINEERING. *Current Pos:* CONSULT, WHITTINGTON ENG, 82- *Personal Data:* b July 19, 20; m 50, Jean Wilhelm; c David, Ann & Brenda. *Educ:* WVa Univ, BSEE, 51. *Honors & Awards:* Centennial Award, Inst Elec & Electronics Engrs, Outstanding Achievement Award, Kaufmann Award, Stand Medallion Award. *Prof Exp:* Lead Elec Engr, Union Carbide, 65-82. *Concurrent Pos:* Chmn, Code Making Panel, Nat Elec Code; eng consult, Union Carbide Corp; WVa Univ Acad Elec Engrs, 92; Am Nat Stand Inst, US Nat Comt, Int Electrotech Comn, 96- *Mem:* Fel Inst Elec & Electronics Engrs; Nat Fire & Protection Asn. *Mailing Add:* Whittington Engr Inc 100 Whittingshire Lane Charleston WV 25312

**WHITTINGTON, STUART GORDON,** THEORETICAL CHEMISTRY. *Current Pos:* from asst prof to assoc prof, 70-80, chmn, 85-88, PROF CHEM, UNIV TORONTO, 80- *Personal Data:* b Chesterfield, Eng, Apr 16, 42; Can & UK citizen; m 64, Ann Fretwell; c Graeme & Megan. *Educ:* Cambridge Univ, BA, 63, PhD(chem), 72. *Prof Exp:* Scientist chem, Unilever Res Lab, UK, 63-66; res fel, Univ Calif, San Diego, 66-67; res fel, Univ Toronto, 67-68; scientist, Unilever Res Lab, UK, 68-70. *Concurrent Pos:* Vis prof, Dept Math, Univ Newcastle, Australia, 77, Dept Math, Fla State Univ, 97; sr res fel, Sci Res Coun, Univ Bristol, 77-78; vis fel, Trinity Col, Oxford, 83-84, vis res fel, Dept Math, Univ Melbourne, Australia, 90, Merton Col, Oxford, 96. *Mem:* Am Math Soc. *Res:* Statistical mechanics; Monte Carlo methods; excluded volume effect in polymers; polymer adsorption and colloid stability; percolation theory; phase transitions and critical phenomena. *Mailing Add:* Dept Chem Univ Toronto Toronto ON M5S 1A1 Can. *E-Mail:* swhittin@alchemy.chem.utoronto.ca

**WHITTINGTON, WESLEY HERBERT,** ESTER PLASTICIZERS FOR POLYMERS. *Current Pos:* TECH SR MGR, C P HALL CO, 78- *Personal Data:* b Basil, Ohio, Dec 1, 33; m 53; c 2. *Educ:* Capital Univ, BS, 61. *Prof Exp:* Asst to chief chem, Precision Rubber Prod Corp, 61-68; develop scientist, B F Goodrich Chem, 68-78. *Mem:* Rubber Div Am Chem Soc. *Res:* Test, study and communicate the use and application of ester plasticizers in rubber and plastics compounds. *Mailing Add:* 5851 W 73rd St PO Box 910 Bedford Park IL 60499-0910

**WHITTLE, CHARLES EDWARD, JR,** PHYSICS, APPLIED MATHEMATICS. *Current Pos:* ASST DIR, INST ENERGY ANALYSIS, OAK RIDGE ASSOC UNIVS, 74- *Personal Data:* b Brownsville, Ky, Mar 8, 31; m 52; c 10. *Educ:* Centre Col, AB, 49; Washington Univ, PhD(nuclear physics), 53. *Prof Exp:* Fulbright & Res Corp grants, State Univ Leiden, 53-54; res scientist, Union Carbide Corp, 54-56; asst & assoc prof physics, Western Ky Univ, 56-60, prof & chmn dept, 60-62; coordr res, Centre Col Ky, 62-64, from assoc dean to dean, 64-72, prof physics, 72-74, Matton chair appl math, 72-74. *Mem:* Am Asn Physics Teachers; Sigma Xi; Phys Soc. *Res:* Nuclear and optical spectroscopy; applied mathematics and geophysics; energy policy analysis and modeling; energy data analysis and validation; geothermal energy assessment; geophysics. *Mailing Add:* 109 Trevose Lane Oak Ridge TN 37830

**WHITTLE, FRANK,** aeronautical engineering; deceased, see previous edition for last biography

**WHITTLE, GEORGE PATTERSON,** WATER TREATMENT, HAZARDOUS WASTE MANAGEMENT. *Current Pos:* PROF CIVIL ENG, UNIV ALA, 67- *Personal Data:* b Eufaula, Ala, July 1, 25; m 63; c 1. *Educ:* Ga Inst Technol, BChE, 46, BIE, 47; Univ Fla, MS, 64, PhD(chem), 66. *Honors & Awards:* Bedell Award, Water Pollution Control Fedn, 77. *Prof Exp:* Chem engr, Hercules Powder Co, 47-49; self-employed, Whittle Lumber Co, 50-53; chemist, Swift & Co, 53-55; chief chemist, Allied Chem Co, 55-57; res engr, Tenn Corp, 57-63. *Mem:* Am Water Works Asn; Am Soc Civil Engrs; Sigma Xi. *Res:* Water quality modeling, hazardous waste management; water treatment and chemistry, pollution control; analytical chemistry of water and wastewater; reaction kinetics of halogen residuals in water. *Mailing Add:* 1305 Heritage Rd Tuscaloosa AL 35406-3016

**WHITTLE, JOHN ANTONY,** ORGANIC CHEMISTRY, BIOCHEMISTRY. *Current Pos:* from asst prof to assoc prof, 69-83, PROF CHEM, LAMAR UNIV, 83- *Personal Data:* b Settle, Yorks, Eng, Mar 13, 42. *Educ:* Univ Glasgow, BSc, 64; Imp Col, dipl, & Univ London, PhD(org chem), 67. *Prof Exp:* Fel, Rutgers Univ, NJ, 67-69. *Concurrent Pos:* Interim chair, Chem Dept, Lamar Univ, 96- *Mem:* Am Chem Soc. *Res:* Biosynthesis of sesquiterpenoids and other natural products; synthesis of sesquiterpenoid ring systems. *Mailing Add:* Dept Chem Lamar Univ PO Box 10022 Lamar Univ Sta Beaumont TX 77710-0022

**WHITTLE, PHILIP RODGER,** ORGANIC CHEMISTRY, FORENSIC CHEMISTRY. *Current Pos:* assoc prof, 70-80, DIR, REGIONAL CRIMINALISTICS LAB, MO SOUTHERN STATE COL, 72-, PROF CHEM, 80- *Personal Data:* b Russell Springs, Ky, July 11, 43; m 67, Donna Hollatz; c Bruce & Brian. *Educ:* Univ Ky, BS, 65; Iowa State Univ, PhD(org chem), 69. *Prof Exp:* NIH fel, Univ Colo, Boulder, 69-70. *Concurrent Pos:* Consult, Analytical Labs; mem, Midwest Asn Forensic Scientists. *Mem:* Am Chem Soc (secy-treas, 66-); Am Soc Crime Lab Dirs; Am Acad Forensic Scientists; Sigma Xi. *Res:* Electrocyclic cyclopropane ring openings; toxicology; modern drug analysis; trace evidence; forensic applications. *Mailing Add:* Dept Chem Mo Southern State Col Joplin MO 64801-1595

**WHITTLESEY, BRUCE R,** MATERIALS SCIENCE, X-RAY CRYSTALLOGRAPHY. *Current Pos:* ASSOC PROF, TEX TECH UNIV, 87- *Personal Data:* b Waterbury, Conn, June 15, 54; m 85. *Educ:* Univ SFla, BA, 78; Univ Tex, Austin, PhD(inorg chem), 85. *Prof Exp:* Assoc, Univ Ill, Urbana, Champaign, 85-87. *Mem:* Am Chem Soc. *Res:* Synthesis and characterization of new inorganic compounds containing transition metals and group 13 elements (aluminum, gallium indium); synthesis of new compounds for use in the preparation of materials having useful electronic properties. *Mailing Add:* Dept Chem & Biochem Tex Tech Univ Box 4260 Lubbock TX 79409-1061. *Fax:* 806-742-1289; *E-Mail:* wdbrw@ttacsl.ttu.edu

**WHITTLESEY, EMMET FINLAY,** MATHEMATICS. *Current Pos:* from instr to assoc prof, 54-65, PROF MATH, TRINITY COL, CONN, 65- *Personal Data:* b Winchester, Mass, Oct 9, 23; m 66, Betty Navratil; c Stanislaus F, Saunders N & Marshall A. *Educ:* Princeton Univ, AB, 48, MA, 56, PhD(math), 57. *Prof Exp:* Instr math, Pa State Univ, 50-51 & Bates Col, 51-54. *Concurrent Pos:* NSF fel, 62-63; Seabury prof. *Mem:* Am Math Soc; Math Asn Am; Sigma Xi. *Res:* Combinatorial topology; functional analysis; integration. *Mailing Add:* 89 Walbridge Rd West Hartford CT 06119. *E-Mail:* finlay.whittlesey@trincoll.edu

**WHITTLESEY, JOHN R B,** MARINE SEISMIC EXPLORATION. *Current Pos:* RETIRED. *Personal Data:* b Los Angeles, Calif, July 21, 27; m 66; c Kim & Karinita. *Educ:* Calif Inst Technol, BS, 48, MS, 50. *Honors & Awards:* Award, Soc Explor Geophys, 65. *Prof Exp:* Instr physics & math, Univ Nev, 50; Ford Found behav sci grant & res asst, Univ NC, 52-54; res mathematician res clin neuropsychiat inst, Med Ctr, Univ Calif, Los Angeles, 57-62, data processing analyst, Brain Res Inst, 62-64; sr mem res staff seismic explor data processing, Ampex Corp, Ray Geophys Co & Petty-Ray Geophys Co, Houston, Tex, 64-80; sr res scientist, Marine Seismic Data Acquisition & Signal Processing, Geosource Inc, 80-86. *Concurrent Pos:* Statist consult numerous behav scientists, Calif, 58-71; NIMH spec res fel brain res inst, Univ Calif, Los Angeles, 63-64. *Mem:* Fel AAAS. *Res:* Mathematics and digital computers applied to psychiatry, brain research, exploration geophysics; time-series analysis; seismic signal processing and air gun signature analysis; laser fusion; digital signal processing; differential geometry and writing chapters for computer-use texts. *Mailing Add:* 5439 Del Monte Dr Houston TX 77056. *Fax:* 713-621-0239

**WHITTON, LESLIE,** PLANT CYTOLOGY, PLANT GENETICS. *Current Pos:* asst prof, 62-64, asst prof bot, 64-68, ASSOC PROF BOT, BRIGHAM YOUNG UNIV, 68- *Personal Data:* b New Bedford, Mass, Sept 1, 23; m 47; c 4. *Educ:* Utah State Univ, BS, 49; Univ Calif, MS, 53; Cornell Univ, PhD, 64. *Prof Exp:* Asst prof hort, Univ Maine, Orono, 56-62. *Mem:* Bot Soc Am; Sigma Xi. *Res:* Cytology, genetics and breeding of small fruit species and native shrub species of the Rocky Mountain region. *Mailing Add:* 1812 N 1450 E Provo UT 84604

**WHITTOW, GEORGE CAUSEY,** PHYSIOLOGY. *Current Pos:* PROF PHYSIOL, SCH MED, UNIV HAWAII, 68-, CHMN DEPT, 85- *Personal Data:* b Milford Haven, UK, Feb 28, 30; m 55; c 1. *Educ:* Univ London, BSc, 52; Univ Malaya, PhD(physiol), 57. *Prof Exp:* Asst lectr physiol, Univ Malaya, 52-54, lectr, 54-59; sr sci officer, Hannah Res Inst, Ayr, Scotland, 59-65; assoc prof physiol, Rutgers Univ, New Brunswick, 65-68. *Mem:* Am Physiol Soc; fel Linnean Soc; Brit Inst Biol. *Res:* Physiology of thermoregulation; thermal ecology. *Mailing Add:* John A Burns Sch Med Univ Hawaii 1960 E-W Rd Honolulu HI 96822. *Fax:* 808-956-5506

**WHITTUM-HUDSON, JUDITH ANNE,** INFECTIOUS DISEASES, MUCOSAL IMMUNITY. *Current Pos:* asst prof, 82-89, ASSOC PROF OPHTHAL, SCH MED, JOHNS HOPKINS UNIV, 89- *Personal Data:* m 84, Alan P Hudson. *Educ:* Wells Col, BA, 69; Univ Conn, PhD(immunol), 80. *Mem:* Am Asn Immunologists; Am Soc Microbiologists; Asn Res Vision & Ophthal; Clin Immunol Soc; Int Mucosal Immunol Soc; Int Soc Neuroimmunol. *Mailing Add:* 457 Wilmer Woods Sch Med Johns Hopkins Univ 600 N Wolfe St Baltimore MD 21287-9142. *Fax:* 410-614-1114; *E-Mail:* jwhittum@ishtar.med.jhu.edu

**WHITTY, ELMO BENJAMIN,** AGRONOMY. *Current Pos:* From asst prof to assoc prof, 66-77, PROF AGRON, UNIV FLA, 77- *Personal Data:* b Lee, Fla, Mar 6, 37. *Educ:* Univ Fla, BSA, 59, MSA, 61; NC State Univ, PhD(soil sci), 65. *Mem:* Am Soc Agron; Plant Growth Regulator Soc Am; Am Peanut Res & Educ Soc. *Res:* Tobacco production; cultural practices; plant growth regulators; plant nutrition. *Mailing Add:* 13815 Millhopper Rd Gainesville FL 32653

**WHITWORTH, CLYDE W,** PHARMACY. *Current Pos:* assoc prof, 66-80, PROF PHARM, UNIV GA, 80- *Personal Data:* b Paulding Co, Ga, Oct 9, 26; m 51; c 3. *Educ:* Univ Ga, BS, 50, MS, 56; Univ Fla, PhD(pharm), 63. *Prof Exp:* From instr to asst prof pharm, Univ Ga, 54-60; asst prof, Northeast La State Col, 63-66. *Concurrent Pos:* Mead Johnson res award, 65-66; William A Webster Co grant prod stability, 72- *Mem:* Am Pharmaceut Asn. *Res:* Factors influencing drug absorption and drug release from external preparations. *Mailing Add:* 390 Greencrest Dr Athens GA 30605

**WHITWORTH, NEIL S,** OBSTETRICS & GYNECOLOGY. *Current Pos:* PROF OBSTET & GYNEC, UNIV MISS MED CTR, 77- *Personal Data:* b San Diego, Calif, Sept 23, 39. *Res:* Obstetrics and gynecology. *Mailing Add:* Dept Obstet & Gynec Univ Miss Med Ctr 2500 N State St MS 39216 Jackson MS 39216

**WHITWORTH, WALTER RICHARD,** aquatic biology, for more information see previous edition

**WHORTON, ELBERT BENJAMIN,** RESEARCH DESIGN & ANALYSIS. *Current Pos:* RES COLLABR, BROOKHAVEN NAT LAB, 82- *Personal Data:* b Stamford, Tex, Nov 10, 38; m 62; c 2. *Educ:* Baylor Univ, BS(math) & BS(physics), 62; Tulane Univ, MS, 64; Okla Univ, PhD(biostatist & med comput), 68. *Prof Exp:* Surv statistician dir, La State Health Dept, 64-65; from asst prof to assoc prof & dir biomet, Univ Vt, 68-72, asst prof math, 69-72;

assoc prof & dir biostatist, Med Br, Univ Tex, Galveston, 72-82. *Concurrent Pos:* Statist consult, Bur Manpower Intel, NIH, 68-73, Nat Cancer Inst, 73-, Dow Chem Co, 73-80 & Ethyl Corp, 81-82; dir, Educ & Res Comput Ctr, Univ Tex Med Br Galveston, 75-81, assoc dean, Grad Sch Biomed Sci, 76-81; vis prof, Med Sch, Univ Vt, 81. *Mem:* Am Statist Asn; Environ Mutagen Soc; Biomet Soc; Sigma Xi. *Res:* Development and evaluation of experimental and non-experimental designs in environmental toxicology mutagenesis research; development of improved methods for statistical evaluation of research results, particularly in genetic toxicology. *Mailing Add:* 20 Colony Park Circle Galveston TX 77551

**WHORTON, M DONALD,** OCCUPATIONAL HEALTH & EPIDEMIOLOGY. *Current Pos:* PRIN, WHORTON, INC, 94- *Personal Data:* b Las Vegas, NMex, Jan 25, 43; m 72, Diana Obrinsley; c Matthew, Laura & Julie. *Educ:* Univ NMex, MD, 68; Johns Hopkins Univ, MPH, 73; Am Bd Internal Med, cert, 75; Am Bd Prev Med Occup Med, cert, 75. *Honors & Awards:* Upjohn Achievement Award; Jean Spensor Felton Award, 96. *Prof Exp:* Instr anat, Sch Med, Univ NMex, 70-71; staff physician, Family Planning Clin, Washington, DC, 71-72; instr, Sch Health Serv, Johns Hopkins Univ, 73-75, instr med, Sch Med, 74-75; assoc dir, Div Emergency Med, Baltimore City Hosps, 74-75; clin asst prof med, Div Ambulatory & Community Med, Sch Med, Univ Calif, San Francisco, 75-77, lectr, Sch Pub Health, Berkeley, 75-79, dir, Labor Occup Health Prog, Inst Indust Relations, Ctr Labor Res & Educ, 75-77, med dir, 77-79, assoc clin prof occup med, Sch Pub Health, 79-87; prin & sr occup physician/epidemiologist, EHA, 78-88; vpres & chief med scientist, ENSR Health Sci, 88-94. *Concurrent Pos:* Resident, Dept Med, Baltimore City Hosp, 71-74; consult, Occup Health Prog, Inst Indust Relations, Univ Calif, Berkeley; mem, Comt Occup Health & Safety, Am Pub Health Asn, 73-74; mem, Study Sect Occup Safety & Health, Ctr Dis Control/Nat Inst Occup Safety & Health, 80-83; mem, Occup Med Pract Comt, Am Occup Med Asn, 82-; corresp, Comt Human Rights, Nat Acad Sci, 83-; mem, Comt Nat Statist, Nat Res Coun, 85-, Panel on Occup Safety & Health Statist, 85-87, Sci Oversight Panel on Ctr Dis Control Select Cancer Study of Vietnam Vets, Inst Med, 88-90; mem, Sci Oversight Panel on Ctr Dis Control Select Cancer Study of Vietnam Vets, Inst Med, 88-90; Comt Health Effects on Indoor Allergens, Inst Med-Nat Acad Sci, 91-93; Comn Behav & Social Sci & Educ, Nat Res Coun, 91-94; mem, Bd Health Prom & Dis Prev, Inst Med, 94- *Mem:* Inst Med-Nat Acad Sci; Am Pub Health Asn; Am Occup Med Asn; Am Col Occup Med; fel Am Col Epidemiol; Soc Occup & Environ Health; AAAS; Int Asn Occup Health; Am Col Occup & Environ Med; Am Pub Health Asn; Am Col Epidmiol. *Res:* Environmental and occupational health issues; occupational reproductive issues. *Mailing Add:* 1135 Atlantic Ave Alameda CA 94501. *Fax:* 510-748-5761

**WHORTON, RAYBURN HARLEN,** PAPER PROCESS CHEMISTRY. *Current Pos:* RETIRED. *Personal Data:* b London, Ark, Apr 28, 31; m 56, Kathryn McMillen; c Mary K, Steven R & Sherry (McMillan). *Educ:* Ark Polytech Col, BS, 53; Univ Ark, MS, 56. *Prof Exp:* Instr chem, Ark Polytech Col, 55-56; res chemist, Crossett Co, 57-62; proj supvr, Ga-Pac Corp, 62-63; sr proj chemist, Int Paper Co, 64-69, sect leader paper develop, 69-77, group mgr paper structure & chem, Erling Riis Res, 77-87. *Mem:* Tech Asn Pulp & Paper Indust. *Res:* Papermaking; surface and internal sizing; printability coatings; paper-plastic combinations; converting processes. *Mailing Add:* 6167 Challen Circle Mobile AL 36608

**WHYBROW, PETER CHARLES,** PSYCHIATRY, ENDOCRINOLOGY. *Current Pos:* RUTH MELTZER PROF PSYCHIAT & CHMN, DEPT PSYCHIAT, UNIV PA, 84- *Personal Data:* b Hertfordshire, Eng, June 13, 39; nat US; div; c 2. *Educ:* Univ London, MB & BS, 62; Royal Col Physicians, dipl, 62; Conjoint Bd Physicians & Surgeons Eng, dipl psychol med, 68. *Hon Degrees:* MA, Dartmouth Col, 74; MA, Univ Pa, 84. *Honors & Awards:* Sr Investr Award, Nat Alliance Res on Schizophrenia & the Depressions, 89. *Prof Exp:* House physician, Med Res Coun-Univ Col Hosp, London, 62; house surgeon, St Helier Hosp, Surrey, Eng, 63; sr house physician, Univ Col Hosp, London, 63-64; house physician, Prince of Wales Hosp, London, 64; resident psychiat, Univ NC, 65-67, instr, 67-68; sci officer, Med Res Coun, Eng, 68-69; from asst prof to prof psychiat, Dartmouth Med Sch, 69-79, chmn dept, 71-78, 71-79, exec dean, 80-83. *Concurrent Pos:* NIMH res fel, Univ NC, 67-68; lectr, Univ Col Hosp Med Sch, London, 68-69; dir res training, Dartmouth Hitchcock Affil Hosps, 69-71, dir psychiat, 70-; consult, Vet Admin Hosp, 70-; Josiah Macy Jr fac scholar, 78-79; vis scientist, Div Psychobiol, NIMH; chmn, Psychiat Test Comt, Nat Bd Med Examrs, 78-; fel, Ctr Advan Study Behav Scis, Stanford Univ, 93-94. *Mem:* Fel Royal Col Psychiat; Am Asn Chmn Depts Psychiat (pres, 77-78); Brit Soc Psychosom Res; fel Am Psychiat Asn; fel Am Col Psychiatrists; Am Col Neuropsychopharm. *Res:* Psychobiology of affective disorders, particularly pharmacologic and endocrinologic aspects of manic-depressive illness. *Mailing Add:* 135 S 19th St Philadelphia PA 19103

**WHYTE, ANNE V T,** GEOGRAPHY. *Current Pos:* dir, Soc Sci Div, 86-92, DIR GEN, ENVIRON & NATURAL RESOURCES DIV, INT DEVELOP RES CTR, OTTAWA, CAN, 92- *Personal Data:* b Thorne, UK, Apr 14, 42; m, Robert D Auger; c David P, Clare A & Joanna C (Burton). *Educ:* Cambridge Univ, BA(Hon), 63, MA, 67, Johns Hopkins Univ, PhD, 71. *Prof Exp:* Res assoc, Dept Geog & Psychol, Univ Bristol, Eng, 68-74; univ lectr, Dept Geog, Univ London, 74-75; assoc prof geog, Univ Toronto, Can, 76-78, dir undergrad environ studies, 78-86. *Concurrent Pos:* Prog specialist MAB prog, Div Ecol Sci, UNESCO, Paris, 84-86; chmn, African Econ Res Consortium Inc, New York, 87-90, Can Nat Comt, UNESCO/MAB, Ottawa, 89-93 & Can Global Change Prog, Ottawa, 90-92. *Mem:* Fel Royal Soc Can; Am Asn Geog; Can Asn Geogrs (vpres, 93, pres, 94); Sigma Xi. *Res:* Geography; author of several books. *Mailing Add:* Mestor Assoc 751 Hamilton Rd Russell ON K4R 1E5 Can

**WHYTE, DONALD EDWARD,** ORGANIC & POLYMER CHEMISTRY, METAL COATINGS. *Current Pos:* PRES, CONSUMER CHEM INC, 85- *Personal Data:* b Regina, Sask, Jan 22, 18; nat US; c 4. *Educ:* Univ Sask, BA, 39, MA, 41; Columbia Univ, PhD(chem), 43. *Prof Exp:* Chemist naval stores, Hercules Powder Co, 43-46; head org res sect, S C Johnson & Son, Inc, 46-52, res serv mgr, 52-57, tech serv mgr, 57-59, dir, serv prod develop, 59-61, appl res dir, 61-64, res mgr, 65-71, prod res mgr int opers, dir res & develop int opers, 74-77, vpres, Int Res & Develop, 77-84. *Concurrent Pos:* Fel, Columbia Univ; consult, Tech One, 90- *Mem:* Am Chem Soc; Am Oil Chem Soc. Am Soc Qual Control. *Res:* Analytical and market research; new product evaluation; new product development of polishes, coating and porelon; polymers; insecticides; insect repellants; synergists and microbiology; development of new consumer and industrial products for overseas introduction; developing overseas research and development laboratories; development of aqueous coatings for metals. *Mailing Add:* 2720 Michigan Blvd Racine WI 53402-4252

**WHYTE, JOHN NIMMO CROSBIE,** TOXIC MICROALGAE, BIVALVE & FISH NUTRITION. *Current Pos:* res scientist, Tech Lab, 67-85, RES SCIENTIST, PAC BIOL STA, DEPT FISHERIES & OCEANS, GOVT CAN, VANCOUVER, 85- *Personal Data:* b Falkirk, Stirlingshire, Scotland, Sept 23, 37; Can & Brit citizen; m 71, Kathleen J Bloomfield; c Christopher J. *Educ:* Heriot-Watt Univ, Edinburgh, Scotland, BSc 61; Univ Edinburgh, Scotland, PhD(chem), 64. *Prof Exp:* Fel, Chem Dept, Univ Alta, Edmonton, 64-66; teaching fel chem, Univ BC, Vancouver, 66-67. *Mem:* Royal Soc Chem; Chem Inst Can; Aquacult Asn Can. *Res:* Biochemistry related to toxic microalgae, nutritional constituents of cultured species of plankton, nutrient transfer in the marine food chian; polysaccharide components of marine benthic algae, chemical indicators of physiological condition of bivalves and fish; nutritional and energy components in larval bivalves and fish influenced by cultivation conditions and diets; biochemical changes resulting from stress in shellfish and fish. *Mailing Add:* Dept Fisheries & Oceans Pac Biol Sta Nanaimo BC V9R 5K6 Can. *Fax:* 250-756-7053; *E-Mail:* whytej@pbs.dfo.ca

**WHYTE, MICHAEL PETER,** INTERNAL MEDICINE, ENDOCRINOLOGY & METABOLISM. *Current Pos:* fel endocrinol, Washington Univ, 76-79, asst prof med, 80-91, asst prof pediat, 82-91, PROF MED & PEDIAT, SCH MED, WASHINGTON UNIV, 91- *Personal Data:* b New York, NY, Dec 19, 46; m 74, Gloria Golenda; c Catherine Alexander. *Educ:* Washington Square Col, NY Univ, BA, 68; State Univ NY, MD, 72. *Honors & Awards:* Fuller Albright Award, Am Soc Bone & Mineral Res, 87. *Prof Exp:* Intern & resident internal med, Dept Med, Bellevue Hosp, New York, 72-74; clin assoc metab neurol, Nat Inst Neurol & Commun Dis & Stroke, NIH, 74-76. *Concurrent Pos:* Consult med staff, St Louis Zoo, 92. *Mem:* Am Soc Clin Invest; Am Soc Bone & Mineral Res; Am Soc Human Genetics; Endocrine Soc; AAAS; Am Soc Cell Biol. *Res:* Calcium metabolism and metabolic bone disease; alkaline phosphatase; bone dysplasias. *Mailing Add:* Barnes-Jewish Hosp St Louis 216 S Kingshighway St Louis MO 63110. *Fax:* 314-454-7999

**WHYTE, THADDEUS E, JR,** GENERAL CATALYSIS. *Current Pos:* tech mgr, 85-87, TECH DIR RES & DEVELOP, PQ CORP, 87- *Personal Data:* b Washington, DC, Dec 8, 37; m 59, Lucille O'Daniel; c 2. *Educ:* Georgetown Univ, BS, 60; Howard Univ, MS, 62, PhD(phys chem), 65. *Prof Exp:* Phys chemist, Nat Bur Stand, 62-63; res chemist, Howard Univ, 63-64; nuclear chemist, USAF, 64-67; sr res chemist & group leader, Mobil Res & Develop Corp, 67-76; dir indust chem res & develop, Air Prod & Chem, 76-79; managing dir, Catalytic Assocs, 79-85. *Concurrent Pos:* Lectr, Grad Sch, Sacramento State Col, 65-67, Gloucester Co Col, 69-70 & W Valley Community Col, 82-83. *Mem:* Am Chem Soc; Am Inst Chemists; Am Inst Chem Eng. *Res:* Industrial chemistry; zeolite synthesis and catalysis; petrochemicals; petroleum research. *Mailing Add:* Whytech Enterprises Inc 7366 E Parkside Dr Scottsdale AZ 85260. *Fax:* 610-825-1421

**WIANT, HARRY VERNON, JR,** FORESTRY. *Current Pos:* PROF FORESTRY, WVA UNIV, 72- *Personal Data:* b Burnsville, WVa, Nov 4, 32; m 54; c 2. *Educ:* Univ WVa, BSF, 54; Univ Ga, MF, 59; Yale Univ, PhD(forestry), 63. *Prof Exp:* Jr forester, US Forest Serv, 57; asst prof forestry, Humboldt State Col, 61-65; prof & asst to dean, Stephen F Austin State Col, 65-72. *Mem:* Soc Am Foresters. *Res:* Concentration of carbon dioxide near forest floor; ecology and silviculture of redwood; chemical and mechanical control of undesirable hardwoods; prediction of site quality; volume determinations and forest inventory; silviculture of southern forest trees; dendrological techniques; forest measurements. *Mailing Add:* Div Forestry WVa Univ PO Box 6125 Morgantown WV 26506-0001. *Fax:* 304-293-2441; *E-Mail:* u0267@wvnvm.wvnet.edu

**WIATR, CHRISTOPHER LOUIS,** INDUSTRIAL MICROBIOLOGY-BIOCORROSION & BIODEPOSITION, FOOD & WATER MICROBIOLOGY. *Current Pos:* sr microbiologist, Nalco Chem Co, 85-87, sr res microbiologist, 87-88, group leader microbiol & deposit control, Water Div, 88-91, GROUP LEADER PULP & PAPER, NALCO CHEM CO, 91- *Personal Data:* b Chicago, Ill, Jan 5, 48; m 78, Jeanne L Malecki; c Kelli, Christopher, Kaycee, Kirby & Nicholas. *Educ:* Ill Benedictine Col, BS, 69; Ill Inst Technol, MS, 74; Univ Ill, Chicago, PhD(microbiol), 85. *Prof Exp:* Teacher biol & advan placement biol, St Rita High Sch, 69-74; res microbiologist, Swift & Co, 74-75, lab mgr, 75-76, dir res & qual assurance, Derby Foods, Swift-Eckrich, 76-79. *Concurrent Pos:* Lab instr, Univ Ill, 79, 80, 82, 83, guest lectr, 82, 83. *Mem:* Sigma Xi (pres-elect, 89-90, pres, 90-91); Am Soc Microbiol; Soc Indust Microbiol; Am Chem Soc; Tech Asn Pulp & Paper Inst. *Res:* Study and control of the microbes in biofilms attached to surfaces; capabilities transferred genetically within the population; biocorrosion caused by anaerobic bacteria; granted five US patents. *Mailing Add:* Calgon Corp Box 1346 Pittsburgh PA 15230. *Fax:* 630-305-2982

**WIATROWSKI, CLAUDE ALLAN,** AUTOMATION, INTERACTIVE MULTIMEDIA. *Current Pos:* PRES, MT AUTOMATION CORP, 93- *Personal Data:* b Chicago, Ill, Dec 27, 46; m 67, Margaret Ammeson; c Kevin & Karen. *Educ:* Ill Inst Technol, BS, 68; Univ Ariz, MS, 70, PhD(elec eng), 73. *Prof Exp:* Consult geophys, 71-73; design engr microcomput, Burr Brown Res Corp, 73-75; asst prof elec eng, Univ Colo, 75-81; res & develop, Scott Sci, 82, chief scientist, 83-84; vpres, Parkcon Inc, 86-93. *Concurrent Pos:* Res asst, Dept Physics, Ill Inst Technol, 67-68; res asst, Dept Elec Eng, Univ Ariz, 68-73. *Mem:* Asn Comput Mach. *Res:* Personal computer applications in instrumentation, automation and control; applications of multimedia software. *Mailing Add:* PO Box 6020 Woodland Park CO 80866-6020

**WIBERG, DONALD M,** CONTROL & BIOMEDICAL ENGINEERING. *Current Pos:* from asst prof to prof eng, 65-94, prof anesthesia, 80-94, EMER PROF, UNIV CALIF, LOS ANGELES, 94- *Personal Data:* b Battle Creek, Mich, Sept, 20, 36; m 60, Merideth Green; c Erik M, Kristin A & Kenneth C. *Educ:* Calif Inst Technol, BS, 59, MS, 60, PhD(eng), 65. *Prof Exp:* Sr design engr, Gen Dynamics/Convair, 64-65. *Concurrent Pos:* Consult, Douglas Aircraft Co, 66-69 & R & D Assocs, 72-74; Fulbright sr res fel, Denmark, 76-77, Norway, 83-84; consult, Aerospace Corp, 81-90, Rockwell Sci, 89-92; legis asst, Off Sen Tom Harkin, 95; cong fel, Inst Elec & Electronics Engrs, 95. *Mem:* Fel Inst Elec & Electronics Engrs; Sigma Xi. *Res:* System modelling and parameter identification; biomedical systems, especially respiratory and cardiovascular modelling; optimum control of distributed parameter systems; nuclear reactor kinetics and control; aerospace control. *Mailing Add:* Elec Eng Dept Univ Calif Los Angeles CA 90024-1594. *Fax:* 310-206-4833; *E-Mail:* wiberg@ee.ucla.edu

**WIBERG, KENNETH BERLE,** ORGANIC CHEMISTRY. *Current Pos:* prof, Yale Univ, 60-68, chmn dept, 68-71, Whitehead prof, 68-90, EUGENE HIGGINS PROF CHEM, YALE UNIV, 90- *Personal Data:* b Brooklyn, NY, Sept 22, 27; m 51; c 3. *Educ:* Mass Inst Technol, BS, 48; Columbia Univ, PhD(chem), 50. *Honors & Awards:* Boomer Mem lectr, Univ Alta, 59; Award, Am Chem Soc, 62, J F Norris Award Phys Org Chem, 73; Cope Scholar Award, Am Chem Soc, 88; Pauling Medal, Am Chem Soc, 94. *Prof Exp:* Instr chem, Univ Wash, Seattle, 50-52, from asst prof to assoc prof, 52-57; vis prof, Harvard Univ, 57-58; prof, Univ Wash, Seattle, 58-60. *Concurrent Pos:* Sloan fel, 58-62; Guggenheim fel, 61-62. *Mem:* Nat Acad Sci; AAAS; Am Chem Soc; Royal Soc Chem; Am Acad Arts & Sci. *Res:* Stereochemistry and kinetics of organic reactions, particularly oxidation reactions and molecular rearrangements; synthesis and reactions of highly strained compounds. *Mailing Add:* 160 Carmalt Rd Hamden CT 06517-1904

**WIBERLEY, STEPHEN EDWARD,** ANALYTICAL CHEMISTRY. *Current Pos:* instr chem, Rensselaer Polytech Inst, 46-48, res assoc, US AEC contract, 48-50, from asst prof to assoc prof analytical chem, 50-57, assoc dean, Grad Sch, 64-65, dean, 65-79, vprovost grad prog & res, 69-79, chair, Dept Chem, 83-88, PROF ANALYTICAL CHEM, RENSSELAER POLYTECH INST, 57- *Personal Data:* b Troy, NY, May 31, 19; m 42; c 2. *Educ:* Williams Col, AB, 41; Rensselaer Polytech Inst, MS, 48, PhD(chem), 50. *Prof Exp:* Sr chemist, Congoleum Nairn, Inc, 41-44; analytical chemist, Gen Elec Corp, 46-48. *Concurrent Pos:* Vis physicist, Brookhaven Nat Labs, 50; consult, Imp Color Chem & Paper Corp, Socony-Mobil Oil Co, Inc, Huyck Felt Co, Schenectady Chem, Inc & Nat Gypsum Co. *Mem:* AAAS; Am Chem Soc; Sigma Xi; Am Asn Univ Profs. *Res:* Instrumental analysis; analysis of radioactive elements; oil shale hazardous wastes. *Mailing Add:* 1676 Tibbitts Ave Troy NY 12180-3726

**WICANDER, EDWIN REED,** PALEONTOLOGY, GEOLOGY. *Current Pos:* ASST PROF GEOL, CENT MICH UNIV, 76- *Personal Data:* b San Francisco, Calif, July 15, 46; m 75. *Educ:* San Diego State Univ, BS, 69; Univ Calif, Los Angeles, PhD(geol), 73. *Mem:* Soc Econ Paleontologists & Mineralogists; Paleont Soc; Sigma Xi; Am Asn Stratig Palynologists. *Res:* Micropaleontology. *Mailing Add:* Dept Geol Cent Mich Univ 100 W Preston Rd Mt Pleasant MI 48859-0001

**WICIIA, MAX S,** ONCOLOGY. *Current Pos:* from asst prof to assoc prof, 80-88, DIR, COMPREHENSIVE CANCER CTR, UNIV MICH, ANN ARBOR, 87-, PROF INTERNAL MED, DIV HEMAT & ONCOL, 88- *Personal Data:* b New York, NY, Mar 24, 49; m, Sheila Crowley; c Jason & Allyson. *Educ:* State Univ NY, Stony Brook, BS, 70; Stanford Univ, MD, 74; Am Bd Internal Med, dipl. *Prof Exp:* Intern internal med, Univ Chicago Hosps & Clins, 74-75, from jr to sr resident, 75-77; res assoc, Lab Pathophysiol, Nat Cancer Inst, NIH, 77-79, fel clin oncol, 78-80, investr lab pathophysiol, 79-80. *Concurrent Pos:* Consult, Warner Lambert Co, 80-; mem, Tumor Metastasis, Extracellular Matrix & Reproductive Endocrinol Progs, Univ Mich, 82-, dir, Div Hemat & Oncol, Simpson Mem Res Inst, 84-93, mem, Prog Cellular & Molecullar Biol, 84-; vis prof numerous univs, 85-90; sci adv, Mt Sinai Med Ctr, 88-93, Univ Colo Cancer Ctr, 90; grantee, NIH 91-, Am Cancer Soc, 92, Suntory Res Inst, 92-93; mem, Prostate Cancer Study Sect, Nat Cancer Inst, 92; assoc ed, Molecular & Cellular Differentiation, 93. *Mem:* Am Asn Cancer Res; Am Fedn Clin Res; Am Soc Cell Biol; Am soc Hemat; Am Soc Clin Invest; Am Soc Clin Oncol. *Res:* Human mammary cell growth inhibitor and methods of production and use; regulation of cell growth and differentiation; molecular mechanisms of tumor metastasis. *Mailing Add:* Univ Mich 102 Observatory Dr NE Ann Arbor MI 48109-2020

**WICHER, KONRAD J,** IMMUNOLOGY. *Current Pos:* Prof, 74-86, EMER PROF MICROBIOL, MED SCII, STATE UNIV NY, BUFFALO, 86- *Personal Data:* b Siemianowice, Poland, Feb 20, 24; m; c 2. *Educ:* Med Sch Rokitnica, MD, 57, PhD(immunol), 62; Am Bd Med Microbiol, dipl, 74.

*Concurrent Pos:* Dir clin microbiol & immunol, Erie Co Lab, Buffalo, 67-79; dir clin microbiol, Wadsworth Res Ctr, NY State Dept Health, 79-83. *Mem:* Am Acad Allergy; Am Soc Microbiol; Am Asn Immunologists; Am Soc Clin Pathologists. *Res:* Immunopathology of syphilis. *Mailing Add:* Div Labs Res NY State Dept Health Empire State Plaza Albany NY 12201. *Fax:* 518-473-1326

**WICHER, VICTORIA,** CLINICAL IMMUNOLOGY. *Current Pos:* RES SCIENTIST, NY STATE DEPT HEALTH, 79- *Personal Data:* b Cordoba, Arg, Mar 19, 33. *Educ:* Nat Univ Bordova, Arg, PhD(biochem), 60. *Prof Exp:* From instr to asst prof, Dept Pediat, Sch Med Cordoba, Arg, 60-63, dir clin biochem, 63-67; res assoc, Sch Med, 67-72, asst prof, Dept Microbiol Sch Med, prof staff, Ctr Immunol, State Univ NY, Buffalo, 76-79. *Mem:* Am Asn Immunologist; Am Soc Microbiol; NY Acad Sci. *Res:* Immunopathology of sexually transmitted diseases. *Mailing Add:* Div Lab & Res PO Box 22002 NY State Dept Health Empire State Plaza Albany NY 12201-2002

**WICHERN, DEAN WILLIAM,** STATISTICS. *Current Pos:* prof bus, 84-85, assoc dean, Col Bus Admin, 88-95, JOHN E PEARSON PROF BUS, TEX A&M UNIV, 85- *Personal Data:* b Medford, Wis, Apr 29, 42; m 68, Dorothy Rutkowski; c Michael & Andrew. *Educ:* Univ Wis-Madison, BS, 64, MS, 65, PhD(statist), 69. *Prof Exp:* From asst to assoc prof bus, Univ Wis-Madison, 69-76, chmn, Dept Quant Anal, 75-78, prof bus, 76-84. *Concurrent Pos:* Vis mem, US Army Math Res Ctr, Madison, Wis, 78-79. *Mem:* Am Statist Asn; Inst Mgt Sci; Royal Statist Soc. *Res:* Time series analysis; experimental design; applications of statistical methods in business. *Mailing Add:* 9217 Riverstone Ct College Station TX 77845

**WICHMANN, EYVIND HUGO,** THEORETICAL PHYSICS. *Current Pos:* from asst prof to assoc prof, 57-67, PROF PHYSICS, UNIV CALIF, BERKELEY, 67- *Personal Data:* b Stockholm, Sweden, May 30, 28; nat US; m 51; c 2. *Educ:* Inst Tech, Finland, AB, 50; Columbia Univ, AM, 53, PhD, 56. *Prof Exp:* Mem staff physics, Inst Advan Study, 55-57. *Mem:* Am Phys Soc. *Res:* Quantum field theory and quantum electrodynamics. *Mailing Add:* Dept Physics Univ Calif Berkeley CA 94720-0001

**WICHNER, ROBERT PAUL,** ENGINEERING SCIENCE. *Current Pos:* DEVELOP RES ENGR, OAK RIDGE NAT LAB, 55- *Personal Data:* b Pecs, Hungary, Apr 29, 33; US citizen; m 54; c 2. *Educ:* City Col New York, BS, 54; Univ Cincinnati, MS, 55; Univ Tenn, PhD(eng sci), 64. *Res:* Experimental and theoretical turbulence research; two-phase flow fluid dynamics and heat transfer; thermal-hydraulic analysis of nuclear reactors; analysis and modeling of thermal discharges. *Mailing Add:* 104 Burgess Lane Oak Ridge TN 37830

**WICHOLAS, MARK L,** INORGANIC CHEMISTRY. *Current Pos:* From asst prof to assoc prof, 67-79, PROF CHEM, WESTERN WASH UNIV, 79-, DEPT CHMN, 82- *Personal Data:* b Lawrence, Mass, June 11, 40; div; c Leslie & Bertrand. *Educ:* Boston Univ, AB, 61; Mich State Univ, MS, 64; Univ Ill, PhD(chem), 67. *Mem:* Am Chem Soc. *Res:* Physical inorganic chemistry; coordination chemistry of transition metals; organometallic chemistry. *Mailing Add:* Dept Chem Western Wash Univ Bellingham WA 98225. *Fax:* 206-650-2826

**WICHTERMAN, RALPH,** zoology; deceased, see previous edition for last biography

**WICK, DARREN DUANE,** RING THEORY. *Current Pos:* ASST PROF MATH, MILLSAPS COL, 95- *Personal Data:* b Springfield, Ohio, Apr 10, 62; m 89, Julia K Subler. *Educ:* Purdue Univ, BS, 84; Utah State Univ, MS, 89; Univ Ore, PhD(math), 95. *Prof Exp:* Propulsion performance engr, USAF, 84-87. *Mem:* Am Math Soc; Math Asn Am. *Res:* Generalizations of monomial algebras and quasi-hereditary rings; representation theory and homology of Artinian rings. *Mailing Add:* 4226 Athens Dr Jackson MS 39211. *Fax:* 601-974-1397; *E-Mail:* wickdd@okra.millsaps.edu

**WICK, EMILY LIPPINCOTT,** ORGANIC CHEMISTRY, ACADEMIC ADMINISTRATION. *Current Pos:* RETIRED. *Personal Data:* b Youngstown, Ohio, Dec 9, 21. *Educ:* Mt Holyoke Col, AB, 43, MA, 45; Mass Inst Technol, PhD(org chem), 51. *Hon Degrees:* ScD, Mt Holyoke Col, 72. *Prof Exp:* Instr chem, Mt Holyoke Col, 45-46; res assoc org chem, Mass Inst Technol, 51-53; org chemist, Flavor Lab, Arthur D Little, Inc, 53-57; res assoc food sci, Mass Inst Technol, 57-59, asst prof food chem, 59-63, from assoc prof to prof, 63-73, assoc dean student affairs, 65-72; prof chem & dean fac, Mt Holyoke Col, 73-80, asst to the pres, Long Range Planning, 81-86. *Mem:* AAAS; Am Chem Soc; Inst Food Technol. *Res:* Chemistry of food and natural products. *Mailing Add:* 37 Atlantic Ave Rockport MA 01966-1651

**WICK, JAMES ROY,** ENTOMOLOGY. *Current Pos:* RETIRED. *Personal Data:* b Henry Co, Iowa, Dec 17, 23; m 42, Ruby Kuhlenbeck; c 2. *Educ:* Iowa Wesleyan Col, BS, 48; Kans State Col, MS, 50; Iowa State Col, PhD(entom), 54. *Prof Exp:* Instr biol, Iowa State Col, 52-54, asst prof, 54-59; assoc prof, Northern Ariz Univ, 59-64, prof zool & chmn, Dept Biol Sci, 64-97. *Mem:* AAAS; Am Inst Biol Sci; Am Entom Soc; Sigma Xi. *Res:* Insect histology and developmental anatomy. *Mailing Add:* 2128 S Linmar Ct Flagstaff AZ 86001. *E-Mail:* james.wick@nau.edu

**WICK, O(SWALD) J,** METALLURGICAL & MINING ENGINEERING. *Current Pos:* RETIRED. *Personal Data:* b Fargo, NDak, July 15, 14; m 41; c 3. *Educ:* Mont Sch Mines, BS, 36, MS, 37. *Prof Exp:* Assoc metall, Col Mines, Univ Wash, Seattle, 37-42; gen supt mercury mine, Pac Mining Co, Wash, 42; metallurgist, Metall Lab, Puget Sound Naval Shipyard, 42-50; metallurgist pile technol, Gen Elec Co, 50-54, sr engr, 54-56, head prod metall, 56, mgr plutonium metall, Hanford Labs, 56-62, mgr metall develop, 62-65; mgr, Pac Northwest Lab, Battelle Mem Inst, 65-66, dep mgr, Metall Dept, 66-68, assoc mgr, Chem & Metall Div, 68-71, staff engr, 71-85, consult, Mat & Chem Applns Dept, 85-94. *Concurrent Pos:* Tech adv, US Deleg Second Int Conf Peaceful Uses Atomic Energy, Geneva, 58. *Mem:* Am Inst Mining, Metall & Petrol Engrs; Am Soc Metals. *Res:* Plutonium metallurgy; metal fabrication; nuclear fuel; mineral dressing. *Mailing Add:* 2201 Putnam St Richland WA 99352

**WICK, TIMOTHY M,** CHEMICAL ENGINEERING. *Current Pos:* Asst prof, 88-94, ASSOC PROF CHEM ENG, GA INST TECHNOL, 94- *Personal Data:* b St Paul, Minn. *Educ:* Univ Colo, Boulder, BS, 83; Rice Univ, PhD(chem eng), 88. *Honors & Awards:* Am Soc Hemat Award, 93. *Concurrent Pos:* Lily Found teaching fel, 91-92; DuPont Young fac award, 91-92. *Mem:* Am Inst Chem Engrs; AAAS; Biomed Eng Soc; NAm Soc Bionephrol; Sigma Xi. *Mailing Add:* Sch Chem Eng Ga Inst Technol 778 Atlantic Dr Atlanta GA 30332-0100

**WICK, WILLIAM QUENTIN,** coastal ecosystem management; deceased, see previous edition for last biography

**WICKE, BRIAN GARFIELD,** physical chemistry, for more information see previous edition

**WICKE, HOWARD HENRY,** TOPOLOGY. *Current Pos:* PROF MATH, OHIO UNIV, 70- *Personal Data:* b Chicago, Ill, Aug 29, 24; m 45; c 4. *Educ:* Univ Iowa, PhD(math), 52. *Prof Exp:* Instr math, Lehigh Univ, 52-54; mem staff, Sandia Corp, 54-61, supvr, 61-70. *Mem:* Am Math Soc; Math Asn Am. *Res:* General topology; point-set topology; set theory; applied mathematics. *Mailing Add:* Dept Math Ohio Univ Athens OH 45701-2979

**WICKELGREN, WARREN OTIS,** NEUROPHYSIOLOGY. *Current Pos:* asst prof, 70-76, ASSOC PROF PHYSIOL, UNIV COLO MED CTR, DENVER, 76- *Personal Data:* b Munster, Ind, Oct 15, 41; m 65; c 2. *Educ:* Univ Mich, Ann Arbor, AB, 63; Yale Univ, PhD(psychol), 67. *Prof Exp:* NIH trainee, Yale Univ, 67-69, asst prof physiol, 69-70. *Concurrent Pos:* NIH res career develop award, Univ Colo Med Ctr, Denver, 71. *Mem:* Soc Neurosci; Am Physiol Soc. *Res:* Organization of simple vertebrate nervous systems; neurophysiology of learning. *Mailing Add:* Dept Physiol Med Sch Univ Colo 4200 E Ninth Ave Denver CO 80262-0001

**WICKER, EVERETT E,** NUCLEAR SCIENCE. *Current Pos:* from asst technologist to technologist, 47-54, from supvry technologist to res technologist, 54-64, ASSOC RES CONSULT, RES LAB, US STEEL CORP, 64- *Personal Data:* b Lockport, NY, Apr 6, 19; m 43; c 2. *Educ:* Univ Pittsburgh, BS, 41; Carnegie-Mellon Univ, MS, 57. *Prof Exp:* Physicist, Kennametal, Inc, 41-42 & 46-47. *Mem:* Am Phys Soc; Am Nuclear Soc. *Res:* Neutron and charged particle activation analysis; nuclear reactor materials; nuclear and reactor physics; industrial and research uses of radioisotopes and radiation. *Mailing Add:* 815 William Penn Ct Pittsburgh PA 15221

**WICKER, ROBERT KIRK,** PHYSICAL INORGANIC CHEMISTRY, SCIENCE EDUCATION. *Current Pos:* from asst prof to assoc prof, 67-78, PROF CHEM, WASHINGTON & JEFFERSON COL, 78- *Personal Data:* b Altoona, Pa, Mar 4, 38; m 61; c 3. *Educ:* Juniata Col, BS, 60; Univ Del, MS, 63, PhD(phys chem), 66. *Prof Exp:* Asst prof chem, Davis & Elkins Col, 65-67. *Concurrent Pos:* Consult, US Dept Energy & Pittsburgh Energy Technol Ctr, Pa Dept Educ, NSF & pvt indust. *Mem:* AAAS; Am Chem Soc; Sigma Xi. *Res:* Thermodynamic properties of nonaqueous electrolyte solutions; preparation and structure determinations of copper complexes; surface area measurements of catalysts; receptor models of acid precipitation; conversion of waste methane gas. *Mailing Add:* Dept Chem Washington & Jefferson Col 60 S Lincoln St Washington PA 15301-4812

**WICKER, THOMAS HAMILTON, JR,** ORGANIC CHEMISTRY, POLYMER CHEMISTRY. *Current Pos:* RETIRED. *Personal Data:* b Orlando, Fla, Nov 19, 23; m 49; c 3. *Educ:* Univ Fla, BS, 44, MS, 48, PhD(org chem), 51. *Prof Exp:* From assoc res chemist to sr res chemist, Tenn Eastman Co, 51-76, res assoc, 77-86. *Mem:* Am Chem Soc; Sigma Xi. *Res:* 2-cyanoacrylate adhesives; condensation polymers; organic chemistry. *Mailing Add:* 4619 Mitchell Rd Kingsport TN 37664

**WICKERHAUSER, MILAN,** BIOCHEMISTRY. *Current Pos:* dir, Am Red Cross Nat Fractionation Ctr, Blood Res Lab, 70-79, sr res scientist, 66-85, head, Plasma Fractionation Sect, 68-85, CONSULT PLASMA PROD DEVELOP, AM RED CROSS, 85- *Personal Data:* b Zemun, Yugoslavia, Aug 28, 22; m 56; c 2. *Educ:* Chem engr, Univ Zagreb, 46, PhD, 61. *Prof Exp:* Develop chemist, Inst Immunol, Yugoslavia, 46-53, head, Dept Serum & Toxoid Purification, 53-57, head, Dept Human Plasma Fractionation, 57-62; immunochemist, Immunol, Inc, Ill, 63; res assoc fractionation plasma protein & blood coagulation studies, Hyland Labs, Calif, 64-66. *Concurrent Pos:* WHO fel, Wellcome Physiol Res Lab, Eng, Lister Inst Prev Med, London & State Serum Inst, Copenhagen, 50. *Mem:* Am Asn Blood Banks; Int Soc Blood Transfusion; Int Soc Thrombosis & Haemostasis; AAAS. *Res:* Isolation and characterization of plasma proteins with special emphasis on the large scale methodology; blood coagulation; immunoglobulins; development of large-scale plasma fractionation methods. *Mailing Add:* 5021 Acacia Ave Bethesda MD 20814

**WICKERSHAM, CHARLES EDWARD, JR,** SPUTTER DEPOSITION OF THIN FILMS, IC METALLIZATION. *Current Pos:* VPRES ENG, TOSOH SMD, INC, 90- *Personal Data:* b Terre Haute, Ind, Oct 26, 51; m 74; Bonnie; c Katherin, Charles & Margaret. *Educ:* Rose-Hulman Inst Technol, BS, 73; Univ Ill, MS, 76, PhD(metall eng), 78. *Prof Exp:* Sr assoc eng, IBM, 77; res scientist, Battelle Mem Inst, 77-80, sr res scientist, 80-83; res mgr, Specialty Metals Div, Varian Assocs, 83-86, eng mgr, 86-90. *Concurrent Pos:* Consult, Battelle Mem Inst, 83-84. *Mem:* Am Vacuum Soc; Am Soc Metals Int. *Res:* Sputtering target metallurgical structure effects on thin film properties; computer simulation of sputtering processes; thin film properties and sputtering target manufacturing. *Mailing Add:* 571 Arden Rd Columbus OH 43214

**WICKERSHAM, EDWARD WALKER,** REPRODUCTIVE PHYSIOLOGY, HUMAN SEXUALITY. *Current Pos:* asst prof zool, 64-68, ASSOC PROF BIOL, PA STATE UNIV, 68- *Personal Data:* b Kelton, Pa, Apr 26, 32; m 59; c 3. *Educ:* Pa State Univ, BS, 57, MS, 59; Univ Wis, PhD(dairy physiol), 62. *Prof Exp:* NIH trainee endocrinol, Univ Wis, 62-63; asst prof biol, WVa Univ, 63-64. *Concurrent Pos:* Cert sex educr, Am Asn Sex Educr, Counselors & Therapists. *Mem:* Brit Soc Study Fertil; Soc Study Reproduction; Am Asn Sex Educr, Counselors & Therapists. *Res:* Mammalian reproductive physiology and endocrinology; physiology of fertility regulation; biological and health aspects of human sexuality. *Mailing Add:* Dept Biol 208 Mueller Lab Pa State Univ University Park PA 16802-5301

**WICKES, HARRY E,** MATHEMATICS. *Current Pos:* instr math, 57-63, form asst prof to assoc prof, 64-75, PROF MATH, BRIGHAM YOUNG UNIV, 75- *Personal Data:* b Portland, Ore, June 24, 25; m 49; c 3. *Educ:* Brigham Young Univ, BS, 50, MEd, 54; Harvard Univ, MEd, 62; Colo State Col, EdD, 67. *Prof Exp:* Teacher high sch, Mont, 50-51, Idaho, 51-54, prin elem & high sch, 54-57. *Mem:* Math Asn Am; Nat Coun Teachers Math. *Res:* Mathematics education. *Mailing Add:* 1733 W 80 S Provo UT 84601-3850

**WICKES, WILLIAM CASTLES,** PHYSICS, ASTRONOMY & COMPUTER SCIENCE. *Current Pos:* MEM TECH STAFF & PROJ MGR, CORVALLIS DIV, HEWLETT-PACKARD CO, 81- *Personal Data:* b Lynwood, Calif, Nov 25, 46; m 71; c 2. *Educ:* Univ Calif, Los Angeles, BS, 67; Princeton Univ, MA, 69, PhD(physics), 72. *Prof Exp:* From res assoc to instr physics, Princeton Univ, asst prof, 75-78; asst prof physics, Univ Md, 78-81. *Mem:* Am Astron Soc; Sigma Xi. *Res:* Double star interferometry; experimental and theoretical cosmology and quantum mechanics; computer science. *Mailing Add:* Hewlett-Packard 1000 NE Circle Blvd Corvallis OR 97330

**WICKHAM, DONALD G,** INORGANIC CHEMISTRY. *Current Pos:* CONSULT, 93- *Personal Data:* b Beaverton, Ore, Feb 24, 22; m 54, Monica R Woodman; c Clarissa & Clifford. *Educ:* Univ Denver, BS, 47, MS, 50; Mass Inst Technol, PhD(inorg chem), 54. *Prof Exp:* Chemist, Lincoln Lab, Mass Inst Technol, 54-57, sect leader, 57-60; mem staff, Res Labs, Hughes Aircraft Co, 60-61; mgr mat res & develop, Components Div, Ampex Comput Prod Co, 61-65, mgr ferrite memory-core develop, 65-93. *Mem:* Am Crystallog Asn. *Res:* Inorganic solid state chemistry; magnetic materials; inorganic syntheses; electronic ceramics. *Mailing Add:* 6146 Trancas Canyon Rd Malibu CA 90265

**WICKHAM, M GARY,** HISTOLOGY, LIGHT & ELECTRON MICROSCOPY. *Current Pos:* assoc prof ocular anat, Northeastern State Univ, Tahlequah, Okla, 79-82, assoc prof biol, 79-85, dir, Biosci Res Facil, 81-88, asst res & vpres acad affairs, 85-88, prof biol, 85-88, PROF OPTOM, NORTHEASTERN STATE UNIV, TAHLEQUAH, OKLA, 88- *Personal Data:* b Ft Morgan, Colo, Dec 23, 42; m 65, Irene Wilhelm. *Educ:* Colo State Univ, BS, 64, MS, 67; Wash State Univ, PhD(zool), 72. *Prof Exp:* Fisheries aide, Colo Game & Fish Dept, 62-65; res asst, Colo Coop Fish Unit, 65-67; teaching asst morphogenesis, Dept Zool, Wash State Univ, 67-71, res asst, 68-70; res physiologist, Vet Admin Med Ctr, Gainesville, Fla, 71-74 & dir, Core EM Facil, San Diego, Calif, 74-79. *Concurrent Pos:* NSF fel, Friday Harbor Marine Lab, Univ Wash, 70; Nat Defense Educ Act fel, Wash State Univ, 71; asst prof, Dept Ophthal, Univ Fla, Gainesville, 72-74; asst res biologist & dir ophthal res, Dept Surg, Univ Calif, San Diego, 74-79; pres, Univ Fac Asn, Northeastern State Univ, 89-91. *Mem:* AAAS; Am Asn Zool Parks & Aquariums; Am Inst Biol Sci; Am Soc Zoologists; Asn Res Vision & Ophthal; Sigma Xi. *Res:* Comparative morphology and functional morphology of the structures of the anterior segment of the mammalian eye; cornea, iris, sclera, trabecular meshwork, ciliary body; computer-based morphometry; recruitment of minority students to research careers. *Mailing Add:* PO Box 1456 Tahlequah OK 74465-1456. *Fax:* 918-458-2104

**WICKHAM, WILLIAM TERRY, JR,** TECHNICAL MANAGEMENT. *Current Pos:* PROF, HEIDELBERG COL, TIFFIN, OHIO, 77- *Personal Data:* b Cleveland, Ohio, May 28, 29; m 52; c 3. *Educ:* Heidelberg Col, AB, 51; Case Inst Technol, MS, 54, PhD(org chem), 56. *Prof Exp:* Instr, Case Inst Technol, 55-56; res chemist, Owens-Ill Glass Co, 56-58; group leader, Dow Chem Co, 58-62; tech mgr, Celanese Plastics Co, 62-67; dir res, Southern Div, Dayco Corp, 67-72, vpres res & develop, 72-76; tech dir, Crosby Chem Inc,

Picaynne, 76-77. *Concurrent Pos:* Consult tech mgt, Gen Motors Mercurs Inc, Dayco Corp & Hercules Inc, 77- *Mem:* Am Chem Soc; Am Phys Soc; Am Inst Chemists; Sigma Xi. *Res:* Research administration; science adminstration; technical management; structure; manufacture; research managment. *Mailing Add:* 54 Glen View Terr Tiffin OH 44883-3420

**WICKLER, STEVEN JOHN,** ENERGETICS, THERMOGENESIS. *Current Pos:* VIS ASST PROF, DEPT ANIMAL PHYSIOL, UNIV CALIF, DAVIS, 79- *Personal Data:* b Volga, SDak, May 17, 52. *Educ:* Univ Calif, Riverside, BA, 74; Univ Mich, MS, 77, PhD(zool), 79. *Mem:* Am Physiol Soc; Am Soc Zoologists. *Res:* Examine whole animal, tissue, and biochemical adaptations with particular emphasis on energetics and thermogenesis. *Mailing Add:* Dept Animal Sci Calif Polytech Univ Pomona CA 91768. *Fax:* 909-869-4454

**WICKLIFF, JAMES LEROY,** PLANT BIOCHEMISTRY, PHOTOBIOLOGY. *Current Pos:* asst prof bot & bact, 65-69, assoc prof biol sci, 69-93, EMER PROF BIOL SCI, UNIV ARK, FAYETTEVILLE, 94- *Personal Data:* b Knoxville, Iowa, Nov 14, 31; m 56, Mary J Hamilton; c Daniel L, David E & Diana S (Hicks). *Educ:* Iowa State Univ, BS, 55, PhD(plant physiol), 62. *Prof Exp:* Assoc bot & plant path, Iowa State Univ, 62-65. *Mem:* AAAS; Am Soc Plant Physiol; Am Inst Biol Sci. *Res:* Chlorophyll biochemistry; photosynthesis; photophysiology of higher plants. *Mailing Add:* 1215 Columbus Blvd Fayetteville AR 72701

**WICKLOW, DONALD THOMAS,** MYCOLOGY, MYCOTOXINS. *Current Pos:* res scientist mycol, 77-85, LEAD SCIENTIST, NAT CTR AGR UTILIZATION RES, USDA, 85- *Personal Data:* b San Francisco, Calif, June 22, 40; div, Constance Kirchhoff; c Cameron & Brandon. *Educ:* San Francisco State Col, BA, 62, MA, 64; Univ Wis, PhD(bot), 71. *Honors & Awards:* Alexopoulous Prize, Mycol Soc Am, 80. *Prof Exp:* Instr biol, Univ Wis Ctr-Waukesha, 69-70; asst prof, Univ Pittsburgh, 70-76. *Concurrent Pos:* Mem, Adv Panel Rcol & Ecosyst Dtudies, NSF, 78-81; organizing comt, Third Int Symp Microbiol & Ecol, 83; co-chairperson, Ann Corn Dry Milling Conf, 92-; mem, Ecol Subcomt, 5th Intern, Mycol Cong, 94. *Mem:* Fel Brit Mycol Soc; Mycol Soc Am; Mycol Soc Japan; Fel Am Acad Microbiol. *Res:* Ecology of fungal communities, their organization and role in both native and man-managed ecosystems; ecology of mycotoxin producing fungi; chemistry of fungus and insect interaction; natural products. *Mailing Add:* Nat Ctr Agr Utilization Res 1815 N University St Peoria IL 61604

**WICKLUND, ARTHUR BARRY,** EXPERIMENTAL HIGH ENERGY PHYSICS. *Current Pos:* fel, 70-73, asst physicist, 73-76, PHYSICIST, ARGONNE NAT LAB, 76- *Personal Data:* b Dec 8, 42; US citizen; m 74. *Educ:* Harvard Univ, BA, 64; Univ Calif, Berkeley, PhD(physics), 70. *Prof Exp:* Res asst high energy physics, Univ Calif, Berkeley, 65-70. *Mem:* Am Phys Soc. *Res:* Strong interaction phenomenology; production mechanisms in few body reactions. *Mailing Add:* 3511 N Freemont St Chicago IL 60657

**WICKMAN, HERBERT HOLLIS,** COLLOID CHEMISTRY. *Current Pos:* PROG DIR, DIV MAT RES, NSF, 87- *Personal Data:* b Omaha, Nebr, Sept 30, 36; m 85; c 2. *Educ:* Univ Omaha, AB, 59; Univ Calif, Berkeley, PhD(chem), 64. *Prof Exp:* Mem tech staff, Chem Physics Res Lab, Bell Tel Labs, NJ, 64-70; assoc prof, Ore State Univ, 70-79, prof chem, 80-87. *Mem:* Am Chem Soc; Am Phys Soc; Biophys Soc; Sigma Xi. *Res:* Magnetism, liquid crystals, membrane biophysics. *Mailing Add:* Div Mat Res NSF 4201 Wilson Blvd No 1065S Arlington VA 22230

**WICKNER, SUE,** PROTIEN STUDIES, BIOCHEMISTRY. *Current Pos:* RES CHEMIST, NIH, 76- *Personal Data:* b Washington, DC, Apr 16, 45. *Res:* Protein Studies; biochemistry. *Mailing Add:* ONCI Bldg 37 Rm 2D19 NIH 37 Convert Dr MSC 4255 Bethesda MD 20892-0001

**WICKNER, WILLIAM TOBEY,** BIOCHEMISTRY. *Current Pos:* JAMES C CHILCOTT DISTINGUISHED PROF & CHMN, DEPT BIOCHEM, DARTMOUTH MED SCH, 93- *Personal Data:* b Wallkill, NY, Mar 13, 46; c 2. *Educ:* Yale Univ, BA, 67; Harvard Univ, MD, 73. *Honors & Awards:* Fac Res Award, Am Cancer Soc, 79. *Prof Exp:* Sr res fel, Dept Biochem, Med Sch, Stanford Univ, 74-76; from asst prof to prof, Dept Biol Chem & Molecular Biol Inst, Univ Calif, Los Angeles, 76-93. *Concurrent Pos:* Graub fel, Cystic Fibrosis Found, 71-73; Mellon fel, 74-76; Guggenheim fel, 82-83; co-chmn, Membrane Molecular Biol Gordon Conf, 87; mem, Cell Biol Study Sect, NIH, 87-91, chmn, 89-91. *Mem:* Nat Acad Sci; fel Am Soc Microbiol. *Mailing Add:* Dept Biochem Dartmouth Med Sch 7200 Vail Bldg Hanover NH 03755-3844

**WICKRAMASINGHE, HEMANTHA KUMAR,** SCANNING PROBE MICROSCOPY & NANOTECHNOLOGY, SENSORS FOR MANUFACTURING & PROCESS CONTROL. *Current Pos:* mgr phys measurements, Mfg Res Dept, 84-96, chief scientist, 92-94, MGR PHYS SCI, T J WATSON RES CTR, IBM, 97- *Personal Data:* b Colombo, Sri Lanka, May 31, 49; US citizen; m 73, Sophie Marie de la Porte; c Lucille & Anita. *Educ:* Univ London, BSc, 70, PhD(electronic & elec eng), 74. *Honors & Awards:* Vladimir Z Zworykin Premium for Contrib to Acoust Micros, Inst Elec & Electronics Engrs, 83, Morris E Leeds Award for Pioneering Contrib to Nanoscale Measurement of Magnetic, Electrostatic, Thermal & Optical Surface Properties, 92. *Prof Exp:* Res assoc, Electronic & Elec Eng Dept, Univ Col, Univ London, 74-75; Appl Physics Dept, W W Hansen Labs, Stanford Univ, 75-78, lectr, Electronic & Elec Eng Dept, 78-83. *Concurrent Pos:* Consult, Hirst Res Ctr, Gen Elec Co, UK, 80-83. *Mem:* Fel Inst Elec & Electronics Engrs; fel Am Phys Soc; fel Royal Micros Soc. *Res:* Novel scanning probe microscopes and their applications to nanotechnology,

materials science and biology; in-situ measurement sensors and techniques aimed at improving the capability and/or efficiency of manufacturing lines. *Mailing Add:* T J Watson Res Ctr IBM PO Box 218 Yorktown Heights NY 10598. *Fax:* 914-945-4006; *E-Mail:* wick@watson.ibm.com

**WICKREMA SINHA, ASOKA J,** BIOCHEMISTRY, ORGANIC CHEMISTRY. *Current Pos:* res scientist chem & biochem, 69-75, SR RES SCIENTIST, RES DIV, UPJOHN CO, 75- *Personal Data:* b Colombo, Ceylon, Sept 8, 37; US citizen. *Educ:* Univ London, BSc, 61; Univ Birmingham, MSc, 64, PhD(org chem), 66. *Prof Exp:* Fel biochem, Univ Birmingham, 66-67; staff scientist, Worcester Found Exp Biol, 67-69. *Mem:* Am Chem Soc; The Chem Soc; Brit Biochem Soc. *Res:* Chemical synthesis; carbonium ion chemistry; biosynthesis and metabolism of steroids; in vivo and in vitro metabolism; analytical methods and assay development; metabolism absorption, distribution and excretion of drugs; isolation and structure elucidation; radiotracer techniques. *Mailing Add:* 3537 Tamsin Ave Kalamazoo MI 49008

**WICKS, CHARLES E(DWARD),** CHEMICAL ENGINEERING. *Current Pos:* From asst prof to prof, 54-89, head dept, 70-89, EMER PROF CHEM ENG, ORE STATE UNIV, 89- *Personal Data:* b Prineville, Ore, July 9, 25; m 48; c 3. *Educ:* Ore State Col, BS, 50; Carnegie Inst Technol, MS, 52, PhD, 54. *Concurrent Pos:* Chem engr, US Bur Mines, 56-58, proj leader, 58-68; consult, US Bur Mines, 56-68, Pac Power & Light Co, 58-60, Year-in-Indust, E I du Pont de Nemours & Co, 64-65 & Ore Metall Corp, 66-; NSF fel, Univ Wis, 60-61; expert witness prod reliability, var law firms; distiguished scholar exchange to People's Repub China, Nat Acad Sci, 84. *Mem:* Am Inst Chem Engrs; Am Soc Eng Educ. *Res:* Waste water treatment; simultaneous heat and mass transfer phenomena. *Mailing Add:* 3222 NW Gumwood Ave Corvallis OR 97330

**WICKS, FREDERICK JOHN,** SERPENTINE MINERALS, ASBESTOS. *Current Pos:* asst cur, Royal Ont Mus, 70-75, assoc cur, 75-80, cur-in-chg, Dept Mineral, 87-92, CUR MINERAL, ROYAL ONT MUS, 80- *Personal Data:* b Winnipeg, Man, Nov 22, 37; div; c Claire E. *Educ:* Univ Man, BSc, 60, MSc, 65; Oxford Univ, DPhil(mineral), 69. *Honors & Awards:* Hawley Award, Mineral Asn Can, 77 & 78. *Prof Exp:* Geologist, Giant Yellowknife Mines Ltd, 60 & 61; consult mineralogist, govt & indust, 62; mineralogist, Man Hwys Br, 63-65 & Geol Surv Can, 67. *Concurrent Pos:* Adj prof, Dept Earth Sci, Univ Man, Winnipeg, 77; assoc prof, Dept Geol, Univ Toronto, 80-; mineral consult, Royal Comn Matters Health & Safety Arising from Use of Asbestos, Ont, 82-83. *Mem:* Mineral Asn Can (secy, 73-75, vpres, 91-93, pres 94-); fel Geol Asn Can; fel Mineral Soc Am; Clay Minerals Soc. *Res:* Structure, chemistry and paragenesis of the serpentine minerals; asbestos deposits; geochemistry and paragenesis of Colombian emerald deposits; thermal and evolved gas analysis; atomic force microscopy of layered structures; microbeam x-ray diffraction. *Mailing Add:* Royal Ont Mus 100 Queen's Park Toronto ON M5S 2C6 Can. *Fax:* 416-586-5814; *E-Mail:* rom!rommin!fred@zoo.toronto.ca

**WICKS, GEORGE GARY,** MATERIALS SCIENCE. *Current Pos:* Engr, 69-70, RES METALLURGIST, SAVANNAH RIVER LAB, E I DU PONT DE NEMOURS & CO, INC, 75- *Personal Data:* b Copaigue, NY, June 26, 45; m 69; c 1. *Educ:* Fla State Univ, BS, 67, MS, 69; Harvard Univ, SM, 71; Mass Inst Technol, PhD(eng mat), 75. *Res:* Structure and science of glass and amorphous materials; immobilization of radioactive waste in glass matrices. *Mailing Add:* Dept Ceramic Eng Clemson Univ Clemson SC 29634-0907

**WICKS, WESLEY DOANE,** REGULATION OF TRANSCRIPTION. *Current Pos:* dept head, 80-92, PROF, DEPT BIOCHEM, UNIV TENN, 80- *Personal Data:* b Providence, RI, Feb 13, 36; m 59, Nancy Schlag; c Stephen, Andrew & James. *Educ:* Bates Col, BS, 57; Harvard Univ, MA, 59, PhD(med sci), 64. *Prof Exp:* Staff mem biochem, Biol Div, Oak Ridge Nat Lab, Tenn, 65-69; staff mem, Div Res, Nat Jewish Hosp, Denver, 69-72; assoc prof, Univ Colo, Denver, 72-78, prof pharmacol, Med Ctr, 78-80. *Concurrent Pos:* Am Cancer Soc fel, Biol Div, Oak Ridge Nat Lab, Tenn, 63-65; hon fac mem, Dept Biosci, Fed Univ Pernambuco, Recife, Brazil, 68-72. *Mem:* Am Soc Biochem & Molecular Biol. *Res:* Control of eukaryotic gene expression; DNA-protein interactions; protein phosphorylation. *Mailing Add:* Dept Biochem Walters Life Sci Bldg Rm F425 Univ Tenn Knoxville TN 37996-0840. *Fax:* 423-974-6306

**WICKS, ZENO W, JR,** polymer chemistry, for more information see previous edition

**WICKSON, EDWARD JAMES,** PLASTICS FORMULATING & PLASTICIZERS, OXO ALCOHOL APPLICATIONS. *Current Pos:* PRES, WICKSON PROD RES, LTD, 86- *Personal Data:* b New York, NY, Jan 25, 20; m 52, Ann M Stapleton; c Barbara (Vogelhuber), Edward J (deceased), Thomas S, John P & Mary Ann (Marino). *Educ:* Univ Calif, Berkeley, BS, 42. *Prof Exp:* Analytical chemist, Gen Chem Co, Calif, 42-43; chemist, Celanese Corp Am, NJ, 46-50; admin asst to lab dir, Vitro Corp Am, 51-54; sr chemist, Chicopee Mfg Co, 54-55; sr chemist, Enjay Labs, Esso Res & Eng Co, 55-56, group leader, 56-60, res assoc, 60-61, head, Chem Sect, 61-69, vinyl indust assoc, Enjay Chem Co, 69-71, sr res assoc, Enjay Chem Lab, 71-75, chief scientist plasticizers, Esso Chem Europe, 75-78, chief prod applns scientist, Exxon Chem Co, 78-86. *Mem:* Am Chem Soc; fel Soc Plastics Engrs. *Res:* Plasticizcrs; chemical specialties; oxo alcohols; trialkylacetic acids; propylene polymers. *Mailing Add:* 7973 Walden Rd Baton Rouge LA 70808. *Fax:* 504-769-3628; *E-Mail:* dinp4ever@aol.com

**WICKSTEN, MARY KATHERINE,** BIOLOGY, INVERTEBRATE ZOOLOGY. *Current Pos:* asst prof, 80-88, ASSOC PROF BIOL, TEX A&M UNIV, 88- *Personal Data:* b San Francisco, Calif, Mar 17, 48. *Educ:* Humboldt State Col, BA, 70, MA, 72; Univ Southern Calif, PhD(biol), 77. *Prof Exp:* Teaching asst biol, Humboldt State Col, 72 & Univ Southern Calif, 73-75 & 76-77; scientist marine biol, Bur Land Mgt Southern Calif Benthic Studies & Analysis, 75-76; res assoc marine biol, Los Angeles Harbor Proj, 77-80. *Concurrent Pos:* Consult systematist, King Harbor Proj, 74-, Gulf Alaska Offshore Surv, 76-77, Bur Land Mgt Southern Calif Benthic Studies & Analysis Seasonal Study, 76- & Bur Land Mgt Southern Calif Mussel Bed Surv, 77- *Mem:* Crustaceon Soc; Sigma Xi. *Res:* Behavior, systematics and zoogeography of decapod crustaceans of the eastern Pacific Ocean. *Mailing Add:* Dept Biol Tex A&M Univ College Station TX 77843. *Fax:* 409-845-2891; *E-Mail:* wicksten@bio.tamu.edu

**WICKSTROM, CONRAD EUGENE,** MICROBIAL ECOLOGY, PHYCOLOGY. *Current Pos:* ASST PROF BIOL SCI, KENT STATE UNIV, 81- *Personal Data:* b Modesto, Calif, Sept 3, 43; m 77; c 3. *Educ:* Calif State Univ, Chico, BA, 65, MA, 68; Univ Ore, PhD(biol), 74. *Prof Exp:* Instr, Emory Univ, 73-74, asst prof biol, 74-81. *Concurrent Pos:* Prin investr NSF grant, 78-80 & 82-83; prin investr, Nat Oceanic & Atmospheric Admin, 85-86. *Mem:* AAAS; Am Soc Microbiol; Am Soc Limnol & Oceanog; Ecol Soc Am; Phycol Soc Am; Int Soc Limnol. *Res:* Biotic components of nitrogen cycle, especially asymbiotic nitrogen fixation; biotic and abiotic control of microbial community structure and function; natural thermal systems and thermal enrichments; aquatic biology. *Mailing Add:* Dept Biol Sci Kent State Univ Main Campus PO Box 5190 Kent OH 44242-0001

**WICKSTROM, ERIC,** BIOPHYSICAL CHEMISTRY. *Current Pos:* prof, Dept Pharmacol, 92-96, PROF, DEPT MICROBIOL & IMMUNOL, THOMAS JEFFERSON UNIV, 97- *Personal Data:* b Chicago, Ill, Dec 21, 46; m 67, Lois June Sinsheimer; c Erica L & Eileen A. *Educ:* Calif Inst Technol, BS, 68; Univ Calif, Berkeley, PhD(chem), 72. *Prof Exp:* Res asst chem, Univ Calif, Berkeley, 68-72; res assoc molecular, cellular & develop biol, Univ Colo, Boulder, 73-74; asst prof chem, Univ Denver, 74-81; asst prof chem & biochem molecular biol & surg, Univ SFla, 82-87, assoc prof, 87-91, prof, 91-92. *Concurrent Pos:* Europ molecular biol orgn fel, Univ Leiden, 84; guest researcher, Nat Cancer Inst, 86 & Max Planck Inst Molecular Genetics, Berlin, 86; res grants, NIH, NSF, Am Cancer Soc, Leukemia Soc Am, US Army Res & Develop Command, Am Found AIDS Res; site visit team mem, Nat Cancer Inst, 89-90; consult, Genta Ins, 89-, Life Sci, 89-; organizer, Int Union Biochem, Nat Cancer Inst Conf Nucleic Acid Therapeut, 91. *Mem:* Am Chem Soc; Am Soc Biochem & Molecular Biol; Biophys Soc; Am Asn Cancer Res; Int Soc Nuclear Acid Chem. *Res:* Antisense DNA therapeutics for oncogenes and viral genes; protein synthesis initiation, RNA-protein interactions. *Mailing Add:* Dept Microbiol & Immunol Thomas Jefferson Univ 1025 Walnut St Suite 420 Philadelphia PA 19107-5541. *Fax:* 215-955-4580; *E-Mail:* ewick@lac.jci.tju.edu

**WIDDEN, PAUL RODNEY,** SOIL MICROBIOLOGY. *Current Pos:* Asst prof, 73-76, ASSOC PROF MICROBIAL ECOL, CONCORDIA UNIV, SIR GEORGE WILLIAMS CAMPUS, 76-, CHAIR, 89- *Personal Data:* b London, Eng, Sept 23, 43; m 67; c 3. *Educ:* Univ Liverpool, BSc Hons, 65; Univ Calgary, PhD(mycol), 71. *Concurrent Pos:* Nat Res Coun Can operating grant, 75-91; Univ res grant, Imp Oil Ltd, 78-81, Que Agr & Fisheries grant, 89-91, Que Govt Infrastructure grant, 89-92; vis scientist, Inst Terestrial Ecol, Merlewood, UK, 81-82. *Mem:* Can Soc Microbiologists; Ecol Soc Am; Mycol Soc Am. *Res:* The distribution of fungi in tundra and temperate forest soils; effects of environment on the distribution of soil fungi; crude oil degradation by arctic soil fungi; fungal decomposition of cellulose in forest soils; vesicular-arbuscular Mycorrhizae in Maple Forest soils. *Mailing Add:* Dept Biol Sir George Williams Campus Concordia Univ 1455 De Maisoneuve Blvd W Montreal PQ H3G 1M8 Can

**WIDDOWSON, KATHERINE LOUISA,** DESIGN & SYNTHESIS OF ENZYME INHIBITORS & ANTAGONISTS OF G-COUPLED PROTEIN RECEPTORS. *Current Pos:* ASSOC SR INVESTR, SMITH KLINE BEECHAM, 92- *Personal Data:* b Jan 30, 65; Can citizen. *Educ:* Reed Col, BA, 86; Calif Inst Technol, PhD(org chem), 92. *Mem:* Am Chem Soc. *Res:* Design and synthesis of antagonists for the I1-8 receptor; computer aided design of agonists for two hematopoeitic receptors; carbon-carbon bondo forming reactions using silicon as a template. *Mailing Add:* Smith Kline Beechman 709 Swedeland Rd UW 2420 King of Prussia PA 19406-2711

**WIDEBURG, NORMAN EARL,** BIOCHEMISTRY. *Current Pos:* RETIRED. *Personal Data:* b Chicago, Ill, Mar 8, 33; m 58; c 4. *Educ:* Ill Inst Technol, BS, 54; Univ Wis, MS, 56. *Prof Exp:* Biochemist, Abbott Labs, 58-95. *Mem:* AAAS; Am Chem Soc; Am Soc Microbiol. *Res:* Microbial transformations; fermentation; antimicrobial agents; enzymology. *Mailing Add:* 2704 W Cheyenne Rd Waukegan IL 60087

**WIDEMAN, CHARLES JAMES,** GEOPHYSICS. *Current Pos:* asst prof, 68-73, ASSOC PROF GEOPHYS & CHMN DEPT, MONT COL MINERAL SCI & TECHNOL, 73- *Personal Data:* b Walkermine, Calif, Feb 7, 36; m 63; c 2. *Educ:* Colo Sch Mines, BSc, 58, MSc, 67, PhD(geophys), 75. *Prof Exp:* Sr geophysicist, Westinghouse Elec Corp, 67-68. *Mem:* Seismol Soc Am. *Res:* Local seismicity; seismic risk analysis and earth strain studies; gravity investigations over and near the Boulder Batholith of Southwestern Montana. *Mailing Add:* Dept Geophys Mont Tech 1300 W Park St Butte MT 59701-8997

**WIDEMAN, CYRILLA HELEN,** PHYSIOLOGY, BIOCHEMISTRY. *Current Pos:* assoc prof, 72-77, PROF BIOL, JOHN CARROLL UNIV, 77- *Personal Data:* b Toledo, Ohio. *Educ:* Notre Dame Col, Ohio, BS, 49; Univ Notre Dame, MS, 60; Ill Inst Technol, PhD(biol), 70. *Prof Exp:* High sch teacher natural sci, Notre Dame Acad, Elyria Cath High Sch, 49-56; instr biol & chem, Notre Dame Col, 56-61, asst prof biol, 61-67; grad asst, Ill Inst Technol, 67-70; fel biochem & physiol, Cleveland Clin, 70-72. *Concurrent Pos:* NIH fel, 70-72; NSF & John Carroll Univ grant, 74. *Mem:* AAAS; Am Inst Biol Sci; NY Acad Sci; Soc Neurosci. *Res:* Neuroendocrinological and biochemical relationships underlying brain behavior patterns with special emphasis on the limbic system, especially hippocampal formation. *Mailing Add:* Dept Biol John Carroll Univ 20700 N Park Blvd Cleveland OH 44118-4520

**WIDEMAN, LAWSON GIBSON,** CATALYSIS, POLYMER CHEMISTRY. *Current Pos:* staff res chemist, Goodyear Tire & Rubber Co, 67-71, sr res chemist, 71-84, group leader, 83-87, assoc scientist, 84-87, RES & DEVELOP ASSOC, RES DIV, GOODYEAR TIRE & RUBBER CO, 87- *Personal Data:* b Morrelton, Mo, July 17, 43; m 65, Peggy J Carr; c Paula, Mary & Lynn. *Educ:* Univ Mo, Rolla, BS, 66, MS, 67; Univ Akron, PhD(chem), 71. *Prof Exp:* Teaching asst, Univ Mo, Rolla. *Concurrent Pos:* Mem, Goodyear Sci Adv Coun, 80-, chmn, Chem Control Adv Coun, 85-; part-time mem chem fac, Univ Akron, 81-85. *Mem:* Am Chem Soc; Sigma Xi; Catalysis Soc. *Res:* Homogeneous and heterogeneous catalysis; polymer modifications; new monomers; homo- and heterogeneous hydrogenation reactions; modification of compounded rubber to give improved properties; preparation of chemicals with the proper structure to improve the performance of compounded rubber in various applications; granted 55 US patents; author of 10 international publications. *Mailing Add:* 82 N Village View Tallmadge OH 44278-2040

**WIDEMAN, ROBERT FREDERICK, JR,** AVIAN PHYSIOLOGY, RENAL PHYSIOLOGY. *Current Pos:* ASST PROF AVIAN PHYSIOL, POULTRY SCI DEPT, PA STATE UNIV, 81- *Personal Data:* b Dallas, Tex, June 16, 49; m 71; c 1. *Educ:* Univ Del, BA, 71; Univ Conn, MS, 74, PhD(physiol), 78. *Prof Exp:* Fel physiol, Col Med, Univ Ariz, 78-81. *Mem:* AAAS; Am Soc Zoologists; Am Physiol Soc; Poultry Sci Asn; Sigma Xi. *Res:* Avian renal and endocrine physiology; endocrinological regulation of renal calcium and phosphate transport; renal and endocrine microanatomy. *Mailing Add:* Dept Poultry Sci Univ Ark 0-402 Poultry Sci Ctr Fayetteville AR 72701. *Fax:* 814-865-5691

**WIDENER, EDWARD LADD, SR,** MATERIALS SCIENCE, INDUSTRIAL & MANUFACTURING ENGINEERING. *Current Pos:* ASSOC PROF MECH ENG TECHNOL, PURDUE UNIV, 78- *Personal Data:* b Madison, SDak, Dec 23, 26; m 52, Martha A Born; c Marjorie, Edward, William & Cora. *Educ:* Purdue Univ, West Lafayette, BS, 49, BS, 51; Univ Kans, MS, 62. *Prof Exp:* Fuel engr, US Steel Corp, 51-52; design engr, Union Carbide Corp, 52-60; develop engr, E I du Pont de Nemours Co, 62-68; process engr, Kimberly-Clark Corp, 68-75; proj engr, Continental Group, Inc, 75-78. *Concurrent Pos:* Lab instr, United Asn Welders & Pipefitters, 79-89; plastics consult, Steel Parts Co & Insilco Corp, 80-81; prog evaluator, Accreditation Bd Eng & Technol, 84-90; panelist, NSF, 90-91; eng lectr & metals lab instr, Univ Tech Malaysia, 95-96. *Mem:* Am Soc Eng Educ; Am Soc Mech Engrs; Instrument Soc Am; Am Soc Mat Int; Tech Asn Pulp & Paper Indust. *Res:* Materials labs; waste disposal and packaging; energy conservation; materials recycling. *Mailing Add:* Mech Eng Technol Dept Knoy 119 Purdue Univ West Lafayette IN 47907-1417. *Fax:* 765-494-6219; *E-Mail:* elwidener@tech.purdue.edu

**WIDERA, GEORG ERNST OTTO,** ENGINEERING MECHANICS. *Current Pos:* DEPT HEAD MECH & INDUST ENG, COL ENG, 91- *Personal Data:* b Dortmund, Ger, Feb 16, 38; US citizen; m 74, Kristel Kornas; c Erika & Nicholas. *Educ:* Univ Wis-Madison, BS, 60, MS, 62, PhD(eng mech), 65. *Honors & Awards:* Pressure Vessel & Piping Award & Medal, Am Soc Mech Engrs, 95. *Prof Exp:* From asst prof to prof mech eng, Univ Ill, Chicago, 65-92, head dept, 83-92. *Concurrent Pos:* Alexander von Humboldt fel, Univ Stuttgart, 68-69, vis prof, 68; vis scientist, Argonne Nat Lab, 68; vis prof, Univ Wis, Milwaukee, 73-74 & Marquette Univ, 78-79; assoc ed, J Pressure Vessel Technol, 77-81, tech ed, 83-93, assoc ed, Appl Mech Revs, 87-93; consult var indust orgn; chmn, Pressure Vessel Res Comt, Am Soc Mech Engrs, 82-87, mem bd, Pressure Technol Codes & Stand; chmn, Subcomt Design Procedures Cylindrical Shells, Pressure Vessel Res Coun, Welding Res Coun, 84-87, Comt, Reinforced Openings & External Leads, 87-90, Comt Shells & Ligaments, 93-96, prog chmn, Pressure Vessel Piping Div, Am Soc Mech Engrs, 85-89, vchmn, 89-90, chmn, 90-91; chmn, Am Reg Comt, 88-, Int Coun Pressure Vessel Technol, 92-96. *Mem:* Fel Am Soc Mech Engrs (vpres, 93-96); Ger Soc Appl Math & Mech; Soc Mfg Engrs; Am Soc Eng Educ; Soc Plastics Engrs; Am Soc Mech Int; Fr Pressure Vessel Asn. *Res:* Plates and shells; composite materials; mechanics of deformation processing; pressure vessels and piping. *Mailing Add:* Dept Mech & Indust Eng Col Eng 1515 W Wisconsin Ave PO Box 1881 Milwaukee WI 53201-1881. *Fax:* 414-288-1647; *E-Mail:* widerag@vms.csd.mu.edu

**WIDERQUIST, V(ERNON) R(OBERTS),** ELECTRICAL ENGINEERING. *Current Pos:* RETIRED. *Personal Data:* b Ft Myers, Fla, Sept 21, 22; m 49; c 3. *Educ:* Ga Inst Technol, BS, 43, MS, 48. *Prof Exp:* Res prof, Eng Exp Sta, Ga Inst Technol, 46-56; proj mgr, Defense Systs Group, TRW Inc, 56-86. *Mem:* Inst Elec & Electronics Engrs; Sigma Xi. *Res:* Program and general management. *Mailing Add:* PO Box 58333 Houston TX 77258-8333

**WIDESS, MOSES B,** GEOPHYSICS. *Current Pos:* CONSULT, 73- *Personal Data:* b Sverdlovsk, Russia, Sept 21, 11; nat US; m 35, Anneliese Vogel; c Paul R & James B. *Educ:* Calif Inst Technol, BS, 33, MS, 34, PhD(elec eng), 36. *Honors & Awards:* Kauffman Gold Medal Award, Soc Explor Geophys, 77. *Prof Exp:* Party chief, Western Geophys Co, Calif, 36-42; consult geophysicist, Amoco Prod Co, 42-73. *Mem:* Soc Explor Geophys; Am Geophys Union. *Res:* Geophysical interpretation and methods. *Mailing Add:* 5910 Horsemans Canyon Dr No 6B Walnut Creek CA 94595

**WIDGER, WILLIAM RUSSELL,** PHOTOSYNTHESIS, MEMBRANE PROTEINS. *Current Pos:* ASST PROF BIOENERGETICS, DEPT BIOCHEM & BIOPHYS, UNIV HOUSTON, UNIVERSITY PARK, 86- *Educ:* State Univ NY, Albany, PhD(chem), 79. *Prof Exp:* Res assoc, Lilly Hall Life Sci, Purdue Univ, 84-86. *Res:* Bioenergetics. *Mailing Add:* Dept Biochem & Biophys Sci Univ Houston Houston TX 77204-0001

**WIDGOFF, MILDRED,** ELEMENTARY PARTICLE PHYSICS, ASTRO PARTICLE PHYSICS. *Current Pos:* from res asst prof to res assoc prof, 58-74, exec officer dep, 68-81, PROF PHYSICS, BROWN UNIV, 74- *Personal Data:* b Buffalo, NY, Aug 24, 24; c Eve W & Jonathan W. *Educ:* Univ Buffalo, BA, 44; Cornell Univ, PhD(physics), 52. *Prof Exp:* Asst physics, Manhattan Proj, 44-45; assoc physics, Brookhaven Nat Lab, 52-54; res fel, Harvard Univ, 55-58. *Concurrent Pos:* Consult, Cambridge Electron Accelerator, 56-59. *Mem:* Fel Am Phys Soc. *Res:* Cosmic rays; medium and high energy particle physics; muons and neutrinos from astrophysical sources. *Mailing Add:* 10 Watson Ave Barrington RI 02806. *E-Mail:* mw@brownvm. edu

**WIDHOLM, JACK MILTON,** PLANT PHYSIOLOGY, GENETICS. *Current Pos:* asst prof physiol, Dept Agron, 68-73, assoc prof, 73-77, PROF PLANT PHYSIOL, DEPT AGRON, UNIV ILL, URBANA, 77- *Personal Data:* b Watseka, Ill, Mar 11, 39; m 64; c 3. *Educ:* Univ Ill, BS, 61; Calif Inst Technol, PhD(biochem), 66. *Prof Exp:* Res chemist, Int Minerals & Chem Corp, 65-68. *Mem:* Am Soc Plant Physiol; Tissue Cult Asn; Scand Soc Plant Physiol; Am Soc Agron; AAAS; Int Asn Plant Tissue Cult; Int Asn Plant Molecular Biol. *Res:* Plant biochemistry and genetics, especially genetic manipulation, control of amino acid biosynthesis and photorespiration. *Mailing Add:* Dept Agron Univ Ill 1102 S Goodwin Ave Urbana IL 61801-4709

**WIDIN, KATHARINE DOUGLAS,** BIOLOGY. *Current Pos:* CONSULT URBAN FORESTRY, 82- *Personal Data:* b Cleveland, Ohio, Oct 1, 52; m 74. *Educ:* Kenyon Col, AB, 74; Univ Minn, MS, 77, PhD(phytopath), 80. *Prof Exp:* Lectr biol & microbiol, Curry Col, Milton Mass, 80-81; asst prof biol, microbiol & bot, 81-82. *Concurrent Pos:* Lectr entom & plant dis, Mass Bay Community Col, 80-82; consult, Plant Insect & Dis Clins, Regional Garden Ctrs, 81- *Mem:* Am Phytopath Soc; Mycol Soc Am; Sigma Xi. *Mailing Add:* 13457 Sixth St N Stillwater MN 55082

**WIDLANSKI, THEODORE SOLOMON,** BIO-ORGANIC CHEMISTRY, ENZYMOLOGY. *Current Pos:* adj prof biochem & molecular biol, asst prof, 90, ASST PROF CHEM, IND UNIV, 89- *Personal Data:* b New York, NY, May 23, 56; m, Martha Jacobs; c Benjamin & Esther. *Educ:* Columbia Univ, BA, 82; Harvard Univ, MA, 83, PhD(chem), 89. *Concurrent Pos:* Du Pont fel, Harvard Univ, 84-85; consult, Amira Inc, 90-, Marion Merrell Dow, 94; fel, Inst Molecular & Cellular Biol, Ind Univ Sch Med, 91-; Camille Dreyfus Teacher-Scholar Award, 94; Am Cancer Soc Jr Fac Res Award, 94- *Mem:* Am Chem Soc; AAAS. *Res:* Design and development of enzyme inhibitors related to the treatment and study of cancer and acquired immune deficiency syndrome. *Mailing Add:* Dept Chem Ind Univ Bloomington IN 47405-4001. *Fax:* 812-855-8300; *E-Mail:* twidlans@iubacs

**WIDMAIER, ERIC PAUL,** PHYSIOLOGICAL STRESS, METABOLISM. *Current Pos:* asst prof, 88-94, ASSOC PROF BIOL, BOSTON UNIV, 94- *Personal Data:* b New York, NY, May 14, 57; m 79, Maria Van Rauenstein; c Richard & Caroline. *Educ:* Northwestern Univ, BA & MS, 79, Univ Calif, San Francisco, PhD(endocrinol), 84. *Prof Exp:* Fel endocrinol, Worcester Found Exp Biol, 84-86, Salk Inst, 86-88. *Mem:* Am Diabetes Asn; Am Physiol Soc; Endocrine Soc. *Res:* Endocrine and nervous compensatory responses to stress; control of energy balance; neuroendocrinology; control of hypothalamic/pituitary/adrenal axis in normal and metabolically-stressed animals; effects of glucose and fats on hormone secretion. *Mailing Add:* Dept Biol Boston Univ 5 Cummington St Boston MA 02215. *Fax:* 617-353-6340; *E-Mail:* widmaier@bio.bu.edu

**WIDMAIER, ROBERT GEORGE,** BIOCHEMISTRY, PHARMACEUTICAL CHEMISTRY. *Current Pos:* vpres tech dir, 88-90, VPRES & CHIEF INNOVATION OFFICER, PENWEST, 90- *Personal Data:* b Riverside, NJ, June 18, 48; m 77; c 4. *Educ:* ECarolina Univ, BS, 70; Purdue Univ, PhD(biochem), 76. *Prof Exp:* Res asst biochem, Purdue Univ, 71-74; res biochemist basic food sci, Res & Develop, Kraft Inc, 76-79; vpres, tech dir & res & develop, Kurth Malting Co, 79-83; res biochemist, Great Western Malting Co, 83-88. *Mem:* Am Chem Soc; Inst Food Technologists; Am Asn Pharmaceut Scientists; AAAS. *Res:* Flavor development in cultured food products; enzyme analysis; clinical diagnosis; drug metabolism; immunology; agricultural biotechnology research in small grains and cereal crops, applications of enzymes and biopolymers in product development for foods and food ingredients. *Mailing Add:* Penwest 777 108th Ave NE Suite 2390 PO Box 1688 Bellevue WA 98004-5193

**WIDMANN, FRANCES KING,** PATHOLOGY. *Current Pos:* asst prof, 71-73, assoc dir, 71-73, DIR, SCH MED TECHNOL, DUKE UNIV, 73-, ASSOC PROF PATH, SCH MED, 73-; ASST CHIEF LAB SERV, VET ADMIN HOSP, 72- *Personal Data:* b Boston, Mass, July 23, 35; div; c 2. *Educ:* Swarthmore Col, BA, 56; Western Res Univ, MD, 60; Am Bd Path, dipl & cert anat & clin path, 65, cert immunohemat, 73. *Honors & Awards:* John Elliott Award, Am Asn Blood Banks, 84. *Prof Exp:* Intern, Cleveland Metrop Gen Hosp, Ohio, 60-61; resident anat & clin path, Sch Med, Univ NC, Chapel Hill, 61-64; resident clin path, Norfolk Gen Hosp, Va, 64-65; staff pathologist, 65-66; from instr to asst prof path, Sch Med, Univ NC, Chapel Hill, 66-70. *Mem:* Am Asn Blood Banks. *Res:* Blood banking and medical education, especially in clinical pathology and medical technology training. *Mailing Add:* Dept Path Duke Univ Durham NC 27710

**WIDMAYER, DOROTHEA JANE,** ZOOLOGY, MICROBIAL GENETICS. *Current Pos:* instr zool, Wellesley Col, 61-63, from asst prof to assoc prof biol, 63-74, prof, 74-75, KENAN PROF BIOL, WELLESLEY COL, 75-, CHMN, DEPT BIOL SCI, 72- *Personal Data:* b Washington, DC, Oct 10, 30. *Educ:* Wellesley Col, BA, 53, MA, 55; Ind Univ, PhD(zool), 62. *Prof Exp:* Instr biol, Simmons Col, 55-57. *Concurrent Pos:* NSF sci fac fel, Inst Animal Genetics, Univ Edinburgh, 67-68; grant, Ascent of Man, Res Corp, 74. *Mem:* AAAS; Sigma Xi; Am Soc Zool; Soc Protozool. *Res:* Gene action and cytoplasmic inheritance in Paramecium aurelia. *Mailing Add:* Dept Biol Sci Wellesley Col Wellesley MA 02181-8203

**WIDMER, ELMER ANDREAS,** HELMINTHOLOGY, MEDICAL PARASITOLOGY. *Current Pos:* assoc prof environ & trop health, Loma Linda Univ, 67-71, chmn dept, 67-78, interim assoc dean, 70-80, assoc dean acad affairs, Sch Health, 80-82, chmn dept, 84-88, PROF ENVIRON & TROP HEALTH, LOMA LINDA UNIV, 71- *Personal Data:* b Dodge, NDak, Apr 27, 25; m; c 2. *Educ:* Union Col, Nebr, BA, 51; Univ Colo, MA, 56; Colo State Univ, PhD(zool), 65; Univ NC, MPH, 74. *Prof Exp:* Teacher, High Sch, 52-53; from instr to assoc prof biol, La Sierra Col, 53-67. *Concurrent Pos:* Fel, Sch Med, La State Univ, 66; WHO fel, Africa, 71. *Mem:* Am Inst Biol Sci; Nat Environ Health Asn; Am Soc Parasitol; Am Soc Trop Med & Hyg; Wildlife Dis Asn; Sigma Xi; Soc Vector Ecol. *Res:* Reptilian parasitology; tropical helminthology; host-parasite interactions. *Mailing Add:* Dept Biol Col Arts & Sci La Sierra Univ Riverside CA 92515-8247

**WIDMER, KEMBLE,** GEOLOGY. *Current Pos:* RETIRED. *Personal Data:* b New Rochelle, NY, Feb 26, 13; m 39; c 2. *Educ:* Lehigh Univ, AB, 37; Princeton Univ, MA, 47, PhD(geol), 50. *Prof Exp:* From instr to asst prof geol, Rutgers Univ, 48-50; assoc prof & chmn dept, Champlain Col, NY, 50-53; prin geologist, Div Sci, Bur Geol & Topog, NJ Dept Environ Protection, 53-58, nuclear indust coordr, 63-68, state geologist, 58-80, nuclear indust coordr, 63-74. *Concurrent Pos:* Tech consult, US Mil Acad, 63-81; seminar assoc, Columbia Univ; mem, Adv Comt on Water Data for Pub Use, US Geol Surv, 76-80. *Mem:* AAAS; Geol Soc Am; Am Inst Mining, Metall & Petrol Eng. *Res:* Areal, economic, Pleistocene and engineering geology. *Mailing Add:* 228 King George Rd Pennington NJ 08534-2324

**WIDMER, RICHARD ERNEST,** HORTICULTURE. *Current Pos:* RETIRED. *Personal Data:* b West New York, NJ, June 19, 22; m 49; c 3. *Educ:* Rutgers Univ, BS, 43, MS, 49; Univ Minn, PhD(hort), 55. *Honors & Awards:* Alex Laurie Award, Soc Am Florists, 81. *Prof Exp:* Instr hort, Univ Minn, St Paul, 49-55, from asst prof to assoc prof, 55-64, prof hort, 64-88. *Concurrent Pos:* Fulbright study grant, Agr Inst, Ireland, 68-69; AID consult, Hassan II Inst Agron & Vet Med, Rabat, Morocco, 73; sr res fel, NZ Nat Res Adv Coun, Levin Hort Res Ctr, 80-81; consult, Integrated Agr Prod & Mkt Proj, Philippines, 83. *Mem:* Fel Am Soc Hort Sci; Int Hort Soc. *Res:* Physiological studies of commercial greenhouse crops; breeding of garden chrysanthemums; ornamental horticulture. *Mailing Add:* 1275 Raymond Ave St Paul MN 55108-1817

**WIDMER, ROBERT H,** AERONAUTICAL ENGINEERING, SYSTEMS ENGINEERING. *Current Pos:* RETIRED. *Personal Data:* b Hawthorne, NJ, May 17, 16; m 45; c 2. *Educ:* Rensselaer Polytech Inst, BS, 38; Calif Inst Technol, MS, 39. *Hon Degrees:* ScD, Tex Christian Univ, 67. *Honors & Awards:* Field of Sci Award, Air Force Asn, 49; Spirit of St Louis Medal, Am Soc Mech Engrs, 63; Reed Aeronaut Medal, Am Inst Aeronaut & Astronaut, 83. *Prof Exp:* Chief aerodyn, Ft Worth Div, Gen Dynamics Corp, 49-51, asst chief engr tech design, 51-59, chief engr, 59-61, vpres res & eng, 61-71, vpres res & eng, Convair Div, Ft Worth & San Diego, 71-74, corp vpres sci & eng, St Louis, 74-81; consult, 81-96. *Concurrent Pos:* Mem, Comts Aerodyn & Propulsion, Nat Adv Comt Aeronaut, 48-58; mem bd dirs, Univ Tex Eng Found, 56-68, Tex Christian Univ Res Found, 73-77 & Southern Methodist Univ Found Sci & Eng, 73-; consult res & eng, Off Asst Secy Defense, 58-64 & USAF Sci Adv Bd, 54-58; chmn, Peer Comn Aero/Astro, Nat Acad Eng, 81-84. *Mem:* Nat Acad Eng; fel Am Inst Aeronaut & Astronaut; Nat Soc Prof Engrs; Air Force Asn. *Mailing Add:* 4765 Overton Woods Dr Ft Worth TX 76109

**WIDMER, WILBUR JAMES,** ENVIRONMENTAL ENGINEERING, LIMNOLOGY. *Current Pos:* from instr to prof, 48-88, EMER PROF CIVIL ENG, UNIV CONN, 88- *Personal Data:* b West New York, NJ, Oct 20, 18; m 50, Pearl Gilmore; c Frederick, Wilbur & Mark. *Educ:* Cooper Union, BCE, 46; Mass Inst Technol, SM, 48. *Honors & Awards:* Bedell Award Water Pollution Control, Water Pollution Control Fedn, 72. *Prof Exp:* Technician, Gibbs & Cox, Inc, NY, 43-47. *Concurrent Pos:* Consult, Conn State Water Resources Comn, 50-52, C W Riva Co, RI, 50-63 & J M Minges Assocs, Conn, 59-63; res asst, Mass Inst Technol, 56-57; NSF sci fac fel biol oceanog, Narragansett Marine Lab, RI, 64-66; WHO assignment as prof sanit eng,

WPakistan Univ Eng & Technol, Lahore & sanit eng adv, Govt Pakistan, 68-70; sanit eng consult in Brazil, Pan-Am Health Orgn, 72; sanitary eng consult, WHO, Egypt, Saudia Arabia & Sudan, 79. *Mem:* Fel Royal Soc Health; fel Am Soc Civil Engrs; Am Soc Limnol & Oceanog; Am Water Works Asn; Am Acad Environ Engrs; Water Pollution Control Fedn. *Res:* Eutrophication and pollution ecology of fresh and marine waters; waste water treatment systems. *Mailing Add:* 61 Meadowood Rd Storrs CT 06268

**WIDMOYER, FRED BIXLER,** horticulture; deceased, see previous edition for last biography

**WIDNALL, SHEILA EVANS,** AERONAUTICAL ENGINEERING, FLUID MECHANICS. *Current Pos:* SECY AIR FORCE, USAF, 93- *Personal Data:* b Tacoma, Wash, July 13, 38; m 60; c 2. *Educ:* Mass Inst Technol, BS, 60, MS, 61, ScD(aeronaut eng), 64. *Hon Degrees:* ScD, New Eng Col, 75, Lawrence Univ, 87, Cedar Crest Col, 88, Smith Col, 90. *Honors & Awards:* Lawrence Sperry Award, Am Inst Aeronaut & Astronaut, 72; Outstanding Achievement Award, Soc Woman Engrs, 75. *Prof Exp:* Res asst aerodyn, Mass Inst Technol, 61-64, Ford fel, 64-66, from asst prof to prof aeronaut, 64-93, chairperson, women fac, 76-77, head, Dynamics Div, Dept Aeronaut & Astronaut, 78-79,. *Concurrent Pos:* Consult several industs; dir univ res, US Dept Transp, Washington, DC, 74-75; mem space & aeronaut bd, Nat Acad Eng, 75-78; mem adv comt, NSF, USAF & US Dept Transp; mem bd gov, USAF Acad, 78-; assoc ed, J Appl Mech, 83- *Mem:* Nat Acad Eng; fel Am Inst Aeronaut & Astronaut; fel Am Phys Soc; Soc Women Engrs; fel AAAS; Am Soc Mech Engrs. *Res:* Unsteady aerodynamics; aeroelasticity; aerodynamic noise; turbulence; applied mathematics; vortex flows; numerical analysis; aerospace; transportation; aerodynamics and fluid mechanics; acoustics; noise and vibration. *Mailing Add:* 1670 Air Force Pentagon Washington DC 20330. *Fax:* 703-693-7553; *E-Mail:* widnall@af.pentagon.mil

**WIDNELL, CHRISTOPHER COURTENAY,** CELL BIOLOGY, BIOCHEMISTRY. *Current Pos:* assoc prof, 69-77, prof anat & cell biol, 77-93, PROF CELL BIOL & PHYSIOL, SCH MED, UNIV PITTSBURGH, 93- *Personal Data:* b London, Eng, May 19, 40; m 65, Anne Ewing; c Katherine L & Nicholas A. *Educ:* Cambridge Univ, BA, 62; Univ London, PhD(biochem), 65. *Honors & Awards:* Price Orator, Am Gynec & Obstet Soc, 86. *Prof Exp:* Res assoc cell biol, Rockefeller Univ, 66-68; staff mem biochem, Nat Inst Med Res, London, Eng, 68-69. *Concurrent Pos:* Jane Coffin Childs fel, Univ Chicago, 65-66; ed, Arch Biochem & Biophys, 72-; sr Fogarty int fel, Int Inst Cellular & Molecular Path, Brussels, 78-79; mem, Cell Biol Panel, NSF, 83-87; John Simon Guggenheim Mem fel, 87-88. *Mem:* Am Soc Biol Chem; Am Soc Cell Biol; Brit Biochem Soc; AAAS; Asn Anatomists; hon mem Am Gynec & Obstet Soc. *Res:* Membrane structure and function; synthesis and assembly of membrane components; endocytosis and membrane recycling; host cell response to viral infection. *Mailing Add:* Dept Cell Biol & Physiol Univ Pittsburgh Sch Med 3550 Terrace St Pittsburgh PA 15261. *Fax:* 412-648-1441; *E-Mail:* cwidnell@pitt.edu

**WIDNER, JIMMY NEWTON,** CROP BREEDING. *Current Pos:* VPRES AGR, SOUTHERN MINN BEET COOP, RENVILLE, MINN, 89- *Personal Data:* b Clovis, NMex, Feb 10, 42; m 64; c 2. *Educ:* NMex State Univ, BS, 64; NDak State Univ, PhD(agron), 68. *Prof Exp:* Plant breeder, Great Western Sugar Co, Colo, 68-72; res mgr, Northern Ohio Sugar Co, 72-75; sr plant breeder, Great Western Sugar Co, 75- *Mem:* Am Soc Agron; Crop Sci Soc Am; Am Soc Sugar Beet Technol. *Res:* Development of improved varieties and hybrids of sugar beets. *Mailing Add:* Southern Minn Sugar Co PO Box 500 Renville MN 56284

**WIDNER, WILLIAM RICHARD,** PHYSIOLOGY, BACTERIOLOGY. *Current Pos:* RETIRED. *Personal Data:* b Baxter Co, Ark, Apr 24, 20; m 43; c 1. *Educ:* Eastern NMex Univ, AB, 42; Univ NMex, MS, 48, PhD, 52. *Prof Exp:* Lab asst biol, Eastern NMex Univ, 42; asst, Univ NMex, 46-48; biomed researcher, Los Alamos Sci Lab, 48-50; asst, Univ NMex, 50-52; indust hygienist, Sandia Corp, 52-55; teacher, Albuquerque Indian Sch, NMex, 55-56; prof biol & head dept, Howard Payne Col, 56-59; asst prof biol & bact, Baylor Univ, 59-64, prof biol, 64-88. *Mem:* AAAS; Am Soc Microbiol; Sigma Xi (treas, 73-74). *Res:* Cell mitoses and growth of normal and malignant tissues; effects of ionizing radiations on living cells; radiation produced cataracts; bacterial metabolism. *Mailing Add:* 2532 Eldridge Lane Waco TX 76710

**WIDNESS, JOHN ANDREW,** ERYTHROPOIESIS IN THE FETUS & NEWBORN. *Current Pos:* assoc prof, 88-92, PROF PEDIAT, UNIV IOWA HOSPS & CLINS, 92- *Personal Data:* b Takoma Park, Md, Feb 28, 46; c Laura, Ben & Jane. *Educ:* Amherst Col, BA, 68; Duke Univ, MD, 72. *Prof Exp:* Instr pediat, Brown Univ, 78-79, asst prof, 79-86, assoc prof, 86-88. *Mem:* Am Acad Pediat; Am Fedn Clin Res; Soc Pediat Res; Am Pediat Soc; Perinatal Res Soc; Europ Soc Pediat Res. *Res:* Fetal and neonatal hypoxia, anemia, erythropoiesis and erythropoietin physiology; fetal circulatory, metabolic and endocrine function in diabetic pregnancies; development aspect of erythropoiesis. *Mailing Add:* 200 Hawkins Dr W222-1 GH Iowa City IA 52242-1083. *Fax:* 319-356-8669

**WIDOM, BENJAMIN,** STATISTICAL MECHANICS, THERMODYNAMICS. *Current Pos:* from instr to prof, 54-83, GOLDWIN SMITH PROF CHEM, CORNELL UNIV, 83- *Personal Data:* b Newark, NJ, Oct 13, 27; m 53, Joanne McCurdy; c Jonathan, Michael & Elisabeth. *Educ:* Columbia Univ, AB, 49; Cornell Univ, PhD(chem), 53. *Hon Degrees:* DSc, Univ Chicago, 91. *Honors & Awards:* Boris Pregel Award, NY Acad Sci, 76;

Langmuir Award, Am Chem Soc, 82, Hildebrand Award, 92; Bakhuis Roozeboom Medal, Royal Neth Acad Scis, 94. *Prof Exp:* Res assoc chem, Univ NC, 52-54. *Concurrent Pos:* Guggenheim & Fulbright fels, 61-62; NSF sr fel, 65; Guggenheim fel, 69; van der Waals prof, Univ Amsterdam, 72; vis prof, Harvard Univ, 75, Katholieke Univ, Leuven, 88, Univ d' Aix Marseille III, 95; IBM prof, Oxford Univ, 78; NATO/Heineman fel, 83; Lorentz prof, Leiden Univ, 85; Fulbright fel, 90. *Mem:* Nat Acad Sci; Am Phys Soc; Am Chem Soc; NY Acad Sci; Am Acad Arts & Sci; Am Philos Soc. *Res:* Phase transitions; statistical mechanics; complex fluids, including surfactant and polymer solutions, interfacial properties. *Mailing Add:* Dept Chem Cornell Univ Ithaca NY 14853. *Fax:* 607-255-4137; *E-Mail:* bw24@cornell.edu

**WIDOM, HAROLD,** CONVOLUTION & PSEUDODIFFERENTIAL OPERATORS, RANDOM MATRICES. *Current Pos:* PROF MATH, UNIV CALIF, SANTA CRUZ, 68- *Personal Data:* b Newark, NJ, Sept 23, 32; c Barbara, Jennifer & Steven. *Educ:* Univ Chicago, SM, 52, PhD(math), 55. *Prof Exp:* From instr to prof math, Cornell Univ, 55-68. *Concurrent Pos:* Res fels, NSF, 59-60 & Sloan Found, 61-63; Guggenheim res fel, 67-68 & 72-73. *Mem:* Am Math Soc. *Res:* Operator theory, specifically Tueplitz, Wiener-Hopt and pseudodifferential operators; problems in random matrix theory. *Mailing Add:* Dept Math Univ Calif Santa Cruz Santa Cruz CA 95064. *E-Mail:* widom@ucsc.edu

**WIDRA, ABE,** MICROBIOLOGY. *Current Pos:* RETIRED. *Personal Data:* b Philadelphia, Pa, Jan 17, 24; m 52, Anita J Hesch; c Ken, Len, Marlene & Jon. *Educ:* Brooklyn Col, BA, 48; Univ Fla, MS, 52; Univ Pa, PhD(med microbiol), 54; Am Bd Med Microbiol, dipl, 69. *Prof Exp:* Tech asst bact & serol, Philadelphia Gen Hosp, 49-50; res assoc cytol & cytogenetics, Univ Pa, 54-55; instr bact & immunol, Univ NC, 55-59, asst prof, 59-64; assoc prof microbiol, Med Ctr, Univ Ill, Chicago, 64-92. *Concurrent Pos:* Consult med mycol, Presby-St Luke's Hosp, Chicago, 66-80. *Mem:* Am Soc Microbiol. *Res:* Medical mycology; wound healing; synthetic skin. *Mailing Add:* 3321 Glenwood Circle Holiday FL 34691-2528

**WIDRLECHNER, MARK PETER,** GERMPLASM CONSERVATION. *Current Pos:* HORTICULTURIST, AGR RES SERV, USDA, 83- *Personal Data:* b Berwyn, Ill, Dec 12, 57. *Educ:* Mich State Univ, BS, 77; Univ Ill, MS, 80; Univ Minn, PhD(hort), 82. *Concurrent Pos:* Asst prof USDA collabr hort & agron, Iowa State Univ, 83-; chmn res comn, Am Rhododendron Soc, 91-95. *Mem:* Am Soc Hort Sci; Am Asn Bot Gardens & Arboreta; Soc Econ Bot; Am Rhododendron Soc; Am Chestnut Found (vpres, 87-91). *Res:* Methods of ex situ germplasm conservation; evaluation of new landscape plants for north central US; evaluation of nectar plants as honeybee forage. *Mailing Add:* Iowa State Univ Plant Introd Sta Ames IA 50011

**WIDROW, BERNARD,** ELECTRICAL ENGINEERING. *Current Pos:* PROF ELEC ENG, STANFORD UNIV, 59- *Personal Data:* b Norwich, Conn, Dec 24, 29. *Educ:* Mass Inst Technol, BS, 51, MS, 53, ScD, 56. *Honors & Awards:* Centennial Medal, Inst Elec & Electronics Engrs, 84, Alexander Graham Bell Medal, 86, Neural Networks Pioneer Medal, 91. *Mem:* Nat Acad Eng; Int Neural Network Soc (pres, 89-90); fel Inst Elec & Electronics Engrs. *Mailing Add:* Info Systs Lab Stanford Univ Durand 139 Stanford CA 94305-9510. *Fax:* 650-723-8473

**WIDSTROM, NEIL WAYNE,** QUANTITATIVE GENETICS, PLANT BREEDING. *Current Pos:* RES GENETICIST PLANTS, AGR RES SERV, USDA, 64- *Personal Data:* b Hecla, SDak, Nov 11, 33; m 60; c 2. *Educ:* SDak State Univ, BS, 59, PhD(plant breeding), 62. *Prof Exp:* Fel genetics, NC State Univ, 63-64. *Mem:* AAAS; fel Am Soc Agron; fel Crop Sci Soc Am; Genetics Soc Am; Am Genetic Asn. *Res:* Plant genetics; genetics of resistance to insects by plants; resistance in corn to aflatoxin contamination. *Mailing Add:* Insect Biol & Pop Mgt Res Lab PO Box 748 Tifton GA 31793. *Fax:* 912-387-2341; *E-Mail:* nwidstru@tifton.cpes.peachnet.edu

**WIE, CHU RYANG,** SEMICONDUCTOR MATERIALS & DEVICES, HIGH RESOLUTION X-RAY DIFFRACTION OF SEMICONDUCTOR STRUCTURES. *Current Pos:* from asst prof to assoc prof, 85-93, PROF ELEC ENG, STATE UNIV NY, BUFFALO, 93- *Personal Data:* b Jangheung, Korea, Apr 25, 57; m 85, Jisoon Kim; c Benjamin J & Samuel C. *Educ:* Chonnam Nat Univ, Korea, BS, 80; Seoul Nat Univ, Korea, MS, 82; Calif Inst Technol, PhD(appl physics), 85. *Prof Exp:* Res fel physics, Calif Inst Technol, 85. *Concurrent Pos:* Vis assoc, Calif Inst Technol, 86; NSF eng initiation award, 87 & presidential young investr award, 88; vis assoc prof, Pohang Inst Sci Technol, Korea, 93. *Mem:* Am Phys Soc; Mat Res Soc; Sigma Xi; NY Acad Sci; Soc Photo-Optical Instrumentation Engrs; Inst Elec & Electronics Engrs. *Res:* X-ray rocking curve analysis of semiconductor heterostructures; materials and devices of lattice-mismatched III-V heterostructures; semi-insulating III-V materials; strained resonant tunneling structures; electrical and optical characterization of semiconductors. *Mailing Add:* Dept Elec & Comput Eng State Univ NY 201 Bonner Hall Buffalo NY 14260. *Fax:* 716-645-5964; *E-Mail:* elewie@ubvms.cs.buff.edu

**WIEBE, DONALD,** ENGINEERING, RAIL TRANSPORTATION EQUIPMENT. *Current Pos:* mgr, 64-76, vpres res & eng, 76-86, CONSULT, RAIL TRANSP, 86- *Personal Data:* b Indicott, Nebr, June 30, 23; m 45; c 2. *Educ:* WVa Univ, BS, 49, MS, 59. *Honors & Awards:* Arnold Stucki Award, Am Soc Mech Engrs, 89. *Prof Exp:* Res engr, Joy Mfg Co, 49-51, mgr, Exp Sta, 51-53; asst prof mining eng, WVa Univ, 51-53; mgr eng mech, Astronuclear Lab, Westinghouse Elec Corp, 63-64. *Concurrent Pos:* Adv comm mech & aerospace eng, WVa Univ, 82-93; mem, Environ Trans Operating Bd, Am Soc Mech Engrs. *Mem:* Soc Exp Mech; Air Pollution

Control Asn; Am Inst Mining, Metall & Petrol Engrs; fel Am Soc Mech Engrs; Instrument Soc Am. *Res:* Product engineering and development; mining, industrial-dust collection; applied research; experimental mechanics; railcar suspension development; holder of 30 US letters patents and 49 foreign patents relating to mining, industrial and rail transport equipment. *Mailing Add:* 106 Woodland Rd Sewickley PA 15143

**WIEBE, JOHN,** HORTICULTURE. *Current Pos:* DIR, PLANT INDUST DIV, ALTA DEPT AGR, EDMONTON, 76- *Personal Data:* b Sask, June 3, 26; m 47; c 6. *Educ:* Ont Agr Col, BSA, 51; Cornell Univ, MS, 53, PhD, 55. *Prof Exp:* Res scientist, Hort Res Inst, Ont Dept Agr, 55-76. *Res:* Viticulture and physiology. *Mailing Add:* Dept Practical Theol Can Mennonite Bible Col 600 Shaftesbury Blvd Winnipeg MB R3P 0M4 Can

**WIEBE, JOHN PETER,** ENDOCRINOLOGY, CONTRACEPTION. *Current Pos:* asst prof physiol, 72-77, from asst prof to assoc prof, 74-85, PROF ZOOL & PHYSIOL, UNIV WESTERN ONT, 85- *Personal Data:* b Neu-Sconsee, Ukraine, Aug 28, 38; Can citizen; m 64; c 2. *Educ:* Univ BC, BSc, 63, PhD(physiol), 67. *Prof Exp:* Nat Res Coun Can res fel zool, Univ Leeds, 68-69; asst prof endocrinol, Tex A&M Univ, 70-72. *Mem:* AAAS; Can Soc Cell Biol; Can Biochem Soc; Soc Study Reproduction; Am Soc Andrology; Soc Adv Contraception. *Res:* Steriods; contraception; reproductive endocrinology. *Mailing Add:* Dept Zool Univ Western Ont London ON N6A 5B1 Can

**WIEBE, LEONARD IRVING,** BIONUCLEONICS, RADIOPHARMACEUTICAL CHEMISTRY. *Current Pos:* Asst prof pharmaceut chem bionucleonics, Univ Alta, 70-73, assoc prof, 73-78, chmn, Res Reactor Comt, 74-89, chmn, Bionucleonics Div, 74-75 & 87-90, PROF RADIOPHARM CHEM, UNIV ALTA, 78-, ASSOC DEAN RES, 90- *Personal Data:* b Swift Current, Sask, Oct 14, 41; m 64, Grace McIntyre; c 3. *Educ:* Univ Sask, BSP, 63, MSc, 66; Univ Sydney, PhD(drug metab), 69. *Honors & Awards:* McNeil Prize, 87. *Concurrent Pos:* Sessional lectr, Univ Sask, 65-66 & Univ Sydney, 73; fel, Univ Alta, 69-70; AUH fel, 76; von Humboldt fel, Ger Cancer Res Ctr, 76-77; res assoc, Cross Cancer Inst, 78-; vis prof, PMAC, Searle & MRC, 86; dir biomed & health, Australian Nuclear Sci Technol Orgn, 90; hon liason prof, Peoples Univ Bangladesh. *Mem:* Asn Fac Pharm Can; Int Soc Antiviral Res; Can Asn Radiopharm Sci; Soc Nuclear Med; Can Soc Pharm Scientists; Can Radiopharm Sci Asn. *Res:* Production of short-lived radionuclides for incorporation into radiopharmaceuticals for use in diagnostic nuclear medicine; emphasis is on radiohalogenated pyrimidine nucleosides and nitroimidazole radiosensitizers for oncology and virology; antiviral and antitumor nucleosides. *Mailing Add:* Fac Pharm & Pharm Sci Univ Alta Edmonton AB T6G 2N8 Can. *Fax:* 403-492-8241; *E-Mail:* leonard.wiebe@ualberta.ca

**WIEBE, MICHAEL EUGENE,** CELL BIOLOGY, VIROLOGY. *Current Pos:* sr scientist, Cell Cult Res & Develop, Genentech Inc, 84-88, assoc dir med & analytical chem, 88-90, dir qual control, 90-96, SR DIR QUAL CONTROL, GENETECH INC, 96- *Personal Data:* b Newton, Kans, Oct 1, 42; m 65, Rebecca A Doak; c Brandon & Thomas. *Educ:* Sterling Col, BS, 65; Univ Kans, PhD(microbiol), 71. *Prof Exp:* Fel microbiol, Duke Univ Med Ctr, 71-73; asst prof, Med Col, Cornell Univ, 73-81, adj assoc prof, 81-84; assoc dir, Blood Derivatives Prog, New York Blood Ctr, 80-83, assoc investr, Lindsley F Kimball Res Inst, 80-84, dir, Leukocyte Prod, 83-84. *Concurrent Pos:* Mem, Subcomt Interrelationships among Catalogued Arboviruses, Am Comt Arthropod-born Viruses, 77-80; prin investr contracts, US Army Med Res & Develop Command, 77-81; mem, Crit Rev Microbiol Adv Bd, 82-86; mem bd trustees, Sterling Col, Kans, 90-, chmn bd trustees, 94- *Mem:* Am Soc Microbiol; Am Soc Virol; AAAS; Parenteral Drug Asn. *Res:* Molecular virology and cell biology; production of human therapeutics by genetically engineered mammalian cells; quality control of genetically engineered biopharmaceuticals. *Mailing Add:* Qual Control Dept Genentech Inc 460 Pt San Bruno Blvd South San Francisco CA 94080. *Fax:* 650-225-8944; *E-Mail:* wiebe.michael@gene.com

**WIEBE, PETER HOWARD,** BIOLOGICAL OCEANOGRAPHY, MARINE BIOLOGY. *Current Pos:* asst scientist, 69-74, assoc scientist, 74-84, SR SCIENTIST BIOL OCEANOG, WOODS HOLE OCEANOG INST, 84- *Personal Data:* b Salinas, Calif, Oct 2, 40; m 68; c 2. *Educ:* Ariz State Col, Flagstaff, BS, 62; Scripps Inst Oceanog, Univ Calif, San Diego, PhD(biol oceanog), 68. *Prof Exp:* Fel biol oceanog, Hopkins Marine Sta, Stanford Univ, 68-69. *Concurrent Pos:* Numerous NSF grants & Off Naval Res contracts. *Mem:* Am Soc Limnol & Oceanog; AAAS. *Res:* Quantitative ecology of zooplankton with emphasis on the biological and physical-chemical factors which act to regulate the distribution and abundance of oceanic populations and communities. *Mailing Add:* 99 Rockledge Dr North Falmouth MA 02556

**WIEBE, RICHARD PENNER,** MATHEMATICAL LOGIC. *Current Pos:* RETIRED. *Personal Data:* b Pittsburgh, Pa, Jan 5, 28; m 56, Tobey Margolis; c Albert & Karl. *Educ:* Univ Ill, Urbana, BS, 49, MS, 51; Univ Calif, Berkeley, PhD(philos), 64. *Prof Exp:* Instr philos, Johns Hopkins Univ, 60-62; asst prof math, St Mary's Col, Calif, 63-88. *Res:* Foundations of mathematics; semantics; philosophy of science and mathematics. *Mailing Add:* 852 Contra Costa Ave Berkeley CA 94707-1920

**WIEBE, ROBERT A,** PETROLOGY. *Current Pos:* Asst prof, 66-73, ASSOC PROF GEOL, FRANKLIN & MARSHALL COL, 73-, CHMN DEPT, 76- *Personal Data:* b San Mateo, Calif, Nov 2, 39; m 65. *Educ:* Stanford Univ, BS, 61; Univ Wash, Seattle, MS, 63; Stanford Univ, PhD, 66. *Concurrent Pos:*

NATO fel, Univ Edinburgh, 72-73. *Mem:* Geol Soc Am; Mineral Soc Am. *Res:* Igneous and metamorphic petrology; mineralogy; plutonic igneous rocks of the Northern Appalachians; the Nain Anorthosite-Adamellite complex. *Mailing Add:* Dept Geol Franklin & Marshall Col Box 3003 Lancaster PA 17604-3003

**WIEBE, WILLIAM JOHN,** MICROBIAL ECOLOGY, ANAEROBIC METABOLISM. *Current Pos:* asst prof, 67-72, assoc prof, 72-77, PROF MICROBIOL, UNIV GA, 77- *Personal Data:* b San Mateo, Calif, Mar 14, 35; m 60; c 3. *Educ:* Stanford Univ, BA, 57; Univ Wash, PhD(fisheries), 65. *Prof Exp:* Fel microbiol & electron micros, Georgetown Univ, 65-67. *Concurrent Pos:* Vis prof, Div Fisheries & Oceanog, Commonwealth Sci & Indust Res Orgn, 75, officer-in-chg, 79-82; mem, Panel Adv Comt Ecol & Ecosyst, NSF, 78, Sci Comt Coral Reefs, Pac Sci Asn, 79. *Mem:* Am Soc Microbiol; Am Soc Limnol & Oceanog; Australian Soc Microbiol; Western Naturalist Asn; Int Soc Coral Reefs. *Res:* Marine microbial ecology in nearshore coastal and estuarine environments; salt marsh sediment fermentation; sulfate reduction and methanogenesis, in coastal zones and coral reefs; macrophyte decomposition and nitrogen fixation. *Mailing Add:* 9927 Cypress Shadow Ave Tampa FL 33647

**WIEBUSCH, CHARLES FRED,** ACOUSTICS. *Current Pos:* mem tech staff, Bell Tel Labs, Inc, 27-45, sta apparatus engr, 45-51, dir, Underwater Systs Lab, 51-62, exec dir, Outside Plant & Underwater Systs Div, 62-67. *Personal Data:* b Perry, Tex, Mar 11, 03; m 26. *Educ:* Univ Tex, BA, 24, MA, 25. *Honors & Awards:* Emile Berliner Award, Audio Eng Soc, 69; VAdmiral Charles B Martell Tech Award, Nat Security Indust Asn, 79. *Prof Exp:* Instr physics, Univ Tex, 25-27. *Concurrent Pos:* Consult acoust, 67-; mem, Comt Undersea Warfare, Nat Acad Sci, 53-74, chmn, Comt Underwater Commun, 68-70. *Mem:* Fel Acoust Soc Am; Inst Elec & Electronics Engrs. *Res:* Sources, transmission and measurement of underwater sounds; recording and reproduction of speech and music; architectural acoustics; management of research and engineering. *Mailing Add:* 700 John Ringling Blvd Apt N206 Sarasota FL 34236

**WIEBUSCH, F B,** PERIODONTOLOGY. *Current Pos:* prof oral diag & therapeut & chmn dept, 54-71, PROF PERIODONT & ASST DEAN CONTINUING EDUC, MED COL VA, 71- *Personal Data:* b Brenham, Tex, Aug 26, 23. *Educ:* Univ Tex, BBA, 43, DDS, 47; Am Bd Periodont, dipl. *Prof Exp:* Pub health dent consult, State Health Dept, Tex, 47-51. *Concurrent Pos:* Consult, Vet Admin Hosps, Richmond & Salem, Va. *Mem:* Am Dent Asn; Am Acad Periodont; fel Int Col Dent; fel Am Col Dent; Am Acad Dent Med. *Res:* Periodontics. *Mailing Add:* 300 W Franklin St Richmond VA 23220

**WIEBUSH, JOSEPH ROY,** ANALYTICAL CHEMISTRY, MARINE CHEMISTRY. *Current Pos:* CONSULT, 77-; DIR, GASSER ASSOC, INC. *Personal Data:* b Lancaster, Pa, Oct 18, 20; m 43, Dorothy Miller; c James P. *Educ:* Franklin & Marshall Col, BS, 41; Univ Md, MS, 51, PhD(chem), 55. *Prof Exp:* Supvr, Explosives Dept, Hercules Powder Co, 41-43, chemist, 46-48; asst chem, Univ Md, 48-51; res chemist, Mead Corp, Ohio, 55-56; dir res, Nat Inst Drycleaning, 56-60; from assoc prof to prof chem, US Naval Acad, 60-81, chmn dept, 66-77. *Concurrent Pos:* Adj prof, Univ Cent Fla, 81-89. *Mem:* Am Chem Soc; Sigma Xi. *Res:* Fluorescence analysis; toxicity of organic solvents; analytical techniques for trace elements; marine corrosion and fouling; oceanographic applications; environmental pollution; general chemistry texts. *Mailing Add:* 1830 Ramie Rd Clermont FL 34711

**WIECH, NORBERT LEONARD,** BIOCHEMICAL PHARMACOLOGY. *Current Pos:* sect head biochem pharm, Merrell Int, Strasbourg, France, 72-74, sect head biochem pharmacol, Merrell Res Ctr, 67-85, ASSOC SCIENTIST PROJ ADMIN & RES DIRECTION, MERRELL-DOW, CINCINNATI, 85- *Personal Data:* b Chicago, Ill, Mar 13, 39; m 61, 85; c 3. *Educ:* Univ Notre Dame, BS, 60, MS, 63; Tulane Univ, PhD(biochem), 66. *Prof Exp:* Res assoc nutrit, Sch Pub Health, Harvard Univ, 66-67. *Concurrent Pos:* Adj assoc prof exp med, Univ Cincinnati, 78-, asst prof chem, 81- *Mem:* AAAS; Am Oil Chemists Soc; Am Chem Soc; NY Acad Sci; Am Diabetes Asn. *Res:* Membrane receptors; neuropharmacology; carbohydrate-lipid metabolism in health and disease. *Mailing Add:* 10 Overshot Ct Phoenix MD 21131

**WIECHELMAN, KAREN JANICE,** BIOPHYSICAL CHEMISTRY. *Current Pos:* from asst prof to assoc prof chem, Univ Southwestern La, 76-90, chmn dept, 88-, prof chem, 90-, PROF MATH, UNIV SOUTHWESTERN LA. *Personal Data:* b Central City, Nebr, Apr 30, 47; m 70; c 1. *Educ:* Univ Nebr, BS, 69, PhD(biochem), 73. *Prof Exp:* Res assoc biophys, Univ Pittsburgh, 73-76. *Concurrent Pos:* Coun Undergrad Res. *Res:* Use of fluorescence techniques to investigate various biological systems; cryoprotection of proteins. *Mailing Add:* Dept Chem Univ Southwestern La PO Box 44370 Lafayette LA 70504-9998

**WIECZOREK, GERALD FRANCIS,** GEOTECHNICAL ENGINEERING, GEOLOGIC HAZARD & RISK ASSESSMENT. *Current Pos:* Res civil engr, Br Geol Risk Assessment, Menlo Park, Calif, 78-87, dep chief eng, Off Earthquakes, Volcanoes & Eng, Reston, Va, 87-90, RES CIVIL ENGR, BR GEOL RISK ASSESSMENT, US GEOL SURV, RESTON, VA, 90- *Personal Data:* b Schenectady, NY, Oct 25, 49; m 75; c 1. *Educ:* Univ Calif, Berkeley, BS, 71, MS, 72, ME, 74, PhD(geol eng), 78. *Mem:* Int Asn Eng Geologists; Asn Eng Geologists; Am Soc Civil Engrs. *Res:* Models ground water fluctuation and reactivation of landslides for improved means of assessing probability of landsliding. *Mailing Add:* US Geol Surv Nat Ctr 12201 Sunrise Valley Dr Mail Stop 955 Reston VA 20192

**WIED, GEORGE LUDWIG,** OBSTETRICS & GYNECOLOGY. *Current Pos:* from asst prof to assoc prof, Univ Chicago, 54-65, actg chmn dept, 74-75, prof obstet & gynec, 65-, prof path, 67-, dir, Schs Cytotechnol & Cytocybernet, 59-, EMER PROF, SCH MED, UNIV CHICAGO. *Personal Data:* b Carlsbad, Czech, Feb 7, 21; wid. *Educ:* Charles Univ, Prague, MD, 44. *Honors & Awards:* Surgeon Gen Cert Merit, 52; Goldblatt Cytol Award, 61; George N Papanicolaou Cytol Award, 70. *Prof Exp:* Intern, County Hosp, Carlsbad, Czech, 45; resident obstet & gynec, Univ Munich, 46-48; asst, Univ Berlin, 48-52, co-chmn dept, 53. *Concurrent Pos:* Ed-in-chief, Acta Cytologica, 57-; ed, Monogr Clin Cytol, 64-; ed-in-chief, J Reproductive Med, 67-; ed-in-chief, Analytical & Quant Cytol, 79- *Mem:* Am Soc Cytol (pres, 65-66); Am Soc Cell Biol; Int Acad Cytol (pres elect, 74-77, pres, 77-80); Ger Soc Obstet & Gynec; Ger Soc Cytol. *Res:* Cytopathology; exfoliative cytology; biological image processing. *Mailing Add:* 1640 E 50th Pl Chicago IL 60615-3161

**WIEDEMAN, VARLEY EARL,** BOTANY, ECOLOGY. *Current Pos:* from asst prof to assoc prof, 64-74, PROF PLANT ECOL, UNIV LOUISVILLE, 64- *Personal Data:* b Oklahoma City, Okla, Mar 14, 33; m 63; c 2. *Educ:* Univ Okla, BS, 57, MS, 60; Univ Tex, PhD(bot), 64. *Prof Exp:* Chemist-biologist, USPHS, 59-61. *Mem:* Am Water Resources Asn; AAAS; Sigma Xi. *Mailing Add:* 12503 Urton Lane Louisville KY 40243

**WIEDEMANN, ALFRED MAX,** PLANT ECOLOGY. *Current Pos:* MEM FAC BIOL, EVERGREEN STATE UNIV, 70- *Personal Data:* b Chicago, Ill, Nov 24, 31; c 2. *Educ:* Utah State Univ, BS, 60, MS, 62; Ore State Univ, PhD(bot), 66. *Prof Exp:* Asst prof bot, Ore State Univ, 65-67, asst prof range mgt, 70; sci fac gen sci, N Geelong High Sch, Victoria, Australia, 69-70. *Concurrent Pos:* Lectr bot, Univ Malaya, 67-68; fel, Commonwealth Sci & Indust Res Orgn, Australia-NSF, 68-69. *Mem:* Ecol Soc Am; Brit Ecol Soc. *Res:* Vegatation of interior and coastal sand dunes; identification and description of natural areas. *Mailing Add:* 19021 Marble St SW Rochester WA 98579

**WIEDEMEIER, HERIBERT,** INORGANIC CHEMISTRY. *Current Pos:* asst prof, 64-67, assoc prof phys chem, 67-72, PROF CHEM, RENSSELAER POLYTECH INST, 72- *Personal Data:* b Steinheim, WGer, Aug 4, 28; nat US. *Educ:* Univ Muenster, BS, 54, MSc, 57, DSc, 60. *Honors & Awards:* Medal Except Sci Achievement, NASA, 74. *Prof Exp:* Asst inorg & phys chem, Univ Muenster, 56-58, instr, 58-60; res assoc chem, Univ Kans, 60-62; res assoc, Univ Muenster, 62-63; res assoc, Univ Kans, 63-64. *Mem:* AAAS; Am Chem Soc; Ger Chem Soc. *Res:* Growth of single crystals of metal chalcogenides; crystal growth mechanism and morphology; thermodynamic and kinetic studies of condensation and vaporization processes of inorganic materials at elevated temperatures; crystal growth in zero-gravity. *Mailing Add:* Dept Phys Chem Rensselaer Polytech Inst 110 Eighth St Troy NY 12180-3522

**WIEDENBECK, MARCELLUS LEE,** NUCLEAR PHYSICS. *Current Pos:* RETIRED. *Personal Data:* b Lancaster, NY, Oct 11, 19; m 46; c 6. *Educ:* Canisius Col, BS, 41; Univ Notre Dame, MS, 42, PhD(physics), 45. *Prof Exp:* Instr physics, Univ Notre Dame, 44-46; from asst prof to prof physics, Univ Mich, Ann Arbor, 46-87. *Mem:* Am Phys Soc. *Res:* Nuclear spectroscopy; beta ray and alpha ray spectra; coincidence methods; spectroscopy of some heavy nuclei. *Mailing Add:* 3786 Elizabeth Rd Ann Arbor MI 48103

**WIEDENHEFT, CHARLES JOHN,** CHEMISTRY. *Current Pos:* RES SPECIALIST, MONSANTO RES CORP, 67- *Personal Data:* b Sandusky, Ohio, Oct 23, 41. *Educ:* Capital Univ, BS, 63; Case Western Res Univ, MS, 65, PhD(chem), 67. *Mem:* AAAS; Am Chem Soc. *Res:* Coordination compounds of the actinide ions; thermal analysis. *Mailing Add:* 85 Springwood Dr Springboro OH 45066-1038

**WIEDENMANN, LYNN G,** POLYMER CHEMISTRY, ORGANIC CHEMISTRY. *Current Pos:* PROF CHEM, BLACK HAWK COL, 69- *Personal Data:* b Moline, Ill, Apr 21, 28; m 56; c 4. *Educ:* Ill Wesleyan Univ, BS, 50; Univ Iowa, MS, 52, PhD(org chem), 55. *Prof Exp:* Asst chemist, Rocky Mountain Arsenal, 55-57; res chemist, Tex-US Chem Corp, 57-60; res chemist, Rock Island Arsenal, 60-69. *Mem:* Am Chem Soc; Sigma Xi. *Res:* Polymer synthesis; high temperature resistant elastomers; boron and stereoregular butadiene polymers; butadiene derivatives; antioxidants; organic phosphorus compounds; dibenzopyrylium compounds. *Mailing Add:* 2387 Fifth St East Moline IL 61244-2742

**WIEDER, GRACE MARILYN,** INFRARED & RAMAN SPECTROSCOPY. *Current Pos:* instr, Brooklyn Col, 62-65, asst prof, 66-77, assoc prof, 78-91, EMER PROF CHEM, BROOKLYN COL, 92- *Personal Data:* b New York, NY, May 10, 28. *Educ:* Univ Vt, BA, 49; Mt Holyoke Col, AM, 51; Polytech Inst Brooklyn, PhD(phys chem), 61. *Prof Exp:* Res assoc chem, Univ Southern Calif, 60-62. *Concurrent Pos:* Vis scientist, Univ Wash, 70-71. *Mem:* Am Chem Soc; Am Phys Soc; Sigma Xi. *Res:* Stability constants and spectra of donor-acceptor complexes; Raman and infrared spectra of crystals; author of general chemistry laboratory manuals. *Mailing Add:* 66-22 Fleet St Apt 5K Forest Hills NY 11375-4162

**WIEDER, HAROLD,** OPTICAL PHYSICS. *Current Pos:* RETIRED. *Personal Data:* b Cleveland, Ohio, July 18, 27; m 63; c 3. *Educ:* Univ Rochester, BS, 50, MA, 57, MS, 58; Case Inst Technol, PhD(physics), 64. *Prof Exp:* Engr, Sarnoff Res Ctr, RCA Labs, 50-54; physicist, Parma Res Ctr, Union Carbide Corp, 57-61; physicist, Watson Res Ctr, 63-68, San Jose Lab,

68-82, & IBM Corp, 63-82. *Res:* Optical, magneto-optic, photoconductive, and structural properties of ordered and disordered films; transient thermal and thermomagnetic techniques; mode coupling and intra-cavity laser effects; level crossing and anticrossing spectroscopy. *Mailing Add:* 20175 Knollwood Dr Saratoga CA 95070

**WIEDER, HARRY H,** III-V SEMICONDUCTING COMPOUNDS, HETEROJUNCTIONS & QUANTUM WELLS. *Current Pos:* adj prof elec eng, 81-82, prof in residence, Elec & Comput Eng Dept, 82-95, EMER PROF, UNIV CALIF, SAN DIEGO, 95- *Personal Data:* b Romania, June 4, 19; US citizen; m 49, Dora C Perl; c Mark, Jonathan & Daniel. *Educ:* Univ Calif, Los Angeles, BS, 49. *Hon Degrees:* DSc, Colo State Univ, Ft Collins, 79. *Honors & Awards:* Charles Babbage Prize, Brit Inst Elec Engrs, 75; Gold Medal, Welch Award, Am Vacuum Soc, 83. *Prof Exp:* Mgr & head, Electronic Mat Sci Div, Naval Ocean Systs Ctr, 73-81. *Concurrent Pos:* Chair, Electronic Mat Processing Div, Am Vacuum Soc, 79-80; affil fac mem, Colo State Univ, Ft Collins, 80-94; vis prof, Univ Duisburg, Ger, 86. *Mem:* Fel Am Phys Soc; fel Inst Elec & Electronics Engrs; Mat Res Soc; fel Am Vacuum Soc. *Res:* Synthesis, characterization and prototype device fabrication of quantum confined heterostructures. *Mailing Add:* Univ Calif San Diego ECE-0407 La Jolla CA 92093-0407

**WIEDER, IRWIN,** MOLECULAR BIOPHYSICS, SPECTROSCOPY. *Current Pos:* OWNER, SCIENETICS, 92- *Personal Data:* b Cleveland, Ohio, Sept 26, 25; m 53, Lois J Fink; c Adam, Shawnee, Melanie & Eric. *Educ:* Case Inst Technol, BS, 50; Stanford Univ, PhD(physics), 56. *Prof Exp:* Asst, Stanford Univ, 51-56; res physicist, Westinghouse Elec Corp, 56-60 & Varian Assocs, 60-61; dir res, Interphase Corp, 61-66; prin scientist, Carver Corp, 66-69; NIH spec fel, Dept Biol Sci, Stanford Univ, 70-71; vis prof, Dept Electronics, Weizmann Inst Sci, Israel, 71-73; pres & tech dir, Anal Radiation Corp, 74-81; sci consult, Baxter Health Care, 82-91. *Mem:* Soc Sci Explor; Inst Elec & Electronics Engrs. *Res:* Magnetic resonance; microwave-optical effects; optical pumping in gases, liquids and solids; masers and lasers; energy transfer in biological systems; immunofluorescent, laser induced fluorescent and fluorescent antibody spectroscopy; time gated fluorescent spectroscopy. *Mailing Add:* 459 Panchita Way Los Altos CA 94022. *Fax:* 650-941-1225

**WIEDER, KENNETH J,** immunology, for more information see previous edition

**WIEDER, SOL,** PHYSICS. *Current Pos:* assoc prof, 67-75, PROF PHYSICS, FAIRLEIGH DICKINSON UNIV, 75- *Personal Data:* b Bronx, NY, Jan 6, 40; m 63; c 3. *Educ:* City Col New York, BS, 61; NY Univ, MS, 62, PhD(physics), 66. *Prof Exp:* Lectr physics, City Col New York, 62-64; instr, NY Univ, 64-65; instr, Bronx Community Col, 65-66; mem tech staff, Bell Tel Labs, Inc, 66-67; asst prof, NY Univ, 67. *Mem:* Am Phys Soc; Am Geophys Union; Am Asn Physics Teachers. *Res:* Many-particle physics; geophysics; solar energy. *Mailing Add:* Fairleigh Dickinson Univ Math & Comput Sci Becton Hall Rm 300 Teaneck NJ 07666

**WIEDERHOLD, EDWARD W(ILLIAM),** CHEMICAL & NUCLEAR ENGINEERING, ENVIRONMENTAL ENGINEERING. *Current Pos:* RETIRED. *Personal Data:* b Clermont Co, Ohio, Nov 4, 21. *Educ:* Ohio State Univ, BChE, 49. *Prof Exp:* Chem engr, AEC, 50-52; chem engr, Mound Lab, Monsanto Co, 52-58, res chemist, 58-59, sr res chemist, 59-68; first officer, Div Nuclear Safety & Environ Protection, Int Atomic Energy Agency, Vienna, Austria, 68-72; pvt pract, 72-78 & 80-91; contract engr & systs develop engr, Gen Devices Inc, 78-80. *Res:* Industrial waste disposal; reactor coolants; cryogenics; environmental science. *Mailing Add:* 1380 Baldwin Rd Milford OH 45150

**WIEDERHOLD, MICHAEL L,** SENSORY PHYSIOLOGY. *Current Pos:* DIR, RES OTORHINOLARYNGOL & ASSOC PROF SURG & PHYSIOL, UNIV TEX HEALTH SCI CTR, SAN ANTONIO, 82- *Personal Data:* b Milwaukee, Wis, Aug 2, 39. *Educ:* Mass Inst Technol, PhD(commun & biophys), 67. *Mailing Add:* Dept ORL Univ Tex Health Sci Ctr 7703 Floyd Curl Dr San Antonio TX 78284-7777. *Fax:* 210-567-5167; *E-Mail:* wiederhold@uthscsa.edu

**WIEDERHOLD, PIETER RIJK,** physics, electrical engineering, for more information see previous edition

**WIEDERHOLT, WIGBERT C,** NEUROLOGY, NEUROEPIDEMIOLOGY. *Current Pos:* neurologist-in-chief, Dept Neurosci, 73-83, chmn dept, 78-83, PROF NEUROSCI, UNIV CALIF, SAN DIEGO, 72- *Personal Data:* b Warmbrunn, Ger, Apr 22, 31; US citizen; c 3. *Educ:* Univ Freiburg, MD, 55. *Honors & Awards:* S Weir Mitchell Award, Am Acad Neurol, 65. *Prof Exp:* Asst to staff neurol, Mayo Clin, 65; from asst prof to assoc prof med, Ohio State Univ, 66-72, chief clin neurophysiol, 69-72. *Mem:* AAAS; fel Am Acad Neurol; Am Neurol Asn; Am EEG Soc; Am Asn Electromyog & Electrodiag (secy-treas, 71-76, pres, 77-78). *Res:* Neuroepidemiology. *Mailing Add:* Univ Cal San Diego Dept Neurosci 0624 9500 Gilman Dr La Jolla CA 92093. *E-Mail:* wwiederholt@ucsd.edu

**WIEDERHORN, SHELDON M,** MECHANICAL PROPERTIES OF CERAMICS. *Current Pos:* INST SCIENTIST, MAT SCI & ENG LAB, NAT INST STAND & TECHNOL, 88- *Personal Data:* b May 4, 33. *Educ:* Columbia Univ, BS, 56; Univ Ill, MS, 58, PhD(chem eng), 60. *Honors & Awards:* Silver Medal, Dept Com, 70, Gold Medal, 82; Ross Coffin Purdy

Award, Am Ceramic Soc, 71, Morey Award, 77; Sosman Lectr, Am Ceramic Soc, 85; Dow Distinguished Lectr Mat Sci & Eng, 88. *Prof Exp:* Res engr, E I du Pont de Nemours & Co, 60-63; res chemist, Inorg Mat Div, Nat Bur Stand, Washington, DC, 63-68, sect chief, Phys Properties Sect, Gaithersburg, Md, 68-76, chief, Fracture & Deformation Div, 76-77, dep div chief, 77-81, group leader, Mech Properties Group, Ceramics Div, 81-88. *Concurrent Pos:* Presidential young investr award panelist, 85. *Mem:* Nat Acad Eng; Am Ceramic Soc. *Res:* Elucidation of the mechanisms of fracture in glass and other brittle ceramics; structural materials. *Mailing Add:* Nat Inst Stand & Technol Bldg 223 Rm B309 Gaithersburg MD 20899. *Fax:* 301-926-8349

**WIEDERICK, HARVEY DALE,** PHYSICS. *Current Pos:* PROF PHYSICS, ROYAL MIL COL CAN, 78- *Personal Data:* b Wetaskiwin, Can, May 10, 37; m 63; c 3. *Educ:* Royal Mil Col Can, BSc, 59; Johns Hopkins Univ, MAT, 64; Queen's Univ, Ont, PhD(physics), 68. *Prof Exp:* Fel physics, Univ Toronto, 68-69; lectr, Royal Mil Col Can, 69-73, asst prof, 74-77; exchange teacher, Royal Mil Col Sci, Eng, 73-74; Nuffield Found res fel, Univ Kent, Canterbury, Eng, 77-78. *Concurrent Pos:* Defence Res Bd Can grant, 70- *Res:* Electrical properties of ferroic materials. *Mailing Add:* Dept Physics Royal Mil Co PO Box 1700 Office Kingston ON K7K 7B4 Can

**WIEDERSICH, H(ARTMUT),** MATERIALS SCIENCE, SOLID STATE PHYSICS. *Current Pos:* RETIRED. *Personal Data:* b Glatz, Ger, Apr 22, 26; US citizen; m 60, Ione Marinoui. *Educ:* Univ Gottingen, BS, 50, Dr rer nat(physics & metall), 54. *Prof Exp:* Res engr, Res Labs, Westinghouse Elec Corp, 54-60; res specialist, Atomics Int Div, NAm Aviation, Inc, 60-62, mem tech staff, Sci Ctr, NAm Rockwell Int, 62-70, group leader, 70-71; group leader, Argonne Nat Lab, 71-82, sr metallurgist, Mat Sci Div, 71-96, assoc div dir, 82-89. *Concurrent Pos:* Adj prof, Dept Mat Sci, Univ Southern Calif, 66-70; assoc ed, Am Inst Physics Appl Physics Lett, 89-90, ed, 90- *Mem:* Fel Am Soc Metals; Mat Res Soc; Am Phys Soc. *Res:* Defects and transport processes in solids, radiation effects on processes in, and microstructure and properties of materials; dislocation theory; defects in solids; magnetic structures by the Mossbauer effect; radiation damage; oxidation processes. *Mailing Add:* 126-16 S 83rd Ave Palos Park IL 60464

**WIEDMAN, HAROLD W,** PHYTOPATHOLOGY. *Current Pos:* from asst prof to assoc prof, 61-69, prof biol sci, 69-, EMER PROF BIOL SCI, CALIF STATE UNIV, SACRAMENTO, 69- *Personal Data:* b Palermo, Calif, Jan 11, 30. *Educ:* Chico State Col, AB, 52; Ore State Col, PhD(bot), 56. *Prof Exp:* Asst, Ore State Col, 53-56; asst plant pathologist, NMex State Univ, 56-58 & State Dept Agr, Calif, 58-59; asst prof bot, Humboldt State Col, 59-61. *Mem:* Am Phytopath Soc; Bot Soc Am. *Res:* Soil-borne diseases; biological control; diseases of vegetables and cotton. *Mailing Add:* Dept Biol Sci Calif State Univ 6000 J St Sacramento CA 95819-2605

**WIEDMEIER, VERNON THOMAS,** PHYSIOLOGY. *Current Pos:* asst prof, 71-75, ASSOC PROF PHYSIOL, MED COL GA, 75- *Personal Data:* b Harvey, NDak, Jan 10, 35; m 57; c 4. *Educ:* NDak State Teachers Col, Valley City, BS, 59; NDak State Univ, MS, 61; Marquette Univ, PhD(physiol), 68. *Prof Exp:* Instr biol, NPark Col, 60-61; asst prof, St Ambrose Col, 61-64. *Concurrent Pos:* NIH trainee, Univ Va, 69-70 & fel, 70-71. *Mem:* Am Physiol Soc. *Res:* Myocardial metabolism and the regulation of coronary blood flow. *Mailing Add:* Dept Physiol Med Col Ga 1120 15th St Augusta GA 30901-3181

**WIEDOW, CARL PAUL,** high voltage phenomena, magnetics, for more information see previous edition

**WIEGAND, CLYDE E,** high energy physics; deceased, see previous edition for last biography

**WIEGAND, CRAIG LOREN,** IRRIGATION, SALINITY. *Current Pos:* Res soil scientist, Agr Res Serv, USDA, 60-78, dir, Rio Grande Soil & Water Res Ctr, 69-78, tech adv, Sci & Educ Admin-Agr Res, 73-80, SR SCIENTIST, AGR RES SERV, USDA, 80- *Personal Data:* b Santa Rosa, Tex, Jan 11, 33; m 62, V Marguerite Johnson; c Jeanne & Stan. *Educ:* Tex A&M Univ, BS, 55, MS, 56; Utah State Univ, PhD(soil physics), 60. *Concurrent Pos:* Mid-career fel, Woodrow Wilson Sch Pub & Int Affairs, Princeton Univ, 74-75; foreign specialist in Japan, 88. *Mem:* Fel AAAS; fel Am Soc Agron. *Res:* Plant physiology; irrigation water management; plant-water relations; crop modeling; earth observation satellite data applications to agriculture; remote sensing; developer of spectral components analysis for relating spectral vegetation indices to crop condition and yield. *Mailing Add:* Remote Sensing Res Unit Agr Res Serv USDA 2413 E Bus Hwy 83 Weslaco TX 78596

**WIEGAND, DONALD ARTHUR,** MECHANICAL PROPERTIES OF SOLIDS. *Current Pos:* supvr res physicist, 79-90, RES PHYSICIST, ENERGETIC MAT DIV, ARMAMENT RES DEVELOP & ENG CTR, 90- *Personal Data:* b Rochester, NY, July 21, 27; m 59; c 2. *Educ:* Cornell Univ, BEE, 52, MEE, 53, PhD(eng physics), 56. *Prof Exp:* Asst & assoc physics, Cornell Univ, 55-56; res physicist, Carnegie Mellon Univ, 56-59, from asst prof to assoc prof physics, 59-68; res physicist, Feldman Res Lab, Picatinny Arsenal, 68-79. *Concurrent Pos:* Fulbright grant, Darmstadt Tech Univ, WGer, 60-61. *Mem:* Am Phys Soc; Mat Res Soc. *Res:* Imperfections in solids; luminescence; photo-conductive processes; optical absorption; x-ray diffraction; x-ray photoelectron spectroscopy; metastable solids; mechanical properties of solids. *Mailing Add:* Energetic Mats Div Armament Res Develop & Eng Ctr Bldg 3002 Picatinny Arsenal NJ 07806-5000. *Fax:* 973-724-5869; *E-Mail:* dwiegand@pica.army.mil

**WIEGAND, GAYL,** ORGANIC CHEMISTRY. *Current Pos:* From asst prof to assoc prof, 65-77, dept chair, 90-92, PROF CHEM, IDAHO STATE UNIV, 77- *Personal Data:* b Estherville, Iowa, July 18, 39. *Educ:* Univ Iowa, BS, 61; Univ Mass, PhD(org chem), 65. *Mem:* Am Chem Soc; Sigma Xi. *Res:* Mechanisms of organic like reactions occurring at elements other than carbon; organosulfur chemistry; kinetics of slow chemical reactions; geothermal energy prospecting; science for the non-specialist. *Mailing Add:* Dept Chem Idaho State Univ Pocatello ID 83209-0009. *Fax:* 208-236-4373; *E-Mail:* wieggayl@isu.edu

**WIEGAND, OSCAR FERNANDO,** PLANT PHYSIOLOGY. *Current Pos:* RETIRED. *Personal Data:* b Mex, Nov 3, 21; US citizen; m 49; c 5. *Educ:* Univ Tex, BA, 50, MA, 52, PhD(cell physiol, chem), 56. *Hon Degrees:* Dr, Univ Guadalajara, 65. *Prof Exp:* Asst prof biol, ETex State Col, 56-57; asst prof pharmacol, Univ Tex Southwest Med Sch, 57-60, vis lectr, Univ Tex, Austin, 60-62, from asst prof to prof zool, 77-87. *Concurrent Pos:* Smith-Mundt fel & vis prof, Univ Guadalajara, 61-62, distinguished prof, 62, gen coord model univ develop prog, 63-67; mem study group for reform & improv educ, Latin Am Univ, 61-71; head consult, Univ Reform Model, Cath Univ Rio de Janeiro, 61-71; consult univ reform prog, Agency Int Develop-Govt Brazil, 66-70. *Mem:* Am Soc Pharmacol & Exp Therapeut; Soc Gen Physiol. *Res:* Photomorphogenesis, growth physiology and tropisms; water and electrolyte equilibria in tissues; histamine reactions; tracer technique; respiromtery; growth methods for plant tissues. *Mailing Add:* 6107 Grass Hollow Austin TX 78750

**WIEGAND, SYLVIA MARGARET,** COMMUTATIVE ALGEBRA. *Current Pos:* from instr to prof, 72-87, PROF MATH, UNIV NEBR, LINCOLN, 87- *Personal Data:* b Cape Town, SAfrica, Mar 8, 45; US citizen; m 66, Roger; c David & Andrea. *Educ:* Bryn Mawr Col, AB, 66; Univ Wash, MA, 67; Univ Wis, PhD(algebra), 72. *Prof Exp:* Teaching asst math, Univ Wis, 67-72. *Concurrent Pos:* Vis assoc prof, Univ Conn, 78-79 & Univ Wis, 85-86; vis prof for women award, NSF, 92-93. *Mem:* Am Math Soc; Math Asn Am; Asn Women Math (pres). *Res:* Commutative algebra work on the prime spectrum of a Noetherian ring; direct sum decompositions; cancellation problem for one-dimensional rings; completions of a normal excellent local domain. *Mailing Add:* Dept Math Univ Nebr Lincoln NE 68588-0323. *Fax:* 402-472-8466; *E-Mail:* swiegand@math.unl.edu

**WIEGANDT, HERBERT F(REDERICK),** CHEMICAL ENGINEERING. *Current Pos:* from asst prof to prof, 47-87, EMER PROF CHEM ENG, CORNELL UNIV, 87- *Personal Data:* b Newaygo, Mich, Jan 4, 17; m 44; c 2. *Educ:* Purdue Univ, BSChE, 38, MSE, 39, PhD(chem eng), 41. *Prof Exp:* Asst process develop, Eng Exp Sta, Purdue Univ, 38-41; chem engr, Stand Oil Co, Ind, 41-44 & Armour Res Found, Ill Inst Technol, 44-47. *Concurrent Pos:* Fulbright Award to France, 60-61; Monsanto Chem Co, 52, & French Petrol Inst, 61 & 64; tech adv, Compagnie Francaise Raffinage, Paris, 72-82. *Mem:* AAAS; Am Chem Soc; Am Inst Chem Engrs. *Res:* Desalination; petroleum processes; extractions; distillation; crystallization. *Mailing Add:* 106 Hampton Rd Ithaca NY 14850

**WIEGEL, JUERGEN K W,** THERMOPHILIC ANAEROBES, ANAEROBIC DEGRADATION OF CHLORINATED AROMATICS. *Current Pos:* res assoc, Dept Biochem, Univ Ga, 77-79, vis assoc prof, Dept Microbiol, 82-85, assoc prof, 85-90, PROF, DEPT MICROBIOL, UNIV GA, 90- *Personal Data:* b Berlin-Spandeey, Ger, Apr 2, 41; US & Ger citizen; m 66, Heide Ziekora; c Markus & Michaela. *Educ:* Univ Gottingen, Ger, MS, 69, PhD(microbiol), 73, DrSc(microbiol), 83. *Prof Exp:* Chemist, Inst Microbiol, Univ Giottingen, 69-73, microbiologist & chemist, 73-84. *Concurrent Pos:* Adj prof, Dept Ecol, Univ Ga, 83-, Dept Biochem, 89-; Fulbright travel grantee, Iceland, 92; managing ed, J Extremophiles. *Mem:* Am Soc Microbiol; Soc Indust Microbiol; Int & Pan Am Soc Biodeterioration; Soc Gen Microbiol. *Res:* Ecology, systematic, physiology, biochemistry and desciption of new thermophilic anaerobic bacteria including novel anaerobic alkali thermophiles; degredation of chlorinated aromatic compounds in anaerobic sediments, enrichment and pure cultures; microbial interactions, biochemistry of key enzymes; genus Xanthobacter; thermoanaerobacter. *Mailing Add:* Dept Microbiol Univ Ga Athens GA 30602-2605. *Fax:* 706-542-2674; *E-Mail:* jwiegel@uga.cc.uga.edu

**WIEGEL, ROBERT L,** OCEAN ENGINEERING. *Current Pos:* Jr res engr, Univ Calif, Berkeley, 46-52, lectr civil eng, 56-60, assoc prof, 60-63, asst dean, 63-72, assoc res engr, 52-60, actg dean, 72-73, prof, 63-87, EMER PROF CIVIL ENG, UNIV CALIF, BERKELEY, 87- *Personal Data:* b San Francisco, Calif, Oct 17, 22; m 48, Anne Pearce; c John M, Carol E & Diana L. *Educ:* Univ Calif, BS, 43, MS, 49. *Honors & Awards:* Res Prize, Am Soc Civil Engrs, 62; Moffatt-Nichol Harbor Am Coastal Eng Award, 78; Outstanding Civilian Serv Medal, US Army CEngr, 85; Int Coastal Eng Award, 85. *Concurrent Pos:* Dir, Calif State Tech Serv Prog, 65-68; pres, Int Comt Oceanic Resources, 72-75; mem comt earthquake eng res, Nat Acad Eng, mem, Marine Bd, 75-81; consult; mem, Comt on Beach Nourishment & Protection, Nat Res Coun, 92- *Mem:* Nat Acad Eng; hon mem & fel Am Soc Civil Engrs; fel AAAS; Permanent Int Asn Navig Cong; Sigma Xi; hon mem Int Eng Comt on Oceanic Resources. *Res:* Ocean and coastal engineering; technology transfer. *Mailing Add:* 409 O'Brien Hall Univ Calif Berkeley CA 94720. *Fax:* 510-642-9143

**WIEGERS, KARL EUGENE,** SOFTWARE ENGINEERING & MANAGEMENT, SOFTWARE PROCESS ENGINEERING. *Current Pos:* res scientist, Eastman Kodak Co, 79-84, software engr, 84-90, software mgr, 90-93, software qual engr, 93-95, SOFTWARE PROCESS ENGR, EASTMAN KODAK CO, 95- *Personal Data:* b Feamcom AFB, Japan, Oct

4, 53; US citizen; m 88, Christine Zambito. *Educ:* Boise State Col, BS, 73; Univ Ill, Urbana-Champaign, MS, 75, PhD(org chem), 77. *Prof Exp:* Vis asst prof org chem, Univ Ill, Urbana-Champaign, 77-78, postdoctoral res assoc, 78-79. *Mem:* Inst Elec & Electronics Engrs Comput Sci; Asn Comput Mach. *Res:* Management and technical practices that can be, and have been, applied to improve the quality of products created by, and processes used by, a software development group. *Mailing Add:* 31 Canterbury Trail Fairport NY 14450-8783. *E-Mail:* kwiegers@acm.org

**WIEGERT, PHILIP E,** BIOMEDICAL ENGINEERING, ORGANIC CHEMISTRY. *Current Pos:* CONSULT, ANGIODYNAMICS, INC, 93- *Personal Data:* b Antigo, Wis, Apr 7, 27; m 59; c 6. *Educ:* Univ Wis, BS, 50; Univ Ill, MS, 51, PhD, 54. *Prof Exp:* Chemist, Mallinckrodt Chem Works, Mallinckrodt Med Inc, 54-61, group leader, 61-66, asst dir pharmaceut chem, 66-74, plant mgr, 74-77, dir res & develop, Mallinckrodt Crit Care, 77-86, dir qual control & regulatory affairs, 86-89, consult, 89-90; consult, Sheridan Cathether Co, 91-92. *Mem:* Am Chem Soc; Chem Soc; Am Soc Testing & Mat; Asn Advan Med Instrumentation; Soc Plastic Engrs. *Res:* X-ray contrast media; opium alkaloids; pharmaceutical chemicals; medical devices; standards development. *Mailing Add:* 2 Horicon Ave Glens Falls NY 12801-2655

**WIEGERT, RICHARD G,** ECOLOGY. *Current Pos:* from asst prof to assoc prof, 62-71, PROF ZOOL, UNIV GA, 71- *Personal Data:* b Toledo, Ohio, Sept 9, 32; div; c 2. *Educ:* Adrian Col, BS, 54; Mich State Univ, MS, 58; Univ Mich, PhD(zool), 62. *Hon Degrees:* DSc, Adrian Col, 76. *Prof Exp:* Instr zool, Univ Mich, 61-62; NSF grants, Yellowstone Nat Park, 68-85 & Sapelo Island Salt Marsh, 75-95. *Mem:* AAAS; Am Soc Mammal; Ecol Soc Am; Brit Ecol Soc; Am Soc Naturalists; Estuarine Res Fedn. *Res:* Plant and animal ecology, particularly problems of population and community energy utilization; population density regulation; interspecies competition; systems ecology and modeling the dynamics of thermal spring and estuarine communities. *Mailing Add:* Dept Ecol Bio Sci Bldg Univ Ga Athens GA 30601-2602

**WIEGMAN, DAVID L,** HYPERTENSION, EXERCISE. *Current Pos:* ASST DEAN & ASSOC PROF PHYSIOL, HEALTH SCI CTR, UNIV LOUISVILLE, 81- *Educ:* Ind Univ, PhD(physiol), 73. *Mailing Add:* Dept Physiol & Biophys Health Sci Ctr Univ Louisville Med Sch Louisville KY 40292-0001. *Fax:* 502-588-6849; *E-Mail:* dlwiegoi@ulkyum.bitnet

**WIEGNER, ALLEN W,** SPINAL CORD INJURY, FUNCTIONAL ELECTRICAL STIMULATION. *Current Pos:* assoc med, 78-80, assoc neurol, 80-87, ASST PROF NEUROL, HARVARD MED SCH, 87-; COMPUT SPECIALIST, WEST ROXBURY VET ADMIN MED CTR, 96- *Personal Data:* b Bethlehem, Pa, July 22, 47; c Benjamin. *Educ:* Mass Inst Technol, SB & SM, 70, PhD(elec eng), 78. *Prof Exp:* Comn officer, USPHS, 70-72; biomed engr, West Roxbury Vet Admin Med Ctr, 87-96. *Concurrent Pos:* Lectr, Dept Elec Eng & Comput Sci, Mass Inst Technol, 79-; asst biomed engr, Mass Gen Hosp, 80- *Mem:* Inst Elec & Electronics Engrs; Biomed Eng Soc; Soc Neurosci; Rehab Eng Soc NAm. *Res:* Role of muscle and reflex in movement and movement disorders, tremor; nonlinear behavior of resting and active muscle; functional electrical stimulation, especially in persons with spinal cord injury; rehabilitation aids. *Mailing Add:* IRM Vet Admin Med Ctr 940 Belmont St Brockton MA 02401. *E-Mail:* wiegner.allen@brockton.va.gov

**WIELAND, DENTON R,** PETROLEUM ENGINEERING. *Current Pos:* sr prod mgr, 79-80, GEN SUPVR, CHEVRON, 80- *Personal Data:* b Yorktown, Tex, Oct 28, 27; m 54; c 2. *Educ:* Agr & Mech Col, Tex, BS, 53, MS, 56, PhD, 58. *Prof Exp:* Asst prof petrol eng, Univ Tulsa, 57-61, assoc prof & actg head dept, 61-64; dir tech develop, Dowell Div, Dow Chem Co, 64-68, supvr, Customer Serv, 68-69, mgr, Sales Develop Dept, 72-76, mgr eng, 72-76; consult, 76-78; proj leader well completions, Osco, 78-79. *Mem:* Am Inst Mining, Metall & Petrol Engrs; Sigma Xi. *Res:* Physical chemistry of petroleum engineering. *Mailing Add:* Hwy 979 Calvert TX 77837

**WIEMAN, CARL E,** AUTOMATIC, MOLECULAR & OPTICAL PHYSICS. *Current Pos:* assoc prof, 84-87, chmn, 93-95, PROF PHYSICS, UNIV COLO, 87-, FEL JOINT INST LAB ASTROPHYS, 85- *Personal Data:* m, Sarah Gilbert. *Educ:* Mass Inst Technol, BS, 73; Stanford Univ, PhD(physics), 77. *Honors & Awards:* Rosenthal Mem Lectr, Yale & Columbia Univs, 88; E O Lawrence Award, Dept Energy, 93; Davisson-Germer Prize, Am Phys Soc, 94; Fritz London Prize, Int Union Pure & Appl Scis, 96; Newcomb-Cleveland Prize, AAAS, 96; Richtmyer Mem Lectr Award, Am Asn Physics Teachers, 96; King Faisal Int Prize for Sci, 97. *Prof Exp:* Asst res scientist physics, Univ Mich, 77-79, asst prof, 79-84. *Mem:* Nat Acad Sci; fel Am Phys Soc; Am Asn Physics Teachers; Optical Soc Am. *Res:* High resolution laser spectroscopy, parity nonconservation in atoms, laser cooling and trapping of neutral atoms, very low energy atomic collisions. *Mailing Add:* Joint Inst Lab Astrophys Dept Physics Univ Colo Boulder CO 80309-0440. *Fax:* 303-492-8994; *E-Mail:* cwieman@jila.colorado.edu

**WIEMER, DAVID F,** ORGANOPHOSPHORUS CHEMISTRY, CHEMICAL ECOLOGY. *Current Pos:* from asst to assoc prof, 78-89, PROF CHEM, UNIV IOWA, 89- *Personal Data:* b Burlington, Wis, Mar 17, 50; m 72, Barbara; c Andrew, Kathryn & Jennifer. *Educ:* Marquette Univ, BS, 72; Univ Ill, PhD(org chem), 76. *Prof Exp:* NIH fel, Cornell Univ, 76-78. *Concurrent Pos:* A P Sloan Found fel, 85-89; vis scientist, Scripps Inst Oceanogr, 86. *Mem:* Am Chem Soc; Sigma Xi; AAAS; Am Soc Pharmacog. *Res:* Isolation, characterization, and synthesis of biologically active natural products; synthetic methodology based on organo phosphorus chemistry; chemical ecology. *Mailing Add:* Dept Chem Univ Iowa Iowa City IA 52242. *Fax:* 319-335-1270; *E-Mail:* david_wiemer@uiowa.edu

**WIEMEYER, STANLEY NORTON,** WILDLIFE TOXICOLOGY. *Current Pos:* Res wildlife biologist, Patuxent Wildlife Res Ctr, 66-92, RESOURCE CONTAMINANT SPECIALIST, US FISH & WILDLIFE SERV, 92- *Personal Data:* b Santa Rosa, Calif, Nov 7, 40; m 68, Lois J Stille; c Alicia. *Educ:* Humboldt State Col, BS, 63, MS, 67. *Mem:* Wildlife Soc; Am Ornithologist's Union; Soc Environ Toxicol & Chem; Wilson Ornith Soc; Raptor Res Found. *Res:* Effects of environmental contaminants, including pesticides, metals and PCBs, on birds with major emphasis on birds of prey; captive breeding of birds of prey. *Mailing Add:* US Fish & Wildlife Serv 4600 Kietzke Lane Suite 125C Reno NV 89502. *Fax:* 702-784-5870; *E-Mail:* stanley_wiemeyer@fws.gov

**WIEN, RICHARD W, JR,** PHYSICAL CHEMISTRY, PHOTOGRAPHIC SCIENCE. *Current Pos:* sr res chemist photog sci, Eastman Kodak, 71-79, proj leader, Photog Technol Div, 79-85, tech assoc, 86-89, prof qual dir & prof imaging, 89-94, MGR COM SYSTS, KODAK PROF, EASTMAN KODAK, 94- *Personal Data:* b Bay Co, Fla, May 17, 45; m 68, Judith Plunkett; c Mary J & Stephanie. *Educ:* Purdue Univ, BS, 67; Stanford Univ, PhD(phys chem), 71. *Honors & Awards:* Pub Serv Medal, NASA, 95; Hero of Chem, Am Chem Soc, 96. *Prof Exp:* NSF fel phys chem, Stanford Univ, 67-71. *Concurrent Pos:* Nat tour speaker, Am Chem Soc, 78- *Mem:* Am Chem Soc. *Res:* Improvement of photographic speed of color reversal films; development of new high speed color photographic systems; development of professional negative-positive photographic systems; development of measures of product quality as used by customers; responsible for growth in the commercial market. *Mailing Add:* 44 Hilltop Dr Pittsford NY 14534. *Fax:* 716-588-6322; *E-Mail:* rwwien@kodak.com

**WIENER, EARL LOUIS,** INDUSTRIAL ENGINEERING, PSYCHOLOGY. *Current Pos:* asst prof psychol & indust eng, 62-66, PROF MGT SCI & ADJ PROF PSYCHOL, UNIV MIAMI, 66- *Personal Data:* b Shreveport, La, May 30, 33; m 55, 80; c 2. *Educ:* Duke Univ, BA, 55; Ohio State Univ, MA, 59, PhD(psychol, indust eng), 61. *Prof Exp:* Asst, Aviation Psychol Lab, Ohio State Univ, 58-59, opers res group, 59-60, res assoc, Systs Res Group, 60-61. *Mem:* Fel Human Factors Soc (pres, 88-89); fel Am Psychol Asn; Soc Eng Psychol; Am Inst Indust Engrs. *Res:* Human factors; aviation safety; human vigilance and monitoring; effect of human performance on systems performance; traffic safety. *Mailing Add:* Dept Mgt Sci Univ Miami PO Box 248237 Coral Gables FL 33124

**WIENER, HARVEY L,** BIOCHEMICAL PHARMACOLOGY, NEUROCHEMISTRY. *Current Pos:* RES INVESTR, BRISTOL-MYERS SQUIBB, 93- *Personal Data:* b New York, NY, Nov 30, 59. *Educ:* Fordham Univ, BS, 81; Ohio State Univ, PhD(physiol chem), 86. *Honors & Awards:* Travel Award, Am Soc Neurochem, 88; New Investr Award, Am Asn Cols Pharm, 90. *Prof Exp:* Postdoctoral res assoc, Cornell Univ Med Col, 86-87; res scientist, N S Kline Inst Psychiat Res, 87-89; asst prof pharmacol & toxicol, St Johns Univ, 89-93. *Concurrent Pos:* Adj res asst prof, Mt Sinai Sch Med, 89- *Mem:* Am Chem Soc; Am Soc Biochem & Molecular Biol; Am Soc Pharmacol & Exp Therapeut; Soc Neurosci; NY Acad Sci. *Res:* Receptor pharmacology and drug discovery for neurodegenerative disorders and psychobiological disorders. *Mailing Add:* Bristol-Myers Squibb Co 5 Research Pkwy Dept 408 Wallingford CT 06492-7660. *Fax:* 203-284-7569; *E-Mail:* hwiener@ussmtp.bms.com

**WIENER, JOSEPH,** PATHOLOGY, CELL BIOLOGY. *Current Pos:* chmn, Dept Path, 78-90, PROF PATH, WAYNE STATE UNIV, 90- *Personal Data:* b Toronto, Ont, Sept 21, 27; m 54, Judith Ross; c Carolyn L & Adam L. *Educ:* Univ Toronto, MD, 53. *Prof Exp:* Assoc path, Col Physicians & Surgeons, Columbia Univ, 60-63, asst prof, 63-68; prof path & attend pathologist, NY Med Col, 68-78; chmn, Dept Path, Detroit Gen Hosp, 78-90. *Concurrent Pos:* Chief path, Detroit Rec Hosp/Univ Health Ctr, 78-91; chief path, Huttel Hosp, 84-91. *Mem:* Am Soc Cell Biol; Am Soc Invest Path; US/Can Acad Path; Coun High Blood Pressure Res; Col Am Pathologists. *Res:* Vascular biology; cardiovascular disease, human and experimental. *Mailing Add:* Dept Path 9374 Scott Wayne State Univ Sch Med 540 E Canfield Ave Detroit MI 48202-1908. *Fax:* 313-577-0057

**WIENER, ROBERT NEWMAN,** CHEMISTRY. *Current Pos:* asst prof, 58-62, ASSOC PROF CHEM, NORTHEASTERN UNIV, 62- *Personal Data:* b New York, NY, Aug 27, 30; m 54; c 3. *Educ:* Harvard Univ, AB, 51; Univ Pa, MS, 53, PhD, 56. *Prof Exp:* Asst instr chem, Univ Pa, 51-54; instr, Rutgers Univ, 55-58. *Mem:* Am Phys Soc. *Res:* Physical chemistry; molecular spectroscopy. *Mailing Add:* Dept Chem Northeastern Univ 360 Huntington Ave Boston MA 02115-5096

**WIENER, RUSSELL WARREN,** AEROSOL PHYSICS, AEROSOL EXPOSURE. *Current Pos:* phys scientist, 87-90, chief, Aerosol Physics & Methods Br, 90-96, ACTG DIR, AIR MEASUREMENT RES DIV, NAT EXPOSURE RES LAB, US ENVIRON PROTECTION AGENCY, 96- *Personal Data:* b New York, NY, June 23, 52; m 82, Martha E Smith; c Benjamin & Victoria. *Educ:* Emory Univ, BS, 74, MS, 78; Univ Cincinnati, PhD(environ health), 87. *Prof Exp:* Res technician II, Dept Environ Sci & Eng, Univ NC, Chapel Hill, 78-79; aerosol technologist, Gen Elec Aircraft Engine Bus Group, 84-86. *Concurrent Pos:* Adj asst prof air, radiation & indust hyg, Dept Environ Sci & Eng, Univ NC, Chapel Hill, 89-; adj assoc prof, Marine, Earth & Atmospheric Sci Dept, NC State Univ, 95- *Mem:* Am Asn Aerosol Res; Am Indust Hyg Asn; Am Acad Indust Hyg. *Res:* Aerosol research in the areas of assessing human exposure to particulate matter through physical analysis; study of ambient aerosol sampling dynamics through static, wind tunnel and ambient sampling experiments. *Mailing Add:* 251 Indian Trail Chapel Hill NC 27514. *Fax:* 919-541-0239; *E-Mail:* wiener.russell@epamail.epa.gov

**WIENER, SIDNEY,** MATERIALS SCIENCE. *Current Pos:* RETIRED. *Personal Data:* b New York, NY, Nov 17, 22; m 44, Beatrice Swartz; c Stephen P & Terri L. *Educ:* Univ Calif, Los Angeles, BS, 47; Univ Calif, Berkeley, PhD(biochem), 52. *Prof Exp:* Exploitation engr, Prod Lab, Shell Oil Co, 52-56; mem tech staff, Airborne Systs Labs, Space & Commun Group, Hughes Aircraft Co, 57-60, group head org mat, Res & Develop Div, 60-62, sect head, 62-65, asst dept mgr mat tech, 65-70, mgr space & commun group support activ, 70-73, mgr proj control, 74-78, sr staff engr, Components & Mat Labs, 78, sr scientist prod assurance eng, 78-80, mgr mat, processes & radiation eng, 80-82. *Mem:* Am Chem Soc; Sigma Xi; Planetary Soc. *Res:* Physical chemistry and elucidation of structure of nucleic acid using enzymatic reactions and acid-base relations; technical administration in materials. *Mailing Add:* 5609 Edgemere Dr Torrance CA 90503-1820

**WIENER, STANLEY L,** INTERNAL MEDICINE, EXPERIMENTAL PATHOLOGY. *Current Pos:* CHIEF SECT GEN MED, SCH MED, UNIV ILL, CHICAGO, 89- *Personal Data:* b New York, NY, Nov 5, 30; m 53; c 3. *Educ:* Univ Rochester, AB, 52; Sch Med, Univ Rochester, MD, 56. *Prof Exp:* From asst prof to prof med, State Univ NY, Stony Brook, 61-72; assoc dir res & educ, Long Island Jewish-Hillside Med Ctr, 72-73, assoc dir med, 73-78; chmn, Dept Med, ETenn State Univ, 78-81, Col Med, 81-89. *Concurrent Pos:* Chmn res comt, Am Heart Asn, NY State Affil, 7375. *Mem:* Am Soc Exp Path; Am Soc Exp Biol & Med; Am Fedn Clin Res. *Res:* In vivo studies of fibroblast activation and growth control; studies of neutrophil chemotaxis and enzyme release into inflammatory liquid; mechanism of pain in sickle cell disease; prevention of hip fracture in the elderly using padded underwear; infectious disease. *Mailing Add:* 631 Alexandria Dr Naperville IL 60565

**WIENKE, BRUCE RAY,** THEORETICAL PHYSICS, COMPUTATIONAL PHYSICS. *Current Pos:* staff mem, Los Alamos Nat Lab, 71-72, staff mem comput physics, 72-78, staff mem comput math, Los Alamos Sci Lab, 79, physicist, Mission Res Corp, 80, SECT LEADER COMPUT PHYSICS, LOS ALAMOS NAT LAB, 81- *Personal Data:* b Chicago, Ill, Sept 21, 40; m 81. *Educ:* Univ Wis, BS, 63; Marquette Univ, MS, 65; Northwestern Univ, PhD(physics), 71. *Honors & Awards:* Bausch & Lomb Sci Award, 58. *Prof Exp:* Teaching asst physics, Northwestern Univ & Marquette Univ, 63-67; res asst theoret physics, Northwestern Univ, 70-71. *Concurrent Pos:* Staff mem, Argonne Nat Lab, 66-68; consult, Square D Co, Milwaukee, 66-72 & Prof Asn Diving Instrs, 77-; instr, Col Santa Fe, 76- *Mem:* Am Phys Soc; Am Nuclear Soc; Soc Indust & Appl Math; Am Acad Mech; Int Oceanog Soc. *Res:* Theoretical particle and nuclear physics; transport theory and applications for neutral and charged particles; computational physics and numerical methodology; mathematical physics and computing science. *Mailing Add:* 24 Via Brisa Santa Fe NM 87501. *Fax:* 505-665-4939

**WIENKER, CURTIS WAKEFIELD,** PHYSICAL ANTHROPOLOGY. *Current Pos:* From lectr to assoc prof, 72-91, assoc dean, 88-93, PROF ANTHROP, UNIV SFLA, 91- *Personal Data:* b Seattle, Wash, Feb 3, 45; div; c Heather. *Educ:* Univ Wash, BA, 67; Univ Ariz, MA, 70, PhD(anthrop), 75. *Concurrent Pos:* Prin investr, 75-78; consult. *Mem:* Am Asn Phys Anthrop; Sigma Xi; Human Biol Asn; Am Acad Forensic Sci. *Res:* Living human biological variation; human evolution; Black population biology; cultural influences on human biology; biomedical anthropology; forensic anthropology; Cuban population biology. *Mailing Add:* SOC 107 Univ SFla Tampa FL 33620-8100. *Fax:* 813-974-2668; *E-Mail:* cwienker@cfrvm.cfr.usf.edu

**WIENS, DARRELL JOHN,** EARLY HEART DEVELOPMENT. *Current Pos:* ASST PROF BIOL, UNIV NORTHERN IOWA, 88- *Personal Data:* b Hutchinson, Kans, Feb 9, 50; m 75, Arleen Cook; c Eric & Galen. *Educ:* Bethel Col, BA, 72; Univ Kans, MA, 75; Kans State Univ, PhD(cell & develop biol), 82. *Prof Exp:* Instr biol, Bethel Col, 75-77; adj prof, Ctr Res & Advan Studies, Nat Polytech Inst, Mexico City, 82-83; asst prof biol, Fresno Pac Col, Calif, 83-84; fel, Stanford Univ Med Sch, 84-86; researcher, OARDC, Ohio State Univ, 86-88. *Concurrent Pos:* Prin investr, Am Heart Asn, 90-91 & 91-92; assoc, NASA-Univ Joint Venture in Space Res grant, 92-95, prin investr, NASA, 96-; co-investr, NSF IG, 95-97. *Mem:* Am Soc Cell Biol; Fedn Am Soc Exp Biol; AAAS; Sigma Xi; Am Asn Univ Prof; Am Soc Space & Gravitational Biol; Soc Develop Biol. *Res:* Early heart development including expression of actins, collagen, fibronectin and the effects of specific drugs and microgravity; ultrastructure and immunocyto architecture of early precardiac and heart cells; mammary epithelial cell differentiation and morphogenesis and involution. *Mailing Add:* Dept Biol Univ Northern Iowa Cedar Falls IA 50614. *Fax:* 319-273-2893; *E-Mail:* wiens@cobra.uni.edu

**WIENS, DELBERT,** SYSTEMATIC BIOLOGY. *Current Pos:* RETIRED. *Personal Data:* b Munich, NDak, July 9, 32; m 55; c 3. *Educ:* Pomona Col, BA, 55; Univ Utah, MS, 57; Claremont Grad Sch, PhD(bot), 61. *Prof Exp:* Instr biol, Univ Colo, 60-62, asst prof, 62-64; from asst prof to assoc prof bot, Univ Utah, 67-74, prof biol, 74- *Concurrent Pos:* Fulbright lectr & hon prof, Univ Guayaquil, 64-65; mem, Flora of Ceylon Proj, 68; vis lectr, Flinders Univ SAustralia, 72. *Mem:* AAAS; Am Soc Plant Taxon; Bot Soc Am; Int Asn Plant Taxon; Soc Study Evolution. *Res:* Systematics, biogeography, chromosome systems and pollination ecology of flowering plants, particularly the mistletoe family. *Mailing Add:* c/o Prof Clyde Calvin Dept Biol Portland State Univ Portland OR 97207

**WIENS, JOHN ANTHONY,** DESERT ECOLOGY, LANDSCAPE ECOLOGY. *Current Pos:* PROF ECOL, COLO STATE UNIV, 86- *Personal Data:* b Moscow, Idaho, Sept 29, 39; m 61, 84; c 4. *Educ:* Univ Okla, BS, 61; Univ Wis, MS, 63, PhD(zool), 66. *Prof Exp:* From asst prof to prof zool, Ore

State Univ, 66-78; distinguished prof, Univ NMex, 78-86. *Concurrent Pos:* NSF res grant, 67-69 & 74-; Am Philos Soc res grant, 72-75; vis prof, Colo State Univ, 73-77; Nat Oceanic Atmospheric Admin res contract, 75-81; US Forest Serv res contract, 76-81; ed, The Auk, 76-84; Fulbright sr scholar, Australia, 84-85; Dept Energy grant, 88-; vis prof, Univ Oslo, 89; US MAB grant, 90- *Mem:* Am Soc Naturalists; fel Am Ornith Union (treas, 74-78); Ecol Soc Am; Animal Behav Soc; Brit Ecol Soc; Copper Ornith Soc; Int Asn Ecol; Wilson Ornith Soc. *Res:* Vertebrate community structure and behavioral ecology; population modeling and analysis; methods of habitat description and analysis; landscape ecology; scaling in ecological systems; desert ecology; seabird ecology. *Mailing Add:* Dept Biol Colo State Univ Ft Collins CO 80523-0001

**WIER, CHARLES EUGENE,** ECONOMIC GEOLOGY. *Current Pos:* VPRES, HOOSIER MINING CO, 85- *Personal Data:* b Jasonville, Ind, May 15, 21; m 49; c 3. *Educ:* Ind Univ, AB, 43, AM, 50, PhD(econ geol), 55. *Honors & Awards:* Gordon H Wood Mem Award, 90. *Prof Exp:* Geologist & head, Coal Sect, Ind Geol Surv, 49-75; assoc prof geol, Ind Univ, Bloomington, 65-75; mgr coal explor, Amax Int Coal Co, 75-76, vpres, 76-85. *Mem:* Geol Soc Am; Soc Econ Geol; Am Asn Petrol Geol; Am Inst Mining, Metall & Petrol Engrs; Sigma Xi. *Res:* Pennsylvanian stratigraphy; coal resources and coal petrology; environmental geology. *Mailing Add:* 8023 S Zikes Rd Bloomington IN 47401-9178

**WIER, DAVID DEWEY,** electrical engineering; deceased, see previous edition for last biography

**WIER, JACK KNIGHT,** PHARMACOGNOSY. *Current Pos:* RETIRED. *Personal Data:* b Cairo, Nebr, Aug 31, 23; m 47. *Educ:* Univ Wis, PhB, 45; Univ Nebr, BS, 56; Univ Wash, Seattle, MS, 59, PhD(pharmacog), 61. *Prof Exp:* From asst prof to assoc prof pharmacog, Univ NC, Chapel Hill, 61-87. *Concurrent Pos:* Consult, F W Dodge Co Div, McGraw-Hill, Inc, 65-69. *Mem:* Am Soc Pharmacog (secy, 70-79, pres, 79-81); Am Pharmaceut Asn; Acad Pharmaceut Sci; Sigma Xi. *Res:* Metabolic products of macrofungi; biosynthesis of indole alkaloids in higher plants. *Mailing Add:* 415 Long Leaf Dr Chapel Hill NC 27515

**WIER, JOSEPH M(ARION),** ELECTRICAL ENGINEERING. *Current Pos:* RETIRED. *Personal Data:* b Amsterdam, Mo, Mar 2, 24; m 48; c 2. *Educ:* Iowa State Col, BS, 49, MS, 50; Univ Ill, PhD(elec eng), 56. *Prof Exp:* Instr elec eng, Iowa State Col, 50; asst digital comput lab, Univ Ill, 50-51, res assoc, 51-56; mem tech staff, AT&T, 56-59, head switching systs study dept, 59-72, data mgt systs dept, 72-77, qual theory & systs dept, 77-80, head customer equip qual dept, Bell Tel Labs, 80-82, customer equip qual dept, AT&T, 83-84, consult qual, 84-87. *Mem:* AAAS; Inst Elec & Electronics Engrs. *Res:* Electronic digital computers; data communications; data management systems; systems theory. *Mailing Add:* 41 E Larchmont Dr Colts Neck NJ 07722

**WIER, WITHROW GIL,** ION CONCENTRATIONS. *Current Pos:* asst prof, 82-87, ASSOC PROF PHYSIOL, UNIV MD SCH MED, 87- *Personal Data:* b San Diego, Calif, Oct 10, 50. *Educ:* Utah State Univ, BS, 72; Univ Utah, PhD(physiol), 78. *Honors & Awards:* Louis N Katz Prize, AMA, 79. *Prof Exp:* Res fel, Dept Pharmacol, Mayo Found, 78-79; from instr to asst prof pharmacol, Mayo Med Sch, 79-82. *Concurrent Pos:* Established investr, Am Heart Asn, 85-90; mem, Coun Basic Sci, AMA. *Mem:* AMA; Biophys Soc; Soc Gen Physiologists; Am Physiol Soc; foreign mem Physiol Soc UK. *Res:* Measurement of intracellular ion concentrations in living cells; excitation-contraction coupling in mammalian heart. *Mailing Add:* Dept Physiol Univ Md Sch Med 665 W Baltimore St 590 HH Baltimore MD 21201. *Fax:* 410-706-8341; *E-Mail:* gil@wgwabumdedu

**WIERENGA, PETER J,** SOIL PHYSICS, SOIL SCIENCE. *Current Pos:* PROF & DEPT HEAD SOIL, WATER SCI & ENVIRON SCI, UNIV ARIZ, 88- *Personal Data:* b Uithuizen, Neth, June 27, 34; m 63; c 3. *Educ:* State Agr Univ, Wageningen, BS, 61, MS, 63; Univ Calif, Davis, PhD(soil sci), 68. *Honors & Awards:* Westhafer Award, NMex State Univ, 82. *Prof Exp:* Res water scientist, Univ Calif, Davis, 65-68; from asst prof to prof agron, NMex State Univ, 68-88. *Concurrent Pos:* Consult, Battelle Northwest, Los Alamos Sci Lab, Sandia Labs, EGG, Off Technol Assessment US Cong & Environ Protection Res Inst; assoc ed, Soil Sci Soc Am Water Resource Res; vis scientist, Nat Ctr Sci Res, Mech Inst, Grenoble, France, 75-76; vis prof, ETH, Zurich & Switz; res award, Col Agr, NMex State Univ, 77. *Mem:* Fel Am Soc Agron; fel Soil Sci Soc Am; Am Geophys Union; Neth Royal Soc Agr Sci; fel AAAS; Int Soc Soil Sci. *Res:* Measurement and simulation of transfer processes in soils, such as movement of water, heat and salts; irrigation management; trickle irrigation; characterization of vadose zone processes. *Mailing Add:* Soil & Water Sci Dept 429 Shantz Bldg Univ Ariz Tucson AZ 85721. *Fax:* 520-621-1647; *E-Mail:* wierenga@ag.arizona.edu

**WIERENGA, WENDELL,** ORGANIC CHEMISTRY. *Current Pos:* SR VPRES RES, PHARMACEUT RES DIV, WARNER-LAMBERT CO, 90- *Personal Data:* b Hudsonville, Mich, Feb 5, 48; m 68; c 2. *Educ:* Hope Col, BA, 70; Stanford Univ, PhD(org chem), 73. *Prof Exp:* Res scientist org chem, Exp Chem Res, Upjohn Co, 74-78, head cancer res, 81-82, dir cancer & viral res, 82-90. *Concurrent Pos:* Am Cancer Soc fel, Dept Chem, Stanford Univ, 73-74. *Mem:* Am Chem Soc; Am Asn Cancer Res. *Res:* Design and synthesis of biologically and medicinally important organic compounds. *Mailing Add:* 5694 Plymouth Rd 248 Ann Arbor MI 48105

**WIERENGO, CYRIL JOHN, JR,** ORGANIC CHEMISTRY. *Current Pos:* PROF CHEM, UNIV W ALA, 96- *Personal Data:* b Picayune, Miss, Mar 7, 40; m 62, Mary Spence; c Cyril J III & Marcy. *Educ:* Univ Southern Miss, BA, 62, MS, 64; Miss State Univ, PhD(chem), 74. *Prof Exp:* Res chemist, Dow Chem Co, 64-67; prof chem, Miss Univ Women, 67-93. *Mem:* Am Chem Soc; Sigma Xi. *Res:* Synthesis and chemistry of bis-heterocyclic compounds. *Mailing Add:* 121 Lynn Dr Columbus MS 39702

**WIERMAN, JOHN C,** PERCOLATION, RANDOM GRAPHS. *Current Pos:* from asst prof to assoc prof, 81-87, PROF MATH SCI, JOHNS HOPKINS UNIV, 87-, CHAIR, 88- *Personal Data:* b Prosser, Wash, June 30, 49; m 71, Susan S Graupmann; c Adam C. *Educ:* Univ Wash, BS, 71, PhD(math), 76. *Prof Exp:* Asst prof math, Univ Minn, 76-81. *Concurrent Pos:* Sr res fel, Inst Math & Its Appln, Univ Minn, 87-88. *Mem:* Fel Inst Math Statist; Am Statist Asn; Am Math Soc; Math Asn Am; Bernoulli Soc; Sigma Xi. *Res:* Exact determination and bounding methods for critical probabilities and critical exponents in percolation models; random graphs; probabilistic methods in combinatorics. *Mailing Add:* Math Sci Dept Johns Hopkins Univ 34th & Charles St Baltimore MD 21218. *Fax:* 410-516-7459; *E-Mail:* wierman@brutus.mts.jhu.edu

**WIERSMA, DANIEL,** soil science; deceased, see previous edition for last biography

**WIERSMA, JAMES H,** ANALYTICAL CHEMISTRY, GENERAL ENVIRONMENTAL SCIENCES. *Current Pos:* asst prof chem, 68-72, ASSOC PROF CHEM, UNIV WIS, GREEN BAY, 72- *Personal Data:* b Beaver Dam, Wis, Jan 4, 40; m 61; c 1. *Educ:* Wis State Univ, Oshkosh, BS, 61; Univ Mo, Kansas City, MS, 65, PhD(chem), 68. *Prof Exp:* Clin chemist, Mercy Hosp, Oshkosh, 61-62; USPHS traineeship water chem, 67-68. *Mem:* AAAS; Sigma Xi; Am Chem Soc. *Res:* Environmental sciences especially related chemistry and development of analytical methods; groundwater quality. *Mailing Add:* RM ES 317 Univ Wis Green Bay WI 54311-7001

**WIERWILLE, WALTER W(ERNER),** HUMAN FACTORS & INDUSTRIAL ENGINEERING. *Current Pos:* assoc prof elec & indust eng & opers res, 71-73, PROF ELEC & INDUST ENG & OPERS RES, VA POLYTECH INST & STATE UNIV, 73- *Personal Data:* b Cincinnati, Ohio, July 3, 36; m 61; c 2. *Educ:* Univ Ill, Urbana, BSEE, 58; Cornell Univ, PhD(elec eng), 61. *Prof Exp:* Res asst comput ctr, Cornell Univ, 60-61, assoc electronics engr, Avionics Dept, Physics Div, Cornell Aeronaut Lab, 61-63, res electronics engr, 63-65, prin electronics engr, 65-67, head dynamic systs sect, 67-69; supvry scientist, Sanders Assocs, 69-70, mgr, Electronic Counter-Measures Systs Group, 70-71. *Concurrent Pos:* Consult, NY Transit Authority, Gen Motors Corp, 74- & USN, 77- *Mem:* Sr mem Inst Elec & Electronics Engrs; fel Human Factors Soc; Soc Indust & Appl Math; sr mem Am Inst Indust Engrs. *Res:* Command and control; workspace layout; human performance modeling; man-machine system simulation; human operator workload; vehicle handling; operator/system interface design. *Mailing Add:* Dept Indust Eng & Oper Res Va Polytech Inst & State Univ Whittemore Hall Blacksburg VA 24061

**WIESBOECK, ROBERT A,** ORGANOMETALLIC CHEMISTRY. *Current Pos:* staff scientist, US Steel Corp, 63-68, res scientist, 68-70, mgr chem, 70-74, MGR ATLANTA RES CTR, US STEEL CORP, 74- *Personal Data:* b Frankfurt, Ger, Jan 19, 30; m 50; c 2. *Educ:* Munich Tech Univ, BS, 55, PhD(chem), 57. *Prof Exp:* NSF fel phys org chem, Ga Inst Technol, 58-59; res chemist, Redstone Res Div, Rohm and Haas Co, 59-63. *Mem:* AAAS; Am Chem Soc. *Res:* Organic and inorganic fluorine chemistry of nitrogen, phosphorous and sulphur. *Mailing Add:* 5912 Oakleaf Dr Stone Mountain GA 30087-5799

**WIESCHAUS, ERIC F,** DROSOPHILA MELANOGASTER. *Current Pos:* from asst prof to assoc prof, 81-87, PROF MOLECULAR BIOL, PRINCETON UNIV, 87-, SQUIBB PROF MOLECULAR BIOL, 93- *Personal Data:* b June 8, 47. *Educ:* Univ Notre Dame, Ind, BS, 69; Yale Univ, PhD(biol), 74. *Honors & Awards:* Nobel Prize in Physiol or Med, 95. *Prof Exp:* Res fel, Zool Inst, Univ Zurich, 75-78; group leader, Europ Molecular Biol Lab, Ger, 78-81. *Concurrent Pos:* Fel, Lab Mme Gans, Laboratoire de Genetique Moleculaire, France, 76; vis researcher, Lab Peter Bryant, Ctr Pathobiol, Univ Calif, Irvine, 77; sci adv coun, Damon Runyon-Walter Winchell Cancer Fund, 87-92. *Mem:* Nat Acad Sci; fel Am Acad Arts & Sci. *Res:* Contributed articles to professional journals. *Mailing Add:* Dept Molecular Biol Princeton Univ Princeton NJ 08544

**WIESE, ALLEN F,** WEED SCIENCE. *Current Pos:* Prof, 53-90, EMER PROF WEED SCI, AGR EXP STA, TEX A&M UNIV, 90- *Personal Data:* b Eyota, Minn, Dec 16, 25; m 48, Joan Hanson; c David, Beth & Ann. *Educ:* Univ Minn, BS, 49, MS, 51, PhD(agron), 53. *Honors & Awards:* Res Award, Weed Sci Soc Am, 80, Tex A&M Univ, 80. *Concurrent Pos:* Agr consult. *Mem:* AAAS; fel Am Soc Agron; fel Weed Sci Soc Am; Soil Sci Soc Am; fel Crop Sci Soc Am. *Res:* Weed control methods in crop production including no-tillage. *Mailing Add:* Tex Agr Exp Sta Bushland TX 79012. *Fax:* 806-358-8846

**WIESE, ALVIN CARL,** NUTRITION. *Current Pos:* RETIRED. *Personal Data:* b Milwaukee, Wis, Aug 13, 13; m 44, Hazel M Kuntz; c Jon L & Ray A. *Educ:* Univ Wis, BS, 35, MS, 37, PhD(biochem), 40. *Prof Exp:* Asst biochem, Univ Wis, 35-40; instr chem, Okla Agr & Mech Col, 40-42; spec res assoc, Univ Ill, 42-45, spec asst animal nutrit, 45-46; prof agr biochem & head dept, Univ Idaho, 46-72, prof biochem, 72-78, emer prof biochem, 78. *Mem:* AAAS; Am Chem Soc; Soc Exp Biol & Med; Poultry Sci Asn; Am Inst Nutrit. *Res:* Nutritional biochemistry; enzymology; effect of fluorides on enzymes; air pollution; trace minerals. *Mailing Add:* 649 N Eisenhower Moscow ID 83843

**WIESE, HELEN JEAN COLEMAN,** MEDICAL ANTHROPOLOGY. *Current Pos:* Asst prof, 72-80, ASSOC PROF BEHAV SCI, COL MED, UNIV KY, 80- *Personal Data:* b San Antonio, Tex, Dec 10, 41; m 75. *Educ:* Univ Wis, Milwaukee, BA, 63; Stanford Univ, MA, 64; Univ NC, Chapel Hill, PhD(anthrop), 72. *Mem:* Soc Appl Anthrop; Soc Med Anthrop; Am Anthrop Asn; Asn Behav Sci Med Educ; Inst Soc Ethics Life Sci. *Res:* Cross-cultural variation in acceptable body image; effects of pharmaceutical counseling on patient compliance with chemotherapy for congestive heart failure; attitudes toward various contraceptive devices; rates of gonorrhea in two Kentucky counties. *Mailing Add:* Dept Behav Sci Univ Ky Col Med 800 Rose St Lexington KY 40536-0001

**WIESE, JOHN HERBERT,** GEOLOGY, HYDROLOGY & WATER RESOURCES. *Current Pos:* RETIRED. *Personal Data:* b Los Angeles, Calif, Jan 15, 17; m 90, Margaret Warren; c Lynn K & Patricia J. *Educ:* Univ Calif, Los Angeles, AB, 40, MA, 41, PhD(struct geol), 47. *Prof Exp:* Geologist, US Geol Surv, 41-48; geologist, Richfield Oil Co, 48-59, supvr explor res, 59-66, sr geologist, Atlantic Richfield Co, 67-73; consult geologist, 73-87. *Concurrent Pos:* Vis indust prof, Southern Methodist Univ, 70-73. *Res:* Geology of Nevada; petroleum exploration; sedimentology; landslides; continental shelf resources; geology of central California coast. *Mailing Add:* 158 Oak Wood Rd Kerrville TX 78028

**WIESE, MAURICE VICTOR,** PLANT PATHOLOGY, CROP LOSS ASSESSMENT. *Current Pos:* RES PROF & CROP LOSS COORDR, UNIV IDAHO, 78- *Personal Data:* b Columbus, Nebr, Sept 22, 40; m 63; c 3. *Educ:* Univ Nebr, BS, 63, MS, 65; Univ Calif, PhD(plant path), 69. *Prof Exp:* Asst prof plant path, Mich State Univ, 69-74, assoc prof & wheat pathologist, 74-78. *Mem:* Am Phytopath Soc; Am Soc Agron; Crop Sci Soc Am; Sigma Xi. *Res:* Pathogenesis, etiology and control of wheat diseases; assessment of losses in crops; comprehensive yield models; crop management. *Mailing Add:* Dept Plant Sci Univ Idaho 375 S Line St Moscow ID 83843-4140

**WIESE, RICHARD ANTON,** SOIL FERTILITY. *Current Pos:* assoc prof agron, 67-74, PROF AGRON, UNIV NEBR, LINCOLN, 74- *Personal Data:* b Howells, Nebr, Apr 3, 28; m 54; c 8. *Educ:* Univ Nebr, BS, 54, MS, 56; NC State Univ, PhD, 61. *Prof Exp:* From asst prof to assoc prof soil fertil, Univ Wis, 61-67. *Mem:* Am Soc Agron; Soil Sci Soc Am. *Res:* Plant nutrition as effected by soil release of nutrients. *Mailing Add:* 6316 Tanglewood Ct Lincoln NE 68516

**WIESE, ROBERT GEORGE, JR,** GEOLOGY. *Current Pos:* mem staff, Geol Dept, 64-70, PROF GEOL & CHMN DEPT, MT UNION COL, 70- *Personal Data:* b Boston, Mass, Sept 14, 33; m 58; c 4. *Educ:* Yale Univ, BS, 55; Harvard Univ, AM, 57, PhD(geol), 61. *Prof Exp:* Explor geologist, New Park Mining Co, 60-63; explor geologist, US Smelting Refining & Mining Co, 63-64. *Concurrent Pos:* Consult geologist. *Mem:* Am Inst Prof Geologists; Geol Soc Am; Am Inst Mining, Metall & Petrol Eng; Mineral Asn Can; Soc Econ Geol; Nat Asn Geol Teachers; assoc Sigma Xi. *Res:* Petrology and geochemistry of White Pine copper deposit, Michigan; petrology of wallrock alteration; genesis of mineral deposits; coal geology, exploration, development; trace elements in coal; x-ray analysis of raw materials for ceramics. *Mailing Add:* 135 Overlook Dr Alliance OH 44601-3918

**WIESE, WARREN M(ELVIN),** ENGINEERING MANAGEMENT, REFRIGERATION & AIR CONDITIONING. *Current Pos:* RETIRED. *Personal Data:* b Rochester, Minn, Apr 14, 29; m 48; c 4. *Educ:* Univ Minn, BS, 50, MS, 52. *Honors & Awards:* Springer Award, Soc Automotive Engrs, 59, McFarland Award, 95, Medal of Honor, 96. *Prof Exp:* Teaching asst, Univ Minn, 50-52; res engr, Gen Motors Res Labs, 52-55, sr res engr, 56-65, sr liaison engr, 66-67, mgr air conditioning & automotive prod eng, Frigidaire Div, 67-72, asst chief engr, 72-75, chief engr, Delco Air Conditioning Div, 75-81, chief engr, Harrison Radiator Div, Gen Motors Corp, 81-91. *Concurrent Pos:* Pres, Delco Air Recreation Asn, 75-83; Comn Chlorofluorocarbon in Stratosphere, Nat Acad Sci, 79. *Mem:* Fel Soc Automotive Engrs. *Res:* Engine combustion; fuel antiknock characteristics; deposit-induced ignition; engine rumble; vehicle exhaust emission; technical liaison; residential and automotive air conditioning systems; air conditioning compressors. *Mailing Add:* 5244 Lewiston Rd Lewiston NY 14092

**WIESE, WOLFGANG LOTHAR,** ATOMIC PHYSICS, PLASMA PHYSICS. *Current Pos:* res physicist, Nat Bue Stand, 60-62, chief, Plasma Spectros, 62-77, CHIEF, ATOMIC PHYSICS DIV, NAT INST STAND & SECT TECHNOL, 78- *Personal Data:* b Tilsit, Ger, Apr 21, 31; nat US; m 57, Gesa Ladehoff; c Margrit & Cosima. *Educ:* Univ Kiel, BS, 54, PhD(physics), 57. *Hon Degrees:* DSc, Univ Kiel, Ger, 93. *Honors & Awards:* Gold Medal, US Dept Com, 71, A V Astin Measurement Sci Award, 92, Distinguished Career Sci Award, Wash Acad Sci, 92. *Prof Exp:* Res assoc physics, Univ Md, 58-59. *Concurrent Pos:* Lectr, Univ Calif, Los Angeles, 63-64; Guggenheim fel, Max Planck Inst, Munich, Ger, 66-67; Humboldt award, Ger, 86. *Mem:* Fel Optical Soc Am; Int Astron Union; fel Am Phys Soc; fel, Wash Acad Sci. *Res:* Experimental plasma spectroscopy; determination of atomic transition probabilities; measurements of plasma line broadening; evaluation and compilation of spectroscopic data. *Mailing Add:* 8229 Stone Trail Dr Bethesda MD 20817. *Fax:* 301-990-1350; *E-Mail:* wolfgang.wiese@nist.gov

**WIESEL, TORSTEN NILS,** NEUROBIOLOGY, VISUAL PROCESSING. *Current Pos:* HEAD, LAB NEUROBIOL, ROCKEFELLER UNIV, 83-, VINCENT & BROOKE ASTOR PROF, 83- *Personal Data:* b Upsala, Sweden, June 3, 24; div. *Educ:* Karolinska Inst, Sweden, MD, 54. *Hon Degrees:* Var from US & foreign univs, 67-90. *Honors & Awards:* Nobel Prize in Med, 81; Jules Stein Award, Trustees Prev of Blindness, 71; Dr Jules C Stein Award, Res to Prev Blindness, 71; Rosenstiel Award, 72; Friedenwald Award, Asn Res Vision & Ophthal, 75; Karl Spencer Lashley Prize, Am Philos Soc, 77; Louisa Gross Horwitz Prize, Columbia Univ, 78; Dickson Prize, Univ Pittsburgh, 79; Ledlie Prize, Harvard Univ, 80. *Prof Exp:* Instr physiol, Royal Caroline Medico-Surg Inst & asst, Dept Child Psychiat, Hosp, 54-55; fel, John Hopkins Univ Sch, 55-58, asst prof ophthal-physiol, 58-59; assoc neurophysiol & neuropharmacol, Harvard Med Sch, 59-60, asst prof, 60-64, asst prof neurophysiol, Dept Psychiat, 64-67, prof physiol, 67-68, prof neurobiol, 68-74, chmn dept, 73-84, Robert Winthrop prof, 74-84. *Mem:* Nat Acad Sci; Inst Med-Nat Acad Sci; Am Acad Arts & Sci; Swed Physiol Soc; AAAS; Am Neurol Soc; Am Physiol Soc. *Res:* Neurophysiology, especially the visual system. *Mailing Add:* Rockefeller Univ 1230 York Ave New York NY 10021

**WIESENDANGER, HANS ULRICH DAVID,** TECHNOLOGY TRANSFER, PHYSICAL CHEMISTRY. *Current Pos:* SR ASSOC, STANFORD UNIV, 84- *Personal Data:* b Zurich, Switz, Jan 13, 28; nat US; m 54; c 4. *Educ:* Swiss Fed Inst Technol, dipl, 51, DrScTech, 54. *Prof Exp:* Tech adv inst phys ther, Zurich Univ, 53-55; fel, Univ Calif, Los Angeles, 55-56; sr res chemist, Kaiser Aluminum & Chem Corp, 57-59; phys chemist, Stanford Res Inst, 59-66; mkt mgr sci instrument dept, Electronics Assocs, Inc, 66-70; dir mkt, Uthe Technol Int, 70-72; dir int mkt, Barnes-Hind Pharmaceut, Inc, 72-74; consult, 74-75; dir mkt, Plessy Environ Systs, Inc, 75-77; dir int mkt, Chemetrics Corp, 77-81; pres, Orbiotech, Inc, 81-83. *Concurrent Pos:* Consult, 54-55, 71-77 & 81- *Mem:* Am Chem Soc. *Res:* Surface chemistry; ultra high vacuum; radiochemistry; isotopes; tracer methods; catalysis; instrumentation; mass spectrometry; semiconductor processing equipment; process control; environmental monitoring; clinical laboratory instrumentation; clinical chemistry; technoeconomics; international marketing; long range planning; technology assessment and transfer; new ventures; acquisitions and business opportunities analysis; technology licensing; science communications. *Mailing Add:* 1151 Buckingham Dr Los Altos CA 94024

**WIESENFELD, JAY MARTIN,** ULTRA-FAST OPTOELECTRONICS, OPTICAL COMMUNICATIONS TECHNOLOGY. *Current Pos:* fel, Bell Labs, 78-80, MEM TECH STAFF, AT&T BELL LABS, 80- *Personal Data:* b New Brunswick, NJ, Sept 24, 50; m 79, Kay Granstrom; c David & Eric. *Educ:* Harvard Univ, AB & AM, 72; Univ Calif, Berkeley, PhD(chem), 78. *Mem:* Inst Elec & Electronics Engrs; Am Phys Soc; Optical Soc Am; Sigma Xi. *Res:* Generation of ultrashort laser pulses; Ultra-high-speed optoelectronic devices; optical communications; transient behavior of optically excited semiconductor and molecular systems; generation of ultrashort laser pulses. *Mailing Add:* AT&T Bell Labs Dept B10 11164 Rm Hoh L-111 Crawford Hill Lab PO Box 400 Holmdel NJ 07733

**WIESENFELD, JOEL,** CIVIL ENGINEERING, MECHANICS. *Current Pos:* from instr to prof, Rutgers Univ, 46-88, chmn, Dept Civil & Environ Eng, 70-80, asst dean freshman, 80-88, EMER PROF CIVIL ENG, RUTGERS UNIV, 88- *Personal Data:* b New York, NY, Apr 9, 18; m 45; c 2. *Educ:* City Col New York, BCE, 40; Mass Inst Technol, SM, 41; Polytech Inst Brooklyn, PhD(appl mech), 53. *Prof Exp:* Stress analyst, Curtiss-Wright Corp, NJ, 41-45; sr stress analyst, Repub Aviation Corp, NY, 45-46. *Mem:* Am Soc Civil Engrs; Am Soc Eng Educ; Nat Soc Prof Engrs; Am Water Works Asn. *Res:* Structural design and analysis; computer techniques applied to structural problems; construction engineering; water distribution system operation. *Mailing Add:* 311 Valentine St Highland Park NJ 08904

**WIESENFELD, JOHN RICHARD,** CHEMICAL KINETICS, PHOTOCHEMISTRY. *Current Pos:* DEAN SCI, FLA ATLANTIC UNIV, 95- *Personal Data:* b New York, NY, July 26, 44. *Educ:* City Col New York, BS, 65; Case Inst Technol, PhD(chem), 69; Cambridge Univ, MA, 70. *Prof Exp:* USAF fel phys chem, Cambridge Univ, 69-70, NSF fel, 70-71, Stokes res fel, Pembroke Col, 70-72; from asst prof to prof chem, Cornell Univ, 72-95, chmn 85-88, dep vpres res, 88-90, vpres planning, 90-95. *Concurrent Pos:* US Hon Ramsay fel, Ramsay Mem Trust, UK, 71; Henry & Camille Dreyfus teacher-scholar, 77-82; Alfred P Sloan Found res fel, 77-79; coun chem res, Gov Bd, 87-91; trustee, Assoc Univs Inc, 89-92. *Mem:* Fel AAAS; Am Chem Soc. *Res:* Gas phase kinetics of atoms and molecules in defined quantum states; energy storage and transfer in chemical lasers; environmental chemistry. *Mailing Add:* Dept Chem Fla Atlantic Univ PO Box 3091 777 Glades Rd Boca Raton FL 33431. *Fax:* 607-255-2990; *E-Mail:* jrw4@cornell.edu

**WIESER, HELMUT,** SPECTROSCOPY, PHEROMONE ACTION CHEMISTRY. *Current Pos:* Session instr, 66-68, from asst prof to assoc prof, 68-80, PROF CHEM, UNIV CALGARY, 80-, ASSOC DEPT HEAD, 88- *Personal Data:* b Austria, July 4, 35; Can citizen; m 67; c 2. *Educ:* Univ BC, BSc, 62; Univ Alta, PhD(chem), 66. *Concurrent Pos:* Dozent fel, Alexander von Humboldt Found, Ger, 74, 75. *Mem:* Fel Chem Inst Can; Sigma Xi. *Res:* Molecular spectroscopy and structure; infrared and Raman spectroscopy; vibrational circular dichroism spectroscopy, ab initio molecular force fields; mode of pheromone action pheromones in forest pest management. *Mailing Add:* Dept Chem Univ Calgary Calgary AB T2N 1N4 Can

**WIESMEYER, HERBERT,** MICROBIOLOGY. *Current Pos:* asst prof, 62-67, ASSOC PROF MOLECULAR BIOL, VANDERBILT UNIV, 67- *Personal Data:* b Chicago, Ill, Jan 12, 32; m 54; c 2. *Educ:* Univ Ill, BS, 54; Washington Univ, St Louis, PhD, 59. *Prof Exp:* NSF fel, Johns Hopkins Univ, 59-61; fel, McCollum-Pratt Inst, 61; NATO fel, 61-62. *Mem:* Am Soc Microbiol; Genetics Soc Am; Sigma Xi. *Res:* Bacterial physiology. *Mailing Add:* 205 Woodmont Circle Nashville TN 37205

**WIESNER, J(EROME) B,** electrical engineering, arms control; deceased, see previous edition for last biography

**WIESNER, LEO,** PHYSICS, ELECTRONICS ENGINEERING. *Current Pos:* ENG CONSULT, 78- *Personal Data:* b Vienna, Austria, May 3, 13; nat US; m 58, Rakoma Lipshitz; c Claire. *Educ:* Univ Vienna, PhD, 37. *Prof Exp:* Res physicist, Harlem Hosp, NY, 39-43 & Int Electronics Indust, Inc, 43-45; electronics engr, Tuck Electronic Corp, 45-47 & Devenco Inc, 47-51; sr gyro engr, Reeves Instrument Corp, 51-62; mgr appl sci, Technol Group, Timex Corp, Waterbury, 62-78. *Mem:* Am Phys Soc; Inst Elec & Electronics Engrs. *Res:* Electro-optical displays; electronic watches; gyros, accelerometers and related inertial devices. *Mailing Add:* 115-01 Grosvenor Rd Richmond Hill NY 11418

**WIESNER, LOREN ELWOOD,** SEED PHYSIOLOGY. *Current Pos:* RES LEADER, NAT SEED STORAGE LAB, AGR RES STA, USDA, 89- *Personal Data:* b Estelline, SDak, Nov 13, 38; m 59; c 3. *Educ:* SDak State Univ, BS, 60, MS, 63; Ore State Univ, PhD(agron), 71. *Honors & Awards:* Seed Sci Award, Crop Sci Soc Am; Merit Award, Asn Off Seed Analysts. *Prof Exp:* Asst agron, SDak State Univ, 63, asst co agt, 63-64; asst prof seed technol, Mont State Univ, 64-68; res asst agron, Ore State Univ, 68-70; from assoc prof to prof seed physiol, Mont State Univ, 70-89. *Mem:* Fel Am Soc Agron; fel Crop Sci Soc Am; Asn Off Seed Analysts; Asn Off Seed Cert Agencies; Sigma Xi. *Res:* Seed research related to production, technology, physiology and ecology. *Mailing Add:* 1111 S Mason St Ft Collins CO 80521-4500

**WIESNER, RAKOMA,** biochemistry, for more information see previous edition

**WIESNET, DONALD RICHARD,** HYDROLOGY & GEOLOGY, REMOTE SENSING. *Current Pos:* CONSULT, 90- *Personal Data:* b Buffalo, NY, Feb 7, 27; m 52, Evelyn E Jordan; c Andrew, Elizabeth, Peter & Ellen. *Educ:* State Univ NY, Buffalo, BA, 50, MA, 51. *Prof Exp:* Asst, Univ Buffalo, 50-51; geologist, US Geol Surv, 52-54, chief manuscript rev sect, 54-55, geophys br, 56-57, asst to geol map ed, 57-59, asst chief br tech illustrations, 59-61, geohydrol map ed, 61-64, proj geologist, 65-67; oceanogr, Naval Oceanog Off, 67-68, res hydrologist, Nat Environ Satellite Data & Info Serv, 68-71, sr res hydrologist, 71-80, chief, Land Sci Br, 80-82; exec dir, Satellite Hydrol Inc, 82-90. *Concurrent Pos:* Mem comt hydrol, US Water Resources Coun, 68-71; rapporteur remote sensing of hydrol elements, Comn Hydrol, World Meteorol Orgn, 72-76; mem work group remote sensing in hydrol, US Nat Com, Int Hydrol Decade, 72-76; mem remote sensing comt, Int Field Year on Great Lakes, 72-75; prin investr, Landsat-1 & 2, NASA, 72-76 & Heat Capacity Map Mission Satellite, 78-80; bd dir, Am Water Resources Asn, 80-82, Antarctican Soc, 83-85 & Potomac Reg, Am Soc Photogram & Remote Sensing, 90-94; int comt remote sensing & data transmission for hydrol, Int Asn Hydrol Res, 81-; vpres, Eastern Snow Conf, 82, pres, 83. *Mem:* Fel Geol Soc Am; fel Am Soc Photogram & Remote Sensing; Int Glaciol Soc; Antarctican Soc; Am Geophys Union. *Res:* Satellite hydrology; remote sensing of hydrologic parameters such as snow, ice, soil moisture, floods, coastal hydrology and ground water; hydrologic maps; disaster studies such as floods, earthquakes, hurricanes and droughts. *Mailing Add:* 601 McKinley St NE Vienna VA 22180-3555. *Fax:* 703-281-0216

**WIEST, STEVEN CRAIG,** ORNAMENTAL HORTICULTURE, PLANT PHYSIOLOGY. *Current Pos:* asst prof, 80-83, ASSOC PROF, DEPT HORT, KANS STATE UNIV, 83- *Personal Data:* b Harrisburg, Pa, Aug 4, 51. *Educ:* Cornell Univ, BS, 73, MS, 75, PhD(agron), 79. *Honors & Awards:* Kenneth Post Award, Am Soc Hort Sci, 78, Alex Laurie Award, 81. *Prof Exp:* Res asst ornamental hort, Cornell Univ, 73-77, res asst agron, 77-78; asst prof hort, Rutgers Univ, NB, 78-80. *Mem:* Am Soc Plant Physiologists; Am Soc Hort Sci. *Res:* Biophysical and biochemical responses of plant cells to environmental stresses, especially those stresses induced directly by such meteorological conditions as low and high temperatures and drought. *Mailing Add:* Hort/Forestry/Rec Res Kans State Univ 2021 Throckmorton Hall Manhattan KS 66506-5506. *Fax:* 785-532-6949; *E-Mail:* wiest@ksuvm.ksu.edu

**WIEST, WALTER GIBSON,** BIOCHEMISTRY. *Current Pos:* RETIRED. *Personal Data:* b Price, Utah, Feb 16, 22; m 48; c 7. *Educ:* Brigham Young Univ, AB, 48; Univ Wis, MS, 51, PhD(biochem), 52. *Prof Exp:* Asst biochem, Univ Wis, 48-52; from instr to assoc prof, Univ Utah, 52-64; assoc prof, Wash Univ, 64-68, prof biochem obstet & gynec, Sch Med, 68-87. *Concurrent Pos:* USPHS spec fel, Univ Cologne, 59-60. *Mem:* Am Soc Biol Chem; Endocrine Soc; Soc Gynec Invest. *Res:* Biosynthesis, metabolism and mode of action of steroid hormones, especially progesterone; application of radioisotopic techniques to steroid biochemistry. *Mailing Add:* 2896 S Fort Pierce Dr St George UT 84770

**WIETING, TERENCE JAMES,** PHYSICS. *Current Pos:* Nat Acad Sci-Nat Res Coun res assoc, 69-71, head, Optical Interactions Sect, 81-90, LEAD, DIRECTED ENERGY EFFECTS BR, NAVAL RES LAB, 90- *Personal Data:* b Chicago, Ill, Sept 4, 35; m 70, Anna Elisabeth Burgunole; c Nicole, Andrea & Karin. *Educ:* Mass Inst Technol, BS, 57; Harvard Univ, BD, 62; Cambridge Univ, PhD(physics), 69. *Prof Exp:* Res staff mem physics, Naval Supersonic Lab, Mass Inst Technol, 58-60; res scientist, Mithras, Inc, Mass, 62-63. *Concurrent Pos:* Invited prof, Fed Polytech, Lausanne, Switz, 77-78, 85-86. *Mem:* Am Phys Soc; Sigma Xi; AAAS. *Res:* Microwave interactions; physics of low-dimensional materials; Raman scattering; lattice dynamics. *Mailing Add:* US Naval Res Lab Code 6650 Washington DC 20375. *E-Mail:* wieting@ccfsun.nrl.navy.mil

**WIEWIOROWSKI, TADEUSZ KAROL,** FERTILIZER TECHNOLOGY, SULFUR TECHNOLOGY. *Personal Data:* b Sopot, Poland, Nov 3, 35; US citizen; m 62; c 2. *Educ:* Loyola Univ, La, BS, 59; Tulane Univ, PhD(chem), 65. *Prof Exp:* Asst mgr res & develop, Freeport Minerals Co, 59-81; vpres & dir res & develop, Freeport Res & Eng Co, 81-90. *Mem:* Am Chem Soc. *Res:* Inorganic and physical chemistry; process development; hydrometallurgy; management of chemical research and development; solvent extraction. *Mailing Add:* 2620 Danbury Dr New Orleans LA 70131-3846

**WIFF, DONALD RAY,** POLYMER PHYSICS, MARKETING RESEARCH. *Current Pos:* SECT HEAD, GENCORP INC, 85- *Personal Data:* b Youngstown, Ohio, Feb 19, 36; m 62, Carol J Skipper; c David S, Devin D & Daniel D. *Educ:* Capital Univ, BS, 58; Kent State Univ, MA, 60; Tex A&M Univ, PhD(physics), 67; Univ Dayton, MBA, 80. *Prof Exp:* Instr physics, Tex A&M Univ, 60-67; res assoc prof physics, Univ Dayton Res Inst, 67-70, res physicist, 70-73, res assoc, 73-76, prin investr, 76-85. *Mem:* Am Phys Soc; Am Mgt Asn; Soc Advan Mat & Process Eng; Brit Inst Physics; Europ Phys Soc; Rheology Soc; Crystallog Asn; Soc Plastics Eng; Am Chem Soc. *Res:* Theoretical polymer physics; electronic energy band calculation of cubic boron nitride via APW method; molecular weight distribution from ultracentrifugation via ill pased problem regularization methods; molecular composites; in-situ composites; dynamic mechanical recalculation spectra using linear viscoelasticity theory; liquid crystals as reinforcement, nonlinear optical polymers. *Mailing Add:* 2650 Mayfair Circle Akron OH 44312. *Fax:* 330-794-6375; *E-Mail:* wiff@iris.gencorp.com

**WIGEN, PHILIP E,** SOLID STATE PHYSICS, MAGNETISM. *Current Pos:* assoc prof, 65-71, PROF PHYSICS, OHIO STATE UNIV, 71- *Personal Data:* b LaCrosse, Wash, May 11, 33; m 54, Bonnie Ackerman; c Beth F, Karen E & Sandra M. *Educ:* Pac Lutheran Col, BA, 55; Mich State Univ, PhD(physics), 60. *Prof Exp:* Assoc res scientist, Lockheed Res Labs, Calif, 60-63, res scientist, 63-65. *Concurrent Pos:* Consult, Res Labs, Battelle Mem Inst, 67-70, Drackett Co, 71-74, A F Avionics Lab, WPAB, 74-78 & Airtron/Litton, 81-; vis prof, Univ Osaka, Japan, 73, Univ Osnabruck, WGer, 86, Univ Zurich, Switz, 87; vis scientist, Phillips Res Lab, Hamburg, WGer, 79. *Mem:* Fel Am Phys Soc; Am Asn Physics Teachers; Inst Elec & Electronics Eng; AAAS; Am Asn Univ Professors; Sigma Xi. *Res:* Magnetism in metals and insulators; ferromagnetic resonance; chaos in magnetism. *Mailing Add:* Dept Physics Ohio State Univ 174 W 18th Ave Columbus OH 43210. *Fax:* 614-292-7557; *E-Mail:* wigen@ohstpy.ohio__state.edu

**WIGFIELD, DONALD COMPSTON,** CHEMICAL TOXICOLOGY, ENVIRONMENTAL CHEMISTRY. *Current Pos:* asst prof, Carleton Univ, 69-72, assoc prof, 72-78, dir, Ottawa-Carleton Inst Res & Grad Studies Chem, 81-84, PROF CHEM, CARLETON UNIV, 78- *Personal Data:* b Godalming, Eng, June 13, 43; m 66; c 2. *Educ:* Univ Birmingham, BSc, 64; Univ Toronto, PhD(org chem), 67. *Hon Degrees:* DSc, Univ Birmingham, 87. *Prof Exp:* Fel, Univ BC, 67-68, teaching fel, 68-69. *Concurrent Pos:* Vis assoc prof, Univ Victoria, 75-76. *Mem:* Soc Environ Toxicol Chem; fel Royal Soc Chem; fel Chem Inst Can. *Res:* Chemical reaction mechanisms. *Mailing Add:* Dept Chem Carleton Univ Ottawa ON K1S 5B6 Can

**WIGFIELD, YUK YUNG,** PESTICIDE RESIDUES IN FOODS, NITROSAMINE CONTAMINATION IN PESTICIDE FORMULATIONS. *Current Pos:* chemist, 62 & 63-87, RES SCIENTIST, LAB SERVS DIV, AGR & AGR-FOOD CAN, 87- *Personal Data:* b Hong Kong, Jan 30, 40; Can Citizen; div; c Edward & Michael. *Educ:* Hong Kong Baptist Col, BSc, 62; St Francis Xavier Univ, MA, 64; Univ BC, PhD(reaction mechanism), 69. *Prof Exp:* Chemist, Bur Environ Health, Health & Welfare Can, 63. *Concurrent Pos:* Fel, Dept Chem, Univ Ottawa, 69-71. *Mem:* Can Soc Agron. *Res:* Develop residue analytical methodologies for pesticides in fruits and vegetables using gas liquid chromatography, high-performance liquid chromatography, surface-free energy and high-performance capillary electrophoresis. *Mailing Add:* Agr & Agr-Food Can Bldg 22 Ottawa ON K1A 0C6 Can. *Fax:* 613-992-5819; *E-Mail:* ag520843@ncccott.agr.ca

**WIGGANS, DONALD SHERMAN,** BIOCHEMISTRY. *Current Pos:* from asst prof to assoc prof, 54-61, PROF BIOCHEM, UNIV TEX HEALTH SCI CTR, DALLAS, 61- *Personal Data:* b Lincoln, Nebr, July 14, 25; m 51, Barbara Tarrant; c David, Richard, John & Scott. *Educ:* Univ Nebr, BSc, 49; Univ Ill, PhD(chem), 52. *Prof Exp:* Instr biochem, Yale Univ, 52-54. *Concurrent Pos:* Vis prof, Southern Methodist Univ, 64-66 & Univ Tex, Arlington, 67-74. *Mem:* Am Chem Soc; Am Soc Biol Chemists; Soc Exp Biol & Med; Am Inst Nutrit. *Res:* Intermediary metabolism of amino acids and peptides; mechanism of protein synthesis. *Mailing Add:* 4129 Northview Dallas TX 75229

**WIGGER, H JOACHIM,** medicine, pathology, for more information see previous edition

**WIGGERS, ERNIE P,** WILDLIFE BIOLOGY. *Current Pos:* ASSOC PROF, UNIV MO, COLUMBIA. *Personal Data:* b SC, Apr 28, 53. *Educ:* Clemson Univ, BS, 75, MS, 79; Tex Tech Univ, PhD(range & wildlife sci), 83. *Concurrent Pos:* Prog leader, Fisheries & Wildlife, 94- *Mem:* Wildlife Soc. *Res:* Species-habitat relationships; white-tailed deer management in urban and rural environments. *Mailing Add:* Sch Nat Resources 112 Stephens Hall Univ Mo Columbia MO 65211. *E-Mail:* ernie__wiggers@muccmail.missouri.edu

**WIGGERS, HAROLD CARL,** PHYSIOLOGY. *Current Pos:* RETIRED. *Educ:* Western Res Univ, PhD(physiol), 35. *Prof Exp:* Prof physiol, Albany Med Col, 47-53, pres & dean, 53-77. *Mailing Add:* 2015 F Quail Ridge Rd Greenville NC 27858

**WIGGERT, BARBARA NORENE,** BIOCHEMISTRY, VISUAL SCIENCE. *Current Pos:* NIH fel, Nat Eye Inst, 75-76, staff fel, 76-78, res chemist biochem, 78-85, SECT CHIEF, NAT EYE INST, NIH, 85- *Personal Data:* b Cleveland, Ohio, Jan 7, 38; m 58; c 4. *Educ:* Univ Wis-Madison, BA, 59; Harvard Univ, PhD(biochem), 63. *Prof Exp:* Fel biochem, Dept Physiol Chem, 63-65. *Mem:* Am Chem Soc; Asn Res Vision & Ophthal; Sigma Xi; Am Soc Biol Chemists. *Res:* Uptake, binding and translocation of retinoids, such as vitamin A and its analogs, into ocular tissues. *Mailing Add:* NIH Lab Retinal Cell & Molec Biol Bldg 6 Rm 338 6 Center Dr MSC 2740 Bethesda MD 20892-2740. *Fax:* 301-402-0750; *E-Mail:* bwq@cu.nih.gov

**WIGGIN, EDWIN ALBERT,** CHEMISTRY. *Current Pos:* EXEC VPRES, ATOMIC INDUST FORUM, 54- *Personal Data:* b Exeter, NH, Aug 11, 21; m 47; c 2. *Educ:* Univ NH, BS, 43. *Prof Exp:* Asst, SAM Labs, Columbia Univ, 43-45; res chemist, Carbide & Carbon Chem Co, 45-48; chief tech develop br, Isotopes Div, AEC, 48-54. *Concurrent Pos:* Mem Adv Comt Indust Info, AEC, 53-54, mem Adv Comt Isotope & Radiation Develop, 58-60 & 70-72. *Mem:* AAAS; Am Chem Soc; Am Nuclear Soc; Inst Nuclear Mat Mgt. *Res:* Application of atomic energy and radioactive by-products. *Mailing Add:* 17 Meadowcroft Ct Gaithersburg MD 20879

**WIGGINS, ALVIN DENNIE,** MATHEMATICAL STATISTICS. *Current Pos:* from asst prof to assoc prof biostatist, 69-82, prof statist, 82-91, EMER PROF STATIST, UNIV CALIF, DAVIS, 91- *Personal Data:* b Harrisburg, Ill, May 5, 22; m 50, Margaret L Deal; c Michael, Karl, Phillip, Frederick, Elizabeth & Andrew. *Educ:* Univ Calif, Berkeley, AB, 51, MA, 53, PhD(statist), 58. *Prof Exp:* Res asst statist & assoc biostatist, Sch Pub Health, Univ Calif, Berkeley, 54-57; instr math, Ctr Grad Studies, Univ Wash, 58-63; assoc res biostatistician & lectr biostatist, Sch Pub Health, Univ Calif, Berkeley, 63-69. *Concurrent Pos:* Sr statistician, Hanford Labs Oper, Gen Elec Co, 57-63; dir, Statist Lab, Univ Calif, Davis, 87-89; pres, San Francisco Bay Area Chap, Am Statist Asn, 87-88. *Mem:* Inst Math Statist; Biomet Soc; Am Statist Asn; fel Royal Statist Soc. *Res:* Mathematical models of biological phenomena; statistical theory of estimation; application of stochastic processes to problems of health, medicine and biology; design and analysis of experiments; stochastic differential equations in biology. *Mailing Add:* Div Statist Univ Calif Davis CA 95616. *E-Mail:* adwiggins@ucdavis.edu

**WIGGINS, CARL M,** TRANSIENT ELECTROMAGNETIC INTERFERENCE, LASER & OPTICAL SYSTEMS ANALYSIS. *Current Pos:* Staff mem, BDM Int, Inc, 73-75, assoc mgr, 75-80, sr staff, 80-85, prin staff, 85-89, SR PRIN SCIENTIST, BDM INT, INC, 89- *Personal Data:* b Jackson, Miss, Aug 5, 41; m 65; c 1. *Educ:* Lamar Univ, BS, 64; Sam Houston State Col, MS, 66. *Mem:* Sr mem Inst Elec & Electronics Engrs Power Eng Soc; sr mem Nat Asn Radio & Telecommun Engrs. *Res:* Transient electromagnetic interference in electric power systems including measurment, analysis, modeling and simulation; fault location; laser, optical, and electro-optical systems analysis. *Mailing Add:* 606 Fernwood Dr Friendswood TX 77546

**WIGGINS, EARL LOWELL,** physiology; deceased, see previous edition for last biography

**WIGGINS, ERNEST JAMES,** PHYSICAL CHEMISTRY, CHEMICAL ENGINEERING. *Current Pos:* RETIRED. *Personal Data:* b Trenton, Ont, Nov 25, 17; m 45; c 2. *Educ:* Queen's Univ, Ont, BSc, 38; McGill Univ, PhD(phys chem), 46. *Hon Degrees:* Dr, Athabasca Univ Alta, Can, 94. *Prof Exp:* Supt, Eng Develop Sect, Atomic Energy Proj, Nat Res Coun, 46-48; head, Munitions & Eng Sect, Suffield Exp Sta, Defense Res Bd, 48-52; sr chemist, Stanford Res Inst, 52-58; head, Chem Div, Sask Res Coun, 58-61; asst dir, Chem Div, Ont Res Found, 61-62; dir res, Res Coun Alta, 62-77, consult mem, Alta Oil Sands Technol & Res Authority, 77-94. *Mem:* Am Chem Soc; Arctic Inst NAm; Chem Inst Can; Brit Soc Chem Indust; Sigma Xi. *Res:* Chemical process development; environmental studies; energy resource development. *Mailing Add:* 8208 117th St NW Edmonton AB T6G 1R2 Can

**WIGGINS, GLENN BLAKELY,** ENTOMOLOGY, FRESHWATER BIOLOGY. *Current Pos:* prof, 68-92, EMER PROF ZOOL, UNIV TORONTO, 92-; EMER CUR, ROYAL ONT MUS, 92- *Personal Data:* b Toronto, Ont, Jan 29, 27; m 49, E Carol Staples; c 3. *Educ:* Univ Toronto, BA, 49, MA, 50, PhD, 58. *Honors & Awards:* Gold Medal for Outstanding Achievement, Entom Soc Can, 92. *Prof Exp:* Asst biologist, Nfld Fisheries Res Sta, Fisheries Res Bd Can, 50-51; asst cur, Dept Entom, Royal Ont Mus, 52-61, from asst cur in chg to cur in chg, 61-76, cur, 64-92. *Concurrent Pos:* Vis prof, Univ Minn, 70, 72 & 74, Univ Mont, 81 & Univ Osaka, Japan, 88;

mem sci comt, Biol Surv Can, 76-91; vpres, Biol Coun Can, 82-84. *Mem:* Fel Entom Soc Can (vpres, 79-80, pres, 81-82); NAm Benthol Soc; Entom Soc Am. *Res:* Systematic entomology, especially Trichoptera; aquatic entomology; biology of temporary pools; domiciliary invertebrates; evolution. *Mailing Add:* Dept Entom Royal Ont Mus 100 Queen's Park Toronto ON M5S 2C6 Can. *Fax:* 416-586-5863

**WIGGINS, JAMES WENDELL,** SEISMIC IMAGING, IMAGE PROCESSING. *Current Pos:* sr res geophysicist, 84-88, mgr geophys res & develop, 88-92, SR SCIENTIST, WESTERN GEOPHYS DIV, WESTERN ATLAS INT, INC, 92- *Personal Data:* b Fayette, Ala, May 9, 42; m 64, Joan Kornegay; c 2. *Educ:* Univ Ala, BS, 63; Johns Hopkins Univ, PhD(physics), 68. *Prof Exp:* Res assoc physics, Johns Hopkins Univ, 68-69, biophys, 69-73, NIH spec fel, 73-74, from asst prof to assoc prof biophys, 74-81; sr res geophysicist, Gulf Res & Develop Co, 82-84. *Mem:* Soc Explor Geophysicists; Am Phys Soc; AAAS; Europ Asn Explor Geophysicists; Soc Indust & Appl Math; Inst Elec & Electronics Engrs; Asn Comput Mach. *Res:* Methods of data collection and processing in seismic imaging; computer modeling of geological structure; image processing techniques applicable to geological, biological and other areas. *Mailing Add:* Western Geophys PO Box 2469 Houston TX 77252

**WIGGINS, JAMES WILLIAM,** INORGANIC CHEMISTRY. *Current Pos:* asst prof, 69-73, PROF CHEM & INORG CHEM, UNIV ARK, LITTLE ROCK, 73-, ASSOC DEAN, COL SCI, 80-, ASSOC DEAN, COL HEALTH RELATED PROFESSIONS, 83- *Personal Data:* b Paris, Ark, Mar 5, 40. *Educ:* Univ Ark, Fayetteville, BS, 62; Univ Fla, PhD(chem), 66. *Prof Exp:* Res grant, Univ Calif, Riverside, 66-68; interim asst prof chem, Univ Fla, 68-69. *Mem:* Am Chem Soc. *Res:* Boron-nitrogen-carbon chemistry, synthesis of compounds; mechanisms of reactions leading to unusual structures; water quality in Arkansas and the effect of changing the stream beds on the water quality. *Mailing Add:* Dept Chem Univ Ark Little Rock AR 72204

**WIGGINS, JAY ROSS,** CARDIAC PHARMACOLOGY. *Current Pos:* asst dir pharmacol, Berlex Labs, Inc, 82, assoc dir cardiac & biochem pharmacol, 82-84, pharmacol, 84-89, asst dir, 89-91, ASSOC DIR DIAG IMAGING, BERLEX LABS, INC, 91- *Personal Data:* b Baltimore, Md, Apr 12, 47; m 87, Patrice Bell; c Katherine, Thomas & Ryan. *Educ:* Bucknell Univ, BS, 69; Columbia Univ, PhD(pharmacol), 75. *Prof Exp:* Res assoc, Rockefeller Univ, 73-75; from asst prof to assoc prof pharmacol, Univ SFla, 76-81. *Mem:* AAAS; Am Soc Pharmacol & Exp Therapeut; Am Heart Asn. *Res:* Contrast echocardiography; electrophysiology and pharmacology of cardiac arrhythmias; mechanisms of excitation-contraction coupling in cardiac muscle. *Mailing Add:* Berlex Labs Inc 300 Fairfield Rd Wayne NJ 07470-7358

**WIGGINS, JOHN,** HEAVY ION PHYSICS. *Current Pos:* staff, 83-93, RES SCIENTIST LIGHT STREAM, BERANEK & NEWMAN INC, CAMBRIDGE, 93- *Personal Data:* b Bellevue, Nebr, Oct 25, 49; m 77. *Educ:* Univ Ga, BS, 75; Ind Univ, Bloomington, MS, 80, PhD(physics), 81. *Prof Exp:* Res asst, Cyclotron Facil, Ind Univ, 75-81, res assoc, 81; res staff, Lab Nuclear Sci, Mass Inst Technol, 81-83. *Mem:* Sigma Xi; NY Acad Sci; Am Phys Soc; AAAS; Am Asn Physics Teachers. *Res:* Experimental intermediate energy nuclear physics; reaction mechanism of protons with nuclei, excitation and decay of giant resonances in nuclei and decay of nuclei at high excitation; nuclear structure and properties from proton and heavy ion induced reactions. *Mailing Add:* 27 Paine St Wellesley MA 02181

**WIGGINS, JOHN H(ENRY), JR,** STRUCTURAL DYNAMICS, GEOPHYSICS. *Current Pos:* PRES, CRISIS MGT CORP, 87- *Personal Data:* b Tulsa, Okla, May 12, 31; m 78; c 2. *Educ:* Stanford Univ, BS, 53; St Louis Univ, MS, 55; Univ Ill, PhD(civil eng), 61. *Honors & Awards:* Moisseiff Award, Am Soc Civil Engrs, 65. *Prof Exp:* Physicist space weapons ctr, USAF, 55-58; sr res engr, Jersey Prod Res Co, 61-64; tech prog dir sonic boom & earthquake effects, res div, John A Blume & Assocs, 64-66; tech dir environ res, Datacraft Inc, 66; pres, J H Wiggins Co, 66-85. *Mem:* Am Inst Aeronaut & Astronaut; Soc Explor Geophysicists; Am Soc Mech Engrs; Am Inst Mining, Metall & Petrol Engrs; Am Geophys Union; Earthquake Eng Res Inst. *Res:* Nuclear weapons effects; earthquake engineering and seismology; oil well drilling and exploration geophysics; sonic boom effects; risk assessment; crisis management. *Mailing Add:* 1650 S Pacific Coast Hwy Redondo Beach CA 90277

**WIGGINS, JOHN SHEARON,** SPACE PHYSICS, SYSTEMS ENGINEERING. *Current Pos:* RETIRED. *Personal Data:* b Chicago, Ill, Feb 8, 15. *Educ:* Earlham Col, AB, 36; Calif Inst Technol, MS, 38; Univ Southern Calif, PhD(physics), 56. *Prof Exp:* Lectr physics, Univ Southern Calif, 41-43; from instr to asst prof, Univ Redlands, 44-46; asst prof, Univ Okla, 46-50; lectr physics, Univ Southern Calif, 50-56, asst prof, 57-58; mem tech staff, Semiconductor Div, Hughes Aircraft Co, 58-63; mem tech staff, Space Sci Dept, TRW Systs, 65-80, mem tech staff, Space & Technol Group, 80-92. *Concurrent Pos:* UNESCO vis prof, Concepcion Univ, Chile, 64. *Mem:* Am Phys Soc; Sigma Xi. *Res:* Photoelectric; electron microscopy; optical, beta-ray and gamma-ray spectroscopy; linear accelerator; semiconductor devices; space physics; space science instrumentation; payload design, test and integration; radiation damage and measurement; spacecraft charging; spacecraft operations engineering. *Mailing Add:* 900 E Harrison Ave Apt D-16 Pomona CA 91767

**WIGGINS, PETER F,** NUCLEAR ENGINEERING. *Current Pos:* asst prof nuclear eng, US Naval Acad, 62-71, assoc prof naval systs eng, 71-76, chmn dept, 76-81, PROF NAVAL SYSTS ENG, US NAVAL ACAD, 76- *Personal Data:* b New York, NY, July 18, 35; m 65; c 2. *Educ:* State Univ NY Maritime Col, BMarE, 58; NY Univ, MME, 61; Univ Md, PhD(nuclear eng), 70. *Prof Exp:* Asst inst eng, State Univ NY Maritime Col, 58-61; asst prof eng sci, State Univ NY Agr & Technol Col, Farmingdale, 61-62. *Concurrent Pos:* NSF sci fac fel, 69-70. *Mem:* Am Soc Eng Educ; Soc Naval Archit & Marine Engrs; Am Nuclear Soc; Am Soc Nuclear Engrs; Sigma Xi. *Res:* Neutron activation analysis; capture gamma ray studies using isotopic source californium-252 for mineral exploration. *Mailing Add:* 1016 Harbor Dr Annapolis MD 21403

**WIGGINS, RICHARD CALVIN,** NEUROCHEMISTRY, DEVELOPMENTAL NEUROBIOLOGY. *Current Pos:* FAC, DEPT ANAT, WVA UNIV HEALTH SCI CTR. *Personal Data:* b Portsmouth, Va, June 26, 45; m 75; c 2. *Educ:* Duke Univ, BS, 67, PhD(anat), 73. *Prof Exp:* Res assoc neurol, Sch Med, Univ Miami, 72-73; res assoc neurochem, Med Sch, Univ NC, 73-75; from asst prof to assoc prof neurobiol & anat, Med Sch, Univ Tex, 76-88, prof, 88- *Concurrent Pos:* NIH res career develop award, 79. *Mem:* Am Soc Neurochem; Int Soc Neurochem; Am Soc Neurosci; Am Asn Anatomists; Int Soc Develop Neurosci. *Res:* Biological chemistry of myelin; effects of environmental perturbation and drug abuse on brain development. *Mailing Add:* Dept Anat WVa Univ Health Sci Ctr PO Box 9128 Morgantown WV 26506

**WIGGINS, ROGER C,** INTERNAL MEDICINE. *Current Pos:* from asst prof to assoc prof, 81-90, CHIEF NEPHROLOGY & DIR, O'BRIEN RENAL CTR, UNIV MICH, ANN ARBOR, 88-, PROF 90- *Personal Data:* b Tetbury, Eng, May 26, 45. *Educ:* Cambridge Univ, BA, 68; Middlesex Hosp Med Sch, London, BChir, 71, MBS, MB & MA, 72. *Honors & Awards:* Leopold Hudson Prize, 71; William Henry Rean Prize, 71; Jerome W Conn Distinguished Res Award, 84. *Prof Exp:* House physician, Dept Med, Middlesex Hosp, London, 71-72; house surgeon, Ipswich & ESuffolk Hosp, 72; sr house officer, Hammersmith Hosp, Middlesex Hosp & Brompton Hosp, 72-74; res registr, Middlesex Hosp Sch Med, 75-76; fel, Scripps Clin & Res Found, 76-78, res assoc, 78-79, asst mem I, 79-81. *Concurrent Pos:* Berkeley fel, Gonville & Caius Col, 76; dir, Nephrol Training Prog, NIH, 88-; assoc ed, J Am Soc Nephrology. *Mem:* Fel Royal Col Physicians; Am Asn Pathologists; Am Asn Immunologists; Am Soc Nephrology; Am Fedn Clin Res; Am Soc Clin Invest. *Res:* Nephrology. *Mailing Add:* Nephrology Div Univ Mich 3914 Taubman Ctr Ann Arbor MI 48109-0364

**WIGGINS, THOMAS ARTHUR,** OPTICS. *Current Pos:* from asst prof to prof, 53-86, EMER PROF PHYSICS, PA STATE UNIV, 87- *Personal Data:* b Indiana, Pa, Feb 24, 21; m 53; c 2. *Educ:* Pa State Univ, BS, 42, PhD(physics), 53; George Washington Univ, MS, 49. *Prof Exp:* Instr physics, George Washington Univ, 48-50. *Mem:* Fel Am Phys Soc; fel Optical Soc Am. *Res:* Light beam propagation; physical optics; spontaneous and stimulated light scattering. *Mailing Add:* 104 Davey Lab Dept Physics Pa State Univ University Park PA 16802

**WIGGINS, VIRGIL DALE,** PALYNOLOGY. *Current Pos:* explor palynologist, 59-69, sr explor palynologist, Alaskan Div, 69-81, STAFF EXPLOR PALYNOLOGIST, WESTERN REGION, CHEVRON USA, 81- *Personal Data:* b Tulsa, Okla, June 25, 31; m 52; c 3. *Educ:* Univ Okla, BS, 57, MS, 62. *Prof Exp:* Sr palynological technician, Sun Oil Co Prod Res, 58-59. *Concurrent Pos:* Alaskan mem, Int Palynological Comn Working Group P3, 74-; mem bd dirs, Am Asn Stratig Palynologists, 83-85. *Mem:* Am Asn Stratig Palynologists. *Res:* Application of palynology to arctic petroleum exploration. *Mailing Add:* 3048 Naranja Dr Walnut Creek CA 94598

**WIGH, RUSSELL,** MEDICINE, RADIOLOGY. *Current Pos:* RETIRED. *Personal Data:* b Weehawken, NJ, Nov 17, 14; m 39; c 3. *Educ:* Rutgers Univ, BS, 35; Harvard Med Sch, MD, 39. *Honors & Awards:* Cert of Merit, Am Roentgen Ray Soc, 51. *Prof Exp:* Asst demonstr radiol, Jefferson Med Col, 46-49, instr, 49-50, assoc, 50, asst prof, 50-52; asst prof, Col Physicians & Surgeons, Columbia Univ, 52-54, assoc prof, 54-56; prof & chmn dept, Med Col Ga, 56-63; dir, Dept Radiol, Bartholomew Co Hosp, 63-71; assoc prof radiol, Sch Med, Ind Univ, Indianapolis, 72-77; from prof to emer prof radiol, Med Col Ga, 77-85. *Concurrent Pos:* Consult, Vet Admin Hosps, New York, 55-56 & Augusta, Ga, 56-63 & Battey State Hosp, Rome, 56-62; clin prof, Sch Med, Univ Louisville, 61-72. *Mem:* Radiol Soc NAm; AMA; fel Am Col Radiol. *Res:* Photofluorographic detection of silent gastric neoplasms; clinical radiological investigations of various body systems. *Mailing Add:* 3601 Burning Tree Ct Augusta GA 30907-9503

**WIGHT, HEWITT GLENN,** SYNTHETIC ORGANIC CHEMISTRY. *Current Pos:* PROF CHEM, CALIF POLYTECH STATE UNIV, SAN LUIS OBISPO, 52- *Personal Data:* b Murray, Utah, Feb 8, 21; m 43, 81, Azarm Ghahreman; c Judith, Michael, Marilyn & Ronald. *Educ:* Univ Utah, BS, 43; Univ Calif, PhD(chem), 55. *Mem:* Am Chem Soc. *Res:* Chemical education; organic syntheses; synthesis of potential pharmaceuticals. *Mailing Add:* Dept Chem Calif Polytech State Univ San Luis Obispo CA 93407

**WIGHT, JERALD ROSS,** RANGE SCIENCE. *Current Pos:* RANGE SCIENTIST, AGR RES SERV, USDA, 65- *Personal Data:* b Brigham City, Utah, Oct 5, 31; m 54, Mary Jo Chadwick; c Michael D, Mark E, Lora L (Knoll), Teresa A (Olsen), Tamara L (Pyfer), Janna D (Syle), Jerilyn K (Nyborg). *Educ:* Utah State Univ, BS, 53, MS, 59; Univ Wyo, PhD(range sci), 66. *Prof Exp:* Lab technician olericult, Univ Calif, 58-63. *Concurrent Pos:*

Affil prof, Univ Idaho. 84- *Mem:* Soil Conserv Soc Am; fel Soc Range Mgt. *Res:* Plant, soil, climate and animal relationships in range ecosystems, with emphasis on development and evaluation of rangeland simulation models. *Mailing Add:* 11864 Reutzel Boise ID 83709

**WIGHTMAN, ARTHUR STRONG,** MATHEMATICAL PHYSICS. *Current Pos:* from instr to prof, 49-71, Thomas D Jones prof math physics, 71-92, EMER PROF, PRINCETON UNIV, 92- *Personal Data:* b Rochester, NY, Mar 30, 22; m 77, Ludmilla Popova; c Robin L. *Educ:* Yale Univ, BA, 42; Princeton Univ, PhD(physics), 49. *Hon Degrees:* DSc, Swiss Fed Inst Technol, 69; Gottingen, 86. *Honors & Awards:* Dannie Heineman Prize in Math Physics, Am Phys Soc, 69. *Prof Exp:* Instr physics, Yale Univ, 43-44. *Concurrent Pos:* Nat Res Coun fel, Inst Theoret Physics, Copenhagen, 51-52; NSF fel, Copenhagen & Naples, 56-57; vis prof, Paris, 57, Inst Advan Study Sci, Bures-sur-Yvette, 63-64 & 68-69, Ecole Polytechnique, 77-78 & Univ Adelaide, Australia, 82. *Mem:* Nat Acad Sci; AAAS; Am Math Soc; Am Phys Soc; Fedn Am Sci (treas, 54-56); Royal Soc Arts & Sci. *Res:* Elementary particle physics; quantum field theory; mathematical physics; functional analysis. *Mailing Add:* Dept Physics Princeton Univ Box 708 Princeton NJ 08544

**WIGHTMAN, FRANK,** PLANT PHYSIOLOGY. *Current Pos:* RETIRED. *Personal Data:* b Padiham, Eng, Jan 22, 28; Can citizen; m 56; c 5. *Educ:* Univ Leeds, BSc, 48, PhD(plant physiol), 54. *Hon Degrees:* DSc, Univ Leeds, 81. *Prof Exp:* Sr sci officer plant physiol, Agr Res Coun Unit, Wye Col, Univ London, 52-58; Nat Res Coun Can fel, Nat Res Coun Lab, Univ Sask, Can, 58-59; from assoc prof to prof biol, Carleton Univ, 60-90, chmn dept, 68-71. *Concurrent Pos:* Nuffield Found vis fel, Univ Col, Univ London, 65-66; vis prof, Univ Lausanne, Switz, 66, Univ Calif, Santa Cruz, 74-75 & Commonwealth Sci & Indust Res Orgn Lab, Adelaide, Australia, 82-83. *Mem:* Can Soc Plant Physiol (pres, 79-80); Am Soc Plant Physiol; Brit Soc Exp Biol; Scand Soc Plant Physiol; fel Royal Soc Can. *Res:* Biosynthesis and physiological activity of indole and phenyl plant growth hormones; characterization of enzymes catalyzing aromatic amino acid metabolism; characterization of hormonal substances regulating flower formation and lateral root initiation. *Mailing Add:* 136 Leopolds Dr Ottawa ON K1V 7E3 Can

**WIGHTMAN, JAMES PINCKNEY,** COLLOID & SURFACE CHEMISTRY, ADHESION SCIENCE. *Current Pos:* from asst prof to prof chem, 62-87, ALUMNI DISTINGUISHED PROF, VA POLYTECH INST & STATE UNIV, 87- *Personal Data:* b Ashland, Va, May 14, 35; m 56, Juanita Kinsey; c Debra E, Sharon A, William H & James P Jr. *Educ:* Randolph-Macon Col, BS, 55; Lehigh Univ, MS, 58, PhD(chem), 60. *Honors & Awards:* Pub Serv Award, NASA, 86; Adhesives Award, Adhesives Age, 91; Adhesive & Sealant Coun Award, 93. *Prof Exp:* Res assoc fuel sci, Pa State Univ, 60-62. *Concurrent Pos:* Vis res prof, Univ Bristol, 75-76. *Mem:* Am Chem Soc; Sigma Xi; Adhesion Soc (pres, 88-90); Int Asn Colloid & Interface Scientists. *Res:* Thermodynamics of adhesion; electron spectroscopic chemical analysis of solids surfaces; surface chemistry focuses on the interaction of liquids with solid surfaces and on the characterization of those solids, applications include metal/polymer interfaces, carbon fiber/polymer matrix adhesion, and composite/composite bonding. *Mailing Add:* Dept Chem 0212 Va Polytech Inst State Univ Blacksburg VA 24061-0212

**WIGHTMAN, ROBERT HARLAN,** ORGANIC CHEMISTRY. *Current Pos:* asst prof, 65-69, ASSOC PROF ORG CHEM, CARLETON UNIV, 69- *Personal Data:* b Ottawa, Ont, Jan 24, 37; m 61; c 3. *Educ:* Univ NB, BSc, 58, PhD(org chem), 62. *Prof Exp:* Nat Res Coun Can overseas fel org chem, Imp Col, Univ London, 62-63; res assoc, Stanford Univ, 63-65. *Mem:* Am Chem Soc; Chem Inst Can. *Res:* New synthetic organic methods; syntheses of organic compounds of biological and theoretical interest. *Mailing Add:* Dept Chem Carleton Univ Ottawa ON K1S 5B6 Can

**WIGHTON, JOHN L(ATTA),** MECHANICAL ENGINEERING. *Current Pos:* RETIRED. *Personal Data:* b Vancouver, BC, June 15, 15. *Educ:* Univ BC, BA, 35, BASc, 44; Univ Mich, MSE, 52, PhD(mech eng), 55. *Prof Exp:* Design engr, Hudson Bay Mining & Smelting Co, Man, 44-47; dist engr, B F Sturtevant Co, Ont, 47-49; design engr, Consol Mining & Smelting Co, BC, 49-51; proj engr, Standard Oil Co, Ind, 55-58; dir labs mech eng, Univ BC, 58-67; dir labs, dept mech eng, Ahmadu Bello Univ, Nigeria, 67-69; dir eng labs, fac eng, Univ Regina, 69-82. *Concurrent Pos:* Lab consult, mech eng dept, Chulalongkorn Univ, Bangkok, Nat Polytech Sch, Ecuador, 74-75, Tehran Polytech, Iran, 76-77, Univ Americas, Puebla, Mex, 81 & Chulalongkorn Univ, Bangkok, 83. *Mem:* Am Soc Eng Educ; Sigma Xi. *Res:* Heating and ventilating; fluid dynamics; particle technology; laboratory management and development. *Mailing Add:* 14980 101A Ave Suite 311 Surrey BC V3R 0T1 Can

**WIGINGTON, RONALD L,** INFORMATION SYSTEMS. *Current Pos:* RETIRED. *Personal Data:* b Topeka, Kans, May 11, 32; m 51, Margaret E Willey; c Linda A, Carol L, David A & Brian K. *Educ:* Univ Kans, BS, 53, PhD(elec eng), 64; Univ Md, MS, 59; Harvard Bus Sch, AMP, 77. *Honors & Awards:* Nat Capitol Award, D C Coun Engrs & Archit Socs, 67. *Prof Exp:* Mem tech staff, Bell Tel Labs, Inc, 53-54; supvry electronic engr, Nat Security Agency, US Dept Defense, 54-65, sr engr, 65-68; dir res & develop, Chem Abstr Serv, Am Chem Soc, 68-84, dep exec dir Wash oper, 84-86, dir chem abstracts serv, 86-91, dir info technol, 91- *Concurrent Pos:* Lectr technol mgt, Am Univ, 67-68; mem, Task Group Comput Use, Int Coun Sci Unions, 68-77, Comt Data Sci & Technol & Comn Coord Bibliog Control, 75-; consult, Dept Defense, 68-; mem comput sci & eng bd, Nat Acad Sci, 69-72; adj assoc prof comput info sci, Ohio State Univ, 70-78, mem adv bd, Dept Comput Sci,

88-90; trustee, Online Comput Libr Ctr, 78-92, chmn bd, 84-87; mem bd dirs, Nat Fedn Abstracting & Indexing Serv, 79-84, pres, 92; mem, Nat Res Coun Panel, Off Stand Reference Data, Nat Bur Stand, 80-86. *Mem:* Inst Elec & Electronics Engrs; Am Chem Soc; Sigma Xi. *Res:* High speed instrumentation; transmission line theory; electronic devices, techniques for switching, storage of information; computer system organization; design evaluation; displays and man-machine communications; simulation; computerized information systems; research and development management; general management; information systems and networks. *Mailing Add:* 2470 Wibledon Rd Columbus OH 43220. *Fax:* 614-447-3767; *E-Mail:* rlw78@cas.org

**WIGINTON, DAN ALLEN,** GENE REGULATION & EXPRESSION, GENE STRUCTURE. *Current Pos:* res asst prof, 84-86, asst prof, 86-93, ASSOC PROF, UNIV CINCINNATI & CHILDREN'S HOSP RES FOUND, 93- *Personal Data:* b Coleman, Tex, Mar 12, 49; m 74, Diane Foye; c Allen, Erin & Amy. *Educ:* Abilene Christian Univ, BS, 72; Univ Tex, Austin, PhD(biochem), 78. *Prof Exp:* Fel, Univ Ky, 78-80; chemist, Vet Admin Hosp, San Antonio, Tex, 80-84. *Concurrent Pos:* Fel, Univ Tex Health Sci Ctr, 80-84; fac mem, develop biol prog, grad prog, Univ Cincinnati, 89- *Mem:* Am Soc Biochem & Molecular Biol. *Res:* Gene regulation related to human adenosine deaminase- enhancer, promoter, structure and interaction; relationship of adenosine deaminase and severe combined immunodeficiency disease and its treatment-mutations, expression, gene theory. *Mailing Add:* Children's Hosp Res Found Elland & Bethesda Aves CHRF 2032 Cincinnati OH 45229-3039

**WIGLE, ERNEST DOUGLAS,** MEDICINE, CARDIOLOGY. *Current Pos:* from asst prof to assoc prof, 66-72, PROF MED, UNIV TORONTO, 72- *Personal Data:* b Windsor, Ont, Oct 30, 28; m 58; c 5. *Educ:* Univ Toronto, MD, 53; FRCP(C), 58. *Prof Exp:* McLaughlin Found fel cardiol, Univ Toronto, 59-60; sr res assoc, Ont Heart Found, 63-66. *Concurrent Pos:* Dir cardiovasc unit, Toronto Gen Hosp, 64-72, dir div cardiol, 72-; fel coun clin cardiol, Am Heart Asn, 65- *Mem:* Fel Am Col Physicians; Asn Am Physicians; Am Soc Clin Invest; Am Fedn Clin Res; Can Soc Clin Invest. *Res:* Muscular subaortic stenosis, hemodynamics, pharmacology and electrocardiography; hemodynamics of acute valvular insufficiency; cardiomyopathy; ventricular aneurysm; heart catheterization; automated assessment of left ventricular function; ritral valve prolapse. *Mailing Add:* Gen Div Eaton N12-217 Toronto Hosp 200 Elizabeth St Toronto ON M5G 2C4 Can

**WIGLER, MICHAEL H,** MEDICAL GENETICS. *Current Pos:* HEAD, MAMMALIAN CELL GENETICS SECT, COLD SPRING HARBOR LAB, NY, 78- *Personal Data:* b New York, NY, Sept 3, 47. *Educ:* Princeton Univ, BA, 70; Rutgers Univ, MMS, 72; Columbia Univ, PhD(microbiol), 78. *Honors & Awards:* Pfizer Biomed Award, 85; Lifetime Res Prof Award, Am Chem Soc, 86; Drew Award in Biomed Res, Ciba-Geigy, 86; G H A Clowes Mem Award for Cancer Res, 91. *Prof Exp:* Staff assoc, Inst Cancer Res, Columbia Univ, 78. *Concurrent Pos:* Am Bus for Cancer res award, 82; outstanding investr award, NIH, 85; adj prof, Dept Genetics, Col Physicians & Surgeons, Columbia Univ, 88- *Mem:* Nat Acad Sci. *Res:* Mammalian cell genetics; cancer research; author of numerous publications. *Mailing Add:* Cold Spring Harbor Lab PO Box 100 Cold Spring Harbor NY 11724

**WIGLER, PAUL WILLIAM,** CANCER CHEMOTHERAPY, PHARMACEUTICAL CHEMISTRY. *Current Pos:* assoc prof res, 66-68, res prof, 68-78, PROF MED BIOL, MEM RES CTR, UNIV TENN, KNOXVILLE, 78- *Personal Data:* b New York, NY, Aug 26, 28; m 85, Frances K Patterson; c David, Stephen, Michael, Daniel, Anne (Sprague) & Carole (Patterson). *Educ:* Queens Col, NY, BS, 50; Brooklyn Col, MA, 52; Univ Calif, Berkeley, PhD(biochem), 58. *Prof Exp:* Jr res biochemist, Virus Lab, Univ Calif, Berkeley, 58; NIH chem fel, Univ Wis, 58-60; from asst prof to assoc prof, Sch Med, Univ Okla, 60-66. *Concurrent Pos:* Biochemist, Okla Med Res Found, 60-63, assoc mem, 63-66; Pub Health Serv res career develop award, 66. *Mem:* Am Soc Biol Chemists; Am Chem Soc. *Res:* Kinetics of cell membrane transport; reversal mechanisms in multidrug resistance of cancer cells. *Mailing Add:* Dept Med Biol Mem Res Ctr Univ Tenn Med Ctr Knoxville TN 37920. *Fax:* 423-544-9527

**WIGLEY, NEIL MARCHAND,** MATHEMATICAL ANALYSIS. *Current Pos:* assoc prof, 70-74, prof, 74-96, EMER PROF MATH, UNIV WINDSOR, 96- *Personal Data:* b Mt Vernon, Wash, Feb 16, 36; c 4. *Educ:* Univ Calif, Berkeley, BA, 59, PhD(math), 63. *Prof Exp:* Staff mem math, Los Alamos Sci Lab, 63-65; asst prof, Univ Ariz, 65-67; assoc prof, Univ NC, 67-68; fel, Alexander von Humboldt Found, Univ Bonn, 68-70. *Mem:* Am Math Soc. *Res:* Partial differential equations. *Mailing Add:* Dept Math Univ Windsor Windsor ON N9B 3P4 Can

**WIGNALL, GEORGE DENIS,** POLYMER PHYSICS, SMALL ANGLE SCATTERING. *Current Pos:* SR RES SCIENTIST POLYMER, STRUCT VIA SMALL-ANGLE SCATTERING, OAK RIDGE NAT LAB, 79- *Personal Data:* b Bradford, Eng, June 16, 41; m 70; c 2. *Educ:* Univ Sheffield, BS, 62, PhD(physics), 66. *Prof Exp:* Fel, Harwell Atomic Energy Ctr, 66-68, Calif Inst Technol, 68-69; lab mgr, Imp Chem Industs, Ltd, 69-79. *Mem:* Am Chem Soc; fel Am Phys Soc; Am Crystallog Asn. *Res:* Structure of synthetic polymers and blends including molecular configuration and domain structure; small angle x-ray and neutron scattering. *Mailing Add:* Solid State Div Bldg 7962 Oak Ridge Nat Lab PO Box X Oak Ridge TN 37831-6393. *E-Mail:* gdw@ornlstc

**WIGNER, EUGENE PAUL,** invariants, philosophical implications of physics; deceased, see previous edition for last biography

**WIGODSKY, HERMAN S,** BIOETHICS, EPIDEMIOLOGY. *Current Pos:* CLIN PROF PATH, HEALTH SCI CTR, UNIV TEX, 70- *Personal Data:* b Sioux City, Iowa, June 12, 15. *Educ:* Northwestern Univ, PhD(physiol), 40, MD, 41. *Mem:* AMA; Am Physiol Soc; Soc Exp Biol Med. *Mailing Add:* Dept Path Univ Tex Health Sci Ctr 7703 Floyd Curl Dr San Antonio TX 78284-7750. *Fax:* 210-567-6729

**WIGTON, ROBERT SPENCER,** MEDICINE. *Current Pos:* prof, 46-77, EMER PROF NEUROL & PSYCHIAT, COL MED, UNIV NEBR, OMAHA, 77- *Personal Data:* b Omaha, Nebr, Nov 1, 11; m 37; c 2. *Educ:* Univ Nebr, BSc, 32, MA & MD, 35. *Prof Exp:* Instr, Sch Med, Univ Pa, 38-42. *Concurrent Pos:* Fel neurol, Hosp Univ Pa, 37-40; resident, Pa Hosp, 40-42; consult, Union Pac RR, 53-77. *Mem:* AAAS; AMA; Am Psychiat Asn. *Res:* Clinical neuropsychiatry; neurophysiology in relation to behavior. *Mailing Add:* 601 S 38th Ave Omaha NE 68105-1103

**WIIG, ELISABETH HEMMERSAM,** SPEECH PATHOLOGY. *Current Pos:* PROF COMMUN DIS, BOSTON UNIV, 70-; KNOWLEDGE RES INST GROUP. *Personal Data:* b Esbjerg, Denmark, May 22, 35; US citizen; m 58; c 2. *Educ:* State Sem Enmdrupborg, Denmark, BS, 56; Case Western Res Univ, MA, 60, PhD(speech path), 67. *Prof Exp:* Instr phonetics, Univ Bergen, Norway, 60-64; asst prof speech path, Univ Mich, 68-70. *Concurrent Pos:* NIH fel, Univ Mich, 67-68. *Mem:* Am Am Speech & Hearing Asn; Coun Except Children; Acad Aphasia. *Res:* Language disorders and learning disabilities; acquired aphasia in adults; congenital language disorders in children. *Mailing Add:* 5211 Vicksburg Dr Arlington TX 76017-4941

**WIITA, PAUL JOSEPH,** ASTROPHYSICS, THEORETICAL PHYSICS. *Current Pos:* assoc prof physics, 86-93, PROF ASTRON, GA STATE UNIV, 93-, DIR GRAD STUDIES, 94- *Personal Data:* b Bronx, NY, Feb 18, 53; m 78, Brinda Umberkoman; c Arun & Neil. *Educ:* Cooper Union, NY, BS, 72; Princeton Univ, MA, 74, PhD(physics), 76. *Honors & Awards:* Compton lectr, Enrico Fermi Inst, Univ Chicago, 77. *Prof Exp:* Res asst physics, Princeton Univ, 75-76; res assoc, Enrico Fermi Inst, Univ Chicago, 76-79; asst prof astron, Univ Pa, 79-86. *Concurrent Pos:* Instr, Adler Planetarium, Chicago, 77; NSF-NATO fel, Inst Astron, Univ Cambridge, 77-78; vis fel, Copernicus Astron Ctr, Warsaw, 78 & Tata Inst Fundamental Res, India, 81, 82 & 85; vis prof, Indian Inst Sci, 86-87, Tata Inst Fund Res, India, 89, 90, 93 & 95. *Mem:* Am Phys Soc; Am Astron Soc; Royal Astron Soc; Int Astron Union. *Res:* Problems in theoretical astrophysics, including radio galaxies, quasars, relativistic beams, black holes, rotating stars, star formation and planetary system formation. *Mailing Add:* Dept Physics & Astron Ga State Univ Atlanta GA 30303-3083. *Fax:* 404-651-1389; *E-Mail:* wiita@chara.gsu.edu

**WIITALA, STEPHEN ALLEN,** ALGEBRA, COMPUTER SCIENCE. *Current Pos:* asst prof, 80-82, ASSOC PROF MATH, NORWICH UNIV, 82- *Personal Data:* b Vancouver, Wash, Oct 3, 46; m 68; c 1. *Educ:* Western Wash Univ, BAEd, 68, MA, 71; Dartmouth Col, PhD(math), 75. *Prof Exp:* Asst prof math, Nebr Wesleyan Univ, 75-80. *Mem:* Am Math Soc; Math Asn Am. *Res:* Quadratic forms on vector spaces of characteristic two; representation theory of finite groups; mathematics and computer science education. *Mailing Add:* Dept Sci Norwich Univ Northfield VT 05663

**WIITANEN, WAYNE ALFRED,** BIONICS, COMPUTER SCIENCES. *Current Pos:* STAFF RES SCIENTIST, COMPUT SCI DEPT, GEN MOTORS RES LABS, 80- *Personal Data:* b Detroit, Mich, May 6, 35; m 73; c 3. *Educ:* Harvard Univ, AB, 68, MA, 69, PhD(biol), 72. *Prof Exp:* Consult comput sci, 67-68; vpres, Mgt Eng Inc, 69-71; asst prof biol, Univ Ore, 71-77, asst prof comput sci, 73-77, assoc prof biol, 77-80, interim dir univ comput, 77-80. *Mem:* AAAS. *Res:* Applications of computers and mathematics to biological problems with special emphasis on the mammalian nervous system; dynamical biological systems simulation; neural networks. *Mailing Add:* 293 Hiscock St Ann Arbor MI 48103

**WIJNEN, JOSEPH M H,** PHYSICAL CHEMISTRY, PHOTOCHEMISTRY. *Current Pos:* RETIRED. *Personal Data:* b Wittem, Neth, Sept 22, 20; US citizen; m 67; c 2. *Educ:* Cath Univ Louvain, Lic Sci, 46, Dr Sci(chem), 48. *Prof Exp:* Lectr chem, Cath Univ Louvain, 48-49; Nat Res Coun Can fel photochem, 49-51; res assoc, NY Univ, 51-53; Nat Res Coun Can res officer, 53-55; res assoc chem, Celanese Corp Am, 55-58; sr fel photochem, Mellon Inst, 58-63; prof chem, Hunter Col, 63-91, chmn dept, 81-83 & 85-88, actg assoc provost, 88-91. *Concurrent Pos:* Consult, US Bur Mines, Pittsburgh, Pa, 61-63; NSF res grants, 67-69 & 70-72; vis prof, Univ Bonn, 69-70, Univ Amsterdam, 76-77 & Algerian Petrol Inst, 83-84. *Mem:* Am Chem Soc; Nat Combustion Inst; fel Am Inst Chemists. *Res:* Primary processes in photochemical reactions; free radical reactions; kinetics of free radical induced polymerization reactions. *Mailing Add:* 608 Wyndham Rd Teaneck NJ 07666

**WIJSMAN, ELLEN MARIE,** STATISTICAL GENETICS, HUMAN GENETICS. *Current Pos:* RES ASSOC PROF MED GENETICS & BIOSTATIST, UNIV WASH, 87- *Personal Data:* b Oakland, Calif, Apr 19, 54; m 80, Ethan Merritt; c Loren. *Educ:* Mich State Univ, BS, 75; Univ Wis-Madison, PhD(genetics), 81. *Prof Exp:* Fel, Stanford Univ, 81-84, res assoc, 84-87. *Concurrent Pos:* Consult DNA forensic anal, 88-; supvry comt, Collab Studies Genetics of Asthma, NIH, 92- *Mem:* Genetical Soc NAm; Am Soc Human Genetics; Biometric Soc; Int Soc Genetic Epidemiol. *Res:* Methods and applications of statist genetics to human disorders; genetics of Alzheimers disease, Werners syndrome, lipid disorders; human population genetics. *Mailing Add:* 5719 Ann Arbor Ave NE Seattle WA 98105. *E-Mail:* wijsman@u.washington.edu

**WIJSMAN, ROBERT ARTHUR,** MATHEMATICAL STATISTICS. *Current Pos:* from asst prof to assoc prof, 57-65, prof statist, 65-90, EMER PROF, UNIV ILL, URBANA, 90- *Personal Data:* b Hague, Neth, Aug 20, 20; US citizen; m 53; c 3. *Educ:* Delft Inst Technol, Neth, Ir, 45; Univ Calif, PhD(physics), 52. *Prof Exp:* Lectr med physics, Univ Calif, 52-53, instr math, 53-54, res statistician, 54-55, lectr statist & pub health, 55-56, actg asst prof statist, 56-57. *Concurrent Pos:* Vis prof, Columbia Univ, 67-68; vis scholar Univ Wash, 94- *Mem:* Inst Math Statist; Am Math Soc; Am Statist Asn. *Res:* Sequential and multivariate analysis. *Mailing Add:* Dept Statist Univ Washington Seattle WA 98195

**WIKEL, STEPHEN KENNETH,** PARASITOLOGY, INFECTIOUS DISEASES. *Current Pos:* PROF ENTOM & ENDOWED CHAIR AGR BIOTECHNOL, OKLA STATE UNIV, 91- *Personal Data:* b Apr 11, 45; m 94. *Educ:* Univ Sask, Can, PhD(immunol), 77. *Honors & Awards:* Fac Res Award, Sigma Xi. *Prof Exp:* Prof microbiol & immunol, Sch Med, Univ NDak, 83-91, Chester Fritz distinguished profG, 87-91. *Concurrent Pos:* Adj prof microbiol & molecular genetics, Okla State Univ. *Mem:* Sigma Xi; Am Asn Immunologists; Am Soc Parasitologists, Soc; Jector Ecologists. *Res:* Immunoparasitology, immunology of arthropod nector-animal host-pathogen interactions. *Mailing Add:* Dept Entom 127 Nobles Res Ctr Stillwater OK 74078-0001. *Fax:* 405-744-6954

**WIKJORD, ALFRED GEORGE,** ENVIRONMENTAL IMPACT ANALYSES, WASTE MANAGEMENT. *Current Pos:* res officer, Analytical Sci Br, 70-80, head, Nuclear Waste Immobilization Sect, 80-86, MGR ENVIRON & SAFETY ASSESSMENT BR, WHITESHELL LABS, ATOMIC ENERGY CAN LTD, 86- *Personal Data:* b Flin Flon, Man, July 15, 43; m 68, Margaret Tarr; c 2. *Educ:* Univ Man, BSc, 64, MSc, 65; McGill Univ, PhD(chem), 69. *Prof Exp:* NATO sci fel, Strasbourg Macromolecular Res Ctr, France, 69-70. *Mem:* Chem Inst Can; Can Nuclear Soc; Soc Risk Analysis; Can Radiation Protection Asn. *Res:* Chemistry of nuclear reactors; heavy water production; management of nuclear wastes; environmental impact assessment of waste disposal. *Mailing Add:* AECL Whiteshell Lab Pinawa MB R0E 1L0 Can. *Fax:* 204-753-2455

**WIKMAN-COFFELT, JOAN,** BIOCHEMICAL CARDIOLOGY. *Current Pos:* RETIRED. *Personal Data:* b Chicago, Ill, June 9, 29; m 70, Robert. *Educ:* Alverno Col, Milwaukee, BS, 59; St Mary's Col, Winona, Minn, MS, 65; St Louis Univ, PhD(biochem), 69. *Prof Exp:* Instr, St Mary's Col, Winona, Minn, 62-63; teaching asst, St Louis Univ, 64-68; fel res, Baylor Col Med, 68-70; asst prof biochem, Univ Okla Med Sch, 70-72; asst prof biol chem, Univ Calif Med Sch, Davis, 72-77, asst res biochemist, 77-80, assoc res biochemist, Cardiovasc Res Inst & Dept Med, 80-96, prof cardiol, 89-96. *Concurrent Pos:* NIH res fel, Baylor Univ, 68-70; NIH grant, Centro Mex & Univ Mex, 70-72; co-dir & coordr, res proj, NIH, 72-77; career develop award, 78-85. *Mem:* AAAS; Am Physiol Soc; Am Col Cardiol; Am Chem Soc; Sigma Xi; Am Heart Asn. *Res:* Preservation of the heart for transplantation; long-term preservation of organs for transplantation; awarded two patents; intracellular calcium in the beating heart. *Mailing Add:* 1610 Redwood Lane Davis CA 95616. *Fax:* 530-756-5290

**WIKSWO, JOHN PETER, JR,** BIOPHYSICS, MEDICAL PHYSICS. *Current Pos:* from asst prof to assoc prof, 77-88, PROF PHYSICS, VANDERBILT UNIV, 88-, A B LEARNED PROF LIVING STATE PHYSICS, 91- *Personal Data:* b Lynchburg, Va, Oct 6, 49; m 70, Julia L Knopp; c Matthew & Sarah. *Educ:* Univ Va, BA, 70; Stanford Univ, MS, 73, PhD(physics), 75. *Honors & Awards:* IR-100 Award, 84. *Prof Exp:* Res fel cardiol, Med Sch, Stanford Univ, 75-77. *Concurrent Pos:* Res fel, Bay Area Heart Res Comt, 75-77; Alfred P Sloan res fel, 80-82; John Simon Guggenheim fel, 92-93. *Mem:* Am Phys Soc; Am Heart Asn; Biophys Soc; Inst Elec & Electronics Engrs; Sigma Xi; Am Asn Physicis. *Res:* Application of electric and magnetic measurements and electromagnetic theory to study propagation of electrical activity in cardiac and smooth muscle; development of instrumentation and analysis techniques for biomagnetism, electrophysiology and non-destructive testing. *Mailing Add:* Dept Physics & Astron Vanderbilt Univ Box 1807 Sta B Nashville TN 37235. *Fax:* 615-322-4977; *E-Mail:* wikswojp@ctrvax.vanderbilt.edu

**WIKTOROWICZ, JOHN EDWARD,** INSTRUMENTATION. *Current Pos:* scientist, 89-90, STAFF SCIENTIST & GROUP LEADER BIOSEPARATIONS, APPL BIOSYSTS, INC, 90- *Personal Data:* b Nairobi, Kenya, Dec 23, 49; US citizen; m 72, Michelle Zgonina; c Alexis M, Sloane J & Conner J. *Educ:* Ill Inst Technol, BS, 74; Univ Tex, Galveston, PhD(human genetics & biol chem), 78. *Honors & Awards:* Nat March of Dimes Merit Award, 78. *Prof Exp:* Res fel, Calif Inst Technol, 78-81; res assoc, Scripps Clin & Res Inst, 81-82; asst prof biochem, Va Polytech Inst & State Univ, 82-89. *Concurrent Pos:* Consult, Automated Dynamics Corp, 82-85 & Unigen, 89. *Mem:* Am Soc Biochem & Molecular Biol; Protein Soc. *Res:* Protein structure-function relationships; separation and analytical chemistry; biochemical analyses; capillary electrophoresis. *Mailing Add:* Perkin Elmer Corp 850 Lincoln Center Dr Foster City CA 94404-1128

**WIKUM, DOUGLAS ARNOLD,** ECOLOGY, BIOLOGY. *Current Pos:* assoc prof, 76-80, PROF BIOL, UNIV WIS, STOUT, 80- *Personal Data:* b Stoughton, Wis, Oct 3, 33; m 58; c 4. *Educ:* Univ Wis, Stevens Point, BS, 61, Univ SDak, MA, 65; Univ NDak, PhD(biol), 72. *Prof Exp:* Prof biol, Univ Wis, Stout, 66-74; ecologist, Stone & Webster Eng Corp, Boston, 74-76. *Concurrent Pos:* Consult ecologist, NUS Corp, Pittsburgh, Pa, 73; res, US Forest Serv, 7-81; co-investr, ELF Commun Syst Ecol Monitoring Prog Wetland Studies, 83-89; investr, Water Qual Assessment Fresh-Water Cult Atlantic Salmon, 88-89. *Mem:* Am Inst Biol Sci; Ecol Soc Am; Sigma Xi. *Res:* Chemical and physical properties of soils; plant community structure; wetlands; black spruce growth; waste water disposal in bog ecosystems. *Mailing Add:* 616 Oak Ridge Ct Menomonie WI 54751

**WILANSKY, ALBERT,** MATHEMATICS. *Current Pos:* RETIRED. *Personal Data:* b St John's, Nfld, Sept 13, 21; nat US; m 69, Rose Sherman; c Eleanor, Kathryn, Laura, Leslie & Carole. *Educ:* Dalhousie Univ, MA, 44; Brown Univ, PhD(math), 47. *Honors & Awards:* Ford Prize, Math Asn Am, 69. *Prof Exp:* Demonstr physics, Dalhousie Univ, 42-44; instr math, Brown Univ, 46-48; from asst prof to prof, Lehigh Univ, 48-78, univ distinguished prof math, 78-92. *Concurrent Pos:* Consult, Frankford Arsenal, 57-58; Fulbright vis prof, Reading Univ, 72-73, London Univ, 73, Tel Aviv Univ, 81, Univ Berne, Switz, 81. *Mem:* Math Asn Am. *Res:* Pure mathematics; analysis; summability; linear topological space; Banach algebra; functional analysis. *Mailing Add:* Dept Math Lehigh Univ Bethlehem PA 18015

**WILBARGER, EDWARD STANLEY, JR,** PHYSICS, FLUIDS. *Current Pos:* RETIRED. *Personal Data:* b Billings, Mont, Feb 21, 31; m 59; c 2. *Educ:* Va Mil Inst, BS, 52; US Naval Postgrad Sch, MS, 56, Univ Calif, Santa Barbara, PhD, 80. *Prof Exp:* Chief, Indust Hyg Sect, Off Surgeon Gen, US Army, 56-58; engr physicist, Proj Res Aviation Med, US Naval Med Res Inst, 58-59; engr physicist, Bioastronaut Res Unit, Ord Missile Command, US Army, Redstone Arsenal, 59, chief inspections, Health & Safety Br, Off Chief Engrs, 59-60; head bioinstrumentation group, Gen Motors Corp, 60-62, sr res physicist, Aerospace Opers Dept, AC Electronics Defense Res Labs, 62-71, sr res physicist, 71-75, head anal & design, Delco Electronics Div, 75-83, mgr, Aerophysics Range Facil, Aerophys Dept, Delco Systs Opers, 83-88. *Concurrent Pos:* Lectr fluid mech & heat transfer, Univ Calif, Santa Barbara, 79-81 & 88; mem, Nat Res Coun, Nat Acad Sci, 86-; res & eng consult, 88-. *Mem:* Sigma Xi; Am Acad Mech; NY Acad Sci. *Res:* Control engineering; measurement methods; physiological response to stress; design and fabrication of control systems; mobility systems analysis for off-road vehicles; analysis and design of auto safety systems; computational fluid dynamics; hypervelocity interior ballistics and fluid dynamics; hypervelocity impact. *Mailing Add:* 3830 Center Ave Santa Barbara CA 93110

**WILBER, CHARLES GRADY,** PHYSIOLOGY. *Current Pos:* prof zool, 67-86, DIR FORENSIC SCI LAB, COLO STATE UNIV, 74- *Personal Data:* b Waukesha, Wis, June 18, 16; m 52; c Maureen, Charles, Michael, Thomas (deceased), Kathleen, Aileen & John. *Educ:* Marquette Univ, BSc, 38; Johns Hopkins Univ, MA, 41, PhD(gen physiol), 42. *Prof Exp:* Lab asst zool, Marquette Univ, 38-39; asst, Johns Hopkins Univ, 40-42; from instr to assoc prof physiol & div biol labs, St Louis Univ, 42-52; asst prof, Fordham Univ, 46-49; chief animal ecol br, Chem Corps Med Labs, US Army Chem Ctr, Md, 52-56, comp physiol br, Chem Res & Develop Labs, 56-60; prof physiol & dean, Grad Sch, Kent State Univ, 61-64; dir marine labs & prof, Univ Del, 64-67. *Concurrent Pos:* Leader, Fordham Arctic Exped, 48; assoc, Univ Pa, 53-60; prof lectr, Loyola Col, 57-60; mem corp, Marine Biol Lab, Woods Hole; mem panel environ physiol, US Dept Army; mem life sci comt, Nat Acad Sci-Air Res & Develop Command; consult, USPHS; dep coroner, Larimer Co, Colo; dir, Ecol Consults, Inc, 72-74; toxicologist, Thorne Ecol Inst, 72-74; Wellcome vis prof basic med sci, Ohio Med Sch, 84-85; distinguished scholar criminal justice, Albany State Col, Ga, 93. *Mem:* Fel Am Acad Forensic Sci; Am Physiol Soc; fel NY Acad Sci; Sigma Xi. *Res:* Biochemistry of body fluids; chemistry of metabolism; comparative aspects of environmental physiology; climatic adaption; forensic biology; wound ballistics; environmental quality; environmental pathology; comparative toxicology; oceanography; application of science to the needs of the law; wound ballistics and environmental and forensic toxicology; biological impact of noxious ambient factors on Homo Sapiens; organophosphorous toxicology, eg nerve gas. *Mailing Add:* 900 Edwards Ft Collins CO 80524. *Fax:* 970-491-0649

**WILBER, DAVID JAMES,** CARDIOLOGY, ELECTROPHYSIOLOGY. *Current Pos:* PROF MED & DIR CLIN ELECTROPHYSIOL, UNIV CHICAGO HOSPS, 94- *Personal Data:* b Ft Atkinson, Wis, Apr 1, 51; m 92, Sandra Reynertson. *Educ:* Univ Wis, BS, 73; Northwestern Univ, MD, 77. *Prof Exp:* Intern internal med, Northwestern Med Sch, 77-78, resident, 78-80, instr, 80-81; fel cardiol, Univ Mich Hosp, 82-84; assoc med & cardiol, Harvard Med Sch, 84-86; asst prof med, Med Ctr, Loyola Univ, 86-90, assoc prof, 90-94. *Concurrent Pos:* NIH training grant, 84, Am Heart Asn, 92-94. *Mem:* Fel NAm Soc Pacing & Electrophysiol; fel Am Col Cardiol; fel Am Heart Asn; Am Fedn Clin Res; NY Acad Sci; Cardiac Electrophysiol Soc. *Res:* Mechanism of clinical arrhythmias; catheter ablation; post infarction risk stratification. *Mailing Add:* Univ Chicago Hosps Sect Cardiol 5758 S Maryland MC 9024 Chicago IL 60637

**WILBER, JOE CASLEY, JR,** CHEMISTRY, SCIENCE EDUCATION. *Current Pos:* assoc prof, 73-80, PROF CHEM, PAUL D CAMP COMMUNITY COL, 80- *Personal Data:* b Jonesboro, Ark, Feb 28, 29; m 51. *Educ:* Memphis State Col, BS, 50, MA, 53; Univ Ga, EdD, 61. *Prof Exp:* Teacher pub schs, Tenn, 50-51 & 53-56; teacher & chmn Dept Sci, pub sch, Ga, 56-59; from asst prof to assoc prof chem, Ga Southern Col, 60-70; teacher chem & chmn Dept Sci, Wingate Col, 70-73. *Mem:* AAAS. *Res:* General chemistry; qualitative analysis, a non-sulfide scheme. *Mailing Add:* 22219 Deer Lane Franklin VA 23851

**WILBER, LAURA ANN,** AUDIOLOGY, SPEECH PATHOLOGY. *Current Pos:* PROF AUDIOL, NORTHWESTERN UNIV, EVANSTON, ILL, 78- *Personal Data:* b Memphis, Tenn, May 26, 34. *Educ:* Univ Southern Miss, BS, 55; Gallaudet Col, MS, 58; Northwestern Univ, PhD(audiol), 64. *Prof Exp:* Teacher hard of hearing & deaf, McKinley Elem Sch, Bakersfield, Calif, 55-57; speech therapist & coordr spec educ, US Army Dependent Sch Syst, Heidelberg, Ger, 57-61; res asst audiol, Northwestern Univ, 61-64; asst res audiologist, Univ Calif, Los Angeles, 64-70; asst prof, Albert Einstein Col Med, 70-75, dir hearing & speech serv, 75-76, assoc prof rehab med, 71-77. *Concurrent Pos:* Spec instr, Calif State Col, Los Angeles & Univ Southern Calif, 65-70; dir audiol clin, Hosp, Univ Calif, Los Angeles, 68-69; chmn, Clin Sch-Coun NY, 72-73; mem, Dir Hosp Speech & Hearing, Prog Asn & Soc Ear, Nose & Throat Advan in Children; US rep, Int Stand Orgn; mem, Am Nat Stand Inst; adj assoc prof, City Univ New York, 74-76; actg chmn commun dis, Northwestern Univ, 81. *Mem:* Fel Am Speech & Hearing Asn; fel Acoust Soc Am; Am Auditory Soc; Am Acad Audiol. *Mailing Add:* Dept Commun Sci Northwestern Univ 633 Clark St Evanston IL 60208-0001

**WILBERGER, JAMES ELDRIDGE,** HEAD INJURY. *Current Pos:* CLIN ASSOC PROF NEUROSURG, WVA UNIV, 87-; ASSOC PROF SURG-NEUROSURG, MED COL PA, 88- *Personal Data:* b Richmond, Va, May 5, 52. *Educ:* Univ Richmond, BA, 74; Med Col Va, MD, 78. *Concurrent Pos:* Dir neurosurg, Allegheny Gen Hosp, 84-; consult neurosurg, New Medico Rehab Facil, 86-, Harmcoville Rehab Inst, 86- *Mem:* Am Asn Neurol Surgeons; Am Col Sports Med; Nat Head Injury Found. *Res:* Neurotransmitted in head injury, studying the derangement in neurotransmitted following severe head injury and correlating with clinical outcome. *Mailing Add:* Allegheny Gen Hosp 320 E N Ave Pittsburgh PA 15212-4772

**WILBORN, WALTER HARRISON,** HUMAN ANATOMY. *Current Pos:* assoc prof, 73-75, PROF ANAT, COL MED, UNIV S ALA, & DIR EM CTR, 76- *Personal Data:* b Arbyrd, Mo, May 20, 35; m; c 3. *Educ:* Harding Col, BA, 57; St Louis Univ, MS, 62; Univ Tenn, PhD(anat), 67. *Prof Exp:* From asst prof to assoc prof anat, Med Ctr, Univ Ala, Birmingham, 67-73. *Concurrent Pos:* NIH & others res grants, 67- *Mem:* Am Asn Anat; Am Soc Cell Biol; Histochem Soc; Am Asn Path. *Res:* Ultrastructure and cytochemistry; cutaneous pathology; secretory mechanisms; reproductive biology. *Mailing Add:* Struct Res Ctr 120 Novatan Rd Mobile AL 33608. *Fax:* 334-649-9752

**WILBRAHAM, ANTONY CHARLES,** HAZARDOUS WASTE MANAGEMENT. *Current Pos:* from asst prof to prof, 68-93, EMER PROF CHEM, SOUTHERN ILL UNIV, EDWARDSVILLE, 93- *Personal Data:* b Chester, Eng, July 26, 36; m 65; c 1. *Educ:* Carlett Park Col, Eng, cert chem & physics, 59; Royal Soc Chem, grad chem, 62, res dipl chem, 65, FRSC, 72. *Prof Exp:* Analytical technician chem, Shell Refining Co, Eng, 53-60; vis asst prof, Eckerd Col, 67-68. *Concurrent Pos:* Res fel chem, Univ Manchester, 73-74; vis scientist, Environ Safety Group, Harwell, Eng, 84. *Mem:* Fel Royal Soc Chem; Am Chem Soc. *Res:* Chemical hazardous waste disposal methods. *Mailing Add:* Dept Chem Southern Ill Univ Edwardsville IL 62026-1002

**WILBUR, DANIEL SCOTT,** RADIOPHARMACEUTICAL DEVELOPMENT, NUCLEAR MEDICINE. *Current Pos:* ASSOC PROF, UNIV WASH, 90- *Personal Data:* b Bath, NY, Mar 18, 50; m 74; c 1. *Educ:* Portland State Univ, BS, 73; Univ Calif, Irvine, PhD(chem), 78. *Prof Exp:* Mem res staff, Los Alamos Nat Lab, 78-84; head, Radiochem Sect, Neorx Corp, 84-86, dir, Radiopharmaceut Chem, 86-90. *Concurrent Pos:* Adj prof, Chem Dept, Univ NMex, 81-82. *Mem:* Am Chem Soc; Soc Nuclear Med; Am Asn Cancer Res. *Res:* Development of new radiopharmaceuticals, including design and synthesis of potential radiopharmaceuticals with concurrent studies involving new radiolabeling techniques; development of radiolabeled monoclonal antibodies for tumor diagnosis and treatment. *Mailing Add:* 2121 N 35th Box 358750 Seattle WA 98103-9103

**WILBUR, DAVID WESLEY,** BIOPHYSICS, MEDICINE. *Current Pos:* MEM, MED ONCOL, DEPT INTERNAL MED, LOMA LINDA UNIV, 76-; CHIEF ONCOL & HEMAT SECT, PETTIS MEM VET HOSP, LOMA LINDA, 80- *Personal Data:* b Hinsdale, Ill, Dec 15, 37; m 68; c 4. *Educ:* Pac Union Col, BA, 61; Univ Calif, Berkeley, PhD(biophys), 65; Loma Linda Univ, MD, 71; Am Bd Internal Med, cert, 75. *Prof Exp:* Biophysicist, Lawrence Radiation Lab, Univ Calif, 65-67; asst prof physiol & biophys, Sch Med, Loma Linda Univ, 67-69, med intern, 71-72, med resident, 72-74, res assoc biomath, 69-74; Am Cancer Soc med oncol clin fel, Roswell Park Mem Inst, 74-76. *Concurrent Pos:* Donner fel, 61-62. *Mem:* Am Col Physicians; Am Soc Clin Oncol; Sigma Xi; AMA. *Res:* Cancer chemotherapy; management of infection in neutropenic patients; role of immunology in cancer. *Mailing Add:* PO Box 291 Loma Linda CA 92354-0291

**WILBUR, DONALD LEE,** NEUROENDOCRINOLOGY. *Current Pos:* ASSOC PROF ANAT, MED UNIV SC, 76- *Personal Data:* b Chicago, Ill, Apr 28, 42; c 2. *Educ:* Ind State Univ, BS, 68, MA, 70; Med Univ SC, PhD(anat), 74. *Prof Exp:* Asst prof anat, Sch Med, Tex Tech Univ, 74-76. *Concurrent Pos:* Consult, Environ Protection Agency, 78- *Mem:* Am Asn Anatomists; Histochem Soc; Sigma Xi. *Res:* Electron microscopic, immunocytochemical studies of the pituitary gland and circumventricular organs, correlated with radioimmunoassayable levels of circulating hormones; mechanisms of hormone synthesis and release. *Mailing Add:* Dept Anat Med Univ SC 171 Ashley Ave Charleston SC 29425

**WILBUR, DWIGHT LOCKE,** gastroenterology; deceased, see previous edition for last biography

**WILBUR, HENRY MILES,** ZOOLOGY, ECOLOGY. *Current Pos:* B F D RUNK PROF BIOL, PROF ENVIRON SCI & DIR, MOUNTAIN LAKE BIOL STA, UNIV VA, 91- *Personal Data:* b Bridgeport, Conn, Jan 25, 44; m 67, 81, Rebecca Burchell; c 3. *Educ:* Duke Univ, BS, 66; Univ Mich, Ann Arbor, PhD(zool), 71. *Honors & Awards:* Stoye Award, Am Soc Ichthyol & Herpet, 70; MacArthur Award, Ecol Soc Am, 95. *Prof Exp:* Jr fel, Univ Mich Soc Fels, Div Reptiles & Amphibians, Mus Zool, Univ Mich, Ann Arbor,

71-73; from asst prof to assoc prof, Duke Univ, 73-82, prof zool & chmn, 82-91. *Concurrent Pos:* NSF grad fel, 67-69; Edwin S George scholar, Edwin S George Res, Mich, 68-69. *Mem:* AAAS; Ecol Soc Am; Soc Study Evolution; Brit Ecol Soc; Am Soc Ichthyol & Herpet; Am Soc Naturalists (pres, 96); Soc Study Reptiles & Amphibians. *Res:* Evolutionary ecology; evolution of species interactions and life histories; conservation biology. *Mailing Add:* Dept Biol Gilmer Jall Univ Va Charlottesville VA 22903-2477. *Fax:* 804-982-5626; *E-Mail:* hmw3q@virginia.edu

**WILBUR, JAMES MYERS, JR,** ORGANIC CHEMISTRY. *Current Pos:* assoc prof, 63-66, PROF CHEM, SOUTHWEST MO STATE UNIV, 66- *Personal Data:* b Philadelphia, Pa, Oct 31, 29; m 60; c 3. *Educ:* Muhlenberg Col, BS, 51; Univ Pa, PhD, 59. *Prof Exp:* Res chemist, J T Baker Chem Co, NJ, 51-53; NIH fel cancer chemother, Univ Minn, 58-60; res chemist, E I du Pont de Nemours & Co, 60-62; fel, Univ Ariz, 62-63. *Mem:* Am Chem Soc. *Res:* Medicinal chemistry; cancer chemotherapy; organic mechanisms; polymers. *Mailing Add:* 3636 S Britian Ave Springfield MO 65807-8678

**WILBUR, KARL MILTON,** physiology; deceased, see previous edition for last biography

**WILBUR, L(ESLIE) C(LIFFORD),** MECHANICAL ENGINEERING. *Current Pos:* from assoc prof to prof, 57-86, dir, Nuclear Reactor Facil, 59-86, EMER PROF MECH ENG, WORCESTER POLYTECH INST, 86-, EMER CHMN, NUCLEAR REACTOR FACIL, 86- *Personal Data:* b Johnston, RI, May 12, 24; m 50, Gertrude Widmer; c Clifford, Kenneth, Ted & Christopher. *Educ:* Univ RI, BS, 48; Stevens Inst Technol, MS, 49. *Prof Exp:* From instr to asst prof mech eng, Duke Univ, 49-57. *Mem:* Fel Am Soc Mech Engrs. *Res:* Nuclear reactor technology; neutron activation analysis. *Mailing Add:* 94 Parkway N Brewer ME 04412

**WILBUR, LYMAN D,** RIVER DIVERSION, CONSTRUCTION. *Current Pos:* RETIRED. *Personal Data:* b Los Angeles, Calif; m 25, 85, Pauline Jordan; c Olive G Waugh. *Educ:* Stanford Univ, BA, 21. *Hon Degrees:* LLD, Col Idaho, 62; DSc, Univ Idaho, 67. *Prof Exp:* Draftsman & asst eng field eng, City San Francisco, 21-24; designer, Merced Irrig Dist, 24-26; design eng, East Bay Munic Utility Dist, 26-29; asst to chief consult eng, Mid Asia Water Econ Serv, 29-31; dist engr eng, Morrison-Knudsen Co, Inc, 32-39, div engr, 40-42, dist mgr, 42-47, chief eng, 47-52, vpres eng, 53-60, vpres foreign oper, 60-65, vpres, 65-70; consult, 71-77. *Concurrent Pos:* Exec vpres, pres & chmn, Int Eng Co, Inc, Div Morrison-Knudsen Co, Inc, 56-70, construct mgr, 39-41, resident partner, 65-66. *Mem:* Nat Acad Eng; hon mem Am Soc Civil Engrs; Nat Soc Prof Engrs; Soc Am Mil Engrs. *Mailing Add:* 4502 Hillcest Dr Boise ID 83705-2857

**WILBUR, PAUL JAMES,** MECHANICAL ENGINEERING. *Current Pos:* From asst prof to assoc prof, 68-75, PROF MECH ENG, COLO STATE UNIV, 75- *Personal Data:* b Ogden, Utah, Nov 8, 37; m 60; Twyla A Beck; c Wendy & Dagny. *Educ:* Univ Utah, BS, 60; Princeton Univ, PhD(aeronaut & mech sci), 68. *Concurrent Pos:* Nuclear Power engr, US AEC. *Mem:* Am Soc Mech Engrs; Am Inst Aeronaut & Astronaut. *Res:* Electric propulsion in space applications; ion implantation. *Mailing Add:* 1500 Teakwood Ct Ft Collins CO 80525

**WILBUR, RICHARD SLOAN,** MEDICINE. *Current Pos:* CHIEF EXEC OFFICER & CHMN BD, INST CLIN INFO, 94- *Personal Data:* b Boston, Mass, Apr 8, 24; m 51; c 3. *Educ:* Stanford Univ, BA, 43, MD, 46; John Marshall Law Sch, JD, 90. *Prof Exp:* Intern, San Francisco Co Hosp, 46-47; resident, Stanford Med Sch, 49-51 & Univ Pa Hosp, 51-52; mem staff, Palo Alto Med Clin, 52-69; dep exec vpres, AMA, Chicago, 69-71 & 73-74; asst secy defense health & environ, 71-73; sr vpres, Baxter Travenol Labs, Inc, Deerfield, Ill, 74-76; exec vpres, Coun Med Specialty Socs, 76-92; pres & chief exec officer, Medic Alert Found US, 92-94. *Concurrent Pos:* Asst clin prof med, Med Sch, Stanford Univ, 52-69 & Med Sch, Georgetown Univ, 71-; bd dirs, Palo Alto Med Res Found, 60-69; chief, Med Staff, Palo Alto Hosp, 63-64; pres, Santa Clara Co Med Soc, 65; mem bd trustees, Am Soc Internal Med, 66-69; chmn coun, Calif Med Asn, 68-69; mem bd gov, Am Red Cross, 71-73 & Am Col Legal Med, 96; chmn bd dirs, Med Alert US, 83-84, Med Alert Int, 86-92; bd dir, Nat Health Coun, 93-94, Am Electrodiag Med, 93- *Mem:* Inst Med-Nat Acad Sci; hon fel Int Col Dent; fel Am Col Physicians; Am Gastroenterol Asn; fel Am Col Physician Execs (pres, 88-89); fel Am Col Legal Med; Soc Med Admin; Am Soc Gastrointestinal Endoscopy; AMA; Soc Med Consults Armed Forces. *Mailing Add:* Inst Clin Info 207 Westminister Suite 201 Lake Forest IL 60045

**WILBUR, ROBERT DANIEL,** AGRICULTURAL RESEARCH MANAGEMENT, PLANT PROTECTION. *Current Pos:* RETIRED. *Personal Data:* b Glendale, Calif, May 7, 31; m 52; c 3. *Educ:* Calif State Polytech Col, BS, 54; Iowa State Univ, PhD(animal nutrit, bact), 59. *Prof Exp:* Asst nutrit & bact, Iowa State Univ, 54-59, fel, 59; res nutritionist, Am Cyanamid Co, 59-67, group leader nutrit & physiol, 67-76, mgr pesticides res, 76-80, mgr animal res, 80-81, dir int plant indust, 81-95. *Concurrent Pos:* Consult, tech mgt. *Mem:* AAAS; Am Soc Animal Sci. *Res:* Nutrition and physiology of domesticated animals; crop physiology. *Mailing Add:* 1 Lupine Lane Titusville NJ 08560

**WILBUR, ROBERT LYNCH,** PLANT TAXONOMY. *Current Pos:* from asst prof to assoc prof, 57-70, chmn dept, 71-78, PROF BOT, DUKE UNIV, 70- CUR, HERBARIUM, 57- *Personal Data:* b Annapolis, Md, July 4, 25; m 55, Jeanne Doucette; c Martha, Ralph, Ellen, Mark, Margaret & Lenore.

*Educ:* Duke Univ, BS, 46, AM, 48; Univ Mich, PhD, 52. *Prof Exp:* Asst bot, Duke Univ, 46-47, Univ Hawaii, 47-48 & Univ Mich, 48-52; asst prof, Univ Ga, 52-53; asst prof & cur herbarium, NC State Col, 53-57. *Mem:* Am Soc Plant Taxon; Int Asn Plant Taxon; Torrey Bot Club. *Res:* Systematics and phytogeography of vascular plants; flora of the southeastern United States and Central America; campanulaceae; gentianaceae; ericaceae. *Mailing Add:* Dept Bot Duke Univ Durham NC 27706-2582

**WILBURN, NORMAN PATRICK,** CHEMICAL & ELECTRICAL ENGINEERING. *Current Pos:* RETIRED. *Personal Data:* b Whittier, Calif, Mar 28, 31; m 56; c 4. *Educ:* Calif Inst Technol, BS, 53, MS, 54, PhD, 58. *Prof Exp:* Engr, Hanford Labs, Gen Elec Co, 58-65; res assoc, Pac Northwest Labs, Battelle Mem Inst, 65-70; res assoc, Hanford Eng Develop Labs, Westinghouse Co, 70-75, mgr, 76-80, adv engr, 81-87, Battelle-Northwest, 87-88. *Concurrent Pos:* Consult. *Res:* Development of mathematical models of chemical and thermohydraulic processes; development of on-line digital computer systems; software engineering; large scale scientific software development; consultant in software quality assurance. *Mailing Add:* 1922 Harris Ave Richland WA 99352

**WILCE, ROBERT THAYER,** BOTANY. *Current Pos:* from instr to prof, 59-76, PROF BOT, UNIV MASS, AMHERST, 76- *Personal Data:* b Carbondale, Pa, Dec 9, 24; m 56. *Educ:* Univ Scranton, BS, 50; Univ Vt, MS, 52; Univ Mich, PhD(bot), 57. *Prof Exp:* Instr bot, Univ Mich, 57-58, fel, Horace Rackham Grad Sch, 58-59. *Mem:* Phycol Soc Am. *Res:* Systematic morphology, distribution and ecology of the attached algae of arctic and subarctic areas, especially the Canadian eastern arctic and northwest Greenland. *Mailing Add:* Dept Bot 221 Morrill Sci Ctr Univ Mass Amherst Campus Amherst MA 01003-0025

**WILCHINSKY, ZIGMOND WALTER,** POLYMER PHYSICS. *Current Pos:* RETIRED. *Personal Data:* b New York, NY, Aug 26, 15; m 40; c 1. *Educ:* Rutgers Univ, BS, 37, MS, 39; Mass Inst Technol, PhD(physics), 42. *Prof Exp:* Asst physics, Rutgers Univ, 37-39; mem staff radiation lab, Mass Inst Technol, 42-45; sect head, US Naval Res Lab, Washington, DC, 43-46; sr res assoc, Exxon Chem Co, 46-79; consult, 79-82. *Mem:* Am Phys Soc; Am Chem Soc; Am Crystallog Asn. *Res:* Structure of plastics; rubber technology; x-ray diffraction; physical chemistry of catalysts; adsorption; development of microwave generators; vacuum tube development. *Mailing Add:* 301 S Wood Ave Linden NJ 07036-0002

**WILCOCK, DONALD F(REDERICK),** BEARING & LUBRICATION, RESEARCH & DEVELOPMENT. *Current Pos:* PRES, TRIBOLOCK INC, 78- *Personal Data:* b Brooklyn, NY, Sept 24, 13; m 38, Marjorie Ferris; c Donald E. *Educ:* Harvard Univ, BS, 34; Univ Cincinnati, DEngSci, 40. *Honors & Awards:* Nat Hersey Award, Am Soc Mech Engrs, 73, Centennial Medal, 81, Wilcock Award, 89. *Prof Exp:* Res chemist, Sherwin-Williams Co, Ill, 39-42 & Res Lab, Gen Elec Co, NY, 42-45; eng group leader, Thomson Lab, 45-53; mgr, Mat & Chem Process Eng Serv Dept, Gen Eng Lab, Gen Elec Co, 53-60, consult engr, Ord Dept, 60-65; dir bearings, lubricant & seal technol, Mech Technol Inc, 65-68, dir technol develop, 69-78. *Mem:* Fel Am Soc Mech Engrs; fel Am Soc Lubrication Engrs. *Res:* Air bearings; magnetic bearings; bearing design and testing; lubricant testing and development. *Mailing Add:* Tribolock Inc 40 Autumn Dr Slingerlands NY 12159

**WILCOX, BENSON REID,** CARDIOVASCULAR SURGERY, THORACIC SURGERY. *Current Pos:* From instr to assoc prof, 63-71, PROF SURG, UNIV NC, CHAPEL HILL, 71-, CHIEF, DIV CARDIOTHORACIC SURG, 69- *Personal Data:* b Charlotte, NC, May 26, 32; m 59, Lucinda Holderness; c Adelaide, Alexandra, Melissa & Reid. *Educ:* Univ NC, Chapel Hill, BA, 53, MD, 57. *Concurrent Pos:* NIH fel, Bethesda, MD, 60-62 & grant, 68-74; Markle scholar, John & Mary Markle Found, 67. *Mem:* Am Asn Thoracic Surg; Am Col Surg; Am Surg Asn; Soc Thoracic Surg; Soc Univ Surg; Thoracic Surg Dir Asn. *Res:* Application of biomathematical and engineering principles to the study of the circulation; pulmonary circulation in heart disease; surgical anatomy of congenital heart disease. *Mailing Add:* Dept Surg 108 Burnett-Womack Bldg Univ NC CB7065 Chapel Hill NC 27599-7065. *Fax:* 919-966-3475

**WILCOX, BRUCE ALEXANDER,** conservation biology, sustainable development, for more information see previous edition

**WILCOX, CALVIN HAYDEN,** MATHEMATICS. *Current Pos:* PROF MATH, UNIV UTAH, 71- *Personal Data:* b Cicero, NY, Jan 29, 24; m 47; c 3. *Educ:* Harvard Univ, AB, 51, AM, 52, PhD(math), 55. *Prof Exp:* Mathematician, Air Force Cambridge Res Ctr, 53-55; from instr to assoc prof math, Calif Inst Technol, 55-61; prof math & mem, US Army Math Res Ctr, Univ Wis, 61-66; prof math, Univ Ariz, 66-69 & Univ Denver, 69-71. *Concurrent Pos:* Vis prof, Inst Theoret Physics, Univ Geneva, 70-71; Univ Liege, 73; Univ Stuttgart, 74, 76-77, Kyoto Univ, 75, ed, Rocky Mountain J Math, 75-78; Alexander von Humboldt Found US sr scientist award, 76-77; Fed Polytech, Lausanne, 79, Univ Bonn, 80. *Mem:* AAAS; Am Math Soc; Soc Indust & Appl Math. *Res:* Applied mathematics and mathematical physics, especially theories of wave propagation and scattering in classical and quantum physics; boundary value problems for partial differential equations. *Mailing Add:* 807 N Juniper Point Dr Salt Lake City UT 84103

**WILCOX, CHARLES FREDERICK, JR,** PHYSICAL CHEMISTY, ORGANIC CHEMISTRY. *Current Pos:* from instr to assoc prof, 57-74, PROF CHEM, CORNELL UNIV, 74- *Personal Data:* b Providence, RI, July 20, 30; m 57; c 3. *Educ:* Mass Inst Technol, BS, 52; Univ Calif, Los Angeles, PhD(org chem), 57. *Prof Exp:* NSF fel, Harvard Univ, 57. *Concurrent Pos:* Guggenheim fel, 66-67; vis prof, Calif Inst Technol, 67; asst ed, J Am Chem Soc, 65-66. *Mem:* Am Chem Soc; Chem Soc. *Res:* Physical aspects of organic chemistry. *Mailing Add:* Dept Chem Cornell Univ Ithaca NY 14853-0001

**WILCOX, CHARLES HAMILTON,** THEORETICAL PHYSICS, ENGINEERING MANAGEMENT. *Current Pos:* sr mem tech staff & assoc mgr theoret studies dept, Res Labs, Hughes Aircraft Co, 53-67, mgr tech planning, Aerospace Group, 67-70, dir corp independent res & develop, 70-74, DIR ENG & PROG DEVELOP, AEROSPACE GROUPS, HUGHES AIRCRAFT CO, 74- *Personal Data:* b Rochester, NY, May 21, 29. *Educ:* Duke Univ, BS, 50; Univ Ill, MS, 52; Univ Southern Calif, 70. *Prof Exp:* Res physicist & lectr physics, Eng Exp Sta, Ga Inst Technol, 52-53. *Concurrent Pos:* Lectr, Univ Southern Calif, 55-59 & Univ Calif, Los Angeles, 61-63; consult, Stanford Res Inst, 73-76. *Mem:* AAAS; Am Phys Soc; Inst Elec & Electronics Engrs; Sigma Xi; Inst Mgt Sci. *Res:* Scattering and diffraction of electromagnetic waves; radiowave propagation and geophysics; technology planning and development. *Mailing Add:* 10520 Draper Ave Los Angeles CA 90064-4410

**WILCOX, CHARLES JULIAN,** DAIRY SCIENCE. *Current Pos:* asst prof & assoc geneticist, 59-71, EMER PROF DAIRY SCI & GENETICIST, UNIV FLA, 71- *Personal Data:* b Harrisburg, Pa, Mar 28, 30; m 55, Eileen L Armstrong; c Marsha L (Mastriforte) & Douglas E. *Educ:* Univ Vt, BS, 50; Rutgers Univ, MS, 55, PhD(animal genetics), 59. *Prof Exp:* Res asst dairy sci, Rutgers Univ, 50, 53-55 & 56-59. *Concurrent Pos:* Owner & mgr dairy farm, 55-56. *Mem:* Am Dairy Sci Asn; Am Soc Animal Sci; Latin Am Asn Animal Prod; Am Registry Prof Animal Scientists; Brazil Soc Genetics. *Res:* Quantitative genetics of productive traits of farm animals, including milk yield and composition, reproductive performance, birth weights, gestation lengths, heat tolerance, type conformation, disease resistance, maternal and fetal effects, life span and livability. *Mailing Add:* Dairy Sci Dept Univ Fla Gainesville FL 32611-0920. *Fax:* 904-392-5595

**WILCOX, CHRISTOPHER STUART,** NEPHROLOGY, CLINICAL PHARMACOLOGY. *Current Pos:* ASST PROF MED CLIN PHARMACOL, BRIGHAM & WOMEN'S HOSP, 80-; DIV NEPHROLOGY & HYPERTENSION, VET ADMIN MED CTR, GAINESVILLE. *Personal Data:* b UK, Sept 15, 42; m 64; c 2. *Educ:* Oxford Univ, BA, 66, BMBCh & MA, 68; London Univ, PhD(med & physiol), 74. *Prof Exp:* House physician gen med, Middlesex Hosp, 69; house surgeon surg & urol, Cent Middlesex Hosp, 69-70; clin asst med hypertension & nephrology, Middlesex Hosp, 70-75. *Concurrent Pos:* House physician neurol, Middlesex Hosp, 70; lectr neurol studies, 70-71; house physician chest dis, Brompton Hosp, 70; asst prof med, Harvard Med Sch, 80- *Mem:* Physiol Soc; Brit Pharmacol Soc; Renal Asn; Am Fedn Clin Res; Am Soc Nephrology. *Res:* Regulation of body fluids and electrolytes and renal vascular resistance; hypertension; autonomic insufficiency; chronic kidney disease. *Mailing Add:* Dept Nephrol & Hypertension Georgetown Univ Med Ctr 3800 Reservoir Rd NW PHC F6003 Washington DC 20007. *Fax:* 352-375-3730

**WILCOX, CLIFFORD LAVAR,** DAIRY HUSBANDRY. *Current Pos:* Asst dairying, Univ Minn, 56-59, instr dairy husb, 60, exten dairy specialist, 60-65, asst dir agr exp sta, 68-72, supt, Agr Exp Sta, 65-90, EMER PROF, UNIV MINN, 90- *Personal Data:* b Archer, Idaho, Apr 15, 25; m 45; c 5. *Educ:* Utah State Univ, BS, 51; Univ Minn, MS, 57, PhD(dairy husb), 59. *Mem:* Am Dairy Sci Asn. *Res:* Dairy cattle breeding. *Mailing Add:* 1048 E Elm St St George UT 84790

**WILCOX, DONALD BROOKS,** INDUSTRIAL ENGINEERING. *Current Pos:* PVT CONSULT & EXPERT WITNESS, 75- *Personal Data:* b Walden, NY, Feb 23, 11; m 35; c 3. *Educ:* Pa State Univ, BS, 33; Ga Inst Technol, MS, 39; Emory Univ, LLB, 52. *Prof Exp:* Instr mech eng, Ga Inst Technol, 36-40, instr indust eng, 46-52; assoc prof & actg head dept, Univ Ala, 41-42; prof, Univ Fla, 52-75. *Concurrent Pos:* Consult, Fla Indust Comn. *Mem:* Am Soc Eng Educ; Am Inst Indust Engrs; Am Soc Safety Engrs; Soc Advan Mgt; Am Soc Prof Engrs. *Res:* Accident prevention engineering; engineering contracts and specifications; engineering economy and law. *Mailing Add:* 2716 NW 39th Dr Gainesville FL 32606

**WILCOX, ETHELWYN BERNICE,** nutrition; deceased, see previous edition for last biography

**WILCOX, FRANK H,** GENETICS. *Current Pos:* PROF LIFE SCI, IND STATE UNIV, TERRE HAUTE, 67- *Personal Data:* b Norwich, Conn, June 15, 27; m 60; c 2. *Educ:* Univ Conn, BS, 51; Cornell Univ, MS, 53, PhD(animal genetics), 55. *Prof Exp:* Assoc prof poultry physiol, Univ Md, 55-67. *Concurrent Pos:* Poultry sci travel award to World Poultry Cong, Australia, 62; USPHS res fel, 75-76; vis investr, Jackson Lab, 75-76. *Mem:* World Poultry Sci Asn. *Res:* Biochemical genetics, especially electrophoretic variants in vertebrates. *Mailing Add:* 60 Heritage Dr Terre Haute IN 47803

**WILCOX, GARY LYNN,** BIOCHEMICAL GENETICS. *Current Pos:* VCHMN, XOMA CORP, 89- *Personal Data:* b Ventura, Calif, Jan 7, 47; m 70; c 2. *Educ:* Univ Calif, Santa Barbara, BA, 69, MA, 72, PhD(molecular biol), 72. *Prof Exp:* Res assoc biol, Univ Calif, Santa Barbara, 72-74; asst prof, Univ Calif, Los Angeles, 74-77, assoc prof bact, 77-80, prof microbiol, 80-84; pres & chief exec officer, Int Genetic Eng, Inc, 82-89. *Concurrent Pos:* Am Can Soc fac res award, 77. *Mem:* Am Soc Microbiol; Genetics Soc Am; Am Soc Biol Chemists; Sigma Xi. *Res:* Protein nucleic acid interactions; genetic engineering; expression of heterologous proteins in microorganisms. *Mailing Add:* ICOS 22021 20th Ave SE Bothell WA 98021

**WILCOX, GEORGE LATIMER,** NEUROPHARMACOLOGY, NEUROCHEMISTRY. *Current Pos:* ASSOC PROF PHARMACOL, UNIV MINN, 77- *Educ:* Univ Colo, PhD(aerospace eng sci), 75. *Mailing Add:* Dept Pharmacol 3-249 Millard Hall Univ Minn 435 Delaware St SE Minneapolis MN 55455-0347. *Fax:* 612-625-8408; *E-Mail:* george@lenfi.med.omnedu

**WILCOX, GERALD EUGENE,** SOIL FERTILITY. *Current Pos:* RETIRED. *Personal Data:* b Wautoma, Wis, July 17, 25; m 49; c 3. *Educ:* Univ Wis, BS, 49, MS, 51, PhD, 53. *Prof Exp:* Asst agronomist, Northern La Hill Farm Exp Sta, La State Univ, 53-57; from assoc prof to prof hort & agron, Purdue Univ, Lafayette, 57-90. *Concurrent Pos:* Plant nutritionist, US Agency Int Develop, Brazil, 75-77. *Mem:* Soil Sci Soc Am; Am Soc Hort Sci; Int Soil Sci Soc. *Res:* Mineral nutrition and fertilization of vegetable crops, especially tomatoes and potatoes; soil fertility; culture and mechanization of tomato production; nutrient film technique for tomato, lettuce and cucumber production. *Mailing Add:* 128 N Beldon Dr Carmel IN 46032

**WILCOX, HARRY HAMMOND,** ANATOMY. *Current Pos:* from asst prof to prof, 52-67, EMER PROF ANAT, UNIV TENN, MEMPHIS, 83- *Personal Data:* b Canton, Ohio, May 31, 18; m 41, June Freed; c Joyce (Graff), Margaret (Smith) & James H. *Educ:* Univ Mich, BS, 39, MS, 40, PhD(zool), 48. *Prof Exp:* Assoc prof biol, Morningside Col, 47-48; assoc anat, Sch Med, Univ Pa, 48-52. *Mem:* Am Soc Zool; Am Asn Anat; Sigma Xi. *Res:* Effects of aging on the nervous system; internal ear; central nervous system pathways. *Mailing Add:* 1031 Marcia Rd Memphis TN 38117

**WILCOX, HENRY G,** BIOCHEMISTRY, PHARMACOLOGY. *Current Pos:* PROF PHARMACOL, UNIV TENN. *Personal Data:* b Hornell, NY, Jan 26, 33; m 66; c 2. *Educ:* Univ Fla, PhD(biochem), 64. *Prof Exp:* Asst prof, Vanderbilt Univ, 68-74, assoc prof pharmacol, 74-77; assoc prof pharmacol, Univ Mo, 77- *Concurrent Pos:* NIH fel pharmacol, Vanderbilt Univ, 64-67. *Res:* Plasma lipoprotein metabolism, structure and function; methodology for lipoprotein isolation and analysis; hormonal control of lipid metabolism and transport. *Mailing Add:* Dept Pharmacol Univ Tenn 301 Crowe Bldg Memphis TN 38163-0001

**WILCOX, HOWARD ALBERT,** physics, environmental management; deceased, see previous edition for last biography

**WILCOX, HOWARD JOSEPH,** MATHEMATICS. *Current Pos:* from asst prof to assoc prof, 72-78, chmn dept, 76-80, PROF MATH, WELLESLEY COL, 78- *Personal Data:* b Plattsburgh, NY, Oct 20, 39. *Educ:* Hamilton Col, AB, 61; Univ Rochester, PhD(math), 66. *Prof Exp:* Asst prof math, Univ Conn, 65-67; asst prof, Amherst Col, 67-70. *Mem:* Am Math Soc; Math Asn Am. *Res:* Topological groups; general topology. *Mailing Add:* Dept Math Wellesley Col Wellesley MA 02181-8289

**WILCOX, HUGH EDWARD,** PLANT PHYSIOLOGY, GROWTH & DEVELOPMENT. *Current Pos:* from assoc prof to prof, Col Environ Sci & Forestry, State Univ NY, 54-85, EMER PROF FORESTRY, STATE UNIV NY, 86- *Personal Data:* b Manchester, Calif, Sept 2, 16; m 38, Elizabeth Bufford; c Irene, Janet, Kenneth, Linda & Carol. *Educ:* Univ Calif, BS, 38, PhD, 50; Syracuse Univ, MS, 40. *Prof Exp:* Asst, Col Forestry, State Univ NY, Syracuse, 38-40; technician, Dept Forestry, Univ Calif, 41-42; physicist, Radiation Lab, 42-45; physicist & ord engr, US Naval Ord Test Sta, 45-46; assoc prof forest prod & wood technologist, Ore State Col, 46-50; res assoc & proj leader, Res Found, State Univ NY, 50-54. *Mem:* Fel AAAS; Soc Am Foresters; Bot Soc Am; Am Soc Plant Physiol. *Res:* Growth periodicity; dormancy; physiology of cambial activity; wound healing and regeneration; growth and differentiation of roots; mycorrhizae. *Mailing Add:* 814 Mountain Meadows Dr Ashland OR 97520. *Fax:* 315-470-6934

**WILCOX, JAMES RAYMOND,** GENETICS, AGRONOMY. *Current Pos:* Res geneticist, Inst Forest Genetics, Forest Serv, USDA, 61-66, res geneticist, 66-76, SUPV RES GENETICIST, AGR RES SERV, USDA, PURDUE UNIV, WEST LAFAYETTE, 76- *Personal Data:* b Minneapolis, Minn, Jan 20, 31; m 55, Mary Roepke; c Barbara J & Steven B. *Educ:* Univ Minn, BA, 53, MS, 59; Iowa State Univ, PhD(plant genetics), 61. *Honors & Awards:* Meritorious Serv Award Soybean Prod Res, Am Soybean Asn, 82; Prosoja Award, World Soybean Res Conf IV, 89. *Mem:* Fel AAAS; fel Am Soc Agron; Am Genetic Asn; fel Crop Sci Soc Am; Am Soybean Asn. *Res:* Soybean breeding and genetics; genetic control of fatty acid biosynthesis and protein accumulation in soybeans; genetic control of pathegen resistance in soybean. *Mailing Add:* Rm 2343 Lilly Hall Purdue Univ Dept Agron West Lafayette IN 47907-1150. *Fax:* 765-494-6508; *E-Mail:* jwilcox@dept.agry.purdue.edu

**WILCOX, JOSEPH CLIFFORD,** FOOD SCIENCE, FOOD MICROBIOLOGY. *Current Pos:* OWNER & PRES, J C WILCOX ASSOC, 82- *Personal Data:* b McLean, Ill, June 18, 30; m 52; c 2. *Educ:* Univ Ill, BS, 52, MS, 54. *Prof Exp:* Bacteriologist, Armour & Co, 56-58, sect head sausage develop, Res & Develop Dept, Food Res Div, 58-76; mgr food prod develop,

Grocery Prods Div, Miles Lab, Inc, 76-82. *Mem:* AAAS; Inst Food Technologists. *Res:* Bacteriological, chemical and radiological warfare decontamination; application of bacteriological principles in development and study of food products and associated problems; fresh, semidry and dry sausage items; utilization of nonmeat proteins; cholesterol-free food analog products; product and process development and sanitation audits; microbiological and sanitation audits; sensory evaluation; code dating and shelf-life determination; quality control; industrial real estate; technical service; nutritional labeling. *Mailing Add:* 6864 Halligan Ave E Worthington OH 43085-2618

**WILCOX, KENT WESTBROOK,** VIROLOGY. *Current Pos:* Asst prof, 79-86, ASSOC PROF MICROBIOL, MED COL WIS, 86- *Personal Data:* b NC, 1945. *Educ:* Duke Univ, BS, 67; Johns Hopkins Univ, MA, 69, PhD(microbiol), 74. *Mem:* Am Soc Microbiol; AAAS. *Res:* Regulation of viral gene expression in cells infected by herpes simplex virus. *Mailing Add:* Dept Microbiol Med Col Wis 8701 Watertown Plank Rd Milwaukee WI 53226-3548

**WILCOX, LEE ROY,** ALGEBRA, SCIENCE EDUCATION. *Current Pos:* from asst prof to prof, 40-77, dir, Ctr Educ Develop, 69-77, EMER PROF MATH, ILL INST TECHNOL, 77- *Personal Data:* b Chicago, Ill, June 8, 12; m 40, Virginia Johnson; c Robert H & Jean M (Hibben). *Educ:* Univ Chicago, SB, 32, SM, 33, PhD(math), 35. *Prof Exp:* Mem sch math, Inst Advan Study, 35-36, asst, 36-38; instr math, Univ Wis, 38-40. *Concurrent Pos:* Vis instr math, Univ Chicago, 36. *Mem:* Am Math Soc; Math Asn Am; Sigma Xi. *Res:* Theories of semi-modular and topological lattices; foundations of mathematics; abstract algebra; mathematics education. *Mailing Add:* 1404 Forest Ave Wilmette IL 60091-1634

**WILCOX, LOUIS VAN INWEGEN, JR,** ecology, for more information see previous edition

**WILCOX, LYLE C(HESTER),** SYSTEMS ENGINEERING, COMPUTER SCIENCE. *Current Pos:* PROVOST, JAMES MADISON UNIV, 84- *Personal Data:* b Lansing, Mich, Aug 8, 32; m 52; c 3. *Educ:* Tri-State Col, BSEE, 54; Mich State Univ, MSEE, 58, PhD(elec eng), 63. *Prof Exp:* Fac mem elec eng, Tri-State Col, 52-54 & Mich State Univ, 55-63; dir opers, Vet Admin, Ark, 64-65; assoc prof elec eng & Draper prof elec & mech eng, Clemson Univ, 65-66, head dept elec eng, 66-72, assoc dean prof studies, 70-73, prof elec & comput eng, 66-80, dean eng, Col Eng, 73-80; pres, Univ Southern Colo, 80-84. *Concurrent Pos:* NSF fac fel, 59-61; Ford Found fel, 62-63. *Mem:* AAAS; Inst Elec & Electronics Engrs; Am Soc Mech Engrs. *Res:* Application of systems theory to problems in control and biomedical and operations research; design and use of specialized instrumentation for data acquisition systems used in the study of multi-terminal components; general digital analog simulation from the hybrid point of view. *Mailing Add:* James Madison Univ 301 Wilson Hall Harrisonburg VA 22807

**WILCOX, MARION WALTER,** engineering mechanics; deceased, see previous edition for last biography

**WILCOX, MERRILL,** PLANT PHYSIOLOGY. *Current Pos:* from asst prof to assoc prof, 60-72, PROF AGRON, UNIV FLA, 72- *Personal Data:* b Milwaukee, Wis, Oct 10, 29; m 62; c 2. *Educ:* Univ Md, BS, 52, MS, 54; NC State Univ, PhD(agron, plant physiol), 61. *Prof Exp:* Biol aide marine biol, Chesapeake Biol Lab, Univ Md, 56-57. *Concurrent Pos:* Grants, Am Cancer Soc, 63-66, NSF, 63-65 & Geigy Chem Corp, 70-78. *Mem:* AAAS; Am Soc Plant Physiol; Weed Sci Soc Am; Scand Soc Plant Physiol; Am Chem Soc; Int Palm Soc. *Res:* Structure-activity relationships and metabolism of herbicides and plant growth regulators; abscission by Glyoxime; tobacco growth regulation by flumetralin; hybridization in cocosoid palms. *Mailing Add:* 2911 NW 30th Terr Gainesville FL 32605

**WILCOX, NEIL L,** SCIENCE POLICY MANAGEMENT, PUBLIC HEALTH POLICY & ADMINISTRATION. *Current Pos:* vet med reviewer, Div Therapeut Drugs Non-Food Animals, Companion & Wildlife Drugs Br, Ctr Vet Med, 90, dir, Off Animal Care & Use, Off Dir, 90-94, SR SCI POLICY OFFICER, OFF SCI/OFF OPERS/OFF COMNR, US FOOD & DRUG ADMIN, 94- *Personal Data:* m, Phyllis King; c Ryan, Sara & Mollly. *Educ:* Mich State Univ, BS, 68, DVM, 71; Univ Mich, MPH, 89. *Prof Exp:* Assoc vet, Plaza Vet Hosp, Mich, 71-74; owner-operator, Wilcox Vet Hosp, Mich, 74-89. *Concurrent Pos:* Bd trustee, Oaklawn Hosp, 77-88, pres & bd dirs, 88; pres, Oaklawn Health Servs, 77-78; mem, Interagency Res Animal Coun, Ctr Vet Med Animal Care & Use Comt, Coord Comt Animal Res, USPHS & Interagency Coord Comt Validation Alternative Methods; chair, Interagency Regulatory Alternatives Group; mem, Subcomt Toxicol, Food & Drug Admin Sci Bd. *Mailing Add:* US Food & Drug Admin HF-32 Rm 17-35 5600 Fishers Lane Rockville MD 20857

**WILCOX, PAUL DENTON,** CERAMIC ENGINEERING, METALLURGY. *Current Pos:* RETIRED. *Personal Data:* b Salt Lake City, Utah, Mar 4, 35; m 61; c 1. *Educ:* Univ Utah, BS, 58, PhD(ceramic eng), 62. *Honors & Awards:* Dept Energy Award, Improving Qual, 88. *Prof Exp:* Supvr active ceramic mat div, Sandia Labs, 62-80, supvr initiating & pyrotech, 80-92. *Concurrent Pos:* Adj prof, Univ NMex, 69-70. *Mem:* Am Ceramic Soc; Int Pyrotech Soc. *Res:* Piezoelectrics; ferroelectrics; glass; glass ceramics; thermoelectrics; acoustic surface waves; ceramic varistors; materials science technology; explosives and propellants; pyrotechnics. *Mailing Add:* 1501 Cedar Ridge Dr NE Albuquerque NM 87112

**WILCOX, RAY EVERETT,** GEOLOGY. *Current Pos:* RETIRED. *Personal Data:* b Janesville, Wis, Mar 31, 12; m 42, Mary Jane Marks; c Peter R, Anne M, Susan J & Stephen M. *Educ:* Univ Wis, PhB, 33, PhM, 37, PhD(geol), 41. *Prof Exp:* Geologist, State Geol Surv, Wis, 35-39 & Jones & Laughlin Steel Corp, 41-42; geologist, US Geol Surv, 46-84. *Mem:* AAAS; fel Geol Soc Am; fel Mineral Soc Am. *Res:* Igneous petrology; volcanology; volcanic ash chronology; petrographic methods; optical crystallography. *Mailing Add:* 3590 Estes St Wheat Ridge CO 80033-5933

**WILCOX, ROBERTA ARLENE,** MEDICAL STATISTICS. *Current Pos:* RETIRED. *Personal Data:* b Hopkinton, RI, Nov 12, 32. *Educ:* Univ RI, BS, 54; Johns Hopkins Univ, ScM, 58. *Prof Exp:* Biostatistician, State Dept Health, NY, 57-59; res statistician, Lederle Labs, Am Cyanamid Co, 59-66; sr biostatistician, Med Div, Ciba-Geigy Corp, 66-72; sr res scientist, Pfizer Cent Res, Pfizer, Inc, 72-77; prin biostatistician, Alcon Labs, Inc, 79-92. *Mem:* Am Statist Asn; Biomet Soc; NY Acad Sci. *Res:* Experimental design and analysis applicable to medical and drug research. *Mailing Add:* 6908 Wilton Dr Ft Worth TX 76133-6131

**WILCOX, RONALD BRUCE,** BIOCHEMISTRY, ENDOCRINOLOGY. *Current Pos:* from asst prof to assoc prof, 65-73, PROF BIOCHEM, SCH MED, LOMA LINDA UNIV, 73- *Personal Data:* b Seattle, Wash, Sept 23, 34; m 58, Susan Folkenberg; c Deanna & Lisa. *Educ:* Pac Union Col, BS, 57; Univ Utah, PhD(biochem), 62. *Prof Exp:* Res fel med, Mass Gen Hosp & Harvard Med Sch, 62-65. *Mem:* Endocrine Soc; Am Thyroid Asn. *Res:* Biochemistry and metabolism of hormones. *Mailing Add:* Dept Biochem Loma Linda Univ Sch Med Loma Linda CA 92354. *Fax:* 909-824-4887; *E-Mail:* bwilcox@ccmail.llu.edu

**WILCOX, RONALD ERWIN,** GEOLOGY. *Current Pos:* CONSULT, 88- *Personal Data:* b Ft Wayne, Ind, Jan 6, 29; m 59; c 3. *Educ:* Iowa State Univ, BS, 50, MS, 52; Columbia Univ, PhD(petrol), 58. *Honors & Awards:* President's Award, Am Asn Petrol Geologists, 75. *Prof Exp:* Asst geol, Iowa State Univ, 50-52 & Columbia Univ, 52-54; res geologist, Humble Oil & Refining Co, 56-64; sr res geologist, Esso Prod Res Co, 64-72; lectr, Univ Houston, 72-75; adj prof, 75-76; assoc prof, Inst Environ Studies, La State Univ, 77-88. *Concurrent Pos:* Consult geologist, 72- *Mem:* Fel AAAS; fel Geol Soc Am; Am Asn Petrol Geologists; Am Geophys Union; Sigma Xi. *Res:* Structural geology; petrology; structure of continental margins; salt tectonics; orogenic belts; metamorphism. *Mailing Add:* PO Box 25096 Baton Rouge LA 70894-5096. *E-Mail:* evwile@unix1.sncc.lsu.edu

**WILCOX, ROY CARL,** PHYSICAL METALLURGY. *Current Pos:* ASSOC PROF MAT, AUBURN UNIV, 69- *Personal Data:* b Alexandria, Va, Feb 4, 33; m 65; c 2. *Educ:* Va Polytech Inst, BS, 55, MS, 59; Univ Mo, Rolla, PhD(metall eng), 62. *Prof Exp:* Metallurgist, Naval Ord Lab, 55-56; instr metall, Va Polytech Inst, 57-59, 62, assoc prof, 62-68, assoc dir, Continuing Educ Ctr, 68-69. *Mem:* Am Soc Metals; Am Inst Mining, Metall & Petrol Engrs; Sigma Xi. *Res:* Deformation of textures of cobalt; study of titanium-aluminum alloys; fracture studies of adhesive bonded joints. *Mailing Add:* Dept Mech Eng 201 Ross Hall Auburn Univ Auburn AL 36830

**WILCOX, THOMAS JEFFERSON,** PHYSICS. *Current Pos:* SR SCIENTIST, LOGICON RDA, 92- *Personal Data:* b San Francisco, Calif, Oct 2, 42; m 72; c 2. *Educ:* Univ Calif, Berkeley, BA, 64; Univ Calif, Los Angeles, MS, 66, PhD(physics), 72. *Prof Exp:* Res physicist plasma/particle physics, Univ Calif, Los Angeles, 72-73; mem tech staff plasma physics, TRW Systs Group, 73-75; mem tech staff physics, R&D Assocs, 75-82; sr scientist, Sci Applications Inc, 82-84, Res & Develop Labs, 84-86, Pac Sierra Res Corp, 86-89, TRW Space & Technol Group, 89-92. *Mem:* Am Phys Soc. *Res:* Plasma physics; radiation transport; optics; electromagnetism; mathematical physics. *Mailing Add:* 235 N Kenter Ave Los Angeles CA 90049. *E-Mail:* twilcox@logicon.com

**WILCOX, W(ILLIAM) R(OSS),** CHEMICAL ENGINEERING, MATERIALS SCIENCE. *Current Pos:* RETIRED. *Personal Data:* b Manhattan, Kans, Jan 14, 35; m 68, Liya L Sahagian; c Russell, Holly, Kathy & William Jr. *Educ:* Univ Southern Calif, BEng, 56; Univ Calif, Berkeley, PhD(chem eng), 60. *Prof Exp:* Instr chem eng, Univ Calif, Berkeley, 60; mem tech staff, Pac Semiconductors Inc, 60-62; mem tech staff, Aerospace Corp, 62-65, head crystal technol sect, 65-68; assoc prof mat sci & chem eng, Univ Southern Calif, 68-74, prof, 74-75; prof chem eng, Clarkson Univ, 75-97, dir, Ctr Advan Mat Processing, 85-91 & Ctr Crystal Growth in Space, 86-94, dean eng, 87-96. *Concurrent Pos:* Consult, NASA, var industs & univs; mem exec comt, Am Asn Crystal Growth, 70-91 & 93-97; mem, Comt Space Res. *Mem:* Fel Am Inst Chem Engrs; Am Soc Eng Educ; Am Asn Crystal Growth (vpres, 84-87); fel AAAS; Int Astronaut Fedn. *Res:* Crystal growth, materials processing in space and on large centrifuges; directional solidification of metal alloys and semiconductors. *Mailing Add:* Clarkson Univ Potsdam NY 13699-5814. *Fax:* 315-268-3833; *E-Mail:* wilcox@agent.clarkson.edu

**WILCOX, W WAYNE,** FOREST PRODUCTS PATHOLOGY, WOOD BIODETERIORATION. *Current Pos:* from asst to assoc forest prod pathologist, 64-77, lectr, 64-75, FOREST PROD PATHOLOGIST & PROF FORESTRY, UNIV CALIF, BERKELEY, 77- *Personal Data:* b Berkeley, Calif, Oct 28, 38; m 60, Margaret Starkweather; c Melissa Margaret & Wynn William. *Educ:* Univ Calif, Berkeley, BS, 60; Univ Wis-Madison, MS, 62, PhD(plant path), 65. *Honors & Awards:* Forest Prod Res Soc Award, 65. *Prof Exp:* Plant pathologist, US Forest Prod Lab, Wis, 60-64. *Concurrent Pos:* Fulbright-Hays sr fel, Ger, 73-74. *Mem:* Forest Prod Soc; fel Int Acad Wood Sci; Soc Wood Sci & Technol; Am Inst Biol Sci; Int Asn Wood Anatomists.

Res: Wood deterioration; microscopy of wood decay; ability to detect, diagnose and evaluate early stages of decay in structures. *Mailing Add:* Forest Prod Lab Univ Calif 1301 S 46th St Richmond CA 94804. *Fax:* 510-215-4299; *E-Mail:* www@nature.berkeley.edu

**WILCOX, WAYNE F,** PLANT PATHOLOGY. *Current Pos:* asst prof, 84-90, ASSOC PROF, NY STATE AGR EXP STA, CORNELL UNIV, 90- *Personal Data:* b Newman, Calif, July 1, 50; m 69, Linda T Pembroke; c Miranda C & Holly C. *Educ:* Univ Calif, Davis, BS, 77, MS, 78, PhD, 82. *Honors & Awards:* Ciba-Geigy Award, Am Phytopath Soc, 93. *Prof Exp:* Asst exten prof, Univ Ky, 82-84. *Concurrent Pos:* Dept exten leader, Cornell Univ; state liasion rep, Nat Impact Assessment Prog; secy, Deciduous Tree Fruit Dis Workers, Am Phytopath Soc, 84-85, chmn, 85-86, jour ed, 85-92, mem exten comt, 88-90. *Mem:* Am Phytopath Soc; Am Soc Hort Sci. *Res:* Biological control of phytophthora by trichoderma and by gliocladium; elucidation of role of phytophthora species as casual agents of root rot of fruit crops, particularly their interaction with soil water status as it effects pathogenesis. *Mailing Add:* Dept Plant Path Cornell Univ NY State Agr Exp Sta Barton Lab Geneva NY 14456

**WILCOX, WESLEY C,** MICROBIOLOGY. *Current Pos:* RETIRED. *Personal Data:* b St Anthony, Idaho, July 19, 25; m 48; c 4. *Educ:* Univ Utah, BA, 51, MS, 55; Univ Wash, PhD(microbiol), 58. *Prof Exp:* Donner fel med res, Western Res Univ, 58-59, USPHS fel prev med, 59-60; assoc microbiol, Univ Pa, 60-62, asst prof, 62-63; prof, Univ Vt, 63-65; prof, Univ Pa, 65-, chmn dept, 76-, head, Lab Microbiol, 80- *Concurrent Pos:* Res career develop award, Univ Pa, 60-63. *Mem:* Am Asn Immunologists; Am Soc Microbiol. *Res:* Virology; immunology; biochemistry. *Mailing Add:* 2302 Bridgewater Ct Chester Springs PA 19425

**WILCOX, WESLEY CRAIN,** AGRONOMY, BOTANY. *Current Pos:* RETIRED. *Personal Data:* b Bloomington, Ill, Apr 8, 26; m 48, Jean Hale; c Barbara, Anne, Joan, Sarah & Martha. *Educ:* Univ Ill, BS, 50, MS, 51. *Prof Exp:* Field supvr, Found Dept, Ciba Seed Div, 51-55, corn breeder, Res Dept, 55-66, mgr spec proj res, 66-71, dir, Qual Assurance Dept, 71-91. *Mem:* Soc Com Seed Technologists; Am Soc Agron; Crop Sci Soc Am; Sigma Xi. *Res:* High quality seed of hybrid corn, sorghum, soybeans and farm seeds. *Mailing Add:* 29 Norbloom Normal IL 61761

**WILCOX, WILLIAM JENKINS, JR,** ISOTOPE SEPARATION, STRATEGIC PLANNING. *Current Pos:* RETIRED. *Personal Data:* b Harrisburg, Pa, Jan 26, 23; m 46; c 3. *Educ:* Washington & Lee Univ, BA, 43; Univ Tenn, MS, 58. *Prof Exp:* Chemist, Tenn Eastman Corp, 43-48; chemist, Union Carbide Corp, 48-49, tech asst to lab dir, 49-55, head dept physics, 55-67, prog mgr, 67-69, prod plants tech dir, Nuclear Div, 69-81; sr staff consult, Martin Marietta Energy Systs, Inc, 81-86. *Concurrent Pos:* Mgt consult, 86- *Mem:* AAAS; Am Chem Soc; Sigma Xi; fel Am Inst Chemists; NY Acad Sci. *Res:* Isotope separation processes, research and development; structure of porous materials; materials development. *Mailing Add:* 412 New York Ave Oak Ridge TN 37830-5219

**WILCOXSON, ROY DELL,** PLANT PATHOLOGY. *Current Pos:* Asst prof, 57-66, PROF PLANT PATH, UNIV MINN, ST PAUL, 66- *Personal Data:* b Columbia, Utah, Jan 12, 26; m 49, Iva Wall; c Bonnie, Paul, Karren & John. *Educ:* Utah State Univ, BS, 53; Univ Minn, MS, 55, PhD(plant path), 57. *Concurrent Pos:* Spec staff mem, Rockefeller Found; vis prof, Indian Agr Res Inst, New Delhi; dir, Morocco Proj, Univ Minn, 83-87; adj prof, Inst Agron & Vet Med, Hassan II, Rabat, Movac, 85- *Mem:* Fel Am Phytopath Soc; fel Indian Nat Acad Sci; fel Indian Phytopath Soc; AAAS. *Res:* Diseases of forage crops and cereal crops; cereal rust diseases. *Mailing Add:* Dept Plant Path Univ Minn St Paul MN 55101

**WILCZEK, FRANK ANTHONY,** THEORETICAL PHYSICS. *Current Pos:* PROF, SCH NATURAL SCI, INST ADVAN STUDY, 88- *Personal Data:* b Queens, NY, May 15, 51; m 73, Elizabeth Devine; c Amity & Mira. *Educ:* Univ Chicago, BS, 70; Princeton Univ, MA, 72, PhD(physics), 74. *Honors & Awards:* MacArthur Fel, 81-85; Sakurai Prize, Am Phys Soc, 86; Dirac Medal, United Nations Educ Sci & Cult Orgn, 94. *Prof Exp:* Asst prof physics, Princeton Univ, 74-77; mem, Inst Advan Studies, 77-78; assoc prof physics, Princeton Univ, 78-80; prof, Inst Theoret Physics, Univ Calif, Santa Barbara, 80-88. *Concurrent Pos:* Prof, Princeton Univ, 80- *Mem:* Nat Acad Sci; Am Acad Arts & Sci. *Res:* High energy physics; quantum field theory. *Mailing Add:* Sch Natural Sci Inst Advan Study Princeton NJ 08540

**WILCZYNSKI, JANUSZ S,** OPTICAL DESIGN & INSTRUMENTATION. *Current Pos:* Mgr tech optics, 62-83, sr mgr, Lithography & Packaging Eng Group, 83-86, DIR PACKAGING TECHNOL, IBM T J WATSON RES LAB, 86-, DIR, ADVAN PACKAGING TECHNOL LAB, 88-; STAFF, WILC INSTRUMENTS, 93- *Personal Data:* b May 12, 29; m 76, Brahna Lauger. *Educ:* Mining Acad, Cracow, Inz dipl, 54; Jagellonian Univ, MSc, 57; Univ London, PhD(physics), 61. *Honors & Awards:* Richardson Medal, Optical Soc Am, 88. *Concurrent Pos:* Fel, IBM, 81. *Mem:* Nat Acad Eng; fel Optical Soc Am; Int Soc Optical Eng. *Res:* Sub-half micron optical stepper; optical instrumentation; microlithography; normal incidence x-ray telescope; author of 37 publications; granted 43 patents. *Mailing Add:* Wilc Instruments 11 Rue du Soleil Sandia Park NM 87047. *Fax:* 505-286-8273; *E-Mail:* wilczyn@ibm.net

**WILCZYNSKI, WALTER,** NEUROETHOLOGY, SENSORY PROCESSING. *Current Pos:* from asst prof to assoc prof, 83-95, PROF PSYCHOL, UNIV TEX, 95- *Personal Data:* b Trenton, NJ, Sept 18, 52. *Educ:* Lehigh Univ, BS & BA, 74; Univ Mich, PhD(neurosci), 78. *Prof Exp:* Fel neurobiol, Cornell Univ, 79-83. *Concurrent Pos:* Prin investr, Univ Tex, NSF & NIMH grants, 84-; vis scientist, Smithsonian Trop Res Inst, 87, 90 & 95. *Mem:* Soc Neurosci; Am Soc Zoologists; Int Soc Neuroethol; AAAS. *Res:* Investigate the neural mechanism of acoustic communication and reproductive social behavior in anuran amphibians; research combines anatomical and physiological techniques to determine how acoustic information is represented and used by the peripheral auditory system and central nervous system. *Mailing Add:* Dept Psychol Univ Tex Austin TX 78712

**WILD, BRADFORD WILLISTON,** OPTOMETRY, OPTICS. *Current Pos:* PROF & DEAN, SCH OPTOM, MED CTR, UNIV ALA, BIRMINGHAM, 74- *Personal Data:* b Fall River, Mass, Dec 5, 27; m 77. *Educ:* Brown Univ, AB, 49; Columbia Univ, BS, 51, MS, 52; Ohio State Univ, PhD(physiol optics), 59. *Hon Degrees:* DOS, Southern Calif Col Optom. *Prof Exp:* From instr to assoc prof optom & physiol optics, Ohio State Univ, 59-69; dean, Col Optom, Pac Univ, 69-74. *Concurrent Pos:* Res optometrist, Gen Vision Sect, US Naval Med Res Lab, Conn. *Mem:* Am Optom Asn; Am Acad Optom (pres, 78-80). *Res:* Physiological optics, especially retinal interaction, border phenomena and problems of visibility. *Mailing Add:* 3298 Hillard Dr Birmingham AL 35243

**WILD, GAYNOR (CLARKE),** NEUROCHEMISTRY, BIOCHEMISTRY OF FERTILIZATION. *Current Pos:* asst prof, 67-85, ASSOC PROF BIOCHEM, SCH MED, UNIV NMEX, 85-, ASSOC PROF NEUROL, 87- *Personal Data:* b Winner, SDak, Nov 10, 34; m 58, 73, 87; c 2. *Educ:* SDak Sch Mines & Technol, BS, 55; Tulane Univ, PhD(biochem), 62. *Prof Exp:* Fel biochem, Clayton Found Biochem Inst, Univ Tex, 62-63; res assoc, Rockefeller Univ, 63-65, asst prof, 65-67. *Concurrent Pos:* Consult, Los Alamos Nat Lab, 83-87. *Mem:* Am Soc Biol Chemists; Soc Neurosci. *Res:* Neurochemistry; enzymology; lipid biochemistry; sperm acrosome autoantigens and enzymes. *Mailing Add:* Dept Biol Murray State Univ 1101 Meadow Lane Murray NM 87131-0001

**WILD, GENE MURIEL,** BIOCHEMISTRY. *Current Pos:* RETIRED. *Personal Data:* b Fremont, Nebr, Oct 15, 26; m 48; c 4. *Educ:* Iowa State Univ, BS, 48, MS, 50, PhD(biochem), 53. *Prof Exp:* Sr biochemist, Eli Lilly & Co, 53-73, res scientist, 73-89. *Res:* Purification process research in antibiotics; chemical analysis and chromatography of antibiotics and related materials. *Mailing Add:* 7455 Jewel Lane Indianapolis IN 46285

**WILD, JAMES ROBERT,** MOLECULAR BIOLOGY. *Current Pos:* asst prof genetics, Tex A&M Univ, 75-80, assoc prof biochem & genetics, 80-84, prof chmn biochem, 87-90, exec assoc dean acad progs, Col Agr & Life Sci, 89-92, chmn fac genetics, 93-95, PROF & HEAD DEPT BIOCHEM/BIOPHYS, TEX A&M UNIV, 94- *Personal Data:* b Sedalia, Mo, Nov 24, 45; m 73, Ann L Brenner; c Kalli A. *Educ:* Univ Calif, Davis, BA, 67; Univ Calif, Riverside, PhD(biol), 71. *Prof Exp:* Res biochemist, Univ Calif, Riverside, 72; microbiologist, Naval Med Res Inst, Nat Naval Med Ctr, 72-75. *Concurrent Pos:* Consult, 90- *Mem:* Am Soc Microbiol; Genetics Soc Am; Am Chem Soc; Sigma Xi; AAAS; Am Soc Biochem Molecular. *Res:* Pyrimidine biosynthesis; nucleotide biosynthesis enzyme-based biorimediation; regulation of gene expression and gene structure; function relationships. *Mailing Add:* Dept Biochem & Biophys Tex A&M Univ College Station TX 77843-2128. *Fax:* 409-845-9274; *E-Mail:* wild@bigraf.tamu.edu

**WILD, JOHN FREDERICK,** NUCLEAR CHEMISTRY. *Current Pos:* RES CHEMIST, LAWRENCE LIVERMORE LAB, 69- *Personal Data:* b Erie, Pa, June 20, 42; m 66; c 2. *Educ:* Pa State Univ, BS, 64; Mass Inst Technol, PhD(nuclear chem), 68. *Prof Exp:* Res chemist, Knolls Atomic Power Lab, 68-69. *Mem:* Am Chem Soc. *Res:* Nuclear chemistry with emphasis on decay and chemical properties of isotopes of elements above Z 96; spontaneous fission; heavy-ion reaction mechanisms. *Mailing Add:* Lawrence Livermore Lab Livermore CA 94551

**WILD, JOHN FREDERICK,** PHYSICS. *Current Pos:* from asst prof to assoc prof, 62-91, EMER PROF PHYSICS, WORCESTER POLYTECH INST, 92- *Personal Data:* b Wallingford, Conn, Nov 30, 26; m 65, Mary Grady; c Margaret, John & Moira. *Educ:* Yale Univ, BS, 50, MS, 51, PhD(physics), 58. *Prof Exp:* From instr to asst prof physics, Trinity Col, Conn, 57-62. *Mem:* Am Phys Soc; Am Asn Physics Teachers; Sigma Xi. *Res:* Wave functions for valence electron of neutral caesium for Fermi-Thomas central field; quantum mechanics; color vision; Foucault knife-edge test; tuned percussion instruments; solar heating. *Mailing Add:* 16 Cavour Circle West Boylston MA 01583

**WILD, JOHN JULIAN,** CLINICAL MEDICINE, ULTRASOUND. *Current Pos:* DIR MED DIAG ULTRASOUND, MEDICO-TECHNOL RES INST, MINNEAPOLIS, 65- *Personal Data:* b Syndenham, Eng, Aug 11, 14; US citizen; m 68, Valerie Grosenick; c Ellen L, John & Douglas. *Educ:* Cambridge Univ, BA, 36, MA, 40, MB, MD, 42, PhD(investigative med), 71. *Honors & Awards:* Pioneer Award, Am Inst Ultrasound Med, 78; Japan Prize Med Imaging, Sci & Technol Found Japan, 91. *Prof Exp:* Res assoc, Dept Surg, Univ Minn, 46-51, res assoc med diag ultrasound, Dept Elec Eng, 51-53; dir res, St Barnabas Hosp, Minneapolis, 53-60; dir medico-technol res unit, Minn Found, St Paul, 60-63. *Concurrent Pos:* Res fel, Marion Ordway Found, St Paul, 46-47 & USPHS, 47-49; prin investr, Nat Adv Cancer Coun, 50-60,

Nat Heart Inst, 57-60 & Gen Med Sci Div, 62-63. *Mem:* Fel Am Inst Ultrasound Med; AMA; hon mem Brit Inst Radiol; hon mem Japan Soc Ultrasound Med; hon mem World Fedn Ultrasound Med. *Res:* Physical detection of disease and deteriorative processes; ultrasonic pulse-echo tissue characterization, cancer detection and diagnosis of the breast and colon; pulse-echo measurement of biological tissues. *Mailing Add:* 4262 Alabama Ave S Minneapolis MN 55416

**WILD, ROBERT LEE,** SOLID STATE PHYSICS. *Current Pos:* from asst prof to prof, 53-88, chmn dept, 63-68, EMER PROF PHYSICS, UNIV CALIF, RIVERSIDE, 88- *Personal Data:* b Sedalia, Mo, Oct 9, 21; m 43, F Elleta Wheeler; c James R, Janet G & Margaret N. *Educ:* Cent Mo State Univ, BS, 43; Univ Mo, Columbia, MA, 48, PhD(physics). 50. *Honors & Awards:* Outstanding Physics Achievement Award, Phil Phys Soc, 86. *Prof Exp:* Asst instr physics, Univ Mo, 49; asst prof, Univ NDak, 50-53. *Concurrent Pos:* NSF fel, Univ Ill, 59-60; vis prof, Tech Univ Denmark, 67-68 & Univ Munster, Ger, 75; Fulbright lectr, Univ Philippines, 81-82; pres, SCalif Sect, Am Asn Physics Teachers, 85-87. *Mem:* Am Phys Soc; Am Asn Physics Teachers; Sigma Xi. *Res:* Small angle x-ray scattering by liquids and solids; optical and transport properties of solids. *Mailing Add:* Dept Physics Univ Calif Riverside CA 92521

**WILD, WAYNE GRANT,** PHYSICS, MATHEMATICS. *Current Pos:* RETIRED. *Personal Data:* b Waterville, Kans, Aug 9, 17; m 39; c 4. *Educ:* SDak State Univ, BS, 40; Univ Wis, MS, 48; Univ Ill, MA, 67. *Prof Exp:* Prof physics & head dept, Buena Vista Col, 48-67, chmn natural sci div, 53-67; assoc prof physics, Univ Wis, Stevens Point, 67-69, assoc prof math, 69-82. *Mem:* Sigma Xi; Am Math Asn. *Res:* Thermionic emission. *Mailing Add:* 22 Little Dr Bella Vista AR 72714

**WILDASIN, HARRY LEWIS,** BIOCHEMISTRY, AGRICULTURAL ECONOMICS. *Current Pos:* OWNER, WILDASIN ASSOCS, 83- *Personal Data:* b York Co, Pa, Oct 10, 23; m 45, 70, Deitrich; c David E. *Educ:* Pa State Univ, BS, 43, PhD(biochem & microbiol), 50. *Prof Exp:* Asst prof dairying, Univ Conn, 49-52; dir qual control, Whiting Milk Co, Boston, 52-57; dir qual control & govt rels, H P Hood Inc, Boston, 57-83. *Mem:* Am Dairy Sci Asn; NY Acad Sci; Nat Environ Health Asn; Am Pub Health Asn; Sigma Xi. *Res:* Frozen milk; lactose; milk proteins; surface active agents; antibiotics; salmonella; radioactive elements in milk; vitamin D in milk. *Mailing Add:* Wildasin Assocs 23 Oxbow Rd Lexington MA 02173-6613. *Fax:* 781-861-6856

**WILDE, ANTHONY FLORY,** PHYSICAL CHEMISTRY. *Current Pos:* res chemist, US Army Natick Labs, 63-68, RES CHEMIST, US ARMY MAT TECHNOL LAB, 68- *Personal Data:* b New York, NY, May 16, 30; m 72. *Educ:* Yale Univ, BS, 52; Ind Univ, PhD(phys chem), 59. *Prof Exp:* Res chemist, Monsanto Res Corp, 59-63. *Mem:* Am Chem Soc; AAAS; NY Acad Sci. *Res:* Polymer rheology, especially dynamic mechanical and optical properties of organic polymers and elastomers; stress wave propagation, fracture and energy dissipation in materials; dielectric and piezoelectric properties of organic polymers; sorption and diffusion of liquids in polymers. *Mailing Add:* 20 Sunset Dr Framingham MA 01701-7933

**WILDE, BRYAN EDMUND,** FORENSIC ENGINEER, MATERIALS SELECTION. *Current Pos:* RETIRED. *Personal Data:* b Salford, Lancashire, UK, Nov 8, 34; US citizen; m 56; c 4. *Educ:* Royal Inst Chem, AGRIC, 59, 61, PhD(phys chem), 64; Rennselaer Polytech, NY, PhD(math), 66. *Prof Exp:* Mgr mat sci, Phys Chem Div, Exide Batteries, 59-64; supvr mat sci, Corrosion Res Lab, RPI, 64-66; lead scientist mat sci, Gen Elec Nucleonics Lab, 66-68; head, Corrosion Tech Div, US Steel, 68-84; prof & dir, Fontana Corrosion Ctr, Ohio State Univ, 84-95. *Concurrent Pos:* Nat chmn, Nat Asn Corrosion Engrs, Res in Progress, 78, Gordon Res Conf-Corrosion, 86; pres, NAm Corrosion Construct, Inc, 83-; distinguished vis scholar, UN Develop Prog, China, 86. *Mem:* Am Soc Metals; Mat Res Soc; Electrochem Soc; fel Inst Corrosion Sci & Tech. *Res:* Corrosion, electrochemistry, environmental by induced degradation of materials, composite corrosion, hydrogen obsorption into materials, fracture. *Mailing Add:* 6077 W Central Park Florence OR 97439

**WILDE, CARROLL ORVILLE,** MATHEMATICS. *Current Pos:* RETIRED. *Personal Data:* b Elmhurst, Ill, June 5, 32; m 52, 71; c 3. *Educ:* Ill State Univ, BS, 58; Univ Ill, Urbana, PhD(math), 64. *Prof Exp:* Instr math, SDak Sch Mines & Technol, 58-59 & Col Wooster, 59-61; asst prof, Univ Minn, Minneapolis, 64-68; from assoc prof to prof math, Naval Postgrad Sch, 68-92, chmn dept, 76-83, fac chmn, 90-91. *Concurrent Pos:* Vis prof, US Mil Acad, West Point, 79-80, 84-85; prog dir, NSF, 89-90. *Mem:* Nat Coun Teachers Math; Math Asn Am; Sigma Xi; Soc Indust & Appl Math. *Res:* Scientific computation. *Mailing Add:* PO Box 482 Carmel CA 93921

**WILDE, CHARLES EDWARD, JR,** biology; deceased, see previous edition for last biography

**WILDE, CHARLES EDWARD, III,** PROTEIN STRUCTURE, INFECTIOUS DISEASES. *Current Pos:* Asst prof, 78-86, ASSOC PROF MICROBIOL & IMMUNOL, SCH MED, UNIV IND, 86- *Personal Data:* b 1946. *Educ:* Univ Calif, Berkeley, PhD(molecular biol), 75. *Mem:* Am Soc Microbiol; Am Asn Immunologists; AAAS. *Mailing Add:* Dept Microbiol & Immunol Sch Med Ind Univ 635 Barnhill Dr Indianapolis IN 46202-5120

**WILDE, D(OUGLASS) J(AMES),** OPTIMIZATION, COMPUTATIONAL GEOMETRY. *Current Pos:* assoc prof, Stanford Univ, 63-67, prof chem eng, 67-72, assoc dean 78-80, PROF MECH ENG DESIGN, STANFORD UNIV, 72- *Personal Data:* b Chicago, Ill, Aug 1, 29; m 56, Jane Paul; c Nicholas P. *Educ:* Carnegie Inst Technol, BS, 48; Univ Wash, MS, 56; Univ Calif, PhD, 60. *Honors & Awards:* Lanchester Prize, Opers Res Soc Am, 68; Maynard Prize, Am Inst Indust Engrs; Design Automation Award, Am Soc Mech Engrs, 88. *Prof Exp:* Chem engr, Pittsburgh Coke & Chem Co, 48-50 & Union Oil Co, 54-56; asst, Univ Calif, 57-58, instr chem eng, 58-59, lectr, 59-60; Fulbright lectr, Nat Advan Sch Chem Industs, 60-61; asst prof, Univ Tex, 61-62. *Concurrent Pos:* Vis assoc prof, Yale Univ, 63; vis prof, PUC, Rio de Janeiro, 77, Univ Sydney, Australia, 84 & Cent Sch Arts & Mfrs, Paris, 84. *Mem:* Am Soc Mech Engrs. *Res:* Optimization theory; optimal design. *Mailing Add:* Dept Mech Eng Stanford Univ Stanford CA 94305

**WILDE, DANIEL UNDERWOOD,** INFORMATION STORAGE & RETRIEVAL, LARGE DATABASE SYSTEMS. *Current Pos:* from assoc dir to dir, 66-85, PRES, NERAC INC, 85- *Personal Data:* b Wilmington, Ohio, Dec 27, 37; m 83, Helen L Herrington. *Educ:* Univ Ill, BS, 60; Mass Inst Technol, MS, 61, PhD(elec eng), 66. *Honors & Awards:* Pub Serv Award, NASA, 75. *Prof Exp:* Res instr med, Boston Univ Med Sch, 64-66; asst prof bus admin, Univ Conn, 66-69, from assoc prof to prof indust admin, 69-76. *Concurrent Pos:* Consult, Am Soc Metals, 68-72; bd mem, Conn State Libr Sci Curric Comt, 74-78; panel mem, Off Technol Asessment, US Cong, 76. *Mem:* Asn Info Dissemination Ctrs (treas, 76-79, pres, 79-81); Spec Libr Asn; Int Coun Sci Info; Sigma Xi. *Res:* Investigate and develop efficient computerized information dissemination and retrieval systems; study and purpose ways to enhance the usefulness of scientific and technical information; author of one book. *Mailing Add:* NERAC Inc 1 Technology Dr Tolland CT 06084

**WILDE, GARNER LEE,** GEOLOGY. *Current Pos:* CONSULT GEOLOGIST, 86- *Personal Data:* b Spring Creek, Tex, Sept 29, 26; m 51; c 2. *Educ:* Tex Christian Univ, BA, 50, MA, 52. *Hon Degrees:* DSc, Tex Christian Univ, 76. *Prof Exp:* Jr geologist, Humble Oil & Refining Co, Exxon Co, USA, 52-53, from assoc paleontologist to paleontologist, 53-63, sr res geologist, 63-67, prof geologist, 67-71, prof geologist, Hq Staff, 71-76, sr explor geologist, 76-81; mgr, Explor Div, Permian Basin, Harper Oil Co, 81-85. *Concurrent Pos:* Lectr, Case Western Res Univ, 63; vis lectr, Tex Tech Univ, 67, 78 & Univ Mo, 69; mem bd dirs, Cushman Found Foraminiferal Res, 70-75, pres, 74-75; vis lectr, Kans State Univ, 71 & Rensselaer Polytech Inst, 71; adj prof geol, Tex Christian Univ, 76-; hon mem, Permian Basin Sect, Soc Econ Paleontologists & Mineralogists. *Mem:* Fel Geol Soc Am; Soc Econ Paleontologists & Mineralogists; Am Asn Petrol Geologists. *Res:* Stratigraphic and paleontological studies on late Paleozoic Fusulinid Foraminifera, Calcareous algae and Mesozoic Calcareous Microfossils; carbonate facies; over 50 publications in fusulinid biostratigraphy, carbonate sedimentation. *Mailing Add:* 5 Auburn Ct Midland TX 79705

**WILDE, GERALD ELDON,** ENTOMOLOGY. *Current Pos:* ASSOC PROF ENTOM & RES ENTOMOLOGY, AGR RES STA, KANS STATE UNIV, 66- *Personal Data:* b Ballinger, Tex, Dec 7, 39. *Educ:* Tex Tech Col, BS, 62; Cornell Univ, PhD(entom), 66. *Prof Exp:* Res asst entom, Cornell Univ, 62-66. *Mem:* Entom Soc Am. *Res:* Economic entomology; field crops insects. *Mailing Add:* Dept Entom Waters Hall Kans State Univ Manhattan KS 66506-4000

**WILDE, KENNETH ALFRED,** PHYSICAL CHEMISTRY. *Current Pos:* CONSULT, RADCAN CORP, 88- *Personal Data:* b Cedar City, Utah, Mar 4, 29; m 61; c 2. *Educ:* Univ Utah, BS, 50, PhD(chem), 53. *Prof Exp:* Res chemist, Redstone Res Labs, Rohm and Haas Co, 53-70, res chemist, Res Div, 70-75; sr scientist, Radian Corp, 75-78; consult, 78-88. *Mem:* Am Chem Soc. *Res:* High temperature thermodynamics and kinetics; aerothermodynamics; mass transfer process simulation; solution thermodynamics and process simulation; adsorption and chromatography simulation. *Mailing Add:* 3604 Laurel Ledge Lane Austin TX 78731-4048. *E-Mail:* 102545.1676@compuserve.com

**WILDE, PAT,** OCEANOGRAPHY. *Current Pos:* CONSULT, 88- *Personal Data:* b Chicago, Ill, Sept 25, 35. *Educ:* Yale Univ, BS, 57; Harvard Univ, AM, 61, PhD(geol), 65. *Prof Exp:* Geologist, Shell Oil Co, 57-59; res geologist, Scripps Inst Oceanog, 60-62; lectr ocean eng, Univ Calif, Berkeley, 64-68, res engr, 64-66, res oceanogr, 66-75, asst prof, 68-75, res scientist & oceanogr, Lawrence Berkeley Lab, 75-82, res marine scientist, Dept Paleont, 82-89, lectr ocean eng, 75-88. *Concurrent Pos:* Consult, Coastal Res Panel Earthquake Eng, Nat Acad Eng, 65-67; adv tech adv bd, Dept Eng, City & Co San Francisco, 70-74; vis prof, Inst Geol, Tech Univ Berlin, Ger, 89-90; Alexander von Humboldt sr fel, 89; assoc dir, Off Naval Res, Tokyo, Japan, 94-96. *Mem:* Geol Soc Am; Am Geophys Union. *Res:* Marine electrochemistry; sediment transport in marine environments; chemostratigraphy of black shales. *Mailing Add:* 1735 Highland Pl No 28 Berkeley CA 94709. *E-Mail:* patwilde@dnai.com

**WILDE, RICHARD EDWARD, JR,** STATISTICAL MECHANICS, HUMAN GENOME. *Current Pos:* from asst prof to prof, 63-95, EMER PROF CHEM, TEX TECH UNIV, 95- *Personal Data:* b Los Angeles, Calif, Jan 7, 31; m 60, Sophia Mueller; c 3. *Educ:* Univ Calif, Los Angeles, BS, 56; Univ Wash, PhD(chem), 61. *Prof Exp:* Res assoc, Johns Hopkins Univ, 61-63. *Concurrent Pos:* Vis prof, Univ Durham, Eng, 86. *Mem:* Am Chem Soc; Am Phys Soc. *Res:* Textbook writing in areas of statistical mechanics and the human genome; heterogeneous photocatalysis. *Mailing Add:* Dept Chem Tex Tech Univ Lubbock TX 79409. *E-Mail:* methsilane@aol.com

**WILDE, WALTER SAMUEL,** medical physiology, for more information see previous edition

**WILDEMAN, THOMAS RAYMOND,** ANALYTICAL CHEMISTRY, GEOCHEMISTRY. *Current Pos:* asst prof, 67-73, assoc prof, 73-79, PROF CHEM, COLO SCH MINES, 79- *Personal Data:* b Madison, Wis, May 11, 40; m 65; c 2. *Educ:* Col St Thomas, BS, 62; Univ Wis, PhD(phys chem), 67. *Honors & Awards:* Nat Eng Excellence Award, Consult Engrs Coun Am, 90. *Prof Exp:* Lectr chem, Univ Wis, 66-67. *Concurrent Pos:* Consult, US Geol Surv, 70-; chmn, Geochem Div, Am Chem Soc, 81, 82, prog chmn, Educ Div, 97-; consult environ chem, 84- *Mem:* Am Chem Soc; Geochem Soc; Am Soc Surface Mining & Reclamation; AAAS. *Res:* Properties of trace elements in solids and liquids; isotopic, radiochemical and atomic analysis; geochemistry of trace elements in rocks and waters; passive treatment technology. *Mailing Add:* Dept Chem Colo Sch Mines Golden CO 80401-1888

**WILDENTHAL, BRYAN HOBSON,** PHYSICS. *Current Pos:* vpres acad affairs, 92-94, PROVOST & VPRES ACAD AFFAIRS, UNIV TEX, DALLAS, 94- *Personal Data:* b San Marcos, Tex, Nov 4, 37; m, Adele Sutton; c Rebecca, Bryan, Lora, Kerry & Andrea. *Educ:* Sul Ross State Col, BA, 58; Univ Kans, PhD(physics), 64. *Prof Exp:* Res assoc physics, Rice Univ, 64-66; US AEC fel, Oak Ridge Nat Lab, 66-68; asst prof, Tex A&M Univ, 68-69; from assoc prof to prof physics, Mich State Univ, 69-83; prof & dept head, physics & atmospheric sci, Drexel Univ, 83-87; dean, Col Arts & Sci, Univ NMex, 87-92. *Concurrent Pos:* Sr US fel, Humboldt Found, Univ Munich, 73; vis scientist, Brookhaven Nat Lab, 74, Max Planck Inst Nuclear Physics, Heidelberg, 76, Soc Heavy Ion Res, Darmstadt, 77 & Los Alamos Nat Lab, 79; vis prof, Univ Paris, 77, Univ Oxford, 79 & Univ Manchester, 80; fel, John Simon Guggenheim Mem Found, 77; exec secy, Nuclear Sci Adv Comt, NSF, 78. *Mem:* Fel Am Phys Soc; Sigma Xi. *Res:* Study of the low lying quantum states of atomic nuclei via direct reaction experiments and shell model theory. *Mailing Add:* Off Provost Univ Tex Dallas Richardson TX 75083-0688

**WILDENTHAL, KERN,** PHYSIOLOGY, INTERNAL MEDICINE. *Current Pos:* from asst prof to prof physiol & internal med, Univ Tex Southwestern Med Ctr, Dallas, 70-75, dean, Grad Sch Biomed Sci, 76-80, dean med sch, 80-86, PROF INTERNAL MED & PHYSIOL & PRES, UNIV TEX SOUTHWESTERN MED CTR, DALLAS, 86- *Personal Data:* b San Marcos, Tex, July 1, 41; m 64, Margaret Dehlinger; c Pamela & Catherine. *Educ:* Sul Ross Col, BA, 60; Univ Tex Southwestern Med Sch, Dallas, MD, 64; Cambridge Univ, PhD(cell physiol), 70. *Prof Exp:* Intern, Bellevue Hosp-NY Univ, 64-65; resident & cardiol fel, Parkland Hosp-Univ Tex Southwestern Med Sch, Dallas, 65-67; guest scientist, Nat Heart Lung & Blood Inst, Bethesda, 67-68; vis scientist, Strangeways Res Lab, Cambridge Univ, 68-70. *Concurrent Pos:* Guggenheim Found Fel, Univ Cambridge, Eng, 75-76. *Mem:* Am Soc Clin Invest; Int Soc Heart Res; Royal Soc Med Gt Brit; Am Physiol Soc; Am Col Cardiol; Asn Am Physicians. *Res:* Cardiac physiology and metabolism. *Mailing Add:* Off Pres Univ Tex Southwestern Med Ctr 5323 Harry Hines Blvd Dallas TX 75235-9002. *Fax:* 214-648-8690

**WILDER, CLEO DUKE,** VERTEBRATE ZOOLOGY. *Current Pos:* ASSOC PROF BIOL, MURRAY STATE UNIV, 69- *Personal Data:* b Macon, Ga, Sept 24, 25; m 50; c 2. *Educ:* Univ NC, AB, 48; Univ Tenn, MS, 51; Univ Fla, PhD, 62. *Prof Exp:* Instr biol, Presby Col, SC, 51-53; asst, Univ Fla, 55-57 & 58-59; asst prof, Memphis State Univ, 59-62; asst zool, Va Polytech Inst, 62-69. *Mem:* Am Soc Ichthyologists & Herpetologists; Soc Study Amphibians & Reptiles; Sigma Xi; Herpetologists' League. *Res:* Taxonomy, ecology, distribution, behavior and evolution of amphibians and reptiles; ecology of stream drainage systems and cypress swamps in western Kentucky. *Mailing Add:* Dept Biol Sci Murray State Univ Murray KY 42071-3310

**WILDER, DAVID RANDOLPH,** CERAMIC ENGINEERING, MATERIALS. *Current Pos:* From instr to prof, Iowa State Univ, 55-91, chmn dept, 61-64, head dept, 64-75, chmn, Dept Mat Sci & Eng, 75-91, EMER PROF CERAMIC ENG, IOWA STATE UNIV, 91- *Personal Data:* b Lorimor, Iowa, June 11, 29; m 51, Donna Moore; c Susan, Michael, Margaret & Bruce. *Educ:* Iowa State Univ, BS, 51, MS, 52, PhD(ceramic eng), 58. *Concurrent Pos:* Jr ceramic engr, Ames Lab, Iowa State Univ, 52-55, ceramic engr, 55-57, res assoc, 57-58, engr, 58-61, sr engr, 61-66, div chief, Ceramic & Mech Eng Div, 66-73, sr engr, Ames Lab, Dept Energy, 73-81. *Mem:* Am Soc Eng Educ; fel Am Ceramic Soc; Nat Inst Ceramic Engrs. *Res:* High temperature properties and processing of ceramic materials. *Mailing Add:* 1214 Ridgewood Ames IA 50012

**WILDER, HARRY D(OUGLAS),** PULP & PAPER SCIENCE, CHEMICAL ENGINEERING. *Current Pos:* RETIRED. *Personal Data:* b Westfield, Wis, Aug 22, 32; m 59; c David, Lynn & Leigh. *Educ:* Univ Wis, BS, 55; Inst Paper Chem, MS, 57, PhD, 60. *Prof Exp:* Res aide chem eng, Inst Paper Chem, 59-65; asst dir res & develop, Albemarle Paper Co, Va, 66, dir, 67-68; dir pulp & paper res, Ethyl Corp, 68-76; sr sci assoc, Scott Paper Co, 77-79, chief res assoc, 79. *Mem:* Am Inst Chem Engrs; Tech Asn Pulp & Paper Indust. *Res:* Pulping methods and rates; pulp bleaching; pulping and bleaching chemical generation; pulping research; fiber properties research. *Mailing Add:* 2027 Ridge Rd Elverson PA 19520. *Fax:* 610-469-9774

**WILDER, JAMES ANDREW, JR,** MATERIALS SCIENCE, GLASS SCIENCE. *Current Pos:* MEM STAFF GLASS CERAMIC RES, SANDIA LABS, 78- *Personal Data:* b Washington, DC, Dec 19, 50; m 73. *Educ:* Cath Univ Am, BSE, 73, MSE, 75, Phd(mat sci), 78. *Mem:* Am Ceramic Soc; Inst Elec & Electronics Engrs. *Res:* Phase separation and crystallization in glass; glass-to-metal sealing. *Mailing Add:* Sandia Nat Lab PO Box 5800 MS 0328 Dept 2674 Albuquerque NM 87185

**WILDER, JOSEPH R,** SURGERY. *Current Pos:* PROF SURG, MT SINAI SCH MED, 67- *Personal Data:* b Baltimore, Md, Oct 5, 20; c 5. *Educ:* Dartmouth Col, BS, 42; Columbia Univ, MD, 45. *Prof Exp:* Chief & dir, Surg Serv, Wright Patterson Hosp, 52-54; fel cardiovasc res, Karolinska Inst, Sweden, 54-55; asst prof surg, NY Med Col, 55-58; dir gen surg, Hosp Joint Dis & Med Ctr, 59-80. *Concurrent Pos:* Med adv, NY State Legis, 65-75; examr, Am Bd Surg, 70-75; consult, US Off Econ Opportunity, 75-80. *Mem:* Am Bd Surg; Fel Am Col Surgeons; AMA. *Res:* Selective surgical intervention in management of penetrating wounds of the abdomen. *Mailing Add:* 1 Gustave L Levy Pl New York NY 10029-6504

**WILDER, PELHAM, JR,** ORGANIC CHEMISTRY. *Current Pos:* From instr to prof chem, Duke Univ, 49-68, prof chem & pharmacol, 68-87, univ distinguished serv prof, 87-90, EMER UNIV DISTINGUISHED SERV PROF CHEM, DUKE UNIV, 90- *Personal Data:* b Americus, Ga, July 20, 20; m 45, Sterly Lebey; c Alma A, Pelham III & Sterly L. *Educ:* Emory Univ, AB, 42, MA, 43; Harvard Univ, MA, 47, PhD(org chem), 50. *Concurrent Pos:* Consult, NSF, 60-68, E I du Pont de Nemours & Co, Inc, 66-69 & Res Triangle Inst, 68-; Gov Sci Adv Comt, 62-64; mem, Advan Placement Chem Comt, Col Entrance Exam Bd, 68-74, chmn, 69-74, mem, Advan Placement Standing Comt, 69-72; assoc, Comt Prof Training, Am Chem Soc. *Mem:* Am Chem Soc; Sigma Xi. *Res:* Stereochemical studies; kinetic, thermodynamic control and mechanism of organic reactions; quantitative structure-activity relationship studies in pharmacology. *Mailing Add:* 2514 Wrightwood Ave Durham NC 27705-5830

**WILDER, RONALD LYNN,** ANIMAL MODELS OF ARTHRITIS, RHEUMATOID ARTHRITIS. *Current Pos:* res assoc immunol, Nat Inst Allergy & Infectious Dis, NIH, 76-79, clin assoc, 79-81, sr investr rheumatology, Arthritis Br, 81-92, CHIEF, INFLAMMATORY JOINT DIS SECT, NIH, 92- *Personal Data:* b Long Beach, Calif, Feb 10, 47; m 69, Souter; c Jason & Wendy. *Educ:* Univ Calif, Los Angeles, BS, 69, MD & PhD(molecular biol), 74. *Prof Exp:* Intern med, Univ Calif, San Diego, 74-75, resident, 75-76. *Mem:* Am Asn Immunologists; Am Col Physicians; Am Col Rheumatology; Sigma Xi; Clin Immunol Soc; Am Soc Clin Invest. *Res:* Etiology and pathogenesis of chronic erosive forms of arthritis; animal models of arthritis; genetics and neuroendocrine mechanisms. *Mailing Add:* Arthritis & Rheumatism Br Nat Inst Arthritis Musculoskeletal & Skin Dis NIH Bldg 10 Rm 9N228 Bethesda MD 20892. *Fax:* 301-402-0012; *E-Mail:* wilderr@arb.niams.nih.gov

**WILDEY, ROBERT LEROY,** LUNAR & PLANETARY PHOTOMETRY, PLANETARY SCIENCE. *Current Pos:* from assoc prof to prof astrophysics & astron, 72-80, PROF MATH PHYSICS & ASTRON, NORTHERN ARIZ UNIV, 82-; ASTROPHYSICIST, BR ASTROGEOL, US GEOL SERV, 85- *Personal Data:* b Los Angeles, Calif, Aug 22, 34; m 59, Diana H Skolfield; c Robert B, Wendy C & Herbert C. *Educ:* Calif Inst Technol, BS, 57, MS, 58, PhD(astron), 62. *Honors & Awards:* Cert of Appreciation, NASA Apollo Prog, 69- *Prof Exp:* Res engr, Jet Propulsion Lab, Calif Inst Technol, 59-60, res fel & lectr astron & geol, Mt Wilson & Palomar Observ & Div Geol Sci, Calif Ist Technol, 62-65. *Concurrent Pos:* Consult, United Electrodyn Corp, 62-63, Aeronutronics Div, Ford Motor Co, 63-64 & World Book Encycl Sci Serv, 63-64; vis prof, Univ Calif, Berkeley, 66; mem planetary astron panel, Space Sci Bd, Nat Acad Sci, 67-69. *Mem:* Am Astron Soc; Am Geophys Union; fel Geol Soc Am; Int Astron Union; fel Royal Astron Soc; fel Explorers Club. *Res:* Observational approach to stellar and galactic evolution; co-pioneer (with B C Murray and J A Westphal) of cryogenic far-infrared, infrared studies substantiating Jupiter as a star, discovered hot satellite shadow phenomenon, first detection of far-infrared radiation from a star; Apollo and Mariner-Mars experimenter; gravitation and cosmology; photoclinometry; automated digital photogrammetry and photoclinometry; radiative transfer theory; synthetic aperture radar signal processing; invention of radarclinometry; comprehensive-spectrometry of the moon for Earth observing system post-launch calibration. *Mailing Add:* Northern Ariz Univ Dept Physics & Astron PO Box 6010 Flagstaff AZ 86011. *E-Mail:* wildey@bohr.phy.nau.edu

**WILDFEUER, MARVIN EMANUEL,** FERMENTATION PRODUCTS, ANTIBIOTIC PURIFICATION DEVELOPMENT. *Current Pos:* sr chemist, 68-80, RES SCIENTIST, ELI LILLY & CO, 80- *Personal Data:* b Bronx, NY, Apr 16, 36; m 67; c 2. *Educ:* Queen's Col, NY, BS, 57; Iowa State Univ, MS, 59; Univ Del, PhD(chem), 63. *Prof Exp:* NIH fel molecular biol, Univ Calif, San Diego, 63-65; res scientist, Sansum Clin & Res Found, 65-67. *Mem:* Am Chem Soc. *Res:* Responsible for production scale antibiotic purification technology, especially macrolide, beta-lactam and polyether antibiotics; development of new isolation procedures from fermentation broth; antibiotic derivatization. *Mailing Add:* 3575 Canterbury Dr Lafayette IN 47905

**WILDI, BERNARD SYLVESTER,** ORGANIC CHEMISTRY. *Current Pos:* CONSULT, 82- *Personal Data:* b Columbus, Ohio, May 23, 20. *Educ:* Ohio State Univ, BSc, 43, PhD(org chem), 48. *Prof Exp:* Res chemist, Nat Defense Res Comt, Ohio State Univ, 43-44 & Manhattan Proj, Los Alamos Sci Lab, NMex, 44-47; Nat Res Coun fel, Harvard Univ, 48-49; mem fac, Fla State Univ, 49-50; mem staff life sci, Monsanto Co, 50-53, group leader, 53-65, mgr, 65-69, distinguished sci fel, 69-82. *Mem:* AAAS; Am Chem Soc. *Res:* Structure of natural products; chemical spectroscopy; organic synthesis. *Mailing Add:* 1234 Folger St Louis MO 63122-1233

**WILDIN, MAURICE W(ILBERT),** HEAT TRANSFER, THERMAL ENERGY. *Current Pos:* From asst prof to prof, 61-72, chmn dept, 68-73, PROF MECH ENG, UNIV NMEX, 72- *Personal Data:* b Hutchinson, Kans, June 24, 35; m 58, Mary A Christiansen; c Molly & Milly. *Educ:* Univ Kans, BSME, 58; Purdue Univ, MSME, 59, PhD(mech eng), 63. *Concurrent Pos:* Staff mem, Jet Propulsion Lab, Pasadena, 67-68 & Sandia Nat Lab, Albuquerque, 84-85; assoc ed, J Solar Energy Eng, 89-92; consult to several firus on stratified thermal storage. *Mem:* Am Soc Heating Refrig & Air Conditioning Engrs; Am Soc Mech Engrs; Int Solar Energy Soc; Am Solar Energy Soc; Sigma Xi. *Res:* Thermal storage in stratified water tanks; building energy use; ground coupled blot pumps. *Mailing Add:* 720 Montclaire Dr NE Albuquerque NM 87110. *Fax:* 505-268-7650; *E-Mail:* wildin@unm.edu

**WILDING, LAWRENCE PAUL,** SOIL SCIENCE, AGRONOMY. *Current Pos:* PROF SOIL SCI, TEX A&M UNIV, 76- *Personal Data:* b Winner, SDak, Oct 1, 34; m 56, Gladys Dora Milne; c Charles William, Linda Kay, Doris Bertha & David Lawrence. *Educ:* SDak State Univ, BSc, 56, MSc, 59; Univ Ill, PhD(soils), 62. *Honors & Awards:* Res Award, Soil Sci Soc Am, 87; Superior Serv Award Surface Mine Reclamation Res, USDA. *Prof Exp:* Asst agron, SDak State Univ, 56-59; Campbell Soup Co fel plant sci, Univ Ill, 59-62; from asst prof to prof agron, Ohio State Univ, 62-76. *Concurrent Pos:* Fel, Univ Guelph, 72; consult, USAID, El Salvador, Sudan, Niger & Cameroon, 78-85, Rockefeller Found China, 87 & 89. *Mem:* Fel Am Soc Agron; fel Soil Sci Soc Am; Int Soil Sci Soc; fel AAAS; Soil Conserv Soc Am. *Res:* Soil classification and genesis among different climatic, chronologic and topographic sequences; origin, depth distributions, properties and radiocarbon age of soil opal phytoliths; statistical variability in soil physical and chemical parameters; clay mineralogy; sediment mineralogy and soil erosion; microfabric and micropedology of soil habitats; international agriculture; land evaluation; environmental quality; wetlands quantification. *Mailing Add:* Dept Soil & Crop Sci Tex A&M Univ College Station TX 77843-2474. *Fax:* 409-862-1712; *E-Mail:* wilding@tamu.edu

**WILDMAN, GARY CECIL,** POLYMER CHEMISTRY. *Current Pos:* VPRES RES & DEVELOP, SCHEARING-PLOUGH HEALTHCARE PRODS, 83- *Personal Data:* b Middlefield, Ohio, Nov 25, 42; m 65, Nancy Jackson; c Deborah & Eric. *Educ:* Thiel Col, AB, 64; Duke Univ, PhD(phys chem), 70. *Prof Exp:* Res chemist, Hercules Inc, 68-71; from assoc prof to prof polymer sci, Univ Southern Miss, 71-83, chmn dept, 71-75, dean, Col Sci & Technol, 76-83. *Mem:* Am Chem Soc; Sigma Xi; Fedn Socs Paint Technol; Soc Plastics Engrs. *Res:* Structure-property relationships of synthetic polymers; x-ray diffraction studies of single crystals and polymeric materials; surface coatings; development and testing of medical devices. *Mailing Add:* 8857 Aldershot Dr Germantown TN 38139. *Fax:* 901-320-5044

**WILDMAN, GEORGE THOMAS,** COST CONTROL, RESOURCE MANAGEMENT. *Current Pos:* Chem engr, Merck & Co, Inc, 57-62, sr chem engr, 62-65, engr assoc, 65-68, res fel, 68-72, sect mgr, Chem Eng Res & Develop Dept, 72-77, tech serv mgr, 77-80, mfg mgr, 80-84, tech oper mgr, 84-87, tech oper dir, Mfg Div, 87-92, TECH OPER & ENG DIR, MERCK & CO, INC, 92- *Personal Data:* b Grasmere, NH, Nov 14, 35. *Educ:* Univ NH, BS, 57; NY Univ, MS, 62; Mass Inst Technol, ScD(chem eng), 73. *Concurrent Pos:* Educ counr, Mass Inst Technol, 75-; tech steering comt, Ctr Chem Process Safety, 88- *Mem:* Am Inst Chem Engrs; Am Chem Soc. *Res:* Organic chemical process research and development; heterogeneous catalysis; synthesis of heterocyclic compounds; antibiotic synthesis; natural products isolation and purification; chemical reactivity evaluation; process safety management; regulatory affairs; new manufacturing technology. *Mailing Add:* 2068 Old Raritan Rd Westfield NJ 07090-4712

**WILDMANN, MANFRED,** MECHANICAL ENGINEERING, COMPUTER SYSTEMS. *Current Pos:* mgr, Mech Sect, Sunnyvale, 62-69, mgr, Terabit Memory Systs Dept, 69-73, MGR, RES DEPT, AMPEX CORP, REDWOOD CITY, 73- *Personal Data:* b Karlsruhe, Ger, Apr 16, 30; US citizen; m 54; c 3. *Educ:* City Col NY, BS, 54; Univ Calif, Los Angeles, MS, 57. *Prof Exp:* Res specialist inertial guidance, Autonetics Div, NAm Aviation, Inc, Calif, 54-62. *Mem:* Am Soc Mech Engrs. *Res:* Lubrication, handling and control of flexible media; large computer memory systems; gas lubrication; foil bearing; inertial components. *Mailing Add:* 1860 Camino De Los Robles St Menlo Park CA 94025

**WILDNAUER, RICHARD HARRY,** DERMATOLOGY, PHARMACEUTICALS. *Current Pos:* PRES, NEOSTRATA CO, INC, 95- *Personal Data:* b New Kensington, Pa, Feb 14, 40; m 66; c 1. *Educ:* St Vincent Col, BS, 62; WVa Univ, PhD(biochem), 66; Rider Col, MBA, 74. *Prof Exp:* Fel, Univ Kans, 66-67; sr scientist, Johnson & Johnson Res Labs, 67-73, sr group leader, 73-77; new prod dir, McNeil Pharmaceut, 77-79; dir new prod develop, Janssen Pharmaceut, 79-82, vpres res & develop, 82-88; vpres technol & bus develop, Johnson & Johnson, 88-92; pres, Baker Cummeur Dermat, 92-95. *Mem:* NY Acad Sci; Soc Invest Dermat; Med Mycol Soc Am; Am Acad Dermat; Sigma Xi. *Res:* Skin physiology and biochemistry; membrane transport properties; wound healing; physical polymer characterizations; medical mycology; pharmaceutical new product development; clinical trials. *Mailing Add:* 6 Pilgrim Run East Brunswick NJ 08816

**WILDS, ALFRED LAWRENCE,** ORGANIC CHEMISTRY. *Current Pos:* from instr to prof 40-85, EMER PROF CHEM, UNIV WIS-MADISON, 85- *Personal Data:* b Kansas City, Mo, Mar 1, 15; wid. *Educ:* Univ Mich, BS, 36, MS, 37, PhD(org chem), 39. *Prof Exp:* Asst chem, Univ Mich, 37-39, DuPont fel, 39-40. *Concurrent Pos:* Co-off investr, Nat Defense Res Comt, Univ Wis-Madison, 42-45; Guggenheim fel, 57. *Mem:* AAAS; Am Chem Soc;

Royal Soc Chem. *Res:* Organic synthesis; integrated syntheses, stereochemistry of catalysis hydrogenations, metal reductions; synthesis of natural products, steroids, hormone analogs; reactions of diazoketones; nuclear magnetic resonance studies. *Mailing Add:* 302 Robin Pkwy Madison WI 53705

**WILDS, PRESTON LEA,** OBSTETRICS & GYNECOLOGY, MATERNAL-FETAL MEDICINE. *Current Pos:* RETIRED. *Personal Data:* b Aiken, SC, Dec 18, 26; m 50, 63; c 4. *Educ:* Yale Univ, BA, 49; Univ Pa, MD, 53; Am Bd Obstet & Gynec, dipl, 62. *Prof Exp:* Asst obstet & gynec, Sch Med, La State Univ, 54-57; pvt pract, SC, 57-59; clin instr, Med Col Ga, 59, from instr to prof, 59-78; prof obstet & gynec, Eastern Va Med Sch, 78-94; regional perinatal clin, Va Dept Health, 84-92. *Mem:* Fel Am Col Obstet & Gynec; AMA. *Res:* Programmed instruction; fetal physiology. *Mailing Add:* 1305 Windsor Point Rd Norfolk VA 23509-1311

**WILDUNG, RAYMOND EARL,** GEOCHEMISTRY, ENVIRONMENTAL SCIENCES. *Current Pos:* sr res scientist, Battelle Pac Northwest Labs, 67-71, prog leader, mgr, Environ Chem Sect, 75-85, assoc mgr environ, 85-86, mgr, Environ Sci Dept, 86-, PROF DIR ENVIRON SCI, BATELLE PAC NORTHWEST NAT LABS. *Personal Data:* b Van Nuys, Calif, Feb 24, 41; m 61; c 2. *Educ:* Calif State Polytech Col, San Luis Obispo, BS, 62; Univ Wis-Madison, MS, 64, PhD(soil sci), 66. *Honors & Awards:* E O Lawrence Award. *Prof Exp:* NIH fel, Univ Wis-Madison, 66-67. *Concurrent Pos:* Grants, USDA, 68-70, Environ Protection Agency, 68-71, US Dept Energy, 68-; Nat Inst Environ Health Sci, 71-82; affil prof, Wash State Univ & Calif State Univ; Comt Accessory Elements, chmn, Oil Shale Panel, Comt Soil as Mineral Resource, Nat Acad Sci; mem, Exec Comt Coord Solid Waste Mgt, US Dept Energy; Nuclear Regulatory Comn, 84-87. *Mem:* AAAS; Am Chem Soc; Am Soc Agron; Int Soc Soil Sci; Soil Sci Soc Am; Soc Environ Geochem & Health. *Res:* Soil-sediment science; over 250 publications on developing a fundamental understanding of geochemical and metabolic processes controlling pollutant behavior as a basis for assessing environmental impacts of energy development, focus on intergrated effects; fate and behavior of pesticides, residuals, trace metals and metal complex behaviour in soils plants radionuclides, subsurface environment and waters. *Mailing Add:* 2632 Harris Ave Richland WA 99352

**WILE, HOWARD P,** research administration; deceased, see previous edition for last biography

**WILEMSKI, GERALD,** PHYSICAL CHEMISTRY, STATISTICAL MECHANICS. *Current Pos:* STAFF SCIENTIST, LAWRENCE LIVERMORE NAT LAB, 93- *Personal Data:* b Dunkirk, NY, Oct 15, 46; div; c Eric. *Educ:* Canisius Col, BS, 68; Yale Univ, PhD(chem), 72. *Prof Exp:* Res assoc, Dept Eng & Appl Sci, Yale Univ, 72-74; res assoc & vis asst prof chem, Dartmouth Col, 74-77; prin scientist, Phys Sci Inc, 77-85, prin res scientist, 85-93. *Concurrent Pos:* Vis prof, Inst CNR TAE, Messina, Italy, 86, 87, 88, 89 & 90. *Mem:* Am Phys Soc; AAAS; Sigma Xi; Am Chem Soc; Am Asn Aerosol Res. *Res:* Statistical mechanics; thermodynamics; electrochemical systems; polymer solutions; nucleation phenomena, aerosols, colloidal suspensions. *Mailing Add:* Lawrence Livermore Nat Lab PO Box 808 Livermore CA 94551-9900. *E-Mail:* wilemski1@llnl.gov

**WILEN, SAMUEL HENRY,** organic chemistry; deceased, see previous edition for last biography

**WILENSKY, JACOB T,** GLAUCOMA, OPHTHALMOLOGY. *Current Pos:* from asst to assoc prof, 74-86, PROF OPHTHAL, COL MED, UNIV ILL, 86-, INTERIM HEAD, DEPT OPHTHAL & VISUAL SCI, 95- *Personal Data:* b New Orleans, La, Aug 16, 42; m 76; c 3. *Educ:* Tulane Univ, BA, 64, MD, 68. *Honors & Awards:* Sr Honor Award, Am Acad Ophthal. *Prof Exp:* Intern med, Mt Sinai Hosp NY, 68-69; res ophthal, Tulane Univ, Affil Hosp, 69-72; fel glaucoma, Sch Med, Washington Univ, 72-73. *Concurrent Pos:* Dir, Glaucoma Serv, Eye & Ear Infirmary, Univ Ill, 77-; vis prof, Hadassah Univ Hosp, Jerusalem, 79; prin investr, Natural Hist Angle-Closure Glaucoma Suspects Study, 80-86. *Mem:* Am Acad Ophthal; Am Glaucoma Soc; Asn Res Vision & Ophthal; Am Ophthal Soc. *Res:* Diagnosis and therapy of glaucoma with an emphasis on laser techniques and the testing of new drugs. *Mailing Add:* 1855 W Taylor Chicago IL 60612-7242

**WILENSKY, ROBERT,** COMPUTER SCIENCE. *Current Pos:* PROF COMPUT SCI, UNIV CALIF, BERKELEY, 78-, CHAIR DEPT, 93- *Personal Data:* b Brooklyn, NY, Mar 26, 51. *Educ:* Yale Univ, BA, 72, PhD(comput sci), 78. *Mem:* Asn Comput Mach; fel Am Asn Artificial Intel. *Res:* Artificial intelligence and the simulation behavior; natural language process; computer situation of human thought processes. *Mailing Add:* 560 Spruce St Berkeley CA 94707

**WILENSKY, SAMUEL,** DATA CONVERSION DESIGN, RADIATION EFFECTS ON ELECTRONICS. *Current Pos:* DIR ENG, HYBRID SYSTS, 68- *Personal Data:* b Savannah, Ga, July 9, 37; m 70; c 2. *Educ:* Mass Inst Technol, BS, 59. *Prof Exp:* Asst prof nuclear eng, Mass Inst Technol, 64-65; res assoc nuclear eng, Mass Gen Hosp, 65-68. *Concurrent Pos:* Asst prof, Harvard Med Sch, 65-68. *Res:* Design and development of data conversion products. *Mailing Add:* 419 Silver Hill Rd Concord MA 01742

**WILES, ANDREW J,** MATHEMATICS. *Current Pos:* PROF MATH, PRINCETON UNIV, 82- *Personal Data:* b Eng, 1952. *Educ:* Oxford Univ, Eng, BS; Cambridge Univ, Eng, PhD(math). *Honors & Awards:* Math Award, Nat Acad Sci, 96; MacArthur Fel, John D & Catherine T MacArthur Found, 97. *Prof Exp:* From asst prof to assoc prof math, Harvard Univ, Cambridge, Mass. *Mem:* Nat Acad Sci. *Res:* Discovery of solution for Pierre de Fermats last theory of 1637. *Mailing Add:* Dept Math Princeton Univ Princeton NJ 08544

**WILES, DAVID M,** POLYMER CHEMISTRY. *Current Pos:* PRES, PLASTICHEMM CONSULT, 90- *Personal Data:* b Springhill, NS, Dec 28, 32; m 57, Valerie Joan Rowlaids; c Gordan & Sandra. *Educ:* McMaster Univ, BSc, 54, MSc, 55; McGill Univ, PhD(phys chem), 57. *Honors & Awards:* Dunlop Lectr Award, Chem Inst Can, 81; Textile Sci Award, Textile Tech Fedn Can, 80. *Prof Exp:* Nat Res Coun Can & Can Ramsay Mem fels, Univ Leeds, 57-59; asst res officer, High Polymer Sect, Nat Res Coun Can, 59-61, assoc res officer, 61-67, sr res officer, 67-74, head, Textile Chem Sect, 66-86, dir, Div Chem, 75-90. *Mem:* Am Chem Soc; Fiber Soc; Chem Inst Can; Can Inst Textile Sci; Royal Soc Chem; fel Royal Soc Can. *Res:* Polymerization kinetics and mechanisms; synthesis of stereoregular polymers; polymer structure; photodegradation of fiber forming macromolecules; polymer stabilization; fiber morphology; modification of fibers; polymer surface studies; microbiological deterioration; composites; high temperature thermoplastics. *Mailing Add:* 3965 Juan de Fuca Terr Victoria BC V8N 5W9 Can. *Fax:* 250-472-2546

**WILES, DONALD ROY,** NUCLEAR INORGANIC CHEMISTRY. *Current Pos:* CONSULT, RADIOACTIVE WASTE DISPOSAL, 90- *Personal Data:* b Truro, NS, Aug 30, 25; m 52, Elisabeth Lilly; c Anne, Karen & Peter. *Educ:* Mt Allison Univ, BSc, 46, BEd, 47; McMaster Univ, MSc, 50; Mass Inst Technol, PhD(chem), 53. *Prof Exp:* Chemist, Eldorado Mining & Refining Ltd, Can, 47-48; res assoc radiochem, Chem Inst, Oslo, Norway, 53-55; res assoc metall chem, Univ BC, 55-59; from asst prof to assoc prof nuclear inorg chem, Carleton Univ, 59, prof chem, 69-90, emer prof, 90-97. *Concurrent Pos:* Vis scientist, Inst Hot Atom Chem, Nuclear Res Ctr, Karlsruhe, Ger, 69-70; chmn, Chem Dept, Carleton Univ, 79-87; adv, Univ Jayapura, Indonesia, 96 & 97. *Mem:* Am Chem Soc; fel Chem Inst Can; Royal Soc Chem; Norweg Chem Soc. *Res:* Dissolution kinetics of metals and oxides; hot atom chemistry in organic solids; nuclear fission; radiochemistry; environmental radiochemistry of radium, thorium; Mossbauer spectroscopy; analytical radiochemistry of radium and thorium; radioanalytical chemistry of radium and thorium, especially in environmental soil, mine waters and water. *Mailing Add:* Dept Chem Carleton Univ 1125 Colonel By Dr Ottawa ON K1S 5B6 Can. *Fax:* 613-520-3749; *E-Mail:* dwiles@ccs.carleton.ca

**WILES, MICHAEL,** PARASITOLOGY, FRESHWATER ECOLOGY. *Current Pos:* from asst prof to assoc prof, 67-80, PROF FRESHWATER ECOL, ST MARY'S UNIV, NS, 80- *Personal Data:* b Sheffield, Eng, May 8, 40; m 63; c 2. *Educ:* Univ Leeds, BSc, 62, PhD(zool), 65. *Prof Exp:* Res scientist, Fisheries Res Bd, Can, 65-67. *Mem:* Can Soc Zool; Brit Soc Parasitol. *Res:* Parasites of freshwater and marine fishes of Eastern Canada; diseases and parasites of reef fishes and turkles in Bermuda; marine ecology. *Mailing Add:* Dept Biol St Mary's Univ Robie St Halifax NS B3H 3C3 Can

**WILES, ROBERT ALLAN,** INDUSTRIAL ORGANIC CHEMISTRY. *Current Pos:* RETIRED. *Personal Data:* b Quincy, Mass, Apr 6, 29; m 51; c 5. *Educ:* Univ NH, BS, 51, MS, 55; Mass Inst Technol, PhD(chem), 58. *Prof Exp:* Res chemist, Sun Oil Co, 57-59; res chemist, Solvay Process Div, Allied Chem Co, Allied Corp, 59-64, res supvr, 64-70, res supvr, Indust Chem Div, 66-68, mgr process res, 71-80, mgr, Specialty Chem Div, 60-80, sr res assoc, 81-82. *Mem:* Am Chem Soc. *Res:* Fluorochemicals and process research and development. *Mailing Add:* 10 Bishops Blvd Apt 101 Holly Hill FL 32117

**WILETS, LAWRENCE,** THEORETICAL PHYSICS, NUCLEAR PHYSICS. *Current Pos:* from assoc prof to prof, 58-95, EMER PROF THEORET PHYSICS, UNIV WASH, 95- *Personal Data:* b Oconomowoc, Wis, Jan 4, 27; m 76, Vivian R Wolf; c Ilanna (Schwalbe), Edward E & James D. *Educ:* Univ Wis, BS, 48; Princeton Univ, MA, 50, PhD(physics), 52. *Honors & Awards:* Alexander von Humboldt Sr Scientist Award. *Prof Exp:* Res assoc theoret physics, Proj Matterhorn, Princeton Univ, 51-53; res assoc, Lawrence Livermore Lab, Univ Calif, 53; NSF fel, Inst Theoret Physics, Copenhagen, 53-55; mem staff, Los Alamos Sci Lab, 55-58; mem, Inst Advan Study, Princeton, 57-58. *Concurrent Pos:* NSF sr fel, Weizmann Inst Sci, 61-62; vis prof, Princeton Univ, 69 & Calif Inst Technol, 71; J S Guggenheim fel, Univ Lund & Weizmann Inst Sci, 76-77; Nordita prof, Univ Lund, 76; sabbatical vis, Lawrence Berkeley Lab & Stanford Linear Acc, 87-88; Sir Thomas Lyle res fel, Univ Melbourne, 89. *Mem:* Fel Am Phys Soc; fel AAAS; Am Asn Univ Professors; Fedn Am Scientists. *Res:* Atomic and nuclear structure and reactions; nuclear substructure, especially the role of quarks and quantum chromodynamics in nuclear physics; meson physics; manybody theory; heavy ions and fission; soliton bag model. *Mailing Add:* Dept Physics Box 351560 Univ Wash Seattle WA 98195-1560. *Fax:* 206-685-0635; *E-Mail:* wilets@uwaphast.bitnet

**WILEY, ALBERT LEE, JR,** RADIATION MEDICINE. *Current Pos:* PROF & CHMN, DEPT RADIATION ONCOL & DIR, CANCER CTR, EASTERN CAROLINA UNIV SCH MED, GREENVILLE, 88- *Personal Data:* b Forest City, NC, June 9, 36; m 60; c 4. *Educ:* NC State Univ, BN, 58; Univ Rochester, MD, 63; Univ Wis-Madison, PhD(radiobiol & nuclear eng), 72; Am Bd Radiol, cert, 68; Am Bd Nuclear Med, cert, 75; Am Bd Sci Nuclear Med, cert, 80. *Prof Exp:* Nuclear engr, Nuclear Prod Div, Lockheed Aircraft, Ga, 58; intern med & surg, Med Ctr, Univ Va, 63-64; Nat Cancer Inst fel radiation ther, Med Ctr, Stanford Univ, 64-65, radiation ther & nuclear med, Univ Wis Hosps, 65-68; med dir, US Naval Radiol Defense Lab, San Francisco, Calif, 68-70; asst prof radiation ther, Univ Tex, M D Anderson Hosp, Houston, 72-73; assoc prof radiol & human oncol, 76-79, assoc dir & clin dir radiation oncol & prof human oncol, radiol & med physics, Med Sch, Univ Wis-Madison, 79-88. *Concurrent Pos:* Vis prof, Cent Hosp & Radiation Clins, Univ Helsinki, 79 & Univ Linkoping, Sweden, 86; consult, Nat Cancer Inst, 81 & Adv Comt Reactor Safeguards, Nuclear Regulatory Comn, 81-; tech adv, Dept Health & Human Serv, State Wis, 81-; mem bd dirs, Am Bd Sci Nuclear Med, 87-, Wis Gov Biotechnol Bd, Wis Radioactive Waste Bd & US Dept Vet Affairs Oncol Bd, 90- *Mem:* Soc Nuclear Med; Health Physics Soc; Inst Elec & Electronics Engrs; Am Soc Law & Med; fel Am Col Prev Med; Am Soc Radiation Oncologists. *Res:* New radiation techniques in the treatment of cancer of pancreas and biliary tract; the use of nuclear medicine, nuclear magnetic resonance and computerized tomography for improving the quality control and optimization of cancer treatment; use of nuclear reactors in medical research and health physics of radiation accidents; biological dosimetry. *Mailing Add:* Watson Clin Rad Therapy Ctr Box 95000 Lakeland FL 33805

**WILEY, BILL BEAUFORD,** MICROBIOLOGY, IMMUNOLOGY. *Current Pos:* from asst prof to prof, 62-88, EMER PROF MICROBIOL, MED CTR, UNIV UTAH, 88- *Personal Data:* b St Joseph, Mo, Nov 12, 23; m 45, Avis M Dew; c Karen S & Sharon M. *Educ:* Univ Kans, BA, 49, MA, 50; Univ Rochester, PhD(microbiol), 56. *Prof Exp:* Asst dir, Rochester Health Bur Labs, Med Ctr, Univ Rochester, 50-56; asst prof microbiol, Univ Sask, 56-62. *Concurrent Pos:* Med Res Coun Can fel, Univ Sask, 57-62; Nat Inst Allergy & Infectious Dis fel, Univ Utah, 63- *Mem:* AAAS; Can Soc Microbiol; Am Soc Microbiol; NY Acad Sci; Sigma Xi. *Res:* Encapsulation and virulence of Staphylococcus aureus staphylococcal scalded skin syndrome; sphingomyelinases of staphylococcal toxins. *Mailing Add:* 4041 Lisa Dr Salt Lake City UT 84124

**WILEY, DON CRAIG,** BIOPHYSICS. *Current Pos:* Asst prof biochem & molecular biol, Harvard Univ, 71-75, assoc prof biochem, 75-80, chmn biophysics, 80-92, chmn, Dept Biochem & Molecular Biol, 92-95, PROF BIOCHEM & BIOPHYS, HARVARD UNIV, 79- *Personal Data:* b Akron, Ohio, Oct 21, 44. *Educ:* Tufts Univ, SB, 66; Harvard Univ, PhD(biophys), 71. *Hon Degrees:* Dr, Univ Leiden, Neth, 95. *Honors & Awards:* K F Lectr, Univ Calif, San Francisco, 86; John T Edsall Lectr, Harvard Univ, 87; Harvey Lectr, NY Acad Sci, 88; Cetus Lectr, Univ Calif, Berkeley, 89; Marchon Vis Lectr, Univ Newcastle upon Tyne, 89; Charlton Lectr, Tufts Univ, 90; William B Coley Award, 92; Emil Von Behring Prize, 93; Passano Found Award, 93; Gairdner Found Int Award, 94; Albert Lasker Basic Med Res Award, 95; Searle Distinguished Lectr, Northwestern Univ, 95; Nelson Med Lectr, Univ Calif, Davis, 96; Rose Payne Distinguished Scientist Award, 96. *Concurrent Pos:* Jane Sloan Coffin Fund grant, Harvard Univ, 72-73; fel, Europ Molecular Biol, 76; investr, Howard Hughes Med Inst, 87- *Mem:* Fel Nat Acad Sci; AAAS; Am Chem Soc; Am Crystallog Asn; Am Soc Virol; Biophys Soc; Protein Soc; fel Am Acad Arts & Sci; Am Philos Soc; Am Soc Biochem & Molecular Biol. *Res:* X-ray diffraction; structure of macromolecules and assemblies of macromolecules; viral membrane glycoproteins. *Mailing Add:* Dept Biochem Harvard Univ Howard Hughes Med Inst 7 Divinity Ave Cambridge MA 02138

**WILEY, DOUGLAS WALKER,** organic chemistry, synthetic organic chemistry; deceased, see previous edition for last biography

**WILEY, E(DWARD) O(RLANDO), III,** ICHTHYOLOGY, SYSTEMATIC BIOLOGY. *Current Pos:* From asst cur to cur fishes, 76-88, CUR, MUS NATURAL HIST, UNIV KANS, 88-, PROF BIOL SCI, 88- *Personal Data:* b Corpus Christi, Tex, Aug 15, 44; m 77, Karen S Carpenter; c 3. *Educ:* Southwest Tex State Univ, BS, 66; Sam Houston State Univ, MS, 72; City Univ New York, PhD(biol), 76. *Honors & Awards:* Stoye Award Ichthyol, Am Soc Ichthyologists & Herpetologists, 76. *Concurrent Pos:* Prof biol sci, Mus Natural Hist, Univ Kans, 78-88; res assoc, US Mus Natural Hist, 80- *Mem:* Am Soc Ichthyologists & Herpetologists; Soc Syst Biol. *Res:* Phylogenetic relationships of fishes; theory and practice of phylogenetic systematics; evolutionary theory and its relationship to systematics and biogeography; molecular systematics of fishes. *Mailing Add:* Nat Hist Mus Dycke Hall Univ Kans Lawrence KS 66045. *E-Mail:* wiley@kuhub.cc.ukans.edu

**WILEY, JACK CLEVELAND,** COMPUTER-AIDED ENGINEERING. *Current Pos:* sr res engr, 72-79, mgr eng analysis, 80-89, PRIN ENGR, DEERE & CO TECH CTR, 89- *Personal Data:* b Evansville, Ind, Mar 17, 40; m 65, Joyce Kale; c Jason & Alice. *Educ:* Purdue Univ, Lafayette, BS, 62, PhD(eng sci), 68; Univ Ill, Urbana, MS, 64. *Prof Exp:* Asst prof theoret & appl mech, Univ Ill, Urbana, 67-72. *Concurrent Pos:* Presidential exchange exec, US Dept Com, 79-80. *Mem:* Am Soc Mech Engrs; Am Soc Agr Engrs. *Res:* Mechanical system analysis; mechanism and vehicle mechanics; mechanical computer aided engineering; tractor performance; soil dynamics. *Mailing Add:* 3732 40th Street Ct 3300 River Dr Moline IL 61265. *Fax:* 309-765-3807; *E-Mail:* wileyj@de.deere.com

**WILEY, JAMES C, JR,** RADIO-CHEMICAL SYNTHESIS. *Current Pos:* Technician, Midwest Res Inst, 62-65, jr chemist, 65-68, asst chemist, 68-71, assoc chemist, 71-76, sr chemist, 76-81, prin chemist, 81-85, GROUP LEADER, MIDWEST RES INST, 85-, TECH OPERS MGR, CHEMSYN SCI LAB, 85- *Personal Data:* b Higginsville, Mo, Mar 4, 38; m 62; c 2. *Educ:* Univ Mo, Kansas City, BS, 68. *Concurrent Pos:* Prin investr, Nat Cancer Inst, 76- *Mem:* Am Chem Soc; AAAS; Sigma Xi. *Res:* Synthesis of labeled and unlabeled carcinogenic polycyclic aromatic hydrocarbon metabolites. *Mailing Add:* Chemsyn Sci Labs 13605 W 96th Terr Lenexa KS 66215-1253

**WILEY, JOHN DUNCAN,** SOLID STATE PHYSICS. *Current Pos:* PROF ELEC & COMPUT ENG, UNIV WIS-MADISON, 76-, CHMN, MAT SCI PROG, 82- *Personal Data:* b Nashville, Tenn, Mar 23, 42. *Educ:* Ind Univ, BS, 64; Univ Wis, MS, 65, PhD(physics), 68. *Honors & Awards:* Alexander Von Humboldt Award, 74 & 75. *Prof Exp:* Mem tech staff, Optical & Magnetic Mat Dept, Bell Tel Labs, 68-74; res assoc, Max Planck Inst Solid State Res, 74-75. *Concurrent Pos:* Fel, NSF, 64-66. *Mem:* Am Vacuum Soc; Am Phys Soc; Inst Elec & Electronics Engrs. *Res:* Transport properties of semiconductors; optical properties of semiconductors; growth and characterization of semiconductor crystals. *Mailing Add:* Univ Wis Rm 150 Bascomb Hall 500 Lincoln Dr Madison WI 53706

**WILEY, JOHN ROBERT,** NUCLEAR CHEMISTRY. *Current Pos:* ASSOC PROF CHEM, PERMIAN BASIN, UNIV TEX, 89- *Personal Data:* b San Angelo, Tex, Oct 10, 46; m 68; c 2. *Educ:* Univ Houston, BS, 69; Purdue Univ, PhD(nuclear chem), 74. *Prof Exp:* Res chem separations, Savannah River Plant, E I du Pont de Nemours & Co, Inc, 74-89. *Concurrent Pos:* Int Atomic Energy Agency, Vienna, 85-87. *Mem:* Am Chem Soc; AAAS; Sigma Xi. *Res:* Management of nuclear plant wastes; toxic chemical waste; gas phase negative ions. *Mailing Add:* 3502 Meadowridge Midland TX 79707-4507

**WILEY, JOHN W,** MEDICINE. *Current Pos:* ASST PROF INTERNAL MED & GASTROENTEROL, UNIV MICH, 87- *Personal Data:* b Portland, Ore, Aug 26, 49. *Educ:* Claremont-McKenna Col, BA, 71; Ore Health Sci Univ, MD, 80. *Mem:* Am Gastroenterol Soc; Am Col Physicians; Am Fedn Clin Res; Am Motility Soc; Cent Soc Clin Res. *Res:* Neurohormonal regulation of neural transmission; motility problems of the gastrointestinal tract. *Mailing Add:* Univ Mich Med Ctr 5056 Christine Dr Ann Arbor MI 48109-0682

**WILEY, LORRAINE,** PLANT PHYSIOLOGY. *Current Pos:* asst prof, 72-76, assoc prof, 76-81, PROF BIOL, CALIF STATE UNIV, FRESNO, 81- *Personal Data:* b Sacramento, Calif. *Educ:* Sacramento State Col, AB, 64; Univ Calif, Davis, MS, 66, PhD(plant physiol), 71. *Prof Exp:* Asst prof bot, Howard Univ, 71-72. *Concurrent Pos:* Res botanist, Univ Calif, Davis, 71. *Mem:* Am Soc Plant Physiol. *Res:* Plant protein metabolism; seed physiology; stress physiology. *Mailing Add:* Dept Biol Calif State Univ 2555 E San Ramon Fresno CA 93740-8034

**WILEY, LYNN M,** DEVELOPMENTAL BIOLOGY. *Current Pos:* MEM FAC, UNIV CALIF, DAVIS, 80- *Personal Data:* b Tucson, Ariz, Feb 24, 47; div. *Educ:* Univ Calif, Irvine, BS, 68, MS, 71; Univ Calif, San Francisco, PhD(anat), 75. *Prof Exp:* Cell biologist mammalian develop, San Francisco Med Ctr, Univ Calif, 75-78; mem fac, Univ Va, 78-80. *Concurrent Pos:* Res Career Develop Award, NIH, 80-84. *Mem:* Am Soc Gravitational & Space Biol; Soc Develop Biol; Am Soc Cell Biol. *Res:* Cell surface in early mammalian development; origin of primary germ layers; regulation of cell determination; cell polarity; effect of ionizing radiation on gametes. *Mailing Add:* Dept Obstet & Gynec Calif Primate Res Ctr Univ Calif Davis CA 95616. *Fax:* 530-752-5300

**WILEY, MICHAEL DAVID,** ORGANIC CHEMISTRY. *Current Pos:* From asst prof to assoc prof, 68-84, PROF & CHAIR, CALIF LUTHERAN UNIV, 84- *Personal Data:* b Long Beach, Calif, Nov 28, 39; div; c David M & Heather J. *Educ:* Univ Southern Calif, BS, 61; Univ Wash, PhD(org chem), 69. *Concurrent Pos:* SRC res assoc, Univ Liverpool, Eng, 81; instr org chem, Sci Inst, Capital Univ, 93. *Mem:* AAAS; Am Chem Soc; Royal Soc Chem. *Res:* Reaction mechanisms; carbcations. *Mailing Add:* Dept Chem Calif Lutheran Univ Thousand Oaks CA 91360. *Fax:* 805-493-3479; *E-Mail:* wiley@clumv1.callutheran.edu

**WILEY, RICHARD G,** ELECTRONIC INTELLIGENCE & SIGNAL PROCESSING. *Current Pos:* FOUNDER & VPRES, RES ASN SYRACUSE, 86- *Personal Data:* b Windridge, Pa, Aug 25, 37; m 60; c 6. *Educ:* Carnegie Mellon Univ, BSEE, 59, MSEE, 60, Syracuse Univ, PhD(elec engr), 75. *Prof Exp:* Staff consult, Syracuse Res Corp, Syracuse, NY. *Mem:* Fel Inst Elec & Electronics Engrs. *Res:* Radar and electronic intelligence. *Mailing Add:* Res Asn Syracuse 6780 Northern Blvd East Syracuse NY 13057. *Fax:* 315-455-8037

**WILEY, RICHARD HAVEN,** chemistry; deceased, see previous edition for last biography

**WILEY, RICHARD HAVEN, JR,** SOCIOBIOLOGY, ETHOLOGY. *Current Pos:* asst prof, 71-76, assoc prof, 76-81, PROF BIOL, UNIV NC, CHAPEL HILL, 81- *Personal Data:* b Wilmington, Del, June 14, 43; m 71, Minna Spencer; c 2. *Educ:* Harvard Univ, BA, 65; Rockefeller Univ, PhD(animal behav), 70. *Prof Exp:* Fel animal behav, Rockefeller Univ, 70-71. *Concurrent Pos:* Res grants, NIMH & NSF, 69-83; mem bd dir, NC Bot Garden & Orgn Trop Studies, 78-; mem, Pop Biol Adv Panel, NSF, 80-83; mem, Scholarly Studies Rev Panel, Smithsonian Inst, 87-88 & 96-. *Mem:* Fel Animal Behav Soc; Int Soc Behav Ecol; Soc Study Evolution; Am Soc Naturalists; fel Am Ornithologists Union. *Res:* Evolution and ecology of vertebrate social organization; behavioral mechanisms of aggression and affiliation; acoustic communication by birds and primates. *Mailing Add:* Dept Biol Univ NC Chapel Hill NC 27599-3280. *Fax:* 919-962-1340

**WILEY, ROBERT A,** MEDICINAL CHEMISTRY. *Current Pos:* DEAN, COL PHARM, UNIV IOWA, 84- *Personal Data:* b Ann Arbor, Mich, Sept 5, 34; m 55; c 3. *Educ:* Univ Mich, BS, 55; Univ Calif, San Francisco, PhD(pharmaceut chem), 62. *Prof Exp:* From asst prof to prof med chem, Univ Kans, 62-84. *Mem:* Am Chem Soc; Am Pharmaceut Asn; Soc Toxicol. *Res:* Relationship between biological activity and chemical properties among drugs; chemical aspects of drug metabolism. *Mailing Add:* 26 Riverview Dr NE Iowa City IA 52240-7973

**WILEY, ROBERT CRAIG,** FOOD PROCESSING, FOOD ENGINEERING. *Current Pos:* from asst prof to assoc prof, 53-69, chmn, Food Sci Interdepartmental Prog, 84-89, PROF HORT, UNIV MD, COLLEGE PARK, 69- *Personal Data:* b Washington, DC, Nov 14, 24; m 51; c 3. *Educ:* Univ Md, BS, 49, MS, 50; Ore State Univ, PhD(food tech), 53. *Honors & Awards:* Woodbury Res Award co-recipient, 61, 62; H W Wiley Medal, US Food & Drug Admin, 81. *Prof Exp:* Asst, Ore State Univ, 51-52; food specialist, US Dept Navy, 53. *Concurrent Pos:* Fulbright-Hays sr lectr, Univ Belgrade, Yugoslavia, 79; chair, Fruit & Veg Technol Div, Inst Food Technol, 88; vis prof, Mid East Tech Univ, Turkey, 89; consult, USAID, Morocco, 90. *Mem:* Am Soc Hort Sci; fel Inst Food Technol. *Res:* Measurement of polysaccharides, fatty acids and enzymes in fruits and vegetables; aroma analyses of fruits; thermal processing of foods; ultrafiltration; reverse osmosis of fruit and vegetable juices; minimally processed refrigerated foods. *Mailing Add:* Dept Hort Food Sci Prog Univ Md Col Agr College Park MD 20742-0001

**WILEY, RONALD GORDON,** NEUROSCIENCE. *Current Pos:* STAFF PHYSICIAN & CHIEF, LAB EXP NEUROL, VET ADMIN MED CTR, NASHVILLE, 82-, ASSOC PROF NEUROL, 87-, ASSOC PROF PHARMACOL, 88- *Personal Data:* b Akron, Ohio, Mar 21, 47; m 93, Virginia F Haile; c Elizabeth A, Kathleen S, Allison C & Christopher A. *Educ:* Northwestern Univ, BS, 72, MD, 75, PhD(pharmacol), 75; Am Bd Psychiat & Neurol, dipl, 81; Am Bd Internal Med, dipl, 81. *Honors & Awards:* Sigma Xi Res Award, 72; G D Searle Res Award, 74; Roche Award in Neurosci, 72. *Prof Exp:* Intern & resident internal med, Peter Bent Brigham Hosp, 75-77; resident neurol, NY Hosp, 77-80; fel neurol, Cornell Univ Sch Med, 80-82; instr pharmacol & asst prof neurol, Vanderbilt Univ Sch Med, Univ Hosp, 82-84. *Concurrent Pos:* Assoc attend neurol, LaGuardia Hosp, NY, 80-; ed neurol, Med Info Systs, 84-; asst prof pharmacol, Vet Admin Med Ctr, Nashville, 84-88; chief, Neuro-Oncol Serv, Med Ctr & vis staff neurol, Vanderbilt Univ Sch Med, Univ Hosp, 84-92; assoc ed, J Neurocytol. *Mem:* Soc Neurosci; NY Acad Sci; AAAS; Am Acad Neurol; Cent Soc Neurol Res; Int Soc Neuroimmunol; Am Neurol Asn. *Res:* Suicide-transport; development and testing of axonally transported cytotoxins as tools for making experimental neural lesions; reaction of the central nervous system to selective loss of motor neurons; modelling neurodegenerative disorders using anti-neuronial immunotoxials. *Mailing Add:* Neurol Serv Vet Admin Med Ctr 1310 24th Ave S Nashville TN 37212-2637. *Fax:* 615-321-6380; *E-Mail:* wileyrg@vanderbilt.edu

**WILEY, RONALD LEE,** CARDIOPULMONARY PHYSIOLOGY. *Current Pos:* asst prof, 67-71, assoc prof zool & physiol, 71-76, PROF ZOOL, MIAMI UNIV, 76- *Personal Data:* b Dayton, Ohio, Oct 4, 37; m 81; c 1. *Educ:* Miami Univ, Ohio, BS, 59; Univ Ky, PhD(physiol, biophys), 66. *Prof Exp:* Teacher, Talawanda High Sch, Ohio, 59-62; instr physiol & NIH fel, Marquette Univ, 66-67. *Concurrent Pos:* Mem med staff, McCullough-Hyde Mem Hosp, Oxford, Ohio, 73-; from asst prof to prof, Sch Med, Wright State Univ, Dayton, 74-80. *Mem:* Am Physiol Soc; Sigma Xi; Am Col Sports Med. *Res:* Control of blood pressure; hypertension. *Mailing Add:* Dept Zool Miami Univ Oxford OH 45056. *Fax:* 513-529-6900

**WILEY, SAMUEL J,** COMPUTER APPLICATIONS IN INSTRUCTION. *Current Pos:* Chmn, Dept Math, 82-90, ASSOC PROF, LASALLE UNIV, PHILADELPHIA, 70- *Personal Data:* b Philadelphia, Pa, May 27, 39; m; c 5. *Educ:* St Josephs Univ, BS, 61; Villanova Univ, MA, 63; Temple Univ, PhD, 70. *Mem:* Math Asn Am; Inst Elec & Electronics Engrs Comput Soc; Asn Comput Mach. *Res:* Computer applications in instruction. *Mailing Add:* Dept Math LaSalle Univ 6511 N Sixth St Philadelphia PA 19126-3808

**WILEY, WILLIAM CHARLES,** ENGINEERING, PHYSICS. *Current Pos:* RETIRED. *Personal Data:* b Monmouth, Ill, Aug 7, 24; m 44, Margaret Kurtz; c Kurt M & Mark S. *Educ:* Univ Ill, BS, 49. *Prof Exp:* Dir, Appl Physics Lab, Bendix Corp, 49-68, assoc dir, Planning Res Labs, 68-69, asst gen mgr, Sci Instruments & Equip Div, 69-71; vpres & chief tech officer, Leeds & Northrup Co, 71-85. *Concurrent Pos:* Dir, Univ City Sci Ctr. *Mem:* Fel Instrument Soc Am; AAAS; fel Inst Elec & Electronics Engrs; Indust Res Inst. *Res:* Advanced sensing techniques; electronics; instrumentation; mass spectrometry; electron multipliers. *Mailing Add:* 1631 Meadowview Dr Medford OR 97504-4507

**WILEY, WILLIAM RODNEY,** microbiology, biochemistry; deceased, see previous edition for last biography

**WILFONG, ROBERT EDWARD,** CHEMISTRY, FIBER SCIENCE. *Current Pos:* RETIRED. *Personal Data:* b Wayne Co, Ill, Jan 3, 20; m 38, Miriam Horner; c Sharon P (Walters), Robert F, Jonathan E, Miriam W (Mitten) & David E. *Educ:* Univ Wis, BS, 41, MS, 42, PhD(phys chem), 44. *Hon Degrees:* LLD, Eastern Nazarene Col, 70. *Honors & Awards:* Award of Merit, Nat Defense Res Coun. *Prof Exp:* Investr, Nat Defense Res Coun, 42-44; res chemist, E I du Pont de Nemours & Co, Inc, Va, 44-48, res supvr, 48-51, res mgr, 51-53, tech supt, 53-59, lab dir, 59-64, tech mgr, 64-71, tech dir, 71-83. *Mem:* Am Chem Soc. *Res:* Photosynthesis; submarine detection; kinetics of rocket propellant decomposition; modified rocket propellants; infrared spectroscopy; new textile fibers, orlon, nylon and dacron; aromatic polyamides; research management. *Mailing Add:* 117 Deer Cove Rd Hampstead NC 28443

**WILFORD, JOHN NOBLE, JR,** SCIENCE COMMUNICATIONS. *Current Pos:* sci reporter, NY Times, 65-73, asst nat ed, 73-75, dir sci news, 75-79, SCI CORRESP, NY TIMES, 79- *Personal Data:* b Murray, Ky, Oct 4, 33; m 66, Nancy Everett Watts; c Nona. *Educ:* Univ Tenn, BS, 55; Syracuse Univ, MA, 56. *Hon Degrees:* DHL, RI Col, 87; DSc, Middlebury Col, 91. *Honors & Awards:* Press Award, Nat Space Club, 74; Westinghouse Sci Writing Award, AAAS, 83; McGraw Lectr, Princeton Univ, 85; Ralph Coats Roe Medal, Am Soc Mech Engrs, 95. *Prof Exp:* Reporter, Wall St J, NY, 56 & 59-61; contrib ed, Time Mag, NY, 62-65. *Concurrent Pos:* Int reporting fel, Columbia Univ, 61-62; ed, Scientists at Work, 79; distinguished prof jour, Univ Tenn, Knoxville, 89-90; vis journalist, Duke Univ, 84; counr, Am Geog Soc, 94; dir's visitor, Inst Advan Study, 95. *Mem:* Nat Asn Sci Writers; Am Geog Soc. *Mailing Add:* 229 W 43rd St New York NY 10036-3913

**WILFRET, GARY JOE,** PLANT BREEDING, GENETICS. *Current Pos:* from asst geneticist to assoc geneticist, 69-79, GENETICIST, AGR RES & EDUC CTR, UNIV FLA, BRADENTON, 79- *Personal Data:* b Sacramento, Calif, Oct 13, 43; m 86, Nancy Wehrheim; c Catherine & David. *Educ:* Univ Hawaii, BS, 65, PhD(hort), 68. *Honors & Awards:* Silver Seal, Nat Fedn Garden Clubs; Gold Medal & Lifetime Achievement Award, NAm Gladiolus Coun. *Prof Exp:* Asst prof biol, Ga South Col, 68-69. *Mem:* Am Soc Hort Sci; Am Asn Trop Biol; Bot Soc Am; Tissue Cult Asn; Am Hort Soc. *Res:* Breeding of ornamental plants for disease resistance and adaptation to subtropical conditions; effect of growth regulations on ornamental plants. *Mailing Add:* 4606 Tournament Blvd Sarasota FL 34243. *Fax:* 941-751-7639

**WILGRAM, GEORGE FRIEDERICH,** PHYSIOLOGY, DERMATOLOGY. *Current Pos:* PROF DERMAT, TUFTS UNIV, 67- *Personal Data:* b Vienna, Austria, Apr 12, 24; nat US; m 56; c 3. *Educ:* Univ Vienna, MD, 51; Univ Toronto, MA, 53, PhD, 57. *Prof Exp:* Lectr physiol, Univ Toronto, 57-58; asst prof exp path, Univ Chicago, 58-59; res assoc dermat, Harvard Med Sch, 59-60, asst prof, 61-67. *Mem:* Am Soc Exp Path; Soc Exp Biol & Med; Am Heart Asn. *Res:* Genetics of keratinization and pigmentation. *Mailing Add:* 59 Eustis St Arlington MA 02174-7638

**WILGUS, DONOVAN RAY,** ORGANIC CHEMISTRY. *Current Pos:* From assoc res chemist to supv res chemist, 51-66, SR RES ASSOC, CHEVRON RES CO, 66- *Personal Data:* b La Plata, Mo, Aug 11, 21; m 52; c 3. *Educ:* Northeast Mo State Teachers Col, AB, 42; Univ Colo, PhD, 51. *Mem:* Am Chem Soc. *Res:* Diels-Alder reaction; lubricating oil additives; synthetic oils. *Mailing Add:* 2912 Cindy Ct Richmond CA 94803-3230

**WILHEIT, THOMAS TURNER,** MICROWAVE PHYSICS, ATMOSPHERIC PHYSICS. *Current Pos:* PROF METEOROL, TEX A&M UNIV, 89- *Personal Data:* b Dallas, Tex, Apr 10, 41; m 66; c 1. *Educ:* Univ South, BA, 63; Washington Univ, St Louis, MA, 67; Mass Inst Technol, PhD(physics), 70. *Prof Exp:* Physicist microwave, Goddard Space Flight Ctr, 71-89. *Concurrent Pos:* Resident res assoc, Nat Acad Sci, 70-71. *Mem:* Inst Elec & Electronics Engrs; Am Meterol Soc; AAAS. *Res:* Passive microwave remote sensing of the earth's surface and atmosphere. *Mailing Add:* 12827 Tall Timber Dr College Station TX 77845

**WILHELM, ALAN ROY,** MICROBIOLOGY, VIROLOGY. *Current Pos:* from asst prof to assoc prof, 69-77, PROF BIOL SCI, CALIF STATE UNIV, CHICO, 77- *Personal Data:* b Buffalo, NY, Oct 30, 36. *Educ:* Stanford Univ, AB, 58; Univ Wis, Madison, MS, 65, PhD(bact), 67. *Prof Exp:* Microbiologist, US Army, 67-69. *Mem:* Sigma Xi; AAAS; Am Soc Microbiol. *Res:* Arboviruses; herpes viruses; viral infection of poikilothermic cells. *Mailing Add:* Dept Biol Sci Calif State Univ Chico 101 Orange St Chico CA 95929-0001

**WILHELM, DALE LEROY,** NUCLEAR CHEMISTRY. *Current Pos:* RETIRED. *Personal Data:* b Greenview, Ill, June 20, 26; m 51, Norma Mathews; c Teresa, Laura, Hoyte & Kyle. *Educ:* Univ Ill, BS, 51; Univ Tenn, MS, 52, PhD(chem), 54. *Prof Exp:* From asst prof to assoc prof chem, Univ WVa, 54-63; assoc prof, Cornell Col, 63-66; prof chem, Liberal Arts Col, Ohio Northern Univ, 66-91, asst dean, 73-78, chmn, Chem Dept, 74-78, vpres acad affairs, 78-91. *Mem:* Am Chem Soc; Sigma Xi. *Res:* Heteropolyanions; electrophoresis in stabilized media. *Mailing Add:* 4748 Coach Rd Columbus OH 43220-2961. *E-Mail:* fc-cc87a@prodigy.com

**WILHELM, DALLAS E, JR,** MAMMALOGY. *Current Pos:* ASSOC PROF & CHAIR, BIOL DEPT, HASTINGS COL, 79- *Personal Data:* b Sterling, Kans, Sept 5, 42. *Educ:* Kans State Univ, BA, 64, MS, 66; Tex Tech Univ, PhD(zool), 77. *Prof Exp:* Instr biol, Baker Univ, 66-68; asst prof & chair, Lincoln Mem Univ, 76-79. *Mem:* Am Soc Mammalogists; Southwestern Asn Naturalists; Nat Asn Biol Teachers; Sigma Xi. *Mailing Add:* Dept Biol Hastings Col Hastings NE 68901

**WILHELM, HARLEY A,** metallurgy; deceased, see previous edition for last biography

**WILHELM, JAMES MAURICE,** MICROBIOLOGY, MOLECULAR BIOLOGY. *Current Pos:* RES FEL, WYETH-AYERST RES, 84- *Personal Data:* b Redfield, SDak, May 20, 40; m 69. *Educ:* SDak Sch Mines & Technol, BS, 62; Case Western Res Univ, PhD (biochem), 68. *Prof Exp:* Am Cancer Soc fel biophys, Univ Chicago, 68-70; asst prof microbiol, Sch Med, Univ Pa, 70-73; asst prof microbiol, Sch Med, Univ Rochester, 73-79, assoc prof, 79-84. *Mem:* Am Soc Cell Biol; Am Soc Microbiol. *Res:* Protein synthesis; control of viral replication; cell biology. *Mailing Add:* Wyeth-Ayerst Res PO Box 8299 Philadelphia PA 19101

**WILHELM, PETER G,** AERONAUTICAL & ASTRONAUTICAL ENGINEERING. *Current Pos:* Radio frequency engr, unit head & sect head, Satellite Tech Br, Nat Res Lab, 59-65, br head, 65-76, head, Space Technol Ctr, 76-81, supt, Space Systs Div, 81-84, supt, Space Systs & Technol Div, 84-86, DIR, NAVAL CTR SPACE TECHNOL, NAT RES LAB, 86- *Personal Data:* b New York, NY, July 26, 35. *Educ:* Purdue Univ, BS, 57. *Prof Exp:* Proj engr, Stewart-Warner Electronics, 57-59. *Concurrent Pos:* Served, Cong Mandated Launch Mobilization Study, 94; served, Study Resusable Launch Vehicles, Nat Res Coun, 95. *Mem:* Nat Acad Eng; fel Am Inst Aeronaut & Astronaut. *Res:* Systems engineering for space systems, particular interest in lowering cost of space systems including launch vehicles and smaller satellites. *Mailing Add:* Naval Res Lab 4555 Overlook Ave SW Washington DC 20375-5353

**WILHELM, RUDOLF ERNST,** ALLERGY, IMMUNOLOGY. *Current Pos:* CHIEF, ALLERGY SECT, OAKWOOD HOSP, 77-; ALLERGY SPECIALIST, ALLERGY ASSOCS, DEARBORN, 77- *Personal Data:* b Hanover, Ger, Dec 26, 26; US citizen; m 52; c 3. *Educ:* Univ Ill, Chicago, MD, 51; Am Bd Internal Med, dipl, 61. *Prof Exp:* Asst resident internal med, Detroit Receiving Hosp, Mich, 52-53; resident allergy, Roosevelt Hosp Inst, NY, 57; resident internal med, Henry Ford Hosp, Detroit, 58-59; instr med, Sch Med, La State Univ, New Orleans, 59-60; asst prof med, Sch Med, Wayne State Univ, 60-64, from asst prof to assoc prof dermat, 64-77. *Mem:* Fel Am Col Physicians; fel Am Acad Allergy. *Res:* Delayed-type allergic skin reactions such as atopic eczema and contact dermatitis; methods and mechanics of allergy hyposensitization injections; anti-allergic drug treatment; methods of medical education in allergy and internal medicine; interface between traditional medicine and alternative medicine in the treatment of allergic illnesses. *Mailing Add:* 751 S Military Rd Dearborn MI 48124-2107

**WILHELM, SCOTT M,** ARTHRITIS RESEARCH. *Current Pos:* SR STAFF SCIENTIST, INST BONE & CARTILAGE METLAB MECHANISM ARTHRITIS RES, 89- *Personal Data:* b Columbus, Ohio, Apr 4, 53. *Res:* Arthritis. *Mailing Add:* Miles Res Ctr Miles Inc Inst Bone & Cartilage Metab 400 Morgan Lane West Haven CT 06516

**WILHELM, STEPHEN,** PLANT PATHOLOGY. *Current Pos:* From instr & jr plant pathologist to prof & plant pathologist, 48-84, EMER PROF PLANT PATH, UNIV CALIF, BERKELEY, 84- *Personal Data:* b Imperial Co, Calif, Apr 19, 19; m 50, Elizabeth Wilson; c Stephen P & George N. *Educ:* Univ Calif, AB, 42, PhD(plant path), 48. *Concurrent Pos:* Guggenheim fel, 58-59. *Mem:* Sigma Xi; fel Am Phytopath Soc; Am Soc Hort Sci. *Res:* Verticilium wilt; diseases of small fruit; root infecting fungi; soil fumigation. *Mailing Add:* 1394 Casa Vallecita Alamo CA 94507-1111

**WILHELM, WILBERT EDWARD,** INTEGER PROGRAMMING, OPTIMIZATION. *Current Pos:* PROF, DEPT INDUST ENG, TEX A&M UNIV, 89- *Personal Data:* b Pittsburgh, Pa, Oct 24, 42; m 63, Vida Meadows; c Sheryl & Byron. *Educ:* WVa Univ, BS, 64; Va Polytech Inst, MS, 70, PhD(indust eng & opers res), 72. *Honors & Awards:* David F Baker Distinguished Res Award, Inst Indust Engrs, 96. *Prof Exp:* Mfg prog, Gen Elec Co, 64-67, spec mfg admin, 67-69; NSF fel & instr, Va Polytech Inst, 69-72; from asst prof to assoc prof, Ohio State Univ, 72-88. *Concurrent Pos:* NSF fel, 69-72; consult, 73-; prin investr, NSF, 83-, Grumman Aerospace Corp, 85-, IBM, 88; dir, OR Div IIE, 88-89 & Tex Advan Technol Prog, 91-93 & 96-98; vpres publ, Inst Indust Engrs, 97- *Mem:* Fel Am Inst Indust Engrs; Opers Res Soc Am; Soc Mfg Engrs; Math Prog Soc. *Res:* Basic research in integer and linear programming and development of specialized methods to resolve problems associated with management of oil spill clean up operations, assembly system design, design for assembly and scheduling; author of numerous publications. *Mailing Add:* Dept Indust Tex A&M Univ College Station TX 77843-3131. *E-Mail:* wilhelm@tamu.edu

**WILHELM, WILLIAM JEAN,** STRUCTURAL & CIVIL ENGINEERING. *Current Pos:* DEAN & PROF, COL ENG, WICHITA STATE UNIV, 79- *Personal Data:* b St Louis, Mo, Oct 5, 35; m 57, Patricia Zietz; c William J Jr, Robert G, Andrew J, Mary E (Castleberry) & David E. *Educ:* Ala Polytech Inst, BME, 58; Auburn Univ, MS, 63; NC State Univ, PhD(struct eng), 68. *Honors & Awards:* Joe W Kelly Award, Am Concrete Inst, 86, Henry L Kennedy Award, 95. *Prof Exp:* Struct engr, Palmer & Baker Engrs, Inc, 58-59 & 59-60; instr eng graphics, Auburn Univ, 60-61 & 62-64; teaching asst civil eng, NC State Univ, 64-67; from asst prof to prof civil eng, WVa Univ, 67-79, assoc chmn dept, 70-74, chmn dept, 74-79. *Concurrent Pos:* NSF grants, 69-73; Am Iron & Steel Inst res grant, 68-73; Expanded Shale Clay & Slate Inst res grant, 71 & 72; chmn, Civil Eng Div, Am Soc Eng Educ, 77-78 & Rels Indust Div, 84-85; chmn, Comt Curricula & Accreditation, Am Soc Civil Engrs, 82-83; chmn, Educ Activ Comt, Am Concrete Inst, 83-88, mem bd dir, 86-89 & chmn conv comt, 89-96; mem, Eng Accreditation Comn & Accreditation Bd Eng & Technol, 85-90. *Mem:* Fel Am Concrete Inst; fel Am Soc Civil Engrs; Am Soc Eng Educ; Nat Soc Prof Engrs; sr mem Soc Women Engrs. *Res:* Reinforced and prestressed concrete with particular emphasis on torsional and bond behavior for both normal weight and light-weight aggregate concrete; engineering education. *Mailing Add:* Dean Col Eng Wichita State Univ Wichita KS 67260-0044. *Fax:* 316-978-3853; *E-Mail:* bwilhelm@engr.twsu.edu

**WILHELMY, JERRY BARNARD,** NUCLEAR CHEMISTRY, NUCLEAR PHYSICS. *Current Pos:* group leader, Nuclear Chem & Analysis, 92-94, MEM STAFF NUCLEAR CHEM, LOS ALAMOS SCI LAB, 72-, FEL, 82- *Personal Data:* b Sewickley, Pa, July 31, 42; m 64, Sharon Larson. *Educ:* Univ Ariz, BSChE, 64; Univ Calif, Berkeley, PhD(nuclear chem), 69. *Prof Exp:* Fel nuclear chem, Lawrence Berkeley Lab, 69-72. *Concurrent Pos:* Vis res scientist, Weizman Inst, 78-79; fel, Max Planck Inst Kernphysik, 78-82, assoc group leader res, 79-82. *Mem:* Am Chem Soc; Am Phys Soc. *Res:* Properties of nuclear fission; fission barriers; fission product spectroscopy, fission produced neutrons; neutrino physics; heavy ion reactions. *Mailing Add:* Los Alamos Nat Lab MS J514 Los Alamos NM 87545. *Fax:* 505-665-4955; *E-Mail:* 079746%incdp3@lanl.gov

**WILHITE, DOUGLAS LEE,** PHYSICAL CHEMISTRY, QUANTUM CHEMISTRY. *Current Pos:* res assoc photog sci, Imaging Systs Dept, Res & Develop Div, 73-93, res assoc, Med Prods Dept, Res & Develop Div, 93-96, SR RES ASSOC, RES & DEVELOP DIV, STERLING DIAG IMAGING, E I DU PONT DE NEMOURS & CO, BREVARD, NC, 96- *Personal Data:* b Owensboro, Ky, July 29, 44; m 67, Bettie M Bommarito; c Douglas B, Benjamin A & Matthew J. *Educ:* Univ Mo, Columbia, BS, 66; State Univ NY, Stony Brook, PhD(phys chem), 71. *Prof Exp:* Fel quantum chem, Aerospace Res Labs, Wright-Patterson AFB, Ohio, 71-73. *Concurrent Pos:* Vis res chemist, Technol Inc, 71-72; Nat Res Coun assoc, 72-73. *Mem:* Am Phys Soc. *Res:* Development of new precipitation processes for AgX microcrystals used in photographic systems; design of more efficient photographic systems; study of fundamental phenomena associated with the photographic process. *Mailing Add:* 49 Kentwood Lane Pisgah Forest NC 28768

**WILHITE, ELMER LEE,** PERFORMANCE ASSESSMENT, PLUTONIUM CHEMISTRY. *Current Pos:* Chemist, Savannah River Lab, E I Du Pont de Nemours & Co, Inc, 69-79, res chemist, 79-80, tech supvr, Environ Monitoring, 80-81, res supvr, Analytical Develop Div, 81-84, res staff chemist, 84-89, ADV SCIENTIST, SAVANNAH RIVER LAB, WESTINGHOUSE SAVANNAH RIVER CO, 89- *Personal Data:* b Owensboro, Ky, July 29, 44; m 66, Bonnie McCarroll; c Joel, Sarah & Rachel. *Educ:* Univ Mo, BS, 66; Washington Univ, MA, 69. *Mem:* Am Chem Soc; Health Physics Soc; Am Nuclear Soc. *Res:* Environmental assessment of transuranic element migration from buried solid waste; melting and off-gas processing of high-level defense nuclear waste; solidification of low-level and hazardous waste; performance assessment of low-level waste disposal. *Mailing Add:* 773-43A Savannah River Technol Ctr Westinghouse Savannah River Co Aiken SC 29808. *Fax:* 803-725-4704; *E-Mail:* elmer.wilhite@srs.gov

**WILHM, JERRY L,** LIMNOLOGY, ECOLOGY. *Current Pos:* PROF ZOOL, DEPT ZOOL, OKLA STATE UNIV, 66-, HEAD DEPT, 81- *Personal Data:* b Kansas City, Kans, Apr 27, 30; m 55; c 2. *Educ:* Kans State Teachers Col, BS, 52, MS, 56; Okla State Univ, PhD(zool), 65. *Prof Exp:* Teacher high sch, Kans, 56-62; US AEC fel, Oak Ridge, Tenn, 65-66. *Concurrent Pos:* Biol consult, Am Inst Biol Sci Film Series, 61-62; Fulbright fel, NZ, 79. *Mem:* Am Soc Limnol & Oceanog; Ecol Soc Am. *Res:* Biological effects of oil refinery effluents. *Mailing Add:* Dept Zool Okla State Univ Stillwater OK 74078-0002

**WILHOFT, DANIEL C,** ZOOLOGY. *Current Pos:* From instr to assoc prof, 62-69, chmn, Dept Zool & Physiol, 69-75, PROF ZOOL, RUTGERS UNIV, NEWARK, 69- *Personal Data:* b Newark, NJ, Nov 16, 30; m 51; c 2. *Educ:* Rutgers Univ, AB, 56; Univ Calif, Berkeley, MA, 58, PhD(zool), 63. *Mem:* AAAS; Am Soc Zool; fel Zool Soc London. *Res:* Ecology of fresh-water turtles; reptilian endocrinology. *Mailing Add:* Dept Biol Sci Rutgers Univ Newark Campus 175 University Ave Newark NJ 07102-1814

**WILHOIT, EUGENE DENNIS,** PHYSICAL CHEMISTRY. *Current Pos:* From res chemist to sr res chemist, Polychem Dept, E I Du Pont de Nemours & Co, 56-67, admin asst, Technol Dept, 67, asst div supt, 69, div supt res, 69-75, gen tech supt, 75-81, tech fel, 81-87, res fel, 87-94, RES CONSULT, E I DU PONT DE NEMOURS & CO, INC, 94- *Personal Data:* b Frankfort, Ky, Jan 28, 31; m 58, Verla Walton; c Michael. *Educ:* Univ Ky, BS, 53, PhD(phys chem), 56. *Mem:* AAAS; Am Chem Soc. *Res:* Electrochemistry and electrolytic conductance; reactions and synthesis of polymer intermediates; nonaqueous solutions; oxidation mechanisms and catalysis. *Mailing Add:* 213 Tracy Lane Victoria TX 77904-1525

**WILHOIT, JAMES CAMMACK, JR,** ENGINEERING MECHANICS. *Current Pos:* from asst prof to prof, 54-81, EMER PROF MECH ENG, RICE UNIV, 81- *Personal Data:* b Tulsa, Okla, Dec 22, 25; m 49, Louise LeGros; c James P, Ann (Sparker), John H & Joan L. *Educ:* Rice Inst, BS, 48; Tex A&M Univ, MS, 51; Stanford Univ, PhD(eng mech), 54. *Prof Exp:* Instr mech eng, Tex A&M Univ, 49-51; sr aerophys eng, Convair, Tex, 53-54. *Mem:* Am Soc Mech Engrs. *Mailing Add:* 9225 McCowans Ferry Rd Versailles KY 40383

**WILHOIT, RANDOLPH CARROLL,** EVALUATION THERMODYNAMIC PROPERTIES. *Current Pos:* ASSOC PROF CHEM & ASSOC DIR THERMODYN RES CTR, TEX A&M UNIV, 64- *Personal Data:* b San Antonio, Tex, Oct 16, 25; m 48, Martha Stoker; c Lawrence, Sharon & Marlene. *Educ:* Trinity Univ, Tex, AB, 47; Univ Kans, MA, 49; Northwestern Univ, PhD, 52. *Prof Exp:* Fel phys chem, Univ Ind, 52-53; asst prof, Tex Tech Col, 53-57; assoc prof, NMex Highlands Univ, 57-60, prof, 60-64. *Concurrent Pos:* Assoc ed, J Chem & Eng Data, Am Chem Soc, 71- *Mem:* AAAS; Am Chem Soc. *Res:* Thermochemistry; molecular structure; energetics of biochemical reactions; estimation of thermodynamic properties. *Mailing Add:* Thermodyn Res Ctr Tex A&M Univ College Station TX 77843-3111. *Fax:* 409-847-8590; *E-Mail:* wilhoit@trchp1.tamu.edu

**WILHOLD, GILBERT A,** PHYSICS, MECHANICS. *Current Pos:* RETIRED. *Personal Data:* b East St Louis, Ill, Dec 9, 34; m 82, Marjorie Carr; c Joseph, Gilbert Jr, Sherrie-Gail, Edward, Stephanie & Becky (Jenkins). *Educ:* St Louis Univ, BS, 57. *Prof Exp:* Engr, McDonnell Aircraft Corp, Mo, 57-60 & Chrysler Corp, Ala, 60-62; engr, Marshall Space Flight Ctr, NASA, 62-63, tech asst analytical & theoret acoust, 63, tech asst to lab dir, 63-66, dep br chief unsteady fluid mech, 66-69 & Unsteady Gas Dynamics Br, 69-77, asst, Aeropys Div, 77-95. *Concurrent Pos:* Consult to pvt firms, fed, state & local govt & univs. *Res:* Acoustic noise generated by rocket exhausts and air flow over space vehicle surfaces during flight; random process theory and application; data reduction and analysis; aeroelasticity; fluid mechanics; structural dynamics and vibrations; sonic boom and its environmental effects; unsteady fluid flow in high performance pumps and aeroelastically induced loads; computational fluid dynamics and numerical analysis. *Mailing Add:* 815 Point of Pines Guntersville AL 35976

**WILIMOVSKY, NORMAN JOSEPH,** ICHTHYOLOGY, FISHERIES. *Current Pos:* RETIRED. *Personal Data:* b Chicago, Ill, Sept 9, 25; m 47; c 4. *Educ:* Univ Mich, BS, 48, MA, 49; Stanford Univ, PhD, 56. *Prof Exp:* Head, Fish & Game Off, Mil Govt, Bavaria, Ger, 46; assoc ichthyologist, Fisheries Surv Brazil, 50-51; prin investr, Arctic Invests, Stanford Univ, 51-54, res assoc, 55-56; chief marine fisheries invests, US Fish & Wildlife Serv, Alaska, 56-60; assoc prof fisheries & zool, Univ BC, 60-64, dir, Inst Fisheries, 63-66, prof fisheries, 64- *Concurrent Pos:* Mem, Comt Proj Chariot, AEC, 60-66; staff specialist, US Coun Marine Resources & Eng Develop, 67-68; mem, Environ Protection Bd, 70-76. *Mem:* Fel AAAS; Am Soc Ichthyol & Herpet; Am Fisheries Soc; Am Soc Limnol & Oceanog; fel Arctic Inst NAm. *Res:* Systematics of fishes; fishery population dynamics; ecology of ice; development and management of fisheries; history of biological exploration; resource policy formulation. *Mailing Add:* 5611 Olympic St Vancouver BC V6N 1Z4 Can

**WILK, LEONARD STEPHEN,** ELECTRICAL ENGINEERING, INSTRUMENTATION. *Current Pos:* STAFF ENGR, CHARLES STARK DRAPER LAB, INC, 74-; PRES, ADAMS ASSOCS, 92- *Personal Data:* b Adams, Mass, Sept 29, 27; m, Christine Porto; c Stephen J, Justin S & Katherine E. *Educ:* Mass Inst Technol, SB & SM, 55. *Prof Exp:* Group leader missile guid, Instrumentation Lab, Mass Inst Technol, 55-60, asst dir space guid, 60-67, assoc dir instrumentation, Measurement Systs Lab, 67-74. *Concurrent Pos:* Lectr, Dept Aeronaut & Astronaut, Mass Inst Technol, 85- *Mem:* AAAS. *Res:* Inertial navigation and guidance; system analysis and testing; gravity gradiometry; magnetic suspension systems; control systems; experimental tests of gravitation theories; configuration management; detectors for high energy physics; fiber optic alignment; arms control; alignment transfer. *Mailing Add:* 555 Tech Sq MS 37 Cambridge MA 02139. *Fax:* 781-729-3247; *E-Mail:* wilk@draper.com

**WILK, RICHARD D,** ENERGY CONVERSION, COMBUSTION. *Current Pos:* asst prof, 89-94, ASSOC PROF, UNION COL, 94-, CHAIR, MECH ENG DEPT, 96- *Personal Data:* b Philadelphia, Pa, Nov 14, 57. *Educ:* Drexel Univ, BS, 80, MS, 82, PhD(mech eng), 86. *Honors & Awards:* Ralph R Teetor Award, Soc Automotive Engrs, 91. *Prof Exp:* Proj engr, Philadelphia Elec Co, 80; grad res asst, Drexel Univ, 81-86, staff res scientist, 86-89. *Concurrent Pos:* Adj prof, Temple Univ, 87-88; consult, Olin Chem, 88, Wright Malta Corp, 93; vis scholar, Rensselaer Polytech Inst, 96. *Mem:* Am Soc Mech Engrs; Soc Automotive Engrs; Am Soc Eng Educ; Int Solar Energy Soc; Combustion Inst; Am Chem Soc. *Res:* Combustion, energy conversion and utilization; solar energy, alternative fuels, alternative and advanced energy systems; hydrocarbon oxidation, chemical kinetic modeling, air pollution control, environmental remediation. *Mailing Add:* 807 Union St Schenectady NY 12308-2311. *E-Mail:* wilkr@union.edu

**WILK, SHERWIN,** BIOCHEMISTRY, PHARMACOLOGY. *Current Pos:* assoc prof, 69-80, PROF PHARMACOL, MT SINAI SCH MED, 80- *Personal Data:* b New York, NY, Aug 25, 38; m 63; c 2. *Educ:* Syracuse Univ, BS, 60; Purdue Univ, MS, 62; Fordham Univ, PhD(biochem), 67. *Prof Exp:* Res asst biochem, Mt Sinai Hosp, 62-67. *Concurrent Pos:* NIH fel, Sch Med, Cornell Univ, 67-69; NIH res career develop award, Mt Sinai Sch Med, 69- *Mem:* AAAS; Am Soc Pharmacol & Exp Therapeut; Am Soc Neurochem; Am Chem Soc; Sigma Xi. *Res:* Metabolism of gamma glutamyl compounds; peptidases and proteinases in the central nervous system; metabolism of catecholamines in central nervous system. *Mailing Add:* Mt Sinai Sch Med 10 E 102nd St New York NY 10029-5205. *Fax:* 212-831-0114

**WILK, WILLIAM DAVID,** INORGANIC CHEMISTRY. *Current Pos:* From asst prof to assoc prof, 68-78, PROF CHEM, CALIF STATE COL, DOMINGUEZ HILLS, 78- *Personal Data:* b Pittsburgh, Pa, Mar 6, 42; m 70; c 3. *Educ:* Thiel Col, BA, 64; Northwestern Univ, PhD(chem), 68. *Mem:* Royal Soc Chem; Nat Sci Teachers Asn. *Res:* Ligand substitution effects on cobalt III complexes. *Mailing Add:* Chem Calif State Univ Dominguez Hills 1000 E Victoria St Carson CA 90747

**WILKE, CHARLES R,** CHEMICAL ENGINEERING. *Current Pos:* from instr to assoc prof, Univ Calif, Berkeley, 46-53, chmn dept, 53-63, prof, 53-87, RES ASSOC, LAWRENCE BERKELEY LAB, UNIV CALIF, BERKELEY, 50-, EMER CHEM ENG, 53- *Personal Data:* b Dayton, Ohio, Feb 4, 17; m 45. *Educ:* Univ Dayton, BS, 40; State Col Wash, MS, 42; Univ Wis, PhD(chem eng), 44. *Honors & Awards:* Colburn Award, Am Inst Chem Engrs, 51, Walker Award, 65, Founders Award, 86. *Prof Exp:* Assoc engr, Union Oil Co, Calif, 44-45; instr chem eng, State Col Wash, 45-46. *Concurrent Pos:* Indust consult, 52-; commencement speaker, Univ Dayton, 61; mem adv bd, Petrol Res Fund, 64-67; mem, Calif Bd Registr Prof Engrs, 64-72, pres, 67-68. *Mem:* Nat Acad Eng; AAAS; Am Inst Chem Engrs; Am Chem Soc; Am Soc Eng Educ. *Res:* Mass transfer operations; separation and purification of materials; biochemical engineering; kinetics and scale-up of microbial processes. *Mailing Add:* Dept Chem Eng 313 Gilman Hall Univ Calif Berkeley CA 94720

**WILKE, FREDERICK WALTER,** MATHEMATICS. *Current Pos:* asst prof, 65-73, ASSOC PROF MATH, UNIV MO, ST LOUIS, 73- *Personal Data:* b Pana, Ill, Sept 13, 33; m 56; c 4. *Educ:* Drury Col, AB, 54; Washington Univ, MA, 59; Univ Mo, Columbia, MA, 60, PhD(math), 66. *Prof Exp:* Instr math, Southwest Mo State Col, 63-65. *Mem:* Am Math Soc; Math Asn Am. *Res:* Finite projective planes, especially translation planes. *Mailing Add:* Dept Math & Comput Sci Univ Mo St Louis MO 63121-4499

**WILKE, ROBERT NIELSEN,** CHEMICAL INFORMATION, INFORMATION ANALYSIS. *Current Pos:* SR RES SCIENTIST, AMOCO CORP, 80- *Personal Data:* b San Diego, Calif, July 7, 41; m 73; c 2. *Educ:* San Diego State Univ, BS, 64; Case Western Res Univ, PhD(org chem), 71. *Prof Exp:* Res assoc electrochem, Youngstown State Univ, 71-72, cancer res, Univ Chicago, 72-74; sr chemist, Velsicol Chem Corp, 74-80. *Mem:* Am Chem Soc. *Res:* Retrieval and analysis of information related to petroleum industry. *Mailing Add:* 329 S Cuyler Ave Oak Park IL 60302

**WILKEN, DAVID RICHARD,** BIOCHEMISTRY. *Current Pos:* RETIRED. *Personal Data:* b Amarillo, Tex, Feb 20, 34; m 55; c 3. *Educ:* Blackburn Col, BA, 55; Univ Ill, MS, 58; Mich State Univ, PhD(biochem), 60. *Prof Exp:* From asst prof to assoc prof biochem, Okla State Univ, 62-66; asst prof, Univ Wis-Madison, 66-72, assoc prof physiol chem, 72- *Concurrent Pos:* Nat Found fel, Inst Enzyme Res, Univ Wis, 60-62; res chemist, Lab Exp Path, Vet Admin Hosp, 66- *Mem:* Am Soc Biol Chem; Am Chem Soc. *Res:* Diabetes; glycoprotein biosynthesis; pantothenic acid metabolism; enzymology. *Mailing Add:* 3659 County Hwy F Blue Mounds WI 53517

**WILKEN, DIETER H,** SYSTEMATIC BOTANY. *Current Pos:* from asst prof to assoc prof, 73-96, PROF BOT, COLO STATE UNIV, 96- *Personal Data:* b Los Angeles, Calif, Apr 12, 44. *Educ:* Calif State Univ, Los Angeles, BA, 67; Univ Calif, Santa Barbara, PhD(biol), 71. *Prof Exp:* Res asst, Los Angeles State & Co Arboretum, 66-67; asst prof biol, Occidental Col, 71-73. *Concurrent Pos:* Cur, Colo State Univ Herbarium, 73- *Mem:* Bot Soc Am; Am Soc Plant Taxon; Int Soc Plant Taxon. *Res:* Systematics of higher plants within field of cytology, biochemistry, anatomy and breeding behavior; ecology and evolutionary dynamics of populations. *Mailing Add:* Santa Barbara Bot Garden 1212 Mission Canyon Rd Santa Barbara CA 93105

**WILKEN, DONALD RAYL,** PURE MATHEMATICS. *Current Pos:* from asst prof to assoc prof, 68-75, PROF MATH, STATE UNIV NY, ALBANY, 75- *Personal Data:* b New Orleans, La, Apr 25, 38; m 58; c 1. *Educ:* Tulane Univ, BS, 58, PhD(math), 65; Univ Calif, Los Angeles, MA, 62. *Prof Exp:* NSF fel, Brandeis Univ, 65-66; instr math, Mass Inst Technol, 66-68. *Res:* Functional and complex analysis. *Mailing Add:* Dept Math State Univ NY Albany NY 12203-3032

**WILKEN, LEON OTTO, JR,** PHARMACEUTICS, BIOPHARMACEUTICS. *Current Pos:* from assoc prof to prof, 63-91, head, Pharmaceut Div, 73-91, EMER PROF PHARM, AUBURN UNIV, 91- *Personal Data:* b Waterbury, Conn, Oct 21, 24; m 46. *Educ:* Loyola Univ, La, BS, 51, PhD(pharm), 82; Univ Tex, MS, 53, PhD(pharm), 63. *Prof Exp:* Spec instr pharm, Univ Tex, 53-63. *Concurrent Pos:* Pharm consult, Vet Admin Hosp, Tuskegee, Ala, 74- *Mem:* Am Asn Cols Pharm; Am Pharmaceut Asn; Am Chem Soc; Acad Pharm Sci. *Res:* Sustained release delivery systems, assay of pharmaceuticals from drug delivery systems and biological fluids by high-pressure liquid chromatography; methods of enhancing bioavailability of difficult soluble drugs; development of oral vaccines, stability studies. *Mailing Add:* Dept Pharm Sci 401 Pharm Bldg Auburn Univ Auburn AL 36849

**WILKENFELD, JASON MICHAEL,** SOLID STATE PHYSICS. *Current Pos:* VPRES, S CUBED DIV, MAXWELL LAB INC, 89- *Personal Data:* b Brooklyn, NY, May 28, 39; m 62, Holly Phelps; c Kyla & Justin. *Educ:* Columbia Col, AB, 60; NY Univ, MS, 65, PhD(physics), 72. *Prof Exp:* Programmer analyst, Syst Develop Corp, 63; res asst physics, Radiation & Solid State Lab, NY Univ, 65-70; fel physics, New Eng Inst, 70-72; staff physicist, IRT Corp, 73-77, group leader, 77-78, dept mgr, 78-89. *Concurrent Pos:* Lectr physics, Hunter Col, City Univ New York, 66-69 & NY Univ, 69. *Mem:* Am Phys Soc. *Res:* Nuclear and space radiation effects in materials and systems; electrical properties of dielectrics; positron annihilation as a morphological probe; space sensor technology. *Mailing Add:* Maxwell Lab Inc 2501 Yale SE Suite 300 Albuquerque NM 87106. *Fax:* 619-576-7710; *E-Mail:* jason@scubed.com

**WILKENING, DEAN ARTHUR,** NUCLEAR STRATEGIES, ARMS CONTROL. *Current Pos:* DIR, FORCE EMPLOY PROG, NAT DEFENSE RES INST, 83- *Personal Data:* b Raleigh, NC, Sept 21, 50. *Educ:* Univ Chicago, BA, 72; Harvard Univ, PhD(physics), 81. *Prof Exp:* Ford Found fel, Ctr Sci & Int Affairs, Harvard Univ, 81-83. *Mem:* Am Phys Soc. *Res:* Strategic theater forces; arms control proposals. *Mailing Add:* 3330 Purdue Ave Los Angeles CA 90066. *Fax:* 310-451-6960

**WILKENING, GEORGE MARTIN,** ENVIRONMENTAL HEALTH, ENVIRONMENTAL SCIENCES. *Current Pos:* EXEC DIR, ENVIRON & OCCUP HEALTH SCI INST, 90- *Personal Data:* b New York, NY, Dec 31, 23; m 50; c 5. *Educ:* Queen's Col, NY, BS, 49; Columbia Univ, MS, 50. *Prof Exp:* Indust hygienist, State Health Dept, Va, 50-51; indust hygienist, Esso Res & Eng Co, 52-56, sr indust hygienist, Esso Stand Oil Co, 56-61; asst chief indust hygienist, Humble Oil & Ref Co, 61-63; dir environ health, Mgt & Safety Ctr, AT&T Bell Labs, 80-90. *Concurrent Pos:* Lectr, Columbia Univ, 59-; chmn, Laser Hazards Stand Comt, 68-; mem, Environ Radiation Adv Comt, Environ Protection Agency, 67-; tech electronic prod radiation stand comt mem, HEW, 68-; mem, Nat Coun Radiation Protection & Measurements, 73-; chmn, Tech Comt Lasers, Int Electrotech Comn, 73-; chmn, Sci Comt Microwaves, Nat Coun Radiation Protection & Measurements, 75; mem, Study Group on Non-Ionizing Radiations, Int Radiation Protection Asn, 75, Nat Acad Sci-Nat Res Coun, Comt on Biosphere Effects Extremely Low Frequency Radiation, 76- & Panel on Effects Radiation from Pave Paws Radar, 78; adj prof environ med, NY Univ, 83-; consult, Armed Forces Epidemiol Bd, Dept Defense, Washington, DC, 77; mem, Electromagnetic Radiation Mgt Adv Coun, Nat Telecommun & Info, 79- *Mem:* AAAS; Sigma Xi; Acoust Soc Am; Am Indust Hyg Asn; fel NY Acad Sci; Bioelectromagnetics Soc. *Res:* Dosimetry of exposure to electromagnetic radiations, including acoustical noise; industrial toxicology; biological effects of chemical, physical and biological agents in the environment; development of standards for permissible levels of exposure to environmental agents. *Mailing Add:* 101 Cottonwood Ct Doylestown PA 18901

**WILKENING, LAUREL LYNN,** METEORITICS, PLANETARY SCIENCES. *Current Pos:* PROF EARTH SYST SCI & CHANCELLOR, UNIV CALIF, IRVINE, 93- *Personal Data:* b Richland, Wash, Nov 23, 44; m 74, Godfrey T Sill. *Educ:* Reed Col, BA, 66; Univ Calif, San Diego, PhD(chem), 70. *Hon Degrees:* DSc, Univ Ariz, 96. *Honors & Awards:* Nininger Meteorite Award, Ariz State Univ, 70. *Prof Exp:* Am Asn Univ Women fel, Tata Inst Fundamental Res, India & Max Planck Inst Chem, 71; res assoc chem, Enrico Fermi Inst, Univ Chicago, 72-73; from asst prof to prof, 73-88, head, Dept Planetary Sci & dir, Lunar & Planetary Lab, Univ Ariz, 81-83, vprovost, 83-85, vpres res & dean, Grad Col, 85-88; prof geol sci, Univ Wash, 88-, provost & vpres acad affairs, 88- *Concurrent Pos:* Vchmn, Nat Comn Space, 85-86. *Mem:* AAAS; fel Meteoritical Soc; Am Geophys Union; Asn Women Sci. *Res:* Chemistry and mineralogy of meteorites, asteroids and comets; cosmochemistry; meteorites and their relationship to asteroids, comets and the formation of the solar system; nature of asteroidal surfaces through theoretical studies and studies of meteorites which probably once resided on the surface of asteroids. *Mailing Add:* Admin 501 Univ Calif Irvine CA 92717. *Fax:* 714-824-2087; *E-Mail:* laurelw@uci.edu

**WILKENING, MARVIN C,** ANIMAL NUTRITION, BIOCHEMISTRY. *Current Pos:* dir, Tech Serv, Nebr, 67-75, NONRUMINANT NUTRITIONIST & CONSULT, CONAGRA, INC, 75- *Personal Data:* b Malone, Tex, July 1, 20; m 43; c 4. *Educ:* Univ Tex, AB, 41; Agr & Mech Col, Tex, MS, 47. *Hon Degrees:* ScD, Athens Col, 56. *Prof Exp:* Res chemist, Dow Chem Co, Tex, 41-44; asst to dir res, Security Mills, Tenn, 47-50; dir res, Ala Flour Mills, 50-66. *Mem:* Fel AAAS; Am Chem Soc; Am Soc Animal Sci; Poultry Sci Asn. *Res:* Application of basic animal nutrition and management research. *Mailing Add:* 4312 Autum Leaves Trail SE Decatur AL 35603

**WILKENING, MARVIN H,** RADON & DAUGHTER PRODUCTS. *Current Pos:* from assoc prof to prof physics & geophys & head dept & dean grad studies, 48-83, EMER PROF PHYSICS, NMEX INST MINING & TECHNOL, 84- *Personal Data:* b Oak Ridge, Mo, Mar 13, 18; m 42, Ruby Barks; c Laurel Sill & Wes. *Educ:* Southeast Mo State Univ, BS, 39; Ill Inst Technol, MS, 43, PhD(nuclear physics), 49. *Prof Exp:* Teacher high sch, Mo, 39-41; physicist, Manhattan Proj, 42-45; instr physics, Ill Inst Technol, 46-48. *Concurrent Pos:* Mem, Fermi Group at First Nuclear Reactor, Chicago, 42; mem, Subcomn Ions, Aerosols & Radioactiv, Int Comt Atmospheric Elec, 76-80; mem, Nat Coun Radiation Protection, SC61, 79-88; mem, NMex Radiation Tech Adv Coun, 81-87; Chicago Pile Exp, Soc Nuclear Med, 77. *Mem:* Fel AAAS; fel Am Phys Soc; Am Geophys Union; Am Meteorol Soc; Health Physics Soc; NY Acad Sci. *Res:* Radon and its daughter products; atmospheric electricity-ions and aerosols related to natural atmospheric radioactivity. *Mailing Add:* 1218 South Dr Socorro NM 87801

**WILKENS, GEORGE A(LBERT),** CHEMICAL ENGINEERING. *Current Pos:* CONSULT ACRYLIC PLASTICS, 74- *Personal Data:* b North Bergen, NJ, June 29, 09; m 46; c 2. *Educ:* Columbia Univ, AB, 29, BS, 30, CE, 31, PhD(chem eng), 33. *Prof Exp:* From res chemist to chief chemist, Arlington Plant, Polychem Dept, E I du Pont de Nemours & Co, Inc, Wilmington, 33-57, plastics consult, Chestnut Run Lab, 57-74. *Mem:* Am Chem Soc; Am Inst Chem Engrs; Am Soc Testing & Mat. *Res:* Agitation; organic synthesis; cellulose plastics; acrylic and dental resins; dyes; pigments; polymerization. *Mailing Add:* 213 Sypherd Dr Oaklands Newark DE 19711-3626

**WILKENS, JERREL L,** INVERTEBRATE NEUROPHYSIOLOGY. *Current Pos:* from asst prof to assoc prof, 69-81, PROF BIOL, UNIV CALGARY, 81- *Personal Data:* b Lorraine, Kans, Aug 5, 37; m 68; c 2. *Educ:* Univ Ottawa, Kans, BA, 59; Tulane Univ, MSc, 61; Univ Calif, Los Angeles, PhD(zool), 67. *Prof Exp:* NIMH fel, Brain Res Inst, Univ Calif, Los Angeles, 67-68. *Mem:* Soc Neurosci; Can Soc Zool. *Res:* Neuronal activity associated with hormone release; neurophysiology of crustacean motor systems; brachiopod neuromuscular physiology; invertebrate muscle physiology. *Mailing Add:* Dept Biol Univ Calgary Calgary AB T2N 1N4 Can

**WILKENS, JOHN ALBERT,** POLLUTION PREVENTION, LIFE CYCLE ASSESSMENT. *Current Pos:* from res engr to sect supvs, RES ASSOC, E I DU PONT DE NEMOURS. *Personal Data:* b New York, Oct 28, 47; m 77, Lucile Shanes; c Christopher. *Educ:* Cornell Univ, BS, 69, MChE, 71; Mass Inst Technol, PhD(chem eng), 77. *Prof Exp:* Chem engr emission testing, US Environ Protection Agency, 70-72. *Mem:* Am Inst Chem Engrs; Am Chem Soc; Sigma Xi; Catalysis Soc. *Res:* Pollution prevention; life cycle assessment; process development; reactor engineering. *Mailing Add:* 138 Round Hill Rd Kennett Square PA 19348-2608

**WILKENS, LON ALLAN,** NEUROBIOLOGY. *Current Pos:* from asst prof to assoc prof, 75-87, PROF BIOL, UNIV MO, ST LOUIS, 88-, CHMN DEPT, 89- *Personal Data:* b Ellsworth, Kans, Sept 7, 42; m 65; c 3. *Educ:* Univ Kans, Lawrence, BA, 65; Fla State Univ, PhD(physiol), 70. *Prof Exp:* Fel neurobiol, Univ Tex, Austin, 70-73; asst prof biol, Bryn Mawr Col, 73-75. *Concurrent Pos:* Res fel, Dept Neurobiol, Res Sch Biol Sci, Australian Nat Univ, 80-82. *Mem:* Am Soc Zoologists; Soc Neurosci; AAAS. *Res:* Neurobiology and behavior of invertebrates, including sensory physiology and central processing of tactile and extraretinal information in decapod crustaceans; visual system physiology and escape behaviors in bivalve molluscs. *Mailing Add:* Dept Biol Univ Mo 8001 Natural Bridge Rd St Louis MO 63121-4401

**WILKENS, LUCILE SHANES,** CHEMICAL ENGINEERING. *Personal Data:* b Kansas City, Mo, May 19, 50; m 77, John A; c Christopher A. *Educ:* Washington Univ, BS, 72; Mass Inst Technol, PhD(chem eng), 77. *Prof Exp:* Res engr, E I Du Pont de Nemours & Co, Inc, 77-84, independent consult, 85-89. *Mem:* Am Inst Chem Engrs; Am Chem Soc; Sigma Xi. *Res:* Colloid and surface chemistry; rheology; cryogenics; heat and mass transfer. *Mailing Add:* 138 Round Hill Rd Kennett Square PA 19348-2608

**WILKERSON, CLARENCE WENDELL, JR,** TOPOLOGY. *Current Pos:* PROF MATH, WAYNE STATE UNIV, 77- *Personal Data:* b Laredo, Tex, Aug 12, 44; m 65; c 2. *Educ:* Rice Univ, BA, 66, PhD(math), 70. *Prof Exp:* Asst prof math, Univ Hawaii, Manoa, 70-72; res assoc, Swiss Fed Inst Technol, 72-73; res assoc, Carleton Univ, 73-74; instr, Univ Pa, 74-75, asst prof math, 75-77. *Concurrent Pos:* Alfred P Sloan fel, 78-82. *Mem:* Am Math Soc. *Res:* Algebraic topology and homotopy theory of Lie groups, H-spaces and associated spaces. *Mailing Add:* Dept Math Purdue Univ West Lafayette IN 47907-1968

**WILKERSON, JAMES EDWARD,** CARDIOLOGY, SPORTS MEDICINE. *Current Pos:* med dir, Post-Cardiac Care Unit, 95, MED DIR, CARDIAC REHAB, VALLEY BAPTIST MED CTR, TEX, 95-, NON-INTERVENTIONAL CARDIOL, 96-; OWNER, AMERIFIT CORP, 75-; VPRES RES, HYDROTONICS THER CORP, 86- *Personal Data:* b Kingsville, Tex, Oct 2, 45; m 85; Eileen M Leeds; c Michelle Kathryn (Miller). *Educ:* Rice Univ, BS, 67; Univ Ore, MA, 68, MS, 69, PhD(physiol), 70; Univ Miami, MD, 87. *Prof Exp:* Asst res physiologist, Inst Environ Stress, Univ Calif, Santa Barbara, 70-75; dir exercise physiol, Univ Ind, 75-85; from med intern to resident, Univ Miami, Jackson Mem Hosp, 87-90, fel, Div Cardiovasc Dis, 90-93; fel, Div Cardiovasc Dis, Univ Miami, 90-93; instr, Univ Miami Sch Med, 91-93. *Concurrent Pos:* NIH fel, 70-71; sr res fel, Santa Barbara Co Heart Asn, 71-72; dir, Clin Chem Labs, Inst Environ Stress, 72-75; instr, Univ Calif Exten, 74-75; asst prof, Dept Phys Educ, Ind Univ, 75-79, adj asst prof, Dept Physiol, 76-79; fac mem, Safety Eng Sch, USN, 76-83; vis prof, Schs Med & Phys Educ & Sport, Univ Helwan, Egypt, 78, Sch Med, Kuwait Univ, 79; chmn, Sci Subcomt, US Olympic Track & Field Develop Comt, 79-80; vis assoc prof, Dept Environ Sci, Johns Hopkins Univ, 83-84; res physiologist, Sch Aerospace Med, USAF, 84-85; admitting physician, Vet Admin Med Ctr, 89-93, Palm Beach Gardens Hosp, 90-91; consult physician, Hospicenter Hosp, 93-; dir, Valley Diag Med & Surg Clin, 93-, cardiologist, 93-; pres & chmn bd dirs, 96-; staff physician, Valley Baptist Med Ctr, 93-, Dolly Vansant Mem Hosp, 94- *Mem:* Am Physiol Soc; NY Acad Sci; Am Col Sports Med; Am Col Physicians; Sigma Xi; Aerospace Med Asn; AAAS; Aerospace Physiol Soc; Am Col Cardiol; Am Col Sports Med; AMA; Am Soc Echocardiol; Fedn Am Socs Exp Biol. *Res:* Exercise and environmental effects on cardiovascular and pulmonary functions of humans as they age, including endocrine, plasma volume, muscle biochemical and thermoregulatory effects; author of numerous publications. *Mailing Add:* Dept Cardiol Valley Diag Clin 2220 Haine Dr Harlingen TX 78550-8599. *Fax:* 956-425-7189

**WILKERSON, JOHN CHRISTOPHER,** PHYSICAL OCEANOGRAPHY. *Current Pos:* SR PROJ SCIENTIST, NAT OCEANIC & ATMOSPHERIC ADMIN, 77- *Personal Data:* b Washington, DC, Mar 15, 26; m 58, Anneliese Driessen; c Scott & Suzanne. *Educ:* Univ Md, BS, 51. *Honors & Awards:* Bronze Medal, Dept Com, 92. *Prof Exp:* Phys oceanogr, US Naval Oceanog Off, 60-62, from proj scientist to sr proj scientist, 62-67, proj mgr, 67-77. *Res:* Remote sensing; aircraft platforms; data management; oceanographic satellite validation. *Mailing Add:* 4834 Butterworth Pl NW Washington DC 20016. *Fax:* 301-763-8231

**WILKERSON, ROBERT C,** PHYSICS, MATHEMATICS. *Current Pos:* RETIRED. *Personal Data:* b Orange, Tex, June 25, 18; m 42, Evedyne Andrews; c 1. *Educ:* Univ Okla, BS, 41. *Prof Exp:* Seismic comput, Geophys Party, Stanolind Oil & Gas Co, Okla, 41-43; spectroscopist, Sinclair Rubber Inc, Tex, 43-47; Res & Develop Div, Celanese Chem Co, 47-49, group leader phys instruments, 49-55, analytical res, 55, head, Analytical Sect, 55-65, admin mgr, Tech Ctr, 65-84. *Mem:* Coblentz Soc. *Res:* Application of physical instruments in analytical support of organic chemistry research and development; development of application of computer systems for management information data and for technical information storage and retrieval systems; thirty-four publications. *Mailing Add:* 221 Rosebud Corpus Christi TX 78404

**WILKERSON, ROBERT DOUGLAS,** PHARMACOLOGY. *Current Pos:* assoc prof, 79-88, PROF, MED COL OHIO, 88- *Personal Data:* b Wilson, NC, Aug 5, 44; m 95, Carol Reichenbach; c Rob, Julie, Christopher, Patrick & Brian. *Educ:* Univ NC, Chapel Hill, BS, 67; Med Univ SC, MS, 69, PhD(pharmacol), 72. *Prof Exp:* From asst prof to assoc prof, Col Med, Univ SAla, 73-79. *Concurrent Pos:* Assoc vpres res, Med Col Ohio, 91- *Mem:* AAAS; Am Soc Pharmacol & Exp Therapeut; Am Heart Asn. *Res:* Cardiovascular pharmacology. *Mailing Add:* Dept Pharmacol PO Box 10008 Med Col Ohio Toledo OH 43699. *E-Mail:* dwilkerson@cutter.mcd.edu

**WILKERSON, THOMAS DELANEY,** plasma physics, space physics, for more information see previous edition

**WILKES, CHARLES EUGENE,** CHEMISTRY. *Current Pos:* From res chemist to sr chemist, BF Goodrich Co, 64-69, sect leader, 69-73, sr res assoc, 73-74, sect mgr, Corp Res New Technol, 74-78, dir, Technol Assessment & Planning, 78-81, DIR CORP RES, RES CTR, B F GOODRICH CO, 81- *Personal Data:* b Worcester, Mass, Oct 9, 39; m 61; c 4. *Educ:* Worcester Polytech Inst, BS, 61; Princeton Univ, PhD(phys chem), 64. *Mem:* Am Chem Soc. *Res:* Chemical physics; polymer characterization; x-ray diffraction; molecular spectroscopy; lab automation. *Mailing Add:* 2141 Pilgrim Way Akron OH 44313

**WILKES, GARTH L,** POLYMER SCIENCE. *Current Pos:* prof chem eng, 78-81, F W B PROF, VA POLYTECH INST & STATE UNIV, 81-, DIR, MAT ENG SCI PROG. *Personal Data:* b Syracuse, NY, May 22, 42; div; c 2. *Educ:* State Univ NY, BS, 64; Univ Mass, Amherst, MS, 67, PhD(phys chem), 69. *Honors & Awards:* Award for Creative Polymer Chem, Am Chem Soc, 87. *Prof Exp:* From asst to assoc prof chem eng, Princeton Univ, 69-78. *Concurrent Pos:* Res assoc, Textile Res Inst, 74-; Turner Alfrey prof, Midland Molecular Inst, 93. *Mem:* Am Inst Chem Eng; Am Chem Soc. *Res:* Property of synthetic and biopolymers; structure property behavior of synthetic and natural polymers. *Mailing Add:* Dept Chem Eng Va Polytech Inst Blacksburg VA 24061

**WILKES, GLENN RICHARD,** INORGANIC CHEMISTRY. *Current Pos:* RES SCIENTIST, EASTMAN KODAK CO, 66- *Personal Data:* b Houtzdale, Pa, Mar 25, 37; m 61; c 2. *Educ:* Pa State Univ, BS, 60; Univ Wis, PhD(inorg chem), 65. *Prof Exp:* Scholar, Univ Calif, Los Angeles, 65-66. *Mem:* Am Chem Soc; Am Crystallog Asn; Royal Soc Chem. *Res:* Crystal and molecular structure determination of organometallic compounds by single crystal x-ray diffraction studies; synthesis of metal carbonyls and their derivatives. *Mailing Add:* 1102 Shoemaker Rd Webster NY 14580-8719

**WILKES, HILBERT GARRISON, JR,** ECONOMIC BOTANY. *Current Pos:* from asst prof to assoc prof, 70-83, PROF BIOL, UNIV MASS, BOSTON, 83- *Personal Data:* b Los Angeles, Calif, Oct 2, 37; m 78. *Educ:* Pomona Col, BA, 59; Harvard Univ, PhD(biol), 66. *Prof Exp:* Asst prof biol, Tulane Univ, 66-70. *Concurrent Pos:* Mem, World Maize Germplasm Comn, Rockefeller Found & Food & Agr Orgn; Indo-Am fel, India, 78-79; Maize res fel, Int Maize & Wheat Improv Ctr, Mex, 85-86; chmn, Ctr Vulnerability Comn, Nat Res Coun, 87-89. *Mem:* Soc Study Econ Bot (secy, 73-75 & 75-77); Bot Soc Am; Soc Econ Bot (pres, 85); Indian Bot Soc; fel AAAS; Crop Sci Soc. *Res:* Evolution under domestication in cultivated plants, especially maize and its wild relatives, teosinte and tripsacum; conservation biology. *Mailing Add:* Dept Biol Col II Univ Mass 100 Morrissey Blvd Boston MA 02125. *Fax:* 617-287-6650

**WILKES, JAMES C,** BIOLOGY. *Current Pos:* RETIRED. *Personal Data:* b Mar 13, 21; US citizen; m 45; c 6. *Educ:* Troy State Col, BS, 48; Univ Tenn, MS, 50; Univ Ala, PhD(bot), 54. *Prof Exp:* Prof biol, Tenn Wesleyan Col, 50-51; prof & head dept, Jacksonville State Univ, 52-56; ed adv med sci, Sch Aviation Med, Air Univ, 56-57; prof & head, Dept Biol, Huntingdon Col, 57-60 & Miss State Col Women, 60-66; head dept, Troy State Univ, 58-77, prof biol, 66- *Res:* Bryophytes; radiation biology. *Mailing Add:* 113 Woodland Circle Troy AL 36081-3941

**WILKES, JAMES OSCROFT,** CHEMICAL ENGINEERING, DIGITAL COMPUTING. *Current Pos:* from instr to assoc prof, Univ Mich, Ann Arbor, 60-70, chmn dept, 71-77, Arthur F Thurnau prof, 89-92, asst dean eng, 90-95, PROF CHEM ENG, UNIV MICH, ANN ARBOR, 70-, ASST DEAN ENG, 90- *Personal Data:* b Southampton, Eng, Jan 24, 32; m 56, Mary A Gibson. *Educ:* Cambridge Univ, BA, 54, MA, 60; Univ Mich, MS, 56, PhD(chem eng), 63. *Prof Exp:* Demonstr chem eng, Cambridge Univ, 57-60. *Concurrent Pos:* Assoc, Trinity Col Music, London, Eng, 51. *Mem:* Soc Petrol Engrs; Am Inst Chem Engrs; Sigma Xi; Am Soc Eng Educ. *Res:* Applied numerical methods; fluid mechanics and heat transfer; metal casting; polymer processing; gas storage; two-phase flow. *Mailing Add:* 805 Colliston Rd Ann Arbor MI 48105. *E-Mail:* wilkes@engin.umich.edu

**WILKES, JOHN BARKER,** PETROLEUM CHEMISTRY. *Current Pos:* RETIRED. *Personal Data:* b Berkeley, Calif, Jan 17, 16; m 38; c 2. *Educ:* Univ Calif, BS, 37; Stanford Univ, PhD(chem), 48. *Prof Exp:* Chemist, Poultry Prod Cent Calif, 37-40; res chemist, Chevron Res Co, 48-62, sr res chemist, 62-65, sr res assoc, 65-83. *Concurrent Pos:* US Army, Ord Dept, 40-45. *Mem:* Am Chem Soc; AAAS. *Res:* Kinetics; thermodynamics; catalysis; chemicals from petroleum; solubility theory. *Mailing Add:* 1570 Kingwood Dr Hillsborough CA 94010

**WILKES, JOHN STUART,** ELECTROCHEMISTRY, ORGANIC CHEMISTRY. *Current Pos:* res chemist, 73-75, TECH DIR, FRANK J SEILER RES LAB, USAF ACAD, 78- *Personal Data:* b Panama, Mar 6, 47; m 71, Laurie Campbell. *Educ:* State Univ NY, Buffalo, BA, 69; Northwestern Univ, Evanston, MS, 71, PhD(chem), 73. *Prof Exp:* Asst prof chem, Univ Colo, Denver, 76-78. *Mem:* AAAS; Am Chem Soc; Electrochem Soc. *Res:* Electrochemistry in molten salts; electroorganic synthesis, thermal decompostion of explosives and propellants. *Mailing Add:* 2845 Palmer Divide Rd Larkspur CO 80118. *Fax:* 719-472-3649; *E-Mail:* wilkesjs%fjsrl%usafa@pcmail.usafa.af.mil

**WILKES, JOSEPH WRAY,** computer science, industrial engineering; deceased, see previous edition for last biography

**WILKES, KENNETH EARL,** HEAT TRANSFER & THERMODYNAMICS, THERMAL INSULATION. *Current Pos:* SR STAFF MEM & PROG MGR, OAK RIDGE NAT LAB, 87- *Personal Data:* b Huntington, WVa, June 6, 44; m, Rose Pennington. *Educ:* Duke Univ, BS, 66; Purdue Univ, MS, 68; Ohio State Univ, MS, 71, PhD(physics), 78. *Prof Exp:* Mech engr, Battelle Mem Inst, 68-77; res assoc, Owens-Corning Tech Ctr, 77-86. *Mem:* Am Soc Mech Engrs; Am Soc Testing & Mat; Am Soc Heating, Refrig & Air Conditioning Engrs; Am Phys Soc; Am Ceramic Soc. *Res:* Heat transfer; thermophysical properties of matter; thermal insulation properties; thermal measurements and modeling; energy conservation. *Mailing Add:* 605 Laurel Valley Rd Knoxville TN 37922

**WILKES, MAURICE V,** COMPUTER SCIENCE. *Current Pos:* head, Comput Lab, 46-80, EMER PROF COMPUT TECHNOL, CAMBRIDGE UNIV, 86- *Personal Data:* b Dudley, Eng, June 26, 13. *Educ:* Cambridge Univ, MA, 34, PhD, 37. *Honors & Awards:* Turing Award, Asn Comput Mach; Harry Goode Mem Award, Am Fedn Info Processing Soc, Eckert-Mauchly Award; McDowell Award, Inst Elec & Electronics Engrs; Faraday Medal, Inst Elec Engrs, London. *Prof Exp:* Sr consult engr, Digital Equip Corp, 80-86. *Concurrent Pos:* Mem res strategy, Olivetti Res Bd, 86-90, consult, 90- *Mem:* Foreign assoc Nat Acad Sci; foreign assoc Nat Acad Eng; fel Royal Soc; foreign hon mem AAAS. *Mailing Add:* 130 Nuntingdon Rd Cambridge CB2-3QG England

**WILKES, RICHARD JEFFREY,** PARTICLE ASTROPHYSICS. *Current Pos:* Res assoc & instr physics, Univ Wash, 74-79, res sci & tech dir, 79-84, sr res assoc, 84-88, res assoc prof, 88-91, RES PROF, UNIV WASH, 91- *Personal Data:* b Chicago, Ill, Oct 18, 45; m 70; c 2. *Educ:* Univ Mich, BSE, 67; Univ Wis, MS, 69, PhD(physics), 74. *Mem:* Am Phys Soc. *Res:* High energy cosmic ray spectra and interactions; elementary particle physics using nuclear emulsion analysis; image analysis; acoustics. *Mailing Add:* Dept Physics Box 351560 Univ Wash Rm B303 Seattle WA 98195-0001

**WILKES, STANLEY NORTHRUP,** PARASITOLOGY, MARINE ZOOLOGY. *Current Pos:* asst prof, 66-71, ASSOC PROF ZOOL, NORTHERN ARIZ UNIV, 71- *Personal Data:* b Corvallis, Ore, Jan 3, 27; m 58; c 3. *Educ:* Ore State Univ, BS, 50, MS, 57, PhD(zool), 66. *Prof Exp:* Aquatic biologist, Res Div, Ore Fish Comn, 50-51 & 56-60; asst prof biol, E Carolina Col, 65-66. *Mem:* Am Soc Parasitol; Am Micros Soc; Sigma Xi. *Res:* Taxonomy, life history studies and distribution of parasitic copepods of fishes, elasmobranchs and invertebrates; taxonomy of monogenetic Trematoda; taxonomy and ecology of marine invertebrates and fishes. *Mailing Add:* 3836 N Paradise Rd Flagstaff AZ 86004

**WILKES, STELLA H,** ENZYMOLOGY. *Current Pos:* RETIRED. *Educ:* La State Univ, MS, 50. *Prof Exp:* Sr lectr, Inst Occup Med, Tex A&M Univ, 85-86. *Mailing Add:* 9552 River Rd College Station TX 77845

**WILKES, WILLIAM ROY,** ISOTOPE SEPARATION, FUSION TECHNOLOGY. *Current Pos:* CONSULT, W2TECH SERV, 92- *Personal Data:* b Harvey, Ill, Feb 15, 39; m 59, Holly Halburt; c 3. *Educ:* DePauw Univ, AB, 59; Univ Ill, MS, 61, PhD(physics), 66. *Prof Exp:* Asst prof physics, Wake Forest Univ, 65-67; sr res physicist, Monsanto Res Corp, 67-74, res specialist, 74-77, group leader, 77-79, mgr isotope separation, Mound Lab, 79-92. *Concurrent Pos:* Adj assoc prof physics, Wright State Univ, 90- *Mem:* AAAS. *Res:* Cryogenic isotope separation; tritium technology; liquid helium; superconductivity. *Mailing Add:* PO Box 756 Saluda NC 28773

**WILKI, GUNTHER,** CHEMISTRY. *Current Pos:* RETIRED. *Personal Data:* b Heidelberg, Ger, Feb 23, 25; m, Dagmar Kind. *Honors & Awards:* Willard Gibbs Medal, Am Chem Soc, 91. *Prof Exp:* Prof chem, Ruhr Univ, 63-90; dir, MP1 Coal Res, 69-93. *Concurrent Pos:* Dean, Dept Chem, Max Planck Inst Coal Res, 68-69. *Mem:* Fel Am Chem Soc; Ger Acad Scientists; foreign mem Royal Dutch Acad Sci. *Mailing Add:* Max Planck Inst Coal Res Kaiser-Wilhelm Platz 1 45470 Mulheim an der Ruhr Germany

**WILKIE, BRUCE NICHOLSON,** IMMUNOLOGY, VETERINARY MEDICINE. *Current Pos:* from asst prof to assoc prof, 73-80, PROF IMMUNOL, UNIV GUELPH, 80-, CHMN, DEPT MICROBIOL & IMMUNOL, 87-, DIR, ANIMAL RES CTR, GUELPH-WATERLOO RES, 87- *Personal Data:* b Perth, Scotland, Jan 19, 41; Can citizen; m 66; c 1. *Educ:* Univ Guelph, DVM, 65; Cornell Univ, PhD(immunol), 71. *Prof Exp:* Res asst path, NY State Vet Col, Cornell Univ, 71; asst prof immunol, Univ Bern, 71-73. *Mem:* Can Soc Immunol; Am Asn Immunologists; Int Soc Animal Genetics. *Res:* Veterinary immunology and immunopathology. *Mailing Add:* Dept Vet Microbiol & Immunol Univ Guelph Guelph ON N1G 2W1 Can. *Fax:* 519-767-0809

**WILKIE, CHARLES ARTHUR,** POLYMER DEGRADATION & STABILIZATION. *Current Pos:* from asst prof to assoc prof, 67-86, PROF CHEM, MARQUETTE UNIV, 86- *Personal Data:* b Detroit, Mich, Nov 21, 41; m 64, Nancy DeCaluwe; c Christine, Stephen & Richard. *Educ:* Univ Detroit, BS, 63; Wayne State Univ, PhD(inorg chem), 67. *Concurrent Pos:* Fulbright scholar, Free Univ of Brussels, 91-92. *Mem:* Am Chem Soc; AAAS; Sigma Xi. *Res:* Flame retardants; polymer chemistry; thermal decomposition and flame retardation. *Mailing Add:* Dept Chem Marquette Univ Milwaukee WI 53233. *Fax:* 414-288-3300; *E-Mail:* wilkiec@vms.csd.mu.edu

**WILKIE, DAVID SCOTT,** NATURAL RESOURCE MANAGEMENT, TROPICAL CONSERVATION ECOLOGY. *Current Pos:* UN ENVIRON PROG FAC ENVIRON MGT, TUFTS UNIV, 90- *Personal Data:* b Edinburgh, Scotland, June 5, 55. *Educ:* Stirling Univ, Scotland, BSc, 77; Univ Mass, Amherst, MS, 82, PhD(conserv biol), 87. *Prof Exp:* Res fac, Univ Utah, 87-89. *Res:* Social ecology of tropical forest hunter-gatherers and farmers, particularly their natural resource exploitation and management practices. *Mailing Add:* 4601 Connecticut Ave NW Washington DC 20008. *E-Mail:* davidw@rsrch.cfm.tufts.edu

**WILKIE, DONALD W,** MARINE BIOLOGY. *Current Pos:* aquarium dir, 65-93, AQUARIUM CUR, SCRIPPS INST OCEANOG, 93- *Personal Data:* b Vancouver, BC, June 20, 31; m 56, 80, Patricia A Archer; c 3. *Educ:* Univ BC, BA, 60, MSc, 66. *Prof Exp:* Asst res biologist, BC Fish & Game Dept, 60-61; asst cur, Vancouver Pub Aquarium, 61-63; cur, Philadelphia Aquarium, Inc, 63-65. *Concurrent Pos:* Aquarium consult. *Mem:* Am Asn Zool Parks & Aquariums; Am Cetacean Soc; Am Asn Ichthyol & Herpet; Am Asn Mus. *Res:* Pigmentation and coloration of fishes; aquariology and methods of public education in aquaria and museums. *Mailing Add:* 4548 Cather Ave San Diego CA 92122

**WILKIN, JONATHAN KEITH,** CLINICAL PHARMACOLOGY, DERMA PHARMACOLOGY. *Current Pos:* DIR, DIV DERMAT, OHIO STATE UNIV, 88- *Personal Data:* b Columbus, Ohio, Oct 8, 45; m 67; c 2. *Educ:* Ohio State Univ, BA, 67, MS, 71, MD, 74. *Prof Exp:* Tech asst, Franz Theodore Stone Inst Hydrobiol, Ohio, 65-68; teaching asst zool, Ohio State Univ, 67-71; asst prof dermat, Univ Tex Med Sch, 78-82 & MD Anderson Hosp & Tumor Inst, 80-82; from assoc prof to prof dermat, pharmacol & toxicol, Med Col Va, 82-88. *Concurrent Pos:* Chief dermat, Vet Admin Med Ctr, 82-88. *Res:* Cutaneous vascular pharmacology and physiology; dermatopharmacology; transdermal drug delivery systems; effects of topical and systemic drugs on the skin. *Mailing Add:* Div Derm Rm 4731 UHC 456 W Tenth Ave Columbus OH 43210-1240

**WILKIN, LOUIS ALDEN,** ORGANIC CHEMISTRY. *Current Pos:* From chemist to sr chemist, Tenn Eastman Co, 65-75, develop assoc, 75-76, group leader, 76-88, DEVELOP ASSOC, TENN EASTMAN CO, 88- *Personal Data:* b Bath, Maine, Mar 5, 39; m 60; c 3. *Educ:* The Citadcl, BS, 60; Clemson Univ, MS, 62, PhD(org chem), 65. *Mem:* Am Chem Soc. *Res:* Novel rearrangements of acetylenic alcohols and esters upon treatment with basic alumina. *Mailing Add:* 1505 Watauga St Kingsport TN 37660

**WILKIN, PETER J,** PHYSIOLOGY. *Current Pos:* HEAD, DEPT BIOL, PURDUE UNIV, CALUMET, 79- *Personal Data:* b Yeoville, Eng, Nov 28, 43; m; c 2. *Educ:* Univ Ill, PhD(physiol & biophys), 71. *Mem:* Am Physiol Soc; Entom Soc Am; Nature Conservancy (treas, 86-); Sierra Club. *Res:* Human and insect physiology. *Mailing Add:* Dept Biol & Chem Purdue Univ North Central Campus Westville IN 46391-9528. *Fax:* 219-785-5355

**WILKINS, BERT, JR,** CHEMICAL ENGINEERING. *Current Pos:* ASSOC PROF CHEM ENG, LA STATE UNIV, BATON ROUGE, 68-, COORDR ENERGY PROGS, 75- *Personal Data:* b Hattiesburg, Miss, Oct 8, 34; m 57; c 2. *Educ:* Ga Inst Technol, BChE, 58, MS, 61, PhD(chem eng), 65. *Prof Exp:* Sr engr, Lockheed-Ga Co Div, Lockheed Aircraft Corp, 63-64; sr engr, Humble Oil & Ref Co, 65-67; asst prof chem eng, Univ Mo, Columbia, 67-68. *Concurrent Pos:* NASA-Am Soc Eng Educ fac fel, NASA Manned Spacecraft Ctr, Tex, 68, 69; consult, 70-; mem, Environ Adv Panel, Gulf Universal Res Corp, 70-; NASA grant, La State Univ, Baton Rouge, 70-, NSF grant, 71- *Mem:* AAAS; Am Inst Chem Engrs. *Res:* Applied mathematics; transport phenomena; process design; bioengineering; ecological systems analysis. *Mailing Add:* 10341 Parkview Dr Baton Rouge LA 70815

**WILKINS, BRIAN JOHN SAMUEL,** PHYSICAL METALLURGY. *Current Pos:* RETIRED. *Personal Data:* b London, Eng, Feb 28, 37; Can citizen; m 61, Sylvia A Albone; c Simon, Elizabeth & Michael. *Educ:* Univ London, BSc, 58, PhD(metall), 61. *Prof Exp:* Sci off fuel element develop, Dounreay Exp Reactor Estab, UK Atomic Energy Auth, 61-64; assoc researcher, Off Mat Develop, Atomic Energy Can Ltd Res, Whiteshell Labs, 64-80, sr researcher, Off Mat & Mech, 80, sect head mat & eng anal, 80-97. *Res:* Materials development; mathematical modelling (thermomechanical behavior, diffusion, deformation and fracture of solids) applied to reactor safety and nuclear waste management programs. *Mailing Add:* Atomic Energy Can Ltd Res Whiteshell Labs Pinawa MB R0E 1L0 Can

**WILKINS, BRUCE TABOR,** RESOURCE EXTENSION ADMINISTRATION. *Current Pos:* exten specialist, Cornell Univ, 63-67, asst prof, 67-73, assoc prof, 73-80, PROF NATURAL RESOURCES, CORNELL UNIV, 80- *Personal Data:* b Greenport, NY, June 21, 31; m 56; c 3. *Educ:* Cornell Univ, BS, 52, PhD(resource planning), 67; Mont State Univ, MS, 56. *Prof Exp:* Res biologist, Mont Fish & Game Dept, 56-59; county agr agent, Broome County Exten Serv, NY, 59-63. *Concurrent Pos:* Prog leader, NY Sea Grant Adv Serv, 72-86, assoc dir, 75-86; vis prof, Univ BC, 74; vis Sea Grant prof, Ore State Univ, 75 & Univ Hawaii, 81. *Mem:* Wildlife Soc; Am Fisheries Soc; Am Asn Univ Profs. *Res:* Relationships of human demands and natural resources, especially fish and wildlife resources; resource policy, particularly marine and recreational policy issues. *Mailing Add:* Dept Natural Resources Fernow Hall Cornell Univ Ithaca NY 14853

**WILKINS, CHARLES LEE,** ANALYTICAL CHEMISTRY. *Current Pos:* PROF CHEM, UNIV CALIF, RIVERSIDE, 81- *Personal Data:* b Los Angeles, Calif, Aug 14, 38; m 66. *Educ:* Chapman Col, BS, 61; Univ Ore, PhD(chem), 66. *Prof Exp:* From asst prof to assoc prof, Univ Nebr, Lincoln, 67-76, prof chem, 76-81. *Concurrent Pos:* Vis assoc prof, Univ NC, Chapel Hill, 74-75. *Mem:* Am Chem Soc; Am Soc Mass Spectros; Soc Appl Spectros. *Res:* Fourier transform infrared spectrometry; Fourier transform mass spectrometry; nuclear magnetic resonance spectroscopy and computer applications to chemical problems and laboratory automation. *Mailing Add:* Dept Chem Univ Calif Riverside CA 92521-0001. *Fax:* 909-787-4713

**WILKINS, CLETUS WALTER, JR,** ORGANIC CHEMISTRY, POLYMER CHEMISTRY. *Current Pos:* Mem tech staff mat res, Bell Labs, 76-84, supvr composite mat, 84-88, tech mgr mat develop, 88-93, HEAD ANALYTICAL TECHNOL, BELL LABS, 93- *Personal Data:* b Asheville, NC, June 23, 45; m 69, Patricia A Potticlo; c Cletus & Grica. *Educ:* Morgan State Univ, BS, 69; Pa State Univ, MS, 74, PhD(chem), 76. *Mem:* Am Chem Soc; AAAS. *Res:* Photochemistry in thin polymer films; solid state photochemistry; organometallic chemistry; surface characterization; semiconductor material; metallization and dielectrics. *Mailing Add:* 9582 E Cortez St Scottsdale AZ 85260

**WILKINS, CURTIS C,** PHYSICAL CHEMISTRY. *Current Pos:* assoc prof, 65-70, PROF CHEM, WESTERN KY UNIV, 70- *Personal Data:* b La Crosse, Wis, Oct 28, 35; m 54; c 3. *Educ:* Wis State Univ, BS, 57; Mich State Univ, PhD(chem), 64. *Prof Exp:* Asst prof chem, WVa Wesleyan Col, 62-65. *Concurrent Pos:* NSF res participation fel, Univ Tenn, 65. *Mem:* Am Chem Soc. *Res:* Dilute solution properties of stereo-regular polymers; flame photometry studies of trace elements. *Mailing Add:* Dept Chem Western Ky Univ Bowling Green KY 42101

**WILKINS, DANIEL R,** NUCLEAR ENGINEERING. *Current Pos:* former head, Advan Boiling Water Reactor Prog, gen mgr, Dept Nuclear Power Syst Eng, GEN MGR, DEPT NUCLEAR SERV & PROJ, GEN ELEC. *Educ:* Case Inst Technol, BS; Mass Inst Technol, SM & ScD(nuclear eng). *Honors & Awards:* George Westinghouse Gold Medal, Am Soc Mech Engrs, 92; Mark Mills Award, Am Nuclear Soc. *Mem:* Am Nuclear Soc. *Res:* Contributed over 30 technical papers to science journals. *Mailing Add:* Gen Elec Co Nuclear Energy 175 Curtner Ave No 835 San Jose CA 95125-1014

**WILKINS, EBTISAM A M SEOUDI,** BIOENGINEERING & BIOSENSORS, CHEMICAL ENGINEERING. *Current Pos:* MEM FAC, UNIV NMEX, 78-, PROF CHEM & NUCLEAR ENG. *Personal Data:* b Monofia, Egypt, Mar 10, 45; US citizen; m 74; c 2. *Educ:* Cairo Univ, BSc, 65, MSc, 68; Univ Va, MSc, 73, PhD(chem eng), 76. *Prof Exp:* Res eng metall, Nat Res Ctr, Cairo, Egypt, 65-68; res specialist biomed eng, Div Biomed Eng, Univ Va, 69-73, res asst chem eng, Dept Chem Eng, 73-76; fel bioenergetics, Dept Kinesiology, Simon Fraser Univ, 76-77; fel, Dept Chem Eng, Univ BC, 77-78. *Concurrent Pos:* Fulbright fel, 88. *Mem:* Am Inst Chem Engrs. *Res:* Waste treatment (bioreactors); solar energy; biomedical sensors (glucose); environmental technology and biotechnology; patentee in field; published numerous articles. *Mailing Add:* Dept Chem Eng Univ NMex Albuquerque NM 87131-0002

**WILKINS, HAROLD,** horticulture, plant physiology, for more information see previous edition

**WILKINS, J ERNEST, JR,** NUCLEAR ENGINEERING. *Current Pos:* DISTINGUISHED PROF APPL MATH & MATH PHYSICS, CLARK ATLANTA UNIV, 90- *Personal Data:* b Chicago, Ill, Nov 27, 23; m 47, 84, Maxine Grundy; c Sharon W (Hill) & J Ernest III. *Educ:* Univ Chicago, SB, 40, SM, 41, PhD(math), 42; NY Univ, BME, 57, MME, 60. *Prof Exp:* Instr math, Tuskegee Inst, 43-44; from assoc physicist to physicist, Manhattan Proj, Metall Lab, Univ Chicago, 44-46; mathematician, Am Optical Co, 46-50; sr mathematician, Nuclear Develop Corp Am, 50-55, mgr, Physics & Math Dept, 55-57, asst mgr res & develop, 58-59 & mgr, 59-60; asst chmn, Theoret Physics Dept, Gen Atomic Div, Gen Dynamics Corp, 60-65, asst dir lab, 65-70; distinguished prof appl math physics, Howard Univ, 70-77; assoc gen mgr, EG&G Idaho, Inc, 77-80, dep gen mgr, 80-84. *Concurrent Pos:* Fel,

Argonne Nat Lab, 84-85; adj prof mech eng, Ga Inst Technol, 95- *Mem:* Nat Acad Eng; Am Math Soc; Optical Soc Am; fel Am Nuclear Soc (pres, 74-75); Soc Indust & Appl Math; fel AAAS; Math Asn Am. *Res:* Differential and integral equations; bessel functions; nuclear reactors; calculus of variations. *Mailing Add:* 587 Virginia Ave NE No 612 Atlanta GA 30306

**WILKINS, JUDD RICE,** MICROBIOLOGY, BIOENGINEERING. *Current Pos:* RETIRED. *Personal Data:* b Chicago, Ill, Dec 12, 20; m 50, Mary; c 2. *Educ:* Univ Ill, BS, 46, MS, 47, PhD(bact), 50. *Honors & Awards:* Spec Achievement & Outstanding Performance Awards, NASA, 76. *Prof Exp:* Asst prof, Med Sch, Univ SDak, 50-51; res investr, Upjohn Co, 51-57; sr res scientist, Booz-Allen Appl Res, 57-64; dept head bact, Eye Res Found, Bethesda, Md, 64-66; res microbiologist, NASA Langley Res Ctr, 66-82. *Mem:* Am Soc Microbiol. *Res:* Pollution monitoring; microbial detection methods; instrumentation development; life support systems; man in closed environments; electrochemistry; operations research; mathematical models. *Mailing Add:* 281 LittleTown Quarter Williamsburg VA 23185

**WILKINS, MAURICE HUGH FREDERICK,** NEUROBIOLOGY, BIOPHYSICS. *Current Pos:* MEM FAC, KINGS COL, LONDON, 46- *Personal Data:* b Pongaroa, NZ, Dec 15, 16; m 59, Patricia A Chidgey; c Sarah (Fenella), George H, Emily L (Una) & William H. *Educ:* St Johns Col, Cambridge, PhD, 40. *Hon Degrees:* LLD, Univ Glasgow 72; DSc, Birmingham Univ & Trinity Col, Dublin, 92. *Honors & Awards:* Nobel Prize for Physiol & Med, 62; Albert Lasker Award, Am Pub Health Asn, 60. *Prof Exp:* Researcher, Manhattan Proj, Univ Calif, Berkeley, 44; lectr, St Andrews Univ, 45; dep dir, Biophys Unit, Med Res Coun, 55-70, dir, 70-72, prof molecular biol, 62-70, prof biophys, 70-81, dir, Neurobiol Unit, 72-74; dir, Med Res Coun Neurobiol Unit, 74-80. *Mem:* Fel Royal Soc; Brit Biophys Soc; hon mem Am Soc Biol Chemists; foreign hon mem Am Acad Arts & Sci; Brit Soc Social Responsibility Sci (pres, 69-91). *Res:* Structure of nerve membranes and x-ray diffraction analysis of structure of DNA; development of electron trap theory of phosphorescence and thermo-luminescence; light microscopy techniques for cyto-chemical research, including use of interference microscope for dry mass determination in cells. *Mailing Add:* King Col Strand London WC2R 2LS England

**WILKINS, RALPH G,** INORGANIC CHEMISTRY. *Current Pos:* head dept, 73-76, PROF CHEM, NMEX STATE UNIV, 76- *Personal Data:* b Southampton, Eng, Jan 7, 27; m 84; c 2. *Educ:* Univ Southampton, BSc, 47, PhD(chem), 50; Univ London, DSc(chem), 61. *Prof Exp:* Res chemist, Imp Chem Indust, Eng, 49-52; res assoc inorg chem, Univ Southern Calif, 52-53; from lectr to sr lectr, Sheffield Univ, 53-62; guest prof, Max Planck Inst Phys Chem, 62-63; prof, State Univ NY, Buffalo, 63-73. *Mem:* Am Chem Soc; Royal Soc Chem. *Res:* Mechanisms of transition metal complexes and metalloenzyme reactions. *Mailing Add:* 8 Upper Rosemary Hill Kenilworth Warwickshire England

**WILKINS, RAYMOND LESLIE,** RESEARCH MANAGEMENT. *Current Pos:* RETIRED. *Personal Data:* b Boston, Mass, Jan 13, 25; m 50; c 2. *Educ:* Univ Chicago, AB, 51, MS, 54, PhD(chem), 57. *Prof Exp:* Sr scientist, Rohm & Hass Co, 56-68, head, Instrument Technol Lab, 68-73, mgr, Chem Process Res Dept, 74-78, mgr, Process Control Anal Dept, 79-81, mgr spec proj, 82-92. *Concurrent Pos:* Mem, Pa Gov Sci Adv Comt, 69-75, chmn, Health Care Delivery Panel, 69-71. *Mem:* Electron Micros Soc Am; NY Acad Sci; fel Royal Micros Soc; Am Chem Soc. *Res:* Correlation of the microstructure of heterogeneous organic plastics, polymers and emulsions with their gross properties; mechanisms of polymer formation; sustainable strategies for applying advanced control systems to chemical processes. *Mailing Add:* Pennswood Village D102 Newtown PA 18940-2401

**WILKINS, ROGER LAWRENCE,** CHEMICAL PHYSICS. *Current Pos:* RETIRED. *Personal Data:* b Newport News, Va, Dec 14, 28; m 55; c 1. *Educ:* Hampton Inst, BS, 51; Howard Univ, MS, 52; Univ Southern Calif, PhD(chem physics), 67. *Prof Exp:* Aeronaut scientist, NASA, Ohio, 52-55; sr tech specialist, Rocketdyne Div, NAm Aviation, Inc, 55-60; sr staff scientist, Aerophys Dept & Aerodyn & Propulsion Res Lab, Aerospace Corp, 60-80, sr staff scientist, Chem Kinetics Dept, Aerophys Lab, 80-91. *Mem:* Combustion Inst. *Res:* Chemical lasers; application of quantum, statistical and classical mechanics to treatment of energy transfer processes in chemical reactions; application of computers to calculate properties of molecules from first principles. *Mailing Add:* 4641 Don Zarembo Dr Los Angeles CA 90008

**WILKINS, RONALD WAYNE,** PHYSICS, COMPUTER SCIENCE. *Current Pos:* MEM STAFF PLASMA PHYSICS, LOS ALAMOS SCI LAB, 77- *Personal Data:* b Roscoe, Tex, Aug 29, 43; m 66; c 1. *Educ:* Harvard Univ, AB, 65; Univ Ill, Urbana, MS, 67, PhD(physics), 73. *Prof Exp:* Fel physics, Univ Kans, 73-75; mem staff, Ind Univ, 75-77. *Mem:* Am Phys Soc. *Res:* Solid state physics, especially equation of state computer control and data acquisition. *Mailing Add:* Los Alamos Nat Lab PO Box 1663 MS B255 Los Alamos NM 87545. *Fax:* 505-665-7793

**WILKINS, TRACY DALE,** MOLECULAR BIOLOGY, BIOTECHNOLOGY. *Current Pos:* from asst prof to prof, 72-85, DEPT HEAD MICROBIOL, VA POLYTECH INST & STATE UNIV, 85- *Personal Data:* b Sparkman, Ark, July 25, 43. *Educ:* Univ Ark, BS, 65; Univ Tex, Austin, PhD(microbiol), 69. *Prof Exp:* Fel pharmacol, Univ Ky Med Ctr, 69-71. *Mem:* Am Soc Microbiol; Soc Intestinal Microbiol & Dis (pres-elect, 88-89, pres, 89-91). *Res:* Anaerobic microbiology of the intestine; colitis; toxins; degradation of xenobiotics and production of carcinogens by intestinal bacteria. *Mailing Add:* Ctr Biotechnol Va Polytech Inst & State Univ PO Box 0308 Blacksburg VA 24063-0001

**WILKINSON, BRIAN JAMES,** MICROBIAL PHYSIOLOGY & BIOCHEMISTRY, MEDICAL MICROBIOLOGY. *Current Pos:* from asst prof to assoc prof, 79-85, PROF MICROBIOL & CHEM, ILL STATE UNIV, 85- *Personal Data:* b Huddersfield, Eng, Aug 10, 46; m 87, Jane L Gramoli; c Joseph G, Mary O & Lou. *Educ:* Univ Col Wales, BSc, 67; Univ Sheffield, PhD(microbiol), 71. *Prof Exp:* Res assoc biochem & microbiol, Univ Ky, 70-73; res fel biochem, Cambridge Univ, 73-76; asst prof med & microbiol, Univ Minn, 76-78. *Concurrent Pos:* Broodbank res fel, Cambridge Univ, 73-76; mem, Spec NIH Study Sect, 85; vis prof, Hull Univ, 86; chair, Div K Microbial, Physiol & Metab, Am Soc Microbiol, 95-96. *Mem:* Am Soc Microbiol; fel Am Acad Microbiol. *Res:* Bacterial cell surface, nature and role in pathogenicity; staphylococcal methicillin resistance; staphylococcal osmoregulation; bacterial stress physiology. *Mailing Add:* Dept Biol Sci Ill State Univ Normal IL 61790-4120. *Fax:* 309-438-3722; *E-Mail:* bjwilkin@ itstu.edu

**WILKINSON, BRUCE H,** SEDIMENTOLOGY. *Current Pos:* asst prof, 73-79, ASSOC PROF GEOL, UNIV MICH, ANN ARBOR, 79- *Personal Data:* b Lancaster, Pa, June 2, 42. *Educ:* Univ Wyo, BS, 65, MS, 67; Univ Tex, PhD(geol), 74. *Prof Exp:* Geologist asst oil shale, US Geol Surv, 65; geologist petrol, Gulf Oil Co, 67-69. *Mem:* Geol Soc Am; Sigma Xi. *Res:* Source and distribution of Holocene sediments of the Texas Gulf Coast and of Michigan; source and distribution of contemporary lacustrine carbonates; evolution; oceanic chemistry. *Mailing Add:* CC Little Bldg Ann Arbor MI 48109-1063

**WILKINSON, BRUCE W(ENDELL),** CHEMICAL & NUCLEAR ENGINEERING. *Current Pos:* from asst prof to prof, 65-90, assoc dir, Div Eng Res, 81-89, EMER PROF CHEM ENG, MICH STATE UNIV, 90- *Personal Data:* b Shelby, Ohio, Aug 9, 28; m 53; c 2. *Educ:* Ohio State Univ, BChE, 51, PhD(chem eng), 58. *Prof Exp:* Chem engr, Dow Chem Co, 54-59, staff asst, 59-63, proj coordr, 63-65. *Mem:* Am Inst Chem Engrs; Am Nuclear Soc; Am Soc Eng Educ; Sigma Xi; Nat Soc Prof Engrs. *Res:* Radioisotope applications; nuclear fuel processing; nuclear power; energy; environmental effects of energy. *Mailing Add:* 29 Hickory Hollow Circle Crossville TN 38555

**WILKINSON, DANIEL R,** PLANT PATHOLOGY, PLANT BREEDING. *Current Pos:* PLANT PATHOLOGIST, PIONEER HI-BREED INT, INC, 67- *Personal Data:* b Glasgow, Ky, May 30, 38; m 61; c 2. *Educ:* Western Ky Univ, BS, 61; Clemson Univ, MS, 63; Univ Ill, PhD(plant path), 67. *Mem:* Am Phytopath Soc. *Res:* Breeding for disease and insect resistance; genetics. *Mailing Add:* Dept Corn Breeding Pioneer Hi-Bred Int Inc 7301 NW 62nd St Johnston IA 50131-0085. *Fax:* 515-253-2221

**WILKINSON, DAVID IAN,** BIOCHEMISTRY. *Current Pos:* NIH res grant & res fel chem, res assoc biochem, 63-73, ADJ PROF DERMAT, SCH MED, STANFORD UNIV, 73- *Personal Data:* b Cookstown, Northern Ireland, Dec 17, 32; m 57; c 2. *Educ:* Queens Univ, Belfast, BS, 54, PhD(chem), 57. *Prof Exp:* USPHS res fel chem, Wayne State Univ, 57-58 & Univ Calif, Los Angeles, 58-59; res chemist, Brit Drug Houses, Eng, 59-61. *Concurrent Pos:* Fulbright fel, 57-59; NIH res grant dermat, Sch Med, Stanford Univ, 71-73. *Mem:* Chem Soc; Am Chem Soc; Soc Invest Dermat. *Res:* Skin lipids; prostaglandins; metabolism of fatty acids in skin; polyunsaturated fatty acids. *Mailing Add:* 1029 Vernier Pl Stanford CA 94305-1006

**WILKINSON, DAVID TODD,** PHYSICS, EXPERIMENTAL COSMOLOGY. *Current Pos:* from instr to prof, 63-87, chmn dept, 87-90, PROF PHYSICS, PRINCETON UNIV, 90- *Personal Data:* b Hillsdale, Mich, May 13, 35; m 86, Eunice Dowell; c Wendy & Kenton. *Educ:* Univ Mich, BSE, 57, MSE, 59, PhD(physics), 62. *Hon Degrees:* PhD, Univ Chicago, 96. *Prof Exp:* Lectr physics, Univ Mich, 62-63. *Concurrent Pos:* Alfred P Sloan Found fel, 66-68; John Simon Guggenheim fel, 77-78. *Mem:* Nat Acad Sci; Am Acad Arts & Sci; fel Am Phys Soc; Am Astron Soc; Am Asn Physics Teachers. *Res:* Atomic physics, properties of electrons and positrons; gravitation and relativity; primeval galaxies; cosmic microwave radiation. *Mailing Add:* Physics Dept PO Box 708 Princeton Univ Princeton NJ 08544-0708

**WILKINSON, EUGENE P DENNIS,** SAGE OPERATION OF NUCLEAR ELECTRIC GENERATING PLANTS. *Current Pos:* CONSULT, 84- *Personal Data:* b Long Beach, Calif, Aug 10, 18; m 42, Janice Edith Thwli; c Dennis Eugene, Stephen James, Marion Lynn & Rodney David. *Educ:* San Diego State Col, BA, 38. *Honors & Awards:* Golden Fleece Award, 55; George Westinghouse Gold Medal, Am Soc Mech Engrs, 83; Oliver Townsend Medal, 84; Uranium Inst Gold Medal, 89; Henry Dewolf Smyth Nuclear Statesman Medal, Am Nuclear Soc, 94. *Prof Exp:* From ensign to vadm, USN, 40-74; exec vpres, Data Design Labs, 76-80; pres & chief exec officer, Inst Nuclear Power Opers, 80-84; emer pres, chmn bd, bd dir, Mgt Analysis Corp. *Concurrent Pos:* Mem Ed Adv on Resource Develop Environ Inc, 81-; chmn bd, MDM Eng Corp, 94- *Mem:* Nat Acad Eng; Am Nuclear Soc; Am Soc Naval Engrs. *Res:* Design, construction, operation and management of nuclear electric generating plants. *Mailing Add:* 1449 Crest Rd Del Mar CA 92014

**WILKINSON, GEOFFREY,** chemistry; deceased, see previous edition for last biography

**WILKINSON, GRANT ROBERT,** PHARMACOLOGY. *Current Pos:* assoc prof, 71-77, PROF PHARMACOL, SCH MED, VANDERBILT UNIV, 77- *Personal Data:* b Derby, Eng, Aug 27, 41; US citizen; m; c 4. *Educ:* Univ Manchester, BSc, 63; Univ London, PhD(pharmaceut chem), 66. *Prof Exp:* Asst prof pharm, Col Pharm, Univ Ky, 68-71. *Concurrent Pos:* USPHS fel, Univ Calif, San Francisco, 66-68. *Mem:* Fel AAAS; Am Soc Pharmacol & Exp Therapeut; NY Acad Sci; fel Am Acad Pharmaceut Sci; Am Soc Clin Pharmacol Ther. *Res:* Clinical pharmacology; application of analytical methodology, drug metabolism and pharmacokinetics. *Mailing Add:* Dept Pharmacol Vanderbilt Univ Sch Med Nashville TN 37232-6602. *Fax:* 615-322-4707

**WILKINSON, HAROLD L,** MEMBRANE TRANSPORT. *Current Pos:* Asst prof, 78-89, ASSOC PROF BIOL, MILLIKIN UNIV, 89- *Personal Data:* b Santa Barbara, Calif, Apr 12, 41; m 66; c 6. *Educ:* Univ Ill, PhD(physiol), 76. *Mem:* Sigma Xi; Am Physiol Soc. *Mailing Add:* Dept Biol Millikin Univ 1184 W Main Decatur IL 62522

**WILKINSON, JACK DALE,** MATHEMATICS, EDUCATION. *Current Pos:* PROF MATH, UNIV NORTHERN IOWA, 62- *Personal Data:* b Ottumwa, Iowa, Jan 27, 31; m 53; c 5. *Educ:* Univ Northern Iowa, BA, 52, MA, 58; Iowa State Univ, PhD(math, educ), 70. *Concurrent Pos:* Consult, 64-; mem, bd dir, Nat Coun Teachers Math & Exec Comt, bd, Nat Coun Accreditation Teacher Educ; rep, Nat Col Athletic Asn. *Mem:* Am Educ Res Asn. *Res:* Activity learning; attitudes toward mathematical learning; learning styles in mathematics education; problem solving and applications of mathematics in the elementary and junior high schools; attracting under represented groups in to mathematics; developing and implementing a better set of linkages between preservice teacher education; the student teaching experience; the initial year(s) of teaching after graduation. *Mailing Add:* Dept Math Univ Northern Iowa Cedar Falls IA 50614-0506

**WILKINSON, JOHN EDWIN,** ANALYTICAL & ENVIRONMENTAL CHEMISTRY, GOVERNMENT & REGULATORY AFFAIRS. *Current Pos:* DIR, GOVT AFFAIRS, VULCAN CHEM, 87- *Personal Data:* b Tacoma, Wash, Nov 11, 42; m 64; c 2. *Educ:* Univ Puget Sound, BS, 64, MS, 76. *Prof Exp:* Mgr environ relations & sr analytical chemist, tech dir, Dept Sci & Technol, Reichhold Chem Inc, 66-85; consult environ & regulatory affairs, 85-87. *Concurrent Pos:* Chlorodioxin specialist, Am Wood Preservers Inst, 73-, chmn, Environ Progs Task Group, 78-; assoc, Chem Mfrs Asn, Halogenated Solvents Indust Alliance, Chlorine Inst, 85- *Mem:* Am Chem Soc; Am Wood Preservers Inst; AAAS. *Res:* Chlorodioxins present in chlorophenols; kemetic and analytical chemical study in the reduction of chlorodioxins in pentachlorophenol; phenol formaldehyde; urea formaldehyde; polyester resins. *Mailing Add:* Vulcan Chem 1899 L St Suite 500 Washington DC 20036

**WILKINSON, JOHN PETER DARRELL,** INFORMATION SYSTEMS. *Current Pos:* RETIRED. *Personal Data:* b Englewood, NJ, Nov 24, 38. *Educ:* Cambridge Univ, BA Hons, 60, MA, 64; Yale Univ, MEng, 61, DEng, 64. *Prof Exp:* Specialist dynamics, NAm Aviation, 64-67; consult struct, Space Div, 67-68; mech engr solid mech, Corp Res & Develop, Gen Elec Co, 68-72, mgr solid mech, 72-79, mgr liaison oper, 79-80, mgr res & develop appln oper, 80-83, mgr info syst oper, 83-92. *Concurrent Pos:* Adj prof, Polytech Inst NY, 71-72. *Mem:* Am Soc Mech Engrs. *Res:* Structural vibrations; dynamics; mechanical behavior of materials; fracture mechanics; information systems. *Mailing Add:* PO Box 388 Schoharie NY 12157

**WILKINSON, JOHN WESLEY,** MATHEMATICAL STATISTICS. *Current Pos:* chmn opers res & statist, 70-76, PROF MGT, RENSSELAER POLYTECH INST, 70- *Personal Data:* b Bexley, Ont, Nov 1, 28; m 53; c 2. *Educ:* Queen's Univ, Ont, BA, 50, MA, 52; Univ NC, PhD(math statist), 56. *Prof Exp:* Statistician, Can Industs, Ltd, 52-53; asst prof math, Queen's Univ, Ont, 56-58; res mathematician, Res Labs, Westinghouse Elec Corp, 58-64, fel mathematician, 64-65; prof statist, 65-70. *Concurrent Pos:* Consult, Can Industs, Ltd, 56-58, Watervliet Arsenal, Bendix Corp, Kamyr, Inc, 72-, Shaker Res Corp, 72-, NY State Depts Transp, Health, Budget, 72- & NY State Legis Comn Expenditure Rev; assoc ed, Technometrics, 70-77, ed, 78-80. *Mem:* Inst Math Statist; Inst Mgt Sci; Am Inst Decision Sci; Am Soc Qual Control; fel Am Statist Asn. *Res:* Statistical design of experiments; statistical inference; mathematical modeling; statistical applications to problems of environment and energy. *Mailing Add:* Dept Decision Sci Rensselaer Polytech Inst 110 Eighth St Troy NY 12180-3590

**WILKINSON, MICHAEL KENNERLY,** SOLID STATE PHYSICS. *Current Pos:* res physicist, Oak Ridge Nat Lab, 50-64, assoc dir, 64-72, dir, Solid State Div, 72-86, sr adv, 86-91, CONSULT, OAK RIDGE NAT LAB, 91- *Personal Data:* b Palatka, Fla, Feb 9, 21; m 44, Virginia Sleap; c Robert W, William M & Elizabeth (Sowell). *Educ:* The Citadel, BS, 42; Mass Inst Technol, PhD(physics), 50. *Prof Exp:* Res assoc, Res Lab Electronics, Mass Inst Technol, 48-50. *Concurrent Pos:* Neely vis prof, Ga Inst Technol, 61-62 & adj prof, 62-91. *Mem:* Fel AAAS; fel Am Phys Soc; Am Crystallog Asn; Sigma Xi. *Res:* Neutron diffraction and spectrometry; magnetic properties of solids; dynamical properties of crystal lattices; x-ray diffraction; physical electronics. *Mailing Add:* 124 E Morningside Dr Oak Ridge TN 37830

**WILKINSON, PAUL KENNETH,** BIOPHARMACEUTICS, PHARMACODYNAMICS. *Current Pos:* MGR PHARMACEUT DEVELOP, JANSSEN RES TECHNOL CTR, 91- *Personal Data:* b Oneonta, NY, Oct 19, 45; m 67; c 3. *Educ:* Univ Conn, BS Pharm, 69; Univ Mich, Ann Arbor, MS & PhD(pharm), 75. *Prof Exp:* Dep chief pharmacist,

USPHS, 69-71; asst, Sch Pharm, Univ Mich, Ann Arbor, 71-75; asst prof, Sch Pharm, Auburn Univ, 75-76; asst prof pharmaceut, Sch Pharm, Univ Conn, 76-82; from res fel to sr res fel, MSDRL, Merck & Co, Rahway, NJ, 82-88; mgr pharmaceut develop, R P Scherer Corp, Ann Arbor, Mich, 88-89; mgr pharmaceut develop, Mediventure, Inc, 89-91. *Mem:* Am Pharmaceut Asn; Acad Pharmaceut Sci; Am Asn Cols Pharm; Sigma Xi; AAAS. *Res:* Pharmaceutical development, novel dosage forms and delivery systems. *Mailing Add:* Janssen Res Technol Ctr 655 Phoenix Dr Ann Arbor MI 48108

**WILKINSON, PAUL R,** ECOLOGY. *Current Pos:* RETIRED. *Personal Data:* b Calcutta, India, Apr 16, 19; m 47; c 5. *Educ:* Cambridge Univ, BA, 41, MA, 45, PhD, 68. *Prof Exp:* Entomologist, Colonial Insecticide Res Unit, Uganda, 46-49; res officer, Commonwealth Sci & Indust Res Orgn, Australia, 50-62; res scientist, Can Dept Agr, 62-84. *Mem:* Acarolog Soc Am; Entom Soc Am; Entom Soc Can. *Res:* Acarology, ecology, physiology and control of ticks and biting flies. *Mailing Add:* 305 Ortona St Lethbridge AB T1J 4K9 Can. *E-Mail:* zebra@agt.net

**WILKINSON, R L,** AGRICULTURE. *Concurrent Pos:* Fel Award, Agr Inst Can, 92. *Mailing Add:* 1971 Casa Marcia Crescent Victoria BC V8N 2X5 Can

**WILKINSON, RALPH RUSSELL,** ECONOMICS & SMALL BUSINESS. *Current Pos:* ASST PROF, CLEVELAND CHIROPRACTIC COL, 87- *Personal Data:* b Portland, Ore, Feb 20, 30; m 56, Evelyn M Wickman. *Educ:* Reed Col, BA, 53; Univ Ore, Eugene, PhD(phys chem), 62; Univ Mo, Kansas City, MBA, 74. *Prof Exp:* Sr res chemist, Sprague Elec Co, Tektronix Inc, MacDermid Inc & Chemagro Agr Div, Mobay Chem Corp, 61-72; res chemist, US Vet Hosp, 73-75; assoc chemist technol assessment, Midwest Res Inst, 75-80; sr scientist, 80-84; asst prof, Rockhurst Col, 85-86. *Mem:* Am Chem Soc; Sigma Xi. *Res:* Technology and risk assessment; organotins; aryl phosphates; chemical economics; pesticides; PCBs; biodegradation; hazardous wastes. *Mailing Add:* 7911 Charlotte St Kansas City MO 64131

**WILKINSON, RAYMOND GEORGE,** ORGANIC CHEMISTRY. *Current Pos:* RETIRED. *Personal Data:* b Duluth, Minn, June 2, 22; m 48, Kathleen R Iffland; c Lynn, Karen & Michael. *Educ:* Harvard Univ, BS, 43; Univ Mich, MS, 48, PhD(org chem), 52. *Prof Exp:* From res chemist to sr res chemist, Lederle Div, Am Cyanamid Co, 51-62, group leader process improv, 62-66; asst to managing ed, Sub Index Div, Chem Abstracts Serv, Ohio State Univ, 66-68; sr res chemist, Lederle Div, Am Cyanamid Co, 68-84, consult, 84-86. *Mem:* Am Chem Soc; Am Humanist Asn. *Res:* Synthesis of steroids, tetracyclines and their degradation products; antituberculosis agents; antimalarials; antitumor; immunomodulating agents; granted over 27 patents. *Mailing Add:* 7 Surrey Lane Montvale NJ 07645

**WILKINSON, ROBERT CLEVELAND, JR,** ENTOMOLOGY, ECOLOGY. *Current Pos:* RETIRED. *Personal Data:* b Grand Rapids, Mich, Oct 2, 23; m 48; c 3. *Educ:* Mich State Univ, BS, 49, MS, 50; Univ Wis, PhD(entom), 61. *Prof Exp:* Entomologist, State Dept Agr, Mich, 51-53; supvr, Off State Entomologist, Wis, 53-57; res asst entom, Univ Wis, 57-60; from asst entomologist to assoc entomologist, Univ Fla, 60-70, prof entom, 71-89. *Concurrent Pos:* Res grants, St Regis Paper Co, Prosper Energy Corp, US Navy, Buckeye Cellulose Corp, Ford Found, SE Coastal Plains Comn, Southern Forest Dis & Insect Res Coun, Ctr Trop Agr, US Forest Serv. *Mem:* AAAS; Entom Soc Am; Soc Am Foresters; Entom Soc Can. *Res:* Forest entomology; bionomics of pine sawflies and bark beetles. *Mailing Add:* 2224 NW 15th Ave Gainesville FL 32605

**WILKINSON, ROBERT E,** INFLUENCE OF ENVIRONMENT & PESTICIDES ON PLANT GROWTH & DEVELOPMENT, INFLUENCE OF EPICUTICULAR WAXES ON LEAF RUST GROWTH. *Current Pos:* assoc prof, 65-72, PROF, AGR EXP STA, UNIV GA, 72- *Personal Data:* m 51, Evelyn G; c Olney T & Randall D. *Educ:* Univ Ill, BS, 50; Univ Okla, MS, 52; Univ Calif, Davis, PhD(plant physiol), 56. *Prof Exp:* Plant physiologist, Agr Res Serv, USDA, Clarkedale, Ark, 57-62, Los Lunas, NMex, 62-65. *Concurrent Pos:* Fulbright fel appl ecol, Finland, 74-75 & Yugoslavia, 75; consult, Univ Sao Paulo, Brazil, 84. *Mem:* Am Soc Plant Physiol; Weed Sci Soc Am; Coun Agr Sci & Technol; fel Am Inst Chemists. *Res:* Response of plants to environmental stress and herbicide mechanism of action; absorption of herbicides, mineral ions and biochemical responses in plant growth regulators, isoprenoids, waxes, pigments and influence of above on preinfestation stage of rusts; total ecology of plant (big and little) growth. *Mailing Add:* 655 Laura Dr Griffin GA 30224. *Fax:* 770-229-3215

**WILKINSON, ROBERT HAYDN,** INSTRUMENTATION. *Current Pos:* RETIRED. *Personal Data:* b Keighley, Eng, Feb 10, 26; m 56; c 4. *Educ:* Univ London, BSc, 48; Syracuse Univ, MEE, 61; Mass Inst Technol, ScD(instrumentation), 65. *Prof Exp:* Apprentice engr, Keighley Lifts, Ltd, Eng, 41-47, jr engr, 47-48; sci officer, Radar Res Estab, 49-51; engr, Eng Elec Co, 51-53; engr, Short Bros & Harland, Northern Ireland, 53-54; sr engr, Air Arm Div, Westinghouse Elec Corp, 54-59; prin engr, Link Div, Gen Precision Inc, 58-61; prin engr, CS Draper Lab, Inc, Mass Inst Technol, 61-62, engr, 62-90. *Concurrent Pos:* Lectr, Northeastern Univ, 65-67. *Mem:* Inst Elec & Electronics Engrs; Brit Inst Elec Eng. *Res:* Thermal errors in instruments; methods of measurement of instrument parameters; analog function generator techniques; design of electromechanical sensors; design of servos and controls; measurement and modelling of instrument noise processes. *Mailing Add:* 330 Waverly Ave Newton MA 02158

**WILKINSON, RONALD CRAIG,** FOREST GENETICS, PHYSIOLOGY. *Current Pos:* RETIRED. *Personal Data:* b Augusta, Ga, Oct 1, 43; m 67. *Educ:* Univ Wash, BS, 65; Yale Univ, MF, 66; Mich State Univ, PhD(forest genetics), 70. *Prof Exp:* Res plant geneticist, Northeastern Forest Exp Sta, US Forest Serv, 70-95. *Mem:* Phytochem Soc NAm. *Res:* Comparative physiology of species, ecological races and hybrids; natural variation and adaptation; genetic and physiological resistance to insects and diseases; biochemical systematics. *Mailing Add:* 12 Corduroy Rd Essex Junction VT 05452

**WILKINSON, STANLEY R,** AGRONOMY, SOIL SCIENCE. *Current Pos:* res soil scientist, Pasture Res Lab, 60-65, RES SOIL SCIENTIST, SOUTHERN PIEDMONT CONSERV RES CTR, AGR RES SERV, USDA, 65- *Personal Data:* b West Amboy, NY, Mar 28, 31; m 57, Jean Saye; c Rachael, Ralph & Augusta. *Educ:* Cornell Univ, BS, 54; Purdue Univ, MS, 56, PhD(soil fertil, plant nutrit), 61. *Prof Exp:* Instr soil fertil & plant nutrit, Purdue Univ, 57-60. *Concurrent Pos:* Res scientist, Univ Ga. *Mem:* Fel Am Soc Agron; Soil Sci Soc Am; Int Soc Soil Sci; Sigma Xi; fel Soil & Water Conserv Soc. *Res:* Mineral nutrient requirements of forage grasses and legumes; modelling growth and nutrient uptake; competitive phenomena between forage species; grazing systems research; land application of wastes and environmental quality; grass tetany fescue toxicosis research. *Mailing Add:* Southern Piedmont Conserv Res Ctr 1420 Experiment Station Rd Watkinsville GA 30677. *Fax:* 706-769-8962; *E-Mail:* wilkinson@uga.cc.uga. edu

**WILKINSON, THOMAS LLOYD, JR,** ADHESIVE BONDING TECHNOLOGY, STRUCTURAL TESTING. *Current Pos:* Test engr, Reynolds Metals Co, 63-66, develop engr, 66-67, sr develop engr, 67-73, develop proj dir, 73-80, sr develop proj dir, 80-85, supvrcomposites & surface technol, 85-87, supvr eng test, 87-93, SECT SUPVR APPL ENG & EXP MECH, REYNOLDS METALS CO, 93- *Personal Data:* b Richmond, Va, Dec 14, 39; m 72, Maxine Doyle; c Margaret & Douglas. *Educ:* Va Commonwealth Univ, BS, 63; Univ Richmond, MC, 76. *Concurrent Pos:* Chmn long range planning, Am Soc Testing & Mat, 89- *Mem:* Am Soc Testing & Mat; Am Soc Metals Int; fel Am Inst Chemists; Am Welding Soc. *Res:* Adhesives technology; organic coatings; structural testing; developments in plastics and composite structures; author of numerous publications and three booklets on adhesive bonding. *Mailing Add:* Corp Technol Ctr 13203 N Enon Church Rd Chester VA 23831. *Fax:* 804-751-2453; *E-Mail:* tlwilkin@lanmail.rue.com

**WILKINSON, THOMAS PRESTON,** EDUCATION ADMINISTRATION, RESOURCE MANAGEMENT. *Current Pos:* From lectr to asst prof, 67-73, ASSOC PROF GEOG, CARLETON UNIV, 73-, DIR CONTINUING EDUC, 85- *Personal Data:* b Gisburn, Eng, Mar 14, 41; m 66; c 2. *Educ:* Univ Durham, BSc, 63; Univ Newcastle, PhD(geomorphol), 72. *Concurrent Pos:* Vis lectr, Univ Liverpool, 72-73. *Res:* Fluvial geomorphology; geography curricula; environmental management. *Mailing Add:* Dept Geog 1125 Conelby Dr Carleton Univ Ottawa ON K1S 5B6 Can

**WILKINSON, THOMAS ROSS,** MICROBIOLOGY. *Current Pos:* DEAN ACAD AFFAIRS, AGR SCI, CLEMSON UNIV. *Personal Data:* b Baltimore, Md, Aug 20, 37; m 65; c 3. *Educ:* Univ Notre Dame, BS, 59; Univ Md, College Park, MS, 62; Wash State Univ, PhD(microbiol), 70. *Prof Exp:* Technician aerobiol, Naval Biol Lab, Univ Calif, Berkeley, 65-66; from asst prof to prof path & immunol, SDak State Univ, 70-81, head, Dept Microbiol, 75-81; assoc dean, Col Agr, assoc dir, Agr Exp Sta & prof microbiol, NDak State Univ, 81- *Mem:* Sigma Xi; Am Soc Microbiol; NY Acad Sci. *Res:* Rapid isolation technique for Listeria monocytogenes; survival of pathogens on metal surfaces; miniature cell systems for virus isolation and epidemiology of enclosed environments; epidemiology of Listeria and pathogenesis of Listeria L-forms; alcohol fuel production by a small farm scale plant. *Mailing Add:* 124 Long Hall Dept Biol Sci Clemson Univ Clemson SC 29634

**WILKINSON, W(ILLIAM) C(LAYTON),** ELECTROMAGNETIC ENGINEERING. *Current Pos:* RETIRED. *Personal Data:* b Teftc, Ind, Dec 17, 14; m 46, Virginia M Corio; c W Clayton, Penelope A, Henry T & Matthew A. *Educ:* Purdue Univ, BSEE, 41. *Prof Exp:* Res engr, RCA Victor Co, RCA Corp, 41-42 & RCA Labs, 42-61, eng supvr, Missile & Surface Radar Div, 61-77, eng supvr astro electronics, 77-80; pres, Space Antenna Tech Inc, 80-93. *Mem:* Sr mem Inst Elec & Electronics Engrs; Sigma Xi. *Res:* Computer aided design of antennas and microwave systems for space communications satellites and systems. *Mailing Add:* 55 Littlebrook Rd N Princeton NJ 08540

**WILKINSON, WILLIAM H(ADLEY),** MECHANICAL ENGINEERING, THERMODYNAMIC SYSTEMS. *Current Pos:* proj engr, Battelle Mem Inst, 56-58, asst consult, 58-60, assoc staff engr, 60-64, fel, 64-70, prin mech engr, 70-80, SR RES SCIENTIST, COLUMBUS LABS, BATTELLE MEM INST, 80- *Personal Data:* b Galt, Ont, Dec 1, 27; US citizen; m 51, Leona Cone; c Mary L (deceased), William W, G Frederick, R Andrew & Charles H. *Educ:* Rensselaer Polytech Inst, BME, 49, MME, 52. *Prof Exp:* Instr mech eng, Rensselaer Polytech Inst, 49-55, asst prof, 55-56. *Concurrent Pos:* Engr, Am Locomotive Co, 53-54. *Mem:* Soc Automotive Engrs; Am Soc Mech Engrs; Am Soc Heating, Refrig & Air-Conditioning Engrs. *Res:* Thermodynamic cycles and conversion systems; flow phenomena; comfort conditioning; advanced system synthesis and modeling; mechanisms; gearing; advanced vehicle propulsion systems; absorption systems and liquid desiccant hybrids. *Mailing Add:* Battelle Mem Inst Columbus Labs 505 King Ave Columbus OH 43201. *Fax:* 614-424-3534

**WILKINSON, WILLIAM KENNETH,** POLYMER CHEMISTRY & VASCULAR IMPLANTS, ULTRA FILTRATION & REINFORCEMENT FIBERS. *Current Pos:* CONSULT. *Personal Data:* b Newcastle, Ind, Jan 17, 18; m 42; c Bill, Ric, Randy, Jay & Alan. *Educ:* DePauw Univ, AB, 40; Northwestern Univ, MS, 47, PhD(org chem), 48. *Prof Exp:* Training supvr, Trojan Powder Co, 41-43; res chemist, Firestone Tire & Rubber Co, 43-45; from res chemist to res fel, E I Du Pont de Nemours & Co, 48-65, res fel, Benger Lab, Textile Fibers Dept, 65- *Concurrent Pos:* Pres, Kenwil Consult. *Mem:* Am Chem Soc. *Res:* Rubber and textile fibers; ultra fibration; spandex; carbon fibers; 87 patents. *Mailing Add:* 1010 Glenwood Blvd Waynesboro VA 22980-3411. *Fax:* 504-946-8651

**WILKINSON, WILLIAM LYLE,** OPERATIONS RESEARCH. *Current Pos:* RETIRED. *Personal Data:* b Sikeston, Mo, Jan 18, 21; m 45, 69, 89; c 6. *Educ:* US Naval Postgrad Sch, BS & MS, 55. *Prof Exp:* Sr staff scientist, George Washington Univ, 65-83. *Concurrent Pos:* Lectr, Univ Calif, Los Angeles, 65-66. *Mem:* Opers Res Soc Am. *Res:* Transportation networks in logistics research; computer-based management information systems; quantitative evaluation of weapon systems and tactics; man-computer systems; military sciences. *Mailing Add:* 1309 Alps Dr McLean VA 22102-1501

**WILKNISS, PETER EBERHARD,** OCEANOGRAPHY, RADIOCHEMISTRY. *Current Pos:* PRES, POLAR KYBERNETES INT, LLC, 97- *Personal Data:* b Berlin, Ger, Sept 28, 34; US citizen; m 63, Edith Koester; c Peter & Sandra. *Educ:* Munich Tech Univ, MS, 59, PhD(radiochem), 61. *Honors & Awards:* Presidential Citation, Am Inst Architects, 93. *Prof Exp:* Res asst, Tech Univ Munich, Ger, 59-61; res chemist, radiol protection officer, US Naval Ord Sta, 61-64, head, Nuclear Chem Br, 64-66, res oceanogr, US Naval Res Lab, 66-70, head geochem sect, 70-75; prog mgr, Nat Ctr Atmosphere Res Prog, NSF, 75-76, prog mgr, Ocean Sediment Coring Prog, 76-80, team mgr, Ocean Drilling Proj Team, 80, dir, Div Ocean Drilling Progs, 80-81, sr sci assoc, 81-82, dep asst dir, Sci, Technol & Int Affairs Directorate, 82-84, dir, Div Polar Progs, 84-93, sr sci assoc, Geo Directorate, 93-97. *Concurrent Pos:* Nat Res Coun, Polar Res bd liasion mem, 84-; head, Chem Oceanog Br, US Naval Res Lab, 71-73, chmn, Radiol Comt, 74-75; mem, Comt Atmospheric Chem & Radioactivity, Am Meteorol Soc, 75-78; mem, Interagency Comt Atmospheric Sci, 75-76; mem, NASA Space Sta Adv Comt, 88-93. *Mem:* AAAS; Sigma Xi; Am Geophys Union; Antarctican Soc. *Res:* Radio and nuclear chemistry, solid propellants, oceanography, marine geochemistry, satellite images applied to meteorology, air/sea interactions; anthropogenic impact on the global environment, natural radioactivity in the troposphere; radiochemistry applied to oceanography. *Mailing Add:* 8814 Stockton Pkwy Alexandria VA 22308. *Fax:* 703-780-0016

**WILKOFF, LEE JOSEPH,** MICROBIOLOGY, BIOCHEMISTRY. *Current Pos:* sr microbiologist, 64-70, HEAD, CELL BIOL DIV, SOUTHERN RES INST, 70- *Personal Data:* b Youngstown, Ohio, Oct 17, 24; m 53; c 1. *Educ:* Roosevelt Univ, BS, 48; Univ Chicago, PhD(microbiol), 63. *Prof Exp:* Chemist, H Kramer & Co, 48-49; res asst biochem, Ben May Lab Cancer Res, Univ Chicago, 49-52 & Dept Med, 54-60; biochemist, Vet Admin Hosp, Hines, Ill, 52-54; dir, Microbiol Lab, Woodard Res Corp, 63-64. *Mem:* AAAS; Am Asn Cancer Res; Soc Exp Biol & Med; Am Soc Microbiol; Tissue Cult Asn; Sigma Xi. *Res:* Cell biology and chemotherapy of tumor cells; effect of anticancer drugs on the kinetic behavior of tumor cells; cellular sites of action of anticancer agents. *Mailing Add:* 1813 Old Creek Trail Birmingham AL 35216

**WILKOV, ROBERT SPENCER,** computer science, for more information see previous edition

**WILKOWSKE, HOWARD HUGO,** DAIRY BACTERIOLOGY. *Current Pos:* RETIRED. *Personal Data:* b Zachow, Wis, Sept 10, 17; m 48; c 3. *Educ:* Tex Tech Col, BS, 40, MS, 42; Iowa State Col, PhD, 49. *Prof Exp:* Assoc prof dairy mfg & assoc dairy technologist, Agr Exp Sta, Inst Food & Agr Sci, Univ Fla, 50-57, asst dir, Agr Exp Sta, 57-68, asst dean res, 68-79, dir internal energy mgt, 80-81. *Concurrent Pos:* Mem adv coun, Ctr Trop Agr, US AID dairy specialist, Costa Rica, 58, Ghana, 69 & Venezuela, 71. *Mem:* AAAS; Am Soc Microbiol; Am Dairy Sci Asn. *Res:* Antibiotics in dairy products; continuous and automatic manufacture of fermented dairy products; bacteriophage of dairy microorganisms; agricultural research administration. *Mailing Add:* 1040 SW 11th St Gainesville FL 32601

**WILKS, ALAN DELBERT,** CHEMICAL RESEARCH & TECHNOLOGY. *Current Pos:* dir phys chem & surface sci, 84-88, dir mat sci, EMS Sector, 88-89, VPRES CHEM & PROCESS TECHNOL, ALLIED-SIGNAL, INC, 89- *Personal Data:* b Liberal, Kans, Sept 4, 43; m 67, Irvana S Keagy; c Jolin R. *Educ:* Univ Kans, BS, 65; Univ Iowa, PhD(analytical chem), 70. *Prof Exp:* Chemist, UOP Res Ctr, Des Plaines, Ill, 69-76, group leader, Catalysis Div, 76-77, mgr catalysis res, 77-84. *Concurrent Pos:* Consult, Los Alamos Nat Lab, 90- *Mem:* Am Chem Soc; Am Vacuum Soc; Am Ceramic Soc; NY Acad Sci. *Res:* Analytical chemistry; granted 5 patents. *Mailing Add:* 1201 West Cleven Dr Mt Prospect IL 60056

**WILKS, DANIEL S,** STATISTICAL METEOROLOGY & CLIMATOLOGY, APPLIED DECISION THEORY. *Current Pos:* ASSOC PROF ATMOSPHERIC SCI, CORNELL UNIV, 87- *Personal Data:* b Long Beach, Calif, July 26, 52. *Educ:* Univ Calif, Berkeley, BS, 75, MS, 77; Ore State Univ, PhD(atmospheric sci), 86. *Concurrent Pos:* Mem, Probability & Statist Comt, Am Meteorol Soc, 91- *Mem:* AAAS; Am Meteorol Soc. *Res:* Atmospheric sciences. *Mailing Add:* Dept Soil Crop & Atmospheric Sci Cornell Univ Ithaca NY 14853

**WILKS, JOHN WILLIAM,** CELL BIOLOGY, ONCOLOGY. *Current Pos:* Sr res scientist reproductive endocrinol & fertil res, Upjohn Co, 70-85, sr scientist, 85-93, assoc dir, 93-96, SR SCIENTIST CANCER & INFECTIOUS DIS RES, UPJOHN CO, 97- *Personal Data:* b Kenosha, Wis, July 5, 44; m 84, Nancy Oleksy. *Educ:* Univ Wis-Madison, BS, 66; Cornell Univ, PhD(physiol), 71. *Concurrent Pos:* Vis assoc prof, Dept Cell Biol, Baylor Col Med, 81. *Mem:* Endocrine Soc; AAAS; Am Asn Cancer Res; Am Soc Cell Biol; Metastasis Res Soc. *Res:* Discovery of anti-cancer pharmaceutical therapies; tumor angiogenesis; matrix metalloproteinases; cell cycle regulation. *Mailing Add:* Cancer Res Pharmacia & Upjohn, Inc Kalamazoo MI 49001. *Fax:* 616-833-0992; *E-Mail:* john.w.wilks@am.pnu.com

**WILKS, LOUIS PHILLIP,** CHEMISTRY. *Current Pos:* RETIRED. *Personal Data:* b Dayton, Ohio, June 28, 13; m 38; c 3. *Educ:* Univ Dayton, BS, 35. *Prof Exp:* Instr chem, Univ Dayton, 35; res chemist, Thomas & Hochwalt Lab, 35-38. *Concurrent Pos:* Consult, 78- *Mem:* AAAS; Am Chem Soc. *Res:* Products from petrochemical by-products; agricultural chemicals; research management and corporate planning. *Mailing Add:* 1906 Mirmar Munster IN 46321-2719

**WILKUS, EDWARD VINCENT,** ELECTRICAL INSULATION POLYMERIC COMPOSITES, ORGANIC-METALLIC POLYMERS. *Current Pos:* CHIEF EXEC OFFICER, FLOW ENTERPRISES, 93- *Personal Data:* b Albany, NY, Feb 14, 23; div; c Lisa, Gail, Nyla & Ward. *Educ:* Siena Col, BS, 48; Rensselaer Polytech Inst, PhD(org chem), 63. *Prof Exp:* Chemist & prod supvr, GAF Corp, 48-56; develop chemist silicones, Gen Elec Co, 56-67, res engr, 67-88; mgr advan res & develop, Elec Cable Co, 88-93. *Concurrent Pos:* Consult, Elec Cable Co, 88- & Gen Elec Co, 88- *Mem:* Sigma Xi; Am Chem Soc; Am Inst Chem Engrs; Plastics Int Orgn. *Res:* Chemical and polymer composites development and production; silicone products; processes and electrical insulations from almost all commercial polymers; test methodologies to shorten production development time; awarded 53 US patents. *Mailing Add:* FWW Enterprises c/o ECC Co 15 Franklin St PO Box 429 Seymour CT 06483-0429. *Fax:* 203-888-6037

**WILL, CLIFFORD MARTIN,** THEORETICAL ASTROPHYSICS, GENERAL RELATIVITY. *Current Pos:* assoc prof, 81-85, PROF PHYSICS, WASHINGTON UNIV, ST LOUIS, 85-, CHMN PHYSICS, 91- *Personal Data:* b Hamilton, Ont, Can, Nov 13, 46; m 70; c 2. *Educ:* McMaster Univ, BSc, 68; Calif Inst Technol, PhD(physics), 71. *Prof Exp:* Instr physics, Calif Inst Technol, 71-72; fel, Enrico Fermi Inst, Univ Chicago, 72-74; asst prof physics, Stanford Univ, 74-81. *Concurrent Pos:* Res fel, Calif Inst Technol, 71-72; Sloan Found res fel, 75-79; fel, Mellon Found, 78-79; chmn, Comt Accuracy Time Transfer in Satellite Systs, Nat Acad Sci, 84-86; mem exec comt, Am Phys Soc, 88-90; div assoc ed, Phys Rev Letters, 89-92; mem, Task Force Rev Mod Physics, Am Phys Soc, 92-93, Educ Comt, 94-97; J S Guggenheim Found fel, 96-97, J W Fulbright fel, 96-97. *Mem:* Fel Am Phys Soc; Am Astron Soc; Sigma Xi; Int Astron Union; Int Soc Gen Relativity & Gravitation; Am Asn Physics Teachers. *Res:* General relativity theory and its applications to astrophysics; gravitational radiation; black holes; cosmology; experimental tests of general relativity. *Mailing Add:* Dept Physics Washington Univ 1 Brookings Dr Campus Box 1105 St Louis MO 63130. *Fax:* 314-935-6219; *E-Mail:* cmw@wuphys.wustl.edu

**WILL, FRIT GUSTAV,** electrochemistry, for more information see previous edition

**WILL, FRITZ, III,** ANALYTICAL CHEMISTRY. *Current Pos:* RETIRED. *Personal Data:* b Richmond, Va, Oct 24, 26; m 54, Betty Ramey; c Fritz IV & Kathrine E (Rutledge). *Educ:* Univ Va, BS, 49, MS, 51, PhD(chem), 53. *Honors & Awards:* Medal, Am Inst Chemists, 49. *Prof Exp:* Asst chem, Univ Va, 47-51; res chemist, Res Labs, Aluminium Co Am, 53-65; res chemist, Phillip Morris, Inc, 65-69, mgr, Analytical Chem Div, Philip Morris Res Ctr, 69-79, mgr beverage res & develop, 80-81, coordr analytical chem tobacco process, 82-85. *Mem:* Am Chem Soc; Soc Appl Spectros; Sigma Xi. *Res:* Analytical methods; spectrophotometry; ultraviolet and visual absorption spectroscopy; nuclear magnetic resonance spectroscopy. *Mailing Add:* 2301 Astoria Dr Richmond VA 23235

**WILL, JAMES ARTHUR,** PHYSIOLOGY. *Current Pos:* from asst prof to assoc prof, Univ Wis-Madison, 67-74, chmn dept, 74-78, dir, Grad Sch Res Animal Resources Ctr, 81-90, PROF VET SCI, UNIV WIS-MADISON, 74-, PROF ANESTHESIOL, MED SCH, 80-; VPRES, CLARION PHARMACEUT INC, MADISON, WIS, 93- *Personal Data:* b Wauwatosa, Wis, Nov 2, 30; m 53; c 3. *Educ:* Univ Wis, BS, 52, MS, 53, PhD(vet sci), 67; Kans State Univ, DVM, 60. *Prof Exp:* Vet, Columbus Vet Hosp, Wis, 60-67. *Concurrent Pos:* NIH spec fel, New Med Sch, Univ Liverpool, 72-73; mem, Coun Basic Sci & Circulation, Am Heart Asn; mem, Comt Primary Pulmonary Hypertension, WHO; consult to domestic & foreign co. *Mem:* AAAS; Am Vet Med Asn; fel Royal Soc Med London; Asn Am Vet Med Col (pres); Am Physiol Soc; Soc Exp Biol & Med. *Res:* Cardiopulmonary physiopathology, particularly relationship between function and disease under natural and altered environmental conditions or with impairment of function by a disease process and pharmacology of smooth muscle. *Mailing Add:* Dept Animal Health & Biomed Sci Univ Wis 1655 Linden Dr Madison WI 53706-1519. *Fax:* 608-262-7420; *E-Mail:* jaw@ahabs.wisc.edu

**WILL, JOHN JUNIOR,** hematology; deceased, see previous edition for last biography

**WILL, PAUL ARTHUR,** FOOD SCIENCE & TECHNOLOGY. *Current Pos:* Asst prof, 78-85, ASSOC PROF & DIR, SUL ROSS STATE UNIV, 85-; INSTR MEAT SCI, OKLA STATE UNIV, 78- *Personal Data:* b Weslaco, Tex, Feb 9, 46; m 70; c 2. *Educ:* Tex A&M Univ, BS, 70; Okla State Univ, MS, 74, PhD(food sci), 78. *Mem:* Am Meat Sci Asn; Inst Food Technologists; Am Animal Sci Asn; Sigma Xi. *Res:* Efficiency of red meat production; palatibility of the produced product; method of fabrication and processing; physical and chemical properties of meat. *Mailing Add:* Dept Animal Sci Sul Ross State Univ 400 N Harrison St Alpine TX 79832-0001

**WILL, PETER MILNE,** COMPUTER SCIENCE, ELECTRICAL ENGINEERING. *Current Pos:* DIR DESIGN STRATEGY, H P CORP, 85- *Personal Data:* b Peterhead, Scotland, Nov 2, 35; m 59; c 3. *Educ:* Aberdeen Univ, BScEng, 58, PhD(elec eng), 60. *Honors & Awards:* Joseph Engelberger Award Robotics, 89. *Prof Exp:* Mem res staff automatic control, Res Labs Assoc Elec Industs, Ltd, Eng, 61-62; proj leader indust electronics & control, AMF Brit Res Labs, 62-64; sr res physicist, Morehead Patterson Res Ctr, Am Mach & Foundry Co, Conn, 64-65; mem res staff comput sci, T J Watson Res Ctr, IBM Corp, 65-80; dir prod systs eng, Schlumberger Well Serv, 80-85. *Concurrent Pos:* Lectr, Univ Conn, Stamford Exten, 66-71; mem, Eng Res Ctr Eval Group, 89; mem, Info Sci & Tech Comn, DARPA, 87-; mem, Comput Sci & Tech Bd, Nat Acad Sci, 82-86. *Mem:* Inst Elec & Electronics Engrs. *Res:* Application of computers to non-traditional fields; image processing; bandwidth compression; robotry; robot vision; multispectral imagery. *Mailing Add:* 4676 Admiralty Way ISI Marina Del Rey CA 90292

**WILLARD, DANIEL,** ELEMENTARY PARTICLE PHYSICS, MILITARY OPERATIONS RESEARCH. *Current Pos:* opers res analyst, 64-93, SPEC ASST SPEC AIR & MISSILE DEFENSE, OFF UNDER SECY US ARMY, 94- *Personal Data:* b Baltimore, Md, Aug 22, 26; m 58, Linda Zeller; c Daniel S & Theodore Z. *Educ:* Yale Univ, BS, 49, MS, 50; Mass Inst Technol, PhD(physics), 54. *Prof Exp:* Res assoc physics, Brookhaven Nat Lab, 54-55; instr, Swarthmore Col, 55-58; assoc prof, Va Polytech Inst, 58-61; opers res analyst, Opers Res Off, Johns Hopkins Univ, 61 & Res Analysis Corp, Va, 61-64. *Concurrent Pos:* Consult, Langley Res Ctr, NASA, 59-61; adv, Math & Comput Sci Prog, Army Res Off. *Mem:* Am Phys Soc; Mil Opers Res Soc. *Res:* Cosmic rays; heavy unstable particles; radio astronomy; mathematical models of combat; operations research; systems analysis; missile defense systems. *Mailing Add:* SAUS-OR Undersecy Army 102 Army Pentagon Washington DC 20310-0102. *E-Mail:* willad@hqda.army.mil

**WILLARD, DANIEL EDWARD,** ENVIRONMENTAL ECOLOGY. *Current Pos:* ASSOC PROF, SCH PUB & ENVIRON AFFAIRS, IND UNIV, BLOOMINGTON, 77- *Personal Data:* b Cincinnati, Ohio, Oct 24, 34; m 78; c 3. *Educ:* Stanford Univ, AB, 60, Univ Calif, Davis, PhD(zool), 66. *Prof Exp:* Lectr biol, Univ Tex, Austin, 66-67, asst prof bot & zool, 67-70; asst prof, Univ Wis-Madison, 70-72, assoc scientist, 72-77. *Concurrent Pos:* Lectr, San Diego Zool Soc, 60; vis asst prof, Inst Marine Sci, Univ Ore, 72-73; consult, Ore Pub Utility Comn, 75-76 & Wis Attorney Gen Off, 73- *Mem:* Ecol Soc Am; Human Ecol Soc; AAAS; Am Behav Soc; Am Inst Biol Sci. *Res:* Impacts of energy development on biological systems; dynamics of wetlands; human impact on wildlife; management of endangered species; ecological regulation. *Mailing Add:* Dept Pub Admin Ind Univ Bloomington IN 47405

**WILLARD, HARVEY BRADFORD,** NUCLEAR PHYSICS. *Current Pos:* CONSULT, 87- *Personal Data:* b Worcester, Mass, Aug 9, 25; m 50, Isabella Rallis; c Karl P & Karen E (Willard-Gallo). *Educ:* Mass Inst Technol, SB, 48, PhD(physics), 50. *Prof Exp:* Physicist, Oak Ridge Nat Lab, 50-57, co-dir, High Voltage Lab, 57-63, assoc dir, Physics Div, 63-67; chmn, Dept Physics, Case Western Res Univ, 67-71, dean sci & vprovost, Case Inst Technol, 70-76, prof physics, 67-81; head nuclear sci, NSF, 81-86, dir, Div Physics, 86-87. *Mem:* AAAS; fel Am Phys Soc. *Res:* Nuclear scattering; reaction and polarization phenomena; energy levels of nuclei; the few nucleon problem; Van de Graaff accelerators; medium energy studies of proton-proton scattering and meson production with polarized beams and targets. *Mailing Add:* 875 Waterside Lane Bradenton FL 34209. *E-Mail:* hbwillard@aol.com

**WILLARD, JAMES MATTHEW,** HYDROLOGY & WATER RESOURCES. *Current Pos:* asst prof, 75-77, asst dean arts & sci, 81-84, ASSOC PROF BIOL, CLEVELAND STATE UNIV, 77- *Personal Data:* b St Johnsbury, Vt, Nov 18, 39; m 61, Marjorie A Masten; c 3. *Educ:* St Michael's Col, Vt, AB, 61; Cornell Univ, PhD(biochem), 67. *Honors & Awards:* Fulbright Award, 88-89. *Prof Exp:* Res assoc biochem, Case Western Res Univ, 66-69; asst prof biochem, Col Med, Univ Vt, 69-75. *Mem:* Am Soc Biol Chemists. *Res:* Preparation and effect of certain analogues of phosphoribosyl pyrophosphate on de novo purine synthesis; zeolites as dietary supplement; dietary use of fructose; predictive method of catalysis (intermedion theory); restoration of biotic condition with zeolite of acid water. *Mailing Add:* Dept Biol Cleveland State Univ 1983 E 24th St Cleveland OH 44115-2403

**WILLARD, JOHN ELA,** physical chemistry; deceased, see previous edition for last biography

**WILLARD, MARK BENJAMIN,** NEUROBIOLOGY. *Current Pos:* Teaching fel anat & biochem, 71-74, from asst prof to assoc prof, 74-85, PROF ANAT NEUROBIOL & BIOCHEM, SCH MED, WASHINGTON UNIV, 85- *Personal Data:* b Chicago, Ill, Feb 18, 43. *Educ:* Oberlin Col, BA, 65; Univ Wis, PhD(biochem), 71. *Res:* Role of regulation of neuronal gene expression in controlling the development and regeneration of the cells of the nervous system. *Mailing Add:* Dept Anat Sch Med Washington Univ 660 S Euclid Ave St Louis MO 63110-1010

**WILLARD, PAUL EDWIN,** organic chemistry; deceased, see previous edition for last biography

**WILLARD, PAUL W,** HAY AND ASSESSMENT RISK ASSESSMENT. *Current Pos:* supvr, Toxicol Serv, 78-80, MGR PROD REGULATORY TOXICOL, 3M CO, 80- *Personal Data:* b Marshalltown, Iowa, Mar 21, 33; m 52; c 4. *Educ:* Iowa State Univ, BS, 55; Univ Iowa, PhD(physiol), 59; Ind Univ, MBA, 68; Am Bd Toxicol, dipl, 81. *Prof Exp:* Nat Heart Inst fel physiol, Lankenau Hosp, Philadelphia, Pa, 59-61; sr scientist, Div Pharmacol Res, Eli Lilly & Co, 61-69; clin res coordr, Med Prods Div, 3M Co, 69-75; dir regulatory affairs, Medtronic Inc, 75-77. *Concurrent Pos:* Adj prof environ health, Univ Minn, 81- *Mem:* Soc Toxicol; Am Col Toxicol; Am Indust Hyg Asn; Am Conf Chem Labeling. *Res:* Cardiovascular pharmacology, physiology and toxicology; regulatory affairs; industrial toxicology; product toxicology. *Mailing Add:* Toxicol Serv 220-2E 3M Ctr St Paul MN 55144-0001. *E-Mail:* pwwillard@mmm.com

**WILLARD, ROBERT JACKSON,** GEOLOGY, RESEARCH ADMINISTRATION. *Current Pos:* RETIRED. *Personal Data:* b Brockton, Mass, Mar 21, 29; m 54, Emma Raad; c David C & Barbara (Foster). *Educ:* Boston Univ, AB, 51, AM, 53, PhD(geol), 58. *Prof Exp:* Instr geol, Wellesley Col, 56-57; from instr to asst prof, Univ Ark, 57-63; geologist, US Bur Mines, 63-67, head, Fabric Analysis Lab, 68-74, geologist & contract tech proj officer, Advan Mining Div, 74-76, staff engr, Minerals Environ Tech, Hq, 77-78, geologist & contract tech proj off, Environ Assessment & Ground Control Div, 78-79, staff scientist, Off Res Dir, Twin Cities Res Ctr, 80-95. *Concurrent Pos:* Nat Park Serv study grant, 60-61; mem, Collegium Distinguished Alumni, Col Libr Arts, Boston Univ. *Mem:* Fel Geol Soc Am; Soc Mining Metall & Explor Inc. *Res:* Petrofabrics and electron fractography applications in rock mechanics; improvements in longwall mining techniques and equipment; seabed mining technology; relation of rock fabric to various deformation and fragmentation tests; analysis of Vermont and New York state industry; evaluation of coal deposits in the Narragansett Basin of Massachusetts and Rhode Island. *Mailing Add:* 6736 Garfield Ave S Minneapolis MN 55423

**WILLARD, THOMAS MAXWELL,** INORGANIC CHEMISTRY, ANALYTICAL CHEMISTRY. *Current Pos:* Chmn dept, 65-95, FAC MEM, FLA SOUTHERN COL, 64-, PROF CHEM, 81- *Personal Data:* b Beaumont, Tex, Aug 30, 37; m 59, Barbara Youngblood; c William W & Barbara E (Lancaster). *Educ:* Lamar Univ, BS, 59; Tulane Univ, PhD(inorg chem), 64. *Concurrent Pos:* Rotary Int Group Study exchange fel, Japan, 73; Danforth Found assoc, 80- *Mem:* Am Chem Soc; Sigma Xi. *Res:* Interactions between very weak acids and very weak bases in non-polar media. *Mailing Add:* Dept Chem Fla Southern Col 111 Lake Hollingsworth Dr Lakeland FL 33801-5698. *Fax:* 941-680-4208

**WILLARD, WILLIAM KENNETH,** ECOLOGY. *Current Pos:* PROF ZOOL & CHMN, DEPT BIOL, TENN TECHNOL UNIV, 75- *Personal Data:* b Hagerstown, Md, Nov 5, 29; m 61; c 2. *Educ:* Univ Ga, BSF, 57, MS, 60; Univ Tenn, PhD(zool), 65. *Prof Exp:* From asst prof to assoc prof zool, Clemson Univ, 65-75. *Mem:* AAAS; Ecol Soc Am; Am Inst Biol Sci; Sigma Xi. *Res:* Effects of radiations on populations; fate of radioactive materials in the environment; population dynamics; ecosystem analysis; radiation ecology; bioenergetics of food chain relationships; ecological strategies in mammalian population dynamics. *Mailing Add:* 619 Alberta Ave Cookeville TN 38501

**WILLARDSON, LYMAN S(ESSIONS),** AGRICULTURAL ENGINEERING. *Current Pos:* PROF AGR & IRRIG ENG, UTAH STATE UNIV, LOGAN, 74- *Personal Data:* b Ephraim, Utah, May 10, 27; m 48, Vivian Berrey; c Lyman W, Kathleen, Timothy M, Mark B, Paul B & Laura. *Educ:* Utah State Univ, BSCE, 50, MSCE, 55; Ohio State Univ, PhD(agr eng), 67. *Honors & Awards:* R J Tipton Award, Am Soc Civil Engrs, 92. *Prof Exp:* Irrig engr, United Fruit Co, 52-54, Agr Exp Sta, Univ PR, 54-57; agr engr, Agr Res Serv, USDA, Ohio, 57-67, res leader drainage, Imp Valley Conserv Res Ctr, 67-74. *Concurrent Pos:* Proj leader, On-Farm Water Mgt, Dominican Repub; mem comt, F17.65 Land Drainage, Am Soc Testing & Mat; mem bd dirs, US Comt Irrigation & Drainage & Int Comn Irrigation & Drainage; dir, Rocky Mountain Sect, Am Soc Agr Engrs, chmn comt, SW-231 Drainage Res; chmn, I&D Div Res Comt, Am Soc Civil Engrs. *Mem:* AAAS; Am Soc Civil Engrs; Am Soc Agr Engrs; Nat Soc Prof Engrs; Int Comn Irrig & Drainage; Am Soc Testing & Mat. *Res:* Engineering research on problems associated with irrigation and drainage of agricultural lands; drainage and salinity of irrigated lands. *Mailing Add:* Dept Biol & Irrig Eng Utah State Univ Logan UT 84322-4105. *Fax:* 435-797-1248; *E-Mail:* fath8@cc.usu.edu

**WILLARDSON, ROBERT KENT,** SOLID STATE PHYSICS. *Current Pos:* PRES, WILLARDSON CONSULT, 91- *Personal Data:* b Gunnison, Utah, July 11, 23; m 47, Beth M Bennett; c Amanda M (Ballou), Elizabeth A (Engar) & Jennie L. *Educ:* Brigham Young Univ, BS, 49; Iowa State Col, MS, 51. *Prof Exp:* Res physicist, Ames Lab, AEC, 49-51; prin physicist, Battelle Mem Inst, 51-56, asst chief, Phys Chem Div, 56-60; chief scientist, Res Ctr, Bell & Howell Co, 60-64, dir solid state res, 64-67, dir mat res, 67-69, gen mgr, Electronic Mat Div, 69-73, pres, Electronic Mat Corp, 73; asst to gen mgr, Electronic Mat Div, Cominco Am Inc, 73-77, mgr electronic mat, Div Sales, 77-81, mgr planning, 81-82; pres, Willardson Consult, 83 & 87; pres, Cryscon Techs, 84-86; tech dir, EniChem Am, 88-91. *Concurrent Pos:* Co-ed, Semiconductors & Semimetals, 66- *Mem:* Am Phys Soc; Electrochem Soc; Am Chem Soc; Inst Elec & Electronics Engrs. *Res:* Preparation, electrical and optical properties of high purity metals, alloys and semiconductors; analysis, control and effects of impurities and lattice defects in these materials; electronic transport phenomena in semiconductors. *Mailing Add:* 12722 E 23rd Ave Spokane WA 99216-0327

**WILLBANKS, EMILY WEST,** COMPUTER SCIENCE, MATHEMATICS. *Current Pos:* RETIRED. *Personal Data:* b Ft Lauderdale, Fla, Nov 25, 30; m 59. *Educ:* Duke Univ, BS, 52; Univ NMex, MS, 57. *Prof Exp:* Eng aide math, Pratt-Whitney Aircraft Co, 52-54; staff mem math & comput, Los Alamos Nat Lab, 54-90. *Mailing Add:* 217 Barranca Rd Los Alamos NM 87544

**WILLCOTT, MARK ROBERT, III,** ORGANIC CHEMISTRY. *Current Pos:* from asst prof to assoc prof, 65-73, PROF CHEM, UNIV HOUSTON, 73- *Personal Data:* b Muskogee, Okla, July 23, 33; m 55; c 4. *Educ:* Rice Univ, BA, 55; Yale Univ, MS, 59, PhD(chem), 63. *Prof Exp:* Asst prof chem, Emory Univ, 62-64. *Concurrent Pos:* NIH fel, Univ Wis, 64-65; Guggenheim fel, 72-73; consult, Upjohn Co, 65- & Aldrich Chem Co, 72-; adj prof med, Baylor Col Med, 78-; adj prof chem, Rice Univ, 81- *Mem:* Am Chem Soc; Royal Soc Chem. *Res:* Thermal rearrangements of organic compounds; nuclear magnetic resonance spectroscopy; magnetic resonance imaging; nuclear magnetic resonances in medicine. *Mailing Add:* Dept Radiol Div Nuclear Med Univ Tex Med Br 31 University Blvd Galveston TX 77555-0709. *Fax:* 408-772-3229

**WILLCOX, ALFRED BURTON,** MATHEMATICS. *Current Pos:* EXEC DIR, MATH ASN AM, 68- *Personal Data:* b Sioux Rapids, Iowa, Sept 18, 25; m 48; c 4. *Educ:* Yale Univ, MA, 49, PhD(math), 53. *Prof Exp:* From instr to prof math, Amherst Col, 53-68, exec dir, Comt Undergrad Prog Math, 63-64. *Concurrent Pos:* Vis asst prof, Univ Chicago, 57-58; vis lectr, Uppsala Univ, Sweden, 67-68. *Mem:* Fel AAAS; Am Math Soc; Math Asn Am (vpres, 64-66); Nat Coun Teachers Math; Soc Indust & Appl Math. *Res:* Banach algebras. *Mailing Add:* 860 Inverrary Ct Annapolis MD 21401-6906

**WILLDEN, CHARLES RONALD,** geology, for more information see previous edition

**WILLE, JOHN JACOB, JR,** CELL & SKIN BIOLOGY, GENETICS. *Current Pos:* mgr, 89-91, DIR SKIN RES, BRISTOL MYERS SQUIBB/CONVATEC, 91- *Personal Data:* b New York, NY, June 24, 37; m; c Chris, Julia, Rachel & Konrad. *Educ:* Cornell Univ, BA, 60; Univ Ind, PhD(genetics), 65. *Prof Exp:* Resident res assoc cell biol, Biol Div, Argonne Nat Lab, 65-66, fel, 66-68; asst prof biol sci, Univ Cincinnati, 68-72; NIH spec fel, Univ Chicago, 72-73; res assoc, Dept Biophys, 73-75; asst prof zool & physiol, La State Univ, 75-80; sr res assoc & asst prof, Dept Cell Biol, Mayo Clin, 80-85, fel, 80-82; sr scientist & head cell biol, Southern Res Inst, 85-89. *Concurrent Pos:* Consult, Ross Labs-Abbott, Columbus, Ohio, 89-90; exec consult, Hy-Gene, Inc, 89- *Mem:* Am Asn Cancer Res; NY Acad Sci; Soc Invest Demat; Controlled Release Soc. *Res:* Developmental genetics of unicellular organisms; molecular biology of biological rhythms; cancer cell biology; pathogenic mechanisms of uroepithal cells; cancer chemo prevention rehioid cell function; epithelial and skin biology; tissue engineering. *Mailing Add:* Convatec/Bristol Myers Squibb Co 200 Headquarters Park Dr Skillman NJ 08558. *Fax:* 908-281-2636; *E-Mail:* jwille@usccmail.vscc.bms.com

**WILLE, LUC THEO,** STATISTICAL PHYSICS. *Current Pos:* from asst prof to assoc prof physics, 88-95, PROF PHYSICS, FLA ATLANTIC UNIV, 95- *Personal Data:* b Ghent, Belg, Dec 8, 56; m 83, Isabelle Verschelde; c Angelique & Vincent. *Educ:* State Univ Ghent, BSc, 80, PhD(physics), 83, MS, 85. *Honors & Awards:* Laureate, Royal Acad Sci, Belg, 88. *Prof Exp:* Fel asst physics, State Univ Ghent, 83-85; sr res assoc, Daresbury Lab, Sci & Eng Res Coun, UK, 85-87; fel asst mat sci, Univ Calif, Berkeley, 87-88. *Concurrent Pos:* Consult, Lawrence Livermore Nat Lab, 89-91; vis prof, Univ Nancy, France, 91-93, Univ Strasbourg, France, 93-96. *Mem:* Am Phys Soc; NY Acad Sci; Mat Res Soc; Soc Indust & Appl Math; Sigma Xi. *Res:* Phase transformations and structural stability of solids, especially superconductors; electronic structure of solids and clusters; self-organization in complex systems. *Mailing Add:* Dept Physics Fla Atlantic Univ Boca Raton FL 33431. *Fax:* 561-367-2662; *E-Mail:* willel@acc.fau.edu

**WILLEBOORDSE, FRISO,** analytical chemistry; deceased, see previous edition for last biography

**WILLEFORD, BENNETT RUFUS, JR,** INORGANIC CHEMISTRY. *Current Pos:* from asst prof to prof, 50-84, EMER PROF CHEM, BUCKNELL UNIV, 84- *Personal Data:* b Greenville, SC, Oct 28, 21. *Educ:* Emory Univ, BA, 43; Univ Wis, MS, 49, PhD(phys chem), 50. *Prof Exp:* Jr chemist, Shell Develop Co, 43-46; asst, Univ Wis, 46-50. *Concurrent Pos:* Res fel, Univ Minn, 56-57; consult, US Fish & Wildlife Serv, 60-64; NSF sci fac fel, Univ Munich, 62-63; res assoc, Univ NC, Chapel Hill, 69-70; guest prof, Inorg Chem Lab, Univ Oxford, Eng, 77-78, Anorganisch-Chem Inst, Tech Univ Munchen, 78, 83, 84 & Univ Cambridge, Eng, 85; Fulbright lectr, Univ Poona, India, 85-86; vis prof, Earlham Col, Richmond, Ind, 86-87, Baylor Univ, Waco, Tex, 88; Fulbright lectr, Cuttington Univ Col, Liberia, WAfrica, 89-90; chem teacher, Kodaikanal Int Sch, India, 93. *Mem:* Am Chem Soc. *Res:* Structure of metal coordination compounds; organometallic chemistry. *Mailing Add:* Dept Chem Bucknell Univ Lewisburg PA 17837. *Fax:* 717-524-1739; *E-Mail:* willefrd@bucknell.edu

**WILLEKE, GENE E,** CIVIL ENGINEERING. *Current Pos:* DIR & PROF, INST ENVIRON SCI, MIAMI UNIV, OHIO, 77- *Personal Data:* b Dola, Ohio, Sept 5, 34; m 62, Carol A Blomquist; c Andrew G & Jonathan C. *Educ:* Ohio Northern Univ, AB, 56, BS, 57; Stanford Univ, MS, 60, PhD(civil eng), 69. *Prof Exp:* Civil engr, Madison Eng Asn, 57; hydraul res engr, US Bur Pub Rds, Wash, 60-62; supvr sanit engr, USPHS, Chicago, 62-65; actg asst prof, Stanford Univ, 68-70; prof, Ga Inst Technol, 70-77. *Concurrent Pos:* Grantee, Hwy Res Bd, 71. *Mem:* Am Soc Civil Engrs; Nat Asn Environ Profs; Nat Soc Prof Engrs; Am Geophys Union; Am Meteorol Soc; Asn Am Geogrs; Am Soc Eng Educ. *Res:* Civil engineering. *Mailing Add:* Inst Environ Sci Miami Univ 102 Boyd Hall Oxford OH 45056

**WILLEKE, KLAUS,** AEROSOL SCIENCE & TECHNOLOGY, INDUSTRIAL HYGIENE. *Current Pos:* assoc prof environ health & adj prof chem eng, 76-81, PROF ENVIRON HEALTH, UNIV CINCINNATI, 81-, ADJ PROF INDUST ENG, 87- *Personal Data:* b Essen, Ger, Mar 26, 41; m 68; c 1. *Educ:* Univ NH, BS, 63; Stanford Univ, MS, 64, PhD(aeronaut & astronaut), 69; Von Karman Inst, dipl, 66. *Prof Exp:* Fel, Max Planck Inst Plasma Physics, Ger, 69-70; asst prof mech eng, Univ Minn, 70-76. *Concurrent Pos:* Vis asst prof, Dept Chem Eng, Kyoto Univ, Japan, 73; mem, Occup Safety & Health Study Sect, Nat Inst Occup Safety & Health, 78-80; assoc dir, Dept Environ Health, Univ Cincinnati, 86- *Mem:* Am Indust Hyg Asn; AAAS; Air Pollution Control Asn; Am Asn Aerosol Res. *Res:* Particle classification and measurement; aerosol generation and sampling; asbestos fibers; particle deposition in lung; therapeutic aerosols; respirator protection of workers; dust control. *Mailing Add:* Dept Molekulargenetik Inst Genet Univ Bonn Romerstr 164 53117 Bonn Germany

**WILLEMOT, CLAUDE,** PLANT LIPID METABOLISM, STRESS PHYSIOLOGY. *Current Pos:* RES SCIENTIST PLANT PHYSIOL, FOOD RES & DEVELOP CTR, ST HYACINTHE CAN DEPT AGR, 67- *Personal Data:* b Ghent, Belg, Dec 26, 33; Can citizen; m 66, Joan Glenn; c Annick, Alain, Catherine & Patrick. *Educ:* McGill Univ, MSc, 63, PhD(plant physiol), 64. *Prof Exp:* Nat Res Coun Can fel, Nat Inst Agr Res, Versailles, France, 64-65 & Univ Calif, Davis, 65-67; Dept Sci & Indust Res, NZ, 79-80. *Concurrent Pos:* Lectr, Fac Agr, Laval Univ, 68-; assoc ed, Can J Biochem, 75-79. *Mem:* Can Soc Plant Physiol (secy-treas, 71-72, secy, 72-73); Am Soc Plant Physiol; Can Soc Hort Sci; Am Soc Hort Sci; Inst Food Technol. *Res:* Plant lipid metabolism; postharvest physiology chilling injury. *Mailing Add:* Univ Laval Envirotron Pavillon Comtois Cite Univ Quebec PQ G1K 7P4 Can. *Fax:* 418-656-7871; *E-Mail:* stawi@hermes.ulaval.ca

**WILLEMS, JAN C,** MATHEMATICAL SYSTEMS THEORY, SYSTEMS ENGINEERING. *Current Pos:* PROF, UNIV GRONINGEN, NETH, 73- *Personal Data:* b Bruges, Belg, Sept 18, 39; m 65; c 2. *Educ:* Univ Ghent, Electromech Engr, 63; Univ RI, MSc, 65; Mass Inst Technol, PhD(elec eng), 68. *Prof Exp:* Asst prof elec eng, Mass Inst Technol, 68-73. *Concurrent Pos:* Sr vis fel, Dept Appl Math & Theoret Physics, UK Sci Res Coun, 70-71. *Mem:* Fel Inst Elec & Electronics Engrs; Soc Indust & Appl Math; Dutch Math Soc. *Res:* Control theory; stability theory; optimal control; mathematical system theory. *Mailing Add:* Univ Groningen Math Inst Postbox 800 Groningen 9700 AV Netherlands

**WILLEMS, NICHOLAS,** CIVIL & STRUCTURAL ENGINEERING. *Current Pos:* asst prof, Univ Kans, 60-61, from instr to prof, 61-75, chmn dept, 72-75, PROF CIVIL ENG, UNIV KANS, 75- *Personal Data:* b Aardenburg, Neth, Jan 6, 24; US citizen; m 48; c 5. *Educ:* Delft Univ Technol, MSc, 46; Univ Pretoria, MComm, 53; Univ Kans, PhD(eng mech), 63. *Prof Exp:* Asst engr, Hague Munic, 46-48; engr, Transvaal Prov Rd Dept, 48-51; construct engr, SAfrican Coal & Oil Corp, 51-52; resident engr, van Niekerk, Kleyn & Edwards, 52-54, jr partner & consult, 54-60. *Concurrent Pos:* Consult, indust, state & fed govt, 60-67; Ford Found grant, 63. *Mem:* Am Soc Civil Engrs; Sigma Xi. *Res:* Structural analysis; plates; shells; dynamic loading; vibrations and matrix analysis. *Mailing Add:* 208 Arizona Pl Lawrence KS 66049

**WILLEMSEN, HERMAN WILLIAM,** PHYSICS. *Current Pos:* SCIENTIST PHYSICS, BELL NORTHERN RES, 79- *Personal Data:* b Huissen, Holland, Dec 23, 45; Can citizen; m 80; c 2. *Educ:* Univ Waterloo, BSc, 70; Univ Toronto, MSc, 72, PhD(physics), 75. *Prof Exp:* Res assoc physics, Univ Toronto, 75-76; res assoc, Argonne Nat Lab, 76-79. *Mem:* Can Asn Physicists; Am Phys Soc. *Res:* Superconductivity; phase transitions; defects in insulators; mass memory systems; opto electronic devices. *Mailing Add:* Nortel Northern Telecom PO Box 3511 Sta C Ottawa ON K1Y 4H7 Can

**WILLEMSEN, ROGER WAYNE,** PHYSIOLOGICAL ECOLOGY, BOTANY. *Current Pos:* FIELD DEVELOP MGR, RHONE POULENC INC, 85- *Personal Data:* b Oskaloosa, Iowa, Jan 14, 44; m 66; c 3. *Educ:* Cent Col, Iowa, BA, 66; Kans State Col, Pittsburg, Kans, MS, 68; Univ Okla, PhD(bot), 71. *Prof Exp:* Grants, Rutgers Univ, New Brunswick, 72-73; asst prof bot, 71-78; mem staff, Lilly Res Labs, 78-85. *Mem:* Entom Soc Am; Am Phytopath Soc; Weed Sci Soc Am. *Res:* Physiology and ecology of weed seed germination; allelopathy; old-field succession; agricultural pest control. *Mailing Add:* 2512 W Sierra Ave Fresno CA 93711

**WILLEN, ERICH H,** HIGH ENERGY PHYSICS. *Current Pos:* Physicist, 76-86, SR PHYSICIST, BROOKHAVEN NAT LAB, 86- *Personal Data:* b Westminster, MD, 36. *Educ:* Western Md Col, BS, 58; Johns Hopkins Univ, PhD(physics), 63. *Mem:* Am Phys Soc; NY Acad Sci; AAAS. *Res:* High energy physics. *Mailing Add:* Brookhaven Nat Lab Bldg 902A Upton NY 11973-5000

**WILLENBERG, HARVEY JACK,** MICROGRAVITY MATERIALS SCIENCE. *Current Pos:* CHIEF SCIENTIST, BOEING DEFENSE & SPACE GROUP, 93-, MGR SPACE FUTURES, 93- *Personal Data:* b New York, NY, Sept 8, 45; m 71, Elke Knoop; c Robert, Heidi & David. *Educ:* Harvey Mudd Col, BS, 67; Univ Wash, MS, 71, MSE, 72, PhD(nuclear eng), 76. *Prof Exp:* Sr engr, Westinghouse-Hanford, 72-76; staff scientist,

Battelle-Northwest Labs, 76-79; scientist, Math Sci Northwest, 79-82. *Concurrent Pos:* Indust adv, Univ Ala, Huntsville. *Mem:* Am Inst Aeronaut & Astronaut; Am Astronaut Soc. *Res:* Physics and technology development and applications of magnetically-confined thermonuclear plasmas to power generation; two-phase compressible fluid dynamics with heat and mass transfer; materials science and applications under microgravity conditions. *Mailing Add:* 932 W St NW Auburn WA 98001. *Fax:* 253-773-6624; *E-Mail:* harvey.j.willenberg@.boeing.com

**WILLENBROCK, FREDERICK KARL,** engineering education, technology public policy; deceased, see previous edition for last biography

**WILLENS, RONALD H,** HARDWARE SYSTEMS, COMPUTERS. *Current Pos:* VPRES OPERS, LIVINGSTON ENTERPRISES, 90- *Personal Data:* b Chicago, Ill, 1931. *Educ:* Calif Inst Tech, BS, 53, MS, 54, PhD(physics), 61. *Mem:* Fel Am Phys Soc. *Res:* Hardware systems; computers. *Mailing Add:* Livingston Enterprises 4464 Willow Rd Pleasanton CA 94588-8519

**WILLER, RODNEY LEE,** STEREOCHEMISTRY, ENERGETIC MATERIALS. *Current Pos:* DIR TECHNOL, GAYLORD CHEM CORP, SLIDELL, LA, 93- *Personal Data:* b Albany, Ore, Nov 27, 48. *Educ:* ECarolina Univ, BS, 70, MS, 74; Univ NC, PhD(org chem), 76. *Prof Exp:* Res assoc, Mich State Univ, 76-78; asst prof, Tex Tech Univ, 78-80; res chemist, Org Chem, Naval Weapons Ctr, 80-84; sr scientist, Thiekel Corp, Elkton, Md, 84-93. *Mem:* Am Chem Soc; Sigma Xi; AAAS; NY Acad Sci. *Res:* Development of environmentally safe solvents based on dimethyl sulfoxide to replace chlorofluorocarbons; aprotic solvent specialist. *Mailing Add:* Gaylord Chem Corp PO Box 1209 Slidell LA 70459-1209. *Fax:* 504-649-0068

**WILLERMET, PIERRE ANDRE,** LUBRICATION, TRIBOLOGY. *Current Pos:* RES SCIENTIST, ENG & RES STAFF, FORD MOTOR CO, 72- *Personal Data:* b Mineola, NY, Aug 21, 41; m 63; c 2. *Educ:* Widener Univ, BS, 67; Univ Pa, PhD(phys chem), 72. *Concurrent Pos:* Assoc ed, J Synthetic Lubrication. *Mem:* Sigma Xi; Soc Automotive Engrs; Soc Tribologists & Lubrication Engrs. *Res:* Tribology; chemistry of friction and wear in lubricated contacts; thermo oxidative degradation of hydrocarbons and lubricant additives; friction losses in automotive engines and drive trains. *Mailing Add:* 36123 Roycroft Livonia MI 48154

**WILLERSON, JAMES THORNTON,** CARDIOVASCULAR DISEASES. *Current Pos:* PROF MED, HEALTH SCI CTR, UNIV TEX, 76-, DIR, DIV CARDIOL, 77- *Educ:* Baylor Col Med, MD, 65. *Mem:* Inst Med-Nat Acad Sci. *Mailing Add:* Dept Internal Med Univ Tex Med Sch 6431 Fannin Rm 1-150 Houston TX 77225-0708. *Fax:* 713-794-4160

**WILLETT, COLIN SIDNEY,** PHYSICAL SCIENCE, LASERS. *Current Pos:* MEM STAFF, DEFENSE RES TECHNOL, INC, 88- *Personal Data:* b Danbury, Eng, Jan 11, 35; US citizen; c 2. *Educ:* City Univ London, BS, 63; Univ London, PhD(physics), 67. *Prof Exp:* Physicist lasers, Harry Diamond Labs, Dept Army, Adelphi, 67-88. *Res:* Atomic collision processes; gas discharge physics; laser systems research and analysis. *Mailing Add:* 12351 Frederick Rd W Friendship Ellicott City MD 21794

**WILLETT, DOUGLAS W,** MATHEMATICS. *Current Pos:* assoc prof, 66-72, PROF MATH, UNIV UTAH, 72- *Personal Data:* b Adams Co, NDak, May 25, 37; m 59; c 6. *Educ:* SDak Sch Mines & Technol, BS, 59; Calif Inst Technol, PhD(math), 63. *Prof Exp:* From asst prof to assoc prof math, Univ Alta, 62-66. *Concurrent Pos:* Vis prof, Univ Alta, 71-72. *Mem:* Soc Indust & Appl Math; Can Math Cong. *Res:* Ordinary differential equations and mathematical analysis. *Mailing Add:* Dept Math Univ Utah 237 John Widstoe Salt Lake City UT 84112-1193

**WILLETT, HILDA POPE,** MICROBIOLOGY. *Current Pos:* Instr microbiol, Sch Med, Duke Univ, 48-50, assoc, 50-52, from asst prof to assoc prof, 52-64, PROF BACT, SCH MED, DUKE UNIV, 64-, DIR, GRAD STUDIES, 80- *Personal Data:* b Decatur, Ga, July 15, 23; m 56; c 2. *Educ:* Woman's Col Ga, AB, 44; Duke Univ, MA, 46, PhD(microbiol), 49. *Mem:* Am Soc Microbiol; Am Acad Microbiol. *Res:* Physiology of Mycobacterium tuberculosis. *Mailing Add:* Dept Microbiol & Immunol Duke Univ Sch Med PO Box 3020 Durham NC 27702-3020

**WILLETT, JAMES DELOS,** CHEMISTRY. *Current Pos:* grants assoc, NIH, 80-81, staff asst dep dir, 81-82, spec asst to dir, 82-84, health sci adminr, biomed res model develop, Animal Resources Prog, 84-85, CHIEF, BIOL MODELS & MAT RESOURCES SECT, ANIMAL RESOURCES PROG, NIH, 85- & CHIEF, OFF PROG PLANNING & EVAL, DIV RES RESOURCES, 87- *Personal Data:* b Stockton, Calif, Jan 16, 37; c 2. *Educ:* Univ Calif, Berkeley, BA, 59; Mass Inst Technol, PhD(org chem), 65. *Prof Exp:* Jr chemist res, Merck, Sharp & Dohme Res Labs, 59-61; fel chem, Stanford Univ, 65-68; asst prof chem, Univ Idaho, 68-73, assoc prof chem, 73-78, prof chem & biochem, 78-80. *Concurrent Pos:* NIH fel, 65-68; NIH career develop award, Nat Inst Aging, 75-80. *Mem:* Am Chem Soc; Soc Nematologists; Am Aging Asn; AAAS; Tissue Cult Asn. *Res:* Nematodes as models for the study of the effects of senescence on hormonal control systems. *Mailing Add:* George Mason Univ 7946 Donegan Dr Mahassas VA 22110

**WILLETT, JOSEPH ERWIN,** PLASMA PHYSICS. *Current Pos:* assoc prof, 65-81, PROF PHYSICS, UNIV MO, COLUMBIA, 81- *Personal Data:* b Albany, Mo, June 9, 29; m 55, Mary E McCown; c Cynthia J, Lori J & Julie A. *Educ:* Univ Mo, BA, 51, MA, 53, PhD(physics), 56. *Prof Exp:* From asst to instr physics, Univ Mo, 53-55, Stewart fel, 55; physicist & aeronaut res engr, US Naval Ord Lab, Md, 56-58; res scientist, McDonnell Aircraft Corp, 58-61; instr, McDonnell Eve Sch, 60-61; staff scientist, Gen Dynamics, Ft Worth, Tex, 61-65. *Concurrent Pos:* Instr & adj prof, Tex Christian Univ, 62-64. *Mem:* Am Phys Soc. *Res:* Theoretical studies of the interaction of electromagnetic waves with plasmas; electrostatic and hydromagnetic waves; stimulated raman and brillouin scattering; instabilities in magnetized plasmas; plasma heating; controlled fusion; free-electron lasers. *Mailing Add:* 509 Rockhill Rd Columbia MO 65201. *Fax:* 573-882-4195

**WILLETT, LYNN BRUNSON,** ANIMAL TOXICOLOGY, DAIRY SCIENCE. *Current Pos:* from asst prof to assoc prof, 71-84, assoc chair, Dept Dairy Sci, 86-94, PROF DAIRY SCI, OHIO AGR RES & DEVELOP CTR, OHIO STATE UNIV, 84-, PROF ANIMAL SCI, 94- *Personal Data:* b Colorado Springs, Colo, Aug 2, 44; m 66, Cynthia Huser; c Kristine L & Lisa L. *Educ:* Colo State Univ, BS, 66; Purdue Univ, Lafayette, MS, 68, PhD(animal physiol), 71. *Concurrent Pos:* Consult, LBW Educ Serv, 74-; ed, Pharmacol & Toxicol Sect, J Animal Sci, 80-83. *Mem:* Am Dairy Sci Asn; Am Soc Animal Sci; Soc Toxicol; Coun Agr Sci & Technol. *Res:* Pharmacokinetics; metabolism and toxicity of heavy metals, halogenated hydrocarbons, particularly organochlorine pesticides, polybrominated biphenyls and polychlorinated biphenyls by cattle, defining routes of environmental exposure; steroid hormone relationships in cattle. *Mailing Add:* Ohio Agr Res & Develop Ctr Ohio State Univ 1680 Madison Ave Wooster OH 44691-4096. *Fax:* 330-263-3949; *E-Mail:* willett.2@osu.edu

**WILLETT, NORMAN P,** MICROBIOLOGY. *Current Pos:* assoc prof, Sch Pharm, Temple Univ, 66-73, head dept, 67-87, prof & chair microbiol, Sch Dent, 73-87, DENT EDUC COORDR, SCH DENT, TEMPLE UNIV, 87-, PROF, DEPT MICROBIOL & IMMUNOL, SCH MED. *Personal Data:* b Paterson, NJ, Apr 13, 28; m 56; c 3. *Educ:* Rutgers Univ, BS, 49; Syracuse Univ, MS, 52; Mich State Univ, PhD(microbiol), 55. *Prof Exp:* Asst dent med, Harvard Univ, 55-57; sr res microbiologist, Squibb Inst Med Res, 57-60; res microbiologist, Bzura, Inc, 60-62; sr res assoc, Lever Brothers, 62-63; chief microbiologist, Food & Drug Res Inc, 63; res assoc, Sch Vet Med, Univ Pa, 63-66. *Mem:* AAAS; Am Soc Microbiol; Am Chem Soc; NY Acad Sci; Am Asn Dent Schs; Am Inst Biol Sci; Soc Infectious Control in Dent; Int Asn Dent Res; Sigma Xi. *Res:* Biochemical basis of pathogenicity; physiology of streptococci and microbes; biochemistry and microbiology of organic acid and antibiotic fermentation; chemotherapy; streptococcal toxins; infection control; macrophage actuation. *Mailing Add:* Dept Microbiol & Immunol Temple Univ Sch Med 3400 N Broad St Philadelphia PA 19140. *Fax:* 215-7788

**WILLETT, RICHARD MICHAEL,** mathematics, for more information see previous edition

**WILLETT, ROGER,** PHYSICAL CHEMISTRY, CHEMICAL PHYSICS. *Current Pos:* From instr to assoc prof, Wash State Univ, 62-72, chmn, Dept Chem, 74-80, chmn, Chem Physics Prog, 84-86, PROF CHEM, WASH STATE UNIV, 72-, CHMN DEPT, 92- *Personal Data:* b Northfield, Minn, July 13, 36; m 57, Thelma Hanson; c 6. *Educ:* St Olaf Col, BA, 58; Iowa State Univ, PhD(chem, physics), 62. *Concurrent Pos:* Vis prof, Univ Zurich, 80; Fulbright scholar, Leiden, Neth, 81; dir, Advan Study Inst, NATO, 83, ed, proc, 85. *Mem:* Am Chem Soc; Am Crystallog Asn; Sigma Xi. *Res:* X-ray diffraction and crystallography; magnetic susceptibility and interactions; chemical bonding; molecular and electronic structure; electronic spectra and electron spin resonance studies of transition metal ions; phase transitions. *Mailing Add:* Dept Chem Wash State Univ 1 E Stadium Way Pullman WA 99164-0001

**WILLETTE, ROBERT EDMOND,** medicinal chemistry, organic chemistry, for more information see previous edition

**WILLEY, CLIFF RUFUS,** SOIL PHYSICS. *Current Pos:* chief, Solid Waste Serv, 73-74, CHIEF, TECH SERV, DEPT NATURAL RESOURCES, MD ENVIRON SERV, 74- *Personal Data:* b Hornell, NY, Nov 20, 35; m 57; c 5. *Educ:* Cornell Univ, BS, 57, MS, 59; Univ Wis-Madison, PhD(soil physics), 62. *Prof Exp:* Soil scientist, Agr Res Serv, USDA, 62-73. *Concurrent Pos:* Assoc prof agr eng, NC State Univ, 67-73. *Mem:* Sigma Xi. *Mailing Add:* 1028 Old Bay Ridge Rd Annapolis MD 21403

**WILLEY, DANIEL ROBERT,** LOW TEMPERATURE STUDIES OF GAS PHASE COLLISIONS. *Current Pos:* ASST PROF PHYSICS, ALLEGHENY COL, 89- *Personal Data:* b Sioux City, Iowa, Jan 9, 58; m 79; c 4. *Educ:* Dartmouth Col, AB, 80; Duke Univ, MA, 87, PhD(physics), 89. *Concurrent Pos:* Young Investr Award, NSF, 92. *Mem:* Am Phys Soc. *Res:* Spectroscopic studies of low temperature gas phase molecular collisions in a quasi-equilibrium environment. *Mailing Add:* Dept Physics Allegheny Col Meadville PA 16335. *E-Mail:* dwilley@alleg.edu

**WILLEY, GORDON RANDOLPH,** AMERICAN ARCHAEOLOGY. *Current Pos:* RETIRED. *Personal Data:* b Chariton, Iowa, Mar 7, 13; m 38, Katherine W Whaley; c Alexandra & Winston. *Educ:* Univ Ariz, AB, 35, AM, 36; Columbia Univ, PhD, 42; Harvard Univ, AM, 50. *Hon Degrees:* LittD, Cambridge Univ, 77, Univ Ariz, 81, Univ NMex, 84. *Honors & Awards:*

Medal, Viking Fund, 53; Gold Medal, Archaeol Inst Am, 73; Alfred V Kidder Medal for Achievement in Am Archaeol, 74; Huxley Medal, Royal Anthrop Inst London, 79; Golden Plate Award, Am Acad Achievement, 87. *Prof Exp:* Archaeol asst, Nat Park Serv, Macon, Ga, 36-38; archaeologist, La State Univ, 38-39; archaeol field supvr, Peru, 41-42; instr anthrop, Columbia Univ, 42-43; anthropologist, Bur Am Ethnol Smithsonian Inst, 43-50; Bowditch prof archaeol, Harvard Univ, 50-87, chmn, Dept Anthrop, 54-57, sr prof anthrop, 83-87. *Concurrent Pos:* Vis prof Am archaeol, Cambridge Univ, 62-63; overseas fel, Churchill Col, Cambridge Univ, 68-69. *Mem:* Nat Acad Sci; fel Am Anthrop Asn (pres, 61); fel Am Acad Arts & Sci; fel Soc Am Archaeol (pres, 68); Am Philos Soc; Royal Anthrop Inst, Eng & Ireland; Brit Acad. *Res:* Prehistoric settlement investigations in Peru, Guatemala and Belize. *Mailing Add:* 25 Gray Gardens E Cambridge MA 02138-1401

**WILLEY, JOAN DEWITT,** MARINE CHEMISTRY, ANALYTICAL CHEMISTRY. *Current Pos:* from asst prof to assoc prof, 77-86, interim dean, Grad Sch, 94-95, PROF CHEM & MARINE SCI, UNIV NC, WILMINGTON, 86- *Personal Data:* b Summit, NJ, May 10, 48; m 70, Charles F Stehman; c 2. *Educ:* Duke Univ, BSc, 69; Dalhousie Univ, PhD(chem oceanog), 75. *Honors & Awards:* Dreyfus scholar, 97. *Prof Exp:* Fel geochem, Mem Univ Nfld, 74-75; vis scientist marine geol, Bedford Inst, 76-77. *Concurrent Pos:* Consult, Am Inst Chemists. *Mem:* Am Chem Soc; AAAS; Oceanog Soc; Am Geophys Union; Sigma Xi. *Res:* Sediment and interstitial water chemistry in estuaries, including seasonal variations; marine chemistry of silica; reactions between sediments and seawater; rainwater composition in coastal areas; impact of rainwater on surface seawater productivity. *Mailing Add:* Dept Chem Univ NC 601 S College Rd Wilmington NC 28403-3297

**WILLEY, ROBERT BRUCE,** ANIMAL BEHAVIOR, INSECT BIOGEOGRAPHY. *Current Pos:* ASSOC PROF BIOL, UNIV ILL, CHICAGO, 65- *Personal Data:* b Long Branch, NJ, Sept 15, 30; m 56, Ruth Lippitt. *Educ:* NJ State Teachers Col, BA, 52; Harvard Univ, PhD(biol), 59. *Honors & Awards:* President's Stewardship Award, Nature Conservancy, 88. *Prof Exp:* Teacher high sch, NJ, 52-54; from asst prof to assoc prof biol, Ripon Col, 59-65. *Concurrent Pos:* Res grants, Sigma Xi, 62 & 67, NSF, 64-69, 72-74 & 75-76; mem bd trustees, Rocky Mountain Biol Lab, 63-88, vpres, 72-76, pres, 77-84. *Mem:* Am Soc Zool; Soc Study Evolution; Entom Soc Am; Orthopterists Soc; Animal Behav Soc; Soc Am Naturalists. *Res:* Invertebrate behavior; interspecific behavior and evolution of sympatric insect populations; animal communication systems; insect biogeography and speciation. *Mailing Add:* Dept Biol Sci M/C 066 Univ Ill 845 W Taylor St Chicago IL 60607-7057

**WILLEY, RUTH LIPPITT,** PHYCOLOGY, LIMNOLOGY. *Current Pos:* asst prof, 65-71, ASSOC PROF BIOL SCI, UNIV ILL, CHICAGO, 71- *Personal Data:* b Wickford, RI, May 11, 28; m 56, Robert. *Educ:* Wellesley Col, BA, 50; Radcliffe Col, PhD(biol), 56. *Honors & Awards:* President's Stewardship Award, Nature Conservancy, 88. *Prof Exp:* Docent mus educ, Peabody Mus Natural Hist, Yale Univ, 50-52; instr zool, Wellesley Col, 56-57; res fel ophthal, Mass Eye & Ear Infirmary, 57-58; comm histologist, Triarch Prod, 59-60. *Concurrent Pos:* Mem, Rocky Mountain Biol Lab, Colo, 58-, secy, 66-68, mem bd trustees, 75-78, environ officer, 79-85. *Mem:* Am Soc Limnol Oceanog; Am Soc Cell Biol; Am Micros Soc; Entom Soc Am; Phycol Soc Am; Am Soc Parasitologists. *Res:* Ultrastructure, ecology and phylogeny of euglenoid algae; ecology of epibiotic interactions among freshwater organisms; distribution of salamanders and incidence of paedomorphy in high altitude ponds. *Mailing Add:* 222 E Gothic Ave Gunnison CO 81230. *Fax:* 312-413-2435

**WILLHAM, RICHARD LEWIS,** ANIMAL BREEDING, LIVESTOCK HISTORY. *Current Pos:* from assoc prof to prof animal sci, 66-79, C F Curtiss distinguished prof, 79-93, REGENT PROF AGR, IOWA STATE UNIV, 93- *Personal Data:* b Hutchinson, Kans, May 4, 32; m 54, Esther Burkhart; c Karen (Conley) & Oliver Lee. *Educ:* Okla State Univ, BS, 54; Iowa State Univ, MS, 55, PhD(animal breeding), 60. *Honors & Awards:* Am Soc Animal Sci Breeding & Genetics Award, 78; Am Soc Animal Sci Indust Serv Award, 86; Nat Cattleman's Asn Res Award, 86. *Prof Exp:* Asst prof animal sci, Iowa State Univ, 59-63; assoc prof animal sci, Okla State Univ, 63-66. *Concurrent Pos:* AEC grant, Iowa State Univ, 59-63; beef breeding res, Agr Exp Sta, 66-96. *Mem:* Fel Am Soc Animal Sci. *Res:* Beef cattle breeding; evaluation of the results of selection and crossbreeding; Beef Improvement Federation work with national sire evaluation program development in beef industry; guest curator of art exposition titled - Art About Livestock. *Mailing Add:* 239 Kilpec Hall Dept Animal Sci Iowa State Univ Ames IA 50011. *Fax:* 515-294-2401

**WILLHITE, CALVIN CAMPBELL,** TOXICOLOGY, TERATOLOGY. *Current Pos:* STAFF TOXICOLOGIST, DEPT TOXIC SUBSTANCE CONTROL, STATE OF CALIF, BERKELEY, 85- *Personal Data:* b Salt Lake City, Utah, Apr 27, 52. *Educ:* Utah State Univ, BS, 74, MS, 77; Dartmouth Col, PhD(pharmacol), 80. *Honors & Awards:* Frank R Blood Award, Soc Toxicol, 86. *Prof Exp:* Albert J Ryan Found fel, Med Sch, Darmouth Col, 77-80; teaching fel toxicol, Dept Pharmacol, Col Med, Health Sci Ctr, Univ Ariz, Tucson, 80; res pharmacol, Toxicol Res Unit, Western Regional Res Ctr, USDA, Berkeley, 80-85. *Concurrent Pos:* Adj asst prof, Toxicol Prog, Utah State Univ, Logan, 84-87, adj assoc prof, 88-90; prin investr, Nat Inst Child Health & Human Develop grant, 85-88; US Environ Protection Agency Health Effects Task Group, Nat Sanitation Found, 86-88; co-prin investr, March of Dimes Res grant, 87-91; mem, Human Health Toxics Rev Comt, Ariz Dept Environ Quality, 89-90, TLV Comt, Am Conf Govt Indust Hygienists, 89-; invited lectr, Instituto di Chimica Biologica, Universita di Palermo Policlinico, Palermo, Mondelo, Italy, 91, Italian Ministry Labour & Social Welfare, Rome, 93; chair, Animals in Res Comt, Soc Toxicol, 91-94, Pub Affairs Comt, Teratology Soc, 92-95; Hoffmann LaRoche grant, 92-94; consult, SRI Int. *Mem:* Soc Toxicol; Teratology Soc; Am Conf Govt Indust Hygienists. *Res:* Embryotoxicity, pharmacokinetics, & placental transfer of cancer chemopreventive retinoids, antiviral nucleosides, industrial chemicals and environmental pollutants; pathogenesis of congenital malformations; identification and risk assessment of teratogenic agents. *Mailing Add:* Dept Toxic Substances Control Calif 700 Heinz St Bldg F Suite 200 Berkeley CA 94710

**WILLHITE, GLEN PAUL,** CHEMICAL & PETROLEUM ENGINEERING. *Current Pos:* from assoc prof, 69-88, ROSS H FORNEY DISTINGUISHED PROF CHEM & PETROL ENG, UNIV KANS, 88-, CHMN DEPT, 88- *Personal Data:* b Waterloo, Iowa, July 18, 37; m 59; c 5. *Educ:* Iowa State Univ, BS, 59; Northwestern Univ, PhD(chem eng), 62. *Honors & Awards:* Distinguished Achievement Award for Petrol Engr Fac, Soc Petrol Engrs, 81; Lester C Uren Award, 86; Distinguished Mem Soc Petrol Engrs, 86. *Prof Exp:* From res scientist to sr res scientist, Continental Oil Co, 62-70. *Concurrent Pos:* Co-dir, Tertiary Oil Recovery Proj, 74-; consult, Off Technol Assessment, 76-78. *Mem:* Am Inst Chem Engrs; Soc Petrol Engrs; Am Chem Soc. *Res:* Transport processes in porous media; environmental heat transfer; numerical solutions of partial differential equations; enhanced oil recovery processes. *Mailing Add:* 2903 Schwarz Rd Lawrence KS 66044-4843

**WILLHOIT, DONALD GILLMOR,** HAZARDOUS WASTE MANAGEMENT. *Current Pos:* asst prof radiol health, Sch Pub Health, 64-68, ASSOC PROF ENVIRON SCI, UNIV NC, CHAPEL HILL, 68-, DIR HEALTH & SAFETY, 74- *Personal Data:* b Kansas City, Mo, Feb 5, 34; m 56; c 4. *Educ:* William Jewell Col, AB, 56; Univ Wash, 58; Univ Pittsburgh, ScD(radiation health), 64. *Prof Exp:* Assoc scientist & health physicist, Westinghouse Testing Reactor, 58-60; radiation safety off, Univ Pittsburgh, 60-61, teaching fel, 61-64. *Mem:* Health Physics Soc. *Res:* Public policy of low-level radioactive and hazardous waste disposal. *Mailing Add:* Dept Environ Sci Univ NC Chapel Hill NC 27599-8140. *Fax:* 919-962-0227

**WILLIAM, JAMES C, JR,** RENAL PHYSIOLOGY, EPITHELIAL TRANSPORT. *Current Pos:* ASSOC PROF, DEPT ANAT, IND UNIV. *Educ:* Cornell Univ, PhD(physiol), 83. *Prof Exp:* Teaching fel, 83-86, instr nephrology, Univ Ala, Birmingham, 86-; Dept Anat & Cell Biol, Med Univ SC. *Mailing Add:* Dept Anat Ind Univ 635 Barnhill Rd Indianapolis IN 46202-5120

**WILLIAMS, AARON, JR,** PHYSICAL GEOGRAPHY. *Current Pos:* instr, 67-69, asst prof, 71-77, ASSOC PROF GEOG, UNIV S ALA, 77-, DIR, COASTAL WEATHER RES CTR, 88- *Personal Data:* b Newark, NJ, Jan 29, 42. *Educ:* Fla State Univ, BS, 65; Univ Mo, MA, 67; Univ Okla, PhD(geog), 71. *Prof Exp:* Meteorologist, US Weather Bur, 66. *Mem:* Am Asn Geog; Am Meteorol Soc. *Res:* Climatology of coastal and tropical environments; radar climatology. *Mailing Add:* Dept Geol & Geog Life Sci Bldg Rm 136 Univ SAla Mobile AL 36688

**WILLIAMS, ALAN EVAN,** ISOTOPE GEOCHEMISTRY, GEOTHERMICS. *Current Pos:* Res geochemist, 79-80, asst res geochemist, 80-90, ASSOC RES GEOCHEMIST, INST GEOPHYS & PLANETARY PHYSICS, UNIV CALIF, RIVERSIDE, 90-, GEOCHEMIST, 90-, ASSOC PROF GEOCHEM, 91- *Personal Data:* b Mechanicsburg, Pa, Oct 4, 52. *Educ:* Juniata Col, ScB, 74; Brown Univ, MSc, 76, PhD(geol), 80. *Concurrent Pos:* Vis lectr, Univ Redlands, 80; adj lectr, Univ Calif, Riverside, 81- *Mem:* Am Geophys Union; Geol Soc Am; Geothermal Resources Coun. *Res:* Stable isotopic constraints on systems of water-rock interaction: geothermal systems, ore bodies, shallow intrusives, and ophiolites. *Mailing Add:* Dept Earth Sci Univ Calif 900 University Ave Riverside CA 92521-0001

**WILLIAMS, ALBERT J, JR,** electrical engineering, for more information see previous edition

**WILLIAMS, ALBERT JAMES, III,** OCEANOGRAPHY, OCEAN ENGINEERING. *Current Pos:* Investr, Woods Hole Oceanog Inst, 69-71, asst scientist, 71-75, assoc scientist, 75-87, SR SCIENTIST, APPL OCEAN PHYSICS & ENG, WOODS HOLE OCEANOG INST, 87- *Personal Data:* b Philadelphia, Pa, Oct 17, 40; m 63, Isabelle Phillips; c Helen I. *Educ:* Swarthmore Col, BA, 62; Johns Hopkins Univ, PhD(physics), 69. *Concurrent Pos:* Assoc ed, J Marine Environ Eng, 93-; co-chief ed, J Atmospheric & Oceanic Eng, 94- *Mem:* Am Geophys Union; Inst Elec & Electronics Engrs; Oceanog Soc; Am Meteorol Soc. *Res:* Ocean microstructure, mixing and thermohaline convection; stress and velocity structure in the benthic boundary layer; oceanographic, optical, acoustic, and electronic instrumentation. *Mailing Add:* Box 308 12 Nobska Circle Woods Hole MA 02543. *E-Mail:* awilliams@whoi.edu

**WILLIAMS, ALBERT SIMPSON,** PLANT PATHOLOGY, HORTICULTURE. *Current Pos:* RETIRED. *Personal Data:* b York Co, SC, Jan 23, 24; m 46, Stella Senn; c Alice W (Curry). *Educ:* Emory Univ, AB, 48; Univ Tenn, MS, 49; NC State Univ, PhD(plant path), 54. *Prof Exp:* Asst prof biol, Athens Col, 50; plant pathologist, State Plant Bd, Miss, 50-51; asst, NC State Univ, 51-54; assoc prof plant path, Va Polytech Inst, 54-68; exten prof plant path, Univ Ky, 68-75, prof & chmn, Hort & Landscape Archit Dept, 75-89. *Concurrent Pos:* Host, Flower & Garden Tours, Univ Ky, 92- *Mem:* Am Phytopath Soc; Am Soc Nematol; Soc Europ Nematol; Am Soc Hort Sci. *Mailing Add:* 790 Cindy Blair Way Lexington KY 40503-3459

**WILLIAMS, ANN HOUSTON,** MARINE COMMUNITY ECOLOGY, BENTHIC ECOLOGY. *Current Pos:* prog adminr, 90-96, DIR, CHAP PROGS, SIGMA XI, 96- *Personal Data:* b Red Bank, NJ, Dec 18, 43; m 76, Delbert E. *Educ:* Univ SC, BS, 65; Duke Univ, MAT, 72; Univ NC, PhD(zool), 77. *Prof Exp:* Res assoc, Marine Lab, Duke Univ, 77-78; asst prof biol, Southwestern Univ, Memphis, 78-80; from asst prof to assoc prof marine biol, Auburn Univ, 80-90. *Concurrent Pos:* Prin investr, NSF grant, 75-77, NSF EPSCOR grant, 86-88; vis prof, Dauphin Island Sea Lab, 81-85; res fel, AAAS-Environ Protection Agency, 83; Ala Exp Sta grants, 85-90 & 89-94. *Mem:* Sigma Xi; Ecol Soc Am; AAAS. *Res:* Competitive interactions in shallow coral reef communities; predator-prey interactions in salt marsh communities; predator-prey interactions of seagrass communities. *Mailing Add:* Sigma Xi Hq PO Box 13975 Research Triangle Park NC 27709. *Fax:* 919-549-0090; *E-Mail:* awilliams@sigmaxi.org

**WILLIAMS, ANNA MARIA,** MICROBIOLOGY. *Current Pos:* res asst bact, Madison, 50-54, proj assoc, McArdle Mem Inst Cancer Res, 55-57, res assoc med, Sch Med, 57-64, from asst prof to prof biol sci, 64-90, EMER PROF BIOL SCI, UNIV WIS-PARKSIDE, 90- *Personal Data:* b Tampa, Fla, June 29, 27. *Educ:* Univ Ala, BS, 48; Univ Wis, MS, 51, PhD(bact), 54. *Prof Exp:* Antibiotics lab supvr, Merck & Co, Inc, 48-50. *Concurrent Pos:* Fulbright res grant, Biophys Res Group, Univ Utrecht, 54-55. *Mem:* AAAS; Am Chem Soc; Am Soc Microbiol; Sigma Xi. *Res:* Science education; applied microbiology. *Mailing Add:* Univ Wis-Parkside Kenosha WI 53141-2000. *E-Mail:* anna.williams@uwp.edu

**WILLIAMS, ARTHUR E,** CIVIL ENGINEERING. *Current Pos:* CHIEF ENGRS COMDR, US ARMY CORPS ENGRS, WASHINGTON, 92- *Personal Data:* m, Carole Waite; c Scott, Christina & Cheryl. *Educ:* St Lawrence Univ, BA, 60; Rensselaer Polytech Inst, BSCE, 62; Stanford Univ, MCE, 69. *Hon Degrees:* Din Eng, Rensselaer Univ, 94. *Mailing Add:* Dept Army Chief Engrs 20 Massachusetts Ave NW Washington DC 20314

**WILLIAMS, ARTHUR ROBERT,** SOLID STATE PHYSICS. *Current Pos:* fel, 68-69, staff physicist, Watson Res Ctr, 69-90, PROG DIR, SCALABLE COMPUTING SOLUTIONS, IBM CORP, 90- *Personal Data:* b Feb 20, 41; US citizen; m 62, Sandra Dantona; c Christopher, Gregory & Laura. *Educ:* Dartmouth Col, AB, 62; Harvard Univ, PhD(solid state physics), 69. *Prof Exp:* Appl mathematician, Info Res Inc, Mass, 67-68. *Concurrent Pos:* Tech Mkt, Thinking Machines Corp, 89-90. *Mem:* Am Phys Soc. *Res:* Effective one-electron theory of optical, mechanical and magnetic properties of solids. *Mailing Add:* IBM T J Watson Res Ctr PO Box 218 Yorktown Heights NY 10598. *E-Mail:* willama@watson.ibm.com

**WILLIAMS, AUSTIN BEATTY,** SYSTEMATIC ZOOLOGY. *Current Pos:* SYST ZOOLOGIST, NAT SYSTS LAB, NAT MARINE FISHERIES SERV, 71- *Personal Data:* b Plattsburg, Mo, Oct 17, 19; m 46, Jean McNicol; c David M. *Educ:* McPherson Col, AB, 43; Univ Kans, PhD(zool), 51. *Honors & Awards:* US Dept Com Spec Achievement Award, Nat Oceanic & Atmospheric Admin, 83-84. *Prof Exp:* Asst genetics, Univ Wis, 43-44; teacher pub schs, Kans, 44-46; shrimp investr, Inst Fisheries Res, Univ NC, 51-52, asst prof, 52-55; asst prof, Univ Ill, 55-56; assoc prof, Inst Fisheries Res, Univ NC, 56-63, prof, Inst Marine Sci, 63-71. *Concurrent Pos:* Adj prof, Univ NC, Chapel Hill, 71-80. *Mem:* Fel AAAS; Am Soc Zool; Ecol Soc Am; Soc Syst Zool (secy, 85-88); Estuarine Res Fedn (secy, 72-73, vpres, 80-81, pres, 83-85). *Res:* Taxonomy; ecology; life histories of decapod crustacea; estuarine ecology; fossil decapod crustacea. *Mailing Add:* Nat Systs Lab Nat Mus Nat Marine Fisheries Serv Washington DC 20560. *Fax:* 202-357-1896; *E-Mail:* mnhiv025@sivm.si.edu

**WILLIAMS, BENJAMIN HAYDEN,** anatomy, orthodontics, for more information see previous edition

**WILLIAMS, BENNIE B,** MATHEMATICS. *Current Pos:* RETIRED. *Personal Data:* b Scranton, Tex, Jan 16, 22; m 48, Betty B Williams; c Blake, Jo N (Lovelace), Bradley & Brent. *Educ:* Howard Payne Col, BA, 48; Univ Tex, MA, 53, PhD(math), 66. *Prof Exp:* From instr to asst prof math, Howard Payne Col, 48-61; from asst prof to assoc prof math, Univ Tex, Arlington, 66-88. *Mem:* Am Math Soc; Math Asn Am. *Res:* Foundations of mathematics; ordinary differential equations. *Mailing Add:* 3405 Halifax Dr Arlington TX 76013

**WILLIAMS, BERNARD LEO,** MEDICAL DEVICES, DRUG DELIVERY SYSTEMS. *Current Pos:* prin scientist, 88-92, RES FEL, R W JOHNSON PHARM RES INST, 92- *Personal Data:* b Newark, NJ, Nov 7, 30; m 54, Frances B Gorbley; c Eric, Mark, Andrew & Gregory. *Educ:* Rutgers Univ, BSc, 54, PhD(polymer phys chem), 59. *Prof Exp:* Sr scientist, Am Cyanamid Co, 69-74; group leader, Ortho Pharm Corp, 74-82, prin scientist, 82-88. *Concurrent Pos:* Co-adj assoc prof, Univ Col, Rutgers Univ, 64-78, Dept Chem, 78-82, Col Eng, 82- *Mem:* Am Chem Soc; NY Acad Sci; Am Soc Testing & Mat. *Res:* Medical devices and drug delivery systems, pharmaceutical package/product stability and interaction and the establishment of the appropriate acceptance specifications for such polymer based systems to support all regulatory requirements. *Mailing Add:* EGAM Enterprises 1393 Mallard Dr Martinsville NJ 08836-2134

**WILLIAMS, BETTY L,** compounds on the cardiovascular system, for more information see previous edition

**WILLIAMS, BOBBY JOE,** PHYSICAL ANTHROPOLOGY, POPULATION GENETICS. *Current Pos:* from asst prof to prof, 65-91, EMER PROF ANTHROP, UNIV CALIF, LOS ANGELES, 91- *Personal Data:* b Idabel, Okla, Nov 3, 30; m 57, Charlene Dale; c Kimberlyn, Jennifer, Derrik & Aaron. *Educ:* Univ Okla, BA, 53, MA, 57; Univ Mich, PhD(anthrop, human genetics), 65. *Prof Exp:* Asst prof anthrop, Univ Wis-Milwaukee, 63-65. *Concurrent Pos:* Vpres, Am Asn Phys Anthrop, 87-88. *Mem:* AAAS; Am Anthrop Asn; Am Asn Phys Anthrop. *Res:* Human population genetics; human evolution; population processes in simple societies. *Mailing Add:* Dept Anthrop Univ Calif Los Angeles CA 90024

**WILLIAMS, BROWN F,** SOLID STATE PHYSICS. *Current Pos:* VPRES, SOLID STATE RES, 87- *Personal Data:* b Evanston, Ill, Dec 22, 40; c 2. *Educ:* Univ Calif, Riverside, BA, 62, MA, 64, PhD(physics). 66. *Prof Exp:* Mem tech staff, RCA Labs, 66-68, leader electron emission, 68-70, mgr electro-optics lab, 70-73, head quantum electronics res, 73-77, dir energy systs res lab, 77-79, staff vpres, display & energy systs, 79-87. *Mem:* Fel Inst Elec & Electronics Engrs; Sigma Xi; AAAS; Am Phys Soc. *Res:* Electro-optic devices; optical information recording; solar energy; television picture tubes; electron optics. *Mailing Add:* 27 Honeybrook Dr Princeton NJ 08540-7408

**WILLIAMS, BRYAN,** INTERNAL MEDICINE. *Current Pos:* RETIRED. *Personal Data:* b Longview, Tex, July 28, 25. *Educ:* Southwestern Univ, MD, 47. *Prof Exp:* Asst resident, Mass Mem Hosp, 50-51, chief resident, 53-54; clin asst, Harvard Univ, 55-56; clin asst prof, Southwestern Univ, 63-66, assoc dean student affairs, 66-90, assoc dean alumni affairs, 90-94. *Mem:* Inst Med-Nat Acad Sci. *Mailing Add:* 3419 Dartsmouth Dallas TX 75205

**WILLIAMS, BYRON LEE, JR,** ORGANIC CHEMISTRY. *Current Pos:* RETIRED. *Personal Data:* b Guantanamo Bay, Cuba, Aug 29, 20; m 42; c 3. *Educ:* ETex State Teachers Col, BS, 40, MS, 42; Univ Okla, PhD(org chem), 53. *Prof Exp:* Teacher pub sch, Tex, 40-42; chem engr, Chem Warfare Serv, US Dept Army, 42-44, chem engr, Chem Corps, 46-47; assoc prof chem, ETex State Teachers Col, 47-41; asst, Res Found, Univ Okla, 51-53; assoc prof chem, ETex State Teachers Col, 53-54; res chemist, Monsanto Co, 54-59, from asst dir res to assoc dir res, Plastics Div, 59-64, dir, Process Tech & Eng Dept, Hydrocarbons Div, 64-65, dir res, Hydrocarbons & Polymers Div, 65-67, dir, Corp Res Dept, 67-76; gen mgr, Technol Div, Monsanto Textiles Co, 76-81, feedstock transition, Monsanto Co, 81-82; teacher, Maryville Col, 82-87; adj prof, Wash Univ, 88-92. *Mem:* Am Chem Soc. *Res:* Isolation, chemical characterization and identification of flavonoid type chemical compounds from selected natural products using ion exchange, adsorption and paper chromatography; synthesis of pigments and demethylation studies; hydrolytic enzyme studies of natural glycosides. *Mailing Add:* 1139 Jo Carr Dr St Louis MO 63017

**WILLIAMS, CALVIT HERNDON,** ENVIRONMENTAL HEALTH & SAFETY. *Current Pos:* PRIN SCIENTIST, LAB DIR & GROUP LEADER, RADIAN INT, 77-84 & 85- *Personal Data:* b Houston, Tex, Dec 28, 36; div; c Sabina, Terence, Russel & Damon. *Educ:* Univ St Thomas, Tex, BA, 58; Brown Univ, PhD(chem), 64; Am Bd Indust Hyg, dipl, 79. *Prof Exp:* Fel chem, Rice Univ, 64-66; tech staff mem, Sandia Labs, 66-70; asst prof chem, State Univ Campinas, Brazil, 71-76; lab dir, Aer-Aqua Labs, 76-77. *Concurrent Pos:* Financial planning, IDS-Am Express, 84-85. *Mem:* Sigma Xi; Am Chem Soc; fel Am Indust Hyg Asn; Air & Waste Mgt Asn; Am Soc Safety Engrs; NY Acad Sci. *Res:* High energy crossed-molecular-beam reaction kinetics; thermodynamics of high temperature processes; mass spectrometry and gas chromatography applied to environmental and biomedical analysis; chemical aspects and comprehensive practice of industrial hygiene; occupational and environmental health and safety. *Mailing Add:* Radian Int 8501 N Mo-Pac Blvd PO Box 201088 Austin TX 78720. *Fax:* 512-345-9684; *E-Mail:* herndon__williams@radian.com

**WILLIAMS, CAROL ANN,** CELESTIAL MECHANICS, NON-LINEAR DYNAMICS. *Current Pos:* from asst prof to assoc prof astron, 68-79, ASSOC PROF MATH, UNIV SFLA, TAMPA, 79- *Personal Data:* b Stratford, NJ, Oct 3, 40. *Educ:* Conn Col, BA, 62; Yale Univ, PhD(astron), 67. *Prof Exp:* Assoc res engr & consult, Jet Propulsion Lab, 64, 65, 84; part-time instr physics, Conn Col, 66-67; res staff astronr, Yale Univ, 67-68. *Concurrent Pos:* Adj assoc prof astron, Univ Fla, 73-; ed, Celestial Mech, 80-87; lectr, Am Astron Soc, 82-86; consult, Space Telescope Sci Inst, 83; mathematician, Nat Bur Stand, 85- *Mem:* Am Astron Soc; Sigma Xi; Int Astron Union. *Res:* Celestial mechanics: lunar and planetary theory, three body problem, resonance problem; applied mathematics: perturbation theory with special functions; astrometry: systematic errors in plate reduction and in star catalogs. *Mailing Add:* 4202 E Fowler Ave Tampa FL 33620-5700

**WILLIAMS, CAROLE A,** CARDIOVASCULAR PHYSIOLOGY. *Current Pos:* Asst prof, 79-85, ASSOC PROF PHYSIOL, E TENN STATE UNIV, 85- *Personal Data:* b New Haven, Conn, July 31, 47. *Educ:* Albertus Magnus Col, AB, 69; St Louis Univ, PhD(physiol), 77. *Mem:* Am Physiol Soc; AAAS. *Mailing Add:* Dept Physiol Tenn State Univ Col Med PO Box 70576 Johnson City TN 37614-0576. *Fax:* 423-929-6249

**WILLIAMS, CARROLL BURNS, JR,** FOREST ENTOMOLOGY. *Current Pos:* ADJ PROF, DEPT FOREST & RESOURCE MGT, COL NATURAL RESOURCES, UNIV CALIF, BERKELEY, 88- *Personal Data:* b St Louis, Mo, Sept 24, 29; m 58; c 3. *Educ:* Univ Mich, BS, 55, MS, 57, PhD(forestry), 63. *Prof Exp:* Entomologist, Pac Northwest Forest & Range Exp Sta, US Forest Serv, Ore, 57-58, res forester, 58-60, forestry sci lab, 61-65, res entomologist, Pac Southwest Forest & Range Exp Sta, Calif, 65-68, leader insect impact proj, Forest Insect & Dis Lab, Northeastern Exp Sta, Conn, 68-72, res entomologist, Pac Southwest Forest & Range Exp Sta, Calif, 72-84, proj leader, Pioneering Res Unit, Integrated Mgt Systs Forest Insect & Dis, 75-84, proj leader, Pest Impact Assessment Technol, 85-88. *Concurrent Pos:* Lectr, Sch Forestry, Yale Univ, 69-71; consult, NSF, 71-74. *Mem:* Soc Am Foresters; AAAS; Entom Soc Am. *Res:* Evaluate and predict impact of forest insect and disease on forest resources; modelling pest management systems; computer simulation experiments of insect and disease control techniques and strategies; forest management decision models; urban forestry; environment and social structure. *Mailing Add:* 145 Mulford Hall Univ Calif Berkeley CA 94720. *Fax:* 510-643-5438; *E-Mail:* cbw88@nature

**WILLIAMS, CHARLES HADDON, JR,** BIOCHEMISTRY, ENZYMOLOGY. *Current Pos:* res chemist, 63-74, coordr res, 77-79, SUPVRY RES CHEMIST, GEN MED RES, DEPT VET AFFAIRS MED CTR, ANN ARBOR, 74-; PROF BIOL CHEM, UNIV MICH, ANN ARBOR, 79- *Personal Data:* b Washington, DC, June 29, 32; m 62, Angela Murison; c Stephen C & Patrick T. *Educ:* Univ Md, BS, 56; Duke Univ, PhD(biochem), 61. *Prof Exp:* Am Cancer Soc fel, Dept Biochem, Univ Sheffield, 61-63; from instr to assoc prof, Univ Mich, Ann Arbor, 63-79. *Concurrent Pos:* Res career scientist, Vet Admin. *Mem:* AAAS; Am Chem Soc; Am Soc Biol Chemists; Sigma Xi. *Res:* Mechanism of action and structure of flavoproteins; roles of various amino acid residues in catalysis by flavoproteins and in their structures. *Mailing Add:* Dept Biochem Univ Mich Ann Arbor MI 48109-0606. *Fax:* 313-761-7693; *E-Mail:* chaswill@umich.edu

**WILLIAMS, CHARLES HERBERT,** MALIGNANT HYPERTHERMIA, SEPTIC SHOCK. *Current Pos:* ASSOC PROF BIOCHEM, SCH MED, TEX TECH UNIV, 82- *Personal Data:* b Aurora, Mo, Jan 21, 35; m 56, Dolores B Vieten; c Nathan, Gregory D & Rachelle A. *Educ:* Univ Mo, Columbia, BS, 57, MS, 67, PhD(agr chem), 68. *Honors & Awards:* Fulbright Lectr, Univ San Marcos, Peru, 71. *Prof Exp:* Grad res asst agr chem, Univ Mo, Columbia, 63-68, assoc prof biochem, Dept Biochem & Med, 73-76, res assoc, Sinclair Exp Med Res Farm, 76-78, fel toxicol, 79, res assoc human nutrit, 81, Cancer Res Ctr, 82; fel enzymol, Inst Enzyme Res, Univ Wis-Madison, 68-70, asst prof bichem, 70-72, Dept Anesthesiol, 70-73; dir qual control, Medico Industs, Elmwood, Kans, 79-80; dir anesthesiol res, Dept Anesthesiol & Biochem, 82-86. *Concurrent Pos:* Adj assoc prof biochem, Dept Chem, Univ Tex, 83-; dir surg res, Dept Surg & Biochem, 86-92. *Mem:* Am Physiol Soc; Am Soc Biol Chemists. *Res:* Physiology and pharmacology of temperature regulation; metabolism and endocrinology of catecholamines; biophysics of membrane calcium regulation, for example, calcium channels, gene mapping of the MH gene. *Mailing Add:* Dept Biochem & Anesthesiol 4800 Albata Ave El Paso TX 79905. *Fax:* 915-545-6656; *E-Mail:* aneechw@ttuhsc.edu

**WILLIAMS, CHARLES MELVILLE,** PHYSIOLOGY, GENETICS. *Current Pos:* Assoc prof animal physiol, Univ Sask, 55-67, head dept, 75-83, prof animal sci, 77-92, EMER PROF ANIMAL SCI, UNIV SASK, 92- *Personal Data:* b Regina, Sask, Mar 18, 25; m 53; c Allan B, Catherine A (Greer) & Charlotte L (Wass). *Educ:* Univ BC, BSA, 49, MSA, 52, Ore State Col, PhD(genetics), 55. *Honors & Awards:* Order of Can. *Mem:* Am Soc Animal Sci; Can Soc Animal Prod; fel Agr Inst Can. *Res:* Effect of low environmental temperatures on farm animals. *Mailing Add:* 1 Moxon Crescent Saskatoon SK S7N 3B8 Can. *Fax:* 306-966-4151

**WILLIAMS, CHRISTINE,** PREVENTIVE CARDIOLOGY. *Current Pos:* prof pediat, 85-92, DIR, CHILD HEALTH CTR & CHIEF, DIV HEALTH PROM, NY MED COL, 92- *Personal Data:* b Miami, Fla, Mar 20, 43; m 66, Gary M; c Walter, Jeffrey & Ingrid. *Educ:* Univ Pittsburgh, BS, 63, MD, 67; Harvard Univ, MPH, 69. *Honors & Awards:* Preventive Cardiol Acad Award, NIH, 87-92. *Prof Exp:* Resident, Johns Hopkins Sch Hyg & Pub Health, 70-71, vis scientist, Karolinska Inst, Stockholm, 71-72; resident pediat, Hosp Med Col Pa, 72-73, pediatrician, Children & Youth Comprehensive Care Clin, 74-75; dir child health, Am Health Found, 75-80; dep comnr health, Westchester Co Dept Health, 81-85. *Mem:* Am Acad Pediat; Am Pub Health Asn; Am Soc Prev Cardiol; Am Heart Asn. *Res:* Preventive cardiology. *Mailing Add:* Am Health Found 1 Dana Rd Valhalla NY 10595

**WILLIAMS, CHRISTOPHER NOEL,** GASTROENTEROLOGY. *Current Pos:* lectr, Dalhousie Univ, 69-72, from asst prof to assoc prof, 72-82, head, Gastroenterol, 81, DIR, GASTROINTESTINAL RES LAB, DALHOUSIE UNIV, 71-, PROF MED, 82-; ASSOC PHYSICIAN, VICTORIA GEN HOSP, 76- *Personal Data:* b York, Eng, Dec 25, 35; Can citizen; m 60, Beryl Stephenson; c Amanda, Jennifer, Russell & Beverly. *Educ:* Royal Col Physicians & Surgeons London, MRCS & LRCP, 60; Royal Col Physicians & Surgeons Can, FRCP(C), 68; FACP, 76. *Prof Exp:* Fel med, Univ Pa, 69-70, instr med, 70-71; asst physician med, Victoria Gen Hosp, 69-76. *Concurrent Pos:* MacLaughlin fel, Univ Pa, 69-70, Med Res Coun fel, 70-71; consult gastroenterol, Camp Hill Hosp, Halifax, 73-; grants in aid, Med Res Coun Can, 71- & Nat Health & Welfare Can, 73-; consult, Halifax Infirmary, 78-; co-ed, Can J Gastroenterol, 87-; gov, Atlantic Provinces, Am Col Gastroenterol, 87-92, 94-; mem, Comt Gastroenterol, USPD, 91-; vis res lectr, Can Asn Gastroenterol, 92- *Mem:* Am Col Physicians; Can Asn Gastroenterol (pres, 86-); Am Col Gastroenterol; Am Gastroenterol Asn; Am Asn Study Liver Dis; Can Asn Study Liver. *Res:* Detailed kinetic studies of bile acid metabolism in health and disease, particularly liver and inflammatory bowel disease; application of 3-alpha, 7-beta, 7-alpha, 12-alpha hydroxysteroid dehydrogenases to bile analysis; controlled therapeutic doing that in liver and inflammatory bowel disease. *Mailing Add:* Div Gastronentrol Dept Med Rm 4090 Dickson Bldg Victoria Gen Hosp 1278 Tower Rd Halifax NS B3H 2Y9 Can

**WILLIAMS, CHRISTOPHER P S,** PEDIATRICS, MEDICINE. *Current Pos:* ASSOC PROF PEDIAT, CRIPPLED CHILDREN'S DIV, MED SCH, UNIV ORE, 68- *Personal Data:* b Medford, Ore, Oct 12, 31; m 57; c 3. *Educ:* Univ Ore, BA, 53, MD, 58. *Prof Exp:* Asst prof pediat, Sch Med, Univ Wash, 62-68. *Res:* Medical education. *Mailing Add:* Crippled Childrens Div Ore Health Sci Univ PO Box 574 Portland OR 97207-0574

**WILLIAMS, CLAYTON DREWS,** THEORETICAL PHYSICS, SOLID STATE PHYSICS. *Current Pos:* Asst prof, 61-64, ASSOC PROF PHYSICS, VA POLYTECH INST & STATE UNIV, 64- *Personal Data:* b St Louis, Mo, Oct 22, 35; m 59; c 4. *Educ:* Rice Inst, BA, 57; Wash Univ, PhD(physics), 61. *Mem:* Am Phys Soc. *Res:* Many-body problem; solid-state theory. *Mailing Add:* Dept Physics Va Polytech Inst & State Univ Blacksburg VA 24061. *Fax:* 540-231-7511

**WILLIAMS, CLYDE MICHAEL,** physiology; deceased, see previous edition for last biography

**WILLIAMS, COLIN JAMES,** physical chemistry, inorganic chemistry, for more information see previous edition

**WILLIAMS, CONRAD MALCOLM,** SOLID STATE PHYSICS. *Current Pos:* PROF PHYSICS, MORGAN STATE UNIV, BALTIMORE, MD, 93- *Personal Data:* b Warsaw, NC, Mar 1, 36; m 67; c 1. *Educ:* Morgan State Col, BS, 58; Howard Univ, MS, 65, PhD(physics), 72. *Honors & Awards:* Sigma Xi Pure Sci Award, Naval Res Lab, 79. *Prof Exp:* Res solid state physicist, Div Math Sci, US Naval Res Lab, 60-80; div sci personnel improv, NSF, 80-81, prog dir solid state phys, Div Mat Res, 81-82; head appl magnetics, Mat Sci & Technol Div, Naval Res Lab, 82-93. *Concurrent Pos:* Adj prof physics, Howard Univ, 74-80, adj prof elec eng, 80- *Mem:* Sigma Xi; fel Am Phys Soc; Inst Elec & Electronics Engrs. *Res:* Solid state physics; physics of metals; ferromagnetism (thin films and bulk materials); low temperature; low temperature properties; irradiation effects metals; metal alloys; semiconductors; ion implantation in the ferromagnetic films. *Mailing Add:* Dept Physics Morgan State Univ Baltimore MD 21239

**WILLIAMS, CURTIS ALVIN, JR,** IMMUNOBIOLOGY, CELL BIOLOGY. *Current Pos:* dean natural sci, State Univ NY, 69-80, prof, 69-93, chmn dept, 80-90, EMER PROF BIOL, STATE UNIV NY, PURCHASE, 94- *Personal Data:* b Moorestown, NJ, June 26, 27; m 60, Marjorie King; c Jennifer, Scott & Elisabeth W (Schmidt). *Educ:* Pa State Univ, BS, 50; Rutgers Univ, PhD(zool), 54. *Honors & Awards:* Founders Award, Electrophoresis Soc, 82. *Prof Exp:* Waksman fel & USPHS fel, Pasteur Inst, Paris, 52-54, USPHS fel, Carlsberg Lab, Copenhagen, 54-55; res assoc microbiol, Rockefeller Inst, 55-57; with Nat Inst Allergy & Infectious Dis, 57-60; from asst prof to assoc prof biochem genetics, Rockefeller Univ, 60-69. *Concurrent Pos:* Adj prof, Rockefeller Univ, 70-78 & Sch Med, NY Univ, 76-88; hon res fel neuroimmunol, Univ Col, London, 78; vis res fel cell biol, Albert Einstein Col Med, 79-80; mem bd dirs, Neuberger Mus Art, 82-93; vis prof neurobiol, Univ Southern Calif, Los Angeles, 85; trustee, Wenner-Gren Found Anthrop, 91- *Mem:* Fel AAAS; Soc Neurosci; Sigma Xi; Am Soc Microbiol; Am Asn Immunol; Int Soc Neuroimmunol; fel NY Acad Sci. *Res:* Neurobiology; immunology; cellular biology; neural and behavioral effects of inflammation in the central nervous system. *Mailing Add:* Dept Biol State Univ NY Purchase NY 10577. *Fax:* 914-251-6635; *E-Mail:* cwill@purvid.purchase.edu

**WILLIAMS, CURTIS CHANDLER, III,** CHEMICAL ENGINEERING. *Current Pos:* RETIRED. *Personal Data:* b New York, NY, Sept 30, 26; wid; c Richard & Susan. *Educ:* Yale Univ, BEng, 48; Mass Inst Technol, SM, 50, ScD(chem eng), 53. *Honors & Awards:* Cert of Appreciation, Am Petrol Inst, 77. *Prof Exp:* Engr, Emeryville Res Ctr, Shell Develop Co, 53-59, supvr process eng, 59-64, sr technologist, Mfg Res Dept, 64-65, head, Petrol Processing Dept, Emeryville Res Ctr, 65-67, chief technologist, Wood River Refinery, Ill, 67-71, mgr facil, 71-74, mgr process eng-refining, 74-82, mgr process eng-separations, 82-93, mgr separations, 92-93. *Concurrent Pos:* Chmn, Tech Data Comt, API Refining Dept, 65-; mem bd dirs, Heat Transfer Res Inc, 75-93, Fractionation Res Inc, 75-94. *Mem:* AAAS; Am Chem Soc; fel Am Inst Chem Engrs. *Res:* Design of petroleum refining and petrochemical processes. *Mailing Add:* 13606 Pinerock Lane Houston TX 77079-5914. *Fax:* 713-467-2641

**WILLIAMS, DANIEL CHARLES,** CELL BIOLOGY, BONE BIOLOGY. *Current Pos:* sr scientist, 76-81, RES SCIENTIST, LILLY RES LABS, 82-, GROUP LEADER BONE BIOL, 86- *Personal Data:* b Compton, Calif, Dec 15, 44; m 64; c 2. *Educ:* Calif State Univ, Long Beach, BS, 67; Iowa State Univ, PhD(cell biol), 72. *Prof Exp:* Res engr microbiol, NAm Aviation Inc, 67; instr cell & develop biol, Kans State Univ, 72-74; asst prof develop biol, Univ Notre Dame, 74-76. *Concurrent Pos:* NIH fel, 67-71 & 72-74; consult, BioInfo Assocs, 72-74. *Mem:* Am Soc Bone & Mineral Res; Am Soc Cell Biol; Electron Micros Soc Am. *Res:* Structure-function relationships and control mechanisms associated with cellular and developmental processes especially skeletal tissue; bone biology. *Mailing Add:* Eli Lilly & Co Lilly Corp Ctr Indianapolis IN 46285

**WILLIAMS, DANIEL FRANK,** NONGAME WILDLIFE MANAGEMENT, ENDANGERED SPECIES CONSERVATION & RECOVERY. *Current Pos:* From asst prof to assoc prof biol sci, 71-80, PROF ZOOL SCI, CALIF STATE UNIV, STANISLAUS, 80- *Personal Data:* b Redmond, Ore, Nov 20, 42; c 2. *Educ:* Cent Wash State Col, BA, 66; Univ NMex, MS, 68, PhD(zool), 71. *Concurrent Pos:* Res assoc, Carnegie Mus

Natural Hist; assoc ed, Mammalian Species, 78-82, coordr, US Fish & Wildlife Serv, San Joaquin Valley Endangered Species Recovery Planning Prog, 92- *Mem:* Am Soc Mammal; Ecol Soc Am; Wildlife Soc; Soc Conserv Biol; Soc NW Vertebrate Zool. *Res:* Systematics and evolution of mammals; ecology of mammals; evolution of chromosome morphology in mammals; conservation of mammals; plant/animal interactions - effects on plant productivity; multispecies conservation planning. *Mailing Add:* Dept Biol Sci Calif State Univ Stanislaus Turlock CA 95382

**WILLIAMS, DANIEL JAMES,** MAIN GROUP STRUCTURAL & SYNTHETIC CHEMISTRY, ENVIRONMENTAL INORGANIC CHEMISTRY. *Current Pos:* PROF CHEM, KENNESAW STATE UNIV, 77- *Personal Data:* b Cleveland, Ohio, May 8, 48; m 70, Martha W Comstock. *Educ:* Hiram Col, BA, 70; Univ Ga, PhD(inorg chem), 74. *Prof Exp:* Strosacker teaching res fel, Baldwin-Wallace Col, 75-77. *Concurrent Pos:* Vis prof, Georgetown Univ, 75, 76 & 77. *Mem:* Fel Am Inst Chemists; Am Chem Soc; Am Soc Limnol & Oceanog. *Res:* Synthesis and characterization of main group inorganic complexes of groups 15 and 16 metal halides; chalcogen heterocycles; environmental research involves acid input to urban wetlands via bulk deposition. *Mailing Add:* Dept Chem Kennesaw State Univ 1000 Chastain Rd Kennesaw GA 30144-5591. *Fax:* 770-423-6674; *E-Mail:* dwilliam@ksumail.kennsaw.edu

**WILLIAMS, DARRYL MARLOWE,** HEMATOLOGY. *Current Pos:* PROF MED, TEX TECH UNIV, LUBBOCK, 90- *Personal Data:* b Denver, Colo, Apr 3, 38; m 66, Susan A Moore; c Carol, Peter & Sarah. *Educ:* Baylor Univ, MS & MD, 64, Colo State Univ, BS, 93. *Prof Exp:* House officer med, Affil Hosps, Baylor Univ, 64-66; Univ Utah, 66-68, fel hemat, 68-73, asst prof med, 73-77; from assoc prof to prof med, La State Univ, 77-90. *Concurrent Pos:* Chief hemat & oncol, La State Univ, Shreveport, 77-85, asst dean res, 81-85, assoc dean acad affairs, 85-86, dean, 86-90; dean, HSC Sch Med, Tex Tech Univ, 90- *Mem:* Am Col Physicians; Am Soc Hemat; Am Inst Nutrit; Am Soc Clin Nutrit; Am Fedn Clin Res; Sigma Xi. *Res:* Biological effects of copper; manifestations of copper deficiency; interactions of copper, iron, and hemoglobin synthesis. *Mailing Add:* Shadow Mountain Dr 304 El Paso TX 79912. *Fax:* 806-743-3021; *E-Mail:* somdmw@hlmbb183.1.lhsc.ttu.edu

**WILLIAMS, DAVID ALLEN,** ANALYTICAL MEDICINAL CHEMISTRY. *Current Pos:* asst prof biochem, Mass Col Pharm, 69-77, assoc prof, 77-84, chmn, Dept Chem & Physics, 81-84, PROF MED CHEM, MASS COL PHARM, 84-, DEAN GRAD STUDIES, 88- *Personal Data:* b Wakefield, Mass, Dec 22, 38; m 62, Gail Morand; c Kristine, Karen, David Jr & Kathleen. *Educ:* Mass Col Pharm, BS, 60, MS, 62; Univ Minn, Minneapolis, PhD(med chem), 68. *Prof Exp:* Sr scientist, Med Chem Div, Mallinckrodt Chem Works, 67-69. *Concurrent Pos:* Vis prof, Univ Strathclyde, Glasgow, 86. *Mem:* Fel Am Inst Chemists; Am Chem Soc; Am Asn Col Pharm; Am Asn Pharmaceut Scientists. *Res:* Stereochemistry of drug action; high performance liquid chromatography analytical methods development; drug stability and compatibility; photo stability of pharmaceuticals. *Mailing Add:* Mass Col Pharm 179 Longwood Ave Boston MA 02115. *Fax:* 617-732-2737; *E-Mail:* dwilliams@mcp.edu

**WILLIAMS, DAVID BERNARD,** ENGINEERING, MATERIALS SCIENCE. *Current Pos:* from asst prof to assoc prof, 76-83, PROF METALL & MAT ENG, LEHIGH UNIV, 83-, CHMN, 92- *Personal Data:* b Leeds, Eng, July 25, 49; m 76; c 3. *Educ:* Cambridge Univ, BA, 70, MA, 73, PhD(mat sci), 74. *Honors & Awards:* Burton Medal, Electron Micros Soc Am, 84. *Prof Exp:* Sci Res Coun fel mat sci, Cambridge Univ, 74-76. *Mem:* Micros Soc Am; Am Soc Metals; Am Inst Metals Engrs; Meteoritical Soc; fel Royal Micros Soc; fel Inst Metals UK; Microbeam Analysis Soc. *Res:* Application of transmission and scanning transmission electron microscopy to the study of phase transformations in metals and ceramics. *Mailing Add:* Dept Mat Sci & Eng Lehigh Univ Whitaker Lab 5 E Packer Ave Bethlehem PA 18015-3195

**WILLIAMS, DAVID CARY,** NUCLEAR CHEMISTRY, NUCLEAR PHYSICS. *Current Pos:* MEM TECH STAFF, SANDIA LABS, 66- *Personal Data:* b Santa Monica, Calif, June 22, 35; m 62. *Educ:* Harvard Univ, AB, 57; Mass Inst Technol, PhD(nuclear chem), 62. *Prof Exp:* Fel nuclear chem, Princeton Univ, 62-64; mem staff, Los Alamos Sci Lab, 64-66. *Mem:* Am Nuclear Soc; AAAS; Am Phys Soc; Am Chem Soc; Sigma Xi. *Res:* Nuclear reactions, nuclear decay schemes and nuclear reaction spectroscopy; fast reactor safety research; statistical models of nuclear reactions; atmospheric tracer studies. *Mailing Add:* Sandia Nat Labs-MS0739 Albuquerque NM 87185

**WILLIAMS, DAVID DUDLEY,** FRESHWATER ECOLOGY, INVERTEBRATE ZOOLOGY. *Current Pos:* from asst prof to assoc prof, 77-88, PROF ZOOL, UNIV TORONTO, 88- *Personal Data:* b Laugharne, Wales, June 22, 48; Brit & Can citizen; m 72, Nancy E Williams; c Sian S & James O. *Educ:* Univ Wales, BSc, 69, DSc, 89; Univ Waterloo, MSc, 72, PhD(biol & ecol), 75. *Prof Exp:* Nat Res Coun fel, Pac Biol Sta, 75-77. *Concurrent Pos:* Mem, Sci Comt, Biol Surv Can, 80-90; mem, Pop Biol Comt, Nat Sci & Eng Res Coun, 84-87. *Mem:* Fel Royal Entom Soc; Freshwater Biol Asn; Brit Ecol Soc; Entom Soc Can; NAm Benthological Soc. *Res:* Aquatic invertebrate ecology, primarily running water communities; predator-prey relationships; colonization dynamics; aquatic entomology; faunal distribution patterns. *Mailing Add:* Div Life Sci Univ Toronto 1265 Military Trail Scarborough ON M1C 1A4 Can. *E-Mail:* caddis@lake.scar.utoronto.ca

**WILLIAMS, DAVID FRANCIS,** MEDICAL ENTOMOLOGY. *Current Pos:* RES ENTOMOLOGIST, MED & VET ENTOM RES LAB, USDA, GAINESVILLE, FLA, 77- *Personal Data:* b New Orleans, La, Sept 4, 38; m 64, Sylvia Smith; c Andrea & Chris. *Educ:* Univ Southwest La, BS, 64, MS, 67; Univ Fla, PhD(entom), 69. *Honors & Awards:* Cert Merit, USDA, 77, Super Serv, 82, Invention Award, 85. *Prof Exp:* Asst prof biol, Greensboro Col, 69-71; res entomologist, WFla Arthropod Res Lab, State Fla, 71-74; location & res leader, Fed Exp Sta, Sci & Educ Admin-Agr Res, USDA, St Croix, 74-77. *Concurrent Pos:* Adj asst prof entom, Univ Fla, 79-; expert witness, 87- *Mem:* Entom Soc Am; Sigma Xi. *Res:* Development and evaluation of chemicals, bait formulations, equipment for methods of control of the imported fire ant and the pharaoh's ant; ecology, population dynamics and developmental biology of the imported fire ant; biology, population dynamics and control of biting flies affecting man and animals. *Mailing Add:* USDA-Agr Res Serv PO Box 14565 Gainesville FL 32604. *Fax:* 352-374-5818; *E-Mail:* dfw@gnv.ifas.ufl.educ

**WILLIAMS, DAVID G(ERALD),** SYSTEMS ANALYSIS, UNDERWATER ACOUSTICS. *Current Pos:* PHYSICIST SYSTS ANALYSIS, NAVAL UNDERWATER SYSTS CTR, 71- *Personal Data:* b Hackensack, NJ, Feb 6, 35; m 76; c 2. *Educ:* Univ Mich, BSE, 58, MA 62, PhD(physics), 66. *Prof Exp:* Sr scientist underwater acoust, Gen Dynamics/Elec Boat, 65-69; systs analyst, Mystic Oceanog Co, 69-71. *Concurrent Pos:* Instr physics, SE Br, Univ Conn, 67-69. *Mem:* Acoust Soc Am; Inst Elec & Electronics Engrs. *Res:* Military systems analysis; war gaming and tactical development; systems performance modelling. *Mailing Add:* Naval Underwater Systs Ft Trumbell New London CT 06340

**WILLIAMS, DAVID JAMES,** PHYSICAL CHEMISTRY. *Current Pos:* HEAD LAB, EASTMAN KODAK CO, 83- *Personal Data:* b Syracuse, NY, Feb 20, 43; m 65; c 3. *Educ:* Le Moyne Col, NY, BS, 64; Univ Rochester, PhD(phys chem), 68. *Prof Exp:* Scientist, Xerox Corp, 68-75, mgr phys chem, Corp Res Labs, 75-83. *Mem:* Am Chem Soc; Am Phys Soc. *Res:* Mechanistics of photogeneration and transport of electronic charge in organic and polymeric materials; pulsed nuclear magnetic resonance; electron spin resonance; electrical measurements; optical spectroscopy. *Mailing Add:* Eastman Kodak Co Rochester NY 14650-2110

**WILLIAMS, DAVID JAMES,** HORTICULTURE, PLANT PHYSIOLOGY. *Current Pos:* from asst prof to assoc prof, 74-86, PROF HORT, UNIV ILL, 86- *Personal Data:* b Glendora, NJ, Mar 19, 47; m 70; c 3. *Educ:* Del Valley Col, BS, 69; Rutgers Univ, MS, 71, PhD(hort), 74. *Prof Exp:* Res asst hort, Rutgers Univ, 69-74, teaching asst, 70-74. *Concurrent Pos:* Res grants, J M Rhoades Co, 77-78, NCent Region Pesticide Impact Assessment Prog, 78-79, 79-80 & 80-81, Abbott Labs, ICI & Stauffer Chem Co, Monsanto, Valent, 84-, Ill Dept Agr, 85-, Ill Dept Energy & Natural Resources, 89-90. *Mem:* Am Soc Hort Sci; Weed Sci Soc Am; Int Plant Propagators Soc; Int Soc Arboricult. *Mailing Add:* Hort Dept Univ Ill 1301 W Gregory Dr Urbana IL 61801-3608

**WILLIAMS, DAVID JOHN,** GENERAL POLYMER SCIENCE & TECHNOLOGY, HIGH TECHNOLOGY POLYMERS. *Current Pos:* PRES, PST, INT, 89- *Personal Data:* b Salem, Mass, Mar 2, 37; div; c 2. *Educ:* Lehigh Univ, BS, 59; Case Western Res Univ, MS, 62, PhD(polymer sci), 64. *Prof Exp:* Prof chem eng, City Col, City Univ New York, 64-74; tech asst, Res & Develop Div, prod mgr, Plastics Div, Am Hoechst Corp, 74-84; res prof & proj mgr, Polymer Sci & Eng Div, Univ Mass, 84-87. *Concurrent Pos:* Part time teaching polymer sci & technol, Tufts Univ, 77-79, Clark Univ, 83, Northeastern Univ, 84, Worcester Polytech Inst, 88, 90; consult, Polymer Sci & Technol, 84- *Mem:* Soc Plastic Indust; Am Chem Soc; Soc Plastics Engrs; Soc Advan Mat & Process Eng; Sigma Xi; AAAS. *Res:* High performance polymers; polymer blends; rubber toughened polymers; expandable polymers; free radical polymerization technology; structure-property relationships; general electrical and aerospace applications. *Mailing Add:* PO Box 1543 Stowe VT 05672-1543

**WILLIAMS, DAVID JOHN, III,** THERIOGENOLOGY. *Current Pos:* from assoc prof to prof, 66-89, EMER PROF VET MED & SURG, COL VET MED, UNIV GA, 90- *Personal Data:* b Cordele, Ga, Sept 22, 27; m 48, Mary C Mace; c Mary C, David J IV & Mace W. *Educ:* Univ Ga, DVM, 53, BSA, 61; Auburn Univ, MS, 63; Royal Vet Col, Sweden, FRVC, 65; Am Col Theriogenologists, dipl, 71. *Prof Exp:* Pvt pract vet med, 53-60; instr vet med & surg, Sch Vet Med, Univ Ga, 61; from instr to assoc prof, Auburn Univ, 61-66. *Concurrent Pos:* Am Vet Med Asn fel, 64-65; Auburn Univ grant, 65-66; Animal Dis res grants, 67-70, 71-72. *Mem:* Am Vet Med Asn; Soc Theriogenologists; emer mem Am Col Theriogenologists; Sigma Xi. *Res:* Bovine and equine reproduction; fat necrosis of bovine as influenced by ecological system. *Mailing Add:* 1361 Robin Hood Rd Watkinsville GA 30677

**WILLIAMS, DAVID L,** PHARMACOLOGY. *Current Pos:* PROF PHARMACOL, STATE UNIV NY, STONY BROOK, 74- *Personal Data:* b Pa, Feb 22, 46. *Res:* Pharmacology. *Mailing Add:* Dept Pharm Sci State Univ NY Stony Brook NY 11794

**WILLIAMS, DAVID LEE,** geophysics, oceanography, for more information see previous edition

**WILLIAMS, DAVID LLEWELYN,** METAL PHYSICS. *Current Pos:* Nat Res Coun Can fel, Univ BC, 60-62, from instr to assoc prof, 62-71, assoc dean grad studies, 75-81, head dept, 82-87, PROF PHYSICS, UNIV BC, 71- *Personal Data:* b Hawarden, Wales, Apr 25, 37; m 62; c 2. *Educ:* Univ Col NWales, BSc, 57; Cambridge Univ, PhD(superconductivity), 60. *Concurrent Pos:* Nat Res Coun sr fel, Copenhagen Univ & Bristol Univ, 69-70; Killam fel, SIN, Switz, 78-79. *Mem:* Can Asn Physicists. *Res:* Nuclear magnetic resonance; positron annihilation in metal single crystals; muon spin rotation. *Mailing Add:* Dept Physics Univ BC 325-6224 Agriculture Rd Vancouver BC V6T 1Z1 Can

**WILLIAMS, DAVID LLOYD,** DRUG DELIVERY, ELECTROCHEMISTRY. *Current Pos:* STAFF SCIENTIST, GENETICS INST, 92- *Personal Data:* b Springfield, Mass, Aug 15, 35; m 64, Virginia Tingley. *Educ:* Trinity Col, BS, 57; Northwestern Univ, PhD(anal chem), 62. *Prof Exp:* Sr res chemist, Monsanto Co, 61-69; Am Hosp Supply Corp, 69-70; res assoc dent, Tufts Univ, 70; prog mgr biomed, Abcor Inc, 70-80; res dir, Biotek Inc, 80-84; staff consult, A D Little, 84-85; sr scientist, Giner Inc, 85-88, Copley Pharmaceut, 88-92. *Concurrent Pos:* Consult, Joslin Diabetes Found, 74-80, Moleculon, 85; vis lectr, Salem State Col, 90-91. *Mem:* Am Chem Soc; Int Asn Dent Res; Sigma Xi; Biomat Soc; Controlled Release Soc. *Res:* Dental drug delivery (enzymes, antibiotics, and fluoride) caries measurement instrumentation; wound dressings; microencapsulation; electrochemical instrumentation (lithium, carbon monoxide, enzyme electrodes); protein drug delivery. *Mailing Add:* 258 Haverhill St Reading MA 01867. *Fax:* 978-474-4646

**WILLIAMS, DAVID NOEL,** MATHEMATICAL PHYSICS. *Current Pos:* asst prof theoret physics, 67-74, ASSOC PROF PHYSICS, UNIV MICH, ANN ARBOR, 74- *Personal Data:* b Lewisburg, Tenn, Oct 10, 34; m 56; c 2. *Educ:* Maryville Col, BA, 56; Univ Calif, Berkeley, PhD(theoret physics), 64. *Prof Exp:* Engr, Lockheed Missile Systs Div, Calif, 56-58; fel, Swiss Fed Inst Technol, 63-65, Nuclear Res Ctr, Saclay, France, 65-66 & Inst Adv Study, Princeton Univ, 66-67. *Mem:* Am Phys Soc. *Res:* Holomorphic, Lorentz covariant functions; analytic S matrix theory; analytic parametrization of higher spin scattering amplitudes; applications of functional analysis in the scattering theory and quantum field theory of elementary particles. *Mailing Add:* 1238 Westport Rd Ann Arbor MI 48103-2572

**WILLIAMS, DAVID TREVOR,** ENVIRONMENTAL CHEMISTRY. *Current Pos:* Res scientist food chem, Foods Directorate, 69-75, RES SCIENTIST ENVIRON CHEM, ENVIRON HEALTH DIRECTORATE, HEALTH & WELFARE CAN, 75- *Personal Data:* b Slough, Eng, Oct 4, 40. *Educ:* Univ Bristol, BSc, 61; Queen's Univ, MSc, 63, PhD(chem), 66. *Mem:* Royal Soc Chem; Chem Inst Can. *Res:* Identification of organic contaminants in air and drinking water; effects of water treatment procedures on the organic contaminants of drinking water. *Mailing Add:* Environ Health Directorate Tunneys Pasture Ottawa ON K1A 0L2 Can

**WILLIAMS, DEAN E,** speech pathology, audiology; deceased, see previous edition for last biography

**WILLIAMS, DONALD BENJAMIN,** BIOLOGY. *Current Pos:* from asst prof to assoc prof, 61-81, PROF, VASSAR COL, 81- *Personal Data:* b New York, NY, Aug 8, 33; m 56; c 2. *Educ:* Maryville Col, BA, 55; Emory Univ, MS, 57, PhD(biol), 59. *Prof Exp:* From asst prof to assoc prof biol, Maryville Col, 58-61. *Mem:* Soc Protozool; Am Micros Soc; Sigma Xi. *Res:* Ecology, physiology, ultrastructure and genetics of ciliated protozoa; factors influencing ciliate cyst induction and development. *Mailing Add:* 78 Mallard Dr Merritt NC 28556

**WILLIAMS, DONALD ELMER,** X-RAY CRYSTALLOGRAPHY. *Current Pos:* assoc prof, 67-71, PROF CHEM, UNIV LOUISVILLE, 71- *Personal Data:* b Kansas City, Mo, Mar 7, 30. *Educ:* William Jewell Col, AB, 50; Iowa State Univ, PhD(chem), 64. *Prof Exp:* Res asst chem, Iowa State Univ, 57-62, from asst chemist to assoc chemist, 62-67. *Concurrent Pos:* Vis prof, Univ Auckland, NZ, 73; State Univ Utrecht, Neth, 80-81; prog officer, Chem Div, NSF, 88-89. *Mem:* Am Chem Soc; Am Crystallog Asn; Am Phys Soc. *Res:* Intermolecular forces in crystals; crystal mechanics; molecular clusters. *Mailing Add:* Dept Chem Univ Louisville Louisville KY 40292

**WILLIAMS, DONALD HOWARD,** INORGANIC CHEMISTRY, NUCLEAR ENERGY ISSUES. *Current Pos:* dir summer sch, Hope Col, 72-78, col trustee, 76-80, chmn, Chem Dept, 79-82, PROF CHEM, HOPE COL, 69-, DIR, INST ENVIRON QUAL, 70- *Personal Data:* b Ellwood City, Pa, Mar 9, 38; m 60; c 2. *Educ:* Muskingum Col, BS, 60; Ohio State Univ, PhD(inorg chem), 64. *Prof Exp:* Asst prof chem, Univ Ky, 64-69. *Concurrent Pos:* Grants, Res Corp, NY, 65-; Water Resources Inst, US Dept Interior, 66-68; Petrol Res Found, Joyce Found & W K Kellogg Found; consult, local industs, Ottawa Co, US Dept Energy & Nuclear Energy Inst; chmn, Mich Low Level Radioactive Waste, Bd Govs. *Mem:* Am Chem Soc; Inst Environ Sci; Nat Sci Teachers Asn; AAAS; Am Nuclear Soc. *Res:* Stereochemistry of transition metal complexes; photochemistry; energy sources; communication of risk. *Mailing Add:* Dept Chem Hope Col Holland MI 49422-9000. *Fax:* 616-395-7118; *E-Mail:* williams@hope.edu

**WILLIAMS, DONALD J,** SPACE PHYSICS, SPACE PLASMA PHYSICS. *Current Pos:* prin staff physicist, 82-89, dir, 90-96, CHIEF SCIENTIST, MILTON S EISENHOWER RES & TECHNOL DEVELOP CTR, APPL PHYSICS LAB, JOHNS HOPKINS UNIV, 96- *Personal Data:* b Fitchburg, Mass, Dec 25, 33; m 53, Priscilla M Gagnon; c Steven J, Craig M & Eino S. *Educ:* Yale Univ, BS, 55, MS, 58, PhD(nuclear physics), 62. *Honors & Awards:* Leigh Page Mem Prize, Yale Univ, 58; Nat Oceanic & Atmospheric Admin Res & Achievement Award, 74. *Prof Exp:* Sr staff physicist, Appl Physics Lab, Johns Hopkins Univ, 61-65; sect head auroral & trapped radiation, Goddard Space Flight Ctr, NASA, 65-68, head, Particle Physics Sect, 68-69, head, Particle Physics Br, 69-70; dir, Space Environ Lab, Environ Res Labs, Nat Oceanic & Atmospheric Admin, 70-82. *Concurrent Pos:* Prin investr, several satellite experiments incl Int Sun Earth Explorer Prog, Galileo Prog & ISTP Prog, NASA; pres, Int Asn Geomagnetism & Aeronomy, 91-95. *Mem:* Fel Am Geophys Union; Am Phys Soc; Int Asn Geomagnetism & Aeronomy (pres). *Res:* Planetary magnetospheres; earth's trapped particle population and magnetic field configuration; solar flares and cosmic rays; interplanetary physics; interaction of interplanetary medium with Earth's environment; space plasma instabilities; published numerous papers in professional journals; editor of two books; co-author of book on Quantitative Aspects of Magnetospheric Physics. *Mailing Add:* Appl Physics Lab Johns Hopkins Univ Johns Hopkins Rd Laurel MD 20707. *Fax:* 301-953-6904; *E-Mail:* djw@aplcomm.jhuapl.edu

**WILLIAMS, DONALD ROBERT,** ORGANIC CHEMISTRY, POLYMER CHEMISTRY. *Current Pos:* res chemist plastics, 78-87, PLASTICS PLANT DEVELOP CHEMIST, ROHM & HAAS CO, 87- *Personal Data:* b Morristown, NJ, June 12, 48; m 70; c 3. *Educ:* Brown Univ, ScBChem, 70; Mass Inst Technol, ScM, 72; Colo State Univ, PhD(chem), 78. *Prof Exp:* Res chemist dent polymers, Kendall Co, 72-74. *Res:* Asymmetric synthesis; polymer research (continuous flow, emulsion polymerizations, extrusion). *Mailing Add:* 426 Merion Dr Newton PA 18940-1649

**WILLIAMS, DONALD SPENCER,** NETWORK DESIGN. *Current Pos:* CHIEF ENGR, SPACE & DEFENSE DIV, TRW INC, 80- *Personal Data:* b Pasadena, Calif, May 28, 39. *Educ:* Harvey Mudd Col, BS; Carnegie-Mellon Univ, MS, PhD(comput sci). *Prof Exp:* Supv, Learning Res & Develop Ctr, Univ Pittsburgh, 65-67; consult, 67-69; staff engr, Comput Systs Div, RCA Corp, 69-72; prin investr, Jet Propulsion Lab, Calif Inst Technol, 72-80. *Mem:* AAAS; Asn Comput Mach; Audio Eng Soc; Nat Fire Protection Asn; Inst Elec & Electronics Engrs; Soc Motion Picture & TV Engrs. *Res:* Design and management of computer centers, national communications facilities, voice and data, and conference facilities; network design; man-machine communications; robotics and theater operations. *Mailing Add:* PO Box 40700 Pasadena CA 91114

**WILLIAMS, DONNA J,** COMPUTER SCIENCES. *Current Pos:* instr math & comput sci, 81-83, asst prof, 89-93, ASSOC PROF COMPUT SCI, DEPT MATH & COMPUT SCI, STETSON UNIV, 93- *Personal Data:* b Lakeland, Fla, Dec 6, 41. *Educ:* Harding Univ, BS, 63; Univ Fla, MA, 66; Univ Cent Fla, PhD(comput sci), 89. *Prof Exp:* Sci programmer, Martin Marietta, 63-64; res mathematician, Denver Res Inst, 65-67; instr comput sci, Rollins Col, 84-85. *Concurrent Pos:* Fulbright scholar, Teachers Col Freeburg, Ger, 95-96. *Mem:* Asn Comput Mach; Inst Elec & Electronics Engrs Comput Soc. *Mailing Add:* Dept Math & Comput Sci Stetson Univ 421 N Woodland Blvd Unit 8330 De Land FL 32720. *E-Mail:* donna.williams@stetson.edu

**WILLIAMS, DOUGLAS EDWARD,** HEMATOLOGY. *Current Pos:* Vpres & dir biol sci, 92-94, SR VPRES DISCOVERY RES, IMMUNEX CORP, 94- *Educ:* State Univ NY, Buffalo, PhD, 84. *Res:* Hematology. *Mailing Add:* Sr Vpres Discovery Res Immunex Corp 51 University St Seattle WA 98101

**WILLIAMS, DOUGLAS FRANCIS,** GEOLOGICAL OCEANOGRAPHY. *Current Pos:* asst prof, 77-85, PROF GEOL & MARINE SCI & CHMN DEPT GEOL, UNIV SC, 85- *Personal Data:* b Long Branch, NJ, Dec 14, 48; m 75. *Educ:* Brown Univ, BA, 71; Univ RI, PhD(oceanog), 76. *Prof Exp:* Res assoc geochem, Dept Geol Sci, Brown Univ, 76-77. *Mem:* Am Asn Petrol Geologists; Am Geophys Union; Geol Soc Am; Sigma Xi. *Res:* Marine micropaleontology; stable isotope geochemistry of carbonates; paleoclimatology. *Mailing Add:* Dept Geol Univ SC Columbia SC 29208

**WILLIAMS, DUANE ALWIN,** CHEMICAL ENGINEERING. *Current Pos:* RETIRED. *Personal Data:* b Marshfield, Wis, Apr 6, 35; m 92, Darlene M Poquette; c Gary, Jeffrey, Michael & Mark. *Educ:* Univ Wis-Madison, BS, 56, MS, 57, PhD(chem eng), 61. *Prof Exp:* Tech serv engr lubricant additives, Enjay Labs, 57-58; fel, Univ Wis-Madison, 61-62; res chem engr pulp & paper, Kimberly-Clark Corp, 62-64; sr res engr, analytical mgr & dir explor res, Rocket Res Corp, 64-71; sr res scientist pulp & paper, Kimberly-Clark Corp, 71-76, mgr, 76-84, dir res & develop, 84-91, dir major proj, 91-93. *Mem:* Am Inst Chem Engrs. *Res:* Solid waste management; reaction control systems and gas generation systems for aerospace and commercial applications; pulp mill unit operations; thermal radiation; solar energy utilization; consumer products research and development. *Mailing Add:* 1301 N Mayer St Menasha WI 54952-1404

**WILLIAMS, DUDLEY,** MOLECULAR SPECTROSCOPY, PLANETARY ATMOSPHERES. *Current Pos:* regent's distinguished prof, 64-82, EMER PROF PHYSICS, KANS STATE UNIV, 82- *Personal Data:* b Covington, Ga, Apr 12, 12; m 37; c 2. *Educ:* Univ NC, AB, 33, MA, 34, PhD(physics), 36. *Prof Exp:* Instr physics, Univ Fla, 36-38, asst prof phys sci, 38-41; staff mem, Radiation Lab, Mass Inst Technol, 41-43; asst prof physics, Univ Okla,

43-44; staff mem, Los Alamos Sci Lab, Calif, 44-46; from assoc prof to prof physics, Ohio State Univ, 46-63, actg chmn dept, 52-53 & 58-59; prof & head dept, NC State Univ, 63-64. *Concurrent Pos:* Guggenheim fel, Univ Amsterdam & Oxford Univ, 56; NSF sr fel, Univ Liege, 61-62. *Mem:* Fel Am Phys Soc; fel Optical Soc Am (vpres, 77, pres-elect, 78, pres, 79); Am Asn Physics Teachers. *Res:* Infrared spectroscopy; microwave transmission; mass spectroscopy; nuclear and atmospheric physics; planetary atmospheres; determination of nuclear magnet moments. *Mailing Add:* 120 Longview Dr Manhattan KS 66502

**WILLIAMS, E(DGAR) P,** MISSILE DESIGN, HYPERSONIC AERODYNAMICS. *Current Pos:* RETIRED. *Personal Data:* b Pierpont, Ohio, Aug 17, 18; div, Esther Elliott; c Katherine, Ruth, Carol & Edna. *Educ:* Oberlin Col, AB, 40; Calif Inst Technol, MS & AeroEng, 42. *Prof Exp:* Asst wind tunnel, Calif Inst Technol, 40-42; aerodyn engr, Douglas Aircraft Co, 42-48; head missiles aerodyn, Rand Corp, 49-55, head aerodyn, 56-63; chief, Aeromech Br, McDonnell Douglas Astronaut Co, 63, chief engr, Aero-Thermodyn Dept, 64-66, staff asst to dir advan missile & reentry systs, 67-72, sr staff engr, 72-74; engr, CDI Corp, 77-78; design specialist, Pomona Div, Gen Dynamics, 78-84; engr specialist, B-2 Div, Northrop Corp, 84-93. *Concurrent Pos:* Lectr, Univ Calif, Los Angeles, 56-58. *Mem:* Assoc fel Am Inst Aeronaut & Astronaut; Sigma Xi. *Res:* Aerodynamics, particularly hypersonic aerodynamics, glide and reentry vehicles. *Mailing Add:* 6721 Cory Dr Huntington Beach CA 92647

**WILLIAMS, EBENEZER DAVID, JR,** TEXTILE CHEMISTRY. *Current Pos:* from res chemist to sr res chemist, E I Du Pont de Nemours & Co, Inc, 52-63, tech supvr, 63-66, res assoc, 66-74, sr res fel, 86, Du Pont fel fibers, Textile Res Lab, 88-92, CONSULT, DUPONT FIBERS, 93- *Personal Data:* b Nanticoke, Pa, June 30, 27; m 54; Florence L Meshkov; c Susan L. *Educ:* Swarthmore Col, AB, 47; Univ Pa, MA, 49, PhD(org chem), 52. *Prof Exp:* Asst instr chem, Univ Pa, 47-52. *Mem:* Am Chem Soc; Sigma Xi; Am Asn Advan Tension Control; Fiber Soc. *Res:* Polymer chemistry; synthetic textiles; mechanism of dyeing; dyeing technology of synthetic fibers. *Mailing Add:* 820 Summerset Dr Hockessin DE 19707

**WILLIAMS, EDDIE ROBERT,** MATHEMATICS. *Current Pos:* ASST PROF MATH, NORTHERN ILL UNIV, 70-, SR VPRES FINANCE & FACIL, 96- *Personal Data:* b Chicago, Ill, Jan 6, 45; m 69, King; c Karen (Baker), Craig D & Evan J. *Educ:* Ottawa Univ, BA, 66; Columbia Univ, PhD(math), 71. *Prof Exp:* Instr math, Intensive Summer Studies Prog, Columbia Univ, 70. *Concurrent Pos:* Asst to vpres acad affairs, San Diego State Univ. *Mem:* NY Acad Sci; Am Math Soc. *Res:* Pure mathematics; several complex variable theory; mathematics education; mathematics for the disadvantaged student. *Mailing Add:* Div Finance & Facil Northern Ill Univ Lowden Hall 109 De Kalb IL 60115. *Fax:* 815-753-1950; *E-Mail:* ewilliam@niu.edu

**WILLIAMS, EDMOND BRADY,** BIOCHEMISTRY, ORGANIC CHEMISTRY. *Current Pos:* ASSOC PROF CHEM, COL ST CATHERINE, 80-, CHAIR, 90- *Personal Data:* b Charlotte, NC, Aug 12, 43; m 67; c 2. *Educ:* Duke Univ, BS, 65; Univ NC, Chapel Hill, PhD(org chem), 70. *Prof Exp:* NIH fel microbiol, Med Ctr, Univ Calif, San Francisco, 70-72; fel chem, Univ Ariz, 72-73; instr, Baylor Univ, 73-74; asst prof chem, Univ Wis-Oshkosh, 74-80. *Mem:* Am Chem Soc; Sigma Xi; AAAS. *Res:* Synthesis of peptides; protein isolation and modification; enzyme kinetics. *Mailing Add:* 1985 Palace Ave St Paul MN 55105-1731

**WILLIAMS, EDWARD ASTON,** PLASMA PHYSICS, INERTIAL CONFINEMENT FUSION. *Current Pos:* PHYSICIST, LAWRENCE LIVERMORE LAB, 83- *Personal Data:* b UK, Oct 20, 47; m, Marlene Noble. *Educ:* Cambridge Univ, BA, 68; Princeton Univ, PhD(physics), 73. *Prof Exp:* Res assoc, Univ Colo, 73-75; mem, Inst Advan Study, Princeton, NJ, 75-77; scientist, Univ Rochester, 77-83. *Mem:* Fel Am Phys Soc; Am Asn Physics Teachers. *Res:* Plasma physics interactions. *Mailing Add:* L472 LLNL UCL Box 5508 Livermore CA 94550. *Fax:* 510-423-9969; *E-Mail:* williams@icf.llnl.gov

**WILLIAMS, EDWARD JAMES,** biopharmaceutics, pharmacokinetics, for more information see previous edition

**WILLIAMS, EDWIN BRUCE,** PHYTOPATHOLOGY. *Current Pos:* RETIRED. *Personal Data:* b Ladoga, Ind, Nov 3, 18; m 40; c 1. *Educ:* Wabash Col, AB, 50; Purdue Univ, MS, 52, PhD(plant path), 54. *Prof Exp:* From asst prof to prof plant path, Purdue Univ, Lafayette, 54-84, plant pathologist, 54-84. *Mem:* Am Phytopath Soc; Am Pomol Soc. *Res:* Genetics of Venturia inaequalis; breeding apples for disease resistance. *Mailing Add:* 801 S 12th Lafayette IN 47907

**WILLIAMS, ELLEN D,** SURFACE STRUCTURE, SURFACE MASS TRANSPORT. *Current Pos:* Res assoc, Physics Dept, Univ Md, College Park, 81-83, from asst prof to assoc prof, 83-91, assoc prof, Inst Phys Sci & Technol, 90-91, PROF, PHYSICS DEPT & INST PHYS SCI & TECHNOL, UNIV MD, COLLEGE PARK, 91-, DIR, CHEM PHYSICS PROG, 93- *Personal Data:* b Oshkosh, Wis, Dec 5, 53; m 80, Neil Gehrels; c Thomas & Emily. *Educ:* Mich State Univ, BS, 76; Calif Inst Technol, PhD(chem), 82. *Honors & Awards:* Presidential Young Investr, NSF, 84; Young Investr Award, Off Naval Res, 86; Maria Goeppert Mayer Award, Am Phys Soc, 90. *Concurrent Pos:* Exec comt, Surface Sci Div, Am Vacuum Soc, 89-90; comt mem, Status Women Physics, Am Phys Soc, 90-92; mem at large, Exec Comt,

93-, Div Condensed Matter Physics, Am Phys Soc, 94- *Mem:* Fel Am Vacuum Soc; fel Am Phys Soc; Sigma Xi; Am Chem Soc. *Res:* Experimental studies of solid surfaces; determination of mechanism of surface mass transport; two-dimensional phase transition & equilibrium crystal shape; stability and formation of nanostructures; electromigration. *Mailing Add:* Dept Physics Univ Md College Park MD 20742. *Fax:* 301-314-9465

**WILLIAMS, ELMER LEE,** PHYSICAL CHEMISTRY. *Current Pos:* RETIRED. *Personal Data:* b Ironton, Ohio, Apr 14, 29; m 57, Mary A Schrader; c Mark E, Ann E (Huffman) & Kristofer K. *Educ:* Ohio Univ, BS, 51, MS, 55; Ind Univ, PhD(phys chem), 59. *Prof Exp:* Asst chem, Ind Univ, 55-58; develop engr, Sylvania Elec Prods Inc Div, Gen Tel & Electronics Corp, 58-60; phys chemist, Owens-Ill, Inc, 60-79; proj mgr, Midland-Ross Corp, 79-84; dir, Gas Chromatography/Mass Spectrometry Facil, Bowling Green State Univ, 86-96. *Concurrent Pos:* Consult, 84- *Mem:* Am Chem Soc. *Res:* Diffusion of ions and atoms in glass and molten silicates; oxygen of mass 18 work and tracer work in the solid state; semiconductors; gas lasers; gas discharge displays; propose, plan and manage research and development engineering projects in energy and glass furnace areas; gas chromatography/mass spectrometry analysis. *Mailing Add:* 3615 Maple Way Dr Toledo OH 43614

**WILLIAMS, EMMETT LEWIS,** SOLID STATE PHYSICS, SCANNING ELECTRON MICROSCOPY. *Current Pos:* CONSULT, 90- *Personal Data:* b Lynchburg, Va, June 6, 33; m 57, Mary Austin; c Deborah, Robert & Martha. *Educ:* Va Polytech Inst, BS, 56, MS, 62; Clemson Univ, PhD(mat eng), 66. *Prof Exp:* Assoc aircraft engr, Lockheed-Ga Co, 56-57; mat engr, Atomic Energy Div, Babcock & Wilcox Co, 57-59; asst prof metall eng, Va Polytech Inst, 59-64; res asst ceramic eng, Clemson Univ, 64-65; res scientist, Union Carbide Nuclear Corp, 65-66; prof physics, Bob Jones Univ, 66-79, chmn dept, 73-79; mat engr, Continental Tel Labs, 79-81; scientist, Lockheed-Ga Co, 81-90. *Concurrent Pos:* Consult, Inland Motors, 61-64; Leaders Am Sci, 66, Continental Tel Labs, 70-72, Polysci Corp & Electrotech Corp; ed, Creation Res Soc Quart, 83-88. *Mem:* Creation Res Soc (vpres, 72-83, pres, 93-); Sigma Xi. *Res:* Solid state, surface physics; thermodynamics; formation of limestone stalactites in laboratory; thermodynamics of living organisms; failure analysis of metallic structures; geomorphology. *Mailing Add:* 7312 Club Crest Dr Flowery Branch GA 30542-5590

**WILLIAMS, ERNEST EDWARD,** herpetology, ecology, for more information see previous edition

**WILLIAMS, ERNEST HERBERT, JR,** POPULATION BIOLOGY OF BUTTERFLIES, CHEMICAL ECOLOGY OF BUTTERFLIES. *Current Pos:* from asst prof to assoc prof, 84-94, PROF BIOL, HAMILTON COL, 94- *Personal Data:* b Washington, DC, Aug 24, 46; m 79, Sharon J Flynn; c Timothy K & Catherine A. *Educ:* Trinity Col, Conn, BS, 68; Princeton Univ, MA, 70, PhD(biol), 76. *Prof Exp:* Asst prof biol, Wellesley Col, 76-83. *Concurrent Pos:* Vis res specialist, Univ Calif, Davis, 80-81; vis assoc prof, Cornell Univ, 90; chmn, Environ Studies Prog, Hamilton Col, 93-94. *Mem:* Ecol Soc Am; Soc Study Evolution; Soc Conserv Biol; Lepidopterists Soc; Sigma Xi; Coun Undergrad Res. *Res:* Population biology of butterflies and chemical ecology of butterflies and their host plants; publications on butterflies and ecology for the general public. *Mailing Add:* Dept Biol Hamilton Col Clinton NY 13323. *E-Mail:* ewilliam@hamilton.edu

**WILLIAMS, EUGENE G,** GEOLOGY, MINERALOGY. *Current Pos:* instr, Pa State Univ, 54-55, res assoc, 56-57, from asst prof to prof, 57-85, EMER PROF GEOL, PA STATE UNIV, 85- *Personal Data:* b New Haven, Conn, June 9, 25; m 52; c 2. *Educ:* Lehigh Univ, BA, 50; Univ Ill, MS, 52; Pa State Univ, PhD, 57. *Prof Exp:* Instr geol, Kent State Univ, 52-53. *Mem:* Geol Soc Am; Am Asn Petrol Geol. *Res:* Stratigraphy and petrography of upper Paleozoic rocks of eastern United States. *Mailing Add:* 628 Outer Dr State College PA 16801

**WILLIAMS, EUGENE H(UGHES),** chemical engineering, for more information see previous edition

**WILLIAMS, EVAN THOMAS,** ANALYTICAL CHEMISTRY. *Current Pos:* vpres acad affairs, 92-95, PROF CHEM, LEWIS & CLARK COL, 92-, ASST TO PRES, 95- *Personal Data:* b New York, NY, May 17, 36; m 59, Lise Jacobsen; c Elisabeth C & John R. *Educ:* Williams Col, BA, 58; Mass Inst Technol, PhD(chem), 63. *Prof Exp:* Civil engr, Res Estab Riso, Roskilde, Denmark, 63-65; from asst prof to prof chem, Brooklyn Col, 65-92, chmn dept, 81-84, dean undergrad studies, 89-92. *Concurrent Pos:* Consult, Geosci Instruments Corp, 66-72; mem exec bd, New York City Coun Environ, 73-76; chmn, Brooklyn Col Fac Coun, 77-85; bd trustees, Packer Col Inst, 78-87; mem, Citizen's Adv Comt, Brooklyn Navy Yard Resource Recovery Plant, 81-92. *Mem:* AAAS; Am Chem Soc; Am Phys Soc; Sigma Xi. *Res:* Trace element analysis; environmental applications; proton-induced x-ray emission. *Mailing Add:* Lewis & Clark Col 0615 SW Palatine Hill Rd Portland OR 97219-7879. *E-Mail:* etw@lclark.edu

**WILLIAMS, F(ORD) CAMPBELL,** CHEMICAL ENGINEERING. *Current Pos:* vpres, 70-93, vpres technol, 80-89, CONSULT, NATRON CONSULTORIA E PROJECTOR SA, 93- *Personal Data:* b Nanaimo, BC, Dec 28, 21; m 55, Ileana H Zander; c Cristina W (Figueiredo) & Ronald. *Educ:* Univ BC, BASc, 43, MASc, 46; Univ Iowa, PhD(chem eng), 48. *Prof Exp:* Instr chem eng, Univ Iowa, 47-48; asst prof, Univ Calif, 48-52; prof chem eng & tech consult, Nat Petrol Coun, Brazil, 52-55; head prof & head res, Petroleo Brasileiro SA, 55-65; consult chem engr, Consult Indust Assoc, 65-70. *Concurrent Pos:* Dir, Alcomat-Cia Sucro Alcooleira de Mato Grosso, 93- *Mem:* Am Inst Chem Engrs; Sigma Xi. *Res:* Phase equilibria; extraction; petroleum process and product development; engineering design; process research; continuous fermentation. *Mailing Add:* Natron-Consultoria e Projetos S A Rua DOM Gerardo 42 7th Floor Rio de Janeiro Brazil. *Fax:* 55-21-253-3662

**WILLIAMS, FLOYD JAMES,** GEOLOGY. *Current Pos:* RETIRED. *Personal Data:* b Electra, Tex, Jan 9, 20; m 49, Betty Bray; c Susan & Bruce. *Educ:* Univ Calif, BS, 43; Colo Sch Mines, MS, 51; Columbia Univ, PhD(geol), 58. *Prof Exp:* Mining engr, Bradley Mining Co, Idaho, 43; mining engr, Idaho-Md Mines Corp, Calif, 46-47; explosives engr, Hercules Powder Co, 47-48; chief, Reconnaissance Sect, Salt Lake Explor Br, Div Raw Mat, USAEC, 52-54; geologist, Standard Oil Co, Calif, 56-58; assoc prof geol, Univ Redlands, 58-66; supvr spectrog, Kaiser Steel Corp, Calif, 66-72; head, Dept Geol, San Bernardino Valley Col, 72-76, assoc prof, 76-80, chmn, Div Sci, 80-95, prof geol, 80-95. *Concurrent Pos:* NSF fel & res assoc geol & geophys, Univ Calif, Berkeley, 63-64; consult geol, City of San Bernardino, Calif, 74- *Mem:* Geol Soc Am; AAAS; Am Geophys Union; Sigma Xi. *Res:* Criteria for active faults, earthquake prediction. *Mailing Add:* 130 Sunridge Way Redlands CA 92373

**WILLIAMS, FORMAN A(RTHUR),** COMBUSTION, FLUID DYNAMICS. *Current Pos:* PROF ENG PHYSICS & COMBUSTION, DEPT APPL MECH & ENG SCI, UNIV CALIF, SAN DIEGO, 89-, DIR CTR ENERGY & COMBUSTION RES, 91- *Personal Data:* b New Brunswick, NJ, Jan 12, 34; m 55, 78; c 6. *Educ:* Princeton Univ, BSE, 55; Calif Inst Technol, PhD(eng sci), 58. *Honors & Awards:* Silver Combustion Medal, Combustion Inst, 78; Bernard Lewis Gold Medal, Combustion Inst, 90. *Prof Exp:* Asst prof mech eng, Harvard Univ, 58-64; mem tech staff, Inst Defense Analysis, 63-64; from assoc prof to prof aerospace eng, Univ Calif, San Diego, 64-81; Robert H Goddard prof, Dept Mech & Aerospace Eng, Princeton Univ, 81-88. *Concurrent Pos:* NSF fel, Imp Col, Univ London, 62; Guggenheim fel, Univs Sydney & Madrid, 70-71; vis prof, Sydney Univ, 70, Univ Colo, 77, lectr, Assoc Physics, Univ Provence, Marseille, 77; Alexander von Humboldt US sr scientist award, 82. *Mem:* Nat Acad Eng; Am Phys Soc; fel Am Inst Aeronaut & Astronaut; Soc Indust & Appl Math; Combustion Inst; foreign corresp mem Nat Acad Eng Mex; Sigma Xi. *Res:* Aerothermochemistry; combustion theory; heat and mass transfer; fire research; mathematical methods. *Mailing Add:* Dept Appl Mech & Eng Sci Univ Calif San Diego La Jolla CA 92093-0310

**WILLIAMS, FRANCIS,** fisheries, biological oceanography, for more information see previous edition

**WILLIAMS, FRANK LYNN,** CHEMICAL ENGINEERING, CATALYSIS. *Current Pos:* DEAN ENG, UNIV ALASKA, 92- *Personal Data:* b Peoria, Ill, Oct 6, 45. *Educ:* Northwestern Univ, BS, 68; Stanford Univ, MS, 70, PhD(chem eng), 73. *Honors & Awards:* Kokes Award, NAm Catalysis Soc, 74. *Prof Exp:* Res engr catalysis, Gen Motors Res Labs, 72-77; asst prof chem eng, Univ NMex, 77-80, assoc prof, 80-92. *Concurrent Pos:* Consult, Sandia Nat Labs, 77- *Mem:* Am Inst Chem Engrs; Am Chem Soc; Am Vacuum Soc; NAm Catalysis Soc. *Res:* Methane recovery from coalbeds; heterogenous surface chemistry during catalytic reactions; in-situ energy production; methane recovery from coalbeds. *Mailing Add:* Univ Alaska 349 Duckering Fairbanks AK 99775-0001

**WILLIAMS, FRED DEVOE,** MICROBIOLOGY, EDUCATION. *Current Pos:* from asst prof to prof bact, 64-91, chmn, Dept Microbiol, 81-91, EMER PROF MICROBIOL, IOWA STATE UNIV, 91- *Personal Data:* b New York, NY, Dec 16, 36; div; c 3. *Educ:* Rutgers Univ, BA, 60, MS, 62, PhD(bact), 64. *Prof Exp:* Instr bact, Rutgers Univ, 63-64. *Concurrent Pos:* Consult, SC Comt High Educ, 88; chmn adv bd, Soil Technol Corp, 87-88. *Mem:* AAAS; Am Soc Microbiol; Sigma Xi. *Res:* Ecology of microorganisms and the function of extracellular polysaccharides; physiology and biochemistry of microbial behavior. *Mailing Add:* Condomminium Allende No 2 ESO Allende Y Bel Dominquez LaPaz 23000 Mexico

**WILLIAMS, FRED EUGENE,** FOOD INTAKE CONTROL, DENTAL EDUCATION. *Current Pos:* Asst prof, 72-77, ASSOC PROF PHYSIOL, BAYLOR COL DENT, 77- *Personal Data:* b Wichita Falls, Tex, Oct 23, 41; m 64; c 2. *Educ:* Arlington State Col, BS, 64; Baylor Univ, PhD(physiol), 72. *Mem:* Sigma Xi; AAAS; Am Physiol Soc; Am Asn Dental Schs. *Res:* Effects of liver denervation, hypothalamic lesions, hormones and other chemical agents on feeding behavior. *Mailing Add:* Baylor Col Dent 3302 Gaston Ave Dallas TX 75246-2098

**WILLIAMS, FREDERICK MCGEE,** QUANTITATIVE THEORETICAL & APPLIED ECOLOGY. *Current Pos:* ASSOC PROF BIOL, PA STATE UNIV, UNIVERSITY PARK, 70- *Personal Data:* b Washington, DC, Jan 10, 34; m, Marina Johns; c Kathryn, David, Elaine & Evan. *Educ:* Stanford Univ, AB, 55; Yale Univ, PhD(biol), 65. *Prof Exp:* Asst prof biol, Lehigh Univ, 63-64; from asst prof to assoc prof zool, Univ Minn, Minneapolis, 64-70. *Concurrent Pos:* NASA-Am Inst Biol Sci fel, 65-66; chmn, Grad Prog Ecol, Pa State Univ, 74-80; enological consult, Nittany Valley Winery, 84-89; chmn, Quant Ecol Option, Ecol Prog, Pa State Univ, 85; pres, Nittany EcoSysts Group Consult, 90-; impact consult, Pa Power & Light, 86-91. *Mem:* Am Soc Naturalists; AAAS; Ecol Soc Am; Am Soc Zool; Am Inst Biol Sci; Int Soc Ecol Model; Sigma Xi. *Res:* Theoretical population dynamics;

environmental impact consulting; statistics of environment impact; competition and predation; modelling fish populations; electronic biomonitoring; constructed wetlands for acid mine drainage remediation; modelling deep sea thermal vents. *Mailing Add:* Dept Biol Pa State Univ University Park PA 16802. *Fax:* 814-865-9131; *E-Mail:* fmw@psu.edu

**WILLIAMS, FREDERICK WALLACE,** ANALYTICAL CHEMISTRY. *Current Pos:* Nat Acad Sci-Nat Res Coun fel, 65-66, res chemist, 66-73, supv res chemist, 73-94, DIR NAVY TECHNOL CTR SAFETY & SURVIVABILITY, US NAVAL RES LAB, DC, 94- *Personal Data:* b Cumberland, Md, Sept 24, 39; m 64; c William, Jennie & Mary-Beth. *Educ:* Univ Ala, BS, 61, MSc, 63, PhD(chem), 65. *Honors & Awards:* E O Hulbert Award, US Naval Res Lab Sci & Eng, 81, E E O Award, 83, Navy Meritorious Award, 93. *Concurrent Pos:* Tech dir, USS Shadwell. *Mem:* AAAS; Am Chem Soc; Combustion Inst. *Res:* Fundamental mechanisms of combustion, fire safety, scaling and modeling. *Mailing Add:* 13408 Colwyn Rd Ft Washington MD 20022. *Fax:* 202-767-1716; *E-Mail:* fwilliams@ifd.nrl.navy. mil

**WILLIAMS, FREDRICK DAVID,** POLYMER CHEMISTRY, COMPUTER SCIENCES. *Current Pos:* asst prof, 65-69, ASSOC PROF CHEM, MICH TECHNOL UNIV, 69-, DIR, CTR TEACHING EXCELLENCE, 90- *Personal Data:* b Winnipeg, Man, Sept 1, 37; m 64; c 3. *Educ:* Univ Man, BSc, 59, MSc, 61, PhD(chem), 62. *Prof Exp:* Ital Govt res scholarship, Inst Indust Chem, Milan Polytech Inst, 62-63; res chemist, Allis-Chalmers Mfg Corp, 63-65. *Mem:* Am Chem Soc. *Res:* Polymer chemistry. *Mailing Add:* Dept Chem & Chem Eng Mich Technol Univ Houghton MI 49931

**WILLIAMS, G(EORGE) BRYMER,** CHEMICAL ENGINEERING. *Current Pos:* from asst prof to assoc prof chem eng, 48-56, PROF CHEM & METALL ENG, UNIV MICH, ANN ARBOR, 56- *Personal Data:* b Denver, Colo, Oct 17, 13; m 40; c 3. *Educ:* Univ Mich, BS, 36, PhD(chem eng), 49. *Prof Exp:* Chem engr, M W Kellogg Co, NY, 40-47. *Mem:* Am Chem Soc; fel Am Inst Chem Engrs; Chem Inst Can; Sigma Xi. *Res:* Process design; natural resource utilization; petroleum processing. *Mailing Add:* Dept Chem Eng Univ Mich Ann Arbor MI 48109-2136

**WILLIAMS, GARETH,** APPLIED MATHEMATICS. *Current Pos:* assoc prof, 73-76, PROF MATH, STETSON UNIV, 76- *Personal Data:* b Rhos, Wales, Apr 28, 37; US citizen; m 65; c 2. *Educ:* Univ Wales, BSc, 59, PhD(math), 62. *Prof Exp:* Asst prof math, Univ Fla, 62-65; from asst prof to assoc prof, Univ Denver, 65-73. *Mem:* Am Math Soc; Tensor Soc Gt Brit; Am Math Asn; Soc Indust & Appl Math. *Res:* Relativity; differential geometry; mathematical models; computer science; linear algebra. *Mailing Add:* Dept Math Stetson Univ 421 N Woodland Box 8345 De Land FL 32720-3777

**WILLIAMS, GARETH PIERCE,** PLANETARY ATMOSPHERES, METEOROLOGICAL MODELING. *Current Pos:* Res meteorologist, 64-74, SR RES SCIENTIST, GEOPHYS FLUID DYNAMICS LAB, NAT OCEANIC & ATMOSPHERIC ADMIN, 74- *Personal Data:* b Llandudno, Wales, Oct 16, 39; m 64; c 2. *Educ:* Univ Wales, BSc, 61, PhD(appl math), 64, DSc, 76. *Concurrent Pos:* Vis fel, Dept Appl Math & Theoret Physics, Cambridge Univ, UK, 79-80; vis prof, Geophys Fluid Dynamics Prog, Princeton Univ, 80-83; Comn Planetary Atmospheres, Int Asn Meteorol Atmospheric Physics, 83-90; vis fel, Japan Soc Prom Sci, 89. *Mem:* Fel Am Meteorol Soc. *Res:* Dynamics of planetary atmospheres, particular Earth and Jupiter; computer modeling of planetary atmospheres; theories for great red spot of Jupiter. *Mailing Add:* US Dept Agr Comm/NOAA Geophys Fluid Dynamics PO Box 308 Princeton NJ 08542

**WILLIAMS, GARY LYNN,** REPRODUCTIVE ENDOCRINOLOGY, REPRODUCTIVE PHYSIOLOGY. *Current Pos:* PROF PHYSIOL REPRODUCTION & GROWTH, AGR EXP STA, TEX A&M UNIV, 89-, FAC MEM, CTR ANIMAL BIOTECHNOL, INST BIOSCI & TECHNOL, 94-, ADJ PROF, TEX A&M UNIV, KINGSVILLE, 95- *Personal Data:* b Carlsbad, NMex, Feb 25, 50; m 80, Lorraine Zeller; c John R & Andrea L. *Educ:* NMex State Univ, BS, 72, MS, 74; Univ Ariz, PhD(animal physiol), 78. *Prof Exp:* From asst prof to assoc prof physiol & endocrinol, Dept Animal Sci, NDak State Univ, 78-84. *Mem:* Am Soc Animal Sci; Soc Study Reproduction; Endocrine Soc; Am Physiol Soc; AAAS; Found Biomed Res. *Res:* Reproductive endocrinology of the postpartum bovine; neuroendocrine-ovarian relationships; nutritional modulation of hypothalamo-hypophyseal-ovarian axis. *Mailing Add:* Tex A&M Univ Agr Res Sta HCR-2 Box 43C Beeville TX 78102

**WILLIAMS, GARY MURRAY,** PATHOLOGY, TOXICOLOGY. *Current Pos:* res assoc prof, 75-80, RES PROF PATH, NY MED COL, 80-; DIR MED SCI & CHIEF, DIV PATH & TOXICOL, AM HEALTH FOUND, 75- *Personal Data:* b Regina, Sask, May 7, 40; US citizen; m 66, Julia C Lundberg; c Walter, Jeffery & Ingrid. *Educ:* Washington & Jefferson Col, BA, 63; Univ Pittsburgh, MD, 67. *Honors & Awards:* Sheard-Sanford Award, Am Soc Clin Path, 67; Arnold J Lehman Award, Am Soc Toxicol, 82. *Prof Exp:* Instr path, Med Sch, Harvard Univ, 67-69; staff assoc, Nat Cancer Inst, 69-71; asst prof, Fels Res Inst & Med Sch, Temple Univ, 71-75. *Concurrent Pos:* From intern to resident path, Mass Gen Hosp, 67-69; Int Agency Res on Cancer res training fel, Wenner-Gren Inst, Stockholm, Sweden, 71-72. *Mem:* Am Asn Cancer Res; Soc Toxicol; Soc Toxicol Path. *Res:* Genetic, toxic and carcinogenic effects of chemicals, especially pharmaceuticals. *Mailing Add:* Am Health Found 1 Dana Rd Valhalla NY 10595. *Fax:* 914-592-3522; *E-Mail:* williamsgm@pol.net

**WILLIAMS, GENE R,** PLANT PHYSIOLOGY, PLANT BIOCHEMISTRY. *Current Pos:* asst prof, 65-68, ASSOC PROF BOT, IND UNIV, BLOOMINGTON, 68- *Personal Data:* b Yuba City, Calif, Nov 10, 32; m 54, 69; c 2. *Educ:* Univ Calif, BS, 57, MS, 59, PhD(plant physiol), 63. *Prof Exp:* Lectr bot, Univ Calif, 61-62; Am Cancer Soc fel biochem, Biol Div, Oak Ridge Nat Lab, 63-65. *Mem:* AAAS; Am Soc Plant Physiol. *Res:* Plant metabolism, protein and nucleic acid synthesis, amino acid activation and chloroplast development; effects of light on plant development. *Mailing Add:* Dept Biol Ind Univ Bloomington IN 47405

**WILLIAMS, GEORGE, JR,** BOTANY. *Current Pos:* PROF BIOL, SOUTHERN UNIV, BATON ROUGE, 63- *Personal Data:* b Benton, La, June 15, 31; m 57. *Educ:* Southern Univ, BS, 57; Univ NH, MS, 59, PhD(bot), 63. *Prof Exp:* Asst bot, Univ NH, 57-63. *Mem:* Am Soc Plant Physiol; Sigma Xi. *Res:* Plant growth as modified by light quality and chemical factors, particularly growth hormones. *Mailing Add:* 1340 Bayberry Ave Baton Rouge LA 70807

**WILLIAMS, GEORGE ABIAH,** SOLID STATE PHYSICS, NUCLEAR MAGNETIC RESONANCE. *Current Pos:* assoc prof, 64-70, assoc chmn dept, 74-83, PROF PHYSICS, UNIV UTAH, 70- *Personal Data:* b Brooklyn, NY, Apr 1, 31; div; c 3. *Educ:* Colgate Univ, BA, 52; Univ Ill, PhD, 56. *Prof Exp:* Res assoc physics, Stanford Univ, 56-59; mem tech staff, Bell Tel Labs, NJ, 59-63; vis asst prof physics, Cornell Univ, 63-64. *Concurrent Pos:* NSF res grant, 72-74; USAF Off Sci Res grant, 65-70; vis prof physics, Univ Minn, 79 & Univ Calif, Berkeley, 80. *Mem:* Am Phys Soc. *Res:* Wave propagation in solid state plasmas; plasma effects in solids; nuclear magnetic resonance and nuclear quadrupole resonance in amorphous semiconductors. *Mailing Add:* Dept Physics Univ Utah 201 J Fletcher Bldg Salt Lake City UT 84112. *Fax:* 801-581-4246

**WILLIAMS, GEORGE CHRISTOPHER,** ZOOLOGY. *Current Pos:* assoc prof, 60-66, PROF BIOL SCI, STATE UNIV NY, STONY BROOK, 66- *Personal Data:* b Charlotte, NC, May 12, 26; m 50; c 4. *Educ:* Univ Calif, Berkeley, AB, 49, MA, Los Angeles, 52, PhD, 55. *Hon Degrees:* ScD, Queen's Univ, Kingston, Ont, 95. *Honors & Awards:* Ecologist of the Year, Ecol Soc Am, 89; Elliot Award, Nat Acad Sci, 92. *Prof Exp:* From instr to asst prof natural sci, Mich State Univ, 55-60. *Concurrent Pos:* Adj prof, Queen's Univ, Kingston, Ont. *Mem:* Nat Acad Sci; Soc Study Evolution; Am Soc Ichthyol & Herpet; Am Soc Naturalists; Arctic Inst NAm; AAAS. *Res:* Evolution; marine ecology; ichthyology; animal behavior; population genetics. *Mailing Add:* 7 Yorktown Rd Setauket NY 11785

**WILLIAMS, GEORGE HARRY,** COMPUTER SCIENCE. *Current Pos:* PROF ELEC ENG & COMPUT SCI, UNION COL, 70- *Personal Data:* b Schenectady, NY, Nov 7, 42; m 67; c 1. *Educ:* Union Col, BSEE & BA, 65; Yale Univ, MS, 66, PhD(eng, appl sci), 70. *Concurrent Pos:* NSF res initiation grant, Union Col, 71-72; prin investr grant, NSF, 72-73. *Mem:* Inst Elec & Electronics Engrs; Asn Comput Mach; Sigma Xi. *Res:* Automata theory, logic design, computer-aided design and artificial intelligence. *Mailing Add:* Dept Elec Eng & Comput Sci Steinmetz Hall 210 Union Col Schenectady NY 12308

**WILLIAMS, GEORGE KENNETH,** MATHEMATICS. *Current Pos:* RETIRED. *Personal Data:* b Detroit, Mich, July 8, 32; m 54; c Kenna, Barbara, Terri & Scott. *Educ:* Univ Ky, BAE, 55, MA, 58; Univ Va, PhD(math), 64. *Prof Exp:* Teacher high sch, Mich, 55-56; asst prof math, James Madison Univ, 58-60 & Univ Notre Dame, 64-68; from assoc prof to prof, Rhodes Col, 68-97. *Mem:* Am Math Soc; Math Asn Am. *Res:* Complex analysis; topology. *Mailing Add:* Dept Math Rhodes Col 2000 N Pkwy Memphis TN 38112

**WILLIAMS, GEORGE NATHANIEL,** INORGANIC CHEMISTRY, ORGANIC CHEMISTRY. *Current Pos:* instr, 72-75, ASST PROF CHEM, SAVANNAH STATE COL, 78- *Personal Data:* b Kingsland, Ga, May 17, 47; m 70; c 1. *Educ:* Savannah State Col, BS, 69; Tuskegee Inst, MS, 72; Howard Univ, PhD(inorg chem), 78. *Prof Exp:* Lab technician chem, Union Camp Corp, 70. *Mem:* Am Chem Soc; Am Inst Chemists. *Res:* Metal incorporation and the anation reactions of porphyrins. *Mailing Add:* Savannah State Univ Box 20149 Savannah GA 31404

**WILLIAMS, GEORGE RAINEY,** MEDICINE. *Current Pos:* from asst prof to prof, Okla Univ, 58-96, chmn, Dept Surg, 74-96, interim dean, Col Med, 81-82, 85-86 & 88-89, CLIN PROF SURG, UNIV OKLA, 96- *Personal Data:* b Atlanta, Ga, Oct 25, 26; m 50; c 4. *Educ:* Northwestern Univ, BS, 47, BMed, 50, MD, 51. *Prof Exp:* Instr surg, Johns Hopkins Hosp, 57-58. *Concurrent Pos:* Markle scholar, 60. *Mem:* Soc Univ Surg; Am Surg Asn; Soc Vascular Surg; Am Asn Thoracic Surg; Am Col Surgeons. *Mailing Add:* Dept Surg Health Sci Ctr Univ Okla PO Box 26307 Oklahoma City OK 73126

**WILLIAMS, GEORGE RONALD,** BIOCHEMISTRY. *Current Pos:* asst prof, Banting & Best Dept Med Res, Univ Toronto, 56-61, assoc prof biochem, 61-66, prof, 66-93, chmn dept, 70-77, chmn, Div Life Sci, 78-83, prin, Scarborough Campus, 84-89, EMER PROF BIOCHEM, UNIV TORONTO, 93- *Personal Data:* b Liverpool, Eng, Jan 4, 28; Can citizen; m 52; c 3. *Educ:* Univ Liverpool, PhD(biochem), 51, DSc, 69. *Prof Exp:* Worshipful Co Goldsmith's traveling fel, Banting & Best Dept Med Res, Univ Toronto, 52-53; res assoc, Johnson Found Med Biophys, Univ Pa, 53-55; Med Res Coun res assoc path, Oxford Univ, 55-56. *Concurrent Pos:* Vis prof geochem, Lamont-Doherty Geol Observ, Columbia Univ, 77-78; vis prof biochem, Univ

Victoria, 89-90. *Mem:* Can Biochem Soc (pres, 71-72); fel Royal Soc Can. *Res:* Geobiochemistry; environmental homeostasis; control systems in biochemical and geochemical reaction networks. *Mailing Add:* 15 Bournville Dr West Hill ON M1C 1E3 Can

**WILLIAMS, GEORGE W,** BIOSTATISTICS. *Current Pos:* VPRES, BIOSTATIST & RES INFO MGT, MERCK RES LABS, WEST POINT, PA, 92- *Personal Data:* b Nashville, Tenn, Oct 31, 46; m, Wanda Mead; c Alec, Stacy & Carol. *Educ:* Bucknell Univ, BS, 68; George Washington Univ, MA, 70; Univ NC, PhD(biostatist), 72. *Prof Exp:* From asst prof to prof biostatist, Univ Mich, Ann Arbor, 72-80. *Concurrent Pos:* Chmn, Dept Biostatist, Cleveland Clin, Cleveland, Ohio, 80-92. *Mem:* Soc Clin Trials; Am Statist Asn; Biomet Soc; Soc Epidemiol Res. *Res:* Clinical trials; statistical methods in epidemiology. *Mailing Add:* 4918 Fawn Ct Doylestown PA 18901. *Fax:* 610-397-2788; *E-Mail:* george_williams@maruk.com

**WILLIAMS, GERALD ALBERT,** MEDICAL RESEARCH, ENDOCRINOLOGY. *Current Pos:* from asst prof to prof, 59-86, EMER PROF MED, UNIV ILL COL MED, 86- *Personal Data:* b Plankinton, SDak, Apr 1, 21; m 50, Dorothy Burks; c Jeffrey, Douglas & Jonathan. *Educ:* SDak State Col, BS, 45; George Washington Univ, MD, 49. *Prof Exp:* Instr med, Sch Med, Univ Va, 57-59. *Concurrent Pos:* Chief nuclear med serv & endocrinol sect, Vet Admin West Side Hosp, Chicago, 59-86; attend physician, Univ Ill Hosp, 59-86, chief endocrinol, 67-86; fac mem, AOA, student selection, 78-86. *Mem:* Am Fedn Clin Res; fel Am Col Physicians; Endocrine Soc; Soc Exp Biol & Med; Cent Soc Clin Res. *Res:* Parathyroid physiology; calcium metabolism; thyroid disorders. *Mailing Add:* Rte 1 PO Box 136A Keezletown VA 22832

**WILLIAMS, GERALD D,** RADIOLOGY, MAGNETIC RESONANCE. *Current Pos:* Res assoc, Dept Radiol, 86-92, FAC RESEARCHER MAGNETIC RESONANCE MED, PA STATE UNIV, M S HERSHEY MED CTR, 92- *Personal Data:* b New York, NY, Sept 27, 55; m 90, Jessica Ying; c 7. *Educ:* Brooklyn Col, BS, 77; Univ Va, PhD(chem), 86. *Mem:* Int Soc Magnetic Resonance Med; Am Chem Soc. *Res:* Radiology; magnetic resonance applied to medicine. *Mailing Add:* Dept Radiol Pa State Univ M S Hershey Med Ctr PO Box 850 Hershey PA 17033

**WILLIAMS, GLEN NORDYKE,** COMPUTER SCIENCE, CIVIL ENGINEERING. *Current Pos:* from asst prof to assoc prof, 69-87, PROF COMPUT SCI, TEX A&M UNIV, 87- *Personal Data:* b Port Arthur, Tex, Nov 15, 38; m 60; c 5. *Educ:* Tex A&M Univ, BS, 60, MEng, 61, PhD(civil eng), 65. *Prof Exp:* Systs engr, IBM Corp, 65. *Mem:* Am Soc Civil Engrs; Inst Elec & Electronics Engrs; Asn Comput Mach. *Res:* Fluid networks; slope stability; numerical analysis; computer applications; information systems. *Mailing Add:* Comput Sci Dept MS 3112 Tex A&M Univ College Station TX 77843

**WILLIAMS, GRAHEME JOHN BRAMALD,** STRUCTURAL CHEMISTRY, CRYSTALLOGRAPHY. *Current Pos:* prod mgr, 81-86, vpres, 86-89, PRES, ENRAF-NONIUS SERV CO, 89-; CHEMIST, BROOKHAVEN NAT LAB, 81- *Personal Data:* b Auckland, NZ, Jan 8, 42; m 69; c 1. *Educ:* Univ Auckland, BSc, 66, MSc Hons, 67; Univ Alta, PhD(biochem), 72. *Prof Exp:* Fel chem, Univ Montreal, 72-73; res assoc chem, 73-78, assoc chemist, 78-80. *Mem:* Am Crystallog Asn; Am Chem Soc; Am Mineral Soc. *Res:* Application of crystallography to structural problems in chemistry and biochemistry, enzymes, drugs and metabolites; crystallographic technique, improved computational methods and instrumentation. *Mailing Add:* ENRAF-NONIUS Co 390 Central Ave Bohemia NY 11716

**WILLIAMS, GWYNNE,** squeeze casting to produce aluminum alloy & metal matrix composite products, systems approach to material & design trade-offs in product engineering, for more information see previous edition

**WILLIAMS, HAROLD,** GEOLOGY. *Current Pos:* from assoc prof to prof geol, 68-84, UNIV RES PROF, MEM UNIV NFLD, 84- *Personal Data:* b St John's, Nfld, Mar 14, 34; m 58; c 3. *Educ:* Mem Univ Nfld, BSc, 56, MSc, 58; Univ Toronto, PhD(geol), 61. *Honors & Awards:* Gov Gens Medal, 56; Past Pres Medal, Geol Asn Can, 76; R J W Douglas Medal, Can Soc Petrol Geologists, 81; Willet G Miller Medal, Royal Soc Can, 87; Logan Medal, Geol Asn Can, 88. *Prof Exp:* Res scientist, Geol Surv Can, Ont, 61-68. *Concurrent Pos:* Killam scholar & fel, 76-79. *Mem:* Royal Soc Can; Geol Soc Am; fel Geol Asn Can; Am Asn Petrol Geologists; Can Soc Petrol Geologists. *Res:* Regional geology; ophiolite suites; continental margins; Appalachian geology; tectonics of Atlantic border lands and North American continent. *Mailing Add:* Dept Earth Sci Mem Univ Nfld St John's NF A1B 3X5 Can. *Fax:* 709-737-2589

**WILLIAMS, HARRY EDWIN,** MECHANICAL ENGINEERING. *Current Pos:* assoc prof, 67-71, PROF ENG, HARVEY MUDD COL, 71- *Personal Data:* b Los Angeles, Calif, Mar 11, 30; m 55; c 4. *Educ:* Univ Santa Clara, BME, 51; Calif Inst Technol, MS, 52, PhD(mech eng), 56. *Prof Exp:* Fulbright scholar math, Univ Manchester, 56-57; res engr, Jet Propulsion Lab, Calif Inst Technol, 57-60; from asst prof to assoc prof eng, Harvey Mudd Col, 60-66; liaison scientist, Off Naval Res, London, 66-67. *Concurrent Pos:* Consult, Jet Propulsion Lab, Calif Inst Technol, 60-66 & 68-71 & Naval Weapons Ctr, China Lake, 72- *Mem:* Am Soc Mech Engrs. *Res:* Analysis of linear and elastic shells and thin rings. *Mailing Add:* Dept Eng Harvey Mudd Col 301 E 12th St Claremont CA 91711-5994

**WILLIAMS, HARRY THOMAS,** THEORETICAL PHYSICS. *Current Pos:* from asst prof to assoc prof, 74-83, PROF PHYSICS, WASHINGTON & LEE UNIV, 83- *Personal Data:* b Hampton, Va, July 22, 41; m 75; c 5. *Educ:* Univ Va, BS, 63, PhD(physics), 67. *Prof Exp:* Res assoc nuclear physics, Nat Bur Stand, 67-69; guest prof, Univ Erlangen-Nurenberg, 70; staff scientist, Kaman Sci Div, Kaman Sci Corp, 71-73. *Concurrent Pos:* Assoc dean col, Washington & Lee Univ, 86-89. *Mem:* Sigma Xi. *Res:* Effect of baryon resonance admixtures in nuclear wave function upon nuclear properties and reactions; CLEBSCH-Gordon algebra in SU2 and SU3. *Mailing Add:* Rte 6 Box 44 Lexington VA 24450. *Fax:* 540-463-8884; *E-Mail:* williams.ht@wlu.edu

**WILLIAMS, HEATHER,** NEUROETHOLOGY. *Current Pos:* asst prof, 88-94, ASSOC PROF BIOL, WILLIAMS COL, 94- *Personal Data:* b Spokane, Wash, July 27, 55; m 86, Patrick D Dunlavey; c Maria G & Alan P. *Educ:* Bowdoin Col, AB, 77; Rockefeller Univ, PhD, 85. *Honors & Awards:* MacArthur Found Fel, 93. *Prof Exp:* Watson fel, Hebrew Univ, Eilat, Israel, 77-78; asst prof, Rockefeller Univ Field Res Ctr, Millbrook, NY, 86-88. *Concurrent Pos:* Adj prof, Rockefeller Univ, 88-; mem, Course Setting Team, US Orienteering/World Championships, Harriman State Park, NY, 93. *Mem:* Soc Neurosci; Int Soc Neuroethology; Animal Behav Soc; Sigma Xi; Am Ornithol Union; Cooper Ornithol Soc. *Res:* Neuroethology; Zebra finches song organization; central control of song timing and organization; sexual dimorphism in song perception; kinship and song model salience; laterality; mechanisms of dialect maintenance. *Mailing Add:* Dept Biol Williams Col Williamstown MA 01267

**WILLIAMS, HENRY WARRINGTON,** ZOOLOGY, ANIMAL BEHAVIOR. *Current Pos:* Assoc prof, 64-70, chmn, Div Natural Sci & Math, 73-79, PROF & CHAIR BIOL, WESTMINSTER COL, MO, 70- *Personal Data:* b Dallas, Tex, July 10, 34; m 58; c 4. *Educ:* Southern Methodist Univ, BS, 55; Utah State Univ, MS, 61, PhD(behav), 66. *Concurrent Pos:* Vis prof ecol, Col Natural Resources, Utah State Univ, Logan, 78- *Mem:* AAAS; Animal Behav Soc; Am Ornith Union; Cooper Ornith Soc; Am Asn Univ Prof (pres, 67-68 & 74-75). *Res:* Investigations in the field of animal behavior with particular concern for sound communication in avian species. *Mailing Add:* Biol Dept Westminster Col 501 Westminster Ave Fulton MO 65251-1230

**WILLIAMS, HIBBARD E,** METABOLISM. *Current Pos:* dean, 80-92, PROF INTERNAL MED, SCH MED, UNIV CALIF, DAVIS, 80- *Personal Data:* b Utica, NY, Sept 28, 32; m 82, Sharon; c Robin & Hans. *Educ:* Cornell Univ, AB, 54, MD, 58. *Prof Exp:* Intern & asst resident med, Mass Gen Hosp, 58-60; clin assoc arthritis & metab dis & sr asst surgeon, NIH, 60-62; resident med, Mass Gen Hosp, 62-63; chief resident & teaching asst, Sch Med, Harvard Univ, 63-64, instr, 64-65; from asst prof to assoc prof, Sch Med, Univ Calif, San Francisco, 65-72, prof, 72-78; prof med & chmn dept, Cornell Med Col, 78-80. *Concurrent Pos:* Markle scholar, 68-73; chief med serv, San Francisco Gen Hosp, 71-78; physician-in-chief, NY Hosp, 78-80. *Mem:* Am Soc Clin Invest (sccy-treas); Asn Am Physicians; Am Fedn Clin Res; AAAS; fel Am Col Physicians. *Res:* Calcium oxalate renal stone disease; oxalate metabolism and transport. *Mailing Add:* Sch Med TB-150 Univ Calif Davis CA 95616

**WILLIAMS, HUGH COWIE,** MATHEMATICS, COMPUTER SCIENCE. *Current Pos:* ASSOC PROF COMPUT SCI, UNIV MAN, 70- *Personal Data:* b London, Ont, July 23, 43; m 67; c 1. *Educ:* Univ Waterloo, BSc, 66, Math, 67, PhD(math), 69. *Prof Exp:* Nat Res Coun Can fel, York Univ, 69-70. *Res:* Application of the computer to problems arising in the theory of numbers. *Mailing Add:* Dept Comput Sci Univ Man Winnipeg MB R3T 2N2 Can

**WILLIAMS, HUGH HARRISON,** EXPERIMENTAL HIGH ENERGY PHYSICS. *Current Pos:* from asst prof to assoc prof, 74-82, PROF PHYSICS, UNIV PA, 82- *Personal Data:* b Boston, Mass, Dec 4, 44; m 70; c 2. *Educ:* Haverford Col, BS, 66; Stanford Univ, PhD(physics), 72. *Prof Exp:* Res assoc physics, Brookhaven Nat Lab, 71-73, assoc physicist, 73-74. *Concurrent Pos:* Mem high energy physics adv panel, 80-84; mem, Fermilab Physics Adv Comt, 82-86, chmn, 84-86; chmn, SSC Detector Res & Develop Comt, 87-91; mem, SSC Policy Adv Comt, 90-; Alfred P Sloan fel. *Mem:* Am Phys Soc. *Res:* Experimental study of elementary particles, their nature and interactions, with particular emphasis on the study of weak interactions; high energy proton antiproton interactions. *Mailing Add:* 1236 Arwyn Lane Gladwyne PA 19035

**WILLIAMS, HULEN BROWN,** PHYSICAL CHEMISTRY. *Current Pos:* From instr to prof, La State Univ, 43-90, admin asst to dean, 52-56, dean, Col Chem & Physics, 68-82, HEAD, DEPT CHEM, LA STATE UNIV, BATON ROUGE, 56-, EMER PROF CHEM, 90- *Personal Data:* b Lauratown, Ark, Oct 8, 20; m 42, 71, Michaela B Loose; c James B & Virginia J. *Educ:* Hendrix Col, AB, 41; La State Univ, MS, 43, PhD(chem), 48. *Honors & Awards:* Coates Award, Am Chem Soc, 63. *Concurrent Pos:* Consult, chem indust, govt, legal prof & educ. *Mem:* Am Chem Soc. *Res:* Light scattering of latices; proteins; protein metal complexes; organic reaction mechanisms; geochemistry. *Mailing Add:* 470 Castle Kirk Dr Baton Rouge LA 70808-6011

**WILLIAMS, JACINTA B,** MOLECULAR BIOLOGY, PHARMACOLOGY. *Current Pos:* SR RES BIOCHEMIST, MERCK SHARP & DOHME LABS, 88- *Personal Data:* b New Orleans, La, Jan 29, 56. *Res:* Molecular biology; pharmacology. *Mailing Add:* Dept Pharmacol WP42-300 Merck Sharp & Dohme Labs Sunneytown Pike WP44C-2 West Point PA 19486

**WILLIAMS, JACK,** SCIENCE POLICY. *Current Pos:* DIR, OFF TECHNOL PARTNERSHIPS, NAT INST STAND & TECHNOL, 94-, DEP DIR TECHNOL SERVS, 97- *Personal Data:* b Brookline, Mass, Mar 7, 39; m 67, Penelope Ann Grimes; c Megan. *Educ:* Tufts Univ, BA, 60; Fletcher Sch Law & Diplomacy, MA, 61; Univ SAfrica, PhD(econs), 71. *Prof Exp:* Dir, Off Productivity, Technol & Innovation, Dept Com, 84-90, Off Technol & Policy, 90-94. *Concurrent Pos:* Bd mem, Fed Lab Consortium. *Res:* Government-industry research and development partnerships; export expansion through standards and conformity assessment. *Mailing Add:* Nat Inst Stand & Technol Dept Com Rte 270 Bldg 820 Gaithersburg MD 20899. *E-Mail:* jack.williams@nist.gov

**WILLIAMS, JACK A,** ORGANIC GEOCHEMISTRY. *Current Pos:* CHEMIST, RES CTR, AMOCO PROD CO, 57- *Personal Data:* b Wichita, Kans, June 29, 26; m 49; c 4. *Educ:* Univ Kans, AB, 50, PhD(org chem), 54. *Prof Exp:* Chemist, Stand Oil Co, Ind, 53-57. *Res:* Organic geochemistry of petroleum and associated sedimentary substances. *Mailing Add:* 7317 E 59th St Tulsa OK 74145

**WILLIAMS, JACK L R,** ORGANIC CHEMISTRY. *Current Pos:* RETIRED. *Personal Data:* b Namoa, Alta, Oct 25, 23; nat US; m 50; c 5. *Educ:* Univ Alta, BSc, 46; Univ Ill, PhD(org chem), 48. *Prof Exp:* Spec asst, Off Rubber Res, Univ Ill, 46-48; Du Pont fel, Univ Wis, 48-49; res chemist, Eastman Kodak Co, 49-55, from res assoc to sr res assoc, 55-68, sr lab head, 68- *Concurrent Pos:* Pres, Weiller & Williams Co Ltd. *Mem:* Am Chem Soc. *Res:* Organic synthesis; rubber chemistry; high pressure reactions; oxo synthesis; catalytic hydrogenation; high polymer chemistry; organic photochemistry; photochemistry of boron. *Mailing Add:* Box 16 Namao AB T0A 2N0 Can

**WILLIAMS, JACK MARVIN,** INORGANIC CHEMISTRY, STRUCTURAL CHEMISTRY. *Current Pos:* Resident res assoc neutron & x-ray diffraction analysis, 66-68, from asst chemist to chemist, 68-77, SR CHEMIST & GROUP LEADER, CHEM & MAT SCI DIV, ARGONNE NAT LAB, 77- *Personal Data:* b Delta, Colo, Sept 26, 38; m 58; c 3. *Educ:* Lewis & Clark Col, BS, 60; Wash State Univ, MS, 64, PhD(phys-inorg chem), 66. *Concurrent Pos:* Guest prof, Univ Copenhagen, Denmark, 80 & 85, Univ Mo, 80 & 81; chmn, Gordon Res Conf Inorg Chem, 80. *Mem:* Am Crystallog Asn; Am Chem Soc; Am Phys Soc; AAAS. *Res:* Inorganic chemistry and neutron and x-ray diffraction as applied to the elucidation of the nature of chemical bonding; synthesis and characterization of synthetic metals and superconductors; chemical bonding. *Mailing Add:* 4801 Montgomery Ave Downers Grove IL 60515

**WILLIAMS, JACK RUDOLPH,** SONAR & UNDERWATER ACOUSTICS, RADAR RESEARCH. *Current Pos:* pres, Diag Retrieval Systs Calif, Inc, 82-92, VPRES RES & TECHNOL, DIAG RETRIEVAL SYSTS, INC, 79- *Personal Data:* b Goldsboro, NC, Sept 24, 29; m 61, Najiya Moroz; c Turan. *Educ:* NC State Univ, BSEE, 56; Univ Calif, Los Angeles, MSEE, 67; Calif Coast Univ, PhD (eng). *Prof Exp:* Res engr, Naval Res Lab, 54-56; dept mgr, TRW, Inc & Space Technol Labs, 56-63; dir anti-submarine warfare progs, Interstate Electronics Corp, 63-79. *Concurrent Pos:* Mcm Frigate Study Comt, NATO Armaments Group, 81-84. *Mem:* Sr mem Inst Elec & Electronics Engrs; Acoust Soc Am; Soc Motion Picture & TV Engrs; Navy League; Naval War Col Found; Nat Security Indust Asn. *Res:* Research and equipment development in sonar and radar systems; statistical methods of signal processing; systems based on fourier and modern processing techniques; shallow underwater surveillance systems; numerous publications in these areas. *Mailing Add:* DRS Electronics Systs 138 Bauer Dr Oakland NJ 07436

**WILLIAMS, JAMES C(LIFFORD), III,** AEROSPACE ENGINEERING. *Current Pos:* head dept, 80-92, PROF AEROSPACE ENG, AUBURN UNIV, 80- *Personal Data:* b Ocala, Fla, Oct 11, 28; m 51, 92, Carol A Dougherty; c Sharon Ann & James Wiley. *Educ:* Va Polytech Inst, BS, 51, MS, 55; Univ Southern Calif, PhD(eng), 62. *Prof Exp:* Aeronaut res intern, Nat Adv Comt Aeronaut, 51; teaching fel fluid mech, Va Polytech Inst, 53-54; aeronaut engr, NAm Aviation Co, Inc, 54-57; res scientist, Univ Southern Calif, 57-62; prof aerospace eng, NC State Univ, 62-80, assoc head, Dept Mech & Aerospace Eng, 72-80. *Concurrent Pos:* Consult, Systs Corp Am, Calif, 58-, Tech Prod Div, Waste King Corp, 60-61, Marquardt Corp, 61-64, Guid & Control Div, Litton Systs, Inc, 62-64, Corning Glass Co, NC, 64-65, Missile & Space Systs Div, Douglas Aircraft Co, Calif, 65-66 & Northrop Space Lab, Ala, 66-72. *Mem:* Assoc fel Am Inst Aeronaut & Astronaut; Am Soc Mech Engrs; Am Soc Eng Educ. *Res:* Boundary layer theory including internal viscous flows; gas dynamics; magnetohydrodynamics; aerodynamics. *Mailing Add:* Dept Aerospace Eng Auburn Univ Auburn AL 36849-5338

**WILLIAMS, JAMES CARL,** ANIMAL PARASITOLOGY. *Current Pos:* From instr to assoc prof, 57-78, PROF VET PARASITOL, LA STATE UNIV, BATON ROUGE, 78- *Personal Data:* b Covington, La, 1935; m 63; c 4. *Educ:* Southeastern La Col, BS, 57; La State Univ, Baton Rouge, MS, 62; La State Univ Med Ctr, New Orleans, PhD(med parasitol), 69. *Honors & Awards:* Doyle Chambers Res Award, 93; Distinguished Vet Parasitologist Award, Am Asn Vet Parasitologists, 95. *Concurrent Pos:* Co-ed-in-chief, Vet Parasitol, 95- *Mem:* Am Asn Vet Parasitologists; World Asn Advan Vet Path; Am Soc Parasitol. *Res:* Epidemiology of parasitism in ruminants; chemotherapy and management control of parasitism in ruminants. *Mailing Add:* Dept Vet Sci La State Univ Baton Rouge LA 70803-6002. *Fax:* 504-388-0400; *E-Mail:* jwilli3@lsuvm.sncc.lsu.edu

**WILLIAMS, JAMES CASE,** METALLURGY, MATERIALS SCIENCE. *Current Pos:* GEN MGR, ENG MAT TECHNOL LABS, GEN ELEC AIRCRAFT ENGINES, 88- *Personal Data:* b Salina, Kans, Dec 7, 38; m 60, Joanne Rufener; c Teresa & Patrick. *Educ:* Univ Wash, BS, 62, MS, 64, PhD(metall eng), 68. *Honors & Awards:* Adams Award, Am Welding Soc, 79; Albert Sauveur Lectr, 83; Gold Medal, Am Soc Metals, 92; Leadership Award, Metall Soc, Am Inst Mining, Metall & Petrol Engrs, 93. *Prof Exp:* Res engr metall, Boeing Co, 62-68; mem tech staff, Rockwell Sci Ctr, 68-70, group leader, 70-73; prog mgr technol, Aerospace Group Staff, Rockwell Int, 73-75; pres, Mellon Inst, 81-83; from assoc prof to prof metall, Carnegie-Mellon Univ, 75-81, dean eng, 83-88. *Concurrent Pos:* Consult, USAF Mat Lab & Los Alamos Nat Lab, 75-, Westinghouse Co, 77-, Gen Elec Co, 81- & Hoeganaes Corp, 84-; adv, USAF Off Sci Res, 76-; chmn US deleg, Int Ti Conf, Moscow, 76; co-chmn, US deleg, Int Ti Conf, Kyoto, 80; comt mem, First Fusion Mat Panel, Int Energy Agency; chmn, Nat Mat Adv Bd, Pa State Univ; mem adv bd, Sch Eng, Univ Va; dir, Wheeling Pittsburgh Steel Co, 87-91; trustee, Ore Grad Inst Sci & Technol. *Mem:* Nat Acad Eng; Am Inst Mining, Metall & Petrol Engrs; Am Soc Metals Int. *Res:* Physical metallurgy of Ti alloys; phase transformations; fracture and fatigue; electron microscopy; strengthening mechanisms; microstructure especially property relationships, powder metallurgy, welding, materials processing, materials applications in turbine engines. *Mailing Add:* Gen Elec Aircraft Engines MDH85 Newman Way Cincinnati OH 45215. *Fax:* 513-243-3526; *E-Mail:* jimcwilliams@ae.ge.com

**WILLIAMS, JAMES D,** ELECTRICAL ENGINEERING, SOLID STATE PHYSICS. *Current Pos:* staff mem, Sandia Corp, 63-66, proj leader adv develop, 66-67, proj leader hybrid microcircuits, 67-68, proj leader semiconductor devices, 68-69, div supvr semiconductor circuits, 69-75, DIV SUPVR, INTRUSION DETECTION SYSTS, SANDIA CORP, 75- *Personal Data:* b Pratt, Kans, June 8, 32; m 56; c 4. *Educ:* Mass Inst Technol, BS & MS, 60; Purdue Univ, PhD(elec eng), 63. *Prof Exp:* Engr, Gen Radio Co, Mass, 57-59; asst elec eng, Mass Inst Technol, 59-60; instr, Purdue Univ, 60-63. *Concurrent Pos:* Instr, Franklin Inst, Boston, 59-60; assoc prof, Univ NMex, 67-68. *Mem:* Inst Elec & Electronics Engrs; Am Phys Soc; Am Soc Testing & Mat; Am Vacuum Soc; Sigma Xi. *Res:* Hybrid microcircuits; development of thin film processes and devices for application of components to hybrid microcircuits; development of semiconductor devices and integrated circuits for use in complex weapon systems; intrusion detection systems. *Mailing Add:* PO Box 5800 US 0765 Albuquerque NM 87185

**WILLIAMS, JAMES E,** NUTRITION. *Current Pos:* PROF NUTRIT & BEEF CATTLE STUDIES, UNIV MO, 80- *Personal Data:* b Moorefield, WVa, June 19, 49. *Res:* Nutrition. *Mailing Add:* Dept Animal Sci Univ Mo 115 Animal Sci Res Ctr Columbia MO 65211-0001

**WILLIAMS, JAMES EARL, JR,** PHYSICAL CHEMISTRY. *Current Pos:* OPERS DIR, DSSC, CARNEGIE MELLON UNIV, 91- *Personal Data:* b Freeport, Pa, June 1, 38; m 58, Judith Mussano; c Jacqueline, Jeri & James. *Educ:* Univ Pittsburgh, BS, 65, MS, 72. *Prof Exp:* Scientist chem, Aluminum Co Am, 65-73, sr scientist, 73-75, group leader chem, 73-79, sect head, 79-90. *Mem:* Am Chem Soc; Electrochem Soc; Aluminum Asn; Steel Struct Painting Coun; Sigma Xi; Fedn Socs Coating Technol. *Res:* Leading the development of understanding materials and processes for advanced data storage systems; magnetic recording substrates, media and wearlayers; recording head/media tribology; thin films, magnetic recording. *Mailing Add:* Carnegie Mellon Univ DSSC Pittsburgh PA 15213-3890. *Fax:* 412-268-3497

**WILLIAMS, JAMES G,** COMPUTER SCIENCES. *Current Pos:* MEM TECH STAFF, MITRE CORP, 79- *Personal Data:* b Atascedero, Calif, Nov 4, 44; m 66, 77, 85. *Educ:* Carleton Col, BA 66; Univ Calif, Berkeley, PhD(math), 71. *Prof Exp:* From asst prof to assoc prof, Bowling Green State Univ, 72-76. *Mem:* Am Math Soc; Asn Comput Sci; Asn Symbolic Logic. *Res:* Program verification including automated theorem proving, formal verification theory, development of formal logical systems and application-independent user-interface translation software; software development methodology; computer security. *Mailing Add:* Mitre Burlington Rd A128 Bedford MA 01730

**WILLIAMS, JAMES GERARD,** GEODYNAMICS, SOLAR SYSTEM DYNAMICS. *Current Pos:* RES SCIENTIST, JET PROPULSION LAB, CALIF, 69- *Personal Data:* b New Kensington, Pa, Apr 12, 41. *Educ:* Calif Inst Technol, BS, 63; Univ Calif, Los Angeles, PhD(planetary & space sci), 69. *Prof Exp:* Mem tech staff, NAm Rockwell, 62-68. *Mem:* Int Astron Union; Am Geophys Union; Am Astron Soc. *Res:* Lunar laser range data; orbit of moon; rotations of earth and moon; dynamical evolution of asteroid orbits; asteroid families; main belt morphology; planet crossing asteroids. *Mailing Add:* Jet Propulsion Lab MS 328-332 4800 Oak Grove Dr Pasadena CA 91109

**WILLIAMS, JAMES HENRY, JR,** AGRONOMY, PLANT BREEDING & GENETICS. *Current Pos:* from asst prof to prof, 52-85, EMER PROF AGRON, E CAMPUS, UNIV NEBR, LINCOLN, 85- *Personal Data:* b Los Angeles, Calif, July 14, 18; m 39, Mary Heard; c William G & Robert G. *Educ:* Ore State Col, BS, 49; Iowa State Col, MS, 50, PhD(agron), 52. *Honors & Awards:* Soybean Prod Award, Am Soybean Asn. *Prof Exp:* Res assoc, Iowa State Col, 49-52. *Mem:* Fel Am Soc Agron; Crop Sci Soc Am; Soc Econ Bot; AAAS; Coun Agr Sci & Technol; Sigma Xi. *Res:* Soybean breeding; established first soybean breeding project at Nebraska Agriculture Experimental Stations; developed soybean cultivars with emphasis on drought tolerance, response to irrigation and cultural practices. *Mailing Add:* 5800 Earl Dr Lincoln NE 68505-2321

**WILLIAMS, JAMES HENRY, JR,** MECHANICAL ENGINEERING. *Current Pos:* assoc prof, 70-80, PROF MECH ENG, MASS INST TECHNOL, 80-, PROF TEACHING EXCELLENCE, SCH ENG, 91- *Personal Data:* b Newport News, Va, Apr 4, 41; c 2. *Educ:* Mass Inst Technol, SB, 67, SM, 68; Univ Cambridge, PhD(mech eng), 70. *Honors & Awards:* Charles F Bailey Awards, Bronze, 61, Silver, 62, Gold, 63; Teetor Award, Soc Automotive Engrs, 74; Den Hartog Award, 81. *Prof Exp:* Apprentice machinist, Newport News Shipbuilding & Dry Dock Co, 60-61, apprentice designer, 61-65, mech designer, 65, sr design engr, 68-70. *Concurrent Pos:* NSF res initiation grant, Mass Inst Technol, 72-74, du Pont-Young fac grant, 72-73, Edgerton prof, 73-75; Charles F Hopewell fac fel, 93. *Res:* Applied mechanics and materials, shell theory; earthquake isolation research, nondestructive evaluation and composite materials. *Mailing Add:* Dept Mech Eng Rm 3-360 77 Massachusetts Ave Cambridge MA 02139

**WILLIAMS, JAMES HUTCHISON,** OBSTETRICS & GYNECOLOGY. *Current Pos:* From instr to assoc prof, 55-70, assoc dir, Inst Perinatal Studies, 60-64 & Ctr Perinatal Studies, 65-70, PROF OBSTET & GYNEC, OHIO STATE UNIV, 70-, ASSOC DEAN COL MED, 61- *Personal Data:* b Westerville, Ohio, Feb 20, 22; m 43; c 4. *Educ:* Otterbein Col, AB, 44; Ohio State Univ, MD, 46, MMSc, 52; Am Bd Obstet & Gynec, dipl. *Mem:* Fel Am Col Surg; fel Am Col Obstet & Gynec. *Res:* Perinatal morbidity and mortality; selection of medical students; medical student evaluation in education. *Mailing Add:* 320 Virgil Ct Irvine CA 92715-4053

**WILLIAMS, JAMES LOVON, JR,** weed science, plant physiology, for more information see previous edition

**WILLIAMS, JAMES MARVIN,** NUCLEAR & CHEMICAL ENGINEERING. *Current Pos:* div leader, Systs, Analysis & Assessment Div, 78-79, asst dir planning & analysis, 79-86, DEP DIR, INDUST APPLNS OFF, LOS ALAMOS NAT LAB, 86- *Personal Data:* b Denver, Colo, Apr 27, 34; m 61; c 2. *Educ:* Univ NMex, BS, 57, MS, 64. *Prof Exp:* Staff mem, Los Alamos Sci Lab, 60-69; chief, Systs Studies Br, Off Safeguards & Mat Mgt, US AEC, 69-72; group leader, Laser Div, Los Alamos Sci Lab, 72-74; asst dir develop & technol, Off Magnetic Fusion Energy, Dept Energy, 74-78. *Mem:* Am Nuclear Soc. *Res:* Development of fusion plasma heaters, magnets and materials; interdisciplinary policy research and analysis; technology assessment; energy systems modeling and economic analysis; strategic planning; technology transfer; economic development. *Mailing Add:* 2022 Valencia Dr Albuquerque NM 87125

**WILLIAMS, JAMES THOMAS,** MEDICINE. *Current Pos:* fel endocrinol, Howard Univ, 65-67, asst prof, 67-74, assoc prof, 74-85, PROF MED, HOWARD UNIV, 85- *Personal Data:* b Martinsville, Va, Nov 10, 33; m 62, Jacqueline C Shepard; c Lawrence D & Laurie C. *Educ:* Howard Univ, BS, 54, MD, 58; Am Bd Internal Med, dipl, 67, 74 & 80, cert endocrinol & metab, 72. *Prof Exp:* Intern, Philadelphia Gen Hosp, 58-59; resident internal med, DC Gen Hosp, 59-60 & Freedmen's Hosp, 60-62 & 64-65. *Mem:* Fel Am Col Physicians; Endocrine Soc; Am Diabetes Asn. *Res:* Clinical endocrinology and metabolic diseases. *Mailing Add:* Dept Med Howard Univ Hosp 2041 Georgia Ave NW Washington DC 20060. *Fax:* 202-865-3632

**WILLIAMS, JEAN PAUL,** analytical chemistry, for more information see previous edition

**WILLIAMS, JEFFREY F,** PARASITOLOGY, IMMUNOLOGY. *Current Pos:* from asst prof to assoc prof microbiol, 71-77, dean res vet med, 77-79, PROF MICROBIOL & PUB HEALTH ASST, MICH STATE UNIV, 77- *Personal Data:* b Bristol, Eng, Aug 28, 42; m 64. *Educ:* Univ Bristol, BVSc, 64; Univ Pa, PhD(parasitol), 68. *Prof Exp:* Parasitologist, Pan-Am Health Orgn, Buenos Aires, Arg, 68-71. *Concurrent Pos:* Dir, Sudan Proj on Collaborative Res on Trop Dis, 79- *Mem:* Brit Soc Immunol; Am Soc Parasitol; Royal Soc Trop Med; Am Soc Trop Med. *Res:* Mechanisms of resistance to helminth infections in domestic animals and man. *Mailing Add:* Dept Microbiol 178 Giltner Hall Mich State Univ East Lansing MI 48824-1101

**WILLIAMS, JEFFREY TAYLOR,** SYSTEMATIC ICHTHYOLOGY, BIOGEOGRAPHY. *Current Pos:* COLLECTION MGR, NAT MUS NATURAL HIST, SMITHSONIAN INST, 83- *Personal Data:* b Honolulu, Hawaii, Apr 10, 53; m 75, Karen Anderson; c Kendra N & Jenna C. *Educ:* Fla State Univ, BS, 75; Univ SAla, MS, 79; Univ Fla, PhD(zool), 86. *Concurrent Pos:* Adj prof, Collin Co Community Col, 90-93. *Mem:* AAAS; Am Soc Ichthyologists & Herpetologists; Sigma Xi; Soc Syst Biol. *Res:* Systematics, biogeography and biodiversity in marine ecosystems with emphasis on tropical marine fishes. *Mailing Add:* Div Fishes Mus Nat Hist Smithsonian Inst Washington DC 20560

**WILLIAMS, JEFFREY WALTER,** ENZYMOLOGY, PROTEIN CHEMISTRY. *Current Pos:* sr scientist, 85-87, DIR MFG, PROMEGA CORP, 87- *Personal Data:* b Monroe, Wis, Oct 4, 51; m 73; c 1. *Educ:* Univ Wis-Madison, BS, 73, PhD(pharmacol biochem), 77. *Prof Exp:* Postdoctoral fel biochem, Australian Nat Univ, 77-79; res fel chem, Univ Sussex, 79-80; asst prof med chem, Ohio State Univ, 80-85; sr scientist, Promega Corp, 85-87, dir mfg, 87-92. *Mem:* Am Soc Biochem & Molecular Biol; AAAS; Soc Ind Microbiol. *Res:* Mechanisms of enzymatic microbiol detoxification of toxic metals; enzymology of DNA modification. *Mailing Add:* Roche Molecular Syst 1080 US Hwy 202 Somerville NJ 08876

**WILLIAMS, JIMMIE LEWIS,** ENVIRONMENTAL AUTOMOTIVE EMISSIONS CONTROL TECHNOLOGY, ENVIRONMENTAL STATIONARY EMISSIONS CONTROL TECHNOLOGY. *Current Pos:* Sr res scientist, 83-89, res assoc, 89-94, TECH LEADER, CORNING INC, 91-, SR RES ASSOC CHEM, 94- *Personal Data:* b Indianola, Miss, June 3, 53. *Educ:* Jackson State Univ, BS, 75; Yale Univ, MS, 77; Univ Calif, Riverside, PhD(inorg chem), 83. *Mem:* Am Chem Soc; Am Ceramic Soc; Air & Waste Mgt Asn; Soc Automotive Engrs; fel Am Inst Chemists; Sigma Xi. *Res:* Automotive and stationary emissions control, the use of extruded honey ceramic subtrates as catalyst supports for the above applications and extended use for chemical process and refining industries; author of several publications; granted 9 US patents. *Mailing Add:* Corning Inc Sullivan Pk DV-19 Corning NY 14831-0001. *Fax:* 607-974-2172

**WILLIAMS, JIMMY CALVIN,** microbiology & biochemistry, infectious diseases, for more information see previous edition

**WILLIAMS, JOEL LAWSON,** POLYMER CHEMISTRY. *Current Pos:* HEAD, MAT SCI DEPT, BECTON DICKINSON RES CTR, RESEARCH TRIANGLE PARK, NC, 74-, HEAD, MAT RES DEPT. *Personal Data:* b Sarecta, NC, Nov 10, 41; m 62, Linda Farmer; c Joel L II & Jessica G. *Educ:* NC State Univ, BS, 65, MS, 67, PhD(polymer sci), 70. *Prof Exp:* Sr chemist polymer res, Camille Dreyfus Lab, Res Triangle Inst, 62-74. *Concurrent Pos:* Adj prof chem eng, NC State Univ, 72-, biomed eng, Duke Univ, 83- & Univ Utah, 89- *Mem:* Am Chem Soc; Soc Plastics Engrs; Soc Biomed. *Res:* Permeability and diffusion in membranes, polymer synthesis and characterization with special emphasis on the utilization of radiation chemistry as a tool for graft modification of polymeric substrates, ionic polymerization, high-energy irradiation applications, irradiation grafting and blood compatibility of polymers. *Mailing Add:* Becton Dickinson Res Ctr Box 12016 Research Triangle Park NC 27709

**WILLIAMS, JOEL MANN, JR,** POLYMER SCIENCE, FOAMS CRITICAL FLUID CLEANING. *Current Pos:* mem staff, 72-93, COMFORCE, LOS ALAMOS NAT LAB, 94- *Personal Data:* b Suffolk, Va, Apr 6, 40; m 62, Mary C Gregory; c Catherine R & Michael G. *Educ:* Col William & Mary, BS, 62; Northwestern Univ, Evanston, PhD(org chem), 66. *Honors & Awards:* Fed Lab Consortium Technol Transfer Award, 88. *Prof Exp:* NSF fel, Univ Minn, Minneapolis, 66-67; asst prof chem, 67-68; res chemist, Benger Lab, E I du Pont de Nemours & Co, Inc, Va, 68-72; consult, Gv Med Inc, Minn, 86-91, Shell Develop, Tex, 91-93. *Mem:* Sigma Xi. *Res:* Environmental chemistry associated with the disposal of energy related wastes; trace element release from coals, oil shales, uranium and their associated coal and coal wastes, especially trace elements of environmental concern; wastes; geothermal energy and uranium mill tailings; microcellular organic foams, deposition of organic films; supercritical fluid cleaning. *Mailing Add:* JMC Williams Consults 51 Zuni Los Alamos NM 87544

**WILLIAMS, JOEL QUITMAN,** PHYSICS. *Current Pos:* From asst prof to assoc prof, 46-49 & 51-70, prof, 70-83, EMER PROF PHYSICS, GA INST TECHNOL, 83- *Personal Data:* b Lake Charles, La, Mar 6, 22; m 47; c 2. *Educ:* Centenary Col, BS, 43; Ga Inst Technol, MS, 48; Duke Univ, PhD(physics), 52. *Mem:* Am Phys Soc; Sigma Xi. *Res:* Microwave spectroscopy. *Mailing Add:* 2792 Dover Rd Atlanta GA 30327

**WILLIAMS, JOHN A(RTHUR),** hydromechanics, civil engineering, for more information see previous edition

**WILLIAMS, JOHN ALBERT,** ASTRONOMY. *Current Pos:* ASSOC PROF PHYSICS, ALBION COL, 70- *Personal Data:* b Springfield, Ill, Mar 28, 37; m 59; c 2. *Educ:* Univ Mich, AB, 49; Univ Calif, Berkeley, PhD(astron), 63. *Prof Exp:* NSF fel, Univ Calif, Berkeley & Princeton Univ, 63-64; from instr to asst prof astron, Univ Mich, Ann Arbor, 64-70. *Mem:* AAAS; Am Astron Soc. *Res:* Photometry of astronomical objects; quantitative spectral classification; interstellar matter. *Mailing Add:* Dept Physics Albion Col Albion MI 49224

**WILLIAMS, JOHN ANDREW,** PHYSIOLOGY. *Current Pos:* PROF PHYSIOL & MED & CHMN, DEPT PHYSIOL, UNIV MICH, ANN ARBOR, 87- *Personal Data:* b Des Moines, Iowa, Aug 3, 41; m 65, Christa Smith; c Rachel & Matthew. *Educ:* Cent Wash State Col, BA, 63; Univ Wash, MD & PhD(physiol, biophys), 68. *Honors & Awards:* Hoffman La Roche Prize, 85. *Prof Exp:* Staff assoc, Clin Endocrinol Br, Nat Inst Arthritis & Metab Dis, 69-71; from asst prof to prof physiol, Univ Calif, San Francisco, 79-87. *Concurrent Pos:* NIH fel, Dept Pharmacol, Univ Utah, 68-69; Helen Hay Whitney Found fel, Univ Cambridge, 71-72; USPHS grants, Univ Calif, San Francisco, 73-88, Univ Mich, 88-; assoc dir, Cell Biol Res Lab, Mt Zion Hosp & Med Ctr, San Francisco, 79-; ed, Am J Physiol, 85-91; trustee, Friends Sch Detroit, 90-; counr, Am Physiol Soc, 96-98; assoc ed, J Clin Invest, 97- *Mem:* Endocrine Soc; Am Soc Cell Biol; Am Physiol Soc; Am Soc Clin Investr; Am Gastroenterol Asn; Am Pancreatic Asn. *Res:* Cellular physiology; regulation of function of the exocrine pancreas by hormones and neurotransmitters. *Mailing Add:* Dept Physiol Univ Mich Ann Arbor MI 48109. *Fax:* 313-936-8813; *E-Mail:* jawillms@umich.edu

**WILLIAMS, JOHN C,** zoology; deceased, see previous edition for last biography

**WILLIAMS, JOHN COLLINS, JR,** ORGANIC CHEMISTRY, PHYSICAL & THEORETICAL CHEMISTRY. *Current Pos:* from asst prof to assoc prof chem, 72-85, chair coun, 78-79, dept chair, 83-86 & 92-95, PROF, RI COL, 83- *Personal Data:* b Jackson, Tenn, Jan 19, 45; m 84, Jane Bodine; c Matthew, Camille & Sarah. *Educ:* Millsaps Col, BS, 67; Tulane Univ, PhD(chem), 72. *Prof Exp:* Instr chem, Sch Arts & Sci, Tulane Univ, 68-71. *Concurrent Pos:* Vis res assoc, La State Univ, 79-80; consult org synthesis, Scott Labs, Inc, 83-84; NSF PRF fel, Brown Univ, 83, 86, 87 & 88, vis prof, 86-87. *Mem:* Am Chem Soc; Sigma Xi. *Res:* Synthetic, physical and theoretical chemistry and cytotoxicity of organophosphorus heterocycles; polarography; educational approaches to introductory organic chemistry; organometallic chemistry; mastery learning. *Mailing Add:* Dept Phys Sci RI Col 600 Mt Pleasant Providence RI 02908-1924

**WILLIAMS, JOHN DELANE,** STATISTICS, EDUCATIONAL PSYCHOLOGY. *Current Pos:* from asst prof to assoc prof, 66-71, PROF STATIST, UNIV NDAK, 71- *Personal Data:* b Ordway, Colo, Oct 26, 38; m 80, Jole A Wells; c Diane, Brian & Delane. *Educ:* Univ Northern Colo, BA, 59, MA, 60, PhD(appl statist), 66; Fielding Inst, MA, 93, PhD(clin psychol), 94. *Honors & Awards:* Sigma Xi Award. *Prof Exp:* Instr math, Western Wyo Community Col, 62-65. *Concurrent Pos:* Statist consult, Proj Reclamation, 76-81; vis consult, Comput Ctr, Univ NDak, 72-82; psychologist, N Star Psychol Serv, 92- *Mem:* Am Statist Asn; Am Educ Res Asn; Am Psychol Asn; Sigma Xi. *Res:* Applied statistics in multiple linear regression; statistical application in educational psychology; life span development and gerontology. *Mailing Add:* Univ NDak PO Box 7189 Grand Forks ND 58202. *Fax:* 701-777-4392; *E-Mail:* jwilliams@plains.nodak.edu

**WILLIAMS, JOHN F, JR,** internal medicine, cardiology, for more information see previous edition

**WILLIAMS, JOHN FREDERICK,** CHEMISTRY. *Current Pos:* STATE CHEMIST & DIR LAB, GA DEPT AGR, 80- *Personal Data:* b York, SC, May 14, 23; m 45, 70, Katherine C Forehand; c John F, Frederick L, Dabney & Katherine. *Educ:* Univ SC, BS, 44; Clemson Univ, MS, 51; Univ Va, PhD(chem), 54. *Prof Exp:* Instr chem, Clemson Univ, 49-51; sr chemist analytical chem, Res Dept, Liggett & Myers Tobacco Co, 54-60, res supvr analytical chem, Res Dept, Liggett & Myers Inc, 60-80. *Mem:* Am Chem Soc; Coblentz Soc; Soc Appl Spectros; Asn Food & Drug Officials; Asn Off Analytical Chemists. *Res:* Development and application of chromatographic, spectrophotometric, automatic and classical methods of analysis in the study of natural products. *Mailing Add:* 1479 Leafmore Pl Decatur GA 30033. *Fax:* 404-656-9380

**WILLIAMS, JOHN PAUL,** INORGANIC CHEMISTRY, CHEMICAL EDUCATION. *Current Pos:* asst prof, 85-90, ASSOC PROF CHEM, MIAMI UNIV, HAMILTON, 90- *Personal Data:* b Laramie, Wyo, Aug 11, 46; m 67, Virginia Bruce; c Elizabeth J & Douglas L. *Educ:* Univ Wyo, BS, 69, MS, 70; Ohio State Univ, PhD(inorg chem), 75. *Prof Exp:* Fel inorg chem, Univ Wis, 75-76; mem staff chem, Univ Cincinnati, 76-77; mem staff inorg chem, Ind Univ-Purdue Univ, Indianapolis, 77-79; asst prof chem, Univ Cincinnati, 79-85. *Mem:* Am Chem Soc. *Res:* Hands-on pre-college science activities. *Mailing Add:* 8774 Constance Lane Cincinnati OH 45231. *Fax:* 513-863-1655; *E-Mail:* jpwilliams@mosler.ham.muohio.edu

**WILLIAMS, JOHN RODERICK,** ORGANIC CHEMISTRY, ORGANIC SYNTHESIS. *Current Pos:* from asst prof to assoc prof, 68-81, PROF ORG CHEM, TEMPLE UNIV, 81- *Personal Data:* b Birmingham, Eng, July 5, 40; m 74, Janice Karoglan; c Joanna B & Angela S. *Educ:* Univ Western Australia, BSc, 62; Univ NSW, PhD(org chem), 66. *Prof Exp:* Vis fel org photochem, NIH, 66-67; NIH fel & res assoc, Columbia Univ, 67-68. *Concurrent Pos:* Vis prof, State Univ Ghent, Belg, 81. *Mem:* Am Chem Soc; fel The Chem Soc. *Res:* Synthesis of natural products; synthesis of enzyme inhibitors; synthesis of affinity labels; new synthetic methods; photochemistry; marine and steroid chemistry. *Mailing Add:* 273 Winding Way Merion Station PA 19066-1225. *Fax:* 215-204-1532

**WILLIAMS, JOHN RUSSELL,** SURFACE CHEMISTRY, LUBRICATION & TRIBOLOGY. *Current Pos:* GROUP LEADER & PRIN MEM TECH STAFF, CHARLES STARK DRAPER LAB, 77- *Personal Data:* b Hartford, Conn, Oct 1, 48; m 71, Barbara A Breen; c Genevieve, Luke, Neal & Alexis. *Educ:* Boston Univ, BA, 70; Brandeis Univ, PhD(org chem), 77. *Mem:* Am Chem Soc. *Res:* Organic synthesis; fluorine chemistry; ball bearing lubricants; slip ring lubricants; gas bearing lubrication; the friction, wear and electrical properties of lubricants for sliding electrical contacts; precision cleaning; environmental chemistry; chemical sensors; surface analysis. *Mailing Add:* 70 Outlook Dr Lexington MA 02139. *Fax:* 617-258-4656; *E-Mail:* jrw1786@draper.com

**WILLIAMS, JOHN WATKINS, III,** CYTOGENETICS. *Current Pos:* from asst prof to assoc prof, 71-79, PROF GENETICS & EMBRYOL, TUSKEGEE UNIV, 79- *Personal Data:* b Alexandria, La, Mar 11, 42; m 70. *Educ:* Univ Southwestern La, BS, 65; La State Univ, MS, 68, PhD(genetics zool), 71. *Prof Exp:* Res assoc genetics, La State Univ, 68-70. *Mem:* AAAS; Int Soc Differentiation; Sigma Xi. *Res:* Amphibian cytogenetics and chromosomal banding patterns in the Rana pipiens complex with emphasis on chromosomal markers in species from different geographic regions; banding of amphibian chromosomes. *Mailing Add:* Dept Biol Tuskegee Inst Tuskegee Institute AL 36088

**WILLIAMS, JOHN WESLEY,** ORGANIC CHEMISTRY. *Current Pos:* SR RES CHEMIST, STAUFFER CHEM CO, 79- *Personal Data:* b Mobile, Ala, Dec 31, 44; m 67; c 2. *Educ:* Univ Ala, BS, 67; Univ Ill, MS, 70, PhD(org chem), 73. *Prof Exp:* Rockefeller Found fel, Dept Entom, Univ Ill, 73-75; sr chemist org chem, Abbott Labs, 75-79. *Mem:* Am Chem Soc; AAAS. *Res:* Synthetic organic chemistry especially industrial and agricultural fungicides and bactericides. *Mailing Add:* 1021 Crestview Dr San Carlos CA 94070-3445

**WILLIAMS, JOHN WHARTON,** ENGINEERING GEOLOGY. *Current Pos:* from asst prof to assoc prof, 76-84, PROF & CHMN, DEPT GEOL, SAN JOSE STATE UNIV, 84- *Personal Data:* b Wichita, Kans, May 3, 45; m 68, Margaret Pratt; c Adam. *Educ:* Col William & Mary, BS, 67; Stanford Univ, MS, 68, PhD(geol), 70. *Prof Exp:* Geologist, Calif Div Mines & Geol, 71-76. *Mem:* AAAS; Geol Soc Am; Asn Eng Geologists. *Res:* Detection, analysis and delineation of geologic hazards to provide for the proper location and construction of engineering works. *Mailing Add:* 1021 Crestview Dr San Carlos CA 94070. *Fax:* 408-924-5053; *E-Mail:* johnww@sjsuvm1.sjsu.edu

**WILLIAMS, JOSEPH FRANCIS,** immunopharmacology & pharmacokinetics, drug metabolism in liver & brain; deceased, see previous edition for last biography

**WILLIAMS, JOSEPH LEE,** FOOD CHEMISTRY, LIPID CHEMISTRY. *Current Pos:* SR SCIENTIST, RES & DEVELOP DIV, KRAFTCO CORP, 72- *Personal Data:* b New Bern, NC, Nov 2, 36; m 62; c 4. *Educ:* Morehouse Col, BS, 60; Tuskegee Inst Technol, MS, 62; Univ Ill, Urbana, PhD(food sci), 70. *Prof Exp:* George Washington Carver fel, Carver Found, Tuskegee Inst Technol, 60-62; chemist, Monsanto Co, 63-66; USPHS fel, Burnsides Res Lab, Univ Ill, 68-70; dir multidisciplinary labs, Sch Vet Med, Tuskegee Inst Technol, 70-72. *Concurrent Pos:* Consult & mgr, Audiovisual & Multimedia Learning Resource Ctr Sci & Med Student & Individualized Study Progs, Tuskegee Inst Technol, 70-72; Ninth Ann George Washington Carver lectr, 71. *Mem:* Fel AAAS; Am Chem Soc; Am Oil Chem Soc; fel Am Inst Chemists; Inst Food Technologists. *Res:* Food science and lipid chemistry as it relates to the feeding of the public; biochemical utilization by man and the nutritional impact upon man; flavor constituents in edible oils, shelf life of products; correlation of physical and sensory method for evaluation of flavor components in edible oils; application of chemometrics to edible oil quality. *Mailing Add:* 1279 Arbor Ave Highland IL 60035-2901

**WILLIAMS, JOY ELIZABETH P,** bacteriology, biochemistry, for more information see previous edition

**WILLIAMS, JUDY ANN,** NEUROENDOCRINOLOGY. *Current Pos:* asst prof, 91-96, ASSOC PROF BIOL, SOUTHEASTERN OKLA STATE UNIV, 96- *Personal Data:* b Ft Lauderdale, Fla, Dec 30, 47; m 80, Jerry L; c Joanna, David & Douglas. *Educ:* Univ Ala, Huntsville, BS, 82; Univ NTex, MS, 84; Tex Woman's Univ, PhD(biol), 88. *Prof Exp:* Fel, Univ, NTex, 89-90, Tex Woman's Univ, 90-91. *Concurrent Pos:* Adj prof, El Centro Col, 89-90. *Mem:* AAAS; Soc Neurosci; Sigma Xi. *Res:* Effects of peri-natal hormones on development of the dopaminergic system and its relationship to gender differences in schizophrenia. *Mailing Add:* PO Box 4184 Durant OK 74701. *Fax:* 580-920-7476; *E-Mail:* jwilliams@sosu.edu

**WILLIAMS, JULIAN CARROLL,** INBORN ERRORS OF METABOLISM, MEDICAL GENETICS. *Current Pos:* ASSOC PROF PEDIAT, SCH MED, UNIV SOUTHERN CALIF, 87-; HEAD, DIV GEN MED, CHILDRENS HOSP LOS ANGELES, 90- *Personal Data:* b Dallas, Tex, Aug 31, 45. *Educ:* Rice Univ, Houston, BA, 67; Mass Inst Technol, MS, 68; Univ Calif, Berkeley, PhD(comp biochem), 71; Wash Univ, MD, 74. *Prof Exp:* Intern pediat, Childrens Hosp, St Louis, 74-75, resident, 75-76, fel med gen, 76; fel, Dept Med, Univ Calif, San Diego, 77; asst prof, Dept Pediat, Wash Univ Sch Med, 78-79; from asst prof to assoc prof, Sch Med, Health Sci Ctr, Univ Tex, Houston, 79-87, assoc prof biochem & molecular biol, 85-87. *Res:* Diagnosis and treatment of inborn errors of metabolism; defects of fatty acid, organic acid and ammonia catabolism; diagnosis of inborn errors via analytic chemistry techniques, characterization of the enzymes involved and application of cDNA methods. *Mailing Add:* Div Med Genetics Childrens Hosp Los Angeles 4650 Sunset Blvd Los Angeles CA 90027. *Fax:* 213-665-5937

**WILLIAMS, KEITH A,** SILICONE RUBBER & SILICONE GEL, MANUFACTURE OF INTERNAL & EXTERNAL BREAST PROSTHESES. *Current Pos:* CHIEF CHEMIST, GT PRODS, 94- *Personal Data:* b Turlock, Calif, Oct 27, 57; m 79, Virginia Wolfe; c Kathrine & Elizabeth. *Educ:* Calif Polytech State Univ, BS, 79; Univ Calif, PhD(chem), 83. *Prof Exp:* Lectr chem & org chem, Calif Polytech State Univ, 83-84; vis res chemist, Dept Physics, Univ Calif, Santa Barbara, 84-86; mgr mats res, Adm Mats Corp, Santa Barbara, 86-88; res & develop mgr, Mentor Polymer Technol Co, 88-93, gen mgr, 93-94. *Mem:* Am Chem Sol. *Res:* Development of room temperature and low temperature vulcanizing silicone rubbers and gels for both industrial and medical applications; current medical activities are for external applications only. *Mailing Add:* GT Prods 501 Industrial Blvd Grapevine TX 76051. *Fax:* 817-421-1211; *E-Mail:* keithw@fastlane.net

**WILLIAMS, KENNETH BOCK,** PLANT TAXONOMY, ZOOLOGY. *Current Pos:* Asst prof, 67-73, ASSOC PROF BIOL, ABILENE CHRISTIAN COL, 73- *Personal Data:* b Petersburg, Tex, Jan 18, 30; m 52; c 2. *Educ:* Abilene Christian Col, BS, 50; Univ Tex, MA, 59; Univ Ariz, PhD(bot), 67. *Res:* Biosystematic studies in the Gramineae. *Mailing Add:* Dept Biol Abilene Christian Univ Box 27868 Abilene TX 79699-8035

**WILLIAMS, KENNETH L,** ZOOLOGY. *Current Pos:* assoc prof, 66-79, PROF ZOOL & BIOL, NORTHWESTERN UNIV, 79- *Personal Data:* b Saybrook, Ill, Sept 4, 34; m 54, Viola Stoehr; c Michele, Christine & Kimberly. *Educ:* Univ Ill, Urbana, BS, 60, MS, 61; La State Univ, Baton Rouge, PhD(zool), 70. *Prof Exp:* Instr comp anat & biol, Millikin Univ, 62-64. *Concurrent Pos:* Sigma Xi grant, La State Univ, 66; NSF fel, Northwestern State Univ, 68, Sigma Xi grant, 71; US Forest Serv grants, 79 & 80. *Mem:* Am Soc Ichthyol & Herpet; Soc Study Amphibians & Reptiles; Japan Snake Inst; Herpet League. *Res:* Systematics and anatomy. *Mailing Add:* Dept Biol Sci Northwestern State Univ Natchitoches LA 71497-0003

**WILLIAMS, KENNETH STUART,** MATHEMATICS. *Current Pos:* from asst prof to assoc prof, 66-75, chmn dept, 80-84, PROF MATH, CARLETON UNIV, 75- *Personal Data:* b Croydon, Eng, Aug 20, 40; m 62, Carole A Lowe; c Helen, Jonathan & Joanna. *Educ:* Univ Birmingham, BSc, 62, DSc, 79; Univ Toronto, MA, 63, PhD(math), 65. *Prof Exp:* Lectr math, Univ Manchester, 65-66. *Mem:* Math Asn Am; Can Math Soc; Am Math Soc. *Res:* Theory of numbers. *Mailing Add:* Dept Math & Statist Carleton Univ Colonel By Dr Ottawa ON K1S 5B6 Can. *Fax:* 613-788-3536; *E-Mail:* williams@ccs.carleton.ca

**WILLIAMS, LANSING EARL,** PLANT PATHOLOGY. *Current Pos:* lab asst, Ohio State Univ, 50-52, from instr to prof, 54-88, assoc chmn dept, 68-88, EMER PROF, DEPT BOT & PLANT PATH, OHIO STATE UNIV, 88- *Personal Data:* b Spencer, WVa, Aug 8, 21; m 46; c 2. *Educ:* Morris Harvey Col, BSc, 50; Ohio State Univ, MSc, 52, PhD(bot, plant path), 54. *Prof Exp:* Lab asst, Morris Harvey Col, 49-50. *Mem:* AAAS; Am Phytopath Soc; Sigma Xi; Nat Res Soc. *Res:* Corn viruses and stalk rot; mycotoxins; relation of soil fungal flora to soil-borne plant pathogens. *Mailing Add:* 1559 Morgan St Wooster OH 44691

**WILLIAMS, LARRY G,** AGRICULTURAL ENGINEERING. *Current Pos:* From asst prof to prof, 56-90, EMER PROF AGR ENG, UNIV IDAHO, 90- *Personal Data:* b Moscow, Idaho, Jan 8, 35; m 56; c 2. *Educ:* Univ Idaho, BS, 56, MS, 59. *Mem:* Am Soc Agr Eng. *Res:* Agricultural mechanization and automation; materials handling and agricultural processing. *Mailing Add:* PO Box 314 Kilauea HI 96754-0314

**WILLIAMS, LARRY GALE,** MOLECULAR BIOLOGY. *Current Pos:* asst prof, 71-86, ASSOC PROF BIOL, KANS STATE UNIV, 87- *Personal Data:* b Lincoln, Nebr, Sept 28, 39; m 62; c 2. *Educ:* Univ Nebr, Lincoln, BS, 61, MS, 63; Calif Inst Technol, PhD(biochem), 68. *Prof Exp:* NIH fel bot, Univ Mich, Ann Arbor, 67-71. *Mem:* Sigma Xi. *Res:* Biology education. *Mailing Add:* Div Biol Kans State Univ 232 Ackert Hall Manhattan KS 66506-4901

**WILLIAMS, LAWRENCE ERNEST,** NUCLEAR MEDICINE, BIOPHYSICS. *Current Pos:* IMAGING PHYSICIST, CITY OF HOPE, DUARTE, CALIF, 80-, RES SCIENTIST, 93- *Personal Data:* b Youngstown, Ohio, Nov 29, 37; m 66, Sonia Bredmeyer; c Erica & Beverley. *Educ:* Carnegie-Mellon Univ, BS, 59; Univ Minn, Minneapolis, MS, 62, PhD(physics), 65; Am Bd Radiol, cert radiol physics, 74. *Honors & Awards:* Exhibit Gold Medalist, Soc Nuclear Med, 83. *Prof Exp:* Sr sci officer, Rutherford High Energy Lab, Eng, 65-68; asst prof physics, Western Ill Univ, 68-70; from asst prof to assoc prof radiol, Univ Minn, Minneapolis, 73-80. *Concurrent Pos:* NIH spec fel nuclear med, Nuclear Med Clin, Univ Minn, Minneapolis, 71-73; NIH grant, 74, 88-91 & 93-; consult, Jet Propulsion Lab; adj assoc prof med physics, Univ Calif, Los Angeles, adj prof med physics, 92-; bd dirs, Epidaurus Corp, 85-87; prof, Eurotech Res Univ, Palo Alto, Ca, 85-; ed, Nuclear Med Physics, CRC Press, 87; chmn, Tush Group Radionuclide Dosimetry, Am Asn Physicists Med, 93- *Mem:* Soc Nuclear Med; Sigma Xi; Am Asn Physicists in Med; Am Col Radiol; NY Acad Sci; Soc Comput Applns Radiol; fel Am Col Angiol. *Res:* Immunological imaging; phospholipid vesicles; biodistributions of radiolabeled compounds; image enhancement. *Mailing Add:* Diag Radiol City of Hope Duarte CA 91010-0269. *Fax:* 626-301-8468; *E-Mail:* lwilliams@smtplink.com.org

**WILLIAMS, LEAH ANN,** DEVELOPMENTAL BIOLOGY. *Current Pos:* from instr to asst prof, 59-73, chairperson, Dept Biol, 86-91, ASSOC PROF BIOL, WVA UNIV, 73- *Personal Data:* b Clarksburg, WVa, July 20, 32. *Educ:* WVa Univ, AB, 54, MS, 58, PhD(biol), 70. *Prof Exp:* Instr anat & physiol, Exten, Pa State Univ, 58-59; instr gen zool, anat & physiol, WLiberty State Col, 59. *Concurrent Pos:* NSF sci fac develop grant, 77-78; PI-NEI NIH, 82-85. *Mem:* AAAS; Am Soc Zool; Soc Develop Biol; Sigma Xi. *Res:* Regeneration; control mechanisms in the regenerative processes in the eyes of newts; evolutionary studies of the lens proteins. *Mailing Add:* Dept Biol WVa Univ PO Box 6057 Morgantown WV 26506-0001

**WILLIAMS, LELAND HENDRY,** MATHEMATICS, COMPUTER SCIENCE. *Current Pos:* RETIRED. *Personal Data:* b Columbia, SC, Feb 24, 30; m 52; c 2. *Educ:* Univ SC, BS, 50; Univ Ga, MS, 51; Duke Univ, PhD(math), 61. *Prof Exp:* Mathematician, Redstone Arsenal, 51-53; res assoc math & vis asst prof, Duke Univ, 60-62; math consult comput, Fla State Univ, 62-64, asst prof math, 62-66, asst dir, Comput Ctr, 64-66, asst prof math, Univ, 62-66; dir comput ctr & assoc prof math, Auburn Univ, 66-70; pres & dir, Triangle Univs Comput Ctr, 70-88; comput resources architect, Naval Res Lab, 88-95. *Concurrent Pos:* Assoc dir & lectr, NSF Comput Inst, Fla State Univ, 66; adj assoc prof math, Duke Univ, Univ NC, Chapel Hill & NC State Univ, 70-; dep dir, Edinburgh Regional Comput Ctr & vis prof, Univ Edinburgh, Scotland, 76-77. *Mem:* Am Sci Affil; Asn Comput Mach; Sigma Xi. *Res:* Numerical analysis; nonnumeric mathematical computation; computation center management. *Mailing Add:* 8432 Porter Lane Alexandria VA 22308. *Fax:* 703-404-8498; *E-Mail:* williams9@ccf.nrl.navy.mil

**WILLIAMS, LESLEY LATTIN,** PHYSICAL CHEMISTRY. *Current Pos:* From asst prof to assoc prof, 68-78, PROF CHEM, CHICAGO STATE UNIV, 78- *Personal Data:* b New Bedford, Mass, Aug 10, 39. *Educ:* Hollins Col, AB, 61, Univ Wis-Madison, PhD(chem), 68. *Concurrent Pos:* Lectr, Univ Md, Munich Campus, 71-72. *Mem:* Sigma Xi; Am Phys Soc. *Res:* Nuclear magnetic resonance relaxation mechanisms in inorganic fluorides, including solvent effects; computer assisted instruction in chemistry; hexafluorides. *Mailing Add:* Chem Chicago State Univ 95th & King Dr Chicago IL 60628

**WILLIAMS, LEWIS DAVID,** CHEMISTRY. *Current Pos:* asst lab dir, 73-80, LAB DIR, DDI PHARMACEUT, INC, MOUNTAIN VIEW, 80- *Personal Data:* b Hopkinsville, Ky, Apr 2, 44; m 86, Marilyn Benner; c 2. *Educ:* Univ Chicago, BS, 66; Harvard Univ, PhD(org chem), 71. *Prof Exp:* Atholl McBean fel chem, Stanford Res Inst, 70-71; Presidential intern, Western Regional Res Lab, Agr Res Serv, USDA, Albany, 72-73. *Mem:* Am Chem Soc. *Res:* Physical organic chemistry; structure-reactivity relationships; biochemistry. *Mailing Add:* 37709 Arlene Ct Fremont CA 94536-3714

**WILLIAMS, LEWIS THOMAS (RUSTY),** CARDIOLOGY. *Current Pos:* PRES, CHIRON TECHNOL, 94-; PROF MED, UNIV CALIF, SAN FRANCISCO. *Personal Data:* b 1949. *Educ:* Duke Univ, MD, 78; Am Bd Internal Med, cert, 81. *Mem:* Nat Acad Sci. *Mailing Add:* Cardiovasc Res Inst Box 0130-L1332 Univ Calif 505 Parnassus Ave San Francisco CA 94143-0130

**WILLIAMS, LORING RIDER,** inorganic chemistry; deceased, see previous edition for last biography

**WILLIAMS, LOUIS GRESSETT,** FRESH WATER ECOLOGY, ALGOLOGY. *Current Pos:* prof, 67-79, EMER PROF BIOL, UNIV ALA, TUSCALOOSA, 79- *Personal Data:* b Owensboro, Ky, Oct 28, 13; m 42; c 2. *Educ:* Marshall Univ, AB, 37; Duke Univ, MA, 40, PhD(biol), 48. *Honors & Awards:* Jefferson Award, 51. *Prof Exp:* Asst, Marshall Col, 37-38; teacher high sch, Fla, 39-40 & NC, 40-41; asst, Duke Univ, 46-47; instr bot, Univ NC, 48; assoc prof biol, Furman Univ, 48-58; in-chg, USPHS Plankton Prog, Nat Water Qual Network, Ohio, 58-65; in-chg, Plankton Prog, Nat Water Qual Lab, Minn, 65-67. *Concurrent Pos:* Carnegie grant, 49; Ford Found fel, Univ Calif, 51-52. *Mem:* Fel AAAS; Bot Soc Am; Am Soc Limnol & Oceanog; Ecol Soc Am; Phycol Soc Am. *Res:* Water quality assessment by species diversity and toxicity bioassay on the Great Lakes and major rivers of the United States; pollution assessment from radionuclides in the environment. *Mailing Add:* 5501 Dove Creek Ave Northport AL 35476

**WILLIAMS, LUTHER STEWARD,** MOLECULAR BIOLOGY. *Current Pos:* from sr sci adv to dir, 89-90, ASST DIR, EDUC & HUMAN RESOURCES, NSF, 90- *Personal Data:* b Sawyerville, Ala, Aug 19, 40; m 63, Constance M; c Mark S & Monique M. *Educ:* Miles Col, BA, 61; Atlanta Univ, MS, 63; Purdue Univ, PhD(molecular biol), 68. *Hon Degrees:* DSc, Purdue Univ, 87, Univ Louisville, 92. *Prof Exp:* Lab instr biol, Spelman Col, 61-62; lab instr, Atlanta Univ, 62-63, instr, 63-64, pres & prof, 84-87; teaching asst, Purdue Univ, 64-66; Am Cancer Soc fel, State Univ NY, Stony Brook, 68-69; asst prof, Atlanta Univ, 69-70; asst prof biol sci, Purdue Univ, West Lafayette, 70-73, assoc prof, 73-80, asst provost, 76-, prof, 80-; dean grad sch & prof, Dept Biol, Washington Univ, St Louis, 80-83; vpres acad affairs & prof, Univ Colo, 83-84; from asst to dir & dep dir, Nat Inst Gen Med Sci, NIH, 87-89. *Concurrent Pos:* NSF teaching asst, 62-63; NIH career develop award, Purdue Univ, 71-75; assoc prof biol, Mass Inst Technol, 73-74; mem, Microbiol Training Comt, Nat Inst Gen Med Sci, 71-74; chmn, MARC Prog, Nat Inst Gen Med Sci, 75-76. *Mem:* AAAS; Am Soc Microbiol; NY Acad Sci; Am Chem Soc; Am Soc Biol Chem & Molecular Biol; fel Am Acad Microbiol. *Res:* Physiological role of aminoacyl-transfer RNA synthetases and transfer RNA's in bacterial metabolism. *Mailing Add:* NSF 4201 Wilson Blvd Arlington VA 22230

**WILLIAMS, LYMAN O,** STRUCTURAL GEOLOGY. *Current Pos:* RETIRED. *Personal Data:* b State College, Pa, Apr 1, 34; m 63; c 2. *Educ:* Univ Ga, BS, 56; Univ Iowa, MS, 59, PhD(geol), 62. *Prof Exp:* Explor geologist, Calif Co, 61-63; asst prof geol, Monmouth Col, 63-64; assoc prof, Eastern Tenn State Univ, 64-69; assoc prof, Monmouth Col, 69-73, prof, 73-, dept chmn, 77- *Concurrent Pos:* Prof geol, Phillips Univ, Enid, Okla. *Mem:* Geol Soc Am. *Res:* Petrology and structure of crystalline rock terranes; remote sensing of environment. *Mailing Add:* 4221 Bayview Pt Traverse City MI 49684

**WILLIAMS, LYNN ROY,** MATHEMATICS. *Current Pos:* asst prof, 75-77, ASSOC PROF MATH, IND UNIV, SOUTH BEND, 77-, ASSOC DEAN, 92- *Personal Data:* b Detroit, Mich, Apr 23, 45; m 84, Julie Jenkins; c 3. *Educ:* King Col, BA, 67; Univ Ky, MA, 68, PhD(math), 71. *Prof Exp:* Asst prof math, La State Univ, Baton Rouge, 71-75. *Mem:* Am Math Soc. *Res:* Functional analysis; Hp theory; harmonic analysis; statistics. *Mailing Add:* Ind Univ Lib Arts & Sci 1700 Mishawaka Ave PO Box 7111 South Bend IN 46634-7111. *E-Mail:* lwilliams@vines.iusb.indiana.edu

**WILLIAMS, M COBURN,** PLANT PHYSIOLOGY. *Current Pos:* RETIRED. *Personal Data:* b Osage City, Kans, Jan 28, 29; m 53, Marilyn J Williams; c Jane A & Sue E. *Educ:* Kansas State Univ, BS & MS, 51; Univ Ill, PhD(agron), 56. *Prof Exp:* Plant physiologist, Agr Res Serv, USDA, 56-89. *Mem:* Weed Sci Soc Am. *Res:* Biochemical and physiological research on poisonous range weeds, especially methods of chemical control and identification toxic compounds; Astragalus, Delphinium, Lupinus, Lotus. *Mailing Add:* 1427 E 800 N Logan UT 84321

**WILLIAMS, MARION PORTER,** FOOD SCIENCE. *Current Pos:* SR VPRES TECHNOL, WELCH'S, 92- *Personal Data:* b Salem, Ind, Jan 24, 46; m 68, Paula. *Educ:* Purdue Univ, BS, 68, PhD(food sci), 73. *Prof Exp:* From sr food scientist to sr res scientist, Carnation Co, 73-75, mgr int res & prod develop, 75-78, asst dir prod develop, Res Labs, 78; dir new prod develop, Res Ctr, Anderson Clayton Foods, 78-81; dir prod develop, Kraft Inc, 81-85, vpres prod develop, Res & Develop, 85-89, vpres technol, Grocery Prod Group, 90-92. *Mem:* Inst Food Technologists; Indust Res Inst. *Res:* Development of new products and maintenance/improvement of current product lines; manufacturing, engineering. *Mailing Add:* 99 Bigelow Dr Sudbury MA 01776

**WILLIAMS, MARK ALAN,** VIROLOGY, GLYCOBIOLOGY. *Current Pos:* SR STAFF SCIENTIST, CYTEL CORP, 90- *Personal Data:* b Muncie, Ind, Jan 16, 60. *Educ:* Ind Univ, BS, 82; Northwestern Univ, PhD(biochem, molecular biol & cell biol), 88. *Prof Exp:* Nat Res Sci Asn trainee, La Jolla Cancer Res Found, 88-89, vis fel, 89-90. *Mem:* Am Soc Cell Biol; Soc Complex Carbohydrates. *Res:* Cloning and expression of carbohydrate synthetic enzymes; project management for therapeutic, recombinant protein drug candidates. *Mailing Add:* Cytel Corp 3525 John Hopkins Ct La Jolla CA 92121

**WILLIAMS, MARSHALL HENRY, JR,** PHYSIOLOGY, INTERNAL MEDICINE. *Current Pos:* vis asst prof physiol, 55-59, assoc prof med & physiol, 59-66, PROF MED, ALBERT EINSTEIN COL MED, 66- *Personal Data:* b New Haven, Conn, July 15, 25; m 48; c 4. *Educ:* Yale Univ, BS, 45, MD, 47. *Prof Exp:* Intern, Presby Hosp, New York, 47-48, asst resident med, 48-49; asst resident, New Haven Hosp, Conn, 49-50, asst, 50; chief respiratory sect, Dept Cardiorespiratory Dis, Army Med Serv Grad Sch, Walter Reed Army Hosp, 52-55; dir, Cardiorespiratory Lab, Grasslands Hosp, Valhalla, NY, 55-59. *Concurrent Pos:* NIH trainee, New Haven Hosp, Conn, 50; dir chest serv, Bronx Munic Hosp Ctr, New York, 59- *Mem:* AAAS; Am Physiol Soc; Am Thoracic Soc; Am Soc Clin Invest; Am Heart Asn. *Res:* Respiratory and clinical cardiopulmonary physiology. *Mailing Add:* Albert Einstein Col Med 1300 Morris Park Ave Bronx NY 10461-1975

**WILLIAMS, MARSHALL VANCE,** TUMOR BIOLOGY, VIROLOGY. *Current Pos:* from asst prof to PROF, DEPT MED MICROBIOL & IMMUNOL, OHIO STATE UNIV, 82-, MEM, COMPREHENSIVE CANCER CTR, 82- *Personal Data:* b Memphis, Tenn, Mar 22, 48; m 70, Marilyn Liebenrood; c Laurie M & Jennifer L. *Educ:* Memphis State Univ, BS, 70, MS, 73; Univ Ga, PhD(microbiol), 76. *Prof Exp:* Cancer res scientist I, Roswell Park Mem Inst, 76-78; asst prof microbiol, Kirksville Col Osteop Med, Mo, 78-82. *Concurrent Pos:* Adj asst prof, NE Mo State Univ, 79-82; consult, Bio-Diesel Fuels Iowa Inc, 81-82; sci adv, Int Inst Immunopath, Inc. *Mem:* Am Soc Microbiol; AAAS; Am Soc Pharmacol & Exp Therapeut; Am Soc Cancer Res; Am Soc Biochem & Molecular Biol; Environ Mutagen Soc. *Res:* Deoxyuridine metabolism in neoplastic cells and cells infected with herpes simplex virus; development of antiviral agents; mammalian cell mutagenesis. *Mailing Add:* Dept Med Microbiol & Immunol Ohio State Univ 333 W Tenth Ave 2078 Graves Hall Columbus OH 43210

**WILLIAMS, MARTHA E,** INFORMATION SCIENCES. *Current Pos:* DIR, INFO RETRIEVAL RES LAB, & PROF INFO SCI, COORD SCI LAB, UNIV ILL, 72-, AFFIL, COMPUT SCI DEPT, 79- *Personal Data:* b Chicago, Ill. *Educ:* Barat Col, AB, 55; Loyola Univ, MA, 57. *Honors & Awards:* Award of Merit, Am Soc Info Sci; Watson Davis Award. *Prof Exp:* Assoc chemist, Chem Dept, ITT Res Inst, 61, asst supvr, 61-68, mgr, Info Sci, 62-72, Comput Search Ctr, 68-72. *Concurrent Pos:* Mem, comt chem info, 70-73, chmn & mem, large data base subcomt, 71-73, ad hoc panel, Info Storage & Retrieval, 77, Numerical Data Adv Bd, 79-82, Nat Res Network Rev Comt, 87-88, Nat Res Coun & Nat Acad Sci; ed, Ann Rev Info Sci & Technol, 75-, Comput Readable Databases: A Directory & Data Sourcebook, 76-87 & Online Rev, 77-; vpres, Eng Info, Inc, 78-80, chmn bd, 80-88; mem bd regents, Nat Libr Med, 78-82, chmn bd, 81-82; hon fel, Inst Info Scientists, London, Eng, 85. *Mem:* Fel AAAS; Am Chem Soc; Am Soc Info Sci (pres-elect, 86-87, pres, 87-88); Asn Comput Mach; Asn Sci Info Dissemination Ctr (vpres, 71-73, pres, 75-77, past pres, 77-79); fel Inst Info Scientists Gt Brit. *Res:* Online retrieval systems; computer readable databases; systems analysis and design; chemical information systems; electronic publishing. *Mailing Add:* 2134 Sandra Lane Monticello IL 61856

**WILLIAMS, MARY ANN,** NUTRITION, BIOCHEMISTRY. *Current Pos:* from instr to asst prof, 55-63, assoc prof, 63-75, PROF NUTRIT, UNIV CALIF, BERKELEY, 75- *Personal Data:* b Albany, NY, May 18, 25. *Educ:* Iowa State Col, BS, 46; Cornell Univ, MS, 50; Univ Calif, PhD, 54. *Prof Exp:* Asst pathologist, Univ Ky, 49-51; asst nutrit, Univ Calif, 51-54; res assoc, McCollum-Pratt Inst, Johns Hopkins Univ, 54-55. *Concurrent Pos:* Guggenheim fel, 63-64. *Mem:* AAAS; Am Chem Soc; Am Inst Nutrit; Soc Exp Biol & Med; Biochem Soc; Am Soc Biochem & Molecular Biol. *Res:* Essential fatty acid metabolism and functions. *Mailing Add:* Dept Nutrit Sci 119 Morgan Hall Univ Calif Berkeley CA 94720. *Fax:* 510-642-0535

**WILLIAMS, MARY BEARDEN,** PHILOSOPHY OF SCIENCE. *Current Pos:* mem hon fac, Freshman Honors Prog, 76-78, dir, Ctr Sci & Cult, 84-89, ASSOC PROF LIFE & HEALTH SCI, UNIV DEL, 78- *Personal Data:* b Lexington, Ky, Aug 29, 36. *Educ:* Reed Col, BA, 58; Univ Pa, MA, 61; Univ London, PhD(math biol) & DIC, 67. *Prof Exp:* Res assoc biomath, Univ Tex M D Anderson Hosp & Tumor Inst, 63-64; asst prof, NC State Univ, 67-73; vis asst prof hist & philos sci, Ind Univ, 73-74; asst prof philos, Ohio State Univ, 74-76. *Mem:* Soc Study Evolution; Philos Sci Asn; Soc Syst Zool; Sigma Xi; Am Philos Asn. *Res:* Axiomatization of evolutionary theory; logical status of evolutionary predictions; evolution of population self-regulation; philosophy of biology; bioethics; medical ethics. *Mailing Add:* Univ Del Newark DE 19716

**WILLIAMS, MARY CAROL,** PULMONARY CYTOLOGY, CELL BIOLOGY. *Current Pos:* PROF ANAT, UNIV CALIF, SAN FRANCISCO, 76- *Educ:* Univ Calif, San Francisco, PhD(anat), 71. *Mailing Add:* Boston Univ Sch Med 80 E Concord St Boston MA 02118-2394. *Fax:* 617-638-5298

**WILLIAMS, MARY CAROL,** INDUSTRIAL HYGIENE, SAFETY ENGINEERING. *Current Pos:* mus guide, 77-78, chem technician, 78-85, STAFF MEM, LOS ALAMOS NAT LAB, 85- *Personal Data:* b Norfolk, Va, Nov 29, 42; m 62, Joel M; c Reine & Michael. *Educ:* Univ NMex, BUS, 82, MS, 85. *Prof Exp:* Med technologist, St Mary's Hosp, Minneapolis, 66-68 & E I DuPont, Waynesboro, Va, 68-72. *Mem:* Soc Appl Spectros; Am Indust Hyg Asn; Am Soc Safety Engr. *Res:* Ergonomics/Human factors and safety engineering. *Mailing Add:* 51 Zuni Los Alamos NM 87544. *E-Mail:* mcwms@lanl.gov

**WILLIAMS, MARY CARR,** STEROID CHEMISTRY. *Current Pos:* RETIRED. *Personal Data:* b Port Arthur, Tex, Dec 25, 26; m 51; c David. *Educ:* Tex Woman's Univ, BA & BS, 49; St Mary's Univ, MS, 75. *Prof Exp:* Res chemist lipid metab, Dept Biochem & Biophys, Tex A&M Univ, 49-63; res scientist, Southwest Found Res & Educ, 63-78; assoc found scientist steriod metab, Dept Clin Sci & Reproductive Biol, Southwest Found Biomed Res, 78-81, assoc found scientist lipid metab, Dept Cardiopulmonary Dis, 82-83, sr res assoc, Dept Physiol & Med, 83-90; res assoc, Dept Pharmacol, Health Sci Ctr, Univ Tex, San Antonio, 91-96. *Res:* Metabolism of natural and synthetic steroid hormones; chromatography of steroids and lipoproteins; metabolism of lipoproteins; analysis of chemotherapy agents by high-power liquid chromatography. *Mailing Add:* 116 Elm Spring Lane San Antonio TX 78231-1413

**WILLIAMS, MARYON JOHNSTON, JR,** CLINICAL ENGINEERING. *Current Pos:* SR ENGR, CONDITION ANALYZING CORP, 93- *Personal Data:* b Griffin, Ga, Jan 14, 46; m; c 2. *Educ:* Ga Inst Technol, BEE, 68; Rutgers Univ, MS, 70, PhD(biomed eng), 72. *Prof Exp:* From instr to asst prof biomed eng & med, Med Col Ga, 72-77; tech dir, Biomed Eng Shared Technol, affil, NJ Hosp Asn, 77-82 & Hosp Eng Logistics & Planning Inc, 82-90; exec dir, Am Tekdyne, Inc, 91-93. *Concurrent Pos:* Lectr physiol, Med Col Ga, 75-77. *Mem:* Sr mem Biomed Eng Soc; sr mem Inst Elec & Electronics Engrs. *Res:* Developed uniquely powered piezo-electric heart assist device; studied control characteristics of artificial heart assist devices; consult on pulmonary function and exercise testing equipment; develop computerized database systems for hospitals. *Mailing Add:* 21 Quaker Rd Princeton Junction NJ 08550-1615

**WILLIAMS, MAX L(EA), JR,** MECHANICS OF FRACTURE. *Current Pos:* prof eng & dean sch eng, 73-85, EMER DEAN & DISTINGUISHED SERV PROF ENG, UNIV PITTSBURGH, 85- *Personal Data:* b Aspinwall, Pa, Feb 22, 22; m 67; c 3. *Educ:* Carnegie Inst Technol, BS, 42; Calif Inst Technol, MS, 47, AeE, 48, PhD, 50. *Honors & Awards:* Adhesion Res Award, Am Soc Testing & Mat, 75; Solid Rocket Tech Achievement Award, Am Inst Aeronaut & Astronaut, 88. *Prof Exp:* Lectr aeronaut, Calif Inst Technol, 48-50, res fel, 50-51, from asst prof to prof, 51-65; prof eng & dean eng, Univ Utah, 65-73, distinguished prof eng, 73. *Concurrent Pos:* Ed in chief, Int J Fracture, 65-; mem exec comt, Int Cong Fracture, 65-; sci dir, NATO Advan Study Inst, Italy, 67; mem biomat adv comt, Nat Inst Dent Res, 67-70; mem chem rocket adv comt, NASA, 68-73; pres, Utah Eng & Develop Corp, 69-79; mem eng adv comn, NSF, 69-72; NSF sr fel, Imp Col, Univ London, 71-72; nat lectr, Sigma Xi, 72; mem nat mat adv bd, Nat Res Coun & chmn, Comt Mat Struct & Design, 75-77; assoc mem, Defense Sci Bd, 75-76, 82-85; consult & lectr in field, co-founder & dir Terra Tek, Inc, Salt Lake City, 73-77; adv, Regional Indust Develop Corp, Pittsburgh, 73-83; chmn, Pa Adv Comn I-79 Bridge Failure, 77; dir, MPC Corp, Pittsburgh, 74-86; chmn struct design task group, Coop Automotive Res Prog, Off Sci & Tech Policy, 78-79; dir, US Nat Comn World Energy Conf, 79-83; founding chmn bd dirs, BCR Nat Lab, Univ Pittsburgh, 83-85; Gen Lew Allen vis prof aeronaut, USAF Inst Technol, 85-87; mem, USAF Sci Adv Bd, 85-89, adv, 90-; sci adv, USAF Acquisition Logistics Ctr, 87-88; consult, Off Under Secy Defense, 70-, & Dept State, 73-81; mem, Nat Eng Adv Bd, Mercer Univ, 88- *Mem:* AAAS; fel Soc Exp Mech; Am Chem Soc; assoc fel Am Inst Aeronaut & Astronaut; Am Soc Eng Educ; Soc Rheology; hon fel Int Cong Fracture. *Res:* Continuum mechanics with application to fracture of solids and interaction with chemical structure of materials. *Mailing Add:* Benedum Eng Hall Univ Pittsburgh Pittsburgh PA 15261

**WILLIAMS, MAX W,** PLANT PHYSIOLOGY, HORTICULTURE. *Current Pos:* RETIRED. *Personal Data:* b Cardston, Alta, Aug 24, 30; US citizen; m 54, 82; c 5. *Educ:* Utah State Univ, BSc, 54, MSc, 57; Wash State Univ, PhD(hort), 61. *Prof Exp:* Res asst, Utah State Univ, 54-55; actg supt, Utah Tree Fruit Exp Sta, 55-58; res asst, Wash State Univ, 58-61; res leader & plant physiologist, Agr Res Serv, USDA, 61-95. *Concurrent Pos:* Adv fruit prod, Chile, Arg, Australia, NZ, France, Eng, Holland, Italy, Romania, Poland, Yugoslavia, Israel & Mex. *Mem:* Am Soc Hort Sci; Int Soc Hort Sci. *Res:* Chemical thinning of apples; growth retardants; cytokinins; auxins. *Mailing Add:* 1907 Skyline Dr Wenatchee WA 98801-2379

**WILLIAMS, MERLIN CHARLES,** METEOROLOGY, ENGINEERING. *Current Pos:* DIR, OFF WEATHER MODIFICATION PROGS, ENVIRON RES LABS, NAT OCEANIC & ATMOSPHERIC ADMIN, 74- *Personal Data:* b Howard, SDak, July 20, 31; m 59; c 4. *Educ:* SDak State Univ, BS, 53; Univ Chicago, cert, 54; Univ Wyo, MS, 62; Stanford Univ, MSA, 81. *Prof Exp:* Instr civil eng, SDak State Univ, 57-58; instr & res asst weather eng, 58-59; engr, US Bur Reclamation, 59-61; asst civil eng, Univ Wyo, 61-62, proj dir weather modification res, 62-66; dir weather modification res, Fresno State Col Found, 66-71; dir, SDak State Weather Control Comn, 71-74. *Concurrent Pos:* Consult adv bd weather modification, NSF, 75- *Mem:* Am Soc Civil Engrs; Am Meteorol Soc; Am Geophys Union; Weather Modification Asn (pres, 69). *Res:* Water resources research to investigate increasing water supplies, including weather modification research, fluid mechanics and hydrology; basic hydrometeorological studies; mountain meteorology; snow physics; hurricane modification (abatement), boundary layer dynamics. *Mailing Add:* 6387 Niwot Rd Longmont CO 80503

**WILLIAMS, MICHAEL,** NEUROCHEMISTRY, PHARMACOLOGY. *Current Pos:* sr res neurochemist, 76-80, RES FEL PHARMACOL, MERCK INST, 80-; AREA HEAD NEUROSCI, ABBOTT LABS, 89- *Personal Data:* b London, Eng, Jan 3, 47. *Educ:* Univ London, BSc, 71, PhD(neurochem), 74. *Prof Exp:* Res assoc neurochem, Univ NC, Chapel Hill, 74-76; staff, Ciba-Geigy Pharmaceut. *Mem:* Am Soc Pharmacol & Exp Therapeut; Soc Neurosci; AAAS; Am Soc Neurochem. *Res:* Synaptic transmission; receptor function; cyclic nucleotides and protein phosphorylation. *Mailing Add:* Dept Neurosci Abbott Labs D-469 Abbott Park IL 60064-3500. *Fax:* 847-937-9195

**WILLIAMS, MICHAEL C(HARLES),** RHEOLOGY, VISCOELASTICITY. *Current Pos:* PROF CHEM ENG, UNIV ALTA, 90-; EMER PROF, UNIV CALIF, BERKELEY, 90- *Personal Data:* b Milwaukee, Wis, June 11, 37. *Educ:* Univ Wis-Madison, BS, 59, MS, 60, PhD(chem eng), 64. *Prof Exp:* Fel, Inst Theoret Sci, Univ Ore, 64-65; from asst prof to prof chem eng, Univ Calif, Berkeley, 65-89. *Concurrent Pos:* Vis prof rheology, Univ Nat Del Sur, Bahia Blanca, Arg, 70; chmn, Career Guid Comt, San Francisco Bay Area Eng Coun, 70-73; consult, pvt indust, govt & litigation; prin investr, numerous res grants & contracts, Nat Sci Eng Res Coun, NSF, NIH, NASA, Off Naval Res & Petrol Res Fund; fac scientist, Ctr Advan Mat, Lawrence Berkeley Lab, 83-89; bd dirs, Can Rheology Group, 91-97, Can Soc Chem Eng, 92-95. *Mem:* Am Inst Chem Engrs; Am Chem Soc; Soc Rheology; Soc Plastics Engrs; Can Rheology Group; Can Soc Chem Eng. *Res:* Viscoelastic fluid phenomena; rheology of polymer melts and solutions, suspensions and fluidized beds; mechanical and thermodynamic properties of solid and liquid block copolymers; polymer composites; blood rheology, hemolysis, sickle-cell capillary flow. *Mailing Add:* Dept Chem & Mat Eng Univ Alta Edmonton AB T6G 2G6 Can. *Fax:* 403-492-2881

**WILLIAMS, MICHAEL D,** NUCLEAR ENGINEERING. *Current Pos:* res assoc magnetohydrodynamics, 66-68, mem staff, 68-70, MEM STAFF, LOS ALAMOS SCI LAB, 75- *Personal Data:* b Covina, Calif, May 19, 39; m 71. *Educ:* Univ Calif, Los Angeles, BS, 61, MS, 63, PhD(nuclear eng), 66. *Prof Exp:* Assoc astrodynamics, Systs Develop Corp, 61; mem tech staff, Space Tech Labs, Inc, 63; res coord, John Muir Inst Environ Studies, 70-75. *Mem:* AAAS. *Res:* Air contaminant dispersion and effects. *Mailing Add:* Rte 5 Box 229A Santa Fe NM 87501-9805

**WILLIAMS, MICHAEL EUGENE,** VERTEBRATE PALEONTOLOGY. *Current Pos:* CUR VERT PALEONT, CLEVELAND MUS NATURAL HIST, 76- *Personal Data:* b Ina, Ill, Aug 4, 40; m 68. *Educ:* Mo Sch Mines & Metall, Rolla, BS, 63; Univ Kans, MS, 72, PhD, 79. *Mem:* Soc Vert Paleont; Paleont Soc; Int Paleont Union. *Res:* Paleozoic fishes with special emphasis on chondrichthyans; sedimentation and environments of deposition of various black shale units; cyclic events in the geological record; KT extinction event and methods of choosing between computing ideas. *Mailing Add:* Cleveland Mus Natural Hist 1 Wade Oval Dr Cleveland OH 44106

**WILLIAMS, MICHAEL LEDELL,** ENTOMOLOGY, SYSTEMATICS. *Current Pos:* ASSOC PROF, DEPT ZOOL-ENTOM, AUBURN UNIV, 73-, ASSOC PROF, DEPT ENTOM, 86- *Personal Data:* b Paragould, Ark, Sept 11, 43; m 63; c 2. *Educ:* Ark State Univ, BS, 67; Va Polytech Inst & State Univ, MS, 69, PhD(entom), 72. *Prof Exp:* Asst entomologist, Md Dept Agr, 71-73. *Concurrent Pos:* Chmn, Entom Sect, Auburn Univ, 83-86. *Mem:* Entom Soc Am; Sigma Xi. *Res:* Insular speciation of scale insects of the Galapagos Islands; systematics and morphology of New World Coccidae (Homoptera: Coccoidea); natural host plant resistance to scale insects; scale insects of Alabama; insects of ornamental plants. *Mailing Add:* Dept Entom Auburn Univ 328 Funchess Hall Auburn AL 36849-3501

**WILLIAMS, MICHAEL MAURICE RUDOLPH,** STOCHASTIC PROCESSES. *Current Pos:* reader, Univ London, Eng, 66-70, prof, 70-86, chmn, 80-86, EMER PROF, UNIV LONDON, ENG, 86-; PRIN SCIENTIST, ELECTROWATT ENG SERV (UK) LTD, 89- *Personal Data:* b Croydon, Eng, Dec 1, 35; Brit citizen; m 58, Ann Betty; c Nicholas & Victoria. *Educ:* Univ London, BSc, 58, PhD(nuclear eng), 62, DSc, 68. *Honors & Awards:* Arthur Holly Compton Award, Am Nuclear Soc, 94. *Prof Exp:* Res engr nuclear eng, Cent Elec Generating Bd, 61-62; res assoc, Brookhaven Nat Lab, 62-63; lectr, Univ Birmingham, Eng, 63-65; prof, Univ Mich, 86-89. *Concurrent Pos:* Ed, Annals Nuclear Energy. *Mem:* Fel Am Nuclear Soc; Inst Nuclear Engrs (vpres, 72-75); fel Inst Physics; fel Royal Soc Arts. *Res:* Neutron transport theory; random processes in nuclear systems; aerosol physics with special references to nuclear reactor safety; radioactive waste; coagulation and deposition aerosols in closed compartments. *Mailing Add:* 2A Lytchgate Close South Croydon Surrey CR2 0DX England. *Fax:* 44-81-680-5354

**WILLIAMS, MORRIS EVAN,** NON-METALLIC MATERIALS, COATINGS. *Current Pos:* MAT & PROCESS ENG SPECIALIST, LOCKHEED MISSILES & SPACE CORP, 86- *Personal Data:* b Los Angeles, Calif, Nov 27, 46; m 83, Judith Plotnick. *Educ:* Polytech N London, UK, Grad Royal Soc Chem, 74; Univ Lancaster, UK, PhD(polymer chem),

78. *Prof Exp:* Res scientist, Van Leer Res Labs, 71-77; paint chemist, Crown Decorative Prod, 78-79; sr chemist, Prods Res Co, 79-82; mem tech staff, Hughes Aircraft Co, 83; eng specialist, Northrop Electronics, 83-86. *Mem:* Royal Soc Chem; Am Chem Soc; Am Inst Chemists; Soc Advan Mat & Process Eng. *Mailing Add:* 1179 Kent Ave Sunnyvale CA 94087-5008

**WILLIAMS, MYRA NICOL,** molecular biophysics, molecular modeling, for more information see previous edition

**WILLIAMS, NATHANIEL ADEYINKA,** FREEZE-DRYING PHARMACEUTICALS, PROTEIN-PEPTIDE FORMULATION. *Current Pos:* PRIN SCIENTIST, R W JOHNSON PHARMACEUT RES INST, 93- *Personal Data:* b Nigeria, July 14, 51; m 77, Iyabo. *Educ:* Obafemi Awolowo Univ, Nigeria, BPharm, 75; Univ Wis, Madison, MS, 80, PhD(pharm), 82. *Prof Exp:* Scientist, Smithkline-Beecham, 82-84; asst prof pharm & chem, Obafemi Awolowo Univ, 84-86; res fel, Univ Mich, Ann Arbor, 86-88; sr res scientist, Abbott Labs, North Chicago, 88-93. *Mem:* Am Asn Pharmaceut Scientists; Parenteral Drug Asn. *Res:* Freeze-drying and its applications to pharmaceuticals; thermal and electrokinetic characterization of freezing solutions; protein and peptide formulation and stabilization; biophysical studies of surfactants. *Mailing Add:* B-260 Res Rte 202 R W Johnson Pharmaceut Res Inst Raritan NJ 08869

**WILLIAMS, NEAL THOMAS,** ENGINEERING PHYSICS. *Current Pos:* PRES, PLATRONICS-SEALS, INC, CLIFTON, 66- *Personal Data:* b East Orange, NJ, Mar 16, 21; m 48; c 2. *Educ:* Cornell Univ, AB, 48. *Prof Exp:* Supvr magnetron eng, Westinghouse Elec Co, 42-44, develop engr, 48-51; res assoc, Radiation Lab, Columbia Univ, 44-48, assoc res physicist, 52; mem tech staff, Bell Tel Labs, Inc, 51-52; chief engr, L L Constantin & Co, 52-53; res engr, T A Edison, Inc, 53-60; chief engr, Seal-A-Metic, Inc, 60-65; div mgr, Platronics, Inc, 65-66. *Mem:* Am Phys Soc; sr mem Inst Elec & Electronics Engrs; NY Acad Sci. *Res:* Microwave magnetrons and electronics; traveling wave tubes and backward oscillators; radar duplexers; gas discharges; metal-ceramic seals; low voltage x-rays. *Mailing Add:* 5 Skyline Dr PO Box 1002 Hopatcong NJ 07843

**WILLIAMS, NOREEN,** BIOENERGETICS, MOLECULAR BIOLOGY. *Current Pos:* Fel, Sch Med, 81-84, RES ASSOC, MCCOLLUM PRATT INST, JOHNS HOPKINS UNIV, 84- *Personal Data:* b Brunswick, Maine, June 21, 55; m 81; c 2. *Educ:* Univ Maine Orono, BS, 77; NY Univ, PhD(biol & biochem), 81. *Mem:* Biophys Soc; NY Acad Sci; AAAS; US Bioenergetics Group. *Res:* Molecular cloning and mechanism studies of energy-linked systems; mitochondrial and bacterial ATPases; enzyme II mannose of the phosphotransferase system in Escherichia coli. *Mailing Add:* Dept Microbiol Med Sch State Univ NY 253 Biomed Res Bldg Buffalo NY 14214. *Fax:* 716-831-2158

**WILLIAMS, NORMAN DALE,** PLANT GENETICS. *Current Pos:* SUPVRY GENETICIST & RES LEADER, AGR RES SERV, USDA, 56- *Personal Data:* b Nebr, Nov 4, 24; m 47, Elaine E Kuster; c David N & Curtis A. *Educ:* Univ Nebr, BS, 51, MS, 54, PhD(agron), 56. *Prof Exp:* Assoc genetics, Argonne Nat Lab, 54-56, res assoc, 56. *Concurrent Pos:* Adj prof, NDak State Univ, 61- *Mem:* Fel AAAS; Am Soc Agron; Am Genetic Asn; fel Crop Sci Soc Am; Genetics Soc Am. *Res:* Genetic studies of host-parasite relationships, especially wheat and wheat stem rust; mutation induction. *Mailing Add:* USDA-ARS Northern Crop Sci Lab Box 5677 University Sta Fargo ND 58105-5677. *Fax:* 701-239-1869; *E-Mail:* williamm@fargo.ars.usda.gov

**WILLIAMS, NORMAN EUGENE,** CELL BIOLOGY. *Current Pos:* Instr, 57-59, from asst prof to assoc prof, 59-67, PROF BIOL, UNIV IOWA, 67- *Personal Data:* b Grove City, Pa, July 29, 28; m 53, 72, Ruth Jaeckel; c Christopher, Paula & Kayla (deceased). *Educ:* Youngstown Univ, AB, 52; Brown Univ, ScM, 54; Univ Calif, Los Angeles, PhD(zool), 58. *Concurrent Pos:* NIH ser fel, Carlsberg Found, Denmark, 63-64 & Dept Biol Struct, Univ Wash, 66-67. *Mem:* Soc Protozoologists (pres, 84-85); Am Soc Cell Biol. *Res:* Cellular development; synthesis and assembly of cell surface. *Mailing Add:* Dept Biol Sci Univ Iowa Iowa City IA 52242

**WILLIAMS, NORMAN S W,** ADVANCED LASER-BASED DIAGNOSTICS, ENVIRONMENTAL TECHNOLOGY. *Current Pos:* PROF SPECTROS & SPECTROMETRY, SOLID STATE PHYSICS, FAC APPL SCI & ENG, UNIV TORONTO, 90-, PROF DEVELOP, 90- *Personal Data:* Can citizen. *Educ:* Univ Waterloo, BASc Hons, 74, MASc, 76; Univ BC, PhD(chem eng & fluid mech), 83. *Prof Exp:* Res scientist & proj leader, Dept Nat Defense Res Estab Valcartien, 83-87; prof & fac mem, Appl Sci & Eng Technol, Seneca, Col, 88-90. *Concurrent Pos:* Prin eng & sci advan technol & mgt consult, 87-; prog consult & adv, Fac Continuing Educ, Sch Eng Tech, Seneca Col, 90-; bus consult & trainer, Community Bus Ctr, Toronto, 93- *Mem:* Asn Prof Engrs Ont. *Res:* Advanced laser-based diagnostic techniques; environmental management and engineering; process simulation and control; advanced statistical methods/techniques; statistical approaches in modern business decisions. *Mailing Add:* 37 Barrymore Rd Scarborough ON M1J 1W1 Can

**WILLIAMS, NORRIS HAGAN,** PLANT TAXONOMY, CHEMICAL ECOLOGY. *Current Pos:* assoc cur, 81-84, CUR VASCULAR PLANTS, UNIV FLA, 84-, CHMN NATURAL SCI, 85- *Personal Data:* b Birmingham, Ala, Mar 31, 43; m 70, Nancy Fraser; c Matthew I & Luke F. *Educ:* Univ Ala, BS, 64, MS, 67; Univ Miami, PhD(biol), 71. *Prof Exp:* From asst prof to assoc

prof biol, Fla State Univ, 73-81. *Mem:* Am Soc Plant Taxonomists; Soc Study Evolution; Asn Trop Biol; Int Asn Plant Taxon; Int Soc Chem Ecol; Am Orchid Soc. *Res:* Systematics and evolution of Orchidaceae; chemical attraction of insects to flowers. *Mailing Add:* Nat Sci Dept Fla Mus Nat Hist Gainesville FL 32611. *Fax:* 352-846-0287

**WILLIAMS, PATRICIA BELL,** CARDIOVASCULAR PHARMACOLOGY, OCULAR PHARMACOLOGY. *Current Pos:* asst prof, 72-78, assoc prof, 78-86, PROF PHARMACOL, EASTERN VA MED SCH, 86- *Personal Data:* b Detroit, Mich. *Educ:* Col Pharm, Univ Mich, BS, 68; Med Col Va, Va Commonwealth Univ, PhD(pharmacol), 72. *Prof Exp:* Lab asst pharmacol, Health Sci, Med Col Va, Va Commonwealth Univ, 68-70, teaching asst, 70-71. *Concurrent Pos:* Consult, United Drug Abuse Coun & Health Adv Coord Comt, Model Cities Comprehensive Health Sci Proj, 72; lectr, Sch Continuing Educ, Univ Va, 72; Tidewater Heart Asn res grant, 75; Am Heart Asn/Va Affil res grant, 76-77 & 87-93; Nat Inst Heart Lung & Blood Inst grant, 76-82; res grants, Am Heart Asn, 83-87, Lions Eye Bank & Res Ctr, 84-, Alzheimer's Res Found Tidewater, 85-89; Basic Sci Coun, Am Heart Asn; Alzheimer's & Related Dis Res Fund/Commonwealth Va, 86; Alzheimer's & Related Dis Assoc/Nat Hq, 86-90; adj prof chem, Old Dominion Univ, 90- *Mem:* Fel Am Col Clin Pharmacol; Asn Women in Sci; Am Heart Asn; Am Soc Pharmacol & Exp Therapeut; Asn Res Vision & Ophthal. *Res:* Cardiovascular pharmacology and physiology of vascular smooth muscle with particular interest in the etiology and treatment of hypertension, peripheral vascular disease and the cell biology of vascular endothelium and calcium-mediated events; topical therapy of opthalmologic disease; geriatrics; granted 4 US patents. *Mailing Add:* Dept Pharmacol Eastern Va Med Sch PO Box 1980 Norfolk VA 23501. *E-Mail:* williams@borg.evms.edu

**WILLIAMS, PATRICK KELLY,** ECOLOGY. *Current Pos:* Asst prof, 73-80, ASSOC PROF BIOL, UNIV DAYTON, 80- *Personal Data:* b San Angelo, Tex, July 31, 43; m 68. *Educ:* Univ Tex, Austin, BA, 66; Univ Minn, Minneapolis, MS, 69; Ind Univ, Bloomington, PhD(zool), 73. *Mem:* Ecol Soc Am; Am Soc Mammalogists; Am Soc Ichthyologists & Herpetologists; Sigma Xi. *Res:* Experimental population ecology on rodents with emphasis on natural regulation and management. *Mailing Add:* Dept Biol Univ Dayton 300 College Park Dayton OH 45469-0001

**WILLIAMS, PAUL HUGH,** PLANT PATHOLOGY, PLANT GENETICS. *Current Pos:* From asst prof to assoc prof, 62-71, PROF PLANT PATH, UNIV WIS-MADISON, 71- *Personal Data:* b Vancouver, BC, May 6, 38; m 63. *Educ:* Univ BC, BSA, 59; Univ Wis, PhD(plant path), 62. *Honors & Awards:* Jakob Eriksson Medal, Swed Acad Sci, 81. *Concurrent Pos:* J S Guggenheim fel, 77-78. *Mem:* Am Phytopath Soc; Am Genetics Asn; Am Soc Hort Sci. *Res:* Genetics and cytology of host-parasite relations and resistance breeding for disease resistance in vegetables; crucifer genetics. *Mailing Add:* Dept Plant Path 284 Russell Lab Univ Wis-Madison 1630 Linden Dr Madison WI 53706-1520

**WILLIAMS, PETER J,** SOIL PHYSICS, GEOTECHNICAL SCIENCE. *Current Pos:* assoc prof, 69-71, PROF GEOG, CARLETON UNIV, 71-, DIR GEOTECH SCI LABS, 79- *Personal Data:* b Croydon, Eng, Sept 27, 32; m 57, Kari Fuglesang; c Eric D, Beatrice A & Inger E. *Educ:* Cambridge Univ, BA, 54, MA, 58; Univ Stockholm, Fil Lic & Fil Dr, 69. *Prof Exp:* Res officer, Soil Mech Sect, Div Bldg Res, Nat Res Coun Can, 57-69. *Concurrent Pos:* Royal Norweg Coun Sci & Indust Res fel, Norweg Geotech Inst, 63-65; lectr several univs in UK, Sweden, Norway, US & Can; consult & geotech adv, Northern Pipelines, Can Govt; vis scholar, Scott Polar Res Inst, Univ Cambridge, UK, 75-76, 82-83 & 89-90, 94; prin investr, Major Int Indust & Govt Sponsored Projs, 82- *Mem:* Can Asn Geog; Norweg Geotech Soc; Can Geotech Soc. *Res:* Physics of freezing soils and application to engineering and environment, especially Northern pipelines and other geotechnical and environmental issues; geomorphology, especially frost action; author of textbooks and general interest book. *Mailing Add:* Geotech Sci Labs Carleton Univ Ottawa ON K1S 5B6 Can. *Fax:* 613-520-9005; *E-Mail:* peter_williams@carleton.ca

**WILLIAMS, PETER M,** chemical oceanography; deceased, see previous edition for last biography

**WILLIAMS, PHILIP CARSLAKE,** ANALYTICAL CHEMISTRY, CEREAL PULSE UTILIZATION & EVALUATION. *Current Pos:* RES SCIENTIST, GRAIN RES LAB, CAN GRAIN COMN, 65- *Personal Data:* b Mountain Ash, Wales, May 26, 33; Can citizen; m 4. *Educ:* Univ Wales, BS, 54, PhD(agr biochem), 58. *Prof Exp:* Res officer, Agr Res Inst, Wagga Wagga, NSW, 58-64; fel cereal chem, Nat Res Coun Can, 64-65. *Concurrent Pos:* Consult, Int Ctr Agr Res Dry Areas, Syria, 75-, Int Develop Res Ctr, 74- *Mem:* Am Asn Cereal Chemists. *Res:* Near-infrared reflectance spectroscopic analysis of cereal grains, oilseals, pulses, and derived products; planning and design of large-scale analytical operations; applied statistical analysis; imunograph; 117 scientific publications. *Mailing Add:* Grain Res Lab 1404-303 Main St Winnipeg MB R3C 3G8 Can

**WILLIAMS, PHLETUS P,** MICROBIOLOGY, BIOCHEMISTRY. *Current Pos:* Microbiologist, Beef Cattle Res Br, Animal Husb Res Div, USDA, Md, 59-60, Dairy Cattle Res Br, 60-61, Beef Cattle Res Br, 61-64, prof bact, 72-73, MICROBIOLOGIST, METAB & RADIATION RES LAB, NDAK STATE UNIV SCI & EDUC ADMIN-AGR RES, USDA, 64-, ADJ PROF BACT, 73- *Personal Data:* b Junior, WVa, Aug 3, 33; m 60; c 3. *Educ:* Davis & Elkins Col, BS, 55; Univ Md, MS, 59; NDak State Univ, PhD(animal nutrit), 68.

*Mem:* AAAS; Am Soc Animal Sci; Am Soc Microbiol; Brit Soc Gen Microbiol. *Res:* Development of rumen protozoal controlled bovines; chemical, physiological, cultural and metabolical study of rumen bacteria and protozoa; microbial metabolic fate studies with lipoidal and pesticidal compounds. *Mailing Add:* 2132 Friley Rd Ames IA 50014

**WILLIAMS, QUENTIN CHRISTOPHER,** HIGH PRESSURE EXPERIMENTATION, CHEMICAL CONSTRAINTS ON DEEP EARTH STRUCTURE. *Current Pos:* Res geophys, Inst Tectonics, 88-91, asst prof, 91-95, ASSOC PROF, DEPT EARTH SCI, UNIV CALIF, SANTA CRUZ, 95- *Personal Data:* b Wilmington, Del, Jan 1, 64; m 87, Elise Knittle; c Byron F & Alanna K. *Educ:* Princeton Univ, AB, 83; Univ Calif, Berkeley, PhD(geol), 88. *Concurrent Pos:* Fac affil, Inst Tectonics, Univ Calif, Santa Cruz, 91-; pres fac fel, NSF, 93. *Mem:* Am Geophys Union; AAAS. *Res:* High pressure properties of minerals, melts and fluids; properties of Earth's mantle and core; chemical evolution of the terrestrial planets; role of water and carbon dioxide in the deep earth. *Mailing Add:* Dept Earth Sci Univ Calif Santa Cruz CA 95064. *Fax:* 408-459-2127; *E-Mail:* quentw@rupture.ucsc.edu

**WILLIAMS, RALPH C, JR,** INTERNAL MEDICINE, IMMUNOLOGY. *Current Pos:* PROF MED & CHMN DEPT, SCH MED, UNIV NMEX, 69- *Personal Data:* b Washington, DC, Feb 17, 28; m 51; c 4. *Educ:* Cornell Univ, AB, 50, MD, 54. *Prof Exp:* Guest investr immunol, Rockefeller Inst, 61-63; from asst prof to prof med, Med Sch, Univ Minn, Minneapolis, 63-69. *Concurrent Pos:* Consult, Bur Hearings & Appeals, Soc Security Admin, 65- *Mem:* Am Rheumatism Asn; Am Fedn Clin Res; Am Soc Clin Invest; Am Asn Immunol; Soc Exp Biol & Med; Am Chem Soc. *Res:* Rheumatic diseases; immunopathology; immunoglobulin abnormalities and their relation to disease. *Mailing Add:* Dept Med Univ Fla Box 277 JHMHC Gainesville FL 32610. *Fax:* 904-392-8483

**WILLIAMS, RALPH EDWARD,** PHYTOPATHOLOGY. *Current Pos:* PLANT PATHOLOGIST FOREST PEST MGT, FOREST SERV, USDA, 70- *Personal Data:* b Ontario, Ore, July 20, 43; m 63. *Educ:* Univ Idaho, BS, 65, MS, 69; Wash State Univ, PhD(plant path), 72. *Prof Exp:* Res asst plant path, Dept Plant Sci, Univ Idaho, 65-66, Wash State Univ, 66-68; res plant pathologist, Forest Serv, USDA, 67-70; weed control specialist, Latah County, Idaho, 70. *Mem:* Optical Soc Am. *Res:* Developed growth impact methodology; conducted survey and analyzed survey data for root disease centers in forests of northern Idaho and western Montana; developed models for root disease center occurrence; designed and established root disease management evaluations. *Mailing Add:* 507 Goodwin Dr Richardson TX 75081

**WILLIAMS, RAY CLAYTON,** PERIODONTOLOGY, MICROBIOLOGY. *Current Pos:* PROF & CHAIR, UNIV NC SCH DENT. *Personal Data:* b Louisville, Ky, July 17, 44. *Educ:* Samford Univ, AB, 66; Univ Ala, Birmingham, DMD, 70; Harvard Univ, cert periodont, 73. *Prof Exp:* Res fel periodont, Sch Dent Med, Harvard Univ, 70-73; res fel microbiol, Forsyth Dent Ctr, Boston, Mass, 70-74; from instr to asst prof, Sch Dent Med, Harvard Univ, 74-85, actg chmn dept, 82-83, chmn dept, 83-, assoc prof periodont, 85- *Concurrent Pos:* Consult, WRoxbury Vet Admin Hosp, Mass, 77-80, attend physician, 80-; consult, Children's Hosp Med Ctr, 81- *Mem:* Am Acad Periodont; Int Asn Dent Res; Am Soc Microbiol. *Res:* Pharmacologic interception of periodontal diseases; nuclear medicine. *Mailing Add:* Dept Periodont CB 7450 Brauer Hall Univ NC Sch Dent Chapel Hill NC 27599

**WILLIAMS, RAYMOND CRAWFORD,** VETERINARY ANATOMY. *Current Pos:* instr, 46-54, from asst prof to prof, 54-92, EMER PROF ANAT & HISTOL, SCH VET MED, TUSKEGEE UNIV, 92- *Personal Data:* b Kansas City, Mo, Sept 22, 24; m 59, Shirley Walton; c Sherelle. *Educ:* Kans State Col, DVM, 46; Cornell Univ, MS, 55, PhD, 61. *Prof Exp:* Asst vet, UN Relief & Rehab Admin, 46. *Concurrent Pos:* Vis prof, Cornell Univ, 75; external examr, Univ Ibadan, Nigeria, 76-77; mem, Fulbright Life Adv Comt, 82-85. *Mem:* AAAS; Am Vet Med Asn; Am Asn Vet Anat; World Asn Vet Anat; Southern Soc Anatomists. *Res:* Descriptive vertebrate anatomy; fetal size and age relationships; dentition development; anatomical museum methods. *Mailing Add:* 706 Patterson St Tuskegee AL 36088

**WILLIAMS, REDFORD BROWN, JR,** BEHAVIORAL MEDICINE, PSYCHOSOMATIC MEDICINE. *Current Pos:* from asst prof psychiat & med to assoc prof psychiat, 72-78, PROF PSYCHIAT, DUKE UNIV MED CTR, 78-, DIR, BEHAV MED RES CTR, 85-, PROF PSYCHOL, 91- *Personal Data:* b Raleigh, NC, Dec 14, 40; m 63, Virginia Parrott; c Jennifer & Lloyd. *Educ:* Harvard Univ, AB, 63; Yale Univ Sch Med, MD, 67. *Honors & Awards:* Upjohn Distinguished Scientists Award, Soc Behav Med. *Prof Exp:* Intern & resident internal med, Yale-New Haven Hosp & Med Ctr, 67-70; clin assoc clin psychophysiol, NIH, 70-72; adj prof epidemiol, Sch Pub Health, Univ NC, Chapel Hill, 89- *Concurrent Pos:* Assoc prof med, Duke Univ Med Ctr, 81-; prin investr, NIMH res scientist develop award, 74-84 & 84-89, Nat Heart Lung & Blood Inst, 76-91; mem, Behav Med Study Sect, NIH, 79-82; consult, President's Biomed & Behav Res Panel, 75-76; lectr, Japanese Psychosomatic Soc, 83; vis scientist, USSR Cardiol Res Ctr, 87. *Mem:* Fel Soc Behav Med (pres, 83-84); Am Psychosomatic Soc (pres, 92-93); Acad Behav Med Res (pres, 95-96); Am Col Neuropsychopharmacol; Soc Psychophysiol Res; Am Heart Asn. *Res:* Behavioral medicine, identification of biobehavioral factors that play a role in the etiology, pathogenesis and course of coronary heart disease, with particular emphasis on type A behavior, hostility and anger; application of behavioral interventions in prevention and treatment of medical illness. *Mailing Add:* Box 3926 Duke Univ Med Ctr Durham NC 27710. *Fax:* 919-681-8960; *E-Mail:* rbw@bmrc.duke.edu

**WILLIAMS, REED CHESTER,** ANALYTICAL CHEMISTRY. *Current Pos:* PRIN RES SCIENTIST, DUPONT-MERCK CO, 90- *Personal Data:* b Chicago, Ill, June 10, 41. *Educ:* Lawrence Univ, BA, 63; Univ Wash, PhD(chem), 68. *Prof Exp:* Res chemist, E I Du Pont de Nemours & Co, Inc, 68-90. *Mem:* Am Chem Soc; Sigma Xi. *Res:* Analytical chemistry; application of high speed liquid column chromatography to the separation and quantitation of complex mixtures. *Mailing Add:* 51 Fox Den Rd Newark DE 19898

**WILLIAMS, RICHARD,** PHYSICAL CHEMISTRY. *Current Pos:* RETIRED. *Personal Data:* b Chicago, Ill, Aug 5, 27; m 61, Alma Eusebietti; c Elena, Cristina & Matthew. *Educ:* Miami Univ, AB, 50; Harvard Univ, PhD(phys chem), 54. *Honors & Awards:* Callinan Prize, Electrochem Soc; NJ Inventor's Hall of Fame; Fulbright lectr, Sao Carlos Sch Eng, 69. *Prof Exp:* Instr chem, Harvard Univ, 55-58; mem tech staff, RCA Labs, 58-91. *Mem:* Fel Am Phys Soc; Brazilian Acad Sci. *Res:* Electrical properties of insulators; liquid crystals; luminescence of organic molecules; physical chemistry of surfaces. *Mailing Add:* 25 Wheat Sheaf Lane Princeton NJ 08540. *Fax:* 609-734-2762

**WILLIAMS, RICHARD, JR,** ANIMAL SCIENCE. *Current Pos:* INSTR & ANIMAL SCIENTIST, ALCORN STATE UNIV, 70-, INSTR COOP EXTEN, 89- *Personal Data:* b Centerville, Miss, Jan 31, 47; m 81, Voletta A Polk; c Sharon, TeAndrea, Orland & DeVeron. *Educ:* Alcorn State Univ, BS, 70; Miss State Univ, MS, 76. *Prof Exp:* Forestry specialist, Ore State Univ, Portland, 66-67. *Res:* Animal science. *Mailing Add:* Alcorn State Univ Agr Res Prog 1000 Asu Dr No 330 Lorman MS 39096

**WILLIAMS, RICHARD ALVIN,** ELECTRICAL ENGINEERING, COMPUTER SCIENCE. *Current Pos:* SR ENGR SPECIALIST, LOCKHEED MARTIN, 87- *Personal Data:* b Canton, Ohio, July 21, 36; m 72, Dawn E (Shoemaker); c Mark, Matthew, Dylan & Collin. *Educ:* Ohio State Univ, BSEE, 59, MSc, 61, PhD(elec eng), 65. *Prof Exp:* Staff mem reliability eng, Sandia Corp, NMex, 59-60; assoc supvr, Electrosci Lab, Ohio State Univ, 60-68, asst prof elec eng, 66-68; assoc prof elec eng, Univ Akron, 68-89; eng specialist, Goodyear Aerospace Corp, 79-86. *Res:* Communications; communication satellite systems; computers, simulation programming and application; environmental engineering; electric power systems; transportation; aerospace electronics; geographic information systems; geophysical data bases; aircraft/vehicle simulation. *Mailing Add:* 7540 Fawn Dr NW North Canton OH 44720-6831. *Fax:* 330-796-4050

**WILLIAMS, RICHARD ANDERSON,** ADVANCED STRUCTURAL MATERIALS & COMPOSITES. *Current Pos:* RETIRED. *Personal Data:* b Akron, Ohio, July 21, 31; m 96, Elizabeth Elechko; c 5. *Educ:* Wabash Col, AB, 53; Univ Rochester, PhD(chem), 57. *Prof Exp:* Res chemist, Patent Div, E I Du Pont de Nemours & Co, 56-60, sr res chemist, Nylon Tech Div, 60-68, supvr res, Qiana Tech Div, 68-71, supvr res & develop, Orlon-Lycra Tech Div, 71-72, patent supvr, Patent Liaison Div, Textile Fibers Dept, 72-77, develop assoc, Carpet Fibers Tech Div, 77-84, patent assoc, 84-86, sr patent assoc, Textile Fibers Dept, 87-89, intellectual property mgr, DuPont Fibres, 89-91. *Res:* Olefin-forming elimination reactions; polymer chemistry; synthetic fibers and applications. *Mailing Add:* 819 Morris Rd Hockessin DE 19707

**WILLIAMS, RICHARD JOHN,** SCIENCE ADMINISTRATION, PLANETARY & EARTH SCIENCES. *Current Pos:* RETIRED. *Personal Data:* b Hazleton, Pa, May 24, 44; m 66. *Educ:* Lehigh Univ, BA, 66; Johns Hopkins Univ, MA, 68, PhD(geochem), 70; Univ Houston, MA, 83. *Honors & Awards:* Sigma Xi. *Prof Exp:* Space scientist lunar studies, NASA Hq, 70-73, sr space scientist lunar & planetary studies, 73-78, supvry space scientist, 79-87, sr oper mgt engr, 88-94. *Mem:* Am Inst Aeronaut & Astronaut; Am Geophys Union; AAAS; Nat Mgt Asn. *Res:* Theoretical and experimental petrology; space industrialization; science and technology policy. *Mailing Add:* 11907 Winterthur Lane No 108 Reston VA 20191

**WILLIAMS, RICHARD KELSO,** MATHEMATICS. *Current Pos:* From asst prof to assoc prof, 65-77, chmn dept, 78-80, PROF MATH, SOUTHERN METHODIST UNIV, 77- *Personal Data:* b Chattanooga, Tenn, Oct 20, 38; m 66, Kathryn Webb; c Samuel Webb & Joseph Mark. *Educ:* Vanderbilt Univ, BA, 60, MA, 62, PhD(math), 65. *Mem:* Math Asn Am; Am Math Soc. *Res:* Complex function theory; topology. *Mailing Add:* Dept Math Southern Methodist Univ Dallas TX 75275-0001

**WILLIAMS, RICHARD STANLEY,** NANOMATERIALS, QUANTUM ELECTRONICS. *Current Pos:* from asst prof to assoc prof, 80-86, vchmn, 91-93, PROF PHYS CHEM, UNIV CALIF, LOS ANGELES, 86-; PRIN LAB SCIENTIST, DIR BASIC RES, HEWLETT-PACKARD LABS, 95- *Personal Data:* b Kodiak, Alaska, Oct 27, 51; m 90, Jennifer Kao. *Educ:* Rice Univ, BA, 74; Univ Calif, Berkeley, MS, 76, PhD(chem), 78. *Prof Exp:* Mem tech staff, AT&T Bell Labs, 78-80. *Concurrent Pos:* Frontier Mat Res Prog, Rikagaku Kenkyusho (Inst Physics & Chem Res Japan) Wako-shi, Saitma, Japan, 87-; res award, Camille & Henry Dreyfus Found, 83, Alfred P Sloan Found, 84; adv, AONO Atomcraft Proj, Tsukuba, Japan, 89-94; lectr, Pepperdine Univ Bus Sch, 89-94. *Mem:* Am Chem Soc; Am Phys Soc; Am Vacuum Soc; Mat Res Soc; AAAS. *Res:* Chemistry and physics of nanometer-scale materials, with emphasis on those properties that may yield useful electronic or optical structures. *Mailing Add:* Hewlett-Packard Labs 3500 Deer Creek Rd Palo Alto CA 94304-1392. *E-Mail:* stan__williams@hpl.hp.com

**WILLIAMS, RICHARD SUGDEN, JR,** SATELLITE GLACIOLOGY, PLANETARY VOLCANIC GEOMORPHOLOGY. *Current Pos:* RES GEOLOGIST, US GEOL SURV, 71- *Personal Data:* b New York, NY, Dec 6, 38; m 60, Mary E Davis; c Jonathan & Christopher. *Educ:* Univ Mich, Ann Arbor, BS, 61, MS, 62; Pa State Univ, PhD(geol), 65. *Honors & Awards:* Alan Gordon Mem Award, 78; Meritorious Serv Award, Am Soc Photogram & Remote Sensing, 79. *Prof Exp:* Proj scientist geol, Air Force Cambridge Res Labs, USAF, 65-68, res geologist, 68-69, br chief, 69-71. *Concurrent Pos:* Assoc ed, J Photogram Eng & Remote Sensing, 76-77; 2nd dep, 1st dep & dir, Remote Sensing Appln Div, Am Soc Photogram & Remote Sensing, 76-79; expert consult, World Glacier Monitoring Serv, UNESCO, 82-; sci corresp, Dagens Nyheter, Stockholm, Sweden, 83-90; mem, Gov Coun, Int Glaciol Soc, 83-87; chief sci ed, Annals of Glaciol, 86-87; mem, Joint Satellite Mapping & Remote Sensing Comt, Am Soc Photogram Eng & Remote Sensing, Am Congr Surv & Mapping, 87-; mem, US Global Chg Res Prog, Working Group Global Chg & Comt Earth & Environ Sci, Fed Coord Coun Sci Educ & Technol, Off Sci & Tech Policy & Exec Off Pres, 87-91; mem, Earth Sci Educ, K-12, Framework Steering Comt, Am Geol Inst, 88-91 & Comt Res & Explor, Nat Geol Surv, 90-; mem-at-large, Sect E, Geol & Geog, AAAS, 89-92; adj prof, World Affairs Prog, Sch Foreign Serv, Georgetown Univ, 92-; mem, Comt Global Environ Chg, Am Geophys Union, 93- *Mem:* Fel Geol Soc Am; fel Iceland Sci Soc; Am Geophys Union; Int Glaciol Soc; AAAS; Am Soc Photogram & Remote Sensing. *Res:* Satellite/aerial remote sensing of dynamic geomorphic processes; volcanoes and glaciers with emphasis on Iceland; landsat data to monitor global environmental change on the Earth's surface; author of over 180 publications. *Mailing Add:* US Geol Surv 384 Woods Hole Rd Woods Hole MA 02543-1598. *Fax:* 508-540-6490; *E-Mail:* rwilliam@nobska.er.usgs.gov

**WILLIAMS, RICHARD TAYLOR,** SOLID STATE PHYSICS. *Current Pos:* PHYSICIST, NAVAL RES LAB, 69- *Personal Data:* b Tarboro, NC, May 27, 46. *Educ:* Wake Forest Univ, BS, 68; Princeton Univ, MA, 71, PhD(physics), 74. *Mem:* Am Phys Soc; AAAS. *Res:* Effects of ionizing radiation in insulating solids, particularly time-resolved studies of exciton self-trapping and defect formation in halide crystals; vacuum-ultraviolet spectroscopy of solids. *Mailing Add:* Dept Physics Wake Forest Univ Box 7507 1834 Reynold A Rd Winston-Salem NC 27106. *Fax:* 919-759-6142

**WILLIAMS, RICKEY JAY,** PHYSICAL INORGANIC CHEMISTRY. *Current Pos:* from asst prof to assoc prof, Midwestern State Univ, 71-80, prof & head, Dept Chem, Physics, Geol & Geophys, 80-82, chem prog coordr, 82-85, actg chmn chem, 85-86, PROF CHEM, MIDWESTERN STATE UNIV, 86- *Personal Data:* b Muskogee, Okla, May 13, 42; m 70, Jeanne Freemen; c Deborah K (Piland), Gregory S & Jay L. *Educ:* Tex Christian Univ, BA, 64, MD, PhD(phys chem), 68. *Prof Exp:* Fel, Los Alamos Sci Lab, 68-70 & Baylor Univ, 70-71. *Mem:* Am Crystallog Asn; Am Chem Soc; Sigma Xi. *Res:* Crystal structure studies of inorganic compounds; heavy metal determinations in environmental samples. *Mailing Add:* 2417 Fain St Wichita Falls TX 76308-2998

**WILLIAMS, ROBERT ALLEN,** NUCLEAR CHEMISTRY. *Current Pos:* Res assoc nuclear chem, 72-73, presidential intern, 73-74, STAFF MEM NUCLEAR CHEM, LOS ALAMOS SCI LAB, UNIV CALIF, 74- *Personal Data:* b Cleveland, Ohio, Apr 25, 45. *Educ:* Oberlin Col, BA, 66; Carnegie-Mellon Univ, MS, 69, PhD(nuclear chem), 72. *Mem:* Am Chem Soc; Am Phys Soc; Sigma Xi. *Res:* Pionic nuclear reactions; neutron activation analysis; nuclear spectroscopy; computer applications; data acquisition software systems. *Mailing Add:* 1063 48th St Los Alamos NM 87544

**WILLIAMS, ROBERT CALVIN,** ANALYTICAL CHEMISTRY, PHYSICAL CHEMISTRY. *Current Pos:* res specialist, 79, sr res & develop chemist, 79-83, RES & DEVELOP ASSOC, BF GOODRICH CHEM GROUP, 83- *Personal Data:* b Key West, Fla, May 1, 44; m 69; c 1. *Educ:* Univ Kans, BS, 66; Univ Wis-Madison, PhD(phys chem), 72. *Prof Exp:* Instr chem, Univ Nebr-Lincoln, 72-74; sr chemist, Cent Res Labs, 3M Co, 74-79. *Concurrent Pos:* Res assoc, Univ Nebr-Lincoln, 72-74. *Mem:* Am Chem Soc; Am Phys Soc; Soc Appl Spectros; Coblentz Soc; Am Soc Testing Mat. *Res:* Analytical applications of fourier transform infrared spectroscopy; computer-coupled instrumentation and instrumental methods of analysis; molecular specroscopy, particularly infrared and mass spectroscopy; infrared normal coordinate analysis; polymer characterization. *Mailing Add:* BF Goodrich 9921 Brecksville Rd Brecksville OH 44141-3201

**WILLIAMS, ROBERT EUGENE,** ASTRONOMY. *Current Pos:* DIR, SPACE TELESCOPE SCI INST, 93- *Personal Data:* b Dunsmuir, Calif, Oct 14, 40; m 61, Elaine C Eckwall; c Scott F. *Educ:* Univ Calif, Berkeley, AB, 62; Univ Wis, PhD, 65. *Honors & Awards:* Dorothy Klumpke Roberts Prize, 62; Alexander von Humboldt Award, Ger Govt, 91; Heinz Pagels Mem Lectr, 95; Stanford Bunyon Lectr, 95; Princeton Evnin Lectr, 97. *Prof Exp:* From asst prof to prof, Univ Ariz, 65-83; vis res assoc, Europ Soc Observ, 83-84; Nat Res Coun sr res fel, NASA-Ames Res Ctr, 84-85; dir, Cerro Tololo Int Am Observ, Chile, 85-93. *Concurrent Pos:* Fulbright prof, Univ London, 71-72, sr Fulbright prof, 72-73; chmn, US Nat Fulbright Comn Astron, 74-78; mem, Cerro Tololo Int Am Observ Telescope Allocation Comt, 76-78; mem, Kitt Peak Nat Observ Telescope Allocation Comt, 78-80; mem, NSF Minority Grad Fel Panel, 82-85; adj prof, Johns Hopkins Univ, 93-; mem, Nat Res Coun Space Studies Bd, 95- *Mem:* Int Astron Union; Am Astron Soc. *Res:* Author of over 100 professional papers. *Mailing Add:* Space Telescope Sci Inst 3700 San Martin Dr Baltimore MD 21218-2410

**WILLIAMS, ROBERT FONES,** TOPOLOGY, CHAOTIC DYNAMICAL SYSTEMS. *Current Pos:* PROF MATH, UNIV TEX, AUSTIN, 87- *Personal Data:* b Bessemer, Ala, July 27, 28; div; c Ellen L. *Educ:* Univ Tex, BA, 48; Univ Va, PhD(math), 54. *Prof Exp:* Asst prof math, Fla State Univ, 54-55; vis lectr, Univ Wis, 55-56; asst prof, Purdue Univ, 56-59; NSF fel & mem, Inst Adv Study, 59-61; asst prof, Univ Chicago, 61-63; from asst prof to prof math, Northwestern Univ, Evanston, 63-87. *Concurrent Pos:* NSF grant, Univ Geneva, 68-69 & Inst Advan Sci Study, Bures-sur-Yvette, France, 70, 72-73; grant, Inst Pure & Appl Math, Rio de Janeiro, 75, 81 & 86. *Mem:* Am Math Soc; Math Asn Am; AAAS; Coun Am Math Soc. *Res:* Transformation groups; topological dynamics; global analysis; differentiable dynamical systems; symbolic dynamics; strange attractors; chaos knot theory. *Mailing Add:* Dept Math Univ Tex Austin TX 78712-1082. *E-Mail:* bob@math.utexas.edu

**WILLIAMS, ROBERT H,** NUCLEAR ENERGY POLICY, BIOENERGY. *Current Pos:* SR RES SCIENTIST, CTR ENERGY & ENVIRON STUDIES & HEAD, TECHNOL ASSESSMENT/ENERGY POLICY ANALYSIS GROUP, PRINCETON UNIV, 75- *Personal Data:* b June 23, 40. *Educ:* Yale Univ, BS, 62; Univ Calif, Berkeley, PhD(theoret physics), 67. *Honors & Awards:* Leo Szilard Award, Am Phys Soc, 88; Sadi Carnot Award, US Dept Energy, 91; MacArthur Fel, 93; Joan Hodges, Queneau Palladium Medal, Nat Audubon Soc & Am Asn Eng Soc, 95. *Prof Exp:* Asst prof physics, Univ Mich, Ann Arbor, 71-72; chief scientist, Ford Found Energy Policy Proj, 72-75. *Concurrent Pos:* Vis prof environ sci, Dept Sci, Technol & Soc, Univ Utrecht, Neth. *Mem:* Fel Am Phys Soc. *Res:* Identify and develop long range global energy strategies; energy technology assessment; changing role of basic materials in industrialized societies; efficient energy use; nuclear energy; bioenergy; wind energy; photovoltaic energy; high-temperature solar thermal technology; hydrogen energy; cogeneration; advanced gas turbines for power generation; fuel cells and alternative fuels for transportation. *Mailing Add:* Ctr Energy & Environ Studies Princeton Univ Eng Quadrangle Princeton NJ 08544

**WILLIAMS, ROBERT HACKNEY,** ORGANIC CHEMISTRY. *Current Pos:* RETIRED. *Personal Data:* b Providence, RI, Jan 3, 15; m 42, Grace Elizabeth Berger; c Bruce L & Holly A. *Educ:* Univ NC, AB, 35, MA, 37; Temple Univ, PhD(chem), 53. *Prof Exp:* Res chemist, Mobil Res & Develop Lab, 38-42, sr res chemist, Cent Res Div Lab, 46-72, asst to admin mgr, Cent Res Div, 72-75. *Concurrent Pos:* Vchmn, Punta Gorda-Charlotte Water & Sewer Bd, 78-81; mem water adv bd, Southwest Fla Regional Planning Coun, 78-81. *Mem:* Am Chem Soc; Am Inst Chem; Sigma Xi. *Res:* Petroleum additives; hydrocracking; lube oil manufacture and composition; radiation chemistry of hydrocarbons; application of nuclear radiation to petroleum processing; radiation and photochemical induced organic chemical reactions; oxidation of hydrocarbons. *Mailing Add:* 23033 Westchester Blvd Apt F-515 Port Charlotte FL 33980-8468

**WILLIAMS, ROBERT J(AMES),** INDUSTRIAL ENGINEERING. *Current Pos:* assoc prof, 63-77, PROF ENG DESIGN & ECON EVAL, UNIV COLO, BOULDER, 77- *Personal Data:* b Iron Mountain, Mich, Sept 12, 23; m 47; c 4. *Educ:* Mich State Univ, BSME, 47, MSME, 53. *Prof Exp:* Instr mech eng, Univ Colo, 48-51; sr indust engr, Boeing Airplane Co, 51-54; from asst prof to assoc prof mech eng, Univ Colo, 52-61, chmn dept, 56-61; indust cngr, Fry & Assocs, 61-63. *Concurrent Pos:* Consult, Vet Admin Hosp, Seattle, 53, Boeing Airplane Co, 58, Mountain States Tel & Tel Co, 59-, Babcock & Wilcox Co, Ohio, 60 & Govt of India, 61-63. *Mem:* Am Soc Mech Engrs; Am Soc Eng Educ; Am Inst Indust Engrs; Opers Res Soc Am. *Res:* Process engineering; engineering economics. *Mailing Add:* 3021 14th St Boulder CO 80304

**WILLIAMS, ROBERT JACKSON,** physiology, biophysics, for more information see previous edition

**WILLIAMS, ROBERT K,** ENTOMOLOGY, CELL BIOLOGY. *Current Pos:* RETIRED. *Personal Data:* b Ft Worth, Tex, Jan 6, 28; m 52; c 3. *Educ:* Agr & Mech Col Tex, BS, 48, MS, 56, PhD(entom), 59. *Prof Exp:* Asst co agent in training, Agr Exten Serv, Agr & Mech Col, Tex, 48, asst co agent, Agr Exten Serv & Wood Co, 48, Agr Exten Serv & Bowie Co, 50 & Agr Exten Serv & Eastland Co, 52-54, res ast entomologist, Col, 54-58; prof biol, ETex State Univ, 58- *Concurrent Pos:* NSF Col Sci Improv Prog grant, Dept Physiol Chem, Univ Wis, 69-70. *Res:* Physiology; cell physiology; rotaria. *Mailing Add:* 808 Greenbrook Allen TX 75002

**WILLIAMS, ROBERT L,** PSYCHIATRY, NEUROLOGY. *Current Pos:* chmn, Dept Psychiat, Baylor Col Med, 72-90, prof psychiat, 72-92, actg chmn, Neural Dept, 76-77, prof neurol, 76-92, EMER PROF PSYCHIAT & NEUROL, BAYLOR COL MED, 92- *Personal Data:* b Buffalo, NY, July 22, 22; m 49, Shirley Miller; c Karen L. *Educ:* Alfred Univ, BA, 44; Albany Med Col, Union Univ, NY, MD, 46. *Honors & Awards:* E B Bowis Award, Am Col Psychiatrists. *Prof Exp:* Chief, Air Force Neurol Ctr, Lackland AFB Hosp, 52-55, chief neuropsychiat serv, 53-55, chief consult, Off Surgeon Gen, USAF, 55-58; from assoc prof to prof psychiat & neurol, Col Med, Univ Fla, 58-72, chmn, Dept Psychiat, 64-72. *Concurrent Pos:* Mem, Nat Adv Ment Health Coun & Nat Adv Neurol Dis & Blindness Coun, 55-58; Fla rep, Comn Ment Illness, Southern Regional Educ Bd, 64-72, chmn, 71-72; psychiat consult, Indust Security Prog, Dept Defense & consult psychiat & neurol, Surgeon Gen, USAF, 66-; pres, Benjamin Rush Soc, 86-88; mem, Accreditation Coun Grad Med Educ, Residency Rev Comt Psychiat, 88-93. *Mem:* Am Asn Chmn Depts Psychiat (pres, 84-85); AMA; fel Am Psychiat Asn; fel Am Acad Neurol; Am Electroencephalog Soc; fel Am Col Psychiatrists (pres, 82-83). *Res:* Psychophysiology of sleep; medical education. *Mailing Add:* 1744 South Blvd Houston TX 77098. *Fax:* 713-523-7968; *E-Mail:* rwilli3541@aol.com

**WILLIAMS, ROBERT LAWRENCE,** MEDICINE, PUBLIC HEALTH. *Current Pos:* ASST PROF FAMILY MED, CASE WESTERN RES UNIV, 90-; DIR FAMILY PRACT, METRO-HEALTH CTR COMMUNITY HEALTH & DEPT FAMILY MED, METROHEALTH CLEMENT CTR, 90- *Personal Data:* b San Antonio, Tex, May 13, 51; m, Carol Elizabeth Garner; c Meredith Nizhoni, Chloe Meaalofa & Colin Vaughn. *Educ:* Univ Tex, Austin, BA, 73; Baylor Col Med, MD, 77; Harvard Univ, MPH, 90; Am Bd Family Pract, cert, 80. *Prof Exp:* Resident family mem, Univ Rochester-Highland Hosp, 77-80; field med officer, Crownpoint Indian Health Serv, 80-83, clin dir & chief staff hosp, 81-84, coordr, Emergency Med Servs, 83-85; chief consult, Family Med, Navajo Area Indian Health Serv, 85-87; chief, Outpatient Servs, Nat Hosp Western Samoa, 87-88. *Concurrent Pos:* Mem, Navajo Area Indian Health Serv Clin Servs Coord Comt, 81; clin instr family med, Univ Colo, 81-87; chair, Med Ethics Comt, Crownpoint Indian Health Serv Hosp, 83-87; prin investr, Indian Health Serv Res Grant, 84-85; mem, NAm Primary Care Res Group Interest Community Oriented Primary Care, 91-, chair, 93-; prin investr, Ohio Bd Regents, 91, Ohio Acad Family Physicians Found, 91, 93; mem, Clin Servs Comt, City Cleveland Healthy Family Health Start Proj, 92-; consult, Residency Training Grant, Bur Health Prof, Dept Med Educ, Richmond Heights Gen Hosp, 93-94; Fulbright scholar, Univ Natal, Durban, SAfrica, 96-97; Robert Wood Johnson Found scholar, 96- *Mailing Add:* Dept Family Med Case Western Res Univ 11001 Cedar Suite 306 Cleveland OH 44106

**WILLIAMS, ROBERT LEROY,** physics, for more information see previous edition

**WILLIAMS, ROBERT LLOYD,** INDUSTRIAL ENGINEERING, OPERATIONS RESEARCH. *Current Pos:* PROF INDUST & SYSTS ENG & CHMN DEPT, OHIO UNIV, 67- *Personal Data:* b Coshocton, Ohio, Mar 16, 33; m 59; c 4. *Educ:* Ohio State Univ, BS & MS, 60, PhD(indust eng), 64. *Prof Exp:* Res assoc & instr indust eng, Ohio State Univ, 60-64. *Concurrent Pos:* Chmn, Z-94 comt indust eng terminology, Am Nat Stand Inst, 66-; Hwy & Econ Growth res grant, 66-69; res contract, effects Hwy Warning Signs, 78-82. *Mem:* Am Inst Indust Engrs; Opers Res Soc Am. *Res:* Transportation systems. *Mailing Add:* Dept Indust & Systs Eng Ohio Univ Stocker Eng Ctr Rm 268 Athens OH 45701-2979

**WILLIAMS, ROBERT SANDERS,** MOLECULAR BIOLOGY, CARDIOVASCULAR PHYSIOLOGY. *Current Pos:* PROF MED, SOUTHWESTERN MED CTR, UNIV TEX, 90- *Personal Data:* b Athens, Ga, Oct 4, 48; m 73; c 3. *Educ:* Princeton Univ, AB; Duke Univ, MD, 74. *Honors & Awards:* Young Investr Award, Am Col Cardiol, 79, 81. *Prof Exp:* Asst prof med, Duke Univ, 80-86, asst prof physiol, 82-90, assoc prof med, 86-90. *Concurrent Pos:* Vis prof biochem, Oxford Univ, Eng, 84-85; mem, Coun Basic Sci, Am Heart Asn; Fogarty Int fel, 84-85. *Mem:* Am Fed Clin Res; Am Soc Clin Invest; Am Physiol Soc; Am Col Cardiol; Asn Am Physicians. *Res:* Mitochondial biogenesis in striated muscles; regulation of gene expression by contractile activity in striated muscles. *Mailing Add:* Univ Tex Southwestern Med Ctr 5323 Harry Hines Blvd Dallas TX 75235-8573

**WILLIAMS, ROBERT WALTER,** EXPERIMENTAL HIGH-ENERGY PHYSICS. *Current Pos:* prof, 59-90, EMER PROF PHYSICS, UNIV WASH, 90- *Personal Data:* b Palo Alto, Calif, June 3, 20; m 46, 58, 69, Erica Lehman; c Paul, David & Eric. *Educ:* Stanford Univ, AB, 41; Princeton Univ, MA, 43; Mass Inst Technol, PhD(physics), 48. *Prof Exp:* Lab asst, Princeton Univ, 41-42; from jr physicist to assoc physicist, Manhattan Proj, Princeton Univ & Los Alamos Sci Lab, 42-46; res assoc, Mass Inst Technol, 46-48, from asst prof to assoc prof, 48-59. *Concurrent Pos:* Sci assoc, Europ Orgn Nuclear Res, 67-68, 74-75, 81-82 & 88-; trustee, Univ Res Asn, 78-84. *Mem:* Fel Am Phys Soc; fel Am Acad Arts & Sci. *Res:* Elementary particle physics using high-energy accelerators; cosmic rays; elementary particles, especially properties of the muon; neutrino and electron-positron collider physics. *Mailing Add:* Physics Dept Univ Wash Box 351560 Seattle WA 98195-1560

**WILLIAMS, ROBIN,** COMPUTER SCIENCE, DISTRIBUTED PROCESSING. *Current Pos:* mgr distrib comput, IBM Res, 72-80, mgr, Database & Distrib Systs Dept, 80-83, mgr, Off Systs Dept, 83-90, MGR IMAGE & MULTIMEDIA SYSTS, IBM RES, 90- *Personal Data:* b Southampton, Eng, July 10, 41; US citizen; m 65, Maryke; c Heather & Jennifer. *Educ:* Univ London, BSc, 62; NY Univ, MS, 68, PhD(comput sci), 71. *Prof Exp:* Staff mem optical character recognition, Mullard Res Labs, Philips Co, Eng, 62-64; staff mem comput memories, Philips Res Labs, 64-67; asst prof & instr comput sci, NY Univ, 67-72. *Mem:* Asn Comput Mach; fel Inst Elec & Electronics Engrs. *Res:* Computer graphics; distributed processing; computer aided publishing; image systems; digital video. *Mailing Add:* Dept K52/803 IBM Almaden Res Ctr 650 Harry Rd San Jose CA 95120-6099

**WILLIAMS, ROBIN O('DARE),** METALLURGY, THERMODYNAMICS. *Current Pos:* RETIRED. *Personal Data:* b Greensboro, NC, Dec 26, 27; m 53; c 4. *Educ:* Univ Tenn, BS, 48, MS, 50; Carnegie-Mellon Univ, PhD(metall), 55. *Prof Exp:* Metallurgist, Oak Ridge Nat Lab, 48-51, consult, 51-54; res assoc, Res Lab, Gen Elec Co, 54-56; sr res supvr, Cincinnati Milacron, 56-59; metallurgist, Oak Ridge Nat Lab, 59-88. *Res:* Preferred orientation of deformed metals; precipitation hardening of alloys; stored energy of deformation; structure and thermodynamics of solid solutions; x-ray diffraction; order-disorder; software development and data reduction; spinodal decomposition; coherent phase equilibria. *Mailing Add:* 906 W Outer Dr Oak Ridge TN 37830

**WILLIAMS, ROBLEY COOK,** biophysics, electron microscopy; deceased, see previous edition for last biography

**WILLIAMS, ROBLEY COOK, JR,** PHYSICAL BIOCHEMISTRY, CYTOSKELETON BIOCHEMISTRY. *Current Pos:* assoc prof, 76-85, PROF MOLECULAR BIOL, VANDERBILT UNIV, 85- *Personal Data:* b Ann Arbor, Mich, Oct 15, 40; m 68, June Henrich; c Elliot & Ruth. *Educ:* Cornell Univ, BA, 62; Rockefeller Univ, PhD(phys biochem), 68. *Prof Exp:* Nat Inst Arthritis & Metab Dis fel, State Univ NY, Buffalo, 67-68; from asst prof to assoc prof biol, Yale Univ, 69-76. *Concurrent Pos:* Mem study sect biophys & biophys chem, NIH, 77-81, chmn, 79-81; fac assoc, US Antarctic Res Prog, McMurdo Sta, 79 & 81, Palmer Sta, 85 & 91. *Mem:* Am Soc Cell Biol; Am Chem Soc; Biophys Soc; Am Soc Biol Chemists. *Res:* Protein-protein association, structure-function relationships in proteins, assembly and function of microtubules and intermediate filaments, protein folding. *Mailing Add:* Dept Molecular Biol Vanderbilt Univ Nashville TN 37235

**WILLIAMS, ROGER LEA,** CLINICAL PHARMACOLOGY, INTERNAL MEDICINE. *Current Pos:* ASSOC DIR SCI & MED AFFAIRS, FOOD & DRUG ADMIN, 91- *Personal Data:* b Hamilton, Ohio, Jan 5, 41; c 2. *Educ:* Oberlin Col, BA, 63; Univ Chicago, MD, 67. *Prof Exp:* Intern med, Univ Chicago Hosps & Clins, 67-68, resident, 67-71; fel clin pharmacol, Univ Calif, San Francisco, 74-77, asst prof med & pharm, 77-91. *Concurrent Pos:* Consult, Rev Panel New Drug Regulation, HEW, 76-77 & Task Force, Calif Citizen Action Group, 77-78. *Mem:* Am Fedn Clin; Am Soc Clin Pharmacol & Therapeut. *Res:* Clinical research drug risk and efficacy for new and established drug products; academic clinical drug investigation. *Mailing Add:* Ctr Drug Eval & Res HFD 5600 Fishers Lane Rockville MD 20857

**WILLIAMS, ROGER NEAL,** ENTOMOLOGY. *Current Pos:* assoc prof, 74-82, PROF ENTOM, OHIO AGR RES & DEVELOP CTR & OHIO STATE UNIV, 82- *Personal Data:* b Amityville, NY, Apr 3, 35; m 59; c 3. *Educ:* Tex Tech Univ, BS, 57; La State Univ, MS, 64, PhD(entom), 66. *Prof Exp:* Res trainee entom, United Brands Co, Honduras, 58-62; res asst, La State Univ, 62-66; res entomologist, IRI Res Inst, Brazil, 66-68; asst prof, Ohio State Univ, Brazil, 68-73. *Mem:* Entom Soc Am; Int Orgn Biol Control; Soc Entom Brazil. *Res:* Biology and control of small fruit insect pests with chemicals and natural enemies; biological control of insect tropical pastures and ranges; natural enemies, chemical control and attractants of sap beetles; pest management tropical crops; cocoa, bananas and other horticultural crops. *Mailing Add:* 1455 McNutt Dr Wooster OH 44691

**WILLIAMS, ROGER RICHARD,** CARDIOVASCULAR GENETICS, PREVENTIVE MEDICINE. *Current Pos:* from asst prof to assoc prof, 76-85, PROF INTERNAL MED, UNIV UTAH MED SCH, 85- *Personal Data:* b Ogden, Utah, Aug 11, 44; m 68; c 7. *Educ:* Weber State Col, BS; Univ Utah Col Med, MD, 71. *Prof Exp:* Med resident internal med, Duke Univ Med Ctr, 71-73; res assoc cancer epidemiol, Nat Cancer Inst, 73-74 & cardiovasc epidemiol, Nat Heart-Lung Inst, 74-75; investr, cardiovascular epidemiol, Nat Heart, Lung & Blood Inst, 75-76. *Concurrent Pos:* Mem & chmn, Epidemiol & Dis Control Sect, NIH, 78-84; prin investr, Cardiovascular Genetics Res Clin, Sch Med, Univ Utah, 77-, dir, 80-; chmn, Pharm & Therapeut Comt, Univ Utah Hosp, 80-; chmn, Coord Coun Diabetes Control Prog, Utah State Dept Health, 84- *Res:* Genetic and environmental determinants of early heart attacks and high blood pressure. *Mailing Add:* 50 N Medical Dr Salt Lake City UT 84132-1001

**WILLIAMS, ROGER STEWART,** CLINICAL NEUROLOGY, NEUROPATHOLOGY. *Current Pos:* instr, 73-78, ASST PROF NEUROL, HARVARD MED SCH, 78- *Personal Data:* b San Diego, Calif, Feb 15, 41; m 74; c 4. *Educ:* Emory Univ, MD, 66. *Prof Exp:* Med intern, Grady Mem Hosp, Atlanta, Ga, 66-67, med resident, 67-68; med officer, US Navy, 68-70; neurol resident, Mass Gen Hosp, Boston, Mass, 70-73. *Concurrent Pos:* Res fel neurol, Mass Gen Hosp, 73-76; res fel neurosci, Joseph P Kennedy Jr Mem Found, 74-76; assoc neurologist, McLean Hosp, Belmont, Mass, 75-; clin assoc neurol, Mass Gen Hosp, 75-; investr, Schizophrenia Res Found of the Scottish Rite, 75-80; asst neurol, Mass Gen Hosp, 78-87; assoc prof med, Univ Wash Med Sch, 87- *Mem:* Am Acad Neurol; Epilepsy Found Am; Soc Neurosci. *Res:* Experimental neuropathology of the developing nervous system. *Mailing Add:* Billings Clin 2825 Eighth Ave N Billings MT 59101-0909

**WILLIAMS, ROGER TERRY,** DYNAMIC METEOROLOGY. *Current Pos:* assoc prof, 68-74, PROF METEOROL, NAVAL POSTGRAD SCH, 74- *Personal Data:* b Covina, Calif, June 15, 36; m 64, Jan Pitts; c Deborah, Peter, Sarah & Joshua. *Educ:* Univ Calif, Los Angeles, AB, 59, MS, 61, PhD(meteorol), 63. *Prof Exp:* Ford Found fel, Univ Calif, Los Angeles, 63-64; res assoc meteorol, Mass Inst Technol, 64-66; asst prof, Univ Utah, 66-68. *Concurrent Pos:* Mem, FGGE Adv Panel, Nat Res Coun, 74-80. *Mem:* AAAS; fel Am Meteorol Soc. *Res:* Numerical weather prediction; dynamics of the atmosphere and other geophysical systems; application of numerical methods; dynamics of atmospheric waves and fronts; tropical cyclones. *Mailing Add:* Dept Meteorol Naval Postgrad Sch Monterey CA 93943

**WILLIAMS, RONALD LEE,** pharmacology, medicine, for more information see previous edition

**WILLIAMS, RONALD LLOYDE,** PHYSICAL CHEMISTRY, ENVIRONMENTAL CHEMISTRY. *Current Pos:* RES CHEMIST, GEN MOTORS RES LABS, 72- *Personal Data:* b Northfield, Minn, May 7, 44; m 64; c 2. *Educ:* St Olaf Col, BA, 66; Iowa State Univ, PhD(phys chem), 70. *Prof Exp:* Fel, Univ Calif, Irvine, 70-72. *Mem:* Am Chem Soc; Soc Automotive Engrs; Air & Waste Mgt Asn. *Res:* Reaction kinetics; hot atom reactions; unreplaned emissions from tires, brakes, refrigeration systems and diesel automobiles; wastewater treatment. *Mailing Add:* 4018 Hillside Royal Oak MI 48073-6263

**WILLIAMS, RONALD WENDELL,** SOLID STATE PHYSICS. *Current Pos:* from asst prof to assoc prof, 70-79, PROF ELEC ENG, UNIV VT, 79- *Personal Data:* b Atlanta, Ga, Nov 9, 39; m 63; c 3. *Educ:* Christian Bros Col, BSc, 62; Iowa State Univ, PhD(physics), 66. *Prof Exp:* Instr physics, Iowa State Univ, 66-67; staff scientist, Oak Ridge Nat Lab, 67-70. *Res:* Band structure and transport properties of metals; digital systems; very large scale integrated circuit design. *Mailing Add:* Dept Elec Eng Univ Vt Votey Bldg Burlington VT 05405-0156

**WILLIAMS, ROSS EDWARD,** PHYSICS. *Current Pos:* pres, 74-94, CHMN BD, OCEAN & ATMOSPHERIC SCI INC, 94- *Personal Data:* b Carlinville, Ill, June 28, 22; m 58, Madeline Peters; c Katherine, Robert (deceased) & Ross Jr. *Educ:* Bowdoin Col, BS, 43; Columbia Univ, MA, 47, PhD(physics), 55. *Prof Exp:* Sr res engr, Sperry Prod Inc, 47-49; consult physicist, Paul Rosenberg Assocs, 53-60; sr res assoc, Oceanog Acoust & Signal Processing, Hudson Labs, Columbia Univ, 60-65, asst dir, 65-66, assoc dir, 66-74, prof ocean eng, 68-74. *Concurrent Pos:* Mem, Comt Undersea Warfare, Nat Res Coun-Nat Acad Sci; consult, Naval Res Lab & Nat Acad Sci; chmn bd dirs, Ocean & Atmospheric Sci, Inc, 68- *Mem:* Fel Acoust Soc Am; Am Phys Soc; Am Soc Photogram; sr mem Inst Elec & Electronics Engrs. *Res:* Oceanography; acoustic propagation; surveillance system design; signal processing techniques; aerial reconnaissance; automatic mapping; optical data processing; electronic design. *Mailing Add:* 23 Alta Pl Centuck PO Yonkers NY 10710

**WILLIAMS, ROY EDWARD,** HYDROGEOLOGY. *Current Pos:* asst prof, 66-70, PROF HYDROGEOL & HYDROGEOLOGIST, UNIV IDAHO, 70- *Personal Data:* b Cookeville, Tenn, Feb 12, 38; m 59. *Educ:* Ind Univ, Bloomington, BSc, 61, MA, 62; Univ Ill, Urbana, PhD(hydrogeol), 66. *Prof Exp:* Teaching asst phys geol, Ind Univ, Bloomington, 63-64; teaching asst eng geol, Univ Ill, Urbana, 64-66. *Concurrent Pos:* Res asst, Ill State Geol Surv, 64-66; grants, Idaho Water Resources Res Inst & Univ Idaho Res Comt, 66- & Idaho Short Term Appl Res Fund, 68- *Mem:* Am Geophys Union; Sigma Xi. *Res:* Studies of pollution of ground and surface water and the relation between ground water flow systems and certain engineering problems. *Mailing Add:* Dept Geol Univ Idaho Moscow ID 83844-3022

**WILLIAMS, ROY LEE,** ORGANIC CHEMISTRY. *Current Pos:* ASST PROF PHARMACOL, EASTERN VA MED SCH, 77- *Personal Data:* b Portsmouth, Va, Feb 20, 37; m 57; c 1. *Educ:* Col William & Mary, BS, 60; Univ Del, PhD(org chem), 65. *Prof Exp:* Res chemist, Am Cyanamid Co, NJ, 64-65; from asst prof to assoc prof, Old Dominion Univ, 65-73, prof chem, 73-77. *Concurrent Pos:* Consult, Chem & Physics Br, Langley Res Ctr, NASA, Va, 65-; res grant, Army Res Inst, Walter Reed Hosp, Washington, DC, 66-68. *Mem:* Am Chem Soc; fel The Chem Soc; Int Soc Heterocyclic Chem. *Res:* Heterocyclic, organic synthesis, including heterocyclic polymers; medicinals; synthetics. *Mailing Add:* Dept Chem Old Dom Univ Norfolk VA 23508-8501

**WILLIAMS, RUSSELL RAYMOND,** PARASITOLOGY, INVERTEBRATE ZOOLOGY. *Current Pos:* from asst prof to prof, Waynesburg Col, 63-88, chmn dept, 70-88, premed adv, 73-88, EMER PROF BIOL, WAYNESBURG COL, 88- *Personal Data:* b Lost Creek, WVa, Apr 11, 26; m 53; c 3. *Educ:* Ohio State Univ, BSc, 55, MSc, 57, PhD(zool), 63. *Prof Exp:* Lab unit operator, B F Goodrich Chem Co, 45-50; from asst instr to instr zool, Ohio State Univ, 57-63. *Concurrent Pos:* Res Corp grant, 64-66; vis prof, Univ Northern Colo, 68-; partic, Res Corp Conf for New Sci Chmn, 71. *Mem:* AAAS; Am Soc Parasitol; Wildlife Dis Asn; Am Micros Soc; Am Inst Biol Sci. *Res:* Life history and taxonomic studies on trematodes. *Mailing Add:* 511 Ross St Waynesburg PA 15370

**WILLIAMS, RUTH JEANNETTE,** STOCHASTIC PROCESSES & THEIR APPLICATIONS, STOCHASTIC NETWORKS. *Current Pos:* PROF MATH, UNIV CALIF, SAN DIEGO, 84- *Personal Data:* b Melbourne, Australia, Mar 7, 55. *Educ:* Univ Melbourne, Australia, BS, 76, MS, 78; Stanford Univ, PhD(math), 83. *Honors & Awards:* Presidential Young Investr Award, NSF, 87. *Prof Exp:* Mem Courant Inst Math Sci, NY Univ, 83-84. *Concurrent Pos:* Prin investr, NSF grants, 84-; Alfred P Sloan res fel, Sloan Found, 88; assoc ed, Annals Probability 88-96, SIAM J Appl Math, 96-, Annals Appl Prob, 97-, Elect J Probability & Electronic Commun Probability, 95-; coun mem-at-large, Am Math Soc, 91-93, western sect prog comt, 93-94, invited address, 94; invited address, Inst Math Statist, 94. *Mem:* Am Math Soc; fel Inst Math Statist; AAAS. *Res:* Stochastic processes and their applications, including work on the foundational theory for reflected Brownian motions in polyhedral domains which arise as approximate models of queueing networks, symmetric reflected diffusions and a book on stochastic integration. *Mailing Add:* Dept Math Univ Calif San Diego 9500 Gilman Dr La Jolla CA 92093-0112

**WILLIAMS, S JEFFRESS,** COASTAL & MARINE GEOLOGY. *Current Pos:* COORDR COASTAL & MARINE GEOL PROG, US GEOL SURV, 96- *Personal Data:* b Washington, DC, Apr 25, 45. *Educ:* Allegheny Col, BS, 67; Lehigh Univ, MS(geol), 69. *Mem:* Geol Soc Am; Am Geophys Union; Soc Sedimentary Geol. *Mailing Add:* Coastal & Marine Geol Prog US Geol Surv 915 Nat Ctr Reston VA 20192

**WILLIAMS, SAM B,** RESEARCH ADMINISTRATION. *Current Pos:* PRES & CHIEF EXEC OFFICER, WILLIAMS INT CORP, 54- *Honors & Awards:* Nat Medal of Technol, 95. *Mem:* Nat Acad Eng. *Mailing Add:* Williams Int Corp 2280 W Maple RD PO Box 200 Walled Lake MI 48390-0500

**WILLIAMS, SANKEY VAUGHAN,** HEALTH SERVICES RESEARCH, CLINICAL EPIDEMIOLOGY. *Current Pos:* From asst prof to assoc prof med, Univ Pa, 77-89, assoc prof health care systs, 87-89, PROF HEALTH CARE SYSTS, UNIV PA, 89-, PROF MED, HOSP UNIV PA, 89-, SOL KATZ PROF MED, 92- *Personal Data:* b San Antonio, Tex, Apr 15, 44; m 72, Constance Hess; c Elizabeth H & Jennifer L. *Educ:* Princeton Univ, AB, 66; Harvard Univ, MD, 70. *Concurrent Pos:* Sr fel, Leonard Davis Inst Health Econs, Univ Pa, 76-; comnr, Prospective Payment Assessment Comn, US Cong Off Technol Assessment, 88-91; ed, J Gen Internal Med, 94- *Mem:* Soc Med Decision Making (pres, 85-86); Soc Gen Internal Med; master Am Col Physicians. *Res:* Conduct projects that examine the organization, financing and delivery of health care in the United States using the methods of clinical epidemiology and health services research; patient classification systems, decision analysis and cost-effectiveness studies. *Mailing Add:* Div Gen Internal Med Silverstein 3 Hosp Univ Pa Philadelphia PA 19104

**WILLIAMS, SCOTT WARNER,** MATHEMATICS. *Current Pos:* from asst prof to assoc prof, 71-85, PROF MATH, STATE UNIV NY, BUFFALO, 85- *Personal Data:* b Staten Island, NY, Apr 22, 43; c 3. *Educ:* Morgan State Col, BS, 64; Lehigh Univ, MS, 67, PhD(math), 69. *Prof Exp:* Instr, Pa State Univ, 68-69, res assoc, 69-71. *Concurrent Pos:* Ford Found sr res fel, 80-81; NSF res grant, 83-87; Fulbright lectr, Czech, 86-87; adj prof math, Beijing Teachers, China, 88- *Mem:* Am Math Soc; Nat Asn Mathematicians. *Res:* General topology, completeness, paracompactness, linearly ordered spaces and Baire spaces; algebra, groups and categories; logic; set theory; independence results; topological dynamics. *Mailing Add:* 44 Highgate Ave Buffalo NY 14214-1409

**WILLIAMS, SIDNEY ARTHUR,** MINERALOGY. *Current Pos:* CONSULT, 82- *Personal Data:* b Ann Arbor, Mich, Dec 26, 33; m 57; c 1. *Educ:* Mich Technol Univ, BS, MS, 57; Univ Ariz, PhD(mineral), 62. *Prof Exp:* Instr mineral, Mich Technol Univ, 60-61, asst prof, 61-63; mineralogist, Silver King Mines, Inc, 63-65; dir res explor geol, Phelps Dodge Corp, 65-82. *Concurrent Pos:* Mineralogist, Brit Mus Natural Hist, 71. *Mem:* Fel Mineral Soc Am; Mineral Asn Can; Brit Mineral Soc; Soc Econ Geol; Mineral Soc Japan. *Res:* Descriptive mineralogy and crystallography; petrology of altered rocks related to ore deposits. *Mailing Add:* 1243 E 16th St Douglas AZ 85607

**WILLIAMS, STANLEY A,** THEORETICAL PHYSICS. *Current Pos:* from asst prof to assoc prof, 63-76, PROF PHYSICS, IOWA STATE UNIV, 76- *Personal Data:* b Lawrence, Kans, May 14, 32; m 58, Shirley Buck; c Constance & Mark. *Educ:* Nebr Wesleyan Univ, BA, 54; Rensselaer Polytech Inst, PhD(physics), 62. *Prof Exp:* NSF fel, Univ Birmingham, 62-63. *Concurrent Pos:* Assoc scientist, Ames Lab, 63-67, scientist, 67- *Mem:* Am Phys Soc; Am Asn Physics Teachers. *Res:* Mathematical physics, principally the application of group theoretic techniques to nuclear and elementary particle physics; structure of fission fragment nuclei. *Mailing Add:* Dept Physics Iowa State Univ Ames IA 50011

**WILLIAMS, STANLEY CLARK,** ECOLOGY, MEDICAL ENTOMOLOGY. *Current Pos:* From asst prof to assoc prof, 67-74, PROF BIOL, SAN FRANCISCO STATE UNIV, 74- *Personal Data:* b Long Beach, Calif, Aug 24, 39; m 65, Roxanna Berlin; c Lisa M, Thomas S & Erin B. *Educ:* San Diego State Col, AB, 61, MA, 63; Ariz State Univ, PhD(zool), 68. *Concurrent Pos:* Res assoc, Calif Acad Sci, 67-; NSF grants, Mex, 68-72; lectr, Moss Landing Marine Sta, 72-73; mem Int Ctr Arachnological Documentation; ecol consult, Mill Valley, Calif; dir, WPoint Acad Sci; vis prof biol, USAF Acad, 92-93; fel, Calif Acad Sci; mem, Classification Soc NAm, Pac Coast Entomol Soc. *Mem:* Am Arachnology Soc; Brit Arachnology Soc; Soc Syst Biol; Asn Biologist Comput (pres, 85-); Int Ctr Arachnology. *Res:* Invertebrate ecology; scorpion systematics; urban ecology; medical entomology; biostatistics and data analysis. *Mailing Add:* Dept Biol San Francisco State Univ 1600 Holloway Ave San Francisco CA 94132-1722. *Fax:* 415-338-2295; *E-Mail:* Williams@sfsuvaxl.sfsu.edu

**WILLIAMS, STEPHEN EARL,** SOIL MICROBIOLOGY, SOIL BIOCHEMISTRY. *Current Pos:* from asst prof to assoc prof, 76-86, PROF SOILS, UNIV WYO, 86-, DEPT HEAD, 93- *Personal Data:* b Borger, Tex, Apr 27, 48; m 75. *Educ:* NMex State Univ, BS, 70, MS, 72; NC State Univ, PhD(soil sci), 77. *Prof Exp:* Plant physiologist soils, Rocky Mountain Forest & Range Exp Sta, Forest Serv, USDA, Albuquerque, NMex, 72; res & teaching assoc, NC State Univ, 75-76. *Concurrent Pos:* Prin investr, US Dept Energy, Laramie Energy Technol Ctr, Wyo, 77- *Mem:* Am Soc Agron; Soil Sci Soc Am. *Res:* Symbiotic associations between plants and microorganisms such as mycorrhizae and symbiotic nitrogen fixation; revegetation of devastated lands; sustainability of ancient agricultural technologies; rungeland soil health. *Mailing Add:* Dept Plant Soil & Insect Sci Univ Wyo PO Box 3354 Laramie WY 82071

**WILLIAMS, STEPHEN EDWARD,** MEMBRANE PHYSIOLOGY, MOLECULAR BIOLOGY. *Current Pos:* from asst prof to assoc prof, 73-85, PROF BIOL, LEBANON VALLEY COL, 85- *Personal Data:* b St Louis, Mo, Oct 9, 42; m 68; c 1. *Educ:* Cent Col, Mo, BA, 64; Univ Tenn, Knoxville, MS, 66; Wash Univ, PhD(biol), 71. *Prof Exp:* Lectr plant physiol, Cornell Univ, 70-73. *Mem:* Am Soc Plant Physiol; Bot Soc Am. *Res:* Chloroplast DNA phylogenetics of droseraceae; electrophysiology, plant sensory physiology, excitable plant cells; carnivorous plants, especially Droseraceae, electron microscopy. *Mailing Add:* Dept Biol Lebanon Valley Col Annville PA 17003-1404. *Fax:* 717-867-6124

**WILLIAMS, STEVEN FRANK,** FISHERIES, ICHTHYOLOGY. *Personal Data:* b Tacoma, Wash, May 8, 44; m 66, Sandra Quinlin; c Robert Q. *Educ:* Univ Wash, BS, 66; Univ Calif, Los Angeles, MA, 68; Ore State Univ, PhD(fisheries), 74. *Prof Exp:* Res biologist fisheries, US Peace Corps, Chile, 68-70. *Concurrent Pos:* Res asst fisheries, Ore State Univ, 70-74. *Mem:* Am Fisheries Soc. *Res:* Natural distribution and abundance of fishes and factors which affect them; hydroacoustics and fish distribution; ichthyo plankton. *Mailing Add:* Dept Biol St Cloud State Univ MS-229 Fourth Ave St Cloud MN 56301-4498. *Fax:* 320-255-4166; *E-Mail:* stevew@stigger.stcloud.msus. edu

**WILLIAMS, STUART K, II,** CELL-TRANSPLANTATION. *Current Pos:* PROF SURG, UNIV ARIZ HEALTH SCI CTR, 91- *Personal Data:* b Wilmington, Del, Apr 3, 52. *Res:* Cell-transplantation. *Mailing Add:* Dept Surg Univ Ariz Health Sci Ctr 1501 N Campbell Ave Tucson AZ 85724-5084

**WILLIAMS, TAFFY J,** IMMUNOLOGY, BIOCHEMISTRY. *Current Pos:* VPRES RES, MAGAININ PHARMACEUT INC, 92- *Res:* Immunology; biochemistry. *Mailing Add:* Panax Pharmaceut Inc 425 Park Ave 27th Fl New York NY 10022

**WILLIAMS, TERENCE HEATON,** NEUROANATOMY, ELECTRON MICROSCOPY. *Current Pos:* PROF ANAT & HEAD DEPT, COL MED, UNIV IOWA, 73- *Personal Data:* b Oldham, Eng, Jan 5, 29; m 56; c 3. *Educ:* Univ Manchester, MB, ChB, 53; Univ Wales, PhD(anat), 60. *Hon Degrees:* DSc, Univ Manchester, 77. *Prof Exp:* House surgeon, Manchester Univ & Royal Infirmary, 53-54; jr registr surg, London Hosp, 55-56; asst lectr anat, Univ Col, Dublin, 57-58; lectr, Univ Wales, 58-61; lectr & sr lectr exp neurol, Univ Manchester, 61-68; vis lectr electron micros nerv syst, Harvard Med Sch, 65-66; prof neuroanat, Sch Med, Tulane Univ, 68-73. *Concurrent Pos:* Brit Med Res Coun traveling fel, Harvard Med Sch, 64-65; Peck Sci Res award; NIH res awards, 69- *Mem:* Soc Neurosci; Am Asn Anat; Anat Soc Gt Brit & Ireland. *Res:* Neuropeptidergic systems; plasticity of nervous system; small intensely fluorescent cells of sympathetic ganglia; electromicroscopy of the nervous system. *Mailing Add:* Dept Anat Univ Iowa Col Med 1-470 Basic Sci Bldg Iowa City IA 52248

**WILLIAMS, THEODORE BURTON,** ASTRONOMY. *Current Pos:* asst prof, 79-85, ASSOC PROF, DEPT PHYSICS & ASTRON, RUTGERS UNIV, 85- *Personal Data:* b Youngstown, Ohio, Sept 9, 49; m 71, Janet L Bank; c Peter & Emily. *Educ:* Purdue Univ, BS, 71; Calif Inst Technol, PhD(astron), 75. *Prof Exp:* Res assoc astron, Princeton Univ, 75-77, mem res staff, 77-79. *Mem:* Am Astron Soc; Int Astron Union. *Res:* Structure and dynamics of individual galaxies; development of astronomical instrumentation. *Mailing Add:* Dept Physics & Astron Rutgers Univ PO Box 849 Piscataway NJ 08855-0849. *Fax:* 732-932-4343; *E-Mail:* williams@fenway.rutgers.edu

**WILLIAMS, THEODORE J(OSEPH),** AUTOMATIC CONTROL, CHEMICAL ENGINEERING. *Current Pos:* PROF ENG & DIR, LAB APPL INDUST CONTROL, PURDUE UNIV, 65- *Personal Data:* b Black Lick, Pa, Sept 2, 23; m 46, Isabel A McAnulty; c Theodore J Jr, Mary M, Charles A & Elizabeth A. *Educ:* Pa State Univ, BS, 49, MS, 50, PhD(chem eng), 55; Ohio State Univ, MSEE, 56. *Honors & Awards:* Sir Harold Hartley Medal, Inst Measure & Control, London, 75; Silver Core Award, Int Fedn Info Processing, 77; Albert F Sperry Founder Medal, ISA, 90. *Prof Exp:* Asst prof chem eng, USAF Inst Technol, 53-56; sr eng supvr, Monsanto Co, 56-65. *Concurrent Pos:* Vpres, Simulation Coun, 60-62; vis prof automatic control, Wash Univ, 62-65; vpres, Am Automatic Control Coun, 63-65, pres, 65-67; supvr lectr, Int Fedn Automatic Control, Basel, Switz, 63 & Warsaw, Poland, 69; mem bd gov, Am Fedn Info Processing Socs, 65-80, pres, 76-80; plenary lectr, Conf Chem Eng Frankfort, Ger, 70. *Mem:* Fel Instrument Soc (vpres, 65-67, pres, 69); Am Chem Soc; Am Soc Eng Educ; fel Am Inst Chem Engrs; Inst Elec & Electronics Engrs; fel AAAS; fel Inst Measurement & Control; fel Am Inst Chemists. *Res:* Industrial process dynamics and automatic control; application of digital computers to industrial process control and management; theory of separation processes, particularly distillation. *Mailing Add:* 208 Chippewa St West Lafayette IN 47906-2123

**WILLIAMS, THEODORE P,** BIOPHYSICS, NEUROSCIENCE. *Current Pos:* assoc prof biol sci, Fla State Univ, 66-73, actg chmn dept, 70-71, co-dir, Psychobiol Prog, 71-74, PROF BIOL SCI, FLA STATE UNIV, 73-, DIR, INST MOLECULAR BIOPHYS, 85- *Personal Data:* b Marianna, Pa, May 24, 33; m 56; c 5. *Educ:* Muskingum Col, BS, 55; Princeton Univ, MA, 57, PhD(phys chem), 59. *Honors & Awards:* Alexander von Humboldt Sr Scientist Award. *Prof Exp:* Res assoc chem, Brown Univ, 59-61, fel psychol, 61-63, asst prof biol & med sci, 63-66. *Concurrent Pos:* Prin investr of numerous NIH, NSF & Dept Energy grants. *Mem:* Asn Res Vision & Ophthal. *Res:* Visual processes; sensory mechanisms; fast chemical reactions. *Mailing Add:* Dept Biol Sci Fla State Univ Tallahassee FL 32306-4075

**WILLIAMS, THEODORE ROOSEVELT,** ANALYTICAL CHEMISTRY. *Current Pos:* from instr to assoc prof, 59-66, PROF CHEM, COL WOOSTER, 66- *Personal Data:* b Washington, DC, Oct 23, 30; m 54; c 4. *Educ:* Howard Univ, BS, 52; Pa State Univ, MS, 54; Univ Conn, PhD, 60. *Honors & Awards:* Mfg Chemists Asn Award, 78; Martha Holden Jennings Found Award, 79; Percy L Julian Award, Nat Orgn Prof Advan Black Chemists & Chem Engrs, 90. *Prof Exp:* Asst instr chem, Univ Conn, 56-59; Case Western Res Univ Med Sch, 87-88. *Concurrent Pos:* Res assoc, Harvard Univ, 67-68, Sloan vis prof chem, 69-70; vis prof, Univ Conn, 72-73, Case Western Res Univ, 77-78 & Carnegie-Mellon Univ, 82-83; chmn anal div grad fel comt, Am Chem Soc, 73-; res award, Asn Independent Col & Univ Ohio, 89. *Mem:* Am Chem Soc. *Res:* Electroanalytical chemistry; analysis of biological tissues. *Mailing Add:* Chem Dept Col Wooster Wooster OH 44691-2363

**WILLIAMS, THEODORE SHIELDS,** VETERINARY MEDICINE. *Current Pos:* RETIRED. *Personal Data:* b Kansas City, Kans, June 2, 11; m 36; c 2. *Educ:* Kans State Univ, DVM, 35; Iowa State Univ, MS, 46. *Prof Exp:* Col vet, Prairie View State Col, 36; vet inspector, Meat Inspection Div, USDA, 36-45; head dept, Tuskegee Inst, 45-51, dean sch, 47-72, prof, Sch Vet & Med, 45-81, emer prof path & parasitol, emer dean, 81. *Concurrent Pos:* Consult, Vet Admin Hosp, Tuskegee, Ala; vis prof path, NY State Vet Col, Cornell Univ, 73. *Mem:* Am Asn Vet Med Cols (pres, 69-70); Am Vet Med Asn. *Res:* Pathological lesions associated with tissue invading migratory parasites in animals. *Mailing Add:* 2501 Bulls Ave Tuskegee AL 36088-2907

**WILLIAMS, THOMAS ALAN,** HERPETOLOGY. *Current Pos:* from instr to asst prof, 81-88, ASSOC PROF BIOL, NCENT COL, 88- *Personal Data:* b Salem, Ore, Sept 28, 47; m 71; c 1. *Educ:* Willamette Univ, BA, 71; Drake Univ, MA, 75; Wash State Univ, PhD(zool), 84. *Prof Exp:* From instr to asst prof biol, Ricker Col, 74-77. *Mem:* Am Soc Ichthyologists & Herpetologists; Soc Study Amphibians & Reptiles; Herpetologists League. *Res:* Biology of salamander granular glands; their structure, function, development and relevance to salamander systematics. *Mailing Add:* Dept Biol NCent Col 30 N Brainard St Naperville IL 60540-4607. *E-Mail:* taw@nccsep.noctrl.edu

**WILLIAMS, THOMAS FFRANCON,** PHYSICAL CHEMISTRY & RADIATION CHEMISTRY, RADICAL ION CHEMISTRY & ELECTRON SPIN RESONANCE SPECTROSCOPY OF TRAPPED RADICALS. *Current Pos:* from asst prof to prof, 61-74, DISTINGUISHED SERV PROF CHEM, UNIV TENN, KNOXVILLE, 74- *Personal Data:* b Denbighshire, Wales, Jan 30, 28; m 59, Astra Silvia Birins; c Ifor R & Gwyn D. *Educ:* Univ London, BSc, 49, PhD(chem), 60. *Prof Exp:* From sci officer to prin sci officer, Chem Div, Atomic Energy Res Estab, Harwell, Eng, 49-61. *Concurrent Pos:* Assoc, Northwestern Univ, 57-59; NSF vis scientist, Kyoto Univ, 65-66; Guggenheim fel, Royal Inst Technol, Sweden, 72-73; consult, Pac NW Nat Lab, 96-97. *Mem:* Am Chem Soc; Royal Soc Chem; Sigma Xi; Radiation Res Soc. *Res:* Electron spin resonance studies of trapped radicals; free radical reactions at low temperature; electronic structure of radicals; radiation chemistry; radiation-induced ionic polymerization; radical cations. *Mailing Add:* Dept Chem Univ Tenn Knoxville TN 37996-1600. *Fax:* 423-974-3454; *E-Mail:* tfwilliams@utk.edu

**WILLIAMS, THOMAS FRANKLIN,** GERIATRIC MEDICINE, DIABETES. *Current Pos:* ATTEND PHYSICIAN, MONROE COMMUNITY HOSP, 91-; EMER PROF MED, UNIV ROCHESTER, 92- *Personal Data:* b Belmont, NC, Nov 26, 21; m 51, Catharine C Catlett; c Mary (Wright) & Thomas N. *Educ:* Univ NC, BS, 42; Columbia Univ, MA, 43; Harvard Univ, MD, 50. *Hon Degrees:* DSc, Med Col Ohio, 87, Univ NC, 91. *Honors & Awards:* Gustav & Lienhard Award, Inst Med-Nat Acad Sci, 96. *Prof Exp:* Asst chem, Columbia Univ, 42-43; asst med, Johns Hopkins Univ, 51-53 & Boston Univ, 53-54; from instr to prof, Sch Med, Univ NC, 56-68; prof, Univ Rochester, 68-83; dir, Monroe Community Hosp, 68-83; dir, Nat Inst Aging, NIH, 83-91; asst surg gen, USPHS, 83-91. *Concurrent Pos:* Res fel, Sch Med, Univ NC, 54-56, Markle scholar, 57-61; fel physiol, Vanderbilt Univ, 66-67; distinguished physician, Dept Vets Affairs, Vet Admin Med Ctr, Canandaigua, NY, 95-98. *Mem:* Inst Med-Nat Acad Sci; fel AAAS; Am Geriat Soc; fel Am Pub Health Asn; fel Am Col Physicians; fel Geront Soc Am; Asn Am Physicians. *Res:* Diseases of metabolism, especially for chronic illness and aging; diabetes mellitues; biomedical, clinical and psychosocial aspects of aging; health services research and development. *Mailing Add:* Monroe Community Hosp Rochester NY 14620

**WILLIAMS, THOMAS HENRY,** STRUCTURAL CHEMISTRY. *Current Pos:* res chemist, 63-74, res fel, 75-84, NUCLEAR MAGNETIC RESONANCE RES INVESTR, HOFFMANN-LA ROCHE INC, NUTLEY, 85- *Personal Data:* b Jamaica, WI, Apr 21, 34; m 67; c 2. *Educ:* Univ WI, BSc, 56; Yale Univ, MS, 60, PhD(chem), 61. *Prof Exp:* Fel Univ Notre Dame, NJ, 61-62. *Mem:* Am Chem Soc; Sigma Xi. *Res:* Structural elucidation of natural products; applications of nuclear magnetic resonance spectroscopy in organic chemistry; diastereomeric solute-solute interaction of enantiomers; drug and vitamin D3 metabolites. *Mailing Add:* 7 Patten Terr Cedar Grove NJ 07009-1919

**WILLIAMS, THOMAS HENRY LEE,** REMOTE SENSING, GEOGRAPHIC INFORMATION SYSTEMS. *Current Pos:* ASSOC PROF GEOG & DIR, GEOSCI REMOTE SENSING GROUP, COL GEOSCI, UNIV OKLA, 86-, DIR, COOP INST APPL REMOTE SENSING, 87-, ASSOC DEAN GEOSCI, 89- *Personal Data:* b Deganwy, Wales, UK, May 31, 51; m 73, Naila Mendes; c Owen-John, Samantha & Gareth. *Educ:* Univ Bristol, Eng, BSc, 72, PhD(geog), 77. *Prof Exp:* From asst prof to assoc prof geog, Univ Kans, 77-86. *Concurrent Pos:* Consult, UNESCO, Haryana Agr Univ, India, 78-79 & Nat Park Serv, 79; intra-univ prof, Dept Elec Eng, Univ Kans, 83-84, researcher, Radar Systs & Remote Sensing Lab, 83-86. *Mem:* Assoc fel Inst Math & Applns UK; Am Soc Photogram & Remote Sensing. *Res:* Remote sensing of renewable resources with emphasis on digital analysis and interpretation of visible and microwave satellite images; applications of expert systems techniques to image understanding. *Mailing Add:* Col Geosci Sarkeys Energy Ctr Ste 710 Univ Okla Norman OK 73019-0628. *Fax:* 405-325-3148; *E-Mail:* lwilliams@geoaom.gcn.uoknor.edu

**WILLIAMS, TIMOTHY C,** BEHAVIOR, ETHOLOGY. *Current Pos:* PROF BIOL, SWARTHMORE COL, 76-, DEPT CHMN, 85- *Personal Data:* b New York, NY, May 7, 42; m 64; c 2. *Educ:* Swarthmore Col, BA, 64; Harvard Univ, AM, 66; Rockefeller Univ, PhD(animal behav), 68. *Prof Exp:* Asst prof biol, State Univ NY, Buffalo, 69-75. *Concurrent Pos:* Scientist, Woods Hole Oceanog Inst, 68-74; investr, Marine Biol Labs, 75-78. *Mem:* Sigma Xi. *Res:* Radar studies of bird orientation and migration, especially over major oceans. *Mailing Add:* Dept Biol Swarthmore Col 500 College Ave Swarthmore PA 19081-1390

**WILLIAMS, TODD ROBERTSON,** POLYMER CHEMISTRY. *Current Pos:* sr chemist med chem, 3M Co, 72-77, supvr biomat res, 77-79, res specialist, 79-86, SR RES SPECIALIST, 3M CO, 86- *Personal Data:* b Washington, DC, Nov 3, 45; m 67; c 1. *Educ:* Cornell Univ, AB, 67; Univ Calif, Los Angeles, PhD(org chem), 71. *Prof Exp:* Fel, Syntex Res Co, 71-72. *Mem:* Am Chem Soc. *Res:* Optical polymers; microreplication. *Mailing Add:* 3025 Lake Elmo Ave N Lake Elmo MN 55042

**WILLIAMS, TOM VARE,** PLANT BREEDING, PLANT PATHOLOGY. *Current Pos:* PROJ LEADER & VEG BREEDER, NORTHRUP KING CO, 77- *Personal Data:* b Philadelphia, Pa, Dec 27, 38; m 63; c 4. *Educ:* Univ Conn, BS, 60; Rutgers Univ, MS, 63, PhD(plant breeding), 66. *Prof Exp:* Agronomist, Soil Conserv Serv, USDA, 66-67; res horticulturist, Birds Eye Div, Gen Foods Corp, 67-70; res dir seed dept, Agr Chem Div, FMC Corp, 70-77. *Concurrent Pos:* Vine Crops Adv Comt, Fla Hort Soc. *Mem:* Am Soc Hort Sci. *Res:* Vegetable variety development. *Mailing Add:* 2329 Pinewoods Circle Naples FL 33942

**WILLIAMS, VERNON,** MATHEMATICS, EDUCATION. *Current Pos:* PROF MATH, SETON HALL UNIV, 80- *Personal Data:* b Augusta, Ga, Nov 10, 26; m 69; c 1. *Educ:* Paine Col, BA, 49; Univ Mich, Ann Arbor, MA, 54; Okla State Univ, EdD, 69. *Prof Exp:* Instr, Paine Col, 49-54 & Fla A&M Univ, 54-56; from asst prof to assoc prof, Southern Univ, Baton Rouge, 56-69, prof math, 69-80. *Concurrent Pos:* Adv, Math Sect, La Educ Asn, 71- *Mem:* Am Math Asn. *Res:* Number theory; educational technology as devoted to higher education as well as secondary education. *Mailing Add:* Dept Math Seton Hall Univ S Orange Ave South Orange NJ 07079-2697

**WILLIAMS, VICK FRANKLIN,** ANATOMY. *Current Pos:* assoc prof, 73-79, PROF ANAT, UNIV TEX HEALTH SCI CTR, SAN ANTONIO, 79- *Personal Data:* b Pittsburg, Tex, Apr 30, 36; m 62, Dorothy J Rodina; c Dorothy Jean & Sara W (Heilbronner). *Educ:* Austin Col, BA, 58; Univ Tex, MD & PhD(anat), 64. *Prof Exp:* Intern path, Charity Hosp La, New Orleans, 64-65; from instr to asst prof anat, Southwestern Med Sch, Univ Tex, Dallas, 65-70; assoc prof anat, Dent Sch, Univ Tex, San Antonio & Univ Tex Med Sch, San Antonio, 70-73. *Concurrent Pos:* Consult, Dept Surg, Brooke Army Med Ctr, Ft Sam, Houston, Tex, 72-78; mem anat bd, State Tex, 81-; mem fac, Head & Neck Anat Oral Surg Residents, Wilford Hall, USAF Med Ctr, Lackland AFB, Tex, 87-; vis prof anat, Christian Med Col, Vellore, India, 93-94. *Mem:* World Med Asn; Am Asn Anat; Sigma Xi; Am Asn Clin Anatomists. *Res:* Ultrastructure of the central nervous system of mammals. *Mailing Add:* 7703 Floyd Curl Dr Univ Tex Health Sci Ctr San Antonio TX 78284-7762. *Fax:* 210-567-3803; *E-Mail:* williamsv@utmscsa.edu

**WILLIAMS, W JON-ALLAN,** PHYSIOLOGY, CARDIOVASCULAR RESEARCH. *Current Pos:* res assoc, 90-93, STAFF SCIENTIST PHYSIOL, JOHNSON SPACE CTR, NASA, 93- *Personal Data:* b Los Angeles, Calif, Aug 12, 52. *Res:* Physiology; cardiovascular research. *Mailing Add:* Nat Res Coun Biomed Oper & Res Br NASA Johnson Space Krug Life Sci Physiol Lab MC SD561 Houston TX 77058

**WILLIAMS, WALTER JACKSON, JR,** ELECTRICAL ENGINEERING. *Current Pos:* CONSULT, 87- *Personal Data:* b Elkhart, Ind, Jan 17, 25; wid; c David, Eileen & Valerie. *Educ:* Purdue Univ, Lafayette, BS, 48, MS, 50, PhD(elec eng), 54. *Prof Exp:* Instr, Purdue Univ, 50-54; from engr to prin engr, Fed Lab, IT&T Corp, 54-60; chmn, Dept Elec Eng, Ind Inst Technol, 61-64, dean eng, 63-67, vpres & acad dean, 67-75, interim pres, 70-71; sr tech adv, IT&T Corp, Ft Wayne, 75-80, dir eng, 80-81, tech dir, Aerospace-Optical Div, 81-87. *Concurrent Pos:* Consult, IT&T Corp, Magnavox Co & Bowmar Instrument Corp; Eng Accreditation Comn, Accreditation, Bd Eng & Tech, 90- *Mem:* Inst Elec & Electronics Engrs; Nat Soc Prof Engrs; Am Soc Eng Educ. *Res:* Systems analysis with emphasis on feedback control. *Mailing Add:* 8707 Stellhorn Rd Ft Wayne IN 46815-4410

**WILLIAMS, WALTER MICHAEL,** CLINICAL PHARMACOLOGY, INTERNAL MEDICINE. *Current Pos:* asst prof, 79-82, ASSOC PROF PHARMACOL, UNIV LOUISVILLE, 82- *Personal Data:* b Birmingham, Ala, Aug 14, 43; m 72; c 2. *Educ:* Univ Louisville, BS, 65, PhD(pharmacol), 70, MD, 74; Am Bd Internal Med, dipl, 77. *Prof Exp:* Resident internal med, Univ Pittsburgh, 74-77; teaching fel clin pharm, Univ Chicago, 77-79. *Mem:* Sigma Xi; Am Soc Pharmacol & Exp Therapeut; Soc Exp Biol & Med; Am Physiol Soc; NY Acad Sci. *Res:* Clinical pharmacology; basic and clinical studies of drug elimination (metabolism and excretion). *Mailing Add:* Dept Pharmacol & Toxicol Univ Louisville Louisville KY 40292-0001. *Fax:* 502-588-7868

**WILLIAMS, WAYNE WATSON,** ENGINEERING, GEOLOGY. *Current Pos:* from assoc prof to prof, 65-92, EMER PROF CIVIL ENG, KANS STATE UNIV, 92- *Personal Data:* b Powersville, Mo, Dec 14, 22; m 44; c 7. *Educ:* Iowa State Univ, BS, 51, MS, 53. *Prof Exp:* Res asst soils, Eng Exp Sta, Iowa State Univ, 51-53; found engr, Des Moines, Iowa, 53-65. *Concurrent Pos:* NSF res asst, Tex A&M Univ, 67; vis prof, Univ Houston, 77-78. *Mem:* Am Soc Civil Engrs. *Res:* Foundations of structures; shearing resistance; swelling clays; deep foundation; building and construction failures; construction litigation. *Mailing Add:* 11420 Riley St Oberland KS 66210

**WILLIAMS, WENDELL STERLING,** SOLID STATE PHYSICS, MATERIALS SCIENCE. *Current Pos:* EMER PROF PHYSICS, MAT SCI & ENG & BIOENG, EMER DIR, PROG ANCIENT TECHNOL & ARCHAEOL MAT, UNIV ILL, URBANA. *Personal Data:* b Lake Forest, Ill, Oct 27, 28; m 52, Dorothy Watt; c Jennifer & Laura. *Educ:* Swarthmore Col, BA, 51; Cornell Univ, PhD(physics), 56. *Prof Exp:* Physicist, Leeds & Northrup Co, 51; asst, Cornell Univ, 52-55; physicist, Union Carbide Corp, 56-65, 66-67; sr res vis, Dept Metall, Cambridge Univ, 65-66; from assoc prof to prof physics, ceramic eng & bioeng, Univ Ill, Urbana, 67-87, co-chmn, Bioeng Comt, 71, prin investr, Mat Res Lab, 67-87, dir, Prog Ancient Technol & Archaeol Mat, 80-87; prof, Dept Mat Sci & Eng & prof physics & biomed eng, Case Western Res Univ, 87-95, chmn, Dept Mat Sci & Eng, 87-91. *Concurrent Pos:* NSF lectr, Univ PR, 61; mem, Mat Sci Comt, Argonne Ctr Educ Affairs, Argonne Nat Lab, 71-; mem adv comt, Metals & Ceramics Div, Oak Ridge Nat Lab, 72-74, mem & chmn adv comt, High Temperature Mat Lab, 75-79; task coordr energy res, Div Mat Res, NSF, 74-75; consult, Kennametal Inc, sect head metall & mat, Div Mat Res, NSF, 77-78; counr, Mat Res Soc, 78 & 79; study dir, Study of Nat Educ Policies Sci, Nat Res Coun, 80; sabbatical vis, Dept Mat Sci & Eng, Imp Col, London, 82, Dept Mat, Oxford Univ, 93. *Mem:* AAAS; fel Am Phys Soc; fel Am Ceramic Soc; Bioelec Repair & Growth Soc (pres, 88-89); Mat Res Soc; Minerals Metals & Mat Soc. *Res:* Electrical, thermal and mechanical properties of refractory hard metals; high-strength fibers; defects in solids; low and high temperature thermal conductivity; electrical properties of bone; electrical modification of osteoporosis; implant materials; archaeological materials. *Mailing Add:* Physics Dept Univ Ill Urbana IL 61801. *Fax:* 217-344-5272; *E-Mail:* w___willms@staff.uiuc.edu

**WILLIAMS, WESLEY M,** BIOCHEMISTRY. *Current Pos:* VIS SCIENTIST BIOCHEM, NIH, 92- *Personal Data:* b Waltham, Mass, Mar 6, 46. *Res:* Biochemistry. *Mailing Add:* Lab Neurosci NIH Bldg 10 Rm 6C103 NIH Bethesda MD 20892-0001

**WILLIAMS, WILLIAM ARNOLD,** AGRONOMY, BIOMATHEMATICS. *Current Pos:* Instr, 51-53, from asst prof to assoc prof, 54-64, PROF AGRON, UNIV CALIF, DAVIS, 65- *Personal Data:* b Johnson City, NY, Aug 2, 22; m 43; c 3. *Educ:* Cornell Univ, BS, 47, MS, 48, PhD(agron), 51. *Concurrent Pos:* Fulbright scholar, Australia, 60; Rockefeller fel, Cent & SAm, 66; mem staff, NSF Res Vessel Alpha Helix, Amazon Exped, 67. *Mem:* Fel Am Soc Agron; fel Crop Sci Soc Am; Soil Sci Soc Am; Am Soc Plant Physiol; Ecol Soc Am; Am Statist Asn; Brit Ecol Soc; Math Asn Am; Am Math Soc; Soc Range Mgt. *Res:* Systems analysis of annual-type range growth and utilization; competition for nutrients and nutrient cycling, especially sulfur and nitrogen; range and agronomic applications of multivariate data analysis techniques. *Mailing Add:* Dept Agron & Range Sci Univ Calif Davis CA 95616-5224

**WILLIAMS, WILLIAM DONALD,** PHYSICAL CHEMISTRY. *Current Pos:* Assoc prof chem, 54-63, PROF CHEM & CHMN, DEPT PHYS SCI, HARDING COL, 63- *Personal Data:* b Macon, Ga, Apr 22, 28; m 52; c 4. *Educ:* Harding Col, BS, 50; Univ Ky, MS, 52, PhD(chem), 54. *Mem:* AAAS; Am Chem Soc. *Res:* Chemistry and kinetics of flames. *Mailing Add:* 11 Harding Dr Searcy AR 72143

**WILLIAMS, WILLIAM JAMES,** ELECTRICAL ENGINEERING, PHYSIOLOGY. *Current Pos:* lectr elec eng, Univ Mich, Ann Arbor, 64-65, asst prof elec eng & bioeng, 65-69, assoc prof elec, comput eng & bioeng, 69-73, dir, Bioelec Sci Lab, 68-83, PROF ELEC & COMPUT ENG & BIOENG, UNIV MICH, ANN ARBOR, 73- *Personal Data:* b Rio Grande, Ohio, May 9, 35; m 61; c 2. *Educ:* Ohio State Univ, BEE, 58; Univ Iowa, MS, 61, PhD(elec eng), 63; Univ Mich, MS, 66. *Prof Exp:* Res engr, Battelle Mem Inst, 58-60; teaching asst elec eng, Univ Iowa, 60-63; sr res specialist commun theory, Emerson Elec Mfg Co, 63-64. *Concurrent Pos:* Rackham fel & award, 66-67; vis scientist, Sch Med, Johns Hopkins Univ, 74. *Mem:* Inst Elec & Electronics Engrs; Soc Neurosci. *Res:* Electrical and communication biophysics; neurocybernetics; application of signal processing and systems analysis techniques to biological problems, particularly the nervous system; computer applications. *Mailing Add:* 5650 Warren Rd Ann Arbor MI 48105-9425

**WILLIAMS, WILLIAM JOSEPH,** MEDICINE, BIOCHEMISTRY. *Current Pos:* chmn dept, 69-92, PROF MED, STATE UNIV NY HEALTH SCI CTR, 69- *Personal Data:* b Bridgeton, NJ, Dec 8, 26; m 89, Karen A Hughes; c Susan L, William P & Sarah R. *Educ:* Univ Pa, MD, 49. *Prof Exp:* Intern, Hosp Univ Pa, 49-50; sr instr microbiol, Sch Med, Western Res Univ, 52-54; resident med, Hosp Univ Pa, 54-55; assoc med, Sch Med, Univ Pa, 55-56, from asst prof to prof, 56-69. *Concurrent Pos:* Am Cancer Soc fel physiol chem, Sch Med, Univ Pa, 50-52, Am Philos Soc Daland fel res clin med, 55-57; Markle scholar, 57-62; USPHS res career develop award, 63-68; asst prof, Sch Med, Wash Univ, 59-60; mem hemat training comt, Nat Inst Arthritis & Metab Dis, 64-68, res career prog comt, 68-72 & thrombosis adv comt, 69-73, chmn, 71-73; mem adv coun, Nat Arthritis Metab & Digestive Dis, NIH, 75-79; vis prof, Med Dept, Monash Univ, Melbourne, Australia, 80; vis scientist, Walter & Eliza Hall Med Res, Melbourne, Australia, 80. *Mem:* Am Soc Hemat; Am Soc Clin Invest; Am Fedn Clin Res; Am Soc Biol Chem; Asn Am Physicians. *Res:* Internal medicine; hematology; blood coagulation; blood cell metabolism. *Mailing Add:* Dept Med State Univ NY Health Sci Ctr 750 E Adams St Syracuse NY 13210. *Fax:* 315-464-5797

**WILLIAMS, WILLIAM LANE,** ANATOMY. *Current Pos:* prof & chmn dept, 58-80, EMER PROF ANAT, MED CTR, UNIV MISS, 80- *Personal Data:* b Rock Hill, SC, Dec 23, 14. *Educ:* Wofford Col, BS, 35; Duke Univ, MA, 39; Yale Univ, PhD(anat), 41. *Prof Exp:* Asst anat, Sch Med, Yale Univ, 39-40, instr, 42-43; instr, Sch Med & Dent, Univ Rochester, 41-42; asst prof, Sch Med, La State Univ, 43-45; from asst prof to assoc prof, Univ Minn, Minneapolis, 45-58. *Concurrent Pos:* Donner Found fel anat, Sch Med, Yale Univ, 42-43; asst vchancellor, Med Ctr, Univ Miss, 75-80. *Mem:* Am Soc Exp Path; Am Physiol Soc; Soc Exp Biol & Med; Am Asn Anat; Am Inst Nutrit. *Res:* Endocrinology, experimental pathology; nutrition; cardiovascular disease; hepatic liposis. *Mailing Add:* 3975 Interstate 55 Apt J2 Jackson MS 39216

**WILLIAMS, WILLIAM LAWRENCE,** BIOCHEMISTRY, ANIMAL PHYSIOLOGY. *Current Pos:* CONSULT HUMAN INFERTILITY, 84- *Personal Data:* b St Cloud, Minn, June 14, 19; div; c 2. *Educ:* Univ Minn, BS, 42; Univ Wis, MS, 47, PhD(biochem), 49. *Prof Exp:* Asst prof biochem, NC State Univ, 49-50; res biochemist, Lederle Lab, 50-59; from res assoc prof to res prof, 60-76, mem fac biochem, Univ Ga, 76-84. *Concurrent Pos:* NIH career develop award, 62-, res grant, 64-67, training grant, 65-70; indust consult; dir, Reprod Res Labs. *Mem:* Am Soc Biol Chem; Brit Soc Study Fertil; Soc Study Reprod; Am Fertil Soc; Am Physiol Soc. *Res:* Animal reproduction. *Mailing Add:* Univ Ga 330 Stoneland Dr Athens GA 30606-2456

**WILLIAMS, WILLIAM ORVILLE,** MATHEMATICS, MECHANICS. *Current Pos:* asst prof, 66-70, assoc prof, 70-76, PROF MATH, CARNEGIE-MELLON UNIV, 76- *Personal Data:* b Carlsbad, NMex, Oct 19, 40; m 60. *Educ:* Rice Univ, BA, 62, MS, 63; Brown Univ, PhD(appl math), 67. *Prof Exp:* Assoc res engr, Houston Res Lab, Humble Oil & Ref Co, 64. *Mem:* Soc Natural Philos; Am Math Soc; Math Asn Am. *Res:* Foundations of continuum mechanics; thermodynamics. *Mailing Add:* Dept Math Carnegie-Mellon Univ 5000 Forbes Ave Pittsburgh PA 15213-3890

**WILLIAMS, WILLIE, JR,** THERMAL PHYSICS. *Current Pos:* Assoc prof, 79-84, CHAIR, DEPT PHYSICS, LINCOLN UNIV, 76-, PROF, 84- *Personal Data:* b Independence, La, Mar 24, 47; c 1; c Willie B III. *Educ:* Southern Univ, BS, 70; Iowa State Univ, Ms, 72, PhD(physics), 74. *Honors & Awards:* Lindback Award for Outstanding Scientist, White House Initiative, 88. *Concurrent Pos:* Mem fac physics, Lincoln Univ, 74-, chmn, Math & Sci Div, 78-, founder, dir & prin investr, Laser Progs, Lincoln Advan Sci, Eng & Reinforcement Prog, 80-, bd mem, Women's Tech Prog, Lincoln Univ Urban Ctr, 80-, dir, Lincoln Univ Nuclear Energy Training Fel Prog, 85-; vis prof, Ctr Teaching Innovation, Drexel Univ, 75; liaison officer, Nat Asn Equal Opportunity Higher Educ, 87- *Mem:* Am Asn Physics Teachers; NY Acad Sci; AAAS; Nat Geog Soc; Sigma Xi. *Res:* Experimental studies of low temperature transport phenomena in metals and metal alloys. *Mailing Add:* 448 W Baltimore Pike West Grove PA 19390

**WILLIAMS, WILLIE ELBERT,** MATHEMATIC STATISTICS, COMPUTER SCIENCE. *Current Pos:* ASSOC PROF MATH, FLA INT UNIV, 73- *Personal Data:* b Jacksonville, Tex, June 6, 27; m 51; c 2. *Educ:* Huston-Tillotson Col, BS, 52; Tex Southern Univ, MS, 53; Mich State Univ, PhD(math educ), 72. *Prof Exp:* Teacher math, Lufkin Independent Schs, 53-59 & Case Western Res Univ, 64-73; dept chmn, Cleveland Bd Educ, 60-73. *Mem:* Math Asn Am; Nat Coun Teachers Math. *Res:* Teacher effectiveness in mathematics and how children learn mathematics. *Mailing Add:* Dept Math Fla Int Univ University Park Miami FL 33199-0001

**WILLIAMS-ASHMAN, HOWARD GUY,** BIOCHEMISTRY. *Current Pos:* prof biochem & physiol, 69-73, Maurice Goldblatt prof, 73- 91, EMER MAURICE GOLDBLATT PROF BIOL SCI, PRITZKER SCH MED, UNIV CHICAGO, 91- *Personal Data:* b London, Eng, Sept 3, 25; nat US; m 59, Elisabeth Bachli; c Anne C, Christina (deceased), Charlotte & Geraldine. *Educ:* Cambridge Univ, BA, 46; Univ London, PhD, 49. *Honors & Awards:* Amory Prize, Am Acad Arts & Sci, 75. *Prof Exp:* Biochemist, Chester Beatty Res Inst, Eng, 49-50; from asst prof to prof biochem, Univ Chicago, 53-64; prof pharmacol & exp therapeut & prof reprod biol, Sch Med, Johns Hopkins Univ, 64-69. *Concurrent Pos:* Am Cancer Soc scholar, 53-57; USPHS res career award, 62-64. *Mem:* Am Soc Biol Chem; fel Am Acad Arts & Sci. *Res:* Mechanism of hormone action; reproductive physiology; chemical pathology. *Mailing Add:* Ben May Inst Pritzker Sch Med Univ Chicago 5421 S Cornell Ave Chicago IL 60615

**WILLIAMS-BLANGERO, SARAH ANN,** GENETIC MANAGEMENT, GENETIC EPIDEMIOLOGY. *Current Pos:* Postdoctoral scientist, 87-90, from asst scientist to assoc scientist, 90-96, SCIENTIST, SW FOUND BIOMED RES, 96- *Personal Data:* b Greenwich, Eng, Apr 26, 62; m 84, John Blangero. *Educ:* Case Western Res Univ, BA, 84, MA, 84, PhD(bioanthrop), 87. *Concurrent Pos:* Prin investr, Nat Ctr Res Resources, NIH, 92-; assoc ed, Am J Phys Anthrop, 92-96; adj assoc prof anthrop, Univ Kans, 93- *Mem:* Am Asn Phys Anthropologists; Am Asn Lab Animal Sci; Am Soc Primatologists; Am Soc Human Genetics; Am Soc Trop Med & Hyg; Human Biol Asn. *Res:* Genetic management; population and quantitative genetics of nonhuman primates; genetic epidemiological approaches in animal colony management; genetic determinants of susceptibility to infectious disease. *Mailing Add:* SW Found Biomed Res PO Box 760549 San Antonio TX 78245-0549. *Fax:* 210-670-3317; *E-Mail:* sarah@darwin.sfbr.org

**WILLIAMSON, ALAN R,** IMMUNOLOGY. *Current Pos:* VPRES BASIC RES IMMUNOL, MERCK SHARP & DOHME RES LABS, 87- *Res:* Immunology. *Mailing Add:* Immunol & Inflamation Res Merck Res Lab Rahway NJ 07065-0900

**WILLIAMSON, ARTHUR ELRIDGE, JR,** ELECTROOPTICS. *Current Pos:* RETIRED. *Personal Data:* b Montgomery, Ala, July 6, 26; m 51; c 2. *Educ:* Auburn Univ, BEP, 50, MS, 51. *Prof Exp:* Res engr, NAm Aviation Inc, 51-52; instr physics, Univ Richmond, 52-53; res physicist, Southern Res Inst, 53-55; asst physics & res proj dir, Ga Inst Technol, 55-59; chief, Electrooptics Lab, Martin Marietta Corp, 59-73; head, Electro Optics Sect, Southern Res Inst, 73-88; secy & treas, Southern Res Tech Inc, 88-89. *Mem:* Am Phys Soc; Optical Soc Am. *Res:* Optics. *Mailing Add:* 501 Benbow Dr Birmingham AL 35226

**WILLIAMSON, ASHLEY DEAS,** AEROSOL MECHANICS & CHEMISTRY. *Current Pos:* sr chemist, 79-80, sect head, 81-84, DIV HEAD, SOUTHERN RES INST, 85- *Personal Data:* b Columbus, Ga, June 16, 47; m 73, Barbara Bauer; c Matthew & Heather. *Educ:* Emory Univ, BS, 68; Calif Inst Technol, PhD(chem), 76. *Prof Exp:* Sci & eng asst, US Army Chem Ctr, Edgewood Arsenal, Md, 69-71; res & teaching asst, Calif Inst Technol, 71-75; scientist, Oak Ridge Nat Lab, 75-79. *Mem:* Am Chem Soc; Air & Waste Mgt Asn; Am Asn Aerosol Res. *Res:* Air pollution control and measurement; particulate sampling, characterization and measurement; chemical and physical transformation of condensible vapors in process emissions; laser spectroscopy; multiphoton excitation and ionization; mass spectrometry; gaseous ion chemistry; vacuum ultraviolet spectroscopy; radon measurement and mitigation; indoor air quality studies. *Mailing Add:* 4415 Debardeleben Ave Fairfield AL 35064. *Fax:* 205-581-2448

**WILLIAMSON, CHARLES ELVIN,** BIO-ORGANIC CHEMISTRY, ONCOLOGY. *Current Pos:* PRES, JUNGLE-GEMS, INC, 79- *Personal Data:* b Portsmouth, Va, Dec 5, 26; m 52; c 6. *Educ:* Col William & Mary, BS, 50; Johns Hopkins Univ, PhD(bio-org chem), 70. *Prof Exp:* Res chemist, Res Labs, Edgewood Arsenal, 52-79. *Concurrent Pos:* Res assoc, Sinai Hosp Baltimore, 55-80 & Sch Med, Johns Hopkins Univ, 72- *Res:* Microenvironmental forces at biologic binding sites; reactions at cell surfaces; hydrophobic and electrostatic catalyses; neoplastic changes and cancer chemotherapy; tissue culture and micropropagation of plants. *Mailing Add:* 210 E Ring Factory Rd Bel Air MD 21014

**WILLIAMSON, CLARENCE KELLY,** MICROBIOLOGY. *Current Pos:* from asst prof to assoc prof, Miami Univ, 55-63, chmn, Dept Microbiol, 62-72, dean, Col Arts & Sci, 71-82, exec vpres acad affairs & provost, 82-85, PROF MICROBIOL, MIAMI UNIV, 63- *Personal Data:* b McKeesport, Pa, Jan 19, 24; m 51; c 2. *Educ:* Univ Pittsburgh, BS, 49, MS, 51, PhD, 55. *Prof Exp:* Instr bact, Sch Pharm, Univ Pittsburgh, 51-55. *Concurrent Pos:* Consult, Warren-Teed Prod Co, 54-64; consult ed, World Publ Co, 65-68; mem, Comt Arts & Sci, Nat Asn State Univ & Land-Grant Col, 75- *Mem:* AAAS; Am Soc Microbiol; fel Am Acad Microbiol; Coun Cols of Arts & Sci (pres, 77-78). *Res:* Microbic dissociation, Pseudomonas aeruginosa; classification and polysaccharides of viridans streptococci; post-streptococcal nephritis. *Mailing Add:* 104 McKee Ave Oxford OH 45056-9025

**WILLIAMSON, CLAUDE F,** NUCLEAR PHYSICS. *Current Pos:* res physicist, Lab Nuclear Sci, 66-75, SR RES SCIENTIST, LAB NUCLEAR SCI & DEPT PHYSICS, MASS INST TECHNOL, 75- *Personal Data:* b Henderson, Tex, Mar 29, 33; m 59, M Delaine Hays. *Educ:* Univ Tex, BS, 55, MA, 56, PhD(physics), 59. *Prof Exp:* Physicist, Saclay Nuclear Res Ctr, France, 60-62; res asst prof nuclear physics, Nuclear Physics Lab, Univ Wash, 62-66. *Concurrent Pos:* Detailee, US Dept Eng, 84-86. *Mem:* AAAS; Am Phys Soc. *Res:* Fast neutron physics; nuclear reaction gamma rays; nuclear and nucleon structure by electron scattering. *Mailing Add:* Mass Inst Technol Rm 26-431 77 Massachusetts Ave Cambridge MA 02139. *Fax:* 617-258-5440; *E-Mail:* cfw@mitlns.mit.edu

**WILLIAMSON, CRAIG EDWARD,** AQUATIC ECOLOGY, POPULATION BIOLOGY. *Current Pos:* Asst prof, Lehigh Univ, 81-87, assoc prof biol, 87-91, assoc prof earth & environ sci, 91-93, PROF EARTH & ENVIRON SCI, LEHIGH UNIV, 93- *Personal Data:* b Boston, Mass, July 20, 53; m 74; c 2. *Educ:* Dartmouth Col, AB, 75, PhD(biol), 81; Mt Holyoke Col, MA, 77. *Mem:* AAAS; Ecol Soc Am; Am Soc Limnol & Oceanog; Sigma Xi; Int Asn Theoret Appl Limnol. *Res:* Comparative limnology; role of ultraviolet radiation and selective predation in structuring freshwater zooplankton communities. *Mailing Add:* Dept Earth & Environ Sci Lehigh Univ Bethlehem PA 18015-3188. *Fax:* 610-758-3677; *E-Mail:* cew0@lehigh.edu

**WILLIAMSON, DAVID G,** BIOSTATISTICS, EPIDEMIOLOGY. *Current Pos:* chief statist consult, Systs Develop Sect, Div Surveillance & Epidemiol, 87-91, CHIEF, STATIST & EPIDEMIOL BR, CTR DIS CONTROL, 91-, ASSOC DIR SCI, DIV PREV RES & ANALYTIC METHODS, 96- *Personal Data:* b Savannah, Ga, Apr 21, 51. *Educ:* Ga Inst Technol, BS, 73; Ga Southern Univ, MS, 78; Va Polytech Inst & State Univ, MS, 80; Emory Univ, PhD(biostatist), 87. *Prof Exp:* Math statistician, Environ Protection Agency, 80-81; res assoc, La State Univ Med Sch, 81-84. *Concurrent Pos:* Adj prof, Dept Biostatist & Dept Epidemiol, Emory Univ, 93. *Mem:* Am Pub Health Asn; Biometric Soc; Am Statist Asn. *Mailing Add:* Epidemiol Prog Off CDC 1600 Clifton Rd NE MS D01 Atlanta GA 30333. *Fax:* 404-639-4463; *E-Mail:* dxw2@epo.em.cdc.gov

**WILLIAMSON, DAVID GADSBY,** CHEMICAL KINETICS. *Current Pos:* from asst prof to assoc prof, 68-76, PROF CHEM, CALIF POLYTECH STATE UNIV, SAN LUIS OBISPO, 76- *Personal Data:* b Honolulu, Hawaii, June 12, 41; m 63; c 2. *Educ:* Univ Colo, Boulder, BA, 63; Univ Calif, Los Angeles, PhD(phys chem), 66. *Prof Exp:* Chemist, Nat Bur Stand, Colo, 63;

teaching & res asst chem, Univ Calif, Los Angeles, 63-66; fel, Nat Res Coun Can, 67-68. *Concurrent Pos:* Res grant, Environ Protection Agency, 72. *Mem:* Am Chem Soc. *Res:* Ozone chemistry and the chemistry of free radicals of importance to atmospheric chemistry; development of energy sources alternate to petroleum products. *Mailing Add:* Chem Dept Calif State Polytech Col San Luis Obispo CA 93407

**WILLIAMSON, DAVID LEE,** GENETICS. *Current Pos:* assoc prof, 71-81, PROF ANAT SCI, STATE UNIV NY, STONY BROOK, 81- *Personal Data:* b Humboldt, Nebr, July 17, 30; m 68; c 3. *Educ:* Nebr State Teachers Col, Peru, AB, 52; Univ Nebr, MS, 55, PhD(zool), 59. *Prof Exp:* Instr biol, Dana Col, 55-56; Fulbright scholar, Lab Genetics, Gif-sur-Yvette, France, 59-60; asst prof genetics, Univ Utah, 60-61; NIH fel, Yale Univ, 61-64; res fel, Med Col Pa, 64-66, asst prof, 66-71. *Mem:* AAAS; Am Soc Microbiol; Genetics Soc Am; Int Orgn Mycoplasmology. *Res:* Maternally inherited traits in Drosophila; biology of spiroplasmas. *Mailing Add:* Dept Anat Sci State Univ NY Health Sci Sch Med 100 N Colls Rd Stony Brook NY 11794-0001

**WILLIAMSON, DENIS GEORGE,** BIOCHEMISTRY. *Current Pos:* Med Res Coun fel, 68-71, lectr, 71-72, from asst prof to assoc prof, 72-81, PROF BIOCHEM, UNIV OTTAWA, 81- *Personal Data:* b Trail, BC, June 9, 41; m 62; c 3. *Educ:* Univ BC, BSc, 63, PhD(biochem), 68. *Mem:* Can Biochem Soc. *Res:* Metabolism of steroid hormones; purification and characterization of steroid dehydrogenases; estrogen receptors. *Mailing Add:* Dept Biochem Univ Ottawa 451 Smyth Rd Ottawa ON K1N 6N5 Can

**WILLIAMSON, DONALD ELWIN,** INSTRUMENTATION, BIOMEDICAL ENGINEERING. *Current Pos:* RETIRED. *Personal Data:* b Lansing, Mich, Oct 24, 13; m 40; c 3. *Educ:* Carleton Col, AB, 35; Univ Mich, MS, 36. *Prof Exp:* Res physicist, Dept Eng Res, Univ Mich, 36, res engr, 44-45; mgr, Profilometer Div, Physicists Res Co, 36-44; res engr, Lincoln Park Industs, 45-47; chief engr & assoc dir res, Baird Assocs, Inc, Mass, 47-52; pres & treas, Williamson Develop Co, 53-60; sci adv to pres, Cordis Corp, 60-79. *Concurrent Pos:* Chmn, Gordon Res Conf Instrumentation, 56. *Mem:* Am Soc Mech Engrs; Optical Soc Am. *Res:* Roughness measurement; optics; infrared instruments; physiological and cardiovascular instrumentation. *Mailing Add:* 1531 Trevino Ave Coral Gables FL 33134

**WILLIAMSON, EDWARD L,** NUCLEAR ENGINEERING. *Current Pos:* RETIRED. *Honors & Awards:* Bernard F Langer Codes & Stand Award, Am Soc Mech Engrs, 90. *Prof Exp:* Staff, Gulf Power Co, Pensacola, Fla, 49-65; staff mem & sr vpres design eng, Southern Co Serv Inc, 65-88. *Concurrent Pos:* Adj prof mech eng, Univ Ala, Birmingham. *Mem:* Fel Am Soc Mech Engrs. *Mailing Add:* 1834 Canyon Rd Birmingham AL 35216-1722

**WILLIAMSON, EDWARD P,** ELECTRICAL ENGINEERING, COMMUNICATIONS. *Current Pos:* from asst prof to assoc prof, 65-96, EMER PROF ELEC ENG & COMPUT SCI, TULANE UNIV, 97- *Personal Data:* b Lee Co, Fla, July 1, 33; m 58, Nancy Uhrich; c Randall, Michael & Scott. *Educ:* Univ Fla, BEE, 55, MSE, 60, PhD(elec eng), 65. *Prof Exp:* Engr, Bendix Radio Div, 55-56. *Concurrent Pos:* Res engr, Gulf South Res Inst, 66; res scientist, Kaman Nuclear Div, Colo, 67; NASA fac fel, 74. *Mem:* Inst Elec & Electronics Engrs. *Res:* Digital communications systems; statistical communication theory; communication system signal design and modulation techniques; optimization, estimation and decision theory as applied to communication and radar systems; satellite communication systems; communication channel modelling. *Mailing Add:* Dept Elec Eng & Comput Sci Tulane Univ New Orleans LA 70118. *Fax:* 504-865-5526

**WILLIAMSON, FRANCIS SIDNEY LANIER,** zoology, public health administration, for more information see previous edition

**WILLIAMSON, HANDY, JR,** ECONOMIC DEVELOPMENT, MANPOWER PLANNING & TRAINING. *Current Pos:* PROF AGR ECON & HEAD DEPT, UNIV TENN, 88- *Personal Data:* b Louin, Miss, Oct 24, 45; m 68, Barbara H; c Lilla-Marie J. *Educ:* Tenn State Univ, MS, 69; Univ Mo, MS, 71, PhD(agr econ), 74; Alcorn State Univ, BS, 67. *Honors & Awards:* Outstanding Black Agr Economist, Am Agr Econs Asn, 90. *Prof Exp:* Assoc prof & assoc regional dir, Agr Econ & Rural Res, Tuskegee Univ, 74-77; assoc prof & res dir, Agr Res, Tenn State Univ, 77-85; dep dir, Res & Univ Rel, Agency Int Develop, 85-88. *Concurrent Pos:* Consult, numerous govt agencies, 74-90; mem, Nat Rural Develop Comn, 75-77 & US Joint Coun Food & Agr Sci, 82-83; bd dirs, Asn State Univ Dirs Int Agr Progs, 84, Va Bus Develop Ctr, 87 & United Methodist Found, 94-97; agency liaison, White House Comn Hist Black Cols, 85-90; owner & chief exec officer, Willco Int; chmn, Am Agr Econs Asn, 90-92. *Mem:* Am Agr Econs Asn; Southern Agr Econs Asn; Nat Asn Agr Econ Adminrs; AAAS; Coun Agr Sci & Technol; Asn Int Agr & Rural Develop; Agr Econs Dept Heads. *Res:* Regional economic development manpower economics and the small firm sector; demographic, historical and empirical analysis; impact assessment; design, evaluation and institution building; author or co-author of numerous scientific and professional publications. *Mailing Add:* 12108 E Ashton Ct Knoxville TN 37922

**WILLIAMSON, HAROLD E,** PHARMACOLOGY. *Current Pos:* from instr to assoc prof, 60-70, PROF PHARMACOL, COL MED, UNIV IOWA, 70- *Personal Data:* b Racine, Wis, Aug 8, 30; m 57, Joan Chase; c Timothy, Julie & Eric. *Educ:* Univ Wis, BS, 53, PhD(pharmacol, toxicol), 59. *Prof Exp:* Res asst pharmacol, Univ Wis, 55-59, proj assoc, 59-60. *Mem:* AAAS; Am Soc

Pharmacol & Exp Therapeut; Int Soc Nephrology; Soc Exp Biol & Med; Am Soc Nephrology; fel Am Col Clin Pharmacol. *Res:* Renal pharmacology and physiology, especially the effect of diuretics and hormones on electrolyte and water transport. *Mailing Add:* Dept Pharmacol Univ Iowa Col Med Iowa City IA 52242-1109. *Fax:* 319-335-8579; *E-Mail:* Bitnet: cmdhwpwy@uiamvs

**WILLIAMSON, HUGH A,** PHYSICS. *Current Pos:* from asst prof to assoc prof, 67-74, PROF PHYSICS, CALIF STATE UNIV, FRESNO, 74- *Personal Data:* b Kemp, Tex, Aug 11, 32; m 56; c 4. *Educ:* North Tex State Univ, BA, 54; Univ Tex, PhD(physics, math), 62. *Prof Exp:* Res scientist, Molecular Physics Res Lab & Mil Physics Res Lab, Univ Tex, 60-63, res fel, 62-63; res scientist, Res Lab, United Aircraft Corp, 63-65, sr res scientist, 65-67. *Res:* Atomic and molecular structure; gaseous electronics; electron scattering processes off neutral atoms including elastic, inelastic and free-free scattering processes. *Mailing Add:* Dept Physics Calif State Univ 2345 E San Ramon Fresno CA 93740-0001

**WILLIAMSON, JAMES LAWRENCE,** animal science, animal nutrition, for more information see previous edition

**WILLIAMSON, JERRY ROBERT,** ORGANIC CHEMISTRY, POLYMER CHEMISTRY. *Current Pos:* asst prof, 67-70, ASSOC PROF CHEM, EASTERN MICH UNIV, 70- *Personal Data:* b Danville, Ill, Feb 14, 38; m 65, Karen Horner; c 1. *Educ:* Univ Ill, Urbana, BA, 60; Univ Iowa, MS, 63, PhD(org polymer chem), 64. *Prof Exp:* Petrol Res Fund res fel polymer res, Univ Iowa, 61-62, teaching asst gen & org chem, 62-64; asst prof chem & actg chmn div sci, Jarvis Christian Col, 64-66; res fel, Tex Christian Univ, 66-67. *Concurrent Pos:* Partic, State Tech Serv Prog, Mich, 67-69; consult hazardous chem safety, off training serv, J T Baker Chem Co, Phillipsburg, NJ. *Mem:* AAAS; Am Chem Soc. *Res:* Organic polymer chemistry, thermally stable materials; polymer analysis via gel permeation chromatography. *Mailing Add:* 1020 Louise St Ypsilanti MI 48197

**WILLIAMSON, JOHN HYBERT,** GENETICS. *Current Pos:* PROF & CHMN, DEPT BIOL, DAVIDSON COL, 78- *Personal Data:* b Clarkton, NC, Apr 28, 38; m 63; c 3. *Educ:* NC State Col, BS, 60; Cornell Univ, MS, 63; Univ Ga, PhD(zool), 66. *Prof Exp:* Fel biol, Oak Ridge Nat Lab, 66-67; fel life sci, Univ Calif, Riverside, 67-69; from asst prof to prof zool, Univ Calgary, 69-81, acad admin officer, Biol Dept, 74-76, head dept, 76-78. *Mem:* Genetics Soc Can; Genetics Soc Am. *Res:* Chromosome mechanics; radiation biology; developmental genetics; enzymology. *Mailing Add:* Dept Biol Davidson Col PO Box 1719 Davidson NC 28036-1719

**WILLIAMSON, JOHN RICHARD,** BIOCHEMISTRY, BIOPHYSICS. *Current Pos:* PROF BIOCHEM, SCH MED, UNIV PA, 75- *Personal Data:* b Coventry, Eng, Sept 18, 33; m 61; c 3. *Educ:* Oxford Univ, BA, 56, MA, 59, PhD(biochem), 60. *Prof Exp:* Dept demonstr biochem, Oxford Univ, 60-61; independent investr, Baker Clin Res Lab, Harvard Univ, 61-63; assoc phys biochem, 63-65, from asst prof to prof phys biochem, Johnson Res Found, 65-76. *Concurrent Pos:* USPHS fel, 61-63; Am Heart Asn grant, 66-72; NIH res grants & contract, 71-; estab investr, Am Heart Asn, 67-72, mem coun basic sci. *Mem:* Am Soc Biol Chem; Am Diabetes Asn; Brit Biochem Soc; NY Acad Sci; Am Physiol Soc. *Res:* Mode of action of hormones and drugs; control of metabolic pathways; effect of hormones on cells and hormone interactions in animal cells; role of anion transport across mitochondrial membranes; myocardial ischemia. *Mailing Add:* Dept Biochem & Biophys Rm 601 Univ Pa 37th & Hamilton Walk Philadelphia PA 19104-6089. *Fax:* 215-898-9918

**WILLIAMSON, JOHN S,** HYBRID ANTIBIOTIC PRODUCTION, DESIGN OF ANTICANCER CHEMOTHERAPEUTICS. *Current Pos:* ASST PROF MED CHEM, UNIV MISS, 89- *Personal Data:* b Jackson, Miss, Oct 24, 58; m 83; c 3. *Educ:* Univ Miss, BS, 82; Univ Iowa, PhD(med chem & natural prod), 87. *Prof Exp:* Postdoctoral fel biol, Yale Univ, 87-89. *Concurrent Pos:* Asst res prof, Res Inst Pharmaceut Sci, 90-; Am Soc Pharmacog young investr award, 90; Am Asn Cols Pharm young investr award, 91. *Mem:* Am Chem Soc; Am Soc Microbiol; AAAS; Soc Indust Microbiologists; Am Soc Pharmacog. *Res:* Exploitation of microbiol biosynthetic and catabolic enzymatic systems for use as alternative synthetic reagents. *Mailing Add:* Dept Med Chem Sch Pharm Univ Miss University MS 38677

**WILLIAMSON, JOHN W,** MECHANICAL ENGINEERING. *Current Pos:* from asst prof to assoc prof mech eng, 64-77, PROF MECH ENG & MAT SCI, VANDERBILT UNIV, 77- *Personal Data:* b Tulsa, Okla, Oct 26, 33; m 61; c 3. *Educ:* Univ Okla, BSc, 55; Ohio State Univ, MSc, 59, PhD(mech eng), 65. *Prof Exp:* Test engr, NAm Aviation, Inc, 56-57; instr mech eng, Ohio State Univ, 57-60, 61-64, res asst, 60-61. *Concurrent Pos:* Consult, Aerospace Struct Div, Avco Corp, 66- & E I du Pont de Nemours & Co, Inc, 69. *Mem:* Am Soc Eng Educ; Am Soc Mech Engrs. *Res:* Fluid mechanics, specifically aspects of turbulent fluid flow; energy utilization studies. *Mailing Add:* Dept Mech Eng PO Box 1592 Sta B Vanderbilt Univ Nashville TN 37235

**WILLIAMSON, KENNETH DALE,** PHYSICAL CHEMISTRY. *Current Pos:* RETIRED. *Personal Data:* b Drumright, Okla, Sept 4, 20; m 46, Dorothy Dale; c Dale A, Kent A & Lance M. *Educ:* Univ Okla, BS, 47, MS, 48; Univ Tex, PhD(chem), 54. *Prof Exp:* Chemist, Petrol Exp Sta, US Bur Mines, Okla, 48-50; spec instr chem, Univ Tex, 53; res chemist, Union Carbide Corp, 53-66, group leader res, 66-71, res scientist, 71-85. *Concurrent Pos:* Asst prof, Morris

Harvey Col, 56-59 & WVa State Col, 62-64; adj prof, Col Grad Studies, WVa, 71; chmn, Kanawha Valley Sect, Am Chem Soc, 84. *Mem:* AAAS; Am Chem Soc; Sigma Xi; NAm Catalyst Soc. *Res:* Physical properties of gas hydrates; physical properties of pure compounds and mixtures; thermodynamics; calorimetry; kinetics of pyrolysis of hydrocarbons; catalysis; 12 scientific publications and three US patents. *Mailing Add:* 1022 Sand Hill Dr St Albans WV 25177

**WILLIAMSON, KENNETH L(EE),** ORGANIC CHEMISTRY, MICROSCALE EXPERIMENTS. *Current Pos:* from asst prof to assoc prof, 61-69, dept chmn, 78-81, PROF CHEM, MT HOLYOKE COL, 69-, MARY E WOOLLEY PROF, 84- *Personal Data:* b Tarentum, Pa, Apr 13, 34; m 56, Louise Hoerner; c Christopher, Tania & Kevin. *Educ:* Harvard Univ, BA, 56; Univ Wis, PhD(org chem), 60. *Prof Exp:* NIH fel, Stanford Univ, 60-61. *Concurrent Pos:* Mem grad fac, Univ Mass, 62-; vis prof, Cornell Univ, 66; NSF sci fac fel & fel, Univ Liverpool, 68-69; vis assoc, Calif Inst Technol, 75 & 82; secy, Exp Nuclear Magnetic Resonance Spectros Confs, 73-78, chmn, 79; fel, John Simon Guggenheim Found, 75-76; vis prof, Univ Utah, 76, Oxford Univ, Eng, 76 & 83, Dartmouth Col, 86-87, Harvard Univ, 89-90, Trondheim Univ, Univ Strasbourg, Basel Univ, Univ Amsterdam, 91-92, Univ Canterbury, NZ & Univ Auckland, 94; mem, Comt Hazardous Substances in the Labs, Nat Res Coun, 81-82. *Mem:* Am Chem Soc; Sigma Xi; AAAS. *Res:* Conformational analysis by means of nuclear magnetic resonance spectroscopy; Xenon nuclear magnetic resonance; carbon relaxation time studies; microscale organic experiments. *Mailing Add:* Dept Chem Mt Holyoke Col South Hadley MA 01075. *Fax:* 413-538-2327; *E-Mail:* kwilliam@mhc.mtholyokc.edu

**WILLIAMSON, LURA C,** NEUROBIOLOGY. *Current Pos:* SR STAFF FEL NEUROBIOL, NIH, 92- *Personal Data:* b Idaho, Aug 4, 53. *Res:* Neurobiology. *Mailing Add:* Lab Develop Neurobiol NICHD NIH Bldg 49 Rm 5A38 Bethesda MD 20892-4480

**WILLIAMSON, LUTHER HOWARD,** PHYSICAL CHEMISTRY, OIL FIELD CHEMISTRY. *Current Pos:* TECH SERV CONSULT, TEX SERV, 85- *Personal Data:* b Osyka, Miss, Oct 9, 36; m 57; c 3. *Educ:* La State Univ, BS, 59, MS, 62, PhD(phys chem), 65. *Prof Exp:* Res chemist corrosion, Mobil Res & Develop Corp, 65-70, sr res chemist corrosion, Water Chem, 70-78; staff engr corrosion, Mat Eng, Super Oil Co, 78-85. *Concurrent Pos:* Adj instr corrosion, Univ Tex, Tyler, 93- *Mem:* Am Chem Soc; Nat Asn Corrosion Engrs; Soc Petrol Engrs. *Res:* Surface chemistry; corrosion, corrosion inhibition, electrochemistry of corrosion; hydrogen embrittlement; sulfide stress corrosion cracking; water chemistry, oilfield chemistry, chemistry of scale formation; water pollution, air pollution; environmental science. *Mailing Add:* 10666 CR 290 Tyler TX 75707

**WILLIAMSON, PATRICK LESLIE,** CYTOLOGY, BIOCHEMISTRY. *Current Pos:* from asst prof to assoc prof, 77-89, PROF BIOL, AMHERST COL, 89- *Personal Data:* b Dickinson, NDak, Apr 15, 48; m 70; c 2. *Educ:* Beloit Col, BA, 70; Harvard Univ, MS, 71, PhD(molecular biol), 74. *Prof Exp:* Staff fel, NIH, 74-77. *Concurrent Pos:* Adj prof, Molecular & Cell Biol Prog, Univ Mass; Fogarty sr int fel, 90. *Mem:* Am Soc Cell Biol. *Res:* Cell biology; structure and function of the plasma membrane of eukaryote cells; alterations of same in leukemia and sickle cell disease. *Mailing Add:* Dept Biol Amherst Col A103 Webster Amherst MA 01002-0001

**WILLIAMSON, RALPH EDWARD,** plant physiology; deceased, see previous edition for last biography

**WILLIAMSON, RICHARD CARDINAL,** ELECTROOPTICAL DEVICES, SURFACE ACOUSTIC WAVES. *Current Pos:* mem tech staff, Lincoln Lab, Mass Inst Technol, 70-74, assoc group leader, 74-80, group leader, 80-95, SR STAFF, LINCOLN LAB, MASS INST TECHNOL, 95- *Personal Data:* b Minocqua, Wis, Sept 10, 39; m 61, Christine Bauer; c 4. *Educ:* Mass Inst Technol, BS, 61, PhD(physics), 66. *Honors & Awards:* Centennial Award, Inst Elec & Electronics Engrs, 84, Career Achievement Award, 85. *Prof Exp:* Staff scientist, Electronics Res Ctr, NASA, 65-70. *Mem:* Fel Inst Elec & Electronics Engrs; Am Phys Soc; Optical Soc Am; Sigma Xi. *Res:* Electrooptical devices and applications; optical signal processing; surface acoustic waves and their use in signal processing; ultrasonic investigations; phase transitions; low-temperature physics. *Mailing Add:* Lincoln Lab Mass Inst Technol PO Box 73 Lexington MA 02173. *Fax:* 781-981-5793; *E-Mail:* williamson@ll.mit.edu

**WILLIAMSON, RICHARD EDMUND,** MATHEMATICS. *Current Pos:* instr, 56-58, from asst prof to assoc prof, 58-66, PROF MATH, DARTMOUTH COL, 66- *Personal Data:* b Chicago, Ill, May 23, 27; m 50. *Educ:* Dartmouth Col, AB, 50; Univ Pa, AM, 51, PhD, 55. *Prof Exp:* Res asst, Univ Pa, 55-56. *Concurrent Pos:* Res fel, Harvard Univ, 60-61. *Mem:* Am Math Soc. *Res:* Analysis. *Mailing Add:* 66 Elm St Norwich VT 05055-9446

**WILLIAMSON, ROBERT BRADY,** MATERIAL SCIENCE ENGINEERING, FIRE PROTECTION ENGINEERING. *Current Pos:* PROF CIVIL ENG, UNIV CALIF, BERKELEY, 68- *Personal Data:* b New Rochelle, NY, Nov 19, 33; m 59; c 3. *Educ:* Harvard Univ, AB, 56, SB, 59, PhD(appl physics), 65. *Prof Exp:* Asst prof civil eng, Mass Inst Technol, 65-68. *Mem:* Am Soc Civil Engrs; Am Soc Testing & Mat; Soc Fire Protection Engrs; Mat Res Soc; Combustion Inst. *Res:* Morphology of solidified materials; fracture of materials; fire research and testing; theory of learning and programmed instruction. *Mailing Add:* Dept Civil Eng 760 Davis Hall Univ Calif Berkeley CA 94720-1710

**WILLIAMSON, ROBERT ELMORE,** AGRICULTURAL MECHANIZATION, MACHINERY MANAGEMENT. *Current Pos:* assoc prof, 78-81, PROF AGR ENG, CLEMSON UNIV, 81- *Personal Data:* b York Co, SC, Nov 8, 37; m 64, Eva Simpson; c Margaret Edye & Robert Elmore, Jr. *Educ:* Clemson Univ, BS, 59, MS, 64; Miss State Univ, PhD(eng), 72. *Prof Exp:* Res assoc, Miss State Univ, 66-71; asst prof, Univ Ga, 71-78. *Mem:* Am Soc Agr Engrs; Am Soc Eng Educ; Sigma Xi. *Res:* Fruit and vegetable mechanization; equipment and techniques for chemical application; machinery management and machine systems for agriculture production; precision agriculture. *Mailing Add:* Agr & Biol Eng Dept Clemson Univ Clemson SC 29634-0357. *Fax:* 834-656-4074; *E-Mail:* bwllmsn@clemson.edu

**WILLIAMSON, ROBERT EMMETT,** GEOMETRY, TOPOLOGY. *Current Pos:* ASSOC PROF MATH, CLAREMONT GRAD SCH, 69- *Personal Data:* b Ashland, Kans, June 9, 37; m 82, K M Davis; c Brian, David & Joan. *Educ:* Univ Ariz, BS, 59; Univ Calif, Berkeley, PhD(math), 63. *Prof Exp:* Mem, Inst Advan Study, 63-65; vis prof, Univ Warwick, 65-66; asst prof, Yale Univ, 66-69. *Concurrent Pos:* Nat Acad Sci-Air Force Off Sci Res fel, 63-64. *Mem:* Am Math Soc. *Res:* Algebraic model of surgery; combiatorial cobordism theory. *Mailing Add:* Dept Math Claremont Grad Sch Claremont CA 91711. *E-Mail:* williamr@cgsvax.claremont.edu

**WILLIAMSON, ROBERT KEITH,** SYSTEMS ANALYSIS & GUIDANCE, NAVIGATION & CONTROL. *Current Pos:* controls analyst & eng specialist, Aerospace Corp, 67-77, mgr, Control Anal Dept, 77-80, dir, Control Technol Dept, 81-90, PRIN DIR SYST ANALYSIS & SIMULATION SUBDIV, AEROSPACE CORP, 90- *Personal Data:* b Hollywood, Calif, June 18, 40; m 63, Sandra Jo DiNardo; c Jennifer, Michael, Kristen & Julie. *Educ:* Univ Calif, Los Angeles, BS, 62, MS, 64, PhD(eng), 69. *Prof Exp:* Mem tech staff, Guid Dept, TRW Systs, 63-67. *Concurrent Pos:* Lectr random vibrations, Uiv Southern Calif, 80-81; lectr control dynamics, Calif State Univ, Long Beach, 81-85; secy, Guid, Navig & Control Tech Comt, Am Inst Aeronaut & Astronaut, 82-86, mem, Guid, Navig & Control Panel Mil Space Syst Tech Plan, 82-84. *Mem:* Assoc fel Am Inst Aeronaut & Astronaut; Soc Photo-Instrumentation Engrs; Am Astronaut Soc. *Res:* Satellite attitude dynamics and control with emphasis in spacecraft structural dynamics, controls interactions and robotics. *Mailing Add:* 20007 Redbeam Ave Torrance CA 90503. *E-Mail:* williamson@courier8mac.aero.org

**WILLIAMSON, ROBERT MARSHALL,** PHYSICS. *Current Pos:* PROF PHYSICS, OAKLAND UNIV, 62- *Personal Data:* b Madison, Wis, Feb 2, 23; m 50; c 2. *Educ:* Univ Fla, BS, 43, PhD(physics), 51. *Prof Exp:* Res assoc, Duke Univ, 51-53, from asst prof to assoc prof physics, 53-62. *Concurrent Pos:* Fulbright lectr, Univ Catania, 59-60. *Mem:* Am Phys Soc; Am Asn Phys Teachers; Acoust Soc Am. *Res:* Nuclear spectroscopy; musical acoustics. *Mailing Add:* Dept Physics Oakland Univ Rochester MI 48309-4401. *Fax:* 313-370-3408

**WILLIAMSON, ROBERT SAMUEL,** PHYSICS. *Current Pos:* Tutor, Queens Col, 52-56, instr, 56-60, from asst prof to assoc prof, 60-68, from asst dean to assoc dean admin, 68-72, PROF PHYSICS, QUEENS COL, NY, 68- *Personal Data:* b Cincinnati, Ohio, June 18, 22. *Educ:* Queens Col, BS, 45; NY Univ, MS, 48; Polytech Inst Brooklyn, PhD(physics), 57. *Mem:* Am Phys Soc; Am Asn Physics Teachers; Am Crystallog Asn; Inst Elec & Electronics Engrs; Sigma Xi. *Res:* X-ray crystallography; electronics. *Mailing Add:* 47-26 196th Pl Flushing NY 11358

**WILLIAMSON, SAMUEL JOHNS,** NEUROMAGNETISM, MAGNETIC SENSOR TECHNOLOGY. *Current Pos:* assoc prof, 71-77, PROF PHYSICS, NY UNIV, 77-, PROF PHYSIOL & NEUROSCI, SCH MED, 84-, UNIV PROF, 90- *Personal Data:* b West Reading, Pa, Nov 6, 39; m 66, Joan Brockman. *Educ:* Mass Inst Technol, SB, 61, ScD(physics), 65. *Hon Degrees:* ScD, NJ Inst Technol, 85; DTech, Helsinki Univ Technol, 94. *Prof Exp:* Staff mem, Francis Bitter Nat Magnet Lab, Mass Inst Technol, 65-66; Nat Acad Sci-Nat Res Coun fel, Dept Physics of Solids, Fac Sci, Univ Paris, Orsay, France, 66-67; mem tech staff, NAm Aviation Sci Ctr, 67-70; lectr physics, Univ Calif, Santa Barbara, 70-71. *Concurrent Pos:* Fulbright sr res scholar, 79-80; chmn, 7th Int Conf Biomagnetism, 89. *Mem:* Fel Am Phys Soc; Sigma Xi; AAAS; Soc Neurosci; Inst Elec & Electronics Engrs. *Res:* Studies of the magnetic field produced by neural activity of the human brain to elucidate sensory, motor, and cognitive processes and the areas of the brain that support them; magnetic source imaging. *Mailing Add:* Physics Dept NY Univ 2 Washington Pl New York NY 10003-1804. *Fax:* 212-995-4011

**WILLIAMSON, STANLEY GILL,** MATHEMATICS. *Current Pos:* From asst prof to assoc prof, 65-75, PROF MATH, UNIV CALIF, SAN DIEGO, 75- *Personal Data:* b Manhattan, Kans, Aug 28, 38; m 65. *Educ:* Calif Inst Technol, BS, 60; Stanford Univ, MS, 62; Univ Calif, Santa Barbara, PhD(math), 65. *Mem:* Soc Indust Appl Math. *Res:* Combinatorial analysis; computation. *Mailing Add:* Dept Comput Sci & Eng Univ Calif San Diego La Jolla CA 92093

**WILLIAMSON, STANLEY MORRIS,** CHEMISTRY. *Current Pos:* Asst prof chem, Univ Calif, Berkeley, 61-65, from asst prof to assoc prof, 65-74, PROF CHEM, UNIV CALIF, SANTA CRUZ, 74-, DEAN GRAD DIV, 72- *Personal Data:* b Chattanooga, Tenn, Mar 18, 36; m 66. *Educ:* Univ NC, BS, 58; Univ Wash, PhD(chem), 61. *Mem:* AAAS; Am Chem Soc; Royal Soc Chem. *Res:* Fluorine chemistry of compounds of sulfur, nitrogen, oxygen and xenon including preparations and properties. *Mailing Add:* Dept Chem Univ Calif Santa Cruz CA 95064-1099

**WILLIAMSON, SUSAN,** MATHEMATICS. *Current Pos:* from asst prof to assoc prof, 65-71, dean col, 73-75, PROF MATH, REGIS COL, MASS, 71- *Personal Data:* b Boston, Mass, Dec 29, 36. *Educ:* Radcliffe Col, AB, 58; Brandeis Univ, AM, 61, PhD(math), 63. *Prof Exp:* Instr, Cardinal Cushing Col, 62-63; asst prof math, Boston Col, 63-64; scholar hist sci, Harvard Univ, 64-65. *Mem:* Am Math Soc; Math Asn Am; Asn Women Math. *Res:* Associative algebras; commutative rings; women's higher education; biographical research. *Mailing Add:* 37 Hagen Rd Newton Centre MA 02159-2730

**WILLIAMSON, THOMAS GARNETT,** NUCLEAR ENGINEERING. *Current Pos:* dir, Reactor Facil, 77-79, chmn, Nuclear Eng & Eng Physics Dept, 77-90, PROF NUCLEAR ENG, UNIV VA, 60-; SR SCIENTIST, WESTINGHOUSE SAVANNAH RIVER LABS, 90- *Personal Data:* b Quincey, Mass, Jan 27, 34; m 61; c 3. *Educ:* Va Mil Inst, BS, 55; Rensselaer Polytech Inst, MS, 57; Univ Va, PhD(physics), 60. *Prof Exp:* Nuclear engr, Alco Prod, Inc, NY, 57-58. *Concurrent Pos:* Consult, Gen Atomic Div, Gen Dynamics Corp, 66 & Combustion Eng, Conn, 71, 72; mem, Syst Nuclear Safety & Operating Comt, Va Elec & Power Co, 75-90; mem reactor safety comt, Babcock & Wilcox Co, 76-90; sabbatical leave, Nat Bur Stand, Md, 84-85. *Mem:* Fel Am Nuclear Soc. *Res:* Radioactive isotope usage; neutron activation analysis; radiation shielding; reactor physics. *Mailing Add:* 217 Colleton Ave SE Aiken SC 29801

**WILLIAMSON, WALTON E, JR,** FLIGHT MECHANICS, OPTIMIZATION. *Current Pos:* mem tech staff, 74-84, SUPVR, ADV SYSTS DIV, SANDIA LABS, ALBUQUERQUE, 84- *Personal Data:* b Corpus Christi, Tex, May 21, 44; m 65, Judy R Wimbish; c Walton R & Jill R. *Educ:* Stanford Univ, BS, 66; Univ Tex, Austin, MS, 67, PhD(aerospace eng), 70. *Prof Exp:* Asst prof optimal control, Univ Tex, Austin, 70-74. *Mem:* Am Inst Aeronaut & Astronaut. *Res:* Numerical methods for optimal control; shuttle reentry optimization; hypersonics; ballistic and maneuvering reentry vehicles; hypersonic vehicle flight testing. *Mailing Add:* Sandia Labs Orgn 9814 PO Box 5800 MS 0303 Albuquerque NM 87185-0303. *Fax:* 505-844-0094

**WILLIAMSON, WILLIAM, JR,** ATOMIC PHYSICS, TRANSPORT THEORY. *Current Pos:* asst prof physics & astron, 65-69, assoc prof, 69-75, PROF PHYSICS, UNIV TOLEDO, 75- *Personal Data:* b Newport, RI, Jan 20, 34; m 57; c 2. *Educ:* San Francisco State Col, BA, 55; Univ Calif, Berkeley, MA, 58; Univ Colo, PhD(physics), 63. *Prof Exp:* Physicist, US Naval Radiol Defense Lab, Calif, 56-58; Fulbright fel, Frascati Labs, Italy, 61-62; asst physics, Univ Colo, 62-63; fel, Inst Sci & Technol, Univ Mich, 63-64, instr, 64-65. *Concurrent Pos:* Vis prof, Univ Adelaide, 71-72; consult, Sandia Nat Labs, Livermore, Calif. *Mem:* Am Phys Soc; Am Asn Physics Teachers; AAAS. *Res:* Nonlinear differential equations (applied). *Mailing Add:* Physics-Astron Univ Toledo Toledo OH 43606. *Fax:* 419-537-2723

**WILLIAMSON, WILLIAM BURTON,** HETEROGENEOUS CATALYSIS. *Current Pos:* SR RES SCIENTIST SCI RES, FORD MOTOR CO, 76- *Personal Data:* b Frederick, Okla, Apr 29, 46; m 67; c 3. *Educ:* Tex Tech Univ, BS, 69; Tex A&M Univ, PhD(phys chem), 76. *Mem:* Am Chem Soc; Sigma Xi. *Res:* Basic and applied laboratory research on potential automotive emission catalysts (heterogeneous catalysis) for the reduction of nitric oxide and oxidation of carbon monoxide and hydrocarbons. *Mailing Add:* 2521 W Elgin Broken Arrow OK 74012-2212

**WILLIAMSON, WILLIAM O(WEN),** CERAMICS, PETROLOGY. *Current Pos:* assoc prof ceramic tech, 59-65, prof ceramic sci, 65-76, EMER PROF CERAMIC SCI, PA STATE UNIV, UNIVERSITY PARK, 76- *Personal Data:* b Luton, Eng, Jan 30, 11; m 58, Olive Z Tucker; c 1. *Educ:* Univ London, BSc, 30 & 31, PhD(geol), 33, DSc(geol, indust chem), 58. *Prof Exp:* Chief asst ceramics, North Staffordshire Col Technol, Eng, 34-42; res chemist, Univ Birmingham, 42-45; prof officer ceramics, Univ Witwatersrand, 45-47; prin res officer, Chem Res Labs, Commonwealth Sci & Indust Res Orgn, Australia, 47-59. *Mem:* Fel Am Ceramic Soc; fel Royal Soc Chem. *Res:* Solid state technology; rheology and surface chemistry; high temperature reactions; materials in ancient and modern cultures. *Mailing Add:* 116 Steidle Pa State Univ University Park PA 16802

**WILLIARD, PAUL GREGORY,** ORGANIC CHEMISTRY, STRUCTURAL CHEMISTRY. *Current Pos:* from asst prof to assoc prof, 79-92, PROF CHEM, BROWN UNIV, 92- *Personal Data:* b Mt Carmel, Pa, Dec 18, 50; m 79; c 2. *Educ:* Bucknell Univ, BS & MS, 72; Columbia Univ, MPhil, 74, PhD(chem), 76. *Prof Exp:* NIH trainee chem, Mass Inst Technol, 76-78, fel, 78-79. *Concurrent Pos:* res career develop awards, NIH, 88-93. *Mem:* Am Chem Soc; Am Crystallog Asn. *Res:* Total synthesis of natural products; synthetic methods; x-ray crystallography. *Mailing Add:* Dept Chem Box H Brown Univ Providence RI 02912. *Fax:* 401-863-2594; *E-Mail:* paul____ williard@brown.edu

**WILLIFORD, WILLIAM OLIN,** MATHEMATICAL STATISTICS. *Current Pos:* SR BIOSTATISTICIAN, COOP STUDIES PROG COORD CTR, VET ADMIN HOSP, MD, 77- *Personal Data:* b San Pedro, Calif, July 18, 33; m 71; c 2. *Educ:* Pepperdine Col, BA, 57; Fla State Univ, MS, 59; Va Polytech Inst & State Univ, PhD(statist), 67. *Prof Exp:* Instr math, Fla State Univ, 59-62; asst prof, Roanoke Col, 62-63; NIH fel, 64-67; asst prof statist, Univ Ga, 67-76, asst prof comput sci, 74-76. *Mem:* Am Statist Asn; Inst Math Statist; Biomet Soc; Math Asn Am; Soc Clin Trials; Sigma Xi. *Res:* Bayesian estimation; discrete and modified discrete distributions; cooperative clinical trials. *Mailing Add:* Coop Studies Prog Support Ctr Vet Hosp Perry Point MD 21902

**WILLIG, MICHAEL ROBERT,** QUANTITATIVE BIOLOGY. *Current Pos:* ASST PROF BIOL, TEX TECH, 83- *Personal Data:* b Pittsburgh, Pa, June 7, 52. *Educ:* Univ Pittsburgh, BS, 74, PhD(biol), 82. *Prof Exp:* Res fel ecol, Brazilian Nat Acad Sci, 76-78; vis prof terrestrial ecol, LaRoch Col, 79; asst prof ecol & biomet, Loyola Univ, 81-83. *Concurrent Pos:* Res fel, Dept Energy, PR, 81, 82 & 84. *Mem:* Ecol Soc Am; Am Soc Naturalists; Soc Study Evolution; Am Soc Mammalogists; AAAS. *Res:* Application of statistical techniques to answer questions of interest in population biology, ecology, behavior and evolution including population estimation, biogeography, conservation and mammalian systematics. *Mailing Add:* Dept Biol Sci Tex Tech Univ MS 3131 Lubbock TX 79409- 3131

**WILLIGER, ERVIN JOHN,** PLASTICS CHEMISTRY, RUBBER CHEMISTRY. *Current Pos:* SR RES CHEMIST, BRECKSVILLE RES & DEVELOP CTR, B F GOODRICH CO, 73- *Personal Data:* b Szeged, Hungary, June 18, 27; US citizen; m 51; c 4. *Educ:* Budapest Tech Univ, dipl chem eng, 50. *Prof Exp:* Res assoc polymers, Inst Plastics Res, Budapest Tech Univ, 50-56; res & develop chemist, Naugatuck Chem, US Rubber Co, 57-63; polymer chemist, Lucidol Div, Wallace & Tiernan, Inc, 63-65; sr res chemist, Res Ctr, Gen Tire & Rubber Co, 65-69; mgr tech serv & mkt, Union Process Co, Akron, 69-73. *Mem:* Nat Soc Prof Engrs; Am Chem Soc; Soc Plastics Engrs. *Res:* Preparative polymer chemistry of thermoplastics and thermosets; structure behavior study of reinforced plastics; preparation and application of unsaturated polyesters and epoxy resins; study of peroxides and other free radical sources; toughening and fatigue of reinforced composites; technology of liquid elastomers; rubber compounding; adhesives and coatings; vinyl technology; compounding and processing testing. *Mailing Add:* 665 Fairwood Dr Tallmadge OH 44278-2029

**WILLIGES, GEORGE GOUDIE,** PLANT PATHOLOGY, PLANT TAXONOMY. *Current Pos:* assoc prof, 61-77, chmn dept, 77-80, CUR HERBARIUM, TEX A&I UNIV, 71-, PROF BIOL, 77- *Personal Data:* b Sioux City, Iowa, May 18, 24; m 47; c 1. *Educ:* Univ Corpus Christi, BA, 55; Tex A&I Univ, MA, 59; Tex A&M Univ, PhD(plant path), 69. *Prof Exp:* Teacher biol, Sinton Independent Sch Dist, 55-60. *Concurrent Pos:* Mem bd dir, Tex Systs Natural Labs, 77. *Mem:* AAAS; Am Phytopath Soc. *Res:* Pathogenic variability, physiological and environmental effects on growth and reproduction of Sclerotium rolfsii; Fusarium diseases of cacti. *Mailing Add:* 831 W Alice Ave Kingsville TX 78363

**WILLIGES, ROBERT CARL,** HUMAN FACTORS ENGINEERING. *Current Pos:* PROF INDUST ENG & PSYCHOL, VA POLYTECH INST & STATE UNIV, 76- *Personal Data:* b Richmond, Va, Mar 19, 42; m 65; c 1. *Educ:* Wittenberg Univ, AB, 64; Ohio State Univ, MA, 66, PhD(eng psychol), 68. *Honors & Awards:* Jerome H Ely Award, Human Factors Soc, 74. *Prof Exp:* Asst human factors, Ohio State Univ, 64-68; from asst prof to assoc prof aviation & psychol, Univ Ill, 68-76. *Concurrent Pos:* Asst dir human factors, Hwy Traffic Safety Ctr, Univ Ill, 68-70, assoc head human factors, Aviation Res Lab, 72-76; mem hwy res bd, Nat Acad Sci, 68-70; ed, Human Factors, 76-79. *Mem:* Human Factors Soc (pres, 82-83); Am Psychol Asn; Inst Indust Engrs. *Res:* Research methodology; human performance research; computer-augmented training; human-computer interface; design of computer-generated displays. *Mailing Add:* Va Tech Dept Indust & Systs Eng Blacksburg VA 24063-0118

**WILLINGHAM, ALLAN KING,** BIOCHEMISTRY. *Current Pos:* asst prof, 76-78, ASSOC PROF BIOCHEM, KIRKSVILLE COL OSTEOP MED, 78- *Personal Data:* b Washington, DC, July 11, 41; m 67. *Educ:* George Washington Univ, BS, 63; St Louis Univ, PhD(biochem), 70. *Prof Exp:* Fel biochem, Res Inst Hosp Joint Dis, New York, 70-71; instr, Univ Nebr, Omaha, 71-75, asst prof biochem, Col Med, 75-76. *Concurrent Pos:* USPHS res grant, Nat Heart, Lung & Blood Inst, 74-80; res grant, Am Osteop Asn, 81-82. *Mem:* AAAS; Sigma Xi. *Res:* Interconversion of phylloquinone and its 2, 3-epoxide and its relationship to the vitamin K-dependent carboxylation of glutamic acid residues to form active clotting proteins; post-translational synthesis and secretion of vitamin K-dependent clotting proteins. *Mailing Add:* Dept Biochem Kirksville Col Osteop Med 800 W Jefferson St Kirksville MD 63501-1497. *Fax:* 660-626-2483

**WILLINGHAM, FRANCIS FRIES, JR,** TAXONOMIC BOTANY, ORNAMENTAL HORTICULTURE. *Personal Data:* b Winston-Salem, NC, June 3, 42; m 70, Christine Wheeldon. *Educ:* Univ NC, Chapel Hill, AB, 65; Wake Forest Univ, MA, 67, PhD(biol), 73. *Prof Exp:* Instr biol, Pine Crest Prep Sch, 67-69 & Salem Col, 69-71; plant taxonomist, Dept Hort, Callaway Gardens, Ga, 73-74, dir greenhouse opers, 74-78; gen mgr, Res Farms, Houston, Tex, 79-80; pres, Phytotech, Inc, 81-89; managing partner, Turtle Pond Nurseries, 89-95. *Concurrent Pos:* Instr philos sci, Gov's Sch NC, 69-72; Hort Res Inst grant, 77-78. *Mem:* Bot Soc Am; Am Fern Soc; Am Soc Plant Taxonomists; Am Soc Hort Sci; Sigma Xi; Nat Soc Environ Consult. *Res:* Taxonomy of ornamental horticulture plant materials; environmental site assessments. *Mailing Add:* 6302 Cherry Hills Rd Houston TX 77069. *Fax:* 713-350-4278

**WILLINGHAM, MARK C,** CELL BIOLOGY, PATHOLOGY. *Current Pos:* res fel, Dept Path, Med Univ SC, 69-70, resident anat path, 70-71, dir, Immunopath Sect, Div Anat Path, Dept Path & Lab Med, 91-93, DIR, DIV RES, DEPT PATH & LAB MED, MED UNIV SC, 94- *Personal Data:* b Charleston, SC, Jan 16, 46; m 71, Susan Davis; c Christopher, Meredith & Jonathan. *Educ:* Col Charleston, SC, BS, 65; Med Univ SC, MD, 69. *Honors & Awards:* Dir's Award, NIH, 91; Pierce Immunotoxin Award, 95. *Prof Exp:* Res assoc, Nat Cancer Inst, NIH, 71-75, sr investr, 75-80, chief, Ultrastruct Cytochem Sect, Lab Molecular Biol, 80-91. *Mem:* AAAS; Electron Micros

Soc Am; Am Soc Cell Biol; Histochem Soc; US Acad Path; Can Acad Path; Am Soc Investigative Path. *Res:* Cell and molecular biology of malignancy, with an emphasis on morphological techniques in the pathology of neoplasia. *Mailing Add:* Med Univ SC Dept Path & Lab Med 171 Ashley Ave Charleston SC 29425. *Fax:* 803-792-9762; *E-Mail:* willingm@musc.edu

**WILLIS, CARL BERTRAM,** PLANT PATHOLOGY. *Current Pos:* RETIRED. *Personal Data:* b Charlottetown, PEI, Nov 27, 37; m 62, L Gayle MacWilliams; c Rodney G & Jeffrey W. *Educ:* McGill Univ, BSc, 59; Univ Wis-Madison, PhD(plant path), 62. *Prof Exp:* Res scientist plant path Agr Can, 62-85, res coordr, 85-88, dir gen & res coordr, 88-91, dir, Res Sta, 91-96. *Mem:* Can Phytopath Soc; fel Agr Inst Can; Can Soc Agron; Can Soc Hort Sci. *Res:* Forage crops diseases; factors affecting root rots of forage legumes. *Mailing Add:* 128 England Circle Charlottetown PE C1E 1V7 Can. *Fax:* 902-566-6821

**WILLIS, CARL RAEBURN, JR,** PHARMACY, PHARMACEUTICAL CHEMISTRY. *Current Pos:* dir, Drug Regulatory Affairs, 79-83, sr dir res & develop, 83-84, VPRES OPERS, BERLEX LABS, INC, 84- *Personal Data:* b Madison, Wis, Apr 5, 39; m 80, Candace Oldham; c Bryan, Alexandra, Heather & Shannon. *Educ:* Purdue Univ, BS, 61, MS, 64, PhD(indust pharm), 66. *Prof Exp:* Teaching asst bionucleonics & mfg pharm, Purdue Univ, 61-62; teaching assoc pharmaceut chem, 62-63; sr pharmaceut chemist, Warren-Teed Pharmaceut, Inc, Rohm & Haas Co, 66-69; supvr prod develop, Pharm Res & Develop Div, Ciba Pharmaceut Co, 69, mgr process & mat technol, 70-71; mgr prod develop, Pharmaceut Div, Ciba-Geigy Corp, 71-72; assoc dir, Drug Regulatory Affairs, Sterling Drug Inc, 72-76, dep dir, 76-78; dir, Drug Regulatory Affairs, Cooper Labs, Inc, 78-79. *Mem:* AAAS; Am Pharmaceut Asn; Acad Pharmaceut Sci; Am Chem Soc; Sigma Xi; Am Asn Pharmaceut Scientists. *Res:* Industrial pharmacy; pharmacokinetics; biopharmaceutics; pharmaceutical dosage form research and development; package materials research and development; drug regulatory affairs. *Mailing Add:* Berlex Labs Inc 300 Fairfield Rd Wayne NJ 07470-7358

**WILLIS, CHARLES ALGERT,** NUCLEAR REACTOR SAFETY. *Current Pos:* TECH ASST TO DIR, NUCLEAR REGULATORY COMN, 86- *Personal Data:* b Versailes, Mo, July 7, 31; m 58, Wynnora King; c Charles K, Damon E & Loretta A. *Educ:* Northwestern La Univ, BS, 56, MS, 57. *Honors & Awards:* Distinguished Serv Award, Korean Govt, 76; Outstanding Serv Award, Philippine Govt, 79. *Prof Exp:* Radiol engr, Lockheed, 58-61; nuclear safety engr, Gen Elec, 61-63; supvr, Kinetics, Shielding & Safety Atomics Int, 63-68; group engr nuclear safety, McDonnell-Douglas, 68-71; mgr, Nuclear Eng Dept, Potomac Elec Power Co, 71-72; health physicist stand develop, Atomic Energy Comn, 72-74, Nuclear Regulatory Comn, 76-77; hon dir, Philippine Assoc Radiation Protection, 78-79; leader, Effluent Treat Syst Nuclear Regulatory Comn, 79-86. *Concurrent Pos:* Reactor safety expert & adv to Korean Govt, Int Atomic Energy Agency, 74-76, adv to Philippine Govt, 77-79; dir, Korean Nuclear Soc, 75-76, Health Physics Soc, 94-; adj asst prof radiation sci, Georgetown Univ, 89-; lectr radiation sci & radioactive waste, Woodson Assocs, 89- *Mem:* Fel Health Phys Soc; AAAS; Korean Nuclear Soc; Philippine Asn Radiation Protection. *Res:* Over 100 technical papers and publications. *Mailing Add:* 8607 Hidden Hill Lane Potomac MD 20854. *Fax:* 301-504-1137

**WILLIS, CHARLES RICHARD,** PHYSICS. *Current Pos:* From asst prof to assoc prof, 57-65, PROF PHYSICS, BOSTON UNIV, 68- *Personal Data:* b Watertown, NY, July 7, 28; m 54; c 2. *Educ:* Syracuse Univ, BA, 51, PhD, 58. *Mem:* Am Phys Soc; Am Asn Univ Physicists. *Res:* Statistical mechanics; laser physics; classical many-body problems; quantum optics; solid state physics. *Mailing Add:* Dept Physics Boston Univ 590 Commonwealth Ave Boston MA 02215. *Fax:* 617-353-9393

**WILLIS, CHRISTOPHER JOHN,** INORGANIC CHEMISTRY. *Current Pos:* lectr, 61-62, from asst prof to assoc prof, 62-82, PROF CHEM, UNIV WESTERN ONT, 82- *Personal Data:* b Sutton, Eng, June 6, 34; m 60; c 3. *Educ:* Cambridge Univ, BA, 55, PhD(chem), 58, MA, 59. *Prof Exp:* Fel chem, Univ BC, 58-60, lectr, 60-61. *Mem:* Chem Inst Can. *Res:* Synthesis and study of fluorinated alchols, alkoxides and related fluorinated ligands. *Mailing Add:* Dept Chem Univ Western Ont London ON N6A 5B7 Can

**WILLIS, CLIFFORD LEON,** GEOLOGY. *Current Pos:* RETIRED. *Personal Data:* b Chanute, Kans, Feb 20, 13; m 47, Serreta Thiel; c David G. *Educ:* Univ Kans, BS, 39; Univ Wash, PhD(geol), 50. *Prof Exp:* Geophysicist, Carter Oil Co, 39-42, geologist, 46-47; instr geol, Univ Wash, 50-52, asst prof, 53-54; chief geologist, Harza Eng Co, Chicago, 54-68, vpres, 68-81. *Concurrent Pos:* Consult geologist, US, Turkey, Greece, Iraq, Jordon, Iran, Pakistan, Belgian Congo, Iceland, Colombia, Venezuela, Ethiopia, Arg, El Salvador & Honduras, 51-84. *Mem:* Fel Geol Soc Am; Am Inst Mining, Metall & Petrol Engrs; fel Brit Geol Soc; Am Asn Petrol Geol. *Res:* Engineering geology; structural geology; geophysics. *Mailing Add:* 4795 E Quail Creek Dr Tucson AZ 85718

**WILLIS, CLIVE,** PHYSICAL CHEMISTRY. *Current Pos:* RES OFFICER PHYS CHEM, NAT RES COUN CAN, 73- *Personal Data:* b London, Eng, July 31, 39; Can citizen; m 62; c 2. *Educ:* Univ Liverpool, BSc Hons, 61, PhD(phys chem), 64. *Prof Exp:* Fel, Univ Calif, Los Angeles, 64-65; res assoc chem physics, Comn Atomic Energy, 65-66; res officer phys chem, Atomic Energy Can Ltd, 66-71; lectr chem, Univ WI, 71-73. *Mem:* Chem Inst Can. *Res:* Laser chemistry; gas phase kinetics; photochemistry; radiation chemistry; discharge phenomena. *Mailing Add:* Nat Res Coun 100 Sussex Dr Ottawa ON K1A 0R6 Can

**WILLIS, D(ONALD) ROGER,** AERONAUTICAL SCIENCE. *Current Pos:* RETIRED. *Personal Data:* b Sutton Coldfield, Eng, Feb 12, 33; m 57; c 2. *Educ:* Oxford Univ, BA, 53, MA, 57; Princeton Univ, MSE, 57, PhD(aeronaut eng), 59. *Prof Exp:* Res assoc aeronaut sci, Royal Inst Technol, Sweden, 59-61 & Princeton Univ, 61-63; from asst prof to prof eng sci, Univ Calif, Berkeley, 63-91. *Concurrent Pos:* Guggenheim fel, 66. *Mem:* Soc Indust & Appl Math. *Res:* Mathematical theory of rarefied gas dynamics; numerical fluid dynamics. *Mailing Add:* Dept Mech Eng Univ Calif Berkeley CA 94720

**WILLIS, DAVID EDWIN,** geophysics, geology, for more information see previous edition

**WILLIS, DAVID LEE,** BIOLOGY, RADIATION BIOLOGY. *Current Pos:* from asst prof to assoc prof, Ore State Univ, 62-71, chmn dept, 69-85, prof, 71-87, asst to dean sci, 86-87, EMER PROF RADIATION BIOL, ORE STATE UNIV, 87- *Personal Data:* b Pasadena, Calif, Mar 15, 27; m 50, Earline L Fleischman; c Dave Jr, Paul & Daniel. *Educ:* Biola Univ, BTh, 49, BA, 51; Wheaton Col, Ill, BS, 52; Calif State, Univ Long Beach, MA, 54; Ore State Univ, PhD(radiation biol), 63. *Prof Exp:* Teacher high sch, Calif, 52-57; instr biol, Fullerton Col, 57-61. *Concurrent Pos:* Consult, Comn Undergrad Educ Biol Sci, NSF, 66-70; vis investr, Oak Ridge Nat Lab, 68-69; consult, Portland Gen Elec Co, 70-72; Life Systs, Inc, 84-85, SENES, 91-97 & Cotter Corp, 92; mem, Hanford Health Effects Panel, Richland, WA, 1986. *Mem:* Health Physics Soc; fel Am Sci Affiliation (pres, 75); Radiation Res Soc. *Res:* Freshwater radioecology; radionuclide metabolism; radiation effects on reptiles and amphibians; general applications of radiotracer techniques to biology; radionuclides in drinking water. *Mailing Add:* Radiation Ctr Ore State Univ Corvallis OR 97331

**WILLIS, GROVER C, JR,** PHYSICAL CHEMISTRY, ELECTROCHEMISTRY. *Current Pos:* from asst prof to prof, 57-92, EMER PROF PHYS & ANALYTICAL CHEM, CALIF STATE UNIV, CHICO, 92- *Personal Data:* b Kansas City, Mo, May 25, 21; m 41; c 3. *Educ:* Whittier Col, BA, 52; Univ Ore, MA, 55, PhD(chem), 57. *Prof Exp:* Petrol inspector, Gen Petrol Corp, Calif, 41-43; chemist, W C Hardesty Co, 46-51; assoc, Univ Ore, 53-55, res assoc, 55-57. *Mem:* Am Chem Soc. *Res:* Anodic oxide formation kinetics; mechanism; reaction rates, thermodynamics, adsorption phenomena and diffusion processes at dropping mercury electrodes; electrochemical instrumentation. *Mailing Add:* 612 Acacia Lane Chico CA 95926

**WILLIS, GUYE HENRY,** SOIL CHEMISTRY. *Current Pos:* RES SOIL SCIENTIST, SOIL & WATER POLLUTION RES DIV, AGR RES SERV, USDA, 65- *Personal Data:* b Los Angeles, Calif, July 1, 37; m 60, Phyllis Payne; c Michael Guye & Mark Charles. *Educ:* Okla State Univ, BS, 61; Auburn Univ, MS, 63, PhD(soil chem), 65. *Mem:* Am Soc Agron; Soil Sci Soc Am; Am Chem Soc; Am Soc Agr Engrs. *Res:* Fate of agricultural chemicals, including pesticides and fertilizers, in the environment; soil chemistry-plant nutrition relationships. *Mailing Add:* Univ Sta PO Box 25071 Baton Rouge LA 70894-5071

**WILLIS, HAROLD LESTER,** SCIENCE EDUCATION. *Current Pos:* AGR WRITER, ACRES USA, 83-; GRAPHIC ARTIST, SCWN GROUP, 95- *Personal Data:* b McPherson, Kans, Oct 20, 40. *Educ:* Emporia Kans State Univ, BA, 62; Univ Kans, PhD(entom), 66. *Prof Exp:* From asst prof to prof biol, Univ Wis-Platteville, 78-81; agr environ consult, 81-; ed, 83-86. *Mem:* AAAS. *Res:* Bionomics, taxonomy and zoogeography of Nearctic tiger beetles; author of books and articles on sustainable agriculture. *Mailing Add:* 623 Vine St Wisconsin Dells WI 53965

**WILLIS, ISAAC,** DERMATOLOGY. *Current Pos:* PROF MED DERMAT, MOREHOUSE SCH MED, 81- *Personal Data:* b Albany, Ga, July 13, 40; m 65; c 2. *Educ:* Morehouse Col, BS, 61; Howard Univ, MD, 65. *Honors & Awards:* Frontiers Int Award, 84. *Prof Exp:* Assoc dermat, Sch Med, Univ Pa, 69-70; head internal med res team & dermatologist, Letterman Army Inst, US Army Med Corps, 70-72; res assoc & clin instr dermat, Sch Med, Univ Calif, 70-72; asst prof med dermat, Sch Med, Johns Hopkins Univ, 72-73; asst prof, Vet Admin Hosp-Atlanta, 73-75, assoc prof med dermat, Sch Med, Emory Univ & chief dermat, Vet Admin Med Ctr-Atlanta, 75-81. *Concurrent Pos:* Asst attend physician, Philadelphia Gen Hosp, 69-70; Dermat Found res award, Univ Pa, 70; attend physician, Univ Calif Med Ctr, 70-72; attend physician, Johns Hopkins Hosp, Baltimore City Hosps & Good Samaritan Hosp, 72-73; consult & lectr dermat, Bur Med & Surg, US Dept Navy, 72-75; consult asst to prof dermat, Howard Univ Col Med, 72-; mem, Formulary Task Force, Nat Prog Dermat, Am Fedn Clin Res; mem, Gen Med & Study Sect, NIH, 85-89; med dir, McWill Res Lab; mem, Sci Rev Panel Health Res, US Environ Protection Agency, 86- & Inst Rev Bd, West Paces Ferry Hosp, 88- *Mem:* Am Med Asn; Nat Med Asn; Am Acad Dermat; Am Fedn Clin Res; Am Dermat Asn; Soc Inst Dermat; Am Photobiol Asn; NY Acad Sci. *Res:* Phototherapy, photochemotherapy; acute and chronic effects of ultraviolet light, including carcinogenesis; effects of light on bacteria and fungi, and effects of heat and humidity on skin. *Mailing Add:* Northwest Med Ctr Suite 342 3280 Howell Mill Rd NW Atlanta GA 30327-4111

**WILLIS, JACALYN GIACALONE,** behavioral ecology, for more information see previous edition

**WILLIS, JAMES STEWART, JR,** PHYSICS. *Current Pos:* RETIRED. *Personal Data:* b West Point, NY, Feb 9, 35; m 59; c 2. *Educ:* US Mil Acad, BS, 58; Rensselaer Polytech Inst, MS, 64, PhD(physics), 66. *Prof Exp:* US Army, 58-, from instr to prof physics, US Mil Acad, 70-88. *Mem:* AAAS; Am Asn Physics Teachers; Am Soc Eng Educ; Am Phys Soc. *Res:* Type II superconductivity; electron spin resonance studies on color centers and other defects in crystals. *Mailing Add:* PO Box 327 Washington VA 22747

**WILLIS, JEFFREY OWEN,** HIGH PRESSURE PHYSICS, SUPERCONDUCTIVITY & MAGNETISM. *Current Pos:* fel, Los Alamos Sci Lab, 78-79, MEM STAFF, LOS ALAMOS NAT LAB, 80- *Personal Data:* b Long Branch, NJ, June 1, 48; m 69. *Educ:* Univ Ill, Urbana-Champaign, BS, 70, MS, 71, PhD(physics), 76. *Prof Exp:* Res assoc, Naval Res Lab, Nat Res Coun, 75-77. *Mem:* Am Phys Soc; Sigma Xi. *Res:* Magnetic and superconductive properties of metals, under conditions of ultralow temperatures and high pressures; low temperature, specific heat of metals. *Mailing Add:* Los Alamos Nat Lab MS K763 STC Los Alamos NM 87545-0001. *Fax:* 505-665-3164

**WILLIS, JOHN STEELE,** MEMBRANE TRANSPORT, THERMAL TOLERANCE & SENSITIVITY. *Current Pos:* prof zool & physiol, 91-95, PROF CELLULAR BIOL & PHYSIOL, UNIV GA, ATHENS, 95- *Personal Data:* b Long Beach, Calif, Jan 19, 35; m 58, Judith Horwitz. *Educ:* Univ Calif, Berkeley, AB, 56; Harvard Univ, AM, 58, PhD(biol), 61. *Prof Exp:* Nat Heart Inst fel biochem, Oxford Univ, 61-62; from asst prof to assoc prof physiol, Univ Ill, Urbana, 62-72, prof, 72-91, prof nutrit sci, 81-91. *Concurrent Pos:* Nat Inst Gen Med Sci res grantee, 63-91; mem, Physiol Study Sect, NIH, 69-73; consult, Basic Sci Rev Bd, Vet Admin, 75-78; assoc ed, Am J Physiol Cell, 76-81. *Mem:* Soc Gen Physiol; Am Soc Zool; Am Physiol Soc; Sigma Xi; Am Inst Nutrit; fel AAAS. *Res:* Cation transport in relation to thermal and metabolic adaptation. *Mailing Add:* Dept Cellular Biol Univ Ga Athens GA 30602. *E-Mail:* jswillis@cb.uga.edu

**WILLIS, JUDITH HORWITZ,** DEVELOPMENTAL BIOLOGY, INSECT PHYSIOLOGY. *Current Pos:* head, Dept Zool, 90-93, PROF, UNIV GA, 90- *Personal Data:* b Detroit, Mich, Jan 2, 35; m 58, John S. *Educ:* Cornell Univ, AB, 56; Harvard Univ, AM, 57, PhD(biol), 61. *Prof Exp:* USPHS res fel, Harvard Univ, 60-61 & Oxford Univ, 61-62; from instr to prof entom, Univ Ill, Urbana, 77-90. *Concurrent Pos:* Mem, Aging Review Comt, NIH, 76-80; mem, Coun Comt Affairs, AAAS, 77-80 & 79-80, chairperson, Sect D, 87-88; prog dir cellular physiol, Nat Acad Sci, 83; mem, Coun & Exec Bd, Tissue Cult Asn, 86-90. *Mem:* AAAS; Entom Soc Am; Soc Develop Biol; Soc In Vitro Biol. *Res:* Gene action in insect metamorphosis, cuticular proteins, insect tissue culture. *Mailing Add:* Dept Cellular Biol Univ Ga Athens GA 30602

**WILLIS, LLOYD L, II,** BIOLOGY. *Current Pos:* asst prof, 74-77, ASSOC PROF BIOL, PIEDMONT VA COMMUNITY COL, 77- *Personal Data:* b Frederick, Okla, June 10, 43; m 67, Margaret Spurlin; c Karen L & Sarah (Terrill). *Educ:* Phillips Univ, BS, 65; Univ Va, MEd, 67. *Prof Exp:* Teacher gen sci, Roanoke City Pub Sch Syst, 65-68; sci teacher, Pickens Co Pub Sch, 68-69; asst prof biol, Va Western Community Col, 69-70; res asst, Bot Dept, Univ NC, 70-73. *Mem:* Am Inst Biol Sci; Ecol Soc Am; Nat Sci Teachers Asn; Soc Col Sci Teachers; Am Rhododendron Soc; Nat Asn Biol Teachers. *Res:* Science education biology; innovative teaching techniques; development of required out of class activities; development of independent study courses; development of support-services for part-time faculty in biology. *Mailing Add:* Piedmont Va Community Col Rte 6 Box 1 Charlottesville VA 22901. *Fax:* 804-971-8232; *E-Mail:* lw2d@jade.pvcc.cc.va.us

**WILLIS, LYNN ROGER,** RENAL PHARMACOLOGY. *Current Pos:* PROF PHARMACOL & MED, SCH MED, UNIV IND, 83- *Personal Data:* b Oct 2, 42; m 66; c 3. *Educ:* Univ Iowa, PhD(pharmacol), 70. *Mem:* Am Soc Pharmacol & Exp Therapeut; Am Soc Nephrol; Int Soc Nephrol. *Res:* Hypertension and renal function. *Mailing Add:* Dept Pharmacol MS 346-A Ind Univ Sch Med 635 Barnhill Dr Indianapolis IN 46202-5120

**WILLIS, PARK WEED, III,** CARDIOVASCULAR DISEASES, INTERNAL MEDICINE. *Current Pos:* prof internal med, 79-96, dir, Div Cardiol, 79-95, EMER PROF, COL HUMAN MED, MICH STATE UNIV, 96- *Personal Data:* b Seattle, Wash, Nov 18, 25; m 48, Christine Boone Weavor; c Park Weed III, Carol Lee, Edwin A, Christin E (Yorker), Sarah A (Leonard) & Elizabeth A (Kimberly). *Educ:* Univ Pa, MD, 48. *Honors & Awards:* Jacob Ehrenzeller Award, 82. *Prof Exp:* Intern, Pa Hosp, 48-50; resident internal med, Univ Hosp & Med Sch, Univ Mich, Ann Arbor, 52-53; jr clin instr, Med Sch, 53-54, from instr to assoc prof, 54-65, asst prof postgrad med, 57-59, dir, Div Cardiol, 69-77, prof internal med, 65-79. *Concurrent Pos:* Attend physician, Vet Admin Hosp, Ann Arbor, 54-59, consult, 59-79; consult health serv, Univ Mich, 56-79. *Mem:* Asn Univ Cardiologists (pres, 79-80); fel Am Col Cardiol; fel Am Col Physicians; Am Fed Clin Res; fel Coun Clin Cardiol & Epidemiol, Am Heart Asn; Cent Soc Clin Res. *Res:* Clinical cardiology mitral valve prolapse, venovs thromboembolism, coronary heart disease epidemiology, congestive heart failure, disorders of lipid metabolism. *Mailing Add:* A205 Clin Ctr Mich State Univ East Lansing MI 48824-1313. *E-Mail:* 21770pww@msu.edu

**WILLIS, ROBERT D,** ATOMIC PHYSICS. *Current Pos:* CONSULT, 91-; RES SCIENTIST, MANTECH ENVIRON. *Personal Data:* b Independence, Mo, Apr 23, 48. *Educ:* Denison Univ, BS, 70; Duke Univ PhD(physics), 76. *Prof Exp:* Fel, Naval Res Lab, Nat Res Coun, 77-79; asst geophysicist, Scripps Inst Oceanog, 79-84; from scientist to sr scientist, Atom Sci, Inc, 84-91. *Mem:* Am Geophys Union; Am Phys Soc. *Res:* Alter sensities tracing analysis; laser spectroscopes, math spectroscopy and isotopic geochemistry. *Mailing Add:* 411 Landerwood Lane Chapel Hill NC 27514

**WILLIS, RONALD PORTER,** GEOLOGY. *Current Pos:* RETIRED. *Personal Data:* b Cowley, Wyo, Sept 20, 26; m 53; c 5. *Educ:* Univ Wyo, BS, 52, MA, 53; Univ Ill, PhD(geol), 58. *Prof Exp:* Geologist, Richfield Oil Corp, 53-55; asst, Univ Ill, 55-57; geologist, Richmond Explor Co, 58-61; chief geologist, Bahrain Petrol Co, 61-65; regional geologist, Amoseas, Tripoli, Libya, 65; geologist, Chevron Oil Co, Okla, 65-67; prof geol, Univ Wis-Eau Claire, 67- *Concurrent Pos:* Fulbright lectr, Univ Benin, Nigeria, 76-77. *Mem:* Geol Soc Am; Am Asn Petrol Geol. *Res:* Stratigraphy; sedimentation; petroleum geology. *Mailing Add:* 1804 Lehman St Eau Claire WI 54701

**WILLIS, ROY F,** SOLID STATE PHYSICS. *Current Pos:* PROF PHYSICS & DIR, CTR MAT PHYSICS, PA STATE UNIV, 87- *Personal Data:* b Eng, Apr 23, 42; m; c 2. *Educ:* Univ Leicester, UK, BSc, 63, PhD, 67. *Prof Exp:* Res fel, Cavendish Lab, Univ Cambridge, 67-69; res scientist, Europ Space Res Orgn, 69-70; Royal Soc res fel, Cavendish Lab, Cambridge, 79-81; dir undergrad studies math physics, Clare Col, Univ Cambridge, 79-88, sr lectr, Dept Physics, 81-86, reader physics, 86-87. *Mem:* Fel Am Phys Soc; Brit Faraday & Chem Soc. *Res:* Solid state physics of surface and low dimensional thin film systems; MBE engineering of novel materials-strained lattice semiconductors, superconductors and metastable magnetic solids; electron spectroscopy-scanning tunneling microscopy, photoelectron spectroscopy, vibrational electron-energy-loss spectroscopy; materials physics using synchrotron radiation light source facilities. *Mailing Add:* 1359 Penfield Rd State College PA 16802

**WILLIS, SUZANNE EILEEN,** ELEMENTARY PARTICLE PHYSICS. *Current Pos:* assoc prof, 88-96, PROF, NORTHERN ILL UNIV, 96- *Personal Data:* b New Brunswick, NJ, May 25, 51; m 88, Jonathan Reich; c Leo R. *Educ:* Mt Holyoke Col, BA, 72; Yale Univ, MPhil, 74, PhD(physics), 79. *Prof Exp:* Res assoc, Fermi Nat Accelerator Lab, 79-82; from asst prof to assoc prof, Dept Physics, Univ Okla, 82-88. *Mem:* Am Phys Soc; AAAS; Sigma Xi; Am Asn Physics Teachers. *Res:* Elementary particle physics; production and decay of charm and heavy quarks; rare decay modes of the muon; neutrino oscillations and decay. *Mailing Add:* Dept Physics Univ Northern Ill De Kalb IL 60115. *Fax:* 815-753-8565; *E-Mail:* willis@niumep.physics.niu.edu

**WILLIS, WILLIAM DARRELL, JR,** NEUROPHYSIOLOGY, NEUROANATOMY. *Current Pos:* PROF ANAT & PHYSIOL & CHIEF COMP NEUROBIOL, MARINE BIOMED INST, MED BR, UNIV TEX, GALVESTON, 70-, DIR INST, 78-, ASHBEL SMITH PROF & CHMN DEPT ANAT & NEUROSCI, 86- *Personal Data:* b Dallas, Tex, July 19, 34; m 60, Jean C Schini; c Thomas D. *Educ:* Tex A&M Univ, BS & BA, 56; Univ Tex, MD, 60; Australian Nat Univ, PhD(physiol), 63. *Honors & Awards:* F W L Kerr Award, Am Pain Soc; Bristol-Myers Squibb Award, Distinguished Achievement In Pain Res, 93. *Prof Exp:* From asst prof to prof anat, Southwestern Med Sch, Univ Tex, Dallas, 63-70, chmn dept, 64-70. *Concurrent Pos:* NIH res fel, Australian Nat Univ, 60-62 & Univ Pisa, 62-63; Nat Inst Neurol Dis & Blindness res grant, 63-; mem, Neurol B Study Sect, NIH, 68-72, chmn, 70-72, mem, Neurol Dis Prog, Proj Rev Comt, 72-76; chief ed, J Neurophysiol, 78-83; Florence & Marie Hall fel, 84-85; Alexander von Humboldt Sr US Scientist Award, 84-85; Jacob K Javits Award, Nat Inst Neurol & Commun Dis & Stroke, 85-; mem, Nat Adv Neurol Dis & Stroke Coun, NIH, 88-91; field ed, J Neurosci Lett, 76-93, sect ed, J Exp Brain Res, 90-93; ed-in-chief, J Neurosci, 93- *Mem:* AAAS; Am Asn Anat; Am Physiol Soc; Am Pain Soc (treas, 78-81, pres, 82-83); Soc Neurosci (pres, 84-85); Int Asn Study Pain. *Res:* Electrophysiology of the vertebrate spinal cord; somatic sensory pathways; pain mechanisms and descending control of pain transmission. *Mailing Add:* St Louis Univ Sch Med 301 Univ Blvd Galveston TX 77555-1069. *E-Mail:* wow@mbian.utmb.edu

**WILLIS, WILLIAM J,** PHYSICS. *Current Pos:* EUGENE HIGGINS PROF PHYSICS, COLUMBIA UNIV, 91- *Personal Data:* b Ft Smith, Ark, Sept 15, 32; m 58; c 5. *Educ:* Yale Univ, BS, 54, PhD, 58. *Prof Exp:* Physicist, Brookhaven Nat Lab, 58-65; prof physics, Yale Univ, 65-73; physicist, Europ Coun Nuclear Res, Geneva, Switz, 73-91. *Concurrent Pos:* Physicist, Europ Orgn Nuclear Res, 61-62. *Mem:* Am Phys Soc. *Res:* Elementary particle physics; weak interactions of strange particles, resonances and high energy collisions; hard parton processes; direct photon and lepton production; ultra relativistic heavy ion collisions. *Mailing Add:* Nevis Labs Columbia Univ PO Box 137 Irvington NY 10533

**WILLIS, WILLIAM VAN,** INORGANIC CHEMISTRY, ANALYTICAL CHEMISTRY. *Current Pos:* ASSOC PROF CHEM, CALIF STATE UNIV, FULLERTON, 67- *Personal Data:* b Morganton, NC, Oct 15, 37. *Educ:* Ga Inst Technol, BS, 60; Univ Tenn, MS, 63, PhD(chem), 66. *Prof Exp:* Res assoc radiation & radiochem, Eng Exp Sta, Ga Inst Technol, 59-61; sci writer nuclear decontamination, Univ Tenn, 63-64; USAEC res fel, 66-67. *Concurrent Pos:* Mem, State Regional Water Qual Control Bd. *Mem:* Am Chem Soc. *Res:* Neutron activation analysis; radiochemical tracer analysis; transition metal transport in biological systems. *Mailing Add:* Chem Dept Calif State Univ 800 N State College Blvd Fullerton CA 92631

**WILLISON, JH MARTIN,** CONSERVATION BIOLOGY, PROTECTED AREAS MANAGEMENT. *Current Pos:* from asst prof to assoc prof, Dalhousie Univ, 80-89, assoc dean grad studies, 90-91, chair, Biol Dept, 91-96, PROF, DALHOUSIE UNIV, CAN, 89-, PROF BIOL & ENVIRON STUDIES, 96- *Personal Data:* m 78, Marjorie Hanlon; c Meghan & Kathleen. *Educ:* St Andrews Univ, Scotland, BSc, 66; Nottingham Univ, Eng, PhD(biol), 73. *Prof Exp:* Sci officer, Nottingham Univ, Eng, 66-74; Killam postdoctoral fel, Dalhousie Univ, Can, 74-76; res fel, Univ NC, Chapel Hill, 76. *Concurrent Pos:* Dir, Sci & Mgt Protected Areas Asn, 92- *Res:* Diverse aspects of nature conservation policy including management methods of protected areas, biodiversity monitoring, protected areas advocacy and politics, marine conservation, marine protected areas, outdoor education and urban ecology. *Mailing Add:* Sch Resource & Environ Studies Dalhousie Univ Halifax NS B3H 3E2 Can. *Fax:* 902-494-3736; *E-Mail:* martin. willison@dal.ca

**WILLISTON, JOHN STODDARD,** NEUROSCIENCES. *Current Pos:* from asst prof to assoc prof, 70-82, PROF BIOL, SAN FRANCISCO STATE UNIV, 82- *Personal Data:* b Ft Madison, Iowa, July 23, 34; m 61. *Educ:* Univ Wis-Madison, BS, 61; Calif State Univ, San Francisco, MA, 65; Univ Southern Calif, PhD(physiol, psychol), 68. *Prof Exp:* NIMH fel, Univ Calif, San Francisco, 68-70. *Concurrent Pos:* Res physiologist, Univ Calif, San Francisco, 76-78. *Mem:* AAAS; Int Brain Res Orgn; Soc Neurosci. *Res:* Neurological substrates of behavioral plasticity; neuroelectrical activity; psychotrophic drugs; distribution of volume conducted event related electrical potentials their generators and clinical applications; natural and artificial learning and associational systems. *Mailing Add:* 133 Westgate Dr San Francisco CA 94112

**WILLITS, CHARLES HAINES,** ORGANIC CHEMISTRY. *Current Pos:* RETIRED. *Personal Data:* b Camden, NJ, June 25, 23; m 45, Mary Grant; c James H II & Anne W (Hoyle). *Educ:* Wheaton Col, Ill, BS, 44; Ohio State Univ, MS, 48; Ore State Univ, PhD(org chem), 55. *Prof Exp:* Res engr, Battelle Mem Inst, 48-51; from asst prof to prof chem, Rutgers Univ, Camden, 55-90, actg chmn dept, 60-69, chmn dept, 70-87. *Mem:* Am Chem Soc; Am Sci Affil. *Res:* Synthesis of purine derivatives; mechanism of Hofmann degradation of amides; Fries rearrangement of higher esters. *Mailing Add:* Dept Chem Rutgers Univ Camden NJ 08102

**WILLITS, RICHARD ELLIS,** DAIRY MICROBIOLOGY, FOOD SAFETY. *Current Pos:* VPRES RES & DEVELOP, ARGENTO FOODS, 95- *Personal Data:* b Indianapolis, Ind, Dec 5, 37; m 60, Abbie Strong; c Ross & Catherine. *Educ:* Purdue Univ, BS, 61, MS, 62, PhD(dairy microbiol), 64. *Prof Exp:* Asst prof & res assoc, Ore State Univ, 64-65; develop scientist, Pillsbury Co, 65-79; dir res, Universal Food Corp, 79-90; dir appln, Haarman & Reimer Corp, 90-93; gen mgr, Deibel Labs Inc, 93-95. *Mem:* Inst Food Technol; Soc Food & Drink Technol. *Res:* Microbiology of foods with emphasis on safety and stability; extension or shelflife through use of mulitiple factors such as water activity, preservatives, etc; fate of food poisoning organisms in various food systems. *Mailing Add:* PO Box 111 305 Pine St Elkhart Lake WI 53020. *Fax:* 608-241-2252

**WILLKE, THOMAS ALOYS,** MATHEMATICAL STATISTICS. *Current Pos:* assoc prof, 66-72, dir statist lab, 71-73, actg dean, 83-84, PROF MATH, OHIO STATE UNIV, 72-, VPROVOST, COL ARTS & SCI, 73- *Personal Data:* b Rome City, Ind, Apr 22, 32; m 54; c 6. *Educ:* Xavier Univ, Ohio, AB, 54; Ohio State Univ, MS, 56, PhD(math), 60. *Prof Exp:* Res mathematician, Nat Bur Stand, 61-63; asst prof math, Univ Md, 63-66. *Concurrent Pos:* Lectr, Univ Md, 61-63. *Mem:* Math Asn Am; Inst Math Statist; Am Statist Asn. *Res:* Design and analysis of experiments. *Mailing Add:* 4375 Mumford Dr Columbus OH 43220-4438

**WILLMAN, JOSEPH F(RANK),** ELECTRICAL ENGINEERING, UNDERWATER ACOUSTICS. *Current Pos:* RETIRED. *Personal Data:* b Brownsville, Tex, Dec 3, 31; m 56; c 3. *Educ:* Univ Tex, BS, 57, MS, 58, PhD(elec eng), 62. *Prof Exp:* Aerophys engr, Gen Dynamics/Ft Worth, 58-61; res engr, Defense Res Lab, Univ Tex, 61-62; sr res engr, Southwest Res Inst, 62-69; spec res assoc, Appl Res Labs, Univ Tex, Austin, 69-80, asst dir, 80-89, proj mgr, 89-93. *Mem:* Sigma Xi; Inst Elec & Electronics Engrs; Acoust Soc Am. *Res:* Systems analysis; signal processing; underwater acoustics; sonar systems; radar systems; radio wave propagation; the ionosphere; electromagnetic compatibility. *Mailing Add:* 7607 Mesa Dr Austin TX 78731

**WILLMAN, VALLEE L,** SURGERY. *Current Pos:* Sr instr, 57-58, from asst prof to assoc prof, 58-64, PROF SURG, SCH MED, ST LOUIS UNIV, 64-, CHMN DEPT, 69- *Personal Data:* b Greenville, Ill, May 4, 25; m 52; c 9. *Educ:* Univ Ill, BS, 47; St Louis Univ, MD, 51; Am Bd Surg, dipl, 57; Bd Thoracic Surg, dipl, 61. *Concurrent Pos:* McBride fel cancer, Sch Med, St Louis Univ, 56-57; attend physician, Vet Admin Hosp, St Louis Univ Hosp & St Marys Hosp, 57- *Mem:* Soc Univ Surg; Am Surg Asn; Am Physiol Soc; Int Cardiovasc Soc; Am Asn Thoracic Surg. *Res:* Cardiovascular surgery and extracorporeal circulation; author or coauthor of over 210 publications. *Mailing Add:* St Louis Univ Sch Med St Louis Univ Hosp 3635 Vista Ave at Grand Blvd Box 15250 St Louis MO 63110-0250. *Fax:* 573-771-1945

**WILLMANN, ROBERT B,** astrophysics, for more information see previous edition

**WILLMARTH, WILLIAM W(ALTER),** FLUID MECHANICS, TURBULENT FLOW. *Current Pos:* RETIRED. *Personal Data:* b Highland Park, Ill, Mar 25, 24; m 59; c 4. *Educ:* Purdue Univ, BS, 49; Calif Inst Technol, MS, 50, PhD(aeronaut eng), 54. *Honors & Awards:* Off Naval Res Fluid Dynamics Prize, Am Phys Soc, 89. *Prof Exp:* From res fel to sr res fel aeronaut eng, Calif Inst Technol, 54-58; from assoc prof to prof aeronaut eng, Univ Mich, Ann Arbor, 58-90. *Concurrent Pos:* Consult, Rand Corp, 54-66, Gen Motors Res Lab, 70-74, Bendix Aerospace Systs Div, 73-76, Bendix Res Labs, 75-77, Lear Siegler, 81-85 & Spalding, 83-85; vis fel, Joint Inst Lab Astrophys, Boulder, 63-64. *Mem:* Fel Am Inst Aeronaut & Astronaut; fel Am Phys Soc.

*Res:* Condensation of gases; transonic flow; turbulent boundary layer; unsteady aerodynamics; aerodynamic sound; scientific instruments for fluid mechanical measurements; structure of turbulence; turbulent drag reduction; vorticity interaction with free surface; applied aerodynamics. *Mailing Add:* 765 Country Club Rd Ann Arbor MI 48105

**WILLMERT, KENNETH DALE,** MECHANICAL ENGINEERING, SYSTEMS DESIGN & SYSTEMS. *Current Pos:* From asst prof to assoc prof, 70-85, chmn, Mech & Aeronaut Eng Dept, 85-91, PROF MECH ENG, CLARKSON UNIV, 85- *Personal Data:* b Kossuth Co, Iowa, Oct 25, 42; m 68, Carol Seeger; c Leslie & Brian. *Educ:* Iowa State Univ, BS, 64; Case Inst Technol, MS, 66; Case Western Res Univ, PhD(mech eng), 70. *Mem:* Am Soc Mech Engrs; Am Inst Aeronaut & Astronaut; Asn Comput Mach; Am Soc Eng Educ. *Res:* Mechanical design; optimization applied to mechanical and structural systems; kinematic analysis and synthesis; finite element techniques applied to vibration problems. *Mailing Add:* Dept Mech Eng Clarkson Univ Potsdam NY 13699. *Fax:* 315-268-6438; *E-Mail:* willmert@ dactyls.soe.clarkson.edu

**WILLMES, HENRY,** NUCLEAR PHYSICS. *Current Pos:* from asst prof to assoc prof, 69-80, PROF PHYSICS, UNIV IDAHO, 80-, CHMN DEPT, 75- *Personal Data:* b Bocholt, Ger, Aug 30, 39; US citizen; m 66; c 3. *Educ:* Univ Calif, Los Angeles, BS, 61, MA, 62, PhD(physics), 66. *Prof Exp:* Res physicist, Aerospace Res Labs, Wright-Patterson AFB, 65-68. *Mem:* Am Phys Soc; Sigma Xi. *Res:* Few nucleon systems; nuclear structure; applications of nuclear technology. *Mailing Add:* 2152 Arbor Crest Rd Moscow ID 83843-9106. *Fax:* 208-885-6173

**WILLMOTT, CORT JAMES,** CLIMATOLOGY, QUANTITATIVE METHODS. *Current Pos:* Lectr geog & climat, 76-77, from asst prof to assoc prof, 77-87, PROF GEOG & CLIMAT, DEPT GEOG & OCEANOG PROG, UNIV DEL, 87-, DEPT CHAIR GEOG, 89-, DIR, UNIV CTR CLIMATIC RES, 92- *Personal Data:* b Oakland, Calif, Dec 18, 46; m 68, Patricia A May; c Abby E & Julia C. *Educ:* Calif State Univ, Hayward, BA, 69, MA, 72; Univ Calif, Los Angeles, PhD(geog), 77. *Concurrent Pos:* Prin co-prin investr, NASA grants, 80-97 & NSF grants, 83-97; vis scholar, Dept Geog, Univ Victoria, 83 & Dept Meterol, Univ Md, 84; vis scientist climat, Lab Atmospheres, Goddard Space Flight Ctr, NASA, Greenbelt, Md, 85; chair, Asn Am Geographers, Climate Specialty Group, 86-88; chair prog comt, 1989 Ann Meeting, Am Asn Geographers, 88-89, chair, Comt Electronic Commun, 94-97; mem, Asn Am Geographers Hons Comt, 89-90 & NSF's Geog, Regional Sci Panel, 88-90; mem prog comt, 27th Cong Int Geog Union, 90-92; assoc ed, Annals Asn Am Geographers, 91-93; assoc dir, Del's Space Grant Prog, Univ Del, 92-, dir, Environ Sci Progs, Col Arts & Sci, 93-; mem, Rediscovery Geog Comt, Nat Res Coun, Nat Acad Sci, 93-96; mem, Expert Panel on Climat & consult, Ctr Nuclear Waste Regulatory Analyses, Nuclear Regulatory Comn, Southwest Res Inst, San Antonio, Tex, 93; vis scholar, Nat Ctr Geog Info & Anal, Univ Calif, Santa Barbara, 95-96. *Mem:* Asn Am Geographers; Am Meteorol Soc; Sigma Xi; Am Geophys Union. *Res:* Land-surface influences on climate and climatic change at the continental and global scales; statistics and computational methods. *Mailing Add:* Dept Geog Univ Del Newark DE 19716

**WILLMS, CHARLES RONALD,** BIOCHEMISTRY. *Current Pos:* assoc prof, 64-68, chmn dept, 68-75, PROF CHEM, SOUTHWEST TEX STATE UNIV, 68- *Personal Data:* b Rupert, Idaho, June 26, 33; m 55, Dianne; c Deborah, Kathryn, Frederick & Emily. *Educ:* Univ Tex, BA, 55; Southwest Tex State Col, MA, 56; Tex A&M Univ, PhD(biochem), 59. *Prof Exp:* Asst prof chem, Southwest Tex State Col, 59-62; res scientist assoc, Clayton Found Biochem Inst, Univ Tex, 62-64. *Mem:* AAAS; Am Chem Soc; Sigma Xi. *Res:* Enzyme and protein chemistry; carbohydrate metabolism; organic synthesis of biochemical analogues that are ligands for formation of platinum complexes. *Mailing Add:* Dept Chem Southwest Tex State Univ San Marcos TX 78666

**WILLNER, ALAN ELI,** OPTICAL COMMUNICATIONS, UNIVERSITY EDUCATION. *Current Pos:* ASSOC PROF, DEPT ELEC ENG SYSTS, COMMUN SCI INST, UNIV SOUTHERN CALIF, 92-, ASSOC DIR, CTR PHOTONIC TECHNOL, 94- *Personal Data:* b Brooklyn, NY, Nov 16, 62; m 91, Michelle F Green. *Educ:* Yeshiva Univ, BA, 82; Columbia Univ, MS, 84, PhD(elec eng), 88. *Honors & Awards:* Armstrong Found Mem Prize. *Prof Exp:* Grad res asst, Microelectronics Sci Lab & Ctr Telecommun Res, Columbia Univ, 84-88; mem tech staff, Crawford Hill Lab, Photonics Networks & Components Res, AT&T Bell Lab, 88-90, Bell Commun Res, 90-92. *Concurrent Pos:* Instr, Columbia Univ, 87; prin investr, NSF young investr award, 92-, ILX Lightwave Corp, 92, NSF & Advan Res Proj Agency & Powell Found, 93-; mem, Standing Tech Comt, Optical Commun & Technol, Inst Elec & Electronics Engrs Lasers & Electro-Optics Soc, 92-94, Optical Networks, 93-94; vchmn, Optical Commun Group, Tech Coun, Optical Soc Am, 93-; chmn & mem bd gov, Standing Tech Comt, Optical Commun, Inst Elec & Electronics Engrs Lasers & Electro-Optics Soc, 94-; consult, New Focus, Inc, Sunnyvale, Calif & Info Presentation Technologies, Inc, San Luis Obispo, Calif; Packard Found fel sci & eng. *Mem:* Sr mem Inst Elec & Electronics Engrs; Sigma Xi; Optical Soc Am; Soc Photo-Instrumentation Engrs. *Res:* Photonics for future networks in an international gigabit-per-second data highway; advancing the fundamental capabilities of wave-length-division-multiplexing WDM which provides significant capacity enhancement by simultaneously transmitting many independent high-speed channels on different wavelengths; wavelength routing and the use of revolutionary erbium-doped fiber optic amplifiers for WDM transmission; publications include 81 papers, 3 patents, and several book chapters. *Mailing Add:* EEB 538 Dept Elec Eng-Systs Univ Southern Calif Los Angeles CA 90089-2565. *Fax:* 213-740-8729; *E-Mail:* willner@ solar.usc.edu

**WILLNER, DAVID,** ORGANIC CHEMISTRY. *Current Pos:* sr res scientist, Bristol Labs, 66-82, SR RES SCIENTIST II, PHARMACEUT RES & DEVELOP DIV, BRISTOL-MYERS-SQUIBB CO, 82- *Personal Data:* b Vienna, Austria, July 2, 30; m 54; c 2. *Educ:* Hebrew Univ, Israel, MSc, 56, PhD(org chem), 59. *Prof Exp:* From res asst to res assoc org chem, Weizmann Inst, 59-64; scientist, New Eng Inst Med Res, Conn, 64-66. *Concurrent Pos:* Asst org chem, Bar-Ilan Univ, Israel, 57-59, lectr org chem & reaction mechanism, 62-63; fel, Dept Chem, Univ Southern Calif, 59-61 & Calif Inst Technol, 61-62. *Mem:* Am Chem Soc; AAAS. *Res:* Medicinal chemistry; structure elucidation and synthesis of natural products and physiological active compounds, antibiotics and gastrointestinal pharmacodynamic agents; reaction mechanisms; antitumor agents; drug targeting. *Mailing Add:* 9 Raelin Rd Hamden CT 06514

**WILLNER, STEVEN P,** INFRARED OBSERVATION, INSTRUMENTATION. *Current Pos:* ASTRONR, SMITHSONIAN ASTROPHYS OBSERV, 81- *Personal Data:* b Louisville, Ky, 1950. *Educ:* Harvard Col, AB, 71; Calif Inst Technol, PhD(astron), 76. *Prof Exp:* Physicist, Univ Calif, San Diego, 76-81. *Concurrent Pos:* Sci ed, Astrophys J, 96- *Mem:* Int Astron Union; Am Astron Soc. *Res:* Star formation and activity in galactic nuclei; infrared observation; instrument design, development and construction. *Mailing Add:* 60 Garden St Cambridge MA 02138. *E-Mail:* swillner@cfa.harvard.edu

**WILLOUGHBY, ANNE D,** PEDIATRICS. *Current Pos:* Epidemiol fel & spec asst pediat, Pregnancy & Perinatology Br, BR CHIEF, PEDIAT, ADOLESCENT & MATERNAL AIDS BR, NAT INST CHILD HEALTH & HUMAN DEVELOP. *Educ:* Cornell Univ, MD; Univ Calif, Berkeley, MPH. *Res:* Epidemiology, natural history, pathogenesis, clinical manifestation, treatment and prevention of HIV infection and disease in pregnant women, mothers, women of reproductive age, infants, children, adolescents and families. *Mailing Add:* NIH Nat Inst Child Health & Human Develop Pediat Adolescent & Maternal Aids Br 6100 Executive Blvd Bldg 61E Rm 4B11H Rockville MD 20892

**WILLOUGHBY, RALPH ARTHUR,** MATHEMATICS. *Current Pos:* RETIRED. *Personal Data:* b Santa Rosa, Calif, Aug 15, 23; m 47, Nona Christensen; c Carol Lynn & Ann W (Abers). *Educ:* Univ Calif, AB, 47, PhD(math), 51. *Prof Exp:* From asst prof to assoc prof math, Ga Inst Technol, 51-55; mem staff, Atomic Energy Div, Babcock & Wilcox Co, 55-57; mem staff, Math Sci Dept, Thomas J Watson Res Ctr, IBM Corp, 57-90. *Concurrent Pos:* Res partic, Math Panel, Oak Ridge Nat Lab, 54, consult, 54-55. *Mem:* Soc Indust & Appl Math. *Res:* Numerical analysis. *Mailing Add:* 4467 Terra Granada Dr Apt 2B Walnut Creek CA 94595-4031

**WILLOUGHBY, RUSSELL A,** VETERINARY MEDICINE. *Current Pos:* RETIRED. *Personal Data:* b Tilston, Man, July 7, 33; m 54; c 3. *Educ:* Univ Toronto, DVM, 57; Cornell Univ, PhD(vet path), 65. *Prof Exp:* Pvt pract vet med, Grenfell, Sask, 57-61; asst prof clin vet med, Ont Vet Col, Toronto, 61-62; res asst vet path, Cornell Univ, 62-65; assoc prof, Univ Guelph, 65-67, assoc dean res, 79-83, chmn, Dept Clin Studies, 83-86, prof clin vet med, Ont Vet Col, 67-90, dir, Equine Res Ctr, 86-90. *Mem:* Am Vet Med Asn; Am Asn Vet Clinicians; Can Vet Med Asn; Am Col Vet Internal Med (secy, 72-81). *Res:* Environmental effects on animals, including heavy metal toxicity, the effects of intensification and the interaction between pollutants and infectious agents. *Mailing Add:* RR No 2 Alora ON N0B 1S0 Can

**WILLOUGHBY, SARAH MARGARET C(LAYPOOL),** CHEMICAL ENGINEERING, POLYMER CHEMISTRY. *Current Pos:* from asst prof to assoc prof chem, 54-83, assoc dir, Ctr Microcrystal Polymer Sci, 75-79, EMER PROF, DEPT CHEM, UNIV TEX, ARLINGTON, 84- *Personal Data:* b Bowling Green, Ky, Oct 15, 17; div; c 2. *Educ:* Univ Western Ky, BS, 38; Purdue Univ, PhD(chem eng), 50. *Prof Exp:* Chemist, Devoe-Raynolds Co, Inc, 40-42; jr engr, Curtiss-Wright Corp, 42-44; res chemist, Monsanto Chem Co, 50-52. *Concurrent Pos:* Pres, Sigma Xi, Univ Tex, Arlington, 66-68; lectr & educator mem, Dallas Soc, Fedn Socs Paint Technol, 74-83; consult protective coatings, Albert Halff Eng Co, 80-86; sci book rev, J Appl Hem, 82. *Mem:* Sigma Xi; fel Am Inst Chem; Am Chem Soc; NY Acad Sci. *Res:* Protective coatings; organic polymer chemistry; education in chemical engineering; professional registration standards. *Mailing Add:* 1630 Pecan Park Dr Arlington TX 76012-3030

**WILLOUGHBY, STEPHEN SCHUYLER,** MATHEMATICS EDUCATION. *Current Pos:* PROF MATH, UNIV ARIZ, 87- *Personal Data:* b Madison, Wis, Sept 27, 32; m 54, Helen S Shapiro; c Wendy V (Gallen) & Todd A. *Educ:* Harvard Univ, AB, 53, AMT, 55; Columbia Univ, EdD(math educ), 61. *Honors & Awards:* Lifetime Achievment Medal for Leadership in Math Educ, Inst Nat Coun Teachers Math. *Prof Exp:* Teacher math & sci, Newton Pub Schs, Mass, 54-57; teacher math, Greenwich Pub Schs, Conn, 57-59; instr educ & math, Univ Wis, Madison, 60-61, asst prof, 61-65; prof educ & math, NY Univ, 65-87, chmn, Dept Math Educ, 67-87. *Concurrent Pos:* Author & consult; chmn, Coun Sci Soc Pres, 88; chmn, US Nat Comn Math Instr, 90-94. *Mem:* Math Asn Am; Nat Coun Teachers Math (pres, 82-84); Coun Sci Soc Pres. *Res:* Learning and teaching mathematics. *Mailing Add:* Dept Math Univ Ariz Tucson AZ 85721

**WILLOUGHBY, WILLIAM FRANKLIN,** IMMUNOPATHOLOGY, AEROSPACE MEDICINE. *Current Pos:* DIR, DEPT LAB, COOK CO HOSP, 92-; PROF, DEPT PATH, RUSH UNIV SCH MED, 93- *Personal Data:* b Washington, DC, Feb 4, 36; m 75; c 5. *Educ:* Johns Hopkins Univ, AB, 57, MD, 65, PhD(microbiol), 65. *Honors & Awards:* Edward E Osgood Prize Med Res, E E Osgood Found, 73. *Prof Exp:* Res fel immunopath, Scripps Clin Res Found, 67-69; asst prof path, Case Western Res Univ, 69-72; dir, Va Mason Res Ctr, 72-75; assoc prof, Johns Hopkins Univ Sch Med, 75-87; prof & chmn, Dept Path, Univ SC Sch Med, 87-92. *Concurrent Pos:* Fel, Arthritis Found, 67-69; mem, Path A Study Sect & Spec Study Sect, NIH, 83-86; consult, Cotton, Inc, 80-83; mem, Comt Byssinosis, Nat Acad Sci, 81-82 & Comt Irritants & Vesicants, 83-84; USAFR, Maj Gen & Dep Surgeon Gen Res Affairs, USAF, 90-95. *Mem:* Am Asn Immunologists; Am Asn Pathologists; Int Acad Path; Am Thoracic Soc; AAAS; Soc USAF Flight Surgeons; Am Soc Cell Biologists; Reticuloendotheliol Soc; Asn Path Chmn; Soc Med Consults Armed Forces. *Res:* Immunopathology; mechanisms of inflammation, particularly as they affect the lung; macrophage function, including their release of soluble mediators of inflammation. *Mailing Add:* Cook Co Hosp Hektoen Bldg 627 S Wood Chicago IL 60612

**WILLOWS, ARTHUR OWEN DENNIS,** NEUROPHYSIOLOGY. *Current Pos:* MEM STAFF, NEUROBIOL PROG, NSF, 80- *Personal Data:* b Winnipeg, Man, Mar 26, 41; m 63; c 3. *Educ:* Yale Univ, BS, 63; Univ Ore, PhD(biol), 67. *Prof Exp:* Asst prof, Univ Ore, 67-68, res assoc neurophysiol, 68-69; from asst prof to assoc prof, Univ Wash, 69-75, prof zool, 75-80, dir, Friday Harbor Labs, 73-80. *Mem:* Soc Gen Physiol; Soc Neurosci; Am Physiol Soc. *Res:* Neuroethology; neurophysiological basis of behavior. *Mailing Add:* Friday Harbor Labs Univ Wash 620 University Rd Friday Harbor WA 98250

**WILLS, CHRISTOPHER J,** GENETICS, BIOLOGY. *Current Pos:* assoc prof, 72-78, PROF BIOL, UNIV CALIF, SAN DIEGO, 78- *Personal Data:* b London, Eng, Mar 23, 38; m 65; c Anne Marie. *Educ:* Univ BC, BA, 60, MSc, 62; Univ Calif, Berkeley, PhD(genetics), 65. *Prof Exp:* NIH fel genetics, Univ Calif, Berkeley, 65-66; asst prof biol, Wesleyan Univ, 66-72. *Concurrent Pos:* NIH res grant, 67; Guggenheim fel, 77-78; var grants, NSF, NIH & Dept Energy. *Mem:* AAAS; Genetics Soc Am; Am Soc Naturalists. *Res:* Maintenance of genetic variability in natural populations; regulation of yeast isoenzymes; evolutionary trees; molecular evolution; diversity of complex ecosystems, DNA polymorphisms. *Mailing Add:* Dept Biol Univ Calif San Diego La Jolla CA 92093. *E-Mail:* cwills@ucsd.edu

**WILLS, DONALD L,** GEOLOGY, PETROLEUM GEOLOGY. *Current Pos:* dir finance & bus, 79-84, EMER CHMN & PROF GEOL, MONMOUTH COL, 84- *Personal Data:* b Peoria, Ill, May 12, 24; m 72, Cindy B Wills; c 2. *Educ:* Univ Ill, BS, 49, MS, 51; Univ Iowa, PhD(geol), 71. *Prof Exp:* Assoc dir, Ill Dept Conserv, 77-80. *Concurrent Pos:* Environ consult, 71-; petrol geologist consult. *Mem:* Am Inst Prof Geol; Sigma Xi; Nat Asn Geol Teachers; Geol Soc Am. *Res:* Biostratigraphic studies of Mississippian Chesterian series. *Mailing Add:* 1048 E Euclid Ave Monmouth IL 61462

**WILLS, GENE DAVID,** PLANT PHYSIOLOGY, BIOCHEMISTRY. *Current Pos:* PLANT PHYSIOLOGIST WEED CONTROL, DELTA BR EXP STA, 67- *Personal Data:* b Birmingham, Ala, Apr 11, 34; m 66; c 2. *Educ:* Auburn Univ, BS, 57, MS, 62; Okla State Univ, PhD(bot), 67. *Prof Exp:* Asst bot, Auburn Univ, 59-62 & Okla State Univ, 63-66. *Mem:* Weed Sci Soc Am; Sigma Xi. *Res:* Chemical weed control including studies on ecology and anatomy of weeds and effects of environment on translocation and toxicity of radiolabeled and non-radiolabeled herbicides in weeds. *Mailing Add:* Delta Br Exp Sta PO Box 197 Stoneville MS 38776

**WILLS, GEORGE B(AILEY),** CHEMICAL ENGINEERING. *Current Pos:* PROF CHEM ENG, VA POLYTECH INST & STATE UNIV, 64- *Personal Data:* b Canton, Mo, Nov 24, 28; m 54; c 3. *Educ:* Mass Inst Technol, BS, 54; Univ Wis, MS, 55, PhD(chem eng), 62. *Prof Exp:* Engr, Mallinckrodt Chem Works, 55-57 & Bjorksten Res Labs, 57-61; asst res engr, Phillips Petrol Co, 61-64. *Concurrent Pos:* Consult, A O Smith Corp, 60 & Electrotech Corp, 66- *Mem:* AAAS; Am Inst Chem Engrs; Am Chem Soc; Sigma Xi. *Res:* Mass transfer; electrochemistry; catalysis. *Mailing Add:* Dept Chem Eng Va Polytech Inst & State Univ 142A Randolph Hall Blacksburg VA 24061

**WILLS, JAMES E, JR,** PHYSICS. *Current Pos:* chmn dept, 64-72, prof, 64-79, EMER PROF PHYSICS, UNIV NC, ASHEVILLE, 80- *Personal Data:* b Tucumcari, NMex, Mar 20, 16. *Educ:* Miss Col, BA, 36; Univ Va, MA, 38; Univ Tex, PhD(physics), 56. *Prof Exp:* Instr physics, Ga Sch Technol, 38-39; asst prof, Baylor Univ, 46-51; from assoc prof to prof, Stetson Univ, 56-64. *Mem:* Am Phys Soc; Sigma Xi. *Res:* Fast neutron spectroscopy. *Mailing Add:* 36 Mockingbird Rd Swannanoa NC 28778

**WILLS, JOHN G,** THEORETICAL PHYSICS. *Current Pos:* from asst prof to assoc prof, 64-76, PROF PHYSICS, IND UNIV, BLOOMINGTON, 76- *Personal Data:* b Greeley, Colo, Feb 4, 31; m 54, Beverly E Howerton; c Debra, Mechele, Kristine, Joanne & Michael. *Educ:* San Diego State Col, AB, 53; Univ Wash, MS, 56, PhD(physics), 63. *Prof Exp:* Staff mem, Los Alamos Sci Lab, 56-60. *Mem:* Am Phys Soc. *Res:* Nuclear theory; elementary particle theory; scattering theory. *Mailing Add:* 3624 E Morningside Dr Bloomington IN 47408. *Fax:* 812-855-5533; *E-Mail:* wills@ucs.indiana.edu

**WILLS, NANCY KAY,** PHYSIOLOGY. *Current Pos:* ASSOC PROF, DEPT PHYSIOL & BIOPHYS, UNIV TEX MED BR, 87- *Personal Data:* b Wytheville, Va, Aug 27, 49. *Educ:* Ohio State Univ, BS, 71; Univ Va, MA, 73, PhD(physiol psychol), 77. *Prof Exp:* Res asst neurophysiol, Dept Physiol & Brain Res Inst, Univ Calif, Los Angeles, 74-76; fel physiol, Med Br, Univ Tex, 76-77; fel physiol, Med Sch, 77-80, res assoc fac physiol, Yale Univ, 80-87. *Concurrent Pos:* NIH fel, 78-80. *Mem:* Biophys Soc; Soc Gen

Physiologists; NY Acad Sci; Am Physiol Soc; Asn Women Sci. *Res:* Electrophysiology and cell biology of ion transport across epithelia. *Mailing Add:* Dept Physiol & Biophys Univ Tex Med Br Galveston TX 77555. *Fax:* 409-772-3381; *E-Mail:* nkwills@utmbeach

**WILLS, WIRT HENRY,** DISEASES OF ORNAMENTALS. *Current Pos:* From asst prof to prof, 54-68, EMER PROF PLANT PATH, VA POLYTECH INST & STATE UNIV, 90- *Personal Data:* b Petersburg, Va, Feb 12, 24; m 54; c 4. *Educ:* Univ Richmond, BA, 50; Duke Univ, MA, 52, PhD(bot), 54. *Mem:* Am Phytopath Soc. *Res:* Ecology of root diseases; biological control of fungal pathogens in soil-less media. *Mailing Add:* 907 Preston Ave Blacksburg VA 24060

**WILLSON, ALAN NEIL, JR,** ELECTRICAL ENGINEERING. *Current Pos:* asst dean grad studies, Sch Eng & Appl Studies, 77-81, PROF ENG & APPL SCI, UNIV CALIF, LOS ANGELES, 72-, ASSOC DEAN ENG, 87- *Personal Data:* b Baltimore, Md, Oct 16, 39; m 62; c Catherine E, Deborah F & David A. *Educ:* Ga Inst Technol, BEE, 61; Syracuse Univ, MSEE, 65, PhD(elec eng), 67. *Honors & Awards:* Guillemin-Cauer Award, Inst Elec & Electronics Engrs, 78, WRG Baker Award, 94; George Westinghouse Award, Am Soc Eng Educ, 82. *Prof Exp:* Instr, Syracuse Univ, 65-67; assoc engr, IBM Corp, 61-64; mem tech staff, Math & Statist Res Ctr, Bell Labs, 67-72. *Concurrent Pos:* Ed, Inst Elec & Electronics Engrs Trans Circuits & Systs, 77-79. *Mem:* Fel Inst Elec & Electronics Engrs; Soc Indust & Appl Math; Am Soc Eng Educ; Sigma Xi. *Res:* Nonlinear circuit theory; digital filter design; theory and applications of digital signal processing, including implementation; neural networks. *Mailing Add:* Univ Calif Box 951600 7400 Boelter Hall Los Angeles CA 90095. *Fax:* 310-206-4061; *E-Mail:* willson@ee.ucla.edu

**WILLSON, CARLTON GRANT,** RADIATION CHEMISTRY, POLYMER SYNTHESIS. *Current Pos:* PROF, DEPT CHEM ENG & DEPT CHEM & BIOCHEM, UNIV TEX, AUSTIN, 93- *Personal Data:* b Vallejo, Calif, Mar 30, 39; m 75, Deborah Merritt; c William & Andrew. *Educ:* Univ Calif, Berkeley, BS, 62, PhD(chem), 73; San Diego State Univ, MS, 69. *Honors & Awards:* Humboldt Sr Scientist Award, 88; Chem Mat Award, Am Chem Soc, 90, Carothers Award, 92 & Coop Res Award Polymer Sci, 93. *Prof Exp:* Chemist, Aerojet Gen Corp, Sacramento, 62-64; instr chem & math, Fairfax High Sch, Los Angeles, 65-66; asst prof chem, Long Beach State Univ, 74-75, Univ Calif, San Diego, 76-78; mgr, Res Lab, IBM Corp, 78-93. *Concurrent Pos:* IBM fel, 85. *Mem:* Nat Acad Eng; Sigma Xi; Am Soc Eng Educ; AAAS; Am Phys Soc; Soc Plastic Engrs; Am Chem Soc. *Res:* Synthetic and mechanistic studies associated with radiation sensitive organic materials, monomers and polymers and their application to resist materials. *Mailing Add:* Dept Chem Eng CPE 3 474 Univ Tex Austin TX 78712-1062. *E-Mail:* willson@che.utexas.edu

**WILLSON, CLYDE D,** ORGANIC CHEMISTRY, MOLECULAR BIOLOGY. *Current Pos:* INSTR LIFE SCI, LANEY COL, 69- *Personal Data:* b Omaha, Nebr, May 7, 35; m 54; c 4. *Educ:* Univ Calif, Berkeley, BA, 56, PhD(chem), 60. *Prof Exp:* NIH fel bact genetics & protein synthesis, Pasteur Inst, Paris, 60-62; asst prof biochem, Univ Calif, Berkeley, 62-68, res fel entom, Miller Inst, 68-69. *Concurrent Pos:* Vis prof biol, Brandeis Univ, 74-75. *Res:* Heterocyclic organic chemistry; bacterial enzyme regulation and genetic control; characterization of messenger RNA; biochemistry of communication substances in insects. *Mailing Add:* Dept Biol Laney Col 900 Fallon St Oakland CA 94607-4808

**WILLSON, DONALD BRUCE,** CHEMISTRY & MANUFACTURING OF ADVANCED CERAMICS, EXTRACTIVE METALLURGY. *Current Pos:* MGR CHEM MFG TECHNOL, CABOT, 95- *Personal Data:* b Bloomington, Ind, Oct 25, 41; m 65, Sarah L Martin; c Judith L, Keith R, Kevin B & Anna G. *Educ:* Geneva Col, BA, 63; Tufts Univ, PhD(chem), 69. *Prof Exp:* Res assoc, Air Force Off Sci Res, Geneva Col, 69; chemist, Kawecki-Berylco Indusrs, Inc, Pa, 70-73, proj leader-group leader, 74; tech mgr, M&R Refractory Metals Inc, Winslow, 75-76, tech dir, 76-81; staff res eng, Anaconda Minerals Co, 81-83, sr res scientist, 83-85; tech advisor, Ceralox, Arco Chem Co, 85-86; plant mgr, Ceralox Corp-Div VistaChem 6, 86-87, mgr res & develop, 87-95. *Concurrent Pos:* Extractive metallurgy consult. *Mem:* Am Chem Soc; Am Ceramic Soc. *Res:* Development and production of advanced ceramics and materials; management of manufacturing technology incorporating research and development, quality and safety advances to enhance department profitability; extractive metallurgy and physical, inorganic and analytical chemistry of the refractory, transition, rare earth and noble metals and their compounds; advanced ceramics materials. *Mailing Add:* 129 Fairfield Dr Barto PA 19504

**WILLSON, JOHN ELLIS,** DIRECT ANIMAL CARE, ALTERNATIVES TO ANIMAL USE IN RESEARCH & TESTING. *Current Pos:* RETIRED. *Personal Data:* b Scranton, Pa, May 4, 29; m 55, June D Isgate; c Judith H (Davies), Laura A & Peter T. *Educ:* Pa State Univ, BS, 50; Cornell Univ, DVM, 54; Am Bd Toxicol, dipl, 81. *Prof Exp:* Gen pract, Williamsport, Pa, 54; med bacteriologist, US Army Ft Detrick, Md, 57; intern, Angell Mem Animal Hosp, Boston, Mass, 57-58, mem staff, 58-61; head, Dept Pharmacol, John L Smith Mem Cancer Res, Chas Pfizer & Co, Inc, NJ, 61-63; sr pathologist, Johnson & Johnson Res Found, 63-66, asst dir, 66-82, mgr, 82-88, corp dir animal care & use, 88-96. *Concurrent Pos:* Mem coun accreditation, Am Asn Accreditation Lab Animal Care, 72-76; mem adv coun, Inst Lab Animal Resources, Div Biol Sci, Assembly Life Sci, Nat Res Coun-Nat Acad Sci, 74-77; chmn, Testing Safety Guidelines Task Force, Cosmetic Toiletry & Fragrance Asn, 77-80; mem adv coun, NY State Col Vet Med, Cornell Univ, 80-86; adv, Vet Med Educ Comt, NJ, 87-; mem, Animal Welfare Comt, Am Vet Med Asn, 91-97. *Mem:* Am Vet Med Asn; Soc

Toxicol; Am Asn Indust Vet; Am Asn Lab Animal Sci; fel Acad Toxicol Sci. *Res:* Methods of safety evaluation of medical devices, drugs and chemicals; responsible animal use, animal welfare and alternatives to animal use in research and testing. *Mailing Add:* 42 Addison Dr Basking Ridge NJ 07920

**WILLSON, JOHN TUCKER,** anatomy, for more information see previous edition

**WILLSON, LEE ANNE MORDY,** ASTRONOMY, ASTROPHYSICS. *Current Pos:* From instr to assoc prof, 73-88, PROF ASTROPHYS, DEPT PHYSICS, IOWA STATE UNIV, 88- *Personal Data:* b Honolulu, Hawaii, Mar 14, 47; m 69; c 2. *Educ:* Harvard Univ, AB, 68; Univ Mich, MS, 70, PhD(astron), 73. *Concurrent Pos:* Annie J Cannon Award, Am Astron Soc, 80-81; mem, Steering Comt, Sect D, AAAS, 87-; chmn, Comt Status Women in Astron, Am Astron Soc, 87-89; dir-at-large, Assoc Univ Res Astron, 90- *Mem:* Int Astron Union; Am Astron Soc; AAAS. *Res:* Problems of stellar atmospheres, particularly theories of mass loss, extended atmospheres, and variable stars. *Mailing Add:* Physics & Astron Iowa State Univ Ames IA 50011-0001

**WILLSON, MARY FRANCES,** ECOLOGY, EVOLUTION. *Current Pos:* RES ECOLOGIST, US FOREST SERV, 89-; ADJ PROF ZOOL & BOT, WASH STATE UNIV, PULLMAN, 90-; ADJ PROF BIOL & WILDLIFE, UNIV ALASKA, FAIRBANKS. *Personal Data:* b Madison, Wis, July 28, 38; wid. *Educ:* Grinnell Col, BA, 60; Univ Wash, PhD(zool), 64. *Prof Exp:* From asst prof to assoc prof zool, Univ Ill, Urbana-Champaign, 65-77, prof ecol, ethology & evolution, 77-90. *Concurrent Pos:* Vis prof, Univ Minn, 78, 80, 82 & 84, Monash Univ, 86. *Mem:* Ecol Soc Am; Am Ornith Union; Brit Ecol Soc; Cooper Ornith Soc; Am Soc Naturalists; Soc Study Evolution; Asn Trop Biol; AAAS. *Res:* Evolutionary ecology. *Mailing Add:* Forestry Sci Lab 2770 Sherwood Lane Juneau AK 99801

**WILLSON, PHILIP JAMES,** HIGH TEMPERATURE CHEMISTRY, CERAMICS. *Current Pos:* STAFF SCIENTIST & OWNER, WILLSON ENTERPRISE, INC, 88- *Personal Data:* b Detroit, Mich, Apr 23, 26; m 48, 76, Eileen W Ei; c Philip J Jr, Ellen E, Carol (D'Joung), Susan Ei & David Ei. *Educ:* Wayne State Univ, BA, 51. *Prof Exp:* Technician electronics, USN, 45-46 & Gen Motors Corp, 48-50; chemist, Chrysler Corp, 51-55, res supvr chem, 56-88. *Mem:* Soc Automotive Engrs. *Res:* High temperature structural ceramic materials for turbine engine applications; automotive catalysts for emission control; friction studies; granted four US patents. *Mailing Add:* Willson Enterprise 709 Mt Vernon Royal Oak MI 48073-5206

**WILLSON, RICHARD ATWOOD,** GASTROENTEROLOGY, HEPATOLOGY. *Current Pos:* asst prof, 73-77, ASSOC PROF MED, UNIV WASH, 77-; HEAD, DIV GASTROENTEROL, HARBORVIEW MED CTR, SEATTLE, 73- *Personal Data:* b Minneapolis, Minn; m 75, Bettina Dordoni; c Stuart, Duncan & Vanessa. *Educ:* Univ Minn, BA, 58, BS, 59, MD, 62, MS, 69, Am Bd Internal Med, cert, 70. *Prof Exp:* Intern, Mary Fletcher Hosp, 62-63; resident internal med, Univ Vt, 63-64; resident, Mayo Clin, 66-68, NIH res fel gastroenterol, 68-71; res fel, Liver Unit, Dept Med, King's Col Hosp Med Sch, London, 72-73. *Mem:* Am Gastroenterol Asn; Am Asn Study Liver Dis; Am Fedn Clin Res. *Res:* Treatment of acute fulminant hepatic failure and the study of hepatic injury secondary to drugs and drug metabolism; treatment of viral hepatitis. *Mailing Add:* Dept Med Univ Wash Seattle WA 98195

**WILLSON, WARRACK GRANT,** FUEL ENGINEERING, PHYSICAL CHEMISTRY. *Current Pos:* MGR, FUELS PROCESS CHEM DIV, ENERGY RES CTR, UNIV NDAK, 83- *Personal Data:* b San Francisco, Calif, July 15, 43; m 63; c 2. *Educ:* Univ Northern Colo, BA, 65; Univ Wyo, PhD(chem, physics), 71. *Prof Exp:* Asst prof phys chem, Upper Iowa Col, 70-71; res scientist coal gasification, Univ Wyo, 71-73; res engr reactor eng, E I du Pont de Nemours & Co, Inc, 73-76; group leader coal chems, Occidental Res Corp, Calif, 76-78; proj mgr coal liquefaction, 78-79, mgr gasification & liquefaction, Dept Energy, Grand Forks Energy Technol Ctr, NDak, 79-83. *Concurrent Pos:* Adj prof chem eng, Univ NDak, 80- *Mem:* Am Chem Soc; Sigma Xi. *Res:* Conversion of abundant domestic fossil resources and carbonaceous wastes into economically and environmentally acceptable alternate energy sources through combustion, gasification and liquefraction; high pressure/temperature reaction engineering and process development. *Mailing Add:* PO Box 82488 Fairbanks AK 99708

**WILLWERTH, LAWRENCE JAMES,** PLASTICS CHEMISTRY. *Current Pos:* TECH MGR CHEM-PLASTICS, K J QUINN & CO INC, MALDEN, MASS, 66-, DIR TECH APPLNS, 85- *Personal Data:* b Melrose, Mass, Oct 3, 32; m 56; c 3. *Educ:* Lowell Technol Inst, BS, 72, MS, 75. *Prof Exp:* Jr chemist plastics, Nat Polychem Inc, Mass, 55-60; chemist, Avco Corp, Mass, 60-66. *Concurrent Pos:* Instr polymer characterization, Eve Div, Lowell Technol Inst, 72- *Mem:* Am Chem Soc; Am Inst Chemists; Soc Plastics Engrs. *Res:* Research and development of polyurethane plastics; attainment of specific properties through rearrangement and addition of various species to the polymer backbone. *Mailing Add:* 160 Flamingo Rd Edgewater FL 32141-7206. *E-Mail:* lwillwerth@aol.com

**WILMER, HARRY A,** PSYCHIATRY. *Current Pos:* EMER PROF PSYCHIAT, UNIV TEX HEALTH SCI CTR, 72- *Personal Data:* b New Orleans, La, Mar 5, 17; m 45, Jane Harris; c Harry, John, Thomas, James & Mary. *Educ:* Univ Minn, BS, 38, MS, 40, MD, 41, PhD(path), 44. *Honors & Awards:* Rollin Cutts Prize Surg. *Prof Exp:* Chief psychiat, Palo Alto Clin,

Calif, 49-51; consult psychiat, Mayo Clin, 57-58; prof psychiat, Sch Med, Univ Calif, 64-69; sr psychiatrist, Scott & White Clin, Temple, Tex, 69-72. *Concurrent Pos:* Consult, Mayo Clin, Mayo Found, 57-58 & Dept Corrections, State Calif, 61-65; ed, Hosp & Community Psychiat, 65-68; Guggenheim fel, Jung Inst, Zurich Switz, 69-70; dir, Int Film Festival-Symp Cult & Psychiat, Univ Tex Health Sci Ctr, 71-78; pres & dir, Inst Humanities, Salado, Tex, 80- *Mem:* Am Psychiat Asn; Int Asn Analytical Psychologists; Am Acad Psychoanalysis; Am Col Psychiatrists; Inter-regional Soc Anal Psychologists; Sigma Xi; fel Nat Res Coun Med Sci. *Res:* Therapeutic community; dreams and Jungian psychology. *Mailing Add:* 506 S Ridge Rd Salado TX 76571. *Fax:* 254-947-9293

WILMER, MICHAEL EMORY, INFORMATION SCIENCE. *Current Pos:* VPRES, PEARSON ELECTRONICS. *Personal Data:* b Washington, DC, Oct 11, 41. *Educ:* Cath Univ Am, BSEE, 63, MSEE, 67, PhD(elec eng), 68. *Prof Exp:* Prin scientist image processing, Palo Alto Res Ctr, Xerox Corp, 67- *Mem:* Sigma Xi; Inst Elec & Electronics Engrs. *Res:* Digital processing of images and speech for enhancement, compression and recognition. *Mailing Add:* 1111 Portola Rd Portola Valley CA 94028-7254

WILMORE, JACK H, KINESIOLOGY. *Current Pos:* PROF KINSESIOLOGY, UNIV TEX, AUSTIN, 85- *Personal Data:* b Apr 23, 38. *Res:* Kinesiology. *Mailing Add:* 3409 Sanderling Tr Austin TX 78746-6646

WILMOT, GEORGE BARWICK, PHYSICAL CHEMISTRY. *Current Pos:* Res chemist, Naval Ord Sta, 54-73, RES CHEMIST, NAVAL SURFACE WEAPONS CTR, 73- *Personal Data:* b Waterbury, Conn, Oct 27, 28; m 53; c 7. *Educ:* Rensselaer Polytech Inst, BS, 51; Mass Inst Technol, PhD(phys chem), 54. *Mem:* AAAS; Am Chem Soc; Am Phys Soc; Sigma Xi. *Res:* Infrared and Raman spectroscopy; propellants, explosives, combustion; thermodynamics; lasers. *Mailing Add:* 6722 Amhurst Rd Bryans Road MD 20616-9747

WILMOT, THOMAS RAY, VECTOR ECOLOGY, INTEGRATED PEST MANAGEMENT. *Current Pos:* ENTOMOLOGIST, MIDLAND CO MOSQUITO CONTROL, 84- *Personal Data:* b Great Falls, Mont, Sept 9, 53; m; Gail A Ballard; c Lacey A & Eric T. *Educ:* Mont State Univ, BS, 75; Ore State Univ, MS, 78; Univ Calif, Los Angeles, MPH, 84, PhD(epidemiol), 86. *Prof Exp:* Grad res asst, Ore State Univ, 76-78; grad teaching asst econ entom, 77; mgr, Yakima Co Wash Mosquito Control Dist, 78-80; grad res assoc, Univ Calif, Los Angeles, 81-84. *Concurrent Pos:* Consult, US Agency Int Develop, 88 & USN, 91; adj lectr genetics entom, Saginaw Valley State Univ, Mich, 88- & epidemiol, Ferris State Univ, Mich, 90. *Mem:* Am Mosquito Control Asn; Soc Vector Ecol; Entom Soc Am; Am Soc Trop Med & Hyg. *Res:* Biology and control of arthropod vectors of disease agents; ecology of immature stages and its relationship to population dynamics and disease transmission. *Mailing Add:* 3219 Milford St Midland MI 48642. *Fax:* 517-687-7914

WILMOTH, BENTON M, HYDROLOGY, WATER RESOURCES. *Current Pos:* HYDROGEOLOGIST, US ENVIRON PROTECTION AGENCY, 66- *Personal Data:* b Big Stone Gap, Va, July 4, 25; m 48, Tressia P; c Benton M, Susan K & Linda A. *Educ:* WVa Univ, AB, 50, MS, 56. *Prof Exp:* Geologist, US Geol Surv, 52-66. *Concurrent Pos:* Coordr emergency removal hazardous mats release to hydrol environ; regist & lic prof geologist, State NC. *Mem:* Geol Soc Am; Am Inst Prof Geologists. *Res:* Ground water availability and quality control in the central Appalachian regions of US; stabilization and removal of unnatural hazardous chemical releases threatening the quality of the natural hydrogeologic environment. *Mailing Add:* 104 Martha Dr St Clairsville OH 43950

WILMOTTE, RAYMOND M, TELECOMMUNICATION. *Current Pos:* RETIRED. *Personal Data:* b Paris, France, Aug 13, 01. *Educ:* Univ Cambridge, Eng, BA, 21, MA, 23, ScD(mech sci), 58. *Prof Exp:* Consult engr, self-employed, 32-83; tech analyst, Fed Commun Comn, 74-92. *Concurrent Pos:* Fel Wash Acad Sci. *Mem:* fel Inst Elec & Electronics Engrs. *Res:* Introduction of telecommunication technology; expected application in private and public use. *Mailing Add:* 1701 N Troy St No 375 Arlington VA 22201

WILMS, ERNEST VICTOR, ENGINEERING MECHANICS. *Current Pos:* ASSOC PROF CIVIL ENG, UNIV MAN, 68- *Personal Data:* b Winnipeg, Man, Apr 21, 36. *Educ:* Univ Man, BSc, 58; Univ Ill, MS, 60, PhD(theoret & appl mech), 63. *Prof Exp:* Res engr, Can Armament Res & Develop Estab, 58-59; from res asst to res assoc theoret & appl mech, Univ Ill, Urbana, 59-62; asst prof mech eng, Univ Sask, 62-64; res engr, Babcock & Wilcox Res Ctr, Ohio, 64-65; from asst prof to assoc prof eng mech, Univ Ala, 65-68. *Concurrent Pos:* Consult, Army Res Off, NC, 67-68. *Mem:* Am Inst Aeronaut & Astronaut. *Res:* Solid and fluid mechanics; dynamics and vibrations. *Mailing Add:* Dept Civil Eng Univ Man Winnipeg MB R3T 2N2 Can

WILMS, HUGO JOHN, JR, electrical engineering, undersea warfare, for more information see previous edition

WILMSEN, CARL WILLIAM, ELECTRICAL ENGINEERING. *Current Pos:* from asst prof to assoc prof, 66-77, PROF ELEC ENG, COLO STATE UNIV, 77- *Personal Data:* b Galveston, Tex, Nov 20, 34; m 60; c Steven K & Erik K. *Educ:* Tex A&M Univ, BS, 56; Univ Tex, Austin, BS, 60, MS, 62, PhD(elec eng), 67. *Prof Exp:* Test engr, Gen Dynamics Corp, 56-59; res engr,

Tracor, Inc, 60-62. *Mem:* Am Phys Soc; Am Vacuum Soc; Inst Elec & Electronics Engrs. *Res:* Optoelectronic integrated circuits; surface emitting lasers heterojunction optoelectronic devices; Auger and XPS analysis; oxide growth on semiconductor. *Mailing Add:* Dept Elec Eng Colo State Univ Ft Collins CO 80523. *Fax:* 970-491-2249; *E-Mail:* wilmsen@longs.lance. colostate.edu

WILNER, GEORGE DUBAR, HEMATOLOGY, PATHOLOGY. *Current Pos:* PROF MED & PHYSIOL, ALBANY MED COL, 88- *Personal Data:* b New York, NY, Dec 7, 40. *Educ:* Northwestern Univ, BS, 62, MD, 65. *Honors & Awards:* Res Career Develop Award, NIH. *Prof Exp:* From instr to prof path, Col Physicians & Surgeons, Columbia Univ, 69-78; prof path & assoc prof med, Wash Univ, Sch Med, 78-88. *Concurrent Pos:* Res career develop award, Nat Heart, Lung & Blood Inst, NIH. *Mem:* Am Heart Asn; Am Soc Clin Invest; Am Soc Hemat; Am Asn Blood Banks; Am Asn Path. *Res:* Hemostasis and thrombosis; immunology/immunochemistry of fibrin (ogen); non-hemostatic function of thrombin; transfusion medicine. *Mailing Add:* Albany Med Col Dept Med & Physiol Div Hemat A-52 47 New Scotland Ave Albany NY 12208. *Fax:* 518-262-4337; *E-Mail:* gwilner@ gateway.amc.edu

WILSDORF, HEINZ G(ERHARD) F(RIEDRICH), MATERIALS SCIENCE, PHYSICS. *Current Pos:* prof mat sci, Univ Va, 63-66, chmn dept, 63-76, Wills Johnson prof, 66-87, William G Reynolds prof, 87-91, EMER PROF MAT SCI, UNIV VA, 91- *Personal Data:* b Pennekow, Ger, June 25, 17; nat US; m 50, Doris Kuhlmann. *Educ:* Univ Berlin, Dipl, 44; Univ Gottingen, Dr rer nat, 47; Univ Witwatersrand, DSc, 54. *Honors & Awards:* Alberta Easton White Distinguished Teacher Award, Am Soc Metals Int, 95. *Prof Exp:* Res asst physics, Univ Gottingen, 47-49; prin res officer, Nat Phys Lab, SAfrica, 50-56; tech dir, Solid State Sci Labs, Franklin Inst, Pa, 56-63. *Concurrent Pos:* Mem, Space Processing Ad Hoc Adv Subcomt, NASA, 75-79; Gauss prof, Univ Gottingen, Ger, 83; dir, Light Metals Ctr, Univ Va, 84-91. *Mem:* Fel Am Soc Metals Int; fel Am Phys Soc; Sigma Xi. *Res:* Metallurgy; x-ray crystallography; electron diffraction; electron microscopy; metal physics, especially plastic deformation and fracture; thin films; high temperature aluminum alloys; dispersion hardening. *Mailing Add:* Dept Mat Sci & Eng Univ Va Charlottesville VA 22901

WILSEY, NEAL DAVID, MAGNETIC RESONANCE, SEMICONDUCTOR MATERIALS. *Current Pos:* res physicist solid state physics, US Naval Res Lab, 67-74, head, Electronic Mat Sect, Radiation Effects Br, 74-79, head, Radiation Interactions Sect, Semiconductors Br, 80-88, mem strategic planning staff, 88-90, head, Semiconductors Br, 90, HEAD, ELECTRONIC MAT BR, US NAVAL RES LAB, 90- *Personal Data:* b Tunkhannock, Pa, July 27, 37; m 92, Zelma L Koon; c Kevin, David, Craig & Keith. *Educ:* Hartwick Col, BA, 61; Colo State Univ, MS, 64, PhD(physics), 67. *Prof Exp:* Instr physics, Colo State Univ, 66-67. *Concurrent Pos:* Instr, Univ Md, 71-72; vis scientist, Inst Study Defects Solids, State Univ NY, Albany, 78-79. *Mem:* Am Phys Soc; Mat Res Soc; Minerals Metals & Mat Soc. *Res:* Radiation effects, defects in solids; electronic materials. *Mailing Add:* US Naval Res Lab Code 6870 Washington DC 20375-5347. *E-Mail:* wilsey@estd.nrl.navy.mil

WILSHIRE, HOWARD GORDON, ENVIRONMENTAL GEOLOGY, SURFACE PROCESSES. *Current Pos:* GEOLOGIST, US GEOL SURV, 61- *Personal Data:* b Shawnee, Okla, Aug 19, 26; m 84, Jane E Nielson; c 3. *Educ:* Univ Okla, BA, 52; Univ Calif, Berkeley, PhD(geol), 56. *Honors & Awards:* Meritorious Serv Award, Dept Interior. *Prof Exp:* Lectr geol, Univ Sydney, 56-60; res fel, Australian Nat Univ, 61. *Mem:* Geol Soc Am; AAAS; Am Geophys Union. *Res:* Structure and petrology of igneous rocks; petrology and processes of the upper mantle; effects of human uses of arid lands and rates of recovery. *Mailing Add:* US Geol Surv 345 Middlefield Rd Menlo Park CA 94025. *E-Mail:* wilshire@mojeve.wr.usgs.gov

WILSON, ALAN C, HEART DISEASE, LIPID METABOLISM. *Current Pos:* adj prof med, 88-89, ASSOC PROF CLIN MED, UNIV MED & DENT NJ, ROBERT W JOHNSON MED SCH, 89- *Personal Data:* b Kampala, Uganda, July 30, 45; m 76; c 3. *Educ:* Univ Aberdeen, Scotland, PhD(biochem), 72. *Prof Exp:* Adj prof, 79-88. *Mem:* Am Inst Nutrit; Biochem Soc Eng; Biochem Soc Can; Am Soc Biochem & Molecular Biol. *Res:* Atherosclerosis, hyperlipidemia and risk factors for myocardial infarction; time trends in myocardiol infaction outcomes and treatment. *Mailing Add:* Dept Med MEB 589 Univ Med & Dent NJ New Brunswick NJ 08903-0019

WILSON, ALBERT E, NUCLEAR ENGINEERING. *Current Pos:* prof & chmn dept, Idaho State Univ, 66-76, dean sch eng, 76-83, prof eng, 76-94, EMER PROF ENG, IDAHO STATE UNIV, 94- *Personal Data:* b Glenwood Springs, Colo, Jan 17, 27; m 52; c 5. *Educ:* Univ Colo, BS, 50; Univ NMex, MS, 59; Univ Okla, PhD(eng sci), 64. *Prof Exp:* Physicist, Nat Bur Stand, 51-55; staff mem, Los Alamos Sci Lab, 55-59; from instr to asst prof nuclear eng, Univ Okla, 59-66. *Concurrent Pos:* Mem, Sci & Technol Adv Comt, Argonne Nat Lab, 81-88. *Mem:* Am Nuclear Soc; Am Soc Eng Educ; Nat Soc Prof Engrs. *Res:* Nuclear engineering education, especially instrumentation, kinetics and control of nuclear reactor systems. *Mailing Add:* PO Box 4178 McCall ID 83638

WILSON, ALEXANDER D, MECHANICAL ENGINEERING. *Current Pos:* supt prod develop, 86-90, SUPT TECH SERV, LUKENS STEEL CO, 90- *Personal Data:* b Corning, NY, Sept 12, 45; m 68, Elizabeth Nelson; c Zachary & Bartholomew. *Educ:* Mass Inst Technol, BS, 67, MS, 89. *Prof Exp:*

Mat engr, Westinghouse Elec Corp, 71-74. *Mem:* Fel Am Soc Metals Int; Am Inst Mining Metall & Petrol Engrs; Am Iron & Steel Inst; Am Soc Civil Engrs; Am Soc Testing & Mat. *Res:* Investigating the influence of chemistry and processing on the microstructure, properties, and behavior of carbon and alloy plate steels. *Mailing Add:* ARC Bldg Lukens Steel Co Modena Rd Coatesville PA 19320

**WILSON, ANDREW ROBERT,** PLASMA PHYSICS. *Current Pos:* prog mgr plasma physics, 71-83, VPRES, MAXWELL LABS, SYSTS, SCI & SOFTWARE, 83- *Personal Data:* b Dublin, Ireland, Sept 13, 41; US citizen; m 68. *Educ:* Trinity Col, Univ Dublin, BA, 62, MA, 65; Oxford Univ, DPhil(physics), 68. *Prof Exp:* Fr Govt boursier nuclear physics, Inst Fourier, Grenoble, 62-63; fel solid state physics, Lincoln Lab, Mass Inst Technol, 68-70; systs engr, Elec Supply Bd, Dublin, Ireland, 70-71. *Mem:* Am Phys Soc; Inst Elec & Electronics Engrs. *Res:* Hydromagnetic theory; system generated electromagnetic theory; radiation transport. *Mailing Add:* Maxwell Labs 8888 Balboa Ave San Diego CA 92123-1506. *Fax:* 619-755-0474

**WILSON, ANDREW STEPHEN,** ASTRONOMY. *Current Pos:* from asst prof to assoc prof, 81-86, PROF ASTRON, UNIV MD, COLLEGE PARK, 86- *Personal Data:* b Doncaster, Eng, Mar 26, 47; m 75; c Daniel & Caroline. *Educ:* Univ Cambridge, BA, 69, MA & PhD(radio astron), 73. *Prof Exp:* Res fel radio astron, State Univ Leiden, 73-75; res fel astron, Univ Sussex, 75-78. *Concurrent Pos:* Astronr, Space Telescope Sci Inst, 92- *Mem:* Fel Royal Astron Soc; fel Am Astron Soc; Int Astron Union; Int Union Radio Sci. *Res:* Crab nebula; radio sources; active galactic nuclei. *Mailing Add:* Dept Astron Univ Md College Park MD 20742

**WILSON, ANGUS,** RUBBER CHEMISTRY. *Current Pos:* RETIRED. *Personal Data:* b Mexico, Maine, Aug 13, 20; m, Doris Huff; c Ann M & Lea S. *Educ:* Georgetown Univ, BS, 41. *Prof Exp:* Control & analytical chemist, E I du Pont de Nemours & Co, Inc, 41-43; prod supvr, Joseph E Seagrams & Sons, Inc, 47-48; control lab supvr, Govt Lab, Univ Akron, 49-52; rubber chemist, US Army Natick Res & Develop Command, 52-68, head rubber technol group, 68-74, head, Rubber & Plastics Group, 74-80. *Mem:* Am Chem Soc. *Res:* Development of methods of testing rubber and elastomeric materials; compounding of phosphazene elastomers; evaluation of experimental elastomers for possible end item applications. *Mailing Add:* 8 Bowdoin Rd Ipswich MA 01938

**WILSON, ARCHIE FREDRIC,** PULMONARY DISEASES, PULMONARY PHYSIOLOGY. *Current Pos:* from asst prof to assoc prof, 70-79, vchmn dept, 78-82, PROF INTERNAL MED, UNIV CALIF, IRVINE, 79- *Personal Data:* b Los Angeles, Calif, May 7, 31; m 66; c 2. *Educ:* Univ Calif, Los Angeles, BA, 53; Univ Calif, San Francisco, MD, 57, PhD(physiol), 67. *Prof Exp:* Asst prof internal med, Univ Calif, Los Angeles, 67-70. *Mem:* Am Col Chest Physicians; Am Fedn Clin Res; Am Col Physicians. *Res:* Asthma; airway physiology and pathophysiology; bronchodilator aerosols; assessment of cardiovascular physiology by breathing tests; exercise. *Mailing Add:* Dept Pulmonary Med Univ Calif Sch Med Irvine CA 92717. *Fax:* 714-456-8349; *E-Mail:* poludocs@uci.edu

**WILSON, ARCHIE SPENCER,** CHEMISTRY. *Current Pos:* assoc chmn dept, 71-78, prof, 71-89, EMER PROF CHEM, UNIV MINN, MINNEAPOLIS, 89- *Personal Data:* b Tekoa, Wash, Jan 19, 21; m 44, Ivon M Teeter; c Andrea Lou, Ronald Spencer & Steven Daniel. *Educ:* Iowa State Univ, BS, 46; Univ Chicago, MS, 50, PhD, 51. *Prof Exp:* Asst chem, Iowa State Univ, 43-46; res assoc, Gallium Proj, US Dept Navy, 48-49; asst, Univ Chicago, 49-50; instr chem, Univ Nebr, 50-51; sr scientist, Gen Elec Co, 51-65; sr res scientist, Pac Northwest Labs, Battelle Mem Inst, 64-71. *Concurrent Pos:* US sci adv, Int Conf Peaceful Uses Atomic Energy, Geneva, 58; mem, US-UK Ruthenium Conf, 58. *Mem:* Am Chem Soc; fel AAAS; Nat Sci Teachers Asn. *Res:* Crystal structure of compounds of uranium; ruthenium chemistry; solvent extraction of the actinide elements. *Mailing Add:* 14833 58th Pl W Edmonds WA 98026. *E-Mail:* aswilson@scn.org

**WILSON, ARMIN GUSCHEL,** ORGANIC CHEMISTRY, MEDICINAL CHEMISTRY. *Current Pos:* RETIRED. *Personal Data:* b Sapulpa, Okla, Dec 13, 16; m 43; c 2. *Educ:* Rice Inst, BA, 39, MA, 41; Harvard Univ, PhD(org chem), 45. *Prof Exp:* Org chemist, Off Sci Res & Develop, Harvard Univ, 45-47 & Merck & Co, Inc, NJ, 47-52; dept head, Res Div, Bristol-Myers Co, 52-68; chmn math & sci, Mercer Co Community Col, 68-69; teacher & counr urban univ prog, Grad Sch Educ, Livingston Col, Rutgers Univ, NB, 69-72, prof acad found, 72-79. *Concurrent Pos:* Instr, Union Jr Col; chmn, Gordon Conf Med Chem, 67. *Mem:* Am Chem Soc; fel NY Acad Sci. *Res:* Synthetic organic chemistry; structure-action relationships of drugs; reaction mechanisms; photochemistry; nature of science; relationship of science and poetry. *Mailing Add:* 4 Ingleton Circle Kennett Square PA 19348

**WILSON, ARNOLD,** CONCRETE MATERIALS RESEARCH, CONCRETE THIN SHELL RESEARCH & DESIGN. *Current Pos:* PROF CIVIL ENG, BRIGHAM YOUNG UNIV, 57- *Personal Data:* b Payson, Utah, Feb 1, 33; m 52, Joyce Hutchings; c Dennis, Sharon, Diana, Kerry, Craig, Christine, Kendall, Mark, Annette & Michael. *Educ:* Brigham Young Univ, BES, 57, MS, 62; Okla State Univ, PhD(civil eng), 73. *Honors & Awards:* William A Cordon Award, Intermountain Chap Am Concrete Inst, 86. *Concurrent Pos:* Struct engr, Wilson-Calder Corp, 72- *Mem:* Fel Am Concrete Inst; Am Soc Civil Engrs; Int Asn Shell & Spatial Structures; Sigma Xi. *Res:* Concrete dome and hyperbolic paraboloid thin shell structures; air supported forms for building concrete thin shell structures; space station construction utilizing composite thin shell and gas supported forms; prestressed concrete floating roof; spherical thin shell concrete water tanks. *Mailing Add:* 415 E Maple Mapleton UT 84664. *Fax:* 801-378-4449

**WILSON, BARBARA ANN,** DETECTORS, PHOTONICS. *Current Pos:* tech supvr, 88-91, dep sec mgr, 91-95, JET PROPULSION LAB, 95- *Personal Data:* b Lafayette, Ind, Sept 7, 48; m 91, Blair F Lewis. *Educ:* Mt Holyoke Col, BA, 68; Univ Wis-Madison, PhD(physics), 78. *Prof Exp:* Assoc physics, Univ Wis-Madison, 78; mem tech staff, AT&T Bell Labs, 78-86, tech supvr, 86-88. *Mem:* Fel Am Phys Soc; sr mem Inst Elec & Electronics Engrs; Mat Res Soc. *Res:* Development of new instruments for observing planet earth from space including spectroscopy and laster sensing. *Mailing Add:* Jet Propulsion Lab MS 300-331 4800 Oak Grove Dr Pasadena CA 91109. *Fax:* 818-393-0046; *E-Mail:* barbara.a.wilson@jpl.nasa.gov

**WILSON, BARRY WILLIAM,** CELL BIOLOGY, NEUROBIOLOGY. *Current Pos:* asst prof poultry husb & animal physiol & asst biologist, Exp Sta, Univ Calif, Davis, 62-68, assoc prof avian sci & animal physiol & assoc biologist, 68-72, chair, Dept Avian Sci, 91-96, PROF AVIAN SCI, ANIMAL PHYSIOL & ENVIRON TOXICOL, UNIV CALIF, DAVIS, 72- *Personal Data:* b Brooklyn, NY, Aug 20, 31; m 56, Joyce A Sisson; c Sean M. *Educ:* Univ Chicago, BA, 50; Ill Inst Technol, BS & MS, 57; Univ Calif, Los Angeles, PhD(zool), 62. *Prof Exp:* Asst zool, Ill Inst Technol, 56-57; asst, Univ Calif, Los Angeles, 57-58, USPHS cardiovasc trainee, 58, fel, 59-61, jr res zoologist, 62. *Mem:* Am Soc Cell Biol; Soc Neurosci; Soc Develop Biol; Soc Toxicol; Tissue Cult Asn; Sigma Xi; Soc Environ Toxicol & Chem; Am Cell Soc. *Res:* Cell growth and development; emphasis on muscle and nerve using cell culture and intact animals; regulation of acetylcholinesterase and other molecules of nerve, muscle; muscle disorders, dystrophy, pesticide action and ecotoxicology. *Mailing Add:* Dept Avian Sci Univ Calif Davis CA 95616. *Fax:* 530-752-3394; *E-Mail:* bwwilson@ucdavis.edu

**WILSON, BASIL W(RIGLEY),** coastal engineering, physical oceanography; deceased, see previous edition for last biography

**WILSON, BENJAMIN JAMES,** MICROBIOLOGY, TOXICOLOGY. *Current Pos:* from asst prof to prof, 63-85, EMER PROF BIOCHEM, SCH MED, VANDERBILT UNIV, 85- *Personal Data:* b Pennsboro, WVa, Jan 7, 23; m 78, Nancy Ligon; c Suzanne (Hadley), Barbara (Bryant), James C & Rebecca. *Educ:* Univ WVa, AB, 43, MS, 47; George Washington Univ, PhD(microbiol), 55. *Prof Exp:* Dir clin lab, Hopemont Sanitarium, State WVa, 47-49; med bacteriologist, Biol Warfare Labs, Ft Detrick, 49-51, chief microbiol br, Spec Oper Div, 51-59; assoc prof biol, David Lipscomb Col, 59-65. *Concurrent Pos:* Prin investr, NIH, 59-83; consult nutrit sect, Off Int Res, NIH, 65-67 & Food & Drug Admin, 72-78; mem subcomt toxicants occurring naturally in foods, Nat Acad Sci, 68-74; contrib ed, Nutrit Reviews, 73-; mem adj fac, Col Vet Med, Univ Tenn, Knoxville, 79-84. *Mem:* Am Soc Microbiol; Am Chem Soc; Soc Toxicol; NY Acad Sci; Sigma Xi. *Res:* Mycotoxins; natural toxicants; microbial toxins; higher plant toxic metabolites. *Mailing Add:* 1515 Leatherwood Rd White Bluff TN 37187

**WILSON, BOBBY L,** TRANSITION METAL CHEMISTRY, COORDINATION CHEMISTRY. *Current Pos:* From asst prof to assoc prof chem, Tex Southern Univ, 76-85, assoc dean, 86-87, head dept, 87-89, interim dean, Col Arts & Sci, 89-90, vpres acad affairs, 90-92, provost, 92-93, PROF CHEM, TEX SOUTHERN UNIV, 85- *Personal Data:* m, Mary A Maull; c Anthony, Melanie, Malissa & Malinda. *Educ:* Ala State Univ, BS, 66; Southern Univ, MS, 72; Mich State Univ, PhD(chem), 76. *Honors & Awards:* First White House Initiative Fac Award for Excellence in Sci & Technol, 88. *Concurrent Pos:* Vis prof, Exxon Res & Eng, 82-83. *Mem:* Am Chem Soc; Sigma Xi; Nat Orgn Prof Advan Black Chemists & Chem Engrs. *Res:* Synthesis of unusual metal-centered complexes of early first, second, and third row transition elements and evaluation of these metal complexes; coal liquefaction catalysts; use of transition metal complexes as models in an effort to reduce lunar materials such as titanium ilmenite and rutile with the production of molecular oxygen. *Mailing Add:* Tex Southern Univ 3100 Cleburne St Houston TX 77004

**WILSON, BRAYTON F,** BOTANY, FORESTRY. *Current Pos:* asst prof, 67-72, ASSOC PROF FORESTRY, UNIV MASS, AMHERST, 72- *Personal Data:* b Cambridge, Mass, May 27, 34; m 60; c 2. *Educ:* Harvard Univ, AB, 55, MF, 57; Australian Forestry Sch, dipl forestry, 59; Univ Calif, Berkeley, PhD(bot), 61. *Prof Exp:* Forest botanist, Harvard Univ, 61-67. *Mem:* AAAS; Bot Soc Am; Am Soc Plant Physiol. *Res:* Tree growth. *Mailing Add:* Dept Forestry Univ Mass Amherst Campus Amherst MA 01003-0002

**WILSON, BURTON DAVID,** ORGANIC CHEMISTRY. *Current Pos:* RETIRED. *Personal Data:* b Los Angeles, Calif, Oct 20, 32; m 58; c 3. *Educ:* Univ Calif, Los Angeles, BS, 54; Univ Ill, PhD, 58. *Prof Exp:* Chemist, Eastman Kodak Co, 57-89. *Mem:* Am Chem Soc. *Res:* Development and production problem solving on chemicals for photographic end uses. *Mailing Add:* 430 Woodland Lane Webster NY 14580-1665

**WILSON, BYRON J,** INORGANIC CHEMISTRY. *Current Pos:* from asst prof to assoc prof, 65-72, PROF CHEM, BRIGHAM YOUNG UNIV, 72- *Personal Data:* b Jackson, Wyo, Feb 2, 31; m 58; c 7. *Educ:* Idaho State Univ, BS, 56; Southern Ill Univ, MA, 58; Univ Wash, PhD(chem), 61. *Prof Exp:* Asst prof chem, Vanderbilt Univ, 61-65. *Mem:* Am Chem Soc. *Res:* Inorganic free-radical research; paper deterioration research. *Mailing Add:* Dept Chem Brigham Young Univ Provo UT 84602

**WILSON, CARL C,** FOREST FIRE MANAGEMENT & RESEARCH. *Current Pos:* FOREST FIRE CONSULT, 78- *Personal Data:* b Halfway, Ore, Mar 17, 15; m 42; c 2. *Educ:* Univ Idaho, BS, 39; Univ Calif, Berkeley, MS, 41. *Prof Exp:* Fire control asst, Lassen Nat Forest, US Forest Serv, Calif, 46-49 & Plumas Nat Forest, 49, forester, Angeles Nat Forest, 49-55, res forester & proj leader forest fire res, Calif Forest Exp Sta, 56-57, chief, Forest Fire Res Div, 57-62, asst dir forest fire & eng res & chief, Forest Fire Lab, Pac Southwest Forest & Range Exp Sta, 62-73, asst dir & nat fire specialist, Coop Fire Control, State & Pvt Forestry, US Forest Serv, 73-78. *Concurrent Pos:* Consult fire mgt, Food & Agr Orgn-UN Environ Prog, UN, Rome, Italy, 75, Calif Dept Forestry, 78-80 & Ministry Natural Resources, Ont Can, 80. *Mem:* Soc Am Foresters; Am Soc Range Mgt; Am Forestry Asn. *Res:* Forest fire science; detection and control of forest fires for the protection of the human environment; author or coauthor of more than 40 technical papers in forestry and forest fire management. *Mailing Add:* 3 Maybeck Twin Dr Berkeley CA 94708

**WILSON, CAROL MAGGART,** PHARMACOGENETICS, BIOCHEMICAL GENETICS. *Current Pos:* res assoc, 74-76, instr, 76-78, ASST PROF PHARMACOL & INTERNAL MED, HEALTH SCI CTR, SOUTHWESTERN MED SCH, UNIV TEX, DALLAS, 78- *Personal Data:* b Burley, Idaho, Oct 26, 36; m 59, Arthur M; c 2. *Educ:* Northwestern Univ, BA, 58; Wayne State Univ, PhD(biochem), 63. *Prof Exp:* Fel microbiol, Emory Univ, 63-64, biochem, 64-66; asst prof chem, Wheaton Col, 67-68; clin chemist, RI Hosp, 69-70; res assoc molecular biol, Univ Tex, Dallas, 71-73. *Mem:* Sigma Xi; Fedn Am Socs Exp Biol; Endocrine Soc. *Res:* Control of eukaryotic gene expression. *Mailing Add:* Univ Tex Southwestern Med Ctr 5323 Harry Hines Blvd Dallas TX 75235

**WILSON, CARROLL KLEPPER,** MATHEMATICS. *Current Pos:* from assoc prof to prof math, 46-83, actg chmn, Div Math & Natural Sci, 56-60, head dept, 60-74, EMER PROF MATH, EASTERN NMEX STATE UNIV, 83- *Personal Data:* b Denton, Tex, Aug 24, 17; m 41; c 2. *Educ:* NTex State Col, BA, 37; Univ Tex, MA, 40. *Prof Exp:* Teacher pub schs, Tex, 37-41; instr radar, US Civil Serv, 41-43. *Mem:* Math Asn Am. *Res:* Analysis. *Mailing Add:* 1321 S Avenue A Portales NM 88130

**WILSON, CHARLES B,** MEDICINE. *Current Pos:* PROF NEUROSURG, UNIV CALIF, SAN FRANCISCO, 68- *Personal Data:* b Neosho, Mo, Aug 31, 29; m 56; c 3. *Educ:* Tulane Univ, BS, 51, MD, 54. *Prof Exp:* Resident path, Tulane Univ, 55-56, instr neurosurg, 60-61; resident, instr, La State Univ, 56-60; instr, La State Univ, 61-63; from asst prof to prof, Univ Ky, 63-68. *Mem:* Am Asn Neurol Surg; Am Asn Neuropath; Soc Neurol Surg. *Res:* Brain tumor chemotherapy. *Mailing Add:* Dept Neurosurg Univ-Calif Med Ctr Dept NS San Francisco CA 94143

**WILSON, CHARLES ELMER,** NOISE CONTROL, MACHINE DESIGN. *Current Pos:* PROF MECH ENG, MACH DESIGN, MECHANISMS & NOISE CONTROL, NJ INST TECHNOL, 56- *Personal Data:* b Passaic, NJ, Aug 2, 31; m 58, Elizabeth Weisenbachen; c Susan (Cuthbert), Laura (Porter) & Jennifer (Crysson). *Educ:* NJ Inst Technol, BS, 53, MS, 58; NY Univ, MS, 62; Polytech Inst NY, PhD(mech eng), 70. *Prof Exp:* Engr, Otis Elevator Co, 53-54; armament & electron officer, USAF, 54-56; engr, Bendix Corp, 56. *Concurrent Pos:* Prin investr, NSF, NASA & other foundations & industs, 64-81; legal expert & consult mach design, var indust firms, 65-; legal expert & consult noise control, Indust Firms & Govt Agencies, 72-; vis fel, Inst Sound & Vibration Res, Univ Southampton, Eng, 77. *Mem:* Inst Noise Control Eng; Sigma Xi. *Res:* Community noise; industrial noise control; hearing protection; transportation noise prediction and control; adhesives and vibration; author of texts in noise control, kinematics, and dynamics of machinery, machine design. *Mailing Add:* Dept Mech Eng NJ Inst Technol University Heights Newark NJ 07102. *Fax:* 973-642-4282

**WILSON, CHARLES NORMAN,** MATERIALS SCIENCE, PHYSICAL CHEMISTRY. *Current Pos:* SR SCIENTIST CERAMIC NUCLEAR MAT, RES & DEVELOP, WESTINGHOUSE HANFORD CO, 74- *Personal Data:* b Seattle, Wash, Mar 28, 47. *Educ:* Univ Wash, BS, 69, MS, 70, PhD(ceramic eng), 74. *Prof Exp:* Ceramic engr glass technol, Penberthy Electromelt Co, Seattle, Wash, 68-69. *Mem:* Am Ceramic Soc. *Res:* Fabrication and characterization of ceramic materials including oxide nuclear fuels, boron carbide, ceramic nuclear waste forms, and lithium ceramics for fusion reactor tritium breeding; solar cell materials characterization; biomaterials and bone physical chemistry; testing of spent nuclear fuel as a wasteform for disposal in geologic repositories. *Mailing Add:* 362 Driftwood Ct Richland WA 99352

**WILSON, CHARLES OREN,** CLINICAL CHEMISTRY. *Current Pos:* RETIRED. *Personal Data:* b Salt Lake City, Utah, May 9, 26; m 83, Marjorie Lansley; c Deborah L, Sarah L, Stephen O & Paul M. *Educ:* Stanford Univ, BS, 49; Univ Southern Calif, MS, 59. *Prof Exp:* Prod chemist, Transandino Co, Calif, 49-51; res chemist, Nat Bur Stand, 51-52; sr res chemist, Olin Mathieson Chem Corp, NY, 52-54 & Calif, 54-59; sr res chemist, Nat Eng Sci Corp, 59-61 & Am Potash & Chem Corp, 61-68; chemist, Xerox MDO-Electro-Optical Systs, Inc, 68-69 & Int Chem & Nuclear Corp, 69-70; mgr qual control, Reagents Qual Control, Abbott Diag Chem & Instrumentation, 70-77, tech specialist, 77-83, biochemist, Clin Chem Prod, Anal Systs, 83-92. *Concurrent Pos:* Consult, 67- *Mem:* Am Chem Soc. *Res:* Organoboron and organophosphorus chemistry; exotic fuels and polymers; infrared spectroscopy; mass spectrometry; rare earth research; solvent cal extraction; C-14 radioactive organic synthesis; quality control and research of clinical diagnostic reagents; 25 publications in professional chemistry journals. *Mailing Add:* 174 Barcelona Way Prescott AZ 86303

**WILSON, CHARLES R,** GEOPHYSICS. *Current Pos:* Prof physics, 59-, EMER PROF PHYSICS, GEOPHYS INST, UNIV ALASKA. *Personal Data:* b Baltimore, Md, Jan 25, 29; m 3. *Educ:* Case Inst Technol, BS, 51; Univ NMex, MS, 56; Univ Alaska, PhD(geophys), 63. *Concurrent Pos:* Fulbright grant, Paris, 63-64; vis scientist, Nat Ctr Atmospheric Res, 68-69. *Mem:* Am Geophys Union. *Res:* Magnetic storms; geomagnetic micropulsations; auroral infrasonics. *Mailing Add:* Geophys Inst PO Box 757320 Univ Alaska Fairbanks AK 99775-7320

**WILSON, CHARLES WOODSON, III,** PHYSICS. *Current Pos:* RETIRED. *Personal Data:* b Columbus, Ohio, Nov 20, 24; m 48; c 4. *Educ:* Univ Mich, BSE, 47, MS, 48; Wash Univ, PhD(physics), 52. *Prof Exp:* Res assoc, Stanford Univ, 52; res physicist, Prod Dept, Res Div, Texaco Inc, 52-56; physicist, Res & Develop Dept, Chem Div, Union Carbide Corp, 56-62, res scientist, 62-64, group leader, 64-65; prof physics & polymer sci, head, Physics Dept & res assoc, Inst Polymer Sci, Univ Akron, 65-89. *Mem:* AAAS; Am Phys Soc; Am Asn Physics Teachers; Sigma Xi. *Res:* Nuclear and electron spin resonance; high polymer physics; energy utilization and conservation. *Mailing Add:* Dept Physics Univ Akron 309 S Rose Blvd Akron OH 44313

**WILSON, CHRISTINE SHEARER,** ANTHROPOLOGY. *Current Pos:* ASSOC, DIV HUMAN NUTRIT, DEPT INT HEALTH, SCH PUB HEALTH, JOHNS HOPKINS UNIV, BALTIMORE, 96- *Personal Data:* b Orleans, Mass. *Educ:* Brown Univ, BA, 50; Univ Calif, Berkeley, PhD(nutrit, anthrop), 70. *Prof Exp:* Asst ed, Nutrit Rev, Sch Pub Health, Harvard Univ, 51-56; nutrit analyst, USDA, 57-58; asst res nutritionist, Univ Calif, San Francisco, 70-71, res assoc nutrit anthrop, 71-74, asst res nutritionist, 74, lectr, 74-86, asst res nutritionist, Dept Epidemiol & Int Health, 75-86, lectr, Prog Med Anthrop, 77-86, res assoc, 87-96. *Concurrent Pos:* Consult, Soc Nutrit Educ, 71-72, 79 & 81; USPHS spec res fel, 72-73; lectr, Dept Anthrop, Univ Calif, Riverside, 73; vis prof, Dept Family Studies, Univ Guelph, 78; vis asst prof, Home Econ Dept, San Francisco State Univ, 79; mem, Behav Factors Panel, USDA Competitive Grants Prog, 79; contrib ed, Nutrit Rev, 79-87; assoc ed, Ecol Food & Nutrit, 88-91, co-ed-in-chief, 91- *Mem:* Fel Am Anthrop Asn; Am Inst Nutrit; Soc Med Anthrop; Soc Nutrit Educ; Coun Nutrit Anthrop; Soc Int Nutrit Res. *Res:* Food in the culture; social influences on nutritional status; ethnographic field research on diet and nutritional health; dietary methodology; diet and cancer; food choices and change. *Mailing Add:* PO Box 3178 Annapolis MD 21403-0178. *Fax:* 410-280-0654

**WILSON, CHRISTOPHER,** INFECTIOUS DISEASE, PEDIATRICS. *Current Pos:* ASST PROF MED, ORTHOP HOSP, UNIV WASH, 79- *Educ:* Univ Calif, MD. *Mailing Add:* Dept Pediat & Immunol Univ Wash Box 356320 Seattle WA 98195-6320. *Fax:* 206-543-3184

**WILSON, CLARK ROLAND,** GEODESY. *Current Pos:* chmn, Dept Geol Sci, 90-95, PROF GEOPHYS, DEPT GEOL SCI, UNIV TEX, 76- *Personal Data:* b Hollywood, Calif, Apr 6, 49; m 76, Ellin Fredrick; c Kirsten & Sissel. *Educ:* Univ Calif, San Diego, BA, 70, MS, 73, PhD(earth sci), 75. *Prof Exp:* Res asst, Scripps Inst Oceanog, 70-75. *Concurrent Pos:* Prin investr, NSF, 78-84, NASA, 85-; mem, Comt Earth Studies, Nat Res Coun, 92-; assoc ed, J Geophys Res, 92-; prog scientist, Mission to Planet Earth, NASA, 96-97. *Mem:* Am Geophys Union; Soc Explor Geophysicists. *Res:* Space geodesy; earth rotation variations and their geophysical origins; exploration geophysics; seismic data processing. *Mailing Add:* Dept Geol Sci Univ Tex Austin TX 78712. *Fax:* 512-471-9425; *E-Mail:* clarkw@maestro.geo.utexas.edu

**WILSON, CLAUDE LEONARD,** mechanical engineering; deceased, see previous edition for last biography

**WILSON, CLYDE LIVINGSTON,** SOIL PHYSICS. *Current Pos:* RETIRED. *Personal Data:* b Ohio, July 29, 22; m 51, Betty Bosse; c Elizabeth & Craig. *Educ:* Ohio State Univ, BS, 47, BAE, 48, PhD(agron), 52. *Prof Exp:* Asst soils, Ohio State Univ, 48-52; from res agronomist to res specialist, Monsanto Co, 52-72, sr res specialist, 72-79, agron systs mgr, 79-82, agr equip eng mgr, 82-86, litigation consult, 86-87. *Mem:* Am Soc Agron; Am Soc Agr Engrs; Soil Sci Soc Am; Weed Sci Soc Am; Coun Agr Sci & Technol. *Res:* Saturated water flow in tiled lands; chemical soil conditioners; herbicide investigations. *Mailing Add:* 1530 Lynkirk Lane Kirkwood MO 63122

**WILSON, COLON HAYES, JR,** RHEUMATOLOGY, INTERNAL MEDICINE. *Current Pos:* from asst prof to assoc prof rheumatology, 66-73, asst prof phys med, 66-74, PROF MED, MED SCH, EMORY UNIV, 74-, DIR, DIV RHEUMATOLOGY & IMMUNOL, 66- *Personal Data:* b Marshallberg, NC, Apr 10, 32; m 56; c 3. *Educ:* Duke Univ, BA, 52, MD, 56. *Prof Exp:* From intern to asst resident med, Univ Va Hosp, 56-58; resident, Edward J Meyer Mem Hosp, Buffalo, NY, 61-63; res instr, State Univ NY, Buffalo, 64-66. *Concurrent Pos:* Fel, Buffalo Gen Hosp, State Univ NY, Buffalo, 63-66; Nat Inst Arthritis & Metab Dis prog grant, Edward J Meyer Mem Hosp, Buffalo; actg med dir, Arthritis Found, 77-79. *Mem:* Am Fedn Clin Res; Am Rheumatism Asn; Reticuloendothelial Soc; fel Am Col Physicians. *Res:* Significance of various patterns of antinuclear antibody fluorescence with respect to specific diagnosis and prognosis on various collagen vascular diseases; the efficacy of early synovectomy in rheumatoid arthritis in prevention of late deformity and preservation of function. *Mailing Add:* 69 Butler St SE Atlanta GA 30303-3056

**WILSON, COYT TAYLOR,** PLANT PATHOLOGY. *Current Pos:* RETIRED. *Personal Data:* b Fulton, Miss, July 27, 13; m 36, Alma I Brackeen; c Patricia A & Kenneth W. *Educ:* Ala Polytech Inst, BS, 38, MS, 41; Univ Minn, PhD(plant path), 46. *Honors & Awards:* Award named in honor, Coyt T Wilson Distinguished Serv Award, Am Peanut Res & Educ Soc. *Prof Exp:* Instr bot, Ala Polytech Inst, 40-41; instr plant path, Univ Minn, 41-43; asst plant pathologist, Exp Sta, Auburn Univ, 44-47; prof plant path & plant pathologist, 47-51, asst dean, Col Agr & assoc dir, Agr Exp Sta, 51-64; from assoc dir to dir, Va Agr Exp Sta, 64-66; assoc dean, Res Div, Va Polytech Inst & State Univ, 66-71, exec assoc dean, 71-78, dir agr & life sci res, 66-78. *Concurrent Pos:* AID short term res consult, Ministry Agr, Iran, 60, Turkey, 66 & EPakistan, 68. *Res:* Developed control measures for peanut and potato diseases. *Mailing Add:* 2010 Linwood Lane NW Blacksburg VA 24060

**WILSON, CURTIS MARSHALL,** plant biochemistry, for more information see previous edition

**WILSON, CYNTHIA,** CLIMATOLOGY. *Current Pos:* consult climat, Ottawa, 76-87, CONSULT CLIMAT, GILLINGHAM, 88- *Personal Data:* b Gillingham, Eng, Aug 31, 26; Can citizen. *Educ:* Univ London, BA, 47, teachers dipl, 48; McGill Univ, MSc, 58; Laval Univ, PhD, 72. *Honors & Awards:* Darton Prize, Royal Meteorol Soc, 63. *Prof Exp:* Teacher grammar sch, Eng, 48-54; res asst meteorol & climat, Meteorol Res Group, McGill Univ, 54-62; asst prof climat, Inst Geog, Laval Univ, 64-67, assoc prof climat & researcher, Ctr Nordic Studies, 67-75. *Concurrent Pos:* Expert, Cold Regions Res & Eng Lab, US Army, 62-66; contract, Meteorol Serv Can, 66-68. *Mem:* Am Meteorol Soc; Can Meteorol Soc; Arctic Inst NAm; Royal Meteorol Soc. *Res:* Meteorology and climatology of cold regions; climate of Quebec; surface energy exchanges of southeast coast Hudson Bay; historical climatology of Hudson/James Bay and eastern Canada. *Mailing Add:* 90 Holmside Gillingham Kent ME7 4BE England

**WILSON, DANA E,** INTERNAL MEDICINE & CLINICAL GERIATRICS, ENDOCRINOLOGY & METABOLISM. *Current Pos:* from asst prof to assoc prof, 71-85, PROF MED, SCH MED, UNIV UTAH, 85- *Personal Data:* b Chicago, Ill, Oct 5, 37; m 79, Carolyn Flowers; c Catherine, Dana Jr & Stephen. *Educ:* Oberlin Col, AB, 57; Western Res Univ, MD, 62. *Prof Exp:* Intern & asst resident internal med, Boston City Hosp, Mass, 62-64, sr resident, 66-67; clin assoc allergy & infectious dis, NIH, 64-66; asst prof clin nutrit & human metab, Mass Inst Technol, 69-71. *Concurrent Pos:* Fel diabetes & metab, Thorndike Mem Lab, Harvard Med Sch, 67-69. *Mem:* AAAS; Am Fedn Clin Res; Am Diabetes Asn. *Res:* Diabetes and metabolism; lipoproteins and lipid transport. *Mailing Add:* Dept Med Univ Utah Salt Lake City UT 84112. *Fax:* 801-582-8930; *E-Mail:* minerals@xmission.com

**WILSON, DARCY BENOIT,** IMMUNOLOGY, IMMUNOBIOLOGY. *Current Pos:* Assoc, 63-65, from asst prof to assoc prof path & med genetics, 66-74, PROF PATH & HUMAN GENETICS, SCH MED, UNIV PA, 74-; DIR BASIC SCI, LA JOLLA INST EXP MED, SAN DIEGO REGIONAL CANCER CTR, 92- *Personal Data:* b Rhinebeck, NY, May 14, 36; m 57; c 3. *Educ:* Harvard Univ, AB, 58; Univ Pa, PhD(zool), 62. *Prof Exp:* Res fel transplantation immunol, Wistar Inst, Univ Pa, 62-63, res fel med genet, Sch Med, 65-66; Helen Hay Whitney Found fel, 64-67; USPHS career develop award, 67-72. *Mem:* Am Asn Immunol. *Res:* Immunology of tissue transplantation, particularly immunologic behavior of lymphoid cells in vitro and in vivo. *Mailing Add:* Sidney Kimmel Cancer Ctr 3099 Science Park Rd 200 San Diego CA 92121

**WILSON, DAVID BUCKINGHAM,** PROTEIN CHEMISTRY, CELLULASE ENGINEERING. *Current Pos:* from asst prof to assoc prof, 67-83, PROF BIOCHEM, CORNELL UNIV, 83- *Personal Data:* b Cambridge, Mass, Jan 15, 40; m 63, Nancy Heffelfinger; c Allison, Ashley & Laurie. *Educ:* Harvard Univ, BA, 61; Stanford Univ, PhD(biochem), 65. *Prof Exp:* Jane Coffin Childs fel biochem, Sch Med, Johns Hopkins Univ, 65-67. *Mem:* Am Soc Biol Chemists; Am Soc Microbiol; AAAS. *Res:* Regulation of gene expression in microorganisms; bacterial membrane biochemistry and genetic engineering; mechanisms of host cell lysis by bacteriophage lambda; cloning of thermophillic cellulase genes; mechanism of cellulose degredation by bacterial cellulases; metal transport in bacteria. *Mailing Add:* Cornell Univ Biotechnol Bldg Rm 458 Ithaca NY 14853. *Fax:* 607-255-2428

**WILSON, DAVID E,** MATHEMATICS. *Current Pos:* from asst prof to assoc prof, 70-88, PROF MATH, WABASH COL, 88- *Personal Data:* b Meade, Kans, Aug 5, 29; m 56; c 2. *Educ:* Kans State Col, Pittsburg, AB, 51, MS, 54; Univ Kans, PhD(math), 67. *Prof Exp:* Asst prof math, Univ Hawaii, 61-65. *Mem:* Am Math Soc; Math Asn Am. *Res:* Quasiconformal mappings in n-space. *Mailing Add:* Dept Math Wabash Col 301 W Wabash Ave Crawfordsville IN 47933

**WILSON, DAVID F,** BIOCHEMISTRY, OXYGEN METABOLISM IN VIVO & IN VITRO. *Current Pos:* USPHS fel phys biochem, Johnson Res Found, 64-67, Pa Plan scholar, Sch Med, 67-69, res assoc, 67-68, from asst prof to assoc prof, 68-80, PROF BIOCHEM & BIOPHYS, MED SCH, UNIV PA, 80- *Personal Data:* b Wray, Colo, Mar 28, 38; m 62, 87, Anna Pastuszko; c Margaret P & Peter P. *Educ:* Colo State Univ, BS, 59; Ore State Univ, PhD(biochem), 64. *Honors & Awards:* Eli Lilly Award, Am Chem Soc, 71. *Mem:* Am Soc Biol Chemists; Biophys Soc. *Res:* Mitochondrial electron transport and energy conservation; cellular energy metabolism; amino acid neurotransmitter function; regulation of tissue energy metabolism and the oxygen dependence of oxidative phosphorylation; hypoxia/ischemia and reperfusion injury in the brain. *Mailing Add:* Dept Biochem & Biophys Univ Pa Med Sch Philadelphia PA 19104-6059. *Fax:* 215-573-3787

**WILSON, DAVID FRANKLIN,** NEUROPHYSIOLOGY. *Current Pos:* from asst prof to assoc prof, 69-78, PROF ZOOL, MIAMI UNIV, 78- *Personal Data:* b Queens Village, NY, Feb 23, 41; m 65; c 3. *Educ:* Hofstra Univ, BA, 63; Univ Del, MA, 66, PhD(biol sci), 68. *Prof Exp:* USPHS fel, Northwestern Univ, 68-69. *Concurrent Pos:* USPHS grants, 70-72, 73-75 & 87-88 & 89-91. *Mem:* Am Physiol Soc; Soc Neurosci. *Res:* Examination of neuromuscular transmission using intracellular recording techniques. *Mailing Add:* Dept Zool Miami Univ 500 E High St Oxford OH 45056-1602

**WILSON, DAVID GORDON,** GAS-TURBINE & TURBOMACHINERY DESIGN, HUMAN-POWERED VEHICLES & TOOLS. *Current Pos:* assoc prof thermodyn, dynamics & design, 66-71, prof mech eng, 71-94, EMER PROF MECH ENG, MASS INST TECHNOL, 94- *Personal Data:* b Sutton Coldfield, UK, Feb 11, 28; m 88, Ellen C Warner; c John M, Erica (Sears) & Susan S. *Educ:* Univ Birmingham, BSc, 48; Univ Nottingham, PhD(heat transfer), 53. *Honors & Awards:* Hall Prize, Brit Inst Mech Engrs, 54, Weir Prize, 55; IR-100 Prize, 74. *Prof Exp:* Sr res asst fluid mech & heat transfer, Univ Nottingham, 52-53; sr gas turbine engr, Brush Elec Eng Co, Ltd, UK, 53-55; Commonwealth Fund fel, Mass Inst Technol & Harvard Univ, 55-57; sr gas turbine designer, Ruston & Hornsby, Ltd, UK, 57-58; sr lectr thermodyn, fluid mech & mach design, Univ Ibadan, 58-60; tech dir, UK, 60-61, tech dir & vpres, Northern Res & Eng Corp, Mass, 61-66. *Concurrent Pos:* Ed, Human Power. *Mem:* Am Soc Mech Engrs; Brit Inst Mech Engrs; Int Human-Powered-Vehicle Asn; Am Soc Eng Educ. *Res:* Heat transfer and fluid dynamics, especially with regard to turbomachinery; economic and design studies in solid-waste treatment, legislation and transportation and highway safety; solid-waste management; science of human-powered vehicles; turbomachinery design. *Mailing Add:* Mass Inst Technol Rm 3-445 Cambridge MA 02139. *E-Mail:* dgwilson@mit.edu

**WILSON, DAVID J,** PHYSICAL CHEMISTRY. *Current Pos:* prof chem, 69-96, prof environ eng, 77-96, EMER PROF ENVIRON ENG, VANDERBILT UNIV, 96-; SR RES FEL, ECKENFELDER, INC, 96- *Personal Data:* b Ames, Iowa, June 25, 30; m 52; c 5. *Educ:* Stanford Univ, BS, 52; Calif Inst Technol, PhD(chem), 58. *Prof Exp:* From instr to prof chem, Univ Rochester, 57-69. *Concurrent Pos:* Alfred P Sloan fel, 64-66. *Mem:* Am Chem Soc; AAAS. *Res:* Energy transfer in gases; homogeneous gas reactions; pesticide and heavy metal residues; foam flotation; math modelling of unit operations in environmental engineering; hazardous waste site remediation. *Mailing Add:* Eckenfelder Inc 227 French Landing Nashville TN 37228. *Fax:* 615-256-8332

**WILSON, DAVID LOUIS,** NEUROSCIENCES, BIOLOGY OF AGING & BIOLOGY OF MIND & CONSCIOUSNESS. *Current Pos:* From asst prof to prof physiol & biophys, Univ Miami, 72-81, dep dean acad affairs, Med Sch, 82-85, assoc provost res & dean, Grad Sch, 83-85, dean, Col Arts & Sci, 85-91, PROF PHYSIOL & BIOPHYS, MED SCH, UNIV MIAMI, 81-, PROF BIOL, 85-, CHAIR FAC SENATE, 96- *Personal Data:* b Washington, DC, Jan 11, 43; m 67, Margaret Gibbons; c Mariah. *Educ:* Univ Md, College Park, BS, 64; Univ Chicago, PhD(biophys), 69. *Concurrent Pos:* Helen Hay Whitney fel, Calif Inst Technol, 69-72; NIH grant, 72-74, 75-78, 78-81 & 80-86, NSF grant, 82-85 & Am Fedn Aging Res Grant, 93-94. *Mem:* AAAS; Am Physiol Soc; Soc Neurosci; Geront Soc Am. *Res:* Testing theories of aging; studies on the biological and physical basis of mind and consciousness. *Mailing Add:* Dept Biol Univ Miami PO Box 249118 Coral Gables FL 33124. *Fax:* 305-284-3039; *E-Mail:* dwilson@umiami.ir.miami.edu

**WILSON, DAVID MERL,** MYCOTOXIN CONTAMINATION, FUNGAL PHYSIOLOGY. *Current Pos:* from asst prof to assoc prof, 73-82, PROF PLANT PATH, COASTAL PLAIN STA, UNIV GA, 82- *Personal Data:* b Mosca, Colo, May 25, 41; m 66, Susan M Hay; c Keri & Mark. *Educ:* Colo State Univ, BS, 64, MS, 66, PhD(plant path). 68. *Honors & Awards:* Res Award, Sigma Xi, 77. *Prof Exp:* Fel plant path, NC State Univ, 68-69; asst prof bot, Univ Vt, 69-73. *Concurrent Pos:* Assoc referee, Asn Analytical Chemists, 74-; assoc ed, Phytopath J, Am Phytopath Soc, 85-87 & Plant Dis, 90-92. *Mem:* Am Chem Soc; Am Peanut Res & Educ Asn; Am Phytopath Soc; Asn Off Analytical Chemists; Sigma Xi. *Res:* Mycotoxin contamination of foods and feeds; definition of ways fungi grow in and contaminate commodities with toxic fungal metabolites; analytical chemistry and mycology; control and elimination of toxic fungal metabolites from foodstuffs. *Mailing Add:* 702 W 12th St Tifton GA 31794-3309. *Fax:* 912-386-7285

**WILSON, DAVID ORIN,** soil microbiology, plant nutrition, for more information see previous edition

**WILSON, DEBORAH E,** MICROBIOLOGY. *Current Pos:* CHIEF, OCCUP SAFETY & HEALTH BR, DIV SAFETY, NIH, 93- *Personal Data:* b Washington, DC, Jan 19, 56. *Educ:* Mary Washington Col, BS, 78; Univ NC, MPH, 82, PhD(microbiol), 88. *Mailing Add:* Occup Safety & Health Br Bldg 13 3RO4 13 South Dr MSC 5760 Bethesda MD 20892

**WILSON, DELANO D,** ALTTERNATING CURRENT TRANSMISSION. *Current Pos:* RETIRED. *Personal Data:* b Great Falls, Mont, Apr 15, 34; m 59, Marilyn A Harant; c R David, Leslie A & Christian W. *Educ:* Mont State Univ, BS, 59. *Prof Exp:* Analytical engr, Gen Elec, 59-61, engr-in-charge, TNA, 61-64, sr engr, 64-69, mgr alternating current transmission, 69-72, mgr engr studies & proj, 72-74; prin engr, Power Technol Inc, 74-86, pres, 86-94, chmn, 88-95. *Concurrent Pos:* Vpres-treas, Technol Assessment Group, 80-85; pres, Hydropower Technol Inc. *Mem:* Fel Inst Elec & Electronics Engrs; Am Nat Stand Inst; Int Conf Large High Voltage Systs. *Res:* Application of compact transmissions line; application of high phase order transmission. *Mailing Add:* Power Technol Inc PO Box 1058 Schenectady NY 12301

**WILSON, DON ELLIS,** MAMMALOGY, SYSTEMATICS. *Current Pos:* chief, Biol Surv, Nat Mus Natural Hist, 79-90, DIR, BIODIVERSITY PROGS, SMITHSONIAN INST, 90- *Personal Data:* b Davis, Okla, Apr 30, 44; m 62, Kathleen Hayes; c Wendy & Kristy. *Educ:* Univ Ariz, BS, 65; Univ NMex, MS, 67, PhD(biol), 70. *Honors & Awards:* Gerrit S Miller Award, 92. *Prof Exp:* Fel ecol, Univ Chicago, 70-71; zoologist, Nat Fish & Wildlife Lab, 71-73; chief mammal sect, US Fish & Wildlife Serv, 73-79. *Concurrent Pos:* Vis prof, Univ Md, 75, 83 & 84; ed, J Mammal, 76-81. *Mem:* Am Soc Mammalogists (vpres, 84-86, pres, 86-88); AAAS; Soc Syst Zool; Asn Trop Biol (pres, 92). *Res:* Systematics and ecology of new world mammals. *Mailing Add:* Nat Mus Natural Hist Washington DC 20560. *Fax:* 202-786-2934; *E-Mail:* mnhvz050@sivm.si.edu

**WILSON, DONALD ALAN,** BIOCHEMISTRY, MICROBIAL PHYSIOLOGY. *Current Pos:* assoc, 66-67, asst prof, 67-70, ASSOC PROF MICROBIOL, CHICAGO MED SCH, 70- *Personal Data:* b San Francisco, Calif, Sept 16, 30; m 57; c 3. *Educ:* San Jose State Col, BA, 59; Western Res Univ, PhD(microbiol), 65. *Prof Exp:* Fel microbiol, Pioneering Res Div, US Army Natick Labs, 65-66. *Res:* Microbial enzymology. *Mailing Add:* Dept Microbiol Finch Univ Chicago Med Sch 3333 Green Bay Rd North Chicago IL 60064-3037

**WILSON, DONALD ALFRED,** DENDROCHRONOLOGY, ENTOMOLOGY. *Current Pos:* PRES, LAND & BOUNDARY CONSULTS, INC, 78- *Personal Data:* b Greenville, Maine, Mar 31, 41; m 67; c Richard D & Stephen J. *Educ:* Univ Maine, BS, 65; Univ NH, MS, 67. *Honors & Awards:* Surv Excellence Award, Nat Soc Prof Surveyors, Am Cong Surv & Mapping, 84. *Prof Exp:* Instr forestry, Dept Forestry Resources, Univ NH, 67-68; instr forestry surv, Sch Forest Resources & Dept Civil Eng, Univ Maine, 68-74; pres, Border Land Consults, 74-78. *Concurrent Pos:* Lectr, Am Cong Surv & Mapping, 75-87, NH Land Surveyors Asn, 75-, Maine Soc Land Surveyors, 75- & Univ NH, 77- *Mem:* Am Forestry Asn; Coleopterists' Soc; Lorquin Entom Soc. *Res:* Collection and study of Coleoptera, primarily Cicindelidae, Cerambycidae, Cleridae, Scarabaeidae, Carabidae (Elaphrus) and some aquatic families; taxonomy; ecology; taxonomy and parasitology of nymphal cicindelidae. *Mailing Add:* 84 Main St PO Box 322 Newfields NH 03856

**WILSON, DONALD BENJAMIN,** FORAGE CROPS. *Current Pos:* RETIRED. *Personal Data:* b Rowley, Alta, June 12, 25; m 48; c 4. *Educ:* Univ Alta, BSc, 50; Utah State Univ, MS, 54; Ore State Univ, PhD(farm crops), 60. *Prof Exp:* Res officer, Agr Can Res Sta, Lethbridge, 50-68, head, Plant Sci Sect, 68-88. *Concurrent Pos:* Coordr, Forage Crops, chmn, Expert Comt Forage Crops; actg dir, Res Sta, Lethbridge. *Mem:* Can Soc Agron; Agr Inst Can. *Res:* Forage crop production and animal grazing; management of irrigated pastures and administration of agricultural research. *Mailing Add:* 1714 21st St S Lethbridge AB T1K 2H7 Can

**WILSON, DONALD EDWARD,** MEDICAL SCHOOL ADMINISTRATION, GASTROENTEROLOGY. *Current Pos:* DEAN, SCH MED, UNIV MD, 91- *Personal Data:* b Worcester, Mass, Aug 28, 36; m, Patricia Littell; c 4. *Educ:* Harvard Col, BS, 58; Tufts Univ Sch Med, MD, 62. *Prof Exp:* Prof & chmn, Dept Med, State Univ NY Health Sci Ctr, Brooklyn, 80-91. *Concurrent Pos:* Mem, Gen Clin Res Ctr Comt, NIH, 87-91; scholar acad admin & health policy, Asn Acad Health Ctr, 91-93; mem, Proj 3000, 2000 Implementation Comt, Asn Am Med Cols, 92-; mem, Vis Comt, Harvard Sch Pub Health, 92-; mem, Bd Dirs, Alliance End Childhood Lead Poisoning, 92- *Mem:* Inst Med-Nat Acad Sci; Am Gastroenterol Asn; Asn Acad Minority Physicians; Asn Am Physicians; Am Fedn Clin Res. *Res:* Effect of prostaglandins on gastric acid secretion and peptic ulcer disease in man; protective effect of prostaglandins on experimental hepatic damage. *Mailing Add:* Sch Med Univ Md 655 W Baltimore St Rm 14-029 Baltimore MD 21201-1559. *E-Mail:* drwilson@schmedol.ab.umd.edu

**WILSON, DONALD LAURENCE,** medicine; deceased, see previous edition for last biography

**WILSON, DONALD RICHARD,** ORGANIC CHEMISTRY, POLYMER CHEMISTRY. *Current Pos:* PRES, ADVAN POLYMER TECHNOL, INC, NJ, 85- *Personal Data:* b Plaistow, NH, Feb 8, 36; m 56; c 3. *Educ:* Univ Wash, BS, 58; Univ Calif, Los Angeles, PhD(org chem), 62. *Prof Exp:* From res chemist to sr res chemist, E I du Pont de Nemours & Co, Inc, Del, 61-67; sr scientist, Xerox Corp, Webster, 67, res mgr org & polymer chem, 68, develop mgr org & polymer mat, 68-70, technol prog mgr advan xerography, 70-71, prin scientist xerographic mat, 71-72, mgr explor graphic sci, 72-75; res dir chem & catalysis, Celanese Res Co, NJ, 75-82; dir corp res, Pennwalt Corp, Pa, 83; vpres res & secy, Chem Systs Res, Inc, 84. *Mem:* Am Chem Soc; NAm Membrane Soc; Asn Res Dir (pres, 84-85). *Res:* Organic and polymer synthesis-reaction mechanisms; stereochemistry; organometallics; textile fiber chemistry; high temperature fibers; xerography; xerographic imaging materials; membrane systems; conductive polymers; liquid crystal polymers. *Mailing Add:* 1911 Jefferson Davis Hwy CM-1 5-D17 Arlington VA 22202

**WILSON, DONELLA JOYCE,** RED CELL MEMBRANE PROTEINS, HEMOGLOBINAPATHY-SICKLE CELL ANEMIA & MALARIA. *Current Pos:* SCI PROG DIR, AM CANCER SOC, 93- *Personal Data:* b Milwaukee, Wis, July 28, 51. *Educ:* Johnston Col, BA, 73; Purdue Univ, MS, 79, PhD(molecular biol), 81; Tex Southern Univ, MS, 77. *Prof Exp:* Res assoc, Harvard Med Sch, 81-83; fel, Mass Inst Technol, 83-85; assoc prof cell & molecular biol, Meharry Med Col, 85-93. *Concurrent Pos:* Vis asst prof, Univ Mass, 83-85; Mary Ingraham Bunting fel, Radcliffe Col, 83-85; vis scientist, Fedn Am Soc Exp Biol, 87- *Mem:* Am Soc Cell Biol; AAAS; NY Acad Sci; Am Soc Microbiologists. *Res:* Study of red cell development, using the cell surface membrane protein glycophorin as a model, we studied its role in RBC differentiation and its role in malaria and sickle cell anemia. *Mailing Add:* Am Cancer Soc 1599 Clifton Rd NE Atlanta GA 30329-4243. *Fax:* 404-321-4669

**WILSON, DORIS BURDA,** ANATOMY, EMBRYOLOGY. *Current Pos:* assoc prof, 75-77, PROF SURG & ANAT, SCH MED, UNIV CALIF, SAN DIEGO, 77- *Personal Data:* b Cleveland, Ohio, July 1, 37; m 68, Wilfred J. *Educ:* Ohio Wesleyan Univ, BA, 59; Radcliffe Col, MA, 60; Harvard Univ, PhD(biol), 63. *Prof Exp:* Teaching fel biol, Harvard Univ, 60-62; asst prof zool, San Diego State Col, 63-65; asst prof anat, Sch Med, Stanford Univ, 65-69; res anatomist & lectr, Sch Med, Univ Calif, San Diego, 69-73; assoc prof anat, Sch Med, Univ Calif, Davis, 73-75. *Concurrent Pos:* Fulbright vis prof, Taiwan, 70-71. *Mem:* AAAS; Histochem Soc; Teratology Soc; Am Soc Zool; Am Asn Anat. *Res:* Developmental biology; neuroembryology; teratology. *Mailing Add:* Dept Surg/Anat 0604 Univ Calif San Diego La Jolla CA 92093-0604

**WILSON, DWIGHT ELLIOTT, JR,** GENETICS. *Current Pos:* RETIRED. *Personal Data:* b Greensburg, Pa, June 7, 32; m 53; c 4. *Educ:* Yale Univ, BS, 53, PhD(biophys), 56. *Prof Exp:* From asst prof to assoc prof, Rensselaer Polytech Inst, 56-68, prof biol, 68-, chmn, Dept Biol, 87- *Concurrent Pos:* NIH fel, 66-67. *Mem:* Am Soc Human Genetics; AAAS. *Res:* Somatic cell genetics. *Mailing Add:* 14 Tides End Lane Orleans MA 02653

**WILSON, EDMOND WOODROW, JR,** PHYSICAL CHEMISTRY. *Current Pos:* from asst prof to assoc prof, 70-79, PROF PHYS CHEM, HARDING UNIV, 79- *Personal Data:* b Selma, Ala, Jan 18, 40; m 65, Elizabeth Kennemer; c Stephanie J. *Educ:* Auburn Univ, BS, 62; Univ Ala, Tuscaloosa, MS, 65, PhD(phys chem), 68. *Prof Exp:* Temporary instr gen chem, Univ Ala, Tuscaloosa, 66-68; res assoc biophys chem, Univ Va, 68-70. *Concurrent Pos:* Vis assoc prof, Okla State Univ, 77. *Mem:* Am Chem Soc; Sigma Xi; Calorimetry Conf. *Res:* Calorimetry and spectroscopy of biological molecules containing transition metal ions; synthesis and characterization of luminescent ruthenium compounds. *Mailing Add:* 100 Red Oak Lane Searcy AR 72143-0001. *Fax:* 501-279-4706; *E-Mail:* wilson@acs.harding.edu

**WILSON, EDWARD L,** FINITE ELEMENTS, COMPUTERS. *Current Pos:* RETIRED. *Personal Data:* b Ferndale, Calif, Sept 5, 31. *Educ:* Univ Calif, Berkeley, BS, 54, MS, 59, DEng(civil eng), 63. *Prof Exp:* Sr res engr, Aerojet Gen Corp, 63-65; from asst prof to prof civil eng, Univ Calif, Berkeley, 65-88. *Mem:* Nat Acad Eng; Am Soc Civil Engrs. *Mailing Add:* Dept Civil Eng Univ Calif Berkeley CA 94720

**WILSON, EDWARD MATTHEW,** RESEARCH ADMINISTRATION. *Current Pos:* DEP ADMINR, COOP STATE RES SERV, USDA, 88- *Personal Data:* b Retreat, Jamaica, Dec 19, 37; US citizen; m 62, Celia E Smith; c Mark S & Joni-Louise. *Educ:* McGill Univ, BS, 64, MS, 66; Ohio State Univ, PhD(dairy sci), 69. *Honors & Awards:* Meritorious Exec Presidential Rank, US Pres, 92. *Prof Exp:* Asst prof, Tuskegee Univ, 69-73; prin physiologist, Coop State Res Serv, 73-74; dean, Coop Res & Exten, Lincoln Univ, 74-85, dean, Col Appl Sci & Technol, 80-85. *Concurrent Pos:* Sr scientist, Devres Inc, 84; dir, Livestock Mgt Prog, USAID. *Res:* Immunogenetic variation of cattle breeds; genetic polymorphisms in blood serum transferrins and certain milk proteins; immunochemical studies of bovine seminal plasma proteins. *Mailing Add:* USDA/Coop State Res Educ & Exten Agr Box 2220 Washington DC 20250-2220. *Fax:* 202-401-4888

**WILSON, EDWARD NATHAN,** RIEMANNIAN GEOMETRY, SCIENCE POLICY. *Current Pos:* from instr to assoc prof, Washington Univ, 68-87, dean, Grad Sch Art & Sci, 83-93, dean, Univ Col, 86-88, PROF, WASHINGTON UNIV, 87-, CHMN, MATH DEPT, 95- *Personal Data:* b Warsaw, NY, Dec 2, 41; m 41, Mary K Schooling; c Nathan & Emily. *Educ:* Cornell Univ, BA, 63; Stanford Univ, MS, 65; Washington Univ, PhD(math), 71. *Prof Exp:* Instr, Woodrow Wilson intern prog, Ft Valley State Col, 65-67, Univ Calif, 70-71, Brandeis Univ, 71-73. *Mem:* Am Math Soc; Math Asn Am. *Res:* Lie theory specifically in differential geometry and harmonic analysis; structure of homogeneous Reimannian manifolds with non-positive currature; study of Riemannian Nilmanifolds which are isospectral but not isometric. *Mailing Add:* Math Dept Washington Univ Campus Box 1146 St Louis MO 63130. *Fax:* 314-935-6839; *E-Mail:* enwilson@math.wustl.edu

**WILSON, EDWARD OSBORNE,** BEHAVIORAL BIOLOGY. *Current Pos:* Soc Fels jr fel, Harvard Univ, 53-56, from asst prof to prof zool, 56-76, Frank B Baird Jr prof sci, 76-90, Mellon prof sci, 90-94, PELLEGRINO UNIV PROF, HARVARD UNIV, 94- *Personal Data:* b Birmingham, Ala, June 10, 29; m 55, Irene Kelley; c Catherine I. *Educ:* Univ Ala, BS, 49, MS, 50; Harvard Univ, PhD(biol), 55. *Hon Degrees:* Numerous from US & foreign univs & cols. *Honors & Awards:* Cleveland Prize, AAAS, 67; Mercer Award, Ecol Soc Am, 71; Founders' Mem Award, Entom Soc Am, 72; Nat Med of Sci, 76; Leidy Medal, 78; Carr Medal, 78; Pulitzer Prize, Gen Nonfiction, 79 & 91; Tyler Prize, Environ Achievement, 84; L O Howard Award, Entom Soc Am, 85; Nat Zool Park Medal, 87; Ecol Inst Prize, Ger, 87; Crafoord Prize, Royal Swed Acad, 90; Gold Medal World Wide Fund Nature, 90; Henry Shaw Medal, Mo Bot Garden, 93; Int Prize Biol, Govt Japan, 93. *Prof Exp:* Biologist, State Dept Conserv, Ala, 49. *Concurrent Pos:* Mem expeds, WIndies & Mex, 53, New Caledonia, 54, Australia & New Guinea, 55, Ceylon, 55 & Surinam, 61; Charles and Martha Hitchcock Prof, Univ Calif, Berkeley, 72; John Simon Guggenheim fel, 77, Comt Selection, 82-; bd dir, World Wildlife Fund, 84-90. *Mem:* Nat Acad Sci; fel Am Acad Arts & Sci;

fel Am Philos Soc; Soc Study Evolution (pres, 73); Am Genetic Asn; German Acad Sci; hon mem Brit Ecol Soc; Acad Humanism; Royal Soc London. *Res:* Classification, ecology and behavior of ants; specialization; general sociobiology; chemical communication in animals; biogeography. *Mailing Add:* Mus Comp Zool Harvard Univ Cambridge MA 02138. *Fax:* 617-495-2315

**WILSON, ELIZABETH ALLEN,** PETROLEUM GEOLOGY, COASTAL GEOLOGY. *Current Pos:* OWNER, METHANE RESOURCES GROUP, LLC, 80- *Personal Data:* b Bridgeport, Conn, Jan 6, 50; m, John T; c Edward A. *Educ:* Mt Holyoke Col, AB, 72; Univ Del, MS, 74, PhD(geol), 78. *Prof Exp:* Geologist petrol, Shell Oil Co, 77-80. *Mem:* Am Asn Petrol Geologists; Soc Econ Paleontologists & Mineralogists; Int Asn Sedimentologists; Sigma Xi. *Res:* Coal bed methane; sequence stratigraphy; Depositional environment; coal bed methane. *Mailing Add:* 720 Emerson St Denver CO 80218

**WILSON, ELIZABETH MARY,** MOLECULAR BIOLOGY. *Current Pos:* ASSOC PROF ENDOCRINOL, UNIV NC, 83- *Educ:* Vanderbilt Univ, PhD(biochem), 74. *Res:* Endocrinology; gene regulation. *Mailing Add:* Dept Pediat & Biochem Univ NC MacNider Bldg CB 7500 Rm 374 Med Sci Bldg Chapel Hill NC 27599-7500. *Fax:* 919-966-2203

**WILSON, ELWOOD JUSTIN, JR,** ORGANIC CHEMISTRY. *Current Pos:* PRES, HERBTEC, INC, 82- *Personal Data:* b New York, NY, Nov 28, 17; m 41; c 4. *Educ:* Princeton Univ, AB, 38, MA, 40, PhD(chem), 41. *Prof Exp:* Corn Industs Res Found fel, NIH, 41-42; proj engr, Sperry Gyroscope Co, NY, 42-44; sr chemist, Exp, Inc, 46-47, secy, 47-49, vpres, 49-54; res dir, Detroit Controls Co, 54-59; pres, Adv Tech Labs Div, Am-Standard, 59-64; pres, E J Wilson Assocs, Inc, 64-; pres, Epoxon Prods, Inc, 71-82. *Concurrent Pos:* Vpres, Flight Res, Inc, 53-54; chmn & dir, Data Cartridge, Inc, 65-67. *Mem:* AAAS; Am Chem Soc. *Res:* Proteins; carbohydrates; fuels; combustion; synthetic organic chemistry; interior ballistics; rockets; petrochemicals; aerospace instruments; nuclear reactors; general and technical management; building specialties. *Mailing Add:* PO Box 7617 Menlo Park CA 94028

**WILSON, ERIC LEROY,** MATHEMATICS. *Current Pos:* From instr to prof math, 62-96, chmn dept, 73-76 & 78-81, EMER PROF MATH, WITTENBERG UNIV, 96- *Personal Data:* b Sharon, Pa, Mar 17, 35; m 59; c 2. *Educ:* Westminster Col, Pa, BS, 57; Vanderbilt Univ, PhD(math), 66. *Concurrent Pos:* Asst prof, Univ South, 67-68; prof, Univ Essex, Eng, 81-82; vis scholar, Vanderbilt Univ, 84, 85 & 86. *Mem:* Math Asn Am; Nat Speleol Soc. *Res:* Loop isotopy; graph theory. *Mailing Add:* 115 Cumberland Ave S Rugby TN 37733

**WILSON, EUGENE M,** PLANT PATHOLOGY. *Current Pos:* PROF GEOG, UNIV SOUTHERN ALA. *Personal Data:* b Buckhannon, WVa, May 4, 28; m 51; c 2. *Educ:* Univ WVa, BS, 51, MS, 54; Univ Calif, PhD(plant path), 58. *Prof Exp:* Asst plant path, Univ WVa, 51 & Univ Calif, 54-58; plant pathologist, Cent Res Lab, United Fruit Co, Mass, 58-60; technologist, Shell Chem Co, 60-72; plant pathologist pesticide regulation, US Environ Protection Agency, 72-73, chief plant path sect, Off Pesticide Progs, 73-74, prod mgr, 74- *Mem:* Am Phytopath Soc. *Res:* Physiology of fungi; plant disease control; host parasite relationship; biological control of plant pests. *Mailing Add:* Dept Geog & Geol Univ Southern Ala 307 University Dr Mobile AL 36688-0001

**WILSON, EUGENE MADISON,** CIVIL ENGINEERING. *Current Pos:* assoc prof, 74-79, PROF CIVIL ENG, UNIV WYO, 79-; DIR, WYO TECHNOL TRANSFER CTR. *Personal Data:* b Cheyenne, Wyo, July 25, 43; m 65, Lelia L Clarkson; c James S, Eugene J & Tracy L (Brown). *Educ:* Univ Wyo, BS, 65, MS, 66; Ariz State Univ, PhD(civil eng, transp), 72. *Prof Exp:* Petrol engr, Texaco, Inc, 66-67; instr civil eng & staff asst transp, Ariz State Univ, 68-69; transp planner, Ariz Hwy Dept, 69-70; asst prof civil eng & res assoc transp, Univ Iowa, 70-74. *Concurrent Pos:* Mem, Transp Res Bd, Nat Acad Sci-Nat Res Coun. *Mem:* Am Soc Civil Engrs; Am Planning Asn; Inst Transp Engrs. *Res:* traffic assignment; public transportation planning; behavioral and sensitivity studies in transportation; traffic engineering operations and safety. *Mailing Add:* Dept Civil Eng PO Box 3295 Laramie WY 82071

**WILSON, EVELYN H,** organic chemistry, for more information see previous edition

**WILSON, EVERETT D,** PHYSIOLOGY, ENDOCRINOLOGY. *Current Pos:* assoc prof, 62-64, dean, Col Sci, 65-79, PROF, SAM HOUSTON STATE UNIV, 64- *Personal Data:* b Covington, Ind, July 13, 28; div; c 4. *Educ:* Ind State Teachers Col, BS, 50, MS, 51; Purdue Univ, PhD(physiol, endocrinol), 60. *Prof Exp:* Teacher pub sch, Ind, 48-50 & 55-56, supvr, 56-57; asst biol, Purdue Univ, 57-58, res asst, 58-60; asst prof zool, Southern Ill Univ, 60-61. *Concurrent Pos:* Lalor res fel, 61; NATO fel, Nat Med Res Inst, 62; chief, Grants Br Pop & Reproduction Ctr, Nat Inst Child Health, NIH, 71-72; adv, Oak Ridge Pop Res Inst, 72-74. *Mem:* Am Soc Zoologists; Endocrine Soc; Am Soc Animal Sci; Brit Soc Study Fertil. *Res:* Factors affecting mammalian reproduction. *Mailing Add:* Dept Sci Sam Houston State Univ Huntsville TX 77341

**WILSON, EWEN M,** AGRICULTURAL ECONOMICS. *Current Pos:* DIV CHIEF, AGR & FINANCIAL STATIST, US DEPT COMMERCE, 94- *Personal Data:* b Kenya, Africa, July 29, 44. *Educ:* Univ London, BS, 65; WVa Univ, MA, 70; NC State Univ PhD(econ), 73. *Mem:* Am Agr Econ Asn; Nat Asn Bus Economists. *Mailing Add:* Agr & Financial Statist Div Dept Commerce 437 Iverson Mall Washington DC 20233

**WILSON, F WESLEY, JR,** MATHEMATICS, ATMOSPHERIC SCIENCES. *Current Pos:* TECH STAFF, LINCOLN LAB, MASS INST TECHNOL, 90- *Personal Data:* b Washington, DC, Apr 22, 39. *Educ:* Univ Md, College Park, BS, 61, PhD(math), 64. *Prof Exp:* Res assoc math, Div Appl Math, Brown Univ, 64-66; asst prof, Univ Mich, Ann Arbor, 66-67; from asst prof to prof math, Univ Colo, Boulder, 67; quant analyst, Nat Ctr Atmospheric Res, Boulder, 87-90. *Concurrent Pos:* Vis assoc prof, Univ Md, College Park, 70-71. *Mem:* Soc Indust & Appl Math; Am Meteorol Soc. *Res:* Applications of differential topology to problems of nonlinear ordinary differential equations; numerical methods for solving differential equations, multidimensional interpolation and applications in meterology and geophysical data analysis. *Mailing Add:* 49 Circle Dr Waltham MA 02154

**WILSON, FOREST RAY, II,** HUMAN PHYSIOLOGY, GERONTOLOGY. *Current Pos:* From asst prof to assoc prof, 73-89, PROF PHYSIOL, BAYLOR UNIV, 89- *Personal Data:* b Wichita Falls, Tex, Aug 1, 41. *Educ:* Tex Wesleyan Col, BA, 66; Tex Christian Univ, MS, 69; Univ Ill, PhD(physiol), 73. *Concurrent Pos:* Prin investr, Monsanto Found Cancer Res grant, 77-; dir, Masters Clin Geront Prog, Baylor Univ, prof, Inst Biomed Studies. *Mem:* AAAS; Am Zool Soc; Sigma Xi; Isozyme Soc. *Res:* Effects of cations on atherogenesis; many physiological problems faced by man including prostaglandins, extra-renal sites of erythropoietin production, lethality of megadoses of vitamines. *Mailing Add:* PO Box 97388 Baylor Univ Waco TX 76798-7388. *Fax:* 254-755-2969; *E-Mail:* ray__wilson@baylor.edu

**WILSON, FRANK B,** SPEECH, AUDIOLOGY. *Current Pos:* RETIRED. *Personal Data:* b Detroit, Mich, Jan 8, 29; m 50; c 7. *Educ:* Bowling Green Univ, BS, 50; Northwestern Univ, PhD, 56. *Prof Exp:* Speech & hearing clinician, Cerebral Palsy Ctr, Ohio, 51-53, actg dir, 52-53; res asst, Lang Inst, Northwestern Univ, 55-57; asst prof speech, St Louis Univ, 57-59; coordr speech & hearing, Spec Dist for Educ & Training Handicapped Children, St Louis Co, Mo, 59-65; dir, Div Speech Path, Dept Otolaryngol, Jewish Hosp St Louis, Mo, 66-72; dir res, Spec Sch Dist St Louis Co, 73-77; prof & dean rehab med, Univ Alta, 77- *Concurrent Pos:* Consult, US Off Res, 63-; assoc prof, Wash Univ, 68. *Mem:* Fel Am Speech & Hearing Asn; Am Cleft Palate Asn. *Res:* Articulatory behavior of the retarded child and the efficacy of speech therapy; hearing deviation among orthopedically handicapped children; basis of nonorganic articulation disorders in children; voice disorders in school-age children. *Mailing Add:* 2011 36th St Bellingham WA 98226

**WILSON, FRANK CHARLES,** POLYMER CHEMISTRY, X-RAY CRYSTALLOGRAPHY. *Current Pos:* RETIRED. *Personal Data:* b Ironwood, Mich, June 29, 27; m 50; c 3. *Educ:* Ripon Col, AB, 52; Mass Inst Technol, BS, 52, PhD(phys chem), 57. *Prof Exp:* Res assoc, Polymer Prod Dept, E I Du Pont De Nemours & Co Inc, 57- *Mem:* Am Chem Soc; Am Crystallog Asn. *Res:* Structure and morphology of polymers and polymer blends by wide-angle and small-angle x-ray diffraction techniques. *Mailing Add:* 1410 Emory Rd Wilmington DE 19803

**WILSON, FRANK CRANE,** MEDICINE, ORTHOPEDIC SURGERY. *Current Pos:* from instr to prof, 64-92, KENAN PROF ORTHOP SURG, SCH MED, UNIV NC, CHAPEL HILL, 92- *Personal Data:* b Rome, Ga, Dec 29, 29; m 51, Ann; c Jennifer, Anna & Robin. *Educ:* Vanderbilt Univ, AB, 50; Med Col Ga, MD, 54; Am Bd Orthop Surg, dipl, 67. *Honors & Awards:* Nicholas Andry Award, 72; Thomas Jefferson Award, 92. *Prof Exp:* Instr orthop surg, Columbia Univ, 63. *Concurrent Pos:* Markle scholar, 66-71; chief, Div Orthop Surg, NC Mem Hosp, 67- *Mem:* Am Col Surg; Asn Am Med Col; Am Acad Orthop Surgeons; Am Orthop Asn; Acad Orthop Soc. *Res:* Trauma; infections of bones and joints; arthritis. *Mailing Add:* Univ NC Sch Med 266 Burnett Womack Bldg Chapel Hill NC 27599

**WILSON, FRANK DOUGLAS,** PLANT GENETICS, PLANT TAXONOMY. *Current Pos:* plant geneticist, 57-93, BIOL SCI COLLABR, WESTERN COTTON RES LAB, AGR RES SERV, USDA, 93- *Personal Data:* b Salt Lake City, Utah, Dec 17, 28; m 50, Beverly A Urry; c Kerry, Leslie, Eileen, John, Gregory, Cynthia, Angela & David. *Educ:* Univ Utah, BS, 50, MS, 53; Wash State Univ, PhD(bot), 57. *Honors & Awards:* Cotton Genetics Award, Nat Cotton Coun Am, 92. *Prof Exp:* Asst biol & genetics, Univ Utah, 51-53; asst bot, Wash State Univ, 53-56, asst agron, 56, jr animal scientist, 56-57. *Concurrent Pos:* Consult, Agron Exp Sta, Int Coop Admin, Cuba, 59-; plant explor, Puerto Rico, 74, EAfrica, 75 & Galapagos Islands, 85; vis scientist, CSIRO, Canberra, Australia, 94- *Mem:* Asn Taxon Study Trop African Flora. *Res:* Insect resistance in cotton; taxonomy of Hibiscus section Furcaria. *Mailing Add:* USDA Western Cotton Res Lab Cotton & Insect Unit 4135 E Broadway Rd Phoenix AZ 85040. *Fax:* 602-379-4509; *E-Mail:* fwilson@asrr.arsusda.gov

**WILSON, FRANK JOSEPH,** ANATOMY, CELL BIOLOGY. *Current Pos:* from asst prof to assoc prof anat, 72-87, PROF NEUROSCI & CELL BIOL, ROBERT WOOD JOHNSON MED SCH, UNIV MED & DENT NJ, 87- *Personal Data:* b Pittsburgh, Pa; c 2. *Educ:* St Vincent Col, BA, 64; Univ Pittsburgh, PhD(anat, cell biol), 69. *Prof Exp:* Muscular Dystrophy Asn fel, Univ Birmingham, 70-72. *Mem:* Am Asn Anatomists; AAAS; Am Soc Cell

Biol; Soc Neurosci. *Res:* Immunochemistry and biochemistry of the contractile proteins. *Mailing Add:* Dept Neurosci & Cell Biol Robert Wood Johnson Med Sch 675 Hoes Lane Piscataway NJ 08854-5635. *Fax:* 732-463-4029

**WILSON, FRED E,** ENDOCRINOLOGY. *Current Pos:* asst prof zool, 65-71, assoc prof biol, 71-90, PROF BIOL, KANS STATE UNIV, 90- *Personal Data:* b Lenexa, Kans, Dec 23, 37; m 61; c 1. *Educ:* Univ Kans, BA, 58, MA, 60; Wash State Univ, PhD(zoophysiol), 65. *Prof Exp:* Instr biol, Lewis & Clark Col, 60-61. *Concurrent Pos:* Physiologist, Agr Exp Sta, Kans State Univ, 65-79; consult, Oak Ridge Grad Sch Biomed Sci, Univ Tenn, 78. *Mem:* Fel AAAS; Am Soc Zoologists; Int Soc Neuroendrocinol; Endocrine Soc; Soc Study Reproduction. *Res:* Avian reproductive physiology; neuroendocrine control of annual reproductive cycles; photoperiodism. *Mailing Add:* 2016 Somerset Sq Manhattan KS 66503

**WILSON, FRED LEE,** INTERNET & WEB DEVELOPMENT, THEORETICAL PHYSICS. *Current Pos:* PRES, PHYSICS ORG, 96- *Personal Data:* b Detroit, Mich, Sept 5, 38; m 67, Jimmie Joan Bennett; c Robert Bennett & Joel Frederich. *Educ:* Murray State Univ, BA, 59; Univ Kans, PhD(physics), 64. *Prof Exp:* Analyst, US Army Sci & Technol Ctr, 65-66; sr res, Exxon Prod Res, 66-69; prof physics & sci policy, Rochester Inst Technol, 69-96. *Concurrent Pos:* Foreign expert, Shanghai Univ Technol, 87 & 89. *Mem:* Am Phys Soc; Sigma Xi. *Res:* Organization of scientific information and telecommunications technology to support and facilitate international cooperation in science. *Mailing Add:* PO Box 60207 San Angelo TX 76906. *Fax:* 716-383-8854; *E-Mail:* flwgsh@ritvax.isc.rit.edu

**WILSON, FREDERICK ALLEN,** GASTROENTEROLOGY. *Current Pos:* PROF, DEPT MED GASTROENTEROL, MED SCH, UNIV SC. *Personal Data:* b Winchester, Mass, Aug 22, 37; m 62; c 2. *Educ:* Colgate Univ, Hamilton, NY, 59; Albany Med Col, NY, MD, 63. *Prof Exp:* Intern med, Hartford Hosp, Conn, 63-64, residency, 64-66; fel gastroenterol, Albany Med Col, NY, 66-67; chief gastroenterol, US Army Hosp, Ft Jackson, SC, 67-69; fel gastroenterol, Southwestern Med Sch, Univ Tex, Dallas, 69-72; asst prof med, Vanderbilt Univ, Nashville, 72-76, assoc prof, 76-82; prof med, Milton S Hershey Med Ctr, Pa State Univ, Hershey, 82- *Mem:* Am Gastroenterol Asn; Am Fedn Clin Res; Am Asn Study Liver Dis; Am Soc Clin Invest. *Res:* Gastroenterology involving the cellular and subcellular aspects of bile acid intestinal transport. *Mailing Add:* Dept Med Gastroent Rm 916 Clin Sci Bldg Univ SC Med Sch 171 Ashley Ave Charleston SC 29425

**WILSON, FREDERICK SUTPHEN,** FAMILY MEDICINE. *Current Pos:* RETIRED. *Personal Data:* b Trenton, NJ, Feb 12, 27; m 50; c 3. *Educ:* Dickinson Col, ScB, 48; Thomas Jefferson Univ, MD, 53. *Prof Exp:* Dir clin invest, McNeil Labs, 69-71, dir med serv, 71-74; asst prof community med, Med Ctr, Temple Univ, 74-95. *Concurrent Pos:* Physician-in-chief & dir, Family Pract Ctr/Family Pract Residency Prog, Abington Mem Hosp, 74-; med dir, William H Rorea, Inc, 76- *Mailing Add:* 1338 Jercho Rd Abington PA 19001

**WILSON, G DENNIS,** EXERCISE PHYSIOLOGY, SPORTS MEDICINE. *Current Pos:* PROF INTERDEPT PHYSIOL, AUBURN UNIV, 73-, HEAD, DEPT HEALTH & HUMAN PERFORMANCE, 81- *Personal Data:* b Jackson, Tenn, Sept 20, 46; m 67, Dianne Jacobs; c Trenton Jacobs. *Educ:* Union Univ, Jackson, Tenn, BS, 68; Univ Tenn, Knoxville, MS, 70, EdD, 73. *Prof Exp:* Teacher-coach biol & phys educ, Oak Ridge High Sch, Orlando, Fla, 68-69 & teacher-coach phys educ, West High Sch, Knoxville, Tenn, 69-70; instr, Univ Tenn, Knoxville, 70-73. *Concurrent Pos:* Pres, Southeastern Am Col Sports Med, 77-78; chmn res coun, Southern Dist, Am Alliance Health Phys Educ, Recreation & Dance, 79-80 & Position Stands Rev Panel, Nat Fitness Test Rev Comt, Res Consortium, 83-; chmn continuing educ coun, Am Col Sports Med, 80-83; lectr, US Sports Acad, Saudi Arabia & Bahran, 83 & Am Col Sports Med, People to People Prog, People's Repub China, 85; mem exec coun, Int Coun Sports Sci & Phys Educ; chmn, Comt Competitive Safeguards & Med Aspects of Sports, Nat Col Athletic Asn. *Mem:* Fel Am Col Sports Med; fel Am Alliance Health, Phys Educ & Dance. *Res:* Use of exercise and training to minimize disease processes such as CHD and obesity, and maximize performance with special emphasis on cardiovascular and metabolic responses to resistive forms of training. *Mailing Add:* Dept Health & Human Performance MC 2050 Auburn Univ Auburn AL 36849. *Fax:* 334-844-4025

**WILSON, GARY AUGUST,** MOLECULAR GENETICS, MICROBIOLOGY. *Current Pos:* dir microbiol res, 80-87, corp dir sci & technol, 87-91, DIR SCI & TECHNOL PHARM RES, MILES INC, 91- *Personal Data:* b Chicago, Ill, Dec 13, 42; m 65; c 1. *Educ:* Ill State Univ, Normal, BS, 65; Univ Chicago, MS, 68, PhD(microbiol), 70. *Prof Exp:* Fel, Sch Med, Univ Rochester, 70-72, from instr to asst prof microbiol, 72-78, assoc prof, 78-80. *Concurrent Pos:* Am Cancer Soc res grant, 72-, fac res award, 79; vis asst prof, Inst Gulbenkian de Ciencia, Portugal, 74, vis prof, 76; mem biotechnol adv comt, Pharmaceut Mfg Asn, 89- *Mem:* Am Soc Microbiol; AAAS; Sigma Xi. *Res:* DNA mediated transformation in Bacillus subtilis; restriction endonucleases; gene cloning. *Mailing Add:* 345 St Ronan St New Haven CT 06511

**WILSON, GEOFFREY LEONARD,** ACOUSTICS. *Current Pos:* RETIRED. *Personal Data:* b London, Eng, Oct 26, 24; nat US; m 55; c 2. *Educ:* Oxford Univ, BA, 45, MSc, & MA, 49; Loughborough Univ, PhD, 75. *Honors & Awards:* Centennial Medal, Inst Elec & Electronics Engrs, 84. *Prof Exp:* Sci off, Royal Naval Sci Serv, Brit Admiralty, Clarendon Lab, Oxford Univ,

44-48, H M Underwater Detection Estab, 48-51 & Torpedo Exp Estab, 52-53; design engr, Can Westinghouse Co, Ont, 53-59; from asst prof to assoc prof eng res, Pa State Univ, 59-85; BP Am distinguished prof math & physics, Johnson C Smith Univ, 85-90. *Concurrent Pos:* Vis res fel, Loughborough Univ Technol, Eng, 68-69; mem, Grad Fac Acoust, Pa State Univ, 75-85; vis scientist, Inst Nat Sci Appliquees, Lyon, France, 82. *Mem:* Acoust Soc Am; fel Audio Eng Soc; sr mem Inst Elec & Electronics Engrs; fel Brit Inst Elec Engrs; fel Brit Inst Acoust. *Res:* Acoustics, especially underwater acoustics and transducer and array design. *Mailing Add:* 441 W Nittany Ave State College PA 16801-4057. *E-Mail:* glw4@psu.edu

**WILSON, GEORGE PETER,** INDUSTRIAL & MANUFACTURING ENGINEERING. *Current Pos:* asst prof, 67-75, ASSOC PROF INDUST ENG, TECH UNIV NS, 75-, DEPT HEAD, 76- *Personal Data:* b Truro, NS, Dec 8, 39; m 67; c 4. *Educ:* Tech Univ, NS, BEng, 62; Univ Birmingham, Eng, MSc, 64. *Prof Exp:* Indust engr, Can Nat Railways, 65-67. *Concurrent Pos:* Asst dir, Atlantic Indust Res Inst, 65-76, dir, 76-; pres, Wilson Fuel Co Ltd, 74- & Appl Comput Systs Ltd, 75-, Wentworth Valley Develop Ltd. *Mem:* Inst Indust Engrs; Can Opers Res Inst; fel Eng Inst Can. *Res:* Development of industrial engineering technology for application in smaller sized industry. *Mailing Add:* PO Box 1000 Halifax NS B3J 2X4 Can

**WILSON, GEORGE PORTER, III,** VETERINARY SURGERY, ANATOMY. *Current Pos:* RETIRED. *Personal Data:* b Flint, Mich, Nov 10, 27; c 4. *Educ:* Univ Ill, BS, 51; Univ Pa, VMD, 55; Ohio State Univ, MSc, 59. *Prof Exp:* Intern vet med, Angell Mem Animal Hosp, 55-56; from instr to prof vet clin sci, Col Vet Med, Ohio State Univ, 55-88, prof microbiol, 67-87. *Concurrent Pos:* Ohio State Univ Develop Fund grant, 67-; Mark Morris Found grant, 68; Am Cancer Soc instnl grant, 68-69; vis scientist, Nat Cancer Inst, Environ Epidemiol Br, 78 & Armed Forces Inst Path, 79. *Mem:* AAAS; Am Vet Med Asn; Am Col Vet Surg; NY Acad Sci. *Res:* Veterinary surgery, especially cancer research as related to immunology and epidemiology. *Mailing Add:* PO Box 141127 Columbus OH 43214

**WILSON, GEORGE RODGER,** AGRICULTURE, ANIMAL SCIENCE. *Current Pos:* RETIRED. *Personal Data:* b Commercial Point, Ohio, July 10, 23; m 46; c 4. *Educ:* Ohio State Univ, BS, 48, MS, 56, PhD(animal sci), 63. *Prof Exp:* Co agent, Butler Co, Ohio, 48-54; from asst prof to prof animal sci, Ohio State Univ, 54-85. *Mem:* Am Soc Animal Sci. *Res:* Animal breeding, physiology and production. *Mailing Add:* 1767 Glen Ave Columbus OH 43212

**WILSON, GEORGE SPENCER,** BIOCHEMISTRY. *Current Pos:* PROF CHEM & PHARMACEUT CHEM, UNIV KANS, 87- *Personal Data:* b Bronxville, NY, May 23, 39; m 64. *Educ:* Princeton Univ, BA, 61; Univ Ill, MS, 63, PhD, 65. *Prof Exp:* NIH fel, Univ Ill, 65-66, instr, 66-67; asst prof, Univ Ariz, 67-72, assoc prof, 72-80, prof chem, 80-87. *Mem:* Fel AAAS; Sigma Xi; Electrochem Soc. *Res:* Analytical applications of biochemical reactions; electrochemical synthesis of unusual or unstable products; flow injection analysis; immunology. *Mailing Add:* 625 N 750 Rd Lawrence KS 66047-9560

**WILSON, GERALD GENE,** CHEMICAL ENGINEERING, GAS TECHNOLOGY. *Current Pos:* RETIRED. *Personal Data:* b Blue Hill, Nebr, Mar 18, 28; m 52, Philomene V Grens; c Virginia A, Diana M, Fredrick P & Thomas M. *Educ:* Univ Kans, BS, 49; Ill Inst Technol, MS & MGas Tech, 51. *Honors & Awards:* Award of Merit, Am Gas Asn, 66, Louis A Sarkes Mem Award, 89, Silver Award Merit, 92. *Prof Exp:* Engr, North Shore Gas Co, 51-55; assoc chem engr, Inst Gas Technol, Ill Inst Technol, 55-56, supvr dist res, 56-60, sr dist engr, 60-63, coordr indust educ, 63-65, mgr indust educ, 65-69, asst dir educ, 69-77, dir indust educ, 77-93. *Concurrent Pos:* Mem subcomt on distribution design & develop, Oper Sect, Am Gas Asn, 62- *Res:* Internal pipeline coatings; sealants for cast iron bell joints; gas industry leak control technology; techniques for solution of network flow problems; pipeline flow behavior; engineering economics. *Mailing Add:* 2307 Buckingham Ave Westchester IL 60154

**WILSON, GERALD LOOMIS,** ELECTROMAGNETICS, ELECTROMECHANICS. *Current Pos:* From asst prof to assoc prof elec eng, Mass Inst Technol, 65-75, dir, Elec Power Systs Eng Lab, 75-80, head, Dept Elec Eng & Comput, 78-81, dean eng, 81-91, PROF ELEC & MECH ENG, MASS INST TECHNOL, 91- *Personal Data:* b Springfield, Mass, Apr 29, 39; m 58; c 3. *Educ:* Mass Inst Technol, SB, 61, SM, 63, ScD(mech eng & magnetohydrodynamics), 65. *Concurrent Pos:* Ford Found fel, 65-66; consult, Dynatech Corp, 65-66 & Am Elec Power Serv Corp, Mass, 66-67. *Mem:* Nat Acad Eng; fel Inst Elec & Electronics Engrs. *Res:* Magnetohydrodynamic energy conversion; electrohydrodynamics; electromechanics; electric power engineering. *Mailing Add:* Sch Eng Bldg 4 Rm 205 Mass Inst Technol 77 Massachusetts Ave Cambridge MA 02139

**WILSON, GLYNN,** pharmacology, for more information see previous edition

**WILSON, GOLDER NORTH,** BIOCHEMISTRY, GENETICS. *Current Pos:* ASSOC PROF, SOUTHWESTERN MED CTR, UNIV TEX, 88-, DIR, DIV PEDIAT GENETICS & METAB, ENDOWED PROF PEDIAT GENETICS. *Personal Data:* b Frederick, Okla, Oct 29, 44; m 88, Donna Tose; c Ben, Dan, Sarah & Shamus. *Educ:* Univ Ill, BS, 66; Univ Chicago, PhD(biochem), 70, MD, 72. *Prof Exp:* Intern pediat, New Eng Med Ctr, 72-73; res assoc hemat, NIH, 73-75; resident pediat, Univ Mich, 75-76, fel, 76-77, asst prof, 77-84; assoc prof, McGill Univ, 85-87; staff physician,

William Beaumont Hosp, 87-88. *Mem:* Am Soc Human Genetics. *Res:* Human congenital anomalies; human genetic disease. *Mailing Add:* Southwestern Med Ctr Univ Tex 5323 Harry Hines Blvd Dallas TX 75235-9063. *Fax:* 214-648-8617; *E-Mail:* wilson@utsw.swmed.edu

**WILSON, GORDON, JR,** POLYMER CHEMISTRY. *Current Pos:* assoc prof, 61-65, head, Dept Chem, 65-78, PROF CHEM, WESTERN KY UNIV, 65- *Personal Data:* b Bowling Green, Ky, Sept 13, 25; m 53; c 2. *Educ:* Western Ky State Col, BS, 47; Univ Ky, MS, 49; Purdue Univ, PhD(org chem), 58. *Prof Exp:* Instr chem, Univ Minn, Duluth, 49-54; res chemist, Dow Chem Co, 57-61. *Mem:* AAAS; Am Chem Soc; Sigma Xi. *Res:* Organic fluorine compounds; polymer chemistry, especially polymer bound catalysts. *Mailing Add:* 2113 Grandview Bowling Green KY 42101-3776

**WILSON, GREGORY BRUCE,** cellular immunology, inborn errors of metabolism, for more information see previous edition

**WILSON, GUSTAVUS EDWIN,** BIOCHEMISTRY. *Current Pos:* dept head chem, Univ Akron, 84-96, interim assoc dean arts & sci, 93, actg vprovost res, 93-94, PROF CHEM, UNIV AKRON, 84-, SPEC ASST TO PRES, 97- *Personal Data:* b Philadelphia, Pa, Oct 6, 39; m 61; c Kristine S, Karin E, Jennifer L & Kiersten B. *Educ:* Mass Inst Technol, SB, 61; Univ Ill, PhD(org chem), 64. *Prof Exp:* From inst to asst prof chem, Polytech Inst Brooklyn, 64-69; from assoc prof to prof, Polytech Inst NY, 69-80; prof chem; Clarkson Univ, 80-84. *Concurrent Pos:* From adj assoc prof to adj prof, Rockefeller Univ, 72-80; vis assoc prof, Sch Med, Univ Pa, 74-76; vis prof, Wash Univ, 78-80. *Mem:* Am Clin Soc; Royal Soc Chem; AAAS; Am Soc Biochem & Molecular Biol; Sigma Xi; NY Acad Sci. *Res:* Magnetic resonance studies of bacterial cell wall metabolism and protein structure. *Mailing Add:* Dept Chem Univ Akron Akron OH 44325-3601. *Fax:* 330-972-7370; *E-Mail:* gewilson@iakron.edu

**WILSON, HAROLD ALBERT,** MICROBIOLOGY. *Current Pos:* assoc prof bact, Univ, & assoc bacteriologist, Exp Sta, 47-57, prof & bacteriologist, 57-72, EMER PROF BACT, WVA UNIV, 72- *Personal Data:* b Tilton, Ill, Oct 10, 05; m 37; c 2. *Educ:* La State Univ, BS, 32, MS, 33; Iowa State Col, PhD(soil microbiol), 37. *Prof Exp:* Prof agr, Panhandle Agr & Mech Col, 35-36; instr & asst, Iowa State Col, 37-38; prof agron, Southwestern La Inst, 38-44; soil conservationist, Soil Conserv Serv, USDA, 44-47. *Mem:* Am Soc Agron; Am Soc Microbiol; Soil Sci Soc Am. *Res:* Microbiology of sanitary landfills and sewage decomposition in acid mine water; microbiology of strip mine (coal) spoil. *Mailing Add:* 1011 Boathouse Ct Raleigh NC 27615-5801

**WILSON, HAROLD FREDERICK,** ORGANIC CHEMISTRY. *Current Pos:* CONSULT, 84- *Personal Data:* b Columbiana, Ohio, Aug 15, 22; m 49, Alice Steer; c Janice, Deborah, James & Kathleen. *Educ:* Oberlin Col, AB, 47; Univ Rochester, PhD(chem), 50. *Prof Exp:* Res chemist, Rohm & Haas Co, 50-57, lab head, 57-63, res supvr, 63-68, from asst dir res to dir res, 68-72, vpres, 72-83, chief sci officer, 81-83. *Concurrent Pos:* Mem bd dirs, Indust Res Inst, 79-82 & Coun Chem Res, 81; chmn, US Nat Comt, Int Union Pure & Appl Chem, 82-84, Finance Comt, 81-89. *Res:* Insecticides; herbicides; growth regulators. *Mailing Add:* 214 Gilmore Ave Merchantville NJ 08109. *Fax:* 609-663-0561; *E-Mail:* hwilson@aol.com

**WILSON, HARRY DAVID BRUCE,** ECONOMIC GEOLOGY. *Current Pos:* RETIRED. *Personal Data:* b Winnipeg, Man, Nov 10, 16; m 41, Marjorie May Singleton; c Terry, Wendy (Powers) & Mary (Brett). *Educ:* Univ Man, BSc, 36; Calif Inst Technol, MS, 39, PhD, 42. *Honors & Awards:* Barlow Medal, Can Inst Mining & Metall. *Prof Exp:* Res & explor geologist, Int Nickel Co, Can, 41-47; asst prof geol, Univ Man, 47-49; geologist, Africa & Europe, 49-51; assoc prof geol, Univ Man, 51-57, head dept, 65-72, prof geol, 57-81. *Concurrent Pos:* Mem, Nat Res Coun Can, 69-72; consult, Falconbridge Nickel Mines Ltd & Selco Mining Co Ltd; dir, Selco Mining Co Ltd & Man Mineral Resources Ltd. *Mem:* Soc Econ Geologists (pres, 76); Geol Soc Am; Geol Asn Can (pres, 65-66); Can Inst Mining & Metall; Royal Soc Can. *Res:* Geology and geochemistry of ore deposits; structure and origin of continental crust. *Mailing Add:* 602-255 Wellington Crescent Winnipeg MB R3M 3V4 Can. *Fax:* 204-474-1042

**WILSON, HARRY W(ALTON), JR,** CHEMICAL ENGINEERING. *Current Pos:* RETIRED. *Personal Data:* b Homestead, Pa, Nov 15, 24; m 47; c 2. *Educ:* Univ Pittsburgh, BSChE, 48. *Prof Exp:* Develop engr, Goodyear Tire & Rubber Co, 48-50; process engr, Koppers Co, Inc, 50-56; sect head process develop, Callery Chem Co Div, Mine Safety Appliances Co, 56-64, mgr process eng, 64-68, mgr eng, 88-92. *Mem:* Am Inst Chem Engrs. *Res:* Chemical process development; new process design. *Mailing Add:* 151 Hidden Acres Lane Valencia PA 16059

**WILSON, HENRY R,** REPRODUCTIVE PHYSIOLOGY, ENVIRONMENTAL PHYSIOLOGY. *Current Pos:* Asst prof poultry, Univ Fla, 62-67, asst poultry physiologist, 62-67, assoc prof & assoc poultry physiologist, 67-74, PROF & POULTRY PHYSIOLOGIST, UNIV FLA, 74- *Personal Data:* b Webbville, Ky, Mar 6, 36; m 59; c 2. *Educ:* Univ Ky, BS, 57, MS, 59; Univ Md, PhD(poultry physiol), 62. *Mem:* Soc Exp Biol & Med; Soc Study Reproduction; Wildlife Soc; Poultry Sci Asn; World Poultry Sci Asn; Sigma Xi. *Res:* Reproduction in male chickens; heat tolerance in chickens; delaying sexual maturity in chickens; management techniques, fertility and hatchability; game birds. *Mailing Add:* Dept Dairy & Poultry Sci Univ Fla PO Box 110920 Gainesville FL 32611-0920

**WILSON, HOWARD LE ROY,** MATHEMATICS. *Current Pos:* RETIRED. *Personal Data:* b Salem, Ore, Dec 8, 32; m 60; c 3. *Educ:* Willamette Univ, BA, 54; Univ Ill, MS, 60, PhD(educ), 66. *Prof Exp:* Teacher high sch, Ore, 55-56; from instr to asst prof math, Eastern Ore Col, 56-64; from asst prof to assoc prof math & sci educ, Ore State Univ, 64-80, prof math & math educ, 80-97. *Concurrent Pos:* Expert in math, Field Sta, Papua, New Guinea, UN Educ Sci & Cult Orgn, 71-73. *Mem:* Nat Coun Teachers Math; Math Asn Am; Am Asn Univ Professors. *Res:* Mathematics education and teacher training. *Mailing Add:* Dept Math Ore State Univ 368 Kidder Hall Corvallis OR 97331-4601

**WILSON, HOWELL KENNETH,** MATHEMATICS. *Current Pos:* assoc prof, 69-73, chair, Dept Math, Statist & Comput Sci, 76-81, PROF MATH, SOUTHERN ILL UNIV, EDWARDSVILLE, 73- *Personal Data:* b Savannah, Ga, Aug 28, 37; c Pamela L (McCraney) & Howell K Jr. *Educ:* Ga Inst Technol, BS, 60; Univ Minn, PhD(math), 64. *Prof Exp:* From asst prof to assoc prof math, Ga Inst Technol, 64-69. *Mem:* Am Soc Qual Control; Asn Automated Reasoning. *Res:* Triadic logic; stability theory for ordinary differential equations. *Mailing Add:* Dept Math & Statist Southern Ill Univ EDWS Box 1653 Edwardsville IL 62026-0001. *Fax:* 618-692-3174

**WILSON, HUGH DANIEL,** SYSTEMATIC BOTANY, ETHNOBOTANY. *Current Pos:* from asst prof to assoc prof, 77-90, PROF BIOL, TEX A&M UNIV, 90- *Personal Data:* b Alliance, Ohio, Aug 15, 43; m 70; c 1. *Educ:* Kent State Univ, BA, 70, MA, 72; Ind Univ, Bloomington, PhD(bot), 76. *Honors & Awards:* W H Fulling Award, Soc Econ Bot, 81. *Prof Exp:* Asst prof bot, Univ Wyo, 76-77. *Mem:* Am Soc Plant Taxonomists; Soc Econ Bot; fel AAAS; Bot Soc Am. *Res:* Angiosperm biosystematics with emphasis on species complexes that include domesticated taxa. *Mailing Add:* Dept Biol Tex A&M Univ College Station TX 77843. *Fax:* 409-862-1977; *E-Mail:* h-wilson@tamu.edu

**WILSON, HUGH REID,** VISUAL PSYCHOPHYSICS, NEURAL MODELING. *Current Pos:* Fel, 69-72, from instr to asst prof, 72-80, PROF OPHTHAL & VISUAL SCI, UNIV CHICAGO, 85- *Personal Data:* b Ft Monmouth, NJ, Apr 20, 43; m 94, Frances Wilkinson. *Educ:* Wesleyan Univ, Conn, BA, 65; Univ Chicago, MA, 68, PhD(chem physics), 69. *Honors & Awards:* Res Career Develop Award, NIH. *Concurrent Pos:* NIH grant, 78-95; NSF grants, 82-85. *Mem:* Asn Res Vision & Ophthal; AAAS; fel Optical Soc Am; Soc Neurosci. *Res:* Processing of spatial and motion information by the human visual system; stereopsis and binocular vision; mathematical models of human visual functions and form vision. *Mailing Add:* Dept Ophthal Univ Chicago 939 E 57th St Chicago IL 60637. *E-Mail:* hrw6@midway.uchicago.edu

**WILSON, IRWIN B,** BIOCHEMISTRY. *Current Pos:* RETIRED. *Personal Data:* b Yonkers, NY, May 8, 21; m 52; c 2. *Educ:* City Col New York, BS, 41; Columbia Univ, AM, 47, PhD(phys chem), 48. *Honors & Awards:* Asn Res Nerv & Ment Dis Award, 58. *Prof Exp:* Jr chemist, Picatinny Arsenal, NJ, 42; res assoc, Columbia Univ, 42-45; chemist, Union Carbide & Carbon Corp, 45; instr chem, City Col New York, 46-49; assoc, Col Physicians & Surgeons, Columbia Univ, 48-49; from asst prof to prof biochem, 49-66; prof chem, Univ Colo, Boulder, 66-88. *Mem:* Am Chem Soc; Am Soc Biol Chem; Am Acad Neurol. *Res:* Enzymology; protein chemistry; nerve function; peptide hormones. *Mailing Add:* 1938 Pearl St No 202 Boulder CO 80302

**WILSON, J(AMES) W(OODROW),** CHEMICAL ENGINEERING, MATHEMATICS. *Current Pos:* from asst prof to prof, 49-77, EMER PROF CHEM ENG, NAVAL POSTGRAD SCH, 77- *Personal Data:* b Commerce, Tex, Apr 5, 16; m 43; c 3. *Educ:* Stephen F Austin State Col, BA, 35; Univ Tex, BS, 39; Agr & Mech Col, Tex, MS, 41. *Prof Exp:* Instr chem, Agr & Mech Col, Tex, 42; instr chem eng, Columbia Univ, 46-49. *Mem:* Am Chem Soc; Am Inst Chem Engrs. *Res:* Explosives; rocket propellants; heat transfer; thermodynamics; fuels and lubricants. *Mailing Add:* 3435 Oak Cluster Rd San Antonio TX 78253-9227

**WILSON, JACK,** AERONAUTICAL ENGINEERING. *Current Pos:* SR ENG SPECIALIST, NYMA INC, CLEVELAND, 94- *Personal Data:* b Sheffield, Yorkshire, Eng, Jan 5, 33; m 96, Carol Blixen; c Tanya R & Cara. *Educ:* Imp Col, London, BS, 54; Cornell Univ, MS, 58, PhD(aeronaut eng), 62. *Honors & Awards:* Manly Mem Award, Soc Automotive Engrs, 95. *Prof Exp:* Sr sci officer, Royal Aircraft Estab, 62-63; prin res scientist, Avco-Everett Res Lab, 63-72; vis prof, Inst Fluid Mech, Marseille, France, 72-73; sr scientist, Univ Rochester, 73-80; sr res assoc, Sohio/BP Am, Cleveland, 80-90; sr eng specialist, Sverdrup Technol, Inc, Cleveland, 90-94. *Mem:* Sr mem Am Inst Aeronaut & Astronaut. *Res:* Gas-dynamic laser; application of high speed flow to gas laser media; development of antimony dopant sources; measurement of air ionization rate at very high speeds; wave rotor development. *Mailing Add:* Nyma Inc 2001 Aerospace Pkwy Cleveland OH 44142. *Fax:* 216-977-1269; *E-Mail:* towilson@scivax.lerc.nasa.gov

**WILSON, JACK BELMONT,** PLANT PATHOLOGY. *Current Pos:* RETIRED. *Personal Data:* b Morgantown, WVa, Dec 1, 21; m 43; c 6. *Educ:* WVa Univ, BS, 53, MS, 54, PhD(plant path), 57. *Prof Exp:* Instr plant path, Univ Md, 56-57, asst prof, 57-62; res plant pathologist, Potato Handling Res Ctr, USDA, Maine, 62-67; assoc prof plant path & exten plant pathologist & entomologist, WVa Univ, 67-69; asst br chief, Hort Crops Res Br, Mkt Qual Res Div, USDA, 69-73, asst area res dir, NE Region, Agr Res Serv, 73-74, area dir, N Atlantic Area, NE Region, Fed Res, Sci & Educ Agency, 74-85. *Concurrent Pos:* Assoc prof, Univ Maine, 66-67. *Mem:* Am Phytopath Soc; Potato Asn Am; Europ Asn Potato Res. *Res:* Diseases of potatoes and ornamental plants; plant disease and insect diagnosis. *Mailing Add:* 115 E Main St Trumansburg NY 14886

**WILSON, JACK CHARLES,** ALGEBRA. *Current Pos:* RETIRED. *Personal Data:* b Waterloo, Iowa, Dec 17, 28; m 48; c 4. *Educ:* Iowa State Teachers Col, BA, 51; Univ Iowa, MS, 54; Case Western Res Univ, PhD(math), 60. *Prof Exp:* Instr math, Cent Col, Iowa, 53-56; asst prof, Fenn Col, 56-59; assoc prof, Cent Col, Iowa, 59-65 & Earlham Col, 65-70; prof math, Univ NC, Asheville, 70-96. *Mem:* Am Math Soc; Math Asn Am. *Res:* Pure mathemtics; functions on algebras. *Mailing Add:* 19 Nichols Hill Dr Asheville NC 28804

**WILSON, JACK LOWERY,** ANATOMY. *Current Pos:* From instr to asst prof, 68-74, ASSOC PROF ANAT, MED UNITS, UNIV TENN, MEMPHIS, 74- *Personal Data:* b Looxahoma, Miss, June 24, 43; m 66; c 3. *Educ:* Univ Southern Miss, BS, 64; Univ Miss, MS, 67, PhD(anat), 68. *Mem:* Am Asn Anat. *Res:* Relations of age and sex hormones to the dietary induction, high fat and low protein components of cardiac and hepatic lesions in mice, also study of the fine structure of these lesions; cerebrovascular spasm. *Mailing Add:* Dept Anat Univ Tenn Col Med 800 Madison Ave Memphis TN 38163

**WILSON, JACK MARTIN,** PHYSICS. *Current Pos:* dir & prof physics, Ctr Innovation Undergrad Educ, 90-95, DEAN UNDERGRAD & CONTINUING EDUC, RENSSELAER POLYTECH INST, 95-, PROF PHYSICS & ENG SCI, 96- *Personal Data:* b Camp Atterbury, Ind, June 29, 45; m 90, Judi Chang; c John, Jessica, Erika & Gretchen. *Educ:* Thiel Col, AB, 67; Kent State Univ, MA, 70, PhD(physics, math), 72. *Prof Exp:* From asst prof to assoc prof physics, Sam Houston State Univ, 72-79, chair dept, 79-82; guest scientist, State Univ NY, Stony Brook, 82-84; prof physics, Univ Md, College Park, 84-90. *Concurrent Pos:* Exec officer, Am Asn Physics Teachers, 82-90; mem educ comt, Am Phys Soc, 82-89; ed, Am Asn Physics Teachers Announcer, 82-90; dir, Md Univ Proj Physics & Educ Technol, 84-89; dir, Cuple Nat Consortium, 90-; dir site comt, Statewide Syst Initiative, NSF, 91. *Mem:* Am Phys Soc; Am Asn Physics Teachers; AAAS; Sigma Xi. *Res:* Computing in physics and education. *Mailing Add:* Dean Undergrad & Continuing Educ Rensselaer Polytech Inst Troy NY 12180. *Fax:* 518-276-4061

**WILSON, JAMES ALBERT,** physiology, biochemistry, for more information see previous edition

**WILSON, JAMES BLAKE,** APPLIED MATHEMATICS. *Current Pos:* RETIRED. *Personal Data:* b Albion, Mich, Feb 9, 24; m 49; c 4. *Educ:* Univ Fla, BS, 48, PhD(appl math), 57; Cornell Univ, MS, 51. *Prof Exp:* Instr mech, Cornell Univ, 50; instr, Dept Ord, US Mil Acad, 51-54; asst math, Univ Fla, 54-56; from asst prof to prof math, NC State Univ, 57-87, asst head, 78-87. *Mem:* Am Math Soc; Math Asn Am. *Res:* Mechanics; numerical analysis. *Mailing Add:* 1311 Greenwood Circle Cary NC 27511-5829

**WILSON, JAMES DENNIS,** risk analysis, for more information see previous edition

**WILSON, JAMES FRANKLIN,** MICROBIOLOGY, GENETICS. *Current Pos:* prof, 64-91, EMER PROF BIOL, UNIV NC, GREENSBORO, 91- *Personal Data:* b Christopher, Ill, Oct 27, 20; m 43; c 2. *Educ:* Southern Ill Univ, BS, 44; Iowa State Col, MS, 46; Stanford Univ, PhD, 59. *Prof Exp:* Instr biol, Hartnell Col, 46-64. *Mem:* AAAS; Genetics Soc Am; Sigma Xi. *Res:* Application of microsurgical techniques to the study of heterocaryosis and cytoplasmic heredity in Neurospora crassa. *Mailing Add:* Dept Biol Univ NC 312 Eberhart Bldg Greensboro NC 27412-5001

**WILSON, JAMES LARRY,** FISHERIES MANAGEMENT, AQUACULTURE. *Current Pos:* From asst prof to assoc prof, 70-83, assoc dir, Grad Prog Ecol, 88-96, PROF FISHERIES, DEPT FORESTRY, WILDLIFE & FISHERIES, UNIV TENN, 83- *Personal Data:* b Jackson, Tenn, Feb 9, 42; m 85, Debbie Danner; c Ben & Sarah. *Educ:* Union Univ, BS, 64; Univ Fla, MS, 67; Univ Tenn, PhD(zool), 70. *Honors & Awards:* Outstanding Serv to Fisheries Award, Am Fisheries Soc, 85. *Concurrent Pos:* Lectr, Tech Aqua Biol Sta, Career Awareness Inst, 78-79; vis scientist prog, Tenn Acad Sci, 83-; chmn regional res proj S-168, USDA/Coop State Res Serv, 84-86; co-chair, Tech Comt, Southern Reg Agr Ctr, 88-; pres, Southern Div, Am Fisheries Soc, 93-94. *Mem:* Am Fisheries Soc; Sigma Xi. *Res:* Management strategies for improvement of game fish yields in Tennessee waters; develop methods for economic rearing and marketing of aquatic animals with economic potential (aquaculture); maximizing production of commercially raised fishes. *Mailing Add:* Dept Forestry Wildlife & Fisheries Univ Tenn PO Box 1071 Knoxville TN 37901-1071

**WILSON, JAMES LEE,** GEOLOGY & CARBONATE GEOLOGY. *Current Pos:* CONSULT, 86- *Personal Data:* b Waxahachie, Tex, Dec 1, 20; m 44, Della Moore; c James L Jr, Burney G & Dale R (deceased). *Educ:* Univ Tex, BA, 42, MA, 44; Yale Univ, PhD(geol), 49. *Prof Exp:* Jr geologist, Carter Oil Co, 43-44; assoc prof geol, Univ Tex, 49-52; res geologist, Shell Develop Co & Shell Int Res, 52-66; Wiess prof geol, Rice Univ, 66-78; prof geol, Univ Mich, 79-86. *Concurrent Pos:* Vis prof, Mex, WGer, Turkey, Italy & Can. *Mem:* Fel Geol Soc Am; Paleont Soc; hon Soc Econ Paleont & Mineral (pres, 75-76); hon Am Asn Petrol Geol. *Res:* Cambrian paleontology; Paleozoic biostratigraphy; carbonate petrography and petrology; sedimentology of carbonate strata; tectonics and sedimentation. *Mailing Add:* 1316 Patio Dr New Braunfels TX 78130. *Fax:* 830-625-3319; *E-Mail:* mrgrey@sat.net

**WILSON, JAMES M,** CERAMIC POWDER SYNTHESIS & CHARACTERIZATION, DIELECTRIC MATERIALS & PROPERTIES. *Current Pos:* MEM STAFF, FERRO CORP, 81- *Personal Data:* b Cuba, NY, June 10, 50; m 72; c 3. *Educ:* Syracuse Univ, BA, 88. *Prof Exp:* Jr engr, AVX Inc, 72-76; eng supvr, Mepco Electra Inc, 76-81. *Mem:* Am Ceramics Soc; Nat Inst Ceramic Engrs. *Res:* Dielectric materials for uses in the ceramic capacitor industry. *Mailing Add:* Transelco Div Ferro Corp 1789 Transelco Dr Penn Yan NY 14527

**WILSON, JAMES R,** THEORETICAL ASTROPHYSICS. *Current Pos:* RETIRED. *Personal Data:* b Berkeley, Calif, Oct 21, 22; m 49; c 5. *Educ:* Univ Calif, BS, 43, PhD(physics), 52. *Prof Exp:* Physicist, Sandia Corp, 52-53; physicist, Lawrence Livermore Lab, Univ Calif, 53-88. *Mem:* Fel Am Phys Soc; AAAS; Int Astron Union. *Res:* Astrophysics; gravitational radiation; relativity; nuclear physics. *Mailing Add:* 2993 Chateau Way Livermore CA 94550-6845. *Fax:* 510-422-3389

**WILSON, JAMES RUSSELL,** BEHAVIORAL BIOLOGY. *Current Pos:* from asst prof to assoc prof, 69-84, PROF PSYCHOL, UNIV COLO, BOULDER, 84- *Personal Data:* b Pittsburgh, Pa, Jan 10, 33. *Educ:* Univ Calif, Berkeley, AB, 59, PhD(psychol), 68. *Prof Exp:* Res psychologist, Univ Calif, Berkeley, 63-66; res assoc psychol, Univ Colo, Boulder, 66-68; instr psychol, Univ Calif, Santa Cruz, 69. *Concurrent Pos:* Assoc researcher, Univ Hawaii, 74- *Mem:* Behav Genetics Asn; Res Soc Alcoholism. *Res:* Genetic analysis of behavioral phenotypes, including aggression, sexual behavior, alcohol use and cognitive abilities. *Mailing Add:* Dept Psychol Univ Colo Box 345 Boulder CO 80309-0345

**WILSON, JAMES WILLIAM,** MEDICINAL CHEMISTRY. *Current Pos:* RETIRED. *Personal Data:* b Rice, Va, Oct 21; m 44; c 4. *Educ:* Hampden-Sydney Col, BS, 41; Univ Va, MS, 44, PhD(org chem), 46. *Prof Exp:* Asst chem, Univ Va, 41-43; res chemist, Smith Kline & French Labs, 46-53, asst sect head org chem, 53-54, head med chem sect, 54-66, staff dir, 66-67, assoc dir chem, 67-85. *Mem:* AAAS; Am Chem Soc; NY Acad Sci; Am Inst Chem. *Res:* Medicinal chemistry; analgesics; cardiovascular drugs; psychopharmacological, diuretic and anti-inflammatory agents. *Mailing Add:* 15 Kinterra Rd Wayne PA 19087-4717

**WILSON, JAMES WILLIAM,** MATHEMATICS EDUCATION, TEACHER EDUCATION IN MATHEMATICS. *Current Pos:* assoc prof, 74-78, PROF MATH EDUC, UNIV GA, 78- *Personal Data:* b Linwood, Kans, Sept 12, 36; m 60; c 3. *Educ:* Kans State Teachers Col, BS, 58 & MA, 60; Stanford Univ, MS, 64 & PhD(math educ), 67; Notre Dame, MS, 65. *Prof Exp:* Teacher math & biol, Marion City Sch, 58-60; instr math, Roosevelt High Lab Sch, 61-62; from res asst to res assoc, Stanford Univ, 62-68; from asst prof to assoc prof math educ, Univ Ga, 68-74; prog mgr, NSF, 74-75. *Concurrent Pos:* Chair, Spec Int Theory Math Educ, Am Educ Res Asn, 68-70; ed, J Res Math Educ, 76-82; bd dirs, Nat Coun Teachers Math, 78-81, Sch Sci & Math Asn, 74-76; consult, Nat Assessment Educ Progress, 68-84; vis prof, St Michaels Col, Winvoski, Vt, 67, Univ Tex, San Antonio, 81, Univ Hawaii, 82, ETenn State Univ, 86-88 & Southern Ill Univ, 87-88. *Mem:* Am Educ Res Asn; Nat Coun Teachers Math; Math Asn Am; Sch Sci & Math Asn. *Res:* Development of abilities in mathematical problem-solving. *Mailing Add:* Univ Ga 290 Hampton Ct Athens GA 30605. *Fax:* 706-542-4551; *E-Mail:* jwilson@moe.coe.uga.edu

**WILSON, JAMES WILLIAM ALEXANDER,** ELECTRICAL ENGINEERING, SPACECRAFT SYSTEMS. *Current Pos:* elec engr, Gen Elec Co, 76-78, unit mgr power circuits & drives, 78-81, br mgr power circuits & systs, 81-84, consult, Res & Develop Strategic Anal, 84-85, mgr, Planning Oper, 86-88, mgr, Power Controls Prog, 88-89, mgr, Control Systems Lab, 89-92, MGR, AEROSPACE PROGS, GEN ELEC CO, 92- *Personal Data:* b Glasgow, Scotland, Dec 24, 44; m 70; c 3. *Educ:* Heriot-Watt Univ, BSc, 67; Univ Edinburgh, PhD(elec eng), 71. *Prof Exp:* Fel elec eng, Univ Toronto, 71-73; sr engr static power conversion, Reliance Elec Co, Cleveland, 73-76. *Mem:* Inst Elec & Electronics Engrs; assoc mem Brit Inst Elcc Engrs. *Res:* Development of advanced solid-state power conversion techniques and applications. *Mailing Add:* Gen Elec Co Res & Develop KW-D278 PO Box 8 Schenectady NY 12301

**WILSON, JEAN DONALD,** ENDOCRINOLOGY, INTERNAL MEDICINE. *Current Pos:* from instr to assoc prof, 60-68, PROF INTERNAL MED, SOUTHWESTERN MED CTR, UNIV TEX, DALLAS, 68- *Personal Data:* b Wellington, Tex, Aug 26, 32. *Educ:* Univ Tex, BA, 51, MD, 55; Am Bd Internal Med, dipl, 64. *Honors & Awards:* Oppenheimer Award, Endocrine Soc, 72, Fred C Koch Award, 93; Amory Prize, Am Acad Arts & Sci, 77; Eugene Fuller Award, Am Urol Asn, 83; Lita Annenberg Hazen Award, 86; Dale Medal, Soc Endocrinol, 91. *Prof Exp:* From intern to asst resident internal med, Parkland Mem Hosp, Dallas, 55-58; clin assoc clin biochem, Nat Heart Inst, 58-60. *Concurrent Pos:* Estab investr, Am Heart Asn, 60-65; ed, J Clin Invest, 72-77. *Mem:* Nat Acad Sci; Inst Med-Nat Acad Sci; Asn Am Physicians; Am Soc Clin Invest; Royal Col Physicians London; Am Acad Arts & Sci. *Res:* Mechanism of action of steroid hormones; sexual differentiation; androgen physiology. *Mailing Add:* Dept Internal Med Southwestern Med Ctr Univ Tex Dallas TX 75235-8857. *Fax:* 214-648-8917; *E-Mail:* jwils1@mednet.swmed.edu

**WILSON, JEFFREY PAUL,** BREEDING CROPS FOR DISEASE RESISTANCE. *Current Pos:* Plant pathologist, 87-88, RES PLANT PATHOLOGIST, COASTAL PLAIN EXP STA, AGR RES SERV, USDA, 88- *Personal Data:* b Chicago, Ill, Dec 12, 59; m 92, Joan Chambless; c Cliff

R, Ryan T & Wade Boutwell. *Educ:* Purdue Univ, BS, 82, MS, 85, PhD(plant path), 87. *Concurrent Pos:* Assoc ed, Phytopath, 92-94. *Mem:* Am Phytopath Soc; Crop Sci Soc Am; Am Soc Agron; Sigma Xi; Am Forage & Grassland Coun. *Res:* Breeding forage grasses for disease resistance through evaluation of pathogen populations, exotic plant germplasm and introgression into improved lines. *Mailing Add:* Agr Res Serv USDA Coastal Plain Exp Sta Tifton GA 31793. *Fax:* 912-391-3701; *E-Mail:* jwilson@tifton.cpes.peachnet.edu

**WILSON, JERRY D(ICK),** SCIENCE WRITING, PHYSICS. *Current Pos:* assoc prof, 79-85, PROF PHYSICS, LANDER COL, 80- *Personal Data:* b Coshocton, Ohio, May 6, 37; div; c 2. *Educ:* Ohio Univ, BS, 62, PhD(physics), 70; Union Col, MS, 65. *Prof Exp:* Mat behav physicist dielectrics, Gen Elec Co, 63-66; lectr physics, Ohio Univ, 75-78. *Concurrent Pos:* Fel, Ohio Acad Sci, 72. *Mem:* Am Asn Physics Teachers; Nat Sci Teachers Asn; Am Med Technologists. *Res:* Science writing and science teaching, particularly for non-science students. *Mailing Add:* Dept Sci & Math Lander Univ 320 Stanley Ave Greenwood SC 29649-2099

**WILSON, JERRY LEE,** BIOCHEMISTRY. *Current Pos:* from asst prof to assoc prof, 69-84, PROF CHEM, CALIF STATE UNIV, SACRAMENTO, 84- *Personal Data:* b Heavener, Okla, Jan 30, 38; m 61; c 2. *Educ:* Okla State Univ, BS, 61; Univ Okla, PhD(chem), 67. *Prof Exp:* USPHS res fel, Univ Calif, Davis, 67-69. *Mem:* Am Chem Soc; Sigma Xi. *Res:* Plant biochemistry; enzymology; protein chemistry. *Mailing Add:* Chem Calif State Univ 6000 J St Sacramento CA 95819

**WILSON, JOE BRANSFORD,** BACTERIOLOGY. *Current Pos:* RETIRED. *Personal Data:* b Dallas, Tex, June 29, 14; m 44; c 2. *Educ:* Univ Tex, BA, 39; Univ Wis, MS, 41, PhD(bact), 47; Am Bd Microbiol, dipl. *Prof Exp:* Instr bact, Univ Tex, 39; asst, Univ Wis-Madison, 39-42, from instr to assoc prof, 46-55, prof bact, 55-81, assoc dean grad sch, 65-69, chmn dept, 68-73, prof med microbiol, 77-81. *Concurrent Pos:* Mem tech adv panel, Off Asst Secy Defense, 52-63. *Mem:* Fel AAAS; Am Soc Microbiol; Soc Exp Biol & Med; Am Asn Immunol; fel Am Acad Microbiol; Sigma Xi. *Res:* Metabolism and pathogenesis of Brucella, Cocci, Vibrio and Leptospira. *Mailing Add:* 36 Pebblebrook Lane Wimberley TX 78676-2711

**WILSON, JOE ROBERT,** CIVIL & CONSTRUCTION ENGINEERING. *Current Pos:* RETIRED. *Personal Data:* b Colfax, La, Apr 5, 23; m 44; c 3. *Educ:* US Naval Acad, BS, 44; Rensselaer Polytech Inst, MCE, 48; Univ Tex, PhD(civil eng), 67. *Prof Exp:* Co commander, Naval Construct Battalion 105 & US Naval Civil Eng Corps, 48-50, proj engr, Pub Works Ctr, Va, 50-52, dir design div, Potomac River Naval Command Pub Works, 52-53, mgr construct div, Off Charge Construct, Spain, 53-55, dir pub works, Naval Air Sta, Ala, 56-58, staff engr, Off Chief Naval Opers, 58-60, dir pub works, Naval Sta, CZ, 60-62, dist civil engr, 15th Naval Dist, 62-64; prof civil eng, La Tech Univ, 66-86, head dept, 75-86. *Mem:* Fel Am Soc Civil Engrs; Water Pollution Control Fedn; Am Soc Eng Educ. *Res:* Hydraulics; water pollution control systems; mixing and dispersion phenomena. *Mailing Add:* 421 Audubon Dr Ruston LA 71270

**WILSON, JOHN CLELAND,** small computers, for more information see previous edition

**WILSON, JOHN COE,** GEOLOGY APPLIED ECONOMIC & ENGINEERING. *Current Pos:* GEN MGR INFO MGT, APPL RESOURCES LTD, 86- *Personal Data:* b Manhattan, KS, Jul 16, 31; m 55; c 2. *Educ:* Calif Inst Technol, BS, 53, PhD(geol), 61; Univ Kans, MS, 55. *Prof Exp:* Explor geologist, Bear Creek, Mining Co, 61-64; res geologist, Explor Serv Dept, Kenecott Copper Corp, 64-68, chief geol res, 68-71, dir explor res, 71-77; mgr explor, Anaconda Minerals Co, 77-86. *Concurrent Pos:* Prog mgt develop, Harvard Bus Sch, 73. *Mem:* Soc Econ Geologist; Soc Mining Engrs; fel Geol Soc Am. *Res:* Origin and discovery on metalliferous ore deposits; efficient intergration of ore deposit exploration concepts with exploration databases to yield mineral discoveries. *Mailing Add:* 2800 S University Blvd No 3 Denver CO 80210

**WILSON, JOHN D(OUGLAS),** ELECTRICAL ENGINEERING, COMPUTER ENGINEERING. *Current Pos:* assoc prof, 67-76, head dept, 78-84, PROF ELEC ENG, ROYAL MIL COL CAN, 76- *Personal Data:* b Edinburgh, Scotland, Aug 21, 35; m 57, Kathleen L Wolff; c Alisdair L, Linda M (Deodato) & Niegel I. *Educ:* Univ Edinburgh, BSc, 56; Univ London (UCWI), PhD(elec eng), 67. *Prof Exp:* Electronic engr, Bristol Aircraft Ltd, Eng, 56-59; lt (RN), 59-62; lectr elec eng, Univ WI, 62-67. *Concurrent Pos:* Can Defence Res Bd grant, 68-; vis prof, Univ Maine, Orono, 85-86; mem, Can Accreditation Vis Team, 82-83 & 85-86. *Mem:* Sr mem Inst Elec & Electronics Engrs. *Res:* Microcomputer applications; acoustic emission studies in aircraft structures; computer aided diagnostics; expert systems; intelligent systems. *Mailing Add:* Dept Elec & Comput Eng Royal Mil Col Can Kingston ON K7K 5L0 Can. *Fax:* 613-544-8107; *E-Mail:* wilsonj@rmc.ca

**WILSON, JOHN DRENNAN,** PHYSIOLOGY, RADIOBIOLOGY. *Current Pos:* asst prof, 72-76, ASSOC PROF RADIOBIOL, MED COL VA, 76- *Personal Data:* b Peoria, Ill, Mar 29, 38; m 67; c 1. *Educ:* Carleton Col, BA, 60; Univ Ill, Urbana, MS, 63, PhD(physiol), 66. *Prof Exp:* Res assoc radiobiol, Univ Tex, Austin, 66-72. *Mem:* AAAS; Radiation Res Soc. *Res:* Lethal and mutagenic effects of radiation on microorganisms; effects of accelerated particles on mammalian systems. *Mailing Add:* Dept Radiol Box 615 Va Commonwealth Univ Sch Med Med Col Va Richmond VA 23298-1900

**WILSON, JOHN EDWARD,** NEUROCHEMISTRY, ENZYMOLOGY. *Current Pos:* From asst prof to assoc prof, 67-75, chmn, Biochem Dept, 89-94, PROF BIOCHEM, MICH STATE UNIV, 75- *Personal Data:* b Ft Wayne, Ind, Apr 27, 39; m 64, Sandra Lilegdon; c John, Jason & James. *Educ:* Univ Notre Dame, BS, 61; Univ Ill, MS, 62, PhD(biochem), 64. *Honors & Awards:* Javits Nuerosci Investr Award, 85, 92. *Concurrent Pos:* NSF fel, Univ Ill, Urbana, 64-65. *Mem:* Am Soc Biol Chem; Am Soc Neurochem; Int Soc Neurochem; Am Chem Soc; fel AAAS. *Res:* Brain hexokinase; brain mitochondria; regulation of energy metabolism in brain. *Mailing Add:* Dept Biochem Mich State Univ Wilson Rd Rm 301 East Lansing MI 48824-1319. *E-Mail:* wilsonj@pilot.msu.edu

**WILSON, JOHN ERIC,** BIOCHEMISTRY. *Current Pos:* from asst prof to assoc prof, Univ NC, 50-60, prof biochem, 65-89, dir, Neurobiol Prog, 72-73, EMER PROF, SCH MED, UNIV NC, CHAPEL HILL, 90- *Personal Data:* b Champaign, Ill, Dec 13, 19; m 47, Marion R Heaton; c Kenneth H, Douglas C & Richard M. *Educ:* Univ Chicago, SB, 41; Univ Ill, MS, 44; Cornell Univ, PhD(biochem), 48. *Prof Exp:* Asst chem, Univ Ill, 41-44; asst biochem, Med Col, Cornell Univ, 44-48, res assoc, 48-50. *Concurrent Pos:* Consult, Oak Ridge Nat Lab, 54-57; Kenan prof, Univ Utrecht, Neth, 78, external examr, Univ Malaya, 88. *Mem:* Fel AAAS; Am Chem Soc; Am Soc Biol Chem & Molecular Biol; Am Soc Neurochem; Soc Neurosci; Int Soc Neurochem. *Res:* Effects of experience and behavior on brain metabolism; neurochemistry. *Mailing Add:* 214 Spring Lane Chapel Hill NC 27514-3540

**WILSON, JOHN F,** MEDICINE, PATHOLOGY. *Current Pos:* pathologist & dir labs, 69-87, CONSULT, PRIMARY CHILD RENS HOSP, 88-; ELECTRON MICROSCOPIST, LDS HOSP, SALT LAKE CITY, 88- *Personal Data:* b Niagara Falls, NY, Dec 23, 22; m 50; c 8. *Educ:* Univ Cincinnati, MD, 52. *Prof Exp:* Intern pediat, Univ Ark Hosp, 52-53; resident, Children's Hosp, Cincinnati, Ohio, 55-57; instr, Univ Cincinnati, 57-58; from instr to asst prof pediat, Univ Utah, 58-68, from instr to asst prof path, 67-87, assoc prof pediat, 73-87. *Concurrent Pos:* Smith Kline & Fr fel hemat, 57-59; from co-prin investr to prin investr gastrointestinal tract in iron deficiency anemia NIH grants, 61-66, prin investr, copper metab in acute leukemia, 63-64; mem comn child nutrit, Food & Nutrit Bd, Nat Res Coun, 64-66; resident path, Univ Utah, 66-69; assoc prog dir, Children's Cancer Study Group A, NIH, Univ Utah, 70-77, path of record, Non-Hodgkins Lymphoma Study, 77-83; mem, Lymphoma Panel, NIH, 78-83. *Mem:* AMA; Am Soc Hemat; Am Fedn Clin Res; Am Soc Clin Path; Col Am Path; Path Soc Gt Brit & Ireland. *Res:* Iron and copper metabolism in iron deficiency; childhood malignancies; childhood non-Hodgkins lymphoma. *Mailing Add:* 1761 Countryside Dr Salt Lake City UT 84106

**WILSON, JOHN H,** BIOCHEMISTRY, GENETICS. *Current Pos:* Asst prof, 73-79, assoc prof, 79-88, PROF BIOCHEM, BAYLOR COL MED, 88- *Personal Data:* b July 27, 44; US citizen; m 77, Lynda Thomas; c James J. *Educ:* Wabash Col, AB, 66; Calif Inst Technol, PhD(biochem, genet), 72. *Prof Exp:* Damon Runyon fel biochem, Med Ctr, Stanford Univ, 71-73. *Mem:* Fel AAAS. *Res:* Recombinational repair and gene stability. *Mailing Add:* Dept Biochem Baylor Col Med 1 Baylor Plaza Houston TX 77030-3489. *Fax:* 715-795-5487; *E-Mail:* johnhwilson@tmcbcm.edu

**WILSON, JOHN NEVILLE,** PHYSICS, RESOURCE MANAGEMENT. *Current Pos:* RETIRED. *Personal Data:* b Portland, Maine, June 13, 18; m 44, Dorothy Finley; c Melissa (Atkinson), Elizabeth (Axford) & Kathleen (Post). *Educ:* Rice Univ, BA, 40; Harvard Univ, AM, 41. *Prof Exp:* Res chemist, E I du Pont de Nemours & Co, Va, 41, res physicist, 42-43, tech specialist, Manhattan Dist, Del, 43-44, sr supvr, Wash, 44-45, res physicist, Va, 45-50, tech specialist, Del, 50-51, SC, 51-53, res supvr, Appl Physics Div, Savannah River Plant, 53, res mgr, 54-70, supt Planning & Anal Dept, Savannah River Plant, 70-80. *Concurrent Pos:* Asst physicist, Nat Defense Res Comt, Radio & Sound Lab, Univ Calif, 41-42; assoc physicist, Clinton Labs, Tenn, 44. *Mem:* Soc Rheology; Sigma Xi. *Res:* Rayon spinning, yarn structure and physical testing; health physics; oceanography; radiation and chemical process instrumentation; electronics; non-destructive testing; computer models for finance and control of large industrial plant and laboratory. *Mailing Add:* 700 Da Vega Dr Box 40 Lexington SC 29073-9676

**WILSON, JOHN PHILLIPS,** MATHEMATICS. *Current Pos:* RETIRED. *Personal Data:* b Stamford, Conn, June 5, 16; m 40, Ray O'Fallon; c Kathy S (Bingley). *Educ:* Univ Southern Miss, BA, 57; Johns Hopkins Univ, MEd, 60, MS, 70. *Prof Exp:* Res staff asst, Ballistic Anal Lab, Inst Coop Res, Johns Hopkins Univ, 57-62, res assoc, 62-67, res scientist, 67-69; sr res analyst, Thor Div, Falcon Res & Develop Co, Baltimore, 69-81. *Concurrent Pos:* Consult mil opers analysis, 81-85. *Mem:* Am Defense Preparedness Asn. *Res:* Military operations analysis: target vulnerability, weapon lethality, weapons systems evaluation, terminal ballistic evaluation of large caliber weapons; geo and celestial navigation for surface vessels; merchant marine industry-shipboard operations. *Mailing Add:* 102 Kenilworth Park Dr Apt 3C Towson MD 21204-2262

**WILSON, JOHN RANDALL,** PHYSICAL CHEMISTRY. *Current Pos:* RETIRED. *Personal Data:* b Miami, Fla, June 12, 34; m 59; c 3. *Educ:* Univ Fla, BS, 56; Univ Wis, MS, 59, PhD(chem), 65. *Prof Exp:* Asst prof chem, Franklin Col, 59-62, Miami Univ, 64-67 & Asheville-Biltmore Col, 67-68; assoc prof chem, Shippensburg Univ, 68-72, chmn dept, 77-81, prof, 72-, chmn dept, 85- *Mem:* Am Chem Soc. *Res:* Radiation chemistry; mechanisms of exchange reactions; photochemistry; scientific education in Latin America. *Mailing Add:* 80 Hassinger Rd Newburg PA 17240

**WILSON, JOHN SHERIDAN,** COAL PROCESSES. *Current Pos:* res supvr, Combustion Res & Develop Br, Res & Develop Admin, 76-77, asst dir, Energy Conversion & Utility Div, 77-79, DIR, COAL PROJ MGT DIV, MORGANTOWN ENERGY TECH CTR, US DEPT ENERGY, 79- *Personal Data:* b Morgantown, WVa, June 17, 44; m 65; c 4. *Educ:* WVa Univ, BS, 66, MS, 68, PhD(chem eng), 75. *Prof Exp:* Proj leader & engr, Bur Mines, US Dept Interior, 68-76. *Concurrent Pos:* Proj mgr, Combustion Res & Develop Br, Res & Develop Admin, Dept Energy, 76. *Mem:* Am Chem Soc; Am Soc Mech Engrs; Sigma Xi. *Res:* Coal combustion and furnace analysis; design and operation of fluidized-bed coal combustion; coal gasification; environmental effluent control from coal conversion and utilization processes. *Mailing Add:* 1004 Grand St Morgantown WV 26505-6919

**WILSON, JOHN T,** PEDIATRICS, CLINICAL PHARMACOLOGY. *Current Pos:* PROF PEDIAT, MED & PSYCHIAT & CHIEF, SECT CLIN PHARMACOL, SCH MED, LA STATE UNIV, 78-, DIR, CHILDREN'S CLIN RES CTR. *Personal Data:* b Gainesville, Tex, Apr 27, 38; m 62, Catherine Jacobs; c John, Lauren & Abigail. *Educ:* Tulane Univ La, BS, 60, MS & MD, 63; Am Bd Pediat, cert, 75. *Prof Exp:* From intern to resident clin pediat, Palo Alto-Stanford Med Ctr, Palo Alto, Calif, 63-65; res assoc biochem pharmacol, Univ Iowa, 65-66; res assoc biochem pharmacol & endocrinol, Nat Inst Child Health & Human Develop, Bethesda, Md, 66-68; attend pediatrician & dir, Lab Perinatal Med Pharmacol, Children's Hosp, San Francisco, 69-70; assoc prof, Med Sch, Vanderbilt Univ, 70-77. *Concurrent Pos:* Fel neonatal med & dir, Lab Develop Pharmacol, Children's Hosp, San Francisco, 68-69; NIH res career develop award, 69 & 72; lectr, Med Ctr, Univ Calif, San Francisco, 69-70; res assoc, J F Kennedy Ctr, 70-; mem, Task Force Drugs Breast Milk, WHO. *Mem:* AAAS; Soc Pediat Res; Am Soc Pharmacol & Exp Therapeut; Am Soc Clin Pharmacol & Therapeut; fel Am Acad Pediat; Am Asn Pharmaceut Scientists; Am Fedn Clin Res; Int Soc Study Xenobiotics; Sigma Xi; Am Col Clin Pharmacol. *Res:* Pediatric clinical pharmacology, drug metabolism. *Mailing Add:* Dept Pediat LSU Med Center PO Box 33932 Shreveport LA 71130-3932. *Fax:* 318-675-7845

**WILSON, JOHN THOMAS, JR,** ENVIRONMENTAL MEDICINE, PREVENTIVE MEDICINE. *Current Pos:* CONSULT, 87- *Personal Data:* b Birmingham, Ala, June 2, 24; m 68. *Educ:* Howard Univ, BS, 46; Columbia Univ, MD, 50; Univ Cincinnati, ScD(indust med), 56. *Prof Exp:* Physician, Div Indust Hyg, NY State Dept Labor, 55-56 & Sidney Hillman Health Ctr, NY, 56-57; chief bur occup health, Santa Clara Co Health Dept, Calif, 57-61; life sci adv, Lockheed Aircraft Corp, 61-67, head, Biol Sci Res Labs, Lockheed Missiles & Space Co, 67-69; asst prof community & prev med, Sch Med, Stanford Univ, 69-71; prof community health pract & chmn dept, Col Med, Howard Univ, 71-74; prof environ health & chmn dept, Sch Pub Health & Community Med Univ Wash, 74-80, prof & dir, 80-87. *Concurrent Pos:* Nat Med Fel fel, 53-55; fel indust med, Univ Cincinnati, 53-56; lectr, Sch Pub Health, Univ Calif, Berkeley, 59-61. *Mem:* Fel Indust Med Asn; fel Am Col Physicians; Am Acad Occup Med; Am Indust Hyg Asn. *Res:* Occupational and environmental medicine; toxicology; industrial hygiene. *Mailing Add:* Comn Med Sch Pub Health Univ Wash Seattle WA 98195

**WILSON, JOHN THOMAS,** GROUND WATER MICROBIOLOGY. *Current Pos:* MICROBIOLOGIST, RES LAB, R S KERR ENVIRON, US ENVIRON PROTECTION AGENCY, 79- *Personal Data:* b El Paso, Tex, Apr 30, 47; m 81; c 4. *Educ:* Baylor Univ, BS, 69; Univ Calif, Berkeley, MA, 71; Cornell Univ, PhD(microbiol), 78. *Prof Exp:* Res assoc, Agron Dept, Cornell Univ, 78, IPA to RSKERL res, 78-79. *Concurrent Pos:* Adj assoc prof, Rice Univ, 81-83 & 83-; mem, Hydrol Sect, Am Geophys Union, 83-; adv, Water Sci & Technol Libr Reidel, 84-; assoc ed, Environ Toxicol Chem, J Indust Microbiol & J Contaminant Hydrol, 85- *Mem:* Am Soc Microbiol; Soc Indust Microbiol. *Res:* Biological processes that control behavior of organic contaminants in the subsurface environment, including ground water; activities that promote biological reclamation of polluted subsurface environments; hazardous waste microbiology. *Mailing Add:* Med Ctr La State Univ PO Box 33932 Shreveport LA 71130-3932

**WILSON, JOHN WILLIAM,** HIGH ENERGY HEAVY ION INTERACTIONS, BIOPHYSICS. *Current Pos:* Aerospace technologist simulation, 63-70, space scientist space physics, 70-75, SR RES SCIENTIST ENERGY SYSTS, LANGLEY RES CTR, NASA, 75- *Personal Data:* b Arkansas City, Kans, Aug 6, 40; m 62, Delores Gelino; c John P. *Educ:* Kans State Univ, BS, 62; Col William & Mary, MS, 69, PhD(physics), 75. *Concurrent Pos:* Adj asst prof physics, Old Dom Univ, 75-80, adj assoc prof, 80-85, adj prof, 85-95. *Mem:* Radiation Res Soc. *Res:* High-energy heavy ion reaction theory; high-energy transport theory; health physics aspects of high-altitude aircraft and space operations and dosimetry; nuclear induced plasmas and radiolysis; nuclear pumped and electral pumped laser kinetics; solar pumped laser kinetics. *Mailing Add:* NASA 8 W Taylor Rd Hampton VA 23681-0001. *E-Mail:* john.w.wilson@larc.nasa.gov

**WILSON, JOHN WILLIAM, III,** ZOOGEOGRAPHY, PALEONTOLOGY. *Current Pos:* Asst prof, 72-78, ASSOC PROF BIOL, GEORGE MASON UNIV, 78- *Personal Data:* b New York, NY, May 10, 43; m 66. *Educ:* Amherst Col, BA, 66; Univ Chicago, PhD(evolutionary biol), 72. *Mem:* AAAS; Soc Study Evolution; Soc Vert Paleont; Am Soc Mammal; Ecol Soc Am. *Res:* Zoogeography of mammals; latitudinal gradients; paleoecology of mammals; changes in resource utilization of mammals during late Cretaceous and Cenozoic; Pleistocene extinctions. *Mailing Add:* Dept Biol George Mason Univ 4400 University Dr Mail Stop 3E1 Fairfax VA 22030

**WILSON, JOSEPH,** MEDICAL BACTERIOLOGY. *Current Pos:* RETIRED. *Personal Data:* b Trenton, NJ, Apr 25, 25. *Educ:* Univ Notre Dame, BS, 48; Univ Tex, MA, 51, PhD(bact), 54. *Prof Exp:* From instr to assoc prof biol, St Edward's Univ, 48-59, dean col, 51-58, dir testing & guid, 58-59; from asst prof to assoc prof biol, Univ Notre Dame, 59-71; prof pediat, Baylor Col Med, 71-76; prof biol, Univ Portland, 76-78, pres, 78-81; dir spec progs, Univ San Francisco, 81-82; prof biol, King's Col, 82-89; pres, Holy Cross Col, 90- *Concurrent Pos:* Vis prof, Univ Ulm, Ger, 69-70 & Baylor Col Med, 70-71. *Mem:* Transplantation Soc; Radiation Res Soc; Am Soc Microbiol; Soc Exp Biol & Med; Soc Exp Hemat. *Res:* Germfree life; protection against radiation damage; role of the thymus; clinical gnotobiology and immunology; gastrointestinal microflora. *Mailing Add:* Church Ascension 2111 Linn Williamsport PA 17701

**WILSON, JOSEPH EDWARD,** POLYMER CHEMISTRY. *Current Pos:* ADJ PROF PHYSIOL, TEX COL OSTEOP MED, 87- *Personal Data:* b Hannibal, Mo, Jan 8, 20; m 45; c 4. *Educ:* Univ Chicago, BS, 39; Univ Rochester, PhD(phys chem), 42. *Prof Exp:* Res chemist, Goodyear Aircraft Corp, 42-46, Argonne Nat Lab, 46-47 & Firestone Tire & Rubber Co, 47-50; sr chemist, Bakelite Co Div, Union Carbide & Carbon Corp, 50-57 & J T Baker Chem Co, 57; develop supvr, Atlas Powder Co, 58-61; proj mgr, Kordite Co, 61-64; res dir, Pollock Paper Div, St Regis Paper Co, 64-67; from assoc prof to prof phys chem, Bishop Col, 67-87. *Concurrent Pos:* Plastics consult, 67- *Mem:* Am Chem Soc; Soc Plastics Eng. *Res:* Photochemistry; polymerization; stability of polymers; radiation chemistry of plastics; synthesis of blood-compatible plastics for use in artificial organs. *Mailing Add:* 9827 Brockbank Apt 136 Dallas TX 75220-2906

**WILSON, JOSEPH WILLIAM,** ORGANIC CHEMISTRY. *Current Pos:* asst prof, 63-70, ASSOC PROF CHEM, UNIV Ky, 70- *Personal Data:* b Massena, NY, Apr 11, 34; m 73; c 3. *Educ:* Mass Inst Technol, BS, 56; Ind Univ, PhD(chem), 61. *Prof Exp:* Res assoc, Univ Wis, 61-63. *Mem:* Am Chem Soc. *Res:* Organic photochemistry. *Mailing Add:* Chem Dept Univ Ky Lexington KY 40506-0002. *Fax:* 606-323-1069; *E-Mail:* jwilson@ukcc.uky.edu

**WILSON, KARL A,** PLANT BIOCHEMISTRY & MOLECULAR BIOLOGY. *Current Pos:* asst prof & assoc fel, Ctr Biochem Res, State Univ NY, 76-80, asst prof & assoc fel semantic cell genetics & Biochem, 80-83, assoc prof, 83-91, co-dir biochem prog, 84-88, DIR BIOCHEM PROG, STATE UNIV NY, BINGHAMTON, 89-, PROF BIOCHEM, 91-, ASSOC CHAIR BIOL SCI, 92- *Personal Data:* b Buffalo, NY, Jan 19, 47; m 74, Anna Letan; c Kathleen. *Educ:* State Univ NY, Buffalo, BA, 69, PhD(biochem), 73. *Prof Exp:* Res assoc biochem, Roswell Park Mem Inst, 73-74, Purdue Univ, West Lafayette, 74-76. *Concurrent Pos:* NSF grad fel, 69-72. *Mem:* AAAS; Sigma Xi; Am Soc Plant Physiol; Am Chem Soc; Am Soc Biochem Molecular Biol. *Res:* Mechanism, molecular biology and physiology of proteases and their protein inhibitors; molecular evolution of proteins and protein sequencing; physiology of seed germination; nitrogen metabolism in plants. *Mailing Add:* Dept Biol Sci State Univ NY PO Box 6000 Binghamton NY 13902-6000. *Fax:* 607-777-6521; *E-Mail:* kwilson@binghamton.edu

**WILSON, KATHERINE WOODS,** air pollution, for more information see previous edition

**WILSON, KATHRYN JAY,** PLANT CELL BIOLOGY, PLANT MORPHOLOGY. *Current Pos:* Asst prof, 76-82, ASSOC PROF BIOL, IND UNIV-PURDUE UNIV, INDIANAPOLIS, 82- *Personal Data:* b Virginia, Minn, June 21, 48; m 69. *Educ:* Univ Wis-Madison, BA, 71; Ind Univ, Bloomington, MA, 76, PhD(plant sci), 76. *Concurrent Pos:* Res grants, Ind Univ-Purdue Univ, NSF, Whitehall. *Mem:* AAAS; Am Soc Plant Physiologists; Am Bot Soc; Sigma Xi. *Res:* Embryogenesis in plant tissue culture; development of non-articulated laticifer system of the Asclepiadaceae, with special emphasis on cytodifferentiation of the laticifer as a unique cell type in whole plants and tissue culture. *Mailing Add:* Sch Sci LD 3220 402 N Blackford St Indianapolis IN 46202

**WILSON, KENNETH ALLEN,** PLANT MORPHOLOGY, SYSTEMATIC BOTANY OF PTERIDOPHYTES. *Current Pos:* from asst prof to assoc prof, Calif State Univ, 60-67, assoc dean, Sch Lett & Sci, 66-73, prof, 67-94, EMER PROF BOT, CALIF STATE UNIV, 94- *Personal Data:* b Rio de Janeiro, Brazil, Apr 15, 28; US citizen. *Educ:* Miami Univ, BA, 51; Univ Hawaii, MS, 53; Univ Mich, PhD(bot), 58. *Prof Exp:* Botanist, Gray Herbarium & Arnold Arboretum, Harvard Univ, 57-60. *Concurrent Pos:* Res assoc, Natural Hist Mus Los Angeles Co & BP Bishop Mus, Honolulu, Hawaii. *Mem:* Bot Soc Am; Am Soc Plant Taxon; Am Fern Soc; Brit Pteridological Soc. *Res:* Taxonomy; pteridophytes; Hawaiian cultivated and naturalized ferns. *Mailing Add:* Dept Biol Calif State Univ 18111 Nordhoff St Northridge CA 91330-8303. *Fax:* 818-885-2034; *E-Mail:* kwilson@vax.csun.edu

**WILSON, KENNETH CHARLES,** CIVIL ENGINEERING, FLUID MECHANICS. *Current Pos:* assoc prof, 71-80, PROF CIVIL ENG, QUEENS UNIV, ONT, 80- *Personal Data:* b Vancouver, BC, Feb 9, 37; m 62, Vilborg Sveinbjarnardottir; c Bjarni & Signy. *Educ:* Univ BC, BASc, 59; Univ London, MSc & DIC, 61; Queens Univ, Ont, PhD(civil eng), 65. *Prof Exp:* Hydraul engr, Ingledow, Kidd & Assocs, BC, 61-63 & Int Power & Eng, 65-66; consult hydraul engr, Dept External Affairs, Govt Can, 66-68; sr hydraul engr, T Ingledow & Assocs, Consult Engrs, 68-70. *Concurrent Pos:* Distinguished lect award, Int Freight Pipeline Soc, 95. *Mem:* Eng Inst Can; Int Freight Pipeline Soc. *Res:* Sediment transport in rivers, canals and pipelines; blockage, plug flow and sliding beds in pipelines; author of one book and co-author of one book. *Mailing Add:* Dept Civil Eng Queens Univ Kingston ON K7L 3N6 Can. *Fax:* 613-545-2128; *E-Mail:* wilson@civil.queensu.ca

**WILSON, KENNETH GEDDES,** PHYSICS. *Current Pos:* HAZEL C YOUNGBERG TRUSTEES DISTINGUISHED PROF, OHIO STATE UNIV, 88- *Personal Data:* b Waltham, Mass, June 8, 36. *Educ:* Harvard Univ, BS, 56; Calif Inst Technol, PhD(physics), 61. *Hon Degrees:* DSc, Harvard Univ, 81. *Honors & Awards:* Nobel Prize Physics, 82; Dannie Heinemann Prize, 73; Boltzmann Medal, 75; Wolf Prize, 80; Franklin Medal, 82; A C Eringen Medal, 84; Aneesur Rahnan Prize, 93. *Prof Exp:* Jr fel, Harvard Univ, 59-62; Ford Found fel, Europ Orgn Nuclear Res, Geneva, Switz, 62-63; from asst prof to prof physics, Cornell Univ, 63-74, James A Weeks prof, 74-88, dir, Ctr Theory & Simulation Sci & Eng, 85-88. *Concurrent Pos:* Mem staff, Stanford Linear Accelerator Ctr, 69-70; mem, Comt Phys Sci, Math & Appln, Nat Acad Sci, 90-, Comt Fed Role Educ Res, 90-; co-prin investr syst change, NSF. *Mem:* Nat Acad Sci; Am Phys Soc; Am Philos Soc; Am Acad Arts & Sci. *Res:* Elementary particle theory. *Mailing Add:* Dept Physics 4138 Smith Lab Ohio State Univ 174 W 18th Ave Columbus OH 43210-1106

**WILSON, KENNETH GLADE,** BOTANY. *Current Pos:* PROF BOT, MIAMI UNIV, 67- *Personal Data:* b Payson, Utah, May 18, 40; m 59; c 3. *Educ:* Univ Utah, BS, 62, PhD(molecular biol), 68. *Prof Exp:* Reliability engr, Hercules Powder, 62-63. *Concurrent Pos:* Pres, Modular Genes Miami. *Mem:* Int Soc Plant Molecular Biol; Am Soc Plant Physiologists; Sigma Xi; Tissue Cult Asn. *Res:* The molecular biology of organelles with special interest in the analysis of chloroplast mutations and function of the genes controlling mitochondrial cytochrome oxidase function; investigating the cpDNA of the genus Hosta which is well recognized for its mutant chloroplasts; the sequence of the cox II gene is being studied in carrot and related dicots; tissue culture is being used to produce mutant plants for the plastid investigations and as a source of biologicals; production of specialty compounds is limited to members of the family Apocynaceae. *Mailing Add:* Dept Bot Miami Univ 500 E High St Oxford OH 45056-1618

**WILSON, KENNETH SHERIDAN,** MYCOLOGY & ECOLOGY, PLANT PATHOLOGY. *Current Pos:* asst, 52-53, from instr to prof, 54-87, EMER PROF BIOL SCI, PURDUE UNIV, CALUMET CAMPUS, 87- *Personal Data:* b Waterloo, Iowa, May 1, 24; m 48, 62, Regina Vilutis; c 1. *Educ:* Colo Col, BS, 49; Univ Wyo, MS, 50; Purdue Univ, PhD(mycol), 54. *Prof Exp:* Asst, Colo Col, 46-49 & Univ Wyo, 49-50. *Mem:* AAAS; Mycol Soc Am; Bot Soc Am; Soc Indust Microbiol; Am Soc Microbiol; Sigma Xi. *Res:* Mycological taxonomy; plant taxonomy; plant morphology; microbiological ecology. *Mailing Add:* 189 W 150 N Rd Valparaiso IN 46385

**WILSON, KENT RAYMOND,** CHEMICAL PHYSICS. *Current Pos:* asst prof phys chem, 65-71, assoc prof, 71-77, PROF PHYS CHEM, UNIV CALIF, SAN DIEGO, 77- *Personal Data:* b Philadelphia, Pa, Jan 14, 37; m 67, Lana Legallet; c 2. *Educ:* Harvard Col, AB, 58; Univ Strasbourg, dipl, 59; Univ Calif, Berkeley, PhD(chem), 64. *Prof Exp:* Res fel chem, Harvard Univ, 64-65; res chemist, Nat Bur Stand, 65. *Concurrent Pos:* Sloan res fel, 70-72. *Mem:* Am Phys Soc; Am Chem Soc. *Res:* Molecular dynamics of chemical reactions, particularly in solution; specialized computer systems for solution of scientific problems; computer animation; archaeological chemistry; quantum control of matter using tailored ultrafast light pulses; ultrafast x-ray and electron diffraction; molecular dynamics of chemical processes; visualization in chemistry and physics. *Mailing Add:* Dept Chem Univ Calif San Diego 9500 Gilmand Dr La Jolla CA 92093-0339. *Fax:* 619-534-7654; *E-Mail:* krwilson@ucsd.edu; krwilson@ucsd.bitnet

**WILSON, L BRITT,** NEURAL CONTROL OF THE CIRCULATION, SPINAL CORD NEUROTRANSMITTERS. *Current Pos:* FAC, DEPT PHYSIOL, SCH MED, UNIV SOUTHERN ALA. *Personal Data:* b Amarillo, Tex, Sept 10, 60; m; c 1. *Educ:* WTex State Univ, BS, 83; La State Univ Med Ctr, PhD(physiol), 88. *Prof Exp:* Grad asst physiol, La State Univ Med Ctr, 84-88; postdoctoral fel, Southwestern Med Ctr, Univ Tex, 88-91, asst instr physiol, 91- *Mem:* Am Physiol Soc; Soc Neurosci; Sigma Xi. *Res:* Neural control of the circulation, with emphasis on spinal cord neurochemistry. *Mailing Add:* Dept Physiol Univ Southern Ala Sch Med MSB 3024 Mobile AL 36688-0002. *Fax:* 214-648-3566; *E-Mail:* maass@ utsw.edu

**WILSON, L KENNETH,** exploration geology; deceased, see previous edition for last biography

**WILSON, LARRY EUGENE,** ANALYTICAL CHEMISTRY. *Current Pos:* from asst prof to assoc prof, 69-96, EMER PROF CHEM, OHIO UNIV, LANCASTER, 96- *Personal Data:* b Wapakoneta, Ohio, Nov 17, 35; m 58, Julia Henry; c Steven B & Katherine B. *Educ:* Ohio State Univ, BSc, 57, PhD(analytical chem), 62. *Prof Exp:* Analytical chemist, Dow Chem Co, Mich, 63-64; asst prof chem, Mich State Univ, 64-65; analytical chemist, Dow Chem Co, Mich, 65-66, supvr, Control Lab, 66-67, coordr lab technician training, 67-69. *Mem:* Am Chem Soc. *Res:* Acid-base equilibria; methods of teaching. *Mailing Add:* 2185 Sunnyhill Lancaster OH 43130

**WILSON, LAUREN R,** INORGANIC CHEMISTRY, ENVIRONMENTAL CHEMISTRY. *Current Pos:* PROF CHEM & VCHANCELLOR ACAD AFFAIRS, UNIV NC, ASHEVILLE, 87- *Personal Data:* b Yates Center, Kans, May 4, 36; m 59; c 2. *Educ:* Baker Univ, BS, 58; Univ Kans, PhD(inorg chem), 63. *Prof Exp:* Asst prof chem, Ohio Wesleyan Univ, 63-70, chmn dept, 70-77, prof chem, 70-87, dean acad affairs, 77-85, actg provost, 85-86, exec asst to pres, 86-87. *Concurrent Pos:* Vis prof, Ohio State Univ, 68 & 76-77; mem staff, Oak Ridge Nat Lab, 72-73. *Mem:* Am Chem Soc; Royal Soc Chem; AAAS; Coun Undergrad Res; Am Asn Higher Educ. *Res:* Synthesis of transition metal compounds; electrocatalysis of chemically modified electrodes; metal ions in natural and biological systems. *Mailing Add:* 22 Maywood Rd Asheville NC 28804

**WILSON, LAURENCE EDWARD,** INORGANIC CHEMISTRY. *Current Pos:* RETIRED. *Personal Data:* b Aberdeen, SDak, June 29, 30; m 57; c 3. *Educ:* Western Wash Col Educ, BA, 52; Univ Wash, PhD(chem), 57. *Prof Exp:* Instr chem, Amherst Col, 56-59; from asst prof to assoc prof, San Jose State Col, 59-63; from assoc prof to prof chem, Kalamazoo Col, 63-92, chmn dept, 63-88. *Mem:* AAAS; Am Chem Soc. *Mailing Add:* 3408 Olney Kalamazoo MI 49006-2834

**WILSON, LAWRENCE ALBERT, JR,** CHEMICAL & PETROLEUM ENGINEERING. *Current Pos:* RETIRED. *Personal Data:* b Mt Hope, WVa, Mar 19, 25; m 49; c 3. *Educ:* Purdue Univ, BS, 49, PhD(chem eng), 52. *Prof Exp:* Engr, Staple Develop Plant, Am Viscose Corp, 52-53, develop supvr, 53-54; res engr, Gulf Res & Develop Co, 54-56, group leader petrol res, 56-62, sr res engr, 62-66, sect supvr, 66-72, staff engr, 72-76, mgr, Prod Res Dept, 76-81, coordr processing appln, 81-85. *Concurrent Pos:* Lectr, Univ Pittsburgh, 64-81. *Mem:* Am Chem Soc; Am Inst Mining, Metall & Petrol Engrs. *Res:* Petroleum production. *Mailing Add:* 118 Woodshire Rd Greenville PA 16125

**WILSON, LEE,** ENVIRONMENTAL RESOURCES & HYDROLOGY. *Current Pos:* PRES, LEE WILSON & ASSOCS INC, 73- *Personal Data:* b Wichita Falls, Tex, Apr 15, 42; m 69; c 1. *Educ:* Yale Univ, BA, 64; Columbia Univ, PhD(geol), 71. *Mem:* Geol Soc Am; Am Geophys Union; Am Water Resources Asn. *Res:* Applied research related to development and protection of water and other environmental resources. *Mailing Add:* PO Box 931 Santa Fe NM 87504. *E-Mail:* lwasf@vsa.net

**WILSON, LENNOX NORWOOD,** FLUID DYNAMICS, ACOUSTICS. *Current Pos:* actg head aerospace eng, 78-79, chmn, 81-87, PROF AEROSPACE ENG, IOWA STATE UNIV, 73- *Personal Data:* b Quebec City, Que, Feb 15, 32; US citizen; m 58; c 3. *Educ:* Univ Toronto, BASc, 53, MASc, 54, PhD(aerophys), 59. *Prof Exp:* Res asst, Inst Aerophys, Univ Toronto, 53-59; res engr, Armour Res Found, Ill, 59-62; head aerochem, Defense Res Labs, Gen Motors Corp, Calif, 62-66; mgr fluid dynamics & acoust, IIT Res Inst, Ill, 66-71; prof mech & aerospace eng, Univ Mo, Columbia, 71-73. *Mem:* Assoc fel Am Inst Aeronaut & Astronaut. *Res:* Turbulence; combustion; shock tubes; chemical kinetics; aerodynamic noise; noise control; engineering acoustics; aerodynamics. *Mailing Add:* Dept Aerospace Eng Iowa State Univ 2080 Black Eng Ames IA 50011

**WILSON, LEONARD GILCHRIST,** HISTORY OF MEDICINE, BIOLOGICAL SCIENCE. *Current Pos:* PROF HIST MED & HEAD DEPT, UNIV MINN, MINNEAPOLIS, 67- *Personal Data:* b Orillia, Ont, June 11, 28; m 69, Adelia K Hans; c 1. *Educ:* Univ Toronto, BA, 49; Univ London, MSc, 55; Univ Wis, PhD(hist sci), 58. *Prof Exp:* Lectr biol, Mt Allison Univ, 50-53; vis instr hist sci, Univ Calif, 58-59; vis asst prof, Cornell Univ, 59-60; from asst prof to assoc prof hist med, Sch Med, Yale Univ, 60-67. *Concurrent Pos:* Mem, US Nat Comt Hist Geol, 85-88. *Mem:* Fel AAAS; Am Asn Hist Med; Am Hist Asn; Hist Sci Soc; Brit Soc Hist Sci; Int Acad Hist Sci. *Res:* History of biology; history of physiology in the seventeenth century; history of fever; history of geology. *Mailing Add:* Dept Hist Med Univ Minn 420 Delaware St SE PO Box 506 Minneapolis MN 55455

**WILSON, LEONARD RICHARD,** GEOLOGY, PALYNOLOGY. *Current Pos:* prof, Univ Okla, 57-62, res prof, 62-67, George Lynn Gross res prof 68-78, EMER PROF GEOL & GEOPHYS, UNIV OKLA, 68-; CUR MICROPALEONT & PALEOBOT, OKLA MUS NATURAL HIST, 71- *Personal Data:* b Superior, Wis, July 23, 06; m 30; c 2. *Educ:* Univ Wis, PhB, 30, PhM, 32, PhD(bot), 36. *Honors & Awards:* VI Gunnar Erdtman Int Medal, Palynology Soc India, 73. *Prof Exp:* Res assoc asst, Wis Geol & Natural Hist Surv, 31-35; from instr to prof geol & bot, Coe Col, 35-46; prof geol & head dept geol & mineral, Univ Mass, 46-56; prof geol, NY Univ, 56-57. *Concurrent Pos:* Melhaup scholar, Ohio State Univ, 39-40; consult, Carter Oil Co, 46-56; leader, Am Geog Soc Greenland Ice Cap Exped, 53; res assoc, Am Mus Natural Hist, 57-78; geologist, Okla Geol Surv, 57-78, emer geologist, 78-; adj prof, Univ Tulsa; consult, Jersey Prod Res Corp, 56-62, Humble Oil Co, 63-64 & Sinclair Oil Co, 63-69; consult geologist, 78- *Mem:* Fel Geol Soc Am; Am Bot Soc; Am Asn Petrol Geol; hon mem Nat Asn Geol Teachers; hon mem Am Asn Stratig Palynologists. *Res:* Stratigraphic and paleoecologic palynology. *Mailing Add:* 933 Wilson St Norman OK 73072

**WILSON, LESLIE,** PHARMACOLOGY, BIOCHEMISTRY. *Personal Data:* b Boston, Mass, June 29, 41; m 89, Carla Van Wingerden; c 2. *Educ:* Mass Col Pharm, BS, 63; Tufts Univ, PhD(pharmacol), 67. *Prof Exp:* Asst prof pharmacol, Sch Med, Stanford Univ, 69-75; from assoc prof to prof biochem, Univ Calif, Santa Barbara, 75-91, chair, Dept Biol Sci, 87-91. *Concurrent Pos:* USPHS fel, Univ Calif, Berkeley, 67-69; Nat Inst Neurol Dis & Stroke res grant, 70-; mem, Molecular Biol Study Sect, NIH, 78-82; mem, Am Cancer Soc Cell & Develop Biol Sci Adv Comt, 84-89, res grant, 87-; assoc ed, Biochem, 91- *Mem:* AAAS; Am Soc Pharmacol & Exp Therapeut; Am Soc Cell Biol; Am Soc Biochem & Molecular Biol. *Res:* Mechanism and regulation of microtubule assembly and function; mechanism of action of antimitotic chemical agents; cell biology. *Mailing Add:* Dept Biol Sci Univ Calif Santa Barbara CA 93106-0001. *Fax:* 805-893-8284; *E-Mail:* wilson@lifesci.ucsb.edu

**WILSON, LINDA S (WHATLEY),** CHEMISTRY, RESEARCH & EDUCATION ADMINISTRATION. *Current Pos:* PRES, RADCLIFFE COL, 89- *Personal Data:* b Washington, DC, Nov 10, 36; m 57, 70, Paul A; c Helen K (Whatley) & Beth A. *Educ:* Tulane Univ, BA, 57; Univ Wis,

PhD(inorg chem), 62. *Hon Degrees:* LHD, Newcomb Col, Tulane Univ & Univ Md, College Park, 93. *Prof Exp:* Res assoc inorg chem, Univ Wis, 62; Nat Inst Dent Res trainee phys chem & res assoc molecular spectros, Univ Md, 62-64, res asst prof, 64-67; vis res fel, Univ Southampton, 67; vis asst prof, Univ Mo, St Louis, 67-68; asst to vchancellor res, Wash Univ, 68-69, asst vchancellor res, 69-74, assoc vchancellor res, 74-75; assoc vchancellor res, Univ Ill, Urbana, 75-85, assoc dean, Grad Col, 78-85; vpres res, Univ Mich, 85-89. *Concurrent Pos:* Mem, Gen Res Support Adv Comt, NIH, 71-75, chmn, 74-75; mem, Comt Govt Relations, Nat Asn Cols & Univ Bus Officers, 71-77, chmn, 73-75; co-chmn, Panel Eval Div Res Resources, NIH, 75-76; mem, Procurement Policy Adv Comt, Energy Res & Develop Admin, 76-77, Bd-Coun Comt Chem & Pub Affairs, Am Chem Soc, 78-82, Nat Adv Coun Res Resources, NIH, 78-80 & Nat Comn Res, 78-80; mem dirs adv coun, NSF, 80-89; mem, Comt Gov & Asn Affairs, Coun Grad Schs, 81-84; mem, Comt Govt Univ Rel Support Sci, Nat Acad Sci, 81-83; mem, Task Force Meeting Res Costs, NIH, 81-83 & adv bd, Nat Coalition Sci & Technol, 83-87; mem bd dirs, Asn Biomed Res, 83-86 & AAAS, 84-88; vis fel, Sci Policy Res Unit, Univ Sussex, Eng, 84; acad vis, London Sch Econ & Polit Sci, 84; coun mem, govt-univ-indust res round table, Nat Acad Sci, 84-88; mem, Coun, Inst Med, 86-89; mem, Energy Res adv Bd, Dept Energy, 86-90; mem bd dir, Mich Mat Processing Inst, 85-89 & Mich Biotechnol Inst, 86-89; mem, Task Force 1990's, NSF, 87-88, Comt Govt-Indust Res Collab Biomed Res & Educ, 88-89, Ad Hoc Comt NIH Directorship, 89-90 & Adv Comt Educ & Human Resources, NSF, 90-93; chair, Off Sci & Eng Personnel, Nat Res Coun, 90-96; mem bd dirs or trustees, Mass Gen Hosp, 92-, Boston Mus Sci, 92- & Citizen's Financial Group, 96- *Mem:* Inst Med-Nat Acad Sci; fel AAAS; Nat Coun Res Adminr; Soc Res Adminr; Am Chem Soc. *Res:* Molecular spectroscopy; spectroscopic studies of molecular interactions; charge transfer complexes; coordination compounds and hydrogen bonded species; optical studies at high pressures; science policy; research policy; author of numerous technical publications. *Mailing Add:* Radcliffe Col 10 Garden St Cambridge MA 02138. *Fax:* 617-496-3179

**WILSON, LON JAMES,** INORGANIC CHEMISTRY, BIOINORGANIC CHEMISTRY. *Current Pos:* from asst prof to assoc prof, 73-84, PROF CHEM, RICE UNIV, 85- *Personal Data:* b Mojave, Calif, Sept 4, 44. *Educ:* Iowa State Univ, BS, 66; Univ Wash, PhD(inorg chem), 71. *Prof Exp:* Teaching asst chem, Univ Wash, 66-68; vis asst prof, Univ Ill, 71-73. *Concurrent Pos:* NIH fel, Univ Ill, 71-73. *Mem:* Chem Soc; Am Chem Soc. *Res:* Magnetic and redox properties of transition metal compounds; Mossbauer spectroscopy; iron, copper and nickel containing metalloproteins and their synthetic analogs; lanthanide coordination chemistry. *Mailing Add:* Dept Chem Rice Univ PO Box 1892 Houston TX 77251-1892

**WILSON, LORENZO GEORGE,** HORTICULTURE, VEGETABLE CROPS. *Current Pos:* PROF HORT & EXTEN HORT SPECIALIST VEG CROPS, HORT DEPT, NC STATE UNIV, 75- *Personal Data:* b Appleton, NY, July 25, 38; m 62; c 3. *Educ:* Cornell Univ, BS, 61; Wash State Univ, MS, 64; Mich State Univ, PhD(hort), 69. *Prof Exp:* Res assoc postharvest physiol, United Fruit Co, 63-66, postharvest physiologist, 69-75. *Concurrent Pos:* Consult, banana & root crop prod, & postharvest produce handling, Cent & SAm; Gov's Task Force, Farm Econ; mem, Sci & Technol Comt, United Fresh Fruit & Veg Asn; Cong Sci fel, Am Soc Hort Sci, Washington, DC, 90-91. *Mem:* Am Soc Hort Sci; Sigma Xi; Potato Asn Am. *Res:* Investigations to determine optimum cultural practices for potato and sweet potato production in North Carolina, including the use of fertilizers, pesticides and harvesting, handling and storage techniques for enhanced quality maintenance; bananas. *Mailing Add:* 508 Ramblewood Dr Raleigh NC 27609

**WILSON, LORNE GRAHAM,** SOIL PHYSICS, HYDROLOGY. *Current Pos:* from asst hydrologist to hydrologist, 62-94, EMER HYDROLOGIST, WATER RESOURCES RES CTR, UNIV ARIZ, 94- *Personal Data:* b Saskatoon, Sask, Oct 23, 29; US citizen; m 57; c 2. *Educ:* Univ BC, BS, 51; Univ Calif, MS, 57, PhD(soil sci), 62. *Prof Exp:* Asst specialist irrig drainage, Univ Calif, 56-58. *Res:* Survey of drainage problems in San Joaquin Valley, California; simultaneous flow of air and water during infiltration in soils; subsurface flow characteristics during natural and artificial recharge in stratified sediments. *Mailing Add:* Dept Hydrol Univ Ariz Harshbarger Bldg Tucson AZ 85721

**WILSON, LOUIS FREDERICK,** ENTOMOLOGY. *Current Pos:* RETIRED. *Personal Data:* b Milwaukee, Wis, Nov 22, 32; m 56; c 4. *Educ:* Marquette Univ, BS, 55, MS, 57; Univ Minn, PhD(entom), 62. *Prof Exp:* Instr cytol & parasitol, Marquette Univ, 54-57; state entomologist, Minn, 58; from asst prof to assoc prof forestry & entom, Mich State Univ, 67-85; prin insect ecologist, NCent Forest Exp Sta, US Forest Serv, 58-90; prof forestry & enton, Mich State Univ, 85-90. *Mem:* Entom Soc Am; Entom Soc Can. *Res:* Insect ecology and behavior; population dynamics; insect impact. *Mailing Add:* 29350 Sam Way Punta Gorda FL 33982

**WILSON, LOWELL D,** ENDOCRINOLOGY, BIOLOGICAL CHEMISTRY. *Current Pos:* from asst prof to assoc prof, 68-77, PROF MED & BIOL CHEM, SCH MED, UNIV CALIF, DAVIS, 77- *Personal Data:* b Pampa, Tex, May 11, 33; m 60; c 2. *Educ:* Univ Calif, Berkeley, AB, 55; Univ Chicago, MD, 60; Univ Southern Calif, PhD(biochem), 68. *Prof Exp:* From instr to asst prof med, Sch Med, Univ Southern Calif, 66-68. *Mem:* Endocrine Soc; Am Fedn Clin Res; Am Chem Soc; Am Soc Biol Chem. *Res:* Biochemistry; metabolic control processes; hormone action. *Mailing Add:* Dept Internal Med & Biol Chem Sch Med Univ Calif MSIA Rm 4418 Davis CA 95616-5224

**WILSON, LOWELL L,** ANIMAL SCIENCES, ANIMAL WELFARE. *Current Pos:* assoc prof animal prod, 66-71, PROF ANIMAL SCI, PA STATE UNIV, UNIVERSITY PARK, 71- *Personal Data:* b Egan, Ill, Jan 3, 36; m 55, Mary E Crea; c 3. *Educ:* Wis State Univ, BS, 60; SDak State Univ, MS, 62, PhD(animal sci), 64. *Honors & Awards:* Meat Animal Mgt Award, Am Soc Animal Sci, 73. *Prof Exp:* Livestock specialist, Purdue Univ, 64-66. *Concurrent Pos:* Consult var firms US & Foreign. *Mem:* AAAS; Am Genetic Asn; Am Soc Animal Sci; Am Meat Sci Asn; Am Dairy Sci. *Res:* Animal welfare and behavior; public perceptions of animal agricultural methods; beef cattle and sheep behavior; forage utilization with ruminants; recycling of waste materials through ruminants. *Mailing Add:* Dept Dairy & Animal Sci Pa State Univ 324 Henning Bldg University Park PA 16802. *Fax:* 814-863-6040

**WILSON, LYNN O,** APPLIED MATHEMATICS. *Current Pos:* DISTINGUISHED MEM TECH STAFF, BELL LABS, 70- *Personal Data:* b Wilmington, Del, July 9, 44. *Educ:* Oberlin Col, AB, 65; Univ Wis, PhD(appl math), 70. *Mem:* Soc Indust & Appl Math; Sigma Xi; Inst Mgt Sci. *Res:* Mathematical physics; marketing science. *Mailing Add:* AT&T Rm 7C-517 Murray Hill NJ 07974. *E-Mail:* low@ulysses.att.com

**WILSON, MABEL F,** analytical chemistry; deceased, see previous edition for last biography

**WILSON, MCCLURE,** RADIOLOGY. *Current Pos:* RETIRED. *Personal Data:* b Ogden, Utah, July 30, 24; m 50; c 2. *Educ:* Univ Ark, BS, 47, MD, 48. *Prof Exp:* From asst prof to assoc prof radiol, Med Br, Univ Tex, 55-63; radiologist, Scott & White Clin, Temple, Tex, 63-64; assoc prof Med Br, Univ Tex, Galveston, 64-69, prof, 69- *Mem:* AMA; Radiol Soc NAm; Am Roentgen Ray Soc. *Mailing Add:* Med Br Univ Tex 2626 Ave O Galveston TX 77550-7828

**WILSON, MARJORIE PRICE,** medicine; deceased, see previous edition for last biography

**WILSON, MARK ALLAN,** INVERTEBRATE PALEONTOLOGY, EVOLUTION. *Current Pos:* from instr to assoc prof, 81-92, PROF GEOL, COL WOOSTER, OHIO, 93- *Personal Data:* b Berkeley, Calif, Nov 26, 56; m 76, Gloria Miller; c Amy & Theodore. *Educ:* Col Wooster, Ohio, BA, 78; Univ Calif, Berkeley, PhD(paleont), 82. *Prof Exp:* Res geologist, Chevron Oil Field Res Co, 78; teaching asst paleont, Univ Calif, Berkeley, 79-81. *Concurrent Pos:* Vis prof earth sci, Oxford Univ; tech ed, J Paleontol, 86- *Mem:* Paleont Soc; Sigma Xi; AAAS; Palaeont Asn. *Res:* Paleozoic invertebrate fossil communities in relation to sedimentary environments, paleoecology of encrusting and coelobite communities; taxonomy of adherent foraminifera and bryozoans, application of paleoecology to biostratigraphy; carbonate petrology; evolution. *Mailing Add:* Dept Geol Col Wooster Wooster OH 44691. *E-Mail:* mwilson@acs.wooster.edu

**WILSON, MARK CURTIS,** ENTOMOLOGY. *Current Pos:* RETIRED. *Personal Data:* b Ware, Mass, Sept 19, 21. *Educ:* Univ Mass, BS, 44; Ohio State Univ, MS, 46. *Prof Exp:* Field aide, Div Truck Crops Invests, Bur Entom & Plant Quarantine, USDA, 45; asst zool, Ohio State Univ, 44-47; from asst prof to prof entom, Purdue Univ, W Lafayette, 47-87. *Concurrent Pos:* Consult, Adv Comt, Alfalfa Seed Coun, Food & Agr Orgn, Rumania, 71. *Mem:* Entom Soc Am. *Res:* Insect pest management; economic insect thresholds; host plant resistance. *Mailing Add:* 800 Cove Cay Dr Unit 2B Clearwater FL 34620-1206

**WILSON, MARK VINCENT HARDMAN,** VERTEBRATE PALEONTOLOGY. *Current Pos:* from asst prof to assoc prof zool, 75-88, PROF BIOL SCI, UNIV ALTA, 88- *Personal Data:* b Toronto, Ont, Feb 11, 46; m 70; c 4. *Educ:* Univ Toronto, BSc, 68, MSc, 70, PhD(geol), 74. *Prof Exp:* Asst prof biol, Queen's Univ, Kingston, Ont, 74-75. *Concurrent Pos:* Res assoc, Dept Vert Palaeont, Royal Ont Mus, 74-; mem, Alta Paleontol Adv Comt, 78-81 & 88-90; assoc ed, Paleontographica Canadiana, 81- & J Vert Paleont, 89-91; adj assoc prof geol, Univ Alta, 81-88, adj prof, 88- *Mem:* Soc Vert Paleont; Am Soc Ichthyologists & Herpetologists; Soc Syst Biol; Geol Asn Can; Paleont Soc; Paleont Asn. *Res:* Fossil fishes, especially faunal and phylogenetic studies of Tertiary freshwater teleosts; zoological systematics; paleoecology of lacustrine sediments, taphonomy of freshwater organisms; Tertiary insects; anatomy and phylogeny of recent fishes. *Mailing Add:* Dept Biol Sci Univ Alta Edmonton AB T6G 2E9 Can. *Fax:* 403-492-9234

**WILSON, MARLENE ANN,** INTERACTIONS BETWEEN HORMONE & NEUROTRANSMITTER SYSTEMS, NEURAL ADAPTATIONS TO CHRONIC DRUG EXPOSURE. *Current Pos:* asst prof, 88-94, ASSOC PROF PHARMACOL, SCH MED, UNIV SC, 94- *Personal Data:* b Cleveland, Ohio, June 22, 56. *Educ:* Muskingum Col, New Concord, Ohio, BS(chem) & BS(biol), 78; Univ Ill, Champaign-Urbana, PhD(neurobiol), 85. *Prof Exp:* Lab technician anesthesia res, Mass Gen Hosp, 79; teaching asst techniques in biol psychol, Univ Ill, 80-85 & res asst psychol, 80-82; fel, Dept Psychiat, Yale Univ Sch Med, 85-88; instr, Nurse Anesthesia Pharmacol Course, Univ SC, Richland Mem Hosp, 88-93. *Mem:* Soc Neurosci; Am Soc Pharmacol & Exp Therapeut; Int Soc Psychoneuroendocrinol; Southeastern Pharmacol Soc. *Res:* How gender- and stress-related factors modify responses to benzodiazepines and antidepressants, including the neuronal adaptations associated with chronic exposure to these drugs; assessment of alterations in the gamma-aminobutyric acid- benzodiazepine receptor complex using biochemical and electrophysiological techniques. *Mailing Add:* Univ SC Sch Med Columbia SC 29208. *Fax:* 803-733-3197; *E-Mail:* marlene@med.sc.edu

**WILSON, MARLENE MOORE,** HUMAN ANATOMY, NEUROENDOCRINOLOGY. *Current Pos:* from asst prof to assoc prof, 76-90, chair, Dept Phys & Life Sci, 86-93, PROF BIOL, UNIV PORTLAND, 90-, SPEC ASST TO DEAN SCI, 93- *Personal Data:* b Austin, Tex, July 4, 47; m 70; c Colin M. *Educ:* Univ St Thomas, BA, 69; Baylor Col Med, PhD(anat), 75. *Prof Exp:* Res asst neuropharmacol, Med Sch, Univ Tex, San Antonio, 69-70; res assoc neuroendocrinol, Health Sci Ctr, Univ Ore, 74-75, res fel endocrinol, 75-76. *Concurrent Pos:* Teaching asst, Baylor Col Med, 70-72; instr anat, Health Sci Ctr, Univ Ore, 74-75; clin res asst prof med, Ore Health Sci Univ, 79-; consult, Providence Med Ctr, 79-84. *Mem:* Am Asn Anatomists; Endocrine Soc; Am Physiol Soc; Soc Neurosci; Geront Soc Am. *Res:* Regulation of pituitary secretion of ACTH by the nervous system; circadian rhythmicity and the role of the hippocampus in regulating the pituitary-adrenal axis; stress and health. *Mailing Add:* 6700 N Richmond Portland OR 97203. *E-Mail:* wilson@uofport.edu

**WILSON, MARTIN,** CHEMISTRY. *Current Pos:* RETIRED. *Personal Data:* b Berlin, Ger, June 12, 13; US citizen; m 47; c 2. *Educ:* Univ Geneva, DSc(constitution of starch), 39. *Prof Exp:* Res chemist, Palestine Potash Co, 43-48, Bonneville Ltd, Utah, 48-55, Kennecott Copper Corp, Utah, 55-56 & Nat Potash Co, NMex, 56; from res chemist to sr res chemist, US Borax Res Corp, 56-62, sr scientist, 62-79; consult, 79. *Mem:* Am Chem Soc. *Res:* Potash refining; phase equilibrium; beneficiation of fluorspar ores and molybdenite ores. *Mailing Add:* 3172 Via Vista No A Laguna Hills CA 92653-2742

**WILSON, MARVIN CRACRAFT,** PHARMACY, PHARMACOLOGY. *Current Pos:* asst prof, 70-73, assoc prof, 73-80, PROF PHARMACOL, SCH PHARM, UNIV MISS, 80- *Personal Data:* b Wheeling, WVa, Aug 7, 43; m 66; c 2. *Educ:* WVa Univ, BS, 66; Univ Mich, Ann Arbor, PhD(pharmacol), 70. *Prof Exp:* Res assoc, Dept Psychiat, Univ Chicago, 70. *Concurrent Pos:* Mem, Int Study Group Invest Drugs as Reinforcers. *Mem:* Sigma Xi; Am Asn Cols Pharm; Am Soc Pharmacol & Exp Therapeut; Soc Stimulus Properties Drugs. *Res:* Neurochemical, neurophysiological and neuropharmacological factors which mediate psychomotor stimulant self-administration behavior; pharmacokinetics of stimulant self-administration; effects of central nervous system drugs on positively and negatively reinforced behavior and group behavior of non-human primates. *Mailing Add:* Dept Pharmacol Sch Pharm Univ Miss University MS 38677-9999

**WILSON, MASON P, JR,** FLUID MECHANICS, HEAT TRANSFER. *Current Pos:* assoc prof fluid mech & heat transfer, 68-76, PROF MECH ENG & APPL MECH & DIR, UNIV RI, 76- *Personal Data:* b Albany, NY, Jan 15, 33; wid; c 2. *Educ:* State Univ NY, Albany, BS, 57; Univ Conn, MS, 60, PhD(mech eng), 68. *Prof Exp:* Mathematician, Res & Develop Lab, Elec Boat Div, Gen Dynamics Corp, 57-58, engr, 58-62; sr analytical engr advan propulsion group, Pratt & Whitney Aircraft, United Aircraft Corp, 62-64, admin supvr heat transfer, 64; res engr, Neptune Res Lab, Neptune Meter Co, 64-68. *Concurrent Pos:* Consult, Neptune Res Lab, Neptune Meter Co, 68- *Mem:* Am Soc Mech Engrs. *Res:* Fluidics; thermodynamics; thermophysical & environmental properties; flow instrumentation. *Mailing Add:* Dept Mech Eng & Appl Mech Univ RI Wales Hall Kingston RI 02881

**WILSON, MATHEW KENT,** physical chemistry, for more information see previous edition

**WILSON, MAUREEN O,** RETROVIRAL ONCOLOGY, CLINICAL RESEARCH ADMINISTRATION. *Current Pos:* chemist, 76-86, admin officer, 86-93, ASST DIR, NAT CANCER INST, 93- *Personal Data:* b Boston, Mass, Feb 20, 54; m 87, James H; c Lisa M & Karen F. *Educ:* Wellesley Col, BA, 75; Am Univ, PhD(biochem), 83. *Prof Exp:* Res assoc, Meloy Labs, 75-76. *Mem:* Fel Am Inst Chemists; NY Acad Sci; Grad Women Sci. *Res:* Molecular, biological and immunological study of oncogenes and products for the development of clinical tools. *Mailing Add:* Nat Cancer Inst 31 Ctr Dr Bldg 31 Rm 4A48 Bethesda MD 20892. *Fax:* 301-402-1508

**WILSON, MERLE R(OBERT),** MECHANICAL ENGINEERING. *Current Pos:* RETIRED. *Personal Data:* b Rochester, NY, July 16, 32; m 56; c 4. *Educ:* Cleveland State Univ, BME, 55. *Prof Exp:* Study engr, Pipe Mach Co, 53-54; asst engr, Bell Aircraft Co, 54; assoc mech engr, Cornell Aeronaut Lab, 55-63, res engr, 63-66; sr reliability engr, Moog Inc, 66-70, sr design engr, 70-88, engr group leader, 88-90, eng sect head, 90-97. *Res:* Design and evaluation of servo valves, servo actuators and servo actuation systems relating to military, space and commercial applications; stress and fatigue analysis; finite element analysis and fracture mechanics; design and evaluation of test techniques for purposes of product development and design verification. *Mailing Add:* 186 Breezewood Common East Amherst NY 14051

**WILSON, MICHAEL FRIEND,** CARDIOLOGY, NUCLEAR MEDICINE. *Current Pos:* ASSOC CHIEF STAFF RES, VET ADMIN HOSP, OKLAHOMA CITY, 76-, PROF MED & ASSOC PROF NUCLEAR MED, 76-, DIR NUCLEAR CARDIOL, OKLA MEM HOSP & OKLAHOMA CITY VET ADMIN MED CTR, 79- *Personal Data:* b Morgantown, WVa, Jan 13, 27; m 54; c 5. *Educ:* WVa Univ, AB, 49; Univ Pa, MD, 53. *Prof Exp:* From intern to resident med, Presby Hosp, Philadelphia, 53-55; resident physician internal med, Med Ctr, Temple Univ, 55-57; from asst prof to assoc prof physiol & biophys, Col Med, Univ Ky, 60-65; prof physiol & biophys & chmn dept, Med Ctr, WVa Univ, 65-76, clin prof med, 73-76. *Concurrent Pos:* Fel physiol & cardiol, Med Ctr, Temple Univ, 57-58; res fel physiol & biophys, Sch Med, Univ Wash, 58-60; NIH fel, 59-60; vis prof, Sch Med, Univ Nottingham, 72-73. *Mem:* Fel Am Col Cardiol; Am

Physiol Soc; Shock Soc; Pavlovian Soc NAm; Am Heart Asn; Fedn Am Soc Exp Biol. *Res:* Neurocirculatory control, cardiovascular dynamics and behavior correlates; myocardial contractility and cardiac function; coronary artery disease. *Mailing Add:* Dept Cardiol Millard Fillmore Hosp 3 Gates Circle Buffalo NY 14209

**WILSON, MICHAEL JOHN,** CELL BIOLOGY, MALE REPRODUCTIVE BIOLOGY. *Current Pos:* res assoc, Univ Minn, 73-75, asst prof, 75-82, ASSOC PROF LAB MED & PATH, UNIV MINN, MINNEAPOLIS, 82-; RES BIOCHEMIST, VET ADMIN MED CTR, MINNEAPOLIS, 76- *Personal Data:* b Iowa City, Iowa, June 3, 42; m 69, Martha Swartzwelter; c Matthew. *Educ:* St Ambrose Col, BA, 64; Univ Iowa, MS, 67, PhD(zool), 71. *Prof Exp:* NIH fel biochem, Harvard Univ, 71-73. *Concurrent Pos:* Raine vis prof, Univ Western Australia, 96. *Mem:* Am Soc Androl; Am Soc Cell Biol; Endocrine Soc; Soc Study Reproduction. *Res:* Prostate cancer and prostate diseases; the role of proteases and peptidases in normal and pathological changes of tissue organization of the prostate; constituents of prostatic fluid as markers of prostate disease and in semen function. *Mailing Add:* Res Serv Vet Admin Med Ctr 1 Veterans Dr Minneapolis MN 55417. *Fax:* 612-725-2093; *E-Mail:* wilso042@maroon.tc.umn.edu

**WILSON, MIRIAM GEISENDORFER,** MEDICINE, PEDIATRICS. *Current Pos:* PROF PEDIAT, SCH MED, UNIV SOUTHERN CALIF, 69- *Personal Data:* b Yakima, Wash, Dec 3, 22; m 47, Howard J; c 5. *Educ:* Univ Wash, BS, 44, MS, 45; Univ Calif, MD, 50; Am Bd Pediat, dipl, 57; Am Bd Med Genetics, dipl, 82. *Prof Exp:* Chief genetics div & dir cytogenics lab, Pediat Pavilion, Los Angeles Co-Univ Southern Calif Med Ctr, 65-87. *Mem:* Am Acad Pediat; Am Pediat Soc; Am Soc Human Genetics; AMA; Am Col Med Genetics. *Res:* Medical genetics and cytogenetics; medical problems of the newborn and premature infant; growth and development of the infant and child; maternal and child health. *Mailing Add:* Dept Pediat Los Angeles Co-Univ Southern Calif Med Ctr Los Angeles CA 90033. *Fax:* 213-226-5049

**WILSON, MONTE DALE,** GEOLOGY. *Current Pos:* dean arts & sci, 85-86, prof, 69-97, EMER PROF GEOL, BOISE STATE UNIV, 97- *Personal Data:* b Pomeroy, Wash, Nov 16, 38; m 62, Helen L Grainge; c Monte D Jr & Tima L. *Educ:* Brigham Young Univ, BS, 62; Univ Idaho, MS, 68, PhD(geol), 70. *Prof Exp:* Geophysicist, Can Magnetic Reduction, Ltd, Alta, 62-63 & US Army Ballistic Res Labs, 63-65; teacher high schs, Idaho, 65-67; instr geol, Univ Idaho, 68-69. *Concurrent Pos:* Mem, Idaho Bd Registration Prof Geologists, 75-80; Fulbright sr fel, Univ Salzburg, 81-82. *Mem:* Int Mountain Soc; Am Quaternary Asn; Nat Asn Geol Teachers; Geol Soc Am. *Res:* Earth science education; environmental geology. *Mailing Add:* Dept Geosci Boise State Univ Boise ID 83725. *Fax:* 208-385-4061; *E-Mail:* mwilson@trex.idbsu.edu

**WILSON, NANCY KEELER,** ENVIRONMENTAL SCIENCE. *Current Pos:* res chemist, US Environ Protection Agency, 74-81, chief, Anal Methods Res Sect, 81-91, chief, Human Exposure Res Br, 91-95, RES CHEMIST & SR SCI ADV, US ENVIRON PROTECTION AGENCY, 95- *Personal Data:* b Walton, NY, Apr 20, 37; m 59, James F; c 3. *Educ:* Univ Rochester, BS, 59; Carnegie-Mellon Univ, MS, 62, PhD(chem), 66. *Honors & Awards:* Sigma Xi. *Prof Exp:* Res assoc chem, Ohio State Univ, Columbus, 66-67; res assoc & lectr chem, Univ NC, Chapel Hill, 67-69; sr staff fel chem, Nat Inst Environ Health Sci, 70-74. *Concurrent Pos:* Instr, Point Park Jr Col, 62-63; lectr math, Carnegie-Mellon Univ, 63-65; fac affil, Colo State Univ, 76-77. *Mem:* Am Chem Soc; Am Inst Chemists; Sigma Xi. *Res:* Applications of spectroscopic techniques to problems in physical organic chemistry; environmental chemistry, toxicology and metabolism; author or coauthor of over 200 publications. *Mailing Add:* 6319 Mimosa Dr Chapel Hill NC 27514-9747

**WILSON, NIGEL HENRY MOIR,** TRANSPORTATION. *Current Pos:* Res asst, 66-68, from instr to assoc prof, 68-82, PROF CIVIL ENG, MASS INST TECHNOL, 82- *Personal Data:* b Kent, Eng, Aug 8, 44; m 70; c 1. *Educ:* Imp Col, Univ London, BSc, 65; Mass Inst Technol, SM, 67, PhD(civil eng), 69. *Concurrent Pos:* Consult, Mass Bay Trans Authority, Budget Off, 85-86; mem, Transp Res Bd; vis prof planning, Dept Civil Eng, Stanford Univ, 77-78. *Res:* Transportation systems analysis; urban transportation; public transportation. *Mailing Add:* Dept Civil Eng Mass Inst Technol 77 Massachusetts Ave Cambridge MA 02139-4307

**WILSON, NIXON ALBERT,** ACAROLOGY. *Current Pos:* from asst prof to assoc prof, 69-75, PROF BIOL, UNIV NORTHERN IOWA, 75- *Personal Data:* b Litchfield, Ill, May 20, 30; m 63, Nell Hines; c Stephen & David. *Educ:* Earlham Col, BA, 52; Univ Mich, MWM, 54; Purdue Univ, PhD(entom), 61. *Prof Exp:* Animal ecologist, Plague Res Lab, Hawaii State Dept Health, 61-62; acarologist, B P Bishop Mus, 62-69. *Concurrent Pos:* USPHS res grants, B P Bishop Mus, 67-69; grants, Univ Northern Iowa, 69-; res assoc, Fla State Collection Arthropods, Fla Dept Agr & Consumer Serv, 70-; zool ed, J Iowa Acad Sci, 76-91; guest investr, Mus Zool, Nat Univ Mexico, 82; Iowa Sci Found grant, 86-87. *Mem:* Am Soc Mammal; Am Soc Parasitol; Acarological Soc Am; Entomol Soc Am. *Res:* Ectoparasites of vertebrates, especially ticks, mites and fleas. *Mailing Add:* Dept Biol Univ Northern Iowa Cedar Falls IA 50614-0421. *Fax:* 319-273-7125

**WILSON, OLIN C(HADDOCK),** astronomy, optics; deceased, see previous edition for last biography

WILSON, OSCAR BRYAN, JR, PHYSICS. *Current Pos:* assoc prof, 57-62, PROF PHYSICS, NAVAL POSTGRAD SCH, 62- *Personal Data:* b Tex, Aug 15, 22; m 45; c 3. *Educ:* Univ Tex, BS, 44; Univ Calif, Los Angeles, MA, 48, PhD, 51. *Prof Exp:* Mem tech staff, Hughes Aircraft Co, 51-52; physicist, Soundrive Engine Co, 52-57. *Concurrent Pos:* Vis prof, ISEN, Lille, France, 89-90. *Mem:* AAAS; Am Phys Soc; Acoust Soc Am; Inst Elec & Electronics Engrs; Sigma Xi. *Res:* Engineering acoustics; underwater acoustics. *Mailing Add:* Dept Physics Naval Postgrad Sch Monterey CA 93943

WILSON, P DAVID, STATISTICS, BIOMATHEMATICS. *Current Pos:* asst prof, Dept Surg, Med Sch, Ctr Study Trauma, Univ Md, 72-74, asst prof, Dept Epidemiol & Prev Med, 74-81, ASSOC PROF, DEPT EPIDEMIOL & PREV MED, MED SCH, UNIV MD, BALTIMORE, 81-87 & 89- *Personal Data:* b Roswell, NMex, Oct 4, 33; m 65; c 1. *Educ:* Univ Colo, Boulder, BA, 56; Univ Minn, Minneapolis, MS, 63; Johns Hopkins Univ, PhD(biostatist), 70. *Prof Exp:* Res assoc, Med Sch, Univ Md, Baltimore, 64-66; consult, Dept Surg, Ctr Study Trauma, Med Sch, Univ Md, Baltimore, 67-70; asst prof biomet, Med Col Va, 70-71; math statistician, Bur Drugs, Food & Drug Admin, HEW, 71-72; assoc prof, Dept Epidemiol & Biostatist, Col Pub Health, Univ SFla, Tampa, 87-88. *Concurrent Pos:* Prin investr res grants in hypertension, 85-86; comput brain metab, 86-88; consult nuclear med, Johns Hopkins Univ, 86-; longitudinal data analysis, 91-94; Nat Res Serv Awards fel, USPHS, 82-83. *Mem:* Biomet Soc; Am Statist Asn. *Res:* Mathematics, statistics and computing in biomedical research. *Mailing Add:* Dept Epidemiol & Prev Med Univ Md Sch Med 655 W Baltimore Baltimore MD 21201-1559

WILSON, PAUL ROBERT, MATHEMATICS. *Current Pos:* ASSOC PROF MATH, ROCHESTER INST TECHNOL, 80- *Personal Data:* b Chicago, Ill, Oct 25, 39. *Educ:* Univ Cincinnati, BA, 61, MA, 62; Univ Ill, PhD(math), 67. *Prof Exp:* Asst prof math, Univ Nebr, Lincoln, 67-71; asst prof math, Alma Col, 71-80. *Mem:* Am Math Soc. *Res:* Algebra, statistics. *Mailing Add:* Dept Math Rochester Inst Technol Rochester NY 14623-5640

WILSON, PEGGY MAYFIELD DUNLAP, SURFACE CHEMISTRY, OIL FIELD CHEMISTRY. *Current Pos:* PRES, STONE GAP INDUST CORP, 94- *Personal Data:* b Austin, Tex, Mar 24, 27; m 75, William W III. *Educ:* Univ Tex, BS, 48, PhD(chem), 52. *Prof Exp:* Spec instr chem, Univ Tex, 52-53; sr res technologist, Mobil Res & Develop Corp, 53-67, res assoc, 67-84, mgr, Anal Serv, 84-85 & Corrosion, Well Stream Processing & Core Anal, 85-89. *Concurrent Pos:* Dir, Stone Gap Indust Corp, 68-; State Republican Committeewoman, 71-80; dir, JayBee Mfg Co, 80-88; regent, ETex State Univ, 81-87; mem adv coun, Col Natural Sci Found, Univ Tex, Austin, 87-90; pres, Greater Duncanville Indust Corp, 94-; pres, Cedar Hill Econ Devel Corp, 94-96. *Mem:* Am Chem Soc; Soc Petrol Engrs. *Res:* Interfacial tension and contact angles; tertiary oil recovery; corrosion; wellstream processing; rock properties; management of research in these topics. *Mailing Add:* 1819 W Belt Line Rd Cedar Hill TX 75104-5615

WILSON, PERRY BAKER, ACCELERATOR PHYSICS, HIGH POWER MICROWAVE TUBES & COMPONENTS. *Current Pos:* res assoc, High Energy Physics Lab, Stanford Univ, 59-64, assoc dir opers, 64-68, sr res assoc, 69-74, PROF APPL RES, STANFORD LINEAR ACCELERATOR CTR, STANFORD UNIV, 74- *Personal Data:* b Norman, Okla, Feb 24, 27; m 82, Gerda von Steht; c Perry F & John A. *Educ:* Wash State Univ, BS, 50, MS, 52; Stanford Univ, PhD(physics), 58. *Honors & Awards:* Particle Accelerator Technol Prize, Inst Elec & Electronics Engrs, 91. *Prof Exp:* Staff physicist, Linfield Res Inst, Ore, 58-59. *Concurrent Pos:* Vis scientist, Europ Orgn, Nuclear Res, Geneva, Switz, 68-69, 77-78; consult, Gen Atomic Div, Gen Dynamics Corp, Calif, 63-64, Phys Electronics Labs, 64, Varian Assocs, 74-77, Western Res Corp, 82-83 & Rocketdyne Div, Rockwell Int Corp, 87-89, STI Optronics, 91, Duly Res Inc, 91-94. *Mem:* Sr mem Inst Elec & Electronics Engrs; Sigma Xi; fel Am Phys Soc. *Res:* Theory and design of linear electron accelerators and storage rings for high energy particle physics; theory and design of high power rating factor sources components for electron linacs. *Mailing Add:* Stanford Linear Accelerator Ctr PO Box 4349 MS-26 Stanford CA 94309-4349

WILSON, PHILO CALHOUN, STRATIGRAPHY, MARINE GEOLOGY. *Current Pos:* assoc prof, Col Oneota, State Univ NY, 63-64, chmn dept, 67-73 & 76-84, prof earth sci, 64-78, distinguished teaching prof, 78-85, EMER DISTINGUISHED TEACHING PROF, COL ONEOTA, STATE UNIV NY, 85- *Personal Data:* b Westfield, Mass, Jan 29, 24; m 47; c 3. *Educ:* Williams Col, AB, 48; Cornell Univ, MS, 50; Wash State Univ, PhD(stratig), 54. *Prof Exp:* From geologist to staff geologist, Sohio Petrol Co, 54-60; area geologist, Champlin Oil Co, 60-63. *Concurrent Pos:* Mem selection panels rev NSF proposals, 65-66 & 70. *Mem:* Am Asn Petrol Geol. *Res:* Sedimentation; regional stratigraphic analysis; Pennsylvanian system of Wyoming. *Mailing Add:* 2 Gull Lane Orleans MA 02653

WILSON, RAY FLOYD, ANALYTICAL CHEMISTRY, PHYSICAL CHEMISTRY. *Current Pos:* from assoc prof to prof, 53-88, chmn chem, 85-87, LLOYD L WOODS DISTINGUISHED PROF CHEM, TEX SOUTHERN UNIV, 88- *Personal Data:* b Lee Co, Tex, Feb 20, 26; m 57, Faye D Gray; c Ray Jr, Freddie, Roy & Mercedes. *Educ:* Houston-Tillotson Col, BS, 50; Tex Southern Univ, MS, 61; Univ Tex, PhD(chem), 53, JD, 72. *Prof Exp:* Asst, Univ Tex, 51-53. *Concurrent Pos:* Grants, Res Corp, 53-55, NSF, 54, 56, Welch Found, 57-68, Environ Protection Agency, 66-73, NASA 73- & Agency Toxic Substances & Dis Registry, 92- *Mem:* Am Chem Soc; Soc Environ Geochem & Health; Nat Org Prof Advan Black Chemists & Chem Engrs. *Res:* Interaction of platinum elements with certain organic reagents; electrochemical study of the interaction of selected transition elements with certain organic reagents. *Mailing Add:* Chem Dept Tex Southern Univ 3506 Arbor Houston TX 77004-6423. *Fax:* 713-527-7824

WILSON, RAYMOND GALE, PROBLEMS OF NUCLEAR WAR & DISARMAMENT, HIROSHIMA & NAGASAKI EXPERIENCE. *Current Pos:* EMER PROF PHYSICS, ILL WESLEYAN UNIV, 62- *Personal Data:* m 56, 85, Akiko Omoto; c Laura, Timothy, David, Aya & Taiyo. *Educ:* Univ Ill, BS, 58, MS, 60; Univ Ariz, PhD(optical sci), 71. *Prof Exp:* Instr physics/ chem, Mid-Pac Inst, 60-62. *Concurrent Pos:* Vis scholar, Hiroshima Jogakuin Univ, 83, 86, 89, 92 & 95. *Mem:* Am Asn Physics Teachers; Optical Soc Am; Int Peace Res Asn; Peace Studies Asn Japan. *Res:* Fourier optical transform techniques in contemporary optics; searching for solution to world war-peace problem based upon J R Oppenheimer's conjecture. *Mailing Add:* 20 Linda Lane Normal IL 61761. *Fax:* 309-556-3864; *E-Mail:* rwilson@titan.iwu.edu

WILSON, RICHARD, PHYSICS. *Current Pos:* from asst prof to assoc prof, 55-61, PROF PHYSICS, HARVARD UNIV, 61- *Personal Data:* b London, Eng, Apr 29, 26; m 52, Andree D Dumund; c 6. *Educ:* Oxford Univ, BA, 46, MA & DPhil(physics), 49; Harvard Univ, MA, 56. *Honors & Awards:* Forum Award, Am Phy Soc, 90; Distinguished Achievement Award, Soc Risk Anal, 93. *Prof Exp:* Res lectr physics, Christ Church, Oxford Univ, 48-53, res officer, Clarendon Lab, 53-55. *Concurrent Pos:* Res assoc, Univ Rochester, 50-51 & Stanford Univ, 51-52; Guggenheim fel, 61 & 69; Fulbright fel, 61 & 69; trustee, Univs Res Asn, 68-74; consult, Energy Res Develop Agency, 75-77, Nuclear Regulatory Comn, 75-, Elec Power Res Inst, 75-76, & Energy Eng Bd, Nat Acad Sci, 82-91; vis prof, Univ Grenoble, 81; dir, Regional Ctr Global Environ Change, 90-93. *Mem:* Am Phys Soc; Am Acad Arts & Sci; Soc Psychol Res; Soc Risk Anal; NY Acad Arts & Sci. *Res:* Elementary particle physics; environmental physics. *Mailing Add:* Harvard Univ Cambridge MA 02138. *Fax:* 617-495-0416; *E-Mail:* wilson@huhepl.harvard.edu

WILSON, RICHARD BARR, PATHOLOGY, ELECTRON MICROSCOPY. *Current Pos:* resident path, Univ Nebr Hosp, 53-57, assoc, Col Med, 57-62, from asst prof to assoc prof, 62-70, prof path, Dept Path, microbiol & anat, Col Med & head electron micros sect, Eppley Inst Cancer Res, 70-89, EMER PROF PATH & MICROBIOL, UNIV NEBR MED CTR, 89- *Personal Data:* b Lincoln, Nebr, Apr 21, 21; m 48, Charlotte Brown; c Thomas D & Cheryl A. *Educ:* Univ Nebr, AB, 43, MD, 45; Am Bd Path, dipl, 57. *Prof Exp:* Staff physician, Univ Nebr, Lincoln, 47-52. *Concurrent Pos:* Attend pathologist, Vet Admin Hosp, Omaha, 60-89. *Mem:* Col Am Path; Am Soc Clin Path; Int Acad Path; Am Soc Nephrology. *Res:* Renal disease and biopsies; electron microscopy of human biopsies; morphological studies; animal carcinogenesis; ultrastructure of human neoplasms. *Mailing Add:* 727 Leewood Dr Omaha NE 68154-2943

WILSON, RICHARD HANSEL, PLANT PHYSIOLOGY, BIOCHEMISTRY. *Current Pos:* field scientist, 78-92, COM TECHNOLOGIST, FIELD DEVELOP, EASTERN REGION, SANDOZ CROP PROTECTION, 92- *Personal Data:* b Madison, Wis, Aug 18, 39; m 64, Pat; c Pamela & Mark. *Educ:* Carleton Col, BA, 61; NC State Univ, MS, 64; Ore State Univ, PhD(plant physiol), 67. *Prof Exp:* USPHS fel plant physiol, Univ Ill, Urbana, 67-68; asst prof, Univ Tex, Austin, 68-74; res specialist, Monsanto Chem Co, 74-78. *Mem:* Weed Soc Am. *Res:* Herbicides. *Mailing Add:* Sandoz Crop Protection 1300 E Touhy Ave Des Plaines IL 60018-3304

WILSON, RICHARD HOWARD, ZOOLOGY, ANIMAL BEHAVIOR. *Current Pos:* from instr to assoc prof, 66-90, PROF BIOL, UNIV WIS, STOUT, 90- *Personal Data:* b Spearville, Kans, June 24, 42; m 62; c 1. *Educ:* Kans State Univ, BS, 64, MS, 65; Utah State Univ, PhD(zool), 71. *Prof Exp:* Instr, Prince Makonnen Sec Sch, 65-66. *Mem:* AAAS; Animal Behav Soc; Am Ornith Union; Cooper Ornith Soc; Wilson Ornith Soc; Sigma Xi. *Res:* Animal communication; display postures and signaling mechanisms in birds. *Mailing Add:* 1319 Oakwood Ave Menomonie WI 54751-2915

WILSON, RICHARD LEE, ENTOMOLOGY, HOST PLANT RESISTANCE. *Current Pos:* RES ENTOMOLOGIST, AGR RES SERV, IOWA STATE UNIV, USDA, AMES, 80- *Personal Data:* b Marshalltown, Iowa, Sept 18, 39; m 60, Sally E Ladd; c Jeffrey S, John B & Sarah J (Anderson). *Educ:* Univ Northern Iowa, BA, 61; Tex A&M Univ, MS, 65; Iowa State Univ, PhD(entom), 71. *Prof Exp:* Teacher, Independent Sch Dist, Iowa, 65-68; res entomologist, Agr Res Serv, USDA, Phoenix, Ariz, 71-77 & Okla State Univ, 77-80. *Mem:* Entom Soc Am; Sigma Xi. *Res:* Host plant resistance; evaluation of plant introduction germplasm for resistance to several insect pests. *Mailing Add:* Regional Plant Introduction Sta Iowa State Univ Ames IA 50011. *Fax:* 515-294-4880; *E-Mail:* rlwilson@iastate.edu

WILSON, ROBERT BURTON, COMPARATIVE PATHOLOGY. *Current Pos:* CONSULT, 88- *Personal Data:* b Salt Lake City, Utah, June 29, 36; m 62, Janet D McMurdie; c Robert B Jr & Janet D. *Educ:* Utah State Univ, BS, 58; Wash State Univ, DVM, 61; Univ Toronto, PhD(physiol), 67. *Honors & Awards:* Mary Mitchell Res Award, 63. *Prof Exp:* Intern vet med, Angell Mem Animal Hosp, 62-63; asst prof animal sci, Brigham Young Univ, 63-64; res investr, Hosp Sick Children, 64-67, asst scientist, 67-69; assoc prof nutrit & animal path, Mass Inst Technol, 69-73; prof vet path, Univ Mo, 73-76; prof microbiol & path & chmn dept, Wash State Univ, 76-83, dean, Col Vet Med, 83, 88. *Concurrent Pos:* Lectr physiol, Univ Toronto, 67-69; mem, Coun on Arteriosclerosis, Am Heart Asn. *Mem:* Am Vet Med Asn; Am Inst Nutrit; Am Heart Asn. *Res:* Nutrition; diabetes; carcinogenesis; cardiovascular diseases; experimental pathology of nutrition and cardiovascular diseases; education; critical thinking. *Mailing Add:* Col Vet Med Wash State Univ Pullman WA 99164-7040. *Fax:* 509-335-8529; *E-Mail:* rwilson@vetmed.wsu.edu

**WILSON, ROBERT E**, STELLAR ASTROPHYSICS, BINARY STARS. *Current Pos:* prof physics & astron, 75-79, PROF ASTRON, UNIV FLA, 79- *Personal Data:* b Norristown, Pa, Jan 16, 37; div; c 2. *Educ:* Univ Pa, AB, 58, MS, 60, PhD(astron), 63. *Prof Exp:* Asst prof astron, Georgetown Univ, 63-66; Nat Res Coun sr res assoc, Inst Space Studies, 72-74; from assoc prof to prof astron, Univ SFla, 66-75. *Concurrent Pos:* Consult, Goddard Space Flight Ctr, NASA, 65-70; res grants, NASA, 66-69, 76-78, NSF, 70-73, 77-79, 80-81, 83-84 & 85-87; Shapley vis lectr, Am Astron Soc, 81-; Sr Scientist Award, Alexander von Humboldt Found, 79. *Mem:* Am Astron Soc; Int Astron Union; Royal Astron Soc; Astron Soc Pac. *Res:* Theory and observation of binary stars; stellar structure and evolution. *Mailing Add:* Dept Astron Univ Fla 211 SSRB Gainesville FL 32611-2002

**WILSON, ROBERT E(LWOOD)**, CHEMICAL ENGINEERING. *Current Pos:* RETIRED. *Personal Data:* b Decatur, Ill, July 2, 26; m 49. *Educ:* Univ Ill, AB, 48, BS, 49, PhD(chem eng), 52; Univ Minn, MS, 50. *Prof Exp:* Proj leader eng res, Corn Prod Refining Co, 52-54; from assoc prof to prof chem eng, Univ Dayton, 54-61, head dept, 54-61, dir, Col Eng Grad Prog, 58-61; mgr eng & develop, Thomas J Lipton, Inc, 61-62, assoc dir develop, 62-64; dir res & develop, Int Minerals & Chem Corp, Ill, 64-67; sr vpres & mem bd dirs, Heidrick & Struggles Inc, Chicago, 67-86. *Concurrent Pos:* Consult, USAF, 55-56, USN, 59-60 & Eng Exp Sta, Univ Wis, 59-60. *Mem:* Am Soc Eng Educ; Inst Nuclear Mgt; Am Inst Chem Engrs. *Res:* Fluid mechanics; high temperature; bioengineering and transport processes. *Mailing Add:* 1926 Wolf Laurel Dr Sun City Center FL 33573

**WILSON, ROBERT EUGENE**, ECOLOGY, GENERAL BIOLOGY. *Current Pos:* from asst prof to assoc prof, 63-70, PROF BIOL, ETEX STATE UNIV, 70- *Personal Data:* b Denton, Tex, Apr 16, 32; m 56; c 3. *Educ:* North Tex State Univ, BS, 52, MS, 56; Univ Tex, PhD(microbiol), 63. *Prof Exp:* Instr biol, Col Arts & Indust, 56-59. *Res:* Cytotoxicity of staphylococcal toxins towards mammalian cells in vitro; changes in serum proteins following x-irradiation; effects of electromagnetic fields on plants and animals; ecology of northeastern Texas pine-oak forests. *Mailing Add:* Dept Biol Sci ETex State Univ Commerce TX 75428-9998

**WILSON, ROBERT FRANCIS**, THORACIC SURGERY, CARDIOVASCULAR SURGERY. *Current Pos:* from instr to assoc prof, 63-71, PROF SURG, SCH MED, WAYNE STATE UNIV, 71- *Personal Data:* b Scranton, Pa, Aug 9, 34; m 72; c 7. *Educ:* Lehigh Univ, BA, 57; Temple Univ, MD, 58. *Concurrent Pos:* Markle scholar acad med; pres med staff, Detroit Gen Receiving Hosp, 72-74; dir, affil prog thoracic surg, Sch Med, Wayne State Univ, 71-89, asst dean, Detroit Gen Hosp Affairs, Wayne State Univ, 72-76; chief sect thoracic & cardiovasc surg, Harper Hosp, 72-89. *Mem:* Soc Univ Surg; Am Asn Thoracic Surg; Am Asn Surg Trauma; Am Col Surg; Am Col Chest Physicians; Am Surg Asn. *Res:* Shock; respiratory failure; fluid and electrolytes; trauma. *Mailing Add:* UHC 4201 St Antoine Sch Med Wayne State Univ Detroit MI 48201

**WILSON, ROBERT G**, chemistry, biochemistry; deceased, see previous edition for last biography

**WILSON, ROBERT GRAY**, ELECTRONICS, NUCLEAR PHYSICS. *Current Pos:* SR MEM TECH STAFF, RES LABS, HUGHES AIRCRAFT CO, 63- *Personal Data:* b Wooster, Ohio, Apr 7, 34; m 57; c 2. *Educ:* Ohio State Univ, BSc, 56, PhD(physics), 61. *Prof Exp:* Prin physicist, Battelle Mem Inst, 54-58; res asst, Res Found, Ohio State Univ, 58-60; sr physicist, NAm Aviation/Rocketdyne, 61-63. *Mem:* Am Phys Soc; Inst Elec & Electronics Eng. *Res:* Ion implantation; semiconductor devices and integrated circuits; electron and ion emission from surfaces; scanning acoustic microscopy; experimental low energy nuclear physics. *Mailing Add:* 20513 Gresham St Winnetka CA 91306

**WILSON, ROBERT HALLOWELL**, ENVIRONMENTAL HEALTH. *Current Pos:* RETIRED. *Personal Data:* b Baltimore, Md, July 30, 24; m 48; c 2. *Educ:* Univ Rochester, BS, 45; Am Bd Indust Hyg, cert, 62. *Prof Exp:* Jr scientist, Atomic Energy Proj, Univ Rochester, 46-51, instr indust hyg & toxicol & asst scientist, 51-56, scientist, 56-62, chief engr, 62-76, asst prof radiation biol & biophys, 56-83, chief environ health & safety & chief safety officer, 75-89, asst prof toxicol, Sch Med & Dent, 83-89. *Mem:* AAAS; Am Nuclear Soc; Health Physics Soc; Am Indust Hyg Asn. *Res:* Generation, sampling and behavior of aerosols; control of radiation hazards; air safety considerations of nuclear weapons transport and storage; environmental impact of mercury. *Mailing Add:* 84 S Main St Pittsford NY 14534

**WILSON, ROBERT JOHN**, RADIOLOGICAL PHYSICS, NUCLEAR MEDICINE. *Current Pos:* asst prof radiol, 69-72, assoc prof nuclear med, 72-78, PROF RADIOLOGY, UNIV TENN, MEMPHIS, 78- *Personal Data:* b St Louis, Mo, Apr 23, 35; m 57; c 5. *Educ:* St Mary's Univ, Tex, BS & BA, 56; Washington Univ, St Louis, PhD(physics), 63. *Prof Exp:* Res assoc physics, Washington Univ, 63-66; res physicist, US Naval Radiol Defense Lab, San Francisco, 66-69. *Mem:* Am Asn Physicists Med; Am Phys Soc; Soc Nuclear Med; Am Col Radiol; Radiol Soc NAm; Sigma Xi. *Mailing Add:* 217 Fleur De Lis CV Memphis TN 38117

**WILSON, ROBERT LEE**, MATHEMATICS. *Current Pos:* prof, 58-79, EMER PROF, OHIO WESLEYAN UNIV, 79- *Personal Data:* b Champaign, Ill, Mar 7, 17; m 40; c 4. *Educ:* Univ Fla, AB, 38; Univ Wis, MA, 40, PhD(math), 47. *Prof Exp:* Asst math, Univ Wis, 39-41, 46-47; from instr to asst prof, Univ Tenn, 47-56; sr aerophys engr, Gen Dynamics/Convair, Tex,

56-58. *Concurrent Pos:* Adj prof, Tex Christian Univ, 56-58; vis prof & dir comput ctr, Univ Ibadan, 66-68, Univ Western Australia, 80 & Washington & Lee Univ, 81; gov, Math Asn Am, 75-77. *Mem:* Am Math Soc; Math Asn Am; Nat Coun Teachers Math. *Res:* Galois theory; computing. *Mailing Add:* 6000 Riverside Dr Apt A-339 Friendship Village Dublin OH 43017

**WILSON, ROBERT LEE**, LIE ALGEBRAS. *Current Pos:* from asst prof to assoc prof, 71-80, PROF MATH, RUTGERS UNIV, NEW BRUNSWICK, 80-, CHAIR, 90- *Personal Data:* b Washington, DC, Jan 16, 46; m 67; c 2. *Educ:* Am Univ, BA, 65; Yale Univ, PhD(math), 69. *Prof Exp:* Instr math, Courant Inst Math Sci, NY Univ, 69-71. *Mem:* Am Math Soc; Math Asn Am. *Res:* Lie algebras over fields of prime characteristic; Kac-Moody Lie algebras. *Mailing Add:* Dept Math Rutgers Univ New Brunswick NJ 08903-2101

**WILSON, ROBERT LEE, JR**, MATHEMATICS. *Current Pos:* PROF MATH, UNIV WIS-MADISON, 90-, DIR MATH OUTREACH, 90- *Personal Data:* b Auburn, Ala, Jan 3, 42; m 62; c 2. *Educ:* Ohio Wesleyan Univ, BA, 62; Univ Wis-Madison, MA, 63, PhD(math), 69. *Prof Exp:* Asst prof math, Univ Wis-Madison, 69-75; prof math & comput sci, Washington & Lee Univ, 75-84; sr scientist, Zilog Corp, 84-87; prin engr & scientist, Ford Aerospace Corp, 87-90. *Mem:* Am Math Soc; Math Asn Am. *Res:* Combinatorics; graph theory; universal algebra; microcomputers; generalizations of group theory. *Mailing Add:* Dept Math Van Vleck Hall Univ Wis 480 Lincoln Dr Madison WI 53706-1388

**WILSON, ROBERT NORTON**, MATHEMATICAL PHYSICS, ATMOSPHERIC PHYSICS. *Current Pos:* PRES, DAVID B RES, 89- *Personal Data:* b Walla Walla, Wash, Oct 7, 27; m 55; c 1. *Educ:* Whitman Col, AB, 48; Stanford Univ, MS, 50, PhD(physics, math), 60. *Prof Exp:* Res scientist microwaves, Kane Eng Labs, Calif, 60-65, atmospheric physics, Lockheed Res Lab, 65-71, Radiative Transfer & Hydrodynamics, Mission Res Corp, 71-75, New Millennium Assocs, 75-82; eng consult, Sundstand Corp, 83-89. *Mem:* Am Phys Soc; Am Inst Physics. *Res:* Electronics reliability, transient radiation effects on electronics, electromagnetic propagation; multiple quantum effect physics; non-equilibrium statistical mechanics; hydrodynamics; magnetohydrodynamics; radiation physics; acoustic gravitation waves; interaction of electromagnetic radiation with relativistically moving plasma fronts; ground water flow; optical fluorescence detection systems. *Mailing Add:* 16 W Mountain Dr Santa Barbara CA 93103

**WILSON, ROBERT PAUL**, BIOCHEMISTRY, FISH NUTRITION. *Current Pos:* from asst prof to assoc prof biochem, 69-77, head biochem dept, 79-89, PROF BIOCHEM, MISS STATE UNIV, 77- *Personal Data:* b Revere, Mo, Dec 28, 41; m 62; c 3. *Educ:* Univ Mo, Columbia, BSEd, 63, MS, 65, PhD(biochem), 68. *Honors & Awards:* Res Award, Catfish Farmers Am, 81. *Prof Exp:* Instr agr chem, Univ Mo, Columbia, 68-69. *Concurrent Pos:* Vis prof, Inst Marine Biochem, Aberdeen, Scotland, 84. *Mem:* Am Inst Nutrit; Catfish Farmers Am. *Res:* Comparative biochemistry and nutrition of channel catfish; fish nutrition in general. *Mailing Add:* Miss State Univ Dept Biochem PO Box 9650 Mississippi State MS 39762. Fax: 601-325-8664

**WILSON, ROBERT RATHBUN**, PHYSICS. *Current Pos:* CONSULT, 82- *Personal Data:* b Frontier, Wyo, Mar 4, 14; m 40; c 3. *Educ:* Univ Calif, AB, 36, PhD(physics), 40. *Hon Degrees:* MA, Harvard Univ, 46; DSc, Notre Dame, Univ Bonn, WGer, Harvard, 86, Weslayan, 87. *Honors & Awards:* Elliot Cresson Medal, Franklin Inst; Nat Medal Sci, 73; Fermi Award, 84; del Regato Medal Med, 89. *Prof Exp:* From instr to asst prof physics, Princeton Univ, 40-46, in tech chg isotron develop proj, 42-43; physicist, Los Alamos Sci Lab, 43-46, leader cyclotron group, 43-44, head exp res div, 44-46; assoc prof physics, Harvard Univ, 46-47; prof physics & dir, Lab Nuclear Studies, Cornell Univ, 47-67; Ritzma prof, Dept Physics & Enrico Fermi Inst Nuclear Studies, Univ Chicago, 67-80, dir, Fermi Nat Accelerator Lab, 67-78; Michael Pupin prof, Columbia Univ, 80-82. *Concurrent Pos:* Mem, Comt Atomic Casualties, Nat Res Coun, 48-51; exchange prof, Univ Paris, 54-55; mem, Steering Comt, Proj Sherwood, US AEC, 58-; Fulbright fel, 61; chmn bd trustees, Aspen Physics Ctr, 85. *Mem:* Nat Acad Sci; Am Phys Soc (pres, 85); Am Acad Arts & Sci; Am Philos Soc. *Res:* Nuclear and particle physics. *Mailing Add:* 916 Stewart Ave Ithaca NY 14850

**WILSON, ROBERT STEPHEN**, RING THEORY, MATH EDUCATION. *Current Pos:* LECTR MATH, SONOMA STATE UNIV, 78- *Personal Data:* b Springfield, Ill, Nov 9, 45; m 93, Shirley Jenner; c Abigale, Stephen, Tara, Ashley, Jared & David. *Educ:* Univ Calif, Santa Barbara, BA, 69, MA, 70, PhD(math), 72. *Prof Exp:* Instr math, Univ Tex, Austin, 72-75, Mendocino Community Col, 77-82; troubleshooter, US Census Bur, 76. *Concurrent Pos:* Instr math, Santa Rosa Jr Col, 79-91. *Mem:* Math Asn Am; Am Math Soc. *Res:* Structure theorems for finite rings. *Mailing Add:* Math Dept Sonoma State Univ Rohnert Park CA 94928. *E-Mail:* steve.wilson@sonoma.edu

**WILSON, ROBERT STEVEN**, PHYSICAL CHEMISTRY. *Current Pos:* ATTY. *Personal Data:* b Hartford, Conn, Dec 26, 39; m 66; c 3. *Educ:* Brown Univ, BS, 62, PhD(phys chem), 68; Northern Ill Univ, JD, 84. *Prof Exp:* Fel phys chem, Yale Univ, 68-69; asst prof, Northern Ill Univ, 69-73, assoc prof, 73- *Concurrent Pos:* Res prof, Solid State Sci Div, Argonne Nat Lab, 71-; fel theoret physics, Lorentz Inst, Leiden, Holland. *Mem:* Am Phys Soc; Am Chem Soc; Am Bar Asn; Sigma Xi. *Res:* Statistical mechanics of irreversible processes; optical properties of impurity systems; critical transport properties of fluids; molecular dynamics; computer simulation. *Mailing Add:* 104 N Main St Sycamore IL 60178

**WILSON, ROBERT WARREN,** VERTEBRATE PALEONTOLOGY. *Current Pos:* Rose Morgan vis prof, 77, ASSOC MUS NATURAL HIST, UNIV KANS, 77-, EMER PROF, 80- *Personal Data:* b Oakland, Calif, July 26, 09; wid; c Robert C & Margaret L. *Educ:* Calif Inst Technol, BS, 30, MS, 32, PhD(vert paleontol), 36. *Honors & Awards:* Arnold Guyot Mem Award, Nat Geog Soc, 74. *Prof Exp:* Asst geol, Calif Inst Technol, 30-34, fel, 37-39, Sterling res fel, Yale Univ, 36-37; from instr to asst prof geol, Univ Colo, 39-46, Nat Res Coun fel, 46-47; assoc prof zool & assoc cur vert paleont, Univ Kans, 47-61; prof, SDak Sch Mines & Technol, 61-75, emer prof paleont & dir mus geol, 75; vis prof, Tex Tech Univ, 75-77. *Concurrent Pos:* Guggenheim fel, London, 56-57; Fulbright sr res scholar, Univ Vienna, 67-68; sr res fel, Carnegie Museum Natural Hist, 81; corresp, Natural Hist Museum, Wien, 82- *Mem:* Fel Geol Soc Am; Paleont Soc; Soc Vert Paleont (secy-treas, 54, pres, 55); Am Soc Mammal. *Res:* Tertiary and late cretaceous mammalian faunas. *Mailing Add:* 5207 Windsor Place Lawrence KS 66049

**WILSON, ROBERT WOODROW,** RADIO ASTRONOMY, MOLECULAR CLOUDS. *Current Pos:* SR SCIENTIST, HARVARD SMITHSONIAN CTR ASTROPHYS, 94- *Personal Data:* b Houston, Tex, Jan 10, 36; m 58, Elizabeth; c 3. *Educ:* Rice Univ, BA (Hons), 57; Calif Inst Technol, PhD(physics), 62. *Honors & Awards:* Nobel Prize in Physics, 78; Herschel Medal, Royal Astron Soc, London; Henry Draper Medal, Nat Acad Sci. *Prof Exp:* Res fel radio astron, Calif Inst Technol, 62-63; mem tech staff, Bell Labs, 63-76, head, Wireless Technol Res Dept, 76-94. *Concurrent Pos:* Adj prof, Princeton Univ, NJ. *Mem:* Nat Acad Sci; Am Acad Arts & Sci; Am Phys Soc; Int Union Radio Sci; Am Astron Soc; Int Astron Union. *Res:* Problems related to the galaxy; absolute flux and background temperature measurements; millimeter-wave measurements of interstellar molecules; structure of nearby molecular clouds. *Mailing Add:* Harvard Smithsonian Ctr Astrophys 60 Garden St No 42 Cambridge MA 02138

**WILSON, RONALD HARVEY,** EXPERIMENTAL SOLID STATE PHYSICS. *Current Pos:* Physicist, Flight Propulsion Lab, Gen Elec Co, 58-59, res trainee, Physics Res Lab, 59-61, physicist, Gen Eng Lab, 61-62, PHYSICIST, GEN ELEC RES & DEVELOP CTR, 63- *Personal Data:* b Belle Fourche, SDak, Oct 2, 32; m 55; c 3. *Educ:* SDak State Univ, BS, 56, MS, 58; Rensselaer Polytech Inst, PhD(physics), 64. *Prof Exp:* Physicist, Flight Propulsion Lab, Gen Elec Co, 58-59, res trainee, Physics Res Lab, 59-61, physicist, Gen Eng Lab, 61-62. *Concurrent Pos:* Teaching asst physics, Rensselaer Polytech Inst, 62-63. *Mem:* AAAS; Am Phys Soc; Electrochem Soc. *Res:* Physics and properties of thin films; physics of semiconductor devices; semiconductor processing; energy conversion processes; photoelectrochemistry; solar energy. *Mailing Add:* 1049 Parkwood Blvd Schenectady NY 12308

**WILSON, RONALD L,** PHARMACOLOGY. *Current Pos:* chief, Admin Compliance Br, Ctr Drugs, 74-84, DIR HEALTH ASSESSMENT POLICY STAFF, FOOD & DRUG ADMIN, 84- *Personal Data:* b Birmingham, Ala, Dec 2, 40. *Educ:* Stanford Univ, BS, 62; Am Univ, MPA, 83. *Mem:* Am Pharmaceut Asn. *Mailing Add:* Food & Drug Admin 5600 Fisher's Lane 15-22 Rockville MD 20857

**WILSON, RONALD WAYNE,** botany, mycology; deceased, see previous edition for last biography

**WILSON, RUBY LEILA,** NURSING. *Current Pos:* Asst prof, 59, 68, dean, Sch Nursing, 71-84, PROF NURSING & MED, SCH MED, DUKE UNIV, 71-, ASST TO CHANCELLOR, 84- *Personal Data:* b Punxsutawney, Pa, May 29, 31. *Educ:* Univ Pittsburgh, BS, 54; Western Res Univ, MS, 59; Duke Univ, PhD(higher educ admin), 68. *Hon Degrees:* Dr, Mahadol Univ, Bangkok, Thailand, 97. *Concurrent Pos:* Asst prof, Rockefeller Found, 68-71. *Mem:* Inst Med-Nat Acad Sci; fel Acad Nursing. *Mailing Add:* Off Chancellor Health Box 3243 Duke Univ Med Ctr Durham NC 27710

**WILSON, RUSSELL B,** PATHOLOGY. *Current Pos:* PRES, AUTO IMMUNE TECH, 95- *Personal Data:* b Ky, Dec 18, 58. *Prof Exp:* Asst prof path, Tulane Med Ctr, 91-95. *Res:* Pathology. *Mailing Add:* Auto Immune Tech 144 Elks Pl New Orleans LA 70112

**WILSON, RUSSELL H,** INTERNAL MEDICINE, PULMONARY MEDICINE. *Current Pos:* ASSOC PROF INTERNAL MED, SOUTHWESTERN MED CTR, UNIV TEX, 54-65, 74- *Personal Data:* b Okla, Oct 31, 12; m 57, Elizabeth Johnson; c Mary, Anne & John. *Educ:* Univ Okla, BS, 38, MD, 40; Med Univ Minn, MS, PhD(med), 53. *Prof Exp:* Asst prof med, Univ Minn, 51-54; from chmn, Univ NDak, 65-73. *Res:* Internal medicine. *Mailing Add:* Dept Internal Med Southwestern Med Ctr Univ Tex 6218 Walnut Hill Lane Dallas TX 75230

**WILSON, SAMUEL H,** BIOCHEMISTRY. *Current Pos:* PROF, DEPT HUMAN BIOL CHEM & GENETICS & DIR, SEALY CTR MOLECULAR SCI, MED BR, UNIV TEX, 92- *Personal Data:* b Washington, DC, Aug 5, 39; c 2. *Educ:* Univ Denver, AB, 61; Harvard Univ, MD, 68. *Prof Exp:* Fel, Dept Biochem, Dartmouth, Med Sch, 67-68 & Lab Biochem Genetics, NIH, 68-70; res scientist, Lab Biochem, Nat Cancer Inst, NIH, 70-85, chief, Nucleic Acid Enzym Sect, 86-91. *Concurrent Pos:* Fel, Houston Advan Res Ctr, 93- *Mem:* Am Asn Cancer Res; AAAS; Am Chem Soc; Am Soc Cell Biol; Am Soc Biol Chemists. *Res:* Biomedical studies of mammalian DNA replication and repair proteins; molecular basis of mutagenesis. *Mailing Add:* Univ Tex Med Br Sealy Ctr Molecular Sci 301 University Blvd Galveston TX 77555-1068. *Fax:* 409-772-6334

**WILSON, SLOAN JACOB,** INTERNAL MEDICINE. *Current Pos:* from asst prof to assoc prof med, 46-59, prof, 59-70, EMER PROF INTERNAL MED, UNIV KANS MED CTR, KANSAS CITY, 70- *Personal Data:* b Dallas, Tex, Jan 22, 10; m 48; c 4. *Educ:* Wichita State Univ, AB, 31, MS, 32; Univ Kans, BS, 34, MD, 36; Am Bd Internal Med, dipl, 48. *Prof Exp:* From intern to asst resident, Ohio State Univ Hosp, 36-38, resident res med, 38-39, instr path, 39-40. *Mem:* AAAS; Soc Exp Biol & Med; fel AMA; fel Am Col Physicians; Am Soc Hemat. *Res:* Blood hematology. *Mailing Add:* Kingswood Manor 1000 Wornall Rd Apt 1206 Kansas City MO 64114

**WILSON, STEPHEN ROSS,** SYNTHETIC ORGANIC CHEMISTRY, COMPUTATIONAL CHEMISTRY. *Current Pos:* assoc prof, 80-86, PROF ORG CHEM, NY UNIV, 86- *Personal Data:* b Oklahoma City, Okla, Mar 13, 46; m 67, Susan Hirsch; c Sonia & Paul. *Educ:* Rice Univ, BA, 69, MA, 72, PhD(org chem), 72. *Prof Exp:* NIH fel org chem, Calif Inst Technol, 72-74; from asst prof to assoc prof org chem, Ind Univ, Bloomington, 74-80. *Concurrent Pos:* Sigma Xi res award, Rice Univ, 72. *Mem:* Mat Res Soc; Am Soc Mass Spectrometry; Am Chem Soc. *Res:* Development of new approaches to the synthesis of naturally occurring compounds of biological significance; electrospray mass spectrometry; fullerene chemistry; combinatorial chemistry. *Mailing Add:* Dept Chem NY Univ Washington Square New York NY 10003. *E-Mail:* wilson@scires.nyu.edu

**WILSON, STEPHEN W,** TAXONOMY OF PLANTHOPPERS. *Current Pos:* from asst prof to assoc prof, 82-89, PROF BIOL, CENT MO STATE UNIV, WARRENSBURG, 89-, CHMN, BIOL DEPT, 92- *Personal Data:* b Hackensack, NJ, Feb 6, 52; div; c 1. *Educ:* Rutgers Univ, BS, 73; Southwest Mo State Univ, MA, 75; Southern Ill Univ, PhD(zool), 80. *Prof Exp:* Asst prof biol, Calif State Univ, Chico, 80-82. *Mem:* Entom Soc Am. *Res:* Systematics and ecology of planthoppers (Homoptera: Fulgoroidea) with emphasis on Delphacidae. *Mailing Add:* Dept Biol Cent Mo State Univ Warrensburg MO 64093. *Fax:* 660-543-8006

**WILSON, STEVEN PAUL,** NEUROCHEMISTRY. *Current Pos:* asst prof, 85-89, ASSOC PROF, DEPT PHARMACOL, UNIV SC SCH MED, COLUMBIA, SC, 89- *Personal Data:* b New Castle, Pa, Oct 12, 50; m 72; c 1. *Educ:* Univ Pittsburgh, BS, 72; Duke Univ, PhD(biochem), 76. *Prof Exp:* Guest worker, Nat Heart, Lung & Blood Inst, NIH, 76-78, staff fel, 78-79; vis scientist, Dept Med Biochem, Wellcome Res Labs, Burroughs Wellcome Co, Research Triangle Park, NC, 79-81; asst med res prof, Dept Pharm, Duke Univ Med Ctr, Durham, NC, 82-85. *Concurrent Pos:* Fel neurol, Sch Med & Dent, George Washington Univ, 76-78; vis assoc prof, Dept Molecular Genetics & Biochem, Univ Pittsburgh Sch Med, 94-95. *Mem:* Soc Neurosci; Am Soc Neurochem; Am Soc Pharmacol Exp Ther. *Res:* Neuropeptide biosynthesis and processing; gene therapy in the nervous system. *Mailing Add:* Dept Pharmacol Univ SC Sch Med Columbia SC 29208. *Fax:* 803-733-3197; *E-Mail:* swilson@med.scarolina.edu

**WILSON, TERRANCE M,** VETERINARY MEDICINE, PATHOLOGY. *Current Pos:* vet pathologist & head, Pathobiol Sect, 87-89, VET PATHOLOGIST & HEAD, PARASITOL & CLIN PATH SECT, NAT VET SERVS LAB, USDA, AMES, IOWA, 89-; ASSOC PROF, DEPT PATH, COL VET MED, IOWA STATE UNIV, 89- *Educ:* Cornell Univ, BS, 59, MS, 66, DVM, 67; Ont Vet Col, PhD(vet path), 71; Am Col Vet Pathologists, cert, 72. *Prof Exp:* Vet asst, US fish & Wildlife Serv, Pribilof Islands, Alaska, 64; vet, NSF & Harvard Univ, Antarctica, 67-68; vet pathologist, Vet Lab, Ont Ministry Agr & Food, Guelph, Can 71-74; proj dir & vet pathologist, Vet Diag Lab, Pan Am Health WHO, Barbados, 74-80; assoc prof, Pa State Univ, 80-86. *Concurrent Pos:* Lectr, comp path, Ont Vet Col, 67-74, path lob instr, 67-74; vet consult, Pan Am Health Orgn, WHO, Surinam, SAm, 73, Mobile Vet Diag Lab, 76-80, lect, 78-80; lectr, Vet Path, Comp Path, Div Health Sci, Barbados Community Col, Univ WI, Bridgetown, 75-80; vet path consult, Vet & Livestock Div, Ministry Agr, Govt St Vincent & Montserrat, 76-80; lectr, Vet Path Comp Path, Pa State Univ, 80-86, Int Agr, 80-86; lectr, Int Vet Med, Sch Vet Med, Univ Pa, 80-89; vet pathologist, Mycotoxin Res Unit, Nat Inst Nutrit Dis, Tygerberg, SAfrica, 83-86. *Mem:* US Animal Health Asn; Am Asn Vet Lab Diagnosticians; Am Vet Med Asn; Can Asn Vet Pathologists. *Res:* Toxic effects of selenium on the nervous system in swine; mycotoxin, fumonisin. *Mailing Add:* 4706 Rams Horn Row Ellicott City MD 21042

**WILSON, THEODORE A(LEXANDER),** AERONAUTICAL ENGINEERING, BIOMECHANICS. *Current Pos:* from asst prof to assoc prof aeronaut & eng mech, 64-72, PROF AEROSPACE ENG & MECH, UNIV MINN, MINNEAPOLIS, 72- *Personal Data:* b Elgin, Ill, June 20, 35. *Educ:* Cornell Univ, BEngPhysics, 58, PhD(aeronaut eng), 62. *Prof Exp:* Res scientist, Avco-Everett Res Lab, 62-63 & Jet Propulsion Lab, 63-64. *Mem:* Am Physiol Soc. *Res:* Respiratory mechanics; acoustics; fluid mechanics. *Mailing Add:* Dept Aerospace Eng & Mech Univ Minn Minneapolis MN 55455

**WILSON, THOMAS EDWARD,** ENVIRONMENTAL & CHEMICAL ENGINEERING. *Current Pos:* CONSULT POLLUTION CONTROL & WATER TREATMENT, GREELEY & HANSEN, 70- *Personal Data:* b Chicago, Ill, Feb 20, 42; m 66, Cheryl A Wegener; c Christopher T & Scott D. *Educ:* Northwestern Univ, BS, 64, MS, 67; Ill Inst Technol, PhD(environ eng), 69. *Honors & Awards:* Thurston E Larson Award, Int Soc Am Water Works Asn. *Prof Exp:* Asst prof environ eng, Rutgers Univ, NB, 67-70. *Mem:* Am Inst Chem Engrs; Int Asn Water Pollution Res; Water Environ Fedn; Am Soc Civil Engrs; Am Water Works Asn; Sigma Xi. *Res:* Pollution control; advanced water treatment; physical-chemical treatment processes; industrial waste treatment; treatment plant operations; nutrient removal; water treatment; biosolids processes. *Mailing Add:* 922 Shoreline Dr Barrington IL 60010

**WILSON, THOMAS G(EORGE),** ELECTRICAL ENGINEERING. *Current Pos:* assoc prof, 59-63, chmn dept, 64-70, PROF ELEC ENG, DUKE UNIV, 63- *Personal Data:* b Annapolis, Md, Jan 19, 26; m 49; c 3. *Educ:* Harvard Univ, AB, 47, SM, 49, ScD(elec eng), 53. *Prof Exp:* Physicist, US Naval Ord Lab, 48, elec engr, US Naval Res Lab, 49-53; mgr res & develop, Magnetics, Inc, 53-59. *Mem:* Inst Elec & Electronics Engrs; Sigma Xi. *Res:* Magnetic devices, materials and amplifiers; nonlinear electromagnetics; energy conversion. *Mailing Add:* Dept Elec Eng Duke Univ Durham NC 27706

**WILSON, THOMAS HASTINGS,** PHYSIOLOGY. *Current Pos:* assoc physiol, 57-59, from asst prof to assoc prof, 59-68, PROF PHYSIOL, HARVARD MED SCH, 68- *Personal Data:* b Philadelphia, Pa, Jan 31, 25; m 52; c 4. *Educ:* Univ Pa, MD, 48; Sheffield Univ, 51-53, PhD(biochem), 53. *Hon Degrees:* MA, Harvard Univ. *Prof Exp:* Instr physiol, Univ Pa, 49-50; instr biochem, Wash Univ, 56-57. *Mem:* Am Soc Biol Chem; Am Physiol Soc; Brit Biochem Soc; Am Acad Arts & Sci. *Res:* Active transport of materials across cell membranes. *Mailing Add:* Dept Physiol & Biophys Harvard Med Sch 25 Shattuck St Boston MA 02115-6092

**WILSON, THOMAS KENDRICK,** PLANT MORPHOLOGY. *Current Pos:* assoc prof, 68-74, PROF BOT, MIAMI UNIV, 74- *Personal Data:* b Highland Park, Mich, June 2, 31; m 52; c 5. *Educ:* Ohio Univ, BS, 53, MS, 55; Ind Univ, PhD(bot), 58. *Prof Exp:* Asst bot, Ohio Univ, 53-55 & Ind Univ, 55-58; from asst prof to assoc prof, Univ Cincinnati, 58-68. *Mem:* AAAS; Bot Soc Am; Int Soc Plant Morphol; Int Asn Plant Taxon. *Res:* Comparative morphology of angiosperms; origin and phylogeny of vascular plants; evolution. *Mailing Add:* Dept Bot Miami Univ Oxford OH 45056

**WILSON, THOMAS LAMONT,** HIGH POWER BROADCAST TRANSMITTERS. *Current Pos:* CONSULT, DIELECTRIC HEATING, 77- *Personal Data:* b Salt Lake City, Utah, June 4, 14; m 37; c 2. *Educ:* Univ Utah, BS, 40; Univ Louisville, MS, 63. *Honors & Awards:* Achievement Award, Inst Elec & Electronics Engrs, 79 & Centennial Medal, 84. *Prof Exp:* Elec engr, Elec Div, Fed Tel & Radio, 41-46; mgr, eng & develop, Chemetron Corp, 46-77. *Concurrent Pos:* Tech adv, US Nat Comt Int Electrotech Comm, 75-88. *Mem:* Fel Inst Elec & Electronics Engrs. *Res:* Dielectric heating uses; high frequency high power for industrial heating applications. *Mailing Add:* 1407 Ormsby Lane Louisville KY 40222-3827

**WILSON, THOMAS LEE,** PHYSICAL CHEMISTRY, GENERAL MATHEMATICS. *Current Pos:* CONSULT, 76- *Personal Data:* b Wyoming, Ohio, Nov 4, 09; m 37; c 2. *Educ:* Col Wooster, BS, 30; Univ Wash, MS, 34; Univ Chicago, PhD(chem), 35. *Prof Exp:* Res chemist, Gen Labs, US Rubber Co, 35-42, dept head, 42-54, admin asst, Res & Develop Dept, 54-58, mgr res ctr, 58-65; from asst prof to assoc prof chem, Montclair State Col, 66-76, chmn dept, 71-73, dean, Sch Math & Sci, 73-76. *Mem:* AAAS; Am Chem Soc; fel Am Inst Chem. *Res:* Oceanography; reaction rates of gaseous decomposition; rubber and inorganic chemistry. *Mailing Add:* 7 Rockbrook Dr Camden ME 04843-1616

**WILSON, THOMAS LEON,** NEUTRINO & GAMMA-RAY ASTROPHYSICS, QUANTUM COSMOLOGY & COSMIC RAYS. *Current Pos:* Aerospace engr, 65-76, RES PHYSICIST, JOHNSON SPACE CTR, NASA, 76- *Personal Data:* b Alpine, Tex, May 21, 42; m 78, Joyce Krevosky; c Kenneth & Bailey. *Educ:* Rice Univ, BA, 64, BSc, 65, MA, 74, PhD(theoret physics), 76. *Honors & Awards:* Hugo Gernsback Award, Inst Elec & Electronics Engrs. *Concurrent Pos:* Astronaut instr, Apollo Skylab Prog, 65-72; fel, NASA, 69-76; co-investr, Skylab Prog, NASA, 70-73. *Mem:* Am Phys Soc; NY Acad Sci; AAAS. *Res:* Theoretical analysis of mechanisms for gamma-ray bursts from accretion of exotic matter onto neutron stars; detection of relic dark matter in the galaxy; neutrino tomography of the planet earth; "chesire cat" effect in quantum mechanics; pathological problems in relativistic wave equations; neutrino astronomy; physics and astrophysics from a lunar base. *Mailing Add:* NASA Johnson Space Ctr-SN Houston TX 77058. *Fax:* 281-483-5347; *E-Mail:* twilson@ems.jsc.nasa.gov

**WILSON, THOMAS PUTNAM,** HETEROGENOUS CATALYSIS. *Current Pos:* RETIRED. *Personal Data:* b New York, NY, Sept 4, 18; m 44, 80, Margaret Hutchinson; c Mark Kinloch. *Educ:* Amherst Col, BA, 39; Harvard Univ, PhD(chem physics), 43. *Prof Exp:* Res chemist, Manhattan Proj, M W Kellogg Co, NJ, 43-44; res chemist, Kellex Corp, 44-45; res chemist, Manhattan Proj & S A M Labs, Chems & Plastics Div, Union Carbide Corp, 45-46 & 46-62, asst dir res, 62-72, res assoc, 72-73, corp res fel, Res & Develop Dept, Ethylene Oxide/Glycol Div, 73-82. *Mem:* Am Chem Soc; Catalysis Soc. *Res:* Kinetics and catalysis; catalytic reaction mechanisms; ethylene polymerization; catalyst development and characterization. *Mailing Add:* 701 Myrtle Rd South Charleston WV 25314-1117

**WILSON, THORNTON ARNOLD,** AERONAUTICS. *Current Pos:* RETIRED. *Personal Data:* b Sikeston, Mo, Feb 8, 21; m 44; c 3. *Educ:* Iowa State Col, BS, 43; Calif Inst Technol, MS, 48. *Honors & Awards:* James Forrestal Award, Nat Security Indust Asn, 75; Wright Bros Trophy, 79; Collier Trophy, Fed Aviation Admin, 82; Daniel Guggenheim Medal & Nat Acad Sci Award. *Prof Exp:* Mem staff, Boeing Co, 43-57, asst chief tech staff & proj eng mgr, 57-58, vpres & mgr Minuteman Br, Aerosace Div, 62-64, vpres opers & planning, 64-66, exec vpres & dir, 66-68, pres, 68-72, chief exec officer, 69-86, chmn bd, 72-87, emer chmn & mem bd dirs, 87- *Concurrent Pos:* Sloan fel, Mass Inst Technol, 52-53; mem bd gov, Iowa State Univ Found; bd dirs, PACCAR Inc, Hewlett-Packard Co & Weyerhaeuser Co. *Mem:* Nat Acad Eng; fel Am Inst Aeronaut & Astronaut; Aerospace Indust Asn. *Res:* Mechanics; aeronautical and astronautical engineering. *Mailing Add:* 126 SW 171st St Seattle WA 98166

**WILSON, TIMOTHY M,** THEORETICAL SOLID STATE PHYSICS. *Current Pos:* from asst prof to assoc prof physics, 69-78, asst dir exten, Col Arts & Sci, 77-79, assoc dir exten, 79-82, PROF PHYSICS, OKLA STATE UNIV, 78- *Personal Data:* b Columbus, Ohio, Aug 3, 38; m Linda L McAninch; c Michael. *Educ:* Univ Fla, BS, 61, PhD(chem physics), 66. *Prof Exp:* Fel solid state physics, Univ Fla, 66-68, asst prof chem, 68-69. *Concurrent Pos:* Res staff mem, Solid State Div, Oak Ridge Nat Lab, 74-75. *Mem:* Am Phys Soc; Sigma Xi. *Res:* Theoretical studies of the optical and magnetic properties of impurities and defects in crystalline solids; band theory of semiconductors and insulators. *Mailing Add:* Dept Physics Okla State Univ Stillwater OK 74078. *Fax:* 405-744-6811; *E-Mail:* phystmw@mvs.ucc. okstate.edu

**WILSON, VICTOR JOSEPH,** NEUROPHYSIOLOGY. *Current Pos:* Res assoc, 56-58, from asst prof to prof neurophysiol, 58-69, PROF NEUROPHYSIOL, ROCKEFELLER UNIV, 69- *Personal Data:* b Berlin, Ger, Dec 24, 28; m 53, Isa Hermer; c 2. *Educ:* Tufts Col, BS, 48, MS, 49; Univ Ill, PhD(physiol), 53. *Mem:* Am Physiol Soc; Soc Neurosci; Int Brain Res Org. *Res:* Organization and synaptic transmission in the central nervous system, particularly the spinal cord and brain stem; vestibular system. *Mailing Add:* Rockefeller Univ 1230 York Ave New York NY 10021-6399. *Fax:* 212-327-8530

**WILSON, VINCENT L,** CHEMICAL CARCINOGENESIS, GENE REGULATION. *Current Pos:* ASSOC PROF & CLAIRBORNE CHAIR ENVIRON TOXICOL, INST ENVIRON STUDIES, LA STATE UNIV, 94-, ADJ ASSOC PROF, DEPT ZOOL, 95-, ADJ ASSOC PROF, DEPT PHARMACOL, PHYSIOL & TOXICOL, SCH VET MED, 95- *Personal Data:* b Kentfield, Calif, Dec 4, 50; m 74, Laurie K Kerr. *Educ:* Sonoma State Univ, BS, 73; Univ Calif, Davis, MS, 76; Ore State Univ, PhD(pharmacol & toxicol), 80. *Prof Exp:* Chemist, Cent Path Lab, Inc, Santa Rosa, Calif, 72-73; analytical chemist, Environ Protection Agency, Corvallis Environ Res Lab, Corvallis, Ore, 78-80; chem & viral carcinogenesis training fel, Univ Southern Calif Comprehensive Cancer Ctr & Children's Hosp, Los Angeles, Calif, 80-82; sr staff fel, Nat Cancer Inst, NIH, Bethesda, Md, 82-88; assoc prof, Dept Path, Univ Colo Med Sch, Denver, 88-95; dir molecular genetics & oncol, Childrens Hosp, Denver, 88-94. *Concurrent Pos:* Vis scientist, Danish Cancer Soc, Lab Environ Carcinogenesis, Fibiger laboratoriet, Copenhagen, Denmark, 86. *Mem:* Am Chem Soc; Am Asn Cancer Res; Am Soc Cell Biol; Am Soc Human Genetics; AAAS; Sigma Xi. *Res:* Pharmacology and toxicology of cancer chemotherapeutic agents, radiation therapy, and environmental pollutants with emphasis on mechanisms in mutation and carcinogenesis; determination of genetic controls involved in the physiologic and perturbed processes of embryogenesis, differentiation, aging, and carcinogenesis; basic research in the inherent functions and controlling systems of DNA; genetic markers of diagnostic and prognostic value in the clinical care of cancer patients. *Mailing Add:* 3435 W 101st Pl Westminster CO 80030

**WILSON, VOLNEY COLVIN,** PLASMA PHYSICS, THERMAL PHYSICS & NUCLEAR REACTORS. *Current Pos:* RETIRED. *Personal Data:* b Evanston, Ill, Feb 27, 10; wid; c 2. *Educ:* Northwestern Univ, BS, 32; Ohio State Univ, MA, 34; Univ Chicago, PhD(physics), 38. *Prof Exp:* Instr physics, Univ Chicago, 38-41; res assoc radar res, Mass Inst Technol Radiation Lab, 41-42; res assoc nuclear energy, Univ Chicago, 41-44; res assoc atomic bomb, Los Alamos Lab, NMex, 44-45; res assoc physics, Gen Elec Res Lab, 45-72. *Mem:* Fel Am Phys Soc; fel Am Nuclear Soc. *Res:* Cosmic ray research; nuclear instrumentation; nuclear reactor design; magnetic materials; thermionic emission and gas discharge; invented thermionic converter. *Mailing Add:* 2446 Del Norte Dr SW Suite A Albuquerque NM 87105

**WILSON, W STEPHEN,** ALGEBRAIC TOPOLOGY. *Current Pos:* assoc prof, 77-80, chair, Dept Math, 93-96, PROF, JOHNS HOPKINS UNIV, 80- *Personal Data:* b Iowa City, Iowa, Nov 11, 46; m 90, Norma J Kriger; c Saul Kriger. *Educ:* Mass Inst Technol, SB, 68, SM, 69, PhD(math), 72. *Prof Exp:* Instr, Princeton Univ, 72-74, asst prof, 74-78. *Concurrent Pos:* Mem, Inst Advan Study, Princeton, 74-75 & 77-78; vis asst prof, Univ Calif, San Diego, 75; Alfred P Sloan res fel, 77-79; vis sr mathematician, Oxford Univ, 78; vis prof, Hebrew Univ, Tata Inst Fundamental Res, Osaka City Univ, 80-81, Porto Univ, 82, Kupto Univ, 83-84, IMPA, Rio de Janiero, Univ Witwatersrand, Univ Melbourne, Nat Taiwan Univ & Rims Kyoto Univ, 83-84. *Mem:* Am Math Soc. *Res:* Developed Brown-Peterson homology and Morava K-theory into useful tools for algebraic topologists; homotopy theory, Complex Cobordism. *Mailing Add:* Dept Math Johns Hopkins Univ 3400 N Charles St Baltimore MD 21218-2689

**WILSON, WALTER DAVIS,** ASTRONOMY, COMPUTERS IN PHYSICS. *Current Pos:* PROF PHYSICS, CALIF POLYTECH STATE UNIV, SAN LUIS OBISPO, 69- *Personal Data:* b Merced, Calif, Oct 20, 35; m 59, Gail Garden; c Kenneth M, Douglas F & Catherine A. *Educ:* Univ Calif, Berkeley, BS, 57, PhD(nuclear eng), 66. *Prof Exp:* Chem engr, Aerojet Gen Nucleonics, Calif, 58-59; mem tech staff high-altitude nuclear effects, Aerospace Corp, 65-69. *Concurrent Pos:* Tech consult, Sci Applns, Inc, Calif, 71-75. *Mem:* Am Asn Physics Teachers. *Res:* Use of computers in lower division physics education; alternatives to the lecture in lower division physics education; nuclear reactor theory. *Mailing Add:* Dept Physics Calif Polytech State Univ San Luis Obispo CA 93407

**WILSON, WALTER ERVIN,** RADIOLOGICAL PHYSICS. *Current Pos:* USTUR, WASH STATE UNIV-TC, 95- *Personal Data:* b Salem, Ore, Apr 1, 34. *Educ:* Willamette Univ, BA, 56; Univ Wis, MS, 58, PhD(physics), 61. *Prof Exp:* Radiation physicist, Pac Northwest Labs, Battelle Mem Inst, 64-95.

Concurrent Pos: Fel, Basel Univ, 61-62 & Univ Wis, 62-64; coordr, Radiol Sci Prog, Univ Wash, Tri-Cities Univ Ctr, 88-91. Mem: Am Phys Soc. Res: Radiation effects and radiological sciences; radiation transport calculations; computer science; programming languages; numerical analysis. Mailing Add: 221 Enterprise Dr Richland WA 99352

**WILSON, WALTER LEROY,** PHYSIOLOGY. Current Pos: RETIRED. Personal Data: b Phoenixville, Pa, Sept 1, 18; m 44; c 2. Educ: Pa State Teachers Col, West Chester, BS, 41; Univ Pa, PhD(zool), 49. Prof Exp: Biologist, Off Sci Res & Develop, Univ Pa, 43-44, asst instr zool, 46-47; biologist, Manhattan Proj, Columbia Univ, 44-46; instr physiol & biophys, Col Med, Univ Vt, 49-52, from asst prof to assoc prof, 52-65; prof biol sci, Oakland Univ, 65-83. Concurrent Pos: Lectr, Middlebury Col, 52-53; mem corp, Marine Biol Lab, Woods Hole. Mem: Am Physiol Soc; Soc Gen Physiol; Am Soc Zoologists. Res: Effects of high temperature on living systems; protoplasmic viscosity changes during cell division; the release of anticoagulant substances from living cells and the inhibitory action of these anticoagulants on cell division; role of cellular cortex in stimulation and cell division. Mailing Add: 743 Cambridge Dr Rochester Hills MI 48309

**WILSON, WALTER LUCIEN, JR,** MATHEMATICS. Current Pos: RETIRED. Personal Data: b Montgomery, Ala, Apr 26, 27; m 47; c 2. Educ: Univ Ala, AB, 50, MA, 51; Univ Calif, Los Angeles, PhD(math), 59. Prof Exp: Res engr, NAm Aviation, Inc, Calif, 59-60; assoc prof math, Univ Ala, 60-89. Mem: Am Math Soc; Math Asn Am. Res: Calculus of variations; numerical analysis; linear programming. Mailing Add: 15 Highridge Circle Tuscaloosa AL 35405

**WILSON, WALTER R,** ENGINEERING PHYSICS. Current Pos: Test engr, Res Lab, 41-42, develop engr, Transformer & Allied Prod Lab, 42-49, elec sect head, Switchgear & Control Lab, 49-54, mgr eng res, 54-56, mgr eng, High Voltage Switchgear Dept, 56-61, consult engr, 61-68, mgr elec & mech eng res, Power Delivery Div, 68-76, SR CONSULT & STAND ENGR, GEN ELEC CO, 76- Personal Data: b South Bend, Ind, May 3, 19; m 44; c 3. Educ: Univ Mich, BS, 41. Honors & Awards: Alfred Noble Prize, Am Soc Civil Engrs, 44. Concurrent Pos: US deleg, Int Electro-Tech Comn, Madrid, 59-72. Mem: Nat Soc Prof Engrs; Am Mgt Asn; fel Inst Elec & Electronics Engrs; Sigma Xi. Res: High voltage electrical power equipment; dielectrics, magnetics, gaseous discharges and electric contact phenomena; electrical and mechanical instrumentation. Mailing Add: 1 Rabbit Run Wallingford PA 19086-6217

**WILSON, WILBUR WILLIAM,** PHYSICAL CHEMISTRY. Current Pos: Asst prof, 74-80, PROF CHEM, MISS STATE UNIV, 80- Personal Data: b Ferriday, La, Jan 10, 48; m 69; c 2. Educ: Northeast La State Col, BS, 69; Univ NC, PhD(phys chem), 73. Mem: Am Chem Soc; Sigma Xi. Res: Laser light scattering by macromolecules. Mailing Add: 1544 Hillbrook St Starkville MS 39759-9254

**WILSON, WILFRED J,** EMBRYOLOGY. Current Pos: RETIRED. Personal Data: b Ferndale, Calif, Mar 4, 30; m 68. Educ: Sacramento State Col, AB, 52; Univ Calif, Davis, MA, 58, PhD(zool), 64. Prof Exp: Teaching asst zool, Univ Calif, Davis, 58-61, assoc, 61-63; from asst prof to assoc prof, San Diego State Univ, 63-70, prof biol, 70- Concurrent Pos: Shell merit fel, Stanford Univ, 69; Fulbright lectr, US Dept State, Nat Taiwan Univ, 70-71; vis lectr, Burma, 71. Mem: Am Soc Zool. Res: General and invertebrate biology; crustacean water balance; teaching methods in human biology; early animal development. Mailing Add: 1788 Oak Creek Dr Apt 404 Palo Alto CA 94305

**WILSON, WILLIAM AUGUST,** neuropsychology, for more information see previous edition

**WILSON, WILLIAM CURTIS,** PLANT PHYSIOLOGY. Current Pos: RETIRED. Personal Data: b Orlando, Fla, Dec 29, 27; m 52; c 1. Educ: Cornell Univ, BS, 49; Univ Fla, MAgr, 58, PhD(fruit crops), 66. Prof Exp: Asst mgr agr res, Fla Agr Res Inst, 57-61; adj assoc horticulturist, Citrus Exp Sta, Agr Res & Educ Ctr, Univ Fla, 66-77; res scientist II, Fla Dept Citrus, 77-80, res scientist III, 80-91. Concurrent Pos: Merck & Co grant, 69; Julian C Miller award, Asn Southern Agr Workers, Inc, 66; Ciba-Geigy grants, 70-72; adj assoc prof, Agr Res & Educ Ctr, Univ Fla, 74-81, adj horticulturist, 81-91. Mem: Am Soc Hort Sci; Int Soc Citricult; Plant Growth Regulator Soc Am (secy, 80-81). Res: Abscission chemicals to facilitate easier removal of citrus fruit to aid mechanical or hand harvesting; acidity reduction and cold hardy chemicals; fresh fruit research. Mailing Add: 1616 Villa Ct Marco Island FL 34145

**WILSON, WILLIAM D,** parasitology; deceased, see previous edition for last biography

**WILSON, WILLIAM DAVID,** NUCLEIC ACID STRUCTURE & INTERACTIONS, ANTI-CANCER DRUG DESIGN. Current Pos: from asst prof to prof, 71-84, REGENTS PROF CHEM, GA STATE UNIV, 84- Personal Data: b Wilmington, NC, June 28, 44; m 66; c 2. Educ: Univ NC, BS, 66; Purdue Univ, PhD(chem), 70. Honors & Awards: Fac Develop Award, Am Cancer Soc. Prof Exp: Fel chem, Purdue Univ, 71. Concurrent Pos: Dir, Lab Biol Sci, Ga State Univ, 79-82; vis prof, Univ Fla, 80 & Inst Cancer Res, London, 88. Mem: Am Chem Soc; Biophys Soc. Res: Biophysical chemistry of nucleic acid structure and interactions; interactions of drugs and model compounds which bind to nucleic acids by very different mechanisms. Mailing Add: Dept Chem Ga State Univ University Plaza Atlanta GA 30303. Fax: 404-651-1416

**WILSON, WILLIAM DENNIS,** SOLID STATE PHYSICS. Current Pos: res physicist, 69-, div supvr, Theoret Div, 74-, SR RES SCIENTIST, LIVERMORE NAT LABS & SANDIA NAT LABS. Personal Data: b New York, NY, July 20, 40; m 60, 73; c 2. Educ: Queens Col, NY, BS, 63, MA, 65; City Univ New York, PhD(physics), 67. Prof Exp: Res physicist, Queens Col, NY, 67 & 68-69; fel physics, City Univ New York, 67-68. Concurrent Pos: Consult, Lawrence Radiation Lab, Calif, 67-69. Mem: Am Phys Soc. Res: Interatomic potentials; defects in solids; hydrogen and helium in metals; diffusion. Mailing Add: 7036 Corte Del Oro Pleasanton CA 94566

**WILSON, WILLIAM ENOCH, JR,** ATMOSPHERIC CHEMISTRY. Current Pos: chief atmospheric aerosol res sect, Environ Protection Agency, 71-75, chief aerosol res br, 75-77, sci dir, Regional Field Studies Off, 77-88, actg dir, Emission Measurements & Characterization Div, 81-87, DIR ATMOSPHERIC CHEM & PHYSICS DIV, ENVIRON PROTECTION AGENCY, 80- Personal Data: b El Dorado, Ark, Jan 15, 33; m 63; c 2. Educ: Hendrix Col, BA, 53; Purdue Univ, PhD(phys chem), 57. Honors & Awards: Silver Medal, Environ Protection Agency, 78. Prof Exp: Instr chem, Wis State Univ-La Crosse, 55-56; Fulbright res fel, Inst Technol, Munich, Ger, 57-58; sr chemist, Appl Physics Lab, Johns Hopkins Univ, 58-67; assoc fel, Battelle Mem Inst, 67-71. Concurrent Pos: Adj prof, Environ Sci & Eng Dept, Sch Pub Health, Univ NC, 73-; prog mgr, Coop Res Atmospheric Sci, People's Rep China, 80-; mem bd dirs, Am Asn Aerosol Res, 84-87; vis prof, Peking Univ, People's Repub China, 86. Mem: AAAS; Am Chem Soc; Am Meteorol Soc; Sigma Xi; Air Pollution Control Asn; Int Aerosol Res Assembly (secy, 86-); Am Asn Aerosol Res. Res: Sources, formation, dynamics, transport, removal, and effects of atmospheric pollutants; atmospheric chemistry and physics; molecular spectroscopy; chemical kinetics and thermodynamics pertinent to combustion, propulsion, and air pollution. Mailing Add: US Environ Protection Agency MD-52 Research Triangle Park NC 27711

**WILSON, WILLIAM EWING,** molecular pharmacology, for more information see previous edition

**WILSON, WILLIAM JAMES FITZPATRICK,** STELLAR EVOLUTION, MASS LOSS. Current Pos: FEL & INSTR PHYSICS & ASTRON, UNIV CALGARY, 77- Personal Data: b Aberdeen, Scotland, Feb 13, 46; Can citizen; m 81; c 2 Anna & Michael. Educ: Univ BC, BSc, 68; Univ Waterloo, MSc, 70; Univ Calgary, PhD(astrophys), 77. Mem: Can Astron Soc. Res: Computation of stellar evolution from the zero-age main sequence to helium exhaustion, with mass loss due to radiation pressure and convective and rotational turbulent pressure; Wesselink radii of dwarf cepheid variable stars. Mailing Add: Dept Physics Univ Calgary 2500 University Dr Calgary AB T2N 1N4 Can

**WILSON, WILLIAM JOHN,** MILLIMETER WAVE RADIOMETERS, MICROWAVE SPECTROMETERS. Current Pos: GROUP SUPVR, JET PROPULSION LAB, 80-, SR RES ENGR, 87- Personal Data: b Spokane, Wash, Dec 16, 39; m 62. Educ: Univ Wash, BS, 61; Mass Inst Technol, MS, 63, PhD(elec eng), 70. Prof Exp: mem staff, Space Div, USAF, 64-67; mem tech staff, Aerospace Corp, 70-80; asst prof elec eng, Univ Tex, Austin, 76-77. Mem: Sr mem Inst Elec & Electronics Engrs, Microwave Theory & Tech Soc; Union Radio Sci; Int Astron Union. Res: Development of low-noise millimeter-wave and submillimeter-wave radiometers and systems for aircraft and spacecraft which have applications for Earth remote sensing and astrophysics; development of analog and digital microwave spectrometers for spaceborne radiometers. Mailing Add: Jet Propulsion Lab 4800 Oak Grove Dr Bldg 168-327 Pasadena CA 91109

**WILSON, WILLIAM MARK DUNLOP,** agriculture, animal science, for more information see previous edition

**WILSON, WILLIAM PRESTON,** PSYCHIATRY. Current Pos: from assoc prof to prof, Med Ctr, 58-85, dir, Neurophysiol Labs, 58-82, EMER PROF PSYCHIAT, DUKE UNIV, 85-; DIR, INST CHRISTIAN GROWTH, GRAHAM, NC. Personal Data: b Fayetteville, NC, Nov 6, 22; m 51; c 5. Educ: Duke Univ, BS, 43, MD, 47. Honors & Awards: Ephraim McDowell Award, Am Orthopsychiat Asn. Prof Exp: Intern, Gorgas Hosp, CZ, 47-48; staff psychiatrist, State Hosp, Raleigh, NC, 48-49; instr psychiat & asst resident, Sch Med, Duke Univ, 49-52, resident neurol, 52, assoc psychiat & chief resident, 52-54, asst prof psychiat, 55-58. Concurrent Pos: Fel med, Duke Univ, 52-54; NIH fel, Montreal Neurol Inst, McGill Univ, 54-55; assoc prof & dir, Psychiat Res Labs & consult, Hogg Found, Med Br, Univ Tex, 58-60; dir, Psychiat Res Labs & staff psychiatrist, Vet Admin HOsp, 58-79; mem, Am Bd Qual EEG, 69-, secy-treas, 71-74. Mem: AAAS; AMA; Am Psychiat Asn; Am Psychopath Asn; Asn Res Nerv & Ment Dis; Sigma Xi. Res: Clinical psychiatry and neurochemistry; clinical and experimental neurophysiology; electroencephalography. Mailing Add: 1209 Virginia Ave Durham NC 27705. Fax: 910-570-1392; E-Mail: 73661.2554@compuserve.com

**WILSON, WILLIAM ROBERT DUNWOODY,** TRIBOLOGY, PLASTICITY. Current Pos: PROF MECH ENG, NORTHWESTERN UNIV, 81- Personal Data: b Belfast, Northern Ireland, Sept 11, 41; US citizen; m 67, Elizabeth Gent; c 2. Educ: Belfast Tech Col, HNC, 64; Queens Univ, Belfast, BS, 63, PhD(mech eng), 67. Honors & Awards: Colwell Award, Soc Automotive Engrs, 93; Blackall Award, Am Soc Mech Engrs, 96. Prof Exp: Student apprentice, Harland & Wolff Ltd, Belfast, 59-63; sr res scientist, Colubus Div, Battelle Mem Inst, 67-71; prof, Univ Mass, Amherst, 71-81. Concurrent Pos: Dir, Ctr Mgf Eng, 83, ctr Surface Eng & Tribol, 95-; assoc dir, Steel Resource Ctr, 86-93. Mem: Am Soc Mech Engrs; Soc Mfg Engrs;

Soc Tribologists & Lubrication Engrs. *Res:* Manufacturing processes and tribology in particular lubrication of metal forming processes, computer-aided design for manufacture. *Mailing Add:* Mech Eng Dept Northwestern Univ Evanston IL 60201-2970. *Fax:* 847-491-3915; *E-Mail:* w-wilson@nwu.edu

**WILSON, WILLIAM STANLEY,** OCEANOGRAPHY. *Current Pos:* asst adminr ocean servs & coastal zone mgt, 92-97, NAT OCEANIC & ATMOSPHERIC ADMIN, 97- *Personal Data:* b Alexander City, Ala, June 5, 38; m 73, Anne M Stout; c Lauren. *Educ:* William & Mary Col, BS, 59, MA, 65; Johns Hopkins Univ, PhD, 72. *Honors & Awards:* Antarctica Service Medal, 61; Ocean Scientist Award, Am Geophys Union, 84; Remote Sensing Soc Award, 92. *Prof Exp:* Marine biol collector, Va Inst Marine Sci, 59-62, comput systs analyst, 64-65; comput systs analyst, Chesapeake Bay Inst, 65-66; phys oceanog prog mgr, Off Naval Res, 72-78; chief oceanic processes prog, NASA, 79-89, prog scientist earth observ syst, 89-92. *Mem:* Am Meteorol Soc; Am Geophys Union; Oceanog Soc; Sigma Xi; Coastal Soc. *Res:* Ocean sciences; coastal management ranging from nautical charts for marine transportation to conservation of marine protected areas. *Mailing Add:* Dept Com NOAA 14th & Constitution Ave NW Washington DC 20230. *Fax:* 301-713-4269; *E-Mail:* Omnet: s.wilson.ocean

**WILSON, WYNDHAM HOPKINS,** INTERNAL MEDICINE, MEDICAL ONCOLOGY. *Current Pos:* Fel oncol, 84-88, spec asst to dir, 88-95, SR INVESTR, NAT CANCER INST, 96- *Personal Data:* b San Francisco, Calif, May 12, 51. *Educ:* Stanford Univ, BA, 75, MS, 75, PhD(neurosci), 81, MD, 81. *Mem:* Am Soc Clin Oncol; Am Soc Hemat. *Res:* Clinical/translational studies on the treatment of lymphomas; emphasis on mechanisms of drug resistance and the role of cytoleinrs in treatment. *Mailing Add:* Bldg 10 Rm 12N-226 NIH 9000 Rockville Pike Bethesda MD 20892. *Fax:* 301-402-2359

**WILSON-FOWLER, DONA JANE,** NEUROENDOCRINOLOGY. *Current Pos:* from instr to prof, 65-88, EMER PROF, WESTERN MICH UNIV, 88- *Personal Data:* b Muncie, Ind, May 8, 28; div; c 2. *Educ:* Purdue Univ, BS, 55, MS, 62, PhD, 65. *Prof Exp:* Res asst plant physiol, Purdue Univ, 54-55, cardiac res, 56-57; assoc res anal chemist, Eli Lilly Co, 57-60; asst zool & biol, Purdue Univ, 60-62 & physiol & ecol, 62-65. *Concurrent Pos:* Guest Scientist, Labs, Genetics, Evolution & Biomet, Nat Ctr Sci Res, Gif-sur-Yvette, France; vis scholar, Biol Dept, Univ Ariz, 80-81 & 87; vis scientist, Argonne Nat labs, 83-; prog dir & reviewer bull, Am Meteorol Soc. *Mem:* AAAS; Am Inst Biol Sci; Am Soc Zool; Int Soc Chronobiol; Am Meteorol Soc; Am Arachnologists; Int Soc Chronobiol; Am Soc Chronobiol; Am Soc Photobiol; Sigma Xi. *Res:* Cellular regulation; environmental factors that influence the regulatory functions of invertebrates, chiefly arachnids, experimental parameters involved, including the analysis of neurosecretions and locomotion as cyclic phenomena; monochromatic light receptors in tissue culture. *Mailing Add:* 8692 N Little Oak Lane Tucson AZ 85704

**WILT, FRED H,** DEVELOPMENTAL BIOLOGY. *Current Pos:* assoc prof, 64-71, prof zool, 71-90, PROF MOLECULAR CELL BIOL, UNIV CALIF, BERKELEY, 90- *Personal Data:* b South Bend, Ind, Dec 12, 34; m 57, 87, Diane; c Laura, Jason & Emily. *Educ:* Ind Univ, AB, 56; Johns Hopkins Univ, PhD(biol), 59. *Honors & Awards:* Fel, AAAS; NIH Merit Award. *Prof Exp:* Fel, Carnegie Inst Technol, 59-60; assoc prof biol, Purdue Univ, 60-64. *Concurrent Pos:* NIH spec fel, 63-64; fel, Guggenheim Found, 75. *Mem:* Soc Develop Biol; Am Soc Cell Biol; AAAS; biomineralization. *Res:* Regulation of gene expression; roll of cell interaction and nucleo-cytoplasmic interactions during embryonic development. *Mailing Add:* Dept Molecular Cell Biol 371 LSA Univ Calif Berkeley CA 94720-0001. *Fax:* 510-643-6791; *E-Mail:* wilt@garnet.berkeley.edu

**WILT, MICHAEL,** ELECTROMAGNETIC METHODS IN GEOPHYSICS, GEOPHYSICS APPLIED TO HYDROLOGY-OIL EXPLORATION WITH ELECTROMAGNETIC METHODS. *Current Pos:* STAFF SCIENTIST, LAWRENCE LIVERMORE NAT LAB, 89- *Personal Data:* m 81, Gloria Chua; c Katharine. *Educ:* Univ Calif, Riverside, BS, 73, MS, 75, Univ Calif, Berkeley, PhD(geophys eng), 89. *Prof Exp:* Geologist, Phillips Petrol, 75; geophysicist, Geonomics Inc, 76-77; staff scientist, Lawrence Berkeley Lab, 77-84. *Mem:* Soc Explor Geophysicists; Am Geophys Union; Geothermal Resources Coun. *Res:* Developing a method to do underground imaging of the electrical resistivity distribution; using electromagnetic methods and applying the technology to burcholes in oil field and environmental clean-up applications. *Mailing Add:* 1206 Newell Ave Walnut Creek CA 94596. *Fax:* 510-422-3013; *E-Mail:* wiltz@unl.gov

**WILT, PAXTON MARSHALL,** MOLECULAR SPECTROSCOPY. *Current Pos:* From asst prof to assoc prof, 67-76, PROF CHEM PHYSICS, CENTRE COL KY, 76- *Personal Data:* b Louisville, Ky, July 8, 42; m 67. *Educ:* Centre Col Ky, BA, 64; Vanderbilt Univ, PhD(physics), 67. *Concurrent Pos:* Consult, Res Corp Am, 67. *Res:* Molecular vibration-rotation spectres of small polyatomic molecules. *Mailing Add:* 1064 Argyl Dr Danville KY 40422

**WILTBANK, WILLIAM JOSEPH,** HORTICULTURE, PLANT PHYSIOLOGY. *Current Pos:* res asst, Univ Fla, 64-68, from asst prof to assoc prof, 68-79, actg chmn dept, 77-79 & 84-86, PROF FRUIT CROPS, UNIV FLA, 79-, ASST CHMN DEPT, 86- *Personal Data:* b Clifton, Ariz, Jan 1, 27; m 47; c 5. *Educ:* NMex State Univ, BSAgr, 50; Univ Fla, PhD(fruit crops), 67. *Honors & Awards:* Gourley Award, Am Soc Hort Sci, 71. *Prof Exp:* Instr voc agr, NMex State Dept Voc Educ, 50-53; instr hort, NMex State Univ, 53-54, ext horticulturist, 54-59; hort adv, US Agency Int Develop, Costa Rica, 59-64. *Mem:* Am Soc Hort Sci; Am Inst Biol Sci; Int Soc Hort Sci; Int Soc Citricult; AAAS. *Res:* Physiology of plant reproduction; plant tolerance to temperature and water stress; mineral nutrition of plants. *Mailing Add:* 3726 SW Fourth Pl Gainesville FL 32607

**WILTON, DONALD ROBERT,** ELECTRICAL ENGINEERING. *Current Pos:* PROF ELEC ENG, UNIV HOUSTON, 83- *Personal Data:* b Lawton, Okla, Oct 25, 42; m 65; c 3. *Educ:* Univ Ill, Urbana, BS, 64, MS, 66, PhD(elec eng), 70. *Prof Exp:* Mem tech staff, Ground Systs Group, Hughes Aircraft Co, 65-67; prof elec eng, Univ Miss, 70-83. *Concurrent Pos:* Vis prof, Syracuse Univ, 77-78. *Mem:* Inst Elec & Electronics Engrs; Electromagnetics Soc; Sigma Xi. *Res:* Electromagnetic theory; numerical methods applied to electromagnetics; antennas. *Mailing Add:* Dept Elec Eng Univ Houston 4800 Calhoon Houston TX 77204-0001

**WILTSCHKO, DAVID VILANDER,** TECTONICS, TECTONOPHYSICS. *Current Pos:* from asst prof to assoc prof, 84-94, dir, Ctr Tectonophysics, 89-94, PROF STRUCT GEOL, TEX A&M UNIV, 94- *Personal Data:* b Portland, Ore, Feb 5, 49; m 81, Sherry I Bame; c Alexander B & Elicia B. *Educ:* Univ Rochester, BA, 71; Brown Univ, MSc, 74, PhD(geol), 78. *Prof Exp:* Vis asst prof, Univ Mich, 77-79, asst prof struct geol, 79-84. *Mem:* Geol Soc Am; Am Geophys Union; Am Asn Petrol Geol. *Res:* Tectonics of mountain belts, focusing on the mechanics of continental structures; theoretical model of thrust sheet motion; mechanisms of fault zones; flow of fluids in deforming rock; original veins. *Mailing Add:* Dept Geol & Geophysics Tex A&M Univ College Station TX 77843-3115. *E-Mail:* d.wiltschko@.tamu.edu

**WILTSCHKO, WOLFGANG,** ZOOLOGY. *Current Pos:* Sci asst, 67-69, asst prof, 70-73, PROF ZOOL, JW GOETHE UNIV, 75- *Personal Data:* b Aug 21, 38; m 68, Roswitha Brill; c Carsten. *Educ:* JW Goethe Univ, PhD, 67, Habilitation, 72. *Honors & Awards:* Eliot Coues Award, Am Ornithologists Union, 94. *Concurrent Pos:* Vis fel, Cornell Univ, NY, 74-75. *Mem:* Fel Am Ornith Soc; Int Ornith Cong; Int Soc Neuroethol; Ger Soc Ornith (vpres, 86-92); Ger Soc Zool. *Res:* Contributed articles to professional journals; orientation of animals in space and time. *Mailing Add:* Dept Zool JW Goethe Siesmayerstr 70 60323 Frankfurt am Main Germany

**WILTSE, JAMES CORNELIUS,** MILLIMETER WAVES, LASERS. *Current Pos:* PRIN RES ENGR, ENG EXP STA, GA INST TECHNOL, 78- *Personal Data:* b Tannersville, NY, Mar 16, 26; m 50; c 2. *Educ:* Rensselaer Polytech Inst, BEE, 47, MEE, 52; Johns Hopkins Univ, PhD(eng), 59. *Prof Exp:* Engr, Gen Elec Co, 47-48; instr elec eng, Rensselaer Polytech Inst, 48-51; instr, Johns Hopkins Univ, 53-54, res assoc, 54-58; mgr microwaves & antennas, Electronic Commun, Inc, 59-63, dir advan develop, 63-64; prin scientist & mgr microwaves, radar, optics & lasers, Martin Marietta Corp, 64-73, dir res & technol, 73-78, dir electronics eng, 76. *Concurrent Pos:* Instr, Naval Reserve Off Sch, Fla, 66-69; mem vis comt, Dept Elec Eng, Univ Fla, 69-70, 73 & 78; mem external adv comt, Ga Inst Technol, 76-78. *Mem:* Fel Inst Elec & Electronics Engrs. *Res:* Microwave and millimeter wave technology, antennas, electromagnetic theory, lasers, infrared and electro-optics with applications to radar, communications, guidance and electronic countermeasures; guided wave propagation; microwave and millimeter-wave technology and communications; lasers, infrared, and optics; quantum electronics; atmospheric propagation; radiometry; radar; antennas; signal processing. *Mailing Add:* Ga Technol Res Inst 400 Tenth St Atlanta GA 30332

**WILTSHIRE, CHARLES THOMAS,** AQUATIC ECOLOGY. *Current Pos:* From asst prof to assoc prof, 66-76, PROF BIOL & CHMN, DIV NATURAL SCI, CULVER-STOCKTON COL, 76- *Personal Data:* b Kansas City, Mo, Apr 5, 41; m 62; c 4. *Educ:* Culver-Stockton Col, BA, 63; Drake Univ, MA, 65; Univ Mo-Columbia, PhD(zool), 73. *Mem:* AAAS; Am Soc Zoologists; Nat Sci Teachers Asn. *Res:* Taxonomy and natural history of conchostracans, such as Cyzicus; ecology of the middle Mississippi River. *Mailing Add:* Off Vp res Acad Affairs Culver-Stockton Col College Hill Canton MO 63435-1257

**WIMALASENA, JAY,** CANCER RESEARCH, MOLECULAR ENDOCRINOLOGY. *Current Pos:* asst prof, 81-83, ASSOC PROF & DIR IMMUNOL, UNIV TENN MED CTR, 92- *Personal Data:* b Sri Lanka, June 7, 48; US citizen; m 72, Sunimal. *Educ:* Univ Southampton, BSc, 69; Univ Colo, PhD(pharmacol), 78. *Prof Exp:* Fel, NIH, 78-80; asst prof, Lehigh Univ, 86-87, Univ Nebr Med Sch, 87-92. *Concurrent Pos:* Prin investr, Univ Tenn, 82-85, Univ Nebr Med Ctr, 86-89, Univ Tenn Med Ctr, 90- *Mem:* Am Asn Cancer Res; Am Soc Biochem & Molecular Biol; Endocrine Soc; Soc Gynec Invest; Soc Study Reproduction; Fertil Soc. *Res:* Elucidation of the signal transduction pathways by which hormones, growth factors and alcohol modulate growth and function of ovarian cancer cells and gonadal and placental cells. *Mailing Add:* Univ Tenn Med Ctr Dept Obstet-Gynec 1924 Alcoa Hwy Knoxville TN 37920-6999. *Fax:* 423-544-6863

**WIMBER, DONALD EDWARD,** BOTANY, CYTOLOGY. *Current Pos:* from assoc prof to prof, 63-90, EMER PROF BIOL, UNIV ORE, 90- *Personal Data:* b Greeley, Colo, Jan 2, 30; m 86, Carol Cogswell; c Erica & Carmel. *Educ:* San Diego State Col, BA, 52; Claremont Col, MA, 54, PhD(bot), 56. *Honors & Awards:* Gold Medal, Am Orchid Soc, 93; Westonbirt Medal, Royal Hort Soc, 94; Hudlow Medal, Cymbidium Soc Am, 95. *Prof Exp:* Res assoc, Dos Pueblos Orchid Co, 54-57; res collabr, Brookhaven Nat Lab, 57-60, asst biologist, 61-63; res collabr, Royal Cancer Hosp, 60-61. *Concurrent Pos:* NIH fel, 58-61, career develop award, 66-71. *Mem:* Bot Soc Am. *Res:* Genetics and cytology of orchids. *Mailing Add:* Dept Biol Univ Ore Eugene OR 97403-1210

**WIMBERLY, C RAY,** HEAT TRANSFER, THERMODYNAMICS. *Current Pos:* DIR INT ACTIV, EMBRY RIDDLE UNIV, 91- *Personal Data:* b Wichita Falls, Tex, Aug 2, 36; m 59; c 2. *Educ:* Tex A&M Univ, BS, 61, PhD(mech eng), 68; Univ Ala, MS, 65. *Prof Exp:* Sr engr, Boeing Co, 61-64; proj engr, Marshall Space Flight Ctr, NASA, 64-67; sr specialist, LTV Aerospace Corp, 67-70; asst prof mech eng, Va Mil Inst, 70-73; prof mech eng, Univ Miss, 73-79; prof & head, Dept Mech Eng, Mont State Univ, 79-82; dean mech eng, La Tech Univ, 82-87; dean eng, Memphis State Univ, 87-91. *Concurrent Pos:* Fac fel, Manned Space Craft Ctr, NASA, 71-72; prin investr, US Army Res Off, 74-76 & 79; consult eng, Battelle Mem Inst-US Army Missile Command, 75 & Comput Sci Corp, 78. *Mem:* Am Soc Mech Engrs; Am Soc Eng Educ; Sigma Xi. *Res:* Engineering and research in flight dynamics, gas dynamics, fluid mechanics, heat transfer, laser technology, combustion, and associated areas with application to numerous flight and non-flight thermal and fluid dynamic systems. *Mailing Add:* 392 Brown Pelican Dr Daytona Beach FL 32119

**WIMBUSH, MARK,** PHYSICAL OCEANOGRAPHY. *Current Pos:* FROM ASSOC PROF TO PROF PHYS OCEANOG, GRAD SCH OCEANOG, UNIV RI, 77- *Personal Data:* b Nairobi, Kenya, June 26, 36; US citizen; m 66, Reiko Uemura; c Adam Chihiro & Julian Jiro. *Educ:* Oxford Univ, BA, 57, MA, 64; Univ Hawaii, MA, 63; Univ Calif, San Diego, PhD(phys oceanog), 69. *Prof Exp:* Res assoc phys oceanog, Inst Geophys & Planetary Physics, La Jolla, 69-70; NSF fel, Inst Oceanog Sci, Eng, 70-71; from asst prof to assoc prof, Nova Univ, 71-77. *Mem:* Am Geophys Union; Oceanog Soc. *Res:* Oceanic turbulence, tides and waves; dynamics of shelf and slope regions and interaction of bottom boundary layer flow with underlying sediment; equatorial oceanography; Kuroshio dynamics. *Mailing Add:* Grad Sch Oceanog Univ RI Narragansett RI 02882-1197. *Fax:* 401-874-6728; *E-Mail:* markw@ono.gso.uri.edu

**WIMENITZ, FRANCIS NATHANIEL,** PHYSICS, ENGINEERING. *Current Pos:* scientist, 87-90, CONSULT, WEAPONS EFFECTS SURVIVABILITY/VULNERABILTIY, KAMAN SCI, 90- *Personal Data:* b Philadelphia, Pa, Mar 9, 22; m 53, Edmeera Bortner; c Lisa R. *Educ:* Temple Univ, BA, 49, MA, 51. *Prof Exp:* Physicist acoust, Nat Bur Stand, 51-53; physicist mine fuze develop, Diamond Ord Fuze Lab, 53-58; res supvr nuclear weapons effects, Harry Diamond Labs, 58-64, chief, Nuclear Weapon Effects Br, 64-70, chief, Nuclear Weapons Effects Prog Off, 70-80; fac mem, George Washington Univ, 80-81; assoc sr scientist, Kaman Tempo, 81-87. *Mem:* AAAS. *Res:* Nuclear weapons effects; radiation transport; nuclear weapons electromagnetic pulse measurement; operations research; nuclear weapons effects simulation. *Mailing Add:* 1024 Chiswell Lane Silver Spring MD 20901

**WIMER, BRUCE MEADE,** INTERNAL MEDICINE, HEMATOLOGY. *Current Pos:* ASSOC PROF MED & HEMAT, TEX TECH UNIV HEALTH CTR, 82- *Personal Data:* b Tuckerton, NJ, Aug 31, 22; m 50; c 3. *Educ:* Franklin & Marshall Col, BS, 43; Jefferson Med Col, MD, 46; Am Bd Internal Med, dipl, 56; Am Bd Hemat, dipl, 72. *Prof Exp:* Intern, Jefferson Med Col, 46-47, resident internal med &hemat, 48-51; asst internal med & hemat, Guthrie Clin, Sayre, Pa, 53-59; pvt pract, Summit, NJ, 59-61; assoc med dir, Squibb Inst Med Res, 61-62; chief hemat & oncol, Lovelace Bataan Med Ctr, 62-81. *Mem:* AMA; fel Am Col Physicians; Am Soc Hemat; Int Soc Hemat. *Res:* Cancer immunotherapy, especially adoptive leukocyte therapy and application of PHA as biological response modifier; therapeutic applications of bone marrow curettage; heparin-induced thrombocytopenie-thrombosis; hemolytic characteristics of the McLeod phenotype. *Mailing Add:* JBM W Immunotherapeutics 1609 Catron Ave SE Albuquerque NM 87123

**WIMER, CYNTHIA CROSBY,** BEHAVIORAL & NEURAL GENETICS. *Current Pos:* RETIRED. *Personal Data:* b Boston, Mass, Oct 23, 33; m 57, Richard E; c John, Luke & Mark. *Educ:* Wellesley Col, BA, 55; McGill Univ, MA, 58; Rutgers Univ, PhD(psychol), 61. *Prof Exp:* Res assoc phychol, Inst Develop Studies, NY Med Col, 61 & Jackson Lab, 63-69; assoc res scientist, Div Neurosci, Beckman Res Inst, City of Hope, 69-90; statist consult, Bayshore Data Serv, 91-95. *Res:* Behavior genetics; biometrics; neuroanatomical correlates of behavior. *Mailing Add:* 166 Bayshore Dr Morro Bay CA 93442

**WIMER, DAVID CARLISLE,** ANALYTICAL & PHARMACEUTICAL CHEMISTRY, ORGANIC & INORGANIC CHEMISTRY. *Current Pos:* RETIRED. *Personal Data:* b Champaign, Ill, July 20, 26; m 55, Gwen Hill; c Beth M (McLain). *Educ:* Univ Ill, BS, 51. *Prof Exp:* From chemist to sr chemist, Abbott Labs, North Chicago, 51-65, group leader invest drugs res, 65-70, analytical res chemist, 70-80, sr analytical chemist, Analytical Res Dept, 80-87. *Mem:* Sigma Xi. *Res:* Acid-base interactions; non-aqueous solvent chemistry; functional group analysis, particularly organic nitrogen functions; thin layer chromatography; organic and inorganic qualitative analysis; ultraviolet absorption spectra of inorganic and organic compounds; ion chromatography. *Mailing Add:* 2312 11th St PO Box 245 Winthrop Harbor IL 60096-1511

**WIMER, LARRY THOMAS,** INSECT PHYSIOLOGY. *Current Pos:* asst prof, 64-70, assoc prof, 70-77, PROF BIOL & CHMN DEPT, UNIV SC, 77- *Personal Data:* b Stuttgart, Ark, Dec 20, 36; m 59; c 3. *Educ:* Phillips Univ, BA, 57; Rice Inst, MA, 59; Univ Va, PhD(physiol), 63. *Prof Exp:* Instr biol, Northwestern Univ, 62-64. *Mem:* AAAS; Am Soc Zoologists. *Res:* Insect developmental physiology; hormonal regulation of developmental metabolic systems. *Mailing Add:* Dept Biol Univ SC Col Main Campus Columbia SC 29208-0001

**WIMER, RICHARD E,** BEHAVIORAL GENETICS, NEUROGENETICS. *Current Pos:* RETIRED. *Personal Data:* b Tulare, Calif, Apr 8, 32; m 57; c 3. *Educ:* San Jose State Col, AB, 52; Ohio Univ, MSc, 53; McGill Univ, PhD(psychol), 59. *Prof Exp:* Instr psychol, Douglass Col, Rutgers Univ, 58-60; sr res assoc psychiat, NY Med Col, 60-61; assoc staff scientist, Jackson Lab, 61-65, staff scientist, 65-69; sr res scientist & chief, Behav & Neural Genetics Sect, Div Neurosci, City of Hope Med Ctr, 69-92. *Mem:* AAAS; Behav Genetics Asn; Sigma Xi. *Res:* Genetic variations in brain structure and correlated behavioral function. *Mailing Add:* 166 Bayshore Dr Morro Bay CA 93442

**WIMMER, DONN BRADEN,** COMBUSTION CHEMISTRY, FUEL CHEMISTRY. *Current Pos:* Res chemist, 51-65, sr res chemist, 65-77, SECT SUPVR COMBUSTION, PHILLIPS PETROL CO, 77- *Personal Data:* b Pittsburg, Kans, Oct 14, 27; m 49; c 3. *Educ:* Univ Kans, BS, 50, MS, 51. *Honors & Awards:* Arch T Colewell Award, Soc Automotive Engrs, 74. *Concurrent Pos:* Mem, Eng & Sci Adv Comt, Coord Res Coun, Air Qual Comt, Am Petrol Inst, 76- *Mem:* Int Inst Combustion. *Res:* Reciprocating engine combustion and atmospheric photochemistry. *Mailing Add:* 6705 Abbey Rd Bartlesville OK 74006

**WIMMER, ECKARD,** MOLECULAR BIOLOGY, VIROLOGY. *Current Pos:* assoc prof, 74-79, PROF MICROBIOL, SCH MED, STATE UNIV NY, STONYBROOK, 79-, CHMN DEPT, 84- *Personal Data:* b Berlin, Germany, May 22, 36; m 65; c 2. *Educ:* Univ Gottingen, dipl chem, 59, PhD(org chem), 62. *Prof Exp:* Asst org chem, Univ Gottingen, 62-64; res fel biochem, Univ BC, 64-66; res assoc molecular biol, Univ Ill, 66-68; from asst prof to assoc prof microbiol, Sch Med, St Louis Univ, 68-74. *Concurrent Pos:* Vis prof, Mass Inst Technol, 69. *Mem:* Am Soc Microbiol; AAAS. *Res:* Molecular biology of animal viruses; biochemistry of nucleic acids and proteins; cell biology; the elucidation of the chemical structure of the poliovirion; mechanisms involved in polio polyprotein processing by proteases and in RNA replication; immunogenic properties, mechanism of entry into the cell, and the molecular basis of pathogencity of the poliovirion. *Mailing Add:* Dept Microbiol Sch Med State Univ NY Stony Brook NY 11794

**WIMPEE, CHARLES F,** MOLECULAR BIOLOGY & EVOLUTION OF PHOTOSYNTHESIS, EVOLUTION OF BIOLUMINESCENCE. *Current Pos:* asst prof, 86-91, ASSOC PROF, DEPT BIOL SCI, UNIV WIS-MILWAUKEE, 92- *Personal Data:* b Syracuse, NY, Mar 12, 53; m 76, Barbara Brown; c 3. *Educ:* Univ Calif, Los Angeles, BA, 75, PhD(biol), 84; Univ Ga, MS, 78. *Prof Exp:* Researcher, Brookhaven Nat Lab, 84-86. *Concurrent Pos:* Affil, Ctr Great Lakes Studies, 88- *Mem:* AAAS; Int Soc Plant Molec Biol; Am Soc Microbiol. *Res:* Symbiosis, molecular evolution, and gene regulation; molecular biology and evolution of chloroplasts and the molecular biology, evolution and ecology of marine luminous bacteria. *Mailing Add:* Dept Biol Sci Univ Wis PO Box 413 Milwaukee WI 53201. *Fax:* 414-229-3926; *E-Mail:* cwimpee@csd.uwm.edu

**WIMPRESS, GORDON DUNCAN, JR,** RESEARCH ADMINISTRATION. *Current Pos:* RETIRED. *Personal Data:* b Riverside, Calif, Apr 10, 22; m 46; c 3. *Educ:* Univ Ore, BA, 46, MA, 51; Univ Denver, PhD(gen semantics), 58. *Hon Degrees:* LLD, Monmouth Col, 70; LHD, Tusculum Col, 71. *Prof Exp:* Instr jour, Whittier Col, 46-51; asst to pres, Colo Sch Mines, 51-59; pres, Monticello Col, 59-64, Monmouth Col, 64-70 & Trinity Univ, 70-77; vchmn, bd gov, Southwest Found Biomed Res, 77-82, pres, 82-92. *Concurrent Pos:* Consult, Burlington Northern RR, 67- & Valero Energy Corp, 85-; exec consult, Donald W Reynolds Found, 83-90. *Mailing Add:* 11102 Whisper Ridge San Antonio TX 78230-3614

**WIMS, ANDREW MONTGOMERY,** PHYSICAL CHEMISTRY, X-RAY DIFFRACTION. *Current Pos:* SR STAFF RES SCIENTIST, GEN MOTORS RES LAB, 69- *Personal Data:* b Phila, Pa, Apr 29, 35; m 59, Sara Chandler; c Joyce, Angela, Cheryl & Brian. *Educ:* Howard Univ, BS, 57, MS, 59, PhD, 67. *Prof Exp:* Res chemist, Nat Bur Stand, 60-68. *Mem:* Am Chem Soc; Sigma Xi. *Res:* Characterization of materials by electron microscopy; electron spectroscopy; x-ray diffraction; data analysis using computer methods. *Mailing Add:* Analytical Chem Dept Gen Motors Res Labs 12 Mile Mound Rd Warren MI 48090-9055. *Fax:* 810-986-0817

**WINANS, RANDALL EDWARD,** PHYSICAL ORGANIC CHEMISTRY. *Current Pos:* Fel, 75-77, from asst chemist to chemist, 77-89, GROUP LEADER, ARGONNE NAT LAB, 80-, SR CHEMIST, 90- *Personal Data:* b Battle Creek, Mich, Jan 11, 49; m 75, Vida Jue; c Adrienne, Amy & Alyssa. *Educ:* Mich Technol Univ, BS, 71; Cornell Univ, MS, 73, PhD(chem), 76. *Honors & Awards:* Storch Award Fuel Sci, Am Chem Soc, 88. *Concurrent Pos:* Consult, Gas Res Inst, 79-80, Helene Curtis, 83. *Mem:* Am Chem Soc; AAAS. *Res:* Organic chemistry of coals and other fossil fuels; applications of mass spectrometry, microwave induced plasma emission spectroscopy, and synchrotron x-ray absorption spectroscopy; preparation of catalytic materials and battery carbons. *Mailing Add:* Chem Div Argonne Nat Lab Argonne IL 60439

**WINAWER, SIDNEY J,** INTERNAL MEDICINE, GASTROENTEROLOGY. *Current Pos:* asst prof, 66-72, CLIN ASSOC PROF MED, MED COL, CORNELL UNIV, 72- *Personal Data:* b New York, NY, July 9, 31. *Educ:* NY Univ, BA, 52; State Univ NY, MD, 56. *Prof Exp:* Asst med, Harvard Med Sch, 62-64, instr, 65-66. *Concurrent Pos:* Fel med, Boston City Hosp, 62-64, assist physician, 65-66; NIH spec fel, 65-67; asst physician, NY Hosp, 66-, dir, Gastrointestinal Lab, 72-; asst clinician, Sloan-Kettering Inst. *Mem:* Fel Am Col Physicians; Am Gastroenterol Asn;

Am Soc Gastrointestinal Endoscopy; Am Fedn Clin Res; Am Col Gastroenterol. *Res:* Clinical investigation in gastrointestinal diseases, particularly morphology, physiology, cell proliferation and other aspects of gastritis; malabsorptive studies such as massive bowel resection; clinical and investigative aspects of gastrointestinal and liver cancer. *Mailing Add:* Mem One Sloan-Kettering Cancer 1275 York Ave New York NY 10021-6007

**WINBORN, WILLIAM BURT,** ANATOMY. *Current Pos:* asst prof, 68-69, ASSOC PROF ANAT, HEALTH SCI CTR, UNIV TEX, SAN ANTONIO, 69- *Personal Data:* b Victoria, Tex, Oct 6, 31; m 53; c 1. *Educ:* Univ Tex, BS, 56; La State Univ, PhD(anat), 63. *Prof Exp:* From instr to asst prof anat, Med Units, Univ Tenn, Memphis, 63-68. *Mem:* AAAS; Electron Micros Soc Am; Am Soc Cell Biol; Am Asn Anatomists. *Res:* Electron microscopic studies of Islets of Langerhans and of the gastrointestinal tract; cytochemistry of the gastrointestinal tract. *Mailing Add:* Dept Cell & Struct Biol Univ Tex Health Sci Ctr 7703 Floyd Curl Dr San Antonio TX 78284-7762

**WINBOW, GRAHAM ARTHUR,** ACOUSTICS, PETROLEUM ENGINEERING. *Current Pos:* sr res physicist geophys, Exxon Prod Res Co, 78-80, res specialist, 80-81, res supvr, 81-85, SR RES ASSOC, EXXON PROD RES CO, 85- *Personal Data:* b Sedgley, Eng, Oct 31, 43; m 77, Virginia Leicht; c Alexander & Victoria. *Educ:* Cambridge Univ, BA, 65, PhD(physics), 68. *Prof Exp:* Sci Res Coun fel, Univ London, 68-69; NATO fel, Europ Orgn Nuclear Res, Geneva, Switz, 69-70; sr res assoc, Daresbury Lab, Warrington, Eng, 70-75; fel physics, Rutgers Univ, 75-78. *Mem:* Am Phys Soc; Soc Explor Geophys; Soc Indust & Appl Math; Acoust Soc Am. *Res:* Data acquisition and image processing technology for oil/gas exploration; theoretical physics. *Mailing Add:* Exxon Prod Res Co PO Box 2189 Houston TX 77252-2189

**WINBURY, MARTIN M,** PHARMACOLOGY, PHYSIOLOGY. *Current Pos:* PRES, INTERPHARM, 86- *Personal Data:* b New York, NY, Aug 4, 18; m 42; c 2. *Educ:* Long Island Univ, BS, 40; Univ Md, MS, 42; NY Univ, PhD(physiol), 51. *Prof Exp:* Economist, US Bur Mines, 42-44; mem staff biochem & pharmacol, Merck Inst Therapeut Res, 44-47; pharmacologist, Div Biol Res, G D Searle & Co, 47-55; sr pharmacologist, Schering Corp, 55-58, dir dept pharmacol, 58-61, assoc dir biol res, 61; dir, Dept Pharmacol, Warner Lambert Co, 61-80, dir Sci Develop, 80-86. *Concurrent Pos:* Mem vis fac, Col Physicians & Surgeons, Columbia Univ; mem vis fac, Rutgers Univ; lectr, Univ Mich Med Sch. *Mem:* NY Acad Sci; Am Soc Pharmacol & Exp Therapeut; Am Chem Soc; Am Heart Asn; Am Col Cardiol. *Res:* Pharmacology and physiology of cardiovascular, coronary and autonomic agents; distribution myocardial flow; microcirculation. *Mailing Add:* Pharm-Ex PO Box 8335 Ann Arbor MI 48107. *Fax:* 313-996-1748

**WINCH, FRED EVERETT, JR,** FORESTRY, SILVICULTURE. *Current Pos:* from asst prof to prof forestry, Cornell Univ, 43-76, actg head, Dept Natural Resources, 72-73, actg assoc dir agr exten, 73-74, EMER PROF FORESTRY, CORNELL UNIV, 76-; CONSULT, FOREST MGT & ENVIRON MGT, 76- *Personal Data:* b Mass, June 16, 14; m 39; c 4. *Educ:* Univ Maine, BS, 36; Cornell Univ, MS, 37. *Prof Exp:* Forestry specialist, Soil Conserv Serv, USDA, 38-40; farm planning technician, 40-43. *Mem:* Fel Soc Am Foresters. *Res:* Plantation establishment and early growth; maple syrup and Christmas tree production; forest recreation, resource development and conservation; land use inventory analysis and planning; forest tax impacts. *Mailing Add:* Warner Rd Box 312 Bradford NH 03221

**WINCHELL, HARRY SAUL,** MEDICAL PHYSICS, NUCLEAR MEDICINE. *Current Pos:* CONSULT, 79- *Personal Data:* b Coaldale, Pa, Mar 1, 35; m 64; c 4. *Educ:* Bucknell Univ, BA, 54; Hahnemann Med Col, MD, 58; Univ Calif, Berkeley, PhD(biophys), 61. *Hon Degrees:* DSc, Bucknell Univ, 72. *Honors & Awards:* George Von Hevesy Award, Europ Orgn Nuclear Med, 69. *Prof Exp:* Intern, San Francisco Hosp, Univ Calif, 58-59; univ fel, Univ Calif, Berkeley, 59-61; resident, Mt Sinai Hosp, NY, 61-62; assoc res physician, Donner Lab, Univ Calif, Berkeley, 62-73, lectr med physics, Univ, 66-73; exec vpres & dir res & develop, Medi-Physics, Inc, 72-78, consult, 78-79. *Concurrent Pos:* NSF fel, Univ Calif, Berkeley, 59-60; NIH fel, 60-61; spec consult, Sealab II Exp, La Jolla, Calif, 65. *Mem:* Fel Am Col Physicians; Soc Nuclear Med. *Mailing Add:* One Via Oneg Lafayette CA 94549-2923

**WINCHELL, ROBERT E,** MINERALOGY, CRYSTALLOGRAPHY. *Current Pos:* assoc prof, 66-72, PROF GEOL & MINERAL, CALIF STATE UNIV, LONG BEACH, 72- *Personal Data:* b Wichita, Kans, Sept 21, 31; m 58; c 3. *Educ:* Stanford Univ, BS, 56; Mich Col Mining & Technol, MS, 59; Ohio State Univ, PhD(mineral), 63. *Prof Exp:* Jr eng geologist, Bridge Dept, Calif Div Hwys, 57-58; res scientist, AC Spark Plug Div, Gen Motors Corp, 63-66. *Mem:* Mineral Soc Am; Brit Mineral Soc. *Res:* Mineral synthesis and characterization; optical, x-ray and morphological crystallography; x-ray diffraction; electron microscopy; phase equilibrium studies; crystal chemistry, growth and structure analysis; solid state and materials science. *Mailing Add:* 6411 Weber Circle Huntington Beach CA 92647

**WINCHESTER, ALBERT MCCOMBS,** biology; deceased, see previous edition for last biography

**WINCHESTER, JAMES FRANK,** MEDICINE. *Current Pos:* From asst prof to assoc prof, 78-86, dir, Nephrology Div, 88-94, PROF MED, GEORGETOWN UNIV MED CTR, 87- *Personal Data:* b Glasgow, Scotland, Mar 24, 44. *Educ:* Glasgow Univ, MBChB, 69, MD, 80; Royal Col Physicians, MRCP, 72, FRCP, 82. *Mem:* Int Soc Peritoneal Dialysis (secy & treas, 83-); Am Soc Nephrol; Nat Kidney Found; Int Soc Nephrol; Am Found Clin Res. *Res:* Nutrition and renal disease; drug poisoning; artificial organs; hypertension; general nephrology; telemedicine. *Mailing Add:* Georgetown Univ Hosp 3800 Reservoir Rd NW Washington DC 20007

**WINCHESTER, JOHN W,** OCEANOGRAPHY. *Current Pos:* chmn dept, 70-76, PROF OCEANOG, FLA STATE UNIV, 70- *Personal Data:* b Chicago, Ill, Oct 8, 29; m 58; c 1. *Educ:* Univ Chicago, AB, 50, SM, 52; Mass Inst Technol, PhD(chem), 55. *Prof Exp:* Fulbright grant, Neth, 55-56; from asst prof to assoc prof geochem, Mass Inst Technol, 56-66; assoc prof meteorol & oceanog, Univ Mich, Ann Arbor, 67-69, prof oceanog & asst dir, Great Lakes Res Div, 69-70. *Mem:* Am Chem Soc; Geochem Soc; Geol Soc Am; Am Geophys Union; Sigma Xi. *Res:* Atmospheric and marine geochemistry. *Mailing Add:* 2405 Delgado Dr Tallahassee FL 32304-1303

**WINCHESTER, RICHARD ALBERT,** AUDIOLOGY, SPEECH PATHOLOGY. *Current Pos:* DIR, DIV COMMUN DIS & RES AUDIOLOGIST, CHILDREN'S HOSP, PHILADELPHIA, 63-; ASST PROF AUDIOL, SCH MED, UNIV PA, 64- *Personal Data:* b Denver, Colo, Nov 20, 21; m 47; c 3. *Educ:* Univ Denver, BA, 47, MA, 48; Univ Southern Calif, PhD(audiol, speech path), 57. *Prof Exp:* Resident audiol & speech path, Orthop Hosp, Los Angeles, 48-50; asst prof, Univ Denver, 50-53; res audiologist, Walter Reed Army Med Ctr, 53-54; dir hearing & speech clin, Vet Admin Hosp, San Francisco, 54-55, res audiologist, Vet Admin Regional Off, Los Angeles, 55-58; asst prof audiol, Sch Med, Temple Univ, 59-63. *Concurrent Pos:* Dir audiol & speech path, Otologic Group Philadelphia, 59-66; consult, Pa Acad Ophthal & Otolaryngol, 60-; spec lectr, Univ Md, 63-64. *Mem:* AAAS; Am Speech & Hearing Asn; assoc fel Am Acad Ophthal & Otolaryngol; Am Cleft Palate Asn; Am Audiol Soc. *Res:* Speech in deafness; auditory perception in brain injury; nonorganic deafness; deafness in otosclerosis; congenital mixed deafness; hearing patterns in vestibular disorders; central auditory functions; sound spectrography and cleft palate speech; auditory behavior in infancy and early childhood. *Mailing Add:* 764 Inverness Dr West Chester PA 19380

**WINCHESTER, ROBERT J,** IMMUNOLOGY, GENETICS. *Current Pos:* CHMN, DEPT RHEUMATICS, HOSP JOINT DIS, 86- *Personal Data:* b Yonkers, NY, Jan 27, 37. *Educ:* Cornell Univ, MD, 63. *Prof Exp:* Prof med, Rockefeller Univ, 60-79, Mt Sinai Sch Med, 80-86; PROF MED, NY UNIV, 86- *Mailing Add:* Dept Med Columbia Univ Col PS 630 W 168th St BHS 116 New York NY 10032-3702. *Fax:* 212-305-9078

**WINCHURCH, RICHARD ALBERT,** IMMUNOLOGY, MICROBIOLOGY. *Current Pos:* ASSOC PROF, SCH MED, JOHNS HOPKINS UNIV, 77- *Personal Data:* b Newark, NJ, June 18, 36; m 61; c 2. *Educ:* Seton Hall Univ, AB, 58, MS, 67; Rutgers Univ, PhD(microbiol), 70. *Prof Exp:* Sr scientist microbiol, Smith, Kline & French Labs, 70-71, assoc sr investr pharmacol, 71-73; staff fel immunol, Baltimore Cancer Res Ctr, Nat Cancer Inst, 73-76, sr staff fel, 76-77. *Mem:* Am Asn Immunologists; Soc Leukocyte Biol; AAAS. *Res:* Cellular immunology; zinc metabolism; trauma; gerontology; infectious diseases. *Mailing Add:* Johns Hopkins Univ Allergy & Asthma Ctr 5501 Hopkins Bayview Circle Baltimore MD 21224-6819. *Fax:* 410-550-7998

**WINCKLER, JOHN RANDOLPH,** PHYSICS. *Current Pos:* from asst prof to prof, 49-86, EMER PROF PHYSICS, UNIV MINN, MINNEAPOLIS, 86- *Personal Data:* b North Plainfield, NJ, Oct 27, 16; m 43; c 5. *Educ:* Rutgers Univ, BS, 42; Princeton Univ, PhD(physics), 46. *Hon Degrees:* Doctor, Univ Paul Sabatier, France, 72. *Honors & Awards:* Space Sci Award, Am Inst Aeronaut & Astronaut, 62; Arctowski Medal, Nat Acad Sci, 78. *Prof Exp:* Res physicist, Johns-Manville Corp, NJ, 37-42; instr physics, Palmer Lab, Princeton Univ, 46-49. *Concurrent Pos:* Guggenheim fel, Meudon Observ, 65-66; mem, Math & Phys Sci Div Comt, NSF; Fulbright fel, Univ Paul Sabatien, France, 85. *Mem:* Nat Acad Sci; fel AAAS; fel Am Phys Soc; fel Am Geophys Union; Int Acad Astronaut. *Res:* High speed flow of gases and shock waves; geomagnetic effects and energy spectrum of primary cosmic rays; atmospheric total radiation; solar produced cosmic rays and energetic processes in solar flares; geomagnetic storm influences on energetic particles in the magnetosphere; space plasma physics, active experiments. *Mailing Add:* Sch Physics 116 Church St SE Minneapolis MN 55455. *Fax:* 612-624-4578

**WINCKLHOFER, ROBERT CHARLES,** POLYMER PHYSICS. *Current Pos:* RETIRED. *Personal Data:* b Newark, NJ, Dec 14, 26; m 49; c 2. *Educ:* Columbia Univ, BS, 53. *Prof Exp:* Engr, Cent Res Lab, Allied Fibers, 53-61, group leader, 61-64, res supvr, 64, Fibers Div, Tech Dept, 64-68, mgr res, 68-70, tech dir heavy denier nylon, 70-72, tech dir advan technol, 72-77, res assoc, 77-84, mgr high performance fibers, Allied Fibers, 84-92. *Mem:* AAAS; Fiber Soc; Marine Technol Soc. *Res:* Fiber polymer physics; crystallization kinetics; polymer characterization; differential thermal analysis of polymers. *Mailing Add:* 4753 Stornoway Dr Richmond VA 23234

**WINDEKNECHT, THOMAS GEORGE,** COMPUTER SCIENCE, SYSTEMS ENGINEERING. *Current Pos:* assoc dean eng, 84-85, PROF ENG, OAKLAND UNIV, MICH, 81- *Personal Data:* b Owosso, Mich, Feb 13, 35; m 58; c 3. *Educ:* Univ Mich, BSE, 58, MSE, 59; Case Western Reserve Univ, PhD(systs eng), 64. *Prof Exp:* Mem tech staff systs eng, Space Technol Labs, Inc, 59-62; from asst prof to assoc prof, Case Western Res Univ, 64-70; prof elec eng, Mich Technol Univ, 70-72; prof info & comput sci, Ga Inst Technol, 72-73; prof math sci, Memphis State Univ, 73-81. *Concurrent Pos:*

NSF grant, Case Western Res Univ, 67-69 & Mich Technol Univ, 70-72. *Mem:* Asn Comput Mach; Inst Elec & Electronics Engrs. *Res:* Formal methods in computer programming; microcomputer programming and graphics; dynamic system theory. *Mailing Add:* Comput Sci & Eng Dept Oakland Univ Rochester MI 48309

**WINDELL, JOHN THOMAS,** AQUATIC BIOLOGY. *Current Pos:* assoc prof, 66-70, PROF BIOL, UNIV COLO, BOULDER, 70-; CONSULT. *Personal Data:* b Hammond, Ind, Apr 4, 30; m 59; c 3. *Educ:* Ind Cent Col, BS, 53; Ind Univ, MA, 58, PhD(limnol), 65. *Prof Exp:* Teacher, Griffith High Sch, 55-58; asst prof biol, Ind Cent Col, 58-62; assoc zool, Ind Univ, Bloomington, 62-65; asst prof, Ind Univ NW, 65-66. *Concurrent Pos:* Ind Univ fac fel, 66; partic, Int Symp Biol Basis Freshwater Fish Prod, Reading, Eng, 66. *Mem:* AAAS; Am Soc Limnol & Oceanog; Wetland Soc Am; Am Fisheries Soc; Sigma Xi. *Res:* Ecological physiology; biological basis of fish production; food consumption in fishes; conversion coefficients and the ecology of fishes; fish physiology, feeding, digestion, nutrition, population ecology, stream and wetland biology and habitat restoration. *Mailing Add:* Aquatic & Wetland Co 1655 Walnut Suite 205 Boulder CO 80302

**WINDELS, CAROL ELIZABETH SCHRENK,** PHYTOPATHOLOGY. *Current Pos:* From jr scientist to scientist, Dept Plant path, Univ Minn, 73-84, asst prof plant path, 84-89, ASSOC PROF PLANT PATH, NW EXP STA, UNIV MINN, CROOKSTON, 89- *Personal Data:* b Long Prarie, Minn, July 12, 48; div. *Educ:* St Cloud State Univ, BA, 70; Univ Minn, MS, 72, PhD(plant path), 80. *Honors & Awards:* Distinguished Serv Award, N Cent Div, Am Phytopath Soc, 94. *Concurrent Pos:* Counr-at-large, Am Phytopath Soc, 90-93; adj prof, NDak State Univ, 92- *Mem:* Am Phytopath Soc (secy-treas, 87-90, vpres, 96-97, pres-elect, 97-98, pres, 98-99); Can Phytopath Soc; Int Soc Plant Path; Mycol Soc Am; Sigma Xi; Am Soc Sugar Beet Technologists. *Res:* Ecology and taxonomy of fusarium species; root rot, stalk rot, and other diseases of corn; ecology and control of seedling and root diseases of sugarbeet. *Mailing Add:* 211 ARC NW Exp Sta Univ Minn Crookston MN 56716. *Fax:* 218-281-8603; *E-Mail:* cwindels@mail.crk.umn.edu

**WINDER, CHARLES GORDON,** GEOLOGY, GENERAL EARTH SCIENCES. *Current Pos:* Lectr, Univ Western Ont, 53-56, from asst prof to assoc prof, 56-64, head dept, 65-71, prof, 64-87, EMER PROF GEOL, UNIV WESTERN ONT, 87- *Personal Data:* b Ottawa, Ont, June 13, 22; m 48, Freida J Clark; c Nancy J (Holmes) & Paula D (Blain). *Educ:* Univ Western Ont, BSc, 49; Cornell Univ, MS, 51, PhD(geol), 53. *Mem:* Fel Geol Asn Can; sr fel Geol Soc Am; Sigma Xi. *Res:* Relationship between science and Christianity; explain major theories of science which can be understood in Judaic Christian scriptures (age of the earth, biological evolutions). *Mailing Add:* Dept Earth Sci Univ Western Ont London ON N6A 5B7 Can. *Fax:* 519-661-3198; *E-Mail:* cwinder@julian.uwo.ca

**WINDER, DALE RICHARD,** SOLID STATE PHYSICS. *Current Pos:* asst prof, 60-64, ASSOC PROF PHYSICS, COLO STATE UNIV, 64- *Personal Data:* b Marion, Ind, Aug 27, 29; m 53. *Educ:* DePauw Univ, AB, 51; Univ Nebr, MA, 54; Case Inst Technol, PhD(physics), 57. *Prof Exp:* Lab & teaching asst physics, DePauw Univ, 50-51, Univ Nebr, 51-54 & Case Inst Technol, 54-57; physicist, Nat Carbon Res Labs, Union Carbide Corp, 57-60. *Concurrent Pos:* Physicist, Boulder Lab, Nat Bur Stand, 62-69; Idaho Nuclear Corp-Asn Western Univs fac appointee, 67. *Mem:* Am Phys Soc; Am Asn Physics Teachers; Am Crystallog Asn; Sigma Xi. *Res:* Photoelectric effect; lattic dynamics; crystal growth; radiation damage; nuclear fuels and moderators; transport property measurements. *Mailing Add:* 1430 W Oak St Ft Collins CO 80521-2348

**WINDER, ROBERT OWEN,** COMPUTER SCIENCE, TECHNICAL MANAGEMENT. *Current Pos:* RETIRED. *Personal Data:* b Boston, Mass, Oct 9, 34; m 83, Kathleen Colvin; c Katherine & Amy. *Educ:* Univ Chicago, AB, 54; Univ Mich, BS, 56; Princeton Univ, MS, 58, PhD(math), 62. *Honors & Awards:* David Sarnoff Award, 76. *Prof Exp:* Engr comput, RCA Corp, 57-58, mem tech staff, RCA Labs, 58-69, head group, 69-75, dir microprocessors, Solid State Div, 75-78; mgr work sta develop, Exxon Off Systs, Syntex Comput Systs, 78-85, vpres, 85-88; mgr prod develop, Intel Corp, 88-95. *Mem:* Fel Inst Elec & Electronics Engrs. *Res:* Threshold logic; computer architecture; plate tectonics. *Mailing Add:* 5555 E Rockridge Rd Phoenix AZ 85018. *E-Mail:* winder@asu.edu

**WINDER, WILLIAM W,** ENDOCRINOLOGY, EXERCISE PHYSIOLOGY. *Current Pos:* assoc prof, 82-86, PROF ZOOL, BRIGHAM YOUNG UNIV, 86-, THOMAS L MARTIN PROF. *Personal Data:* b Vernal, Utah, Sept 12, 42; m 64; c 8. *Educ:* Brigham Young Univ, BS, 66, PhD(zool), 71. *Prof Exp:* Teaching fel, Wash Univ Sch Med, 71-74, asst prof, 73-79; assoc prof physiol, Univ SDak Sch Med, 79-82, head, physiol & pharmacol sect, 81-82. *Concurrent Pos:* Prin investr liver metab, NIH grant, 78-89; Res Career Develop Award, NIH, 79-83; prin investr NIII grants, muscle lactate, 88-94, muscle malonyl-CoA, 92-97. *Mem:* Endocrine Soc; Am Physiol Soc; Am Col Sports Med. *Res:* Hormonal regulation of liver and muscle glycogenolysis; gluconeogenesis during exercise; muscle acetyl-CoA carboxylase, malonyl-CoA and regulation of fatty acid oxidation in muscle. *Mailing Add:* Dept Zool Brigham Young Univ Provo UT 84602. *Fax:* 801-378-7423; *E-Mail:* winderw@acdi.byu.edu

**WINDHAGER, ERICH E,** PHYSIOLOGY, BIOPHYSICS. *Current Pos:* from asst prof to prof physiol, 63-78, CHMN, DEPT PHYSIOL, MED COL, CORNELL UNIV, 73-, MAXWELL M UPSON PROF PHYSIOL & BIOPHYS, 78- *Personal Data:* b Vienna, Austria, Nov 4, 28; US citizen; m 56; c 2. *Educ:* Univ Vienna, MD, 54. *Honors & Awards:* Homer W Smith Award. *Prof Exp:* Fel biophys, Harvard Med Sch, 56-58; instr physiol, Med Col, Cornell Univ, 58-61; vis scientist, Biochem Inst, Univ Copenhagen, 61-63. *Concurrent Pos:* Career scientist, Res Coun NY, 63-71 & Irma Hirschl Found, 73-78; sect ed, Am J Physiol, 69-74. *Mem:* Am Physiol Soc; Biophys Soc; Int Soc Nephrology; Harvey Soc; Am Soc Nephrology. *Res:* Renal tubular transfer of electrolytes; electrophysiology of the nephron; micropuncture techniques and nephron function; kidney, water and electrolytes. *Mailing Add:* Dept Physiol Cornell Univ Med Col 1300 York Ave New York NY 10021-4805

**WINDHAM, CAROL THOMPSON,** NUTRITIONAL BIOCHEMISTRY, NUTRITION EDUCATION. *Current Pos:* ASSOC PROF NUTRIT, DEPT NUTRIT & FOOD SCI, UTAH STATE UNIV, 83- *Personal Data:* b Houston, Tex, Mar 14, 48; m 70; c 2. *Educ:* Rice Univ, BA, 70; Utah State Univ, PhD(nutrit), 82. *Mem:* Sigma Xi; Soc Nutrit Educ; AAAS; Am Dietetic Asn; assoc Am Inst Nutrit. *Res:* Evaluation of dietary status of national and international populations; establishment of reliable, documented food composition data bases; determination of food supply, human requirement and dietary standards for vitamin A; development of scientifically based nutrition education materials. *Mailing Add:* 1429 Regal Oaks Ct Mobile AL 36609-2207. *Fax:* 435-750-2379; *E-Mail:* cwind@usc

**WINDHAM, MICHAEL PARKS,** MATHEMATICS. *Current Pos:* from asst prof to assoc prof, 71-86, PROF MATH, UTAH STATE UNIV, 86- *Personal Data:* b Houston, Tex, Sept 23, 44; m 70; c 2. *Educ:* Rice Univ, BA, 66, MA & PhD(math), 70. *Prof Exp:* Instr math, Univ Miami, 70-71. *Mem:* Soc Indust & Appl Math; Math Asn Am; Am Math Soc; Classification Soc NAm. *Res:* Cluster analysis; numerical optimization. *Mailing Add:* 330 Lauralin Dr Logan UT 84321

**WINDHAM, RONNIE LYNN,** ANALYTICAL CHEMISTRY. *Current Pos:* MGR ANALYTICAL SERV, AUSTIN LABS, HUNTSMAN CORP, 93- *Personal Data:* b Jasper, Tex, Mar 2, 43; m 72, Dorothy Belk; c Christopher & Lee. *Educ:* Pan Am Univ, BA, 65; Eastern NMex Univ, MS, 69; Tex A&M Univ, PhD(anal chem), 71. *Prof Exp:* Proj chemist, Jefferson Chem Co, 71-81; supvr analytical chem, Austin Labs, Texaco Chem Co, 81-93. *Mem:* Am Chem Soc; Am Soc Qual Control. *Res:* Atomic absorption spectrophotometry; ion chromatography; trace analysis. *Mailing Add:* 11608 January Dr Austin TX 78753

**WINDHAM, STEVE LEE,** horticulture; deceased, see previous edition for last biography

**WINDHAUSER, MARLENE M,** CHOLESTEROL METABOLISM, DIETARY FIBERS. *Current Pos:* RES DIETITIAN, PENNINGTON BIOMED RES CTR, 91-, DIR, METAB KITCHEN, 91- *Personal Data:* b Lincoln, Nebr, Mar 20, 54; m 75; c Bret. *Educ:* Colo State Univ, BS, 75, MS, 77; La State Univ, PhD(physiol), 88. *Prof Exp:* Nutritionist, Miss State Bd Health, 78-79; clin dietitian, NMiss Retardation Ctr, 79-81, food serv dir, 81-82; asst mgr, Residence Food Serv, La State Univ, 82-83, res assoc, 89-91. *Mem:* Am Inst Nutrit; Am Dietetic Asn; Am Heart Asn. *Res:* Cholesterol metabolism as affected by dietary fats, rice bran, rice bran oil and other dietary fibers. *Mailing Add:* 2826 Dakin Ave Baton Rouge LA 70820

**WINDHOLZ, THOMAS BELA,** ORGANIC CHEMISTRY. *Current Pos:* RETIRED. *Personal Data:* b Arad, Romania, Jan 10, 23; US citizen; m 48, Martha Schillinger; c Veronica & Maya. *Educ:* Univ Cluj, MS, 47. *Prof Exp:* Res chemist, Chinoin Pharmaceut Co, Budapest, 48-50; sr res chemist, Res Inst Pharmaceut Indust, 51-54, sect head, 55-56; res chemist, Res Labs, Celanese Corp Am, NJ, 57-59; sr res chemist, Merck & Co, 60-63, sect head, 64-69, assoc dir, 70-72, dir, Int Regulatory Affairs, 72-75, dir, Proj Planning & Mgt, 75-80, sr dir human health prod develop, Res Labs, 81-85. *Mem:* Am Chem Soc. *Res:* Synthetic organic chemistry; steroids and other natural products; medicinal chemistry, metabolism; international relations and management. *Mailing Add:* 400 E 56th St Apt 24B New York NY 10022

**WINDHOLZ, WALTER M,** NUMERICAL ANALYSIS. *Current Pos:* SR MATHEMATICIAN, SCI APPL INT, INC, 83- *Personal Data:* b Gorham, Kans, Apr 25, 33; m 61; c 3. *Educ:* Ft Hays Kans State Col, AB, 53; Kans State Univ, MS, 58. *Prof Exp:* Mathematician, Thiokol Chem Corp, Utah, 61-65; mathematician, Kaman Sci Corp, 65-83. *Mem:* Math Asn Am. *Res:* Applied mathematics; structural dynamics; computational electromagnetics. *Mailing Add:* 1555 Gatehouse Circle Apt A1 Colorado Springs CO 80904-2922

**WINDHORN, THOMAS H,** SEMICONDUCTOR DEVICES, LASER DIODES. *Current Pos:* PRIN ENGR, KNOWLES ELECTRONICS, INC, 93- *Personal Data:* b New Ulm, Minn, Dec 28, 47. *Educ:* Mankato State Col, BS, 73; Univ Ill, Urbana-Champaign, MS, 77, PhD(elec eng), 82. *Prof Exp:* Res assoc, Elec Eng Res Lab, Univ Ill Urbana-Champaign, 82; res staff scientist, Lincoln Lab, Mass Inst Technol, 82-87; res staff engr, Amoco Corp Res Ctr, 87-93. *Mem:* Inst Elec & Electronics Engrs; Am Phys Soc. *Res:* Gallium arsenide lasers on Si substrates; surface-emitting diode laser arrays in gallium arsenide; development of high-power diode lasers. *Mailing Add:* 41W577 Farview Rd Elburn IL 60119

**WINDISCH, RITA M,** CLINICAL CHEMISTRY. *Current Pos:* Chief clin chemist path, 65-80, DEP CHIEF CLIN CHEM & CRITICAL CARE PATH, MERCY HOSP, 80- *Personal Data:* b Pittsburgh, Pa. *Educ:* Duquesne Univ, BS, 60, PhD(chem), 64. *Concurrent Pos:* Clin prof, Sch Med Technol, Carlow Col, 65-; clin prof, Sch Med Technol, Duquesne Univ, 69-; med staff affil, Div Clin Chem & Critical Care, Dept Path, Mercy Hosp, 69- *Mem:* Am Asn Clin Chemists; Am Chem Soc. *Res:* Diabetes, clinical chemistry and toxicology. *Mailing Add:* 25 Thorncrest Dr Pittsburgh PA 15235-5215

**WINDLER, DONALD RICHARD,** PLANT TAXONOMY. *Current Pos:* From asst prof to assoc prof, 69-77, PROF BIOL, TOWSON STATE UNIV, 77-, CUR HERBARIUM, 69-, CHMN DEPT, 84- *Personal Data:* b Centralia, Ill, Feb 4, 40; div; c 1. *Educ:* Southern Ill Univ, Carbondale, BS, 63, MA, 65; Univ NC, Chapel Hill, PhD(bot), 70. *Concurrent Pos:* Nat Defense Educ Act fel, 65-68; actg dean, Col Natural & Math Sci, Towson State Univ, 87-90. *Mem:* Int Asn Plant Taxonomists; Am Soc Plant Taxon; Torrey Bot Club; Sigma Xi; Soc Econ Bot. *Res:* Systematics of Leguminosae, Crotalaria, Mucuna and Neptunia; flora of Maryland and Delaware; lichens of Maryland; plant distribution in the Eastern United States. *Mailing Add:* Biol Dept Towson State Univ 8000 York Rd Baltimore MD 21204-7010

**WINDOM, HERBERT LYNN,** OCEANOGRAPHY, GEOCHEMISTRY. *Current Pos:* Prof oceanog, 68-93, ACTG DIR, SKIDAWAY INST OCEANOG, 94- *Personal Data:* b Macon, Ga, Apr 23, 41; m 63, Patricia Woodruff; c Kevin & Elizabeth. *Educ:* Fla State Univ, BS, 63; Univ Calif, San Diego, MS, 65, PhD(earth sci), 68. *Concurrent Pos:* Mem, Group Experts Methods Stand & Intercalibration. *Mem:* Am Soc Limnol & Oceanog; Int Coun Explor Sea; Am Geophys Union; Oceanog Soc. *Res:* Marine environmental quality; chemical oceanography; marine biogeochemistry of trace elements; marine sediments; environmental effects of dredging. *Mailing Add:* Skidaway Inst Oceanog 10 Ocean Sci Circle Savannah GA 31411. *Fax:* 912-598-2310; *E-Mail:* herb@skio.peachnet.edu

**WINDSOR, DONALD ARTHUR,** INFORMATION SCIENCE, BIOLOGICAL DIVERSITY. *Current Pos:* RES DIR, SCI AESTHETICS INST, 69- *Personal Data:* b Chicago, Ill, Mar 22, 34; m 63, 69; c 4. *Educ:* Univ Ill, Urbana, BS, 59, MS, 60; State Univ NY, Binghamton, MS, 82. *Prof Exp:* Unit leader, Prod Develop Dept, Norwich Eaton Pharmaceut, 66-67, sect chief, 67-74; info scientist, Procter & Gamble, 74-94. *Concurrent Pos:* Ed, The Kingbird, J Orinthol NY State. *Mem:* AAAS; Am Soc Info Sci; Nature Conserv; Soc Conserv Biol; Am Birding Asn; Hawk Migration Asn NAm. *Res:* Applications of general systems principles to the investigation of real-world phenomena; preservation of biological diversity; roles of parasites and other symbionts in ecosystems; ornithological information for New York State. *Mailing Add:* Sci Aesthetics Inst PO Box 604 Norwich NY 13815-0604

**WINDSOR, JOHN GOLAY, JR,** ENVIRONMENTAL CHEMISTRY, MARINE SCIENCE. *Current Pos:* ASSOC PROF CHEM OCEANOG, FLA INST TECHNOL, 82- *Personal Data:* b Chester, Pa, Nov 20, 47. *Educ:* PMC Col, Pa, BS, 69; Col William & Mary, MA, 72, PhD(marine sci), 77. *Prof Exp:* Res asst, Va Inst Marine Sci, 72-74; res assoc, Mass Inst Technol, 76-78; sr proj scientist, Northrop Servs, Inc, 78-82. *Mem:* Am Chem Soc; AAAS; Marine Technol Soc. *Res:* Application of modern instrumental methods, for example gas chromatography and mass spectrometry to trace organic analysis of environmental mixtures such as air, soil, water and sediments; development of environmental education programs. *Mailing Add:* 410 Banyan Way Melbourne FL 32951-2018

**WINDSOR, MAURICE WILLIAM,** PHOTOCHEMISTRY, PHOTOSYNTHESIS. *Current Pos:* prof & chmn dept, 71-74, PROF PHYS CHEM & MAT SCI, WASH STATE UNIV, 74- *Personal Data:* b Kent, Eng, Feb 28, 28; m 53; c 3. *Educ:* Univ Cambridge, BA, 52, PhD(phys chem), 55, MA, 57. *Prof Exp:* Res assoc, Calif Inst Technol, 55-58, Univ Sheffield, Eng, 56-67; mgr, Chem Sci Dept, TRW Systs, Redondo Beach, Calif, 58-71. *Concurrent Pos:* Sr scholar, Royal Exhib of 1851, 56-58; guest scientist, Nat Bur Standards, 58-59; prin investr, Sch Aerospace Med, Off Naval Res, Army Res Off, Air Force Off Sci Res, Nat Sci Found, 60-; consult, Appl Photophysics, London Eng, 74-77; sr vis fel, Royal Inst, London, Eng, 78-79, Tech Univ, Berlin, 85; vis prof, Univ Paris, Orsay, 79, Univ Cambridge, 84-85, Tech Univ, Berlin, 85. *Mem:* AAAS; Am Chem Soc; Royal Soc Chem London; Royal Inst London; Inter-Am Photochem Soc; Sigma Xi. *Res:* Laser photochemistry and photobiophysics; design and development of instrumentation for ultrafast (nanosecond to picosecond) flash photolysis and kinetic spectroscopy; study of primary events, including electron transfer, in photosynthesis and related model systems. *Mailing Add:* 720 SW City View St Pullman WA 99163

**WINDSOR, RICHARD ANTHONY,** BEHAVIORAL SCIENCE, PUBLIC HEALTH EVALUATION. *Current Pos:* PROF, SCH PUB HEALTH & EDUC & SR SCIENTIST, COMPREHENSIVE CANCER CTR, UNIV ALA, BIRMINGHAM, 77- *Personal Data:* b Baltimore, Md, Aug 7, 43; c 1. *Educ:* Morgan State Univ, BS, 69; Univ Ill, MS, 70, PhD(educ res & evaluation), 72; Johns Hopkins Univ, MCH, 76. *Prof Exp:* Asst prof, Col Educ, Ohio State Univ, 72-75; asst prof pub health, Sch Hyg & Pub Health, Johns Hopkins Univ, 76-77. *Concurrent Pos:* Prin investr, Nat Ctr Health Serv Res, Nat Cancer Inst, Nat Heart, Lung & Blood Inst, Ctr Dis Control; sr res fel fac med, Univ Edinburgh; vis prof, Community Med, Epidemiol & Social Res, Univ Manchester, 84, Univ Western Australia. *Mem:* Am Pub Health Asn; Soc Pub Health Educ (vpres, 79, pres elect, 80, pres, 81); Soc Behav Med; Int Union Health Educ (pres elect, 82-85, pres, 85-88). *Res:* Smoking cessation interventions for pregnant women; public health; maternal and child health; evaluation health services research. *Mailing Add:* 2640 Alta Vista Dr Birmingham AL 35243. *Fax:* 205-975-4411

**WINE, JEFFREY JUSTUS,** NEUROSCIENCES. *Current Pos:* NIH fel, Dept Biol Sci, 71-72, from asst prof to assoc prof, 72-86, PROF PSYCHOL, STANFORD UNIV, 86- *Personal Data:* b Pittsburgh, Pa, Feb 10, 40; m 66, Marlene; c Nina & Jenny. *Educ:* Univ Pittsburgh, BS, 66; Univ Calif, Los Angeles, PhD(psychol), 71. *Mem:* Soc Neurosci; Int Brain Res Orgn; Soc Exp Biol; AAAS; Am Physiol Soc. *Res:* Cystic fibrosis; neurophysiological and neuroanatomical analysis of invertebrate behavior. *Mailing Add:* Cystic Fibrosis Res Lab Stanford Univ Stanford CA 94305-2130. *Fax:* 650-725-5699; *E-Mail:* wine@stanford.edu

**WINE, PAUL HARRIS,** PHYSICAL & ATMOSPHERIC CHEMISTRY. *Current Pos:* from res scientist to sr res scientist, 77-86, PRIN RES SCIENTIST, TECH RES INST, GA INST TECHNOL, 86-, HEAD, PHYS & ATMOSPHERIC CHEM BR, 86-, PROF, GA TECH SCHS CHEM, BIOCHEM, EARTH & ATMOSPHERIC SCI, 92- *Personal Data:* b Detroit, Mich, Mar 18, 46; m 74, Carol L Marchich; c Jeremy & Jacob. *Educ:* Univ Mich, BS, 68; Fla State Univ, PhD(phys chem), 74. *Prof Exp:* Robert A Welch fel chem, Univ Tex, Dallas, 74-76. *Concurrent Pos:* Sr ed, J Phys Chem, 94- *Mem:* Am Chem Soc; Am Phys Soc; Am Geophys Union; Inter-Am Photochem Soc; Sigma Xi. *Res:* Gas phase kinetics; photochemistry; reaction dynamics; lasers; spectroscopy; atmospheric chemistry. *Mailing Add:* Sch Chem & Biochem Ga Inst Technol Atlanta GA 30332-0400. *E-Mail:* pw7@prism.gatech.edu

**WINE, RUSSELL LOWELL,** STATISTICS. *Current Pos:* from assoc prof to prof, 57-85, EMER PROF STATIST, HOLLINS COL, 85- *Personal Data:* b Indian Springs, Tenn, Aug 17, 18; m 42, Ruth Crumpacker; c 3. *Educ:* Bridgewater Col, BA, 41; Univ Va, MA, 45; Va Polytech Inst, PhD(statist), 55. *Prof Exp:* Instr math, Univ Va, 43-45, Amherst Col, 45-46 & Univ Okla, 46-47; asst prof, Washington & Lee Univ, 47-52; assoc prof statist, Va Polytech Inst, 55-57. *Mem:* Fel AAAS; Am Statist Asn; Sigma Xi. *Res:* Least squares; design of experiments; sample surveys; author of two books. *Mailing Add:* 4510 Cloverdale Rd Roanoke VA 24019

**WINEBURG, ELLIOT N,** BEHAVIORAL MEDICINE. *Current Pos:* ASSOC PSYCHIAT, MT SINAI SCH MED, 67-, ASST PROF, 74- *Personal Data:* b Hornell, NY, May 22, 28; m 57; c 3. *Educ:* Univ Rochester, BA, 48; Fordham Univ, MA, 50; Univ Zurich, MD, 56. *Prof Exp:* Instr psychol, Hunter Col, 49-59. *Concurrent Pos:* Asst attend psychiat & dir courses hypnother, Mt Sinai Hosp, 62-; attend psychiat, Parkway Hosp, 65-; vis mem, Albert Einstein Col Med, 74-; dir, Asn Biofeedback Med Group, 79- *Mem:* Fel Am Psychiat Asn; Am Soc Clin Hypn; Biofeedback Soc Am; AMA; Soc Clin & Exp Hypn; Asn Appl Psychophysiol & Biofeedback. *Res:* Treatment of stress related disorders of psychological and physical origin; specific use of biofeedback and hypnotherapy as applied to stress related diseases. *Mailing Add:* 145 W 58th St New York NY 10019

**WINEFORDNER, JAMES D,** ANALYTICAL CHEMISTRY. *Current Pos:* from asst prof to assoc prof, 59-67, PROF CHEM, UNIV FLA, 67- *Personal Data:* b Geneseo, Ill, Dec 31, 31; m 57; c 3. *Educ:* Univ Ill, BS, 54, MS, 55, PhD(anal chem), 58. *Honors & Awards:* Meggers Award in Spectros, 69; Analytical Chem Award, Am Chem Soc, 73 & 91, Chem Instrumentation Award, Analytical Div, 78, Spectrochem Analysis Award, 87; Theophilus Redwood Award, 81; Torbern Bergman Award, 87; Talanta Gold Medal, 93; Robert Boyle Medal Analytical Chem, Royal Soc Chem, 96. *Prof Exp:* Fel, Univ Ill, 58-59. *Mem:* Soc Appl Spectros; Am Chem Soc; hon mem Japan Soc Analytical Chem. *Res:* Atomic, ionic and molecular emission; absorption; fluorescence spectroscopy; gas chromatographic detectors; trace analysis. *Mailing Add:* Dept Chem Univ Fla Gainesville FL 32611

**WINEGARD, WILLIAM CHARLES,** METALLURGY. *Current Pos:* DIR, HOMEWOOD CORP & HOMEWOOD HEALTH SCI CTR. *Personal Data:* b Hamilton, Ont, Sept 17, 24; m 47, Elizabeth Jaques; c William, Charles & Kathryn. *Educ:* Univ Toronto, BASc, 49, MASc, 50, PhD(metall), 52. *Hon Degrees:* LLD, Univ Toronto, 71, Laurentian Univ, 82, McMaster Univ, 95; DEng, Mem Univ, 76; DSc, Baptist Univ, Hong Kong, 93. *Honors & Awards:* Alcan Award, Can Inst Mining & Metall, 67. *Prof Exp:* Spec lectr, Univ Toronto, 50-52, from asst prof to prof metall, 54-67, asst dean sch grad studies, 64-67; pres & vchancellor, Univ Guelph, 67-75; vchmn, Ont Coun Univ Affairs, 76-77, chmn, 77-82. *Concurrent Pos:* Vis prof, Cambridge Univ, 59-60; consult, Ont Fire Marshall, 50-65, A D Lettle Inc, 60-67; ed, Can Metall Quart, 64-67; pres, Can Bur Int Educ, 71-73; gov, Int Develop Res Ctr, 74-80; fel, Univ Guelph, 78; mem, Govt Ont Res Found, 78-80; min sci, Govt Com, 89-93. *Mem:* Fel Am Soc Metals. *Res:* Solidification of pure metals and alloys; grain boundary migration. *Mailing Add:* PO Box 127 Guelph ON N1H 6J6 Can. *Fax:* 519-822-1092

**WINEGARTNER, EDGAR CARL,** COMBUSTIBILITY OF SOLIDS. *Current Pos:* CONSULT FUEL TECHNOL, 86- *Personal Data:* b Cleveland, Ohio, Jan 28, 27; m 49, Beverly Lebenstein; c Penny A & Becky J. *Educ:* Ohio State Univ, BMetE, 49. *Prof Exp:* Plant engr beryllium prod, Brush Beryllium Co, 49-51; res engr corrosion, Exxon Co, 51-62; res engr wood technol, Exxon Res & Eng Co, 62-65, res assoc coal combustion, 65-85. *Mem:* Fel Am Soc Mech Engrs; Soc Mining Engrs; Am Soc Metals; Combustion Inst; Nat Asn Corrosion Engrs. *Res:* Investigation of combustion related properties of coal and solid by-products from synthetic fuels, including combustibility, fouling and slagging; size preparation of coal for synthetic fuels processes. *Mailing Add:* 408 Rollingwood Rd Baytown TX 77521

**WINEGRAD, ALBERT IRVIN,** IMMUNOLOGY. *Current Pos:* intern, 52-53, resident immunol, 53-55, RESIDENT, HOSP UNIV PA, 57-, PROF MED. *Personal Data:* b Philadelphia, Pa. *Prof Exp:* Resident endocrinal, Peter Bent Brigham Hosp, Boston, 55-57. *Res:* Immunology; endocrinology. *Mailing Add:* 3400 Spruce St Philadelphia PA 19104

**WINEGRAD, SAUL,** PHYSIOLOGY. *Current Pos:* from asst prof to assoc prof, 62-69, PROF PHYSIOL, SCH MED, UNIV PA, 69- *Personal Data:* b Philadelphia, Pa, Mar 15, 31; m 63, Dilys Pegler; c Naomi & Gwyneth. *Educ:* Univ Pa, BA, 52, MD, 56. *Prof Exp:* Intern, Peter Bent Brigham Hosp, 56-57; sr asst surgeon, NIH, 57-59; surgeon, 60-61; fel, Nat Heart Inst, 59-60; hon res assoc, Univ Col, Univ London, 61-62. *Concurrent Pos:* Assoc, Sch Med, George Washington Univ, 58-61; NSF sr fel, Univ Col, Univ London, 71-72; Guggenheim fel. *Mem:* Am Physiol Soc; Soc Gen Physiol; Biophys Soc; Cardiac Muscle Soc; Int Soc Heart Res. *Res:* Cardiovascular and muscle physiology; cardiac cell function. *Mailing Add:* Sch Med Univ Pa Richards Bldg G4 Philadelphia PA 19104-6085. *Fax:* 215-898-2671

**WINEHOLT, ROBERT LEESE,** ORGANIC CHEMISTRY. *Current Pos:* RES ASSOC, CROMPTON & KNOWLES, 77- *Personal Data:* b York, Pa, Sept 20, 39; m 62; c 3. *Educ:* Gettysburg Col, AB, 61; Univ Del, PhD(org chem), 66. *Prof Exp:* Fel, Duke Univ, 66; sr chemist, Hoffman LaRoche, Inc, 67-73, Mallinckrodt, Inc, 73-76. *Mem:* Am Chem Soc. *Res:* Process development for organic chemicals to plant production. *Mailing Add:* 2631 Filbert Ave Reading PA 19606-2143

**WINEK, CHARLES L,** TOXICOLOGY, PHARMACOLOGY. *Current Pos:* from asst prof pharmacol & toxicol to assoc prof toxicol, 63-69, PROF TOXICOL, DUQUESNE UNIV, 69-; CHIEF TOXICOLOGIST, ALLEGHENY CO CORONER'S OFF, 66- *Personal Data:* b Erie, Pa, Jan 13, 36; m 60; c 3. *Educ:* Duquesne Univ, BS, 57, MS, 59; Ohio State Univ, PhD(pharmacol), 62. *Prof Exp:* Res assoc phytochem, Ohio State Univ, 59-62; res toxicologist, Procter & Gamble Col, 62-63. *Concurrent Pos:* Consult, Dept Anesthesiol, St Francis Hosp, 67-; mem panel ther, Poison Control Ctrs, Dept Health; mem adv comt lab act, Pa Dept Health; mem adv bd, Drug Res Proj, Franklin Inst, Philadelphia; fac mem, Bur Narcotics & Dangerous Drugs, Police Educ Prog; adj prof, Sch Med, Univ Pittsburgh; ed at large toxicol, Marcel Dekker, Inc, NY; ed, Toxicol Newslett, Sch Pharm, Duquesne Univ; ed, Toxicol Ann, 74. *Mem:* Soc Toxicol; Am Acad Forensic Sci; Acad Pharmaceut Sci; Am Asn Poison Control Ctrs; Drug Info Asn. *Res:* Toxicity of antifungal agents; safety evaluations; rapid methods of toxicological analyses. *Mailing Add:* Duquesne Univ Pittsburgh PA 15219

**WINELAND, DAVID J,** ATOMIC PHYSICS. *Current Pos:* physicist, 75-95, FEL, NAT INST STAND & TECHNOL, 95- *Personal Data:* b Milwaukee, Wis, Feb 24, 44. *Educ:* Univ Calif, Berkeley, BA, 65; Harvard Univ, MA, 66, PhD, 70. *Honors & Awards:* Dept Commerce Gold Medal (shared), 85; Samuel Wesley Stratton Award (shared), Nat Inst Stand & Technol, 89; Davisson-Germer Prize, Am Phys Soc, 90; William F Meggers Award, Optical Soc Am, 90. *Prof Exp:* Res assoc, Univ Wash, 70-75. *Concurrent Pos:* Proj leader, Ion Storage Group, 79-; affil fac, Colo State Univ, 85-93; fel, Nat Inst Stand & Technol, 88. *Mem:* Nat Acad Sci; fel Am Phys Soc; fel Am Optical Soc; Sigma Xi; AAAS. *Mailing Add:* Div 847 Nat Inst Stand & Technol 325 Broadway Boulder CO 80303. *E-Mail:* dwineland@nist.gov

**WINEMAN, ALAN STUART,** APPLIED MECHANICS, APPLIED MATHEMATICS. *Current Pos:* From asst prof to assoc prof, 64-75, PROF APPL MECH, UNIV MICH, 75- *Personal Data:* b Wyandotte, Mich, Nov 17, 37; m 64, Carol Frank; c Daniel & Lara. *Educ:* Univ Mich, BSE, 59; Brown Univ, PhD(appl math), 64. *Mem:* Am Acad Mech; Soc Rheology; Am Soc Mech Engrs; Soc Natural Philos. *Res:* Viscoelasticity; numerical methods; nonlinear elasticity; continuum mechanics; mechanical and polymer engineering. *Mailing Add:* Dept Mech Eng & Appl Mech Univ Mich Ann Arbor MI 48109. *Fax:* 313-764-4256; *E-Mail:* lardan@engin.umich.edu

**WINEMAN, ROBERT JUDSON,** BIO-ORGANIC CHEMISTRY, BIOMATERIALS. *Current Pos:* RETIRED. *Personal Data:* b Chicago, Ill, 1919; m 44; c 5. *Educ:* Williams Col, AB, 41; Univ Mich, MS, 42; Harvard Univ, PhD(chem), 49. *Prof Exp:* Chemist, E I du Pont de Nemours & Co, 42-43; res chemist, Monsanto Chem Co, 49-53, res group leader, 54-60, Monsanto Res Corp, Mass, 60-61, dir, Boston Lab, 61-69; dir biomed res labs, Am Hosp Supply Corp, 69-70; assoc chief, Artificial Kidney-Chronic Uremia Prog, Nat Inst Arthritis, Metab & Digestive Dis, 70-78, dir, Chronic Renal Dis Prog, Nat Inst Arthritis, Diabetes, Digestive & Kidney Dis, 79-82; dir spec proj, Nat Nephrology Found, 82-92. *Concurrent Pos:* Instr, Northeastern Univ, 52-53. *Mem:* AAAS; Am Chem Soc; Am Soc Artificial Internal Organs. *Res:* Organic synthesis; steroids; amino acids; sulfur compounds; medical devices; artificial organs. *Mailing Add:* Box 306 East Orleans MA 02643-0306

**WINEMILLER, KIRK OWEN,** AQUATIC ECOSYSTEMS, FOOD WEBS. *Current Pos:* asst prof, 92-96, ASSOC PROF, DEPT WILDLIFE & FISHERIES, TEX A&M UNIV, 96- *Personal Data:* b Mansfield, Ohio, Apr 4, 56. *Educ:* Miami Univ, BA, 78, MS, 81; Univ Tex, Austin, PhD(zool), 87. *Prof Exp:* Asst instr, Dept Zool, Univ Tex, Austin, 81-87, lectr, 87-88 & 90; res assoc, Oak Ridge Nat Lab, Environ Sci Div, Univ Tenn, 90-92. *Concurrent Pos:* Cur fishes, TNHC, Tex Mem Mus, 88-89; Fulbright res assoc, Zambia Dept Fisheries, Zambia, 89; vis grad fac, Univ Okla, 94- *Mem:* Sigma Xi; Am Soc Ichthyol & Herpet; Ecol Soc Am; Soc Am Naturalists; Am Fisheries Soc; Am Inst Biol Sci; Soc Int Ecol; Soc Conserv Biol. *Res:* Author of numerous publications; regulation of populations and community structure; aquatic, flood plain and estuarine ecosystems; life history theory; reproductive biology of fishes; tropical fish systematics; fisheries management. *Mailing Add:* Dept Wildlife & Fisheries Sci Tex A&M Univ College Station TX 77843-2258

**WINER, ALFRED D,** BIOCHEMISTRY. *Current Pos:* ASSOC PROF BIOCHEM, MED CTR, UNIV KY, 65- *Personal Data:* b Lynn, Mass, Dec 24, 25; m 55; c 2. *Educ:* Northeastern Univ, BS, 48; Purdue Univ, MS, 50; Duke Univ, PhD(biochem), 57. *Prof Exp:* Instr org chem, Univ Mass, 50-51; USPHS fel, Med Nobel Inst, Sweden, 58-60. *Concurrent Pos:* USPHS career develop award, 60-70. *Mem:* Am Chem Soc; Am Soc Biol Chemists. *Res:* Mechanism of action of dehydrogenase-coenzyme complexes; hormonal effects on enzymes in spermatogenesis. *Mailing Add:* 871 Edgewater Dr Lexington KY 40502

**WINER, ARTHUR MELVYN,** ATMOSPHERIC CHEMISTRY, AIR POLLUTION. *Current Pos:* Asst res chemist, Univ Calif, Riverside, 71-75, assoc res chemist, 76-80, asst dir, Air Pollution Res Ctr, 78-86, res chem, 80-89, PROF & DIR ENVIRON SCI PROG, UNIV CALIF, LOS ANGELES, 89-; CONSULT, 86- *Personal Data:* b New York, NY, May 5, 42; m 78, Judy Vickers; c Elizabeth A & Andrew M. *Educ:* Univ Calif, Los Angeles, BS, 64; Ohio State Univ, PhD(phys chem), 69. *Mem:* Air & Waste Mgt Asn; AAAS; Am Chem Soc. *Res:* Air toxics; indoor air pollution; regional human exposure modeling; air pollution policy; vehicle emissions; biogenic hydrocarbon emissions; air quality trends. *Mailing Add:* Sch Pub Health Univ Calif Los Angeles CA 90024. *Fax:* 310-206-3358; *E-Mail:* amwiner@ucla.edu

**WINER, BETTE MARCIA TARMEY,** PHYSICS, POWER SYSTEM ENGINEERING. *Current Pos:* GEN ENGR & SR STAFF PHYSICS & ENG, US DEPT TRANSP VOLPE, NAT TRANSP SYSTS CTR, 88- *Personal Data:* b Boston, Mass, Feb 21, 40; m 63; c 2. *Educ:* Univ Mass, BS, 61; Univ Md, PhD(physics), 69. *Prof Exp:* Staff physics, Lincoln Labs, Mass Inst Technol, 59-63, staff, Nat Magnet Labs, 70-72; engr anal, Bedford Labs, Raytheon, 72-74; sr staff physics & eng, Arthur D Little, Inc, 74-88. *Concurrent Pos:* Vis prof, Univ Md, Catonsville, 69- & Univ Lowell, 70-72. *Mailing Add:* US Dept Transp Volpe Nat Transp Systs Kendall Sq Cambridge MA 02142

**WINER, HERBERT ISAAC,** FORESTRY. *Current Pos:* RETIRED. *Personal Data:* b New York, NY, Sept 19, 21; m 43, 70, Hannah Bress Breitman; c Lise, Laura, Daniel & David. *Educ:* Yale Univ, BA, MF, 49, PhD, 56. *Prof Exp:* Instr forestry, Sch Forestry, Yale Univ, 52-56, asst prof lumbering, 56-64; sci consult, Pulp & Paper Res Inst Can, 63-64, forester, 64-65; sr forester, 65-71, dir, Logging Res Div, 71-75, res dir, 75-76, sr forest engr, Eastern Div, Forest Eng Res Inst Can, 76-78; mgr woodlands oper res, 79-84, mgr woodlands resource progs, Mead Corp, 84-87; lectr, Yale Sch Forestry & Environ Studies, 88-96. *Concurrent Pos:* Mem, Int Union Forest Res Orgns. *Mem:* Soc Am Foresters; Can Inst Forestry; Forest Hist Soc (pres, 87-90); Sigma Xi. *Res:* Forest management; forest history. *Mailing Add:* PO Box 2987 New Haven CT 06515-0087. *Fax:* 203-387-9282

**WINER, JEFFERY ALLAN,** NEUROANATOMY, NEUROSCIENCES. *Current Pos:* MEM FAC, DEPT PHYSIOL & ANAT, UNIV CALIF, 80- *Personal Data:* b Minneapolis, Minn, Nov 16, 45. *Educ:* Univ Ariz, BA, 67; Univ Tenn, PhD(physiol psychol), 74. *Prof Exp:* Fel neuroanat, Dept Psychol, Duke Univ, 74-76; res assoc, Dept Anat, Harvard Med Sch, 76-77; res assoc neuroanat, Health Ctr, Univ Conn, 77-80. *Concurrent Pos:* NIMH fel, USPHS, 74-77. *Mem:* Soc Neurosci. *Res:* Neuroanatomy of the central auditory and visual systems, including Golgi, electron microscopic and axoplasmic transport methods applied to the morphology and development of the auditory thalamus, midbrain and cerebral cortex. *Mailing Add:* Dept Molec & Cell Biol Univ Calif Berkeley CA 94720-3200

**WINER, RICHARD,** CHEMICAL ENGINEERING. *Current Pos:* RETIRED. *Personal Data:* b Rochester, NY, Sept 16, 16; m 42, Serena Stein; c Harley S & Ronna (Chalvet). *Educ:* Univ Ill, BS, 39; Univ Del, MFA, 91. *Prof Exp:* Tech asst, Radford Ord Works, Hercules Powder Co, Va, 42-45, chem engr, Hercules Inc, Exp Sta, Del, 45-46, supvr propellant dept, Allegany Ballistics Lab, 46-53, dir develop, propellants & rockets, 53-59, asst plant mgr, 59-63, dir develop, Chem Propulsion Div, 63-66, dir eng & res, Indust Systs Dept, 66-77, dir, Res Ctr, 78-81. *Mem:* AAAS; Am Chem Soc. *Res:* Solid propellants; rockets; chemical research. *Mailing Add:* 211 Churchill Dr Wilmington DE 19803-4203

**WINER, WARD OTIS,** MECHANICAL ENGINEERING, PHYSICS. *Current Pos:* from assoc prof to prof, 69-84, REGENTS PROF MECH ENG, GA INST TECHNOL, 84-, DIR, G W WOODRUFF SCH MECH ENG, 88- *Personal Data:* b Grand Rapids, Mich, June 27, 36; m 57; c 4. *Educ:* Univ Mich, BSE, 58, MSE, 59, PhD(mech eng), 62; Cambridge Univ, PhD(physics), 64. *Honors & Awards:* Melville Medal, Am Soc Mech Engrs, 75; Tribology Gold Medal, 86, Charles R Richards Award, 88. *Prof Exp:* Demonstr, Univ Cambridge, 61-63; from asst to assoc prof mech eng, Univ Mich, 63-69. *Concurrent Pos:* Consult var indust. *Mem:* Nat Acad Eng; Am Soc Lubrication Engrs; fel Am Soc Mech Engrs; fel AAAS. *Res:* Tribology; high pressure lubricant rheology; fluid mechanics; heat transfer. *Mailing Add:* Sch Mech Eng Ga Inst Technol Atlanta GA 30332-0405. *Fax:* 404-894-1658

**WINESTOCK, CLAIRE HUMMEL,** ORGANIC CHEMISTRY. *Current Pos:* sci adminr, 86-91, SR SCI OFFICER, HOWARD HUGHES MED INST, 91- *Personal Data:* b US, July 7, 32; m 56; c Jennifer Luna. *Educ:* Univ Utah, BS, 52; Univ Wis, PhD(org chem), 56. *Prof Exp:* Res assoc biochem, Columbia Univ, 56-59; res fel chem, Univ Utah, 59, res assoc biochem, Col Med, 60-61, res instr, 61-65; grants assoc, NIH, 65-66, health scientist adminr, Nat Inst Arthritis & Metab Dis, 66-69, exec secy & referral officer, virol study sect, Div Res Grants, NIH, 69-86. *Mem:* AAAS; Am Chem Soc; Sigma Xi. *Res:* Organic synthesis; chemistry of natural products; science administration. *Mailing Add:* 5707 Glenwood Rd Bethesda MD 20817

**WINET, HOWARD,** IMPLANTOLOGY, FRACTURE HEALING. *Current Pos:* ASSOC PROF RES ORTHOP, DEPT ORTHOP, UNIV SOUTHERN CALIF, 80-, ASSOC PROF RES BIOMED ENG, 96- *Personal Data:* b Chicago, Ill, Sept 13, 37; m 68, Carol K Kasper; c Evan & Wendy. *Educ:* Univ Ill, BS, 59; Univ Calif, Los Angeles, MA, 62, PhD(biophys & cell physiol), 69. *Prof Exp:* Res fel eng sci, Calif Inst Technol, 69-73, res biophysicist eng sci, 73-77; assoc prof physiol, Southern Ill Univ, Carbondale, 77-80. *Concurrent Pos:* Adv, Nat Sci Comt, Calif State Comn Teacher Preparation & Licensing, 72-77; vis res assoc eng sci, Calif Inst Technol, 78-; mem spec reproduction study sect, NIH, 78-; prin investr res grant, NIH, 78-; NIH Fogarty fel, Gothenburg Univ, Sweden, 85. *Mem:* Microcirculatory Soc; Am Physiol Soc; Orthop Res Soc; Soc Exp Biol Med Eng; Soc Biomat. *Res:* Biophysical fluid mechanics of muco-ciliary systems, transit and propulsion of gametes; blood form in bone, vascular role in osteogenesis; wound healing in bone; bone-implant interaction; cytokine effects on bone. *Mailing Add:* c/o Orthop Hosp Univ Southern Calif Med 2400 S Flower St Los Angeles CA 90007. *Fax:* 213-742-1515; *E-Mail:* hwinet@hsc.usc.edu

**WINETT, JOEL M,** COMPUTER & MANAGEMENT SCIENCE. *Current Pos:* prod mgr, 81-82, dir comput opers, 82-88, DIR QUALITY ASSURANCE, BGS SYSTS, 89- *Personal Data:* b Boston, Mass, Mar 1, 38; m 65, Ruth Schiff; c Barbara (Richman), Rachel & Carol. *Educ:* Mass Inst Technol, BSEE, 60, EE, 65; Columbia Univ, MSEE, 61. *Prof Exp:* Mem comput systs group, Lincoln Lab, Mass Inst Technol, 61-73, mem radar systs group, 73-74; mgr sci comput, Analytical Sci Corp, 74-79; mgr sci appl support, Sanders Assoc, 79-81. *Concurrent Pos:* Instr, Northeastern Univ, 67-69. *Res:* Effective use of computers for scientific and commerical applications; interactive operating systems emphasizing human engineered control language; user documentation and training aids; system measurement and operations procedures; software testing and quality assurance. *Mailing Add:* Ten Berkeley Rd Framingham MA 01701

**WINEY, KAREN IRENE,** POLYMER ELECTRON MICROSCOPY, POLYMER RHEOLOGY. *Current Pos:* ASST PROF, DEPT MAT SCI & CHEM ENG, UNIV PA, 92- *Personal Data:* b Abington, Pa, Aug 1, 63. *Educ:* Cornell Univ, BS, 85; Univ Mass, Amherst, MS, 89, PhD(polymer sci), 91. *Prof Exp:* Postdoctoral fel, AT&T Bell Labs, 91-92. *Concurrent Pos:* Young investr award, NSF, 94. *Mem:* Am Chem Soc; Am Phys Soc; Soc Rheology; Am Soc Mat; Mat Res Soc; Micros Soc Am. *Res:* Structure-property relationships in amorphous polymers and polymer blends, particularly random and block copolymers; polymer microscopies; polymer rheology. *Mailing Add:* 3231 Walnut St Philadelphia PA 19104-6272. *Fax:* 215-273-2128

**WINFIELD, JOHN BUCKNER,** IMMUNOLOGY, RHEUMATOLOGY. *Current Pos:* assoc prof, 78-81, PROF INTERNAL MED, UNIV NC, CHAPEL HILL, 81-, CHIEF, DIV IMMUNOL & RHEUMATOLOGY, 78-, DIR, THURSTON ARTHRITIS RES CTR, 82-, SMITH PROF INTERNAL MED, 86- *Personal Data:* b Kentfield, Calif, Mar 19, 42; m 69, Teresa McGrath; c Ann, Becky & Virginia. *Educ:* Williams Col, BA, 64; Cornell Univ, MD, 68. *Prof Exp:* Intern internal med, New York Hosp, 68-69; staff assoc immunol, NIH, 69-71; resident, 71-73, instr, 74-75, assoc prof internal med, Univ Va, 76-78. *Concurrent Pos:* Fel immunol, Rockefeller Univ, 73-75; fel, Arthritis Found, 73-76, sr investr, 76-79. *Mem:* Fel Am Col Physicians; Am Rheumatology Asn; Am Asn Immunol; Am Soc Clin Invest; Asn Am Prof; Am Clin Climatol Asn. *Res:* Clinical immunology; auto immune diseases; fibromyalgia, chronic pain and fatigue syndromes. *Mailing Add:* Div Immunol & Rheumatology Univ NC 3330 Thurston Bldg Chapel Hill NC 27599-0001. *Fax:* 919-966-1739

**WINFREE, ARTHUR T,** BIOMATHEMATICS, PHYSICAL CHEMISTRY. *Current Pos:* PROF ECOL & EVOLUTIONARY BIOL, UNIV ARIZ, 85-, REGENTS PROF, 89- *Personal Data:* b St Petersburg, Fla, May 5, 42; m 83, Ji-Yun Yang; c Erik & Rachael. *Educ:* Cornell Univ, BS, 65; Princeton Univ, PhD(biol), 70. *Honors & Awards:* MacArthur Fel, 84-89; Einthoven Award Cardiol, 89. *Prof Exp:* Asst prof math biol, Univ Chicago, 69-72; from assoc prof to prof biol, Purdue Univ, 78-85. *Concurrent Pos:* Res career develop award, NIH, 73-78; assoc ed, Ecol & Ecol Monographs, 73-77, J Theoret Biol, 77-82, Physica D, 86-91; dir res, Inst Natural Philos, 77-88; Japan Soc Prom Sci fel, Osaka, 81; J S Guggenheim mem fel, 82. *Res:* Dynamics and timing in biological clocks; discovery of phase singularities and their roles in jet-lag, in sudden cardiac death, and in self-organization of biological and chemical excitable media; medical physics. *Mailing Add:* Dept Ecol & Evolutionary Biol Univ Ariz 1600 E University Blvd Tucson AZ 85721-0001. *E-Mail:* art@cochise.biosci.edu

**WINFREY, J C,** ORGANIC CHEMISTRY, ANALYTICAL CHEMISTRY. *Current Pos:* staff, 77-80, DIR HYDROCARBON SERV, SOUTHERN PETROL LABS, 80- *Personal Data:* b Post, Tex, Feb 10, 27; m 47; c 1. *Educ:* ETex State Teachers Col, BS & MS, 49. *Prof Exp:* Teacher high sch, Tex, 49-51; chemist, Eagle-Picher Lead Co, 51 & Lone Star Gas Co, 51-56; res chemist, Dow Chem Co, 56-62; analytical chemist, Res Dept, Signal Oil & Gas Co, 62-68; analytical sect supvr res mgt, Signal Chem Co, 69-71; chief chemist, Geneva Industs, Inc, 71-73; gen mgr & corp secy, Analytical Serv, Inc, 73-75; consult, 75-76; lab mgr, Val Verde Corp, 76-77. *Concurrent Pos:* Mem, Adv Comt Proj, 44, Am Petrol Inst, 68-71; analytical consult, Haines & Assocs, 71. *Mem:* Am Chem Soc; Am Soc Testing Mat. *Res:* Instrumental analytical chemistry; organic synthesis of amines and epoxides; gas chromatography; thin layer chromatography; liquid chromatography; mass spectrometry; infrared spectrometry; computer applications in analytical chemistry; spectrochemical analysis of used lube oils. *Mailing Add:* 5215 Georgi Lane Houston TX 77092-5511

**WING, BRUCE LARRY,** BIOLOGICAL OCEANOGRAPHY. *Current Pos:* chief investr oceanog, 75-80, task leader oceanog, 81-82, FISHERY RES BIOLOGIST, AUKE BAY LAB, NAT MARINE FISHERIES SERV, 83- *Personal Data:* b Coeur d'Alene, Idaho, Aug 7, 38. *Educ:* San Diego State Col, AB, 60; Univ RI, PhD(oceanog), 76. *Honors & Awards:* C Y Conkel Award, Auke Bay Fisheries Lab, 77. *Prof Exp:* Fishery biologist zooplankton, US Bur Com Fisheries, 62-75. *Concurrent Pos:* Lectr, Univ Alaska Southeast, 87. *Mem:* Fel Am Inst Fishery Res Biologists; AAAS; Am Fisheries Soc; Am Soc Limnol & Oceanog; Sigma Xi. *Res:* Effect of environmental variation on plankton composition and fishery productivity; taxonomy of Alaskan marine invertebrates; ellobiopsids. *Mailing Add:* Nat Marine Fisheries Serv 11305 Glacier Hwy Juneau AK 99801-8626

**WING, EDWARD JOSEPH,** INFECTIOUS DISEASES, IMMUNOLOGY. *Current Pos:* asst prof, Sch Med, Univ Pittsburgh, 77-81, assoc prof med, 82-88, vchmn, Dept Med, PROF MED, SCH MED, UNIV PITTSBURGH, 89-, INTERIM CHMN, DEPT MED, 95- *Personal Data:* b Mineola, NY, June 19, 45; m 67; c 2. *Educ:* Williams Col, BA, 67; Harvard Med Sch, MD, 71. *Prof Exp:* Resident med, Peter Bent Brigham Hosp, Boston, Mass, 71-73; asst surgeon, USPHS, 73-75; fel infectious dis, Stanford Univ Sch Med, 75-77. *Concurrent Pos:* Prin investr, NIH, 83-; interim physician in chief, Montefiore Univ Hosp, 90-94. *Mem:* Infectious Dis Soc Am; fel Am Fedn Clin Res; Am Soc Microbiol; Am Asn Immunologists; Reticuloendothelial Soc. *Res:* Immunology and pathogenesis of experimental listeria monocytogenes infection as a model of infections by intracellular pathogens; role of various cytokines, particularly the colony-stimulating factors in the stimulation of host defenses to microbial pathogens. *Mailing Add:* Dept Med Univ Pittsburgh Med Ctr 1200 Scaife Hall 3550 Terrace St Pittsburgh PA 15261

**WING, ELIZABETH S,** ZOOLOGY. *Current Pos:* Asst cur zoo-archaeol, 61-74, from asst prof to assoc prof anthrop, 70-90, COURTESY PROF ANTHROP & ZOOL, UNIV FLA, 90- *Personal Data:* b Cambridge, Mass, Mar 5, 32; m 57, James E; c 2. *Educ:* Mt Holyoke Col, BA, 55; Univ Fla, MS, 57, PhD(zool), 62. *Honors & Awards:* Fryxwll Award, Soc Am Archaeol, 96. *Concurrent Pos:* NSF grants, 61-, co-investr, 61-64; Caribbean Res Prog grant, 64 & 65; Ctr Latin Am Studies res grant, 66; US rep, Int Congress Archaeozool; pres, Soc Ethnobiology; assoc cur, Fla Mus Natural Hist, 74-78, cur, 78- *Mem:* Am Soc Mammal; Soc Am Archaeol; AAAS. *Res:* Identification and analysis of faunal remains excavated from archeological sites in Southeastern United States and Latin America; prehistoric subsistence and animal domestication in the Andes and West Indies. *Mailing Add:* Fla Mus Natural Hist Univ Fla Gainesville FL 32611

**WING, G(EORGE) MILTON,** APPLIED MATHEMATICS. *Current Pos:* RETIRED. *Personal Data:* b Rochester, NY, Jan 21, 23. *Educ:* Univ Rochester, BA, 44, MS, 47; Cornell Univ, PhD(math), 49. *Prof Exp:* Scientist, Los Alamos Sci Lab, Univ Calif, 45-46, mem staff, 51-58, 81-87; instr math, Univ Rochester, 46-47; instr, Univ Calif, Los Angeles, 49-51, asst prof, 51-52; assoc prof, Univ NMex, 58-59; mem staff, Sandia Corp, 59-64; prof math, Univ Colo, 64-66 & Univ NMex, 66-73; vis prof, Tex Tech Univ, 75-76; prof, Southern Methodist Univ, 77-81, chmn, 77-78. *Concurrent Pos:* Consult, Los Alamos Sci Lab, 58-59 & 64-81; Sandia Corp, 58-59, E H Plesset Assocs, 58-59 & 65-69 & Rand Corp, 58-65; mem, Panel Phys Sci & Eng, Comt Undergrad Prog Math, 63-67; assoc, Los Alamos Sci Lab, 87-93. *Mem:* AAAS; Am Math Soc; Math Asn Am; Soc Indust & Appl Math. *Res:* Transport theory; integral equations. *Mailing Add:* 302 Calle Estado Santa Fe NM 87501-1020

**WING, JAMES,** NUCLEAR CHEMISTRY. *Current Pos:* RETIRED. *Personal Data:* b Highland Park, Mich, July 8, 29; m 57, Dorothy C Lee; c Kimberly J & Jonathan J. *Educ:* Univ Tenn, BS, 51; Purdue Univ, MS, 53, PhD(chem), 56. *Prof Exp:* Asst chemist, Argonne Nat Lab, 55-65, assoc chemist, 65-69; res chemist, Analysis Div, Nat Bur Stand, 69-75; nuclear chemist, US Nuclear Regulatory Comn, 75-78, sr chem engr & proj mgr, 78-87; reliability & risk analyst, 87-95. *Concurrent Pos:* Fulbright lectr, Chinese Univ Hong Kong, 64-65; free-lance translr, 75- *Mem:* Am Chem Soc; fel Am Sci Affil. *Res:* Nucleidic mass systematics; nuclear activation analysis; cross sections and mechanisms of nuclear reactions; radioactivities of new isotopes; radiochemical separation; computer automation of laboratory experiments; probabilistic safety assessment of nuclear power plants. *Mailing Add:* 15107 Interlachen Dr Unit 1014 Silver Spring MD 20906-5635. *E-Mail:* jameswing1@juno.com

**WING, JANET E (SWEEDYK) BENDT,** NUCLEAR REACTOR SAFETY ANALYSIS. *Current Pos:* RETIRED. *Personal Data:* b Detroit, Mich, Oct 12, 25; div; c 4. *Educ:* Wayne State Univ, Detroit, BS, 47; Columbia Univ, MS, 50. *Prof Exp:* Engr, Gen Motors, 44-48; mathematician, Manhattan Proj, Columbia Univ, 50-51; mem res staff, Los Alamos Nat Lab, 51-57 & 68-91, asst group leader, 80-84, assoc group leader, 88-91. *Concurrent Pos:* Proj leader, Los Alamos Nat Lab, 78-81. *Mem:* Women Sci & Eng; AAAS; Sigma Xi. *Res:* Mathematical modeling and computer solutions of physical systems; radiation-hydrodynamics and transport theory; applications to nuclear weapon design and testing; underground containment of nuclear explosions; pulsations of Cepheid stars. *Mailing Add:* 107 Tuyo Los Alamos NM 87544

**WING, JOHN FAXON,** NAVAL ARCHITECTURE, MARINE ENGINEERING. *Current Pos:* sr engr, Booz-Allen & Hamilton, Inc, 64-65, proj engr, 65-66, prin engr, 66-67, res dir, 67-70, vpres, 70-72, sr vpres, 72-81, MANAGING OFFICER TRANSP CONSULT, BOOZ-ALLEN & HAMILTON, INC, 81- *Personal Data:* b Lincoln, Nebr, Jan 27, 34; m 56; c 4. *Educ:* Mass Inst Technol, BS, 55; Harvard Univ, MBA, 57. *Prof Exp:* Proj engr, Alcoa Steamship Co, 57-61; engr, Shipbldg Div, Bethlehem Steel Co,

61-64. *Concurrent Pos:* Lectr, Univ Mich, 66. *Mem:* Soc Naval Archit & Marine Engrs; Sigma Xi. *Res:* Management consulting in transportation; research and analysis of maritime operations. *Mailing Add:* 7810 Stratford Rd Bethesda MD 20814

**WING, OMAR,** ELECTRICAL ENGINEERING, COMPUTER SCIENCE. *Current Pos:* from instr to assoc prof, 56-76, PROF ELEC ENG, COLUMBIA UNIV, 76- *Personal Data:* b Detroit, Mich, Mar 2, 28; m 53; c 2. *Educ:* Univ Tenn, BS, 50; Mass Inst Technol, MS, 52; Columbia Univ, DEng, 59. *Prof Exp:* Asst elec eng, Mass Inst Technol, 50-52; mem tech staff, Bell Tel Labs, NJ, 52-56. *Concurrent Pos:* Fulbright vis lectr, Inst Electronics, Chiao Tung Univ, 61; Ford Found eng resident, Thomas J Watson Res Ctr, Int Bus Mach Corp, 65-66; vis prof, Tech Univ Denmark, 73. *Mem:* Inst Elec & Electronics Engrs. *Res:* Network theory; computer design of networks; design automation; computer simulation of systems; distributed parameter networks; digital filters; computer analysis of large networks. *Mailing Add:* Flat 4b Residence No 6 Chinese Univ Hong Kong Shatin NT People's Republic of China

**WING, RENA R,** EPIDEMIOLOGY, PHYSIOLOGY. *Current Pos:* PROF PHYSIOL, SCH MED, UNIV PITTSBURGH, 92- *Personal Data:* b New York, NY, Oct 31, 45. *Res:* Epidemiology; physiology. *Mailing Add:* Dept Psychiat Univ Pitts Sch Med Western Psychiat Inst & Clin 3811 O'Hara St Pittsburgh PA 15213-2593

**WING, ROBERT FARQUHAR,** ASTRONOMY, STELLAR PHOTMETRY & SPECTROSCOPY. *Current Pos:* From asst prof to assoc prof, 67-76, PROF ASTRON, OHIO STATE UNIV, 76- *Personal Data:* b New Haven, Conn, Oct 31, 39; m 63, Ingrid McCowen; c Sylvia (Onder), Roger V & James D. *Educ:* Yale Univ, BS, 61; Univ Calif, Berkeley, PhD(astron), 67. *Concurrent Pos:* Mem bd, Asn Univs for Res in Astron Inc, 81-87; dir, Perkins Observ, 90-92; chair, Working Group Peculiar Red Giants, Int Astron Union, 91-; counr, Am Asn Variable Star Observers, 94-96. *Mem:* Int Astron Union; Am Astron Soc; fel Royal Astron Soc; Astron Soc Pac; Am Asn Variable Star Observers. *Res:* Spectroscopy and photometry of cool stars, including Mira variables; infrared spectra; determination of chemical composition and effective temperature; chromospheres of cool stars; space astronomy; infrared flux calibration; galactic structure; stellar content of nearby galaxies. *Mailing Add:* Dept Astron Ohio State Univ Columbus OH 43210. *E-Mail:* wing.1@osu.edu

**WING, WILLIAM HINSHAW,** ATOMIC PHYSICS, LASER SPECTROSCOPY. *Current Pos:* assoc prof physics, 74-78, PROF PHYSICS & OPTICAL SCI, UNIV ARIZ, 78- *Personal Data:* b Ann Arbor, Mich, Jan 11, 39; c 2. *Educ:* Yale Univ, BA, 60; Rutgers Univ, New Brunswick, MS, 62; Univ Mich, Ann Arbor, PhD(physics), 68. *Honors & Awards:* Alexander von Humboldt Sr Scientist Award. *Prof Exp:* Res staff physicist, Yale Univ, 68-70, res assoc physics, 70-72, asst prof, 72-74. *Concurrent Pos:* Res Corp Cottrell grant, 71; Nat Bur Stand, US Dept Com Precision Measurement grants, 74 & 80; Am Chem Soc petrol res grant, 77; vis prof & Joint Inst Lab Astrophys fel, Univ Colo, 79-80 & Mass Inst Technol, 80; assoc prof, Ecole Normale Superieure, 81; J S Guggenheim fel, 80-81; chmn, Comt Fundamental Constants, Nat Data Adv Bd, Nat Res Coun, 83-86; mcm, exec comt, Div Atomic Molecular & Optical Physics, Am Phys Soc, 84-87. *Mem:* Fel Am Phys Soc; Inst Elec & Electronics Engrs; fel Optical Soc Am; Sigma Xi; NY Acad Sci; Am Chem Soc. *Res:* Fundamental physical constants; simple atomic and molecular physics; lasers; particle beams; chemical physics; computer sciences; molecular physics. *Mailing Add:* Phys Dept Univ Ariz Tucson AZ 85721. *Fax:* 202-647-9103

**WINGARD, CHRISTOPHER JON,** COMPARATIVE ANIMAL PHYSIOLOGY. *Current Pos:* FEL SMOOTH MUSCLE, DEPT PHYSIOL, UNIV VA, CHARLOTTESVILLE, 91- *Personal Data:* b Canton, Ohio, Nov 30, 62. *Educ:* Hiram Col, BA, 84; Univ Akron, MS, 86; Wayne State Univ, PhD(biol), 91. *Prof Exp:* Animal Keeper II, Sea World Ohio Inc, Aurora, 86; lab analyst, ERT Testing Serv Inc, Highland Park, Mich, 88-91. *Concurrent Pos:* Field lab instr, Bermuda Biol Sta Res, Wayne State Univ, 88-91, instr, Dept Biol, 88-90, lab instr, 90; adj fac, Pedemont Community Col. *Mem:* Am Soc Zoologists; Am Physiol Soc; Int Soc Optical Eng; Biophy Soc. *Res:* Animal physiology; development and application of thermal and oxygen imaging systems in the eludification of energetics of physiologial processes; contractile system regulation and control; physiology of aquatic organisms and their response to environmental perturbations; energetic process associated with smooth muscle contration. *Mailing Add:* Dept Physiol Health Sci Ctr Univ Va Box 449 Charlottesville VA 22908

**WINGARD, DEBORAH LEE,** EPIDEMIOLOGY. *Current Pos:* asst prof, 80-86, ASSOC PROF, DIV EPIDEMIOL, DEPT FAMILY & PREV MED, UNIV CALIF, SAN DIEGO, 86- *Personal Data:* b San Diego, Calif, Aug 20, 52; m 76, Pierre Vaughn; c Brendan & Kyle. *Educ:* Univ Calif, Berkeley, BA, 74, MS, 76, PhD(epidemiol), 80. *Prof Exp:* Res specialist, Social Res Group, Sch Pub Health, Univ Calif, Berkeley, 76-77; epidemiologist, Human Pop Lab, Calif State Dept Health Serv, 77-78. *Concurrent Pos:* Epidemiologist, Lipid Res Clin, Calif, 81-84; consult, DES Action USA, 82-; Nat Inst Aging, 86-; prin investr, NIA Grant, 84-89, 85-88, 90-93, AARP Grant, 88-89; consult fac, San Diego State Univ, 85-; co-prin investr, NIADDK grant, 83-, NIH grant, 93- *Mem:* Soc Epidemiol Res; Am Pub Health Asn; Am Heart Assoc; Asn Women Sci; Am Diabetes Asn; NAm Menopause Soc. *Res:* The interaction of biological and pyschosocial factors in the maintenance of health, through the study of sex differences in morbidity and mortality. *Mailing Add:* Dept Family & Prev Med Univ Calif San Diego 9500 Gilman Dr La Jolla CA 92093-5003

**WINGARD, PAUL SIDNEY,** PHYSICAL GEOLOGY. *Current Pos:* RETIRED. *Personal Data:* b Akron, Ohio, Jan 10, 30; m 53; c 5. *Educ:* Miami Univ, AB, 52, MS, 55; Univ Ill, PhD(geol), 61. *Prof Exp:* Instr geol, Kans State Univ, 57-61, asst prof, 61-66; assoc prof & asst dean lib arts, Univ Akron, 66-67, prof geol & assoc dean, Col Arts & Sci, 67-92. *Mem:* AAAS; Geol Soc Am. *Res:* Geochronology and geology of south central Maine; geology of central and southern Colorado; post-Pleistocene geology and life of northern Ohio. *Mailing Add:* 3904 Kent Rd Stow OH 44224

**WINGARD, ROBERT EUGENE, JR,** organic chemistry, polymer chemistry, for more information see previous edition

**WINGATE, CATHARINE L,** radiological physics, medical physics, for more information see previous edition

**WINGATE, FREDERICK HUSTON,** GEOLOGY, BOTANY. *Current Pos:* PALYNOLOGICAL CONSULT, 85- *Personal Data:* b Provo, Utah, Dec 21, 32; m 71. *Educ:* Univ Utah, BS, 56, MS, 61; Univ Okla, PhD(bot), 74. *Prof Exp:* Subsurface geologist oil explor, Chevron Oil Co, 61-66; western region palynologist biostratig, Cities Serv Co, 73-85. *Mem:* Am Asn Stratig Palynologists. *Res:* Palynology, involving organic- and siliceous-walled microfossil studies with application to solution of bistratigraphic and hydrocarbon generation problems. *Mailing Add:* 3052 S Ivan Way Denver CO 80227

**WINGATE, MARTIN BERNARD,** obstetrics & gynecology, for more information see previous edition

**WINGE, DENNIS R,** PROTEIN CHEMISTRY. *Current Pos:* HEAD, RES LAB, DIV HEMAT, UNIV UTAH, 79- *Personal Data:* b Marshall, Minn, Apr 5, 47. *Educ:* Duke Univ, PhD(biochem), 75. *Mem:* Am Soc Biol Chemists; AAAS. *Mailing Add:* Dept Biochem & Med Univ Utah Med Ctr 50 N Medical Dr Salt Lake City UT 84132-0001. *Fax:* 801-585-5469; *E-Mail:* drw@hemoncol.med.utah.edu

**WINGELETH, DALE CLIFFORD,** CLINICAL CHEMISTRY, ORGANIC CHEMISTRY. *Current Pos:* FORENSIC CHEMIST & TOXICOLOGIST, CHEMATOX LAB, INC, 77- *Personal Data:* b Cleveland, Ohio, June 8, 43; c 3. *Educ:* Cleveland State Univ, BES, 66; Univ Colo, Boulder, PhD(inorg chem), 70. *Prof Exp:* Clin biochemist, St Joseph Hosp, Denver, 70-72; clin chemist, St Lawrence Hosp, Mich, 72; forensic chemist, Poisonlab Inc, 72, vpres & tech dir, Poisonlab Div, Chemed Corp, 72-77. *Mem:* Am Chem Soc; Royal Soc Chem; Am Asn Clin Chemists; Forensic Sci Soc; Am Indust Hyg Asn. *Res:* Inorganic hydrides; clinical toxicology. *Mailing Add:* Chematox Lab Inc 5401 Western Ave Boulder CO 80301-2730

**WINGENDER, RONALD JOHN,** ANALYTICAL CHEMISTRY, ENVIRONMENTAL ANALYSIS. *Current Pos:* MGR, ANALYTICAL SERV, DEXTER CORP, 89- *Personal Data:* b Menominee, Mich, Sept 30, 36; m 91, Doris Worthington; c J Jay & Alyssa J. *Educ:* Univ Wis, BS, 59, PhD(anal chem), 69; Univ Iowa, MS, 61. *Prof Exp:* Chemist, Forest Prod Lab, 61-64; chemist, Ansul Co, Wis, 69, mgr analysis res, 69-72; sect head chem, Indust Bio-Test Labs, 72-78; lab & res dir, Clin Bio-Tox Labs, 78-79; chemist, Argonne Nat Lab, 79-87, assoc group leader, 87-89. *Mem:* Sigma Xi; Am Chem Soc. *Res:* Proton nuclear magnetic resonance of cobalt II and nickel II aminopolycarboxylic acid and polyamine complexes; development of pesticide residue analytical procedures; development of analytical procedures for trace organic pollutants; applications of gas chromtography/mass spectrometry and liquid chromatography/mass spectrometry analysis in polymeric coatings; development of analytical procedures for drugs in biological fluids; analysis of polymeric coating systems; PC computer applications. *Mailing Add:* 17587 Dartmoor Dr Grayslake IL 60030. *E-Mail:* wingende@interaccess.com

**WINGER, MILTON EUGENE,** MATHEMATICS, STATISTICS. *Current Pos:* assoc prof, 71-78, PROF MATH, UNIV NDAK, 78-, ADV DEPT STATIST, 71-, CHMN DEPT MATH, 84- *Personal Data:* b Mayville, NDak, Aug 28, 31; m 54; c 2. *Educ:* Mayville State Col, BS, 53; Univ NDak, MS, 56; Iowa State Univ, PhD(statist), 72. *Prof Exp:* Inspector eng, US Army CEngr, 57; asst prof math, Univ NDak, 60-68; instr statist, Iowa State Univ, 68-70. *Concurrent Pos:* Statist consult, Inst Appl Math & Statist, 74-80; vis lectr, Inst Math Statist, 74-82; assoc ed, Col Math J, 82- *Mem:* Math Asn Am; Am Statist Asn; Am Asn Univ Profs. *Mailing Add:* 623 24th Ave S Grand Forks ND 58201

**WINGER, PARLEY VERNON,** AQUATIC BIOLOGY, FISHERIES. *Current Pos:* leader, Field Res Sta Aquatic Biol, Nat Fishery Contaminant Res Ctr, Nat Biol Surv, 78-95, FISHERY BIOLOGIST, PATUXENT WILDLIFE RES CTR, US GEOL SURV, 96- *Personal Data:* b Driggs, Idaho, Dec 11, 41; m 67, Alexis Passino; c Shane & Amanda. *Educ:* Idaho State Univ, BS, 66, MS, 68; Brigham Young Univ, PhD(aquatic biol), 72. *Prof Exp:* Res assoc aquatic biol, Brigham Young Univ, 72-73; asst prof, Tenn Technol Univ, 74-78. *Concurrent Pos:* Prin investr fisheries, Ctr Health & Environ Studies, Brigham Young Univ, 72-74 & Tenn Valley Authority, 74-76; adj asst prof, Univ Ga, 78- *Mem:* Am Fisheries Soc; Freshwater Biol Asn; NAm Benthic Soc; Soc Int Limnol; Soc Environ Toxicol Chem. *Res:* Effects of habitat alteration on aquatic ecosystems; mitigation techniques to enhance aquatic environments; effect of acid mine drainage and chemical contaminants on aquatic populations; population dynamics of benthic macroinvertebrates; toxicity of aquatic sediments. *Mailing Add:* USGS-Biol Resources Div Patuxent Wildlife Res Ctr Sch Forest Resources Univ Ga Athens GA 30602. *Fax:* 706-546-2109; *E-Mail:* parley_winger@nbs.gov

**WINGERT, LOUIS EUGENE,** CHEMICAL ENGINEERING. *Current Pos:* RES CHEM ENGR, KIMBERLY-CLARK CORP, NEENAH, 68- *Personal Data:* b Kimball, SDak, Feb 3, 24; m 52; c 3. *Educ:* SDak Sch Mines & Technol, BS, 44. *Prof Exp:* Res engr, Deere & Co, Ill, 46-47; chem engr, Duro Tank Co, 47-48; bd plant engr, US Gypsum Co, Ohio, 48-51, qual supvr, 51-53, qual supt, Que, 53-57; sr chem engr, Minn Mining & Mfg Co, 57-68. *Mem:* Am Chem Soc. *Res:* Gypsum products; thermographic copy paper; lime; paper coatings. *Mailing Add:* 323 N Potomac St Hagerstown WI 21740

**WINGET, CARL HENRY,** FOREST ECOLOGY, TREE PHYSIOLOGY. *Current Pos:* DIR GEN, PAC FORESTRY CTR, VICTORIA, BC, 95- *Personal Data:* b Noranda, Que, Sept 28, 38; m 64, Madeleine Roy; c Julie, Marian & Jeffrey. *Educ:* Univ NB, BScF, 60; Univ Wis, MSc, 62, PhD(forestry, bot), 64. *Prof Exp:* Prof forestry & geod, Laval Univ, 67-73; dir, Laurentian Forestry Res Ctr, Can Forest Serv, 78-82, dir gen, Res & Tech Servs, 82-88, dir gen, Ont Region, 88-95. *Mem:* Can Inst Forestry. *Res:* Forest resource management; silviculture of tolerant northern hardwoods. *Mailing Add:* Natural Resources Can Forest Serv Pac Forestry Ctr 506 W Burnside Rd Victoria BC V8Z 1M5 Can. *Fax:* 705-759-5720

**WINGET, CHARLES M,** AEROSPACE SCIENCES. *Current Pos:* res scientist, NASA, 63-67, proj scientist, Biosatellite Proj, 67-85, res scientist, Neurosci Br, payload proj scientist, Shuttle EOM-1/2 mission & sci coordr for space sta, Adv Progs Off, 85-86, sec payload scientist & IML-1 payload scientist, 86-92, SR PAYLOAD SCIENTIST, NASA-AMES RES CTR, MOFFETT FIELD, CALIF, 92- *Personal Data:* b Garden City, Kans, Dec 26, 25; m, Katherine Barkas; c Jean A, Jo A, Steven & Eleni. *Educ:* San Francisco State Col, BA, 51; Univ Calif, PhD, 57. *Honors & Awards:* Paul Bert Award Physiol Res, 77; Arnold D Tuttle Mem Award, Aerospace Med Asn, 82. *Prof Exp:* Chemist poultry husb, Univ Calif, 51-53, res asst, 53-56, jr res poultry physiologist, 56-57, res fel, 57-59; assoc prof avian physiol, Ont Agr Col, Univ Guelph, 59-63. *Concurrent Pos:* Nat Inst Neurol Dis & Blindness fel, 57-59; lectr, Univ Calif, Davis, 64-; prof pharmacol, Sch Pharm, Fla A&M Univ, 75-; bd regents distinguished vis scholar, Sch Pharm, Fla Agr & Mech Univ, Tallahassee, 78; consult, Sports Med Div, US Olympic Comt, 82-84; mem, Adv Comt for Minority Insts, Res Ctrs in Minority Insts Prog, NIH, 85- *Mem:* Poultry Sci Asn; Biophys Soc; Aerospace Med Asn; Int Soc Chronobiol; Am Physiol Soc; Sigma Xi. *Res:* Rhythms and social schedule; hypokinesis and drugs in humans; bird and monkey response to change in photoperiod; physiological changes associated with aeronautical environment; biotelemetry; biorhythm data acquisition and reduction; chronopharmacology; space medicine. *Mailing Add:* Space Life Sci 236-5 NASA Ames Res Ctr Moffett Field CA 94035-1000. *Fax:* 650-604-3159

**WINGET, GARY DOUGLAS,** PLANT BIOCHEMISTRY, PLANT PHYSIOLOGY. *Current Pos:* asst prof, 66-71, ASSOC PROF BIOL SCI, UNIV CINCINNATI, 71- *Personal Data:* b Dayton, Ohio, Mar 27, 39; m 60; c 3. *Educ:* Miami Univ, AB, 61, MA, 63; Mich State Univ, PhD(bot), 68. *Prof Exp:* Res chemist, Mound Lab, Monsanto Res Corp, 63-64. *Concurrent Pos:* Vis assoc prof biochem, molecular & cell biol, Cornell Univ, 75. *Mem:* Am Soc Photobiol; Am Chem Soc; Am Soc Plant Physiologists; Sigma Xi. *Res:* Inhibitors of photosynthesis; mechanism of photophosphorylation; physiological action of phlorizin. *Mailing Add:* Dept Biol Sci Univ Cincinnati Cincinnati OH 45221-0001

**WINGET, ROBERT NEWELL,** AQUATIC ECOLOGY, BIOLOGY. *Current Pos:* Res assoc aquatic ecol, 70-85, assoc prof biol, PROF, BRIGHAM YOUNG UNIV, HAWAII, 86- *Personal Data:* b Monroe, Utah, July 11, 42; m 64; c 7. *Educ:* Univ Utah, BS, 67, MS, 68, PhD(biol sci), 70. *Concurrent Pos:* Proj dir insect control, Div Parks & Recreation, State of Utah, 69-71; consult water qual mgt, US Forest Serv, Intermountain Region, 72-; consult, Cent Utah Proj, US Bur Reclamation, 73-, Vaughn Hansen Assocs, Utah, 77-78 & Sandia Proj, Eastern NMex Univ, 77-78; dir thermal study, Utah Power & Light Co, 74-76, consult aquacult, 77-86; consult impact analysis, Westinghouse Corp, 74-76; consult water qual, Eyring Res Inst, 75-83, stream reclamation, Coastal States Energy Co, 79-88, water qual, Getty Mineral Resources Co, 80-85 & Homestake Mining Co, 81-85; prog bd, Hawaii Erwin Educ Asn, 89- *Mem:* Am Sci Teachers Asn; Home Econ Educ Asn; NAm Benthol Soc. *Res:* Environmental impact analyses, especially fisheries resources, water quality and water quality standards; aquaculture using thermal effluents; macroinvertebrate community dynamics. *Mailing Add:* 55430 Moana St Laie HI 96762

**WINGFIELD, EDWARD CHRISTIAN,** physics, science administration, for more information see previous edition

**WINGO, CHARLES S,** NEPHROLOGY, EPITHELIAL TRANSPORT. *Current Pos:* Asst prof, 81-86, ASSOC PROF NEPHROLOGY, UNIV FLA, 86- *Personal Data:* b Ruston, La, Oct 5, 49. *Educ:* La State Univ, MD, 75. *Mem:* Am Physiol Soc; Am Col Physicians; Am Fedn Clin Res; AAAS; Am Soc Nephrology; NY Acad Sci. *Mailing Add:* Dept Med Div Nephrology & Hyperten 111G Univ Fla Vet Admin Med Ctr Gainesville FL 32610-0224. *Fax:* 352-375-3730

**WINGO, CURTIS W,** entomology; deceased, see previous edition for last biography

**WINGROVE, ALAN SMITH,** ORGANIC CHEMISTRY. *Current Pos:* PROF CHEM, TOWSON STATE UNIV, 73- *Personal Data:* b Hanford, Calif, Mar 4, 39; m 94, Eileen W. *Educ:* Univ Calif, Berkeley, BS, 60; Univ Calif, Los Angeles, PhD(chem), 64. *Prof Exp:* NSF fel, 64-65; asst prof chem, Univ Tex, Austin, 65-71; lectr & sci researcher & writer, 71-73. *Res:* Chemistry of second row elements and participation in solvolysis and base-catalyzed cleavages; destabilized carbonium ions; carbenophiles; stereochemistry; synthetic methods. *Mailing Add:* Dept Chem Towson State Univ 8000 York Rd Towson MD 21252. *E-Mail:* etohal@aol.com

**WINHOLD, EDWARD JOHN,** PHYSICS. *Current Pos:* from asst prof to assoc prof, 57-69, PROF PHYSICS, RENSSELAER POLYTECH INST, 69- *Personal Data:* b Brantford, Ont, Jan 3, 28; nat US; m 51; c 3. *Educ:* Univ Toronto, BA, 49; Mass Inst Technol, PhD(physics), 53. *Prof Exp:* Asst physics, Mass Inst Technol, 49-53, res staff mem, Lab Nuclear Sci, 53-54; from instr to asst prof physics, Univ Pa, 54-57. *Concurrent Pos:* Vis staff mem, Atomic Energy Res Estab, Harwell, Eng, 68-69 & lab nuclear sci, Mass Inst Technol, 82. *Mem:* Am Phys Soc. *Res:* Experimental nuclear and intermediate energy physics. *Mailing Add:* Dept Physics Rensselaer Polytech Inst 110 Eighth St Troy NY 12180

**WINHOLTZ, ROBERT ANDREW,** DIFFRACTION STRESS MEASUREMENT. *Current Pos:* ASST PROF MECH & AERONAUT ENG, UNIV MO, 91- *Personal Data:* b Kearney, Nebr, July 8, 61. *Educ:* Univ Nebr, Lincoln, BS, 83, MS, 85; Northwestern Univ, PhD(mat sci), 91. *Concurrent Pos:* Res scientist, Res Reactor Ctr, Univ Mo, 91- *Mem:* Metall Soc; Am Soc Metals; Neutron Scattering Soc Am; Sigma Xi. *Res:* Measurement and effects of residual and applied stresses in materials using diffraction methods. *Mailing Add:* 261C Res Reactor Columbia MO 65211. *Fax:* 573-882-3443; *E-Mail:* winholtz@showme.missouri.edu

**WINIARZ, MAREK LEON,** FACTORY MEASUREMENT SYSTEMS USING MACHINE VISION, ALGORITHM DEVELOPMENT FOR DIGITAL SYSTEMS. *Current Pos:* METROL SPECIALIST, QUAL TECHNOL CTR, GEN ELEC, 90- *Personal Data:* b Tczew, Poland, Sept 6, 51; m 76; c 2. *Educ:* Purdue Univ, BS, 74, MS, 76. *Prof Exp:* Grad teaching asst physics, Purdue Univ, 74-75, grad res asst mech eng, Herrick Labs, 75-76; engr, Ford Motor Co, 76-79; engr & shop foreman, Seaco Indust, 80; test engr, Teledyne McCormick-Selph, 81; consult engr, 82; mgr design eng, BDM Int, 82-90. *Concurrent Pos:* Consult, Pol-Mart Int, 89- *Mem:* Instrument Soc Am; Am Soc Mech Engrs; Soc Automotive Engrs. *Res:* Dimensional and pressure metrology; sensor development for ultra-precision measurements; validation and calibration of sensors. *Mailing Add:* 9838 Forest Glen Dr Cincinnati OH 45242

**WINICK, HERMAN,** SYNCHROTRON RADIATION, FREE ELECTRON LASERS. *Current Pos:* dep dir, 73-92, dep assoc dir, 92-95, RES PROF APPL PHYSICS, STANFORD UNIV, 92-, ASST DIR, STANFORD SYNCHROTRON RADIATION LAB, 95- *Personal Data:* b New York, NY, June 27, 32; m 53, Renee Feldman; c Alan L, Lisa F & Laura J. *Educ:* Columbia Univ, AB, 53, PhD(physics), 57. *Honors & Awards:* Alexander von Humboldt Sr Scientist Prize, 85; Technol Award, Dept Energy, 87. *Prof Exp:* Asst physics, Columbia Univ, 53-54, asst, Nevis Cyclotron Lab, 54-57; res assoc & instr physics, Univ Rochester, 57-59; res fel, Cambridge Electron Accelerator, Harvard Univ, 59-65, sr res assoc & lectr, 65-73, asst dir, 73. *Concurrent Pos:* Adj prof, Suranaree Univ Technol, Thailand. *Mem:* Fel Am Phys Soc; AAAS. *Res:* Meson scattering; bremstrahlung research; accelerator design and development; colliding beams; synchrotron radiation production; free electron lasers. *Mailing Add:* 853 Tolman Dr Stanford CA 94305. *Fax:* 650-926-4100; *E-Mail:* winick@slac.stanford.edu

**WINICK, JEREMY ROSS,** UPPER ATMOSPHERE. *Current Pos:* PHYSICIST, OPTICAL INFRARED TECHNOL DIV, AIR FORCE GEOPHYS LAB, 82- *Personal Data:* b Washington, DC, Aug 24, 47; m 73; c 2. *Educ:* Univ Rochester, BS, 69; Harvard Univ, PhD(chem physics), 76. *Prof Exp:* Res assoc, Lab Atmospheric & Space Physics, Univ Colo, 76-80; Nat Res Coun resident & res assoc, Aeronomy Lab, Environ Res Lab, Nat Oceanic & Atmospheric Admin, Boulder, 80-81. *Mem:* Am Geophys Union. *Res:* Model atomic and molecular processes that lead to infrared radiation in the upper atmosphere; analysis of field measurements to validate models; kinetics and radiation in upper atmosphere; modeling of upper atmosphere emissions. *Mailing Add:* 10 Paul Revere Rd Acton MA 01720

**WINICK, MYRON,** PEDIATRICS, NUTRITION. *Current Pos:* ROBERT R WILLIAMS PROF NUTRIT, PROF PEDIAT & DIR INST HUMAN NUTRIT, COL PHYSICIANS & SURGEONS, COLUMBIA UNIV, 72-, DIR, CTR NUTRIT, GENETICS & HUMAN DEVELOP, 75- *Personal Data:* b New York, NY, May 4, 29; m 64; c 2. *Educ:* Columbia Univ, AB, 51; Univ Ill, Urbana, MS, 52; State Univ NY Downstate Med Ctr, MD, 56. *Honors & Awards:* E Mead Johnson Award Pediat Res, 70; Osborne & Mendel Award, Am Inst Nutrit, 76; Agnes Higgins Award, March Dimes Birth Defects Found, 83. *Prof Exp:* From asst resident pediat to chief resident, Med Col, Cornell Univ, 57-60; Bank Am-Giannini Found fel, Stanford Univ, 62-63, attend pediatrician & instr pediat, Med Col, 63-64; asst prof, Med Col, Cornell Univ, 64-68, from assoc prof to prof 68-71, Birth Defects Treat Ctr, 64-71. *Concurrent Pos:* NIH spec fel, 63-64; dir, Birth Defects Treatment Ctr, 64-71; vis prof, Univ Chile, 67; USPHS Career Develop Award, 69-71; mem comt Nutrit, Brain Develop & Behav, Nat Acad Sci, 71-79 & Food & Nutrit Bd, 82-; consult, Pan-AM Health Orgn, 66- *Mem:* Soc Pediat Res; Am Pediat Soc; Am Inst Nutrit; Am Soc Clin Nutrit; Am Acad Pediat; Soc Exp Biol & Med. *Res:* Effects of early malnutrition on subsequent growth and development, particularly of the brain; study of brain growth and subsequent behavior. *Mailing Add:* 317 W 83rd St New York NY 10024. *Fax:* 212-799-0688

**WINICOUR, JEFFREY,** THEORETICAL PHYSICS. *Current Pos:* ASSOC PROF PHYSICS, UNIV PITTSBURGH, 72- *Personal Data:* b Providence, RI, Apr 12, 38; m 64; c 1. *Educ:* Mass Inst Technol, BS, 59; Syracuse Univ, PhD(physics), 64. *Prof Exp:* Res asst, Syracuse Univ, 59-64; res physicist, Aerospace Res Labs, 64-72. *Concurrent Pos:* Res assoc, Ctr Philos Sci, 77- *Mem:* Am Phys Soc. *Res:* General relativity; equations of motion; gravitational radiation. *Mailing Add:* Dept Physics Univ Pittsburgh Pittsburgh PA 15260

**WINICOV, HERBERT,** ORGANIC CHEMISTRY, WATER PURIFICATION. *Current Pos:* CHEM SPECIALIST, MAINE YANKEE. *Personal Data:* b Brooklyn, NY, Mar 14, 35; c 2. *Educ:* Univ Pa, BA, 56; Univ Wis, PhD(chem), 61. *Prof Exp:* Sr chemist, Smith, Kline & French Labs, 60-68, sr investr, 68-86. *Mem:* AAAS; Sigma Xi; Am Chem Soc. *Mailing Add:* Little River Cove PO Box 345 East Boothbay ME 04544-0345

**WINICOV, ILGA,** NUCLEIC ACID BIOCHEMISTRY, MOLECULAR GENETICS. *Current Pos:* from asst prof to assoc prof, 79-95, PROF MICROBIOL & BIOCHEM, SCH MED, UNIV NEV, RENO, 95- *Personal Data:* b Riga, Latvia, May 16, 35; US citizen; m 79, Rodney E Harrington; c Eric & Mark. *Educ:* Univ Pa, Philadelphia, AB, 56, PhD(microbiol), 71; Univ Wis-Madison, MS, 58. *Prof Exp:* Assoc, Inst Cancer Res, Philadelphia, 72-74, res assoc, 74-76; res asst prof biochem, Fels Inst & Dept Biochem, Sch Med, Temple Univ, Philadelphia, 76-79. *Concurrent Pos:* Vis scientist, NIH, 80-81; vis scholar, Univ Calif Los Angeles, 91. *Mem:* Am Soc Microbiol; Am Soc Biol Chemists; Am Asn Cancer Res; Int Soc Plant Molecular Biol; Soc Plant Physiol. *Res:* Eucaryotic gene expression at the level of RNA transcription and processing; characterization of processing products and enzymes in cultured mammalian cells; stress elicited plant gene expression; cloroplast gene regulation; salt-tolerance in plants. *Mailing Add:* Dept Biochem Sch Med Univ Nev Reno NV 89557. *Fax:* 702-784-1620

**WINICOV, MURRAY WILLIAM,** CHEMICAL ANTIMICROBIAL SUBSTANCES. *Current Pos:* chemist, West Chem Prod Inc, 56-75, res dir, 75-80, res dir, West Agrochem Div, 80-83, vpres res & develop, 83-84, vpres res & develop, West Agro Inc, 84-91, SR RES ASSOC, WEST AGRO INC, DIV ALFA LAVAL, INC, 92- *Personal Data:* b New York, NY, July 4, 28; m, Elsie Lota; c 2. *Educ:* Univ Pa, BS, 49; Brooklyn Polytech Inst, MS, 59. *Prof Exp:* Chemist, Sloan-Kettering Inst, 49-50, Indust Toxicol Labs, 50-53 & Barret Div, Allied Chem & Dye, 53-56. *Mem:* Am Chem Soc; Am Soc Microbiol; AAAS. *Res:* Formulation of chemical antimicrobials, especially iodine, to maximize effectiveness as disinfectants, sanitizers, and sterilizing agents; development of products for use as human topicals, health care personnel handwash, and bovine teat dips. *Mailing Add:* 4609 Charlotte St Kansas City MO 64110-1521. *Fax:* 816-472-1197

**WINICUR, DANIEL HENRY,** chemical physics, for more information see previous edition

**WINICUR, SANDRA,** CELL & HUMAN PHYSIOLOGY, ANIMAL BIOLOGY. *Current Pos:* Asst prof, 70-77, ASSOC PROF BIOL, IND UNIV, SOUTH BEND, 77- *Personal Data:* b New York, NY, Oct 4, 39; c 2. *Educ:* Hunter Col, BA, 60; Univ Conn, MS, 63; Calif Inst Technol, PhD(biochem), 71. *Mem:* Nat Asn Biol Teachers. *Res:* Variations in salivary amylase activity; science & literature. *Mailing Add:* Dept Biol Ind Univ PO Box 7111 South Bend IN 46634-7111

**WINIKOFF, BEVERLY,** PUBLIC HEALTH, NUTRITION. *Current Pos:* med assoc, 78-84, SR MED ASSOC, INT PROGS, POP COUN, 84- *Personal Data:* b New York, NY, Aug 26, 45; m 73, Michael C Alpert; c Hilary & Lindsay. *Educ:* NY Univ, MD, 71; Harvard Univ, AB, 66, MPH, 73. *Prof Exp:* Intern, Gen Rose Mem Hosp, Denver, 71-72; res fel, Dept Nutrit, Sch Pub Health, Harvard Univ, 73-74; prog assoc & nutrit specialist, Rockefeller Found, 74-75, asst dir health sci, 75-78. *Mem:* Am Pub Health Asn. *Res:* Development and implementation of nutrition policies and programs; lactation; maternal child health; contraception and abortion. *Mailing Add:* 333 E 30th St New York NY 10016. *Fax:* 212-755-6052

**WINJE, RUSSELL A,** power electronics, for more information see previous edition

**WINJUM, JACK KEITH,** FOREST CULTURE. *Current Pos:* RES SCIENTIST POTENTIAL FOREST MGT MITIGATION MEASURE GLOBAL WARMING, NAT COUN PAPER INDUST AIR & STREAM IMPROV, US ENVIRON PROTECTION AGENCY, CORVALLIS, ORE, 87- *Personal Data:* b Platte, SDak, Feb 5, 33; m 54; c 3. *Educ:* Ore State Univ, BS, 55; Univ Wash, MS, 61; Univ Mich, PhD(forest ecol), 65. *Prof Exp:* Forester, US Forest Serv, 55; forest technologist, Forestry Res Ctr, Weyerhaeuser Co, 58-63, regeneration ecologist, 63-73, mgr forest regenerator res, 73-77, forest cult res, Technol Ctr, 77-80, Mt St Helen's Res & Develop, Western Forestry Res Ctr, 80-85, air pollution and forest effects, Nat Acid Precipitation Assessment Prog, 86-87. *Concurrent Pos:* Affil assoc prof, Col Forest Resources, Univ Wash, Seattle, 80-85. *Mem:* Soc Am Foresters; Sigma Xi. *Res:* Cone and seed yield of Douglas fir; ecology of forest nurseries; stock handling and field out planting of seedlings in the regeneration period of Douglas fir management; forest regeneration ecology; air pollution and forest effects; managing forests to mitigate global warming; assessment of the carbon budget of Brazil. *Mailing Add:* 2905 W 13th Pl Corvallis OR 97330

**WINKEL, CLEVE R,** BIOCHEMISTRY, ORGANIC CHEMISTRY. *Current Pos:* Chmn, Div Nat Sci, 72-77, chmn dept chem, 84-91, PROF CHEM, RICKS COL, 59- *Personal Data:* b Logan, Utah, Mar 20, 32; m 55, Vera Stevens; c 9. *Educ:* Utah State Univ, BS, 54, MS, 55; Brigham Young Univ, PhD, 70. *Honors & Awards:* Catalyst Award, Chem Mfg Asn, 78. *Res:* Enzymology; enzyme mechanism; medical biochemistry. *Mailing Add:* Dept Chem Ricks Col 525 S Center St Rexburg ID 83460-0001

**WINKELHAKE, JEFFREY LEE,** IMMUNOCHEMISTRY, PHARMACOLOGY. *Current Pos:* VPRES PHARMACEUT DEVELOP, ANERGEN INC, 93- *Personal Data:* b Champaign, Ill, Oct 5, 45. *Educ:* Univ Ill, Urbana-Champaign, BS, 67, MS, 69, PhD(immunochem), 74. *Prof Exp:* Res asst immunol, Walter Reed Army Inst Res, 69-72; res assoc fel cell biol, Jane Coffin Childs Mem Fund Med Res, Salk Inst Biol Studies, 74-76; from asst prof to prof microbiol, Med Col Wis, 76-84; dir pharmacol, Cetus Corp, 84-90; sr dir progs & proj, Cytelcorp, 90-93. *Concurrent Pos:* Instr hemat & serol, US Army Med Training Ctr, San Antonio, 69-70; assoc scientist, Ctr Great Lakes Res, Univ Wis, Milwaukee, 78-84. *Mem:* Am Chem Soc; Am Asn Immunologists; Am Asn Cancer Res; Am Soc Biol Chemists; Am Col Rheumatol. *Res:* Immunoglobulin effector functions; homeostasis of immune effector systems; evolutionary aspects; protein and carbohydrate pharmacology; antibody and lymphokine metabolism; biological response modifiers - immunopharmacology; biopharmaceutical drug development; autoimmune disease. *Mailing Add:* 301 Penobscot Dr Redwood CA 94063

**WINKELMAN, JAMES W,** PATHOLOGY, HOSPITAL ADMINISTRATION. *Current Pos:* PROF PATH, HARVARD MED SCH, 86-, VPRES & DIR LABS, BRIGHAM & WOMEN'S HOSP, 86- *Personal Data:* b Brooklyn, NY, Oct 29, 35; m 77, Rina Lavie; c Elizabeth, Claudia, Recha & Zev. *Educ:* Univ Chicago, AB, 55; Johns Hopkins Sch Med, MD, 59. *Hon Degrees:* MA, Harvard Med Sch, 90. *Prof Exp:* Asst prof path, Sch Med, NY Univ, 65-67; asst dir, Bio-Sci Labs, 67-70, vpres & dir, 70-72, pres & dir, 72-77; exec vpres & dir, Nat Health Labs, 77-80; prof & actg chmn, State Univ NY Health Sci, 80-85, dir labs, 85-86. *Concurrent Pos:* Assoc clin prof path, Los Angeles Med, Univ Calif, 69-80. *Mem:* Am Asn Pathologists; fel Col Am Pathologists; Acad Clin Lab Physicians & Scientists; Am Asn Clin Chemists; Am Fedn Clin Res; AMA. *Res:* Porphyrin uptake in tumors and photodynamic therapy; noninvasive measurements in clinical testing; fiscal analysis of policy and procedures in clinical laboratories. *Mailing Add:* Brigham & Women's Hosp Harvard Med Sch 75 Francis St Boston MA 02115

**WINKELMANN, FREDERICK CHARLES,** COMPUTER ANALYSIS, BUILDING ENERGY USE. *Current Pos:* res assoc, 72-75, STAFF SCIENTIST, APPL SCI DIV, LAWRENCE BERKELEY LAB, UNIV CALIF, 76- *Personal Data:* b Brooklyn, NY, Apr 11, 41; m 68; c 2. *Educ:* Mass Inst Technol, BS, 62, PhD(physics), 68. *Prof Exp:* Res assoc physics, Lab Nuclear Sci, Mass Inst Technol, 68-69, Stanford Linear Accelerator Ctr, 69-72 & Carleton Univ, Ottawa, Can, 75-76. *Concurrent Pos:* Vis scientist, Group RAMSES, Nat Ctr Sci Res, Orsay, France, 82-83. *Mem:* Am Soc Heating, Refrig & Air Conditioning Engrs. *Res:* Development of software for computer analysis of energy use in buildings. *Mailing Add:* 1815 San Juan Ave Berkeley CA 94707

**WINKELMANN, JOHN ROLAND,** VERTEBRATE ZOOLOGY, MAMMALOGY. *Current Pos:* Asst prof, 63-80, ASSOC PROF BIOL, GETTYSBURG COL, 80- *Personal Data:* b Champaign, Ill; m 62; c 2. *Educ:* Univ Ill, Urbana, BS, 54; Univ Mich, Ann Arbor, MA, 60, PhD(zool), 71. *Concurrent Pos:* Fac fel grant for res in Mex, Gettysburg Col, 72-73. *Mem:* AAAS; Soc Study Evolution; Am Soc Mammal. *Res:* Biology of nectar-feeding bats. *Mailing Add:* Dept Biol Gettysburg Col 300 N Washington St Gettysburg PA 17325-1400

**WINKELMANN, RICHARD KNISELY,** DERMATOLOGY, DERMATOPATHOLOGY. *Current Pos:* from instr to assoc prof dermat, 56-65, assoc prof anat, 64-73, Robert H Kieckhefer prof 75-80, PROF DERMAT, MAYO GRAD SCH MED, UNIV MINN, 65-, PROF ANAT, 73- *Personal Data:* b Akron, Ohio, July 12, 24; c 4. *Educ:* Univ Akron, BS, 47; Marquette Univ, MD, 48; Univ Minn, PhD(dermat), 56. *Prof Exp:* Res assoc chem, Wash Univ, 49, res assoc anat, 50; asst pub health officer, USPHS, Ala, 52-54. *Concurrent Pos:* Fel dermat, Mayo Grad Sch Med, 51-52 & 54-56; instr & res assoc, Med Col, Univ Ala, 53-54; consult, dept dermat, Mayo Clin, 56-, chmn dept, 70-75; assoc ed, Invest Dermat, 60-63, 69-72, Dermatol Digest, 65-70, Mayo Clin Proceedings, 68-69; mem bd dirs, Am Acad Dermat, 67-79 & Soc Invest Dermat, 69-70; ed, Dermatol Digest, 71-74; mem, Int Comt Dermat, 72-; Health, Educ & Welfare, Food & Drug Admin. *Mem:* Am Acad Dermat; fel Am Col Physicians; Am Soc Dermatopathologists (pres, 77); Am Asn Anatomists; Am Fedn Clin Res; AAAS; Am Asn Phys Anthropologists; Sigma Xi; Soc Invest Dermat (vpres, 69-70, pres, 70-71); AMA; hon mem NAm Clin Dermat Soc. *Res:* Anatomy; pathobiology; biology of skin. *Mailing Add:* 200 First St Rochester MN 55905-0001

**WINKELSTEIN, ALAN,** HEMATOLOGY, IMMUNOLOGY-CLINICAL. *Current Pos:* from asst prof to assoc prof, 69-80, PROF MED & HEMAT, UNIV PITTSBURGH SCH MED, 80- *Personal Data:* b New York, NY, May 27, 35; m 59; c 2. *Educ:* Univ Mich, BS, 57; State Univ NY, MD, 61. *Prof Exp:* Intern & resident internal med, Univ Calif Los Angeles Sch Med, 61-63; resident internal med, Univ Wash, Seattle, 63-64; fel hemat, Univ Calif Los Angeles Med Sch, 64-67, asst prof hemat, 66-67. *Concurrent Pos:* Actg chief div hemat, Univ Pittsburgh Sch Med, 90-91; mem, Immunol Sci Study Sect, NIH, 84-88; mem, Biobehav/Clin subcomt, Drug Abuse AIDS Res Rev Comt, NIDA, 84- *Mem:* Am Soc Hemat. *Res:* Lymphocyte biology-lymphoprolifrative responses, flow cytometry, immune deficiencies including those associated with HIV infection activities of immuno-suppressive compounds and lymphocyte stimulatory activities of interleukins in vitro. *Mailing Add:* Montefiore Univ Hosp 200 Lothrop St N804 Pittsburgh PA 15213. *Fax:* 412-648-6393

**WINKELSTEIN, JERRY A,** PEDIATRIC IMMUNOLOGY, COMPLEMENT. *Current Pos:* DIR, DIV IMMUNOL, JOHNS HOPKINS HOSP, 80-, PROF PEDIAT, 83- *Personal Data:* b Syracuse, NY, Sept 5, 40; m 69; c Beth & Amy. *Educ:* Syracuse Univ, BA, 61; Albert Einstein Col Med, MD, 65. *Honors & Awards:* Mead Johnson Award, Am Acad Pediat; Lifetime Achievement Award, Modell Found. *Mem:* Am Asn Immunol; Am Soc Clin Invest; Am Pediat Soc; Soc Pediat Res; Infectious Dis Soc; Am Soc Microbiol. *Res:* Biology and genetics of the complement system. *Mailing Add:* Dept Pediat CMSC 1103 John Hopkins Hosp 601 N Wolfe St Baltimore MD 21205

**WINKELSTEIN, WARREN, JR,** MEDICINE, EPIDEMIOLOGY. *Current Pos:* prof, Sch Pub Health, Univ Calif, Berkeley, 68-91, assoc dean, 70-71, actg dean, 71-72, dean, 72-81, head, Epidemiol Prog, 87-90, EMER PROF EPIDEMIOL, DEPT BIOMED & ENVIRON HEALTH SCI, UNIV CALIF, BERKELEY, 91-, ACTG DIR, INT ENVIRON EPIDEMIOL INST, 94- *Personal Data:* b Syracuse, NY, July 1, 22; m 47, Veva Kerrigan; c 3. *Educ:* Univ NC, BA, 43; Syracuse Univ, MD, 47; Columbia Univ, MPH, 50; Am Bd Prev Med, dipl. *Honors & Awards:* Abraham Lilienfeld Award, Am Pub Health Asn, 92. *Prof Exp:* Dist health officer, Erie Co Health Dept, NY, 50-51; regional rep, Pub Health Div, Tech & Econ Mission, Mutual Security Agency, Cambodia, Laos & Viet Nam, 51-53; dir, Div Commun Dis Control, Erie Co Health Dept, NY, 53-56; from asst prof to prof prev med, Sch Med, State Univ NY, Buffalo, 56-69, chief, Dept Epidemiol, Chronic Dis Res Inst, 57-63. *Concurrent Pos:* Spec res fel, Nat Heart Inst, 56-67, career develop award, 62-68; Buswell res fel, Univ Buffalo, 58-59; dep health comnr, Erie Co Health Dept, 59-62; mem, Heart Dis Control Prog Adv Comt & Air Pollution Training Comt, USPHS, 62-65, Subcomt, Nat Comt Health Statist, 65-68, Res Comt, Am Heart Asn, 66-71, Nat Air Qual Criteria Adv Comt, 69-72, Comn Natural Resources, Nat Res Coun & Ad Hoc Working Group Epidemiol, Nat Cancer Inst, 75-77, Bd Sci Adv, Nat Inst Occup Safety & Health, 83-87 & Adv Comt, III Int Conf AIDS, 86-87; from assoc prof to prof epidemiol, Dept Prev Med, State Univ NY, Buffalo, 62-68; asst managing ed, AM J Epidemiol, 65-75; chmn, Panel Arsenic Studies, Am Pub Health Asn, 75-76 & Panel Experts Arch Pub Health, 79; consult, WHO, 76, Dept Health, NY, 84, Nat Acad Sci & USPHS, 86 & 87; adj prof, Dept Epidemiol, Sch Pub Health, Univ Mich, 93- *Mem:* Sr mem Inst Med-Nat Acad Sci; fel Am Pub Health Asn; fel Am Col Prev Med; fel AAAS; Am Heart Asn; Am Epidemiol Soc (pres, 76-77); fel Infectious Dis Soc Am; Soc Epidemiol Res; Int Epidemiol Asn; Int Environ Epidemiol Soc. *Res:* Epidemiology of cardiovascular diseases; air pollution and cancer; author of 148 technical publications. *Mailing Add:* Dept Epidemiol Univ Calif Sch Pub Health Berkeley CA 94720. *Fax:* 510-643-5163

**WINKER, JAMES A(NTHONY),** LIGHTER-THAN-AIRCRAFT, METEOROLOGY. *Current Pos:* CONSULT, 91- *Personal Data:* b Randall, Minn, Dec 16, 28; m 53, Marlene Modjeske; c David, Jeffrey, Gregory, Ted & Jennifer. *Educ:* Univ Minn, BAeroE & BBA, 52. *Prof Exp:* Jr engr, Mech Div, Gen Mills, Inc, 51-54; sr engr, Raven Industs, Inc, 56-60, chief engr, 60-66, res mgr, 66-68, vpres, Appl Technol Div, 68-91. *Concurrent Pos:* Expert witness, lighter-than-air aircraft. *Mem:* Fel Am Inst Aeronaut & Astronaut. *Res:* Scientific ballooning; atmospheric decelerators; aerial recovery systems; earth and space inflatables; history of balloon technology. *Mailing Add:* 2805 Poplar Dr Sioux Falls SD 57105

**WINKLER, BARRY STEVEN,** VISION, RETINAL PHYSIOLOGY. *Current Pos:* asst prof, 71-78, ASSOC PROF BIOL SCI, OAKLAND UNIV, 78-, ASSOC DIR, RES & ACAD DEVELOP, 83- *Personal Data:* b New York, NY, Apr 17, 45; m 66; c 2. *Educ:* Harpur Col, BA, 65; State Univ NY Buffalo, MA, 68, PhD(physiol), 71. *Prof Exp:* Instr physiol, Sch Med, State Univ NY Buffalo, 70-71. *Mem:* Am Physiol Soc; Soc Neurosci; Asn Res Vision & Ophthal; AAAS; Soc Res Adminr; Nat Coun Univ Res Adminr. *Res:* Physiology of the retina; analysis of ionic and metabolic contributions to photoreceptor potentials. *Mailing Add:* Eye Res Inst Oakland Univ Rochester MI 48309-4401. *Fax:* 313-370-2006

**WINKLER, BRUCE CONRAD,** BIOCHEMISTRY. *Current Pos:* asst prof, 78-82, ASSOC PROF CHEM, UNIV TAMPA, 82- *Personal Data:* b Milwaukee, Wis, Sept 25, 37; m 59; c 2. *Educ:* Valparaiso Univ, BA, 59; Iowa State Univ, MS, 62; Univ Okla, PhD(biochem), 67. *Prof Exp:* Instr chem, Cent State Univ, 62-64; fel biochem, Univ Alta, 67-69; asst prof biochem, Kansas City Col Osteop Med, 69-73, actg chmn dept, 73-78. *Res:* Muscle phosphorylase; clinical chemistry, especially proteins and enzymes; protein electrophoresis. *Mailing Add:* Dept Sci Univ Tampa 401 Kennedy Blvd Tampa FL 33606-1496

**WINKLER, DELOSS EMMET,** POLYMER CHEMISTRY. *Current Pos:* RETIRED. *Personal Data:* b Atchison, Kans, Feb 4, 14; m 41; c 2. *Educ:* Univ Kans, AB, 36, MA, 39, PhD(chem), 41. *Prof Exp:* Teacher high sch, Kans, 36-37; asst instr chem, Univ Kans, 37-39; chemist, Shell Develop Co, 41-70; real estate salesman, 71-72; chemist, Beckman Instruments, 72-79. *Concurrent Pos:* Consult, Polymer Chem & Technol, 79- *Mem:* Am Chem Soc. *Res:* Vapor phase catalysis; plastics; rubber; oxidation of hydrocarbons; chromatographic polymers for separation of amino acids and polymers for solid phase synthesis of peptides. *Mailing Add:* 3234 Rossmoor Pkwy No 1 Walnut Creek CA 94595

**WINKLER, ERHARD MARIO,** ENVIRONMENTAL GEOLOGY. *Current Pos:* from instr to prof geol, 48-80, EMER PROF GEOL, UNIV NOTRE DAME, 80- *Personal Data:* b Vienna, Austria, Jan 8, 21; nat US; m 53, Isolde Konig; c Gabriela & Manfred. *Educ:* Univ Vienna, PhD, 45. *Honors & Awards:* E B Burwell Jr Award, Geol Soc Am, 75. *Prof Exp:* Asst eng geol, Vienna Tech Univ, 40-45; sci asst geol, Vienna Tech Univ, 46-48. *Mem:* Fel AAAS; fel Geol Soc Am. *Res:* Decay of stone monuments. *Mailing Add:* 17635 Juday Dr South Bend IN 46635

**WINKLER, HERBERT H,** MICROBIOLOGY, BIOCHEMISTRY. *Current Pos:* prof, 78-80, PROF & VCHMN MICROBIOL, COL MED, UNIV SALA, 81- *Personal Data:* b Highland Park, Mich, June 18, 39; m 61, Schuler; c Elizabeth. *Educ:* Kenyon Col, BA, 61; Harvard Univ, PhD(physiol), 66. *Hon Degrees:* DSc, Kenyon Col, 88. *Prof Exp:* NSF fel physiol chem, Sch Med, Johns Hopkins Univ, 66-68; from asst prof to assoc prof microbiol, Sch Med, Univ Va, 68-77. *Concurrent Pos:* NIH res career develop award. *Mem:* Am Soc Microbiol; Am Soc Biol Chemists; Am Soc Rickettsiology (pres, 83-85); Am Asn Immunol. *Res:* Transport of molecules across biological membranes; biology of rickettsiae. *Mailing Add:* Dept Microbiol Univ SAla Col Med Mobile AL 36688-0001. *Fax:* 334-460-7269

**WINKLER, JAMES DAVID,** PHARMACY, BIOCHEMISTRY. *Current Pos:* Postdoctoral fel, 87-89, SR SCIENTIST, SMITHKLINE BEECHAM, 89- *Personal Data:* b Flint, Mich, Oct 24, 54; m 80; c 3. *Educ:* Princeton Univ, BA, 76; Med Col Pa, PhD(pharmacol), 87. *Concurrent Pos:* Assoc prof, Med Col Pa, 87- *Mem:* AAAS; Am Soc Pharmacol & Exp Therapeut; Inflammation Res Asn; NY Acad Sci. *Res:* Mechanisms of inflammation; focus on biochemical mediator of inflammation processes. *Mailing Add:* Dept Pharmacol Smithkline Beecham L532 PO Box 1539 King of Prussia PA 19406-0939. *Fax:* 610-270-5381

**WINKLER, LEONARD P,** ELECTRICAL ENGINEERING, COMPUTER SCIENCES. *Current Pos:* ASSOC PROF ENG SCI, COL STATEN ISLAND, CITY UNIV NEW YORK, 77- *Personal Data:* b New York, NY. *Educ:* Polytech Inst Brooklyn, BSEE, 65, MSEE, 67, PhD(elec eng), 71. *Prof Exp:* Res fel, Polytech Inst Brooklyn, 69-70; asst prof eng sci, Richmond Col, NY, 70-77. *Concurrent Pos:* NSF res grant, 72. *Mem:* Inst Elec & Electronics Engrs; Sigma Xi. *Res:* Traffic control; microcomputers; communications-computer systems; numerical optimization techniques; stochastic processes. *Mailing Add:* Col Staten Island Staten Island NY 10314

**WINKLER, LINDA IRENE,** GRAVITATIONAL PHYSICS, PRECISION MEASUREMENTS. *Current Pos:* ASST PROF PHYSICS, APPALACHIAN STATE UNIV, 93- *Personal Data:* b Easton, Pa, Jan 14, 59. *Educ:* Univ NC, Chapel Hill, BS, 81; Carnegie Mellon Univ, MS, 83; Univ Va, PhD(physics), 89. *Prof Exp:* Mem tech staff, Bell Commun Res, 88-90; asst prof physics, Stockton State Col, 90-93. *Mem:* Am Phys Soc; Sigma Xi; Astron Soc Pac. *Res:* Investigating weak effects predicted outside Einstein's Theory of Relativity using benchtop instruments; anomalous spin-dependent forces using a torsion balance; designing a novel noise-cancellation scheme for removing seismic noise in torsion balances. *Mailing Add:* Dept Physics Appalachain State Univ 572 Rivers St Boone NC 28608. *E-Mail:* winklerli@appstate.edu

**WINKLER, LOUIS,** ASTRONOMY. *Current Pos:* ASST PROF, PA STATE UNIV, 64- *Personal Data:* b Elizabeth, NJ, Sept 7, 33; m 57; c 1. *Educ:* Rutgers Univ, BS, 55; Adelphi Univ, MS, 59; Univ Pa, PhD(astron), 64. *Prof Exp:* Engr, Am Bosch Arma Corp, 56-59; proj engr, Philco Corp, 59-64. *Mem:* Am Astron Soc. *Res:* Archaeoastronomy; astronomy and astrology of early America; United States of America seismic histories. *Mailing Add:* Dept Astron Pa State Univ 525 Davey Lab University Park PA 16802-6305

**WINKLER, MARJORIE EVERETT,** PROTEIN PURIFICATION, PROTEIN CHARACTERIZATION. *Current Pos:* scientist, 82-89, SR SCIENTIST, RECOVERY SCI, GENENTECH INC, 89- *Personal Data:* b Suffern, NY, July 19, 54; m 87, Paul F Hohenschuh; c William E, Charles T & Abigail M. *Educ:* State Univ NY, Buffalo, BS, 75, PhD(chem), 80. *Prof Exp:* NIH fel, Mass Inst Technol, 80-82. *Mem:* Am Chem Soc; Sigma Xi. *Res:* Develop processes to recover and characterize clinically relevant recombinant proteins from bacterial and mammalian cell cultures. *Mailing Add:* Genentech Inc 460 Point San Bruno Blvd South San Francisco CA 94080. *Fax:* 650-225-3880; *E-Mail:* winkler.marge@gene.com

**WINKLER, MARTIN ALAN,** IMMUNOASSAYS FOR TRYPANUSOMA CRUZI INFECTION, IDENTIFICATION & PURIFICATION OF ANTIGENS RELEVANT TO TUMOR OR PROTOZOAN IMMUNOTHERAPY. *Current Pos:* sr res biochemist, 89-95, SR RES ANALYTICAL CHEMIST, ABBOTT LABS, 95- *Personal Data:* b Ft Stockton, Tex, June 8, 50; m 78, Janet K Phillips. *Educ:* Univ Tex, Austin, BA, 74, PhD(immunogenetics), 78. *Prof Exp:* Am Cancer Soc fel, Rockefeller Univ, 78-80, res assoc 80-81; from res asst to res assoc, St Jude Childrens Res Hosp, 81-87; staff scientist, Biotherapeutics, Inc, 87-89. *Concurrent Pos:* Consult, Am Col Testing, 89-90. *Mem:* AAAS; Sigma Xi; Am Asn Immunologists; Am Chem Soc; Am Soc Trop Med & Hyg. *Res:* Development of immunoassays and confirmatory schemes for detection of seropositivity by infection of Trypanosoma cruzi; protein eptide analysis by MALDI-TOP mass spectrometry and capillary eletropharesis. *Mailing Add:* Dept 4P2 Bldg R13 Abbott Labs North Chicago IL 60064. *E-Mail:* martin__winkler@compuserve.com

**WINKLER, MARTIN KENNETH,** SPACE TRANSPORTATION & LAUNCH VEHICLE ENGINEERING, FLIGHT MECHANICS. *Current Pos:* PRES & CHIEF EXEC OFFICER, CUBIC DEFENSE SYSTS, 96- *Personal Data:* b New York, NY, Apr 8, 43; m 66, Olivia Cuadras; c David & Jacqueline (Gordon). *Educ:* Cornell Univ, BEE, 64; Univ Calif, San Diego, MS, 68. *Prof Exp:* Vpres & gen mgr, Space Systs Div, Gen Dynamics, 64-93, Teledyne Ryan Aeronaut, 93-96. *Mem:* Assoc fel Am Inst Aeronaut & Astronaut; sr mem Inst Elec & Electronics Engrs. *Res:* Management of diversified aerospace and defense companies; system design of launch vehicles, cruise missiles and airplanes; optimization theory as applied to guidance and trajectories of launch vehicles. *Mailing Add:* 1349 Caminito Halago La Jolla CA 92037

**WINKLER, MATTHEW M,** CELL BIOLOGY. *Current Pos:* PRES, AMBION, INC, 89- *Personal Data:* b Boston, Mass, June 22, 52. *Educ:* Univ Calif, Berkeley, PhD(zool), 79. *Prof Exp:* Instr embryol, Marine Biol Lab, Woods Hole, 83; asst prof zool, Univ Tex, 83-88, assoc prof, 88-91. *Concurrent Pos:* Adj assoc prof zool, Univ Tex. *Mailing Add:* Ambion Inc 2130 Woodward St Austin TX 75744-0001

**WINKLER, MAX ALBERT,** PHYSICS, MATHEMATICS. *Current Pos:* MEM STAFF PHYSICS, LOS ALAMOS SCI LAB, 62- *Personal Data:* b San Antonio, Tex, May 19, 31; m 53; c 4. *Educ:* St Mary's Univ, BS, 57; Univ Tex, Austin, MA, 62. *Prof Exp:* Physicist, Gen Elec Co, 57-59. *Res:* Optical engineering; lens design; nondestructive testing. *Mailing Add:* 2318 33rd St No A Los Alamos NM 87544

**WINKLER, NORMAN WALTER,** BIOCHEMISTRY, DERMATOLOGY. *Current Pos:* CHIEF, DERMAT SERV, SBUFFALO MERCY HOSP, 76- *Personal Data:* b Englewood, NJ, May 28, 35; m 80; c 2. *Educ:* Univ Rochester, AB, 57; Univ Chicago, MD, 65, PhD(biochem), 70. *Prof Exp:* Res asst fibrinolysis, Sloan-Kettering Inst Cancer Res, 58-59; from intern to resident internal med, Univ Chicago Hosps & Clins, 68-70; USPHS fel dermat, Med Sch, Univ Ore, 70-72; chief dermat serv, Buffalo Vet Admin Hosp, 73-76. *Concurrent Pos:* Asst prof dermat, Sch Med, State Univ NY, Buffalo, 72-76. *Mem:* AAAS; Am Acad Dermat; Soc Invest Dermat. *Res:* Enzymology; membrane receptors in cutaneous disease; keratinocyte differentiation. *Mailing Add:* 4174 N Buffalo St Orchard Park NY 14127-2415

**WINKLER, PAUL FRANK,** ASTROPHYSICS. *Current Pos:* From asst prof to assoc prof physics, Middlebury Col, 69-81, chmn dept, 80-88, chmn, Div Natural Sci, 88-93, asst to pres, 93-96, PROF PHYSICS, MIDDLEBURY COL, 81- *Personal Data:* b Nashville, Tenn, Nov 10, 42; m 83, Janet P Beers; c Katharine, Johanna, Sarah & Nathan. *Educ:* Calif Inst Technol, BS, 64; Harvard Univ, AM, 65, PhD(physics), 70. *Concurrent Pos:* Vis scientist, Mass Inst Technol, 73-74, res affil, 74-78, vis scientist, 78-80; sr vis fel, Inst Astron, Cambridge Univ, 85-86; vis resident astronr, Cerro Tololo Inter Am Observ, 90-91 & 96-97; vis fel, Joint Inst Lab Astrophys, 91. *Mem:* Am Phys Soc; Am Astron Soc; Int Astron Union; Coun Undergrad Res. *Res:* Supernova remnants; galactic and extragalactic x-ray sources; atomic and molecular physics. *Mailing Add:* Dept Physics Middlebury Col Middlebury VT 05753. *Fax:* 802-443-2072; *E-Mail:* winkler@middlebury.edu

**WINKLER, PETER MANN,** COMPUTABILITY. *Current Pos:* from asst prof to assoc prof, 77-89, PROF MATH & COMPUT SCI, EMORY UNIV, 89-, RES MGR, MATH & THEORET COMP SCI, BELLCORE, 89- *Personal Data:* b Pasadena, Calif, Nov, 9, 46; m 73; c 2. *Educ:* Harvard Univ, BA, 68; Yale Univ, PhD(math), 75. *Prof Exp:* Mathematician, Dept Defense, 68-70; asst prof math, Stanford Univ, 75-77. *Concurrent Pos:* Consult math, Navig Sci, Inc, 78-; Humboldt fel, T H Darmstadt, 84-85. *Mem:* Am Math Soc; Math Asn Am; Soc Indust Appl Math. *Res:* Combinatorics; theoretical computer science. *Mailing Add:* AT&T Bell Labs 2-D-147 600 Mountain Ave Murray Hill NJ 07974-0636

**WINKLER, ROBERT LEWIS,** STATISTICS. *Current Pos:* IBM res prof, 84-85, Calvin Bryce Hoover prof, 85-89, JAMES B DUKE PROF, DUKE UNIV, 89-, SR ASSOC DEAN FAC & RES, 91- *Personal Data:* b Chicago, Ill Feb 12, 43; m 64, Dorothy M Hespen; c Kevin M & Kristin L. *Educ:* Univ Ill, BS, 63; Univ Chicago, PhD, 66. *Prof Exp:* From asst prof to prof quant bus analysis, Ind Univ, Bloomington, 66-80, distinguished prof, 80-84. *Concurrent Pos:* Vis assoc prof, Univ Wash, Seattle, 70-71; consult, 70-; vis scientist, Nat Ctr Atmospheric Res, Boulder, 72; res scientist, Inst Appl Systs Analysis, Austria, 73-74; vis prof, Stanford Univ, 74, Europ Inst Admin Affairs, France, 80-81 & 90-91. *Mem:* Fel Am Inst Decision Sci; fel Am Statist Asn; Inst Mgt Sci; Int Inst Forecasters (pres, 89-90). *Res:* Statistics; Bayesian inference and decision. *Mailing Add:* Fuqua Sch Bus Duke Univ Box 90120 Durham NC 27708

**WINKLER, ROBERT RANDOLPH,** ORGANIC CHEMISTRY. *Current Pos:* from asst prof to assoc prof, 61-85, PROF ORG CHEM, OHIO UNIV, 85- *Personal Data:* b Washington, DC, June 16, 33; m 55; c 3. *Educ:* Univ Md, BS, 55; Univ Mich, MS, 60, PhD(org chem), 62. *Prof Exp:* Phys sci aide plant indust sta, Agr Res Serv, USDA, Md, 55, chemist, 57-58; teaching asst & res fel, Univ Mich, 58-61. *Mem:* Sigma Xi; AAAS; Am Chem Soc. *Res:* Chemical education; mechanism and stereochemistry of carbonyl condensation reactions. *Mailing Add:* 7727 N Blackburn Rd Ohio Univ Athens OH 45701-9382

**WINKLER, SHELDON,** DENTISTRY. *Current Pos:* prof removable prosthodontics & chmn dept, 79-86, asst dean advan studies, continuing educ & res, 87-89 & 93-95, chmn, Dept Prosthodontics, 93-96, PROF PROSTHODONTICS, TEMPLE UNIV, PHILADELPHIA, 79- *Personal Data:* b New York, NY, Jan 25, 32; m 61, Sandra M Cohen; c Mitchell & Lori. *Educ:* NY Univ, BA, 53, DDS, 56. *Honors & Awards:* Int Educ Award, Int Cong Oral Implantologists, 92; Jour Award, Int Col Dentists, 93. *Prof Exp:* From instr to asst prof denture prosthesis, Col Dent, NY Univ, 58-68; asst prof removable prosthodontics, State Univ NY, Buffalo, 68-70, assoc prof, 70-79. *Concurrent Pos:* Dir mat res, CMP Industs, Inc, 63-65, consult, 65-66; lectr, New York Community Col, 67-68; consult, Coe Labs, Inc, Ill, 67-87; consult dent auxiliary training progs, Bd Coop Educ Serv, Cheektowaga, NY, 70-79; consult, Dent Lab Technol, Erie Community Col, Buffalo, NY, 78-; mem, Bd Consults, Quintessence Int, 80-81; consult, Personal Prod Div, Lever Bros Co, NY, 81-, Dent Schs, Asuncion, Paraguay, Valparaiso, Santiago & Chile, 81-, Off Atty Gen, Commonwealth, Pa, 83-, Dent Schs, Bangkok, Thailand & Alexandria, Egypt, 82-, Vet Admin Med Ctr, Philadelphia, Pa, 88-; ed, Implant Dent, 91- *Mem:* Fel Am Col Dent; Am Prosthodont Soc; Am Dent Asn; Am Acad Plastics Res Dent; Int Cong Oral Implantologists. *Res:* Dental resins and alloys; preservation and embedment of specimens in methyl methacrylate; demineralization of bone; geriatric dentistry; laser radiation applications in dentistry; increasing the bond strength of ceramometal restorations. *Mailing Add:* Sch Dent 3223 N Broad St Philadelphia PA 19140. *Fax:* 215-707-2802

**WINKLER, VIRGIL DEAN,** GEOLOGY. *Current Pos:* GEOL ADV, LAGOVEN SA, 76- *Personal Data:* b Danvers, Ill, Feb 9, 17; m 43, Ana Balza; c Moraima & Kelvin. *Educ:* Univ Ill, AB & BS, 38, MS, 39, PhD(geol), 41. *Prof Exp:* Instr geol, Univ Ill, 38-39; paleontologist, Creole Petrol Corp, 41-45, chief paleontologist, 45-55, paleont coordr, 55-56, eval geologist, 56-61, eval & opers geologist, 61-63, spec studies & eval geologist, 63-76. *Concurrent Pos:* Prof, Cent Univ Venezuela, 58-59 & 66- *Mem:* AAAS; Paleont Soc; Soc Econ Paleont & Mineral; Geol Soc Am; Asn Geol, Mineral & Petrol, Venezuela (vpres, 54-55, secy-treas, 59-60); Am Asn Petrol Geologists. *Res:* Paleontology of Paleozoic rocks; world-wide occurrence of oil; Mesozoic and Cenozoic stratigraphy of Venezuela. *Mailing Add:* Aptdo 80537 Prados del Este Caracas 1080A Venezuela

**WINKLES, JEFFREY A,** MOLECULAR BIOLOGY. *Current Pos:* SCIENTIST MOLECULAR BIOL, AM RED CROSS, 90- *Personal Data:* b Coatesville, Pa, Feb 18, 22. *Res:* Molecular biology. *Mailing Add:* JH Holland Lab Am Red Cross 15601 Crabbs Branch Way Rockville MD 20855-2743

**WINN, ALDEN L(EWIS),** ELECTRONICS. *Current Pos:* from asst prof to prof, 48-83, chmn dept, 52-67, EMER PROF ELEC ENG, UNIV NH, 83- *Personal Data:* b Portsmouth, NH, Jan 26, 16; m 41; c 2. *Educ:* Univ NH, BS, 37; Mass Inst Technol, MS, 48. *Prof Exp:* Engr & acct phys plant eval, New Eng Gas & Elec Syst, 37-40; asst elec eng, Mass Inst Technol, 45-47, instr, 47-48. *Mem:* Am Soc Eng Educ; Inst Elec & Electronics Engrs. *Res:* Oceanographic instrumentation; semiconductor devices and circuits. *Mailing Add:* 1 Churchill Rd Durham NH 03824

**WINN, C BYRON,** AERONAUTICAL ENGINEERING, ELECTRICAL ENGINEERING. *Current Pos:* assoc prof, 67-77, assoc dir, Univ comput Ctr, 70-77, PROF MECH ENG, COLO STATE UNIV, 77-, HEAD DEPT, 83- *Personal Data:* b Canton, Mo, Nov 21, 33; m 58; c 3. *Educ:* Univ Ill, Urbana, BS, 58; Stanford Univ, MS, 60, PhD(aeronaut eng), 67. *Honors & Awards:* Tech Paper Award, Am Inst Aeronaut & Astronaut, 67. *Prof Exp:* Engr, Lockheed Missiles & Space Co, 58-60; engr, Martin Marietta Co, 60-62; engr Lockheed Missiles & Space Co, 62-63; res asst, Stanford Univ, 63-67. *Concurrent Pos:* NASA res grant satellite geodesy, Colo State Univ, 67-71, remote sensing in hydrol, 70-72, Off Water Resources res grant optimal control of storm sewer syst, 70-72; consult, Space Res Corp, Que, 70-72, MEPPSCO, Inc, Mass, 71 & USAF, Wright-Patterson AFB, 71-72; vis assoc prof, Univ Newcastle, NSW, 72; dir, Energy Analysis & Diag Ctr, Colo State Univ, 84- & Mfg Excellence Ctr, 88- *Mem:* Am Inst Aeronaut & Astronaut; Am Soc Mech Engrs. *Res:* Optimal control theory and applications; satellite geodesy; simulation; solar energy. *Mailing Add:* Dept Mech Eng Colo State Univ Ft Collins CO 80523-1374

**WINN, EDWARD BARRIERE,** TECHNICAL & GENERAL CORPORATE MANAGEMENT, CHEMICAL INDUSTRY. *Current Pos:* INDEPENDENT CONSULT STRATEGIC & TECH MGT & SCI PUBL VENTURES, 97- *Personal Data:* b Baltimore, Md, Dec 27, 22; m 49, Joan Pilchard; c Edward Jr, Anne, Chloe & Thomas. *Educ:* Univ SC, BSc, 46; Univ Va, MSc, 47; Univ Minn, PhD(physics), 50. *Prof Exp:* Elec engr, Westinghouse Elec Corp, 46; res assoc, Univ Minn, 48-50; res physicist, Textile Fibers Dept, E I du Pont de Nemours & Co, 50-57, res supvr, 57-62, tech mgr, du Pont de Nemours Int, SA, 62-70; managing dir, Techinter SA, Geneva, 71-74; asst to managing dir, SNIA Viscosa SpA, Milan, 74-76; mgr diversification, SIPE Nobel SpA, Milan, 76-77; mgr, Diamond Shamrock France, 78-80; Europ dir, Process Indust Div, SRI Int, Zurich, Switz, 80-88; Europ dir, Kansai Res Inst, Prangins, Switz, 89-96. *Concurrent Pos:* Sr staff consult, Arthur D Little, Ltd, 78. *Mem:* Am Phys Soc; Am Chem Soc; Sigma Xi; Soc Sci Explor; Int Soc Cryptozool. *Res:* Physics of high polymers; textile fibers; processing and applications technology of synthetic fibers; physics of electrical insulating materials; electrical insulation technology; industrial and technical marketing; new business ventures in textile, polymers and chemicals; several science papers published and granted one patent. *Mailing Add:* 5-17 Carn Castle Gate St Catharines ON L2N 5V4 Can. *Fax:* 905-937-0939

**WINN, HENRY JOSEPH,** IMMUNOLOGY. *Current Pos:* IMMUNOLOGIST, MASS GEN HOSP, 73-; SR ASSOC SURG, HARVARD MED SCH, 77- *Personal Data:* b Lowell, Mass, Mar 2, 27; m 53; c 6. *Educ:* Ohio State Univ, BA, 48, MS, 50, PhD(bact), 52. *Prof Exp:* Fel med & bact, Ohio State Univ, 52-54; fel chem, Calif Inst Technol, 54-55; res assoc, Jackson Mem Lab, 55-57, staff scientist, 57-65; assoc immunologist, Mass Gen Hosp, 65-73; asst prof bact, 65-70, assoc prof microbiol & molecular genetics, 69-77. *Mem:* Am Asn Immunologists. *Res:* Immunology of homotransplantation; immunogenetics. *Mailing Add:* Dept Surg Mass Gen Hosp Boston MA 02114

**WINN, HOWARD ELLIOTT,** biological oceanography, behavior-ethology; deceased, see previous edition for last biography

**WINN, HUGH,** CHEMICAL & MATERIALS ENGINEERING. *Current Pos:* mgr nose cone design eng, Missile & Space Vehicle Dept, 55-58, mgr res opers & applns, Aerosci Lab, 58-59, mgr data processing & comput, 59-63, mgr corp eng, 63-71, mgr eng, Lamp Glass Dept, 71-78, PROJ MGR GLASS RESOURCE PLANS & PROG, LAMP GLASS PROD DEPT, GEN ELEC CO, 78- *Personal Data:* b St Louis, Mo, Apr 7, 18; m 39; c 2. *Educ:* Mich Col Mining & Technol, BS, 40; Case Inst Technol, MS, 44, PhD(chem eng), 48. *Prof Exp:* Res engr, Saran Develop Lab, Dow Chem Co, 41-42; asst prof chem eng & dir plastics lab, Case Inst Technol, 42-48; group leader, Firestone Tire & Rubber Co, 48-50 & Defense Res Div, 50-55. *Concurrent Pos:* Consult, Martin Co, Md, 42, Ohio Chem Co, 44-47 & Frankford Arsenal, 55-58. *Mem:* Am Chem Soc; Soc Plastics Engrs; Am Inst Chem Engrs; Sigma Xi. *Res:* Plastics formulation; evaluation and fabrication; rubber oxidation, compounding and evaluation; high explosive effects; space environment; engineering design and space vehicles; scientific computation and test data reduction; materials and processes. *Mailing Add:* 6524 Kingswood Dr Mayfield OH 44124-4228

**WINN, JOHN STERLING,** MATRIX ISOLATION SPECTROSCOPY, WEAKLY BOUND MOLECULES. *Current Pos:* PROF CHEM, DARTMOUTH COL, 82- *Personal Data:* b Lexington, Va, Oct 8, 47; c John C. *Educ:* Mass Inst Technol, SB(chem) & SB(physics), 69; Univ Calif, Berkeley, PhD(chem), 73. *Prof Exp:* Fel, Harvard Univ, 73-75; prof chem, Univ Calif, Berkeley, 75-82. *Concurrent Pos:* Prin investr, Lawrence Berkeley Lab, 77-82. *Mem:* Am Chem Soc; Am Phys Soc; Sigma Xi. *Res:* Intermolecular interactions studied by high resolution matrix isolation spectroscopy, theoretical lineshape analysis and gas phase spectroscopy of vibrational motion. *Mailing Add:* Dept Chem Dartmouth Col Hanover NH 03755. *Fax:* 603-646-3946; *E-Mail:* JWinn@dartmouth.edu

**WINN, MARTIN,** MEDICINAL CHEMISTRY. *Current Pos:* SR CHEMIST, ABBOTT LABS, 65- *Personal Data:* b Brooklyn, NY, Jan 25, 40; m 66, Barbara Gill; c Joshua & David. *Educ:* Cooper Union Univ, BChE, 61; Northwestern Univ, PhD(org chem), 65. *Mem:* Am Chem Soc. *Res:* Pharmaceuticals; heterocycles; antihypertensive drugs; endothlin antagonists. *Mailing Add:* Dept 47V AP 10 Abbott Labs Abbott Park IL 60064. *Fax:* 847-938-1674; *E-Mail:* marty.winn@abbott.com

**WINN, WILLIAM PAUL,** ATMOSPHERIC PHYSICS & INSTRUMENTATION. *Current Pos:* from asst prof to assoc prof, 70-77, chmn dept, 77-82, PROF PHYSICS, NMEX INST MINING & TECHNOL, 82-, CHMN, LANGMUIR LAB ATMOSPHERIC RES, 85- *Personal Data:* b Los Angeles, Calif, Apr 24, 39. *Educ:* Univ Calif, Berkeley, BS, 61, PhD(physics), 68. *Prof Exp:* Fel physics, Nat Ctr Atmospheric Res, 66-70. *Mem:* Am Geophys Union; Am Asn Physics Teachers; AAAS; Am Meteorol Soc. *Res:* Thunderstorms. *Mailing Add:* Dept Physics NMex Inst Mining & Technol Socorro NM 87801. *Fax:* 505-835-5707; *E-Mail:* winn@kestrel.nmt.edu

**WINNICK, JACK,** CHEMICAL ENGINEERING. *Current Pos:* Cramer Wilson La Pierre prof eng, 79-80, PROF CHEM ENG, GA INST TECHNOL, 79- *Personal Data:* b Chicago, Ill, Sept 20, 37. *Educ:* Univ Ill, BS, 58; Univ Okla, MS, 60, PhD(chem eng), 63. *Honors & Awards:* Krupp Prize Energy Res, 83. *Prof Exp:* From asst prof to assoc prof chem eng, Univ Mo-Columbia, 63-67, prof, 71-79. *Concurrent Pos:* NSF res grants, 64-94; consult, NASA Manned Spacecraft Ctr, 66-76, Life Syst Inc, 75-78, Combustion Eng, Giner Inc, 86- & Grove Eng, 90-; vis prof, Univ Calif, Berkeley, 69-70, 77 & 84-85, Univ Calif, Los Angeles, 76; Petrol Res Fund grant, 70-73; NASA grants, 72-83; Dept Energy grant, 77- *Mem:* Am Inst Chem Engrs; Am Chem Soc; AAAS; Sigma Xi. *Res:* Photoelectrochemistry; electrochemical membrane seperation; electrochemical engineering; fuel cells. *Mailing Add:* Dept Chem Eng Ga Inst Technol Atlanta GA 30332

**WINNIE, DAYLE DAVID,** MECHANICAL ENGINEERING, ELECTRONICS. *Current Pos:* sr res engr, 69-81, STAFF ENGR ELECTROMECH, SOUTHWEST RES INST, 81- *Personal Data:* b Brandon, Wis, July 20, 35; m 57; c 2. *Educ:* Univ Wis, BS, 58. *Prof Exp:* Aircraft maintenance officer, Charleston AFB, SC, 59-60; prod engr electromech design, Centralab Div, Globe Union Inc, Milwaukee, 60-64; develop engr automatic processing equip, Stoelting Bros Co, Kiel, 64-69. *Mem:* Sigma Xi; Am Soc Mech Engrs. *Res:* Electromechanical design; spaceflight mass measurement equipment; automatic machinery design and development; automatic direction finding systems; sub-sea hyperbaric and single atmosphere systems; geophysical anomaly detection systems; automated continuous dairy processing equipment. *Mailing Add:* Southwest Res Inst 6220 Culebra Rd San Antonio TX 78228

**WINNIE, GLENNA BARBARA,** PEDIATRIC PULMONOLOGY. *Current Pos:* asst prof pediat, 82-90, HEAD PEDIAT PULMONOLOGY SECT, ALBANY MED COL, 82-, ASSOC PROF PEDIAT, 90- *Personal Data:* b Lansing, Mich; m 90, Jeffrey A Cooper; c Robert J Cooper & David J Cooper. *Educ:* Mich State Univ, BS, 73; Vanderbilt Univ, MD, 77; Am Bd Pediat, dipl. *Prof Exp:* Resident pediat, Case Western Res Univ, Babies & Childrens Hosp, 77-79, fel pediat pulmonology, 79-82. *Concurrent Pos:* Dir, Albany Pediat Pulmonology & Cystic Fibrosis Ctr, 82-; res grants, Nat Cystic Fibrosis Found, 84-86 & 88-90, NIH, 87-93. *Mem:* Am Acad Pediat; Am Thoracic Soc. *Res:* Description of role of Epstein Barr virus in pulmonary cxacerbations in cystic fibrosis. *Mailing Add:* Childrens Hosp 3705 Fifth Ave Pittsburgh PA 15213

**WINNIFORD, ROBERT STANLEY,** PHYSICAL CHEMISTRY. *Current Pos:* from asst prof to assoc prof, 63-77, chmn dept, 71-80, PROF CHEM, WHITWORTH COL, WASH, 77- *Personal Data:* b Portland, Ore, Oct 10, 21; m 44; c 4. *Educ:* Ore State Col, BS, 43; Calif Inst Technol, MS, 48; Univ Tenn, PhD, 51. *Prof Exp:* Instr chem, Univ Tenn, 47-49; res chemist, Calif Res Corp, Standard Oil Co Calif, 51-63. *Mem:* Am Chem Soc; Sigma Xi. *Res:* Colloid and surface chemistry; nonaqueous solutions; asphalt chemistry and rheology. *Mailing Add:* 41096 Nichol Dr Sweet Home OR 97386-1692

**WINNIK, FRANCOISE MARTINE,** FLUORESCENCE & SPECTROSCOPY, LIPOSOMES. *Current Pos:* ASSOC PROF, DEPT CHEM, PHYSICS & ASTRON, MCMASTER UNIV, 93- *Personal Data:* b Mulhouse, France, Mar 2, 52. *Educ:* Ecole Nat Superieure Chim, Ingenieur Chimiste, 74; Univ Toronto, PhD(org chem), 79. *Prof Exp:* Fel carbohydrate chem, Dept Med Genetics, Univ Toronto, 79-81; mem res staff org & polymer chem, Xerox Res Ctr Can, 81-93. *Concurrent Pos:* Lectr, Dept Chem, Univ Toronto, 83-84; vis scientist, Tokyo Inst Technol, 85-86, Frontier Res Prog, Saitama, Japan, 93-94. *Mem:* Am Chem Soc; Chem Inst Can. *Res:* Design and properties of materials used in printing technologies; application of luminescence techniques in polymer science; study of structure-properties relationships of hydrophobic polymers in water; interactions of liposomes and polymers, ferrofluids, polysaccarides. *Mailing Add:* Dept Chem Physics & Astron McMaster Univ 1280 Main St W Hamilton ON L8S 4M1 Can. *Fax:* 905-540-1310; *E-Mail:* winnikf@mcmaster.ca

**WINNIK, MITCHELL ALAN,** ORGANIC CHEMISTRY, PHOTOCHEMISTRY. *Current Pos:* asst prof, 70-75, assoc prof, 75-80, PROF ORG CHEM, UNIV TORONTO, 80- *Personal Data:* b Milwaukee, Wis, July 17, 43; m 80. *Educ:* Yale Univ, BA, 65; Columbia Univ, PhD(org chem), 69. *Honors & Awards:* A A Vernon Mem Lectr, Northeastern Univ, 83; Xerox Lectrs, Victoria Univ, BC, Can, 87. *Prof Exp:* USPHS fel, Calif Inst Technol, 69-70. *Concurrent Pos:* Assoc prof, Univ Bordeaux, 77-78; world trade fel, Int Bus Mach Corp, San Jose, 82; fel, Japan Soc Prom Sci, Tokyo Inst Technol, 85-86. *Mem:* Inter-Am Photochem Soc; Am Chem Soc; Chem Inst Can. *Res:* Polymer conformation and dynamics; luminescence techniques in polymer science; new techniques for the study of interfaces in polymer materials; polymer colloids. *Mailing Add:* Dept Chem Univ Toronto Toronto ON M5S 1A1 Can

**WINNINGHAM, JOHN DAVID,** MAGNETOSPHERIC PHYSICS. *Current Pos:* MGR, EXP SPACE PHYSICS, SOUTHWEST RES INST, SAN ANTONIO, TEX, 80- *Personal Data:* b Mexia, Tex, Dec 28, 40; m 63; c 1. *Educ:* Tex A&M Univ, BS, 63, MS, 65, PhD(physics), 70. *Prof Exp:* From res asst to res sci asst physics, Univ Tex, Dallas, 66-71, res assoc, 71-73, res scientist, 73-80. *Concurrent Pos:* Consult, Los Alamos Sci Lab, Univ Calif, 74- *Mem:* Am Geophys Union. *Res:* Investigation of the source and acceleration mechanisms of corpuscular fluxes that produce the aurora and concomitant physical processes by means of rocket and satellite instruments. *Mailing Add:* Southwest Res Inst PO Box 28510 San Antonio TX 78228-0510

**WINOGRAD, ISAAC J,** PALEOCLIMATOLOGY, HYDROGEOLOGY. *Current Pos:* RES HYDROLOGIST, DEPT INTERIOR, US GEOL SURV, 71- *Personal Data:* b Stanford, Conn, Feb 6, 31. *Educ:* Brooklyn Col, BS, 53; Columbia Univ, MS, 58; Univ Ariz, PhD(geochem), 71. *Honors & Awards:* Meinzer Award, Geol Soc Am, 88. *Prof Exp:* Hydrologist, 53-70. *Mem:* Fel Am Geophys Union; AAAS. *Mailing Add:* US Geol Surv 432 Nat Ctr Reston VA 20192. *Fax:* 703-648-5832; *E-Mail:* ijwinogr@usgs.gov

**WINOGRAD, NICHOLAS,** ANALYTICAL CHEMISTRY. *Current Pos:* prof, 79-85, EVAN PUGH PROF CHEM, PA STATE UNIV, 85- *Personal Data:* b New London, Conn, Dec 27, 45. *Educ:* Rensselaer Polytech Inst, BS, 67; Case Western Res Univ, PhD(chem), 70. *Honors & Awards:* Tex Instruments Found Founders Prize, 84. *Prof Exp:* Asst prof, Purdue Univ, West Lafayette, 70-75, assoc prof chem, 75-79. *Concurrent Pos:* Consult, Shell Develop Co, 77; Guggenheim fel, 77-78; mem, Adv Bd Anal Chem, 86-88, NSF Chem Adv Bd, 87-90. *Mem:* Am Chem Soc; Electrochem Soc; fel AAAS. *Res:* Characterization of solid surfaces; x-ray photoelectron spectroscopy; secondary ion mass spectrometry; theory of ion impact phenomena on solids. *Mailing Add:* Dept Chem Pa State Univ 184 Mat Res Inst Bldg University Park PA 16802

**WINOGRAD, SHMUEL,** THEORETICAL COMPUTER SCIENCE. *Current Pos:* mem res staff, 61-81, dir, Mat Sci Dept, T J Watson Res Ctr, 81-95, FEL, IBM, 95- *Personal Data:* b Tel Aviv, Israel, Jan 4, 36; m 58, Elaine R Tates; c Daniel & Sharon. *Educ:* Mass Inst Technol, BS & MS, 59; NY Univ, PhD(math), 68. *Hon Degrees:* Dr, Acad Grenoble, Nat Polytech Inst, 87, Technion, Israel, 92. *Honors & Awards:* W Wallace McDowell Award, Inst Elec & Electronics Engrs, 74, Comput Pioneer Award, 82. *Prof

*Exp:* Res asst, Mass Inst Technol, 59-61. *Concurrent Pos:* Adj prof math, Courant Inst Math Sci, NY Univ, 68; Mackay lectr, Univ Calif, Berkeley, 67-68; vis prof, The Technion, Israel, 72-; Int Bus Mach Corp fel, 72; chmn appl math, Comput Sci & Statist Sect, Nat Acad Sci, 87. *Mem:* Nat Acad Sci; fel Inst Elec & Electronics Engrs; Asn Comput Mach; Am Math Soc; Math Asn Am; Am Acad Arts & Sci; Soc Indust & Appl Math. *Res:* Computer mathematics; reliable computations; complexity of computations. *Mailing Add:* Math Sci Dept T J Watson Res Ctr PO Box 218 Yorktown Heights NY 10598. *Fax:* 914-945-3434; *E-Mail:* swin@watson.ibm.com

**WINOGRAD, TERRY ALLEN,** COMPUTER SCIENCE. *Current Pos:* from asst prof to assoc prof, 74-89, PROF COMPUT SCI DEPT, STANFORD UNIV, 89- *Personal Data:* b Takoma Park, Md, Feb 24, 46; m 68. *Educ:* Colo Col, BA, 66; Mass Inst Technol, PhD(appl math), 70. *Hon Degrees:* DSc, Colo Col, 86. *Prof Exp:* Instr math & asst prof elec eng, Mass Inst Technol, 70-74. *Concurrent Pos:* Consult, Palo Alto Res Ctr, Xerox Corp, 73-, Action Technol, Inc, Alameda, Calif, Hermenet, Inc, San Francisco, Xerox Palo Alto Res Ctr, spec consult to pres, Fuji Xerox, Japan & to Fr Govt; mem, Comput Sci & Eng Res Study Panel Artificial Intel, NSF, 75; vis asst prof, Comput Sci Dept, Stanford Univ, 73-74; Mellon Jr fac fel, 77; mem, Spec Interest Group on Comput & Soc, Asn Comput Mach & Nat Bd, Computer Prof for Social Responsibility, 84- *Mem:* Asn Comput Ling; Inst Elec & Electronics Engrs; Union Concerned Scientists; Comput Prof Social Responsibility (pres, 87-90); Asn Comput Mach; Am Asn Artificial Intel. *Res:* Artificial intelligence; computational linguistics; cognitive modelling; author of numerous books and articles. *Mailing Add:* 746 Esplanada Way Palo Alto CA 94305-1901

**WINOKUR, GEORGE,** GENETICS, EPIDEMIOLOGY. *Current Pos:* prof psychiat & head dept, 71-90, PAUL W PENNINGROTH PROF, PSYCHIAT, COL MED, UNIV IOWA & DIR, IOWA PSYCHIAT HOSP, 90- *Personal Data:* b Philadelphia, Pa, Feb 10, 25; m 51, Betty Stricklin; c Patricia, Kenneth & Thomas. *Educ:* Johns Hopkins Univ, BA, 44; Univ Md, MD, 47; Am Bd Psychiat & Neurol, dipl, 53. *Honors & Awards:* Hofheimer Prize Psychiat Res, Am Psychiat Asn, 72; Res Affective Dis Prize, Anna-Monika Found, Switz, 73; Samuel W Hamilton Award, Am Psychopath Asn, 77; Paul Hoch Award, 81; Joseph Zubin Award, 92; Leonard Cammer Award, Columbia Col Physicians & Surgeons, 80; Gold Medal Award, Soc Biol Psychiat, 84; Achievement Award, Am Acad Clin Psychiat; Lifetime Res Award, Nat Depressive & Manic Depressive Asn, 90; Lifetime Achievement Award, Int Soc Psychiat Genetics, 93. *Prof Exp:* Intern med, Church Home & Hosp, 47-48; resident asst, Seton Inst, 48-50; resident neuropsychiat, Univ Iowa Col Med, 50-51, instr psychiat, 51-55, from asst prof to prof, 55-71, prof psychiat & head dept, 71-90. *Concurrent Pos:* From asst psychiatrist to assoc psychiatrist, Barnes Hosp, 55-71; attend, Malcolm Bliss Psychiat Hosp; ed, J Affective Disorders, 78-; co-ed, Europ Archives Psychiat & Neurol Sci, 85-; foreign ed, Psychiat Fennica, 85-; managing ed, Europ Archives Psychiat & Neurol Sci, 86-93. *Mem:* Am Acad Clin Psychiatrists; fel Am Psychiat Asn; Am Col Neuropsychopharmacol; Int Group Study Affective Dis; Am Psychopath Asn; Swiss Psychiat Asn. *Res:* Sexual variables in psychiatric patients and controls; genetics and epidemiological studies of psychiatric diseases. *Mailing Add:* Psychiat Univ Iowa Iowa City IA 52242-1000. *Fax:* 319-353-3003

**WINOKUR, ROBERT MICHAEL,** ZOOLOGY. *Current Pos:* ASST PROF BIOL, UNIV NEV, LAS VEGAS, 78- *Personal Data:* b Minneapolis, Minn, July 2, 42; m 88. *Educ:* Macalester Col, BA, 65; Ariz State Univ, MA, 67; Univ Utah, PhD(biol), 72. *Honors & Awards:* Dwight D Davis Award, Am Soc Zoologists, 73. *Prof Exp:* Teaching fel biol, Univ Utah, 67-72, asst res prof, 72-73; instr zool, Univ New Eng, Australia, 74-78. *Mem:* Am Soc Zoologists; Am Soc Ichthyologists & Herpetologists; Soc Study Amphibians & Reptiles. *Res:* Comparative morphology of lower vertebrates with emphasis on the microscopic anatomy and integumentary specialization of reptiles and amphibians. *Mailing Add:* Dept Biol Sci Univ Nev 4505 S Maryland Pkwy Las Vegas NV 89154-9900

**WINREICH, DANIEL,** NEUROBIOLOGY. *Current Pos:* asst prof, 74-77, ASSOC PROF PHARMACOL, SCH MED, UNIV MD, BALTIMORE, 74- *Personal Data:* b Claremont, France, June 6, 42; US citizen; m 36; c 2. *Educ:* Bethany Col, BS, 64; Univ Utah, PhD(pharmacol), 70. *Prof Exp:* Res asst neuropharmacol, Sandoz Pharmaceut, Inc, 64-65; NSF fel, City of Hope Nat Med Ctr, 70-72, NIMH fel, 73-74. *Concurrent Pos:* Extramural reviewer, NSF, 73-, Neurobiol Study Sect, 80-81; NSF res grant, 74-83. *Mem:* Neurosci Soc. *Res:* Identification and regulation of neurotransmitter and neuromodulator substances in single nerve cells; cellular autonomic neuropharmacology. *Mailing Add:* Dept Pharmacol & Exp Therapeut Univ Md 655 W Baltimore St Rm 4002 Baltimore MD 21201-1509

**WINRICH, LONNY B,** COMPUTER SCIENCE. *Current Pos:* prof, 85-96, chmn dept, 86-90, EMER PROF COMPUT SCI, UNIV NDAK, 96- *Personal Data:* b Eau Claire, Wis, July 10, 37; m 89, Sandra Donaldson; c 5. *Educ:* Wis State Univ, Eau Claire, BS, 60; Univ Wyo, MS, 62; Iowa State Univ, PhD(appl math), 68. *Prof Exp:* Physicist, Boulder Labs, Nat Bur Stand, 60-62; mathematician, Aerospace Div, Honeywell, Inc, 62-64; instr math & comput sci, Iowa State Univ, 64-68; asst prof comput sci, Univ Mo, Rolla, 68-71; from assoc prof to prof, Univ Wis-La Crosse, 71-85, chmn dept, 71-79. *Concurrent Pos:* Consult, Mctadynamics, 90. *Mem:* Inst Elec & Electronics Engrs; Sigma Xi; Asn Comput Mach; Am Asn Artificial Intel. *Res:* Application of intelligent systems to software testing; software maintenance and documentation; intelligent systems; systems level testing. *Mailing Add:* 606 S Fourth St Grand Forks ND 58201. *Fax:* 701-772-1363; *E-Mail:* winrich@ cr.und.edu

**WINSBERG, GWYNNE ROESELER,** EPIDEMIOLOGY. *Current Pos:* PRES, GRW ASSOCS INC, 81- *Personal Data:* b Chicago, Ill, Nov 28, 30; m 50; c Jeri L & William F. *Educ:* Univ Chicago, MS, 62, PhD(biopsychol), 67. *Prof Exp:* Instr biol, Univ Chicago, 65-67; asst prof anat, Med Sch, Northwestern Univ, Chicago, 67-71, asst prof community health & prev med, 71-76; assoc prof community & family med & assoc dean, Stritch Sch Med, Loyola Univ, Chicago, 76-81; assoc prof prev med, Univ Ill, 82-87; assoc prof psychiat, Rush Presby St Lukes Med Ctr, 89-93. *Concurrent Pos:* Lectr, Ill Col Optom, 62-67; consult, Ill Dept Ment Health, 69-72; USPHS grant, Fac Inst Med Care Orgn, Univ Mich, 73 & 74; Nat Endowment Humanities grant, Univ Pa, 74; spec asst to regional health adminr, Region V, USPHS, 74-76; secy, bd trustees, North Communities Health Plan, Inc, Evanston, 76-; sr policy analyst, Off Secy, Dept Health Human Serv, Washington, DC, 79-81; vpres, Efficient Health Systs, Inc, Skokie, Ill, 86-87. *Mem:* Am Pub Health Asn; Am Med Care Review Asn; Group Health Asn Am. *Res:* Social and medical epidemiology; medical care organization; health policy and legislation; mental health and long term care benefits; corporate health care benefits and cost containment. *Mailing Add:* 5533 N Glenwood Chicago IL 60640. *Fax:* 773-561-9553

**WINSKE, DAN,** SPACE PHYSICS, PLASMA SIMULATION. *Current Pos:* staff mem, Appl Theoret Physics Div, 83-95, DEP GROUP LEADER, PLASMA PHYSICS APPLNS GROUP, LOS ALAMOS NAT LAB, 95- *Personal Data:* b East Chicago, Ind, Feb 24, 46. *Educ:* Purdue Univ, BS, 68; Univ Ill, Champaign-Urbana, MA, 69, PhD(physics), 74. *Prof Exp:* Staff mem, Controlled Thermonuclear Res Div, Los Alamos Sci Lab, 74-79; sr res assoc, Plasma & Fusion Studies Lab, Univ Md, 79-83. *Concurrent Pos:* Consult, Off Fusion Energy, Dept Energy, 83; vis scientist, Observatoire de Paris Meudon, 83; assoc ed, J Geophys Res, 89-; prin investr, NASA Space Plasma Theory Prog, Los Alamos Nat Lab, 89-96. *Mem:* Fel Am Phys Soc; Am Geophys Union; Inst Elec & Electronics Engrs. *Res:* Numerical modeling and theoretical analysis of space and laboratory plasmas; study of collisionless shock waves, plasma microinstabilities, and dusty plasmas using particle and hybrid plasma simulation methods. *Mailing Add:* MS B259 XPA Los Alamos Nat Lab Los Alamos NM 87545

**WINSLOW, ALFRED EDWARDS,** ORGANIC CHEMISTRY, POLYMERS & LIQUID PHENOLIC RESINS. *Current Pos:* RETIRED. *Personal Data:* b Clinton, Mass, Oct 8, 19; m 44; c 2. *Educ:* Worcester Polytech Inst, BS, 41; Mass Inst Technol, PhD(org chem), 47. *Prof Exp:* Jr chemist, Tenn Eastman Corp, 44-45; asst, Sugar Res Found, Mass Inst Technol, 45-47; res chemist, Union Carbide Chem Co, 47-64; sr res chemist, Borden Chem Co, 64-86. *Mem:* Am Chem Soc. *Res:* Water soluble polymers; condensation polymerizations; reactions in aqueous media; binders; resin analyses; manufacturing procedures and quality control. *Mailing Add:* 2500 Glenwood Park New Albany IN 47150-1542

**WINSLOW, CHARLES ELLIS, JR,** CHEMICAL ENGINEERING. *Current Pos:* RETIRED. *Personal Data:* b Norfolk, Va, July 2, 28; m 50; c 2. *Educ:* Va Polytech Inst, BS, 50; NC State Univ, MS, 52, PhD(chem eng), 56. *Prof Exp:* Chem engr, Va Chem Inc, 56-58, group leader, 58-64, mgr process develop, 64-72, assoc dir res, 72-75, dir develop, 75-90. *Mem:* Am Inst Chem Engrs. *Res:* Inorganic and organic process development and equipment design; chemistry of sulfur dioxide bases on or derived from reducing agents. *Mailing Add:* 1308 W Oceanview Ave Norfolk VA 23503

**WINSLOW, DOUGLAS NATHANIEL,** CIVIL ENGINEERING. *Current Pos:* ASSOC PROF CIVIL ENG, PURDUE UNIV, 73- *Personal Data:* b Lakewood, Ohio. *Educ:* Purdue Univ, BSCE, 64, MSCE, 69, PhD(construct mat), 73. *Mem:* Am Concrete Inst; Am Soc Testing & Mat; Am Ceramic Soc. *Res:* Microstructure, durability and test methods for various construction materials (cement, concrete, bricks and bituminous mixtures); mercury intrusion porosimetry. *Mailing Add:* 2886 Bridgeway Dr West Lafayette IN 47906-5251

**WINSLOW, FIELD HOWARD,** ORGANIC CHEMISTRY, POLYMER CHEMISTRY. *Current Pos:* CONSULT, 87- *Personal Data:* b Proctor, Vt, June 10, 16; m 45; c 3. *Educ:* Middlebury Col, BS, 38; RI State Col, MS, 40; Cornell Univ, PhD(org chem), 43. *Prof Exp:* Res chemist, Manhattan Proj, Columbia Univ, 43-45; mem tech staff, Bell Labs, Inc, 45-87. *Concurrent Pos:* Adj prof, Stevens Inst Technol, 64-67; ed, Macromolecules, 67- *Mem:* Fel AAAS; Am Chem Soc. *Res:* Photochemistry; organic semiconductors; polymer morphology and chemical reactivity; deterioration and stabilization of rubbers and plastics; fluorocarbons. *Mailing Add:* Jessica Lane Warren NJ 07059. *Fax:* 908-582-3609

**WINSLOW, GEORGE HARVEY,** PHYSICS. *Current Pos:* RETIRED. *Personal Data:* b Washington, DC, June 21, 16; m 44; c 2. *Educ:* Carnegie Inst Technol, BS, 38, MS, 39, DSc, 46. *Prof Exp:* Instr physics, Carnegie Inst Technol, 38, res physicist, 43-46; assoc physicist, Argonne Nat Lab, 46-81. *Mem:* Am Phys Soc. *Res:* Magnetic moments by molecular beams; high speed deformation of metals; shaped charges; solid state; attempts to find requantization of space quantized atoms at collision; alpha decay theory high temperature physical chemistry. *Mailing Add:* 3004 N Ridge Rd No 301 Ellicot City MD 21043

**WINSLOW, LEON E,** MATHEMATICAL ANALYSIS. *Current Pos:* PROF COMPUT SCI, UNIV DAYTON, 81- *Personal Data:* b Centralia, Ill, Nov 17, 34; m 59; c 6. *Educ:* Marquette Univ, BS, 56, MS, 60; Duke Univ, PhD(math), 65. *Prof Exp:* Comput Ctr, 58-59; prin physicist, Battelle Mem Inst, 57-58; instr math, Rockhurst Col, 59-60; asst, Duke Univ, 60-64, res assoc spec projs numerical analysis, 64-65; asst prof math, Rockhurst Col, 65-66; asst prof comput sci, Univ Notre Dame, 66-72; assoc prof comput sci, Wright State Univ, 72-81. *Mem:* Inst Elec & Electronics Engrs; Asn Comput Mach. *Res:* Systems analysis. *Mailing Add:* 2255 Andrew Rd Dayton OH 45440

**WINSLOW, RAIMOND L,** THEORETICAL BIOLOGY. *Current Pos:* ASST PROF BIOMED, JOHNS HOPKINS UNIV, 91- *Personal Data:* b Portland, Maine, Nov 6, 55. *Educ:* Western Polytech Inst, BS, 78; Johns Hopkins Univ, MS, 80, PhD(theoret biol), 85. *Prof Exp:* Fac mem eng, Minn Univ, 89-91. *Mem:* Soc Neurosci; Am Inst Chemists. *Mailing Add:* Biomed Eng Johns Hopkins Univ 3400 N Charles St Baltimore MD 21218-2608

**WINSOR, FREDERICK JAMES,** METALLURGY. *Current Pos:* CONSULT, 85- *Personal Data:* b Ilion, NY, Aug 22, 21; m 42; c 5. *Educ:* Rensselaer Polytech Inst, BMetE, 42, MMetE, 44, PhD(metall), 46. *Prof Exp:* Asst, Rensselaer Polytech Inst, 42-46; res metallurgist, Armour Res Found, 46-48; supvr welding res, Standard Oil Co, Ind, 48-51; res engr, E I du Pont de Nemours & Co, 51-59; mgr welding lab, Foster Wheeler Corp, 59-69, dir, Welding Develop Lab, 69-85. *Mem:* Am Soc Metals; Am Welding Soc. *Res:* Welding and metallurgical research and development; manufacturing and fabrication engineering. *Mailing Add:* Two Birchwood Terr Fanwood NJ 07023

**WINSOR, LAURISTON P(EARCE),** ELECTRICAL ENGINEERING. *Current Pos:* RETIRED. *Personal Data:* b Johnston, RI, Dec 30, 14; m 42, Agnes; c Chester, Mary (Schenk) & Ruth (Martin). *Educ:* Brown Univ, ScB, 36; Harvard Univ, MS, 37, ScD(elec eng), 46. *Prof Exp:* Asst elec eng, Grad Sch Eng, Harvard Univ, 38-40; instr, Case Inst Technol, 40-46; from asst prof to assoc prof, 46-53, prof elec eng, Rensselaer Polytech Inst, 53-, dir spec projs, Off Continuing Studies, 72-78, emer prof, Rensselaer Polytech Inst, 79- *Mem:* Am Soc Eng Educ; Inst Elec & Electronics Engrs. *Res:* Electromechanical energy conversion and control; arc reignition. *Mailing Add:* 463 Garfield Rd Troy NY 12180

**WINSOR, NIELS K,** PLASMA PHYSICS, GENERAL PHYSICS. *Current Pos:* SR ACCDUST PHYSICIST, TETRA CORP, 94- *Personal Data:* b Albany, NY, 41. *Educ:* Mass Inst Technol, BS, 63; Dartmouth Col, MS, 65; Princeton Univ, PhD(physics), 69. *Prof Exp:* Dir computational sci, GT Devices, 82-94. *Mem:* Fel Am Phys Soc. *Mailing Add:* Tetra Corp 3701 Hawkins St NE Albuquerque NM 87109

**WINSTEAD, JACK ALAN,** TOXICOLOGY, BIOCHEMISTRY. *Current Pos:* CONSULT, 82- *Personal Data:* b Dixon, Ky, June 13, 32; m 56, Mary A Purdy; c Katherine, Karen & Sheri. *Educ:* Univ Ky, BS, 54; Okla State Univ, MS, 59; Univ Ill, PhD(chem), 64. *Prof Exp:* Res officer chem, Mat Lab, USAF Acad, 59-62, res chemist, Sch Aerospace Med, 64-68, Frank J Seiler Res Lab, 68-70, dir, Directorate Chem Sci, 70-72, dep dir, Toxic Hazards Div, Aerospace Med Res Lab, Wright-Patterson AFB, 72-75; prof assoc, Nat Acad Sci, 75-78; dir toxicol rev, Cosmetic, Toiletry & Fragrance Asn, 78-80; prin scientist, Health Effects & Bioassay Div, Tracor Jitco, 80-82. *Mem:* Am Soc Biol Chemists; Am Chem Soc. *Res:* Structure and function of proteins; radiation biochemistry; organic synthesis and toxicology. *Mailing Add:* 6971 E Costilla Pl Englewood CO 80112

**WINSTEAD, JANET,** MYCOLOGY. *Current Pos:* ASSOC PROF BIOL, JAMES MADISON UNIV, VA, 69- *Personal Data:* b Wichita Falls, Tex, Mar 13, 32. *Educ:* Midwestern Univ, BS, 53; Ohio Univ, MS, 55; Univ Tex, Austin, PhD(bot), 70. *Prof Exp:* Instr biol, Ky Wesleyan Col, 56-57; asst prof, Atlantic Christian Col, 57-65. *Mem:* Am Inst Biol Sci; Mycol Soc Am; Sigma Xi. *Res:* Monospore culture of myxomycetes. *Mailing Add:* Biol James Madison Univ Harrisonburg VA 22807-0001

**WINSTEAD, JOE EVERETT,** BOTANY, ECOLOGY. *Current Pos:* from asst prof to assoc prof, 72-78, PROF BIOL, WESTERN KY UNIV, 78- *Personal Data:* b Wichita Falls, Tex, Mar 17, 38; c 2. *Educ:* Midwestern Univ, BS, 60; Ohio Univ, MS, 62; Univ Tex, Austin, PhD(bot), 66. *Prof Exp:* Instr biol, Delta Col, 62. *Concurrent Pos:* Adj prof, Tenn Tech, 74-90. *Mem:* Ecol Soc Am; Bot Soc Am; Sigma Xi. *Res:* Ecotype differentiation of plant species; natural revegetation of stripmines; differentiation of wood cell types and wood anatomy; environmental physiology. *Mailing Add:* Dept Biol Western Ky Univ Bowling Green KY 42101-3576. *Fax:* 502-745-6856

**WINSTEAD, MELDRUM BARNETT, JR,** ORGANIC CHEMISTRY. *Current Pos:* from asst prof to prof, 69-71, EMER PROF CHEM, BUCKNELL UNIV, 91- *Personal Data:* b Lincolnton, NC, Oct 19, 26; m 59; c 3. *Educ:* Davidson Col, BS, 46; Univ NC, Chapel Hill, MA, 49, PhD(chem), 52. *Honors & Awards:* USPHS Award, Nat Inst Gen Med Sci, 74 & 77. *Prof Exp:* Instr chem, Davidson Col, 46-47; asst, Univ NC, 47-50. *Concurrent Pos:* Res grants, DuPont res fel, 51-52, Res Corp, 54-56, AAAS, 59-60 & Petrol Res Fund, 61-62; consult, Glyco Chem, Inc, 58 & Sadtler Res Labs, 59-70; vis chem assoc, Calif Inst Technol, 67-68; USPHS spec res fel, 67-68; res assoc, Lawrence Berkeley Lab, Univ Calif, Berkeley, 68-69; vis scientist, Medi-Physics, Inc, Calif, 72-78, Sloan-Kettering Cancer Ctr, 81, Israel Resources Corp, Ltd, Haifa, Israel, 81-82; Bucknell fac res fel, 70-71 & 78-79. *Mem:* Sigma Xi; Am Chem Soc. *Res:* Organic medicinals; preparation and scintigraphic study of pharmaceuticals containing short-lived radiocarbon-11. *Mailing Add:* RR 1 Box 395 Lewisburg PA 17837

**WINSTEAD, NASH NICKS,** PLANT PATHOLOGY. *Current Pos:* From asst prof to assoc prof, NC State Univ, 53-60, provost & vchancellor, 74-90, actg chancellor, 81-82, PROF PLANT PATH, NC STATE UNIV, 60-, EMER PROVOST & VCHANCELLOR, 90- *Personal Data:* b Durham, Co, NC, June 12, 25; m 49, Geraldine K; c Karen. *Educ:* NC State Col, BS, 48, MS, 51; Univ Wis, PhD(plant path), 53. *Honors & Awards:* Res Award, Sigma Xi, 60. *Concurrent Pos:* Phillips Found internship acad admin, Ind Univ, 65-66; dir, Inst Biol Sci & asst dir res, NC Agr Exp Sta, 65-67, asst provost, NC State Univ, 67-73, assoc provost, 73-74; mem, Comt Planned Res Basic Bio-sci during manned earth-orbiting missions, Am Inst Biol Sci-NASA, 65-67; mem bd dirs, Consortium Coop Raleigh Cols, 68-90, pres, 71-83 & 83-85; mem, Educ Telecommun Comt, Nat Asn State Univ & Land Grant Col, 80-85; trustee, NC Sch Sci & Math, 85-90; trustee, NC Wesleyan Col, 88-97, emer trustee, 97- *Mem:* Fel AAAS; Am Phytopath Soc; Am Inst Biol Sci; Sigma Xi. *Res:* Vegetable diseases; breeding for resistance; physiology of parasitism. *Mailing Add:* 1109 Glendale Dr Raleigh NC 27612

**WINSTEIN, BRUCE DARRELL,** PHYSICS. *Current Pos:* sr res assoc, Enrico Fermi Inst, Univ Chicago, 72-76, Arthur H Compton lectr, 76, from asst prof to assoc prof, 76-83, PROF, DEPT PHYSICS & ENRICO FERMI INST, UNIV CHICAGO, 83-, SAMUEL K ALLISON DISTINGUISHED SERV PROF, 97- *Personal Data:* b Los Angeles, Calif, Sept 25, 43; m 79, Joan; c Keith & Allison. *Educ:* Univ Calif, Los Angeles, BA, 65; Calif Inst Technol, PhD(physics), 70. *Prof Exp:* Res physicist, Max Planck Inst Physics & Astrophys, Munich, Ger, 70-72. *Concurrent Pos:* Consult physicist, CalTech Synchrotron Group, 70; mem sub panel, New Fac US High Energy Physics Prog, HEPAP, 83, US High Energy Physics Res Prog, 90; chmn, Physics Superconducting Super Collider Study Group, 83-84, Comt Elementary Particles, Nat Acad Sci-Nat Res Coun, 96-; vis prof, Physics Dept, Stanford Linear Accelerator Ctr, 85-86; vis scientist, Fermilab, 90- *Mem:* Nat Acad Sci; fel Am Phys Soc. *Res:* Physics education. *Mailing Add:* Univ Chicago Enrico Fermi Inst 5640 Ellis Ave Chicago IL 60637-1433

**WINSTEN, SEYMOUR,** BIOCHEMISTRY. *Current Pos:* DIR LABS, MOSS REHAB HOSP, 75- *Personal Data:* b Jersey City, NJ, June 14, 26; m 49; c 3. *Educ:* Rutgers Univ, AB, 48, PhD(microbiol, physiol), 56; NY Univ, MSc, 50; Am Bd Clin Chem, dipl. *Honors & Awards:* John Gunther Reinhold Award, 68. *Prof Exp:* Asst, Merck Inst Therapeut Res, 50-56; assoc microbiol, Univ Pa, 56-57; head dept chem, Albert Einstein Med Ctr, 57-86. *Concurrent Pos:* Consult, Atlantic City Hosp, Surgeon Gen US & Walson Gen Hosp; assoc prof biochem, Sch Med, Temple Univ, 70-76; consult, Deborah Heart & Lung Ctr, 65-75. *Mem:* Fel Am Asn Clin Chem; Am Chem Soc. *Res:* Clinical chemistry; immunochemistry; chemical diagnosis of disease; mycology; endocrine chemistry and its relationship to various disease processes; nuclear magnetic resonance. *Mailing Add:* 218 Preston Rd Flourtown PA 19031

**WINSTON, ANTHONY,** POLYMER CHEMISTRY. *Current Pos:* from asst prof to prof, 59-92, chmn dept, 86-90, EMER PROF CHEM, WVA UNIV, 92- *Personal Data:* b Washington, DC, Dec 5, 25; m 52, Lois Eney; c Anthony Jr, Richard, Robert & David. *Educ:* George Washington Univ, BS, 50; Duke Univ, MA, 52, PhD, 55. *Prof Exp:* Res chemist, Armstrong Cork Co, 54-59. *Concurrent Pos:* Res assoc, Water Res Inst, WVa Univ, 75-82. *Mem:* Am Chem Soc. *Res:* Polymer synthesis and reactions; metal complexing polymers; selective chelating ion exchange resins; polymers for medical applications; stereochemistry; polymer-drug combinations. *Mailing Add:* Dept Chem WVa Univ Morgantown WV 26506-6045. *Fax:* 304-293-4904; *E-Mail:* awins@wvnvm.wvnet.edu

**WINSTON, ARTHUR WILLIAM,** PHYSICS, MATHEMATICS. *Current Pos:* PRES, WINCOM CORP, 79- *Personal Data:* b Toronto, Ont, Feb 11, 30; US citizen; m 49; c 4. *Educ:* Univ Toronto, BASc, 51; Mass Inst Technol, PhD(physics), 54. *Prof Exp:* Eng physicist, Nat Res Coun Can, 49-51; res asst, Mass Inst Technol, 51-54; sr engr, Schlumberger Well Surv Corp, 54-57; sr engr, Nat Res Corp, 57-59; chief scientist, Allied Res Assocs, Inc, 59-61; pres, Space Sci, Inc, 61-65; pres, Ikor, Inc, 65-75, chmn, 75-79. *Concurrent Pos:* Lectr, Northeastern Univ, 57-65, adj prof, 65-; mem, Int Dept Com First Trade Mission to Europe on Pollution Controls; judge, Mass State Sci Fair; chmn, Northeast Elec & Eng, 60. *Mem:* Am Inst Aeronaut & Astronaut; Inst Elec & Electronics Engrs; Am Geophys Union; Am Phys Soc; Am Inst Mining, Metall & Petrol Engrs. *Res:* Electromagnetic propagation and measurements; nuclear physics applied to geophysics; thin film technology; microprocessors; pollution control devices and systems. *Mailing Add:* 7 Wainwright Rd Apt 15 Winchester MA 01890-2388

**WINSTON, DONALD,** GEOLOGY. *Current Pos:* From instr to assoc prof, 61-76, PROF GEOL, UNIV MONT, 76- *Personal Data:* b Washington, DC, Apr 4, 31; m; c 2. *Educ:* Williams Col, BA, 53; Univ Tex, MA, 57, PhD(geol), 63. *Mem:* AAAS; Soc Econ Paleont Mineral; Geol Soc Am; Geol Asn Can. *Res:* Stratigraphy and sedimentation, particularly Precambrian rocks; Cambrian paleontology; sedimentary petrology, particularly carbonate petrology of Pennsylvanian rocks and modern carbonate areas. *Mailing Add:* Dept Geol Univ Mont Missoula MT 59801

**WINSTON, FLAURA K,** PEDIATRICS. *Current Pos:* Resident, 91-94, ATTENDING PHYSICIAN, CHILDRENS HOSP PHILADELPHIA. *Personal Data:* b July 24, 61; m, Ira; c Zachary & Andrew. *Educ:* Univ Pa, BS, 83, MS, 84, PhD(sci & eng), 89, MD, 90. *Honors & Awards:* Melville Medal, Am Soc Mech Engr, 95; Achievement Award, Sect Injury & Poison Prev, Am Acad Pediat, 96. *Prof Exp:* Postdoctoral, Johns Hopkins Univ, 94-95. *Concurrent Pos:* Comt mem, Comn Injury Prev & Control, Inst Med-Nat Acad Sci; asst prof pediat, Sch Med, Univ Pa; adj asst prof health policy & mgr, Sch Hyg & Pub Health, Johns Hopkins Univ. *Mem:* Am Acad Pediat; Asn Advan Automotive Med; Am Pharmaceut Asn; Am Pub Health Asn; Am Soc Mech Engrs; Soc Automotive Engrs. *Res:* Injury as the cause of death or disability in children; biomechanical epidemiology. *Mailing Add:* Childrens Hosp Philadelphia 34th St & Civic Center Blvd Philadelphia PA 19104. *Fax:* 215-590-5425

**WINSTON, HARVEY,** PHYSICAL CHEMISTRY. *Current Pos:* RETIRED. *Personal Data:* b Newark, NJ, Aug 11, 26; m 86, Jessamine Ural; c 2. *Educ:* Columbia Univ, AB, 45, MA, 46, PhD(chem), 49. *Prof Exp:* Asst chem, Columbia Univ, 45-49; Jewett fel, Univ Calif, 49-50, instr, 50-51; asst prof, Univ Calif, Los Angeles, 51-52; mem tech staff, Hughes Aircraft Co, 52-58, mgr, Mat Res Lab, Semiconductor Div, 58-60; assoc dir, Quantum Electronics Lab, Quantatron, Inc, 61, vpres, Quantum Tech Labs, Inc, 61-63; mgr, Hughes Res Labs, 63-69, sr scientist, Chem Physics Dept, 69-89. *Mem:* Fel Am Phys Soc; sr mem Inst Elec & Electronics Engrs. *Res:* Solid state spectroscopy; lasers and laser systems; semiconductor physics and devices. *Mailing Add:* 1450 San Remo Dr Pacific Palisades CA 90272-2737

**WINSTON, HUBERT,** PROCESS CONTROL. *Current Pos:* asst prof chem eng, 75-77, assoc prof, 83-86, ASST DEAN & DIR ACAD AFFAIRS, COL ENG, NC STATE UNIV, 86- *Personal Data:* b Wash, DC, May 29, 48. *Educ:* NC State Univ, BS, 70, MS, 73, PhD(chem eng), 75. *Prof Exp:* Sr res engr & res specialist, Exxon Prod Res Co, 77-83. *Mem:* Am Inst Chem Engrs; Am Soc Eng Educ; Instrument Soc Am; Nat Orgn Black Chemists & Chem Engrs. *Mailing Add:* 4412 Seaforth Ct Raleigh NC 27606

**WINSTON, JUDITH ELLEN,** SYSTEMATICS, MARINE ECOLOGY. *Current Pos:* DIR RES & COLLECTIONS, VA MUS NATURAL HIST, 93- *Personal Data:* b Haverhill, Mass, Mar 11, 45; c Eliza C. *Educ:* Brown Univ, AB, 66; Univ NH, MS, 70; Univ Chicago, PhD(geophys sci), 74. *Prof Exp:* Fel & invert biologist marine ecol & bryozoan syst, Smithsonian Marine Sta, Linkport, 74-76; asst prof marine ecol & bryozoan systs, Indian River Community Col, 76-77; assoc res scientist marine ecol & bryozoan systs, Johns Hopkins Univ, 77-80; from asst cur to assoc cur, Am Mus Natural Hist, 80-91, cur & chmn marine ecol & bryozoan systs, Dept Invertebrates, 91-92. *Concurrent Pos:* Adj prof, City Univ New York, 89- *Mem:* Fel AAAS; Am Asn Mus; Am Soc Zoologists; Soc Syst Zool; Soc Conserv Biol. *Res:* Bryozoan systematics, ecology and evolution of colonial organisms oryozoans, taxonomic procedure and nomenclature, and history of science; field work; scuba duty; traveling duty; laboratory; underwater macro-photography and video recording. *Mailing Add:* Va Mus Natural Hist 1001 Douglas Ave Martinsville VA 24112. *Fax:* 540-632-6487

**WINSTON, PAUL WOLF,** BIOLOGY. *Current Pos:* RETIRED. *Personal Data:* b Chicago, Ill, Aug 9, 20; m 48; c 1. *Educ:* Univ Mass, BS, 48; Northwestern Univ, MS, 50, PhD, 52. *Prof Exp:* Instr, Brown Univ, 51-52; from instr to prof biol, Univ Colo, Boulder, 52-90. *Mem:* AAAS; Soc Environ Geochem & Health. *Res:* Humidity relations and water balance of terrestrial arthropods, especially cuticular control of water exchange with air; physiology of molybdenum and toxicity of chronic exposure to trace metals in mammals. *Mailing Add:* 650 S 41st St Boulder CO 80303

**WINSTON, PHILIP ELDRIDGE, JR,** PAPER COATINGS TECHNOLOGY, PAINT & COATINGS TECHNOLOGY. *Current Pos:* SR RES CHEMIST, KELCO DIV, MERCK & CO INC, 77- *Personal Data:* b Austin, Tex, Feb 28, 35; m 68, Sylvia Thomas; c Scott & Jennifer. *Educ:* Univ Tex, Austin, BS, 58. *Prof Exp:* Res chemist, Penn Indust Chem Corp, 63-68, Shell Chem Co, 68-71; sr chemist, PPG Indust Inc, 71-77. *Mem:* Tech Asn Pulp & Paper Indust; Am Asn Textile & Color Chemists; Fedn Soc Coating Technol. *Res:* Development of edible films and barrier coatings for food and industrial application; formulation of waterborne clear industrial coatings; development of products for waterborne thermoplastic and thermosetting systems; formulation of water-based high solids paper coatings; water-soluble polymers; granted 5 US patents. *Mailing Add:* 3570 Trenton Ave San Diego CA 92117. *Fax:* 619-467-6571; *E-Mail:* pwinston@kelco.com

**WINSTON, ROLAND,** EXPERIMENTAL PHYSICS, PARTICLE PHYSICS. *Current Pos:* from asst prof to assoc prof, 64-75, chair, Dept Physics, 89-95, PROF PHYSICS, UNIV CHICAGO, 75- *Personal Data:* b Moscow, USSR, Feb 12, 36; US citizen; m 57, Patricia Le Gette; c Joseph, John & Gregory. *Educ:* Shimer Col, BA, 53; Univ Chicago, BS, 56, MS, 57, PhD(physics), 63. *Honors & Awards:* Charles Greeley Abbot Award, Am Solar Energy Soc, 87-; Krause Medal, Franklin Inst, 96. *Prof Exp:* Asst prof physics, Univ Pa, 63-64. *Concurrent Pos:* Sloan Found fel, 67-69; Guggenheim fel, 77-78. *Mem:* Fel Am Phys Soc; Am Solar Energy Soc; AAAS; Int Solar Energy Soc; Am Optical Soc. *Res:* Elementary particle physics; leptonic decays of hyperons; muon physics, especially hyperfine effects in muon capture by complex nuclei; solar energy concentrators; infra-red detectors; optics of visual receptors. *Mailing Add:* Dept Physics Univ Chicago 5640 S Ellis EF1-381 Chicago IL 60637. *Fax:* 773-702-6317

**WINSTON, VERN,** VIROLOGY, CELL CULTURE. *Current Pos:* ASST PROF MICROBIOL, IDAHO STATE UNIV, 81- *Personal Data:* b Gordon, Nebr, Apr 30, 48; m 70; c 2. *Educ:* Univ Nebr-Lincoln, BS, 70, PhD(microbiol), 76. *Prof Exp:* Res assoc, Kans State Univ, 76-80. *Mem:* Am Soc Microbiol; Sigma Xi. *Res:* Viral diseases of fish; immunodiagnostic methods of identifying infectious pancreatic necrosis virus; immunodiagnostic methods of identifying infectious hematopoietic necrosis virus. *Mailing Add:* Dept Microbiol & Biochem Idaho State Univ 921 S 58th Ave Pocatello ID 83209-0001

**WINSTROM, LEON OSCAR,** PHYSICAL CHEMISTRY, TEXTILE CHEMISTRY. *Current Pos:* CONSULT, 80- *Personal Data:* b Holland, Mich, Apr 8, 12; m 38, Mary Kaltenbaugh; c Carol L (Moskowitz), William L & Leon O Jr. *Educ:* Hope Col, AB, 34; Carnegie Inst Technol, MS, 37, DSc(phys chem), 38. *Honors & Awards:* Schoellkopf Medal, 66. *Prof Exp:* Instr, Carnegie Inst Technol, 37-38; res chemist, Nat Aniline Chem Div, Allied Chem Corp, 38-53, asst supvr, 53-57, sr scientist, 57-58, group leader, 58-64, res supvr, 64-68, sr res assoc, Spec Chem Div, 68-71; mgr res & develop, Flock Div, Malden Mills, Lawrence, 71-80. *Mem:* Am Chem Soc. *Res:* Vapor and liquid phase hydrogenation and oxidation; ammination by reduction; recovery of organic oxidation products. *Mailing Add:* 57 Maple St East Aurora NY 14052-1712

**WINTER, ALEXANDER J,** IMMUNOBIOLOGY, BACTERIOLOGY. *Current Pos:* assoc prof, 63-66, PROF VET MICROBIOL, NY STATE VET COL, CORNELL UNIV, 66- *Personal Data:* b Vienna, Austria, June 21, 31; nat US; m 59; c 3. *Educ:* Univ Ill, DVM, 55; Univ Wis, PhD(med & vet path), 59. *Prof Exp:* From asst to assoc prof vet sci, Pa State Univ, 59-63. *Concurrent Pos:* Mem, Bacteriol & Mycol Sect, NIH, 71-75. *Mem:* Infectious Dis Soc Am; Am Soc Microbiol; Am Asn Immunologists; Am Col Vet Microbiologists. *Res:* Brucellosis. *Mailing Add:* NY State Col Vet Med Cornell Univ Ithaca NY 14853-0001. *Fax:* 607-253-3419

**WINTER, CHARLES GORDON,** BIOCHEMISTRY, MEMBRANES. *Current Pos:* asst prof, 66-73, actg chmn, 89-90, ASSOC PROF BIOCHEM, SCH MED, UNIV ARK, LITTLE ROCK, 73-, ASSOC DEAN RES, COL MED, 94- *Personal Data:* b Hanover, Pa, Dec 28, 36; m 58, Betty A Fuhrman; c David, Douglas & John. *Educ:* Juniata Col, BS, 58; Univ Mich, MS, 63, PhD(biochem), 64. *Prof Exp:* Technician, Metab Res Unit, Univ Mich, Ann Arbor, 58-60; Childs Mem Fund Med Res fel phys chem, Sch Med, Johns Hopkins Univ, 64-66. *Concurrent Pos:* Hon res assoc, Harvard Univ, 78-79. *Mem:* Am Soc Biochem & Molecular Biol; AAAS; Am Chem Soc; Biophys Soc. *Res:* Structure and function of membrane transport ATPases. *Mailing Add:* Dept Biochem & Molecular Biol Univ Ark Col Med Little Rock AR 72205. *E-Mail:* cgwinter@life.uams.edu

**WINTER, CHARLES HARTGER,** CHEMISTRY. *Current Pos:* Asst prof, 88-94, career develop chair, 95-96, ASSOC PROF INORG CHEM, WAYNE STATE UNIV, 94- *Personal Data:* b Grand Rapids, Mich, Nov 3, 59; m 85, Julia English Doan; c Peter & Anne. *Educ:* Hope Col, BS, 82; Univ Minn, PhD(chem), 86. *Concurrent Pos:* Consult, Ford Motor Co, 96- *Mem:* Am Chem Soc; Mat Res Soc; AAAS. *Res:* Organometallic and materials chemistry; development of new source compounds for film depositions; study of chemical vapor deposition processes; preparation and characterization of permetalated aromatic compounds. *Mailing Add:* Dept Chem Wayne State Univ Detroit MI 48202. *Fax:* 313-577-1377; *E-Mail:* cwinter@sun.science.wayne.edu

**WINTER, CHESTER CALDWELL,** UROLOGY. *Current Pos:* Levy prof, 88-88, PROF UROL, COL MED, OHIO STATE UNIV, 60- *Personal Data:* b Cazenovia, NY, June 2, 22; m 83, Mary; c Paul, Ann & Jane. *Educ:* Univ Iowa, BA, 43, MD, 46; Am Bd Urol, dipl. *Prof Exp:* Asst prof surg, Sch Med, Univ Calif, Los Angeles, 57-60. *Concurrent Pos:* Mem staff, Univ Hosp, 60- & Riverside Methodist Hosp, 82- *Mem:* Am Urol Asn; Am Col Surg; Soc Univ Urol; Soc Univ Surg; Am Asn Genito-Urinary Surg; Urol Invest Forum. *Res:* Urological surgery; renal hypertension; diagnostic isotopes in urology; priapism; incontinence; vesico-ureteral reflux. *Mailing Add:* 6425 Evening St Worthington OH 43085-3054

**WINTER, DAVID ARTHUR,** BIOMEDICAL ENGINEERING, ELECTRICAL ENGINEERING. *Current Pos:* from assoc prof to prof, 74-94, DISTINGUISHED EMER PROF KINESIOL, UNIV WATERLOO, 94- *Personal Data:* b Windsor, Ont, June 16, 30; m 58, Judith M Wilson; c Merriam, Andrew & Bruce. *Educ:* Queen's Univ, Ont, BSc, 53, MSc, 61; Dalhousie Univ, PhD(physiol), 67. *Honors & Awards:* Career Investigators Award, Can Soc Biomech, 90. *Prof Exp:* From lectr to asst prof elec eng, Royal Mil Col, Ont, 58-63; from asst prof to assoc prof, Tech Univ, Nova Scotia, 63-69; assoc prof surg, Univ Man, 69-74, adj prof elec eng, 70-74. *Concurrent Pos:* Can Coun fel med, eng & sci, Dalhousie Univ, 66-68. *Mem:* Fel Inst Elec & Electronics Engrs; Can Med & Biol Eng Soc (pres, 70-74); Int Soc Electrophys Kinesiol; Int Soc Biomech; Can Soc Biomech. *Res:* Signal processing of biological signals; medical image processing; electromyography; biomechanics; locomotion studies; assessment pathological gait; balance control in normals, elderly and balance-impaired. *Mailing Add:* Dept Kinesiol Univ Waterloo Waterloo ON N2L 3G1 Can. *Fax:* 519-746-6776

**WINTER, DAVID F(ERDINAND),** SHOCK & INDUCED VOLTAGES & CURRENT IN DAIRY COWS, MITIGATION OF STRAY VOLTAGE. *Current Pos:* PVT CONSULT, 86- *Personal Data:* b St Louis, Mo, Nov 9, 20; m 44, Betty J Turner; c Suzanne & Sharie (Chappeau). *Educ:* Washington Univ, BS, 42; Mass Inst Technol, MS, 48. *Prof Exp:* Mem staff, Radiation Lab, Mass Inst Technol, 42-45; res assoc & asst prof elec eng, Washington Univ, 48-51, assoc prof, 51-54, affil prof, 54-64; sr engr, Spec Contract, US Naval Ord Plant, Ind, 50-52, proj head, 52-53; consult, Moloney Elec Co, 51-54, sect engr electronics, 54-57, vpres, chief engr & dir res, 55-66, vpres res & develop, 66-73, vpres eng, central Moloney Div, Colt Indust, 73-74; vpres res & develop, ITT Blackburn, 74-86. *Mem:* Fel Inst Elec & Electronics Engrs; Am Soc Agr Eng; Nat Soc Prof Engrs; Sigma Xi. *Res:* High voltage magnetic components for power industry; specialized high power radar and communications; electrical connectors for power industry; electronic grounding for animal confinement with stray voltage; power distribution line grounding; relation of primary neutral voltage and current in dairy cattle; response of dairy cattle to shock current. *Mailing Add:* 629 Meadowridge Lane St Louis MO 63122-3021. *Fax:* 314-821-1865

**WINTER, DAVID JOHN,** MATHEMATICS. *Current Pos:* from asst prof to assoc prof, 68-74, PROF MATH, UNIV MICH, ANN ARBOR, 74- *Personal Data:* b Painesville, Ohio, May 2, 39; m 65; c 1. *Educ:* Antioch Col, BA, 61; Yale Univ, MS, 63, PhD(math), 65. *Prof Exp:* Instr math, Yale Univ, 65-67; NSF fel, Univ Bonn, 67-68. *Concurrent Pos:* Vis assoc prof, Calif Inst Technol, 72-73. *Mem:* Am Math Soc. *Res:* Algebra. *Mailing Add:* Dept Math Univ Mich Ann Arbor MI 48109-0001

**WINTER, DAVID LEON,** RESEARCH ADMINISTRATION. *Current Pos:* PRES, GEN PHARM. *Personal Data:* b New York, NY, Nov 10, 33; m 73; c 5. *Educ:* Columbia Col, AB, 55; Wash Univ, MD, 59. *Honors & Awards:* Hans Berger Prize, Am Electroencephalog Soc, 64. *Prof Exp:* Surg intern, Sch Med, Wash Univ, 59-60; Nat Inst Neurol Dis & Blindness fel, Baylor Univ, 60-62; med res officer, Nat Inst Neurol Dis & Blindness, 62-64; neurophysiologist, Walter Reed Army Inst Res, 64-66, chief dept neurophysiol, 66-71; dep dir life sci, Ames Res Ctr, Moffett Field, Calif, 71-74, dir life sci, NASA HQ, DC, 74-79; dir, 79-84, vpres med res, Sandoz Inc, 84-85; vpres clin res & develop, Sandoz Pharmaceut Corp, 85-89, vpres sci & external affairs, 89- *Mem:* AAAS; Am Physiol Soc; Soc Neurosci; Aerospace Med Asn; Am Soc Clin Pharmacol & Therapeut. *Res:* Somatosensory systems; visceral reflexes; autonomic nervous system; psychophysiology; aerospace physiology; drug development. *Mailing Add:* Sangstat Med Corp 1505 Adams Dr Menlo Park CA 94043

**WINTER, DONALD CHARLES,** OPTICS. *Current Pos:* Mem res staff optics, 72-74, sect ha head optics technol, 74-77, MGR, OPTICS DEPT, TRW DEFENSE & SPACE SYSTS GROUP, 77- *Personal Data:* b Brooklyn, NY, June 15, 48; m 69; c 2. *Educ:* Univ Rochester, BS, 69; Univ Mich, MS, 70, PhD(physics), 72. *Mem:* Optical Soc Am. *Res:* High energy laser optics; optical components; laser diagnostics; interferometry and optical testing; optical system design and optimization. *Mailing Add:* 608 14th St Manhattan Beach CA 90266

**WINTER, DONALD F,** APPLIED MATHEMATICS. *Current Pos:* PROF MATH, ENG & COMPUT SCI, UNIV REDLANDS, 86- *Personal Data:* b Buffalo, NY, Oct 6, 31; div; c 3. *Educ:* Amherst Col, BA, 54; Harvard Univ, MA, 59, PhD(appl physics), 62. *Prof Exp:* Mathematician, Air Force Cambridge Res Labs, 54-56; engr, Missile Systs Lab, Sylvania Elec Prod, Inc, 56-58, eng specialist, Appl Res Lab, 58-62, sr eng specialist, 62-63; mem staff, Geo-astrophys Lab, Boeing Sci Res Labs, 63-70; assoc prof, Ctr Quant Sci & Dept Oceanog, Univ Wash, 70-74, prof oceanog & appl math, 74-86. *Concurrent Pos:* Vis lectr, Univ Manchester, 66-67. *Mem:* Am Math Soc; AAAS; Am Geophys Union; Soc Indust & Appl Math. *Res:* Applied and numerical analysis; methods of mathematical physics with applications to general engineering; hydrodynamical and biological processes in oceanography; growth and transport processes in biological systems. *Mailing Add:* Eng-Univ Redlands 1200 E Colton Ave PO Box 3080 Redlands CA 92373-0999. *Fax:* 909-793-2029

**WINTER, HARRY CLARK,** BIOCHEMISTRY. *Current Pos:* lectr biol chem, 75-87, ASST RES SCIENTIST, UNIV MICH, ANN ARBOR, 87- *Personal Data:* b New Britain, Conn, Feb 26, 41; m 77, Dorothy Cox. *Educ:* Pa State Univ, BS, 62; Univ Wis, MS, 64, PhD(biochem), 67. *Prof Exp:* NSF fel cell physiol, Univ Calif, Berkeley, 67-68; asst prof biochem, Pa State Univ, 68-75. *Mem:* Am Chem Soc; Am Soc Plant Physiologists; Am Soc Biol Chemists. *Res:* Biological nitrogen fixation; glycobiology; biosynthetic pathways of plants and bacteria; enzyme mechanisms. *Mailing Add:* Univ Mich Med Sch 1301 Catherine Rd M5323 0606 Ann Arbor MI 48109-0606. *Fax:* 313-763-4581

**WINTER, HENRY FRANK, JR,** PHYSIOLOGY. *Current Pos:* Asst prof, 65-72, assoc prof physiol, 73-80, PROF PHYSIOL & BIOMED SCI, SCH DENT MED, WASHINGTON UNIV, 80- *Personal Data:* b Wooster, Ohio, Dec 25, 36. *Educ:* Case Inst Technol, BSc, 58; Baylor Univ, MSc, 62, PhD(physiol, biochem, anat), 65. *Mem:* AAAS; Am Physiol Soc; Int Asn Dent Res. *Res:* Oral biology, neurophysiology; instrumentation for medical research; growth and development. *Mailing Add:* 556 Ridge Ave Webster Groves MO 63119-4272

**WINTER, HERBERT,** CONTROL & ELECTRICAL ENGINEERING. *Current Pos:* RETIRED. *Personal Data:* b Vienna, Austria, July 31, 24; US citizen; m 46, Elisabeth R Bauer; c Judith A (Siewert) & David E. *Educ:* City Col New York, BEE, 49; Univ Mich, MSE, 50. *Prof Exp:* Instr elec eng, City Col New York, 49; engr, Bell Aerospace Textron, 50-54, syst engr, 54-57, group chief systs oper & preliminary design, 57-59, dynamic analytical hypersonic glider, 59-60, supvr preliminary design electromech systs, 60-65, prin scientist, 66-87. *Mem:* Inst Elec & Electronics Engrs; Am Inst Navig. *Res:* Application of optimal control and filtering to inertial navigation; optimization of oceanic air traffic; computer simulation of atmospheric propagation of laser beams; design of gravity gradiometer systems. *Mailing Add:* 75 Chateau Terr Snyder NY 14226-3929

**WINTER, HORST HENNING,** POLYMER ENGINEERING, RHEOLOGY. *Current Pos:* assoc prof, 79-84, PROF CHEM ENG, UNIV MASS, AMHERST, 84- *Personal Data:* b Stuttgart, Ger, Sept 9, 41; m 69, Karin Eckert; c Dirk, Lisa, Caroline & Peter. *Educ:* Univ Stuttgart, Dr-Ing, 73. *Prof Exp:* Privatdozent rheology, Univ Stuttgart, 76-79. *Concurrent Pos:* DFG Fel, Univ Wis-Madison, 73-74; vis prof, Univ Minn, 78 & Max Planck Inst, Polymerforschung, Mainz, Ger, 87-88 & 93; ed, Rheologica Acta, 89- *Mem:* Soc Rheology; Soc Plastics Eng; Polymer Processing Soc; Deutsche Rheologische Gesellschaft; Am Inst Chem Engrs. *Res:* Rheology and processing behavior of complex polymeric materials such as gels, liquid crystalline polymers, block-copolymers, polymer blends and filled polymers; rheo-optical methods; rheological constitutive equations. *Mailing Add:* Dept Chem Univ Mass Univ Mass 159 Goessmann Lab Amherst MA 01003-3110. *E-Mail:* winter@ucsvax.ucs.umass.edu

**WINTER, J BURGESS,** METALLURGY. *Honors & Awards:* Daniel C Jackling Award, Soc Mining, Metall & Explor, 95. *Mailing Add:* 7400 N Oracle Rd Suite 200 Tucson AZ 85704

**WINTER, JEANETTE E,** MICROBIOLOGY. *Current Pos:* Instr, 64-68, asst prof, 68-71, ASSOC PROF MICROBIOL, MED SCH, NY UNIV, 71- *Personal Data:* b New York, NY, Dec 19, 17. *Educ:* Brooklyn Col, BA, 37; NY Univ, PhD(microbiol), 60. *Mem:* AAAS; Am Soc Microbiol. *Res:* Mechanism of competence for DNA uptake in bacterial transformation; role of nucleases in DNA integration during bacterial transformation of streptococci. *Mailing Add:* Dept Microbiol NY Univ Sch Med 550 First Ave New York NY 10016-6481

**WINTER, JEREMY STEPHEN DRUMMOND,** PEDIATRICS, ENDOCRINE PHYSIOLOGY. *Current Pos:* from asst prof to assoc prof, 67-78, PROF PEDIAT, UNIV MAN, 78-; PROF PEDIAT, UNIV ALTA, CAN, 90- *Personal Data:* b Duncan, BC, Dec 11, 37; m 61; c 2. *Educ:* Univ BC, MD, 61; Am Bd Pediat, dipl, 67; FRCP(C), 68. *Prof Exp:* Intern & resident, Montreal Gen, Montreal Children's & Royal Victoria Hosp, 61-64; instr pediat, Univ Pa, 64-67; endocrinologist, Health Sci Ctr, Winnipeg, 71-90. *Concurrent Pos:* NIH fel endocrinol, Children's Hosp Philadelphia, 64-67; Med Res Coun grant, Univ Man, 67-; consult, St Boniface Hosp, 67-; scientist, Queen Elizabeth II Res Found, 72. *Mem:* Endocrine Soc; Soc Pediat Res; Can Soc Clin Invest; Am Fedn Clin Res; Can Pediat Soc. *Res:* Physiology of the pituitary-gonadal axis during fetal life, childhood and puberty. *Mailing Add:* Univ Alberta Dept Peds 263 Univ Alberta Hosp Edmonton AB T6G 2R7 Can

**WINTER, JERROLD CLYNE, SR,** PHARMACOLOGY. *Current Pos:* Asst prof, 67-71, assoc prof, 71-76, PROF PHARMACOL, STATE UNIV NY, BUFFALO, 76- *Personal Data:* b Erie, Pa, March 25, 37; m 60; c 4. *Educ:* Univ Rochester, BS, 59; State Univ NY, PhD(pharmacol), 66. *Res:* Behavioral pharmacology. *Mailing Add:* 102 Farber Hall State Univ NY Buffalo NY 14214-3000. *Fax:* 716-829-2801

**WINTER, JOHN HENRY,** GEOARCHAEOLOGY, PHYSICAL ANTHROPOLOGY. *Current Pos:* CHMN, DEPT CHEM, PHYSICS & EARTH SCI, ROCKVILLE CTR, MOLLOY COL, NY. *Personal Data:* b New York, NY, Sept 1, 47; m 90, Takako Inara; c Allen & Valerie. *Educ:* Northern Ariz Univ, BA, 69, MA, 73; Columbia Univ, EdD, CTAS, 89. *Concurrent Pos:* Field sta archaeologist, Bahamian Field Sta, San Salvador Island, Bahamas, 80; dir, Int Asn Caribbean Archaeologists, 87-89; adj assoc prof, Teachers Col, Columbia Univ, NY, 91- *Mem:* Nat Sci Teachers Asn; Nat Asn Geol Teachers; Soc Am Archaeol. *Res:* Palaeopathology of the prehistoric peoples of the Bahamas; geoarchaeology of the Bahamas; environmental conditions of the prehistoric period within the Bahamas. *Mailing Add:* Dept Chem Physics & Earth Sci Molloy Col 1000 Hempstead Ave Rockville Centre NY 11570. *E-Mail:* winjo01@molloy.edu

**WINTER, JOSEPH,** PHYSICAL METALLURGY. *Current Pos:* ASSOC DIR METALL DEPT, METALS RES LABS, OLIN CORP, 60- *Personal Data:* b New York, NY, July 26, 29; c 2. *Educ:* NY Univ, BME, 53, MS, 55, EngScD, 58. *Honors & Awards:* John M Olin Award. *Prof Exp:* Assoc res scientist metall, Res Div, NY Univ, 52-60. *Concurrent Pos:* Adj instr, Cooper Union, 56-61; adj assoc prof, New Haven Col, 62-70. *Mem:* Am Soc Metals; Am Inst Mining, Metall & Petrol Engrs; Brit Inst Metals. *Res:* Solid state bonding; nonferrous physical metallurgy. *Mailing Add:* 88 Vista Terr New Haven CT 06515-2402

**WINTER, KARL A,** RUMINANT NUTRITION. *Current Pos:* RETIRED. *Personal Data:* b Yarmouth, NS, Dec 18, 28; m 57; c 3. *Educ:* McGill Univ, BSc, 53, MSc, 56; Ohio State Univ, PhD(ruminant nutrit), 62. *Prof Exp:* Grain salesman, Toronto Elevators Ltd, 55-57; res officer ruminant nutrit, Agr Can, 57-65; field res mgr, Tuco Prod Co, Upjohn Co, 65-68; res scientist cattle nutrit, Res Sta, Res Br, Agr Can, 68-88, spec adv-livestock, 88-89, asst dir, 90-91. *Concurrent Pos:* Adj prof, Atl Vet Col, Univ Prince Edward Island, Charlottetown. *Mem:* Can Soc Animal Sci (pres, 81-82); Agr Inst Can (vpres, 76-77 & 80-81); Am Soc Animal Sci. *Res:* Nutrition of ruminant animals, especially the young calf; utilization of non-protein nitrogen and agricultural wastes in cattle feeding and trace elements in ruminant nutrition. *Mailing Add:* Dunedin RR3 Cornwall PE C0A 1H0 Can

**WINTER, MILDRED M,** EDUCATIONAL ADMINISTRATION. *Current Pos:* EXEC DIR, PARENTS AS TEACHERS NAT CTR INC, ST LOUIS. *Educ:* Harris Teachers Col, BA; Univ Mo, MEd. *Honors & Awards:* Spec Award, Nat Soc Behav Pediat, 92; Charles A Dana Pioneering Achievements Health & Educ Inst Med Award, Nat Acad Sci, 95. *Concurrent Pos:* Teacher & consult, Mo, 62-68; developer & dir, Ferguson-Florissant Parent Child Early Educ Prog, Mo, 69-72; dir, Early Childhood Educ Mo Dept Elem & Sec Educ, 72-84; sr lectr, Dept Elem & Early Childhood Educ, Univ Mo. *Res:* Published articles in professional journals. *Mailing Add:* Parents as Teachers Nat Ctr Inc 10176 Corp Sq Dr Suite 230 St Louis MO 63132

**WINTER, NICHOLAS WILHELM,** THEORETICAL CHEMISTRY, THEORETICAL PHYSICS. *Current Pos:* atomic & molecular physicist, 76-, CONSENSED MATTER PHYSICIST, LAWRENCE LIVERMORE LAB. *Personal Data:* b Birmingham, Ala, Mar 7, 43; m 65; c 2. *Educ:* Northern Ill Univ, BS, 65; Calif Inst Technol, PhD(chem & physics), 70. *Prof Exp:* Atmospheric physicist, Jet Propulsion Lab, 71-73 & Aerospace Corp, 73-76. *Concurrent Pos:* Fel, Battelle Mem Inst, 69-71; consult, Lawrence Livermore Lab, 71-75; res assoc, Calif Inst Technol, 72-75. *Mem:* Am Phys Soc. *Res:* Molecular structure; potential energy surfaces; excited states; reaction dynamics as applied to atmospheric and laser physics. *Mailing Add:* Lawrence Livermore Lab PO Box 808 L-50 Livermore CA 94557

**WINTER, OLAF HERMANN,** CHEMICAL ENGINEERING, CHEMISTRY. *Current Pos:* CONSULT, 93- *Personal Data:* b Erfurt, Ger, Dec 1, 33. *Educ:* Brunswick Tech Univ, BS, 57; Hannover Tech Univ, MS, 60, PhD(chem eng), 63; Univ Akron, MBA, 69. *Prof Exp:* Sr res engr, Res Div, Goodyear Tire & Rubber Co, 63-71; asst to vpres res, Hydrocarbon Res Inc, Trenton Lab, Dynalectron Corp, 72-73; prin engr, 73-80, sr prin engr, process technol planning, Lummus Co, Combustion Eng, Inc, 80-84; technol mgr, H-R Int, Inc, 84-85; consult, 85-86; mgr, Chem Process Res Waste Mgt, Waste Mgt, Inc, 86-87; supvry engr, Brown & Root Braun, Halliburton Co, 88-93. *Concurrent Pos:* Teacher, Berlitz Sch Lang, 65-71. *Mem:* Am Chem Soc; Am Inst Chem Engrs; Ger Chem Soc. *Res:* Novel processing methods and equipment; pollution control; gasification and liquefaction of coal; hazardous waste treatment systems; economic evaluations; process planning; facilities planning for petroleum, petrochemical and chemical complexes; feasibility and marketing studies; identification of future technological and economic trends; technology assessments; evaluation of competing processes and licensors. *Mailing Add:* 343 Pioneer Dr Apt 1701 E Glendale CA 91203-1786

**WINTER, PETER,** SCIENCE POLICY, RESOURCE MANAGEMENT. *Current Pos:* ED, CAN BIOTECH NEWS, 86- *Personal Data:* b Sheffield, Eng, Nov 4, 46; m 82, Carole Cheetham; c Ainsley. *Educ:* Univ London, BSc, 74, MSC, 76. *Prof Exp:* Ed, Morgan Grampian, 72-76; lectr psychol & jour, Bromley Col Technol, 76-78; consult, 79-82; exec dir, Biomass Energy Inst, 82-86. *Concurrent Pos:* Ed, Int Environ & Safety, 78-80; consult commun, 78-82. *Mem:* Can Sci Writers Asn; Indust Biotechnol Asn Can. *Res:* Biotechnolog; science policy and financing intellectual property. *Mailing Add:* Can Biotech News 20 Stonepark Lane Nepean ON K2H 9P4 Can

**WINTER, PETER MICHAEL,** ANESTHESIOLOGY. *Current Pos:* PROF & CHMN DEPT ANESTHESIOL & CRITICAL CARE MED SCH MED, UNIV PITTSBURGH, 79-, ANESTHESIOLOGIST-IN-CHIEF, UNIV HEALTH CTR HOSP, PITTSBURGH, 79- *Personal Data:* b Sverdlovsk, Russia, Aug 5, 34; US citizen; m 64; c 2. *Educ:* Cornell Univ, AB, 58; Univ Rochester, MD, 62; Am Bd Anesthesiol, dipl, 72. *Prof Exp:* USPHS rcs fcl, Harvard Univ, 65-66; res assoc physiol, State Univ NY Buffalo, 66-67, asst res prof anesthesiol, 67-69; assoc prof anesthesiol, Sch Med, Univ Wash, 69-74, prof, 74-79; chief anesthesiol serv, Vet Admin Hosp, Seattle, 78-79. *Concurrent Pos:* Consult, Virginia Mason Res Ctr, Seattle, 69-; Nat Heart & Lung Inst grant, Sch Med, Univ Wash, 71-74, res career develop award, 72-77. *Mem:* Am Col Chest Physicians; AMA; Am Soc Anesthesiol; Asn Univ Anesthetists; NY Acad Sci. *Res:* Respiration therapy; critical care medicine; hyperbaric physiology; oxygen toxicity. *Mailing Add:* Dept Anesthesiol 1385 Scaife Hall Univ Pittsburgh Sch Med Pittsburgh PA 15261-2013

**WINTER, ROBERT JOHN,** PEDIATRIC ENDOCRINOLOGY. *Current Pos:* asst prof, 75-81, ASSOC PROF PEDIAT ENDOCRINOL, CHILDREN'S MEM HOSP & NORTHWESTERN UNIV, CHICAGO, 81-, DIR MED EDUC, 85- *Personal Data:* b Toledo, Ohio, Oct 13, 45; m 72; c 1. *Educ:* Amherst Col, BA, 67; Northwestern Univ, MD, 71. *Prof Exp:* Intern pediat, Hartford Hosp, Conn, 71-72; resident pediat, Boston City Hosp, 72-73; fel pediat endocrinol, Johns Hopkins Univ, 73-75. *Mem:* Endocrine Soc; Am Diabetes Asn; Acad Pediat; Lawson Wilkins Pediat Endocrine Soc; Soc Pediat Res; Asn Am Med Cols. *Res:* Disorders of growth and of glucose homeostasis; primarily clinical research; research in medical education. *Mailing Add:* Northwestern Univ Med Sch 303 E Chicago Ave Chicago IL 60611-3008

**WINTER, ROLAND ARTHUR EDWIN,** ORGANIC CHEMISTRY, POLYMER CHEMISTRY. *Current Pos:* Res chemist, J R Geigy AG, Basel, Switz, 65-66, res assoc, Geigy Chem Corp, NY, 66-69, group leader, 69-70, Ciba-Geigy Corp, 70-72, sr staff scientist, 72-78, res mgr, 79-86, res fel, 86-88, SR RES FEL, CIBA-GEIGY CORP, 88- *Personal Data:* b Reval, Estonia, Aug 29, 35; US citizen; m 59; c 3. *Educ:* Stuttgart Tech Univ, Cand chem, 57; Harvard Univ, AM, 61, PhD(org chem), 65. *Mem:* Am Chem Soc; Sigma Xi. *Res:* Synthetic organic chemistry; heterocyclic chemistry; high temperature polymers, resins, light stabilizing additives and antioxidants for polymers. *Mailing Add:* 23 Banksville Rd Armonk NY 10504

**WINTER, ROLF GERHARD,** nuclear physics, elementary particle physics; deceased, see previous edition for last biography

**WINTER, RUDOLPH ERNST KARL,** ORGANIC CHEMISTRY. *Current Pos:* ASSOC PROF ORG CHEM, UNIV MO, ST LOUIS, 69- *Personal Data:* b Vienna, Austria, Nov 27, 35; US citizen; m 64; c 3. *Educ:* Columbia Univ, AB, 57; Johns Hopkins Univ, MA, 59, PhD(org chem), 64. *Prof Exp:* NIH fel chem, Karlsruhe Tech Univ, 62-63 & Harvard Univ, 63-64; asst prof org chem, Polytech Inst Brooklyn, 64-69. *Concurrent Pos:* Vis res prof, Swiss Fed Univ, Zurich, 75-76. *Mem:* Am Chem Soc; Chem Soc. *Res:* Chemistry of naturally occurring substances, especially terpenes and sesquiterpenes; isolation, structure, reactions and synthesis of natural substances; chemical ecology; photochemical and thermal reactions. *Mailing Add:* Dept Chem Univ Mo St Louis 8001 Natural Bridge Rd St Louis MO 63121-4499

**WINTER, STEPHEN SAMUEL,** SCIENCE EDUCATION. *Current Pos:* chmn dept, 71-78 & 84-90, PROF EDUC, TUFTS UNIV, 71- *Personal Data:* b Vienna, Austria, Feb 27, 26; US citizen; m 51; c 3. *Educ:* Albright Col, BS, 48; Columbia Univ, PhD(phys chem), 53. *Prof Exp:* Res chemist, Atlas Powder Co, 52-53; asst prof chem, Northeastern Univ, 53-58; asst prof chem & educ, Univ Minn, 58-61; from assoc prof to prof educ, State Univ NY Buffalo, 61-71. dir teacher educ, 68-71. *Concurrent Pos:* NSF fac fel, Harvard Univ, 57-58, consult, Proj Physics, 64-70; consult & hon assoc prof, Univ Paraguay, 65; consult, Div Sci Teaching, UNESCO, 69-71. *Mem:* Nat Sci Teachers Asn; Nat Asn Res Sci Teaching; Asn Educ Teachers Sci (pres, 66-67). *Res:* Measurements of outcomes of science instruction; science curriculum in elementary and secondary schools. *Mailing Add:* 10 Fairmont St Belmont MA 02178-2919

**WINTER, STEVEN RAY,** AGRONOMY, PLANT PHYSIOLOGY. *Current Pos:* Asst prof, 71-78, ASSOC PROF CROP PROD, TEX A&M UNIV, 78- *Personal Data:* b Belvidere, Ill, Jan 16, 44; m 70. *Educ:* Univ Ill, BS, 66, MS, 68; Purdue Univ, PhD(agron), 71. *Mem:* Am Soc Agron; Am Soc Sugar Beet Technol. *Res:* Production and physiology of sugar beets on the Texas high plains. *Mailing Add:* 6006 Garden Lane Amarillo TX 79106

**WINTER, WILLIAM KENNETH,** PHYSICS. *Current Pos:* RETIRED. *Personal Data:* b Manitowoc, Wis, Apr 26, 26; m 63, Norma J Bittle; c Billie K & Nicki L. *Educ:* Univ Wis, BA, 50; Kans State Col, MS, 52, PhD(physics), 56. *Prof Exp:* Res physicist, Phillips Petrol Co, 56-85. *Mem:* AAAS; Soc Petrol Eng. *Res:* Develop mathematical models for petroleum reservoir simulation. *Mailing Add:* 2312 SE Hill Dr Bartlesville OK 74006

**WINTER, WILLIAM PHILLIPS,** PROTEIN CHEMISTRY. *Current Pos:* SR BIOCHEMIST, CTR SICKLE CELL DIS, ASSOC PROF, DEPT MED & GRAD DEPT GENETICS, MED SCH, HOWARD UNIV, 77- *Personal Data:* b Uniontown, Pa, Aug 17, 38; m 60; c 2. *Educ:* Pa State Univ, University Park, BS, 60, MS, 62, PhD(biochem), 65. *Prof Exp:* Instr biochem, Pa State Univ, University Park, 63-65; res assoc, Univ Wash, 65-67, actg asst prof, 67-69; res assoc, Med Sch, Univ Mich, Ann Arbor, 69-73, asst res scientist, 73-75, assoc res scientist human genetics, 75-77. *Concurrent Pos:* NIH fel, Univ Wash, 65-66, Am Cancer Soc fel, 66-67; investr, Howard Hughes Med Res Inst, 67-69. *Mem:* Am Soc Human Genetics; AAAS; Am Chem Soc; Am Soc Hemat; NY Acad Sci. *Res:* Structure and function of hemoglobin and other human blood proteins; structural abnormalities in proteins in inherited and congenital disease; therapy for sickle cell anemia. *Mailing Add:* Howard Univ Ctr Sickle Cell Dis 2121 Georgia Ave NW Washington DC 20001-3028

**WINTER, WILLIAM THOMAS,** X-RAY FIBER DIFFRACTION, COMPUTATIONAL CHEMISTRY. *Current Pos:* ASSOC PROF CHEM, STATE UNIV NY, COL ENVIRON SCI & FORESTRY, 88- *Personal Data:* b New York, NY, Nov 14, 44; m 69, Helen Dalmaso. *Educ:* State Univ NY Col Environ Sci & Forestry, BS, 66, PhD(phys chem), 74. *Prof Exp:* Res assoc biol, Purdue Univ, 73-77; from asst prof to assoc prof chem, Polytech Univ, 77-87, assoc head dept, 82-84. *Concurrent Pos:* Vis asst prof biol, Purdue Univ, 75-77; lectr polymer characterization, Ethicon Div, Johnson & Johnson, 79, 87; res scientist, Ctr Res Plant Macromolecules, Grenoble, France, 84-85; consult & vis scientist, Xerox Res Ctr, Can, 85, 86; vis prof, Univ Grenoble, 87, 90; vis scientist, Agr & Food Res Ctr, Norwich, UK, 88; treas, Cellulose, Paper & Textile Div, Am Chem Soc, 90-92. *Mem:* Am Chem Soc; Soc Complex Carbohydrates; Sigma Xi. *Res:* Structural studies of biologically or physically significant macromolecules by X-ray diffraction, computer aided modelling methods, and solid-state nuclear magnetic resonance; bacterial and seed gum polysaccharides. *Mailing Add:* 315 Baker Lab State Univ NY Col Environ Sci & Forestry Syracuse NY 13210-2786. *Fax:* 315-470-6856; *E-Mail:* wtwinter@mailbox.syr.edu

**WINTERBERG, FRIEDWARDT,** THEORETICAL PHYSICS. *Current Pos:* assoc prof, 63-68, PROF PHYSICS, UNIV NEV, RENO, 68- *Personal Data:* b Berlin, Ger, June 12, 29; c Astrid. *Educ:* Univ Frankfurt, MS, 53; Univ Goettingen, PhD(nuclear physics), 55. *Honors & Awards:* Gold Medal, Hermann Oberth-Wernher von Braun Int Space Flight Found, 79. *Prof Exp:* Group leader theoret physics, Res Reactor, Hamburg, Ger, 55-59; asst prof plasma physics & relativity, Case Univ, 59-63. *Mem:* Am Phys Soc; hon mem Lilienthal Oberth Soc; corresp mem Int Acad Astronaut. *Res:* Neutron physics; plasma physics; magnetohydrodynamics; intense relativistic electron and ion beams; thermonuclear microexplosions and inertial confinement fusion; nuclear rocket propulsion; relativity; elementary particle physics; energy research. *Mailing Add:* Desert Res Inst & Dept Physics Univ & Community Col Syst Nev Reno NV 89507. *Fax:* 702-673-7397

**WINTERBOTTOM, RICHARD,** BIOGEOGRAPHY, PHYLOGENETICS. *Current Pos:* from asst cur to assoc cur, 78-84, CUR ICHTHYOL, ROYAL ONT MUS, TORONTO, 84- *Personal Data:* b Livingstone, Zambia, Sept 30, 44; Brit & Can citizen; m 71, Irina Donskov; c Marina & David. *Educ:* Univ Cape Town, SAfrica, BSc, 67; Queen's Univ, Kingston, Ont, PhD(biol), 71. *Honors & Awards:* Jessup Award, Acad Nat Sci, Philadelphia, 69; Stoye Award, Am Soc Ichthyologists & Herpetologists, 71. *Prof Exp:* Postdoctoral fel, Smithsonian Inst, Washington DC, 71-72 & Nat Mus Can, Ottawa, 72-73; sr lectr ichthyol, Smith Inst, Rhodes Univ, SAfrica, 73-77. *Concurrent Pos:*

Adj asst prof, Univ Toronto, 79-86, assoc prof, 86-90, prof, 90-; consult, Mako Films Ltd, Toronto, 80. *Mem:* Can Soc Zoologists; Am Soc Ichthyologists & Herpetologists (gov, 78-83); Soc Syst Zoologists; Zool Soc Southern Africa; Japan Soc Ichthyol; fel Willi Hennig Soc. *Res:* Systematics, anatomy, phylogeny and biogeography of fishes, primarily the coral reef perciforms of the Indo-Pacific ocean; coral reef ecology; larval fish recruitment; the theory of phylogenetic interpretation. *Mailing Add:* Ctr Biodiversity & Con Biol Royal Ont Mus 100 Queen's Park Toronto ON M5S 2C6 Can. *Fax:* 416-586-5863; *E-Mail:* rickw@zoo.toronto.edu, rickw@rom.on.ca

**WINTERBOTTOM, W L,** METALLURGY. *Current Pos:* Staff scientist, 62-80, PRIN RES SCIENTIST, SCI LAB, FORD MOTOR CO, 80-, MGR, MAT SYSTS RELIABILITY DEPT. *Personal Data:* b Pittsburgh, Pa, Sept 27, 30; m 51; c 4. *Educ:* Drexel Inst Technol, BSc, 58; Carnegie Inst Technol, PhD(metall), 62. *Mem:* Am Inst Mining, Metall & Petrol Engrs; Am Soc Mat; Soc Automotive Eng; fel Am Soc Metals Int. *Res:* Surface physics; evaporation of solids; vapor-solid interactions; condensation and nucleation; catalysis; gas monitoring devices; metal joining; fluxless vacuum brazing of aluminum, elec packaging design. *Mailing Add:* 30106 Pipers Lane Ct Farmington MI 48334-4358

**WINTERCORN, ELEANOR STIEGLER,** AUDIOLOGY, SPEECH PATHOLOGY. *Current Pos:* RETIRED. *Personal Data:* b Morristown, NJ, Jan 15, 35; m 58, Richard. *Educ:* Rockford Col, BA, 56; Univ Wis, MS, 58; Univ Md, PhD, 69. *Prof Exp:* Clin instr speech path & phonetics, Rockford Col, 56-57; speech & hearing therapist, El Paso Cerebral Palsy Treatment Ctr, 58-59; audiologist, Vet Admin Med Ctr, 60-66, supvre clin audiol, 66-70, asst chief audiol & speech path serv, 71-80, chief audiol & speech path serv, 80-96. *Concurrent Pos:* Mem, Res Comt Hearing Aid Eval Processes, Am Speech & Hearing Asn, 66-67; Vet Admin rep, Comt Hearing, Bioacoust & Biomech, Nat Res Coun-Nat Acad Sci, 68-71; res assoc & Vet Admin rep, Comt Hearing, Bioacoust Lab, Univ Md, 68-72; res asst prof, Univ Md, 73-; dir, Vet Admin Nat Hearing Aid Testing Prog, 75- *Mem:* Sigma Xi. *Res:* Hearing aids; speech intelligibility. *Mailing Add:* 109 Juniper Hills Williamsburg VA 23188

**WINTERHALDER, KEITH,** REVEGETATION ECOLOGY, SOIL-PLANT RELATIONSHIPS. *Current Pos:* lectr, 65-69, asst prof, 69-80, ASSOC PROF BIOL, LAURENTIAN UNIV, 80- *Personal Data:* b Burrington, Eng, Apr 14, 35; Can citizen. *Educ:* Univ Wales, BSc Hons, 56; New Eng Univ, Australia, MSc, 70. *Prof Exp:* Demonstr bot, Univ New Eng, 59-60, lectr, 60-62; sr res asst, Univ Liverpool, 62-65. *Concurrent Pos:* Chmn, veg enhancement tech adv comt, Sudbury, Can, 78-86. *Mem:* Can Bot Asn (treas, 84-86, 89); Can Land Reclamation Asn (vpres, 86-87); Ecol Soc Australia; Brit Ecol Soc; Am Soc Surface Mining & Reclamation; Soc Ecol Restoration. *Res:* Plant-soil relationships; soil biology; industrially-disturbed sites; plant distribution in northern Ontario. *Mailing Add:* Dept Biol Laurentian Univ Sudbury ON P3E 2C6 Can

**WINTERLIN, WRAY LAVERNE,** ENVIRONMENTAL CHEMISTRY. *Current Pos:* lab staff res assoc, Univ Calif, Davis, 59-65, specialist, 65-78, actg dept chmn, 72-73, environ chemist, Dept Environ Toxicol, 78-92, EMER PROF, UNIV CALIF, DAVIS, 92- *Personal Data:* b Sioux City, Iowa, July 20, 30; m 56; c 3. *Educ:* Univ Nebr, Lincoln, BS, 54, MS, 57. *Prof Exp:* Forestry aide, US Forestry, Calif Inst Technol, Pasadena, 56-57; jr chemist, Dept Water Resources, Calif Bryte, 58-59. *Concurrent Pos:* Prin investr, US Environ Protection Agency, NIH, USDA & other projs, 69-; vis scholar, US Environ Protection Agency, Research Triangle Park, NC, 74-75; vis prof, Cairo, Egypt, 82. *Mem:* Am Chem Soc; Sigma Xi; Soc Environ Toxicol & Chem; AAAS. *Res:* Development of analytical methods for trace quantities of environmental agents, primarily pesticides; isolation and confirmation of trace organics in environmental samples; metabolism and transformation of biologically active agents and waste disposal of pesticides. *Mailing Add:* 1931 Amador Davis CA 95616

**WINTERNHEIMER, P LOUIS,** BOTANY. *Current Pos:* RETIRED. *Personal Data:* b Evansville, Ind, Feb 9, 31; m 51; c 2. *Educ:* Purdue Univ, West Lafayette, BS, 53; Univ Iowa, MS, 55; Ind Univ, Bloomington, PhD(bot), 71. *Prof Exp:* From assoc prof to prof biol, Univ Evansville, 57-96. *Mem:* Am Bot Soc. *Res:* Biosystematic studies of Oenothera biennis and other species. *Mailing Add:* 1515 Redwing Dr Evansville IN 47715

**WINTERNITZ, WILLIAM WELCH,** MEDICINE. *Current Pos:* PROF & CHMN, DEPT INTERNAL MED, COL COMMUNITY HEALTH SCI, UNIV ALA, 77- *Personal Data:* b New Haven, Conn, June 21, 20; m 49, 84; c 3. *Educ:* Dartmouth Col, AB, 42; Johns Hopkins Univ, MD, 45. *Prof Exp:* From instr to asst prof med & physiol, Yale Univ, 52-59; from assoc prof to prof med, Col Med, Univ Ky, 59-77. *Mem:* Endocrine Soc; AMA; Am Diabetes Asn. *Res:* Endocrine regulation of metabolism. *Mailing Add:* Sch Med Univ Ala PO Box 870326 Tuscaloosa AL 35487-0326

**WINTERS, ALVIN L,** VIRAL PATHOGENESIS, ANTIVIRAL IMMUNOMODULATION. *Current Pos:* ASSOC PROF BIOL SCI, UNIV ALA, 80- *Personal Data:* b Enumclaw, Wash, Aug 26, 39; m 60, Patricia Bass; c Anthony L & Brian R. *Educ:* Kans State Teachers Col, BA, 64; Kans State Univ, MA, 68, PhD(virol), 69. *Prof Exp:* Instr biol, Kans State Univ, 69; asst prof microbiol, Univ Pa, 71-74 & Univ SFla, Tampa, 75-80. *Concurrent Pos:* Fel, Univ Pa, 69-71. *Mem:* Am Soc Microbiol; Sigma Xi; Am Soc Virol; Int Soc Antiviral Res. *Res:* Biochemistry of adenovirus pathogenesis. *Mailing Add:* Dept Biol Sci PO Box 870344 Tuscaloosa AL 65487-0344. *Fax:* 205-348-1786; *E-Mail:* awinters@biology.as.ua.edu

**WINTERS, C(HARLES) E(RNEST),** NUCLEAR ENGINEERING. *Current Pos:* CONSULT, 78- *Personal Data:* b Pratt, Kans, July 15, 16; m 41, Mary Tyler; c 4. *Educ:* Kans State Col, BS, 37; ScD, Mass Inst Technol, 42. *Prof Exp:* Chem engr, Mallinckrodt Chem Works, Mo, 40-43; prin engr, Manhattan Dist, US AEC, 43-47; sect chief, Technol Div, Oak Ridge Nat Lab, Carbide & Carbon Chem Co, 47-49, dept head, Eng Res & Develop Technol Div, 49-51, dir, Exp Eng Div, 51-53, asst res dir, 53-55, asst lab dir, Union Carbide Nuclear Co, 55-61; res dir, Parma Res Lab, Ohio, Union Carbide Corp, 62-66, gen mgr, Fuel Cell Dept, 63-69, asst to vpres, Washington, DC, 69-78. *Mem:* Am Chem Soc; fel Am Nuclear Soc; Am Inst Chem Engrs. *Res:* Electrochemical and nuclear engineering; energy generation. *Mailing Add:* 8800 Fernwood Rd Bethesda MD 20817

**WINTERS, EARL D,** ELECTROCHEMISTRY, ELECTRONIC PACKAGING. *Current Pos:* TECH CONSULT, 89- *Personal Data:* b Rio Grande, Ohio, Aug 28, 37; m 60; c 1. *Educ:* Ohio Wesleyan Univ, BA, 59; Mass Inst Technol, PhD(phys chem), 65. *Prof Exp:* Mem tech staff, Bell Labs, Inc, 65-89. *Mem:* Electrochem Soc; Electroplaters Soc. *Res:* Electrodeposition, etching and corrosion of metals. *Mailing Add:* 923 W Sawmill Rd Quakertown PA 18951-2909

**WINTERS, HARVEY,** MICROBIOLOGY, BIOCHEMISTRY. *Current Pos:* From instr to asst prof, 69-75, assoc prof, 75-79, PROF BIOL, FAIRLEIGH DICKINSON UNIV, 79- *Personal Data:* b Paterson, NJ, Aug 23, 42; m 65; c 1. *Educ:* Fairleigh Dickinson Univ, BS, 64, MS, 66; Columbia Univ, PhD(chem biol), 71. *Honors & Awards:* Roon Award, Soc Paint Technol, 73. *Mem:* Am Soc Microbiol; Soc Indust Microbiol; Sigma Xi. *Res:* Microbiology of aqueous coatings; microbiofouling of marine surfaces; desalination. *Mailing Add:* Dept Biol Fairleigh Dickinson Univ 1000 River Rd Teaneck NJ 07666-1914

**WINTERS, KEN C,** ADOLESCENT DRUG ABUSE, COMPULSIVE GAMBLING. *Current Pos:* ASSOC PROF PSYCHIAT, UNIV MINN, 89- *Personal Data:* b Minneapolis, Minn, Mar 31, 53; m 77, Mary Russell; c Libby & Johanna. *Educ:* Univ Minn, BA, 76; State Univ NY, Stonybrook, PhD(clin psychol), 82. *Prof Exp:* Res scientist, Dept Phychiat, State Univ NY, Stony Brook, 82-84; clin psychologist, Cent Minn Ment Health Ctr, 84-85; sr res scientist, Amherst H Wilder Found, 85-89. *Concurrent Pos:* Psychotherapist, 82-; instr, Dept Psychol, St Cloud State Univ, 84; prin investr, Nat Inst Drug Abuse, Univ Minn, 87-; dir, Ctr Adolescent Substance Abuse, 89- *Mem:* Am Psychol Asn; Nat Coun Compulsive Gambling. *Res:* Study the assessment and treatment of adolescent drug abuse, with a particular focus on the development of standardized and clinically oriented assessment instruments and interviews; prevalence of gambling problems and the effectiveness of the treatment of compulsive gamblers; clinical assessment and health services evaluation. *Mailing Add:* Univ Minn 420 Delaware St SE PO Box 393 Minneapolis MN 55455. *Fax:* 612-626-5591; *E-Mail:* winte001@umn.edu

**WINTERS, LAWRENCE JOSEPH,** ORGANIC CHEMISTRY. *Current Pos:* PROF CHEM & CHMN DEPT, VA COMMONWEALTH UNIV, 72- *Personal Data:* b Chicago, Ill, June 11, 30; m 61; c 3. *Educ:* Wash Univ, AB, 53; Univ Kans, PhD(chem), 59. *Prof Exp:* Asst chem, Univ Kans, 56-58; fel, Fla State Univ, 59-61; from asst prof to prof, Drexel Univ, 61-72, actg chmn dept, 68-69, asst dean grad sch, 69-71. *Mem:* Am Chem Soc. *Res:* Bipyridine chemistry; organic reaction mechanisms; structure-activity relationships; aliphatic nitro-compounds. *Mailing Add:* Dept Chem Va Commonwealth Univ PO Box 2006 Richmond VA 23216-2006

**WINTERS, MARY ANN,** BIOCHEMISTRY. *Current Pos:* CHANCELLOR, DIOCESE PHOENIX, 93- *Personal Data:* b Paterson, NJ, Nov 14, 37. *Educ:* Seton Hill Col, BA, 67; Univ Pittsburgh, PhD(biochem), 72. *Prof Exp:* Teacher elem & high schs, Pa & Ariz, 56-66; from instr to assoc prof chem, Sisters Charity Seton Hall, 67-81, admin, 81-93. *Mem:* Am Chem Soc; Leadership Conf Women Religious USA. *Res:* Purification of nucleic acid synthesizing enzymes and the isolation and identification of nucleic acids. *Mailing Add:* Our Lady Perpetual Help Convent 7634 Second St Scottsdale AZ 85251

**WINTERS, RAY WYATT,** PHYSIOLOGICAL PSYCHOLOGY. *Current Pos:* Asst prof, 69-74, assoc prof, 74-80, PROF PSYCHOL, UNIV MIAMI, 80- *Personal Data:* b Takoma Park, Md, Feb 17, 42; m 67. *Educ:* Mich State Univ, BS, 64, MA, 66, PhD(psychol), 69. *Concurrent Pos:* NIH & NSF instnl grants, 69-, NIH grant, 72-80. *Mem:* Optical Soc Am. *Res:* Human psychophysical research in conjunction with animal neurophysiology, especially sensory systems and vision. *Mailing Add:* Dept Psychol Univ Miami PO Box 248106 Miami FL 33124-8106

**WINTERS, ROBERT WAYNE,** PEDIATRICS, NUTRITION. *Current Pos:* PRES, WINTERS ASSOCS INC, 91- *Personal Data:* b Evansville, Ind, May 23, 26; m 48, 76; c 1. *Educ:* Ind Univ, AB, 48; Yale Univ, MD, 52. *Honors & Awards:* E Mead Johnson Prize, 66; Borden Award, 74. *Prof Exp:* Intern pediat, Univ Calif, 52-53; from asst to chief resident, Univ NC, 54-56; res fel med, Univ NC, 56-58; asst prof physiol, Univ Pa, 58-61; from assoc prof to prof pediat, Col Physicians & Surgeons, Columbia Univ, 61-81; exec vpres, Health Dine, Home Nutrit Support Inc, 81-86, chief exec officer, 86-89, med dir & vpres, 89-91. *Concurrent Pos:* Res fel, Univ Calif, 53-54; res fel biochem, Univ Pa, 58-60. *Mem:* Soc Pediat Res; Am Soc Clin Invest; Am Pediat Soc; Am Acad Pediat; Am Physiol Soc; Asn Am Physiol. *Res:* Renal and acid base physiology; metabolism of water and electrolytes; intravenous nutrition. *Mailing Add:* Winters Assocs Inc PO Box 188 Mendham NJ 07945

**WINTERS, RONALD HOWARD,** PHARMACOLOGY. *Current Pos:* DEAN HEALTH RELS, UNIV ARK, 82- *Personal Data:* b Los Angeles, Calif, Apr 13, 42; m 76; c 2. *Educ:* Calif State Univ, Northridge, BA, 63; Ore State Univ, PhD(pharmacol), 69. *Prof Exp:* Biochemist, Riker Labs, Inc, 64-65; asst to dean undergrad studies, Sch Pharm, Ore State Univ, 72-74, from instr to assoc prof pharmacol, 68-76, asst dean, 74-76; assoc dean, Col Health Related Prof, Wichita State Univ, 77-82. *Concurrent Pos:* Res grants, Ore Heart Asn & Ore Educ Coord Coun, 70-72. *Mem:* AAAS; Sigma Xi; NY Acad Sci; Am Soc Allied Health Professions. *Res:* Cardiovascular pharmacology; anesthesia. *Mailing Add:* Col Health Related Prof Med Sci Univ Ark Med Sch 4301 W Markham Slot 619 Little Rock AR 72205

**WINTERS, RONALD ROSS,** NUCLEAR PHYSICS, ASTROPHYSICS. *Current Pos:* Assoc prof physics, Denison Univ, 66-80. *Personal Data:* b Marion, Va, June 4, 41; m 60; c 2. *Educ:* King Col, AB, 63; Va Polytech Inst & State Univ, PhD(physics), 67. *Concurrent Pos:* Consult, Oak Ridge Nat Lab, 72-74; dir, Sci Semester prog, Great Lakes Col Asn, 75- *Mem:* Sigma Xi; Asn Advan Physics Teaching. *Res:* Measurement of neutron capture cross sections; s-process nucleosynthesis; origin of the earth-moon system. *Mailing Add:* 820 Broadway W Granville OH 43023-1207

**WINTERS, STEPHEN SAMUEL,** GEOLOGY. *Current Pos:* from asst prof to assoc prof, Fla State Univ, 49-66, dean, Div Basic Studies, 64-84, dir honors prog, 67-85, prof, 66-85, serv prof, 85-89, EMER PROF GEOL, FLA STATE UNIV, 89- *Personal Data:* b New York, NY, June 29, 20; m 43, Doris Rosenblum; c Philip & Martha. *Educ:* Rutgers Univ, BA, 42; Columbia Univ, MA, 48, PhD(geol), 55. *Prof Exp:* Instr geol, Rutgers Univ, 48-49. *Mem:* Fel Geol Soc Am; Am Asn Petrol Geol; Sigma Xi; Hist Earth Sci Soc; Nat Asn Geol Teachers. *Res:* Stratigraphy and invertebrate paleontology of late Paleozoic. *Mailing Add:* Fla State Univ Dept Geol 205 Carraway Bldg Tallahassee FL 32306-3026

**WINTERS, WALLACE DUDLEY,** NEUROPHARMACOLOGY, CLINICAL PHARMACOLOGY. *Current Pos:* PROF FAMILY PRACT, PHARMACOL, PSYCHIAT, & EMERGENCY MED, SCH MED, UNIV CALIF, DAVIS, 71- *Personal Data:* b New York, NY, June 20, 29; m 53; c 4. *Educ:* George Washington Univ, AB, 50; Univ Mich, Ann Arbor, MA, 52; Univ Wis-Madison, PhD(pharmacol), 54; Med Col Wis, MD, 58; Am Bd Med Toxicol, dipl, 77. *Honors & Awards:* A E Bennet Award, Soc Biol Psychiat, 66. *Prof Exp:* Asst pharmacol, Univ Mich, Ann Arbor, 51-52 & Univ Wis-Madison, 52-54; instr, Med Col Wis, 54-58; intern, Milwaukee Hosp, Wis, 58-59; ment health trainee neuropharmacol, Univ Calif, Los Angeles, 59-61, res pharmacologist, 61-63, assoc prof pharmacol, Sch Med, 63-68, prof pharmacol & psychiat, 68-71. *Concurrent Pos:* Ment Health Prog rep pharmacol, Univ Calif, Los Angeles, 61-71, mem, Brain Res Inst & chmn ment health training prog, Educ Comt, 65-71, mem brain res adv comt, 70-71; mem, Preclin Psychopharmacol Res Rev Comt, 65-69. *Mem:* AAAS; Am Soc Pharmacol & Exp Therapeut; fel Am Asn Clin Toxicol; Am Asn Poison Control Centers. *Res:* Neuropharmacological action of central nervous system acting drugs; models of psychosis; scheme of anesthetic, excitant, hallucinogen and convulsant drug action; circadian and seasonal rhythm and drug actions; melatonin and analgesia. *Mailing Add:* 44865 S El Macero Dr El Macero CA 95618-1035

**WINTERS, WENDELL DELOS,** VIROLOGY, IMMUNOLOGY. *Current Pos:* ASSOC PROF MICROBIOL, SCH MED, UNIV TEX HEALTH SCI CTR, SAN ANTONIO, 76- *Personal Data:* b Herrin, Ill; div; c 3. *Educ:* Univ Ill, Urbana, BS, 62, MS, 66, PhD(med microbiol), 68. *Prof Exp:* Res asst med microbiol, Univ Ill Col Med, 63-65, teaching asst, 65-68; vis scientist, Nat Inst Med Res, London, 68-71; asst prof surg & med microbiol, Sch Med, Univ Calif, Los Angeles, 71-76. *Concurrent Pos:* Biochemist, Chicago Bd Health, 63-68; microbiologist, Presby St Lukes Hosp, Chicago, 65-68; Med Res Coun Eng grant, Nat Inst Med Res, London, 68-69; Damon Runyon Mem Fund Cancer Res fel, 70-71; consult, Vet Admin Hosp, Sepulveda, Calif, 71-76 & Audie Murphy Mem Vet Admin Hosp, 78-; mem, bd dirs, Aloe Res Found, 90; prog chmn & mem bd dirs, Bioelec Growth & Repair Soc; cong chmn, Int Cong Phytopath. *Mem:* Am Asn Immunologists; Am Asn Cancer Res; Am Soc Microbiol; Tissue Cult Asn; Brit Soc Gen Microbiol; Bioelectromagnetics Soc; Bioelectric Growth & Repair Soc; Soc Exp Biol Med; fel Am Acad Microbiol. *Res:* Mechanisms of virus assembly; immune responses to bacterial, viral and cancer antigens plus immunotherapy substances; characterization of bioactive phytotherapeutic substances; electromagnetic field exposure effects on immunomodulation, embryonic/fetal development and neoplastic marker oncogenes. *Mailing Add:* Dept Microbiol Sch Med Univ Tex Health Sci Ctr 7703 Floyd Curl Dr San Antonio TX 78284-7758. *Fax:* 210-567-6612

**WINTERSCHEID, LOREN COVART,** MEDICAL SCHOOL ADMINISTRATION. *Current Pos:* Asst surg, Univ Wash, 57-58, from instr to assoc prof, 58-72, asst dean clin affairs, 72-80, prof surg, Sch Med, 72-89, assoc dean, 80-89, ASSOC DEAN ADMIN, SCH MED, UNIV WASH, 89- *Personal Data:* b Manhattan, Kans, Oct 5, 25; m 48; c 6. *Educ:* Willamette Univ, BA, 48; Univ Pa, PhD(microbiol), 53, MD, 54. *Concurrent Pos:* Resident surgeon, Affil Hosps, Univ Wash, 55-62; NIH fel, 57-60; mem bd trustees, Willamette Univ, 60-; attend surgeon, Univ & King Co Hosps, Seattle, 63. *Mem:* AMA. *Res:* General surgery. *Mailing Add:* Sch Med SC-61 Univ Wash 3900 7th Ave NE Seattle WA 98195-0001

**WINTERSTEIN, SCOTT RICHARD,** WILDLIFE BIOMETRY, POPULATION DYNAMICS. *Current Pos:* ASST PROF WILDLIFE ECOL, DEPT FISHERIES & WILDLIFE, MICH STATE UNIV, 86- *Personal Data:* b Charleston, SC, Aug 25, 55. *Educ:* Northern Ariz Univ, BS, 77; NMex State Univ, MS, 80, PhD(biol), 85; NC State Univ, MSt, 86. *Prof Exp:* Vis prof, Dept Exp Statis, La State Univ, 85-86. *Mem:* Am Ornithologists Union; Biomet Soc; Soc Conserv Biol; Wildlife Soc; Cooper Ornith Soc; Wilson Ornith Soc. *Res:* Dynamics of fish and wildlife populations; statistical methods for sampling fish and wildlife populations; experimental design and statistical analysis; mathematical modeling; conservation biology. *Mailing Add:* Dept Fisheries & Wildlife Mich State Univ 13 Natural Resources Bldg East Lansing MI 48824

**WINTHROP, JOEL ALBERT,** APPLIED MATHEMATICS, ELECTRICAL ENGINEERING. *Current Pos:* CONSULT, 80- *Personal Data:* b Elizabeth, NJ, Oct 30, 42. *Educ:* Univ Calif, BA, 64, MA, 70, PhD(math), 71, MEE, 78. *Prof Exp:* Asst prof math, Univ Mo, 71-76; mem tech staff, Bell Tel Labs, 77-80. *Mem:* Am Math Soc; Math Asn Am; Soc Indust & Appl Math; Inst Elec & Electronics Engrs; Sigma Xi. *Res:* Digital signal processing. *Mailing Add:* PO Box 21 Little Silver NJ 07739

**WINTHROP, JOHN T,** HOLOGRAPHY, OPHTHALMIC LENS DESIGN. *Current Pos:* CONSULT, 86-87 & 89- *Personal Data:* b Evanston, Ill, Feb 7, 38; m 59; c 1. *Educ:* Univ Ill, BS, 60; Univ Mich, MS, 62, PhD(physics), 66. *Prof Exp:* Postdoctoral, Univ Mich Inst Sci & Technol, 66-67; res physicist, Am Optical, 67-78, chief scientist, 78-86, vpres prod develop, 87-88. *Mem:* Optical Soc Am; Sigma Xi. *Res:* Optical diffraction, coherence theory and design of progressive-addition ophthalmic lenses; research in physics, reality problem and origin of physical law. *Mailing Add:* PO Box 185 Stevensville MT 59870-0185

**WINTHROP, STANLEY OSCAR,** ORGANIC CHEMISTRY. *Current Pos:* RETIRED. *Personal Data:* b Cowansville, Que, June 22, 27; m 56; c 3. *Educ:* McGill Univ, BEng, 48; Ga Inst Technol, MS, 49; Univ Tex, PhD(org chem), 51. *Prof Exp:* Res chemist, Sterling-Winthrop Res Inst, 52-54; head med chem, Ayerst Res Labs, 54-64; dir res & develop, Lever Bros, Can, 64-69; sci adv, Off Sci & Technol, Can Dept Indust, Trade & Com, 69-71; dir gen, Air Pollution Control Directorate, Can Dept Environ, 71-77, dir env, Environ Impact Control Directorate, 77-82, sr adv environ health, Dept Health & Welfare, 82-88. *Mem:* Fel Can Inst Chem; Can Res Mgt Asn. *Res:* Pharmaceuticals; nitrogen heterocycles; fats and oils; detergents; research administration. *Mailing Add:* 1510 Riverside Dr Apt 2702 Ottawa ON K1G 4X5 Can

**WINTNER, CLAUDE EDWARD,** ORGANIC CHEMISTRY. *Current Pos:* assoc prof, 69-76, PROF CHEM, HAVERFORD COL, 76- *Personal Data:* b Princeton, NJ, Apr 8, 38; m 67; c 2. *Educ:* Princeton Univ, AB, 59; Harvard Univ, MA, 60, PhD(chem), 63. *Honors & Awards:* Lindback Award, 82. *Prof Exp:* From instr to asst prof, Yale Univ, 63-68; asst prof, Swarthmore Col, 68-69. *Concurrent Pos:* Acad guest, Swiss Fed Inst Technol, Zurich, 72-73, 76-77 & 89-90; vis prof chem, Harvard Univ, 84-85, 95-97. *Mem:* Am Chem Soc. *Res:* Organic synthesis; chemical education. *Mailing Add:* 25 Railroad Ave Haverford PA 19041

**WINTON, CHARLES NEWTON,** SOFTWARE ENGINEERING, SIMULATION. *Current Pos:* assoc prof math sci, 74-82, dean comput info systs, CIS, 89-91, PROF COMPUT SCI, UNIV NFLA, 83-, DEAN, COMPUT SCI & ENG, 94- *Personal Data:* b Raleigh, NC, Sept 22, 43; m 66; c 2. *Educ:* NC State Univ, BS, 65; Univ NC, Chapel Hill, MA & PhD(math), 69. *Prof Exp:* Asst prof math, Univ SC, 69-84; assoc prof comput sci, Univ SFla, 82-83. *Mem:* Inst Elec & Electronics Engrs; Asn Comput Mach; Math Asn Am. *Res:* Medical systems simulation; prototype-based system specification; ring structure theory, including quotient objects and various torsion theories. *Mailing Add:* Dept Comput Sci Univ NFla Jacksonville FL 32224. *Fax:* 904-646-2988; *E-Mail:* cwinton@unf.edu

**WINTON, HENRY J,** ELECTRICAL ENGINEERING. *Current Pos:* assoc prof, 61-76, PROF ELEC ENG, ROSE-HULMAN INST TECHNOL, 76- *Personal Data:* b Guthrie, Okla, Mar 29, 29; m 55; c 3. *Educ:* Purdue Univ, Lafayette, BS, 50; Univ Ill, Urbana, MS, 55; Univ Santa Clara, PhD(elec eng), 70. *Prof Exp:* Engr, Sperry Gyroscope Co, NY, 57-60. *Mem:* Inst Elec & Electronics Engrs; Am Soc Eng Educ. *Res:* Modeling and computer simulation of biological control systems. *Mailing Add:* Dept Elec Eng Rose-Hulman Inst Technol 5500 Wabash Ave Terre Haute IN 47803

**WINTON, RAYMOND SHERIDAN,** MOLECULAR SPECTROSCOPY. *Current Pos:* asst prof math & physics, 72-81, PROF ELEC ENG, MISS STATE UNIV, 81- *Personal Data:* b Raleigh, NC, Jan 4, 40; m 73. *Educ:* NC State Univ, BS, 62; Duke Univ, PhD(physics), 72. *Prof Exp:* Physicist electro-optics, US Army Electronics Command, 65-67. *Mem:* Sigma Xi; Am Phys Soc; Math Asn Am; Inst Elec & Electronics Engrs. *Res:* High precision measurements in microwave molecular spectroscopy and saturation effects in molecular absorption spectra. *Mailing Add:* Eng Sch Miss State Univ Mississippi State MS 39762-5660

**WINTROUB, HERBERT JACK,** PHYSICS, ELECTRONICS. *Current Pos:* head, Commun Sci Dept, Electronics Res Lab, 68-91, DISTINGUISHED ENGR, AEROSPACE CORP, 91- *Personal Data:* b Omaha, Nebr, Aug 22, 21; m 48; c 3. *Educ:* Univ Southern Calif, BS, 50. *Prof Exp:* Mem tech staff, Hughes Aircraft Co, 50-57; sr engr, Litton Indust, 57-58; mem sr tech staff, Space Tech Lab, TRW, Inc, 58-63, mem tech staff, Electronics Res Lab. *Concurrent Pos:* Consult, Sch Med, Univ Southern Calif, 65-, adj asst prof, 69-; mem adv group on electron devices, Dept Defense. *Mem:* Inst Elec & Electronics Engrs; Air Force Asn; Armed Force Commun & Electronics Asn.

*Res:* Electronic systems research and development in radar, communications, command and control; millimeter-wave systems investigations; applications of electronics to medical research; space systems, microwave/millimeter-wave, receiver, signal processor and transmitter subsystems; management of solid-state device applications research. *Mailing Add:* Aerospace Corp PO Box 92957 M1-928 Los Angeles CA 90009. *Fax:* 310-336-6225; *E-Mail:* lwintroub@courier8.aero.org

**WINTSCH, ROBERT P,** METAMORPHIC GEOLOGY, STRUCTURE PETROLOGY. *Current Pos:* Asst prof, 75-81, ASSOC PROF, GEOL, DEPT GEOL, IND UNIV, 81- *Personal Data:* b Toronto, Can, Aug 15, 46; m; c 1. *Educ:* Beloit Col, BA, 69; Brown Univ, PhD(geol), 75. *Concurrent Pos:* Vis prof Inst Tech, Zurich, 81, Dept Earth Sci, Univ Leeds, 82, Dept Geol Sci, Univ Mich, 85, US Geol Surv, 88-89. *Mem:* Geol Soc Am; Am Geophys Union; Mineral Soc Am. *Mailing Add:* 1005 E Hunter Ave Bloomington IN 47401

**WINTZ, P(AUL) A,** electrical engineering, for more information see previous edition

**WINTZ, WILLIAM A, JR,** CIVIL ENGINEERING. *Current Pos:* RETIRED. *Personal Data:* b Carville, La, June 7, 15; m 42; c 8. *Educ:* La State Univ, BS, 36, MS, 38; Mass Inst Technol, SM, 51. *Prof Exp:* From instr to prof civil eng, La State Univ, Baton Rouge, 41-80. *Mem:* Am Soc Civil Engrs; Am Soc Eng Educ; Water Pollution Control Fedn; Am Water Works Asn. *Res:* Sanitary engineering; advanced surveying. *Mailing Add:* 1991 Hollydale Ave Baton Rouge LA 70808

**WINZENREAD, MARVIN RUSSELL,** MATHEMATICS, MICROCOMPUTERS EDUCATION. *Current Pos:* from asst prof to assoc prof, 69-82, PROF MATH & COMPUT SCI, CALIF STATE UNIV, HAYWARD, 82- *Personal Data:* b Indianapolis, Ind, Nov 22, 37; m 60; c 2. *Educ:* Purdue Univ, BS, 60; Univ Notre Dame, MS, 64; Ind Univ, Bloomington, EdD(math educ), 69. *Prof Exp:* Teacher high sch, Ind, 60-63; from instr to asst prof math, Northwest Mo State Col, 64-67; lectr, Ind Univ Indianapolis, 69. *Res:* Mathematics in the inner city school. *Mailing Add:* 43 Cork Rd Alameda CA 94502

**WINZER, STEPHEN RANDOLPH,** electronic ceramics, transducers, for more information see previous edition

**WIORKOWSKI, JOHN JAMES,** STATISTICS. *Current Pos:* assoc prof statist, 75-81, asst vpres, 85-91, PROF, UNIV TEX, DALLAS, 81-, ASSOC VPRES, ACAD AFFAIRS, 91- *Personal Data:* b Chicago, Ill, Sept 30, 43; m 66; c Fleur. *Educ:* Univ Chicago, BS, 65, MS, 66, PhD(statist), 72. *Prof Exp:* Asst prof statist, Grad Prog Health Care Admin, US Army-Baylor Univ, 68-71; res assoc, Univ Chicago, 71-73; asst prof, Pa State Univ, 73-75. *Concurrent Pos:* Assoc dir, Statist Consult & Coop Res Ctr, Pa State Univ, 73-74, dir, 74-75; consult, Fed Energy Admin, 75; asst vpres, Acad Affairs, 79-; prog head, Math Sci, 78-79; fel acad admin, Am Coun Educ, 81-82. *Mem:* Sigma Xi; Am Statist Asn; Biomet Soc; Inst Math Statist. *Res:* Interest in applied statistics, specifically biostatistics, linear models, time series analysis, genetic statistics. *Mailing Add:* 9922 Lincolnshire Ct Rockwall TX 75087. *Fax:* 972-690-2276; *E-Mail:* wiorkow@utdallas.edu

**WIPKE, W TODD,** CHEMISTRY, THEORETICAL CHEMISTRY. *Current Pos:* assoc prof, 75-81, PROF, UNIV CALIF, SANTA CRUZ, 81- *Personal Data:* b St Charles, Mo, Dec 16, 40; c 2. *Educ:* Univ Mo, Columbia, BS, 62; Univ Calif, Berkeley, PhD(chem), 65. *Honors & Awards:* Alexander von Humbolt Award, 87; Comput Chem Award, Am Chem Soc, 87, Skolnik Award, 91. *Prof Exp:* Res fel chem, Harvard Univ, 67-69; asst prof, Princeton Univ, 69-75. *Concurrent Pos:* NIH res fel, Harvard Univ, 68-69; NIH spec res resource grant, Princeton Univ, 70-75 & Merck prof develop grant, 70-75; consult, Merck, Sharp & Dohme, 70-80, Molecular Design Ltd, 77-94; mem bd adv, Chem Abstr Serv, 70-73; dir, NATO Advan Study Inst Comput Rep & Manipulation Chem Info, 73; mem, Nat Res Coun Comt Nat Res Comput Chem, 74-77; cofounder, Molecular Design Ltd, 77. *Mem:* Am Chem Soc; Royal Soc Chem; Asn Comput Mach; Am Asn Artificial Intel. *Res:* Organic synthesis; computer assisted design of organic syntheses; computer assisted prediction of metabolism; computer drug design; artificial intelligence in chemistry; molecular engineering. *Mailing Add:* Dept Chem Univ Calif Santa Cruz CA 95064. *Fax:* 408-459-2935

**WIREMAN, KENNETH,** GENETICS & ZOOLOGY, ANATOMY. *Current Pos:* PROF BIOL & CHAIR, NATURAL SCI DEPT, SOUTHEASTERN COL, 77-, CHAIR, SCI DIV, 79- *Personal Data:* b Waldo, Ky, Jan 18, 32; m 54, Betty J Schomer; c Sandra J (Callan), Janice S (Albritton). *Educ:* Ashland Univ, BS, 60; Univ Utah, MS, 66, PhD(biol), 71. *Prof Exp:* Instr chem-physics, Millersburg High Sch, 60-61; Manchester High Sch, 61-63; instr phys sci-math, Rittman High Sch, 63-65; prof biol, Bethany Col, 67-77. *Concurrent Pos:* Consult, ICI Univ, Irving, Tex. *Mem:* AAAS; Am Math Soc; Nat Geog Soc; Am Mus Natural Hist; Nat Wildlife Asn. *Res:* General and human genetics. *Mailing Add:* Dept Sci Southeastern Col 1000 Longfellow Blvd Lakeland FL 33801-6034. *Fax:* 941-646-2372

**WIRSEN, CARL O, JR,** MARINE MICROBIOLOGY, OCEANOGRAPHY. *Current Pos:* RES SPECIALIST MICROBIOL, WOODS HOLE OCEANOG INST, 68- *Personal Data:* b Arlington, Mass, Aug 11, 42; c 2. *Educ:* Univ Mass, BS, 64; Boston Univ, MA, 66. *Prof Exp:*

Res assoc microbiol, Harvard Univ, 66-68. *Mem:* Am Soc Microbiol; Am Soc Limnol & Oceanog; Sigma Xi. *Res:* The role of microorganisms in the deep sea environment and how the environmental parameters of temperature and pressure influence their activities; microbiological studies of deep sea hydrothermal vents. *Mailing Add:* Dept Biol Woods Hole Oceanog Inst Woods Hole MA 02543. *Fax:* 508-457-2169; *E-Mail:* cwirsen@whoi.edu

**WIRSZUP, IZAAK,** MATHEMATICS. *Current Pos:* from instr to prof, 49-85, EMER PROF MATH, UNIV CHICAGO, 85- *Personal Data:* b Wilno, Poland, Jan 5, 15; US citizen; m 49; c 1. *Educ:* Univ Wilno, Mag Philos, 39; Univ Chicago, PhD(math), 55. *Honors & Awards:* Quantrell Award, Univ Chicago, 58. *Prof Exp:* Lectr math, Tech Inst, Wilno, Poland, 39-41; dir bur studies & spec statist, Cent Soc Purchase; dir Soc Anonyme des Monoprix, France, 46-49. *Concurrent Pos:* Dir Surv East Europ Math Lit, proj Univ Chicago, under NSF grant, 56-83; consult sch math study group, Yale Univ & Stanford Univ, 60, 61 & 66; Ford Found consult, Univ Math Progs, Colombia, SAm, 65 & 66; mem, US Comn Math Instr, 69-73; adv math, Encyclopaedia Britannica, 71-; dir, NSF Surv Appl Soviet Res Math Educ, 85-; prin investr, Univ Chicago Sch Math Proj, 83-; dir, Int Math Educ Resource Ctr, Univ Chicago, 88- *Mem:* Am Math Soc; Math Asn Am; NY Acad Sci; AAAS. *Res:* Mathematical analysis; international mathematics education. *Mailing Add:* Dept Math Eckhart Hall Univ Chicago 1118 E 58th St Chicago IL 60637-1538

**WIRTA, ROY W(ILLIAM),** REHABILITATION BIOMEDICAL ENGINEERING, BIOMECHANICS. *Current Pos:* RETIRED. *Personal Data:* b Big Lake, Wash, Mar 27, 21; m 46; c 3. *Educ:* Univ Wash, BSME, 47. *Prof Exp:* Test engr, Gen Elec Co, 47-48, develop engr, Gen Eng Lab, 48-52, process engr, 52-56, mech engr, 56-57, sr engr, Hanford Atomic Prod Oper, 57-61, electromech systs engr, Ord Dept, 61-64; sr eng specialist, Biocybernetics Lab, Philco-Ford Corp, Pa, 64-67; sr res scientist, Rehab Eng Ctr, Moss Rehab Hosp, Philadelphia, 67-77; biomech engr, Biomechanics, 77-86. *Concurrent Pos:* Res biomed engr, Vet Admin Med Ctr, San Diego, Calif, 78-86. *Mem:* Am Soc Mech Engrs. *Res:* Electromechanical devices; mechanical arts; integrated man-machine systems; human locomotion; measurement of impaired human performance. *Mailing Add:* 5570 Rab St La Mesa CA 91942-2461

**WIRTH, HENRY E,** CHEMISTRY. *Current Pos:* RETIRED. *Personal Data:* b Bellingham, Wash, June 4, 08; m 31, Naomi Thomas; c Thomas H, John W & Kathryn (Hansen). *Educ:* Univ Wash, Seattle, BSc, 29, PhD(chem), 34. *Prof Exp:* From asst prof to assoc prof chem, NDak Agr Col, 34-39; from asst prof to assoc prof, Ohio State Univ, 39-50; chmn, Syracuse Univ, 50-65, prof, 50-73. *Mem:* Am Chem Soc; Am Inst Chemists; Sigma Xi; fel AAAS. *Mailing Add:* 701 Oaknoll Dr Apt 208 Iowa City IA 52246

**WIRTH, JAMES BURNHAM,** PHYSIOLOGICAL PSYCHOLOGY, PSYCHIATRY. *Current Pos:* resident, 75-77, clin dir in-patient servs, 85-93, ASST PROF PSYCHIAT, JOHNS HOPKINS HOSP, 77-, DIR EATING & WEIGHT DIS PROG, 91- *Personal Data:* b New Milford, NJ, Jan 15, 41; c 3. *Educ:* Cornell Univ, AB, 63, MD, 67; Cambridge Univ, PhD(physiol), 75. *Prof Exp:* Intern med, Cornell Univ Hosps, 67-68; resident neurol, Cleveland Metrop Gen Hosp, 68-69; fel physiol psychol, Inst Neurol Sci, Univ Pa, 71-73; res physiol, Cambridge Univ, 73-75. *Concurrent Pos:* Mem panel neurol behav, Nat Inst Neurol & Cardiovasc Dis & Stroke, 78. *Mem:* Am Physiol Soc; Am Psychiat Asn; Sigma Xi; Eastern Physiol Asn. *Res:* Ingestive behavior, especially thirst, hunger and sodium appetite; anorexia nervosa. *Mailing Add:* Dept Psychiat & Behav Sci Meyer 4-181 600 N Wolfe St Baltimore MD 21205

**WIRTH, PETER JAMES,** CHEMICAL CARCINOGENESIS. *Current Pos:* staff fel, 75-88, SR SCIENTIST, NAT CANCER INST, NIH, 89- *Personal Data:* m; c 1. *Educ:* St Benedict's Col, BS, 70; Univ Kans, PhD(med chem), 74. *Prof Exp:* Fel, Univ Wash, 74-75. *Mem:* Soc Toxicol; Am Asn Cancer Res; Am Chem Soc; Am Soc Pharmacol & Exp Therapeut. *Res:* Analysis of polypeptide (protein) alterations during chemical carcinogenesis. *Mailing Add:* Bldg 37 Rm 3C28 Nat Cancer Inst-NIH Bethesda MD 20892-0001. *Fax:* 301-496-0734; *E-Mail:* peter@elsie.nci.nih.gov

**WIRTHLIN, MILTON ROBERT, JR,** PERIODONTICS, EPIDEMIOLOGY. *Current Pos:* assoc clin prof, 86-96, CLIN PROF, UNIV CALIF, SAN FRANCISCO, 96- *Personal Data:* b Little Rock, Ark, July 13, 32; m 54, Joan Krieger; c Michael, Steven, Laurie, David & Alna. *Educ:* Univ Calif, DDS, 56, MS, 68; Am Bd Periodont, dipl, 74. *Honors & Awards:* Milton & Mary Gabbs Prize in Dent, 56; Am Acad Dent Med Cert Merit, 56. *Prof Exp:* US Navy gen dent officer, 56-68; exec officer, First Dent Co, Fleet Marine Force, 68-69, Third Dent Co, 73-74; head periodont, Naval Dent Clin, Long Beach, CA, 69-73; chief epidemiol, Naval Dent Res Inst, Great Lakes, Ill, 74-76, comdg officer, 76-81; comdg officer, Naval Regional Dent Ctr, San Francisco, 81-83; asst chief staff, Naval Med Co, Southwestern Region, 83-85; assoc prof, Univ Pac, 85-86. *Concurrent Pos:* Spec proj officer, Bur Med & Surg, USN, 64-65; Dir fel, Naval Dent Clin, Long Beach, 71-72, consult periodont, Naval Regional Med Ctr, Great Lakes, Ill, 74-76; clin asst prof periodont, Univ Southern Calif, 70-73; Comt Nat Health Legis, Western Soc Periodont, 72-73; clin asst prof periodont, Univ Ill, 77-81. *Mem:* Am Dent Asn; Int Asn Dent Res; fel Int Col Dentists; Am Acad Periodont. *Res:* Periodontal new attachment therapy through biological treatment of diseased root surfaces; dental care delivery; experimental atherosclerosis effect on supporting tissues of teeth; application of growth factors to wound healing. *Mailing Add:* Sch Dent Univ Calif PO Box 0762 San Francisco CA 94143

**WIRTSCHAFTER, JONATHAN DINE,** OPHTHALMOLOGY, NEUROLOGY. *Current Pos:* PROF OPHTHAL, NEUROL & NEUROSURG, COL MED, UNIV MINN, 77- *Personal Data:* b Cleveland, Ohio, Apr 9, 35; m 59, Carol Lavenstein; c Jacob, Benjamin, Joshua, David & Brooke. *Educ:* Reed Col, BA, 56; Harvard Med Sch, MD, 60; Linfield Col, MS, 63. *Prof Exp:* Intern, Philadelphia Gen Hosp, 60-61; resident neurol, Good Samaritan Hosp, Portland, Ore, 61-63; resident ophthal, Johns Hopkins Hosp, 63-66; fel neurol, New York Neurol Inst, Columbia-Presby Med Ctr, New York, 66-67; from asst prof to assoc prof ophthal & neurol, Col Med, Univ Ky, 67-72, dir div ophthal, 67-74, prof ophthal & neurol, 72-77, chmn dept ophthal, 74-77. *Concurrent Pos:* Vis prof, Hadassah Hosp & Hebrew Univ Jerusalem, 73-74; consult surgeon, Vet Admin Hosp, Minneapolis, Minn, 77-; sect ed, Survey of Ophthal, 83- *Mem:* Fel Am Acad Ophthal; fel Am Col Surg; Asn Res Vision & Ophthal; Am Ophthal Soc; NAm Neuro-Ophthal Soc (pres). *Res:* Clinical neuro-ophthalmology; optic nerve; experimental pathology and pharmacology; facial spasms. *Mailing Add:* Dept Ophthal Univ Minn Hosp Box 493 420 Delaware St SE Minneapolis MN 55455-0501. *Fax:* 612-626-3119; *E-Mail:* wirtsch@maroon.tc.umn.edu

**WIRTZ, GERALD PAUL,** SOLID STATE ELECTROCHEMISTRY, CATALYSIS. *Current Pos:* sr staff mem, Mat Res Lab, 68-80, ASSOC PROF CERAMIC ENG, UNIV ILL, URBANA, 68- *Personal Data:* b Wisconsin Rapids, Wis, Dec 22, 37; m 61; c 3. *Educ:* St Norbert Col, BS, 59; Marquette Univ, BME, 61; Northwestern Univ, PhD(mat sci), 66. *Honors & Awards:* Fulbright-Hayes lectr, Univ Aveiro, 80. *Prof Exp:* Res scientist, Airco Speer Div, Air Reduction Co, Inc, 66-68. *Concurrent Pos:* vis lectr, Mideast Tech Univ, Ankara Turkey, 80. *Mem:* Am Ceramic Soc; Sigma Xi. *Res:* Phase equilibria and transformations; magnetic oxides; materials for thick-film hybrid microcircuitry; metallic conductivity in oxides; defect chemistry of oxides; solid electrolytes; high temperature fuel cells. *Mailing Add:* 1752 County Rd 1650 N Urbana IL 61802

**WIRTZ, JOHN HAROLD,** NATURAL HISTORY, VERTEBRATE ZOOLOGY. *Current Pos:* RETIRED. *Personal Data:* b Sheboygan, Wis, Nov 13, 23; m 50. *Educ:* Loyola Univ, Ill, BS, 52; Univ Wyo, MS, 54; Ore State Univ, PhD, 61. *Prof Exp:* From asst prof to assoc prof natural hist & gen biol, Portland State Univ, 57-88. *Mem:* AAAS; Nat Audubon Soc. *Res:* Visual behavior, mobility and orientation in sciurid rodents. *Mailing Add:* 28700 SW Farmington Rd Hillsboro OR 97123

**WIRTZ, RICHARD ANTHONY,** MECHANICAL ENGINEERING. *Current Pos:* Asst prof, 70-76, ASSOC PROF & EXEC OFFICER MECH ENG, CLARKSON COL TECHNOL, 76- *Personal Data:* b New Brunswick, NJ, Aug 16, 44; m 66; c 1. *Educ:* Newark Col Eng, BSME, 66; Rutgers Univ, MS, 68, PhD(heat transfer), 71. *Concurrent Pos:* Prin investr grants, 73-80. *Mem:* Assoc Am Soc Mech Engrs; Am Phys Soc; Sigma Xi. *Res:* Numerical and physical experiments on free convection heat transfer. *Mailing Add:* 688 Tumbleweed Circle Incline Village NV 89451

**WIRTZ, WILLIAM OTIS, II,** MAMMALOGY. *Current Pos:* from asst prof to assoc prof zool, 68-88, PROF BIOL, POMONA COL, 88- *Personal Data:* b Montclair, NJ, Aug 16, 37; m 72, Helen Spaulding. *Educ:* Rutgers Univ, BA, 59; Cornell Univ, PhD(ecol, evolutionary biol), 68. *Prof Exp:* Res cur, Smithsonian Inst, 62-66. *Mem:* Am Soc Mammalogists; Ecol Soc Am; Wildlife Soc; Am Ornithologists Union; Asn Field Ornithologists. *Res:* Mammalian population ecology and behavior; fire ecology; predator ecology; carnivores and raptors; evolution and systematics of mammals. *Mailing Add:* Dept Biol Pomona Col 609 N College Ave Claremont CA 91711. *Fax:* 909-621-8878; *E-Mail:* wwirtz@pomona.edu

**WISBY, WARREN JENSEN,** FISHERY BIOLOGY, BEHAVIOR OF MARINE ORGANISMS. *Current Pos:* RETIRED. *Personal Data:* b Denmark, Nov 14, 22; US citizen; m 62, Audra B; c Douglas V, Mark S, Stephanie W (Nissen) & Karen E. *Educ:* Univ Wis, BA, 48, MA, 50, PhD(zool), 52. *Prof Exp:* Res assoc zool, Univ Wis, 52-59; assoc prof marine biol, Inst Marine Sci, Univ Miami, 59-65; dir, Nat Fisheries Ctr & Aquarium Dept Interior, 65-72; adj prof, Inst Marine Sci, Sch Marine & Atmospheric Sci, Univ Miami, 65-72, assoc dean, 72-80, interim dean, 80-82, assoc dean, 82-90. *Mem:* Am Fisheries Soc; Am Soc Zool; Animal Behav Soc; Sigma Xi. *Res:* Behavior and sensory physiology of marine organisms. *Mailing Add:* 555 S Luna Ct No 312 Hollywood FL 33021

**WISCHMEIER, WALTER HENRY,** SOIL CONSERVATION. *Current Pos:* from assoc prof to prof, 65-76, EMER PROF AGR ENG, PURDUE UNIV, WEST LAFAYETTE, 76- *Personal Data:* b Lincoln, Mo, Jan 18, 11; m 47; c 2. *Educ:* Univ Mo, BS, 53; Purdue Univ, MS, 57. *Honors & Awards:* Superior Serv Awards, USDA, 59 & 73; Hugh Hammond Bennett Award, Soil Conserv Soc Am, 77. *Prof Exp:* Researcher, Soil & Water Conserv Res Div, Agr Res Serv, USDA, 40-61, res invests leader soil erosion, Corn Belt Br, 61-72, tech adv water erosion, NCent Region, 72-75. *Concurrent Pos:* Consult, soil erosion prediction & control, 76- *Mem:* Am Soc Agron; fel Soil Conserv Soc Am; Am Soc Agr Eng; Soil Sci Soc Am. *Res:* Soil and water conservation; quantitative relationship of soil erosion to rainfall characteristics, topographic features, management, productivity level and factor interactions; conservation farm planning; runoff and soil-loss prediction equations. *Mailing Add:* 2009 Indian Trail Dr West Lafayette IN 47906

**WISCHMEYER, CARL R(IEHLE),** ELECTRICAL ENGINEERING. *Current Pos:* TECH REP, WERSI ELECTRONIC ORGANS, 84- *Personal Data:* b Terre Haute, Ind, Oct 2, 16; m 45; c 3. *Educ:* Rose Polytech Inst, BS, 37, EE, 42, ScD, 70; Yale Univ, MEng, 39. *Prof Exp:* Lab asst elec eng, Yale Univ, 37-39; instr, Rice Inst Technol, 39-45; mem tech staff, Bell Tel Labs, Inc, 45-47; from asst prof to prof elec eng, Rice Univ, 47-68, master, Baker Col, 56-68, dir continuing studies, 68; dir educ, Bell Tel Labs, 68-84. *Concurrent Pos:* Consult to indust, 43-68; NSF grant, Eindhoven Technol Univ, 62; mem tech staff, Bell Tel Labs, 63-64, 68-84; bd mgrs, Rose Polytech Inst, 63-67. *Mem:* Am Soc Eng Educ; fel Inst Elec & Electronics Engrs; Am Soc Train & Develop Engrs; Sigma Xi. *Res:* Radio; electronics; instruments and equipment. *Mailing Add:* 1311 Oyster Point Dr Sugar Land TX 77478-4211

**WISCOMBE, WARREN JACKMAN,** ATMOSPHERIC PHYSICS. *Current Pos:* PHYS SCIENTIST, GODDARD SPACE LAB CTR, NASA, 83- *Personal Data:* b St Louis, Mo, Feb 4, 43; m 84, Helenka Novak; c Tom, Juliet, Elaine & Natasha. *Educ:* Mass Inst Technol, SB, 64; Calif Inst Technol, MS, 66, PhD(appl math), 70. *Prof Exp:* Res scientist, Systs Sci Software, 69-74; res scientist, Nat Ctr Atmospheric Res, 74-80; assoc prof, NY Univ, 80-83. *Mem:* Am Meteorol Soc. *Res:* Radiative transfer in planetary atmospheres, particularly bearing on climate problems. *Mailing Add:* Climate Radiation Br Code 913 NASA Goddard Space Flight Ctr Greenbelt MD 20771

**WISDOM, JACK LEACH,** NON-LINEAR DYNAMICS, PLANETARY DYNAMICS. *Current Pos:* res scientist, 84-85, from asst prof to assoc prof, 85-90, PROF, DEPT EARTH, ATMOSPHERIC & PLANET SCI, MASS INST TECHNOL, 90- *Personal Data:* b Lubbock, Tex, Jan 28, 53; m 81; c 4. *Educ:* Rice Univ, BS, 76; Calif Inst Technol, PhD(physics), 81. *Honors & Awards:* Harold C Urey Prize, Div Planet Sci, Am Astron Soc, 86; Helen B Warner Prize, Am Astron Soc, 87; MacArthur Fel, John D & Catherine T MacArthur Found, 94. *Prof Exp:* NATO fel, Observatoire de Nice, France, 81-82; res assoc, Univ Calif, Santa Barbara. *Concurrent Pos:* Presidential young investr, 88-93. *Mem:* Am Astron Soc; Am Acad Arts & Sci. *Res:* Application of modern non-linear dynamics to the dynamics of the solar system. *Mailing Add:* 54-414 Mass Inst Technol Dept EAPS Cambridge MA 02139. *Fax:* 617-253-2886; *E-Mail:* wisdom@mit.edu

**WISE, BRADLEY C,** PHARMACOLOGY. *Current Pos:* ASSOC PROF PHARMACOL, FIDIA-GEORGETOWN INST NEUROSCI, 89- *Personal Data:* b Needham, Mass, Mar 1, 53. *Res:* Pharmacology. *Mailing Add:* Fidia-Georgetown Inst Neurosci 3900 Resevoir Rd NW Washington DC 20007-2187

**WISE, BURTON LOUIS,** NEUROSURGERY. *Current Pos:* CONSULT, 85- *Personal Data:* b New York, Nov 24, 24; m 59; c 3. *Educ:* Columbia Univ, AB, 44; New York Med Col, MD, 47. *Prof Exp:* Clin instr neurol surg, Univ Calif San Francisco, 54, from instr to assoc prof, 55-68, vchmn dept, 65-68, assoc clin prof neurosurg, Sch Med, 68-77; chief dept neurosci, Mt Zion Hosp & Mt Zion Neurol Inst, 75-85. *Concurrent Pos:* Attend neurol surgeon, Ft Miley Vet Admin Hosp, San Francisco, 54-68 & San Francisco Gen Hosp, 58-69; consult neurosurgeon, Laguna Honda Home & Langley Porter Neuropsychiat Inst, 57-68 & Letterman Army Hosp, 58-; chief neurosurg, Mt Zion Hosp & Mt Zion Neurol Inst, 70-74. *Mem:* Am Asn Neurol Surg; AMA; Am Col Surg; Am Fedn Clin Res. *Res:* Metabolic responses to central nervous system lesions; brain stem mechanisms in salt and water homeostasis; effects of hypertonic solutions on cerebrospinal fluid pressure; neuroendocrinology; pediatric neurosurgery and hydrocephalus. *Mailing Add:* 2186 Geary Blvd San Francisco CA 94115-3455

**WISE, C DAVID,** BIOCHEMISTRY, NEUROPSYCHOPHARMACOLOGY. *Current Pos:* DIR, OFF TECHNOL INFO SYSTS, NAT INST ALLERGY & INFECTIOUS DIS, NIH, 96- *Personal Data:* b Lisbon, Ohio, Mar 19, 35; m 65, Edythe Sahm; c Andrew & Kenneth. *Educ:* Susquehanna Univ, BA, 58; Univ Pa, PhD(biochem), 66. *Mailing Add:* NIAID/NIH Off Technol Info Systs Bldg 31 Rm 7A32 9000 Rockville Pike Bethesda MD 20892. *Fax:* 301-402-0120; *E-Mail:* dw22a@nih.gov

**WISE, CHARLES DAVIDSON,** INVERTEBRATE ZOOLOGY, ORNITHOLOGY. *Current Pos:* RETIRED. *Personal Data:* b Huntington, WVa, June 13, 26; m 47, Juanita Meadows; c Sandra L. *Educ:* WVa Univ, AB & MS, 50; Univ NMex, PhD(invert zool), 62. *Prof Exp:* Asst zool, Marshall Univ, 50-51; teacher high sch, WVa, 51-53; instr biol, Amarillo Col, 55-57; res scientist, Inst Marine Sci, Univ Tex, 58-60; asst biol, Univ NMex, 60-61; from asst prof to prof biol, Ball State Univ, 61-91. *Concurrent Pos:* Ind State rep, 66-68; Ind State senator, 68-72; mem, Int Comt Recent Ostracoda, 63-73. *Mem:* Nat Audubon Soc; Sigma Xi. *Res:* Ecology; biological oceanography; marine and freshwater ostracods, especially taxonomy and ecology; ornithology. *Mailing Add:* Dept Biol Ball State Univ Muncie IN 47306

**WISE, DAVID HAYNES,** POPULATION & COMMUNITY ECOLOGY, SOIL ECOLOGY. *Current Pos:* asst prof, 76-81, ASSOC PROF BIOL SCI, UNIV MD, BALTIMORE COUNTY, 81- *Personal Data:* b Mineral Wells, Tex, Apr 28, 45; m 67; c 2. *Educ:* Swarthmore Col, BA, 67; Univ Mich, MS, 69, PhD(zool), 74. *Prof Exp:* Instr biol, Albion Col, 69-70; lectr zool, Univ Mich, 70-71; asst prof biol, Univ NMex, 74-76. *Concurrent Pos:* Alexander von Humboldt fel, Univ Göttinger, Ger, 85-86. *Mem:* Ecol Soc Am; Am Arachnol Soc; Soc Study Evolution; Brit Arachnol Soc; US Soil Ecol Soc. *Res:* Population dynamics and regulation of population density; experimental field studies of competition and predation; life history evolution. *Mailing Add:* 6855 Mount Horeb Rd Lexington KY 40511

**WISE, DAVID STEPHEN,** FUNCTIONAL PROGRAMMING LANGUAGES, HEAP BASED MULTIPROCESSING. *Current Pos:* from asst prof to assoc prof, 77-87, PROF COMPUT SCI, IND UNIV, 87- *Personal Data:* b Findlay, Ohio, Aug 10, 45; m 71; c 2. *Educ:* Carnegie Inst Technol, 67; Univ Wis, MS, 69, PhD(comput sci), 71. *Prof Exp:* Lectr comput sci, Univ Edinburgh, 71-72. *Concurrent Pos:* Vis assoc prof comput sci, Ore State Univ, 83-84; prin scientist, Computer Res Lab, Tektronix Labs, 87; chair, Spec Interest Group Prog Lang, Asn Comput Mach, 89-91. *Mem:* Asn Comput Mach. *Res:* Functional (or applicative) programming; developing parallel algorithms, architectures, hardware, and programming style, unified to deliver parallel processing to non-specialists. *Mailing Add:* Ind Univ 215 Lindley Hall Bloomington IN 47405

**WISE, DONALD L,** CELL PHYSIOLOGY. *Current Pos:* from instr to assoc prof, 58-66, chmn dept, 72-87, PROF BIOL, COL WOOSTER, 66- *Personal Data:* b Indianapolis, Ind, May 27, 29; m 52; c 4. *Educ:* Wabash Col, AB, 51; NY Univ, MS, 54, PhD, 58. *Prof Exp:* Instr natural sci, Univ Chicago, 57-58. *Concurrent Pos:* Staff biologist, Comn Undergrad Educ Biol, 67-68; vis prof, George Washington Univ, 67-68; vis prof, Case Western Res Univ, 76-77 & Univ Miami, 85-86; consult & examr, N Cent Asn Col & Schs, 75- *Mem:* Soc Protozool; Sigma Xi. *Res:* Protozoan, bacterial and cellular metabolism and physiology. *Mailing Add:* 7763 Cameron Circle Ft Myers FL 33912

**WISE, DONALD U,** GEOLOGY. *Current Pos:* prof geol, Univ Mass, Amherst, 69-80. *Personal Data:* b Reading, Pa, Apr 21, 31; m 65; c 2. *Educ:* Franklin & Marshall Col, BS, 53; Calif Inst Technol, MS, 55; Princeton Univ, PhD(geol), 57. *Prof Exp:* From asst prof to prof geol, Franklin & Marshall Col, 57-68; chief scientist & dep dir, NASA Apollo Lunar Explor Off, 68-69. *Concurrent Pos:* Pa Geol Surv, 65-66, Geotech & Power Cos Seismic Risk, 72-, Nuclear Regulation Comn, 76-80, various oil co, 73-; vis scientist, Max Planck Inst, Heidelberg, 75 & Univ Rome, 76. *Mem:* AAAS; Geol Soc Am; Am Geophys Union. *Res:* Structural geology; structure and basement features of the middle Rocky Mountains; flow mechanics of rocks; structures of the Appalachian Piedmont; regional fracture analysis; lunar and planetary geology. *Mailing Add:* Dept Geo Sci Franklin & Marshall Col PO Box 3003 Lancaster PA 17604-3003

**WISE, DWAYNE ALLISON,** CYTOGENETICS, CELL BIOLOGY. *Current Pos:* MEM FAC, DEPT BIOL SCI, MISS STATE UNIV, 80- *Personal Data:* b Lewisburg, Tenn, Feb 5, 45; m 66; c 1. *Educ:* David Lipscomb Col, BA, 67; Fla State Univ, MS, 70, PhD(genetics), 72. *Prof Exp:* Res fel cytogenetics, Health Sci Ctr, Univ Tex, 73-74; instr zool, Duke Univ, 74-75, res assoc cell biol, 75-80. *Concurrent Pos:* NIH fel, 75-77. *Mem:* Sigma Xi; Am Soc Cell Biol; Asn Southeastern Biologists. *Res:* Investigation of the control of chromosome distribution at meiosis and mitosis; nonrandom segregation; mechanism of chromosome movement; spindle function. *Mailing Add:* 1200 S Montgomery St Starkville MS 39759-1136. *Fax:* 601-325-7939; *E-Mail:* daw1@ra.msstate.edu

**WISE, EDMUND MERRIMAN, JR,** MICROBIAL BIOCHEMISTRY, CLINICAL RESEARCH & DEVELOPMENT OF DRUGS & BIOTECHNOLOGICALS. *Personal Data:* b Jersey City, NJ, Aug 10, 30; m 52, Cynthia Worrell; c Nancy & John. *Educ:* Oberlin Col, BA, 52; Harvard Univ, PhD(biochem), 63. *Prof Exp:* Jr biologist, Parke, Davis & Co, 54-55; NIH fel, Med Sch, Tufts Univ, 64-66, from instr to asst prof molecular biol & microbiol, 65-73; Sr res microbiologist, Burroughs-Wellcome Co, 73-92, sr sci adv, Infectious Dis & Immunol Dept, 92-95. *Concurrent Pos:* NIH fel, Med Sch, Harvard Univ, 63-64. *Mem:* AAAS; Am Chem Soc; Am Soc Microbiol; NY Acad Sci; Sigma Xi. *Res:* Control of enzyme activity; bacterial cell wall synthesis and degradation; design of enzyme inhibitors; discovery, review and development of licensing-in candidate drugs and biologicals; clinical research on drugs for infectious diseases. *Mailing Add:* 1139 Burning Tree Dr Chapel Hill NC 27514

**WISE, EDWARD NELSON,** CHEMISTRY, RESEARCH ADMINISTRATION. *Current Pos:* RETIRED. *Personal Data:* b Athens, Ohio, May 30, 15; m 36; c 2. *Educ:* Ohio Univ, BS, 37, MS, 38; Univ Kans, PhD(chem), 53. *Prof Exp:* Teacher chem & physics, Gallia Acad High Sch, 38-42; qual control chemist, Baker & Adamson Div, Gen Chem Co, 42; supvr, Stand Lab, WVa Ord Works, 42-45; res engr graphic arts, Battelle Mem Inst, 45-47; mem staff analytical instrumentation, Los Alamos Sci Lab, 47-50; tech asst, Hercules Powder Co, 51; from asst prof to prof chem, Univ Ariz, 52-81, from assoc coordr to coordr res, 64-72. *Mem:* Am Chem Soc. *Res:* Electrophoretic deposition of natural and synthetic rubbers; halftone and color separation techniques in the graphic arts; electrostatic image formation and development; xerography; analytical instrumentation; automatic titrimetry and coulometric analysis. *Mailing Add:* 6914 Sesame Lane Tucson AZ 85704-1850

**WISE, EVAN MICHAEL,** PAPERMAKING, PULPING. *Current Pos:* MGR OPERS RES & DEVELOP, JEFFERSON SMURFIT CORP, CCA, 85- *Personal Data:* b Cleveland, Ohio, May 15, 52; m 75, Diane Weinberg; c Ryan D & Tara R. *Educ:* Miami Univ, BS, 74; Univ NFla, MBA, 79. *Prof Exp:* Pulp mill supt, St Regis Paper Co, 74-83; prod mgr, Jacksonville Kraft Paper Co, 83-85. *Concurrent Pos:* Adj prof, Univ NFla, 76; mem, Paper Chem Water Treat Specialist Group, Paper Indust Mgt Asn; mem, Water Removal Comt, Tech Asn Pulp & Paper Indust; indust liaison, Forest Prods Lab. *Mem:* Tech Asn Pulp & Paper Indust. *Res:* Implementing new developments into current operating systems; innovative ways to produce paper and board products; recycled paper production; team management implementation; problem solving of processes involving pulping, paper and board making and paper recycling. *Mailing Add:* 1332 Old Dominion Naperville IL 60540

**WISE, GARY E,** CELL BIOLOGY. *Current Pos:* PROF & CHMN, DEPT ANAT, LA STATE UNIV, VET SCH MED, 92- *Personal Data:* b Yuma, Colo, July 30, 42; m 62; c 2. *Educ:* Univ Denver, BA, 64; Univ Calif, Berkeley, PhD(zool), 68. *Prof Exp:* NIH fel cell biol, Univ Colo, Boulder, 69-71; from asst prof to assoc prof biol, Univ Miami, Sch Med, 72-82; prof & chmn, Dept Anat & Cell Biol, Tex Col Osteop Med, 82-89, prof, 89-92. *Mem:* Am Soc Cell Biol; Am Asn Anatomists; Int Asn Dent Res. *Res:* Cellular basis of tooth eruption, role of sickled erythrocyte membranes in vaso-occlusion. *Mailing Add:* La State Univ Sch Vet Med Baton Rouge LA 70803-8408

**WISE, GEORGE HERMAN,** ANIMAL NUTRITION, ANIMAL PHYSIOLOGY. *Current Pos:* prof animal indust, NC State Univ, 49-51, head nutrit sect, 49-66, William Neal Reynolds prof, 51-74, EMER PROF ANIMAL SCI, NC STATE UNIV, 74- *Personal Data:* b Saluda, SC, July 7, 08; m 37; c 4. *Educ:* Clemson Col, BS, 30; Univ Minn, MS, 32, PhD(dairy husb), 37. *Honors & Awards:* Award, Am Feed Mfrs Asn, 48; Borden Award, 49; Award of Honor, Am Dairy Sci Asn, 66. *Prof Exp:* Asst dairy husb, Univ Minn, 33-36; assoc, Clemson Col, 37-44; from assoc prof to prof, Kans State Col, 44-47; assoc prof, Iowa State Col, 47-49. *Concurrent Pos:* Mem, Comt Animal Nutrit, Nat Res Coun, 51-53; consult, State Exp Sta Div, Agr Res Serv, USDA, 55-62; study leave, Univ Calif, Davis, 66-67. *Mem:* Fel Am Soc Animal Sci; Am Dairy Sci Asn (vpres, 63-64, pres, 64-65). *Res:* Nutrition and physiology of animals. *Mailing Add:* 229 Woodburn Rd Raleigh NC 27695-0001

**WISE, HAROLD B,** SOCIAL MEDICINE, INTERNAL MEDICINE. *Current Pos:* ASSOC PROF COMMUNITY HEALTH, ALBERT EINSTEIN COL MED, 70- *Personal Data:* b Hamilton, Ont, Feb 14, 37. *Educ:* Univ Toronto, MD, 61. *Prof Exp:* Physician, Prince Albert Clin, Sask, Can, 62-63; resident, Kaiser Found Hosp, San Francisco, Calif, 63-64; Montefiore Hosp & Med Ctr, Bronx, NY, 64-65; actg dir ambulatory serv & home care, Morrisania City Hosp, 65-66; dir, Health Ctr, Dr Martin Luther King Jr Health Ctr, 66-71. *Concurrent Pos:* Dir, Internship & Residency Prog Social Med, Montefiore Hosp & Med Ctr, 69-, dir, Inst Health Team Develop, 72-; dir, Family Ctr Health; dir anal & develop health teams, Montefiore Hosp & Med Ctr, 71-77. *Mem:* Inst Med-Nat Acad Sci. *Res:* Research into the family and the healing processes. *Mailing Add:* 988 Fifth Ave New York NY 10021

**WISE, HENRY,** STRUCTURAL CHEMISTRY. *Current Pos:* chmn, Chem Dynamics Dept, 55-71, dir, Catalysis Lab, 71-84, SCI FEL, SRI INT, 84- *Personal Data:* b Ciechanow, Poland, Jan 14, 19; nat US; m 96; c 6. *Educ:* Univ Chicago, SB, 41, SM, 44, PhD(phys chem), 47. *Honors & Awards:* Fulbright Award, 65; McBean Award, 83. *Prof Exp:* Res assoc, Univ Chicago, 41-46; dir field lab, NY Univ, 46-47; scientist, Nat Adv Comt Aeronaut, Ohio, 47-49; phys chemist, Calif Inst Technol, 49-55; adj prof mat sci & eng, Stanford Univ, 84-93. *Concurrent Pos:* Lectr, Sch Eng, Stanford Univ, 60-; vis prof, Israel Inst Technol, 65; vis prof, Univ Calif, Berkeley, 77-78; mem comt motor vehicle emission, Nat Acad Sci; vis prof chem eng, Univ Calif, Berkeley, 80-81. *Mem:* Am Chem Soc; Am Phys Soc; Catalysis Soc; Chem Soc. *Res:* Heterogeneous catalysis; chemical kinetics; surface chemistry. *Mailing Add:* Mat Sci & Eng Dept Stanford Univ Stanford CA 94305

**WISE, HUGH EDWARD, JR,** INDUSTRIAL ORGANIC CHEMISTRY, WASTEWATER TREATMENT TECHNOLOGY. *Current Pos:* ENVIRON SCIENTIST, INDUST TECHNOL DIV, US ENVIRON PROTECTION AGENCY, 78- *Personal Data:* b Lafayette, Ind, Oct 12, 30. *Educ:* Vanderbilt Univ, BA, 52; Univ Fla, PhD(chem), 61. *Prof Exp:* Proj leader, Tech Serv Lab, Union Carbide Corp, NY, 61-66, proj specialist, 66-68; res chemist, Nalco Chem Co, Ill, 68-70; res chemist, 70-71, field serv supvr, res & develop, Waste Treat Div, Clow Corp, 71-77. *Mem:* Am Chem Soc; Water Environ Fedn. *Res:* Environmental science and engineering; waste treatment technology; occurrence and predictability of regulated chemicals in wastewater; industrial process chemistry. *Mailing Add:* US Environ Protection Agency 4303 401 M St SW Washington DC 20460

**WISE, JOHN JAMES,** PHYSICAL INORGANIC CHEMISTRY, CHEMICAL ENGINEERING. *Current Pos:* Res engr, Mobil Res & Develop Corp, 53-55, sr res engr, 56-62, group leader appl res, 65-68, asst mgr appl res, 68-69, supvr appl develop, 69-76, mgr process res & develop, 76-77, vpres planning, 77-84, mgr process & prod res & develop, 84-87, VPRES RES, MOBIL RES & DEVELOP CORP, 87- *Personal Data:* b Cambridge, Mass, Feb 28, 32; m 67; c 2. *Educ:* Tufts Univ, BS, 53; Mass Inst Technol, PhD(chem), 65. *Mem:* Nat Acad Eng; AAAS; Am Inst Chem Engrs; Am Chem Soc. *Res:* Catalysis related to petroleum and petrochemical processes. *Mailing Add:* Res Dept Mobil Res & Develop Corp PO Box 480 Paulsboro NJ 08066-0480. *Fax:* 609-224-3912; *E-Mail:* jjwise@pau.mobil.com

**WISE, JOHN P,** FISHERIES BIOLOGY, MARINE BIOLOGY. *Current Pos:* CONSULT, CTR MARINE CONSERV, WASHINGTON, DC, 87- *Personal Data:* b Boston, Mass, Feb 9, 24; m 60, Beatrice M Donnelly; c John P, Charles W & Beatrice M. *Educ:* Suffolk Univ, AB, 50; Univ NH, MS, 53. *Prof Exp:* Fishery res biologist, US Bur Com Fisheries, Woods Hole, Mass, 53-60; tech asst officer, Food & Agr Orgn, UN, Rome, Italy, 60-65; chief, Atlantic Tuna Fisheries Res, Nat Marine Fisheries Serv, Miami, 65-73, sr res specialist, 73-74, chief, Resource Assessment Div, 75-77, Data Mgt & Statist Div, 77-78, Prog Eval Staff, Washington, DC, 78-81; biostatistician, Int Comn Conserv Atlantic Tunas, Madrid, Spain, 81-86. *Concurrent Pos:* Consult, Food & Agr Orgn UN, Offshore/Sea Develop Corp, US Agency Int Develop, Heritage Found & KCA Res Inc; adv & comt mem, Univ Miami & Am Univ; adv to res fels, Nat Res Coun, Brazil. *Mem:* AAAS; fel Am Inst Fishery Res Biol; Sigma Xi. *Res:* Stocks of marine animals, involving studies of ecology, growth rates, mortality rates, predation and parasitology, directed at eventual exploitation by man for optimum sustainable yield; approximately 100 publications in assessment of living marine resources, marine biology and oceanography. *Mailing Add:* 4545 Connecticut Ave NW Washington DC 20008

**WISE, LAWRENCE DAVID,** ORGANIC CHEMISTRY. *Current Pos:* res assoc, 77-82, sr res assoc, 82-90, SECT DIR, ORG CHEM, WARNER-LAMBERT/PARKE DAVIS RES, 90-, DIR, PSYCHIAT DIS CHEM, PARKE-DAVIS RES, 93- *Personal Data:* b Canton, Ohio, Oct 13, 40; m 67; c 3. *Educ:* Manchester Col, BA, 62; Ohio State Univ, MS, 64, PhD(org chem), 67. *Prof Exp:* Res scientist org chem, Goodyear Tire & Rubber Co, 67-69; res scientist org chem, Warner-Lambert Res Inst, 69-77. *Mem:* Am Chem Soc; Soc Neurosci. *Res:* Synthetic organic chemistry, particularly heterocycles directed toward drug design. *Mailing Add:* Parke Davis Res 2800 Plymouth Rd Ann Arbor MI 48105-2430. *Fax:* 313-996-5229; *E-Mail:* wisel@aa.wl.com

**WISE, LOUIS NEAL,** agronomy; deceased, see previous edition for last biography

**WISE, MATTHEW NORTON,** HISTORY OF PHYSICS, HISTORY OF SCIENCE. *Current Pos:* lectr, 75-78, ASST PROF HIST, UNIV CALIF, LOS ANGELES, 78- *Personal Data:* b Tacoma, Wash, Apr 2, 40; m 65. *Educ:* Pac Lutheran Univ, BS, 62; Wash State Univ, PhD(physics), 68. *Prof Exp:* Asst prof physics, Auburn Univ, 67-69 & Ore State Univ, 69-71; NSF sci fac fel hist of sci, Princeton Univ, 71-72. *Mem:* Am Phys Soc; Am Asn Physics Teachers; Hist Sci Soc. *Res:* History of nineteenth and twentieth century physical sciences. *Mailing Add:* 129 Dickinson Hall Princeton NJ 08544-1017

**WISE, MILTON BEE,** ANIMAL NUTRITION. *Current Pos:* RETIRED. *Personal Data:* b Newland, NC, July 17, 29; m 51; c 3. *Educ:* Berea Col, BS, 51; NC State Col, MS, 53; Cornell Univ, PhD(animal nutrit), 57. *Prof Exp:* Lab supvr, Berea Col, 47-51; asst, NC State Col, 52-53, res assoc, 53-54; asst, Cornell Univ, 54-55, instr animal husb, 55-57; from asst prof to prof animal sci, NC State Univ, 57-70; prof animal sci & head dept, Va Polytech Inst & State Univ, 70-94. *Mem:* Am Soc Animal Sci; Sigma Xi. *Res:* Mineral and nutrient metabolism; forage utilization; physiology of digestion. *Mailing Add:* 150 Spring Valley Rd Seneca SC 29678

**WISE, RALEIGH WARREN,** RESEARCH ADMINISTRATION, RUBBER CHEMISTRY. *Current Pos:* PRES, WISE-SULLIVAN, INC, 91- *Personal Data:* b Plainfield, NJ, Sept 30, 28; m 57, Mamie E Addington. *Educ:* Univ Va, BS, 51. *Honors & Awards:* Banbury Award, Am Chem Soc, 87. *Prof Exp:* Analytical chemist, Monsanto Chem Co, 51-53, analytical res chemist, 54-56, res group leader, 56-65, res sect mgr, 65-71, group mgr, Instrument & Equip Div, 71-74, dir, 74-75, dir technol, Rubber Chem Div, 75-87, consult, 87-91. *Mem:* Am Chem Soc; Instrument Soc Am. *Res:* Instrumentation; chemical and elastomer research. *Mailing Add:* 12755 Cold Stream Dr Ft Myers FL 33912

**WISE, RICHARD MELVIN,** ORGANIC CHEMISTRY. *Current Pos:* RETIRED. *Personal Data:* b Greentown, Ohio, Sept 27, 24; m 68, Vera Daughnbaugh; c 3. *Educ:* Mt Union Col, BS, 49; Ohio State Univ, PhD(org chem), 55. *Prof Exp:* Res chemist, Gen Corp, 55-58, sr res chemist, 58-72, res scientist, 72-87. *Mem:* Am Chem Soc. *Res:* Organic research; synthesis of monomers; preparation of polymerization catalysts and polymers; tire cord adhesives; emulsion rubbers. *Mailing Add:* 2780 Wright Rd PO Box 459 Uniontown OH 44685-0459

**WISE, ROBERT IRBY,** BACTERIOLOGY, INTERNAL MEDICINE. *Current Pos:* EMER MAGEE PROF MED, JEFFERSON MED COL, 75- *Personal Data:* b Barstow, Tex, May 19, 15; m 40, Mary C Dosterschill; c Robert I Jr, Joyce (Beene) & John K. *Educ:* Univ Tex, BA, 37, MD, 50; Univ Ill, MS, 38, PhD(bact), 42; Am Bd Internal Med, dipl, 57. *Hon Degrees:* DSc, Thomas Jefferson Univ, 80. *Prof Exp:* Asst, Div Animal Genetics, Exp Sta, Univ Ill, 38-39, asst instr bact, 39-42; dir, Wichita City-County Pub Health Lab, Tex, 42-43; dir, Houston Pub Health Lab, 43; asst prof bact, Sch Med, Univ Tex, 43-46, dir bact & serol labs, Univ Hosp, 46-50; asst surgeon, USPHS Hosp, New Orleans, La, 50-51; fel med, Univ Minn, 51-53, asst prof, 53-54, asst prof med & bact, 54-55; from asst prof to assoc prof med, 55-59, Magee prof med & head dept, 59-75; asst chief med staff, Vet Admin Med & Regional Off Ctr, Togus, 75-77, chief staff, 77-84. *Concurrent Pos:* Bacteriologist, Univ Hosp, Univ Minn, 57-59; assoc mem comn streptococcal dis, Armed Forces Epidemiol Bd, 58-66; physician-in-chief, Thomas Jefferson Univ Hosp, 59-75; mem bd trustees, Magee Mem Hosp, Philadelphia, 59-75 & Drexel Univ, 66-75; mem, Greater Philadelphia Comt Med-Pharmaceut Sci, 63-75, chmn, 70-74; mem adv comt, Inter-Soc Comt Heart Dis Resources, 67-70; mem bd-adv comt registry of tissue reaction, Univs Assoc Res & Educ Path Inc, 70-75; mem exec comt, Int Cong Internal Med, 71; mem, Nat Brucellosis Tech Comn, 76-79. *Mem:* Am Fedn Clin Res; fel Am Col Physicians; Asn Am Physicians; Am Infectious Dis Soc; Sigma Xi. *Res:* Infectious diseases; chemotherapy; antibiotics. *Mailing Add:* 5814 Williamsburg Landing Dr Williamsburg VA 23185

**WISE, ROBERT J,** HEMATOLOGY. *Current Pos:* ASST PROF MED, BRIGHAM & WOMENS HOSP, 93- *Personal Data:* b Indianapolis, Ind, Oct 18, 53. *Res:* Hematology. *Mailing Add:* Dept Hemat LMRC-610 Brigham & Womens Hosp 75 Francis St Boston MA 02115-6195

**WISE, SHERWOOD WILLING, JR,** GEOLOGY, PALEONTOLOGY. *Current Pos:* asst prof, 71-75, assoc prof, 75-80, PROF GEOL, FLA STATE UNIV, 80- *Personal Data:* b Jackson, Miss, May 31, 41; m 65. *Educ:* Washington & Lee Univ, BS, 63; Univ Ill, MS, 65, PhD(geol), 70. *Prof Exp:* NSF fel, Swiss Fed Inst Technol, 70-71. *Concurrent Pos:* NSF res grant, 72-; res grant, Petrol Res Fund, 73-81; sci ed, Initial Reports Deep Sea Drilling Proj, 77, 83; co-chief, Deep Sea Drilling Proj, 83, 88; mem, ad hoc comt Antarctic Geoscience, Nat Acad Sci, 83-86; pres, N Am Micropaleontol Sect, Soc Econ Paleontologists & Mineralogists, 86-87; mem, Southern Oceans Panel, Ocean Drilling Project, 87-; chair, Res Comt, SEPM, 88-90; mem, USSAC Comt & Info Handling Panel, Joint Oceanog Inst. *Mem:* Fel AAAS; Am Asn Petrol Geologists; Soc Econ Paleontologists & Mineralogists; Geol Soc Am; Swiss Geol Soc. *Res:* Skeletal ultrastructure; taxonomy and biostratigraphy of fossil calcareous nannoplankton, diatoms and silico flagellates; early diagenesis of carbonate and siliceous sediment; circum-Antarctic and Atlantic marine geology. *Mailing Add:* Dept Geol 3026 Fla State Univ Tallahassee FL 32306

**WISE, WILLIAM CURTIS,** PHYSIOLOGY, COMPUTER SCIENCE. *Current Pos:* from asst prof to assoc prof, Med Univ SC, 68-80, asst to acad vpres, Acad Info Mgt, 85-91, chief info off, Med Ctr, 87-88, PROF PHYSIOL, MED UNIV SC, 80-, ACAD RES COMPUT SPECIALIST, 91- *Personal Data:* b Louisville, Ky, Nov 24, 40; m 63; c 2. *Educ:* Transylvania Univ, AB, 63; Univ Ky, PhD(physiol & biophys), 67. *Prof Exp:* Physiologist, McDonnell-Douglas Corp, 67-68. *Concurrent Pos:* Koebig Trust grant physiol, Med Univ SC, 72-73; Nat Cancer Inst res career develop award, 74-79. *Mem:* Sigma Xi; Am Physiol Soc; Soc Gen Physiologists; Biophys Soc; Shock Soc. *Res:* Endotoxic shock; septic shock; renal and acid-base physiology; computers in education. *Mailing Add:* Dept Physiol Med Univ SC 171 Ashley Ave Charleston SC 29425-2258. *Fax:* 803-792-4423; *E-Mail:* curtis_wise@smtpgw.musc.edu

**WISE, WILLIAM STEWART,** MINERALOGY, PETROLOGY. *Current Pos:* RETIRED. *Personal Data:* b Carson City, Nev, Aug 18, 33; m 55; c 3. *Educ:* Stanford Univ, BS, 55, MS, 58; Johns Hopkins Univ, PhD(geol), 61. *Prof Exp:* Instr geol, Stanford Univ, 58 & Johns Hopkins Univ, 60-61; from asst prof to prof geol, Univ Calif, Santa Barbara, 61-94, assoc dean, Col Lett & Sci, 79-81, dean, Acad Skills, 81-94. *Concurrent Pos:* Consult, US Geol Surv, 65-67 & Argonne Nat Lab, 79- *Mem:* Fel Geol Soc Am; fel Mineral Soc Am; Mineral Asn Can; Mineral Soc Gt Brit; Sigma Xi. *Res:* Paragenesis of minerals, principally zeolites and associated minerals, barium silicates; petrology of oceanic volcanoes. *Mailing Add:* 4575 Nueces Dr Santa Barbara CA 93110

**WISECARVER, KEITH DOUGLAS,** MULTIPHASE REACTORS. *Current Pos:* asst prof, 87-92, ASSOC PROF CHEM ENG, UNIV TULSA, 92- *Personal Data:* b Columbus, Ohio, Sept 14, 57; m 86, Diane Chen; c Adam & Amy. *Educ:* Ohio State Univ, BS, 79, MS, 83, PhD(chem eng), 87. *Prof Exp:* Prod develop engr, Firestone Tire & Rubber, 79-80; process engr, Mat Concepts Inc, 80-81. *Concurrent Pos:* Consult, Amoco Prod Co, 88-89, John Zink Co, 89. *Mem:* Am Inst Chem Engrs; Sigma Xi. *Res:* Hydrodynamics and transport phenomena in multiphase reactors, biochemical reaction engineering, hydrometallurgy and adsorptive separations. *Mailing Add:* 3038 S Utica Ave Tulsa OK 74114. *E-Mail:* che_kw@vax1.utulsa.edu

**WISEMAN, BILLY RAY,** ENTOMOLOGY, HORTICULTURE. *Current Pos:* res entomologist, Southern Grain Insects Lab, 67-84, INSECT BIOL POP MGR, RES LAB, AGR RES SERV, USDA, 84- *Personal Data:* b Sudan, Tex, Mar 28, 37; m 63, Gladys M Striegler; c William S II & Amy L. *Educ:* Tex Tech Col, BS, 59; Kans State Univ, MS, 61, PhD(entom), 67. *Honors & Awards:* Bussart Mem Award, 90. *Prof Exp:* Res asst host plant resistance, Kans State Univ, 59-61 & 64-66; res entomologist, Southern Grains Invests, Okla, 66-67. *Concurrent Pos:* Mem grad fac, Univ Ga & Univ Fla; courtesy prof, grad courses in plant resistance to insects, Univ Fla. *Mem:* Fel Entom Soc Am; Sigma Xi; Coun Agr Sci & Technol. *Res:* Entomological research in host plant resistance of small grains, corn, sorghum and vegetable crops and the insects attacking these crops, including feeding stimulants, deterrents, food utilization, behavior, biology and mechanisms of resistance; published over 300 articles. *Mailing Add:* IBPMRL PO Box 748 Tifton GA 31794-0748

**WISEMAN, CARL D,** PHYSICAL METALLURGY. *Current Pos:* RETIRED. *Personal Data:* b Chicago, Ill, Oct 25, 25; m 49, Ruth A; c Dulcie A, Carl Jr & Clayton L. *Educ:* Southern Methodist Univ, BS, 50; Univ Calif, MS, 55, PhD(metall), 57. *Prof Exp:* Res engr, Calif, 51-57; metallurgist, Gen Elec Co, 57-59 & Tex Instruments, Inc, 59-64; from assoc prof to prof eng mech, Univ Tex, Arlington, 64-91. *Mem:* Am Soc Metals; Am Inst Mining, Metall & Petrol Engrs; Sigma Xi. *Res:* Plastic deformation of metals; nuclear reactor metallurgy; metal failure analysis; metallurgy of semiconductors and thermoelectric materials; surfaces of solids to fields of research. *Mailing Add:* Dept Mech Eng Univ Tex Arlington TX 76019

**WISEMAN, EDWARD H,** BIOCHEMISTRY, PHARMACOLOGY. *Current Pos:* res chemist, Pfizer Inc, 61-64, supvr biochem pharmacol, 64-67, asst to res vpres, 67, mgr biochem pharmacol, 67-71, dir pharmacol, 71-76, EXEC DIR RES ADMIN, PFIZER INC, 76- *Personal Data:* b Portsmouth, Eng, Nov 14, 34; m 57; c 4. *Educ:* Univ Birmingham, BSc, 56, PhD(org chem), 59. *Prof Exp:* Fel, Ohio State Univ, 60. *Mem:* Am Rheumatism Asn; Am Soc Pharmacol & Exp Therapeut. *Res:* Non-steroidal anti-inflammatory agents; biochemistry of metabolic diseases. *Mailing Add:* Pfizer Inc Groton CT 06340-5196. *Fax:* 860-441-4735

**WISEMAN, GEORGE EDWARD,** INORGANIC CHEMISTRY, ORGANIC CHEMISTRY. *Current Pos:* chmn dept chem, 59-66, assoc grad dean, Conolly, 66-71, prof, 59-86, EMER PROF CHEM, LONG ISLAND UNIV, 87- *Personal Data:* b Brooklyn, NY, May 28, 18; m 45; c 3. *Educ:* St Peter's Col, BS, 40; Polytech Inst Brooklyn, PhD(chem), 56. *Prof Exp:* Assoc prof chem, St John's Univ, NY, 46-59. *Mem:* Am Chem Soc; fel Am Inst Chemists. *Res:* Preparation, properties and structures of organoselenium compounds; heterocyclic compounds; metallic derivatives of aromatic hydrocarbons. *Mailing Add:* 106 Conn Ave Massapequa NY 11758-4503

**WISEMAN, GORDON G,** PHYSICS. *Current Pos:* from instr to prof, 43-87, EMER PROF PHYSICS, UNIV KANS, 87- *Personal Data:* b Livingston, Wis, Feb 24, 17; m 42; c 2. *Educ:* SDak State Univ, BS, 38; Univ Kans, MS, 41, AM, 47, PhD(physics), 50. *Prof Exp:* Instr physics, Culver-Stockton Col, 41-43. *Mem:* Am Phys Soc; Am Asn Physics Teachers. *Res:* Dielectrics; absorption microspectrophotometry; ferroelectricity. *Mailing Add:* Dept Physics Univ Kans Lawrence KS 66044

**WISEMAN, GORDON MARCY,** BACTERIOLOGY. *Current Pos:* RETIRED. *Personal Data:* b Winnipeg, Man, Feb 24, 34; m 56. *Educ:* Univ Man, BSc, 56, MSc, 61; Univ Edinburgh, PhD(bact), 63, DSc, 74. *Prof Exp:* Demonstr, Fac Med, Univ Man, 57-59, from asst prof to prof med microbiol, 65-90. *Concurrent Pos:* Med Res Coun fel bact, Fac Med, Univ Man, 64 & scholar, 65-70. *Mem:* Am Soc Microbiol; Can Soc Microbiol. *Res:* Neisseria gonorrhoeae; adhesion to host cells in relation to pathogenicity and virulence. *Mailing Add:* 3517 Vialoux Dr Winnipeg MB R3E 0A5 Can

**WISEMAN, H(ARRY) A(LEXANDER) B(ENJAMIN),** ENGINEERING MECHANICS. *Current Pos:* RETIRED. *Personal Data:* b Montreal, Que, Dec 27, 24; m 44; c 1. *Educ:* Univ Sask, BSc, 47; Wash State Univ, MS, 49; Pa State Univ, PhD(eng mech), 54. *Prof Exp:* Instr, Wash State Univ, 47-49; asst & res assoc, Pa State Univ, 49-54; res officer, Nat Res Coun Can, 54-55; assoc prof eng, Univ Del, 55-58; prof civil & mech eng, Univ Miami, 58-76, prof biomed eng, Sch Med, 70-76, prof mech eng, 76- *Mem:* Am Soc Eng Educ; Am Soc Mech Engrs; Nat Soc Prof Engrs; Am Soc Metals; Am Soc Artificial Internal Organs; Sigma Xi. *Res:* Biaxial and triaxial stress and strain relations; prestressed concrete; solid state studies of ultra high pressures; electron microscope metallography; high velocity stress-strain phenomena; photo stress and elasticity; biomedical engineering. *Mailing Add:* 508 Caligula Ave Miami FL 33146

**WISEMAN, JEFFREY STEWART,** ENZYME INHIBITION, LEUKOTRIENE BIOSYNTHESIS. *Current Pos:* DEPT HEAD BIOCHEM, GLAXO WELLCOME, INC, 88-, DIR WORLD-WIDE RES INFO. *Personal Data:* b Athens, Ohio, Dec 8, 48; m 74; c 2. *Educ:* Ohio Univ, BS, 70; Harvard Univ, PhD(chem), 74. *Prof Exp:* Teaching fel, Stanford Univ, 75-76 & Brandeis Univ, 76-78; sr biochemist, Merrell Dow Res Inst, 79-88. *Mem:* Am Soc Biol Chemists. *Res:* Design and characterization of enzyme inhibitors; mechanisms of action of enzymes of therapeutic interest. *Mailing Add:* Glaxo Wellcome Inc PO Box 13398 5 Moore Dr Research Triangle Park NC 27709

**WISEMAN, JOHN R,** ORGANIC CHEMISTRY, SYNTHETIC ORGANIC & NATURAL PRODUCTS CHEMISTRY. *Current Pos:* from asst prof to assoc prof, 66-76, PROF CHEM, UNIV MICH, 76- *Personal Data:* b Patriot, Ohio, May 4, 36; m 56; c 3. *Educ:* Univ Colo, BS, 57; Stanford Univ, PhD(chem), 65. *Prof Exp:* NSF fel chem, Univ Calif, Berkeley, 64-65, lectr, 65-66, fel, 66. *Concurrent Pos:* Grants, Petrol Res Fund, 68-73; Res Corp grant, 68-69; Am Cancer Soc grant, 72-77, Nat Cancer Inst, 78-80. *Mem:* AAAS; Am Chem Soc; Royal Soc Chem. *Res:* Strain of bicyclic bridgehead alkenes; reaction of carbonium ions; synthesis of natural products. *Mailing Add:* Dept Chem Univ Mich Ann Arbor MI 48109

**WISEMAN, LAWRENCE LINDEN,** DEVELOPMENTAL BIOLOGY. *Current Pos:* from asst prof to assoc prof biol, 71-77 CHMN DEPT, 81-, PROF BIOL, COL WILLIAM & MARY, 86- *Personal Data:* b Galion, Ohio, Apr 27, 44; c 2. *Educ:* Hiram Col, AB, 66; Princeton Univ, MA, 69, PhD(biol), 70. *Prof Exp:* Nat Cancer Inst fel, Princeton Univ, 70-71. *Concurrent Pos:* Vis scientist, Human Leukemia Prog, Ont Cancer Inst, Toronto, 74-75; spec asst to pres, Univ Colo, 87-88; Am Coun Educ fel, 87-88. *Mem:* AAAS; Soc Develop Biol; Am Soc Zool; Am Soc Cell Biol; Int Soc Develop Biologists. *Res:* Cell adhesion, cell movement; vertebrate embryology. *Mailing Add:* Dept Biol Col William & Mary Williamsburg VA 23185. *Fax:* 757-221-6483; *E-Mail:* llwise@mail.wm.edu

**WISEMAN, PARK ALLEN,** ORGANIC CHEMISTRY. *Current Pos:* from asst prof to assoc prof, 47-56, head dept, 65-69, prof, 56-81, EMER PROF CHEM, BALL STATE UNIV, 81- *Personal Data:* b Amsden, Ohio, Dec 29, 18; m 42; c 1. *Educ:* DePauw Univ, AB, 40; Purdue Univ, MA, 42, PhD(org chem), 44. *Prof Exp:* Asst org & phys chem, Purdue Univ, 40-42, Monsanto Chem Co res fel org chem, 44-46; res chemist, Firestone Tire & Rubber Co, Ohio, 46-47. *Concurrent Pos:* NSF vis prof, Tech Inst Northwestern Univ, 69-70. *Mem:* AAAS; Am Chem Soc. *Res:* High pressure oxidation of hydrocarbons; catalytic vapor-phase oxidation of hydrocarbons; fluorine chemistry; organic synthesis and natural products. *Mailing Add:* 4204 W University Muncie IN 47304-3656

**WISEMAN, RALPH FRANKLIN,** MICROBIOLOGY. *Current Pos:* RETIRED. *Personal Data:* b Washington, DC, Sept 1, 21; m 51, Millicent Becker; c Carmen D & Eve J. *Educ:* Univ Md, BS, 49; Univ Hawaii, MS, 53; Univ Wis, PhD(bact), 56. *Prof Exp:* Lab asst, Nat Cancer Inst, 39-42, bacteriologist, Nat Inst Dent Res, 49-51; asst, Univ Wis, 53-55; instr, Univ Ky, 55-56, from instr to prof microbiol, 56-87. *Concurrent Pos:* Vis prof, Hacettepe Univ, Turkey, 68-69 & Rega Inst Med Res, Cath Univ, Louvain, Belg, 69. *Mem:* Am Soc Microbiol; Asn Gnotobiotics; fel Am Acad Microbiol; Sigma Xi. *Res:* Intestinal microbiology; germ free-like characteristics in antibiotic-treated animals; animal-microbial ecosystems; water quality. *Mailing Add:* Morgan Sch Biol Sci Rm 1 Frazee Hall Univ Ky Lexington KY 40506

**WISEMAN, ROBERT S,** ILLUMINATING ENGINEERING, ELECTRICAL ENGINEERING. *Current Pos:* RETIRED. *Personal Data:* b Robinson, Ill, Feb 27, 24; m 47; c 1. *Educ:* Univ Ill, BSEE, 48, MSEE, 50, PhD(elec eng), 54. *Prof Exp:* Instr & asst prof elec eng, Miss State Col, 48-51; chief, Res Sect, US Army Eng Res & Develop Lab, 51-58, chief, Warfare Vision Br, 58-65; dir, Combat Surv, Night Vision & Target Acquisition Labs, US Army Electronics Command, 65-68, dep for labs, 68-71, dir, Res & Develop/Army Electronics Labs, 71-78, tech dir, 78-79; dep sci & technol, Darcom, 79-80; dir, Electronics Lab, Orlando Div, Martin Marietta Aerospace, 81-83, dep dir res & develop, 83-84, dir, Electro-Optics Dept, 84-93, exec vpres mkt res. *Concurrent Pos:* Mem, Comt Vision, Nat Res Coun, 54-78. *Mem:* Fel Inst Elec & Electronics Engrs; Am Inst Aeronaut & Astronaut; fel Illum Eng Soc. *Res:* Night vision; combat surveillance and target acquisition; electronics/signals warfare; atmospheric sciences; electronic technology and devices; illuminating engineering; electro-optics. *Mailing Add:* 8451 Bay Hill Blvd Orlando FL 32819

**WISEMAN, WILLIAM H(OWARD),** CHEMICAL ENGINEERING. *Current Pos:* RETIRED. *Personal Data:* b Chillicothe, Ohio, May 11, 29; m 50; c 2. *Educ:* Ohio State Univ, BSChE, 53; Lawrence Col, MS, 55, PhD, 58. *Prof Exp:* Asst tech dir, WVa Pulp & Paper Co, 58-59; asst paper mill supt, 59-61; prod mgr bd div, Brunswick Pulp & Paper Co, Ga, 61-65, asst gen prod mgr, 65-69, opers mgr, 69-71; plant mgr, Continental Can Co, 71-77, vpres & gen mgr bleached opers, 77-85. *Concurrent Pos:* Consult, 85- *Mem:* Tech Asn Pulp & Paper Indust. *Res:* Pulp and paper technology. *Mailing Add:* 2203 Terrace Rd Augusta GA 30904

**WISEMAN, WILLIAM JOSEPH, JR,** OCEANOGRAPHY. *Current Pos:* Chmn dept marine sci, 87-90, from asst prof to assoc prof, 71-80, PROF MARINE SCI, COASTAL STUDIES INST, LA STATE UNIV, BATON ROUGE, 80-, PROF OCEANOG & COASTAL SCI, 87- *Personal Data:* b Summit, NJ, June 16, 43; m 65; c 3. *Educ:* Johns Hopkins Univ, BES, 64, MS, 66, MA, 68, PhD(oceanog), 69. *Prof Exp:* Instr geol, Univ NH, 69-70, asst prof earth sci, 70-71. *Concurrent Pos:* Chmn dept, La State Univ, 77-80 & 85-87. *Mem:* Am Geophys Union; Inst Elec & Electronics Engrs; Am Meteorol Soc; Oceanog Soc. *Res:* Estuarine and nearshore circulation. *Mailing Add:* Coastal Studies Inst La State Univ Baton Rouge LA 70803-0001

**WISER, CYRUS WYMER,** AQUATIC ECOLOGY, PHYSIOLOGY. *Current Pos:* assoc prof, 56-61, PROF BIOL, MID TENN STATE UNIV, 61- *Personal Data:* b Wartrace, Tenn, Jan 14, 23; m 45; c 3. *Educ:* Harding Col, BS, 45; George Peabody Col, MA, 46; Vanderbilt Univ, PhD(biol), 56. *Prof Exp:* Instr biol, David Lipscomb Col, 46-49; assoc prof, Jacksonville State Teachers Col, 49-51, 53-54; vis asst prof, Vanderbilt Univ, 54-55. *Mem:* Sigma Xi. *Res:* Physiology, aquatic ecology and limnology; population studies of ponds and lakes; accumulation of radioactive isotopes by aquatic organisms. *Mailing Add:* 814 Minerva Dr Murfreesboro TN 37130-5232

**WISER, EDWARD H(EMPSTEAD),** AGRICULTURAL ENGINEERING. *Current Pos:* From instr to prof agr eng, 57-76, PROF BIOL & AGR ENG, NC STATE UNIV, 76- *Personal Data:* b Fatehgarh, India, Jan 21, 31; US citizen; m 57; c 2. *Educ:* Iowa State Univ, BS, 53; NC State Univ, MS, 58, PhD(agr eng), 64. *Mem:* Am Geophys Union; Am Soc Agr Engrs; Am Soc Agron; Soil Conserv Soc Am; Sigma Xi. *Res:* Prediction of water yield from agricultural watersheds; computer simulation of precipitation and streamflow; statistical methods in hydrology. *Mailing Add:* 404 Dixie Trail Raleigh NC 27607

**WISER, HORACE CLARE,** MATHEMATICS. *Current Pos:* From asst prof to assoc prof, 61-74, PROF MATH, WASH STATE UNIV, 74- *Personal Data:* b Lewiston, Utah, Jan 26, 33; m 53; c 4. *Educ:* Univ Utah, BA, 53, PhD(math), 61; Univ Wash, BS, 54. *Mem:* Am Math Soc; Math Asn Am. *Res:* Undergraduate mathematics curriculum; point set topology. *Mailing Add:* 775 SE Derby St Pullman WA 99163

**WISER, JAMES ELDRED,** ANALYTICAL CHEMISTRY. *Current Pos:* PROF CHEM & HEAD DEPT CHEM & PHYSICS, MID TENN STATE UNIV, 46- *Personal Data:* b Wartrace, Tenn, Dec 31, 15; m 41; c 1. *Educ:* Mid Tenn State Col, BS, 38; Peabody Col, MA, 40, PhD(sci educ), 47. *Prof Exp:* Teacher high sch, Fla, 38-39 & Ala State Teachers Col, 40-41; teacher physics, Vanderbilt Univ, 42; teacher chem & physics, David Lipscomb Col, 42-46. *Concurrent Pos:* Instr, Peabody Col, 44; NSF panelist, 64, 68 & 71. *Mem:* AAAS; emcr mem Am Chem Soc; Am Inst Chem. *Res:* Food chemistry; educational psychology. *Mailing Add:* 6682 Miller Johnson Rd Christiana TN 37037-9764

**WISER, MARK FREDERICK,** MOLECULAR PARASITOLOGY. *Current Pos:* ASST PROF MED PROTOZOOL CELL BIOL METHODS, DEPT TROP MED, TULANE UNIV SCH PUB HEALTH, 89- *Personal Data:* b Louisville, Ky, Nov 9, 56; m 77, Juanita Steele; c Ellen, Mary & Anthony. *Educ:* Franklin Col, BA, 78; Univ Minn, PhD(cell biol), 83. *Prof Exp:* Fel, Max Planck Inst Cell Biol, Heidelberg, 83-86; assoc res scientist, Dept Pharmacol, Yale Univ Sch Med, 87-88. *Mem:* Am Soc Trop Med & Hyg; AAAS; Soc Protozoologist. *Res:* Molecular and cellular biology of host-parasite interactions and in particular how the malarial parasite alters the host erythrocyte membrane. *Mailing Add:* Tulane Univ Sch Pub Health 1430 Tulane Ave New Orleans LA 70112-2699. *E-Mail:* wiser@mailhost.tcs.tulane.edu

**WISER, NATHAN,** theoretical physics, material science, for more information see previous edition

**WISER, THOMAS HENRY,** CLINICAL PHARMACY. *Current Pos:* PROF PHARM & ASST DEAN, PURDUE UNIV SCH PHARM & PHARMICOL SCI, 91- *Personal Data:* b Minneapolis, Minn, May 17, 46. *Educ:* Univ Minn, BS, 71, PharmD, 73. *Prof Exp:* Pharmacist, 71-87; asst prof clin pharm, Sch Pharm, Univ MD, 73-87, assoc dir primary care prog, Sch Med, 75-87; prof pharm pract, Campbell Univ Sch Pharm, 87-91. *Concurrent Pos:* Clin pharm practitioner, Univ Md Hosp, 73-, clin pharm consult, 73-, co-dir, Anticoagulant clin, 76-, co-dir, Therapeut Probs Clin, 77-; clin pharm consult, Loch Raven Vet Admin Hosp, 74-, Baltimore City Jail, 77-, Critical Care Nurses' Asn, 78- & Am Pharmaceut Asn Policy Comt Prof Affairs, 78-; mem, Md Comn Nursing, 75-76. *Mem:* Am Pharmaceut Asn; Am Asn Col Pharm; Am Asn Hosp Pharmacists. *Res:* Ambulatory care; medical audits; clinical pharmacy services; drug utilization; adverse reactions; patient education. *Mailing Add:* 668 Hawthorne Dr Carmel IN 46033

**WISER, WENDELL H(ASLAM),** FUEL ENGINEERING, PHYSICAL CHEMISTRY. *Current Pos:* assoc prof, 65-69, chmn dept, 66-70, PROF FUELS ENG, UNIV UTAH, 69- *Personal Data:* b Fairview, Idaho, Dec 16, 22; m 47; c 5. *Educ:* Univ Utah, BS, 49, PhD(fuel eng), 52. *Honors & Awards:* Henry H Storch Award, Am Chem Soc, 78. *Prof Exp:* Res assoc explosives res, Univ Utah, 52-53; asst prof chem eng, Brigham Young Univ, 55-58; pres, Church Col, NZ, 60-65. *Concurrent Pos:* Consult, Power Plant Div, Boeing Airplane Co, 56-58; US ed, Fuel, 70-78. *Mem:* Am Inst Aeronaut & Astronaut; fel Brit Interplanetary Soc; Am Chem Soc. *Res:* Jet engine fuels; rocket propellants; production of liquid and gaseous fuels from coal. *Mailing Add:* Dept Chem & Fuels Eng Univ Utah Salt Lake City UT 84112

**WISER, WINFRED LAVERN,** OBSTETRICS & GYNECOLOGY. *Current Pos:* PROF & CHMN OBSTET & GYNEC, SCH MED, UNIV MISS, 76- *Personal Data:* b Wartrace, Tenn, June 14, 26; m 74; c 2. *Educ:* Middle Tenn Univ, BS, 49; Univ Tenn, MD, 52. *Prof Exp:* Intern, John Gaston Hosp, 53; resident obstet & gynec, Sch Med, Univ Miss, 62; asst prof, Med Ctr, Univ Miss, 67-68; assoc prof, Ctr Health Sci, Univ Tenn, 68-73, prof, 73-76. *Concurrent Pos:* Dir gynec, Ctr Health Sci, Univ Tenn, 68-76, dep chmn obstet & gynec, 71-76, actg chmn, 74-76; consult staff, Vet Admin Hosp & Methodist Rehab Ctr, 76- *Mem:* AMA; Am Soc Fertil & Steril; Am Col Surgeons; Am Col Obstetricians & Gynecologists; Sigma Xi. *Res:* Gynecology; congenital anomalies of the uterus; infertility. *Mailing Add:* Dept Obstet & Gynec Dept Univ Miss Sch Med OB/GYN 2500 N State St Jackson MS 39216-4505

**WISHMAN, MARVIN,** POLYMER STABILIZATION, SYNTHETIC FIBER PROCESSES. *Current Pos:* br mgr, 68-70, RES DIR, PHILLIPS PETROL CORP, 70- *Personal Data:* b New York, NY, Apr 24, 25; m 53, Nan Liver; c Lisa Bess. *Educ:* NY Univ, University Heights, BA, 49; NY Univ, Washington Square, PhD(org chem), 54. *Prof Exp:* Res chemist, Indust Rayon Corp, 55-56; group leader & res mgr, Am Cyanamid, 56-68. *Mem:* Am Chem Soc. *Res:* Synthetic fibers; acrylic fibers; polypropylene fibers; fiber additives and fiber processes to achieve specific properties. *Mailing Add:* 4 Whittington Ct Greenville SC 29615-2621

**WISHNER, KATHLEEN L,** ENDOCRINOLOGY, PEDIATRICS. *Current Pos:* asst prof, Dept Biomed Chem, Sch Pharm, 70-72, asst clin prof, Dept Med, 81-84, ASSOC CLIN PROF, UNIV CALIF, 84- *Personal Data:* b Modesto, Calif, June 11, 43; m 73, William Grishner; c Jeffrey & Michael. *Educ:* San Francisco State Univ, BA, 63; Univ Calif, San Francisco, PhD(nutrit), 68; Univ Southern Calif, MD, 76. *Prof Exp:* Asst prof, Div Nutrit, Univ Minn, St Paul, 68-70. *Concurrent Pos:* Prin investr, NIH supported proj, 69-73 & 79-81, co-investr, 69-72; physician endocrinol, Pasadena Diabetes & Endocrinol Med Group, 81-; mem, Panel Space Sta Oper Med, Am Inst Biol Sci, 83-85; mem, Space Sta Health Maintenance Fac Consult Comt, NASA, 84-85, Space Adv Panel, 85; mem, Sci Adv Panel for Simplesse, Nutra-Sweet Co, 87-90; bd dirs, Am Diabetes Asn, 88- *Mem:* Fel Am Acad Pediat; Am Diabetes Asn (pres-elect, 93-94); Am Dietetics Asn; Am Inst Nutrit; Am Soc Clin Nutritionists. *Res:* Lipo-protein metabolism; dietary factors affecting chylo micron metabolism and the effect of heparin disposition on lipo protein metabolism. *Mailing Add:* Pasadena Diabetes & Edocrinol Med Group 675 S Arroyo PKwy No 420 Pasadena CA 91105-3265. *Fax:* 626-577-6835

**WISHNER, LAWRENCE ARNDT,** BIOCHEMISTRY, ANIMAL BEHAVIOR-ETHOLOGY. *Current Pos:* from asst prof to assoc prof, Mary Wash Col, 61-68, chmn dept, 67-71, asst dean, 71-77, PROF CHEM, MARY WASH COL, 68- *Personal Data:* b New York, NY, Sept 7, 32; m 82; c 2. *Educ:* Univ Md, BS, 54, MS, 61, PhD(food chem), 64. *Prof Exp:* Asst, Dairy

Dept, Univ Md, 57-61. *Mem:* Am Chem Soc; Am Oil Chem Soc; Am Inst Chem; NY Acad Sci; Sigma Xi. *Res:* Light-induced oxidation of milk; thermal oxidation of fats; autoxidation of tissue lipids in vivo; biological antioxidants; behavior and life history of the eastern chipmunk. *Mailing Add:* 1645 Heatherstone Dr Fredericksburg VA 22407-4845

**WISHNER, RICHARD,** ELECTRICAL ENGINEERING. *Current Pos:* ASST DIR, INFO SYSTS OFF, DEPT DEFENSE, 94- *Personal Data:* b Nov 1, 34. *Educ:* Univ Ill, PhD (elec eng), 60. *Mailing Add:* DARPA Rm 705 3701 N Fairfax Dr Arlington VA 22203-1714

**WISHNETSKY, THEODORE,** FOOD TECHNOLOGY, CRYOGENICS. *Current Pos:* RETIRED. *Personal Data:* b New York, NY, July 5, 25; m 48; c 2. *Educ:* Cornell Univ, BS, 49, MS, 50; Univ Mass, PhD(food technol), 58. *Prof Exp:* Res assoc, NY Agr Exp Sta, Geneva, 50-54; chemist, Eastman Chem Prod, Inc, 58-62; sr scientist, Air Prod & Chem, Inc, Pa, 62-68; assoc prof food sci, Mich State Univ, 68-92. *Mem:* Inst Food Technol. *Res:* Fruit and vegetable processing; processing and marketing of frozen foods; mechanism of changes in frozen foods; application of cryogenic technology to processing problems; low-temperature preservation of foods; controlled atmospheres; packaging. *Mailing Add:* 732 Tarleton East Lansing MI 48823

**WISHNIA, ARNOLD,** BIOPHYSICAL CHEMISTRY, MOLECULAR BIOLOGY. *Current Pos:* ASSOC PROF CHEM, STATE UNIV NY, STONY BROOK, 66- *Personal Data:* b New York, NY, July 1, 31; m 52; c 3. *Educ:* Cornell Univ, AB, 52; NY Univ, PhD(biochem), 57. *Prof Exp:* Res assoc chem, Yale Univ, 56-59; from asst prof to assoc prof biochem, Dartmouth Med Sch, 59-66. *Concurrent Pos:* USPHS sr fel, Dept Natural Philos, Univ Edinburgh, 67. *Mem:* Am Soc Biol Chemists; Am Chem Soc; Biophys Soc. *Res:* Ribosome chemistry. *Mailing Add:* Dept Chem State Univ NY Stony Brook NY 11794. *Fax:* 516-632-7960; *E-Mail:* wishnia@bchmi.suny.edu

**WISHNICK, MARCIA M,** PEDIATRICS, GENETICS & DEVELOPMENTAL DISORDER. *Current Pos:* res assoc pharmacol, Sch Med, NY Univ Med Ctr, 71, asst prof, 71-82, clin assoc prof, 83-87, actg dir, Div Human Genetics, 81-90, CLIN PROF PEDIAT, NY UNIV MED CTR, 87- *Personal Data:* b New York, NY, Oct 10, 38; m 60, Stanley; c 1. *Educ:* Barnard Col, BA, 60; NY Univ, PhD(biochem), 70, MD, 74. *Prof Exp:* Chemist, Lederle Labs, Am Cyanamid Co, 60-66; assoc biochem, Pub Health Res Labs, City New York, 70-71. *Concurrent Pos:* Resident pediat, NY Univ-Bellevue Med Ctr, 74-77, asst attend pediatrician, 77-82, assoc attend pediatrician, 83-87, attend pediatrician, 87-; attend, Mt Sinai, Lenox Hill; assoc attend, Beth Israel. *Mem:* AAAS; Am Soc Human Genetics; AMA; Am Med Women's Asn; fel Am Acad Pediat. *Res:* Inborn errors in metabolism; craniofacial disorders; growth and development. *Mailing Add:* 157 E 81st St No 1A New York NY 10028. *Fax:* 212-628-8147

**WISIAN-NEILSON, PATTY JOAN,** CHEMISTRY. *Current Pos:* asst prof, 84-90, ASSOC PROF, SOUTHERN METHODIST UNIV, 90- *Personal Data:* b Cuero, Tex, Aug 22, 49; m 76; c 2. *Educ:* Tex Lutheran Col, BS, 71; Univ Tex Austin, PhD(inorg chem), 76. *Prof Exp:* Res assoc, Duke Univ, 76-78; res assoc, Univ Tex, Arlington, 78; res assoc, 79-80, res scientist, Tex Christian Univ, 80-84. *Concurrent Pos:* Prin investr, Army Res Off grant, Tex Christian Univ, 80-84, Southern Methodist Univ, 84-; vis asst prof, Mass Inst Technol, 84-85; NSF-VPW grant, 84-85; prin investr, Am Chem Soc-Petro Res Found, 88- *Mem:* Am Chem Soc; Sigma Xi. *Res:* Synthesis and characterization of new polymers derived from poly(alky-arylphosphazenes); synthesis of new diiron complexes with low-coordinate phosphorus ligands. *Mailing Add:* Dept Chem Southern Methodist-Univ Dallas TX 75275

**WISLER, DAVID CHARLES,** AEROSPACE ENGINEERING, TURBOMACHINERY AERODYNAMICS. *Current Pos:* Res engr, Res & Develop Ctr, Schnectady, 65-67, MGR, AERODYN RES LAB, GE AIRCRAFT ENGINES, EVENDALE, OHIO, 85- *Personal Data:* b Pottstown, Pa, Apr 21, 41; m 64, 80, Beth E Howard; c Scott D, Cheryl L, Daniel J, Chad & Christen. *Educ:* Pa State Univ, BS, 63; Cornell Univ, MS, 65; Univ Colo, PhD (aerospace), 70. *Honors & Awards:* Melville Medal, Am Soc Mech Engrs, 89, Gas Turbine Award, 90 & 92. *Concurrent Pos:* Adj prof, Iowa State Univ, Ames, 87-; chmn, Turbomach Comt, Am Soc Mech Engrs, 93- *Mem:* Assoc fel Am Inst Aeronaut & Astronaut; Am Soc Mech Engrs. *Res:* Mixing in axial compressors; unsteady aerodynamics; advanced aerofoil design; boundary layer studies. *Mailing Add:* GE Aircraft Engines 1 Neumann Way MD A411 Cincinnati OH 45215

**WISLOCKI, PETER G,** METABOLISM, ENVIRONMENTAL TOXICOLOGY. *Current Pos:* res fel, Merck, Sharp & Dohme, 78-83, sr res fel, 83-87, dir, 88-93, SR DIR, MERCK RES LAB, 93- *Personal Data:* b Derby, Conn, Jan 21, 47; m 72, Mary K Anderson; c Daniel & Andrew. *Educ:* Fairfield Univ, BS, 68; Univ Wis, PhD(exp oncol), 74. *Prof Exp:* Fel, Hoffmann-La Roche, Inc, 74-76; vis scientist, 76-77; asst prof, Eppley Inst Res Cancer, 77-78. *Mem:* Am Chem Soc. *Res:* Metabolic activation of carcinogens; binding of reactive intermediates to DNA and protein; toxicological significance of protein bound adducts; metabolism, environmental fate and ecological effects of pesticides; animal drugs. *Mailing Add:* Merck & Co Rahway NJ 07065. *Fax:* 732-594-1449

**WISMAN, EVERETT LEE,** POULTRY SCIENCE. *Current Pos:* County agr agent, 47-48, PROF POULTRY SCI, VA POLYTECH INST & STATE UNIV, 52- *Personal Data:* b Woodstock, Va, Oct 1, 22; m 48; c 3. *Educ:* Va Polytech Inst & State Univ, BS, 46; Cornell Univ, MS, 49; Pa State Univ, PhD(biochem, poultry husb), 52. *Concurrent Pos:* Bd trustees, Sci Mus of Va, 77-80. *Mem:* Am Poultry Sci Asn; Am Inst Nutrit; Asn Acad Sci (pres, 79); AAAS. *Res:* Role of antibiotics, arsenicals and other feed additives in chick growth stimulation; evaluation of animal by-products in poultry rations. *Mailing Add:* 107 Faystone Dr Blacksburg VA 24060

**WISMAR, BETH LOUISE,** ANATOMY, MEDICAL EDUCATION. *Current Pos:* Instr embryol & histol, Col Med, 61-63, asst prof anat, Col Med & Col Arts & Sci, 63-69, ASSOC PROF ANAT, COL MED & COL ARTS & SCI, OHIO STATE UNIV, 69- *Personal Data:* b Cleveland, Ohio, Feb 18, 29. *Educ:* Western Reserve Univ, BSc, 51, MSc, 57; Ohio State Univ, PhD(anat), 61. *Concurrent Pos:* Fac, Creative Prob Solving Inst; consult prob solving & decision making; assoc ed, J Creative Behav. *Mem:* Am Asn Anatomists; Sigma Xi. *Res:* Pulmonary morphology in adult respiratory distress syndrome and sepsis with emphasis on the role of intravascular macrophages; relationship of cognitive style to learning and problem solving abilities of medical students. *Mailing Add:* 4063 Fairfax Dr Columbus OH 43220

**WISMER, MARCO,** polymer chemistry, for more information see previous edition

**WISMER, ROBERT KINGSLEY,** X-RAY CRYSTALLOGRAPHY, CHEMICAL EDUCATION. *Current Pos:* from asst prof to assoc prof, 76-85, chmn dept, 83-87, PROF CHEM, MILLERSVILLE UNIV, 85- *Personal Data:* b Atlantic City, NJ, June 18, 45; m 70, Debbie E Grindem; c Michael, Mary & Karen. *Educ:* Haverford Col, BS, 67; Iowa State Univ, PhD(phys chem), 72. *Prof Exp:* Instr chem, Iowa State Univ, 72; systs analyst comput sci, Ames Lab, Energy Res & Develop Admin, 73; asst prof chem, Luther Col, Iowa, 73-74; asst prof chem, Denison Univ, 74-76. *Mem:* Am Chem Soc; AAAS; Am Crystallog Asn; Sigma Xi. *Res:* Solution of the phase problem through deconvolution of the Patterson function, especially development of techniques adaptable to small computers; general chemistry and qualitative analysis author. *Mailing Add:* Dept Chem Millersville Univ Millersville PA 17551

**WISNER, ROBERT JOEL,** ALGEBRA. *Current Pos:* assoc prof, 63-70, head dept math, 70-77, PROF MATH SCI, NMEX STATE UNIV, 70- *Personal Data:* b Hannibal, Mo, Jan 18, 25; m 47; c 4. *Educ:* Univ Ill, BS, 48, MS, 49; Univ Wash, PhD(math), 53. *Prof Exp:* Assoc math, Univ Wash, 51-53, res mathematician, Pub Opinion Lab, 52-53; instr math, Univ BC, 53-54; from asst prof to assoc prof, Haverford Col, 54-60; assoc prof, Mich State Univ, Oakland, 60-63. *Concurrent Pos:* Consult, Burroughs Corp, 57-58; NSF fel & mem, Inst Advan Study, 59-60; ed, Rev, Soc Indust & Appl Math, 59- *Mem:* Am Math Soc; Soc Indust & Appl Math; Math Asn Am; Am Statist Asn; Can Math Cong. *Res:* Rings; Abelian groups; number theory. *Mailing Add:* Dept Math Sci NMex State Univ PO Box MB Las Cruces NM 88003-0105

**WISNIESKI, BERNADINE JOANN,** PHYSICAL BIOCHEMISTRY. *Current Pos:* Damon Runyon Mem Fund fel, Univ Calif, Los Angeles, 71-73, Celeste Durand Rogers Mem Found fel, 73-74, actg asst prof, 74-75, from asst prof to assoc prof microbiol, 75-90, PROF MICROBIOL & MOLECULAR GENETICS, UNIV CALIF, LOS ANGELES, 90- *Personal Data:* b Baltimore, Md, Feb 26, 45; m 80. *Educ:* Univ Md, College Park, BS, 67; Univ Calif, Berkeley, PhD(genetics), 71. *Concurrent Pos:* Mem, Jonsson Comprehensive Cancer Ctr, Univ Calif, Los Angeles, 75-, assoc mem, Molecular Biol Inst, 75-; res career develop award, USPHS, 76-81. *Mem:* AAAS; Sigma Xi; Biophys Soc. *Res:* Function and physical structure of animal cell membranes; membrane alterations; photoreactive probes, spin labels and protein insertion into membranes; membrane fusion induced by viral proteins; protein toxins; immunology; tumor necrosis factor. *Mailing Add:* Dept Microbiol & Molecular Genetics Univ Calif 405 Hilgard Ave Los Angeles CA 90095. *Fax:* 310-206-5231

**WISNIEWSKI, HENRY MIROSLAW,** NEUROPATHOLOGY, PATHOLOGY. *Current Pos:* DIR, NY STATE INST BASIC RES, STATEN ISLAND, 76-; PROF PATH, STATE UNIV NY DOWNSTATE MED CTR, HEALTH SCI CTR, BROOKLYN, 76-; ADJ PROF, DEPT PSYCHIAT, NY UNIV MED CTR. *Personal Data:* b Luszkowko, Poland, Feb 27, 31; US citizen; m 54; c 2. *Educ:* Med Acad, Gdansk, MD, 55; Med Acad, Warsaw, PhD, 60, docent, 65. *Hon Degrees:* DSc, Med Sch, Gdansk, Poland, 91; Col Staten Island, 92, Med Sch, Poznan, Poland, 96. *Honors & Awards:* Weil Award, Am Asn Neuropathologists, 69, Moore Award, 72; Alfred Jurzykowski Found Award in Neurobiol, 96. *Prof Exp:* Resident res fel, Med Acad, Gdansk, Poland, 55-58; from asst to assoc prof neuropath, head of lab & assoc dir, Inst Neuropath, Polish Acad Sci, Warsaw, 58-66; from res assoc to prof path, Albert Einstein Col Med, Yeshiva Univ, 66-75; dir, Demyelinating Dis Unit, Med Res Coun, Newcastle-upon-Tyne, Eng, 74-76. *Concurrent Pos:* Vis neuropathologist, Univ Toronto, 61-62; vis scientist, Lab Neuropath, Nat Inst Neurol Dis & Blindness, 62-63; Health Res Coun New York career scientist award, 70-72; Nat Multiple Sclerosis Soc fel, 71-74; NIH fel, 72-77; consult, Merck Labs, Rahway, NJ, 72-74. *Mem:* Am Asn Neuropath (pres, 84); Polish Asn Neuropath; fel AAAS; Soc Exp Neuropath; World Fedn Neurol; foreign mem Polish Acad Sci; Brit Soc Neuropathologists; Can Asn Neuropathologists; Asn Res Nervous & Ment Dis; Am Asn Ment Retardation; Int Soc Develop Neurosci; Am Soc Neurosci; Sigma Xi; Int Soc Neuropath. *Res:* Light and ultrastructural studies of the pathological brain; experimental neuropathology; synaptic and axonal pathology; developmental neurobiology; mental retardation; pre and senile dementia; multiple sclerosis and other human and experimental demyelinating diseases; neuronal fibrous protein pathology; Down syndrome and Alzheimer disease; blood-brain barrier; neurotoxicology; author or co-author of 640 publications. *Mailing Add:* NY State Inst Basic Res 1050 Forest Hill Rd Staten Island NY 10314

**WISOTZKY, JOEL,** DENTISTRY, DENTAL RESEARCH. *Current Pos:* assoc prof res dent med, Sch Dent, Case Western Res Univ, 59-63, prof med & dir dent res, 63-72, prof oral biol, 63-85. dir grad training & res, 72-78, EMER PROF, SCH DENT, CASE WESTERN RES UNIV, 86- *Personal Data:* b Chicago, Ill, Feb 17, 23; m 49; c 3. *Educ:* Cent YMCA Col, BS, 45; Loyola Univ, DDS, 47; Univ Rochester, PhD(exp path), 56. *Prof Exp:* Pvt pract, 48-49; sr asst dent surgeon, Fed Correctional Inst, Tex, 49-51; fel, Univ Rochester, 51-56; res assoc exp path, Dent Med Div, Colgate-Palmolive Co, 56-59; hon assoc res specialist, Bur Biol Res, Rutgers Univ, 57-59. *Concurrent Pos:* USPHS res fel, 52-56, career develop award, 59-65. *Res:* Cariology; aging changes in oral tissues; phosphorescence of oral structures; electro-physiology; theoretical oral biology; myofibroblast function studies. *Mailing Add:* 301 Andover Pl S No 173 Sun City Center FL 33573

**WISSBRUN, KURT FALKE,** POLYMER SCIENCE, RHEOLOGY. *Current Pos:* CONSULT, 90- *Personal Data:* b Brackwede, Ger, Mar 19, 30; nat US. *Educ:* Univ Pa, BS, 52; Yale Univ, MS, 53, PhD(phys chem), 56. *Honors & Awards:* Bingham Medal, Soc Rheology. *Prof Exp:* Dreyfus fel, Univ Rochester, 55-57; res chemist, Celanese Res Co, 57-60, group leader, 60-62, res assoc, 62-72, sr res assoc, 72-90. *Concurrent Pos:* Adj prof chem eng, Univ Del, 74- *Mem:* Am Chem Soc; Soc Rheology; Sigma Xi. *Mailing Add:* One Euclid Ave Apt 4E Summit NJ 07901. *Fax:* 908-273-9605; *E-Mail:* kwiss63@mail.idt.net

**WISSEMAN, CHARLES LOUIS, JR,** MEDICAL MICROBIOLOGY. *Current Pos:* asst prof med, 57-74, PROF MICROBIOL & HEAD DEPT, SCH MED, UNIV MD, BALTIMORE CITY, 54- *Personal Data:* b Seguin, Tex, Oct 2, 20; m 41; c 4. *Educ:* Southern Methodist Univ, BA, 41; Kans State Col, MS, 43; Southwestern Univ, MD, 46; Am Bd Path, dipl; Am Bd Microbiol, dipl. *Prof Exp:* Chief chemotherapeut res sect, Dept Virus & Rickettsial Dis, Army Med Serv Grad Sch, Walter Reed Army Med Ctr, DC, 48-54, asst chief dept, 52-54. *Concurrent Pos:* Instr med, Sch Med, Georgetown Univ & actg dir bact & serol labs, Univ Hosp, 50-54; dep dir comn rickettsial dis, Armed Forces Epidemiol Bd, 57-59, dir, 59-72; consult, Surgeon Gen, US Army, NIH, WHO & Pan-Am Health Orgn. *Mem:* Am Soc Microbiol; Infectious Dis Soc Am; Am Soc Trop Med & Hyg; Am Soc Clin Invest; Am Asn Immunol. *Res:* Infectious diseases; viral and rickettsial diseases; pathogenesis and immunity. *Mailing Add:* 40 Cedar Knoll Rd Cockeysville MD 21030-2321

**WISSEMAN, WILLIAM ROWLAND,** PHYSICS. *Current Pos:* mem tech staff, 60-75, br mgr, 75-84, ASSOC LAB DIR, TEX INSTRUMENTS, INC, 84- *Personal Data:* b Halletsville, Tex, Nov 2, 32; m 59; c 3. *Educ:* NC State Univ, BNuclearEng, 54; Duke Univ, PhD(physics), 59. *Prof Exp:* Res assoc & instr physics, Duke Univ, 59-60. *Mem:* Am Phys Soc; fel Inst Elec & Electronics Engrs. *Res:* Electromagnetic wave propagation in solids; properties of semiconductors; solid state microwave sources. *Mailing Add:* 5747 Melshire Dr Dallas TX 75230

**WISSIG, STEVEN,** ELECTRON MICROSCOPY, MICROVASCULAR PERMEABILITY. *Current Pos:* PROF MICROS ANAT, UNIV CALIF, 58- *Educ:* Yale Univ, PhD(anat), 56. *Mailing Add:* Dept Anat Univ Calif 1334-S Sch Med San Francisco CA 94143-0452. *Fax:* 415-476-4845

**WISSING, THOMAS EDWARD,** FRESH WATER ECOLOGY. *Current Pos:* from asst prof to assoc prof, 69-78, PROF ZOOL, MIAMI UNIV, 78- *Personal Data:* b Milwaukee, Wis, Aug 15, 40; m 69, Holly Dunlop; c Katherine. *Educ:* Marquette Univ, BS, 62, MS, 64; Univ Wis-Madison, PhD(zool), 69. *Prof Exp:* Asst aquatic ecol, Marquette Univ, 62-63, asst gen biol, 63-64; asst gen zool, Univ Wis, 64-65, Fed Water Pollution Control Adm. *Concurrent Pos:* Res assoc, Tex A&M Univ, 70; sci ed, Fisheries, Bull Am Fisheries Soc, 84-; ed, Ohio J Sci, 85-88; co-ed, Trans Am Fish Soc, 89-92. *Mem:* Am Fisheries Soc; Sigma Xi; Am Inst Biol Sci; NAm Benthological Soc. *Res:* Fisheries biology; ecology. *Mailing Add:* Dept Zool Miami Univ Oxford OH 45056. *Fax:* 513-529-6900; *E-Mail:* wissing@msmail.muohio.edu

**WISSLER, EUGENE H(ARLEY),** BIOMEDICAL ENGINEERING & SIMULATION. *Current Pos:* From asst prof to prof chem eng, Univ Tex, 57-67, chmn dept, 69-70, assoc dean, Col Eng, 70-76, assoc dean grad studies, 82-93, PROF CHEM ENG, UNIV TEX, AUSTIN, 67- *Personal Data:* b Cherokee, Iowa, Dec 18, 27; m 51, Patricia Nysren; c Gerhardt E, Konrad P & Neyra L (Thore). *Educ:* Iowa State Univ, BS, 50; Univ Minn, PhD(chem eng), 55. *Concurrent Pos:* NSF fac fel, Univ Mich, 61-62; consult. *Mem:* Am Inst Chem Engrs; Am Soc Mech Engrs; Aerospace Med Asn. *Res:* Heat and mass transfer in the human; development of computer models for prediction of human responses to exercise and environmental stress. *Mailing Add:* 4704 Ridge Oak Dr Austin TX 78731

**WISSLER, ROBERT WILLIAM,** PATHOLOGY. *Current Pos:* asst path, 41-43, from instr to prof, 43-72, chmn dept, 57-72, Donald N Pritzker, 72-77, DISTINGUISHED SERV PROF PATH, SCH MED, UNIV CHICAGO, 77- *Personal Data:* b Richmond, Ind, Mar 1, 17; m 40, Elizabeth A Polk; c Barbara, Mary, David & John. *Educ:* Earlham Col, AB, 39; Univ Chicago, MS, 43, PhD(path), 46, MD, 48; Am Bd Path, dipl, 51. *Hon Degrees:* DSc, Earlham Col, 59; MD, Univ Heidelberg, 73; Siena, 82; DSc, NJ, 82, Ohio State, 90. *Honors & Awards:* H P Smith Award, Am Soc Clin Path, 76; Joseph B Goldberger Award, Am Med Asn, 79; Gold Headed Cane Award, Am Asn Pathol, 83; Distinguished Achievement Award, Soc Cardiovasc Pathol, 87. *Prof Exp:* Asst chem, Earlham Col, 38-39. *Concurrent Pos:* Intern, Chicago Marine Hosp, 49-50; mem path study sect, USPHS, 57-61, consult, Surgeon Gen Path Training Comt, 63-68; mem comt path, Nat Acad Sci-Nat Res Coun, 58-69, chmn, 62-69; consult, Armed Forces Inst Path, 61-72, chmn sci adv comt, 66-67; secy-treas, Am Asn Chmn Med Sch Dept Path, 63-64, pres, 67-68; chmn coun arteriosclerosis, Am Heart Asn, 65-66; vpres-dir, Univs Assoc Res & Educ Path, Inc, 65, pres, 69-71; chmn ad hoc comt animal models, Artificial Heart-Myocardial Infarction Prog, Nat Heart Inst & mem Vet Admin Eval & Rev Comt, Res in Path & Lab Med, 66; vchmn bd trustees, Am Asn Accreditation on Lab Animal Care, 67, chmn, 72-74; trustee, Am Bd Path, 68-, secy, 74; mem path adv coun, Vet Admin, 70-74; mem adv comt, Life Sci Res Off, 71-; mem nat adv food comt, Food & Drug Admin, 72-74; pres, Am Bd Pathol, 79-80. *Mem:* Soc Exp Biol & Med; Am Soc Exp Path (vpres, 60-61, pres, 61-62); AMA; Am Asn Path & Bact (vpres, 67, pres, 68-69); Am Asn Cancer Res. *Res:* Protein, lipid nutrition and metabolism; cardiovascular disease; experimental induction and regression of atherosclerosis; cellular immunological reactions including tumor immunity; immunohistochemistry of atherosclerosis; lipoprotein arterial wall cell interaction. *Mailing Add:* Dept Path MC 3083 Univ Chicago Billings Hosp 5841 S Maryland Ave Chicago IL 60690-0414. *Fax:* 773-702-1258

**WISSNER, ALLAN,** ORGANIC CHEMISTRY. *Current Pos:* RES CHEMIST, LEDERLE LABS, AM CYANAMID CO, 74- *Personal Data:* b New York, NY, Nov 14, 45; m 78; c 3. *Educ:* Long Island Univ, BS, 67; Univ Pa, PhD(org chem), 71. *Prof Exp:* NIH fel chem, Cornell Univ, 72-74. *Mem:* Am Chem Soc. *Res:* Medicinal chemistry. *Mailing Add:* Oncol & Immunol Sect Lederle Labs Pearl River NY 10965-1299

**WISSOW, LENNARD JAY,** CHEMISTRY. *Current Pos:* treas, 59-60, CHIEF CHEMIST, J & H BERGE, INC, 58-, PRES, 60- *Personal Data:* b Philadelphia, Pa, May 23, 21; m 46; c 2. *Educ:* Pa State Col, BS, 42; Duke Univ, AM, 43, PhD(org chem), 45. *Prof Exp:* Asst instr chem & asst org chem res, Duke Univ, 43-45; res org chemist, Publicker, Inc, 45; res & develop chemist, Nat Foam Syst, Inc, Pa, 46-47; sr res & develop chemist, Merck & Co, Inc, 47-51; head develop res, Otto B May, Inc, 51-58. *Mem:* Am Chem Soc; Am Inst Chem; AAAS; Sigma Xi; NY Acad Sci. *Res:* Synthetic organic chemistry; fine organic chemicals and processes; pharmaceuticals; vat dyestuffs and intermediates; research and sales administration. *Mailing Add:* Tierra Del Mar S 951 Desota Rd Apt 435 Boca Raton FL 33432-7743

**WIST, ABUND OTTOKAR,** ELECTRONICS ENGINEERING, CHEMICAL CATALYSTS. *Current Pos:* asst prof comput sci & biophys, 73-83, ASST PROF RADIOL, VA COMMONWEALTH UNIV, 83- *Personal Data:* b Vienna, Austria, May 23, 26; US citizen; m 63, Suzanne S; c John & Bundy. *Educ:* Graz Tech Univ, BS, 48; Univ Vienna, MS, 50, PhD(non-equilibrium thermodyn), 51. *Prof Exp:* Technician physics, Vienna Tech Univ, 51-52; res & develop engr, Radiowerke Wien, Austria, 52-54 & Siemens & Halske AG, WGer, 54-58; dir res & develop, Brinkmann Instruments & sr scientist, Fisher Sci, Inc, 64-69; res assoc, Grad Sch Pub Health, Univ Pittsburgh, 70-72 & Dept Chem, 72-73. *Concurrent Pos:* Adj prof chem, Va Commonwealth Univ, 76-77; US deleg in biomed eng, China, 87 & 93, Russia, 93; adj prof physics, 88-; chmn, Conf Clin Appln Mod Imaging Technol, Int Soc Optical Eng, 93 & 94. *Mem:* Sr mem Inst Elec & Electronics Engrs; Am Chem Soc; NY Acad Sci; Am Asn Phsicists Med; Biomed Eng Soc; Sigma Xi; assoc mem Am Col Radiol. *Res:* Radiation physics; solid state devices; new computer systems; biomedical engineering; precision and automatic instrumentation in chemistry, physics, medicine and radiology; published book "Electronic Design of Microprossor Based Instrumentation; 70 scientific publications; 10 patents. *Mailing Add:* 9304 Farmington Dr Richmond VA 23299-5336

**WISTRAND, HARRY EDWIN,** POPULATION GENETICS, MOLECULAR EVOLUTION. *Current Pos:* From asst prof to assoc prof, 74-96, assoc dean col, 87-91, PROF BIOL & DEPT CHAIR, AGNES SCOTT COL, 96- *Personal Data:* b Aug 2, 46; m 70, Penny Rush. *Educ:* Austin Col, BA, 68; Univ NTex, MA, 70; Ariz State Univ, PhD(zool), 73. *Concurrent Pos:* Grantee, NSF, 94. *Mem:* Soc Study Evolution; Sigma Xi; Genetics Soc Am; Am Soc Naturalists; AAAS. *Res:* In situ hybridization of amylase; esterase; alcohol dehydrogenase to drosophila chromosomes; chromosomal changes in drosophila. *Mailing Add:* Dept Biol Agnes Scott Col Decatur GA 30030-3797. *E-Mail:* hwistrand@ness.agnesscott.edu

**WISTREICH, GEORGE A,** MICROBIOLOGY, ELECTRON MICROSCOPY. *Current Pos:* from instr to asst prof biol, 61-71, dir Allied Health Sci Progs, 68-, chmn dept, 72-, ASSOC PROF LIFE SCI, E LOS ANGELES COL, 71-, PROF MICROBIOL, 73- *Personal Data:* b New York, NY, Aug 12, 32; m 57; c 2. *Educ:* Univ Calif, Los Angeles, AB, 57, MS, 61; Univ Southern Calif, PhD(bact), 68. *Prof Exp:* Res asst zool, Univ Calif, Los Angeles, 58-60, res virologist, 60-61. *Concurrent Pos:* Aerospace consult, Garrett Corp, Calif, 66-67; lectr, Upward Bound Prog, East Los Angeles Col, 68- *Mem:* Am Soc Microbiol; Am Inst Biol Sci; NY Acad Sci; fel Am Inst Chem; fel Royal Soc Health; fel Am Acad Microbiol; fel Linnean Soc London. *Res:* Insect pathology; virology and tissue culture; cytology and cytochemistry; undergraduate education in biological sciences; electron microscopy. *Mailing Add:* 9351 Cresta Dr Los Angeles CA 90035-4118

**WISTREICH, HUGO ERYK,** BUSINESS MANAGEMENT. *Current Pos:* vpres technol, 64-75, pres, 75-91, EMER PRES, B HELLER & CO, 91- *Personal Data:* b Jasto, Poland, Aug 8, 30; nat US; m 58; c 3. *Educ:* Inst Agr Tech, France, Ingenieur, 53; Rutgers Univ, MS, 57, PhD(food tech), 59. *Prof Exp:* Dir res, Reliable Packing Co, 58-60, Preservaline Mfg Co, 60-63 & Dubuque Packing Co, 63-64. *Mem:* AAAS; Am Chem Soc; Inst Food Technol; Am Meat Sci Asn. *Res:* Meat curing; electrical anesthesia in animals; food analysis; nutrition; food-meat biochemistry; bacteriology. *Mailing Add:* 8450 Southbridge Dr Ft Myers FL 33912

**WISWALL, RICHARD H, JR,** PHYSICAL CHEMISTRY. *Current Pos:* RETIRED. *Personal Data:* b Peabody, Mass, Mar 7, 16; m 46; c 5. *Educ:* Harvard Univ, AB, 37; Princeton Univ, PhD(chem), 41. *Prof Exp:* Chemist, Am Cyanamid Co, NJ, 40-43 & Union Carbide & Carbon Chem Corp, 46-49; chemist, Brookhaven Nat Lab, 49-79. *Concurrent Pos:* Consult, 79- *Mem:* Am Chem Soc; fel Am Nuclear Soc. *Res:* Chemistry of nuclear energy production; fluorine chemistry; fused salts; metal hydrides; energy storage. *Mailing Add:* 331 Beaver Dam Rd Brookhaven NY 11719

**WIT, ANDREW LEWIS,** CARDIOVASCULAR PHYSIOLOGY, PHARMACOLOGY. *Current Pos:* assoc, 70-71, from asst prof to assoc prof, 71-81, PROF PHARMACOL, COL PHYSICIANS & SURGEONS, COLUMBIA UNIV, 81- *Personal Data:* b Oceanside, NY, Jan 18, 42; m 65; c 3. *Educ:* Bates Col, BS, 63; Columbia Univ, PhD(pharmacol), 68. *Prof Exp:* Res physiologist, USPHS Hosp, Staten Island, NY, 68-70. *Concurrent Pos:* Res assoc, Rockefeller Univ, 70-71, vis asst prof, 71-74, adj assoc prof, 74-; NIH grants, 70-; NY Heart Asn sr investr, Columbia Univ, 71-75, Am Heart Asn grant in aid, 72-76. *Mem:* Am Heart Asn; Am Fedn Clin Res; Soc Gen Physiol; Am Physiol Soc; Int Soc Res Cardiac Metab. *Res:* Cardiac electrophysiology, pharmacology and arrhythmias. *Mailing Add:* Col Physicians & Surgeons Columbia Univ Dept Pharmacol 630 W 168th St New York NY 10032

**WIT, LAWRENCE CARL,** PHYSIOLOGICAL ECOLOGY. *Current Pos:* From asst prof to assoc prof, 76-88, PROF ZOOL, AUBURN UNIV, 88- *Personal Data:* b Chicago, Ill, May 12, 44; m 68; c 3. *Educ:* Wheaton Col, BS, 66; Western Ill Univ, MS, 68; Univ Mo, PhD(zool), 75. *Concurrent Pos:* Assoc dean, Col Sci & Math, 91- *Mem:* AAAS. *Res:* Physiological mechanisms regulating mammalian and reptilian hibernation. *Mailing Add:* 1042 Stage Rd Auburn AL 36830

**WITCHER, WESLEY,** PLANT PATHOLOGY. *Current Pos:* prof forest path, 60-78, veg pathologist, 81-88, EMER PROF FOREST PATH, CLEMSON UNIV, 88- *Personal Data:* b Chatham, Va, July 9, 23; m 55, Shirley Wyatt; c Laura Lea (Goldstein) & Steven. *Educ:* Va Polytech Inst, BS, 49, MS, 58; NC State Col, PhD(plant path), 60. *Prof Exp:* Instr voc agr, Pittsylvania County Sch Bd, 49-54; asst county agent, Exten Serv, Va Polytech Inst, 54-56; asst, NC State Col, 57-60. *Mem:* Am Phytopath Soc; Soc Nematol. *Res:* Fungus-nematode complex of tobacco; diseases of highbush blueberries; forest diseases; vegetable diseases. *Mailing Add:* 1125 Old Seneca Rd Central SC 29630

**WITCOFSKI, RICHARD LOU,** RADIATION BIOLOGY, NUCLEAR MEDICINE. *Current Pos:* Res asst, 57-61, from instr to prof, 61-73, PROF RADIOL, BOWMAN GRAY SCH MED, 73- *Personal Data:* b Peiping, China, Mar 29, 35; US citizen; m 56; c 2. *Educ:* Lynchburg Col, BS, 56; Vanderbilt Univ, MS, 60; Wake Forest Univ, PhD(anat), 67. *Mem:* Soc Nuclear Med; Health Physics Soc; Radiation Res Soc; Am Asn Physicists Med. *Res:* Low dose levels-radiation biology. *Mailing Add:* 729 Elderwood Ave Winston-Salem NC 27103-3413. *Fax:* 910-716-2029

**WITCZAK, ZBIGNIEW J,** CARBOHYDRATES & NATURAL PRODUCTS CHEMISTRY, CARBOHYDRATE-BASED DRUGS. *Current Pos:* ASST PROF NATURAL PROD CHEM, SCH PHARM, UNIV CONN, 91- *Personal Data:* b Zgierz, Poland, July 13, 47; m 74; c 2. *Educ:* Med Acad, Lodz, Poland, MS, 72, PhD(org chem & natural prod), 79. *Prof Exp:* Res asst org chem, Dept Org Chem, Med Acad Lodz, 73-75, asst lectr, 75-79, asst prof, 79-81; res assoc carbohydrate chem, Dept Biochem, Purdue Univ, 81-83 & Dept Food Sci, 83-87; sr res chemist, A E Staley Mfg Co, Decatur, Ill, 87-91. *Concurrent Pos:* NIH res participation fel, 81-82. *Mem:* Am Chem Soc; Sigma Xi; Am Soc Pharmacog. *Res:* Chemistry of carbohydrates, particularly thio and seleno-sugars; synthesis of new carbohydrate sweeteners; synthetic carbohydrate chemistry; natural products chemistry; chemistry of levogiucosenone and other carbohydrate synthons; carbohydrate drugs and therapeutics; L-fucosidase inhibitors as anti-cancer agents. *Mailing Add:* Univ Conn Sch Pharm 372 Fairfield Rd U-92 Storrs CT 06269-2092. *Fax:* 860-486-4998; *E-Mail:* witczak@uconnvm.uconn.edu

**WITELSON, SANDRA FREEDMAN,** NEUROPSYCHOLOGY, COGNITIVE NEUROANATOMY. *Current Pos:* from asst prof to assoc prof, 69-77, PROF, DEPT PSYCHIAT, SCH MED, MCMASTER UNIV, 77- *Personal Data:* b Montreal, Que, Feb 24, 40. *Educ:* McGill Univ, BSc, 60, MSc, 62, PhD(psychol), 66. *Honors & Awards:* Morton Prince Award, Am Psychopath Asn, 76; John Dewan Award, Ont Ment Health Found, 78; Clarke Inst Res Fund Prize, Univ Toronto, 78. *Prof Exp:* Lectr psychol, Yeshiva Univ, 66; NIMH res fel, Sch Med, NY Univ, 66-68; instr, NY Med Col, 68-69. *Concurrent Pos:* Ont Ment Health Found res grant, McMaster Univ, 70-84, assoc mem, Dept Psychol, 76- & Dept Biomed Sci, 83-; US NIH, Nat Inst Neurol Dis & Stroke contract & grants, 77-; Nat Res Coun grants, 89-; chair, Social Issues Comt, Soc Neurosci, 93- *Mem:* Fel AAAS; fel Can Psychol Asn; fel Am Psychol Asn; Am Psychol Soc; Int Neuropsychol Soc;

Soc Neurosci; fel Royal Soc Can. *Res*: Perception; cognition; language; brain function; developmental psychology; functional neuroanatomy; sex differences; dyslexia; hemispheric specialization; sexual orientation; brain imaging. *Mailing Add*: Dept Psychiat McMaster Univ Hamilton ON L8N 3Z5 Can

**WITHAM, CLYDE LESTER,** POWDER & PARTICLE TECHNOLOGY, AEROSOL SCIENCE. *Current Pos*: Chem engr, 73-81, sr chem engr, 81-82, PROG MGR, FINE PARTICLE TECHNOL, SRI INT, 82- *Personal Data*: b Los Angeles, Calif, Jan 15, 48; m 71; c 4. *Educ*: Brigham Young Univ, BS, 73; Stanford Univ, MS, 77. *Mem*: Am Inst Chem Engrs; Am Chem Soc; Am Asn Aerosol Res; Soc Plastics Engrs. *Res*: Applied research in fine particle and aerosol technology including product development, process development and air pollution; atomizer development; military smoke; protective equipment and aerosol detection; powder handling; particle size determination; fillers in polymers; pharmaceutical development (especially aerosol drug delivery); air pollution control; industrial hygiene. *Mailing Add*: 13728 Paseo Bonita Poway CA 92064. Fax: 650-859-2813

**WITHAM, FRANCIS H,** PLANT PHYSIOLOGY. *Current Pos*: from asst prof to assoc prof biol, 66-79, prof & head, Dept Hort, 79-88, PROF PLANT PHYSIOL, DEPT HORT, PA STATE UNIV, 89- *Personal Data*: b Waltham, Mass, Apr 26, 36; m 61; c 3. *Educ*: Univ Mass, BS, 58, MA, 60; Ind Univ, PhD(plant physiol), 64. *Prof Exp*: Lectr plant physiol, Ind Univ, 63-64. *Mem*: Am Soc Plant Physiol. *Res*: Biosynthesis, chemistry and mechanism of action of phytohormones and their interaction with nucleic acids. *Mailing Add*: Dept Hort Pa State Univ 102 Tyson Bldg University Park PA 16802-4200

**WITHAM, P(HILIP) ROSS,** MARINE TURTLE RESEARCH, SPINY LOBSTER RESEARCH. *Current Pos*: ADJ PROF, FLA ATLANTIC UNIV, 93- *Personal Data*: b Stuart, Fla, Apr 11, 17; m 45, Mabel Blasko; c Chester R, Steven P, Timothy D & Julie (Hartwiger). *Educ*: Univ SFla, BS, 73; Univ Okla, MS, 76. *Honors & Awards*: Commendation, Gov & Cabinet of Fla, 86. *Prof Exp*: Proj leader spiny lobster res, Fla Dept Natural Resources, 63-71, marine turtle coordr, 71-87; res assoc, Rosentiel Sch Marine & Atmospheric Sci, Univ Miami, 87-91. *Concurrent Pos*: Mem, Sea Turtles-Dredging Task Force, CEngr, 85-87, Restore Coast Task Force, State Fla, 86 & Southeast Region Marine Turtle Recovery Team, Calif, 87. *Mem*: Am Soc Zoologists; Am Soc Ichthyologists & Herpetologists; Am Inst Fisheries Res Biologists; fel Explorers Club. *Res*: Management of marine turtles nesting in unbalanced areas; developing methodology for increasing oceanic stocks of marine turtles. *Mailing Add*: 1457 NW Lake Pt Stuart FL 34994

**WITHBROE, GEORGE LUND,** ASTROPHYSICS, SOLAR PHYSICS. *Current Pos*: dir, Space Physics Div, 91-, SCI PROF DIR, SUN EARTH COMET, NASA HQ, WASHINGTON, DC, 91- *Personal Data*: b Green Bay, Wis, Dec 14, 38; m 64; c 2. *Educ*: Mass Inst Technol, BS, 61; Univ Mich, MS, 63, PhD(astron), 65. *Prof Exp*: Res fel astron, Harvard Univ, 65-69, res assoc, 69-76; astrophysicist, Smithsonian Astrophys Observ, 73-91, assoc dir, Ctr Astrophys. *Concurrent Pos*: Lectr, Harvard Univ, 70-; mem, Sci Adv Comt, NASA, 75- & Comt Solar & Space Physics, Space Sci Bd, 81-84; chair, Solar Physics Div, Am Astron Soc, 90-92. *Mem*: Int Astron Union; Am Astron Soc; Am Geophys Union. *Res*: Interpretation of solar and stellar visible, radio and EUV radiation; determination of solar chemical abundances; temperature density structure of solar atmosphere and terrestrial atmosphere; development of plasma diagnostic techniques. *Mailing Add*: NASA HQ Off Space Sci Div Code S Washington DC 20546

**WITHEE, WALLACE WALTER,** AERONAUTICAL ENGINEERING. *Current Pos*: RETIRED. *Personal Data*: b Minneapolis, Minn, Mar 12, 13; m 38; c 3. *Educ*: Univ Minn, BS, 34. *Prof Exp*: Engr, Boeing Co, 36-38; layout engr, Consol Vultee, 38-40, group leader, 40-42, asst proj engr, 42-49, design specialist, 49-50, sr design group engr, 50-53, chief flight test engr, Gen Dynamics/Convair, 53-54, sr design group engr, 54-55, chief exp flight test, 55-56, asst chief flight test, 56-57, asst chief engr, Gen Dynamics/Astronaut, 57-60, sr asst chief engr, 60-61, vpres res, develop & eng, 61-62, vpres eng, 62-65, dir test opers, Gen Dynamics/Convair Aerospace, 65-66, dept prog dir advan intercontinental ballistic missile, 66-67, prog dir manned orbital space systs, 67-68, dir mil space progs, 68, dir advan space systs, 68-71, prog dir, res & applications modules, 71, dir res & applications progs, 72-76, subcontract proj dir, 76-78, dir energy progs & consult, Gen Dynamics/Convair Aerospace, 78-86. *Concurrent Pos*: Mem, Aircraft Powerplant Activity Comt, Soc Automotive Engrs, Aerospacecraft Activity Comt, Astronaut Planning Comt, Eng Activity Bd, Reading Comt, Prog Planning Comt, chmn, Nat Aeronaut & Space Eng Meeting, 68; chmn, Tech Comt Flight Testing, Am Inst Aeronaut & Astronaut. *Mem*: Assoc fel Am Inst Aeronaut & Astronaut; Soc Automotive Engrs; Inst Environ Sci; Am Astronaut Soc; Am Nuclear Soc. *Res*: Technical management in the aerospace industry from conception of missile to system development; author of several publications. *Mailing Add*: 4858 Butterfly Lane La Mesa CA 91941

**WITHER, ROSS PLUMMER,** PULP & PAPER TECHNOLOGY. *Current Pos*: RETIRED. *Personal Data*: b Portland, Ore, Dec 29, 22; m 92, Martha Aspitarte; c William, Janice & Bonnie. *Educ*: Univ Ore, BS, 47, MA, 49; Stanford Univ, PhD(chem), 56. *Prof Exp*: Sr res chemist, Cent Res Div, Crown Zellerbach Corp, 55-85. *Mem*: Am Chem Soc; Tech Asn Pulp & Paper Indust; Sigma Xi. *Res*: Cellulose chemistry; pulp and paper research; paper coatings research; specialty papers development. *Mailing Add*: 1526 NE Fourth Ave Camas WA 98607

**WITHERELL, EGILDA DEAMICIS,** RADIOLOGICAL PHYSICS, NUCLEAR MEDICINE. *Current Pos*: RETIRED. *Personal Data*: b Fall River, Mass, Nov 1, 22; m 56, Dana Grover. *Educ*: Mass Inst Technol, SB, 44; Am Bd Radiol, dipl, 53; Am Bd Health Physics, dipl, 60. *Prof Exp*: Mem staff physics, Radiation Lab, Mass Inst Technol, 44-45, mem staff math, Dynamic Anal & Control Lab, 46-47; asst instr chem, Northeastern Univ, 45-56; radiol physicist, Cancer Res Inst, New Eng Deaconess Hosp, Boston, Mass, 47-66 & Peter Bent Brigham Hosp, 66-67; radiol physicist, Newton Wellesley Hosp, Newton Lower Falls, 67-86. *Mem*: Am Col Radiol; Am Asn Physicists Med. *Res*: Radiological physics. *Mailing Add*: PO Box 757 49 Bess Rd Needham MA 02192

**WITHERELL, MICHAEL STEWART,** ELEMENTARY PARTICLE PHYSICS. *Current Pos*: from asst prof to assoc prof, 81-86, PROF, UNIV CALIF, SANTA BARBARA, 86- *Personal Data*: b Toledo, Ohio, Sept 22, 49. *Educ*: Univ Mich, BS, 68; Univ Wis, MA, 70, PhD(physics), 73. *Honors & Awards*: Panofsky Prize, Am Phys Soc. *Prof Exp*: Instr, Princeton Univ, 73-75, asst prof, 75-81. *Concurrent Pos*: Guggenheim Fel. *Mem*: Am Phys Soc. *Res*: Counter and spark chamber experiments in elementary particle physics. *Mailing Add*: Dept Physics Univ Calif Santa Barbara CA 93106

**WITHERELL, PETER CHARLES,** REGULATORY ENTOMOLOGY, PLANT QUARANTINE TREATMENTS. *Current Pos*: ASST DIR, OXFORD PLANT PROTECTION CTR, OXFORD, NC, 95- *Personal Data*: b Athol, Mass, Sept 23, 43; m 81, Beatriz Gonzales; c Tina, Phil & Melissa. *Educ*: Univ Mass, Amherst, BS, 65; Univ Calif, Davis, MS, 70, PhD(entom), 73. *Prof Exp*: Res entomologist, Univ Calif, Davis, 73-74; asst res dir, Dadant & Sons Inc, Hamilton, Ill, 75-77; grain inspector, Fed Grain Inspection Serv, USDA, Baltimore, 77-78, plant protection & quarantine officer, Laredo, Tex, 78-81, sta supvr, Methods Develop Sta, Miami, Fla, 81-85, asst ctr dir, Methods Develop Ctr Animal & Plant Health Inspection Serv, Plant Protection & Quarantine, Hoboken, NJ, 85-95. *Concurrent Pos*: Mem, Interagency Comt, Africanized Honey Bees & Parasitic Bee Mites, USDA, 88-91. *Mem*: Orgn Prof Employees Dept Agr; Entom Soc Am; Sigma Xi. *Res*: Quarantine entomology; inspection; fumigation; methyl bromide alternatives; heat and cold; treatment of commodities in the import export trade. *Mailing Add*: Oxford Plant Protection Ctr Plant Protection & Quarantine Animal & Plant Health Inspection Serv USDA 901 Hillsboro St Oxford NC 27565

**WITHERINGTON, BLAIR ERNEST,** BIOLOGICAL CONSERVATION. *Current Pos*: MARINE RES ASSOC, FLA MARINE RES INST, 92- *Personal Data*: b Jacksonville, Fla, July 19, 62. *Educ*: Univ Cent Fla, BS, 84, MS, 86; Univ Fla, PhD(zool), 92. *Prof Exp*: Teaching & res asst zool dept, Univ FL, 89-92. *Concurrent Pos*: Adj asst prof, Dept Zool, Univ Fla, 92- *Res*: Biology and conservation of sea turtles; studies of hatching behavior and dispersal, adult nesting ecology and mitigation of photo pollution effects. *Mailing Add*: 7865-B SE Courtney Terr Hobe Sound FL 33455

**WITHERS, HUBERT RODNEY,** RADIATION ONCOLOGY. *Current Pos*: PROF RADIOTHER, UNIV CALIF, LOS ANGELES, 80- *Personal Data*: b Stanthorpe, Australia, Sept 21, 32; m 59, Janet Macfie; c Genevieve. *Educ*: Univ Queensland, MBBS, 56; Univ London, PhD(path), 65, DSc, 82. *Honors & Awards*: Finzi Prize, Brit Inst Radiol, 74; Failla Award, Radiation Res Soc, 88; Erskine lectr, Radiol Soc NAm, 88; del Regato Medal, Am Radium Soc, 90, Janeway Medal, 94; H S Kaplan Distinguished Scientist Award, Int Asn Radiation Res, 91; Gold Medal, Am Soc Ther Radiol Oncol, 92. *Prof Exp*: Res fel, Univ Queensland, 63-65; vis res scientist, Nat Cancer Inst, 66-68; from assoc prof to prof radiother, Univ Tex, 68-80. *Concurrent Pos*: Gaggin res fel, Univ Queensland, 63-66; dir, Inst & Oncol, Univ NSW, Sydney, 89-91. *Mem*: Am Col Radiol; Am Soc Therapeut Radiol & Oncol; Radiation Res Soc; Am Radium Soc; Am Asn Cancer Res; Royal Australasian Col Radiol; hon mem Polish Oncol Asn; fel Am Col Radiol; hon mem Europ Soc Therapeut Radiation Oncol. *Res*: Precise quantitation of normal tissue responses to irradiation as used for treatment of cancer; measurement of kinetics of metastatic spread of cancer. *Mailing Add*: Dept Radiation Oncol Ctr Health Sci Univ Calif Los Angeles CA 90095

**WITHERS, JAMES C,** COMPOSITE MATERIALS, REINFORCEMENTS. *Current Pos*: CHIEF EXEC OFFICER, MER CORP, 85- *Personal Data*: b Buna, Tex, Nov 5, 34; m 56; c 3. *Educ*: Am Univ, BS, 58; Clayton Univ, PhD(chem), 80. *Prof Exp*: Pres, Gen Technol Inc, 61-71; chmn, Deposits & Composites Inc, 71-76; pres, Pora Inc, 76-81; mgr, Arco Metals Co, 81-85. *Concurrent Pos*: Grad fac, VPI, 68-71. *Mem*: Mat Res Soc; Am Ceramic Soc; Am Soc Metals. *Res*: Author of over 60 publications; granted over 24 patents. *Mailing Add*: Mer Corp 7960 S Kolb Rd Tucson AZ 85706

**WITHERS, STEPHEN GEORGE,** ENZYMOLOGY, CARBOHYDRATE CHEMISTRY. *Current Pos*: from asst prof to assoc prof, 82-91, PROF, DEPT CHEM, UNIV BC, CAN, 91-, PROF BIOCHEM, DEPT BIOCHEM, 91- *Personal Data*: b Britain, 1953; Brit & Can citizen. *Educ*: Bristol Univ, UK, BSc, 74, PhD(chem), 77. *Honors & Awards*: Merck Award, Can Soc Chem, 89; Corday Morgan Medal, Royal Soc Chem UK, 90; Rutherford Medal, Royal Soc Can, 93. *Prof Exp*: Fel, Dept Biochem, Univ Alta, 77-79, prof asst, 79-82. *Mem*: Am Chem Soc; Can Soc Chem; Can Biochem Soc. *Res*: Mechanism of enzyme action, particularly of glycosyl transfer reactions; applications of nuclear magnetic resonance to biochemistry; applications of fluorinated sugars. *Mailing Add*: Univ BC Chem Dept 0236 Main Mall Vancouver BC V6T 1Z1 Can. Fax: 604-822-2847; E-Mail: witmeds@unixg.ubc.ca

**WITHERSPOON, JAMES DONALD,** DEVELOPMENT OF NEW PROGRAMS FOR HEALTH SCIENCES. *Current Pos:* adj prof biol, Grand Canyon Col, 82-83, chmn, Dept Natural Scis, 85-92; coordr allied health, Grand Canyon Univ, 92-94; PROF BIOL, GRAND CANYON COL, 83-; ASSOC DEAN, COLL SCI & ALLIED HEALTH, GRAND CANYON UNIV, 94- *Personal Data:* b Springfield, Mo, Dec 19, 33; m 58, Rebecca Hutto; c Sarah & John. *Educ:* Purdue Univ, BS, 55, MS, 60, PhD(physiol), 63. *Prof Exp:* From instr to asst prof biol, Western Md Col, 60-68; assoc prof biol, Southwestern-Memphis Col, 68-76; free-lance writer, Phoenix, AZ, 76-82. *Concurrent Pos:* Consult, Doubleday & Co, 60-62, Narco Bio-Systs, 72-76; vis prof physiol, Ba Nong Agr Col, China, 88; adj prof community med, Kirksville Osteop Med Col, 91- *Mem:* AAAS; Am Inst Biol Sci. *Res:* Preparation for start of new programs in the health sciences; educational administration; major writing of materials related to educational programs in science and medicine, and books on physiology, anatomy, general biology, and science on the internet. *Mailing Add:* 17122 Grande Blvd Fountain Hills AZ 85268. *Fax:* 602-589-2716; *E-Mail:* jdw@grand-canyon.edu

**WITHERSPOON, JOHN PINKNEY, JR,** RADIATION ECOLOGY, PLANT ECOLOGY. *Current Pos:* RETIRED. *Personal Data:* b Hamlet, NC, Feb 28, 31; m 52, Ulilla Ann Treon; c Michael, Sharon, Susan, Robert & Patricia. *Educ:* Emory Univ, BS, 52, MS, 53; Univ Tenn, PhD(bot), 62. *Prof Exp:* Res asst biol, Emory Univ, 55-57; health physicist, Oak Ridge Nat Lab, 62, ecologist, 62-91. *Concurrent Pos:* Adj prof, Univ Tenn, 76-; mem, Nat Acad Sci, 81; mem comt, Nat Coun Radiation Protection & Measurements, 83-84; environ effects ed, Nuclear Safety, 83- *Mem:* Ecol Soc Am; Health Physics Soc. *Res:* Radiological impact assessments of nuclear fuel cycle facilities; environmental health physics. *Mailing Add:* 123 Windham Rd Oak Ridge TN 37830-8319

**WITHERSPOON, PAUL A(DAMS), JR,** GEOLOGICAL & PETROLEUM ENGINEERING. *Current Pos:* prof petrol eng, 57-65, PROF GEOL ENG, UNIV CALIF, BERKELEY, 65-, HEAD EARTH SCI DIV & ASSOC DIR, LAWRENCE BERKELEY LAB, 77- *Personal Data:* b Pittsburgh, Pa, Feb 9, 19; m 46; c 3. *Educ:* Univ Pittsburgh, BS, 41; Univ Kans, MS, 51; Univ Ill, PhD(geol, phys chem), 57. *Honors & Awards:* Robert E Horton Award, Am Geophys Union, 69; O E Meinzer Award, Geol Soc Am, 76. *Prof Exp:* Petrol prod engr, Phillips Petrol Co, 41-42 & 45-47, chem process engr, 42-45, petrol reservoir engr, 47-49; asst instr petrol eng, Univ Kans, 49-51, head div petrol eng, State Geol Surv, Ill, 51-57. *Concurrent Pos:* Mem subpanel nuclear waste disposal, panel on rock mech probs, US Nat Comn Rock Mech, Nat Res Coun, 77-78. *Mem:* Am Geophys Union; Geol Soc Am; Am Asn Petrol Geol; Am Inst Mining, Metall & Petrol Engrs; Sigma Xi. *Res:* Flow of fluids in porous and fractured rocks; regional groundwater flow; well hydraulics; underground storage of fluids; radioactive waste isolation; geothermal systems. *Mailing Add:* 1824 Monterey Ave Berkeley CA 94707-2544

**WITHINGTON, HOLDEN W,** ENGINEERING. *Current Pos:* RETIRED. *Mem:* Nat Acad Eng. *Mailing Add:* 8000 SE 20th Mercer Island WA 98040

**WITHNER, CARL LESLIE, JR,** PLANT MORPHOGENETICS, ORCHID TAXONOMY & PHYSIOLOGY. *Current Pos:* from instr to prof biol, Brooklyn Col, 48-78, dep chmn dept, 60-64, actg chmn dept, 64-65, EMER PROF BIOL, BROOKLYN COL, 78- *Personal Data:* b Indianapolis, Ind, Mar 3, 18; m 41, Patricia Maxwell; c Dennis Maxwell, Rika d'Almeida & Holly N (Johnson). *Educ:* Univ Ill, BA, 41; Yale Univ, MS, 43, PhD(bot), 48. *Honors & Awards:* Gold Medal for Distinguished Achievement in Sci & Educ, Am Orchid Soc, 90; Silver Medal, Orchid Digest Corp. *Prof Exp:* Asst instr bot, Yale Univ, 41-43, asst, 46-47. *Concurrent Pos:* Resident investr orchids, Brooklyn Bot Garden, 49-76; Guggenheim fel, 61-62; accredited judge, Am Orchid Soc, 61-; orchid consult, NY Bot Garden, 76-79; instr hort, Bellingham Voc-Tech Sch, 79-80; res assoc, Western Wash Univ, 82- *Mem:* Bot Soc Am; Am Soc Plant Physiol; hon mem Am Orchid Soc. *Res:* Orchids; physiology of higher plants in relation to growth and development. *Mailing Add:* 2015 Alabama St Bellingham WA 98226-3709

**WITHROW, CLARENCE DEAN,** PHARMACOLOGY. *Current Pos:* Res instr, 59-63, from instr to asst prof, 63-70, ASSOC PROF PHARMACOL, COL MED, UNIV UTAH, 70- *Personal Data:* b Hutchinson, WVa, Mar 6, 27; m 53; c 3. *Educ:* Davis & Elkins Col, BS, 48; Univ Utah, MS, 55, PhD(pharmacol), 59. *Mem:* AAAS; Am Soc Pharmacol & Exp Therapeut; Sigma Xi. *Res:* Acid-base metabolism, particularly intracellular pH regulation; renal pharmacology; mineralocorticoids; polarography. *Mailing Add:* Dept Pharmacol Univ Utah Col Med 410 Chipeta Way 215 Salt Lake City UT 84108

**WITHSTANDLEY, VICTOR DEWYCKOFF, III,** MOLECULAR SPECTROSCOPY. *Current Pos:* RETIRED. *Personal Data:* b New York, NY, Sept 1, 21; m 58, Violet Pucek; c Suzanne, June & Carolyn. *Educ:* Cornell Univ, BA, 50; Univ Calif, Berkeley, MA, 52; Pa State Univ, DEd(physics), 66, PhD(physics), 72. *Prof Exp:* Asst seismologist, Geotech Corp, Tex, 52-56; res asst underwater acoust, Ord Res Lab, Pa State Univ, 59-62; instr math, Juniata Col, 66-67; res assoc, Ctr Air Environ Studies, Pa State Univ, 69-73; prin scientist, Scitek, Inc, 74-75; instr phys sci, Pa State Univ, 75-77; staff scientist, Bacharach Instrument Co, Pittsburgh, 78-80; consult, Ctr Consult, State Col Pa, 80-83; sr physicist, Dept Defense, 84-94. *Mem:* Am Phys Soc. *Res:* Seismic wave and underwater sound studies; magnetic anisotropies of single crystals; computer analysis of time series; optical engineering; infrared spectroscopy of molecules; remote sensing for geophysical and environmental studies; optics; computer-component physics; co-holder of one US patent. *Mailing Add:* 127 W Whitehall Rd State College PA 16801

**WITIAK, DONALD T,** ORGANIC CHEMISTRY, MEDICINAL CHEMISTRY. *Current Pos:* assoc prof, 67-71, chmn dept, 73-82, PROF MED CHEM, COL PHARM, OHIO STATE UNIV, 71-, KIMBERLY PROF PHARMACOL, 85-, ASSOC DIR BASIC RES, COMPREHENSIVE CANCER CTR, 87- *Personal Data:* b Milwaukee, Wis, Nov 16, 35; m 55; c 2. *Educ:* Univ Wis, BS, 58, PhD(med chem), 61. *Honors & Awards:* Smith Kline & French Lectr, Div Med Chem, Univ Pittsburgh, 81. *Prof Exp:* From asst prof to assoc prof med chem, Univ Iowa, 61-67. *Concurrent Pos:* NIH fel, 59-61 & mem med chem A study sect, 80-83; consult, Diamond-Shamrock Corp, Ohio, 76-79, Schering Corp, NJ, 77-80 & Adria Labs, Inc, 80-87, Marion Labs, 86-88, G D Searl Co, 85-86, Nova Labs, 89-; rep chem teachers sect, house deleg, Am Asn Col Pharm, 75-76 & chmn, 80-81; vchmn, Div Med Chem, Am Chem Soc, 83, chmn, 84, counr, 90-92; distinguished vis lectr, Col Pharm, Univ Houston, 85; res achievement award, Am Pharmaceut Asn Found-Acad Pharmaceut Sci, 85. *Mem:* Am Chem Soc; Am Pharmaceut Asn; fel Acad Pharmaceut Sci; Am Asn Col Pharm; Sigma Xi; fel Am Asn Pharmaceut Scientists. *Res:* Synthesis of biologically active compounds; stereostructure activity relationships; antiatheroslerotic drugs; central nervous system drugs; carcinogenesis and anticancer agents; chemical synthesis of targets in the antineoplastic, antimetastatic, antiatherogenic, antiaggregatory, carcinogenesis, central and peripheral nervous system areas; assess mechanisms of transformation of synthesized polycyclic aromatic hydrocarbons in tissue culture; analogues of various rationally designed compounds which block the abortifacient activity of PGF2, antilipidemic and antiaggregatory aci-reductone redox compounds, bis dioxopiperazine compounds; preparation of bis alkylating agents as solid tumor specific antineoplastic drugs. *Mailing Add:* Dept Med Chem Col Pharm Ohio State Univ 500 W 12th Ave Columbus OH 43210

**WITKIN, EVELYN MAISEL,** MICROBIAL GENETICS & DNA REPAIR, MUTAGENESIS. *Current Pos:* prof biol sci, Douglass Col, 71-79, Barbara McClintock prof genetics, 79-91, EMER PROF, WAKSMAN INST MICROBIOL, RUTGERS UNIV, 91- *Personal Data:* b New York, NY, Mar 9, 21; wid; c 2. *Educ:* NY Univ, AB, 41; Columbia Univ, MA, 43, PhD(zool), 47. *Hon Degrees:* DSc, NY Med Col, 78, Rutgers Univ, 95. *Honors & Awards:* Waksman Lectr, 59; Prix Charles-Leopold Mayer, Inst France Acad Sci, 77; Environ Mutagenesis Soc Award, 90. *Prof Exp:* Res assoc bact genetics, Carnegie Inst, 46-49, mem staff genetics, 49-55; assoc prof med, Col Med, Downstate Med Ctr, State Univ NY, 55-69, prof, 69-71. *Concurrent Pos:* Am Cancer Soc fel, 47-49; Miller vis prof, Univ Calif, Berkeley, 91. *Mem:* Nat Acad Sci; Am Soc Microbiol; Genetics Soc Am; Am Acad Arts & Sci. *Res:* Mechanism of spontaneous and induced mutation in bacteria; genetic effects of radiation; enzymatic repair of DNA damage. *Mailing Add:* One Firestone Ct Princeton NJ 08540

**WITKIN, STEVEN S,** IMMUNOLOGY, REPRODUCTIVE BIOLOGY. *Current Pos:* ASSOC PROF, MED COL, CORNELL UNIV, 81- *Personal Data:* b Brooklyn, NY, Oct 19, 43; m 86; c 3. *Educ:* Hunter Col, BA, 65; Univ Conn, MS, 67; Univ Calif, Los Angeles, PhD(microbiol), 70. *Prof Exp:* Staff assoc, Inst Cancer Res, Columbia Univ, 72-74; assoc, Sloan-Kettering Inst Cancer Res, 74-81. *Concurrent Pos:* Fel, Roche Inst Molecular Biol, Nutley, NJ, 70-72. *Mem:* AAAS; Am Soc Microbiol; Soc Gyn Invest; Am Asn Immunologists; Am Fertil Soc; Obstet-Gynec Infectious Dis Soc. *Res:* Reproductive immunology; cancer; spermatozoa. *Mailing Add:* Dept Obstet/Gynec Cornell Univ Med Col 515 E 71st St New York NY 10021-4895. *Fax:* 212-746-8799

**WITKIND, IRVING JEROME,** STRUCTURAL GEOLOGY, STRATIGRAPHY. *Current Pos:* GEOLOGIST, US GEOL SURV, 46- *Personal Data:* b New York, NY, Mar 28, 17; m 42. *Educ:* Brooklyn Col, BA, 39; Columbia Univ, MA, 41; Univ Colo, PhD(geol), 56. *Mem:* Geol Soc Am. *Res:* Pleistocene geology; localization of sodium sulfate; geologic mapping for environmental purposes in Price 1 degree x 2 degree AMS Sheet, Central Utah; localization of uranium minerals; laccolithic mountains of southeastern Utah and central Montana; stratigraphy and structural geology of southwestern Montana and southeastern Idaho; salt diapirism in central Utah. *Mailing Add:* 30 Ammons St Lakewood CO 80226-1322

**WITKOP, BERNHARD,** BIOLOGICAL CHEMISTRY, PHYSIOLOGICAL CHEMISTRY. *Current Pos:* vis scientist, NIH, 51-53, chemist, 53-55, chief, Lab Chem, 57-88, inst scholar, 88-93, CHIEF SECT METABOLITES, NAT INST ARTHRITIS, METAB & DIGESTIVE DIS, NIH, 55-, EMER SCHOLAR, 94- *Personal Data:* b Freiburg, Ger, May 9, 17; nat US; m 45, Marlene Prinz; c Cornelia, Phyllis & Thomas. *Educ:* Univ Munich, PhD(org chem), 40, ScD, 46. *Hon Degrees:* PhD, Univ Munich, 90. *Honors & Awards:* Paul Karrer Prize, Univ Zurich, 71; Kun-Ni-To, Order of Sacred Treasure, Emperor of Japan, 76. *Prof Exp:* Privat docent, Univ Munich, 46-47; Mellon Found fel, Harvard Univ, 47-48, instr, 48-50, USPHS spec fel, 50-51. *Concurrent Pos:* Mem, Nat Acad Sci-Nat Res Coun, 59-62; vis prof, Kyoto Univ, 61 & Univ Freiburg, 62; mem, Bd Int Sci Exchange, Nat Acad Sci, 75-77; adj prof, Med Sch, Univ Md, Baltimore, 78-; Alexander von Humboldt US sr scientist award, Univ Hamburg, 79; Paul Ehrlich Award Comt, Frankfurt, Ger, 80- *Mem:* Nat Acad Sci; hon mem Pharmacol Soc Japan; Am Acad Arts & Sci; Am Chem Soc; Leopoldina Ger Acad Res Natural Sci; hon mem Chem Soc Japan; hon mem Biochem Soc Japan. *Res:* Alkaloids; arrow and mushroom poisons; oxidation mechanisms; peroxides; ozonides; intermediary and labile metabolites; nonenzymatic selective cleavage of proteins and enzymes; photochemistry of amino acids and nucleotides; venoms of amphibians; biochemical mechanisms; dynamics of modified homopolynucleotides; stimulation of interferon. *Mailing Add:* 3807 Montrose Dr Chevy Chase MD 20815-4701

**WITKOP, CARL JACOB, JR,** human genetics, oral pathology; deceased, see previous edition for last biography

**WITKOVSKY, PAUL,** SENSORY PHYSIOLOGY. *Current Pos:* MEM STAFF, DEPT OPHTHAL, NY UNIV MED CTR. *Personal Data:* b Chicago, Ill, May 24, 37; m 64. *Educ:* Univ Calif, Los Angeles, BA, 58, MA, 60, PhD(physiol), 62. *Prof Exp:* NIH fel neurophysiol, Sci Res Inst, Caracas, Venezuela, 62-63; instr ophthal, Columbia Univ, 64-65, from asst prof to assoc prof physiol, 65-73; prof anat sci, State Univ NY Stony Brook, 75- *Concurrent Pos:* Res grants, Nat Inst Neurol Dis & Blindness, 64- & Nat Coun Combat Blindness, 66-67. *Mem:* AAAS; Asn Res Vision & Ophthal; Biophys Soc; Soc Neurosci. *Res:* Central nervous system organization of tactile sensation; neurophysiological organization of the retina. *Mailing Add:* 9 Pearson St Brooklyn NY 11234

**WITKOWSKI, JOHN FREDERICK,** ENTOMOLOGY. *Current Pos:* ENTOMOLOGIST, UNIV NEBR, 75- *Personal Data:* b Beatrice, Nebr, Apr 30, 42; m 74; c 1. *Educ:* Univ Nebr, BSc, 65, MSc, 70; Iowa State Univ, PhD(entom), 75. *Prof Exp:* Res rep agr chem, Chemagro Corp, 70-72; res assoc entom, Iowa State Univ, 72-75. *Mem:* Entom Soc Am. *Res:* The biology and chemical control of insects damaging corn and soybeans. *Mailing Add:* RR 1 Wayne NE 68787

**WITKOWSKI, JOSEPH THEODORE,** ORGANIC CHEMISTRY, MEDICINAL CHEMISTRY. *Current Pos:* RES CHEMIST, SCHERING CORP, 77- *Personal Data:* b Ft Worth, Tex, Oct 29, 42; m 65; c 1. *Educ:* NTex State Univ, BS, 65, MS, 66; Univ Utah, PhD(chem), 70. *Prof Exp:* Res chemist, Nucleic Acid Res Inst, ICN Pharmaceut, Inc, 69-77. *Mem:* Am Chem Soc; Int Soc Heterocyclic Chem. *Res:* Medical chemistry; design and synthesis of cardiovascular agents. *Mailing Add:* Schering Corp K15 2A 2545 2015 Galloping Hill Rd Kenilworth NJ 07033-1310

**WITKOWSKI, MARK ROBERT,** MID & NEAR INFRARED ANALYSIS OF LIQUIDS & GASES, ATMOSPHERIC ANALYSIS OF VOLATILE ORGANIC COMPOUNDS. *Current Pos:* STAFF SCIENTIST, COM ASSOCS INT INC, 92- *Personal Data:* b McKeesport, Pa, Feb 24, 66; m 92, Lorraine Fox. *Educ:* Univ Pittsburgh, BS, 88; Kans State Univ, PhD(analytical chem), 92. *Prof Exp:* Res asst, Kans State Univ, 88 & 92. *Mem:* Soc Appl Spectros; Am Chem Soc; Coblentz Soc. *Res:* Applying near infrared spectrometry to analyze different vapor and condensed phase samples, these samples range from hydrocarbons to chlorinated hydrocarbons; this work will be applied to using near infrared spectrometry for remote monitoring of these types of compounds. *Mailing Add:* Forsgate Terr Annandale NJ 08801. *Fax:* 785-532-6666

**WITKOWSKI, ROBERT EDWARD,** MICROANALYTICAL CHEMISTRY, PLASMA CHEMICAL VAPOR DEPOSITION. *Current Pos:* assoc engr mass spectros, Westinghouse Res Labs, 67-71, engr liquid metal technol, 71-75, sr engr liquid metal technol, 75-80, FEL SCIENTIST ADVAN MAT, WESTINGHOUSE SCI & TECHNOL CTR, 80- *Personal Data:* b Glassport, Pa, Jan 9, 41; m 63, Anna M Novakowski; c Mark R & Gregory E. *Educ:* Univ Pittsburgh, BS, 62, MS, 73, PhD, 88. *Honors & Awards:* Jacquet-Lucas Award & Gold Medal, 78. *Prof Exp:* Res asst phys measurements, Mellon Inst, Pittsburgh, 62-63, jr fel infrared spectros, 63-67. *Concurrent Pos:* Res assoc, Sect Minerals, Carnegie Mus Natural Hist, Pittsburgh, 74-; res scientist, US Antarctic Res Prog, Antarctic Search for Meteorites Proj, 83-88; prin investr, Naval Weapons Ctr Prog, Optical Qual Diamond Films, 89-93. *Mem:* Am Chem Soc; Sigma Xi. *Res:* Sodium corrosion and mass transport studies via advanced instrumental microanalytical techniques; South Pole atmospheric particle collection and characterization; microwave excited and DC plasma jet reactor chemistry; chemical vapor deposition technology. *Mailing Add:* 633 Shadyside Dr West Mifflin PA 15122-3228. *Fax:* 412-256-1348

**WITKUS, ELEANOR RUTH,** BIOLOGY. *Current Pos:* from instr to assoc prof bot & bact, 44-74, chmn dept, 72-78, PROF BIOL SCI, FORDHAM UNIV, 71- *Personal Data:* b New York, NY, July 11, 18. *Educ:* Hunter Col, BA, 40; Boston Univ, MA, 41; Fordham Univ, PhD(cytol), 44. *Prof Exp:* Instr zool, Marymount Col, NY, 43-44. *Mem:* Bot Soc Am; Torrey Bot Club (corresp secy, 53-56); Sigma Xi. *Res:* Botanical cytology. *Mailing Add:* Dept Biol Fordham Univ Bronx NY 10458

**WITLIN, BERNARD,** MICROBIOLOGY. *Current Pos:* from assoc prof to prof bact, 50-71, EMER PROF BACT & PUB HEALTH, PA COL OPTOM, 71-, EMER PROF PHARM, COL PHARM & SCI, 81- *Personal Data:* b Philadelphia, Pa, July 18, 14; m 44; c 2. *Educ:* Univ Calif, Los Angeles, AB, 36; Philadelphia Col Pharm, MSc, 38, DSc(bact, pub health), 40; Am Bd Clin Chem, dipl. *Prof Exp:* Res bacteriologist, Sharp & Dohme, Inc, Pa, 38-40; dir, Barlin Labs, 40-41; bacteriologist, USPHS, US Dept Army & USN, 41-46 & Mellon Inst, 46-50. *Concurrent Pos:* Prof, Philadelphia Col Pharm & Sci, 40-81; assoc prof microbiol & pub health, Philadelphia Col Osteopath Med, 50-68; clin pathologist, 52-81, emer pathologist, Metrop Hosp, Philadelphia, 81- *Mem:* AAAS; Am Soc Microbiol; Am Pub Health Asn; Am Asn Clin Chemists; Sigma Xi (pres, 71-72). *Res:* Antiseptics and disinfectants; water purification; blood banks; serology. *Mailing Add:* Kennedy House Apt No 1820 1901 John F Kennedy Blvd Philadelphia PA 19103

**WITMAN, GEORGE BODO, III,** CELL MOTILITY. *Current Pos:* staff scientist, 81-82, sr scientist, 83-90, DIR, MALE FERTILITY PROG, WORCESTER FOUND BIOMED RES, SHREWSBURY, MASS, 85-, PRIN SCIENTIST, 90- *Personal Data:* b Upland, Calif, July 19, 45; m 69, Rita Ricciutti; c George B, Anthony R & Andrew J. *Educ:* Univ Calif, Riverside, BA, 67; Yale Univ, PhD(cellular & develop biol), 72. *Prof Exp:* NIH fel cell biol, Whitman Lab, Univ Chicago, 72-73; NIH fel molecular biol, Lab Molecular Biol & Biophys, Univ Wis-Madison, 73-74; asst prof, dept biol, Princeton Univ, 74-81; assoc prof, Dept Anat, Univ Mass Med Ctr, Worcester, 85-; adj prof, Dept Cell Biol, Univ Mass Med Ctr, Worcester, 92- *Mem:* AAAS; Am Soc Biochem Molecular Biol; Am Soc Cell Biol; Micros Soc Am; Genetics Soc Am; Protein Soc; Soc Study Reproduction. *Res:* Structure, composition, function and development of cell organelles; male reproduction; cell motility; cilia and flagella; microtubule-based force production; sperm maturation and motility. *Mailing Add:* Worcester Found Biomed Res 222 Maple Ave Shrewsbury MA 01545

**WITMER, EMMETT A(TLEE),** aerodynamics, structural dynamics, for more information see previous edition

**WITMER, GARY WILLIAM,** VERTEBRATE DAMAGE MANAGEMENT, WILDLIFE HABITAT RELATIONSHIPS. *Current Pos:* RES WILDLIFE BIOL & PROJ LEADER, ANIMAL & PLANT HEALTH INSPECTION SERV, NAT WILDLIFE RES CTR, USDA, 91- *Personal Data:* b Hamtramck, Mich, Sept 28, 51; m 85, Vicki Lynn Ellis; c Brian & Sarah. *Educ:* Univ Mich, BS, 73, MS, 74; Purdue Univ, MS, 76; Ore State Univ, PhD(wildlife sci), 81. *Prof Exp:* Postdoctoral res assoc, Ore State Univ, 81-84; staff scientist & proj leader, Argonne Nat Lab, 84-88; asst prof, Pa State Univ, 88-91. *Concurrent Pos:* Adj assoc prof, Wash State Univ, 92-; affil assoc prof, Univ Idaho, 94-; chair, 95 Group, Agr Res Sta, Wash Res Coun, 94. *Mem:* Wildlife Soc; Northwest Sci Asn; Nat Animal Damage Control Asn. *Res:* Methods of vertebrate damage management; technology transfer in wildlife damage management; wildlife-habitat relationships; predator-prey relationships. *Mailing Add:* 813 Alyson Dr Ft Collins WA 99164-6410

**WITMER, HEMAN JOHN,** VIROLOGY, BIOCHEMISTRY. *Current Pos:* asst prof, 72-77, ASSOC PROF BIOL SCI, UNIV ILL, CHICAGO CIRCLE, 77- *Personal Data:* b Bayonne, NJ, Apr 5, 44; m 70; c 2. *Educ:* Delaware Valley Col, BS, 65; Ind Univ, Bloomington, PhD(microbiol), 69. *Prof Exp:* NIH fel, McArdle Lab, Univ Wis-Madison, 69 & Ind Univ, Bloomington, 69-71; vis asst prof microbiol, 71, asst prof, Med Ctr, 71-72. *Res:* Controls of gene expression of coliphage T4; biosynthesis of unusual bases in DNA. *Mailing Add:* 123 N Taylor Ave Oak Park IL 60302

**WITMER, RICHARD E,** REMOTE SENSING, GEOGRAPHIC INFORMATION SYSTEM TECHNOLOGY. *Current Pos:* res coordr, Geog Prog, US Geol Surv, 74-77, asst chief, 77-80, chief geog prog 80, chief, Off Geog Res, Nat Mapping Div, 80-82, chief, Off Geog & Cartog Res, 82-84, asst div chief plans & opers, 84-89, asst div chief prog budget & admin, 89-95, assoc div chief progs & finances, 95, ACTG CHIEF, NAT MAPPING DIV, US GEOL SURV, 95- *Personal Data:* b Swarthmore, Pa, 1942. *Educ:* Univ Fla, BS, 62, MS, 64, PhD(geog & geol), 67. *Prof Exp:* Instr geog, Colo State Univ, Fla State Univ & Univ Tenn, 64-74. *Res:* Geographic applications of remote sensing; geographic information system technology; land use and land cover mapping; federal land management policy and history. *Mailing Add:* US Geol Surv Reston VA 22092

**WITMER, WILLIAM BYRON,** INORGANIC CHEMISTRY, PHYSICAL CHEMISTRY. *Current Pos:* CONSULT & OWNER, WITMER ASSOC, ENVIRON HEALTH SAFETY & MGT SERVS, 85- *Personal Data:* b Clarksville, Tex, June 29, 31; m 55, Rosemary Michie; c Margaret A, Lora E & William B Jr. *Educ:* Tex A&M Univ, BS, 52, MS, 58, PhD(chem), 60. *Prof Exp:* Res chemist, Chemstrand Res Ctr, Monsanto Co, NC, 59-64; sr res chemist, 64, supvr, Spec Anal Lab, Textiles Div, Ala, 64-65, supt, Tech Lab, 65-68, supt qual control, Decatur Plant, 68-70, qual control mgr, Lingen Plant, Monsanto (Deutschland), GMBH, WGer, 70-73, supt, Tech Dept, Sand Mountain Plant, 73-79; training specialist, Tex Eng Exten Serv, Occup & Environ Safety Training Div, Tex A&M Univ Syst, 87-95; dir, Osha Tng Inst, SW Educ Ctr, 94-95. *Concurrent Pos:* Supt, Environ Health & Safety, Pensacola Plant, Monsanto Textiles, 79-82; mgr, Environ Analysis Sci Ctr & Contracts, Mon Res Corp, 82-83, assoc dir, Dayton Lab, 83, mgr, Nuclear Opers, Mound Facil, 83-85; owner, Witmer Assocs, Environ & Mgt Servs, 85- *Mem:* Am Soc Qual Control; Am Chem Soc. *Res:* Amine-halogen complexes; polymer characterizition techniques; polymer properties related to synthetic fiber production; investigation of cause, course of a hypersensitivity pneumonities like disease among employees in an industrial setting; environmental health; health and safety; emergency response. *Mailing Add:* 1408 Country Club Rd Argyle TX 76226. *E-Mail:* byronwitmer@worldnet.att.net

**WITORSCH, RAPHAEL JAY,** PHYSIOLOGY, TOXICOLOGY. *Current Pos:* from asst prof to assoc prof, 70-88, PROF PHYSIOL, MED COL VA, VA COMMONWEALTH UNIV, 88- *Personal Data:* b New York, NY, Dec 12, 41; m 64; c 2. *Educ:* NY Univ, AB, 63; Yale Univ, MS, 65, PhD(physiol), 68. *Prof Exp:* USPHS trainee, Sch Med, Univ Va, 68-69, NIH fel, 69-70. *Concurrent Pos:* Dir first yr med curric, Med Col Va, 75-77; co-investr, NIH Grant Breast Cancer, 75-78; prin investr, NIH grant prolactin binding in normal & neoplastic prostate, 78-85. *Mem:* Endocrine Soc; Am Physiol Soc; Soc Exp Biol & Med; Histochem Soc; Am Soc Andrology. *Res:* Endocrinology; immunohistochemistry; hormone receptors in normal and neoplastic tissues; endocrine toxicology; nature of the hormone prolactin and its interaction with its target tissue; cytoxicity; apoptosis. *Mailing Add:* Dept Physiol Box 980551 Med Col Va Richmond VA 23298-0551. *E-Mail:* witorsch@ruby.vcu.edu

**WITRIOL, NORMAN MARTIN,** OPTICS, CHEMICAL PHYSICS. *Current Pos:* from asst prof to assoc prof, 77-84, PROF PHYSICS, LA TECH UNIV, 85- *Personal Data:* b Brooklyn, NY, June 9, 40; m 66; c Daniel & Jennifer. *Educ:* Polytech Inst Brooklyn, BS, 61; Brandeis Univ, MA, 64, PhD(physics), 68. *Prof Exp:* Res physicist, Phys Sci Lab, US Army Missile Command, 68-77. *Concurrent Pos:* Asst prof, Univ Ala, Huntsville, 70-77; consult, Columbus Labs, Battelle Mem Inst, 78-79, Naval Res Lab, 85-89, Ballistic Res Lab, 89-90, Chem Res, Develop & Eng Ctr, 89, 91- *Mem:* Am Phys Soc; Optical Soc Am. *Res:* Light scattering from particulate matter; computer modeling and simulation of the ignition process and the chemical kinetics in reactive gases; multiphoton processes; design of robotic vision systems; fabrication of micro-opto-mechanical systems; micro-optical switches; micro-motors. *Mailing Add:* La Tech Univ PO Box 3169 Tech Sta Ruston LA 71272. *E-Mail:* witriol@latech.edu

**WITSCHARD, GILBERT,** ORGANIC CHEMISTRY. *Current Pos:* GROUP LEADER, OXY CHEM, BURLINGTON, NJ, 86- *Personal Data:* b Morehead City, NC, Mar 13, 33; m 60; c 3. *Educ:* Queens Col, BS, 57; Univ Pittsburgh, PhD(org chem), 63. *Prof Exp:* Res chemist, Hooker Chem Corp, Niagara Falls, 63-70, sr res chemist, 70-84; compound develop mgr, Oxy Chem, Burlington, NJ, 84-86. *Mem:* Am Chem Soc; Soc Plastic Engr. *Res:* Organo-phosphorus chemistry; fire retardance; polymer synthesis; polymers stabilization; powder coatings; polyvinyl chloride. *Mailing Add:* 85 Richboro Rd Newtown PA 18940-1534

**WITSCHI, HANSPETER R,** PATHOLOGY, ENVIRONMENTAL HEALTH. *Current Pos:* PROF & ASSOC DIR, TOXIC SUBSTANCES RES & TEACHING PROG, UNIV CALIF, DAVIS, 87- *Personal Data:* b Berne, Switz, Mar 17, 33; US citizen; m 63; c 2. *Educ:* Univ Berne, MD, 60; Am Bd Toxicol, dipl, 80; Acad Toxicol Sci, dipl, 82. *Honors & Awards:* Educ Award, Soc Toxicol, 91. *Prof Exp:* Asst path, Inst Forensic Med, Univ Berne, 61-64; res fel, Toxicol Res Unit, Med Res Coun, 65-66; res fel exp path, Univ Pittsburgh, 67-69; from asst prof to assoc prof toxicol & pharmacol, Fac Med, Univ Montreal, 69-77; sr res staff mem, Biol Div, Oak Ridge Nat Lab, 77-87. *Concurrent Pos:* Assoc ed, Toxicol Appl Pharmacol, 78-86; ed USA, Toxicol, 78-; mem, toxicol study sect, Div Res Grants, NIH, 80-84, rev comt, Nat Inst Environ Health Sci, 86-90, chmn, 89-90; sci adv bd, subcomt Health Effects, Rel Risk Reduction Proj, US Environ Protection Agency; sci rev panel, State Calif Air Resources Bd; bd mem, Am Bd Toxicol, 88-92. *Mem:* Am Soc Pharmacol & Exp Therapeut; Soc Exp Biol & Med; Soc Toxicol; Am Col Toxicol. *Res:* Experimental toxicology; biochemical pathology; interaction of drugs and toxic agents with organ function at the cellular level; pulmonary carcinogenesis; air pollutants and lung disease. *Mailing Add:* Toxics Prog ITEH Univ Calif Davis CA 95616-5224. *Fax:* 530-752-5300

**WITSENHAUSEN, HANS S,** APPLIED MATHEMATICS. *Current Pos:* RETIRED. *Personal Data:* b Frankfurt, Ger, May 6, 30; US citizen; m 61; c 3. *Educ:* Free Univ Brussels, ICME, 53, lic sc phys, 56; Mass Inst Technol, SM, 64. *Prof Exp:* Asst elec eng, Free Univ Brussels, 53-57; appln engr, European Ctr, Electronic Assoc, Inc, 57-60, sr engr, Res Div, 60-63; res asst control theory & Lincoln Lab assoc, Electronic Systs Lab, Mass Inst Technol, 63-65; mem tech staff, Math Res Ctr, AT&T Bell Labs, 66-90; sr vis scientist, Lab Info & Decision Sci, Mass Inst Technol, 90-93; vis lectr, Princeton Univ, 94. *Concurrent Pos:* Vis prof, Mass Inst Technol, 73; Vinton Hayes sr fel, Harvard Univ, 75-76. *Mem:* Am Math Soc. *Res:* System theory; optimization; geometry; inequalities; information. *Mailing Add:* 137 Beechwood Rd Summit NJ 07901

**WITT, ADOLF NICOLAUS,** ASTROPHYSICS. *Current Pos:* From asst prof to prof astron, Univ Toledo, 67-89, assoc dir, Ritter Observ, 72-76, dir, 76-79, chmn dept phys & astron, 79-81, DISTINGUISHED UNIV PROF ASTRON, UNIV TOLEDO, 89- *Personal Data:* b Bad Oldesloe, Ger, Oct 17, 40; m 67; c 2. *Educ:* Univ Hamburg, Vordiplom, 63; Univ Chicago, PhD(astrophys), 67. *Honors & Awards:* Sigma Xi Award. *Concurrent Pos:* Vis fel, Lab Atmospheric & Space Physics, Univ Colo, Boulder, 75-76; vis prof, Max Planck Inst Astron, Heidelberg, Ger, 82. *Mem:* AAAS; Am Astron Soc; Int Astron Union. *Res:* Interstellar matter; photometry; astronomical instrumentation; radiative transfer; scattering by dust; photoluminescence of solids; laboratory astrophysics. *Mailing Add:* Dept Physics & Astron Univ Toledo Toledo OH 43606. *Fax:* 419-530-2723; *E-Mail:* awitt@anwsun.astro.utoledo.edu

**WITT, AUGUST FERDINAND,** AEROSPACE SCIENCE. *Current Pos:* Prof mat sci, 72-90, TDK prof, 90-93, MEM STAFF, MASS INST TECHNOL, 60-, FORD PROF ENG, 93- *Personal Data:* b Innsbruck, Austria, 1931; M; c 3. *Educ:* Univ Innsbruck, PhD(phys chem), 59. *Honors & Awards:* Exner Medal for Outstanding Contrib to Sci & Technol, Austria, 76; Space Processing Award, Am Inst Aeronaut & Astronaut, 92. *Concurrent Pos:* Chmn, Electronic Mat Working Group, NASA, 82-89. *Mem:* Am Asn Crystal Growth; Sigma Xi. *Res:* Engineering; materials science. *Mailing Add:* Mass Inst Technol 77 Massachusetts Ave Cambridge MA 02139

**WITT, CHRISTOPHER JOHN,** SIMULATION TECHNOLOGY, ELECTRONIC PROTOTYPING. *Current Pos:* sect head, Guid & Control, Grumman Aerospace Corp, 63-67, eng mgr, 67-72, mgr & dir, Elec Systs Ctr, 72-87, DIR, CORP DEVELOP LABS, GURMMAN CORP, 87- *Personal Data:* b Flushing, NY, Dec 24, 31; m 58, Clara E Scheuing; c Erika L, Christopher F & Lyssa A. *Educ:* Polytech Univ, BEE, 53, MEE, 54. *Honors & Awards:* Region 1 Award for Technol Appln to Aerospace, Inst Elec & Electronics Engrs, 93. *Prof Exp:* Sr engr, Sperry Gyroscope Co, 56-63. *Concurrent Pos:* Adj prof systs eng, State Univ NY, Stony Brook, 82-86; mem, ad hoc comt Ultra Reliable Elec, AIA, 88-90; mem, Res & Eng Comt,

Nat Security Indust Asn, 91; chmn, Int Technol. *Mem:* Inst Elec & Electronics Engrs; Sigma Xi. *Res:* Magnetics; mag amp and mag pulse modulators; inertial component design; space telescope and space telescope control system design; application of high temperature superconductivity and diamond thin films to electronics. *Mailing Add:* 8 White Oak Tree Rd Laurel Hollow NY 11791-1210

**WITT, DONALD JAMES,** VIROLOGY, TISSUE CULTURE. *Current Pos:* NIH fel, Dept Cellular Virol & Molecular Biol, Med Sch, 78-80, virologist, 80, MGR BIOCHEM & MOLECULAR BIOL, RES INST, UNIV UTAH, 80- *Personal Data:* b Chicago, Ill, May 13, 49; m 73; c 2. *Educ:* Loyola Univ, BS, 71; Ohio State Univ, MS, 73, PhD(virol), 76. *Prof Exp:* Res assoc, Dept Entom, Ohio State Univ, 76-77; sr scientist, Crop Protection Div, Sandoz Inc, 77-78. *Mem:* Am Soc Microbiol; Soc Invert Path; Sigma Xi. *Res:* Molecular biology of infectious disease agents, especially viruses; development of diagnostic technology for the identification of infectious disease agents; development of artificial vaccines; application of microorganisms to regulate pest insect populations. *Mailing Add:* 107 S Corncrib Ct Cary NC 27513-5407

**WITT, DONALD REINHOLD,** CHEMISTRY. *Current Pos:* Res chemist, 50-62, GROUP LEADER CHEM, PHILLIPS PETROL CO, 62- *Personal Data:* b LeMars, Iowa, Apr 15, 23; m 50; c 4. *Educ:* Westmar Col, BS, 48; Univ SDak, MA, 50. *Mem:* Am Chem Soc. *Res:* Polymerization of olefins and diolefins to solid polymers; catalyst development related to such reactions. *Mailing Add:* 4909 Harvard Dr Bartlesville OK 74006

**WITT, ENRIQUE ROBERTO,** ORGANIC CHEMISTRY. *Current Pos:* CONSULT ENVIRON SCI, 86- *Personal Data:* b Buenos Aires, Arg, May 10, 26; nat US; m 55; c 2. *Educ:* Univ Buenos Aires, Lic, 51, DrChem, 53. *Prof Exp:* Technician, E R Squibb & Sons, Arg, 51-52; res chemist, Arg AEC, 53-55; res assoc, Celanese Chem Co, 56-86. *Mem:* AAAS; Am Chem Soc; Soc Econ Bot. *Res:* Synthetic lubricants; phosphorus compounds; polyester technology; environmental maintenance; anaerobic biological treatment of industrial wastes. *Mailing Add:* 1037 Brock Corpus Christi TX 78412-3343

**WITT, HOWARD RUSSELL,** ELECTRICAL ENGINEERING. *Current Pos:* assoc prof eng, 67-71, asst dean sch eng, 69-75, PROF ENG, OAKLAND UNIV, 71-, ASSOC DEAN SCH ENG, 75- *Personal Data:* b Morden, Man, July 12, 29; m 56; c 3. *Educ:* Univ Toronto, BASc, 53; Princeton Univ, MSE, 59; Cornell Univ, PhD(elec eng), 62. *Prof Exp:* Asst prof elec eng, Cornell Univ, 62-67. *Mem:* Inst Elec & Electronics Engrs; Am Soc Eng Educ; Sigma Xi. *Mailing Add:* Sch Eng Oakland Univ Rochester MI 48063

**WITT, JOHN, JR,** ORGANIC CHEMISTRY. *Current Pos:* asst head chem process develop, Nutrasweet Co, 62-69, mgr spec synthesis & process develop, 69-72, mgr, synthesis develop, 72-78, dir chem develop, 78-81, sr dir, 81-94, VPRES, NUTRASWEET RES & DEVELOP, NUTRASWEET CO, 94- *Personal Data:* b Muskegon, Mich, Oct 5, 35; m 64; c 2. *Educ:* Mich State Univ, BS, 57; Univ Ill, PhD(org chem), 61; Univ Chicago, MBA, 78. *Prof Exp:* Res chemist, Ethyl Corp, 60-62. *Mem:* Am Chem Soc. *Res:* Organic synthesis; steroids; heterocyclics; amino acids. *Mailing Add:* 2425 Swainswood Dr Glenview IL 60025

**WITT, PATRICIA L,** CYTOKINES. *Current Pos:* PROF, NAT SCI CANCER CTR, STEPHENS COL. *Educ:* Univ Wis-Madison, PhD(cell biol), 80. *Prof Exp:* Asst scientist, Univ Wis-Madison, 83-89, assoc scientist, 89-90; asst res prof, Dept Microbiol, Med Col Wis, 90-93, assoc res prof, 93- *Mem:* Int Soc Interferon Res; Am Asn Cancer Res; Int Soc Inteferon & Cytokine Res. *Res:* Protein induction by interferons and cyytokines in cancer and AIDS. *Mailing Add:* Nat Sci Cancer Ctr Stephens Col Columbia MO 65215. *E-Mail:* pwitt@its.mcw.edu

**WITT, PETER NIKOLAUS,** PHARMACOLOGY. *Current Pos:* RETIRED. *Personal Data:* b Berlin, Ger, Oct 20, 18; m 49; c 2. *Educ:* Univ T bingen, MD, 46. *Honors & Awards:* Buergi Award, 56. *Prof Exp:* Asst, Univ T bingen, 45-49; sr asst, Univ Berne, 49-56, privat-docent, 56; from asst prof to assoc prof pharmacol, Col Med, State Univ NY Upstate Med Ctr, 56-66; dir div res, NC Dept Ment Health, 66-81. *Concurrent Pos:* Rockefeller fel, Harvard Med Sch, 52-53; Lederle med fac award, 57-59; adj prof, NC State Univ & Univ NC, Chapel Hill, 66-81. *Mem:* Am Soc Pharmacol & Exp Therapeut; Ger Pharmacol Soc; Swiss Pharmacol Soc. *Res:* Effect of drugs on web building behavior of spiders; invertebrate behavior; effect of cardioactive drugs on ion movements in heart muscle; objective testing of fine motor behavior in healthy and diseased human subjects under the influence of drugs. *Mailing Add:* 619 Tower St Raleigh NC 27607-7360

**WITT, ROBERT MICHAEL,** MEDICAL PHYSICS, RADIOLOGICAL SCIENCES. *Current Pos:* PHYSICIST NUCLEAR MED, VET ADMIN MED CTR, 77- *Personal Data:* b Waukesha, Wis, Oct 3, 42; m 71; c 2. *Educ:* Univ Wis-Milwaukee, BS, 64; Univ Wis-Madison, MS, 66, PhD(radiol sci), 75. *Prof Exp:* Proj assoc med physics, Dept Radiol, Univ Wis-Madison, 75-77. *Concurrent Pos:* Asst prof radiol, Med Ctr, Ind Univ, Indianapolis, 77- *Mem:* Am Asn Physicists Med; AAAS; Soc Nuclear Med; Health Physics Soc; Inst Elec & Electronics Engrs; Int Soc Optical Eng. *Res:* Medical image communication, storage and management; quantitative and qualitative medical imaging. *Mailing Add:* Nuclear Med 115 Roudebush Vet Admin Med Ctr Indianapolis IN 46202

**WITT, WILLIAM,** BOTANY. *Current Pos:* PROF AGRON, UNIV KY, LEXINGTON. *Honors & Awards:* Ciba Plant Protection Award, Weed Sci Soc Am, 94. *Res:* Weeds. *Mailing Add:* Univ Ky N 122 Agr Sci Ctr N Lexington KY 40546

**WITTBECKER, EMERSON LAVERNE,** POLYMER CHEMISTRY, TEXTILE CHEMISTRY. *Current Pos:* RETIRED. *Personal Data:* b Freeport, Ill, Feb 25, 17; m 56, Margaret E Ryan; c Alan E & Carl E. *Educ:* Univ Ill, AB, 39; Pa State Univ, MS, 41, PhD(org chem), 42. *Prof Exp:* Jr res assoc pioneering res, Textile Fibers Dept, E I Du Pont de Nemours & Co, Inc, 46-52, res assoc, 52-55, res mgr, 55-60, Orlon-Lycra res, 60-64, dir, Carothers Lab, 64-77. *Mem:* Am Chem Soc. *Res:* Condensation polymers; fibers; low temperature polymerizations, leading to nomex aramid, keviar aramid and lycra spandex fibers. *Mailing Add:* 8071 Glenbrooke Lane Sarasota FL 34243

**WITTCOFF, A HAROLD,** ORGANIC CHEMISTRY, INDUSTRIAL CHEMICAL EDUCATION. *Current Pos:* SCI ADV, CHEM SYST INC, 81- *Personal Data:* b Marion, Ind, July 3, 18; m 46, Dorothy Brochin; c Ralph G & Theodore A. *Educ:* DePauw Univ, AB, 40; Northwestern Univ, PhD(org chem), 43; Harvard Univ, cert mgt, 64. *Honors & Awards:* Minn Award, Am Chem Soc, 76. *Prof Exp:* Head, Chem Res Dept, Gen Mills Chem, Inc, 43-56, dir chem res, 56-68, vpres chem res & develop, 68-69, vpres & dir corp res, 69-78; dir res & develop, Koor Chem Ltd, Beer-Sheva, Israel, 78-81. *Concurrent Pos:* Adj prof chem, Univ Minn, 73-81. *Mem:* Am Chem Soc; Am Oil Chem Soc; Fedn Socs Paint Technol; Com Develop Asn; Inst Food Technol; Sigma Xi. *Res:* Phosphatides; polymers; protective coatings; resins and plastics; research adminstration; author or co-author of five books. *Mailing Add:* Chem Syst Inc 303 S Broadway Tarrytown NY 10591. *Fax:* 914-631-8851

**WITTE, JOHN JACOB,** PREVENTIVE MEDICINE, PEDIATRICS. *Current Pos:* ASST, STATE HEALTH OFF DIS CONTROL & AIDS PREV, FLA, 82- *Personal Data:* b Passaic, NJ, Mar 10, 32; m 68, 79; c 3. *Educ:* Hope Col, AB, 54; Johns Hopkins Univ, MD, 59; Harvard Univ, MPH(microbiol), 66. *Prof Exp:* Intern & resident pediat, Johns Hopkins Univ, 59-62; med epidemiologist infectious dis, Bur Health Educ, Dis Control, 62-65, asst chief immunization br, 66-70, chief, 70-74, dir, Immunization Div, 74-77, med dir, 77-82. *Concurrent Pos:* Consult, Adv Comt Immunizing Agents, Can, 69- & Adv Comt Epidemiol, Can, 69- *Mem:* Fel Am Acad Pediat; Infectious Dis Soc; Am Col Preventive Med; Am Pub Health Asn. *Res:* Epidemiology of communicable and chronic diseases; smoking related diseases; development and field testing of vaccines; complications of vaccine administration; AIDS epidemiology and clinical trials. *Mailing Add:* Dept Health Rehab Serv Dist 15 337 N Fourth St Suite A Ft Pierce FL 34950

**WITTE, LARRY C(LAUDE),** MECHANICAL ENGINEERING, MATHEMATICS. *Current Pos:* from asst prof to assoc prof, Univ Houston, 67-73, chmn dept, 72-76 & 88-93, PROF MECH ENG, UNIV HOUSTON, 73- *Personal Data:* b Jonesboro, Tex, Apr 27, 39; m 62; c 2. *Educ:* Arlington State Col, BSME, 63; Okla State Univ, MSME, 65, PhD(mech eng), 67. *Honors & Awards:* Herbert Allen Award, Am Soc Mech Engrs, 75. *Prof Exp:* Assoc aerodyn engr, Ling-Temco-Vought, Inc, 63-65; res assoc, Argonne Nat Lab, 65-66, asst mech eng, 66-67. *Concurrent Pos:* Heat transfer consult. *Mem:* Assoc fel Am Inst Astronaut & Aeronaut; Am Nuclear Soc; fel Am Soc Mech Engrs; Am Soc Heating Refrig & Air Conditioning Engrs. *Res:* Boiling heat transfer; high flux heat transfer processes; explosive vapor formation; natural convection in irregular enclosures; thermodynamic efficiency of heat exchangers. *Mailing Add:* 6135 Birchmont Dr Houston TX 77092-2323. *Fax:* 713-743-4503; *E-Mail:* witte@jetson.uh.edu

**WITTE, MICHAEL,** ORGANIC CHEMISTRY, POLLUTION CHEMISTRY. *Current Pos:* RETIRED. *Personal Data:* b Poland, Mar 15, 11; nat US; m 40, Louise Wujek; c 4. *Educ:* Loyola Univ, Ill, BS, 37; Univ Ill, MS, 38, PhD(org chem), 41. *Prof Exp:* Asst chem, Univ Ill, 38-41; res chemist, Nat Aniline Div, Allied Chem Corp, 41-47; prod supvr, Gen Aniline & Film Corp, 46-54, prod mgr, NJ, 54-56; pres, Simpson Labs, Inc, 57-59; pres, Carnegies Fine Chem Div, Rexall Drug & Chem Corp, 59-60; pres, M Witte Assocs, 60-87. *Concurrent Pos:* Chem consult; Dept Energy grantee, Solar Energy Proj, 80-81. *Mem:* Am Chem Soc. *Res:* Pharmaceutical intermediates; dyestuffs manufacture; biochemistry; chemical management; solar energy. *Mailing Add:* 3674 N Laurelwood Loop Beverly Hills FL 34465

**WITTE, OWEN NEIL,** LEUKEMIA & MOLECULAR IMMUNOLOGY. *Current Pos:* from asst prof to assoc prof, 80-86, PROF MICROBIOL & MOLECULAR GENETICS & INVESTR, HOWARD HUGHES MED INST, UNIV CALIF, LOS ANGELES, 86-, PRES'S CHAIR DEVELOP IMMUNOL, 89- *Personal Data:* m, Jami McLaughlin; c Gabrielle M. *Educ:* Cornell Univ, BS, 71; Stanford Univ, MD, 76. *Honors & Awards:* Allison Eberlin Fund Award, 89; Milken Family Med Found Award, 90; Rosenthal Award, Am Asn Cancer Res, 91; Kenneth B McCredie Mem lectr, Leukemia Soc Am, 92; Dameshek Prize, Am Soc Hemat, 93. *Prof Exp:* Fel, Ctr Cancer Res, Mass Inst Technol, 76-80. *Concurrent Pos:* Rev, Virol Study Sect, NIH, 82-83, mem, 85-89; fel, Am Cancer Soc, Calif Div, 83-86; Cancer Res Coord Comt, Univ Calif, 84-87; Nat Rev Panel, Leukemia Soc Am, 88-92; numerous invited lectureships. *Mem:* Nat Acad Sci; Am Soc Clin Invest; Am Soc Microbiol; Am Soc Hemat; Am Asn Cancer Res; fel Am Acad Arts & Sci; Am Asn Immunologists. *Res:* Development of the immune response; growth regulation of hematopoietic stem cells by the abl oncogene and other mechanisms. *Mailing Add:* Univ Calif Los Angeles Howard Hughes Med Inst 5-748 MRL 10833 Le Conte Ave Los Angeles CA 90024-1662. *E-Mail:* owenw@microbio.lifesci.ucla.edu

**WITTEBORN, FRED CARL,** PHYSICS, ASTROPHYSICS. *Current Pos:* res scientist, 69-70 & 75-89, CHIEF ASTROPHYS BR, NASA AMES RES CTR, 70-74 & 90- *Personal Data:* b St Louis, Mo, Dec 27, 34; m 57, Nancy Durham; c Fred J. *Educ:* Calif Inst Technol, BS, 56; Stanford Univ, MS, 58, PhD(physics), 65. *Prof Exp:* Res assoc physics, Stanford Univ, 65-68. *Concurrent Pos:* Vis scholar, Stanford Univ, 70-75. *Mem:* Am Phys Soc; Am Astron Soc; Astron Soc Pac. *Res:* Infrared astronomy; gravity; atomic physics; low temperature physics. *Mailing Add:* 2071 Madelaine Ct Los Altos CA 94024. *Fax:* 650-604-6779; *E-Mail:* witteborn@ssa1.arc.nasa.gov

**WITTEBORT, JULES I,** physics, materials science; deceased, see previous edition for last biography

**WITTEKIND, RAYMOND RICHARD,** ORGANIC CHEMISTRY. *Current Pos:* PATENT LAWYER, AM HOECHST CORP, SOMERVILLE, 78- *Personal Data:* b Jamaica, NY, May 9, 29; m 60. *Educ:* Polytech Inst Brooklyn, BS, 51; Columbia Univ, AM, 55, PhD, 59; Seton Hall Univ, JD, 77. *Prof Exp:* Res chemist, McNeil Labs, Inc, 58-61; scientist, Warner-Lambert Res Inst, 61-73, sr scientist, 73-74; patent lawyer, Hoffman-LaRoche Inc, Nutley, 74-78. *Mem:* Am Chem Soc. *Res:* Synthesis of fused ring heterocyclic compounds; stereochemistry and mechanism of organic reactions. *Mailing Add:* 30 Valley View Dr Morristown NJ 07960

**WITTELES, ELEONORA MEIRA,** THIN FILM DEPOSITION TECHNOLOGY, HIGH ENERGY X-RAY OPTICS. *Current Pos:* chief scientist, 92-93, PRES, WORLD-WIDE INNOVATIVE TECHNOL CORP, 93- *Personal Data:* b Jerusalem, Israel, July 14, 38; nat US. *Educ:* Fordham Univ, BS, 62, MS, 63; NY Univ, MS, 65; Yeshiva Univ, PhD(physics), 69. *Prof Exp:* Postdoctoral fel, Bar Ilan Univ, 69; dir, Res Lab, Atlantic Richfield Co, 80-84; sr res scientist, Hughes Aircraft Co, 84-86; prog mgr, Aerojet Electrosyst Corp, 88-90, Rockwell Int, 90 & Summa Technol, 91-92; exec dir, Summa Int Res Inst, 92-93. *Concurrent Pos:* Prin investr, Marshall Space Flight Ctr, NASA, 94-97, Ballistic Missile Defense Orgn, 95 & NSF, 96. *Mem:* Inst Elec & Electronics Engrs; Am Phys Soc; Optical Eng Soc. *Res:* Thin film deposition process for ultra thin ultra smooth thin film of metals oxides carbides nitrides and ceramics; multilater high energy xray optics; solid state medical devices; inventor of new method for deposition of films and coatings; patentee in field. *Mailing Add:* PO Box 4722 Palos Verdes CA 90274. *Fax:* 310-541-3131; *E-Mail:* witc@juno.com

**WITTELS, BENJAMIN,** PATHOLOGY, BIOCHEMISTRY. *Current Pos:* Assoc prof, 60-70, PROF PATH, MED CTR, DUKE UNIV, 70- *Personal Data:* b Minneapolis, Minn, Jan 22, 26; m 55; c 2. *Educ:* Univ Minn, BA, 48, MD, 52; Am Bd Path, dipl, 57; Am Bd Clin Path, dipl, 70. *Mem:* Am Asn Path & Bact; Am Col Path. *Res:* Cardiac metabolism; hematology. *Mailing Add:* Dept Path Duke Med Ctr Durham NC 27710

**WITTELS, MARK C,** MINERALOGY, SOLID STATE PHYSICS. *Current Pos:* CHIEF, SOLID STATE PHYSICS & MAT CHEM BR, DIV MAT SCI, US DEPT ENERGY, 74- *Personal Data:* b Minneapolis, Minn, July 14, 21; m 51; c 3. *Educ:* Univ Minn, BS, 47; Mass Inst Technol, PhD(geol, ceramic eng), 51. *Prof Exp:* Staff scientist, Oak Ridge Nat Lab, 51-63; sr solid state physicist, US AEC, 63-74. *Concurrent Pos:* Vis prof, Wash Univ, 68-69. *Mem:* Mineral Soc Am; Am Crystallog Asn; Am Phys Soc. *Res:* Radiation effects in crystalline solids and in lunar materials; x-ray diffraction instrumentation; crystal growth techniques; defects in crystals; stored energy in reactor-irradiated graphite. *Mailing Add:* 8309 Still Spring Ct Bethesda MD 20817

**WITTEMANN, JOSEPH KLAUS,** dentistry, psychology, for more information see previous edition

**WITTEN, ALAN JOEL,** FLUIDS. *Current Pos:* Mem staff, Thermal-Hydraulics Group, 75-78, mgr, Coal Gasification Environ Proj, 78-80, LEADER, APPL PHYS SCI GROUP, OAK RIDGE NAT LAB, 80- *Personal Data:* b Malden, Mass, Dec 11, 49; m 75; c 1. *Educ:* Univ Rochester, BS, 71, MS, 72, PhD(mech eng), 75. *Mem:* Am Geophys Union. *Res:* Geophysical fluid dynamics; ekman layers; diffusion equation with random ejection; atmospheric transport in complex terrain. *Mailing Add:* 3308 Riverwalk Ct Norman OK 73072

**WITTEN, EDWARD,** PHYSICS. *Current Pos:* PROF, SCH NATURAL SCI, INST ADVAN STUDY, 87- *Personal Data:* b Aug, 1951. *Educ:* Brandeis Univ, BA, 71; Princeton Univ, MA, 74, PhD, 76. *Hon Degrees:* PhD, Hebrew Univ, Jerusalem, 93, Columbia Univ, 96. *Honors & Awards:* MacArthur Fel, 82; Einstein Medal, Einstein Soc Berne, Switz, 85; Award Phys & Math Sci, NY Acad Sci, 85; Dirac Medal, Int Ctr Theoret Physics, 85; Alan T Waterman Award, NSF, 86; Fields Medal Math, 90. *Prof Exp:* Fel, Harvard Univ, 76-77, jr fel, Harvard Soc Fels, 77-80; prof physics, Princeton Univ, 80-87. *Mem:* Fel Nat Acad Sci; fel Am Phys Soc; fel Am Acad Arts & Sci. *Res:* Natural sciences. *Mailing Add:* Sch Natural Sci Inst Advan Study Olden Lane Princeton NJ 08540

**WITTEN, GERALD LEE,** SCIENCE EDUCATION. *Current Pos:* ASSOC PROF PHYS SCI, EMPORIA KANS STATE COL, 62- *Personal Data:* b Davies County, Mo, May 12, 29; m 51; c 3. *Educ:* Kans State Teachers Col, 56, MS, 58, EdS(phys sci), 62. *Prof Exp:* Teacher high sch, Kans, 56-62. *Mem:* Nat Sci Teachers Asn; Am Asn Physics Teachers. *Res:* Development of take home laboratory exercises for high school physics and general education physical science classes. *Mailing Add:* 206 S Union St Emporia KS 66801

**WITTEN, LOUIS,** THEORY OF GRAVITATION-GENERAL RELATIVITY. *Current Pos:* head dept physics, 68-74, prof, 68-91, EMER PROF PHYSICS, UNIV CINCINNATI, 91- *Personal Data:* b Baltimore, Md, Apr 13, 21; m 91, Francis de Lange; c Edward, Celia, Matthew & Jesse. *Educ:* John Hopkins Univ, BE, 41, PhD(physics), 51; NY Univ, BS, 44. *Prof Exp:* Res assoc, Princeton Univ, 51-53, Univ Md, 52-53; staff scientist, Lincoln Lab, Mass Inst Technol, 53-54; prin scientist, Res Inst Advan Study, Martin Marietta Corp, Md, 54-65, assoc dir, 65-68. *Concurrent Pos:* Adj prof, Drexel Univ, 56-68; Fulbright lectr, Weizmann Inst Sci, Israel, 64-65; trustee, Gravity Res Found, 66-, vpres, 72- *Mem:* AAAS; Am Phys Soc; Am Math Soc; Am Asn Physics Teachers. *Res:* General theory of relativity; theory of particles and fields. *Mailing Add:* Dept Physics Univ Cincinnati Cincinnati OH 45221. *E-Mail:* witten@ucbeh.san.uc.edu

**WITTEN, MARK LEE,** RESPIRATORY PHYSIOLOGY, INHALATION TOXICOLOGY. *Current Pos:* res asst prof, 90-93, RES ASSOC PROF, DEPT PEDIAT, UNIV ARIZ, 93- *Personal Data:* b Amarillo, Tex, June 23, 53; m 88, Christine; c Brandon. *Educ:* Emporia State Univ, BS, 75; Ind Univ, PhD(physiol), 83. *Prof Exp:* Fel, Dept Physiol, Univ Ariz, 83-88; instr med, Harvard Med Sch, 88-90. *Concurrent Pos:* Co-prin investr, Shriners Burns Inst, 89-; prin investr, USAF Off Sci Res, 91-, Dept Defense, 92-, Upjohn Pharmaceut, 92-, US Army Med Res & Develop Command, 93-; consult, NASA, 93- *Mem:* Am Physiol Soc; AAAS; NY Acad Sci; Soc Critical Care Med; Am Thoracic Soc; Soc Toxicol. *Res:* Effects of environmental toxins on lung function; acute smoke-induced lung injury and the subsequent development of acute respiratory distress syndrome; effect of chronic inhalation of hydrocarbons on lung function. *Mailing Add:* Dept Pediat Univ Ariz Tucson AZ 85724-0001. *Fax:* 520-626-3636

**WITTEN, MAURICE HADEN,** PHYSICS EDUCATION. *Current Pos:* from instr to assoc prof, 60-69, chmn dept, 69-89, PROF PHYSICS, FT HAYS STATE UNIV, 69- *Personal Data:* b Jamesport, Mo, Dec 5, 31; wid; c Barry, Brenda & Carmen. *Educ:* Emporia State Univ, BA, 56; Univ Nebr, Lincoln, MA, 60; Univ Iowa, PhD(sci educ, physics), 67. *Prof Exp:* Engr, Int Business Mach Corp, 56-57. *Concurrent Pos:* NSF sci fac fel, 65-66. *Mem:* Am Asn Physics Teachers; Nat Sci Teachers Asn. *Res:* Nuclear emulsion techniques; physics education. *Mailing Add:* 101 W 33rd St Hays KS 67601. *Fax:* 785-628-4096

**WITTEN, THOMAS ADAMS,** THEORETICAL PHYSICS, SOFT CONDENSED MATTER. *Current Pos:* PROF PHYSICS, UNIV CHICAGO, 89- *Personal Data:* b Raleigh, NC, Aug 24, 44. *Educ:* Reed Col, AB, 66; Univ Calif, San Diego, PhD(physics), 71. *Prof Exp:* Instr physics, Princeton Univ, 71-74; foreign collabr, Comn Atomic Energy, Saclay, France, 74-75; asst prof physics, Univ Mich, Ann Arbor, 75-82; res assoc, Exxon Corp Res, Annandale, NJ, 82-89. *Mem:* Fel Am Phys Soc. *Res:* Renormalization scaling symmetry in condensed matter; mechanics of tenuous structures. *Mailing Add:* James Franck Inst Univ Chicago 5640 S Ellis Ave Chicago IL 60637. *Fax:* 773-702-0947; *E-Mail:* t__witten@uchicago.edu

**WITTENBACH, VERNON ARIE,** PLANT PHYSIOLOGY, HERBICIDE ACTION. *Current Pos:* Res biologist, Cent Res & Develop Dept, SR RES BIOLOGIST, AGR PROD DEPT, E I DU PONT DE NEMOURS & CO, 83- *Personal Data:* b Belding, Mich, Dec 13, 45; m 68; c 2. *Educ:* Mich State Univ, BS, 68, MS, 70, PhD(hort), 74. *Mem:* Am Soc Plant Physiologists; Am Soc Hort Sci. *Res:* Mechanism of action of herbicides. *Mailing Add:* 609 Greenbank Rd Wilmington DE 19808

**WITTENBERG, ALBERT M,** PHYSICAL ELECTRONICS. *Current Pos:* CONSULT, 89- *Personal Data:* b Newark, NJ; m 61, Agnes Offenbach; c David H & Susan. *Educ:* Union Col, NY, BS, 47; Johns Hopkins Univ, PhD(physics), 55. *Prof Exp:* Mem tech staff physics, Bell Labs, 55-89. *Mem:* Am Phys Soc; Sigma Xi. *Res:* Atomic structure of diatomic molecules; gaseous electronics; radiative heat transfer; optical spectroscopy; photoconductivity; interconnection technology; electron beam and solid state display systems. *Mailing Add:* 19 Exeter Rd Short Hills NJ 07078

**WITTENBERG, BEATRICE A,** BIOCHEMISTRY, PHYSIOLOGY. *Current Pos:* from asst prof to assoc prof physiol, 64-85, PROF PHYSIOL & BIOPHYS, ALBERT EINSTEIN COL MED, 85- *Personal Data:* b Berlin, Ger, Nov 6, 28; US citizen; m 54; c 3. *Educ:* Univ Toronto, BA, 49, MA, 50; Western Reserve Univ, PhD(pharmacol), 54. *Prof Exp:* Res assoc physiol, Western Reserve Univ, 54-55; cancer res, Delafield Hosp, NY Univ, 55-56. *Mem:* Am Soc Physiologists; Am Soc Biol Chem. *Res:* Heme proteins; oxygen supply; isolated adult heart cells. *Mailing Add:* Dept Physiol & Biophys Albert Einstein Col Med 1300 Morris Park Ave Bronx NY 10461. *Fax:* 718-828-1377

**WITTENBERG, JONATHAN B,** BIOCHEMISTRY, PHYSIOLOGY. *Current Pos:* from asst prof to prof, 55-96, PROF PHYSIOL, ALBERT EINSTEIN COL MED, 96- *Personal Data:* b New York, NY, Sept 19, 23; m 54, Beatrice A Karger; c David, William & Rebecca. *Educ:* Harvard Univ, BS, 45; Columbia Univ, MA, 46, PhD, 50. *Prof Exp:* From instr to asst prof biochem, Western Res Univ, 52-55. *Concurrent Pos:* NIH res fel, 52-96. *Res:* Porphyrins; swimbladders; retia mirabilia; oxygen transport; myoglobin; heme proteins; hemoglobin. *Mailing Add:* Dept Physiol Albert Einstein Col Med Bronx NY 10461-1924. *Fax:* 718-430-8811; *E-Mail:* bwitten@aecom.yu.edu

**WITTER, JOHN ALLEN,** FOREST ENTOMOLOGY, FOREST STRESS. *Current Pos:* from asst prof to assoc prof forest entom, 72-84, PROF FORESTRY, SCH NATURAL RESOURCES, UNIV MICH, ANN ARBOR, 84- *Personal Data:* b Jamestown, NY, Sept 2, 43; m 71; c 1. *Educ:* Va Polytech Inst, BS, 65, MS, 67; Univ Minn, St Paul, PhD(entom), 71. *Prof Exp:* Res technician entom, Southeastern Forest Exp Sta, US Forest Serv, 66-67; res asst, Univ Minn, St Paul, 67-71, res fel, 71-72, instr forest entom, 72. *Mem:* Entom Soc Am; Entom Soc Can; Soc Am Foresters; AAAS. *Res:* Insect impact; forest tree stress; risk rating systems; technology transfer; intensive forestry; defoliators; gypsy moth; spruce budworm; tent caterpillars. *Mailing Add:* Sch Natural Resources Dana Bldg Univ Mich Main Campus 430 University Ave Ann Arbor MI 48109-1115

**WITTER, LLOYD DAVID,** FOOD MICROBIOLOGY, FOOD SCIENCE. *Current Pos:* from asst prof to assoc prof, 56-67, PROF FOOD MICROBIOL, UNIV ILL, URBANA, 67- *Personal Data:* b Chicago, Ill, May 15, 23; m 50, Carolyn Schlueter; c Bart D, Beth E & Janet L. *Educ:* Univ Wash, Seattle, BS, 45, MS, 50, PhD(microbiol), 53. *Prof Exp:* Asst microbiol, Univ Wash, Seattle, 52-53; res chemist, Continental Can Co, Ill, 53-56. *Concurrent Pos:* Vis prof appl biochem, Univ Nottingham, Eng, 72; vis prof food microbiol, Univ Montevideo, Uruguay, 77; vis prof, Polytech South Bank London, 80; vis scientist, Food Res Asn, Eng, 80. *Mem:* Fel Am Acad Microbiol; Am Soc Microbiol; Am Dairy Sci Asn; fel Inst Food Technol; NY Acad Sci. *Res:* Microbiology of food and dairy products; psychrophilic bacteria; bacterial growth on solid surfaces; heat resistance and injury of bacteria; food fermentations; osmoregution in microorganisms. *Mailing Add:* 406 W Pennsylvania Ave Urbana IL 61801. *Fax:* 217-244-2517

**WITTER, RICHARD L,** POULTRY PATHOLOGY. *Current Pos:* Res vet, Regional Poultry Res Lab, 64-75, DIR, AVIAN DIS & ONCOL LAB, AGR RES SERV, USDA, 75-; CLIN PROF, MICH STATE UNIV, 71- *Personal Data:* b Bangor, Maine, Sept 10, 36; m 62; c 2. *Educ:* Mich State Univ, BS, 58, DVM, 60; Cornell Univ, MS, 62, PhD, 64. *Honors & Awards:* Am Asn Avian Path Award, 68, 82, 87 & 92; Res Award, Poultry Sci Asn, 71; Res Award, Sigma Xi, 75; Res Award, CPC Int, Inc, 76; Res Award, Mfg Asn Am Feed, 79; Bart Rispens Res Award, World Vet Poultry Asn, 83; Distinguished Serv Award, USDA, 85; Upjohn Achievement Res Award, Am Asn Avian Path, 92. *Concurrent Pos:* Asst prof, Mich State Univ, 64-71. *Mem:* Am Vet Med Asn; Am Asn Avian Path; Conf Res Workers Animal Dis; Poultry Sci Asn; Sigma Xi. *Res:* Epizootiology and control of poultry diseases, especially virology and pathology; viral-induced neoplasia, especially Marek's disease and lymphoid leukosis of chickens. *Mailing Add:* 3606 E Mt Hope Rd East Lansing MI 48823-5338

**WITTERHOLT, EDWARD JOHN,** CROSSWELL TOMOGRAPHY, BOREHOLE GEOPHYSICS. *Current Pos:* MGR BOREHOLE GEOPHYS, B P EXPLOR PROD CO, 84- *Personal Data:* b Osceola Mills, Pa, Nov 12, 35; m 57; c 5. *Educ:* Manhattan Col, BS, 57; Brown Univ, ScM, 59, PhD(appl math), 64. *Prof Exp:* Res proj mathematician, Schlumberger Technol Corp, 63-75; supvr analysis & calibration, Seismograph Serv Corp, Tulsa, 75-78; res mgr borehole geophys, Cities Serv Co, 78-83, res mgr appl geophys, 83; mgr petrophysics, Cities Serv Oil & Gas, 83-84. *Concurrent Pos:* Adj prof math, Univ Tulsa, 78-80; lectr, Am Asn Petrol Geologists, 82- *Mem:* Am Phys Soc; Acoust Soc Am; Soc Petrol Engrs; Soc Explor Geophysicists; Soc Prof Well Log Analysts; Soc Petrol Engr; Technol Comm; Soc Prof Log Analysts (pres, Tulsa chap, 80). *Res:* Cross well tomography; reservoir delineation and monitoring; borehole geophysics; production geophysics; well logging; production logging; rock physics. *Mailing Add:* 2400 Old South Dr Richmond TX 77469

**WITTERHOLT, VINCENT GERARD,** ORGANIC CHEMISTRY. *Current Pos:* res chemist, Org Chem Dept, E I Du Pont De Nemours & Co Inc, 58-68, res supvr, 69-73, sr supvr sulfur colors area, Chamber Works, 73-74, chief supvr, Azo Lab, 74-75, div head, Chem Dyes & Pigments Dept, Jackson Lab, 75-80, res supvr, biochem dept, 81-84, from res fel to sr res fel, 84-89, Du Pont fel, 89-94, DISTINGUISHED SCIENTIST, AGRICHEM PROD, E I DU PONT DE NEMOURS & CO, INC, 94- *Personal Data:* b New York, NY, Sept 24, 32; m 54, Alice E Zaborowski; c 6. *Educ:* Queens Col, City Univ NY, BS, 53; Purdue Univ, PhD(org chem), 58. *Mem:* Am Chem Soc. *Res:* Dyes product and process development; agricultural product and process development (herbicides, fungicides, and insecticides). *Mailing Add:* Du Pont Agr Prod Exp Sta E I Du Pont de Nemours & Co Inc Wilmington DE 19880-0402. *Fax:* 302-695-3347

**WITTERS, ROBERT DALE,** PHYSICAL CHEMISTRY. *Current Pos:* from asst prof to assoc prof, 65-78, PROF CHEM, COLO SCH MINES, 78- *Personal Data:* b Cheyenne, Wyo, May 2, 29; m 87, Brenda Marlow. *Educ:* Univ Colo, BA, 51; Mont State Univ, PhD(phys chem), 64. *Prof Exp:* Chemist, E I Du Pont de Nemours & Co, 51-53; asst prof chem, State Univ NY Col Plattsburgh, 59-62 & Mont State Univ, 62-63; res fel, Harvey Mudd Col, 64-65. *Concurrent Pos:* Brown innovative teaching grant, 75. *Mem:* Am Chem Soc; Am Crystallog Asn; Sigma Xi. *Res:* X-ray crystallography. *Mailing Add:* Dept Chem Colo Sch Mines Golden CO 80401. *E-Mail:* rwitters@mines.edu

**WITTICK, JAMES JOHN,** ANALYTICAL CHEMISTRY, QUALITY CONTROL. *Current Pos:* Chemist, Merck Sharp & Dohme Res Labs, NJ, 55-57, group leader phys & analytical res, 57-60, unit head pharmaceut analysis, Pa, 60-62, sr res chemist, 65-68, res fel, 68-70, assoc dir qual control, 70-80, DIR QUAL CONTROL OPERS, MERCK CHEM DIV, MERCK & CO, INC, 80- *Personal Data:* b New York, NY, Aug 17, 30; m 56; c 4. *Educ:* Col Holy Cross, BS, 52; Tufts Univ, MS, 55; Univ Pa, PhD(chem), 66. *Mem:*

Am Chem Soc; AAAS. *Res:* Purity and structure determination of organic compounds; pharmaceutical analysis; electro-analytical chemistry; x-ray diffraction; chromatography. *Mailing Add:* 401 Stonybrook Dr Bridgewater NJ 08807-1962

**WITTIE, LARRY DAWSON,** LARGE PARALLEL & DISTRIBUTED COMPUTER SYSTEMS, MICROPROCESSORS & COMPUTER ARCHITECTURE. *Current Pos:* assoc prof, 82-86, PROF, DEPT COMPUT SCI, STATE UNIV NY, STONY BROOK, 87- *Personal Data:* b Bay City, Tex, Mar 9, 43; m 72, Diane Fischer; c Lea & Loren. *Educ:* Calif Inst Technol, BS, 66; Univ Wis-Madison, MS, 67, PhD(comput sci), 73. *Prof Exp:* Systs programmer, Calif Inst Technol, 63-66 & IBM Corp, Sunnyvale, 66; NASA trainee comput sci, Univ Wis-Madison, 66-69, res asst, 69-72; asst prof comput sci, Purdue Univ, 72-73; from asst prof to prof, State Univ NY, Buffalo, 73-81. *Concurrent Pos:* Nat lectr, Asn Comput Mach, 78-79 & 79-80; prin investr, NSF, 77-, Air Force, 82-, NASA, 82-, Navy, 88-; sci adv, Army, 81; consult industry, 77- *Mem:* Asn Comput Mach; Sigma Xi; Inst Elec & Electronics Engrs; Soc Neurosci. *Res:* Latency hiding methods for large networks and parallel computers; distributed operating systems; parallel information processing in networks of millions of microcomputers; simulation of large brain models; neural distributed memory mechanisms. *Mailing Add:* Dept Comput Sci State Univ NY Z4400 Comput Sci Bldg Stony Brook NY 11794-4400. *Fax:* 516-632-8334; *E-Mail:* lw@sbcs.sunysb.edu

**WITTIG, CURT,** CHEMISTRY. *Current Pos:* PROF, CHEM DEPT, UNIV SOUTHERN CALIF, LOS ANGELES. *Honors & Awards:* Herbert Broida Atomic Molecular Chem Physics Prize, Am Phys Soc, 93. *Mailing Add:* Chem Dept Univ Southern Calif University Park Los Angeles CA 90007

**WITTIG, GEORG FRIEDRICH KARL,** chemistry; deceased, see previous edition for last biography

**WITTIG, GERTRAUDE CHRISTA,** HISTORY OF SCIENCE, INSECT PATHOLOGY. *Current Pos:* assoc prof biol sci, 68-75, PROF BIOL SCI, SOUTHERN ILL UNIV, EDWARDSVILLE, 75- *Personal Data:* b Glauchau, Ger, Oct 4, 28; US citizen. *Educ:* Univ Tuebingen, Dr rer nat(zool, bot, biochem), 55. *Prof Exp:* Teacher, Musterschule Glauchau, Ger, 46-47 & Preuniv Sch Neckarsulm, 55; Ger Res Asn prin investr, Zool Inst, Univ Tuebingen, 56-58; res fel entom, Univ Calif, Berkeley, 58-59; microbiologist, Insect Path Pioneering Lab, Entom Res Div, Agr Res Serv, USDA, Md, 59-62; res microbiologist, Forestry Sci Lab, Pac NW Forest & Range Exp Sta, US Forest Serv, Ore, 62-68. *Concurrent Pos:* Lalor Found fel, 58; Ger Acad Exchange Serv & Ministry Educ Baden-Wuerttemberg res grants, 58; Fulbright travel grant, 58-59; consult, Univ Ariz, 61; adj assoc prof, Ore State Univ, 62-68. *Mem:* AAAS; Hist Sci Soc; Entom Soc Am; Am Inst Biol Sci; Micros Soc Am; Soc Integrative & Comp Zool. *Res:* Biological ultrastructure; morphology and histology of insects; insect pathology; history of science, especially gender studies; soil microanthropods. *Mailing Add:* Dept Biol Sci Southern Ill Univ Edwardsville IL 62026-1651. *Fax:* 618-692-3174

**WITTIG, KENNETH PAUL,** COMPARATIVE PHYSIOLOGY. *Current Pos:* from asst prof to assoc prof biol, 74-80, chmn dept, 79-83, chmn, Long Range Planning, 83-84, PROF BIOL & DEAN SCI, SIENA COL, 84- *Personal Data:* b Pittsburgh, Pa, Aug 19, 46; m 69, Jane Lachmaier. *Educ:* St Vincent Col, BS, 68; Kent State Univ, PhD(animal physiol), 74; State Univ NY, Albany, MBA, 84. *Prof Exp:* Teacher biol & chem, St Thomas Aquinas High Sch, 68-69. *Mem:* AAAS; Sigma Xi; Coun Undergrad Res; Am Soc Zoologists; NY Acad Sci. *Res:* Investigation of the neuroendocrine control of calcium metabolism in the crayfish; salt metabolism in amphibians. *Mailing Add:* Info & Technol Serv Siena Col 515 Loudon Rd Loudonville NY 12211. *E-Mail:* wittig@siena.bitnet

**WITTING, HARALD LUDWIG,** PLASMA PHYSICS. *Current Pos:* PHYSICIST, GEN ELEC RES & DEVELOP CTR, 64- *Personal Data:* b Duisburg, Ger, Sept 23, 36; US citizen; m 60, Joyce Ismert; c David, Karen & Peter. *Educ:* Mass Inst Technol, BS & MS, 59, ScD(plasma), 64. *Mem:* AAAS; Am Phys Soc; Sigma Xi. *Res:* Gas discharges; electrodes; plasma light sources. *Mailing Add:* 11 Wendy Lane Burnt Hills NY 12027-9755

**WITTING, JAMES M,** PHYSICAL OCEANOGRAPHY, HYDRODYNAMICS. *Current Pos:* SR RES ASSOC, APPL RES LAB, PA STATE UNIV, STATE COL, 93- *Personal Data:* b Chicago, Ill, Jan 14, 38; m 62; c 3. *Educ:* John Carroll Univ, BS, 59, MS, 60; Mass Inst Technol, PhD(physics), 64. *Prof Exp:* Assoc physicist, IIT Res Inst, 64-66, res physicist, 66; asst prof hydrodyn, Dept Geophys Sci, Univ Chicago, 66-70; phys sci adminr, Off Naval Res, US Naval Res Lab, 70-73, oceanogr, Phys Oceanog Prog, 72-73, head, Phys Oceanog Br, 73-84; dir, Advan Technol Opers Ctr, ARC Prof Serv, Rockville, Md, 84-93. *Mem:* Am Phys Soc; Am Geophys Union. *Res:* Waves in dispersive media; water waves; undular bores; numerical modeling of oceanic circulation. *Mailing Add:* 9400 Athens Rd Fairfax VA 22030

**WITTING, LLOYD ALLEN,** NUTRITION, LIPID CHEMISTRY. *Current Pos:* sr chemist, Supelco Inc, 76-77, tech dir biochem res & mfg, 77-84, DIR REGULATORY COMPLIANCE, SUPELCO INC, 84- *Personal Data:* b Chicago, Ill, May 18, 30; m 56; c 3. *Educ:* Univ Ill, BS, 52, MS, 53, PhD, 56. *Honors & Awards:* Merit Award, Am Oil Chem Soc, 85. *Prof Exp:* Asst food technol, Univ Ill, 52-55; assoc biochemist, Am Meat Inst Found, Chicago, 55-57; proj assoc physiol chem, Univ Wis, 57-59; med res assoc, Mendel Res Lab, Elgin State Hosp, Ill, 59-68, actg dir, 68-70, res scientist, 69-72; assoc

prof food sci & technol, Tex Woman's Univ, 72-74; consult, NTex Educ & Training Coop, Inc, 75-76. *Concurrent Pos:* Asst prof, Col Med, Univ Ill, 62-72. *Mem:* Am Inst Nutrit; Am Oil Chem Soc; Am Soc Biol Chemists. *Res:* High performance liquid chromatography; polyunsaturated fatty acids; glycolipids; clinical and animal nutrition; chemistry and biochemistry of lipids; tocopherol; gas chromatography. *Mailing Add:* 249 Oakley Dr State College PA 16803. *Fax:* 814-359-5459

**WITTKE, DAYTON D,** NUCLEAR & MECHANICAL ENGINEERING. *Current Pos:* mgr, Opers Tech Support Serv, 74-77, mgr generating sta eng, 77-80, mgr, Eng Div, 80-85, VPRES, OMAHA PUB POWER DIST, 85- *Personal Data:* b Matador, Tex, Oct 9, 32; m 56; c 5. *Educ:* Brigham Young Univ, BES, 56; Univ Ill, MS, 61, PhD(nuclear eng), 66. *Prof Exp:* Mech engr, Atomic Prod Div, Gen Elec Co, Wash, 56; res asst nuclear eng, Univ Ill, Urbana, 63-65; from asst prof to assoc prof mech & nuclear eng, Univ Nebr, Lincoln, 65-74. *Concurrent Pos:* Tech consult, Omaha Pub Power Dist, 67-74; consult, Wittke & Assocs, 70- *Mem:* Am Nuclear Soc; Am Soc Mech Engrs; Am Soc Eng Educ; Nat Soc Prof Engrs. *Res:* Heat transfer and fluid flow problems associated with nuclear engineering applications. *Mailing Add:* 15204 Lloyd Circle Omaha NE 68144

**WITTKE, JAMES PLEISTER,** OPTICAL PHYSICS. *Current Pos:* MEM TECH STAFF, RCA LABS, 55- *Personal Data:* b Westfield, NJ, Apr 2, 28; m 52; c 2. *Educ:* Stevens Inst Technol, ME, 49; Princeton Univ, MA, 52, PhD(physics), 55. *Prof Exp:* Instr physics, Princeton Univ, 54-55. *Mem:* Fel Am Phys Soc; Inst Elec & Electronics Engrs; Optical Soc Am; Sigma Xi. *Res:* Microwave spectroscopy; masers; lasers; fiber optics; optical instrumentation. *Mailing Add:* 244 Russell Rd Princeton NJ 08540

**WITTKE, PAUL H,** ELECTRICAL ENGINEERING. *Current Pos:* res assoc statist commun theory, Queen's Univ, 60-65, asst prof elec eng, 65-67, prof & head dept elec eng, 77-86, assoc dean res, 90-93, ASSOC PROF ELEC ENG, QUEEN'S UNIV, ONT, 67-, HEAD COMMUN GROUP, 68- *Personal Data:* b Toronto, Ont, Aug 17, 34; m 60; c 2. *Educ:* Univ Toronto, BASc, 56; Queen's Univ, Ont, MSc, 62, PhD(elec eng), 65. *Prof Exp:* Defense sci serv officer radar, Defence Res Telecommun Estab, Ont, 56-60. *Concurrent Pos:* Acad vis, Imp Col, Univ London, 71-72; vis prof, Space Systs Sect, Commun Res Ctr, Ottawa & Nat Univ Singapore, 82-83; chmn, Can Nat Comt, Int Union Radio Sci, 87-93, chmn, Comn C, 93-96; dir, AstroCom Assocs, Inc, 93- *Mem:* Inst Elec & Electronics Engrs; Int Union Radio Sci. *Res:* Radar signal processing; statistical communication theory; digital communications systems. *Mailing Add:* Dept Elec Eng Queen's Univ Kingston ON K7L 3N6 Can. *E-Mail:* wittkep@post.queensu.ca

**WITTKOWER, ANDREW BENEDICT,** ATOMIC PHYSICS. *Current Pos:* PRES, SOITEE USA, INC & SUPERIOR DESIGN INC, 91- *Personal Data:* b London, Eng, Nov 7, 34; m 57, Mary Shotter; c David & Elizabeth. *Educ:* McGill Univ, BSc, 55; Cambridge Univ, MSc, 59; Univ London, PhD(atomic physics), 67. *Honors & Awards:* Semmy Award, Semiconductor Equip Mfrs Inst, 86. *Prof Exp:* Proj physicist, High Voltage Eng Corp, 59-64, res physicist, 64-67, assoc dir res, 67-71; sr vpres, Extrion Corp, 71-75, mkt & asst gen mgr, Extrion Div, Varian Assoc, 75-78; vpres & gen mgr, Nova Assoc, 78-80, Ion Implementation Div, Eaton Corp, 80-83; pres, Zymet Corp, 83-85; bd chmn, IBIS Tech Corp, 87-91. *Mem:* Fel Am Phys Soc; fel Brit Inst Physics. *Res:* Atomic physics applied to the development of ion accelerators; author or coauthor of over 100 publications. *Mailing Add:* 352 Granite St Rockport MA 01966. *Fax:* 978-531-2758

**WITTLE, JOHN KENNETH,** INORGANIC CHEMISTRY, ANALYTICAL CHEMISTRY. *Current Pos:* Inorg chemist, Gen Elec Co, 67-68, proj engr, 68-72, mgr polymer technol, 72-75, MGR, DIELECTRIC MAT LAB, GEN ELEC CO, 75- *Personal Data:* b Lancaster, Pa, July 20, 39; c 1. *Educ:* Franklin & Marshall Col, AB, 62; Purdue Univ, Lafayette, PhD(inorg chem), 68. *Concurrent Pos:* Secy, Indust & Electro Petroleum Inc. *Mem:* AAAS; Am Chem Soc; Royal Soc Chem; Am Inst Mining, Metall & Petrol Eng; Am Soc Mech Engrs. *Res:* Insulation systems for electrical systems; decomposition of electrical insulation under electrical stress; materials application. *Mailing Add:* 1740 Conestoga Rd Chester Springs PA 19425-1810

**WITTLE, LAWRENCE WAYNE,** PHYSIOLOGY. *Current Pos:* asst prof, 70-77, ASSOC PROF BIOL, ALMA COL, 77-, CHMN BIOL, 77- *Personal Data:* b Mt Joy, Pa, Nov 20, 41; m 64, 77; c 2. *Educ:* Lebanon Valley Col, BS, 63; Univ Va, PhD(biol), 68. *Prof Exp:* NIH fel, Inst Marine Sci, Univ Miami, 68-70. *Mem:* AAAS; Am Soc Zool; Int Soc Toxinology; Sigma Xi. *Res:* Physiological and pharmacological properties of marine toxins; parathyroid physiology of uradele amphibians. *Mailing Add:* Dept Biol Alma Col 614 W Superior St Alma MI 48801-1511

**WITTLIFF, JAMES LAMAR,** MOLECULAR ENDOCRINOLOGY, CLINICAL BIOCHEMISTRY. *Current Pos:* prof biochem & chmn dept, Sch Med & Dent, 76-83, DIR, HORMONE RECEPTOR LAB, JAMES GRAHAM BROWN CANCER CTR, UNIV LOUISVILLE, 76- *Personal Data:* b Taft, Tex, June 15, 38; m 62; c 2. *Educ:* Univ Tex, Austin, BA, 61, PhD(molecular biol), 67; La State Univ, MS, 63. *Honors & Awards:* George Grannis Award Excellence in Res, Nat Acad Clin Biochem, 85; Special Award, Cath Med Col, Korea, 85; SKBL Award, Clin Ligand Assay Soc, 88; Pfizer Lectr, Montreal Gen Hosp, Can, 90. *Prof Exp:* USPHS fel biochem regulation, Oak Ridge Nat Lab, Tenn, 67-69; asst prof biochem, Sch Med & Dent, 69-74, assoc prof biochem & head sect endocrine biochem, Cancer Ctr,

Univ Rochester, 75-76. *Concurrent Pos:* Vis prof, Univ Dusseldorf, Institut fur Physiologische Chemie II, WGer, 74, Univ Innsbruck Frauenklinik, Austria, 76, SAfrican Asn Clin Biochemists, 82, Wolmarans Lab, Univ Pretoria, RSA, 88; vis prof biochem, La State Univ Sch Med, Shreveport, 79; fel, Nat Acad Clin Biochem, 84; spec lectureship, Cath Med Ctr, Seoul, Korea, 85; distinguished vis prof, SAfrican Inst Med Res, Johannesburg, 86; vis lectr, Univ Zimbabwe, Harare, 86; ed-in-chief, Clin Biochem, 89; MDS health lectureship award, Can Soc Clin Chem, 89. *Mem:* AAAS; Am Chem Soc; Am Asn Cancer Res; Am Soc Biol Chemists; Endocrine Soc; fel Nat Acad Clin Biochem; hon mem SAfrican Asn Clin Biochemists. *Res:* Hormonal control of protein and nucleic acid synthesis; role of specific hormone receptors in target cell response. *Mailing Add:* Hormone Receptor Lab James Graham Brown Cancer Ctr Univ 529 S Jackson St Louisville KY 40202. *Fax:* 502-588-8008

**WITTMAN, JAMES SMYTHE, III,** MANAGEMENT, NUTRITION. *Current Pos:* PROF, ROCK VALLEY COL, 81- *Personal Data:* b Ft Bragg, NC, Mar 1, 43; m 86, Valarie Lathom; c 4. *Educ:* La Col, BA, 64; Tulane Univ, PhD(biochem), 70; Fairleigh Dickinson Univ, MBA, 78. *Prof Exp:* Chemist, Southern Regional Res Lab, USDA, 64-65; org chemist, US Customs Lab, La, 65-66; asst biochemist, Hoffmann-La Roche Inc, 68-70, sr biochemist, 70-77, clin res scientist, 77-79; tech dir, Batter-Lite Foods Inc, 80-81. *Concurrent Pos:* Consult food indust, 81- *Res:* Reduced-calorie food formulations; fructose; biochemical nutrition; regulation of intermediary metabolism and protein synthesis; clinical studies, vitamin E and calorie sweeteners; computers in management. *Mailing Add:* Dept Bus Rock Valley Col 3301 N Mulford Rockford IL 61114-5699

**WITTMAN, WILLIAM F,** ORGANIC CHEMISTRY. *Current Pos:* Sr res chemist, 3M Co, 64-72, patent liaison specialist & patent agent, 72-76, patent & info supvr, 77, patent & res admin mgr, 78-82, staff intellectual property scientist, 85, CORP INTELLECTUAL PROPERTY SCIENTIST, 3M CO, 90- *Personal Data:* b Pittsburgh, Pa, Oct 10, 37; m 64; c 6. *Educ:* Carnegie Inst Technol, BS, 59; Univ Nebr, PhD(org chem), 65. *Res:* Pharmaceutical, agrichemical, biomaterials and biopolymer patents. *Mailing Add:* 10341 Hadley Ct N White Bear Lake MN 55110

**WITTMANN, HORST RICHARD,** RESEARCH ADMINISTRATION, GENERAL PHYSICS. *Current Pos:* DIR, ELECTROMAGNETICS & RELIABILITY, ROME LABS, HANSCOM AFB, 96- *Personal Data:* b Worms, Ger, Jan 31, 36; US citizen; div; c Ute, Thomas & Michael. *Educ:* Graz Uni, PhD(physics),64. *Prof Exp:* Asst exp physics, Graz Univ,63-64; space physicist, Boelkow, Ger, 64-66; res scientist quantum electronics, Phys Sci Lab, Missile Command, Redstone Arsenal, Ala, 66-70; chief, Elec Br, US Army Res Off, 70-75, asst dir, Electronics Div, 75-84; dir electronics & mat sci, Air Force Off Sci Res, 84-96. *Concurrent Pos:* Res asst, Duke Univ, 71-73; adj prof, NC State Univ, 75-84; Secy Army fel, 77; Fulbright fel, Tech Univ, Vienna, Austria, 77-78. *Mem:* Am Phys Soc; fel Inst Elec & Electronics Engrs; fel AAAS. *Res:* Semiconductor lasers; solid state electronics; 3-5 compounds. *Mailing Add:* Air Force Rome Lab 31 Grenier St Hanscom AFB MA 01731-3010

**WITTMER, MARC F,** SEMICONDUCTOR MATERIALS. *Current Pos:* RES STAFF MEM SOLID STATE PHYSICS, IBM, INC T J WATSON RES CTR, 81- *Personal Data:* b Basel, Switz, May 4, 45. *Educ:* Univ Basel, Switz, dipl, 70, PhD(solid state physics), 75. *Prof Exp:* Res scientist, solid state physics, Calif Inst Technol, 75-77; physicist res & develop, Brown Boveri Co, Baden, Switz, 77-81; res asst solid state physics, Swiss Fed Inst Technol, Zurich, 81. *Mem:* Inst Elec & Electronics Engrs; Mat Res Soc; Swiss Phys Soc; Europ Phys Soc; Sigma Xi. *Res:* Research in electronic and materials properties of metal- semiconductor interfaces and reactions, in contact and interconnect structures and materials for VLSI, in fabrication and properties of epitaxial layers on semiconductor materials. *Mailing Add:* Colonel Greene Rd Yorktown Heights NY 10598

**WITTMUSS, HOWARD D(ALE),** AGRICULTURAL ENGINEERING. *Current Pos:* asst soil physics, 52-56, asst prof agr eng, 56-58, ASSOC PROF AGR ENG, UNIV NEBR, LINCOLN, 58- *Personal Data:* b Papillion, Nebr, July 15, 22; m 50; c 3. *Educ:* Univ Nebr, BS, 47, MS, 50, PhD(soil physics, agr eng), 56. *Prof Exp:* Construct engr, Diamond Eng Co, Nebr, 47-49; irrig engr, Irrig Res Div, Soil Conserv Serv, USDA, 49-50. *Mem:* Am Soc Agr Engrs; Soil Conserv Soc Am. *Res:* Irrigation efficiency; soil structure; tillplant system of corn production; land shaping; soil and water conservation. *Mailing Add:* 1808 Morningside Dr Lincoln NE 68506

**WITTNEBERT, FRED R,** mechanical engineering; deceased, see previous edition for last biography

**WITTNER, MURRAY,** PHYSIOLOGY, PARASITOLOGY. *Current Pos:* Instr path & parasitol & consult path, 56-57, PROF PATH & PARASITOL & DIR PARASITOL LABS, ALBERT EINSTEIN COL MED, 67- *Personal Data:* b New York, NY, Apr 23, 27; m 55; c 2. *Educ:* Univ Ill, ScB, 48, ScM, 49; Harvard Univ, PhD, 55; Yale Univ, MD, 61. *Concurrent Pos:* Career scientist, Health Res Coun, New York, 67-; attend physician, Bronx Munic Hosp Ctr, Lincoln Hosp & Albert Einstein Col Med Hosp; dir, Trop Dis Clin, Lincoln Hosp & Bronx Munic Hosp Ctr. *Mem:* Soc Protozool; Am Soc Cell Biol; Am Asn Path & Bact; Am Soc Zool; Am Soc Parasitol; Sigma Xi. *Res:* Physiology and biochemistry of oxygen poisoning; physiology of parasites; experimental pathology. *Mailing Add:* 6 Pheasant Run Larchmont NY 10538-3423

**WITTROCK, DARWIN DONALD,** HELMINTHOLOGY, ELECTRON MICROSCOPY. *Current Pos:* PROF BIOL, UNIV WIS, EAU CLAIRE, 76- *Personal Data:* b Primghar, Iowa, Oct 20, 49; m 79; c 2. *Educ:* Univ Northern Iowa, BA, 71; Iowa State Univ, MS, 73, PhD(parasitol), 76. *Mem:* Am Soc Parasitologists; Am Micros Soc. *Res:* Ultrastructural studies on organ systems of digenetic trematodes and helminthological surveys from mammals. *Mailing Add:* Dept Biol Univ Wis PO Box 4004 Eau Claire WI 54702-4004. *E-Mail:* wittrod@uwec.edu

**WITTRY, DAVID BERYLE,** SEMICONDUCTOR PHYSICS, ELECTRON OPTICS. *Current Pos:* from asst prof to assoc prof, 59-69, PROF MAT SCI & ELEC ENG, UNIV SOUTHERN CALIF, 69- *Personal Data:* b Mason City, Iowa, Feb 7, 29; m 55; c 5. *Educ:* Univ Wis, BS, 51; Calif Inst Technol, MS, 53, PhD(physics), 57. *Prof Exp:* Res fel, Calif Inst Technol, 57-59. *Concurrent Pos:* Consult, Appl Res Labs Inc, 58-83, Hughes Aircraft, 58-59, Exp Sta, E I Du Pont de Nemours & Co, 62-71, NAm Aviation, 61-63, Gen Tel & Electronics Res Labs, 66-72, Electronics Res Div, Rockwell Int, 76-81, Atlanta Richfield Co Corp Technol Lab, 81-, Jet Propulsion Lab, 85- & Microbean Inc, 88-; Guggenheim fel, Univ Cambridge, 67-68; vis prof, Univ Osaha prefecture, 74 & Ariz State Univ, 81; consult, Atlanta Richfield Co Corp Technol Lab, 81-, Jet Propulsion Lab, 85-, Microbean Inc, 88-; coun mem, Microbean Analysis Soc, 70-72, pres, 88; dir phys sci, Electron Micros Soc Am, 79-87, pres, 82-84. *Mem:* Am Phys Soc; Electron Micros Soc Am; Microbeam Analysis Soc; Sigma Xi. *Res:* Scanning electron microprobe instrumentation; quantitative electron probe microanalysis, electron microprobe applications to solid state electronics, electron spectroscopy in TEM, secondary ion mass spectrometry; x-ray optics. *Mailing Add:* 1036 S Madison Pasadena CA 91106-4365

**WITTRY, ESPERANCE,** biology, for more information see previous edition

**WITTRY, JOHN P(ETER),** AERONAUTICAL & ASTRONAUTICAL ENGINEERING. *Current Pos:* RETIRED. *Personal Data:* b Aurora, Ill, Sept 6, 29; m 51; c 6. *Educ:* St Louis Univ, BS, 51; USAF Inst Technol, MS, 56; Univ Mich, AAE, 62. *Prof Exp:* USAF, 51-, proj off aircraft nuclear propulsion, Res & Develop Command, Wright-Patterson AFB, Ohio, 56-58, adv propulsion technologist, AEC, Hq, Germantown, Md, 58-60, instr astronaut, USAF Acad, 62-72, assoc prof astronaut & head astronaut & comput sci, 73-78, prof & head, Dept Astronautics & Comput Sci, 73-78, chmn eng div & vdean fac, USAF Acad, 78-84; acad dean, Calif Maritime Acad, 84-92. *Mem:* Am Soc Eng Educ. *Res:* Space nuclear power systems; astrodynamics; inertial guidance and control systems. *Mailing Add:* 309 Mountain Vista Ct Santa Rosa CA 95409

**WITTWER, JOHN WILLIAM,** PERIODONTICS. *Current Pos:* assoc prof, 69-75, PROF PERIODONT, SCH DENT, UNIV LOUISVILLE, 75- *Personal Data:* b Columbus, Ohio, Apr, 35; m 59; c 3. *Educ:* Ohio State Univ, DDS, 59, MSc, 65. *Prof Exp:* Instr periodont, Ohio State Univ, 61-64; asst prof, Sch Dent, Loyola Univ Chicago, 66-69. *Mem:* Am Acad Periodont. *Mailing Add:* Sch Dent Univ Louisville Louisville KY 40292. *E-Mail:* jwwitt01@ulkyvm.louisville.edu

**WITTWER, LELAND S,** animal nutrition; deceased, see previous edition for last biography

**WITTWER, ROBERT FREDERICK,** SILVICULTURE. *Current Pos:* ASSOC PROF FORESTRY, OKLA STATE UNIV, 82- *Personal Data:* b Boonville, NY, Sept 18, 40; m 68, Joan Bauer; c Robin, Roberta & Robert. *Educ:* State Univ NY Col Environ Sci & Forestry, BS, 66, PhD(forestry), 74. *Prof Exp:* Forester, NY State Dept Environ Conserv, 66-69; NDEA fel, State Univ NY Col Environ Sci & Forestry, 69-73; from asst prof to assoc prof forestry, Univ Ky, 74-80. *Mem:* Soc Am Foresters. *Res:* Forest soil productivity; forest fertilization; nutrient cycling; nutrition of forest trees. *Mailing Add:* Dept Forestry Okla State Univ Stillwater OK 74078. *E-Mail:* rfw1124@okway.okstate.edu

**WITTWER, SYLVAN HAROLD,** HORTICULTURE. *Current Pos:* RETIRED. *Personal Data:* b Hurricane, Utah, Jan 17, 17; m 38, Maurine Cottle; c Laree (Farrar), Alice (Sowards), Arthur & Carl. *Educ:* Utah State Agr Col, BS, 39; Univ Mo, PhD(hort), 43. *Honors & Awards:* Campbell Award, AAAS, 57; Tanner Lectr Award, Inst Food Technol, 80; Am Farm Bur Fedn Serv Award, 82. *Prof Exp:* Asst, Univ Mo, 40-43, instr hort, 43-46; from asst prof to emer prof hort, Mich State Univ, 46-86, dir, Agr Exp Sta, 65-83; agr mgt consult, USAID-Belize, 87-89. *Concurrent Pos:* Consult, Rockefeller Found, Mex, 68-69, Ford Found, Ceylon, 69- & UN Develop Prog, 71-; mem agr bd, Nat Acad Sci, 71-73; chmn bd agr & renewable resources, Nat Acad Sci-Nat Res Coun, 73-77; climate res bd, Nat Acad Sci, Nat Res Coun, 78-83; mem, US Cong Food Adv Bd, Off Technol Assessment, 77-82, Liaison Comt, food & agr, Int Inst Appl Systs Anal, 77-81, NASA Adv Coun, space & terrestrial appl, 78-82 & V I Lenin All-Union Acad of Agr Sci, USSR, 78-; tech adv agr adv groups, UNDP-Egypt, 86 & 90, China, 80, 81, 83, 85, 87 & 89. *Mem:* Fel AAAS; Soc Develop Biol; Am Soc Hort Sci; Am Soc Plant Physiol; Bot Soc Am. *Res:* Physiology of reproduction in horticulture; plant growth regulators for improving fruit set and control flowering; nutrition of horticultural crops; radioisotopes in mineral nutrition of plants; agricultural communications; minimizing agricultural production; biological limits in agricultural productivity. *Mailing Add:* Box 1169 1590 Wittwer Ave Logandale NV 89021-1169. *Fax:* 702-398-3975

**WITULSKI, ARTHUR FRANK,** POWER ELECTRONICS, RESONANT POWER CONVERSION. *Current Pos:* asst prof power electronics, Dept Elec & Comput Eng, 89-95, ASSOC PROF, UNIV ARIZ, 95- *Personal Data:* b Denver, Colo, May 27, 58. *Educ:* Univ Colo, BS, 81, MS, 86, PhD(elec eng), 88. *Prof Exp:* Design engr, Storage Technol Corp, 81-83; teaching asst power electronics, Dept Elec & Comput Eng, Univ Colo, 83-84, res asst, 84-88, res assoc, 88-89. *Mem:* Inst Elec & Electronics Engrs. *Res:* Power electronics, especially resonant and quasi-resonant dc-dc switching converters and regulators; high-power-factor ac to dc conversion; distributed electronic power systems; high-frequency magnetic circuit components; high voltage dc power for transmitters. *Mailing Add:* Dept Elec & Comput Eng Univ Ariz Tucson AZ 85721

**WITZ, DENNIS FREDRICK,** MICROBIOLOGY. *Current Pos:* RES ASSOC MICROBIOL, PHARMACIA & UPJOHN CO, 67- *Personal Data:* b Milwaukee, Wis, Dec 10, 38; div; c Ben, Wendy, Brian & Dawn. *Educ:* Carroll Col, Wis, BS, 61; Univ Wis-Madison, MS, 64, PhD(bact), 67. *Mem:* Am Soc Microbiol; Soc Indust Microbiol. *Res:* Process of biological nitrogen fixation by microorganisms; biosynthesis of antibiotics and secondary metabolites; production of antibiotics by fermentation. *Mailing Add:* 1400-89-1 Pharmacia & Upjohn Co Kalamazoo MI 49002

**WITZ, GISELA,** CANCER. *Current Pos:* from asst prof to assoc prof, 80-93, PROF ENVIRON & COMMUN MED, ROBERT WOOD JOHNSON MED SCH, UNIV MED & DENT NJ, 93- *Personal Data:* b Breslau, Ger, Mar 16, 39; US citizen. *Educ:* NY Univ, BA, 62, MS, 65, PhD(phys org chem), 69. *Prof Exp:* Fel biochem, Sloan-Kettering Inst Cancer Res, 69-70; assoc res scientist cancer res, NY Univ, Med Ctr, 70-73, res scientist environ med, 73-77, asst prof environ med, 77-80; asst prof commun med, Rutgers Med Sch, 80-86. *Concurrent Pos:* Assoc dir, Joint Grad Prof Toxicol, UMDNJ-Robert Wood Johnson Med Sch, 92- *Mem:* NY Acad Sci; Am Asn Cancer Res; Am Chem Soc; Sigma Xi; Soc Toxicol; fel Oxygen Soc; Int Soc Free Radical Res. *Res:* Chemical carcinogenesis; mode of action of tumor promoters; mechanism of benzene hematoxicity and mechanisms of oxidant injury. *Mailing Add:* 240 Lurline Dr Basking Ridge NJ 07920. *Fax:* 732-445-0119; *E-Mail:* witz@eohsti.rutgers.edu

**WITZ, RICHARD L,** AGRICULTURAL ENGINEERING. *Current Pos:* from asst prof & asst agr engr to assoc prof agr eng & assoc agr engr, 45-57, prof 57-83, EMER PROF AGR ENG, EXP STA, NDAK STATE UNIV, 83- *Personal Data:* b New Lisbon, Wis, Jan 12, 16; m 41, Marjorie V Hoover; c John & Fred. *Educ:* Univ Wis, BS, 39; Purdue Univ, MS, 42. *Honors & Awards:* George W Kable Award, Am Soc Agr Engrs. *Prof Exp:* Asst, Purdue Univ, 39-42; exten specialist, Mich State Univ, 42-45. *Mem:* Fel & sr mem Am Soc Agr Engrs; Am Soc Eng Educ. *Res:* Rural electrification; building design; sewage disposal; farm water treatment. *Mailing Add:* 1525 N Eighth St Fargo ND 58102

**WITZEL, DONALD ANDREW,** VETERINARY PHYSIOLOGY. *Current Pos:* RETIRED. *Personal Data:* b Artesian, SDak, Sept 9, 26. *Educ:* Univ Minn, BS, 53, DVM, 57; Iowa State Univ, MS, 65, PhD(vet physiol), 70. *Prof Exp:* Res vet physiol, Nat Animal Dis Lab, Agr Res Serv, USDA, 61-72, vet med officer physiol & toxicol, Vet Toxicol & Entom Res Lab, 72-90. *Concurrent Pos:* Consult, Baylor Col Med, 72-74. *Mem:* AAAS; Am Vet Med Asn; NY Acad Sci; Am Soc Vet Physiologists & Pharmacologists. *Res:* Electrophysiological studies of the visual system of domestic animals as related to toxicological problems. *Mailing Add:* 3720 Sweetbriar Dr Bryan TX 77802

**WITZELL, O(TTO) W(ILLIAM),** MECHANICAL ENGINEERING. *Current Pos:* RETIRED. *Personal Data:* b Baltimore, Md, Nov 14, 16; m 42, Virginia Deck. *Educ:* Johns Hopkins Univ, BE, 37; Purdue Univ, MSME, 49, PhD, 51. *Prof Exp:* Marine engr, US Maritime Comn, 40-46; from instr to prof mech eng, Purdue Univ, 46-64; prof & chmn dept, Univ Calif, Santa Barbara, 64-66; dean, Grad Sch, Drexel Univ, 66-83, prof mech eng, 76-83. *Concurrent Pos:* Consult, US Steel Corp, 57- & Allison Div, Gen Motors Corp, 58-59; prog dir, off inst prog, NSF, 62-63; pres, Asian Studies Found, 82-83. *Mem:* AAAS; Am Soc Mech Engrs; Am Soc Eng Educ. *Res:* Determination of physical and chemical thermodynamic properties. *Mailing Add:* 9306 Pebble Creek Dr Tampa FL 33647

**WITZEMAN, JONATHAN STEWART,** POLYMER CHEMISTRY, ORGANIC CHEMISTRY. *Current Pos:* asst to chmn & chief exec officer, 96-97, RES ASSOC, EASTMAN CHEM CO, KINGSPORT, TENN, 85-, MGR, CHEM RES, EASTMAN CHEM EUROPE. *Personal Data:* b Phoenix, Ariz, June 18, 57; m 80, Kerry A Miller; c 2. *Educ:* Northern Ariz Univ, BS, 79; Univ Calif, Santa Barbara, PhD(org chem), 84. *Prof Exp:* Assoc, Dept Chem, Univ Chicago, 84-85. *Concurrent Pos:* Postdoctorate, Univ Chicago, 84-85; adj prof, Dept Chem, ETenn State Univ, Johnson City, 91. *Mem:* Am Chem Soc; Sigma Xi. *Res:* Mechanistic study of reactions of industrial importance; development of new monomers, crosslinkers and polymers for coating applications. *Mailing Add:* Eastman Chem Co PO Box 511 Kingsport TN 37662

**WITZGALL, CHRISTOPH JOHANN,** OPERATIONS RESEARCH, NUMERICAL ANALYSIS. *Current Pos:* actg chief, Opers Res Div, 79-82, MATHEMATICIAN, CTR COMPUT APPL MATH, NAT INST STAND & TECHNOL. *Personal Data:* b Hindelang, Ger, Feb 25, 29; US citizen; m 64; c 3. *Educ:* Univ Munich, PhD(math), 58. *Prof Exp:* Res assoc math, Princeton Univ, 59-60, Univ Mainz, 60-62 & Argonne Nat Lab, 62; mathematician, Nat Bur Standards, 62-66 & Boeing Co, 66-73. *Concurrent* *Pos:* Vis prof, Univ Tex, Austin, 71 & Univ Wurzburg, 72; assoc ed, Math Prog, 73-82. *Mem:* Soc Indust & Appl Math; AAAS; Am Math Soc; Opers Res Soc Am. *Res:* Further development of operations research, numerical analysis and programming languages as needed for planning and systems applications; computational geometry. *Mailing Add:* Ctr Comput Appl Math Nat Inst Stand & Technol Gaithersburg MD 20899-0001. *E-Mail:* Witzgall@cam.nist.gov

**WITZIG, WARREN FRANK,** NUCLEAR ENGINEERING, PHYSICS. *Current Pos:* EMER PROF & DEPT HEAD, PA STATE UNIV, UNIVERSITY PARK, 86- *Personal Data:* b Detroit, Mich, Mar 26, 21; m 42, Bernadette Sullivan; c 4. *Educ:* Rensselaer Polytech Inst, BS, 42; Univ Pittsburgh, MS, 44, PhD(physics), 52. *Prof Exp:* Res engr, Westinghouse Elec Corp, 42-46, from engr & scientist to proj mgr, Bettis Labs, 46-60; sr vpres & dir, NUS Corp, 60-67; prof nuclear eng & head dept, PA State Univ, University Park, 67-86. *Concurrent Pos:* Mem nuclear stand bd, US Am Stand Inst, 65; mem comt radioactive waste mgt, Nat Acad Sci; mem, Pa Gov Adv Comt Nuclear Energy & Asn Am Univs Rev Comt on EBR II Fast Breeder Reactor; bd dirs, Gen Pub Utilities Nuclear Corp, 84-93; mem, PSE&G, Nuclear Oversight Comt, 83-91; Tu Operating Rev Comt, 85-; Tenn Valley Auth Nuclear Safety Rev Bd, 86-91; chmn, Westinghouse Nuclear Safety & Environ Oversight Comt, 88-93, INPO Accreditation Bd, 93-96; res reactor safeguards comt, Pa State. *Mem:* Inst Elec & Electronics Engrs; fel Am Nuclear Soc; Am Phys Soc; fel AAAS; Sigma Xi. *Res:* Nuclear reactor engineering and physics; reactor safety; nuclear safeguards; nuclear fuel costs; reactor plant siting; reactor design and operation; operator training and environmental oversite. *Mailing Add:* 1330 Park Hills Ave E State College PA 16803

**WITZLEBEN, CAMILLUS LEO,** PATHOLOGY. *Current Pos:* dir path, 73-96, PATHOLOGIST, CHILDREN'S HOSP, PHILADELPHIA, 96- *Personal Data:* b Dickinson, NDak, Apr 20, 32; m 56; c 6. *Educ:* Univ Notre Dame, BS, 53; St Louis Univ, MD, 57. *Prof Exp:* Resident path, St Louis Univ, 57-60; NSF fel, Hosp Sick Children, London, Eng, 60-61; fel, Harvard Univ, 61-62; dir labs, Children's Hosp Med Ctr Northern Calif, 64-66; dir labs, Cardinal Glennon Mem Hosp Children, St Louis, 66-73; prof path & pediat, Univ Pa, 73-96. *Concurrent Pos:* Capt, USAF, 62-64; consult, San Francisco Gen Hosp, 64-66; asst prof, Univ Calif, 64-66; from asst prof to prof, St Louis Univ, 66-73; NIH res grant, 68-74. *Mem:* Pediat Path Soc; Am Asn Study Liver Dis. *Res:* Hepatobiliary system; pediatric disease. *Mailing Add:* Path Med Pediat Univ Pa Childrens Hosp 34th St & Civic Center Blvd Philadelphia PA 19104

**WITZMAN, SORIN,** SYSTEM RELIABILITY, FAILURE PREDICTION-ANALYSIS. *Current Pos:* MEM SCI STAFF, BELL NORTHERN RES, 85- *Personal Data:* b Bucharest, Romania, June 6, 49, Can citizen. *Educ:* Polytech Inst Bucharest, Romania, BSc, 71, MSc, 72; Technion, Israel Inst Technol, MEng, 73. *Prof Exp:* Res engr, Res & Design Inst Food Indust, 72-75; res asst, Technion, Isreal Inst Technol, 75-79; mgr eng dept, Taasan Ltd, 79-80; sr develop engr, TAT Aero Equip Indust, 80-84. *Res:* Correlation between the temperature field and device reliability/failure; methodologies for predicting reliability/temperature field of electronic devices; electronic devices failure mechanisms. *Mailing Add:* PO Box 3511 Sta C Ottawa ON K1Y 4H7 Can. *Fax:* 613-763-5692

**WITZMANN, FRANK A,** MUSCLE PHYSIOLOGY & BIOCHEMISTRY, EXERCISE PHYSIOLOGY. *Current Pos:* ASST PROF BIOL, IND UNIV-PURDUE UNIV, COLUMBUS, 85- *Personal Data:* b Bucyrus, Ohio, June 6, 54; m 77; c 2. *Educ:* Defiance Col, BA, 76; Ball State Univ, MS, 78; Marquette Univ, PhD(biol), 81. *Prof Exp:* Asst prof biol, Marquette Univ, 81-82; asst prof, Defiance Col, 82-85. *Mem:* Sigma Xi; Am Col Sports Med. *Res:* Role of humoral mechanisms in muscle atrophy and endocrine influence on muscle; qualitative changes induced in skeletal and cardiac muscle by anabolic steroids and growth hormone. *Mailing Add:* Ind Univ-Purdue Univ Columbus 4601 Central Ave Columbus IN 47203

**WIXOM, ROBERT LLEWELLYN,** METABOLISM, NUTRITION & BIOCHEMISTRY. *Current Pos:* from assoc prof to prof, 64-92, EMER PROF BIOCHEM, SCH MED, UNIV MO, COLUMBIA, 92- *Personal Data:* b Philadelphia, Pa, July 6, 24; m 49, 86, Patricia McMillin; c David G & Richard L. *Educ:* Earlham Col, AB, 47; Univ Ill, PhD(biochem), 52. *Prof Exp:* Asst biochem, Univ Ill, 48-52; from instr to assoc prof, Sch Med, Univ Ark, 52-64. *Concurrent Pos:* Fel, Univ Ill, 55; Lalor Found res fel, 58; spec res fel, NIH, 70-71; res serv fel, 78-79; res develop fel, Univ Mo, 86. *Mem:* AAAS; Am Soc Biochem & Molecular Biol; Am Chem Soc; Soc Exp Biol & Chem; Am Inst Nutrit; Sigma Xi; Protein Soc. *Res:* Requirements of essential amino acids in man; glycine serine in chick nutrition; biosynthesis of amino acids in microorganisms and plants; inborn errors of amino acid metabolism; total parenteral administration of amino acids; role of histidine in man; relation of iron/ferritin/hemosiden; role of ubiquitin in protein degradation; educational aspects of environmental concerns. *Mailing Add:* Dept Biochem Sch Med DC 008-200 Univ Mo Columbia MO 65212. *Fax:* 573-884-4597

**WIXSON, BOBBY GUINN,** AQUATIC BIOLOGY, ENVIRONMENTAL ENGINEERING. *Current Pos:* actg provost, Clemson Univ, 83, dean, Int Progs, 85-87, dean, Col Sci, 87-96, EMER DEAN, CLEMSON UNIV, 97- *Personal Data:* b Abilene, Tex, Mar 19, 31; m 52; c 2. *Educ:* Sul Ross State Col, BS, 60, MA, 61; Tex A&M Univ, PhD(biol oceanog), 67. *Prof Exp:* Asst instr sci, Sul Ross State Col, 58-60, instr, 60-61, dir col planetarium & asst to dean of men, 59-61; asst oceanog, Tex A&M Univ, 61-63, asst aquatic biol, 63-65, asst water pollution res, 65-67; from asst prof to prof environ health, Univ MoRolla, 67-87, dir, Int Ctr, 69-84. *Concurrent Pos:* Consult, UN

Environ Prog, US Environ Protection Agency; Proj Hope, Brazil; secy-treas, US Found Int Econ Policy. *Mem:* Nat Water Pollution Control Fedn; Am Water Resources Asn; Soc Environ Geochem & Health (pres, 78-81); Sigma Xi. *Res:* Aquatic pollution and industrial waste disposal problems; environmental, earth and marine sciences. *Mailing Add:* 4698 S Forest Ave Springfield MO 65810

**WIXSON, ELDWIN A, JR,** MATHEMATICS OF FINANCE. *Current Pos:* assoc prof, 66-69, chmn dept, 66-83, acad dean, 83-86, PROF MATH, PLYMOUTH STATE COL, 69- *Personal Data:* b Winslow, Maine, Nov 30, 31; m 54, 76; c 6. *Educ:* Univ Maine, BS, 53; Colby Col, MST, 62; Temple Univ, MSEd, 62; Univ Mich, PhD, 69. *Prof Exp:* Teacher, High Sch, Maine, 53-54 & 57-60; TV teacher, Maine Dept Educ, 60-61; teacher, High Sch, Maine, 62-63; assoc prof math, Keene State Col, 63-65. *Concurrent Pos:* Pvt financial consult, 66- *Mem:* Math Asn Am; Nat Coun Teachers Math. *Res:* Mathematics education, especially at the undergraduate college level; financial matters, especially annuities of all types and real estate or business financing. *Mailing Add:* Dept Math MSC29 Plymouth State Col Plymouth NH 03264-1600

**WLODEK, STANLEY T,** METALLURGY, PHYSICAL METALLURGICAL & MATERIALS SCIENCE ENGINEERING. *Current Pos:* PRES, GAMMA PRIME CONSULT, 93- *Personal Data:* b Haiduki, Poland, Sept 23, 30; US citizen; m 55; c 3. *Educ:* Queens Univ, Ont, BSc Hons, 52; Mass Inst Technol, SM, 54, ScD, 56. *Prof Exp:* Unit mgr, Metals Res Lab, Union Carbide Corp, 56-60, AEBG, 60-64 & Graham Lab, Jal Steel, 64-69; unit mgr, Gen Elec Aircraft Engines, 60-64, mgr proc develop, GE TTL Lab, 79-85, sr staff engr, 85-93; res dir, Cabot Corp, Kokomo, Ind, 69-79. *Mem:* Fel Am Soc Metals Inc; Minerals Metals & Mat Soc. *Res:* Physical and process metallurgy of high performance Ni, Co and Fe base alloys: corrosion and coating technology; structural studes of super alloys to elucidate structure- property interactions, particulary of jet engine alloys; failure analysis. *Mailing Add:* Gamma Prime Consults 17810 Pueblo Vista Lane San Diego CA 92127-1272

**WNUK, MICHAEL PETER,** ENGINEERING MECHANICS, FRACTURE MECHANICS. *Current Pos:* PROF ENG MECH, UNIV WIS, 82- *Personal Data:* b Katowice, Poland, Sept 12, 36; US citizen; m 64; c Jennifer. *Educ:* Tech Univ Krakow, MS, 59, PhD, 62; Jolgiellonian Univ Krakow, MS, 65. *Prof Exp:* Asst prof physics, Tech Univ Krakow, 59-64, assoc prof, 64-66; from asst prof to assoc prof mech eng, SDaK State Univ, 66-82. *Concurrent Pos:* Sr res fel, Calif Inst Technol, 67-68; distinguished vis scholar, Cambridge Univ, 68-70; vis scholar, Cambridge Univ, UK, 70-71, Acad Mining & Metall, Krakow, 74, Moscow State Univ, Russ, 91 & Technion Israel Technol Inst, 92; Nat Acad Sci sponsored vis prof & co-ed of proceedings, Fac Technol & Metall, Univ Belgrade, 80; vis prof, Northwestern Univ, 80-81; Fulbright Scholar, 91. *Mem:* Sigma Xi; NY Acad Sci. *Res:* Solid mechanics with particular emphasis on mechanics of fracture; initiation and subsequent propagation of fracture in non-linear range of material behavior (ductile and time-dependent fracture); computational mechanics. *Mailing Add:* 3436 Dousman Apt D Milwaukee WI 53212-1751. *Fax:* 414-229-6958; *E-Mail:* mpw@alpham.csd.uwm.edu

**WOBESER, GARY ARTHUR,** WILDLIFE PATHOLOGY. *Current Pos:* Assoc prof, 73-78, PROF VET PATH, WESTERN COL VET MED, UNIV SASK, SASKATOON, 78- *Personal Data:* b Regina, Sask, Feb 12, 42; m 65, Amy G Kendall; c Keith & Bruce. *Educ:* Univ Toronto, BSA, 63; Univ Guelph, MSc, 66, DVM, 69; Univ Sask, PhD(vet path), 73. *Concurrent Pos:* Co-dir, Can Coop Wildlife Health Ctr, 92- *Mem:* Wildlife Dis Asn; Can Vet Med Asn; Am Asn Vet Lab Diagnosticians; Wildlife Soc. *Res:* Diseases of wildlife, with particular emphasis on infectious, degenerative and toxic problems. *Mailing Add:* Dept Vet Path Western Col Vet Med Univ Sask Saskatoon SK S7N 0W0 Can

**WOBSCHALL, DAROLD C,** ELECTRONIC INSTRUMENTATION, SENSORS. *Current Pos:* VPRES, SENSOR PLUS, 90- *Personal Data:* b Wells, Minn, Feb 24, 32; m 57, Katrina; c 3. *Educ:* St Olaf Col, BA, 53; State Univ NY, Buffalo, MA, 60, PhD(biophys), 66. *Prof Exp:* Res assoc physics, Univ Buffalo, 58-60; assoc physicist, Cornell Aeronaut Lab, 60-62; cancer res scientist, Roswell Park Mem Inst, 66-67; from asst prof to assoc prof eng, State Univ NY, Buffalo, 67-85; pres, Index Electronics Inc, 85-90. *Concurrent Pos:* NIH spec fel, 66-67. *Mem:* Am Phys Soc; Biophys Soc; Inst Elec & Electronics Engrs. *Res:* Sensors; bioengineering; electronics instrumentation. *Mailing Add:* 25 Blossom Heath Williamsville NY 14221. *Fax:* 716-831-0212

**WOBUS, REINHARD ARTHUR,** GEOLOGY. *Current Pos:* from asst prof to prof, 66-85, dept head, 88-96, EDNA MCCONNELL CLARK PROF GEOL, WILLIAMS COL, 85- *Personal Data:* b Norfolk, Va, Jan 11, 41; m 67, Sheridan Whitcher; c Erik R & Cameron W. *Educ:* Wash Univ, AB, 62; Harvard Univ, MA, 63; Stanford Univ, PhD(geol), 66. *Concurrent Pos:* Geologist, Cent Regional Geol Br, US Geol Surv, 67-86; vis prof geol, Colo Col, 76, 82-83; instr geol field course, Colo State Univ, 77-84; coun, Council Undergrad Res, 87-89. *Mem:* Fel Geol Soc Am; Nat Asn Geol Teachers; Am Geophys Union; Sigma Xi; Mineral Soc Am; Coun Undergrad Res. *Res:* Igneous and metamorphic petrology; Precambrian geology of Southern Rocky Mountains; mid-tertiary volcanism in central Colorado. *Mailing Add:* Dept Geol Williams Col Williamstown MA 01267. *Fax:* 413-597-4116; *E-Mail:* reinhard.a.wobus@williams.edu

**WODARCZYK, FRANCIS JOHN,** MOLECULAR DYNAMICS, SPECTROSCOPY. *Current Pos:* PROG DIR, NSF, 90- *Personal Data:* b Chicago, Ill, Dec 11, 44. *Educ:* Ill Inst Technol, BS, 66; Harvard Univ, AM, 67, PhD(chem), 71. *Prof Exp:* Lectr chem, Harvard Univ, 69; res assoc, Univ Calif, Berkeley, 71-73; res chemist, Cambridge Res Labs, USAF, 73-77, prog mgr, Off Sci Res, 77-78; mem tech staff, Rockwell Int Sci Ctr, 78-85; prog mgr, USAF Off Sci Res, 85-90. *Concurrent Pos:* Lectr, Univ Calif, Berkeley, 73. *Mem:* Am Chem Soc; AAAS; Sigma Xi. *Res:* Atomic and molecular spectroscopy; energy transfer and reaction kinetics; laser physics and chemistry; surface analysis; thin film coatings research. *Mailing Add:* Chem Div NSF 4201 Wilson Blvd Arlington VA 22230. *Fax:* 703-306-0534; *E-Mail:* fwodarcz@nsf.gov

**WODARSKI, JOHN STANLEY,** RESEARCH ADMINSTRATION, HEALTH SCIENCES. *Current Pos:* ASSOC VPRES RES & GRAD STUDIES, UNIV AKRON, 88- *Personal Data:* b Philadelphia, Pa, Feb 27, 43; m 64; c 1. *Educ:* Fla State Univ, BS, 65; Univ Tenn, MSSW, 67; Wash Univ, St Louis, Mo, PhD(social work), 70. *Prof Exp:* Instr sociol, Sam Houston State Univ, 67-68; asst prof social work, George Warren Brown Sch Social Work, Wash Univ, 70-74; assoc prof social work, Sch Social Work, Univ Md, 75-78; prof social work & dir res ctr, Sch Social Work, Univ Ga, 78-88. *Concurrent Pos:* Res dir, Ctr Studies Crime & Delinquency, NIMH, 70-75; adj fac res scientist, Inst Behav Res & Ctr Social Orgn Sch, Johns Hopkins Univ, 75-77; prin investr, spec progs proj grants, Univ Ga, 78-80, grad sch fac award, 79, res found grant, 80-82 & 82-83, social work training br grant, NIMH, 79-83, social work educ br grant, 83-86, Ga Dept Human Resources grant, 82-83, Ford Found grant, 82-83, Edna McConnell-Clark Found, Ga Alliance Children & Trust Fund, Atlanta grant, 83-84, US dept transp grant, 83-86 & Gov emergency fund grant, Ga state, 84-85; co-prin investr, Ga Dept Human Resources grant, 81-84 & Ga Dept Community Affairs grant, 83-84; prin investr grants, US Dept Educ, Univ Affil Prog, 86-88, Edward W Hazen Found, 86-87, US Dept Health & Human Serv, 87-; res assoc, Dept Health & Human Serv, 86-88. *Mem:* Am Psychol Asn; Am Sociol Asn; Asn Advan Behav Ther; Coun Social Work Educ; Nat Asn Social Workers; Nat Coun Crime & Delinquency. *Res:* Mental health programs with emphasis on the provision of services to rural areas and social work training for minorities; services for children and youth, specifically in regard to family violence and prevention of alcohol abuse; aging with emphasis on training social workers to work with older adults; health; school social work; projects on energy conservation for college campuses, comprehensive treatment for college and high school students who abuse alcohol, treatment for families with runaway children and evaluation of different child welfare procedures. *Mailing Add:* 8541 Quincy Ct East Amherst NY 14051

**WODICKA, VIRGIL O,** FOOD TECHNOLOGY. *Current Pos:* RETIRED. *Personal Data:* b St Louis, Mo, Mar 5, 15; m 41; c 2. *Educ:* Rutgers Univ, PhD(food sci), 56. *Prof Exp:* Food technol consult, 75-89. *Mem:* Inst Food Technol; Am Soc Qual Control; Am Chem Soc; Am Asn Cereal Chemists; Am Oil Chemists Soc; AAAS; Am Inst Nutrit. *Mailing Add:* 1307 Norman Pl Fullerton CA 92631-2045

**WODZICKI, ANTONI,** GEOLOGY. *Current Pos:* from asst prof to assoc prof, econ geol & mineral, 77-88, PROF ECON GEOL, WESTERN WASH UNIV, 88- *Personal Data:* b Krakow, Poland, July 15, 34; US citizen; m 62; c 4. *Educ:* Univ Otago, NZ, BE, 56; Univ Minn, MS, 61; Stanford Univ, PhD(geol), 65. *Prof Exp:* Geologist econ geol, NZ Geol Surv, 54-75, geologist petrol, 58-59; vis asst prof mineral & geochem, Portland State Univ, 75-76; vis asst prof mineral & econ geol, Univ Ore, 76-77. *Concurrent Pos:* Actg chief petrologist, NZ Geol Surv, 69-70; mem mineral resources comt, NZ Nat Develop Conf, 69-70; hon lectr, Victoria Univ, Wellington, 74-75; proj geologist, Nat Uranium Resource Eval, 78-80 & Wilderness Study Area Assessment, 82-83; exchange fel, Polish Acad Sci, 85; geol consult, Haitian Govt, 88. *Mem:* Royal Soc NZ; NZ Geol Soc; NZ Geochem Group (chmn, 71-73); Polish Geol Soc. *Res:* Field geology, economic geology, petrology, geochemistry and particularly the application of these disciplines to the finding, evaluation and understanding of the origin of ore deposits. *Mailing Add:* 311 Parkridge Rd Bellingham WA 98225

**WODZINSKI, RUDY JOSEPH,** MICROBIAL BIOCHEMISTRY. *Current Pos:* prof biol sci, Univ Cent Fla, 70-75 & 77-89, Gordon J Barnett prof environ sci, 75-77, PROF MOLECULAR BIOL & MICROBIOL, UNIV CENT FLA, 89- *Personal Data:* b Chicago, Ill, June 12, 33; m 56, Mildred Lipinski; c Steven, Michael & Carol. *Educ:* Loyola Univ, Ill, BS, 55; Univ Wis, MS, 57, PhD(bact), 60. *Prof Exp:* Asst bact, Univ Wis, 55-60; sr res scientist, Squibb Inst Med Res, New Brunswick, NJ, 60-62; res microbiologist, Int Minerals & Chem Corp, Ill, 62-64; supvr microbial biochem, 64-68, mgr animal sci, 68-70. *Concurrent Pos:* Consult microbiol of the eye, Frontier Contact Lenses, 76-81, viruses in waste water, Worldco, 77-80, methane generation, Anaerobic Energy Systs, Inc, 78-82, fermentation-biotechnol, William Underwood Co, 76-83, Pet Inc, 83-85, biotechnol investments, G K Scott & Co, 82-84, Rooney PAC, Ch2-Hill, 89-; nat coun, Fla Br, Am Soc Microbiol, 78-81, vchmn, Environ, Gen & Appl Microbiol, 76-77, chmn, 77-78, med bd, Pub Sci Affairs, 85-94, Comt Agr, Food & Indust Microbiol, 79-85, chmn, 85-94, counr, Environ, Gen & Appl Div, 85-; mem bd dirs & secy-treas, Convert-EDA, 87-93 & Energy Develop Assocs, 87-93, Gov Energy Res Task Force, State Fla, 80- *Mem:* Am Soc Microbiol; fel Am Acad Microbiol; Sigma Xi. *Res:* Enzymology; molecular biology; virology; microbial genetics and physiology; fermentation; available moisture requirements of microorganisms; water and waste microbiology. *Mailing Add:* Dept Molecular Biol & Microbiol Univ Cent Fla Orlando FL 32816-2360

**WOEHLER, KARLHEINZ EDGAR,** PHYSICS. *Current Pos:* assoc prof physics, 65-72, chmn dept physics & chem, 74-79, PROF PHYSICS, NAVAL POSTGRAD SCH, 72-, CHMN DEPT, 87- *Personal Data:* b Berlin, Ger, June 5, 30; m 56; c 1. *Educ:* Univ Bonn, BS, 53; Aachen Tech Univ, Dipl, 55; Univ Munich, PhD(physics), 62. *Prof Exp:* Physicist commun technol, Siemens & Halske, Ger, 55-59; res assoc plasma physics, Max Planck Inst Physics, 59-62; asst prof physics, US Naval Postgrad Sch, 62-64; sr res assoc, Inst Plasma Physics, 64-65. *Concurrent Pos:* Consult physicist, Atomics Int Div, NAm Aviation, Inc, 63-64; Nat Acad Sci res grant, Res Labs, NASA, 66; consult, Naval Electronics Lab Ctr, Calif, 68, 69 & 72. *Mem:* Am Phys Soc; AAAS; Sigma Xi. *Res:* Plasma physics; general relativity and cosmology. *Mailing Add:* Dept Physics US Naval Postgrad Sch Monterey CA 93940

**WOEHLER, MICHAEL EDWARD,** IMMUNOLOGY, MEDICAL MICROBIOLOGY. *Current Pos:* mem staff, 80-92, PRES, PHARMACIA, INC, 92- *Personal Data:* b Appleton, Wis, Feb 16, 45. *Educ:* Northwestern Univ, BA, 67; Marquette Univ, PhD(microbiol), 71. *Prof Exp:* Fel biochem, Univ Ga, 71-74; mem tech staff immunol, GTE Labs, Inc, 74-80. *Mem:* Am Soc Microbiol; AAAS; Sigma Xi; NY Acad Sci. *Res:* Immunology, specifically structure function relationships of immunoglobulins G and E antibodies. *Mailing Add:* Pharmacia Biotech Inc 800 Centennial Ave Piscataway NJ 08854

**WOEHLER, SCOTT EDWIN,** NUCLEAR MAGNETIC RESONANCE, FOURIER TRANSFORM INFRARED. *Current Pos:* at Dept Chem, 92-, MMR SPECTROSCOPIST, COL PHARM, UNIV MICH, ANN ARBOR. *Personal Data:* b Albany, Ga, Sept 19, 52; m 89; c 1. *Educ:* Ill Benedictine Col, BS, 74; Univ Mich, MS, 77; Univ Louisville, PhD(chem), 86. *Prof Exp:* Sales & serv engr, Tret-O-Lite, St Louis, 77-79; res asst phys chem, Univ Ky, 79-82; fel biochem, Ga State Univ, 87-88; nuclear magnetic resonance specialist, Purdue Univ, 88-90, Northwestern Univ, 90-92. *Concurrent Pos:* Consult, Molecular Modeling Workshop, Fac Southeastern US Cols, 89. *Res:* Electron self exchange through nuclear magnetic resonance; polymer reactions through Fourier Transform Infrared. *Mailing Add:* Col Pharm Univ Mich Ann Arbor MI 48109

**WOELFEL, JULIAN BRADFORD,** DENTISTRY. *Current Pos:* PROF DENT, COL DENT, OHIO STATE UNIV, 48- *Personal Data:* b Baltimore, Md, Dec 17, 25; m 48; c 3. *Educ:* Ohio State Univ, DDS, 48. *Honors & Awards:* Int Asn Dent Res Award, 67. *Concurrent Pos:* Consult & Am Dent Asn res assoc, Nat Bur Stands, 57-63; consult, Vet Admin Hosp, Dayton, Ohio, 66-69 & Fed Penitentiary, Chillicothe, 65-66; pres, Carl O Boucher Prosthodontic Conf, 67- *Mem:* Am Prosthodont Soc; Am Dent Asn; Int Asn Dent Res; fel Am Col Dent; Acad Denture Prosthetics; Sigma Xi. *Res:* Prosthodontic dentistry; denture base resins; clinical evaluation of complete dentures; electromyography; jaw and denture movement; mandibular motion in three dimensions; accuracy of impression materials; soft and hard tissue and facial dimension changes beneath complete dentures during six years; computer analysis of mandibular resorption. *Mailing Add:* 4345 Brookie Ct Columbus OH 43214-2903

**WOELKE, CHARLES EDWARD,** FISHERIES, MARINE ECOLOGY. *Current Pos:* RETIRED. *Personal Data:* b Seattle, Wash, Jan 8, 26; m 47; c 2. *Educ:* Univ Wash, BS, 50, PhD(fisheries), 68. *Prof Exp:* Aquatic biologist, Ore Fisheries Comn, 50-51; fisheries biologist, 51-64, res scientist fisheries, 68-75; chief res & develop, Wash Dept Fisheries, 75-79; asst to dir, Intergovt Affairs, 79-82; consult biologist, 82-92. *Concurrent Pos:* Affil prof, Univ Wash, 69- *Mem:* Fel Am Inst Fishery Res Biol; Nat Shellfisheries Asn. *Res:* Molluscan commercial shellfish; bioassays with bivalve embryos; development of in situ bioassays with bivalve larvae; development of water quality standards and criteria; biometrics and ecological systems analysis. *Mailing Add:* 1608 Sullivan Dr NW Gig Harbor WA 98335

**WOELKERLING, WILLIAM J,** BOTANY. *Current Pos:* PROF, DEPT BOT, LATROBE UNIV, AUSTRALIA. *Honors & Awards:* Gerald W Prescott Award, Phycol Soc Am, 89. *Mailing Add:* Dept Bot LaTrobe Univ Bundoora Victoria 3063 Australia

**WOERNER, DALE EARL,** ANALYTICAL CHEMISTRY. *Current Pos:* from asst prof to assoc prof, 58-66, PROF CHEM, UNIV NORTHERN COLO, 66- *Personal Data:* b Oak Hill, Kans, Jan 15, 26; m 50; c 6. *Educ:* Kans State Univ, BS, 49; Univ Ill, MS, 51, PhD(analytical chem), 53. *Prof Exp:* Asst chem, Univ Ill, 49-53; assoc prof, Hanover Col, 53-55; from asst instr to asst prof, Kans State Univ, 55-58. *Mem:* Am Chem Soc; Sigma Xi. *Res:* Amperometric titrations; spectroscopy. *Mailing Add:* 2028 Buena Vista Ct Greeley CO 80631

**WOERNER, ROBERT LEO,** LASER ISOTOPE SEPARATION, FUSION TARGET FABRICATION. *Current Pos:* DIR STRATEGY & PLANNING, PAC BELL, 91- *Personal Data:* b Evanston, Ill, Apr 21, 48. *Educ:* Mass Inst Technol, SB & SM, 71, PhD(physics), 74. *Prof Exp:* Fel liquid helium, Dept Physics, Mass Inst Technol, 74-75; mem tech staff physics, Bell Tel Labs, Holmdel, NJ, 75-76; physicist, Lawrence Livermore Lab, 76-84. *Mem:* Am Phys Soc. *Res:* Integrated experiments to demonstrate the atomic vapor laser isotope separation process. *Mailing Add:* 2535 Chateau Way Livermore CA 94550

**WOESE, CARL R,** EVOLUTION, BACTERIA PHYLOGENY. *Current Pos:* assoc prof microbiol, Univ Ill, 64-69, prof biophys, 72-79, prof genetic & develop, 73-86, PROF MICROBIOL, CTR ADVAN STUDY, UNIV ILL, 69-, PROF BIOL, SCH LIFE SCI, 87- *Personal Data:* b Syracuse, NY, July 15, 28; c 2. *Educ:* Amherst Col, AB, 50; Yale Univ, PhD(biophys), 53. *Hon Degrees:* DSc, Amherst Col, 85 & Syracuse Univ, 94. *Honors & Awards:* Storer Lectr, Univ Calif, Davis, 79; Karl August Forester Lectr, Johannes-Gutenberg Univ, Ger, 82; John D & Catherine T MacArthur Award, 84; Leeuwenhoek Medal, 90; Twenty-Third Brown-Hazen Lectr Award, 92; Roger W Stanier Mem Lectr, Univ Calif, Berkeley, 93. *Prof Exp:* Res assoc biophys, Yale Univ, 55-60; biophysicist, Res Lab, Gen Elec, 60-63. *Mem:* Nat Acad Sci; fel Am Acad Art & Sci; corresp mem Dutch Soc Hyg & Microbiol; Max-Planck Soc; Can Inst Advan Res; fel Am Acad Microbiol. *Res:* Molecular mechanism of translation and on the evolution of the cell; phylogeny of microorganisms and the nature of the universal common ancestor. *Mailing Add:* Dept Microbiol Univ Ill 371 Morill Hall 601 S Goodwin Ave Urbana IL 61801

**WOESSNER, DONALD EDWARD,** NUCLEAR MAGNETIC RESONANCE & IMAGING. *Current Pos:* ADJ ASST PROF, SOUTHWESTERN MED CTR, UNIV TEX, 92- *Personal Data:* b Milledgeville, Ill, Oct 6, 30; m 58, Rebecca A Patchin; c Richard D. *Educ:* Carthage Col, AB, 52; Univ Ill, PhD(chem), 57. *Honors & Awards:* W T Doherty Award, Am Chem Soc, 75. *Prof Exp:* Asst phys chem, Univ Ill, 55-57, fel chem, 57-58; sr res technologist, Dallas Res Lab, Mobil Res & Develop Corp, 58-62, res assoc, 62-84, sr res assoc, 84-92. *Concurrent Pos:* Assoc ed, J Chem Physics, 71-73 & J Magnetic Resonance, 80- *Mem:* AAAS; Am Phys Soc; NY Acad Sci; Am Chem Soc; Soc Magnetic Resonance; Int Soc Magnetic Resonance Med. *Res:* Use of nuclear magnetic resonance to analyze structure and motions in solids, liquids and heterogeneous systems; conventional liquid and solid measurements; magic angle spinning and cross polarization; magic angle spinning of solids and absorbed materials; nuclear magnetic resonance imaging and spectroscopy of biological materials. *Mailing Add:* Rogers Magnetic Resonance Ctr Univ Tex Southwestern Med Ctr 5801 Forest Park Rd Dallas TX 75235-9085. *Fax:* 214-648-5881; *E-Mail:* dwoess@mednet.swmed.edu

**WOESSNER, JACOB FREDERICK, JR,** BIOCHEMISTRY. *Current Pos:* res asst prof biochem, Univ Miami, 56-64, assoc prof, 64-72, assoc prof med, 72-80, PROF BIOCHEM, SCH MED, UNIV MIAMI, 72-, PROF MED, 80- *Personal Data:* b Pittsburgh, Pa, May 8, 28; m 53, Nina Butler; c Jeffrey & Katharine. *Educ:* Valparaiso Univ, BA, 50; Mass Inst Technol, PhD(biochem), 55. *Honors & Awards:* Int Geigy Rheumatism Prize, 81; Roussel-Osteoarthritis Res Soc Prize, 94. *Prof Exp:* Lilly fel natural sci, Univ Mich, 55-56. *Concurrent Pos:* Investr, Labs Cardiovasc Res, Howard Hughes Med Inst, Fla, 56-71; vis scientist, Max Planck Inst Protein & Leather Res, 61-62; mem, Gen Med B Study Sect, NIH, 71-75. *Mem:* Am Chem Soc; Geront Soc; Am Rheumatism Asn; Am Soc Biol Chemists; Biochem Soc; Soc Study Reprod. *Res:* Formation, metabolism and aging of connective tissue; matrix metalloproteinases; tissue resorption; arthritis; cervical dilation. *Mailing Add:* Univ Miami Sch Med R-127 PO Box 016960 Miami FL 33101. *Fax:* 305-243-3955; *E-Mail:* woessne@mednet.med.miami.edu

**WOESSNER, RONALD ARTHUR,** FORESTRY, GENETICS. *Current Pos:* mgr, forest productivity, 81-88, MGR, LANDS & FOREST PRODUCTIVITY, MEAD CORP, 88- *Personal Data:* b Pittsburgh, Pa, Apr 27, 37; m 56, Gayle Jones; c Ronald, Laura & Derek. *Educ:* WVa Univ, BS, 63; NC State Univ, MS, 66, PhD(forest genetics), 68. *Honors & Awards:* Merit Award Forestry Res, Tex Forestry Asn. *Prof Exp:* Asst prof plant & forest sci, Tex A&M Univ, 68-74, assoc prof forestry, 74, assoc geneticist, Tex Forest Serv, 68-74; supv res & devel, Jari Florestal, Amazon Basin, Nat Bulk Carriers Inc, 74-81. *Mem:* Soc Am Foresters; AAAS; Sigma Xi; Commonwealth Forestry Asn; Int Soc Trop Foresters. *Res:* Genetic improvement of pine and hardwood species, temperate and tropical; quantitative genetics of forest trees; provenance and progeny testing; seed orchards, genotype-environment interactions; inter-population crossing; wood density, nurseries and regeneration; herbicides for site preparation and release. *Mailing Add:* 6109 Ascot Way Columbus GA 31909. *Fax:* 706-571-7471

**WOESTE, FRANK EDWARD,** WOOD CONSTRUCTION, SYSTEM SIMULATION & RELIABILITY. *Current Pos:* from asst prof to assoc prof, 77-90, PROF WOOD ENG RES, VA TECH, BLACKSBURG, 90- *Personal Data:* b Alexandria, Ky, Feb 11, 48. *Educ:* Univ Ky, BSAE, 70, MSAE, 72; Purdue Univ, PhD(agr eng), 75. *Prof Exp:* Vis asst prof wood eng res, Wood Res Lab, Purdue Univ, West Lafayette, 75-77. *Mem:* Forest Prod Res Soc; Am Soc Testing & Mat; Am Soc Agr Engrs; Truss Plate Inst. *Res:* Engineered wood trusses; lumber properties research; farm structures research; light-frame building fire research. *Mailing Add:* Dept Biol Systs Eng Polytech Inst & State Univ Seitz Hall Blacksburg VA 24061

**WOFFORD, IRVIN MIRLE,** AGRONOMY. *Current Pos:* MGR AGR PUB RELS, KAISER AGR CHEM, 64- *Personal Data:* b White Co, Ga, Dec 11, 16; m 38. *Educ:* Univ Ga, BSA, 48; Univ Fla, MSA, 49; Mich State Col, PhD(farm crops), 53. *Prof Exp:* Instr agron, Univ Fla, 49-51, asst agronomist, Exp Sta, 53-56; asst, Mich State Col, 51-53; dir agron, Southern Nitrogen Co, Inc, 56-64. *Mem:* Am Soc Agron. *Res:* Crop management and production; fertilizer studies; variety testing; date of planting; rotations; plant population studies. *Mailing Add:* 1325 Lavon Ave Savannah GA 31406

**WOFSY, LEON,** CHEMISTRY, IMMUNOLOGY. *Current Pos:* Prof, 64-, EMER PROF IMMUNOL, UNIV CALIF, BERKELEY. *Personal Data:* b Stamford, Conn, Nov 23, 21; m 42; c 2. *Educ:* City Col New York, BS, 42; Yale Univ, MS, 60, PhD(chem), 61. *Mem:* Am Chem Soc. *Res:* Study of antibody specificity; mechanisms of cellular differentiation. *Mailing Add:* Dept Microbiol & Cell Biol Univ Calif Berkeley CA 94720-3200

**WOFSY, STEVEN CHARLES,** ATMOSPHERIC CHEMISTRY, AQUATIC CHEMISTRY. *Current Pos:* lectr, 74-77, assoc prof, Div Appl Sci, 77-82, SR RES FEL, HARVARD UNIV, 82- *Personal Data:* b New York, NY, June 24, 46. *Educ:* Univ Chicago, BS, 66; Harvard Univ, PhD(chem), 71. *Honors & Awards:* MacIlwane Award, Am Geophys-Union, 81. *Prof Exp:* Res assoc, Smithsonian Astrophys Observ, 71-74. *Concurrent Pos:* Res assoc, Nat Acad Sci-Nat Res Coun, 71-73. *Mem:* Am Geophys Union; AAAS; Am Soc Limnol & Oceanog. *Res:* Photochemistry and biogeochemistry of atmospheric gases; gases and nutrients in marine and fresh waters; human impact on the global environment. *Mailing Add:* Div Eng & Appl Sci Pierce Hall Rm 100A Harvard Univ Cambridge MA 02138

**WOGAN, GERALD NORMAN,** PHARMACOLOGY. *Current Pos:* res assoc food toxicol, 61-62, from asst prof to assoc prof, 62-68, PROF TOXICOL, MASS INST TECHNOL, 68-, DIR, DIV TOXICOL, 88- *Personal Data:* b Altoona, Pa, Jan 11, 30; m 57; c 2. *Educ:* Juniata Col, BS, 51; Univ Ill, MS, 53, PhD(physiol), 57. *Prof Exp:* Instr physiol, Univ Ill, 56-57; asst prof, Rutgers Univ, 57-61. *Concurrent Pos:* Assoc ed, J Toxicol & Environ Health, 75-79; bd trustees, Int Life Sci Inst, 85-92; sect ed, J Environ Path, Toxicol & Oncol, 92. *Mem:* Nat Acad Sci; Inst Med-Nat Acad Sci; Am Soc Pharmacol & Exp Therapeut; Soc Toxicol; Am Asn Cancer Res; AAAS; fel Am Acad Microbiol; Repub Singapore Cancer Soc; Japan found Promy Cancer Res; Am Soc Microbiol; Am Soc Prev Oncol; Am Inst Nutrit; Am Col Toxicol; Am Chem Soc; Sigma Xi. *Res:* Chemical carcinogenesis; physiological and biochemical responses to toxic substances; mechanisms of action of carcinogens and mutagens; environmental carcinogenesis. *Mailing Add:* Div Toxicol Rm 26-009 Mass Inst Technol Cambridge MA 02139

**WOGEN, WARREN RONALD,** MATHEMATICS. *Current Pos:* Assoc prof, 69-80, PROF MATH, UNIV NC, CHAPEL HILL, 80- *Personal Data:* b Forest City, Iowa, Feb 19, 43; m 67; c 2. *Educ:* Luther Col, Iowa, BA, 65; Ind Univ, Bloomington, MS, 67, PhD(math), 69. *Concurrent Pos:* Vis prof, Ind Univ, 76. *Mem:* Am Math Soc; Math Asn Am. *Res:* Operator theory and operator algebras. *Mailing Add:* Dept Math Univ NC Chapel Hill NC 27599-3250

**WOGMAN, NED ALLEN,** NUCLEAR CHEMISTRY, PHYSICAL CHEMISTRY. *Current Pos:* Sr res scientist, Battelle Pac NW Lab, 65-68, mgr radiol chem, 68-72, res assoc, 72-79, mgr radiol chem, 79-86, MGR TECHNOL DEVELOP, BATTELLE PAC NW LAB, 86- *Personal Data:* b Spokane, Wash, Oct 25, 39; m 72, Nancy Neuman; c 3. *Educ:* Wash State Univ, BS, 61; Purdue Univ, PhD(phys chem), 66. *Concurrent Pos:* Lectr, Joint Ctr Grad Study, Wash State Univ, Univ Wash, Ore State Univ, 72-; mem sci comt, Nat Coun Radiation Protection, 73- *Mem:* Am Chem Soc; fel Am Nuclear Soc. *Res:* Rates and mechanisms of biological, meteorological, oceanographic and ecological processes studied using natural and artificial radionuclides, development of sensitive multidimensional gamma-ray spectrometer systems for trace radionuclide measurements; neutron, alpha, and beta detection systems; low background radiation detector development. *Mailing Add:* 3408 S Irby Kennewick WA 99337. *Fax:* 509-376-2373

**WOGRIN, CONRAD A(NTHONY),** ELECTRICAL ENGINEERING, COMPUTER SCIENCE. *Current Pos:* dir, Univ Comput Ctr, 67-85, chmn comput sci, 85-86, PROF COMPUT & INFO SCI, UNIV MASS, AMHERST, 67- *Personal Data:* b Denver, Colo, Apr 16, 24; m 51; c 3. *Educ:* Yale Univ, BE, 49, MEng, 51, DEng, 55. *Prof Exp:* From instr to assoc prof elec eng, Yale Univ, 51-66. *Concurrent Pos:* Consult, Mitre Corp, 61-65, Goddard Space Flight Ctr, 65-72 & United Aircraft Corp Syst Ctr, 66-70. *Mem:* AAAS; Inst Elec & Electronics Engrs; Asn Comput Mach. *Res:* Digital computers; computer systems and languages; information and control systems; digital image processing. *Mailing Add:* Dept Comput Sci Univ Mass Amherst MA 01002

**WOHL, ELLEN EVA,** FLUVIAL GEOMORPHOLOGY, QUATERNARY PALEOHYDROLOGY. *Current Pos:* Asst prof geol, 89-95, ASSOC PROF GEOL, COLO STATE UNIV, 89- *Personal Data:* b Cleveland, Ohio, Nov 10, 62. *Educ:* Ariz State Univ, BS, 80; Univ Ariz, PhD(geol), 88. *Honors & Awards:* Cole Mem Award, Geol Soc Am, 94. *Mem:* Geol Soc Am; Am Geophys Union; Sigma Xi; Am Quaternary Asn. *Res:* Physical processes occurring within river channels. *Mailing Add:* Dept Earth Resources Colo State Univ Ft Collins CO 80523. *Fax:* 970-491-6307; *E-Mail:* ellenw@picea.cnr.colostate.edu

**WOHL, MARTIN H,** MARKETING, NEW PRODUCT DEVELOPMENT. *Current Pos:* mgr bus develop, 86-93, CONSULT, MONSANTO CHEM CO, 93- *Personal Data:* b New York, NY, Feb 12, 35; m 57, Suzanne Cassell; c Jeffrey & Eric. *Educ:* Cornell Univ, BChE, 57. *Prof Exp:* Res engr, Plastics Div, Monsanto Co, 57-63, res specialist, Plastic Prod & Resins Div, 63-68, tech group leader process develop, 68-70, tech supt film, Fabricated Prod Div, Monsanto Com Prod Co, 70-75, mgr, Res & Technol, Fabricated Prod Div, Monsanto Plastics & Resins Co, 75-78, proj dir, New Prod Develop Dept, 78-83, proj dir, Plastics Div, Monsanto Polymer Prod Co, 83-86. *Mem:* Am Inst Chem Engrs; Soc Plastic Engrs; Soc Automotive Engrs; Soc Advan Mat & Process Eng; Soc Mfg Engrs. *Res:* Process development in the field of high

polymers; fluid flow and heat transfer to non-Newtonian fluids; research and engineering administration; advanced composites; engineering plastics; lead acid batteries. *Mailing Add:* 14185 Cross Trails Dr Chesterfield MO 63017-3308. *E-Mail:* mhw089@aol.com

**WOHL, PHILIP R,** ecological modeling, dynamical systems; deceased, see previous edition for last biography

**WOHL, RONALD A,** ORGANIC CHEMISTRY, MEDICINAL CHEMISTRY. *Current Pos:* sr org chemist, 74-76, sect head org chem, 76-82, ASST DIR MED CHEM, BERLEX LABS, 82- *Personal Data:* b Basel, Switz, Nov 25, 36. *Educ:* Univ Basel, PhD(org chem), 65. *Prof Exp:* Lectr org chem, Univ Basel, 65-66; res assoc, Yale Univ, 66-67; asst prof, Rutgers Univ, 67-74. *Mem:* Am Chem Soc. *Res:* Stereochemistry; cardiovascular drugs. *Mailing Add:* Berlex Labs Inc 300 Fairfield Rd Wayne NJ 07470

**WOHLEBER, DAVID ALAN,** CHEMISTRY. *Current Pos:* PRES, D A WOHLEBER, INC, 92- *Personal Data:* b Pittsburgh, Pa, Oct 1, 40; m 61; c 4. *Educ:* Univ Pittsburgh, BS, 62; John Carroll Univ, MS, 67; Kent State Univ, PhD(chem), 70. *Prof Exp:* Chemist analytical chem, Develop Lab, Stand Oil Co, Ohio, 61-63, chemist polymer chem, Res Lab, 63-66; sr res scientist phys chem, Aluminum Co Am, 70-74, sect head, 74-79, mgr, Extractive Metall Div, 79-81, mgr, Process Chem & Physics Div, 81-84, tech consult, Alcoa Tech Ctr, 84-87, sr tech specialist, 88-92. *Mem:* Sigma Xi; Am Soc Qual Control. *Res:* Chlorination technology; inorganic and physical chemistry of alumina refining and aluminum smelting; physical adsorption; polymer synthesis and characterization. *Mailing Add:* 2150 Spooky Hollow Rd Lower Burrell PA 15068

**WOHLFORD, DUANE DENNIS,** GEOLOGY, PETROLOGY. *Current Pos:* Asst prof geol, 64-74, ASSOC PROF, STATE UNIV NY COL, ONEONTA, 74-, PROF EARTH SCI. *Personal Data:* b Newcastle, Ind, May 20, 37; m 66; c 3. *Educ:* Univ Wis, BS, 59; Univ Colo, PhD(geol), 65. *Mem:* AAAS; Geol Soc Am. *Res:* Petrology of the Precambrian rocks of the southern Adirondack Mountains of New York. *Mailing Add:* Dept Earth Sci State Univ NY Col Oneonta Oneonta NY 13820-4015

**WOHLFORT, SAM WILLIS,** analytical chemistry, technical management, for more information see previous edition

**WOHLPART, KENNETH JOSEPH,** FOOD TECHNOLOGY, AGRICULTURAL PRODUCTS INSPECTION. *Current Pos:* FOOD INSPECTOR, PA DEPT AGR, 86- *Personal Data:* b New York, NY. *Educ:* St Bonaventure Univ, BS, 53; Purdue Univ, MS, 58. *Prof Exp:* Res asst anal chem, Union Carbide Corp, 55-56; asst food technologist food prod develop, Gen Foods Corp, 57-60; food pilot plant mgr, Beech Nut Foods, 60-63; sr food technologist, Prod Eng Div, Aluminum Co Am, 63-86. *Mem:* Inst Food Technologists. *Res:* Product-package interaction; sensory evaluation; package-process development. *Mailing Add:* 4113 Impala Dr Pittsburgh PA 15239

**WOHLRAB, HARTMUT,** BIOCHEMISTRY. *Current Pos:* staff scientist, 72-81, SR SCIENTIST, BOSTON BIOMED RES INST, 81-; RES ASSOC, DEPT BIOL CHEM & MOLECULAR PHARMACOL, HARVARD MED SCH, 73- *Personal Data:* b Berlin, WGer, July 2, 41; m 67; c 2. *Educ:* Rensselaer Polytech Inst, BS, 62; Stanford Univ, PhD(biophys), 68. *Prof Exp:* Asst biochem, Univ Munich, 70-72. *Concurrent Pos:* Estab investr, Am Heart Asn, 73-78; adj prof, Inst Gen Path, Cath Univ, Rome, Italy, 88- *Mem:* Geront Soc; Biophys Soc; Fedn Europ Biochem Socs; Am Aging Asn; AAAS; Am Soc Biol Chem & Molecular Biol. *Res:* Mitochondrial biochemistry; biochemistry of developing and aging, or senescent, tissues; function and molecular structure of membrane transport proteins. *Mailing Add:* Boston Biomed Res Inst 20 Staniford St Boston MA 02114-2500. *Fax:* 617-523-6649; *E-Mail:* wohlrab@bbri.eri.harvard.edu

**WOHLSCHLAG, DONALD EUGENE,** MARINE ECOLOGY, SUBLETHAL STRESSES ON FISHES. *Current Pos:* prof zool & dir, 65-70, prof zool & marine studies, 70-86, EMER PROF, MARINE SCI INST, UNIV TEX, 86- *Personal Data:* b Bucyrus, Ohio, Nov 6, 18; m 43; c 3. *Educ:* Heidelberg Col, BS, 40; Ind Univ, PhD, 49. *Prof Exp:* Lab asst chem & zool, Heidelberg Col, 40-41; res assoc limnol, Univ Wis, 49; from asst prof to prof biol, Stanford Univ, 49-65. *Concurrent Pos:* Prin investr Arctic fisheries, Off Naval Res & Arctic Inst NAm, 52-55; prin investr Antarctic fisheries biol, NSF, 58-65; prin investr Gulf coastal fishery biol res, several funding sources, 65-85; coord comt, Nat Acad Sci, Nat Res Coun, Int Biol Prog, 67-70, consult, Interoceanic Canal, 69-70; consult, NSF Tundra Biome Panel, Off Polar Prog, 71-74, Inst Ecol, 74-; ed, Contrib Marine Sci, Univ Tex Marine Sci Inst, 75-88. *Mem:* AAAS; Am Fisheries Soc; Am Soc Limnol & Oceanog; Am Soc Zoologists; Ecol Soc Am. *Res:* Ecology of fishes; metabolism and growth; population dynamics; toxic stresses. *Mailing Add:* 625 E Ave C Port Aransas TX 78373

**WOHLTMANN, HULDA JUSTINE,** PEDIATRIC DIABETES & ENDOCRINOLOGY. *Current Pos:* asst prof, 65-70, PROF PEDIAT, MED UNIV SC, 70- *Personal Data:* b Charleston, SC, Apr 10, 23. *Educ:* Col Charleston, BS, 44; Med Col SC, MD, 49; Am Bd Pediat, dipl, 55. *Prof Exp:* From instr to asst prof pediat, Sch Med, Wash Univ, 53-61, USPHS spec res fel biochem, 61-63. *Mem:* AAAS; fel Am Acad Pediat; Am Diabetes Asn; Endocrine Soc; Am Pediat Soc; Am Fedn Clin Res. *Res:* Pediatric metabolism and endocrinology; tight metabolic control of diabetes mellitus in children and adolescents and assessing the effects in later development. *Mailing Add:* 280 N Hobcaw Dr Mt Pleasant SC 29464

**WOISARD, EDWIN LEWIS,** TECHNICAL MANAGEMENT, OPERATIONS RESEARCH. *Current Pos:* RETIRED. *Personal Data:* b Newark, NJ, Jan 21, 26; m 53, 69, Doris Bradshaw; c Kevin, Casimir, Brian, Lisa, Kathleen, Mary Ellen & Jennifer. *Educ:* Drew Univ, BA, 50; Lehigh Univ, MS, 52, PhD(physics), 59. *Prof Exp:* Instr physics, Moravian Col, 56-59; assoc res physicist, Res Lab, Whirlpool Corp, 59-61; proj leader, Weapons Systs Eval Div, Inst Defense Analysis, 61-67; exec vpres, John D Kettelle Corp, 67-70; asst, Navy Net Assessment & Midrange Objectives, Off Chief Naval Opers, US Navy, 71-79; prin scientist, Ramcor Inc, 79-89; dir advan technol, Unmanned Aerial Vehicle Prog Off, Gen Dynamics Corp, 90; sr staff, Strategic Analysis, Inc, 91-93. *Concurrent Pos:* Consult, 70-71. *Mem:* Res Soc Am; Sigma Xi; AAAS; Opers Res Soc Am; Mil Pers Res Soc. *Res:* Thermoelectricity; solid state physics; microwave absorption; systems and defense analysis; planning and management of research and development; technology review and assessment. *Mailing Add:* 42909 Nashua St Ashburn VA 20147-3640. *Fax:* 703-724-0524; *E-Mail:* mizusiz@mediasoft.net

**WOJCICKI, ANDREW,** INORGANIC CHEMISTRY, ORGANOMETALLIC CHEMISTRY. *Current Pos:* from asst prof to assoc prof, 61-69, PROF INORG CHEM, OHIO STATE UNIV, 69- *Personal Data:* b Warsaw, Poland, May 5, 35; nat US; m 68; c 2. *Educ:* Brown Univ, BS, 56; Northwestern Univ, PhD(chem), 60. *Prof Exp:* Asst chem, Northwestern Univ, 56-58, assoc, 59; NSF fel inorg chem, Univ Nottingham, 60-61. *Concurrent Pos:* Vis assoc prof, Case Western Reserve Univ, 67; US sr scientist award, Humboldt Found, Ger, 75-76; Guggenheim Found fel, 76; vis scholar, Univ Calif, Berkeley, 84; vis prof, Univ Bologna, Italy, 88. *Mem:* AAAS; Am Chem Soc; Royal Soc Chem. *Res:* Synthesis and mechanism of reactions of inorganic and organometallic compounds. *Mailing Add:* Chem Dept Ohio State Univ 120 W 18th Ave Columbus OH 43210

**WOJCICKI, STANLEY G,** HIGH ENERGY PHYSICS. *Current Pos:* from asst prof to assoc prof, 66-74, PROF PHYSICS, STANFORD UNIV, 74- *Personal Data:* b Warsaw, Poland, Mar 30, 37; US citizen; m 61. *Educ:* Harvard Univ, AB, 57; Univ Calif, Berkeley, PhD(physics), 62. *Prof Exp:* Physicist, Lawrence Radiation Lab, Univ Calif, 61-66. *Concurrent Pos:* NSF fel, 64-65; Alfred P Sloan Found fel, 68-72; Guggenheim fel, 73-74; Alexander von Humboldt sr scientist award, 80. *Mem:* Fel Am Phys Soc. *Res:* Resonances in high energy physics; candle power violation; electron-positron annihilations; muon production in hedronic interactions. *Mailing Add:* Dept Physics Stanford Univ Stanford CA 94305

**WOJCIECHOWSKI, BOHDAN WIESLAW,** CHEMICAL ENGINEERING, CATALYSIS. *Current Pos:* from asst prof to assoc prof chem eng, 65-72, PROF CHEM ENG, QUEEN'S UNIV, ONT, 72- *Personal Data:* b Wilno, Poland, Jan 29, 35; Can citizen; m 59; c 2. *Educ:* Univ Toronto, BASc, 57, MASc, 58; Univ Ottawa, PhD(phys chem), 60. *Prof Exp:* Fel photolysis, Nat Res Coun, 60-61; fel kinetics, Univ Ottawa, 61-62; sr res chemist, Res & Develop, Socony Mobil Oil Co, Inc, 62-65. *Concurrent Pos:* UN Develop Prog tech expert, Brazil, 72; consult to petrol indust, catalyst mfrs. *Mem:* AAAS; Sigma Xi; fel Chem Inst Can; Am Inst Chem Engrs; Catalysis Soc; Can Soc Chem Eng. *Res:* Kinetics; catalysis; absorption; petroleum refining; process design; oceanography; recovery of oils from sand and shale; mathematical systems for highly coupled reactions; Fischer Tropsch synthesis. *Mailing Add:* Dept Chem Eng Queen's Univ Kingston ON K7L 3N6 Can

**WOJCIECHOWSKI, NORBERT JOSEPH,** DRUG INFORMATION. *Current Pos:* from asst prof to assoc prof pharmaceut, 66-86, PROF CLIN PHARM, COL PHARM, UNIV TENN, 86- *Personal Data:* b Evanston, Ill, Aug 4, 27; m 54. *Educ:* Univ Ill, BS, 51, MS, 61; Loyola Univ, PhD(pharmacol), 67. *Prof Exp:* Sr anal chemist chem, Abbott Labs, Inc, 51-56; grad asst pharmacol, Stritch Sch Med, Loyola Univ, 61-66. *Concurrent Pos:* Instr pharmacol, Col Basic Sci, Univ Tenn, 66-80; asst prof pharmacol, 80-89; assoc ed, Drug & Therap Lett, Drug Info Ctr, Univ Tenn, 82-90; consult, Bur Medicaid-Formulary Adv Comt, Tenn Dept Health & Environ, 86- *Mem:* Sigma Xi; Am Asn Col Pharm; Am Pharm Asn. *Res:* Cardiovascular pharmacology - antiarrhythmic activity of compounds in isolated atrial tissue; antihypertensive studies in hypertensive rats; written reviews and evaluations of new drugs. *Mailing Add:* 945 Green Oaks Dr Memphis TN 38117

**WOJCIK, ANTHONY STEPHEN,** DESIGN AUTOMATION, ARTIFICIAL INTELLIGENCE. *Current Pos:* chmn 86-95, PROF, COMPUT SCI DEPT, MICH STATE UNIV, 86- *Personal Data:* b Chicago, Ill, Sept 18, 45; m 69, Paula Valaitis; c Laura & Jeffrey. *Educ:* Univ Ill, Urbana-Champaign, BS, 67, MS, 68, PhD(comput sci), 71. *Prof Exp:* From asst prof to prof comput sci, Ill Inst Technol, 71-86, chmn dept, 78-84. *Concurrent Pos:* Mem tech staff, Bell Tel Labs, 74; resident assoc, Argonne Nat Lab, 82- *Mem:* Asn Comput Mach; Inst Elec & Electronics Engrs. *Res:* Computer architecture; reliable design of digital systems; design automation of digital systems; logic design; multiple-valued logic; artificial intelligence. *Mailing Add:* Dept Comput Sci Mich State Univ A714 Wells Hall East Lansing MI 48824. *E-Mail:* wojcik@cps.msu.edu

**WOJCIK, JOHN F,** PHYSICAL CHEMISTRY. *Current Pos:* from asst prof to assoc prof, 77-83, chmn chem, 90-94, PROF CHEM, VILLANOVA UNIV, 84- *Personal Data:* b Ashley, Pa, Nov 12, 38; m 60; c 6. *Educ:* King's Col, Pa, BS, 60; Cornell Univ, PhD(phys chem), 65. *Prof Exp:* Asst prof chem, St Francis Col, Pa, 65-66. *Concurrent Pos:* Petrol Res Fund res grant, 66-68. *Mem:* Am Chem Soc; Sigma Xi. *Res:* Cyclodextrin chemistry; nature of the hydrophobic bond; fast reactions by temperature jump; classical experimental physical chemistry. *Mailing Add:* Chem Dept Villanova Univ Villanova PA 19085-1699

**WOJNAR, ROBERT JOHN,** IMMUNOBIOLOGY, BIOCHEMISTRY. *Current Pos:* SR RES INVESTR, GH BESSE LAAR, 87- *Personal Data:* b Thompsonville, Conn, Jan 29, 35; m 58; c 3. *Educ:* Univ Conn, BA, 56, MS, 60, PhD(biochem), 64. *Prof Exp:* NIH fel, Yale Univ, 63-65; staff scientist, Worcester Found Exp Biol, 65-68; from res investr to sr investr biochem immunol, Squibb Inst Med Res, 68-86. *Mem:* AAAS; NY Acad Sci. *Res:* Cellular immunology; inflammation; nucleic acids; immunopharmacology; allergy and drug hypersensitivity; steroid biology. *Mailing Add:* 147 Oak Creek Rd Hightstown NJ 08520

**WOJNOWSKI, DANIEL ALLEN,** FAILURE ANALYSIS, INDUSTRIAL CONSULTING. *Current Pos:* staff engr, 88-90, sr engr, 90-92, PROJ MGR, ENG SYST INC, 92- *Personal Data:* b Chicago, Ill, Apr 15, 59; m 85, Janis Vacca; c Meghan. *Educ:* Univ Ill, Urbana, BS, 81, MS, 83; Univ Ill, Chicago, PhD(metall), 94. *Prof Exp:* Staff engr, Packer Eng Assoc, 83-87; instr, Triton Col, 87-88. *Concurrent Pos:* Instr struct analysis, Aurora Univ, 84-85. *Mem:* Am Soc Metals Int; Am Welding Soc; Nat Soc Prof Engrs; Struct Engrs Asn. *Res:* Phase transformations in chromium-molybdenum-vanadium rotor steels. *Mailing Add:* 3851 Exchange Ave Aurora IL 60504

**WOJTAL, STEVEN FRANCIS,** ROCK STRAIN MEASUREMENT DEFORMATION MECHANISMS, KINEMATICS. *Current Pos:* From instr to assoc prof, 79-88, PROF GEOL, OBERLIN COL, 88- *Personal Data:* b Albany, NY, Oct 3, 52; m 85. *Educ:* Brown Univ, BS, 74; Johns Hopkins Univ, MA, 76, PhD(geol), 82. *Concurrent Pos:* Chair, Dept Geol, Oberlin Col, 89-93; assoc ed, J Structural Geol, 91- *Mem:* Geol Soc Am; Am Geophys Union; Sigma Xi; Int Asn Struct/Tectonic Geologists. *Res:* Examining naturally-occurring rock structures using theoretical models from continuum mechanics and using experimental data on the physical properties of crystalline aggregates and continuous media. *Mailing Add:* Dept Geol Oberlin Col 52 W Lorrain St Oberlin OH 44074. *Fax:* 440-775-8886

**WOJTKOWSKI, PAUL WALTER,** ORGANIC CHEMISTRY. *Current Pos:* res chemist, Pioneering Res Lab, Textile Fibers Dept, E I DuPont de Nemours & Co, 74-76, res chemist, Petrochem Dept, 76-79, sr res chemist, Feedstocks Div, Cent Res & Develop Dept, 80-82, SR RES ASSOC, AGR PROD DEPT, E I DU PONT DE NEMOURS & CO, 82- *Personal Data:* b Buffalo, NY, May 16, 45. *Educ:* State Univ NY, Buffalo, BA, 67; Univ Notre Dame, PhD(org chem), 71. *Prof Exp:* Assoc, Iowa State Univ, 71-73 & Squibb Inst Med Res, Princeton, NJ, 73-74. *Mem:* Am Chem Soc; Sigma Xi. *Res:* Organic chemistry; organoboranes; low temperature organic photochemistry; insect chemistry; synthesis of beta-lactam antibiotics; condensation polymers and their fibers; heterogeneous catalysis; agricultural chemical process development. *Mailing Add:* DuPont Agri Prod Stine-Haskell Res Ctr PO Box 30 Newark DE 19714. *Fax:* 302-366-5738

**WOJTOWICZ, JOHN ALFRED,** INDUSTRIAL CHEMISTRY, WATER TREATMENT. *Current Pos:* CONSULT, 91- *Personal Data:* b Niagara Falls, NY, Oct 12, 26; div; c Carrie, Chris & Janice. *Educ:* Univ Buffalo, BA, 54; Niagara Univ, MS, 66. *Prof Exp:* Analyst chem analysis, E I Du Pont de Nemours & Co, Inc, 45-50, develop analyst chem analysis & process develop, 50-54, develop chemist, 54-56; res chemist inorg synthesis & chem kinetics, 56-61, sr res chemist org synthesis & process develop, 61-71, res assoc inorg & org synthesis & process develop, consult scientist, 77-85, sr consult scientist, inorg & synthesis process & prod develop & water treatment, 85-91. *Mem:* Am Chem Soc; Sigma Xi; Int Ozone Asn. *Res:* Organic and inorganic synthesis; process and product development in the areas of hypochlorites and chloroisocyanurates. *Mailing Add:* 60 Philson Ct Cheshire CT 06410-3225. *Fax:* 203-272-1479

**WOJTOWICZ, PETER JOSEPH,** THEORETICAL PHYSICS, MATHEMATICAL MODELING. *Current Pos:* RETIRED. *Personal Data:* b Elizabeth, NJ, Sept 22, 31; m 53; c 3. *Educ:* Rutgers Univ, BSc, 53; Yale Univ, MS, 54, PhD(phys chem), 56. *Prof Exp:* Mem tech staff & theoret chem physicist, RCA Labs, 56-78, head electron optics & deflection res, 78-84; sr mem tech staff, David Sarnoff Res Ctr, 84-92. *Mem:* Fel Am Phys Soc. *Res:* Statistical mechanics; theory of liquid and solid states; theory of magnetism and properties of magnetic substances; liquid crystals; electron optics and magnetic deflection in display systems. *Mailing Add:* 721 Rosedale Rd Princeton NJ 08540

**WOLAK, JAN,** MECHANICAL ENGINEERING. *Current Pos:* from asst to prof mech eng, 65-90, EMER PROF MECH ENG, UNIV WASH, 90- *Personal Data:* b Lubasz, Poland, Mar 8, 20; US citizen; m 59; c 3. *Educ:* Univ London, BSc, 50; Wash Univ, MS, 60; Univ Calif, Berkeley, PhD(mech eng), 65. *Prof Exp:* Col apprenticeship, AEI-Gen Elec Co, Eng, 50-52, steam turbine design engr, 52-56; lectr mech eng, Wash Univ, 56-60; assoc, Univ Calif, Berkeley, 60-63, asst res specialist, Inst Eng Res, 63-65. *Concurrent Pos:* Fac fel, NASA, 79-80; res consult, Boeing Com Airplane Co, 85- *Mem:* Am Soc Mech Engrs; Brit Inst Mech Engrs; Am Soc Eng Educ; fel Soc Mfg Engrs. *Res:* Mechanical behavior of materials; metal removal and forming processes; erosion by abrasive particles; evaluation of large plastic strains; friction and wear. *Mailing Add:* 4028 NE 92nd St Seattle WA 98115

**WOLAVER, LYNN E(LLSWORTH),** ENGINEERING, MATHEMATICS. *Current Pos:* electronic engr, Wright Air Develop Ctr, USAF, 50-51, electronic scientist, 51-56, aero-res engr, Aerospace Res Labs, 56-63, dep dir, Appl Math Lab, 63-67, dir, 67-71, chmn dept syst eng & assoc dean res, 71-79, PROF, AIR FORCE INST TECHNOL, USAF, 63-, DEAN RES, 79- *Personal Data:* b Springfield, Ill, Mar 10, 24; m 49; c 2. *Educ:* Univ Ill, BS, 49, MS, 50; Univ Mich, PhD(info & control eng), 64. *Prof Exp:* Instr elec eng,

Univ Ill, 49-50. *Concurrent Pos:* Lectr eve sch, Wright State Univ, 64-71; mem, Midwestern Simulation Coun, 53- *Mem:* NY Acad Sci; Inst Elec & Electronics Engrs; Soc Indust & Appl Math; fel Brit Interplanetary Soc; Am Soc Eng Educ; AAAS; Biofeedback Soc Am. *Res:* Navigation; astrodynamics; simulation; nonlinear systems analysis; modeling nonlinear systems driven by random noise; bioengineering; motion sickness research. *Mailing Add:* 1380 Timberwyck Ct Fairborn OH 45324

**WOLBARSHT, MYRON LEE,** BIOPHYSICS, BIOMEDICAL ENGINEERING. *Current Pos:* PROF OPHTHAL & BIOMED ENG, ASSOC PROF PHYSIOL, PSYCHOL DEPT, DUKE UNIV, ASST DIR INT CARDIAC CATHETERIZATION, DEPT MED, 84- *Personal Data:* b Baltimore, Md, Sept 18, 24; div; c 3. *Educ:* St Johns Col, AB, 50; Johns Hopkins Univ, PhD (biol biophys), 58; Am Bd Laser Surg, dipl, 85. *Honors & Awards:* Mark Award, Am Soc Laser Med & Surg. *Prof Exp:* Chief physicist, Naval Med Res Inst, 58-68. *Concurrent Pos:* Guest scientist, Naval Med Res Inst, 54-58; res assoc, Psychiat Inst, Med Sch, Univ Md, 54-60; res fel biol, Johns Hopkins Univ, 58-63; consult, York Hosp, Pa, 63-68; mem exec panel, Nat Res Coun Armed Forces Comt Vision, 63-; chmn, Eye Hazards Subcomt, Laser Safety Comt, Am Nat Stand Inst, 68; lectr, Psychol Dept, Duke Univ, 68-; US rep, Tech Comt 76 Laser Safety, Int Electro Tech Comn, 76-; mem, US Nat Comt Photobiol, 78-; mem bd, Am Soc Laser Med & Surg, 82-90; vis scientist, Mass Gen Hosp, Wollman Lab, 82-90, Mass Inst Technol, Dept Physics, 90- *Mem:* Am Physiol Soc; Inst Elec & Electronics Engrs; Soc Gen Physiol; Optical Soc Am; fel Royal Soc Med; Am Soc Laser Med & Surg; fel Laser Inst Am (pres, 82-83); foreign mem Finnish Soc Sci & Arts; fel Soc Photog & Instrumentation Engrs. *Res:* Laser safety; biomedical engineering applications to ophthalmology; structure and function of sense organs, especially vision, chemoreception, mechanoreception; electrophysiology of central nervous system; laser surgery. *Mailing Add:* Dept Psychol Duke Univ Box 9008 Durham NC 27708-0086

**WOLBER, WILLIAM GEORGE,** INSTRUMENT ENGINEERING. *Current Pos:* sr tech adv, 81-86, chief tech off, 86-89, CHMN, INVENTION REV COMT, CUMMINS ELECTRONICS CO, 85-, EXEC ENGR, 90- *Personal Data:* b Detroit, Mich, Feb 19, 27; m 50, Velma F Campbell; c Paul K, William G Jr, Teresa A (Enstis), Robert A & Andrew J. *Educ:* Univ Mich, BS (chem eng) & BS (eng math), 49, MS, 50. *Honors & Awards:* Corp Tech Achievement Award, Bendix Corp, 75. *Prof Exp:* Engr-group leader, Uniroyal Tire Div, 50-54; proj engr-prog mgr, Bendix Res Labs, 54-62, dept mgr, 62-66, sr prin engr, 66-73, sr res planner, 73-76, sr res consult, 76-81. *Concurrent Pos:* Chmn, Invention & Patent Comt, Bendix Res Labs, 74-78, corp gatekeeper-instr, Bendix Corp, 77-81; reader, Soc Automotive Engrs; NSF peer grant reviewer, 80-; mem, bd dirs, Weed Instrument, 84-92; consult expert, Teltech, 90- *Mem:* Soc Automotive Engrs. *Res:* Research and development in measuring instruments and sensors; their application to control systems such as automobile engine control; theory and practice of precision instrument calibration. *Mailing Add:* 3151 Sumac Ct Columbus IN 47203. *Fax:* 812-377-5744

**WOLBERG, DONALD LESTER,** VERTEBRATE PALEONTOLOGY. *Current Pos:* EXEC DIR SPEC PROJ, ACAD NAT SCI, 93- *Personal Data:* b New York, NY, Dec 18, 45; c 7. *Educ:* NY Univ, BA, 68; Univ Minn, PhD (geol), 78. *Prof Exp:* Curator & teaching asst geol, NY Univ, 67-69; ed, Encyclopedia Britannica, 69-71; teaching assoc, Univ Minn, 71-75; ed & geologist, Minn Geol Survey, 75-76; geologist, Nat Biocentric, Inc, 76-77; asst prof, Univ Wis-River Falls, 77-78; paleontologist, NMex Bur Mines & Mineral Resources, 78-93. *Concurrent Pos:* Res assoc, Minn Messenia Exped Greece, 71-73; contract writer & ed, Encyclopedia Britannica, 71-73; ed, J Paleont; mem, NMex Coal Surface Mining Comn, 82-; mem, Paleont Collecting Guidelines Comt, Nat Acad Sci; mem, Govt Liason Comt, Soc Vert Paleont; adj assoc prof geol, Geosci Dept, NMex Inst Mining & Technol; bd dirs, Geronimo Springs, Mus, San Juan Basin Regional Coal Team & Environ Legis & Regulations. *Mem:* Soc Vert Paleont; Soc Econ Paleontologists & Mineralogists; Paleont Soc; Asn Geoscientists Int Develop; Sigma Xi; Int Soc Cryptozool; Paleont Res Inst; Geol Soc Am. *Res:* Late Mesozoic and early Tertiary stratigraphy; paleontolgy and paleoecology of North America. *Mailing Add:* Acad Nat Sci 1900 Benjamin Franklin Pkwy Philadelphia PA 19103

**WOLBERG, GERALD,** IMMUNOLOGY, MICROBIOLOGY. *Current Pos:* RETIRED. *Personal Data:* b New York, NY, Aug 18, 37; m 67, Marilynn Goldstein; c Alison S & Lori M. *Educ:* NY Univ, BA, 58; Univ Ky, MS, 63; Tulane Univ, PhD (immunol), 67. *Prof Exp:* Fel immunol, Pub Health Res Inst, City New York, 67-68, NIH fel, 68-70; mem staff, Wellcome Res Labs, Burroughs Wellcome Co, 70-95. *Mem:* Am Asn Immunol; Am Soc Microbiol; Sigma Xi. *Res:* Immunosuppression; immunoactivation; septic shock. *Mailing Add:* Glaxo Wellcome Co 1109 Troon Ct Cary NC 27511. *Fax:* 919-315-8747; *E-Mail:* usbwczjc@ibmmail.com

**WOLBERG, WILLIAM HARVEY,** SURGERY, ONCOLOGY. *Current Pos:* resident surg, 57-61, chmn gen surg, 72-75, from instr to assoc prof, 61-71, PROF SURG, UNIV WIS-MADISON, 71- *Personal Data:* b July 10, 31; US citizen; m 55; c 6. *Educ:* Univ Wis-Madison, BS, 53, MD, 56. *Prof Exp:* Intern, Ohio State Univ, 56-57. *Concurrent Pos:* Consult merit rev bd oncol, Vet Admin, 72. *Mem:* Am Asn Cancer Res; Am Col Surg; Asn Acad Surg; Western Surg Asn. *Res:* Nucleic acid synthesis in human tumors; immune response to human tumors. *Mailing Add:* Dept Surg Univ Wis 600 Highland Ave Madison WI 53792-0001

**WOLCOTT, THOMAS GORDON,** PHYSIOLOGICAL ECOLOGY, BIOTELEMETRY. *Current Pos:* asst prof zool, 72-78, assoc prof, 78-85, PROF MARINE, EARTH & ATMOSPHERIC SCI, NC STATE UNIV, 85- *Personal Data:* b San Diego, Calif, Dec 22, 44; m 68, Donna L Riley; c Renee C & Nathaniel R. *Educ:* Univ Calif, Riverside, BA, 66; Univ Calif, Berkeley, PhD (zool), 71. *Prof Exp:* Vis asst prof biol, Univ Calif, Riverside, 71-72. *Concurrent Pos:* NSF, Nat Oceanog & Atmospheric Admin grants, 77-80, 83-86 & 89-; res assoc, Smithsonian Environ Res Ctr, 85- *Mem:* AAAS; Am Soc Zoologists; Am Soc Limnol & Oceanog; Sigma Xi; Crustacean Soc; Int Soc Biotelemetry. *Res:* Physiological ecology of marine invertebrates and terrestrial crabs; behavioral biotelemetry and instrumentation development, transports and recruitment of planktonic larvae using "smart" drifters. *Mailing Add:* 18 Henderson St Raleigh NC 27607-7055. *Fax:* 919-515-7802

**WOLD, AARON,** INORGANIC CHEMISTRY. *Current Pos:* assoc prof, 63-67, prof eng & chem, 67-80, VERNON K KRIEBLE PROF CHEM, BROWN UNIV, 80- *Personal Data:* b NY, May 8, 27; m 57; c 3. *Educ:* Polytech Inst Brooklyn, BS, 46, MS, 48, PhD (chem), 52. *Prof Exp:* Res assoc chem, Univ Conn, 51-52; from instr to asst prof, Hofstra Col, 52-56; mem staff, Lincoln Lab, Mass Inst Technol, 56-63. *Concurrent Pos:* Ed, J Solid State Chem, 68-75; assoc ed, Inorg Chem, 74-76 & Mat Res Bull, 77-; consult, Exxon Res & Develop Labs, 76-, Dow Chem Co, Midland, Mich, 80-83, Gen Telephone Labs, Waltham, Mass, 80- & Kodak, 85- *Mem:* Am Chem Soc; Sigma Xi. *Res:* Solid state chemistry of rare earths and transition elements; new synthetic techniques for the optimization of transparent far infrared chalcogenides and phosphides; preparation and properties of new superconductors; development of new techniques for the preparation of thin films. *Mailing Add:* 1520 High Hawk Rd East Greenwich RI 02818-1317

**WOLD, DONALD C(LARENCE),** NEUTRINO & GAMMA-RAY ASTROPHYSICS, ACOUSTICS OF SPEECH. *Current Pos:* assoc prof physics, Univ Ark, 69-74, head dept, 70-74, chmn dept physics & astron, 74-89, PROF PHYSICS, UNIV ARK, LITTLE ROCK, 74-; ADJ PROF, MED SCI, UNIV ARK, 85- *Personal Data:* b Fargo, NDak, Sept 24, 33; m 56, Shelley Thurman; c Sara, Steven & Sheila. *Educ:* Univ Wis-Madison, BA, 55, MA, 57; Ind Univ, Bloomington, PhD (physics), 68. *Honors & Awards:* Donaghey Urban Mission Award, 79. *Prof Exp:* Lectr physics, Forman Christian Col, WPakistan, 58-63, head dept, 61-63; asst res physicist, Univ Calif, Los Angeles, 68-69. *Concurrent Pos:* Proj dir energy conserv plan, State Ark, 76-77; HEW res fel, 78. *Mem:* Acoust Soc Am; Am Phys Soc; Am Asn Physics Teachers; Asn Comput Mach; Inst Elec & Electronics Engrs. *Res:* Study of cosmic rays, astrophysical sources and high-energy particle interactions; acoustics and perception of speech to investigate the properties of physiologically significant acoustical features of the voice. *Mailing Add:* Dept Physics & Astron Univ Ark 2801 S University Ave Little Rock AR 72204

**WOLD, FINN,** BIOCHEMISTRY, PROTEIN SCIENCE. *Current Pos:* ROBERT A WELCH PROF CHEM, MED SCH, UNIV TEX, HOUSTON, 82- *Personal Data:* b Stavanger, Norway, Feb 3, 28; nat US; m 53; c 2. *Educ:* Okla State Univ, MS, 53; Univ Calif, PhD (biochem), 56. *Prof Exp:* Res assoc biochem, Univ Calif, 56-57; from asst prof to assoc prof, Univ Ill, 57-66; prof biochem, Med Sch, Univ Minn, Minneapolis, 66-74; head dept, Univ Minn, St Paul, 74-79, prof biochem, 74-81. *Concurrent Pos:* Lalor res award, 58; Guggenheim fel immunochem, London, Eng, 60-61; USPHS res career develop award, 61-66; vis prof chem, Nat Taiwan Univ, 71; consult, biochem & molecular biol fel rev comt, Nat Inst Gen Med Sci, 66-70 & biochem training comt, 71-74; consult, biochem & biophys res eval comt, Vet Admin, 69-71 & res serv merit rev basic sci, 72-75; consult, res personnel comt, Am Cancer Soc, 74-77; vis prof biochem, Rice Univ, 74; consult, adv comt on nucleic acids & protein synthesis, Am Cancer Soc, 79-82; vis prof II, Univ Tromsoe, Norway, 91. *Mem:* AAAS; Am Soc Biol Chemists; Am Chem Soc; Protein Soc. *Res:* Protein chemistry; physical, chemical and biological properties of proteins and glycoproteins; relation of protein structure and function; mechanism of enzyme action. *Mailing Add:* Dept Biochem Molecular Biol Med Sch Univ Tex PO Box 20708 Houston TX 77225-0708. *Fax:* 713-794-4150; *E-Mail:* fwold@utmmq.med.uth.tmc.edu

**WOLD, RICHARD JOHN,** marine geophysics, for more information see previous edition

**WOLD, WILLIAM S M,** ADENOVIRUS, GENE THERAPY. *Current Pos:* Postdoctoral fel, Inst & Molecular Virol, St Louis Univ, 73-75, instr, 75-76, asst prof, 76-79, assoc prof, 79-86, prof, 86-92, PROF & CHMN, DEPT MOLECULAR MICROBIOL & IMMUNOL, ST LOUIS UNIV, 92- *Personal Data:* b Pine Falls, Manitoba, Feb 12, 44; m 67, Susan Ann Lees; c Loralee J, Jessica A, William G & Jonathan E. *Educ:* Univ Manitoba, Winnipeg, BSc, 65, MSc, 68, PhD (microbiol), 73. *Honors & Awards:* NIH Res Career Develop Award, 80. *Concurrent Pos:* Can Med Res Coun postdoctoral fel, 73; consult, Can Nat Cancer Inst, Nat Sci & Eng Res Coun Can & Can Cystic Fibrosis Found, 90- & Genetic Ther Inc, 94-; Cancer Res Campaign Lectr, Brit Biochem Soc, 94. *Mem:* Am Soc Microbiol; Am Soc Virol; AAAS; Int Soc Antiviral Res. *Res:* Molecular mechanisms allowing adenovirus to counteract immunosurveillance; adenovirus proteins regulating cell death and signal transduction; adenovirus vectors for gene therapy. *Mailing Add:* 1402 S Grand Blvd St Louis MO 63104. *Fax:* 314-773-3403; *E-Mail:* woldws@slu.edu

**WOLDA, HINDRIK,** POPULATION ECOLOGY, PHYSIOLOGICAL ECOLOGY. *Current Pos:* SR RES SCIENTIST, INDEPENDENT CONTRACTOR, 92- *Personal Data:* b Wageningen, Neth, May 24, 31; m 58, Trientje Smit; c Hetty, Willem D, Jacob & Marianne. *Educ:* Univ Groningen,

Neth, BSc, 55, MSc, 58, PhD(ecol), 63. *Honors & Awards:* Bur Dirs Award Smithsonian, Trop Res Inst, 77; Award, Smithsonian Inst, 84. *Prof Exp:* Teaching asst ecol, Univ Groningen, 58-60, sci officer, 60-63, sr sci officer, 63-68, reader, 68-71; biologist, Smithsonian Trop Res Inst, 71-91. *Concurrent Pos:* Res fel ecol, Univ Sydney, Australia, 64-65; vis prof, Univ Wash, 88. *Mem:* Japanese Soc Pop Res; Ecol Soc Am; Linnean Soc London; Royal Entom Soc London; Royal Dutch Acad Sci. *Res:* Temporal and spatial variations in abundance of tropical insect species; diapause in tropical insects; population ecology of insects; community studies of tropical forests; seasonality and stability of insect populations. *Mailing Add:* 1626 106th Ave SE Bellevue WA 98004

**WOLDEGABRIEL, GIDAY,** GEOLOGY. *Current Pos:* Postdoctoral fel, 87-90, contractor/collabr, 90-92, MEM TECH STAFF, LOS ALAMOS NAT LAB, 92- *Personal Data:* b Mai Misham/Adwa, Ethiopia, Sept 3, 55; m 94, Almaz Berhane Tesfamichael. *Educ:* Addis Ababa Univ, Ethiopia, BS, 78, MS, 80; Case Western Res Univ, PhD(geol), 87. *Prof Exp:* Lectr, Addis Ababa Univ, 80-82. *Mem:* Am Geophys Union. *Res:* Volcanology; rift tectonics; geochemistry; alteration processes in high- and low-teemperature environments; published more than 30 peer-reviewed articles. *Mailing Add:* 45 Paige Circle Los Alamos NM 87544-3638. *Fax:* 505-665-3285; *E-Mail:* wgiday@lanl.gov

**WOLDEGIORGIS, GEBRETATEOS,** ION TRANSPORT, LIPID METABOLISM. *Current Pos:* assoc res prof, 93-94, ASSOC PROF, DEPT CHEM, BIOCHEM & MOLECULAR BIOL, ORE GRAD INST SCI & TECHNOL, PORTLAND, 94- *Personal Data:* b Asmara, Eritrea; m 94, Asefash T Gebremariam; c Mathew. *Educ:* Haile Sellassie Univ, Addis Ababa, Ethiopia, BS, 69; Univ Wis-Madison, MS, 73, PhD(nutrit biochem), 76. *Prof Exp:* Asst chem, Haile Sellassie Univ, Addis Ababa, Ethiopia, 69-70; res asst biochem, Univ Wis-Madison, 70-76, res assoc med, 76-80, proj assoc, 80-81, from asst scientist to assoc scientist med, 81-91; res assoc prof pharmacol, Med Col Ohio, Toledo, 91-93. *Concurrent Pos:* Vis scientist biochem, Inst Med Biochem, Univ Oslo, Norway, 85, Mich State Univ, East Lansing, 90. *Mem:* Am Soc Biol Chemists; AAAS. *Res:* Membrane ion transport and bioenergetics; membrane protein structure-function relationships and molecular biology; lipid metabolism and chemistry; protein chemistry and intermediary metabolism. *Mailing Add:* Dept Chem Biochem & Molecular Biol Ore Grad Inst Sci & Technol 20000 NW Walker Rd PO Box 91000 Portland OR 97291-1000. *Fax:* 503-690-1464; *E-Mail:* gwoldeg@admin.ogi.edu

**WOLDSETH, ROLF,** ATOMIC PHYSICS, NUCLEAR PHYSICS. *Current Pos:* RETIRED. *Personal Data:* b Trondheim, Norway, Jan 18, 30; US citizen; m 55; c 4. *Educ:* Tech Univ Norway, BSc, 55; Washington Univ, St Louis, PhD(physics), 65. *Prof Exp:* Res physicist, Joint Estab for Nuclear Energy Res, Norway, 55-56; asst prof physics, Rensselaer Polytech Inst, 63-67 & Wake Forest Univ, 67-70; dir, Appln Lab, Kevex Corp, Foster City, Calif, 70-91. *Mem:* Am Phys Soc. *Res:* Positron annihilation; x-ray spectra; photo-nuclear reactions; fast neutron induced reactions. *Mailing Add:* 116 Gold Hunter Ct San Mateo CA 94404

**WOLEN, ROBERT LAWRENCE,** PHARMACOLOGY. *Current Pos:* res scientist, Lilly Res Labs, 62-65, res assoc pharmacol, 65-75, RERS ADV PHARMACOL, LILLY LAB CLIN RES, 75-; ASSOC PROF PHARMACOL, UR SCH MED, IND UNIV, INDIANAPOLIS, 73- *Personal Data:* b New York, NY, May 20, 28. *Educ:* West Chester State Col, BS, 50; Univ Del, MS, 51, PhD(biochem), 60. *Prof Exp:* Lectr atomic energy, Oak Ridge Inst Nuclear Studies, 60-61; lab dir biochem, Res Inst, St Joseph Hosp, 61-62. *Mem:* Am Chem Soc; Sigma Xi; Am Soc Pharmacol & Exp Therapeut; Am Asn Clin Chemists; Am Soc Chem Pharmacol & Therapeut. *Res:* Phase I clinical pharmacology including drug metabolism, pharmacokinetics, drug interactions and therapeutic drug analysis. *Mailing Add:* Dept Pharmacol Ind Univ Sch Med 7306 Laurel Dr Indianapolis IN 46227-5341

**WOLF, A(LFRED) A(BRAHAM),** ELECTRICAL ENGINEERING, BIOMEDICAL ENGINEERING. *Current Pos:* PRES, PRIME RES CORP, MD, 78- *Personal Data:* b Philadelphia, Pa, July 21, 35; m 57, Enid Gordon; c Marcus M & Laurence J. *Educ:* Drexel Univ, BSc, 53; Univ Pa, MSc, 54, PhD(elec eng), 58; Univ Juarez, Mex, ScD(biomed), 77, MD, 78. *Prof Exp:* Head anal group, Anti-Submarine Div, US Naval Air Develop Ctr, 49-54; asst prof elec eng, Univ Pa, 54-59; chief scientist & tech asst to vpres, Gen Dynamics-Electronics, 59-61; dir res, Emerson Radio & Phonograph Corp, Md, 61-63; distinguished prof elec eng, chmn grad res & actg dir, Sch Continuing Educ, Drexel Univ, 63-65; coordr & tech dir, Aerospace Systs Div, Radio Corp Am, Mass, 65-67; assoc tech dir res, Naval Ship Res & Develop Ctr, 67-78, sr sci adv, Navy Dept, 74-78. *Concurrent Pos:* Lectr, Drexel Univ, 58-59, vis prof, 65-66; vis assoc prof, Univ Rochester, 59-61; asst secy, Int Mil Electronics Conf, DC, 62, secy, 63; vis prof, Univ Md, 67-68; vis prof, George Washington Univ, 68-69, adj prof, 72- *Mem:* Sr mem Inst Elec & Electronics Engrs; Sigma Xi (vpres, 60-61). *Res:* Mathematical theory of nonlinear systems; stochastic processes; theory of physical and human systems; mathematical analysis; superconductivity; high temperature superconducting organic compounds with high critical fields; etiology and pathogenesis of cancer; mechanism of division of biological cells; mathematical biology; biological effects of magnetic and electromagnetic fields on humans; author of fourteen prize winning papers on nonlinear systems theory, stochastic processes biological effects of electromagnetic and magnetic fields, and superconductivity. *Mailing Add:* 562 Ferry Pt Rd Annapolis MD 21403

**WOLF, ALBERT ALLEN,** ELEMENTARY PARTICLE PHYSICS. *Current Pos:* CONSULT, 89- *Personal Data:* b Nashville, Tenn, Sept 2, 35; m 56; c 4. *Educ:* Vanderbilt Univ, BA, 58, MA, 60; Ga Inst Technol, PhD(physics), 66. *Prof Exp:* Physicist, Aladdin Electronics Div, Aladdin Industs, Inc, 58; engr, Sperry Rand, Inc, 59-61; instr physics, Ga Inst Technol, 61-64; from asst prof to prof physics, Davidson Col, 65-89, chmn dept, 83-89. *Concurrent Pos:* Guest prof, Univ Ulm, WGer, 71-72. *Mem:* Am Phys Soc; Am Asn Physics Teachers; Am Chem Soc. *Res:* Quantization of non-linear fields; computer simulation. *Mailing Add:* 6600 Alexander Rd Charlotte NC 28270

**WOLF, ALFRED PETER,** ORGANIC CHEMISTRY, NUCLEAR CHEMISTRY. *Current Pos:* Dir, Cyclotron-PET Prog, 76-93, MEM STAFF, CHEM DEPT, BROOKHAVEN NAT LAB, 51-, DIR, CYCOTRON-PET PROG, 93- *Personal Data:* b New York, NY, Feb 13, 23; m 46, Elizabeth H; c Roger O. *Educ:* Columbia Univ, BA, 44, MA, 48, PhD(chem), 52. *Hon Degrees:* PhD, Univ Uppsala, Sweden, 83. *Honors & Awards:* Award, Am Chem Soc, 71; Aebersold Award, Soc Nuclear Med, 81; GV Hevesy Medal, Hevesy Found, 86; JK Javits Neurosci Investr Award, 86; Esselen Award, 88; Georg Charles de Hevesy Pioneer Award, Soc Nuclear Med, 91; Distinguished Scientist Award, Inst Clin PEF, 96. *Concurrent Pos:* Adj prof, Columbia Univ, 53-82; ed, J Labelled Compounds, 65-; consult, Univ Mass, 65-66, Philip Morris, 66-, NIH, 66 & Int Atomic Energy Agency, 69-; adv, Ital Nat Res Coun, 69-; mem, Eval Panel, Nat Bur Stand, 72-; consult, Nat Bur Stand, 72-76 & adv panel chem, Nat Res Coun, 77-80; ed, Radiochim Acta, 77- & assoc ed, J Nuclear Med, 78-81; Japan Soc Prom Sci fel, 79 & 84; vis comn, Atomic Res Ctr, Julich, Ger, 80-91 & Los Alamos Nat Lab, 81-85; chmn, Chem Dept, Brookhaven Nat Lab, 82-87. *Mem:* Nat Acad Sci; Royal Soc Chem; Soc Ger Chem; Soc Nuclear Med; Am Chem Soc; Collegium Int Neuropsychopharmacol. *Res:* Radiopharmaceutical research and nuclear medicine; organic reaction mechanisms; chemical effects of nuclear transformations; chemistry of carbon-11, nitrogen-13, oxygen-15, fluorine-18 and iodine-123; accelerators for nuclide production and radiopharmaceutical production. *Mailing Add:* PO Box 1043 Setauket NY 11733. *Fax:* 516-344-7902

**WOLF, BARRY,** BIOCHEMICAL GENETICS. *Current Pos:* From asst prof to assoc prof, 78-85, PROF HUMAN GENETICS & PEDIAT, MED COL VA, 85-, PROF BIOCHEM & MOLECULAR BIOPHYS, 96-, VCHAIR PEDIAT RES, 96- *Personal Data:* b Chicago, Ill, June 19, 47; m 71, Gail Ross; c 2. *Educ:* Univ Ill, BS, 69, PhD(biol chem) & MD, 74; Am Bd Pediat, dipl, 79; Am Bd Med Genetics, dipl, 82, cert clin genetics & clin biochem genetics. *Honors & Awards:* Borden Award Nutrit, Am Inst Nutrit, 87; E Mead Johnson Award Pediat Res, Am Acad Pediat. *Concurrent Pos:* Residency, Children's Mem Hosp, Northwestern Univ, 74-76; fel, Human Genetics, Yale Univ Sch Med, 76-78. *Mem:* Am Soc Clin Invest; Soc Pediat Res; Am Soc Human Genetics; Soc Inherited Metab Dis; Soc Study Inborn Errors Metab; Am Soc Clin Nutrit; Am Inst Nutrit. *Res:* Inherited genetic and metabolic diseases particularly the vitamin-responsive disorders; biochemical and clinical characterization of the biotin-responsive disorder and biotinidase deficiency. *Mailing Add:* Dept Human Genetics & Pediat Med Col Va PO Box 980033 Richmond VA 23298. *Fax:* 804-828-3760; *E-Mail:* bwolf@gems.vcu.edu

**WOLF, BENJAMIN,** SOIL CHEMISTRY, SOIL & PLANT ANALYSIS. *Current Pos:* CONSULT, DR WOLF'S AGR LABS, 49- *Personal Data:* b Deerfield, NJ, Dec 2, 13; m 40; c 2. *Educ:* Rutgers Univ, BS, 35, MS, 38, PhD(soil chem), 40. *Prof Exp:* Asst instr soil chem, Rutgers Univ, New Brunswick, 40-41; soil chemist, Seabrook Farms Co, 41-49. *Concurrent Pos:* Consult veg & floricult crops, Cent Am, SAm & Caribbean; assoc ed, Commun Soil Sci & Plant Anal, 70- *Mem:* Fel AAAS; Soil Sci Soc Am; Am Soc Hort Sci; Am Chem Soc. *Res:* Soil and plant analysis; herbicides; fluid fertilizer. *Mailing Add:* Dr Wolf's Agr Labs 6851 SW 45th St Ft Lauderdale FL 33314-3239

**WOLF, BENJAMIN,** MICROBIOLOGY. *Current Pos:* From asst instr to asst prof, 57-69, assoc prof, 69-80, PROF MICROBIOL, SCH VET MED, UNIV PA, 80- *Personal Data:* b Detroit, Mich, June 27, 26; m 52; c 2. *Educ:* Wayne State Univ, BS, 49; Univ Mich, MS, 52; Univ Pa, PhD(microbiol), 59. *Mem:* Am Soc Microbiol. *Res:* Medical microbiology; immunology. *Mailing Add:* Dept Pathobiol Univ Pa 3800 Spruce St Philadelphia PA 19104-6008. *Fax:* 215-898-9923

**WOLF, BEVERLY,** MICROBIOLOGY. *Current Pos:* RETIRED. *Personal Data:* b Chicago, Ill, Jan 14, 35. *Educ:* Univ Colo, BA, 55; Univ Calif, Los Angeles, PhD(biochem), 59. *Prof Exp:* Guest investr, Rockefeller Inst, 59-61; res assoc, Harvard Univ, 61-63; asst res biologist, Univ Calif, Berkeley, 65-72; vis asst prof, Mills Col, 72-73; sr scientist, Cetus Corp, 73-82. *Res:* Biochemical genetics of neurospora; genetical transformation of pneumococcus; origin and direction of deoxyribonucleic acid synthesis in Escherichia coli; temperature sensitive DNA synthesis mutants of Escherichia coli; microbial antibiotic production. *Mailing Add:* 5825 Huntington Ave Richmond CA 94804

**WOLF, CAROL EUWEMA,** COMPUTER THEORY, COMPUTER SCIENCE EDUCATION. *Current Pos:* assoc prof, 86-93, PROF COMPUT SCI, PACE UNIV, 93-, CHMN DEPT, 88-, ASSOC DEAN, SCH COMPUT SCI & INFO SYSTS, 93- *Personal Data:* b New Castle, Pa, June 11, 36; m 58, Edward L; c Douglas & David. *Educ:* Swarthmore Col, BA, 58; Cornell Univ, MA, 62, PhD(math), 64. *Prof Exp:* Asst prof math, State Univ NY, Brockport, 68-75; asst prof comput sci, Iowa State Univ, 75-86. *Mem:* Asn Comput Mach; Math Asn Am; Asn Women Math; Inst Elec & Electronics Engrs Comput Soc. *Res:* Model high school computer science curriculum; computer science. *Mailing Add:* Dept Comput Sci Pace Univ One Pace Plaza New York NY 10038. *Fax:* 212-346-1863; *E-Mail:* wolf@pace.edu

**WOLF, CHARLES TROSTLE,** MATHEMATICS. *Current Pos:* RETIRED. *Personal Data:* b West Reading, Pa, Mar 20, 30; m 53, Virginia Slabach; c Diane, Susan & Amy. *Educ:* Millersville State Col, BS, 53; Univ Del, MS, 59. *Prof Exp:* Teacher, Pequea Valley High Sch, 53-56; asst math, Univ Del, 56-58; asst prof, Shippensburg State Col, 58-61; assoc prof math, Millersville Univ, 61-91. *Res:* Modern mathematics. *Mailing Add:* 1605 Oregon Pike Lancaster PA 17601

**WOLF, CLARENCE J,** POLYMERIC DURABILITY & LONG TERM AGING, EXTRATERRESTIAL STUDIES. *Current Pos:* PROF MAT SCI & CHEM ENG, WASHINGTON UNIV, ST LOUIS, 93- *Personal Data:* b St Louis, Mo, Nov 11, 31; m 87, Daisy J Craig; c Linda L, John M, Michael D, Karen F, Katherine A & Susan M. *Educ:* Univ Mo, Columbia, BS, 53; Purdue Univ, PhD (phys chem), 57. *Prof Exp:* Sr radiation chemist, Union Carbide Res Labs, 57-61; scientist, McDonnell Douglas Res Lab, 61-70, mgr res, 70-72, chief scientist, 72-78, prin scientist, 78-83, res fel & staff mgr, 83-91; prof & sr investr, Mich Molecular Inst, Midland, 91-93. *Concurrent Pos:* Assoc prof physics, Univ Col, Washington Univ, 65-72, adj prof mats sci, 88-91; gen chmn, Gordon Res Conf Composites, 86; affil prof chem eng, Mich Technol Univ, 91- *Mem:* Am Chem Soc; Am Soc Composites; Planetary Soc. *Res:* Long term stability and aging of polymeric and composite materials; thermal stability and the effect of fluids on the lifetime of materials subjected to external accelerating factors; kinetics of polymer reactions; aging/stability of electrical insulation; aging of silicone breast implants. *Mailing Add:* 1125 Wood Summit Ballwin MO 63021. *Fax:* 314-935-7211; *E-Mail:* ajw@mccf.wustl.edu

**WOLF, DALE DUANE,** AGRONOMY. *Current Pos:* asst prof, 67-71, ASSOC PROF AGRON, VA POLYTECH INST & STATE UNIV, 71- *Personal Data:* b Alma, Nebr, June 16, 32; m 52; c 4. *Educ:* Univ Nebr, BSc, 54, MSc, 57; Univ Wis, PhD(agron), 62. *Prof Exp:* Asst prof agron, Univ Conn, 62-67. *Mem:* Am Soc Agron; Crop Sci Soc Am. *Res:* Forage crops; plant physiology. *Mailing Add:* Crop & Soil Environ Scis Va Polytech Inst & State Univ Blacksburg VA 24061

**WOLF, DALE E,** AGRONOMY. *Current Pos:* CHMN, DAYNEL INT LLC, 95- *Personal Data:* b Kearney, Nebr, Sept 6, 24; m 45; c 4. *Educ:* Univ Nebr, BSc, 43; Rutgers Univ, PhD(farm crops, weed control), 49. *Hon Degrees:* DSc, Univ Nebr, 86, Univ Pedro Henriquez Ureha Dom Repub, 92. *Prof Exp:* Asst farm crops, Rutgers Univ, 46-49, assoc prof & assoc res specialist, 49-50; agronomist, USDA, 47-50; asst mgr agr chem res, E I Du Pont de Nemours & Co, Inc, 50-54, mgr, 54-56, asst dist sales mgr, 56-59, dist sales mgr, 60-64, sales mgr biochem, Del, 64-67, mgr, Planning Div, 67-68, asst dir, Agr Div, 68-70, dir, Indust Specialities Div, 71-72, dir mkt agrichem, 72-75, asst gen mgr, Biochem Dept, 75-78, gen mgr, Biochem Dept, 78-79, vpres biochemicals, 79-95,. *Concurrent Pos:* Chmn bd, Endo Lab Inc, Subsid E I DuPont de Nemours & Co Inc, 79-95. *Mem:* Am Soc Agron; Nat Agr Chem Asn; Pharmaceut Mfg Asn. *Res:* Agricultural chemicals; weed control; pharmaceuticals. *Mailing Add:* PO Box 3825 Greenville DE 19807. *Fax:* 302-654-9653

**WOLF, DANIEL STAR,** ocean engineering, finite element methods, for more information see previous edition

**WOLF, DIETER,** THEORETICAL MATERIALS SCIENCE. *Current Pos:* SR SCIENTIST, ARGONNE NAT LAB, 86- *Personal Data:* b Sindelfingen, WGer, Nov 3, 46. *Educ:* Univ Stuttgart, Diplom, 70, Dr rer nat(physics), 73. *Honors & Awards:* Max-Planck Res Award, 93. *Prof Exp:* Res assoc mat sci, Max Planck Inst Metal Res, Stuttgart, 72-74; res asst prof physics, Univ Utah, 74-77; asst scientist, Mat Sci Div, 77-79, scientist, 79-86. *Concurrent Pos:* Pvt lectr, Univ Dort, WGer, 79- *Mem:* Am Phys Soc; Sigma Xi; Am Ceramic Soc; Mat Res Soc. *Res:* Diffusion in crystals; theory of magnetic resonance and relaxation; atomic, molecular and defect motions in metals, metal oxides and ionic crystals studied by nuclear magnetic resonance; Mossbauer effect and quasielastic neutron scattering; computer simulation and theory of solid interfaces, grain boundaries and point defects; mechanical properties of materials; computer simulations of nanocrystalline materials. *Mailing Add:* Div Mat Sci Argonne Nat Lab Argonne IL 60439. *Fax:* 630-252-4798; *E-Mail:* dieter_wolf@qmgate.anl.gov

**WOLF, DON PAUL,** BIOCHEMISTRY, REPRODUCTIVE BIOLOGY. *Current Pos:* PROF OBSTET & GYNEC, UNIV FERTIL CONSULT, 86-, PROF PHYSIOL & PHARM, 86-, DIR ANTHROP, 86- *Personal Data:* b Lansing, Mich, Aug 8, 39; m 67; c 2. *Educ:* Mich State Univ, BS, 61, MS, 62; Univ Wash, PhD(biochem), 67. *Prof Exp:* Fel biochem, Univ Geneva, 67-68 & Univ Calif, Davis, 68-71; asst prof obstet & gynec & biophys, Univ Pa, 71-77, assoc prof, 77-; prof, Dept Obstet & Gynec, Univ Tex Health Sci Ctr; scientist, Ore Regional Primate Res Ctr. *Mem:* AAAS; Am Fertil Soc; Soc Study Reproduction; Am Soc Cell Biol; Am Soc Biol Chemists. *Res:* Characterization of reproductive processes; the role of cortical granules in fertilization and early development; sperm excluding mechanism operative in animal ova; isolation and characterization of cervical and tracheal mucin. *Mailing Add:* Ore Health Sci Univ Fertil Consult 1750 SW Harbor Way Suite 100 Portland OR 97201-5133

**WOLF, DUANE CARL,** SOIL MICROBIOLOGY. *Current Pos:* assoc prof, 79-81, prof, 81-96, UNIV PROF SOILS, UNIV ARK, FAYETTEVILLE, 96- *Personal Data:* b Springfield, Mo, Apr 7, 46; m 90, Nancy A Nowak; c Douglas C. *Educ:* Univ Mo, Columbia, BS, 68; Univ Calif, Riverside, PhD(soils), 73. *Prof Exp:* Asst prof soils, Univ Md, College Park, 73-78. *Mem:* Fel Am Soc Agron; fel Soil Sci Soc Am; Am Soc Microbiol; AAAS; Sigma Xi. *Res:* Bioremediation of petroleum-contaminated soil; degradation of organic chemicals in soil; microbiology and biochemistry of nitrogen transformations in soil. *Mailing Add:* Dept Agron Univ Ark Fayetteville AR 72701. *Fax:* 501-575-7465; *E-Mail:* dwolf@comp.uark.edu

**WOLF, EDWARD D,** NANOFABRICATION PROCESSES. *Current Pos:* prof & dir, Nat Res & Resource Facil Submicron Struct, 78-88, EMER PROF, NAT NANOFABRICATION FACIL, CORNELL UNIV, 91- *Personal Data:* b Quinter, Kans, May 30, 35; m 55, Marlene K Simpson; c Julie, LeAnn & Shelly. *Educ:* McPherson Col, BS, 57; Iowa State Univ, PhD(phys chem), 61. *Prof Exp:* Res assoc, Princeton Univ, 61-62; sr chemist, Atomics Int Div, NAm Aviation, Inc, 63-64; res specialist, 65, mem tech staff, Sci Ctr Div, 64-65; mem tech staff, Hughes Res Labs, Malibu, 65-67, sr staff chemist, 67-72, sect head electron beam surface physics, 72-74, sr scientist, 74-78. *Concurrent Pos:* Res assoc, Univ Calif, Berkeley, 68; vis prof, Eng Dept, Cambridge Univ, 86-87; guest prof, Tech Univ Vienna, Austria, 87; co-founder & chmn bd, Boilistics Inc, 86-90; mem bd, Phyton, Inc & Cornell Res Found. *Mem:* Am Phys Soc; Electron Micros Soc Am; fel Inst Elec & Electronics Eng; Mat Res Soc; fel Am Inst Chemist. *Res:* Field emission and scanning electron microscopy; scanning electron beam diagnostics and microfabrication; nanolithographic and nanofabrication processes. *Mailing Add:* 1691 Taughannock Blvd Trumansburg NY 14886. *Fax:* 607-255-8601; *E-Mail:* wolf@nnf.cornell.edu

**WOLF, EDWARD LINCOLN,** CONDENSED MATTER PHYSICS, TUNNELING SPECTROSCOPY. *Current Pos:* prof, Dept Physics, 86-95, PROF PHYSICS, POLYTECH UNIV, 86- *Personal Data:* b Cocoa, Fla, Nov 22, 36; m 58, Carol Euwema; c Douglas W & David L. *Educ:* Swarthmore Col, AB, 58; Cornell Univ, PhD(exp physics), 64. *Prof Exp:* Fel physics, Dept Physics & Coord Sci Lab, Univ Ill, Urbana, 64-66, res assoc, 67; sr physicist, Res Labs, Eastman Kodak Co, Rochester, 68-75; assoc prof, 75-80, prof physics, Ames Lab, Iowa State Univ, 81-85. *Concurrent Pos:* Vis fel, Cavendish Lab, Univ Cambridge, 73-74, Univ Pa, 81, IBM, Corp Watson Res, 82; program dir condensed matter physics, NSF, 96-97. *Mem:* Fel Am Phys Soc; AAAS. *Res:* Superconductivity; electron tunneling; physics of surfaces and interfaces; ultra high vacuum; superconducting proximity effect; photoemission spectroscopy and electron energy loss spectroscopy; scanning tunneling microscopy; superconductivity; high Tc superconductivity. *Mailing Add:* Dept Physics Polytechnic Univ 6 Metrotech Ctr Brooklyn NY 11201. *E-Mail:* ewolf@duke.pdg.edu

**WOLF, ELIZABETH ANNE,** NUCLEAR PHYSICS. *Current Pos:* from asst prof to prof, 79-94, chair dept, 87-93, EMER PROF PHYSICS, SOUTHERN CONN STATE UNIV, 94- *Personal Data:* b Leeds, UK; US citizen; m 54, Werner P; c Peter & Mary A. *Educ:* Oxford Univ, BA, 51, PhD(nuclear physics), 55. *Prof Exp:* Dept demonstr physics, Clarendon Lab, Oxford Univ, 52-55, res staff, Lab Archaeol, 55-56; res assoc physics, Biophys Lab, Harvard Med Sch, 56-57; lectr, Univ Conn, Waterbury, 75-79. *Concurrent Pos:* Newsletter ed, New Eng Sect, Am Phys Soc, 81-86; hon sr res physicist, Churchill Hosp, Oxford, UK, 84. *Mem:* Am Phys Soc; Am Asn Physics Teachers; Am Asn Physicists Med. *Res:* Experimental nuclear physics; deuteron-deuteron interaction; inelastic neutron scattering; measurement of very low level radiation; pulmonary edema detection by back scattering of gamma radiation. *Mailing Add:* Physics Dept Southern Conn State Univ New Haven CT 06515

**WOLF, EMIL,** MATHEMATICAL PHYSICS, OPTICS. *Current Pos:* assoc prof optics, 59-61, prof physics, 61-87, prof optics, 78-87, WILSON PROF OPTICAL PHYSICS, UNIV ROCHESTER, 87- *Personal Data:* b Prague, Czech, July 30, 22. *Educ:* Bristol Univ, BSc, 45, PhD(physics), 48; Univ Edinburgh, DSc(physics), 55. *Honors & Awards:* Frederic Ives Medal, Optical Soc Am, 77; Albert A Michelson Medal, Franklin Inst, 80; Max Born Award, Optics Soc Am, 87; Marconi Medal, Ital Nat Res Coun, 87. *Prof Exp:* Res asst optics, Cambridge Univ, 48-51; res asst & lectr math physics, Univ Edinburgh, 51-54; res fel theoret physics, Univ Manchester, 54-59. *Concurrent Pos:* Vis scientist, NY Univ, 57; Guggenheim fel & vis prof, Univ Calif, Berkeley, 66-67; vis prof, Univ Toronto, 74-75; ed, Progress in Optics. *Mem:* Fel Optical Soc Am (pres, 78); fel Am Phys Soc; fel Brit Inst Physics; hon mem Optical Soc India; fel Franklin Inst; Optics Soc Am; hon mem Optical Soc Am. *Res:* Theoretical optics; electromagnetic theory; co-author of book. *Mailing Add:* Dept Physics & Astron Univ Rochester Rochester NY 14627

**WOLF, ERIC R,** PEASANT STUDIES, COMPLEX SOCIETIES. *Current Pos:* distinguished prof, 71-92, EMER DISTINGUISHED PROF, H LEHMAN COL, CITY UNIV NEW YORK, 92- *Personal Data:* b Vienna, Austria, Feb 1, 23; US citizen; m 71, Sydel Finfer Silverman; c John D & Daniel J. *Educ:* Queens Col, BA, 46; Columbia Univ, PhD(anthrop), 51. *Hon Degrees:* LLD, Univ Mich, 92, Dr, Univ Vienna, 93, Univ Amsterdam, 97. *Honors & Awards:* I I Staley Prize, Sch Am Res, 88; Distinguished Lectr Award, Am Anthrop Asn, 89; MacArthur Found Fel, 90-95. *Prof Exp:* Vis asst prof, Univ Ill, 52-54; asst prof, Univ Va, 55-58; vis asst prof, Yale Univ, 58-59; assoc prof, Univ Chicago, 59-61; prof, Univ Mich, 61-71. *Mem:* Nat Acad Sci; Am Acad Arts & Sci. *Res:* Comparative study of peasantry; integration of culturally marked groups into complex societies. *Mailing Add:* 4 Blueberry Hill Rd Irvington NY 10533-1402

**WOLF, ERIC W,** SYSTEMS SCIENCE, LIBRARY AUTOMATION. *Current Pos:* PRIN SCIENTIST, FIAT LUX, 91- *Personal Data:* b Frankfurt am Main, Ger, Feb 20, 22; US citizen; m 49; c 2. *Educ:* City Col New York, BEE, 49; Ohio State Univ, MS, 51. *Prof Exp:* Electronic scientist, Wright Air Develop Ctr, 49-53; res engr, Lincoln Lab, Mass Inst Technol, 53-59; tech adv tech ctr, Supreme Hq Allied Powers Europe, Hague, 59-60; dir comput prog, Data & Info Systs Div, Int Tel & Tel Corp, 61-62, tech dir, 62-65; tech dir, Naval Command Systs Support Activity, 65-70; sr scientist, Bolt Beranek & Newman Inc, 70-80, mgr wash opers, Commun Systs Div, 80-87, prog mgr, 87-91. *Mem:* Comput Soc; Commun Soc; Inst Elec & Electronics Engrs. *Res:* Design and development of computer-based information systems; computer communications; computer networks; information management; man-machine interaction in natural language. *Mailing Add:* Fiat Lux 6300 Waterway Dr Falls Church VA 22044-1316

**WOLF, FRANK JAMES,** ORGANIC CHEMISTRY. *Current Pos:* Sr chemist, Merck & Co, Inc, 42-59, asst dir microbiol, Merck Sharp & Dohme Res Labs, 59-70, dir animal drug metab & radiochem, 70-77, SR SCIENTIST, MERCK SHARP & DOHME RES LABS, 78- *Personal Data:* b Xenia, Ohio, Nov 7, 16; m 42; c 3. *Educ:* Miami Univ, AB, 38; Univ Ill, PhD(org chem), 42. *Concurrent Pos:* Asst, Nat Defense Res Comt, 41-42. *Mem:* Am Soc Pharmacol & Exp Therapeut; Am Chem Soc. *Res:* Phthalides; substituted sulfaquinoxalines; benzotriazines; antibiotics; vitamin B-12; catalysis; biochemical separations; animal and human drug metabolism; animal tissue residue; mass spectroscopy; biochemical toxicology; pharmacokinetics. *Mailing Add:* 38 Genesee Trail Westfield NJ 07090-2706

**WOLF, FRANK LOUIS,** MULTIVARIATE ANALYSIS. *Current Pos:* from instr to prof, 52-90, EMER PROF MATH, CARLETON COL, 90- *Personal Data:* b St Louis, Mo, Apr 18, 24; m 47, Joy Gifford; c Joan, Allison, Barbara & Jon. *Educ:* Wash Univ, BS, 44, MA, 48; Univ Minn, PhD(math), 55. *Prof Exp:* Tech supvr chem eng, Carbon & Carbide Chem Corp, Tenn, 44-46; instr math, St Cloud State Col, 49-51. *Concurrent Pos:* NSF fel, 60-61. *Mem:* AAAS; Math Asn Am; Am Statist Asn. *Res:* Multivariate descriptive statistics; statistical education. *Mailing Add:* 12 Bunday Ct Northfield MN 55057. *E-Mail:* fwolf@carleton.edu

**WOLF, FRANKLIN KREAMER,** INDUSTRIAL ENGINEERING, OPERATIONS RESEARCH. *Current Pos:* assoc prof, 70-77, PROF INDUST ENG & CHMN, WESTERN MICH UNIV, 77- *Personal Data:* b Norman, Okla, Sept 30, 35; m 62; c 3. *Educ:* Iowa State Univ, BS, 57, PhD(eng valuation, statist), 70; Univ Wis, MS, 62. *Prof Exp:* Officer, US Army CEngrs, 57-59; engr, Rheem Semiconductor, 59-60; res asst, Univ Wis, 60; engr, Martin Co, Denver, 61-64; asst prof indust eng, Iowa State Univ, 64-70. *Mem:* Am Inst Indust Engrs; Am Soc Eng Educ; Inst Mgt Sci; Opers Res Soc Am; Sigma Xi. *Res:* Engineering economics and study of life estimation and methods of depreciation for capital recovery in regulated industries. *Mailing Add:* Dept Indust Eng Western Mich Univ Kalamazoo MI 49008

**WOLF, FREDERICK TAYLOR,** botany; deceased, see previous edition for last biography

**WOLF, GEORGE,** NUTRITION, BIOCHEMISTRY. *Current Pos:* from assoc prof to prof physiol chem, 62-88, EMER PROF PHYSIOL CHEM, MASS INST TECHNOL, 88-; ADJ PROF NUTRIT SCI, UNIV CALIF, BERKELEY, 88- *Personal Data:* b Vienna, Austria, June 16, 22; nat US; m 48; c 3. *Educ:* Univ London, BSc, 44; Oxford Univ, DPhil, 47. *Honors & Awards:* Osborne-Mendel Award, Am Inst Nutrit, 77. *Prof Exp:* Res fel, Chester Beatty Res Inst, Royal Cancer Hosp, Eng, 47-48, Harvard Univ, 48-50 & Univ Wis, 50-51; from asst prof to assoc prof animal nutrit, Univ Ill, Urbana, 51-62. *Concurrent Pos:* Guggenheim fel, 58-59. *Mem:* Am Soc Biol Chemists; Am Inst Nutrit. *Res:* Metabolism and function of vitamin A and beta-carotene. *Mailing Add:* Dept Nutrit Sci Univ Calif 119 Morgan Hall Berkeley CA 94720-3014. *Fax:* 510-642-0535

**WOLF, GEORGE WILLIAM,** ASTRONOMY. *Current Pos:* PROF ASTRON, SOUTHWEST MO STATE UNIV, 71- *Personal Data:* b Newark, NJ, Jan 15, 43; m 80; c 2. *Educ:* Univ Pa, BA, 65, MS, 67, PhD(astron), 70. *Prof Exp:* Res assoc astron, Mt John Observ, Univ Canterbury, NZ, 68-69. *Concurrent Pos:* NSF fel, 77-78. *Mem:* Am Astron Soc. *Res:* Observational astronomy in the areas of linear and circular polarimetry, spectroscopy and photoelectric photometry of stars. *Mailing Add:* Dept Physics & Astron Southwest Mo State Univ Springfield MO 65804-0027. *E-Mail:* gww836F@vma.smsu.edu

**WOLF, GERALD LEE,** RADIOLOGY. *Current Pos:* PROF RADIOL, UNIV PA MED CTR, 80- *Personal Data:* b Sidney, Nebr, Apr 2, 38; m 64; c 2. *Educ:* Univ Nebr, BS, 62, MS, 64, PhD(physiol & pharmacol), 65; Harvard Univ, MD, 68. *Prof Exp:* Asst prof physiol, Col Med, Univ Nebr, Omaha, 68-69, asst prof physiol & med, 69-71, asst prof pharmacol & radiol & dir radiol res, 71-80. *Concurrent Pos:* Life Ins Med res fel, 64-69; intern, Col Med, Univ Nebr, 68-69; res consult, Omaha Vet Admin Hosp, 69-, clin investr, 70-73. *Mem:* Am Col Radiol; fel Am Soc Clin Pharmacol & Therapeut; Asn Am Med Cols; AMA; Am Soc Pharmacol & Exp Therapeut. *Res:* Renal and endocrine participation in electrolyte homeostasis; physiology of the pump-perfused dog kidney. *Mailing Add:* MGH-NMR Ctr Bldg 149 13th St Charlestown MA 02129-2000. *Fax:* 617-726-7830

**WOLF, HAROLD HERBERT,** PHARMACOLOGY. *Current Pos:* dean, Col Pharm, 76-89, PROF PHARMACOL & TOXICOL, COL PHARM, UNIV UTAH, 76- *Personal Data:* b Quincy, Mass, Dec 19, 34; m 57; c 2. *Educ:* Mass Col Pharm, BS, 56; Univ Utah, PhD(pharmacol, exp psychiat), 61. *Hon Degrees:* LLD, Univ Md, 94. *Honors & Awards:* Distinguished Educ Award, Am Asn Col Pharm, 88. *Prof Exp:* From asst prof to assoc prof, 61-69,

Kimberly prof pharmacol & chmn dept, Col Pharm, Ohio State Univ, 69-76. *Concurrent Pos:* NIH & Alcohol, Drug Abuse & Ment Health Admin res grants, 63-; Am Asn Cols Pharm vis lectr, 64-; mem pharm rev comt, NIH, 69-71; Fulbright-Hays sr scholar, Univ Sains Malaysia, 74; mem, Joint Comn on Prescription Drug Use, 77-80, Biomed Res Support Comt, NIH, 78-79, bd of dir, Am Found for Pharmaceut Educ, 78, comt of pres, Asn Acad Health Ctr, 78; external examr, Univ Sains, Malaysia, 80 & 93, Univ Malaya, 78, 92 & 96; Am Pharmaceut Asn Task Force Educ, 81-84; Comn on Goals, Am Soc Hosp Pharm, 82-84; bd dir, Am Coun on Pharm Educ, 85-88; chmn, Comn Implement Change in Pharmaceut Educ, Am Asn Col Pharm, 89-92, 95-96. *Mem:* AAAS; Am Asn Col Pharm (pres, 78); Am Pharmaceut Asn; fel AAAS; fel Acad Pharmaceut Sci; Am Soc Pharmacol & Exp Therapeut. *Res:* Investigation of effects of drugs on central nervous system; psychotropics, central nervous system stimulants, anticonvulsants, narcotic analgetics, thermoregulation and animal behavior. *Mailing Add:* Univ Utah Col Pharm Salt Lake City UT 84112

**WOLF, HAROLD WILLIAM,** ENVIRONMENTAL HEALTH. *Current Pos:* CONSULT ENGR, 84- *Personal Data:* b Chicago, Ill, July 13, 21; m 44; c 4. *Educ:* Univ Iowa, BS, 49, MS, 50; Univ Calif, Los Angeles, DrPH, 65. *Prof Exp:* From sanit engr to sr sanit engr, Fed Water Pollution Control Admin, USPHS, Calif, 50-68, asst chief res & develop, Water Supply & Sea Resources, Ohio, 68, dir, Div Criteria & Standards, Bur Water Hygiene, Md, 68-70; prof civil eng, Tex A&M Univ, 70-84. *Concurrent Pos:* Res fel, Calif Inst Technol, 60-62; lectr, Univ Calif, Los Angeles, 65-66; dir, Dallas Water Reclamation Res Ctr, 70-75; mem, Nat Drinking Water Adv Coun, 75-79. *Mem:* AAAS; Asn Environ Eng Profs; Am Soc Civil Eng; Am Pub Health Asn. *Res:* Water quality criteria; air-borne pathogens; hazardous waste disposal. *Mailing Add:* 1007 Rose Circle College Station TX 77840

**WOLF, HELMUT,** MECHANICAL ENGINEERING, HEAT TRANSFER. *Current Pos:* RETIRED. *Personal Data:* b Einöd, Ger, Jan 19, 24; US citizen. *Educ:* Case Inst Technol, BSME, 48; Purdue Univ, MSME, 50, PhD(mech eng), 58. *Prof Exp:* Instr mech eng, Purdue Univ, 48-50; develop engr, Eastman Kodak Co, 50-53; res assoc heat transfer, Jet Propulsion Ctr, Purdue Univ, 53-58; prin scientist, NAm Aviation, Inc, 58-61; prof mech eng, Univ Ark, Fayetteville, 61-71, Raymond F. Giffels distinguished prof eng, 71- *Concurrent Pos:* Resident res assoc, Argonne Nat Lab, 64-66; res grant & consult, Cent Transformer Corp, 66-67; staff adv, Inst Reactor Develop, Nuclear Res Ctr, Karlsruhe, WGer, 70-71. *Mem:* Am Soc Mech Engrs; Am Nuclear Soc; Am Soc Eng Educ; Sigma Xi. *Res:* Heat transfer of forced and free-convection shear flows and conduction transfer. *Mailing Add:* 1913 Quail Run Dr NE Albuquerque NM 87122-1141

**WOLF, IRA KENNETH,** MATHEMATICS. *Current Pos:* MEM STAFF, DEPT MATH, STONY BROOK; AT CARDOSO HIGH SCHOOL, BAYSIDE, NY. *Personal Data:* b New York, NY, Nov 14, 42; m 64; c 1. *Educ:* Tufts Univ, BA, 64; Yale Univ, MA, 66; Rutgers Univ, PhD(math), 71. *Prof Exp:* Asst prof math, Brooklyn Col, 71- *Mem:* Math Asn Am. *Res:* Category theory. *Mailing Add:* 12 Rugby Rd Roslyn Heights NY 11577-1821

**WOLF, IRVING W,** CHEMICAL ENGINEERING. *Current Pos:* TEACHER, CHEM DEPT, MENLO SCH, ATHERTON, 91- *Personal Data:* b Nashville, Tenn, July 12, 27; m 54; c 3. *Educ:* Vanderbilt Univ, BE, 47, MS, 49; Ill Inst Technol, PhD(chem eng), 51. *Prof Exp:* Instr chem eng, Ill Inst Technol, 50-51; res & develop engr, Gen Elec Co, 51-55, consult heat transfer, 55-58, proj engr, 58-61; mgr functional films sect, 61-63; head mat res, Ampex Corp, 63-65, mgr mat & devices res, 65-71, corp consult, 71-72, mgr magnetic mat, Magnetic Tape Div, 72-78, mgr plastics & chem eng, 72-91. *Mem:* AAAS; Inst Elec & Electronics Engrs; Electrochem Soc. *Res:* Electrodeposition of magnetic thin films for information storage; vacuum deposition and sputtering of thin films for electronic application. *Mailing Add:* Menlo Sch 50 Valparaiso Ave Atherton CA 94027

**WOLF, JACK KEIL,** ELECTRICAL ENGINEERING. *Current Pos:* prof, 85-94, STEPHEN O RICE PROF ELEC ENG & COMPUT SCI, UNIV CALIF, SAN DIEGO, 94- *Personal Data:* b Newark, NJ, Mar 14, 35; m 55; c 3. *Educ:* Univ Pa, BS, 56; Princeton Univ, MSE, 57, MA, 58, PhD(elec eng), 60. *Prof Exp:* Instr, Syracuse Univ, 60-62; assoc prof elec eng, NY Univ, 63-65; from assoc prof to prof, Polytech Inst Brooklyn, 65-73; chmn, Dept Elec & Comput Eng, Univ Mass, Amherst, 73-75, prof elec eng, 73-84. *Concurrent Pos:* Consult, govt & indust, 63-; NSF sr fel, Univ Hawaii, 71-72; Guggenheim fel, 79-80. *Mem:* Nat Acad Eng; fel Inst Elec & Electronics Engrs. *Res:* Statistical communications theory; algebraic coding theory; magnetic recording; computer networks. *Mailing Add:* 8529 Prestwick Dr LaJolla CA 92037

**WOLF, JAMES S,** METALLURGY. *Current Pos:* RETIRED. *Personal Data:* b Cleveland, Ohio, July 26, 33; m 57. *Educ:* Case Inst Technol, BS, 54, MS, 60; Univ Fla, PhD(metall), 65. *Prof Exp:* Res scientist, Lewis Lab, NASA, 57-69; from assoc prof to prof mat eng, Clemson Univ, 69-93. *Mem:* Am Soc Metals; Am Inst Mining, Metall & Petrol Engrs; Brit Inst Metals; Nat Asn Corrosion Engrs; Sigma Xi. *Res:* High temperature oxidation and deformation of metals and alloys; biomedical materials; secondary metals. *Mailing Add:* Dept Mech Eng Clemson Univ Clemson SC 29634-0921

**WOLF, JAMES STUART,** MEDICINE, SURGERY. *Current Pos:* PROF SURG & CHMN DIV TRANSPLANTATION, NORTHWESTERN UNIV MED SCH, 76-, ASSOC DEAN MED EDUC, 90- *Personal Data:* b Chicago, Ill, Mar 1, 35; m 58; c 2. *Educ:* Grinnell Col, AB, 57; Univ Ill, BS, 59, MD, 61. *Prof Exp:* USPHS res fel transplantation, 64-66, from instr to prof surg,

Med Col Va, 67-76; chief surg, McGuire Vet Admin Hosp, 68-76. *Concurrent Pos:* Attend surgeon, McGuire Vet Admin Hosp, 67-76, Northwestern Mem Hosp, Lakeside Vet Admin Hosp, Evanston Hosp, 76- *Mem:* Transplantation Soc; Am Soc Nephrology; Asn Acad Surg; fel Am Col Surg; Soc Univ Surg. *Res:* Transplantation immunology; clinical and experimental organ transplantation. *Mailing Add:* Dept Surg Northwestern Univ Med Sch 303 E Chicago Ave Chicago IL 60611-3008

**WOLF, JOE,** cell biology, for more information see previous edition

**WOLF, JOSEPH A(LLEN), JR,** APPLIED MECHANICS. *Current Pos:* sr res engr, Eng Mech Dept, Gen Motors Res Labs, 71-80, staff res engr, 80-90, STAFF RES ENGR, GEN MOTORS SYSTS ENG CTR, 90- *Personal Data:* b Tacoma, Wash, Nov 26, 33; m 60, Sally Doyle; c Joseph. *Educ:* Stevens Inst Technol, ME, 55; Univ Calif, Los Angeles, MS, 57; Mass Inst Technol, ScD(mech eng), 67. *Prof Exp:* Mem tech staff, Hughes Aircraft Co, 55-62; asst prof mech & struct, Univ Calif, Los Angeles, 66-71. *Concurrent Pos:* Adj prof, Dept Mech Eng, Wayne State Univ, Detroit, 89- *Mem:* Fel Am Soc Mech Engrs; Am Acad Mech. *Res:* Dynamics; mechanical and structural vibrations; structural-acoustic interaction. *Mailing Add:* 438 S Glenhurst Dr Birmingham MI 48009

**WOLF, JOSEPH ALBERT,** GROUP THEORY, HARMONIC ANALYSIS. *Current Pos:* From asst prof to assoc prof, 62-66, PROF MATH, UNIV CALIF, BERKELEY, 66- *Personal Data:* b Chicago, Ill, Oct 18, 36. *Educ:* Univ Chicago, BS, 56, MS, 57, PhD(math), 59. *Honors & Awards:* Medaille de l'Universite, Univ Liege, 77; Humboldt Prize, Bonn, 94. *Concurrent Pos:* Mem, Inst Advan Study, Princeton, 60-62 & 65-66; prin investr, NSF, 64-; Miller res prof, Univ Calif, 72-73 & 83-84; ed, Geometriae Dedicata, Math Reports, J Math Systs, Estimation & Control, Nova J Algebra & Geom, Lett in Math Physics; hon prof, Nat Univ Cordoba, Arg, 89. *Mem:* Swiss Math Soc; Am Math Soc. *Res:* Use of group theory to study differential geometry, complex manifolds, harmonic analysis, and a few areas in particle physics and control theory. *Mailing Add:* Dept Math Univ Calif Berkeley CA 94720-3840. *E-Mail:* jawolf@math.berkeley.edu

**WOLF, JULIUS,** MEDICINE. *Current Pos:* Chief med serv, 54-72, CHIEF OF STAFF, VET ADMIN HOSP, BRONX, 72-; PROF CLIN MED, MT SINAI SCH MED, 68-, ASSOC DEAN VET ADMIN PROGS, 72- *Personal Data:* b Boston, Mass, Aug 15, 18; m 45; c 3. *Educ:* Boston Univ, SB, 40, MD, 43. *Concurrent Pos:* Assoc clin prof med, Col Physicians & Surgeons, Columbia Univ, 62-68; chmn, Vet Admin Lung Cancer Study Group, 62- *Res:* Lung cancer chemotherapy. *Mailing Add:* Vet Admin Ctr 130 W Kingsbridge Rd Bronx NY 10468-3904

**WOLF, KATHLEEN A,** ENVIRONMENTAL RESEARCH. *Current Pos:* DIR, INST RES & TECH ASSISTANCE, 90- *Personal Data:* b Dallas, Tex, Sept 10, 46. *Educ:* Univ Washington, BS, 68; San Diego State Univ, MS, 71; Univ Southern Calif, PhD(chem), 80. *Prof Exp:* Phys scientist, Rand Corp, 73-87; source reduction, Source Reduction Res Partnership, 88-90. *Concurrent Pos:* Res asst chem, Univ Southern Calif, 76-80, res assoc, 81-83. *Mem:* Am Chem Soc. *Res:* Quantum mechanics; spectroscopy; ozone layer depletion; hazardous waste disposal; risk analysis. *Mailing Add:* 2800 Olympic Blvd Santa Monica CA 90404

**WOLF, KENNETH EDWARD,** microbiology, for more information see previous edition

**WOLF, LARRY LOUIS,** MATING SYSTEMS, FORAGING. *Current Pos:* from asst prof zool to assoc prof biol, 67-76, PROF BIOL, SYRACUSE UNIV, 76- *Personal Data:* b Madison, Wis, Oct 21, 38; m 65, Janet N Sorlien; c Alan M & Frederick I. *Educ:* Univ Mich, BS, 61; Univ Calif, Berkeley, PhD(zool), 66. *Prof Exp:* Assoc zool, Univ Calif, Berkeley, 64-66; Elsie Binger Naumberg res fel ornith, Am Mus Natural Hist, 66-67. *Concurrent Pos:* Ecol adv panel, NSF, 77-79; ed Ecol, Ecological Monographs, 84-87; vis prof, Univ Miami, 82; ed, Behav Ecol, 93- *Mem:* Fel Am Ornith Union; Int Soc Behav Ecol; fel AAAS; Animal Behav Soc. *Res:* Ecological determinants of social systems, principally in birds and insects; community organization; coevolution; plant population biology. *Mailing Add:* Dept Biol Syracuse Univ Syracuse NY 13244-1270. *Fax:* 315-443-2156; *E-Mail:* llwolf@mailbox.syr.edu

**WOLF, LESLIE RAYMOND,** ORGANIC CHEMISTRY, POLYMER CHEMISTRY. *Current Pos:* SR RES CHEMIST, AMOCO OIL CO, 81- *Personal Data:* b East Chicago, Ind, Feb 18, 49; m 72; c 2. *Educ:* Lewis Univ, BA, 71; Pa State Univ, PhD(chem), 74. *Prof Exp:* Chemist, Rohm & Haas Co, 73-78; sr res chemist, DeSoto, Inc, 78-81. *Concurrent Pos:* Lectr chem, Eve Div, LaSalle Col, 74-78, Lewis Univ, 85- *Mem:* Am Chem Soc. *Res:* Fuels research. *Mailing Add:* 3619 Shakespeare Lane Naperville IL 60564. *Fax:* 630-420-4831

**WOLF, LOUIS W,** ENGINEERING MECHANICS, APPLIED MATHEMATICS. *Current Pos:* RETIRED. *Personal Data:* b Saginaw, Mich, May 3, 28; m 52; c 4. *Educ:* Univ Mich, BSE, 52, MSE, 55, PhD(eng mech), 63. *Prof Exp:* Engr, Carrier Corp, 52-54; res assoc eng mech, Univ Mich, 54-61, instr, 55-60; res engr, Systs Div, Bendix Corp, 61-62; from asst prof to assoc prof mech eng, Univ Mich, Dearborn, 62-93. *Mem:* Asn Comput Mach; Soc Indust & Appl Math. *Res:* Fluid mechanics; nonlinear elastic shells; computer technology. *Mailing Add:* 1212 Olivia Ann Arbor MI 48104

**WOLF, LUDWIG, JR,** BLOOD BANKING, DIALYSIS. *Current Pos:* RES & DEVELOP ENGR, BAXTER HEALTH CARE, 72-, DIR ADVAN DEVELOP, 84- *Personal Data:* b Chicago, Ill, July 24, 39; m, Kathleen; c Ximen. *Educ:* Ill Inst Technol, BS, 61, MS, 63, PhD(mech eng), 74. *Prof Exp:* Res engr, Ill Inst Technol, 63-72. *Mem:* Asn Study Med Educ; Am Asn Blood Banks; Am Inst Med & Biol Eng. *Res:* Elimination of virus from blood products and other technologies for improving the quality of blood components; development of disposables for gene therapy and cord blood transplant. *Mailing Add:* 1417 Kirkwall Barrington IL 60010. *Fax:* 847-270-4192; *E-Mail:* wolfl@baxter.com

**WOLF, MARVIN ABRAHAM,** MICROMETEOROLOGY, AIR POLLUTION. *Current Pos:* RETIRED. *Personal Data:* b Syracuse, NY, Dec 26, 25; m 54, Jo A Spohn; c Steven D & Susan D. *Educ:* NMex Inst Mining & Technol, BS, 51; Univ Wash, MS, 62. *Prof Exp:* Assoc res engr, Boeing Airplane Co, Wash, 58-60; res meteorologist, Meteorol Res Inc, Calif, 60-63; physicist, Pac Missile Range, Calif, 63-66; res assoc, Pac Northwest Labs, Battelle-Mem Inst, 66-77; res assoc, Air Res Ctr, Ore State Univ, 77-80, assoc prof, Dept Atmospheric Sci, 80-86; cert consult meteorologist, 82-90. *Concurrent Pos:* Consult, US Dept Energy, 84. *Mem:* Sigma Xi. *Res:* Citizen lobbyist for improved environment and government operations. *Mailing Add:* 654 NW Stewart Pl Corvallis OR 97330-3839

**WOLF, MATTHEW BERNARD,** PHYSIOLOGY. *Current Pos:* ASSOC PROF PHYSIOL, UNIV SC, 76- *Personal Data:* b Los Angeles, Calif, May 5, 35; m 60; c 2. *Educ:* Univ Calif, Los Angeles, BSc, 57, MSc, 62, PhD(physiol), 67. *Prof Exp:* Sr engr, Bendix Corp, 58-63; asst prof biomed eng, Univ Southern Calif, 67-72; assoc prof eng, Univ Ala, Birmingham, 72-76. *Concurrent Pos:* Consult, Rand Corp, 61-72; USPHS fel, 63-67. *Mem:* Am Physiol Soc; Biomed Eng Soc. *Res:* Cell biophysics; ion transport. *Mailing Add:* Dept Physiol Univ SC Sch Med Bldg 1 Columbia SC 29208. *Fax:* 803-733-1523

**WOLF, MERRILL KENNETH,** NEUROBIOLOGY, TISSUE CULTURE. *Current Pos:* prof anat, 72-91, PROF NEUROL, MED SCH, UNIV MASS, 78-, PROF, CELL BIOL, 91- *Personal Data:* b Cleveland, Ohio, Aug 28, 31; m 58, Emily Vaugman. *Educ:* Yale Col, BA, 45; Western Reserve Univ, MD, 56. *Honors & Awards:* Javits Award, NINCDS, 84. *Prof Exp:* Intern med, Peter Bent Brigham Hosp, 56-57; res assoc, Nat Inst Neurol Dis & Blindness, 57-59; res fel neurol, Med Sch, Harvard Univ, 59-64, instr anat, 64-69, asst prof neuropath, 69-71, assoc prof, 71-72. *Concurrent Pos:* Lectr, Med Sch, Harvard Univ, 72-79; vis prof, Sch Med, Stanford Univ, 77. *Mem:* Am Asn Anatomists; Soc Neurosci; Am Soc Neurochem. *Res:* Neurological mutant mice with central nervous system disorders; cytology, genetics, analysis of gene action in double mutant mice. *Mailing Add:* Dept Cell Biol Sch Med Univ Mass 55 Lake Ave N Worcester MA 01655. *Fax:* 508-856-5612

**WOLF, MONTE WILLIAM,** ORGANIC CHEMISTRY. *Current Pos:* ASSOC PROF CHEM, OGLETHORPE UNIV, 78- *Personal Data:* b Whittier, Calif, Sept 1, 49. *Educ:* Univ Calif, Santa Barbara, BS, 71; Univ Southern Calif, PhD(org chem), 76. *Prof Exp:* Res org chem, Univ Calif, San Diego, 76-77; asst prof chem, Bethel Col, Minn, 77-78; vis asst prof, Univ Calif, San Diego, 78. *Mem:* Sigma Xi; Am Chem Soc. *Res:* Photophysical processes of excited state aromatic ketones. *Mailing Add:* Oglethorpe Univ 4484 Peachtree Rd Atlanta GA 30319-2737

**WOLF, NEIL STEPHAN,** PLASMA PHYSICS. *Current Pos:* asst prof, 67-72, chmn, Dept Physics & Astron, 74-77 & 84-88, assoc prof & coordr, Dept Sci, 72-80, PROF PHYSICS, DICKINSON COL, 80-, DIR, DICKINSON CTR EUROP STUDIES, BOLOGNA, ITALY, 88- *Personal Data:* b Brooklyn, NY, Nov 15, 37; m 59, Susan Schorsch; c Debra (Goldstein) & Michael. *Educ:* Queens Col, NY, BS, 58; Stevens Inst Technol, MS, 60, PhD(physics), 66. *Honors & Awards:* Lindbach Award, 83; Merck Lab Develop Award, 89. *Prof Exp:* Res assoc physics, Space Physics Labs, G C Dewey Corp, 65-67. *Concurrent Pos:* Res Corp Frederick Cottrell res grant, 67-; NSF fel, Univ Calif, Irvine, 81, vis assoc prof, 81-82, vis prof, 90-91; vis physicist, Univ Innsbruck, Austria, 83 & Univ Calif, Irvine, 84-88. *Mem:* Am Inst Physics; Fedn Am Scientists. *Res:* Plasma physics related to control of instabilities in plasma immersed in strong magnetic fields; current drive in tokamaks; computer simulation of fully ionized plasmas. *Mailing Add:* Dept Physics Dickinson Col Carlisle PA 17013. *Fax:* 717-245-1642; *E-Mail:* wolf@dickinson.edu

**WOLF, NORMAN SANFORD,** EXPERIMENTAL HEMATOLOGY, CELLULAR AGING. *Current Pos:* assoc prof path & mem radiol sci group, Sch Med, 68-90, PROF PATH & AFFIL PROF COMP MED, SCH MED, UNIV WASH, 90- *Personal Data:* b Kansas City, Mo, July 22, 27; m 67, 76, 95, Susan Herring; c Jeremy. *Educ:* Kans State Univ, BS & DVM, 53; Northwestern Univ, PhD(exp path), 60; Am Col Lab Animal Med, dipl, 55. *Prof Exp:* Dir dept animal care, Med Sch, Northwestern Univ, 53-58; vis scientist & NSF fel, Pasteur Lab, Inst Radium, Paris, 60-61; consult radiation biol, Path & Physiol Sect, Biol Div, Oak Ridge Nat Lab, 61-62; res asst prof exp biol, Baylor Col Med, 62-68. *Concurrent Pos:* Consult, Animal Quarters, Vet Admin Res Hosp, Chicago, 54-60 & Vet Admin Hosp, Seattle, 73-79; vis scientist, P MacCallum Cancer Res Inst, Melbourne, Australia, 88. *Mem:* Am Soc Exp Path; Int Soc Exp Hemat; Am Col Lab Animal Med. *Res:* Hematopoietic regeneration and transplantation following ionizing radiation; immune competence; hemopoietic stem cell identification; control of hematopoiesis by hematopoietic organ stroma; osteoblast proliferation and function; cellular aging studies. *Mailing Add:* Dept Path Univ Wash Sch Med Seattle WA 98195. *Fax:* 206-543-3644

**WOLF, P S,** PHARMACOLOGY. *Current Pos:* MEM STAFF, DEPT CORP DEVELOP, STERLING WINTHROP DRUG INC, DIR LICENSING. *Mailing Add:* 12 Richard Somers Rd Granite Springs NY 10527

**WOLF, PAUL LEON,** PATHOLOGY. *Current Pos:* PROF PATH, UNIV CALIF, SAN DIEGO, 74- *Personal Data:* b Detroit, Mich, Oct 4, 28; m 52; c 3. *Educ:* Wayne State Univ, BA, 48; Univ Mich, MD, 52; Am Bd Path, cert path anat & clin path, 60. *Prof Exp:* Intern, Detroit Receiving Hosp, 52-53; resident path, Wayne State Univ Hosps, 56-60, from asst prof to prof, 60-68; dir, Clin lab, Stanford Univ Med Ctr, 68-74. *Concurrent Pos:* Assoc, Detroit Receiving Hosp; mem staff, Dearborn Vet Admin Hosp. *Mem:* AMA; Am Soc Clin Path; Am Asn Path & Bact; Col Am Path. *Res:* Anatomic pathology; histochemistry; immunopathology; cancer immunology. *Mailing Add:* Univ Hosp 225 W Dickenson San Diego CA 92103-1910

**WOLF, PAUL R,** PHOTOGRAMMETRY,CIVIL ENGINEERING. *Current Pos:* RETIRED. *Personal Data:* b Mazomanie, Wis, June 13, 34; m 59; c 3. *Educ:* Univ Wis-Madison, BSCE, 60, MSCE, 66, PhD(civil eng), 67. *Honors & Awards:* Bausch & Lomb Photogram Award, 66; Talbert Abrams Award III, Am Soc Photogram, 71; Fennel Award, Am Cong Surv & Mapping, 79. *Prof Exp:* Hwy engr, Wis Hwy Comn, 60-63; instr civil eng, Univ Wis-Madison, 63-67; asst prof, Univ Calif, Berkeley, 67-70; assoc prof, Univ Wis-Madison, 70-74, prof civil & environ eng, 74-93. *Concurrent Pos:* Mem, Panel Geod & Cartog, Nat Acad Sci, 72-74. *Mem:* Am Cong Surv & Mapping; Am Soc Photogram; Soc Automotive Engrs. *Res:* Geodesy; cartography; photogrammetry with concentration on close-range and terrestrial applications; accident reconstruction. *Mailing Add:* Dept Civil & Environ Eng Univ Wis Madison WI 53706-1607

**WOLF, PHILIP FRANK,** PHYSICAL ORGANIC CHEMISTRY. *Current Pos:* res chemist, Union Carbide Corp, 65-70, from proj scientist to res scientist, 70-74, group leader org chem, 74-76, sr res scientist, 76-77, assoc dir res & develop, 77-84, DIR RES & DEVELOP, UNION CARBIDE CORP, 84- *Personal Data:* b New York, NY, Apr 12, 38; div; c 3. *Educ:* NY Univ, BS, 60; Columbia Univ, MA, 61, PhD(org chem), 64. *Prof Exp:* Fel org chem, Yale Univ, 64-65. *Mem:* Am Chem Soc; Sigma Xi. *Res:* Studies on oxidation-oxygen transfer mechanisms, substitution reactions of ethylene oxide, free radical telomerization, heterogeneous gas phase kinetics, Diels-Alder reactions and water soluble polymers. *Mailing Add:* 401 Jaguar Lane Bridgewater NJ 08807-2336

**WOLF, RAOUL,** PEDIATRICS, PULMONARY MEDICINE. *Current Pos:* DIR ALLERGY & CLIN IMMUNOL, DEPT ALLERGY & IMMUNOL, WYLER CHILDREN'S HOSP, 79- *Personal Data:* b 1946. *Educ:* Univ Witwatersrand, Johannesburg, SAfrica, MD, 69. *Mailing Add:* Dept Allergy & Immunol La Rabida Children Hosp E 65th St Chicago IL 60649-1395. *Fax:* 773-363-7160

**WOLF, RICHARD ALAN,** SPACE PHYSICS. *Current Pos:* from asst prof to assoc prof space sci, 67-74, PROF SPACE PHYSICS & ASTRON, RICE UNIV, 74- *Personal Data:* b Pittsburgh, Pa, Nov 10, 39; m 71, Helen C Gilbert; c Susan E & Michael D. *Educ:* Cornell Univ, BEngPhys, 62; Calif Inst Technol, PhD(nuclear astrophys), 66. *Prof Exp:* Res fel physics, Calif Inst Technol, 66; mem tech staff, Bel Tel Labs, 66-67. *Concurrent Pos:* Mem, Inst Advan Study, 69 & 74-75. *Mem:* Am Geophys Union. *Res:* Physics of the magnetosphere and ionosphere. *Mailing Add:* Dept Space Physics & Astron Rice Univ Houston TX 77251-1892. *E-Mail:* wolf@alfven.rice.edu

**WOLF, RICHARD CLARENCE,** PHYSIOLOGY, ENDOCRINOLOGY. *Current Pos:* asst prof physiol, Primate Lab, 57-61, assoc prof, 61-66, co-dir, 68-70, MEM ENDOCRINOL-REPRODUCTION PHYSIOL PROG, UNIV WIS-MADISON, 63-, DIR, 70-, PROF PHYSIOL, 66- CHMN DEPT, 71- *Personal Data:* b Lancaster, Pa, Nov 28, 26; m 52; c 2. *Educ:* Franklin & Marshall Col, BS, 50; Rutgers Univ, PhD(zool), 54. *Prof Exp:* Waksman-Merck fel, Rutgers Univ, New Brunswick, 54-55; Milton fel, Sch Dent Med, Harvard Univ, 55-56, USPHS fel, 56-57. *Concurrent Pos:* Mem res career award comt, NIH, 70-72, mem contract res & adv comt, 73-76; mem sci adv bd, Yerkes Regional Primate Res Ctr, Emory Univ, 72-78; consult, Ford Found, 72- *Mem:* Soc Study Reprod; Endocrine Soc; Am Physiol Soc; Brit Soc Endocrinol; Brit Soc Study Fertil. *Res:* Endocrinology of pregnancy. *Mailing Add:* 4205 Manitou Way Madison WI 43711

**WOLF, RICHARD EDWARD, JR,** MOLECULAR BIOLOGY. *Current Pos:* asst prof, 75-80, FROM ASSOC PROF TO PROF BIOL SCI, UNIV MD BALTIMORE CO, 80- *Personal Data:* b Philadelphia, Pa, Mar 22, 41. *Educ:* Univ Cincinnati, BA, 63, MS, 68, PhD(microbiol), 70. *Prof Exp:* Res fel microbiol & molecular genetics, Med Sch, Harvard Univ, 70-73, instr, 73-75. *Res:* Molecular mechanisms of growth rate-dependent regulation of gene expression. *Mailing Add:* 7104 Black Rock Ct Columbia MD 21046-1465

**WOLF, RICHARD EUGENE,** ORGANIC CHEMISTRY, POLYMER CHEMISTRY. *Current Pos:* managing dir, Int & Centres, 91-94 MANAGING DIR, INT, VALSPAR CORP, 91- *Personal Data:* b Dixon, Ill, June 25, 36; m 60; June; c 2. *Educ:* Northern Ill Univ, BSEd, 57; Univ San Francisco, MS, 65; Univ Calif, Berkeley, PhD(chem), 68. *Prof Exp:* Sect leader org synthesis, Desoto Inc, 68-70, mgr, Long Range Res Dept, 70-74, res scientist, 74-77, contract & explor res mgr, 77-79, dir int licensing, 79-87, sr dir int licensing, Desoto, Inc, 87-90. *Concurrent Pos:* Chmn patent comt, DeSoto, Inc, 71-76, chmn basic res comt, 74-76; mem, Patent Rev Comt, Valspar, 91- *Mem:* Am Chem Soc; Fedn Socs Paint Technol; Nat Micrographics Asn; fel Am Inst Chem; Licensing Exec Soc. *Res:* Photochemistry; photoconduction in organic molecules; photopolymerization; emulsion polymerization; coatings technology; water treatment. *Mailing Add:* 210 Tully Pl Prospect Heights IL 60070. *Fax:* 847-520-8501; *E-Mail:* dwolf@valspar.com

**WOLF, ROBERT E,** IMMUNOLOGY, RHEUMATOLOGY. *Current Pos:* PROF MED & CHIEF RHEUMATOLOGY, MED CTR, LA STATE UNIV, 77-; DIR CTR EXCELLENCE ARTHRITIS OVERTON BROOKS VET ADMIN MED CTR, SHREVEPORT, 77- *Personal Data:* b Houston, Tex, Jan 20, 42; m 67, Ann E Killebrew; c Robert E Jr. *Educ:* Baylor Univ, BA, 64; Univ Tex, Galveston, MD, 69, PhD, 73. *Prof Exp:* Resident med, Univ Tex Med Br, Galveston, 69-71; comn officer, USPHS, 71-73; rheumatology fel, Univ Tex Southwestern Med Sch, 73-75, asst prof med, 75-77; res assoc, Dallas Vet Admin Hosp, 75-77. *Mem:* Am Rheumatism Asn; Am Asn Immunologists; Int Soc Immunopharmacol; Soc Leukocyte Biol. *Res:* Aspects of cellular immunology and immuno-pharmacology relating to rheumatic diseases. *Mailing Add:* Dept Med La State Univ Med Ctr PO Box 33932 Shreveport LA 71130-3932

**WOLF, ROBERT LAWRENCE,** physiology, biochemistry, for more information see previous edition

**WOLF, ROBERT OLIVER,** ORAL BIOLOGY. *Current Pos:* RETIRED. *Personal Data:* b Mansfield, Ohio, Mar 14, 25; m 70; c 2. *Educ:* NCent Col, BA, 50; Ohio State Univ, MA, 52, DDS, 58. *Prof Exp:* Res asst physiol genetics, Ohio State Univ, 52-54; res asst oral biol, Col Dent, 57-58; comn officer, USPHS, 58; intern clin dent, USPHS Hosp, New Orleans, La, 58-59; investr salivary physiol & biochem, Human Genetics Br, Nat Inst Dent Res, 59-70, Oral Med & Surg Br, 70-73, Lab Oral Med, 73-77 & Clin Invest Br, 77-81; prin investr, salivary physiol & biochem, Lab Biol Struct, Nat Inst Dent Res, 81-85. *Concurrent Pos:* Clin assoc prof, Sch Dent, Georgetown Univ, 80- *Mem:* Am Dent Asn; Am Soc Human Genetics; Int Asn Dent Res; Am Inst Biol Sci. *Res:* Human and animal salivary physiology, biochemistry, enzymology and genetics, especially isoamylases; human salivary gland disease, diagnosis and treatment. *Mailing Add:* 5515 Johnson Ave Bethesda MD 20817

**WOLF, ROBERT PETER,** ENVIRONMENTAL PHYSICS. *Current Pos:* From asst prof to prof physics, 63-88, DIR ACAD COMPUT, HARVEY MUDD COL, 86- *Personal Data:* b Long Branch, NJ, Oct 27, 39; m 60; c 2. *Educ:* Mass Inst Technol, BS, 60, PhD(physics), 63. *Concurrent Pos:* NSF sci faculty fel, Oxford Univ, 69-70; vis scientist, Mass Inst Technol, 76, Univ Toronto, 79, Stanford, 85-86. *Mem:* Am Phys Soc. *Res:* Energy resources; phase transitions; solar energy development; philosophy of science; chaos; neural networks. *Mailing Add:* Dept Physics Harvey Mudd Col Claremont CA 91711

**WOLF, ROBERT STANLEY,** MATHEMATICAL LOGIC. *Current Pos:* from lectr to assoc prof, 75-85, PROF MATH, CALIF POLYTECH STATE UNIV, SAN LUIS OBISPO, 85- *Personal Data:* b New York, NY, May 14, 46; m 75. *Educ:* Mass Inst Technol, BS, 66; Stanford Univ, MS, 67, PhD(math), 74. *Prof Exp:* Vis asst prof math, Univ Ore, 73-74; vis scholar, Stanford Univ, 74-75. *Mem:* Am Math Soc; Asn Symbolic Logic. *Res:* Continuing study of set theories with intuitionistic logic; theory of infinite games, specifically Almost-Borel games; point-set topology, mathematical biology, artificial intelligence and mathematics education. *Mailing Add:* Dept Math Calif Polytech State Univ San Luis Obispo CA 93407

**WOLF, ROBERT V(ALENTIN),** METALLURGICAL ENGINEERING. *Current Pos:* From instr to prof, 51-94, asst dean, Sch Mines & Metall, 81-89, EMER PROF METALL ENG, SCH MINES, UNIV MO, ROLLA, 94- *Personal Data:* b St Louis, Mo, June 5, 29; m 75. *Educ:* Univ Mo, BS, 51, MS, 52. *Concurrent Pos:* Partner, Askeland, Kisslinger & Wolf, consults. *Mem:* Am Soc Metals; Am Foundrymen's Soc; Am Inst Mining & Metall Engrs; Am Soc Nondestructive Testing; Am Welding Soc; Sigma Xi. *Res:* Metals casting; nondestructive testing. *Mailing Add:* Dept Metall Eng Univ Mo Rolla MO 65401

**WOLF, STANLEY MYRON,** METALLURGICAL ENGINEERING, MATERIALS SCIENCE. *Current Pos:* metallurgist, 77-85, metall engr, 88-90, DIV DIR, US DEPT ENERGY, 90- *Personal Data:* b Washington, DC, July 12, 39; m 63; c Michelle. *Educ:* Va Polytech Inst & State Univ, BS, 60; Cornell Univ, MS, 63; Mass Inst Technol, PhD(metall), 72. *Prof Exp:* Metallurgist res & develop, Mat & Control Div, Tex Instruments, 62-63; researcher, US Army Mat Res Agency, 64-66, chief data processing br, Eighth US Army Hq, 66-67, metallurgist, US Army Mat & Mech Res Ctr, 71-74; metallurgist res, AEC, 74-75; metallurgist, ERDA, 75-77. *Concurrent Pos:* Sr staff scientist, Nat Res Coun, 85-88. *Mem:* Am Inst Metall Engrs; Am Soc Metals; Nat Asn Corrosion Engrs; Am Soc Testing Mat. *Res:* Environmental science and technology; waste characterization, treatment, and disposal; high level, low level, and mixed waste; application of manufacturing methods to waste treatment; materials science and technology; research and development management. *Mailing Add:* US Dept of Energy EM54-CL 19901 Germantown Rd Germantown MD 20874-1290

**WOLF, STEPHEN NOLL,** ACOUSTICS. *Current Pos:* RES PHYSICIST UNDERWATER ACOUST, US NAVAL RES LAB, 71- *Personal Data:* b Biloxi, Miss, Dec 4, 44; m 74; c 2. *Educ:* Lebanon Valley Col, BS, 66; Univ Md, PhD(molecular spectros), 72. *Concurrent Pos:* Exchange scientist, Defence Res Estab Atlantic Dartmouth, NS, Can, 86-88. *Mem:* Sigma Xi; fel Acoust Soc Am. *Res:* At-sea experimental studies of propagation of sound in shallow water. *Mailing Add:* Code 7120 US Naval Res Lab Overlook Ave SW Washington DC 20375-5350

**WOLF, STEVEN L,** REHABILITATION MEDICINE, PHYSICAL THERAPY. *Current Pos:* instr, 69-70, from asst prof to assoc prof, 75-85, PROF REHAB, EMORY UNIV, 85- *Personal Data:* b Chicago, Ill, May 15, 44; m 83, Lois Barnhart; c Josh & Adam. *Educ:* Clark Univ, AB, 65; Boston Univ, MS, 68; Emory Univ, MS, 72, PhD(anat). 73. *Honors & Awards:* Marion Williams Res Award, Am Phys Ther Asn, 80, Golden Pen Award, 83 & Lucy Blair Serv Award, 96. *Prof Exp:* Staff phys ther, USPHS, Boston, 66-68; instr phys ther, Boston Univ, 69-70. *Concurrent Pos:* Assoc ed, F A Davis, Phildelphia & J Head Trauma Rehab, 86-; prin investr, Emory Univ Rehab Res, 74, 82, 83 & 88; Catherine Worthingham fel, Am Phys Ther Asn, 87; bd dirs, Biofeedback Soc Am, 83-86; vis prof, Univ Gothenberg, 87-88; consult, EMPI Inc, 83-87. *Mem:* Biofeedback Cert Inst Am (secy, 81-84, vpres, 85-86 & pres, 87-89); Am Phys Ther Asn; Am Cong Rehab Med; NY Acad Sci; Biofeedback Soc Am; Soc Neurosci; Indust Soc Electrokines; Assoc Appl Psychophysiol & Biofeedback (pres, 91-92). *Res:* Use of physiological monitoring to enhace self-control of movement among patients with neuromuscular disorders; new techniques to achieve sensory-motor integration following central nervous system trauma; enhancing postural stability in older individuals. *Mailing Add:* Ctr Rehab Med 1441 Clifton Rd NE Atlanta GA 30322. *Fax:* 404-712-4809; *E-Mail:* steve@spinal.emory.edu

**WOLF, STEWART GEORGE, JR,** INTERNAL MEDICINE, PHYSIOLOGY. *Current Pos:* DIR, TOTTS GAP MED RES LABS, BANGOR, PA, 58-; PROF MED, TEMPLE UNIV, 77- *Personal Data:* b Baltimore, Md, Jan 12, 14; m 42; c 3. *Educ:* Johns Hopkins Univ, AB, 34, MD, 38. *Hon Degrees:* MD, Gothenburg Univ, 68. *Honors & Awards:* Award, Am Gastroentrol Asn, 42; Hofheimer Prize, Am Psychiat Asn, 52; Hans Selye Award, Am Inst Stress, 88. *Prof Exp:* Intern med, NY Hosp, 38-39, from asst resident to resident, 39-42; from asst prof to assoc prof med, Med Col, Cornell Univ, 46-52; prof med & consult prof psychiat, Sch Med, Univ Okla, 52-67, regents prof med, psychiat, neurol & behav sci, 67-70, head, Dept Med, 52-69, prof physiol, Sch Med, 68-70; prof med, Univ Tex Syst, 70-77; dir, Marine Biomed Inst, 70-77; prof internal med & physiol, Univ Tex Med Br Galveston, 70-77; vpres, Med Affairs & mem staff, St Lukes Hosp, Bethlehem, Pa, 77-82. *Concurrent Pos:* Res fel, Bellevue Hosp, 39-42; Nat Res Coun fel, Cornell Univ, 41-42; assoc vis neuropsychiatrist, Bellevue Hosp, 48-52; asst attend physician in charge psychosom clin, Cornell Univ, 46-52; mem, Comt Psychiat, Nat Res Coun, 48-52; mem, Comt Vet Med Probs, 51-52; head, Psychosom Sect, Okla Med Res Found, 52-, head, Neurosci Sect, 67-70; mem, Spec Study Group, Off Res & Develop, Dept Defense, 52-55; mem, Pharmacol & Exp Therapeut Study Sect, 56-57; mem, Comt Prof Educ, 56-63, chmn, 57-63; mem, Gen Med Study Sect, NIH, 57-61, chmn, Gastroenterol training Grant Comt, 58-61; mem adv comt, Space Med & Behav Sci, NASA, 60-61 & Nat Adv Heart Coun, 61-65; mem, Coun Ment Health, AMA, 60-64; consult, Europ Off, Off Int Res, NIH, 63-64; mem, Adv Comt Admis, Nat Formulary, 65-69; mem bd regents, Nat Libr Med, 65-69, chmn, 68-69; mem, Comt Int Progs, Am Heart Asn, 65-70, chmn, 65-70; mem, Educ & Supply Panel, Nat Adv Comn Health Manpower, 66-67; mem, Nat Adv Environ Health Sci Coun, 78-82; mem bd visitors, Dept Biol, Boston Univ, 78- & Ctr Soc Res, Lehigh Univ, 80-90; chmn, Adv Comt, Francis Clark Wood Inst Hist Med, Col Physicians of Philadelphia, 79-90; mem, Bd Dirs, Inst Advan Studies Immunol & Aging, 84-; mem, Sci Adv Comt, Lehigh Univ, 74-, chmn, 80-89. *Mem:* Am Psychosom Soc (pres, 61-62); Am Gastroenterol Asn (pres, 69-70); fel Am Col Physicians; Pavlovian Soc (pres, 66-67); Am Col Clin Pharmacol & Chemother (pres, 66-67); Am Soc Clin Invest; Asn Am Physicians; distinguished fel, Am Psychiat Asn. *Res:* Gastrointestinal, cardiovascular, sensory and neural physiology. *Mailing Add:* RD 1 Box 1120 G Bangor PA 18013-9801

**WOLF, STUART ALAN,** SOLID STATE PHYSICS. *Current Pos:* res physicist, 72-82, supvry res physicist, 82-86, HEAD, MAT PHYSICS BR, US NAVAL RES LAB, 86- *Personal Data:* b Brooklyn, NY, Sept 15, 43; m 65, Iris Tabachnick; c Lisa & Dori. *Educ:* Columbia Col, AB, 64; Rutgers Univ, MS, 66, PhD(physics), 69. *Prof Exp:* Res assoc physics, Case Western Reserve Univ, 69-72. *Concurrent Pos:* Assoc prof & lectr, George Washington Univ, 79-; panel mem, Interagency Advan Power Group-Superconductivity Panel, 80-; vis scholar, Univ Calif, Los Angeles, 81-82; mem, Elec, Magnetic & Optical Panel, Metall Soc; organizer, Gordon Conf Superconducting Films; NSF Rev panels; adj prof, Col William & Mary, 92-; prog mgr, Advan Res Projs Agency, 93- *Mem:* Fel Am Phys Soc; Am Vacuum Soc; Sigma Xi; Metall Soc. *Res:* Cryogenics; superconductivity; transport properties; vacuum system design; thin films; magnetic shielding; Josephison devices; cuprate superconductors. *Mailing Add:* Naval Res Lab Code 6340 Washington DC 20375-5343. *Fax:* 202-767-1697; *E-Mail:* wolf@anvil.nrl.navy.mil

**WOLF, THOMAS,** ANALYTICAL CHEMISTRY. *Current Pos:* sr res chemist, 66-75, res assoc, 75-84, HEAD RES QUAL ASSURANCE, COLGATE-PALMOLIVE CO, 84- *Personal Data:* b Sept 10, 32; US citizen; m 59, Pat Peacock; c Susan & Lynn. *Educ:* Cambridge Univ, BA, 55, MA, 61; Univ RI, PhD(anal chem), 66. *Prof Exp:* Chemist, Coates Bros, Eng, 55-57; lab supvr, Wymat Corp, NJ, 57-58; chemist, Enthone Inc, Conn, 58-59 & Eltex Res Corp, RI, 59-62. *Concurrent Pos:* Course dir, Ctr Prof Advan, 79- *Mem:* Am Chem Soc; Soc Qual Assurance. *Res:* Liquid chromatography; quality assurance; validation. *Mailing Add:* 609 S Fifth Ave Highland Park NJ 08904-2628

**WOLF, THOMAS MARK,** CHILD-CLINICAL PSYCHOLOGY, BEHAVIORAL MEDICINE. *Current Pos:* assoc prof, 75-82, PROF PSYCHOL, LA STATE UNIV MED SCH, 82- *Personal Data:* b Cincinnati, Ohio, Dec 25, 44; m 69, Valerie B Winchester; c Mark B. *Educ:* Univ Cincinnati, BA, 66; Miami Univ, Ohio, MA, 67; Univ Waterloo, Ont, PhD(psychol), 71. *Honors & Awards:* Dr Ernst Lederle Award Excellence Res, Educ & Patient Care, La State Univ, 93. *Prof Exp:* Asst prof psychol, State Univ NY, Cortland, 70-74, assoc prof, 74-75. *Concurrent Pos:*

Postdoctorate psychol, St Louis Univ, 74-76; consult psychologist, Youth Study Ctr, New Orleans, 77, New Orleans pub schs, 79-80, St Bernard Group Home, 79-86, Cent City Ment Health Clin, 80-89, Asn Cath Charities New Orleans, 87-89, Child & Adolescent Ment Health Prog, 89-96, New Orleans Target Cities Prog, 96- *Mem:* Am Psychol Asn; Soc Behav Med; Asn Am Med Col. *Res:* Perceived mistreatment and health during professional training; lifestyle characteristics stress, coping and health of medical students; health promotion and disease prevention. *Mailing Add:* Dept Psychiat La State Univ Med Ctr 1542 Tulane Ave New Orleans LA 70112. *Fax:* 504-568-8647

**WOLF, THOMAS MICHAEL,** GENETICS EVOLUTION. *Current Pos:* From instr to assoc prof, 80-88, ASSOC PROF BIOL, WASHBURN UNIV, TOPEKA, 88- *Personal Data:* b Highland Park, Mich, Dec 28, 42; c 2. *Educ:* Western Mich Univ, BS, 65; Wayne State Univ, MS, 67, PhD(genetics), 72. *Mem:* Genetics Soc Am; Entom Soc Am. *Res:* Evolutionary biology of petridine pigments in dipterans. *Mailing Add:* Dept Biol Washburn Univ Topeka 1700 SW College Ave Topeka KS 66621-1110

**WOLF, WALTER,** RADIOCHEMISTRY, RADIOPHARMACY. *Current Pos:* DIR RADIOPHARM SERV, LOS ANGELES COUNTY-UNIV SOUTHERN CALIF MED CTR, 70-; PROF BIOMED CHEM, UNIV SOUTHERN CALIF, 70-, DIR RADIOPHARM PROG, 68- *Personal Data:* b Frankfurt, Germany, May 25, 31; US citizen; m 55; c 2. *Educ:* Univ of the Repub, Uruguay, BSc, 49, MS, 52; Univ Paris, PhD, 56. *Honors & Awards:* G Czezniak Prize Nuclear Med, Israel, 80, 86. *Prof Exp:* Asst chem, Univ of the Repub, Uruguay, 51-52; asst chem, Nat Cent Sci Res, France, 55-56, attache, 56; assoc prof org chem & biochem, Concepcion Univ, 56-58; traveling fel, McGill Univ, 58; res assoc, Amherst Col, 58-59; res assoc org chem, Univ Southern Calif, 59-62, vis asst prof pharmaceut chem, 61-62; from asst prof to assoc prof, 62-70, chmn dept biomed chem, 70-74. *Concurrent Pos:* Consult radiopharm, Int Atomic Energy Agency & US Vet Admin. *Mem:* Am Chem Soc; Soc Nuclear Med; Radiation Res Soc; Acad Pharmaceut Sci. *Res:* Non-invasive monitoring of drug biodistribution targeting and metabolism; chemistry and biochemistry of organic iodo compounds; radioiodination; non-invasive magnetic resonance; radiopharmacokinetics; nuclear magnetic resonance. *Mailing Add:* Radiopharm Prog Univ Southern Calif 1985 Zonal Ave Los Angeles CA 90033. *Fax:* 213-342-9804

**WOLF, WALTER ALAN,** BIOCHEMISTRY, EXPERT SYSTEMS. *Current Pos:* asst prof, 85-90, ASSOC PROF COMPUT SCI, ROCHESTER INST TECHNOL, 90-, DEPT CHAIR, 93- *Personal Data:* b New York, NY, Mar 9, 42; m 62; c 2. *Educ:* Wesleyan Univ, BA, 62; Brandeis Univ, MA, 64, PhD(org chem), 67; Rochester Inst Technol, MS, 86. *Prof Exp:* Fel, Mass Inst Technol, 67-70; asst prof biochem, Colgate Univ, 70-77; from asst prof to assoc prof chem, Eisenhower Univ, 77-84. *Concurrent Pos:* Vis prof, Agr & Tech Col, State Univ NY, Morrisville, 71-72, State Agr Exp Sta, Geneva, 80-; ed, Chem Ed Compacts, J Chem Educ; res corp grantee, Colgate Univ, 71-72; grantee, NSF. *Mem:* AAAS; Am Chem Soc; Royal Soc Chem; Asn Comput Mach. *Res:* Pheromone biosynthesis; expert system user interfaces; expert systems. *Mailing Add:* 1229 Birdsey Rd Waterloo NY 13165. *E-Mail:* waw@cs.rit.edu

**WOLF, WALTER J,** BIOCHEMISTRY, PROTEIN CHEMISTRY. *Current Pos:* Assoc chemist, USDA, 56-58, chemist, 58-61, prin chemist, 61-68, leader meal prod res, 68-85, lead scientist, 85-90, PRIN SCIENTIST, NORTHERN REGIONAL RES CTR, USDA, 90- *Personal Data:* b Hague, NDak, May 2, 27; m 49, Mary A Grant; c Julie, Maria, Charles, Martin & Barbara. *Educ:* Col St Thomas, BS, 50; Univ Minn, PhD(biochem), 56. *Concurrent Pos:* Assoc ed, Cereal Chem, 70-73 & Cereal Sci Today, 70-73; consult, Int Nutrit Anemia Consultative Group, Nutrit Found, 81-82; off deleg, US-People's Repub China Soybean Symp, 83; ed, Food Microstruct, 84-94; ed bd, J Sci Food Agr, 88-; mem, US Delegation, codex alimentarius comt veg proteins, 86- *Mem:* AAAS; Am Asn Cereal Chemists; Am Chem Soc; Am Oil Chemists Soc; Inst Food Technologists. *Res:* Isolation and characterization of soybean, jojoba and almond proteins; protein interactions, denaturation and structure; food uses of soybean proteins. *Mailing Add:* Nat Ctr Agr Utilization Res 1815 N University St Peoria IL 61604. *Fax:* 309-681-6638; *E-Mail:* wolfwj@ncaur1.ncaur.gov

**WOLF, WARREN WALTER,** glass science, ceramics engineering, for more information see previous edition

**WOLF, WAYNE ROBERT,** ANALYTICAL CHEMISTRY, REFERENCE MATERIALS & FOOD ANALYSIS. *Current Pos:* Nat Res Coun assoc, 71-72, res chemist, Human Nutrit Res Div, Agr Res Serv, 71-75, RES CHEMIST, FOOD COMPOS LAB, NUTRIT CTR, USDA, 75- *Personal Data:* b Kenton, Ohio, May 18, 43; m 71, Karen Flayler; c Lynne Wolf. *Educ:* Kent State Univ, BS, 65, PhD(chem), 69. *Prof Exp:* Res chemist, Aerospace Res Lab, USAF, Wright-Patterson AFB, Ohio, 67-71. *Concurrent Pos:* USDA-NIST res assoc, SRMP, Nat Inst Standards & Technol, 88-93. *Mem:* AAAS; Am Chem Soc; Asn Orr Anal Chemists Int. *Res:* Instrumental analytical methodology for nutrient content of foods; high accuracy analytical methodology; high performance liquid chromatography; mass spectrometry; isoiopedilution, reference materials. *Mailing Add:* Food Compos Lab Nutrit Ctr USDA Beltsville MD 20705. *Fax:* 301-504-8314; *E-Mail:* wolf@bhnre.usda.gov

**WOLF, WERNER PAUL,** PHYSICS, MAGNETIC MATERIALS. *Current Pos:* from assoc prof to prof physics & appl sci, Yale Univ, 63-76, Becton prof & chmn, Dept Eng & Appl Sci, 76-81, chmn, Coun Eng, 81-84, RAYMOND J WEAN PROF ENG & APPL SCI & PROF PHYSICS, YALE UNIV, 84-, CHMN, DEPT APPL PHYSICS, 90-, DIR EDUC AFFAIRS, 94- *Personal Data:* b Vienna, Austria, Apr 22, 30; nat US; m 54, Elizabeth A Eliot; c Peter P, Mary A (Githa). *Educ:* Oxford Univ, BA, 51, MA & DPhil(physics), 54. *Hon Degrees:* MA, Yale Univ, 65. *Honors & Awards:* Sr US Scientist Award, Alexander von Humboldt Found, 83. *Prof Exp:* Res assoc physics, Clarendon Lab, Oxford Univ, 54-56, Imp Chem Industs res fel, 57-59; res fel appl physics, Harvard Univ, 56-57; univ lectr physics, Oxford Univ, 59-63. *Concurrent Pos:* Consult, Hughes Aircraft Co, E I Du Pont de Nemours & Co, Inc, 57 & Gen Elec Co, 60 & 66-93, Mullard Res Labs, 61, Watson Res Ctr, IBM, 62-66; res collabr, Brookhaven Nat Lab, 66-80; vis prof, Munich Tech Univ, 69; gen conf chmn, Conf Magnetism & Magnetic Mat, 71; sr vis fel, Oxford Univ, 80 & 84; vis fel, Corpus Christi Col, 84, 87 & vis guest fel, Royal Soc London, 87; extenal examr, Dept Physics, Univ Singapore, 94-96; mem, Redesign Eng & Sci Prog Comt, Univ Bridgeport, 95-, BEI Bd Vistors, Fairfield Univ, 96- *Mem:* Fel Am Phys Soc; fel Inst Elec & Electronics Engrs. *Res:* Magnetism; experimental and theoretical study of magnetic materials, especially at low temperatures; magnetic cooling, relaxation, microwave resonance, optical properties, crystal fields and anisotropy; magnetic thermal properties, critical points and magnetic phase transitions; synthesis of new materials and growth of single crystals. *Mailing Add:* Yale Univ Becton Ctr PO Box 208284 New Haven CT 06520-8284. *Fax:* 203-432-4283; *E-Mail:* werner.wolf@yale.edu

**WOLFARTH, EUGENE F,** PHYSICAL ORGANIC CHEMISTRY. *Current Pos:* RETIRED. *Personal Data:* b Washington, DC, June 24, 32; m 57; c 3. *Educ:* Univ Md, BS, 54; Ohio State Univ, PhD(chem), 61. *Prof Exp:* Res chemist, Res & Develop Command, Wright Patterson AFB, Ohio, 57; asst instr chem, Ohio State Univ, 58-60; res assoc, Res Labs, Eastman Kodak Co, 61-76, mgr, Kodak Legal Dept, Litigation Group, 76-82, res adminr, Kodak Res Labs, 82-91. *Res:* Kinetics and reaction mechanisms; organic synthesis; color photography, the mechanisms of development and designing new film systems. *Mailing Add:* 19 Rippingale Rd Pittsford NY 14534

**WOLFE, ALAN DAVID,** BIOCHEMISTRY, TOXICOLOGY. *Current Pos:* Molecular biologist, 58-76, ASST CHIEF BIOCHEM & PRIN INVESTR BIOCHEM, WALTER REED ARMY INST RES, 76- *Personal Data:* b New York, NY, Mar 25, 29; m 69. *Educ:* Queens Col, NY, BS, 52; Mass Inst Technol, SM, 56, George Washington Univ, JD, 62; Univ Md, College Park, PhD(microbiol), 70. *Concurrent Pos:* Secy Army fel, US Dept Defense, 72-73. *Mem:* Am Soc Microbiol; AAAS; Am Chem Soc. *Res:* Molecular biology and pharmacology of organophosphates; biochemistry of bacterial toxins; protein and nucleic acid synthesis; the mode of action of growth inhibitors. *Mailing Add:* Dept Appl Biochem Walter Reed Army Inst Res Washington DC 20012-5100

**WOLFE, ALLAN FREDERICK,** INVERTEBRATE PHYSIOLOGY, HISTOLOGY. *Current Pos:* PROF BIOL, LEBANON VALLEY COL, 68- *Personal Data:* b Olyphant, Pa, Oct 22, 38; m 63, Juliana Zelna; c Allan, David, Susan & Michael. *Educ:* Gettysburg Col, BA, 63; Drake Univ, MA, 65; Univ Vt, PhD(zool), 68. *Mem:* AAAS; Am Soc Zool; Am Inst Biol Sci; Crustacean Soc; Am Micros Soc. *Res:* Histology, cell biology and physiology of Artemia; invertebrate reproductive systems; sensory receptors, behavior. *Mailing Add:* Dept Biol Lebanon Valley Col Annville PA 17003. *Fax:* 717-867-6075; *E-Mail:* wolfe@lvc.edu

**WOLFE, ALLAN MARVIN,** MEDICINE, METABOLISM. *Current Pos:* PRES, VOXELL, 81- *Personal Data:* b New York, NY, Nov 4, 37; m 64; c 3. *Educ:* Cornell Univ, MB, 58; NY Univ, MD, 62. *Prof Exp:* Asst instr med, State Univ NY Downstate Med Ctr, 64-66; diabetes & arthritis consult & chief educ & info control prog, Nat Ctr Chronic Dis Control, 66-68; clin asst prof med, State Univ NY Downstate Med Ctr, 68-72; med dir, Arthritis Found, NY Chap, 68-70; dir med res infrared eng, Barnes Eng Co, 69-71, dir med mkt, 70-71; dir med res devices & instrumentation, Survival Technol Inc, 71-75; vpres res & develop pharmaceut, McGaw Labs Div, Am Hosp Supply Corp, 75-81. *Concurrent Pos:* Prin investr, Voc Rehab Serv, 68-69, Arthritis Ctr Prog, Pub Health Serv, 69-72; Mayor's Orgn Task Force Comprehensive Health Planning, 70-72 & Sudden Cardiac Death & Onset Myocardial Infarction, 71-73; gen partner, Utah Venture Partners, Salt Lake City, 90- *Mem:* AMA; Am Soc Parenteral & Enteral Nutrit. *Res:* Human metabolism; amino acid chemistry; medical devices; parenteral pharmacologic agents. *Mailing Add:* Voxell 26081 Merit Circle Suite 117 Laguna Hills CA 92653

**WOLFE, BARBARA ANN,** ASSISTED REPRODUCTIVE TECHNOLOGY IN DOMESTIC & EXOTIC ENDANGERED SPECIES. *Current Pos:* PHILLIP REED FEL, NAT ZOOL PARK, 94- *Personal Data:* b Albany, NY, May 29, 61. *Educ:* Univ Calif, BS, 83; Tex A&M Univ, DVM, 93, PhD(reproductive physiol), 93. *Prof Exp:* Res asst, Genentech Inc, 83-85. *Mem:* Am Vet Med Asn; Int Embryo Transfer Soc; Int Soc Vet Perinatology. *Res:* Assisted reproduction in endangered species, especially cats, including artificial insemination and embryo transfer, invitro fertilization and embryo micromanipulation. *Mailing Add:* Vet Hosp 1500 Remount Rd Front Royal VA 22630. *Fax:* 202-673-4733

**WOLFE, BERNARD MARTIN,** MEDICINE, BIOCHEMISTRY. *Current Pos:* from asst prof to assoc prof, 70-80, PROF MED, UNIV WESTERN ONT, 80-, PROF BIOCHEM, 97- *Personal Data:* b Killdeer, Sask, Dec 31, 34; m 70, Elene Dukellis; c Deanna M. *Educ:* Univ Sask, BA, 56; Oxford Univ, BM & BCh, 63, MA, 67; McGill Univ, MSc, 67; FRCP(C), 68; Royal Col Physicians & Surgeons, cert Endocrinol & Metab, 85. *Prof Exp:* House physician & surgeon med, Guy's Hosp, London, Eng, 63-64; from jr asst resident to sr asst resident, Royal Victoria Hosp, Montreal, Que, 64-68; Med Res Coun Can centennial fel, Cardiovasc Res Inst, Med Ctr, Univ Calif, San Francisco, 68-70. *Concurrent Pos:* Consult & chief endocrinol & metab, Univ Hosp, London, Ont, 72-87; mem, Coun Arteriosclerosis, Am Heart Asn; hon lectr biochem, Univ Western Ont, 72-; chmn, Can Lipoprotein Conf, 85-86; chmn, Dept Med Div Endocrinol & Metab, Dept Med, Univ Western Ont, 87-91. *Mem:* Can Soc Clin Invest; Can Soc Endocrinol & Metab; Can Med Asn; Can Atherosclerosis Soc. *Res:* Clinical investigation of the effects of diets, hormones and drugs on lipid, carbohydrate and amino acid metabolism in man and experimental animals. *Mailing Add:* 17 Metamora Crescent London ON N6G 1R2 Can. *Fax:* 519-663-3232

**WOLFE, BERTRAM,** ENERGY TECHNOLOGY, BUSINESS MANAGEMENT. *Current Pos:* INDEPENDENT CONSULT, 92- *Personal Data:* b New York, NY, June 26, 27; m 50, Leila A Katz; c Sarah E ( Rothenberg), Donald S & William A. *Educ:* Princeton Univ, BA, 50; Cornell Univ, PhD(nuclear physics), 54. *Honors & Awards:* Henry DeWolf Smyth Nuclear Statesman Award, Am Nuclear Soc, Walter H Zinn Award. *Prof Exp:* Physicist, Eastman Kodak Co, 54-55; physicist, Nuclear Energy Div, Gen Elec Co, 55-56, mgr develop reactor physics, 57-59, mgr conceptual design & anal, 59-64, mgr plant eng & develop, Advan Prod Oper, 64-69; assoc dir, Pac Northwest Labs, Battelle Mem Inst, 69-70; vpres & tech dir, Wadco Corp, 70; gen mgr, Breeder Reactor Dept, Gen Elec Co, 70-73 , Fuel Recovery & Irradiation Prod Dept, 74-78, vpres & gen mgr, Nuclear Energy Progs Dept, 78-84, Nuclear Technol & Fuel Div, 84-87, vpres & gen mgr, Gen Elec Nuclear Energy, 87-92. *Concurrent Pos:* Mem, Nuclear Power Oversight Comt; mem bd dirs, Am Nuclear Energy Coun; mem bd dirs, Nuclear Mgt & Resources Comt. *Mem:* Nat Acad Eng; Am Phys Soc; fel Am Nuclear Soc (pres); AAAS; Sigma Xi; Nat Res Coun. *Res:* Nuclear power technology; advanced energy technology. *Mailing Add:* 15453 Via Vaquero Monte Sereno CA 95030. *Fax:* 408-395-9039; *E-Mail:* wolfeb@jcrema.ne.ge.com

**WOLFE, CARVEL STEWART,** MATHEMATICS, INTEGER PROGRAMMING. *Current Pos:* RETIRED. *Personal Data:* b Minneapolis, Minn, June 11, 27; m 54, Margaret; c Norman, Cynthia & Eileen. *Educ:* Univ Ariz, BS, 50, MS, 51; Walden Univ, PhD, 83. *Prof Exp:* Asst math, Univ Wash, 51-53; asst prof, Shepherd State Col, 53-54; asst, Univ Md, 54-56; from asst prof to assoc prof, US Naval Acad, 56-92. *Mem:* AAAS; Am Math Soc; Math Asn Am. *Res:* Numerical analysis; linear programming; integer programming. *Mailing Add:* 3531 S River Terr Edgewater MD 21037

**WOLFE, CHARLES MORGAN,** ELECTRICAL ENGINEERING, SOLID STATE ELECTRONICS. *Current Pos:* dir, Semiconductor Res Lab, 79-90, Samuel C Sachs prof, 82-90, PROF ELEC ENG, WASHINGTON UNIV, 75- *Personal Data:* b Morgantown, WVa, Dec 21, 35; div; c David M & Diana M. *Educ:* Univ WVa, BSEE, 61, MSEE, 62; Univ Ill, PhD(elec eng), 65. *Honors & Awards:* Electronics Award, Electrochem Soc, 78; Jack A Morton Award, Inst Elec & Electronics Engrs, 90. *Prof Exp:* Mem staff, Lincoln Lab, Mass Inst Technol, 65-75. *Mem:* Nat Acad Eng; Am Asn Univ Prof; fel Inst Elec & Electronics Engrs; Electrochem Soc; AAAS. *Res:* Preparation and characterization of semiconductor materials for solid state devices. *Mailing Add:* Washington Univ Campus Box 1127 St Louis MO 63130

**WOLFE, DAVID M,** HIGH ENERGY PHYSICS. *Current Pos:* from asst prof to assoc prof, 71-79, PROF PHYSICS, UNIV NMEX, 79-, CHMN DEPT, 91- *Personal Data:* b Philadelphia, Pa, Oct 27, 38; div; c 3. *Educ:* Univ Pa, BA, 59, MS, 61, PhD(physics), 66. *Prof Exp:* Res assoc physics, Enrico Fermi Inst, Univ Chicago, 66-69; vis asst prof physics, Univ Wash, 69-71. *Concurrent Pos:* Vis scientist, Brookhaven Nat Lab, Upton, NY, 78-79; sci assoc, CERN, Geneva, Switz, 83-85. *Mem:* Am Phys Soc; Fedn Am Scientists; Sigma Xi. *Res:* Experimental research in the nucleon-nucleon and antinucleon-nucleon interactions. *Mailing Add:* Dept Physics Univ NMex Albuquerque NM 87131. *Fax:* 505-277-1520; *E-Mail:* dwolfe@unmb.unm.edu

**WOLFE, DOROTHY WEXLER,** mathematics, for more information see previous edition

**WOLFE, DOUGLAS ARTHUR,** AQUATIC ECOLOGY & POLLUTION. *Current Pos:* SR SCIENTIST & CONSULT, WOLFE ENVIRON SERVM, 94- *Personal Data:* b Dayton, Ohio, July 6, 39; m 59, Nancy S Meeker; c Cynthia M, Nicholas A & Catherine A. *Educ:* Ohio State Univ, BSc, 59, MSc, 61, PhD(physiol chem), 64; Stanford Univ, MSc, 81. *Prof Exp:* Chief, Biogeochem Prog, Radiobiol Lab, US Bur Com Fisheries, 64-70; dir estuarine res, Atlantic Estuarine Fisheries Ctr, Nat Marine Fisheries Serv, 70-75; staff dir ecol, Nat Oceanic & Atmospheric Admin, 75-55, dept dir, Oute Continental Shelf Environ Assessment Prog, 77-81, dir oper progs, Off Marine Pollution Assessment, 81-83, chief scientist, Ocean Assessment Div, 83-91, chief biol effects, Assessment Br, 91-94. *Concurrent Pos:* From adj asst prof to adj assoc prof, NC State Univ, 66-75; chief scientist I marine biol, Nuclear Tra, PR, 69-70; consult, Panel on Zinc, Nat Acad Sci, 73-75; proj mgr, Energy Proj Fate & Effects Petrol, Nat Oceanic & Atmospheric Admin-Environ Protection Agency, 75-80; mem, Int Comn Study Ecol Effects Amoco Cadiz Oil Spill, Nat Oceanic & Atmospheric Admin-Ctr Nat Exploitation of Oceans, 78-81; head, Marine Pollution Deleg, Nat Ocean & Atmospheric Admin, People's Repub China, 83; Nat Ocean & Atmospheric Admin rep, Sci Group of London Dumping Conv, 83-; affil prof, George Mason Univ, 88-; proj mgr, Fate & Effects Exxon Valdez Oil, Nat Oceanic & Atmospheric Admin, 89-93. *Mem:* Estuarine Res Fedn; Soc Environ

Toxicol & Chem; Am Malacol Union; Am Soc Limnol & Oceanog; Sigma Xi. *Res:* Comparative biochemistry of carotenoids and lipids; ecology and biology of molluscs; biogeochemistry of petroleum, radioisotopes and trace metals in marine environment; ocean dumping and marine waste disposal management. *Mailing Add:* Wolfe Environ Serv 109 Shore Dr Shell Landing Beaufort NC 28516

**WOLFE, EDWARD W,** GEOLOGY. *Current Pos:* GEOLOGIST, US GEOL SURV, 61- *Personal Data:* b Brooklyn, NY, Jan 21, 36; m 56; c 5. *Educ:* Col Wooster, BA, 57; Ohio State Univ, PhD(geol), 61. *Prof Exp:* Instr geol, Col Wooster, 59-61. *Mem:* Int Asn Volcanol & Chem Earth's Interior; Geol Soc Am; Am Geophys Union. *Res:* Areal geology and volcanology. *Mailing Add:* US Geol Surv Cascades Volcano Observ 5400 MacArthur Blvd Vancouver WA 98661

**WOLFE, GENE H,** STATIC CONTROL ELIMINATION, ELECTROSTATIC PRINTING. *Current Pos:* RES PHYSICIST, R R DONNELLEY & SONS, 64- *Personal Data:* b Calumet City, Ill, May 18, 36; c Lynne, Lisa, Gene, Karen, Kimberly & Amy. *Educ:* Univ Ill, BS, 58, MS, 59. *Prof Exp:* Res physicist, IIT Res Inst, 60-64. *Concurrent Pos:* Mem, Comt Static Elec, Nat Fire Protection Asn. *Mem:* Optical Soc Am; Laser Inst Am; Int Soc Optical Eng; Electrostatic Discharge Asn; Nat Fire Protecton Asn. *Res:* Development of equipment utilizing electrostatics for various graphics arts processes, primarily printing; devices and methods to control static electricity. *Mailing Add:* 2971 173rd Pl Lansing IL 60438. *Fax:* 630-322-6711

**WOLFE, GORDON A,** SOLID STATE PHYSICS. *Current Pos:* RETIRED. *Personal Data:* b Chicago, Ill, Sept 8, 31; m 56; c 2. *Educ:* Ill Inst Technol, BS, 60; Univ Mo, MS, 63, PhD(physics), 67. *Prof Exp:* Instr physics, Univ Mo, 64-67; asst prof, Southern Ore State Col, 67-74, assoc prof physics, 74-94. *Mem:* AAAS; Am Asn Physics Teachers. *Res:* Anharmonic effects in crystals. *Mailing Add:* 4250 Hwy 99 S Ashland OR 97520

**WOLFE, HARRY BERNARD,** OPERATIONS RESEARCH. *Current Pos:* Sr staff mem oper res, Mass, 56-63, mgr, San Francisco Opers Res Group, Calif, 63-69, SR STAFF MEM, HEALTH CARE SECT, ARTHUR D LITTLE, INC, MASS, 69- *Personal Data:* b Vancouver, BC, Dec 29, 27; m 52; c 4. *Educ:* Univ BC, BA, 49, MA, 51; Columbia Univ, PhD(physics), 56. *Mem:* Inst Mgt Sci; Opers Res Soc Am; Can Opers Res Soc. *Res:* Health care; hospitals; management science, including inventory and scheduling theory and marketing analysis; nuclear physics. *Mailing Add:* 15 Phinney Rd Lexington MA 02173

**WOLFE, HARVEY,** OPERATIONS RESEARCH, STATISTICS. *Current Pos:* from asst prof to assoc prof, 64-72, chmn, 86, PROF INDUST ENG, UNIV PITTSBURGH, 72- *Personal Data:* b Baltimore, Md, Apr 14, 38; m 59; c 4. *Educ:* Johns Hopkins Univ, BES, 60, MSE, 62, PhD(opers res), 64. *Prof Exp:* Opers res asst, Johns Hopkins Hosp, 60-64, opers res assoc, 64. *Concurrent Pos:* Res assoc, Grad Sch Pub Health, Univ Pittsburgh, 64-67, adj assoc prof, 67-77, prof, 77-, mem grad fac, 66-; consult, Blue Cross Western Pa, 65-, dir res, 67-69; consult, Dept Med & Surg Study Group, Vet Admin, 66-72, Nat Ctr Health Serv Res, Dept HEW, 67-, Social Security Admin, 73- & Blue Cross/Blue Shield Greater New York, 75-; partner, Wolfe-Shuman Consult, 75-; bd dirs, Actronics, Inc, 81- *Mem:* Opers Res Soc Am; Inst Indust Engrs; Am Soc Eng Educ; Inst Mgt Sci. *Res:* Applications of operations research to the health services; manufacturing systems. *Mailing Add:* Dept Indust Eng Univ Pittsburgh 1048 Benedum Hall Pittsburgh PA 15261

**WOLFE, HERBERT GLENN,** DEVELOPMENTAL GENETICS, GENE ACTION. *Current Pos:* from asst prof to assoc prof, 63-70, prof physiol & cell biol, 70-94, EMER PROF PHYSIOL & CELL BIOL, UNIV KANS, 94- *Personal Data:* b Uniontown, Kans, Mar 14, 28; m 50; c 3. *Educ:* Kans State Univ, BS, 49; Univ Kans, PhD(zool), 60. *Prof Exp:* Assoc staff scientist physiol genetics, Jackson Lab, Maine, 60-63. *Concurrent Pos:* Mem genetics standards subcomt, Inst Lab Animal Resources, 65-68; NIH spec res fel, Harwell, Eng, 69-70; vis scientist, Worcester Found for Exp Biol, Shrewsbury, Mass, 77. *Mem:* Soc Develop Biol; Genetics Soc Am; Sigma Xi; Soc Study Reproduction. *Res:* Physiological genetics, specifically genetic control of physiological and developmental processes related to reproduction; blood proteins and hematopoiesis; pigmentation in mice; gene regulation of y chromosome length; reproductive physiology. *Mailing Add:* 1513 Crescent Rd Lawrence KS 66044

**WOLFE, JAMES F,** ORGANIC CHEMISTRY. *Current Pos:* from asst prof to assoc prof, 64-74, dept head, 81-89, PROF CHEM, VA POLYTECH INST & STATE UNIV, 74-, VPROVOST ACAD AFFAIRS, 90- *Personal Data:* b York, Pa, Oct 5, 36; m 59; c 2. *Educ:* Lebanon Valley Col, BS, 58; Ind Univ, PhD(chem), 63. *Prof Exp:* Res assoc, Duke Univ, 63-64. *Mem:* Am Chem Soc. *Res:* Use of multiple anions in organic synthesis; mechanisms of heteroaromatic nucleophilic substitution; synthesis of new CNS agents. *Mailing Add:* Va Polytech Inst 3105 Hahn Hall Blacksburg VA 24061-0212

**WOLFE, JAMES FREDERICK,** POLYMERS. *Personal Data:* b Bell, Calif, Dec 1, 48; m 71; c 1. *Educ:* Occidental Col, Calif, AB, 70; Univ Iowa, PhD(org chem), 75. *Prof Exp:* Vis scientist polymers, Mat Lab, Polymer Br Wright-Patterson AFB, 76; sr polymer chemist, Polymer Syntheses Res, SRI Int, 76-95. *Mem:* Am Chem Soc. *Res:* Defining molecular structural requirements and developing synthesis conditions and techniques to give aromatic, heterocyclic polymers capable of liquid crystalline order; polyphenylene benzo bisthiazole. *Mailing Add:* 130 Del Mar St San Francisco CA 94117

**WOLFE, JAMES H,** MATHEMATICS. *Current Pos:* RETIRED. *Personal Data:* b Salt Lake City, Utah, Jan 7, 22; m 56. *Educ:* Univ Utah, BA, 42; Harvard Univ, MA, 43, PhD(math), 48. *Prof Exp:* Prof math, Univ Utah, 48-94. *Mem:* Am Math Soc. *Res:* Topology and integration theory; matrices. *Mailing Add:* 1525 Emigration Canyon Salt Lake City UT 84108

**WOLFE, JAMES LEONARD,** VERTEBRATE ZOOLOGY, ANIMAL BEHAVIOR. *Current Pos:* ASSOC VPRES & DEAN GRAD SCH, UNIV SALA, 93- *Personal Data:* b Milton, Fla, May 5, 40; m 63, Doris Gillen; c Walter C. *Educ:* Univ Fla, BS, 62; Cornell Univ, PhD(vert zool), 66. *Prof Exp:* Asst prof biol, Univ Ala, 66-68; from asst to assoc prof zool, Res Ctr, Nat Space Technol Lab, Miss State Univ, 68-77, prof zool & adj assoc prof wildlife & fish, 77-81, dir, 81-85; exec dir, Archbold Biol Sta, 85-88; dean, Grad Studies & Res, Emporia State Univ, 88-91, dean, Arts & Sci, 91-93. *Concurrent Pos:* Coun mem, Grad Sch, Coun Southeastern Grad Sch & Nat Coun Univ Res Adminr. *Mem:* Animal Behav Soc; Am Soc Mammal; Ecol Soc Am. *Res:* Ecology and behavior of mammals. *Mailing Add:* Grad Studies & Res Adm 300 Univ SAla Mobile AL 36688. *Fax:* 334-460-6575

**WOLFE, JAMES PHILLIP,** SOLID STATE PHYSICS. *Current Pos:* from asst prof to assoc prof, 76-81, PROF PHYSICS, UNIV ILL, URBANA-CHAMPAIGN, 81- *Personal Data:* b Randolph Field, Tex, July 16, 43; m 66; c 3. *Educ:* Univ Calif, Berkeley, BA, 65, PhD(physics), 71. *Prof Exp:* Asst res physicist, Univ Calif, Berkeley, 71-76. *Concurrent Pos:* Prin investr, Mat Res Lab, Univ Ill, 76-, Cottrell res grant, Res Corp, 77-78, NSF grants, 78- & Air Force Off Sci Res grant, 79-83; prog dir, DOE, Sol St Sci, Univ Ill, 89-91; Humboldt Sr Scientist, 88-89. *Mem:* Fel Am Phys Soc. *Res:* Physics of semiconductors; optical and microwave studies of photo-excited phases; thermal transport in crystals; phonon imaging; electron and nuclear magnetic resonance in solids. *Mailing Add:* 104 Loomis Lab Univ Ill Urbana Champaign 1110 W Green St Urbana IL 61801. *Fax:* 217-244-2278

**WOLFE, JAMES WALLACE,** NEUROPHYSIOLOGY, PSYCHOLOGY. *Current Pos:* RETIRED. *Personal Data:* b Ludlowville, NY, Apr 11, 32; m 54; c 2. *Educ:* Univ Calif, Riverside, BA, 63; Univ Rochester, PhD(psychol), 66. *Prof Exp:* Res psychologist, Army Med Res Lab, Ft Knox, Ky, 66-68; res neurophysiologist sch aerospace med, USAF, 68-88, liason officer, Off Sci Res, Tokyo, Japan, 85-86. *Concurrent Pos:* Lectr, Univ Louisville, 67-68 & St Mary's Univ, Tex, 69-81; adj prof, Univ Tex, San Antonio, 85- *Mem:* Int Brain Res Orgn; Aerospace Med Asn; Barany Soc. *Res:* Cerebellar integration of sensory information; effects of drugs on electrophysiological responses; neurophysiological control of oculomotor function. *Mailing Add:* 9327 S Pass Rd San Antonio TX 78255-2112

**WOLFE, JOHN A(LLEN),** geological & mining engineering, volcanology; deceased, see previous edition for last biography

**WOLFE, JOHN HALL,** GENE THERAPY. *Current Pos:* ASSOC PROF PATH, UNIV PA SCH VET MED, 87- *Personal Data:* b Davenport, Iowa, Oct 16, 47; m 86, Ruth Lamdan. *Educ:* Ripon Col, AB, 69; Univ Pa, VMD, 82, PhD(immunol), 86. *Hon Degrees:* MA, Univ Pa, 93. *Prof Exp:* Fel, Sloan-Kettering Inst Cancer Res, 84-87. *Concurrent Pos:* Vis investr, Jackson Lab, 90-; adj assoc prof, Wistar Inst, 93- *Mem:* AAAS; Am Vet Med Asn; Am Soc Microbiol; Am Soc Human Genetics. *Res:* Somatic cell gene transfer; gene therapy especially using animal homologs of human genetic diseases. *Mailing Add:* Univ Pa Sch Vet Med 3800 Spruce St Philadelphia PA 19104. *Fax:* 215-573-2162

**WOLFE, LAUREN GENE,** PATHOLOGY. *Current Pos:* prof & head path & parasitol, 81-87, PROF & HEAD PATHOBIOL, AUBURN UNIV, 88- *Personal Data:* b Kenton, Ohio, Nov 7, 39; m 66, Virginia Smith. *Educ:* Ohio State Univ, DVM, 63, MS, 65, PhD(vet path), 68; Am Col Vet Path, dipl, 68. *Prof Exp:* Asst prof path, Univ Ill Med Ctr, 68-71; assoc prof microbiol, Rush-Presby-St Luke's Med Ctr, 71-74, prof, 74-81. *Concurrent Pos:* Asst microbiologist, Presby-St Luke's Hosp, 68-71. *Mem:* AAAS; Am Soc Microbiol; Am Asn Pathologists; Am Asn Immunol; Am Asn Cancer Res. *Res:* Tumor pathobiology and immunology; oncology. *Mailing Add:* Dept Pathobiol 166 Greene Hall Auburn Univ Auburn AL 36849-5519

**WOLFE, LEONHARD SCOTT,** BIOCHEMISTRY, NEUROCHEMISTRY. *Current Pos:* from asst prof neurochem to assoc prof neurol & neurosurg, 60-70, PROF NEUROL & NEUROSURG, MONTREAL NEUROL INST, MCGILL UNIV, 70-; DIR, DONNER LAB EXP NEUROCHEM, 65- *Personal Data:* b Auckland, NZ, Mar 23, 26; Can citizen; m 60; c 2. *Educ:* Univ NZ, BSc, 47; Cambridge Univ, PhD(insect physiol, biochem), 52, ScD, 76; Univ Western Ont, MD, 58; FRCP(C), 72, FRSC, 73. *Honors & Awards:* Heinrich Waelsh Lectr, Columbia Univ. *Prof Exp:* Jr lectr zool, Univ Canterbury, 49-50; assoc entomologist, Agr Res Inst, Can Dept Agr, 52-54. *Concurrent Pos:* Nat Res Coun Can med res fel, 59-60; Sister Elizabeth Kenny Found scholar, 60-61; career investr, Med Res Coun Can, 63-, mem, Grants Comt Neurol Sci, 70-74, mem, Priorities Selection & Rev Comt, 72-75; hon lectr biochem, McGill Univ, 60-70, prof biochem, 71-; consult dermat res unit, Royal Victoria Hosp, Montreal, 65-67. *Mem:* Int Brain Res Orgn; Am Soc Biol Chemists; Can Biochem Soc; Can Physiol Soc; Int Soc Neurochem; Soc Neurosci; Am Soc Neurochem. *Res:* Entomology; biology and control of biting flies; insect cholinesterases; metabolism of insecticides; biochemistry and function of complex glycolipids in neurones; membranes; role of lipid anions in excitable tissues; convulsive states; biosynthesis, release and action of prostaglandins and eicosanoids; biochemistry of lipid storage diseases and degenerative neurological diseases. *Mailing Add:* Montreal Neurol Inst & Hosp Rm 778 3801 University St Montreal PQ H3A 2B4 Can. *Fax:* 514-398-8106

**WOLFE, MARTIN S,** TROPICAL MEDICINE. *Personal Data:* b Scranton, Pa, Apr 9, 35. *Educ:* Cornell Med Col, BA, 57, MD, 61; London Sch Trop Med, DCMT, 67. *Concurrent Pos:* Rockefeller Found fel, London, 66-67; trop med consult, 69; mem, Epidemiol Bd, US Armed Forces, 94-96. *Mem:* Fel Am Col Physicians; Am Soc Trop Med & Hyg; Royal Soc Trop Med & Hyg; fel Infectious Dis Soc Am; Int Soc Travel Med. *Mailing Add:* Travelers Med Serv US Dept State 2141 K St NW No 408 Washington DC 20037. *Fax:* 202-331-0240

**WOLFE, PAUL JAY,** EXPLORATION GEOPHYSICS, ENVIRONMENTAL & ENGINEERING GEOPHYSICS. *Current Pos:* asst prof physics, Wright State Univ, 66-71, chmn dept, 72-75, assoc prof, 71-89, PROF PHYSICS & GEOL SCI, WRIGHT STATE UNIV, 89- *Personal Data:* b Mansfield, Ohio, Oct 2, 38; m 60, Carolyn Mogg; c Bruce & Craig. *Educ:* Case Inst Technol, BS, 60, MS, 63, PhD(nuclear physics), 66. *Prof Exp:* Design engr, Lamp Div, Gen Elec Co, 60-61. *Concurrent Pos:* NSF geophysicist fel, US Bur Mines, Denver, 79-80; vis scholar, Flinders Univ S Australia, 90-91. *Mem:* Soc Explor Geophysicists; Environ & Eng Geophys Soc; Am Geophys Union. *Res:* Seismic exploration techniques related to hydrocarbons and coal; shallow geophysical techniques for hydrology, engineering and archeology; subsurface cavity detection with seismic and gravity methods. *Mailing Add:* Dept Geol Wright State Univ 3640 Colonel Glenn Dayton OH 45435-0002. *E-Mail:* wolfe@wright.edu

**WOLFE, PETER E,** ENVIRONMENTAL CONSULTING, HYDROLOGY-GROUND WATER. *Current Pos:* prof, 46-81, EMER PROF GEOL, RUTGERS UNIV, 81- *Personal Data:* b Hammonton, NJ, Apr 27, 11. *Educ:* Rutgers State Univ, BS, 33; Princeton Univ, MA, 40, PhD(geol), 41. *Prof Exp:* Instr geol, Princeton Univ, 38-41, res assoc, 45-46; dir, Nfld Dept Natural Resources, 41-45. *Concurrent Pos:* Vis prof geol, Osmania Univ India, 57-81. *Mem:* Geol Soc Am; Sigma Xi. *Res:* Ground water recycling research; environmental geology. *Mailing Add:* 3202 Nesco Rd Hammonton NJ 08037

**WOLFE, PETER NORD,** PHYSICS. *Current Pos:* RETIRED. *Personal Data:* b Lakewood, Ohio, July 24, 29; m 51; c 3. *Educ:* Ohio Wesleyan Univ, BA, 51; Ohio State Univ, MS, 52, PhD(physics), 55. *Prof Exp:* NSF fel, 54-55; from res physicist to mgr systs physics dept, Res Labs, Westinghouse Elec Corp, 55-72, mgr transformer technol, 72-75, mgr laser fusion activities, 75-78; from staff mem to dep group leader, Los Alamos Nat Lab, 78-90. *Mem:* Inst Elec & Electronics Engrs. *Res:* High power lasers; power technology; applied physics; microwave spectra. *Mailing Add:* 155 Tunyo St Los Alamos NM 87544. *E-Mail:* 73467.1466@compuserve.com

**WOLFE, PHILIP,** APPLIED MATHEMATICS, OPTIMIZATION. *Current Pos:* mem res staff, 66-97, ASST CHMN, MATH SCI DEPT, IBM RES, 86-, EMER MEM STAFF, 97- *Personal Data:* b San Francisco, Calif, Aug 11, 27; m 68, Hallie Flanagan; c Sarah. *Educ:* Univ Calif, AB, 48 & PhD(math), 54. *Honors & Awards:* Von Neumann Theory Prize, Opers Res Soc Am-TIMS, 92. *Prof Exp:* Instr math, Princeton Univ, 54-57; mathematician, Rand Corp, 57-66. *Concurrent Pos:* Prof eng math, Columbia Univ, 68-77; chmn, Math Prog Soc, 78-80, vchmn, 80-82. *Mem:* Fel AAAS; Math Prog Soc; fel Econ Soc. *Res:* Mathematics of optimization; linear and nonlinear programming. *Mailing Add:* 1380 Spring Valley Rd Ossining NY 10562. *Fax:* 914-945-3434; *E-Mail:* dab@watson.ibm.com

**WOLFE, RALPH STONER,** MICROBIAL BIOCHEMISTRY. *Current Pos:* from instr to prof, 53-91, EMER PROF MICROBIOL, UNIV ILL, URBANA, 91- *Personal Data:* b New Windsor, Md, July 18, 21; m 50; c 3. *Educ:* Bridgewater Col, BS, 42; Univ Pa, MS, 49, PhD, 53. *Prof Exp:* Asst instr microbiol, Univ Pa, 47-49, instr, 51-52; asst limnol, Acad Natural Sci, Pa, 49-50. *Concurrent Pos:* NSF fel, 58; Guggenheim fel, 60 & 75. *Mem:* Nat Acad Sci; Am Soc Microbiol; Am Acad Arts & Sci; Am Soc Biol Chemists. *Res:* Metabolism and physiology of bacteria; methanogens; archaebacteria. *Mailing Add:* Dept Microbiol Univ Ill 371 Morrill Hall 601 S Goodwin Urbana IL 61801

**WOLFE, RAYMOND,** SOLID STATE PHYSICS. *Current Pos:* supvr, Magnetic Bubble Mat Group, 67-83, MEM TECH STAFF, BELL TEL LABS, 57-, PHYSICS MAT RES 83- *Personal Data:* b Hamilton, Ont, Apr 8, 27; m 54; c 3. *Educ:* Univ Toronto, BA, 49, MA, 50; Bristol Univ, PhD(physics), 55. *Prof Exp:* Physicist, Eastman Kodak Co, NY, 50-52; physicist, Gen Elec Co, Eng, 54-57. *Concurrent Pos:* Ed, Appl Solid State Sci. *Mem:* Fel Am Phys Soc. *Res:* Theoretical and experimental solid state physics; transport and optical properties of semiconductors and metals; thermoelectric materials and devices; magnetic materials; magnetic bubble devices; magneto-optic materials and devices. *Mailing Add:* AT&T Bell Labs 600 Mountain Ave Rm 3A535 Murray Hill NJ 07974. *Fax:* 908-580-6355

**WOLFE, RAYMOND GROVER, JR,** BIOCHEMISTRY. *Current Pos:* Lalor res fel, 56, from asst prof to prof, 56-83, EMER PROF CHEM, UNIV ORE, 83- *Personal Data:* b Oakland, Calif, June 1, 20; m 46; c 3. *Educ:* Univ Calif, AB, 42, MA, 48, PhD(biochem), 55. *Prof Exp:* Biochemist, Donner Lab, Univ Calif, 48-55; Nat Found Infantile Paralysis fel chem, Univ Wis, 55-56. *Concurrent Pos:* Guggenheim fel, Inst Biochem, Univ Vienna, 63-64; vis prof, Bristol Univ, 70-71; Cornell Univ, 78-79. *Mem:* AAAS. *Res:* Enzyme catalytic mechanism; structure-function relationship of polymeric enzymes; enzyme kinetics and inhibition; protein structure studies, particularly in dehydrogenases. *Mailing Add:* 1473 Luella Eugene OR 97401

**WOLFE, REUBEN EDWARD,** PULSE CODED SIGNAL SYSTEM OPERATIONS FOR TARGET LOCATION & COMMUNICATIONS, MILLIMETER RECEIVER DESIGN CHARACTERISTICS FOR HARDWARE COLLECTORS. *Current Pos:* STAFF ENGR, E SYSTS INC, 90- *Personal Data:* b Schuylkill Haven, Pa, Dec 19, 27; m 60; c 2. *Educ:* Pa State Col, BS, 49; Pa State Univ, BS, 59. *Prof Exp:* Res engr, Sylvania Elec Corp, 50-54; sci adv, Haller, Raymond & Brown Inc, 54-57; prin engr, Topp Industs, 57-59; staff engr, HRB-Singer Corp, 59-87, Singer Corp, 87-88, Hadson Corp, 88-90. *Mem:* Nat Soc Prof Engrs (secy-treas, 73-75); Am Inst Elec Engrs (secy, 66-68). *Res:* Development of linear modulated fast wave electronic beam devices for power spectral density values greater than 50 kilowatts and phase stabilities exceeding six degrees over an octave bandwidth. *Mailing Add:* 150 S Science Park Rd State College PA 16801

**WOLFE, ROBERT KENNETH,** COMPUTER SCIENCE, ENGINEERING. *Current Pos:* PROF INDUST ENG & COMPUT SCI & ENG, UNIV TOLEDO, 73- *Personal Data:* b Chattanooga, Tenn, Sept 5, 29; m 59, Chacharonis; c Robert K Jr & Ann M. *Educ:* Ga Inst Technol, BChE, 52, PhD(chem eng), 56. *Prof Exp:* Res asst chem eng, Ga Inst Technol, 51-52; chem engr, Mallinckrodt Chem Works, 55-60; systs eng mgr comput, IBM, 60-68; opers res mgr planning, Owens Ill, 68-73. *Concurrent Pos:* Tenn Eastman fel, Ga Inst Technol, 52-54; res contracts, Ohio Dept Transp & Fed Hwy Admin, 75-, Edison Indust Systs Ctr, 88-; chmn systs eng PhD prog, Univ Toledo, 76-78. *Mem:* Sigma Xi; sr mem Am Inst Indust Engrs; Am Inst Chem Engrs. *Res:* Development and use of design and decision making models using computers, informations systems and simulation. *Mailing Add:* 4930 Spring Mill Ct Toledo OH 43615. *Fax:* 419-537-2805; *E-Mail:* rwolfe@uofto2.utoledo.edu

**WOLFE, ROGER THOMAS,** ORGANIC CHEMISTRY. *Current Pos:* RETIRED. *Personal Data:* b Mt Vernon, Ill, July 31, 32; m 56; c 2. *Educ:* Bradley Univ, BS, 54; Rensselaer Polytech Inst, PhD(chem), 59; Salmon P Chase Col, JD, 69. *Prof Exp:* Lab asst analytical chem, Bradley Univ, 52-54; asst gen & org chem, Rensselaer Polytech Inst, 54-56; res chemist, Sterling-Winthrop Res Inst, NY, 56-60, from assoc patent agent to patent agent, 60-65, patent agent, Hilton-Davis Chem Co Div, Sterling Drug Co, 65-66, asst dir res & develop, 66-69, vpres res & develop, 70-75, patent attorney, Hilton-Davis Chem Co Div, 69-77, vpres res admin & legal affairs, 75-77, asst to corp dir, Safety & Environ Affairs, Sterling Drug Inc, 77-88, dir sci affairs, 88-89; tech assoc, Eastman Kodak Co, 89-91. *Mailing Add:* 3 Kingsbury Ct New York NY 14618

**WOLFE, SETH AUGUST, JR,** NEUROIMMUNOLOGY, PSYCHONEUROIMMUNOLOGY. *Current Pos:* ASST PROF IMMUNOL & NEUROIMMUNOL, DEPT MED MICROBIOL & IMMUNOL, OHIO STATE UNIV, 90- *Personal Data:* b Baltimore, Md, July 3, 44; m 76; c 2. *Educ:* Dickenson Col, BA, 70; Johns Hopkins Univ, PhD(immunol), 83. *Prof Exp:* Res contractor opthal & immunol, Dept Opthal, Sch Med, Johns Hopkins Univ, 76-81; biologist, Lab Neurochem & Neuroimmunol, Nat Inst Child Health & Human Develop, NIH, 83-84, guest researcher, Clin Immunol Sect, Gerontol Res Ctr, Nat Inst Aging; staff fel, Neurobiol Lab, Neurosci Br, Addiction Res Ctr, Nat Inst Drug Abuse, 86-90. *Mem:* Fedn Am Soc Exp Biol; Am Asn Immunologists; Soc Neurosci; AAAS; NY Acad Sci. *Res:* Receptors and communication molecules shared by the immune, endocrine and central nervous systems; mechanisms of communication and integration of neuroendocrine and immune responses and the involvement of these mechanisms in disease processes and pharmacologic intervention. *Mailing Add:* Dept Med Microbiol & Immunol Graves Hall 2078 Ohio State Univ 333 W Tenth Ave Columbus OH 43210-1239. *Fax:* 614-292-3778; *E-Mail:* wolfe22@oso.edu

**WOLFE, STEPHEN LANDIS,** CELL BIOLOGY. *Current Pos:* RETIRED. *Personal Data:* b Sept 23, 32; m 82; c 3. *Educ:* Bloomsburg State Col, BS, 54; Ohio State Univ, MS, 59; Johns Hopkins Univ, PhD(biol), 62. *Prof Exp:* NIH fel zool, Univ Minn, 62-63; from asst prof to assoc prof, Univ Calif, Davis, 63-82, sr lectr zool, 82-87, emer prof, 87. *Concurrent Pos:* Vis prof, Yale Univ, 73. *Res:* Fine and molecular structure of chromatin. *Mailing Add:* 8015 Masefield Ct West Hill CA 91304

**WOLFE, STEPHEN MITCHELL,** PLASMA PHYSICS, LASER PHYSICS. *Current Pos:* physicist, Francis Bitter Nat Magnet Lab, 77-80,' PHYSICIST, PLASMA FUSION CTR, MASS INST TECHNOL, 80- *Personal Data:* b Winter Haven, Fla, Nov 13, 49; m. *Educ:* Mass Inst Technol, SB, 71, PhD(physics), 77. *Mem:* Am Optical Soc; Am Phys Soc. *Res:* Fusion research; plasma diagnostics; optically pumped lasers; cyclotron resonance masers. *Mailing Add:* Plasma Fusion Ctr Rm NW17-10 Mass Inst Technol 175 Albany St Cambridge MA 02139

**WOLFE, WALTER MCILHANEY,** OBSTETRICS & GYNECOLOGY. *Current Pos:* Asst prof, 65-68, actg chmn dept, 69-72, ASSOC PROF OBSTET & GYNEC, SCH MED, UNIV LOUISVILLE, 80- *Personal Data:* b Baltimore, Md, Aug 15, 21; m 45; c 3. *Educ:* Univ Md, MD, 46; Am Bd Obstet & Gynec, dipl, 57. *Concurrent Pos:* Proj dir family planning, Dept HEW Grant, Louisville Gen Hosp, 71- *Mem:* Am Col Obstet & Gynec. *Res:* Applications of current technological and educational techniques to community reproductive health. *Mailing Add:* Dept Obstet/Gynec Univ Louisville Sch Med Louisville KY 40208

**WOLFE, WILLIAM LOUIS, JR,** OPTICS, ELECTRICAL ENGINEERING. *Current Pos:* RETIRED. *Personal Data:* b Yonkers, NY, Apr 5, 31; m 55; c 3. *Educ:* Bucknell Univ, BS, 53; Univ Mich, MS, 56, MSE, 66. *Prof Exp:* Asst proj engr, Sperry Gyroscope Co, 52-53; from res asst to res assoc infrared & optics, Univ Mich, 53-57, from assoc res engr to res engr, 57-66, lectr elec eng, 62-66; chief engr, Honeywell Radiation Ctr, 66-68, mgr, Lectro-Optics Dept, Honeywell, Inc, 68-69; prof optical sci, Univ Ariz, 69- *Concurrent Pos:* Lectr, Northeastern Univ, 68-69; mem, Panel Comt Undersea Warfare-Assessment Electro Optics, Nat Acad Sci; mem adv comt, Army Res Off, Study Panel on Army Countermine Adv Comt & adv comt, Nat Bur Stand & Air Force Systs Command; consult, var orgn; army sci bd. *Mem:* Fel Optical Soc Am; sr mem Inst Elec & Electronics Engrs; fel Soc Photoelectronic Instrumentation Engrs (pres elect). *Res:* Optical materials for infrared use; radiometry; space navigation using star trackers; electro-optical system design; infrared simulation; infrared reconaissance and surveillance systems; optical scattering. *Mailing Add:* Optical Sci Ctr Univ Ariz Tucson AZ 85721

**WOLFE, WILLIAM RAY, JR,** PHYSICAL CHEMISTRY. *Current Pos:* res chemist cent res dept, 52-60, chemist, Explosives Dept, 60-64, chemist develop dept, 65-68, RES ASSOC, POLYMER PROD DEPT, EXP STA, E I DU PONT DE NEMOURS & CO, INC, 68- *Personal Data:* b Grafton, WVa, Nov 16, 24; m 52; c 2. *Educ:* WVa Wesleyan Col, BS, 49; Western Reserve Univ, MS, 50, PhD(phys chem), 53. *Prof Exp:* Asst phys chem, Western Reserve Univ, 50-52. *Mem:* Am Chem Soc; Sigma Xi. *Res:* Fused salt and aqueous electrochemistry; energy conversion; high temperature chemistry; catalysis; plastics processing; microwave and dielectric film. *Mailing Add:* 1007 Parkside Dr Wilmington DE 19803-5211

**WOLFENBARGER, DAN A,** PLANT BREEDING & GENETICS. *Current Pos:* ENTOMOLOGIST COTTON INSECT RES, AGR RES SERV, USDA, 65- *Personal Data:* b White Plains, NY, Sept 23, 34; m 59, Delores J Williams; c Jay W, Jeff B & Jon A. *Educ:* Univ Fla, BSA, 56; Iowa State Univ, MS, 57; Ohio State Univ, PhD(entom), 61. *Prof Exp:* Entomologist, Agr Exp Sta, Tex A&M Univ, 61-65. *Mem:* Entom Soc Am. *Res:* Activity of and resistance and mode of inheritance to insecticides against tobacco bollworm, beet armyworm, boll weevil, tobacco budworm and sweet potato whitefly; control of cotton insects; sampling of cotton insects; effects of insect growth regulators and biological and chemical insecticides on Heliothis viresceus and Heliocoverpa zea and Spodoptera exigua. *Mailing Add:* 55 Calle Cenizo Brownsville TX 78520. *Fax:* 956-969-4877

**WOLFENBERGER, VIRGINIA ANN,** ENVIRONMENTAL PHYSIOLOGY, BEHAVIORIAL SCIENCE. *Current Pos:* PROF PHYSIOL & CHEM, TEX CHIROPRACTIC COL, 82- *Personal Data:* b Fort Worth, Tex, Sept 15, 48. *Educ:* Univ Tex, Arlington, BS, 70, MA, 73; Tex A&M Univ, PhD(biol), 81; Univ Houston, Clear Lake, MA, 85. *Prof Exp:* Asst prof biol, Xavier Univ La, 81-82. *Res:* Physiological responses of an organism to various environmental stimuli and ecological factors; responses of humans to stresses and other psychological factors. *Mailing Add:* 11215 Sage Trail Dr Houston TX 77089

**WOLFENDEN, RICHARD VANCE,** BIOCHEMISTRY. *Current Pos:* from assoc prof to prof biochem, Sch Med, 70-83, ALUMNI DISTINGUISHED PROF BIOCHEM & NUTRIT, UNIV NC, CHAPEL HILL, 83- *Personal Data:* b Oxford, Eng, May 17, 35; US citizen; m 65; c Peter & John. *Educ:* Princeton Univ, AB, 56; Oxford Univ, BA & MA, 60; Rockefeller Inst, PhD(biochem), 64. *Prof Exp:* Asst prof biochem, Princeton Univ, 64-70. *Concurrent Pos:* Mem, NSF Adv Panel Molecular Biol, 74-77, NIH Study Sect Biorg & Natural Prods, 82-86; vis fel, Exeter Col, Oxford, 69, 76. *Mem:* Fel AAAS; Am Chem Soc; Am Soc Biol Chemists. *Res:* Physical organic chemistry in relation to enzyme-catalyzed reactions. *Mailing Add:* Dept Biochem Univ NC Sch Med Chapel Hill NC 27514

**WOLFENSTEIN, LINCOLN,** THEORETICAL HIGH ENERGY PHYSICS. *Current Pos:* from instr to prof, 48-78, UNIV PROF PHYSICS, CARNEGIE-MELLON UNIV, 78- *Personal Data:* b Cleveland, Ohio, Feb 10, 23; m 43, 57; c 3. *Educ:* Univ Chicago, BS, 43, MS, 44, PhD(physics), 49. *Honors & Awards:* J J Sakurai Prize, Am Phys Soc, 92. *Prof Exp:* Physicist, Nat Adv Comt Aeronaut, 44-46. *Concurrent Pos:* NSF sr fel, Europ Orgn Nuclear Res, Geneva, Switz, 64-65; vis prof, Univ Mich, 70-71; Guggenheim fel, 74-75 & 83-84; mem, Physics Adv Comt, NSF, 74-77; Fairchild vis scholar, Calif Tech, 88. *Mem:* Nat Acad Sci; Am Phys Soc; AAAS. *Res:* Nuclear collisions; weak interactions. *Mailing Add:* Dept Physics Carnegie-Mellon Univ Pittsburgh PA 15213. *E-Mail:* lincoln@defoe.phys.cmu.edu

**WOLFERSBERGER, MICHAEL GREGG,** MEMBRANE BIOLOGY. *Current Pos:* res assoc, 77-84, sr res assoc biol, 85-96, ASSOC PROF BIOL, TEMPLE UNIV, 96- *Personal Data:* b Northampton, Pa, June 14, 44; m 65, Martha. *Educ:* Lebanon Valley Col, BS, 66; Temple Univ, PhD(biochem), 71. *Prof Exp:* Res assoc biochem, Lab Exp Dermat, Albert Einstein Med Ctr, Philadelphia, 71-73, assoc mem div res, 73-75; asst prof, Div Natural Sci & Math, Rosemont Col, 74-77. *Concurrent Pos:* Lectr, Cabrini Col, 76-77 & LaSalle Col, 81-82; consult, Rohm & Haas Co, 79-80 & 83-84; Roche fel Microbiol Inst, Swiss Fed Inst Technol, Zurich, 84-85; vis scientist, Gen Physiol & Biochem, Univ Milan,85; consult, Advan Technol Ctr, Southeastern Pa, 87; prin investr, USDA Comp res grant, 87- & NIH res grant, 90- *Mem:* AAAS; NY Acad Sci; Sigma Xi; Soc Invert Path; Am Soc Biochem & Molecular Biol. *Res:* Mechanism of active solute transport in insect epithelial cells; mechanism of action of insecticidal bacterial toxins. *Mailing Add:* 2158 Bedminster Rd Perkasie PA 18944

**WOLFF, ARTHUR HAROLD,** environmental health; deceased, see previous edition for last biography

**WOLFF, DAVID A,** CELL BIOLOGY, VIROLOGY. *Current Pos:* staff, Nat Inst Dent Res, 79-82, dep asst dir, Off Prog Activ, Nat Inst Gen Med Sci, 82-89, CHIEF, INST RES & AWARDS BR, FOGARTY INT CTR, 89- *Personal Data:* b Cleveland, Ohio, Nov 2, 34; m 58, 76, Linda Heding; c Kurt, Christopher, Andrew & Lauren. *Educ:* Col Wooster, AB, 56; Univ Cincinnati, MS, 60, PhD(microbiol), 65. *Prof Exp:* From asst prof to prof virol & microbiol, Ohio State Univ, 64-78. *Concurrent Pos:* Res grant, 66-69; Am-Swiss Found Sci exchange lectr, Switz, 70; res leave, Univ Uppsala, Sweden, 71 & Basel Univ, 74. *Mem:* AAAS; Am Soc Microbiol; Sigma Xi; Am Soc Virol. *Res:* Viral-induced cytopathic effects and relation of lysosomal enzymes; purification of virus; electron microscopy of virus infected cells; purification of lysosomes; virus interactions with synchronized cells. *Mailing Add:* Chief Int Res & Awards Br Fogarty Int Ctr NIH Bethesda MD 20892. *Fax:* 301-402-0779

**WOLFF, DONALD JOHN,** BIOCHEMISTRY, PHARMACOLOGY. *Current Pos:* Asst prof, 72-80, ASSOC PROF PHARMACOL, RUTGERS MED SCH, COL MED & DENT NJ, 80- *Personal Data:* b New York, NY, Feb 23, 42. *Educ:* Fordham Univ, BS, 63; Univ Wis, PhD(biochem), 69. *Concurrent Pos:* NIH trainee pediat, J P Kennedy, Jr Labs, Med Sch, Univ Wis, 68-72. *Mem:* AAAS. *Res:* Calcium-binding proteins; regulation of cyclic nucleotide metabolism by calcium ion. *Mailing Add:* Dept Pharmacol UMDNJ Robert Wood Johnson Med Sch Box 101 Piscataway NJ 08854

**WOLFF, EDITH CLARKE,** ENZYMOLOGY, ENDOCRINOLOGY. *Current Pos:* RES CHEMIST BIOCHEM, NAT INST DENT RES, 86- *Personal Data:* b Brooklyn, NY, Nov 1, 29; m 55, Jan; c Bretton R & Renee S. *Educ:* Smith Col, BA, 51; Radcliffe Grad Sch Arts & Sci, PhD(biochem), 56. *Prof Exp:* Res asst, Brookhaven Nat Lab, 52, Woods Hole Marine Biol Lab, 53; teaching asst biochem, Harvard Med Sch, 54-55; postdoctoral res fel, Nat Inst Arthritis & Metab Dis, 56-58, Nat Inst Med Res, Mill Hill, Eng, 58-59; res chemist, Nat Inst Dent Res, 59-62; asst to ed & mgr, Ed Off, J Biol Chem, 68-86. *Concurrent Pos:* Co-chair, Comt Equal Opportunities Women, Am Soc Biochem & Molecular Biol, 88-92. *Mem:* Am Soc Biochem & Molecular Biol; Am Soc Cell Biol. *Res:* Action of thyroxine on succinate oxidation; enzymology of carboxypeptidase B and deoxyhypusine synthase; modification of a specific protein lysine to form a unique residue, deoxyhypusine, involved in eukaryotic cell proliferation. *Mailing Add:* Nat Inst Dent Res NIH Bldg 30 Rm 211 Bethesda MD 20892-4340. *Fax:* 301-402-0823; *E-Mail:* wolff@yoda.nidr.nih.gov

**WOLFF, EDWARD A,** ELECTRICAL ENGINEERING. *Current Pos:* head, Syst Study Off, 71-73, ASSOC CHIEF COMMUN & NAVIG DIV, NASA GODDARD SPACE FLIGHT CTR, 73-; SR STAFF MEM, MRJ, INC, 89- *Personal Data:* b Chicago, Ill, Oct 31, 29; m 51; c 3. *Educ:* Univ Ill, BSEE, 51; Univ Md, MS, 53, PhD, 61. *Honors & Awards:* Centennial Medal, Inst Elec & Electronics Engrs, 85. *Prof Exp:* Electronic scientist, US Naval Res Lab, 51-54; proj engr, Md Electronic Mfg Corp, Litton Indust, 56-59 & Electromagnetic Res Corp, 59-61; staff consult & mgr, Space Eng Lab, Aero Geo Astro Corp, Keltec Indust, Inc, Md, 61-65, chief engr, 65-67; vpres, Geotronics, Inc, 67-71. *Concurrent Pos:* Mem, Md Gov Sci Resources Adv Bd, treas, Joint Bd Sci Educ. *Mem:* Nat Soc Prof Engrs; fel Inst Elec & Electronics Engrs; Am Inst Aeronaut & Astronaut; Antennas & Propagation Soc (pres, 77). *Res:* Antennas; microwave components; electromagnetic waves. *Mailing Add:* 1021 Cresthaven Dr Silver Spring MD 20903

**WOLFF, ERNEST N,** GEOLOGY, MINING ENGINEERING. *Current Pos:* PROF EXPLOR ENG & ASSOC DIR, MINERAL INDUST RES LAB, UNIV ALASKA, 69- *Personal Data:* b St Paul, Minn. *Educ:* Univ Alaska, BS, 41; Univ Ore, MS, 59, PhD(geol), 65. *Prof Exp:* Field asst, Alaska Territorial Dept Mines, 39-40; observer geophys, Carnegie Inst Dept Terrestrial Magnetism, 41-46; observer in chg, Univ Alaska, 46-48, res assoc & asst prof mining eng, Sch Mines, 51-57; asst prof geol, Colo State Univ, 59-66; assoc prof geol & mining eng, Univ Alaska, 66-67; assoc prof geol, Colo State Univ, 67-69. *Mem:* Am Inst Mining, Metall & Petrol Engrs; Sigma Xi. *Res:* Economic geology of Alaska; regional Alaskan economics. *Mailing Add:* PO Box 10705 Fairbanks AK 99710-0705

**WOLFF, FREDERICK WILLIAM,** PHARMACOLOGY, MEDICINE. *Current Pos:* prof, 65-90, EMER PROF MED, SCH MED, GEORGE WASHINGTON UNIV, 90- *Personal Data:* b Berlin, Ger, Aug 21, 20; m 64, Katherine Chura; c Susan, Peter & Catherine. *Educ:* Univ Durham, MB, BS, 46, MD, 57. *Hon Degrees:* Georgeian USSR Acad Sci, Dipl, 81. *Prof Exp:* House physician, Royal Victoria Infirmary, Univ Durham, 46-47; house physician, med registr & resident med officer, Southend-on-Sea Gen Hosp, Eng, 47-50; med registr, Whittington Hosp, 53-54; clin pharmacologist, Wellcome Res Inst, 55-59; asst prof med, Sch Med & Endocrine Clin, Johns Hopkins Univ, 59-65; pres, Inst Drug Develop, Washington, DC, 80-86. *Concurrent Pos:* Sr res asst, Post-Grad Med Sch, Univ London & Whittington Hosp, 55-59; consult, Food & Drug Admin, DC & Children's Med Ctr, DC, 71-79. *Mem:* Am Diabetes Asn; Am Soc Pharmacol & Exp Therapeut; Am Fedn Clin Res; Am Heart Asn; Royal Soc Med; Brit Pharmacol Soc. *Res:* Therapeutics; clinical pharmacology; endocrinology; diabetes; hypertension. *Mailing Add:* 10908 Piney Meeting House Rd Potomac MD 20854-1300. *Fax:* 301-299-5292

**WOLFF, GEORGE LOUIS,** GENETICS, TOXICOLOGY. *Current Pos:* chief mammalian genetics br, 72-74, chief div mutagenic res, 74-79, sr sci coordr genetics, 79-88, SR RES SCIENTIST, NAT CTR TOXICOL RES, US FOOD & DRUG ADMIN, 88- *Personal Data:* b Hamburg, Ger, Aug 24, 28; US citizen; m 53, Eleanor Herstein; c Adrienne A & David B. *Educ:* Ohio State Univ, BS, 50; Univ Chicago, PhD(zool), 54. *Prof Exp:* Biologist, Nat

Cancer Inst, 56-58; res assoc, Inst Cancer Res, 58-63, supvr animal colony, 58-68, asst mem, 63-72, geneticist, 68-72. *Concurrent Pos:* USPHS fel, Nat Cancer Inst, 54-56; prof assoc, Nat Acad Sci, 56-57; consult, Am Asn Accreditation Lab Animal Care, 70-75; mem, HEW subcomt, Environ Mutagenesis, 73-81; from asst prof to assoc prof biochem, Univ Ark, 73-89, assoc prof interdisciplinary toxicol, 81-90, prof biochem, 89-, prof interdisciplinary toxicol 90-; assoc ed, Lab Animal Sci, 64-76. *Mem:* Soc Toxicol; Am Asn Cancer Res; Environ Mutagen Soc; Genetics Soc Am; Soc Exp Biol & Med. *Res:* Developmental and molecular genetics of carcinogenic response to environmental toxicants and of obesity; genetic aspects of toxicology; regulation of gene expression in mutant mice. *Mailing Add:* Div Biochem Toxicol Nat Ctr Toxicol Res Jefferson AR 72079. *Fax:* 870-543-7635

**WOLFF, GEORGE THOMAS,** AIR POLLUTION METEOROLOGY & CHEMISTRY. *Current Pos:* sr scientist, Gen Motors Corp, 77-81, group leader, 78-86, sr staff scientist, 81-86, prin scientist & sect mgr, Res Labs, 86-92, PRIN SCIENTIST ENVIRON & ENERGY STAFF, GEN MOTORS CORP, 92- *Personal Data:* b Irvington, NJ, Nov 27, 47; m 72, Carol Wirth; c Elaine, Meg & Kristen. *Educ:* NJ Inst Technol, BSChe, 69; NY Univ, MS, 70; Rutgers Univ, PhD(environ sci), 74. *Honors & Awards:* John Campbell Award, Gen Motors Res Labs, 84, Environmental Achievement Award, 83. *Prof Exp:* Assoc engr, Interstate Sanitation Comn, 73-77. *Concurrent Pos:* Prog chmn, Int Conf Carbonaceous Aerosols, 80; adj prof atmospheric & oceanic sci, Univ Mich, 84-88; tech prog chmn, Air & Waste Mgt Asn, 85, dir, 86-89; consult, Clean Air Sci Adv Comt, US Environ Protection Agency, 85-87 & mem, 87-, chair 93-; adj prof, Sch Pub Health, Univ Mich, 91-; Mich Environ Sci Bd, 92-; mem, Environ Futures Comm, US Environ Protection Agency, 93. *Mem:* Am Meteorol Soc; fel Air & Waste Mgt Asn (vpres, 88-89); Sigma Xi. *Res:* Photochemical smog formation pollutant transport; chemical composition of aerosols; sources of aerosols; effect of aerosol composition on visibility; fate of air pollutants and acid precipitation; effect of pollutants on climate. *Mailing Add:* Gen Motors Pub Policy Ctr Gen Motors Bldg 3044 W Grand Blvd Detroit MI 48202

**WOLFF, GUNTHER ARTHUR,** PHYSICAL CHEMISTRY, SOLID STATE CHEMISTRY. *Current Pos:* G A CONSULT, NPO, 81- *Personal Data:* b Essen, Ger, Mar 31, 18; nat US; m 45; c 2. *Educ:* Univ Berlin, BS, 44, MS, 45; Tech Univ, Berlin, ScD(theoret inorg chem), 48. *Prof Exp:* Res assoc, Fritz-Haber Inst, Ger, 44-50, sci asst head & dep chief, 50-53; consult & sr res scientist, Signal Corps Res & Develop Labs, US Dept Army, NJ, 53-60; sr group leader mat res solid state res dept, Harshaw Chem Co, Ohio, 60-63; dir mat res, Erie Tech Prod, Inc, 63-64; prin scientist, Tyco Labs, Inc, 64-70; consult chemist, Lighting Res & Tech Serv Oper, Gen Elec Co, East Cleveland, 70-77; sr scientist, Epidyne, Inc, 77-78; sr engr, Nat Semiconductor Corp, 78-81. *Concurrent Pos:* Mem comn crystal growth, Int Union Crystallog, 66-75, mem, Am Comt Crystal Growth, 67-72; chmn, Gordon Conf Chem & Metall of Semiconductors, 65; chmn, Int Union Crystallog Topical Meeting Crystal Morphol & Its Rel to Crystal Struc & Environ Conditions, 69. *Mem:* Am Asn Crystal Growth; Am Chem Soc; Electrochem Soc; fel Mineral Soc Am; fel Am Inst Chemists; AAAS; Am Crystallog Asn; Am Ceramic Soc; NY Acad Sci. *Res:* Crystal growth and dissolution, including evaporation and etching; crystal imperfections; electroluminescence and luminescence; semiconductors and ceramics; chemical bonding; solid state chemistry and physics. *Mailing Add:* 3776 N Hampton Rd Cleveland Heights OH 44121-2027

**WOLFF, IVAN A,** RESEARCH ADMINISTRATION, SCIENCE MANAGEMENT. *Current Pos:* RETIRED. *Personal Data:* b Louisville, Ky, Feb 10, 17; m 41, Mary Strawitz; c Martin, Ronald, Harold & James. *Educ:* Univ Louisville, BA, 37; Univ Wis, MA, 38, PhD(org chem), 40. *Prof Exp:* Fel biochem, Univ Wis, 40-41; asst chemist, Northern Regional Res Lab, Bur Agr Chem & Eng, Sci & Educ Admin Agr Res, USDA, 41-42, from assoc chemist to chemist, 43-48, unit leader, 48-54, asst head, Cereal Crops Sect, 54-58, chief, Indust Crops Lab, Northern Utilization Res & Develop Div, Agr Res Serv, 58-69, dir, E Region Res Ctr, Agr Res Serv, 69-80, emer dir, E Region Res Ctr, Agr Res Serv, 81-93, Consult, 93- *Concurrent Pos:* Mem, Subcomt Natural Toxicants Food Protection Comt, Nat Acad Sci-Nat Res Coun, 70-74; consult chem & mgt, 94- *Mem:* Am Chem Soc; Am Oil Chem Soc; Soc Econ Bot (pres, 64-65); Inst Food Technol. *Res:* Biochemistry, nutrition, processing utilization of farm commodities, and the constituents, components and derivatives from them; authored or coauthored over two hundred refereed professional publications and over 20 patents, many book chapters. *Mailing Add:* 1957 N Honore Ave Apt C314 Sarasota FL 34235

**WOLFF, JAN,** BIOCHEMISTRY, ENDOCRINOLOGY. *Current Pos:* from surgeon to sr surgeon, 55-63, chief, Sect Endocrine Biochem, 75-91, MED DIR, NIH, 63-, ASSOC CHIEF, CLIN ENDOCRINOL BR, 65-, LAB BIOCHEM PHARMACOL, 91- *Personal Data:* b Dusseldorf, Ger, Apr 25, 25; US citizen; m 55; c 2. *Educ:* Univ Calif, BA, 45, PhD(physiol, biochem), 49; Harvard Univ, MD, 53. *Prof Exp:* Teaching asst, Univ Calif, 46 & res asst, 46-49; res asst, Harvard Univ, 54-55. *Concurrent Pos:* NSF sr fel, London & Paris, 58-59; vis prof, Univ Naples, 68 & Univ Lyon, 83. *Mem:* Am Thyroid Asn; Am Soc Biol Chemists; Endocrine Soc; Protein Soc. *Res:* Chemistry and biochemistry of tubulin, microtubule assembly, microtubule-associated proteins, and ligands that regulate polymerization such as colchicine and its analogues, vinblastine, calcium and calmodulin and fluorescent probes; properties; activation by calmodulin and host-cell penetration of adenylate cyclase from Bordetella pertussis and its role as a virulence factor; properties and function of biological membranes, particularly thyroid membranes, and the relation of adenylate cyclase to receptors and membrane organization, transport, secretory mechanisms, and tubulin-membrane interactions. *Mailing Add:* NIH Rm 2A23 Bldg 8 Bethesda MD 20892-0001. *Fax:* 301-402-0240

**WOLFF, JOHN B,** BIOPHYSICS. *Current Pos:* RETIRED. *Personal Data:* b Ger, May 5, 25; nat US; m 50, Marion; c 1. *Educ:* Hunter Col, AB, 50; Johns Hopkins Univ, MA, 51, PhD(biol), 55. *Honors & Awards:* Distinguished Serv Award, Biophys Soc, 91. *Prof Exp:* NIH fel, 52-54; biochemist, Smithsonian Inst, 54-58; vis scientist & res assoc, Nat Inst Arthritis & Metab Dis, NIH, 58-60, chemist, Nat Inst Neurol Dis & Blindness, 60-62, health scientist adminr, 62-65, Div Res Grants, 65-90. *Mem:* Fel AAAS; Am Soc Biochem & Molecular Biol; Biophys Soc (treas, 71-78). *Res:* Microbial and plant biochemistry; enzymology. *Mailing Add:* 5609 Roosevelt St Bethesda MD 20817-6739

**WOLFF, JOHN SHEARER, III,** biochemistry, virology, for more information see previous edition

**WOLFF, MANFRED ERNST,** MEDICINAL CHEMISTRY. *Current Pos:* AT ALERGAN PHARMACEUT. *Personal Data:* b Berlin, Ger, Feb 14, 30; nat US; div; c 3. *Educ:* Univ Calif, BS, 51, MS, 53, PhD(pharmaceut chem), 55. *Prof Exp:* Asst, Univ Calif, 52-55; res fel, Univ Va, 55-57; sr med chemist, Smith Kline & French Labs, 57-60; from asst prof to assoc prof pharmaceut chem, Univ Calif, San Francisco, 60-65, prof, 65-, chmn dept, 70- *Concurrent Pos:* Vis prof, Imperial Col Sci, London, 67-68; ed, Burger's Med Chem, 79-81. *Mem:* Am Chem Soc; Am Pharmaceut Asn; fel Am Acad Pharmaceut Sci; Sigma Xi. *Res:* Synthesis of potential anabolic, anti-inflammatory or anti-aldosterone hormone analogs; synthesis of aldosterone, of cardiac glycosides and aglycones; steroid chemistry and biochemistry. *Mailing Add:* 1304 Morningside Dr Laguna Beach CA 92651

**WOLFF, MANFRED PAUL (FRED),** GEOLOGY, SEDIMENTOLOGY. *Current Pos:* assoc prof, 74-81, PROF GEOL, HOFSTRA UNIV, 81- *Personal Data:* b New York, NY, Apr 26, 38; m 88, Suzanne Mosier; c Brian & Mark. *Educ:* Hofstra Univ, BS, 61; Univ Rochester, MS, 63; Cornell Univ, PhD(geol), 67. *Prof Exp:* instr, Cornell Univ, 64-67, from asst prof to assoc prof geol, 67-74, chmn dept, 71-75. *Concurrent Pos:* Wilson P Foss fel, Cornell Univ, 63-65; Am Penrose Bequest grant, Geol Soc Am, 66; mem adv comt, Nassau-Suffolk Regional Planning Bd, 66-69; NSF grant, 69; Hofstra Univ res awards, 75-93; mem sci adv comt on coastal dynamics, NY State Dept Parks & Recreation; exec secy, NY State Geol Asn, 80-91. *Mem:* Geol Soc Am; Soc Econ Paleont & Mineral; Nat Asn Geol Teachers; Sigma Xi. *Res:* Ancient and recent clastic and carbonate depositional environments; hurricane effects on beaches; coastal processes; hurricane effects on coastal stabilization and structures; sedimentology of beaches and barrier islands; nearshore shelf processes. *Mailing Add:* Dept Geol 114 Hofstra Univ Hempstead NY 11550-1090. *Fax:* 516-463-6010; *E-Mail:* geompw@vaxc. hofstra.edu

**WOLFF, MARIANNE,** PATHOLOGY, SURGICAL PATHOLOGY. *Current Pos:* RETIRED. *Personal Data:* b Berlin, Ger; US citizen; m 52, Herbert (deceased); c Jay D & Daniel C. *Educ:* Hunter Col, BA, 48; Columbia Univ, MD, 52. *Prof Exp:* Intern med, Presby Hosp, New York, 52-53; asst resident lab, Mt Sinai Hosp, New York, 53-54, asst resident path, St Luke's Hosp, 54-56; from instr to assoc prof surg path, Col Physicians & Surgeons, Columbia Univ, 56-70, from assoc prof to prof clin surg path, 70-93; assoc surg pathologist, Presby Hosp, New York, 71-82. *Concurrent Pos:* Resident, Presby Hosp, New York, 56-57, asst surg pathologist, 68-71; from asst pathologist to assoc pathologist, Roosevelt Hosp, New York, 57-68; mem, Arthur Purdy Stout Soc Surg Pathologists, 68-; attend pathologist, Morristown Mem Hosp, Morristown, NJ, dir surg path & vchmn, Dept Path, 82-93; anat pathologist, Quest Diag, Inc, 93- *Mem:* US Asn Pathologists; Can Asn Pathologists. *Mailing Add:* 3 London Ct Teaneck NJ 07666-6461. *Fax:* 201-462-4712

**WOLFF, MILO MITCHELL,** PHOTOPOLARIMETRY OF ASTEROIDS, MODELS OF FUNDAMENTAL PARTICLES. *Current Pos:* CHIEF EXEC OFFICER, TECHNOTRAN PRESS, 93- *Personal Data:* b Glen Ridge, NJ, Aug 9, 23; m 54, Lie Ching; c Eric, Jennifer, Douglas, Winston & Lanling. *Educ:* Upsala Col, BS, 48; Univ Pa, MS, 53, PhD(physics), 58. *Hon Degrees:* DSc, Univ Kelania, Sri-Lanka, 92. *Honors & Awards:* Apollo Navig Team Award, 69. *Prof Exp:* Electronic engr, Philco Corp, Pa, 49-51; lectr electronics, Community Col, Temple Univ, 52-53; instr physics, Univ Pa, 58; Univ Ky-Agency Int Develop asst prof, Bandung Tech Inst, Indonesia, 58-61, assoc prof, 62; res physicist, Mass Inst Technol, 63-69; prof physics, Nanyang Univ, Singapore, 70-72; mem tech staff, Aerospace Corp, Los Angeles, 72-75; chief, Sci & Technol Sect, Econ Comn Africa-UN, Addis Ababa, 75-77; mem staff, Int Technol Asn, Long Beach, 78-92. *Concurrent Pos:* Asia Found vis prof physics, Vidyalankara Univ, Ceylon, 66-68; mem, US-Pakistan Sci Surv Team, US NSF, 74; mem methane gas panel, Nat Acad Sci, 74; vis prof, Nanjing Univ, China, 81; vis astronr, Paris Observ, 82. *Mem:* Inst Elec & Electronics Engrs; Am Phys Soc; Sigma Xi. *Res:* Methods of cultural adaptation to technology in traditional societies; technical development in Southeast Asia; the analysis of polarized light scattered from asteriods, moons, and particulate surfaces; numerous publications; electron, natural laws and cosmology. *Mailing Add:* 1124 Third St Manhattan Beach CA 90266. *Fax:* 310-379-7855; *E-Mail:* mwolff@beachnet.gen.ca.us

**WOLFF, NIKOLAUS EMANUEL,** CHEMISTRY, ELECTRONICS. *Current Pos:* TECHNOL CONSULT TO MGT, 76- *Personal Data:* b Munich, Ger, July 7, 21; nat US; m 54; c 3. *Educ:* Munich Tech Univ, Cand, 48; Princeton Univ, MA, 51, PhD(chem), 52. *Prof Exp:* Asst instr, Princeton Univ, 50-52, instr chem, 52-53; res chemist, Jackson Lab & Exp Sta, E I Du Pont de Nemours & Co, 53-58; mem tech staff, Labs, David Sarnoff Res Ctr, RCA Corp, 59-63, head mat processing res, 63-66; assoc lab dir, Process Res & Develop Lab, 67-68; mgr mat progs, Xerox Corp, 68-69, mgr photoreceptor technol, 69-71, mgr mat info technol group, 71-76. *Mem:* Fel AAAS; Am Chem Soc; emer mem Tech Asn Pulp & Paper Indust; fel Am Inst Chemists; Soc Photog Sci & Eng. *Res:* Steroid, fluorine and polymer chemistry; organometallics; electronic properties of organic materials; chemistry of recording media; electrophotography; solid state technology and integrated circuits. *Mailing Add:* PO Box 1003 Hanover NH 03755-1003

**WOLFF, PETER A,** NONLINEAR OPTICS, DILUTED MAGNETIC SEMICONDUCTORS. *Current Pos:* EMER PROF PHYSICS, MASS INST TECHNOL, 94- *Personal Data:* b Oakland, Calif, Nov 15, 23; m 48, Catherine Carroll; c Catherine M & Peter. *Educ:* Univ Calif, Berkeley, BS, 45, PhD(physics), 51. *Prof Exp:* Postdoctoral, Lawrence Radiation Lab, 51-52; mem staff, Bell Labs, 52-65, mem tech staff, 66-70; prof physics, Univ Calif, San Diego, 65-66; prof physics, Mass Inst Technol, 66-88; res Lab Electronics, 76-81, dir, Nat Magnetics Lab, 81-88; fel, NEC Res Inst, 89-94. *Mem:* Fel Am Phys Soc; Am Acad Arts & Sci. *Res:* Semiconductor physics; magnetism; optics; nonlinear optics of semiconductors and diluted magnetic semiconductors. *Mailing Add:* Dept Physics Mass Inst Technol 13-2077 Cambridge MA 02139. *E-Mail:* wolff@slipknot.mit.edu

**WOLFF, PETER HARTWIG,** MEDICINE, PSYCHOBIOLOGY. *Current Pos:* res assoc, 56-61, ASSOC, CHILDREN'S HOSP MED CTR, 61-, DIR RES, 64-; PROF PSYCHIAT, HARVARD MED SCH, 71- *Personal Data:* b Krefeld, Ger, July 8, 26; US citizen; m 62; c 4. *Educ:* Univ Chicago, BS, 47, MD, 50. *Honors & Awards:* Kirby Collier Mem Lectr, Rochester, NY, 63; Helen Sargent Prize, Menninger Found, 66; Felix & Helene Deutsch Prize, Boston Psychoanal Inst, 66; Sandor Rado Lectr, Columbia Univ, 69. *Prof Exp:* Asst psychiat, Harvard Med Sch, 56-59, instr, 58-61, assoc, 61-64, asst prof, 64-71. *Concurrent Pos:* Fel neurophysiol, Univ Chicago, 51-52; instr, Boston Psychoanal Inst, 67- *Mem:* Fel Am Psychiat Asn. *Res:* Developmental psychobiology; biological basis of behavior. *Mailing Add:* Children's Hosp Med Ctr 300 Longwood Ave Boston MA 02115-5737

**WOLFF, ROBERT JOHN,** ARACHNOLOGY, INVERTEBRATE ZOOLOGY. *Current Pos:* ASSOC PROF BIOL & GEOG, TRINITY CHRISTIAN COL, 80- *Personal Data:* b Marquette, Mich, Jan 22, 52; m 74. *Educ:* Hope Col, BA, 74; Western Mich Univ, MA, 76; Univ Wis-Madison, PhD(biol), 85. *Concurrent Pos:* Fac aquatic biol, Au Sable Inst Environ Studies, 86 & 87; mem, Educ Div, Argonne Nat Labs, 89-, res fac, 91; mem educ comn, Am Soc Zoologists, 90-; vis asst prof biol sci, Univ Ill, Chicago, 90; sci educ consult, Ill Sch Dist 161, 90-91; field assoc, Field Mus Natural Hist, 91. *Mem:* Sigma Xi; Am Arachnological Soc; Am Soc Zoologists; Am Inst Biol Sci; Soc Conserv Biol. *Res:* Biology, ecology and taxonomy of spiders and other invertebrates; conservation biology of tarantulas and fauna of natural areas. *Mailing Add:* Trinity Christian Col 6601 W College Dr Palos Heights IL 60463-0929

**WOLFF, ROBERT L,** AGRICULTURE. *Current Pos:* asst prof, 72-77, PROF & DEPT CHMN AGR, SOUTHERN ILL UNIV, CARBONDALE, 77- *Personal Data:* b Marion, Tex, Dec 12, 39; m 60; c 2. *Educ:* Tex A&I Univ, BS, 66; Tex A&M Univ, MS, 68; La State Univ, Baton Rouge, PhD(agr), 71. *Prof Exp:* Asst prof agr, Tex A&I Univ, 66-72. *Mem:* Am Soc Agr Eng. *Res:* Agricultural mechanization. *Mailing Add:* 1412 W Mcguire Rd Makanda IL 62958

**WOLFF, ROGER GLEN,** ROLE OF CONFINING LAYERS. *Current Pos:* RETIRED. *Personal Data:* b Eureka, SDak, Sept 7, 32; m 59, Mary Varga; c Mark R & Steven C. *Educ:* SDak Sch Mines, BS, 58; Univ Ill, MS, 60, PhD(geol), 61. *Prof Exp:* Hydrologist, US Geol Surv, Dept Interior, 61-79, chief res, Water Resources Div, 79-94. *Mem:* Fel Geol Soc Am; Am Geophys Union; Int Asn Hydrologists; Sigma Xi. *Res:* Weathering of rock, impact on water quality; role of confining beds on movement of water and dissolved solutes. *Mailing Add:* PO Box 215 Bluemont VA 20135

**WOLFF, RONALD GILBERT,** VERTEBRATE PALEONTOLOGY, VERTERBRATE MORPHOLOGY. *Current Pos:* asst prof, 73-78, ASSOC PROF ZOOL, UNIV FLA, 78- *Personal Data:* b Lewiston, Idaho, Jan 17, 42; m; c 1. *Educ:* Whitman Col, AB, 64; Univ Ore, MA, 66; Univ Calif, Berkeley, PhD(paleont), 71. *Prof Exp:* Fel anat, Univ Chicago, 71-72, res assoc, 72-73. *Concurrent Pos:* Prin investr grant, Col Arts & Sci, Univ Fla, 77-79 & Div Environ Biol, NSF, 78-83; co-investr grant, Nat Geog Soc, 78-79. *Mem:* Soc Vert Paleont; Paleont Soc; Sigma Xi; Ecol Soc Am; Am Soc Mammalogists; Am Soc Zoologists. *Res:* Population and community ecology of mammals; environment of human evolution; Tertiary and Quaternary vertebrate communities. *Mailing Add:* Dept Zool Univ Fla PO Box 118525 Gainesville FL 32611-8525

**WOLFF, RONALD KEITH,** AEROSOLS IN BIOMEDICINE, MUCOCILIARY CLEARANCE. *Current Pos:* RES SCIENTIST, LILLY RES LABS, 88- *Personal Data:* b Brantford, Ont, July 25, 46; US citizen; m 72, Mary; c Mark, Sarah, Andy & Brian. *Educ:* Univ Toronto, BSc, 68, MSc, 69, PhD(med biophys), 72, Am Bd Toxicol, dipl, 83. *Prof Exp:* Res fel respiratory physiol, McMaster Univ, 73-76; sr scientist, Lovelace Inhalation Toxicol Res Inst, 76-88. *Mem:* Soc Toxicol; Am Indust Hyg Asn; Am Thoracic Soc; Am Physiol Soc; Am Asn Physicists Med; Am Asn Aerosol Res,(pres, 95-99). *Res:* Inhalation toxicology; deposition and clearance of inhaled particles from the lung including effects of toxic agents, inhalation carcinogenesis; drug delivery. *Mailing Add:* Lilly Res Labs PO Box 708 Greenfield IN 46140. *Fax:* 317-277-4783; *E-Mail:* rkw@lilly.com

**WOLFF, SHELDON,** CYTOGENETICS, RADIOBIOLOGY. *Current Pos:* PROF CYTOGENETICS, UNIV CALIF, SAN FRANCISCO, 66-, DIR, LAB RADIOBIOL & ENVIRON HEALTH, 83- *Personal Data:* b Peabody, Mass, Sept 22, 28; m 54; c 3. *Educ:* Tufts Col, BS, 50; Harvard Univ, MA, 51, PhD(biol), 53. *Honors & Awards:* E O Lawrence Award, US AEC, 73; Environ Mutagen Soc Award,82. *Prof Exp:* Biologist, Oak Ridge Nat Lab, 53-66, mem sr res staff, 65-66. *Concurrent Pos:* Mem subcomt radiobiol, Nat Acad Sci-Nat Res Coun, 61-77, space sci bd, 74-78, Comt nuclear sci, 73-75; vis prof, Univ Tenn, 62; mem comt 15 environ biol & chmn panel radiation biol of comt 15, Space Sci Bd, Nat Acad Sci, 62, mem comt postdoctoral fels div biol & agr, 62-65; consult spec facil prog, NSF, 62-64; mem exec comt, Nat Acad Sci-Nat Res Coun Space Biol Summer Study, 68, mem exec comt priorities study for NASA, 70, mem subcomt genetics effects adv comt to Environ Protection Agency, Div Med Sci, 70-; mem safe drinking water comt, Nat Acad Sci, 76-81; prog chmn, XIII Int Cong Genetics; mem comt federal res ionizing radiation & mem comt chem environ mutagens, Nat Res Coun-Nat Acad Sci, 80-81; mem, Mammalian Genetics study Sect, NIH, 80-83; chmn, Health & Environ Res Adv Comt, US Dept Educ, 87- *Mem:* Radiation Res Soc; Bot Soc Am; Am Soc Cell Biol; Sigma Xi; Environ Mutagen Soc (pres, 80). *Res:* Chromosome structure; radiation genetics and cytology; chromosome structure; genetics and cytology. *Mailing Add:* 41 Eugene St Mill Valley CA 94941

**WOLFF, SIDNEY CARNE,** astrophysics, for more information see previous edition

**WOLFF, STEVEN,** ORGANIC CHEMISTRY. *Current Pos:* res leader, 95, RES INVESTR, CHEM SYNTHESIS DEPT, HOFFMANN-LA ROCHE, INC, 87- *Personal Data:* b New York, NY, Apr 15, 43; m 84, L Feigenbaum; c Elizabeth R & Avery M. *Educ:* Williams Col, BA, 65; Yale Univ, PhD(org chem), 70. *Prof Exp:* Fel org chem, Squibb Inst Med Res, 70-71; res assoc, Rockefeller Univ, 71-73, from asst prof to assoc prof org chem, 71-87. *Mem:* Am Chem Soc; Royal Soc Chem; Int Am Photochem Soc; Sigma Xi. *Res:* Mechanistic organic photochemistry; organic synthesis. *Mailing Add:* Hoffmann-La Roche Inc 340 Kingsland St Nutley NJ 07110

**WOLFF, THEODORE ALBERT,** ENTOMOLOGY, MEDICAL PARASITOLOGY. *Current Pos:* TECH STAFF MEM, SANDIA NAT LABS, 81- *Personal Data:* b Philadelphia, Pa, Feb 24, 43; m 62. *Educ:* NMex Highlands Univ, BS, 65; Univ NC, Chapel Hill, MSPH, 69; Univ Utah, PhD(biol), 76. *Prof Exp:* Vol biol, Peace Corps, Malaysia, 65-68; environ scientist entom, NMex Environ Improv Agency, 69-72; teaching fel biol, Univ Utah, 72-74; environ scientist, NMex Environ Improv Agency, 74-76, dir radiation protection prog, 76-81. *Mem:* Assoc Sigma Xi; Am Mosquito Control Asn; Am Pub Health Asn; Health Physics Soc. *Res:* Systematic studies of mountain Aedes mosquitoes; subgenus Ochlerotatus of Arizona and New Mexico; the transportation of radioactive materials. *Mailing Add:* 10443 Fourth St NW Albuquerque NM 87114

**WOLFF, THOMAS E,** CHEMICAL & PATENT INFORMATION, INFORMATION ANALYSIS. *Current Pos:* res chemist, 80-87, staff res chemist, 87-90, SR RES SCIENTIST, AMOCO CORP, 90- *Personal Data:* b Chicago, Ill, Oct 21, 52; m 80, Marcy Epstein; c Ilana & Joseph. *Educ:* Mass Inst Technol, BS, 74; Stanford Univ, PhD(inorg chem), 80. *Prof Exp:* Chemist, Corp Res Lab, Exxon Res & Eng Co, 75-76. *Concurrent Pos:* Patent agent, US Patent & Trademark Off, 93- *Mem:* Am Chem Soc. *Res:* Chemical information* retrieval and analysis; patent searching and analysis; new methods for access to information by researchers; polymer science; polyolefin catalysis; catalytic oxidation for production of polycarboxylic acids. *Mailing Add:* Amoco Corp PO Box 3011 Naperville IL 60566-7011. *E-Mail:* tewolff@amoco.com

**WOLFF, WILLIAM FRANCIS,** ORGANIC CHEMISTRY. *Current Pos:* res chemist, 54-58, sr proj chemist, 58-61, sr res scientist, 61-82, INDEPENDENT RES, STANDARD OIL CO, IND, 82- *Personal Data:* b Newark, NJ, June 17, 21; m 48; c 4. *Educ:* Yale Univ, BS, 47. *Prof Exp:* Res chemist, Standard Oil Co, Ind, 47-53 & Pa Salt Mfg Co, 53-54. *Mem:* AAAS; Am Chem Soc. *Res:* Hydrocarbon polymers; organic sulfur and chlorine compounds; carbons and aromatic complexes; heterogeneous catalysis; electromagnetism. *Mailing Add:* 205 Rich Road Park Forest IL 60466-1611

**WOLFFE, ALAN PAUL,** PROTEIN-NUCLEIC ACID INTERACTIONS, GENE REGULATION. *Current Pos:* prin investr, Lab Molecular Biol, Nat Inst Diabetes Digestive & Kidney Dis, 87-90, CHIEF, LAB MOLECULAR EMBRYOL, NAT INST CHILD HEALTH & HUMAN DEVELOP, NIH, BETHESDA, MD, 90- *Personal Data:* b Burton-on-Trent, Staffordshire, UK, June 21, 59; m 82, Elizabeth Hall. *Educ:* Oxford Univ, BA, 81; Med Res Coun, London, PhD(molecular biol), 84. *Prof Exp:* Postdoctoral molecular biol, Carnegie Inst, Baltimore, Md, 84-86, prin investr, 87. *Mem:* Am Soc Microbiol; AAAS; Am Asn Cancer Res; Am Soc Cell Biol. *Res:* Molecular mechanisms responsible for establishing and maintaining stable states of gene activity; integration of replication, transcription and chromatin assembly especially during early vertebrate development; germ-cell specific gene expression. *Mailing Add:* Lab Molecular Embryol Nat Inst NIH Bldg 6 Rm B1A13 Bethesda MD 20892-2711. *Fax:* 301-402-1323

**WOLFHARD, HANS GEORG,** ATOMIC & MOLECULAR PHYSICS. *Current Pos:* sr res staff, 63-94, EMER INST DEFENSE ANALYSIS, ALEXANDRIA, VA, 94- *Personal Data:* b Basel, Switz, Apr 2, 12; nat US; m 97, Clara Ralston; c George, John & Bernard. *Educ:* Univ Goettingen, Dr Rer Nat(physics), 38. *Honors & Awards:* First General Goodpaster Award for Res, 84. *Prof Exp:* Scientist, Aeronaut Res Sta, Brunswick, Ger, 39-46; res scientist, Imp Col, London, Royal Aircraft Estab, Eng, 46-56 & Bur Mines, 56-59; head, Physics Dept, Reaction Motors Div, Thiokol Chem Corp, Denville, NJ, 59-63. *Mem:* Fel Am Optical Soc; Am Inst Aeronaut & Astronaut; Combustion Inst. *Res:* Combustion research; ballistic missile research. *Mailing Add:* Inst Defense Analysis 1801 N Beauregard St Alexandria VA 22311

**WOLFLE, DAEL (LEE),** SCIENCE POLICY. *Current Pos:* actg dean archit & urban planning, 72-73, prof pub affairs, 70-76, EMER PROF PUB AFFAIRS, GRAD SCH PUB AFFAIRS, UNIV WASH, 76- *Personal Data:* b Puyallup, Wash, Mar 5, 06; m 29, Helen Morrill (deceased 88); c Janet H (Christopherson), Lee M & John M. *Educ:* Univ Wash, BS, 27, MS, 28; Ohio State Univ, PhD(psychol), 31. *Hon Degrees:* DSc, Drexel Inst Technol, 56, Ohio State Univ, 57 & Western Mich Univ, 60; Alumnus Summa Laude Dignatus, Univ Wash, 1979. *Honors & Awards:* Montgomery lectr, Univ Nebr, 59; Walter Van Dyke Bingham lectr, Columbia Univ, 60; Herbert S Langfeld lectr, Princeton Univ, 69. *Prof Exp:* Instr psychol, Ohio State Univ, 29-32; prof, Univ Miss, 32-36; examr biol sci, Univ Chicago, 36-39, from asst prof to assoc prof psychol, 38-45; exec secy, Am Psychol Asn, 46-50; dir, Comn Human Resources & Advan Training, Assoc Res Couns, 50-54; exec officer, AAAS, 54-70. *Concurrent Pos:* Civilian training adminr electronics, US Army Sig Corps, 41-43; tech aide, Off Sci Res & Develop, 44-46; mem or vchmn, Bd Trustees, Russell Sage Found, 61-78; mem or chmn, Bd Trustees, James McKeen Cattell Fund, 62-82; trustee, Pac Sci Ctr Found, 62-80; mem ed adv bd, Sci Yearbk, Encycl Brittanica, 67-77; mem res adv comt, Am Coun Educ, 68-73; trustee, Biosci Info Servs, 68-74; mem or chmn, Geophys Inst Adv Comt, Univ Alaska, 69-93; mem manpower inst, Nat Indust Conf Bd, 70; chmn rev comt sci resources studies, NSF, 72-73 & 82-83; mem comt grad med educ, Asn Am Med Cols, 72-75; mem, US-USSR Joint Group Experts Sci Policy, 73-82; mem comn human resources, Nat Acad Sci-Nat Res Coun, 74-78; mem bd trustees, Biol Sci Curriculum Study, 80-85; mem coun, AAAS, 49-51, 87-88 & 90-, exec officer, 54-70, pres, Pac Div, 92; mem exec comt, Pac Div, 91- *Mem:* AAAS; Am Psychol Asn (exec secy, 46-50); Am Coun Educ (secy, 66-67). *Res:* Education, utilization, mobility, supply and demand trends of scientific and specialized personnel. *Mailing Add:* Grad Sch Pub Affairs Univ Wash DC-13 Box 353055 Seattle WA 98195-3055

**WOLFLE, THOMAS LEE,** LABORATORY ANIMAL SCIENCE, ANIMAL BEHAVIOR. *Current Pos:* DIR INST LAB ANIMAL RESOURCES, NAT ACAD SCI, 88- *Personal Data:* b Eugene, Ore, Apr 24, 36; m 86, Jacquelyn Malmrose; c Thomas L Jr & William T. *Educ:* Tex A&M Univ, BS, 59, DVM, 61; Univ Calif, Los Angeles, MA, 67, PhD(physiol psychol), 70; Am Col Lab Animal Med, dipl, 66. *Honors & Awards:* Commendation Medal, USPHS, 83, Outstanding Serv Medal, 88. *Prof Exp:* Vet primate colony mgt, Sch Aerospace Med, Brooks AFB, Tex, 61-65, chief, Comp Toxicol Lab, Aeromed Res Lab, Holloman AFB, 65-66; chief, Flight Environ Br, Aerospace Med Res Labs, Wright-Patterson AFB, Ohio, 70-73, asst chief, Weapons Effects Br, Sch Aerospace Med, Brooks AFB, Tex, 73-75; vet dir, USPHS, 75-88. *Concurrent Pos:* Adj prof psychol, Wright State Univ, 71-73, consult, Lab Animal Med, 72-73; exec dir, Interagency Res Animal Comt, NIH, 82-88; adj prof vet med, Univ Md, 84- *Mem:* Am Vet Med Asn; Am Vet Soc Animal Behav; Am Asn Lab Animal Sci; Am Soc Primatology; Int Primatological Soc; Asn Primate Vets; Am Soc Lab Animal Practitioners. *Res:* Animal behavior, canine medicine; impact on research and animals of early non-specific environmental influences; identification of animal models of human disease; biological and behavioral effects of housing on laboratory animals; pain and stress in animals. *Mailing Add:* Nat Acad Sci 2101 Constitution Ave NW Washington DC 20418. *Fax:* 202-334-1687; *E-Mail:* twolfle@nas.edu

**WOLFMAN, EARL FRANK, JR,** SURGERY. *Current Pos:* chmn div & dept & assoc dean, 66-78, PROF SURG, SCH MED, UNIV CALIF, DAVIS, 66- *Personal Data:* b Buffalo, NY, Sept 14, 26; m 46, Lois Jeannette Walker; c Nancy J, Carol A & David E. *Educ:* Harvard Univ, BS, 46; Univ Mich, MD, 50; Am Bd Surg, dipl, 58. *Prof Exp:* From instr to assoc prof surg, Med Sch, Univ Mich, 57-66, asst to dean, 60-61, asst dean, 61-64. *Concurrent Pos:* Chief div surg serv, Sacramento Med Ctr, 66-78. *Mem:* Fel Am Col Surgeons; AMA; Soc Surg Alimentary Tract; Asn Acad Surg; Sigma Xi. *Mailing Add:* 44770 N El Macero Dr El Macero CA 95618. *E-Mail:* efwolfman@ucdavis.edu

**WOLFNER, MARIANA FEDERICA,** DROSOPHILA DEVELOPMENT, GENE REGULATION. *Current Pos:* asst prof, 83-89, ASSOC PROF DEVELOP BIOL, SECT GENETICS & DEVELOP, CORNELL UNIV, 89- *Personal Data:* b Caracas, Venezuela, Dec 30, 53; US citizen; m 85, James Rothenbegh; c Miriam & Joshua. *Educ:* Cornell Univ, BA, 74; Stanford Univ, PhD(biochem), 81. *Prof Exp:* Damon Runyon-Walter Winchell Cancer Fund fel, Dept Biol, Univ Calif, San Diego, 81-82; sr fel, Am Cancer Soc, 83. *Mem:* Genetics Soc Am; Int Soc Develop Biol; Soc Develop Biol. *Res:* Molecular genetics of drosophila development; regulation and function of seminal fluid proteins that regulate reproductive efficiency and behavior and the nuclear envelope's role in initiating mitosis in embryos. *Mailing Add:* Dept Genetics Cornell Univ Main Campus Ithaca NY 14853-0001

**WOLFORD, JACK ARLINGTON,** PSYCHIATRY. *Current Pos:* asst prof psychiat, Sch Med, Univ Pittsburgh, 58-69, chief social psychiat, Western Psychiat Inst & Clin, 58-72, dir community ment health, Retardation Ctr, 67-74, prof psychiat, Sch Med, 69-87, psychiatrist-in-chief & actg chmn dept psychiat, Sch Med, 72-73, dir adult serv, Western Psychiat Inst & Clin, 72-87, dir community ment health/ment retardation ctrs, 76-91, PROF EMER, SCH MED, UNIV PITTSBURGH, 87- *Personal Data:* b Brookville, Pa, Dec

5, 17; m 44; c 2. *Educ:* Allegheny Col, AB, 40; Univ Pa, MD, 43; Am Bd Psychiat, dipl, 53. *Prof Exp:* Intern med, Allegheny Gen Hosp, Pittsburgh, Pa, 43; resident psychiat, Warren State Hosp, 44-46, sr psychiatrist, 48-51, clin dir, 51-56; dir, Hastings State Hosp, Nebr, 56-58. *Concurrent Pos:* Resident psychiat, Psychiat Inst & Clin, Pittsburgh, 53; asst prof psychiat, Univ Nebr, 56-58; vis fac sem, Lab Community Psychiat, Harvard Univ; mem, Govs Adv Comt to Dept Welfare & Comn Ment Health; mem commun adv comt, NIMH; mem med adv comt, Gov Adv Comt Ment Health & Ment Retardation, Dept Pub Welfare & Comn Ment Health, 74 & 75, Comprehensive Comt Ment Health Planning, 75 & Pa Asn Community Ment Health & Ment Retardation Ctrs, 75; pres, Group for Advan Psychiat, 77-79; secy, Pa Asn Community Ment Health & Ment Retardation Providers, 80-91. *Mem:* Fel Am Psychiat Asn (vpres, 75); fel Am Col Psychiat; AMA. *Res:* Social and community psychiatry; urban mental health and illness. *Mailing Add:* 450 Avon Dr Pittsburgh PA 15228

**WOLFORD, JAMES C,** MECHANICS, MECHANICAL ENGINEERING. *Current Pos:* from instr to asst prof mech, 54-58, assoc prof kinematics & mach design, 58-63, PROF KINEMATICS & MACH DESIGN, UNIV NEBR, LINCOLN, 63- *Personal Data:* b Fairmont, Nebr, July 20, 20; m 50; c 3. *Educ:* Univ Nebr, BS, 47, MS, 52; Purdue Univ, PhD(kinematics), 56. *Prof Exp:* Test engr, Gen Elec Co, 47-48, design engr, 48-50; design engr, Cecil W Armstrong & Assocs, 50-51. *Mem:* Am Soc Mech Engrs; Am Soc Eng Educ; Sigma Xi. *Res:* Design of machine elements; kinematics of mechanisms. *Mailing Add:* 5801 J St Lincoln NE 68510

**WOLFORD, JOHN HENRY,** AVIAN PHYSIOLOGY, POULTRY SCIENCE. *Current Pos:* PROF POULTRY SCI & DEPT HEAD, VA POLYTECH INST & STATE UNIV, 80- *Personal Data:* b Osgood, Ind, June 11, 36. *Educ:* Purdue Univ, BS, 58; Mich State Univ, MS, 60, PhD(avian physiol), 63. *Prof Exp:* From asst prof to assoc prof poultry sci, Mich State Univ, 63-74; prof animal & vet sci & chmn dept, Univ Maine, Orono, 74-80. *Mem:* Poultry Sci Asn; Sigma Xi; World Poultry Sci Asn. *Res:* Reproductive physiology of the turkey breeder hen; physiological alterations of fatty liver syndrome in laying chickens. *Mailing Add:* 503 Floyd St Blacksburg VA 24060

**WOLFRAM, LESZEK JANUARY,** FIBER SCIENCE, PROTEIN CHEMISTRY. *Current Pos:* dir res, 77-79, VPRES RES, CLAIROL RES LABS, 79- *Personal Data:* b Krakow, Poland, Feb 24, 29; US citizen; m 53; c 2. *Educ:* Politechnika, Lodz, Poland, BSc, 53, MSc, 55; Univ Leeds, PhD(protein chem), 61. *Honors & Awards:* Medal Award, Soc Cosmetic Chemists. *Prof Exp:* Chemist, Gillette Res Lab, Reading, UK, 61-63, sr chemist, ground leader & prin scientist, Gillette Res Inst, Rockville, Md, 63-72; sci liaison officer, Int Wool Secretariat, Australia, 72-73; asst dir res, Personal Care Div, The Gillette Co, Boston, 74-77. *Concurrent Pos:* Assoc ed, J Soc Cosmetic Chemists, 78-79, ed, 79-83. *Mem:* Am Chem Soc; NY Acad Sci; Fiber Soc; Soc Cosmetic Chemists; AAAS. *Res:* Physical chemistry of synthetic polymers and proteins; structure of fibers and biological tissues; evaluative techniques for hair and skin; organ biosurfaces and their properties; structure and properties of melanius. *Mailing Add:* 666 Westover Rd Stamford CT 06902

**WOLFRAM, STEPHEN,** PHYSICS. *Current Pos:* PROF PHYSICS, MATH & COMPUT SCI, UNIV ILL, 86-; PRES & CHIEF EXEC OFFICER, WOLFRAM RES INC, CHAMPAIGN, ILL, 87- *Personal Data:* b London, Eng, Aug 29, 59. *Educ:* Calif Inst Technol, PhD(theoret physics), 79. *Prof Exp:* Staff, Calif Inst Technol, 79-82 & Inst Advan Study, 83-86. *Concurrent Pos:* MacArthur Found fel, 81; ed, J Complex Systs, 87- *Res:* Author of 3 books. *Mailing Add:* Wolfram Res Inc 100 Trade Ctr Dr Champaign IL 61820

**WOLFRAM, THOMAS,** SOLID STATE PHYSICS. *Current Pos:* VPRES & GEN MGR, AMOCO LASER CO, 87- *Personal Data:* b St Louis, Mo, July 27, 36; m; c 5. *Educ:* Univ Calif, Riverside, AB, 59, PhD(physics), 63; Univ Calif, Los Angeles, MA, 60. *Prof Exp:* Mem tech staff, Atomics Int, 60-63; mem tech staff, NAm Rockwell Sci Ctr, 63-68, group leader solid state physics, 68-72, dir physics & chem, Rockwell Int Sci Ctr, 72-74; prof, Univ Mo, Columbia, 74-83, chmn dept, 83- *Concurrent Pos:* Adj prof physics, Univ Calif, Riverside, 68-69; dir, Phys Technol Div, Amoco corp, Napreville, Ill, 83-86. *Mem:* Fel Am Phys Soc. *Res:* Lattice dynamics; spin waves; superconductivity; electronic and optical properties; physics and chemistry of surfaces; catalysis. *Mailing Add:* 2004 Somerset Lane Wheaton IL 60187

**WOLFSBERG, KURT,** RADIOCHEMISTRY, NUCLEAR CHEMISTRY. *Current Pos:* Assoc group leader, Isotope Geochem Group, 80-88, STAFF MEM, RADIOCHEM GROUP, LOS ALAMOS NAT LAB, 59-, SECT LEADER, ISOTOPE GEOCHEM GROUP, 88- *Personal Data:* b Hamburg, Ger, Nov 1, 31; nat US; m 55; c 3. *Educ:* St Louis Univ, BS, 53; Wash Univ, St Louis, MA, 55, PhD(chem), 59. *Concurrent Pos:* Consult aircraft nuclear propulsion comt nuclear measurements & standards, US Air Force, 56-57; mem subcomt radiochem, Nat Acad Sci, 72-76; guest & Fulbright grantee, Univ Mainz, WGer, 74-75; guest scientist, 82, 85; Fulbright award, tech proj officer, Nev Terminal Waste Storage Proj, 78-79. *Mem:* AAAS; Am Chem Soc; fel Am Inst Chemists; Mat Res Soc. *Res:* Emanation techniques; mass and charge distribution in fission; high temperature diffusion of fission products; lanthanide and actinide chemistry; properties of very heavy nuclides; nuclear waste management, sorptive properties of geologic media, migration of radionuclides; geochemistry; solar neutrinos; radiochemical separation. *Mailing Add:* 303 Venado Los Alamos NM 87544-2435

**WOLFSBERG, MAX,** ISOTOPE EFFECTS, CHEMICAL PHYSICS. *Current Pos:* Regents' lectr, 68, chemn dept, 74-80, PROF CHEM, UNIV CALIF, IRVINE, 69- *Personal Data:* b Hamburg, Germany, May 28, 28; nat US; m 57; c 1. *Educ:* Wash Univ, St Louis, AB, 48, PhD(chem), 51. *Prof Exp:* Asst chem, Wash Univ, St Louis, 48-50; assoc chemist, Brookhaven Nat Lab, 51-54, from chemist to sr chemist, 54-69. *Concurrent Pos:* NSF sr fel, 58-59; vis prof chem, Cornell Univ, 63 & Ind Univ, 65; prof, State Univ NY Stony Brook, 66-69; Alexander von Humboldt award, 77; guest prof, Deutsche Forschungspemeinschaft, Univ Ulm, Fed Repub Ger, 86. *Mem:* Am Chem Soc. *Res:* Theoretical chemistry; isotope effects, energy transfer, chemical reactions, electronic structure of molecules and molecular dynamics. *Mailing Add:* Dept Chem Univ Calif Irvine CA 92717

**WOLFSON, ADELE JUDITH,** PROTEOLYTIC ENZYMES & INHIBITORS, PROTEIN DESIGN. *Current Pos:* asst prof, 85-91, ASSOC PROF CHEM, WELLESLEY COL, 91- *Personal Data:* b New York, NY, Apr 15, 50; m 82, Daniel H Seeley; c 2. *Educ:* Brandeis Univ, AB, 71; Columbia Univ, PhD(biochem), 79. *Prof Exp:* Nat Cancer Inst fel, Univ Paris, Bicetre, 79-80; asst prof physiol & biochem, Univ Pittsburgh, 80-83; lectr & mem fac pop sci, Harvard Sch Pub Health, 83-85. *Concurrent Pos:* Prin investr NIH & NSF, 81-83, 83-85 & 89-; asst prof obstet, gynec & biochem, Harvard Med Sch, 84-86; vis scientist, Mass Inst Technol & Brandeis Univ, 89-90; sci scholar, Bunting Inst, Radcliffe Col, 89; career achievement award, NSF, 89; co-chair, Comt Equal Opportunities for Women, Am Soc Women Sci, 92-94. *Mem:* Am Chem Soc; Am Soc Biochem & Molecular Biol; Asn Women Sci; Endocrine Soc. *Res:* Determine whether the reactive region (a loop) from one protein can maintain its structure and, therefore, its function in a new protein environment; transfer construct chimeric proteins with loops from protease inhibitors into a host protein. *Mailing Add:* Dept Chem Wellesley Col 106 Central St Wellesley MA 02181-8284. *Fax:* 781-283-3642; *E-Mail:* awolfson@lucy.wellesley.edu

**WOLFSON, ALFRED M,** plant morphology, evolution; deceased, see previous edition for last biography

**WOLFSON, BERNARD T,** ENERGY CONVERSION & UTILIZATION, BUSINESS OF PROGRAM DEVELOPMENT & MARKETING. *Current Pos:* TECH & MGT CONSULT, 85- *Personal Data:* b Chicago, Ill, Mar 16, 19; m 42, Vera Arlene Easton; c Terry Alan & Randolph Douglas. *Educ:* Ill Inst Technol, BS, 40; Ohio State Univ, MS, 50, PhD, 60. *Prof Exp:* Chem & metall engr, Process Control Dept, Carnegie-Ill Steel Corp, Ind, 40-41; chem engr, Eng & Oper Div, Kankakee Ord Works, Ill, 41-42; tech supvr prod & inspection, Atlas Imp Diesel Engine Co, 42; rotary wing aircraft develop engr, Mech Br, Rotary Wing Unit, Propeller Lab, Wright Patterson AFB, Ohio, 42-44; aeronaut flight test engr, Flight Test Div, Ames Res Ctr, Moffett Field, Calif, 45-46; asst chief rotary wing aerodyn develop eng, Aerodyn Br, Rotary Wing Unit, Aircraft Lab, Wright Patterson AFB, 46-51, sr propulsion res scientist, Fluid Dynamics Res Br, Aerospace Res Lab, 51-61; aerospace propulsion scientist, Propulsion Div, Eng Sci Directorate, Air Force Off Sci Res, 61-66, 67-83, actg dir div, 66-67. *Concurrent Pos:* Mem panels & steering comts, Liquid Rocket Combustion Instability & Solid Rocket Combustion, Interagency Chem Rocket Propellants Group, Dept Defense Advan Res Projs Agency-NASA, 62-; adv panel air-breathing propulsion & power plants, NASA, 65-; ad hoc comt SRAMJET, Supersonic Combustion & Appln, Air Force Systs Command, 65-; Joint Army-Navy-Air Force-NASA Panels Liquid & Solid Rockets & Air-Breathing Combustion; magnetohydrodyn panel & working groups, Interagency Advan Power Group; mem steering group, Joint Army Navy NASA Air Force Interagency Propulsion Comt, 79- *Mem:* Combustion Inst; Am Inst Aeronaut & Astronaut; Sigma Xi. *Res:* Terresterial space and missile propulsion and power generation; chemical explosives; advanced energy systems; new and alternative fuels; environmental and pollutions control; fire and explosion prevention; technical management and marketing consultant and advisor. *Mailing Add:* 4797 Lake Valencia Blvd W Palm Harbor FL 34684-3924. *Fax:* 813-786-3007; *E-Mail:* docwolf12@aol.com

**WOLFSON, JAMES,** PHYSICS. *Personal Data:* b Chicago, Ill, Mar 16, 43; m 71. *Educ:* Grinnell Col, BA, 64; Mass Inst Technol, PhD(physics), 68. *Prof Exp:* Mem staff physics, Lab Nuclear Sci, Mass Inst Technol, 68-70, asst prof physics, 70-76; mem staff, Fermi Nat Accelerator Lab, 76-80. *Mem:* AAAS; Am Phys Soc. *Res:* Experimental high energy physics. *Mailing Add:* 694 Sterling Ct Naperville IL 60540

**WOLFSON, JOSEPH LAURENCE,** NUCLEAR PHYSICS. *Current Pos:* dean sci, 74-80, prof physics, 74-82, ADJ PROF, CARLETON UNIV, OTTAWA, 83- *Personal Data:* b Winnipeg, Man, July 22, 17; m 44; c 2. *Educ:* Univ Man, BSc, 42, MSc, 43; McGill Univ, PhD(physics), 48. *Prof Exp:* Asst res officer physics, Atomic Energy Can, Ltd, Chalk River, 48-55; physicist, Jewish Gen Hosp, Montreal, Que, 55-58; assoc res officer, Nat Res Coun Can, 58-64; prof physics, Univ Sask, 64-74. *Mem:* Am Phys Soc; Can Asn Physicists. *Res:* Nuclear spectroscopy. *Mailing Add:* 951 Blythdale Rd Ottawa ON K2A 3N9 Can

**WOLFSON, KENNETH GRAHAM,** MATHEMATICS. *Current Pos:* From instr to assoc prof, 52-58, chmn dept, 61-75, PROF MATH, RUTGERS UNIV, 60-, DEAN, GRAD SCH, 75- *Personal Data:* b New York, NY, Nov 21, 24; m 47; c 2. *Educ:* Brooklyn Col, BA, 47; Johns Hopkins Univ, MA, 48; Univ Ill, PhD(math), 52. *Mem:* Am Math Soc; Math Asn Am. *Res:* Spectral theory of differential equations; rings of linear transformations; structure of rings. *Mailing Add:* 4565 Cocoplum Way Delray Beach FL 33445-4303

**WOLFSON, LEONARD LOUIS,** QUALITY CONTROL, STERILIZATION. *Current Pos:* CONSULT, LEONARD L WOLFSON, 88- *Personal Data:* b Wilkes Barre, Pa, Dec 13, 19; m 47, Doris; c Mark. *Educ:* Univ Chicago, BS, 50, MS, 51. *Prof Exp:* Microbiologist, Wilson & Co, Chicago, 54-57; group leader microbiol, Nalco Chem Co, Chicago, 57-70; corp dir qual assurance & regulation affairs, Will Ross Inc, Milwaukee, 70-78 & Ipco Corp, White Plains, NY, 78-88. *Concurrent Pos:* Pres, Wilro Sci Labs, 72-78. *Mem:* NY Acad Sci; Am Soc Microbiol; Soc Indust Microbiol. *Res:* Medical and dental devices; quality control; drugs; cosmetics; disinfectants; product development; sterilization. *Mailing Add:* 36 Maple Wood Rd Hartsdale NY 10530

**WOLFSON, RICHARD L T,** SOLAR PHYSICS, SOLAR ENERGY. *Current Pos:* From asst prof to assoc prof, 76-87, chmn, Dept Physics, 88-92, PROF, MIDDLEBURY COL, 87-, ELLIS PROF LIBERAL ARTS, 92- *Personal Data:* b San Francisco, Calif, Apr 13, 47; m 70, Artley Swift; c 2. *Educ:* Swarthmore Col, BA, 69; Univ Mich, MS, 71; Dartmouth Col, PhD(physics), 76. *Concurrent Pos:* Vis scientist, High Altitude Observ, Nat Ctr Atmospheric Res, 80-81 & 86-87, Solar Theory Group, St Andrews Univ Scotland, 93; prin investr, NSF, Dept Energy, NASA; auth. *Mem:* Am Phys Soc; Am Asn Physics Teachers. *Res:* Theoretical work on magnetohydrodynamics of space plasmas, especially in application to the solar corona and solar wind; experimental work on control strategies for solar energy systems; introductory physics and science for nonscientists. *Mailing Add:* Dept Physics Middlebury Col Middlebury VT 05753. *Fax:* 802-388-0739

**WOLFSON, ROBERT JOSEPH,** OTOLARYNGOLOGY. *Current Pos:* PROF OTOLARYNGOL & BRONCHO-ESOPHAGOLOGY, & HEAD DEPT, MED COL PA, 69- *Personal Data:* b Philadelphia, Pa, Sept 11, 29; m 53; c 2. *Educ:* Temple Univ, BA, 52, MS, 61; Hahnemann Med Col, MD, 57. *Mem:* Am Acad Ophthal & Otolaryngol; Am Otol Soc; Am Laryngol, Rhinol & Otol Soc; Royal Soc Med; AMA. *Mailing Add:* Dept Otolaryngol 1920 Chestnut St Suite 700 Philadelphia PA 19103-4625

**WOLFSON, SEYMOUR J,** COMPUTER SCIENCE. *Current Pos:* asst prof, 68-73, ASSOC PROF COMPUT SCI, WAYNE STATE UNIV, 73- *Personal Data:* b Detroit, Mich, Feb 13, 37; m 58; c 4. *Educ:* Wayne State Univ, BS, 59, PhD(physics), 65; Univ Chicago, MS, 60. *Prof Exp:* Res assoc physics, Wayne State Univ, 63-65; sr scientist, Comput Sci Corp, 65-68. *Concurrent Pos:* Consult, Comput Sci Corp, 68-71; Lincorp Corp, 72- & Dept Housing & Urban Develop, 75-; secy, Comput Sci Bd, 74-76 & New York Carpet World, 80; chmn, Nat Comput Conf Bd, 81-82; dir, Word Processing Training Ctr, 81- *Mem:* Am Phys Soc; Asn Comput Mach; Am Arbit Asn; Inst Elec & Electronics Engrs. *Res:* Computer networks and applications; numerical methods. *Mailing Add:* 18803 Hilton Dr Southfield MI 48075-7237. *Fax:* 313-577-6868; *E-Mail:* wolfson@mts.cc.wayne.edu

**WOLFSON, SIDNEY KENNETH, JR,** NEUROSURGERY, BIOMEDICAL ENGINEERING. *Current Pos:* assoc prof neurosurg, 71-77, dir surg res, 74-78, PROF NEUROSURG, UNIV PITTSBURGH, 78-, DIR SURG RES, MONTEFIORE HOSP, 71- *Personal Data:* b Philadelphia, Pa, June 14, 31; m 58; c 3. *Educ:* Univ Pa, AB, 51; Univ Chicago, MD, 58. *Prof Exp:* Resident surg, Univ Pa Hosp, 59-63, asst prof surg res, Sch Med, Univ Pa, 63-68; assoc prof surg, Univ Chicago, 68-71; dir surg res, Michael Reese Hosp & Med Ctr, 68-71. *Concurrent Pos:* Career Develop Award, Nat Heart & Lung Inst, 63; chmn spec study sect, Nat Inst Arthritis & Metab Dis, 74-75; consult, Artificial Heart Assessment Panel, NIH, 74, Med Devices Prog, Nat Heart & Lung Inst, 73-74; Peripheral Vascular Diag Lab, 77- *Mem:* Am Soc Artificial Internal Organs; Am Asn Neurol Surgeons; Soc Acad Surgeons; Soc Neurosci; Am Soc Hypertension; Inst Elec & Electronics Engrs. *Res:* Hypothermia and circulatory arrest; artificial pancreas; cerebral blood flow; computerized patient and data management systems; implantable glucose electrode; epidemiological studies of cerebral ischemia and stroke; relationship of ultrasound imaging and doppler blood flow to risk factors in cardiovascular disease; experimental model of neurogenic hypertension. *Mailing Add:* 205 Buckingham Rd Pittsburgh PA 15215

**WOLGA, GEORGE JACOB,** SPECTROSCOPY MONITORING OF COMBUSTION PRODUCTS, MODERN SPECTROSCOPY INSTRUMENTS. *Current Pos:* from asst prof to assoc prof, 61-68, PROF ELEC ENG & APPL PHYSICS, CORNELL UNIV, 68- *Personal Data:* b New York, NY, Apr 2, 31; div; c 3. *Educ:* Cornell Univ, BEngPhys, 53; Mass Inst Technol, PhD(physics), 57. *Prof Exp:* Asst physics, Mass Inst Technol, 53-56, instr, 57-60, asst prof, 60-61. *Concurrent Pos:* Consult, Gen Elec, Sylvania & US Naval Res Lab, vpres-dir res, Lansing Inst Corp, 64-; head, Laser Physics Br, US Naval Res Lab, 68-70. *Mem:* Am Phys Soc; Inst Elec & Electronics Engrs; Optical Soc Am; Mat Res Soc; Soc Info Display. *Res:* Excited state spectroscopy; molecular physics; quantum electronics; molecular energy transfer and relaxation; modern optical spectroscopic instruments; infrared tunable lasers and spectroscopy; picosecond optoelectronics; laser processing of semiconductors; electroluminescent displays. *Mailing Add:* Sch Elec Eng 412 Phillips Hall Cornell Univ Ithaca NY 14853

**WOLGAMOTT, GARY,** MICROBIOLOGY, IMMUNOLOGY. *Current Pos:* From asst prof to assoc prof, 68-75, PROF MICROBIOL, SOUTHWESTERN OKLA STATE UNIV, 75-, CHMN DEPT, DIV ALLIED HEALTH SCI, 77-, ASSOC DEAN, SCH HEALTH SCI. *Personal Data:* b Alva, Okla, July 23, 40; m 62, Sandy Seibel; c Thad Dean & Dotti D'Lane (Forehand). *Educ:* Northwestern State Col, Okla, BS, 63; Okla State Univ, PhD(microbiol), 68. *Concurrent Pos:* NSF fel, Col Med, Univ Iowa, 71;

NASA-Am Soc Eng Educ fel, Johnson Space Ctr, Houston, Tex; mem, Med Technol Rev Comt, Clin Microbiol Prog Rev Comt & Nat Accrediting Agency Clin Lab Sci. *Mem:* AAAS; Am Soc Microbiol. *Res:* Study of the mode of action of specific chemotherapeutic agents on the activities of microorganisms, including their physiology and microstructure; action of microbial hemolysins on tissue culture cells ultrastructure; virulence analysis of space flown microautoflora from astronauts. *Mailing Add:* Div Allied Health Sci Southwestern Okla State Univ Weatherford OK 73096. *E-Mail:* wolgamg@hostl.swosu.edu

**WOLGEMUTH, CARL HESS,** MECHANICAL ENGINEERING, ENGINEERING EDUCATION. *Current Pos:* from asst prof to assoc prof, Pa State Univ, 63-77, prof mech eng, 77-94, actg dept head, 83-84, assoc dean eng, 84-91, actg dean, 91-92, assoc dean, 92-94, EMER PROF & ASSOC DEAN, PA STATE UNIV, 94- *Personal Data:* b Bareville, Pa, Apr 18, 34; m 54, Lois M Huber; c Thomas E & Andrew K. *Educ:* Pa State Univ, BS, 56; Ohio State Univ, MS, 58, PhD(mech eng), 63. *Honors & Awards:* Ralph R Teetor Award, Soc Automotive Engrs, 65. *Prof Exp:* Instr mech eng, Ohio State Univ, 56-63. *Concurrent Pos:* Mem, Eng Accreditation Comn, 93- *Mem:* Fel Soc Automotive Engrs; Am Soc Eng Educ; Am Soc Mech Engrs; Sigma Xi. *Res:* Application of thermodynamics and heat transfer to the study of power-producing systems; improving engineering education. *Mailing Add:* Pa State Univ 307 Reber University Park PA 16802. *Fax:* 814-863-4749; *E-Mail:* chw1@psu.edu

**WOLGEMUTH, DEBRA JOANNE,** DEVELOPMENTAL BIOLOGY, CELL & MOLECULAR BIOLOGY. *Current Pos:* from asst prof to assoc prof genetics & develop, 80-93, PROF GENETICS & DEVELOP & OBSTET & GYNEC, COLUMBIA UNIV, 93- *Personal Data:* b Lancaster, Pa, July 28, 47; m 70, Richard L Jarashow; c Evan M & Anna C. *Educ:* Gettysburg Col, BA, 69; Vanderbilt Univ, MA, 71; Columbia Univ, MPhil, 72, PhD(human genetics), 77. *Prof Exp:* Res assoc reproductive physiol, Vanderbilt Univ, 71-72; fel RNA synthesis, Sloan-Kettering Inst Cancer Res, 77-78, molecular cell biol, Rockefeller Univ, 78-80. *Concurrent Pos:* Assoc dir, Ctr Reproduction Sci. *Mem:* Am Soc Cell Biol; Soc Develop Biol; Int Soc Develop Biologists; AAAS; NY Acad Sci. *Res:* Cellular and molecular biology of mammalian gametogenesis, fertilization, and early embryogenesis; elucidating the structure of sperm chromatin and the role of oocyte products in the activation of development; cell cycle regulation, homeobox gene structure and function. *Mailing Add:* Dept Genetics & Develop Columbia Univ Col Physicians & Surgeons 630 W 168th St New York NY 10032. *Fax:* 212-305-6084

**WOLGEMUTH, RICHARD LEE,** PHYSIOLOGY, PHARMACOLOGY. *Current Pos:* dir regulatory affairs, 92-95, GROUP DIR NAM REGULATORY AFFAIRS, GLAXO WELLCOME, 95- *Personal Data:* b Lebanon, Pa, June 29, 45; m 68, Cheryl L Hamman; c Brent, Erryl, Christina & Travis. *Educ:* Ashland Col, BSc, 68; Ohio State Univ, MS, 75, PhD(physiol), 75. *Prof Exp:* Jr pharmacologist, Warren-Teed Pharmaceut, Rohm & Haas, 69-74; teaching asst physiol, Ohio State Univ, 73-75; scientist, Rohm & Haas Co, 75-77; sr res scientist drug metab, Adria Labs Inc, 77-82, proj leader, 83-84, mgr pharmacol & med chem, 84-85, dir proj coord, 86-87, dir regulatory affairs new drugs, 88-92. *Concurrent Pos:* Consult, Nat Inst Occup Safety & Health, 75-76 & Poly Sci Inc, 76-79. *Mem:* Soc Exp Biol & Med; Am Soc Cancer Chemother; NY Acad Sci; AAAS; Regulatory Affairs Profs Soc; Drug Info Asn; Am Urol Asn. *Res:* Gastrointestinal physiology especially pancreatic function, proteolytic enzymes and digestion, enteric bacteria; renal stones especially calcium and phosphorus metabolism, mechanism and treatment of benign prostate hypertrophy and urolithiasis; anthracycline metabolism and toxicity; antiemetics. *Mailing Add:* 103 Wood Lily Lane Cary NC 27511. *Fax:* 919-483-5118; *E-Mail:* rlw22242@glaxo.com

**WOLGIN, DAVID L,** PSYCHOPHARMACOLOGY, PSYCHOBIOLOGY. *Current Pos:* from asst prof to assoc prof, 75-85, asst chair psychol, 90-96, PROF PSYCHOL, FLA ATLANTIC UNIV, 85-, CHAIR PSYCHOL, 96- *Personal Data:* b Elizabeth, NJ, Oct 17, 45. *Educ:* Rutgers Univ, BA, 67, PhD(psychol), 73; Vanderbilt Univ, MA, 68. *Prof Exp:* Fel, Inst Neurol Sci, Univ Pa, 72-74; res assoc, Univ Ill, 74-75. *Concurrent Pos:* Prin investr, Nat Inst Drug Abuse, 90- *Mem:* Soc Neurosci; Int Behav Neurosci Soc; Soc Study Ingestive Behav; Soc Stimulus Properties Drugs; Europ Behav Pharmacol Soc. *Res:* Examine the mechanisms by which behavioral variables modify the effects of chronically administered psychoactive drugs; how tolerance and sensitization develop to drugs of abuse. *Mailing Add:* 22141 Primrose Way Boca Raton FL 33433. *E-Mail:* wolgindl@acc.fau.edu

**WOLICKI, ELIGIUS ANTHONY,** NUCLEAR PHYSICS, APPLICATIONS OF NUCLEAR TECHNIQUES & NUCLEAR ACCELERATORS. *Current Pos:* RETIRED. *Personal Data:* b Buffalo, NY, May 10, 27; m 54, Wilma Pitsenbarger; c Karol, Ann, Stasia & Stefanie. *Educ:* Canisius Col, BS, 46; Univ Notre Dame, PhD(physics), 50. *Honors & Awards:* Centennial of Sci Award, Univ Notre Dame, 65. *Prof Exp:* Asst physics, Univ Notre Dame, 46-47, asst, 47-48; res assoc nuclear physics, Univ Iowa, 50-52; nuclear physicist, Nuclear Sci Div, 52-66, consult & actg assoc, 66-77, assoc supt, Radiation Technol Div, 77-81, assoc supt, Condensed Matter & Radiation Sci Div, US Naval Res Lab, 81-84; pres, Wolicki Assocs, Inc, 84-94. *Concurrent Pos:* AEC fel, 48-50. *Mem:* Fel Am Phys Soc; fel Inst Elec & Electronics Engrs. *Res:* Nuclear reactions and applications; electrostatic accelerators; radiation detectors; applications of nuclear radiation, nuclear techniques and ion beam accelerators; radiation damage and radiation effects; radiation hardness assurance; single event upsets in very large scale integrated circuits; radiation effects on electronics. *Mailing Add:* 1310 Gatewood Dr Alexandria VA 22307

**WOLIN, ALAN GEORGE,** FOOD SCIENCE. *Current Pos:* prod improv mgr, 62-67, QUAL COORDR, M&M CANDIES DIV, MARS, INC, 67- *Personal Data:* b New York, NY, Apr 2, 33; m 54; c 4. *Educ:* Cornell Univ, BS, 54, MS, 56, PhD, 58. *Prof Exp:* Sr proj leader yeast tech div, Fleischmann Labs, Standard Brands, Inc, 58-60; head dairy tech lab, Vitex Labs Div, Nopco Chem Co, 60-62. *Concurrent Pos:* Ed, J Appl Microbiol, 72-; mem res comt, Nat Confectioners Asn, 75-, tech comt, Grocery Mfrs Asn, 73- & NJ Pub Health Adv Comn, 73-75. *Mem:* Am Dairy Sci Asn; Am Soc Microbiol; Inst Food Technol; Soc Consumer Affairs Prof; Am Chem Soc. *Res:* Use of radioisotopes in study of food flavors; dairy starter cultures; enzymes; fermentation; antimicrobial agents in milk; food fortification; phosphatase activity of chocolate milk; natural bacterial inhibitors in raw milk. *Mailing Add:* 44 Stonehenge Rd Morristown NJ 07960

**WOLIN, HAROLD LEONARD,** MICROBIOLOGY, CLINICAL CHEMISTRY. *Current Pos:* RETIRED. *Personal Data:* b Brooklyn, NY, June 22, 27; m 56; c 3. *Educ:* Univ Calif, AB, 50, MA, 52; Cornell Univ, PhD(microbiol/biochem), 56. *Prof Exp:* Res scientist, Pac Yeast Prod Co, 56-57; instr, Hahnemann Med Col, 57-59; asst prof microbiol, Col Med & Dent, Seton Hall Univ, 59-63; clin assoc prof microbiol, Col Med & Dent, NJ, 63-95; clin lab, Brookdale Hosp Ctr, Brooklyn, NY, 63-95. *Mem:* Am Soc Microbiol; Brit Soc Gen Microbiol; Am Asn Clin Chem; Nat Acad Clin Biochem. *Res:* Clinical microbiology and chemistry; microbial physiology. *Mailing Add:* 1772 Slocum St Hewlett NY 11557

**WOLIN, LEE ROY,** PSYCHOLOGY, NEUROPHYSIOLOGY. *Current Pos:* asst prof neurosurg, 70-76, ASST CLIN PROF PHYSIOL, CASE WESTERN RES UNIV, 76-; DIR, LAB NEUROPSYCHOL & EEG, OHIO MEMT HEALTH & MENT RETARDATION RES CTR, 73-; ADMIN DIR, DRUG ABUSE TREAT UNIT, CLEVELAND PSYCHIAT INST, 75- *Personal Data:* b Cleveland, Ohio, Dec 8, 27; m 50; c 3. *Educ:* Los Angeles State Col, BS, 50; Cornell Univ, PhD(psychol), 55. *Prof Exp:* Mem fac psychol, Sarah Lawrence Col, 55-59; res assoc develop, Child Study Ctr, Clark Univ, 59-60; res assoc, Cleveland Psychiat Inst, 60-69, dir lab neuropsychol, 69-73. *Concurrent Pos:* Lectr, Lakewood High Exten, Ohio State Univ, 63-66 & Bedford Exten, Cleveland State Univ, 66; lectr, Kent State Univ, 65. *Mem:* AAAS; Am Psychol Asn; NY Acad Sci. *Res:* Neurophysiology of vision; behavioral and neurophysiological manifestations of brain disfunction; perceptual, cognitive and emotional aspects of neuropsychiatric disorders perception. *Mailing Add:* 12228 Fairview Ct Cleveland OH 44106

**WOLIN, MEYER JEROME,** MICROBIAL ECOLOGY, MICROBIAL PHYSIOLOGY. *Current Pos:* CHIEF RES SCIENTIST, DIV LAB & RES, NY STATE HEALTH DEPT, 74-; PROF ENVIRON HEALTH & TOXICOL, GRAD SCH PUB HEALTH SCI, STATE UNIV NY, ALBANY, 85- *Personal Data:* b Bronx, NY, Nov 10, 30; m 55; c 2. *Educ:* Cornell Univ, BS, 51; Univ Chicago, PhD(microbiol), 54. *Prof Exp:* NIH fel microbiol, Univ Minn, 54-55; fel, Univ Ill, Urbana, 55-56, from asst prof to assoc prof dairy sci, 56-67, assoc prof microbiol, 65-67, prof dairy sci & microbiol, 67-74. *Concurrent Pos:* NSF sr fel, Univ Newcastle, 64-65; mem microbial chem study sect, NIH, 71-75; chmn dept environ health & toxicol, Grad Sch Pub Health Sci, State Univ NY, Albany, 85-87. *Mem:* AAAS; Am Chem Soc; Am Soc Microbiol; NY Acad Sci; Am Soc Biol Chem. *Res:* Microbial biochemistry and ecology; fermentations in anaerobic ecosystems; intestinal tract microbiology; interspecies interactions; hydrogen metabolism; methane production. *Mailing Add:* Wadsworth Ctr Labs & Res Empire State Plaza PO Box 509 Albany NY 12201-0509. *Fax:* 518-474-8590; *E-Mail:* meyer.wolin@wadsworth.org

**WOLIN, MICHAEL STUART,** VASCULAR REGULATION, OXYGEN PHYSIOLOGY. *Current Pos:* asst prof, 83-89, assoc prof, 89-95, PROF PHYSIOL, NY MED COL, 95- *Personal Data:* b Brooklyn, NY, Sept 11, 53; m 87, Theresa M Burke; c Joshua M, Seth A, Sarah R. *Educ:* Harpur Col, BA, 75; Yale Univ, MSc, 76, MPhil, 77 & PhD(chem), 81. *Honors & Awards:* Albert Hyman Res Award, Am Heart Asn, 83. *Prof Exp:* Fel, Tulane Univ Sch Med, 81-83, instr pharmacol, 82-83. *Concurrent Pos:* Biomed Res Scholar Awardee, C H Revson Found, 83-85; prin investr, NIH, 84-, Am Lung Asn Grant, 84-86; prog comt, Am Heart Asn Cardiolpulmonary Coun, 85-91, exec comt, 92-94, comt chmn, 96-99; prin investr, Am Heart Asn Grant, 86-93; nat res serv award, NIH, 81-83; estab investr award, Am Heart Asn, 89-, mem res comt, chmn Lung, Respiration & Recessitation Grant Review Comt, 97-; prog comt, Am Thoracic Soc, 90-95; assoc ed, Am J Physiol, Heart & Circulatory Physiol, 93-; mem, Develop Comt, Microcirculatory Soc, 93-; Merit Award, NIH, 96. *Mem:* Am Physiol Soc; Nitric Oxide Soc; Am Heart Asn; Int Soc Free Radical Res; Microcirculatory Soc; Am Thoracic Soc. *Res:* Reconstruction of the regulation of soluble guanylate cyclase; basic mechanisms of vascular regulation by oxygen tension, reactive oxygen metabolites and the intracellular mediator cyclic GMP, with a focus on those which are unique to the pulmonary circulation versus systemic circulations. *Mailing Add:* Dept Physiol NY Med Col Valhalla NY 10595. *Fax:* 914-993-4018

**WOLIN, SAMUEL,** ELECTRONICS, PHYSICS. *Current Pos:* CONSULT SCIENTIST, 80- *Personal Data:* b New York, NY, Feb 12, 09; m 42; c 2. *Educ:* City Col New York, BS, 30, MS, 31; Columbia Univ, AM, 41. *Honors & Awards:* Belden Medal. *Prof Exp:* Instr, Pub Schs, NY, 30-42; instr radio eng, Army Air Force Officers Div, Yale Univ, 42-44; instr elec commun, Radar Sch, Mass Inst Technol, 44-45; radio engr, Victor Div, Radio Corp Am, 45-46; res engr, Bartol Res Found, Franklin Inst, 46-47; electronics engr, US Naval Base Sta, Naval Air Mat Ctr, 47; electronic scientist, US Naval Air Develop Ctr, 47-57; sr electronic engr, McDonnell Aircraft Corp, Mo, 56-60; sr elec engr, Adv Systs Res Dept, Lockheed Electronics Co, 60-61; sr design staff engr, Boeing Co, Pa, 61-63; sr res engr, Brown Engr Co, Ala, 63-66; res engr, Boeing Co, Ala, 66-69; electronic engr, US Army Missile Command, Redstone Arsenal, 69-80. *Mem:* AAAS; sr mem Inst Elec & Electronics Engrs; Soc Indust & Appl Math. *Res:* Electronic systems engineering for space vehicles; guided missiles; aircraft and vertical takeoff and landing; applied electromagnetic theory; antennas; radomes; radio propagation; optics; reliability; applied mathematics. *Mailing Add:* 2205 Wimberly Rd NW Huntsville AL 35816

**WOLINSKY, EMANUEL,** INFECTIOUS DISEASES. *Current Pos:* asst prof med, Case Western Res Univ, 56-62, from asst prof to assoc microbiol, 62-68, prof med, 68-88, prof path, 81-88, EMER PROF MED & PATH, SCH MED, CASE WESTERN RES UNIV, 88- *Personal Data:* b New York, NY, Sept 23, 17; m 47, Marjorie Claster; c Douglas & Peter. *Educ:* Cornell Univ, BA, 38, MD, 41. *Honors & Awards:* Trudeau Medal, 86; Louis Weinstein Award, 95. *Prof Exp:* Intern med, NY Hosp, 43-44, resident, 44-45; asst dir tuberc res, Trudeau Lab, Trudeau Found, 46-56. *Concurrent Pos:* Dir microbiol, Cleveland Metrop Gen Hosp, 59-91; former mem tuberc panel, US-Japan Coop Sci Proj, strep & staph comn, Armed Forces Epidemiol Bd; former assoc ed, Am Rev Respiratory Dis. *Mem:* Am Soc Microbiol; Am Thoracic Soc; Infectious Dis Soc Am. *Res:* Medical microbiology and pulmonary diseases; tuberculosis bacteriology and experimental chemotherapy; infectious diseases. *Mailing Add:* MetroHealth Med Ctr Cleveland OH 44109-1998. *Fax:* 216-778-3328

**WOLINSKY, HARVEY,** MEDICINE, PATHOLOGY. *Current Pos:* CLIN PROF MED, MT SINAI SCH MED, 81- *Personal Data:* b Cleveland, Ohio, June 3, 39; m; c 2. *Educ:* Western Reserve Univ, AB, 60; Univ Chicago, MD & MS, 63, PhD(path), 67. *Prof Exp:* Intern, Univ Chicago Hosps, 63-64; asst resident internal med, Mt Sinai Hosp, Cleveland, Ohio, 64-65; resident chest serv, Bronx Municipal Hosp Ctr, NY, 67-68; assoc, Albert Einstein Col Med, 68-70, assoc path, 69-70, asst prof med & path, 70-73, assoc prof med, 73-77, prof med & path, 77-81. *Concurrent Pos:* USPHS res fel, Univ Chicago Hosps, 65-67; USPHS res career develop award, Nat Heart & Lung Inst, 72-77; assoc attend physician, Bronx Munic Hosp Ctr, NY, 68-71; attend physician, 72-81; mem, Coun Arteriosclerosis, Am Heart Asn, 70- & mem, Coun High Blood Pressure Res, 72-; attend physician, Mt Sinai Hosp & Med Ctr, 81- *Mem:* Am Thoracic Soc; Am Soc Exp Path; Fedn Am Socs Exp Biol; Am Soc Clin Invest; NY Acad Sci; Am Col Cardiol. *Res:* Comparative pathology; structure, function and biochemistry of blood vessels; effects of hormonal and mechanical factors on blood vessel structure. *Mailing Add:* 49 E 96th St New York NY 10128

**WOLINSKY, IRA,** NUTRITION, BIOCHEMISTRY. *Current Pos:* PROF NUTRIT, UNIV HOUSTON, 79- *Personal Data:* b New York, NY, Mar 30, 38; m 65; c 2. *Educ:* City Col New York, BS, 60; Kans Univ, MS, 65, PhD(biochem), 68. *Prof Exp:* Lectr, Hebrew Univ Hadassah Med Sch, 68-74; vis scientist, Dalton Res Ctr, Univ Mo, 74; assoc prof nutrit, Pa State Univ, 74-79. *Mem:* Am Inst Nutrit; Soc Exp Biol & Med; Sigma Xi; Soc Clin Nutrit. *Res:* Nutritional biochemistry of bone; calcium metabolism; sports nutrition. *Mailing Add:* Dept Human Develop Univ Houston 110 Cameron Bldg Houston TX 77204-6861. *Fax:* 713-743-4033

**WOLINSKY, JERRY SAUL,** NEUROVIROLOGY, NEUROIMMUNOLOGY. *Current Pos:* PROF NEUROL, HEALTH SCI CTR, UNIV TEX, HOUSTON, 83-, GRAD FAC VIROL, GRAD SCH BIOMED SCI, 84- *Personal Data:* b Baltimore, Md, Nov 26, 43; m 69, Gerlind Stahler; c Anjak & Jean P. *Educ:* Ill Inst Technol, BS; Univ Ill, MD, 69. *Prof Exp:* From instr to asst prof neurol, Univ Calif, San Francisco, 73-78; assoc prof neurol, Sch Med, Johns Hopkins Univ, 78-83, assoc prof immunol & infectious dis, Sch Hyg & Pub Health, 79-83. *Concurrent Pos:* David M Olkon scholar, 68-69; Basil O'Connor Starter Res grant, 75-78; res assoc neurovirol, Vet Admin Hosp, San Francisco, 75-78; Res Career Develop Award, NIH, 78-83; mem, NIH Immunol Sci study sect, 85-89; mem, Nat Mult Sclerosis Soc study sect, 93- *Mem:* Fel Am Acad Neurol; AAAS; Am Soc Microbiol; Am Neurol Asn; Am Soc Clin Invest; Am Soc Virol. *Res:* Virus and autoimmune diseases of the nervous system. *Mailing Add:* Health Sci Ctr Univ Tex PO Box 20708 Houston TX 77225-0708. *Fax:* 713-745-0768

**WOLINSKY, JOSEPH,** ORGANIC CHEMISTRY. *Current Pos:* from asst prof to assoc prof 58-67, PROF CHEM, PURDUE UNIV, 67- *Personal Data:* b Chicago, Ill, Dec 3, 30; m 51, Sheila L Rubin; c Debra S, Kharry B, Rebecca E, Michael R & Julie B. *Educ:* Univ Ill, BS, 52; Cornell Univ, PhD, 56. *Prof Exp:* Proj assoc, Univ Wis, 56-58. *Mem:* Am Chem Soc. *Res:* Chemistry of terpenes, alkaloids and related natural products. *Mailing Add:* Dept Chem Purdue Univ West Lafayette IN 47907

**WOLK, COLEMAN PETER,** DEVELOPMENTAL MICROBIOLOGY. *Current Pos:* from asst prof to assoc prof, 65-74, dir, Dept Energy Plant Res Lab, 88-92, PROF BOT, MICH STATE UNIV, 74- *Personal Data:* b New York, NY, Sept 28, 36; m 65; c 1. *Educ:* Mass Inst Technol, SB & SM, 58; Rockefeller Inst, PhD(biol), 64. *Honors & Awards:* Darbaker Prize, Bot Soc Am. *Prof Exp:* Nat Acad Sci-Nat Res Coun res fel biol, Calif Inst Technol, 64-65. *Mem:* Am Soc Microbiol; Am Soc Plant Physiol. *Res:* Physiological, biochemical and genetic bases of development and nitrogen fixation in cyanobacteria. *Mailing Add:* 310 Plant Biol-Plant Res Lab Mich State Univ East Lansing MI 48824-1301

**WOLK, ELLIOT SAMUEL,** MATHEMATICS. *Current Pos:* Instr math, Univ Conn, 50-56, chmn dept, 67-73, from asst prof to prof, 56-88, EMER PROF MATH, UNIV CONN, 88- *Personal Data:* b Springfield, Mass, Aug 5, 19; m 50, Eleanor Lisniansky; c Joel, Daniel & Sara (Lisniansky). *Educ:* Clark Univ, AB, 40; Brown Univ, ScM, 47, PhD(math), 54. *Concurrent Pos:* Consult elec boat div, Gen Dynamics Corp, 55-58. *Mem:* Am Math Soc; Math Asn Am. *Res:* Partially ordered sets; general topology. *Mailing Add:* Dept Math Univ Conn Storrs CT 06268. *E-Mail:* wolk@uconnvm.uconn.edu

**WOLK, ROBERT GEORGE,** ORNITHOLOGY, EVOLUTION. *Current Pos:* dir educ, 83-91, prog dir, 91-94, DIR POLICY, NC STATE MUS NATURAL SCI, 94- *Personal Data:* b New York, NY, Mar 10, 31; m 56, Wilhelmina J Klein; c Stephanie E, David P, Jennifer S, Nancy (Baker) & Jonathan G. *Educ:* City Univ NY, BS, 52; Cornell Univ, MS, 54, PhD(vert zool), 59. *Prof Exp:* Asst prof biol, St Lawrence Univ, 57-63; assoc prof vert morphol & behav, Adelphi Univ, 63-67; cur life sci, Nassau County Mus, 67-78; exec dir, Nature Sci Ctr, 78-82; lectr zool, Greensboro Col, 82-83. *Concurrent Pos:* Sci ed, NC Naturalist, 93- *Mem:* Am Ornithologists Union; Brit Ornithologists Union; Am Asn Mus; Sigma Xi; Cooper Ornith Soc; Wilson Ornith Soc. *Res:* Behavioral adaptations and functional morphology of birds; avian vision; reproductive behavior of the black skimmer; evolution, systematics, and distribution of gulls, terns, and skimmers. *Mailing Add:* NC State Mus Nat Sci PO Box 29555 Raleigh NC 27626. *Fax:* 919-733-1573

**WOLKE, RICHARD ELWOOD,** VETERINARY PATHOLOGY. *Current Pos:* asst prof, 70-75, assoc prof ichthyopath, 75-81, PROF AQUACULT & PATH, UNIV RI, 86- *Personal Data:* b East Orange, NJ, June 2, 33; m 64; c 2. *Educ:* Cornell Univ, BS, 55, DVM, 62; Univ Conn, 66, PhD(vet path), 68. *Prof Exp:* Vet, Am Soc Prev Cruelty Animals, 62-63; pvt pract, 63-64; NIH path trainee, Univ Conn, 64-68, res assoc, 68-69, res assoc ichthyopath, 69-70. *Concurrent Pos:* Conn Res Comn grant, Univ Conn, 69-70; Nat Oceanic & Atmospheric Admin Sea grant, Univ RI, 70-80; vis prof, Unit Aquatic Pathobiol, Stirling Univ, Scotland, 78-79; adj prof comp med, Tufts Univ, 81-86. *Mem:* Wildlife Dis Asn; Int Asn Aquatic Animal Med; World Maricult Soc; Sigma Xi; NY Acad Sci. *Res:* Ichthyopathology; comparative pathology; inflammation. *Mailing Add:* Animal Sci Univ RI Kingston RI 02881

**WOLKE, ROBERT LESLIE,** SCIENCE WRITING & EDITING, CONSULTING ON TECHNICAL COMMUNICATION. *Current Pos:* from assoc prof to prof, Univ Pittsburgh, 60-90, dir, Wherrett Lab Nuclear Chem, 61-77 & Univ Off Fac Develop, 77-88, EMER PROF CHEM, UNIV PITTSBURGH, 90- *Personal Data:* b Brooklyn, NY, Apr 2, 28; m, Marlene Parrish; c Leslie A (Wolke). *Educ:* Polytech Inst Brooklyn, BS, 49; Cornell Univ, PhD, 53. *Prof Exp:* Res assoc nuclear chem, Enrico Fermi Inst, Univ Chicago, 53-56; nuclear chemist, Gen Atomic Div, Gen Dynamics Corp, 56-57; from asst prof to assoc prof chem, Univ Fla, 57-60. *Concurrent Pos:* Res partic, Oak Ridge Nat Lab, 58 & 59; vis prof, Univ PR, 70; vis prof, USAID, Univ Oriente, Venezuela, 73; acad dean, Semester at Sea, 82; consult, USIA, Bangladesh, 90. *Mem:* Am Chem Soc; Nat Assn Sci Writers. *Res:* Writing and editing: chemistry and physics, general commentary, food, food science; recoil studies, interaction of energetic ions with matter; natural radioactivity; marine radioactivity; nuclear reactions. *Mailing Add:* Dept Chem Univ Pittsburgh Pittsburgh PA 15260

**WOLKEN, GEORGE, JR,** CHEMICAL PHYSICS, THEORETICAL CHEMISTRY. *Current Pos:* PATENT ATTY & CONSULT, 74- *Personal Data:* b Jersey City, NJ, Nov 11, 44; m 67; c 2. *Educ:* Tufts Univ, BS, 66; Harvard Univ, PhD(chem physics), 71. *Prof Exp:* Fel, Max Planck Inst Aerodyn, Univ Gottingen, 71-72; asst prof chem, Ill Inst Technol, 72-74; mem staff, Battelle Mem Inst, 74-81. *Mem:* Am Chem Soc; Am Phys Soc. *Res:* Theoretical chemical kinetics, both of gas phase reactions and heterogeneous reactions. *Mailing Add:* 6602 Hawthorne St Columbus OH 43085

**WOLKEN, JEROME JAY,** BIOPHYSICS, BIOENGINEERING. *Current Pos:* dir, Biophys Res Lab, Eye & Ear Hosp, Mellon Col Sci, 53-64, head, Dept Biol Sci, 64-67, PROF BIOPHYS, CARNEGIE-MELLON UNIV, 64- *Personal Data:* b Pittsburgh, Pa, Mar 28, 17; m 56, Tobey Holstein; c Ann A, Jonathan, Johanna & Erik A. *Educ:* Univ Pittsburgh, BS, 46, MS, 48, PhD(biophys), 49. *Prof Exp:* Res fel, Mellon Inst, 43-47, Rockefeller Inst, 51-52 & Univ Pittsburgh, Med Sch, 53-65. *Concurrent Pos:* AEC fel, 49-51, Am Cancer Soc fel, 51-53; asst prof sch med, Univ Pittsburgh, 53-57, from assoc prof to prof, 57; Nat Coun Combat Blindness fel, 57; career prof, USPHS, 62-64; guest prof, Pa State Univ, 63; vis prof, Univ Paris, 67-68, Univ Col, Univ London, 71, Pasteur Inst, Paris, 72 & Princeton Univ, 78; vis professorship, Tohoku Univ Med Sch, Sendai, Japan, 88. *Mem:* Fel AAAS; fel Optical Soc Am; Am Chem Soc; fel Am Inst Chemists; Soc Gen Physiol; Am Soc Photobiol; Am Soc Cell Biol; Biophys Soc; fel Explorers Club. *Res:* Biophysics; photobiology, optics and vision; issued 2 patents. *Mailing Add:* 5817 Elmer St Pittsburgh PA 15232. *Fax:* 412-268-7129

**WOLKO, HOWARD STEPHEN,** MECHANICAL ENGINEERING, SOLID MECHANICS. *Current Pos:* RETIRED. *Personal Data:* b Buffalo, NY, Apr 30, 25; m 50, Ruth A Westphal; c Leslie, Kurt, Lindsey & Nels. *Educ:* Univ Buffalo, BS, 49, MS, 53; George Washington Univ, ScD(mech), 67. *Prof Exp:* Design engr, Sci Instruments Div, Am Optical Co, 50-52; res assoc exp mech, Cornell Aeronaut Lab, Cornell Univ, 52-55; chief struct res, Bell Aircraft Corp, 55-59; head solid mech, Eng Sci Directorate, Air Force Off Sci Res, 59-62; chief struct mech, Off Advan Res & Technol, NASA, 62-67; prof mech eng, Tex A&M Univ, 67-72; prof & chmn dept, Memphis State Univ, 72-73; asst dir, Sci & Technol Dept, Nat Air & Space Mus,

Smithsonian Inst, 73-80, spec adv, Aeronaut Dept, 80-93. *Concurrent Pos:* Lectr, Univ Buffalo, 53-59. *Mem:* Soc Eng Sci; Soc Exp Stress Analysis. *Res:* Coupled thermomechanics; continuum mechanics; materials science. *Mailing Add:* 1561 Evers Dr McLean VA 22101

**WOLKOFF, AARON WILFRED,** ANALYTICAL CHEMISTRY. *Current Pos:* PRES, WATERS LTD, 92- *Personal Data:* b Toronto, Ont, Feb 12, 44; m 66, Braverman; c Jodie & Jay. *Educ:* Univ Toronto, BSc, 65, MSc, 67, PhD(org chem), 71. *Prof Exp:* Fel, Inst Environ Sci & Eng, Univ Toronto, 71-72; teaching master math & chem, Seneca Col Appl Arts & Technol, 72-73; res scientist environ analysis, Can Centre Inland Waters, Dept Environ, 73-77. *Mem:* Am Chem Soc; Chem Inst Can. *Res:* Development of new analytical methods on the applications of high pressure liquid chromatography. *Mailing Add:* 3687 Nashua Dr Mississauga ON L4V 1V5 Can. *Fax:* 905-678-9237; *E-Mail:* aaron_wolkoff@waters.com

**WOLKOFF, HAROLD,** MECHANICAL ENGINEERING. *Current Pos:* Prof 51-85, EMER PROF ENG, NEW YORK CITY TECH COL, 85- *Personal Data:* b Brooklyn, NY, June 10, 23; m 49; c 2. *Educ:* Polytech Inst Brooklyn, BME, 49; City Col New York, MBA, 56. *Mem:* Am Soc Eng Educ; Soc Mfg Engrs; Am Indust Arts Asn. *Res:* Strength of materials; engineering drawing. *Mailing Add:* 7069 Rain Forest Dr Boca Raton FL 33434

**WOLL, EDWARD,** MECHANICAL ENGINEERING. *Current Pos:* RETIRED. *Personal Data:* b New York, NY, May 29, 14. *Educ:* Mass Inst Technol, BS, 35; Rensselaer Polytech Inst, ME, 46. *Prof Exp:* Gen mgr, Small Aircraft Dept, Gen Elec Co, 58-63, vpres, Mil Eng Div & Group Eng Div, 68-79, vpres & gen mgr, Group Advan Eng Div, 70-79. *Mem:* Nat Acad Eng; fel Soc Automotive Engrs; fel Am Inst Aeronaut & Astronaut; Am Helicopter Soc. *Mailing Add:* 241 Aspen Circle Lincoln MA 01773

**WOLL, HARRY JEAN,** ELECTRICAL & ELECTRONICS ENGINEERING. *Current Pos:* RETIRED. *Personal Data:* b Farmington, Minn, Aug, 25, 20; m 47, Mary V Cowan; c 2. *Educ:* NDak State Univ, BS, 40; Univ Pa, PhD(elec eng), 53. *Prof Exp:* Asst, Ill Inst Technol, 40-41; res & develop engr, RCA, 41-43, res & develop supvr, 53-58, mgr appl res, 58-63, chief engr, Aerospace Systs Div, 63-69, div vpres gov eng, Govt & Com Systs, 69-75, div vpres & gen mgr, Automated Systs, 75-81, staff vpres & chief engr, Electronic Prod, Systs & Serv, 81-85. *Concurrent Pos:* Chmn, Trustees Moore Sch Elec Eng, Univ Pa, 76-90; chmn, Aerospace Indust Asn Tech Coun, 77 & Inst Elec & Electronics Engrs, Fel Comt, 79-80. *Mem:* Fel AAAS; fel Inst Elec & Electronics & Engrs. *Res:* Linear circuit theory; solid state circuits; communications; electro-optics; aerospace systems; automatic test systems. *Mailing Add:* PO Box 679 Concord MA 01742

**WOLL, JOHN WILLIAM, JR,** MATHEMATICS. *Current Pos:* PROF MATH, WESTERN WASH STATE UNIV, 68- *Personal Data:* b Philadelphia, Pa, May 19, 31; m 52, 84; c 2. *Educ:* Haverford Col, BS, 52; Princeton Univ, PhD, 56. *Prof Exp:* Instr math, Princeton Univ, 56-57; asst prof, Lehigh Univ, 57-58, Univ Calif, 58-61 & Univ Wash, 61-68. *Mem:* Am Math Soc. *Res:* Functional analysis and stochastic processes. *Mailing Add:* Dept Math Western Wash State Univ Bellingham WA 98225-5946

**WOLLA, MAURICE L(EROY),** ELECTRICAL & COMPUTER ENGINEERING. *Current Pos:* PROF, COL INTEGRATED SCI & TECHNOL, JAMES MADISON UNIV, HARRISONBURG, VA, 92- *Personal Data:* b Minot, NDak, May 13, 33; m 53; c 5. *Educ:* NDak State Univ, BS, 56; Mich State Univ, PhD(elec eng), 66. *Prof Exp:* Instr elec eng, NDak State Univ, 56-58 & Mich State Univ, 58-65; assoc prof, Colo State Univ, 65-66; assoc prof elec eng, Clemson Univ, 66-72, prof, 72-85. *Concurrent Pos:* US Dept Interior res grants, 67-69; vis prof, Clemson Univ, 85- *Mem:* Simulation Coun; Inst Elec & Electronics Engrs; Am Soc Eng Educ. *Res:* Analysis and simulation of physical systems; computer sciences; software engineering; educational computing systems; real-time computing systems. *Mailing Add:* ISTA 207 James Madison Univ Harrisonburg VA 22807

**WOLLAN, DAVID STRAND,** SCIENCE POLICY, SOLID STATE PHYSICS. *Current Pos:* physicist, 74-89, SR EXEC SERV, US ARMS CONTROL & DISARMAMENT AGENCY, 89- *Personal Data:* b Boston, Mass, Mar 25, 37; m 79; c 2. *Educ:* Amherst Col, AB, 59; Univ Ill, MS, 61, PhD(physics), 66. *Prof Exp:* Asst prof physics, Va Polytech Inst & State Univ, 66-74. *Mem:* Am Phys Soc; Inst Elec & Electronics Engrs; Sigma Xi. *Res:* Electron and nuclear magnetic resonance in solids; strategic arms control. *Mailing Add:* 6026 Grove Dr Alexandria VA 22307-1139

**WOLLAN, JOHN JEROME,** LOW TEMPERATURE PHYSICS. *Current Pos:* DIR, ACOUSTIC REFRIG PROG, CRYENCO INC, 94- *Personal Data:* b Chicago, Ill, July 7, 42; c 2. *Educ:* St Olaf Col, BA, 64; Iowa State Univ, PhD(physics), 70. *Prof Exp:* Vis asst prof physics, Univ Ky, 70-73; Nat Res Coun assoc physics, Air Force Mat Lab, 73-74; staff mem physics, Los Alamos Sci Lab, 74-84; mgr, Magnetic Eng, Gen Elec Med Systs, 84-91; mgr superconducting technol, Martin Marietta Corp, 91-94. *Mem:* Am Phys Soc. *Res:* Development of thermo acoustically driven orifice pulse tube refrigeration for liquefaction of cryogenic gases. *Mailing Add:* 23529 Shingle Creek Rd Golden CO 80401. *Fax:* 303-371-0267; *E-Mail:* johnw@cryenco.com

**WOLLENBERG, BRUCE FREDERICK,** POWER SYSTEMS OPERATIONS. *Current Pos:* PROF ELEC ENG, UNIV MINN, 89- *Personal Data:* b Buffalo, NY, June 14, 42. *Educ:* Rensselaer Polytech Inst, BEE, 64, MEng, 66; Univ Pa, PhD(systs eng), 74. *Prof Exp:* Engr, Leeds & Northrop Co, 66-70, sr engr, 70-74; sr engr, Power Technologies Inc, 74-89. *Mem:* Sigma Xi; fel Inst Elec & Electronics Engrs. *Res:* Methods for secure and optical operation of electric power systems. *Mailing Add:* Dept Elec Eng Univ Minn 200 Union St SE Minneapolis MN 55455. *Fax:* 612-625-4583; *E-Mail:* wollenbe@ee.umn.edu

**WOLLENSAK, JOHN CHARLES,** ORGANIC CHEMISTRY, ORGANOMETALLIC CHEMISTRY. *Current Pos:* RETIRED. *Personal Data:* b Rochester, NY, Dec 16, 32; m 57; c 5. *Educ:* Col Holy Cross, BS, 54; Mass Inst Technol, PhD(org chem), 58; Mich State Univ, MBA, 80. *Prof Exp:* Res chemist, Ethyl Corp, 58-66, supvr chem res, 66-81, asst to vpres res, 81-83, dir chem res & develop, 83-93. *Mem:* Am Chem Soc; assoc Int Union Pure & Appl Chem. *Res:* Organic synthesis; organometallics; administering research on pharmaceuticals, agricultural chemical intermediates, bromine-containing organics, organometallics, alkylated phenols and anilines, polymer intermediates, long chain olefins and alcohols, antioxidants, and additives for petroleum products. *Mailing Add:* 18 Teaberry Lane Amherst MA 01002

**WOLLER, WILLIAM HENRY,** PHYSICAL PHARMACY, COSMETIC CHEMISTRY. *Current Pos:* Mfg pharmacist drug prod, Alcon Labs Inc, 56-64, res & develop scientist drugs & cosmetics, 65-73, RES & DEVELOP MGR DRUGS & COSMETICS & TECH DIR, DERMAT PROD TEX DIV, DPT LABS INC, NESTLE S A, SWITZ, VPRES RES PROD DEVELOP. *Personal Data:* b San Antonio, Tex, Feb 28, 33; m 58; c 3. *Educ:* Univ Tex, Austin, BS, 55. *Mem:* Am Pharm Asn; Soc Cosmetic Chemists. *Res:* Development of vehicles for organic peroxides for use in the treatment of dermatological disorders; screening alpha hydroxy acids for use in treatment of icthyosis; coal tar fractions. *Mailing Add:* 3314 Yorktown Dr San Antonio TX 78230

**WOLLIN, GOESTA,** CLIMATOLOGY, CHEMISTRY. *Current Pos:* RES CONSULT, HAYWOOD, COMMUNITY COL, CLYDE, NC, 86- *Personal Data:* b Ystad, Sweden, Oct 4, 22; nat US; m 50; c 1. *Educ:* Hermods Col, Sweden, Phil; Columbia Univ, MS, 53. *Prof Exp:* Newspaper reporter, Ystads Allehanda, 39-41; free lance writer, Swedish Newspapers, 45-50; asst, 50-56, Columbia Univ, res scientist, Lamont Geol Observ, Columbia Univ, 56-86. *Mem:* AAAS; NY Acad Sci; Glaciol Soc; Explorers Club. *Res:* Holocene and pleistocene climates and marine sedimentation; micropaleontological research of marine sediments; the relationship between climatic changes and variations in the earth's magnetic field; chemical research on origin of life; inventions for firefighting, agricultural spraying, and snow-skiing. *Mailing Add:* Jones Cove Rd Clyde NC 28721

**WOLLMAN, HARRY,** ANESTHESIOLOGY. *Current Pos:* RETIRED. *Personal Data:* b Brooklyn, NY, Sept 26, 32; m 57, Anne C Hamel; c Julie E, Emily J & Diana L. *Educ:* Harvard Univ, AB, 54, MD, 58; Am Bd Anesthesiol, dipl, 64. *Honors & Awards:* Detur Award. *Prof Exp:* Intern med & surg, Univ Chicago Clins, 58-59; resident, Hosp Univ Pa, 59-63, assoc in anesthesia, Univ, 63-65, from asst prof to prof, 65-70, Robert Dunning Dripps prof anesthesia & chmn dept, Sch Med, Univ PA, 72-87, prof pharmacol, 71-87; sr vpres, acad affairs, dean, Sch Med, Hahnemann Univ, 87-92. *Concurrent Pos:* NIH res trainee, 59-63; Pharmaceut Mfrs Asn fel, 60-61; consult, Vet Admin Hosp, Philadelphia, 63-64, 79- & Valley Forge Army Hosp, 65-66; mem, Pharm & Toxicol Training Grants Comt, NIH, 66-68, Anesthesia Training Grants Comt, 71-73, Surg A Study Sect, 74-78; mem, Anesthesia Drug Panel Drug Efficacy Study, Comt Anesthesia, Nat Acad Sci-Nat Res Coun, 70-71, Comt Adverse Reactions Anesthesia Drugs, 71-72; assoc ed, Anesthesiol, 70-75; prin investr, Anesthesia Res Ctr, Univ Pa 72-78, prog dir anesthesia res training grant, 72-, chmn, Comt Studies Involving Human Beings, 72-76; chmn, Clin Pract Exec Com, 76-80; John Harvard scholar. *Mem:* Am Soc Anesthesiologists; Soc Acad Anesthesia Chmn (pres, 77-78); Am Physiol Soc; Sigma Xi; Asn Univ Anesthetists. *Res:* Circulatory physiology; cerebral blood flow and metabolism; regional blood flow during anesthesia. *Mailing Add:* 13 Hathorn's Hill Woodstock VT 05091. *Fax:* 802-457-1688

**WOLLMAN, LEO,** TRANSSEXUALISM, ACUPUNCTURE THERAPY. *Current Pos:* MED DIR, LEXINGTON ACUPUNCTURE CLINIC, 95- *Personal Data:* b New York City, NY, Mar 14, 14; m 85, Ellen Hershenson; c Arthur & Bryant. *Educ:* Columbia Univ, BS, 34; NY Univ, MS, 38, Royal Col Physicians & Surgeons, Edinburgh, MD, 42; Rochdale Col, PhD, 72. *Hon Degrees:* DSc, Univ Mich, 73. *Honors & Awards:* Jules Weinstein Pioneer in Modern Hypn Award, 64. *Prof Exp:* Pres, Royal Med Soc, 40-41; peripatetic psychiat, World Fed Ment Health, 62-88; dir med, World Med Asn, 64-88, secy; Acad Psychosomat Med, 65-66; ed dent & med, J Am Soc Psychol Dent & Med, 67-84; adv ed hypnosis, Japanese J Hypnosis, 68-88; lic pvt sch teacher, Univ State NY, 73. *Concurrent Pos:* Hon mem, Arg Soc Hypnotherap, 62-88; life mem, NY State marriage, family, child counselor, 70-88; mem Soc Med Jurisprudence, 74-88; fel Am Col Sexologists, 79-88; exec dir, Inst Human Develop, 80-88. *Mem:* AAAS; Am Soc Abdominal Surgeons; Nat Acupuncture Res Soc; Am Soc Law & Med; Am Soc Clin Hypno; Am Soc Psychoprophylax Obstet; Am Med Writers Asn; Am Soc Psychosomat Dent & Med (pres, 66-69); Soc Sci Study Sex (pres, 79-82). *Res:* Transsexualism and transvestism using hypnosis; books on obesity, sexology, marriage, divorce, hypnosis; acupuncture therapy for medical dysphoria. *Mailing Add:* 3813 Poplar Ave Brooklyn NY 11224-1301

**WOLLMAN, SEYMOUR HORACE,** ENDOCRINOLOGY, CYTOLOGY. *Current Pos:* Scientist, 48-85, EMER SCIENTIST THYROID GLAND, PHYSIOL, CELL BIOL & TUMOR, NAT CANCER INST, NIH, 85- *Personal Data:* b New York, NY, May 17, 15; m 44, Cecelia Guntermann; c 3. *Educ:* NY Univ, BS, 35, MS, 36; Duke Univ, PhD(physics), 41. *Hon Degrees:* MD, Univ Goteborg, Sweden, 83. *Honors & Awards:* Dunhill Lectr, 5th Int Thyroid Cong, 65. *Mem:* Am Thyroid Asn (vpres, 70); Am Soc Cell Biol; European Thyroid Asn; Am Physiol Soc. *Res:* Aspects of synthesis and secretion of thyroid hormone; growth and involution of thyroid gland; production of thyroid tumors. *Mailing Add:* NIH Bldg 37 Rm 1E20 Bethesda MD 20892-0037

**WOLLMER, RICHARD DIETRICH,** ECONOMICS, MATHEMATICAL PROGRAMMING. *Current Pos:* PROF, CALIF STATE UNIV, LONG BEACH, 70- *Personal Data:* b Los Angeles, Calif, July 27, 38. *Educ:* Pomona Col, BA, 60; Columbia Univ, MA, 62; Univ Calif, Berkeley, MA, 63, PhD(eng sci), 65. *Prof Exp:* Oper res sci, Rand Corp, 65-70. *Concurrent Pos:* Consult, USAF Adv Bd Int Trans, 68-70; mem, Naval Res Adv Comt, 74-78; lectr, Univ Calif, Los Angeles, 70 & 74; res mathematician, Univ Southern Calif, 73-75; vis assoc prof, Stanford Univ, 76-77; mathematician, Elec Power Res Inst, 77; consult, McDonnell Douglas Corp, 78-80, 85-90 & Logicon, 79-81. *Mem:* Int Fed Oper Res & Mgt Sci. *Res:* Mathematical programming; network flows; dynamic programming; Markov processes; probability and statistics. *Mailing Add:* Dept Info Syst Calif State Univ 1250 Bellflower Blvd Long Beach CA 90840

**WOLLNER, THOMAS EDWARD,** ORGANIC CHEMISTRY, POLYMER CHEMISTRY & MATERIALS SCIENCE. *Current Pos:* Res mgr polymer res, 3M Co, 64-74, lab mgr, 75-77, dir, Chem Res Lab, 77-81 & Indust & Consumer Sector Res Lab, 81-84, res & develop dir, 84-86, res & develop vpres, Indust & Consumer Sector, 86-87, STAFF VPRES, CORP RES LABS, 3M CO, 87- *Personal Data:* b Rochester, Minn, Dec 30, 36; m 58; c 2. *Educ:* St John's Univ, Minn, BA, 58; Wash State Univ, PhD(chem), 64. *Mem:* Am Chem Soc; Sigma Xi; Indust Res Inst. *Res:* Adhesives, binders and coatings; optical and electrical properties of organics. *Mailing Add:* 3M Co 3M Ctr Bldg 220-4E-01 St Paul MN 55144-1000

**WOLLSCHLAEGER, GERTRAUD,** MEDICINE, RADIOLOGY. *Current Pos:* PROF RADIOL & NEURORADIOL, SCH MED, WAYNE STATE UNIV, 73- *Personal Data:* b Muenchen, Ger, Feb 28, 24; US citizen; m 48; c 3. *Educ:* Univ Munich, physicum, 54, MD & PhD, 57; State Univ NY, MD, 65. *Prof Exp:* Instr radiol, Albert Einstein Col Med, 61-64; from asst prof to assoc prof, Sch Med, Univ Mo, Columbia, 64-71; asst chief sect neuroradiol, William Beaumont Hosp, Royal Oak, Mich, 71-72. *Concurrent Pos:* Res fel radiol, Albert Einstein Col Med, Yeshiva Univ, 61-62, NIH spec fel neuroradiol, 62-64; res grant, Univ Mo-Columbia, 64-71; co-dir, NIH spec fel training prog, 67-71, consult, Crippled Children's Serv, 69-71. *Mem:* AAAS; Asn Univ Neuroradiol; Radiol Soc NAm; Inst Elec & Electronics Eng; AMA; Sigma Xi. *Res:* Postmortem cerebral angiography; cerebral microangiography; microtumor-circulation. *Mailing Add:* 5885 Wing Lake Rd Bloomfield Hills MI 48301-1255

**WOLLUM, ARTHUR GEORGE, II,** SOILS, MICROBIOLOGY & ECOLOGY. *Current Pos:* assoc prof soils, 71-76, chmn, Ecol Prog, 85-89, PROF SOILS, NC STATE UNIV, 76- *Personal Data:* b Chicago, Ill, July 26, 37; m 60, Karen E Hanson; c Steven A & Mark H. *Educ:* Univ Minn, BS, 59; Ore State Univ, MS, 62, PhD(soils), 65. *Prof Exp:* Forester, Gifford Pinchot Nat Forest, USDA, 59-60, res forester, Pac Northwest Forest & Range Exp Sta, 60-61; asst soils, Ore State Univ, 64-65, asst prof, 65-67; asst prof, NMex State Univ, 67-71. *Concurrent Pos:* Vis prof, Ohio State Univ, 78-79. *Mem:* Soc Am Foresters; fel Soil Sci Soc Am; Am Soc Microbiol; Sigma Xi; fel Am Soc Agron. *Res:* Microbiology of nodule-formation of nonleguminous plants; ecology of nitrogen fixing plants; nitrogen cycle; microbiology of environmental pollution; rhizobial ecology of stressed environments; bioremediation of environmental sensitive sites. *Mailing Add:* Dept Soil Sci NC State Univ Box 7619 Raleigh NC 27695-0001. *Fax:* 919-515-2167; *E-Mail:* arthur_wollum@nscu.edu

**WOLLWAGE, JOHN CARL,** PAPER CHEMISTRY. *Current Pos:* RETIRED. *Personal Data:* b Chicago, Ill, Oct 11, 14; wid; c 3. *Educ:* Northwestern Univ, BS, 34; Lawrence Col, MS, 36, PhD(paper chem), 38. *Prof Exp:* Mem staff, Res Dept, Hammermill Paper Co, Pa, 36; mem staff chem res, Beveridge-Marvellum Co, Mass, 37; res chemist, Kimberly-Clark Corp, 39-40, 42, tech supt, Mill, 41-42, war prod develop, 43-45, mill mgr, 45-49, asst tech dir, 49-52, dir res, 52-55, mgr Foreign Opers, 55-59, gen mgr Creped Wadding Mfg Processes, Consumer Prod Div, 59-62, vpres mfg, 62-68, vpres, C W Mfg, Res & Eng, 68-71, vpres corp res & eng, 71-73; vpres res, Inst Paper Chem, 73-78; dir, Memline, Inc, Suring, 78-88. *Concurrent Pos:* Tech Asn Pulp & Paper Indus fel, 63-; dir, Upson Co, Lockport, NY, 78-84. *Mem:* Tech Asn Pulp & Paper Indust (pres, 63-64); Am Chem Soc; Can Pulp & Paper Asn; AAAS; Sigma Xi. *Res:* Alum and its effect on hydrogen ion concentration of paper; flocculation of paper making fibers. *Mailing Add:* Nine Lawrence Ct Appleton WI 54911

**WOLLWAGE, PAUL CARL,** PULPING AND BLEACHING CHEMISTRY, ENVIRONMENTAL SCIENCES PULP & PAPER. *Current Pos:* BLEACHING SCIENTIST, WEYERHAUSER TECH CTR, 79- *Personal Data:* b Appleton, Wis, Mar 15, 41; m 65; c 2. *Educ:* St Olaf Col, BA, 63; Inst Paper Chem, MS, 66, PhD(chem), 69. *Prof Exp:* Sr res chemist, St Regis Tech Ctr, 69-79. *Mem:* Tech Asn Pulp & Paper Indust. *Res:* Pulping and bleaching processes; pulp characterization; wood chemicals. *Mailing Add:* Weyerhaeuser Co Weyerhaeuser Tech Ctr 2G25 Tacoma WA 98477

**WOLMA, FRED J,** MEDICINE, SURGERY. *Current Pos:* resident surg, 48-51, from instr to assoc prof, 51-69, chief div gen surg, 67-70, PROF SURG, UNIV TEX MED BR, GALVESTON, 69- *Personal Data:* b Albuquerque, NMex, Dec 10, 16; m 43; c 2. *Educ:* Univ Tex, BA, 40, MD, 43; Am Bd Surg, dipl, 53. *Prof Exp:* Intern, Med Col Va, 43-44, resident surg, 47-48; res physician, St Mary's Infirmary, Galveston, Tex, 46-47. *Concurrent Pos:* Consult, St Mary's Hosp & Galveston, Tex. *Mem:* AMA; Am Col Surg; Soc Surg Alimentary Tract; Am Asn Cancer Res; Am Asn Surg Trauma. *Res:* Clinical medicine; peripheral vascular surgery. *Mailing Add:* 4404 Sherman Galveston TX 77550-8519

**WOLMAN, ERIC,** CANCER CONTROL. *Current Pos:* FAC, DEPT INTERNAL MED & GRAD PROG IN CANCER BIOL, SCH MED, WAYNE STATE UNIV, 92- *Personal Data:* b New York, NY, Sept 25, 31; m 63, Sandra Rosman; c Karin & Alec. *Educ:* Harvard Univ, AB, 53, MA, 54, PhD(appl math), 57. *Prof Exp:* Mem tech staff, AT&T Bell Labs, 57-66, head, Traffic Systs Analysis Dept, 66-68, head, Traffic Res Dept, 68-72, head, Network Eng Dept, 72-77, head, Opers Res Tech & Database Res Dept, 77-80, head, Advan Comput Systs Dept, 81-82, head, Human Performance Eng Dept, 83-87; vpres community res, Mich Cancer Found, 88-91. *Concurrent Pos:* Vis lectr, Harvard Univ, 64; mem, Comt Fire Res, Nat Acad Sci-Nat Res Coun, 66-70; mem ad hoc eval panel, Fire Prog, 71-74, mem eval panel, Inst Appl Technol, 74-78, Nat Eng Lab, Nat Bur Stand, 78-80; mem, Working Group Info Technol, NSF, 80-81; chmn, bd trustees, Soc Indust & Appl Math, 81-82; asst leader, Cancer Control Prog, Prentis Comprehensive Cancer Ctr, 90- *Mem:* Fel AAAS; Am Pub Health Asn; Opers Res Soc Am; Sigma Xi. *Res:* Mathematical modeling and policy research on cancer screening. *Mailing Add:* 7806 Hidden Meadow Terr Potomac MD 20854-1792

**WOLMAN, MARKLEY GORDON,** GEOLOGY. *Current Pos:* Interim provost, 87, 89-90, PROF GEOG & CHMN, DEPT GEOG & ENVIRON ENG, JOHNS HOPKINS UNIV, 58-; GEOLOGIST, US GEOL SURV, 51- *Personal Data:* b Baltimore, Md, Aug 16, 24; m 51, Elaine Mielke; c 4. *Educ:* Johns Hopkins Univ, BA, 49; Harvard Univ, MA, 51, PhD(geol), 53. *Honors & Awards:* Asn Am Geog Award, 72; John Wesley Powell Award, US Geol Surv, 89; Cullum Geog Medal, Am Geog Soc, 89. *Mem:* Nat Acad Sci; Geol Soc Am; Am Geophys Union; Asn Am Geog; Am Acad Arts & Sci; AAAS. *Res:* River morphology; water resources. *Mailing Add:* Dept Geog & Environ Eng Johns Hopkins Univ Baltimore MD 21218. *Fax:* 410-516-8996

**WOLMAN, SANDRA R,** PATHOLOGY, CYTOGENETICS. *Current Pos:* PROF CLIN PATHOL, SCH MED, WAYNE STATE UNIV, GEORGE WASHINGTON UNIV SCH MED & UNIFORMED SERV UNIV HEALTH SCI. *Personal Data:* b New York, NY, Nov 23, 33; m 63, Eric; c Karin & Alec. *Educ:* Radcliffe Col, AB, 55; NY Univ, MD, 59. *Prof Exp:* Intern path, Bellevue Hosp, New York, 59-60, resident, 60-63; asst pathologist, Morristown Mem Hosp, 64-66; asst pathologist, Monmouth Med Ctr, 66-67; asst prof clin path, Sch Med, NY Univ, 67-71; from asst prof to prof, 72-88. *Concurrent Pos:* Teaching fel path, Sch Med, NY Univ, 62-64, Nat Cancer Inst res fel oncol, 63, Children's Cancer Res Found fel, 64; asst pathologist, Bellevue Hosp, 63-64, asst vis pathologist, 67-76, consult pathologist, Morristown Mem Hosp, 66-73; assoc pathologist, Fr & Polyclin Hosps, 70-71; mem, Path B Study Sect, NIH, 76-80; assoc attend pathologist, Bellevue & Univ Hosps, 76-85, attend pathologist, 85-88; mem, Nat Large Bowel Cancer Proj, 80-83, Vet Admin Merit Rev Bd, Basic Med Sci, 82-84; chair, Fac Coun, NY Univ, 85-86, Gordon Conf on Cancer, 88; mem, Breast Cancer Prog, Karmanos Cancer Inst; pres, Women in Cancer Res, 92; dir, Am Asn Cancer Res, 88-91. *Mem:* AAAS; Am Soc Human Genetics; Am Asn Cancer Res; Tissue Cult Asn; Sigma Xi; Am Oncol Asn; Cell Prolif Soc; Am Soc Invest Path. *Res:* Tumor markers; breast cancer; cytogenetics. *Mailing Add:* Path Uniformed Serv Univ Health Servs 4301 Jones Bridge Rd Bethesda MD 20814. *Fax:* 301-295-1640; *E-Mail:* wolmans@erols.com

**WOLNIAK, STEPHEN M,** CELL MOTILITY, SIGNAL TRANSDUCTION. *Current Pos:* ASST PROF PLANT CELL BIOL & OPTICAL PRIN MICROS, UNIV MD, 81- *Educ:* Univ Calif, Berkeley, PhD(bot), 79. *Mailing Add:* Dept Bot Univ Md College Park MD 20742-5815. *Fax:* 301-314-9075

**WOLNY, FRIEDRICH FRANZ,** ORGANIC POLYMER CHEMISTRY. *Current Pos:* chemist, 65-68, group leader, 69-72, mgr resin res, 73-83, VPRES RES, SCHENECTADY CHEM, INC, NY, 84- *Personal Data:* b Troppau, Czech, Aug 24, 31; US citizen; m 56; c 1. *Educ:* Munich Tech Univ, BS, 54, MS, 55. *Prof Exp:* Group leader resin res, Sued-West-Chemie, WGer, 56-58, asst res & develop dir, 59-64. *Mem:* Electrochem Soc WGer; Am Chem Soc; Soc Automotive Engrs. *Res:* Organic polymer chemistry, poly condensation products, phenol formaldehyde resins, applied in friction materials. *Mailing Add:* 686 Plank Rd Clifton Park NY 12065-2097

**WOLOCK, FRED WALTER,** mathematical statistics, for more information see previous edition

**WOLOCK, IRVIN,** MATERIALS ENGINEERING, COMPOSITES. *Current Pos:* supvr mat res engr, Naval Res Lab, DC, 57-73, liaison scientist, Off Naval Res, London, 73-74, SUPVR MAT RES ENGR, NAVAL RES LAB, DC, 74- *Personal Data:* b Baltimore, Md, June 21, 23; m 51; c 3. *Educ:* Johns Hopkins Univ, BS, 43, ME, 49, DrEng, 50. *Prof Exp:* Res asst, SAM Labs, Columbia Univ, 43-44; chemist, Nat Bur Standards, 50-57. *Concurrent Pos:* Ed, J Soc Plastics Engrs, 58-64. *Mem:* Am Soc Testing & Mat; Soc Advan Mat & Process Eng; AAAS; Sigma Xi. *Res:* Failure behavior of plastics and composites; transparent plastics; composites applications. *Mailing Add:* 401 Scott Dr Silver Spring MD 20904

**WOLOS, JEFFREY ALAN,** SOLUBLE MEDIATORS, T-CELLS. *Current Pos:* ASST PROF IMMUNOL, THOMAS JEFFERSON UNIV, 81- *Educ:* NY Upstate Med Ctr, PhD(microbiol), 79. *Mailing Add:* Dept Immunol PO Box 156300 Hoechst Marion Roussel Inc 2110 E Galbraith Rd Cincinnati OH 45237-1641. *Fax:* 513-948-7472

**WOLOSEWICK, JOHN J,** cytoskeleton electron microscopy, for more information see previous edition

**WOLOSEWICZ, RONALD MITCHELL,** DYNAMICS VIBRATION & DESIGN OF MECHANICAL SYSTEMS, FINITE ELEMENT ANALYSIS. *Current Pos:* PRIN ENGR, ROCKWELL GRAPHIC SYSTS, 84- *Personal Data:* b Chicago, Ill, Dec 27, 37; m 77, Christine Borawski; c Andrzej & Isabella. *Educ:* Northwestern Univ, BS, 60, MS, 62, PhD(mech eng), 67. *Prof Exp:* Sr develop engr, Anocut Eng Co, 68-69; sr res engr, Whirlpool Corp, 69-77; mech engr, Argonne Nat Lab, 77-82; mgr eng & mfg, Trak Microcomput Corp, 82-84. *Concurrent Pos:* Fulbright Hayes fel, Polish Acad Sci, Inst Fundamental Res, Warsaw, 66-67; adj prof mech mat, Lake Mich Col, 72-73; adj prof, Mich State Univ Exten, Benton Harbor, 73-76. *Mem:* Fel Am Soc Mech Engrs. *Res:* Design and analysis using analytical computer modeling and experimental techniques for components and mechanical systems. *Mailing Add:* 5410 Country Club Dr La Grange IL 60525

**WOLOSHIN, HENRY JACOB,** radiology; deceased, see previous edition for last biography

**WOLOVICH, WILLIAM ANTHONY,** ELECTRICAL ENGINEERING, CONTROL SYSTEMS. *Current Pos:* from asst prof to assoc prof eng, 70-77, PROF ENG, BROWN UNIV, 77- *Personal Data:* b Hartford, Conn, Oct 15, 37; m 59; c 2. *Educ:* Univ Conn, BS, 59; Worcester Polytech Inst, MS, 61; Brown Univ, PhD(elec sci), 70. *Prof Exp:* Systs analyst, Res Lab, United Aircraft Corp, 59-61; control systs engr, Electronics Res Labs, NASA, 64-70. *Mem:* Inst Elec & Electronics Engrs. *Res:* Linear multivariable control systems; computational methods for the analysis and synthesis of large scale systems; stability and optimization of dynamical systems. *Mailing Add:* Div Eng Brown Univ Providence RI 02912

**WOLPAW, ELIZABETH WINTER,** NEUROCHEMISTRY. *Current Pos:* lectr chem, 84-85, asst prof, 85-91, ASSOC PROF CHEM, SIENA COL, NY, 91-, CHEM DEPT HEAD, 93- *Personal Data:* b New York, NY, Dec 26, 44; m 66, Jonathan R; c David & Jessica. *Educ:* Smith Col, BA, 65; Case Western Res Univ, MSSA, 68; Univ Md, PhD(biochem), 84. *Prof Exp:* Psychiat caseworker, Mt Sinai Hosp, Cleveland, 68-70; res technician, Armed Forces Radiobiol Res Inst, 78-80, Wadsworth Ctr, NY State Dept Health, 80-85. *Concurrent Pos:* Teaching asst, Univ Md, 78-79; lectr, State Univ NY, Albany, 85. *Mem:* Am Chem Soc; Soc Neurosci; Asn Women Sci; Sigma Xi. *Res:* Neurochemistry. *Mailing Add:* Chem Dept Siena Col Loudonville NY 12211. *E-Mail:* wolpaw@siena.edu

**WOLPOFF, MILFORD HOWELL,** PHYSICAL ANTHROPOLOGY. *Current Pos:* assoc prof, 70-78, PROF ANTHROP, UNIV MICH, ANN ARBOR, 78- *Personal Data:* b Chicago, Ill, Oct 28, 42; m 85; c 1. *Educ:* Univ Ill, Urbana, AB, 64, PhD(anthrop), 69. *Prof Exp:* Asst prof anthrop, Case Western Reserve Univ, 68-70. *Concurrent Pos:* NSF res grant, Transvaal Mus, Nat Mus Kenya, 72; NSF grant human evolution, 76-79; NSF, Rackham Found & Nat Acad Sci grants. *Mem:* Fel Am Asn Phys Anthrop; fel Am Anthrop Asn; Sigma Xi. *Res:* Paleoanthropology; human origins and evolution; evolution theory; biomechanics; computer analysis; dental variation; worldwide fossil hominid study. *Mailing Add:* Anthrop-1059LSA Univ Mich Ann Arbor MI 48109-1382

**WOLSEY, LAURENCE ALEXANDER,** MATHEMATICS. *Current Pos:* res fel, Ctr Opers Res & Economet, Cath Univ Louvain, 71-72, from asst prof to assoc prof, 72-89, res dir, 88-91, PROF, CATH UNIV LOUVAIN, 89-, PRES, 93- *Personal Data:* b London, Eng, May 14, 45; m 74, Marguerite L Loute; c Jonathan & Julian. *Educ:* Oxford Univ, BA, 66; Mass Inst Technol, PhD(math), 69. *Honors & Awards:* Orchard-Hays Prize, Math Programming Soc, 88; Lancester Prize, Opers Res Soc Am, 89; Gold Medal, 94. *Prof Exp:* Vis lectr, Manchester Bus Sch, Eng, 69-71. *Concurrent Pos:* Vis sr res fel, London Sch Econs, 78-79; vis prof, Ecole Poly Federale, Switz, 86-87; co-ed, Math Prog, 89- *Mem:* Math Prog Soc; Opers Res Soc Am. *Mailing Add:* Ctr Opers Res & Economet 34 Voie de Roman Pays Louvain-la-Neuve B-1348 Belgium

**WOLSEY, WAYNE C,** INORGANIC CHEMISTRY. *Current Pos:* asst prof chem, 65-72, assoc prof, 72-80, PROF CHEM, MACALESTER COL, 80- *Personal Data:* b Battle Creek, Mich, Nov 12, 36; m 65, Mary Lou Morris; c Carole & Roger. *Educ:* Mich State Univ, BS, 58; Univ Kans, PhD(chem), 62. *Prof Exp:* Sr res chemist chem div, Pittsburgh Plate Glass Co, 62-65. *Concurrent Pos:* Vis asst prof, Ariz State Univ, 71-72; vis sr res fel, Bristol Univ, 78-79; guest scientist, Oak Ridge Nat Lab, 87-88 & 94-95. *Mem:* AAAS; Am Chem Soc; Am Asn Univ Prof; Am Nuclear Soc. *Res:* Coordination compounds; chemistry of chlorine and nitrogen compounds; laboratory computing; chemistry experiments. *Mailing Add:* Dept Chem Macalester Col St Paul MN 55105-1899

**WOLSKY, ALAN MARTIN,** PHYSICS, RESEARCH ADMINISTRATION. *Current Pos:* dir technol eval, 86-89, MEM STAFF, ARGONNE NAT LAB, 75-, SR ENERGY SYSTS SCIENTIST, EES DIV, 85-, ASSOC DIV DIR, ES DIV, 89- *Personal Data:* b Brooklyn, NY, May 17, 43; m 69; c 1. *Educ:* Columbia Col, AB, 64; Univ Pa, MS, 65, PhD(physics), 69. *Prof Exp:* Nat Res Coun fel math physics, Courant Inst Math Sci, NY Univ, 70, vis mem, 71; asst prof physics, Temple Univ, 71-75. *Concurrent Pos:* Prin investr, Argonne Nat Lab, 78- *Mem:* Am Phys Soc; Int Asn Economists. *Res:* Feasibility of reducing petroleum consumption by using biomass as an alternative source of hydrocarbons and by recycling, recovering or upgrading industrial waste materials; feasibility of recovering carbon dioxide from stationary combustion to provide carbon dioxide for enhanced oil recovery; mathematical economics; theory of social choice and input-output analysis; potential uses of high temperature superconductors. *Mailing Add:* 5461 Hillcrest Ave Downers Grove IL 60515

**WOLSKY, ALEXANDER,** HISTORY & THEORIES OF EVOLUTION. *Current Pos:* RETIRED. *Personal Data:* b Budapest, Hungary, Aug 12, 02; US citizen; m 40, Maria de Issekutz; c Catherine (deceased) & Thomas. *Educ:* Univ Budapest, DPhil, 28. *Hon Degrees:* PhD, St Peter's Col, Jersey City, 67. *Prof Exp:* Researcher & dir biol, Biol Res Inst Hungary Acad Tihany, 29-45; prof gen zool, Univ Budapest, 45-48; prin sci officer gen sci, UNESCO, 48-54; prof exp embryol, Fordham Univ, NY, 54-66; prof biol, Marymount Col, Tarrytown, 66-72; adj prof radiation biol, Med Sch, NY Univ, 72-86; adj prof biol, Concordia Univ, Montreal, 87-91. *Mem:* Hungarian Acad Sci; Sigma Xi. *Res:* Analysis of development and regeneration of arthropods (insects, crustaceans) and amphibians, both morphological and physiological (respiration); functions (optics) of the arthropodan eye; evolution (both progressive and regressive) of eyes and the mechanism of evolution in general. *Mailing Add:* 407 Mount Echo Rd RR 4 Sutton Junction PQ J0E 2K0 Can

**WOLSKY, SUMNER PAUL,** PHYSICAL CHEMISTRY. *Current Pos:* PRES, ANSUM ENTERPRISES, INC, 81- *Personal Data:* b Boston, Mass, Aug 21, 26; m 50; c 2. *Educ:* Northeastern Univ, BS, 47; Boston Univ, MA, 49, PhD(chem), 52. *Prof Exp:* Mem res staff, Raytheon Co, 52-61; dir lab phys sci, P R Mallory & Co, Inc, 61-74, dir res & develop lab phys sci, 74-76, vpres res & develop, 76-81. *Mem:* AAAS; Am Chem Soc; Am Phys Soc; Inst Elec & Electronics Engrs; Electrochem Soc. *Res:* Batteries; semiconductors; surface physics; physical electronics; sputtering; thin films; vacuum microbalances; environment; occupational health. *Mailing Add:* 1900 Coconut Rd Boca Raton FL 33432

**WOLSSON, KENNETH,** LINEAR ALGEBRA & CLASSICAL ANALYSIS. *Current Pos:* asst prof, 64-77, ASSOC PROF MATH, FAIRLEIGH DICKINSON UNIV, TEANECK, 77- *Personal Data:* b Paterson, NJ, Oct 12, 33. *Educ:* Brooklyn Col, BS, 54; Columbia Univ, AM, 55; NY Univ, PhD(math), 62. *Prof Exp:* Prin res mathematician, Repub Aviation Corp, 62-63. *Mem:* Am Math Soc; Math Asn Am. *Res:* Partial and ordinary differential equations; exploring the relation between Wronskians and linear dependence of their functions and curvature of manifolds; investigating the separability of functions of several variables. *Mailing Add:* 697 W End Ave 10A New York NY 10025-6823

**WOLSTENHOLME, DAVID ROBERT,** MOLECULAR BIOLOGY, CELL BIOLOGY. *Current Pos:* assoc prof, 70-72, chmn, Dept Biol, 80-83, PROF BIOL, UNIV UTAH, 72- *Personal Data:* b Bury, Eng, Nov 5, 37; m 63. *Educ:* Univ Sheffield, BSc, 58, PhD(genetics), 61, DSc(genetics), 73. *Prof Exp:* Fel zool, Univ Wis, 61-62, res assoc, 62-63; vis lectr genetics, Univ Groningen, 63-64; res fel biol, Beermann Div, Max Planck Inst Biol, 64-67; res assoc, Whitman Lab, Univ Chicago, 67-68; assoc prof, Kans State Univ, 68-70. *Concurrent Pos:* Nat Inst Gen Med Sci res career develop award, Univ Utah, 72-76; mem, Molecular Biol Study Sect, NIH, 73-77. *Mem:* Brit Genetical Soc; Am Soc Cell Biol; Genetics Soc Am. *Res:* Structure, replication, and evolution of animal and plant mitochondrial DNA. *Mailing Add:* Dept Biol Univ Utah 201 S Biol Bldg Salt Lake City UT 84112-1196

**WOLSTENHOLME, WAYNE W,** MUSCARINIC RECEPTORS, OPIOID RECEPTORS. *Current Pos:* INDEPENDENT CONTRACTOR. *Personal Data:* b Philadelphia, Pa, Dec 24, 48; m 85; c 3. *Educ:* Villanova Univ, BS, 70; Temple Univ, MS, 74, PhD(pharmacol), 78. *Prof Exp:* Asst prof pharmacol, Al-Faateh Univ, Tripol, Libya, 78-79; Univ PR Pharm Sch, 80-83; assoc prof, Med Sch, Univ Cent Del Caribe, 83-92. *Concurrent Pos:* Coordr, Comput Facil, Univ Cent del Caribe, 85-91, prin investr, Neurosci Proj, 86-91. *Mem:* Sigma Xi; AAAS. *Res:* Receptor identification of muscarinic receptors in the isolated vasdeferens and neuromodulatory role of opioids and peptides in the same preparation. *Mailing Add:* 2928 Yorkshire Rd Doylestown PA 18901

**WOLSZON, JOHN DONALD,** ANALYTICAL CHEMISTRY. *Current Pos:* ASSOC PROF CHEM, PURDUE UNIV, 63- *Personal Data:* b Chicago, Ill, Jan 27, 29; m 53; c 6. *Educ:* Univ Ill, BS, 51; Pa State Univ, PhD(anal chem), 55. *Prof Exp:* Instr chem, Marshall Univ, 55-58; asst prof, Univ Mo, 58-63. *Mem:* Am Chem Soc; Water Pollution Control Fedn; Am Water Works Asn. *Res:* Methods of chemical analysis; water and waste water chemistry. *Mailing Add:* 132 Hideaway Lane West Lafayette IN 47906

**WOLT, JEFFREY DUAINE,** SOIL & ENVIRONMENTAL CHEMISTRY, RISK ASSESSMENT. *Current Pos:* sr scientist, Environ Chem Lab, 89-94, tech leader & res scientist soil, air & water chem, 94-95, ENVIRON ISSUES MGR, DOWELANCO, 95- *Personal Data:* b Grand Forks, NDak, Oct 18, 51; m 80, Evelyn Richmond; c Kathryn, Raymond & Jared. *Educ:* Colo State

Univ, BS, 73; Auburn Univ, MS, 76, PhD(soil chem), 79. *Prof Exp:* From asst prof to assoc prof plant & soil sci, Univ Tenn, 84-89. *Concurrent Pos:* Consult, 83-; vis scientist award, Am Soc Agron, 89; vis scientist agron & soils, Univ Hawaii, 89-90; adj prof agron, Purdue Univ, 93- *Mem:* Am Soc Agron; Soil Sci Soc Am; AAAS; Sigma Xi; Am Chem Soc. *Res:* Methods development and applications in soil solution chemistry; soil chemistry of pesticides; organic waste management; acid precipitation impacts on plants and soils; solute transport and retention in the vadose zone; environmental risk assessment. *Mailing Add:* Environ Chem Lab DowElanco A-2773 9330 Zionsville Rd Indianapolis IN 46268-1053. *Fax:* 317-337-3235; *E-Mail:* jwolt@elinet1.dowelanco.com

**WOLTER, J REIMER,** OPHTHALMOLOGY, PATHOLOGY. *Current Pos:* res assoc path, 53-56, from asst prof to assoc prof ophthal, 56-64, PROF OPHTHAL, MED SCH, UNIV MICH, ANN ARBOR, 64- *Personal Data:* b Halstenbek, Ger, May 9, 24; US citizen; m 52; c 4. *Educ:* Univ Hamburg, MD, 49. *Prof Exp:* Intern med, Med Sch, Univ Hamburg, 49-50, resident instr ophthal, 50-53. *Concurrent Pos:* Chief ophthal serv, Vet Admin Hosp, Ann Arbor, 62-85; ed, J Pediat Ophthal, 67-81. *Mem:* AMA; Am Ophthal Soc; Am Acad Ophthal & Otolaryngol; Asn Res Ophthal; Ger Ophthal Soc. *Res:* Clinical ophthalmology; ophthalmic pathology. *Mailing Add:* 2565 Bedford Rd Univ Hosp Ann Arbor MI 48104

**WOLTER, JAN D(ITHMAR),** assembly sequence planning, computer-aided mechanical design, for more information see previous edition

**WOLTER, JANET,** MEDICAL ONCOLOGY. *Current Pos:* from asst prof to assoc prof, 71-81, PROF MED, RUSH MED COL, PRESBY-ST LUKE'S MED CTR, 81- *Personal Data:* b Chicago, Ill, Apr 24, 26; m 73. *Educ:* Cornell Col, AB, 46; Univ Ill, MD, 50. *Prof Exp:* Instr med, Univ Ill Col Med, 55-57, clin asst prof, 57-70, asst prof med, 70-71. *Concurrent Pos:* Staff physician respiratory, Univ Ill Hosp, 55-57; tumor clin physician oncol, Univ Ill Res & Educ Hosp, 63; res assoc oncol, Presby-St Luke's Hosp, 63-66, consult oncol, 66; consult oncol, WSuburban Hosp, 66; asst attend physician, Presby-St Luke's Med Ctr, 67-70, assoc attend physician, 70-72, sr attend physician, 72, consult oncol, 72-; consult oncol, Copley Hosp, 72- *Mem:* Am Soc Clin Oncol; Am Asn Cancer Res; Eastern Coop Oncol Group; Nat Surg Adj Breast Proj. *Res:* Cancer chemotherapy. *Mailing Add:* 1753 W Congress Pkwy Chicago IL 60612-3809

**WOLTER, KARL ERICH,** PLANT PHYSIOLOGY. *Current Pos:* RETIRED. *Personal Data:* b New York, NY, Nov 8, 30. *Educ:* State Univ NY Col Forestry, Syracuse, BS, 58; Univ Wis, PhD(plant physiol), 64. *Prof Exp:* Proj leader biodegradation & biotechnol res, Forest Prod Lab, Forest Serv, USDA, 63-86; asst prof & sr scientist, Dept Hort, Univ Wis, 86-97. *Concurrent Pos:* Vis prof, Iowa State Univ, 71-72; Japanese Sci & Technol grant; vis scientist, Tsukuba, Japan, 81-82. *Mem:* Am Soc Plant Physiol; Scand Soc Plant Physiol; Int Plant Growth Substances Asn. *Res:* Growth, differentiation and nutrition of plants and secondary cambium, specifically tree species; host pathogen interactions, action, and characterization of plant cell wall degrading enzymes. *Mailing Add:* 12146 Hwy 59 Evansville WI 53536

**WOLTER, KIRK MARCUS,** SCIENCE ADMINISTRATION, MATHEMATICAL STATISTICS. *Current Pos:* VPRES, A C NIELSEN, 88- *Personal Data:* b Evanston, Ill; m 81, Mary J Vanderford; c Nicole, Alexander & Asilinn. *Educ:* St Olaf Col, BA, 70; Iowa State Univ, MS, 72, PhD(statist), 74. *Honors & Awards:* Bronze Medal & Silver Medal, US Dept Com. *Prof Exp:* Chief, Statist Res Div, US Bur Census, 74-88. *Concurrent Pos:* Prof lectr, George Washington Univ, 75-88. *Mem:* Fel Am Statist Asn; fel Int Statist Inst; Int Asn Surv Statisticians (vpres, 93-); Inst Math Statist; Am Mkt Asn. *Res:* Variance estimation for complex sample surveys; measurement of decennial census undercount; evaluation of statistical programs; statistical policy; statistical administration; design and analysis of marketing research information. *Mailing Add:* 1321 Wild Rose Lane Lake Forest IL 60045

**WOLTERINK, LESTER FLOYD,** BIOPHYSICS. *Current Pos:* from instr to prof physiol, 41-84, asst exp sta, 45-81, EMER PROF PHYSIOL, MICH STATE UNIV, 84- *Personal Data:* b Marion, NY, July 28, 15; m 38, Lillian R Nichols; c Charles P & Timothy J. *Educ:* Hope Col, AB, 36; Univ Minn, MA, 40, PhD(zool), 43. *Prof Exp:* Lab asst, Hope Col, 34-36, Univ Minn, 36-41. *Concurrent Pos:* Assoc physiologist, Argonne Nat Lab, Ill, 48; proj scientist biosatellite proj, Ames Res Ctr, NASA, 65-66; mem, Subcomt Nitrogen Oxides, Nat Acad Sci-Nat Res Coun, 73-75. *Mem:* Biomed Eng Soc; Biophys Soc; Am Physiol Soc; Radiation Res Soc. *Res:* Biological rhythms, oscillatory time series; physiological models. *Mailing Add:* Dept Physiol Mich State Univ 129 Giltner Hall East Lansing MI 48824-1101

**WOLTERS, ROBERT JOHN,** PHARMACEUTICAL CHEMISTRY, PHARMACOLOGY. *Current Pos:* SUPVRY CHEMIST, US FOOD & DRUG ADMIN, ROCKVILLE, 84- *Personal Data:* b St Louis, Mo, Nov 7, 40; m 70, Cameron; c John & Katheen. *Educ:* St Louis Col Pharm, BS, 65; NDak State Univ, MS, 68, PhD(pharmaceut chem), 71. *Mem:* Am Chem Soc; Am Pharmaceut Asn; Sigma Xi. *Res:* Synthesis of potential pharmaceutically active compounds; mescaline analogs. *Mailing Add:* 18645 Hedgegrove Terr Olney MD 20832

**WOLTERSDORF, OTTO WILLIAM, JR,** MEDICINAL CHEMISTRY. *Current Pos:* RETIRED. *Personal Data:* b Philadelphia, Pa, June 19, 35; m 57; c 2. *Educ:* Gettysburg Col, AB, 56; Pa State Univ, MS, 59. *Prof Exp:* Res assoc org synthesis, Merck Sharp & Dohme Res Labs, 59-65, from res chemist to sr res chemist, 65-73, res fel, 73-83, sr res fel, 83-93. *Mem:* Am Chem Soc. *Res:* Organic synthesis; radioisotope synthesis. *Mailing Add:* 200 Dorset Way Chalfont PA 18914-2322

**WOLTHUIS, ROGER A,** CARDIOVASCULAR PHYSIOLOGY. *Current Pos:* VPRES MED PROD, METRICOR INC, 82- *Personal Data:* b Champaign, Ill, Mar 30, 37; m 65; c 2. *Educ:* Univ Mich, BA, 63; Mich State Univ, MS, 65, PhD(physiol), 68. *Prof Exp:* Prin res scientist, Technol Inc, Cardiovasc Res Lab, NASA Johnson Space Ctr, 68-74; chief cardiovasc res internal med, Sch Aerospace Med, Brooks AFB, 74-79; sr staff scientist, Medtronic Inc, 79-81. *Concurrent Pos:* Partic, Apollo & Skylab Med Experiments. *Mem:* Am Col Cardiol; Am Heart Asn; Aerospace Med Asn; Am Physiol Soc; Inst Elec & Electronics Engrs. *Res:* Studies on man's physiological adaptation to normal and zero gravity environments; studies on exercise stress testing for detection of coronary artery disease; studies on hypertension and its treatment; development of fiber optic sensors and systems. *Mailing Add:* Metrilab Inc 15430 NE 162nd Pl Woodinville WA 98072-8911

**WOLTZ, FRANK EARL,** PHYSICAL CHEMISTRY. *Current Pos:* RETIRED. *Personal Data:* b Bethlehem, Pa, Nov 29, 16; m 47, Jean Lawrence; c 2. *Educ:* Bethany Col, WVa, BS, 38; Univ WVa, MS, 40, PhD(chem), 43; Ohio Univ, MS, 70. *Prof Exp:* Mat engr, Westinghouse Elec Corp, Pa, 42-44; lab engr, Goodyear Synthetic Rubber Corp, Ohio, 44-47, res chemist, Goodyear Tire & Rubber Co, 47-50, rubber compounder, 50-53, supvr opers anal, Goodyear Atomic Corp, Piketon, 53-67, supt eng develop, 67-83, supt nuclear criticality safety, 83-85. *Concurrent Pos:* Consult radiation adv bd, Ohio Dept Health, 74- *Mem:* Am Nuclear Soc. *Res:* Electrical insulating varnishes; analytical test methods; rubber manufacture; inert electrode systems; rubber compounding for use in tire manufacturing; fluid flow; material and energy optimization of gaseous diffusion processes; computer control of chemical processes; nuclear criticality safety. *Mailing Add:* 400 E Third St Waverly OH 45690

**WOLTZ, SHREVE SIMPSON,** HORTICULTURE. *Current Pos:* asst horticulturist, Univ Fla, 53-62, assoc plant physiologist, 62-68, plant physiologist, Agr Res & Educ Ctr, Bradenton, 53-62, prof plant physiol, 68-92, EMER PROF PLANT PHYSIOL, UNIV FLA, 68- *Personal Data:* b Clifton, Va, Apr 9, 24; m 47; c 2. *Educ:* Va Polytech Inst, BS, 43; Rutgers Univ, PhD(soils, plant physiol), 51. *Prof Exp:* Dir fertilizer res, Baugh & Sons Co, 51-53. *Mem:* Am Soc Hort Sci; Am Soc Plant Physiol; Am Phytopath Soc; Scand Soc Plant Physiol. *Res:* Plant nutrition; gladiolus and chrysanthemum culture; soil fertility; physiology of disease. *Mailing Add:* Gulf Coast Res & Educ Ctr 5007 60th St E Bradenton FL 34203

**WOLVEN-GARRETT, ANNE M,** regulatory affairs, risk assessment, for more information see previous edition

**WOLVERTON, BILLY CHARLES,** CHEMISTRY. *Current Pos:* ENVIRON & SR SCIENTIST, NAT SPACE TECHNOL LAB, BAY ST LOUIS, MISS, 71- *Personal Data:* b Scott Co, Miss, Oct 13, 32; m 55; c 1. *Educ:* Miss Col, BS, 60; Occidental Univ, PhD(environ eng), 78. *Honors & Awards:* Super Sci Achievement Award, Dept Navy, 65; Sci Technol Utilization Award, Am Inst Aeronaut & Astronaut, 70; Except Sci Serv Medal, NASA, 75. *Prof Exp:* Res asst, Med Ctr, Univ Miss, 60-63; res chemist, US Naval Weapons Lab, 63-65; br chief res chemist, Air Force Armament Lab, 65-71. *Concurrent Pos:* Mem Panel Unconventional Approaches to Aquatic Weed Control & Utilization, Nat Acad Sci, 75- *Mem:* Water Pollution Control Fedn; AAAS; Econ Botany Soc. *Res:* Vascular, aquatic plants as biological filtration systems for removing domestic and industrial pollutants from wastewater; utilization of harvested plant material as renewable sources of feed, fertilizer and methane; converting raw sewage to potable water; use of plants for purifying and revitalizing air inside energy-efficient homes and other closed facilities; converting raw sewage to potable water. *Mailing Add:* 514 Pine Grove Rd Picayune MS 39466

**WOLYNES, PETER GUY,** CONDENSED MATTER CHEMICAL PHYSICS. *Current Pos:* assoc prof, 80-83, PROF CHEM, UNIV ILL, URBANA-CHAMPAIGN, 83-, PROF PHYSICS, 85- *Personal Data:* b Chicago, Ill, Apr 21, 53. *Educ:* Ind Univ, AB, 71; Harvard Univ, PhD(chem physics), 76. *Honors & Awards:* Award in Pure Chem, Am Chem Soc, 86. *Prof Exp:* Fel, Mass Inst Technol, 75-76; asst prof, Harvard Univ, 76-79, assoc prof, 79-80. *Concurrent Pos:* Vis scientist, Max Planck Inst Biophys Chem, 77; vis prof, Inst Molecular Sci, Okazaki, Japan, 82. *Mem:* Nat Acad Sci; Am Chem Soc; NY Acad Sci; AAAS; Am Phys Soc. *Res:* Theory of chemical dynamic phenomena in condensed phases, especially kinetics, tunneling and electronic structure in liquids; theory of the glassy state; biophysical applications. *Mailing Add:* A544 Chem & Life Sci Lab Box 16-16 Dept Chem Univ Ill Urbana-Champaign Urbana IL 61801

**WOLYNETZ, MARK STANLEY,** STATISTICS. *Current Pos:* STATISTICIAN AGR RES, DEPT AGR, CAN, 75- *Personal Data:* b Kitchener, Ont, Nov 11, 45. *Educ:* Univ Waterloo, BMath, 69, MMath, 70, PhD(statist), 74. *Prof Exp:* Statistician rd safety, Ministry Transp Can, 74-75. *Res:* Application of statistical techniques in agriculture research; specifically in problems of categorical data, data screening, censored observations. *Mailing Add:* 1514 Edgecliffe Ottawa ON K1Z 8G1 Can

**WOLYNIC, EDWARD THOMAS,** SPECIALTY CHEMICALS TECHNOLOGY. *Current Pos:* dir process res & develop, 93-94, VPRES RES & DEVELOP, INT SPECIALTY PRODS CORP, 94- *Personal Data:* b Brooklyn, NY, May 29, 48; m, Loraine C Ciardullo; c William. *Educ:* Polytech Inst NY, BS, 69; Princeton Univ, MS, 71, PhD(chem eng), 74. *Prof Exp:* Staff engr, Union Carbide Corp, Bound Brook, NJ, 74-75, supvr, Tarrytown, NY, 75-77, mgr mfg technol, 77-82, assoc dir technol, 82-85, dir, 85-88; vpres res, UOP, Tarrytown, 88-90, vpres, develop, Des Plaines, Ill, 90-92. *Mem:* Am Inst Chem Engrs; Indust Res Inst; Com Develop Asn. *Res:* Chemical engineering; personal care; pharmaceutical; agricultural; industrial polymers. *Mailing Add:* 604 Old Forge Lane Franklin Lakes NJ 07417. *Fax:* 973-628-3886

**WOMACK, EDGAR ALLEN, JR,** ENERGY RESEARCH & DEVELOPMENT. *Current Pos:* sr tech consult reactor plant eng, McDermott Inc, Babcock & Wilcox Co, eng mgr, mgr proj mgt, vpres sales, 75-85, vpres res & develop, 85-93, SR VPRES & CHIEF TECHNOL OFFICER, MCDERMOTT INC, BABCOCK & WILCOX CO, 93- *Personal Data:* b Humboldt, Tenn, Oct 29, 42; m 63, Linda Cochran; c 2. *Educ:* Mass Inst Technol, BS, 63, MS, 65, PhD(physics), 69. *Prof Exp:* Br engr reactor develop, br chief & asst div dir, US AEC Comn, Washington DC, 68-75. *Concurrent Pos:* Lectr, Cath Univ Am, 72-73; guest lectr, Mass Inst Technol, 80-82; pres, Indust Res Inst, 95. *Mem:* Sigma Xi; AAAS; Am Soc Mech Engrs; Indust Res Inst. *Res:* Energy systems, instruments materials and mechanics. *Mailing Add:* 7412 Jade St New Orleans LA 70124. *Fax:* 504-288-8049; *E-Mail:* e.allen.womack@nola.mcdermott.com

**WOMACK, FRANCES C,** genetics, enzymology, for more information see previous edition

**WOMACK, JAMES E,** GENETICS. *Current Pos:* PROF VET PATH & GENETICS, TEX A&M UNIV, 77- *Personal Data:* b Anson, Tex, Mar 30, 41; m 63; c 2. *Educ:* Abilene Christian Col, BS, 64; Ore State Univ, PhD(genetics), 68. *Prof Exp:* From asst prof to assoc prof biol, Abilene Christian Col, 68-73; vis scientist, Jackson Lab, 73-75, staff scientist, 75-77. *Mem:* AAAS; Genetics Soc Am; Am Genetics Asn (pres, 85); Am Soc Human Genetics. *Res:* Comparative gene mapping; somatic cell genetics of cattle; mammalian developmental genetics; gene transfer in animals; mapping the bovine genome. *Mailing Add:* 2105 Farley St College Station TX 77845

**WOMBLE, DAVID DALE,** MOLECULAR BIOLOGY, BIOCHEMISTRY. *Current Pos:* RES ASSOC, CTR MOLECULAR MED, WAYNE UNIV. *Personal Data:* b Coffeyville, Kans, Oct 10, 49; m 72. *Educ:* Ohio Univ, BS, 71; Univ Wis-Madison, PhD(biochem), 76. *Prof Exp:* Trainee biochem, Univ Wis-Madison, 71-75, res asst, 75-76, res assoc molecular biol, 76-77, trainee pathobiol, 77-79, asst scientist molecular biol, 79-81; sr res assoc, Med Sch, Northwestern Univ, 81-86, res asst prof, 86- *Mem:* Am Soc Microbiol; AAAS; Sigma Xi. *Res:* Nuclei acid structure and organization; regulation of replication and genetic expression. *Mailing Add:* Ctr Molecular Med & Gen 5121 Biol Sci Bldg Wayne Univ 5047 Gullen Mall Detroit MI 48202

**WOMBLE, EUGENE WILSON,** MATHEMATICS. *Current Pos:* prof, 70-72, CHARLES A DANA PROF MATH, PRESBY COL, 72- *Personal Data:* b High Point, NC, June 27, 31; m 59; c 4. *Educ:* Wofford Col, BS, 52; Univ NC, Chapel Hill, MA, 59; Univ Okla, PhD(math), 70. *Prof Exp:* Teacher, Kernersville High Sch, 56-58; instr math, Wake Forest Col, 59-61; asst prof, Pfeiffer Col, 61-66; spec instr, Univ Okla, 69-70. *Mem:* Math Asn Am; Nat Coun Teachers Math. *Res:* Foundations of convexity; convexity structures. *Mailing Add:* Dept Math Presby Col 2 Shell Creek Dr Clinton SC 29325

**WOMMACK, JOEL BENJAMIN, JR,** AGRICULTURAL CHEMISTRY. *Current Pos:* Res chemist, E I Du Pont de Nemours & Co, Inc, 68-74, res supvr, 74-76, res mgr, 76-78, gen supvr, 78-79, asst mgr, 80-81, site mgr, 81-84 PLANNING MGR, BIOCHEM DEPT, E I DU PONT DE NEMOURS & CO, INC, 85- *Personal Data:* b Benton, Ky, Dec 5, 42; m 67; c 2. *Educ:* David Lipscomb Col, BS, 64; Vanderbilt Univ, PhD(org chem), 68. *Mem:* Am Chem Soc. *Mailing Add:* 12 Wineberry Dr Hockessin DE 19707-2126

**WONDERGEM, ROBERT,** BIOLOGICAL TRANSPORT, ELECTROPHYSIOLOGY. *Current Pos:* from asst prof to assoc prof, Quillen-Dishner Col Med, E Tenn State Univ, 78-89, PROF PHYSIOL, JAMES H QUILLEN COL MED, E TENN STATE UNIV, 89- *Personal Data:* b Sheboygan, Wis, Jan 17, 50; m 72; c 2. *Educ:* Calvin Col, BS, 72; Med Col Wis, Milwaukee, PhD(physiol), 77. *Prof Exp:* Nat Cancer Inst fel cell biol, McArdle Lab Cancer Res, Univ Wis-Madison, 77-78. *Concurrent Pos:* Prin investr, Mt Desert Island Biol Lab, Maine, 85-91. *Mem:* Am Physiol Soc; Am Soc Cell Biol; Soc Gen Physiologists; Am Asn Study Liver Dis; Biophys Soc. *Res:* Regulation of biological transport and cell volume regulation in liver cells; membrane ion channels and control of cell proliferation. *Mailing Add:* Dept Physiol James H Quillen Col Med ETenn State Univ PO Box 70 576 Johnson City TN 37614-0576. *E-Mail:* wondergem@washington.xtn.net

**WONDERLING, THOMAS FRANKLIN,** agriculture, for more information see previous edition

**WONG, ALAN YAU KUEN,** PHYSICS, BIOPHYSICS. *Current Pos:* Res assoc comput sci, 66-68, lectr biophys, 68-71, from asst prof to assoc prof, 71-84, PROF BIOPHYS, DALHOUSIE UNIV, 84- *Personal Data:* b Hong Kong, Feb 6, 37; Can citizen; m 67, Vivian Wong; c Michele, Andre & Rene. *Educ:* Dalhousie Univ, BSc, 62, MSc, 63, PhD(biophys), 67. *Concurrent Pos:* Can Heart Found fel biophys & bioeng res lab, Dalhousie Univ, 68-71, Med Res Coun Can res scholar, 71-76; fel circulation, Am Heart Asn. *Mem:* Biophys Soc; Soc Math Biol; NY Acad Sci; Biophys Soc Can; Can Physiol Soc; Biomed Engr Soc. *Res:* Excitation-contraction coupling of cardiac muscle; coronary flow; sodium-calcium exchange in excitable tissue; ventricular dynamics; intrathoracic cardiovascular neurons; calcium-2+ regulation in smooth muscle and endothelial cells. *Mailing Add:* Dept Physiol & Biophys Dalhousie Univ Halifax NS B3H 4H7 Can. *Fax:* 902-494-1685; *E-Mail:* awong@biophy.bp.dal.ca

**WONG, ALFRED YIU-FAI,** PLASMA PHYSICS. *Current Pos:* from asst prof to assoc prof physics, 64-72, PROF PHYSICS, UNIV CALIF, LOS ANGELES, 72- *Personal Data:* b Macao, Portugal, Feb 4, 37; m 65. *Educ:* Univ Toronto, BASc, 58, MA, 59; Univ Ill, MSc, 61; Princeton Univ, PhD(plasma physics), 63. *Honors & Awards:* Plasma Physics Res Award, Am Phys Soc, 85. *Prof Exp:* Res assoc plasma physics lab, Princeton Univ, 62-64. *Concurrent Pos:* Sloan res fel, 66-68. *Mem:* Fel Am Phys Soc; Am Geophys Union. *Res:* Waves and radiation from plasmas; nonlinear phenomena; confinement system and space plasmas. *Mailing Add:* Dept Physics Univ Calif Los Angeles 405 Hilgard Ave Los Angeles CA 90095-1547. *Fax:* 310-206-2173; *E-Mail:* awong@physics.ucla.edu

**WONG, ANTHONY SAI-HUNG,** TECHNOLOGY INCUBATOR, SEMICONDUCTOR SENSORS. *Current Pos:* staff scientist electronic mat, Gould Electronics & Technol Ctr, 87, proj mgr, 87, mgr sensors, electronic mat, 888-92, dir, Technol Ctr, 93-95, dir, Strategic Mkt, Technol Ctr, 94-95, VPRES MKT & SALES, POWERDEX DIV, GOULD ELECTRONICS & TECHNOL CTR, 95- *Personal Data:* b Hong Kong, Apr 5, 51; US citizen; m 75, Judy; c 2. *Educ:* San Jose State Univ, BS, 74; Case Western Reserve Univ, MS, 76, PhD(biomed eng), 85. *Prof Exp:* Clin engr med instruments, Vet Admin Hosp, 75-76; process engr & res asst semiconductor sensors, Case Western Reserve Univ, 76-85, res assoc, 85-86; asst prof microelectronics, Cleveland State Univ, 86-87. *Concurrent Pos:* Sensor consult numerous clients, 81-87; integrated circuit lab mgr semiconductor mat, processes, sensors, Case Western Res Univ, 83-84; chmn, Microsensor & Fabrication, Sensors Expo 86, 86. *Mem:* Inst Elec & Electronics Engrs; Am Vacuum Soc; Am Chem Soc; Soc Photo-Optical Instrumentation Engrs; Mat Res Soc. *Res:* Technology management-develop and/or acquire technology for present and future electronic industry; develop semiconductor sensors for industrial and medical applications; technology gate-keeper-keep abreast in new development and chart out strategy for company growth. *Mailing Add:* Gould Electronics Inc Powerdex Div 34099 Melinz Pkwy Eastlake OH 44095-4055. *Fax:* 215-918-6030

**WONG, BING KUEN,** MATHEMATICS. *Current Pos:* chmn dept, 68-84 & 90-92, PROF MATH & COMPUT SCI, WILKES COL, 68-, ASSOC DEAN, SCH SCI & ENG, 92- *Personal Data:* b Shanghai, China, Oct 4, 38; m 66; c 2. *Educ:* Pittsburg State Univ, Kans, AB, 61; Univ Ill, MA, 63, PhD(math), 66. *Prof Exp:* Asst prof math, Univ Western Ill, 65-66; asst prof, Rochester Inst Technol, 66-68. *Mem:* Am Math Soc; Math Asn Am; Asn Comput Mach. *Res:* Analysis. *Mailing Add:* Sch Sci & Eng Wilkes Univ Wilkes-Barre PA 18766-0001. *Fax:* 717-829-2434; *E-Mail:* bwong@wilkes1.wilkes.edu

**WONG, BRENDAN SO,** BIOPHYSICS, PHYSIOLOGY. *Current Pos:* ASSOC PROF, DEPT BIOMED SCI, BAYLOR COL DENT, DALLAS, 83- *Personal Data:* b Hong Kong, Feb 25, 47; US citizen; m 72, Mimi L Chang; c Stephanie. *Educ:* Univ San Francisco, BS, 71; Southern Ill Univ, MA, 74, PhD(biophys), 78. *Prof Exp:* Fel biophys, Nat Inst Neurol & Commun Dis & Stroke, 78-83. *Mem:* Biophys Soc; Am Physiol Soc; Soc Neurosci; Soc Exp Biol Med; Sigma Xi; Int Asn Dent Res. *Res:* Patch-clamp studies on tissue-cultured and dissociated primary cells; electrophysiology of osteoblasts; intracellular calcium signalling with fluorescent dyes; confocal microscopy. *Mailing Add:* Dept Biomed Sci Baylor Col Dent 3302 Gatson Ave Dallas TX 75246. *Fax:* 214-828-8951; *E-Mail:* bwong@tambcd.edu

**WONG, CHAK-KUEN,** DESIGN & ANALYSIS OF ALGORITHMS, COMPUTER-AIDED DESIGN. *Current Pos:* RES STAFF MEM COMPUT SCI, T J WATSON RES CTR, IBM CORP, 69-, MGR DESIGN ALGORITHMS, 85- *Personal Data:* b Macao, China; m 70; c 2. *Educ:* Univ Hong Kong, BA, 65; Columbia Univ, MA, 66, PhD(math), 70. *Honors & Awards:* Outstanding Invention Award, IBM Corp, 71. *Concurrent Pos:* Vis assoc prof, Univ Ill, Urbana, 72-73; vis prof, Columbia Univ, 78-79. *Mem:* Fel Inst Elec & Electronics Engrs; NY Acad Sci; Asn Comput Mach. *Res:* Computer-aided design algorithms; very large scale integration algorithms; analysis of optimum and near-optimum algorithms in computing; application of mathematics to computers and computing. *Mailing Add:* T J Watson Res Ctr IBM Corp PO Box 218 Yorktown Heights NY 10598

**WONG, CHEUK-YIN,** PHYSICS. *Current Pos:* PHYSICIST, OAK RIDGE NAT LAB, 69- *Personal Data:* b Kwangtung, China, Apr 28, 41; m 66, Jeanne P Yang; c Janet, Albert & Lisa. *Educ:* Princeton Univ, AB, 61, MA, 63, PhD(physics), 66. *Prof Exp:* Physicist, Oak Ridge Nat Lab, 66-68; res fel physics, Niels Bohr Inst, Copenhagen, Denmark, 68-69. *Concurrent Pos:* Vis scientist, Mass Inst Technol, 82-83; vis prof, Inst Nuclear Study, Univ Tokyo, Japan, 88. *Mem:* Fel Am Phys Soc. *Res:* Theoretical studies of nuclear properties, nuclear reactions, high energy nucleus-nucleus collisions, particle production and physics of strong fields; dynamics of nuclear fluid; high energy nucleus; nucleus collisions. *Mailing Add:* Oak Ridge Nat Lab Oak Ridge TN 37831-6373. *Fax:* 423-574-4745; *E-Mail:* wongc@ornl.gov

**WONG, CHI SONG,** MATHEMATICAL STATISTICS, OPERATOR THEORY. *Current Pos:* asst prof, 71-73, assoc prof, 73-77, PROF MATH, UNIV WINDSOR, 77- *Personal Data:* b Cheng Tak, Hunan, China, May 26, 38; m 66; c Cheng Chung, Cheng Mei & Cheng Kar. *Educ:* Nat Taiwan Univ, BS, 62; Univ Ore, MS, 66; Univ Ill, Urbana, MS, 67, PhD(functional anal), 69. *Prof Exp:* Tutor, Chinese Univ, Hong Kong, 62-65; asst prof math, Southern Ill Univ, Carbondale, 69-71. *Concurrent Pos:* Vis prof, Nat Tsing Hua Univ, 78-79, Nat Chiao Tung Univ, 85-86, City Univ Hong Kong, 93-94. *Res:* Optimality and inference in multirate analysis; vector majorization; Chinese literature. *Mailing Add:* Dept Math & Statist Univ Windsor Windsor ON N9B 3P4 Can

**WONG, CHI-HUEY,** BIOORGANIC CHEMISTRY, ENZYME TECHNOLOGY. *Current Pos:* ERNEST W HAHN PROF CHEM, SCRIPPS RES INST, 89- *Personal Data:* b Taiwan, Aug 3, 48; m 76, Yieng Lii; c Heather & Andrew. *Educ:* Nat Taiwan Univ, BS, 70, MS, 77; Mass Inst Technol, PhD(chem), 82. *Honors & Awards:* Searle Scholar Award, 85; Presidential Young Investr Award, NSF, 86; Cope Scholar Award, Am Chem Soc, 93; Int Carbohydrate Award, Int Union Pure & Appl Chem, 94. *Prof Exp:* Asst res fel & lectr biochem, Acad Sci & Nat Taiwan Univ, 74-79; fel, Harvard Univ, 82-83; from asst prof org chem to assoc prof, Tex A&M Univ, 83-87, prof chem, 87-89. *Concurrent Pos:* Consult, Abbott Co, Eli Lilly Co & Oncogene Sci Inc. *Mem:* Am Chem Soc; NY Acad Sci; AAAS; Am Acad Arts & Sci. *Res:* Enzymes in organic synthesis; glycotechnology; synthesis of bioactive molecules; enzyme stabilization and functionalization; design and synthesis of enzyme inhibitors. *Mailing Add:* Dept Chem Scripps Res Inst La Jolla CA 92037-1027

**WONG, CHING-PING,** CHEMISTRY. *Current Pos:* mem res staff, AT&T Bell Labs, 77-82, sr mem, 82-87, distinguished mem tech staff, 87-92, FEL, AT&T BELL LABS, 92- *Personal Data:* b Canton, China, Mar 29, 47; m 78, Lorraine Homnack; c Michelle & David. *Educ:* Purdue Univ, BS, 69; Pa State Univ, PhD(org & inorg chem), 75. *Honors & Awards:* Award for Outstanding Contrib, Inst Elec & Electronics Engrs Components, Hybrids & Mfg Technol Soc, 91; Bd Gov Distinguished Serv Award, CPMT, Inst Elec & Electronics Engrs, 92. *Prof Exp:* Scholar, Stanford Univ, 75-77. *Concurrent Pos:* Bd govs, Inst Elec & Electronics Engrs Components, Hybrids & Mfg Technol Soc, 87-89, tech vpres, 90-91, pres, 92-93; chmn, Tech Activities Bd Design Mfg Eng, Inst Elec & Electronics Engrs. *Mem:* Inst Elec & Electronics Engrs Components Hybrids & Mfg Technol Soc (pres, 92-93); Mat Res Soc. *Res:* Integrated device passivation and encapsulation area; application of polymers for device reliability without humeticity; electronic device packaging; granted 30 US and numerous international patents. *Mailing Add:* 38 Friar Lane Freehold NJ 07728

**WONG, CHI-SHING,** CHEMICAL OCEANOGRAPHY. *Current Pos:* head ocean chem, Dept Fisheries & Oceans, 71-89, HEAD, CTR OCEAN BIOGEO CHEM, INST OCEAN SCI, BC, 89- *Personal Data:* b Hong Kong, Sept 1, 34; m 60, Shau-King E Leung; c Adriana H & Calvin J. *Educ:* Univ Hong Kong, BSc, 57, BSc Hons, 58, MSc, 61; Univ Calif, San Diego, PhD(chem oceanog), 68. *Honors & Awards:* Newcomb Cleveland Prize, AAAS, 91. *Prof Exp:* Asst res officer, Fisheries Res Unit, Hong Kong Univ, 58-60; head, Chem Dept, United Col, Hong Kong, 61-62; scientist-in-charge, Weathership Chem Prog, Dept Energy Mines & Resources, BC, 68-71. *Concurrent Pos:* Hon prof, Third Oceanog Inst, Xiamen, China, 85. *Mem:* Fel Royal Soc Chem; fel chem Inst Can; Can Meteorol & Oceanog Soc; Am Geophys Union; Am Soc Limnol & Oceanog; AAAS. *Res:* Use of decadel change in C-13 isotope in the ocean to infer that the ocean is a major sink of fossil-fuel carbon dioxide; Wood burning as a major contribution to atmospheric carbon dioxide; El Nino effects on air-sea carbon dioxide exchange and ocean productivity; Use of lead isotopes to trace pollution in coastal water and to trace ocean circulation; findings on marine pollution by oil and metals. *Mailing Add:* Ctr Ocean Biogeo Chem Inst Ocean Sci Sidney BC V8L 4B2 Can

**WONG, CHIU MING,** ORGANIC CHEMISTRY. *Current Pos:* RETIRED. *Personal Data:* b Canton, China, July 8, 35; m 60; c 2. *Educ:* Nat Taiwan Univ, BSc, 59; Univ NB, PhD(chem), 64. *Prof Exp:* Asst, Univ NB, 64, res fels, 64-65; res fels, Harvard Univ, 65-66; from asst prof to prof org chem, Univ Man, 66-93. *Mem:* Am Chem Soc. *Res:* Synthesis and structure-reactivity studies of anthracycline antitumor antibiotics. *Mailing Add:* 31 Folkestone Blvd Winnipeg MB R3P 0B4 Can

**WONG, CHUEN,** physics, for more information see previous edition

**WONG, CHUN WA,** NUCLEAR FORCES, NUCLEON STRUCTURE. *Current Pos:* actg assoc prof, 70-71, FROM ASST PROF TO PROF PHYSICS, UNIV CALIF, LOS ANGELES, 69- *Personal Data:* b Hong Kong, China, Jan 22, 38; US citizen; m 67; c 2. *Educ:* Univ Calif, Los Angeles, BS, 59; Harvard Univ, AM, 60, PhD(physics), 65. *Prof Exp:* Rcs assoc physics, Princeton Univ, 65-66; Oxford Univ, 66-67 & Saclay, 67-68. *Concurrent Pos:* Alfred P Sloan Found fel, 70-72. *Mem:* Fel Am Phys Soc. *Res:* Description of the properties of atomic nuclei in terms of the fundamental forces acting between their constituents. *Mailing Add:* Dept Physics & Astron Univ Calif Los Angeles CA 90095-1547. *Fax:* 310-206-5668; *E-Mail:* cwong@physics.ucla.edu

**WONG, CHUN-MING,** ORGANIC POLYMER CHEMISTRY. *Current Pos:* staff, 80-89, SR ENG, BOEING COMM AIRPLANE CO, 89- *Personal Data:* b Hong Kong, Brit Crown Colony, Nov 12, 40; m 71. *Educ:* Univ Calif, Berkeley, BS, 65; Wayne State Univ, MS, 66; NDak State Univ, PhD(chem),

73. *Prof Exp:* Chemist, Inmont Corp, 66-70; res chemist, E I du Pont de Nemours & Co, Inc, 74-77; Chrysler Corp, 77-80. *Mem:* Am Chem Soc. *Res:* Low volatile organic compound coatings aimed at reducing pollution. *Mailing Add:* 9250 25th Ave NW Seattle WA 98117

**WONG, DAVID TAIWAI,** BIOCHEMISTRY. *Current Pos:* sr biochemist, Lilly Res Labs, Eli Lilly & Co, 68-72, res biochemist, 73-77, sr res scientist, 78-89, RES ADV, LILLY RES LABS, ELI LILLY & CO, 90- *Personal Data:* b Hong Kong, Nov 6, 35; US citizen; m 63, Christina Lee; c Conrad, Melvin & Vincent. *Educ:* Seattle Pac Col, BS, 60; Ore State Univ, MS, 64; Univ Ore, PhD(biochem), 66. *Honors & Awards:* Outstanding Neuropharmaceut Award, Chinese Neurosci Soc, 91; Discoverers Award, Pharmaceut Mfr Asn, 93; Discover Award for Prozac, Nat Alliance Res Schizophrenia & Depression, 96. *Prof Exp:* Fel biophys chem, Univ Pa, 66-67. *Concurrent Pos:* Adj prof biochem, 86-, neurobiol, 90- *Mem:* NY Acad Sci; Int Soc Neurochem; Am Soc Pharmacol & Exp Therapeut; Sigma Xi; Soc Neurosci; Am Col Neuropsychopharmacol. *Res:* Biochemistry of neurotransmission; synthetic chemicals which block the uptake of specific neurotransmitters investigated as potentially useful therapeutic agents for mental disorders; discoverer of fluoxetine (prozac), tomoxetine and duloxetine for treatment of mental depression; biochemical mechanism of ionophorous agents. *Mailing Add:* Lilly Res Labs Eli Lilly & Co Lilly Corp Ctr Indianapolis IN 46285. *Fax:* 317-276-5546; *E-Mail:* wong__david.t@lilly.com

**WONG, DAVID YUE,** PHYSICS. *Current Pos:* PROF PHYSICS, UNIV CALIF, SAN DIEGO, 67- *Personal Data:* b Swatow, China, Apr 16, 34; US citizen; m 60; c 2. *Educ:* Hardin-Simmons Univ, BA, 54; Univ Md, College Park, PhD(physics), 58. *Prof Exp:* Theoretical physicist, Univ Calif, Berkeley, 58-60, from asst prof to assoc prof, 60-67; provost, Warren Col, 86-94. *Concurrent Pos:* Alfred P Sloan fel, Univ Calif, San Diego, 63-66. *Mem:* Am Inst Physics; Am Phys Soc. *Res:* Theoretical high energy physics. *Mailing Add:* Dept Physics MC-0354 Univ Calif San Diego 9500 Gilman Dr La Jolla CA 92093-0354

**WONG, DENNIS MUN,** CELLULAR IMMUNOLOGY. *Current Pos:* WRITER & PUBLISHER, 91- *Personal Data:* b San Francisco, Calif, Dec 14, 44; m 69. *Educ:* Calif State Univ, San Francisco, BA, 69, MA, 74; Georgetown Univ, PhD(microbiol), 77. *Prof Exp:* Fel, Naval Med Res Inst, 77-79; staff fel, Bur Biologics, Div Blood & Blood Prod, NIH, 80-85; asst prof, Georgetown Univ, 85-87; sr res investr, Walter Reed Army Med Ctr, 87-91. *Mem:* AAAS; Am Soc Microbiol; NY Acad Sci; Am Asn Clin Histocompatibility Testing; Sigma Xi. *Res:* Cellular immunology; human histocompatibility antigens; immunogenetic system; development of hybridoma antibodies against cell surface antigens. *Mailing Add:* 831 Hillcrest Blvd Millbrae CA 94030

**WONG, DEREK,** OPERATIONS RESEARCH, MATHEMATICAL PROGRAMMING. *Current Pos:* SCIENTIST, NCCOSC, 85- *Personal Data:* b Shanghai, China, Jan 22, 46; m 72; c 1. *Educ:* Hong Kong Baptist Col, BSc, 68; Fla State Univ, MS, 75, PhD(statist), 77. *Prof Exp:* Asst prof math prog, Northern Ill Univ, 77-85. *Mem:* Inst Mgt Sci; Am Statist Asn; Inst Math Statist. *Res:* Optimization theory. *Mailing Add:* NCCOSC RDTE Div 53560 Hull St San Diego CA 92152-5001

**WONG, DONALD TAI ON,** IMMUNOLOGY. *Current Pos:* RETIRED. *Personal Data:* b Honolulu, Hawaii, Nov 1, 26; m 54; c 2. *Educ:* St Louis Univ, BS, 49; Wash Univ, PhD(microbiol), 53. *Prof Exp:* Res chemist, Dept Bact Microbial Chem Sect, Walter Reed Army Inst Res, Army Med Ctr, Washington, DC, 52-61; res chemist, Blood Antigen Lab, Div Animal Husb, Agr Res Ctr, Md, 61-65; res chemist, Dept Immunochem, Div Commun Dis & Immunol, Walter Reed Army Inst Res, Army Med Ctr, 65-81. *Mem:* AAAS; Am Chem Soc. *Res:* Oxidative metabolism in microorganisms; alternate pathways and carbon-2-carbon-2 condensation mechanisms; immunoglobulin specifity and structure; mechanisms involved with immediate type hypersensitivity reactions. *Mailing Add:* 5918 Mustang Dr Riverdale MD 20737

**WONG, DOROTHY PAN,** PHYSICAL CHEMISTRY. *Current Pos:* asst prof, 66-67, assoc prof, 68-73, PROF PHYS CHEM, CALIF STATE UNIV, FULLERTON, 70- *Personal Data:* b Nanking, China, July 8, 37; US citizen; m 68. *Educ:* Univ Okla, BS, 57; Univ Minn, MS, 59; Case Inst Technol, PhD(phys chem), 64. *Prof Exp:* Res chemist, Continental Oil Co, 57; assoc chemist, Airforce Midway Lab, Univ Chicago, 59-60; asst prof phys chem, Calif State Col Fullerton, 64-65; res assoc quantum chem, Princeton Univ, 65-66. *Mem:* Am Chem Soc; Am Phys Soc. *Res:* Non-empirical quantum mechanical calculations for geometry of molecules; molecular properties and rotation barriers of nitrogen compounds and for other molecules of current chemical interest. *Mailing Add:* Dept Chem Calif State Univ 800 N State College Blvd Fullerton CA 92631-3547

**WONG, E(UGENE),** ELECTRICAL ENGINEERING, COMPUTER SCIENCE. *Current Pos:* from asst prof to prof elec eng, Elect Eng & Comput Sci Dept, 62-90, chmn, 85-89, EMER PROF ELEC ENG, UNIV CALIF, BERKELEY, 93- *Personal Data:* b Nanking, China, Dec 24, 34; nat US; m 56; c 3. *Educ:* Princeton Univ, BSE, 55, AM, 58, PhD(elec eng), 59. *Honors & Awards:* Systs Award, Asn Comput Mach, 90. *Prof Exp:* Mem res staff, Int Bus Mach Corp, 55-56 & 60-62; NSF fel, Cambridge Univ, 59-60. *Concurrent Pos:* Guggenheim fel, Cambridge Univ, 68-69; consult, Ampex Corp; Vinton Hayes sr fel, Harvard Univ, 76-77; consult, Honeywell, Inc, 78-; assoc dir phys sci & eng, Off Sci & Technol Policies, White House, Washington, DC, 90- *Mem:* Nat Acad Eng; Asn Comput Mach; fel Inst Elec & Electronics Engrs. *Res:* Stochastic processes; data base systems; data base management; stochastic processs, system theory. *Mailing Add:* Dept Elec Eng & Comput Sci Univ Calif Berkeley CA 94720

**WONG, EDWARD CHOR-CHEUNG,** RAS, SYSTEM ARCHITECTURE. *Current Pos:* Jr engr, IBM, 74-75, assoc engr, 75-76, sr assoc engr, 76-79, staff engr, 79-82, develop eng mgr, 82-89, SR ENGR, IBM, 89- *Personal Data:* b Hong Kong, China, Jan 16, 52; US citizen; c Fun-Wah D, Chiu-Wah E & Chun-Wah E. *Educ:* Fordham Univ, BA, 73; Columbia Univ, BS & MS, 74, CSE 80. *Concurrent Pos:* Adj lectr, Columbia Univ, 82; Adj prof, Comput Software Develop Grad Prog, Marist Col, 83- *Mem:* Asn Comput Mach; sr mem Inst Elec & Electronics Engrs. *Res:* Cache design; large system architecture; reliability, availability, serviceability architecture/design, software design/development; algorithms. *Mailing Add:* PO Box 1909 Poughkeepsie NY 12601. *E-Mail:* edwong@vnet.ibm.com

**WONG, EDWARD HOU,** INORGANIC CHEMISTRY. *Current Pos:* from asst prof to assoc prof, 78-89, PROF CHEM, UNIV NH, 89- *Personal Data:* b Hankow, China, Oct 5, 46; c 2. *Educ:* Univ Calif, Berkeley, BS, 68; Harvard Univ, PhD(inorg chem), 74. *Prof Exp:* Res assoc boron chem, Univ Calif, Los Angeles, 74-76; asst prof, Fordham Univ, 76-78. *Concurrent Pos:* St Mary's fel, Durham Univ, UK, 86. *Mem:* Am Chem Soc. *Res:* Transition metal complexes in catalysis; poly-phosphine heterocycles; novel polyamine ligands. *Mailing Add:* Dept Chem Parsons Hall Univ NH Durham NH 03824

**WONG, FULTON,** VISUAL SCIENCES. *Current Pos:* ASSOC PROF, DEPT OPHTHAL & NEUROBIOL, DUKE UNIV, 89- *Personal Data:* b Kwangtung, China, Nov 9, 48; m 76; c 2. *Educ:* Univ Redlands, Calif, BS, 72; Rockefeller Univ, NY, PhD(biophys, neurophysiol), 77. *Prof Exp:* Res assoc vision, Dept Biol Sci, Purdue Univ, 77-78, vis asst prof biol, 78-79; asst prof, Dept Physiol & Biophys, Med Br, Univ Tex, 79-86; assoc prof, Dept Ophthal & Anat & Cell Biol, Univ Ill, Chicago, 86-89. *Concurrent Pos:* Adj res assoc, Rockefeller Univ, 77-78; mem, Marine Biomed Inst, 79-86; vis res scientist neurobiol, Yale Univ, 85-86. *Mem:* AAAS; Soc Gen Physiologists; NY Acad Sci; Sigma Xi; Asn Res Vision & Ophthal. *Res:* Hereditary eye diseases caused by mutations in photoreceptor-specific genes. *Mailing Add:* Dept Ophthal Duke Univ Med Ctr Box 3802 DUMC Durham NC 27710

**WONG, GEORGE SHOUNG-KOON,** ACOUSTICAL MEASUREMENTS, ACCOUSTICAL STANDARDS. *Current Pos:* From asst res officer to assoc res officer, 66-79, group leader acoust stand, 90-95, SR RES OFFICER, NAT RES COUN, CAN, 79-, PROG LEADER, 96- *Personal Data:* b Hong Kong, July 21, 35; Can citizen. *Educ:* Manchester Univ, MSc, 63, PhD, 65. *Concurrent Pos:* Chmn, Int Electrotech Comn Comt TC 29, Can Stand, Coun Subcomt, 85-, Acoust Soc Am Stand Comt S1-Acoust, 90-96, vice chmn, 96-; assoc ed, Acoust Stand News, J Am Statist Asn. *Mem:* Fel Inst Elec Engrs UK; fel Acoust Soc Am; Inst Mech Engrs UK. *Res:* Precision acoustical measurements developed precision primary acoustical standards calibration system; theoretical prediction and experimental confirmation on the variation of the ratio of specific heats in air with humidity and temperature; calculated a new value for the speed of sound and other physical properties in air; published one book. *Mailing Add:* Inst Nat Measurement Stand Nat Res Coun Can Ottawa ON K1A 0R6 Can. *Fax:* 613-990-8765; *E-Mail:* george.wong@nrc.ca

**WONG, GEORGE TIN FUK,** HYDROGEOCHEMISTRY, ENVIRONMENTAL CHEMISTRY. *Current Pos:* Asst prof, 76-82, PROF OCEANOG, OLD DOMINION UNIV, 82-, DOCTORAL PROG DIR, 85- *Personal Data:* b Hong Kong, Nov 29, 49; m 74. *Educ:* Calif State Univ, Los Angeles, BS, 71; Mass Inst Technol, MS, 73; PhD(chem oceanog), 76. *Mem:* Am Soc Limnol & Oceanog; AAAS; Am Geophys Union; Geochem Soc. *Res:* Trace elements; radiogeochemistry; physical and analytical chemistry of natural waters; environmental chemistry; redox chemistry of ground water; hydrogeochemistry. *Mailing Add:* Dept Oceanog Old Dominion Univ Norfolk VA 23529

**WONG, HANS KUOMIN,** PHYSICAL & INORGANIC CHEMISTRY. *Current Pos:* CONSULT, 87- *Personal Data:* b Canton, Kwangtung, China, Apr 30, 36; US citizen; m 67, Frances Tang; c Wilbur & Alan. *Educ:* NDak State Univ, BS, 59; Univ Minn, PhD(phys chem), 65. *Prof Exp:* Sr chemist, Itek Corp, 65-70; sr chemist phys chem, Olivetti Corp Am, 71-80; sr chemist phys chem, Bacharach Inst Co, 80-82; asst prof, Cumberland Col, 83-84; sr chemist, Olin Hunt, 84-87. *Mem:* Am Chem Soc. *Res:* Electrophotography; photoconductivity; dye sensitization mechanism; photochemistry. *Mailing Add:* 1269 Ayala Dr No 4 Sunnyvale CA 94086-5541

**WONG, HARRY YUEN CHEE,** PHYSIOLOGY, ENDOCRINOLOGY & METABOLISM. *Current Pos:* from instr to assoc prof, Sch Med, 51-66, prof physiol & biophys, Grad Sch Arts & Sci, 75-96, DIR ENDOCRINOL & METAB, HOWARD UNIV, 53-, PROF PHYSIOL, COL MED, 66- *Personal Data:* b Kapaa, Hawaii, Oct 23, 16; m 43, Mabel Liu; c William J, Donald & Carol Jean. *Educ:* Okla State Univ, BS, 42; Univ Southern Calif, MS, 47, PhD(endocrinol, physiol), 50. *Prof Exp:* Asst physiol, Univ Southern Calif, 46-48, lab assoc anat, 48-49; assoc prof biol, Andrews Univ, 49-51. *Concurrent Pos:* Dir basic endocrine res, Freedmen's Hosp, 52-60; Consult, Off Surgeon Gen, USAF, 63-; vis prof hormone lab, II Med Clin, Univ Hamburg, 69; vis scientist, Armed Forces Inst Path, Dc, 70 & 82; fel, coun arteriosclerosis, Am Heart Asn; mem, Int Cong Physiol Sci, Int Cong Pharmacol, Int Cong Hormonal Steroids & Int Cong Endocrinol; consult to chief, Dept Med & Clin Sci, Brooks AFB; fel coun arteriosclerosis, Am Heart Asn; vis prof, People's Repub China, 82 & 88, Nanking Med Univ, 88; vis prof, Shanghai Med Univ & Shanghai Inst Cardiovasc Dis, China, 88-89. *Mem:* Am Physiol Soc; Endocrine Soc; NY Acad Sci; AMA; fel Coun Arteriosclerosis; Am Heart Asn. *Res:* Studying the effects of certain tranquilizers and stress on experimental artherosclerosis; various diets on plasma lipids, lipoproteins hormonal changes (automatic computerized transverse axial, corticosterone, catecholamines) and enzyme levels of lecithin-cholesterol acyltransferase and acquisition category. *Mailing Add:* Dept Physiol & Biophys Howard Univ Col Med Washington DC 20059-2337. *Fax:* 202-806-4489

**WONG, HENRY VERNON,** PLASMA PHYSICS. *Current Pos:* RES SCIENTIST, UNIV TEX, AUSTIN, 80- *Personal Data:* b Montego Bay, Jamaica, 1938. *Educ:* Univ Southern Calif, Kingston, BS, 61; Oxford Univ, Eng, PhD(physics), 65. *Mem:* Am Phys Soc. *Mailing Add:* Fusion Res Ctr Univ Tex Austin TX 78712

**WONG, HORNE RICHARD,** SAWFLY SYSTEMATICS, FOREST ENTOMOLOGY. *Current Pos:* res officer, 61-65, res scientist, Can Dept Agr, 66-88, EMER RES SCIENTIST, NORTHERN FOREST RES CTR, CAN DEPT FORESTRY, 89- *Personal Data:* b Hong Kong, Jan 9, 23; Can citizen; m 58; c 3. *Educ:* Univ Man, BSA, 47; Mich State Univ, MS, 50; Univ Ill, PhD(entom), 60. *Prof Exp:* Sr agr asst, Can Dept Agr, 47-48, officer-in-charge forest insect surv, 49-52, res officer, 53-60. *Concurrent Pos:* Mem, Can Comt Common Names Insects, 58-70; pres, Entom Soc Alta, 79. *Mem:* Entom Soc Am; Sigma Xi; Entom Soc Can. *Res:* Systematics, biology and phylogeny of sawflies (Hymenopter, Symphyta); life history and habits of forest insects. *Mailing Add:* 11403-37 B Ave Edmonton AB T6H 0K2 Can

**WONG, JAMES B(OK),** CHEMICAL ENGINEERING, ECONOMICS. *Current Pos:* PRES, JAMES B WONG ASSOC, 81- *Personal Data:* b Canton, China; nat US; m 46, Wai P Lim; c John, Jane D & Julia A. *Educ:* Univ Md, BS, 49, BChE, 50; Univ Ill, MS, 51, PhD(chem eng), 54. *Prof Exp:* Asst chem eng, Univ Ill, 50-53; chem engr, Stand Oil Co, Ind, 53-55; engr, Shell Develop Co, Calif, 55-61; sr planning engr, Chem Group, Dart Indust Inc, 61-64, prin planning engr, 64-66, supvr planning & econ, 66-67, mgr long range planning & econ, 67, chief economist, 67-72, dir econ & opers analysis, 72-78, dir, Int Technol, 78-81; pres, Chinese Am Citizens Alliance Found. *Mem:* Am Chem Soc; Am Inst Chem Engrs. *Res:* Filtration of aerosols; fluid mechanics; process design; economics and planning; technologies on polyethylene, polypropylene, polystyrene and other polymers; general operations analysis; international licensing; technology transfer; technology transfer and product distribution, Asian and Pacific basin regions. *Mailing Add:* 2460 Venus Dr Los Angeles CA 90046

**WONG, JEFFREY TZE-FEI,** BIOCHEMISTRY. *Current Pos:* From asst prof to assoc prof, 65-76, PROF BIOCHEM, FAC MED, UNIV TORONTO, 76- *Personal Data:* b Hong Kong, Aug 5, 37; Can citizen; m 61, Eva Nong; c 3. *Educ:* Univ Toronto, BA, 59, PhD(biochem), 62. *Concurrent Pos:* Med Res Coun Can grant, Univ Toronto, 65- *Mem:* Can Soc Biochem; Am Soc Biochem. *Res:* Enzyme kinetics and mechanism; biochemical evolution; blood substitutes. *Mailing Add:* Dept Biochem Hong Kong Univ Sci & Technol Clearwater Bay Hong Kong People's Republic of China. *Fax:* 852-2358-3978

**WONG, JO YUNG,** TRANSPORT TECHNOLOGY, TRANSPORT SYSTEMS ANALYSIS. *Current Pos:* from asst prof to assoc prof, 68-78, PROF ENG, DEPT MECH & AEROSPACE ENG & DIR, TRANSP TECHNOL RES LAB, CARLETON UNIV, 78-; PRES, VEHICLE SYSTS DEVELOP CORP, 77- *Personal Data:* b Canton, China; Can citizen; m 62; c 1. *Educ:* Tsinghua Univ, China, BSc Hons, 55; Univ Newcastle-upon-Tyne, Eng, PhD(eng), 67, DSc, 86. *Honors & Awards:* Starley Premium Award, Inst Mech Engrs, Eng, 84 & 88. *Prof Exp:* Res assoc eng, Univ Newcastle-upon-Tyne, Eng, 65-67; res engr, Logging Develop Corp, 67-68. *Concurrent Pos:* Assoc ed, J Terramech, 73-; vis prof, Univ Warwick, Eng, 74-75 & Cemoter, Italian Nat Res Coun, 85, 87-; dir, Ottawa-Carleton Inst Mech & Aeronautical Eng, 87-90; consult, govt agencies & industs, NAm, Europ & Asia. *Mem:* Fel Inst Mech Engrs; fel Am Soc Mech Engrs; Soc Automotive Engrs; Int Soc Terrain-Vehicle Systs. *Res:* Ground transport technology; off-road transport technology; road vehicle dynamics and safety; air cushion technology; advanced guided ground transport systems. *Mailing Add:* Dept Sci Carleton Univ 1125 Colonel By Dr Ottawa ON K1S 5B6 Can

**WONG, JOE,** PHYSICAL CHEMISTRY, SOLID STATE SCIENCE. *Current Pos:* CONSULT, 86- *Personal Data:* b Hong Kong, Aug 8, 42; m 69, Mei; c Glenn, Christina & Theresa. *Educ:* Univ Tasmania, BSc, 65, BSc Hons, 66; Purdue Univ, Lafayette, PhD(phys chem), 70. *Hon Degrees:* DSc, Univ Tasmania, 86. *Honors & Awards:* 1st Prize Optical Micros, Am Ceramic Soc, 75 & 77; Dushman Award, General Elec, 84; R&D 100 Award, 90 & 91; Humboldt Award, 91. *Prof Exp:* Analytical chemist, Australian Titan Prod, Tasmania, 62-63; res asst, Electrolytic Zinc Co Australasia, 63-64 & Dept Chem, Univ Tasmania, 64-65; res chemist, Electrolytic Zinc Co Australasia, Tasmania, 66; res asst chem, Walker Lab, Rensselaer Polytech Inst, 66-67 & Purdue Univ, West Lafayette, 67-70; phys chemist, Corp Res & Develop, Gen Elec Co, 70-86. *Concurrent Pos:* Adj lectr chem, Royal Hobart Col, 66; adj prof chem, State Univ NY, Albany, 80-85; sr sci & technol agency fel, 91; consult prof, Stanford Univ, 93- *Mem:* Am Chem Soc; Royal Australian Chem Inst; Am Phys Soc; AAAS; fel Am Inst Chemists. *Res:* Molten salt chemistry; thermodynamic and spectroscopic studies; spectroscopy of simple inorganic glasses; thin films; deposition and structure; impurity diffusion in semiconductors; microstructure of non-ohmic Zn0 ceramics; metallic glasses; EXAFS spectroscopy; coal science; synchrotron radiation research; near edge structure spectroscopy, high resolution electron microscopy, electron energy loss spectroscopy; time-resolved diffraction and x-ray absorption spectroscopy; combustion synthesis; phase transformation. *Mailing Add:* Lawrence Livermore Nat Lab Chem Mat Sci L369 PO Box 808 Livermore CA 94551. *Fax:* 510-423-7040; *E-Mail:* wong@cmsl.llnl.gov

**WONG, JOHN LUI,** MOLECULAR EPIDEMIOLOGY, COAL CHEMISTRY. *Current Pos:* From asst prof to assoc prof chem, 66-74, vchmn dept, 75-76, chmn, 87-88, PROF CHEM, UNIV LOUISVILLE, 74-, ASSOC ONCOL, CANCER CTR, 75-, ASSOC PHARMACOL & TOXICOL. *Personal Data:* b Macau, June 12, 40; US citizen; m 64; c 2. *Educ:* Cheng Kung

Univ, BS, 62; Univ Calif, Berkeley, PhD(org chem), 66. *Concurrent Pos:* Consult, indust & govt, 79- *Mem:* Sigma Xi; Am Chem Soc; Am Asn Cancer Res; fel Am Inst Chemists. *Res:* Chemical carcinogenesis and molecular epidemiology; synthesis of polycyclic amines and natural product analogs; modern coal and environmental studies. *Mailing Add:* Dept Chem Univ Louisville Louisville KY 40292-0001

**WONG, JOHNNY WAI-NANG,** COMPUTER SYSTEMS. *Current Pos:* From asst prof to assoc prof, 75-85, PROF, DEPT COMPUT SCI, UNIV WATERLOO, 85- *Personal Data:* b Hong Kong, Nov 22, 47. *Educ:* Univ Calif, BS, 70, MS, 71, PhD(comput sci), 75. *Res:* Modeling and analysis of computer systems and networks. *Mailing Add:* Dept Comput Sci Univ Waterloo Waterloo ON N2L 3G1 Can

**WONG, K(WEE) C,** WATER TREATMENT, CHEMICAL ETCHING. *Current Pos:* PROJ LEADER, DEXTER ELECTRONIC MAT, 87-, RES ASSOC. *Personal Data:* b Burma; US citizen. *Educ:* Univ Rangoon, Burma, BSc, 65. *Prof Exp:* Chemist, Chamberlain Mfg Co, 71-74; chief chemist, Bonewitz Chem Serv, 74-79; prin chemist, Dart Industs, 79-84; res chemist, Inland Specialty, Great Lakes Chem, 84-87. *Mem:* Am Chem Soc; Royal Soc Chem; fel Am Inst Chemists. *Res:* Improving and finding new processes and products for the printed circuit board industry and wastewater treatment; granted several patents. *Mailing Add:* 19 Wyndmere Dr Londonderry NH 03053

**WONG, KAI-WAI,** PHYSICS. *Current Pos:* from asst prof to assoc prof, 64-72, PROF PHYSICS, UNIV KANS, 72-, DIR HIGH TC LAB, 89- *Personal Data:* b Aug 7, 38; nat US citizen; m, Jane Say; c Hester, Roderick & Kristin. *Educ:* Duke Univ, BS, 59; Northwestern Univ, MS, 60, PhD(physics), 63. *Prof Exp:* Res assoc physics, Northwestern Univ, 63; res assoc, Univ Iowa, 63-64. *Concurrent Pos:* Vis assoc prof, Univ Southern Calif, 69-71; vis prof, Univ Calif, Los Angeles, 72-73 & 79-80; hon prof, Univ Hong Kong, 72. *Mem:* Am Phys Soc; AAAS; NY Acad Sci. *Res:* Theoretical physics; many-body problems; statistical mechanics; high Tc theory and experiment. *Mailing Add:* Dept Physics Univ Kans Lawrence KS 66045

**WONG, KAM WU,** PHOTOGRAMMETRY, GEODETIC SURVEYING. *Current Pos:* From asst prof to assoc prof, 67-76, PROF CIVIL ENG, UNIV ILL, URBANA-CHAMPAIGN, 76- *Personal Data:* b Hong Kong, Mar 8, 40; m 70, Betsy Pendleton; c David & Michael. *Educ:* Univ NB, BSc, 64; Cornell Univ, MSc, 66, PhD(photogram), 68. *Honors & Awards:* Talbert Abrams Award, Am Soc Photogram, 70; Walter L Huber Res Prize, Am Soc Civil Engrs, 71. *Mem:* Am Soc Photogram & Remote Sensing; Am Soc Civil Engrs; Can Inst Geomatics. *Res:* Metric vision; digital photogrammetry; geodetic surveying. *Mailing Add:* Dept Civil Eng Univ Ill 205 N Mathews Ave Urbana IL 61801. *Fax:* 217-333-9464

**WONG, KEITH KAM-KIN,** BIOCHEMISTRY, PHYSIOLOGY. *Current Pos:* RETIRED. *Personal Data:* b Hong Kong, Feb 11, 29; US citizen; m 61; c 2. *Educ:* Southwestern at Memphis, BA, 55; Univ Tenn, MSc, 57; NY Univ, PhD(biol), 69; Monmouth Col, MBA, 85. *Prof Exp:* Res asst chemother, Sloan-Kettering Inst Cancer Res, 57-58; mem staff biochem & drug metab, Worcester Found Exp Biol, 60-63; res assoc biochem pharmacol, Schering Corp, 63-66; res assoc exp hemat, NY Univ, 66-69; sr res investr drug metab, Squibb Inst Med Res, 69-79; sect leader biochem, Wallace Labs, Carter-Wallace Inc, 79-94. *Mem:* AAAS; Am Chem Soc; NY Acad Sci. *Res:* Drug metabolism; biochemical pharmacology; biogenesis of erythropoietin; metabolism of biogenic amines; amino acid activation and transfer; protein synthesis; transformation of nucleic acid. *Mailing Add:* 16 Desmet Ave Milltown NJ 08850

**WONG, KEN,** INORGANIC CHEMISTRY. *Current Pos:* sr chemist, 90-97, TECH ASSOC, SCOTT SPECIALTY GASES, 97- *Personal Data:* m 79, Betty; c Karen. *Educ:* Univ Cambridge, UK, PhD(inorg chem), 79. *Prof Exp:* Lectr, Hong Kong Polytech, 79-81; chemist, Hong Kong Govt Lab, 81-89. *Mem:* Am Chem Soc. *Res:* Cylinder passivation and analytical development. *Mailing Add:* 6141 Easton Rd Scott Specialty Gases Plumsteadville PA 18949. *Fax:* 215-766-2009

**WONG, KIN FAI,** UNIT OPERATIONS, CHEMICAL SAFETY & ENVIRONMENTAL TECHNOLOGY. *Current Pos:* PROG MGR, DIV ENVIRON TECHNOL, US BUR MINES, 93- *Personal Data:* b Kwangtung, China, Nov 6, 44; m 71, Yen-i Wang; c 2. *Educ:* Ariz State Univ, BSE, 65; Univ Ill, Urbana, MS, 67, PhD(chem eng), 70. *Prof Exp:* Res engr process develop, Western Res Ctr, Stauffer Chem Co, 70-76, sr res engr, De Guigne Tech Ctr, 76-79; proj officer, Off Toxic Substances, US Environ Protection Agency, 79-93. *Mem:* Am Inst Chem Engrs. *Res:* Thermodynamics and kinetics; occupational exposure and controls, modelling; process economics; waste product recovery and pollution control; asbestos abatement; prediction and control mining wastes. *Mailing Add:* 8711 Brickyard Rd Potomac MD 20854. *Fax:* 202-501-9957

**WONG, KING-LAP,** PLASMA HEATING & CONFINEMENT, TOKAMAK PHYSICS. *Current Pos:* res assoc, 76-78, res staff, 78-80, res physicist, 80-86, PRIN RES PHYSICIST, PLASMA PHYSICS LAB, PRINCETON UNIV, 86- *Personal Data:* b Canton, China. *Educ:* Chinese Univ, Hong Kong, BSc, 68; Univ Del, MS, 70; Univ Wis, PhD(physics), 75. *Prof Exp:* Res assoc, Columbia Univ, 75-76. *Concurrent Pos:* Prin investr L3/ACT-1 proj, US Dept Energy, 77-84. *Mem:* Fel Am Phys Soc. *Res:* Plasma heating and confinement; adiabatic compression; toroidal plasma confinement; thermonuclear fusion; linear and nonlinear plasma wave phenomena; radio-frequency wave heating and current drive; impurity transport; alfuen instability. *Mailing Add:* Plasma Physics Lab James Forrestal Campus Princeton Univ Princeton NJ 08543. *Fax:* 609-243-2874; *E-Mail:* wong@usc.pppl.gov

**WONG, KIN-PING,** BIOTECHNOLOGY, PHYSICAL CHEMISTRY. *Current Pos:* DEAN & PROF CHEM, SCH NATURAL SCI, CALIF STATE UNIV, 83- *Personal Data:* b China, Aug 14, 41; m 68; c 2. *Educ:* Univ Calif, Berkeley, BS, 64; Purdue Univ, PhD(phys & biol chem), 68. *Prof Exp:* Res fel phys biochem, Med Ctr, Duke Univ, 68-70; from asst prof to assoc prof chem, Univ SFla, Tampa, 70-75; from assoc prof to prof biochem, 75-83, dean grad studies, Univ Kans Med Ctr, 80-83. *Concurrent Pos:* Am Cancer Soc res grant, Univ SFla, Tampa, 70-71; NIH biomed res grant, 71-72, Cottrell res grant, 71-, Damon Runyon cancer res grant, 72-74; USPHS res career develop award, Nat Inst Gen Med Sci, 73; vis scientist, Max Planck Inst Molecular Genetics, 73; Europ Molecular Biol Orgn sr fel, Wsenberg Lab, Univ Uppsala, Sweden, 75; res grants, Nat Inst Gen Med Sci & Nat Heart, Lung & Blood Inst, 74-; vis prof, Univ Tokyo, Hongo, 79; prog dir biophys, NSF, Washington, DC, 82-83; US Dept Com sea grant, 87-, Milheim Found Cancer Res grant, 86-87; adj prof biochem & biophys, Univ Calif, San Francisco, adj prof med, Fresno Med Prog, 86-; Nat Col Sea grant, 87-90; chmn, chief exec officer & pres, RiboGene, Inc, 90-91. *Mem:* Am Soc Biol Chemists; Biophys Soc; Sigma Xi; AAAS; Am Chem Soc; Protein Soc; fel Royal Soc Chemists; fel Am Inst Chemists. *Res:* Physical biochemistry of protein and nucleic acids; mechanism of protein folding; ribosome structure; physicochemical studies of ribosomal proteins and RNAs; the molecular mechanism on the assembly of ribosome; mechanism of RNA folding; development of a potential anti-tumor drug: angiogenesis inhibitor from cartilage; protein aging; chemical carcinogensis. *Mailing Add:* Sch Natural Sci Calif State Univ 2555 E San Ramon Ave Fresno CA 93740-0090

**WONG, KWAN Y,** ELECTRICAL & SYSTEMS ENGINEERING. *Current Pos:* Mem res staff systs, 66-77, mgr, 77-88, JOINT PROG MGR, RES & MFG, INT BUS MACH CORP RES LAB, SAN JOSE, CALIF, 88- *Personal Data:* b Hong Kong, June 12, 37; US citizen; m 66, Polly T Cheng; c Derck & Juliana. *Educ:* Univ NSW, BS, 60, ME, 63; Univ Calif, Berkeley, PhD(elec eng), 66. *Mem:* Sr mem Inst Elec & Electronics Engrs; Sigma Xi. *Res:* Image processing; data compression; pattern recognition; process control; manufacturing systems; quality design and control. *Mailing Add:* IBM Almaden Res Ctr Dept Dpb Bldg B1 650 Harry Rd San Jose CA 95120-6099

**WONG, LAN KAN,** PHARMACEUTICAL RESEARCH & DEVELOPMENT, ANTICANCER AGENTS. *Current Pos:* DIR RES & LAB, PHARMAKON, 82- *Personal Data:* b Hong Kong, Sept 10, 50; US citizen; m 76, Deborah Chung. *Educ:* Calif State Univ, BS, 73; Mass Inst Technol, PhD(chem), 77. *Prof Exp:* Asst prof pharmacol, Ohio State Univ, 77-79; assoc prof pharm sci, Univ Pittsburgh, 79-92, dir pharmaceut analysis, 81-92. *Concurrent Pos:* Prin investr, various pub & govt grants, 78-; prin investr, NIH, 78-91; consult, Hoffman La Roche, 84-97, FMC, 86. *Mem:* Am Soc Mass Spectrometry; Am Chem Soc; AAAS; Am Asn Pharm Scientists; Control Release Soc. *Res:* Design and testing of new drug entities; development of assay methods for drugs and metabolites; phase 1 to 3 clinical studies; controlled release drug delivery. *Mailing Add:* 108 Rolling Meadow East Amherst NY 14051. *E-Mail:* lanwong@compuserv.com

**WONG, MAURICE KING FAN,** MATHEMATICAL PHYSICS. *Current Pos:* from asst prof to assoc prof, 69-79, PROF MATH, FAIRFIELD UNIV, 79- *Personal Data:* b Shanghai, China, Apr 9, 32. *Educ:* Univ Hong Kong, BSc, 54; Berhmans Col, AB, 58, MA, 61; Univ Birmingham, PhD(math physics), 64. *Prof Exp:* Res assoc, Inst Advan Studies, Dublin, 64-65; res fel res, Inst Nat Sci, Woodstock Col, Md, 65-68. *Concurrent Pos:* Fel, St Louis Univ, 69. *Mem:* AAAS; Am Phys Soc; Am Math Soc; Math Asn Am. *Res:* Lie groups; superconductivity; Mossbauer effect; elementary particles; nuclear physics; quantum theory. *Mailing Add:* Dept Math & Comput Sci Fairfield Univ Fairfield CT 06430-7524

**WONG, MING MING,** PARASITOLOGY, PRIMATE PARASITES. *Current Pos:* asst res parasitologist, Univ Calif, Davis, 67-73, assoc res parasitologist, Primate Res Ctr, 73-78, from assoc prof to prof, 78-88, EMER PROF, DEPT PATH, MICROBIOL & IMMUNOL, SCH VET MED, UNIV CALIF, DAVIS, 88- *Personal Data:* b Singapore, Jan 3, 28; US citizen. *Educ:* Wilmington Col, Ohio, BS, 52; Ohio State Univ, MS, 53; Tulane Univ La, PhD(med parasitol), 63. *Prof Exp:* Med technologist, Good Samaritan Hosp, Zanesville, Ohio, 54-55; teacher, Diocesan Girls' Sch, Hong Kong, 55-56; demonstr parasitol & bact fac med, Univ Hong Kong, 56-59; teaching asst med parasitol med sch, Tulane Univ La, 59-63, NIH res fel trop med, 63-64, res assoc, 64-65; res assoc fac med, Univ Malaya, 64-65, lectr parasitol, 65-67. *Concurrent Pos:* WHO res grant, Univ Malaya, 66-67; NIH grants, Primate Res Ctr, Univ Calif, Davis, 70-75. *Mem:* Am Soc Parasitol; Am Soc Trop Med & Hyg; Royal Soc Trop Med & Hyg; Am Heartworm Soc; Am Soc Clin Pathologists; Am Soc Vet Parasites. *Res:* Filariasis; primate parasitology; immunology of parasitic diseases. *Mailing Add:* 2916 Boathouse Ave Davis CA 95616

**WONG, MORTON MIN,** electrochemistry, hydrometallurgy, for more information see previous edition

**WONG, NOBLE POWELL,** FOOD CHEMISTRY, NUTRITION. *Current Pos:* RETIRED. *Personal Data:* b Baltimore, Md, Apr 30, 31; m 61; c 4. *Educ:* Univ Md, BS, 53; Pa State Univ, MS, 58, PhD(dairy sci), 61. *Prof Exp:* Res chem, Food & Drug Admin, 61-66; res chemist, USDA, 66-91. *Mem:* Am Chem Soc; Am Dairy Sci Asn; Inst Food Technol. *Res:* Nutrition and composition of dairy products; bioavailability of minerals. *Mailing Add:* 8716 Camille Dr Potomac MD 20854

**WONG, NORMAN L M,** NEPHROLOGY, PATHOPHYSIOLOGY. *Current Pos:* res assoc, Dept Med, Univ Hosp, Univ BC, 76-83, res med staff, 83-89, asst prof med, 83-89, assoc prof, 89-96, DIR EXP MED, UNIV BC, 94-, PROF, 96- *Personal Data:* b Hong Kong, Jan 14, 45; Can citizen; m, Katherine Si; c Kimberly & Germaine. *Educ:* Sir George Williams Univ, BS, 66; McGill Univ, MS, 69 & PhD(physiol), 72. *Prof Exp:* Fel Renal & Electrolyte Div, McGill Univ, 72-74, lectr, Dept Exp Med & Prof Asst, Renal & Electrolyte Div, 74-76. *Concurrent Pos:* Res med staff, Dept Med, Vancouver Gen, 83- *Mem:* Am Soc Nephrol; Am Physiol Soc; Can Physiol Soc; Can Soc Clin Invest; NY Acad Sci; Int Soc Nephrol. *Res:* Renal micropuncture of mammalian nephron with special emphasis on electrolyte transport, particularly directed at understanding of kidney tubule handling of calcium, magnesium and phosphate in various physiological and pathophysiological states; mechanism of atrial peptide release in viro and vitro; in normal and abnormal physiological conditions. *Mailing Add:* Dept Med Univ BC 2211 Wesbrook Mall Vancouver BC V6T 2B5 Can

**WONG, PATRICK YUI-KWONG,** BIOCHEMISTRY, BIOCHEMICAL PHARMACOLOGY. *Current Pos:* assoc prof, 79-85, PROF, DEPT PHARMACOL, NY MED COL, VALHALLA, 85- *Personal Data:* b Kiangsi, China, Nov 25, 44. *Educ:* Nat Taiwan Norm Univ, BSc, 67; Univ Vt, PhD(biochem), 75. *Prof Exp:* Fel, Med Col Wis, 74-75; instr pharmacol, Col Basic Med Sci, Univ Tenn, Memphis, 75-79. *Concurrent Pos:* Young investr award, NIH, 78-80 & career res develop award, 81-86; spec dent res award, Nat Inst Dent Res, 78-82; vis scientist, Karolinska Inst, Stockholm, Sweden, 82-83. *Mem:* Am Chem Soc; Am Soc Biol Chemists; Am Soc Pharm & Exp Therapeut. *Res:* Control and regulation of leukotrienes and prostaglandin synthesis and metabolism in cardiovascular disorders and inflammation process in arthritis. *Mailing Add:* Dept Cell Biol UM DNJ Sch Osteo-Med Two Med Ctr Dr Stratford NJ 08084

**WONG, PAUL WING-KON,** PEDIATRICS, GENETICS. *Current Pos:* PROF PEDIAT & DIR GENETIC SECT, RUSH MED SCH & PRESBY-ST LUKE MED CTR, CHICAGO, 76- *Personal Data:* US citizen. *Educ:* Univ Hong Kong, MD, 58; Univ Man, MSc, 67; Am Bd Pediat, dipl, 64; Am Bd Genetics, dipl, 82. *Prof Exp:* Instr pediat, Children's Mem Hosp, Northwestern Univ, Chicago, 63-64; from asst prof to prof pediat, Chicago Med Sch, 67-73; prof pediat & dir metab unit, Abraham Lincoln Sch Med, Univ Ill Med Ctr, 73-76. *Concurrent Pos:* USPHS res fel biochem & med genetics, Northwestern Univ, Chicago, 62-64; Children's Res Fund fel, Ment Retardation Res Unit, Royal Manchester Children's Hosp, Eng, 65-67; attend physician, Cook County Hosp, Chicago, Ill, 65-72, consult, 72-; dir infant's aid perinatal res labs & premature & newborn nurseries, Mt Sinai Hosp, 67-73; attend physician, Univ Ill Hosp & Presby-St Luke Med Ctr, 73- *Mem:* Am Pediat Soc; Am Fedn Clin Res; Soc Pediat Res; Am Soc Human Genetics; Cent Soc Clin Res. *Res:* Metabolic diseases; human genetics; atherosclerosis. *Mailing Add:* Dept Pediat Rush Univ 600 S Paulina St Chicago IL 60612. *Fax:* 312-942-6298; *E-Mail:* pwong@rpslmc.edu

**WONG, PETER ALEXANDER,** CHEMICAL INSTRUMENTATION. *Current Pos:* from asst prof to assoc prof, 69-88, PROF CHEM, ANDREWS UNIV, 88- *Personal Data:* b Honan, China, Apr 9, 41; US citizen; m 66, Dixie Barber; c Lenson P. *Educ:* Pac Union Col, BS, 62; Rensselaer Polytech Inst, PhD(chem), 69. *Prof Exp:* US AEC grant, Purdue Univ, 67-69. *Mem:* Am Chem Soc; Sigma Xi. *Res:* Use of microcomputers with chemical instruments; laminescencce properties of molecular assemblies for chemical sensing applications. *Mailing Add:* Dept Chem Andrews Univ Berrien Springs MI 49104. *E-Mail:* wong@andrews.edu

**WONG, PETER P,** NITROGEN FIXATION, CELL-CELL RECOGNITION. *Current Pos:* from asst prof to assoc prof, 76-85, PROF BIOL, KANS STATE UNIV, 85- *Personal Data:* b Shanghai, China, Dec 12, 41; m 64, Susan Lee; c 2. *Educ:* San Francisco State Col, BS, 66; Ore State Univ, BA, 67, PhD(plant physiol), 71. *Prof Exp:* Res assoc biochem, Univ Wis, 70-72; res assoc agr chem, Wash State Univ, 72-74, instr bot, 74-76. *Concurrent Pos:* Prin investr, USDA, 75- *Mem:* Am Soc Plant Physiologists; AAAS; Int Soc Plant Molecular Biol; Am Acad Microbiol. *Res:* Physiology and biochemistry of legume root nodule development; mechanism of recognition between rhizobia and legumes. *Mailing Add:* Div Biol Kans State Univ Manhattan KS 66506

**WONG, PO KEE,** RESEARCH ADMINISTRATION, SCIENCE EDUCATION. *Current Pos:* PRES & CHIEF EXEC OFFICER, SYST RES CO, SOMERVILLE, MASS, 76- *Personal Data:* b Canton City, China, May 5, 34; US citizen; m 65, Ruby Ching; c Adam & Anita. *Educ:* Cheng-Kung Univ, Taiwan, BSc, 56; Univ Utah, MSc, 61; Calif Inst Technol, ME, 66; Stanford Univ, PhD(aeronaut & astronaut), 70. *Prof Exp:* Teaching asst thermodynamics elasticity, Cheng-Kung Univ, 58-59; res & teaching asst appl math & mech eng, Univ Utah, 59-61; res & teaching asst appl math, Calif Inst Technol, 61-65; sr scientist appl mech, Lockheed Missiles & Space Co, 66-68; res asst aeronaut & astronaut eng, Stamford Univ, 68-70; lectr & researcher, Univ Santa Clara, 70 & 71 & Ames Ctr, NASA, 70; engr l, Breeder Reactor Dept, Gen Elec, Sunnyvale, 72-73; specialist engr, Nuclear Serv Co, Campbell, Calif, 73; engr, Stone & Webster Eng Co, Boston, Mass, 74.

*Concurrent Pos:* Teacher math & sci, Hong Kong YMCA Eng Col, 59; consult pressure transducer, Consolidated Electrodynamics Co, 62-65; consult, Flanco Serv, Inc & Air Res Co, Phoenix, 72-73; teacher math & sci, Boston Pub Sch, Mass, 79- *Mem:* Am Soc Mech Engrs; AAAS; Int Asn Struct Mech Reactor Technol; NY Acad Sci; Math Asn Am; Asn Supv & Curric Develop. *Res:* Trajectory solid angle, generalized stream functions, magneto-viscoelasto dynamics and visco-elasto dynamics; formulation and solution of multi-reservoir transient problem; physical economic model by means of the solution of a system of indeterminate structures which provide impacts in science; mathematics and engineering; nonlinear and linear structural systems; Wong's Angles to determine trajectories of objects. *Mailing Add:* 50 Bradley St Somerville MA 02145-2924

**WONG, PUI KEI,** DIFFERENTIAL EQUATIONS. *Current Pos:* from asst prof to assoc prof, 64-72, PROF MATH, MICH STATE UNIV, 72-, ASSOC DEAN COL NATURAL SCI. *Personal Data:* b Canton, China, Nov 7, 35; m 67, Vivian Liao; c Jean. *Educ:* Pac Union Col, BS, 56; Carnegie Inst Technol, MS, 58, PhD(math), 62. *Prof Exp:* Instr math, Carnegie Inst Technol, 60-62; asst prof, Lehigh Univ, 62-64. *Mem:* Math Asn Am; Soc Indust & Appl Math. *Res:* Stability and oscillation theory of differential equation; function-theoretic differential equations; non-linear boundary value problems. *Mailing Add:* Dept Math Wells Hall Mich State Univ East Lansing MI 48825. *E-Mail:* pkwong@msu.edu

**WONG, RODERICK SUE-CHEUN,** MATHEMATICAL ANALYSIS. *Current Pos:* PROF & HEAD, DEPT MATH, CITY UNIV HONG KONG, 94- *Personal Data:* b Shanghai, China, Oct 2, 44; m 76, Edwina C Nee; c Prescilla M & Letitial L. *Educ:* San Diego State Col, AB, 65; Univ Alta, PhD(math), 69. *Prof Exp:* From asst prof to prof math, Univ Man, 69-93, head, Dept Appl Math, 86-93. *Concurrent Pos:* Natural Sci & Eng Res Coun Can grant, Univ Man, 69-93; Killam res fel, Can Coun, 82-84. *Mem:* Can Math Soc (vpres, 91-93); Can Appl Math Soc (pres, 89-90); fel Royal Soc Can; Hong Kong Math Soc (pres, 96-98). *Res:* Asymptotic expansions; special functions. *Mailing Add:* Dept Math City Univ Hong Kong Tat Chee Ave Kowloon Hong Kong People's Republic of China

**WONG, ROMAN WOON-CHING,** ALGEBRA, MATHEMATICS. *Current Pos:* ASSOC PROF MATH, WASHINGTON & JEFFERSON COL, 78- *Personal Data:* b Canton, China, June 17, 48; m 73; c 2. *Educ:* Chinese Univ, Hong Kong, BS, 70; Sam Houston State Univ, MA, 72; Rutgers Univ, PhD(math), 77. *Prof Exp:* Asst prof, Syracuse Univ, 77-78. *Concurrent Pos:* NATO travel grant math conf, Univ Antwerp, 78; res grant, Am Philos Soc, 78-79. *Mem:* Am Math Soc; Math Asn Am. *Res:* Category theory and homological algebra; group rings and free algebras. *Mailing Add:* Dept Math Washington & Jefferson Col Washington PA 15301. *E-Mail:* rwong@washjeff.edu

**WONG, ROSIE BICK-HAR,** BIOCHEMISTRY, IMMUNOLOGY. *Current Pos:* SCIENTIST IMMUNOL, AGR DIV, AM CYANAMID CO, 77-, PRIN RES BIOCHEMIST, 92- *Personal Data:* b Shanghai, China; US citizen; c 2. *Educ:* Mt Mary Col, BSc, 65; Med Col Wis, PhD(biochem), 69. *Honors & Awards:* Am Cyanamid Sci Achievement Award, 83. *Prof Exp:* Res assoc biochem, Rockefeller Univ, 69-71; res assoc virol & immunol, Rutgers State Univ, 71-77. *Mem:* Am Chem Soc; Sigma Xi; Asn Women Sci. *Res:* Protein structure and function relationship; radioimmunoassay, transplantation antigen system in mouse; hybridoma; chicken immunology; immunoassays for environmental analysis; biosensor development. *Mailing Add:* Am Cyanamid Agr Res Ctr PO Box 400 Princeton NJ 08540-0400. *E-Mail:* wongr@pt.cyanamid.com

**WONG, RUTH (LAU),** PATHOLOGY. *Current Pos:* from asst prof to assoc prof, 57-69, PROF PATH, UNIV ILL COL MED, 69- *Personal Data:* b Hong Kong, Nov 25, 25; m 52; c 4. *Educ:* Lingnan Univ, MD, 48. *Prof Exp:* Resident path, Children's Hosp, Wash, DC, 51-52; resident, Duke Univ Hosp, 52-53; resident, Michael Reese Hosp, 53-54; res asst, La Rabida Sanitarium, 55-56; res asst, Univ Chicago, 56-57. *Concurrent Pos:* Fel, Michael Reese Hosp, Chicago, Ill, 54-55. *Mem:* Int Acad Path. *Res:* Surgical pathology; serotonin content of mast and enterochromaffin cells; relationship of mast cells to tissue response; medical information science; data retrieval of pathology records. *Mailing Add:* Dept Path Univ Ill Med Sch 1853 W Polk St Chicago IL 60612-4316

**WONG, S(OON) Y(UCK),** CHEMICAL ENGINEERING. *Current Pos:* tech asst to dir, Continental Oil Co, 56-61, supt process lab, Petrol Prod Res & Develop Div, 61-63, supvr process develop sect, Petrochem Res Div, 64-65, proj coordr, Petrochem Dept, 66-68, asst to mgr, Petrol Prods Res Div, 68-72, tech asst to mgr proj develop, Res & Develop Dept, 72-76, PROJ COORDR, MINING RES DIV, CONTINENTAL OIL CO, 76- *Personal Data:* b San Antonio, Tex, Mar 4, 20; m 49; c 3. *Educ:* Univ Tex, BS & MS, 43, PhD(chem eng), 49. *Prof Exp:* Sr res engr, Skelly Oil Co, 43-46; res assoc, Jefferson Chem Co, 50-53, staff engr, 53-56. *Res:* Minerals extraction and coal processing projects. *Mailing Add:* 160 Spencer Lane San Antonio TX 78201

**WONG, SAMUEL SHAW MING,** PHYSICS, THEORETICAL PHYSICS. *Current Pos:* From asst prof to assoc prof, 69-78, PROF PHYSICS, UNIV TORONTO, 78- *Personal Data:* b Beijing, China, May 10, 37; m 67; c 2. *Educ:* Int Christian Univ, Tokyo, BA, 59; Purdue Univ, MS, 61; Univ Rochester, PhD(theoret physics), 65. *Mem:* Am Phys Soc; Can Asn Physics. *Res:* Nuclear structure theory; intermediate energy nuclear theory, high energy nuclear physics. *Mailing Add:* Dept Physics Univ Toronto Toronto ON L5L 1C6 Can

**WONG, SHAN SHEKYUK,** CLINICAL CHEMISTRY & TOXICOLOGY. *Current Pos:* PROF MED, LOMA LINDA UNIV, LOMA LINDA, 96- *Personal Data:* b Mankassar, Indonesia, May 10, 45; US citizen; m 72, Lee-Jun Chang; c Inyork H & Injune H. *Educ:* Ore State Univ, Corvallis, BSc, 70; Ohio State Univ, Columbus, PhD(biochem), 74. *Honors & Awards:* Samuel A Talbot Mem Award, Biophys Soc, 74. *Prof Exp:* McPherson fel, Ohio State Univ, 72-73; fel, Temple Univ Med Sch, 75-76; asst prof chem, Dennison Univ, 77-78; from asst prof to prof, Univ Mass, Lowell, 78-90; assoc prof path, Univ Tex, Houston, 90-96. *Concurrent Pos:* Vis lectr chem, Ohio State Univ, 77; travel award, Am Asn Clin Chem, 86; young investr award, Acad Clin Lab Physicians & Scientists, 86; assoc sect chief clin chem, Hermann Hosp, 90-92, assoc sect chief forensic toxicol, 91-92, sect chief specimen control, 91-93, sect chief clin chem & forensic toxicol, 92-96; assoc sect chief clin chem & toxicol, Lyndon B Johnson Hosp, 90-92, sect chief, 92-96. *Mem:* Am Asn Clin Chem; Am Soc Biochem & Molecular Biol; NAm Chinese Clin Chem Asn (treas, 92-94; pres elect, 95-96, pres, 96-97); Nat Acad Clin Biochemists; Int Asn Forensic Toxicologists; Int Asn TDM & Clin Toxicol; Am Chem Soc; NY Acad Sci; Sigma Xi. *Res:* Analytical methodology for drug analysis and substances in body fluids; diagnosis of bone resorption and formation. *Mailing Add:* Mineral Metab 151 Vet Admin Med Ctr 11201 Benton St Loma Linda CA 92357

**WONG, SHEK-FU,** atomic physics, molecular physics, for more information see previous edition

**WONG, SHI-YIN,** ORGANIC CHEMISTRY. *Current Pos:* MEM TECH STAFF, HUGHES RES LAB, HUGHES AIRCRAFT CO, MALIBU, CALIF, 69- *Personal Data:* b Hoiping, Canton, China, Apr 27, 41; US citizen; m 67; c 1. *Educ:* Univ Calif, Los Angeles, BS, 64; Univ Southern Calif, PhD(chem), 68. *Concurrent Pos:* Air Force Off Sci Res fel, Hughes Res Lab, 72-73. *Res:* Electrohydrodynamics of liquid crystal; molecular correlation of liquid crystal. *Mailing Add:* 407 W College Los Angeles CA 90012

**WONG, SIU GUM,** OPTOMETRY, PUBLIC HEALTH. *Current Pos:* optom consult, 84-91, CHIEF, AREA OPTOM SERV BR, INDIAN HEALTH SERV, 78- *Personal Data:* b San Francisco, Calif, Feb 21, 47; m 79. *Educ:* Univ Calif, Berkeley, BS, 68, OD, 70, MPH, 72. *Honors & Awards:* Pub Health Serv Commendation Award, 82; Outstanding Serv Medal, USPHS, 85, Unit Commendation, 85, 88 & 90, Meritorious Serv Medal, 89. *Prof Exp:* Res assoc community med, Sch Med, St Louis Univ, 72-73; asst prof optom & pub health, Col Optom, Univ Houston, 73-78. *Concurrent Pos:* Consult, Health Power Assoc, Inc, New Orleans, 74. *Mem:* Fel Am Acad Optom; Am Optom Asn; Am Pub Health Asn. *Res:* Community optometry; quality assurance. *Mailing Add:* Indian Health Serv 505 Marquette Ave NW Suite 1502 Albuquerque NM 87102-2162

**WONG, TANG-FONG FRANK,** THEORETICAL PARTICLE PHYSICS. *Current Pos:* DIST MGR, AT&T, 93- *Personal Data:* b Canton, China, Jan 21, 44; m 69, Rosie; c Adrianne & Julian. *Educ:* Chinese Univ Hong Kong, BSc, 65; Brown Univ, PhD(physics), 70. *Prof Exp:* Res assoc physics, Brookhaven Nat Lab, 69-71; res fel physics, Rutgers Univ, New Brunswick, 71-73, vis asst prof, 73-74, asst prof, 74-78; tech mgr, Bell Labs, 79-92. *Mem:* Am Phys Soc. *Res:* High energy behavior of renormalizable field theories; symmetry and symmetry breaking in field theories; strong interaction phenomenology. *Mailing Add:* 16 Ross Hall Blvd Piscataway NJ 08854. *E-Mail:* fwong@attmail.att.com

**WONG, TING-WA,** ENDOCRINE PATHOLOGY, CELL PATHOLOGY. *Current Pos:* ASSOC PROF PATH, UNIV CHICAGO, 58- *Educ:* Univ Chicago, MD, 57, PhD(org chem), 70. *Mailing Add:* Dept Path Univ Chicago Path 5841 S Maryland Ave Chicago IL 60637-1463

**WONG, TUCK CHUEN,** NUCLEAR MAGNETIC RESONANCE OF SURFACTANT SOLUTION & LIQUID CRYSTALS, NUCLEAR MAGNETIC RESONANCE STUDY OF BIOMOLECULAR STRUCTURE. *Current Pos:* assoc prof teaching & res, 81-89, DIR NUCLEAR MAGNETIC RESONANCE FACIL, UNIV MO, 81-, PROF TEACHING & RES, 89- *Personal Data:* b Canton, Kwangtung, China, Mar 28, 46; US citizen; m 72, Kit L Tang; c Ellen, Denise & Peter. *Educ:* Chinese Univ Hong Kong, BSc, 69; Univ Mich, MS, 71, PhD(chem), 74. *Prof Exp:* Fel res, Dept Chem, Ind Univ, 74-75; Killam fel res, Univ BC, 75-76; asst prof teaching, Dept Chem, Tufts Univ, 76-81. *Concurrent Pos:* Vis prof, Chem Ctr, Univ Lund, Sweden, 87-88; consult, Unilever Res Lab, NJ, 90- *Mem:* Am Chem Soc; Int Soc Magnetic Resonance. *Res:* Nuclear magnetic resonance investigation of micelles, liquid crystals and surfactant/polymer systems; structure and dynamics of biological molecules in solution by multi-dimensional nuclear magnetic resonance, magnetic relaxation and molecular modeling. *Mailing Add:* Chem Dept Univ Mo Columbia MO 65211-0002. *Fax:* 573-882-2754; *E-Mail:* chem1060@mizzou1.missouri.edu

**WONG, VICTOR KENNETH,** LOW TEMPERATURE PHYSICS, HIGH ENERGY SPIN PHYSICS. *Current Pos:* PROF, UNIV MICH, FLINT, 86-, PROVOST & VCHANCELLOR ACAD AFFAIRS, 86- *Personal Data:* b San Francisco, Calif, Nov 1, 38; m 64; c 3. *Educ:* Univ Calif, Berkeley, BS, 60, PhD(physics), 66. *Prof Exp:* Fel physics, Ohio State Univ, 66-67, res assoc, 67-68; lectr, Univ Mich, Ann Arbor, 68-69, asst prof physics, 69-76; from assoc prof to prof physics, Univ Mich, Dearborn, 76-86, chmn physics discipline, 7980, chmn, Dept Natural Sci, 80-83, dean, Col Arts, Sci & Lett, 83-86. *Concurrent Pos:* Adj prof, Univ Mich, Ann Arbor, 92- *Mem:* Am Phys Soc. *Res:* Many-body theory; equilibrium properties of interacting bosons at low temperatures; superfluidity; quantum fluids; critical phenomena; surface

phenomena; and dielectric formulation of Bose liquids; high energy spin physics; Siberian snacks. *Mailing Add:* Off Provost Univ Mich Flint 5074 Fleming 503 Thompson Ann Arbor MI 48109-1340. *E-Mail:* vkw@umich. edu

**WONG, WAI-MAI TSANG,** POLYMER SCIENCE. *Current Pos:* RES SCIENTIST POLYMER SCI, COLUMBUS DIV, BATTELLE MEM INST, 76- *Personal Data:* b Hong Kong, Apr 14, 41; Brit citizen; m 69; c 1. *Educ:* Nat Taiwan Normal Univ, BSc, 65; Univ Guelph, MSc, 69; Case Western Reserve Univ, PhD(macromolecular sci), 74. *Prof Exp:* Teaching asst physics, Nat Taiwan Normal Univ, 64-67; res assoc polymer sci, Case Western Reserve Univ, 74-76. *Mem:* Am Phys Soc. *Res:* Structure-property relationship of synthetic and bio-polymers. *Mailing Add:* 1390 Darcann Dr Columbus OH 43220

**WONG, WANG MO,** CHEMICAL ENGINEERING. *Current Pos:* RETIRED. *Personal Data:* b Canton, Kwangtung, China; US citizen; m 49; c 2. *Educ:* Sun Yat-Sen Univ, BS, 39; Univ Iowa, MS, 49, PhD(chem eng), 54. *Prof Exp:* Chief chem engr, US Rubber Co, Joliet Arsenal, Ill, 55-60; res engr, US Borax & Chem Corp, Calif, 60-61; sr engr, Armour Pharmaceut Co, Kankakee, 61-77; chem engr, Arthur G Mc Kee & Co, 77- *Mem:* Am Chem Soc; Am Inst Chem Engrs. *Res:* Research and process development in bench scale and pilot plant of organic and inorganic chemical process; specialization in continuous process development. *Mailing Add:* 4233 Oakwood Lane Matteson IL 60443

**WONG, WARREN JAMES,** ALGEBRA. *Current Pos:* assoc prof, 64-68, PROF MATH, UNIV NOTRE DAME, 68- *Personal Data:* b Masterton, NZ, Oct 16, 34; m 62, Nellie Gee; c Carole, Frances & Andrea. *Educ:* Univ Otago, NZ, BSc, 55, MSc, 56; Harvard Univ, PhD(math), 59. *Prof Exp:* Lectr math, Univ Otago, NZ, 60-63, sr lectr, 64. *Concurrent Pos:* Vis fel, Univ Auckland, 69; ed, Proceedings Am Math Soc, 88-90. *Mem:* Am Math Soc; Math Asn Am; Australian Math Soc; Sigma Xi. *Res:* Finite group theory; groups of Lietype. *Mailing Add:* Dept Math Univ Notre Dame Notre Dame IN 46556-5683

**WONG, WILLIAM WAI-LUN,** NUTRIENT REQUIREMENTS & CHOLESTERAL METABOLISM DURING INFANCY GROWTH & REPRODUCTION. *Current Pos:* from instr to asst prof, 80-88, ASSOC PROF, BAYLOR COL MED, 88- *Personal Data:* b Kowloon, Hong Kong, Dec 4, 48; m 74, Susannah Lee; c Christina W & Princeton C. *Educ:* Tex Lutheran Col, BS, 72; Tex A&M Univ, MS, 74, PhD(oceanog), 76. *Honors & Awards:* Young Investr Award, Children's Nutrit Res Ctr, USDA/Agr Res Serv, 85. *Prof Exp:* Fel, Tex A&M Univ, 76-78, Robert A Welch fel, 78; res scientist, Global Geochem Corp, 78-80. *Concurrent Pos:* Fel, Am Col Nutrit, 93-; consult, Meretek Diag Inc, 93-; prin investr, Am Soybean Asn, 93- *Mem:* Am Col Nutrit; Am Inst Nutrit; Soc Pediat Res; Europ Soc Pediat Res; Am Soc Clin Nutrit. *Res:* Energy requirements and lipid requirements for optimal growth; development in infants, children and adolescents. *Mailing Add:* USDA/Agr Res Serv Nutrit Res Ctr 1100 Bates St Houston TX 77030-2600. *Fax:* 713-798-7119

**WONG, YIU-HUEN,** PHYSICS, MATERIALS SCIENCE. *Current Pos:* MEM TECH STAFF, BELL LABS, 79- *Personal Data:* b Hong Kong, May 9, 46; m 72. *Educ:* Mass Inst Technol, BS, 67; Univ Wis-Madison, MS, 69, PhD(physics), 73. *Prof Exp:* Res fel, Rutgers Univ, 73-76; asst prof physics, Wayne State Univ, 76-79. *Concurrent Pos:* Co-prin investr grant, Army Res Off, 78-79. *Mem:* Am Phys Soc; Inst Elec & Electronics Engrs; Electrochem Soc. *Res:* Laser spectroscopy of matter; surface and subsurface characterization of solids; transport properties of condensed matter; microelectronics; telecommunication systems. *Mailing Add:* Lucent Technol 600 Mountain Ave Murray Hill NJ 07974

**WONG, YUEN-FAT,** MATHEMATICS. *Current Pos:* ASSOC PROF MATH, DEPAUL UNIV, 64- *Personal Data:* b Kwangtung, China, Sept 22, 35; US citizen; m 62; c 3. *Educ:* Cornell Univ, PhD(math), 64. *Concurrent Pos:* NSF fel, DePaul Univ, 65-67. *Mem:* Am Math Soc. *Res:* Algebraic topology. *Mailing Add:* Dept Math DePaul Univ Byrne Hall Chicago IL 60614-3504

**WONG-RILEY, MARGARET TZE TUNG,** NEUROANATOMY, ANATOMY. *Current Pos:* assoc prof anat, 81-84, PROF ANAT & CELLULAR BIOL, MED COL WIS, 84- *Personal Data:* b Shanghai, China, Oct 20, 41; US citizen; m 70; c 2. *Educ:* Columbia Univ, BS, 65, MA, 66; Stanford Univ, PhD(anat), 70. *Prof Exp:* Asst prof anat & neuroanat, Univ Calif, San Francisco, 73-80, assoc prof anat, 80-81. *Concurrent Pos:* Fight for Sight fel, Univ Wis, 70-71; NIH fel, Lab Neurophysiol, Nat Inst Neurol Dis & Stroke, 72-73; Alexander Ryan Endowment Fund fel, Univ Calif, San Francisco, 74-75; visual sci B study sect, NIH, 80-84; mem, Behav & Neurosci Study Sect 1, NIH, 86-90 & Reviewers Reserve, 90-94; pres, Milwaukee Chap, Soc Neurosci, 88. *Mem:* AAAS; Soc Neurosci; Asn Am Anat. *Res:* Structural and functional organization of the mammalian visual system; functionally related metabolic adjustments in neurons as revealed by cytochrome oxidase histo-and cytochemistry. *Mailing Add:* Dept Anat & Cellular Biol Med Col Wis 8701 Watertown Plank Rd Milwaukee WI 53226

**WONG-STAAL, FLOSSIE,** RETROVIRUSES, AIDS RESEARCH. *Current Pos:* FLORENCE RIFORD CHAIR AIDS RES, PROF MED & BIOL, UNIV CALIF, SAN DIEGO, 90- *Personal Data:* b China; US citizen. *Educ:* Univ Calif, Los Angeles, BA, 68, PhD(molecular biol), 72. *Honors & Awards:*

Howard Gilman Lectr, NY Univ, 85; Outstanding Sci Award, Chinese Med & Health Asn, 87; Harry McFadden Lectr, Univ Nebr Med Ctr, 88; James M Craig Lectr, Univ Ore, 89; Kroc Lectr, Western Asn Physicians, 91; RE Dyer Lectr, NIH, 93; Alexander Wiener Lectr, NY Blood Ctr, 95; Robert T Wong Lectr, Univ Hawaii, 96. *Prof Exp:* Teaching asst, Univ Calif, Los Angeles, 69-70, res asst, 70-72; postdoctoral fel, Univ Calif, San Diego, 72-73; Fogarty fel, Nat Cancer Inst, NIH, 73-75, vis assoc, 75-76, cancer expert, 76-78, sr investr, 78-81; chief, Molecular Genetics Hematopoietic Cells Sect, Lab Tumor Cell Biol, Nat Cancer Inst, 82-89. *Concurrent Pos:* Ed, J AIDS Res & Human Retroviruses, Microbial Pathogenesis, DNA, Cancer Res, Leukemia, 87- *Mem:* Inst Med-Nat Acad Sci; Am Asn Cancer Res; Am Soc Virol; hon mem Am Soc Clin Invest. *Res:* Molecular biology of human pathogenic viruses, cancer and AIDS; mechanisms of gene regulation; novel approaches to gene therapy; molecular vaccines. *Mailing Add:* Dept Med 0665 Univ Calif San Diego 9500 Gilman Dr La Jolla CA 92093-0613

**WONHAM, W MURRAY,** APPLIED MATHEMATICS, SYSTEMS ENGINEERING. *Current Pos:* assoc prof, 70-72, PROF ELEC ENG, UNIV TORONTO, 72- *Personal Data:* b Montreal, Que, Nov 1, 34. *Educ:* McGill Univ, BEng, 56; Cambridge Univ, PhD(eng), 61. *Prof Exp:* Asst prof elec eng, Purdue Univ, 61-62; res mathematician, Res Inst Advan Study, 62-64; assoc prof appl math & eng, Brown Univ, 64-70. *Concurrent Pos:* Consult, Electronics Res Ctr, NASA, Mass, 65-70. *Mem:* Fel Inst Elec & Electronics Engrs; Soc Indust & Appl Math. *Res:* Systems theory. *Mailing Add:* Dept Elec & Computer Eng Univ Toronto 10 Kings Col Rd Toronto ON M5S 1A4 Can

**WONNACOTT, THOMAS HERBERT,** DEMOGRAPHY, ENVIRONMENT & POPULATION. *Current Pos:* Assoc prof math, 66-80, ASSOC PROF STATIST, UNIV WESTERN ONT, 80- *Personal Data:* b London, Ont, Nov 29, 35; m 80, Elizabeth Ellwood; c Rebecca, Cecilia, Dan, Matthew, Kathleen, Marion & David. *Educ:* Univ Western Ont, BA, 57; Princeton Univ, PhD(math statist), 63. *Mem:* Am Statist Asn; Can Pop Soc. *Res:* Statistics in social science, especially population and environmental issues; textbook writing. *Mailing Add:* Dept Statist Univ Western Ont London ON N6A 5B9 Can. *Fax:* 519-661-3813; *E-Mail:* thw@statistics.uwo.ca

**WONSIEWICZ, BUD CAESAR,** METALLURGY. *Current Pos:* VPRES SCI & TECHNOL, US W ADVAN TECHNOL, 88- *Personal Data:* b Buffalo, NY, Aug 23, 41; m 63; c 3. *Educ:* Mass Inst Technol, SB, 63, PhD(metall), 66. *Prof Exp:* Asst prof metall, Mass Inst Technol, 66-67; mem tech staff, Bell Tel Labs, 67-88. *Mem:* AAAS; Am Inst Mining, Metall & Petrol Engrs; Am Soc Metals; Inst Elec & Electronics Engrs; Asn Comput Mach. *Res:* Software engineering; software quality and productivity; software methodology; software project management. *Mailing Add:* US W Advan Tech 4001 Discovery Dr Suite 210 Boulder CO 80303

**WOO, CHIA-WEI,** THEORETICAL PHYSICS. *Current Pos:* PRES, HONG KONG UNIV SCI & TECHNOL, 88- *Personal Data:* b Shanghai, China, Nov 13, 37; m 60, Yvonne M Lo; c dekai J Wu, Deyi Y, De-Hwei M & Detian A. *Educ:* Georgetown Col, BS, 56; Wash Univ, MA, 61, PhD(physics), 66. *Hon Degrees:* LHD, Georgetown Col, 95, DSC, Wash Univ, 96. *Prof Exp:* Appl mathematician, Monsanto Co, Mo, 58-62; res assoc, Wash Univ, 66; asst res physicist, Univ Calif, San Diego, 66-68; from asst prof to prof physics, Northwestern Univ, Evanston, 68-79, chmn dept, 74-79; provost & prof physics, Univ Calif, San Diego, 79-83; pres & prof, San Francisco State Univ, 83-88. *Concurrent Pos:* hon prof, Peking Univ, Shenzhen Univ & Fadan Univ. *Mem:* Fel Am Phys Soc. *Res:* Quantum many body theory; low temperature physics; surface physics; liquid crystals and polymers, nuclear astrophysical calculations, technology transfer and economic development. *Mailing Add:* Hong Kong Univ Sci & Technol Clearwater Bay Kowloon Hong Kong People's Republic of China. *E-Mail:* preswoo@usthk.ust.hk

**WOO, CHUNG-HO,** MATERIALS SCIENCE, SOLID STATE PHYSICS. *Current Pos:* From asst res officer to sr res officer, 77-92, SR PHYSICIST, REACTOR MAT RES, CHALK RIVER LABS, ATOMIC ENERGY CAN LTD, CHALK RIVER, 93- *Personal Data:* b Sept 7, 43; Can citizen; m 68; c 1. *Educ:* Univ Hong Kong, BSc, 67; Univ Calgary, MSc, 69; Univ Waterloo, PhD(physics), 73. *Concurrent Pos:* Vis scientist, Harwell Labs, UK, 78, Max-Planck Inst Metals, Stuttgart, 81 & 84-85 & RZSQ Labs, Denmark, 89-93. *Mem:* Am Soc Testing & Mat. *Res:* Radiation damage; defects and mechanical properties; dislocations and point-defect dislocation interaction; color centers; electronic states in metals; computer simulation and numerical analysis; molecular quantum chemistry; diffusion mechanisms in metals. *Mailing Add:* Whiteshell Labs Atomic Energy Can Ltd Pinawa MB R0E 1L0 Can. *Fax:* 204-753-2455

**WOO, DAH-CHENG,** HYDRAULICS, HYDROLOGY. *Current Pos:* RETIRED. *Personal Data:* b Shanghai, China, Dec 18, 21; US citizen. *Educ:* Hangchow Christian Col, BS, 44; Univ Mich, Ann Arbor, MA, 48, PhD(hydraul eng), 56. *Prof Exp:* Res asst struct & hydraul res, Univ Mich, Ann Arbor, 48-50; design engr, Ayres, Lewis, Norris & May, Consult Engrs, 51-56, hydraul engr, 57-62; proj engr, Univ Mich, Ann Arbor, 56-57; hydraul engr, US Fed Hwy Admin, 62-92, res mgr robotics & automation, 92-96. *Mem:* Am Geophys Union; Am Soc Civil Engrs; Int Asn Hydraul Res; Int Water Resources Asn; Int Asn Automation & Robotics Construct. *Res:* Urban water resources; small watershed hydrology. *Mailing Add:* 2300 Pimmit Dr No 712 Falls Church VA 22043

**WOO, GAR LOK,** ORGANIC CHEMISTRY. *Current Pos:* Res chemist, 62-69, sr res chemist, 69-75, SR RES ASSOC, CHEVRON RES CO, RICHMOND, 75- *Personal Data:* b Canton, China, Jan 14, 35; US citizen; m 64; c 2. *Educ:* Univ Calif, Berkeley, BS, 59; Mass Inst Technol, PhD(org chem), 62. *Mem:* Am Chem Soc. *Res:* Physical organic chemistry, mechanism, stereochemistry and synthesis; exploratory petrochemicals and surfactants; sulfur and organo-sulfur chemistry. *Mailing Add:* 200 Blackfield Dr Tiburon CA 94920-2074

**WOO, GEORGE CHI SHING,** OPTOMETRY. *Current Pos:* asst prof, 70-74, assoc prof, 74-80, PROF OPTOM, UNIV WATERLOO, 80- *Personal Data:* b Shanghai, China, Feb 15, 41; Can citizen; m 67; c 3. *Educ:* Col Optom Ont, OD, 64; Ind Univ, Bloomington, MS, 68, PhD(physiol optics), 70; Melbourne Univ, LOSc, 79. *Hon Degrees:* OD, Univ Waterloo, 87. *Honors & Awards:* Herbert Moss Mem lectr, Int Optom & Optical League, 90. *Prof Exp:* Optometrist, Can Red Cross, 64-66; clin instr optom, Ind Univ, 66-67; dir, Ctr Sight Enhancement, 84-87. *Concurrent Pos:* Res assoc & assoc instr, Ind Univ, 66-70; vis prof, Pa Col Optom, 83; vis scholar, Cambridge Univ, UK, 84; head & prof, Dept Diag Sci, Hong Kong Polytech, 87-89. *Mem:* Am Acad Optom; Can Asn Optom. *Res:* Low vision; photometry; contrast sensitivity function and optics of the eye; refraction; myopia. *Mailing Add:* Sch Optom Columbia St Univ Waterloo Waterloo ON N2L 3G1 Can

**WOO, JAMES T K,** ORGANIC CHEMISTRY, POLYMER CHEMISTRY. *Current Pos:* PROF, EASTERN MICH UNIV, 97- *Personal Data:* b Shanghai, China, June 7, 38; m 67, Liisa Mikkola; c Alex, Anton & Alicia. *Educ:* Wabash Col, BA, 61; Univ Md, PhD(chem), 67. *Prof Exp:* Asst, Univ Md, 61-63, res asst, 63-66, fel, 66-67; res chemist, Dow Chem Co, Mich, 67-71; mem tech staff, Horizon Res Corp, 71-72; sr chemist, Glidden Co, 72-74, scientist, 74-83, sr scientist, 83-96. *Mem:* Am Chem Soc; AAAS; Sigma Xi; Am Inst Chemists. *Res:* Polymer chemistry; graft copolymer; coatings; polymer synthesis. *Mailing Add:* 5733 Wolff Rd Medina OH 44256

**WOO, KWANG BANG,** ROBOTICS & AUTOMATION, INTELLIGENT SYSTEMS. *Current Pos:* assoc dean, Grad Sch, 83-87, PROF ELEC ENG, YONSEI UNIV, 82-, DIR, AUTOMATION TECHNOL RES INST, 93- *Personal Data:* b Kyoto, Japan, Jan 25, 34; m 63, Kum Y Lee; c 2. *Educ:* Yonsei Univ, Korea, BE, 57, ME, 59; Ore State Univ, MS, 62, PhD(elec eng), 64. *Honors & Awards:* Medal Hon, Dong Baek Jang, Repub Korea. *Prof Exp:* Res mem, Sci Res Inst, Ministry Defense, Korea, 57-60; instr elec eng, Yonsei Univ, Korea, 59-60; res assoc, Ore State Univ, 64; asst prof elec eng & biomed eng, Wash Univ & res assoc, Ctr Biol Natural Systs, 66-71; sr staff fel, Off Dept Dir, Div Cancer Treatment, Nat Cancer Inst, 71-76; scientist, Biol Markers Lab, Frederick Cancer Res Ctr, 76-79 & John Hopkins Oncol Ctr, 79-82. *Concurrent Pos:* Fel biophys, Inst Sci Technol, Univ Mich, 65-66; bd mem, Soc Inst Control Engrs Japan, 96-97. *Mem:* AAAS; Inst Elec & Electronics Engrs; Korean Sci Eng Asn Am (pres, 80-81); Biophys Soc; Korean Inst Elec Eng; Korean Asn Automatic Control (pres, 94); Inst Control Automation Systs Engrs (pres, 94-95); Soc Inst Control Engrs Japan. *Res:* Robotics and automation; intelligent systems; tumor-marker interactions; untrasonic imaging; semiconductor manufacturing. *Mailing Add:* Dept Elec Eng Yonsei Univ Seoul 120-749 South Korea. *E-Mail:* kbwoo@bubble.yousei.ac.kr

**WOO, LECON,** POLYMER CHEMISTRY, MEDICAL & HEALTH SCIENCES. *Current Pos:* sr scientist, 82-84, tech dir, 84-92, DISTINGUISHED SCIENTIST, BAXTER HEALTHCARE, 92- *Personal Data:* b Chung Kin, Sept 9, 45; US citizen; m 78, Hung Lo; c Eileen & Raymond. *Educ:* Kans State Univ, BS, 67; Univ Chicago, MS, 73, PhD(chem physics), 73. *Honors & Awards:* I-R 100 Award, 77. *Prof Exp:* Sr chemist, E I du Pont de Nemours & Co, Inc, 73-78; sr res scientist, Atlantic & Richfield, 78-82. *Concurrent Pos:* Consult polymer physics, 78- *Mem:* AAAS; Sigma Xi; Am Chem Soc; Am Inst Physics; Soc Plastics Engrs; NAm Thermal Anal Soc. *Res:* Structure property of synthetic and natural polymers; biomaterial development; dynamic mechanical and rheological properties; fracture properties of polymers. *Mailing Add:* Baxter Healthcare Round Lake IL 60073

**WOO, MING-KO,** GEOGRAPHY, HYDROLOGY. *Current Pos:* from asst prof to assoc prof, 72-83, PROF, DEPT GEOG, MCMASTER UNIV, 83-;PROF HYDROLOGIST, AM INST HYDROL. *Personal Data:* b Hong Kong, 1941. *Educ:* Univ Hong Kong, BA, 64, MA, 67; Univ BC, PhD(hydrol), 72. *Prof Exp:* Res programmer, Int Animal Resource Ecol, Univ BC, 72. *Concurrent Pos:* Grantee, Nat Sci & Eng Res Coun Can, 72-, Inland Waters Directorate, 77-80, Atmospheric Environ Serv, 80-82, Soc Sci & Humanities Res Coun Can, 83-84, Donner Can Found, 82-85, UN Develop Prog, 86 & 90-, Energy, Mines & Resources, 89- & Can Int Develop Agency, 93-; partic var res projs, Environ Can, 73-76, Ont Hydro, 74-78, Indian & Northern Affairs Can, 81-87, Int Develop Res Ctr, 87-89, Atmospheric Environ Serv, 88-89, 89-91 & 92, Wildlife Serv, 89-91, Duck Unltd, 89-91 & Can Elec Asn, 92-93; mem, Permafrost Subcomt, Nat Res Coun Can, 85-91; vis scientist, Inst Glaciol & Geocryol, Chinese Acad Sci, 86 & St Andrews Univ, Scotland, 86; mem, Can Nat Comt, Int Union Geodesy & Geophys, 86-88; chmn, Int Biosphere Prog Comt, Can Asn Geogrs, 89-91; mem, Can Nat Comt, World Climate Res Prog, 92-; consult, Ont Coun Grad Studies, 93; comt mem, Hydrol Sect, Can Geophy Union, 93- *Mem:* Am Geophys Union; Am Meteorol Soc; Can Asn Geogrs; corresp mem Geog Soc China; fel Arctic Inst NAm; fel Royal Canadian Geog Soc. *Res:* Snow accumulation, snow melt and runoff processes; ice problems in northern Canada; hydrological processes as affected by the presence of permafrost in arctic and western Canada; wetland storage and runoff in temperate, sub arctic and arctic environments; stochastic modelling of droughts, floods, and other runoff phenomena; rural water use in the desert fringe of northern Nigeria; tropical soil erosion in southern China; hydrological effects of climatic variability and climate change in Arctic and prairie regions. *Mailing Add:* Dept Geog McMaster Univ 1280 Main St W Hamilton ON L8S 4K1 Can. *Fax:* 905-546-0463

**WOO, NAM-SUNG,** COMPUTER-AIDED VERY-LARGE SCALE INTEGRATED DESIGN, PARALLEL PROCESSING. *Current Pos:* MEM TECH STAFF, AT&T BELL LABS, 83- *Personal Data:* Korean citizen. *Educ:* Seoul Nat Univ, BS, 75; Korea Advan Inst Sci, MS, 77; Univ Md, PhD(comput sci), 83. *Prof Exp:* Design engr, SamSung, GTE Telecommun, Inc, 77-79; lectr comput systs, Dept Comput Sci, Dong-Guk Univ, 79-80; res asst, Univ Md, College Park, 80-83. *Concurrent Pos:* Lectr, Univ Md, College Park, 83. *Mem:* Inst Elec & Electronics Engrs. *Res:* Computer-aided design of very large scale integration and parallel processing; developing a synthesis environment for field programmable gate array. *Mailing Add:* 10225 Willow Creek Rd San Diego CA 92131

**WOO, NORMAN TZU TEH,** MATHEMATICS. *Current Pos:* PROF MATH, CALIF STATE UNIV, FRESNO, 68- *Personal Data:* b Shanghai, China, Sept 28, 39. *Educ:* Wabash Col, BA, 62; Southern Methodist Univ, MS, 64; Wash State Univ, PhD(math), 68. *Mem:* Am Math Soc. *Res:* Number theory of mathematics. *Mailing Add:* Dept Math Calif State Univ Maple & Shaw Ave Fresno CA 93740

**WOO, P(ETER) W(ING) K(EE),** ORGANIC CHEMISTRY, RADIOCHEMISTRY. *Current Pos:* from assoc res chemist to sr res chemist, Parke, Davis & Co, 58-71, res scientist, 71-77, res assoc, 77-94, SR RES ASSOC, PHARMACEUT RES DIV, WARNER-LAMBERT/ PARKE-DAVIS, 94- *Personal Data:* b Canton, China, June 22, 34; m 66, Katherine Liang; c Karen H W, Lena H A & Nelson H Y. *Educ:* Stanford Univ, BS, 55; Univ Ill, PhD(chem), 58. *Honors & Awards:* Award Excellence Indust Chem Res, Am Chem Soc, 83. *Mem:* Am Chem Soc; AAAS; Int Isotope Soc. *Res:* Radiolabeling, synthesis, isolation and structural elucidation of medicinal agents and related metabolites: antibiotics, enzyme inhibitors, anti-inflammatory and anti-hypertensive agents; chemistry of peptides, nucleosides, beta-lactams, aminoglycosides, carbohydrates, heterocycles and macrolides; computer database program development. *Mailing Add:* Park Davis Pharmaceut Res Div Warner Lambert 2800 Plymouth Rd Ann Arbor MI 48105. *Fax:* 313-998-2751; *E-Mail:* woo@aa.wl.com

**WOO, RICHARD,** SPACE PHYSICS, SOLAR PHYSICS. *Current Pos:* Engr, Jet Propulsion Lab, Calif Inst Technol, 64-68, sr engr, 68-73, mem tech staff, 73-81, res scientist, 81-87, SR RES SCIENTIST, JET PROPULSION LAB, CALIF INST TECHNOL, 87- *Personal Data:* b Portland, Ore, June 24, 41; m 64, Bobbie Wong; c Dennis. *Educ:* Univ Wash, BSEE, 62, MSEE, 64. *Concurrent Pos:* Prin investr radio & scintillation exp, Pioneer Venus, Galileo, Mars Observer & Mars Global Surv Missions. *Mem:* Am Geophys Union; Am Astron Soc; Int Radio Sci Union. *Res:* Microwave voltage breakdown; wave propagation through random media; remote sensing of planetary atmospheres, planetary ionospheres and the solar corona with radio propagation; scattering measurements using spacecraft radio signals; published over 70 papers. *Mailing Add:* 203 Mariners View Lane La Canada CA 91011

**WOO, SAVIO L C,** PHENYLKETONURIA, HEPATIC GENE THERAPY. *Current Pos:* PROF & DIR, INST GENE THERAPY & MOLLECULAR MED, MT SINAI SCH MED, 96- *Personal Data:* b Shanghai, China, Dec 20, 44. *Educ:* Loyola Col, BSc, 66; Univ Wash, Seattle, PhD(biochem), 71. *Prof Exp:* Postdoc fel neurol sci, Dept Psychiat, Univ BC, 71-73; res assoc, Baylor Col Med, 73-74, from instr to prof cell biol, 74-96, prof, Inst Molecular Genetics, 85-96. *Concurrent Pos:* Res assoc, Howard Hughes Med Inst, 76-77, assoc investr, 77-79, investr, 79-; mem, Ad Hoc Grant Review Comt, Cystic Fibrosis Found, 81-86, ad hoc NIH Grant Study Sect Physiol Chem, 83, Grant Study Sect Molecular Biol, 83-85, sci adv meeting, Metab Dis Res Prog, Nat Inst Diabetes, Digestive & Kidney Dis, 87, bd sci counr, Nat Inst Child Health & Human Develop, 88-; organizer & chmn, Gordon Res Conf, Colby, Sawgu Col, 85; co-organizer, Serle UCLA Symp, Keystone, Colo, 86; mem, US del human genetics, Sect US-Peoples Rep China Coop Med Health Protocol, Chinese Ministry Pub Health & US Dept Health & Human Serv, 83, US-Japan Coop Prog Recombinant DNA Res, Japanese Ministry Educ & US Dept Health & Human Serv, 87; mem, Internal Adv Comt, Baylor Col Med, 86-, Internal Expert Adv Comt, 87-, Inst Biosafety Comt Recombinant DNA Res, 78-; cell biol res fel prog, 79-, med genetics res fel prog, 85-; dir & organizer, Interdept Grad Training Prog, 87- *Mem:* Inst Med-Nat Acad Sci; NY Acad Sci; Soc Study Inborn Errors Metab; Am Soc Biol Chemists; Am Soc Human Genetics; Am Soc Cell Biol; Soc Inherited Metab Dis; Am Soc Gene Ther. *Res:* Molecular basis of genetic disorders in man, to develop analytical methods for prenatal diagnosis and carrier screening; exploration of possibility of correcting such genetic disorders by somatic gene therapy. *Mailing Add:* Mt Sinai Sch Med 1 Gustave Levy Pl New York NY 10029

**WOO, SAVIO LAU-YUEN,** ORTHOPEDIC SURGERY, MECHANICAL ENGINEERING. *Current Pos:* prof & vchmn orthop surg, 90-92, PROF MECH ENG, UNIV PITTSBURGH, 90-, ALBERT B FERGUSON JR PROF ORTHOP SURG, 93- *Personal Data:* b Shanghai, China, June 3, 42; m 69, Patricia T Cheong; c Kirstin W & Jonathan I. *Educ:* Chicago State Univ, BS, 65; Univ Wash, MS, 66, PhD, 71. *Honors & Awards:* O'Donoghue Award, 90. *Prof Exp:* Res assoc, Univ Wash, Seattle, 68-70; from asst res prof to assoc res prof, Univ Calif, San Diego, La Jolla, 70-75, from assoc prof to prof surg & bioeng, 75-90. *Concurrent Pos:* Prin investr, Vet Admin Med Ctr, San Diego, 72-90, Pittsburgh, 90-; vis prof biomech, Kobe Univ, Japan, 81-82; dir & chief exec officer, M & D Coutts Inst Joint Reconstruct & Res, 84-90; assoc ed, J Orthop Res, 83-92, Math Sci Reports, 90-, Proc Inst Mech Engrs, 90- *Mem:* Fel Am Inst Med & Biol Eng; Nat Acad Eng; Biomed Eng Soc; Am Acad Orthop Surgeons; Orthop Res Soc (pres, 86-87); Am Soc Biomech (pres, 85-86, secy, 77-80); Int Soc Fractures Repair (vpres, 87-90, pres, 90-92); hon mem Can Orthop Res Soc; Europ Orthop Res Soc; Int Soc Biomed. *Mailing Add:* Kaufman Bldg Suite 1010 Univ Pittsburgh 3471 Fifth Ave Pittsburgh PA 15213. *Fax:* 412-687-0802; *E-Mail:* ddenzo@uoi.upmc.edu

**WOO, SHIEN-BIAU,** ATOMIC PHYSICS, MOLECULAR PHYSICS. *Current Pos:* from asst prof to assoc prof, 66-82, trustee, 76-82, PROF PHYSICS, UNIV DEL, 82- *Personal Data:* b Shanghai, China, Aug 13, 37; m 63; c 2. *Educ:* Georgetown Col, BS, 57; Wash Univ, MA, 61, PhD(physics), 64. *Prof Exp:* Instr math, Univ Mo, St Louis, 61-62; res assoc physics, Joint Inst Lab Astrophys, Univ Colo, 64-66. *Concurrent Pos:* Consult, Control Data Corp & Mid-Atlantic Consortium Energy Res, 81 & various law firms, 79-81; prin investr grant, NSF, 78-81 & Asn Res Opthamol, 81-83; Lt Gov, Del, 85-89; inst fel, Kennedy Sch Govt, Harvard Univ, 89. *Mem:* Am Phys Soc; Am Asn Physics Teachers; AAAS. *Res:* Photodetachment of molecular negative ions; photodetachment theory: zero-core-contribution model; international trade imbalance; static-assets-inclusive-general-equilibriam model. *Mailing Add:* Dept Physics Univ Del Newark DE 19711. *Fax:* 302-831-1637

**WOO, TSE-CHIEN,** APPLIED MECHANICS, APPLIED MATHEMATICS. *Current Pos:* assoc prof mech eng, 68-71, prof math, 77-80, PROF MECH ENG, UNIV PITTSBURGH, 71- *Personal Data:* b Nanking, China, Mar 6, 24, US citizen; m 57; c 2. *Educ:* Ord Eng Col, China, BS, 46; Univ Wash, MS, 54; Brown Univ, PhD(appl math), 60. *Prof Exp:* Res asst interior ballistics, Ballistics Res Inst, China, 46-48; res assoc weapon eng, Navy Res Inst, 48-51; sr develop engr, Taiwan Fertilizer Co, 51-52; res asst mech eng, Univ Wash, 53-54; res asst appl math, Brown Univ, 54-60; sr researcher basic eng, Glass Res Ctr, PPG Indust, Inc, 60-62, eng assoc, 62-64, sr eng assoc, 64-67. *Concurrent Pos:* Lectr, Univ Pittsburgh, 60-67; consult, Glass Res Ctr, PPG Indust, Inc, 68-; bd dirs, Mid-West Mech Conf, 71-75, co-chmn, 13th Mid-West Mech Conf, 73. *Mem:* Soc Rheology; Math Asn Am; fel Am Soc Mech Engrs; Sigma Xi; Am Acad Mech; Am Asn Univ Prof. *Res:* Finite elasticity; theory of viscoelasticity and its applications to the thermal stress problems; viscoelastic properties of glass at elevated temperatures. *Mailing Add:* Dept Mech Eng Univ Pittsburgh 3700 Ohara St 644 Benedum Hall Pittsburgh PA 15261

**WOO, YIN-TAK,** TOXICOLOGY, CANCER RESEARCH. *Current Pos:* TOXICOLOGIST, US ENVIRON PROTECTION AGENCY, 88- *Personal Data:* b Shanghai, China, Oct 23, 47; US citizen; m 77; c 2. *Educ:* McGill Univ, Bsc, 70; Univ Toronto, MSc, 71, PhD(biochem & pharmacol), 75; Am Bd Toxicol, dipl, 81. *Honors & Awards:* Bronze Medal, US Environ Protection Agency, 87; J Seifter Mem Award, US Environ Protection Agency, 90. *Prof Exp:* Instr biochem & oncol, dept med, Tulane Univ, 75-79, guest lectr, dept pharmacol, 78-79; sr toxicologist, Sci Applns Int Corp, 79-88. *Concurrent Pos:* Mem, peer rev comt, Ambient Water Qual Criteria Doc, US Environ Protection Agency, Cincinnati, 78-79, consult, struct-activ team, Washington, DC, 82-; co-ed, J Environ Sci Health, Part C, Environ Carcinogenesis Revs, 83-; sect ed, J Am Col Toxicol, Chem Carcinogenesis, 85-; vis prof, Med Col Wis, 85; NCI chem selection working group, 88-; mem workgroup, Nat Acad Sci, 90- *Mem:* Am Asn Cancer Res; Europ Asn Cancer Res; Am Soc Pharmacol & Exp Therapeut; Am Col Toxicol; Soc Toxicol. *Res:* Environmental and industrial chemical carcinogenesis and toxicology; structure-activity relationships analysis; risk assessment; metabolism and reaction mechanisms; chemical induction of cancer; environmental and occupational carcinogenesis; cancer prevention. *Mailing Add:* 5227 Lighthorn Rd Burke VA 22015-1728

**WOOD, ALASTAIR JAMES JOHNSTON,** PHARMACOLOGY, MEDICINE. *Current Pos:* res fel clin pharmacol, Vanderbilt Univ Sch Med, 76-78, asst prof med & pharmacol, 78-82, assoc prof, 82-85, PROF MED & PHARMACOL, VANDERBILT UNIV SCH MED, 85- *Personal Data:* b Edinburgh, Scotland, UK, Oct 13, 46; US citizen; m 72, Margaret Hicks; c Alastair & Iain. *Educ:* Univ St Andrews, MBChB, 70; Royal Col Physicians, UK, MRCP, 76. *Prof Exp:* House physician, Maryfield Hosp, 71; res fel drug monitoring, Dundee Univ, 71-72, med registr, 72-75, lectr therapeut & pharmacol, 75-76. *Concurrent Pos:* Mem, Geront & Geriat Study Sect, 84-88; chmn, Geront & Geriat Rev Comt, NIH, 88-89; ed, Drug Ther Sect, New Eng J Med. *Mem:* Am Soc Clin Invest; fel Am Col Physicians; Am Fedn Clin Res; Am Soc Pharmacol & Exp Therapeut; Am Soc Clin Pharmacol & Therapeut; Brit Pharmacol Soc. *Res:* Control of factors responsible for interindividual variability in the response to drugs. *Mailing Add:* Dept Med & Pharmacol Vanderbilt Univ Sch Med Nashville TN 37232-0001. *Fax:* 615-343-2551

**WOOD, ALBERT D(OUGLAS),** GAS DYNAMICS, ENERGY CONVERSION. *Current Pos:* CONSULT, AEROSPACE & MARINE SYSTEMS, 95- *Personal Data:* b Providence, RI, June 8, 30; m 75, Sherry Scott; c Jeffrey, Maribeth, Jennifer, Scott & Michael. *Educ:* Brown Univ, ScB, 51, PhD(eng), 59; Harvard Univ, MS, 53. *Prof Exp:* Inst eng, Brown Univ, 56-58; staff scientist, Avco Syst Div, Avco Corp, 58-64, chief exp gas dynamics sect, 64-66, prin res scientist, Avco Everett Res Lab, 66-69; fluid dynamicist, Off Naval Res, Boston, 69-81, dir sci, 81, head, Mech Div, Arlington, 81-85, dep dir, Technol Progs, 85-89, dir, Appl Res & Technol, 89-93, dir, Joint Sci & Technol Progs, 93-94, chief scientist, aviation progs, off naval res, Arlington, VA, 94-95. *Res:* Theoretical and experimental aerophysics; high temperature gas dynamics; chemical kinetics; laser technology; aerospace propulsion; ship hydrodynamics. *Mailing Add:* 1130 Secretariat Ct Great Falls VA 22066

**WOOD, ALBERT E(LMER),** VERTEBRATE PALEONTOLOGY. *Current Pos:* from asst prof to prof, 46-70, chmn dept, 62-66, EMER PROF BIOL, AMHERST COL, 70- *Personal Data:* b Cape May Court House, NJ, Sept 22, 10; wid; c A(lbert) F, Roger C & Daniel N. *Educ:* Princeton Univ, BS, 30; Columbia Univ, MA, 32, PhD(geol), 35. *Hon Degrees:* MA, Amherst Col, 54. *Prof Exp:* Asst biol, Long Island Univ, 30-33, tutor, 33-34; from asst geologist to geologist, US Army Engrs, 36-41 & geologist, 46. *Concurrent Pos:* Partic, Paleont Expeds, Western US, 28, 31-32 & 35; dir, Amherst Col Exped, 48,

57, 60, 63, 65 & 68; assoc cur vert paleont, Pratt Mus, Amherst Col, 48-70; NSF sr fel, Naturhistorisches Mus, Basel, Switz, 66-67; vis prof, Dept Paleont, Univ Calif, Berkeley, 72. *Mem:* Fel AAAS; Am Soc Mammalogists; Paleont Soc; fel Geol Soc Am; Soc Study Evolution; hon mem Soc Vert Paleont (secy-treas, 58-59, vpres, 60, pres, 61). *Res:* Rodent and lagomorph classification, paleontology and evolution. *Mailing Add:* 20 E Mechanic St Cape May Court House NJ 08210

**WOOD, ALEXANDER W,** ONCOLOGY. *Current Pos:* distinguished res leader, 87-92, DIR CELL BIOL, DEPT ONCOL, ROCHE RES CTR, 92- *Personal Data:* b Newburgh, NY, Nov 2, 44; m 68, Barbara Curry; c Caroline & Emily. *Educ:* Bates Col, BS, 66; NY Univ, PhD(basic med sci), 71. *Prof Exp:* Res group chief, Hoffmann LaRoche Inc, 81-85. *Concurrent Pos:* Adj prof, NY Univ Med Sch. *Mem:* Am Soc Biochem & Molecular Biol; Am Asn Cancer Res; Am Soc Pharmacol & Exp Therapeut. *Res:* Oncogenes and tumor suppressor genes. *Mailing Add:* Dept Oncol Bldg 86 Roche Res Ctr Bldg 123 Rm 2111 Nutley NJ 07110-1150. *Fax:* 973-235-4795

**WOOD, ALLEN D(OANE),** MECHANICAL ENGINEERING. *Current Pos:* RETIRED. *Personal Data:* b Englewood, NJ, Aug 16, 35; m 57; c 4. *Educ:* Purdue Univ, BSME, 57, MSME, 61, PhD(mech eng), 63. *Prof Exp:* Res Scientist, Lockheed Res Lab, 63-92. *Mem:* Am Inst Aeronaut & Astronaut. *Res:* Instrumentation for remote measurement of automobile exhaust emissions; environmental pollution studies; electrically-powered vehicles; infrared systems; spectroscopy; lasers; shock tubes; gas dynamics. *Mailing Add:* 3212 Cowper St Palo Alto CA 94306

**WOOD, ALLEN JOHN,** ELECTRICAL ENGINEERING. *Current Pos:* RETIRED. *Personal Data:* b Milwaukee, Wis, Oct 1, 25; m 49; c 2. *Educ:* Marquette Univ, BEE, 49; Ill Inst Technol, MSEE, 51; Rensselaer Polytech Inst, PhD(elec eng), 59. *Prof Exp:* Engr, Allis Chalmers Mfg Co, Wis, 49-50; asst, Ill Inst Technol, 50-51; eng analyst, Gen Elec Co, 51-59; mem tech staff, Hughes Aircraft Co, 59-60; sr engr, Elec Utility Eng Oper, Gen Elec Co, 60-69; prin consult, chief financial officer & mem bd dir, Power Technol, Inc, 69-91. *Concurrent Pos:* Adj prof, Rensselaer Polytech Inst, 66- *Mem:* AAAS; Nat Soc Prof Engrs; Inst Elec & Electronics Engrs; Am Nuclear Soc. *Res:* Engineering analysis of complex technical or economic systems; business and system planning simulations and studies. *Mailing Add:* 901 Vrooman Ave Schenectady NY 12309

**WOOD, ANNE MICHELLE,** MICROBIAL ECOLOGY, PHYTOPLANKTON ECOLOGY. *Current Pos:* ASST PROF, UNIV ORE, 90- *Personal Data:* b Cleveland, Ohio, Aug 4, 51; m, Russell Lande. *Educ:* Univ Corpus Christi, BA, 73; Univ Ga, PhD(zool), 80. *Honors & Awards:* Provasoli Prize, 88. *Prof Exp:* Res asst, Cent Power & Light, 73; engr tech II, Tex Water Qual Bd, 73-74; teaching asst, Univ Ga, 74-78; instr, 78, res asst, 76-80; fel, Univ Chicago, 81-84, res asst prof, 84-89, res assoc prof, 89-90. *Concurrent Pos:* Consult, Cent Power & Light, 73-75 & LGL, Inc, 78; NIH trainee, 81-83; fel, Am Asn Univ Women, 83-84; lectr, Col Univ Chicago, 83-90; adj scientist, Bigelow Lab Ocean Sci, 84- *Mem:* Am Soc Limnol & Oceanog; Phycol Soc Am; Ecol Soc Am; Oceanog Soc Diatom Res; Sigma Xi. *Res:* Plankton ecology and evolution, particularly the effect of environmental parameters on production, distribution and physiology; production and fate of dissolved organic carbon, bacteria/algal interactions. *Mailing Add:* Dept Biol Univ Ore Eugene OR 97403. *Fax:* 541-346-2364; *E-Mail:* miche@darkwing.uoregon.edu

**WOOD, BETTY J,** molecular biology, for more information see previous edition

**WOOD, BOBBY EUGENE,** CONTAMINATION-OPTICAL EFFECTS, THERMOPHYSICAL PROPERTIES OF CRYOGENIC SURFACES. *Current Pos:* ENGR AEROSPACE, SVERDRUP TECH, 80- *Personal Data:* b Martinsville, Va, May 9, 39; m 65, Anna Howard; c Kenneth W & Barry E. *Educ:* Berea Col, BA, 61; Vanderbilt Univ, MA, 64. *Prof Exp:* Engr aerospace, Aro, Inc, 64-80. *Mem:* Optical Soc Am; Am Inst Aeronaut & Astronaut; Inst Environ Sci; Int Soc Optical Eng. *Res:* Optical properties of materials, especially radiative properties of condensed gases on cryogenically cooled optical components; contamination and contaminant optical effects; contaminant monitoring device testing; satellite component testing and flight data analysis. *Mailing Add:* Sverdrop Tech MS 6400 Arnold AFB TN 37389-6400. *Fax:* 615-454-6348; *E-Mail:* wood@hap.arnold.af.mil

**WOOD, BRUCE,** MATHEMATICS, MECHANICAL ENGINEERING. *Current Pos:* asst prof, 67-71, ASSOC PROF MATH, UNIV ARIZ, 71- *Personal Data:* b Kintnersville, Pa, Apr 9, 38; m 63; c 2. *Educ:* Pa State Univ, BS, 60; Univ Wyo, MS, 64; Lehigh Univ, PhD(math), 67. *Prof Exp:* Asst air pollution control engr, Bethlehem Steel Corp, 60-62; asst math, Univ Wyo, 63-64 & Lehigh Univ, 64-67. *Mem:* Am Math Soc. *Res:* Linear approximation theory; summability theory; theory of complex variables; linear positive operators. *Mailing Add:* Dept Math Univ Ariz Tucson AZ 85721

**WOOD, BRUCE WADE,** TREE NUT PHYSIOLOGY, BREEDING & HORTICULTURE. *Current Pos:* Horticulturist, Sci Educ, 79-91, LAB DIR, AGR RES SERV, USDA, 91- *Personal Data:* b Morganfield, Ky, Oct 22, 51; m 75, Kathryn Thomas; c 5. *Educ:* Univ Ky, BS, 73, MS, 75; Mich State Univ, PhD(forestry), 79. *Mem:* Am Soc Hort Sci; Int Soc Hort Sci. *Res:* Maximizing nut production efficiency of nut trees by regulating growth. *Mailing Add:* USDA Southeastern Fruit & Tree Nut Res Lab Byron GA 31008. *Fax:* 912-956-2929

**WOOD, BYARD DEAN,** mechanical engineering, heat transfer & solar energy, for more information see previous edition

**WOOD, CALVIN DALE,** NUCLEAR PHYSICS, SHOCK HYDRODYNAMICS. *Current Pos:* RETIRED. *Personal Data:* b Salt Lake City, Utah, July 13, 33; m 55, Dixie Bates; c 5. *Educ:* Univ Calif, Berkeley, AB, 57, PhD(high energy physics), 61. *Prof Exp:* Res asst high energy physics, Lawrence Radiation Lab, Univ Calif, Berkeley, 58-61, physicist, 61-62; asst prof physics, Univ Utah, 62-64; sr design physicist, Lawrence Livermore Lab, 64-93. *Concurrent Pos:* Expert witness, accident reconstruction; Crown Zellerbach Scholar, 57; UN nuclear prog inspector, Iraq, 91. *Mem:* Am Phys Soc; Ital Phys Soc; Sigma Xi. *Res:* Shock hydrodynamics; neutron cross sections; high speed digital computers; nuclear processes; chemical high explosives; material properties under high strain rates; high speed optics; equations of state. *Mailing Add:* Lawrence Livermore Lab PO Box 808 L-170 Livermore CA 94551

**WOOD, CARL EUGENE,** MARINE ECOLOGY, INVERTEBRATE ZOOLOGY. *Current Pos:* ASSOC PROF INVERT & MARINE BIOL, TEX A&I UNIV, 69- *Personal Data:* b Alice, Tex, Aug 28, 40; m 73; c 3. *Educ:* Tex A&M Univ, BS, 62, MS, 65; PhD(fisheries), 69. *Prof Exp:* Fishery technician, Nat Marine Fisheries Serv, 63-64; res asst limnol, Tex A&M Univ, 65-67; limnologist, Tenn Valley Authority, 67-69. *Concurrent Pos:* Maricult consult, Flato Corp, 73-74. *Mem:* Am Soc Limnol & Oceanog; Fedn Estuarine Res. *Res:* Marine invertebrate ecology; shrimp of the suborder Natantia systematics; primary productivity of estuaries. *Mailing Add:* Dept Biol Box 158 Tex A&I Univ 700 University Blvd Kingsville TX 78363-8203

**WOOD, CARLOS C,** AERONAUTICAL ENGINEERING. *Current Pos:* RETIRED. *Personal Data:* b Turloc, Calif, June 19, 13. *Educ:* Col Pac, BA, 33; Calif Inst Technol, MSME, 34, MSAE, 35. *Prof Exp:* Mem eng staff, Douglas Aircraft Corp, 37-42, chief preliminary design, Douglas Aircraft Eng, Santa Monica, 42-55, chief engr, Long Beach Div, 55-59, dir advan eng planning, 59-60; eng mgr & vpres, Sikorsky Aircraft Div, United Aircraft Corp, 60-70, consult, 70-75. *Concurrent Pos:* Dir & vpres, Claude C Wood & Co, Lodi, Calif, 46-81; mem sci adv bd, USAF; mem aerospace eng bd, Nat Acad Eng. *Mem:* Emer mem Nat Acad Eng; emer fel Am Inst Aeronaut & Astronaut. *Mailing Add:* 145 Bonniebrook Dr Napa CA 94558

**WOOD, CAROL SAUNDERS,** MATHEMATICAL LOGIC. *Current Pos:* vis instr math, 70-71, asst prof, 73-80, assoc prof, 80-86, PROF, WESLEYAN UNIV, 86-, CHAIR, 90- *Personal Data:* b Pennington Gap, Va, Feb 9, 45. *Educ:* Randolph-Macon Woman's Col, AB, 66; Yale Univ, PhD(math), 71. *Prof Exp:* Gast dozent math, Univ Erlangen-Nurnberg, WGer, 71-72; lectr, Yale Univ, 72-73; res assoc prof, Dept Math, Rutgers Univ, New Brunswick, NJ, 85-86. *Concurrent Pos:* Vis, Inst Advan Study, Princeton, 82, 85-86; vis mem, MSRI, Berkeley, 89-90. *Mem:* Am Math Soc; Math Asn Am; Asn Symbolic Logic; Asn Women Math (pres, 91-93). *Res:* Application of model theory to algebra. *Mailing Add:* Dept Math Wesleyan Univ Middletown CT 06459-0128

**WOOD, CARROLL E, JR,** BOTANY. *Current Pos:* assoc cur, 54-70, MEM, FAC ARTS & SCI, HARVARD UNIV, 63-, CUR, ARNOLD ARBORETUM, 70-, PROF BIOL, 72- *Personal Data:* b Roanoke, Va, Jan 13, 21. *Educ:* Roanoke Col, BS, 41; Univ Pa, MS, 43; Harvard Univ, AM, 47, PhD(biol), 49. *Prof Exp:* Instr biol, Harvard Univ, 49-51; from asst prof to assoc prof bot, Univ NC, 51-54. *Concurrent Pos:* Lectr biol, Harvard Univ, 64-72. *Mem:* Am Soc Plant Taxon; Bot Soc Am; Int Asn Plant Taxon. *Res:* Flora of southeastern United States; biosystematics and taxonomy of flowering plants. *Mailing Add:* 64 W Rutland Sq Boston MA 02118

**WOOD, CHARLES,** EXPERIMENTAL SOLID STATE PHYSICS. *Current Pos:* RETIRED. *Personal Data:* b London, Eng, Nov 6, 24; US citizen; m 50; c 3. *Educ:* Univ London, BSc, 51, MSc, 55, PhD(physics), 62. *Prof Exp:* Physicist, Gen Elec Res Labs, Eng, 51-53 & Electronic Tubes Ltd, 53-54; dep group leader, Caswell Res Lab, Plessey Co, 54-56; group supvr, Res Div, Philco Corp, Pa, 56-60; sect head solid state prod group, Kearfott Div, Gen Precision Instruments, NJ, 60-61; dir thermoelec, Intermetallic Prod, Inc, 61-63; mgr, Mat Res Dept, Xerox Corp Res Labs, NY, 63-67; head, Dept Physics, Northern Ill Univ, 67-70, prof, 67-90. *Mem:* Am Phys Soc; Sigma Xi. *Res:* Semiconductors; photoconductors; thin films; crystal growth; Hall-effect devices; thermoelectricity; electrophotography. *Mailing Add:* 3795 Berwick Dr La Canada Flintridge CA 91011

**WOOD, CHARLES D,** automotive engineering, for more information see previous edition

**WOOD, CHARLES DONALD,** pharmacology, for more information see previous edition

**WOOD, CHARLES EVANS,** FETAL PHYSIOLOGY & ENDOCRINOLOGY. *Current Pos:* asst prof, 83-88, assoc prof, 88-93, PROF PHYSIOL, UNIV FLA, 93- *Personal Data:* b San Francisco, Calif, May 14, 52; m 79, Maureen Keller; c Margaret, Charles & Sarah. *Educ:* Univ Calif, Berkeley, AB, 74, San Francisco, PhD(endocrinol), 80. *Prof Exp:* Fel, Cardiovasc Res Inst, Univ Calif, San Francisco, 80-83. *Mem:* Am Physiol Soc; Endocrine Soc. *Res:* Cortisol negative feedback control of fetal and adult adrenocorticotrophic hormone secretion; cardiovascular mechanoreceptor and chemoreceptor control of adrencorticotrophic hormone, cortisol, renin and vasopressin secretion. *Mailing Add:* Dept Physiol Univ Fla PO Box 100274 JHM C Gainesville FL 32610-0274. *Fax:* 904-392-8340; *E-Mail:* wood@nerum.nerdc.ufl.edu

**WOOD, CHRISTOPHER MICHAEL,** COMPARATIVE PHYSIOLOGY. *Current Pos:* from asst prof to assoc prof, 76-85, PROF BIOL, MCMASTER UNIV, 85- *Personal Data:* b Manchester, Eng, Feb 21, 47; Brit & Can citizen; m 71; c 2. *Educ:* Univ BC, BSc, 68, MSc, 71; Univ E Anglia, PhD(comp physiol), 74. *Prof Exp:* Fel, Univ Calgary, 74-76. *Mem:* Soc Exp Biol; Am Soc Zool; Can Soc Zool; AAAS. *Res:* Circulation, respiration, gas exchange, acid base regulation, osmoregulation and homeostasis in teleost fish and decapod crustaceans; environmental acid and heavy metal toxicology of fishes. *Mailing Add:* Dept Biol 1280 Main St West McMaster Univ Hamilton ON L8S 4K1 Can

**WOOD, CORINNE SHEAR,** physical anthropology, medical anthropology, for more information see previous edition

**WOOD, CRAIG ADAMS,** COMPUTER SCIENCE, MATHEMATICS. *Current Pos:* PROF COMPUT SCI & CHMN DEPT, STEPHEN F AUSTIN STATE UNIV, 79- *Personal Data:* b Rochester, NY, Jan 31, 41; m 64; c 2. *Educ:* Col Wooster, BA, 62; Fla State Univ, MS, 63, PhD(math), 67. *Prof Exp:* Instr math, Fla State Univ, 67-68; from asst prof to assoc prof, Okla State Univ, 68-73, NASA res grant, 69-70; assoc prof math sci & head div, Univ Houston, Victoria Campus, 73-76, assoc prof comput sci & math & dir, Comput Ctr, 77-78, prof, 78-79. *Concurrent Pos:* Am Coun Educ fel, Acad Admin, 76-77. *Mem:* Asn Comput Mach. *Res:* Commutative ring theory in algebra; algebraic equations in numerical analysis; computer graphics and applications. *Mailing Add:* Comput Sci Dept Stephen F Austin State Univ PO Box 13063 Nacogdoches TX 75962-3063

**WOOD, DARWIN LEWIS,** PHYSICS, CHEMISTRY. *Current Pos:* RETIRED. *Personal Data:* b East Orange, NJ, July 21, 21; m 45; c 6. *Educ:* Princeton Univ, AB, 42; Ohio State Univ, PhD(physics, physiol), 50. *Prof Exp:* Physicist, Rohm & Haas Co, 42-46; fel, Univ Mich, 50-52, asst prof physics, 53-56; mem tech staff, Chem Dept, Bell Labs, Inc, 56-88. *Mem:* Fel Optical Soc Am. *Res:* Polymers; proteins; optics; spectroscopy; crystal spectra; ions in crystals. *Mailing Add:* 46 Fox Run Murray Hill NJ 07974

**WOOD, DAVID,** CHROMATOGRAPHY, DOCUMENTATION. *Current Pos:* RETIRED. *Personal Data:* b Woodlawn, Ill, Oct 10, 28; m 58, Gloria Caskey; c Claire, Anita (Gerace) & Bruce David. *Educ:* Univ Ill, BS, 50; Univ Wis, PhD(chem), 56. *Prof Exp:* Chemist, Velsicol Chem Corp, 50-52, Spencer Kellogg & Sons, Inc, 56-59; asst chem, Univ Wis, 52-56; assoc res chemist, Sterling-Winthrop Res Inst, 59-75, group leader, 75-88, sect head, 88-90, asst res dir analytical sci, Sterling Res Group, 90-93. *Mem:* Am Chem Soc; Sigma Xi. *Res:* Synthetic organic chemistry; synthesis of pharmaceuticals. *Mailing Add:* 22 Bellwood Way Castleton on Hudson NY 12033-9558

**WOOD, DAVID ALVRA,** PATHOLOGY. *Current Pos:* EMER PROF PATH, SCH MED & EMER DIR, CANCER RES INST, UNIV CALIF, SAN FRANCISCO, 72- *Personal Data:* b Flora Vista, NMex, Dec 21, 04; m 37; c 5. *Educ:* Stanford Univ, AB, 26, MD, 30. *Honors & Awards:* Am Cancer Soc Award, 50; Col Am Pathologists Award, 58; Lucy Wortham James Award, James Ewing Soc, 70. *Concurrent Pos:* Historian, Am Asn Cancer Educ, 81-, historian, Am Cancer Soc, Calif div, 86-; consult, 77. *Mem:* Fedn Am Socs Exp Biol; Am Cancer Soc (pres, 56-57); Am Asn Cancer Res; Col Am Pathologists (pres, 52-55); Asn Am Cancer Insts (pres, 70-72); Sigma Xi. *Res:* Neoplastic diseases; dual pulmonary circulation; exfoliative cytology; evaluation of cancer education in medical and dental schools; oral contraceptives and tumors of the breast, epidemiological and morphological correlations. *Mailing Add:* 54 Commonwealth Ave San Francisco CA 94118-2602

**WOOD, DAVID BELDEN,** TECHNICAL MANAGEMENT, ASTRONOMY. *Current Pos:* mem tech staff, Theater C 3 Systs, 80-92, LEAD ENGR, INT COMMAND, CONTROL & COMMUN, MITRE CORP, 92- *Personal Data:* b Glendale, Calif, Nov 15, 35; m 83, Monique Maisonpierre; c Glenn, Steven & Arnold. *Educ:* Univ Calif, Berkeley, AB, 57, PhD(astron), 63. *Prof Exp:* Mem tech staff astron, Bellcomm, Inc, 67-69, supvr astrophys, 69-71; mem adv plans staff, Goddard Space Flight Ctr, NASA, 71-76, opers res analyst, Appln Systs Analysis Off, 76-80. *Mem:* AAAS; Sigma Xi. *Res:* Eclipsing binary stars; extragalactic research; photoelectric photometry; space astronomy; operations research; computer modeling; computer sciences. *Mailing Add:* 709 Larchwood Dr Brea CA 92821

**WOOD, DAVID COLLIER,** PROTEIN PURIFICATION, RECOMBINANT PROTEIN TECHNOLOGY. *Current Pos:* STAFF SCIENTIST, MONSANTO CORP RES, MONSANTO CO, ST LOUIS, MO, 85- *Personal Data:* b Jacksonville, Fla, Sept 7, 54; m 88, Linda Lahman; c Andrei & Julia. *Educ:* Duke Univ, BS, 76; Univ NC, PhD(protein chem), 81. *Prof Exp:* Postdoctoral fel, Dept Microbiol, Univ Ala, Birmingham, 81-84. *Mem:* Am Chem Soc; Protein Soc. *Res:* Protein biochemistry; purification and characterization of proteins from heterologous expression systems; structure-function analysis via mutagenesis and active-site modification. *Mailing Add:* Monsanto Co AA4E 700 Chesterfield Pkwy N St Louis MO 63198-0001. *Fax:* 314-537-7223; *E-Mail:* dcwood@ccmail.monsanto.com

**WOOD, DAVID DUDLEY,** LYMPHOKINES, IMMUNOREGULATION. *Current Pos:* US REP CARDIOVAS RES, 92- *Personal Data:* b Wilmington, Del, May 3, 43; m 64; c 2. *Educ:* Harvard Univ, BA, 65; Rockefeller Univ, PhD(cell biol), 70. *Prof Exp:* Sr res biologist, Merck Sharp & Dohme Res Labs, 72-75, res fel, 75-81, sr res fel, 81-82, assoc dir, 82-83; dir, Immunol,

Ayerst Labs Res Inc, 83-87; dir, Inst Arthritis & Autoimmunity, Miles Inc, 87-92. *Mem:* Am Asn Immunologists; NY Acad Sci; Int Soc Immunopharmacol. *Res:* Interleukin-1, immunoregulation, cartilage and bone metabolism. *Mailing Add:* Bayer Inc 400 Morgan Lane West Haven CT 06516-4134. *Fax:* 203-931-5353

**WOOD, DAVID LEE,** FOREST ENTOMOLOGY. *Current Pos:* from lectr entom & asst entomologist to prof entom & entomologist, Univ Calif, 60-94, assoc dean, Grad Div, 83-85, chmn, Dept Entom Sci, 85-90, EMER PROF ENTOM & PROF, GRAD SCH, UNIV CALIF, 94- *Personal Data:* b St Louis, Mo, Jan 8, 31; m 60, Caroline Westervelt; c Catherine & Jonathan. *Educ:* State Univ NY Col Envrion Sci & Forestry, Syracuse Univ, BS, 52; Univ Calif, Berkeley, PhD(entom), 60. *Honors & Awards:* Founders Award Mem Lectr, Entom Soc Am, 86. *Prof Exp:* Asst entomologist, Boyce Thompson Inst Plant Res, 59-60. *Mem:* AAAS; Sigma Xi; Entom Soc Am; Soc Am Foresters; fel Entom Soc Can. *Res:* Forest insect behavior and pest management; insect-host relationships, especially host selection behavior, insect pheromones and host resistance with special emphasis on bark beetles; insert, fungus, tree interactions. *Mailing Add:* Div Insect Biol Univ Calif 201 Wellman Hall Berkeley CA 94720. *Fax:* 510-642-7428; *E-Mail:* bigwood@nature.berkeley.edu

**WOOD, DAVID OLIVER,** BACTERIAL GENETICS. *Current Pos:* PROF MICROBIOL, UNIV SALA, 79- *Personal Data:* b Rome, Ga. *Educ:* Berry Col, BA, 72; Med Col Ga, MS, 75, PhD(microbiol), 78. *Prof Exp:* Res fel microbiol, Med Col, Va Commonwealth Univ, 77-79. *Mem:* Am Soc Microbiol; Am Soc Rickettsiology & Rickettsial Dis. *Res:* Molecular basis of bacterial pathogenicity; genetic analysis of Rickettsia prowazekii. *Mailing Add:* Dept Microbiol & Immunol Col Med Univ SAla 307 University Blvd Mobile AL 36688

**WOOD, DAVID ROY,** SPECTROSCOPY. *Current Pos:* asst prof, 67-74, ASSOC PROF PHYSICS, WRIGHT STATE UNIV, 74- *Personal Data:* b Mar 3, 35; US citizen; m 67. *Educ:* Friends Univ, AB, 56; Univ Mich, MS, 58; Purdue Univ, PhD(physics), 67. *Prof Exp:* Instr physics, Friends Univ, 58-59; instr math & physics, Scattergood Sch, 59-61; res assoc physics, Purdue Univ, 67. *Mem:* Optical Soc Am. *Res:* Experimental atomic spectroscopy; analysis of the energy level structure of the lead atom and ion; Fabry-Perut interferometry and Zeeman effect analysis; spectral line profiles in the vacuum ultraviolet; spectra of multiply-ionized atoms. *Mailing Add:* 1813 Shady Lane Dayton OH 45432

**WOOD, DAVID S(HOTWELL),** MATERIALS SCIENCE. *Current Pos:* RETIRED. *Personal Data:* b Akron, Ohio, May 21, 20; m 45, Constance L Simonsess; c Alison J. *Educ:* Calif Inst Technol, BS, 41, MS, 46, PhD(mech eng), 49. *Honors & Awards:* Richard L Templin Award, Am Soc Testing & Mat, 50. *Prof Exp:* Asst, Calif Inst Technol, 42-44; staff engr, Univ Calif, 44-46; asst mach design, Calif Inst Technol, 46-49, lectr, 49-50, from asst prof to assoc prof mech eng, 50-61, prof mat sci, 61-88, assoc dean students, 68-74. *Mem:* AAAS; Am Soc Mech Engrs; Am Soc Metals; Am Inst Mining, Metall & Petrol Engrs; Sigma Xi. *Res:* Plastic strain waves in metals; mechanical properties of metals subjected to dynamic loading; dislocations in crystals. *Mailing Add:* 590 Elm Ave Sierra Madre CA 91024-1244

**WOOD, DAVID WELLS,** MATERIALS SCIENCE, PHYSICAL CHEMISTRY. *Current Pos:* MGR MAT & PROCESSES, MCDONNELL DOUGLAS CORP, 87- *Personal Data:* b Amesville, Ohio, May 22, 38; m 70; c Amanda. *Educ:* Univ Pac, BS, 60, MS, 61; Univ Utah, PhD(ceramic eng), 65. *Prof Exp:* Petrol Res Fund grant calorimetry, Univ Pac, 60-61; Army res grant high pressure chem, 63-65; res chemist, E I du Pont de Nemours & Co, Inc, 65-68; proj leader composites, Burlington Industs, 68-70, sr res chemist, Corp Res & Develop, 70-77, mem tech staff, Indust Div, 77-78, mgr qual control, Indust Div, 78-79; mgr new prod, Hexcel Corp, Dublin, Calif, 79-85, res assoc, 85-87. *Mem:* AAAS; Am Chem Soc; Am Ceramic Soc; NAm Thermal Anal Soc; Soc Advan Mat & Process Eng. *Res:* Solid state chemistry and physics relating to polymers in the form of plastics and fibers or in conjunction with each other in composites; electrochemistry. *Mailing Add:* McDonnell Douglas Helicopter Corp 5000 E McDonnell Rd MS 530/B336 Mesa AZ 85215-9797

**WOOD, DERICK,** COMPUTER SCIENCE. *Current Pos:* PROF COMPUT SCI, UNIV WATERLOO, 82- *Personal Data:* b Bolton, Eng, July 19, 40. *Educ:* Univ Leeds, BS, 63, dipl electronic comput, 64, PhD(math), 68. *Prof Exp:* Comput asst, Univ Leeds, 64-68; asst res scientist, Courant Inst Math Sci, NY Univ, 68-70; from asst prof to assoc prof comput sci, McMaster Univ, 70-78, prof, 78-82. *Mem:* Asn Comput Mach; Am Math Soc; Can Info Processing Soc; Inst Elec & Electronics Engrs; Europ Asn Comput Sci. *Res:* Formal language theory; data structure theory; analysis of algorithms; computational geometry; very large scale integration theory. *Mailing Add:* Dept Comput Sci Clearwater Bay Kowloon Hong Kong People's Republic of China

**WOOD, DON JAMES,** FLUID MECHANICS. *Current Pos:* PROF CIVIL ENG, UNIV KY, 66- *Personal Data:* b Northeast, Pa, July 28, 36; m 59; c 2. *Educ:* Carnegie Inst Technol, BS, 58, MS, 59, PhD, 61. *Honors & Awards:* Huber Res Prize, Am Soc Civil Engrs, 75; Western Elec Fund, Am Soc Eng Educ, 76. *Prof Exp:* Asst prof eng mech, Clemson Univ, 61-62; asst prof civil eng, Duke Univ, 62-66. *Concurrent Pos:* Res engr & consult, NASA, 63-66. *Mem:* Am Soc Civil Engrs; Am Soc Mech Engrs; Soc Eng Sci; Am Inst Aeronaut & Astronaut; Am Soc Eng Educ. *Res:* Fluid transients; water hammer problems; water distribution systems; hydrotransport. *Mailing Add:* Dept Civil Eng Univ Ky Lexington KY 40506

**WOOD, DONALD EUGENE,** nuclear physics, for more information see previous edition

**WOOD, DONALD ROY,** PLANT BREEDING, GENETICS. *Current Pos:* RETIRED. *Personal Data:* b Keats, Kans, Apr 17, 21; m 43; c 2. *Educ:* Kans State Col, BS, 43; Colo State Univ, MS, 49; Univ Wis, PhD, 56. *Prof Exp:* From asst prof agron & asst agronomist to prof agron & agronomist, Colo State Univ, 47-86. *Concurrent Pos:* Asst, Univ Wis, 50-51; res assoc, Univ Calif, 60-61; res assoc, Inst Nutrit Cent Am, Panama, 74. *Mem:* Fel AAAS; Genetics Soc Am; Genetics Soc Can; Am Soc Agron; Am Phytopath Soc. *Res:* Dry field bean breeding; dry bean disease resistance; breeding for improved nutritional value. *Mailing Add:* 1920 Sheeley Dr Ft Collins CO 80526

**WOOD, EARL HOWARD,** PHYSIOLOGY, AEROSPACE MEDICINE. *Current Pos:* assoc prof physiol, 42-60, prof, 42-82, EMER PROF PHYSIOL & MED, MAYO GRAD SCH MED, UNIV MINN, 82-, CONSULT, MAYO CLIN, 42- *Personal Data:* b Mankato, Minn, Jan 1, 12; m 36, Ada Peterson; c Phoebe W (Busch), Mark, Guy & Earl A. *Educ:* Macalester Col, BA, 34; Univ Minn, BS, 36, MS, 39, PhD(physiol), 40; MD, 41. *Hon Degrees:* DSc, Macalester Col, 50; DMed, Univ Bern, 82. *Honors & Awards:* Mayo Distinguished Lectr Med Sci, 78; Alza lectr, Biomed Eng Soc, 78; John Phillips Mem Award, Am Col Physicians, 83; Res Award, Aerospace Med Asn, 83; Carl Wiggers Award & Daggo Award; Am Physiol Soc; Res Achievement & Gold Heart Awards, Am Heart Asn; Stewart Mem Lectr, Royal Aeronaut Soc, London, 88; C Ludwig Ehremuinz Award, Ger, 89. *Prof Exp:* Instr physiol, Univ Minn, 39-40; Nat Res Coun fel pharmacol, Univ Pa, 41-42; instr pharmacol, Harvard Med Sch, 42. *Concurrent Pos:* Sci consult to Surgeon Gen, Aeromed Ctr, USAF, Heidelberg, 46; career investr, Am Heart Asn, 61-; vis scientist, Univ Bern, 65-66 & Univ Col, Univ London, 72-73, Univ Kiel, 73 & 75 & McGill Univ, 86; distinguished lectr, Am Col Chest Physicians, 74; Am Physiol Soc travel award, Int Physiol Cong, Oxford Univ; mem, first med teaching deleg China, Am Col Physicians; Humboldt sr scientist award, 83; on-site consult, Defense & Civil Inst Environ Med, 92-94. *Mem:* AAAS; Am Physiol Soc (pres, 80-81); Soc Exp Biol & Med; Am Heart Asn; hon fel Am Col Cardiol; Am Soc Clin Invest; Royal Neth Acad Arts & Sci; Biomed Eng Soc (pres elect); Cent Soc Clin Invest; Aerospace Med Asn. *Res:* Electrolyte metabolism of cardiac and voluntary muscle; glucose reabsorption in amphibian kidney; effect of cardiac glycoside on electrolyte metabolism; cardiopulmonary effects of gravitational and inertial forces, aerospace medicine; computer based quantitative imaging techniques; cardiovascular and respiratory physiology of man; instrumental and computer based techniques and procedures for detection and quantitation of acquired and congenital cardiovascular diseases and compensatory reactions to various types of circulatory stress. *Mailing Add:* Mayo Rochester MN 55901. *Fax:* 507-284-5036; *E-Mail:* wood.earl@mayo.edu

**WOOD, EDWARD C(HALMERS),** engineering, for more information see previous edition

**WOOD, ERIC F,** ENVIRONMENTAL DATA ANALYSIS, GROUNDWATER ANALYSIS. *Current Pos:* from asst prof to assoc prof, 76-86, PROF WATER RESOURCES, PRINCETON UNIV, 86- *Personal Data:* b Vancouver, BC; c 2. *Educ:* Univ BC, BASc Hons, 70; Mass Inst Technol, SM, 72, ScD, 74. *Honors & Awards:* Robert E Horton Award, Am Geophys Union, 77. *Prof Exp:* Res scholar, Int Inst Appl Systs Analysis, Austria, 74-76. *Concurrent Pos:* Assoc ed, Water Resources Res, 77-82, Rev Geophys, J Forecasting & Appl Math & Computation; mem numerous comts, Am Geophys Union, NASA, Am Meteorol Asn, Nat Acad Sci, NSF & Environ Protection Agency, 77-; dir, Water Resources Prog, Princeton Univ, 80-, actg chmn, Dept Civil Eng, 86-87; vis sr scientist, Inst Hydrol, UK, 83-84; vis prof, Politecnico de Milano, Italy, 88-89. *Mem:* Fel Am Geophys Union; Am Meteorol Soc; Inst Opers Res & Mgt Sci. *Res:* Hydroclimatology with emphasis on land-atmospheric interactions and determining the hydrologic impacts from climate change. *Mailing Add:* Dept Civil Eng Princeton Univ Princeton NJ 08544-1099

**WOOD, EUNICE MARJORIE,** cell biology, electron microscopy, for more information see previous edition

**WOOD, F(REDERICK) B(ERNARD),** ELECTRICAL ENGINEERING. *Current Pos:* RETIRED. *Personal Data:* b Sacramento, Calif, Dec 17, 17; wid; c Fred B & Peter M. *Educ:* Univ Calif, BS, 41, MS, 48, PhD(elec eng), 53. *Prof Exp:* Asst elec eng, Univ Calif, 40-41, asst resonator coupling, 49-52; mem staff radar, Mass Inst Technol, 41-46; staff engr, Res & Develop Lab, IBM Corp, 52-58, staff eng, Advan Systs Develop Div Lab, 59-61, proj engr 61-64, staff engr, 65-70, adv engr, 70-72, adv eng, Systs Develop Div, 72-75, adv engr, Systs Commun Div, 75-76, adv engr, Gen Prod Div, 76-80. *Concurrent Pos:* Mem bd dirs, Comput Social Impact Res Inst, 78-, Earth Regeneration Soc, 83-; adj prof, Union Inst Cincinnati, Ohio, 96- *Mem:* AAAS; Inst Elec & Electronics Engrs; Soc Social Responsibilities Sci; Soc Gen Systs Res; NY Acad Sci; Sigma Xi. *Res:* Development of computer-communication systems; simulation; computer programming; information theory; data communication; cybernetics; philosophy of science. *Mailing Add:* 2346 Lansford Ave San Jose CA 95125. *Fax:* 408-269-7045; *E-Mail:* csiri@ige.apc.org

**WOOD, FERGUS JAMES,** TIDAL DYNAMICS, COASTAL FLOODING. *Current Pos:* RETIRED. *Personal Data:* b London, Ont, May 13, 17; nat US; m 46; c 2. *Educ:* Univ Calif, AB, 38. *Prof Exp:* Asst astron, Univ Mich, 40-42; instr physics & astron, Pasadena City Col, 46-48 & John Muir Col, 48-49; asst prof physics, Univ Md, 49-50; assoc physicist, Appl Physics Lab, Johns Hopkins Univ, 50-55; sci ed, Encycl Americana, 55-60; aeronaut & space res scientist & sci asst to dir, Off Space Flight Progs, NASA, 60-61; prog dir foreign sci info, NSF, 61-62; phys scientist, Off Dir, US Coast & Geod Surv, 62-70; phys scientist, Off Dir, Nat Ocean Surv, Nat Oceanic & Atmospheric Admin, 70-73, res assoc, Off Dir, Nat Ocean Surv, Rockville, Md, 73-77; geophys consult tidal dynamics, 78. *Res:* Environmental geoscience; wind-profile studies over navy ships at sea; perigean and proxigean spring tide analysis and potential for coastal flooding; gravitational-geophysical correlations; science education, history and film documentation. *Mailing Add:* 3103 Casa Bonita Dr Bonita CA 91902

**WOOD, FRANCIS C, JR,** DIABETES, NUTRITION. *Current Pos:* from instr to assoc prof, Sch Med, Univ Wash, 61-92, from asst prog dir to prog dir, Clin Res Ctr, 62-70, assoc dean, 70-76, EMER ASSOC PROF MED, SCH MED, UNIV WASH, 92- *Personal Data:* b Philadelphia, Pa, Oct 20, 28; m 58, 91, Thelma K Philpott; c 2. *Educ:* Princeton Univ, AB, 50; Harvard Med Sch, MD, 54; Am Bd Internal Med, dipl, 63 & 74. *Prof Exp:* Intern, King Co Hosp, Seattle, Wash, 54-55; resident, Vet Admin Hosp, 55-56 & Univ Wash Hosp, 60-61. *Concurrent Pos:* Res fel, Harvard Med Sch & Peter Bent Brigham Hosp, 58-60; chief staff, Seattle Vet Admin Hosp, 70-76; dir physician educ, Providence Med Ctr, Seattle, 76-87. *Mem:* Endocrine Soc; Am Diabetes Asn; fel Am Col Physicians. *Mailing Add:* Dept Med Univ Wash Box 356426 Seattle WA 98195-6426. *Fax:* 206-695-3781

**WOOD, FRANK BRADSHAW,** astronomy, for more information see previous edition

**WOOD, GALEN THEODORE,** NUCLEAR PHYSICS. *Current Pos:* ASSOC PROF PHYSICS, CLEVELAND STATE UNIV, 69- *Personal Data:* b Philadelphia, Pa, Feb 7, 29; m 55; c 3. *Educ:* Wash Univ, BS, 51, PhD(physics), 56. *Prof Exp:* Physicist, Argonne Cancer Res Hosp, Univ Chicago, 55-57; NSF res fel nuclear spectros, Inst Theoret Physics, Univ Copenhagen, 57-59; asst prof physics & res nuclear spectros, Univ Pa, 59-65, NSF res grant radioactive nuclei, 63-65; assoc physicist, Argonne Nat Lab, 65-69. *Mem:* Am Phys Soc. *Res:* Nuclear spectroscopy of radiations from radioactive decay and nuclear reactions, decay scheme, gamma-gamma directional and polarization correlations, magnetic moments, lifetimes and nuclear magnetic hyperfine fields; electron accelerator developments; nuclear spectroscopy. *Mailing Add:* Dept Physics Cleveland State Univ 1983 W 24th St Cleveland OH 44115

**WOOD, GARNETT ELMER,** BIOCHEMISTRY. *Current Pos:* RES CHEMIST, DIV CHEM & PHYSICS, FOOD & DRUG ADMIN, 65- *Personal Data:* b Gloucester, Va, Feb 14, 29; m 53; c 2. *Educ:* Va State Col, BS, 51, MS, 56; Georgetown Univ, PhD(chem), 66. *Prof Exp:* Res microbiologist, Div Vet Med, Walter Reed Army Med Ctr, 56-64. *Concurrent Pos:* Lectr chem, Univ DC, 73- *Mem:* AAAS; NY Acad Sci; Sigma Xi; Am Chem Soc; Am Oil Chemists Soc. *Res:* Chemistry of toxic and deleterious compounds that may arise in certain foods as a result of handling, storage and/or processing. *Mailing Add:* 1717 Verbena St NW Washington DC 20012-1048

**WOOD, GARY WARREN,** IMMUNOLOGY. *Current Pos:* Fel immunol, 71-73, instr path, 73-74, asst prof, 74-79, ASSOC PROF PATH, UNIV KANS MED CTR, 79-, DIR, DIAG IMMUNOL LAB, 73- *Personal Data:* b Rochester, NY, Sept 9, 41. *Educ:* Kalamazoo Col, BA, 63; Univ Mich, MS, 65; State Univ NY Buffalo, PhD(microbiol), 71. *Mem:* Am Asn Immunologists; Sigma Xi; Reticuloendothelial Soc. *Res:* Immunobiology of the maternal/fetal interrelationship; in situ immune response to tumors. *Mailing Add:* Dept Path Univ Kans Med Ctr 39th St & Rainbow Blvd Kansas City KS 66160-7410. *Fax:* 913-588-7073

**WOOD, GENE WAYNE,** WILDLIFE ECOLOGY. *Current Pos:* from asst prof to assoc prof, 74-81, PROF FORESTRY, BELLE W BARUCH RES INST, CLEMSON UNIV, 81- *Personal Data:* b Bedford, Va, Oct 23, 40; m 65; c 2. *Educ:* Va Polytech Inst & State Univ, BS, 63; Pa State Univ, MS, 66, PhD(agron), 71. *Prof Exp:* Instr wildlife mgt, Pa State Univ, University Park, 67-71, asst prof wildlife ecol, 71-74. *Mem:* Ecol Soc Am; Wildlife Soc; Soc Am Foresters. *Res:* Effects of silvicultural practices on animal population and habitat; nutrient distribution in forest ecosystems. *Mailing Add:* Clemson Univ Fisheries & Wildlife Clemson SC 29632-0001

**WOOD, GEORGE MARSHALL,** ENGINEERING SCIENCE, PHYSICS. *Current Pos:* SR RES SCIENTIST & PROJ MGR INSTRUMENTATION, NASA/LANGLEY RES CTR, 59- *Personal Data:* b Fairfield, Conn, Jan 20, 33; m 52, Nancy Litz; c Judith, Nancy & Jennifer. *Educ:* Univ Ga, BS, 59; Rensselaer Polytech Inst, MS, 68, PhD(eng sci), 74. *Concurrent Pos:* Adj assoc prof nuclear eng, Rensselaer Polytech Inst, 75-83; adj assoc prof physics, Univ New Orleans, 82; mgr tethered satellite syst oper, flight exp, NASA Hq, 89-90. *Mem:* Am Inst Aeronaut & Astronaut; Am Soc Mass Spectrometry; Am Chem Soc. *Res:* Develop mass spectrometry and analytical instrumentation for ionization processes and charged particle behavior; surface chemistry; ion physics; metal oxide catalysis; data enhancement through deconvolution methods; on-orbit flight experiments with tethered satellites and polymers. *Mailing Add:* Instrument Res Div NASA/Langley Res Ctr Hampton VA 23665. *Fax:* 757-864-8673; *E-Mail:* g.m.wood@nasa.larg.gov

**WOOD, GERRY ODELL,** INDUSTRIAL HYGIENE, CHEMISTRY. *Current Pos:* Fel, 69-71, STAFF MEM CHEM, LOS ALAMOS NAT LAB, 72- *Personal Data:* b Oklahoma City, Okla, Nov 19, 43; m 65, Linda Killian; c Paul & Julie. *Educ:* Univ Okla, BSCh, 65; Univ Tex, Austin, PhD(phys chem), 69; Am Bd Indust Hyg, cert, 76. *Mem:* Am Indust Hyg Asn; Am Chem

Soc. *Res:* Air sampling techniques; analytical methods development; chemical kinetics; photochemistry; vapor adsorption in sorbent beds; dynamics of gas phase reactions; carbon adsorption of gases and vapors. *Mailing Add:* 2233 37th St Los Alamos NM 87544-2020. *E-Mail:* gerry@beta.lanl.gov

**WOOD, GLEN MEREDITH,** AGRONOMY, PHOTOGRAPHY. *Current Pos:* from assoc prof & assoc agronomist to prof & agronomist, 50-85, actg chmn, Dept Agron, 53-55, EMER PROF PLANT & SOIL SCI, UNIV VT, 85- *Personal Data:* b Dallas, Tex, Apr 17, 20; m 50, Elizabeth Bailey; c Gretchen, Priscilla, Howard, David, Eric, Kristin & Mark. *Educ:* RI State Col, BS, 47; Rutgers Univ, MS, 48, PhD(agr), 50. *Prof Exp:* Asst, Rutgers Univ, 47-50. *Concurrent Pos:* Golf Course Supts Asn Am res grants, 67, 68 & 71-74; assoc prof & assoc agronomist, Wash State Univ, 69-70; tech adv, Vol Tech Asst, 76-; vis prof, Cornell Univ, 80; agronomist, Baptist Haiti Mission, Haiti, 89-90. *Mem:* Am Soc Agron; Crop Sci Soc Am; Nat Audubon Soc; Sierra Club; Nature Conserv. *Res:* Cold hardiness in ladino clover; physiological and environmental studies with birdsfoot trefoil, perennial ryegrass and other forage crops; forage utilization by poultry; turfgrass management; shade and drouth studies with turfgrasses; application of infrared photography to turfgrass research; cold hardiness studies with forage and turfgrasses; marginal land pasture renovation studies using sheep, goats and cattle. *Mailing Add:* RR 2 Box 5550 Jericho VT 05465

**WOOD, GORDON HARVEY,** SCIENTIFIC NUMERIC DATABASES, PHYSICS. *Current Pos:* Res officer, 69-79, RES COUN OFFICER, NAT RES COUN CAN, 80- *Personal Data:* b Trail, BC, Jan 30, 40; m 64, Linda; c Brian & Douglas. *Educ:* Univ BC, BASc, 63, MASc, 65, PhD(physics), 69. *Concurrent Pos:* Exec Secy, Can Nat Comt, Comt Data Sci & Technol, 94-; mem, Nat Res Coun Assoc Comt Tribology, 88-92; secy gen, Comt Data Sci & Technol, 90- *Mem:* Can Asn Physicists; Chem Inst Can; Am Sci Affil. *Res:* Collections of scientific-technical numeric data which can be searched, retrieved and manipulated by computer. *Mailing Add:* Nat Res Coun Can Montreal Rd Ottawa ON K1A 0S2 Can. *Fax:* 613-952-8246; *E-Mail:* gordon.wood@nre.ca

**WOOD, GORDON WALTER,** MASS SPECTROMETRY, SCIENCE EDUCATION. *Current Pos:* from asst prof to assoc prof, 63-75, PROF CHEM, UNIV WINDSOR, 75- *Personal Data:* b NS, Can, Apr 6, 33; m 56; c 2. *Educ:* Mt Allison Univ, BSc, 55, MSc, 56; Syracuse Univ, PhD(org chem), 62. *Prof Exp:* Elem sch teacher, NS, 51-52; chemist, Paints Div, Can Industs Ltd, 56-58; fel with A C Cope, Mass Inst Technol, 62-63. *Concurrent Pos:* Vis assoc res scientist, Space Sci Lab, Univ Calif, Berkeley, 69-70; sr researcher, Dept Med Biochem, Fac Med, Univ Dijon, 76-77; assoc dean, Fac Grad Studies & Res, Univ Windsor, 79-82, dean, 82-85, vpres acad, 85- *Mem:* Am Chem Soc; Asn Educ Teachers Sci; fel Chem Inst Can. *Res:* Applications of field desorption mass spectrometry and fast atom bombardment to problems in organic and biochemistry; science education improvements through revised teacher training curricula. *Mailing Add:* Dept Chem Univ Windsor 401 Sunset Ave Toronto ON N9B 3P4 Can

**WOOD, HAROLD SINCLAIR,** CHEMICAL ENGINEERING. *Current Pos:* head process design gas plant construct, 61-77, CHIEF ENGR, MALONEY-CRAWFORD TANK CORP, 77-; MGR APPLN ENG, ARROW ENG, INC, TULSA. *Personal Data:* b Washington, DC, Aug 4, 22. *Educ:* Cornell Univ, BChE, 44. *Prof Exp:* Asst, Geol Lab, Univ Kans, 41; phys chemist, Univ Okla, 42; chem engr, Standard Oil Co, Ind, 44-50; head supvr eng lab, Res & Develop Dept, Mid-Continent Petrol Corp, 50-55; owner, Remwood Chem Co, Okla, 55-58; process engr, Refining & Chem Div, Bechtel Corp, Calif, 58-61. *Mem:* Am Chem Soc; Am Inst Chem Engrs. *Res:* Commercial desalting unit employing fiberglass as contacting agent; petroleum, natural gas and their products. *Mailing Add:* 217 E 24th St Tulsa OK 74114-1217

**WOOD, HARRY ALAN,** VIROLOGY. *Current Pos:* RES SCIENTIST, BOYCE THOMPSON INST PLANT RES, 68-; ADJ PROF, DEPT ENTOM, CORNELL UNIV, 93- *Personal Data:* b Albany, NY, Apr 24, 41; m 55, Judith Pawlaczyk; c Kirsten M & Tiffany. *Educ:* Middlebury Col, AB, 63; Purdue Univ, MS, 65, PhD(plant virol), 68. *Concurrent Pos:* Chair, recombinant DNA comt, Cornell Univ; vis fel, Univ Calif, Davis, 74-75; Fulbright fel, 81. *Mem:* Soc Invert Path; Am Soc Microbiol; Am Soc Virol; AAAS; Entom Soc Am. *Res:* Physical and biological properties of insect and plant viruses with special interest in insect virus genetics; genetic engineering and field testing of insect viruses; development of genetically enhanced viral pesticides. *Mailing Add:* Boyce Thompson Inst Cornell Univ-Tower Rd Ithaca NY 14853. *E-Mail:* haw5@cornell.edu

**WOOD, HENDERSON KINGSBERRY,** genetics, physiology; deceased, see previous edition for last biography

**WOOD, HOUSTON GILLEYLEN, III,** FLUID DYNAMICS, MECHANICAL ENGINEERING. *Current Pos:* ASSOC PROF MECH & AEROSPACE ENG, SCH ENG & APPL SCI, UNIV VA, CHARLOTTESVILLE, 81- *Personal Data:* b Tupelo, Miss, Oct 4, 44; m 65, 91; c 2. *Educ:* Miss State Univ, BA, 65, MS, 67; Univ Va, PhD(appl math), 78. *Prof Exp:* Engr isotope separation theory, Oak Ridge Gaseous Diffusion Plant, Union Carbide Corp, 67-73; res engr gas centrifuge theory res lab eng sci, Univ Va, 73-77; engr gas centrifuge theory & fluid dynamics, Oak Ridge Gaseous Diffusion Plant, Nuclear Div, Union Carbide Corp, 77-81. *Mem:* Soc Indust & Appl Math; Am Phys Soc; Am Inst Aeronaut & Astronaut; Am Soc Mech Engrs. *Res:* Fluid dynamics; computational methods; centrifugation. *Mailing Add:* Dept Mech Aerospace Eng Univ Va Thornton Hall Charlottesville VA 22903

**WOOD, HOWARD JOHN, III,** ASTRONOMY, PHYSICS. *Current Pos:* PHYSICIST-ASTRON, NASA GODDARD SPACE FLIGHT CTR, 85-, MGR OPTICAL TELESCOPE ASSEMBLY, HUBBLE SPACE TELESCOPE, 90- *Personal Data:* b Baltimore, Md, July 19, 38; m 61, 77; c 3. *Educ:* Swarthmore Col, BA, 60; Ind Univ, MA, 62, PhD(astron), 65. *Prof Exp:* Res asst, Sproul Observ, 57-59, Goethe Link Observ, 58-62 & Lowell Observ, 62-63; from instr to assoc prof astron, Univ Va, 64-70; staff astronr, Europ Southern Observ, Santiago, Chile, 70-75; Fulbright vis prof, Univ Observ, Vienna, 75-77; vis asst prof dept astron, Ind Univ, Bloomington, 78-81; asst to dir, Cerro Tololo, Interam Observ, La Serena, Chile, 82-84; sr scientist, Northrop Serv Inc, NASA-Goddard Space Flight Ctr, 84-85. *Concurrent Pos:* Guest investr, McDonald Observ, 59-60, Lowell Observ, 62-65 & Kitt Peak Nat Observ, 63-69; NSF grants, 66-70, 79-82; guest prof, Univ Observ Vienna, 80-81. *Mem:* Am Astron Soc; Sigma Xi; Int Astron Union; Space Studies Inst. *Res:* Photoelectric and spectrophotometric studies of the Balmer lines in the spectra of the magnetic and related stars; Zeeman spectroscopy of magnetic stars; photometric studies of asteroids; photography of Mars; optical alignment and testing of aerospace optics; optics lead for DIRBE instrument on the cosmic Background Explorer. *Mailing Add:* 15806 Pinecroft Lane Bowie MD 20716-1737

**WOOD, IRWIN BOYDEN,** PARASITOLOGY. *Current Pos:* RETIRED. *Personal Data:* b Concord, NH, Apr 27, 26; m 84; c 3. *Educ:* Univ NH, BS, 49, MS, 51; Kans State Univ, PhD(parasitol), 58. *Honors & Awards:* Sci Achievement Award, Am Cyanamid Co, 86. *Prof Exp:* Asst zoologist, Univ NH, 50; chemist, Cyanamid Agr Res Div, Princeton, 52-54, parasitologist, 54-56, res parasitologist & group leader, Agr Div, 58-64, mgr animal res & develop, Cyanamid Int, 64-74, dir animal prod res & develop, Cyanamid Int, Wayne, 74-77, prin scientist, Parasitic Chemother & Immunol Cyanamid Agr Res Div, Princeton, 77-84, assoc res fel, 84-86, res fel chemother & immunol 87-91, res fel, animal indust prod develop, 91. *Concurrent Pos:* Chmn, Anthelminthic Guidelines Comt, 83- *Mem:* Am Soc Parasitologists; World Asn Advan Vet Parasitologists; Am Asn Vet Parasitologists. *Res:* Chemotherapy and physiology of helminths; host-parasite relations; bacterial chemotherapy; acaricides; animal health and feed product development. *Mailing Add:* PO Box 430826 Big Pine Key FL 33043

**WOOD, JACK SHEEHAN,** ENVIRONMENTAL PHYSIOLOGY. *Current Pos:* RETIRED. *Personal Data:* b St Albans, Vt, Oct 31, 31; m 58; c 2. *Educ:* Univ Maine, Orono, BS, 54; Mich State Univ, MA, 60, PhD(ecol, animal physiol), 63. *Prof Exp:* From asst prof to prof biomed sci, Western Mich Univ, 63-81, dir pub serv, 81-92. *Concurrent Pos:* Water qual dir, Mich SCent Planning & Develop Region, 75- *Mem:* AAAS; Wildlife Soc; Am Inst Biol Sci; Soc Exp Biol & Med. *Res:* Physiological response to adverse environmental conditions, including general systematic stress responses, reproductive inhibition and related phenomena in vertebrates; water quality management. *Mailing Add:* 7635 W Hickory Rd Hickory Corners MI 49060

**WOOD, JACKIE DALE,** PHYSIOLOGY, NEUROBIOLOGY. *Current Pos:* PROF & CHMN, PHYSIOL DEPT, COL MED, OHIO STATE UNIV, COLUMBUS, 85- *Personal Data:* b Picher, Okla, Feb 16, 37; m 56; c Cynthia L (Sill) & Sandra J (Hadley). *Educ:* Kans State Univ, Pittsburg, BS, 64, MS, 66; Univ Ill, PhD(physiol), 69. *Honors & Awards:* Hoffman LaRoche Prize Gastrointestinal Res, 86. *Prof Exp:* Asst prof biol, Williams Col, 69-71; from asst prof to assoc prof physiol, Univ Kans Med Ctr, Kansas City, 71-78, prof, 78-79; prof & chmn, physiol dept, Sch Med, Univ Nev, Reno, 79-85. *Concurrent Pos:* Alexander von Humboldt fel; NIH career develop award, 74. *Mem:* AAAS; Am Gastroenterol Asn; Am Soc Zool; Soc Neurosci; Am Physiol Soc. *Res:* Electrical and synaptic behavior of gastrointestinal nerve cells in relation to control and coordination of secretion; absorption and motor function of the gut in health and disease. *Mailing Add:* Dept Physiol 300 Hamilton Hall Ohio State Univ 1645 Neil Ave Columbus OH 43210-1239. *Fax:* 614-292-4888

**WOOD, JAMES ALAN,** MATHEMATICAL ANALYSIS. *Current Pos:* asst prof, 69-72, ASSOC PROF MATH, VA COMMONWEALTH UNIV, 72- *Personal Data:* b Richmond, Va, Sept 16, 39; m 65; c 1. *Educ:* Georgetown Univ, BS, 61; Univ Va, MA, 63, PhD(math), 66. *Prof Exp:* From instr to asst prof math, Georgetown Univ, 65-69. *Concurrent Pos:* NSF res grant, 68-70 & NSF-Nat Inst Educ grant, 80-82. *Mem:* Am Math Soc. *Res:* Operational calculus and dynamical systems; multiplier theory. *Mailing Add:* Dept Math Sci Va Commonwealth Univ Richmond VA 23284-2014

**WOOD, JAMES BRENT, III,** ORGANIC CHEMISTRY, GENERAL CHEMISTRY. *Current Pos:* ASSOC PROF, PALM BEACH COMMUNITY COL, 83- *Personal Data:* b Oct 25, 42; US citizen; m 69; c 2. *Educ:* Univ Denver, BS, 65; Univ Ariz, MS, 70, PhD(chem), 71. *Prof Exp:* Asst prof chem, Mobile Col, 71-73; assoc prof chem & head dept, Palm Beach Atlantic Col, 73-83, chmn, Div Natural Sci & Math, 76-83. *Concurrent Pos:* Instr physics, Palm Beach Community Col, 74-83; instr chem, Fla Atlantic Univ. *Mem:* Am Chem Soc. *Res:* Chemical education. *Mailing Add:* Palm Beach Community Col 4200 Congress Ave Lake Worth FL 33461-3084

**WOOD, JAMES C, JR,** SOLID STATE PHYSICS. *Current Pos:* head, Dept Sci Teaching Physics & Phys Sci, 73-84, actg head, Nuclear Eng Dept, 78-80, CHMN INDUST & ENG TECHNOL DIV, TRI-COUNTY TECH COL, 84- *Personal Data:* b Spartanburg, SC, Aug 21, 39; m 64; c 2. *Educ:* Clemson Univ, BS, 61, MS, 63; Univ Va, PhD(physics), 66. *Prof Exp:* Res physicist, Cent Res Div, Am Cyanamid Co, Conn, 66-71; sr res scientist, TRW Eastern Res Lab, 71-73. *Concurrent Pos:* Prin investr planning grant, NSF, 94-96, co-prin investr ATE Examplary Fac Develop grant, 95-, co-prin investr ATE Ctr Excellence grant, 96- *Mem:* Am Phys Soc; Am Asn Physics Teachers; Sigma Xi; Am Soc Eng Educators. *Mailing Add:* Tri-County Tech Col PO Box 587 Pendleton SC 29670-0587

**WOOD, JAMES DOUGLAS,** NEUROCHEMISTRY. *Current Pos:* head dept, 68-87, prof, 68-97, EMER PROF BIOCHEM, UNIV SASK, 97- *Personal Data:* b Aberdeen, Scotland, Jan 25, 30; m 56, Leila Nephew; c 3. *Educ:* Aberdeen Univ, BSc, 51, PhD(biochem), 54; Univ Sask, DSc, 85. *Prof Exp:* Res officer, Can Dept Agr, 54-57; assoc scientist, Fisheries Res Bd, Can, 57-61; head, Biochem Group, Defence Res Med Labs, Can, 61-63, head physiol chem sect, 63-68. *Concurrent Pos:* Mem, Med Res Coun, Can, 76-82. *Mem:* Am Soc Neurochem; Int Soc Neurochem; Europ Soc Neurochem. *Res:* Gamma-aminobutyric acid metabolism and function. *Mailing Add:* Dept Biochem 107 Wiggins Rd Saskatoon SK S7N 5E5 Can

**WOOD, JAMES KENNETH,** SYNTHETIC ORGANIC CHEMISTRY. *Current Pos:* From asst prof to assoc prof, 69-82, PROF CHEM, UNIV NEBR, OMAHA, 82- *Personal Data:* b Boulder, Colo, Jan 29, 42; m 66; c 2. *Educ:* Colo State Univ, BS, 64; Kans State Col, MS, 65; Ohio State Univ, PhD(chem), 69. *Mem:* Am Chem Soc; Sigma Xi; Nat Sci Teachers Asn. *Res:* Synthesis of novel and biologically active compounds; development of new synthetic techniques and methods; development of new methods for the resolution of racemates. *Mailing Add:* 1622 Hillside Dr Omaha NE 68114-1619

**WOOD, JAMES LEE,** INORGANIC CHEMISTRY, THERMOCHEMISTRY. *Current Pos:* from asst prof to assoc prof, 66-80, ADJ PROF CHEM, DAVID LIPSCOMB COL, 94- *Personal Data:* b Cordele, Ga, Sept 5, 40; m 60; c 4. *Educ:* Vanderbilt Univ, BA, 62, PhD(inorg chem), 66. *Prof Exp:* Res fel chem, Rice Univ, 65-66. *Concurrent Pos:* Sr fel, Rice Univ, 71-73; Indust Res 100 Award, Indust Res Mag; actg dir, Hazardous Mat Training Inst, State Tenn, 78-; consult hazardous mat, Off Civil Defense. *Mem:* Am Chem Soc. *Res:* Thermodynamics and reaction calorimetry; fluorine chemistry; coordination compounds. *Mailing Add:* 4024 General Bates Dr Nashville TN 37204

**WOOD, JAMES MANLEY, JR,** PHYSICAL CHEMISTRY. *Current Pos:* RETIRED. *Personal Data:* b Birmingham, Ala, July 5, 27; m 53, Marian Hill; c Maura, Heather & Jeffrey. *Educ:* Howard Col, BA, 47; Univ Wis, PhD, 52. *Prof Exp:* Res chemist, La, 52-69; res advisor, Ethyl Corp, 69-92. *Mem:* Am Chem Soc; Electrochem Soc. *Res:* Molecular spectra; electrochemistry of fused salts; high energy batteries; decomposition of organometallic compounds, vapor plating; zeolite chemistry; high temperature chemistry; semiconductor materials; lubricant testing; environmental science. *Mailing Add:* 2440 O Neal Lane Baton Rouge LA 70816

**WOOD, JAMES W,** BIOLOGY. *Current Pos:* RETIRED. *Personal Data:* b Seattle, Wash, Jan 22, 25; m 53; c 2. *Educ:* Univ Wash, BS, 50, MS, 58. *Prof Exp:* Aquatic biologist, Fish Comn Ore, 50-55, fish pathologist, 55-60; fish pathologist, Wash State Dept Fisheries, 60-70, supvr fish cult res, 70-77, fish qual control supvr, 77-86. *Concurrent Pos:* Consult, Int Pac Salmon Fisheries Comn, 64-65, Can Dept Fisheries, 66 & Repub of Chile Dept Fisheries, 70-71. *Mem:* Am Fisheries Soc; Am Inst Fishery Res Biol; Wildlife Dis Asn. *Res:* Infectious and nutritional diseases of salmonid fishes. *Mailing Add:* 8124 NE 157th St Bothell WA 98011

**WOOD, JANET MARION,** ENERGY TRANSDUCTIONS MEDIATED BY MICROBIOL MEMBRANE ENZYMES, METABOLIC REGULATION & OSMO ADAPTATION. *Current Pos:* PROF MICROBIOL, UNIV GUELPH, 77- *Personal Data:* b Vancouver, BC, Aug, 1947. *Educ:* Univ Victoria, BSc, 69; Univ Edinburgh, PhD(biochem), 72. *Prof Exp:* Fel, Cornell Univ, 72-75; res assoc, Nat Res Coun Can, 76. *Concurrent Pos:* Vis prof, Univ Calif, Los Angeles, 83. *Mem:* Am Soc Microbiol; Can Soc Microbiologists; Am Soc Biochem & Molecular Biol; Can Soc Biochem & Molecular Biol; Biophys Soc; Can Biophys Soc. *Res:* Structure, function and regulation of membrane enzymes implicated in bacterial energy transductions, including transport and respiration; the molecular mechanism of osmoregulation in Escherichia coli and the importance of osmoregulation in renal and urinary tract pathogenesis. *Mailing Add:* Dept Microbiol Univ Guelph Guelph ON N1G 2W1 Can. *Fax:* 519-837-1802; *E-Mail:* jwood@micro.uoguelph.ca

**WOOD, JANITH CAROLYN,** FAMILY PRACTICE NURSING & ADMINISTRATION. *Current Pos:* PROF NURSING, UNIV MOBILE, 81-; STAFF NURSE, CHARTER HOSP, 89- *Personal Data:* b Providence, RI, June 25, 48; m 67, Ronald; c Christopher & Heather. *Educ:* Univ SAla, BSN, 78; Univ Ala, Birmingham, MSN, 80, DSN, 90. *Prof Exp:* Staff nurse, Univ SAla, 78-81. *Concurrent Pos:* Prog evaluator, Nat League Nursing, 89- *Mem:* Nat League Nursing; Am Acad Nurse Practrs. *Res:* Nursiing administration and education; concept of caring and how it impacts patient outcomes. *Mailing Add:* 6408 Shetland Ct Mobile AL 36695. *Fax:* 334-679-0875; *E-Mail:* drjcwood@aol.com

**WOOD, JOHN ARMSTEAD,** METEORITICS, PLANETARY SCIENCE. *Current Pos:* assoc dir, Harvard-Smithsonian Ctr Astrophys, 81-86, GEOLOGIST, SMITHSONIAN ASTROPHYS OBSERV, 65- *Personal Data:* b Roanoke, Va, July 28, 32; m 58, 89, Julie M Laffey; c Crispin S & Georgia K. *Educ:* Va Polytech Inst, BS, 54; Mass Inst Technol, PhD(geol), 58. *Honors & Awards:* NASA Medal, 73; J Lawrence Smith Award, Nat Acad Sci, 76; Frederick C Leonard Award, Meteoritical Soc, 78; G K Gilbert Award, Geol Soc Am, 92. *Prof Exp:* Geologist, Smithsonian Astrophys Observ, 59; Am Chem Soc-Petrol Res Fund fel, Cambridge Univ, 59-60; geologist, Smithsonian Astrophys Observ, 60-62; res assoc, Enrico Fermi Inst Nuclear Studies, Univ Chicago, 62-65. *Concurrent Pos:* Res assoc, Harvard Col Observ, 60-; vchmn, Lunar Sample Anal Planning Team, 71-73; prof pract geol, Dept Geol Sci, Harvard Univ, 76-94. *Mem:* Nat Acad Sci; fel Am Geophys Union; Meteoritical Soc (pres, 70-72); Am Astron Soc; Int Astron Union; fel AAAS. *Res:* Study of meteorites as samples of primordial planetary material; lunar petrology and geophysics; origin of the planets; surface mineralogy of Venus. *Mailing Add:* Harvard-Smithsonian Ctr Astrophys 60 Garden St Cambridge MA 02138

**WOOD, JOHN D(UDLEY),** PHYSICAL METALLURGY, MATERIALS SELECTION. *Current Pos:* RETIRED. *Personal Data:* b Brooklyn, NY, Dec 5, 30; m 56, 81; c 6. *Educ:* Case Inst Technol, BS, 53; Lehigh Univ, MS, 59, PhD(metall eng), 62. *Prof Exp:* Student engr, Long Lines Dept, Am Tel & Tel Co, 53-54; prod metallurgist, Kaiser Aluminum & Chem Corp, 56-58; instr phys metall, Lehigh Univ, 60-61; res metallurgist, Alcoa Res Labs, Aluminum Co Am, 61-62; from asst prof to prof metall eng, Lehigh Univ, 62-92. *Concurrent Pos:* Consult, Aluminum Div, Howmet Corp, 65-82; mat engr, Allied Chem Corp, 76-77; course dir & lectr, Ctr Prof Adv, 78- *Mem:* Am Inst Mining, Metall & Petrol Engrs; Am Soc Metals; Am Soc Testing & Mat; Brit Inst Metals. *Res:* Physical metallurgy of aluminum alloys; corrosion and stress corrosion; selection of materials; failure analysis; non-destructive evaluation. *Mailing Add:* 337 Sky Valley Dillard GA 30537

**WOOD, JOHN GRADY,** NEUROBIOLOGY. *Current Pos:* MEM STAFF, DEPT ANAT & CELL BIOL, SCH MED, EMORY UNIV, GA. *Personal Data:* b Atlanta, Ga, Aug 1, 42; m 78; c 2. *Educ:* Ga State Univ, BS, 67; Emory Univ, PhD(anat), 71. *Prof Exp:* Fel neurobiol, Inst Animal Physiol, Cambridge, Eng, 71-73 & City Hope Med Ctr, Duarte, Calif, 73-74; asst prof anat, Univ Tenn, 74-76, assoc prof, 76-80, adj assoc prof anat, Ctr Health Sci, 80- *Concurrent Pos:* Fel, Nat Mult Sclerosis Soc, 71-72 & Mult Sclerosis Soc Gt Brit & Northern Ireland, 72-73; independent res fel neurobiol, Friday Harbor Marine Labs, Friday Harbor, Wash, 74; Alfred P Sloan Found res fel, 76. *Mem:* Am Asn Anat; Soc Neurosci; Am Soc Cell Biol; Am Soc Neurochem; Am Soc Zoologists. *Res:* Synthesis, posttranslational modification and transport of glycoconjugates in neurons; fundamental mechanics of axonal transport; cytochemical and biochemical studies of synapse formation; role of protein phosphorylation systems in neurite outgrowth and synapse formation, particularly in regard to phosphoxylation of cytoskeletal proteins; studies of the segration of cytoskeletal proteins in neurons and mechanisms of cytoskeletal clysfunction in neurodegenerative dieseases such as Alzheimer's disease. *Mailing Add:* Dept Anat & Cell Biol Emory Univ Sch Med Atlanta GA 30322-1100. *Fax:* 404-727-6256

**WOOD, JOHN HENRY,** PHARMACOKINETICS, BIOPHARMACEUTICS. *Current Pos:* prof, 69-89, EMER PROF PHARM, MED COL VA, VA COMMONWEALTH UNIV, 90- *Personal Data:* b Calgary, Alta, Nov 18, 24; nat US; m 50, Mary E Snodgrass; c Alice & Beverly. *Educ:* Univ Man, BSc, 46, MSc, 47; Ohio State Univ, PhD(phys chem), 50. *Prof Exp:* Proj chemist, Colgate-Palmolive Co, 50-53; sr res assoc chem, Rensselaer Polytech Inst, 53-54; proj chemist, Colgate-Palmolive Co, 54-56; group leader, 56-57; head phys chem sect, Prod Div, Bristol-Myers Co, NJ, 57-61, head, Phys Chem Dept, 61-65, asst dir res & develop labs, 65-67, dir chem res, 67-69. *Mem:* Am Chem Soc; fel Am Asn Pharmaceut Sci. *Res:* Drug micellar phenomena; rheology; physical pharmacy; biopharmaceutics and pharmacokinetics; pharmacogenetics; saturation and competitive metabolism. *Mailing Add:* 2300 Cedarfield Pkwy Apt 212 Richmond VA 23233-1941

**WOOD, JOHN HERBERT,** software systems; deceased, see previous edition for last biography

**WOOD, JOHN KARL,** PHYSICS. *Current Pos:* PROF PHYSICS, UTAH STATE UNIV, 56- *Personal Data:* b Logan, Utah, July 8, 19; m 47; c 4. *Educ:* Utah State Agr Col, BS, 41; Pa State Col, MS, 42, PhD(physics), 46. *Prof Exp:* Asst petrol refining, Pa State Univ, 44-46; optical engr, Bausch & Lomb Optical Co, NY, 46-48; from asst prof to assoc prof physics, Univ Wyo, 48-56. *Concurrent Pos:* NSF sci fac fel, Sweden, 66. *Mem:* Am Phys Soc; Am Soc Metals; Optical Soc Am. *Res:* Crystal orientation in metals studies by means of x-rays; Raman spectroscopy; pole figures of the effect of some cold rolling mill variables on low carbon steel; light; molecular and atomic physics; general mathematics; sound. *Mailing Add:* 1359 Juniper Dr Logan UT 84321

**WOOD, JOHN L,** ORGANIC CHEMISTRY. *Current Pos:* ASSOC PROF CHEM, YALE UNIV, 93- *Personal Data:* b Keokuk, Iowa, Dec 4, 61. *Educ:* Univ Colo, BA, 85; Univ Pa, PhD(chem), 91. *Honors & Awards:* NSF Career Award, 96. *Prof Exp:* Postdoctoral fel, Harvard Univ, 91-93. *Concurrent Pos:* Alfred P Sloan Found fel, 97. *Mem:* Am Chem Soc. *Mailing Add:* Dept Chem Yale Univ 225 Prospect St New Haven CT 06520. *Fax:* 203-432-6144; *E-Mail:* john.wood@yale.edu

**WOOD, JOHN LEWIS,** BIOCHEMISTRY. *Current Pos:* CONSULT LIFE SCI, 81- *Personal Data:* b Homer, Ill, Aug 7, 12; m 41; c 2. *Educ:* Univ Ill, BS, 34; Univ Va, PhD(org chem), 37. *Hon Degrees:* DSc, Blackburn Univ, 55. *Prof Exp:* Asst biochem, Med Sch, George Washington Univ, 37-38; asst, Med Col, Cornell Univ, 38-39; assoc chemist, Eastern Regional Res Lab, Bur Agr Chem & Eng, USDA, 41-42; asst biochem, Med Col, Cornell Univ, 42-44, asst prof, 44-46; assoc prof, Col Med, Univ Tenn, Memphis, 46-50, prof biochem, Med Units, 50-71, head dept biochem, 52-55, chmn dept, 55-67, alumni distinguished serv prof biochem, Ctr Health Sci, 71-80, assoc dean, Grad Sch-Med Sci, 78-79, actg dean, 79-80; sr staff scientist, Life Sci Res Off, Fedn Am Soc Exp Biol, 80-81. *Concurrent Pos:* Finney-Howell fel, Harvard Univ, 39-41; Guggenheim fel, 54; USPHS spec res fel, 65; Nat Acad Sci-Polish Acad Sci exchange visitor, 70; vis prof, Rhodes Col, 83. *Mem:*

AAAS; Am Chem Soc; Am Soc Biol Chemists; Soc Exp Biol & Med; Am Asn Cancer Res; Am Asn Univ Prof. *Res:* Biochemistry of amino acids; proteins; carcinogenesis; thiocyano derivatives; sulfur compounds. *Mailing Add:* 49 Sevier St Memphis TN 38111

**WOOD, JOHN MARTIN,** biochemistry, inorganic chemistry, for more information see previous edition

**WOOD, JOHN STANLEY,** CHEMISTRY. *Current Pos:* PROF CHEM, UNIV MASS, AMHERST, 70- *Personal Data:* b Stoke-on-Trent, Eng, Oct 9, 36; m 62; c 2. *Educ:* Univ Keele, BA, 58; Univ Manchester, PhD(chem), 62. *Prof Exp:* Res assoc chem, Mass Inst Technol, 62-64; lectr, Univ Southampton, 64-70. *Mem:* Royal Soc Chem; Am Crystallog Asn. *Res:* Inorganic chemistry; x-ray crystallography; studies of stereochemistries and electron structures of inorganic compounds. *Mailing Add:* Dept Chem Univ Mass Amherst Campus Amherst MA 01003

**WOOD, JOHN WILLIAM,** DIFFERENTIAL TOPOLOGY, TOPOLOGY OF VARIETIES. *Current Pos:* assoc prof, 75-81, dept head, 89-94, PROF MATH, UNIV ILL, CHICAGO, 81- *Personal Data:* b Tacoma Park, Md, Nov 14, 41; m 65, Nancy B; c Nicholas & Stephen. *Educ:* Harvard Univ, BA, 63; Univ Calif, Berkeley, PhD(math), 68. *Prof Exp:* Instr math, Princeton Univ, 68-69, lectr, 70-71, mem, Inst Advan Study, 69-70 & 71; Ritt asst prof, Columbia Univ, 72-75. *Concurrent Pos:* Vis res scholar, Univ Geneva, 72. *Mem:* Am Math Soc. *Res:* Algebraic and differential topology; topology of algebraic varieties. *Mailing Add:* Math Dept 851 S Morgan St Chicago IL 60607. *E-Mail:* jwood@uic.edu

**WOOD, JOSEPH GEORGE,** ANATOMY, NEUROSCIENCE. *Current Pos:* RETIRED. *Personal Data:* b Victoria, Tex, Dec 8, 28; m 82, Jane L Andrews; c Marian. *Educ:* Univ Houston, BS, 53, MS, 58; Univ Tex, Galveston, PhD(anat), 62. *Honors & Awards:* Res Award, Sigma Xi, 62. *Prof Exp:* Asst biol, Univ Houston, 56-58; instr anat, Dent Br, Univ Tex, 61 & Sch Med, Yale Univ, 62-63; asst prof, Sch Med, Univ Ark, 63-66; assoc prof, Univ Tex Med Sch, San Antonio, 66-70, asst dean acad develop, 67-69; prof neurobiol & anat, Univ Tex Med Sch, Houston, 70-88, chmn dept, 70-84; prof & chair anat sci, Univ Okla Health Sci Ctr, 88-93, dir, Okla Ctr Neurosci, 91-94. *Concurrent Pos:* USPHS trainee, Univ Tex, Galveston & Sch Med, Yale Univ, 62-63; mem, Neuroanat Vis Scientist Prog, USPHS, 65-66; consult, vchancellor health affairs, Univ Tex, 68-70; consult, Dept Path & Biol, Univ Minn Col Vet Med, 93-94. *Mem:* Am Asn Anat; Soc Exp Biol & Med; Electron Micros Soc Am; Soc Neurosci; Histochem Soc; Am Soc Cell Biol. *Res:* Histochemistry and cytochemistry of neurons; histochemical and electron microscopic localization of biogenic amines and their relation to nerve function and degeneration. *Mailing Add:* 8638 Old Oak Dr Irving TX 75063

**WOOD, JOSEPH M,** botany, paleobotany; deceased, see previous edition for last biography

**WOOD, KENNETH GEORGE,** LIMNOLOGY. *Current Pos:* RETIRED. *Personal Data:* b Niagara Falls, Ont, Jan 11, 24; nat US; m 48; c 3. *Educ:* Univ Toronto, BA, 47, MA, 49; Ohio State Univ, PhD(hydrobiol), 53. *Prof Exp:* Asst prof biol, Buena Vista Col, 53-55 & RI Col, 55-56; prof, Thiel Col, 56-65; from assoc prof to prof biol, State Univ NY, Col Fredonia, 65-87. *Concurrent Pos:* Sabbatical leave, Calspan Corp, NY, 72-73; Fulbright scholar, Madurai-Kamaraj Univ, Madurai, India, 80-81. *Mem:* NAm Benthological Soc; Int Asn Theoret & Appl Limnol. *Res:* Ecology of aquatic animals; primary productivity; inorganic carbon dioxide. *Mailing Add:* Rte 1 Box 1322 Whigham GA 31797

**WOOD, KRISTIN LEE,** ENGINEERING DESIGN, DESIGN FOR MANUFACTURING. *Current Pos:* ASSOC PROF, UNIV TEX, AUSTIN, 89- *Personal Data:* b Burlington, Colo, Dec 27, 62; m 86; c 1. *Educ:* Colo State Univ, BS, 85; Calif Inst Technol, MS, 86, PhD(mech eng), 89. *Prof Exp:* Engr tech support, Digital Equip Corp, 85; grad teaching asst, Calif Inst Technol, 85-88, grad res asst, 86-89. *Concurrent Pos:* Eng aid A roadway design, Colo Dept Highways, 82-83, eng aide B, 84; lab tutor & monitor, Ctr Comput Asst Eng, Colo State Univ, 84-85. *Mem:* Am Soc Mech Engrs; Am Soc Eng Educ; Inst Elec & Electronics Engrs Computer Soc. *Res:* Design theory; computer-integrated engineering; design for manufacture; applied mechanics in the design of mechanical components, features and assemblies. *Mailing Add:* Dept Mech Eng Univ Tex ETC 5-160 Austin TX 78712-1063

**WOOD, KURT ARTHUR,** VIBRATIONAL SPECTROSCOPY, CONDENSED PHASES. *Current Pos:* ASST PROF CHEM, ST OLAF COL, 81- *Personal Data:* b Springfield, Minn, July 2, 56; m 79. *Educ:* Univ Calif, Davis, BS, 77, Berkeley, PhD(chem), 81. *Mem:* Am Phys Soc; Am Chem Soc; Am Sci Affil. *Res:* Applications of spectroscopy, particularly vibrational spectroscopy, to intra- and intermolecular interactions of molecules in condensed phases; to energy transfer and to the structure of matter. *Mailing Add:* ELF ATocHem N Am 900 First Ave King of Prussia PA 14906-0936

**WOOD, LAWRENCE ARNELL,** physics; deceased, see previous edition for last biography

**WOOD, LEONARD ALTON,** GEOLOGY, GROUND WATER HYDROLOGY. *Current Pos:* RETIRED. *Personal Data:* b Gratiot Co, Mich, Aug 22, 22; m 42, 77, Annie O Grimsley; c Judy K (Robbins), Beth L (Plank-Smotherman) & Penny L (Gittings-Thompson). *Educ:* Mich State Univ, BS, 46. *Prof Exp:* Geologist, Water Resources Div, US Geol Surv, Mich, 46-51, Tex, 52-63, Colo, 63-67, Washington, DC, 67-74 & Reston, Va, 74-80, coordr subsurface waste disposal studies, 71-78, staff hydrologist, Water Resources Div, 67-80; consult hydrogeologist & sr assoc, SS Papadopulos & Assocs, 80-96. *Concurrent Pos:* Chmn, US Nat Comt, Asn Int Hydrogeol, 77-80, Hydrogeol Div, Geol Soc Am, 81-82. *Mem:* Geol Soc Am; Am Asn Petrol Geologists; Am Geophys Union; Asn Eng Geologists; Am Inst Prof Geologists; Asn Int Hydrogeol. *Res:* Occurrence of ground water; relation of ground water to surface water; contamination of ground water; protection of ground water resources. *Mailing Add:* 10406 Hunter Ridge Dr Oakton VA 22124. *Fax:* 301-718-8909; *E-Mail:* lwood4562@aol.com

**WOOD, LEONARD E(UGENE),** CIVIL ENGINEERING. *Current Pos:* from instr to assoc prof, 55-80, PROF CIVIL ENG, PURDUE UNIV, 80- *Personal Data:* b Burr Oak, Kans, June 10, 23; m 47. *Educ:* Kans State Univ, BS & MS, 49; Purdue Univ, PhD(civil eng), 56. *Prof Exp:* Instr appl mech, Kans State Univ, 49-53. *Concurrent Pos:* Consult, Tech Studies Adv Comt, Bldg Res Adv Bd, Nat Acad Sci-Nat Res Coun, 57-61, Conoco, 82-88, Mobile, 85-87, US CEngr, 85, Nat High Inst, 89-91. *Mem:* Hon mem Am Soc Testing & Mat; Asn Asphalt Paving Technol; Am Soc Eng Educ; Transp Res Bd. *Res:* Engineering materials; rock mechanics; corrosion studies; viscoelastic behavior of bituminous mixes; cold and hot recycling of asphalt pavements; compositional studies of asphalts. *Mailing Add:* Sch Civil Eng Purdue Univ 1284 Civil Eng Bldg West Lafayette IN 47907

**WOOD, LEONARD E(UGENE),** ENVIRONMENTAL SCIENCES, GEOLOGY. *Current Pos:* RETIRED. *Personal Data:* b Elwood, Ind, Nov 2, 27; m 58; c 4. *Educ:* Univ Ky, BS, 52, MS, 57; Mich State Univ, PhD(geol), 58. *Prof Exp:* Instr geol, Mich State Univ, 55-58; staff geologist, Mobil Oil Co, 58-61, US Geol Surv, 62-63 & Army Res Off, 63-65; prog mgr environ sci, Adv Res Projs Agency, Thailand, 65-72; chief, environ control group, Off Res, Fed Hwy Admin, 72-83, chief, eng & hwy, oper technol transfers, 83-85. *Concurrent Pos:* Instr exten, Univ Va, 64-65; adv ed, J Develop Areas, 68-72. *Res:* Management in environmental sciences; geology, soils, water resources, vegetation, fauna and meteorology in United States, Europe and Southeast Asia; geologic considerations in excavation; environmental research on high elevations; highways and the bio-environment; highway environmental interface, especially air, noise, water, ecology. *Mailing Add:* 7109 Murray Lane Annandale VA 22003

**WOOD, LINCOLN JACKSON,** SPACE NAVIGATION, TRAJECTORY OPTIMIZATION. *Current Pos:* mem tech staff, Calif Inst Technol, 77-81, tech group supv, 81-89, tech mgr, 89-91, DEP TECH SECT MGR, JET PROPULSION LAB, CALIF INST TECHNOL, 91-, SR MEM TECH STAFF, 92- *Personal Data:* b Lyons, NY, Sept 30, 47. *Educ:* Cornell Univ, BS, 68; Stanford Univ, MS, 69, PhD(aeronaut & astronaut), 72. *Prof Exp:* Staff engr, Hughes Aircraft Co, 74-77. *Concurrent Pos:* Consult, 72-79; Bechtel instr eng, Calif Inst Technol, 72-74, lectr systs eng, 75-76, from vis asst prof to vis assoc prof systs eng, 76-84; assoc ed, J Astronaut Sci, Am Astronaut Soc, 80-83, J Guid, 83-89; mem, Space Flight Mech Comt, Am Astronaut Soc, 80-; chmn, Tech Comt Astrodyn, Am Inst Aeronaut & Astronaut, 86-88. *Mem:* Assoc fel Am Inst Aeronaut & Astronaut; sr mem Am Astronaut Soc; sr mem Inst Elec & Electronics Engrs; AAAS; Sigma Xi. *Res:* Navigation and flight mechanics; authored or co-authored over 30 professional journal articles. *Mailing Add:* Jet Propulsion Lab MS 301-125L 4800 Oak Grove Dr Pasadena CA 91109. *E-Mail:* lincoln.j.wood@jpl.nasa.gov

**WOOD, LOUIS L,** ORGANIC CHEMISTRY. *Current Pos:* CHEM ADV, RHONE-POULENC, SAVAGE, MD, 86- *Personal Data:* b Washington, DC, July 26, 31; m 58, 68; c 3. *Educ:* Univ Del, BS, 53; Ohio State Univ, PhD(org chem), 59. *Prof Exp:* Res chemist, W R Grace & Co, Wash Res Ctr, Clarkville, 58-81; chem adv, Purification Eng Inc, Columbia, Md, 81-86. *Mem:* Am Chem Soc; AAAS. *Res:* Polymers; organic chemical synthesis; textile applications; foam technology; immobilzation of cells; enzymes; monoclonal antibodies. *Mailing Add:* 11760 Gainsborough Rd Potomac MD 20854-3246

**WOOD, LOWELL THOMAS,** HIGH TEMPERATURE SUPERCONDUCTORS, FIBER OPTIC SENSORS. *Current Pos:* asst prof, 69-73, chmn dept, 75-80, ASSOC PROF PHYSICS, UNIV HOUSTON, 73- *Personal Data:* b Ada, Okla, Sept 8, 42; m 66, Marion Means; c 2. *Educ:* Univ Kans, BS, 64; Univ Tex, Austin, PhD(physics), 68. *Prof Exp:* Asst prof physics, Univ Tex, Austin, 68-69. *Concurrent Pos:* NASA grant, Univ Houston, 70-78 & NSF grant, 72-77; mem Col Bd Comt, Vector/Schlumberger, 78-82, sr res scientist, 80-81; assoc dean, NSM, 84-89. *Mem:* Am Phys Soc; Optical Soc Am. *Res:* Optical properties of high temperature superconductors; fiber optic microdistortion sensors; undergraduate laboratory development using computers. *Mailing Add:* Dept Physics Univ Houston 4800 Calhoun Houston TX 77204. *Fax:* 713-743-3589

**WOOD, MARGARET GRAY,** MEDICINE, DERMATOLOGY. *Current Pos:* Assoc, Univ Pa, 53-68, from asst prof to assoc prof, 68-77, prof, 78-89, EMER PROF DERMAT, SCH MED, UNIV PA, 89- *Personal Data:* b Jamaica, NY, May 23, 18; wid; c M Diana, Deirdre (Harper) & Moira D. *Educ:* Univ Ala, BA, 41; Woman's Med Col Pa, MD, 48. *Hon Degrees:* Dr Med Sci, Med Col Pa, 90. *Honors & Awards:* Commonwealth Bd Award, 81. *Concurrent Pos:* Assoc, Grad Div Med Dermat, Univ Pa, 53-66, assoc prof,

66-71; asst vis physician, Philadelphia Gen Hosp, 54-70, consult, 70-77; asst prof, Woman's Col Pa, 58-66, vis asst prof, 66-; consult, Philadelphia Vet Hosp & Dent Sch, Univ Pa, 66- & Vet Sch Med, 70-; peer rev comt, Am Soc Dermatopathol, 78-81; bd corp, Med Col Pa, 79-84, vchmn, 84-; mem & chmn, Libr Comt, Univ Pa, 84-87; bd dirs, Allegheny Health Syst, Inc, 89-, United Hosp, Inc, 91; vchair & bd dirs, St Christophers Hosp Children, 91-; bd dir, Allegheny Health Educ & Res Found, Med Col Pa. *Mem:* Histochem Soc; Soc Invest Dermat; AMA; Am Med Women's Asn; Am Acad Dermat; Int Soc Dermatol. *Res:* Histochemistry; dermatopathology; published 75 articles in peer review journals, Cheysters in 3 books. *Mailing Add:* 6386 Church Rd Philadelphia PA 19151

**WOOD, MAURICE,** FAMILY MEDICINE. *Current Pos:* dir res, 71-87, from assoc prof to prof, 71-88, EMER PROF, DEPT FAMILY PRACT, MED COL VA, 88- *Personal Data:* b Durham Co, Eng, June 28, 22; US citizen. *Educ:* Newcastle upon Tyne, MB & BS, 45; Kings Col Med Sch, Univ Durham, MRC, 66; FRCP(G), 75; Am Bd Family Pract, dipl, 79. *Honors & Awards:* Maurice Wood Res Award, 95. *Prof Exp:* House physician, Newcastle Gen Hosp, 45; house surgeon, Sunderland Royal Infirmary, 46 & Obstet & Gynecol, Queen Elizabeth Hosp Gateshead, 50; maj & sr med officer, Port Said, Mid E Oper, Royal Army Med Corps, 46-49; pvt med pract, South shields, Eng, 50-71. *Concurrent Pos:* Surg registr, Sunderland Royal Infirmary, 46; lectr pract nurse training, N Eastern Fac, Royal Col Gen Practr, 65-71; clin asst, Dept Psychol Med, South Shields Gen Hosp, 66-71; gen pract teaching group, Univ Newcastle, 69-71; mem res comt, N Eastern Fac, Royal Col Gen Practr, 60-70, chmn, Pract Orgn Comt, 69-70, recorder, Nat Collab Study, Med Res Coun, 69-73 & vis patterns gen pract, NE Fac, 70; sr recorder collabor study, Dept Health & Human Serv, UK, 64-67; A D Williams distinguished scholar, 71-72; mem, US Nat Comt Vital & Health Statist, 77-80; M S McCleod vis prof, Univ Adelaide, SAustralia, 82; adv, Data & Commun Comt, Dept Family Pract, Med Col Va, Curric & Eval Comt, Pract Orgn & Mgt Comt & Behav Sci Training, proj dir, Predoc Med Educ Grant Award, 72-80 & Grad Med Educ Grant Award, 76-86, prin investr, Epidemiol Diabetes Study, 80-83, mem, Steering Comt, Family Pract Fac Develop Prog, 78-81 & Chest Pain Study Group, 80-83, prin investr & prog dir family med, 72-86; mem, Res Comt, Soc Teachers Family Med, 71-77, Comt Terminol, 72-79 & Adv Comn Prof & Hosp Activ, 72-79, Mead Johnson Award Comt, Am Acad Family Physicians, 77-79, bd dirs, Ambulatory Sentinel Pract Network & Nat Cancer Inst Task Force, 86-; data rec subcomt chmn, Soc Teachers Family Prac, 72-77; consult, Div Educ, Am Acad Family Physicians, 75-; chmn, Community Oriented Primary Care Study Group, Inst Med-Nat Acad Sci, 83-85; treas bd dirs, Ambulatory Sentinel Pract Network, 86-; reviewer, J Am Med Asn, 80; consult, Nat Comt Vital & Health Statist, 76-77, chmn tech consult panel for Ambulatory Med Care Minimum Data Set, 78-80, NIH, 79-, Nat Ctr Health Statist, 80-; mem, Int Primary Care Res Network, 81-; secy res comt, World Orgn Nat Col, Acad & Acad Asn Gen Practr & Family Physicians, 76-83 & mem, 75-, comt voc, 75-80 & mem, Classification Comt, 83-; mem, Int Primary Care Res Network, 81- *Mem:* Inst Med-Nat Acad Sci; Brit Med Asn (pres, 69-); fel Royal Col Gen Practr; fel Am Acad Family Physicians; Soc Teachers Family Med; Int Epidemiol Asn; NAm Primary Care Res Group; World Orgn Family Doctors. *Res:* Author of over 64 articles. *Mailing Add:* MCV Sta Box 251 Richmond VA 23298-0001

**WOOD, MICHAEL BRUCE,** BONE BLOOD FLOW. *Current Pos:* from asst prof to assoc prof orthod surg, Mayo Grad Sch Med, 79-89, DIR, MAYO MICROSURG TRAINING CTR, MAYO CLIN, 86-, PROF ORTHOP SURG, 89- *Personal Data:* b Glasgow, Mont, Oct 7, 43. *Educ:* Franklin & Marshall Col, AB, 65; McGill Univ, MD, CM, 69. *Honors & Awards:* Henry W Meyending Essay Award, Am Fracture Asn, 74. *Prof Exp:* Asst prof orthod surg, Med Col Ohio, 77-79. *Concurrent Pos:* Consult, Sect Hand Surg, Mayo Clin, 78- *Mem:* Am Acad Orthop Surgeons; Am Soc Surg Hand; Am Soc Reconstructive Microsurg; Int Soc Reconstructive Microsurg. *Res:* Bone blood flow; nerve graft revascularization; microsurgical free tissue transfer. *Mailing Add:* Dept Orthop Mayo Clin Rochester MN 55901

**WOOD, NORMAN KENYON,** ORAL PATHOLOGY, ORAL SURGERY. *Current Pos:* RETIRED. *Personal Data:* b Perth, Ont, Dec 1, 35; m 69; c 4. *Educ:* Univ Toronto, DDS, 58; Cook County Hosp, Chicago, dipl oral surg, 65; Northwestern Univ, MS, 66, PhD(oral path), 68; Am Bd Oral Surg, dipl, 70; Am Bd Oral Path, dipl, 71; Am Bd Oral Med, dipl, 86. *Prof Exp:* Pvt pract, 58-62; res assoc biol mat, Dent Sch, Northwestern Univ, 67-68; asst prof oral path, Loyola Univ, Chicago, 68-70, from assoc prof to prof oral diag, Dent Sch, 70-89, chmn, Dept Oral Diag, Radiol & Path, 70-86; dean fac dent, Univ Alta, 89-95. *Concurrent Pos:* Consult, Hines Vet Admin Hosp, Ill, 71-89. *Mem:* Am Acad Oral Path; Sigma Xi; Am Asn Dent Schs. *Res:* Induction of hamster cheek pouch carcinomas; seeding during incisional biopsy. *Mailing Add:* Fac Dent Univ Alta Edmonton AB T6G 2N8 Can

**WOOD, NORRIS PHILIP,** BACTERIOLOGY. *Current Pos:* from asst prof to assoc prof bact, 63-72, PROF MICROBIOL, UNIV RI, 72-, CHMN DEPT, 70- *Personal Data:* b Binghamton, NY, July 8, 24; m 55; c 2. *Educ:* Hartwick Col, BS, 49; Cornell Univ, MNS, 51; Univ Pa, PhD(microbiol), 55. *Prof Exp:* From asst prof to assoc prof microbiol, Agr & Mech Col Tex, 55-63. *Concurrent Pos:* Res partic, Oak Ridge Nat Lab, 58 & 62; mem, State Adv Comt Regional Med Prog, 66-76. *Mem:* AAAS; Am Chem Soc; Am Soc Microbiol; Sigma Xi. *Res:* Bacterial physiology; intermediary metabolism; chemistry of microorganisms; microbial ecology. *Mailing Add:* 113 White Horn Dr Kingston RI 02881

**WOOD, O LEW,** QUARTZ RESONATOR TRANSDUCERS. *Current Pos:* CHMN & CHIEF EXEC OFFICER, QUARTEX & QUARTZTRONICS, INC, 79- *Personal Data:* b Hurricane, Utah, Apr 26, 36; m 57, Yvonne Silva; c Sharla, Sherri, Brent L & Blaine O. *Educ:* Brigham Young Univ, BS, 58; Univ Calif, Los Angeles, MS, 62; Univ Utah, PhD(radiation biophys), 68. *Honors & Awards:* Gov Medal for Sci & Tech, State Utah, 93. *Prof Exp:* Sr engr, Sperry Utah Co, 62-65; res scientist, Fluidonics Res Lab, ITE-Imperial Corp, 65-67, dir res biomed eng, BioLogics Inc, 67-69; assoc prof & collab environ pollution, Utah State Univ, 69-71; prog dir radiologic technol, Weber State Col, 70-75. *Concurrent Pos:* Consult, O Lew Wood Assocs, 69- *Mem:* Sr mem Inst Elec & Electronics Engrs; sr mem Instrument Soc Am. *Res:* Development of biomedical and air pollution instrumentation; development of quartz resonator transducers to measure force, pressure, temperature, weight and acceleration; management of technology transfer. *Mailing Add:* 811 E Woodshire Circle Murray UT 84107

**WOOD, OBERT REEVES, II,** ELECTRICAL ENGINEERING, QUANTUM ELECTRONICS. *Current Pos:* MEM TECH STAFF LASER RES, BELL LABS, LUCENT TECHNOLS, 69- *Personal Data:* b Sacramento, Calif, Jan 18, 43; c 2. *Educ:* Univ Calif, Berkeley, BS, 64, MS, 65, PhD(elec eng), 69. *Mem:* Am Phys Soc; Optical Soc Am; Inst Elec & Electronics Engrs; AAAS; Sigma Xi. *Res:* Quantum electronics; nonlinear optics; plasma physics. *Mailing Add:* Bell Labs Lucent Technols Murray Hill NJ 07974. *E-Mail:* orw@bell-labs.com

**WOOD, PAUL MIX,** COMPUTER-BASED SYSTEMS ANALYSES. *Current Pos:* RETIRED. *Personal Data:* b Champion, NY, Dec 28, 30; m 55, Eloise Hazard; c Michele & Susan. *Educ:* Syracuse Univ, BS, 56, MS, 58; Rensselaer Polytech Inst, MS, 71, MBA, 75. *Prof Exp:* Opers res analyst, Gen Dynamics Pomona, 62-63, Hamilton Stand, United Aircraft, 63-64 & Tech Opers Res, Inc, 64-65; res scientist, Travelers Res Ctr, Inc, 65-68; res scientist, NY State Dept Health, 68-89 & NY State OASAS, 90-96. *Concurrent Pos:* Mem, Nat Cost Effectiveness Consult Comt, Opers Res Soc Am, 69-72 & Nat Data Comt, Coun Regional Networks Genetics, 86-89; vpres, RPI-MBA Asn, 88-90. *Res:* Computer-based systems analyses for decision support in health and in health systems. *Mailing Add:* 24 N Hill Rd Ballston Lake NY 12019-1314

**WOOD, PETER DOUGLAS,** BIOCHEMISTRY, CHEMISTRY. *Current Pos:* ADJ PROF MED, MED CTR, STANFORD UNIV, 69- *Personal Data:* b London, Eng, Aug 25, 29; m 53; c 1. *Educ:* Univ London, BSc, 52, MSc, 56, PhD(chem), 62, DSc, 72. *Prof Exp:* Chemist, Weston Res Labs, Eng, 52-55; res chemist, Imp Chem Industs Australia & NZ, 56-59; res asst chem, Univ Sask, 59; res assoc, Inst Metab Res, Oakland, Calif, 62-68. *Concurrent Pos:* Fel coun arteriosclerosis, Am Heart Asn, 68; dep dir, Stanford Heart-Dis Prev Prog, 71- *Mem:* Fel Royal Soc Chem; Am Inst Nutrit; Am Soc Clin Nutrit; Am Heart Asn; Am Oil Chem Soc; Sigma Xi. *Res:* Lipid chemistry, metabolism and methodology; exercise. *Mailing Add:* Dept Med Stanford Ctr Res Stanford Univ 730 Welch Rd Suite B Dis Prevention Stanford CA 94305

**WOOD, PETER JOHN,** CARBOHYDRATE CHEMISTRY, FOOD SCIENCE. *Current Pos:* RES SCIENTIST CARBOHYDRATES, FOOD RES INST, 69- *Personal Data:* b Barnard Castle, Durham, Eng, Aug 20, 43. *Educ:* Univ Birmingham, BS, 65, PhD(carbohydrate chem), 69. *Mem:* Am Asn Cereal Chemists. *Res:* Connective tissue glycosaminoglycans; polysaccharides of potato cell wall; rapeseed carbohydrates; oat endosperm cell wall polysaccharides; analytical methodology; use of boronate esters for glc analysis and methanol analysis; dye-binding by polysaccharides; dietary fiber. *Mailing Add:* Res Br Food Res Inst Neatby Bldg Agr Can Ottawa ON K1A 0C6 Can

**WOOD, RANDALL DUDLEY,** BIOCHEMISTRY & ORGANIC CHEMISTRY, LIPID METABOLISM. *Current Pos:* PROF BIOCHEM, TEX A&M UNIV, COLLEGE STATION, 76- *Personal Data:* b Palmer, Ky, Aug 3, 36; m 59, Arlene Baker; c Marjorie (Guidry). *Educ:* Univ Ky, BS, 59, MS, 61; Tex A&M Univ, PhD(biochem), 65. *Prof Exp:* Scientist, Oak Ridge Assoc Univs, 66-70; assoc prof, Stritch Sch Med, Loyola Univ Chicago & Hines Vet Admin Hosp, 70-71; assoc prof med & biochem, Sch Med, Univ Mo-Columbia, 71-76. *Concurrent Pos:* AEC fel, 65-66; consult, Planning & Design Sci & Biotechnol Facil. *Mem:* Am Inst Nutrit; Am Asn Cancer Res; Am Chem Soc; Am Oil Chem Soc; Am Soc Biol Chemists. *Res:* Lipid biochemistry and metabolism of normal, tumor and embryonic tissues; biosynthesis, metabolism and occurrence of alkyl glyceryl ethers and plasmalogens; structural and metabolic relationships between molecular species of various classes; the metabolic fate of unnatural dietary fatty acids in processed foods; lipid metabolism in plants; nutrition; effect of dietary fat on serum cholesterol and serum lipids. *Mailing Add:* Dept Biochem & Biophys Tex A&M Univ College Station TX 77843

**WOOD, RAYMOND ARTHUR,** ZOOLOGY, PARASITOLOGY. *Current Pos:* PROF ZOOL & CHMN DIV, ORANGE CO COMMUNITY COL, 56- *Personal Data:* b Middletown, NY, Nov 28, 24. *Educ:* Mt St Mary's Col, Md, BS, 50; Univ Notre Dame, MS, 53, PhD, 55. *Prof Exp:* Instr & spec lectr anat & physiol, Ind Univ, 54-55; asst prof, Pan Am Col, 55-56. *Concurrent Pos:* NSF grants, Bermuda Biol Sta, 56, Comp Anat Inst, Harvard Univ, 63, Col Biol Inst, Williams Col, 66, Marine Lab, Duke Univ, 65, 67 & Marine Labs, Naples, Italy, 70; Sigma Xi grant, 57. *Mem:* Fel AAAS; Am Soc Parasitologists; Am Soc Zoologists; Soc Syst Zool; fel Royal Soc Trop Med & Hyg. *Res:* Systematics of monogenea. *Mailing Add:* Div Biol Orange Co Community Col 115 South St Middletown NY 10940-6441

**WOOD, REGINALD KENNETH,** COMPUTER PROCESS CONTROL, MODELING & SIMULATION. *Current Pos:* from asst prof to assoc prof, 66-72, PROF CHEM ENG, UNIV ALTA, 72- *Personal Data:* b Unity, Sask, July 12, 37; m 58, Joan Houlgate; c 3. *Educ:* Univ Sask, BE, 58; Univ Alta, MSc, 60; Northwestern Univ, PhD(chem eng), 63. *Prof Exp:* Res engr, Can Chem Co Ltd, 59-60; asst prof chem eng, Univ Ottawa, 63-66. *Concurrent Pos:* Guest worker, Control Eng Div, Warren Spring Lab, Stevenage, Eng, 72-; vis res fel, Comput Aided Design Ctr, Cambridge, Eng, 80-81. *Mem:* Am Inst Chem Engrs; Can Soc Chem Engrs; Instrument Soc Am; Soc Comput Simulation; Am Soc Eng Educ. *Res:* Dynamics and control of chemical and mineral process systems. *Mailing Add:* Dept Chem & Mat Eng Univ Alta Edmonton AB T6G 2G6 Can. *E-Mail:* wood@gpu.srv.ualberta.ca

**WOOD, RICHARD ELLET,** NUCLEAR PHYSICS, ENERGY SYSTEMS. *Current Pos:* RETIRED. *Personal Data:* b Farmington, Utah, Mar 3, 28; m 48; c 5. *Educ:* Univ Utah, BS, 52, PhD(physics), 55. *Prof Exp:* Res assoc neutron cross sects, Brookhaven Nat Lab, 53-54; nuclear engr, Gen Elec Co, 55-56, supvr low power test opers, 56-59, supvr initial eng test opers, 59-60, supvr analysis, Idaho Test Sta, Air Craft Nuclear Propulsion Dept, 60-61, physicist, Atomic Power Equip Dept, 61-62, mgr, Idaho Eng, Nuclear Mat & Propulsion Oper, Idaho Test Sta, 62-68; chief, Nuclear Eng Br, Idaho Opers Off, AEC, 68-74; dir, Reactor Support Div, US Energy Res & Develop Admin, 74-76, dir, Energy & Technol Div, 76-84, asst mgr, Projs & Energy Progs, US Dept Energy, 84-88. *Mem:* Am Nuclear Soc. *Res:* Nuclear engineering and neutron physics. *Mailing Add:* 3184 Chaparral Dr Idaho Falls ID 83404

**WOOD, RICHARD FROST,** PHYSICS. *Current Pos:* RES SCIENTIST & HEAD THEORY SECT, SOLID STATE DIV, OAK RIDGE NAT LAB, 62- *Personal Data:* b Lebanon, Tenn, June 6, 31; m; c 3. *Educ:* Fordham Univ, BS, 53; Ohio State Univ, MS, 56, PhD(physics), 59. *Prof Exp:* Res specialist, Opers Res, NAm Aviation, Inc, 58-60; asst prof physics, Univ Fla, 60-62. *Concurrent Pos:* Vis prof, Univ Uppsala, 60-61, NSF fel, 61-62. *Mem:* AAAS; fel Am Phys Soc. *Res:* Theoretical solid state physics; lattice defects; lattice dynamics; optical properties and electronic structure of solids. *Mailing Add:* Solid State Div Oak Ridge Nat Lab PO Box 2008 Bldg 3025 MS 6032 Oak Ridge TN 37831

**WOOD, RICHARD LEE,** VETERINARY MICROBIOLOGY. *Current Pos:* RETIRED. *Personal Data:* b Ft Dodge, Iowa, Sept 8, 30; m 55; c 3. *Educ:* Univ Mo, Columbia, DVM, 61; Iowa State Univ, MS, 66, PhD(vet microbiol), 70. *Prof Exp:* Vet med officer, Nat Animal Dis Ctr, Agr Res Serv, USDA, 61-91. *Mem:* Am Vet Med Asn; Conf Res Workers Animal Dis; US Animal Health Asn. *Res:* Epizootiology, pathogenesis and immunology of bacterial diseases of swine. *Mailing Add:* 620 River Oak Dr Ames IA 50010

**WOOD, RICHARD LYMAN,** CYTOLOGY. *Current Pos:* PROF ANAT, SCH MED, UNIV SOUTHERN CALIF, 74- *Personal Data:* b Allamore, Tex, Jan 2, 29; m 51; c 2. *Educ:* Linfield Col, BA, 50; Univ Wash, PhD(zool), 57. *Prof Exp:* From instr to asst prof anat, Univ Wash, 59-64; assoc prof, Univ Minn, Minneapolis, 64-70; prof biol struct, Sch Med, Univ Miami, 70-74. *Concurrent Pos:* NIH fel, Univ Wash, 57-59; NIH res grant, Dept Biol Struct, Univ Wash, 60-64 & Dept Anat, Univ Minn, 64-70; NSF res grant, Dept Anat, Univ Southern Calif, 78-82. *Mem:* Am Soc Cell Biol; Am Asn Anat; Electron Micros Soc Am; Soc Develop Biol. *Res:* Cell junctions; cellular biology; animal cytology and histology. *Mailing Add:* Dept Cell & Neurobiol Univ Southern Calif Sch Med 1333 San Pablo St Los Angeles CA 90033-1026. *Fax:* 213-342-3158

**WOOD, ROBERT CHARLES,** ONCOGENESIS. *Current Pos:* asst prof, 64-65, ASSOC PROF MICROBIOL, UNIV TEX MED BR GALVESTON, 65- *Personal Data:* b Lakewood, Ohio, May 7, 29; div. *Educ:* Lehigh Univ, BA, 51, MS, 52; Univ Md, PhD, 55. *Prof Exp:* Sr res microbiologist, Wellcome Res Labs, Burroughs Wellcome & Co, 56-60; asst prof microbiol, Sch Med, George Washington Univ, 60-64. *Concurrent Pos:* Res fel bact physiol, Univ Pa, 55-56. *Mem:* AAAS. *Res:* Folic acid metabolism; glycolipid metabolism; enzymic basis of oncogenesis. *Mailing Add:* 2501 Gulf Freeway Apt 251 League City TX 77573

**WOOD, ROBERT E,** INDUSTRIAL ENGINEERING & OPERATIONS RESEARCH IN FREIGHT RAILROADING. *Current Pos:* mgr indust eng, 82-93, DIR INDUST ENG & OPER RES, NORFOLK SOUTHERN CORP, 93- *Personal Data:* b Philadelphia, Pa, May 16, 38; m 62, Lorna J Jarrell; c Laura E (Dafoe) & David A. *Educ:* Ga Inst Technol, BS, 60, MS, 62, PhD(physics), 65. *Prof Exp:* From asst prof to assoc prof physics, Emory Univ, 64-75; sr opers res analyst, 75-76, mgr indust eng, Southern Rwy Syst, 76-82. *Concurrent Pos:* Consult, Ga Inst Technol, 65, fcl chem, 66; consult, Allied Gen Nuclear Serv, 73-75 & Aston Co, 75-76. *Mem:* AAAS. *Res:* Direct application of management science to railroad managment. *Mailing Add:* Norfolk Southern Corp 125 Spring St Box 110 Atlanta GA 30303

**WOOD, ROBERT HEMSLEY,** PHYSICAL CHEMISTRY. *Current Pos:* From instr to assoc prof, 57-70, chmn dept, 69-71, PROF CHEM, UNIV DEL, 70- *Personal Data:* b Brooklyn, NY, May 8, 32; div; c Michael & Mark. *Educ:* Calif Inst Technol, BS, 53; Univ Calif, PhD(chem), 57. *Honors & Awards:* Huffman Award, 93; R A Robinson Mem Lectr, 95. *Mem:* Am Chem Soc. *Res:* Solution thermodynamics; electrolytes, non-electrolytes, non-aqueous, and high temperature; geochemistry. *Mailing Add:* Dept Chem Univ Del Newark DE 19716

**WOOD, ROBERT M(CLANE),** TECHNICAL MANAGEMENT. *Current Pos:* OWNER, BOB WOOD ENTERPRISES, 93- *Personal Data:* b Ithaca, NY, Apr 4, 28; m 51, Charlotte A Kleinhans; c Ryan Schuyler & Denise Anne (Buysse). *Educ:* Univ Colo, BS, 49; Cornell Univ, PhD(exp physics), 53. *Prof Exp:* Asst elem physics, Cornell Univ, 49-50, asst solid state physics, 51-53; res engr automatic control systs, Douglas Aircraft Co, Santa Monica, 53-54 & Missile & Space Systs Div, 56-63, dep chief engr advan space technol, 63-64, asst dir sci & future systs res & develop, 64-66, dep dir res & develop, 66-71, asst dir detection, designation & discrimination, 71-76, dir res & develop, 76-84, dir advan systs & technol, Space Sta Div, McDonnell Douglas Astronaut Co, 84-93. *Concurrent Pos:* Consult, Flight Refueling, Inc, 55. *Mem:* AAAS; Am Inst Aeronaut & Astronaut; Am Phys Soc. *Res:* Heat transfer; missile and space system design; radar discrimination; research and development management; space station technology. *Mailing Add:* 1727 Candlestick Lane Newport Beach CA 92660. *Fax:* 714-631-3567; *E-Mail:* drbobwood@aol.com

**WOOD, ROBERT MANNING,** ATOMIC PHYSICS, MOLECULAR PHYSICS. *Current Pos:* asst prof, 66-80, ASSOC PROF PHYSICS, UNIV GA, 80- *Personal Data:* b Bronxville, NY, May 13, 38; c 2. *Educ:* Princeton Univ, AB, 60; Univ Wis, PhD(physics), 64. *Prof Exp:* Res assoc physics, Univ Wis, 64-66. *Mem:* Am Phys Soc. *Res:* Ion-atom and ion-molecule collisions. *Mailing Add:* Dept Physics & Astron Univ Ga Athens GA 30602

**WOOD, ROBERT WINFIELD,** RADIATION BIOPHYSICS. *Current Pos:* RETIRED. *Personal Data:* b Detroit, Mich, Dec 29, 31; m 59; c 3. *Educ:* Univ Detroit, BS, 53; Vanderbilt Univ, MA, 55; Cornell Univ, PhD(biophys), 61. *Honors & Awards:* Presidential Meritorious Rank Award, 89; Dept Energy Meritorious Serv Award, 90. *Prof Exp:* Radiol physicist, AEC, 62-73; dir, Phys & Technol Res Div, Off Health & Environ Res, US Dept Energy, 73-91, dir, Med Applns & Biophys Res Div, 91. *Concurrent Pos:* Nat Inst Gen Med Sci fel, 61-62. *Mem:* Health Physics Soc; Radiation Res Soc; Sigma Xi. *Res:* Electron spin resonance, aromatic hydrocarbon negative ions and irradiated biological compounds; radiological physics; dosimetry; biomedical instrumentation. *Mailing Add:* Off Health & Environ Res US Dept Energy Washington DC 20585

**WOOD, RODNEY DAVID,** CHEMICAL & ENVIRONMENTAL ENGINEERING, TECHNICAL MANAGEMENT. *Current Pos:* CONSULT ENGR, 93- *Personal Data:* b Lansing, Mich, Aug 19, 32; wid; c Lawrence R, Thomas K, Catherine B (Fagan) & Elizabeth S (Wilner). *Educ:* Yale Univ, BE, 54; Mich State Univ, MS, 59; Northwestern Univ, PhD(chem eng), 63. *Honors & Awards:* Award, Am Inst Chem Engrs, 64. *Prof Exp:* Instr mech eng, Mich State Univ, 56-59; asst prof, Univ Nebr, 62-64; res engr, Tex Instruments Inc, 64-70; sr engr, Sherwin Williams Chem, 70-72, tech dir, 73-77; dir process eng, Bristol-Myers Squibb Co, 77-80, mgr sterile drugs, 80-86, sr eng specialist, 86-93. *Mem:* Am Chem Soc; Am Inst Chem Engrs; Sigma Xi. *Res:* Thermodynamics, food, and pharmaceutical processing; energy; semiconductors. *Mailing Add:* 4717 Rounding Run Rd Charlotte NC 28277-8624

**WOOD, ROGER CHARLES,** COMPUTER SCIENCE, APPLIED MATHEMATICS. *Current Pos:* from asst prof to assoc prof elec eng, 65-72, chmn dept, 71-75, PROF ELEC ENG & COMPUT SCI, UNIV CALIF, SANTA BARBARA, 72- *Personal Data:* b Minneapolis, Minn, Jan 17, 32; m 54; c 4. *Educ:* Univ Minn, BS, 54, MS, 56; Univ Calif, Los Angeles, PhD(eng), 66. *Prof Exp:* Dynamics engr, Ryan Aeronaut Co, 54-57, sr dynamics engr, 57-58, sr opers res engr, 58-59; res engr, Univ Calif, Los Angeles, 64-65; opers res analyst, Syst Develop Corp, 59-60, sect head, 60-61, opers res scientist, 61-65. *Concurrent Pos:* Consult, GE Tempo, 66-68, Gen Motors Res Lab, 68-73, Human Factors Res Corp, 68-74, Gen Res Corp, 77-80 & USN, 76-; mem bd dir, Concordia Historical Inst Systs, 78- *Mem:* Inst Elec & Electronics Engrs; Opers Res Soc Am; Asn Comput Mach; Simulation Coun. *Res:* Analog, hybrid and digital computer applications; quantization theory; time sharing system scheduling; operations research; communications theory; simulation; computer architecture. *Mailing Add:* Col Eng Univ Calif Santa Barbara CA 93106

**WOOD, SCOTT EMERSON,** PHYSICAL CHEMISTRY, THERMODYNAMICS APPLIED TO CHEMICAL SYSTEMS. *Current Pos:* from assoc prof to prof, Ill Inst Technol, 48-75, admin officer & vchmn dept, 60-62, actg assoc dean for res, 62-64, EMER PROF CHEM, ILL INST TECHNOL, 75- *Personal Data:* b Ft Collins, Colo, Apr 9, 10; m 36, Marie S Simmons; c Edward S. *Educ:* Univ Denver, BS, 30, MS, 31; Univ Calif, PhD(chem), 35. *Prof Exp:* Res assoc chem, Mass Inst Technol, 35-40; from instr to asst prof, Yale Univ, 40-48. *Concurrent Pos:* Consult, Argonne Nat Lab, 60-80, Exxon Nuclear, 74-75 & 78-79; assoc ed, J Chem Phys & sect ed, Chem Abstr, 61-63; vis prof, Univ Col, Dublin, 66-67. *Mem:* AAAS; Am Chem Soc; Am Phys Soc. *Res:* Vapor pressures of nonaqueous solutions; density and coefficient of expansion of solutions; index of refraction; theory and thermodynamics of nonaqueous solutions; chromatography; paper electrochromatography; fused salts. *Mailing Add:* 1575 Belvidere St Apt 116 El Paso TX 79912-2635

**WOOD, SPENCER HOFFMAN,** GEOLOGY. *Current Pos:* asst prof, 78-80, PROF GEOL, BOISE STATE UNIV, 80- *Personal Data:* b Portland, Ore, Nov 18, 38; m 61, Layle Evansen; c 3. *Educ:* Colo Sch Mines, GE, 64; Calif Inst Technol, MS, 70, PhD(geol), 75. *Prof Exp:* Seismol engr, Geophys Serv, Mobil Oil Corp, 64-65, geophysicist, Mobil Oil Libya, Ltd, 65-68; instr geol, Occidental Col, 74-76; geologist, Nat Ctr Earthquake Res, US Geol Surv, 76-77. *Concurrent Pos:* Vis asst prof geol, Univ Ore, 76; vis prof, Chiang Mai Univ, Thailand, 94. *Mem:* Geol Soc Am; Am Geophys Union; Am Asn Petrol

Geologists. *Res:* Hydrogeology, geomorphology, neotectonics, geology of geothermal areas, tephrochronology and obsidian dating; geophysics. *Mailing Add:* Dept Geol & Geophys Boise State Univ 1910 Univ Dr Boise ID 83725. *Fax:* 208-385-4061; *E-Mail:* swood@trex.idbsu.edu

**WOOD, STEPHEN CRAIG,** PHYSIOLOGY. *Current Pos:* from asst prof to prof, Sch Med, 74-87, SR SCIENTIST LOVELACE MED FOUND, NMEX, 87- *Personal Data:* b Cleveland, Ohio, Sept 28, 42; m 67; c 4. *Educ:* Kent State Univ, BS, 64, MA, 66; Univ Ore, PhD(physiol), 70. *Prof Exp:* Res assoc physiol, Nat Res Coun, Submarine Med Res Lab, Groton, Conn, 70-71; asst prof zoophysiol, Aarhus Univ, 71-72; asst prof physiol, Southern Ill Univ, Edwardsville, 72-74. *Concurrent Pos:* Sr vis res fel, Marine Biol Lab, Plymouth, Eng, 72; Danish Natural Sci Res Coun grant, Comoro Islands Coelacanth Exped, 72. *Mem:* Am Physiol Soc; Scand Physiol Soc. *Res:* Diving physiology; comparative physiology of respiration and blood gas transport; metabolism and function of red blood cells; environmental physiology. *Mailing Add:* Dept Physiol E Carolina Univ Sch Med Greenville NC 27858

**WOOD, STEPHEN LANE,** ENTOMOLOGY. *Current Pos:* from asst prof to prof, 56-89, EMER PROF ZOOL & ENTOM, BRIGHAM YOUNG UNIV, 89- *Personal Data:* b Logan, Utah, July 2, 24; m 47, Elizabeth Griffin; c Katherine W (Brown), John G & Marian W (Pickerd). *Educ:* Utah State Univ, BS, 46, MS, 48; Univ Kans, PhD(entom), 53. *Prof Exp:* High sch instr, Utah, 48-50; asst instr biol, Univ Kans, 50-53; syst entomologist, Can Dept Agr, 53-56. *Concurrent Pos:* Vis res prof entom, Univ de Costa Rica, 63-64, Univ de los Andes, Merida, Venezuela, 69-70; ed, Great Basin Naturalist, 70-89. *Mem:* AAAS; Entom Soc Am; Coleopterists' Soc. *Res:* Systematics of Scolytidae and Platypodidae; coleoptera; world fauna. *Mailing Add:* Life Sci Mus Brigham Young Univ Provo UT 84602

**WOOD, SUSAN,** materials science engineering, for more information see previous edition

**WOOD, THOMAS H,** MULTIPLE QUANTUM WELLS. *Current Pos:* DISTINGUISHED MEM TECH STAFF, BELL LABS, 80- *Personal Data:* b Mineola, NY, Apr 17, 53; m 87; c 2. *Educ:* Brown Univ, ScB, 75; Univ Ill, Urbana, MS, 76, PhD(physics), 80. *Mem:* Am Phys Soc; Optical Soc Am; Inst Elec & Electronics Engrs. *Res:* Optoelectronic properties of multiple quantum wells, especially their use as optical modulators; fiber-in-the-loop systems. *Mailing Add:* Bell Labs Rm L115 Crawford Hill Holmdel-Keyport Rd Holmdel NJ 07733-0400. *Fax:* 732-888-7074; *E-Mail:* thw@bell-labs.com

**WOOD, THOMAS HAMIL,** BIOPHYSICS. *Current Pos:* from asst prof to prof, 53-89, EMER PROF PHYSICS, UNIV PA, 89- *Personal Data:* b Atlanta, Ga, June 22, 23; m 51; c 3. *Educ:* Univ Fla, BS, 46; Univ Chicago, PhD(biophys), 53. *Prof Exp:* Res assoc, Univ Chicago, 53. *Concurrent Pos:* NSF sr fel, Inst Radium, Paris, 61-62; vis prof, Univ Leicester, 67-68 & Ein Shams Univ, Cairo, Egypt, 80-81. *Mem:* Biophys Soc; Radiation Res Soc; Genetics Soc Am. *Res:* Effects of radiations on microorganisms; influence of temperature and protective agents; cellular freezing; bacterial conjugation; genetic recombination. *Mailing Add:* 375 Baird Rd Merion PA 19066

**WOOD, THOMAS KENNETH,** BEHAVIORAL ECOLOGY, INSECT SYSTEMATICS. *Current Pos:* PROF, DEPT ENTOM & APPL ECOL, UNIV DEL, 80- *Personal Data:* b Cleveland, Ohio, June 12, 43; m 65; c 2. *Educ:* Wilmington Col, AB, 64; Cornell Univ, PhD(entom), 68. *Prof Exp:* Prof biol, Wilmington Col, 68-80. *Concurrent Pos:* NSF grant, 75-80. *Mem:* Entom Soc Am; Entom Soc Can; AAAS. *Res:* Parental care in insects, host-plant interaction; membracid-ant associations, membracid systematics. *Mailing Add:* Dept Entom & Appl Ecol Townsend Hall Rm 216 Univ Del Newark DE 19716

**WOOD, TIMOTHY E,** ROOT SYMBIOSES, SOIL BIOGEOCHEMISTRY. *Current Pos:* SR ECOLOGIST SOILS ECOL, NATIVE PLANTS, INC, 81- *Personal Data:* b San Francisco, Calif, Aug 27, 48. *Educ:* Univ Calif, Santa Barbara, BA, 70; Yale Univ, MFS, 72, PhD(forest ecol), 80. *Prof Exp:* Res asst forest ecol, Yale Univ, 72-74; res assoc, Wood Hole Marine Biol Lab, 75-76. *Res:* Mineral nutrition of natural plant communities, including root systems, soil chemistry, and soil microbiology; symbiotic root associations involving mycorrhizal fungi, Frankia actomycenes, and Rhizobium bacteria. *Mailing Add:* 1564 E Harrison Ave Salt Lake City UT 84105

**WOOD, TIMOTHY SMEDLEY,** INVERTEBRATE ZOOLOGY. *Current Pos:* Asst prof, 71-76, ASSOC PROF BIOL SCI, WRIGHT STATE UNIV, 76-, DIR, ENVIRON STUDIES PROG, 75- *Personal Data:* b Port Washington, NY, Dec 4, 42; m 64; c 2. *Educ:* Earlham Col, AB, 64; Univ Colo, PhD(zool), 71. *Mem:* AAAS; Am Soc Zoologists; Am Micros Soc; Int Asn. *Res:* Aquatic community ecology; structure and function of animal colonies, with emphasis on the Ectoprocta. *Mailing Add:* Dept Biol Sci Wright State Univ 3640 Colonel Glenn Dayton OH 45435-0001

**WOOD, VAN E(ARL),** PHYSICS. *Current Pos:* Fel, 60-73, prin physicist, 73-89, SR PHYSICIST, COLUMBUS LABS, BATTELLE MEM INST, 89- *Personal Data:* b New York, NY, May 25, 33; m 58, Carol M Hubbard; c Susan H & Heather D. *Educ:* Union Col, BS, 55; Case Inst Technol, MS, 59, PhD(physics), 61. *Concurrent Pos:* Mem, Comt Ferroelectrics, Inst Elec & Electronics Engrs, 80- *Mem:* Am Phys Soc; Inst Elec & Electronics Engrs; Sigma Xi. *Res:* Theoretical solid-state physics, materials science and optics; related applied mathematics. *Mailing Add:* 7332 S Section Line Rd Delaware OH 43015. *Fax:* 614-424-3962

**WOOD, WALLACE D(EAN),** engineering; deceased, see previous edition for last biography

**WOOD, WARREN WILBUR,** GEOCHEMISTRY, GROUND WATER HYDROLOGY. *Current Pos:* RES HYDROLOGIST, US GEOL SURV, 81- *Personal Data:* b Pontiac, Mich, Apr 9, 37; m 61; c 2. *Educ:* Mich State Univ, BS, 59, MS, 62, PhD(geol), 69. *Honors & Awards:* Birdsall distinguished lectr, 88; Keith Anderson Award, 92. *Prof Exp:* Geologist II, Mich Hwy Dept, 62-63; res hydrologist, US Geol Surv, 64-77, asst chief off radiohydrol, 77-78; assoc prof, dept geosci, Tex Tech Univ, 78-81. *Concurrent Pos:* Consult hydrologist, 78-81; pres, GeoChem Software Inc, 93-; ed, Ground Water, 95- *Mem:* Am Geophys Union; fel Geol Soc Am; Nat Ground Water Asn; AAAS. *Res:* Geochemistry of ground water; artificial recharge; solute transport; hydrology of radioactive waste isolation; ground water and geomorphology. *Mailing Add:* US Geol Surv Nat Ctr MS430 Reston VA 20192

**WOOD, WILLIAM BAINSTER,** MEDICINE. *Current Pos:* RETIRED. *Personal Data:* b Surry Co, NC, Feb 7, 31; m 52; c 4. *Educ:* Univ NC, BS, 53, MD, 56. *Prof Exp:* Intern, NC Mem Hosp, Chapel Hill, 56-57, resident internal med, 57-59; assoc physiol, George Washington Univ, 61-63; from instr to assoc prof, Univ NC, Chapel Hill, 63-68, prof med & assoc dean, Sch Med, 84-96. *Concurrent Pos:* Fel chest dis, Sch Med, Univ NC, 59-60; attend physician, consult & dir, Pulmonary Lab, NC Mem Hosp, Chapel Hill, 63-; attend physician, Gravely Sanatorium, 63-; sr scientist, Wrightsville Marine-Biomed Lab, 66-; hon sr lectr, Cardio Thoracic Inst, London, Eng, 73-74; dir med educ & res, Eastern NC Hosp, 74-, med dir, Wilson, NC, 75-77. *Mem:* Am Thoracic Soc; AMA; Am Fedn Clin Res; Am Soc Internal Med; Soc Med Col. *Res:* Pulmonary diseases; morphology of lung in disease; mechanics and control of respiration; effects of hyperbaric atmospheres on respiration; respiratory physiology in deep sea diving; immunological and hypersensitivity lung diseases. *Mailing Add:* 2217 Homestead Rd Chapel Hill NC 27516

**WOOD, WILLIAM BARRY, III,** DEVELOPMENTAL GENETICS, MOLECULAR BIOLOGY. *Current Pos:* chmn, 77-83, PROF, DEPT MOLECULAR, CELLULAR & DEVELOP BIOL, UNIV COLO, 77- *Personal Data:* b Baltimore, Md, Feb 19, 38; m 61; c 2. *Educ:* Harvard Univ, AB, 59; Stanford Univ, PhD(biochem), 63. *Honors & Awards:* US Steel Award, Nat Acad Sci, 69. *Prof Exp:* Air Force Off Sci Res, Nat Acad Sci-Nat Res Coun fel molecular biol, Univ Geneva, 63-64; from asst prof to prof, Calif Inst Technol, 65-77. *Concurrent Pos:* Guggenheim fel, Dept Molecular, Cellular & Develop Biol, Univ Colo, Boulder, 75-76; Merit Award, NIH, 86-95; Lab Molecular Biol, Med Res Coun, Eng, 89-90; mem, Cancer Ctr, Health Sci Ctr, Univ Colo, 95- *Mem:* Nat Acad Sci; AAAS; Am Acad Arts & Sci; Am Soc Biol Chemists; Soc Develop Biol; Genetics Soc Am. *Res:* Invertebrate development genetics; genetic control and molecular biology of axis determination pattern formation and sex determination; developmental genetics of the neuratode Caenorhabditis elegans; determination of sex and cell fates in the early embryo. *Mailing Add:* Univ Colo Campus Box 347 Boulder CO 80309. *Fax:* 303-492-7744

**WOOD, WILLIAM BOOTH,** PHYSIOLOGY. *Current Pos:* from instr to assoc prof, 59-73, PROF PHARMACOL, COL MED, UNIV TENN, MEMPHIS, 73- *Personal Data:* b New York, NY, Sept 9, 22. *Educ:* Ft Hays Kans State Col, MS, 51; Univ Kans, PhD(physiol, anat), 59. *Prof Exp:* Lab asst physiol, Univ Kans, 55-56, asst, 56-58, res assoc, 58, asst instr, 58-59. *Mem:* AAAS; assoc Am Physiol Soc; Am Soc Pharmacol & Exp Therapeut. *Res:* Respiratory physiology and pharmacology of cardiovascular system. *Mailing Add:* Dept Pharmacol Univ Tenn Ctr Health Sci Memphis TN 38163-0001

**WOOD, WILLIAM C,** ONCOLOGY, SURGICAL ONCOLOGY. *Current Pos:* CHMN, DEPT SURG, SCH MED, EMORY UNIV, 91- *Personal Data:* b Fairbury, Ill, May 3, 40. *Educ:* Harvard Univ, MD, 66. *Prof Exp:* Assoc prof surg, Sch Med, Harvard Univ, 82-91; dir, Cancer Ctr, Mass Gen Hosp, 82-91, chief surg oncol, 85-91. *Mem:* Soc Surg Oncol; Am Soc Clin Oncol; Am Asn Immunol. *Mailing Add:* Sch Med Dept Surg Emory Univ Suite B-206 1364 Clifton Rd NE Surg Atlanta GA 30322-1104

**WOOD, WILLIAM EDWIN,** MATERIALS SCIENCE. *Current Pos:* Asst prof, 73-77, assoc prof, 77-81, PROF MAT SCI, ORE GRAD CTR, 81- *Personal Data:* b Plainfield, NJ, Mar 25, 47; m 71; c 3. *Educ:* Univ Notre Dame, BS, 69; Univ Calif, Berkeley, MS, 70, DEngr, 73. *Mem:* Am Soc Metals; Am Welding Soc. *Res:* Physical mechanical metallurgy; alloy developmental design; ferrous and non ferrous materials. *Mailing Add:* PO Box 91000 Portland OR 97291-1000

**WOOD, WILLIAM FULTON,** CHEMISTRY OF MUSHROOM ODORS, CHEMISTRY OF MAMMALIAN GLAND SECRETIONS. *Current Pos:* PROF CHEM, HUMBOLDT STATE UNIV, 76- *Personal Data:* b Los Angeles, Calif, May 19, 42; m 74, Brenda J Thurlow; c Warren J & Britta A. *Educ:* Univ Calif, Santa Barbara, BA, 65, PhD(org chem), 68. *Prof Exp:* Fel, McArdle Lab, Univ Wis, 69-71, Cornell Univ, 71-72; res scientist, Int Ctr Insect Physiol & Ecol, Kenya, 72-75; lectr chem, Calif Polytech State Univ, 76. *Mem:* Am Chem Soc; Int Soc Chem Ecol. *Res:* Identification of the chemicals responsible for the odors of wild mushrooms; identification of chemicals in the defensive spray of the striped skunk, the spotted skunk and the hog-nosed skunk. *Mailing Add:* Chem Dept Humboldt State Univ Arcata CA 95521-4957. *Fax:* 707-826-3279; *E-Mail:* woodw@axe.humboldt.edu

**WOOD, WILLIAM IRWIN,** MOLECULAR BIOLOGY, BIOCHEMISTRY. *Current Pos:* scientist, 82-84, sr scientist, 85-89, STAFF SCIENTIST, GENENTECH, INC, 90- *Personal Data:* b Bloomington, Ind, Nov 8, 47; div. *Educ:* Cornell Univ, BA, 70; Harvard Univ, MA, 71, PhD(biochem), 77. *Prof Exp:* Comn officer comput sci, USPHS, NIH, 71-73, staff fel biochem, 78-81. *Mem:* AAAS; Endocrine Soc. *Res:* Cloning and expression of genes of therapeutic interest including factor VIII, the growth hormone receptor, PTHrP and the IL-8 receptor. *Mailing Add:* Genentech Inc 460 Pt San Bruno Blvd South San Francisco CA 94080-4990

**WOOD, WILLIAM OTTO,** CELL BIOLOGY, BIOPHYSICS. *Current Pos:* RETIRED. *Personal Data:* b Oklahoma City, Okla, Apr 7, 25; m 50, Nadine Knodell; c Sharon L. *Educ:* Southern Methodist, BS, 50;. *Prof Exp:* Indust bacteriologist, Joseph E Seagrams & Sons, Inc, Ky, 50-53; phys chem scientist, Bur Mines, US Dept Interior, Ore, 53-54; serologist, USDA, 59-61; tissue cult res cytologist, Nat Animal Dis Lab, Iowa, 61-64; res biologist, Tissue Cult Res Labs, Biophys Lab, US Dept Army, 64-69, phys sci adminr, 69-74. *Concurrent Pos:* Independent grant, 66-69; chem res coordr, Dept Army, 69-74. *Mem:* Emer mem Soc In Vitro Biol; emer mem Am Soc Cell Biol. *Res:* Comparative studies in tissue culture preservation; in vitro studies of regenerating liver cells wounded by ballistic missles; wounding and hyperbaric oxygenation; biochemistry of "Choisonne" Goat kidney cells in vitro; primary cell culture metabolism in vitro; lymphoid tissue culture for mucosal disease studies; serum specificity for vesicular stomatitis on field samples; serum neutralization method for vesicular stomatitis; the culture of cells from a cloissone goat kidney. *Mailing Add:* 4444 US 98 N Lakeland FL 33809

**WOOD, WILLIAM WAYNE,** MONTE CARLO METHODS IN STATISTICAL MECHANICS. *Current Pos:* staff mem, Los Alamos Nat Lab, 50-57 & 71-81, group leader, 57-71, consult, 91-93, guest scientist, 93-94, consult, 94-95, GUEST SCIENTIST, LOS ALAMOS NAT LAB, 96- *Personal Data:* b Terry, Mont, Nov 1, 24; m 46, Betty J King; c Bernard E, William G, Elisabeth J, Richard L & John F. *Educ:* Mont State Univ, BS, 47; Calif Inst Technol, PhD(chem & physics), 51. *Prof Exp:* From assoc prof to prof physics, Carroll Col, 81-90. *Concurrent Pos:* Vis prof chem, Univ Colo, 69-70. *Mem:* Fel Am Phys Soc; AAAS; Sigma Xi. *Res:* Statistical mechanics of fluids. *Mailing Add:* 72 Manhattan Loop Los Alamos NM 87544. *E-Mail:* wwwood@lanl.gov

**WOOD, WILLIS AVERY,** ENZYMOLOGY, BIOINSTRUMENTATION. *Current Pos:* PRIN SCIENTIST, AGOURON INST, 93- *Personal Data:* b Johnson City, NY, Aug 6, 21; m 47; c 3. *Educ:* Cornell Univ, BS, 47; Ind Univ, PhD(microbiol), 50. *Honors & Awards:* Lilly Award, Am Soc Microbiol, 55. *Prof Exp:* From asst prof to assoc prof dairy bact, Univ Ill, 50-58; prof agr chem, Mich State Univ, 58-61, prof biochem, 61-68, chmn dept biochem, 68-74; dir microbiol & biochem, Salk Inst Biotechnol-Indust Assoc, 82-92. *Concurrent Pos:* Dir, Gilford Instrument Labs, 67-81; mem & chmn adv comt, Nat Inst Dent Res, NIH, 71-78, mem, Nat Caries Adv Comt, 79-80, Nat Adv Dent Res Coun, 86-89; pres, Neogen Corp, 81-82. *Mem:* Am Chem Soc; Am Soc Microbiol (pres, 79); Am Soc Biol Chemists. *Res:* Chemical activities of microorganisms; amino acid metabolism; protein structure; instrumentation; biotechnology-bioconversion. *Mailing Add:* Agouron Institute 505 Coast Blvd S La Jolla CA 92037

**WOODALL, DAVID MONROE,** NUCLEAR ENGINEERING, ENGINEERING PHYSICS. *Current Pos:* PROF NUCLEAR ENG, COL ENG, UNIV IDAHO, 92- *Personal Data:* b Perryville, Ark, Aug 2, 45; m 66, Carol Page Woodall. *Educ:* Hendrix Col, BA, 67; Columbia Univ, MS, 68; Cornell Univ, PhD(appl physics), 76. *Prof Exp:* Nuclear engr, Westinghouse Nuclear Energy Systs, 68-70; asst prof mech eng, Univ Rochester, 74-77; from asst prof to assoc prof nuclear eng, Univ NMex, 77-79, assoc prof & chmn chem & nuclear eng, 80-83, prof, 84-86; group mgr, Physics & Math Group, Idaho Nat Eng Lab, 86-88, dir, Ctr Nuclear Eng & Technol, 88-92. *Concurrent Pos:* Vis, Ctr Nuclear Studies, Nat Univ Mex, 83-84; vis staff, US Dept Energy, Off Space, 91. *Mem:* Am Soc Eng Educ; Am Nuclear Soc; Sigma Xi; Inst Elec & Electronics Engrs. *Res:* Plasma physics; nuclear engineering; reactor physics; applications of plasmas to microelectronic materials processing and space propulsion. *Mailing Add:* 2449 Moscow Mountain Rd Moscow ID 83843. *E-Mail:* woodall@uidaho.edu

**WOODALL, JERRY M,** RESEARCH ADMINISTRATION. *Current Pos:* PROF MICROELECTRONICS, CHARLES WILLIAM HARRISON DIST, PURDUE UNIV, 93- *Personal Data:* b Tacoma Park, Md, Sept 5, 38; m, Susan; c Chandler B, Marshall O, Debra M, Sunny L & Serena J. *Educ:* Mass Inst Technol, BS, 60; Cornell Univ, PhD(elec eng), 82. *Honors & Awards:* Jack A Morton Award, Inst Elec & Electronics Engrs, 84; Solid State Sci & Tech Award, Electrochem Soc, 85; Heinrich Welker Gold Medal, Inst Physics, 88; Medard Welch Award, Am Vacuum Soc, 90. *Concurrent Pos:* Dir, NSF Mat Res Sci & Eng Ctr Technol Enabling Heterostruct Mat. *Mem:* Nat Acad Eng; fel Am Phys Soc; fel Inst Elec & Electronics Engrs; fel Electrochem Soc; fel Am Vacuum Soc (pres-elect, 96-97). *Mailing Add:* Sch Elec & Comput Eng 1285 EE Bldg Purdue Univ West Lafayette IN 47907-1285. *Fax:* 765-494-2706; *E-Mail:* woodall@ech.purdue.edu

**WOODALL, WILLIAM ROBERT, JR,** FUEL CHEMISTRY, ENVIRONMENTAL SCIENCE. *Current Pos:* VPRES, ENVIRON POLICY DEPT, SOUTHERN CO, 91- *Personal Data:* b Augusta, Ga, May 29, 45; m 66; c 2. *Educ:* Univ Ga, BS, 67, MS, 69, PhD(entom), 72. *Prof Exp:* Ecol consult, Ga Power Co, 72, environ specialist, 72-78, supvr, Environ Ctr, 78-80, mgr, Power Supply Labs, 80-84; mgr, Environ Affairs Dept, 84-91, gen mgr, 91. *Mem:* Ecol Soc Am; Soc Power Indust Biologists (pres, 77-78). *Res:*

Thermal effects; ecology of large rivers, their floodplains, oxbow lakes and swamps; invasion of exotic bivalves; entrainment and impingement of aquatic organisms; larval fish and invertebrate drift; nutrient cycling; coal chemistry. *Mailing Add:* 15 Clarendon Ave Avondale Estates GA 30002

**WOODARD, DAVID W,** MICROWAVE & OPTICAL SEMICONDUCTORS, SEMICONDUCTOR MICROFABRICATION. *Current Pos:* res asst, 65-68 & 77-79, SR RES ASSOC, CORNELL UNIV, 79- *Personal Data:* b Philadelphia, Pa, Sept 28, 38; m 62, Susan Brown; c Kenneth & Nathan. *Educ:* Princeton Univ, BS, 62; Rutgers Univ, MS, 64; Cornell Univ, PhD(appl physics), 79. *Prof Exp:* Mem tech staff, RCA Labs, 62-65; prin engr, Cayuga Assocs, Inc, 68-77. *Concurrent Pos:* Consult, Narda Microwave Corp, 77-87 & Simmonds Precision Corp, 87-89, Mission Res, Inc, 91- *Res:* Development of microwave frequency optical sources, modulators, detectors and transistors based on heterojunction; quantum well structures made from alloys of the III-V compound semiconductors GaAs, InAs and AlAs. *Mailing Add:* Cornell Univ Phillips Hall Ithaca NY 14853

**WOODARD, HENRY HERMAN, JR,** GEOLOGY. *Current Pos:* assoc prof geol, Beloit Col, 53-66, chair dept, 55-87, chmn, Div Natural Sci & Math, prof geol, 66-92, EMER PROF, BELOIT COL, 92- *Personal Data:* b Salisbury, Mass, Dec 18, 25; m 49; c 2. *Educ:* Dartmouth Col, AB, 47, AM, 49; Univ Chicago, PhD, 55. *Honors & Awards:* Neil Miner Award, Nat Asn Geol Teachers. *Prof Exp:* Geologist, US Geol Surv, 47-49 & State Develop Comn, Maine, 50-51. *Concurrent Pos:* Geologist, Geol Surv Nfld, 55 & US Geol Surv, 57; coordr, Keck Consortium Geol, 91-94. *Mem:* Geol Soc Am; Geochem Soc; Nat Asn Geol Teachers; Am Geophys Union. *Res:* Diffusion in naturally occurring silicates; geology of Newfoundland and Boulder batholith; structure and petrology of southwestern Maine; contact alteration associated with Tertiary stocks in central Colorado; sanidines from Ordovician of Wisconsin; structural geology and petrology of the eastern contact zone vermilion batholith, Minnesota. *Mailing Add:* Dept Geol Beloit Col Beloit WI 53511-5595. *E-Mail:* woodard@beloit.edu

**WOODARD, JAMES CARROLL,** NUTRITION, COMPARATIVE PATHOLOGY. *Current Pos:* NIH fel, Univ Fla, 65-66, asst prof, 66-70, head, Dir Comp Path, 74-80, assoc prof, 78, PROF PATH, COL MED & VET MED, UNIV FLA, 78- *Personal Data:* b Birmingham, Ala, Nov 19, 33. *Educ:* Auburn Univ, DVM, 58; Mass Inst Technol, PhD(nutrit, path), 65. *Prof Exp:* Parasitologist, Ala Vet Diag Lab, 58-59; instr vet path, Auburn Univ, 61-62; res assoc, Mass Inst Technol, 63-65. *Mem:* Am Vet Med Asn; Int Acad Path; Am Inst Nutrit; Am Soc Exp Path. *Res:* Pathology, biochemical relationships of disease to microscopic pathology. *Mailing Add:* Div Comp & Exp Path Univ Fl Col Vet Med PO Box 100145 Gainesville FL 32610-0145. *Fax:* 904-392-5426

**WOODARD, KENNETH EUGENE, JR,** ELECTROCHEMICAL ENGINEERING. *Current Pos:* sect mgr chloralkali, Olin Corp, 74-75, mgr electrochem develop chloralakali, Chem Group, 75-79, mgr electrochem technol, 79-91, prog mgr han develop, 91-92, dir, Charleston Technol Ctr, Olin Basic Chem Div, 92-93, DIR TECHNOL, OLIN CHLORALKAI PROD DIV, 94- *Personal Data:* b Middletown, Ohio, Oct 7, 42; m 69, Polly S Olinger; c Kenneth J, Kelly E & Colin M. *Educ:* Univ Cincinnati, BS, 65. *Prof Exp:* Prod & develop engr chloralkali, Olin Mathieson Chem Corp, 65-69; prod supvr chloralkali & fluorocarbons, Vulcan Mat Co, 69-74. *Mem:* Electrochem Soc; Int Electrochem Soc; Am Inst Chem Engrs. *Res:* Electrochemical technology applications directed toward customer focused needs. *Mailing Add:* 128 Hummingbird Dr NW Cleveland TN 37312. *Fax:* 423-336-4554

**WOODARD, RALPH EMERSON,** RESEARCH ADMINISTRATION, REACTOR PHYSICS. *Current Pos:* RETIRED. *Personal Data:* b Nelsonville, Ohio, May 27, 21; m 43; c 3. *Educ:* Wittenberg Col, BA, 53; Oak Ridge Sch Reactor Technol, dipl, 57; Indust Col Armed Forces, dipl, 70; George Washington Univ, MSBA, 71. *Prof Exp:* Res physicist, Wright Air Develop Ctr, US Dept Air Force, 53-56, gen physicist, Oak Ridge Nat Lab, 56-57, nuclear physicist, Wright Air Develop Ctr, 57-61, gen engr res & tech plans, Aeronaut Systs Div, 61-63; supvry physicist & dep dir gen physics res lab, Aerospace Res Labs, 63-71, phys sci adminr, 71-75, phys sci adminr, Air Force Wright Aeronaut Labs, 75-79, phys sci adminr, Air Force Mat Lab, 80-82. *Concurrent Pos:* Instr physics, Wittenberg Col, 57-58; lectr, Res Mgt, Air Force Inst Tech, 72-75. *Mem:* Am Phys Soc. *Res:* Laboratory management; plasma physics; solid state physics; mathematics; chemistry; fluid mechanics; metallurgy and ceramics; energy conversion; research management. *Mailing Add:* 1138 Bradford Dr Springfield OH 45503

**WOODARD, RICHARD P,** QUANTUM GRAVITY, QUANTUM FIELD THEORY. *Current Pos:* ASST PROF PHYSICS, UNIV FLA, GAINESVILLE, 89- *Personal Data:* b Kansas City, Kans, Aug 10, 55. *Educ:* Case Western Res Univ, BS, 77; Harvard Univ, AM, 79, PhD(physics), 84. *Prof Exp:* Postdoctoral physics, Univ Tex, Austin, 83-85 & Univ Calif, Santa Barbara, 85-87; res asst prof, Brown Univ, 87-89. *Res:* Quantum gravity in the larger context of Laguargian field theory and elementary particle physics; string field theory and methods of regularization. *Mailing Add:* Physics Dept Univ Fla PO Box 118440 Gainesville FL 32611

**WOODBREY, JAMES C,** TECHNOLOGY DEVELOPMENT, BUSINESS DEVELOPMENT. *Current Pos:* TECHNOL & BUS DEVELOP CONSULT, 89- *Personal Data:* b Sebago Lake, Maine, Oct 16, 34; m 56, Cornelia E Douglass; c Margaret R, Dorrance K & Alison M. *Educ:* Univ Maine, BS, 56; Mich State Univ, PhD(phys chem, physics, org chem), 60.

*Prof Exp:* Sr phys res chemist, Res Div, W R Grace & Co, Md, 60-61; sr res chemist, Plastics Div, Monsanto Co, Mass, 61-65, res projs leader, Cent Res Dept, Mo, 65-67, New Enterprises Div, 67-69, projs mgr, res & develop, 69-76, mgr res & develop, Polymer Prod Co, 77-82, dir res & develop, Electronic Mat Co, 82-89. *Concurrent Pos:* Sci fel, Monsanto Corp, 69-79, corp sr sci fel, 79-89; dir res & mfg & actg chief exec officer, Aspect Systs Corp, 86-89. *Mem:* Am Chem Soc; AAAS; Am Phys Soc; Soc Plastics Engrs. *Res:* Preparations, structures, properties and applications of polymers, composite materials, biomedical materials, photopolymers, photoresists, magnetic resonance, vibrational spectros and solution thermodynamics; magnetic resonance and vibrational spectros; solution thermodynamics; surface physical chemistry. *Mailing Add:* 15255 Kempwood Dr Chesterfield MO 63017

**WOODBRIDGE, JOSEPH ELIOT,** CLINICAL CHEMISTRY, PHYSICAL CHEMISTRY. *Current Pos:* PRES, ALLADIN DIAGNOSTICS INC, 81- *Personal Data:* b Philadelphia, Pa, July 15, 21; m 49; c 6. *Educ:* Princeton Univ, PhD(chem), 48. *Prof Exp:* Chemist, Manhattan Proj, 44; from res chemist to group leader, Atlantic Refining Co, 46-60; dir res, Hartman-Leddon Co, 60-66; res dir, Sadtler Res Labs, Inc, Pa, 66-68; dir clin res, Worthington Biochem Corp, NJ, 68-71; vpres diag prod, Princeton Biomedix Inc, 71-81. *Mem:* Am Chem Soc; Am Asn Clin Chemists; Sigma Xi; Am Soc Clin Pathol. *Res:* Synthetic detergents; petrochemicals; clinical reagents; mass spectrometry. *Mailing Add:* 84 Bayard Lane Princeton NJ 08540-3046

**WOODBURN, MARGY JEANETTE,** FOOD SCIENCE, MICROBIOLOGY. *Personal Data:* b Pontiac, Ill, Sept 5, 28. *Educ:* Univ Ill, Urbana, BS, 50; Univ Wis-Madison, MS, 56, PhD(exp foods), 59. *Honors & Awards:* Borden Award, 76. *Prof Exp:* Instr foods & nutrit, Univ Wis-Madison, 56-57; from assoc prof to prof, Purdue Univ, 59-69; assoc dean res, Ore State Univ, 80-87, assoc dir, Ore Agr Exp Sta, 82-91, prof & head, Dept Nutrit & Food Mgt, Col Home Econ & Educ, 69-94. *Concurrent Pos:* Nat Res Coun res assoc, Ft Detrick, Md, 68; vis prof, Food Res Inst, Univ Wis-Madison. *Mem:* Am Dietetic Asn; Sigma Xi; Am Inst Nutrition; AAAS; Am Asn Family & Consumer Sci. *Res:* Food microbiology; staphylococcal enterotoxins; foodborne pathogenic bacteria; consumer practices influencing food quality and safety. *Mailing Add:* Dept Nutrit & Food Mgt Ore State Univ Milam Hall 108 Corvallis OR 97331-5103. *Fax:* 541-737-0999

**WOODBURN, WILTON A,** MECHANICAL ENGINEERING. *Current Pos:* RETIRED. *Personal Data:* b Pittsburgh, Pa, Nov 2, 26; m 56, Joan Berry; c Susan, Gail & Robert. *Educ:* Carnegie Inst Technol, BS, 47, MS, 56. *Prof Exp:* res engr, Eng Design Div, Alcoa Res Labs, Aluminum Co Am, 47-65 & Fabricating Metall Div, 65-72, eng assoc, 72-80, sr tech specialist, Fabricating Technol Div, Alcoa Tech Ctr, 80-88. *Mem:* Am Soc Mech Engrs. *Res:* Fabricating processes, particularly hot and cold rolling; computerized control for preset, guage and flatness. *Mailing Add:* 15001 Lakeside View Dr No 2504 Fort Myers FL 33919

**WOODBURNE, MICHAEL O,** VERTEBRATE PALEONTOLOGY, STRATIGRAPHY. *Current Pos:* from lectr to assoc prof, 66-77, PROF GEOL, UNIV CALIF, RIVERSIDE, 78- *Personal Data:* b Ann Arbor, Mich, Mar 8, 37; m 60; c 2. *Educ:* Univ Mich, BS, 58, MS, 60; Univ Calif, Berkeley, PhD(paleont), 66. *Prof Exp:* Mus technician vert paleont, Univ Calif, Berkeley, 62-65, mus scientist, 65-66; res assoc, Princeton Univ, 66. *Mem:* Soc Vert Paleont; Paleont Soc; Soc Study Evolution; fel Geol Soc Am. *Res:* Mammalian paleontology, including Australian marsupials; biostratigraphy and paleontology of the Mojave Desert. *Mailing Add:* Dept Earth Sci Univ Calif Riverside CA 92521

**WOODBURNE, RUSSELL THOMAS,** ANATOMY. *Current Pos:* From instr to prof, 36-74, chmn dept, 58-73, EMER PROF ANAT, MED SCH, UNIV MICH, ANN ARBOR, 75- *Personal Data:* b London, Ont, Nov 2, 04; US citizen; m 3. *Educ:* Univ Mich, AB, 32, MA, 33, PhD(anat), 35. *Mem:* Am Asn Anat (secy-treas, 64-72, pres, 74-75); Can Asn Anat. *Res:* Structure of mammalian midbrain; pleura; blood vessels of pancreas, liver, urinary bladder, ureter and urethra. *Mailing Add:* Dept Anat Univ Mich Med Sci II Ann Arbor MI 48109

**WOODBURY, ERIC JOHN,** LASER SYSTEMS. *Current Pos:* RETIRED. *Personal Data:* b Washington, DC, Feb 9, 25; m 46, Naomi F Washburn; c Judith A (Stoeser), Margaret L & John R. *Educ:* Calif Inst Technol, BS, 47, PhD(physics), 51. *Prof Exp:* Asst, Calif Inst Technol, 47-51; mem tech staff, Hughes Aircraft Co, 51-53, group head & sr staff engr, Electronics Dept, Guided Missile Lab, 53-60, sr staff physicist, Radar & Missile Electronics Lab, 61-62, sr scientist, 62-63, asst dept mgr, Laser Develop Dept, 63-66, mgr laser dept, 66-69, mgr laser develop dept, 69-72, mgr tactical laser systs lab, 72-76, chief scientist, Laser Systs Div, 76-79, chief scientist, Electro-Optical Engr Div, 79-81; asst prof, Calif State Univ, Northridge, 82-91. *Concurrent Pos:* Mem indust adv comt, Tech Educ Res Ctr, 72-75; mem local adv comt, Caltech TV proj, The Mech Universe, 82-86. *Mem:* Am Phys Soc; fel Inst Elec & Electronics Engrs; Sigma Xi. *Res:* Noise in electronic systems; application of solid state devices to electronic devices; electronic systems for use in missiles and satellites; experimental nuclear physics; laser systems and components. *Mailing Add:* 18621 Tarzana Dr Tarzana CA 91356-4512

**WOODBURY, GEORGE WALLIS, JR,** PHYSICAL CHEMISTRY. *Current Pos:* from asst prof to assoc prof, 66-74, PROF CHEM, UNIV MONT, 74- *Personal Data:* b Oct 13, 37; US citizen; m 60; c 2. *Educ:* Univ Idaho, BS, 59; Univ Minn, PhD(phys chem), 64. *Prof Exp:* Res assoc chem, Univ Minn, 64-65 & Cornell Univ, 65-66. *Mem:* Am Chem Soc. *Res:* Statistical mechanics of cooperative phenomena and adsorption. *Mailing Add:* Dept Chem Univ Mont Missoula MT 59812

**WOODBURY, JOHN F L,** medicine, for more information see previous edition

**WOODBURY, JOHN WALTER,** PHYSIOLOGY, BIOPHYSICS. *Current Pos:* PROF PHYSIOL, SCH MED, UNIV UTAH, 73- *Personal Data:* b St George, Utah, Aug 7, 23; m 49; c 4. *Educ:* Univ Utah, BS, 43, MS, 47, PhD(physiol), 50. *Prof Exp:* Lab asst physics, Univ Utah, 42-43; staff mem, Radiation Lab, Mass Inst Technol, 43-45; res asst physiol, Univ Utah, 45-47; from instr to asst prof, Sch Med, Univ Wash, 50-57, from assoc prof to prof physiol & biophys, 57-73. *Concurrent Pos:* Mem, NIH Physiol Study Sect, Dept Health & Human Serv, 78-82. *Mem:* AAAS; Am Physiol Soc; Biophys Soc; Inst Elec & Electronics Eng; Soc Neurosci. *Res:* Electrophysiology of excitable tissues; ion transport through membranes; characteristics of anion channels; anion permeability; human voluntary motor performance. *Mailing Add:* Dept Physiol Univ Utah Col Med 410 Chipeta Way Salt Lake City UT 84108-1297

**WOODBURY, MAX ATKIN,** BIOMATHEMATICS, COMPUTER SCIENCE. *Current Pos:* EMER PROF, MED CTR, DUKE UNIV, 66-, PROF COMPUT SCI, 71- *Personal Data:* b St George, Utah, Apr 30, 17; m 47; c 4. *Educ:* Univ Utah, BS, 39; Univ Mich, MS, 40, PhD(math), 48; Univ NC, Chapel Hill, MPH, 77. *Prof Exp:* Instr math, Univ Mich, 47-49; Off Naval Res grant & mem, Inst Advan Study, 49-50; res assoc math & econ, Princeton Univ, 50-52; assoc prof statist, Univ Pa, 52-54; prin investr, Logistics Res Proj, George Washington Univ, 54-56; res prof math, Col Eng, NY Univ, 56-62; prof exp neurol, Med Ctr, 63-65. *Concurrent Pos:* Gov & indust consult, 51-; mem opers res adv coun, New York, 64-68; mem diag radiol adv group, Nat Cancer Inst, 74-77; sr fel, Ctr for Demographic Studies, 75-; mem several nat comts weather modification & NIH & Food & Drug Admin study sects. *Mem:* Fel AAAS; fel Inst Math Statist; fel Am Statist Asn; Sigma Xi. *Res:* Computing; statistics; models in biology and medicine; quantitative models of information about biomedical systems require mathematics, probability and basic sciences for formulation, statistics of estimation of parametrics and testing, computing and numerical analysis for calculation. *Mailing Add:* Duke Univ 2117 Campus Dr Durham NC 27706

**WOODBURY, RICHARD BENJAMIN,** ANTHROPOLOGY, ARCHEOLOGY. *Current Pos:* prof, Univ Mass, 69-81, chmn dept, 69-73, actg assoc provost & dean grad sch, 73-74, EMER PROF ANTHROP, UNIV MASS, 81- *Personal Data:* b West Lafayette, Ind, May 16, 17; m 48, Nathalie F Sampson. *Educ:* Harvard Univ, BS, 39, MA, 42, PhD, 49. *Honors & Awards:* A V Kidder Award, Am Anthrop Asn, 89. *Prof Exp:* Archaeologist, Zaculeu Proj, United Fruit Co, Guatemala, 47-50; assoc prof anthrop, Univ Ky, 50-52; Columbia Univ, 52-58; res assoc prof, Interdisciplinary Arid Lands Prog, Univ Ariz, 59-63; cur archeol & anthrop, US Nat Mus, Smithsonian Inst, 63-69, actg head, Off Anthrop, 65-66, chmn, 66-67. *Concurrent Pos:* Mem, Div Anthrop & Psychol, Nat Res Coun, 54-57; ed, Am Antiquity, 54-58; mem, Comt Desert & Arid Zones Res, SW & Rocky Mountain Div, AAAS, 58-64, vchair, 62-64, Comt Arid Lands, 69-74, secy, 70-72; liaison rep, Comt Recovery Archeol Remains, Smithsonian Inst, 65-69; ed-in chief, Am Anthropologist, 75-78. *Mem:* Fel Am Anthrop Asn; fel AAAS; fel Archeol Inst Am; Soc Am Archeol (treas, 53-54, pres, 58-59); Sigma Xi. *Res:* Archeology; pre-industrial water management in arid lands; history of anthropology. *Mailing Add:* Dept Anthrop Machmer Hall Univ Mass Amherst MA 01003

**WOODBURY, RICHARD C,** SOLID STATE ELECTRONICS. *Current Pos:* from asst prof to assoc prof, 65-72, PROF ELEC ENG, BRIGHAM YOUNG UNIV, 72- *Personal Data:* b Salt Lake City, Utah, Apr 19, 31; m 54; c 6. *Educ:* Univ Utah, BS, 56; Stanford Univ, MS, 58, PhD(elec eng), 65. *Prof Exp:* Engr, Oscilloscope Circuit Design, Hewlett-Packard Co, Calif, 56-59; asst prof elec eng, Brigham Young Univ, 59-62; res assoc, Stanford Electronics Labs, 62-65. *Concurrent Pos:* NSF grants, 68-72; res consult to numerous firms. *Mem:* Inst Elec & Electronics Engrs. *Res:* Magnetic devices; silicon monolithic integrated circuits; silicon and cadmium sulfide photovoltaic cells; radiation hardening of silicon electron voltaic and photovoltaic cells; vacuum microelectronics. *Mailing Add:* 2891 N 175 E Provo UT 84604-3907

**WOODBURY, RICHARD PAUL,** HYDROGEN CYANIDE & SULFUR CHEMISTRY, BIODEGRADATION & CHELATION. *Current Pos:* sr res chemist, 83-89, MGR ORG CHEM RES, HAMPSHIRE CHEM CORP, NASHUA, NH, 89- *Personal Data:* b Kenosha, Wis, Aug 16, 50; m 71, Janet L Hammond; c Elizabeth A & Michael P. *Educ:* Univ Wis-Whitewater, BS, 72; Mich State Univ, PhD(chem), 76. *Prof Exp:* Sr chemist, Borg Warner Chem, 76-83. *Mem:* Am Chem Soc; Am Org Chem Soc. *Res:* Synthesis of biologically important peptides and amino acids; heterocyclic compounds; chelating agents, hydantoins & sulfur specialty chemicals. *Mailing Add:* 9 Woodland Dr Amherst NH 03031-2523. *E-Mail:* rpwo@aol.com

**WOODBURY, ROBERT A,** PHARMACOLOGY. *Current Pos:* RETIRED. *Personal Data:* b Sep 1, 04; US citizen; m; c 3. *Educ:* Univ Kans, BS, 24, MS, 28, PhD(physiol), 31; Univ Chicago, MD, 34. *Prof Exp:* From asst prof to prof pharmacol, Sch Med, Univ Ga, 34-47, chmn, 41-47; prof & chmn, Med Units, Univ Tenn, 47-75. *Concurrent Pos:* Mem, study sect & rev comt, NIH, 65-67. *Mem:* Sigma Xi; Am Soc Physiol; Am Soc Pharmacol & Exp Therapeut. *Res:* Cardiovascular system; autonomic system; uterine pharmacology and physiology. *Mailing Add:* 8696 Pepper Bush Lane Germantown TN 38139

**WOODCOCK, ALFRED HERBERT,** OCEANOGRAPHY. *Current Pos:* res assoc geophys, Hawaii Inst Geophys, 63-72, RES AFFIL, DEPT OCEANOG, UNIV HAWAII, 72-; EMER SCIENTIST, WOODS HOLE OCEANOG INST, 88- *Personal Data:* b Atlanta, Ga, Sept 7, 05; m 41; c 3. *Hon Degrees:* DSc, Long Island Univ, 61. *Prof Exp:* Technician, Woods Hole Oceanog Inst, 31-42, res assoc, 42-46, oceanogr, 46-63. *Mem:* AAAS; fel Am Meteorol Soc; assoc Am Geophys Union. *Res:* Marine meteorology; air-sea interaction; sea-salt nuclei in marine air and their role in cloud, rain and fog formation; Hawaii Alpine Lake, permafrost and mountain breathing studies. *Mailing Add:* 45-090 Namoku St Apt 912 Kaneohe HI 96744-5320

**WOODCOCK, CHRISTOPHER LEONARD FRANK,** CELL BIOLOGY, BIOCHEMISTRY. *Current Pos:* from asst prof to assoc prof, 72-78, PROF ZOOL, UNIV MASS, AMHERST, 78-, DIR CENT MICROS FACIL, 86-, CHMN, DEPT BIOL, 95- *Personal Data:* b Essex, Eng, July 9, 42; m 64; c 3. *Educ:* Univ Col, Univ London, BSc, 63, PhD(bot), 66. *Prof Exp:* Res fel biophys, Univ Chicago, 66-67; res fel bot, Harvard Univ, 67-69, lectr biol, 69-72. *Concurrent Pos:* Fogarty sr int fel, 92-93. *Mem:* Am Soc Cell Biol; Micros Soc Am. *Res:* Cell ultrastructure and function; information processing in cells; chromatin structure and function. *Mailing Add:* Dept Biol Univ Mass Amherst MA 01003. *Fax:* 413-545-1696; *E-Mail:* chris@bio.umass.edu

**WOODCOCK-MITCHELL, JANET LOUISE,** CELL BIOLOGY. *Current Pos:* postdoctoral fel, 81-86, RES ASST PROF, UNIV VT, 86- *Personal Data:* b Barre, Vt, Sept 6, 49; m 75. *Educ:* Univ Conn, BA, 71, MS, 74, PhD(biochem), 79. *Prof Exp:* Postdoctoral fel, Johns Hopkins Univ, 79-81. *Mem:* Am Soc Cell Biol; Am Thoracic Soc. *Res:* Differentiation of lung epithelial cells during development and in repair after lung injury; growth factors and signals inducing differentiation of epithelial cells. *Mailing Add:* Dept Physiol Univ Vt Given Bldg D-206 Burlington VT 05405-0001

**WOODFIELD, F(RANK) W(ILLIAM), JR,** CHEMICAL ENGINEERING. *Current Pos:* RETIRED. *Personal Data:* b Astoria, Ore, Mar 1, 18; m 44, Joyce E Gleeson; c Susan J (Norwood), Dorothy A (Latendresse) & William G. *Educ:* Ore State Col, BS, 39; Columbia Univ, MS, 40. *Prof Exp:* Chem engr process eng & eng res, E I Du Pont de Nemours & Co, Inc, 40-47; increasing responsibility group leader to mgr eng develop, Gen Elec Co, 47-55, mgr reactor mat develop, 55-62, specialist contract admin, 62-63, mgr programming, 64; dep staff mgr programming & tech develop, Pac Northwest Lab, Battelle Mem Inst, 65-66, mgr develop, Fast Flux Test Facil, 67-68, asst lab dir tech serv, 68-70, mgr facil planning & eng, 70-73, prog mgr plenum fill exp, 74; mgr, Res & Technol Ctr, Exxon Nuclear Co Inc, 75-81, mgr logistics, 81-83. *Concurrent Pos:* Chmn, Nuclear Eng Div, Am Inst Chem Engrs, 67. *Mem:* Am Chem Soc; Am Nuclear Soc; Am Inst Chem Engrs. *Res:* Chemical engineering diffusional operations; technical and administrative management of research and development in a broad-spectrum laboratory. *Mailing Add:* 81 McMurray St Richland WA 99352

**WOODFILL, MARVIN CARL,** COMPUTER SYSTEM ENGINEERING. *Current Pos:* from asst prof to prof elec eng, 66-80, PROF COMPUT SCI, ARIZ STATE UNIV, 80- *Personal Data:* b Los Angeles, Calif, June 13, 38; m 80, 88, Marolee D O'Dowd; c 5. *Educ:* Iowa State Univ, BS, 59, MS, 61, PhD(elec eng), 64. *Prof Exp:* Asst prof elec eng, Iowa State Univ, 59-64. *Concurrent Pos:* Engr consult, Sperry Flight Systs, Ariz, 66-67, semiconductor prod div, Motorola, Inc, 68-70, govt electronics div, 71, St Joseph's Hosp & Med Ctr, Phoenix, 70-81 & City Prescott, 79- *Mem:* Inst Elec & Electronics Engrs. *Res:* Development of mini-micro computer systems for engineering, medical and governmental applications. *Mailing Add:* 296 Williamson Valley Rd Prescott AZ 86301. *Fax:* 602-965-2751; *E-Mail:* marvin.woodfill@asu.edu

**WOODFIN, BEULAH MARIE,** BIOCHEMISTRY. *Current Pos:* asst prof, 67-78, ASSOC PROF BIOCHEM, SCH MED, UNIV NMEX, 78- *Personal Data:* b Chicago, Ill, June 22, 36. *Educ:* Vanderbilt Univ, BA, 58; Univ Ill, Urbana, MS, 60, PhD(biochem), 63. *Prof Exp:* Res assoc biochem, Univ Mich, 63-66, instr, 66-67. *Concurrent Pos:* USPHS fel, Univ Mich, 63-65. *Mem:* AAAS; Am Chem Soc; NY Acad Sci; Sigma Xi; Am Soc Biochem Molecular Biol; Protein Soc. *Res:* Interaction of viral proteins with mitochondria; experimental mouse model of Reye's syndrome; ornithine carbamoyl transferase deficiency. *Mailing Add:* Dept Biochem Univ NMex Sch Med Albuquerque NM 87131-5221

**WOODFORD, DAVID A(UBREY),** PHYSICAL METALLURGY. *Personal Data:* b Cleethorpes, Eng, Sept 17, 37; m 61; c 3. *Educ:* Univ Birmingham, BSc, 60, PhD(metall), 63. *Hon Degrees:* DSc, Univ Birmingham, 81. *Honors & Awards:* A H Geisler Award, 72. *Prof Exp:* Res fel, Univ Birmingham, 63-64; res metallurgist, Mat & Processes Lab, Gen Elec Co, 64-73, staff metallurgist, Corp Res & Develop, 73-86; prof mat res, Rensselaer Polytech Inst, 86-95. *Concurrent Pos:* Assoc ed, J Eng Mat & Tech, 74- & Fatigue Eng Mat & Struct, 78- *Mem:* Am Soc Metals; Am Soc Testing & Mat; Am Soc Mech Engrs. *Res:* High temperature mechanical properties; creep and radiation damage; strain aging superplasticity; temper embrittlement; thermal fatigue; cavitation erosion; environmental embrittlement; author or coauthor of 60 publications. *Mailing Add:* 1707 Garden St Santa Barbara CA 43101

**WOODFORD, JAMES,** FORENSIC COMPARISON ANALYSIS, MEDICINAL CHEMISTRY. *Current Pos:* DIR, WEB RES, ATLANTA, GA, 75- *Personal Data:* b Roanoke, Va, Mar 18, 46. *Educ:* Emory Univ, MS, 70, PhD(chem), 73. *Prof Exp:* Postdoctoral, Univ Kans, 73-74; Res assoc chem, Dept Chem, Emory Univ, 74-75. *Concurrent Pos:* Res award, Nat Cancer Inst, 73; vis scientist & guest seminar speaker, Metro Police Forensic Sci Lab, Scotland Yard; lectr chem, Chem Dept, Emory Univ, 76-77; instr clin chem, Sch Pharm, Mercer Univ, 77-78; bd dir, Metrop Atlanta Coun Alcohol & Drugs, 79- *Mem:* Am Chem Soc; AAAS. *Res:* Testing for court purposes; forensic comparison analyses of evidence. *Mailing Add:* PO Box 941156 Atlanta GA 30341

**WOODGATE, BRUCE EDWARD,** ASTROPHYSICS. *Current Pos:* sci systs analyst, 74-75, proj scientist, Solar Maximum Mission, 83-85, ASTROPHYSICIST, GODDARD SPACE FLIGHT CTR, 75-, PRIN INVESTR, SPACE TELESCOPE IMAGING SPECTROG, 85- *Personal Data:* b Eastbourne, Sussex, Eng, Feb 19, 39; m 65, Patricia; c Catherine & Nina. *Educ:* Univ London, BSc, 61, PhD(astron), 65. *Honors & Awards:* NASA Except Sci Achievement Medal, 86. *Prof Exp:* From res asst to res assoc physics, Univ Col, Univ London, 65-71; sr res assoc, Columbia Univ, 71-74, assoc dir, Astrophys Lab, 72-74. *Concurrent Pos:* Mem working group, NASA Outlook for Space Study, 74. *Mem:* Am Astron Soc. *Res:* X-ray astronomy; astronomy of supernova remnants and the interstellar medium; solar physics and solar-terrestrial relations, solar flares; remote sensing of earth resources; solar flare physics using UV and x-ray spectroscopy; supernova remnant and interstellar medium physics using optical narrow bend imaging; evolution of galaxies; space instrumentation, UV, x-ray, optical. *Mailing Add:* Goddard Space Flight Ctr NASA Greenbelt MD 20771. *E-Mail:* woodgate@stars.gsfc.nasa.gov

**WOODHAM, DONALD W,** analytical chemistry, insect rearing, for more information see previous edition

**WOODHAMS, RAYMOND T,** SELF-REINFORCED & ORIENTED PLASTICS, STRUCTURAL FOAMS & ORIENTED COMPOSITES. *Current Pos:* RETIRED. *Personal Data:* m 58, Alice Pauline; c Diane Elizabeth & Linda Lee Mary. *Educ:* Univ Western Ont, BSc, 50, MSc, 51; Polytech Inst Brooklyn, PhD(polymerization kinetics), 54. *Prof Exp:* Mgr chem res, Dunlop Res Ctr, 54-68; prof, Dept Chem Eng & Appl Chem, Univ Toronto, 68-92, emer prof chem eng, 92-97. *Concurrent Pos:* Dir, Chem Eng & Res Consults Ltd, 68-92; prin investr, Mfg Res Corp Ont, 87-93 & Ont Ctr Mat Res, 88-93; prog area leader, Ont Ctr Mat Res, 89-92; vpres, Tribokinetics Inc, 92-96. *Mem:* Soc Plastic Engrs. *Res:* Manufacture of self-reinforced plastics and composites by extrusion and injection molding; new technology applied to the manufacture of biaxially oriented pipes, plastic strapping, plastic wire, oriented profiles, oriented structural foams, plastic lumber, lubricated flow orientation of plastics. *Mailing Add:* 33 The Palisades Toronto ON M6S 2W9 Can. *Fax:* 416-766-6553; *E-Mail:* raymond. woodhams@utoronto.ca

**WOODHOUR, ALLEN F,** VIROLOGY, BACTERIOLOGY. *Current Pos:* RETIRED. *Personal Data:* b Newark, NJ, Feb 21, 30; m 55; c 1. *Educ:* St Vincent Col, AB, 52; Cath Univ Am, MS, 54, PhD(bact), 56. *Prof Exp:* Bacteriologist, Walter Reed Army Inst Res, 56-57; res assoc virol, Charles Pfizer & Co, Inc, 57-60; res assoc, Merck Inst Therapeut Res, 60-64, asst dir, Dept Virus Dis, 64-66, dir viral vaccine res, 66-73, asst dir virus & cell biol res, 68-73, sr dir & asst area head virus cell biol res, 74-78, exec dir bact vaccines & admin affairs, virus & cell biol res, 78-89. *Mem:* AAAS; Am Asn Immunol; Sigma Xi; Int Asn Biol Stand; Am Soc Microbiol. *Res:* Use of adjuvants in immunology; metabolizable vegetable oil water-in-oil adjuvant; respiratory viruses for vaccine development; development of bacterial vaccines; antivirals. *Mailing Add:* 8003 River Pl Carmel CA 93923

**WOODHOUSE, BERNARD LAWRENCE,** PHARMACOLOGY. *Current Pos:* from instr to asst prof, 64-73, assoc prof, 73-79, PROF BIOL, SAVANNAH STATE COL, 79- *Personal Data:* b Norfolk, Va, Aug 14, 36; m 64; c 3. *Educ:* Howard Univ, BS, 58, MS, 63, PhD(pharmacol), 73. *Prof Exp:* Instr zool, A&T Col NC, 63-64. *Concurrent Pos:* Hoffmann-La Roche res grant & NIH res grant, 75- *Res:* Study of the mechanism of the antihypertensive effects of beta adrenergic blocking drugs on various species of animals. *Mailing Add:* Dept Biol Savannah State Col Savannah GA 31404-9702

**WOODIN, SARAH ANN,** MARINE ECOLOGY. *Current Pos:* from res assoc prof to res prof, 80-87, PROF, DEPT BIOL, UNIV SC, 87- *Personal Data:* b New York, NY, Dec 27, 45; m 80, David S Wethey; c 1. *Educ:* Goucher Col, BA, 67; Univ Wash, PhD(marine ecol), 72. *Prof Exp:* Res asst prof ecol, Univ Md, 72-75 & Johns Hopkins Univ, 75-80; asst prof ecol, Johns Hopkins Univ, 75-80. *Concurrent Pos:* Res grant, Div Biol Oceanog, NSF, 74- & Div Systs, 85-88, Div Ecol, 89-92; marine ed, Ecol & Ecological Monographs, 78-81; mem, Animal Resources Comt, NIH, 83-87. *Mem:* Ecol Soc Am; Am Soc Zool; fel AAAS; Am Soc Limnol & Oceanog; Sigma Xi; Soc Study Evolution. *Res:* Benthic ecology; life history strategies of organisms, particularly in fauna; functional morphology of polychaetes. *Mailing Add:* Dept Biol Univ SC Columbia SC 29208

**WOODIN, TERRY STERN,** BIOCHEMISTRY. *Current Pos:* ASSOC PROF, UNIV NEV, RENO, 77- *Personal Data:* b New York, NY, Dec 25, 33; m 54; c 5. *Educ:* Alfred Univ, BA, 54; Univ Calif, Davis, MA, 65, PhD(biochem), 67. *Prof Exp:* Res assoc biochem, Univ Calif, Davis, 67-68; adj asst prof, Univ Nev, Reno, 68-69, asst prof, 69-72; asst prof biochem, Humboldt State Univ, 72-77. *Mem:* AAAS; Am Chem Soc; Sigma Xi; Am Soc Plant Physiologists. *Res:* Sulfate metabolism in fungi; thermophilic fungi; temperature effects on membrane structure and function. *Mailing Add:* Div Undergrad Educ Nat Sci Found 4201 Wilson Blvd Arlington VA 22230

**WOODIN, WILLIAM GRAVES,** ALLERGY. *Current Pos:* from instr to asst prof, 48-54, clin assoc prof, 54-63, CLIN PROF MED, STATE UNIV NY UPSTATE MED CTR, 63-, DIR ALLERGY CLIN, 48- *Personal Data:* b Dunkirk, NY, July 22, 14; m 40, Barbara Mason; c William N & Sarah A (Wethey). *Educ:* Cornell Univ, AB, 36, MD, 39. *Prof Exp:* Intern & asst resident med, Univ Hosps Cleveland, 39-41; asst, Med Col, Cornell Univ, 46, instr, 47-48. *Concurrent Pos:* Fel, Roosevelt Hosp, NY, 47-48; consult hosps, 50- *Mem:* AMA; fel Am Acad Allergy; NY Acad Sci. *Res:* Immunological characteristics of genetically engineered B lactoglobulin. *Mailing Add:* 4 Old Farm Rd Fayetteville NY 13066

**WOODIN, WILLIAM HARTMAN, III,** ZOOLOGY. *Current Pos:* Dir, 54-71, EMER DIR, ARIZ-SONORA DESERT MUS, 72-; PRES, WOODIN LAB, 81- *Personal Data:* b New York, NY, Dec 16, 25; m 48, 77, Elizabeth Thomas; c Peter, John, Michael & W Hugh. *Educ:* Univ Ariz, BA, 50; Univ Calif, MA, 56. *Mem:* Fel AAAS. *Res:* Herpetology; taxonomy; desert ecology. *Mailing Add:* 3600 N Larrea Lane Tucson AZ 85750

**WOODING, FRANK JAMES,** agronomy; deceased, see previous edition for last biography

**WOODING, WILLIAM MINOR,** EXPERIMENTAL STATISTICS, CHEMISTRY. *Current Pos:* CONSULT, 82-; WRITER, 85- *Personal Data:* b Waterbury, Conn, Aug 24, 17; m 53, Nina Peaslee; c Barbara (Bose) & Beth. *Educ:* Polytech Inst Brooklyn, BChemE, 53. *Prof Exp:* Analyst inorg chem, Scovill Mfg Co, Conn, 36-40; technician, Am Cyanamid Co, 41-46, chemist, 46-51, res chemist, 51-56, coordr personnel admin serv, 56-57; asst chief chemist, Revlon, Inc, NY, 57-61, assoc res dir, 61-65; assoc res dir, Carter-Wallace, Inc, 65-67, dir tech serv, Carter Prod Div, 67-75, corp dir statist serv, 75-82. *Mem:* AAAS; Am Chem Soc; fel Am Inst Chemists; fel Am Soc Qual Control; fel Soc Cosmetic Chem; Am Statist Asn; Am Soc Test Mat; Biomet Soc; Soc Clin Trials. *Res:* Experimental design and applied statistics, principally in medical and biological fields; teaching statistical techniques to biomedical personnel; contributed 24 papers to scientific journals. *Mailing Add:* 4690 Maquam Shore Rd Swanton VT 05488. *Fax:* 802-868-7375

**WOODLAND, BERTRAM GEORGE,** STRUCTURAL GEOLOGY, MICRO-FABRICS. *Current Pos:* cur, 63-87, EMER CUR, FIELD MUS NATURAL HIST, 87- *Personal Data:* b Mountain Ash, Wales, Apr 4, 22; m 52; c 2. *Educ:* Univ Wales, BSc, 42; Univ Chicago, PhD(geol), 62. *Prof Exp:* Exp officer, Ministry Home Security, Gt Brit Air Ministry, 43-46; res asst mineral surv, Ministry Town & Country Planning, 46-49; asst res officer, Ministry Housing & Local Govt, 49-54; from instr to asst prof geol, Univ Mass, 54-56; asst prof, Mt Holyoke Col, 56-58; assoc cur, Chicago Natural Hist Mus, 58-62. *Concurrent Pos:* Consult, Petrol Brasileiro Depex, Rio de Janeiro, Brazil, 55-56, Coronet Instrnl Films, 70-80, ITT Res Inst, 75-79, Denoyer-Cappert, 79-80 & Harza Eng Co, 83-84. *Mem:* Fel Geol Soc London; Geol Asn London. *Res:* Metamorphism; igneous rocks; cone-in-cone structure; tectonics and microstructures. *Mailing Add:* 18345 Perth Ave Homewood IL 60430

**WOODLAND, DOROTHY JANE,** PHYSICAL CHEMISTRY. *Current Pos:* prof & head dept, 44-74, EMER PROF CHEM, JOHN BROWN UNIV, 74- *Personal Data:* b Warren, Ohio, Sept 20, 08. *Educ:* Col Wooster, BS, 29; Ohio State Univ, MSc, 30, PhD(chem), 32. *Prof Exp:* Asst, Col Wooster, 28-29 & Ohio State Univ, 29-32; from instr to asst prof chem, Wellesley Col, 32-38; assoc prof & head dept, Western Col, 38-42, prof, 42-44. *Mem:* Emer mem Am Chem Soc; Sigma Xi. *Res:* Surface energy; relation between radius of curvature of droplets and surface energy. *Mailing Add:* 811 W Elgin Woodland Manor Siloam Springs AR 72761

**WOODLAND, JOSEPH,** ENGINEERING, ARTIFICIAL INTELLIGENCE EXPERT SYSTEMS. *Current Pos:* RETIRED. *Personal Data:* b Atlantic City, NJ, Sept 6, 21. *Educ:* Drexel Univ, BS, 47; Syracuse Univ, MME, 56. *Honors & Awards:* Nat Medal Technol, President George Bush, 92. *Prof Exp:* Mech Designer, IBM, 51-54, from staff engr to proj engr, 56-87, sr planner, 87-92; Technol Consult, 92- *Mem:* Am Soc Mech Engrs. *Mailing Add:* 426 Van Thomas Dr Raleigh NC 27615

**WOODLAND, WILLIAM CHARLES,** PHYSICAL CHEMISTRY. *Current Pos:* RETIRED. *Personal Data:* b Highland Park, Mich, Nov 22, 19; m 44; c 3. *Educ:* Col Wooster, BA, 41; Carnegie Inst Technol, MS, 49, DSc(phys chem), 50. *Prof Exp:* Instr org microanal, NY Univ, 49-51; chemist, Jackson Lab, Washington Works, E I Du Pont de Nemours & Co, Inc, Parkersburg, WVa, 51, Chambers Works, NJ, 61-64, color specialist, Parkersburg, WVa, 64-72, sr chemist, 72-84. *Res:* Thermoplastic resins; color technology; specialized analytical chemistry. *Mailing Add:* 9 Ashwood Dr Vienna WV 26105

**WOODLEY, CHARLES LAMAR,** BACTERIAL GENETICS. *Current Pos:* lab technician, 66-72, MICROBIOLOGIST, CTR DIS CONTROL, 72- *Personal Data:* b Atlanta, Ga, Sept 12, 41; m 64; c 1. *Educ:* Ga State Univ, BS, 72, MS, 75; Univ Ga, PhD(microbiol), 80. *Prof Exp:* Lab technician, US Army Nutrit Labs, 64-66. *Mem:* Am Soc Microbiol. *Res:* Genetic aspects of genus mycobacterium; organisms that cause tuberculosis. *Mailing Add:* Ctr Dis Control Mail Stop F08 1600 Clifton Rd Atlanta GA 30333

**WOODLEY, CHARLES LEON,** BIOCHEMISTRY. *Current Pos:* ASST PROF BIOCHEM, UNIV MISS MED CTR, 74- *Personal Data:* b Montgomery, Ala, Jan 22, 44; m 66; c 1. *Educ:* Univ Ala, BS, 66, MS, 68; Univ Nebr, PhD(chem), 72. *Prof Exp:* Res assoc biochem, Univ Nebr, Lincoln, 71-74. *Mem:* Sigma Xi. *Res:* Control of protein synthesis initiation and translation in eukaryotic and viral systems. *Mailing Add:* Dept Biochem Univ Miss Sch Med 2500 N State St Jackson MS 39216-4505

**WOODMAN, DANIEL RALPH,** VIROLOGY, CLINICAL MICROBIOLOGY. *Current Pos:* RETIRED. *Personal Data:* b Portland, Maine, Apr 20, 42; m 67. *Educ:* Univ Maine, Orono, BS, 64; Univ Md, College Park, MS, 66, PhD(microbiol), 72. *Prof Exp:* Asst microbiol, Univ Md, College Park, 64-67; naval officer virol, Deseret Test Ctr, Salt Lake City, 67-69; instr, Univ Col, Univ Md, 70; exec officer, US Naval Unit, Ft Detrick, Md, 71-74, head, Virol Div, 74-78, head, Microbiol Br, Naval Med Res Inst, 78-80, head, Microbiol Sect, Nat Naval Med Ctr, Bethesda, 80- *Mem:* Am Soc Microbiol; Asn Mil Surgeons US; Am Soc Trop Med & Hyg; AAAS. *Res:* Animal virology with a special interest in viral immunology and chemotherapeutics; arbovirus replication and pathogenicity. *Mailing Add:* 3904 Randolph Rd Silver Spring MD 20902

**WOODMAN, PETER WILLIAM,** TOXICOLOGY, CARCINOGENESIS. *Current Pos:* DEP MGR ENVIRON SCI, HALEY & ALDRICH INC, 91- *Personal Data:* b Gloucester, Eng; m; c 2. *Educ:* Univ Bath, B Pharm, Hons, 70, PhD(molecular pharmacol & med chem), 74. *Prof Exp:* Systs analyst pharmaceut mfg, Eli Lilly, Eng, 69; teaching asst pharm & pharmacol, Univ Bath, 70-74; proj assoc oncol, McArdle Lab Cancer Res, 74-76; asst mem biochem & pharmacol, St Jude Childrens Res Hosp, 76-80; tech dir & dept mgr, Health Sci, Dynamac Corp, 80-90; sr assoc, Precepts Inc, 90-91. *Concurrent Pos:* Mem ad hoc, Nat Large Bowel Cancer Proj, Nat Cancer Inst, 76-80; mem SBIR rev bd, Nat Inst Environ Health Sci, 85-88. *Res:* Medicinal, chemical, and environmental risk assessment programs involving evaluation of the metabolism, pharmacology, toxicology, pharmacokinetics, and carcinogenicity of chemical compounds. *Mailing Add:* 27 Stoneymeade Way Acton MA 01720-5676

**WOODMANSEE, DONALD ERNEST,** CHEMICAL ENGINEERING, GEOCHEMISTRY. *Current Pos:* Mgr, Geosci Br, 80-82, CHEM ENGR FUELS RES, GEN ELEC CORP RES & DEVELOP CTR, 67- *Personal Data:* b Lexington, Ky, May 23, 41; m 64; c 2. *Educ:* Univ Del, BChE, 63; Univ Ill, MS, 65, PhD(chem eng), 68. *Honors & Awards:* Industrial Res 100, 77. *Concurrent Pos:* Mgr planning & resources, Mat Labs, Gen Elec Res & Develop Ctr, 83-85. *Mem:* Am Inst Chem Engrs. *Res:* Conversion of fossil fuels to clean energy forms; research on a one ton per hour, twenty atmosphere coal gasifier. *Mailing Add:* 1470 Dean St Schenectady NY 12309

**WOODMANSEE, ROBERT GEORGE,** RANGE ECOLOGY, SYSTEMS ECOLOGY. *Current Pos:* dir, Natural Resource Lab, 84, PROF, DEPT RANGE SCI, COLO STATE UNIV, 82- *Personal Data:* b Albuquerque, NMex, Sept 11, 41; m 63; c 2. *Educ:* Univ NMex, BS, 67, MS, 69; Colo State Univ, PhD(forest ecol & soils), 72. *Prof Exp:* Fel grassland ecol, Colo State Univ, 72-74, sr res ecologist, Natural Resource Ecol Lab, 74-78, asst dir grassland biome, 75-76, assoc prof, Dept Range Sci, 78-82; prog dir, Ecosyst Studies, NSF, 82-84. *Concurrent Pos:* Consult interactions biochem cycles, Steering Comt, Swedish Univ Agr; prin investr, NSF; mem, US Nat Comt-Sci Comt Prob Environ, Med Adv Bd, Exec Comt Asn Ecosyst Res Ctr, Nat Astrological Soc, Comt Planetary Biol & Chem Evol. *Mem:* Ecol Soc Am; Soc Range Mgt; AAAS; Am Inst Biol Sci; Sigma Xi. *Res:* Field experimentation and simulation modeling of nutrient cycling in grassland and agricultural ecosystems; long-term ecological research. *Mailing Add:* 703 E County Rd 68 Ft Collins CO 80524

**WOODRIFF, ROGER L,** MATHEMATICAL & MACHINE MODELS OF THE BRAIN, ILLUMINATION & DISCRETE EVENT MODELS OF LASER DISK JUKE BOX STORAGE SYSTEMS. *Current Pos:* PROF MATH, MENLO COL, 70-; PRES, MENLO RES ASSOC, 85-; CHIEF EXEC OFFICER, BUCKEYE ASSOCS, 87-; PRES & CHIEF EXEC OFFICER, NAEFELS LTD, 96- *Personal Data:* b Bozeman, Mont. *Educ:* Mont State Univ, BS, 64; Univ Wis-Milwaukee, MS, 65; Columbia Pacific Univ, PhD, 97. *Prof Exp:* Asst math, Mont State Univ, 63-64; instructing asst, Univ Wis-Milwaukee, 64-65; vis instr, Mid East Tech Univ, Ankara, 65-67; asst prof, Humboldt State Col, 67-70. *Concurrent Pos:* Comput & educ consult, Menlo Res Assoc, 81-; ed & rev, Math Texts, Harper & Row; Int consult Hardware-Software, Portable Systs. *Mem:* Am Math Soc; Math Asn Am; Am Asn Univ Profs; Am Col Math; Inst Elec & Electronics Engrs. *Res:* Mathematical models of cognition and their implementation as computer programs or computer hardware architecture, particularly cellular and hierarchial paradigms. *Mailing Add:* Menlo Res Assocs 1000 El Camino Atherton CA 94027

**WOODRING, JOSEPH,** INSECT PHYSIOLOGY. *Current Pos:* From instr to assoc prof, 60-70, PROF ZOOL, LA STATE UNIV, BATON ROUGE, 71- *Personal Data:* b Phillipsburg, Pa, Sept 29, 32; m 55; c 2. *Educ:* Pa State Univ, BS, 54; Univ Minn, MS, 58, PhD(entom & zool), 60. *Concurrent Pos:* Humboldt fel, Univ Kiel, 67-68, Univ Dulsseldorf, 89, Univ Ulm, 91, 92 & 93. *Res:* hormonal regulation of metabolism and reproduction; neuropeptides, biogenic amines and juvenile hormone. *Mailing Add:* Dept Zool La State Univ Baton Rouge LA 70803-0001. *Fax:* 504-388-1763; *E-Mail:* zowood@lsuvm

**WOODROW, DONALD L,** STRATIGRAPHY, SEDIMENTOLOGY. *Current Pos:* From asst prof to assoc prof, 65-75, PROF GEOL, HOBART & WILLIAM SMITH COLS, 75- *Personal Data:* b Washington, Pa, Nov 25, 35; m 60; c 2. *Educ:* Pa State Univ, BS, 57; Univ Rochester, MS, 50, PhD(geol), 65. *Concurrent Pos:* NSF res grant, 68-78; Res Corp res grant, 69-75; vis res geologist, Univ Reading, 71-72 & 79-80; consult, var indust orgns, 74-; vis res fel, Univ Rochester, 80-82; adj prof, State Univ NY, Binghamton. *Mem:* Geol Soc Am; Am Asn Petrol Geologists; Soc Econ Paleontologists & Mineralogists; Int Asn Sedimentol. *Res:* Sedimentology of Paralic and lake sediments; Upper Devonian stratigraphy and sedimentology of the northern hemisphere; paleomagnetism of lake sediments; paleomagnetism. *Mailing Add:* Dept Geosci Hobart & William Col Geneva NY 14456

**WOODRUFF, CHARLES MARSH, JR,** ENVIRONMENTAL GEOLOGY & HYDROLOGY. *Current Pos:* CONSULT GEOLOGIST & PRIN, CHARLES WOODRUFF & ASSOCS, 83- *Personal Data:* b Columbia, Tenn, Aug 26, 44; m 73, 87, Patricia M Speier. *Educ:* Vanderbilt Univ, BA, 66, MS, 68; Univ Tex, Austin, PhD(geol), 73. *Prof Exp:* Geologist, Tenn Div Geol, 69-70; res scientist geol, Bur Econ Geol, Univ Tex, Austin, 72-83. *Concurrent Pos:* Geol consult, Coastal Mgt Prog, Tex Gen Land Off, 74-76; lectr, Dept Geol Sci, Univ Tex, Austin, 76-83; lectr, Sch Archit, Dept Community & Regional Planning, Univ Tex, Austin, 87. *Mem:* AAAS; Sigma Xi; Geol Soc Am. *Res:* Assessment of land, water, mineral and energy resources; terrain analysis; assessment of environmental impacts. *Mailing Add:* 711 W 14th St Austin TX 78701-1707

**WOODRUFF, CLARENCE MERRILL,** AGRONOMY, SOIL SCIENCE. *Current Pos:* from instr to prof soils, 38-76, chmn dept, 67-70, EMER PROF AGRON, EXP STA, COL AGR, UNIV MO-COLUMBIA, 76- *Personal Data:* b Kansas City, Mo, Apr 8, 10; m 37, Juanita McCollum; c James M & Robert A. *Educ:* Univ Mo, BS, 32, MA, 39, PhD, 53. *Prof Exp:* Lab technician, Exp Sta, Univ Mo, 32-34; supt in chg soil conserv exp sta, USDA, 34-38. *Concurrent Pos:* Electronic engr, Wright Field, Dayton, Ohio, 42-45. *Mem:* Fel Am Soc Agron; fel Soil Sci Soc Am; assoc Am Geophys Union; Sigma Xi; fel AAAS. *Res:* Symmetrical hydrugraph of ruoff as archetype of curve of growth. *Mailing Add:* 138 Mumford Hall Univ Mo Columbia MO 65211

**WOODRUFF, DAVID SCOTT,** EVOLUTION AND CONSERVATION OF ANIMAL SPECIES. *Current Pos:* assoc prof, 80-86, PROF BIOL, UNIV CALIF, SAN DIEGO, 86-, FAC DIR, EDUC ABROAD PROG, 93- *Personal Data:* b Penrith, Eng, June 12, 43; Australian citizen; m 72; c 2. *Educ:* Univ Melbourne, BSc, 65, PhD(zool), 73. *Prof Exp:* Tutor biol, Trinity Col, Univ Melbourne, 66-69; Frank Knox fel biol, Harvard Univ, 69-71; Alexander Agassiz lectr biogeog, 72, res fel biol, Mus Comp Zool, 73-74; asst prof biol, Purdue Univ, 74-80. *Concurrent Pos:* Lectr ecol, Comn Exten Courses, Harvard Univ, 72-74; dir, Res Initiative & Support Prog Develop Ecol, Purdue Univ, 77-79; coordr, Proj in Conserv Sci, Univ Calif, San Diego, 87- *Mem:* Soc Study Evolution; fel AAAS; Soc Syst Biol; Ecol Soc Am; Soc Conserv Biol. *Res:* Genetics, ecology and evolution of land snails; evolution of animal species including gibbons and chimpanzees; host-parasite coevolution; schistosomiasis; conservation biology with field projects in Thailand. *Mailing Add:* Dept Biol Univ Calif San Diego La Jolla CA 92093-0116. *E-Mail:* dwoodruf@ucsd.edu

**WOODRUFF, EDYTHE PARKER,** TOPOLOGY. *Current Pos:* From asst prof to assoc prof, 71-90, EMER PROF MATH, TRENTON STATE COL, 90- *Personal Data:* b Bellwood, Ill, Jan 15, 28; m 50, Robert W; c Andrew & Jeanne (Kingery). *Educ:* Univ Rochester, BA, 48, MS, 52; Rutgers Univ, New Brunswick, MS, 67; State Univ NY Binghamton, PhD(math), 71. *Concurrent Pos:* Vis, Inst Advan Study, 79-80 & 81. *Mem:* Am Math Soc; Math Asn Am; Asn Women Mathematicians; Sigma Xi. *Res:* Topology of Euclidean 3-space; monotone decompositions, P-lifting; crumpled cubes; shrinkable decompositions. *Mailing Add:* 11 Fairview Ave East Brunswick NJ 08816-2862

**WOODRUFF, GENE L(OWRY),** NUCLEAR ENGINEERING. *Current Pos:* from asst prof to assoc prof, Univ Wash, 65-76, from asst dir to dir, Nuclear Reactor Labs, 65-76, chmn dept, 81-84, dean Grad Sch & vprovost, 84-93, PROF NUCLEAR ENG, UNIV WASH, 76-, PROF CHEM ENG, 93- *Personal Data:* b Conway, Ark, May 6, 34; m 61; c 2. *Educ:* US Naval Acad, BS, 56; Mass Inst Technol, SM, 63, PhD(nuclear eng), 65. *Prof Exp:* Reactor supvr, Mass Inst Technol, 63-65. *Concurrent Pos:* Consult, Pac Northwest Labs, Battelle Mem Inst, 67-70; Math Sci Northwest, 70- & Los Alamos Nat Lab, 77- *Mem:* Am Nuclear Soc. *Res:* Nuclear reactor physics, especially neutron spectra; fusion reactor engineering. *Mailing Add:* 7423 Sunnyside Ave N Seattle WA 98103

**WOODRUFF, HAROLD BOYD,** MICROBIOLOGY. *Current Pos:* PRES, SOIL MICROBIOL ASSOCS, INC, 82- *Personal Data:* b Bridgeton, NJ, July 22, 17; m 42, Jeanette Whitner; c Brian & Hugh. *Educ:* Rutgers Univ, BS, 39, PhD(microbiol), 42. *Honors & Awards:* Charles Thom Award, Soc Indust Microbiol, 73. *Prof Exp:* Asst soil microbiol, Rutgers Univ, 38-42; res microbiologist, Merck Sharp & Dohme Res Labs, 42-46; head res sect, Microbiol Dept, 47-49, from asst dir to dir, 49-57, dir, Microbiol & Natural Prod Res Dept, 57-69, exec dir biol sci, Merck Inst Therapeut Res, 69-73, exec adminr, Merck Sharp & Dohme Res Labs, MSD (Japan) Co, Ltd, 73-82. *Concurrent Pos:* Lectr, US Off Educ; ed, Appl Microbiol, 53-62; mem bd dirs, Am Soc Microbiol Found, 72-74, pres,74; mem bd trustees, Biol Abstracts, 72-77, treas, 74-77; mem sci adv comt, Charles F Kettering Res Lab, 72-75; mem exec bd, US Fedn Cult Collections, 73-76; mem bd trustees, Am Type Cult Collection, 81-87. *Mem:* Am Soc Microbiol (treas, 64-70); Soc Indust Microbiol (pres, 54-56); Am Chem Soc; Am Acad Microbiol; Brit Soc Gen Microbiol; Sigma Xi; AAAS; hon mem Am Soc Microbiol; hon mem Kitasato Inst Japan; hon mem Soc Actinomycetes Japan. *Res:* Antibiotics; physiology of microorganisms; production of chemicals by microorganisms; analytical procedures using microorganisms; isolation of natural products. *Mailing Add:* 797 Valley Rd Watchung NJ 07060

**WOODRUFF, HUGH BOYD,** ANALYTICAL & COMPUTER CHEMISTRY. *Current Pos:* sr res chemist anal chem, Merck Sharp & Dohme Res Labs, 77-82, res fel, 82-85, mgr, 85-88, dir, Dept Comput Resources, 88-94, DIR RES SUPPORT, MERCK RES LABS, 94- *Personal Data:* b Plainfield, NJ, Mar 3, 49; m 73, Sandria Ewers; c Ashley. *Educ:* Trinity Col, BS, 71; Univ NC, PhD(anal chem), 75. *Prof Exp:* Res assoc chem, Ariz State Univ, 75-77. *Concurrent Pos:* Chmn, Comput Div, Am Chem Soc, 89. *Mem:* Am Chem Soc; Coblentz Soc; Drug Info Asn. *Res:* Computer applications in chemistry; pattern recognition; intelligent computer systems for infrared spectral interpretation; computer resource planning. *Mailing Add:* Merck & Co Inc PO Box 2000 RY32-301 Rahway NJ 07065-0900. *Fax:* 732-594-1455; *E-Mail:* hugh__woodruff@merck.com

**WOODRUFF, JAMES DONALD,** OBSTETRICS & GYNECOLOGY. *Current Pos:* From instr to assoc prof gynec, Johns Hopkins Univ, 42-60, from assoc prof to prof gynec & obstet, 60-75, assoc prof path, 63-75, RICHARD W TELINDE PROF GYNEC & PATH, SCH MED, JOHNS HOPKINS UNIV, 75-, HEAD GYNEC PATH LAB, JOHNS HOPKINS HOSP, 51- *Personal Data:* b Baltimore, Md, June 20, 12; m 39; c 3. *Educ:* Dickinson Col, BS, 33; Johns Hopkins Univ, MD, 37. *Concurrent Pos:* Chief gynecologist, Md Gen Hosp, 51-58 & Hosp for Women of Med, 58-62. *Mem:* Int Soc Study Vulvar Dis (pres, 73-75); Am Asn Obstet & Gynec (pres, 77); Am Gynec Soc; fel Am Col Obstet & Gynec. *Res:* Gynecologic pathology; study of functional activity of ovarian neoplasms and vulvar disease. *Mailing Add:* Johns Hopkins Hosp Baltimore MD 21205

**WOODRUFF, JOHN H, JR,** RADIOLOGY. *Current Pos:* clin instr, 50-52, asst prof, 52-54, assoc clin prof, 54-80, ADJ ASSOC PROF RADIOL, UNIV CALIF, LOSANGELES, 80-; CHIEF RADIOL, US VET ADMIN HOSP, SEPULVEDA, 71- *Personal Data:* b Barre, Vt, Dec 14, 11; m 50; c 1. *Educ:* Univ Vt, BS, 35, MD, 38. *Prof Exp:* Intern, US Marine Hosp, 38-39; resident radiol, Mary Fletcher Hosp, 39-40 & Royal Victoria Hosp, 40-41; asst prof, Univ Vt, 42-44; pvt pract, Calif, 46-50. *Concurrent Pos:* Chief radiologist, Los Angeles, Co Harbor Gen Hosp, 52-65; consult, Terminal Island Fed Prison, 57-65 & Long Beach Vet Admin Hosp, 59-68; radiologist, Univ Calif Med Ctr, 65-67; clin prof radiologic serv, Univ Calif, Irvine, 67-68, clin prof radiologic sci, 68-70; chief radiol, San Fernando Vet Admin Hosp, 68-71. *Mem:* Am Roentgen Ray Soc; Radiol Soc NAm; AMA; Am Col Radiol. *Res:* Radiologic aspects of diseases of kidneys, lungs, gastro-intestinal tract and of trauma to the abdomen and its contents. *Mailing Add:* 2618 Palos Verdes Dr W Palos Verdes Estates CA 90274-2861

**WOODRUFF, KENNETH LEE,** MINERAL ENGINEERING, METALLURGY. *Current Pos:* CONSULT, RESOURCE RECOVERY, KENNETH L WOODRUFF & ASSOC, 83- *Personal Data:* b Phoenixville, Pa, Oct 10, 50; m 76, Kathryn M Tapp; c Andrew K & Daniel L. *Educ:* Pa State Univ, BS, 72. *Prof Exp:* Eng asst, Bethlehem Mines Corp, 70-71; staff consult & res engr, Nat Ctr Resource Recovery Inc, 72-75; proj mgr, Wehran Eng Corp, 75-76; pres, Resource Recovery Serv Inc, 76-81; mgr, Bio-Tech Energy Corp, 82-83. *Concurrent Pos:* Tech prog chmn, Ninth Nat Waste Processing Conf, Am Soc Mech Engrs, 78-80; chmn, Solid Waste Proc Div, Am Soc Mech Engrs, 85-86; assoc ed, Solid Waste Handbk, J Wiley & Sons, 86. *Mem:* Am Inst Mining, Metall & Petrol Engrs; Am Inst Chem Engrs; Am Inst Mech Engrs; Am Soc Testing & Mat; Nat Asn Environ Prof; Air & Waste Mgt Asn; Soc Plastics Engrs. *Res:* Energy and materials recovery from municipal and industrial solid waste; unit operations and processes; hazardous waste reclamation and recovery systems; trommel for pre-processing of solid waste for resource recovery. *Mailing Add:* 182 Walton Dr Morrisville PA 19067-0042. *Fax:* 215-736-2225

**WOODRUFF, NEIL PARKER,** AGRICULTURAL ENGINEERING, HIGHWAY CONSTRUCTION. *Current Pos:* STAFF MEM, W/PT CONSULTS, 84- *Personal Data:* b Clyde, Kans, July 25, 19; m 52, Dorothy A Russ; c Timothy C & Thomas S. *Educ:* Kans State Univ, BS, 49, MS, 53. *Honors & Awards:* Hancor Soil Water Eng Award, Am Soc Agr Engrs, 75. *Prof Exp:* Agr engr, Agr Res Serv, USDA, Manhattan, Kans, 49-63, res leader 63-75; consult engr, 75-77; civil engr, Kans Dept Transp, Topeka, 77-79; prof & mem grad fac, Kans State Univ, 63-75, civil engr, Planning Off, 79-84. *Mem:* Fel Am Soc Agr Engrs; Sigma Xi. *Res:* Agricultural engineering; wind erosion and its control; tillage and soil conservation; author and co-author of numerous papers and reports. *Mailing Add:* 12906 Blue Bonnet Dr Sun City West AZ 85375-2538

**WOODRUFF, RICHARD IRA,** DEVELOPMENTAL BIOLOGY, REPRODUCTIVE BIOLOGY. *Current Pos:* from instr to assoc prof, 66-72, PROF BIOL, WEST CHESTER STATE COL, 72- *Personal Data:* b Glen Ridge, NJ, Aug 19, 40; m 62; c 3. *Educ:* Ursinus Col, BS, 62; West Chester State Col, MEd, 65; Univ Pa, PhD(biol), 72. *Prof Exp:* Teacher high sch, 62-66. *Concurrent Pos:* Res fel, Univ Pa, 72- *Mem:* AAAS; Am Soc Zoologists. *Res:* Developmental biology; electrophysiological events during egg formation. *Mailing Add:* Dept Biol West Chester Univ 700 S High St West Chester PA 19383-0002

**WOODRUFF, ROBERT EUGENE,** ENTOMOLOGY. *Current Pos:* EMER ENTOMOLOGIST, FLA STATE COL ARTHROPODS. *Personal Data:* b Kennard, Ohio, July 20, 33; m 54, Nina Evelyn; c Kris & Cheri. *Educ:* Ohio State Univ, BSc, 56; Univ Fla, PhD(entom), 67. *Prof Exp:* Entomologist, Ky State Health Dept, 56-58 & Plant Indust Div, Fla Dept Agr, 58-88. *Concurrent Pos:* Mem, Orgn Trop Studies, NSF, Costa Rica, 64; assoc ed, Fla Entom Soc, 70-82; ed, Coleopterists Bulletin, 71-75; mem bd dirs, NAm Beetle Fauna Proj, 75-81; adj cur Natural Sci, Fla State Mus, 76-; NSF fossil amber insects, Dominican Republic, 77-78; consult, FAD/UN, 87-91, Ill Nat Hist Serv, 89-90, Tex A&M Univ, 89-90; founder, Ctr Syst Entom, pres, 87, 95-96. *Mem:* Entom Soc Am; Soc Syst Zool; Asn Trop Biol; Coleopterists Soc (pres, 78); Sigma Xi. *Res:* Systematic entomology; taxonomy, ethology, ecology of beetles of the family Scarabaeidae, especially myrmecophilous and termitophilous species; fossil amber insects of the Dominican Republic; mineralogy (research on Larimar from Dominican Republic); insects of Grenada (FAO). *Mailing Add:* 3517 NW Tenth Ave Gainesville FL 32605. *Fax:* 352-334-0737

**WOODRUFF, RONNY CLIFFORD,** GENETICS, EVOLUTION. *Current Pos:* from asst prof to assoc prof, Bowling Green State Univ, 77-85, prof biol, 85-, chair, 93-96, DISTINGUISHED RES PROF, 94- *Personal Data:* b Greenville, Tex, Mar 12, 43; m; c 1. *Educ:* ETex State Univ, BS, 66, MS, 67; Utah State Univ, PhD(zool), 72. *Honors & Awards:* Outstanding Young Scientist Award, Sigma Xi, 81; Fulbright Res Award, Kenya, 87. *Prof Exp:* NIH reproduction & develop training grant, Univ Tex, Austin, 71-73, asst prof zool, 73-74; sr res asst genetics, Univ Cambridge, 74-76; res assoc zool, Univ Okla, 76-77. *Concurrent Pos:* Mem, Environ Protection Agency Gene-Tox Comt, 80-83; res career develop award, NIH, 80-85; mem, Comt Stand Drosophilia Assays, Am Soc Testing & Mat, 84-85; Fulbright fel, Kenya, 87; vis res fel, Univ New Eng, Armidale, Australia, 91. *Mem:* Genetics Soc Am; Environ Mutagen Soc; Soc Study Evolution. *Res:* Structure and function of transposable DNA elements in Drosophilia melanogaster; mutagenesis; evolution. *Mailing Add:* Dept Biol Sci Bowling Green State Univ Bowling Green OH 43402

**WOODRUFF, TERESA K,** CELL BIOLOGY. *Current Pos:* fel, 89-91, SCIENTIST, DEPT CELL STRUCT RES & DEVELOP, GENENTECH, INC, 91- *Personal Data:* b Dec 7, 63. *Educ:* Olivet Nazarene Univ, BA, 85; Northwestern Univ, PhD(molecular biol, cellular biol & biochem), 89. *Honors & Awards:* Cornelia Post Channing Mem Award, Abbott Labs, 88. *Prof Exp:* Fel, Abbott Labs, 87. *Concurrent Pos:* Prin investr, NIH, 88; vis lectr, Nat Inst Sci, Beijing, 91. *Mem:* AAAS; Am Chem Soc; Am Fertil Soc; Women Endocrinol; Endocrine Soc; Sigma Xi. *Res:* Method of increasing fertility in females; method of inhibiting follicular maturation in females; TGF-beta supergene family of receptors; granted one US patent. *Mailing Add:* Dept Discovery Res Genentech Inc 1 DNA Way South San Francisco CA 94080

**WOODRUFF, TRUMAN OWEN,** theoretical solid state physics, for more information see previous edition

**WOODRUFF, WILLIAM LEE,** REACTOR PHYSICS. *Current Pos:* NUCLEAR ENGR, ARGONNE NAT LAB, 68- *Personal Data:* b Seward, Nebr, Oct 21, 38; m 63; c 3. *Educ:* Nebr Wesleyan Univ, BA, 60; Univ Nebr, MS, 64; Tex A&M Univ, PhD(nuclear eng), 70. *Prof Exp:* Lab asst & technician physics, Nebr Wesleyan Univ, 60-63, vis lectr, 63-64; instr, Univ Omaha, 64-66. *Concurrent Pos:* Inst Atomic Energy, Brazil, 75- *Mem:* Am Nuclear Soc; Sigma Xi. *Res:* Methods and computer code development and physics analysis for design and safety of liquid metal and gas-cooled fast breeder reactors and for reduced enrichment research reactors. *Mailing Add:* 2905 Hickory Ct Woodridge IL 60517-4545

**WOODS, ALAN CHURCHILL, JR,** SURGERY. *Current Pos:* RETIRED. *Personal Data:* b Baltimore, Md, July 1, 18; m 44; c 4. *Educ:* Princeton Univ, AB, 40; Johns Hopkins Univ, MD, 43; Am Bd Surg, dipl, 51. *Prof Exp:* Intern & asst resident surgeon, Johns Hopkins Hosp, 44-45, from asst resident surgeon to resident surgeon, 48-49, surgeon & surgeon chg, Outpatient Dept, 50; resident surg, Henry Ford Hosp, 45-56; asst, Johns Hopkins Univ, 49, from instr to assoc prof surg, 49-88. *Concurrent Pos:* William Stewart Halsted fel surg, Johns Hopkins Univ, 49-50. *Mem:* Fel Am Col Surgeons; Soc Head & Neck Surg. *Res:* Abdominal, head and neck surgery. *Mailing Add:* 207 Wendover Rd Baltimore MD 21218

**WOODS, ALEXANDER HAMILTON,** IMMUNOLOGY. *Current Pos:* prof immunol, 64-77, ASSOC PROF INTERNAL MED, COL MED, UNIV ARIZ, 64- *Personal Data:* b Tuxedo, NY, July 26, 22; m 56; c 2. *Educ:* Harvard Univ, BS, 44; Johns Hopkins Univ, MD, 52; Am Bd Internal Med, dipl, 60. *Prof Exp:* Instr med, Sch Med, Duke Univ, 55-56; asst prof med & microbiol, Med Ctr, Univ Okla, 58-64. *Concurrent Pos:* Res fel biochem, Duke Univ, 56-58; clin investr, Vet Admin Hosp, Oklahoma City, 59-61; dir res, Vet Admin Hosp, Tuscon, 62-70; assoc chief staff, Vet Admin Hosp, Tuscon, 70-77. *Mem:* AAAS; Am Chem Soc; NY Acad Sci; Brit Biochem Soc. *Res:* Immunochemistry; hematology; cancer chemotherapy. *Mailing Add:* Hughes Aircraft Co Bldg 801-H7 Tucson AZ 85734

**WOODS, ALFRED DAVID BRAINE,** SOLID STATE PHYSICS, LOW TEMPERATURE PHYSICS & NEUTRON SCATTERING. *Current Pos:* RETIRED. *Personal Data:* b St John's, Nfld, July 16, 32; m 54, Doreen McFatridge; c Brian, Elizabeth & Nicola. *Educ:* Dalhousie Univ, BSc, 53, MSc, 55; Univ Toronto, PhD(low temperature physics), 57. *Prof Exp:* Res fel low temperature physics, Univ Toronto, 57-58; res officer solid state physics, Atomic Energy Can Ltd, Res Co, 58-78, head, Neutron & Solid State Physics Br, 71-78, sr adv to the exec vpres, Res Co, 79-86; sr adv strategic tech mgt, Atomic Energy Can Ltd, Res Co, 86-89. *Mem:* Fel Am Phys Soc; fel Royal Soc Can. *Res:* Dynamics of condensed matter using inelastic neutron scattering. *Mailing Add:* Chalet Sur-Los Cupresos 141 Campo Mijas Buzon 453 Mijas Costa E29649 Malaga Spain

**WOODS, ALVIN EDWIN,** FOOD CHEMISTRY, BIOCHEMISTRY. *Current Pos:* From asst prof to assoc prof, 61-69, PROF CHEM, MID TENN STATE UNIV, 69- *Personal Data:* b Murfreesboro, Tenn, Mar 17, 34; m 59; c 2. *Educ:* Mid Tenn State Univ, BS, 56; NC State Univ, MS, 58, PhD(food flavor), 62. *Concurrent Pos:* Consult, Off Int Res, NIH, 65-67. *Mem:* Am Chem Soc; fel Am Inst Chemists; Sigma Xi. *Res:* Enzyme stereochemistry and kinetics; food flavors, metal ions in biological systems; organo phosphorous compounds; bromine in biological systems. *Mailing Add:* Dept Chem Mid Tenn State Univ Murfreesboro TN 37132

**WOODS, CHARLES ARTHUR,** PALEONTOLOGY. *Current Pos:* chmn, Natural Sci, 79-86, CURATOR MAMMAL, FLA MUS NATURAL HIST, 79-; PROF ZOOL, UNIV FLA, 79- *Personal Data:* b Sherman, Tex, Dec 23, 40; m 63, Ellen M Stott; c C Stott, Patricia J & Bryan W. *Educ:* Univ Denver, BA, 64; Univ Mass, PhD(zool), 70. *Prof Exp:* Asst prof zool, Univ Denver, 70-71; assoc prof, Univ Vt, 71-79. *Concurrent Pos:* Consult, govt Haiti, 83-, Mill Pond Press, 85-, Nat Acad Sci, 88-90, govt Pakistan, 90- *Mem:* Am Soc Mammalogists; Sigma Xi. *Res:* Biogeography of new and old world mammals; island biology; biological conservation; birds and mammals of the West Indies; small mammal biology. *Mailing Add:* Fla Mus Natural Hist Univ Fla Gainesville FL 32611. *Fax:* 904-392-8508; *E-Mail:* cawoods@flmnh.ufl.edu

**WOODS, CHARLES WILLIAM,** ORGANIC CHEMISTRY. *Current Pos:* RES CHEMIST, ENTOM RES DIV, USDA, 59- *Personal Data:* b Akron, Ohio, June 1, 28; m 61; c 2. *Educ:* Ohio State Univ, BS, 51; Univ Md, PhD(org chem), 58. *Prof Exp:* Chemist, E I du Pont de Nemours & Co, Ky, 57-58. *Mem:* AAAS; Am Chem Soc; Sigma Xi. *Res:* Synthesis of chemosterilants for insects; synthesis of radioactive organic compounds. *Mailing Add:* 4320 Underwood St Apt M Hyattsville MD 20782

**WOODS, CLIFTON, III,** PHYSICAL INORGANIC CHEMISTRY. *Current Pos:* from asst prof to assoc prof, 74-92, ASSOC DEAN, COL LIBERAL ARTS, UNIV TENN, 90-, PROF CHEM, 92- *Personal Data:* b Mecklenburg Co, NC, Aug 28, 44. *Educ:* NC Cent Univ, BS, 66; NC State Univ, MS, 69, PhD(chem), 71. *Prof Exp:* Asst prof chem, Univ Fla, 71-73, Bowling Green State Univ, 73-74. *Mem:* Am Chem Soc; Sigma Xi. *Res:* Synthesis, characterization, electrochemistry and catalysis of organometallic complexes; synthetic inorganic and organometallic chemistry. *Mailing Add:* Dept Chem Univ Tenn Knoxville TN 37996-1600

**WOODS, DONALD LESLIE,** PLANT BREEDING. *Current Pos:* RES SCIENTIST PLANT BREEDING, RES STA, AGR CAN, 77- *Personal Data:* b London, Eng, Mar 4, 44; Can citizen; m 68; c 2. *Educ:* Univ London, BPharm, 65; MPhil, 68; Univ Man, PhD(plant sci), 71. *Prof Exp:* Res assoc plant breeding, Dept Plant Sci, Univ Man, 71-76; res specialist plant chem, Dept Agron, Univ Minn, 76. *Concurrent Pos:* Overseas aid prog, Kenya, 83 & 84. *Res:* Secondary plant metabolites and their biosynthesis, function, utilization, and environmental and genetic control. *Mailing Add:* Res Sta Agr Can Box 29 Beaverlodge AB T0H 0C0 Can

**WOODS, DONALD ROBERT,** COLLOID & SURFACE CHEMISTRY, TEACHING. *Current Pos:* asst prof, McMaster Univ, 64-68, assoc prof, 68-74, chmn, 79-82, dir, Eng & Mgt Prog, 86-92, PROF CHEM ENG, MCMASTER UNIV, 74- *Personal Data:* b Sarnia, Ont, Apr 17, 35; m 61, Diane Elliott; c Russell (deceased), Suzanna & Cynthia. *Educ:* Queen's Univ, Ont, BSc, 57; Univ Wis, MS, 58, PhD(chem eng), 61. *Hon Degrees:* DSc, Queens Univ, 96. *Honors & Awards:* Ben Dasher Award; Corcoran Award, Am Soc Eng Educ, 93. *Prof Exp:* Instr chem eng, Univ Wis, 59-60, Athlone fel, 61-63. *Concurrent Pos:* C D Howe mem fel, Van't Hoff Lab, State Univ Utrecht, 70-71. *Mem:* Am Inst Chem Engrs; Can Soc Chem Engrs; fel Chem Inst Can; fel Am Inst Chem Engrs. *Res:* Surface behavior; separation of immiscible liquid and liquid-solid systems for waste water treatment and chemical processing; properties of emulsions; stability and separation of emulsions; physical separations; cost estimation; problem solving. *Mailing Add:* Dept Chem Eng McMaster Univ Hamilton ON L8S 4L7 Can. *Fax:* 905-521-1350; *E-Mail:* woodsdr@mcmail.cis.mcmater.ca

**WOODS, EDWARD JAMES,** mathematics, for more information see previous edition

**WOODS, FRANK ROBERT,** HYDRODYNAMICS, GAS DYNAMICS. *Current Pos:* RETIRED. *Personal Data:* b Mt Vernon, NY, June 20, 16; m 42; c 3. *Educ:* NY Univ, BA, 41, MS, 47, PhD(physics), 55. *Prof Exp:* Instr physics, Univ NH, 48-53, from asst prof to assoc prof, 53-57; physicist, Boeing Airplane Co, 57-58; assoc prof physics, Mont State Col, 58-63; lectr aerospace eng & eng physics, Univ Va, 63-73, sr scientist, 63-69, prin scientist, Dept Aerospace Eng & Eng Physics, 69-73; master, Hill Sch, Pottstown, Pa, 73-81; assoc prof physics, Lock Haven State Col, 81-82. *Concurrent Pos:* Adj prof, Millersville Univ Pa, 82-86. *Mem:* Am Phys Soc; Sigma Xi. *Res:* Hydrodynamics; scattering; theoretical hydrodynamics. *Mailing Add:* 301 N Rutland Ave PO Box 374 Brooklyn WI 53521

**WOODS, GEORGE THEODORE,** VETERINARY MEDICINE, PUBLIC HEALTH. *Current Pos:* asst prof vet path & hyg, Univ Ill, 49-59, assoc prof vet microbiol, pub health & res, 59-66, prof, 66-86, EMER PROF VET MICROBIOL & PUB HEALTH, RES COL VET MED, UNIV ILL, URBANA, 86- *Personal Data:* b Tyro, Kans, Aug 21, 24; m 48, Helen Jordan; c David, Jeffrey & Linda. *Educ:* Kans State Univ, DVM, 46; Univ Calif, MPH, 59; Purdue Univ, MS, 60. *Prof Exp:* Inspector animal dis eradication, Ill State Dept Agr, 46-47; supvr lab animal med, Med Sch, Northwestern Univ, 47-48; vet, 48-49; adminr, Dewitt-Piatt Bi-Co Health Dept CI, 88-90. *Concurrent Pos:* Trainee, USPHS, 58-59; adv, Am Coun Health & Sci, 85- *Mem:* Am Vet Med Asn; Asn Teachers Vet Pub Health & Prev Med (pres); Am Asn Food Hyg Veterinarians. *Res:* Preventive veterinary medicine; epidemiology; viral respiratory diseases of cattle and swine; bovine myxovirus para-influenza 3. *Mailing Add:* Dept Vet Pathobiol 503 E Burkwood Ct Urbana IL 61801

**WOODS, GERALDINE PITTMAN,** NEUROEMBRYOLOGY. *Current Pos:* EMER CHMN BD DIRS, HOWARD UNIV, 88- *Personal Data:* b West Palm Beach, Fla; m 45, Robert I; c Jan, Jerri & Robert Jr. *Educ:* Howard Univ, BS, 42; Radcliffe Col, MA, 43; Harvard Univ, PhD(neuroembryol), 45. *Hon Degrees:* DSc, Benedict Col, 77 & Talladega Col, 80; Fisk Univ, 91, Bennett Co, 93; LHD, Meharry Med Col, 88 & Howard Univ, 89. *Honors & Awards:* Kellogg lectr, Univ Ark; Scroll of Merit, Nat Med Asn, 79. *Prof Exp:* Instr biol, Howard Univ, 45-46; spec consult, Nat Inst Gen Med Sci, NIH, 69-87. *Concurrent Pos:* Mem, Nat Adv Coun, Gen Med Sci Inst, NIH, 64-68; chmn, Defense Adv Comt Women in Serv, 68; mem, Gen Res Support Prog Adv Comt, Div Res Resources, NIH, 70-73 & 77-78; mem bd trustees, Calif Mus Found Calif Mus Sci & Indust, 71-; mem air pollution manpower develop adv comt, Environ Protection Agency, 73-75; mem bd dirs, Robert Wood Johnson Health Policy Fels, Inst Med-Nat Acad Sci, 73-78, Nat Comn Cert Physicians Assts, 74-78; mem bd trustees, Atlanta Univ, 74- & mem Calif Post Sect Educ Comn, 74-78; chmn bd trustees, Howard Univ, 75-88, mem bd trustees, 89; pres, Delta Res & Educ Found, 83-88; chmn bd dirs, Howard Univ Found, 84-88; mem bd dirs, Charles R Drew Univ Med & Sci, 91-93; hon chmn, Nat Inst Sci, 85. *Mem:* Inst Med-Nat Acad Sci; AAAS; Fedn Am Scientists; Nat Inst Sci; Am Asn Univ Professors; NY Acad Sci. *Res:* Encouraging the participation of minorities in the regular programs at the National Institutes of Health and developing two programs, Minority Biomedical Research Support Program and Minority Access to Research Careers, that would further assist colleges with minorities move into research and research training to project more participation in health and scientific careers. *Mailing Add:* 22 Hawksmoor Aliso Viejo CA 92656

**WOODS, J(OHN) M(ELVILLE),** CHEMICAL ENGINEERING. *Current Pos:* MEM STAFF, DEPT CHEM ENG, PRAIRIE VIEW A&M UNIV. *Personal Data:* b Denver, Colo, May 14, 22; m 49; c 3. *Educ:* Univ Kans, BS, 43; Univ Wis, PhD(chem eng), 53. *Prof Exp:* Instr chem eng, Univ Wis, 48-50; asst prof, Univ RI, 50-52; asst prof chem eng, Purdue Univ, 52-57, assoc prof, 57-77. *Concurrent Pos:* Consult chem eng, 77- *Mem:* Sigma Xi; Am Chem Soc; Am Inst Chem Engrs. *Res:* Applied reaction kinetics; process simulation and optimization. *Mailing Add:* 5907 Boyce Springs Houston TX 77066-2301

**WOODS, JAMES STERRETT,** TOXICOLOGY, ENVIRONMENTAL EPIDEMIOLOGY. *Current Pos:* HEAD, ENVIRON & OCCUP HEALTH RISK ASSESSMENT PROG, BATTELLE SEATTLE RES CTR, 78-; RES PROF, DEPT ENVIRON HEALTH, UNIV WASH, 79- *Personal Data:* b Lewistown, Pa, Feb 26, 40; m 69, Nancy Fugate; c 1. *Educ:* Princeton Univ, AB, 62; Univ Wash, PhD(pharmacol), 70; Univ NC, MPH, 78; Am Bd Toxicol, dipl, 86. *Prof Exp:* Res assoc pharmacol, Sch Med, Yale Univ, 70-72; head, Biochem Toxicol Sect, Lab Environ Toxicol, Nat Inst Environ Health Sci, NIH, 72-78. *Concurrent Pos:* Chmn sci coun & mem bd dir, Pac Sci Ctr, 81-87, adv comt herbicides, Vet Admin, 87-90; Founding pres, Pac Northwest Asn Toxicol, 84-85; trustee, Seattle Biomed Res Inst, 89-; counr, Soc Toxicol, 90-92; secy, Int Cong Toxicol, 92-95; pres, Am Bd Toxicol, 97-98. *Mem:* Am Asn Cancer Res; Am Soc Pharmacol & Exp Therapeut; Soc Epidemiol Res; Soc Toxicol. *Res:* Biochemical toxicology; environmental epidemiology; biomarkers of toxicant exposures. *Mailing Add:* Battelle Seattle Res Ctr 4000 NE 41st St Seattle WA 98105. *Fax:* 206-528-3550

**WOODS, JAMES WATSON,** medicine, for more information see previous edition

**WOODS, JIMMIE DALE,** MATHEMATICS, STATISTICS. *Current Pos:* dean, Sch Mgt, 90-91, PROF MGT, HARTFORD GRAD CTR, 81-,. *Personal Data:* b Albuquerque, NMex, Oct 8, 33; m 56, Jane R Lewis; c Cindy K (Bonneau), Timmie A & Jimmie D Jr. *Educ:* USCG Acad, BS, 55; Trinity Col, Conn, MS, 63; Univ Conn, PhD(math statist), 68. *Prof Exp:* USCG, 51-81, from instr to assoc prof math, USCG Acad, 60-68, asst head dept, 64-68, prof math & head dept, 68-81. *Mem:* Am Statist Asn; Am Math Soc; Math Asn Am; Am Soc Qual Control. *Res:* Application of matrix techniques to statistical distribution theory; mathematical modeling in management science. *Mailing Add:* 392 Wheeler Rd Stonington CT 06378

**WOODS, JOE DARST,** INORGANIC CHEMISTRY. *Current Pos:* From instr to prof, 52-85, chmn dept, 69-78 & 82-85, EMER PROF CHEM, DRAKE UNIV, 85- *Personal Data:* b Knoxville, Iowa, Jan 2, 23; m 48, Nadine Reed; c John & Miriam. *Educ:* Cent Col, Iowa, BS, 44; Iowa State Univ, MS, 50, PhD(chem), 54. *Honors & Awards:* Fulbright Hays lectr, St Louis Univ, Philippines, 67-68. *Mem:* AAAS; Am Chem Soc; Sigma Xi. *Res:* Mechanism of decomposition of chlorates; radioactive tracers; oxidation of metals; dissolution of metals in acids. *Mailing Add:* 4107 Ardmore Rd Des Moines IA 50310

**WOODS, JOHN WHITCOMB,** membrane traffic through golgi apparatus, for more information see previous edition

**WOODS, JOHN WILLIAM,** IMAGE PROCESSING, VIDEO CODING & PROCESSING. *Current Pos:* PROF & ASSOC DIR, CTR IMAGE PROCESSING RES, RENESSELAER POLYTECH INST, TROY, NY, 76- *Personal Data:* b Washington, DC, Dec 5, 43; m 72, Harriet Hemmerich; c Anne & Christopher. *Educ:* Mass Inst Technol, BS, 65, MS, 67, PhD(commun), 70. *Honors & Awards:* Meritorious Serv Award, Inst Elec & Electronics Engrs, Signal Processing Soc, 90, Tech Achievement Award, 94. *Prof Exp:* Sr engr, Electronics Res Dept, Lawrence Livermore Lab, 73-76. *Concurrent Pos:* Admin Comt, Inst Elec & Electronics Engrs, ASSP Soc, 86-89; vis prof, Delft Univ Technol, Neth, 85-86; dir, Circuits & Signal Processing Prog, NSF, Washington, DC, 87-88. *Mem:* Inst Elec & Electronics Engrs; AAAS; Sigma Xi. *Res:* Image processing including image sequence processing and video coding; author or co-author of over 100 papers and one book. *Mailing Add:* 43 Longview Dr Clifton Park NY 12065. *Fax:* 518-276-6079; *E-Mail:* woods@ecse.rpc.edu

**WOODS, JOSEPH,** electrical engineering, materials science, for more information see previous edition

**WOODS, JOSEPH JAMES,** PHYSIOLOGY. *Current Pos:* From asst prof to assoc prof, Quinnipiac Col, 70-78, chmn, Dept Biol, 79-82, PROF BIOL, QUINNIPIAC COL, 78-, DEAN, SCH ALLIED HEALTH & NATURAL SCI, 88. *Personal Data:* b Camden, NJ, June 21, 43; m 68, Geralding McGettigan; c Christopher, Alisa & Michael. *Educ:* St Jospeh's Col, Pa, BS, 65; Rutgers Univ, PhD(physiol), 71. *Concurrent Pos:* NIH co-investr, 71-89; mem bd dirs, Alzheimer's Resource Ctr Conn. *Mem:* Sigma Xi. *Res:* Human muscle fatigue mechanisms using force and electromyographic indices. *Mailing Add:* Sch Allied Health & Natural Sci Quinnipiac Col 275 Mt Carmel Ave Hamden CT 06518-1961. *Fax:* 203-281-8706

**WOODS, KEITH NEWELL,** MATERIALS SCIENCE, CERAMICS. *Current Pos:* RES MGR, EXXON NUCLEAR CO, INC, 77- *Personal Data:* b Wilmington, Del, Jan 28, 41; m 68; c 2. *Educ:* Stanford Univ, BS, 62; Univ Mich, MSE, 63; Northwestern Univ, PhD(mat sci), 68. *Prof Exp:* Adv res engr, Appl Res Lab, Sylvania Elec Prods, Inc, 68-69; staff ceramist, Res & Develop Ctr, Gen Elec Co, 69-72, tech mgr, Nuclear Fuels Dept, 72-77. *Mem:* Am Ceramic Soc; Am Nuclear Soc. *Res:* Physical properties of crystalline ceramics and glasses; fabrication and irradiation behavior of nuclear fuels. *Mailing Add:* 2020 Harris Ave Richland WA 99352

**WOODS, KENNETH R,** ENERGY, ENVIRONMENT. *Current Pos:* PRES, ENERGY-ENVIRON, INC, 86- *Personal Data:* b Chicago, Ill, Apr 14, 25; m 46; c 2. *Educ:* Northwestern Univ, Evanston, BSME, 48. *Prof Exp:* Res engr, Ingersoll Utility Unit Div, Borg Warner Corp, 48-49; test engr, Underwriter's Labs, Inc, 49-52; responsible charge, Indust Hyg & Radiation Safety Div, Argonne Nat Lab, 52-55; monitoring partner, Thulin, Woods & Isensee, 55-60; pres, Woods & Assocs, Inc, 60-86. *Concurrent Pos:* Prin investr, Am Soc Mech Engrs, Am Inst Architects, Am Soc Heating Refrig & Air Conditioning Eng, Am Soc Bldg & Construct Inspectors & Am Acad Environ Med, 82-87. *Mem:* Am Inst Architects; Am Cong Surv & Mapping; Nat Soc Prof Engrs; Sigma Xi; Int Solar Energy Soc; AAAS. *Res:* Technologies that do more with less in the energy field and promulgate living in harmony with nature in the environmental field. *Mailing Add:* Energy Environment Inc Energy-Environ Inc Naperville IL 60564-8956

**WOODS, KERRY DAVID,** FOREST ECOLOGY, PLANT COMMUNITY ECOLOGY. *Current Pos:* PROF BIOL, BENNINGTON COL, 86- *Personal Data:* b Jacksonville, Ill, Sept 5, 53. *Educ:* Ill Col, BS, 75; Cornell Univ, PhD(ecol), 80. *Prof Exp:* Assoc, Univ Minn, 80-82; asst prof ecol, St Olaf Col, 82-83; res assoc & instr environ studies, Univ Calif, Santa Barbara, 83-86; prof environ sci, Cent Europ Univ, 91. *Concurrent Pos:* Prin investr, NASA, 84-88, Mellon Found, 86, US Forest Serv, 88-92, NSF, 93-; Bullard fel, Harvard Univ. *Mem:* Ecol Soc Am; Brit Ecol Soc; Soc Conserv Biol. *Res:* Long-term community dynamics and tree demography in eastern old-growth forests; biogeography of temperate forests, community consequences of biological invasion. *Mailing Add:* Dept Biol Bennington Col Bennington VT 05201. *E-Mail:* kwoods@benningt.edu

**WOODS, LAUREN ALBERT,** PHARMACOLOGY. *Current Pos:* prof, Va Commonwealth Univ, 81-84, vpres health sci, 70-76 & 81-84, assoc provost, Acad Med Col Va, 77-78, actg vpres health sci, 78-81, EMER PROF PHARMACOL, VA COMMONWEALTH UNIV, 84- *Personal Data:* b Aurora Co, SDak, Spet 10, 19; m 44; c 3. *Educ:* Dakota Wesleyan Univ, BA, 39; Iowa State Col, PhD(org chem), 43; Univ Mich, MD, 49. *Prof Exp:* Asst, Nat Defense Res Comt, Iowa State Col, 43-44; from instr to prof pharmacol, Univ Mich, 46-60, actg chmn dept, 56; prof & head dept, Col Med, Univ Iowa, 60-70. *Mem:* AAAS; Am Chem Soc; Am Soc Pharmacol & Exp Therapeut; NY Acad Sci. *Res:* Metabolism of drugs; chemical structure; biological activity relationships; compounds affecting the central nervous system; mechanisms of development of tolerance and physical dependence to narcotics; radioactive tracer studies; histochemical distribution of drugs. *Mailing Add:* 410 W 12th St PO Box 980613 Va State Med Col Richmond VA 23298-0613

**WOODS, LEWIS CURRY, III,** FISH DOMESTICATION & GENETIC IMPROVEMENT, FISH PHYSIOLOGY REPRODUCTION & NUTRITION. *Current Pos:* dir, Crane Aquacult Facil, Baltimore Gas & Electric, 82-90, DIR & RES LEADER, CRANE AQUACULT FACIL, MD AGR EXP STA, 90- *Personal Data:* b Harrodsburg, Ky, Oct 20, 53. *Educ:* Murray State Univ, BS, 75; Ohio State Univ, MS, 77; NC State Univ, PhD(zool), 83. *Honors & Awards:* Chesapeake Bay Conserv Award, Izaak

Walton League Am, 85; Urban Wildlife Conserv Award, Nat Inst Urban Wildlife, 86; Take Pride in Am Award, US Dept Interior, 86. *Prof Exp:* Fac res asst, Dept Zool, Ohio State Univ, 75-77; fishery supvr, Div Wildlife, Ohio Dept Natural Resources, 77-79; fac res assoc, Dept Zool, NC State Univ, 79-82. *Concurrent Pos:* Guest fisheries scientist, Woods Hole Oceanog Inst, 77; assoc ed, J Progressive Fish-Culturist, 88-90; mem, Fed Qual Assurance Aquacult Comt, US Food & Drug Admin, 90-; chmn, Striped Bass Comt, Am Fisheries Soc, 87-89, Task Force Fishery Chem, 93- *Mem:* Am Fisheries Soc; World Aquacult Soc; Estuarine Res Fedn. *Res:* Development of improved techniques to mature, reproduce and domesticate striped bass in captivity; endocrinology, nutrition, physiology and genetics of striped bass; development of genetic lines and to quantify to progress of improvement for important heritable traits of domestic striped bass progeny. *Mailing Add:* Crane Aquaculture Facil PO Box 1475 Baltimore MD 21203

**WOODS, MARIBELLE,** MICROBIOLOGY. *Current Pos:* RETIRED. *Personal Data:* b Albany, Ga, Aug 16, 19. *Educ:* Univ Chattanooga, BS, 42; Yale Univ, MS, 48. *Prof Exp:* Bioassayer, Chattanooga Med Co, 42-48, pharmacologist, 48-66; pharmacologist, Chattem Drug & Chem Co, 66-78, microbiologist, Chattem, Inc, 78-95. *Concurrent Pos:* Pharmacologist, Brayten Pharmaceut Co, 48-73. *Mem:* NY Acad Sci. *Res:* Laxative action of senna; premenstrual tension; uterine physiology; antacids. *Mailing Add:* 311 Guild Dr Chattanooga TN 37421-3920

**WOODS, MARY,** INORGANIC CHEMISTRY. *Current Pos:* from instr to assoc prof chem, 53-73, PROF CHEM, ROSARY COL, 73- *Personal Data:* b Webster Groves, Mo, Dec 22, 23. *Educ:* Rosary Col, AB, 45; Univ Ill, MA, 47; Univ Wis, PhD(chem), 61. *Prof Exp:* Teacher, Trinity High Sch, Ill, 49-53. *Concurrent Pos:* Consult, Argonne Nat Lab, 75- *Mem:* Am Chem Soc; Sigma Xi. *Res:* Complex ion equilibria and kinetics; kinetics of redox reactions of actinide ions in solution. *Mailing Add:* Dept Natural Sci Rosary Col River Forest IL 60305-1099. *Fax:* 708-366-5360; *E-Mail:* woodssrm@email.rosary.edu

**WOODS, NANCY FUGATE,** WOMENS HEALTH RESEARCH. *Current Pos:* assoc prof physiol, 78-82, 82-84, DIR, CTR WOMEN'S HEALTH RES, UNIV WASH, 89-, PROF, DEPT PARENT & CHILD NURSING, 90-, ASSOC DEAN RES, SCH NURSING, 97- *Educ:* Wis State Univ, BS, 68; Univ Wash, MNurs, 69; Univ NC, PhD(epidemiol), 78. *Honors & Awards:* Distinguished Contrib Nursing Sci Award, Am Nurses Found, 92; Distinguished Contrib Women's Health, Am Psychol Asn, 94; Jean A Kelley Endowed Lectr, Univ Ala, 94. *Prof Exp:* Staff nurse, Sacred Heart Hosp, Wis, 68, Univ Hosp, Wash, 69-70, St Francis Cabrini Hosp, Wash, 70; nurse clinician, Yale New Haven Hosp, 70-71; instr, Grace New Haven Sch Nursing, Duke Univ, 71-72, from instr to assoc prof, 72-78. *Concurrent Pos:* Dir, Off Nursing Res Facil, Univ Wash, 82-84, prof & chairperson, Dept Parent & Child Nursing, 84-90; consult, USPHS, 84-85, Univ Tex, Univ Mont, NIH, 87, Ore Health Sci Univ, 85-87 & 87-89, Nat Ctr Nursing res, 88, Nordic Inst Nursing Sci, 90, Univ NC, Chapel Hill, 90, 91, Univ Ariz, Mont State Univ, 91, Emory Univ, 92; pres scholar, Univ Calif, San Francisco, 85-86; vis prof, Univ Ala, 94. *Mem:* Inst Med-Nat Acad Sci; assoc mem Am Col Epidemiol; fel Am Acad Nursing (pres, 89-91); Am Nursing Asn; Soc Menstrual Cycle Res (vpres, 81-83, pres, 83-85); Am Asn Univ Prof; Am Pub Health Asn; Soc Advan Women's Health Res. *Res:* Author of numerous articles to professional journals and publications. *Mailing Add:* Sch Nursing Ctr Women's Health Res Univ Wash Box 357265 Seattle WA 98195-7265. *Fax:* 206-685-9264

**WOODS, PHILIP SARGENT,** cell & molecular biology, chromosome ultrastructure; deceased, see previous edition for last biography

**WOODS, RALPH ARTHUR,** METALLURGY, WELDING ENGINEERING. *Current Pos:* WELDING ENGR, KAISER ALUMINUM & CHEM CORP, 67- *Personal Data:* b Norwich, Eng, Mar 26, 41; m 66; c 2. *Educ:* Birmingham Univ, BSc, 63, PhD(metall), 66. *Honors & Awards:* C H Jennings Mem Award, Am Welding Soc, 72. *Prof Exp:* Mat engr, Sikorsky Helicopters Div, United Technologies Corp, 66-67. *Mem:* Am Soc Metals. *Res:* Aluminum welding research; aluminum alloy metallurgy; aluminum vacuum brazing. *Mailing Add:* 2292 Camino Brazos Pleasanton CA 94566

**WOODS, RAYMOND D,** GEOLOGY. *Current Pos:* RETIRED. *Personal Data:* b Evangeline, La, Sept 14, 10. *Educ:* Univ Tex, BS, 31, MS, 34. *Prof Exp:* Res geologist, Exxon Corp, asst chief geologist, sr petrol geologist, 32-72. *Concurrent Pos:* Consult, Exxon, 72. *Mem:* Geol Soc Am; Am Asn Petrol Geologists; Soc Econ Paleontologists & Mineralogists. *Mailing Add:* 4100 Jackson Ave Apt 484 Austin TX 78731

**WOODS, RICHARD DAVID,** CIVIL ENGINEERING. *Current Pos:* from asst prof to assoc prof, 67-77, PROF & CHMN CIVIL ENG, UNIV MICH, ANN ARBOR, 77- *Personal Data:* b Lansing, Mich, Sept 4, 35; m 57; c 3. *Educ:* Univ Notre Dame, BSCE, 57, MSCE, 62; Univ Mich, Ann Arbor, PhD(civil eng), 67. *Honors & Awards:* Collingwood Prize, Am Soc Civil Engrs, 68. *Prof Exp:* Proj engr, Air Force Weapons Lab, NMex, 62-63; instr civil eng, Mich Technol Univ, 63-64. *Concurrent Pos:* Consult, 67-; Fed Ger Res Coun vis prof, Inst Soil & Rock Mech, Univ Karlsruhe, 71-72; found eng consult, Consumers Power Co, Mich, 72- *Mem:* Am Soc Civil Engrs; Am Soc Eng Educ; Am Soc Testing & Mat. *Res:* Vibrations of soils; foundations and structures; seismology; earthquake engineering; geophysical methods in environmental geotechnology. *Mailing Add:* 3699 Bradford Sq Dr Ann Arbor MI 48103

**WOODS, ROBERT CLAUDE,** CHEMICAL PHYSICS, INTERSTELLAR CHEMISTRY. *Current Pos:* from asst prof to assoc prof, 67-77, PROF CHEM, UNIV WIS-MADISON, 77- *Personal Data:* b Atlanta, Ga, Mar 24, 40; m 63; c 2. *Educ:* Ga Inst Technol, BS, 61; Harvard Univ, AM, 62, PhD(phys chem), 65. *Honors & Awards:* Nobel Laureate Signature Award, Am Chem Soc, 84. *Prof Exp:* Instr chem, US Naval Acad, 65-67. *Concurrent Pos:* Mem, Comt Atomic & Molecular Physics, Nat Res Coun, 84-; vis prof, Justus-Liebig Univ, Giessen, WGer, 85. *Mem:* Am Chem Soc; Am Phys Soc; Sigma Xi; fel Am Inst Chemists; AAAS. *Res:* Microwave spectroscopy of molecular ions and of transient species present in electrical discharges and related theoretical problems; radioastronomy and the chemistry of the interstellar medium. *Mailing Add:* Chem-Univ Wis 1101 Univ Ave Madison WI 53706

**WOODS, ROBERT JAMES,** RADIATION CHEMISTRY, SCIENCE COMMUNICATIONS. *Current Pos:* from asst prof to prof, 63-95, head Dept Chem, 84-88 EMER PROF CHEM, UNIV SASK, 95- *Personal Data:* b London, Eng, Feb 8, 28; m 58, Margaret E Brand; c Robert S, Catherine F, Margaret A & Elizabeth K. *Educ:* Univ London, BSc, 49, PhD(org chem), 51; Imp Col London, dipl, 51. *Prof Exp:* Nat Res Coun Can fel, Prairie Regional Lab, Sask, 51-53; Univ NZ res fel, Victoria, NA, 53-54; res assoc, Univ Sask, 55-62; sr res fel, Royal Mil Col Sci, Eng, 62-63. *Concurrent Pos:* Vis prof, Saclay Nuclear Res Ctr, France, 72-73. *Mem:* Chem Inst Can; fel Royal Soc Chem. *Res:* Radiation chemistry of organic compounds, both pure and in aqueous solution; radiation safety. *Mailing Add:* Dept Chem Univ Sask 110 Science Pl Saskatoon SK S7N 5C9 Can. *Fax:* 306-966-4730; *E-Mail:* rjwoods@link.ca

**WOODS, ROBERT OCTAVIUS,** VACUUM SCIENCE, FLIGHT INSTRUMENTATION & ROBOTICS. *Current Pos:* SR MEM TECH STAFF, SANDIA NAT LABS, 67- *Personal Data:* b Evanston, Ill, Feb 17, 33; m 65, Judith Neese; c Lisa A & Robert D. *Educ:* Princeton Univ, BSE, 62, MSE, 64, MA, 65, PhD(aerospace & mech sci), 67. *Prof Exp:* Prof engr, Allstates Eng Co. *Concurrent Pos:* Cong sci fel, Am Soc Mech Engrs, 91-92; mem, Senate Comt Govt Affairs. *Mem:* Am Phys Soc; Sigma Xi; fel Am Soc Mech Engrs; fel Brit Interplanetary Soc; AAAS. *Res:* Design of instrument systems for research from flight vehicles: small rockets, aircraft, stratospheric balloons and satellites; atmospheric research. *Mailing Add:* 7513 Harwood Ave NE Albuquerque NM 87110

**WOODS, ROGER DAVID,** THEORETICAL PHYSICS, COMPUTER SCIENCE. *Current Pos:* assoc prof, 65-72, prof, 72-97, EMER PROF PHYSICS, SAN BERNADINO VALLEY COL, 97- *Personal Data:* b Los Angeles, Calif, Mar 28, 24; m 52; c 3. *Educ:* Univ Redlands, AB, 45; Univ Calif, Los Angeles, MA, 49, PhD, 54. *Prof Exp:* Res physicist, Univ Calif, Los Angeles, 54; asst prof physics, Univ Miami, 54-61; assoc prof, Univ Redlands, 61-65. *Mem:* AAAS; Am Phys Soc. *Res:* Nucleon-nuclei scattering; molecular structure; electron structure of atoms; energy bands in solids; generalized theory of gravitation; visible, ultraviolet and infrared spectroscopy; scientific computer application. *Mailing Add:* Dept Physics San Bernardino Valley Col San Bernardino CA 92410-2748

**WOODS, ROY ALEXANDER,** PHYSICS, ELECTRONICS. *Current Pos:* prof, 68-80, EMER PROF PHYSICS, NORFOLK STATE COL, 80- *Personal Data:* b Columbia, Mo, Oct 31, 13; m 34; c 1. *Educ:* Lincoln Univ, Mo, AB, 34; Boston Univ, AM, 46 & 48, EdD, 60. *Prof Exp:* Teacher high schs, Mo, 34-41; instr electronics & radar technician, USN, 42-45; prof physics & chmn div natural sci, Va State Col, 48-68. *Concurrent Pos:* Electronic engr, Lab Electronics Res & Develop, Mass, 52-53, 59-60. *Mem:* Am Asn Physics Teachers. *Res:* Instrumentation for naval radar. *Mailing Add:* 6028 Wesleyan Dr Virginia Beach VA 23455

**WOODS, SHERWYN MARTIN,** PSYCHIATRY, PSYCHOANALYSIS. *Current Pos:* dir grad educ, 63-82, from asst prof to assoc prof, 63-74, PROF PSYCHIAT, SCH MED, UNIV SOUTHERN CALIF, 74-, DIR STUDENT PSYCHIAT SERV, 66-, DIR PSYCHOANALYSIS EDUC, 82- *Personal Data:* b Des Moines, Iowa, June 25, 32; m 71. *Educ:* Univ Wis, BS, 54, MD, 57, PhD(psychoanal), 77; Am Bd Psychiat & Neurol, dipl, 65, cert psychoanal, 77. *Prof Exp:* Intern, Philadelphia Gen Hosp, 57-58; resident, Univ Hosps, Univ Wis Med Sch, 58-61, instr psychiat, Med Sch, 61. *Concurrent Pos:* NIMH career teacher award, 64-66; clin assoc, Southern Calif Psychoanal Inst, 64-68, mem, 68-, instr, 69-, supv & training analyst, 78-; examr, Am Bd Psychiat & Neurol, 67-; consult, Calif Dept Ment Hyg, 70-; pres, Am Asn Dir Psychiat Residency Training, 74-76; chmn, Residency Rev Comt Psychiat, 87-89 & 92-96; Am Psychiat Asn Comt Grad Educ, 85-87. *Mem:* Fel Am Psychiat Asn; Asn Advan Psychother; fel Am Col Psychiat; fel Am Acad Psychoanalysis. *Res:* Medical education; human sexuality; psychotherapy. *Mailing Add:* Univ Southern Calif 1937 Hosp Place Grad Hall Los Angeles CA 90033

**WOODS, STEPHEN CHARLES,** PHYSIOLOGICAL PSYCHOLOGY. *Current Pos:* from asst prof to assoc prof, 72-77, chmn, Dept Psychol, 81-88, PROF PSYCHOL, UNIV WASH, 77-, ASSOC DEAN ACAD PROGS & RES, 92- *Personal Data:* b Pasadena, Calif, Feb 17, 42; m 88, Evelyn Laiche; c 2. *Educ:* Univ Wash, BS, 65, BS, 66, PhD(physiol & psychol), 70. *Prof Exp:* Asst to assoc prof psychol, Columbia Univ, 70-72. *Concurrent Pos:* Mem psychobiol study sect, NSF, 83-86; counr, NAm Asn Study Obesity, 84-86; mem biopsychol study sect, NIH, 86-; pres, Int Cong Physiol Food & Fluid Intake, 86, Soc Study Ingestive Behav, 88-91. *Mem:* Am Diabetes Asn; Soc Neurosci; Soc Study Ingestive Behav (pres 88-89); Am Psychol Soc; Psychonomic Soc. *Res:* Neural and hormonal control of appetite and the regulation of body weight; influence of learning on metabolic processes; numerous articles published in various journals. *Mailing Add:* Dept Psychol Univ Wash 73900 Seventh Ave NE Seattle WA 98195. *Fax:* 206-685-3157; *E-Mail:* swoods@u.washington.edu

**WOODS, STUART B,** SOLID STATE PHYSICS. *Current Pos:* from assoc prof to prof physics, 59-89, assoc dean Fac Grad Studies & Res, 74-83, EMER PROF PHYSICS, UNIV ALTA, 89- *Personal Data:* b Pathlow, Sask, Apr 26, 24; m 49, Willa E McPeak; c W James & Marianne H. *Educ:* Univ Sask, BA, 44, MA, 48; Univ BC, PhD, 52. *Prof Exp:* Res officer physics, Nat Res Coun Can, 52-59. *Concurrent Pos:* Vis prof, Univ Bristol, 66-67 & Univ St Andrews, Scotland, 73-74. *Mem:* Sci Peace. *Res:* Low temperature and solid state physics, chiefly experimental transport properties in solids and high Tc superconductivity. *Mailing Add:* Dept Physics Univ Alta Edmonton AB T6G 2J1 Can. *Fax:* 403-492-4256

**WOODS, THOMAS STEPHEN,** ORGANIC CHEMISTRY. *Current Pos:* res chemist, Biochem Dept, Du Pont Co, 74-79, res supvr, synthesis, 79-80, lab adminr, 80-82, res supvr, formulations, 82-84, licensing mgr, Agr Prod Dept, 85-87, mgr res & develop Europ, Mideast & Africa, Agr Prod Dept, du Pont de Nemours, Paris, 87-90, res mgr, Prod Delivery Systs, Du Pont Agr Prods, 90-96, INT TECHNOL MGR, DU PONT AGR PRODS, NEW DELHI, INDIA, 96- *Personal Data:* b Florence, Ala, Dec 13, 44; m 66, Susan Schweers; c Kathryn S & Leslie G. *Educ:* Auburn Univ, BS, 67; Univ Ill, PhD(org chem), 71. *Prof Exp:* Res chemist, Div Med Chem, Walter Reed Army Inst Res, 72-74. *Concurrent Pos:* Am Crop Protection Asn Rep Europ Crop Protection Asn Specif Expert Team. *Mem:* Am Chem Soc. *Res:* Synthesis of novel organic compounds of biological utility; heterocyclic chemistry; organosulfur and selenium chemistry; theories of tautomerism and resonance; organic photochemistry; agricultural product formulations and delivery systems. *Mailing Add:* Du Pont Agr Prod Exp Sta Bldg 402 Wilmington DE 19880-0402. *Fax:* 302-695-7804; *E-Mail:* woodsts@esvax. email.dupont.com

**WOODS, W(ALLACE) KELLY,** NUCLEAR ENGINEERING. *Current Pos:* RETIRED. *Personal Data:* b Claremore, Okla, Dec 10, 12; m 37; c 4. *Educ:* Stanford Univ, AB, 34; Mass Inst Technol, MS, 36, DSc(chem eng), 40. *Prof Exp:* Instr chem eng, Mass Inst Technol, 36-40; chem engr, Tech Div, Eng Dept, E I du Pont de Nemours & Co, 40-43, tech specialist, Explosives Dept, 43-46; tech & managerial assignments with plutonium prod reactors, Hanford Labs, Gen Elec Co, 46-55, mgr nuclear mat, Vallecitos Atomic Lab, 55-61 & prog, Hanford Labs, 61-63, consult engr, 63-65; consult engr, Douglas United Nuclear, Inc, Wash, 65-71; coordr, Ore Nuclear & Thermal Energy Coun, Ore State Govt, 71-75, energy site coordr, 75-78; prof nuclear eng, Ore State Univ, 78-88. *Mem:* Am Chem Soc; fel Am Nuclear Soc (treas, 59-61); Am Inst Chem Engrs. *Res:* Heat transfer to boiling liquids; fluid flow; irradiation effects in solids. *Mailing Add:* 714 Tillman Ave SE Salem OR 97302. *E-Mail:* kwoods1803@aol.com

**WOODS, WALTER RALPH,** ANIMAL NUTRITION. *Current Pos:* RETIRED. *Personal Data:* b Grant, Va, Dec 2, 31; m 53, Jackie Miller; c Neal & Diana. *Educ:* Murray State Univ, BS, 54; Univ Ky, MS, 55; Okla State Univ, PhD, 57. *Prof Exp:* Instr, Okla State Univ, 56-57; from asst prof to assoc prof animal husb, Iowa State Univ, 57-62; from assoc prof to prof, Univ Nebr, Lincoln, 62-71; head, Dept Animal Sci, Purdue Univ, West Lafayette, 71-85; dean agr & dir, Agr Exp Sta, Kans State Univ, 85-92, dir, Coop Exten Serv, 87-92. *Concurrent Pos:* Asst adminr regional res, Coop State Res Serv, USDA. *Mem:* Am Soc Animal Sci; Sigma Xi. *Res:* Protein and nonprotein nitrogen utilization in beef cattle and sheep; energy utilization as influenced by diet composition and processing. *Mailing Add:* 8318 Strathmore Lane Roanoke VA 24019

**WOODS, WENDELL DAVID,** OPHTHALMOLOGY, ECOSANOIDS. *Current Pos:* Res asst, 63-66, from instr to asst prof, 66-73, ASSOC PROF OPHTHAL, SCH MED, EMORY UNIV, 73- *Personal Data:* b Liberal, Kans, Dec 5, 32; m 64; c 2. *Educ:* Univ Mo, BS, 58, MS, 59, PhD(biochem), 65. *Concurrent Pos:* NIH grant vision, Emory Univ, 72- *Mem:* AAAS; Asn Res Ophthal; Am Chem Soc; Sigma Xi. *Res:* Ecosanoid metabolism in the cornea and in the outflow area of the eye; oxidative effects in glaucoma. *Mailing Add:* Ophthal Res Lab Emery Eye Ctr 1327 Clifton Rd Atlanta GA 30322

**WOODS, WILLIAM A,** knowledge representation, natural language processing, for more information see previous edition

**WOODS, WILLIAM FRED,** AGRICULTURAL ECONOMICS. *Current Pos:* Asst dep admin, 80-85, PUB POLICY SPECIALIST, EXTEN SERV, USDA, 85- *Personal Data:* b Ala. *Educ:* Auburn Univ, BS, 60, MS, 61. *Concurrent Pos:* Mem, Nat Pub Policy Educ Comt. *Mem:* Am Agr Econ Asn. *Res:* Agricultural policy; public policy education; agricultural extension education. *Mailing Add:* 4206 Washington Blvd Apt B Arlington VA 22201

**WOODS, WILLIAM GEORGE,** PHYSICAL ORGANIC CHEMISTRY. *Current Pos:* DIR & CHEM HYG OFFICER, OFF ENVIRON HEALTH & SAFETY, UNIV CALIF, RIVERSIDE, 92-; CONSULT, 92- *Personal Data:* b Superior, Wis, Dec 21, 31; m 52; c Jennifer, Leland & Jeffrey. *Educ:* Univ Calif, Los Angeles, BS, 53; Calif Inst Technol, PhD, 57. *Prof Exp:* Asst, Calif Inst Technol, 53-55; res chemist, Res Lab, Gen Elec Co, 56-58; sr res chemist, US Borax Res Corp, 58-74, mgr agr res & develop, 74-76, sr scientist, 76-92. *Concurrent Pos:* Res officer, Commonwealth Sci & Indust Res Orgn, Melbourne, Australia, 62-63. *Mem:* Am Inst Mining, Metall & Petrol Engrs; Am Chem Soc; Sigma Xi. *Res:* Carbonium ion and pyrolysis mechanism; semi-inorganic polymer systems; semi-empirical molecular orbital calculations; nuclear magnetic resonance spectroscopy; organometallic and organic synthesis; herbicide synthesis and metabolism; direct agricultural research programs; fire retardants and polymer additives; corrosion electro-chemistry; precious metal extractive metallurgy; boron chemistry; boron specification in biological systems; environmental and worker safety. *Mailing Add:* 2922 Las Flores Riverside CA 92503-6106. *Fax:* 909-787-5122; *E-Mail:* william.woods@ucr.edu

**WOODS, WILNA ANN,** CANCER RESEARCH. *Current Pos:* chief, Contract Rev Br, 89-97, DEPT CHIEF, SPEC REV REFERRAL RESOURCES BR, NAT CANCER INST, NIH, 97- *Personal Data:* b Apr 20, 29. *Educ:* Stanford Univ, BA, 51, PhD, 55. *Prof Exp:* Res assoc, Case Western Res Univ, Cleveland, 54-68. *Res:* Cancer; microbiology; chemistry; anatomy; numerous technical publications. *Mailing Add:* NIH Nat Cancer Inst Spec Rev Referral Resources Br EPN Bldg Rm 605 Bethesda MD 20892

**WOODSIDE, DAVID LEVER,** PLASMA PHYSICS RELATED TO DYNAMIC UNIVERSE THEORY, POLYMER CHEMISTRY RELATED TO ELECTRONIC PRODUCTS. *Current Pos:* ENGR, TRITON INC, 80- *Personal Data:* b Mt Holly, NJ, Oct 12, 27. *Educ:* Bucknell Univ, BS, 52; Rutgers Univ, MS, 55, PhD(phys chem), 57. *Mem:* Sigma Xi; Am Chem Soc. *Res:* Theoretical development of the Dynamic Universe to replace the outdated Big Bang Theory. *Mailing Add:* PO Box 646 Marlton NJ 08053

**WOODSIDE, JOHN MOFFATT,** MARINE GEOPHYSICS, GEOLOGY. *Current Pos:* ASSOC PROF, FREE UNIV AMSTERDAM, 89- *Personal Data:* b Toronto, Ont, Jan 23, 41; m 67; c 2. *Educ:* Queen's Univ, BSc, 64; Mass Inst Technol, MSc, 68; Cambridge Univ, PhD(geophys), 76. *Prof Exp:* Tech officer geophys, Geol Surv Can, 64; res asst marine geophys, Woods Hole Oceanog Lab, 66-68; sci officer, Bedford Inst Oceanog, 68-71; res asst, Dept Geod & Geophys, Cambridge Univ, 71-76; res scientist marine geophys, Atlantic Geosci Ctr, Geol Surv Can, 76-89. *Concurrent Pos:* Int Bus Mach Corp fel, Dept Geod & Geophys, Cambridge Univ, 75-76; mem bd dirs, Int Gravity Bur, 78-; sr geophysicist, Proj for Regional Offshore Prospecting in East Asia & Pac, UN, 79-80; coord Int Training Through Res Prog, 91-96; chmn, ESF Network, 92-95. *Mem:* Fel Geol Asn Can; Am Geophys Union; Soc Explor Geophysicists; Am Asn Petrol Geologists; Can Geophys Union; Environ & Eng Geophys Soc; Europ Union Geosci. *Res:* Structural and tectonic aspects of evolution of ocean basins with particular emphasis on neotectonics of collision zones, nature of passive continental margins, and subduction zones; areas of primary interest are Mediterranean Sea, Banda Sea and the Southwestern Pacific; potential fields and seismic methods; deep sea depositional systems; fluid flux through sea floor; mud volcanoes. *Mailing Add:* De Boelelaan 1085 Amsterdam 1081 HV Netherlands. *E-Mail:* nooj@ geo.vu.nl

**WOODSIDE, KENNETH HALL,** PHYSIOLOGY, BIOCHEMISTRY. *Current Pos:* PROF BIOCHEM & CHMN DEPT, NOVA SOUTHEASTERN UNIV, 81- *Personal Data:* b Northampton, Mass, June 18, 38; m 60; c 2. *Educ:* Oberlin Col, AB, 59; Univ Rochester, PhD(biochem), 69. *Prof Exp:* Res assoc physiol, Col Med, Pa State Univ, 68-70, asst prof physiol & head multidiscipline labs, 70-76; asst prof med, Sch Med, Univ Miami, 76-79; res biochemist, Mt Sinai Med Ctr, Miami, 79-81. *Mem:* Am Physiol Soc; AAAS; Sigma Xi. *Res:* Hormonal and non-hormonal regulation of protein biosynthesis and degradation; pulmonary macrophage function. *Mailing Add:* Dept Biochem Nova Southeastern Univ 3200 S University Dr Ft Lauderdale FL 33328. *Fax:* 954-723-1802; *E-Mail:* woodsidek@aol.com

**WOODSIDE, WILLIAM,** PHYSICS, MATHEMATICS. *Current Pos:* from asst prof to assoc prof, 66-95, chmn eng math, 80-95, EMER PROF MATH, QUEEN'S UNIV, ONT, 95- *Personal Data:* b Ft William, Ont, July 5, 31; m 53; c 3. *Educ:* Queen's Univ, Belfast, BSc, 51, MSc, 59, DSc, 62. *Prof Exp:* Asst, Royal Naval Sci Serv, Baldock, Eng, 51 & Toronto, 53; master physics, Ridley Col, Can, 52-55; res officer, Nat Res Coun, Can, 54-58; res physicist, Gulf Res & Develop Co, 58-60; master math, Ridley Col, 60-66. *Mem:* Can Math Soc; Math Asn Am. *Res:* Optimization theory; operations research; mathematics; education; heat transfer in porous media. *Mailing Add:* 633 Pimlic Pl Kingston ON K7M 5Z7 Can. *Fax:* 613-545-2964

**WOODSON, CHARLES R,** SOCIAL WORK, PUBLIC ADMINISTRATION. *Current Pos:* sr pub health analyst, Health Care Homeless Br, Bur Primary Health Care, 92-93, sect chief, Scholar Prog Br, 93-94, actg chief, 94-95, DIR, PUB HOUSING PRIMARY CARE PROG & DEP CHIEF, HEALTH CARE HOMELESS BR, DIV PROG SPEC POP, BUR PRIMARY HEALTH CARE, 95- *Personal Data:* b Louisville, Ky, Feb 22, 42. *Educ:* Lincoln Univ, BS, 63; Univ Louisville, MSW, 69; Univ Southern Calif, MPA, 89. *Prof Exp:* Dir, SFields Residential Juv Treat Ctr, Metrop Social Serv Dept, Am Asn Cols Osteop Med, 69-70, City-County Community Action Comn, 70-71, Off Minority Affairs, Univ La, 71-74, Off Spec Opportunities, 74-79; pub health analyst, Div Community Assistance, Nat Inst Drug Abuse, 79-80, Off Extramural Proj Rev, 80-81; assoc prog coordr, Am Asn State Cols & Univs, 81-82; asst prof & prog coordr, Southern Ill Univ, 82-84, Off Med Educ, Univ Va Sch Med, 83-85; educ specialist, Howard Univ Col Med, 85-86; health scientist adminr, Grants Rev Br, Nat Cancer Inst, 86-88, Off Substance Abuse Prev, 88-92. *Concurrent Pos:* Instr sociol, Bellarmine Col, 73; adj asst prof, Univ Dist Columbia, 81-83, Southern Ill Univ, 82-83; mgt consult, Fed Support Div, Del Green Assoc Inc, 82-83; spec asst dir, Nat Inst Environ Health, 83; asst prof med educ, Univ Va, 84-86. *Mem:* Nat Asn Minority Med Educr. *Res:* Provide direction and administrative guidance to public health programs including organization development, program planning, implementation and evaluation. *Mailing Add:* HRSA/BPHC/DPSP/HCHB 4350 East-West Hwy Bethesda MD 20814. *Fax:* 301-594-2470; *E-Mail:* cwoodson@hesa.ssw.dhhs.gov

**WOODSON, HERBERT H(ORACE),** ELECTRICAL ENGINEERING. *Current Pos:* RETIRED. *Personal Data:* b Stamford, Tex, Apr 5, 25; m 51; c 3. *Educ:* Mass Inst Technol, SB & SM, 52, ScD, 56. *Honors & Awards:* Nikola Tesla Award, Inst Elec & Electronics Engrs, 84. *Prof Exp:* Elec engr, US Naval Ord Lab, Md, 52-54; asst elec eng, Mass Inst Technol, 54-55, from instr to prof, 55-71; Alcoa Found prof, Univ Tex, Austin, 72-75, chmn dept, 71-81, prof elec eng, 71-83, Tex Atomic Energy Found prof, 80-83, dir, Ctr Energy Studies, 77-88, assoc dean develop & planning, Col Eng, 86-87, Ernest H Cockrell Centennial Chair Eng, 87-93, deans chair excellence eng, 88-96. *Concurrent Pos:* Actg dean eng, Univ Tex, Austin, 87-88. *Mem:* Nat Acad Eng; Am Soc Eng Educ; fel Inst Elec & Electronics Engrs. *Res:* Electrical energy conversion and control; power system engineering. *Mailing Add:* 7603 Rustling Rd Austin TX 78731-1333

**WOODSON, JOHN HODGES,** PHYSICAL CHEMISTRY, QUANTUM CHEMISTRY. *Current Pos:* from asst prof to assoc prof, 61-70, PROF CHEM, SAN DIEGO STATE UNIV, 70- *Personal Data:* b Hartford, Conn, May 25, 33; m 60, Karin A Turnbull; c James S, Anne E & Peter G. *Educ:* Wesleyan Univ, BA, 55; Northwestern Univ, PhD(phys chem), 59. *Prof Exp:* Asst prof chem, Wesleyan Univ, 59-61. *Mem:* Am Chem Soc; Sigma Xi. *Mailing Add:* Dept Chem San Diego State Univ San Diego CA 92182-0328. *Fax:* 619-594-4634; *E-Mail:* john.woodson@sdsu.edu

**WOODSON, ROBERT D,** HEMATOLOGY, PHYSIOLOGY & INTERNAL MEDICINE. *Current Pos:* assoc prof, 74-82, PROF MED, UNIV WIS, 82- *Personal Data:* b 1938; m 69, Anne L Hogren; c David, Karen & Lisa. *Educ:* Houghton Col, BA, 59; Univ Chicago, MD, 63. *Prof Exp:* Epidemic intel officer, Ctrs Dis Control, 65-67; instr & fel, Univ Wash, 68-71, asst prof med, 71-74. *Concurrent Pos:* Vis prof, Univ Zurich, Switz, 84-85; Fogarty Int fel, NIH, 84-85. *Mem:* Am Physiol Soc; Am Fedn Clin Res; Am Soc Hemat; Int Soc Oxygen Transport Tissue; Christian Med Soc. *Res:* Control of oxygen delivery; role of oxygen dissociation curve in oxygen transport; hemoglobin-based blood substitutes; platelet alloimmunization; demographics of blood transfusion. *Mailing Add:* Dept Med Univ Wis H4/534 CSC Madison WI 53792

**WOODSON, WILLIAM RANDOLPH,** POST HARVEST PHYSIOLOGY, REGULATION OF GENE EXPRESSION IN PLANTS. *Current Pos:* from asst prof to assoc prof, 85-93, PROF PLANT PHYSIOL, PURDUE UNIV 93- *Personal Data:* b Arkadelphia, Ark, Apr 20, 57; m 79, Susan W Woodson; c Samantha, Patrick & Chloe. *Educ:* Univ Ark, BS, 79; Cornell Univ, MS, 81, PhD(plant physiol), 83. *Prof Exp:* Asst prof, La State Univ, 83-85. *Mem:* Am Soc Hort Sci; Am Soc Plant Physiol; AAAS; Int Soc Plant Molecular Biol. *Res:* Role of the plant hormone ethylene in senescence of flower petals; regulation of ethylene biosynthesis and the regulation of gene expression by ethylene. *Mailing Add:* Bot Bldg Purdue Univ West Lafayette IN 47907-1968. *Fax:* 765-494-0391; *E-Mail:* randy_woodson@mailhost.hort.purdue.edu

**WOODSTOCK, LOWELL WILLARD,** seed physiology, seed vigor & deterioration; deceased, see previous edition for last biography

**WOODWARD, ARTHUR EUGENE,** PHYSICAL CHEMISTRY OF POLYMERS, POLYMER PHYSICS. *Current Pos:* assoc prof chem, 64-66, PROF CHEM, CITY COL NEW YORK, 67- *Personal Data:* b Los Angeles, Calif, Oct 16, 25; m 52; c 1. *Educ:* Occidental Col, BA, 49, MA, 50; Polytech Inst Brooklyn, PhD(phys chem), 53. *Prof Exp:* Asst Occidental Col, 50; US Govt grantee chem, Cath Univ Louvain, 53-54; res fel, Harvard Univ, 54-55; asst prof, Pa State Univ, 55-59, from asst prof to assoc prof physics, 59-64. *Concurrent Pos:* Guggenheim fel, Queen Mary Col, London, 62-63. *Mem:* Am Chem Soc; Am Phys Soc. *Res:* Physical and chemical properties of polymer crystals; nuclear magnetic resonance of high polymers; polymer morphology and infrared spectroscopy. *Mailing Add:* 70 E Tenth St Apt 5H New York NY 10003-5108

**WOODWARD, CLARE K,** BIOCHEMISTRY. *Current Pos:* from asst prof to assoc prof biochem, 72-81, PROF BIOCHEM & BIOL SCI, UNIV MINN, ST PAUL, 81- *Personal Data:* b Houston, Tex, Dec 10, 41; m 67. *Educ:* Smith Col, BA, 63; Rice Univ, PhD(biol), 67. *Prof Exp:* Fel phys chem, Med Sch, Univ Minn, Minneapolis, 68-70, asst prof lab med, 70-72. *Concurrent Pos:* Fel genetics, Univ Minn, St Paul, 67-68. *Mem:* Biophys Soc; Am Soc Biol Chemists. *Res:* Protein chemistry; protein dynamics, hydrogen exchange, NMR; protein folding. *Mailing Add:* Dept Biochem Univ Minn 140 Gortner Hall St Paul MN 55108-1022. *Fax:* 612-625-5780; *E-Mail:* clare@mulbrocbsumnedu

**WOODWARD, DAVID WILLCOX,** PHOTOCHEMISTRY, PHYSICAL CHEMISTRY. *Current Pos:* RETIRED. *Personal Data:* b Oxford, NY, July 24, 13; m 38; c 1. *Educ:* Amherst Col, AB, 34; Harvard Univ, PhD(org chem), 37. *Prof Exp:* Res chemist, Chem Dept, E I du Pont de Nemours & Co, Inc, 37-51, res supvr, Photo Prod Dept, 51-54, res mgr, 45-68, lab dir, Photo Prod Dept, 68-76. *Mem:* Am Chem Soc; Soc Photog Sci & Eng. *Res:* Photography; furane and polymer chemistry; cyanides; nitriles; photochemistry; photopolymerization; dyes. *Mailing Add:* 103 Taylor Lane Kennett Square PA 19348

**WOODWARD, DOW OWEN,** MOLECULAR BIOLOGY. *Current Pos:* assoc prof, 62-74, PROF BIOL, STANFORD UNIV, 74- *Personal Data:* b Logan, Utah, Dec 1, 31; m 56; c 4. *Educ:* Utah State Univ, BS, 56; Yale Univ, MS, 57, PhD(bot), 59. *Prof Exp:* Mem res staff radiobiol, Aerospace Med Ctr, USAF, 59-62. *Mem:* Genetics Soc Am; Am Soc Biol Chemists. *Res:* Biochemical genetics in microorganisms; membrane structure and function; cytoplasmic inheritance; biological rhythms; enzymology. *Mailing Add:* Dept Biol Sci Stanford Univ Stanford CA 94305-5020

**WOODWARD, EDWARD ROY,** surgery; deceased, see previous edition for last biography

**WOODWARD, ERVIN CHAPMAN, JR,** RADIATION PHYSICS. *Current Pos:* PHYSICIST, LAWRENCE LIVERMORE LAB, UNIV CALIF, 52- *Personal Data:* b Long Beach, Calif, Apr 8, 23; m 49; c 2. *Educ:* Univ Calif, PhD(physics), 52. *Mem:* Am Phys Soc. *Res:* Spectroscopy; hyperfine structure; nuclear spin and isotope shift; high speed optics. *Mailing Add:* 3876 Stanford Way Livermore CA 94550

**WOODWARD, FRED ERSKINE,** surface chemistry, organic polymer chemistry; deceased, see previous edition for last biography

**WOODWARD, J GUY,** PHYSICS. *Current Pos:* RETIRED. *Personal Data:* b Carleton, Mich, Nov 19, 14; m 45, Ruth L Errien; c Marcia & Lenore B (Brown). *Educ:* NCent Col, BA, 36; Mich State Col, MS, 38; Ohio State Univ, PhD(physics), 42. *Honors & Awards:* Emile Berliner Award, Audio Eng Soc, 68. *Prof Exp:* Asst physics, Mich State Col, 36-39; asst physics, Ohio State Univ, 39-42; res physicist, Mfg Co, RCA Corp, 42, res engr, 42-72, res fel, RCA Labs, 72-83. *Mem:* Fel AAAS; Acoust Soc Am; Hon Mem Audio Eng Soc (pres, 71-72); fel Inst Elec & Electronics Engrs; Sigma Xi. *Res:* Physical optics; room and music acoustics; radio interference from motor vehicles; underwater sound; electroacoustic transducers; high fidelity phonograph systems; viscometry; video digital and audio magnetic tape recording. *Mailing Add:* 208 Laurel Circle Princeton NJ 08540

**WOODWARD, JAMES FRANKLIN,** EXPERIMENTAL GRAVITATION, PULSAR ASTROPHYSICS. *Current Pos:* PROF HIST SCI, CALIF STATE UNIV, 72- *Personal Data:* b Boston, Mass, Dec 22, 41. *Educ:* Middlebury Col, AB, 64; NY Univ, MS, 69; Univ Denver, PhD(hist sci), 72. *Concurrent Pos:* Adj prof physics, Calif State Univ, 80- *Mem:* Int Soc Gen Relativity & Gravitation; NY Acad Sci; Hist Sci Soc; Astron Soc Pac. *Res:* Experimental investigation of relativistic gravitation; Mach's principle; interrelation of gravity with the other forces of nature. *Mailing Add:* Dept Hist & Physics Calif State Univ Fullerton CA 92634

**WOODWARD, JAMES KENNETH,** pharmacology, for more information see previous edition

**WOODWARD, JOAN STRATTON,** ON SHORE SEA LAB, FLOATING LAB TO ANACAPA ISLAND. *Current Pos:* marine shoreline field instr, 73-97, MARINE BIOLOGIST, UNLIMITED LEARNING CTR, 82- *Personal Data:* b New York, NY, Feb 26, 43; m 65, Lee; c Joanna, Amy, Adam & Anne. *Educ:* Dakota Wesleyan Univ, BA, 65; Univ Calif, Irvine, PhD(marine biol), 70; World Univ, MA, 85. *Prof Exp:* Pop biol teacher, Anahcim Union High Sch Dist, 65-73. *Concurrent Pos:* Consult teacher, Orange Co Marine Sci, 68-70; vis marine biologist, Inst Zen Studies, 84; marine biologist, Los Posas Sea Lab Proj, Pleasant Valley Sch Dist, 87-97; dir commun, Search Assocs, 94-97. *Res:* Life cycle and biometrics of Diamond turbid; on shore lab activities for students; island ecology. *Mailing Add:* 183 Cerro Crest Dr Camarillo CA 93010. *Fax:* 818-787-0110; *E-Mail:* sw@cup.portal.com

**WOODWARD, JOE WILLIAM,** CHEMICAL ENGINEERING. *Current Pos:* CONSULT, E I DU PONT DE NEMOURS & CO, INC, 66-, ASPEN TECHNOL. *Personal Data:* b Teral, Okla, Oct 31, 37; m 58; c 3. *Educ:* Tex A&M Col, BS, 60; Calif Inst Technol, MS, 61, PhD(chem eng), 65. *Prof Exp:* Sr res engr, US Army assigned to Jet Propulsion Lab, NASA, 65-66. *Concurrent Pos:* Fel, Calif Inst Technol, 65-66. *Mem:* Am Inst Chem Engrs; Nat Soc Prof Engrs. *Res:* Polymer processing; rheology; mathematical models; computer process control. *Mailing Add:* 2726 Elizabeth St Port Neches TX 77651

**WOODWARD, LEE ALBERT,** STRUCTURAL GEOLOGY. *Current Pos:* from asst prof to assoc prof, 65-73, chmn dept, 70-76, PROF GEOL, UNIV NMEX, 73- *Personal Data:* b Omaha, Nebr, Apr 22, 31; m 52; c 4. *Educ:* Univ Mont, BA, 58, MS, 59; Univ Wash, PhD(geol), 62. *Prof Exp:* Geologist, US Bur Reclamation, 58 & Pan Am Petrol Corp, 62-63; instr geol, Olympic Col, 63-65. *Concurrent Pos:* NSF fel, 58-61; Monsanto fel, 61-62; assoc ed, Geol Soc Am Bull, 77-82; NATO fel, 73. *Mem:* Geol Soc Am; Am Asn Petrol Geologists; Soc Mining Engrs; Soc Econ Geologists. *Res:* Regional tectonics of western United States; mineral exploration. *Mailing Add:* Dept Geol Univ NMex Albuquerque NM 87106

**WOODWARD, LEROY ALBERT,** PHYSICS. *Current Pos:* res asst prof physics, Eng Exp Sta, 60-63, from asst prof to assoc prof, 63-82, EMER ASSOC PROF PHYSICS, GA INST TECHNOL, 82- *Personal Data:* b Hartford, Conn, Nov 22, 16; m 42; c 2. *Educ:* Ga Inst Technol, BS, 43; Univ Mich, MS, 47. *Prof Exp:* Mem sci staff, US Navy Underwater Sound Lab, Columbia Univ, 44; contract physicist, David Taylor Model Basin, US Dept Navy, DC, 45; from instr to asst prof physics, Ga Inst Technol, 47-51, assoc prof physics & res physicist, Eng Exp Sta, 51-55; res physicist, Scripto, Inc, 55-58, dir res, 58-60. *Mem:* Sigma Xi. *Res:* Optics and optical microscopy. *Mailing Add:* 834 Oakdale Rd NE Atlanta GA 30307

**WOODWARD, PAUL RALPH,** COMPUTATIONAL ASTROPHYSICS. *Current Pos:* PROF ASTRON, UNIV MINN, MINNEAPOLIS, 85-, DIR GRAPHICS & VISUALIZATION, ARMY HIGH PERFORMANCE COMPUT RES CTR, 90- *Personal Data:* b Rockeville Center, NY, Aug 25, 46; m 72, Judith Hansburg; c Thomas & Theodore. *Educ:* Cornell Univ, BA, 67; Univ Calif, Berkeley, PhD, 73. *Prof Exp:* Physicist, Lawrence Livermore Nat Lab, 68-71 comput physicist, 78-85; res assoc, Nat Radio Astron Observ,

Charlottesville, Va, 74-75; res assoc, Observ Leiden Univ, Neth, 75-78. *Mem:* Int Astron Union; Soc Indust & Appl Math; NY Acad Sci. *Res:* Simple line interface calculation fluid interface tracking technique for computational fluid dynamics; animation of computational fluid dynamics data. *Mailing Add:* Univ Minn Army High Performance Comput Res Ctr 1100 Washington Ave S Minneapolis MN 55415

**WOODWARD, STEPHEN COTTER,** PATHOLOGY. *Current Pos:* asst prof, 64-68, ASSOC PROF PATH, SCH MED, GEORGETOWN UNIV, 68-; PATHOLOGIST, HUNTER LAB, SIBLEY HOSP, 68- *Personal Data:* b Atlanta, Ga, July 19, 35; m 57; c 2. *Educ:* Emory Univ, MD, 59. *Prof Exp:* Pathologist, Georgetown Univ Hosp, 64-68. *Concurrent Pos:* Consult, Children's Hosp, 64-, Vet Admin Hosp, 65- & comt skeletal syst, Div Med Sci, Nat Res Coun, 68-; attend pathologist, DC Gen Hosp, 67- *Mem:* Col Am Path; Am Soc Clin Path; Am Soc Exp Path; AMA. *Res:* Fibroplasia; collagen elaboration; effects of endocrine and vulnerary agents upon wound repair; quality control methods for clinical laboratories. *Mailing Add:* Va Med Ctr 1310 24th Ave S Nashville TN 37212-2637

**WOODWARD, TED K,** SEMICONDUCTOR DEVICE PHYSICS, OPTOELECTRONIC DEVICES. *Current Pos:* MEM TECH STAFF, AT&T BELL LABS, 88- *Personal Data:* b Peoria, Ill, Nov 11, 60; m 88. *Educ:* Univ Tex, Austin, BS, 83; Calif Inst Technol, MS, 85, PhD(appl physics), 88. *Mem:* Am Phys Soc; Inst Elec & Electronics Engrs; Optical Soc Am; Sigma Xi. *Res:* Semiconductors; optical, electro-optical and electrical investigations of electronics and opto-electronic materials and devices; quantum electronics and bandgap engineering; photonic switching device research; basic physics of semiconductor materials and devices; fabrication. *Mailing Add:* AT&T Bell Labs Rm 4B-525 Crawfords Corner Rd Holmdel NJ 07733-1988

**WOODWARD, THEODORE ENGLAR,** MICROBIOLOGY, MEDICINE. *Current Pos:* EMER PROF MED, SCH MED, UNIV MD, 83- *Personal Data:* b Westminster, Md, Mar 23, 14; m 38, Celeste C Lauve; c William Englar, Lewis Omer (deceased), R Craig & Celeste. *Educ:* Franklin & Marshall Col, BS, 34; Univ Md, MD, 38; Am Bd Internal Med, dipl. *Hon Degrees:* DSc, Western Med Col, 50, Franklin & Marshall Col, 54, Univ Md, 91, Hahnemann Univ, Philadelphia, 93. *Honors & Awards:* Louis Pasteur Medal, Pasteur Inst, 61; James D Bruce Mem Award, Am Col Physicians, 70; Sir Spencer Lister Award & Medal; Order of Sacred Treasure, Gold & Silver Star, Japan Cooperative Med Sci Prog, 90; Bristol Award, Infectious Dis Soc Am, 91; Edward Kuss Award, 91; Dir Award, Walter Reed Army Inst Award, 92; Distinguished Serv Award, AMA, 95. *Prof Exp:* Asst prof med, Sch Med, Univ Hosp, 46-48, assoc prof med & dir, Sect Infectious Dis, Sch Med, 48-54, prof med & head dept, Sch Med, 54-81, distinguished physician, Vet Admin Hosp, 81-87. *Concurrent Pos:* Instr, Sch Med, Johns Hopkins Univ, 46-48; lectr, 48-60; attend physician, Vet Admin Hosp, 46-48, consult, 48-; consult, State Health Dept, Md, 50; mem, Comt Int Ctrs Med Res & Training, USPHS, 61-62; mem, US Adv Comt, US-Japan Coop Med Sci Prog, 65- *Mem:* Inst Med-Nat Acad Sci; AMA; Am Clin & Climat Asn; Am Asn Physicians; master Am Col Physicians; Am Soc Clin Invest; Am Clin & Climate Asn; NY Acad Sci; Infectious Dis Soc Am(pres-elect, 75, pres, 76). *Res:* Infectious and rickettsial diseases; enteric diseases including typhoid fever; internal medicine. *Mailing Add:* Dept Med Rm N3W40 Univ Md Hosp Baltimore MD 21201. *Fax:* 410-605-7914

**WOODWARD, VAL WADDOUPS,** GENETICS. *Current Pos:* PROF GENETICS, UNIV MINN, ST PAUL, 67- *Personal Data:* b Preston, Idaho, July 26, 27; m 47, 67, Clare Keating; c 3. *Educ:* Utah State Univ, BS, 50; Kans State Univ, MS, 50; Cornell Univ, PhD(genetics), 53. *Prof Exp:* NIH fel & guest assoc biologist, Brookhaven Nat Lab, 53-55; assoc prof genetics, Kans State Univ, 55-58; prof biol & chmn dept, Univ Wichita, 58-61; assoc prof, Rice Univ, 61-67. *Concurrent Pos:* Fel, Birmingham Univ, 62-63, Open Univ, 86-87. *Mem:* AAAS; Am Soc Cell Biol; Genetics Soc Am; Sigma Xi. *Res:* Gene-enzyme transport; cell wall; neurospora; self-assembly of membrane and other organelle proteins; behavior genetics. *Mailing Add:* Genetics & Cell Biol Univ Minn 1445 Gortner Ave St Paul MN 55108-1095

**WOODWARD, WAYNE ANTHONY,** TIME SERIES ANALYSIS, CLASSIFICATION. *Current Pos:* from asst prof to assoc prof, 74-89, PROF & CHAIR, DEPT STATIST SCI, SOUTHERN METHODIST UNIV, 89- *Personal Data:* m 68, Beverly Maeker; c Angela J & Barry A. *Educ:* Tex Tech Univ, BA, 69, MS, 71, PhD(math), 74. *Prof Exp:* Assoc prof biostatist, Univ Tex S Western Med Ctr, 79-81. *Concurrent Pos:* Research award, Sigma Xi, 86. *Mem:* Am Statist Asn. *Res:* Time series analysis, attempting to determine whether there is a trend in global temperature series; transfer function modeling and long memory modeling. *Mailing Add:* Dept Statists Southern Methodist Univ PO Box 750001 Dallas TX 75275. *E-Mail:* woodward@vm.cis.smu.edu

**WOODWELL, GEORGE MASTERS,** ECOLOGY, BOTANY. *Current Pos:* FOUNDER, DIR & PRES, WOODS HOLE RES CTR, 85- *Personal Data:* b Cambridge, Mass, Oct 23, 28; m 55; c 4. *Educ:* Dartmouth Col, AB, 50; Duke Univ, AM, 56, PhD(bot), 58. *Hon Degrees:* DSc, Williams Col, 77, Miami Univ, 84, Carleton Col, 88, Muhlenberg Col, 90 & Dartmouth Col, 96. *Honors & Awards:* NY Bot Garden Sci Award, 75; Distinguished Serv Award, Am Inst Biol Sci, 82; Heinz Environ Prize, Heinz Family Found, 96. *Prof Exp:* From asst prof to assoc prof bot, Univ Maine, 57-61; sr ecologist, Brookhaven Nat Lab, 61-75; founder & dir, Ecosyst Ctr, Marine Biol Lab, 75-85. *Concurrent Pos:* Assoc, Conserv Found, 58-61, mem bd trustees, 75-77; lectr, Sch Forestry, Yale Univ, 67-; founding mem bd trustees, Environ Defense Fund, 67-68 & 73-; founding mem bd trustees, Natural Resources Res Coun, 70-, vchmn 74-, World Wildlife Fund, 70, chmn bd, 80-84; chmn,

Suffolk Co NY Coun Environ Qual, 72; trustee, Conserv Found, 75-77; bd trustees, Sea Educ Asn, 80-84; founding mem bd, World Resources Inst, 82-, bd trustees, Ruth Mott Fund, 84-, chmn, 89-; chmn, Conf Long-term biol consequences nuclear war, 82-83; mem, Conn River Watershed Coun, 84. *Mem:* Nat Acad Sci; Ecol Soc Am (vpres, 67, pres, 77-78); Am Inst Biol Sci; Brit Ecol Soc; fel Am Acad Arts & Sci; Sigma Xi; fel AAAS. *Res:* Structure, function and development of terrestrial and aquatic ecosystems; biotic impoverishment, especially effects of ionizing radiation and other toxins such as pesticides; biotic contributions to the global carbon cycle and climatic change; biotic contributions to the global carbon cycle. *Mailing Add:* Woods Hole Res Ctr 13 Church St PO Box 296 Woods Hole MA 02543

**WOODWICK, KEITH HARRIS,** INVERTEBRATE ZOOLOGY. *Current Pos:* from instr to assoc prof zool, 55-66, chmn dept, 65-69, PROF ZOOL, CALIF STATE UNIV, FRESNO, 66-, COORDR MARINE SCI, 68- *Personal Data:* b Tappen, NDak, Jan 4, 27; m 51; c 3. *Educ:* Jamestown Col, BS, 49; Univ Wash, MS, 51; Univ Southern Calif, PhD(zool), 55. *Prof Exp:* Asst zool, Univ Wash, 49-51; instr, Univ Southern Calif, 54, asst, 54-55. *Mem:* Am Inst Biol Sci; Soc Syst Zool; Sigma Xi. *Res:* Systematics and larval development of polychaetes; Enteropneusta. *Mailing Add:* Dept Biol Calif State Univ Fresno CA 93710

**WOODWORTH, CURTIS WILMER,** ORGANIC CHEMISTRY. *Current Pos:* Res chemist, Am Cyanamid Co, Bound Brook, 68-73, group leader, 73-75, dept head, Lederle Labs, 75-79, SECT DIR, MED RES DIV, AM CYANAMID CO, PEARL RIVER, 79- *Personal Data:* b Reading, Pa, Aug 30, 42; m 64; c 2. *Educ:* Albright Col, BS, 64; Princeton Univ, PhD(chem), 69. *Mem:* Am Chem Soc. *Res:* Structure-reactivity relationships; process research and development on pharmaceuticals and fine chemicals; fermentation; proces development; biotechnology. *Mailing Add:* 16 Westminster Pl Old Tappan NJ 07675-6863

**WOODWORTH, JOHN GEORGE,** NUCLEAR & PLASMA PHYSICS. *Current Pos:* Physicist nuclear physics, 78-85, proj leader, ICF Prog, 86-88, SR SCIENTIST, LAWRENCE LIVERMORE LAB, 88- *Personal Data:* b Lockport, NY, Apr 16, 48; m 78; c 2. *Educ:* Trent Univ, BSc, 72, MSc, 74; Univ Toronto, PhD(physics), 78. *Mem:* Am Phys Soc. *Res:* Intertial confinement fusion. *Mailing Add:* L-481 Lawrence Livermore Nat Lab UCL PO Box 808 Livermore CA 94550

**WOODWORTH, MARY ESTHER,** ANIMAL VIROLOGY, REGULATORY MECHANISMS IN EUKARYOTIC CELLS. *Current Pos:* CHAIR & PROF MICROBIOL, MIAMI UNIV, OXFORD, OHIO, 89- *Personal Data:* b Grand Rapids, Mich. *Educ:* Univ Mich, Ann Arbor, BS, 57; Temple Univ, MS, 65, PhD(biochem), 68. *Prof Exp:* Fel bacteriophage genetics, Univ Mich, 68-72; res assoc DNA topology, Syracuse Univ, NY, 72-73; res scientist tumor virol, Sch Med, Johns Hopkins Univ, 73-76; cancer res scientist, Roswell Park Mem Inst, 77-89, actg chair tumor & cell biol, 83-84; asst prof viral oncol, Roswell Park Div, State Univ NY, Buffalo, 77-86, assoc prof molecular & cell biol, 86-89. *Concurrent Pos:* Prin investr, Nat Cancer Inst, NIH, 77-80 & 80-88; Nat Cancer Inst res career develop award, NIH, 78-83; mem bd dirs, Health Res, Inc, Buffalo, NY, 84-87; Nat Found lectr, Am Soc Microbiol, 89-90, comt mem, Genetic & Molecular Microbiol & Public & Sci Affairs Bd, 90- , chair, Genetic & Molec Microbiol Comt, 91- *Mem:* Am Soc Microbiol; Am Soc Biochem & Molecular Biol; Am Soc Virol; Sigma Xi; Am Asn Univ Women; Am Women Sci. *Res:* Molecular biology of tumor virusus utilizing SV40 as a model system to study the regulation of eukaryotic DNA replication and gene expression. *Mailing Add:* Dept Microbiol Miami Univ Oxford OH 45056. *Fax:* 513-529-2431; *E-Mail:* woodwome@muohio.edu

**WOODWORTH, ROBERT CUMMINGS,** PROTEIN CHEMISTRY, BIOINORGANIC CHEMISTRY. *Current Pos:* from instr to assoc prof, 61-75, PROF BIOCHEM, COL MED, UNIV VT, 75- *Personal Data:* b Cambridge, Mass, Nov 11, 30; m 52; c 3. *Educ:* Univ Vt, BS, 53; Pa State Univ, PhD(chem), 57. *Prof Exp:* Res chemist, Nat Inst Allergy & Infectious Dis, 56-60. *Concurrent Pos:* USPHS fel, Clin Chem Lab, Malmo Gen Hosp, Sweden, 60-61; USPHS spec fel & vis prof, Inorg Chem Lab, Oxford Univ, 68-69; Fogarty Int sr fel, Oxford Univ, 76-77; MRC Can vis scientist, Univ BC, 87-88. *Mem:* Am Chem Soc; Am Soc Biochem & Molecular Biol; Sigma Xi; Am Heart Asn; AAAS; Soc Values Higher Educ. *Res:* Protein structure-function; nature of iron-binding proteins; mechanisms of metal binding and release; role of bound anions, physiological function and structure; protein structure and function. *Mailing Add:* Dept Biochem Univ Vt Given Med Bldg Burlington VT 05405-0068. *Fax:* 802-656-0342; *E-Mail:* rwoodworth@uvmvax.uvm.edu

**WOODY, A-YOUNG MOON,** BIOCHEMISTRY, CHEMISTRY. *Current Pos:* res assoc biochem, 76-87, res assoc prof Biochem, 88-95, RES PROF, DEPT BIOCHEM & MOLECULAR BIOL, COLO STATE UNIV, FT COLLINS, 96- *Personal Data:* b Pyungyang, Korea, Mar 7, 34; US citizen; m 65, Robert W; c Michael R & David M. *Educ:* Univ Calif, Berkeley, BS, 59; Cornell Univ, PhD(biochem), 64. *Prof Exp:* Res assoc chem, Cornell Univ, 64-65; res assoc microbiol, Univ Ill, Urbana, 65-66; res assoc biochem, 67-69; res assoc develop biol, Dept Zool, Ariz State Univ, 72-74. *Mem:* Am Chem Soc; Sigma Xi; Am Soc Biochem & Molecular Biol; Biophys Soc. *Res:* Structure and function of proteins and enzymes; mechanism of RNA polymerase. *Mailing Add:* Dept Biochem & Molecular Biol Colo State Univ Ft Collins CO 80523. *Fax:* 970-491-0494; *E-Mail:* aymw@lamar.colostate.edu

**WOODY, CHARLES DILLON,** NEUROPHYSIOLOGY. *Current Pos:* assoc prof anat, physiol & psychiat, 71-76, PROF ANAT & PSYCHIAT, MENT RETARDATION CTR, NEUROPSYCHIAT INST, UNIV CALIF, LOS ANGELES, 77- *Personal Data:* b Brooklyn, NY, Feb 6, 37; m 59; c 2. *Educ:* Princeton Univ, AB, 57; Harvard Med Sch, MD, 62. *Honors & Awards:* Nightingale Prize, Brit Biol Eng Soc & Int Fedn Med Electronics & Biol Eng, 69. *Prof Exp:* Intern med, Strong Mem Hosp, Univ Rochester, 62-63; resident, Boston City Hosp, Mass, 63-64; res assoc, Lab Neurophysiol, NIH, 64-67, res officer, Lab Neural Control, 68-71. *Concurrent Pos:* Harvard Moseley fel & Nat Acad Sci exchange fel neurophysiol, Inst Physiol, Czech Acad Sci, 67-68; res fel neurol, Harvard Med Sch, 63-64. *Mem:* AAAS; Am Physiol Soc; Soc Neurosci; Biomed Eng Soc. *Res:* Neurophysiology of learning and memory; neurophysiology of learned motor performance; electrophysiologic data analysis by linear filter techniques employing digital computers. *Mailing Add:* Dept Anat & Psychiat Univ Calif Los Angeles Med Ctr 10833 6 Conte Ave Los Angeles CA 90024-1300

**WOODY, CHARLES OWEN, JR,** REPRODUCTIVE PHYSIOLOGY. *Current Pos:* assoc prof, 68-81, PROF ANIMAL SCI, UNIV CONN, 81- *Personal Data:* b Somerville, Tenn, Oct 28, 30; m 60; c 4. *Educ:* Miss State Univ, BS, 57, MS, 59; NC State Univ, PhD(animal sci), 63. *Prof Exp:* Trainee endocrinol, Univ Wis-Madison, 63, proj assoc reproductive physiol, 64-68. *Mem:* Am Soc Animal Sci; Brit Soc Study Fert; Soc Study Reproduction; NY Acad Sci. *Res:* Gamete physiology and in vitro fertilization; testis growth and function. *Mailing Add:* 43 Lynwood Rd Storrs Manfield CT 06268

**WOODY, CRAIG L,** EXPERIMENTAL PARTICLE PHYSICS. *Current Pos:* MEM STAFF, BROOKHAVEN NAT LAB, 79- *Personal Data:* b Baltimore, Md, Mar 26, 51; m 73, Margaret; c Gregory. *Educ:* Johns Hopkins Univ, BA, 73, MA, 74, PhD(physics), 79. *Prof Exp:* Res asst physics, Johns Hopkins Univ, 74-78; res assoc physics, Stanford Linear Accelerator Ctr, 78-79. *Mem:* Am Phys Soc. *Res:* Detectors and instrumentation for high energy particle physics, especially calorimetry and electromagnetic radiation detectors. *Mailing Add:* Brookhaven Nat Lab Physics Dept Bldg 510C Box 5000 Upton NY 11973

**WOODY, ROBERT WAYNE,** BIOPHYSICAL CHEMISTRY, SPECTROSCOPY. *Current Pos:* PROF BIOCHEM, COLO STATE UNIV, 75- *Personal Data:* b Newton, Iowa, Dec 5, 35; m 65, A Young Moon; c Michael & David. *Educ:* Iowa State Col, BS, 58; Univ Calif, Berkeley, PhD(chem), 62. *Prof Exp:* Res assoc phys chem, Cornell Univ, 62-64, Nat Inst Gen Med Sci fel, 63-64; asst prof, Univ Ill, Urbana, 64-70; from assoc prof to prof, Ariz State Univ, 70-75. *Concurrent Pos:* John Simon Guggenheim Mem Fel, 81-82; mem, Molecular & Cellular Biophys Study Sect, NIH, 83-87; Fogarty sr int fel, 88-89 & 95-96. *Mem:* AAAS; Am Chem Soc; Am Soc Biochem & Molecular Biol; Biophys Soc. *Res:* Optical properties of molecules; structure of proteins; protein-nucleic acid interactions; interaction of small molecules with proteins. *Mailing Add:* Dept Biochem & Molecular Biol Colo State Univ Ft Collins CO 80523. *Fax:* 970-491-0494; *E-Mail:* rww@lamar.colostate.edu

**WOODYARD, JAMES DOUGLAS,** ORGANIC CHEMISTRY. *Current Pos:* from asst prof to assoc prof, 67-74, PROF CHEM, WTEX STATE UNIV, 78- *Personal Data:* b San Antonio, Tex, Oct 8, 38. *Educ:* Tex Christian Univ, BA, 61, MA, 63, PhD(chem), 67. *Prof Exp:* NSF fel Univ Ill, Chicago, 66-67. *Mem:* Am Chem Soc; Royal Soc Chem. *Res:* Reaction of carbenes and stereochemistry of carbene reactions; triplet state of organic molecules. *Mailing Add:* Dept Chem WTex A&M Univ Canyon TX 79016

**WOODYARD, JAMES ROBERT,** SEMICONDUCTOR DEVICES, ELECTRONICS ENGINEERING. *Current Pos:* assoc prof, Div Sci & Technol, Col Lifelong Learning, 75-82, ASSOC PROF, DEPT ELEC & COMPUTER ENG, WAYNE STATE UNIV, 83- *Personal Data:* b Pittsburgh, Pa, July 18, 36; m 60; c 4. *Educ:* Duquesne Univ, BEd, 60; Univ Del, MS, 62, PhD(physics), 66. *Prof Exp:* Asst prof physics, Univ Ky, 67-69; mem tech staff, Gen Tel & Electronics Labs, 69-71; asst prof physics, Univ Hartford, 71-72; asst prof, Trenton State Col, 72-75. *Concurrent Pos:* AEC postdoctoral fel, 65-67; Danforth Found assoc, 77-86. *Mem:* AAAS; Am Phys Soc; Am Vacuum Soc; Sigma Xi; Am Asn Physics Teachers; Am Asn Univ Professors; Inst Elec & Electronics Engrs; Mat Res Soc. *Res:* Particle surface interactions; instructional methods; solid state device materials; photovoltaics device and device materials characterization. *Mailing Add:* Dept Elec & Comput Eng Wayne State Univ Detroit MI 48202

**WOOFTER, HARVEY DARRELL,** WEED SCIENCE, ENTOMOLOGY. *Current Pos:* PRES, WOOFTER CONSULTS, INC, 86- *Personal Data:* b Glenville, WVa, Jan 31, 23; m 44, Violet Hill. *Educ:* WVa Univ, BS, 43; Ohio State Univ, MS, 49, PhD(agron), 53. *Prof Exp:* Co agr agt, WVa, 43-44 & 46-48; asst agron, Ohio State Univ, 48-49; res agronomist, Chem Corps Biol Warfare Labs, US Dept Army, Md, 49-54; field res rep, Pittsburgh Coke & Chem Co, 54-56; field res rep, Chemagro Corp, 56-62, asst supvr field res, 62-64; mgr field res, Diamond Alkali Co, 64-66; mgr prod develop, Ciba Agrochem Co, Fla, 66-68; mgr, Fla Res Sta, Velsicol Chem Corp, 68-72, mgr agrochem sta, 72-76, dir res & develop, Maag Agrochem, 76-86. *Mem:* Am Soc Agron; Entom Soc Am; Weed Sci Soc Am; Aquatic Plant Mgt Soc; Plant Growth Regulator Soc Am. *Res:* Weed control; development of new herbicides, insecticides, fungicides, nematocides, bactericides, defoliants, desiccants and plant growth regulators. *Mailing Add:* 3040 Nassau Dr Vero Beach FL 32960

**WOOL, IRA GOODWIN,** BIOCHEMISTRY, MOLECULAR BIOLOGY. *Current Pos:* from asst prof to assoc prof physiol, 57-65, assoc prof biochem, 64-65, PROF BIOCHEM, UNIV CHICAGO, 65-, A J CARLSON PROF BIOL SCI, 73- *Personal Data:* b Newark, NJ, Aug 22, 28; m 61, Barbara Mirecki; c Christopher D & Jonathan A. *Educ:* Syracuse Univ, AB, 49; Univ Chicago, MD, 53, PhD(physiol), 54. *Honors & Awards:* Ginsburg Award, Univ Chicago, 52; Bernstein lectr, Beth Israel Hosp, Harvard Med Sch, 64; Alexander von Humboldt spec fel, Fed Repub Ger, 73-74. *Prof Exp:* Intern med, Beth Israel Hosp, Boston, Mass, 54-55, asst resident, 55-56. *Concurrent Pos:* Fel physiol, Harvard Univ, 56; Commonwealth Fund fel, Univ Chicago, 56-57; vis scientist, Dept Biochem, Cambridge Univ, 60-61; vis prof, Wayne State Univ, 64, 66 & Fla State Univ, 66; Lederle sci lectr, Lederle Labs, 66; vis fac mem, Mayo Grad Sch Med, 66; vis prof, Rutgers Univ, 67; ed, Vitamins & Hormones & J Biol Chem; vis res scientist, Max-Planck Inst Molecular Genetics, Berlin, Ger, 73-74; mem, Molecular Biol Study Sect, NIH, 74-78. *Mem:* AAAS; Brit Biochem Soc; Am Soc Biol Chemists; Am Soc Cell Biol. *Res:* Structure and function of eukaryotic ribosomes; nucleic acid-protein interactions. *Mailing Add:* Dept Biochem & Molecular Biol 920 E 58th St Chicago IL 60637. *Fax:* 773-702-0439; *E-Mail:* irawool@midway. uchicago.edu

**WOOL, RICHARD P,** MATERIALS SCIENCE. *Current Pos:* from asst prof to assoc prof, 77-86, PROF, DEPT MAT SCI, UNIV ILL, 86- *Educ:* Univ Col Cork, Ireland, BSc, 70; Univ Utah, MS, 72, PhD(mat sci & eng), 74. *Prof Exp:* Res asst mat sci & eng, Univ Utah, 70-74; res assoc mech eng, Univ Colo, 74-75; asst prof chem eng, City Col New York, 75-77. *Concurrent Pos:* Guest prof, Polytech Milan, Italy, 84, Polytech Inst, Paris, 91; vpres & dir res & develop, Agri-Tech Industs, 86-89; dir, Degradable Plastics Lab, 87-; resident assoc, Ctr Advan Study, 89; consult & dir, Huaxin Inst Biodegradable Plastics Res, Beijing, 92-; pres, Cara Plastics, 93- *Mem:* Am Chem Soc; Am Inst Chem Engrs; fel Am Phys Soc; Soc Rheology; Soc Plastic Engrs. *Res:* Polymer materials science and engineering; composites; fracture mechanics; strength of polymer interfaces; biodegradable plastics; plastics engineering; polymer characterization; spectroscopy; polymer physics. *Mailing Add:* 702 W Pennsylvania Ave Urbana IL 61801

**WOOLARD, EDGAR S, JR,** INDUSTRIAL & MANUFACTURING ENGINEERING. *Current Pos:* Indust engr, DuPont, Kinston, NC, 57-59, group supvr & indust engr, 59-62, supvr, mfg sect, 62-64, planning supvr, 64-65, staff asst to prod mgr, Wilmington, Del, 65-66, prod supvr, Old Hickory, Tenn, 66-69, eng supt, 69-70, asst plant mgr, Camden, SC, 70-71, plant mgr, Kinston, SC, 71-73, dir, Prod Mkt Div, Wilmington, Del, 73-75, managing dir, Textile Mkt Div, 75-76, mgr, Corp Plans Dept, 76-77, gen dir, Prod & Planning Div, 77-78, gen mgr textile fibers, 78-81, vpres, 81-83, exec vpres, 83-85, vchmn, 85-87, pres & chief operating officer, 87-89, chmn & chief exec officer, 89-96, CHMN, DUPONT WILMINGTON, DEL, 96- *Personal Data:* b Washington, NC, Apr 15, 34; m 56, Peggy Harrell; c Annette & Lyda. *Educ:* NC State Univ, BS, 56. *Honors & Awards:* Int Palladium Medal, Am Sect, Soc Indust Chem, 95. *Mailing Add:* DuPont 1007 Market St Wilmington DE 19898-1226

**WOOLARD, HENRY W(ALDO),** FLUID DYNAMICS, AERODYNAMICS. *Current Pos:* RETIRED. *Personal Data:* b Clarksburg, WVa, June 2, 17; m 41, Helen Waldron; c Shirley & Robert. *Educ:* Univ Mich, BS, 41; Univ Buffalo, MS, 54. *Honors & Awards:* Sci Achievement Award, Air Force Systs Command, 82. *Prof Exp:* Aeronaut engr, Nat Adv Comt Aeronaut, 41-46; from asst prof to assoc prof aeronaut eng, Univ WVa, 46-48, actg head dept, 46-48; res aerodynamicist, Cornell Aeronaut Lab, Inc, 48-57; sr staff engr, Appl Physics Lab, Johns Hopkins Univ, 57-63; sr res specialist, Lockheed-Calif Co, 63-67; mem tech staff, TRW Systs Group, Calif, 67-70; pres, Beta Technol Co, Calif, 70-71; aerospace engr, Flight Dynamics Lab, Wright Patterson AFB, 71-85; eng consult, 85-95. *Concurrent Pos:* Lectr aerodynamics, Univ Buffalo, 55-57. *Mem:* Assoc fel Am Inst Aeronaut & Astronaut; Sigma Xi; Am Soc Mech Engrs. *Res:* Numerous investigations in fluid dynamics and aerodynamics published in various journals and government, industry and university reports. *Mailing Add:* 1249 W Magill Ave Fresno CA 93711-1428. *E-Mail:* 70200.176@compuserve.com

**WOOLCOTT, WILLIAM STARNOLD,** VERTEBRATE ZOOLOGY. *Current Pos:* assoc prof, 55-67, PROF BIOL, UNIV RICHMOND, 67- *Personal Data:* b Coffeyville, Kans, Apr 14, 22; m 46; c 2. *Educ:* Austin Peay State Col, BS, 47; Peabody Col, MA, 48; Cornell Univ, PhD(vert zool), 55. *Prof Exp:* Asst prof biol, Carson-Newman Col, 49-53. *Mem:* Sigma Xi; Am Soc Ichthyol & Herpet. *Res:* Morphological and ecological aspects of fishes. *Mailing Add:* 6804 Lakewood Dr Richmond VA 23229

**WOOLDRIDGE, DAVID DILLEY,** FOREST SOILS, FOREST HYDROLOGY. *Current Pos:* RETIRED. *Personal Data:* b Seattle, Wash, Mar 12, 27; m 48, 70; c 5. *Educ:* Univ Wash, BS, 50, PhD(forestry), 61. *Prof Exp:* Forester, Rayonier Inc, 50-52, res forester, 53-56; res forester, Forest Hydrol Lab, US Forest Serv, Wash, 56-68; assoc prof forest hydrol, Col Forest Resources, Univ Wash, 68-83. *Concurrent Pos:* Asst prof, Univ Wash, 65-68; consult, King County Flood Control Div, 66-; consult local eng firms & US CEngr; res grants, Off Water Resources & Res & US Forest Serv, Wash State Dept Ecol, Environ Protection Agency & Wash State Dept Natural Resources; consult, 83- *Mem:* Sigma Xi; Soc Am Foresters; Soil Sci Soc Am; Am Geophys Union. *Res:* Watershed classification, Thailand; turbidity-suspended sediment relations in forest streams; disposal of stabilized municipal-industrial sewage sludge; impacts of clear-cutting on soil nutrient balance; effects of slash burial on surface water quality; soil properties under pristine western hemlock. *Mailing Add:* 7870 Stines Hill Rd Cashmere WA 98815

**WOOLDRIDGE, DAVID PAUL,** ENTOMOLOGY. *Current Pos:* from asst prof to assoc prof, 68-78, PROF BIOL, PA STATE UNIV, 78- *Personal Data:* b Terre Haute, Ind, Dec 25, 31; m 56. *Educ:* Ind Univ, BS, 56, PhD(zool), 62. *Prof Exp:* Asst prof biol, Wilkes Col, 62-63; asst prof zool, Southern Ill Univ, 63-67; assoc ed, Biol Abstr, 67-68. *Mem:* Coleopterist's Soc. *Res:* Taxonomy of aquatic Coleoptera; systematics of world Limnichidae. *Mailing Add:* Dept Biol Pa State Univ Ogontz Campus 71600 Woodland Rd Abington PA 19001-3990

**WOOLDRIDGE, DEAN E,** PHYSICS, ENGINEERING. *Current Pos:* RETIRED. *Personal Data:* b Chickasha, Okla, May 30, 13; c 3. *Educ:* Univ Okla, BA, MS; Calif Inst Technol, PhD(physics), 36. *Honors & Awards:* Raymond E Hackett Award, 55; Westinghouse Award, AAAS, 63. *Prof Exp:* Mem tech staff, Bell Tel Lab, 36-46; dir electronic res & develop, Hughes Aircraft Co, 46-53; pres, Thompson Ramo Wooldridge Inc, 53-62; res assoc eng, Calif Inst Technol, 62-72. *Concurrent Pos:* Chmn, Study Comt, NIH, 64-65; mem bd trustees, Calif Inst Technol, 75-78. *Mem:* Nat Acad Sci; Nat Acad Eng; Am Phys Soc; Inst Elec & Electronics Engrs; Am Inst Aeronaut & Astronaut. *Mailing Add:* 4545 Via Esperanza Santa Barbara CA 93110

**WOOLDRIDGE, GENE LYSLE,** ATMOSPHERIC SCIENCES, PHYSICS. *Current Pos:* RETIRED. *Personal Data:* b Randalia, Iowa, Apr 16, 24; m 45; c 5. *Educ:* Upper Iowa Col, BS, 44; Mankato State Col, MS, 61; Colo State Univ, PhD(atmospheric sci), 70. *Prof Exp:* Instr physics, Rochester State Jr Col, Minn, 61-62; instr, Mankato State Col, 62-64; asst prof atmospheric sci, 65-67; from assoc prof to prof atmospheric sci, Utah State Univ, 77-87. *Mem:* Am Meteorol Soc. *Res:* Mesoscale circulations and transport processes; mesoscale-macroscale and mesoscale-microscale energy interactions and mechanisms. *Mailing Add:* 1908 Wallenberg Dr Ft Collins CO 80526

**WOOLDRIDGE, KENT ERNEST,** MATHEMATICS. *Current Pos:* Asst prof math, 74-81, ASSOC PROF MATH, CALIF STATE COL, 81- *Personal Data:* b Waukegan, Ill, Apr 23, 42; m 68; c 2. *Educ:* Univ Chicago, BS, 64; Univ Ill, Urbana, PhD(math), 75. *Mem:* Am Math Soc; Math Asn Am. *Res:* Number theory. *Mailing Add:* 787 Sierra View Way Chico CA 95926

**WOOLES, WALLACE RALPH,** PHYSIOLOGY, PHARMACOLOGY. *Current Pos:* PROF PHARMACOL & ASSOC VCHANCELLOR HEALTH AFFAIRS, E CAROLINA UNIV, 70- *Personal Data:* b Lawrence, Mass, Mar 8, 31; m 51; c 5. *Educ:* Boston Col, BS, 58, MS, 61; Univ Tenn, PhD(physiol), 63. *Prof Exp:* From instr to assoc prof pharmacol, Med Col Va, 63-70. *Mem:* AAAS; Soc Toxicol; Int Soc Res Reticuloendothelial Systs; Am Soc Pharmacol & Exp Therapeut; Sigma Xi. *Res:* Radiation injury and lipid metabolism; alcohol and lipid metabolism; reticuloendothelial system and drug metabolism. *Mailing Add:* Dept Pharmacol E Carolina Univ Sch Med Greenville NC 27858-4353. *Fax:* 919-816-3203

**WOOLEVER, PATRICIA,** ENTOMOLOGY. *Current Pos:* from asst prof to assoc prof, 78-87, biol dept head, 83-96, PROF BIOL, NORTHEASTERN STATE UNIV, 87- *Personal Data:* b Dana Point, Calif, 38. *Educ:* Cent State Col, BS, 58; Univ Calif, Berkeley, PhD(entom), 65. *Prof Exp:* Asst specialist, Entom Dept, Univ Calif, Berkeley, 63-68 & 73-74, res entomologist, 75-77; asst prof biol, Cent State Univ, 69-70. *Concurrent Pos:* Dir, NSF-Student Sci Training Prog, Northeastern State Univ, 80-82. *Mem:* AAAS; Sigma Xi; Entom Soc Am. *Res:* Insect neurometamorphosis; haplosporidian parasites of cockroach Malpighian tubules; cricket circadian rythyms; tardigrades. *Mailing Add:* Biol Dept Northeastern State Univ Tahlequah OK 74464. *Fax:* 918-458-2015; *E-Mail:* woolever@cherokee.nsuok.edu

**WOOLF, CHARLES MARTIN,** GENETICS. *Current Pos:* dean, Col Lib Arts, Ariz State Univ, 73-75, assoc prof genetics, 61-64, vpres grad studies & res, 76-79, dean grad col, 76-86, PROF ZOOL ARIZ STATE UNIV, 64- *Personal Data:* b Salt Lake City, Utah, Aug 23, 25; m 50; c 4. *Educ:* Univ Utah, BS, 48, MS, 49; Univ Calif, PhD(genetics), 54. *Prof Exp:* Asst geneticist, Lab Human Genetics, Univ Utah, 50-51, dir, 57-61, res instr genetics, Univ, 53-55, asst prof, 55-59, assoc prof, 59-61. *Mem:* Am Soc Human Genetics (treas, 61-63); Genetics Soc Am. *Res:* Genetics of congenital malformation; consanguinity and genetic effects; drosophila behavior and developmental genetics. *Mailing Add:* 334 E Fremont Dr Tempe AZ 85282

**WOOLF, HARRY,** SCIENCE POLICY. *Current Pos:* dir, 76-87, PROF, INST ADVAN STUDY, 87- *Personal Data:* b New York, NY, Aug 12, 23; c 4. *Educ:* Univ Chicago, BS, 48, MA, 49; Cornell Univ, PhD(hist sci), 55. *Hon Degrees:* DSc, Whitman Col, 79, Am Univ, 82; LHD, Johns Hopkins Univ, 83 & St Lawrence Univ, 86. *Prof Exp:* Instr physics, Boston Univ, 53-55; from asst prof to prof hist, Univ Wash, 55-61; prof hist sci, Johns Hopkins Univ, 61-76, chmn, 6-72, provost, 72-76. *Concurrent Pos:* Instr hist, Brandeis Univ, 54-55; trustee, Assoc Univ Inc, Brookhaven Nat Lab & Nat Radio Astron Observ, 72-; chmn bd, Univ Res Asn, Inc, 79-89; mem, Corp Vis Comt, dept physics, Mass Inst Technol, 79-85, Adv Coun, dept philos, Princeton Univ, 80-84, adv bd, Stanford Humanities Ctr, 81-87, Wissensch-Kol Beriat, Berlin, 81-87 & Sci Adv Bd, Alexander von Humboldt Found, 85- *Mem:* Sigma Xi; fel Am Philos Soc; AAAS; Royal Astron Soc; Hist Sci Soc; fel Am Acad Arts & Sci. *Res:* History of science, with emphasis on physics and astronomy; issues involving the intersection of basic science and education with modern technology. *Mailing Add:* 29 Sergeant St Princeton NJ 08540

**WOOLF, J(ACK) R(OYCE),** MECHANICAL ENGINEERING. *Current Pos:* dean, Univ Tex, Arlington, 57-58, actg pres, 58-59, pres, 59-68, univ prof mech eng, 68-89, EMER PRES, UNIV TEX, ARLINGTON, 68-, EMER PROF MECH ENG, 89- *Personal Data:* b Trinidad, Tex, June 10, 24; m 48, Martha Frazar; c Charles & Mark. *Educ:* Agr & Mech Col, Tex, BS & MS, 48; Purdue Univ, PhD, 51. *Prof Exp:* Asst instr, Agr & Mech Col, Tex, 47-48, prof mech eng & res engr, Eng Exp Sta, 56-57, asst to dean eng, 57; instr, Purdue Univ, 48-51; res engr, Consol Aircraft Co, 51-56. *Concurrent Pos:* Lectr, Southern Methodist Univ, 53-56. *Mem:* Am Soc Mech Engrs; Am Soc Eng Educ. *Res:* Heat transfer; thermodynamics and transfer properties of fluids; aerothermodynamics. *Mailing Add:* 3115 Woodford Dr Arlington TX 76013

**WOOLF, NEVILLE JOHN,** ASTROPHYSICS. *Current Pos:* PROF ASTRON, STEWARD OBSERV, UNIV ARIZ, 74- *Personal Data:* b London, Eng, Sept 15, 32; US citizen; m 72; c 2. *Educ:* Manchester Univ, BSc, 56, PhD(astrophys), 59. *Prof Exp:* Res assoc astron, Lick Observ, Univ Calif, 59-61; res assoc, Princeton Univ, 61-65; assoc prof, Univ Tex, 65-67; prof, Univ Minn, 67-74. *Concurrent Pos:* Dir, Minn Observ, Univ Minn, 67-74; Nat Acad Sci/Nat Res Coun sr fel, NASA Goddard Inst Space Studies, 65-67; actg dir, Flandrau Planetarium, Univ Ariz, 77; actg dir, Mult Mirror Telescope Observ, 78-79. *Mem:* Am Astron Soc; Int Astron Union. *Res:* Astrophysics, observational, theoretical and instrumental. *Mailing Add:* 3336 N Camino Los Brazos Tucson AZ 85750

**WOOLF, WILLIAM BLAUVELT,** mathematics, for more information see previous edition

**WOOLFENDEN, GLEN EVERETT,** ORNITHOLOGY, BEHAVIORAL ECOLOGY. *Current Pos:* from instr to assoc prof zool, 60-70, prof biol, 70-87, DISTINGUISHED RES PROF BIOL, UNIV SFLA, TAMPA, 88- *Personal Data:* b Elizabeth, NJ, Jan 23, 30; m 54; c 3. *Educ:* Cornell Univ, BS, 53; Univ Kans, MA, 56; Univ Fla, PhD(zool), 60. *Honors & Awards:* Brewster Award, Am Ornithol Union, 85. *Prof Exp:* Instr biol, Univ Fla, 59-60. *Concurrent Pos:* Res Soc Am res grant, 61; consult, Encephalitis Res Ctr, Tampa, 61-64; res assoc, Archbold Biol Sta, 70-, Field Mus Natural Hist, 82-; vis prof, Univ Kans, 85, Int Ornithol Cong, 78- *Mem:* Fel Am Ornithologists Union (pres, 86-88); Wilson Ornith Soc; Cooper Ornith Soc; Brit Ornith Union; Animal Behav Soc; corresp fel Ger Ornith Soc. *Res:* Behavioral ecology; communal breeding; long-term study of individually marked birds investigates the demographic and habitat features of cooperative breeding. *Mailing Add:* Dept Biol Univ SFla 4202 Fowler Ave Tampa FL 33620-9951. *Fax:* 941-465-1927

**WOOLFOLK, CLIFFORD ALLEN,** MICROBIOLOGY. *Current Pos:* asst prof, 65-68, ASSOC PROF MICROBIOL, UNIV CALIF, IRVINE, 68- *Personal Data:* b Riverside, Calif, June 5, 35; m 57; c 2. *Educ:* Univ Calif, Riverside, BA, 57; Univ Wash, Seattle, MSc, 59, PhD(microbiol), 63. *Prof Exp:* Res asst microbiol, Univ Wash, 57-59 & 62-63; USPHS fel enzymol lab biochem, Nat Heart Inst, 63-65. *Mem:* AAAS; Am Soc Microbiol; Brit Soc Gen Microbiol; Am Chem Soc; Am Soc Biol Chemists. *Res:* Microbial physiology; hydrogenase and hydrogenase mediated reduction of inorganic compounds; cumulative feedback inhibition of glutamine synthetase from Escherichia coli; bacterial purine oxidizing enzymes. *Mailing Add:* Dept Microbiol & Biochem Univ Calif Irvine CA 92717-0001

**WOOLFOLK, ROBERT WILLIAM,** PHYSICAL CHEMISTRY. *Current Pos:* ASST DIR PROG DEVELOP, SW RES INST, 90- *Personal Data:* b Riverside, Calif, Feb 9, 37; wid; c Nancy (Jellison), Helene, Paula & Andrew. *Educ:* Univ Calif, Riverside, BA, 58; Univ Calif, Berkeley, PhD(phys chem), 64. *Prof Exp:* Staff scientist, Chem Syst Div, United Technol Corp, 63-65; phys chemist & dir bus develop, SRI Int, 65-90. *Mem:* Am Chem Soc; Am Inst Aeronaut & Astronaut; AAAS; Sigma Xi. *Res:* Shock wave phenomenon; gas phase reaction kinetics; photochemistry; fluorine chemistry; explosive sensitivity; nonideal explosions; combustion and marketing research and development. *Mailing Add:* 8801 Aquary Ct Springfield VA 22153. *Fax:* 703-416-0503

**WOOLFORD, ROBERT GRAHAM,** ORGANIC CHEMISTRY. *Current Pos:* From asst prof to prof, Univ Waterloo, 59-96, assoc dean sci, 67-75, assoc chmn, Dept Chem, 77-96, EMER PROF CHEM, UNIV WATERLOO, 96- *Personal Data:* b London, Ont, Apr 14, 33; m 55, Lillian A Ellis; c David & Ken. *Educ:* Univ Western Ont, BSc, 55, MSc, 56; Univ Ill, PhD(org chem), 59. *Concurrent Pos:* Res fel chem, Univ Ill, 56-58. *Mem:* Fel Chem Inst Can. *Res:* Electroorganic chemistry of halogenated carboxylic acids; synthesis of polymers. *Mailing Add:* Dept Chem Univ Waterloo Waterloo ON N2L 3G1 Can

**WOOLHISER, DAVID A(RTHUR),** CIVIL ENGINEERING, AGRICULTURAL ENGINEERING. *Current Pos:* RETIRED. *Personal Data:* b La Crosse, Wis, Jan 21, 32; m 57; c 3. *Educ:* Univ Wis, BS(agr) & BS(civil eng), 55, PhD(civil eng), 62; Univ Ariz, MS, 59. *Honors & Awards:* Robert E Horton Award, Am Geophys Union, 83; Arid Lands Hydrol Award, Am Soc Civil Engrs, 88 & Nat Acad Eng, 90. *Prof Exp:* Asst agr engr, Univ Ariz, 55-58; hydraul engr, Agr Res Serv, USDA, 58-63; asst prof civil eng, Cornell Univ, 63-67; res hydraul engr, Agr Res Serv, USDA, 67-91. *Concurrent Pos:* Mem assoc fac, Dept Civil Eng, Colo State Univ, 70-84; vis prof, Imp Col, London, 77-78, Va Polytech Inst & State Univ, 92, Univ Cordoba, Spain, 93-94 & 96; vis scientist, Inst Hydrol, Wallingford, UK, 77-78; adj prof, Dept Hydrol & Water Resources, Univ Ariz, 81-92; adj prof, Univ Ariz, 81-92; sr res sci, Colo State Univ, 93-94, fac affil, 94. *Mem:* Nat

Acad Eng; Am Soc Civil Engrs; Am Soc Agr Engrs; fel Am Geophys Union. *Res:* Simulation of hydrologic systems, including numerical solutions of unsteady, spatially varied flow; stochastic models of climate. *Mailing Add:* 1631 Barnwood Dr Ft Collins CO 80525

**WOOLLAM, JOHN ARTHUR,** OPTICS, ELECTRICAL ENGINEERING. *Current Pos:* GEORGE HOLMES DISTINGUISHED PROF, DEPT ELEC ENG, UNIV NEBR, 80-, DIR, CTR MICROELECTRONIC & OPTICAL MAT RES, 88-; PRES, J A WOOLAM CO, INC, LINCOLN, NEBR, 89- *Personal Data:* b Kalamazoo, Mich, Aug 10, 39; c Catherine & Susan. *Educ:* Kenyon Col, AB, 61; Mich State Univ, MS, 63, PhD(physics), 67; Case Western Res Univ, MS, 78. *Honors & Awards:* Achievement Awards, NASA/Lewis Res Ctr, 72 & 77. *Prof Exp:* Res physicist mat, Lewis Res Ctr, NASA, 67-74, head, Cryophysics Sect, 74-78, res physicist photovoltaics, 78-80. *Concurrent Pos:* Mem, Interagency Adv Power Group, 70-79; vis scientist, Mat Sci Ctr, Mass Inst Technol, 72 & Francis Bitter Nat Magnet Lab, 77-84; adj scientist, Oberlin Col, 78-; consult, Wright Patterson AFB, 78-82. *Mem:* Fel Am Phys Soc; Am Vacuum Soc; sr mem Inst Elec & Electronics Engrs; Mat Res Soc. *Res:* Thin films physics of solids: electronic properties; semiconductors; dielectrics; surfaces; ellipsometry and polarized light. *Mailing Add:* 2436 Sheridan Blvd Lincoln NE 68502-4042

**WOOLLEY, DONALD GRANT,** AGRONOMY, PHYSIOLOGY. *Current Pos:* RETIRED. *Personal Data:* b Magrath, Alta, Dec 12, 25; m 47; c 5. *Educ:* Utah State Univ, BSc, 51, MSc, 56; Iowa State Univ, PhD(crop physiol), 59. *Prof Exp:* Asst prof agron, Iowa State Univ, 59-60; res officer, Can Dept Agr, 60-63; from assoc prof to prof agron, Col Agr, Iowa State Univ, 63-89, head, Farm Mgt Dept & Classification Officer, 78-80. *Concurrent Pos:* Consult, World Bank, SE Asia, 74-75. *Mem:* Am Soc Agron; Am Soc Crop Sci. *Res:* Crop physiology, climatology and crambe production. *Mailing Add:* 1816 Bel Air Dr Ames IA 50010

**WOOLLEY, DOROTHY ELIZABETH SCHUMANN,** PHYSIOLOGY, PHARMACOLOGY. *Current Pos:* from asst prof to assoc prof physiol & environ toxicol, 65-74, PROF ANIMAL PHYSIOL, UNIV CALIF, DAVIS, 74- *Personal Data:* b Wapakoneta, Ohio, Feb 2, 29; m 50; c 3. *Educ:* Bowling Green State Univ, BS, 50; Ohio State Univ, MS, 56; Univ Calif, Berkeley, PhD(physiol), 61. *Prof Exp:* NSF fel, Univ Calif, Berkeley, 61-62, asst res physiologist, 62-65, lectr physiol, 63-64. *Concurrent Pos:* Lectr, Univ Calif, Sch Med, San Francisco, 60-65. *Mem:* AAAS; Am Physiol Soc; Endocrine Soc; Am Soc Pharmacol & Exp Therapeut. *Res:* Effects of hormones, drugs and neurotoxins on brain electrical activity, neurochemistry and behavior in rats and monkeys. *Mailing Add:* Dept Neurobiol Univ Calif Davis CA 95616-5200. *Fax:* 530-752-5582

**WOOLLEY, EARL MADSEN,** PHYSICAL CHEMISTRY, ANALYTICAL CHEMISTRY. *Current Pos:* assoc prof, 70-77, PROF ANALYTICAL & PHYS CHEM, BRIGHAM YOUNG UNIV, 77-, CHAIR, 89- *Personal Data:* b Richfield, Utah, Apr 10, 42; m 66; c 8. *Educ:* Brigham Young Univ, BS, 66, PhD(phys chem), 69. *Prof Exp:* Nat Res Coun Can fel, Univ Lethbridge, 69-70. *Mem:* Am Chem Soc; Calorimetry Conf. *Res:* Thermodynamics of solutions containing reacting and/or non-reacting components including surfactants, strong electrolytes, acids, bases, and hydrogen bonding species. *Mailing Add:* C304BNSN Brigham Young Univ Provo UT 84602-5700

**WOOLLEY, TYLER ANDERSON,** ZOOLOGY. *Current Pos:* from asst prof to assoc prof, 48-58, PROF ZOOL, COLO STATE UNIV, 58- *Personal Data:* b Los Angeles, Calif, Apr 3, 18; m 80; c 3. *Educ:* Univ Utah, BS, 39, MS, 41; Ohio State Univ, PhD(entom), 48. *Prof Exp:* Sr asst comp anat, Univ Utah, 38-39; asst zool, Ohio State Univ, 46-47, asst instr, 47-48. *Res:* Acarology; Oribatei; taxonomy; biology; invertebrate zoology. *Mailing Add:* 1813 Crestmore Pl Ft Collins CO 80521

**WOOLRIDGE, EDWARD DANIEL,** DENTISTRY, FORENSIC DENTISTRY. *Current Pos:* RETIRED. *Personal Data:* b Jackson, Miss, June 7, 32; m 63; c 2. *Educ:* Lynchburg Col, BS, 53; Med Col Va, DDS, 57; George Washington Univ, MEd, 81; Am Bd Forensic Odontol, dipl, 71. *Honors & Awards:* Commendation Medal, USPHS, 73. *Prof Exp:* Private pract dent, Farmville, Va, 59-62; liaison officer, USCG, NY, 65-66, sr dent officer, 69-74; sr dent officer, USCG Acad, 74-77; chief dent officer, USCG Hq, 77-88. *Concurrent Pos:* Consult, Off Chief Med Examrs, Rockland, NY, 71-, vis asst prof, Med Univ SC, 75-; clin instr, Sch Dent Med, Tufts Univ, 76-; clin field instr, Baltimore Col Dent Surg, Univ Md, 78- *Mem:* Fel Am Col Dent; fel Am Acad Forensic Sci; Soc Med Jurisprudence. *Mailing Add:* Pamlico Beach Belhaven NC 27810

**WOOLRIDGE, ROBERT LEONARD,** MEDICAL BACTERIOLOGY, IMMUNOLOGY. *Current Pos:* RETIRED. *Personal Data:* b Garretson, SDak, Oct 13, 19; m 46; c 1. *Educ:* Univ SDak, BA, 41; Univ Chicago, MSc, 43; Keio Univ, Japan, DSc(microbiol), 60. *Honors & Awards:* Provincial Health Dept Award, Rep China, 66. *Prof Exp:* Res asst path, Sch Med, Univ Chicago, 43-48; microbiologist, US Naval Med Res Unit 4, 48-59 & Unit 2, 59-66; health scientist adminr, US-Japan Coop Med Sci Prog, NIH, 66-68, chief, Dept HEW health scientist liaison officer to Dept State, 71-72, chief prev br, Cancer Control Prog, 72-76, prog dir, Diag Res & Prev, Div Div Cancer Res Resources & Ctrs, 76-78, exec scientist, Univ Asn Res & Educ Pathol, 85-89; consult, 89- *Concurrent Pos:* Res assoc, Univ Chicago, 49-52; asst clin prof, Univ Wash, 61-65; tech consult, WHO, Geneva, 62-66. *Mem:* Fel AAAS; Am Soc Microbiol; Am Sci Prev Oncol; Asia-Pac Acad Ophthal; NY Acad Sci; Am Pharmaceut Asn; Fed Am Soc

Exp Biol. *Res:* Vaccine development; immunological prophylaxis; laboratory diagnosis of respiratory viruses, arboviruses and the trachomainclusion conjunctivitis agents; epidemiology and chemoprophylaxis studies in trachomatous children in the Far East. *Mailing Add:* 2318 Lost Rd Martinsburg WV 25401

**WOOLSEY, GERALD BRUCE,** PHYSICAL CHEMISTRY. *Current Pos:* res chemist, E I DuPont de Nemours & Co, Inc, 67-69, develop supvr, 69-71, res supvr, 71-74, mfg supvr, 74-76, bus specialist, 76-78, STAFF RES CHEMIST, SAVANNAH RIVER PLANT, E I DUPONT DE NEMOURS & CO, INC, 79- *Personal Data:* b Brooks, Ga, Aug 16, 37; m 60; c 3. *Educ:* Univ SC, BS, 60, PhD(phys chem), 67. *Prof Exp:* Chemist, Tenn Corp, Cities Serv Co, 60-63. *Mem:* Am Chem Soc; Sigma Xi. *Res:* Thermodynamics of solutions; hydration in solutions of concentrated electrolytes; amide solutions; polyester films; nuclear waste disposal; nuclear propulsion. *Mailing Add:* 1588 Tri County Rd Brooks GA 30205

**WOOLSEY, MARION ELMER,** MICROBIOLOGY. *Current Pos:* asst prof, 70-76, ASSOC PROF MICROBIOL, UNIV TULSA, 76- *Personal Data:* b Croft, Kans, July 27, 19; m 40; c 3. *Educ:* Univ Tex, Austin, BA, 64, MA, 66, PhD(microbiol), 68. *Prof Exp:* Res assoc immunol, Univ Tex, Austin, 68, asst prof microbiol, 68-70. *Concurrent Pos:* NIH fel, Univ Tex, Austin, 68. *Mem:* Am Soc Microbiol. *Res:* Basic and applied research in medical microbiology, immunology and immunochemistry. *Mailing Add:* 5702 E Seventh St Tulsa OK 74112

**WOOLSEY, NEIL FRANKLIN,** ORGANIC CHEMISTRY OF COAL, ORGANOMETALLIC ARENE CHEMISTRY. *Current Pos:* from asst prof to assoc prof, 65-77, PROF CHEM, UNIV NDAK, 77- *Personal Data:* b Tieton, Wash, Apr 30, 35; m 56, Marilyn E Gill; c Beth, Earl, Spencer, Nathan & Heather. *Educ:* Univ Portland, BS, 57; Univ Wis, PhD(org chem), 62. *Prof Exp:* NSF fel, Imp Col, London, 61-63; res assoc org chem, Iowa State Univ, 63-65. *Mem:* Am Chem Soc; Sigma Xi. *Res:* Reductive cleavage of aryl ethers; organometallic arene chemistry; structure, reactions and analytical chemistry of coal and coal derived materials; nonplanar polycyclic aromatic hydrocarbons related to fullerenes. *Mailing Add:* 1819 N Fourth St Grand Forks ND 58203-1614

**WOOLSEY, ROBERT M,** MEDICINE, NEUROLOGY. *Current Pos:* from instr to assoc prof, 62-75, PROF NEUROL, ST LOUIS UNIV, 75- *Personal Data:* b Chicago, Ill, May 30, 31; m 67; c 1. *Educ:* St Louis Univ, BS, 53, MD, 57. *Prof Exp:* Intern med, St Louis Univ Hosp, 57-58; resident neurol, Univ Mich Hosp, 58-61. *Concurrent Pos:* Fel neuropath, Col Physicians & Surgeons, Columbia Univ, 61-62. *Mem:* AMA; Asn Res Nerv & Ment Dis; Am Acad Neurol; Am Electroencephalog Soc; Am Paraplegia Soc. *Res:* Electroencephalography. *Mailing Add:* 3635 Vista Ave St Louis MO 63110-2539

**WOOLSEY, THOMAS ALLEN,** NEUROSCIENCES. *Current Pos:* from asst prof to assoc prof, Washington Univ Med Sch, 71-83, coordr neural sci prog, 80-84, sr Mcdonnell neuroscientist, McDonnel Ctr Studies Higher Brain Function, 82-97, PROF NEUROL, NEUROSURG, ANAT, NEUROBIOL, CELL BIOL & PHYSIOL, WASHINGTON UNIV MED SCH, 84-, GEORGE H & ETHEL R BISHOP SCHOLAR NEUROSCI, 84- *Personal Data:* b Baltimore, Md, Apr 17, 43; m 69, Cynthia Ward; c Alix W & Timothy W. *Educ:* Univ Wis-Madison, BS, 65; Johns Hopkins Univ, MD, 69. *Honors & Awards:* Pickney J Harman Lectr, Am Asn Anatomists; McKnight Neurosci Develop Award; Jacob Javits Neurosci Investr Award. *Prof Exp:* Intern surg, Barnes Hosp, St Louis, Mo, 69-70. *Concurrent Pos:* NIH fel anat, Med Sch, Wash Univ, 70-71, Nat Inst Neurol Dis & Stroke grant, 72-, consult NIH, NSF; reviewer Brain Res, J Comp Neurol Sci; dir, James L O'Leary Div Exper Neurol & Neurobiol Surg, Med Sch, Washington Univ, 84- *Mem:* Am Asn Anat; Soc Neurosci; Am Neurol Asn; Am Acad Neurol; Microvascular Soc; Develop Neurobiol. *Res:* Structure and function of somatosensory; computer applications to morphology; local cerebral blood flow mechanisms. *Mailing Add:* Lab Exp Neurol & Neurosurg Washington Univ Sch Med Box 8057 St Louis MO 63110. *Fax:* 314-362-8359

**WOOLSON, EDWIN ALBERT,** PESTICIDE CHEMISTRY. *Current Pos:* PRES & DIR CHEM, EPL-BIO-ANALYTICAL SERV, 86- *Personal Data:* b Takoma Park, Md, Oct 2, 41; m 61, Barbara L Wilhelm; c Janice (Doherty), Mark, Michael & Karen (Riley). *Educ:* Univ Md, BS, 63, MS, 66, PhD(soil chem), 69. *Prof Exp:* Analyst soil testing, Univ Md, 62; phys sci aide, USDA, 62-63, chemist, 63-65, analytical chemist, 65-67, res chemist, 67-85; mgr chem, Am Biogenics Corp, 85-86. *Mem:* Am Chem Soc; Am Soc Agron; Soil Sci Soc Am; Weed Sci Soc Am; Coun Agr Sci Technol; Soc Environ Toxicol & Chem. *Res:* Behavior and fate of arsenic, herbicides and insecticides in soil and water; method development for pesticides in soils, plants and water; toxicity of pesticides to plants; impurities in pesticides; bioaccumulation; residue analysis in soil, plants and water. *Mailing Add:* EPL Bio-Analytical Servs Inc PO Box 109 Harristown IL 62537-0109. *Fax:* 217-963-2283; *E-Mail:* ewoclsnw@aplbas.com

**WOOLSTON, DANIEL D,** ELECTRONICS. *Current Pos:* RETIRED. *Personal Data:* b Churchville, NY, Oct 18, 26; m 50; c 2. *Educ:* Iowa State Col, BS, 51. *Prof Exp:* Physicist & electronic scientist, US Naval Ord Lab, 51-63; vpres, Underwater Systs, Inc, 63-75, pres, 75-87. *Mem:* Inst Elec & Electronics Engrs. *Res:* Underwater telemetry; hydroacoustic mine research and development; underwater explosive parameter data gathering and analysis for underwater mine research programs; sediment velocimeter research, design and development of the instrumentation; underwater sound propagation studies. *Mailing Add:* 6427 Morning Time Lane Clarksville MD 21209-1273

**WOOLVERTON, CHRISTOPHER JUDE,** immunoregulation, infection & immunity, for more information see previous edition

**WOOLVERTON, WILLIAM L,** BEHAVIORAL PHARMACOLOGY. *Current Pos:* PROF, UNIV MISS MED CTR, 93- *Personal Data:* b Birmingham, Ala, Nov 28, 50. *Educ:* Univ Chicago, PhD(pharm), 77. *Prof Exp:* From asst prof to assoc prof pharm, Univ Chicago, 80-93. *Concurrent Pos:* Pres, Int Study Group Investigating Drugs as Reinforcers, 85- *Mem:* Am Soc Pharm & Exp Therapeut; Soc Neurosis; Behav Pharm Soc. *Mailing Add:* Dept Psychiat Univ Miss Med Ctr Arthur C Guyton Lab Res Bldg 2500 State St Jackson MS 39216-4505

**WOOSLEY, RAYMOND LEON,** CLINICAL PHARMACOLOGY. *Current Pos:* prof & chmn, Pharmacol Dept, 88-94, PROF PHARMACOL & MED & CHMN, DEPT PHARMACOL, GEORGETOWN UNIV, 94- *Personal Data:* b Roundhill, Ky, Oct 2, 42; m 84, Julianne B; c 2. *Educ:* Western Ky State Univ, BS, 64; Univ Louisville, PhD(pharmacol), 67; Univ Miami, MD, 73. *Honors & Awards:* Rawls-Palmer Award, Am Soc Clin Pharmacol & Therapeut, 90; Carmelia Louise Riker Mem lectr, Ore Health Sci Univ, 95; Distinguished Investr Award, Am Col Clin Pharmacol, 96. *Prof Exp:* Sr pharmacologist, Meyer Labs, Inc, 68-69, dir, Res Pharmaceut, 69-71; from intern to resident med, Vanderbilt Univ Hosp, Vanderbilt Univ, 73-74, fel clin pharmacol, 74-75, from asst prof to prof med & pharmacol, 75-88. *Concurrent Pos:* NIH fel pharmacol, Med Sch, Univ Louisville, 67-68, lectr, 69-71; instr med & clin pharmacol, Vanderbilt Univ, 75; postdoctoral fel, Dept Pharmacol & Med, Vanderbilt Univ, 76-77. *Mem:* Soc Exp Biol & Med; Am Soc Pharmacol & Exp Therapeut; fel Am Col Clin Pharmacol; fel Am Col Physicians; fel Am Col Cardiologists; Sigma Xi; Am Bd Clin Pharmacol (secy-treas, 92-). *Res:* Drug induced lupus erythematosus; and clinical pharmacology of new antiarrhythmic drugs; the actions of antihistamines; author/co-author of over 125 articles; holder of three patents. *Mailing Add:* Dept Pharmacol Georgetown Univ 3900 Reservoir Rd NW Washington DC 20007-2188

**WOOSLEY, ROYCE STANLEY,** ORGANIC CHEMISTRY. *Current Pos:* from asst prof to assoc prof chem, 66-74, chmn dept, 69-75 & 88-89, PROF CHEM, WESTERN CAROLINA UNIV, 74- *Personal Data:* b Caneyville, Ky, June 17, 34; m 59, Marcia Heffernan; c Jennie W (Chase) & Julie S. *Educ:* Western Ky Univ, BS, 56; Univ Conn, MS, 59; Ohio Univ, PhD(org chem), 67. *Prof Exp:* Sect leader tech serv, Olin Mathieson Chem Corp, 58-62. *Mem:* Am Chem Soc; Sigma Xi; Int Union Pure & Appl Chem. *Res:* Chemosystematic studies of spruce-fir forests in the southern appalachcians. *Mailing Add:* Dept Chem & Phys Western Carolina Univ Cullowhee NC 28723. *Fax:* 704-227-7647; *E-Mail:* rwoosley@wpoff.wcu.edu

**WOOSLEY, STANFORD EARL,** ASTROPHYSICS. *Current Pos:* from asst prof to assoc prof, 75-83, PROF ASTRON, LICK OBSERV, UNIV CALIF, SANTA CRUZ, 83-, CHMN DEPT, 89- *Personal Data:* b Texarkana, Tex, Dec 8, 44; div. *Educ:* Rice Univ, BA, 66, MS, 69, PhD(astrophys), 71. *Honors & Awards:* Fel Am Phys Soc. *Prof Exp:* Res assoc, Rice Univ, 71-73; res fel, Calif Inst Technol, 73-75. *Concurrent Pos:* Consult, Lawrence Livermore Lab, 74- & Los Alamos Lab, 88-; NSF & NASA grants, 77-83; mem coun, Am Astron Soc. *Mem:* Am Phys Soc; Am Astron Soc; Int Astron Union. *Res:* Nuclear astrophysics, nucleosynthesis supernovae, gamma-ray bursts. *Mailing Add:* 115 Auburn Ave Santa Cruz CA 95060

**WOOSTER, HAROLD ABBOTT,** INFORMATION SCIENCE. *Current Pos:* RETIRED. *Personal Data:* b Hartford, Conn, Jan 3, 19; m 41, 68, Alice Hammond; c 4. *Educ:* Syracuse Univ, AB, 39; Univ Wis, MS, 41, PhD(physiol chem), 43. *Prof Exp:* Asst, Toxicity Lab, Univ Chicago, 43-46; res assoc, Pepper Lab, Univ Pa, 46-47; sr fel, Mellon Inst, 47-56; dir res commun, Air Force Off Sci Res, 56-59, chief info sci div, 59-62, dir info sci, 62-70; chief res & develop br, Nat Libr Med, Lister Hill Nat Ctr Biomed Commun, 70-74, sr info scientist, 74-85 spec asst prog develop, 74-85. *Concurrent Pos:* Exec secy panel info sci & tech, Comt Sci & Tech Info, Off Dir Defense Res & Eng, 65-66; adj instr, Grad Sch Libr Sci, Drexel Inst Technol, 67. *Mem:* Fel AAAS; Am Soc Info Sci; Sigma Xi. *Res:* Biomedical communications; computer-aided instruction; medical television; information storage and retrieval. *Mailing Add:* 8807 Mead St Bethesda MD 20817-3223

**WOOSTER, WARREN SCRIVER,** OCEANOGRAPHY. *Current Pos:* dir, 79-82, prof, Inst Marine Studies, 76-91, EMER PROF MARINE STUDIES & FISHERIES, SCH MARINE AFFAIRS, UNIV WASH, 91- *Personal Data:* b Westfield, Mass, Feb 20, 21; m 48, Clarissa; c Susan, Daniel & Dana. *Educ:* Brown Univ, BSc, 43; Calif Inst Technol, MS, 47; Univ Calif, PhD, 53. *Prof Exp:* Asst res oceanogr, Scripps Inst, Univ Calif, 51-58, assoc res oceanogr, 58-61; dir off oceanog, UNESCO, 61-63; prof oceanog, Scripps Inst Oceanog, Univ Calif, 63-73, chmn, Grad Dept, 67-69; prof oceanog & dean, Rosenstiel Sch Marine & Atmospheric Sci, Univ Miami, 73-76. *Concurrent Pos:* Dir invests, Coun Hydrobiol Invests, Peru, 57-58; pres, Sci Comm Oceanic Res, 68-72; Int Explor Sea, 82-85; Nat Pac Marine Sci Orgn, 92-96. *Mem:* Fel Am Geophys Union; fel Am Meteorol Soc. *Res:* Descriptive oceanography of the Pacific Ocean; physical, chemical and fishery oceanography; ocean affairs; climate variations and marine ecosystems. *Mailing Add:* Marine Affairs Univ Wash 3707 Brooklyn Ave NE Seattle WA 98105-6715. *Fax:* 206-543-1417; *E-Mail:* wooster@u.washington.edu

**WOOTEN, FRANK THOMAS,** TECHNICAL MANAGEMENT. *Current Pos:* res engr, Res Triangle Inst, 67-71, mgr biomed eng, 71-75, exec asst to pres, 75-80, vpres, 80-89, PRES, RES TRIANGLE INST, 89- *Personal Data:* b Fayetteville, NC, Sept 24, 35; m 62, Linda Walker; c Ashley, Patrick & Laurin. *Educ:* Duke Univ, BS, 57, PhD(elec eng), 64. *Prof Exp:* Sr engr, Electronic Res Lab, Corning Glass Works, 64-67. *Mem:* Asn Advan Med Instrumentation; Inst Elec & Electronics Engrs; Sigma Xi. *Res:* Medical instrumentation; analysis of pulmonary sound; technology transfer; electronics. *Mailing Add:* Res Triangle Inst PO Box 12194 Research Triangle Park NC 27709

**WOOTEN, FREDERICK (OLIVER),** SOLID STATE PHYSICS. *Current Pos:* vchmn, Dept Appl Sci, 72-73, chmn dept, 73-92, PROF APPL SCI, UNIV CALIF, DAVIS, 72-, CHMN COMPUT SCI, 89- *Personal Data:* b Linwood, Pa, May 16, 28; m 52, Jane MacPherson; c Bartley L & Donald B. *Educ:* Mass Inst Technol, BS, 50; Univ Del, PhD(chem), 55. *Prof Exp:* Staff physicist, All Am Eng Co, 54-57; res chemist, Lawrence Livermore Lab, 57-72. *Concurrent Pos:* Vis prof, Drexel Univ, 64; lectr, Univ Calif, Davis, 65-72; vis prof, Chalmers Univ Technol, Sweden, 67-68; consult, Lawrence Livermore Nat Lab, 72-; vis prof, Heriot-Watt Univ, Scotland, 79, Trinity Col, Ireland, 86, Univ Mass, 91, Mich State Univ, 93 & Boston Univ, 96. *Mem:* AAAS; Am Phys Soc; NY Acad Sci; Sigma Xi. *Res:* Structure of amorphous solids. *Mailing Add:* Dept Appl Sci Univ Calif Davis CA 95616

**WOOTEN, JEAN W,** botany, for more information see previous edition

**WOOTEN, MARIE W,** CANCER RESEARCH. *Current Pos:* RES ASSOC, COLD SPRING HARBOR LABS, 85- & UNIV ALA, BIRMINGHAM, 86- *Educ:* Tex Women's Univ, PhD(biochem), 83. *Res:* Protein kinase; oncogenesis. *Mailing Add:* Dept Zool Auburn Univ 331 Funchess Hall Auburn AL 36849-5414. *Fax:* 334-844-9234

**WOOTEN, WILLIS CARL, JR,** POLYMER CHEMISTRY. *Current Pos:* Sr res chemist, Tenn Eastman Co, 51-60, admin asst, 60-65, div head, res lab, 65-75, DIR, POLYMER RES DIV, TENN EASTMAN CO, 76- *Personal Data:* b Homerville, Ga, Mar 9, 22; m 49; c 3. *Educ:* Univ NC, PhD(chem), 50. *Mem:* Am Chem Soc; Sigma Xi. *Res:* Synthetic fibers and plastics; organic chemistry. *Mailing Add:* 105 Pine Lane Chapel Hill NC 27514-4332

**WOOTTEN, HENRY ALWYN,** ASTRONOMY, ASTROPHYSICS. *Current Pos:* SCIENTIST, NAT RADIO ASTRON OBSERV, 82- *Personal Data:* b Salisbury, Md, May 3, 48; m 80, Ida L Darby; c Nathaniel A & James D. *Educ:* Univ Md, BS, 70; Univ Tex, MS, 76, PhD(astron), 78. *Prof Exp:* Res fel astron, Calif Inst Technol, 78-81; res assoc astron, Rensselaer Polytech Inst, 82; vis scientist, Observ Paris, 90, Univ Bordeaux I, 93. *Concurrent Pos:* Mem, Submillimeter Sci Working Group, NASA, 92-; res prof astron, Univ Va, 93- *Mem:* Am Astron Soc; Int Astron Union; Int Aroid Soc. *Res:* Formation and evolution of stars and planetary systems primarily through observations in the infrared through millimeter wavelength bands of dust and molecular emission. *Mailing Add:* Nat Radio Astron Observ 520 Edgemont Rd Charlottesville VA 22903-2475

**WOOTTERS, WILLIAM KENT,** QUANTUM INFORMATION THEORY, QUANTUM CHAOS. *Current Pos:* from asst prof to assoc prof, 82-95, PROF PHYSICS, WILLIAMS COL, 95- *Personal Data:* b Houston, Tex, July 7, 51; m 82; c 2. *Educ:* Stanford Univ, BS, 73; Univ Tex Austin, PhD(physics), 80. *Prof Exp:* Instr & postdoctoral res assoc physics, Univ Tex, Austin, 80-82. *Concurrent Pos:* Vis res assoc, Univ Tex, Austin, 85-86; vis assoc prof, Santa Fe Inst, 89-90. *Mem:* Am Phys Soc; Sigma Xi; Coun Undergrad Res. *Res:* Foundations of quantum mechanics, with special emphasis on optimal measurement strategies, quantum information theory, relation between quantum and classical mechanics, and quantum chaos. *Mailing Add:* Dept Physics Williams Col Williamstown MA 01267

**WOOTTON, JOHN FRANCIS,** BIOORGANIC CHEMISTRY, PROTEIN SCIENCE. *Current Pos:* from asst prof to prof physiol chem, 62-79, assoc dean, Grad Sch, 80-83, PROF BIOCHEM, NY STATE COL VET MED, CORNELL UNIV, 79- *Personal Data:* b Penn Yan, NY, May 31, 29; m 59, Joyce MacMullen; c Jo T, David, Barbara & Bruce. *Educ:* Cornell Univ, BS, 51, MS, 53, PhD(biochem), 60. *Prof Exp:* Clin chemist, Clifton Springs Sanitarium & Clin, NY, 56; Nat Found fel chem, Univ Col London, 60-62. *Concurrent Pos:* Hon res asst, Univ London, 62; vis scientist, Lab Molecular Biol, Univ Postgrad Med Sch, Cambridge, Eng, 69-70, Nat Inst Med Res, Mill Hill, London, 85-86 & 92-93; temp sr res assoc, Stanford Univ Med Sch, 77-78. *Mem:* Am Chem Soc; AAAS; Sigma Xi; Am Soc Biochem & Molecular Biol; Biophys Soc. *Res:* Enzymology; proteolytic enzymes; regulatory & transport proteins; relationship of protein structure to function; synthesis and applications of photolabile compounds; molecular physiology. *Mailing Add:* Dept/Sect Physiol T8-022 VRT Cornell Univ Ithaca NY 14853. *Fax:* 607-253-3851; *E-Mail:* jfw1@cornell.edu

**WOOTTON, PETER,** MEDICAL PHYSICS, RADIOLOGY. *Current Pos:* from asst prof to assoc prof radiol, 64-72, PROF RADIOL, UNIV WASH, 72- *Personal Data:* b Peterborough, Eng, Apr 30, 24; m 47; c 3. *Educ:* Univ Birmingham, BSc, 44. *Prof Exp:* Physicist, Res & Develop Labs, Farrow's Br, Reckitt & Coleman Ltd, 44-48; radiation physicist, Royal Infirmary, Glasgow, Scotland, 48-51; instr radiol physics, Univ Tex M D Anderson Hosp, 51-53; radiation physicist, Tumor Inst, Swedish Hosp, Seattle, Wash, 53-64. *Concurrent Pos:* Instr, Med Sch, Univ Ore, 54-60, Univ Seattle, 56 & Penrose Cancer Hosp, Colorado Springs, Colo, 56-57; clin asst prof & radiation physicist, Univ Wash, 59-64; mem tech adv bd radiation control, Dept Health, Wash, 62-68, comt radiation oncol studies, Nat Cancer Inst, 77-81 & sci comt, 25, Nat Coun Radiation Protection & Measurements, 67-83. *Mem:* Am Asn Physicists Med (pres, 78); Soc Nuclear Med; fel Am Col Radiol; Am Soc

Therapeut Radiol; Brit Inst Physics; Am Col Med Physics. *Res:* Applications of radiation physics in medicine, especially dosimetry of all types of ionizing radiations and the effects of physical parameters such as high pressure oxygen and pulsed radiation in radiobiology; fast neutron therapy. *Mailing Add:* 4633 137th Ave NE Bellevue WA 98005

**WOPSCHALL, ROBERT HAROLD,** PHYSICAL CHEMISTRY. *Current Pos:* RES CHEMIST, E I DU PONT DE NEMOURS & CO, INC, 66- *Personal Data:* b Glendale, Calif, May 1, 40; m 62; c 2. *Educ:* Harvey Mudd Col, BS, 62; Univ Wis, PhD(phys chem), 67. *Mem:* Am Chem Soc; Sigma Xi. *Res:* Stationary electrode polarography; adsorption of electroactive species on electrodes and coupled chemical reactions; photopolymerization; electroless deposition; photoresists; printed circuits manufacturing; photographic science. *Mailing Add:* 1118 S Dolton Ct Wilmington DE 19810-3006

**WORDEN, DAVID GILBERT,** SOLID STATE PHYSICS, PLASMA PHYSICS. *Current Pos:* RETIRED. *Personal Data:* b Minneapolis, Minn, Mar 9, 24; m 47, Elizabeth Hegge; c David & Christine. *Educ:* Earlham Col, AB, 50; Iowa State Univ, PhD(physics), 56. *Prof Exp:* Physicist, Gen Elec Res Lab, 56-61; mgr surface physics sect, Electro-Optical Systs, Inc, 61-65, electron device res sect, 65-66, electron & image device dept, 66-67; chmn, Dept Physics, NDak State Univ, 67-68, prof physics & acad vpres, 68-79; mgr, Univ Relations, Gen Elec Corp Res & Develop, 79-85. *Concurrent Pos:* Assoc part-time prof, Calif State Col, Los Angeles, 65-67. *Res:* Properties of thin films; physical and chemical adsorption; electron emission; ion production on surfaces; low energy gaseous electrical discharges in magnetic fields; university industry relationships; manpower; science and engineering policy. *Mailing Add:* 4028 Chaucer Pl Slingerlands NY 12159

**WORDEN, EARL FREEMONT, JR,** PHYSICAL CHEMISTRY. *Current Pos:* RETIRED. *Personal Data:* b Portsmouth, NH, Nov 30, 31; m 60, Marlys Winter; c Seth L. *Educ:* Univ NH, BS, 53, MS, 55; Univ Calif, Berkeley, PhD(chem), 59. *Honors & Awards:* Louis A Strait Award, Soc Appl Spectros, 85. *Prof Exp:* Chemist, Lawrence Livermore Nat Lab, Univ Calif, 58-96. *Concurrent Pos:* Consult, US Enrichment Corp, Lawrence Livermore Nat Lab. *Mem:* Am Chem Soc; Sigma Xi; Optical Soc Am; Soc Appl Spectros. *Res:* Atomic and molecular optical spectroscopy; laser isotope separation; laser spectroscopy of atoms. *Mailing Add:* Lawrence Livermore Nat Lab Univ Calif MS&I L-463 Livermore CA 94550. *Fax:* 510-422-6007; *E-Mail:* worden1@llnl.gov

**WORDEN, PATRICIA BARRON,** SCIENCE EDUCATION. *Current Pos:* MEM, ARLINGTON SCH COMT, ARLINGTON TWP, 79- *Educ:* Harvard Univ, PhD(biol), 64. *Mailing Add:* 27 Jason St Arlington MA 02174-6446

**WORDEN, PAUL WELLMAN, JR,** PHYSICS. *Current Pos:* Res asst, Stanford Univ, 68-76, scholar, 76-78, res assoc physics, 78-80, SR RES ASSOC, STANFORD UNIV, 80- *Personal Data:* b San Angelo, Tex, Mar 1, 45. *Educ:* Rice Univ, BA, 67; Stanford Univ, MS, 69, PhD(physics), 76. *Concurrent Pos:* Consult, Jet Propulsion Lab, Pasadena, Calif, 83-84. *Mem:* AAAS; Am Phys Soc; Sigma Xi. *Res:* Experimental gravitation; equivalence principle; cryogenic applications to basic research; satellite test of the equivalence principle. *Mailing Add:* 2284 Williams St Palo Alto CA 94306. *E-Mail:* worden@step.stanford.edu

**WORDEN, SIMON PETER,** SOLAR PHYSICS. *Current Pos:* MEM FAC, DEPT ASTRON, UNIV CALIF, LOS ANGELES, 80- *Personal Data:* b Mt Clemens, Mich, Oct 21, 49. *Educ:* Univ Mich, BS, 71; Univ Ariz, PhD(astron), 75. *Prof Exp:* Res asst astron, Kitt Peak Nat Observ, 71-75; astrophysicist, Sacramento Peak Observ, Air Force Geophys Lab, 75-80. *Mem:* Am Astron Soc; Royal Astron Soc. *Res:* The study of large-scale convective motions on the sun and observation and interpretation of stellar phenomena related to solar surface activity; development of techniques for high resolution imaging through the Earth's atmosphere. *Mailing Add:* 6757 N 27th St Arlington VA 22213

**WORDINGER, ROBERT JAMES,** ANATOMY, ELECTRON MICROSCOPY. *Current Pos:* asst prof, 78-80, ASSOC PROF ANAT, TEX COL OSTEOP MED, UNIV NTEX, 80- *Personal Data:* b Philadelphia, Pa, Feb 5, 45; m 74; c 4. *Educ:* Pa State Univ, BS, 67; Clemson Univ, MS, 69, PhD(animal physiol), 72. *Prof Exp:* Fel physiol, Sch Vet Med, Univ Pa, 72-73; asst prof biol, St Bonaventure Univ, 73-76; asst prof path, Sch Med Sci, Univ Ark, 76-77. *Concurrent Pos:* Head histol, Nat Ctr Toxicol Res, 76-77; vchmn, Dept Anat, Tex Col Osteop Med, NTex State Univ, 80- *Mem:* Soc Study Reproduction; Histochem Soc; Am Soc Cell Biol. *Res:* Estrogenic changes in the mammalian reproductive system using histochemistry and electron microscopy; factors influencing in vitro embryo development and differentiation within mammals; implantation. *Mailing Add:* Dept Anat Tex Col Osteop Med 3500 Comp Bowie Blvd Ft Worth TX 76107-2644. *Fax:* 817-735-2610

**WOREK, WILLIAM MARTIN,** HEAT & MASS TRANSFER, ENERGY SYSTEMS. *Current Pos:* PROF & ASSOC DEPT HEAD, UNIV ILL, CHICAGO, 86- *Personal Data:* b Joliet, Ill, May 7, 54; m 85; c 1. *Educ:* Ill Inst Technol, BS, 76, MS, 77 & PhD(mech eng), 80. *Prof Exp:* Instr, Ill Inst Technol, 77-80, vis asst prof mech eng, 80-83, asst prof mech & aero eng, 83-86. *Mem:* Am Soc Mech Engrs; Am Soc Heating, Refrig & Air Conditioning Engrs; Sigma Xi. *Res:* Fundamental heat and mass transfer problems which are related to specific problems encountered in advanced energy systems; design and simulation of hybrid heat transfer components and advanced energy systems. *Mailing Add:* 7613 Queens Ct Downers Grove IL 60516-4478

**WORF, GAYLE L,** PLANT PATHOLOGY. *Current Pos:* plant pathologist, 63-92, EMER PROF, UNIV WIS-MADISON, 92- *Personal Data:* b Garden City, Kans, Nov 17, 29; m 52; c 2. *Educ:* Kans State Univ, BS, 51, MS, 53; Univ Wis, PhD(plant path), 61. *Prof Exp:* County agt, Kans State Univ, 55-58; plant pathologist, Iowa State Univ, 61-63. *Mem:* Am Phytopath Soc. *Res:* Interpreting current research in plant pathology and analyzing its application to field situations; diagnostic procedures; economical appraisal of disease outbreaks; effective control programs. *Mailing Add:* 5601 Russet Rd Madison WI 53711

**WORGUL, BASIL VLADIMIR,** CELL BIOLOGY, RADIATION BIOLOGY. *Current Pos:* Staff assoc, Columbia Univ, 74-75, NIH fel & res assoc cell biol, 75-78, from asst prof to assoc prof, Dept Ophthal, Col Physicians & Surgeons, 78-90, DIR, EYE RADIATION & ENVIRON RES LAB, COLUMBIA UNIV, 85-, PROF RADIATION BIOL, 90-, DIR UKRAINIAN/AM CHERNOBYL OCULAR STUDY. *Personal Data:* b New York, NY, June 30, 47; m 69, Kathleen Hennessy; c Ronald & Suzanne. *Educ:* Univ Miami, BS, 69; Univ Vt, PhD(zool), 74. *Honors & Awards:* Robert E McCormick Res Scholar. *Concurrent Pos:* Consult, Cataract Panel Nat Adv Eye Coun, 80-83; adv, NRCP, 83-; mem, Non-ionizing Radiation Effects Panel, US Dept Labor, 84-86. *Mem:* Soc Gen Physiol; Radiation Res Soc; AAAS; Asn Res Vision & Ophthal; Am Soc Cell Biol; foreign mem Ukrainian Acad Sci; Comt Space Res. *Res:* The cytopathomechanism of radiation cataractogenesis; radiation risk to populations. *Mailing Add:* Col Physicians & Surgeons Eye Radiation & Environ Res Lab Columbia Univ 630 W 168th St New York NY 10032. *Fax:* 212-305-6749; *E-Mail:* bvw1@columbia.edu

**WORK, CLYDE E(VERETTE),** MATERIALS SCIENCE & MECHANICAL ENGINEERING. *Current Pos:* RETIRED. *Personal Data:* b Bridgeport, Nebr, Jan 31, 24; m 48, Elizabeth A Kennedy; c Cathleen D (Draper), Janice K, Richard D & Steven A. *Educ:* Univ Ill, BS, 45, MS, 48, PhD, 52. *Honors & Awards:* Dudley Medal, Am Soc Testing & Mat, 54; Western Elec Award, Am Soc Eng Educ, 68, Distinguished Educator Award, Mech Div, 84; Tatnall Award, Soc Exp Mech, 78, Frocht Award, 93. *Prof Exp:* Asst prof, Univ Ill, 52-53; assoc prof, Rensselaer Polytech Inst, 53-91; head dept, Mich Technol Univ, 57-69, prof eng mech, 57-68, assoc dean eng, 69-84; dean eng, Western New Eng Col, 84-91. *Concurrent Pos:* UNESCO expert eng mat, Maulana Azad Col Technol, Bhopal, India, 68-69; vis prof mech eng, Univ Ilorin, Nigeria, 78-79. *Mem:* Am Soc Testing & Mat; fel Soc Exp Mech (pres, 72-73); Am Soc Eng Educ; Am Acad Mechs. *Res:* Mechanical behavior of engineering materials; fatigue of metals; effects of fluctuation in stress amplitude; temperature time effects; torsional loading. *Mailing Add:* 2 Spencer Ave Guilford CT 06437. *E-Mail:* clydework@aol.com

**WORK, DENNIS M,** PURIFIED WATER SYSTEMS DESIGN, CLEAN ROOM DESIGN FOR PRODUCTION OF PHARMACEUTICAL PRODUCTS. *Current Pos:* PRES, DW TECHNOLOGIES INC, 94- *Personal Data:* b New Castle, Del, Jan 26, 52; m 94, Cheryl E Empson; c Jeffrey M. *Educ:* Univ Del, BEE, 78. *Prof Exp:* Proj engr, Borg Warner Chem, 78-79; prod supvr, EI Dupont, 79-82, proj engr, 82-87; mgr eng, Triad Technologies Inc, 87-89, mgr, Qualification & Validation, 89-91, dir eng, 91-93, vpres & sr consult, 93-94. *Concurrent Pos:* Lectr, Biopharmaceut Facil Design Construct, Fine Particle Soc, 88, Pharmaceut Facil Design & Construct, Int Soc Pharmaceut Engrs, 90; prin lectr, Water & Air Compliance, Interplex USA, 91, Water System Design, 92, Clean Room Heating, Vent & Air Conditioning Design, 93. *Mem:* Int Soc Pharmaceut Engrs; Am Soc Heating Refrig & Air Conditioning Engrs; Nat Fire Protection Asn. *Mailing Add:* 222 W Longsper Dr Wilmington DE 19808. *Fax:* 215-668-4827

**WORK, HENRY HARCUS,** PEDIATRICS, PSYCHIATRY. *Current Pos:* RETIRED. *Personal Data:* b Buffalo, NY, Nov 11, 11; wid; c Henry H III, David C, William B & Stuart R. *Educ:* Hamilton Col, AB, 33; Harvard Univ, MD, 37; Am Bd Pediat, dipl, 47; Am Bd Psychiat & Neurol, dipl, 50, cert child psychiat, 60. *Prof Exp:* Psychiat serv adv, US Children's Bur, 47-49; assoc prof pediat & psychiat, Univ Louisville, 49-55; from assoc prof to prof psychiat, Univ Calif, Los Angeles, 55-72; dep med dir, Am Psychiat Asn, 72-83. *Concurrent Pos:* Pres, Group Advan Psychiat, 80-84. *Mem:* Am Psychiat Asn; fel Am Orthopsychiat Asn; Am Pub Health Asn; Am Acad Pediat; Am Col Psychiat. *Res:* Identification of child with mother and other relatives. *Mailing Add:* 4986 Sentinel Dr Apt 504 7001 Glenbrook Rd Bethesda MD 20816

**WORK, JAMES LEROY,** POLYMER CHEMISTRY, PHYSICAL CHEMISTRY. *Current Pos:* Res scientist, 52-77, RES ASSOC, ARMSTRONG CORK CO, LANCASTER, 77- *Personal Data:* b Lancaster, Pa, Feb 6, 35; m 55; c 2. *Educ:* Franklin & Marshall Col, BA, 62; Univ Del, PhD(phys chem), 70. *Mem:* Am Chem Soc. *Res:* Structure-property relationships in polymers and polymeric composites. *Mailing Add:* 913 Sherry Lane Lancaster PA 17601

**WORK, ROBERT WYLLIE,** spider silk; deceased, see previous edition for last biography

**WORK, STEWART D,** ORGANIC CHEMISTRY. *Current Pos:* from asst prof to assoc prof, 64-73, PROF CHEM, EASTERN MICH UNIV, 73- *Personal Data:* b Chicago, Ill, Oct 17, 37; m 59; c 4. *Educ:* Oberlin Col, AB, 59; Duke Univ, PhD(org chem), 63. *Prof Exp:* Fel, Duke Univ, 63 & Purdue Univ, 63-64. *Concurrent Pos:* Spec asst, Provost, 85- *Mem:* Am Chem Soc; Sigma Xi. *Res:* Base-catalyzed condensation reactions; organo-silicon chemistry. *Mailing Add:* Chem-Eastern Mich Univ Ypsilanti MI 48197

**WORK, TELFORD HINDLEY,** biology, epidemiology; deceased, see previous edition for last biography

**WORK, WILLIAM JAMES,** POLYMER CHEMISTRY, ORGANIC CHEMISTRY. *Current Pos:* CHEMIST POLYMER CHEM, ROHM & HAAS CO, 76- *Personal Data:* b Carmel, Calif, Feb 23, 48; m 76. *Educ:* Univ Santa Clara, BS, 70; Univ Ill, PhD(org chem), 76. *Mem:* Am Chem Soc; AAAS. *Res:* Morphology of polymer blends and composites; synthesis of grafted polymers. *Mailing Add:* 1288 Burnett Rd Huntington Valley PA 19006-2706

**WORKER, GEORGE F, JR,** AGRONOMY, BOTANY. *Current Pos:* RETIRED. *Personal Data:* b Ordway, Colo, June 1, 23; m 47, Donna R Pinkerton; c Deborah (deceased), Kent, Stephanie, Cathy & Mindy. *Educ:* Colo State Univ, BS, 49; Univ Nebr, MS, 53. *Prof Exp:* Asst county agent, Nebr, 49-51, asst in agron, 53; specialist in agron & supt, IMP Valley Agr Ctr, Univ Calif, Davis, 53-87. *Concurrent Pos:* Consult, Kufra Agr Pro, Libya, 67-70, Hawaiian Agron, Iran, 75, N Yeman, 81 & Sahel Area Western Africa, 75. *Mem:* Am Soc Agron. *Res:* Grain sorghum production, plant function, breeding and adaption to desert climate; adaption of other field crops such as barley, sugar beets and flax to southwestern desert areas. *Mailing Add:* PO Box 546 Julian CA 92036

**WORKMAN, GARY LEE,** PHYSICAL CHEMISTRY, NONDESTRUCTIVE TESTING. *Current Pos:* DIR & SR RES SCIENTIST, UNIV ALA, HUNTSVILLE, 80- *Personal Data:* b Birmingham, Ala, Apr 21, 40; m 67, Carol Yavorsky; c Deborah (Jech). *Educ:* Col William & Mary, BS, 64; Univ Rochester, PhD(phys chem), 69. *Prof Exp:* Res fel chem, Ohio State Univ, 69-70; Nat Acad Sci res assoc, Marshall Space Flight Ctr, NASA, 70-72; dir, PBR Electronics, Inc, 72-76; prof sci technol, Athens State Col, 76-80. *Concurrent Pos:* Dir, Mat Proc Lab, 89- *Mem:* Am Phys Soc; Soc Advan Mat & Process Eng; Optical Soc Am; Sigma Xi; sr mem Inst Elec & Electronics Engrs; fel Am Soc Nondestructive Testing. *Res:* Systems interfacing; electrooptics applications; laser welding in space; microgravity materials processing; nondestructive evaluation; materials processing; robotics and industrial automation. *Mailing Add:* Univ Ala RI-A6 Huntsville AL 35899. *Fax:* 205-895-6970

**WORKMAN, JOHN PAUL,** RANGELAND ECONOMICS. *Current Pos:* From asst prof to assoc prof, 70-80, PROF RANGE ECON, UTAH STATE UNIV, 81- *Personal Data:* b Salem, Ore, Feb 18, 43; m 64, Lou J Clayton; c Jeff & Greg. *Educ:* Univ Wyo, BS, 65; Utah State Univ, MS, 67, PhD(range econ), 70. *Concurrent Pos:* Mem, Rangeland Mgt Comt, Nat Acad Sci; mem, Range Sci Panel, NSF; cert range mgt consult, 79- *Mem:* AAAS; Soc Range Mgt; Western Agr Econ Asn. *Res:* Economics of range utilization, range improvement and range livestock production. *Mailing Add:* 2777 N 1600 E North Logan UT 84321

**WORKMAN, MARCUS ORRIN,** INORGANIC CHEMISTRY. *Current Pos:* ASSOC PROF CHEM, THOMAS NELSON COMMUNITY COL, 75- *Personal Data:* b Canton, Ohio, Sept 20, 40. *Educ:* Manchester Col, BA, 62; Ohio State Univ, PhD(inorg chem), 66. *Prof Exp:* Teaching assoc chem, Ohio State Univ, 65-66; res assoc, Northwestern Univ, 66-67; asst prof chem, Univ Va, 67-74. *Concurrent Pos:* Adv Res Projs Agency fel, 66-67. *Mem:* Am Chem Soc. *Res:* Coordination complexes of transition metals with polydentate ligands; complexes with oxide and sulfoxide donor atoms; complexes of lanthanides and actinides. *Mailing Add:* Thomas Nelson Community Col Box 9407 Hampton VA 23670-0407

**WORKMAN, MILTON,** PLANT PHYSIOLOGY. *Current Pos:* RETIRED. *Personal Data:* b Chicago Heights, Ill, Oct 1, 20; m 49; c 6. *Educ:* Colo Agr & Mech Col, BS, 50; Univ Calif, PhD(plant physiol), 54. *Prof Exp:* Asst veg crops, Univ Calif, 50-54; from instr to assoc prof hort, Purdue Univ, 54-63; prof hort, Colo State Univ, 63-85. *Mem:* Fel Am Soc Hort Sci. *Res:* Pre and post harvest physiology. *Mailing Add:* 3033 Moore Lane Ft Collins CO 80526

**WORKMAN, RALPH BURNS,** ECONOMIC ENTOMOLOGY, VEGETABLE CROPS. *Current Pos:* RETIRED. *Personal Data:* b Omaha, Nebr, June 25, 24; m 51; c 4. *Educ:* Colo State Univ, BS, 51, MS, 52; Ore State Univ, PhD(entom), 58. *Prof Exp:* Res asst entom, Colo State Univ, 52-55; from asst entomologist to assoc entomologist, Agr Res Ctr, Univ Fla, 58-85. *Mem:* Entom Soc Am. *Res:* Economic entomology; biology and control of cruciferous and potato insects. *Mailing Add:* 30 Coquina Ave St Augustine FL 32084

**WORKMAN, WESLEY RAY,** ORGANIC CHEMISTRY. *Current Pos:* RETIRED. *Personal Data:* b Mich, Feb 1, 26; m 48; c 4. *Educ:* Mich State Univ, BS, 49, MS, 50; Univ Minn, PhD(org chem), 54. *Prof Exp:* Sr res chemist, 3M Co, 54-68, mgr photog sci & photo chem, 68-72, dir imaging, Res Div, 72-74, dir, Systs Res Lab, 74-78, dir univ rels, Cent Res Labs, 78-85. *Mem:* Am Chem Soc; Soc Photog Scientists & Engrs. *Res:* Photochemistry. *Mailing Add:* 100 W Moore Dr No 76 Pharr TX 78577

**WORKMAN, WILLIAM EDWARD,** ENVIRONMENTAL GEOLOGY. *Current Pos:* CONSULT GEOLOGIST, 79- *Personal Data:* b Richmond, Va, May 13, 41; m 59; c 2. *Educ:* Univ Va, BS, 62, MS, 64; Univ Tex, Austin, PhD(geol), 68. *Prof Exp:* Asst prof geol, Albion Col, 68-73; geoscientist, Palmer & Baker Engrs, Inc, 73-75; supvry environ geologist, US CEngr, Mobile, 75-79. *Concurrent Pos:* Sigma Xi-Sci Res Soc Am grants in aid of res, 63 & 66; geologist C, Va Div Mineral Resources, Charlottesville, 63-; consult, Palmer & Baker Engrs, Inc, 75-; environ consult to var pvt firms, 75- *Mem:* Sigma Xi. *Res:* Regional metamorphism in Llano Uplift, Texas; coastal erosion; engineering geology relative to coastal processes. *Mailing Add:* PO Box 745 Lillian AL 36549. *E-Mail:* drroc@gulftel.com

**WORKMAN, WILLIAM GLENN,** NATURAL RESOURCE ECONOMICS, ENVIRONMENTAL ECONOMICS. *Current Pos:* VIS PROF ECON, UTAH STATE, 96- *Personal Data:* b Sheridan, Wyo, Mar 19, 47; m 72, Jolene Jorgensen; c Ben & Emily. *Educ:* Univ Wyo, BS, 69; Utah State Univ, MA, 72, PhD(resource econ), 78. *Prof Exp:* Res asst econ, Utah State Univ, 69-72; from asst prof to assoc prof, Univ Alaska, 79-90; econ consult & adj prof, Eastern Ore State Col, 90-91, assoc prof econ, 92-96; vis prof agr econ, Ore State Univ, 91-92. *Concurrent Pos:* Assoc economist, Frank Orth & Assocs, Seattle, 80-82; vis assoc prof, Dept Agr & Resource Econ, Univ Md, 85-86. *Mem:* Asn Environ & Resource Econ. *Res:* Economic analysis of land use and public land use policy. *Mailing Add:* 2530 N 2050 E North Logan UT 84321

**WORLEY, DAVID EUGENE,** PARASITOLOGY, PUBLIC HEALTH & EPIDEMIOLOGY. *Current Pos:* from asst prof to assoc prof, 62-72, PROF, VET RES LAB, MONT STATE UNIV, 72- *Personal Data:* b Cadiz, Ohio, Aug 6, 29; m 68, Judith Jacobson; c Timothy & Mark. *Educ:* Col Wooster, AB, 51; Kans State Univ, MS, 55, PhD(parasitol), 58. *Prof Exp:* Assoc res parasitologist, Parke, Davis & Co, 58-62. *Concurrent Pos:* Consult, Brazil & Czech; pres, Rocky Mountain Conf Parasitol, 74-75. *Mem:* Am Soc Parasitol; Wildlife Dis Asn; Am Asn Vet Parasitol; World Asn Advan Vet Parasitol; Polish Acad Sci. *Res:* Zoology; helminthology, including chemotherapy of parasitic infections and helminth life cycles and host-parasite relationships; parasitic zoonoses, especially trichinosis and echinococcosis. *Mailing Add:* Vet Molecular Biol Lab Mont State Univ Bozeman MT 59717. *Fax:* 406-994-4303

**WORLEY, FRANK L, JR,** CHEMICAL ENGINEERING. *Current Pos:* from instr to assoc prof, 61-72, PROF CHEM ENG, UNIV HOUSTON, 72-, ASSOC DEAN ENG, 85- *Personal Data:* b Kansas City, Mo, Oct 9, 29; m 52; c 1. *Educ:* Univ Houston, BS, 52, MS, 59, PhD(chem eng), 65. *Prof Exp:* Chem engr, Nyotex Chem, Inc, 52-55 & Stauffer Chem Co, 55-57; instr chem eng, Univ Houston, 57-59; Fulbright lectr, Univ Guayaquil & Cent Univ Ecuador, 59-61. *Concurrent Pos:* Vis scientist, Div Meteorol, Environ Protection Agency, 71. *Mem:* Fel Am Inst Chem Engrs. *Res:* Modelling of atmospheric dispersion and reactions; air pollution control; computer aided design and analysis; process control. *Mailing Add:* Dept Chem Eng Culler Col Eng Univ Houston Houston TX 77204-4814

**WORLEY, JIMMY WELDON,** COMPETITIVE TECHNICAL INTELLIGENCE. *Current Pos:* sr res chemist, Monsanto Co, 71-75, res specialist, 75-78, res group leader, 78-80, sr res group leader, 80-82, res mgr, Pesticide Residues, 82-84, mgr, Res Process Environ, 84-87, mgr, Chem & Microbiol, 87-89, MGR, PROCESS TECHNOL, MONSANTO CO, ST LOUIS, 89- *Personal Data:* b Bowie, Tex, May 2, 44; m 66, Pam Wood; c Christine, Micah & Amanda. *Educ:* Midwestern State Univ, BS, 66; Univ Ill, Urbana-Champaign, PhD(org chem), 71. *Prof Exp:* Res assoc, Wesleyan Univ, 71. *Mem:* Am Chem Soc. *Res:* Process chemistry research and development to support manufacture of agricultural chemicals. *Mailing Add:* Monsanto Co 800 N Lindbergh Blvd St Louis MO 63167

**WORLEY, JOHN DAVID,** BIOPHYSICAL CHEMISTRY. *Current Pos:* asst prof, 70-77, ASSOC PROF CHEM, ST NORBERT COL, 78- *Personal Data:* b Texarkana, Tex, Dec 10, 38; m 63; c 4. *Educ:* Hendrix Col, BA, 60; Univ Okla, PhD(phys chem), 64. *Prof Exp:* NIH fel biophys chem, Northwestern Univ, 64-66; asst prof chem, Univ Cincinnati, 66-70. *Mem:* Am Chem Soc; Sigma Xi. *Res:* Protein structure and denaturation in solution; solutions of nonelectrolytes; hydrogen bonding. *Mailing Add:* Dept Nat Sci St Norbert Col De Pere WI 54115-2099

**WORLEY, RAY EDWARD,** HORTICULTURE, AGRONOMY. *Current Pos:* asst horticulturist, Ga Coastal Plain Exp Sta, 61-72, assoc horticulturist, 72-80, prof hort, 80-96, actg dept head, 85-87, EMER PROF HORT, GA COASTAL PLAIN EXP STA, 96- *Personal Data:* b Robbinsville, NC, May 4, 32; m 55, Billie J Adams; c David, Diane & Miriam. *Educ:* NC State Col, BS, 54, MS, 58; Va Polytech Inst, PhD(agron), 61. *Honors & Awards:* L M Ware Award, 81; Distinguished Res Award, Sigma Xi, 90; L M Ware Research Award, 92. *Prof Exp:* Asst field crops, NC State Col, 56-58; instr agron, Va Polytech Inst, 58-61. *Mem:* Am Soc Hort Sci. *Res:* Pecan tree nutrition, management and physiology; vegetable and forage nutrition and physiology. *Mailing Add:* Hort Dept Ga Coastal Plain Exp Sta Tifton GA 31794. *Fax:* 912-386-3373; *E-Mail:* rworley@tifton.cpes.peachnet.edu

**WORLEY, RICHARD DIXON,** PHYSICS. *Current Pos:* RETIRED. *Personal Data:* b Little Rock, Ark, Dec 24, 26; m 51; c 2. *Educ:* Hendrix Col, BS, 49; Univ Ark, MA, 51; Univ Chicago, MS, 60; Univ Calif, Berkeley, PhD(physics), 63. *Prof Exp:* Nuclear physicist, Wright-Patterson AFB, Ohio, 51-54; nuclear engr, Douglas Air Craft Co, Calif, 57-59; sr physicist, Lawrence Radiation Lab, Univ Calif, 63-70; Physicist Mason & Hanger, Pantex Plant, Silas Maspm Co, 70-81; prof physics, Dyersburg State Commun Col, 81-91. *Concurrent Pos:* Teacher, Memphis State Univ. *Mem:* Am Phys Soc. *Res:* Characteristic x-ray production by ion bombardment of both polycrystalline and single-crystal targets; atomic beams and the hyperfine interaction; high explosive research and development. *Mailing Add:* 606 Wisteria Dr Sunset Beach NC 28468

**WORLEY, ROBERT DUNKLE,** PHYSICS. *Current Pos:* RETIRED. *Personal Data:* b Trenton, NJ, Jan 24, 25; m 50; c 3. *Educ:* Williams Col, AB, 49; Columbia Univ, AM, 51, PhD, 55. *Prof Exp:* From asst to lectr, Columbia Univ, 50-54; mem staff, Bell Labs, Inc, 54-86, supvr, 60-86. *Mem:* Am Phys Soc; Acoust Soc Am. *Res:* Heat capacities of superconductors; sound transmission in the ocean; operations research; sonar systems. *Mailing Add:* 71 Galway Dr Mendham NJ 07945

**WORLEY, S D,** ORGANIC CHEMISTRY, SOLID STATE PHYSICS. *Current Pos:* from asst to assoc prof, 74-82, PROF ORG CHEM, AUBURN UNIV, 82- *Personal Data:* b Russellville, Ala, Jan 31, 42; m 64; c 2. *Educ:* Auburn Univ, BS, 64; Univ Tex, PhD(chem), 69. *Prof Exp:* Res chemist, Johnson Manned Spacecraft Ctr, 69-72; asst prof phys chem, Cleveland State Univ, 72-73; prog officer, Off Naval Res, 73-74. *Concurrent Pos:* Vis prof chem, Univ Wis, 75, Calif Inst Technol, 78; vis scientist, Nat Bur Standards, 76. *Mem:* Am Chem Soc; AAAS. *Res:* Spectroscopic studies of surfaces and catalysts; synthesis of new water disinfectants; molecular orbital calculations; photoelectron spectroscopy. *Mailing Add:* Dept Chem Auburn Univ Auburn AL 36849

**WORLEY, WILL J,** THEORETICAL MECHANICS, APPLIED MECHANICS. *Current Pos:* From instr to prof, 43-89, EMER PROF THEORET & APPL MECH, UNIV ILL, URBANA, 89- *Personal Data:* b Gibson City, Ill, Aug 2, 19; m 54, Carolyn Juergensmeyer; c James L, Thomas R & Fred B. *Educ:* Univ Ill, BS, 43, MS, 45, PhD, 52. *Concurrent Pos:* Consult, Magnavox Co, Ind, 56-58, Chris-Kaye Mfg Co, Ill, 57, Ill, 56-58, A O Smith Corp, Wis, 59 & attorneys, Ill, 59-; proj dir, Wright Air Develop Ctr Nonlinear Mech Proj, 59-61, NASA Proj, 63-67; consult, Int Bus Mach Corp, NY, 60-61 & 63-64, Calif, 61; chmn, Shock & Vibration Comt, Appl Mech Div, Am Soc Mech Engrs, 62-63, chmn, awards comt, Mach Design Div, 64-65; pres, Worley Systs Inc, 77-; vis fel, Inst Sound & Vibration Res, Univ Southampton, Eng, 79. *Mem:* Am Soc Mech Engrs. *Res:* Acoustical noise reduction; mechanical vibrations and nonlinear mechanics; static and dynamic behavior of plates and shells; optimum structural design; mechanical properties of materials; failure investigation of components and systems; systems approach to prevention and analysis of system failure. *Mailing Add:* 2106 Zuppke A3 Urbana IL 61801-6706

**WORLOCK, JOHN M,** SOLID STATE PHYSICS. *Current Pos:* RES PROF, UNIV UTAH, 92- *Personal Data:* b Kearney, Nebr, Feb 15, 31; div; c 2. *Educ:* Swarthmore Col, BA, 53; Cornell Univ, PhD(physics), 62. *Prof Exp:* NSF fel, 62-63; actg asst prof physics, Univ Calif, Berkeley, 63-64; mem tech staff, Bell Labs, Inc, 64-84; distinguished mem prof staff, Bellcore, 85-91. *Mem:* AAAS; Fedn Am Scientists; fel Am Phys Soc. *Res:* Lattice dynamics; transport and optical properties of non-metallic crystals; light scattering; phase transitions; electron-mole droplets; optical properties of semiconductors; heterostructures; superlattices; microstructures. *Mailing Add:* 1369 Gilmer Dr Salt Lake City UT 84105

**WORMAN, JAMES JOHN,** ORGANIC CHEMISTRY. *Current Pos:* VIS PROF, CHEM DEPT, DARTMOUTH COL, 88- *Personal Data:* b Allentown, Pa, Feb 17, 40; m 61; c 4. *Educ:* Moravian Col, BS, 61; NMex Highlands Univ, MS, 64; Univ Wyo, PhD, 68. *Prof Exp:* Instr chem, Moravian Col, 62-63; res asst, Univ Wyo, 65-67; from asst prof chem to prof, SDak State Univ, 67-88. *Mem:* Am Chem Soc; Royal Soc Chem. *Res:* Theoretical and experimental organic photochemistry, including syntheses and reaction of large ring nitrogen heterocycles. *Mailing Add:* Chem Dept Rochester Inst Technol Col Sci-85 Lomb Mem Dr Rochester NY 14623-5603

**WORMSER, ERIC M,** ENGINEERING PHYSICS. *Current Pos:* PRES, WORMSER SCI CORP, 76- *Personal Data:* b Ger, Apr 30, 21; nat US; m, Linda Birnbaum; c Peter & Thomas. *Educ:* Mass Inst Technol, BS, 42. *Prof Exp:* Test engr, Universal Camera Co, 42-45; physicist, Hillyer Instrument Co, 47-49 & Servo Corp Am, 49-52; chief engr, Barnes Eng Co, 52-58, vpres, 58-68, exec vpres, 68-76. *Concurrent Pos:* Managing trustee, Margot Wormser Found. *Mem:* Optical Soc Am; Inst Elec & Electronics Engrs; Instrument Soc Am; NY Acad Sci; fel Optical Soc Am; fel Can Aeronaut & Space Inst. *Res:* Infrared instruments, systems and detector development. *Mailing Add:* 66 Doral Farm Rd Stamford CT 06902. *Fax:* 203-322-6200

**WORMSER, GARY PAUL,** INFECTIOUS DISEASES, INTERNAL MEDICINE. *Current Pos:* CHIEF INFECTIOUS DIS, NY MED COL, 81-, PROF MED, 85- *Personal Data:* b Wilmington, Del, Jan 17, 47. *Educ:* Univ Pa, BA, 68; Johns Hopkins Univ, MD, 72. *Prof Exp:* Chief infectious dis, Bronx Vet Admin Hosp, 77-81. *Concurrent Pos:* Dir, Ctr Study & Treat AIDS & Lyme Dis Res Ctr, NY Med Col, 85- *Mem:* Am Fedn Clin Res. *Res:* AIDS-HIV infection; lyme disease; infection control. *Mailing Add:* 301 E 79th St New York NY 10021-0951

**WORMSER, HENRY C,** PHARMACEUTICAL CHEMISTRY. *Current Pos:* From asst prof to assoc prof, 65-76, PROF PHARMACEUT CHEM, WAYNE STATE UNIV, 76- *Personal Data:* b Strasbourg, France, Sept 10, 36; US citizen; m 63; c 2. *Educ:* Temple Univ, BSc, 59, MSc, 61; Univ Wis, PhD(pharmaceut chem), 65. *Mem:* Am Chem Soc; Am Pharmaceut Asn. *Res:* Synthesis of model compounds to be used in study of drug-enzyme or drug-receptor site interactions in an effort to determine specific mechanisms of drug activity. *Mailing Add:* Pharm Sci Wayne State Univ 528 Shapero Detroit MI 48202-3940

**WORMUTH, JOHN HAZEN,** BIOLOGICAL OCEANOGRAPHY. *Current Pos:* asst prof, 72-77, assoc prof, 77-, PROF, TEX A&M UNIV. *Personal Data:* b Cobleskill, NY, Dec 9, 44; m 67; c 2. *Educ:* Hope Col, BA, 66; Scripps Inst Oceanog, PhD(oceanog), 71. *Prof Exp:* Biol oceanogr, Intersea Res Corp, 71-72. *Mem:* Am Soc Limnol & Oceanog; Am Geophys Union. *Res:* Ecology and sampling problems associated with cephalopods; neuston communities; zooplankton ecology, particularly pteropods. *Mailing Add:* Dept Oceanog MS3146 Tex A&M Univ College Station TX 77843-3146

**WORNE, HOWARD E,** BIOTECHNOLOGY, MICROBIOLOGY. *Current Pos:* Pres, Worne Biochem, Inc, 72-83, Bioferm Int, 77-83, chmn bd, 72-82, PRES, WORNE BIOTECHNOL INC, 82- *Personal Data:* b Mar 1, 14; m 62, Phyllis Garafolo; c Elinor. *Educ:* Nat Univ Mex, BS, 38; Free Univ Mex, MD, 40; St Andrews Univ, PhD(biol), 57; Nat Polytech Inst, PhD(biochem), 62. *Concurrent Pos:* Pres, Nat Solvents Corp, 42-45, Pharmaceut Industs Inc, 55-62, Enzymes Inc, 62-72, Bioferm Int, 77-83, Phytochemica Ltd, Mont, 85-92; sci dir, Nat Inst Biochem, 43-45; vpres, Pentavir Div, A P DeSanna & Sons, 45-47; chmn, Dept Biochem, Robinson Found, 50-53; sci dir & bd dirs, Robinson Found, 53-55; res coun, Nat Fisheries Inst, 62-72; chmn bd, Enzymes Japan Inc, 69-76, Fermentation Industs Inc, 77-83, Waste-Energy Corp, 84- *Mem:* Fel Am Inst Chemists; Am Inst Biol Sci; Am Soc Microbiol; Soc Indust Microbiol; fel Am Col Bioanalysts; NY Acad Sci; Soc Cosmetic Chemists; Am Phytopath Soc; AAAS. *Res:* Petroleum microbiology; soil microbiology; industrial uses of microorganisms; introduction to microbial biotechnology; published over 150 articles and granted several patents. *Mailing Add:* Eastampton Bus Ctr 1507 US Rte 206 Mt Holly NJ 08060. *Fax:* 609-261-3111

**WOROCH, EUGENE LEO,** MEDICINAL CHEMISTRY. *Current Pos:* vpres, 88-93, DIR, CLARA ABBOTT FOUND, 88-, PRES & DIR, 93- *Personal Data:* b Kenosha, Wis, Mar 18, 22; m 49, Anna J Reppen; c Susan (Sanborn), Wendy (Barmore), Craig & Scott. *Educ:* Univ Wis, BS, 44, MS, 45, PhD(org chem), 48; Univ Chicago, MBA, 71. *Prof Exp:* Proj dir natural prod, Wis Alumni Res Found, 48-49; group leader & consult, Bjorksten Labs, 49; res assoc natural prod, Mayo Clin, 49-51; group leader, Glidden Co, 51-58; head dept org chem res, Abbott Labs, 58-75, dir, Div Antibiotic Res, 75-77, Div Sci Serv, 77-84, Div Chem & Anal Serv, 84-86. *Concurrent Pos:* Vpres & treas, Ill Sci Lect Asn, 80- *Mem:* Am Chem Soc; AAAS; Sigma Xi. *Res:* Natural products; steroids; antibiotics; peptides and structural chemistry. *Mailing Add:* 485 Greenvale Rd Lake Forest IL 60045

**WORONICK, CHARLES LOUIS,** BIOCHEMISTRY, BIOSTATISTICS. *Current Pos:* PRES, WORONICK CONSULT, INC, 95- *Personal Data:* b Meriden, Conn, Dec 4, 30. *Educ:* Univ Conn, BS, 53; Univ Calif, Berkeley, MS, 55; Univ Wis, PhD(biochem), 59. *Honors & Awards:* Joseph Susman Award, Infectious Dis Soc Am. *Prof Exp:* Asst prof chem, Brown Univ, 62-66; assoc non-clin investr path, Pa Hosp, 66-68; biochemist, Hartford Hosp, 68-92, res analyst, Off Res Admin, 92-94. *Concurrent Pos:* NSF fel, 59-61; fel enzyme chem, Nobel Med Inst, Stockholm, 59-62; Nat Cancer Inst fel, 61-62; assoc path, Med Sch, Univ Pa, 66-68; consult staff biochem, Hartford Hosp, 68-94; consult staff clin chem, John Dempsey Hosp, Conn, 75-94; asst prof labs med, Sch Med, Univ Conn, Farmington, 73-94; mem comn toxicol, Clin Chem Div, Subcomt Cholinesterases, Int Union Pure & Appl Chem, 76-81; assoc non-clinical investr, Pa Hosp, Philadelphia, 66-68. *Mem:* Am Asn Clin Chem; fel Nat Acad Clin Biochem. *Res:* Enzyme kinetics; equilibria and mechanisms; immunochemistry; leukocyte function; biostatistics. *Mailing Add:* 61 Lonsdale Ave Meriden CT 06450

**WORRALL, JAMES JOSEPH,** MYCOLOGY, FOREST PATHOLOGY. *Current Pos:* asst prof, 86-92, ASSOC PROF, COL ENVIRON SCI & FORESTRY, STATE UNIV NY, 92- *Personal Data:* b Bad Krevznach, WGer, June 5, 53; US citizen; m 82, Carol Roberts; c Jason W & Jeffrey A. *Educ:* Univ Alaska, Fairbanks, BS, 76; Univ Calif, Berkeley, MS, 78, PhD(plant path), 82. *Prof Exp:* Fel, Alexander von Humboldt Found, 83-85; assoc, Univ NH, 85-86. *Mem:* Am Phytopath Soc; Mycol Soc Am. *Res:* Root diseases of trees and the role of diseases and other agents in ecology of natural forests; types and mechanisms of wood decay. *Mailing Add:* Col Environ Sci & Forestry State Univ NY 320 Bray Hall Syracuse NY 13210-2723. *E-Mail:* jworrall@mailbox.syr.edu

**WORRALL, JOHN GATLAND,** DENDROLOGY. *Current Pos:* ASSOC PROF FORESTRY, UNIV BC, 68- *Personal Data:* b Cleethorpes, Eng, May 22, 38; Can citizen. *Educ:* Univ Durham, BSc, 59; Yale Univ, MF, 64, PhD(forestry), 69. *Mem:* Sigma Xi. *Res:* Environmental control of cambial activity; breakage of dormancy seeds and plants. *Mailing Add:* Fac Forestry 2357 Main Mall Vancouver BC V6T 1W5 Can

**WORRALL, RICHARD D,** CIVIL & TRANSPORTATION ENGINEERING. *Current Pos:* MGR, PEAT MARWICK MITCHELL & CO, 69- *Personal Data:* b Waterloo, Eng, May 31, 38; m 60; c 2. *Educ:* Durham Univ, BSc, 60; Northwestern Univ, MS, 61, PhD(civil eng), 66. *Prof Exp:* Asst traffic engr, City Planning Dept, Newcastle, Eng, 61-62; sr res fel city & transp planning, Lower Swansea Valley Proj, Univ Wales, 62-63; res assoc transp planning & traffic flow theory, Northwestern Univ, Evanston, 63-69. *Concurrent Pos:* Mem, Hwy Res Bd, Nat Acad Sci-Nat Res Coun, 63-, mem comts land use eval, freeway opers & origin-destination, 66- *Mem:* Am Soc Civil Engrs. *Res:* Transportation and city planning; traffic flow theory; transportation systems control. *Mailing Add:* 206 Carrwood Rd Great Falls VA 22066

**WORRALL, WINFIELD SCOTT,** ORGANIC CHEMISTRY. *Current Pos:* RETIRED. *Personal Data:* b Cheltenham, Pa, Jan 12, 21; m 49; c 2. *Educ:* Haverford Col, BS, 42; Harvard Univ, MA, 47, PhD(chem), 49. *Prof Exp:* Res chemist, Monsanto Chem Co, 50-54; from instr to assoc prof chem, Trinity Col, Conn, 54-64; assoc prof chem, State Univ NY Col Plattsburgh, 64-68, assoc prof gen sci studies, 68-77, prof, 78-83. *Res:* Steroids; heterocyclics. *Mailing Add:* 8 Logan Dr Shelburne VT 05482

**WORRELL, FRANCIS TOUSSAINT,** PHYSICS. *Current Pos:* RETIRED. *Personal Data:* b Hartford, Conn, Apr 19, 15; m 48, 72; c 2. *Educ:* Univ Mich, BSE, 36; Univ Pittsburgh, MS, 40, PhD(physics), 41. *Honors & Awards:* Fulbright lectr, Al-Hikma Univ Baghdad, 58-59. *Prof Exp:* Mem staff, Physicists Res Co, Mich, 36-37; asst, Univ Pittsburgh, 37-41; instr, Univ Tenn, 41-42; staff mem, Radiation Lab, Mass Inst Technol, 42-46; res assoc, Inst Metals, Univ Chicago, 46-47; asst prof physics, Rensselaer Polytech Inst, 47-55; assoc prof, DePauw Univ, 55-58; assoc prof, Beloit Col, 59-60; staff mem, Lincoln Lab, Mass Inst Technol, 60-63; prof physics, Univ Lowell, 63-80. *Concurrent Pos:* Vis lectr, Univ Bristol, 72-73 & Mass Maritime Acad, 81. *Res:* Design of experiments; structure of materials; thermionic emission; atmospheric optics. *Mailing Add:* 11 Old Salt Lane Yarmouth Port MA 02675-1234

**WORRELL, JAY H,** PHYSICAL INORGANIC CHEMISTRY, CHEMICAL ENGINEERING. *Current Pos:* from asst to assoc prof, 67-78, PROF CHEM, UNIV SFLA, TAMPA, 78-, DIR, CTR GEN CHEM, 89- *Personal Data:* b Manchester, NH, July 14, 38; m 59, Louise Bowen; c Steven, Cherylann & Carolyn. *Educ:* Univ NH, BS, 61, MS, 63; Ohio State Univ, PhD(inorg chem), 66. *Prof Exp:* Res assoc chem, State Univ NY Stony Brook, 66-67. *Concurrent Pos:* Indust consult; mem bd dirs & ed secy, Inorganic Syntheses Inc; Summer Inst High Sch Teachers; steering comt excellence in math, sci, computer & technol, Univ SFla. *Mem:* Am Chem Soc; Am Inst Chem Engrs. *Res:* Preparation, properties and theory of coordination compounds; stereochemistry and inorganic reaction kinetics for ligand substitution and oxidation reduction processes; applied industrial chemistry; chemical engineering. *Mailing Add:* Dept Chem Univ SFla Tampa FL 33620. *E-Mail:* worrell@chuma.ca.usf.edu

**WORRELL, JOHN MAYS, JR,** MATHEMATICS, MEDICINE. *Current Pos:* PROF MATH, OHIO UNIV, 72-, DIR INST MED & MATH, 75- *Personal Data:* b El Paso, Tex, Oct 3, 33; m 66; c 1. *Educ:* Univ Tex, BA, 54, MD, 57, PhD(math), 61. *Prof Exp:* Intern med, Denver Gen Hosp, Colo, 57-58; instr math, Univ Tex, 58-59; NSF fel, 61-62; mem tech staff math res, Sandia Corp, NMex, 62-72. *Concurrent Pos:* Consult clin med & biomed sci. *Mem:* Am Math Soc; AMA. *Res:* Problems having topological character; clinical medicine; biological processes. *Mailing Add:* 1908 W Wall Midland TX 79701

**WORRELL, WAYNE L,** ELECTRICAL CERAMICS, SENSOR MATERIALS. *Current Pos:* from asst prof to assoc prof, 65-74, PROF MAT SCI, UNIV PA, 74-, ASSOC DEAN, 86- *Personal Data:* b Rock Island, Ill, Oct 25, 37; m 68; c 2. *Educ:* Mass Inst Technol, BS, 59, PhD(metall), 63. *Hon Degrees:* MA, Univ Pa, 71. *Honors & Awards:* Outstanding Achievement Award High Temperature Mat, Electrochem Soc, 88, Carl Wagner Mem Award, 89. *Prof Exp:* Fel metall, Univ Calif, Berkeley, 63-64, lectr, 64-65. *Concurrent Pos:* Chmn comt high temp sci & technol, Nat Acad Sci-Nat Res Coun, 74-77; consult to indust & govt orgns; vis prof, Dept Chem, Univ Calif, Berkeley, 75-76; ed, Prog Solid State Chem, 77-86; mem chem eng, Div Rev Comt, Argonne Nat Lab, 79-86; Japan Soc Prom Sci lect fel, 82; Max Planck Soc fel, Stuttgart, Fed Repub Ger, 82-83. *Mem:* Electrochem Soc; fel Am Soc metals Int; fel Am Ceramic Soc; Am Inst Mining, Metall & Petrol Engrs; Sigma Xi. *Res:* Ceramic sensors; ceramic coatings; corrosion at elevated temperatures; high-temperature materials chemistry; solid state electrochemistry; electrical ceramics. *Mailing Add:* Eng-Univ Pa 3231 Walnut St Philadelphia PA 19104

**WORSHAM, ARCH DOUGLAS,** WEED SCIENCE, ALLELOPATHY. *Current Pos:* From exten asst prof to exten assoc prof, 60-67, assoc prof, 67-69, PROF CROP SCI, NC STATE UNIV, 69- *Personal Data:* b Culloden, Ga, Feb 22, 33; m 56, 82; c 5. *Educ:* Univ Ga, BSA, 55, MS, 57; NC State Univ, PhD(crop sci), 61. *Honors & Awards:* Outstanding Publ Award, Weed Sci Soc Am, 75. *Concurrent Pos:* Res grants, 66-; consult, 67-; ed, S Weed Sci Soc, 69-71, 87-89, vpres, 91. *Mem:* Weed Sci Soc Am; Am Soc Agron; Am Soc Plant Physiologists; Sigma Xi; Int Soc Chem Ecol. *Res:* Pesticides; crop science; weed science; weed biology basic and applied weed science research in agronomic crops and non-tillage crop production and biology and control of specific weeds; weed suppression through allelopathy. *Mailing Add:* Dept Crop Sci Campus Box 7620 Raleigh NC 27645-7620

**WORSHAM, LESA MARIE SPACEK,** PROTEIN ISOLATION CHARACTERIZATION. *Current Pos:* RES ASSOC BIOCHEM, QUILLEN-DISHNER COL MED, E TENN STATE UNIV, 79- *Personal Data:* b Sellersville, Pa, Dec 4, 50; m 73, Paul; c Rebecca & Emily. *Educ:* Ursinus Col, BS, 72; Univ NC Chapel Hill, PhD(chem), 77. *Prof Exp:* Consult atmospheric chem, Res Triangle Inst, 77-78. *Mem:* Am Chem Soc; Sigma Xi; AAAS. *Res:* Subcloning, expression and isolation of hemolysin proteins from ecoli. *Mailing Add:* 415 Autumn Knoll Ct Kingsport TN 37664-5457

**WORSHAM, WALTER CASTINE,** TEXTILE CHEMISTRY. *Current Pos:* vpres & gen mgr, 79-89, PRES, ETHOX CHEM, INC, 89- *Personal Data:* b Turbeville, SC, Aug 17, 38; m 59, Carolyn Wall; c Walter S & Miriam M. *Educ:* Col Charleston, BS, 61; Univ NC, PhD(phys chem), 66. *Prof Exp:*

Chemist, Fiber Industs, Inc, 66-67; chemist, Emery Industs, Inc, Mauldin, 67-75, tech mgr, 75-79. *Mem:* Am Chem Soc; Am Asn Textile Chemists & Colorists. *Res:* Kinetics of photochemical reactions; chemistry of textile processing. *Mailing Add:* PO Box 5094 Sta B Ethox Chem Inc Greenville SC 29606

**WORSLEY, THOMAS R,** MARINE GEOLOGY, BIOSTRATIGRAPHY. *Current Pos:* PROF GEOL, OHIO UNIV, 76- *Personal Data:* b Brooklyn, NY, June 1, 42. *Educ:* City Col New York, BS, 65; Univ Tenn, MS, 67; Univ Ill, PhD(geol), 70. *Prof Exp:* Res prof oceanog, Univ Wash, 70-77. *Concurrent Pos:* NSF grant, 73-75, 75-77 & 77- *Mem:* Soc Econ Paleont & Mineralog. *Res:* Computer application in marine micropaleontology; erosion-sedimentation of the globe. *Mailing Add:* Dept Geol 316 Clippinger Labs Ohio Univ Main Campus Athens OH 45701-2979

**WORSTELL, HAIRSTON G(EORGE),** MECHANICAL ENGINEERING. *Current Pos:* RETIRED. *Personal Data:* b West Plains, Mo, Jan 5, 20; m 44, Betty J Holmes; c Mark H (deceased). *Educ:* Univ Okla, BSME, 50. *Prof Exp:* Design engr, Boeing Aircraft Co, Kans, 50-51; staff engr, Sandia Corp, NMex, 51-53; proj engr, Phillips Petrol Co, Okla, 53-59; staff engr, Los Alamos Sci Lab, 59-66, asst group leader mech eng, 66-67, assoc group leader, 67-72, alt group leader, 72-77, consult, 77-86. *Mem:* Am Vacuum Soc. *Res:* Mechanical design and supervision of fellow engineers in development of large ultra high vacuum linear accelerator systems employing unusual fabrication and metallurgical techniques. *Mailing Add:* 207 McDougal Belen NM 87002

**WORT, ARTHUR JOHN,** microbiology, medicine, for more information see previous edition

**WORTH, DONALD CALHOUN,** SOLAR ENERGY APPLICATIONS, SCIENCE EDUCATION. *Current Pos:* RETIRED. *Personal Data:* b Brooklyn, NY, Oct 20, 23; m 46; c 4. *Educ:* Carnegie Inst Technol, BS, 44; Yale Univ, MS, 48, PhD(physics), 49. *Prof Exp:* Instr physics, Berea Col, 50-52, assoc prof, 52-53; from asst prof to assoc prof, Int Christian Univ, Tokyo, 54-60, dean, Col Liberal Arts, 70-74 & 76-80, prof physics, 60-89. *Concurrent Pos:* Vis asst prof, Ala Polytech Inst, 51; vis assoc prof, Univ Chicago, 53-54; NSF fel, Univ Va, 58-59; vis prof, Univ Wis, 63-64 & State Univ NY Stony Brook, 68-69; vis researcher, Lawrence Berkeley Nat Lab, Univ Calif, 81-82, 86-87. *Mem:* Am Solar Energy Soc. *Res:* Low energy nuclear polarization studies, especially in nucleon-nucleon scattering; physics education; solar energy utilization. *Mailing Add:* 401 Stannage Ave Apt 10 Albany CA 94706-1243

**WORTH, ROBERT MCALPINE,** EPIDEMIOLOGY. *Current Pos:* RETIRED. *Personal Data:* b Kiangsi Prov, China, Aug 27, 24; US citizen; m 51; c 2. *Educ:* Univ Calif, Berkeley, BA, 50, PhD(epidemiol), 62; Univ Calif, San Francisco, MD, 54; Harvard Univ, MPH, 58. *Prof Exp:* Intern med, Southern Pac Hosp, San Francisco, 54-55; resident family pract, San Mateo Community Hosp, 55-56; physician leprosy, Hawaii Dept Health, 56-57, asst chief chronic dis, 57, health officer, 58-60; prof epidemiol, Sch Pub Health, Univ Hawaii, Manoa, 65-85; chief scientist, Agent Orange Progs, Ctr Dis Control, Atlanta, 86-88; chief, Div Commun Dis Control, Dept Health, Hawaii, 88-92. *Concurrent Pos:* Hooper Found res fel, Univ Hong Kong, 61-63. *Mem:* Am Pub Health Asn. *Res:* Leprosy epidemiology and control; disease survey methodology; automation medical record systems for epidemiologic and quality control purposes; public health in modern China. *Mailing Add:* 1747 Iwi Way Honolulu HI 96816

**WORTH, ROY EUGENE,** FUNCTIONAL ANALYSIS, COMPUTER PROGRAMMING. *Current Pos:* asst prof, 68-71, ASSOC PROF MATH, GA STATE UNIV, 71- *Personal Data:* b Broxton, Ga, Mar 24, 38; m 65; c 1. *Educ:* Univ Ga, BS, 60, MA, 62, PhD(math), 68. *Prof Exp:* Asst prof math, WGa Col, 63-68. *Mem:* Math Asn Am. *Res:* Henstock integral. *Mailing Add:* 1399 Vista Leaf Dr Decatur GA 30033

**WORTHEN, HOWARD GEORGE,** pediatrics, biochemistry, for more information see previous edition

**WORTHEN, LEONARD ROBERT,** MICROBIOLOGY. *Current Pos:* asst prof pharm, Univ RI, 57-63, assoc prof pharmacog, 63-70, prof, 70-90, assoc dean, 84-90, DIR ENVIRON HEALTH SCI PROG, UNIV RI, 72-, EMER PROF PHARMACOG & ASSOC DEAN, 90- *Personal Data:* b Woburn, Mass, Dec 28, 25; m 55, M Elizabeth Shumway; c Diane, Lawrence & David. *Educ:* Mass Col Pharm, BS, 50; Temple Univ, MS, 52; Univ Mass, PhD(bact), 57. *Prof Exp:* Instr pharmacol, Sch Nursing, Holyoke Hosp, 55-57. *Mem:* Am Asn Cols Pharm; Am Pharmaceut Asn; Am Soc Pharmacog; Sigma Xi. *Res:* Fungal metabolites, particularly antibiotics and other metabolites of medicinal importance; natural products from marine sources. *Mailing Add:* 145 Kenyon Ave Kingston RI 02879-4243

**WORTHEN, WADE BOLTON,** COMMUNITY ECOLOGY, BIODIVERSITY. *Current Pos:* Asst prof, 88-94, ASSOC PROF BIOL, FURMAN UNIV, 94- *Personal Data:* b Bristol, Pa, Apr 30, 60; m 85, Sharon A Boeglin; c 2. *Educ:* Bucknell Univ, BS, 82; Rutgers Univ, MS, 85, PhD(ecol), 88. *Mem:* Ecol Soc Am; Am Soc Naturalists; Soc Study Evolution; Int Asn Ecol. *Res:* Effects of competition, predation and microenvironment on the structure and diversity of mycophagous fly communities; use of mycophagous fly model systems to study determinants of biodiversity patterns. *Mailing Add:* Dept Biol Furman Univ 3300 Poinsett Hwy Greenville SC 29613-0001. *Fax:* 864-294-2085; *E-Mail:* worthen_wade/furman@furman.edu

**WORTHING, JURGEN,** ENERGY CONSERVATION BY PUBLIC UTILITIES. *Current Pos:* PRES, WORTHING ENTERPRISES, 68- *Personal Data:* b Brooklyn, NY, Aug 11, 24; m 49; c 2. *Educ:* Polytech Inst Brooklyn, BEE, 48. *Prof Exp:* Staff engr, Servomechanisms, Inc, 48-55; staff engr, Repub Aviation Corp, 55; dir eng & sr vpres, Trio Labs, Inc, NY, 55-68; tech dir, NY State Legis Comn Energy Systs, 75-78; tech coun, NY State Energy Comt, 78-84. *Mem:* Sr mem Inst Elec & Electronics Engrs. *Res:* Cable television; medical instrumentation; energy legislation, its effects on production, distribution and use of energy, and socio-economic effects; microcomputer applications. *Mailing Add:* 75 Weaving Lane Wantagh NY 11793

**WORTHINGTON, CHARLES ROY,** BIOPHYSICS. *Current Pos:* prof chem & physics, 69-72, PROF PHYSICS & BIOL, MELLON COL SCI, CARNEGIE-MELLON UNIV, 72- *Personal Data:* b Penola, Australia, May 17, 25; m 59; c 3. *Educ:* Univ Adelaide, PhD(physics), 55. *Prof Exp:* Res assoc crystallog, Polytech Inst Brooklyn, 55-57; staff mem biophys, Biophys Res Unit, Med Res Coun, King's Col, Univ London, 58-61; from asst prof to assoc prof physics, Univ Mich, Ann Arbor, 61-69. *Concurrent Pos:* Consult, Nat Bur Stand, DC, 57-58; Sir Thomas Lyle fel, Univ Melbourne, Australia, 67-68; prof physics, Oxford Res Univ, Open Univ, 87-88 & 93-94, hon res assoc, 92- *Mem:* Biophys Soc; Am Crystallog Asn. *Res:* Membrane structure; molecular organization of biological systems and theories of biological mechanisms; x-ray biophysics and microscopy. *Mailing Add:* Mellon Col Sci Carnegie-Mellon Univ 4400 Fifth Ave Pittsburgh PA 15213

**WORTHINGTON, JAMES BRIAN,** ANALYTICAL CHEMISTRY. *Current Pos:* Res chemist, Diamond Shamrock Corp, 70-72, group leader environ analysis, 72-75, mgr environ analysis & comput serv, 75-76, mgr sci servs, 76-77, dir environ affairs, 77-84, MGR TECHNOL, DIAMOND SHAMROCK CORP, 84- *Personal Data:* b Sandwich, Ill, Nov 29, 43; m 65; c 1. *Educ:* Augustana Col, BA, 65; Purdue Univ, Lafayette, PhD(analytical chem) 70. *Honors & Awards:* Am Inst Chemists Award. *Mem:* Am Chem Soc. *Res:* Kinetic methods of analysis; design of chemical instrumentation; real time computer automation; environmental related analyses. *Mailing Add:* 313 Carmel Valley Way Edmond OK 73003

**WORTHINGTON, JOHN WILBUR,** ELECTRICAL ENGINEERING. *Current Pos:* RETIRED. *Personal Data:* b Lexington, Ky, June 13, 18; m 43; c 2. *Educ:* Univ Ky, BSEE, 49. *Prof Exp:* Tech adv, Tech Training Command, Scott AFB, US Dept Air Force, Ill, 49-51; engr, Wright-Patterson AFB, 51-52, elec engr, Griffis AFB, 52-58, supv elec engr, Ground Elec Eng Installation Agency, 58-60, dep div chief, 60, proj elec engr, Rome Air Develop Ctr, 60-62; elec engr, opers res off, Defense Commun Agency, 62-74, elec engr, Defense Commun Eng Ctr, 74-85. *Mem:* Sr mem Inst Elec & Electronics Engrs. *Res:* Operations research; war gaming; simulation; systems engineering; systems survivability/endurability. *Mailing Add:* 8416 Doyle Dr Alexandria VA 22308

**WORTHINGTON, RICHARD DANE,** MORPHOLOGY, HERPETOLOGY. *Current Pos:* asst prof biol, 69-74, ASSOC PROF BIOL SCI, UNIV TEX, EL PASO, 74- *Personal Data:* b Houston, Tex, Sept 20, 41; m 64. *Educ:* Univ Tex, Austin, BA, 63; Univ Md, MS, 66, PhD(zool), 68. *Prof Exp:* USPHS trainee, Univ Chicago, 68-69. *Mem:* Soc Syst Zool; Soc Study Evolution; Ecol Soc Am; Am Soc Ichthyologists & Herpetologists; Soc Study Amphibians & Reptiles; Am Soc Plant Taxonomists. *Res:* Evolutionary biology of caudate amphibians; mountain floras of the southwest United States; evolutionary morphology; lizard ecology; ecology; floras. *Mailing Add:* Dept Biol Sci Univ Tex 500 W University Ave El Paso TX 79968-8900

**WORTHINGTON, ROBERT EARL,** LIPID CHEMISTRY, FOOD SCIENCE. *Current Pos:* asst prof, 64-76, ASSOC PROF FOOD SCI, GA STA, UNIV GA, 76- *Personal Data:* b Kingston, Ga, Jan 2, 29; m 60; c 3. *Educ:* Berry Col, BSA, 52; NC State Col, MS, 55; Iowa State Univ, PhD(biochem), 62. *Prof Exp:* Res instr agr & biol chem, NC State Col, 55-56; assoc biochem & biophys, Iowa State Univ, 56-61, asst prof animal sci, 61-64. *Mem:* AAAS; Am Chem Soc; Am Oil Chem Soc. *Res:* Lipid chemistry of foods. *Mailing Add:* 979 McDonough Rd Hampton GA 30228-1527

**WORTHINGTON, RONALD EDWARD,** PHARMACOLOGY, CELL BIOLOGY. *Current Pos:* postdoctoral, 82-84, RES SCIENTIST, G D SEARLE, 90- *Personal Data:* b St Louis, Mo, Mar 23, 52; m, Mary J Baird; c Sarah & Megan. *Educ:* Wash Univ, AB, 74, PhD(cell biol), 82. *Prof Exp:* Res assoc, Tex Tech Univ, Health Sci Ctr, 84-86; asst prof, Univ Tenn Med Ctr, Knoxville, 86-90. *Mem:* Am Soc Hemat. *Res:* Cardiovascular drug discovery. *Mailing Add:* Edit Dept Mosby Inc 11830 Westline Dr St Louis MO 63146. *Fax:* 314-694-7517; *E-Mail:* rewort@ccmail.monsanto.com

**WORTHINGTON, THOMAS KIMBER,** LOW TEMPERATURE PHYSICS. *Current Pos:* FEL PHYSICS, RUTGERS UNIV, 75- *Personal Data:* b New York, NY, Aug 4, 47. *Educ:* Franklin & Marshall Col, BA, 69; Wesleyan Univ, PhD(physics), 75. *Mem:* Am Inst Physics; Am Phys Soc. *Res:* Specific heat and thermal conductivity of granular aluminum films; magnetics. *Mailing Add:* 233 Naalae Rd Kula HI 96790

**WORTHINGTON, WARD CURTIS, JR,** MEDICAL HISTORY, MEDICAL SCHOOL ADMINISTRATION. *Current Pos:* from asst prof to prof anat, Med Univ SC, 57-91, from asst dean to assoc dean, 66-77 & 82-91, actg vpres, 75-77, vpres acad affairs, 77-82, emer prof anat, 91, DIR HIST LIBR, MED UNIV SC, 82-, PROF HIST HEALTH SCI, 87- *Personal Data:* b Savannah, Ga, Aug 8, 25; m 47, Floride McDermid; c Ward Curtis III & Amy Lynn. *Educ:* The Citadel, BS, 52; Med Col SC, MD, 52. *Prof Exp:* Intern surg, Boston City Hosp, Mass, 52-53; instr anat, Sch Med, Johns Hopkins Univ, 53-56; asst prof, Col Med, Univ Ill, 56-57. *Concurrent Pos:* NIH spec fel, Dept Human Anat, Oxford Univ, 64-65; chmn, Asn Anat, 69-77, secy-treas & pres, 71-76. *Mem:* AAAS; Am Asn Anat; Endocrine Soc; Am Physiol Soc; Am Asn Hist Med. *Res:* Medical history, anatomy and physiology of pituitary circulation; histology; neuroendocrinology. *Mailing Add:* Waring Hist Libr Med Univ SC 171 Ashley Ave Charleston SC 29425-2201

**WORTHMAN, ROBERT PAUL,** veterinary anatomy, for more information see previous edition

**WORTHY, GRAHAM ANTHONY JAMES,** MARINE MAMMALS. *Current Pos:* asst prof physiol, ecol marine mammals, 90-93, ASSOC PROF, TEX A&M UNIV, GALVESTON, 93- *Personal Data:* b Bournemouth, Eng, Sept 13, 56; Can citizen; div; c Colin. *Educ:* Univ Guelph, BSc, 79, MSc, 82, PhD(environ physiol), 85. *Prof Exp:* Postdoctoral researcher, Univ Calif, Santa Cruz, 87-90. *Concurrent Pos:* Lectr, Univ Calif, Santa Cruz, 87-90. *Mem:* Soc Marine Mammal; Am Soc Mammalogists; Int Asn Aquatic Animal Med; Comp Nutrit Soc. *Res:* Physiological ecology of marine mammals through the study of their energetics growth and nutrition of both captive and wild animals to define; appropriate criteria for care of captive marine mammals. *Mailing Add:* Tex A&M Univ Bldg 303 4700 Ave U Galveston TX 77551. *Fax:* 409-740-4717; *E-Mail:* worthyg@tamug.tamu.edu

**WORTIS, MICHAEL,** THEORETICAL PHYSICS, SOLID STATE PHYSICS & BIOPHYSICS. *Current Pos:* PROF PHYSICS, SIMON FRASER UNIV, 87- *Personal Data:* b New York, NY, Sept 28, 36; US and Can citizen; m 64, Ruth Emerson; c Naomi & Rachel. *Educ:* Harvard Univ, BA, 58, MA, 59, PhD(physics), 63. *Honors & Awards:* Fulbright-Hays Lectr, Pakistan, 78, Morocco 86,. *Prof Exp:* Miller fel physics, Univ Calif, Berkeley, 62-64; NSF fel, Fac Sci, Univ Paris, 64-65; vis prof, Pakistan AEC, WPakistan, 65; res asst prof, Univ Ill, Urbana, 66, from asst prof to prof physics, 66-89. *Concurrent Pos:* A P Sloan Found fel, Univ Ill, Urbana, 67-69; Ford Found consult, Univ Islamabad, WPakistan, 71. *Mem:* Fel Am Phys Soc. *Res:* Statistical physics; magnetic phenomena; phase transitions; phase transitions and related phenomena in strongly coupled and complex systems; surface and interface phenomena; biomembranes; complex fluids. *Mailing Add:* Dept Physics Simon Fraser Univ Burnaby BC V5A 1S6 CAN. *Fax:* 604-291-3592; *E-Mail:* wortis@sfu.ca

**WORTMAN, BERNARD,** BIOCHEMISTRY. *Current Pos:* CONSULT, TECHREVIEW, 84- *Personal Data:* b Brooklyn, NY, Apr 23, 24; m 52; c 3. *Educ:* Syracuse Univ, AB, 48; Univ Tex, MA, 51; Ohio State Univ, PhD(physiol), 55. *Prof Exp:* From res asst to res asst prof ophthal, Sch Med, Wash Univ, 55-65; res assoc prof, Albany Med Col, 65-66; res chemist, Food & Drug Admin, Wash, DC, 66-69; scientist adminr, Nat Eye Inst, 69-80; sci adminr, Nat Inst Aging, 80-82; vis prof, Col Optom, Univ Calif, 82-83; spec asst, Nat Inst Arthritis, Metabolic & Kidney Dis, 83-84; sr staff consult, Fedn Am Socs Exp Biol, 84-87. *Concurrent Pos:* NIH spec fel, 60-61; estab investr, Am Heart Asn, 61-65; vis scientist, Am Physiol Soc, 63; consult to lab serv, Vet Admin Hosp, Albany, 65-66; res assoc prof, Med Sch, George Washington Univ, 67-70. *Mem:* Am Physiol Soc; Soc Gen Physiol. *Res:* Cell physiology; general metabolism of cornea; biosynthesis of sulfated mucopolysaccharides in cornea; biochemistry of connective tissue; macromolecular biochemistry. *Mailing Add:* 6407 Tone Dr Bethesda MD 20817-5815

**WORTMAN, JIMMIE J(ACK),** SOLID STATE PHYSICS, ELECTRONICS. *Current Pos:* PROF, NC STATE UNIV, 80- *Personal Data:* b NC, Feb 23, 36; m 84; c 2. *Educ:* NC State Univ, BS, 60; Duke Univ, MS, 62, PhD(elec eng), 65. *Prof Exp:* Mem tech staff, Bell Tel Labs, 60-62; res engr, Res Triangle Inst, 62-68, mgr, Eng Physics Dept, 68-72, dir, Eng Div, 72-75, dir, Energy & Environ Res Div, 75-80. *Concurrent Pos:* Asst prof, Exten Div, NC State Univ, 62-63, adj prof, 74, prof, 80-85; lectr, Duke Univ, 64-70. *Mem:* Inst Elec & Electronics Engrs; Mat Res Soc; Electrochem Soc. *Res:* Microelectronics, semiconductor device theory and fabrication; thin film phenomena; integrated circuits. *Mailing Add:* Dept Elec & Comput Eng NC State Univ Box 7911 Raleigh NC 27695

**WORTON, RONALD GILBERT,** MEDICAL GENETICS-MUSCULAR DYSTROPHY, HUMAN GENOME PROJECT. *Current Pos:* DIR RES, OTTAWA GEN HOSP, 96- *Personal Data:* m 66, Helen Dixon; c Scott R. *Educ:* Univ Manitoba, BSc, 64, MSc, 65; Univ Toronto, PhD(med biophysics), 69. *Hon Degrees:* Doctorate Honoris Causa, Catholique Univ De Louvain, Belgium, 91. *Honors & Awards:* Gairdner Found Int Award, Gairdner Found, 89; Award Distinction, Muscular Dystrophy Asn, 89; E Mead Johnson Award for Res in Pediats, Pediat Res Soc Am, 91; UK Can Rutherford Lectr, Royal Soc, London, 93. *Prof Exp:* Ass prof to assoc prof, Univ Toronto, 73-84; scientist, Res Inst, Hosp Sick Children, 71-85, geneticist-in-chief, 85-96. *Concurrent Pos:* Prof molecular & med genetics, Univ Toronto, 84-; assoc dir, Can Genetic Dis Network, 90-; head, Can Genome Proj, 92-; vpres, Human Genome Orgn, 93- *Mem:* Genetics Soc Can; Can Col Med Geneticists; Am Soc Human Genetics; Human Genome Orgn (vpres, 93-); fel Royal Soc Can. *Res:* The gene responsible for duchenne muscular dystrophy; the gene's expression and regulation; the protein product and mutations causing the disease; vectors and delivery systems for gene therapy applied to muscle disease. *Mailing Add:* Ottawa Gen Hosp 501 Smyth Rd Ottawa ON K1H 8L6 Can. *Fax:* 416-813-4931

**WORTS, GEORGE FRANK, JR,** GEOLOGY, HYDROGEOLOGY. *Current Pos:* RETIRED. *Personal Data:* b Toledo, Ohio, Apr 24, 16; m 50, Betty Stevens; c 1. *Educ:* Stanford Univ, BS, 39. *Prof Exp:* Geologist, Ground Water Br, US Geol Surv, 40-50, geologist in charge, Long Beach, 52-56, dist geologist, Sacramento, 56-58, br area chief, Pac Coast Area, 58-62, dist chief, Nev, 62-74, part-time, 74-89. *Concurrent Pos:* Water res eval, Azores, Guyana, Philippines, Guam, Israel, Egypt, SKorea & Somalia. *Mem:* Fel Geol Soc Am; Am Geophys Union; Asn Eng Geol. *Res:* National and international hydrology, especially of arid regions; ground-water resources, particularly quantitative analysis, water quality, coastal hydrology and water management; direction of complex hydrologic studies and applied research. *Mailing Add:* 163 Tahoe Dr Carson City NV 89703

**WORZALA, F(RANK) JOHN,** NUCLEAR METALLURGY. *Current Pos:* assoc prof nuclear mat, 67-77, PROF ENG METALL & MINING ENG, UNIV WIS-MADISON, 77- *Personal Data:* b Milwaukee, Wis, Nov 13, 33; m 54; c 9. *Educ:* Univ Wis, BS, 56, MS, 58; Carnegie Inst Technol, MS, 62, PhD(metall eng), 65. *Prof Exp:* Engr, Hanford Labs, Gen Elec Co, Wash, 56-57; engr, Bettis Atomic Power Lab, Westinghouse Elec Corp, 58-65, res scientist, 66-67; NSF fel & res scientist, Grenoble Nuclear Res Ctr, France, 65-66. *Mem:* Am Nuclear Soc; Am Inst Mining, Metall & Petrol Engrs; Am Soc Metals. *Res:* Nuclear materials; irradiation damage in metals; fracture mechanics; applied superconductivity and superconducting materials. *Mailing Add:* 2115 Van Hise Ave Madison WI 53705

**WORZEL, JOHN LAMAR,** geophysics, oceanography, for more information see previous edition

**WOSILAIT, WALTER DANIEL,** PHARMACOLOGY, BIOCHEMISTRY. *Current Pos:* from assoc prof to prof, 65-89, EMER PROF PHARMACOL, SCH MED, UNIV MO-COLUMBIA, 89- *Personal Data:* b Racine, Wis, Feb 4, 24; m 48; c 1. *Educ:* Wabash Col, BA, 49; Johns Hopkins Univ, PhD(biol), 53. *Prof Exp:* Jr instr pharmacol, Western Reserve Univ, 53-56; asst prof, State Univ NY Downstate Med Ctr, 56-63, assoc prof, 63-65. *Concurrent Pos:* USPHS res grant, State Univ NY Downstate Med Ctr, 56-65; USPHS res grant, Sch Med, Univ Mo-Columbia, 65- *Mem:* Am Soc Biol Chemists; Am Soc Pharmacol & Exp Therapeut; Harvey Soc. *Res:* Anticoagulant drug interactions; pharmacokinetics; computer simulations of drug interactions; mathematical modeling of human fetal growth. *Mailing Add:* 2307 Ridgemont Dr Columbia MO 65203-1541

**WOSINSKI, JOHN FRANCIS,** MATERIAL SCIENCE, MINERALOGY. *Current Pos:* mineralogist glass, Corning Glass Works, 58-60, supvr petrog, 61-64, supvr refractories, 65-67, mgr refractories, 67-82, PROJ MGR REFRACTORIES, CORNING GLASS WORKS, 82- *Personal Data:* b North Tonawanda, NY, Dec 30, 30; m 56, Jean A Smith; c John S & Wesley W. *Educ:* Denison Univ, BS, 53; Brown Univ, MS, 58. *Prof Exp:* Geologist mapping, US Geol Surv, 56-57. *Concurrent Pos:* Prin investr Apollo 14-15 mission samples, NASA, 71-72; chmn Refractories Div, Am Ceramic Soc, 78-79; chmn, C-8 Div, Am Soc Testing & Mat, 82-87; consult glass refractory appln, Corning Eng. *Mem:* Geol Soc Am; Sigma Xi; fel Am Ceramic Soc; fel Am Soc Testing & Mat; Soc Glass Technol. *Res:* Develop, test, evaluate and recommend refractory materials used in corporate glass melting endeavors; glass-refractory manufacturing problems and archaeological excavations; develop, issue and monitor corporate refractory material specifications for glass melting. *Mailing Add:* Corning Glass Works HP ME E-5 Corning NY 14831-0001. *Fax:* 607-974-8079

**WOSKE, HARRY MAX,** INTERNAL MEDICINE, CARDIOLOGY. *Current Pos:* assoc dean, 74, prof med & chief med serv, 73-76, CLIN PROF MED, NJ-RUTGERS MED SCH, 77-, ACTG DEAN, 75-; CHIEF CARDIOL, HUNTERDON MED CTR, NJ, 77- *Personal Data:* b Reading, Pa, Feb 26, 24; m 72; c 7. *Educ:* Columbia Univ, AB, 45; Long Island Col Med, MD, 48. *Prof Exp:* Instr med, Sch Med, Univ Pa, 55-57, assoc, 57-64, from adj asst prof to adj assoc prof, 64-69, assoc prof med & assoc dean, 69-73. *Concurrent Pos:* NIH fel cardiol, Sch Med, Univ Pa, 55-57. *Mem:* Fel Am Col Physicians; fel Am Col Cardiol; fel NY Acad Sci. *Res:* Exercise projects. *Mailing Add:* Hunterdon Card Assoc 1100 Wescott Dr Suite 305 Flemington NJ 08822-4605

**WOSKOV, PAUL PETER,** PLASMA DIAGNOSTICS, PROCESS DIAGNOSTICS. *Current Pos:* staff scientist lasers & plasma diag, Francis Bitter Nat Magnet Lab, 76-80, proj leader plasma diag develop, 80-93, PRIN RES ENGR & GROUP LEADER, PLASMA FUSION CTR, MASS INST TECHNOL, 93-, ASSOC DIV HEAD, 94- *Personal Data:* b Montour Falls, NY, Apr 23, 50; m 76, Constance Golba; c Peter & Stephen. *Educ:* Rensselaer Polytech Inst, BS, 72, MS, 74, PhD(electrophysics), 76. *Prof Exp:* Res asst lasers, Rensselaer Polytech Inst, 72-75, asst electromagnetics, 75-76. *Concurrent Pos:* Consult, Xsirius Superconductivity, Inc, 89-94; chmn, 8th Topical Conf High Temperature Plasma Diag, 90. *Mem:* Am Phys Soc; AAAS; Inst Elec & Electronics Engrs. *Res:* Plasma diagnostics of controlled fusion plasmas; development of infrared to millimeter-wave technologies; application of millimeter/submillimeter-wave technologies to process diagnostics; diagnostics for environmental waste remediation processes. *Mailing Add:* Bldg NW16-110 Mass Inst Technol Cambridge MA 02139. *Fax:* 617-253-0700; *E-Mail:* ppw@psfc.mit.edu

**WOSTER, PATRICK MICHAEL,** COMPUTER ASSISTED DRUG DESIGN ANTITRYPANOSOMAL AGENTS. *Current Pos:* lectr, 88-89, ASST PROF MED CHEM, WAYNE STATE UNIV, 89- *Personal Data:* b Omaha, Nebr, Jan 5, 55; m 84, Patricia Karmazin; c Matthew L. *Educ:* Univ Nebr, BS, 78, PhD(med chem), 86. *Prof Exp:* Assoc chem, Rensselaer Polytech Inst, 86; assoc med chem, Univ Mich, 87. *Mem:* Am Chem Soc; Am Asn Cols Pharm. *Res:* Synthesis and biological evaluation of novel, rationally designed enzyme inhibitors as potential therapeutic agents. *Mailing Add:* 539 Shapero Hall Wayne State Univ Detroit MI 48202

**WOSTMANN, BERNARD STEPHAN,** BIOCHEMISTRY, NUTRITION. *Current Pos:* from asst prof to assoc prof, 55-65, PROF, 65-, EMER PROF BIOL SCI, UNIV NOTRE DAME, 87- *Personal Data:* b Amsterdam, Neth, Nov 6, 18; US citizen; m 46; c 5. *Educ:* Univ Amsterdam, BS, 40, MS, 45, DSc, 48. *Prof Exp:* Instr org chem, Univ Amsterdam, 43, instr biochem, 45-48, lectr, 48-50, sci off, 48-55. *Concurrent Pos:* Asst dir, Neth Inst Nutrit, 48-55; Rockefeller res fel, 50-51. *Mem:* AAAS; Am Inst Nutrit; Soc Exp Biol & Med; Asn Gnotobiotics (pres, 66-68); NY Acad Sci. *Res:* Biochemical background of host-contaminant relationship; role of intestinal flora in physiology and nutrition. *Mailing Add:* Dept Biol Sci Lobund Lab Univ Notre Dame Notre Dame IN 46556

**WOTHERSPOON, NEIL,** PHYSICAL CHEMISTRY, INSTRUMENTATION. *Current Pos:* ASST PROF ELECTRO-MECH TECH, CITY TECH COL, CITY UNIV NEW YORK, 86- *Personal Data:* b New York, NY, Oct 24, 30; m 54, Penelope; c Stella. *Educ:* Polytech Inst Brooklyn, BS, 52, PhD, 57; NY Univ, MBA, 82. *Prof Exp:* Res scientist, Radiation & Solid State Lab, NY Univ, 57-68; asst prof biophys & bioeng, Mt Sinai Sch Med, 68-76; sr scientist, Technicon Instruments Corp, 76-85; sr physicist, Dept Health, Bur Radiation Control, NY, 87-91. *Concurrent Pos:* Res scientist, Polytech Univ, Brooklyn, NY. *Mem:* Am Chem Soc; Asn Comput Mach; Inst Elec & Electronics Engrs; Sigma Xi; Am Asn Aerosol Sci. *Res:* Instrumentation for physics, chemistry and biomedical sciences, including optical electronic and computer techniques for automated analysis; analog and digital data acquisition, interfacing and processing. *Mailing Add:* PO Box 021657 Brooklyn NY 11202-1657. *E-Mail:* wothersp@photon.poly. edu

**WOTIZ, HERBERT HENRY,** endocrine biochemistry, for more information see previous edition

**WOTIZ, JOHN HENRY,** HISTORY OF CHEMISTRY. *Current Pos:* chmn dept, 67-69, prof, 67-90, EMER PROF CHEM, SOUTHERN ILL UNIV, 90- *Personal Data:* b Moravska Ostrava, Czech, Apr 12, 19; nat US; m 45, Kathryn Erdody; c Anita, Karen & Vivian. *Educ:* Furman Univ, BS, 41; Univ Richmond, MS, 43; Ohio State Univ, PhD(org chem), 48. *Honors & Awards:* Dexter Award, 82. *Prof Exp:* Asst chem, Univ Richmond, 41-43 & Ohio State Univ, 43-44 & 46-47; from instr to assoc prof, Univ Pittsburgh, 48-57; prof chem & chmn dept, Marshall Univ, 62-67. *Concurrent Pos:* At Fed Security Agency, 44; Nat Acad Sci exchange prof, numerous Far East & Europ Socialist Countries, 69-74; mem, Int Activ Comt, Am Chem Soc, 75-; vis prof & lectr, Japan, 84; pres, Glenview Press, Carbondale, Ill. *Mem:* Hist Sci Soc; Am Chem Soc. *Res:* Propargylic rearrangement; radical ions from vicinal diamines; institutional research in eastern socialist southeast Asian and Pacific Ocean countries; history of chemistry; kekule fictitiou dreams. *Mailing Add:* 903 Glenview Dr Carbondale IL 62901. *Fax:* 618-453-6408

**WOTT, JOHN ARTHUR,** HORTICULTURE, BOTANICAL GARDEN & ARBORETA. *Current Pos:* PROF URBAN HORT, UNIV WASH, SEATTLE, 81-, ASSOC DIR, CTR URBAN HORT, 90-, DIR ARBRETA, WASH PARK ARBORETUM, 93- *Personal Data:* b Fremont, Ohio, Apr 10, 39; m 59; c Christopher P, Timothy E & Holly M. *Educ:* Ohio State Univ, BS, 61; Cornell Univ, MS, 66, PhD(hort), 68. *Prof Exp:* Instr, Coop Exten Serv, Ohio State Univ, 61-64; res asst hort, Cornell Univ, 64-68; from asst prof to assoc prof hort, Purdue Univ, West Lafayette, 68-78, prof 78-81. *Concurrent Pos:* Co exten agent 4-H, Wood Co, Bowling Green, Ohio, 61-64; mem, Home Hort Working Group, Am Soc Hort Sci, 69-85, chmn, 82, chmn, Ornamental & Turf Working Group, 84; mem, Int Plant Propagation, Eastern Region, 70-79, Int pres, 84, int secy treas, 86-; mem, Prod Rev Comt, Am Hort Soc, 79-80. *Mem:* Am Soc Hort Sci; Am Hort Soc; Int Plant Propagators Soc; Am Asn Bot Gardens & Arboreta; Sigma Xi. *Res:* Nutrition of cuttings during propagation; horticultural problems of homeowners, such as foliage plants, annuals and perennials; herbicides in annual flowers; adaptation and use of plants in the urban environment; botanical garden management and curation. *Mailing Add:* Wash Park Arboretum Box 358010 Univ Wash Seattle WA 98195-8010. *Fax:* 206-325-8893

**WOTZAK, GREGORY PAUL,** CHEMICAL ENGINEERING. *Current Pos:* DEAN BUS, REGENTS COL, 90- *Personal Data:* b New York, NY, Dec 12, 44; m 68; c 1. *Educ:* Rensselaer Polytech Inst, BChE, 65; Princeton Univ, MS, 67, PhD(chem eng), 68. *Prof Exp:* From asst prof to assoc prof chem eng, Rensselaer Polytech Inst, 68-77, prof, 77-80; mem fac chem eng, Cleveland State Univ, 80-90. *Mem:* Am Inst Chem Engrs. *Res:* Chemical reaction engineering; stochastic simulation; transport phenomena; chemical physics. *Mailing Add:* 2005 Inwood Terr Schenectady NY 12303

**WOUK, ARTHUR,** MATHEMATICS. *Current Pos:* RETIRED. *Personal Data:* b New York, NY, Mar 25, 24; m 44; c 2. *Educ:* City Col New York, BS, 43; Johns Hopkins Univ, MA, 47, PhD(math), 51. *Prof Exp:* Instr math, Johns Hopkins Univ, 47-50 & Queens Col, NY, 50-52; mathematician, Proj Cyclone, Reeves Instrument Corp, 52-54; supvr, Math Analysis Sect, Missile Systs Lab, Sylvania Elec Prod, Inc, 54-56, sr eng specialist, Appl Res Lab, Sylvania Electronic Systs Div, Gen Tel & Electronics Corp, 56-62; vis prof, Math Res Ctr, Univ Wis, 62-63; from assoc prof to prof appl math, Northwestern Univ, Evanston, 63-72; chmn dept, Univ Alta, 72-77, prof comput sci, 72-83; mathematician, Army Res Off, Triangle Park, NC, 83-89. *Concurrent Pos:* Ed, Commun, Asn Comput Mach, 58-64; consult, Appl Res Lab, Sylvania Electronic Systs Div, Gen Tel & Electronics Corp & Argonne Nat Lab, 63-69; ed, Soc Indust & Appl Math Rev, 63-83. *Mem:* Am Math Soc; Soc Indust & Appl Math; Asn Comput Mach. *Res:* Numerical and functional analysis. *Mailing Add:* 3849 Birchwood Dr Boulder CO 80304-1428

**WOUK, VICTOR,** HIGH POWER ELECTRONICS, ELECTRIC & HYBRID VEHICLES. *Current Pos:* PRES, VICTOR WOUK ASSOCS, 76- *Personal Data:* b New York, NY, Apr 27, 19; m 41; c 2. *Educ:* Columbia Univ, BA, 39; Calif Inst Technol, MS, 40, PhD(elec eng), 42. *Prof Exp:* Res engr, Res Labs, Westinghouse Elec Corp, 42-45; circuit engr, NAm Philips Co, NY, 45-47; pres & chief engr, Beta Elec Corp, 47-57; vpres eng & res, Sorenson & Co, Inc, 57-60; pres, Electronic Energy Conversion Corp, 60-63; gen mgr electronic energy conversion dept, Gulton Industs, Inc, NY, 63-68; dir electronics res, 68-70; pres, Petro-elec Motors, Ltd, 70-76; Consult, E & HVs, 76- *Concurrent Pos:* US rep tech comt elec rd vehicles, Int Electrotech Comn, 69; consult, Dept Energy, 76-81; vpres bd gov, NY Acad Sci; mem gov bd, Metrol Sect, Soc Automotive Engrs, 81- *Mem:* Fel AAAS; Soc Automotive Engrs; Inst Elec & Electronics Engrs; Fedn Am Sci; fel NY Acad Sci (vpres); Sigma Xi. *Res:* Static electricity generation by gasoline; television amplifier and sweep circuits; high voltage power supplies; regulated alternating and direct current power supplies; electronic controls for electric vehicles; electric and hybrid vehicles. *Mailing Add:* 1225 Park Ave New York NY 10128-1758. *Fax:* 914-666-2188

**WOURMS, JOHN P,** CELL BIOLOGY, DEVELOPMENTAL BIOLOGY. *Current Pos:* assoc prof, 77-82, PROF BIOL SCI, CLEMSON UNIV, 82- *Personal Data:* b New York, NY, Apr 30, 37; m 72, Deborah R Deane; c Nicholas S. *Educ:* Fordham Univ, BS, 58, MS, 60; Stanford Univ, PhD(biol), 66. *Prof Exp:* Am Cancer Soc fel, Harvard Univ, 66-68; Nat Res Coun Can grant & asst prof cell develop biol, Dept Biol, McGill Univ, 68-71, res assoc, Dept Path, 71-72; assoc res scientist, NY Ocean Sci Lab, 72-76. *Concurrent Pos:* Vis lectr, Biol Labs, Harvard Univ, 71-72; assoc ed, J Exp Zool, 79-83, Environ Biol Fisheries, 84-, J Morphol, 91-, Acta Zoologica, 97-; prin investr, NSF Grant, 82-84, 87-89, 90-93 & 95-; Guggenheim fel, 84-85; vis prof, Univ Colo, 84-85 & Univ Calif, Santa Cruz, 85; chief scientist, Nat Oceanic & Atmospheric Admin Deep Submersible Dives, 87, 88 & 90. *Mem:* Am Soc Cell Biol; Am Soc Ichthyologists & Herpetologists; Soc Develop Biol; Int Soc Develop Biologists; Marine Biol Asn UK; Am Soc Zoologists. *Res:* Cell differentiation; cell ultrastructure; reproduction and development of fishes and marine invertebrates; oogenesis; ultrastructure and chemistry of extra-cellular matrices; biology of annual fishes; evolution of development; elasmobranch biology; maternal-fetal relationship in viviparous fishes. *Mailing Add:* Dept Biol Sci Clemson Univ Clemson SC 29634-1903. *Fax:* 864-656-0435

**WOVCHA, MERLE G,** BIOCHEMISTRY. *Current Pos:* res scientist, 74-77, sr res scientist, 77-81, SR SCIENTIST, FERMENTATION RES & DEVELOP, UPJOHN CO, 81- *Personal Data:* b Virginia, Minn, Dec 19, 38. *Educ:* Univ Minn, BA, 62, BS, 64, MS, 67, PhD(biochem), 71. *Prof Exp:* NIH fel, Dept Biol Chem, Univ Mich, 71-74. *Mem:* Am Soc Microbiol. *Res:* Microbial sterol bioconversions; streptomycete metabolism and replication; bacteriophage biochemistry. *Mailing Add:* 130 S Prairie Ave Kalamazoo MI 49006-4441

**WOYCHIK, JOHN HENRY,** BIOCHEMISTRY, PHYSIOLOGY. *Current Pos:* RETIRED. *Personal Data:* b Scranton, Pa, Mar 30, 30; m 53; c 2. *Educ:* Univ Scranton, BS, 53; Univ Tenn, MS, 55, PhD(biochem), 57. *Prof Exp:* Chemist, Northern Regional Lab, USDA, 57-63, prin chemist, Eastern Mkt & Res Div, 63-74, chief, Dairy Lab, Eastern Regional Res Ctr, 74-97. *Mem:* Am Chem Soc; Am Dairy Sci Asn; Am Soc Biol Chemists; Inst Food Technologists. *Res:* Isolation and characterization of milk and cereal proteins; glycoproteins; basic research on milk components and dairy product development. *Mailing Add:* USDA Eastern Regional Res Ctr 600 E Mermaid Lane Philadelphia PA 19118

**WOYCHIK, RICHARD P,** MOLECULAR BIOLOGY, BACTERIOLOGY. *Current Pos:* RES SCIENTIST, OAK RIDGE NAT LAB, 87- *Personal Data:* b Arcadia, Wis, Oct 28, 52. *Educ:* Univ Wis-Madison, BS, 77; Case Western Reserve Univ, PhD(molecular biol), 84. *Prof Exp:* Postdoctoral, Harvard Med Sch, 84-87. *Mem:* AAAS; Am Soc Microbiol; Fedn Am Socs Exp Biol. *Res:* Molecular analysis of developmental genes in mice utilizing DNA probes derived from transgenic mice. *Mailing Add:* Biol Div Oak Ridge Nat Lab PO Box 2009 Oak Ridge TN 37831. *Fax:* 423-574-0793; *E-Mail:* woychik@ biovx1.bio.ornl.gov

**WOYCZYNSKI, WOJBOR ANDRZEJ,** MATHEMATICS. *Current Pos:* prof & chmn, Dept Math & Statist, 82-91, DIR, CTR STOCHASTIC & CHAOTIC PROCESSES SCI & TECHNOL, CASE WESTERN RES UNIV, 89- *Personal Data:* b Czestochowa, Poland, Oct 24, 43; m, Elizabeth W Holbrook; c Martin W & Gregory H. *Educ:* Wroclaw Polytech, Poland, MSEE, 66, PhD(math), 68. *Prof Exp:* Asst prof, Inst Math, Wroclaw Univ, 68-72, assoc prof, 72-77; prof, Dept Math, Cleveland State Univ, 77-82. *Concurrent Pos:* Res fel, Inst Math, Polish Acad Sci, Warsaw, 69-76; fel Carnegie-Mellon Univ, 70-72; res grants, NSF, 70, 71, 76, 77, 81 & 87-, Off Naval Res, 85-; vis prof, Aarhus Univ, Denmark, 72, Univ Paris, 73, Univ Wis-Madison, 76, Univ SC, 79, Univ NC, Chapel Hill, 83-84, Gottingen Univ, Ger, 85 & 91, Univ NSW, 88 & Nagoya Univ, Japan, 92 & 93; Vis assoc prof, Northwestern Univ, 76-77; assoc ed, Chemometrics J, 87-, Probability & Math Statist, 88-, Annals Appl Probability, 89- & Stochastic Processes &

Their Applns, 93- *Mem:* Fel Inst Math Statist; Am Math Soc; Am Statist Asn; Polish Math Soc; Polish Inst Arts & Sci. *Res:* Stochastic and chaotic processes; stochastic analysis; statistical physics; stochastic partial differential equations. *Mailing Add:* Dept Math Case Western Res Univ Cleveland OH 44106-7058

**WOYSKI, MARGARET SKILLMAN,** GEOLOGY. *Current Pos:* RETIRED. *Personal Data:* b W Chester, Pa, July 26, 21; m 48, Mark; c Nancy E, William B, Ronald D & Wendelin J. *Educ:* Wellesley Col, BA, 43; Univ Minn, MS, 45, PhD(geol), 46. *Prof Exp:* Instr geol, Univ Minn, 46; geologist, Mo Geol Surv, 46-48; instr geol, Univ Wis, 48-52; lectr, Calif State Col, Long Beach, 63-67; from asst prof to prof geol, Calif State Univ, Fullerton, 67-91, chmn earth sci, 73-76, assoc dean natural sci & math, 81-91. *Mem:* Mineral Soc Am; fel Geol Soc Am. *Res:* Intrusive rocks of central Minnesota; Precambrian sediments of Missouri; laboratory manuals for historical and physical geology; geologic guidebooks of Southern California; source locations of artifacts; petrology of peninsular range batholith. *Mailing Add:* 1843 Kashlan La Habra CA 90631

**WOZAB, DAVID HYRUM,** LIMESTONE HYDROLOGY, IRRIGATION DEVELOPMENT. *Current Pos:* Proj mgr, Food & Agr Orgn, UN, Rome, Italy, 61-80, rep, Tanzania, 80-83, rep, Jamaica & Bahamas, 83-86. *Personal Data:* b Los Angeles, Calif, April 17, 23; m 56; c 1. *Educ:* Univ Southern Calif, BA, 50, MA, 52. *Concurrent Pos:* Consult, World Bank & Jamaican Govt, 87-88, Food & Agr Orgn, UN, 86. *Mem:* fel Geol Soc Am; Am Geophy Union; AAAS; Am Water Works Asn; Nat Water Well Asn; Asn Eng Geol. *Res:* Flow of water in karatified limestone. *Mailing Add:* 8360 SW 97th St Miami FL 33156

**WOZENCRAFT, JOHN MCREYNOLDS,** ELECTRICAL ENGINEERING, COMMUNICATIONS. *Personal Data:* b Dallas, Tex, Sept 30, 25; m 63, Frances P Trask; c John, Colin & Katherine. *Educ:* US Mil Acad, BS, 46; Mass Inst Technol, SM & EE, 51, ScD, 57. *Prof Exp:* Asst elec eng, Mass Inst Technol, 55-57, from asst prof to prof, 57-72, head commun div, Lincoln Lab, 69-72, prof, 74-77; dean res, Naval Postgrad Sch, 72-74, prof elec eng, 77-86. *Mem:* Fel Inst Elec & Electronics Engrs. *Res:* Application of information theory to practical communication problems; algorithmic languages for digital computation. *Mailing Add:* 18160 Cottonwood 108 Sunriver OR 97707

**WOZNIAK, TIMOTHY JAMES,** ANALYTICAL CHEMISTRY. *Current Pos:* sr anal chemist, 87-92, res scientist, 92-95, SR RES SCIENTIST, ELI LILLY & CO, 95- *Personal Data:* b Cleveland, Ohio, May 23, 56; m 85, Janice E Hartman; c Andrew T & Katherine A. *Educ:* Col Wooster, BS, 78; Ind Univ, PhD(anal chem), 84. *Prof Exp:* Res fel, Nat Res Coun-Nat Inst Stand & Technol, 84-85; sr analytical chemist, Merrell Dow Pharmaceut, 85-87. *Concurrent Pos:* Adj prof chem, Butler Univ, 86-; US Patent Comt Rev, 95- *Mem:* Am Asn Pharmaceut Scientists; Asn Off Anal Chemists; Am Chem Soc. *Res:* Investigation of chiral separation mechanisms and application of chiral analysis techniques to the characterization of pharmaceuticals. *Mailing Add:* Lilly Corp Ctr Drop Code 3822 Indianapolis IN 46285. *Fax:* 317-277-5519; *E-Mail:* wozniak@lilly.com

**WOZNIAK, WAYNE THEODORE,** COLOR ANALYSIS. *Current Pos:* res assoc biophys, Am Dent Asn, 75-78, head, Physics Lab, 78-79, lab dir, 79-80, asst secy, 80-89, asst dir, Coun Dent Mat, Instruments & Equip, 89-93, DIR, EVALS CRITERIA, COUN SCIENTIFIC AFFAIRS, AM DENT ASN, 93- *Personal Data:* b Chicago, Ill, Oct 13, 45; m 71, Susan Chester; c Justin, Ethan & Darren. *Educ:* Ill Benedictine Col, BS, 67; Fla State Univ, PhD(phys inorg chem), 71. *Prof Exp:* Res assoc phys chem, Princeton Univ, 71-73; res assoc chem physics, Univ Ill, 73-75. *Concurrent Pos:* Instr, Univ Ill, 74. *Mem:* Am Chem Soc; Int Asn Dent Res; Soc Appl Spec. *Res:* Spectroscopy of dental materials and calcified tissue; color analysis; applications of vibrational spectroscopy to biological systems. *Mailing Add:* Am Dent Asn 211 E Chicago Ave Chicago IL 60611

**WRAIGHT, COLIN ALLEN,** BIOPHYSICS. *Current Pos:* asst prof, 75-81, ASSOC PROF BIOPHYS & BOT, UNIV ILL, URBANA-CHAMPAIGN, 81- *Personal Data:* b London, Eng, Nov 27, 45. *Educ:* Univ Bristol, BSc, 67, PhD(biochem), 71. *Prof Exp:* Fel biophys, State Univ Leiden, 71-72; assoc, Cornell Univ, 72-74; asst prof biol, Univ Calif, Santa Barbara, 74-75. *Mem:* Biophys Soc; AAAS; Am Soc Photobiol. *Res:* Membrane functions and mechanisms of electron and ion transport in biological energy conservation. *Mailing Add:* Dept Plant Biol Univ Ill 161 PABL 1201 W Gregory Dr 190 ERM L Urbana IL 61801. *Fax:* 217-244-1336; *E-Mail:* cawps@vmdcso.uiuc.edu

**WRANGHAM, RICHARD WALTER,** PRIMATE BEHAVIOR, EVOLUTIONARY ECOLOGY. *Current Pos:* PROF ANTHROP, HARVARD UNIV, 89- *Personal Data:* b Leeds, Eng, Nov 8, 48; m 80, Elizabeth Ross; c Ross G, David W & Ian A. *Educ:* Oxford Univ, BA, 70; Cambridge Univ, PhD(zool), 75. *Honors & Awards:* Rivers Medal, Royal Anthrop Inst, 93. *Prof Exp:* From asst prof to assoc prof, Univ Mich, 81-89. *Mem:* Am Acad Arts & Sci. *Res:* Use primate field studies to understand adaptive significance of social relationships and thereby reconstruct hominoid behavioral evolution. *Mailing Add:* Peabody Mus Harvard Univ Cambridge MA 02138-3800. *E-Mail:* wrangham@husc4.harvard.edu

**WRASIDLO, WOLFGANG JOHANN,** polymer chemistry, for more information see previous edition

**WRATHALL, DONALD PRIOR,** PHYSICAL CHEMISTRY. *Current Pos:* EASTMAN GELATINE CORP, 87- *Personal Data:* b Pittsburgh, Pa, Mar 9, 36; m 62; c 4. *Educ:* Brigham Young Univ, BA, 64, PhD(phys chem), 68. *Prof Exp:* NIH fel, Yale Univ, 67-68; sr res chemist, Eastman Kodak Co, 68-87. *Res:* Thermodynamics of reactions at solid-liquid interfaces and with macromolecules in solution. *Mailing Add:* 27 Washington St Peabody MA 01960

**WRATHALL, JAY W,** INORGANIC CHEMISTRY. *Current Pos:* assoc prof, Church Col Hawaii, 69-73, prof & div chmn, 74-85, PROF PHYS SCI, BRIGHAM YOUNG UNIV, HAWAII CAMPUS, 77-, CHMN 74- *Personal Data:* b Salt Lake City, Utah, May 12, 33; m 69; c 7. *Educ:* Brigham Young Univ, BS, 57, MS, 59; Ohio State Univ, PhD(inorg chem), 62. *Prof Exp:* Asst prof chem, Univ Calif, Berkeley, 62-64 & Univ Hawaii, 64-69. *Mem:* Am Chem Soc. *Res:* Coordination chemistry; reactions of coordinated ligands; biological activity of transition metal complexes. *Mailing Add:* Dept Phys Sci Brigham Young Univ Hawaii Campus Laie HI 96762-1295

**WRATHALL, JEAN REW,** GENETICS, CELL BIOLOGY. *Current Pos:* res assoc, 74-75, ASST PROF ANAT, MED COL, GEORGETOWN UNIV, 75- *Personal Data:* b Brooklyn, NY, Dec 3, 42; m 60; c 2. *Educ:* Univ Utah, BS, 64, PhD(genetics, molecular biol), 69. *Prof Exp:* Asst prof biol, State Univ NY Col Geneseo, 69-70; from instr to asst prof genetics, Med Col, Cornell Univ, 70-74. *Concurrent Pos:* Damon Runyon Mem Fund fel, Cornell Univ, 71- *Mem:* AAAS; Soc Develop Biol; Soc Cell Biologists; Tissue Cult Asn; Soc Neurosci. *Res:* Control of differentiated function in eukaryotic cells in culture; abnormal functions in malignant cells in culture; 5-bromodeoxyuridine suppression of melanin synthesis and tumorigenicity of melanoma cells. *Mailing Add:* Dept Anat Georgetown Univ Sch Med 3900 Reservoir NW Washington DC 20007-2187

**WRATHER, JAMES ALLEN,** EFFECT OF TILLAGE ON CROP DISEASES, DEVELOP DISEASE RESISTANT VARIETIES. *Current Pos:* Asst prof, 80-86, ASSOC PROF PLANT PATH, UNIV MO, 86- *Personal Data:* b Cape Girardeau, Mo, Nov 10,48; m 74, Brenda Jones; c Jim & Julie. *Educ:* Cent Methodist Col, BA, 70; Purdue Univ, MS, 72; Univ Mo, PhD(plant path), 79. *Honors & Awards:* Distinguished Serv Award, Southern Soybean Dis Workers, 96. *Concurrent Pos:* Host Plant Resistance Comt, Am Phytopath Soc, 91-93; prin investr soybean dis, USDA, 92- *Mem:* Am Phytopath Soc; Soc Nematol. *Res:* Effects of tillage on diseases of cotton and soybean and searching for resistance in soybean to Macrophomina phaseolina. *Mailing Add:* PO Box 160 Portageville MO 63873. *Fax:* 573-379-5875; *E-Mail:* plantaw@.mizzou1

**WRAY, GRANVILLE WAYNE,** CELL BIOLOGY, BIOCHEMISTRY. *Current Pos:* grants assoc, NIH, 84-85, health scientist adminr, Nat Heart Lung & Blood Inst/NIH, 86-88, DEP DIR EP, NIDR/NIH, 88- *Personal Data:* b Elk City, Okla, Dec 16, 41; m 65; c 1. *Educ:* Phillips Univ, BS, 63; Okla State Univ, MS, 65; Univ Tex, PhD(cell biol), 70. *Honors & Awards:* Mike Hogg Award, 68. *Prof Exp:* Res asst biochem, Okla State Univ, 63-65; res asst, Univ Tex M D Anderson Hosp & Tumor Inst, 65-66; asst prof cell biol, Baylor Col Med, 72-84. *Concurrent Pos:* Damon Runyon Cancer res fel, McArdle Lab Cancer Res, Univ Wis-Madison, 71-72. *Mem:* AAAS; Am Soc Cell Biologists. *Res:* Isolation, morphology and biochemistry of the mammalian metaphase chromosome. *Mailing Add:* NIH 45 Center Dr Natcher Bldg Rm 4AN-32J MSC 6402 Bethesda MD 20892-6402. *Fax:* 301-496-4180

**WRAY, H LINTON,** ENDOCRINOLOGY. *Current Pos:* Asst chief, 77-82, chief, Endocrine & Metab Serv, 82-83, CHIEF, DEPT CLIN INVEST, WALTER REED ARMY MED CTR, 85- *Personal Data:* b Charlotte, NC, Apr 2, 40; m; c 3. *Educ:* Univ Pa, MD, 66. *Mem:* Endocrine Soc; Am Physiol Soc; Am Col Physicians; Am Soc Bone & Mineral Res. *Res:* Hormonal control of calcium metabolism. *Mailing Add:* 4005 Drummond Ave Chevy Chase MD 20815

**WRAY, JAMES DAVID,** ASTRONOMY. *Current Pos:* PRES, SCI TECH ASTRON RES, 85- *Personal Data:* b Norton, Kans, Oct 3, 36; c 1. *Educ:* Univ MNex, BS, 59; Univ Cincinnati, MS, 62; Northwestern Univ, PhD(astron), 66. *Prof Exp:* Res assoc meteoritics, Univ NMex, 62-64, dir, Inst Meteoritics, 66-67; asst prof astron, Northwestern Univ, 67-72; res scientist astron, Univ Tex, Austin, 72-85. *Concurrent Pos:* Consult, Boller & Chivens Div, Perkin-Elmer Corp, 73- *Mem:* Int Astron Union; Am Astron Soc. *Res:* Space astronomy, ultraviolet stellar spectroscopy; extra-galactic research, surface distribution of color in galaxies; digital image processing; numerical data base management and applications. *Mailing Add:* 21200 Todd Valley Rd No 54 Forest Hill CA 95631-9511

**WRAY, JOE D,** MATERNAL & CHILD HEALTH, NUTRITION. *Current Pos:* dep dir, Ctr Pop & Family Health, 81-87, prof, 81-91, EMER PROF CLIN PUB HEALTH, COLUMBIA UNIV, 91-; VIS LECTR, HARVARD SCH PUB HEALTH, 91- *Personal Data:* b Conway, Ark, Sept 30, 26; m 51, Elizabeth Treadwell; c David, Ann, Amy, Emily & Richard. *Educ:* Stanford Univ, BA, 47, MD, 52; Univ NC, MPH, 67; Am Bd Pediat, dipl. *Hon Degrees:* Dr, Hacettepe Univ, Ankara, 83. *Prof Exp:* Intern, Charity Hosp La, New Orleans, 51-52; intern & resident pediat, Grace-New Haven Community Hosp, Conn, 54-56; chief resident, Hacettepe Children's Hosp, Ankara, Turkey, 56-58, assoc pediatrician, 58-61; vis prof pediat, Fac Med, Univ Valle, Cali, Colombia, 61-66; vis prof community med & pediat, Ramathibodi Hosp Med Sch, Mahidol Univ, Bangkok, Thailand, 67-74; fel, Ctr Advan Study Behav Sci, 74-75; vis prof maternal & child health & int health, Harvard Sch

Pub Health, 75-78, sr lectr, 78-81, head, Dept Pop Sci, 78-80, dir, Off Int Health Prog, 79-81. *Concurrent Pos:* Mem field staff health & pop, Rockefeller Found, NY, 60-76; chairperson gov bd, Nat Coun Int Health, 84-86; consult, WHO, UNICEF, USAID, Rockefeller Found, Ford Found & var nat govt orgs. *Mem:* Fel Am Acad Pediat; Am Pub Health Asn. *Res:* Infant and preschool child nutrition; growth and development; nutrition and infection; delivery of health services to children in developing countries; family planning, evaluation of child survival and primary health care programs. *Mailing Add:* 25 Wilkins Station Rd Medford NJ 08055. *E-Mail:* jwraymd@aol.com

**WRAY, JOHN L,** ELECTRONICS ENGINEERING, TECHNICAL MANAGEMENT. *Current Pos:* SR CONSULT, MOLLERUS ENG CORP, 92- *Personal Data:* b Maryville, Mo, June 17, 35; m 58; c Mary (Deauville), Nancy & Carolyn. *Educ:* Univ Mo, Columbia, BS, 57; Stanford Univ, MS, 58; Univ Santa Clara, MBA, 66. *Prof Exp:* Test planning officer, USAF, 58-62; mgr mkt res, Gen Elec Co, 62-78; vpres, Quadrex Corp, 78-84; pres, Systrol, Inc, 84-86; pres, Gooselake Lumber Co, 87-89; vpres, Renewable Resources, 89; sr consult, vpres & chief financial officer, Thomas Res Corp, 90-92. *Mem:* Am Soc Mech Engrs. *Res:* Effects on eyes of thermal energy from nuclear detonations; water jet pumps for boiling water reactors; instrumentation for nuclear reactors. *Mailing Add:* 19992 Buckhaven Lane Saratoga CA 95070

**WRAY, JOHN LEE,** GEOLOGY. *Current Pos:* RETIRED. *Personal Data:* b Charleston, WVa, July 10, 25; m 52; c 1. *Educ:* Univ WVa, BS, 50, MS, 51; Univ Wis, PhD(geol), 56. *Prof Exp:* Teaching asst geol, Univ WVa, 48-51; geologist, WVa State Hwy Dept, 51-53; res asst chem, Univ Wis, 53-56; res assoc, Res Ctr, Marathon Oil Co, 56-86. *Concurrent Pos:* Adj prof geol, Colo Sch Mines, 70-83. *Mem:* Geol Soc Am; Paleont Soc; Am Asn Petrol Geologists; Soc Econ Paleont & Mineral. *Res:* Paleontology; fossil algae; carbonate sedimentology; biostratigraphy. *Mailing Add:* 3755 Chataway Ct Colorado Springs CO 80906-4388

**WRAY, PORTER R,** ENGINEERING. *Current Pos:* RETIRED. *Personal Data:* b Chester, Pa, Jan 21, 13; m 39; c 4. *Educ:* Swarthmore Col, BS, 34. *Prof Exp:* Qual observer, Carnegie Steel Co, 34-36; res asst, Res Lab, US Steel, 36-37; metall serv engr, Carnegie-Ill Steel Corp, 37-41, mgr stainless, 41-43, asst chief metallurgist, Duquesne Works, 43-44, metall engr alloy, US Steel, 44-55, gen mgr metall, 55-69, dir metall eng qual control & serv, 69-78. *Concurrent Pos:* Consult, US State Dept, NATO, 59; mem, Adv Coun, Mat Res Agency, US Army, 66-68; dir, Am Nat Standards Inst, 70-73 & Metal Properties Coun, 74-79; chair, Steel Indust, Am Nat Metric Coun, 75-78. *Mem:* Fel Am Soc Metals; Am Iron & Steel Inst; Soc Automotive Engrs; Am Nat Standards Inst; Am Nat Metric Coun. *Mailing Add:* 1290 Boyce Rd Upper St Clair PA 15241

**WRAY, VIRGINIA LEE POLLAN,** BIOCHEMISTRY. *Current Pos:* RES ASST PROF CELL BIOL, BAYLOR COL MED, 73- *Personal Data:* b Grove, Okla, Mar 20, 40; m 65. *Educ:* Okla State Univ, BS, 62, MS, 66; Univ Tex Grad Sch Biomed Sci Houston, PhD(biochem), 70. *Prof Exp:* Res asst biochem virol, Col Med, Baylor Univ, 66. *Concurrent Pos:* Fel, McArdle Lab Cancer Res, Univ Wis-Madison, 70-72. *Mem:* Am Soc Cell Biologists; Am Chem Soc. *Res:* Membrane biochemistry; composition and function of nuclear and plasma membranes. *Mailing Add:* 7505 Water Lily Way Columbia MD 21046-1422

**WREDE, ROBERT C, JR,** MATHEMATICS. *Current Pos:* from instr to prof, 55-94, EMER PROF MATH, CALIF STATE UNIV, SAN JOSE, 94- *Personal Data:* b Cincinnati, Ohio, Oct 19, 26; m 48, Jeanne Skedden; c Scott, Brian & James. *Educ:* Miami Univ, Ohio, BS, 49, MA, 50; Ind Univ, PhD(math), 56. *Prof Exp:* Instr math, Miami Univ, Ohio, 50-51. *Concurrent Pos:* Consult phys & res lab, Int Bus Mach Corp, Calif, 56-58; Hunter's Point Radiation Lab, 60. *Mem:* Am Math Soc; Math Asn Am. *Res:* Relativity theory; differential geometry; vector and tensor analysis; study of black holes and cosmology. *Mailing Add:* 132 Wingfoot Ct Aptos CA 95003-5428. *Fax:* 408-688-5352

**WREFORD, STANLEY S,** CATALYTIC CHEMISTRY, CARBOXYLATION CHEMISTRY. *Current Pos:* TECH MGR SPECIALTY CHEMICALS, E I DU PONT DE NEMOURS & CO, INC, 80- *Personal Data:* b Detroit, Mich, Mar 18, 49; m 67; c 1. *Educ:* Univ Mich, BS, 70; Mass Inst Technol, PhD(inorg chem), 74. *Prof Exp:* Assoc prof inorg chem, Harvard Univ, 74-78, Univ Toronto, 78-80. *Mem:* Am Chem Soc. *Res:* Homogeneous catalysis of carboxylation reactions. *Mailing Add:* 232 Commercial St Unit D Boston MA 02109-1305

**WRENN, MCDONALD EDWARD,** ENVIRONMENTAL HEALTH, RADIOLOGICAL HEALTH. *Current Pos:* prof pharm & dir, Radiobiol Div, 79-86, DIR, ENVIRON RADIATION & TOXICOL LAB, UNIV UTAH SCH MED, 86- *Personal Data:* b New York, NY, Apr 16, 36; m 67; c 2. *Educ:* Princeton Univ, AB, 58; NY Univ, MS, 62, PhD(nuclear eng, environ health), 67. *Prof Exp:* Res scientist, US Energy Res & Develop Admin, 62-67, from instr to asst prof, 67-72; biomed scientist radiobiol, Div Biomed & Environ Res, 73-75; assoc prof environ med, Med Ctr, NY Univ, 72-79. *Concurrent Pos:* Mem, Nat Coun Radiation Protection & Measurements, 71-; mem & former chmn N-13 comt, Am Nat Standards Inst, 72- *Mem:* Radiation Res Soc; Health Physics Soc; fel Am Pub Health Asn; Am Inst Biol Sci; Am Indust Hygiene Asn. *Res:* Biological effects of environmental agents on man and animals, particularly radiations and radioactive materials; environmental cycling and transport of trace and radioactive elements; mammalian metabolism of actinides and development of environmental radiation detection instruments. *Mailing Add:* Environ Radiation & Toxicol Lab Univ Utah 50 N Med Dr Salt Lake City UT 84132-0001

**WRENN, WILLIAM J,** SYSTEMATICS & TAXONOMY OF CHIGGERS, ECTOPARASITIC MITES ON TERRESTRIAL VERTEBRATES. *Current Pos:* from asst prof to assoc prof, 69-87, PROF BIOL & ENTOM, DEPT BIOL, UNIV NDAK, 87- *Personal Data:* b Los Angeles, Calif, July 18, 35. *Educ:* Calif State Univ, BS, 62, MA, 64; Univ Kans, PhD(entom), 72. *Prof Exp:* Teaching asst biol & zool, Dept Biol, Calif State Univ, 62-64; teaching asst biol & biomet, Entom Dept, Univ Kans, 64-66; teaching asst zool & entom, Univ Mich, Ann Arbor, 66-68. *Concurrent Pos:* Res assoc entom, Natural Hist Mus, Los Angeles County, 80-; adj prof, Calif State Univ, Long Beach, 81. *Mem:* Acarol Soc Am; Entom Soc Am; Soc Syst Zool; Soc Study Evolution; Soc Vector Ecol. *Res:* Systematics of parasitic acarines, especially chiggers; chigger-host relationships, ecology, biology, immune responsiveness and taxonomy, especially of western hemisphere species. *Mailing Add:* Dept Biol Univ NDak PO Box 9019 Grand Forks ND 58202-9019

**WRENSCH, DANA LOUISE,** ACAROLOGY, GENETICS. *Current Pos:* NIH trainee, 72-75, ADJ ASST PROF ENTOM, OHIO STATE UNIV, 78-; ASST PROF BOT & BACT, OHIO WESLEYAN UNIV, 81- *Personal Data:* b Greenwood, Miss, Oct 3, 46; m 74; c 2. *Educ:* Ohio State Univ, BSc, 68, MS, 70, PhD(genetics), 72. *Concurrent Pos:* Consult, IBP, 72 & 73, Ministry Educ & Cult, Brazil, 78; lectr genetics, Ohio State Univ, 82. *Mem:* AAAS; Acarol Soc Am; Am Genetic Asn; Entom Soc Am. *Res:* Population biology and genetics of spider mites. *Mailing Add:* Entom Ohio State Univ 1735 Neil Ave Columbus OH 43210-1220

**WRIDE, W(ILLIAM) JAMES,** CHEMICAL ENGINEERING. *Current Pos:* RETIRED. *Personal Data:* b Garfield, Wash, Dec 3, 21; m 48; c 3. *Educ:* State Col Wash, BS, 43, MS, 46; Iowa State Col, PhD(chem eng), 48. *Prof Exp:* Co-owner, mgr & consult engr, Ames Eng & Testing Serv, 48-51; chem & process engr, Philips Petrol Co, 52-66, mgr, Chem Eng Fundamentals Br, Res & Develop Dept, 66-72, mgr, Eng Res Br, 72-74, process technol consult, 74-77, mgr, eng & technol, Energy Minerals Div, 78-84. *Mem:* Am Inst Chem Engrs. *Res:* Mercaptan formation in petroleum distillates; polyolefin resin process development; petrochemical process optimization; kinetics and mass transfer; process design and economic evaluation; research and development of alternate energy sources. *Mailing Add:* 633 Oakridge Dr Bartlesville OK 74006

**WRIEDT, HENRY ANDERSON,** PHYSICAL CHEMISTRY, METALS. *Current Pos:* RETIRED. *Personal Data:* b Melbourne, Australia, Feb 6, 28; nat US; m 60; c 3. *Educ:* Univ Melbourne, BMetE, 49; Mass Inst Technol, ScD(metall), 54. *Prof Exp:* Asst metall, Mass Inst Technol, 49-53; technologist, Appl Res Lab, US Steel Corp, 53-55, scientist, Edgar C Bain Lab Fund Res, 55-66, sr scientist, 66-72, sr scientist, Res Lab, 72-76, assoc res consult, Res Lab, 76-83; consult, 83-96. *Concurrent Pos:* Ed screener & tech writer, Int Ctr Diffraction Data, 90- *Mem:* Am Inst Mining, Metall & Petrol Engrs. *Res:* Physical chemistry of metals; phase equilbria and gas-metal reactions in metallic systems; thermodynamics of metallic systems. *Mailing Add:* 148 Washington St Pittsburgh PA 15223

**WRIGHT, ALAN CARL,** CHEMISTRY. *Current Pos:* from asst prof to assoc prof, 70-82, chmn, Dept Earth & Phys Sci, 75-78, PROF CHEM, EASTERN CONN STATE UNIV, 82- *Personal Data:* b Bangor, Maine, Aug 16, 39; m 64, Olga Kokkinos; c Kathryn & Marlena. *Educ:* Univ Maine, Orono, BS, 61; Univ Fla, PhD(chem), 66. *Prof Exp:* Res chemist, Cent Res Div, Am Cyanamid Co, 66-69. *Mem:* Am Chem Soc; Sigma Xi; AAAS. *Res:* Development of new laboratory experiments for organic chemistry involving compounds of biological interest. *Mailing Add:* Dept Phys Sci Eastern Conn State Univ Willimantic CT 06226

**WRIGHT, ALDEN HALBERT,** GENETIC ALGORITHMS. *Current Pos:* assoc prof, 83-86, PROF COMPUT SCI, UNIV MONT, 86- *Personal Data:* b Missoula, Mont, Apr 23, 42; m 67, Sally Fant; c Eric & Kevin. *Educ:* Dartmouth Col, BA, 64; Univ Wis-Madison, PhD(math), 69. *Prof Exp:* Vis asst prof math, Univ Utah, 69-70; from asst prof to prof, Western Mich Univ, 70-83. *Mem:* Asn Comput Mach; Inst Elec & Electronics Engrs Comput Soc. *Res:* Theory of genetic algorithms; string search algorithms. *Mailing Add:* Dept Comput Sci Univ Mont Missoula MT 59812

**WRIGHT, ANDREW,** MOLECULAR BIOLOGY. *Current Pos:* PROF MOLECULAR BIOL, MED SCH, TUFTS UNIV, 67- *Personal Data:* b Edinburgh, Scotland, Jan 28, 35; m 57; c 2. *Educ:* Univ Edinburgh, BSc, 57, PhD(biochem), 60. *Prof Exp:* Fel biochem, Univ Minn, 60-62; fel biol, Mass Inst Technol, 63-67. *Mem:* Fedn Am Socs Exp Biol; Sigma Xi; Am Soc Microbiol; Am Acad Microbiol. *Res:* Cell cycle events in bacteria; mechanisms of bacterial pathogenesis. *Mailing Add:* Dept Molecular Biol Tufts Univ Med Sch 136 Harrison Ave Boston MA 02111. *Fax:* 617-956-0337; *E-Mail:* awright@opal.tufts.edu

**WRIGHT, ANTHONY AUNE,** ANIMAL BEHAVIOR, PSYCHOPHYSICS. *Current Pos:* asst prof, Univ Tex, Austin, 71-72, from asst prof to assoc prof, 72-81, PROF NEURAL SCI, SENSORY SCI CTR, UNIV TEX, HOUSTON, 81- *Personal Data:* b Los Angeles, Calif, Jan 4, 43; m 65. *Educ:* Stanford Univ, BA, 65; Columbia Univ, MA, 70, PhD(psychol), 71. *Prof Exp:* Instr psychol, Columbia Univ, 69-71. *Concurrent Pos:* Fogarty sr int fel NZ, 83-84. *Mem:* Psychonomic Soc; Asn Res Vision & Ophthal; Sigma Xi. *Res:* Animal sensory processes; discrimination learning; theoretical psychophysics; color vision; memory cognition. *Mailing Add:* 2615 Pemberton Dr Houston TX 77005

**WRIGHT, ARCHIBALD NELSON,** PHYSICAL CHEMISTRY, PLASTICS FORMULATIONS & PROCESSING. *Current Pos:* SR VPRES ENVIRON & TECHNOL, SYNERGISTICS INDUST, MONTREAL, 78- *Personal Data:* b Toronto, Ont, May 22, 32; m 55, 87, Helene Vincent; c Percival, Adrian, Dawn, Nicolas & Sara-Michele. *Educ:* McGill Univ, BSc, 53, PhD, 57. *Honors & Awards:* IR-100 Award Surface Photopolymerization, 67. *Prof Exp:* Grace Chem fel Prof F S Dainton, Univ Leeds, 57-59; res fel, Prof C A Winkler, McGill Univ, 59-63; phys chemist, 63-68, mgr photochem br, Chem Lab, 68-72, mgr reactions & processes br, 72-73, mgr planning & resources, Mat Sci & Eng, Res & Develop Ctr, Gen Elec Co, 73-78. *Concurrent Pos:* Chmn, Macromolecular & Eng Div, Chem Inst Can, 83-85, Vinyl Div, Soc Plastics Engrs, 88-89, gen chmn, Vinyl Retec, 88, tech prog chmn, Antec, 91; mem bd, Laurention Int Col, Ste Agate-des-Monts, 86-; mem exec comn bd, Can Soc Chem, 88-92; mem, Strategic Grants Panel, Nat Sci & Eng Coun, Can, 88-90, chmn, Comt Formation Fed Network Ctr of Excellence, 89; comt mem, Can Nat, Int Union Pure & Appl Chem, 91-; mem, Soc Plastics Indust Task Force, Revenue Can appln paper, Res & Develop tax credits, 91-92. *Mem:* Am Chem Soc; Am Phys Soc; Royal Soc Chem; AAAS; Chem Inst Can; Int Soc Plastics Engrs (vpres, 93-). *Res:* Gas phase kinetics, especially reactions of hydrogen and nitrogen atoms and excited nitrogen molecules; anionic polymerization; reactions at clean metal surfaces; photolysis; photopolymerization; polymer chemistry; author of 25 referred technical publications; awarded 24 patents. *Mailing Add:* Synergistics Industs Ltd 177 St Andre St St Remi PQ J0L 2L0 Can. *Fax:* 514-454-8600

**WRIGHT, BARBARA EVELYN,** BIOCHEMISTRY, DIFFERENTIATION. *Current Pos:* res dir, Boston Biomed Res Inst, 67-82, RES PROF, DEPT MICROBIOL, UNIV MONT, 82-; DIR, STELLA DUNCAN MEM RES INST, 82- *Personal Data:* b Pasadena, Calif, Apr 6, 26; m 51; c 3. *Educ:* Stanford Univ, PhD(microbiol), 51. *Prof Exp:* Biologist, Nat Heart Inst, 53-61; res assoc, Huntington Labs, Mass Gen Hosp, 61-67. *Concurrent Pos:* Nat Res Coun fel, Carlsberg Lab, Copenhagen, Denmark, 50-51, Childs Mem Fund fel, 51-52; tutor, Harvard Univ & assoc prof, Harvard Med Sch; ed ann rev microbiol, Exp Mycol & J Bact; Found for Microbiol lectr, 70-71; div lectr Miles Lab, 78-79, consult, 80-83; mem, Govenor's Coun Sci & Technol, 83-85; pres, Pac Div, AAAS, 84-85; consult, Advancing Sci Excellence NDak, 86-88. *Mem:* Am Soc Biol Chem; Am Soc Microbiol. *Res:* Biochemical basis of differentiation in the slime mold; kinetic modelling of metabolic networks in steady state and while undergoing transitions, as in aging and development; metabolic models. *Mailing Add:* Div Biol Sci Univ Mont Missoula MT 59812-1002. *Fax:* 406-243-4184

**WRIGHT, BILL C,** SOIL SCIENCE. *Current Pos:* chief, Party Mgt, Agr Res & Technol Proj, Pakistan, 86-92, SR ASSOC, WINROCK INT, 92- *Personal Data:* b Waterford, Miss, June 15, 30; m 59; c 3. *Educ:* Miss State Univ, BS, 52, MS, 56; Cornell Univ, PhD(soil sci), 59. *Honors & Awards:* Farmers Terai Award, 71. *Prof Exp:* From asst prof to assoc prof soil sci, Miss State Univ, 59-64; assoc soil scientist to assoc dir, Indian Agr Prog Rockefeller Found, Int Agr Develop Serv, NY, 64-70, agr proj leader, Turkey, 70-77, prog officer Africa & Middle East, 77-82; sabbatical study, NC State Univ, 82-83; asst dean agr int progs, Okla State Univ, 83-86. *Concurrent Pos:* Mem, Bd Sci & Technol for Int Develop, Nat Acad Sci, 80-82, bd dirs, MidAm Int Agr Consortium. *Mem:* Int Soc Soil Sci; Am Soc Agron; Soil Sci Soc Am; Indian Soc Agron; Indian Soil Sci Soc. *Res:* Soil-phosphorus reactions products; phosphate components of fertilizers; evaluation techniques for fertilizers in field and laboratory; fertilizer use and cultural management of cereal crops in India; wheat production in areas of low rainfall; organization and management of agricultural research and production in developing countries. *Mailing Add:* 2 Guindola Lane Hot Springs Village AR 71909

**WRIGHT, BYRON TERRY,** NUCLEAR PHYSICS. *Current Pos:* from asst prof to assoc prof, 46-56, PROF PHYSICS, UNIV CALIF, LOS ANGELES, 56- *Personal Data:* b Waco Tex, Oct 19, 17; wid; c 3. *Educ:* Rice Univ, BA, 38; Univ Calif, Berkeley, PhD(physics), 41. *Prof Exp:* Physicist, Navy Radio & Sound Lab, Calif, 41-42 & Manhattan Dist, Calif, Tenn & NMex, 42-46. *Concurrent Pos:* Fulbright res scholar, 56-57; Guggenheim fel, 63-64; Ford Found fcl, Europ Orgn Nuclear Res, 63-64. *Mem:* Am Phys Soc. *Res:* Accelerators; nuclear structure. *Mailing Add:* 1225 Chickory Lane Los Angeles CA 90049

**WRIGHT, CHARLES DEAN,** POLYMER CHEMISTRY. *Current Pos:* RETIRED. *Personal Data:* b Yankton, SDak, June 25, 30; m 52; c 4. *Educ:* Augustana Col, SDak, BA, 52; Univ Minn, PhD(org chem), 56. *Prof Exp:* Instr org chem, Univ Minn, 55-56; res chemist, 3M Co, 56-64, mgr res & new prod groups, 64-77, sr res specialist 77-84, scientist, Adhesives, Coatings & Sealers Div, 84-90. *Mem:* Am Chem Soc. *Res:* Stereospecific polymers; oxidizers for rocket fuels; general polymer chemistry; adhesive compounding and testing; adhesion; new business development; relationships of science and Christianity; epoxy chemistry; cyanoacrylate chemistry; granted 22 US patents. *Mailing Add:* 14 Oakridge Dr White Bear Lake MN 55110-1839

**WRIGHT, CHARLES GERALD,** ENTOMOLOGY. *Current Pos:* RETIRED. *Personal Data:* b Boynton, Pa, June 12, 30; m 53; c 1. *Educ:* Univ Md, BS, 51, MS, 53; NC State Univ, PhD(entom), 58. *Prof Exp:* Entomologist, Wilson Pest Control, 58-63; from asst prof to assoc prof, NC State Univ, 63-75, prof entom, 75- *Concurrent Pos:* Vchmn, NC Struct Pest Control Comt, 67-80, mem, 83-89. *Mem:* Entom Soc Am; Nat Asn Cols & Teachers Agr; Sigma Xi. *Res:* Urban and industrial entomology; cockroaches; insecticide movement in structures. *Mailing Add:* Box 7613 NC State Univ Raleigh NC 27695

**WRIGHT, CHARLES HUBERT,** ANALYTICAL CHEMISTRY. *Current Pos:* RETIRED. *Personal Data:* b Appleton City, Mo, Oct 30, 22; m 52; c 5. *Educ:* Univ Mo, PhD(chem), 52. *Prof Exp:* Instr analytical chem, Univ Mo, 52-54; chemist, US Radium Corp, 54-58; analytical group leader, Spencer Chem Co, 58-66; supvr analytical sect, Gulf Res & Develop Co, 66-71; sr res chemist, Pittsburgh & Midway Coal Mining Co, 71-80, res assoc, 80-84. *Mem:* AAAS; Am Chem Soc; Sigma Xi. *Res:* Analytical chemistry of fertilizers, herbicides, polymers and fuels. *Mailing Add:* 6115 W 85th Terr Overland Park KS 66207-1514

**WRIGHT, CHARLES JOSEPH,** SYNTHETIC ORGANIC & NATURAL PRODUCTS CHEMISTRY. *Current Pos:* RETIRED. *Personal Data:* b Montour Falls, NY, May 27, 38. *Educ:* Univ Rochester, BS, 60; Mass Inst Technol, MS, 62. *Prof Exp:* From res chemist to sr res chemist, Eastman Kokak Co, 64-82, res assoc, Res Labs, 82-86, tech assoc sect supvr mass spectrometry, Anal Technol Div, 86-91. *Mem:* Am Soc Mass Spectrometry. *Res:* Mass spectrometry of organic compounds. *Mailing Add:* 1210 Majestic Way Webster NY 14580-9538

**WRIGHT, CHARLES R B,** ALGEBRA, DISCRETE MATHEMATICS. *Current Pos:* from asst prof to assoc prof, 61-72, assoc dean, Col Liberal Arts, 73-77, PROF MATH, UNIV ORE, 72- *Personal Data:* b Lincoln, Nebr, Jan 11, 37; m 90; c 2. *Educ:* Univ Nebr, BA, 56, MA, 57; Univ Wis, PhD(math), 59. *Prof Exp:* Res fel math, Calif Inst Technol, 59-60, instr, 60-61. *Concurrent Pos:* Vis prof math, Mich State Univ, 77. *Mem:* Am Math Soc; Math Asn Am. *Res:* Finite groups and computational group theory. *Mailing Add:* Dept Math Univ Ore Eugene OR 97403-1226

**WRIGHT, CLARENCE PAUL,** GENETICS. *Current Pos:* ASSOC PROF BIOL, WESTERN CAROLINA UNIV, 68- *Personal Data:* b Cliffside, NC, Apr 15, 39. *Educ:* Lenoir-Rhyne Col, BS, 62; Univ Utah, MS, 65, PhD(genetics), 68. *Mem:* Genetics Soc Am. *Res:* Developmental genetics. *Mailing Add:* Dept Biol Western Carolina Univ Cullowhee NC 28723

**WRIGHT, CLIFFORD DEAN,** CELLULAR PHARMACOLOGY, BIOCHEMICAL PHARMACOLOGY. *Current Pos:* RES SCIENTIST III, AMGEN INC, 94- *Personal Data:* b Chicago, Ill, June 30, 54; m 76, Diane Maria Van Haren; c Christian, David, John & Elizabeth. *Educ:* Brigham Young Univ, BS, 77, MS, 79; Univ Minn, PhD(microbiol), 83. *Prof Exp:* From scientist to sr scientist, Warner-Lambert Co, 83-87, from res assoc to sr res assoc, 87-94. *Concurrent Pos:* Mentor-student, Biomed Res Prog, Univ Mich, 91-94; adj prof, Eastern Mich Univ, 91-94. *Mem:* AAAS; Am Soc Microbiol; Inflammation Res Asn; Am Soc Cell Biol. *Res:* Cellular and biochemical pharmacology pertaining to leukocytes and vascular cells and their contributions to the pathogenesis of inflammatory diseases, including arthritis, asthma and acute inflammatory disorders. *Mailing Add:* 7415 Park Circle Boulder CO 80301

**WRIGHT, CURTIS,** ADDICTIVE DISEASES, PUBLIC HEALTH. *Current Pos:* med rev officer, drug abuse staff, Food & Drug Admin, 89-91, supvry med officer, Ctr Drug Eval & Res, 91-93, actg dir, Pilot Drug Div, 93-94, ACTG DIR, ANESTESIA CRITICAL CARE & ADDICTION DRUG PRODS, FOOD & DRUG ADMIN, 94- *Personal Data:* b Chicago, Ill, Oct 29, 49; c 2, Linda Johnson; c Rusty & Erik. *Educ:* Haverford Col, BS, 71; George Washington Univ, MD, 77; Johns Hopkins Univ, MPH, 86. *Prof Exp:* Supv water & wastewater treat, Supvr, Embreeville, Pa, 71; rcs biochemist, NIMH, NIH, 71-73; intern Naval Reg Med Ctr, Va, 77-78 staff, Naval Hosp, Calif, 79, Naval Reg Med Ctr, Japan, 80, Kent & Queen Annes Hosp Emergency rm, 85; staff physician, Bethesda Naval Hosp, 81, Emergency Dept, 83-84, actg head emergency servs, 84; med officer, Tri Serv Alcoholism Recovery Fac, 81-83, head, Med Div, 84-85. *Concurrent Pos:* NSF Res fel, 68-69; res fel behav pharmacol, Johns Hopkins Univ, 87-89. *Res:* Author numerous publications; occupational and preventative medicine; public health; pharmacoepidemiology; substance abuse; prevention detection and management of behavorial disorders in the workplace. *Mailing Add:* Anestia Critical Care & Addition Drug Prold 5600 Fishers Lane HFD-007 (9B-45) CDER Rockville MD 20857

**WRIGHT, DANIEL CRAIG,** PLANT GROWTH REGULATION, TISSUE CULTURE. *Current Pos:* DEAN COMPUT SCI, DEVRY INST, 97- *Personal Data:* b Rockford, Ill, Nov 15, 54; m 76; c 2. *Educ:* WVa Univ, BA, 75; Univ Md, MS, 78 & PhD(bot), 79. *Prof Exp:* Teaching asst bot, Univ Md, 75-78; lab asst, Weed Res Lab, USDA, 78-79; res assoc, Hort Dept, Purdue Univ , 79-81; asst prof bot, Alfred Univ, 81-82; res scientist, Brooklyn Bot Garden, 82-87, res mgr, 87-90; res comput specialist, Dial Corp, 90-94. *Concurrent Pos:* Adj asst prof bot, Pace Univ, 86-90. *Mem:* Am Soc Plant Physiol; Am Soc Hort Sci; Sigma Xi. *Res:* Biochemistry and physiology of plant growth and development; the effects of various herbicides and other growth regulation on woody plant growth. *Mailing Add:* 14815 N Deerskin Dr Fountain Hills AZ 85268

**WRIGHT, DAVID ANTHONY,** DEVELOPMENTAL BIOLOGY, GENETICS. *Current Pos:* RETIRED. *Personal Data:* b Baltimore, Md, Aug 19, 41; m 62; c 3. *Educ:* Univ Md, College Park, BS, 63; Univ Ill, Urbana, MS, 65; Wash Univ, PhD(biol), 68. *Prof Exp:* NIH fel med genetics, Univ Tex M D Anderson Hosp & Tumor Inst Houston, 68-70; asst prof biol, Univ Tex Grad Sch Biomed Sci Houston, 70-75; assoc biologist & asst prof biol, Univ Tex Cancer Ctr, M D Anderson Hosp & Tumor Inst, 75-80, assoc prof molecular genetics, 80-97. *Mem:* AAAS; Am Soc Zoologists; Soc Develop Biol; Genetics Soc Am. *Res:* Patterns and control of gene expression during embryogenesis, especially of enzyme phenotypes in nuclear-cytoplasmic hybrids in amphibians. *Mailing Add:* Dept Molecular Genetics Univ Tex M D Anderson Cancer Ctr 1515 Holcombe Blvd Box 45 Houston TX 77030-2102

**WRIGHT, DAVID GRANT,** TOPOLOGY. *Current Pos:* assoc prof, 83-88, PROF MATH, BRIGHAM YOUNG UNIV, 88- *Personal Data:* b Am Fork, Utah, Aug 21, 46; m 70, Carolyn Savage; c Joel, Rebekah, Brendan, Paul, Emily, Jonathan & Anne. *Educ:* Brigham Young Univ, BS, 70; Univ Wis-Madison, MA, 72 & PhD(math), 73. *Prof Exp:* Lectr math, Univ Wis-Madison, 74; fel math, Mich State Univ, 74-76; from asst prof to assoc prof math, Utah State Univ, 76-83. *Concurrent Pos:* Vis scholar, Univ Utah, 94-95. *Mem:* Am Math Soc. *Res:* Geometric topology including piecewise linear topology and topological embeddings in manifolds, and covering spaces. *Mailing Add:* Dept Math Brigham Young Univ Provo UT 84602. *E-Mail:* wfight@math.byu.edu

**WRIGHT, DAVID LEE,** MATHEMATICS. *Current Pos:* Asst prof math, 75-81, ASSOC PROF MATH, WASHINGTON UNIV, 81- *Personal Data:* b Mattoon, Ill, Dec 1, 49; m 69; c 1. *Educ:* David Lipscomb Col, BA, 71; Columbia Univ, MS, 73, PhD(math), 75. *Mem:* Sigma Xi; Am Math Soc. *Res:* Behavior of polynomial algebras, their automorphisms, their stable structure. *Mailing Add:* Dept Math Washington Univ St Louis MO 63100

**WRIGHT, DAVID PATRICK,** NUCLEAR PHYSICS. *Current Pos:* ASST PROF PHYSICS & MATH, ST EDWARDS UNIV, 77- *Personal Data:* b Pocahontas, Ark, Apr 11, 43; m 75. *Educ:* St Edwards Univ, BS, 65; Univ Tex, Austin, PhD(nuclear physics), 74. *Prof Exp:* Instr math, Univ Tex, Austin, 75-76; vis asst prof physics, Univ Southwestern La, 76-77. *Mem:* Am Phys Soc. *Res:* Nuclear structure; medical physics; energy studies. *Mailing Add:* Sch Natural Sci St Edwards Univ Austin TX 78704

**WRIGHT, DAWN JEANNINE,** MARINE GEOLOGY, GEOGRAPHIC INFORMATION SYSTEMS. *Current Pos:* ASST PROF EARTH SCI & OCEANOG, ORE STATE UNIV, 95- *Personal Data:* b Baltimore, Md, Apr 15, 61. *Educ:* Wheaton Col, BS, 83; Tex A&M Univ, MS, 86, Univ Calif, Santa Barbara, PhD(phys geog), 94. *Concurrent Pos:* Nat Oceanic & Atmospheric Admin postdoctoral fel, Pac Marine Environ Lab, Ore State Univ, 95. *Mem:* Am Geophys Union; Asn Am Geogr; Geol Soc Am; Am Sci Affil. *Res:* Fissuring, faulting, hydrothermal and magnetic processes at mid-ocean ridges; geographic information systems and spatial analysis; processing and interpretation of deep sea maps, videography and photography. *Mailing Add:* Dept Geosci Ore State Univ Corvallis OR 97331-5506. *Fax:* 541-737-1200; *E-Mail:* dawn@dusk.geo.orst.edu

**WRIGHT, DENNIS CHARLES,** BEHAVIORAL NEUROSCIENCE. *Current Pos:* Asst prof, Univ Mo, Columbia, 68-73, assoc chair, 81-85, assoc prof, 73-97, ASSOC PROF PSYCHOL & CHAIR, UNIV MO, COLUMBIA, 94- *Personal Data:* b Flint, Mich, Oct 14, 39. *Educ:* Univ Mich, Ann Arbor, BA, 60; Univ Calif, Berkeley, PhD(psychol), 69. *Mem:* Behav Teratology Soc; Psychonomic Soc; Am Psychol Soc. *Res:* Psychopharmacology; behavioral toxicology/teratology; biochemistry and electrophysiology of learning and memory. *Mailing Add:* Dept Psychol Univ Mo 210 McAlster Hall Columbia MO 65211

**WRIGHT, DEXTER V(AIL),** MECHANICAL ENGINEERING. *Current Pos:* CONSULT ENGR, JRL ENTERPRISES, INC, 96- *Personal Data:* b Milford, Conn, Sept 12, 23; m 44, Helen M Hammon; c David P & Raymond D. *Educ:* Univ Conn, BSEE, 44; Univ Pittsburgh, MSEE, 47. *Prof Exp:* Res engr, Westinghouse Res & Develop Ctr, Westinghouse Sci & Technol Ctr, 44-61, fel engr, 61-66, engr in charge mech vibrations, 66-67, mgr dynamics, 67-90, consult engr, 90-96. *Res:* Vibration of machines and structures; noise control and acoustics; vibration and acoustic instrumentation; structural vibration due to fluid flow. *Mailing Add:* 104 Kings Dale Rd Pittsburgh PA 15221

**WRIGHT, DONALD C,** ORGANIC BIOCHEMISTRY, ANALYTICAL BIOCHEMISTRY. *Current Pos:* GAS CHROMATOGRAPHY/MASS SPECTROMETRY MGR, LANGSTON LABS, LEAWOOD, KANS, 86- *Personal Data:* b Altus, Okla, Sept 27, 51; m 74; c 1. *Educ:* Northeast La Univ, BS, 72; Univ Mo, Columbia, MS, 74; Kans State Univ, PhD(biochem), 78. *Prof Exp:* Res assoc biochem, Miss State Univ, 77-78; assoc prof chem, Eastern Ill Univ, 78-79; chemist, Ill Environ Protection Agency, Springfield, 79-83; independent consult, 83-85; chemist, Southwest Labs, Tulsa, Okla, 85-86. *Mem:* Am Chem Soc. *Res:* Investigator in environmental gas chromatography mass spectrometry (GC/MS); mass spectral techniques combined with capillary gas chromatography; artificial intelligence techniques for processing data streams of organic compound classes by computer. *Mailing Add:* 13301 W 80 Terr Lenexa KS 66215

**WRIGHT, DONALD N,** BACTERIOLOGY, BIOCHEMISTRY. *Current Pos:* assoc prof, 69-74, PROF MICROBIOL, BRIGHAM YOUNG UNIV, 74- *Personal Data:* b Provo, Utah, Dec 6, 35; m 57; c 4. *Educ:* Univ Utah, BS, 58; Iowa State Univ, PhD(bact), 64. *Prof Exp:* Chief bacteriologist & head serol div, Philadelphia Naval Hosp, Pa, 60-62; res bacteriologist, Naval Biol Lab, Calif, 64-69. *Mem:* AAAS; Am Soc Microbiol; Brit Soc Gen Microbiol; Am Oil Chem Soc. *Res:* Physiology of microorganisms, particularly growth, inhibition, taxonomy and aerosol behavior of the Mycoplasma; biochemical responses and growth rate control of microorganisms as a function of their environment. *Mailing Add:* Brigham Young Univ Dept Microbiol 775 WIDB Provo UT 84602

**WRIGHT, DOUGLAS TYNDALL,** STRUCTURAL ENGINEERING. *Current Pos:* pres & vchancellor, 81-93, PROF SYSTS DESIGN ENG, UNIV WATERLOO, 81- *Personal Data:* b Toronto, Ont, Oct 4, 27; m 55; c William, Clyde, Robert, Sarah & Anna. *Educ:* Univ Toronto, BASc, 49; Univ Ill, MSc, 52; Cambridge Univ, PhD(eng). 54. *Hon Degrees:* DEng, Carleton Univ, 67; LLD, Brock Univ, 67, Concordia Univ, 82; DSc, Mem Univ Nfld, 69, McMaster Univ, 93, Queen's Univ, 93; LHD, Northeastern Univ, 85; DU, Strathclyde Univ, 89, Tech Univ Compiegne, France, 92. *Honors & Awards:* Gold Medal, Ont Asn Prof Engrs, 90; Gold Medal, Can Coun Prof Engrs, 92; Chevalier Nat Order of Merit, France, 93. *Prof Exp:* Struct designer, Morrison Hershfield Millman & Huggins, 49-52; lectr assoc prof, Queen's Univ, 54-58; prof civil eng, Univ Waterloo, 58-67, chmn dept, 58-63, dean eng, 59-66; chmn, Ont Comt Univ Affairs, 67-72, chmn, Comn Post Secondary Educ Ont, 69-72, dep prov secy social develop, 72-78, dep minister cult & recreation, 79-80. *Concurrent Pos:* Athlone fel, Trinity Col, 52-54; fel, Australia, 74; consult, Dutch & Mex Pavilions, Expo 67, 65-67, Palacio de Los Deportes, Olympic Games, Mex, 66-68 & Cinesphere Dome Theatre & Forum, Ont Place, 69-70; dir, Bell Can, London Life, Westinghouse Can, Electrohome Ltd, Lac Mineral, Meloche-Monnex, Com-Develop, Geometrica Inc, Visirue Decisions. *Mem:* Fel Eng Inst Can; fel Am Soc Civil Engrs; Inst Pub Admin Can; Int Asn Bridge & Struct Engrs; fel Can Acad Eng. *Res:* Public policy; space frame structures; aseismic design; author of over 60 publications on structural engineering, education and manpower issues. *Mailing Add:* Systs Design Eng Univ Waterloo Waterloo ON N2L 3G1 Can. *Fax:* 519-725-7833

**WRIGHT, ELISABETH MURIEL JANE,** MATHEMATICS. *Current Pos:* RETIRED. *Personal Data:* b Ottawa, Ont, July 28, 26; m 58; c 3. *Educ:* Univ Toronto, BA, 49, MA, 50, cert, 51; Wash Univ, PhD(educ), 57. *Prof Exp:* Specialist schs, Ont, 51-55; asst prof educ, Wash Univ, 57-61, asst prof math, 59-61; from asst prof to prof math, Calif State Univ, Northridge, 63-89. *Concurrent Pos:* Consult, Santa Barbara Schs, 61-62 & Minn Nat Lab, State Dept Educ, 62-67. *Mem:* AAAS; Math Asn Am; Am Educ Res Asn. *Res:* Psychological problems in mathematics education; curriculum development. *Mailing Add:* 97 Tenth St No 3 Cayucos CA 93430

**WRIGHT, ERNEST MARSHALL,** MEMBRANE BIOLOGY, EPITHELIAL TRANSPORT. *Current Pos:* res fel physiol, 66-67, from asst prof to assoc prof, 67-74, PROF PHYSIOL, UNIV CALIF, LOS ANGELES, 74-, CHMN DEPT PHYSIOL, 87- *Personal Data:* b Belfast, N Ireland, June 8, 40; Brit citizen. *Educ:* Univ London, BSc, 61, DSc, 78; Univ Sheffield, England, Ph D(physiol), 64. *Prof Exp:* Res asst physiol, Univ Sheffield, 63-65; res fel biophysics, Harvard Univ, 65-66. *Concurrent Pos:* Mem, physiol study sect, NIH, 82-86, chmn, 83-86; Jacob Javits Neurosci investr, 85- *Mem:* Am Physiol Soc; Am Biophys Soc; Am Nephrology Soc; Am Soc Gen Physiologists; Brit Physiol Soc. *Res:* Transport of solutes and water across epithelial tissues from the kidney, intestine and brain; transport of ions and nutrients (sugars, amino acids, carboxylic acids) across plasma membranes of epithelial cells. *Mailing Add:* Dept Physiol Univ Calif Med Sch Los Angeles CA 90095-1751. *Fax:* 310-206-5661; *E-Mail:* ikusemw@uclamvs

**WRIGHT, EVERETT JAMES,** ORGANIC CHEMISTRY. *Current Pos:* RES CHEMIST, E I DU PONT DE NEMOURS & CO, 57- *Personal Data:* b Meriden, Conn, Sept 20, 29; m 51; c 1. *Educ:* Hobart Col, BS, 51; Univ Del, MS, 54, PhD(chem), 57. *Prof Exp:* Chemist, Olin Industs, 51-52. *Mem:* Am Chem Soc. *Res:* Organic nitrogen heterocycles; aliphatic nitrogen compounds; polymerization; textile chemicals; application techniques; fibers and fabrics; personnel and industrial relations. *Mailing Add:* 216 N Star Rd Newark DE 19711-2935

**WRIGHT, FARRIN SCOTT,** AGRICULTURAL ENGINEERING, PLANT SCIENCE. *Current Pos:* AGR ENGR, USDA, 66- *Personal Data:* b Fallston, NC, Dec 3, 36; m 57, Joyce A Ross; c Susan, Rachel & Anita. *Educ:* Clemson Univ, BS, 59, MS, 61; NC State Univ, PhD(agr eng), 66. *Prof Exp:* Res asst agr eng, Clemson Univ, 57-59; res instr, NC State Univ, 60-66. *Concurrent Pos:* Fel prog, Nat Cotton Coun, 59-60; mem, Suffolk City Sch Bd, 77-87 & 93-94. *Mem:* Am Soc Agr Engrs; Sigma Xi; fel Am Peanut Res & Educ Soc. *Res:* Agricultural research, development of concepts and improvement of peanut production equipment and peanut harvesting machinery; soil and water management-irrigation and conservation tillage. *Mailing Add:* Nat Peanut Res Lab 1011 Forrester Dr SE Dawson GA 31742

**WRIGHT, FARROLL TIM,** STATISTICS, MATHEMATICS. *Current Pos:* from assoc prof to prof math, Univ Mo-Rolla, 75-89, PROF STATIST, UNIV MO, COLUMBIA, 89-, CHMN DEPT, 95- *Personal Data:* b Hume, Mo, June 24, 41; m 65; c 4. *Educ:* Univ Mo, AB, 63, AM, 64, PhD(statist), 68. *Prof Exp:* Asst prof math, Univ Mo-Rolla, 67-68; asst prof statist, Univ Iowa, 68-71, assoc prof, 71-75. *Concurrent Pos:* Prog dir, Probability & Statist, NSF, 81-82. *Mem:* Fel Am Statist Asn; fel Inst Math Statist; Int Statist Inst. *Res:* Order restricted inference; behavior of sums of independent variables; reliability and life testing. *Mailing Add:* Dept Statist Univ Mo Columbia MO 65211. *Fax:* 573-884-5524; *E-Mail:* wright@stat.missouri.edu

**WRIGHT, FRANCIS STUART,** PEDIATRIC NEUROLOGY. *Current Pos:* PROF PEDIAT & NEUROL, OHIO STATE UNIV, 81- *Personal Data:* b Pittsfield, Mass, Feb 24, 29; m 58; c 6. *Educ:* Univ Mass, BS, 51; Univ Rochester, MD, 55; Am Bd Pediat, dipl, 64; Am Bd Psychiat & Neurol, dipl & cert neurol, 66, cert child neurol, 72. *Prof Exp:* From asst prof to prof pediat & neurol, Med Ctr, Univ Minn, Minneapolis, 68-81. *Concurrent Pos:* Fel pediat, Med Ctr, Univ Minn, Minneapolis, 56-58, Nat Inst Neurol Dis & Blindness spec fel pediat neurol, 60-63; consult, Minneapolis Pub Sch Syst, 65-; assoc, Grad Fac, Univ Minn, 67- *Res:* Developmental electrophysiology. *Mailing Add:* Dept Pediat 5123 Bonham Rd Oxford OH 45056

**WRIGHT, FRED BOYER,** MATHEMATICS. *Current Pos:* chmn dept, 68-76, PROF MATH, UNIV NC, CHAPEL HILL, 68- *Personal Data:* b Roanoke, Va, Dec 14, 25; m 48; c 2. *Educ:* Univ NC, BA, 47, MA, 48; Univ Chicago, PhD(math). 53. *Prof Exp:* Instr math, Univ NC, 48-49; sr mathematician adv bd simulation, Univ Chicago, 53-54, consult systs res; from instr to prof math, Tulane Univ, 54-68. *Concurrent Pos:* Vis prof, Cambridge Univ, 58-59 & Northwestern Univ, 63; Sloan Found fel, 58-62; chmn comt regional develop, Nat Acad Sci-Nat Res Coun, 69-71, pregrad fel panel, 71-72; mem math adv panel, NSF, 71-; pregrad fel panel (chmn, 73-74), 71-74; actg chmn opers res curric, Univ NC, Chapel Hill, 72. *Mem:* Am Math Soc; Math Asn Am; London Math Soc; Sigma Xi. *Res:* Algebra; functional analysis; history of math. *Mailing Add:* 5 Buttons Lane Chapel Hill NC 27514-4200

**WRIGHT, FRED(ERICK) D(UNSTAN),** mining engineering; deceased, see previous edition for last biography

**WRIGHT, FRED MARION,** MATHEMATICS. *Current Pos:* from instr to assoc prof, 53-64, PROF MATH, IOWA STATE UNIV, 64- *Personal Data:* b Aurora, Ill, Sept 29, 23; m 47. *Educ:* Denison Univ, BA, 44; Northwestern Univ, MS, 49, PhD(math). 53. *Prof Exp:* Instr math, Denison Univ, 47; asst, Northwestern Univ, 47-51. *Concurrent Pos:* Vis asst prof, Univ Mich, 57-58. *Mem:* Am Math Soc. *Res:* Continued fractions and function theory. *Mailing Add:* Dept Math Rm 462 Carver Iowa State Univ Ames IA 50011

**WRIGHT, FREDERICK FENNING,** MARINE GEOLOGY, ESTUARINE OCEANOGRAPHY. *Current Pos:* CONSULT, 81- *Personal Data:* b Princeton, NJ, Mar 16, 34; m 84, Wanda M Mead; c Paul A & Moss Penelope. *Educ:* Columbia Univ, BS, 59, AM, 61; Univ Southern Calif, PhD(geol). 67. *Prof Exp:* Teaching asst geol, Columbia Univ, 59-61; res asst, Univ Southern Calif, 61-65; eng geologist, Div Water Resources, State of Calif, 65-66; asst prof marine sci, Inst Marine Sci, Univ Alaska, Fairbanks, 66-72, asst prof oceanog & exten oceanogr, Marine Adv Prog, Anchorage, 72-74; oceanog consult, 74-75; dir, Alaska Coastal Mgt Prog, Off Gov, State of Alaska, 75; Alaska OCS res mgt officer, Outer Continental Shelf Environ Assessment Prog, Off Gov, State of Alaska & Nat Oceanic & Atmospheric Agency, 75-81. *Concurrent Pos:* Asst dir, NSF Inst Oceanog, Marine Lab, Tex A&M Univ, 63; Geol Soc Am Penrose res grant, 64-66; dir, NSF Inst Geol Oceanog, Douglas Marine Sta, Univ Alaska, 68. *Mem:* Am Geophys Union; Am Soc Limnol & Oceanog; Arctic Inst NAm. *Res:* Inshore oceanography and sedimentation in subarctic; fisheries oceanography; coastal resource management and planning. *Mailing Add:* PO Box 240537 Douglas AK 99824-0537

**WRIGHT, FREDERICK HAMILTON,** PHYSICS. *Current Pos:* CONSULT, 78- *Personal Data:* b Washington, DC, Dec 2, 12; m 70, Margueritte Walker; c 4. *Educ:* Haverford Col, BA, 34; Calif Inst Technol, PhD(physics), 48. *Prof Exp:* Aerodynamicist, Douglas Aircraft Co, Inc, 40-46; res engr, Jet Propulsion Lab, Calif Inst Technol, 46-59; div mgr & prog mgr, Space Gen Corp, 59-69; mem staff, Aerojet Electrosysts Co, Azusa, 69-78. *Mem:* Am Inst Aeronaut & Astronaut; Am Phys Soc; Inst Elec & Electronics Engrs. *Res:* Sensor systems; fluids; geophysics. *Mailing Add:* 515 Palmetto Dr Pasadena CA 91105

**WRIGHT, GEORGE EDWARD,** MEDICINAL CHEMISTRY. *Current Pos:* assoc prof, Univ Mass, 74-78, actg assoc dean, 78-80, dean grad studies, 80-84, PROF PHARMACOL, MED SCH, UNIV MASS, 78- *Personal Data:* b Milwaukee, Wis, Oct 21, 41; m 65, Donna Draski; c 3. *Educ:* Univ Ill, Chicago, BS, 63, PhD(chem), 67. *Prof Exp:* Sr res asst chem, Univ Durham, 66-68; asst prof med chem, Sch Pharm, Univ Md, Baltimore, 68-74. *Concurrent Pos:* Affil assoc prof chem, Clark Univ, 76-78, affil prof, 78-; vis prof, Inst Exp Physics, Univ Warsaw, 80-81; Fogarty fel, Max Planck Inst Med Res, Heidelberg, Ger, 88-89. *Mem:* Am Chem Soc; Chem Soc; Int Soc Heterocyclic Chem; Int Soc Antiviral Res. *Res:* Synthesis and structure of nucleosides and nucleotides; nuclear magnetic resonance spectroscopy; DNA polymerase inhibitors; oncogene proteins. *Mailing Add:* Dept Pharmacol Univ Mass Med Sch Worcester MA 01655. *Fax:* 508-856-5080

**WRIGHT, GEORGE GREEN,** immunology, microbiology, for more information see previous edition

**WRIGHT, GEORGE JOSEPH,** DRUG METABOLISM, BIOCHEMISTRY. *Current Pos:* PRES, G WRIGHT CONSULT INC. *Personal Data:* b Allendale, Ill, June 4, 31; m 53; c 2. *Educ:* Univ Ill, Urbana, BS, 52, PhD(animal nutrit & biochem). 60. *Prof Exp:* Med researcher human biochem, L B Mendel Res Lab, Elgin State Hosp, Ill, 60-62; biochemist toxicol & indust hyg, Biochem Res Lab, Dow Chem Co, Midland, Mich, 62-67; head, Drug Metab Dept, Merrell-Nat Labs, Richardson-Merrell, Inc, 67-79; dir, Drug Metab, A H Robins Co, 79- *Concurrent Pos:* Lectr chem, Eve Col, Univ Cincinnati, 70-72; consult clin and preclin pharmacol, Walter Reed Army Inst Res & Nat Cancer Inst. *Mem:* AAAS; Soc Toxicol; Am Soc Pharmacol & Exp Therapeut; Am Soc Clin Pharmacol & Therapeut; Sigma Xi. *Res:* Drug disposition; bioavailability; biopharmaceutics; pharmacokinetics; enzymology; toxicology. *Mailing Add:* G Wright Consult Inc 8229 Greg Fox Dr West Chester OH 45069-2195

**WRIGHT, GEORGE LEONARD, JR,** IMMUNOCHEMISTRY, TUMOR IMMUNOLOGY. *Current Pos:* assoc prof, 73-76, DIR IMMUNOL PROG, EASTERN VA MED SCH, 75-, DEP CHMN, DEPT MICRO/IMMUNOL, 86-, PROF DEPT MICROBIOL & IMMUNOL, 76- *Personal Data:* b

Ludington, Mich, Feb 8, 37; m 64; c 2. *Educ:* Albion Col, BA, 59; Mich State Univ, MS, 62, PhD(microbiol, path, biochem), 66. *Honors & Awards:* NIH Career Develop Award, 75-80. *Prof Exp:* Fel immunol & immunochem, Sch Med, George Washington Univ, 66-67; asst prof microbiol & immunochem, 67-73. *Concurrent Pos:* Sigma Xi award sci res, 66; spec consult, Vet Admin Hosp, Wilmington, Del, 66-73; deleg & rapporteur, Tuberc Panel, US-Japan Coop Med Sci Prog, Tokyo, 68 & 70; Hartford Found grant, 68-73; NIH grant, 72-74; Nat Cancer Inst contract, 75-78; Am Cancer Soc grant, 77-79; spec consult, Beckman Instruments; consult, Washington, DC Vet Admin & Children's Hosps; mem subcomt, US-Japan Med Sci Prog Stand Mycobact Antigens. *Mem:* AAAS; Am Asn Cancer Res; Am Soc Microbiol; Am Asn Immunologists; Sigma Xi; Am Urol Asn; Soc Basic Urol Res; Soc Urologic Oncol. *Res:* Separation, isolation and immunobiological characterization of specific mycobacterial antigens; identification and isolation of human prostate tumor-associated antigens; monoclonial antibodies to urogenital cancer cells for diagnosis and patient management. *Mailing Add:* Dept Microbiol & Immunol Eastern Va Med 700 Olney Rd PO Box 1980 Norfolk VA 23501-1980

**WRIGHT, HAROLD E(UGENE),** MECHANICS. *Current Pos:* RETIRED. *Personal Data:* b Hillsdale, Mich, Dec 28, 20; m 49; c 2. *Educ:* Univ Dayton, BME, 49; Univ Cincinnati, MS, 60; Mich State Univ, PhD, 66. *Prof Exp:* From instr to assoc prof mech eng, Univ Dayton, 49-62; from assoc prof to prof mech eng, USAF Inst Technol, 62-82. *Concurrent Pos:* Mech engr, Nat Cash Register Co, 51-52; combustion engr, City of Dayton, 52-53; maintenance dir, Miami Valley Hosp, 53-57. *Mem:* Am Soc Mech Engrs; Am Soc Eng Educ; Nat Soc Prof Engrs. *Res:* Gas dynamics; applied mechanics; heat transfer; shock tubes utilization, both gas and liquid drivers. *Mailing Add:* 7625 Rolling Oak Dr Dayton OH 45459

**WRIGHT, HARRY TUCKER, JR,** PEDIATRICS, EPIDEMIOLOGY. *Current Pos:* From instr to assoc prof, 63-73, PROF PEDIAT, UNIV SOUTHERN CALIF, 73-, HEAD, DIV INFECTIOUS DIS & VIROL, CHILDREN'S HOSP, LOS ANGELES, 75- *Personal Data:* b Louisville, Ky, July 21, 29. *Educ:* Wake Forest Col, BS, 51, MD, 55; Univ Calif, Berkeley, MPH, 75. *Concurrent Pos:* Teaching fel pediat, Case Western Reserve Univ, 58-59; NIH res training grant, 61-64; mem infectious dis comt, Am Acad Pediat. *Mem:* Am Acad Pediat; Am Fedn Clin Res; Soc Pediat Res; Am Pediat Soc; Am Soc Microbiol; fel Infectious Dis Soc. *Res:* Clinical and laboratory studies of cytomegalovirus and other herpes viruses; central nervous system syndromes of viral etiology and newborn infections; virology; hospital acquired infections; infectious disease. *Mailing Add:* Childrens Hosp Los Angeles PO Box 54700 Terminal Annex Los Angeles CA 90054-0700

**WRIGHT, HARVEL AMOS,** MATHEMATICS. *Current Pos:* RETIRED. *Personal Data:* b Mayflower, Ark, July 6, 33; m 54; c 2. *Educ:* Ark State Teachers Col, BS, 54; Univ Ark, MA, 56; Univ Tenn, PhD, 67. *Prof Exp:* Teacher high sch, Ark, 55-56; instr math & physics, Ark State Teachers Col, 56-58; instr math, Univ Tenn, 58-62; physicist, Oak Ridge Nat Lab, 62-74, head, Biol & Radiation Physics Sect, 74-89; pres & bd dirs, Consultec Sci Inc, 89-95. *Concurrent Pos:* Vis scientist, Europ Ctr Nuclear Res, Switz, 71-72. *Mem:* Health Physics Soc; Radiation Res Soc. *Res:* Interaction of radiation with matter; dosimetry of ionizing radiation; plasma physics; theory of real variable. *Mailing Add:* 2435 Smithland Lane Knoxville TN 37932

**WRIGHT, HASTINGS KEMPER,** MEDICINE, PHYSIOLOGY. *Current Pos:* assoc prof, 66-72, PROF SURG, SCH MED, YALE UNIV, 72- *Personal Data:* b Boston, Mass, Aug 22, 28; m 54; c 4. *Educ:* Harvard Univ, AB, 50, MD, 54. *Prof Exp:* Asst prof surg, Western Reserve Univ, 62-66. *Concurrent Pos:* Crile fel surg, Western Reserve Univ, 61-62. *Mem:* AAAS; Soc Univ Surg; Am Fedn Clin Res; Am Gastroenterol Asn; Am Surg Asn. *Res:* Gastrointestinal fluid and electrolyte absorption. *Mailing Add:* Dept Surg Yale Univ Med Sch 333 Cedar St New Haven CT 06510-3289

**WRIGHT, HELEN S,** APPLIED NUTRITION, NUTRITION ASSESSMENT. *Current Pos:* Assoc prof, 75-85, PROF NUTRIT, PA STATE UNIV, 85- *Personal Data:* b Kirkland Lake, Ont, Mar 29, 36. *Educ:* Pa State Univ, PhD(nutrit), 69. *Mem:* Soc Nutrit Educ; Am Inst Nutrit; Am Dietetic Asn. *Mailing Add:* PA State Univ 126 Henderson Bldg S Rm 5 University Park PA 16802

**WRIGHT, HENRY ALBERT,** fire ecology, range management; deceased, see previous edition for last biography

**WRIGHT, HERBERT EDGAR, JR,** QUATERNARY PALEOECOLOGY. *Current Pos:* from asst prof to prof, Univ Minn, 47-74, regents prof geol, ecol & bot, 74-88, dir, 63-91, EMER PROF GEOL, ECOL & BOT, LIMNOL, LIMNOL RES CTR, UNIV MINN, MINNEAPOLIS, 88- *Personal Data:* b Malden, Mass, Sept 13, 17; m 43, Rhea Jane Hahn; c Richard, Jonathan, Andrew & Jeffrey. *Educ:* Harvard Univ, AB, 39, AM, 41, PhD(geol), 43. *Hon Degrees:* DSc, Trinity Col, Dublin, 66; PhD, Lund Univ, Sweden, 87, Univ Minn, 96. *Honors & Awards:* Pomerance Award, Archeol Inst Am, 84; Fryxell Award, Soc Am Archeol, 90; Distinguished Career Award, Geol Soc Am, 89 & 92, Amer Quaternary Asn, 96. *Prof Exp:* Instr geol, Brown Univ, 46-47. *Concurrent Pos:* Geologist, US Geol Surv, DC, 46-47 & 52-53 & Minn Geol Surv, DC, 52-53; mem Boston Col-Fordham archaeol exped, 47; Wenner-Gren fel, 51; mem, archaeol exped, Oriental Inst, 51, 54-55, 60, 63, 64 & 70; Guggenheim Fel, 54-55. *Mem:* Nat Acad Sci; Geol Soc Am; Ecol Soc Am; Am Soc Limnol & Oceonog; Am Quaternary Asn (pres, 71-72). *Res:* Pleistocene geology and paleoecology; vegetation history; paleolimnology. *Mailing Add:* Dept Geol Univ Minn Minneapolis MN 55455. *Fax:* 612-625-3819; *E-Mail:* hew@maroon.tc.umn.edu

**WRIGHT, HERBERT FESSENDEN,** MEDICINAL CHEMISTRY, BIOLOGY & MOLECULAR BIOLOGY. *Current Pos:* RETIRED. *Personal Data:* b Worcester, Mass, July 19, 17; m 41; c 1. *Educ:* Oberlin Col, AB, 40; Cornell Univ, MS, 42, PhD(org chem), 44; Am Inst Chem, cert. *Prof Exp:* Asst chem, Cornell Univ, 42-43, Off Sci Res & Develop antimalarial proj, 43-44; res chemist, Lever Bros Co, Mass, 44-45; res assoc, Mass Inst Technol, 45-46; instr chem, Tufts Col, 46-48; res chemist, Arthur D Little, Inc, 48-49; instr chem, Yale Univ, 49-52; sr res chemist, Olin Industs, 52-54; pres & res dir, W Elsworth Co, Inc, 59-64; from asst prof to assoc prof, Univ New Haven, 64-66, chmn dept, 67-79, dir environ studies, 70-79, prof biol & phys sci, 66-87. *Concurrent Pos:* Consult chem, 54-; dir, Univ Res Insts Conn, 67-77. *Mem:* AAAS; Am Chem Soc; NY Acad Sci; fel Am Inst Chem; Am Inst Biol Sci. *Res:* Synthetic drugs and vitamin A, organic ortho silicate esters; polymers; fungicides; antimetabolites; organic electrode reactions; organic synthetic methods; molecular biology; forensic science; biochemical genetics; nutrition; science education. *Mailing Add:* 1041 Ridge Rd Hamden CT 06517-1620

**WRIGHT, IAN GLAISBY,** synthetic organic chemistry, for more information see previous edition

**WRIGHT, JAMES ARTHUR,** GEOPHYSICS. *Current Pos:* from asst prof to assoc prof physics, 69-82, PROF EARTH SCI, 90- *Personal Data:* b Toronto, Ont, Dec 29, 41; m 70. *Educ:* Univ Toronto, BASc, 64, MSc, 65, PhD(physics), 68. *Prof Exp:* Nat Res Coun Can fel, Brunswick Tech Univ, 68-69. *Concurrent Pos:* Mem geomagnetism subcomt, Assoc Comt Geod & Geophys, Nat Res Coun Can, 71-73, Lithprobe Sub-Comt, 88-92. *Mem:* Can Soc Explor Geophysicists; Geol Asn Can; Am Geophys Union; Soc Explor Geophysicists; Asn Prof Engrs & Geoscientists. *Res:* Geomagnetism and the earth's interior; exploration geophysics; marine heat flow. *Mailing Add:* Dept Earth Sci Mem Univ Nfld St John's NF A1B 3X5 Can

**WRIGHT, JAMES EDWARD,** EXERCISE PHYSIOLOGY. *Current Pos:* SPORTS SCI CONSULT, 96- *Personal Data:* b Little Rock, Ark, Sept 6, 46; m 66; c 2. *Educ:* Fairleigh Dickinson Univ, BS, 69; Miss State Univ, PhD(zool), 73. *Prof Exp:* Asst prof biol sci, Simon's Rock Early Col, 73-75; NIH fel & asst res physiologist exercise & environ physiol, Inst Environ Stress, Univ Calif, Santa Barbara, 75-77; staff, Exercise Physiol Div, US Army Res Inst Environ Med, 77-82; tech ed & spec asst publ, Weider Health & Fitness Corp, Woodland Hills, Calif, 82-96. *Concurrent Pos:* Athletic training & nutrit consult, Sports Sci Consult, Natick, Mass, 78; mem, Int Coun Phys Fitness Res, 80-; assoc ed, Nat Strength Conditioning Asn J, 81- *Mem:* AAAS; Am Col Sports Med. *Res:* Longitudinal and cross sectional investigation of functional physical and physiological changes produced by weight/strength training and body building; anabolic steroid and other ergogenic aid effects on muscle size, strength, endurance and performance; comparative responses of males and females to strength training and bodybuilding; occupational fitness requirements. *Mailing Add:* 17326 Parthenia St Northridge CA 91325

**WRIGHT, JAMES ELBERT,** MEDICAL ENTOMOLOGY, BACTERIOLOGY. *Current Pos:* vpres res & develop, 93-94, CHIEF TECHNOL OFFICER & VPRES, TROY BIOSOURCE, 94- *Personal Data:* b Kerrville, Tex, Oct 7, 40; m 62; c 2. *Educ:* Tex A&M Univ, BS, 63; Ohio State Univ, PhD(med entom, bact), 66; Am Registry Cert Entom, cert. *Prof Exp:* Res asst mosquitoes entom, Ohio State Univ, 63-66, res assoc, 66; res entomologist & res leader, Boll Weevil Res Lab, Sci & Educ Admin-Agr Res, Agr Res Serv, USDA, 66-93, res entomologist, Subtrop Cotton Insect Res Lab; dir entomol, USDA-ARS, Washington, DC. *Concurrent Pos:* Adj prof entomol, Miss State Univ, Tex A&M. *Mem:* Fel AAAS; Entom Soc Am; Am Chem Soc; Soc Invert Path; Am Mosquito Control Asn. *Res:* Insect juvenile and molting hormones interrelationships; insect biochemistry; mosquito biology; diapause mechanisms; livestock arthropods; biting flies; stable fly and horn fly biology; studies on temperature and photoperiod; biology of livestock ticks; insect growth regulators; boll weevil and cotton insects; sterility; nutrition. *Mailing Add:* Troy Biosci 2620 N 37th Dr Phoenix AZ 85009. *E-Mail:* jamesw234@msn.com

**WRIGHT, JAMES EVERETT, JR,** genetics; deceased, see previous edition for last biography

**WRIGHT, JAMES FOLEY,** ENVIRONMENTAL SCIENCES. *Current Pos:* PRES, SW ENVIRON SERV, 91- *Personal Data:* b Tulsa, Okla, Feb 9, 43; div; c 2. *Educ:* Cent State Univ, Okla, BS, 69; Iowa State Univ, PhD(nuclear chem), 74. *Prof Exp:* Fel physics, Ames Lab, Iowa, 74; scientist, Battelle NW Labs, 74-75; mem sci staff weapon planning, Los Alamos Sci Lab, 75-80; pres, Tech Systs, 80-90. *Concurrent Pos:* Dir, Nat Particle-Beam Study Group, 78-79. *Mem:* Am Phys Soc; Inst Elec & Electronics Engrs; Am Chem Soc. *Res:* Directed energy weapons, nuclear weapons, plasma physics, systems analysis; Monte Carlo risk analysis; hydrodynamics; process chemistry; radiation handling and disposal; gamma-ray spectroscopy. *Mailing Add:* PO Box 2991 Midland TX 79702-2991

**WRIGHT, JAMES FRANCIS,** COMPARATIVE PATHOLOGY. *Current Pos:* VET & PATHOLOGIST, NC ZOOL PARK, ASHEBORO, NC, 88- *Personal Data:* b Philadelphia, Pa, Jan 18, 24; m 55; c 3. *Educ:* Univ Pa, VMD, 51; Univ Calif, Davis, PhD(comp path), 69. *Prof Exp:* Vet in-charge animal quarantine, Plum Island Animal Dis Lab, USDA, NY, 54-57; vet, Nat Zool Park, Smithsonian Inst, 57-62; res scientist, USPHS, USAF Radiobiol Lab, Univ Tex, Austin, 62-64, Yerkes Regional Primate Res Ctr, Emory Univ, 64-65 & Radiobiol Lab, Univ Calif, Davis, 65-69; chief toxicol studies sect,

Twinbrook Res Lab, Environ Protection Agency, 69-73, chief path studies sect, Health Effects Res Lab, 73-82. *Concurrent Pos:* Adj assoc prof, Sch Vet Med, NC State Univ, 79-82, vis assoc prof path, 82-92; consult pathologist, NC Zool Park, 82-88; adj vis assoc prof, Vet Med, 83-92. *Mem:* Am Vet Med Asn; Am Asn Zoo Vets; Am Asn Lab Animal Sci; Wildlife Dis Asn; Radiation Res Soc. *Res:* pathology and toxicology; wild & exotic animals; diseases of wild animals. *Mailing Add:* 8508 E Lake Ct Raleigh NC 27613

**WRIGHT, JAMES LOUIS,** AGRONOMY, AGRICULTURAL METEOROLOGY. *Current Pos:* ASSOC PROF RES CLIMATOL & AFFIL PROF SOILS, UNIV IDAHO, 70- *Personal Data:* b Pleasant Grove, Utah, Aug 28, 34; m 58; c 7. *Educ:* Utah State Univ, BS, 59, MS, 61; Cornell Univ, PhD(soil physics), 65. *Prof Exp:* SOIL SCIENTIST, AGR RES SERV, USDA, 65- *Mem:* Am Soc Agron; Soil Sci Soc Am; Sigma Xi. *Res:* Microclimate investigations to determine rate of evaporation of water from agricultural crops using energy balance and micrometeorological approaches. *Mailing Add:* 3795 N 3575 E Kimberly ID 83341

**WRIGHT, JAMES P,** ASTROPHYSICS. *Current Pos:* PROG DIR, DIV ASTROPHYS SCI, NSF, 70- *Personal Data:* b St Petersburg, Fla, Apr 10, 34; m 56; c 4. *Educ:* Univ Fla, BS, 56; Univ Chicago, PhD(chem), 61. *Prof Exp:* NSF-Nat Res Coun assoc, Inst Space Studies, 61-63; vis asst prof math, Math Res Ctr, Univ Wis, 63-64; astrophysicist, Smithsonian Astrophys Observ, 64-70. *Concurrent Pos:* Lectr astron, Harvard Univ, 64-70. *Mem:* Am Astron Soc; Int Astron Union. *Res:* Properties of high temperature gases in electromagnetic fields; theoretical cosmological world models; observable effects of use of general relativity theory; high energy astrophysics. *Mailing Add:* 4119 Woodbine St Chevy Chase MD 20815-5043. *Fax:* 703-306-0910; *E-Mail:* jwright@nsf.gov

**WRIGHT, JAMES R,** SOIL CHEMISTRY. *Current Pos:* RETIRED. *Personal Data:* b Riversdale, NS, July 19, 16; m 42; c 2. *Educ:* McGill Univ, BSc, 40; Mich State Univ, MS, 48, PhD(soil chem), 53. *Hon Degrees:* DSc, Acadia Univ, 80. *Prof Exp:* Asst chemist, NS Dept Agr, 40-41, asst prov chemist, 45-50; head soil genesis sect, Soil Res Inst, Can Dept Agr, 51-61, dir, Kentville Res Sta, 61-78; consult soils & agr, 79-86. *Concurrent Pos:* Lectr, NS Agr Col, 45-50; prof, Acadia Univ, 65-75; asst dir gen, Res Br, Agr Can, 67-68; reg-treas, NS Inst Agrology, 81-85. *Mem:* Am Soc Agron; Soil Sci Soc Am; fel Chem Inst Can; Can Soc Soil Sci (pres, 61-62); fel Agr Inst Can. *Res:* Chemical nature of soil organic matter; soil genesis, fertility and plant nutrition. *Mailing Add:* PO Box 668 Chester NS B0J 1J0 Can

**WRIGHT, JAMES ROSCOE,** ORGANIC CHEMISTRY, TECHNICAL MANAGEMENT. *Current Pos:* RETIRED. *Personal Data:* b White Hall, Md, July 7, 22; m 50, Blanca Guerrero; c James A & Ronald K. *Educ:* Md State Col Salisbury, BSEd, 46; Wash Col, BS, 48; Univ Del, MS, 49, PhD(chem), 51. *Honors & Awards:* Gold Medal Award, Dept Com, 75. *Prof Exp:* Res chemist, SW Res Inst, 51-52 & Chevron Res Corp, Chevron Oil Co, 52-60; from chemist to sr chemist, Nat Bur Stand, 60-66, phys sci adminstr, 66-72, dir, Ctr Bldg Technol, 72-74, dep dir, Inst Appl Technol, 74-76, actg dir, 76-78, dep dir, Nat Eng Lab, 78-85; consult, 85-88. *Concurrent Pos:* Asst prof, Trinity Univ, Tex, 51-52; Comn Sci & Tech fel, US Patent Off, 64-65; del, Int Union Testing & Res Labs Mat & Struct, 68-88; mem, USA/Egypt Working Group, Technol, Res & Develop, 76-78; dir & treas, St Mark Elderly Housing Corp, 87-; dir, Washington DC Chap, Buick Club Am, 91-93. *Mem:* Emer mem Am Chem Soc; Am Soc Testing & Mat; hon mem Int Union Testing & Res Labs Mat & Struct (vice-pres, 79-82, pres, 71-72 & 82-85). *Res:* Organosilicon compounds; radiation effects on organic lubricants; emulsification of petroleum products; photochemical stability of organic building materials; application of performance concept in building research, codes and standards; managerial organization development. *Mailing Add:* 6204 Lone Oak Dr Bethesda MD 20817

**WRIGHT, JAMES SHERMAN,** THEORETICAL CHEMISTRY. *Current Pos:* from asst prof to assoc prof, 70-83, PROF CHEM, CARLETON UNIV, 83-, CHAIR DEPT, 94- *Personal Data:* b Seattle, Wash, Aug 27, 40; m 84; c Julian, Cameron, Meredith & Laura. *Educ:* Stanford Univ, BS, 62; Univ Calif, Berkeley, PhD(chem), 68. *Prof Exp:* Nat Ctr Sci Res, France grant, Fac Sci, Orsay, France, 69-70. *Mem:* Am Chem Soc; Can Soc Chem. *Res:* Theoretical chemistry; unusual chemical structures, molecular reaction dynamics, quantum chemistry, chemical bonding. *Mailing Add:* Dept Chem Carleton Univ 1125 Colonel By Dr Ottawa ON K1S 5B6 Can

**WRIGHT, JEFFERY REGAN,** INFORMATION SYSTEMS, PUBLIC DECISION. *Current Pos:* DIR, IND WATER RESOURCES RES CTR. *Personal Data:* b Spokane, Wash, Nov 25, 50; m 74; c 2. *Educ:* Univ Wash, BA, 75, BSE, 75, MSCE, 77; Johns Hopkins Univ, PhD(environ eng), 82. *Prof Exp:* Res asst prof, Dept Civil Eng, Univ Wash, 76-78; ASSOC PROF CIVIL ENG, SCH CIVIL ENG, PURDUE UNIV, 87- *Concurrent Pos:* Vpres, Omtek Eng, Inc, 83-; dir, Scheduling Systs Res Inst, 85- *Mem:* Am Soc Civil Eng; Opers Res Soc Am; Inst Mgt Sci; Am Soc Eng Educ; Soc Comput Simulation; Am Geophys Union. *Res:* Public systems modeling such as facilities location, project planning and management, scheduling systems; decision support and information systems design and resource acquisition-allocation; development of computer-support systems. *Mailing Add:* Sch Civil Eng Purdue Univ West Lafayette IN 47907-1284

**WRIGHT, JOE CARROL,** ORGANIC CHEMISTRY. *Current Pos:* assoc prof, 66-72, PROF CHEM, HENDERSON STATE UNIV, 72-, DEAN, MATLOCK ELLIS COL ARTS & SCI. *Personal Data:* b Benton, Ark, Feb 6, 33; m 53; c 4. *Educ:* Ouachita Baptist Univ, BS, 54; Univ Ark, MS, 62,

PhD(org mech), 66. *Prof Exp:* Asst prof chem, Mobile Col, 64-66. *Mem:* Am Chem Soc; Royal Soc Chem. *Res:* Isotope effect studies in organic reaction mechanism determinations. *Mailing Add:* Dean Ellis Col Arts & Sci Henderson State Univ Box 7622 Arkadelphia AR 71999-0001

**WRIGHT, JOHN CLIFFORD,** LIMNOLOGY. *Current Pos:* RETIRED. *Personal Data:* b Livingston, Mont, Jan 29, 19; m 95, Gail Wheatley; c John & Jean. *Educ:* Mont State Univ, BS, 41; Ohio State Univ, PhD, 50. *Prof Exp:* From instr to assoc prof, Mont State Univ, 49-61, assoc coordr, Ctr Environ Studies, 71-73, prof bot, 61-81. *Concurrent Pos:* NSF sr fel, 59-60; exec secy, XV Int Cong Limnol, 61-62; dir, Ctr Environ Studies, Mont State Univ, 66-71. *Mem:* AAAS; Ecol Soc Am; Am Soc Limnol & Oceanog; Int Asn Theoret & Appl Limnol. *Res:* Oceanography; ecology. *Mailing Add:* 1111 S Bozeman Ave Bozeman MT 59715-5341

**WRIGHT, JOHN CURTIS,** ANALYTICAL & PHYSICAL CHEMISTRY, SOLID STATE PHYSICS. *Current Pos:* from asst prof to assoc prof, 72-80, PROF CHEM, UNIV WIS, 80- *Personal Data:* b Lubbock, Tex, Sept 17, 43; m 68, Carol Swanson; c Dawna & David. *Educ:* Union Col, BS, 65; Johns Hopkins Univ, PhD(physics), 70. *Honors & Awards:* William F Meggars Award, Soc Appl Spectros, 80; Spectrochem Anal Award, Am Chem Soc, 91. *Prof Exp:* Student fel, Purdue Univ, 70-72. *Mem:* Sigma Xi; Am Chem Soc; Am Phys Soc. *Res:* Lasers in analytical chemistry; fluorescence methods; solid state chemistry; coherent Raman methods; energy transfer and relaxation processes. *Mailing Add:* 1101 University Ave Univ Wis Madison WI 53706

**WRIGHT, JOHN FOWLER,** PHYSICAL CHEMISTRY. *Current Pos:* RETIRED. *Personal Data:* b London, Ont, July 28, 21; US citizen; m 49; c 2. *Educ:* Univ Western Ont, BSc, 45, MSc, 46. *Prof Exp:* Res assoc, Res Labs, Eastman Kodak Co, 46-83. *Mem:* Am Chem Soc. *Res:* Polymer synthesis; surface treatments of polymers; colloid chemistry; surface active agents. *Mailing Add:* 85 Greatwood Circle Fairport NY 14450

**WRIGHT, JOHN JAY,** ATOMIC PHYSICS. *Current Pos:* asst prof, 70-77, PROF PHYSICS, UNIV NH, 77- *Personal Data:* b Torrington, Conn, July 10, 43; m 65; c 2. *Educ:* Worcester Polytech Inst, BS, 65; Univ NH, PhD(physics), 70. *Prof Exp:* Fel lasers, Joint Inst Lab Astrophys, Colo, 69-70. *Mem:* Am Inst Physics; Am Phys Soc; Am Asn Physics Teachers. *Res:* Optical pumping; liquid crystals. *Mailing Add:* Dept Physics Dermitt Hall Univ NH Durham NH 03824

**WRIGHT, JOHN MARLIN,** CHEMICAL INSTRUMENTATION, MAGNETIC RESONANCE. *Current Pos:* assoc specialist, 70-73, specialist & lectr chem, 73-79, SR DEVELOP ENGR CHEM, UNIV CALIF, SAN DIEGO, 79- *Personal Data:* b Long Beach, Calif, Feb 2, 37; m 58; c 2. *Educ:* Calif Inst Technol, BS, 60; Harvard Univ, PhD(chem), 67. *Prof Exp:* Res fel chem, Harvard Univ, 67-70. *Concurrent Pos:* Lectr, Univ Calif, San Diego, 73-76. *Mem:* Am Chem Soc; AAAS. *Res:* Application of nuclear magnetic resonance and mass spectrometry to chemical problems; development of new instrumental techniques. *Mailing Add:* Dept Chem B-014 Univ Calif San Diego La Jolla CA 92093-0314

**WRIGHT, JOHN RICKEN,** BIOINORGANIC CHEMISTRY, NUCLEAR MAGNETIC RESONANCE SPECTROSCOPY. *Current Pos:* PROF CHEM, DEPT PHYS SCI, SOUTHEASTERN OKLA STATE UNIV, 73- *Personal Data:* b Batesville, Ark, Jan 3, 39; m 64, Barbara R Martin; c Karen E & Faron D. *Educ:* Ark State Univ, BS, 60; Univ Miss, MS, 67, PhD(chem), 71. *Prof Exp:* Res assoc, Dept Bot, Wash Univ, 67-68; NIH fel, Fla State Univ, 72-73. *Mem:* Sigma Xi; Am Chem Soc. *Res:* The metabolism and transport of biological forms of copper; bismuth, boron and copper antibody labels for biomedical applications; chemiluminescent/sonochemiluminescent systems. *Mailing Add:* Dept Phys Sci Southeastern Okla State Univ Durant OK 74701. *Fax:* 580-920-7476; *E-Mail:* jwright@sosu.edu

**WRIGHT, JOHNIE ALGIE,** HORTICULTURE. *Current Pos:* RETIRED. *Personal Data:* b Atlas, Ala, Feb 5, 24; m 49; c 2. *Educ:* Tenn Polytech Inst, BS, 47; Iowa State Col, MS, 49; La State Univ, PhD, 60. *Prof Exp:* Asst prof hort, Tenn Polytech Inst, 49-53; from assoc prof to prof hort, La Tech Univ, 53-72, assoc dean, Col Life Sci, 72-77, prof agron & head dept agron & Hort, 77-87. *Concurrent Pos:* Asst, La State Univ, 60. *Mem:* Am Soc Hort Sci. *Res:* Nutrient culture of roses; methods of watering greenhouse roses; container nursery stock studies. *Mailing Add:* 610 Durden Ave Ruston LA 71270

**WRIGHT, JON ALAN,** THEORETICAL PHYSICS, FLUIDS. *Current Pos:* PROF, INST NON-LINEAR SCI, UNIV CALIF, SAN DIEGO, 90- *Personal Data:* b Tacoma, Wash, Jan 18, 38; m 62; c Jeffrey, Allison & Dana. *Educ:* Calif Inst Technol, BS, 59; Univ Calif, Berkeley, PhD(physics), 65. *Prof Exp:* Physicist, Aerospace Corp, 65; res assoc physics, Univ Calif, San Diego, 65-67; from assoc prof to prof, Univ Ill, Urbana, 67-82; prof, La Jolla Inst, 82-90. *Mem:* Am Inst Physics. *Res:* Non-linear physics. *Mailing Add:* Inst Non-linear Sci Univ Calif San Diego CA 92093-0402

**WRIGHT, JOSEPH D,** CHEMICAL ENGINEERING. *Current Pos:* PRES & CHIEF EXEC OFFICER, PULP & PAPER RES INST CAN, 94- *Personal Data:* b Trochu, Alta, Nov 11, 41; m 69, Christiane Gouin; c Thomas J, Heather M, Matthew P & Nicholas J. *Educ:* Univ Alta, BSc, 63; Cambridge Univ, PhD(chem eng), 67. *Prof Exp:* Res engr, Shawinigan Chem Div, Gulf Oil Can, 67-69; from asst prof to assoc prof, McMaster Univ, 69-78, prof chem eng, 78- *Concurrent Pos:* Trustee Comput Aids Chem Eng Educ Corp; exec dir, Sheridan Res Park Asn, 79-82; mgr, Mat Processing Lab, Xerox Res Centre Can, 77-85, Technol Strategy Off, Xerox Corp, 85-86 & Technol & Eng Systs Lab, 86-87; vchmn, Comput & Systs Technol Div, Am Inst Chem Eng, 88-89, chmn, 89-90; chmn, Ont Ctr Mat Res, 88-90; exec bd, Precarn Corp, 88-, Can Res Mgt Asn, 93- *Mem:* Chem Inst Can; Am Inst Chem Engrs; Am Chem Soc; Can Soc Chem Eng. *Res:* Chemical plant simulation and control extending to direct digital control and optimization of chemical plants and simulations; computer process control; specialty materials; management of technology. *Mailing Add:* Pulp & Paper Res Inst Can 570 St Johns Blvd Pointe-Claire PQ H9R 3J9 Can. *Fax:* 514-630-4110; *E-Mail:* wright@paprican.ca

**WRIGHT, JOSEPH WILLIAM, JR,** medicine; deceased, see previous edition for last biography

**WRIGHT, JULIAN,** ATMOSPHERIC SCIENCES. *Current Pos:* FED COORDR METEOROL & DIR, OFF FED COORDR METEOROL SERV & SUPPORTING RES, 92- *Personal Data:* b Jamestown, NY, June 11, 41; m 66, Anne Brantlay. *Educ:* US Naval Acad, BS, 63; US Naval Post Grad Sch, MM, 75. *Prof Exp:* Dir opers, Fleet Numerical Meteorol & Oceanog Ctr, Monterey, 80-83; dir interagency & int affairs, Dept Navy, 88-89; dep asst secy, US Dept Energy, 89-92. *Concurrent Pos:* Chair, Nat Aviation Weather Prog Coun, 92-, Nat Space Weather Prog Coun, 94- *Mem:* Am Meteorol Soc; Armed Forces Commun & Electronics Asn. *Mailing Add:* 8455 Colesville Rd Suite 1500 Silver Spring MD 20910. *Fax:* 301-427-2007; *E-Mail:* julian.wright@nova.gov

**WRIGHT, KENNETH C,** INTERVENTIONAL RADIOLOGY, IMAGING. *Current Pos:* ASST PROF PHYSIOL, SYST CANCER CTR, ANDERSON HOSP, UNIV TEX, 80- *Educ:* Tex A&M Univ, PhD(vet physiol), 77. *Mailing Add:* Dept Exp Diagnostic Radiol Cancer Ctr MD Anderson Hosp Univ Tex 1515 Holcombe Blvd Box 057 Houston TX 77030

**WRIGHT, KENNETH JAMES,** SCIENCE EDUCATION METHODOLOGY, ENVIRONMENTAL SCIENCES. *Current Pos:* chmn, Div Phys Sci, 72-77, PROF CHEM & ENVIRON SCI, NIDAHO COL, 71- *Personal Data:* b Pittsburgh, Pa, Aug 26, 39; m 66, Virginia Brodin; c Kody & Clark. *Educ:* Portland State Univ, BS, 62; Univ Idaho, PhD(inorg chem), 72. *Prof Exp:* Anal & res chemist, Harvey Aluminum Corp, Ore, 63-66. *Concurrent Pos:* NSF trainee chem, Univ Idaho, 67, Nat Defense Educ Act fel, 68-70, consult, Bunker Hill Co, 78-, Coeur d'Alene Hazardous Mat Comt, 86-88; Fulbright exchange teacher chem, Uk, 90-91. *Mem:* Am Chem Soc; Sigma Xi; Nat Sci Teachers Asn; Environ Defense Fund. *Res:* Environmental effects of air and water pollutants; energy resources and conservation; science education methodologies; growth and its ramifications. *Mailing Add:* Div Natural Sci NIdaho Col 1000 WGarden Ave Coeur d'Alene ID 83814. *Fax:* 208-769-7839; *E-Mail:* kjwright@nidc.edu

**WRIGHT, KENNETH OSBORNE,** ASTROPHYSICS. *Current Pos:* RETIRED. *Personal Data:* b Ft George, BC, Nov 1, 11; m 37, 70, Jean M Ellis; c Nora L (Osborne). *Educ:* Univ Toronto, BA, 33, MA, 34; Univ Mich, PhD(astron), 40. *Hon Degrees:* DSc, Nicolas Copernicus Univ, Torun, Poland, 73. *Honors & Awards:* Gold Medal, Royal Astron Soc Can, 33. *Prof Exp:* Asst astron, Univ Toronto, 33-34; asst, Dom Astrophys Observ, 36-40, astromr, 40-60, asst dir, 60-66, dir, 66-76, guest worker, 76-84. *Concurrent Pos:* Lectr, Univ BC, 43-44; spec lectr, Univ Toronto, 60-61; res asst, Mt Wilson & Palomar Observ, 62; chmn assoc comt astron, Nat Res Coun Can, 71-74. *Mem:* Int Astron Union; Am Astron Soc; Royal Astron Soc Can (pres, 64-66); fel Royal Soc Can; Can Astron Soc. *Res:* Stellar radial velocities; observations of stellar line intensities; curves of growth; stellar atmospheres, peculiar A-type stars; observation and analysis of atmospheres of giant eclipsing systems. *Mailing Add:* 202-1375 Newport Victoria BC V8S 5E8 Can

**WRIGHT, LAUREN ALBERT,** GEOLOGY. *Current Pos:* prof geol, 61-85, EMER PROF GEOL, PA STATE UNIV, 85- *Personal Data:* b New York, NY, July 9, 18. *Educ:* Univ Southern Calif, AB, 40, MS, 43; Calif Inst Technol, PhD(geol), 51. *Prof Exp:* From jr geologist to asst geologist, US Geol Surv, 42-46; assoc geologist, State Div Mines, Calif, 47-51, sr mining geologist, 51-54, supv mining geologist, 54-61. *Mem:* Fel Geol Soc Am; Am Soc Econ Geologists; fel AAAS; Sigma Xi. *Res:* Geologic occurrence, origin and economics of industrial minerals; stratigraphic-tectonic evolution of southwestern Great Basin; structural geology; extensional tectonics. *Mailing Add:* 500 E Marylyn Ave Apt E69 State Col University Park PA 16801

**WRIGHT, LEMUEL DARY,** biochemistry; deceased, see previous edition for last biography

**WRIGHT, LEON WENDELL,** ORGANIC CHEMISTRY, FOOD SCIENCE & TECHNOLOGY. *Current Pos:* RETIRED. *Personal Data:* b Los Angeles, Calif, July 16, 23; m 50; c 4. *Educ:* Univ Calif, Los Angeles, BS, 46, MS, 47; Univ Del, PhD(chem), 51. *Prof Exp:* Instr chem, Mont State Col, 47-49 & Univ Del, 49-51; res chemist, Houdry Process Corp, 51-56; from res chemist to sr res chemist, Atlas Chem Indust, Inc, 56-67, prin chemist, Chem Res Dept, 67-70, supvr, Org & Process Res Group, 70-77, prin chemist, ICI US, Inc, 77-86. *Mem:* Am Chem Soc; Sigma Xi. *Res:* Catalytic hydrogenation and hydrogenolysis; hetero and homogeneous activation of hydrogen; isomerization of polyhydric alcohols; carbohydrate conversion processes; sunscreen processes; kinetics, catalysis, process development of carbohydrate conversion processes, monnitol, sorbitol, food and cosmetic chemicals including sun blockers; catalyst development. *Mailing Add:* 215 Oakwood Rd Fairfax Wilmington DE 19803-3132

**WRIGHT, LOUIS E,** THEORETICAL PHYSICS, NUCLEAR PHYSICS. *Current Pos:* from asst prof to assoc prof, 70-80, PROF PHYSICS, OHIO UNIV, 80-, CHAIR, DEPT PHYSICS & ASTRON, 90- *Personal Data:* b Buras, La, Oct 18, 40; m 69, Karin Kindlmann; c Leslie A & Avery R. *Educ:* La State Univ, BS, 61; Duke Univ, PhD(physics), 66. *Prof Exp:* Res assoc physics, Duke Univ, 66; prog mgr theoret physics, US Army Res Off-Durham, 66-69; asst prof physics, Duke Univ, 69-70. *Concurrent Pos:* Vis physicist, Inst Theoret Physics, Univ Frankfurt, 68-69; Alexander von Humboldt fel, Inst Nuclear Physics, Main Univ, 81-82. *Mem:* Am Phys Soc; Sigma Xi; AAAS. *Res:* Theoretical nuclear physics; electron scattering, pion production, virtual photon spectra, bremsstrahlung and pair production. *Mailing Add:* 98 Mulligan Rd Athens OH 45701. *Fax:* 740-593-0433; *E-Mail:* wright@next.phy.ohiou.edu

**WRIGHT, LYNN DONELSON,** COASTAL & ESTUARINE HYDRO DYNAMICS & MORPHODYNAMICS, CONTINENTAL SHELF BOTTOM BOUNDARY LAYERS & SEDIMENT TRANSPORT. *Current Pos:* prof marine sci, 82-94, CHANCELLOR PROF MARINE SCI, VA INST MARINE SCI, COL WILLIAM & MARY, 94-, DEAN SCH MARINE SCI & DIR, 96- *Personal Data:* b Nashville, Tenn, Dec 13, 40; m 65, Jeanne M Eckard; c Lauren K & Shannon G. *Educ:* Univ Miami, BA, 65; Univ Sydney, Australia, MA, 67; La State Univ, PhD(coastal studies & geog), 70. *Prof Exp:* Res assoc, Coastal Studies Inst, La State Univ, 70-71, from asst prof to assoc prof marine sci, 71-74; sr lectr geog, Univ Sydney, Australia, 74-78, assoc prof, 78-82. *Mem:* Am Geophys Union; Oceanog Soc; Estuarine Res Fedn. *Res:* Sediment transport processes and associated morphological changes in continental shelf, estuarine and coastal environments; physical oceanographic processes, boundary layer hydrodynamics and shallow stratigraphy. *Mailing Add:* PO Box 731 Gloucester Point VA 23062. *Fax:* 804-684-7009; *E-Mail:* wright@vims.edu

**WRIGHT, MADISON JOHNSTON,** AGRONOMY. *Current Pos:* RETIRED. *Personal Data:* b Washington, DC, Apr 9, 24; m 54; c 4. *Educ:* Univ NC, BA, 47; Univ Wis, MS, 50, PhD(agron, bot), 52. *Prof Exp:* Asst prof agron, Univ Wis, 52-59; assoc prof, Cornell Univ, 59-68, chmn dept, 70-75, prof agron, 68-89. *Mem:* Am Soc Agron; Crop Sci Soc Am; AAAS; Am Inst Biol Sci. *Res:* Crop management. *Mailing Add:* 212 Texas Lane Ithaca NY 14850

**WRIGHT, MARGARET HAGEN,** NONLINEAR PROGRAMMING, NUMERICAL ANALYSIS. *Current Pos:* mem tech staff, AT&T Bell Labs, 88-97, HEAD, SCI COMP RES DEPT, AT&T BELL LABS LUCENT TECHNOL, 97- *Personal Data:* b San Francisco, Calif; m 65; c 1. *Educ:* Stanford Univ, BS, 64, MS, 65, PhD(comput sci), 76. *Prof Exp:* Develop engr, Sylvania Electron Syst, 65-71; sr res assoc, Stanford Univ, 76-88. *Concurrent Pos:* Mem, Bd Dir, Special Interest Group Numerical Anal, Asn Comput Mach, 79-82; assoc ed, J Sci Statist Comput, Soc Indust & Appl Math, 81- *Mem:* Nat Acad Eng; Soc Indust & Appl Math; Math Prog Soc; Asn Comput Mach. *Res:* Methods for nonlinear programming, particularly unconstrained, linearly constrained and nonlinearly constrained optimization; mathematical software; numerical linear algebra; software library development. *Mailing Add:* AT&T Bell Labs Lucent Technol Rm 2C-462 600 Mountain Ave Murray Hill NJ 07974. *Fax:* 908-582-5857; *E-Mail:* mhw@vescarch.bell-labs.com

**WRIGHT, MARGARET RUTH,** ZOOLOGY. *Current Pos:* from instr to prof, 46-78, EMER PROF ZOOL, VASSAR COL, 78- *Personal Data:* b Rochester, NY, Mar 24, 13. *Educ:* Univ Rochester, AB, 34, MS, 38; Yale Univ, PhD(zool), 46. *Prof Exp:* Asst, Univ Rochester, 36-38; histol technician, Med Sch, Yale Univ, 38-41, asst, Osborn Zool Lab, 42-43; instr biol, Middlebury Col, 43-46. *Concurrent Pos:* Mem exped, Alaska, 36; grant, Nat Inst Neurol Dis & Blindness, 54-64; Vassar Col fels, 54-55, 63-64 & 68-69; cur, Natural Hist Mus, Vassar Col; vis scientist, Marine Biol Asn UK, Plymouth, Devon, 68-69, 76 & 81. *Mem:* Fel AAAS; Am Soc Zool; Sigma Xi; NY Acad Sci; Am Inst Biol Sci. *Res:* Limnology and biogeography; experimental morphology; trophic action in sensory systems; ecology of cladocera; history of science. *Mailing Add:* Dept Biol Vassar Col Poughkeepsie NY 12601

**WRIGHT, MARY LOU,** DEVELOPMENTAL BIOLOGY, ENDOCRINOLOGY. *Current Pos:* TEACHING & RES BIOL, COL OUR LADY ELMS, 58- *Personal Data:* b Milford, Mass, Dec 4, 34. *Educ:* Col Our Lady Elms, BS, 57; Univ Detroit, MS, 66; Univ Mass, PhD(develop biol), 72. *Concurrent Pos:* Sigma Xi Res grant, 73; Res Corp grants, 76-88; consult, NSF, 81-84 & grants; NIH grant, 88-91, 93-97; NSF grant, 93-96. *Mem:* Int Soc Chronobiol; Soc Integrative & Comp Biol; Tissue Cult Asn; AAAS; Sigma Xi; Soc Res Biol Rhythms. *Res:* Hormonal control of amphibian metamorphosis; interactions among various hormones in development; role of melatonin and the light/dark cycle in controlling metamorphosis. *Mailing Add:* Col Our Lady Elms Chicopee MA 01013. *Fax:* 413-592-4871; *E-Mail:* wrightm@elms.cdu

**WRIGHT, MAUREEN SMITH,** ELECTROPHORETIC KARYOTYPING, CLONING. *Current Pos:* Mycotoxin lab technician, 82-84, res geneticist, 90-92, MOLECULAR BIOLOGIST, SOUTHERN REGIONAL RES CTR, AGR RES SERV, USDA, 92- *Personal Data:* b New Orleans, La, Dec 5, 62; m 86, Gregory G; c Jessica C. *Educ:* Xavier Univ, La, BS, 84; La State Univ, Baton Rouge, PhD(molecular biol), 90. *Concurrent Pos:* Adj, prof microbiol, Southern Univ, New Orleans, 91-93. *Mem:* Am Soc Microbiol; Sigma Xi. *Res:* Karyotype analysis of the fungal species Aspergillus; characterization of the biosynthetic pathway of aflatoxin. *Mailing Add:* USDA 1100 Robert E Lee Blvd New Orleans LA 70124. *Fax:* 504-286-4419; *E-Mail:* mswright@nola.srrc.usda.gov

**WRIGHT, MAURICE ARTHUR,** COMPOSITE MATERIALS, FRACTURE MECHANICS. *Current Pos:* PROF & DIR, MAT TECHNOL CTR, SOUTHERN ILL UNIV, CARBONDALE, 84- *Personal Data:* b Coventry, Eng, Aug 2, 35; US citizen; m 60; c 3. *Educ:* Univ Wales, Swansea, UK, BSc, 59, PhD(metall), 62. *Prof Exp:* Staff scientist, Tyco Labs, 62-65; sr scientist, Nat Norton Res Corp, 65-68; from assoc prof to prof, Univ Tenn, 68-84. *Concurrent Pos:* Vis prof, Technischen Hochschule, Aachen, Ger, 73 & USAF Acad, 83-84; Alcoa Found res award, 75-76; dir, Mat Div, Univ Tenn, 76-84, head, Aviations Systs Div, 79-84; consult, Univ Ala, Huntsville, 79, 81 & 84, Sverdrup Technol, Arvin-Calspan, Am Cyanamid & Nat Ctr Mfg Sci, 79, 84 & Los Alamos Weapons Lab, NMex, 80. *Mem:* Am Carbon Soc; Soc Advan Mat & Process Eng. *Res:* Relationships that exist between processing, microstructure and the reality physical and mechanical properties of materials, primarily fiber reinforced composites; basic mechanisms of fatigue and fracture of materials. *Mailing Add:* Mat Technol Ctr Southern Ill Univ MS 4303 Carbondale IL 62901-4303

**WRIGHT, MAURICE MORGAN,** ELECTROCHEMISTRY, HETEROGENEOUS CATALYSIS. *Current Pos:* RETIRED. *Personal Data:* b Assiniboia, Sask, July 29, 16; m 45; c 3. *Educ:* Univ BC, BA & BASc, 38; Princeton Univ, MA, 48, PhD(chem), 52. *Prof Exp:* Res chemist, Cominco, Ltd, 38-45 & 49-81. *Concurrent Pos:* Indust fel, Nat Res Coun Can, 49-52. *Mem:* Sigma Xi; Chem Inst Can. *Res:* Electrowinning and refining of metals; electrolytic hydrogen; ammonia synthesis; physical methods of analysis; deuterium separation, analysis and exchange reactions; reactive metals; anodic films; corrosion; protective coatings; lead-acid battery chemistry. *Mailing Add:* 1454 Willowdown Rd Oakville ON L6L 1X3 Can

**WRIGHT, MELVYN CHARLES HARMAN,** RADIO ASTRONOMY. *Current Pos:* RES ASTRONR, RADIO ASTRON LAB, 72- *Personal Data:* b Leicester, Eng, Sept 1, 44; Brit citizen. *Educ:* Cambridge Univ, BA, 66, MA, 69, PhD(astron), 70. *Prof Exp:* Res assoc astron, Nat Radio Astron Observ, 70-72 & Calif Inst Technol, 72-77. *Mem:* Fel Royal Astron Soc; Am Astron Soc. *Res:* Galactic and extragalactic radio astronomy; design and implementation of radio interferometers. *Mailing Add:* Radio Astron Lab Univ Calif 453 Campbell Hall Berkeley CA 94720-3411

**WRIGHT, MICHAEL GEORGE,** ATOMIC ENERGY. *Current Pos:* res scientist, Atomic Energy Can Ltd, 66-77, br mgr, 77-82, sr adv & asst, 82-84, mgr, Eng Div, 84-86, GEN MGR, ATOMIC ENERGY CAN LTD, 86-, GEN MGR, NUCLEAR OPER. *Personal Data:* b Bristol, UK, Apr 15, 39; m 64, Fiona E Crozier; c Craig & Graeme. *Educ:* Univ Wales, BS, 60; McMaster Univ, MSc, 64. *Prof Exp:* Metallurgist, GE-Simon Carves Atomic Energy Group, Kent, UK, 60-62, Inland Steel Co, Ind, 64-66. *Res:* Metallurgy. *Mailing Add:* Atomic Energy Can Ltd Chalk River Lab Chalk River ON K0J 1J0 Can

**WRIGHT, OSCAR LEWIS,** organic chemistry, physical chemistry; deceased, see previous edition for last biography

**WRIGHT, PAUL ALBERT,** REPRODUCTIVE ENDOCRINOLOGY. *Current Pos:* assoc prof, Univ NH, 58-62, endocrinologist, Agr Exp Sta, 58-68, chmn dept, 63-69, prof, 62-85, EMER PROF ZOOL, UNIV NH, 85- *Personal Data:* b Nashua, NH, June 15, 20; m 43, Claire Wilson; c Loren W, Darryl P & Barton D. *Educ:* Bates Col, SB, 41; Harvard Univ, AM, 42, PhD(endocrinol), 44. *Prof Exp:* Asst biol, Harvard Univ, 42-43, instr, 44-45; instr zool & physiol, Univ Wash, 45-46; instr biol sci, Boston Univ, 46-47; from instr to assoc prof zool, Univ Mich, 47-58. *Mem:* AAAS; Am Soc Zoologists (treas, 65-68); Soc Exp Biol & Med; Soc Study Reproduction. *Res:* Ovulation in the frog; physiology of melanophores of Amphibia; blood sugar studies in lower vertebrates; control of corpus luteum life by the uterus. *Mailing Add:* 20979 Cornell Ave Port Charlotte FL 33952

**WRIGHT, PAUL MCCOY,** PHYSICAL CHEMISTRY. *Current Pos:* from asst prof to prof chem, Wheaton Col, 29-70, actg chmn, Dept Chem & Geol, 39-40, chmn, Dept Geol, 40-59, chmn, Dept Chem, 40-69, dir field camp, SDak, 46-52 & 60, EMER PROF CHEM, WHEATON COL, ILL, 70- *Personal Data:* b Alfalfa Co, Okla, Sept 11, 04; wid, Eleanor Smith Hale; c Margorie E (deceased), Eugene P & Roger L. *Educ:* Wheaton Col, Ill, BS, 26; Ohio State Univ, MS, 28, PhD(phys chem), 30. *Prof Exp:* Asst chem, Wheaton Col, Ill, 25-26; asst gen chem, Ohio State Univ, 26-28, asst phys chem, 28-29. *Mem:* AAAS; Am Chem Soc; fel Am Inst Chemists; fel Am Sci Affil. *Res:* Dimensions of vapor particles; eutectics of explosive mixtures; equilibria of glycerol esters; radiochemistry. *Mailing Add:* Goye Village Apt 416 Tahlequah OK 74464

**WRIGHT, PETER MURRELL,** CIVIL ENGINEERING, ENGINEERING EDUCATION. *Current Pos:* assoc dean eng, 81-85, actg dean archit, 84-88, PROF STRUCT, UNIV TORONTO, 68- *Personal Data:* b Toronto, Ont, Sept 26, 32; m; c 4. *Educ:* Univ Sask, BS, 54, MSc, 61; Univ Colo, Boulder, PhD(struct), 68. *Honors & Awards:* Queen's Can Silver Jubilee Medal, 77. *Prof Exp:* Engr, Dorman-Long Ltd, Eng, 54-57; asst prof struct, Univ Sask, 57-66. *Mem:* Can Soc Civil Engrs (pres, 81-82). *Res:* Automatic design of steel building frames including member selection. *Mailing Add:* Dept Civil Eng Univ Toronto Toronto ON M5S 1A4 Can. *Fax:* 416-978-7046; *E-Mail:* pmw@civ.utoronto.ca

**WRIGHT, PHILIP LINCOLN,** ZOOLOGY. *Current Pos:* From instr to prof, 39-85, chmn dept, 56-69 & 70-71, EMER PROF ZOOL, UNIV MONT, 85- *Personal Data:* b Nashua, NH, July 9, 14; m 39, 89, Hedwig Vogel; c Alden H, Philip L Jr & Ann E (Dwyer). *Educ:* Univ NH, BS, 35, MS, 37; Univ Wis, PhD(zool), 40. *Concurrent Pos:* Ed, Gen Notes & Rev, J Mammal, 66-67; sabbatical leave, Africa, 70; vis Maytag prof zool, Ariz State Univ, 80. *Mem:* Am Soc Mammalogists; Am Soc Zoologists; Wildlife Soc; Am Ornithologists Union; fel AAAS. *Res:* Reproductive cycles of birds and mammals; especially Mustelidae. *Mailing Add:* Dept Biol Sci Univ Mont Missoula MT 59812

**WRIGHT, RAMIL CARTER,** MICROPALEONTOLOGY, BIOSTRATIGRAPHY. *Current Pos:* RES SUPVR, EXXON PROD RES CO, 81- *Personal Data:* b Hastings, Nebr, May 16, 39; m 63. *Educ:* Rice Univ, BA, 60; Univ Ill, MS, 62, PhD(geol), 64. *Prof Exp:* Asst dir, Waterways Exp Sta, Corps Engrs, 64-66; NSF fel, Museo Argentino de Ciencias Naturales, Argentina, 66-67; vis prof, Hamline Univ, St Paul, Minn, 68; from asst prof to assoc prof, Beloit Col, Wis, 68-76; from assoc prof to prof geol, Fla State Univ, 76-81. *Concurrent Pos:* Int Working Group, Int Geol Correlation Proj, 75-78. *Mem:* Geol Soc Am; Paleont Soc; AAAS; Sigma Xi; Soc Econ Paleontologist & Mineralogists. *Res:* Foraminiferal ecology and biostratigraphy; Miocene paleoenvironments. *Mailing Add:* Exxon Prod Res Co Box 2189 Rm 5206 Houston TX 77252-2189

**WRIGHT, RICHARD KENNETH,** COMPARATIVE IMMUNOLOGY. *Current Pos:* PROPERTY MASTER, MOTION PICTURE, 89- *Personal Data:* b Richmond, Ind, Sept 22, 39. *Educ:* San Diego State Univ, BS, 67, MS, 70; Univ Calif, Santa Barbara, PhD(immunol), 73. *Prof Exp:* Teaching asst, San Diego State Univ, 67-69; assoc biol sci, Univ Calif, Santa Barbara, 71-73, res fel, Sch Med, Los Angeles, 73-75, asst res anatomist, 75-81, assoc res, 81-84; dir res & develop, Physicians Labs Inc, 84-89. *Mem:* Int Soc Develop & Comp Immunol (secy & treas, 80-86); Am Soc Zoologists, Div Comp Immunol (secy, 76-79); Am Asn Immunologists; Sigma Xi. *Res:* Development and production of immunological assays for the detection of immediate and delayed type hypersensitivities to dietary proteins and environmental allergens. *Mailing Add:* 1315 Stanford St Apt 1 Santa Monica CA 90404

**WRIGHT, RICHARD N(EWPORT),** CIVIL ENGINEERING, STRUCTURAL ENGINEERING. *Current Pos:* chief struct sect, Nat Inst Stand & Technol, 71-72, dep dir-tech, 72-73, dir, Ctr for Bldg Technol, 74-90, DIR, BLDG & FIRE RES LAB, NAT INST STAND & TECHNOL, 91- *Personal Data:* b Syracuse, NY, May 17, 32; m 59, Teresa Rids; c John, Carolyn, Elizabeth & Edward. *Educ:* Syracuse Univ, BS, 53, MS, 55; Univ Ill, PhD(civil eng), 62. *Honors & Awards:* Gold Medal, US Dept Com, 82; Presidential Award, Illum Eng Soc, 83; Fed Eng Yr, Nat Soc Prof Engrs, 88. *Prof Exp:* Jr engr, Pa RR Co, 53-54; from instr to assoc prof, 57-70, prof civil eng, Univ Ill, Urbana, 70-71 & 73-74. *Concurrent Pos:* Chmn mgt group A, Am Soc Civil Engrs, 78-79, exec comt, Struct Div, 90-94 & chmn, 92-93; mem bd, Int Coun Bldg Res, 80-89, pres, 83-86; chmn, Lighting Res Inst, 82-83, mem bd, 82-84; US chmn, US Japan Panel Wind & Seismic Effects, 83-; mem, Bur Int Union Testing & Res Lab Mat & Struct, 90-95; co-chmn subcom construct, Nat Sci Technol Coun, 94- *Mem:* Fel Am Soc Civil Engrs; Int Union Testing & Res Labs Mat & Struct; Earthquake Eng Res Inst; Sigma Xi; Nat Soc Prof Engrs; fel AAAS. *Res:* Analysis, behavior and design of structures; technologies for the formulation and expression of standards; performance criteria and measurement technology for buildings. *Mailing Add:* Bldg & Fire Res Lab Nat Inst Stand & Technol Gaithersburg MD 20899. *Fax:* 301-975-4032; *E-Mail:* richard.wright@nist.gov

**WRIGHT, RICHARD T,** AQUATIC ECOLOGY. *Current Pos:* PROF BIOL, GORDON COL, 65- *Personal Data:* b Haddonfield, NJ, June 28, 33; m 61, Ann Stone; c Susan, Richard & Karin. *Educ:* Rutgers Univ, AB, 59; Harvard Univ, PhD(biol), 63. *Prof Exp:* NSF fel, Inst Limnol, Univ Uppsala, 63-65. *Concurrent Pos:* NSF res grants, 66-71, 73-79, 80-83, 84-88, 88-91; NSF sci fac fel, Univ Stirling, 69-70; acad chair, Ausable Inst, 82-; Fulbright Scholar award, 96. *Mem:* Fel AAAS; Am Soc Limnol & Oceanog; Am Sci Affil; Estuarine Res Fedn; Ecol Soc Am. *Res:* Factors controlling the density and productivity of planktonic bacteria in estuaries and coastal waters; relationships between biological knowledge and christian thought; authoring environmental sciense text for Prentice Hall. *Mailing Add:* Dept Biol Gordon Col Wenham MA 01984. *Fax:* 978-524-3747; *E-Mail:* wright@gordonc.edu

**WRIGHT, ROBERT ANDERSON,** botany, for more information see previous edition

**WRIGHT, ROBERT L,** ORGANIC CHEMISTRY, RUBBER CHEMISTRY. *Current Pos:* RETIRED. *Personal Data:* b Buckhannon, WVa, Sept 7, 30; m 52; c 1. *Educ:* WVa Wesleyan Col, BS, 52. *Prof Exp:* Analyst trainee, Monsanto Co, 52, res chemist, 55-64, sr res chemist, 64-75, res specialist, 75-80, sr res specialist, 80-89; res consult technol, 90-93. *Mem:* Am Chem Soc. *Res:* Process development; exploratory synthesis in the field of rubber chemicals. *Mailing Add:* 95 Blue Hill Lane Akron OH 44333-3417

**WRIGHT, ROBERT W,** PHYSICAL ORGANIC CHEMISTRY, POLYMER CHEMISTRY. *Current Pos:* group dir synthetic mat, 69-76, MGR ANALYTICAL SCI, CORP RES CTR, INT PAPER CO, 77- *Personal Data:* b Auburn, NY, Aug 2, 32; m 73, Eleanor Dodge. *Educ:* NY State Col Forestry, BS, 59, PhD(chem), 64. *Prof Exp:* Chemist, Owens-Ill, Inc, Ohio, 64-65, res chemist, 65-66, sect leader polymer chem, 66-69. *Mem:* Am Chem Soc; Tech Asn Pulp & Paper Indust; Am Lab Mgr Asn. *Res:* Polymer characterization; analytical chemistry. *Mailing Add:* Int Paper Co Long Meadow Rd Tuxedo Park NY 10987

**WRIGHT, ROGER M,** CHEMICAL ENGINEERING, HEAT TRANSFER. *Current Pos:* SR ENG SPECIALIST, AIRES MFG CO, 61- *Personal Data:* b Long Beach, Calif, Feb 19, 35; m 58; c 2. *Educ:* Univ Calif, Berkeley, BS, 56, PhD(chem eng), 61. *Prof Exp:* Res engr, Lawrence Radiation Lab, Calif, 57-61. *Mem:* Am Inst Chem Engrs; Am Inst Aeronaut & Astronaut. *Res:* Heat transfer, including research in forced-convection boiling, compact heat exchangers and spacecraft thermal radiators; spacecraft environmental control systems; mass-transfer systems; thermal systems design and analysis. *Mailing Add:* 6235 Monita St Long Beach CA 90803-2125

**WRIGHT, ROGER NEAL,** MECHANICAL BEHAVIOR, WIRE PROCESSING. *Current Pos:* from asst prof to assoc prof mat eng, Rensselaer Polytech Inst, 74-83, exec officer, 83-90, actg chmn, 84-86, PROF MAT ENG, RENSSELAER POLYTECH INST, 83-, DIR, HIGH TEMPERATURE TECHNOL PROG, 90- *Personal Data:* b Springfield, Ill, Nov 14, 42; m 67, Patricia Michael; c Sydney & Evan. *Educ:* Mass Inst Technol, BS, 65, DSc(metall), 69. *Honors & Awards:* Mordica Mem Award, Wire Asn Int, 93, Yokelson Medal, 93. *Prof Exp:* Sr res metallurgist, Allegheny Ludlum Res Labs, 68-71; sr engr, Westinghouse Res Labs, 71-74. *Concurrent Pos:* Consult metall & metals processing, var co & govt agencies, 74-; prin investr, NSF, Gen Motors, IBM, Am Iron & Steel Inst, Int Copper Asn & NY State Energy Res & Develop Authority, 76-; chmn, Eng Mat Coun, Soc Mfg Engrs & trustee, Fedn Mat Soc, 80-83; mem, bd dirs, Metall Soc, 83-85. *Mem:* Metall Soc; Am Soc Metals Int; Am Soc Mech Engrs; fel Soc Mfg Engrs; Wire Asn Int. *Res:* Mechanical properties of materials; thermal processing of materials. *Mailing Add:* Dept Mat Sci & Eng Rensselaer Polytech Inst Troy NY 12180. *Fax:* 518-399-2646; *E-Mail:* wrighr@rpi.edu

**WRIGHT, RUSSELL E,** METEOROLOGY. *Current Pos:* RETIRED. *Personal Data:* b Auburn, Ind, May 16, 19. *Educ:* Goshen Col, BS, 40; Univ Wis, PHM, 47; Univ Chicago, MS, 51. *Prof Exp:* Prof math, Napa Valley Col, 70-93. *Mem:* Am Meteorol Soc; Am Math Soc; Math Asn Am. *Mailing Add:* Napa Valley Col 5150 Wild Horse Valley Rd Napa Valley CA 94558-4016

**WRIGHT, RUSSELL EMERY,** MEDICAL ENTOMOLOGY. *Current Pos:* assoc prof, 76-82, PROF, OKLA STATE UNIV, 82- *Personal Data:* b Muscatine, Iowa, June 19, 39; m 63; c 3. *Educ:* Iowa State Univ, BSc, 63, MS, 66; Univ Wis-Madison, PhD(entom), 69. *Prof Exp:* From asst prof to assoc prof entom, Univ Guelph, 69-76. *Mem:* Entom Soc Am; Am Mosquito Control Asn. *Res:* Behavior, biology and control of insect pests of livestock; arthropod borne viruses. *Mailing Add:* Dept Entom Okla State Univ Main Campus Stillwater OK 74078-0001

**WRIGHT, SAMUEL D,** PHAGOCYTOSIS, RECEPTOR & ENDOTOXIN BIOLOGY. *Current Pos:* Asst prof, 84-89, ASSOC PROF, ROCKEFELLER UNIV, 89- *Personal Data:* b Hibbing, Minn, Sept 23, 52; m 80, Patricia A Detmers; c Alex E. *Educ:* Carleton Col, BA, 74; Harvard Univ, PhD(biol), 79. *Mem:* Am Soc Cell Biol; Am Soc Immunologists; Soc Leukocyte Biol; Int Endotoxin Soc. *Res:* Study of receptors on leukocytes that mediate adhesion; migration and phagocytosis; receptors for bacterial endotoxin. *Mailing Add:* Dept Cellular Physiol & Immunol Rockfeller Univ 1230 York Ave Box 303 New York NY 10021-6399. *Fax:* 212-327-7901

**WRIGHT, STEPHEN E,** ONCOLOGY, VIROLOGY. *Current Pos:* CHIEF HEMAT/ONCOL, VET ADMIN MED CTR, AMARILLO, TEX, 87-; ASSOC PROF INT MED, BIOCHEM & MOLECULAR BIOL, TEX TECH UNIV SCH MED. *Personal Data:* b Searcy, Ark, Mar 20, 42; m 65; c 2. *Educ:* Hendrix Col, BA, 63; Univ Ark, MD, 67. *Prof Exp:* Instr med hematol/oncol, Sch Med, Univ Wash, 73-74, asst prof, 74-75; chief oncol, Vet Admin Med Ctr, Salt Lake City, Utah, 75-82, res assoc cancer res, 82-87; asst prof med molecular biol, Col Med, Univ Utah, 75-87. *Res:* Mechanisms of oncogenic transformation; tumor vaccine production; tumor antibody production. *Mailing Add:* Vet Admin Ctr Hemat Oncol Sect 111 6010 Amarillo Blvd W Amarillo TX 79106-1924

**WRIGHT, STEPHEN GAILORD,** CIVIL ENGINEERING. *Current Pos:* From asst prof to assoc prof, 69-84, PROF CIVIL ENG, UNIV TEX, AUSTIN, 84- *Personal Data:* b San Diego, Calif, Aug 13, 43; m 70; c 2. *Educ:* Univ Calif, Berkeley, BS, 66, MS, 67, PhD(civil eng), 69. *Mem:* Am Soc Civil Engrs. *Res:* Soil mechanics and foundations; slope stability; foundations for offshore structures. *Mailing Add:* Dept Civil Eng Univ Tex Austin TX 78712

**WRIGHT, STEVEN JAY,** ENVIRONMENTAL FLUID MECHANICS, HYDRAULIC ENGINEERING. *Current Pos:* PROF CIVIL & ENVIRON ENG, UNIV MICH, 77- *Personal Data:* m 71, Dayle K Wilson; c Glenn T & Daniel B. *Educ:* Wash State Univ, BS, 71, MS, 73; Calif Inst Technol, PhD(civil eng), 77. *Honors & Awards:* Lorenz B Straub Award, St Anthony Falls Lab, 77; J C Stevens Award, Am Soc Civil Engrs, 86; James R Rumsey Award, Water Pollution Control Fedn, 83. *Concurrent Pos:* Int fel, Fed Inst Technol, Zurich, Switz, 84-85; Erskine fel coastal eng, Univ Canterbury Christchurch, NZ, 92. *Mem:* Am Soc Civil Engrs; Am Geophys Union; Int Asn Hydraul Res; Soc Ground Water Scientists & Engrs. *Res:* Contaminant transport processes in surface and ground waters; mixing of turbulent jets and plumes; stratified flow; infiltration processes. *Mailing Add:* 113 EWRE Bldg Univ Mich Ann Arbor MI 48118. *Fax:* 313-763-2275; *E-Mail:* sjwright@engin.umich.edu

**WRIGHT, STEVEN MARTIN,** FLUORINE CHEMISTRY. *Current Pos:* from asst prof to assoc prof, 82-93, PROF, DEPT CHEM, UNIV WIS, STEVENS POINT, 93- *Personal Data:* b Oak Park, Ill, Aug 25, 53; m 75; c 2. *Educ:* Elmhurst Col, BA, 75; Marquette Univ, PhD(inorg chem), 80. *Prof Exp:* Asst prof chem, Lakeland Col, 80-82. *Concurrent Pos:* Vis asst prof, Univ Wis, Milwaukee, 81-82; instr, Marquette Univ, 80-82. *Mem:* Am Chem Soc; AAAS; Sigma Xi; NY Acad Sci. *Res:* New synthetic methods to form new and existing graphite interalation compounds; interalation of fluorides and graphite. *Mailing Add:* Chem Dept Univ Wis Stevens Point WI 54481

**WRIGHT, STUART R(EDMOND),** CHEMICAL ENGINEERING, CHEMISTRY. *Current Pos:* engr, E I Du Pont de Nemours & Co, 54-66, sr res engr, 66-69, res assoc chem, 69-74, res assoc, Div Eng, 74-85, CONSULT, E I DU PONT DE NEMOURS & CO, INC, 85- *Personal Data:* b Calgary, Alta, Aug 13, 23; m 49, Elsie J Pfeil; c Stuart J, Kathryn (Hoover) & James. *Educ:* Univ Alta, BSc, 46, MSc, 47; Northwestern Univ, PhD, 50. *Prof Exp:* Engr, Aluminum Co Can, Ltd, 50-54. *Mem:* Am Inst Chem Engrs; Sigma Xi. *Res:* Industrial chemicals; dye intermediates. *Mailing Add:* 15 Marlton Rd Woodstown NJ 08098-1227

**WRIGHT, SYDNEY COURTENAY,** PHYSICS. *Current Pos:* NSF fel, Enrico Fermi Inst, Univ Chicago, 49-50, res assoc, 50-55, from asst prof to assoc prof, 55-68, PROF PHYSICS, ENRICO FERMI INST, UNIV CHICAGO, 69- *Personal Data:* b Vancouver, BC, Oct 16, 23; m 48; c 3. *Educ:* Univ BC, BA, 43; Univ Calif, PhD(physics), 49. *Concurrent Pos:* Consult, Brookhaven Nat Lab, 53 & Argonne Nat Lab, 57-60. *Mem:* Am Phys Soc. *Res:* Experimental particle physics; particle accelerator design. *Mailing Add:* 5831 S Blackstone Chicago IL 60637

**WRIGHT, TERRY L,** synthetic heterocyclic chemistry, for more information see previous edition

**WRIGHT, THEODORE ROBERT FAIRBANK,** DEVELOPMENTAL GENETICS. *Current Pos:* assoc prof, 65-75, prof biol, 75-95, EMER PROF, UNIV VA, 95- *Personal Data:* b Kodaikanal, India, Apr 10, 28; US citizen; m 51, Eileen Yongen. *Educ:* Princeton Univ, AB, 49; Wesleyan Univ, MA, 54; Yale Univ, PhD(zool), 59. *Honors & Awards:* Wilhelmine E Key lectr, Am Genetics Asn, 92. *Prof Exp:* Asst prof biol, Johns Hopkins Univ, 59-65. *Concurrent Pos:* Mem, Genetics Study Sect, NIH, 72-74; fel, Max Planck Inst Biol, 75-76. *Mem:* Fel AAAS; Genetics Soc Am; Soc Develop Biol. *Res:* Developmental genetics of embryonic mutants in Drosophila; genetic and molecular analysis of the functional organizaion of the genome of Drosophila. *Mailing Add:* Dept Biol Univ Va Charlottesville VA 22903-2477. *E-Mail:* trw3j@virginia.edu

**WRIGHT, THOMAS CARR, JR,** pathology, cell growth control, for more information see previous edition

**WRIGHT, THOMAS L,** PETROLOGY, VOLCANOLOGY. *Current Pos:* AT SMITHSONIAN INST NAT MUS NATURAL HIST, 95- *Personal Data:* b Chicago, Ill, July 26, 35; div; c John & Rececca. *Educ:* Pomona Col, AB, 57; Johns Hopkins Univ, PhD(geol), 61. *Prof Exp:* Geologist, US Geol Surv, Washington, DC, 61-64, staff geologist, Hawaiian Volcano Observ, 64-69, geologist, Geol Div, Washington, DC, 69-74, geologist, Reston, Va, 74-84, scientist-in-charge, Hawaiian Volcano Observ, 84-91, geologist, Hawaiian Hist Studies, 92-93, geologist, Reston Va, 94-95. *Mem:* Mineral Soc Am; Am Geophys Union. *Res:* Petrology of Hawaiian basalt; chemical and stratigraphic study of the basalts of the Columbia River plateau; geology, geophysics, petrology and geochemistry of Kilauea volcano from an historical perspective. *Mailing Add:* Smithsonian Inst Nat Mus Natural Hist NHB-119 Washington DC 20560

**WRIGHT, THOMAS OSCAR,** STRATIGRAPHY, STRUCTURE. *Current Pos:* prog assoc geol, 78-80, PROG DIR STRUCT & TECTONICS, NSF, 80- *Personal Data:* b Jasper, Ala, July 9, 40; m 65. *Educ:* Auburn Univ, BS, 65; George Washington Univ, MS, 71, PhD(geochem), 74. *Prof Exp:* Oceanogr, Nat Oceanog Data Ctr, 65-69; lectr geol, Bryn Mawr Col, 73-75; asst prof geol, Allegheny Col, 75-78. *Concurrent Pos:* Lectr, George Washington Univ, 73-75 & Carbon Lehigh Intermediate Sch Unit, 76-78; proj geologist explor, Cyprus Explor Ltd, 70- *Mem:* Geol Soc Am. *Res:* Geology and geochemistry of sedimentary rocks and modern analogs; teaching of geology; Ordovician clastic rocks of central Appalachians; sedimentology and structure of pre-cambrian and paleozoic rocks; northern Victoria Land; Antarctica. *Mailing Add:* 3531 T St NW Washington DC 20007

**WRIGHT, THOMAS PAYNE,** PHYSICS, PLASMA PHYSICS. *Current Pos:* Staff mem physics, 69-80, SUPVR THEORET DIV, SANDIA NAT LABS, 80- *Personal Data:* b Ft Worth, Tex, Dec 23, 43; m 66; c 3. *Educ:* St Bonaventure Univ, BS, 66; NMex State Univ, MS, 68, PhD(physics), 69. *Mem:* Am Phys Soc. *Res:* Plasma waves and instabilities; electromagnetic theory; theory of kinetic equations; laser-plasma interaction; statistical mechanics; relativistic electron beams; magnetohydrodynamics; intense charged particle beam sources and transport. *Mailing Add:* 341 Big Horn Ridge NE Albuquerque NM 87122

**WRIGHT, THOMAS PERRIN, JR,** TOPOLOGY. *Current Pos:* Assoc prof, 67-, PROF MATH, FLA STATE UNIV. *Personal Data:* b Great Falls, SC, June 23, 39; m 61; c 2. *Educ:* Davidson Col, AB, 60; Univ Wis, MA, 63, PhD(math), 67. *Concurrent Pos:* NSF grant, Fla State Univ, 67-72. *Mem:* Am Math Soc. *Res:* Topology of manifolds. *Mailing Add:* Math Dept 208 Love Bldg Fla State Univ Tallahassee FL 32306-3027

**WRIGHT, THOMAS WILSON,** CONTINUUM MECHANICS. *Current Pos:* MECH ENGR, US ARMY BALLISTIC RES LABS, ABERDEEN PROVING GROUND, 67- *Personal Data:* b Fergus Falls, Minn, Oct 23, 33; m 55; c 3. *Educ:* Cornell Univ, BCE, 56, MCE, 57, PhD(mech), 64. *Prof Exp:* Sr engr struct, AAI Corp, Md, 59-61; asst prof mech, Johns Hopkins Univ, 64-67. *Concurrent Pos:* Adj prof mat sci, Johns Hopkins Univ, 92-93. *Mem:* Soc Natural Philos; Am Soc Mech Engrs; Soc Eng Sci. *Res:* Nonlinear wave propagation and the mechanics of deformable media. *Mailing Add:* 4906 Wilmslow Rd Baltimore MD 21210-2329

**WRIGHT, VERNON LEE,** BIOMETRICS, POPULATION DYNAMICS. *Current Pos:* PROF EXP STATIST, SCH FORESTRY, WILDLIFE & FISHERIES, LA STATE UNIV, BATON ROUGE, 78- *Personal Data:* b Muscatine, Iowa, Feb 20, 41; c Rebecca Dawn, Pamela Marie & Timothy L. *Educ:* Iowa State Univ, BS, 64; Purdue Univ, MS, 66; Wash State Univ, PhD(zool), 71. *Prof Exp:* Fel biomet, Cornell Univ, 70-72; wildlife biometrician, Iowa Conserv Comn, 72-76; conserv res analyst, Ill Dept Conserv, 76-78. *Mem:* Wildlife Soc; Ecol Soc Am; Sigma Xi. *Res:* Sampling from and modeling of naturally occurring populations; statistical aspects of wildlife management and administration; measuring peoples' attitudes toward conservation issues. *Mailing Add:* Sch Forestry Wildlife & Fisheries La State Univ Baton Rouge LA 70803. *Fax:* 504-388-4227

**WRIGHT, WALTER EUGENE,** BIOPHARMACEUTICS. *Current Pos:* RETIRED. *Personal Data:* b Terre Haute, Ind, July 16, 24; m 51, Ruth L Kadell; c 5. *Educ:* Purdue Univ, BS, 48, MS, 50, PhD(pharmaceut chem), 53. *Prof Exp:* Sr biochemist, Eli Lilly & Co, 53-65, res scientist, 65-69, res assoc, 69-86. *Mem:* Am Chem Soc; NY Acad Sci; Am Soc Microbiol; Sigma Xi. *Res:* Intestinal and drug absorption; active transport; study of the absorption, metabolism and excretion of new medicinal agents in experimental animals. *Mailing Add:* 7553 N Audubon Rd Indianapolis IN 46250

**WRIGHT, WAYNE MITCHELL,** ACOUSTICS. *Current Pos:* from asst prof to assoc prof, 62-75, chmn dept, 75-95, PROF PHYSICS, KALAMAZOO COL, 75- *Personal Data:* b Sanford, Maine, July 12, 34; m 59, Mary Urbanowicz; c Catherine, Peter, Laura & Daniel. *Educ:* Bowdoin Col, AB, 56; Harvard Univ, MS, 57, PhD(appl physics), 61. *Prof Exp:* Res fel, Harvard Univ, 61-62. *Concurrent Pos:* Vis prof physics, Naval Postgrad Sch, 69-70; vis prof atmospheric sci, Univ Mich, 79-80; res fel mech eng, Univ Tex Austin, 88-89 & 96. *Mem:* Fel Acoust Soc Am; Am Asn Physics Teachers. *Res:* Physical acoustics; experimental studies of finite-amplitude sound phenomena in air; optoacoustics. *Mailing Add:* Dept Physics Kalamazoo Col Kalamazoo MI 49006-3295. *E-Mail:* wwritht@kzoo.edu

**WRIGHT, WILLIAM BLYTHE, JR,** PHARMACEUTICAL CHEMISTRY. *Current Pos:* RETIRED. *Personal Data:* b Washington, DC, Sept 29, 18; m 48; c 2. *Educ:* Univ Va, BS, 39; Univ Mich, PhD(chem), 42. *Prof Exp:* Resin res chemist, Rohm & Haas Co, Pa, 42-47; pharmaceut res chemist, Bound Brook Labs, Am Cyanamid Co, 47-55 & Lederle Labs, 55-87. *Mem:* Am Chem Soc. *Res:* Coatings; plywood adhesives; ion exchange resins; pharmaceuticals. *Mailing Add:* 18 Clinton Pl Woodcliff Lake NJ 97675-8299

**WRIGHT, WILLIAM F(RED),** mechanical engineering; deceased, see previous edition for last biography

**WRIGHT, WILLIAM HERBERT, III,** STRUCTURAL GEOLOGY. *Current Pos:* PRES, WILDERNESS INTERPRETATION. *Personal Data:* b Newton, Mass, Feb 13, 43; m 92, Mary C Cunningham; c Heather L & William K. *Educ:* Middlebury Col, BA, 65; Ind Univ, Bloomington, MA, 67; Univ Ill, Urbana, PhD(geol), 70. *Prof Exp:* Explor geologist, Chevron Oil Co, Colo, 66; from asst prof to prof geol, Sonoma State Univ, 69-97. *Concurrent Pos:* Vis prof, Wellesley Col, 91; prof, Santa Rosa Jr Col. *Mem:* Nat Asn Geol Teachers; Geol Soc Am; Am Geophys Union. *Res:* Folding, metamorphic structures; structural evolution of mountain belts; structure and geologic history of Calaveras Formation and Sierra Foothills Melange, Sierra Nevada, California; geology of coast ranges-Sonoma County. *Mailing Add:* Sonoma State Univ Dept Geol 1801 E Cotati Ave Rohnert Park CA 94928. *Fax:* 707-664-3012; *E-Mail:* wrightw@sonoma.edu

**WRIGHT, WILLIAM LELAND,** WEED SCIENCE. *Current Pos:* RETIRED. *Personal Data:* b Darbyville, Ohio, Aug 14, 30; m 52, Anita Wendt; c Kimberly D, Scott D & Wendy L. *Educ:* Ohio Univ, BS, 53, MS, 57; Purdue Univ, PhD(plant physiol), 64. *Prof Exp:* Plant physiologist, Dow Chem Co, Tex, 57-58; from plant physiologist to sr plant physiologist, Eli Lilly & Co, 58-65, head plant sci res, 65-72, prod plans adv, Elanco Prod Co, 72-73, regulatory serv adv, 73-74, mgr, Agr Regulatory Serv, 74-76, dir, 76-80, dir, Elanco Govt Affairs, Washington, DC, 80-82, dir, Lilly Int Plant Sci Res, Indianapolis, Ind, 82-85, dir, Discovery Res Plant Sci, 85-87, dir, Qual Assurance Res & Develop, 87-89. *Mem:* Sigma Xi; Am Hort Soc; Am Soc Plant Physiologists; Weed Sci Soc Am. *Res:* Chemical weed control; plant growth regulation, insecticides and aquatic weed control; fate of herbicides in environment; product planning; regulatory affairs; government affairs. *Mailing Add:* 6295 Dover Ct Fishers IN 46038

**WRIGHT, WILLIAM RAY,** SOIL MORPHOLOGY. *Current Pos:* From asst prof to assoc prof, 72-86, chmn, 83-96, PROF SOIL SCI, UNIV RI, 86-, ASSOC DEAN, COL RES & DEVELOP, 96- *Personal Data:* b Iola, Wis, Aug 16, 41; m 63. *Educ:* Wis State Univ-River Falls, BS, 66; Univ Md, College Park, MS, 69, PhD(soils), 72. *Mem:* Am Soc Agron; Soil Sci Soc Am; Soil Conserv Soc Am. *Res:* Soil genesis, classification and land use. *Mailing Add:* Assoc Dean Col Res & Develop Univ RI Kingston RI 02881

**WRIGHT, WILLIAM REDWOOD,** PHYSICAL OCEANOGRAPHY. *Current Pos:* OCEANOGR, ASSOC SCIENTISTS, WOODS HOLE, INC, 79- *Personal Data:* b Philadelphia, Pa, Sept 17, 27; m 56; c 3. *Educ:* Princeton Univ, BA, 50; Univ RI, MS, 65, PhD(oceanog), 70. *Prof Exp:* Teacher, RI Pvt Sch, 50-52; pub info officer, Woods Hole Oceanog Inst, 60-62, res asst phys oceanog, 62-70, asst scientist, 70-75; supvry oceanogr, Northeast Fisheries Ctr, Nat Marine Fisheries Serv, 76-81; pres, Bermuda Biol Sta Res, Inc, 77-86. *Concurrent Pos:* Reporter, Auburn Citizen-Advertiser, NY, 52-54 & Providence J, RI, 54-60. *Res:* Deep circulation of the world oceans; coastal circulation. *Mailing Add:* Box 54 Woods Hole MA 02543

**WRIGHT, WILLIAM ROBERT,** theoretical physics; deceased, see previous edition for last biography

**WRIGHT, WILLIAM V(AUGHN),** MOLECULAR GRAPHICS, COMPUTER ARCHITECTURE. *Current Pos:* vis res assoc prof, 90-91, res prof, 91-96, EMER PROF RES, UNIV NC, CHAPEL HILL, 96- *Personal Data:* b Winston-Salem, NC, Sept 15, 31; m 55, Anne M Carleton; c Audrey (Meyer), David & Wendy. *Educ:* Duke Univ, BSEE, 53; Harvard Univ, SM, 54; Univ NC, PhD(comput sci), 72. *Prof Exp:* Engr, IBM Corp, 58-67, sr engr, Research Triangle Park, 67-90. *Concurrent Pos:* Adj assoc prof comput sci, Univ NC, Chapel Hill, 72-90. *Mem:* Sr mem Inst Elec & Electronics Engrs; Asn Comput Mach; Sigma Xi; Am Crystallog Asn. *Res:* Computer applications in molecular biology; computing systems architecture and implementation. *Mailing Add:* 104 Campbell Lane Chapel Hill NC 27514-7802. *E-Mail:* wright@cs.unc.edu

**WRIGHT, WILLIAM VALE,** ENGINEERING, AERONAUTICS. *Current Pos:* PRES, ENTEG SYSTS INC, 81- *Personal Data:* b Long Beach, Calif, Dec 4, 29; m 71; c 4. *Educ:* Calif Inst Technol, BS, 51, PhD(mech eng, physics), 55. *Prof Exp:* Res asst, Calif Inst Technol, 50-52; mem tech staff, Hughes Aircraft Co, 53-54; mgr semiconductor mats, TRW Semiconductors, Inc, 54-57, mgr, Solid State Div, Electro Optical Systs, Inc, 57-60, vpres, 60-65; dir sci & eng, Environ Sci Serv Admin, 66-68; pres, Flight Test Res, Inc, 68-72; prog develop mgr autonetics, Rockwell Int Corp, 72-75; vpres, COR, Inc, 75-78; dir eng & develop, Ball Corp, 78-80; tech dir, Food Mach Group, FMC Corp, 80-81; assoc prof mech eng technol, Univ NC, Charlotte, 84-89. *Concurrent Pos:* Lectr, Univ Calif, Los Angeles, 55-60; lectr eng, Univ NC, Charlotte, 74-75; NSF fel, 52-53. *Mem:* AAAS; Inst Elec & Electronics Engrs; assoc fel Am Inst Aeronaut & Astronaut. *Res:* Research and engineering management; aeronautics; solid state materials and devices; computer sciences. *Mailing Add:* Enteg Syst Inc PO Box 410327 Charlotte NC 28241

**WRIGHT, WILLIAM W,** REPRODUCTIVE BIOLOGY, ENDOCRINOLOGY. *Current Pos:* Asst prof, 82-88, ASSOC PROF POP DYNAMICS, SCH HYG & PUB HEALTH, JOHNS HOPKINS UNIV, 88- *Personal Data:* b Feb 17, 49. *Educ:* State Univ NY, Binghamton, PhD(biol sci), 78. *Mem:* Am Soc Cell Biol; Soc Study Reproduction. *Res:* Male reproductive biology. *Mailing Add:* Dept Pop Dynamics Johns Hopkins Univ 615 N Wolfe St Rm 3606 Baltimore MD 21205-2103. *Fax:* 410-955-0792

**WRIGHT, WILLIAM WYNN,** PHARMACEUTICAL CHEMISTRY. *Current Pos:* SR SCIENTIST, US PHARMACOPEIA, ROCKVILLE, MD, 79- *Personal Data:* b Baltimore, Md, Aug 13, 23; m 45, Mary T Mead; c 5. *Educ:* Loyola Col, Md, BS, 44; Georgetown Univ, MS, 46, PhD(biochem), 48. *Prof Exp:* Chemist, Nat Bur Stand, Washington, DC, 45; chief, Antibiotic Chem Br, US Food & Drug Admin, 45-55, dir, Antibiotic Control Labs, 55-57, dir, Antibiotic Res, 57-64, dept dir div antibiotics & insulin cert, 64-69, dep dir pharmaceut res & testing, 69-71, dir, Div Drug Biol, 71-75, dep assoc dir pharmaceut res & testing, Bur Drugs, 75-79. *Concurrent Pos:* Mem, WHO Expert Panels on Antibiotics, 60-75 & Biol Stand, 75- *Mem:* Fel AAAS; Am Chem Soc; fel Asn Off Analytical Chemists (pres, 76-77); NY Acad Sci; fel Acad Pharmaceut Sci; Sigma Xi. *Res:* Antibiotic testing by chemical, physical, microbial and biological methods; absorption, excretion, distribution and tissue residues of antibiotics; bacterial susceptibility; pharmaceutical analysis. *Mailing Add:* 1301 Dilston Pl Silver Spring MD 20903-2259

**WRIGHT, WOODRING ERIK,** CELL BIOLOGY, SOMATIC CELL GENETICS. *Current Pos:* PROF CELL BIOL, UNIV TEX SOUTHWESTERN MED CTR, DALLAS, 85- *Personal Data:* b San Francisco, Calif, June 21, 49; m 71; c 2. *Educ:* Harvard Univ, BA, 70; Stanford Univ, PhD(med microbiol), 74, MD, 75. *Honors & Awards:* Lyndon Baines Johnson Award, Am Heart Asn, 78; Merit Award, Nat Inst Aging, 86- *Prof Exp:* Fel, Pasteur Inst, Paris, 75-78; from asst prof to assoc prof, Univ Tex Health Sci Ctr, Dallas, 78-92. *Concurrent Pos:* Prin investr, Am Heart Asn, 78-79 & 80-82, res grants, NIH, 78-, & Muscular Dystrophy Asn, 80-; Nat Inst Aging, Res Career Develop Award, 78. *Mem:* Geront Soc; Am Soc Cell Biol; AAAS. *Res:* Using somatic cell genetic and molecular genetic approaches to probe the mechanisms regulating cell differentiation and aging. *Mailing Add:* Dept Cell Biol Univ Tex Southwestern Med Ctr 5323 Harry Hines Blvd Dallas TX 75235. *Fax:* 214-648-8694; *E-Mail:* wright@utsw.swmed.edu

**WRIGHTON, MARK STEPHEN,** PHOTOCHEMISTRY, INORGANIC CHEMISTRY. *Current Pos:* CHANCELLOR, WASHINGTON UNIV, ST LOUIS, 95- *Personal Data:* b Jacksonville, Fla, June 11, 49; m 68. *Educ:* Fla State Univ, BS, 69; Calif Inst Technol, PhD(chem), 72. *Hon Degrees:* DSc, Univ WFla, 80. *Honors & Awards:* Am Chem Soc Award, 80 & 88; E O Lawrence Award, US Dept Energy, 83; MacArthur Prize, 83; Halperin Award, NY Acad Sci, 83. *Prof Exp:* From asst prof to prof chem, Mass Inst

Technol, 72-81, Frederick G Keyes prof, 81-89, dept head, 87-90, ciba-geigy prof chem, 89-95, provost, 90-95. *Concurrent Pos:* Alfred P Sloan fel, 74-76 & Dreyfus grants, 75-80; mem, Chem Res Eval Panel Air Force Off Sci Res, 76-80; Stand Oil Co Calif vis energy prof, Calif Inst Technol, 77; distinguished vis lectr, Univ Tex, Austin, 77; div ed, J Electrochem Soc, 80-82; mem, Defense Sci Res Coun, Advan Res Projs Agency, 81-; mem chem adv comt, NSF, 84-87; bd, Chem Sci & Technol, NRC, 86-89. *Mem:* Fel AAAS; Am Chem Soc; Electrochem Soc; Am Acad Arts & Sci. *Res:* Excited state processes in transition metal containing molecules; photoelectrochemistry; surface chemistry; catalysis; energy conversion; molecular electronics. *Mailing Add:* Washington Univ Brookings Dr Campus Box 1192 St Louis MO 63130. *Fax:* 314-935-4744

**WRIGLEY, COLIN WALTER,** CEREAL CHEMISTRY. *Current Pos:* exp scientist, Wheat Res Unit, Commonwealth Sci & Indust Res Orgn, 61-63, exp res scientist, 67-69, res scientist, 70-83, OFFICER IN CHARGE, GRAIN QUAL RES LAB, COMMONWEALTH SCI & INDUST RES ORGN, 83- *Personal Data:* b Sydney, Australia, Dec 25, 37; m 59, Janice M Saxby; c Christine (Ferguson), Jennifer (Swanton), Robyn & Margaret (Kemmis). *Educ:* Univ Sydney, BSc, 59, MSc, 61, PhD(agr chem), 67. *Honors & Awards:* H G Smith Medal, Royal Australian Chem Inst, 87, F B Guthrie Medal, 88; Thomas Burr Osborne Medal, Am Asn Cereal Chemists, 92; Harold Perten Prize, Int Asn Cereal Sci & Grain Technol, 94. *Prof Exp:* Postdoctoral fel, Univ Man, 69-70. *Mem:* Fel Royal Australian Chem Inst; Am Asn Cereal Chemists; Int Asn Cereal Sci & Grain Technol; Int Electrophoresis Soc; Australian Biotech Asn; Australian Electrophoresis Soc (pres). *Res:* Contributed over 300 articles to professional journals; patentee in field; invention of gel isoelectric focusing for fractionation of proteins. *Mailing Add:* CSIRO Grain Qual Lab PO Box 7 NorthRyde Sydney NSW 2113 Australia. *Fax:* 612-9490-8419; *E-Mail:* c.wrigley@pi.csiro.au

**WRIST, PETER ELLIS,** PULP & PAPER TECHNOLOGY, ENGINEERING PHYSICS. *Current Pos:* RETIRED. *Personal Data:* b Mirfield, Yorkshire, Eng, Oct 9, 27; m, Mirabelle B Harley; c Denise (Parson), Philip, Lydia (Schweizer), Richard M & Kathryn (Idelson). *Educ:* Cambridge Univ, BA, 48, MA, 52; London Univ, MSc, 52; Harvard Univ, AMP, 67. *Hon Degrees:* DSc, Univ BC, 93. *Honors & Awards:* Howard Smith Award, Can Pulp & Paper Asn, 54, Weldon Gold Medal, 56; Eng Award, Tech Asn Pulp & Paper Indust, 69, Gold Medal, 83. *Prof Exp:* Res physicist, Brit Paper & Bd Indust Res Asn, Kenley, 49-52, Que NShore Paper Co, 52-56; res physicist, Mead Corp, 56-60, assoc dir res, 60-61, dir res, 61-66, mgr res & eng, 66-68, vpres res & eng, 68-72, vpres technol, 72-83; exec vpres, Pulp & Paper Res Inst Can, Que, 83-86, pres & chief exec officer, 86-94, dep chmn bd, 94. *Concurrent Pos:* Chmn, Nat Coun Air & Stream Improv, 72-75; mem, Marcus Wallenberg Prize Selection Comt, 83-91, chmn, 91- *Mem:* Fel Tech Asn Pulp & Paper Indust (vpres, 75-77, pres, 77-79); Can Pulp & Paper Asn; NY Acad Sci. *Res:* Environmental research and policy making with respect to pulp and paper manufacture. *Mailing Add:* Pulp & Paper Res Inst Can 570 St Johns Blvd Pointe Claire PQ H9R 3J9 Can. *Fax:* 514-630-9444; *E-Mail:* wrist@paprican.ca

**WRISTON, JOHN CLARENCE, JR,** BIOCHEMISTRY. *Current Pos:* from asst prof to assoc prof, 55-69, PROF CHEM, UNIV DEL, 69- *Personal Data:* b Boston, Mass, Aug 12, 25; m 45; c 4. *Educ:* Univ Vt, BS, 48; Columbia Univ, PhD(biochem), 53. *Prof Exp:* Nat Found Infantile Paralysis fel & instr biochem, Sch Med, Univ Colo, 53-55. *Mem:* Am Soc Biol Chemists. *Res:* Protein chemistry; structure and mechanism of action of L-asparaginase. *Mailing Add:* Dept Chem Univ Del Newark DE 19711

**WROBEL, JOSEPH JUDE,** CHEMICAL PHYSICS. *Current Pos:* RES PHYSICIST, EASTMAN KODAK CO RES LABS, 75- *Personal Data:* b Chicago, Ill, Mar 18, 47; m 70; c 2. *Educ:* Loyola Univ, Chicago, BS, 68; Univ Fla, PhD(chem physics), 76. *Res:* Image storage and display systems. *Mailing Add:* 29 Red Cedar Dr Rochester NY 14616

**WROBEL, JOSEPH STEPHEN,** SOLID STATE PHYSICS. *Personal Data:* b Syracuse, NY, Aug 15, 39. *Educ:* Syracuse Univ, BS, 61, MS, 64, PhD(physics), 67. *Prof Exp:* Res asst physics, Syracuse Univ, 61-66; mem tech staff, Tex Instruments Inc, 66-86; assoc prof comput sci eng, Univ Ark, 86-91. *Mem:* Asn Comput Mach; Am Phys Soc. *Res:* Semiconductor materials; computer automation; photoconductivity; infrared physics. *Mailing Add:* 10471 SW Campbell Fayetteville AR 72701

**WROBEL, WILLIAM EUGENE,** ENVIRONMENTAL ASSESSMENT, WATER QUALITY. *Current Pos:* vpres opers, 89-92, EXEC VPRES OPERS, ECOTECH, INC, 92- *Personal Data:* b Syracuse, NY. *Educ:* Syracuse Univ, BA, 68; New York Univ, MS, 73. *Prof Exp:* Biologist, NY State Atomic & Space Develop Authority, 69-72; sr proj mgr, Dames & Moore, 72-79; projs dir, VTN Ore, Inc, Subsid VTN Corp, 79-84. *Concurrent Pos:* Vchmn, Bd Dir, TELCO FCU. *Mem:* Am Soc Civil Eng; Asn Environ Health Soils. *Res:* Performance and management of interdisciplinary environmental studies for mining and energy facilities, pipelines, chemical plants, refineries, dredging activities, shoreline and land developments, and pollution control facilities; specializes in soil and groundwater studies for solid and hazardous waste facilities; hazardous waste studies and remediation. *Mailing Add:* 8018 One Calais Ave Suite B Baton Rouge LA 70809

**WROBLEWSKI, JOSEPH S,** BIOLOGICAL OCEANOGRAPHY, FISHERIES OCEANOGRAPHY. *Current Pos:* PROF RES, MEM UNIV NFLD, 89- *Personal Data:* b Chicago, Ill, June 8, 48; m 82, Verna Loder; c 3. *Educ:* Univ Ill, BSc, 70; Fla State Univ, MSc, 72, PhD(oceanog), 76. *Prof*

*Exp:* Asst prof biol oceanog, Dalhousie Univ, 76-84; res scientist, Bigelow Lab Ocean Sci, 84-89. *Concurrent Pos:* Prin investr, Natural Sci & Eng Res Coun Can, 76-, NSF, 80-, Off Naval Res, 84-89; indust res chair, Nat Sci & Eng Res Coun Can, 89-95; adj scientist, Bigelow Lab Ocean Sci, 90- *Mem:* Am Soc Limnol & Oceanog; Sigma Xi; Am Geophys Union. *Res:* Numerical modeling of marine ecosystems; ocean circulation-marine biomass interactions; numerical analysis; applied statistics; fisheries oceanography; aquaculture. *Mailing Add:* Ocean Sci Ctr Mem Univ Nfld St John's NF A1B 3X7 Can. *Fax:* 709-737-8739; *E-Mail:* jwroblew@morgan.ucs.mun.ca

**WROGEMANN, KLAUS,** BIOCHEMISTRY, GENETICS & MOLECULAR BIOLOGY. *Current Pos:* from asst prof to prof, 70-79, PROF BIOCHEM, FAC MED, UNIV MAN, 79-, PROF HUMAN GENETICS, 85- *Personal Data:* b Berlin, Ger, Dec 8, 40; Can citizen; m 67, Dorit Jenckel; c Jens, Mark & Sylvia. *Educ:* Univ Marburg, MD, 66; Univ Man, PhD(biochem), 69. *Honors & Awards:* Rh Inst Award, 82. *Prof Exp:* Intern surg & med, Med Hosp, Hanover, Ger, 70. *Concurrent Pos:* Vis prof, Max-Planck Inst Immunol, Freiburg, Ger, 77-78; vis prof, Inst Molecular Biol, Strasbourg, France, 84-85 & 92-93. *Mem:* Can Biochem Soc; Am Soc Human Genetics; Int Study Group Heart Res; Am Soc Biochem & Molecular Biol; Endocrine Soc. *Res:* Metabolism of normal and dystrophic heart and skeletal muscle; molecular basis of genetic diseases; basic and applied studies of steroid hormone receptors; mapping genetic neuromuscular diseases. *Mailing Add:* Dept Biochem & Molecular Biol Univ Man Winnipeg MB R3E 0W3 Can. *Fax:* 204-783-0864; *E-Mail:* wrogemn@bldghsc.lani.umanitoba.ca

**WROLSTAD, RONALD EARL,** FOOD SCIENCE, AGRICULTURAL CHEMISTRY. *Current Pos:* res assoc, Ore State Univ, 65-66, asst prof, 66-71 assoc prof, 71-80, PROF FOOD SCI, ORE STATE UNIV, 80- *Personal Data:* b Oregon City, Ore, Feb 5, 39; m 77; c 2. *Educ:* Ore State Univ, BS, 60; Univ Calif, Davis, PhD(agr chem), 64. *Prof Exp:* Grad scientist, Unilever Res Lab, Eng, 64-65. *Concurrent Pos:* Sabbatical leave, Plant Dis Div, Dept Sci & Indust Res, Auckland, NZ, 72-73; vis prof, Cornell Univ, 79-80. *Mem:* Inst Food Technol; Am Chem Soc; Sigma Xi. *Res:* Composition of foods as indices of authenticity and quality; sugars; anthocyanin pigments; flavonoids; acids; color degradation; adulteration. *Mailing Add:* Dept Food Sci Ore State Univ Corvallis OR 97331

**WRONSKI, CHRISTOPHER R,** ELECTRICAL ENGINEERING. *Current Pos:* PROF ELEC ENG, DEPT ELEC & COMPUT ENG, PA STATE UNIV, 87- *Educ:* London Univ, BSc, 60, dipl, 63, PhD, 63. *Honors & Awards:* Morris N Liebmann Mem Award, Inst Elec & Electronics Engrs, 84. *Prof Exp:* Mem tech staff, 3M Cent Res Lab, 63-66, RCA Labs, 66-78; Corp Res Labs, Exxon Res & Eng Co, 78-86. *Concurrent Pos:* Vis prof, Kuwait Univ, 79, Mexican Nat Univ, 84, Univ PR, 84, Princeton Univ, 86. *Mem:* Fel Am Phys Soc; fel Inst Elec & Electronics Engrs. *Res:* Melting of submicron crystallites; photoconductivity and electrophotography; semiconductor cold cathodes; heterojunction vidicons; thin film solar cells; amorphous silicon. *Mailing Add:* Elec Eng Dept Pa State Univ 213 Elec Eng West University Park PA 16802

**WROTENBERY, PAUL TAYLOR,** INFORMATION SYSTEMS. *Current Pos:* PVT INVESTR & EXEC CONSULT, 79- *Personal Data:* b Pollok, Tex, Apr 24, 34; m 54; c 2. *Educ:* Univ Tex, BS, 58, MA, 62, PhD(physics, chem), 64. *Prof Exp:* Res scientist, Defense Res Labs, Tex, 58; sr scientist & proj dir, Tracor Inc, 58-64; sci consult & mgr, IBM Corp, Dallas & Washington, DC, 64-68; dir comput serv dept, Tracor Inc, 68, sr vpres & dir, Tracor Comput Corp, 68-70; pres & chmn bd, United Systs Int, 70-74; pres, Equimatics Co, 74-76; dir, Informatics Inc, 74-76, group vpres & dir, 76-79; sr staff to Gov & Dir Budget & Planning, State of Tex, 79-82; chmn Tex State Bd Ins, 89-90. *Res:* Surfaces and solid-liquid interfaces; semiconductor electrolyte interface properties; signal processing; management information systems; systems analysis; strategic planning, management development. *Mailing Add:* 3411 Monte Vista Austin TX 78731

**WRUCKE, CHESTER THEODORE, JR,** GEOLOGY. *Current Pos:* GEOLOGIST, US GEOL SURV, 52- *Personal Data:* b Portland, Ore, Oct 24, 27; m 54; c 3. *Educ:* Stanford Univ, BS, 51, MS, 52, PhD, 66. *Mem:* Geol Soc Am. *Res:* Mineral resource assessment and general geologic studies of areas in the western United States having complex structural settings and igneous rocks. *Mailing Add:* 30 Cima Way Portola Valley CA 94028

**WU, ALAN SEEMING,** PUBLIC HEALTH ADMINISTRATION. *Current Pos:* dir Dent Servs, 69-91, DIR, CHILD & ADOLESCENT DIRECTORATE & DENT OFFICER HEALTH, OTTAWA-CARLETON HEALTH DEPT, 91- *Personal Data:* b Hong Kong, China, June 4, 40; Can citizen. *Educ:* Univ Alta, DDS, 66; Univ Toronto, DDPH, 69. *Concurrent Pos:* Guest lectr, Univ Ottawa, 71- & lectr, Univ Toronto, 84-; chief surveyor, Ont Coun Community Health Accreditation, 81- *Mem:* Can Dent Asn; Can Pub Health Asn. *Mailing Add:* Child & Adolescent Directorate Ottawa-Carleton Regional Health Dept 495 Richmond Rd Ottawa ON K2A 4A4 Can

**WU, ALBERT M,** GLYCO-IMMUNOCHEMISTRY, CARBOHYDRATE CHEMIST. *Current Pos:* PROF GLYCO-IMMUNOCHEM, CHANG-GUNG MED COL, TAU-YUAN, TAIWAN, 89- *Personal Data:* b Tainan, Taiwan, Mar 28, 40; m 72, June H Wu. *Educ:* Nat Taiwan Univ, BS, 65; NY Med Col, PhD(biochem), 75. *Honors & Awards:* Units Award Super Serv, USDA, 89. *Prof Exp:* Staff assoc glyco-immunochem, Dr E A Kabat Lab, Dept Microbiol, Col Physicians & Surgeons, Columbia Univ, New York, NY, 76-79, sr staff assoc, 79-82; assoc prof glyco-immunochem, Dept

Vet Path, Tex A&M Univ, College Sta, Tex, 82-89. *Mem:* Am Soc Biochem & Molecular Biol; Soc Complex Carbohydrates; Sigma Xi. *Res:* Isolation, purification and characterization of glycoproteins; immunochemical studies on the binding properties of antibodies and lectins structural and immunochemical studies on epitopes or antigenic determinants. *Mailing Add:* Dept Molecular & Cell Biol Glyco-Immunochem Lab Chang-Gung Med Col Apt 221 2F Kwei-San Tau-Yuan Taiwan. *Fax:* 86-3-328-3031

**WU, ALFRED CHI-TAI,** THEORETICAL PHYSICS. *Current Pos:* from asst prof to assoc prof, 62-80, PROF PHYSICS, UNIV MICH, ANN ARBOR, 80- *Personal Data:* b Chekiang, China, Jan 24, 33; m 67, Corinne C Huang; c Veda & Yvette. *Educ:* Wheaton Col, BS, 55; Univ Md, PhD(physics), 60. *Prof Exp:* Mem, Inst Advan Study, 60-62. *Concurrent Pos:* John Simon Guggenheim Mem Found fel, 68-69. *Mem:* Am Phys Soc. *Res:* Quantum field theory; particle physics. *Mailing Add:* Dept Physics Univ Mich Ann Arbor MI 48109-1120. *E-Mail:* actwu@umich.edu

**WU, ANNA FANG,** MEDICINE, BIOCHEMISTRY. *Current Pos:* resident, Northwestern Univ, 75-77, instr, 77-79, assoc, 79-80, ASST PROF MED, MED SCH, NORTHWESTERN UNIV, 80- *Personal Data:* b Chengtu, China, Mar 25, 40; US citizen; m 66, Tai Te; c Richard. *Educ:* Cornell Univ, BA, 62; Mass Inst Technol, MS, 65, PhD(chem), 67; Univ Chicago, MD, 74; Am Bd Internal Med, cert, 77. *Prof Exp:* Res assoc biochem, Muscle Inst, 67-68; res assoc, Col Physicians & Surgeons, Columbia Univ, 68-71. *Concurrent Pos:* Med dir employee health, Northwestern Mem Hosp, 79-92. *Mem:* Sigma Xi; Am Col Physicians; Am Occup Med Asn. *Res:* Synthetic peptides; synthetic nucleotides; fractionation of erythrocytes. *Mailing Add:* Dept Med Med Sch Northwestern Univ Chicago IL 60611. *Fax:* 312-335-9774

**WU, CHANGSHENG,** EXPLORATION GEOPHYSICS. *Current Pos:* res geophysicist, Western Geophys Co, 66-69, sr res geophysicist, 69-74, sr staff scientist, 74-84, mgr interpretation & spec processing, 79-84, CHIEF SCIENTIST & MGR INTERPRETATION, CHINA, WESTERN GEOPHYS CO, LITTON INDUSTS, INC, 85- *Personal Data:* b Liaoning, Manchuria, China, Oct 3, 23; nat US; m 55; c 2. *Educ:* Nat Southwestern Assoc Univs, China, 44; Univ Tex, BS, 47; Rice Univ, MA, 63, PhD(geophys), 66. *Prof Exp:* Seismologist, United Geophys Co, 47-51; party chief, Tex Seismog Co, 52-53; rev geophysicist, Precision Explor Co, 53-55 & Ralph E Fair, Inc, 55-56; seismic prospecting expert, Tech Assistance Admin, UN, 57-60; asst geophys, Rice Univ, 62-64. *Mem:* Soc Explor Geophysicists. *Res:* Elastic wave propagation and seismic data interpretation. *Mailing Add:* 2275 Woodland Springs St Houston TX 77077

**WU, CHAU HSIUNG,** PHARMACOLOGY, ELECTROPHYSIOLOGY. *Current Pos:* asst prof, 77-82, ASSOC PROF PHARMACOL, MED SCH, NORTHWESTERN UNIV, 82- *Personal Data:* b Taipei, Taiwan, Feb 10, 41; US citizen; m 66; c 2. *Educ:* Nat Taiwan Univ, BS, 63; Univ Miami, MS, 68, PhD(pharmacol), 71. *Prof Exp:* Res assoc pharmacol, Med Ctr, Duke Univ, 74-75, asst adj prof, 75-76, asst med res prof, 76-77. *Concurrent Pos:* Fel, Med Ctr, Duke Univ, 70-72, Muscular Dystrophy Asn fel, 72-74; NIH res career develop award, 81-86. *Mem:* Am Chem Soc; Biophys Soc; Soc Gen Physiologists; Soc Neurosci; Am Soc Pharmacol & Exp Therapeut; Int Soc Toxinology. *Res:* Mechanisms of action of neurotoxins on membrane ionic channels in nerves and muscles. *Mailing Add:* Dept Pharmacol/Searle 8-477 Northwestern Univ Med Sch 303 E Chicago Ave Chicago IL 60611-3008. *Fax:* 312-503-5349

**WU, CHENG-HSIAO,** SEMICONDUCTOR DEVICES, SOLID STATE PHYSICS. *Current Pos:* assoc prof, 83-91, PROF ELEC ENG, UNIV MO, ROLLA, 91- *Personal Data:* b Lukang, Taiwan, Feb 5, 43; US citizen; div; c 2. *Educ:* Nat Taiwan Univ, BS, 65; Univ Rochester, MS, 67, PhD(physics), 72. *Prof Exp:* Fel physics, New York Univ, 72-74, City Col, City Univ NY, 74-75; vis scientist solid state physics, Max-Planck Inst, Stuttgart, Germany, 75-77; res assoc, Univ Rochester, 78-80; mem tech staff, RCA Lab, Princeton, NJ, 80-83. *Concurrent Pos:* Consult, Xerox Weber Res Ctr, 79-80; vis prof, Inst Theoret Physics, Univ Stuttgart, Ger, 90. *Mem:* Am Phys Soc; Inst Elec & Electronics Engrs; Sigma Xi; NY Acad Sci. *Res:* Random walk theory and transport in disordered materials; semiconductor device modeling; quantum resistor network theory for wave computing; mesoscopic physics and devices. *Mailing Add:* Dept Elec Eng Univ Mo Rolla MO 65401. *Fax:* 573-341-4532; *E-Mail:* chw@ee.emr.edu

**WU, CHENG-WEN,** BIOPHYSICS, BIOCHEMISTRY. *Current Pos:* DIR, INST BIOMED SCI, ACADEMIA SINICA, REPUB CHINA, 88-; PRES, NAT HEALTH RES INST, ROC, 96- *Personal Data:* b Taipei, Taiwan, June 19, 38; m 63, Felicia Y H; c David, Faith & Alert. *Educ:* Nat Taiwan Univ, MD, 64; Case Western Res Univ, PhD(biochem), 69. *Honors & Awards:* Catacosinos Prof Award Cancer Res. *Prof Exp:* Res assoc phys biochem, Cornell Univ, 69-71; from asst prof to assoc prof biophys, Albert Einstein Col Med , 72-78, prof biochem, 78-80; prof pharmacol sci, State Univ NY Stony Brook, 80-90. *Concurrent Pos:* NIH spec fel biophys, Yale Univ, 71-72; Am Cancer Soc res grant, Albert Einstein Col Med, 72-75, NIH res grant, 72-79 & res career develop award, 72-77; Irma T Hirschl Sci Award, 77-82. *Mem:* Am Soc Pharmacol & Exp Therapeut; Am Chem Soc; Am Soc Biochem & Molecular Biol; Biophys Soc; Am Asn Cancer Res. *Res:* Regulation and mechanism of gene expression; carcinogenesis; optical studies of nucleic acid and protein interaction; fast reactions in biological systems; absorption and emission spectroscopy. *Mailing Add:* Nat Health Res Inst No 128 Sect II Yen-chik-Yvan Rd Taipei 11529 Taiwan. *Fax:* 886-2-782-5573

**WU, CHI,** PHOTONIC SWITCHING DEVICES, LASER DOPPLER VELOCIMETRY. *Current Pos:* MEM TECH STAFF, JET PROPULSION LAB, CALIF INST TECHNOL, 97- *Personal Data:* b Xi'An, China, May 19, 63; Can citizen; m 88, Yu-Shien Wang; c Albert, Eric & Kevin. *Educ:* Shandong Univ, China, BS, 82; Univ Toronto, MAS, 91, PhD(elec eng), 95. *Honors & Awards:* Silver Medal, Nat Sci & Eng Res Coun, Can, 95. *Prof Exp:* Instr, Elec Eng Dept, Hebei Univ, China, 82-83; researcher, Inst Semiconductors, Chinese Acad Sci, Beijing, 83-86; vis researcher, Elec Eng Dept, Univ Calif, Santa Barbara, 86-88; sr scientist & proj leader, Bell-Northern Res & Northern Telecom, 92-96. *Mem:* Inst Elec & Electronics Engrs; Optical Soc Am; Int Soc Optical Eng; Photonic Soc Chinese Am. *Res:* Photonic and optoelectronic devices for telecommunication and space exploratory applications; photonic switching, integrated micro laser Doppler velocimetry and integrated laser modulators. *Mailing Add:* M/S 302-231 4800 Oak Grove Dr Pasadena CA 91109. *Fax:* 818-393-4540; *E-Mail:* chi.wu@jpl.nasa.gov

**WU, CHIEN-SHIUNG,** physics; deceased, see previous edition for last biography

**WU, CHIH,** THERMODYNAMICS, HEAT TRANSFER. *Current Pos:* From asst to assoc prof, 66-78, PROF ENG, US NAVAL ACAD, 78-; PROF, JOHNS HOPKINS UNIV, 68- *Personal Data:* b Changsha, China, Apr 13, 36; m 66; c Anna, Joy, Sheree & Patricia. *Educ:* Cheng Kung Univ, Taiwan, BS, 57, MS, 61; Univ Ill, PhD(mech eng), 66. *Concurrent Pos:* Prof, Johns Hopkins Univ, 68- *Mem:* Am Soc Mech Engrs; Am Soc Eng Educ; Chinese Soc Mech Engrs. *Res:* Energy conversion; computer-assisted education; finite-time thermodynamics. *Mailing Add:* 1528 Wild Cranberry Dr Crownsville MD 21032. *Fax:* 410-293-2591; *E-Mail:* wu@sourctic.navy.mil

**WU, CHING-HSONG GEORGE,** CHEMICAL KINETICS & CHEMICAL VAPOR DEPOSITION, DIAMOND THIN FILMS. *Current Pos:* SR RES CHEMIST, SCI RES LAB, FORD MOTOR CO, DEARBORN, 69- *Personal Data:* b Taipei, Taiwan, Apr 22, 39; m 67; c 2. *Educ:* Nat Taiwan Univ, BS, 62; NMex Highland Univ, MS, 65; Univ Calif, Berkeley, PhD(chem), 69. *Mem:* Am Chem Soc; Mat Res Soc. *Res:* Gas phase kinetics; free radical reactions; mechanism of smog formation; energy transfer; mechanism of chemical vapor deposition; three-way catalyst research, characterization, and modeling; cvd diamond films. *Mailing Add:* 30691 Turtle Creek Dr Farmington MI 48331

**WU, CHING-SHENG,** THEORETICAL PLASMA PHYSICS, PLASMA ASTROPHYSICS. *Current Pos:* res prof space plasma-physics, Inst Fluid Dynamics & Appl Math, 68-76, RES PROF SPACE PLASMA PHYSICS, INST PHYS SCI & TECHNOL, UNIV MD, 76- *Personal Data:* b Nanjing, China, Nov 11, 29; US citizen; m 61; c 1. *Educ:* Nat Taiwan Univ, BSE, 54; Va Polytech Inst, MS, 56; Princeton Univ, PhD(plasma physics), 59. *Prof Exp:* Sr scientist, physics sect, Jet Propulsion Lab, Calif Inst Technol, 59-68. *Concurrent Pos:* Vis mem, Atomic Energy Res Estab, UK Atomic Energy Authority, 61-62; vis assoc prof, Dept Math, Mass Inst Technol, 66-67 & Inst Fluid & Appl Math, Univ Md, 67; vis prof, Dept Physics, Nat Taiwan Univ, 68-69 & Fed Univ Rio Grande do Sul, Porto Alegre, Brazil, 77; consult, Nat Aeronaut & Space Admin, 77-84; hon prof, Chinese Acad Sci, 79-; mem adv panel, Nat Natural Sci Found, China, 93- *Mem:* Am Geophys Union; fel Acad Sci; Int Union Radio Sci; Sigma Xi; fel Am Phys Soc. *Res:* Study of radio emission and major plasma processes in solar-terrestrial environment; Investigation of basic plasma instabilities relevant to laboratory and space plasmas. *Mailing Add:* Inst Phys Sci & Technol Univ Md CSS Bldg 224 Rm 4257 College Park MD 20742. *Fax:* 301-434-0355

**WU, CHING-YONG,** INDUSTRIAL ORGANIC CHEMISTRY. *Current Pos:* SR SCIENTIST, INDSPEC CHEM CORP, 88- *Personal Data:* US citizen; m 61, Teng M Hu; c 3. *Educ:* Nat Taiwan Univ, BS, 55; Univ Pittsburgh, PhD(chem), 61. *Prof Exp:* Nat Res Coun Can fel chem, 63-65; fel, Mellon Inst Sci, 65-67; res chemist, Gulf Res & Develop Co, 67-71, sr res chemist, 71-83; sr scientist, Koppers Co, Inc, 83-88. *Mem:* Am Chem Soc; Catalysis Soc. *Res:* Physical organic chemistry and petrochemical research; homogeneous and heterogeneous catalysis, polymer synthesis and new polymerization; development of new chemical process and pilot planting. *Mailing Add:* 104 Wilmer Dr Pittsburgh PA 15238-1608

**WU, CHUANYUE,** extracellula matrix, cell adhesion molecules, for more information see previous edition

**WU, CHUEN-SHANG C,** PROTEIN CONFORMATION, ENZYMOLOGY. *Personal Data:* b Taiwan, July 10, 32; US citizen; m 67; c 1. *Educ:* Univ Calif, Berkeley, PhD(agr chem) 67. *Prof Exp:* Assoc res biochemist, Cardiovasc Res Inst, Univ Calif, San Francisco, 82-92. *Mem:* Am Soc Biochem & Molecular Biol; Protein Soc; Soc Chinese-Am Bioscientists. *Res:* Conformation of peptides and proteins in surfactant solutions; structure-function relationship of acetyleholinesterase. *Mailing Add:* 1004 Rudgear Rd Walnut Creek CA 94596

**WU, CHUN-FANG,** NEUROPHYSIOLOGY, NEUROGENETICS. *Current Pos:* from asst prof to assoc prof, 79-89, PROF BIOL, UNIV IOWA, 89- *Personal Data:* b Fujien, China, Feb 4, 47; m 71; c 3. *Educ:* Tunghai Univ, Taiwan, BS, 69; Purdue Univ, PhD(neurobiol), 76. *Prof Exp:* Res fel neurobiol, Cal Inst Technol, 76-79. *Concurrent Pos:* Vis prof pharmacol, Nat Taiwan Univ, 87 & vis prof physics, Univ Tokyo, 88; assoc ed, J Neurogenetics. *Mem:* Soc Neurosci; Biophys Soc; AAAS; Sigma Xi. *Res:* Genetic analysis of neurophysiological processes; function and development of Drosophila nervous system. *Mailing Add:* Dept Biol Univ Iowa Iowa City IA 52242-1368. *Fax:* 319-335-1103

**WU, CHUNG,** BIOCHEMISTRY. *Current Pos:* RETIRED. *Personal Data:* b Foochow, China, Dec 13, 19; nat US; m 50, Helen Chen; c 4. *Educ:* Fukien Christian Univ, China, BS, 41; Univ Mich, MS, 48, PhD(biol chem), 52. *Prof Exp:* Res asst, Mayo Clin, 52-56; from instr to assoc prof biol chem, Med Sch, Univ Mich, Ann Arbor, 56-86. *Concurrent Pos:* Lectr, summer sem, Academea Sinica, Taiwan, 68. *Mem:* Am Soc Biol Chem; Am Chem Soc; Am Asn Cancer Res. *Res:* Mechanisms of enzyme action; enzymology of cancer; metabolic controls; drug allergy. *Mailing Add:* 731 Hillmont St Santa Rosa CA 95409-2817

**WU, CHUNG PAO,** SOLID STATE ELECTRONICS. *Current Pos:* MEM TECH STAFF INTEGRATED CIRCUIT TECHNOL, SARNOFF RES CTR, RCA CORP, 73- *Personal Data:* b Kwantung, China, May 15, 42; US citizen; m 71; c 3. *Educ:* Yale Univ, BS, 65, MS, 66, PhD(physics), 68. *Prof Exp:* Res physicist, Electron Accelerator Lab, Yale Univ, 68-70; asst prof physics, Nanyang Univ, 70-72. *Mem:* Am Chem Soc; Inst Elec & Electronics Engrs. *Res:* Development of methods which accurately control the generation and implantation of ions in solids; study and characterization of ion implantation and laser annealing techniques for semiconductor device fabrication. *Mailing Add:* Sarnoff Corp CN5300 Washington Rd Princeton NJ 08543-5300

**WU, DAO-TSING,** chemical engineering, for more information see previous edition

**WU, DOLLY Y,** electronics development, particle searches, for more information see previous edition

**WU, ELLEN LEM,** PHYSICAL CHEMISTRY. *Current Pos:* RETIRED. *Personal Data:* b Shanghai, China, Dec 6, 30; m 54; c 2. *Educ:* Carleton Col, BA, 54; Univ Minn, PhD(phys chem), 62. *Prof Exp:* Sr res chemist, Appl Res Div, Mobil Res & Develop Corp, 62-71, res assoc, 71-79, sr res assoc, Process Res & Tecg Serv Div, 79-89. *Mem:* Am Chem Soc; Am Crystallogrs Asn. *Res:* Catalysis research; physicochemical methods employed to elucidate nature of catalysts used in hydrocarbon conversion processes. *Mailing Add:* 1203 Woodruff Rd Glassboro NJ 08028

**WU, EN SHINN,** CHEMICAL PHYSICS. *Current Pos:* asst prof, 74-79, ASSOC PROF PHYSICS, UNIV MD, BALTIMORE CO, 79- *Personal Data:* b Kwangtung, China, Apr 20, 43. *Educ:* Nat Taiwan Univ, BS, 65; Cornell Univ, PhD(appl physics), 72. *Prof Exp:* Res assoc chem, Syracuse Univ, 72-74. *Mem:* Am Phys Soc; Biophys Soc; Sigma Xi; Optical Soc Am. *Res:* General properties of simple fluids and fluid mixtures, in particular, their thermodynamic behaviors near the critical points; the experimental techniques employed are primarily light-scattering and small angle X-ray scattering. *Mailing Add:* Dept Physics Univ Md Baltimore Co Catonsville MD 21228-5329

**WU, FA YUEH,** STATISTICAL PHYSICS. *Current Pos:* from asst prof to prof, 67-89, distinguished prof, 89-92, MATTHEWS DISTINGUISHED PROF PHYSICS, NORTHEASTERN UNIV, 92- *Personal Data:* b China, Jan 5, 32; m 63, Jane Chang; c Yvonne, Yolanda & Yelena. *Educ:* Chinese Naval Col, BS, 54; Nat Tsing Hua Univ, MS, 59; Wash Univ, PhD(physics), 63. *Prof Exp:* Res assoc physics, Wash Univ, 63; asst prof, Va Polytech Inst, 63-67. *Concurrent Pos:* Sr Fulbright res fel, Australian Nat Univ, 73; staff assoc, NSF, 83-84; vis prof, Inst Lorentz, 80, Nat Tsing Hua Univ, 74 & 88, Univ Wash, 87, Ecole Polytech Fed, Laussane, 75, 78, 85, 91, Nat Taiwan Univ, 84, Univ Paris, 92 & 96. *Mem:* Fel Am Phys Soc. *Res:* Many body theory; theory of quantum liquids; statistical mechanics; solid state theory. *Mailing Add:* Dept Physics Northeastern Univ Boston MA 02115. *E-Mail:* fywu@neu.edu

**WU, FELICIA YING-HSIUEH,** MOLECULAR BIOLOGY, BIOCHEMISTRY. *Current Pos:* RES FEL, INST BIOMED SCI, ACADEMIA SINICA, TAIPEI, TAIWAN, 88-, SPEC MED RES CHAIR PROF, NAT SCI COUN, 89- *Personal Data:* b Taipei, Taiwan, Feb 27, 39; US citizen; m 63, Cheng-Wean; c David, Faith & Albert. *Educ:* Nat Taiwan Univ, BS, 61; Univ Minn, MS, 63; Case Western Res Univ, PhD(org chem), 69. *Prof Exp:* Med technician biochem, US Naval Med Res Unit 2, Taipei, Taiwan, 63-65; res asst, Dept Chem, Case Western Res Univ, 65-69; res assoc, Sect Biochem & Molecular Biol, Cornell Univ, 69-71; res assoc pharmacol, Yale Univ, 71-72; instr/assoc biophys, Albert Einstein Col Med, 72-78, asst prof biochem, 78-79; from assoc prof to prof pharmacol sci, State Univ NY, Stony Brook, 80-90. *Concurrent Pos:* Grants, NSF & NIH, 72-93, NIEHS, 82-83; vis prof, Inst Pasteur & Inst Gustave Roussy, Paris, 79-80; Catacosinos prof cancer res, Stony Brook Res Found, 80-90; adj prof pharmacol chem, Univ Calif, San Francisco, 91-; adj prof pharmacol chem, Univ Calif, San Francisco, 91-; ad hoc reviewer, NIH & NSF. *Mem:* Am Soc Biochem & Molecular Biol; Am Biophys Soc; Am Chem Soc; Am Soc Pharmacol & Exp Therapeut; Soc Chinese Biosci Am; Am Asn Cancer Res; Am Inst Chemists; Sigma Xi; Chinese Soc Biochem; Chinese Soc Cell & Molecular Biol; Chinese Soc Genetics; Chinese Oncol Soc; Asn Women Sci; Int Asn Women Biosci; Asia Pac Soc Biosci; Biophys Soc Rol. *Res:* Role of metal ions in gene expression; mechanism of action of anti-tumor drugs; oncosuppressive mechanisms of adeno-associated virus; author or co-author of 87 publications, editor 1 book and 151 abstracts. *Mailing Add:* Inst Biomed Sci Academia Sinica Taipei 11529 Taiwan. *Fax:* 886-2-782-5573; *E-Mail:* bmfwu@ccvax. sinica.edu.tw

**WU, FELIX F,** POWER SYSTEMS. *Current Pos:* ASSOC PROF ELEC ENG & COMPUT SCI, UNIV CALIF, BERKELEY, 78- *Personal Data:* b China, Dec 1, 43; US citizen. *Educ:* Nat Taiwan Univ, BS, 65; Univ Pittsburgh, MS, 68; Univ Calif, Berkeley, PhD(elec eng & comput sci), 72. *Prof Exp:* Asst prof elec eng, Univ Pittsburgh, 72-74, asst prof elec eng & comput sci, Univ Calif, Berkeley, 74-78; engr, Pac Gas & Elec Co, 76-77. *Concurrent Pos:* Consult, Pac Gas & Elec Co, 77-, Solar Energy Res Inst, 80-81, Elec Power Res Inst, 81-82; vis prof, Shanghai Jiao Tung Univ, 80, Swiss Fed Inst Technol, 82. *Mem:* Inst Elec & Electronics Engrs; AAAS. *Res:* Analysis methods for electric power systems planning and operations. *Mailing Add:* Dept Elec Eng & Comput Sci Univ Calif Berkeley CA 94720

**WU, FRANCIS TAMING,** GEOPHYSICS, SEISMOLOGY. *Current Pos:* from asst prof to assoc prof, 70-76, chmn, Dept Geol Sci & Environ Studies, 89-92, PROF GEOPHYS, STATE UNIV NY, BINGHAMTON, 76- *Personal Data:* b Shanghai, China, May 27, 36; m 66, Miriam Brown; c Allison. *Educ:* Nat Taiwan Univ, BS, 59; Calif Inst Technol, PhD(geophys), 66. *Prof Exp:* Asst prof geophys, Boston Col, 68-69. *Concurrent Pos:* Bd dirs, Seismol Soc Am, 86-92; chmn, Data Mgt Commun, IRIS, 93- *Mem:* Am Geophys Union; Seismol Soc Am. *Res:* Faulting as a dynamic phenomenon, its seismic radiation; near source strong ground motion; mechanics of faulting; crustal structures and active tectonics. *Mailing Add:* Dept Geol State Univ NY Binghamton NY 13902-6000. *E-Mail:* wu@sunquakes.geol.binghamton. edu

**WU, GUANLI,** ORGANOMETALLIC CHEMISTRY, SILICON CHEMISTRY. *Current Pos:* DIR INORG CHEM, IMARX PHARMACEUT CORP, 91- *Personal Data:* b Nanjing, China, May 29, 35; m 60, DeKang Shen; c Aijin & Jim X. *Educ:* Dalien Polytech Univ, China, BA, 56; Chem Polytech Inst, Soviet Union, PhD, 62. *Honors & Awards:* Sci Award Sci & Technol of China, 78. *Prof Exp:* Teaching fel chem, Tianjin Univ, China, 56-57; asst prof, Inst Chem Acad Sinica, Beijing, China, 62-78, assoc prof, 78-82 & 83-87; res assoc, Univ Ore, 82-83; res prof, NJ Inst Technol, 88-90. *Res:* Co-inventor on 15 ImaRx patents and author of over 80 publications in journals; key inventor in the development of Sono Rx. *Mailing Add:* 2602 W Aiden St Tucson AZ 85745. *Fax:* 520-791-2437; *E-Mail:* gwu@ imarx.com

**WU, HAI,** MECHANICAL ENGINEERING, APPLIED MECHANICS. *Current Pos:* sr res engr fluid mech heat transfer, Mech Res Dept, Sci Res Lab, Ford Motor Co, 69-75, prin res assoc engr engine analysis, 76-80, prin staff engr, comput modeling & simulation, Control Systs Dept, 80-83, prin staff engr, Fluid & Struct Dynamics, Comput Aided Eng Dept, Systs Res Lab, Eng & Res Staff, 84-86, Safety Anal Dept, 87-90, Safety & NVH Anal Dept, Car Prod Develop, 91-93, MGR, BRAKES TECHNOL & CHASSIS CAE, ADVAN VEHICLE TECHNOL, FORD MOTOR CO, 94- *Personal Data:* b Tunghai, Kiangsu, China, Aug 22, 36; US citizen; m 66, Grace Hsiao-Lee Ma; c Frank H, Carson H & Nelson H. *Educ:* Nat Cheng Kung Univ, Taiwan, BS, 54; Univ Iowa, MS, 63; Case Inst Technol, PhD(fluid mech), 69. *Prof Exp:* Mech engr HVAC design, Syska & Hennessy, Engrs, 65. *Concurrent Pos:* Vis lectr, Detroit Inst Technol, 74. *Mem:* Sigma Xi; Am Soc Mech Engrs. *Res:* Energy management, engine research, automotive safety, lubrication, squeeze films, computer modeling, system optimization, brake technology and structural dynamics. *Mailing Add:* 50150 Hanford Rd Canton MI 48187. *Fax:* 313-845-9295; *E-Mail:* hwu.ford@e-mail.com

**WU, HENRY CHI-PING,** biochemistry; deceased, see previous edition for last biography

**WU, HOFU,** SOLAR ENERGY. *Current Pos:* PROF, CALIF POLYTECH UNIV, POMONA. *Personal Data:* b Taipei, Taiwan, Mar 28, 49; c 2. *Educ:* Tamkang Univ, BArch, 71; Univ Ill, MArch, 75. *Prof Exp:* Lectr archit, Ill Ctr Col, Peoria, 76-77; lectr, Univ Mich, 78-81, asst prof archit, 81-84; asst prof solar archit, Ariz State Univ, 84-92; prof, Col Archit & Urban Planning, Univ Mich, 92- *Concurrent Pos:* Researcher, Archit & Planning Res Lab, Univ Mich, 80-84; dir, Environ Test Lab, Col Archit & Environ Design, 84- *Mem:* Am Soc Heating, Refrig & Air Conditioning; Am Inst Architects; Asn Comput Mach; Int Solar Energy Soc. *Res:* Computer aided energy design for architecture and passive solar heating and cooling strategies for hot and arid region; energy management of large institutional buildings and automatic controls of intelligent buildings. *Mailing Add:* Dept Archit Calif State Polytech Univ 3801 W Temple Ave Pomona CA 91768

**WU, HSIN-I,** ECOLOGICAL PHYSICS, BIOSYSTEMS MODELING. *Current Pos:* from asst prof to assoc prof, 80-87, PROF BIOENG, TEX A&M UNIV, 87- *Personal Data:* b Tokyo, Japan, May 25, 37; m 64, Sancy Y Kiang; c Vernon C (deceased) & Tammy L. *Educ:* Tunghai Univ, Taiwan, BS, 60; Univ Mo, MS, 64, PhD(physics), 67; Tex A&M Univ, MS, 77. *Prof Exp:* From asst prof to assoc prof physics, Southeast Mo State Univ, 67-76; res assoc, Tex A&M Univ, 76-77, res scientist, 77-78, sr res scientist biosysts, 78-80. *Concurrent Pos:* Adj sr res scientist, Gansu Grassland Ecol Res Inst, Lanzhou, China, 88-; fel, Tex Eng Exp Sta, Tex A&M Univ, 90; sr Fulbright scholar, 92; vis prof, Key & Open Lab Bot, NE Forestry Univ, Harbin, China, 93- *Mem:* Int Cong Ecol; Sigma Xi; Int Soc Ecol Modeling. *Res:* Ecological physics; application of saturated rate kinetics in ecological modeling; applied nonlinear dynamics in ecological modelling. *Mailing Add:* Ctr Biosysts Modelling Tex A&M Univ College Station TX 77843-3131. *E-Mail:* wwu@ ie-gate.amu.edu

**WU, HUNG-HSI,** MATHEMATICS. *Current Pos:* from asst prof to assoc prof, 65-73, PROF MATH, UNIV CALIF, BERKELEY, 73- *Personal Data:* b Hong Kong, May 25, 40; US citizen; m 76, Kuniko Weltin; c Colin. *Educ:* Columbia Col, AB, 61; Mass Inst Technol, PhD(math), 63. *Prof Exp:* Res assoc math, Mass Inst Technol, 63-64; mem, Inst Advan Study, 64-65. *Concurrent Pos:* Alfred P Sloan fel, 71-73. *Mem:* Am Math Soc. *Res:* Differential geometry; complex manifolds. *Mailing Add:* Dept Math No 3840 Univ Calif Berkeley CA 94720-3840

**WU, I-PAI,** HYDROLOGY, HYDRAULICS. *Current Pos:* from asst prof to assoc agr engr, 66-76, assoc agr engr, 71-80, PROF AGR ENG, UNIV HAWAII, 76- *Personal Data:* b Chingkaing Kaingsu, China, June 23, 33; m 63; c 2. *Educ:* Nat Taiwan Univ, BS, 55; Purdue Univ, MS, 60, PhD(civil eng), 63. *Prof Exp:* Hydraul engr, Ind Flood Control & Water Resources Comn, 61-62 & 63-64; asst prof civil eng, Chico State Col, 64-66. *Concurrent Pos:* Fulbright prof, Dept Agr Eng, Univ Khartoum, Sudan, 79-80, fac agr eng, Israel Inst Technol, Technion, Haifa, Israel, 86. *Mem:* Am Soc Agr Engrs; Am Soc Civil Engrs; Am Water Resources Asn. *Res:* Small watershed hydrology; hydraulics of surface irrigation; sprinkler irrigation; drip irrigation system design. *Mailing Add:* Dept Bio Syst Eng Univ Hawaii Manoa 3050 Maile Way Honolulu HI 96822

**WU, JAMES CHEN-YUAN,** MECHANICAL ENGINEERING. *Current Pos:* prof aerospace eng, 65-92, EMER PROF, GA INST TECHNOL, 92- *Personal Data:* b Nanking, China, Oct 5, 31; nat US; m 57; c 2. *Educ:* Gonzaga Univ, BS, 54; Univ Ill, MS, 55, PhD(mech eng, appl math), 57. *Prof Exp:* Mech engr, Wah Chang Corp, NY, 54; mem res staff, Mass Inst Technol, 57; asst prof, Gonzaga Univ, 57-59; chief, Res Br, Douglas Aircraft Co, 59-65. *Concurrent Pos:* Europ Atomic Energy Comn sr vis fel, Ispra Res Ctr, Italy, 62-63; consult, Lockheed-Georgia Co, 76- *Mem:* Am Soc Eng Educ; Am Inst Aeronaut & Astronaut; Am Astronaut Soc; Sigma Xi. *Res:* Gas dynamics; thermodynamics; boundary layer theory; viscous flows; numerical analysis. *Mailing Add:* Sch Aerospace Eng Ga Inst Technol Atlanta GA 30332-0150

**WU, JAY Y,** SUPERCONDUCTING MAGNET, SOFTWARE DEVELOPMENT. *Current Pos:* SR ENGR, CRYOMAGNETICS INC, 94- *Personal Data:* b Shanghai; China, Oct 2, 61; m 87, Ye Hong; c Joseph H. *Educ:* Beijing Tsinghua Univ, BS, 85; Tex A&M Univ, MS, 93, PhD(physics), 94. *Mem:* Inst Elec & Electronics Engrs; Am Phys Soc. *Res:* Superconducting magnet, computer engineering and software development. *Mailing Add:* Cryomagnetics Inc 1006 Alvin Weinberg Dr Oak Ridge TN 37830

**WU, JIA-HSI,** PLANT PHYSIOLOGY, VIROLOGY. *Current Pos:* from asst prof to assoc prof cell physiol, 66-80, PROF BIOL SCI, CALIF STATE POLYTECH UNIV, POMONA, 80- *Personal Data:* b Formosa, July 6, 26; m 56; c 1. *Educ:* Univ Taiwan, BA, 50; Cornell Univ, MS, 52; Wash Univ, PhD(bot), 58. *Prof Exp:* Instr plant physiol, Univ Taiwan, 52-55; fel, Univ Wis, 58-59; asst botanist, Univ Calif, Los Angeles, 59-63; asst prof plant physiol, Tex Tech Col, 63-65; asst biologist, Univ Calif, San Diego, 65-66. *Concurrent Pos:* NSF grants, 64-68 & 70-72. *Res:* Cell physiology. *Mailing Add:* 1711 Avenida Monte Vis San Dimas CA 91773

**WU, JIANN-LONG,** RADIOCHEMISTRY, RADIOPHARMACEUTICALS. *Current Pos:* res scientist, 79-84, MGR RES & DEVELOP, MEDI-PHYSICS INC, SUBSID HOFFMANN-LA ROCHE, 84- *Personal Data:* b Chang-hua, Taiwan. *Educ:* Fu-Jen Cath Univ, Taiwan, BS, 68; Northeast La Univ, MS, 72; Va Polytech Inst & State Univ, PhD(chem), 77. *Prof Exp:* Instr anal chem, Chem Dept, Northeast La Univ, 72; fel, Nuclear Med Dept, Med Ctr, Univ Mich, 77-79. *Mem:* Soc Nuclear Med; Am Chem Soc. *Res:* Design, synthesis and development of radiolabeled compounds for organ imaging and biological function studies. *Mailing Add:* 2570 Royal Oaks Dr Alamo CA 94507-2227

**WU, JIE,** SIGNAL TRANSDUCTION, PROTEIN KINASES. *Current Pos:* ASST PROF, H LEE MOFFITT CANCER CTR & RES INST, 95- *Personal Data:* b Xiamen, China, Aug 10, 59; US citizen. *Educ:* Xiamen Univ, China, BS, 82; Univ Kans, PhD(biochem), 88. *Prof Exp:* Res fel, Mem Sloan-Kettering Cancer Ctr, 88-90; postdoctoral fel, Univ Va, 90-94, res asst prof, 94-95. *Concurrent Pos:* Postdoctoral fel, Juv Diabetes Found Int, 92-94; young investr award, Va Affil, Am Diabetes Asn, 93; asst prof, Dept Med Microbiol & Immunol, Univ SFla, 95-, mem, Inst Biomolecular Sci & Inst Aging, 96-, asst prof, Dept Biochem & Molecular Biol, 97-; jr fac res award, Am Cancer Soc, 96- *Mem:* Soc Chinese Bioscientist Am. *Res:* Signal transduction of growth factors and mitogenic phospholipids; regulation of the mitogen-activated protein kinase signaling pathway; characterization of protein kinases and phosphatases; role of reactive oxygen species in cell signaling. *Mailing Add:* H Lee Moffitt Cancer Ctr 12902 Magnolia Dr Tampa FL 33612. *Fax:* 813-979-6700; *E-Mail:* wu@moffitt.usf.edu

**WU, JIN,** FLUID MECHANICS, HYDRAULIC ENGINEERING. *Current Pos:* from assoc prof to prof, 74-80, H FLETCHER BROWN PROF MARINE STUDIES & CIVIL ENG, UNIV DEL, 80-, DIR, AIR-SEA INTERACTION LAB, 80- *Personal Data:* b Nanking, China, Apr 9, 34; m 61; c 3. *Educ:* Nat Cheng Kung Univ, Taiwan, BSc, 56; Univ Iowa, MSc, 61, PhD(mech, hydraul), 64. *Prof Exp:* Res scientist, Hydronautics, Inc, 63-66, sr res scientist, 66-69, head, Fluid Motions Div, 66-72, prin res scientist, 69-74, head, Geophys Fluid Dynamics Div, 72-74. *Concurrent Pos:* Consult, Hydronautics, Inc, 74- & US Naval Res Lab, 80-; adv, Taiwan Hydraulics Lab, Nat Cheng-Kung Univ, Taiwan, 75-; hon prof, Shandong Col Oceanog, China, 81- *Mem:* Nat Acad Eng; Am Soc Civil Engrs; Academia Sinica; Am Geophys Union. *Res:* Geophysical and environmental fluid dynamics; air-sca interaction; coastal and ocean engineering. *Mailing Add:* Air-Sea Interaction Lab Col Marine Studies Univ Del Lewes DE 19958

**WU, JIN ZHONG,** DENSITY FUNCTIONAL THEORY, COMPUTATIONAL PHYSICS. *Current Pos:* CONSULT, 94- *Personal Data:* b Chengdu, China, Jan 5, 45; m 76, Yue P Lu; c Ying J Lu. *Educ:* Beijing Univ, China, BS, 67; Univ Sci & Technol China, MS, 81; Univ Cincinnati, MS, 83, PhD(physics), 88. *Prof Exp:* Assoc engr, Beijing Semiconductor Devices Inst, 70-79; asst researcher, Inst Semiconductors, Chinese Acad Sci, 81; fel assoc, Quantum Theory Proj, Univ Fla, 88-91, asst res scientist, 91-94. *Mem:* Am Phys Soc. *Res:* Electronic properties and structures in films; energy deposition of massive swift particles in ultra-thin films; renormalization of anisotropic Fermi surface of two-dimensional electron systems; semiconductor devices physics and microelectronics; develop films stopping fortran code. *Mailing Add:* 7720 NW 38th Pl Gainesville FL 32606. *Fax:* 904-392-8722; *E-Mail:* wu@qtp.ufl.edu

**WU, JOHN NAICHI,** materials science engineering, for more information see previous edition

**WU, JONATHAN TZONG,** GEOSYNTHETICS, NUMERICAL METHODS. *Current Pos:* from asst prof to assoc prof, 80-94, PROF GEOTECH ENG, UNIV COLO, DENVER, 94- *Personal Data:* b Taipei, Taiwan, Dec 7, 51; US citizen; m 75, Mary S Kang; c Ivan. *Educ:* Nat Taiwan Univ, BS, 74; Va Polytech Inst & State Univ, MS, 76; Purdue Univ, PhD(civil eng), 80. *Honors & Awards:* Outstanding Contrib Geosynthetic Technol, NAm Geosynthetic Soc, 91. *Prof Exp:* Sr engr, Colo Dept Hwy, 84. *Concurrent Pos:* Consult, Colo Dept Hwy, 84-, sr engr, 85; prin investr, Geosynthetic Res Projs, 84-; mem, Soil Placement & Improv Comt, Am Soc Civil Engrs, 87- & Geosynthetic Comt, Nat Res Coun, 91-; vis prof geotech eng, Univ Tokyo, 89. *Mem:* Am Soc Civil Engrs; Int Soc Soil Mech & Found Eng; Int Geotextile Soc; NAm Geotextile Soc; Am Drill Shaft Soc. *Res:* Geosynthetics in earth reinforcement and drainage applications; application of finite element methods in geotechnical engineering; seepage and ground water flow and their effects on earth structures. *Mailing Add:* 15916 E Mercer Circle Aurora CO 80013. *Fax:* 303-556-2368

**WU, JOSEPH M,** GENE REGULATION, DEVELOPMENTAL CONTROL. *Current Pos:* from asst prof to assoc prof, 78-87, PROF BIOCHEM, NY MED COL, 87- *Personal Data:* b China, Aug 1, 47; US citizen; m 76; c 2. *Educ:* McGill Univ, BS, 70; Fla State Univ, MS, 72, PhD(biol sci), 75. *Prof Exp:* Fel, Temple Univ, 76-77, res instr, 77-78. *Concurrent Pos:* Prin investr, NIH grants, 79-88; distinguished vis prof, Guangzhou Med Col, 92- *Mem:* Fed Am Soc Exp Biol; AAAS; Ny Acad Sci; Interferon Soc. *Res:* Molecular mechanism of interferon action; tau protein phosphorylation adn processing; Alzheimer Disease research. *Mailing Add:* Dept Biochem NY Med Col 95 Grasslands Rd Valhalla NY 10595-1600. *Fax:* 914-993-4058

**WU, JOSEPH WOO-TIEN,** ORGANIC CHEMISTRY, ENZYMOLOGY. *Current Pos:* SR SCIENTIST IMMUNOCHEM, INSTRUMENTATION LAB INC, 76- *Personal Data:* b Taiwan; US citizen; c 2. *Educ:* Tainan Cheng-Kung Univ, BS, 65; Worcester Polytech Inst, MS, 69; Univ Pa, PhD(chem), 72. *Prof Exp:* Fel enzymol dept biochem & human genetics, Univ Pa, 72-74; sr chemist bio-org chem, New Eng Nuclear Co, 74-76. *Mem:* Am Chem Soc. *Res:* Modification of protein enzyme surface; organic and enzymatic reaction mechanism and analysis of biochemical compounds by antibody, enzyme and fluorometer. *Mailing Add:* 34 Mount Herman Way West Caldwell NJ 07006-7243

**WU, JULIAN JUH-REN,** NUMERICAL METHODS, FINITE ELEMENT METHODS. *Current Pos:* PROG MGR APPL MATH & MATH SCI, US ARMY RES OFF, 83- *Personal Data:* b Shanghai, China, June 15, 35; US citizen; m. *Educ:* Taiwan Univ, BS, 58; Rice Univ, MS, 62; Columbia Univ, ME, 66; Rensselaer Polytech Inst, PhD(mech), 70. *Prof Exp:* Sr scientist composites, Advan Technol Div, Avco Co, 66-67; proj engr eng analysis, Teledyne Advan Mat Co, 67-68; res assoc mech, Rensselaer Polytech Inst, 68-71; res engr struct dynamics, US Army Watervliet Arsenal, 71-76, res mathematician numerical methods, 76-83. *Concurrent Pos:* Adj prof lasticity & vibrations, Rensselaer Polytech Inst, 76-83; adj prof, Dept Mech Eng, Duke Univ, 84- *Mem:* Soc Appl & Indust Math; Am Soc Mech Engrs; NY Acad Sci; Am Acad Mechanics. *Res:* Analytical and numerical research on nonlinear structural dynamics and stability; nonlinear continuum mechanics; perturbation methods; nonlinear vibrations. *Mailing Add:* US Army Res Off Unit 45002 Box 393 APO AP 96337-0007

**WU, JUN,** CRYSTAL GROWTH, DEFECT ENGINEERING. *Current Pos:* MAT SCIENTIST, GEN INSTRUMENT CO, 94- *Personal Data:* b Shanghai, China, Feb 6, 62. *Educ:* Zhe Jiang Univ, BS, 82; State Univ NY, Stony Brook, PhD(mat sci), 92. *Prof Exp:* Asst engr, Shanghai Non-Ferros Metal & Alloy Res Inst, 82-84; postdoctoral, State Univ NY, Stony Brook, 92-94. *Mem:* Inst Elec & Electronics Engrs. *Res:* Develop new electronic and opto-electronic devices and processes by material science and defect engineering; improve crystal growth processes by computer simulation and experiments. *Mailing Add:* 172 Spruce St Westbury NY 11590

**WU, JUN RU,** ULTRASOUND, BIOSENSORS. *Current Pos:* from asst prof to assoc prof physics, 87-96, assoc prof mech eng, 94-96, PROF PHYSICS & MECH ENG, UNIV VT, 96- *Personal Data:* b Shanghai, China, Apr 5, 44; US citizen; m, Yi Y Lin; c Kathy & Jane. *Educ:* Univ Calif, Los Angeles, MS, 81, PhD(physics), 85. *Honors & Awards:* Nat Sci Progress Award, China, 86. *Prof Exp:* Res assoc, Univ Calif, Los Angeles, 85-87, adj asst prof physics, 86-87. *Concurrent Pos:* Resource mem, Bioeffect Comt, Am Inst Ultrasound Med, 91-95, mem, 95-; mem, Tech Comt Phys Acoust, Acoust Soc Am, 93-

Mem: Fel Acoust Soc Am; fel Am Inst Ultrasound Med; Inst Elec & Electronics Engrs. Res: Understanding of physical laws of acoustic phenomena and their applications in biology and medicine. Mailing Add: Dept Physics Univ Vt Burlington VT 05405. Fax: 802-656-0817; E-Mail: jwu@zoo.uvm.edu

**WU, JUNG-TSUNG,** REPRODUCTIVE BIOLOGY, EMBRYOLOGY. Current Pos: ASST PROF OBSTET & GYNEC, MED SCH, UNIV MASS, 85- Personal Data: b Taiwan, Feb 17, 36; US citizen; m 65; c 2. Educ: Nat Taiwan Univ, BS, 58; Univ Wis-Madison, MS, 66, PhD(endocrinol & reprod biol), 69. Prof Exp: Teaching asst zool, Nat Taiwan Univ, 60-62; fel reprod biol, Med Ctr, Univ Kans, 69-71; res assoc, Worcester Found Exp Biol, 71-72, staff scientist reprod biol, 72-85. Mem: Soc Study Reprod; Am Fertil Soc; AAAS. Res: Implantation; embryo development and transport; hybridization; pathenogenesis; fertilization. Mailing Add: 47 Floral St Shrewsbury MA 01545

**WU, KENNETH KUN-YU,** MEDICAL SCIENCE, BIOLOGY. Current Pos: assoc prof & chief, Coagulation & Thrombosis Unit, 76-81, PROF MED, RUSH MED COL, RUSH PRESBY ST LUKE'S MED CTR, 81- Personal Data: b Kaohsiung, Taiwan, July 6, 41; US citizen; m 69; c 2. Educ: Yale Univ, MS, 69; Nat Taiwan Univ, MD, 66; Univ London, PhD, 97. Prof Exp: From instr to asst prof, Univ Iowa, 73-76. Concurrent Pos: Adv consult, NIH, 76-, mem prog proj rev comt, 76- Mem: Am Asn Immunol; Am Soc Hemat; Am Fedn Clin Res; Int Soc Thrombosis & Hemostasis; Am Soc Biochem & Molecular Biol; Am Soc Clin Invest. Res: Thrombosis and hemostasis; platelet physiology; pathophysiology and biochemistry. Mailing Add: Div Hemat Med Dept Univ Tex 6431 Fanin 5016 MSB Houston TX 77030. Fax: 713-794-4230

**WU, KONRAD T,** GAS-PHASE SPECTROSCOPY, MOLECULAR BEAM CHEMISTRY. Current Pos: from asst prof to assoc prof, 80-92, PROF CHEM, STATE UNIV NY, OLD WESTBURY, 92- Personal Data: b Canton, China, July 1, 48; US citizen; m 74; Angela Lu; c Sabrina & Brandon. Educ: Fu-Jen Catholic Univ, Taiwan, BS, 70; State Univ NY, Albany, PhD(chem), 76. Prof Exp: Res, Univ Tex, Austin, 76-77 & Columbia Univ, 77-78; chemist, Mt Sinai Sch Med fel, 78-80. Concurrent Pos: Vis scholar, Dept Chem, Wesleyan Univ, 83-85; vis prof, State Univ NY, Stony Brook, 87-88. Mem: Fel Int Biog Soc; Am Chem Soc; Am Phys Soc; Sigma Xi. Res: Gas-phase spectroscopy; molecular reaction dynamics; studies of flowing-afterglow and chemiluminescence. Mailing Add: Dept Chem State Univ NY Old Westbury NY 11568-0210

**WU, LANCELOT T L,** DIGITAL SIGNAL PROCESSING, INFORMATION THEORY. Current Pos: DEP GEN, COMP & COMMUN RES LABS, TAIWAN, 89- Personal Data: b Taiwan, China. Educ: Nat Taiwan Univ, BS, 74; State Univ NY, Albany, MS, 78; Columbia Univ, PhD(statist), 82. Prof Exp: Mem tech staff, Bell Labs, Bell Commun Res, 82-83, mem tech staff res, 83-89. Mem: Inst Elec & Electronics Engrs; Sigma Xi. Res: Statistical communications; digital communications; digital signal processing. Mailing Add: Comp & Commun Res Labs Assoc Bldg 111 195 Chung Hsing Rd Sect 4 Chutang Hsin Chu 31015 Taiwan

**WU, LEI,** dynamics properties, phase transition, for more information see previous edition

**WU, LILIAN SHIAO-YEN,** APPLIED MATHEMATICS. Current Pos: RES STAFF APPL MATH, THOMAS J WATSON RES CTR, IBM CORP, 73- Personal Data: b Peiking, China, July 6, 47. Educ: Univ Md, BS, 68; Cornell Univ, MS, 72, PhD(appl math), 74. Concurrent Pos: Vis scientist, Marine Biol Lab, 75-77; adj prof, NY Univ Grad Sch Bus, 88- Mem: Am Statist Asn; Int Inst Forecasters. Res: Business planning and forecasting; population biology. Mailing Add: BB5 Bedford Mews 208 Harris Rd Bedford Hills NY 10507. E-Mail: wul@watson.ibm.com

**WU, LIN,** FISHERIES BIOLOGY, PLANKTON ECOLOGY. Current Pos: RES SCIENTIST, UNIV NH, 92- Personal Data: b Beijin, China, Aug 10, 61; m, Liang Shi; c Edmund W Shi. Educ: Huazhong Agr Univ, BS, 83; Ohio State Univ, MS, 90, PhD(aquatic ecol), 91. Prof Exp: Teaching asst iththyology, Huazhong Agr Univ, 83-85; vol technician, US Fish & Wildlife Serv, 86; res scientist, Nat Water Res Inst Can, 87; res assoc, Ohio State Univ, 90. Concurrent Pos: Lectr gen biol, Ohio State Univ, 91. Mem: Am Fisheries Soc; Am Soc Limnol & Oceanog; Int Asn Theoretical & Appl Limnol. Res: Assessing the effects of stocking alewife on native New Hampshire fish and plankton communities. Mailing Add: 124 Forest Park Durham NH 03824. Fax: 603-862-3784; E-Mail: 1_wu@unhh.unh.edu

**WU, MING-CHI,** BIOCHEMISTRY. Current Pos: ASSOC PROF BIOCHEM, TEX COL OSTEOPATH MED, 82-; ASSOC PROF & VCHMN, DEPT BIOCHEM, UNIV NTEX, 82- Personal Data: b Nantou, Taiwan, Nov 13, 40; US citizen; m 68; c 2. Educ: Nat Taiwan Univ, BS, 63; Univ Wis-Madison, MS, 68, PhD(biochem), 70. Prof Exp: Res fel physiol chem, Sch Med, Johns Hopkins Univ, 69-71; res assoc biochem, Sch Med, Univ Pittsburgh, 71-73; res assoc hemat, Howard Hughes Med Inst, 74-80, asst prof med, Sch Med, Univ Miami, 75-80, assoc prof, 81-82. Mem: Am Chem Soc; Am Fedn Clin Res; Sigma Xi; Am Soc Biol Chemists; Int Soc Exp Ment Hematol. Res: Control of granulopoiesis; proteases from cultured cancer cells. Mailing Add: Dept Biochem Tex Col Osteo Med 3500 Camp Bowie Blvd Ft Worth TX 76107-2690. Fax: 817-735-2133

**WU, MINGDAN,** ENDOTHELIAL FREE RADICAL BIOLOGY, LIPID PEROXIDATION & ANTIOXIDANTS. Current Pos: ASST PROF RES, NY MED COL, 92- Personal Data: b Zhejiang, China, Nov 27, 53; m 88, Ming Sun; c Michael Q S. Educ: EChina Univ Chem Technol, BS, 77, ME, 82; La State Univ, PhD(bioorg chem), 91. Prof Exp: Lectr, EChina Univ Chem Technol, 82-84; teaching asst, La State Univ, 85-87, res asst, 87-91; res fel, Am Health Found, 91-92. Concurrent Pos: Staff scientist, Health Maintenance Prog Inc, 92; prin investr, Am Heart Asn, 93- Mem: AAAS; NY Acad Sci; Am Chem Soc. Res: Reactive oxygen species in atherogenic pathophysiology and viscular endothelial biology; characterization of modified cellular glutathione, sulfhydryls, lipids and LDL by reactive oxygen species. Mailing Add: 37 Judson St Apt 15B Edison NJ 08837. Fax: 914-993-4679

**WU, MIN-YEN,** ELECTRICAL ENGINEERING, COMPUTER SCIENCE. Current Pos: asst prof, 69-74, ASSOC PROF ELEC ENG, UNIV COLO, BOULDER, 74- Personal Data: b Taiwan, China, Oct 1, 40; m 68; c 1. Educ: Nat Taiwan Univ, BS, 62; Univ Ottawa, MSc, 65; Univ Calif, Berkeley, PhD(elec eng), 68. Prof Exp: Actg asst prof elec eng, Univ Calif, Berkeley, 68-69. Concurrent Pos: Independent prof, IBM Corp, Boulder, 72-74, consult, 74-75. Mem: AAAS; Inst Elec & Electronics Engrs. Res: Control and system theory; social and economical systems; mathematical ecology. Mailing Add: Dept Elec & Comp Engr Ecot 349 Univ Colo Boulder CO 80309

**WU, MU TSU,** ORGANIC CHEMISTRY, MEDICINAL CHEMISTRY. Current Pos: sr res chemist, 65-72, res fel, 72-78, SR RES FEL, MERCK & CO, INC, 78- Personal Data: b Changhwa, Taiwan, Oct 25, 29; US citizen; m 57; c 4. Educ: Nat Taiwan Univ, BS, 51; Univ Md, PhD(pharmaceut chem), 61; Tohoku Univ, Japan, DSc(chem), 61. Prof Exp: Res chemist, Ord Res Inst, 51-58; res assoc pharmaceut chem, Univ Md, 58-62, assoc res prof, 64-65; res assoc chem, Univ NH, 62-64. Mem: AAAS; Am Chem Soc; Am Inst Chemists. Res: Synthetic organic and medicinal chemistry. Mailing Add: 35 Lance Dr Clark NJ 07066-2717

**WU, PEI-RIN,** ELECTRICAL ENGINEERING, ELECTROMAGNETISM. Current Pos: SR SCIENTIST, SPARTA INC, 96- Personal Data: b Taoyuan, Taiwan, Feb 16, 35; US citizen; m 58; c 3. Educ: Taipei Inst Technol, dipl, 55; Univ Tenn, MS, 60; Univ Mich, PhD(elec eng), 67. Prof Exp: Engr elec, Sintong Chem Works Inc, 56-59; asst prof elec eng, SDak Sch Mines & Technol, 60-64; res asst, Radiation Lab, Univ Mich, 66-67; sr staff electromagnetics, Lincoln Lab, Mass Inst Technol, 67-96. Mem: Inst Elec & Electronics Engrs. Res: Antennas; electromagnetics; scattering; radar data analysis; radar decoy designs; reentry physics and signatures; satellite signatures; identification; signature discrimination techniques; near-field measurement techniques. Mailing Add: 4 Hiddenwood Path Lincoln MA 01773

**WU, RAY J,** BIOCHEMISTRY. Current Pos: assoc prof, Cornell Univ, 66-72, assoc chmn sect, 75-77, chmn sect, 77-79, PROF BIOCHEM, MOLECULAR & CELL BIOL, CORNELL UNIV, 72- Personal Data: b Peking, China, Aug 14, 28; nat US; m 56; c 2. Educ: Univ Ala, BS, 50; Univ Pa, PhD, 55. Prof Exp: Asst instr biochem, Univ Pa, 51-55, Damon Runyon fel cancer res, 55-57; from asst to assoc, Pub Health Res Inst New York, 57-61, assoc mem, 61-66. Concurrent Pos: NSF sr fel, MRC Lab, Cambridge, Eng, 71; vis assoc prof, Mass Inst Technol, 72; hon res prof, Academia Sinica, China, 82-; hon prof, Peking Med Col, 83-, Fudan Univ, 83- Mem: Am Chem Soc; Sigma Xi; Am Soc Biol Chem; fel Chinese Acad Sci. Res: DNA sequence analysis; cancer research; recombinant DNA research; gene synthesis; enzymology. Mailing Add: Dept Biochem 316 Biotechnol Bldg Cornell Univ Ithaca NY 14853-2703. Fax: 607-255-2428

**WU, RICHARD LI-CHUAN,** MATERIALS SCIENCE ENGINEERING. Current Pos: EXEC VPRES, K SYSTS CORP, 94- Personal Data: b Tainan, Taiwan, Aug 21, 40; m 68; Spring C Kuo; c Joyce S. Educ: Nat Cheng Kung Univ, Taiwan, BS, 63; Univ Kans, PhD(chem), 71. Prof Exp: Res chemist, Aerospace Res Labs, Wright-Patterson AFB, 71-75; adj res prof eng, Chem & Brehm Lab, Wright State Univ, 75-86; prin scientist, UES, 87-94. Concurrent Pos: Adj prof, Dept Physiol & Biophys, Sch Med Wright-State Univ, 93- Mem: Am Chem Soc; Am Mat Res Soc; Sigma Xi; AAAS. Res: Diamond and diamond-like carbon films; thin film coating; mass spectrometry; high temperature chemistry; vaporization processes; ion-molecule reactions; thermodynamics; capacitors; granted one patent. Mailing Add: 384 Merrick Dr Beavercreek OH 45434. Fax: 937-429-1122; E-Mail: rlwu@aol.com

**WU, ROBERT CHUNG-YUNG,** EXTREME ULTRAVIOLET SPECTROSCOPY, LASER NONLINEAR SPECTROSCOPY. Current Pos: fel, Chem Dept, Univ Southern Calif, 73-75, res scientist, Physics Dept, 77-78, asst res prof, 78-88, ASSOC RES PROF, SPACE SCI CTR, UNIV SOUTHERN CALIF, 88- Personal Data: b Kao-Hsiung, Taiwan, Oct 16, 43; US citizen; m 69, Grace Lee; c David, John & Michael. Educ: Nat Taiwan Norm Univ, BS, 68; Univ Ill, MS, 70, PhD(chem), 73. Prof Exp: Fel, Chem Dept, Univ Iowa, 76-77. Concurrent Pos: Consult, Res Div, Nat Tech Systs, 80-82, Rocketdyne Div, Rockwell Int Co, 84-85 & Plasma Lab, Univ Calif, Los Angeles, 88. Mem: Optical Soc Am; Am Geophys Union; Soc Appl Spectros. Res: Molecular autoionization; molecular photodissociation; nonlinear laser spectroscopy; ultraviolet laser generation; photochemical processes in planetary environments; aeronomy. Mailing Add: 923 Adams Ave Montebello CA 90640. Fax: 213-740-6342; E-Mail: robertwu@lism.usc.edu

**WU, ROY SHIH-SHYONG,** CELL BIOLOGY, BIOCHEMISTRY. *Current Pos:* MEM STAFF, NIH, 80- *Personal Data:* b Shanghai, China, Nov 15, 44; US citizen; m 82, Irene C Liang; c Michelle. *Educ:* Univ Calif, Berkeley, AB, 67; Albert Einstein Col Med, Bronx, NY, PhD(biochem), 72. *Prof Exp:* NIH fel develop biol, Dept Zool, Univ Calif, Berkeley, 72-74; fel cell biol, Children's Hosp, Oakland, Calif, 74-75; scientist cell biol, Biotech Res Lab Inc, Rockville, Md, 75-80. *Concurrent Pos:* Lectr, Dept Zool, Univ Calif, Berkeley; peer reviewer grants, NSF & NIH; exec dir, Soc Chinese Bio-Scientists Am, 89-93. *Mem:* AAAS; Am Soc Cell Biol; Am Chem Soc; Am Soc Biochem & Molecular Biol; Sigma Xi; Soc Chinese Bio-Scientists Am; Am Asn Cancer Res. *Res:* Studying the molecular mechanism of coordination of protein and DNA synthesis during cell proliferation; development of new assays for DNA repair enzymes, the methytransferases. *Mailing Add:* CTEP/DCT/NCI/NIH EPN Rm 734 Bethesda MD 20892-0001. *Fax:* 301-480-4663; *E-Mail:* Bitnet: wur@nihcdct1

**WU, SAU LAN YU,** EXPERIMENTAL HIGH ENERGY PHYSICS. *Current Pos:* from asst prof to prof, 77-90, ENRICO FERMI DISTINGUISHED PROF PHYSICS, UNIV WIS-MADISON, 90- *Personal Data:* b Hong Kong, China; US citizen; m 67. *Educ:* Vassar Col, BA, 63; Harvard Univ, MA, 64, PhD(physics), 70. *Hon Degrees:* Numerous from US univs. *Honors & Awards:* Outstanding Jr Investr Award, US Dept Energy, 80; High Energy & Particle Physics Prize, Europ Phys Soc, 95. *Prof Exp:* Res assoc, Mass Inst Technol, 70-72, res physicist, 72-77. *Concurrent Pos:* Vis scientist, Deutsches Elektronen-Synchrotron, 70-72, 77-86, Brookhaven Nat Lab, 72-75, Europ Orgn Nuclear Res, 75-77, 86-; prin investr, US Dept Energy, 77-, investr award, 80; Romnes fel, Univ Wis, 81; Hilldale prof, Univ Wis, 91; gen counr, Am Phys Soc, 97- *Mem:* fel Am Phys Soc; fel Am Acad Arts & Sci. *Res:* Electron-positron colliding beam physics at high energies using the detector TASSO and the machine PETRA to obtain the first evidence of three jet events which signified the existence of gluons; preparation and construction of the new detector ALEPH to study the production and decay of the neutral intermediate boson and the production of the charged intermediate boson; contributed over 250 articles to professional journals. *Mailing Add:* Dept Physics 2531 Sterling Hall Univ Wis 475 N Charter St Madison WI 53706-1507

**WU, SHERMAN H,** ELECTRICAL & SYSTEMS ENGINEERING. *Current Pos:* from asst prof to assoc prof, 65-76, PROF ELEC ENG, MARQUETTE UNIV, 76- *Personal Data:* b Hupeh, China, Aug 21, 38; US citizen. *Educ:* Northwestern Univ, BSEE, 61, MS, 63, PhD(elec eng), 65. *Prof Exp:* Asst engr, Ill Bell Tel Co, 61-62; lectr systs eng, Univ Ill, Chicago, 64; staff engr, TRW Systs Group, Calif, 65. *Concurrent Pos:* NSF grant, 66-68. *Mem:* Inst Elec & Electronics Engrs. *Res:* Nonlinear pulse-modulation in aerospace and physiological systems. *Mailing Add:* Dept Elec Eng & Comput Sci Marquette Univ Haggerty Eng Rm 283 PO Box 1881 Milwaukee WI 53201-1881

**WU, SHI TSAN,** AEROSPACE ENGINEERING. *Current Pos:* from asst prof to assoc prof, 67-72, PROF MECH ENG, UNIV ALA, HUNTSVILLE, 72-, ADJ PROF PHYSICS, 73- *Personal Data:* b Nanchang, China, July 31, 34; m 64; c 3. *Educ:* Nat Taiwan Univ, BS, 56; Ill Inst Technol, MS, 59; Univ Colo, PhD(aerospace eng sci), 67. *Honors & Awards:* Flag Award, Am Inst Aeronaut & Astronaut. *Prof Exp:* Res asst eng sci, Harvard Univ, 59-62; res fel aeronaut, NY Univ, 62-63; asst aerospace eng sci, Univ Colo, 63-64; res asst solar physics, High Altitude Observ, Nat Ctr Atmospheric Res, 64-67. *Concurrent Pos:* Consult, Wyle Labs, 68-; sr Fulbright-Hays Scholar, 75-76; Australia-Am Educ Found prof space physics, La Trobe Univ, Australia, 75-76; solar physics coordr, Study Interplanetary Phenomena & Spec Comt Solar Terrestrial Physics; dir, Ctr Space Plasma & Aeronomic Res, 86-; distinguished prof, Mech/Aeronaut, 90- *Mem:* AAAS; Am Phys Soc; Am Geophys Union; fel Am Inst Aeronaut & Astronaut. *Res:* Plasmadynamics; magnetohydrodynamics and its astrogeophysical applications; boundary layer type flows; kinetic theory; radiative gas dynamics and other fluid mechanics problems; numerical methods, computational field mechanics. *Mailing Add:* Mech Eng Dept Univ Ala Huntsville AL 35899-0001

**WU, SING-CHOU,** STATISTICS, ECONOMETRICS. *Current Pos:* from asst prof to assoc prof, 69-75, PROF STATIST, CALIF STATE POLYTECH UNIV, SAN LUIS OBISPO, 75- *Personal Data:* b China, June 2, 36; m 64; c 2. *Educ:* Nat Taiwan Univ, BA, 59; Utah State Univ, MS, 66; Colo State Univ, PhD(statist), 70. *Prof Exp:* Economist, Bank of China, 61-63; programmer, Comput Ctr, Utah State Univ, 65-66; asst statist, Colo State Univ, 66-69. *Mem:* Am Statist Asn; Chinese Statist Soc; Japan Statist Soc. *Res:* Design of experiment; statistical computation. *Mailing Add:* Dept Statist Bldg 25 Rm 103 Calif Polytech State Univ San Luis Obispo CA 93407

**WU, SING-YUNG,** ENDOCRINOLOGY, NUCLEAR MEDICINE. *Current Pos:* from asst prof to assoc prof, 77-90, PROF RADIOL & MED, UNIV CALIF, IRVINE, 90- *Personal Data:* b Cheng-tu, China, July 5, 39. *Educ:* Univ Wash, PhD(exp path), 69; Johns Hopkins Univ, MD, 72. *Prof Exp:* Intern med, Univ Chicago, 71-72; resident, Univ Calif, Irvine, 72-73; instr, Univ Wash, 73-75; fel, Univ Calif, Los Angeles, 75-77. *Concurrent Pos:* Staff physician, Vet Admin Med Ctr, Long Beach, 77-; chief, Nuclear Consult Serv, 91- *Mem:* Am Thyroid Asn; Soc Nuclear Med; Soc Clin Res; Endocrine Soc; Am Clin Endocrine; fel Am Col Endocrinol. *Res:* Biochemical study of endocrine physiology, the thyroid in particular; clinical application of radioisotopes: radioimmunoassay and radio-immune-detection of pathological foci including cancer; marker for diagnosing congenital hypothyroidism in fetuses (compound w). *Mailing Add:* 5901 E Seventh St 151 Long Beach CA 90822. *Fax:* 562-494-5675

**WU, TAI TE,** BIOCHEMISTRY, MOLECULAR BIOLOGY. *Current Pos:* from assoc prof to prof physics & eng sci, 70-74, prof biochem, molecular & cell biol, Eng Sci & Appl Math, 74-85, PROF BIOCHEM, MOLECULAR BIOL & CELL BIOL, BIOMED ENG, ENG SCI & APPL MATH, NORTHWESTERN UNIV, 85- *Personal Data:* b Shanghai, China, Aug 2, 35; m 66, Anna Fang; c Richard. *Educ:* Univ Hong Kong, MB & BS, 56; Univ Ill, Urbana, BS, 58; Harvard Univ, SM, 59, PhD(eng), 61. *Prof Exp:* Res fel struct mech, Harvard Univ, 61-63; asst prof eng, Brown Univ, 63-65; res assoc biol chem, Harvard Med Sch, 65-66; from asst prof to assoc prof biomath, Med Col, Cornell Univ, 67-70. *Concurrent Pos:* Gordon McKay fel, Harvard Univ, 58; res scientist, Hydronaut, Md, 62; res fel biol chem, Harvard Med Sch, 64; chmn, Comt Biophys, & mem, Comt Biomed Eng, Northwestern Univ, 72-80; res career develop award, NIH, 74; C T Loo scholar, China Inst, 59; vis prof biol, Mass Inst Technol, 83. *Mem:* Am Soc Biochem & Molecular Biol; Am Soc Microbiol; Biophys Soc. *Res:* Structure and functions of macromolecules, especially those of antibodies and related proteins. *Mailing Add:* Dept Biochem Molecular Biol & Cell Biol Northwestern Univ Evanston IL 60208. *Fax:* 847-491-4928; *E-Mail:* t-wu@nwu.edu

**WU, TAI TSUN,** PHYSICS. *Current Pos:* Jr fel, Soc Fels, 56-59, from asst prof to assoc prof, 59-66, GORDON MCKAY PROF APPL PHYSICS, HARVARD UNIV, 66-, PROF PHYSICS, 94- *Personal Data:* b Shanghai, China, Dec 1, 33; m 67, Sau Lan Yu. *Educ:* Univ Minn, BS, 53; Harvard Univ, SM, 54, PhD(appl physics), 56. *Concurrent Pos:* Mem, Inst Advan Study, 58-59, 60-61 & 62-63; vis prof & NSF sr fel, Rockefeller Univ, 66-67; Guggenheim Mem Found fel, Deutsches Elektronen-Synchotron, Hamburg, Ger, 70-71; Kramers prof, Inst Theoret Physics, Univ Utrecht, Neth, 77-78; sci assoc, CERN, Geneva, Switz, 77-78 & 86. *Mem:* Am Acad Arts & Sci. *Res:* Electromagnetic theory; statistical mechanics; elementary particles. *Mailing Add:* Eng Appl Sci Pierce Hall Harvard Univ Cambridge MA 02138-2901

**WU, TAI WING,** CLINICAL BIOCHEMISTRY, CLINICAL DIAGNOSTICS & THERAPEUTICS. *Current Pos:* PROF CLIN BIOCHEM & SURG, FAC MED, UNIV TORONTO, 86- *Personal Data:* b Hong Kong; Can citizen; m 74, Peggy Chang; c Tyan. *Educ:* Chinese Univ Hong Kong, BSc, 66; Univ Toronto, MSc, 68, PhD(biochem), 71. *Honors & Awards:* Meuser Prize; Gold Medal Res Award, Repub China, 93. *Prof Exp:* Med Res Coun Can molecular biol, Univ BC, 71-73; sr res chemist, Res Labs, Eastman Kodak Co, Ny, 73-79, sr res assoc, 79-86. *Concurrent Pos:* Referee publ, Can J Biochem, Nat Res Coun Can, 73-; referee papers, Biochem, J Biol Chem, 73-, Clin Chem, 81-; sr vis fel biotechnol, Cornell Univ, Ithaca, Ny, 84-86, vis prof, Dept Chem, 84-85 & Sch Appl Phys & Eng, 85-86. *Mem:* Biophys Soc; Can Biol Socs; AAAS; Am Asn Clin Chem. *Res:* Discovery and identification of novel and clinically useful enzymes and antioxidants; mechanistic studies of organ transplant rejection; exploration of multiple molecular diagnoses of diseases, especially of the liver, heart, lung and nervous system; protein chemistry and enzymology. *Mailing Add:* 399 Bathurst St MC- 5th Floor Rm 405 Toronto ON M5T 2S7 Can

**WU, TE-KAO,** ELECTRICAL ENGINEERING. *Current Pos:* SR ENGR, TRW, ES&TD, 95- *Personal Data:* b Feng-Shan, Taiwan, Oct 12, 48; m 76, Tsan-Sheng Chang; c Angela & David. *Educ:* Nat Taiwan Univ, BEE, 70; Univ Miss, MS, 73, PhD(elec eng), 76. *Prof Exp:* Res assoc elec eng, Univ Miss, 76-78; scientist & assoc res eng, Lockheed Missiles & Space Co Inc, 78-79; tech staff mem, TRW, 79-80; sr staff engr, Sperry Microwave Electronics, 80-81, Hughes Aircraft, 83-90; tech staff, ECI Inc, 81-83, Jet Propulsion Lab, 90-95. *Concurrent Pos:* Adj prof, Univ SFla, 80-81. *Mem:* Sigma Xi; Inst Elec & Electronics Engrs. *Res:* Electromagnetics; scattering; antennas; microwave biological effects; electromagnetic compatibiligy; electromagnetic pulses; microwave and millimeter circuits and devices; photonics; communications; frequency selective surface; granted 10 US patents. *Mailing Add:* 26911 Springcreek Rd Palos Verdes CA 90275

**WU, THEODORE YAO-TSU,** FLUID MECHANICS, ENGINEERING SCIENCE. *Current Pos:* res fel appl mech, 52-55, from asst prof to prof, 55-96, EMER PROF ENG SCI, CALIF INST TECHNOL, 96- *Personal Data:* b Changchow, China, Mar 20, 24; US citizen; m 50; c 2. *Educ:* Chiao Tung Univ, BS, 46; Iowa State Col, MS, 48; Calif Inst Technol, PhD(aeronaut), 52. *Concurrent Pos:* Mem, Fluid Mech Comt, Am Inst Aeronaut & Astronaut, 49- & Hydrodyn H-5 & H-8 Panels, Soc Naval Architects & Marine Engrs, 63; fac mem, Div Eng & Appl Sci, Calif Inst Technol, Pasedena, 52-; mem, Am Towing Tank Conf, 56-, chmn, 72-74; Guggenheim fel & vis prof, Univ Hamburg, 64-65; mem, Int Towing Tank Conf, Wave Resistance Comt, 67-78, chmn, 77-78; mem, Comt Recommendation US Army Basic Sci Res, Nat Res Coun, 75-78; vchmn, Div Fluid Dynamics, Am Phys Soc; adj prof, Shanghai Jiao Tong Univ, China, 79-; hon prof, Northwestern Polytech Univ, Xian, China, 79- & Harbin Shipbldg Eng Inst, China, 87-; Russell Severance Springer vis prof, Univ Calif, Berkeley, 80; vis fel, Japan Soc Promotion Sci, 82; co-ed, Advan Appl Mech, 82-; consult var co & corp. *Mem:* Nat Acad Eng; fel Am Phys Soc; assoc fel Am Inst Aeronaut & Astronaut; Ger Soc Appl Math & Mech; hon fel Acad Sinica; Sigma Xi; Soc Naval Architects & Marine Engrs; Soc Indust & Appl Math. *Res:* Fluid mechanics of compressible, viscous, heat-conducting fluids, water waves, jets, cavity, wake, boundary layer and stratified flows; biophysical and geophysical fluid mechanics; author of various publications. *Mailing Add:* Dept Eng & Sci 104-44 Calif Inst Technol Pasadena CA 91125. *Fax:* 626-795-9839

**WU, TIEN HSING,** CIVIL ENGINEERING, GEOTECHNICAL ENGINEERING. *Current Pos:* PROF CIVIL ENG, OHIO STATE UNIV, 65- *Personal Data:* b Shanghai, China, Mar 2, 23; nat US; m 52; c 2. *Educ:* St John's Univ, BS, 47; Univ Ill, MS, 48, PhD(civil eng), 51. *Honors &*

*Awards:* US Antartica Serv Medal, 67; State of Art Award, Am Soc Civil Engrs, 90. *Prof Exp:* Civil engr, Deleuw, Cather & Co, Ill, 51-52; State Hwy Div, Ill, 52-53; from asst prof to prof civil eng, Mich State Univ, 53-65. *Concurrent Pos:* Consult geotech eng; vis prof, Norweg Geotech Inst, 59, 68, 76, Univ Mex, 64, Royal Inst Tech, 80, Punjal Agr Univ, 81, SW Jiaotong Univ, 86. *Mem:* Am Soc Civil Engrs; Soc Soil Mech Found Eng. *Res:* Soil mechanics; geotechnical engineering; risk and reliability. *Mailing Add:* Dept Civil Eng Ohio State Univ 2070 Neil Ave Columbus OH 43210. *E-Mail:* twu.26@osu.edu

**WU, TSU MING,** PHYSICS. *Current Pos:* from asst prof to assoc prof, 68-80, PROF PHYSICS, STATE UNIV NY, BINGHAMTON, 80- *Personal Data:* b Taipei, Taiwan, Dec 18, 36; c 2. *Educ:* Univ Taiwan, BS, 59; Univ Pa, PhD(physics), 66. *Prof Exp:* Fel physics, Case Western Reserve Univ, 66-68. *Mem:* Am Phys Soc. *Res:* Many-body problems in solid state physics, especially superconductivity and magnetism; biophysics. *Mailing Add:* Dept Physics State Univ NY Binghamton NY 13902-6000

**WU, WAN CHU,** POLYMERIZATION PROCESSES. *Current Pos:* SR RES & DEVELOP SCIENTIST TECHNOL, BAYER CORP, 96- *Personal Data:* b Jan 26, 47; m, Mun Ya Wong; c San San, Sing Sing, Sian & Sarah. *Educ:* Univ RI, BS, 70; Lehigh Univ, MS, 73, PhD(chem eng), 80. *Prof Exp:* Sr res engr, Monsanto Chem Group, 77-80, res specialist, 80-90, sr res specialist, 90-95, master technologist, 95-96. *Res:* Development of new technology, process and product, of producing rubber-modified styrenic thermo-plastics in an industrial environment. *Mailing Add:* Bayer Corp 730 Worcester St Springfield MA 01151. *Fax:* 413-750-7801; *E-Mail:* wan.wu.b@bayer.com

**WU, WEN PAO,** POLYMERIC FOAM TECHNOLOGY. *Current Pos:* DEVELOP ENG SUPVR, TENNECO PACKAGING, 96- *Personal Data:* b Chang-hwa, Taiwan, Jan 15, 51; US citizen; m 76, Elizabeth E Shen; c Jennifer S, Melissa P & Eric Y. *Educ:* Nat Taiwan Univ, BS, 74; Wash State Univ, MS, 78; Washington Univ, St Louis, MS, 81, DSc, 81. *Prof Exp:* Sr develop engr, Mobil Chem Co, 81-85, eng assoc I, 85-87, eng assoc II, 87-96. *Mem:* Sigma Xi; Soc Plastics Engrs; Am Inst Chem Engrs; Am Chem Soc. *Res:* Polymeric foams technology including extrusion, thermo forming and environmental impact; granted 19 US patents. *Mailing Add:* Tenneco Packaging 102 North St Canandaigua NY 14424-1026. *Fax:* 716-394-8980

**WU, WEN-HSIEN,** PHARMACOLOGY, ALGOLOGY. *Current Pos:* PROF & CHMN ANESTHESIOL & PHARMACOL, NJ SCH MED, 79-, DIR, PAIN MGT CTR, 80- *Educ:* Nat Taiwan Univ, MD, 58. *Mailing Add:* Dept Anesthesiol UMDNJ NJ Med Sch 185 S Orange Ave Newark NJ 07103. *Fax:* 973-504-7825

**WU, WEN-LI,** POLYMER SCIENCE. *Current Pos:* MAT RES ENGR, NAT INST STAND & TECHNOL, 79- *Personal Data:* b Chentu, China, 1945. *Educ:* Mass Inst Technol, PhD(mat sci), 72. *Mem:* Fel Am Phys Soc. *Mailing Add:* Polymer Div Rm B320 Bldg 224 Nat Inst Stand & Technol Gaithersburg MD 20899

**WU, WILLIAM GAY,** MEDICAL MICROBIOLOGY, IMMUNOLOGY. *Current Pos:* from asst prof to assoc prof, San Francisco State Univ, 62-70, chmn, Dept Microbiol, 67-72, chmn, Dept Biol, 76-81, PROF MICROBIOL, SAN FRANCISCO STATE UNIV, 70- *Personal Data:* b Portland, Ore, Feb 5, 31; m 57; c 3. *Educ:* Ore State Univ, BS, 49, MS, 61; Univ Utah, PhD(immunol, cell biol), 62. *Prof Exp:* Lab asst soil microbiol, Ore State Univ, 57-58, res asst vet microbiol, 58-59; res asst immunol, Univ Utah, 59-62. *Concurrent Pos:* Res Corp grants, 64-65; NSF grants, 65-67, NIH grant, 87-; vis prof, Tulane Univ, 70-71; acad vis, Stanford Res Inst, 82. *Mem:* AAAS; Am Soc Microbiol; Am Asn Immunol. *Res:* Study of surface antigens of bacteria; acute disease mechanisms. *Mailing Add:* Dept Biol San Francisco State Univ 1600 Holloway Ave San Francisco CA 94132-1722. *Fax:* 415-338-2295

**WU, WU-NAN,** PHARMACY. *Current Pos:* prin scientist, 88-92, RES FEL DRUG METAB, R W JOHNSON PHARM RES INST, 92. *Personal Data:* b Kaohsiung, Taiwan, Mar 16, 38; US citizen; m 71; c 2. *Educ:* Kaohsiung Med Col, BS, 61; Ohio State Univ, PhD(pharm), 72. *Prof Exp:* Technologist drug analysis, Taiwan Prov Hyg Labs, 62-63; asst pharm, Taipei Med Col, 63-65; specialist, Bristol Res Inst Taiwan, 65-67; res assoc, Col Pharm, Ohio State Univ, 67-72, fel researcher, 74-77; res scientist, McNeil Pharmaceut Inc, 78-79, sr scientist, 79-84, prin scientist drug metab, 85-87. *Concurrent Pos:* Res fel, Col Pharm, Univ Fla, 73-74. *Mem:* Am Chem Soc; Am Pharmacog Soc; Am Asn Pharm Scientist; Int Soc Study Xenobiotics; Am Soc Mass Spectrometry. *Res:* Isolation and structural elucidation of biologically active natural products; drug metabolism and disposition; pharmacokinetics; biotransformation. *Mailing Add:* Dept Drug Metabolism RW Johnson Pharmaceut Res Inst Spring House PA 19477. *Fax:* 215-628-7822

**WU, XIN DI,** thin film deposition & characterization, high temperature superconductors, for more information see previous edition

**WU, XIZENG,** DIAGNOSTIC IMAGING, THEORETICAL PHYSICS. *Current Pos:* fel med physics, 88-89, instr med physics, 89-90, ASST PROF MED PHYSICS, UNIV ALA, BIRMINGHAM, 90- *Personal Data:* b Guiyang, China, Aug 22, 44; m 91, Jieling Yang; c Ying & Xionang. *Educ:* Nanjing Normal Univ, BS, 65; City Univ NY, PhD(physics), 83; Am Bd Radiol, cert, 93. *Prof Exp:* Fel theoret physics, Mass Inst Technol, 83-85;

Univ Cinninati, 85-88. *Mem:* Am Phys Soc; Am Asn Med Physicists; Am Col Radiol. *Res:* Theoretical high energy physics; unification theories in high energy physics; diagnostic imaging author of 20 articles and a book. *Mailing Add:* Dept Radiol Rm JT 1105 Univ Ala Birmingham 619 S 19th St Birmingham AL 35233

**WU, YAO HUA,** ORGANIC CHEMISTRY. *Current Pos:* RETIRED. *Personal Data:* b Soochow, China, July 16, 20; nat US; m 50; c 2. *Educ:* Chiao Tung Univ, BS, 43; Univ Nebr, MS, 48, PhD(org chem), 51. *Prof Exp:* Pharmaceut chemist, Int Chem Works, Shanghai, 43-47; res chemist, Smith-Dorsey Co, 51-53; res chemist, Mead Johnson & Co, 53-60, sr res fel, 60-70, dir chem res, 70-76, dir clin publ, 77-80, dir res planning, 80-83; sr staff mem, Res & Develop Div, Bristol-Myers Pharmaceut, 84-90. *Mem:* Am Chem Soc. *Res:* Synthetic pharmaceuticals. *Mailing Add:* 9200 Farmington Dr Evansville IN 47712

**WU, YING VICTOR,** PHYSICAL CHEMISTRY, BIOCHEMISTRY. *Current Pos:* RES CHEMIST, NAT CTR AGR UTILIZATION RES, USDA, 61- *Personal Data:* b Peking, China, Nov 1, 31; nat US; m 60, Mildred Ling; c Julia. *Educ:* Univ Ala, BS, 53; Mass Inst Technol, PhD(phys chem), 58. *Prof Exp:* Asst phys chem, Mass Inst Technol, 53-57; res assoc chem, Cornell Univ, 58-61. *Mem:* AAAS; Am Chem Soc; Am Asn Cereal Chemists; Am Soc Biochem, Molecular Biol; Inst Food Technologists; Sigma Xi; Protein Soc. *Res:* Physical chemistry of protein, protein structure, cereal protein concentrates and isolates; optical rotatory dispersion; circular dichroism; hydrogen ion equilibria; distillers' grains and solubles; reverse osmosis and ultrafiltration; food science and technology. *Mailing Add:* Nat Ctr Agr Utilization Res 1815 N University St Peoria IL 61604

**WU, YING-CHU LIN (SUSAN),** ENERGY, FLUIDS. *Current Pos:* PRES & CHIEF EXEC OFFICER, ERC INC, 88- *Personal Data:* b Peking, China, June 23, 32; m 59, Jain-Ming; c Ernest E, Albert E & Karen E. *Educ:* Nat Taiwan Univ, BS, 55; Ohio State Univ, MS, 59; Calif Inst Technol, PhD(aeronaut), 63. *Honors & Awards:* Achievment Award, Soc Women Engrs, 85. *Prof Exp:* Engr, Taiwan Hwy Bur, 55-56; sr engr, Electro-Optical Syst, Pasadena, Calif, 63-65; from asst prof to assoc prof, 65-73, prof aerospace, Space Inst, Univ Tenn, 73-88. *Concurrent Pos:* Amelia Earhart fel, 58, 59 & 62; lab mgr, Res & Develop Lab, 77-81, adminr, Energy Conversion Res & Develop Prog, 81-88. *Mem:* Assoc fel Am Inst Aeronaut & Astronaut; fel Am Soc Mech Engrs; Sigma Xi; Soc Women Engrs. *Res:* Magnetohydrodynamic power generation. *Mailing Add:* ERC Inc PO Box 417 Tullahoma TN 37388. *Fax:* 615-454-2042

**WU, YONG-SHI,** QUANTUM FIELD THEORY, TOPOLOGICAL INVESTIGATIONS IN PHYSICS. *Current Pos:* assoc prof, 84-87, PROF PHYSICS, DEPT PHYSICS, UNIV UTAH, 87- *Personal Data:* Hubei, China, Aug 4, 42; m 70; c 2. *Educ:* Peking Univ, MS, 65; Academia Sinica, PhD, 70. *Prof Exp:* Res fel, Inst Physics, 65-78, asst prof, Inst Theoret Physics, 78-80, assoc prof, physics, Academia Sinica, 80-82; res assoc, physics, Dept Physics, Univ Washington, 82-84. *Concurrent Pos:* Vis scientist, Inst Adv Sci Study, Bures sur Yvette, Paris, 79, Inst Theoret Physics, State Univ NY, Stony Brook, 81, Inst Theoret Physics, Univ Calif, Santa Barbara, 86, Inst Solid State Physics, Univ Tokyo, 90; mem Instit Adv Study, Princeton, 81-82. *Mem:* Am Phys Soc. *Res:* Unity of forces and matter by use of quantum field theory and string theory and topological aspects of physical phenomena in various branches of physics from cosmology down to the deepest structure in matter. *Mailing Add:* Tianjin Univ No 3 Bldg 23rd Village Tianjin 300072 People's Republic of China

**WU, YUNG-CHI,** THERMODYNAMICS. *Current Pos:* CHEMIST, NAT INST STAND & TECHNOL, 67- *Personal Data:* b Canton, China, Oct 3, 23; US citizen; m 45; c 2. *Educ:* Sun Yat-Sen Univ, BS, 47; Univ Houston, MS, 52; Univ Chicago, PhD(chem), 57. *Prof Exp:* Chemist, Res & Develop Lab, Portland Cement Asn, 57-62, Watson Res Ctr, IBM Corp, 63-66 & Oak Ridge Nat Lab, 66-67. *Mem:* Electrochem Soc; Am Chem Soc; Sigma Xi. *Res:* Electrolyte solutions; thermodynamics; electrolytic conductivity. *Mailing Add:* Nat Inst Stand & Technol Gaithersburg MD 20899

**WU, YUNG-KUANG,** ELECTRICAL ENGINEERING. *Current Pos:* USAOPTEC, ALEXANDRIA, VA, 89- *Personal Data:* b Chung-li, Taiwan, Dec 15, 33; m 63, Nell Hung; c Melissa & Theodore. *Educ:* Nat Taiwan Univ, BS, 56; Kans State Univ, MS, 60; Univ Mich, PhD(elec eng), 65. *Prof Exp:* Asst res engr, Radiation Lab, Univ Mich, 64-65; from asst prof to prof elec eng, Southeastern Mass Univ, 65-72; mem staff, Lincoln Lab, Mass Inst Technol, 72-74 & Charles Stark Draper Lab, 74-75; res engr, Nat Hwy Traffic Safety Admin, Dept Transp, 75-82; mem tech staff, Mitre Corp, McLean, Va, 83-89. *Mem:* Sr mem Inst Elec & Electronics Engrs. *Res:* Electromagnetic compatibility; radar brake; electronic engine control systems; application of electromagnetic theory such as reentry blackout problems; magnetohydrodynamic boundary-layer control; strategic communications; ballistic missile defense system. *Mailing Add:* USAOPTEC 4501 Ford Ave Alexandria VA 22302. *E-Mail:* wu@optec.army.mil

**WU, ZHEN,** SURFACE SCIENCE. *Current Pos:* PROF PHYSICS, RUTGERS UNIV, 89- *Personal Data:* b Sozhou, China. *Educ:* Columbia Univ, MA, 80, MPhil, 81, PhD(physics), 84. *Prof Exp:* Fel physics, Princeton Univ, 84-85; res physicist, 86-87; res scientist physics, Microelectronics Sci Lab, Columbia Univ, 87-89. *Mem:* Am Phys Soc; Optical Soc Am; AAAS; Am Vacuum Soc. *Res:* Interactions between radiation and matter (such as atoms, molecules, and surfaces of various solids). *Mailing Add:* Rutgers Univ Dept Physics 101 Warren St 361 Smith Hall Newark NJ 07102

**WUBBELS, GENE GERALD,** CHEMISTRY, BIOCHEMISTRY. *Current Pos:* SR VCHANCELLOR ACAD AFFAIRS, UNIV NEBR, KEARNEY, 94- *Personal Data:* b Preston, Minn, Sept 21, 42; m 67, Joyce R Honebrink; c Kristen L, Benjamin G & John C. *Educ:* Hamline Univ, BS, 64; Northwestern Univ, PhD(chem), 68. *Honors & Awards:* Catalyst Awardee, Chem Mfg Asn, 89. *Prof Exp:* From asst prof to prof, Grinnell Col, 68-79, chmn dept, 75-78 & 83-85, prof org & biol chem, 79-, Dack prof, 86-92; provost & prof chem, Wash Col, 92-94. *Concurrent Pos:* Res grant, Am Chem Soc-Petrol Res Fund, 71-73, 74-77, 78-80, 81-83 & 84-86 & NSF, 86-; res assoc, State Univ NY, Col, Buffalo, 74-75; ed, Surv Progress Chem, 80-86; vis prof, Univ Leiden, Neth, 81-82; charter counr, Coun Undergrad Res; prog dir, NSF, 90-92. *Mem:* Am Chem Soc; InterAm Photochem Soc; AAAS. *Res:* Catalytic mechanisms for photosubstitution, photoreduction and photoaddition reactions of aromatic compounds. *Mailing Add:* Univ Nebr 905 W 25th St Founders Hall Rm 1000 Kearney NE 68849. *Fax:* 410-778-7850; *E-Mail:* gene_wubbels@washcoll.edu

**WUCHTER, RICHARD B,** ORGANIC CHEMISTRY. *Current Pos:* group leader process res, 63-70, pollution control chem synthesis, Fluid Process Lab, 70-89, SEPARATIONS RESEARCHER, ROHM & HAAS CO, 90- *Personal Data:* b Wadsworth, Ohio, July 21, 37; m 72, Fay Gauger. *Educ:* Case Western Res Univ, AB, 59; Cornell Univ, PhD(org chem), 63. *Prof Exp:* Asst org chem, Cornell Univ, 60-62. *Mem:* Am Chem Soc. *Res:* Monomer synthesis and process development; plastics; modifiers for plastics; fibers; pollution control and ion exchange syntheses; reactive polymers. *Mailing Add:* 1521 Old Welsh Rd Huntington Valley PA 19006-5833

**WUDL, FRED,** ORGANIC CHEMISTRY, MATERIALS SCIENCE. *Current Pos:* MEM TECH STAFF, BELL LABS, 73-; PROF, UNIV CALIF, SANTA BARBARA, 73- *Personal Data:* b Cochabamba, Bolivia, Jan 8, 41; US citizen; m 67, Linda Raimondo. *Educ:* Univ Calif, Los Angeles, BS, 64; PhD(chem), 67. *Honors & Awards:* A C Cope Scholar Award, Am Chem Soc, 96. *Prof Exp:* Fel org chem, Harvard Univ, 67-68; asst prof, State Univ NY, Buffalo, 68-73. *Concurrent Pos:* Assoc dir, Inst Polymers & Organic Solids, 82- *Mem:* Fel AAAS; Am Chem Soc; Sigma Xi. *Res:* Organic conductors; organic synthesis; heterocycles; organometallic compounds and complexes; polymer science. *Mailing Add:* Dept Chem Univ Calif Santa Barbara CA 93106. *E-Mail:* wvdl@physics.ucsb.edu

**WUEBBLES, DONALD J,** ATMOSPHERIC CHEMISTRY & PHYSICS. *Current Pos:* head dept, 94-96, PROF, DEPT ATMOSPHERIC SCI, UNIV ILL, 94-, DIR ENVIRON COUN, 96- *Personal Data:* b Breese, Ill, Jan 28, 48; m 70, Barbara Yaley; c Ryan, Kevin & Alan. *Educ:* Univ Ill, BS, 70, MS, 72; Univ Calif, PhD, 83. *Prof Exp:* Res scientist, Nat Oceanic & Atmospheric Admin, 72-73; Univ Colo, Boulder, 73; res scientist & group leader, Lawrence Livermore Nat Lab, 73-94. *Concurrent Pos:* Prin investr, Environ Protection Agency, 79-, NASA, 84-; Dept Energy, 84-; sci adv, US deleg, Orgn Econ Coop & Develop, 81; mem adv panel, NASA High Speed Res Prog, 89-; mem, Nat Res Coun Working Group Solar Influences, 90-93, Int Comn Meteorol Upper Atmosphere Working Group Modeling Middle Atmosphere. *Mem:* Am Geophys Union; Am Meteorol Soc; AAAS; Sigma Xi. *Res:* Computational modelling of the physical, chemical, and radiative processes in the atmosphere; atmospheric ozone and anthropogenic effects on it; greenhouse gases and their effects on climate. *Mailing Add:* 3405 S Persimmon Circle Urbana IL 61802. *Fax:* 510-422-5844; *E-Mail:* wuebbles@llnl.gov

**WUENSCH, BERNHARDT J(OHN),** CRYSTALLOGRAPHY, CERAMICS. *Current Pos:* TDK prof mat sci & eng, 85-90, dir, Ctr Mat Sci & Eng, 88-93, FROM ASST PROF TO PROF CERAMICS, MASS INST TECHNOL, 64- *Personal Data:* b Paterson, NJ, Sept 17, 33; m 60, Mary Jane Harriman; c Stefan R & Katrina R. *Educ:* Mass Inst Technol, SB, 55, SM, 57, PhD(crystallog), 63. *Honors & Awards:* Outstanding Educr Award, Am Ceramic Soc, 87. *Prof Exp:* Res fel crystallog, Inst Mineral Petrog, Univ Berne, 63-64. *Concurrent Pos:* Ford fel eng, 64-66; vis prof crystallog, Univ Saarland, Saarbrucken, Ger, 73; adv ed, Physics & Chem Minerals, 76-85; assoc ed, Can Mineralogist, 78-80, ed, Zeit Kristallogr, 81-88; vis scientist, Max Planck Inst fur Festkorperforschung, Ger, 81; USA Nat Comt Crystallography, Nat Acad Sci, 80-82, 89-94. *Mem:* Mineral Asn Can; Am Crystallog Asn; fel Am Ceramic Soc; fel Mineral Soc Am; Electrochem Soc; Mats Res Soc. *Res:* X-ray and neutron diffraction; crystal structure determination; relation between crystal structure and crystal properties; diffusion and point defects; fast-ion conductors. *Mailing Add:* Dept Mat Sci & Eng Mass Inst Technol 77 Massachusetts Ave Cambridge MA 02139-4307. *E-Mail:* wuensch@mit.edu

**WUENSCHEL, PAUL CLARENCE,** GEOPHYSICS. *Current Pos:* res assoc, 55-74, geophysicist & sr scientist, 74-83, GEOPHYS CONSULT, GULF RES & DEVELOP CO, 83- *Personal Data:* b Erie, Pa, May 13, 21; m 50; c 6. *Educ:* Colo Sch Mines, GeolEngr, 44; Columbia Univ, PhD(geol), 55. *Prof Exp:* Res assoc, Columbia Univ, 46-52; dir geol & geophys res, Res, Inc, 52-55. *Mem:* Hon mem Soc Explor Geophys; Seismol Soc Am; Acoust Soc Am; Am Geophys Union; Europ Asn Explor Geophys. *Res:* Seismology; potential, electrical and seismic methods of geophysical exploration. *Mailing Add:* 128 Marian Ave Glenshaw PA 15116-1443

**WUEPPER, KIRK DEAN,** dermatology, experimental dermatopathology; deceased, see previous edition for last biography

**WUERKER, RALPH FREDERICK,** PHYSICS. *Current Pos:* RETIRED. *Personal Data:* div; c Marie Corinne (Ortiz), Matthew Christain & Christopher Kirsch. *Educ:* Occidental Col, BA, 51; Stanford Univ, PhD(physics), 60. *Honors & Awards:* Res Soc Award, TRW Systs, 66. *Prof Exp:* Engr, AiRes, Inc, 56-58; mem tech staff, Res Lab, Ramo-Wooldridge, Inc, 58-59; mem sr staff, Res Lab, Space Technol Labs, Inc, 60-61; mem sr staff, Quantatron Corp, 61-62; mem prof staff, TRW Systs Group, TRW Inc, Redondo Beach, 63-86. *Concurrent Pos:* Consult, Lawrence Livermore Labs, 73-; assoc dir, HIPAS Observ, Fairbanks, Alaska, 86- *Mem:* Am Asn Physics Teachers; Am Phys Soc; Optical Soc Am. *Res:* Holography and coherent optics; plasma particle resonances; superconductivity; electrooptics; lasers; physical optics; plasma physics; electron and general experimental physics; electrodynamic charge particle containment. *Mailing Add:* 887 Gold Springs Pl Westlake CA 91361-2024. *E-Mail:* rwuerker@physics.ucla.edu

**WUEST, JAMES D,** MOLECULAR RECOGNITION, SELF ASSEMBLY. *Current Pos:* PROF CHEM, UNIV MONTREAL, 81- *Personal Data:* b Cincinnati, Ohio, Oct 24, 48; Can & US citizen; m 80, Mary C Larson; c Spencer L. *Educ:* Cornell Univ, AB, 69; Harvard Univ, PhD(org chem), 73. *Honors & Awards:* Merck Sharp & Dohme Award, Can Soc Chem, 88; Rutherford Mem Medal, Royal Soc Can, 92. *Prof Exp:* Asst prof chem, Harvard, 73-79, fel, 80. *Concurrent Pos:* Killam res fel, Can Coun, 92. *Mem:* Am Chem Soc; fel Can Soc Chem; fel Royal Soc Can. *Res:* Design, synthesis, structure, and reactions of new organic, organometallic, and inorganic compounds; use of noncovalent interactions to regulate catalysis, molecular recognition, and the self-assembly of complex structures. *Mailing Add:* Dept Chem Univ Montreal Montreal PQ H3C 3J7 Can. *E-Mail:* wuest@ere.umontreal.ca

**WUEST, PAUL J,** PLANT PATHOLOGY, MYCOLOGY. *Current Pos:* Asst, 58-63, from asst prof to assoc prof, 64-74, PROF PLANT PATH, PA STATE UNIV, 74- *Personal Data:* b Philadelphia, Pa, Feb 26, 37; m 61; c 4. *Educ:* Pa State Univ, BS, 58, PhD(plant path), 63. *Concurrent Pos:* Fel, Univ Guelph, 70-71; agr consult, 70- *Mem:* Am Phytopath Soc; Can Phytopath Soc; Soc Nematol; Mycol Soc Am; Am Mushroom Inst; Sigma Xi. *Res:* Diseases of the commercial mushroom; soil treatment and disease occurrence; fungicide tolerance; epidemiology; pest management; worker exposure to pesticides. *Mailing Add:* Dept Plant Path Penn State Univ 211 Buckhout Lab University Park PA 16802-4507

**WUJEK, DANIEL EVERETT,** BOTANY. *Current Pos:* assoc prof, 68-73, PROF BOT, CENT MICH UNIV, 73-, RES PROF, 78- *Personal Data:* b Bay City, Mich, Oct 26, 39; m 66, Mildred G Andes; c Cynthia & Kassia. *Educ:* Cent Mich Univ, BS, 61, MA, 62; Univ Kans, PhD(bot), 66. *Honors & Awards:* Dimond Award, Bot Soc Am, 75; Darbaker Prize, Bot Soc Am, 95. *Prof Exp:* From asst prof to assoc prof bot, Wis State Univ, La Crosse, 66-68. *Concurrent Pos:* Wis State Univ fac grant, 66-68; NSF grant, 71-72, 76-77 & 87; Cent Mich Univ fac res grant, 71-85; vis prof, Univ Minn, Univ Mont & Univ SFla; pres, Mich Electron Microscopy Forum. *Mem:* AAAS; Bot Soc Am; Am Soc Plant Taxon; Phycol Soc Am; Int Phycol Soc; Aquatic Plant Soc. *Res:* Algal life history studies and electron microscopy, including ecology and relations to water quality; aquatic plant taxonomy; plant taxonomyu. *Mailing Add:* Dept Biol Cent Mich Univ Mt Pleasant MI 48859. *Fax:* 517-774-3462; *E-Mail:* d.wujek@cmich.edu

**WUKELIC, GEORGE EDWARD,** REMOTE SENSING, SPACE PHYSICS. *Current Pos:* Prin physicist, Columbus Div, Battelle Mem Inst, 52-60, sr physicist, 60-72, assoc sect mgr, Space Systs & Appln Sect, 72-77, staff scientist, Water & Land Resources Dept, 77-85, tech group leader remote sensing, 85-93, SR PROG MGR REMOTE SENSING, EARTH & ENVIRON SCI CTR, PAC NW DIV, BATTELLE MEM INST, 94- *Personal Data:* b Steubenville, Ohio, Sept 17, 29; m 55, Leila Mclick; c George W, Michael S & Larry E. *Educ:* WVa Univ, AB, 52. *Mem:* Am Soc Photogram; Am Geophys Union. *Res:* Space; geophysics; remote sensing applications; satellite earth resource surveys; image processing-multispectral data; application for geoscientific, environmental and national security interests. *Mailing Add:* 241 Saint St Richland WA 99352

**WULBERT, DANIEL ELIOT,** MATHEMATICS, FUNCTIONAL ANALYSIS. *Current Pos:* assoc prof, 74-80, PROF MATH, UNIV CALIF, SAN DIEGO, 80- *Personal Data:* b Chicago, Ill, Dec 17, 41; c Kera & Noah. *Educ:* Knox Col, Ill, BA, 63; Univ Tex, MA, 64, PhD(math), 66. *Prof Exp:* Vis asst prof math, Univ Lund, 66-67; asst prof, Univ Wash, 67-74. *Concurrent Pos:* Fel, Univ Lund, 66-67; NSF res grant, 68-; vis prof, Northwestern Univ, 77-80. *Mem:* Am Math Soc. *Res:* Approximation theory; functional analysis. *Mailing Add:* Dept Math Univ Calif San Diego La Jolla CA 92093. *E-Mail:* dwulbert@ucsd.edu

**WULF, RONALD JAMES,** TOXICOLOGY, PHARMACOLOGY. *Current Pos:* DIR BIOL RES, CARTER WALLACE INC, 70- *Personal Data:* b Davenport, Iowa, July 24, 28; m 59; c 3. *Educ:* Univ Iowa, BS, 50, MS, 57; Purdue Univ, PhD(biochem), 64. *Prof Exp:* Res chemist, John Deere & Co, 50-52; asst pharmacol, Univ Iowa, 54-57; res pharmacologist, Lederle Labs, Am Cyanamid Co, NY, 57-61; teaching asst biochem, Purdue Univ, 61-64; assoc prof pharmacol, Univ Conn, 64-70. *Mem:* AAAS; Am Chem Soc; Soc Toxicol. *Res:* Drug safety evaluations; chemically induced fibrinolysis; inhalation toxicology. *Mailing Add:* Carter Wallace Inc Half Acre Rd Cranbury NJ 08512

**WULF, WILLIAM ALLAN,** COMPUTER SCIENCE. *Current Pos:* AT&T PROF ENG, UNIV VA, 88- *Personal Data:* b Chicago, Ill, Dec 8, 39; m 61, Anita K Jones; c 2. *Educ:* Univ Ill, BSc, 61, MSc, 63; Univ Va, DSc(comput sci), 68. *Prof Exp:* Instr comput sci, Univ Va, 63-68; from asst prof to assoc prof, Carnegie-Mellon Univ, 68-75, prof comput sci, 75-81, actg dept head, 78-79; founder & chmn, Tartan Labs, 81-87. *Concurrent Pos:* Chmn, Working Group Syst Implementation Lang, Int Fedn Info Processing, 72-78; assoc ed, Transactions Prog Lang & Systs, 79-; asst dir, NSF, 88-90. *Mem:* Nat Acad Eng (pres, 96-); fel Inst Elec & Electronics Engrs; Int Fedn Info Processing; fel AAAS; Asn Comput Mach; fel Am Acad Arts & Sci. *Res:* Computer languages and their translators, operating systems, methodology and computer architecture. *Mailing Add:* 3897 Free Union Rd Charlottesville VA 22901-9812

**WULFERS, THOMAS FREDERICK,** ORGANIC CHEMISTRY. *Current Pos:* sr res chemist, 72-80, mgr indust prod res, 72-85, MGR LUBRICANTS RES & DEVELOP & VPRES LICENSING, ATLANTIC RICHFIELD CO, ILL, 85- *Personal Data:* b Cape Girardeau, Mo, Oct 4, 39; m 63; c 2. *Educ:* St Louis Univ, BS, 61; Wash Univ, MA, 63; Univ Chicago, PhD(chem), 65. *Prof Exp:* Res chemist, Shell Oil Co, Mo, 65-72. *Mem:* Am Chem Soc. *Res:* Petroleum products research; lubricants formulation and processing. *Mailing Add:* Lyondell-CITCO PO Box 2451 Houston TX 77252-2451

**WULFF, BARRY LEE,** ECOLOGY, BOTANY. *Current Pos:* From asst prof to assoc prof, 70-82, PROF BIOL, EASTERN CONN STATE UNIV, 82- *Personal Data:* b Mt Kisco, NY, Feb 17, 40; m 66; c 2. *Educ:* State Univ NY, Cortland, BS, 65; Col William & Mary, MA, 68; Ore State Univ, PhD(bot), 70. *Concurrent Pos:* Pres, Natural Resources Coun Conn, 76-87. *Mem:* AAAS; Am Bryological & Lichenological Soc; Mycol Soc Am; Sigma Xi. *Res:* Lichens; fungi; marine algae; ecology of cryptogamic plants. *Mailing Add:* 59 Bella Vista Dr North Windham CT 06256

**WULFF, DANIEL LEWIS,** MOLECULAR GENETICS. *Current Pos:* dean, Col Sci & Math, 80-93, PROF BIOL, DEPT BIOL SCI, STATE UNIV NY, ALBANY, 80- *Personal Data:* b Santa Barbara, Calif, Mar 29, 37; m 57, Bonnie Taylor; c Melissa, Mark & Elise. *Educ:* Calif Inst Technol, BS, 58, PhD(chem), 62. *Prof Exp:* Fel, Inst Genetics, Univ Koln, 62-63, & Biol Dept, Harvard Univ, 63-65; from asst prof to prof biol, Dept Molecular Biol & Biochem, Univ Calif, Irvine, 65-79, assoc dean biol sci, 75-79. *Mem:* AAAS; Genetics Soc Am; Am Soc Microbiol; Am Soc Biochem & Molecular Biol. *Res:* Transcriptional and translational control mechanisms in the regulation of gene expression in bacteriophage lambda. *Mailing Add:* 117 Ball Ct Menands NY 12204. *Fax:* 518-442-4767; *E-Mail:* dlw96@cnsvax.albany.edu

**WULFF, JOHN LELAND,** MATHEMATICS. *Current Pos:* From instr to assoc prof, 55-68, chmn dept, 68-71, PROF MATH, CALIF STATE UNIV, SACRAMENTO, 69- *Personal Data:* b Oakland, Calif, Mar 19, 32; m 68, Ruth A Tortora; c Leland J, Nancy L, Susan A & Karen M. *Educ:* Sacramento State Col, AB, 54; Univ Calif, Davis, MA, 57, PhD(math), 66. *Res:* Measure theory and integration. *Mailing Add:* 3644 Lusk Dr Sacramento CA 95821

**WULFF, WOLFGANG,** MECHANICAL & AEROSPACE ENGINEERING, COMPUTER SIMULATION. *Current Pos:* TENURED SCIENTIST, BROOKHAVEN NAT LAB, 74- *Personal Data:* b Darmstadt, Ger, June 16, 33, US citizen; m 64; c 2. *Educ:* Winterthur Inst Technol, Switz, BSME, 58; Ill Inst Technol, MSME, 62, PhD(mech & aerospace eng), 68. *Honors & Awards:* Achievement Award, US Nuclear Regulatory Comn, 89. *Prof Exp:* Proj engr, Escher-Wyss Ltd, Zurich, 58-60 & Eppi Precision Prod, Ill, 60-63; res engr, IIT Res Inst, 63-68; from asst prof to assoc prof mech eng, Ga Inst Technol, 68-74. *Concurrent Pos:* Adj prof, NY Inst Technol, 79-80; chmn, Thermal Hydraulics Div, Am Nuclear Soc, 92-93; consult, Adv Comt Reactor Safeguards, Nat Res Coun, 92-96. *Mem:* Am Soc Mech Engrs; Combustion Inst; NY Acad Sci; Am Nuclear Soc; Sigma Xi; Am Asn Univ Prof. *Res:* Fabric flammability; thermal control of space vehicles; atmospheric vortices; thermohydraulics of reactor systems; nuclear power reactor safety; nuclear power plant simulation. *Mailing Add:* 11 Hamilton Rd Setauket NY 11733. *Fax:* 516-344-2613; *E-Mail:* wulff@bnl.gov

**WULFMAN, CARL E,** THEORETICAL PHYSICS, THEORETICAL CHEMISTRY. *Current Pos:* chmn dept, 61-74, prof, 61-96, EMER PROF PHYSICS, UNIV PAC, 96- *Personal Data:* b Detroit, Mich, Nov 30; m 52, Constance Hart; c Michael, Peter, Andrew & Edward. *Educ:* Univ Mich, BS, 53; Univ London, PhD(org chem), 57. *Prof Exp:* Instr chem, Univ Tex, 56-57; assoc prof, Defiance Col, 57-61. *Concurrent Pos:* Vis mem, Ctr Theoret Studies, Coral Gables, Fla, 67; NSF sci fac fel, Oxford Univ, 67-68; vis prof, Japan Soc Promotion Sci, 74-75, Max Born vis prof, Hebrew Univ, 88; coop res, NZ, Can, Mex & Israel. *Mem:* Am Phys Soc; Am Asn Physics Teachers. *Res:* Transformation properties of dynamical equations; continuous groups; applications to chemical kinetics, atomic and molecular quantum mechanics; dynamical symmetry. *Mailing Add:* Dept Physics Univ of the Pac Stockton CA 95211. *E-Mail:* cwulfman@uop.edu

**WULFMAN, DAVID SWINTON,** SYNTHETIC ORGANIC CHEMISTRY, EXPLOSIVES ENGINEERING. *Current Pos:* from asst prof to prof, 63-91, investr, Rock Mech & Explosives Res Ctr, 88-91, EMER PROF CHEM, UNIV MO, ROLLA, 91-; DIR CHEM RES, TDI, 89-; PRES, D S WULFMAN & ASSOC, 90- *Personal Data:* b Detroit, Mich, Sept 1, 34; m 61, Helga Seifert; c Knud, Eric & Matthew. *Educ:* Helga Seifert; c Knud, Eric & Matthew. *Educ:* Univ Calif, Berkeley, BS, 56; Dartmouth Col, AM, 58; Stanford Univ, PhD(chem), 62; Alliance Francaise, Paris, France, IVe, French, 74. *Prof Exp:* Res asst chem, Univ Mich, 54-56; sr develop engr, Hercules Inc, Utah, 61-63. *Concurrent Pos:*

Consult, Dept Chem, Stanford Univ, 69; lectr, Washington Univ, 70 & Chem Soc France, 75; res assoc, Ctr Nat Res Sci, Ecole Normale Superieure, Paris, 74-75; vis prof, St Marys Univ, Halifax NS, Can, 81-82 & Dalhousie Univ, 84; consult, Metalbright, Burns & Roe, IRECO, Tressler, Soderstrom, Maloney & Priess & Univ Mo, Rolla. *Mem:* Am Chem Soc; Royal Soc Chem; Chem Inst Can; Asn Can Studies US; Soc Explosive Engrs. *Res:* Synthesis and study of theoretically important molecules; homogeneous catalysis; physical organic chemistry; demilitarization of explosive and propellants, new explosives, explosive safety. *Mailing Add:* PO Box 703 Mill Village NS B0J 2H0 Can. *Fax:* 902-677-2293, 314-341-3614

**WULLERT, JOHN R, II,** DISPLAYS FOR GRAPHICS & VIDEO, OPTICAL SIGNAL PROCESSING. *Current Pos:* MEM TECH STAFF, ELECTRONIC DISPLAYS & OPTICAL SIGNAL PROCESSING, BELLCORE, 86- *Personal Data:* b Abington, Pa, Feb 27, 62; m 86. *Educ:* Lafayette Col, BS, 84; Carnegie Mellon Univ, MS, 87. *Mem:* Soc Info Display; Inst Elec & Electronics Engrs; Optical Soc Am. *Res:* Investigating electrical-optical conversions for the purposes of generating images for video displays as well as for generation of inputs to optical signal processing systems. *Mailing Add:* MTS Bellcore 331 Newman Spring Rd 3Z 383 Red Bank NJ 07701

**WULLSTEIN, LEROY HUGH,** BIOGEOGRAPHY, SOIL MICROBIOLOGY. *Current Pos:* from asst prof to assoc prof, 66-75, PROF BIOGEOG, UNIV UTAH, 75-, ASSOC PROF BIOL, 80-, PROF GEOG, 85- *Personal Data:* b Nampa, Idaho, Nov 23, 31; m 56; c 1. *Educ:* Univ Utah, BS, 57; Ore State Univ, MS, 61, PhD(microbiol), 64. *Honors & Awards:* William Skinner Cooper Award, Ecol Soc Am, 87. *Prof Exp:* Asst prof soil sci, Univ BC, 64-66. *Concurrent Pos:* Sr Fulbright res fel nitrogen fixation, Ireland, 72-73; consult, Brookhaven Labs, 74-; mem, Utah Statewater Pollution Control Comn. *Mem:* Am Soc Microbiol; Am Chem Soc; Soil Sci Soc Am. *Res:* Nitrogen transformations; oak biogeography; endemism. *Mailing Add:* Dept Geog Univ Utah Salt Lake City UT 84112

**WUN, CHUN KWUN,** BACTERIOLOGY, BACTERIAL GENETICS. *Current Pos:* from asst instr to instr biol, Springfield Col, 68-70, asst prof, 73-74, adj asst prof, 75-90, ASSOC RES PROF BIOL SPRINGFIELD COL, 81-82, 90- *Personal Data:* b Canton, China, Feb 15, 40; US citizen; m 64; c 2. *Educ:* Chung Chi Col, Chinese Univ Hong Kong, BS, 64; Springfield Col, MS, 69; Univ Mass, Amherst, MS, 71, PhD(lipid chem), 74. *Honors & Awards:* DIFCO AWARD, 76 & 82. *Prof Exp:* Asst educ officer sci, Educ Dept Hong Kong, 65-66; res asst lipid chem, Univ Mass, Amhearst, 70-73, fel, Dept Environs Sci, 75-82; dir, Health Labs, City Springfield, Mass, 87-90. *Concurrent Pos:* Invited Prof, Pasteur Inst, Paris, 97. *Mem:* Fel Am Soc Microbiol; Sigma Xi; Soc Appl Bacteriol. *Res:* Lipid metabolism, particularly triglyceride synthesis and its control in mycobacterium smegmatis; water pollution; the use of fecal sterols as an indicator of fecal pollution of water; column method for rapid extraction and gas-liquid chromatography quantitation of algal chlorophylls; new media for the isolation/identification of E coli and other enteric organisms; rapid procedure for the isolation and drug susceptibility determination of mycobacteria; bacillus subtilis genome studies. *Mailing Add:* Dept Biol & Chem Springfield Col 263 Alden St Springfield MA 01109-3761. *Fax:* 413-748-3761; *E-Mail:* cwun@spfldcoll.edu

**WUNDER, BRUCE ARNOLD,** PHYSIOLOGICAL ECOLOGY, VERTEBRATE ZOOLOGY. *Current Pos:* from asst prof to assoc prof, Colo State Univ,69-84, asst chmn dept, 78-79, 83-84, interim chmn, 84-85, chmn prog ecol studies, 85-87, chmn dept, 85-93, PROF BIOL, COLO STATE UNIV, 84-, INTERIM VPROVOST UNDERGRAD STUDIES, 96- *Personal Data:* b Monterey Park, Calif, Feb 10, 42; m 63; c 2. *Educ:* Whittier Col, BA, 63; Univ Calif, Los Angeles, PhD(vert zool), 68. *Prof Exp:* NIH fel, Inst Arctic Biol, Univ Alaska, 68-69. *Concurrent Pos:* Small mammal ecologist, Biol Res Assocs, Inc & consult, Thorne Ecol Inst, 72-; assoc prof zool, Univ Mich Biol Sta, 76 & 78; prof zool, Univ Mont Biol Sta, 81, 83 & 85; Alexander von Humboldt fel, Frankfurt, Ger, 79-80; prof biol, Rocky Mt Biol Sta, 87 & 90. *Mem:* AAAS; Am Soc Zoologists; Am Soc Mammalogists; Ecol Soc Am; Sigma Xi. *Res:* Temperature regulation and energetics; water balance and mechanisms of evaporative water loss, particularly in vertebrates; feeding strategies and distribution patterns in vertebrates; digestive physiology of vertebrates. *Mailing Add:* Dept Biol Colo State Univ Ft Collins CO 80523

**WUNDER, CHARLES C(OOPER),** PHYSIOLOGY, BIOPHYSICS. *Current Pos:* assoc physiol, 54-56, from asst prof to assoc prof, 56-71, PROF PHYSIOL & BIOPHYS, UNIV IOWA, 71- *Personal Data:* b Pittsburgh, Pa, Oct 2, 28; m 62, Marcia L Barnes; c E Douglas, David B & Donald C. *Educ:* Washington & Jefferson Col, AB, 49; Univ Pittsburgh, MS, 52, PhD(biophys), 54. *Prof Exp:* Asst biophys, Univ Pittsburgh, 49-51. *Concurrent Pos:* NIH res career develop award, 61-66; vis scientist & NIH spec fel, Mayo Clin, 66-67. *Mem:* Soc Exp Biol & Med; Biophys Soc; Am Physiol Soc; Am Soc Gravitational & Space Biol; Am Soc Biomech; Aerospace Med Asn. *Res:* Environmental biophysics of growth and function; gravitational biology; bone strength; blood pressure of human populations. *Mailing Add:* Dept Physiol & Biophys Univ Iowa Iowa City IA 52242. *Fax:* 319-335-7330; *E-Mail:* charles__wunder@uiowa.edu

**WUNDER, WILLIAM W,** POPULATION GENETICS, ANIMAL SCIENCE. *Current Pos:* from asst prof to assoc prof, 68-79, PROF ANIMAL SCI, IOWA STATE UNIV, 79- *Personal Data:* b Lake Park, Iowa, June 4, 30; m 60; c 3. *Educ:* Iowa State Univ, BS, 58; Mich State Univ, MS, 64, PhD(dairy cattle breeding), 67. *Prof Exp:* Asst prof exten dairy sci, Univ Ky, 67-68. *Mem:* Am Dairy Sci Asn; Am Soc Animal Sci. *Res:* Influence of corrective versus random mating on net income and type in Holstein dairy cattle. *Mailing Add:* Dept Animal Sci Iowa State Univ Ames IA 50011-2010

**WUNDERLICH, BERNHARD,** POLYMER CHEMISTRY. *Current Pos:* from assoc prof to prof, 63-88, EMER PROF CHEM, RENSSELAER POLYTECH INST, 88-; PROF CHEM & DISTINGUISHED SCIENTIST, UNIV TENN & OAK RIDGE NAT LAB, 88- *Personal Data:* b Brandenburg, Ger, May 28, 31; nat US; m 53, Adelheid C Felix; c Caryn C & Brent B. *Educ:* Univ Frankfurt, BSc, 54; Northwestern Univ, PhD, 57. *Honors & Awards:* Mettler Award for Thermal Analysis, 71. *Prof Exp:* Instr chem, Northwestern Univ, 57-58; from instr to asst prof, Cornell Univ, 58-63. *Concurrent Pos:* Consult, E I du Pont de Nemours & Co, 63-88; Humboldt fel, 87; adv prof, Fudan Univ, Shanghai, China, 88- *Mem:* Am Chem Soc; fel NAm Thermal Analysis Soc; Int Confedn Thermal Anal; fel Am Phys Soc. *Res:* Physical chemistry of the solid state of high polymers; transitions of high polymers at elevated temperatures and high pressures; thermal analysis. *Mailing Add:* 200 Baltusrol Rd Knoxville TN 37922-3707. *Fax:* 423-974-0652; *E-Mail:* athas@utkvx.utk.edu

**WUNDERLICH, FRANCIS J,** PHYSICAL CHEMISTRY. *Current Pos:* asst prof, 69-, ASSOC PROF PHYSICS, VILLANOVA UNIV. *Personal Data:* b Philadelphia, Pa, Mar 9, 38; m 62; c 5. *Educ:* Villanova Univ, BS, 59; Georgetown Univ, PhD(chem), 64. *Honors & Awards:* Award, Am Inst Chemists, 59. *Prof Exp:* Res asst chem, Villanova Univ, 57-58, instr, 59; instr, Georgetown Univ, 59-61, res assoc, 61-63; fel molecular physics, 63-65; from asst prof to assoc prof physics & chem, Col Virgin Islands, 65-69. *Concurrent Pos:* Dir, NSF Grant, Undergrad Sci Equip Prog, Col Virgin Islands, 65-67; dir, Etelman Astron Observ, 66-67. *Mem:* Am Chem Soc; Royal Soc Chem. *Res:* Theoretical molecular physics; gas phase free radicals; laser-induced gas phase reactions. *Mailing Add:* Dept Physics Villanova Univ 800 Lancaster Ave Villanova PA 19085-1672

**WUNDERLICH, JOHN R,** TUMOR IMMUNOLOGY, CELLULAR IMMUNOLOGY. *Current Pos:* SR INVESTR, NIH, 70- *Educ:* Stanford Univ, MD, 64. *Mailing Add:* 10113 Parkwood Terr Bethesda MD 20814

**WUNDERLICH, MARVIN C,** MATHEMATICS. *Current Pos:* DIR MATH SCI PROG, NAT SECURITY AGENCY, US DEPT DEFENSE, FT MEADE, MD, 88- *Personal Data:* b Decatur, Ill, May 8, 37; m 60; c 2. *Educ:* Concordia Teachers Col, Ill, BS, 59; Univ Colo, PhD(math), 64. *Prof Exp:* Asst prof math, State Univ NY, Buffalo, 64-67; assoc prof math, Northern Ill Univ, 67-72, prof, 72-88. *Concurrent Pos:* NSF res grant, 66-; vis, Univ Nottingham, 72-73. *Mem:* Am Math Soc; Asn Comput Mach. *Res:* Number theory; computing mathematics. *Mailing Add:* 11620 Tuscany Dr Laurel MD 20708

**WUNDERLY, STEPHEN WALKER,** MEASUREMENT OF LOW ENERGY RADIOACTIVITY, SYNTHETIC ORGANIC CHEMISTRY. *Current Pos:* STAFF SCIENTIST, BECKMAN INSTRUMENTS INC, 78- *Personal Data:* b Cleveland, Ohio, May 24, 45; m 69; c 2. *Educ:* Col Wooster, BA, 63; Univ Cincinnati, MS, 71, PhD(chem), 75. *Prof Exp:* Res assoc chem, Univ BC, 74-76, Univ Calif, San Francisco, 76-77 & Univ Southern Calif, 77-78. *Mem:* Am Chem Soc; Am Inst Chem. *Res:* Photochemistry; alkaloid synthesis and biosynthesis; synthesis of polycyclic aromatics; emulsion chemistry and emulsifer properties; chemistry with solid phase supported reagents; detection and measurement of low energy radionuclides; nuclear chemistry. *Mailing Add:* Beckman Instruments 2500 Harbor Blvd Fullerton CA 92634-3100

**WUNDERMAN, IRWIN,** ELECTROOPTICS, ELECTRONIC INSTRUMENTATION. *Current Pos:* RESEARCHER, SCIENTIST & AUTHOR, 71- *Personal Data:* b New York, NY, Apr 24, 31; m 51; c 3. *Educ:* City Col New York, BSEE, 52; Univ Southern Calif, MSEE, 56; Stanford Univ, EEE, 61, PhD(elec eng), 64. *Prof Exp:* Jr engr draftsman, Lockheed-Calif Co, 52, jr engr, 52-53, res engr, 53-56; lab sect leader, Hewlett Packard Co, 56-61, co-founder, Hewlett Packard Assocs, 61-65, lab mgr, Hewlett Packard Corp Labs, 65-67; pres & gen mgr, Cintra Inc, Cintra Physics Int, 67-71. *Mem:* AAAS; sr mem Inst Elec & Electronics Engrs; Optical Soc Am; Am Inst Physics; Sigma Xi; Int Soc Optical Instrumentation Engrs. *Res:* Electrooptics instrumentation; radiometry; photometry; optoelectronic solid state devices and circuits; computer architecture and systems; modeling of nonlinear physical systems; physics of optics and quanta; wave/particle dilemma; photons, granular mechanics and the classical origin of quanta theory in mathematical physics; optoelectronic instrumentation of malignant tissue. *Mailing Add:* 655 Eunice Ave Mountain View CA 94040-3875

**WUNG, PETER Y,** ELECTRICAL MACHINERY DESIGN, CONTROL OF ELECTRIC MACHINERY. *Current Pos:* SR ENG SPECIALIST, EMERSON MOTOR CO, 94- *Personal Data:* b Taiwan, China, Mar 27, 61; US citizen. *Educ:* Univ Ill, Urbana-Champaign, BSEE, 83; Ga Inst Technol, MS, 84, PhD(elec eng), 93. *Prof Exp:* Advan develop engr, Westinghouse Motor Co, 93-94. *Mem:* Inst Elec & Electronics Engrs. *Res:* Machinery design and analysis, specifically in the areas of mitigation of machinery noise, thermal modeling, electromagnetic modeling, synthesis and analysis of electric machinery theory with power electronics and control of electric machinery. *Mailing Add:* 8050 W Florissant Sta 8293 St Louis MO 63136. *Fax:* 314-595-8071; *E-Mail:* wungp@emotors.com

**WUNSCH, ABRAHAM DAVID,** APPLIED MATHEMATICS. *Current Pos:* Asst prof, 69-82, ASSOC PROF ELEC ENG, UNIV LOWELL, 82- *Personal Data:* b Brooklyn, NY, Dec 13, 39; c 2. *Educ:* Cornell Univ, BEE, 61; Harvard Univ, SM, 62, PhD(eng & appl physics). *Mem:* Sigma Xi. *Res:* Electromagnetic theory; antennas; functions of a complex variable. *Mailing Add:* Dept Elec Eng Univ Mass Lowell MA 01854-2882

**WUNSCH, CARL ISAAC,** PHYSICAL OCEANOGRAPHY. *Current Pos:* Lectr oceanog, Mass Inst Technol, 66-67, from asst prof to prof, 67-76, head, Dept Earth & Planetary Sci, 77-81, CECIL & IDA GREEN PROF PHYS OCEANOG, MASS INST TECHNOL, 76- *Personal Data:* b New York, NY, May 5, 41; m 70, Marjory Morkel; c Jared & Hannah. *Educ:* Mass Inst Technol, SB, 62, PhD(geophys), 66. *Honors & Awards:* James B Macelwane Award, Am Geophys Union, 71; Maurice Ewing Medal, 90; Founders Prize, Tex Instruments Found, 75, A G Huntsman Prize, 88. *Concurrent Pos:* Vis sr investr, Cambridge Univ, 69, 74-75 & 81-82; vis prof, Univ Wash, 80 & Harvard Univ, 80; ed, Monographs in Mech & Appl Math, Cambridge Univ Press, 81-89; Fulbright fel, 81-82; Guggenheim Found fel, 81-82; secy, Navy Res Prof, 85-89; sr vis scientist, Geophys Fluid Dynamics Lab, Princeton Univ, 93; vis scientist, CNES/CNRS, Toulouse, France, 94. *Mem:* Nat Acad Sci; Am Geophys Union; Royal Astron Soc; Am Acad Arts & Sci; Soc Indust & Appl Math; Oceanog Soc; Am Meteorol Soc. *Res:* Sea level, general circulation; tides; ocean acoustics; climate; author of several scientific papers and books. *Mailing Add:* Dept Earth Atmospheric & Planetary Sci Rm 54-1524 Mass Inst Technol Cambridge MA 02139. *Fax:* 617-253-4464; *E-Mail:* cwunsch@pond.mit.edu

**WUNZ, PAUL RICHARD, JR,** ORGANIC CHEMISTRY, TEACHING. *Current Pos:* RETIRED. *Personal Data:* b Erie, Pa, Oct 18, 23; m 48, Jane Kyle; c Timothy P, Carol J (Guba) & Stephen K. *Educ:* Pa State Col, BS, 44, MS, 47; Univ Del, PhD(chem), 50. *Prof Exp:* Instr chem, Univ Del, 50; asst prof chem & head dept, Augsburg Col, 50-51; res chemist, Nopco Chem Co, 51-53; res chemist & group leader, Callery Chem Co, 53-57; from asst prof to assoc prof chem, Geneva Col, 57-65; chmn dept, Ind Univ Pa, 65-73, prof chem, 65-87. *Concurrent Pos:* Vis prof, Univ Ariz, 82. *Mem:* Am Chem Soc. *Res:* Synthetic organic chemistry; organometallic compounds; pharmaceuticals, steroids; heterocyclic compounds. *Mailing Add:* 219 Oriole Ave Indiana PA 15701

**WUONOLA, MARK ARVID,** organic chemistry, medicinal chemistry, for more information see previous edition

**WUORINEN, JOHN H, JR,** ELECTRICAL ENGINEERING. *Current Pos:* ED, INT SOLID-STATES CIRCUIT CONF, 89- *Personal Data:* b New York, NY, Aug 9, 31; m 56; c 4. *Educ:* Columbia Univ, AB, 53, MS, 56, PhD(elec eng), 63. *Prof Exp:* Res asst elec eng, Electronics Res Lab, Columbia Univ, 54-56, instr, Univ, 56-62; mem tech staff, Bell Labs, 62-64, supvr digital device integration, 64-68, head, Electronic Subsyst Design Dept, 68-74, head, Memory & Call Progress Syst Dept, 74-80, head, Special Systs Dept, 81-86; prof elec eng, Univ Maine, 86-89, dir, Ctr Eng Studies, 88-90. *Concurrent Pos:* Chmn solid state circuits conf, Inst Elec & Electronics Engrs, 76-77. *Mem:* Inst Elec & Electronics Engrs; Sigma Xi. *Res:* Digital integrated circuits; solid state electronics; digital memory systems; telephone switching. *Mailing Add:* 2 School St Castine ME 04421

**WURDACK, JOHN J,** BOTANY. *Current Pos:* from asst cur to assoc cur, Nat Mus Natural Hist, Smithsonian Inst, 52-60, assoc cur, Div Phanerogams, 60-63, cur bot, 63-90, EMER CUR, NAT MUS NATURAL HIST, SMITHSONIAN INST, 91- *Personal Data:* b Pittsburgh, Pa, Apr 28, 21; m 59; c 2. *Educ:* Univ Pittsburgh, BS, 42; Univ Ill, BS, 49; Columbia Univ, PhD, 52. *Prof Exp:* Asst bot, Univ Pittsburgh, 42; tech asst bot, NY Bot Garden, 49-52. *Concurrent Pos:* Mem exped, Venezuela, 50-59 & 72 & Peru, 62. *Mem:* Am Soc Plant Taxonomists; Torrey Bot Club; Int Asn Plant Taxon. *Res:* Taxonomy of Melastomataceae and flowering plants of northern South America. *Mailing Add:* Dept Bot Nat Mus Natural Hist Smithsonian Inst Washington DC 20560

**WURM, JAROSLAV,** COMPRESSORS & PRIME MOVERS, AIR CONDITIONING & REFRIGERATION. *Current Pos:* ASST DIR, SPACE CONDITIONING RES, INST GAS TECHNOL, 68- *Personal Data:* b Czech, Apr 12, 35; US citizen; m 64, Eva; c Peter & Gabriella. *Educ:* Czech Tech Univ, MS, 58, PhD, 96. *Prof Exp:* Dep head, Compressor Div, Dept Compressor Develop, Czech, 58-66. *Concurrent Pos:* Pres, Air Conditioning Comn, Int Inst Refrig, 83-91. *Mem:* Am Soc Heating Refrig & Air Conditioning Engrs; hon mem Int Inst Refrig; Am Solar Energy Soc; Ger Soc Refrig & Air Conditioning Engrs; Czech Soc Air Conditioning Engrs. *Res:* Energy conversion systems including conceptual, component and systems evaluation; compressors, refrigeration, air conditioning and air quality, prime movers, and heat transfer. *Mailing Add:* Inst Gas Technol 1700 S Mt Prospect Rd Des Plaines IL 60018. *Fax:* 847-768-0510; *E-Mail:* wurmj@igt.org

**WURMSER, LEON,** PSYCHOANALYSIS, DRUG ABUSE. *Personal Data:* b Zurich, Switz, Jan 31, 31; US & Swiss citizen; m 58, Zdenka Koudelova; c 3. *Educ:* Univ Basel, MD, 58. *Honors & Awards:* Lewis B Hill Award, Inst Psychoanal, 75; Egner Prize, Switz, 97. *Prof Exp:* Staff psychiatrist, Sheppard Pratt Hosp, Baltimore, 62-65; dir outpatient, Sinai, 66-69; clin asst prof psychol & dir, Drug Abuse Ctr, Johns Hopkins Univ, 69-71; from assoc prof to prof psychiat, Univ Md, 71-83, dir, Alcohol & Drug Abuse Prog, 77-83. *Concurrent Pos:* Teacher, Switz, Ger, Sweden, Austria. *Mem:* Am Psychiat Asn; Am Psychoanal Asn; Swiss Med Soc; Swiss Psychiat Soc. *Res:* Psychodynamics of compulsive substance abuse; shame, shame conflicts, and defense against shame; the defense against superego; author of over 300 scientific articles. *Mailing Add:* 200 E Joppa Rd Baltimore MD 21286

**WURSIG, BERND GERHARD,** BEHAVIORAL BIOLOGY, MARINE MAMMALOGY. *Current Pos:* PROF & DIR, MARINE MAMMAL RES PROG, TEX, 89- *Personal Data:* b WGermany, Nov 9, 48; m 69, Melany A Camballeira; c Kim & Paul. *Educ:* Ohio State Univ, BSc, 71; State Univ NY,

PhD(behav biol), 78. *Honors & Awards:* Heiser Award, Houston Zool Soc, 91. *Prof Exp:* Fel, NIH & Univ Calif, Santa Cruz, 78-81; staff mem, Moss Landing Marine Labs, 81-89. *Concurrent Pos:* Researcher, Nat Geog Soc, 74-77, biomed res fel, 77. *Mem:* Am Behav Soc; Explorer's Club; Am Soc Mammalogists; Natural Hist Soc; Int Soc Cryptozool; Int Soc Marine Mammal (pres, 90-94). *Res:* Behavior and ecology of cetaceans and pinnipeds; movement and migration patterns of dolphins and whales; field research techniques for cetaceans; comparison of wild and captive dolphin behavior; sociobiology and ecology of mammals. *Mailing Add:* Marine Mammal Res Prog Tex A&M Univ Galveston TX 77553. *Fax:* 409-740-4717; *E-Mail:* wursigb@tamug.tamu.edu

**WURST, GLEN GILBERT,** GENETICS. *Current Pos:* asst prof, 75-84, ASSOC PROF BIOL, ALLEGHENY COL, 84- *Personal Data:* b Mt Holly, NJ, Apr 17, 45; m 82, Paula Coyle. *Educ:* Juniata Col, BS, 67; Univ Pittsburgh, PhD(biol), 75. *Prof Exp:* Teaching asst biol, Univ Pittsburgh, 67-71, teaching fel, 71-75. *Concurrent Pos:* Vis assoc res scientist, Johns Hopkins Univ, 80, 81 & 83-84. *Mem:* Genetics Soc Am; Soc Develop Biol; Sigma Xi; AAAS. *Res:* Developmental genetics of Drosophila Melanogaster. *Mailing Add:* Dept Biol Allegheny Col Meadville PA 16335. *Fax:* 814-337-0988; *E-Mail:* gwurst@alleg.edu

**WURST, GLORIA ZETTLE,** ANIMAL PHYSIOLOGY, EMBRYOLOGY. *Current Pos:* from asst prof to assoc prof, 78-88, PROF ZOOL, WEBER STATE UNIV, 88- *Personal Data:* b Steelton, Pa, Jan 13, 46. *Educ:* Juniata Col, BS, 66; Univ Pittsburgh, MS, 70, PhD(biol), 74. *Prof Exp:* Res assoc zool, Univ Calif, Berkeley, 75-78. *Mem:* AAAS; Am Soc Zoologists; Am Soc Ichthyologists & Herpetologists; Herpetologists' League; Sigma Xi. *Res:* Developmental morphology of pineal complex and pituitary gland in amphibians and reptiles; population genetics and evolution of salamanders. *Mailing Add:* Dept Zool Weber State Univ Ogden UT 84408-0001. *Fax:* 801-626-7445; *E-Mail:* gwurst@cc.weber.edu

**WURST, JOHN CHARLES,** CERAMIC ENGINEERING. *Current Pos:* Sr res ceramist, 57-75, assoc prof, 73-83, ASSOC DIR RES INST, UNIV DAYTON, 75-, PROF, GRAD FAC, 83- *Personal Data:* b Defiance, Ohio, Jan 11, 36; m 58; c 3. *Educ:* Univ Dayton, BME, 57, MEngSc, 68; Univ Ill, Urbana, PhD(ceramic eng), 71. *Concurrent Pos:* Consult mem comt coatings, Mat Adv Bd, Nat Acad Eng, 67-71. *Mem:* Fel Am Ceramic Soc; Sigma Xi; Nat Coun Univ Adminr; Nat Inst Ceramic Engrs; Ceramic Educ Coun. *Res:* High temperature protective coatings; corrosion; infrared transmitting materials; ceramics; sintering. *Mailing Add:* Univ Dayton Res Inst Dayton OH 45469-0101

**WURSTER, CHARLES F,** ENVIRONMENTAL SCIENCES & TOXICOLOGY, ORNITHOLOGY. *Current Pos:* asst prof biol sci, 65-71, assoc prof environ toxicol, Marine Sci Res Ctr, 71-94, EMER PROF ENVIRON SCI, STATE UNIV NY, STONY BROOK, 94- *Personal Data:* b Philadelphia, Pa, Aug 1, 30; m 70, Eva Tank-Nielsen; c Steven H, Nina F & Erik F. *Educ:* Haverford Col, SB, 52; Univ Del, MS, 54; Stanford Univ, PhD(org chem), 57. *Prof Exp:* Asst, Univ Del, 52-54 & Stanford Univ, 54-57; Fulbright fel, Innsbruck Univ, 57-58; res chemist, Monsanto Res Corp, 59-62; res assoc, Dartmouth Col, 62-65. *Concurrent Pos:* Founder & mem bd trustees, Environ Defense Fund, 67-; mem bd dir, Defenders Wildlife, 75-84 & 87-96; vis scientist & spec asst to dir, Nat Cancer Inst, Bethesda, Md, 78-79; vis prof, Dept Chem, Microbiol & Plant Physiol, Univ Bergen, Norway, 81. *Mem:* AAAS. *Res:* Ecological and physiological effects of stable chemical pollutants; chemical pollutants and avian reproduction; environmental protection via legal action; public policy and environmental quality; public interest science; ecological tourism. *Mailing Add:* Marine Sci Res Ctr State Univ NY Stony Brook NY 11794-5000. *Fax:* 516-632-8820; *E-Mail:* cwurster@ccmail.sunysb.edu

**WURSTER, DALE E,** PHARMACY. *Current Pos:* prof pharm & dean Col Pharm, 72-84, interim dean, 91-92, EMER PROF & DEAN, UNIV IOWA, 84-, EMER DEAN, 92- *Personal Data:* b Sparta, Wis, Apr 10, 18; m 44, June M Peterson; c Dale E & Susan G. *Educ:* Univ Wis, BS, 42, PhD, 47. *Honors & Awards:* Res Achievement Award, Am Pharmaceut Asn, 65; George B Kaufman Mem Lectr, Ohio State Univ, 68; Indust Pharm Technol Award, Am Pharmaceut Asn Acad Pharmaceut Sci, 80; Hancher-Finkbine Medal, Univ Iowa, 84; Distinguished Pharmaceut Scientist, Am Asn Pharm Sci, 91. *Prof Exp:* From instr to prof pharm, Univ Wis, 47-71; prof pharm & pharmaceut chem & dean, Col Pharm, NDak State Univ, 71-72. *Concurrent Pos:* Am Asn Cols Pharm-NSF vis scientist, 63-66; consult, USPHS, 66-72; mem, Rev Comt, US Pharmacopoeia, 61-72; sci adv, Wis Alumni Res Found, 68-72; phys sci adminr, USN, 60-63. *Mem:* Acad Pharmaceut Sci (pres, 75); fel Am Pharmaceut Asn; hon mem Rumanian Soc Med Sci; Soc Invest Dermat; Am Asn Cols Pharm; Sigma Xi; Am Asn Hosp Pharmacists; Fed Int Pharmaceut; Controlled Release Soc; fel Am Asn Pharmacol Sci. *Res:* Physical factors influencing dissolution kinetics; diffusion kinetics in biological membranes, drug release mechanisms from pharmaceutical systems, percutaneous absorption, air-suspension microencapsulation coating and granulating technique. *Mailing Add:* 16 Brickwood Knoll RR 6 Iowa City IA 52240

**WURSTER, DALE ERIC, JR,** SURFACE CHEMISTRY, THERMAL ANALYSIS. *Current Pos:* from asst prof to assoc prof, 83-95, PROF, COL PHARM, UNIV IOWA, 96- *Personal Data:* b Madison, Wis, Jan 19, 51; m 75, Pamela A Marvin; c Elizabeth A, Kristin G & D Edward. *Educ:* Univ Wis, BS, 74; Purdue Univ, PhD(phys pharm), 79. *Prof Exp:* Asst prof pharm, Sch Pharm, Univ NC, 79-82. *Concurrent Pos:* Consult, Nat Asn Bd Pharm & Pharmaceut Indust; elected mem, US Pharmacopeial Conv Comt Rev, 95-

*Mem:* Mat Res Soc; Am Chem Soc; Sigma Xi; Am Asn Col Pharm; Am Asn Pharmaceut Scientists. *Res:* Surface phenomena, especially adsorption-desorption thermodynamics; dissolution mechanisms; heats of solution and of interaction; heat evolution upon tablet compression; solution and differential scanning calorimetry; physics of tablet compression; analytical aspects of FTIR. *Mailing Add:* S215 Pharmacy Bldg Univ Iowa Iowa City IA 52242. *Fax:* 319-335-9349; *E-Mail:* dale__e__wurster@uiowa.edu

**WURSTER-HILL, DORIS HADLEY,** cytogenetics, for more information see previous edition

**WURTELE, MORTON GAITHER,** DYNAMIC METEOROLOGY, FORENSIC METEOROLOGY. *Current Pos:* from assoc prof to prof, Univ Calif, Los Angeles, 58-90, vchmn dept, 69-72, chmn dept, 72-76, EMER PROF METEOROL, UNIV CALIF, LOS ANGELES, 90- *Personal Data:* b Harrodsburg, Ky, July 25, 19; m 42, Zivia Syrkin; c Eve Syrkin & Jonathan Syrkin. *Educ:* Harvard Univ, BS, 40; Univ Calif, Los Angeles, MA, 44, PhD, 53. *Prof Exp:* Asst prof meteorol, Mass Inst Technol, 53-58. *Concurrent Pos:* Fulbright grants, Univ Sorbonne, 49 & Hebrew Univ, Israel, 65; NATO sr fel, 62; consult, Atmospheric Sci Lab, White Sands Missile Range, 65-, Jet Propulsion Lab, 78- *Mem:* Fel Am Meteorol Soc; Am Geophysics Union. *Res:* Small- and medium-scale atmospheric motions; sound propagation; atmospheric-ocean interaction; remote sensing; air pollution. *Mailing Add:* Dept Atmospheric Sci Univ Calif Los Angeles CA 90095-1565. *Fax:* 310-206-5219; *E-Mail:* wartele@ucla.edu

**WURTH, MICHELLE JANETTE,** ORGANIC CHEMISTRY, PHOTOGRAPHY. *Current Pos:* ASSOC PROF CHEM, OKLAHOMA CITY UNIV, 68- *Personal Data:* b Highland Park, Ill, Mar 31, 37; c Elisa M & Davis M. *Educ:* Lake Forest Col, BA, 64; Northwestern Univ, Evanston, PhD(org chem), 69. *Mem:* Am Chem Soc. *Res:* Synthesis of new bicyclic heterocyclic compounds; photographic chemistry, especially emulsions and developing agents. *Mailing Add:* 2409 NW 17th St Oklahoma City OK 73107

**WURTH, THOMAS JOSEPH,** CHEMICAL ENGINEERING. *Current Pos:* res engr, Gulf Res & Develop Co, 63-66, sr proj engr, 66-69, planning specialist, Chem Dept, Develop Div, 69-71, dir planning, Develop Div, 71-75, mgr planning & bus analysis spec chem, 75-80, COORDR TECHNOL DEVELOP, SPEC CHEM, GULF OIL CHEM CO, 80- *Personal Data:* b St Louis, Mo, June 13, 28; m 58; c 3. *Educ:* Washington Univ, St Louis, BS, 52; Univ Mo, Kansas City, MBA, 67. *Prof Exp:* Develop engr, Mathieson Chem Corp, NY, 52-53, proj engr, Olin Mathieson Chem Corp, Ill, 53-55, pilot plant supvr, 55-59; process engr, R W Booker & Assoc, Mo, 59-61; process engr, Austin Co, Ill, 61-63. *Mem:* Am Asn Cost Engrs. *Res:* Process development of chemical processes; process design of chemical plants. *Mailing Add:* 5054 Bayou Vista Dr Houston TX 77091

**WURTMAN, JUDITH JOY,** OBESITY, PREMENSTRUAL SYNDROME. *Current Pos:* RES SCIENTIST, MASS INST TECHNOL, 74-, FEL, DEPT BRAIN & COGNITIVE SCI, 74- *Personal Data:* b Brooklyn, NY, Aug 4, 37; m 59; c 2. *Educ:* Wellesley Col, BA, 59; Harvard Univ, MAT, 60; George Washington Univ, PhD(cell biol), 71. *Prof Exp:* Asst prof biol & nutrit, Newton Col, 72-74. *Concurrent Pos:* Consult nutrit educ, Newton Pub Schs, 72-74; NIH fel, 74-76; instr, Radcliffe Seminars-Harvard Exten Courses, 76-; counselor, Obesity Clin, 81-; commentator, Boston TV Sta, 81- *Mem:* Soc Nutrit Educ; Am Dietetic Asn; Nutrit Today; Inst Food Technol; Sigma Xi. *Res:* Regulation of food intake in laboratory animal and human, especially in obesity and other eating disorders. *Mailing Add:* Dept Brain & Cognitive Sci Mass Inst Technol E-25-604 Cambridge MA 02139. *Fax:* 617-253-6882

**WURTMAN, RICHARD JAY,** NEUROSCIENCE, METABOLISM. *Current Pos:* assoc prof, Mass Inst Technol, 67-70, prof endocrinol & metab, 70-80, prof neuroendocrine regulation, 80-94, PROF NEUROPHARMACOL, WHITAKER COL, MASS INST TECHNOL, 84-, DIR, CLIN RES CTR, 85-, CECIL H GREEN DISTINGUISHED PROF, 94- *Personal Data:* b Philadelphia, Pa, Mar 9, 38; m 59, Judith Hirschhorn; c Rachael E & David F. *Educ:* Univ Pa, AB, 56; Harvard Med Sch, MD, 60. *Honors & Awards:* Am Therapeut Soc Prize, 66; Soc Biol Psychiat Prize, 66; John Jacob Abel Award, Am Soc Pharmacol Exp Therapeut, 68; Alvarenga Prize & lect, Col Physicians Philadelphia, 70; Ernst Oppenheimer Prize, Endocrine Soc, 73; Foster Elting Bennett lectr, Am Neurol Asn, 74; Louis B Flexner lectr, 75; Pfizer lectr, State Univ NY Buffalo, 80; Zale lectr, Univ Tex, 80; McCallum lectr, Univ Toronto, 81; Osborne & Mendel Award, 82; Ciba-Geigy Drew Award, 82; Rufus Cole lectr, Rockefeller Univ, 85; Merit Award, Nat Inst Ment Health, 89; Julius Axelrod Distinguished lectr neurosci, 90; Hans Linder Mem lectr, The Weizmann Inst, 93. *Prof Exp:* Intern & asst resident med, Mass Gen Hosp, 60-62; res assoc, Lab Clin Sci, NIMH, 62-64, med res officer, 65-67. *Concurrent Pos:* Josiah Macy, Jr Found fel, Mass Gen Hosp, 60-62; res fel endocrinol, Mass Gen Hosp, 64-65; clin assoc med, Mass Gen Hosp, 65-; vis lectr, Am Chem Soc, 66; lectr, Harvard Med Sch, 69-; mem, Preclin Psychopharmacol Study Sect, NIMH, 71-75; Am Inst Biol Sci Adv panel, Biosci Prog, NASA; res adv bd, Parkinson's Dis, Am Parkinson's Dis Asn, Tourette Syndrome Asn; assoc, Neurosci Res Prog; chmn, Life Sci Adv Comt, NASA, 79-; Sterling vis prof, Boston Univ, 81; invited prof, Univ Geneva, 81; chmn, Air Force Life Sci adv bd, 85-; co-founder & chmn sci adv bd, Interneuron Pharmaceut Inc, Lexington, Mass, 89- *Mem:* Am Physiol Soc; Am Soc Pharmacol & Exp Therapeut; Am Soc Neurochem; Am Soc Biol Chem; Am Soc Clin Invest. *Res:* Neuroendocrinology; neuropharmacology; biological rhythms; pineal gland; catecholamines; amino acid metabolism; effects of nutrition on brain; biological effects of light; acetylcholine; membrane phosphatides; melatonin; neurotransmitters. *Mailing Add:* Dept Brain & Cognitive Sci Mass Inst Technol E 25-604 Cambridge MA 02139. *Fax:* 617-253-6882; *E-Mail:* dick@mit.edu

**WURTZ, ROBERT HENRY,** NEUROPHYSIOLOGY, NEUROPSYCHOLOGY. *Current Pos:* res fel, Lab Neurophysiol, NIH, 65-66, res scientist, Lab Neurobiol, NIMH, 66-78, CHIEF, LAB SENSORIMOTOR RES, NAT EYE INST, NIH, 78- *Personal Data:* b St Louis, Mo, Mar 28, 36; m; c 2. *Educ:* Oberlin Col, AB, 58; Univ Mich, Ann Arbor, PhD(physiol psychol), 62. *Honors & Awards:* Gordon Holmes lectr, Europ Neurosci Soc, 85; James M Sprague lectr, Univ Pa, 86; W Alden Spencer Award, Columbia Univ, 87; George H Bishop lectr, Washington Univ, 88; Clinton N Woolsey lectr, 91; Karl Spencer Lasaley Award, 95; Jonas S Friedenward Award, 96. *Prof Exp:* Res assoc neurophysiol, Washington Univ, 62-65. *Mem:* Nat Acad Sci; Inst Med-Nat Acad Sci; Soc Neurosci (pres, 90-91); Asn Res Vision & Opthal; Am Physiol Soc; Am Acad Arts & Sci. *Res:* Neurophysiological basis of behavior, specifically the physiology of vision and movement. *Mailing Add:* Lab Sensorimotor Res Bldg 49 Rm 2A50 Nat Eye Inst Bethesda MD 20892-4435

**WURZBURG, OTTO BERNARD,** STARCH CARBOHYDRATE CHEMISTRY. *Current Pos:* CONSULT, 80- *Personal Data:* b Grand Rapids, Mich, Aug 1, 15; m 40, Charlotte Donohoe; c Anne (Nordstrom), Jane (Anderson), Gerardine, Gregory K, Otto B III & Robert J. *Educ:* Univ Mich, BS, 38, MS, 39. *Honors & Awards:* Alsberg Schock Mem Award, 86, Corn Refiners Asn, Inc & Am Asn Cereal Chemists, Inc. *Prof Exp:* Chemist & supvr cent control, Nat Starch Prod, Nat Starch & Chem Corp, 39-44, res chemist & supvr starch res, 45-55, assoc res dir, 56-68, vpres res, Starch Div, 68-73, sr vpres, 73-80. *Concurrent Pos:* Mem bd dirs, Customaize Inc, 74-; ed, Modified Starches: Properties & Uses, Food Regulatory. *Mem:* Am Chem Soc; Inst Food Technologists; Am Asn Cereal Chemists. *Res:* Starch; carbohydrates; industrial applications; author. *Mailing Add:* RFD 1 Box 138E St Johnsbury VT 05819-9801

**WUSKELL, JOSEPH P,** CHEMISTRY, PHARMACEUTICAL CHEMISTRY. *Current Pos:* RES ASSOC, UNIV CONN HEALTH CTR, 86- *Personal Data:* b New York, NY, Nov 14, 38. *Educ:* Univ Conn, BA, 60; Univ Minn, PhD(chem), 67. *Prof Exp:* Chemist, Merck Sharp & Dohme Res Labs, 60-62; sr chemist, Ott Chem Co, Corn Prod Co, 67-68; group leader, Quaker Oats Co, 68-83. *Mem:* Am Chem Soc; Royal Soc Chem. *Res:* Organic synthesis and reaction mechaisms. *Mailing Add:* 11 Lowell Rd West Hartford CT 06119

**WUSSOW, GEORGE C,** ORAL SURGERY, ORAL PATHOLOGY. *Current Pos:* RETIRED. *Personal Data:* b Milwaukee, Wis, Mar 10, 23; m 49; c 3. *Educ:* Marquette Univ, DDS, 49. *Prof Exp:* From instr to prof oral surg, Marquette Univ, 53-86, chmn dept, 61-67, lectr, Sch Dent Hyg, 70-86. *Concurrent Pos:* Attend oral surg, Vet Admin Ctr, Wood, Wis & mem consult staff, Milwaukee Co Gen Hosp, 57-; consult, Great Lakes Naval Hosp, 70-; mem adv bd, Milwaukee Area Tech Col, 70- *Mem:* Am Soc Oral Surg; Am Acad Oral Path; fel Am Col Dent; Int Asn Oral Surg; fel Royal Soc Health. *Res:* Clinical evaluation of proteolytic enzymes in the management of impacted mandibular third molars. *Mailing Add:* 521 Dodge St Kewaunee WI 54216

**WUST, CARL JOHN,** IMMUNOLOGY. *Current Pos:* assoc prof, 70-74, PROF MICROBIOL, UNIV TENN, KNOXVILLE, 74-, PROF MED BIOL, 83- *Personal Data:* b Providence, RI, July 2, 28; m 51; c 5. *Educ:* Providence Col, BS, 50; Brown Univ, MSc, 53; Ind Univ, PhD(microbiol), 57. *Prof Exp:* Electron microscopist, Ind Univ, 53-55; NIH fel, Yale Univ, 57-59; biochemist, Biol Div, Oak Ridge Nat Lab, 59-70. *Mem:* AAAS; Am Soc Microbiol; Am Asn Immunologists; Sigma Xi; Soc Exp Biol & Med. *Res:* Leukemia antigens/induced differentiation and induced cell growth; immunity to viral infections. *Mailing Add:* 132 Iroquois Rd Oak Ridge TN 37830-4934. *Fax:* 423-974-4007

**WUTHIER, ROY EDWARD,** BIOCHEMISTRY. *Current Pos:* PROF CHEM, COL ARTS & SCI & COORDR BIOCHEM, COL MED, UNIV SC, 75- *Personal Data:* b Rushville, Nebr, Nov 11, 32; m 56; c 2. *Educ:* Univ Wyo, BS, 54; Univ Wis, MS, 58, PhD, 60. *Honors & Awards:* Biol Mineralization Basic Res Award, Int Asn Dent Res, 82. *Prof Exp:* Asst biochem, Univ Wis, 55-60; res fel, Forsyth Dent Ctr, Harvard Med Sch, 60-63, asst mem staff & assoc biol chem, 63-69; assoc prof biochem, Depts Orthop Surg & Biochem, Col Med, Univ Vt, 69-75. *Concurrent Pos:* Chmn, Gordon Res Conf, Calcium Phosphates, 89. *Mem:* AAAS; Am Soc Biol Chem; Am Chem Soc; Am Soc Bone & Mineral Res; Int Asn Dent Res. *Res:* Mechanism of calcification; lipid and membrane involvement in calcification; role of matrix resicles in calcification; fatty acid metabolism in cartilage. *Mailing Add:* Dept Chem Phys Sci Ctr Univ SC Thomas Jones Bldg 424 Phys Sci Ctr Columbia SC 29208

**WUTHRICH, KURT,** NUCLEAR MAGNETIC RESONANCE SPECTROSCOPY. *Current Pos:* pvt lectr, 69-72, from asst prof to assoc prof, 72-80, PROF BIOPHYS, INST MOLECULAR BIOL & BIOPHYS, EIDGENOSSISCHE TECH HOCHSCHULE, 80-, CHMN BIOL DEPT, 95- *Personal Data:* b Aarberg, Switz, Oct 4, 38; m 63, Marianne Briner; c Bernhard & Karin. *Educ:* Univ Bern & Basel, Switz, dipl, 62, PhD(chem), 64. *Hon Degrees:* Dr, Univ Siena, Italy, 97. *Honors & Awards:* Baker Lectr, Cornell Univ, 83; S Rudin Lectr, Columbia Univ Med Sch, 84; P Bruylants Medal, Louvain Cath Univ, 86; James Shannon Lectr, Mass Gen Hosp, 89; Ada Doisy Lectr, Univ Ill, Urbana, 89; Stein & Moore Award, Protein Soc, 90; Louisa Gross Horwitz Prize, Columbia Univ, 91; John T Edsall Lectr, Harvard Univ, 91; Ira Remsen Mem Lectr, Johns Hopkins Univ, 91; Gilbert Newton Lewis Medal, Univ Calif, Berkeley, 91; Marcel Benoist Prize, Swiss Confederation, 92; William H Stein Mcm Lectr, Rockcfeller Univ, 93; Louis Jeantet Prize for Med, Louis Jeantet Found, Geneva, 93; Adam Neville Lectr,

Univ Dundee, 95; Kaj Linderstrom-Lang Award, Carlsberg Found, 96. *Prof Exp:* Fel, Univ Calif, Berkeley, 65-67; mem tech staff, Bell Tel Labs, Murray Hill, 67-69. *Concurrent Pos:* Mem, Swiss Comn Molecular Biol, 73-76, pres, 77-82; coun mem, secy gen & vpres, Int Union Pure & Appl Biophys, 75-90, mem, Comn Biophys Chem, 96-; lectr numerous univs & schs, 82-; pres, Biophys Sect, Swiss Soc Biochem, 85-88; vis Miller res prof, Univ Calif, Berkeley, 88; scholar in residence, Johns Hopkins Univ, Baltimore, 92; Fairchild distinguished scholar, Calif Inst Technol, Pasadena, 94, vis assoc biol & chem, 95; guest scientist, Scripps Res Inst, Calif, 94. *Mem:* Foreign assoc Nat Acad Sci; Europ Molecular Biol Orgn; foreign fel Indian Nat Sci Acad; hon fel Nat Acad Sci India; foreign hon mem Am Acad Arts & Sci; hon mem Japanese Biochem Soc. *Res:* Determination of the three-dimensional structure of biological macromolecules in solution, using primarily nuclear magnetic resonance spectroscopy; applications in drug design and protein engineering; author of numerous publications. *Mailing Add:* ETH-Honggerberg Inst Molecular Biol & Biophys Zurich CH-8093 Switzerland. *Fax:* 41-1-633-1153

**WUTHRICH, PAUL,** RESEARCH & DEVELOP MINIATURE MECHANICAL DEVICES & SUB-MINIATURE IMPLANT DEVICES. *Current Pos:* CONSULT, 96- *Personal Data:* b Ziefen, Switz, Feb 25, 31; US citizen; m 60, Irmgard Ann Garbe; c Christine & Marc. *Educ:* Univ New Haven BS, 70; Univ Conn, MS, 73. *Prof Exp:* Dir res & develop, Timex Corp, 56-87, staff scientist, 88-96. *Mem:* Optical Soc Am; Physics Soc Am; Instrument Soc Am. *Res:* Research and development watch movements from mechanical to electrical to solid state; director of design and development of 3D Nimslo camera; development of first micro miniature implant infusion and pulse monitor devices; granted 45 patents. *Mailing Add:* 760 Hamilton Ave Watertown CT 06795

**WUTS, PETER G M,** SYNTHETIC ORGANIC CHEMISTRY. *Current Pos:* at UPJOHN CO, 85- *Personal Data:* b Schiedamm, Holland, July 24, 50; US citizen; m 78; c 1. *Educ:* Univ Wash, BS, 73; Northwestern Univ, PhD(chem), 78. *Prof Exp:* Fel chem, Calif Inst Technol, 78-80; asst prof chem, Univ Mich, 80-85. *Concurrent Pos:* NIH fel, 80. *Mem:* Am Chem Soc. *Res:* Development of methodology and process development for drug candidates. *Mailing Add:* UpJohn Co 1500-91-2 Kalamazoo MI 49001. *Fax:* 616-329-9158

**WUTSCHER, HEINZ KONRAD,** CITRUS ROOTSTOCKS, CITRUS NUTRITION. *Current Pos:* RES HORTICULTURIST, AGR RES SERV, USDA, 67- *Personal Data:* b Selztal, Austria, Dec 23, 30; US citizen; m 64, Doris Asako Tanaka; c Heidi & Ralph. *Educ:* Univ Hawaii, Manoa, BSc, 63; Cornell Univ PhD(pomol), 67. *Honors & Awards:* Gold Medal for Genetic Improvement, Fruit Breeding Sect, Am Soc Hort Sci, 97. *Concurrent Pos:* Chmn, Citrus Crops Working Group, Am Soc Hort Sci, 77-80; adj prof fruit crops, Hort Dept, Univ Fla, Gainsville, 87- *Mem:* Fel Am Soc Hort Sci; Int Soc Citricult. *Res:* Development of new citrus rootstocks; investigation of the cause of citrus blight; effects of fertilization regimes on nitrate levels in groundwater; general citrus nutrition problems. *Mailing Add:* US Hort Res Lab 2120 Camden Rd Orlando FL 32803. *Fax:* 407-897-7309

**WUU, TING-CHI,** BIOCHEMISTRY. *Current Pos:* asst prof, 69-74, ASSOC PROF BIOCHEM, MED COL OHIO, 75- *Personal Data:* b Salt Co, China, Sept 27, 34; US citizen; m 62; c 3. *Educ:* Nat Taiwan Univ, BSc, 58, MSc, 60; McGill Univ, PhD(biochem), 67. *Prof Exp:* Prof asst biochem res, McGill Univ, 67-69. *Mem:* AAAS. *Res:* Structure and function of peptides and proteins; brain, peptides and proteins; isolation and characterization of hormone-binding proteins of neurohypophysis; biological, chemical and physical properties of neurophysins and neurosecretory granules; biosynthesis of brain peptides and proteins. *Mailing Add:* Dept Biochem & Molecular Biol Med Col Ohio PO Box 10008 Toledo OH 43699-0008

**WU-WONG, JINSHYUN RUTH,** PROTEIN CHEMISTRY. *Current Pos:* sr res scientist, 88-91, RES INVESTR, ABBOTT LABS, 91- *Personal Data:* b Hong Kong; US citizen. *Educ:* Nat Taiwan Univ, Repub of China, BSc, 77; Ohio State Univ, PhD(biochem), 81. *Prof Exp:* Res assoc, Ohio State Univ, 81 & Chinese Univ, Hong Kong, 82-85; res fel, Univ Tex Med Sch, 85-88. *Concurrent Pos:* Travel fel, Int Union Biochem, 85. *Mcm:* Am Soc Biochem & Molecular Biol; Biochem Soc UK; AAAS. *Res:* Characterization and purification of endothelin converting enzymecs from tissues/cells; endothelin receptor; ligand interaction. *Mailing Add:* Pharmaceut Prod Div D47V AP9 Abbott Labs Abbott Park IL 60064-3500

**WYANT, GORDON MICHAEL,** ANESTHESIOLOGY. *Current Pos:* prof, 54-71, EMER PROF ANESTHESIA, UNIV SASK, 71- *Personal Data:* b Frankfurt, Ger, Mar 28, 14; c 5. *Educ:* Univ Bologna, MD, 38; Royal Col Physicians & Surgeons Eng, dipl, 45; Am Bd Anesthesiol, dipl, 53; Royal Col Physicians & Surgeons Can, dipl anesthesiol, 52, FRCP(C), 63. *Honors & Awards:* Gold Medal, Can Anesthesiol Soc. *Prof Exp:* Asst prof anesthesia, Col Med, Univ Ill, 50-53; asst prof surg & head, Div Anesthesia, Stritch Sch Med, Loyola Univ, Ill, 53-54. *Mem:* Am Soc Anesthesiol; fel Am Geriat Soc; fel Am Col Anesthesiol; Can Anaesthetists Soc. *Res:* Related clinical and basic sciences of anesthesia; principle management. *Mailing Add:* No 11 Rockwood Terr 6000 St Anns Dr Rural Rt 5 Duncan BC V9L 5T1 Can

**WYANT, JAMES CLAIR,** OPTICS. *Current Pos:* from asst prof to assoc prof, 74-79, PROF, OPTICAL SCI CTR, UNIV ARIZ, 79-; PRES, WYKO CORP, 84- *Personal Data:* b Morenci, Mich, July 31, 43; m 71, Louise Doherty; c Clair F. *Educ:* Case Inst Technol, BS, 65; Univ Rochester, MS, 67, PhD(optics), 68. *Honors & Awards:* Gov Award, Soc Photo Optical Instrumentation Engrs, 79; Technol Achievement Award, Int Soc Optical

Eng, 88; Joseph Fraunhofer Award, Optical Soc Am, 92; R & D 100 Award, 93. *Prof Exp:* Optical engr & head, Optical Eng Sect, Itek Corp, 68-74. *Concurrent Pos:* Assoc ed, J Optical Soc Am & Optical Eng, 76-84; bd gov, Soc Photo-Optical Instrumentation Engrs, 78-84; mem, Int Comn Optics, US Nat Comt, Am Inst Physics; mem bd dir, Optical Soc Am, 79-81, mem exec comt, 80-81; vis prof, Univ Rochester, 83; assoc ed, Appl Optics, 83; chmn, Gordon Conf on Holography & Optical Info Processing, 84. *Mem:* Fel Optical Soc Am; fel Soc Photo-Optical Instrumentation Engrs (pres, 86). *Res:* Interferometry; holography; optical testing; optical processing; optical properties of the atmosphere; active optics; application of microcomputer to optics; author of more than 100 publications. *Mailing Add:* Optical Sci Ctr Univ Ariz Tucson AZ 85721. *Fax:* 520-294-1799; *E-Mail:* jcwyant@ccit.arizona.edu

**WYATT, BENJAMIN WOODROW,** CHEMISTRY. *Current Pos:* RETIRED. *Personal Data:* b Farrar, Ga, Dec 24, 16; m 48; c 4. *Educ:* Southwestern Univ, Tex, BS, 37; Univ Tex, MA, 40, PhD(org chem), 43. *Prof Exp:* Tutor chem, Univ Tex, 38-43; assoc mem & asst to patent agent, Sterling-Winthrop Res Inst, 43-50, patent agent, 50-61, from asst dir to assoc dir, 61-74, dir, Patent Div, 74-78, vpres patents, 78-87. *Mem:* Am Chem Soc. *Res:* Organic chemistry. *Mailing Add:* 317 Loudonville Rd Loudonville NY 12211

**WYATT, COLEN CHARLES,** PLANT BREEDING. *Current Pos:* PLANT BREEDER, PETO SEED CO, 72-, SR PLANT BREEDER. *Personal Data:* b Geneva, NY, Dec 10, 27; m 48, Virginia Steinel; c Vicki, Stephen, Bonnie, Jane & Christine. *Educ:* Cornell Univ, BS, 53. *Prof Exp:* Sr res horticulturist, H J Heinz Co, 54-64; univ horticulturist & asst dir maintenance, Bowling Green State Univ, 65-66; plant breeder, Libby McNeill & Libby, Ohio, 67-72. *Res:* Breeding processing and fresh market tomatoes for worldwide production, including the development of disease resistance for tobacco mosaic virus, spotted wilt virus, nematodes bacterial wilt and other major diseases; breeding squash for high vitamin content and disease resistance. *Mailing Add:* 844 Princeton Ct Woodland CA 95695. *Fax:* 530-668-0219

**WYATT, ELLIS JUNIOR,** PARASITOLOGY, INVERTEBRATE ZOOLOGY. *Current Pos:* from asst prof to assoc prof, Hamline Univ, 71-77, chmn dept, 72-82, prof biol, 77-, EMER PROF BIOL, HAMLINE UNIV. *Personal Data:* b Norton, Kans, Oct 30, 30; m 53; c 3. *Educ:* Lewis & Clark Col, BS, 57; Ore State Univ, MS, 61, PhD(zool), 71. *Prof Exp:* Aquatic biologist, Ore State Fish Comn, 57, 58-60 & 61; asst prof biol, Cent Ore Col, 61-65 & 67-68; aquatic biologist, Ore State Fish Comn, 68-71. *Concurrent Pos:* Lab teaching asst, Ore State Univ, 57. *Mem:* AAAS; Am Soc Parasitologists; Am Soc Zoologists; Am Fisheries Soc. *Res:* Parasitic protozoa of fresh water fishes; bacteriology, helminthology, mycology, therapeutics and toxicology of fresh water fishes; ecology of fish parasitism. *Mailing Add:* 801 Meadowood Dr Woodbury MN 55125

**WYATT, GERARD ROBERT,** INSECT BIOCHEMISTRY, MOLECULAR BIOLOGY. *Current Pos:* head dept, 73-75, prof biol, 73-94, EMER PROF BIOL, QUEENS UNIV, ONT, KINGSTON, 96- *Personal Data:* b Palo Alto, Calif, Sept 3, 25; m 51, 85, Mary E Rogers; c Eve (Morton), Graham (Strickland) & Diana (Silver). *Educ:* Univ BC, BA, 45; Cambridge Univ, PhD(natural sci), 50. *Prof Exp:* Sci officer, Insect Path Res Inst, Can Dept Agr, Ont, 50-54; asst prof biochem, Yale Univ, 54-60, from assoc prof to prof biol, 60-73. *Concurrent Pos:* Guggenheim Mem fel, 54; Killam res fel, 85; sci dir, insect biotech can, 90-94. *Mem:* Am Soc Biochem & Molecular Biol; fel Royal Soc Can; Entom Soc Am. *Res:* Composition of nucleic acids; biochemistry and physiology of insects; composition of insect hemolymph; carbohydrate metabolism and regulation; physiology of development; actions of insect hormones; insect vitellogenins; insect molecular biology; juvenile hormone. *Mailing Add:* Dept Biol Queen's Univ Kingston ON K7L 3N6 Can. *Fax:* 613-545-6617; *E-Mail:* wyaltg@biology.queensu.ca

**WYATT, JAMES L(UTHER),** METALLURGICAL ENGINEERING. *Current Pos:* PRES & OWNER, AMBASSADOR INDUSTS INC, 72- *Personal Data:* b Williamsburg, Ky, May 13, 24; m 46; c 2. *Educ:* Univ Ky, BS, 47, MS, 48; Mass Inst Technol, ScD(metall), 53. *Prof Exp:* Instr metall, Univ Ky, 47-48; proj engr, Titanium Div, Nat Lead Co, 48-50; head, Dept Metall Eng, Horizons, Inc, 53-57; consult & assoc, Booz-Allen & Hamilton, 57-61; vpres prog develop, Armour Res Found, 61-63; vpres new prod develop, Joy Mfg Co, Pa, 63-67; vpres corp develop, Nat Gypsum Co, NY, 67-69; Max Factor & Co, Calif, 69-71; pres, Wyatt & Co, 71-72. *Concurrent Pos:* US rep, World Metall Cong Steelmaking, 51. *Mem:* Am Inst Mining, Metall & Petrol Engrs; Am Soc Metals; Marine Technol Soc. *Res:* Extractive and physical metallurgy of titanium, zinc, zirconium, uranium; development of heavy industrial machinery; mining and construction; chemical engineering. *Mailing Add:* 510 NE Golden Harbour Dr Boca Raton FL 33432

**WYATT, JEFFREY RENNER,** ANALYTICAL CHEMISTRY. *Current Pos:* Nat Res Coun res fel, 72-73, RES CHEMIST, NAVAL RES LAB, 73- *Personal Data:* b Hampton, Va, Jan 1, 46; m 69; c 3. *Educ:* Univ Calif, Riverside, AB, 67; Northwestern Univ, Evanston, PhD(chem), 71. *Prof Exp:* Teaching assoc chem, Univ Kans, 71-72. *Mem:* Am Chem Soc; Am Soc Mass Spectrometry. *Res:* Mass spectrometry; chemical dynamics; trace analysis. *Mailing Add:* Naval Res Lab Code 6110 Washington DC 20375-5342

**WYATT, PHILIP JOSEPH,** LIGHT SCATTERING, ELECTROOPTICAL INSTRUMENTS. *Current Pos:* PRES & CHMN, WYATT TECHNOL CORP, 82- *Personal Data:* b Los Angeles, Calif, Apr 16, 32; div; c Geofrey, Monica & Clifford. *Educ:* Univ Chicago, BA, 52, BS, 54; Univ Ill, MS, 56; Fla State Univ, PhD, 59. *Prof Exp:* Staff mem, Los Alamos Sci Lab, 59; prin scientist, Aeronutronic Div, Ford Motor Co, 59-62; dir adv planning, Plasmadyne Corp, 62-63; mem tech staff, DRC Inc, 63-66; sr sci specialist, EG&G, Inc, 66-68; pres & chmn, Sci Spectrum, Inc, 68-82. *Concurrent Pos:* Vis lectr physics, Univ Calif, Santa Barbara, 81-82. *Mem:* Fel Am Phys Soc; fel Optical Soc Am; Am Soc Microbiol; Sigma Xi; Am Chem Soc. *Res:* Light scattering studies of microparticles; development of new assays and identification techniques using resonance light scattering; quality control for beverages and foods using electrooptical techniques; development of light scattering instrumentation; characterization of macromolecules using light scattering techniques. *Mailing Add:* Wyatt Tech Corp PO Box 3003 Santa Barbara CA 93130-3003. *Fax:* 805-965-4898; *E-Mail:* pwyatt@wyatt.com

**WYATT, RAYMOND L,** PLANT MORPHOLOGY, PLANT TAXONOMY. *Current Pos:* from asst prof to assoc prof, 56-75, lectr, NSF Insts Sci Teachers, 59-60, PROF BIOL, WAKE FOREST UNIV, 75- *Personal Data:* b Salisbury, NC, Nov 23, 26; m 52; c 1. *Educ:* Wake Forest Col, BS, 48; Univ NC, MA, 54, PhD, 56. *Prof Exp:* Instr biol, Mars Hill Col, 48-52 & Univ NC, 55-56. *Mem:* AAAS. *Res:* Embryology of Asarum; floral morphology and phylogeny of Aristolochiaceae and Annonaceae; survival of American chestnut in North Carolina. *Mailing Add:* Dept Biol Wake Forest Univ Box 7325 Reynolda Sta Winston-Salem NC 27109

**WYATT, RICHARD JED,** PSYCHOPHARMACOLOGY. *Current Pos:* clin assoc, Lab Clin Psychobiol, NIMH Neurosci Ctr, 67-69, res psychiatrist, Lab Clin Psychopharmacol, 67-69, dir, Div Spec Ment Health Res, 77-87, assoc dir intramural res, 77-87, CHIEF NEUROPSYCHIAT BR, NIMH NEUROSCI CTR, 77- *Personal Data:* b Los Angeles, Calif, June 5, 39. *Educ:* Johns Hopkins Univ, BA, 61, MD, 64; Am Bd Psychiat & Neurol, dipl, 71. *Hon Degrees:* Dr, Univ Centrale Venezuela, 77. *Honors & Awards:* Harry Solomon Res Award, Mass Ment Health Ctr, Boston, 68; A E Bennett Award Clin Psychiat Res, Soc Biol Psychiat, 71; Psychopharmacol Award, Am Psychol Asn, 71; Stanley R Dean Res Award, Am Col Psychiatrists, 82; Daniel Efron Award, Am Col Neuropsychopharmacol, 83; Arthur P Noyes Award Schizophrenia Res, 86. *Prof Exp:* Intern pediat, Western Res Univ Hosp, 64-65; resident psychiat, Mass Ment Health Ctr, Boston, 65-67. *Concurrent Pos:* Teaching asst, Harvard Univ, 65-67; consult, Sch Syst, Falls Church, Va, 69-70, Head Start, Washington, DC, 70-72 & Chestnut Lodge Hosp, 84-; instr, Found Advan Educ Sci, NIH & Washington Sch Psychiat, 71-; assoc prof psychiat, Med Ctr, Stanford Univ, 73-74; clin prof, Med Ctr, Duke Univ, 75-; adj prof psychiat, Uniformed Servs Univ Sch Med, 80-; ed, Foundations of Modern Psychiat, 82- & Psychiat Briefs, 85-; assoc ed, Psychiat, 85-, Am J Psychiat, 88- & Schizophrenia Bull, 88-; vis prof psychiat, Columbia Univ, 87- *Mem:* Fel Am Psychiat Asn; Soc Psychophysiol Study Sleep; Psychiat Res Soc; Soc Biol Psychiat; fel Am Col Neuropsychopharmacol; Am Asn Geriat Psychiat; Asn Clin Psychosocial Res; Int Psychogeriat Asn; Soc Neurosci. *Res:* Etiology and treatment of major psychiatric disorders; neural plasticity; sleep and memory; author of numerous scientific publications. *Mailing Add:* NIMH Neurosci Ctr WAW Build St Elizabeth Hosp Rm 536 Bethesda MD 20032

**WYATT, ROBERT EDWARD,** POPULATION BIOLOGY, PLANT SYSTEMATICS. *Current Pos:* from asst prof to prof bot, 79-93, PROF ECOL, UNIV GA, 93- *Personal Data:* b Charleston, SC, July 15, 50; m 78; c 1. *Educ:* Univ NC, AB, 72; Duke Univ, PhD(bot), 77. *Honors & Awards:* George R Cooley Award, Am Soc Plant Taxonomists, 87. *Prof Exp:* Asst prof biol, Tex A&M Univ, 77-79. *Concurrent Pos:* Vis asst prof biol, Univ Va, 80; mem bd sci adv, Highlands Biol Sta, Highlands, NC; prin investr on grants, Nat Sci Foun & Whitehall Found; Sarah Moss fel, Guggenheim fel. *Mem:* Am Soc Plant Taxonomists; Bot Soc Am; Soc Study Evolution; Ecol Soc Am; Am Soc Naturalists; Am Bryological & Lichenological Soc; Sigma Xi. *Res:* Reproductive biology of plants, especially Asclepias, Arenaria, and Aesculus; population dynamics, breeding systems, pollination and fruit-set; plant biosystematics and evolutionary ecology; population ecology of bryophytes. *Mailing Add:* Bot-Dept Bot Univ Ga Athens GA 30602. *Fax:* 706-542-1805; *E-Mail:* wyatt@dogwood.botany.uga.edu

**WYATT, ROBERT EUGENE,** THEORETICAL CHEMISTRY. *Current Pos:* from asst prof to assoc prof, 67-76, PROF CHEM, UNIV TEX, AUSTIN, 76- *Personal Data:* b Chicago, Ill, Nov 11, 38; m 64; c 1. *Educ:* Ill Inst Technol, 61; Johns Hopkins Univ, MA, 63, PhD(chem), 65. *Honors & Awards:* Prize Medal, Int Acad Quantum Molecular Sci, 80. *Prof Exp:* NSF fel chem, Keele Univ, 65-66 & Harvard Univ, 66-67. *Mem:* AAAS; Am Chem Soc; Am Phys Soc. *Res:* Scattering theory; theoretical chemical dynamics; molecular multiphoton processes. *Mailing Add:* Dept Chem Univ Tex Austin TX 78712-1104. *Fax:* 512-471-8696

**WYATT, ROGER DALE,** MICROBIOLOGY, POULTRY SCIENCE. *Current Pos:* Asst prof, 74-77, ASSOC PROF, DEPT POULTRY SCI, UNIV GA, 77- *Personal Data:* b Albemarle, NC, Apr 16, 48; m 68; c 2. *Educ:* NC State Univ, BS, 70, MS, 72, PhD(microbiol), 74. *Mem:* Poultry Sci Asn; Am Soc Microbiol. *Res:* Biological effects of dietary mycotoxins on poultry and evaluation of antifungal compounds for use in grain and poultry feeds. *Mailing Add:* 195 Edgewood Dr Athens GA 30606

**WYATT, STEPHEN WILSON,** CANCER PREVENTION. *Current Pos:* dep chief, Cancer Prev & Control, Ctr Dis Control, 89-90, chief, 90-91, actg dir, 91-92, dir, 92-94, actg dep dir, 94-95, DIR, DIV CANCER PREV & CONTROL, NAT CTR CHRONIC DIS PREV & HEALTH PROM, CTR DIS CONTROL & PREV, 95- *Personal Data:* b Mayfield, Ky, Aug, 1955; m; c Stephanie. *Educ:* Univ Ky, DMD, 80; Univ Ala, Birmingham, MPH, 85; Univ Ill, MPH, 86. *Honors & Awards:* Pres Citation, Am Acad Dermat, 95. *Prof Exp:* Staff, USPHS, 80-85, consult, 85-86, dep chief, 86-87, consult, 86-88, chief, 87-88, dir, 88-89. *Mem:* Am Pub Health Asn. *Mailing Add:* Ctr Dis Control & Prev 1600 Clifton Rd NE MS K-52 Atlanta GA 30341-3724

**WYBAN, JAMES A,** AQUACULTURE PRODUCTION TECHNOLOGY, INDUSTRY DEVELOPMENT. *Current Pos:* PRIN INVESTR, US MARINE SHRIMP FARMING PROG, 85- & MARINE INSTRUMENTATION PROG, 87- *Personal Data:* b Cleveland, Ohio, Jan 23, 51; m 80; c 2. *Educ:* Northwestern Univ, BS, 73; Univ Hawaii, PhD(zool), 81. *Prof Exp:* Res assoc, Inst Cancer Res & fel, Marine Biol Lab, 78; res asst, Hawaii Inst Marine Biol, 76-81; pres-owner, Northshore Fish & Produce, 81-85; co-mgr, US Aid Coop Res Prog & prin investr, Hawaii Shrimp Prog, 84-85. *Concurrent Pos:* Adj prof, Dept Animal Sci, Univ Hawaii, 87- *Mem:* Am Soc Zool; Fedn Am Scientists; Nat Wildlife Fedn; World Aquaculture Soc. *Res:* Marine shrimp production technology for US commercial application combining economic evaluation, system design and biological performance targeting economic optimization. *Mailing Add:* 487 Half Pile Loop Keaaw HI 96749

**WYCH, ROBERT DALE,** SEED PRODUCTION, AGRONOMY. *Current Pos:* res agronomist, Pioneer Hi-Bred Int Inc, 82-86, prod res mgr, 86-91, Parent Seed Dir, 91-93, PARENT TEST MGR, PIONEER HI-BRED INT INC, 93- *Personal Data:* b Kingsley, Iowa, Mar 3, 48; m 71, Elizabeth Sisson; c Heidi & Aaron. *Educ:* Iowa State Univ, BS, 70; Univ Calif, Davis, MS, 74, PhD(plant physiol), 77. *Prof Exp:* Asst prof small grain physiol, Dept Agron & Plant Genetics, Univ Minn, 77-82. *Concurrent Pos:* Assoc ed, J Prod Agr, 88-90. *Mem:* Am Soc Agron; Crop Sci Soc Am; Plant Growth Regulation Soc Am; Weed Sci Soc Am. *Res:* Influence of genotype and environment on seed corn production; factors affecting corn seed germination. *Mailing Add:* 5220 NW 70th Pl Johnston IA 50131. *Fax:* 515-253-2125; *E-Mail:* wychb@phibred.com

**WYCKOFF, DELAPHINE GRACE ROSA,** MICROBIOLOGY, BACTERIOLOGY. *Current Pos:* from instr to assoc prof bact & bot, 38-57, prof bact, 57-72, EMER PROF BACT, WELLESLEY COL, 72- *Personal Data:* b Beloit, Wis, Sept 11, 06; m 42, John F. *Educ:* Univ Wis, PhB, 27, PhM, 28, PhD(bact), 38. *Prof Exp:* From instr to asst prof bact, NDak Agr Col, 28-37. *Concurrent Pos:* Consult, Traveling Sci Teachers Prog, Oak Ridge Inst Nuclear Studies & Biol Sci Curric Study, Am Inst Biol Sci. *Mem:* Fel AAAS; Am Soc Microbiol; Am Acad Microbiol; Sigma Xi. *Res:* Physiological variation; induced mutations in actinomycetes; bactericidal agents; antibiotics from actinomycetes; biochemical activities of yeasts; marine halophilic bacteria; soil microbiology. *Mailing Add:* 78 Cedar St Newington CT 06111

**WYCKOFF, HAROLD ORVILLE,** physics, for more information see previous edition

**WYCKOFF, HAROLD WINFIELD,** MOLECULAR BIOPHYSICS. *Current Pos:* ASSOC PROF MOLECULAR BIOPHYS, YALE UNIV, 63- *Personal Data:* b Niagara Falls, NY, Dec 3, 26; m 55; c 3. *Educ:* Antioch Col, BS, 49; Mass Inst Technol, PhD(biophys), 55. *Prof Exp:* Res assoc biol, Mass Inst Technol, 55; NIH fel, Cambridge Univ, 56; res physicist, Am Viscose Corp, Pa, 57-63. *Mem:* Am Crystallog Asn; Biophys Soc. *Res:* Structure and function of biological macromolecules, especially enzymes, as determined by x-ray diffraction analysis. *Mailing Add:* Dept Molecular Biophys & Biochem Yale Univ 260 Whitney Ave New Haven CT 06520-8114

**WYCKOFF, JAMES M,** NUCLEAR PHYSICS. *Current Pos:* RETIRED. *Personal Data:* b Niagara Falls, NY, July 3, 24; m 47, 68; c 5. *Educ:* Antioch Col, BS, 48; Univ Rochester, MS, 52. *Honors & Awards:* Metcalf Award, Fed Lab Consortium Technol Transfer, 82; Presidents Award, Technol Transfer Soc, 84. *Prof Exp:* Electronics technician, Airborne Instruments Lab, 46-47; asst physics, Antioch Col, 47-48; res asst, Univ Rochester, 48-51; physicist, Nat Bur Stand, 51-67; health physicist, Stanford Linear Accelerator Ctr, 67-68; physicist, Nat Bur Stand, 68-71, coordr, Radiation Safety Prog, 71-76, liaison, State & Local Govt Affairs, 76- *Concurrent Pos:* Mem comt 22, Nat Coun Radiation Protection & Measurement, 66-72, mem off telecommun policy side effects subcomt, 72-75; mem, Interagency Comt Fed Guid Occup Exposures to Ionizing Radiation, 74-75; rep, Nat Conf State Legislatures' Model Interstate Tech Info Clearinghouse, 76-; exec secy comt, Fed Labs Off Sci & Technol Policy, 76-77; rep, Fed Lab Consortium Technol Transfer, 77- *Mem:* Am Phys Soc; Sigma Xi; Fedn Am Scientists; Technol Transfer Soc (vpres, 83-). *Res:* Detection of high energy x-rays; measurement of attenuation coefficients; induced radioactivity and development of on-line computer system; application of measurements to safe and effective use of x-rays; radioactivity, ultraviolet light, lasers, electromagnetic and ultrasonic radiation sources; development of measurement systems adequate to the protection of those near such radiation sources; review of mechanisms of technology transfer. *Mailing Add:* 24300 Hanson Ct Gaithersburg MD 20882

**WYCKOFF, RALPH WALTER GRAYSTONE,** physical chemistry, biophysics; deceased, see previous edition for last biography

**WYCKOFF, SUSAN,** ASTRONOMY. *Current Pos:* assoc prof, 79-82, PROF PHYSICS, ARIZ STATE UNIV, 82- *Personal Data:* b Santa Cruz, Calif, Mar 18, 41; m 67. *Educ:* Mt Holyoke Col, AB, 62; Case Western Reserve, PhD(astrophys), 67. *Honors & Awards:* Shapley lectr, Am Astron Soc, 85. *Prof Exp:* Post doctoral fel, Univ Mich, 67-68; asst prof physics, Albion Col, 68-70; res assoc astron, Univ Kans, 70-72; Smithsonian res fel, Wise Observ, Tel Aviv Univ, 72-75; prin res fel, Royal Greenwich Observ, 75-78 & 83; vis prof, Dept Astron, Ohio State Univ, 78-79. *Concurrent Pos:* Hon lectr, Women Astron, Smith Col, 78; vis prof, Univ Heidelberg, 80; Millan scholar, Denison Univ, 82; mem, comt comet spectroscopy, Int Astron Union, coun, Am Astron Soc, 85-; discipline specialist spectroscopy & spectrophotometry, Int Halley Watch, NASA, 82-, Space Telescope Working Group Key Projs,

Extra Galactic Astron, 84-88; chmn, Comt Status Women, Am Astron Soc, 84-85; space sci adv comt, Nat Acad Sci, 86-87; adv comt, NSF, 90. *Mem:* Int Astron Union; Royal Astron Soc. *Res:* Cool stars, comets and supernovae; normal and active galaxies; quasars and cosmology. *Mailing Add:* Dept Physics Ariz State Univ Tempe AZ 85287

**WYCOFF, SAMUEL JOHN,** public health, dentistry, for more information see previous edition

**WYDEVEN, THEODORE,** PHYSICAL CHEMISTRY. *Current Pos:* RES SCIENTIST ENVIRON CONTROL SYSTS, NASA AMES RES CTR, 64- *Personal Data:* b Wausau, Wis, Jan 18, 36; m 63; c 2. *Educ:* Marquette Univ, BS, 58; Univ Wash, PhD(phys chem), 64. *Mem:* Am Chem Soc. *Res:* Advanced environmental control systems for purifying water, recycling oxygen and controlling atmospheric trace contaminants; development of plasma polymerized thin film technology. *Mailing Add:* 1130 Revere Dr Sunnyvale CA 94087-2259

**WYETH, NEWELL CONVERS,** PHYSICS. *Current Pos:* SR SCIENTIST, SCI APPLN INT CORP, 79- *Personal Data:* b Wilmington, Del, Oct 13, 46; m 72; c 2. *Educ:* Princeton Univ, AB, 67; Univ Calif, Berkeley, PhD(physics), 74. *Prof Exp:* Physicist appl physics, Eng Physics Lab, E I du Pont de Nemours & Co, 68-69; assoc scientist solid state physics, Inst Energy Conversion, Univ Del, 74-79. *Mem:* Am Phys Soc; AAAS; Math Asn Am. *Res:* Underwater acoustics; biomembrane modeling. *Mailing Add:* Sci Appln Int Corp PO Box 1303 1710 Goodridge Dr McLean VA 22102. *Fax:* 703-893-8753

**WYGANT, J(AMES) F(REDERIC),** CERAMIC ENGINEERING, PETROLEUM TECHNOLOGY. *Current Pos:* RETIRED. *Personal Data:* b Hornell, NY, Aug 4, 19; m 44, Carol Walker; c 7. *Educ:* Alfred Univ, BS, 41, MS, 48; Mass Inst Technol, ScD(ceramics), 50. *Honors & Awards:* Purdy Award, Am Ceramic Soc, 52; Pace Award, Inst Ceramic Engrs, 59. *Prof Exp:* Chemist, Mo Portland Cement Co, 41-43; proj engr, Eng Res Dept, Stand Oil Co, Ind, 50-55, sect head res & develop dept, Am Oil Co, 55-62, asst dir res dept, 62-68, dir, Eng & Explor Res, Res & Develop Dept, 68-71, dir prod & explor res, 71-73; dir corp res, Stand Oil Co, Ind, 73-75, mgr corp serv, 75-79. *Concurrent Pos:* Consult, 79- *Mem:* Fel Am Ceramic Soc; Inst Ceramic Engrs. *Res:* Non-petroleum energy resources and processing; process industry refractories and insulations; industrial research evaluation and management; fireproofing; organic materials of construction; cements and concretes; corrosion protection; carbon; petroleum processing; advanced energy resources; alternative fossil fuels. *Mailing Add:* 1306 Francisco Dr Tallahassee FL 32304

**WYGNANSKI, ISRAEL JERZY,** TURBULENCE. *Current Pos:* PROF FLUID DYNAMICS, TEL-AVIV UNIV, 72- & AEROSPACE ENG, UNIV ARIZ, 85- *Personal Data:* b Warsaw, Poland, June 3, 35; US citizen; m 62; c 2. *Educ:* McGill Univ, Montreal, BEng, 61, MEng, 62, PhD(aerodyn), 64. *Prof Exp:* Asst prof heat transfer, Univ BC, 64-65; sr res scientist, Boeing Sci Res Labs, 65-72. *Concurrent Pos:* Consult, Israel Aircraft Industs, 72-76; chmn, Eng Dept, Tel-Aviv Univ, 72-76, dean fac eng, 77-80; vis prof, Univ Southern Calif, 76-77 & Univ Ariz, 81-83; fel, Inst Advan Study, Berlin, Ger, 90-91. *Mem:* Nat Acad Eng; fel Am Phys Soc; Am Inst Aeronaut & Astronaut. *Res:* Low speed aerodynamics, high life devices, delay of flow separation and drag reduction; turbulent shear flow control and enhancement of mixing. *Mailing Add:* Dept Aerospace & Mech Eng Univ Ariz Tucson AZ 85721

**WYKES, ARTHUR ALBERT,** BIOCHEMICAL PHARMACOLOGY & TOXICOLOGY. *Current Pos:* SR PHARMACOLOGIST & SR DRUG & TOXICOL INFO EXPERT, NAT LIBR MED, NIH, 68- *Personal Data:* b Boston, Mass, May 21, 23; m 56, Mary A Maushak; c Pamela S & Paul A. *Educ:* Univ Ill, BS, 45; Univ Wis, MS, 49; Purdue Univ, PhD(pharmaceut chem, pharmacol, biochem), 57. *Prof Exp:* Res asst biochem, Res Div, Armour & Co, 45-46; res asst biochem, Univ Wis, 47-49; teaching asst pharmaceut chem, Purdue Univ, 49-51; res biochemist, Armour & Co, 51-52; res biochemist, Res Div, Int Minerals & Chem Corp, 52-53; res biochemist, Res Dept, Baxter Labs, Inc, 53-55; teaching asst pharmaceut chem, Purdue Univ, 55-57; sr res biochem pharmacologist, Chem Pharmacol Sect, Abbott Labs, 57-61; chief & supvry res pharmacologist, Chem Pharmacol Sect, USAF Sch Aerospace Med, 61-67; sr pharmacologist, Chem & Life Sci Labs, Res Triangle Inst, 67-68. *Concurrent Pos:* Assoc clin prof pharmacol, Div Pharmacol & Physiol, Med Ctr, Duke Univ, 67-69; vis assoc prof pharmacol, Milton S Hershey Med Ctr, 71-77; consult, Int Life Sci Inst, 84-86. *Mem:* Am Chem Soc; Soc Toxicol; Drug Info Asn; Am Soc Pharmacol & Exp Therapeut; Asn Govt Toxicologists (pres, 92-93); Sigma Xi. *Res:* Drug and toxic agent effects on biological, enzyme and metabolic systems at cellular and subcellular levels, especially as influenced by environmental agents, nutritional factors, other drugs and toxic chemicals; drug interactions; neurochemistry; basic pharmacology and toxicology; enzymology; central nervous system and cardiovascular drugs; drugs of abuse; biogenic amines; psychopharmacology drugs and central nervous system agents; actions of prescription and experimental drugs, nutritional supplements and factors, biotoxins and hazardous chemicals; pharmacology, toxicology, biotechnology products, nutritional agents and their uses; computerized biomedical information systems for query/response activities; specialized information services relevent to toxicology, pharmacology, nutrition, biomedicine and chemistry. *Mailing Add:* 18900 Diary Rd Gaithersburg MD 20879-2123. *Fax:* 301-402-0421

**WYKLE, ROBERT LEE,** BIOCHEMISTRY. *Current Pos:* ASSOC PROF, DEPT BIOCHEM, BOWMAN GRAY SCH MED, 80- *Personal Data:* b Belmont, NC, Mar 17, 40; m 71. *Educ:* Western Carolina Univ, BS, 63; Univ Tenn, Memphis, PhD(biochem), 70. *Prof Exp:* Teacher, Waynesville High Sch, 63-65; teaching asst biochem, Med Sch, Univ Tenn, 65-67; fel, Oak Ridge Assoc Univs, 68-70, assoc scientist, 70-71, scientist, 76-80. *Mem:* Am Soc Biol Chemists. *Res:* Biochemistry and function of lipids in normal and neoplastic cells with special interest in ether-linked lipids. *Mailing Add:* Dept Biochem Wake Forest Univ Med Ctr Med Ctr Bldg Winston-Salem NC 27157-1016. *Fax:* 919-716-7671; *E-Mail:* 806449@bgsmwsl

**WYLD, HENRY WILLIAM, JR,** PHYSICS. *Current Pos:* from asst prof to assoc prof, 57-63, PROF PHYSICS, UNIV ILL, URBANA, 63- *Personal Data:* b Portland, Ore, Oct 16, 28; m 55; c 3. *Educ:* Reed Col, BA, 49; Univ Chicago, MS, 52, PhD(physics), 54. *Prof Exp:* Instr physics, Princeton Univ, 54-57. *Concurrent Pos:* Consult, Space Tech Labs, Inc, Calif, 57-63; NSF sr fel, Oxford Univ, 63-64; Guggenheim fel, Europ Coun Nuclear Res, 71. *Mem:* Am Phys Soc. *Res:* Theoretical high energy and plasma physics. *Mailing Add:* Loomis Lab Physics Univ Ill Urbana-Champaign Urbana IL 61801. *Fax:* 217-333-9819

**WYLDE, RONALD JAMES,** INSTRUMENTATION, PHYSICAL MEASUREMENTS. *Current Pos:* CONSULT, 71- *Personal Data:* b St Louis, Mo, Feb 7, 21; m 47; c 3. *Educ:* Washington Univ, St Louis, BA, 42; Univ Md, MS, 52. *Prof Exp:* Physicist, Underwater Acoust Div, Naval Ord Lab, USB, 42-48, head, Physics Br, Naval Gun Factory, 48-54, supt, Elec Lab, Naval Eng Exp Sta, 54-57, head, Instrumentation Div, 57-63 & Elec Div, US Navy Marine Eng Lab, 63-68, head, Elec Dept, Naval Ship Res & Develop Ctr, 68-71. *Mem:* Sr mem Inst Elec & Electronics Engrs. *Res:* Electronic circuitry of measuring systems; electromechanical transducers; amplitude-modulating transducers; electronic devices for physical measurement; granted 3 US patents in these fields. *Mailing Add:* 5320 18th St-Blvd E Bradenton FL 34203

**WYLER, ALLEN RAYMER,** EPILEPSY, CLINICAL NEUROSURGERY. *Current Pos:* PROF NEUROSURG, UNIV TENN, MEMPHIS, 84-, DIR, EPILEPSY CTR. *Personal Data:* b Seattle, Wash, Sept 3, 43; m 83. *Educ:* Univ Wash, BA, 65, MD, 69. *Prof Exp:* Actg instr neurosurg, Univ Wash, 74-75, from asst prof to assoc prof, Dept Neurol Surg, 75-84; chief neurosurg, Harborview Med Ctr, Seattle, Wash, 77-84. *Concurrent Pos:* Prof, Univ Wash Hosp, Seattle, 74-84; teacher investr neurol, NIH, 77-83; mem staff, Baptist Hosp, Memphis, Tenn, 84- *Mem:* Am League Against Epilepsy; Am Asn Neurol Surgeons; Acad Neurol Surgeons. *Res:* Active clinical and basic neurophysiological investigations into the basic mechanisms of focal epilepsy. *Mailing Add:* 2000 First Ave Apt 2101 Seattle WA 98121

**WYLER, DAVID J,** INFECTIOUS DISEASES, IMMUNOPARASITOLOGY. *Current Pos:* from asst prof to assoc prof, 79-85, PROF MED, SCH MED, TUFTS UNIV, 85- *Personal Data:* b Dec 21, 44; m, Deborah Alport; c Jonathan, Benjamin, Samuel & Anna R. *Educ:* Brown Univ, BA, 66; Harvard Univ, MD, 70. *Prof Exp:* Sr investr, NIH, 76-79; asst prof, John Hopkins Sch Med, 78-79. *Concurrent Pos:* Physician, New Eng Med Ctr, 83-; consult physician, Martha's Vineyard Hosp, 96- *Mem:* AAAS; Am Col Physicians; Am Soc Microbiol; Am Soc Trop Med Hyg; Am Assoc Immunol; Am Soc Clin Invest; Infectious Dis Soc Am. *Res:* Cytokine regulation of pathological fibrogenesis in infectious, allergic and rheumatological disorders. *Mailing Add:* New Eng Med Ctr 750 Washington St NEMCH 041 Boston MA 02111. *Fax:* 617-636-5292; *E-Mail:* david. wyler@es.nemc.org

**WYLER, OSWALD,** MATHEMATICS. *Current Pos:* PROF MATH, CARNEGIE-MELLON UNIV, 65- *Personal Data:* b Scuol, Grisons, Switz, Apr 2, 22; m 60; c 3. *Educ:* Swiss Fed Inst Technol, dipl, 47, Dr sc math, 50. *Prof Exp:* Asst inst geophys, Swiss Fed Inst Technol, 46-50; lectr math, Northwestern Univ, 51-53; from asst prof to assoc prof, Univ NMex, 53-65. *Mem:* Am Math Soc; Math Asn Am; Swiss Math Soc. *Res:* Categorical algebra; categorical topology; theory of convergence spaces; continuous lattices. *Mailing Add:* Dept Math Carnegie-Mellon Univ Pittsburgh PA 15213-3890

**WYLIE, C J,** NUCLEAR ENGINEERING. *Current Pos:* MEM ADV COMT REACTOR SAFEGUARDS, US NUCLEAR REG COMN, 84- *Personal Data:* b Morganton, NC, June 20, 26. *Educ:* Univ SC, BSEE, 50. *Prof Exp:* Chief elec engr, Duke Power Co, NC, 70-84. *Concurrent Pos:* Elec Utility Engr, 84- *Mem:* Fel Inst Elec & Electronics Engrs. *Res:* Electrics and design of power generator plants. *Mailing Add:* 9610 Lawyers Rd Charlotte NC 28227

**WYLIE, CLARENCE RAYMOND, JR,** geometry; deceased, see previous edition for last biography

**WYLIE, DOUGLAS WILSON,** PHYSICS. *Current Pos:* chmn dept, 68-73, PROF PHYSICS, WESTERN ILL UNIV, 68- *Personal Data:* b Saskatoon, Sask, Nov 12, 26; nat US; m 51; c 4. *Educ:* Univ NB, BSc, 47; Dalhousie Univ, MSc, 49; Univ Conn, PhD(solid state physics), 62. *Prof Exp:* Asst, Brown Univ, 49-50; instr, Univ NB, 50-51; from instr to prof, Univ Maine, 51-68. *Mem:* AAAS; Am Phys Soc; Am Asn Physics Teachers. *Res:* Solid state physics; radiation damage; electron spin resonance. *Mailing Add:* 304 Jana Rd Macomb IL 61455

**WYLIE, EVAN BENJAMIN,** HYDRAULICS, CIVIL ENGINEERING. *Current Pos:* from asst prof to assoc prof, 65-70, chmn, 84-94, PROF CIVIL & ENVIRON ENG, UNIV MICH, ANN ARBOR, 70- *Personal Data:* b Sask, Can, Jan 14, 31; US citizen; m 55, Frances E Miller; c 3. *Educ:* Univ Denver, BS, 53; Univ Colo, MS, 55; Univ Mich, PhD(hydraul), 64. *Prof Exp:* Asst engr, City Engr Off, Englewood, Colo, 54-55; jr res off hydraul sect, Div Mech Eng, Nat Res Coun Can, 55-56; struct design engr, Ford Motor Co Can, Ltd, 56-59; asst prof civil eng, Univ Denver, 59-62. *Mem:* Fel Am Soc Civil Engrs; fel Am Soc Mech Engrs; Am Soc Eng Educ; Int Asn Hydraul Res. *Res:* Basic and applied research in fluid transients in closed and open conduits; automotive airbag technology. *Mailing Add:* Dept Civil & Environ Eng Univ Mich 2340 G G Brown Ann Arbor MI 48109-2125. *E-Mail:* ebw@engin. umich.edu

**WYLIE, HAROLD GLENN,** ENTOMOLOGY. *Current Pos:* RETIRED. *Personal Data:* b Wingham, Ont, Oct 15, 27; wid; c Barbara & Linda. *Educ:* Univ Toronto, BA, 49; Univ Oxford, PhD(entom), 53. *Prof Exp:* Res scientist, Belleville, Ont, 49-50 & 51-72, res scientist entom, Can Dept Agr, Winnipeg, 72-87. *Concurrent Pos:* Res scientist, Commonwealth Inst Biol Control, Zurich, 50-51; adj prof entom, Univ Man, 82-88. *Mem:* Hon mem Entom Soc Can. *Res:* Parasitic hymenoptera and diptera; manipulation of insect parasites for pest control; host selection behavior of insect parasites. *Mailing Add:* 643 Silverstone Ave Winnipeg MB R3T 2V8 Can

**WYLIE, KYRAL FRANCIS,** engineering, physics, for more information see previous edition

**WYLIE, RICHARD MICHAEL,** BIOLOGY, NEUROPHYSIOLOGY. *Current Pos:* RES PHYSIOLOGIST, DEPT MED NEUROSCI, WALTER REED ARMY INST RES, 69- *Personal Data:* b Louisville, Ky, June 17, 34; div. *Educ:* Harvard Univ, BA, 56, MA, 58, PhD(biol), 62. *Prof Exp:* Fel neurophysiol, Univ Utah, 62-65, res assoc, 65-66; res assoc, Rockefeller Univ, 66-69. *Mem:* Soc Neurosci; assoc mem Am Physiol Soc. *Res:* Biophysics of sensory mechanisms; mechanisms of sensory discrimination in central nervous systems; integration in sensory and motor systems; neuropharmacology. *Mailing Add:* Div Neurosci Walter Reed Army Inst Res Washington DC 20307

**WYLLIE, GILBERT ALEXANDER,** BIOLOGY, ECOLOGY. *Current Pos:* RETIRED. *Personal Data:* b Saltcoats, Scotland, Jan 11, 28; US citizen; m 57; c 3. *Educ:* Col Idaho, BS, 58; Sacramento State Col, MA, 60; Purdue Univ, PhD(ecol), 63. *Prof Exp:* Assoc prof biol, WTex State Univ, 63-65; asst prof, Boise State Univ, 65-66, assoc prof biol, 66- *Mem:* Ecol Soc Am. *Res:* Effects of environment on morphology, distribution, behavior of invertebrates and lower vertebrates. *Mailing Add:* 306 Parkway Boise ID 83706

**WYLLIE, LORING A,** ENGINEERING. *Current Pos:* CHMN BD, H J DEGENKOLB ASSOC, 86- *Educ:* Univ Calif, BS, 60, MS, 62. *Concurrent Pos:* Consult, var agencies; chmn, Comt Concrete & Masonry Struct, Am Soc Civil Engrs, 81-84; dir, Am Concrete Inst, 85-88, mem, Tech Activ Comt, 82-88 & Comt 318, Stand Bldg Code, 72-; dir, Earthquake Eng Res Inst, 86-89. *Mem:* Nat Acad Eng; fel Am Soc Civil Engrs; fel Am Concrete Inst; Earthquake Eng Res Inst. *Res:* Analysis of existing buildings; design for correction of structural deficiencies; strengthening of buildings for improved seismic performance; author of various publications. *Mailing Add:* H J Degenkolb Assoc 225 Bush St Suite 1000 San Francisco CA 94104. *Fax:* 415-981-3157

**WYLLIE, PETER JOHN,** GEOLOGY, GEOCHEMISTRY. *Current Pos:* chmn & prof geol, Div Geol & Planetary Sci, 83-87, PROF GEOL, CALIF INST TECHNOL, PASADENA, 87- *Personal Data:* b London, Eng, Feb 8, 30; m 56, Romy Blair; c Andrew, Lisa & John. *Educ:* Univ St Andrews, BSc, 52 & 55, PhD, 58. *Hon Degrees:* DSc, Univ St Andrews, 74. *Honors & Awards:* Polar Medal, Her Majesty Queen Elizabeth, 54; Res Award, Mineral Soc Am, 65; Quantrell Award, 79; Wollaston Medal, Geol Soc London, 82; Abraham-Gottlob-Werner Medal, Ger Mineral Soc, 87. *Prof Exp:* Geologist, Brit NGreenland Exped, 52-54; asst lectr geol, Univ St Andrews, 55-56; res asst geochem, Pa State Univ, 56-58, asst prof, 58-59, assoc prof petrol, 61-65, actg head, Dept Geochem & Mineral, 62-63; res fel chem, Leeds Univ, Eng, 59-60, lectr exp petrol, 60-61; prof petrol & geochem, Univ Chicago, 65-83, master phys sci, Col Div & assoc dean col & Phys Sci Div, 72-73, Homer J Livingston Prof, 78-83, chmn geophys sci, 79-82. *Concurrent Pos:* Managing ed, J Petrol, 65-67, ed, J Geol, 67-83, ed-in-chief, Springer-Verlag Monograph Series, 67-; mem, Comn Exp Petrol, Int Union Geol Sci, 70-92; chmn, Award Comt, Mineral Soc Am, 70-71, counr, 70-72; mem subcomt, Penrose Medal Award, Geol Soc Am, 71-73; subcomt, Nat Medal Sci, 80-82, counr, 82-85; mem vis comt, Dept Geol & Geophys, Woods Hole Oceanog Inst, 72; Goldschmidt Medal Comt, Geochem Soc, 72-74, counr, 82-85; mem, Adv Panel Earth Sci, NSF, 75-78, chmn, Earth Sci Div Adv Comt, 79-82; team leader, Basatic Volcanism Study Proj, Lunar & Planetary Inst, 76-79; vpres, Int Mineral Asn, 78-86; mem ed bd, Tectonophys, 78-90; mem, Macelwane Award Comt, Am Geophys Union, 78-80; mem, US Nat Comt Geol, 78-80; mem, US Nat Comt, Int Union Geodesy & Geophys, 80-84; vchmn, Coordn Comt, Int Union Comn Lithosphere, 81-84; mem, Comt Ocean Drilling, Nat Acad Sci, 81-82; mem, Arthur Holmes Medal Comt, Europ Geophys Union, 83; mem adv bd, Sch Earth Sci, Stanford Univ, 83-88; pres, Int Mineral Asn. 86-90; Louis Murray vis fel, Univ Cape Town, 87; chmn, Comt Res Objectives Solid-Earth Sci, Nat Acad Sci, 88-93. *Mem:* Foreign assoc Nat Acad Sci; fel Am Geophys Union; fel Geol Soc Am; hon mem Mineral Soc London; fel Mineral Soc Am; fel Royal Soc London; hon mem Mineral Soc Russia; foreign mem Russ Acad Sci; foreign fel Indian Nat Sci Acad; foreign fel Nat Acad Sci India; foreign mem Chinese Acad Sci; Acad Europ; Int

Union Geod & Geophys (pres, 95). *Res:* Igneous and metamorphic petrology; experimental petrology; high pressure studies on hydrothermal systems; application of phase equilibrium studies to batholiths, andesites, kimberlites, and carbonatites; author of 2 textbooks and one book on geosciences. *Mailing Add:* Calif Inst Technol 1201 E California Blvd Pasadena CA 91125. *E-Mail:* wyllie@caltech.edu

**WYLLIE, THOMAS DEAN,** PLANT PATHOLOGY. *Current Pos:* PROF PLANT PATH, UNIV MO, COLUMBIA, 60- *Personal Data:* b Hinsdale, Ill, Dec 4, 28; m 50; c 3. *Educ:* San Diego State Col, AB, 52; Univ Minn, MS, 57, PhD(plant path), 60. *Mem:* Am Phytopath Soc. *Res:* Mycotoxin and mycotoxicoses research; computer modeling; ecological relationships of non-specific soil borne pathogenic fungi on the soybean. *Mailing Add:* 809 Forest Hill Ct Columbia MO 65203

**WYLLY, ALEXANDER,** OPERATIONS RESEARCH, COMPUTER SCIENCE. *Current Pos:* CONSULT, 73- *Personal Data:* b New York, NY, Sept 2, 20; m 43; c 2. *Educ:* Ga Inst Technol, BS, 41; Mass Inst Technol, SM, 46; Calif Inst Technol, PhD(aerodyn eng), 51. *Prof Exp:* Aerodynamicist, Rand Corp, 46-51, chief missile preliminary designs, 51-54; founder & vpres comput sci, Planning Res Corp, 54-69, vpres pac opers, 69-73. *Concurrent Pos:* Bd dir, Planning Res Corp, 54-74; trustee, Oceanic Found. *Mem:* Am Soc Info Sci. *Res:* Systems analysis; computer systems software design and applications. *Mailing Add:* 1434 Punahou St Apt 930 Honolulu HI 96822-4740

**WYLLYS, RONALD EUGENE,** INFORMATION SCIENCE. *Current Pos:* dean, 82-90, PROF LIBR & INFO SCI, GRAD SCH LIBR & INFO SCI, UNIV TEX, AUSTIN, 72- *Personal Data:* b Phoenix, Ariz, May 14, 30; m 57; c 4. *Educ:* Ariz State Univ, BA, 50; Univ Wis-Madison, PhD(info sci), 74. *Prof Exp:* Mathematician, Dept Defense, Washington, DC, 54-59; assoc, Planning Res Corp, Los Angeles, 59-61; comput systs specialist, Syst Develop Corp, Santa Monica, 61-66; chief systs analyst, Univ Librs, Univ Wis-Madison, 66-69, lectr comput sci, 66-72. *Concurrent Pos:* Assoc math, George Washington Univ, 54-59. *Mem:* AAAS; Am Soc Info Sci; Am Statist Asn; Asn Records Mgrs & Adminrs. *Res:* Information storage and retrieval; statistical linguistics and other programmatic techniques for the analysis of information content. *Mailing Add:* 1306 Belmont Pkwy Austin TX 78703

**WYLY, LEMUEL DAVID, JR,** NUCLEAR PHYSICS. *Current Pos:* from assoc prof to Regent's prof, 49-88, EMER PROF PHYSICS, GA INST TECHNOL, 88- *Personal Data:* b Seneca, SC, Aug 9, 16; m 38; c 2. *Educ:* The Citadel, BS, 38; Univ NC, MA, 39; Yale Univ, PhD(physics), 49. *Prof Exp:* Instr physics, Ga Sch Technol, 39-41, asst prof, 46; asst instr, Yale Univ, 46-48. *Concurrent Pos:* Consult, Oak Ridge Nat Lab, 52- *Mem:* Fel Am Phys Soc; Sigma Xi. *Res:* Nuclear energy levels; proportional and scintillation and solid state detectors; decay schemes of radioactive isotopes and from neutron capture. *Mailing Add:* 962 Canter Rd E Atlanta GA 30324

**WYMA, RICHARD J,** PHYSICAL CHEMISTRY, INORGANIC CHEMISTRY. *Current Pos:* ASSOC PROF CHEM, IND-PURDUE UNIV, INDIANAPOLIS, 70- *Personal Data:* b Grand Rapids, Mich, June 25, 36; m 64; c 3. *Educ:* Hope Col, AB, 58; Univ Mich, MS, 60, PhD(phys chem), 64. *Prof Exp:* Asst prof chem, Geneva Col, 64-69. *Concurrent Pos:* Consult, City Indianapolis & Inst Adv Res, Ind-Purdue Univ, 76-80. *Mem:* Am Chem Soc; Soc Appl Spectros; Coblentz Soc. *Res:* Application of molecular spectroscopy to structure determination and to bounding theories of inorganic systems; chemistry of sulfides, phosphines, boranes and transition metal complexes; chemical education research; methods for solving chemical problems. *Mailing Add:* IUPUI Dept Chem 402 N Blackford St Indianapolis IN 46202-3274. *Fax:* 317-274-4701; *E-Mail:* wyma@chem.iupui.edu

**WYMAN, BOSTWICK FRAMPTON,** MATHEMATICS, ACTUARIAL SCIENCE. *Current Pos:* assoc prof, 72-82, PROF MATH, OHIO STATE UNIV, 82- *Personal Data:* b Aiken, SC, Aug 22, 41; m 75, Linda Curtis; c John & Tracy. *Educ:* Mass Inst Technol, SB, 62; Univ Calif, Berkeley, MA, 64, PhD(math), 66. *Prof Exp:* Instr math, Princeton Univ, 66-68; asst prof, Stanford Univ, 68-72. *Concurrent Pos:* Vis asst prof, Univ Oslo, 70-71; vis assoc prof, Univ Notre Dame, 78-79; vis prof, Univ Genoa, Italy, 88-90. *Mem:* Am Math Soc; Math Asn Am; Inst Elec & Electronics Engrs. *Res:* Algebraic system theory; linear control system design; algebraic number theory. *Mailing Add:* Dept Math Ohio State Univ 231 W 18th Ave Columbus OH 43210

**WYMAN, CHARLES ELY,** BIOMASS CONVERSION, FERMENTATIONS. *Current Pos:* staff engr, Solar Energy Res Inst, 78, sr engr, 78-79, group mgr, 79-81, prog coordr, 78-81, dep div mgr, 81, biotechol br mgr, 84-91, div dir alternate fuels, 91-96; DIR, BIOTECH CTR FUELS & CHEM, NAT RENEWABLE ENERGY LAB, 96- *Personal Data:* b Greenfield, Mass, Oct 23, 44; m 68, Carol J Wroblewski; c Marc E & Kristin L. *Educ:* Univ Mass, BS, 67; Princeton Univ, MA, 69, PhD(chem eng), 71; Univ Denver, MBA, 88. *Prof Exp:* Sr chem engr, Monsanto Co, 71-74; asst prof chem eng, Univ NH, 74-78; mgr process develop, Badger Co Inc, 81-84. *Concurrent Pos:* Affil prof, Agr & Chem Eng, Colo State Univ, 86-; adj prof, Chem Eng & Petrol Refinding Dept, Colo Sch Mines, Golden Colo, 86; bd dir, Colo Inst Res Biotechnol, Colo Advan Technol Inst, 87-; assoc ed, J Solar Energy Eng, 89-; bd dir, Colo Inst Res, Biotechnol Bioprocessing Ctr, 90-; chmn, Res Comt Processes & Prod, Am Inst Chem Engrs, 90-93. *Mem:* Am Chem Soc; Am Inst Chem Engrs; Am Soc Mech Engrs; Int Solar Energy Soc; Sigma Xi. *Res:* Broad background in alternative fuels production and utilization; expertise in fermentations and reactor engineering at bench, pilot, and commercial scales as well as process analysis and modeling; experience in project, program, and line management. *Mailing Add:* Biotechnol Ctr Nat Renewable Energy Lab 1617 Cole Blvd Golden CO 80401

**WYMAN, DONALD,** horticulture; deceased, see previous edition for last biography

**WYMAN, DONALD PAUL,** TECHNICAL MANAGEMENT, ORGANIC CHEMISTRY. *Current Pos:* vpres, 79-87, PRES, ROCHESTER MIDLAND CORP, 87- *Personal Data:* b Cleveland, Ohio, Feb 4, 31; m 54; c 2. *Educ:* Ohio Univ, BS, 53; Mich State Univ, PhD(org chem), 57. *Prof Exp:* Group leader, Lubrizol Corp, 57-61; fel, Mellon Inst, 61-64; res mgr, Borg Warner Chem, 64-68, Scott Graphics, 68-74; tech dir, GAF, 74-79. *Concurrent Pos:* Chmn, T-3A Comt, Nat Asn Corrosion Engrs. *Mem:* AAAS; Am Asn Metals; Am Chem Soc; Nat Asn Corrosion Engrs. *Res:* Polymers; plastics; corrosion and scale inhibitors; disinfectants; organic chemicals. *Mailing Add:* Rochester Midland Corp PO Box 1515 Rochester NY 14621-1515

**WYMAN, GEORGE MARTIN,** CHEMICAL DYNAMICS, PHOTOCHEMISTRY. *Current Pos:* RETIRED. *Personal Data:* b Budapest, Hungary, Oct 13, 21; nat US; m 51, Mary E Truitt; c Barbara W (Pherribo). *Educ:* Cornell Univ, AB, 41, MS, 43, PhD(org chem), 44. *Prof Exp:* Res chemist, Gen Chem Co, 44-45, Gen Aniline & Film Corp, 45-49 & Nat Bur Stand, 49-54; chief, Spectros Sect, Qm Res & Develop Ctr, US Dept Army, 54-57, sci adv, Europ Res Off, 57-60, dir chem div, 60-77, chief, Chem Br, 77-83, dir, Chem & Biol Sci Div, US Army Res Off, 83-85; consult, 85-95. *Concurrent Pos:* Adj prof chem, Univ NC, Chapel Hill, 73-77, 86-95. *Mem:* Am Chem Soc; Int Am Photochem Soc; Europ Photochem Asn. *Res:* Spectrophotometry; cis-trans isomerization of conjugated compounds; organic photochemistry; excited state chemistry of dyes. *Mailing Add:* 2231 Cranford Rd Durham NC 27706. *E-Mail:* mwyman@acpub.duke.edu

**WYMAN, JEFFRIES,** molecular biology, for more information see previous edition

**WYMAN, JOHN E,** CHEMISTRY. *Current Pos:* MEM SCI STAFF, ITEK CORP, 65- *Personal Data:* b Amsterdam, NY, Feb 20, 31; m 52; c 4. *Educ:* Univ Mich, BS, 52, Purdue Univ, MS, 55, PhD, 56. *Prof Exp:* Res chemist, Linde Co, Union Carbide Corp, 56-58, res chemist, Union Carbide Chem Co, 58-59; res chemist, Spec Proj Dept, Monsanto Chem Co, 59-60, res group leader, Monsanto Res Corp, 60-65. *Mem:* Am Chem Soc. *Res:* Photochemistry; complex transition element organometallic chemistry; metal carbonyls; propellant, explosive and inorganic chemistry; graphic arts, film and paper coatings. *Mailing Add:* 17 Monadnock Dr Westford MA 01886-3018

**WYMAN, MILTON,** VETERINARY MEDICINE, OPHTHALMOLOGY. *Current Pos:* RETIRED. *Personal Data:* b Cleveland, Ohio, Oct 11, 30; m 56; c 2. *Educ:* Ohio State Univ, DVM, 63, MS, 64; Am Col Vet Ophthal, dipl. *Prof Exp:* Res assoc ophthal, Cols Med & Vet Med, Ohio State Univ, 62-64, instr vet ophthal, Col Vet Med, 64-66, from asst prof to prof vet ophthal & med, 66-75, chief comp vet ophthal & med, Col Vet Med, 75-92, chief, Small Animal Serv, 72-92, assoc prof ophthal, Col Med, 72-92. *Mem:* Am Soc Vet Ophthal; Am Col Vet Ophthalmologists (past pres); Am Vet Med Asn; Am Asn Vet Clin. *Res:* Congenital ocular defects in dogs and their relationship to man; glaucoma in the basset hound; ocular fundus anomaly in collies; medical application of soft contact lenses in animals and man. *Mailing Add:* 2615 Carriage Rd Powell OH 43065

**WYMAN, RICHARD L,** FACTORS INFLUENCING STRUCTURE OF AMPHIBIAN COMMUNITIES, AMPHIBIAN DECLINES & ENVIRONMENTAL CHANGE. *Current Pos:* EXEC DIR, EDMOND NILES HOUCK PRESERVE & BIOL RES STA, 86- *Personal Data:* b Morristown, NJ, Oct 24, 46; m 80, Marilyn; c Richard, Laurie, Allyson & Jerrine. *Educ:* Panhandle State Univ, BS, 69; Ill State Univ, MS, 70, PhD(ecol/ethology), 73. *Prof Exp:* Prin investr, LMS Engrs, 74-80; asst prof, Hartwick Col, 80-85. *Concurrent Pos:* Chair int comt, Orgn Biol Field Stas, 91-; adj assoc prof, State Univ NY, Albany, 92-; mem, Species Survival Comt, Int Union Conserv Nature & Natural Resources, 93. *Mem:* AAAS; Soc Study Amphibians & Reptiles; Soc Study Evolution; Animal Behav Soc; Org Biol Field Stas. *Res:* Factors effecting amphibian community structure and effects of environmental change on amphibians. *Mailing Add:* Huyck Preserve PO Box 189 Rensselaerville NY 12147-0189

**WYMAN, RICHARD VAUGHN,** GEOLOGICAL ENGINEERING, ECONOMIC GEOLOGY. *Current Pos:* lectr, Univ Nev, 69-74, assoc prof, 74-80, chmn dept, 76-80, prof eng, 80-92, chmn civil & mech eng, 84-90, chmn civil & environ eng, 90-92, EMER PROF CIVIL ENG, UNIV NEV, 92-; PRIN, WYMAN ENG CONSULT, 89- *Personal Data:* b Painesville, Ohio, Feb 22, 27; m 47, Anne Fenton; c William F. *Educ:* Case Western Res Univ, BS, 48; Univ Mich, MS, 49; Univ Ariz, PhD(geol eng), 74. *Prof Exp:* Geologist econ geol, NJ Zinc Co, 49, Cerro de Pasco Corp, 50-52, NJ Zinc Co, 52-53; geologist uranium, Western Gold & Uranium Inc, 53-54, chief geologist, 54-55, gen mgr, 55-57, vpres, 57-59; tunnel supt tunnel construct, Reynolds Elec & Eng Co, 61-63; construct supt, Sunshine Mining Co, 63-65; engr, Reynolds Elec & Eng Co, 65-67, asst mgr, 67-69. *Concurrent Pos:* Pres explor geol, Intermountain Explor Co, 59-92; consult, C K Geoenergy Corp, Latin Am, 77-79; Univ Nev, Las Vegas Senate Res Grant Geothermal, 77-; mem peer rev comt, Nevada Nuclear Waste Isolation Proj, Dept Energy, 78-82. *Mem:* Am Inst Mining Metall & Petrol Engrs; fel Am Soc Civil Engrs; Soc Econ Geol; Geol Soc Am; Asn Eng Geol; Sigma Xi; distinguished mem Soc Mining Engrs; Arctic Inst NAm. *Res:* Ore genesis; tunnel construction and design; hydrology; flood control. *Mailing Add:* 610 Bryant Ct Boulder City NV 89005. *Fax:* 702-293-4424

**WYMAN, ROBERT J,** DEVELOPMENTAL NEUROBIOLOGY, DEVELOPMENTAL GENETICS. *Current Pos:* from asst prof to assoc prof, 66-80, PROF BIOL, YALE UNIV, 80- *Personal Data:* b Syracuse, NY, June 8, 40. *Educ:* Harvard Univ, AB, 60; Univ Calif, Berkeley, MA, 63, PhD(biophys), 65. *Hon Degrees:* MA, Yale Univ. *Prof Exp:* Math analyst, Tech Res Group, Inc, 59; NSF res fel appl sci, Calif Inst Technol, 66. *Concurrent Pos:* Vis scientist, Nobel Inst, Stockholm, 70-71, Med Res Coun, Cambridge, Eng, 74 & Univ Basel, Switz, 77; mem physiol study sect, NIH, 76-80; mem bd sci adv, Microgenesys Corp. *Mem:* Soc Neurosci; Int Brain Res Orgn; Sigma Xi; Brit Soc Exp Biol; Genetics Soc Am. *Res:* Genetics of Drosophila nervous system; neural generation of motor output in insects and vertebrates; insect physiology; molecular cloning of genes necessary for the specificity of neural connectivity; insect oocyte physiology. *Mailing Add:* Dept Biol Yale Univ PO Box 208103 New Haven CT 06520-8103. *Fax:* 203-432-6161; *E-Mail:* rwyman@minerva.cis.yale.edu

**WYMAN, STANLEY M,** medicine, radiology; deceased, see previous edition for last biography

**WYMER, JOSEPH PETER,** industrial engineering, for more information see previous edition

**WYMER, RAYMOND GEORGE,** NUCLEAR CHEMISTRY. *Current Pos:* RETIRED. *Personal Data:* b Colton, Ohio, Oct 1, 27; m 48; c 4. *Educ:* Memphis State Col, BS, 50; Vanderbilt Univ, MA & PhD, 53. *Prof Exp:* Mem staff, Oak Ridge Nat Lab, 53-56; assoc prof, Ga Inst Technol, 56-58; chief nuclear chem, Indust Reactor Labs, 58-59; res chemist, Oak Ridge Nat Lab, 59-62, sect chief, 62-73, assoc dir, 73-82, dir, Chem Technol Div, 73-89. *Concurrent Pos:* Ed, Radiochimica Acta. *Mem:* Am Inst Chem Engrs; Sigma Xi; fel Am Nuclear Soc; Am Chem Soc. *Res:* Colloid, radiation, transuranium element and complex ion chemistry; kinetics; nuclear fuel cycle. *Mailing Add:* 188 Outer Dr Oak Ridge TN 37830

**WYMORE, ALBERT WAYNE,** MATHEMATICAL SYSTEM THEORY, SYSTEMS ENGINEERING. *Current Pos:* OWNER & PRIN SYSTS ENGR, SANDS SYSTS ANALYSIS & DESIGN SYSTS, 87- *Personal Data:* b New Sharon, Iowa, Feb 1, 27; m 49, Muriel L Farrell; c Farrell, Darcy, Melanie & Leslie. *Educ:* Iowa State Univ, BS, 49, MS, 50; Univ Wis, PhD(math), 55. *Prof Exp:* Consult, Pure Oil Co, 55-57; dir, Comput Ctr, Univ Ariz, 57-67, head, Dept Systs Eng, 59-74, prof systs eng, 59-87. *Concurrent Pos:* Consult, RCA, 58 & 73, IBM, San Jose, 60-61, Lockheed, Ga, 69, Centro Agronomotrop de Invest y Ensenanza, Costa Rica, 75-76, Gen Elec Tempo Ctr Advan Studies, 77-78, IBM Fed Syst Div, 82-85, Johannes Kepler, 84-85, Siemens WGer, 86-88 & 90-95, Bellcore, 85-88, Unisys, 88, City Tucson, Dept Energy & Environ, 89-91, Agr Res Serv, USDA, 89-92 & Bechtel, 91, Bullhn, 92, Ecole Nacionale, 93, MRJ, 93, Ariz State Univ, 94, George Washington Univ, 94, NASA, 96. *Mem:* Am Math Soc; Nat Coun Systs Eng. *Res:* Mathematical system theoretic foundations for systems engineering methodology and apply the methodology to the design of bioware/hardware/software systems in the fields of aerospace, agriculture, computers, education, health, information, management, manufacturing, mining, nuclear, telecommunications, transportation, urban planning, water and welfare; author of 3 books. *Mailing Add:* Sands Systs Anal & Design Systs 4301 Camino Kino Tucson AZ 85718-6657

**WYNBLATT, PAUL P,** SURFACE SCIENCE. *Current Pos:* dir, Ctr Study Mat, Carnegie Mellon Univ, 85-88, assoc dean eng, 89-91, head dept, 91-95, PROF MAT SCI & ENG, CARNEGIE MELLON UNIV, 81- *Personal Data:* b Alexandria, Egypt, June 30, 35; US citizen; m 59, Ann Whitehouse; c Deborah A & Michael J. *Educ:* Univ Manchester, BScTech, 56; Israel Inst Technol, MS, 58; Univ Calif, Berkeley, PhD(metall), 66. *Hon Degrees:* Dr, Univ Aix-Marseille, 87. *Honors & Awards:* Andrew Carnegie Lectr, Pittsburgh Chap, Am Soc Metals, 93. *Prof Exp:* Res metallurgist, Israel Atomic Energy Comn Labs, 58-62; staff scientist res staff, Ford Motor Co, 66-81. *Concurrent Pos:* Bd dir, Am Inst Mining Metall & Petrol Engrs, Metall Soc, 77-80; vis prof, Sch Natural Chem, Paris, 87, Univ Aix Marseille III, 88; Von Humboldt Found sr fel, 95-; Lady Davis vis prof, Isreael Inst Tech, 96. *Mem:* Fel Am Soc Metals; Am Vacuum Soc; Am Inst Mining Metall & Petrol Engrs-Metall Soc; Mat Res Soc. *Res:* Equilibrium surface composition of materials; structure and composition of solid-solid interfaces; thermal stability of thin films; two-dimensional phase transitions. *Mailing Add:* Dept Mat Sci & Eng Carnegie Mellon Univ Pittsburgh PA 15213. *Fax:* 412-268-1513; *E-Mail:* pw01@andrew.cmu.edu

**WYNDER, ERNST LUDWIG,** PREVENTIVE MEDICINE, EPIDEMIOLOGY. *Current Pos:* PRES & MED DIR, AM HEALTH FOUND, 69- *Personal Data:* b Ger, Apr 30, 22; nat US. *Educ:* NY Univ, BA, 43; Wash Univ, BS & MD, 50. *Prof Exp:* Intern, Georgetown Univ Hosp, 50; asst prof prev med, Grad Sch Med Sci, Med Col, Cornell Univ, 54-56, assoc prof, 56-69. *Concurrent Pos:* Asst, Sloan-Kettering Inst Cancer Res, 52-54, assoc, 54-60, assoc mem, 60-69, assoc scientist, 69-71; jr asst resident, Mem Hosp for Cancer & Allied Dis, 51-52, sr asst resident, 52-54, clin asst physician, 54-64, asst attend physician, 64-69, consult epidemiologist, 69-; clin vis asst, James Ewing Hosp, 54-64, asst vis physician, 64-68; mem, Task Force Lung Cancer, Tobacco Working Group, 67-; mem, Nat Cancer Plan, 71; ed, Prev Med J, 72. *Mem:* AMA; Am Asn Cancer Res; Am Pub Health Asn; NY Acad Sci. *Res:* Environmental factors affecting major chronic disease development, preventive medical aspects. *Mailing Add:* 860 United Nations Plaza New York NY 10017

**WYNDRUM, RALPH WILLIAM, JR,** ELECTRICAL ENGINEERING, TELECOMMUNICATIONS. *Current Pos:* Mem tech staff, Bell Labs Inc, 63-65, supvr explor circuit appln, 65-69, head loop transmission systs, 69-79, head, Adv Transmission Systs Dept, 79-87, head, Int Loop Systs, dir systs analysis, 87-90, dir, Qual Process Ctr, 90-92, dir qual, software, eng & technol, 92-95, VPRES WORLD SERVS, AT&T LABS, 94-, VPRES TECHNOL, 96- *Personal Data:* b Brooklyn, NY, Apr 20, 37; m 60, Meta Schmidt; c 4. *Educ:* Columbia Univ, BS, 59, MS, 60, MS(bus admin), 78; NY Univ, EngScD, 63. *Concurrent Pos:* Asst prof, NY Univ, 63-64; mem, Nat Basic Sci Comt, 66-70; adj prof, Newark Col Eng, 67-70; prof elec eng & comput sci, Stevens Inst Technol, 81-89; mem bd dirs, Inst Elec & Electronics Engrs, 88-90, vpres publ, 90-91; chmn, Indust Res Qual Dirs Network, 95. *Mem:* Fel Inst Elec & Electronics Engrs. *Res:* Network synthesis; integrated circuit design; telephone transmission design; quality systems; re-engineering. *Mailing Add:* AT&T Labs Rm 3L-324 101 Crawfords Corner Rd Holmdel NJ 07733-3030. *Fax:* 732-949-5309; *E-Mail:* rww@att.com

**WYNEKEN, JEANETTE,** ZOOLOGY. *Current Pos:* RES ASSOC, FLA ATLANTIC UNIV, 90- *Personal Data:* b Bloomington, Ill, July 14, 56. *Educ:* Ill Wesleyan Univ, BA, 78; Univ Ill, PhD(biol), 88. *Prof Exp:* Res assoc, Univ Ill, 88-89. *Mem:* Am Soc Zoologist; Sigma Xi; AAAS; Soc Study Amphibians & Reptiles; Soc Study Evolution; Herpetologists League. *Res:* Understanding how organisms contend with their environments; the behavior, functional morphology and physiology of sea turtles; understanding the adapture significance of characteristics unique to marine turtles or unique to migratory species. *Mailing Add:* 1033 Coral Way Boynton Beach FL 33426

**WYNER, AARON D,** ELECTRICAL ENGINEERING, MATHEMATICS. *Current Pos:* distinguished mem tech staff, Math Sci Res Ctr, 63-74, HEAD, COMMUN ANALYSIS RES DEPT, BELL LABS, 74- *Personal Data:* b New York, NY, Mar 17, 39; m 63, Nusha Zukerman; c Tamar, Abraham, Dena & Yael. *Educ:* Queens Col, NY, BS, 60; Columbia Univ, BS, 60, MS, 61, PhD(elec eng), 63. *Honors & Awards:* Centennial Award, Inst Elec & Electronics Engrs, Shannon Award, 94. *Prof Exp:* Asst prof elec eng, Columbia Univ, 63. *Concurrent Pos:* Consult, T J Watson Res Ctr & IBM Corp, 63; adj prof, Columbia Univ, 64-; Guggenheim fel, 66-67; vis scientist, Weizmann Inst Sci & Israel Inst Technol, 69-70; vis prof, Polytech Inst Brooklyn, 71, Princeton Univ, 83 & 90. *Mem:* Nat Acad Eng; Inst Elec & Electronics Engrs; AAAS. *Res:* Communication theory; information theory; probability. *Mailing Add:* Bell Labs Mountain Ave New Providence NJ 07974. *Fax:* 908-582-3340; *E-Mail:* adw@lucent.com

**WYNGAARD, JOHN C,** FLUID DYNAMICS. *Current Pos:* PROF METEOROL, PA STATE UNIV, 80- *Personal Data:* b Madison, Wis, Dec 4, 38; m 65; c 2. *Educ:* Univ Wis-Madison, BSc, 61, MSc, 62; Pa State Univ, PhD(mech eng), 67. *Prof Exp:* Res physicist, Air Force Cambridge Res Labs, 67-75; physicist, Wave Propagation Lab, Nat Oceanic & Atmospheric Admin, Boulder, 75-79. *Concurrent Pos:* Vis assoc prof atmospheric sci, Univ Wash, 73; fel, Coop Inst Res Environ Sci, Boulder, 75-79; physicist, Mesoscale Res Sect, Nat Ctr Atmospheric Res, 79-91, head, 81-91. *Mem:* Am Meteorol Soc; Am Phys Soc; Sigma Xi. *Res:* The structure and dynamics of turbulent flows, particularly in the lower atmosphere. *Mailing Add:* 300 E Hamilton Ave State College PA 16801. *Fax:* 814-865-3663

**WYNGAARDEN, JAMES BARNES,** BIOCHEMISTRY, METABOLISM. *Current Pos:* EMER PROF, DUKE UNIV, 95- *Personal Data:* b East Grand Rapids, Mich, Oct 19, 24; div; c 5. *Educ:* Univ Mich, MD, 48. *Hon Degrees:* DSc, Univ Mich, 80, Med Col Ohio, 84, Univ Ill, Chicago, 85, George Washington Univ, 86, Univ SC, 89 & Western Mich Univ, 89; PhD, Tel Aviv Univ, 87. *Prof Exp:* Asst pharmacol, Med Sch, Univ Mich, 46-48; mem med house staff, Mass Gen Hosp, 48-52; vis investr, Pub Health Res Inst NY, 53; investr, Nat Heart Inst, 53-54 & Nat Inst Arthritis & Metab Dis, 54-56; assoc prof med & biochem, Sch Med, Duke Univ, 56-61, prof med & assoc prof biochem, 61-65; prof med & chmn dept, Univ Pa, 65-67; Frederic M Hanes prof med & chmn dept, Duke Univ, 67-82; dir, NIH, 82-89; assoc dir, Life Sci Off Sci & Tech Policy, White House, 89-90; dir, Hugo, 90-91; foreign secy, Nat Acad Sci & Indust Med, 90-95. *Concurrent Pos:* Dalton scholar med res, Mass Gen Hosp, 51; consult, Vet Admin Hosp, Durham, NC; consult, Off Sci & Technol, Exec Off Pres, 66-72; mem, Adv Comt Biol & Med, AEC, 67-69; mem adv bd, Howard Hughes Med Inst, 69-82; mem bd sci counrs, Nat Inst Arthritis, Metab & Digestive Dis, 71-74; mem, President's Sci Adv Comt, 72-73; mem exec comn, Assembly Life Sci, 72-77; mem, Coun Govt-Univ-Indust Res Roundtable, Nat Acad Sci, 84-90. *Mem:* Nat Acad Sci; Inst Med-Nat Acad Sci; Am Soc Clin Invest; Am Acad Arts & Sci; Asn Am Physicians (pres, 78-79); fel Royal Col Physicians London; Am Soc Biochem & Molecular Biol. *Res:* Control of purine synthesis; purine metabolism in normal and gouty man; metabolism of iodine and steroids; oxalate synthesis; inborn errors of metabolism/human genetics. *Mailing Add:* 2 Health Pl Durham NC 27705. *Fax:* 919-402-8169

**WYNN, CHARLES MARTIN, SR,** ORGANIC CHEMISTRY. *Current Pos:* from asst prof to prof chem, 79-83, GEN CHEM COORDR, EASTERN CONN STATE UNIV, 83- *Personal Data:* b New York, NY, May 8, 39; m 66, Jean M Boris; c Charles Jr, Joseph, Michelle & Andrew. *Educ:* City Col NY, BChE, 60; Univ Mich, MS, 63, PhD(chem), 65. *Prof Exp:* Instr gen chem, Univ Mich, 65-67; US Peace Corps lectr chem, Malayan Teachers' Col, 67-69; from asst prof to prof phys sci, Oakland Community Col, 69-74, asst to provost, 74-75, chmn dept. *Concurrent Pos:* Vis scholar, Wesleyan Univ, 87. *Mem:* Am Educ Sci Asn. *Res:* Structural directivity in diene synthesis; author of laboratory manuals and natural science textbook. *Mailing Add:* Dept Phys Sci Eastern Conn State Univ Willimantic CT 06226-2295. *Fax:* 860-465-5213

**WYNN, JAMES ELKANAH,** MEDICINAL CHEMISTRY, ANALYTICAL CHEMISTRY. *Current Pos:* from asst prof to assoc prof med chem, 69-77, PROF PHARM, COL PHARM, UNIV SC, 77- *Personal Data:* b Pennington Gap, Va, Feb 7, 42; m 64; c 1. *Educ:* Va Commonwealth Univ, BS, 64, PhD(med chem), 69. *Prof Exp:* Res fel med & analytical chem, Med Col Va, 69. *Concurrent Pos:* Comn prod scholar grant, Col Pharm, Univ SC, 70-71, lectr, Proj Upward Bound, 70- *Mem:* Am Chem Soc; Am Pharmaceut Asn; Am Asn Cols Pharm; Sigma Xi. *Res:* Organic chemistry; cancer chemotherapeutic agents of the alkylating type; synthesis, testing and correlation of activity with physical parameters; mechanism of dimenthyl sulfoxide interaction with isolated enzyme systems; synthesis of agents for urolithiasis treatment. *Mailing Add:* 306 Ayers Circle Summerville SC 29485-3306

**WYNNE, BAYARD EDMUND,** group design making & communication support systems, organizational management & leadership; deceased, see previous edition for last biography

**WYNNE, ELMER STATEN,** CLINICAL MICROBIOLOGY. *Current Pos:* RETIRED. *Personal Data:* b El Paso, Tex, Oct 23, 17; m 38, 78, Opal Marks; c Edith & Frank. *Educ:* Univ Tex, BA, 38, MA, 44, PhD(bact), 48; Am Bd Microbiol, cert microbiol & bact. *Prof Exp:* Asst bact, Univ Tex, 38-39, tutor, 39-42, instr, 46, res assoc, 46-48, res bacteriologist, M D Anderson Hosp & Tumor Inst, 50-58, assoc prof microbiol, Dent Br, 58-59; asst prof, Univ Okla, 48-50; bacteriologist, Sch Aerospace Med, USAF, 59-60, res prof bact & chief microbiol, 60-67, sr microbiologist, 68-69; from assoc prof to prof, St Phillips Col, 70-82, Med Lab Technol & prog dir, 70-82. *Concurrent Pos:* Comdr, Med Serv Corps, US Naval Res. *Mem:* AAAS; Am Soc Microbiol; fel Am Acad Microbiol; Sigma Xi; charter fel Am Acad Microbiol. *Res:* Enteric bacteriology; bacterial antagonism; physiology of Clostridium spore germination; microbiological aspects of cancer research; aerospace microbiology; hand disinfection; live hybrid vaccine for bacillary dysentery. *Mailing Add:* 14802 Iron Liege San Antonio TX 78248-0903

**WYNNE, JAMES J,** PHYSICS. *Current Pos:* res staff mem, IBM Zurich Res Lab, IBM Thomas J Watson Res Ctr, 69-71, mgr nonlinear spectros, 74-76, mgr laser physics & chem, 76-87, mgr biol & molecular sci, 87-93, RES STAFF MEM, IBM THOMAS J WATSON RES CTR, 71- *Personal Data:* b Brooklyn, NY, Mar 19, 43; m 64; c 2. *Educ:* Harvard Univ, AB, 64, MA, 65, PhD(appl physics), 69. *Concurrent Pos:* Vis physicist, Johns Hopkins, 79, Dartmouth, 82, Univ Rochester, 82, Univ Chicago, 83; assoc ed, J Optical Soc Am, 82-83; prog mgr local educ outreach, IBM Thomas J Watson Res Ctr, 90- *Mem:* Nat Acad Sci; fel Optical Soc Am; Am Inst Physics; fel Am Phys Soc; Sigma Xi; Inst Elec & Electronics Engrs. *Res:* Nonlinear optical studies of semiconductors and insulators; study of novel laser systems; excimer laser etching of skin; laser-induced-fluorescence detection of arterial lesions and cluster science; applications of technology to K-12 education. *Mailing Add:* IBM Thomas J Watson Res Ctr Rm 26-118 Yorktown Heights NY 10598

**WYNNE, JOHNNY CALVIN,** PLANT BREEDING, PLANT GENETICS. *Current Pos:* ASSOC DEAN & DIR, NC AGR RES SERV, 91- *Personal Data:* b Williamston, NC, May 17, 43; m 63; c Debbie, Carol, Chris & Alex. *Educ:* NC State Univ, BS, 65, MS, 68, PhD(crop sci), 74. *Honors & Awards:* Bailey Award, Am Peanut Res & Educ Asn; Res Award, Nat Peanut Coun. *Prof Exp:* From instr to assoc prof, NC State Univ, 68-82, prof & head crop sci, 89-91. *Mem:* Am Soc Agron; fel Am Peanut Res & Educ Asn; fel AAAS. *Res:* Improvement of cultivated peanuts through breeding for higher productivity, disease resistance, insect resistance, nitrogen fixation efficacy, and better quality; collaborative research on peanuts in Thailand and the Philippines. *Mailing Add:* NC Agr Res Serv NC State Univ Box 7643 Raleigh NC 27695-7643. *Fax:* 919-515-7745

**WYNNE, KENNETH JOSEPH,** POLYMER SCIENCE. *Current Pos:* PROG MGR, ORG & POLYMERIC MAT, 84- *Personal Data:* b Rumford, RI, Jan 17, 40; m 67; c 2. *Educ:* Providence Col, BS, 61; Univ Mass, Amherst, MS & PhD(chem), 65. *Prof Exp:* Fel inorg chem, Univ Calif, Berkeley, 65-67; asst prof, Univ Ga, 67-73; sci officer, Off Naval Res, 73-83. *Concurrent Pos:* Vis scientist, IBM, San Jose, 83-84; vis scholar, Stanford Univ, 83-84; prog mgr, Solid State Chem, NSF, 88-89. *Mem:* AAAS; Sigma Xi; Am Chem Soc. *Res:* Polymer chemistry; surface polymer chemistry; polymers for optical applications; polymer membranes; electroactive polymers. *Mailing Add:* Off Naval Res Phys Sci Div 800 N Quincy St Arlington VA 22217-5660

**WYNNE, LYMAN CARROLL,** PSYCHIATRY, PSYCHOLOGY. *Current Pos:* chmn dept, 71-77, PROF PSYCHIAT SCH MED & DENT, UNIV ROCHESTER, 71- *Personal Data:* b Lake Benton, Minn, Sept 17, 23; m 47; c 5. *Educ:* Harvard Med Sch, MD, 47; Harvard Univ, PhD(soc psychol), 58. *Hon Degrees:* MD, Oulu Univ, Finland, 89. *Honors & Awards:* Commendation Medal, USPHS, 65, Meritorious Serv Medal, 66; Fromm-Reichmann Award, Am Acad Psychoanal, 66; Hofheimer Prize, Am Psychiat Asn, 66; Salmon Lectr, 73; Stanley R Dean Res Award, Am Col Psychiatrists, 76; McAlpin Res Achievement Award, 77; Distinguished Contributions to Family Ther Res Award, Am Asn Marriage & Family Ther, 82, Distinguished Achievement in Family Ther Res Award, 81, Distinguished Prof Contributions to Family Ther Award, 86. *Prof Exp:* Intern med, Peter Bent Brigham Hosp, Boston, 47-48; USPHS res fel, Harvard Univ, 48-49; Moseley traveling fel, London, Eng, 49-50; Rantoul fel psychol, Harvard Univ, 50; resident, Mass Gen Hosp, 51; resident, NIMH & St Elizabeth Hosp, Washington, DC, 52-53; psychiatrist, Lab Socio-Environ Studies, NIMH, Md, 54, Adult Psychiat, 54-71, chief family studies sect, 57-67, chief adult psychiat br, 61-71. *Concurrent Pos:* Mem fac, Wash Sch Psychiat, 56-71; mem fac, Wash Psychoanal Inst, 60-71, teaching analyst, 66-71; consult &

collab investr, WHO, 65-; mem-at-large, Div Behav Sci, Nat Res Coun, 69-72; psychiatrist-in-chief, Strong Mem Hosp, 71-77; mem rev comt career develop awards, NIMH, 72-76; vis lectr, Am Univ Beirut, 63-64; bd dir, Am Asn Marriage & Family Ther, 92-94, chair, bd trustees, 92-94. *Mem:* Am Psychiat Asn; Psychiat Res Soc; Soc Life Hist Res Psychopath; Am Family Ther Asn (pres, 86-87); Am Asn Marriage & Family Ther. *Res:* Family research and therapy; schizophrenia; cross-cultural studies; child development. *Mailing Add:* Dept Psychiat Univ Rochester Sch Med Ctr 300 Crittenden Blvd Rochester NY 14642. *Fax:* 716-273-1091

**WYNNE, MICHAEL JAMES,** BIOLOGY. *Current Pos:* PROF BIOL, UNIV MICH, ANN ARBOR, 76- *Personal Data:* b St Louis, Mo, Feb 4, 40. *Educ:* Washington Univ, St Louis, BA, 62; Univ Calif, Berkeley, PhD(bot), 67. *Honors & Awards:* Darbaker Prize, Bot Soc Am, 71; G W Prescott Award, Phycol Soc Am, 87. *Prof Exp:* From asst prof biol to assoc prof biol, Univ Tex, Austin, 69-76. *Concurrent Pos:* Instr, Hopkins Marine Sta, Stanford Univ, 68, Friday Harbor Labs, Univ Wash, 70 & 78, Marine Biol Lab, Woods Hole, 71 & 72; vis res assoc, Univ Melbourne Parkville, 81. *Mem:* Int Phycol Soc (pres, 88-89); Phycol Soc Am (secy, 73-75, vpres, 76, pres, 77); Bot Soc Am; Brit Phycol Soc; Am Soc Plant Syst. *Res:* Marine phycology, systematics of marine algae, morphology, and biogeography; the algae floor of Alaska, the Caribbean, and various other regions, particular interest on the red algae order Ceramiales. *Mailing Add:* Dept Biol & Herbarium Univ Mich 7830 N University Ave Ann Arbor MI 48109-1048

**WYNNE-EDWARDS, HUGH ROBERT,** GEOLOGY. *Current Pos:* PRES & CHIEF EXEC OFFICER, BC RES INC, VANCOUVER, 93-; PRES, TERRACY INC, 93- *Personal Data:* b Montreal, Que, Jan 19, 34; m 56, 72, 85; c 4. *Educ:* Aberdeen Univ, BSc, 55; Queen's Univ, Ont, MA, 57, PhD(geol), 59. *Hon Degrees:* DSc, Mem Univ, 75. *Honors & Awards:* Spendiarov Prize, 72. *Prof Exp:* Tech officer geol, Geol Surv Can, 58-59; lectr, Queen's Univ, Ont, 59-61, from asst prof to assoc prof, 61-68, prof geol & head dept geol sci, 68-72; Cominco prof geol & head, Dept Geol Sci, Univ BC, 72-77; asst secy, Ministry State for Sci & Technol, Govt Can, Ottawa, 77-79; sci dir, Alcan Int Ltd, Montreal, 79-80, vpres & chief sci officer, 80-89. *Concurrent Pos:* Vis fel, Aberdeen Univ, 65-66 & Univ Witwatersrand, 72; pres, Can Geosci Coun, 74; UN consult, India, 76; mem sci adv comt, Can Broadcasting Comn, 78-84; mem, Conseil de la Politique Sci, Quebec, 81-; dir, Soquip, 83-; dir & trustee, Sci Coun Can, 83- & Royal Victorial Hosp, 84-88. *Mem:* AAAS; Asn Sci & Technol Community Can (pres, 77); Royal Soc Can. *Res:* Resources and physical environment; science policies. *Mailing Add:* 2080 27th St W Vancouver BC V7V 4L4 Can

**WYNNE-EDWARDS, VERO COPNER,** population structure & natural selection theory; deceased, see previous edition for last biography

**WYNNYCKYJ, JOHN ROSTYSLAV,** AGGLOMERATION, HIGH TEMPERATURE PROCESSES. *Current Pos:* assoc prof, 69-82, PROF CHEM ENG & EXTRACTIVE METALL, UNIV WATERLOO, 82- *Personal Data:* b Ukraine, Nov 4, 32; Can citizen; m 56, Iroida Lebid; c Oksana, Roman & Mychailo. *Educ:* McGill Univ, BEng, 56; Univ Toronto, MASc, 65, PhD(metall), 68. *Honors & Awards:* Plummer Gold Medal, 81. *Prof Exp:* Res engr, Int Nickel Co Can, 56-59; develop supvr, DuPont Can Ltd, 59-64; Nat Res Coun Can fel, Max Planck Inst Phys Chem, 68-69. *Concurrent Pos:* Consult metal extraction; vis scientist, Nat Res Coun, Ottawa, 79; div mineral eng, Commonwealth Sci & Indust Res Orgn, Australia, 84; vis scientist, L Mintek, SAfrica, 92; vis prof, Lviv Polytech Univ, Ukraine, 92. *Mem:* Can Inst Mining & Metall; Minerals, Metals & Mat Soc; Fel Shevchenko Sci Soc. *Res:* Mechanisms of high temperature heterogeneous reactions significant in metals extraction; coal combustion and ash fouling; sintering, selective reduction agglomeration; iron ore pelletizing; silicothermic production of magnesium metal. *Mailing Add:* Dept Chem Eng Univ Waterloo Waterloo ON N2L 3G1 Can. *Fax:* 519-746-4979; *E-Mail:* jrwynnyckyj@chemical.watstar.uwaterloo.ca

**WYNSTON, LESLIE K,** BIOCHEMISTRY. *Current Pos:* from asst prof to assoc prof chem, 65-75, PROF CHEM, CALIF STATE UNIV, LONG BEACH, 75- *Personal Data:* b San Diego, Calif, Jan 5, 34; m 85, Anna Sun; c Lani P (Noreke). *Educ:* San Diego State Univ, BS, 55; Univ Calif, Los Angeles, MS, 58, PhD(physiol chem), 60. *Prof Exp:* Instr biochem, Med Sch, Northwestern Univ, 60-61; lectr, Med Sch, Univ Calif, San Francisco, 61-63; USPHS fel, Max Planck Inst Protein & Leather Res, 63-65. *Concurrent Pos:* Supvr, Metab Res Lab, Chicago Wesley Mem Hosp, 60-61; consult, NAm Aviation, Inc, 65-67; vis prof, Univ Zurich, 71-72; exchange prof, Nat Chung Hsing Univ, Taiwan, 75-76. *Mem:* AAAS; Am Chem Soc; Soc Wine Educr. *Res:* Protein purification and characterization; chemical isolation procedures; chromatographic and electrophoretic methods. *Mailing Add:* Dept Chem & Biochem Calif State Univ Long Beach CA 90840-3903. *Fax:* 562-985-8557

**WYNTER, CARLTON ELLESTON, JR,** CORAL REEF FISH ECOLOGY. *Current Pos:* PRES, NSR, INC, 86- *Personal Data:* b New York, NY, Aug 11, 47; m, Barbara Seruya. *Educ:* Columbia Univ, BA, 68; Princeton Univ, MS, 71, PhD(ecol & evolutionary biol), 93. *Prof Exp:* Pres, Ecosysts Res, 78-94. *Concurrent Pos:* Assoc Educ, Am Mus Nat Hist; sci content dir, Neon Prodns Inc, 93-94. *Res:* Examination of the mechanisms controlling the distribution, behavior and ecology of fishes resident on coral reefs; remote sensing to identify large and small scale patterns. *Mailing Add:* HSR Inc Box 925 Village Sta New York NY 10014-0701

**WYNVEEN, ROBERT ALLEN,** HEALTH PHYSICS, MEDICAL PHYSICS. *Current Pos:* health physics mgr, Argonne Nat Lab, 76-87, assoc mgr, Occup Health & Safety, 82-87, mgr, Environ Health & Safety Dept, 87-91, DIR, ENVIRON SAFETY & HEALTH DIV, ARGONNE NAT LAB, 91- *Personal Data:* b Baldwin, Wis, July 24, 39; m 64, Sylvia Melby; c Jeffrey, Timothy, Stacie & Eric. *Educ:* Univ Wis-River Falls, BS, 61; Rutgers Univ, MS, 63, PhD(radiation biophys), 72. *Prof Exp:* Health physicist, Argonne Nat Lab, 63-65; radiol health physicist, Rutgers Med Sch, Rutgers Univ, 65-76. *Concurrent Pos:* Radiol health physics consult, Colgate-Palmolive Res Ctr, 68-76, Warner-Lambert Res Ctr, 72-76, Ortho Diag & Pharmaceut, Inc, 74-76 & Fusion Energy Corp, 75-76. *Mem:* Am Asn Physicists Med; Nat Health Physics Soc. *Res:* Immediate and transient effects of radiation, especially ionizing, microwave and laser, on biological systems' functions with emphasis on cellular energy production and active transport across membranes; environmental hazard assessment. *Mailing Add:* Environ Safety & Health Div Argonne Nat Lab 9700 S Cass Ave Argonne IL 60439. *Fax:* 630-252-5778; *E-Mail:* lrwynveen@anl.gov

**WYON, JOHN BENJAMIN,** COMMUNITY BASED PUBLIC HEALTH EPIDEMIOLOGY. *Current Pos:* RETIRED. *Personal Data:* b London, Eng, May 3, 18; m 46; c 2. *Educ:* Cambridge Univ, BA, 40, MB, BCh, 42; Harvard Univ, MPH, 53. *Prof Exp:* Med officer, Friends Ambulance Unit, Ethiopia, 43-45; med missionary to India from Church Missionary Soc, London, 47-52; res assoc epidemiol, Sch Pub Health, Harvard Univ, 53-58, instr, 58-60, res fel, 60-61, res assoc pop studies, 61-62, asst prof, 62-66, lectr pop studies & sr res assoc, Ctr Pop Studies, 66-71, sr lectr pop studies, 71-88. *Concurrent Pos:* Field dir, India-Harvard-Ludhiana Pop Study & asst prof, Christian Med Col, Ludhiana, India, 53-60. *Mem:* Am Pub Health Asn. *Res:* Community-oriented approaches to primary health care and population control; community epidemiology; field research on births, deaths and migrations in developing countries; development of local education units to demonstrate implications of population changes. *Mailing Add:* 143 Fairway Rd Chestnut Hill MA 02167

**WYRICK, PRISCILLA BLAKENEY,** BACTERIOLOGY. *Current Pos:* from asst prof to assoc prof, 73-88, PROF SCH MED, UNIV NC, CHAPEL HILL, 88- *Personal Data:* b Greensboro, NC, Apr 28, 40. *Educ:* Univ NC, Chapel Hill, BS, 62, MS, 67, PhD(bact), 71. *Prof Exp:* Technician clin microbiol, NC Mem Hosp, 62-64, asst supvr, 64-65, supvr in chg mycol & mycobact, 65-66. *Concurrent Pos:* Med Res Coun fel, Nat Inst Med Res, London, Eng, 71-73; consult, Dept Hosp Labs, NC Mem Hosp, 73- *Mem:* Am Soc Microbiol; Brit Soc Gen Microbiol; Am Acad Microbiol; AAAS; Am Soc Infectious Dis; Am Sexually Transmitted Dis Asn. *Res:* Pathogenesis of chlamydia; cellular and molecular biology of human clamydial infections; structure-function analyses of bacterial pathogens. *Mailing Add:* Dept Microbiol CB 7290 FLOB Univ NC Sch Med Chapel Hill NC 27599. *Fax:* 919-962-8103; *E-Mail:* pbwyrick@med.unc.edu

**WYRICK, RONALD EARL,** BIOCHEMISTRY, ALLERGY. *Current Pos:* WASH BIOTECH, 92- *Personal Data:* b Kansas City, Mo, Nov 4, 44; m 66; c 4. *Educ:* Calif State Col, Stanislaus, BA, 68; Univ Calif, Davis, PhD(biochem), 74. *Prof Exp:* Indust res allergist, Hollister-Stier, Subsid Miles Inc, Wash, 74-81, vpres sci affairs, 81-84, vpres opers, 84-92. *Res:* Elucidation of allergy mechanisms to provide research directions for potential new treatments for the allergic condition. *Mailing Add:* Wash Biotech E 4503 Red Roan Dr Spokane WA 99217

**WYRICK, STEVEN DALE,** MOLECULAR MODELING, TISSUE CULTURE. *Current Pos:* ASST PROF, UNIV NC, CHAPEL HILL, 82- *Personal Data:* b Greensboro, NC, Oct 23, 51; m 87. *Educ:* Univ NC, Chapel Hill, BS, 74, PhD(med chem), 77. *Prof Exp:* Res assoc med chem, Research Triangle Inst, 78-82. *Mem:* Am Chem Soc; Sigma Xi; AAAS. *Res:* Radiosynthesis, molecular modeling and drug design and synthesis of novel dopamine antagonists and anti-cerebral edema agents. *Mailing Add:* Univ NC Sch Pharm Beard Hall CB 407360 Chapel Hill NC 27599-7360

**WYRTKI, KLAUS,** PHYSICAL OCEANOGRAPHY. *Current Pos:* prof, 64-93, EMER PROF OCEANOG, UNIV HAWAII, 93- *Personal Data:* b Tarnowitz, Ger, Feb 7, 25; m 53, 70, Erika Maassen; c Undine & Oliver. *Educ:* Kiel Univ, PhD(phys oceanog), 50. *Honors & Awards:* Rossenstiel Award, Univ Miami, 81; Maurice Ewing Medal, Am Geophys Union, 89; Sverdrup Gold Medal, Am Meterol Soc, 91; Albert Defant Medal, Ger Meterol Soc, 92. *Prof Exp:* Scientist, Ger Hydrographic Inst, Hamburg, 50-51; res fel oceanog, Kiel Univ, 51-54; scientist, Inst Marine Res, Djakarta, 54-57 & Int Hydrographic Bur, Monaco, 58; res officer, Commonwealth Sci & Indust Res Orgn, Australia, 58-61; res oceanogr, Scripps Inst, Univ Calif, 61-64. *Concurrent Pos:* Ed, Atlas Phys Oceanog, Int Indian Ocean Exped, 65-72; chmn, NPac Exp, 74-82. *Mem:* AAAS; fel Am Geophys Union; fel Am Meteorol Soc; Oceanog Soc. *Res:* General circulation of the oceans; water masses; equatorial circulation; climate change; ocean-atmosphere interaction; El Nino, Sea Level. *Mailing Add:* Dept Oceanog Univ Hawaii Honolulu HI 96822-2336

**WYRWICKA, WANDA,** FEEDING, CONDITIONING. *Current Pos:* RES ANAT, UNIV CALIF, LOS ANGELES, 66- *Personal Data:* b Poland, Sept 8, 12, US Citizen; m 46, Leszek Kolodziejczyk; c 1. *Educ:* Univ Poznan, Poland, PhD(zool), 47. *Honors & Awards:* Pavlovian Soc Award, 77. *Prof Exp:* Neurophysiologist, Nencki Inst, Warsaw, Poland, 47-66. *Concurrent Pos:* Consult, Lab Neuropsychol, Vet Admn Med Ctr, Sepulveda, 66-71; key investr, Ctr Ulcer Res & Educ, Wadsworth Vet Admin Med Ctr, Los Angeles, 74-78. *Mem:* Am Physiol Soc; Soc Neurosci; Pavlovian Soc Am. *Res:* Feeding responses and their representations in the brain; initiation and inhibition of eating; social influences on feeding and food preferences; feeding disorders; articles on conditioning and feeding; books on problems of conditioning, food preferences and brain control of food intake. *Mailing Add:* Univ Calif Sch Med Los Angeles CA 90095

**WYSE, B D,** ORGANIC CHEMISTRY. *Current Pos:* RETIRED. *Personal Data:* b Columbia, SC, July 20, 27; m 52; c 2. *Educ:* Erskine Col, AB, 48; Vanderbilt Univ, MA, 51; Univ SC, PhD(chem), 57. *Prof Exp:* Instr math, Erskine Col, 49-51; chemist, Celanese Corp, SC, 51-53; chemist, Tech Sect, E I Du Pont de Nemours & Co, Inc, 56-61, sr res chemist, 61-92. *Mem:* Am Chem Soc. *Res:* Acrylic polymerization processes and reaction mechanisms; isocyanate chemistry; solution and melt spinning processes of elastomers and polyamides. *Mailing Add:* 4813 Shorewood Dr Chattanooga TN 37416

**WYSE, BONITA W,** DIETETICS, MAMMALIAN PHYSIOLOGY. *Current Pos:* PROF NUTRIT, UTAH STATE UNIV, 81-, DEAN, COL FAMILY LIFE, 86- *Personal Data:* b Lorain, Ohio, Oct 2, 45. *Educ:* Colo State Univ, PhD(nutrit), 77. *Concurrent Pos:* Mem, Arteriosclerosis-Hypertension Lipid Metab Adv Comt, Nat Heart Lung & Blood Inst, NIH, 84-87. *Mem:* Am Dietetic Asn; Exp Sta Comn Orgn & Policy. *Mailing Add:* Dean Off Col Family Life Utah State Univ Logan UT 84322-2900. *Fax:* 435-750-3845; *E-Mail:* bwyse@cc.usu.edu

**WYSE, DAVID GEORGE,** HYPERTENSION RESEARCH, CARDIOELECTROPHYSIOLOGY. *Current Pos:* PROF PHARMACOL & THERAPEUT, UNIV CALGARY, 78-, PROF CARDIOL, 85-; HEAD CARDIOL, FOOTHILLS HOSP, 86-, ASSOC DEAN, CLIN AFFAIRS, FAC MED, 93- *Personal Data:* b Kamloops, BC, Aug 15, 41. *Educ:* McGill Univ, PhD(pharmacol), 69; Univ Calgary, MD, 74. *Concurrent Pos:* Scholar, Alta Heritage Found Med Res. *Mem:* Can Cardiovasc Soc; Can Soc Clin Invest; Am Soc Pharmacol & Exp Therapeut; Can Soc Clin Pharmacol. *Res:* Pataphysiology of hypertension; management of ventricular arrhythmics; antiarrhythmic drugs. *Mailing Add:* Off Assoc Dean Clin Affairs Fac Med Univ Calgary 3350 Hospital Dr NW Calgary AB T2N 4N1 Can. *Fax:* 403-283-5594; *E-Mail:* dgwyse@acs.ucalgary.ca

**WYSE, DONALD L,** AGRONOMY. *Current Pos:* PROF, DEPT AGRON, UNIV MINN, ST PAUL. *Honors & Awards:* Ciba-Geigy/Weed Sci Soc Am Award, Ciba-Geigy Corp, 81. *Mailing Add:* Dept Agron Univ Minn 1991 Buford Ave St Paul MN 55108-1013

**WYSE, FRANK OLIVER,** MATHEMATICS. *Current Pos:* RETIRED. *Personal Data:* b Milwaukee, Wis, Apr 22, 30; m 67; c 4. *Educ:* Harvard Univ, AB, 52; Princeton Univ, AM, 55; Ore State Univ, PhD(math), 64. *Prof Exp:* Instr math, Lehigh Univ, 55-58; from instr to asst prof, Ore State Univ, 58-70; prof & chmn dept, Talladega Col, 70-73; assoc prof math, Clark Col, 73-79; prof math, Oglethorpe Col, 79-80; programmer, Southern Co Servs, 80-92. *Concurrent Pos:* Asst prof, Cleveland State Univ, 66-70. *Mem:* Am Math Soc. *Res:* Algebra; topology. *Mailing Add:* 2555 Moon Mountain Eugene OR 97403-2200

**WYSE, GORDON ARTHUR,** NEUROBIOLOGY. *Current Pos:* from asst prof to prof zool, 66-92, actg dir, Neurosci & Behav Prog, 88-89, PROF BIOL, UNIV MASS, AMHERST, 92- *Personal Data:* b San Jose, Calif, July 12, 40; m 63; c 3. *Educ:* Swarthmore Col, BA, 61; Univ Mich, MA, 63, PhD(zool), 67. *Concurrent Pos:* Nat Inst Neurol Dis & Stroke res grant, 69-78; vis scholar, Stanford Univ, 72-73; vis prof neurobiol, Harvard Med Sch, 82-83; Whitehall Found res grant, 92- *Mem:* AAAS; Am Soc Mammal; Soc Neurosci; Int Brain Res Orgn. *Res:* Comparative neurobiology; neural integration of central and sensory information to control rhythmic and other behavior patterns; neurotransmitters and neuromodulators. *Mailing Add:* Dept Biol Univ Mass Amherst MA 01003-0002. *Fax:* 413-545-3243; *E-Mail:* gwyse@bio.umass.edu

**WYSE, JOHN PATRICK HENRY,** MEDICAL SCIENCE, ANATOMY. *Current Pos:* From asst prof to assoc prof anat, 78-88, ASSOC CLIN PROF, FAC MED, UNIV CALGARY, 88-; PVT PRACTICE, 88- *Personal Data:* b Kamloops, BC, July 28, 48; m 72; c 4. *Educ:* Univ BC, BSc, 71, MD, 75; Univ Calgary, PhD(med sci anat), 78. *Concurrent Pos:* MRC grant, Med Res Coun Can, 78-80; Nat Retinitis Pigmentosa Found Can grant, 78-82; Alta Ment Health grant & Alta Heritage Found med res grant, 81; fel, Med Res Coun, 75-78. *Mem:* Asn Res Vision & Ophthal; Soc Neurosci; Can Asn Anatomists. *Res:* Histological, functional and genetic investigation of inherited ophthalmic defects in the BW rat; dopamine neurochemisty of retina, hypothalamus and nigrostriatal system of BW rat; morphometric investigations of mechanisms regulating rod outer segment renewal in vertebrate retinae. *Mailing Add:* 1632 14th Ave NW No 261B Calgary AB T2N 1M7 Can

**WYSE, ROGER EARL,** PLANT PHYSIOLOGY, BIOCHEMISTRY. *Current Pos:* DEAN & DIR, COL AGR & LIFE SCI, UNIV WIS, 92- *Personal Data:* b Wauseon, Ohio, Apr 22, 43. *Educ:* Ohio State Univ, BSAgr, 65; Mich State Univ, MS, 67, PhD(crop sci), 69. *Honors & Awards:* Arthur Flemming Award, 82. *Prof Exp:* Fel, Mich State Univ, 69-70; plant physiologist, Agr Res Serv, USDA, 70-86; dean res, Cook Col, Rutgers Univ, 86-92. *Mem:* AAAS; Am Soc Plant Physiol; Am Soc Agron; Am Soc Crop Sci. *Res:* Physiological limitations to yield in crop plants; oligosaccharide metabolism and mechanism of sucrose storage in beet roots; biochemical methods of testing for superior breeding lines. *Mailing Add:* Col Agr & Life Sci Univ Wis 140 Agricultural Hall Madison WI 63706. *Fax:* 608-262-4556; *E-Mail:* roger.wyse@ccmail.adp.wisc.edu

**WYSHAK, GRACE,** BIOSTATISTICS. *Current Pos:* LECTR, HARVARD SCH PUB HEALTH & MED SCH, 75- *Personal Data:* b Boston, Mass. *Educ:* Smith Col, BA, 49; Harvard Univ, MSHyg, 56; Yale Univ, PhD(biomet), 64. *Prof Exp:* Res assoc epidemiol, Harvard Univ, 56-60; instr math, Albertus Magnus Col, 64-65; assoc prof biomet, Yale Univ, 65-75. *Concurrent Pos:* NIH res career develop award, 68-72; consult, NIH, 70-, Vet Admin Coop Studies Ctr, 72- & Radcliffe Inst Prog Health Care, 75-77; statist consult, Mass Gen Hosp; lectr, Prev Med, Harvard Med Sch, 78-82, lectr on med, 82- *Mem:* Sigma Xi; Am Statist Asn; Biomet Soc; Am Epidemiol Asn; Int Epidemiol Asn. *Res:* Inheritance of twinning; biometric and epidemiologic methods; statistical methods in virology; statistical applications in psychiatry; cancer epidemiology; statistical applications in reproductive health and in preventive medicine. *Mailing Add:* Pop Studies Harvard Sch Pub Health 677 Huntington Ave Boston MA 02115-6023

**WYSKIDA, RICHARD MARTIN,** INDUSTRIAL ENGINEERING, OPERATIONS RESEARCH. *Current Pos:* from asst prof to assoc prof, 68-78, PROF INDUST ENG, UNIV ALA, HUNTSVILLE, 78- *Personal Data:* b Perrysburg, NY, Sept 2, 35; m 62; c 2. *Educ:* Tri-State Col, BS, 60; Univ Ala, Tuscaloosa, MS, 64; Okla State Univ, PhD(indust eng), 68. *Prof Exp:* Elec engr, Philco Corp, 60-62; aerospace technol, Marshall Space Flight Ctr, NASA, 62-68. *Concurrent Pos:* Consult, Gen Res Corp, Revere, Missile Command, Battelle Mem Inst & Mantech; assoc prof, Ala A&M Univ, 71-76. *Mem:* Am Inst Indust Engrs; Opers Res Soc Am; Am Soc Eng Educ; Inst Mgt Sci. *Res:* Temperature sensitive cushioning systems; routing models; cost estimation models. *Mailing Add:* Dept Indust & Syst Eng & Eng Mgt Univ Ala Huntsville AL 35899

**WYSOCKI, ALLEN JOHN,** INDUSTRIAL ORGANIC CHEMISTRY. *Current Pos:* tech mgr, 77-84, TECH DIR, CHEM PROD DIV, DE SOTO, INC, 84- *Personal Data:* b Chicago, Ill, Dec 22, 36; m 63; c 2. *Educ:* Loyola Univ Chicago, BS, 58; Northwestern Univ, Evanston, PhD(org chem), 63. *Prof Exp:* Res chemist, IIT-Res Inst, 62-64; div res mgr, Soap & Household Prod Div, Armour-Dial, Inc, Phoenix, 64-77. *Mem:* Am Chem Soc. *Res:* Development of detergents and other household products. *Mailing Add:* 715 E Cherry Lane Arlington Heights IL 60004-3217

**WYSOCKI, ANNETTE BERNADETTE,** CELL-EXTRACELLULAR MATRIX INTERACTIONS. *Current Pos:* DIR NURSING RES, NY UNIV MED CTR, 91-, RES ASST PROF, 91- *Personal Data:* b Raleigh, NC, Dec 31, 54; m 87, John. *Educ:* E Carolina Univ, BS, 78, MS, 80; Univ Tex, Austin, PhD(nursing), 86. *Honors & Awards:* Merit Award, Friends of Nat Inst Nursing Res. *Prof Exp:* Staff nurse, Univ Va Med Ctr, 78-79, Seton Med Ctr, Austin, Tex, 81-86; res & teaching asst nursing, Univ Tex, Austin, 82-84, sr res assoc, Univ Southwestern Med Ctr, 86-88, NIH fel, 88-89; NIH fel, Med Col, Cornell Univ, 89-91. *Concurrent Pos:* Mem, Res Comt, Parkland Mem Hosp, Dallas, 87-89, NY Hosp, New York, 90-91; mem, Decubitus Ulcer Panel & Skin Dis Interagency Coord Comt, NIH; Cong Liason Comt, Am Soc Cell Biol. *Mem:* AAAS; NY Acad Sci; Soc Invest Dermat; Am Soc Cell Biol; Wound Healing Soc. *Res:* Clinical and laboratory studies of acute and chronic wound healing; factors leading to the development of chronic wounds; prevention of chronic wounds; cell and extracellular matrix interactions in normal and chronic wound healing; adhesion, integrin receptors and proteolysis. *Mailing Add:* Dept Nursing Ronald O Perelman Dept Dermat NY Univ Med Ctr 560 First Ave New York NY 10016. *Fax:* 212-263-6226; *E-Mail:* wysocki@is2.nyu.edu

**WYSOCKI, CHARLES JOSEPH,** REPRODUCTION, CHEMORECEPTION. *Current Pos:* Fel vomeronasal organ & reproduction, Univ Pa, 78-79, asst mem genes & reproduction, 80-83, assoc mem chem commun & genetics, Monell Chem Senses Ctr, 83-90, RES ASST PROF, DEPT ANIMAL BIOL, SCH VET MED, UNIV PA, 85-, MEM, GENETICS & CHEM COMMUN, 90-, RES PROF, 93- *Personal Data:* b Utica, NY, May 4, 47; m 68, Linda M Moore; c Tracy L, Theresa M & Alexandra C. *Educ:* Col Oswego, State Univ NY, BA, 73; Fla State Univ, Tallahassee, MS, 76, PhD(psychobiol), 78. *Honors & Awards:* Kenji Nakanishi Award in Olfaction, 88. *Concurrent Pos:* Lectr, Dept Biol, Univ Pa, 78-; asst prof, Dept Psychol, Rutgers Univ, 79-80; ed, Focus on Fragrance, 84-92; prin investr, Individual Differences in Human Olfaction, NIH, 85-; co-author, co-prin investr, Nat Geograph Smell Surv. *Mem:* Asn Chemoreception Sci; NY Acad Sci; Sigma Xi; Soc Neurosci. *Res:* Role of genetics in individual differences in odor perception; regulation of reproductive physiology and behavior by odors; analysis of 1.5 million returns of Nat Geograph Smell Survey. *Mailing Add:* Monell Chem Senses Ctr Univ Pa 3500 Market St Philadelphia PA 19104-3308. *Fax:* 215-898-2084; *E-Mail:* wysocki@pobox.upenn.edu

**WYSOCKI, JOSEPH J(OHN),** LIQUID CRYSTAL DEVICES, THIN FILM DEVICES. *Current Pos:* sr res scientist, 67-86, PRIN SCIENTIST, XEROX CORP, 86- *Personal Data:* b Cohoes, NY, Aug 6, 28; m 57; c 3. *Educ:* Mass Inst Technol, BS & MS, 54. *Prof Exp:* Trainee, Naval Ord Lab, 51-54; res engr, RCA Labs, 54-67. *Concurrent Pos:* Instr, Trenton Jr Col, 60-62. *Mem:* Inst Elec & Electronics Engrs. *Res:* Semiconductor and solar cell devices; transistors; diodes; radiation damage to solar cells; lithium-doped, radiation-resistant solar cells; liquid crystals; display devices; thin-film transistors; fabrication; testing and evaluation of solid-state devices of various types; ferroelectric liquid crystals. *Mailing Add:* 544 Crest Circle Webster NY 14580

**WYSOLMERSKI, THERESA,** zoology, developmental biology, for more information see previous edition

**WYSONG, DAVID SERGE,** PLANT PATHOLOGY. *Current Pos:* ASSOC PROF PLANT PATH & EXTEN PLANT PATHOLOGIST, UNIV NEBR, LINCOLN, 64- *Personal Data:* b Glasgow, Ky, Apr 20, 34; m 58; c 5. *Educ:* Colo State Univ, BS, 58, MS, 61; Univ Ill, PhD(plant path), 64. *Mem:* Am Phytopath Soc. *Res:* Practical application of plant pathology. *Mailing Add:* 820 E Sanborn Dr Lincoln NE 68505

**WYSS, JAMES MICHAEL,** NEUROSCIENCE, NEUROANATOMY. *Current Pos:* asst prof anat 79-84, assoc prof cell biol & anat, 84-88, PROF CELL BIOL, UNIV ALA AT BIRMINGHAM, 88-, PROF MED & PSYCHOL, 89- *Personal Data:* b Ft Wayne, Ind, Mar 11, 48; m 73, Gloria F Gardels; c Dana, William & Steven. *Educ:* Concordia Col, Ft Wayne, Ind, BS, 70; Lutheran Sch Theol, Chicago, MDiv, 74; Wash Univ, PhD(psychobiol), 76. *Prof Exp:* Instr biol, Wash Univ, 74-77, teaching fel anat, Wash Univ, 76-79. *Concurrent Pos:* Mem, Neuropsychiat Prog, Univ Ala, Birmingham, 79-, Hypertension Res Prog, 81- *Mem:* AAAS; Soc Neurosci; Am Asn Anatomists; Am Physiol Soc; Am Heart Asn. *Res:* Understanding the mechanisms by which the central and peripheral nervous system participate in the development and maintenance of hypertension; role that the renal nerves and hypothalmus play in hypertension; mechanisms of antonomic control by limbic cortex. *Mailing Add:* Dept Cell Biol Univ Ala Birmingham AL 35294. *Fax:* 205-934-7029; *E-Mail:* jmwyss@uab.edu

**WYSS, MAX,** SEISMOLOGY. *Current Pos:* PROF, GEOPHYS INST, UNIV ALASKA, FAIRBANKS, 91- *Personal Data:* b Zürich, Switz, Sept 10, 39; US citizen; m 70, Ingrid Aufder Heide; c Birgit Gabriella, David Daedalas & Ben Max. *Educ:* Swiss Fed Inst Technol, dipl, 64; Calif Inst Technol, MS, 67, PhD(geophys), 70. *Prof Exp:* Res scientist geophys, Univ Calif, San Diego, 70; res scientist seismology, Lamont-Doherty Geol Observ, Columbia Univ, 70-71, res assoc, 71; from asst prof to prof, Univ Colo, Boulder, 72-91, Cires fel, geol sci, 72-91. *Concurrent Pos:* Ed, Pure & Appl Geophys, 74; vis prof geophys, Univ Karlsruhe, Ger, 75, Fed Inst Technol, Zurich, 79, 80 & Nat Univ Mex, 72; explor geophys, Geotest AG, Bern, Switz, 64; res scientist, Univ Mainz, Mainz, Ger, 65; res asst, Calif Inst Technol, 65-70; vis scientist, Graefenberg Array, Erlangen, Ger, 85-86; sr US scientist award, Alexander von Humboldt, 85-86; chmn, sub-comn earthquake prediction, IASPEI, 87-; mem eval comt, Can Earthquake Prediction, 89-; state seismologist, Alaska, 92-94. *Mem:* Am Geophys Union; Seismol Soc Am. *Res:* Earthquake source mechanism; earthquake predictions; seismic risk. *Mailing Add:* Geophysics Inst Univ Alaska Fairbanks AK 99775. *Fax:* 907-474-7092; *E-Mail:* mark@giseis.alaska.edu

**WYSS, WALTER,** MATHEMATICS, PHYSICS. *Current Pos:* from asst prof to assoc prof math & physics, 68-77, PROF PHYSICS, UNIV COLO, BOULDER, 77- *Personal Data:* b Matzendorf, Switz, Mar 26, 38; m 61, Yvonne; c Christa, Markus, Daniel W & Michelle (Manuela). *Educ:* Swiss Fed Inst Technol, dipl phys, 61, Dr Sc Nat(math physics), 65. *Prof Exp:* Instr physics, Swiss Fed Inst Technol, 61-66; instr, Princeton Univ, 66-68. *Concurrent Pos:* Swiss Nat Found stipend, Princeton Univ, 66-68; res fel, Univ Colo, Boulder, 69-70, NSF res grant, 70-72. *Mem:* Am Math Soc; Int Asn Math Phys; Int Soc Gen Relativity & Gravitation. *Res:* Axiomatic theory of quantized fields; general relativity; functional analysis; infinite parameter lie groups; stochastic processes and combinatorics. *Mailing Add:* 2810 Iliff Boulder CO 80303

**WYSSBROD, HERMAN ROBERT,** PHYSIOLOGY, BIOPHYSICS. *Current Pos:* RETIRED. *Personal Data:* b Louisville, Ky, Oct 17, 41; m 63. *Educ:* Univ Louisville, BEE, 63, PhD(physiol), 68. *Prof Exp:* Asst prof physiol, Mt Sinai Sch Med, 72-73, assoc prof physiol & biophys, 74-89; prof chem, Univ Louisville, 89-92. *Concurrent Pos:* NIH res career develop award, Mt Sinai Sch Med, 72-77; asst prof biophys chem, Mt Sinai Grad Sch Biol Sci, City Univ New York, 68-73; vis asst prof, Rockefeller Univ, 71-73, vis assoc prof, 74-78; investr, NY Heart Asn, 77-81. *Mem:* AAAS; Am Physiol Soc; Am Chem Soc; Soc Exp Biol & Med; NY Acad Sci. *Res:* Conformation-function relationships of biologically active peptides; transmembrane transport. *Mailing Add:* 1237 Larchmont Ave Louisville KY 40214

**WYTTENBACH, CHARLES RICHARD,** DEVELOPMENTAL BIOLOGY. *Current Pos:* asst prof zool, Univ Kans, 66-70, assoc prof, 70-75, chmn dept, 76-83, PROF PHYSIOL & CELL BIOL, UNIV KANS, 75- *Personal Data:* b South Bend, Ind, Jan 28, 33; m 59, Ellen Garnett; c Robert A, Ann G & Rebecca J (Marshall). *Educ:* Ind Univ, AB, 54, MA, 56; Johns Hopkins Univ, PhD(biol), 59. *Prof Exp:* From instr to asst prof anat, Univ Chicago, 59-66. *Concurrent Pos:* Managing ed, Univ Kans Sci Bull, 68-74; mem corp, Marine Biol Lab, Woods Hole, Mass; co-ed, Develop Biol Cnidaria, 74. *Mem:* Soc Develop Biol; Soc Integrative & Comp Biol. *Res:* Developmental biology, particularly mechanisms of insecticide-induced teratogenesis in chicks. *Mailing Add:* Div Biol Sci Univ Kans Haworth Hall Lawrence KS 66045-2106. *Fax:* 785-864-5321

**WYTTENBACH, ROBERT ALAN,** NEUROETHOLOGY. *Current Pos:* POSTDOCTORAL, CORNELL UNIV, 96- *Personal Data:* b Birmingham, Ala, Aug 8, 61. *Educ:* Univ Kans, BA & BS, 84; Oxford Univ, BA, 86; Cornell Univ, PhD(neurobiol & behav), 96. *Mem:* Soc Neurosci. *Res:* Applies paradigms of human psychophysics to hearing in crickets; precedence effect; categorical perception; minimum audible angle. *Mailing Add:* 915 N Cayuga St Ithaca NY 14850. *E-Mail:* rw12@cornell.edu

**WYZGA, RONALD EDWARD,** PUBLIC HEALTH. *Current Pos:* tech mgr, 77-83, PROJ MGR, ELEC POWER RES INST, 75-, SR MGR, 84- *Personal Data:* b New Bedford, Mass, Aug 10, 42; m 69; c 2. *Educ:* Harvard Col, AB, 64; Fla State Univ, MS, 66; Harvard Univ, ScD, 71. *Prof Exp:* Tech staff, Orgn Econ Coop & Develop, 71-75. *Concurrent Pos:* Lectr, Am Col, Paris, 73-75. *Mem:* Am Statist Asn; Biomet Soc; Soc Risk Assessment. *Res:* Environmental risk assessment; health effects of air pollution; environmental cost-benefit analyses. *Mailing Add:* 4690 Smith Grade Santa Cruz CA 95060

**WYZGOSKI, MICHAEL GARY,** POLYMER SCIENCE, MATERIALS ENGINEERING. *Current Pos:* RES ENGR, GEN MOTORS RES LAB, 73- *Personal Data:* b Pontiac, Mich, Dec 25, 43; m 67; c 3. *Educ:* Oakland Univ, BS, 64; Univ Mich, MS, 70, PhD(mat eng), 73. *Prof Exp:* Plastics engr, Dow Chem Co, 66-68. *Mem:* Am Phys Soc; Am Chem Soc. *Res:* Durability of plastic and elastomeric materials, including oxidative and physical aging, stress cracking and ozone cracking; fatigue fracture of composites and unfilled thermoplastics; impact fracture. *Mailing Add:* 1500 Houghton Trail Ortonville MI 48462-8402

# X

**XI, XIAOXING,** THIN FILMS OF METAL OXIDE MATERIALS, HIGH TEMPERATURE SUPERCONDUCTORS. *Current Pos:* ASST PROF PHYSICS, PA STATE UNIV, 95- *Personal Data:* b Beijing, China, Nov 1, 57; m 86, Qi Li; c Joyce. *Educ:* Peking Univ, BSc, 82, PhD(physics), 87. *Honors & Awards:* Career Award, NSF, 97; K C Wang Sci & Technol Award, Chinese Acad Sci, 97. *Prof Exp:* Vis scientist, Karlsruhe Nuclear Res Ctr, Ger, 87-89; res assoc, Rutgers Univ/Bellcore, 89-90; asst res scientist, Univ, Md, 90-95. *Concurrent Pos:* Res scientist, Nat Inst Stand & Technol, 83-94; guest prof, Peking Univ, 93-; mem tech staff, Superconducting Core Technol, 95, consult, 95-96; consult, Sumitomo Elec Indust, 96- *Mem:* Am Phys Soc; Mat Res Soc. *Res:* Material physics in metal oxide thin films underlying their electronic and photonic applications; high temperature superconductors; ferroelectric and magnetic oxide thin film; multilayer heterostructures. *Mailing Add:* Dept Physics Pa State Univ 104 Davey Lab University Park PA 16802. *Fax:* 814-865-3604; *E-Mail:* xi@phys.pbu.edu

**XIANG, JIM,** GENETIC ENGINEERING OF IMMUNOGLOBULIN & CYTOKIN GENES, CANCER BIOTHERAPY. *Current Pos:* res scientist & asst prof, 90-93, RES SCIENTIST & ASSOC PROF, SASKATOON CANCER CTR, UNIV SASK, 93- *Personal Data:* b Shanghai, China, Feb 21, 47; Can citizen; m 76, Tilly Ping; c David. *Educ:* Shanghai Med Univ, MD, 70; Univ Fla, MS, 83, PhD(tumor immunol), 86. *Prof Exp:* Pathologist, Xian Yau Hosp, 74-76, Child & Maternal Hosp, 76-78; res fel, Cancer Inst, China, 78-80; vis scholar, Nat Cancer Inst, NIH, 80-81, fcl, 86-88; res assoc, Mt Sinai Hosp Res Inst, Univ Toronto, 88-90. *Concurrent Pos:* Res scholar, Med Res Coun Can, 91; prin investr, Sask Cancer Found, 91-92, Sask Health Res Bd, 91-93, Med Res Coun Can, 91-96, Nat Cancer Inst Can, 93-96, Sterling Winthrop Res Inst, 93-; honor prof, Norman Bethune Univ Med Scis, 93-; vis prof, Xi An Med Univ, 93- *Mem:* Am Asn Cancer Res; Am Asn Immunol. *Res:* Genetic engineering of immunoglobulin and cytokine genes for cancer therapy; the study of antibody and antigen interaction by site-directed mutagenesis; the study of pathogenesis and biodistribution of tumor associated antigen. *Mailing Add:* Dept Microbiol & Oncol Saskatchewa Cancer Ctr 20 Campus Dr Saskatoon SK S7J 4H4 Can. *Fax:* 306-966-2910

**XIAO, MIN,** LASER & ATOMIC PHYSICS, NONLINEAR & QUANTUM OPTICS. *Current Pos:* asst prof, 90-95, ASSOC PROF PHYSICS, UNIV ARK, 95- *Personal Data:* b Xuzhou City, China; m, Hua Xa; c Lucy & Kathie. *Educ:* Nanjing Univ, China, BS, 82; Univ Tex, Austin, PhD(physics), 88. *Prof Exp:* Postdoctoral assoc, Mass Inst Technol, 88-90. *Concurrent Pos:* Young investr award, NSF, 94. *Mem:* Optical Soc Am. *Res:* Optics; laser physics; nonlinear optics; applications of optical instrumentation. *Mailing Add:* Dept Phys Univ Ark Fayetteville AR 72701

**XIE, JIANMING,** REGULATION OF VASCULAR SMOOTH MUSCLE, ROLE OF NITRIC OXIDE IN HOST DEFENSE RESPONSES. *Current Pos:* RES ASSOC, LA STATE UNIV, MED CTR, NEW ORLEANS, 91- *Personal Data:* b Putian City, Fujian, China, Nov, 22, 60; m 88, Ye Wang. *Educ:* Fujian Med Col, China, BS, 82; Peking Union Med Col, China, MS, 87. *Honors & Awards:* Young Scientist Award, Chinese Pathophysiol Soc, 90. *Prof Exp:* Teaching asst pathophysiol, Fujian Med Col, 82-84; res asst, Chinese Acad Med Sci, 87-88; fel, Cancer Inst, China, 89-91. *Concurrent Pos:* Human physiol res, Chinese 4th Antarctic Sci Exped, 87-88; vis scholar, Univ Tex, Galveston, 88-89; trainee travel award, Am Fedn Clin Invest, 93 & 94. *Mem:* Chinese Path Soc; Am Hypertension Soc; Am Heart Asn; Soc Exp Biol & Med. *Res:* Role of nitric oxide and cytokines in the regulation of vascular smooth muscle and host immunoresponses. *Mailing Add:* 3513 Green Acres Rd Metairie LA 70003. *Fax:* 504-568-4295

**XIE, YA-HONG,** NOVEL PROPERTIES OF SI & GE, MOLECULAR BEAM EPITAXY. *Current Pos:* MEM TECH STAFF, AT&T BELL LABS, MURRAY HILL, NJ, 86- *Educ:* Purdue Univ, BS, 81; Univ Calif, Los Angeles, MS, 84, PhD(elec eng), 86. *Mem:* Mat Res Soc; Inst Elec & Electronics Engrs; Am Phys Soc. *Res:* Increased functionality of Si based materials; optical and electronic crystal growth of GeSi alloys by molecular beam epitaxy; epitaxy of dissimilar materials: stability and relaxation. *Mailing Add:* AT&T Bell Labs MH1E-342 600 Mountain Ave Murray Hill NJ 07974-2070

**XIONG, YIMIN,** SIGNAL TRANSDUCTION, CELL PROLIFERATION & DIFFERENTIATION. *Current Pos:* MED PRACTR, 97- *Personal Data:* b Shanghai, China, May 8, 50. *Educ:* Shanghai Sec Med Univ, MD, 83; Univ Mass, PhD(molecular cell biol), 91. *Prof Exp:* Res assoc, Hoffman-La Roche, 91-97. *Mem:* Am Soc Cell Biol; AAAS. *Res:* Signal transduction in the regulation of cell proliferation and differentiation; gene expression in response to extracellular stimulation in the regulation of epidermal cell proliferation and hair follicle growth. *Mailing Add:* 26 Valley Rd Nutley NJ 07110

**XU, JIANMING,** INSTRUMENTATION SCIENCE, MEASUREMENT & METROLOGY. *Current Pos:* SR DESIGN ENGR, JOHN BEAN CO, 96- *Personal Data:* b WuXi, China, May 29, 57; m 84, Xiaohong Liu; c Ke & Steven H. *Educ:* Zhejiang Univ, China, BS, 82, MS, 84; Univ Ark, PhD(instrumental sci), 96. *Prof Exp:* Asst prof optics & electro-optics, Shanghai Jiao Tong Univ, China, 84-91; sr design engr, Automotive Serv Equip Div, FMC Co, 96. *Concurrent Pos:* Vis researcher, Univ Tokoyo, Japan, 91; consult, Automotive Serv Equip Div, FMC Co, 94-95, Univ Ark, Little Rock, 96-97. *Mem:* Soc Photo-optical Instrumentation Engrs. *Res:* Study of test and measurement for temperature, pressure and high speed spectrum; investigation of new method for measurements and metrology for angle, positioning, dimensional size and surface quality; optical, electro-optic, hardware and software; computer technology in instrumental science. *Mailing Add:* John Bean Co 309 Exchange Ave Conway AR 72032. *E-Mail:* jimmyxu@rocketmail.com

**XU, RENLIANG,** LIGHT SCATTERING, COLLOID PHYSICS. *Current Pos:* STAFF SCIENTIST, SHORT COURSE DIR & LAB MGR, COULTER CORP, 91- *Personal Data:* b Suzhou, China, Oct 20, 54; Can citizen; m 84, Jinglu Cao; c Jennifer. *Educ:* Fudan Univ, China, BS, 82; State Univ NY, Stony Brook, MS, 87, PhD(chem), 88. *Honors & Awards:* Sherwin-William Award, Am Chem Soc, 89. *Prof Exp:* Fel, Dept Chem, Univ Toronto, 88-90, sr tutor chem, 89-91, Nat Sci & Eng Res Coun Can res fel, 90-91. *Concurrent Pos:* Mem, Eng Res Ctr, Particle Sci Technol. *Mem:* Am Chem Soc; Am Phys Soc; Am Soc Testing & Mat. *Res:* Polymer and colloid physics, materials characterization and instrumentation. *Mailing Add:* 1441 SW 102nd Ave Pembroke Pines FL 33025. *Fax:* 305-883-6877; *E-Mail:* ren.xu@internet.com

**XU, XUEMIN,** BIOHEAT TRANSFER. *Current Pos:* ASST PROF ENG SCI, COL STATEN ISLAND, 91- *Personal Data:* b Jangsu, China, Oct 2, 63. *Educ:* Shanghai Med Univ, BS, 86; Univ Ala, Birmingham, MS, 88. *Mem:* Soc Women Eng; Am Soc Mech Engrs. *Mailing Add:* Dept Appl Sci Col Staten Island Rm IN-236 2800 Victoria Blvd Staten Island NY 10314

**XU, YUNJIE,** HIGH RESOLUTION SPECTROSCOPY, MOLECULAR BEAM VAN DER WAALS COMPLEXES & LASER SPECTROSCOPY. *Current Pos:* POSTDOCTORAL FEL, CHEM DEPT, UNIV ALTA CAN, 96- *Personal Data:* b Xiamen, China, Apr 17, 66. *Educ:* Xiamen Univ, China, BSc, 88; Univ BC, PhD(chem), 93. *Prof Exp:* Res assoc spectros, SIMS, Nat Res Coun Can, 93-95. *Res:* Infrared laser spectroscopy of ions and complexes; application of molecular beam techniques and pulsed excitation; emission spectroscopy methods for the study of intermolecular interactions. *Mailing Add:* Dept Chem Univ Alta Edmonton AB T6G 2G2 Can

**XU, ZHENCHUN,** SYNTHESIS OF COMPOUNDS USED AS DRUG DELIVERY SYSTEM, STUDIES ON PHOSPHOLIPIDS. *Current Pos:* SCIENTIST, EMISPHERE TECHNOL, INC, 91- *Personal Data:* b Shanghai, China, Feb 28, 46; m 79, Xinxin Sun; c Ying. *Educ:* Univ Sci & Technol, China, BS, 68; Grad Sch, Acad Sci China, MS, 82; Univ Va, MS, 86; City Univ NY, PhD(org chem), 91. *Prof Exp:* Chemist, Shenyang Glass Works, China, 69-73, Shenyang Inst, Bldg Mat, China, 73-78; res chemist, Inst Environ Chem, Acad Sci China, 78-83. *Mem:* Chinese Asn Sci & Technol USA (vpres, 92-); Am Chem Soc; Chinese Chem Soc. *Res:* Preparation of proteinoids, phospholipids and other materials used as drug delivery systems; permeability of liposomes, phospholipid packing and conformation, new phosphorylating agents, and organic and enzymatic syntheses of carbohydrates. *Mailing Add:* 4310 Kissena Blvd Apt 16H Flushing NY 11355. *Fax:* 914-235-8461

**XU, ZHI XIN,** LUNG DEVELOPMENT MOLECULAR BIOLOGY, PULMONARY SURFACTANT BIOCHEMISTRY. *Current Pos:* fel, 87-89, assoc, 91-94, ASST RES SCIENTIST, YALE UNIV SCH MED, 94- *Personal Data:* b Shanghai, China, Apr 8, 52; m 83, Jue W Bao; c Lijing. *Educ:* Guiyang Med Col, MD, 82; Zhejiang Univ, MS, 85; Shanghai Med Univ, PhD(neonatology), 89. *Prof Exp:* Attend pediatrician, Shanghai Med Univ, 89-91. *Mem:* Am Soc Biochem & Molecular Biol. *Res:* Regulation of gene expression for enzymes involved in fatty-acid synthesis in fetal lung; hormonal control of pulmonary surfactant production during fetal development. *Mailing Add:* Dept Pediat Yale Univ Sch Med 333 Cedar St PO Box 3333 New Haven CT 06510-8064. *Fax:* 203-785-7194

**XU, ZHIFU,** CHEMISTRY. *Current Pos:* RES CHEMIST, PPG INDUSTS INC, 93- *Personal Data:* b Qichun, Hubei, China, Nov 17, 62; m 87, Suzhen Ruan; c Angela R. *Educ:* Wuhan Univ, China, BS, 82; Wuxi Inst Light Chem, MS, 85; Univ Mich, PhD, 92. *Prof Exp:* Res fel, Zhengzhou Inst Technol, China, 85-88; fel, Univ Mich, 93. *Mem:* Am Chem Soc. *Res:* Synthesis and unambiguous characterization of world's largest pure hydrocarbon molecule; efficient synthesis of large-size dendritic molecules. *Mailing Add:* PPG Industs Res Ctr 4325 Rosanna Dr Allison Park PA 15101

**XUAN, JIALUO JACK,** TRIBOLOGY, MAGNETIC RECORDING & DATA STORAGE SYSTEMS. *Current Pos:* sr mgr, Conner Peripherals, Calif, 94-95, SR MGR, SEAGATE/CONNER TECHNOL, CALIF, 95- *Personal Data:* b Shanghai, China, Nov 25, 50; US citizen. *Educ:* Shanghai Univ Technol, China, BS, 79, MS, 82; Okla State Univ, PhD(mech eng), 88. *Prof Exp:* Postdoctoral res fel, Northwestern Univ, Ill, 88-91; sr tribology res & develop engr, Hitadi Metal Technol, Calif, 92-94. *Res:* Advanced data storage devices; surface analysis; laser and optics development for micromachinery on data storage media surfaces; material development and analysis; contact mechanisms; tribology simulation and testing. *Mailing Add:* PO Box 360409 Milpitas CA 95036-0409. *Fax:* 408-263-0782

**XUE, YONGPENG,** spectroscopy, quantum chemistry, for more information see previous edition

**XUE, ZILING,** MATERIALS CHEMISTRY. *Current Pos:* ASSOC PROF, DEPT CHEM, UNIV TENN, 92- *Personal Data:* b Wuxi, China, Dec 18, 59; m 84, Yihui Yang; c Katherine S. *Educ:* Nanjing Univ, China, MS, 82; Univ Calif, Los Angeles, PhD(chem), 89. *Honors & Awards:* Young Investr Award, NSF, 94. *Prof Exp:* Teaching staff chem, Nanjing Col Pharm, 82-83; postdoctoral assoc, Ind Univ, 90-92. *Concurrent Pos:* DuPont young prof, E I du Pont, de Nemours & Co, 95; Camille Dreyfus teacher & scholar, 97. *Mem:* Am Chem Soc; Mat Res Soc. *Res:* Synthesis, structure and reactivity of inorganic and organometallic compounds; mechanism of inorganic and organometallic reactions; molecular approaches to solid-state materials; homogeneous and heterogeneous catalysis. *Mailing Add:* Dept Chem Univ Tenn Knoxville TN 37996

# Y

**YAAKOBI, BARUKH,** ATOMIC & MOLECULAR PHYSICS. *Current Pos:* SR SCIENTIST, LAB LASER ENERGETICS, UNIV ROCHESTER, 74- *Personal Data:* b Petach-Tikva, Israel, Dec 10, 36; US citizen; m 68; c 2. *Educ:* Hebrew Univ, MS, 62, PhD(physics), 67. *Prof Exp:* Scientist magnetic fusion, AEC, France, 70-74. *Concurrent Pos:* Consult, Hampshire Instruments, Rochester, 84- *Mem:* Fel Am Phys Soc. *Res:* Plasma diagnosis using primarily x-ray physics and x-ray spectroscopy as applied to inertially confined fusion research. *Mailing Add:* LAB Laser Energetics Univ Rochester 250 E River Rd Rochester NY 14623-1299

**YABLON, ISADORE GERALD,** ORTHOPEDIC SURGERY. *Current Pos:* from asst prof to assoc prof, 71-78, PROF ORTHOP SURG, BOSTON UNIV SCH MED, 78- *Personal Data:* b Montreal, Que, May 30, 33; m 62; c 2. *Educ:* McGill Univ, BSc, 54; Univ Toronto, MD, 58. *Prof Exp:* Instr orthop, McGill Univ, 67-71. *Concurrent Pos:* Vis surgeon orthop, Univ Hosp, 71- & Boston City Hosp, 71- *Mem:* Am Acad Orthop Surg; Orthop Res Soc; Can Orthop Soc; Can Orthop Res Soc; fel Royal Col Physicians & Surgeons Can. *Res:* Developing technique of joint homografting for clinical application; methods to prevent graft rejection. *Mailing Add:* 720 Harrison Ave No 808 Boston MA 02118-2334

**YABLON, MARVIN,** APPLIED STATISTICS, PATTERN RECOGNITION. *Current Pos:* from asst prof to assoc prof, 78-90, PROF MATH, JOHN JAY COL, 91- *Personal Data:* b New York, NY, Oct 30, 35; m 68, Judith E Goldberg; c Andrew, Cynthia & Yablon. *Educ:* New York Univ, BEE, 57, MEE, 60, MS, 64, PhD(opers res), 77. *Prof Exp:* Res engr, Grumman Corp, 62-69; opers res analyst, Roosevelt Hosp, 73-76; statistician, Med Ctr, New York Univ, 76-78. *Concurrent Pos:* Consult, Med Ctr, New York Univ, 78-82; prof, PhD prog criminal justice, Grad Sch & Univ Ctr, City Univ NY, 88- *Mem:* Sigma Xi; Am Statist Asn; Inst Elec & Electronics Engrs; Opers Res Soc Am; Soc Indust & Appl Math; NY Acad Sci. *Res:* Pattern recognition; applied statistics; stochastic processes; applications of operations research. *Mailing Add:* 35-17 172nd St Flushing NY 11358

**YABLONOVITCH, ELI,** OPTICS, SOLID STATE PHYSICS. *Current Pos:* mem tech staff, 84-90, DISTINGUISHED MEM STAFF, BELLCORE, 90- *Personal Data:* b Puch, Austria, Dec 15, 46; Can citizen. *Educ:* McGill Univ, BSc, 67; Harvard Univ, AM, 69, PhD(appl physics), 72. *Honors & Awards:* Adolph Lomb Medal, Optical Soc Am, 78. *Prof Exp:* Mem tech staff, Bell Labs, 72-74; asst prof appl physics, Harvard Univ, 74-76, assoc, 76-79; res assoc & group head, Exxon Res Ctr, 79-84. *Concurrent Pos:* A P Sloan fel, 78-79. *Mem:* Fel Am Phys Soc; fel Optical Soc Am; sr mem Inst Elec & Electronics Engrs. *Res:* Nonlinear optics; laser-plasma interaction; laser induced chemistry; solar cells; semiconductor surfaces; photonic band structure. *Mailing Add:* Dept Elec Eng Dept 66-147K Engr IV Univ Calif Los Angeles 405 Hilgard Ave Los Angeles CA 90024. *Fax:* 310-206-8495

**YABLONSKI, MICHAEL EUGENE,** MEDICINE, PHYSIOLOGY. *Current Pos:* STAFF MEM, CORNELL UNIV. *Personal Data:* b Minneapolis, Minn, July 11, 40; m 62; c 4. *Educ:* Univ Minn, BS, 65, MD, 67, PhD(physiol), 73. *Prof Exp:* Intern surg, Albert Einstein Col Med, 68; resident physician, Naval Air Develop Ctr, 71-73; resident ophthal, Univ Minn Hosps, 73-76; res ophthalmologist, Mt Sinai Sch Med, 77- *Concurrent Pos:* Glaucoma fel, Wash Univ, St Louis, 76-77. *Res:* Transport physiology; transcapillary exchange; physiology of the eye and vision. *Mailing Add:* Dept Ophthal Univ Nebr Col Med 600 S 42nd St Omaha NE 68198-0001

**YABLONSKY, HARVEY ALLEN,** PHYSICAL CHEMISTRY. *Current Pos:* PROF CHEM, DEPT PHYS SCI, KINGSBOROUGH COL, 69- *Personal Data:* b New York, NY, Nov 24, 33; m 64; c 2. *Educ:* Brooklyn Col, BS, 54, MA, 58; Stevens Inst Technol, MS, 57, PhD(phys chem), 64; Am Inst Chem, cert. *Prof Exp:* Res chemist, NY State Dept Health, 55; lectr chem, Brooklyn Col, 55-56; teaching asst, Stevens Inst Technol, 56-59; lectr, Hunter Col, 60-63; asst prof, US Merchant Marine Acad, 63-64; head dept phys chem, Prod Div, Bristol Myers, 64-69. *Concurrent Pos:* Res biochemist, Messinger Res Found, 56-58; lectr, Hunter Col, 63-64, Rutgers Univ, 67-69; independent consult. *Mem:* Am Chem Soc; fel Am Inst Chem; Sigma Xi. *Res:* Kinetics of redox systems; structure of solutions; sorption at surfaces; complex ion chemistry; fiber and powder rheology; piezoelectricity of biological materials; nonuniform surface photometry; pharmacokinetics. *Mailing Add:* 815 Springfield Ave Cranford NJ 07016

**YABROFF, RONALD M,** PROCESS DEVELOPMENT, PROCESS SAFETY. *Current Pos:* Res engr, E I DuPont de Nemours & Co, Inc, 64-70, patent specialist, 70-71, spec assignment mkt, 71-72, develop engr, Elastomers Dept, Deepwater, NJ, 72-77, develop engr, Elastomers Dept, Ky, 78-80, STAFF ENGR, POLYMER PROD DEPT, E I DU PONT DE NEMOURS & CO, INC, 80- *Personal Data:* b Berkeley, Calif, Apr 24, 37; m 63; c 3. *Educ:* Univ Colo, BS, 59; Cornell Univ, PhD(chem eng), 64. *Mem:* Am Inst Chem Engrs. *Res:* Expression of fluids from fluid-solid combinations; formation of microporous polymeric structures; isocynate manufacture; polychloroprene manufacture; kinetics. *Mailing Add:* 607 Wynard Rd Wilmington DE 19803

**YACHNIN, STANLEY,** INTERNAL MEDICINE, HEMATOLOGY. *Current Pos:* from asst prof to assoc prof, 61-69, head, Sect Hemat-Oncol, 66-81, PROF MED, SCH MED, UNIV CHICAGO, 69- *Personal Data:* b New York, NY, June 28, 30; m 60; c 2. *Educ:* NY Univ, MD, 54; Am Bd Internal Med, dipl, 62. *Prof Exp:* House officer, Peter Bent Brigham Hosp, Boston, Mass, 54-55, jr asst resident med, 55-56, sr resident, 60-61. *Concurrent Pos:* USPHS res fel, Peter Bent Brigham Hosp & Harvard Med Sch, 58-60; Markle scholar acad med, 63-68. *Mem:* AAAS; Am Soc Clin Invest; Am Fedn Clin Res; Am Soc Hemat; Asn Am Physicians. *Res:* Hemolytic anemias; complement; lymphocyte transformation; mitogenic proteins; paroxysmal nocturnal hemoglobinuria; alpha feto protein; cholesterol metabolism and cell growth. *Mailing Add:* Dept Med Univ Chicago Sch Med Chicago IL 60637

**YACHNIS, MICHAEL,** OCEAN ENGINEERING. *Current Pos:* PROF, SCH ENG, GEORGE WASHINGTON UNIV, 70- *Personal Data:* b Athens, Greece, Mar 22, 22. *Educ:* Mil Acad, Greece, BS, 43; Mil Tech Col, Greece, BSCE, 51; George Washington Univ, MS, 56, MA, 62, DSc(struct eng), 68. *Honors & Awards:* Presidential Rank Award, 82. *Prof Exp:* From lieutenant to major, Greek Army Corps Engrs, 43-55; struct eng specialist, Adams Fabricated Steel, 55-56; struct br mgr, Naval Facil Eng Command, 56-63, chief struct engr & ocean eng consult, 63-72, chief engr, 72-88. *Concurrent Pos:* Chmn, Task Comt E, Am Soc Civil Engrs, mem, Coun Ocean Eng; mem, Welding Res Coun, Eng Found. *Mem:* Nat Acad Eng; fel Am Soc Civil Engrs; Soc Mil Engrs; Nat Soc Prof Engrs; Marine Technol Soc; Sigma Xi; Am Welding Soc; Undersea Med Soc. *Res:* Fleet readiness; author of various publications; granted one patent. *Mailing Add:* 4201 Military Rd NW Washington DC 20015

**YACKEL, ERNA BETH,** SOCIOCONSTRUCTIVIST THEORY, ARGUMENTATION & MATHEMATICAL COMMUNICATION. *Current Pos:* PROF MATH EDUC, PURDUE UNIV, CALUMET, 88- *Personal Data:* b Portland, Ore, Feb 13, 39; m 60, James; c Jonathan, Juliet & Carolyn. *Educ:* Dickinson State Col, BS, 57; Univ Minn, MA, 60; Purdue Univ, PhD(math educ), 84. *Concurrent Pos:* Young investr award, NSF, 90-97; monograph ed, J Res Math Educ, 97- *Mem:* Am Educ Res Asn; Nat Coun Teachers Math; Math Asn Am. *Res:* Classroom-based research that focuses on how students learn mathematics, with special emphasis on social interaction and the development of mathematical argumentation. *Mailing Add:* 7035 Knickerbocker Pkwy Hammond IN 46323. *Fax:* 219-989-2750; *E-Mail:* yackeleb@calumet.purdue.edu

**YACKEL, JAMES W,** MATHEMATICS. *Current Pos:* from asst prof to assoc prof, Purdue Univ, 66-76, prof & assoc dean sci, 76-87, vchancellor acad affairs, 87-90, CHANCELLOR, PURDUE UNIV, 90- *Personal Data:* b Sanborn, Minn, Mar 6, 36; m 60, Erna B Seecamp; c Jonathan, Juliet & Carolyn. *Educ:* Univ Minn, BA, 58, MA, 60, PhD(math), 64. *Prof Exp:* John Wesley Young res instr math, Dartmouth Col, 64-66. *Mem:* Am Math Soc; fel AAAS; Inst Math Statist; Math Asn Am. *Res:* Stochastics processes and graph theory; probability theory; combinatorial theory. *Mailing Add:* Purdue Univ Calumet Hammond IN 46323-2094. *Fax:* 219-989-2581

**YACKEL, WALTER CARL,** FOOD SCIENCE & TECHNOLOGY. *Current Pos:* Food technologist consumer prod, 70-75, food scientist, Corp Res, 76-86, APPLNS MGR FOOD & INDUST PROD, A E STALEY MFG CO, 86- *Personal Data:* b Evanston, Ill, Nov 20, 42; m 73. *Educ:* Univ Ill, BS, 65, MS, 68, PhD(food sci), 71. *Mem:* Inst Food Technologists; Sigma Xi. *Res:* Product and process development of food ingredients. *Mailing Add:* 8440 Hickory Dr Argenta IL 62501

**YACOUB, KAMAL,** ELECTRICAL ENGINEERING. *Current Pos:* from asst prof to assoc prof, 66-73, chmn dept, 72-87, PROF ELEC ENG, UNIV MIAMI, 73- *Personal Data:* b Nazareth, Palestine, Nov 11, 32; US citizen; m 64; c 3. *Educ:* Univ Pa, MSEE, 58, PhD(elec eng), 61. *Honors & Awards:*

Res Award, Am Soc Eng Educ. *Prof Exp:* Assoc elec eng, Moore Sch Elec Eng, Univ Pa, 61-63, asst prof, 63-66. *Concurrent Pos:* Chmn, Fac Senate, Univ Miami. *Mem:* Inst Elec & Electronics Engrs; Am Soc Eng Educ; Sigma Xi. *Res:* Acoustic transmission fluctuations in Florida straits; tidal modulation of environmental and acoustic parameters; spectral analysis and modelling of relationships; relationship between partial and multiple coherence functions; estimation through order statistics; time series analysis. *Mailing Add:* Univ Miami PO Box 248294 Coral Gables FL 33124. *Fax:* 305-284-4044

**YACOWITZ, HAL,** INVENTOR OF MEDICAL DEVICES, WILDLIFE CONSERVATION. *Current Pos:* PRES & DIR RES, DR H YACOWITZ & CO, 61-; PRES, DRUG DELIVERY DEVICES, 93- *Personal Data:* b Bronx, NY, Feb 17, 22; m 41, Ann Barnett. c Caryn, Richard & Susan. *Educ:* Cornell Univ, BS, 47, MNS, 48, PhD(animal nutrit), 50. *Prof Exp:* Assoc res biochemist, Parke, Davis & Co, 50-51; from asst prof to assoc prof poultry nutrit, Ohio State Univ, 51-55, assoc prof, Agr Exp Sta, 51-55; head, Nutrit Res Dept, Squibb Inst Med Res, 55-59; dir appl res, Nopco Chem Co, 59-61; dir res, Amburgo Co Inc, 61-79. *Concurrent Pos:* Prin Investr, small bus innovative res, US Govt Nat Inst Environ Health Sci, 87-91; owner, H Yacowitz & Co, nutrit consult lab. *Mem:* Am Chem Soc; fel NY Acad Sci; fel Am Heart Asn; Am Inst Nutrit; Am Asn Lab Animal Sci; Poultry Sci Asn. *Res:* Vitamin B-12 microbiological assays; vitamin interrelationships; antibiotic absorption and effects of dietary antibiotics on chicks and hens; vitamin requirements; antifungal agents; calcium and fat metabolism in man and animals; atherosclerosis; nutritional value of human and animal foods; marine sources of animal protein; developed new animal identification system; patented device for delivering material via skin injections to proximal lymphnodes. *Mailing Add:* Aims Inc 221 Second Ave Piscataway NJ 08854-3519. *Fax:* 732-271-8857

**YADAV, KAMALESHWARI PRASAD,** ANALYTICAL BIOCHEMISTRY. *Current Pos:* PRES, CHEMCO INDUSTS, INC, 74- *Personal Data:* b Burhiatikar, India, Jan 5, 37; m 57; c 2. *Educ:* Univ Bihar, BSc, 59; Univ Mo, MS, 61, PhD(biochem), 66. *Prof Exp:* Instr animal husb, Ranchi Agr Col, Bihar, 59-61; res asst agr chem, Univ Mo, 62-66; res biochemist, Falstaff Brewing Corp, 66-70, sr biochemist, 70-74. *Mem:* Am Soc Brewing Chemists. *Res:* Brewing and fermentation. *Mailing Add:* 1133 Clayton Place Dr St Louis MO 63131

**YADAV, RAGHUNATH P,** ENTOMOLOGY. *Current Pos:* From asst prof to assoc prof entom, 64-74, assoc prof, 74-88, PROF BIOL, SOUTHERN UNIV, BATON ROUGE, 88- *Personal Data:* b Kanpur, India, Jan 2, 35; m 64; c 3. *Educ:* Agra Univ, BS, 56, MS, 58; La State Univ, PhD(entom), 64. *Mem:* Entom Soc Am. *Res:* Artificial diet media for rearing of sugarcane borer; laboratory techniques for the detection of sugarcane borer resistance to insecticides; response of sweet corn hybrids to corn earworm damage in southern central Louisiana; possible antibiosis in sweet corn hybrids to corn earworm. *Mailing Add:* 1416 Kenilworth Pkwy Baton Rouge LA 70808

**YADAVALLI, SRIRAMAMURTI VENKATA,** PHYSICS, ELECTRICAL ENGINEERING. *Current Pos:* DIR RES, SHASTRA INC, 77- *Personal Data:* b Secunderabad, India, May 12, 24; US citizen; m 52. *Educ:* Andhra Univ, India, BS, 42, MS, 45; Univ Calif, MS, 49, PhD(elec eng), 53. *Prof Exp:* Officer in charge, Physics & Chem Labs, Eng Res Dept, Hyderabad, India, 46-48; asst elec eng, Univ Calif, 49-52; mem tech staff, Gen Elec, 53-59; physicist, Stanford Res Inst, 59-67, staff scientist, 67-68, staff scientist eng sci, 68-77. *Concurrent Pos:* Lectr, Univ Calif, 52 & 57-58, res engr, 59; consult engr, Gen Elec, 59; consult, Raytheon Co, 59-62, Litton Indust, 62-64, McGraw Hill Book Co, 62-70 & Rand Corp, 71-78 & 85-87, Misc Orgn, 77- *Mem:* AAAS; Inst Elec & Electronics Engrs; Am Phys Soc; NY Acad Sci; Sigma Xi. *Res:* Stochastic processes; electron and plasma physics; statistical and mathematical physics; electrohydrodynamics; optics; biomathematics. *Mailing Add:* Shastra Inc PO Box 1231 Palo Alto CA 94302

**YADEN, SENKA LONG,** ZOOLOGY, ENVIRONMENTAL HEALTH. *Current Pos:* PROF BIOL, TEX COL, TYLER, 93- *Personal Data:* b Nagaland, India, Apr 21, 35; m 82, Theola Thedford. *Educ:* Wilson Col, Bombay, India, BSc, 56; Univ Bombay, MSc, 58; Univ Minn, PhD(zool), 65. *Prof Exp:* From assoc prof to prof biol, Jarvis Christian Col, 67-81; sr sci assoc pharmacol, TCom, Ft Worth, 81-84; assoc prof basic sci, Parker Col, Irving, Tex, 85-86; assoc prof biol, Talladega Col, Ala, 87-88; prof biol & staff mem, Wiley Col, Marshall, Tex, 88-93, dir, Health Career Opportunity Prog, 88-92. *Concurrent Pos:* Adj fac, Tex State Tech Col, Marshall, 93- *Mem:* AAAS; NY Acad Sci; Am Inst Biol Sci. *Res:* Animal model; hypertension; psychopharmacology; sickle cell. *Mailing Add:* Sci Tex Col Tyler TX 75702-1962

**YADVISH, ROBERT D,** MATERIAL QUALIFICATION OF IN GAAS & INP SUBSTRAITS LASER FABRICATION OF INP LASERS. *Current Pos:* Electronic device processor, 81-82, sr tech asst, electronic device fabrication, 82-86, MEM TECH STAFF, LASER DEVELOP, AT&T BELL LABS, 86- *Educ:* Jersey City State Col, BA, 77, BS, 89. *Res:* Much research was completed on the effects of silicon nitride layers on graphite strip heaters and the recrystallization of the thin film Si on Sio2; the effects of high temperature operation of lattice mached and strained in Ga As/INP quantum well lasers. *Mailing Add:* 142 North St Bayonne NJ 07002

**YAEGER, JAMES AMOS,** HISTOLOGY. *Current Pos:* head dept, 68-78, PROF BIOSTRUCT & FUNCTION, SCH DENT MED, UNIV CONN, 68- *Personal Data:* b Chicago, Ill, Aug 10, 28; m 52, Jean Prosier; c Beverly J, Lynn S, Barbara J & William D. *Educ:* Ind Univ, DDS, 52, MS, 55; Univ Ill,

PhD(anat), 59. *Prof Exp:* Instr anat & clin dent, 55-57; from asst prof to prof histol & head dept, Col Dent, Univ Ill, Chicago, 59-68. *Concurrent Pos:* Resident assoc, Argonne Nat Lab, 63-64; vis prof, Univ Ill; exec dir, Annual Midwest Seminar Dent Med, 64-66; regional ed, Archives Oral Biol, 68-76; mem, Dent Training Comt, Nat Inst Dent Res, 68-72. *Mem:* Am Asn Anat; Int Asn Dent Res. *Res:* Physiology of mastication; mineralized tissues. *Mailing Add:* Dept Biostruct & Function Univ Conn Health Ctr Farmington CT 06030-3705. *Fax:* 860-679-2910

**YAEGER, ROBERT GEORGE,** PARASITOLOGY NUTRITION & MEDICAL ENTOMOLOGY. *Current Pos:* RETIRED. *Personal Data:* b Rochester, NY, Oct 25, 17; m 53, Barbara Fisher; c James, Alyson & Keith. *Educ:* Univ Rochester, AB, 50; Univ Tex, MA, 52; Tulane Univ, PhD(parasitol), 55. *Prof Exp:* Instr bact & parasitol, Med Sch, Univ Tex, 52-54; from instr to prof parasitol & med, Sch Med & Sch Pub Health & Trop Med, Tulane Univ, 55-88. *Concurrent Pos:* Consult biochem & parasitol, NIH, 62-65; consult & trustee, Am Type Cult Collection, 69-80; vis prof, Sch Med, St George Univ, 79-85; consult, AID, 87. *Mem:* Am Soc Parasitol; Am Soc Trop Med & Hyg; Soc Exp Biol & Med; Am Inst Nutrit; Soc Protozool. *Res:* Nutritional and immunological relationships of host and parasite; culture methods; Chagas' disease; other parasitic protozoa which infect man; venomous animals. *Mailing Add:* 6052 Shetland Dr New Orleans LA 70131-3940

**YAES, ROBERT JOEL,** RADIATION ONCOLOGY, THEORETICAL RADIATION BIOLOGY. *Current Pos:* FAC MEM ONCOL, UNIV MD MED SYST, 92- *Personal Data:* b New York, NY, July 11, 42; m 86. *Educ:* Mass Inst Technol, Cambridge, SB, 63, ScD, 67; Mem Univ Nfld, St Johns, BS, 78, MD, 80. *Prof Exp:* Fac assoc physics, Univ Tex, Austin, 68-70; Humboldt Found fel, Johannes Gutenberg Univ, Mainz, Ger, 71-72; asst prof physics, Mem Univ Nfld, 72-76; resident radiation ther, Mem Sloan-Kettering Cancer Ctr, 80-82 & radiation oncol, State Univ NY Downstate Med Ctr, 82-85; fel radiation med, State Univ NY, Stoney Brook, 85-86; asst prof, Univ Ky Med Ctr, 86-92. *Concurrent Pos:* Alexander von Humboldt Stiftung fel, 71; attend radiotherapist, Cent Baptist Hosp, Lexington, Ky, 86-89 & St Claires Med Ctr, Morehead, Ky, 89- *Mem:* Am Soc Therapeut Radiol & Oncol; Radiol Soc NAm; Radiation Res Soc; Am Soc Physicists Med; Am Phys Soc; AMA. *Res:* Mathematical modeling of radiation effects on tumors and on normal tissues; treatment of malignant gliomas with California-252 neutron brachytherapy and hyperfractionation. *Mailing Add:* 419 W Redwood St Baltimore MD 21201

**YAFET, YAKO,** SOLID STATE PHYSICS. *Current Pos:* MEM TECH STAFF, BELL TEL LABS, INC, 60- *Personal Data:* b Istanbul, Turkey, Jan 2, 23; nat US; m 49; c 3. *Educ:* Tech Univ Istanbul, ME, 45; Univ Calif, PhD(physics), 52. *Prof Exp:* Res assoc physics, Univ Ill, 52-54; physicist, Westinghouse Elec Corp Res Labs, 54-60. *Mem:* Fel Am Phys Soc. *Res:* Electronic properties of semiconductors and metals; theoretical solid state physics. *Mailing Add:* 47 Curtiss Pl Maplewood NJ 07040. *Fax:* 908-582-3260

**YAFFE, LAURENCE G,** PHYSICS. *Current Pos:* assoc prof, 88-93, PROF PHYSICS, UNIV WASH, 93- *Personal Data:* b Palo Alto, Calif, Nov 28, 56. *Educ:* Princeton Univ, PhD(physics), 80. *Prof Exp:* Richard Chace Tolman fel theoret physics, Calif Inst Technol, 80-82; asst prof physics, Princeton Univ, 82-88. *Mem:* Am Phys Soc. *Res:* Quantum field theory and elementary particle physics. *Mailing Add:* Dept Physics Univ Wash Seattle WA 98125. *E-Mail:* yaffe@phys.washington.edu

**YAFFE, LEO,** radiochemistry; deceased, see previous edition for last biography

**YAFFE, ROBERTA,** ORGANIC CHEMISTRY. *Current Pos:* TECH REP, ADDITIVES FOR LUBRICANTS, CIBA-GEIGY CORP, 85- *Personal Data:* b Chelsea, Mass, Jan 2, 44. *Educ:* Bryn Mawr Col, AB, 65; Mass Inst Technol, PhD(chem), 70. *Prof Exp:* Teaching asst org chem, Mass Inst Technol, 65-66; sr chemist, Beacon Res Labs, Texaco, Inc, 69-75, res chemist, 75-83, sr res chemist, Petrol Prod Res, 83-85. *Mem:* Am Chem Soc; Am Soc Lubrication Engrs; Nat Lubricating Grease Inst. *Res:* Non-crankcase automotive lubricants; aircraft lubricants; tractor transmission-differential-hydraulic lubricants; lubricant base rocks. *Mailing Add:* PO Box K Glenham NY 12527-1011

**YAFFE, RUTH POWERS,** RADIOCHEMISTRY. *Current Pos:* from asst prof to assoc prof, San Jose State Univ, 57-66, prof, 66-90, coordr, Nuclear Sci Facil, 72-90, EMER PROF, SAN JOSE STATE UNIV, 90. *Personal Data:* b Duluth, Minn, June 4, 27; m 76, Charles B Houser; c Lauren (deVore) & Lawrence G. *Educ:* Macalester Col, BA, 48, PhD(phys chem), 51. *Prof Exp:* AEC fel radiochem, Ames Lab, 51-52; chemist, Oak Ridge Nat Lab, 52-53; instr chem, Univ Tenn, 55-56. *Mem:* Am Chem Soc; Health Physics Soc; Sigma Xi. *Res:* Chemistry of ruthenium; environmental soil and water analysis for radionuclides; fast radiochemistry; nuclear spectroscopy. *Mailing Add:* 1481 Elnora Ct Los Altos CA 94024-6933

**YAFFE, SUMNER J,** PEDIATRICS, CLINICAL PHARMACOLOGY. *Current Pos:* DIR, CTR RES MOTHERS & CHILDREN, NAT INST CHILD HEALTH & HUMAN DEVELOP, NIH, BETHESDA, MD, 81- *Personal Data:* b Boston, Mass, May 9, 23; m 82, Anita Vega; c Steven, Kristine, Jason, Noah, Iaix & Zachary. *Educ:* Harvard Univ, AB, 45, MA, 50; Univ Vt, MD, 54; Am Bd Pediat, dipl, 60. *Honors & Awards:* Jose Albert Mem Lectr, 81. *Prof Exp:* From intern to sr asst resident, Children's Hosp,

Boston, 54-56; exchange resident, St Mary's Hosp, London, Eng, 56-57; from instr to asst prof pediat, Stanford Univ, 59-63; assoc prof, State Univ NY Buffalo, 63-66, prof pediat, 66-75, assoc chmn dept, 69-75; prof pediat & pharmacol, Univ Pa, 75-81; head, Div Clin Pharmacol, Children's Hosp Philadelphia, 75-81. Concurrent Pos: Teaching fel pediat, Harvard Med Sch, 56; Fulbright scholar, St Mary's Hosp, London, Eng, 56-57; res fel metab, Children's Hosp, Boston, 57-59; attend pediatrician, Palo Alto-Stanford Hosp, 59, dir newborn nursery serv, 60, prof dir, Clin Res Ctr Premature Infants, 62; dir, Pediat Renal Clin, Stanford Med Ctr, 60; Am Heart Asn advan res fel, 60; Lederle med fac award, 62; prog dir, Clin Res Ctr Children, 63; prog consult, Nat Inst Child Health & Human Develop, 63, mem, Training Grant Comt, 63 & Reproduction Biol Comt, 65; attend pediatrician, Children's Hosp, Buffalo, 63-75; head, Div Clin Pharmacol, Univ Pa, 75-81. Mem: Soc Pediat Res; Am Acad Pediat; Am Soc Clin Pharmacol & Therapeut; Am Pediat Soc; Am Soc Pharmacol & Exp Therapeut; Perinatal Res Soc; fel Japan Soc Prom Sci. Res: Pediatric clinical pharmacology; neonatal, perinatal, fetal and pediatric pharmacology; developmental pharmacology; drug metabolism; drug disposition in sick infants and children; bilirubin metabolism and binding albumin; drug effects upon the mother, fetus and infant. Mailing Add: Nat Inst Child Health & Human Develop NIH 9000 Rockville Pike Bethesda MD 20892-0001. Fax: 301-480-7773; E-Mail: yaffes@abel.nichd.nih.gov

**YAGER, BILLY JOE,** PHYSICAL ORGANIC CHEMISTRY. Current Pos: from asst prof to assoc prof, 62-71, chmn dept, 75-87, PROF CHEM, SOUTHWEST TEX STATE UNIV, 71- Personal Data: b Cameron, Tex, Dec 16, 32; m 53; c 4. Educ: Southwest Tex State Col, BS, 53; Tex A&M Univ, MS, 60, PhD(chem), 62. Prof Exp: Instr chem, Tex A&M Univ, 61-62. Mem: Am Chem Soc; Sigma Xi. Res: Solvent effects upon saponification rate constants; effect of solvent composition upon activity of reactants. Mailing Add: Dept Chem Southwest Tex State Univ San Marcos TX 78666

**YAGER, JAMES DONALD, JR,** CELL BIOLOGY, GENETICS. Current Pos: PROF & DIR, DIV TOXICOL SCI, JOHNS HOPKINS SCH HYG & PUB HEALTH, 89- Personal Data: b Milwaukee, Wis, Dec 29, 43; m 68, 81; c 3. Educ: Marquette Univ, BS, 65; Univ Conn, PhD(cell/develop biol), 71. Prof Exp: Postdoctoral fel, McAndes Lab Cancer Res, Univ Wis, 71-74; asst prof biol sci, Dartmouth Col, 74-77, asst prof path, Dartmouth Med Sch, 77-80, assoc prof anat & path, 80-81, prof anat, 86-89; assoc prof environ med, NY Univ Med Ctr, 81-83, assoc prof anat, 83-86. Concurrent Pos: Assoc dir, Norris Cotton Cancer Ctr, Dartmouth/Hitchcock Med Ctr, 83-89; actg chair, Dept Pharmacol & Toxicol, Dartmouth Med Sch, 87- 89. Mem: AAAS; Am Asn Cancer Res; Am Soc Cell Biologists; Sigma Xi; Am Asn Pathologists; Soc Toxicol. Res: Carcinogenesis. Mailing Add: Div Toxicol Sci Dept Environ Health Sci Johns Hopkins Sch Hyg & Pub Health 615 N Wolfe St Rm 7032 Baltimore MD 21205-2178. Fax: 410-955-0116

**YAGER, JANICE L WINTER,** genetic toxicology, toxicology, for more information see previous edition

**YAGER, PHILIP MARVIN,** EXPERIMENTAL HIGH ENERGY PHYSICS. Current Pos: From lectr to assoc prof, 68-75, PROF PHYSICS, UNIV CALIF, DAVIS, 81- Personal Data: b Los Angeles, Calif, Aug 5, 38; m 73; c 2. Educ: Univ Calif, Berkeley, BA, 61; Univ Calif, San Diego, MS, 64, PhD(physics), 71. Mem: AAAS; Am Phys Soc; Sigma Xi. Res: Hadronic interactions at high energy. Mailing Add: Dept Physics Univ Calif Davis CA 95616

**YAGER, ROBERT EUGENE,** SCIENCE EDUCATION, PLANT PHYSIOLOGY. Current Pos: Res asst plant physiol, 55-56, from instr to assoc prof, 56-67, PROF SCI EDUC, UNIV IOWA, 67- Personal Data: b Carroll, Iowa, Apr 13, 30; wid; c Laura B & Stuart O. Educ: Univ Northern Iowa, BA, 50; Univ Iowa, MS, 53, PhD, 57. Honors & Awards: R H Carleton Award, Nat Sci Teachers Asn, 77. Concurrent Pos: Dir, Sec Sci Training Prog, NSF, 59-, dir, In-Serv Inst, 61-, dir, Summer Inst, 63-, dir, Acad Yr Prog Sci Supv, Summer Inst In-Serv Teachers, Coop Col Sch Sci Prog & Undergrad Pre-Serv Teacher Educ Prog; ed, J Nat Asn Res Sci Teaching, 64-, scope, sequence & coord dir, 90; pres, Nat Asn Sci Technol Soc; dir, Iowa Chautauqua Prog, 83-, Iowa Scope, Sequence & Coord Proj, STAR Schs Proj. Mem: Nat Asn Res Sci Teaching; Nat Sci Teachers Asn; Nat Asn Biol Teachers; Asn Educ Teachers Sci (pres, 73-74); Sch Sci & Math Asn (pres, 69-70); Nat Asn Sci Technol & Soc (pres, 92-93). Res: Chemical control of abscission processes; science curriculum and development; distance education instructional design and materials development; teacher training, testing and measurement; ecology, science, technology, social efforts; constructivism. Mailing Add: Univ Iowa 259 Lindquist Ctr N Iowa City IA 52242-1529. Fax: 319-335-1188

**YAGGY, PAUL FRANCIS,** AERONAUTICAL & ELECTRICAL ENGINEERING. Current Pos: RETIRED. Personal Data: b Detroit, Mich, Aug 4, 23; m 45; c 4. Educ: San Jose State Col, BSEE, 63. Prof Exp: Aeronaut engr, Ames Res Ctr, NASA, 46-50 & 51-58, aeronaut engr large scale aerodyn br, 58-61, asst br chief, 61-65, tech dir, US Army Aeronaut Res Lab, 65-68, dir lab, 68-72, dir lab, US Army Air Mobility Res & Develop Lab, 72-74. Concurrent Pos: Mem subcomt aircraft aerodyn, NASA, 67-70; mem fluid dynamics panel, Adv Group Aerospace Res & Develop, NATO, 67- Mem: Am Helicopter Soc; Soc Automotive Engrs; assoc fel Am Inst Aeronaut & Astronaut. Res: Aeronautical sciences; aerodynamics; flight vehicles for air mobile systems development. Mailing Add: 1381 Sheffield Ave Campbell CA 95008

**YAGHJIAN, ARTHUR DAVID,** ELECTROMAGNETIC THEORY. Current Pos: RES ENGR, AJ DEVANEY ASSOC, INC, 96- Personal Data: b Jan 1, 43; US citizen; m 73, Lucretia Bailey. Educ: Brown Univ, ScB, 64, ScM, 66, PhD(elec eng), 69. Prof Exp: Asst prof physics & elec eng, Hampton Inst, 69-70; Nat Res Coun res assoc, Nat Bur Standards, 71-73, electronics engr, Electromagnetic Fields Div, 73-82; electronics engr, Electrogmagnetics Directorate, Hanscom AFB, 82-96. Concurrent Pos: Vis scientist, Rome Lab, 80; assoc ed, Inst Elec & Electronics Engrs Trans Antennas & Propagation, 83-86, Radio Sci, 88-89; guest prof, Tech Univ Denmark, 89. Mem: Fel Inst Elec & Electronics Engrs; Sigma Xi; Int Union Radio Scientists; Electromagnetic Soc. Res: Near-field antenna measurements; electromagnetic scattering and radiation. Mailing Add: 115 Wright Rd Concord MA 01742

**YAGI, FUMIO,** MATHEMATICS. Current Pos: RETIRED. Personal Data: b Seattle, Wash, July 14, 17; m 54, Shizuko Nakagawa. Educ: Univ Wash, BS, 38, MS, 41; Mass Inst Technol, PhD(math), 43. Prof Exp: Fel, Inst Advan Study, 43; instr, Univ Wash, 46-49, asst prof, 49-53; mathematician, Ballistic Res Labs, Aberdeen Proving Ground, 53-56; sr res engr, Jet Propulsion Lab, Calif Inst Technol, 56-58, res specialist, 58-63; appl mathematician, Grumman Aircraft Eng Corp, Bethpage, NY, 63-66, mem systs anal staff, 66-67, group supvr systs anal, 67-77. Concurrent Pos: Lectr, Univ Md, 56, Univ Calif, Los Angeles, 57-61 & Adelphi Univ, 63-64 & 66; adj prof, C W Post Col, Long Island Univ, 66-77. Mem: Am Math Soc; Sigma Xi. Res: Analysis; space trajectory and guidance studies; systems performance and error analysis. Mailing Add: 2914 Sahalee Dr E Redmond WA 98053-6353

**YAGI, HARUHIKO,** ORGANIC CHEMISTRY, DRUG METABOLISM. Current Pos: VIS SCIENTIST DRUG METABOLISM & CARCINOGENESIS, LAB BIOORG CHEM, NAT INST ARTHRITIS, DIGESTIVE & KIDNEY DIS, NIH, 71- Personal Data: b Sendai, Japan, June 27, 39; m 69; c 2. Educ: Tohoku Univ, Japan, MS, 65, PhD(synthesis of isoquinoline alkaloid), 68. Prof Exp: Asst org synthesis, Pharmaceut Inst, Tohoku Univ, Japan, 68-69; res asst electrochem, Univ Conn, 69-70; res assoc chem kinetics, Johns Hopkins Univ, 70-71. Concurrent Pos: Fel, Univ Conn, 69-70 & Johns Hopkins Univ, 70-71. Mem: Pharmaceut Soc Japan; Am Chem Soc. Res: Organic synthesis; natural product chemistry; carcinogenesis. Mailing Add: 11 Candlelight Ct Potomac MD 20854-2753

**YAGIELA, JOHN ALLEN,** DENTAL ANESTHESIA, DENTAL PHARMACOLOGY. Current Pos: assoc prof pain control, Sch Dent, Univ Calif, Los Angeles, 82-83, resident anesthesiol, Sch Med, 82-83, assoc dean acad affairs, 85-86, & acad & admin affairs, 86-89, PROF ORAL BIOL, SCH DENT, UNIV CALIF, LOS ANGELES, 83-, PROF ANESTHESIOL, SCH MED, 83- Personal Data: b Washington, DC, July 23, 47; m 70, Dolores Mitchell; c Gregory & Leanne. Educ: Univ Calif, Los Angeles, DDS, 71; Univ Utah, PhD(pharmacol), 75. Prof Exp: From asst prof to assoc prof oral biol, Sch Dent, Emory Univ, 75-82. Concurrent Pos: Consult physician, Dent Serv, Vet Admin, Wadsworth Med Ctr, 83-; chmn, Sect Pharmacol & Therapeut, Am Asn Dent Schs, 83; consult, Coun Dent Therapeut, Am Dent Asn, 87-; chmn, fellowship Comt, Am Dent Soc Anesthesiol, 87-90; chmn, Pharmacol, Toxicol, Therapeut Group, Int Asn Dent Res, 90; ed, Anesthesis Progress, 90-95. Mem: Int Asn Dent Res; Am Asn Dent Schs; fel Am Dent Soc Anesthesiol; Am Dent Asn; AAAS; Am Asn Dent Ed. Res: Pharmacology and toxicology of local anesthetic agents and drugs used in dental anesthesia and sedation. Mailing Add: Ctr Health Sci Sch Dent Univ Calif Los Angeles CA 90095

**YAGLE, RAYMOND A(RTHUR),** NAVAL ARCHITECTURE, OCEAN ENGINEERING. Current Pos: res asst to res engr, Univ Mich, Ann Arbor, 50-54, asst prof eng mech, 55-60, assoc prof naval archit & marine eng, 60-64, prof, 64-76, PROF MARINE ENG, ENG RES INST, UNIV MICH, ANN ARBOR, 76- Personal Data: b Aspinwall, Pa, Dec 29, 23; m 54; c 3. Educ: Univ Mich, BSE, 44, MSE, 47. Prof Exp: Jr engr, Cornell Aeronaut Lab, Inc, 46; res engr, Frederic Flader, Inc, 47. Concurrent Pos: Consult, Rand Corp; chmn ship res comt, Nat Acad Sci-Nat Res Coun. Mem: Marine Technol Soc; Am Soc Naval Engrs; Soc Naval Archit & Marine Engrs. Res: Fuel sprays, atomization and combustion; fluid mechanics generally, resistance studies and naval architecture applications in particular; ship structures; computer applications. Mailing Add: 2707 Brockman Blvd Ann Arbor MI 48104

**YAGUCHI, MAKOTO,** PROTEIN CHEMISTRY, AGRICULTURAL CHEMISTRY. Current Pos: from asst res officer to assoc res officer, 65-77, SR RES OFFICER, DIV BIOL SCI, NAT RES COUN CAN, 77- Personal Data: b Yokohama, Japan, Oct 19, 30; m 60, Mutsuko Obara; c Mariko C. Educ: Tokyo Univ Agr, BAgr, 53; Univ Calif, Davis, MS, 57, PhD(agr chem), 63. Honors & Awards: Japanese Govt Res Award, Foreign Specialists, 87. Prof Exp: Res assoc protein chem, Purdue Univ, 63-64; res food technologist, Univ Calif, Davis, 64-65. Concurrent Pos: Vis scientist, Max-Planck-Inst for Molecular Genetics, Berlin, 74-75; vis prof, Japan Soc Prom Sci, 78. Mem: Protein Soc. Res: Proteins and enzymes from thermophilic and halophilic bacteria; structure and function of cellulases and xylanases; protein and glycoproteins analysis. Mailing Add: Inst Biol Sci Nat Res Coun Ottawa ON K1A 0R6 Can. Fax: 613-952-9092

**YAHIL, AMOS,** ASTROPHYSICS, ASTRONOMY. Current Pos: from asst prof to assoc prof, 77-83, PROF ASTROPHYS, STATE UNIV NY, STONY BROOK, 83- Personal Data: b Tel Aviv, Israel, Nov 28, 43; m 89, Ludmila M Mleczko; c Edna, Ron, Shaul & Uri. Educ: Hebrew Univ, Jerusalem, BSc, 66; Calif Inst Technol, PhD(physics), 70. Honors & Awards: Fullam Award, 82; Guggenheim Award, 84. Prof Exp: Lectr, Tel Aviv Univ, 70-71; mem, Inst Advan Study, 71-73; lectr, Tel Aviv Univ, 73-75, sr lectr, 75-77. Concurrent

*Pos:* Vis fel, Inst Astron, Cambridge, 72, 81 & 84-85; Chercheur invite, Univ Montreal, 75 & 76-77; vis assoc prof, Calif Inst Technol, 77 & 78; vis prof, Nordita, Copenhagen, 81, Res Inst Fundamental Physics, Kyoto Univ, 86, Hebrew Univ, Jerusalem, 90, Observatoire de Paris a Meudon, 91, Inst Astrophys, CEA-Saclay & Univ Paris VII, 92. *Mem:* Am Astron Soc; Int Astron Union. *Res:* Physical cosmology, large-scale structure; dynamics and evolution of clusters of galaxies; galactic structure; stellar collapse; supernovae; molecular clouds. *Mailing Add:* 11 Night Heron Dr Stony Brook NY 11790. *Fax:* 516-632-8240; *E-Mail:* ayahil@sbast3.ess.sunysb.edu

**YAHNER, JOSEPH EDWARD,** SOILS & LAND USE PLANNING. *Current Pos:* Agronomist, Purdue Univ-Brazil Proj, US AID Contract, Vicosa, Brazil, 63-67, assoc prof, 70-78, EXTEN AGRONOMIST, PURDUE UNIV, WEST LAFAYETTE, 67-, PROF AGRON, 78- *Personal Data:* b Chicago, Ill, June 16, 31; m 58; c 3. *Educ:* Purdue Univ, BS, 54; Ore State Univ, MS, 61, PhD(soils), 63. *Mem:* Am Soc Agron; Soil Conserv Soc Am. *Res:* Use of soil maps and soil information in land use planning; on-site waste disposal for homes or small commercial establishments; soil map use for land appraisal. *Mailing Add:* 1825 Greenbriar Ave West Lafayette IN 47906

**YAHNER, RICHARD HOWARD,** WILDLIFE SCIENCES. *Current Pos:* assoc prof, 81-89, PROF, PA STATE UNIV, 89- *Personal Data:* b McKees Rocks, Pa, June 21, 49; m 72; c 2. *Educ:* Pa State Univ, BS, 71; Univ Tenn, MS, 73; Ohio Univ, PhD(zool), 77. *Prof Exp:* Fel, Smithsonian Inst, 77-78; asst prof, Univ Minn, 78-81. *Concurrent Pos:* Wildlife consult. *Mem:* Am Soc Mammalogists; Wildlife Soc. *Res:* Effects of habitat alteration, manipulation, and fragmentation on ecology of vertebrates; habitat management; conservation biology. *Mailing Add:* Dept Wildlife Pa State Univ 205 Forest Resources University Park PA 16802-1009

**YAHR, MELVIN DAVID,** NEUROLOGY. *Current Pos:* HENRY P & GEORGETTE GOLDSCHMIDT PROF NEUROL & CHMN DEPT, MT SINAI SCH MED, 73- *Personal Data:* b New York, NY, Nov 18, 17; m 48; c 4. *Educ:* NY Univ, AB, 39, MD, 43; Am Bd Psychiat & Neurol, dipl, 49. *Honors & Awards:* Golden Plate Award, Am Acad Achievement, 69; Lucy Moses Award, Col Physicians & Surgeons, Columbia Univ, 72; William Hammond Award, Col Med, NY Univ, 79, Solomon A Berson Award, 85. *Prof Exp:* Res asst, Col Physicians & Surgeons, Columbia Univ, 48-50, instr, 50-51, assoc, 51-53, from asst prof to assoc prof neurol, 53-70, from asst dean to assoc dean, 59-73, Merritt prof neurol, 70-73. *Concurrent Pos:* Nat Res Coun res assoc & asst neurologist, Neurol Inst, Presby Hosp, 48-50, asst attend neurologist, 50-53, assoc attend, 53-61, attend, 61-; asst adj neurol serv, Lenox Hill Hosp, 48-49, adj, 49-54, assoc, 54-60; asst neurologist, Montefiore Hosp, 49-51; mem neurol study sect, NIH, 50-; consult, USPHS, 52-55 & Neuro-Psychiat Inst, NJ, 52-59; med dir, Parkinson's Dis Found, 58-73; mem comt drug ther in neurol, Nat Inst Neurol Dis & Blindness, 59-; dir & neurologist-in-chief, Mt Sinai Hosp, NY, 73- *Mem:* Am Epilepsy Soc; Am Neurol Asn; Asn Am Med Cols; Asn Res Nerv & Ment Dis; fel Am Acad Neurol; fel NY Acad Sci; fel NY Acad Med. *Res:* Cause and treatment of epilepsy; cerebro-vascular diseases; Parkinsonism and multiple sclerosis; mechanisms, causes, methods, and treatment of Parkinson's and allied diseases. *Mailing Add:* Mt Sinai MC Dept Neur Box 1139 One Gustave Levy Pl New York NY 10029-6574

**YAKAITIS, RONALD WILLIAM,** ANESTHESIOLOGY. *Current Pos:* STAFF ANESTHESIOLOGIST, KINO COMMUNITY HOSP, TUCSON, 77- *Personal Data:* b Baltimore, Md, Oct 13, 41; m 68; c 2. *Educ:* Loyola Col, BS, 63; Univ Md, MD, 67. *Prof Exp:* Staff instr anesthesia, US Naval Hosp, Oakland, Calif, 71-73; asst prof, Med Univ SC, 73-75; asst prof anesthesia, Univ Ariz Med Ctr, 75-77. *Concurrent Pos:* Consult anesthesia, Univ Calif, San Francisco, 72-73, Vet Admin Hosp, Charleston, SC, 73-75 & Vet Admin Hosp, Tucson, Ariz, 75-; clin assoc, Univ Ariz Med Ctr, 77-; consult, Tucson Hosps Med Educ Prog, 78- *Mem:* Am Soc Anesthesiologists; Int Anesthesia Res Soc; Am Col Physicians; AMA. *Res:* Pulmonary ultramicroscopic and biochemical changes due to oxygen toxicity; cardiovascular drug pharmacokinetics during acid-base imbalance; new techniques for intraoperative anesthetic management. *Mailing Add:* 3390 N Campbell Suite 110 Tucson AZ 85719-2307

**YAKATAN, GERALD JOSEPH,** PHARMACY, DRUG DISCOVERY & DEVELOPMENT. *Current Pos:* PRES/CHIEF EXEC OFF, TANABE RES LABS, USA, 90- *Personal Data:* b Philadelphia, Pa, May 20, 42; m 64, Una Gittleman; c Nicole & Brook. *Educ:* Temple Univ, BS, 63, MS, 65; Univ Fla, PhD(pharmaceut sci), 71. *Prof Exp:* Asst prof pharm, Univ Tex, Austin, 72-76, assoc prof, 76-80, asst dir, Drug Dynamics Inst, 75-80; dir, Pharmacokinetics/Drug Metab, Warner-Lambert Co, 80-83, vpres, prod develop, 83-87; vpres pharmaceut develop, Immunetech Pharmaceuts, 87-90. *Concurrent Pos:* Adj prof pharm, Univ Mich, 81-83; vis prof, Rutgers Univ, 83-87; predoctoral fel, NIH & NSF. *Mem:* Controlled Release Soc; fel Am Asn Pharmaceut Sci; fel Am Col Clin Pharmacol; Drug Info Asn; NY Acad Sci. *Res:* Pharmacokinetics; biopharmaceutics; analysis of drugs in biological fluids; drug stability; drug discovery and development; drug delivery. *Mailing Add:* 13813 Boquita Dr Delmar CA 92014. *Fax:* 619-558-0650

**YAKEL, HARRY L,** X-RAY CRYSTALLOGRAPHY. *Current Pos:* GROUP LEADER METALS & CERAMICS, OAK RIDGE NAT LAB, 53- *Personal Data:* b Brooklyn, NY, July 24, 29. *Educ:* Polytech Inst Brooklyn, BS, 49; Calif Inst Technol, PhD(chem), 52. *Prof Exp:* Fel chem, Calif Inst Technol, 52-53. *Mem:* AAAS; Am Chem Soc; Am Crystallog Asn; Mineral Soc Am; Sigma Xi. *Res:* Structural studies of solids using x-ray diffraction methods. *Mailing Add:* 129 Westlook Circle Oak Ridge TN 37830-4898

**YAKIR, BENJAMIN,** SEQUENTIAL ANALYSIS, QUALITY CONTROL. *Current Pos:* FEL, DEPT BIOSTATIST, UNIV ROCHESTER, 92- *Personal Data:* b Rehovot, Israel, June 29, 60; US citizen; m 91, Lily Morad; c Oren S & Hadar. *Educ:* Hebrew Univ, Israel, BA, 86, PhD(statist), 91. *Prof Exp:* Fel, Math Sci Res Inst, Berkeley, 91-92. *Mem:* Inst Math Statist; Am Statist Asn. *Res:* Optimality and working characteristics of the Shiryayer-Roberts procedure in different settings; inference following random stopping; probabilistic characteristics of scheduling algorithms. *Mailing Add:* 401 University Park Rochester NY 14620. *Fax:* 716-273-1031; *E-Mail:* yakir@biol.bst.rochester.edu

**YAKOVENKO, VICTOR MIKHAILOVICH,** THEORY OF ORGANIC SUPERCONDUCTORS. *Current Pos:* ASST PROF CONDENSED MATTER THEORY, UNIV MD, 93- *Personal Data:* b Donetsk, Ukraine, Mar 24, 61; m 83, Irina Antonova; c Nikolai & Galina. *Educ:* Moscow Phys Tech Inst, dipl physics, 84; Landau Inst Theoret Physics, Moscow, PhD(theoret physics), 87. *Prof Exp:* Researcher, Landau Inst Theoret Physics, Moscow, 87- *Concurrent Pos:* Vis scientist, Solid Physics Lab Orsay, France, 89, Inst Sci Interchange, Turin, Italy, 90, Cambridge Univ, Brit, 91; res assoc, Rutgers Univ, 91-93. *Mem:* Am Phys Soc. *Res:* Study of the behavior of organic quasi-one-dimensional (super) conductors in high magnetic fields including the cascade of magnetic-field-induced spin-density waves, the quantum hall effect and magnetic oscillations. *Mailing Add:* Dept Physics Univ Md College Park MD 20742-4111. *E-Mail:* yakovenk@glue.umd.edu

**YAKOWITZ, SIDNEY J,** STATISTICS, COMPUTER SCIENCE. *Current Pos:* asst prof systs eng, Univ Ariz, 66-68, assoc prof math, 68-71, assoc prof systs eng, 68-, assoc prof, 71-76, PROF INDUST ENG, UNIV ARIZ, 76- *Personal Data:* b San Francisco, Calif, Mar 8, 37; m 63; c 2. *Educ:* Stanford Univ, BS, 60; Ariz State Univ, MS, 65, MA, 66, PhD(elec eng), 67. *Prof Exp:* Fac assoc elec eng, Ariz State Univ, 65-66. *Concurrent Pos:* Nat Res Coun fel, Naval Postgrad Sch, 70-71. *Mem:* Inst Math Statist; Inst Elec & Electronics Engrs. *Res:* Sequential design of statistical experiments; statistical decision theory; applications to adaptive control theory; pattern recognition. *Mailing Add:* Dept Systs Eng Univ Ariz Old Eng Bldg 20 Rm 111 Tucson AZ 85721-0001

**YAKSH, TONY LEE,** NEUROPHARMACOLOGY, NEUROPHYSIOLOGY. *Current Pos:* PROF ANESTHESIOL & PHARMACOL, UNIV CALIF, SAN DIEGO, 88- *Personal Data:* b San Angelo, Tex, June 14, 44; m 74; c 1. *Educ:* Ga Inst Technol, BS, 66; Univ Ga, MS, 68; Purdue Univ, PhD(neurobiol), 71. *Prof Exp:* Res asst, Purdue Univ, 67-71; mem res staff, Biomed Lab, US Army, Edgewood Arsenal, Md, 71-73; asst scientist, Sch Pharm, Univ Wis-Madison, 73-76; vis scientist, Dept Physiol, Univ Col, Univ London, 76-77; assoc consult pharmacol & neurosurg, Mayo Clin, 77-88. *Mem:* Am Physiol Soc; Int Asn Study Pain; Soc Neurosci; Sigma Xi. *Res:* Pharmacology of opiate action; physiology and pharmacology of pain transmission; role of neuropeptides in behavior. *Mailing Add:* Dept Anesthesiol 0818 Univ Calif San Diego 9500 Gilman Dr La Jolla CA 92093-0818

**YAKUBIK, JOHN,** PHARMACEUTICAL CHEMISTRY. *Current Pos:* from scientist to sr scientist, Schering Corp, 55-61, mgr, Pharmaceut Develop Dept, 61-65, dir sci liaison, Schering Labs, 65-71, dir new prod planning, 71-74, dir corp prod develop, Schering Corp, Bloomfield, 74-79, dir bus develop, 79-80, dir int regulatory affairs, 80-81, DIR NEW PROD DEVELOP, PHARMACEUT PROD DIV, SCHERING PLOUGH INT, KENILWORTH, 82- *Personal Data:* b Fords, NJ, Sept 23, 28; m 52; c 2. *Educ:* Rutgers Univ, BS, 49; Purdue Univ, MS, 50, PhD(pharmaceut chem), 52. *Prof Exp:* Res assoc, Squibb Inst Med Res, 52-55. *Mem:* AAAS; Soc Cosmetic Chem; Am Pharmaceut Asn; NY Acad Sci. *Res:* Pharmaceutical product development; pharmaceutical and medicinal chemistry; pharmacology. *Mailing Add:* 65 Stratford Dr Colonia NJ 07067

**YAKUNIN, ALEXANDER F,** MICROBIAL BIOCHEMISTRY & PHYSIOLOGY, REGULATION OF THE SYNTHESIS & ACTIVITY OF PROTEINS. *Current Pos:* fel, 92-96, INV RESEARCHER, UNIV MONTREAL, 96- *Personal Data:* b Perm, Russia, Apr 25, 55; m 74, Nina A Plotnikova; c Fedor & Julia. *Educ:* Moscow State Univ, BS, 78; Inst Microbiol, Moscow, PhD(microbiol), 86. *Prof Exp:* Trainee-researcher, Inst Photosynthesis, Pushchino, 78-80, jr researcher, 80-86, researcher, Inst Soil Sci & Photosynthesis, 86-90, sr researcher, 90-92. *Res:* Biological nitrogen fixation, particularly the mechanism of nitrogenase regulation and nif-specific electron transport systems in phototrophic microorganisms. *Mailing Add:* Dept Microbiol Univ Montreal Montreal PQ H3C 3T7 Can. *Fax:* 514-343-5701; *E-Mail:* iakounia@ere.umontreal.ca

**YAKURA, HIDETAKA,** IMMUNOLOGY, PATHOLOGY. *Current Pos:* DIR, DEPT MICROBIOL & IMMUNOL, TOKYO METROP INST NEUROSCI, 89- *Personal Data:* b Sapporo, Japan. *Educ:* Hokkaido Univ, MD, 72, PhD(path), 78. *Prof Exp:* Res fel immunol, Farber Cancer Ctr, Harvard Med Sch, 76-78; res assoc, Mem Sloan-Kettering Cancer Ctr, 78-83; from asst prof to assoc prof path, Asahikawa Med Col, 83-89. *Concurrent Pos:* Vis investr, Mem Sloan-Kettering Cancer Ctr, 88; assoc scientist, Nat Ctr Neurol & Psychiat, Nat Inst Neurosci, Tokyo, Japan, 91-97. *Mem:* Am Asn Immunologists. *Res:* Regulatory mechanisms of B lymphocyte differentiation; functional analysis of protein tyrosine phosphatases in the immune and the neuronal cells. *Mailing Add:* Tokyo Metrop Inst Neurosci 2-6 Musashidai Fuchu Tokyo 183 Japan. *Fax:* 81-423-21-8678; *E-Mail:* yakura@tmin.ac.jp

**YAKURA, JAMES K,** AERONAUTICAL ENGINEERING. *Current Pos:* staff engr, Aerospace Corp, 66-69, asst dir, 69-71, assoc systs planning dir, 71-72, dir, Vehicle Systs Off, 72-74, dir, Shuttle Interface Off, 75-77, ASSOC DIR, PAYLOAD INTEGRATION OFF, AEROSPACE CORP, EL SEGUNDO, 77- *Personal Data:* b Los Angeles, Calif, Nov 1, 33; m 61; c 3. *Educ:* Univ Calif, Los Angeles, BS, 55, MS, 57; Stanford Univ, PhD(aeronaut), 62. *Prof Exp:* Mem tech staff, Hughes Aircraft Co, 55-58, sr staff engr, 62-65; mem sr staff, Nat Eng Sci Co, 65-66. *Mem:* Am Inst Aeronaut & Astronaut. *Res:* Hypersonic aerodynamics. *Mailing Add:* 7732 Gonzaga Pl Westminster CA 92683

**YALCINTAS, M GUVEN,** HEALTH & MEDICAL PHYSICS, WASTE MANAGEMENT. *Current Pos:* PROJ MGR, OAK RIDGE NAT LAB, 77-, DIR, WASTE MGT TECHNOL TRANSFER. *Personal Data:* b Milas-Mugla, Turkey, Apr 11, 45; Turkish & US citizen; wid; c Banu. *Educ:* Univ Ankara, Turkey, BS, 65; Univ Rochester, MS, 71, PhD(radiation biol-med physics), 74. *Prof Exp:* Fel, Argonne Nat Lab, 74-75; dir med physics & asst prof radiol physics, Izmir Med Sch, 75-76; corp health physicist, EMI Med Inc, 76-77. *Concurrent Pos:* Turkish Atomic Energy grad fel; consult, UN Develop Prog, 79-83; adj prof radiation biol, Tenn Technol Univ, 86-; adj prof, Tusculum Col; dir educ, ERWM Prog, Univ Tenn & Oak Ridge Nat Lab. *Mem:* Am Nuclear Soc; Health Physics Soc. *Res:* Comparison of risk from radiation in diagnostic radiology; development of a telemetry system that provides real life images from a radiation survey on the field; radiation biology; dosimetry; environmental restoration; technology transfer; business development. *Mailing Add:* 147 Inata Circle 2663 London TN 37774. *Fax:* 423-435-3271; *E-Mail:* mgy@ornl.gov

**YALE, CHARLES E,** MEDICINE, SURGERY. *Current Pos:* from asst prof to assoc prof, 64-72, PROF SURG, MED SCH, UNIV WIS-MADISON, 72-, VCHMN DEPT, 73- *Personal Data:* b Aurora, Ill, Mar 21, 25; m 48; c 4. *Educ:* Univ Ill, Urbana, BS, 49; Case Western Res Univ, MD, 55; Univ Cincinnati, DSc, 61. *Prof Exp:* Resident surg, Univ Cincinnati, 56-62, instr, 62-64. *Concurrent Pos:* NIH grant, Univ Wis-Madison, 66-71; clin investr surg, Cincinnati Vet Admin Hosp, 62-64; attend surgeon, Univ Wis Hosps, 64-, dir gnotobiotic lab, Univ Wis-Madison, 65-81. *Mem:* Soc Surg Alimentary Tract; Asn Gnotobiotics (pres, 70-71); Asn Acad Surg; Am Col Surg; AMA; Sigma Xi. *Res:* Gastrointestinal surgery; intestinal obstruction and strangulation; wound healing; surgical infections and septic shock; gnotobiotics; surgery for morbid obesity. *Mailing Add:* Dept Surg Sch Med Univ Wis Clin Sci Ctr 600 Highland Ave Madison WI 53792-0001

**YALE, HARRY LOUIS,** ORGANIC CHEMISTRY. *Current Pos:* RETIRED. *Personal Data:* b Chicago, Ill, Dec 18, 13; m 43; c 3. *Educ:* Univ Ill, BSc, 37; Iowa State Col, PhD(org chem), 40. *Honors & Awards:* Lasker Award. *Prof Exp:* Res chemist, Nat Defense Res Comt, 40-41 & Shell Develop Co, 41-45; res chemist, Squibb Inst Med Res, 46-67, sr res fel, 67-79; consult, 79-88. *Mem:* Am Chem Soc; NY Acad Sci; Swiss Chem Soc. *Res:* Organometallic compounds; quinoline derivatives; furan; high temperature oxidation and chlorination of olefins; chelate compounds; explosives; antituberculous drugs; diuretics; ataractic agents; natural products. *Mailing Add:* 4 New York Ave New Brunswick NJ 08901-1714

**YALE, IRL KEITH,** MATHEMATICS. *Current Pos:* asst prof, 67-73, assoc prof, 73-80, PROF MATH, UNIV MONT, 80- *Personal Data:* b Billings, Mont, Mar 13, 39. *Educ:* Univ Mont, BA, 60; Univ Calif, Berkeley, PhD(math), 66. *Prof Exp:* Instr math, Univ Mont, 64-65; asst prof, Morehouse Col, 66-67. *Mem:* Am Math Soc; Math Asn Am. *Res:* Functional and harmonic analysis. *Mailing Add:* Dept Math Univ Mont Missoula MT 59812-1032

**YALE, PAUL B,** MATHEMATICS. *Current Pos:* from asst prof to assoc prof, 61-74, PROF MATH, POMONA COL, 74- *Personal Data:* b Geneva, NY, Apr 28, 32; m 71; c 5. *Educ:* Univ Calif, Berkeley, BA, 53; Harvard Univ, MA & PhD(math), 59. *Honors & Awards:* Lester R Ford Award, 67. *Prof Exp:* Asst prof math, Oberlin Col, 59-61. *Concurrent Pos:* NSF sci fac fel, 67-68. *Mem:* Am Math Soc; Math Asn Am; Asn Comput Mach. *Res:* Geometry; symmetry; group theory; computer graphics. *Mailing Add:* 448 W Tenth St Claremont CA 91711-6348

**YALE, SEYMOUR HERSHEL,** RADIOLOGY. *Current Pos:* Asst clin dent, Col Dent, Univ Ill, 48-49, from instr to asst prof, 49-54, assoc prof Dept Radiol, 56, prof & head dept, 57-61, admin asst dean, 61-63, from asst dean to actg dean, 63-65, dean, 65-87, EMER DEAN, COL DENT, UNIV ILL, 87- *Personal Data:* b Chicago, Ill, Nov 27, 20; m 43; c 2. *Educ:* Univ Ill, BS, 44, DDS, 45. *Honors & Awards:* Harry Sicher Meml Lect Award, Am Col Stomologic Surgeons, 83. *Concurrent Pos:* Res consult, Hines Vet Admin Hosp, Ill, 59; consult, West Side Vet Admin Hosp, Chicago, 61-, dent proj sect, Nat Inst Radiol Health, 61-, div radiol health, Bur State Serv, 63- & Vet Admin Res Hosp, Chicago, 63-; mem sect comt dent film specifications, US Am Stand Inst, 59-, subcomt 16, Nat Comt Radiation Protection, 63-, gen res support adv comt, HEW, 65-Mayor's Comt Heart, Cancer & Stroke, Chicago & Comt Dent Care Ment Ill, Ill State Dept Ment Health; mem, Grad Fac Dept Radiol, Col Med, Univ Ill, Chicago, Hillel Bd; founder, Ctr Res Periodont Dis & Oral Molecular Biol, 77; organizer & chmn, Nat Conf Hepatitis-B Dent, 82; organizer & dir, Univ Taskforce Primary Health Care Proj, Univ Ill, Chicago; chmn, Univ Ill, Univ Stockholm & Univ Gothenberg Conf Geriatrics, 85; prof dent & health sources mgt, Sch Pub Health, Univ Ill, Chicago, 87- *Mem:* AAAS; Am Dent Asn; Am Acad Dent Radiol; fel Am Col Dent; Int Asn Dent Res; hon fel, Acad Gen Dent; Am Acad Oral Roentgenology; NY Acad Sci; Am Pub Health Asn; Sigma Xi. *Res:* Morphology; radiographic anatomy; radiation biology and control. *Mailing Add:* 155 N Harbor Dr No 1703 Chicago IL 60601

**YALISOVE, STEVEN M,** OPTOELECTRONICS. *Current Pos:* asst prof, 89-95, ASSOC PROF MAT SCI & ENG, UNIV MICH, 95- *Personal Data:* b Wilmington, Nebr, Dec 7, 54. *Educ:* Univ Rochester, BA, 77, MS, 79; Univ Pa, PhD, 86. *Prof Exp:* Aerothermodynamics engr, Gen Elec, 79-80, consult, 80-82; postdoctoral mem tech staff, AT&T Bell Labs, 87-89. *Concurrent Pos:* Fulbright scholar, Univ Amsterdam, 96-97. *Mem:* Am Phys Soc; Am Vacuum Soc; Mat Res Soc; Mat Soc. *Res:* Relationship of atomic structure to electrical, optical and mechanical properties at interfaces and surfaces; growth of expitaxial silicon and silicide thin films in UHV; role of growth conditions on atomic structure and morphology of expitaxial films; role of initial surface topography on evolution of thin film structure; author of numerous publication in field. *Mailing Add:* Dept Mat Sci & Eng Univ Mich 2118 Dow Bldg Ann Arbor MI 48109-2136

**YALKOVSKY, RAFAEL,** OCEANOGRAPHY. *Current Pos:* from asst prof to prof geol, 62-83, EMER PROF GEOL & OCEANOG, BUFFALO STATE UNIV COL, 84- *Personal Data:* b Chicago, Ill, Oct 11, 17. *Educ:* Univ Chicago, BS, 46, MS, 55, PhD(geol), 56. *Honors & Awards:* Silver Pin Award, Am Geophys Union. *Prof Exp:* Geologist, US CEngrs, Wash, 49-50; jr engr, State Div Hwys, Calif, 50-52; jr engr geophys comput, Western Geophys Co, 52-54; assoc geol engr, Crane Co, Ill, 55-56; asst prof geol, Mont State Univ, 56-61 & State Univ NY Col New Paltz, 61-62. *Concurrent Pos:* Res grant, Mont State Univ, 59-60 & 60-61; vis investr, Archives of Indies, Naval Mus Madrid, 59-60 & 68, Span Inst Oceanog, Spain, 59-60 & Royal Span Acad Hist, 68; vis investr, Woods Hole Ocean Inst, 59; vis scientist, US Coast Geodetic Surv Ship Discoverer, 69; sci corresp, Nat Pub Radio, WBFO, 75-78, UN press corresp, Geneva, 75, New York, 73, 76, 77 & 79-81; vis scholar, Univ London Law Sch, 75; Inst Marine Studies, Univ Washington, 75, rep, KPBX, Radio, Spokane, 79-81; mem, Malaspina Exped; chair, UN Conf Law Sea Sem, Cousteau Soc, 78; vis investr, Mus Naval, Madrid, 81-82; freelance sci writer, 84-; lectr, Kings Col London, 87. *Mem:* Fel AAAS; Nat Asn Geol Teachers; Am Geophys Union; fel NY Acad Sci; Nat Sci Teachers Asn; Sigma Xi; Nat Asn Sci Writers; Int Sci Writers Asn. *Res:* Marine geology and geochemistry of marine sediments; water resources; history of science; international law of the sea; public policy. *Mailing Add:* Snug Harbor PO Box 398 Grand Island NY 14072-0398

**YALKOWSKY, SAMUEL HYMAN,** PHARMACEUTICAL CHEMISTRY. *Current Pos:* at COL PHARM, UNIV ARIZ. *Personal Data:* b New York, NY, Dec 5, 42; m 62; c 2. *Educ:* Columbia Univ, BS, 65; Univ Mich, Ann Arbor, MS, 68, PhD(pharm chem), 69. *Prof Exp:* Sr res scientist pharm res, Upjohn Co, 69- *Mem:* Am Asn Pharmaceut Sci; Am Chem Soc. *Res:* Physical chemistry of surfaces and micelles; solubility and related phenomena; drug product formulation. *Mailing Add:* Dept Pharmaceut Sci Univ Ariz Tucson AZ 85721-0001

**YALL, IRVING,** MICROBIAL PHYSIOLOGY. *Current Pos:* from asst prof to assoc prof microbiol, 57-68, prof, 68-83, EMER PROF MICROBIOL & IMMUNOL, UNIV ARIZ, 84- *Personal Data:* b Chicago, Ill, Jan 31, 23. *Educ:* Brooklyn Col, BA, 48; Univ Mo, MA, 51; Purdue Univ, PhD(bact), 55. *Prof Exp:* Asst bact, Univ Mo, 49-51; res fel, Purdue Univ, 54-56, resident res assoc biochem, Argonne Nat Lab, 56-57. *Mem:* Fel AAAS; Am Soc Microbiol; Am Chem Soc. *Res:* Phosphorus metabolism in wastewaters; intermediary metabolism of microorganisms; control of nucleic acids. *Mailing Add:* 6124 E Rosewood Tucson AZ 85711-1637

**YALMAN, RICHARD GEORGE,** INORGANIC CHEMISTRY. *Current Pos:* RETIRED. *Personal Data:* b Indianapolis, Ind, Apr 16, 23; m 44; c 2. *Educ:* Harvard Univ, BS, 43, MA, 47, PhD(chem), 49. *Prof Exp:* Jr chemist, Monsanto Chem Co, 44; res chemist & sr group leader, Mound Lab, 49-50; from asst prof to prof chem, Antioch Col, 50-83, chmn dept, 58 & 61-66, chmn dept, 72-83. *Concurrent Pos:* Consult, Signal Corps, Air Force Off Sci Res Projs, Antioch, 50-58, Monsanto Co, 55 & Kettering Res Lab, 67-71; pres, Mad River Chem Co, 67-; consult, Yellow Springs Instrument Co, 71-72; vis scientist, Electronics Br, Avionics Lab, Wright-Patterson AFB, 79- *Mem:* AAAS; Am Chem Soc; Royal Soc Chem; Indian Chem Soc; Soc Chem Indust. *Res:* Kinetics; metal complexes; high temperature synthesis; metalloporphines; hydrothermal properties of oil shale. *Mailing Add:* 440 San Pasquale St Santa Fe NM 87501

**YALOVSKY, MORTY A,** APPLIED STATISTICS, INFORMATION SYSTEMS. *Current Pos:* Lectr math, McGill Univ, 70-74, asst prof, 74-78, assoc mgt sci, 79-82, assoc dean acad, 83-93, DEAN, CTR CONTINUING EDUC, MCGILL UNIV, 93- *Personal Data:* b Montreal, Que, May 14, 44; m 70, Aviva Miller; c David & Mark. *Educ:* McGill Univ, BSc, 65, MSc, 68, PhD(statist), 76. *Mem:* Am Statist Asn; Statist Soc Can. *Res:* Goodness-of-fit testing; regression models and time series analysis; applications of quantitative techniques to administrative sciences; biostatistics; information systems. *Mailing Add:* Fac Mgt McGill Univ Montreal PQ H3A 1G5 Can. *Fax:* 514-398-3876; *E-Mail:* yalovsky@management.mcgill.ca

**YALOW, A(BRAHAM) AARON,** PHYSICS, MEDICAL BIOPHYSICS. *Current Pos:* from instr to assoc prof, 48-66, prof, 66-83, EMER PROF PHYSICS, COOPER UNION SCH ENG, 83- *Personal Data:* b Syracuse, NY, Sept 18, 19; m 43; c 2. *Educ:* Syracuse Univ, AB, 39; Univ Ill, MS, 42, PhD(physics), 45. *Prof Exp:* Asst physics, Syracuse Univ, 39-41 & Univ Ill, 41-42; asst physicist, Nat Defense Res Comt, 43; asst physics, Univ Ill, 44-45; asst engr, Fed Telecommun Labs, NY, 45-46; asst prof physics, NY State Maritime Col, 47-48. *Concurrent Pos:* Consult physicist, Montefiore Hosp, 46-80. *Mem:* AAAS; Am Phys Soc; Am Asn Physics Teachers; assoc fel Am Col Radiol. *Res:* Neutron resonance absorption and scattering; microwave transmission; medical applications of radioactive isotopes; Mossbauer effect. *Mailing Add:* 3242 Tibbett Ave Bronx NY 10463-3801

**YALOW, ROSALYN SUSSMAN,** MEDICAL PHYSICS. *Current Pos:* sr med investr, 72-92, EMER SR MED INVESTR, VET ADMIN, 92-; EMER PROF, ALBERT EINSTEIN COL MED, YESHIVA UNIV, 85- *Personal Data:* b New York, NY, July 19, 21; m 43; c 2. *Educ:* Hunter Col, AB, 41; Univ Ill, MS, 42, PhD(physics), 45; Am Bd Radiol, dipl, 51. *Hon Degrees:* Fifty-one from US & foreign Univs, 74-92. *Honors & Awards:* Nobel Prize, 77; Lilly Award, Am Diabetes Asn, 61, Banting Medal, 78, Rosalyn S Yalow Res & Develop Award, 78; Fed Woman's Award, 61; Van Slyke Award, Am Asn Clin Chem, 68; Gairdner Found Int Award, 71; Am Col Physicians Award, 71; Koch Award, Endocrine Soc, 72; A Cressy Morrison Award Natural Sci, NY Acad Sci, 75; Boehringer-Mannheim Award, Am Asn Clin Chemists, 75; Sci Achievement Award, AMA, 75; Gratum Genus Humanum Gold Medal, World Fedn Nuclear Med & Biol, 78; G von Heresy Medal, 78; Theobold Smith Award, 82; Nat Medal of Sci, 88. *Prof Exp:* Instr physics, Univ Ill, 44-45; lectr & temp asst prof, Hunter Col, 46-50; physicist & asst chief, Radioisotope Serv, Vet Admin Hosp, Bronx, 50-70, actg chief, Radioisotope Serv, 68-70; res prof, Dept Med, Mt Sinai Sch Med, 68-74, distinguished serv prof, 74-79. *Concurrent Pos:* Consult, Radioisotope Unit, Vet Admin Hosp, Bronx, 47-50 & Lenox Hill Hosp, 52-62; secy, US Nat Comt Med Physics, 63-67; mem, Med Adv Bd, Nat Pituitary Agency, 68-71; chief, Radioimmunassay Ref Lab, Vet Admin Med Ctr, 69-, Nuclear Med Serv, 70-80, sr med investr, 72-; mem Endocrinol Study Sect, NIH, 69-72, Bd Sci Coun, Nat Inst Arthritis, Metab & Digestive Dis, 72-75 & 78-81, Task Force Immunol Dis, Nat Inst Allergy & Infectious Dis, 72-73; Int Atomic Engergy Agency expert, Inst Atomic Energy, Sao Paulo, 70; consult, New York City Dept Health, 72-; mem, Comt Eval Nat Pituitary Agency, Nat Res Coun, 73-74; co-ed, Hormone & Metab Res, 73-; dir, Solomon A Berson Res Lab, Vet Admin Hosp, Bronx, 73-, Solomon A Berson distinguished prof-at-large, Mt Sinai Sch Med, City Univ NY, 86-; Albert Lasker Basic Med Res Award, 76; WHO consult, Radiation Med Ctr, Bombay, 78; distinguished prof at large, Albert Einstein Col Med, Yeshiva Univ, 79-85; chmn, Dept Clin Sci, Montefiore Hosp & Med Ctr, 80-85. *Mem:* Nat Acad Sci; Am Acad Arts & Sci; Endocrine Soc (pres elect, 77-78, pres, 78-79); fel NY Acad Sci; hon mem Am Gastroenterol Asn; foreign assoc Fr Acad Med; Radiation Res Soc; Am Asn Physicists Med; Am Col Radiol; Biophys Soc; Am Diabetes Asn; Am Physiol Soc; Soc Nuclear Med. *Res:* Medical use of radioisotopes, radioimmunoassay and radiation chemistry. *Mailing Add:* Vet Affairs Med Ctr 130 W Kingsbridge Rd Bronx NY 10468

**YAM, LUNG TSIONG,** INTERNAL MEDICINE. *Current Pos:* assoc prof, 74-80, PROF MED, UNIV LOUISVILLE, 80-; CHIEF HEMAT-ONCOL, VET ADMIN HOSP, 74- *Personal Data:* b Canton, China, Apr 16, 36; US citizen; m 64; c 2. *Educ:* Nat Taiwan Univ, MD, 60. *Prof Exp:* From instr to asst prof, Sch Med, Tufts Univ, 67-72; assoc hemat, Scripps Clin & Res Found, 72-74. *Concurrent Pos:* Res assoc, New Eng Med Ctr Hosp, 68-72, head cytol & histochem, 70-72. *Mem:* Am Soc Hemat; Am Soc Histochem & Cytochem. *Res:* Use of morphologic approach to study problems related to hematology-oncology; use of cytochemistry, immunochemistry and electrophoresis for isoenzymes to identify the origin of normal and neoplastic cells. *Mailing Add:* Dept Med Univ Louisville Sch Med 2301 S 3rd St Louisville KY 40292-0001

**YAMADA, EICHI,** ANATOMY, CYTOLOGY. *Current Pos:* prof, 69-83, EMER PROF ANAT, FAC MED, TOKYO UNIV, 83- *Personal Data:* b Fukuoka, Japan, May 17, 22; m 47, Takeko Yoshida; c Machiko S & Sekiko A. *Educ:* Kyushu Imp Univ, MD, 45; DSc, Kyushu Univ, 50. *Honors & Awards:* Setoh Award, Japan Soc Electron Micros, 58; Yamaji Sci Award, Yamaji Sci Found, 67; Brasilian Garibaldi Order, 91; Fujiwara Award, Fujiwara Sci Found, 91. *Prof Exp:* From assoc prof to prof anat, Fac Med, Kyushu Univ, 49-69; prof anat, Sch Med, Kurume Univ, 56-60 & Fukuoka Univ, 83-93. *Concurrent Pos:* Fel, Sch Med, Univ Wash, 54-55; res assoc, Rockefeller Inst Med Res, 58-59; vis prof, Jules Stein Eye Inst, Univ Calif, Los Angeles, 67-68; sr res sci, Sch Med, Yale Univ, 86-91. *Mem:* Am Soc Cell Biol; hon mem Am Asn Anatomists. *Res:* Electron microscopy of cells and tissues; gall bladder epithelium; renal glomerulus; megakaryocyte; centriole; ocular tissue. *Mailing Add:* Hirao 3-9-15 Chuo-ku Fukuoka 810 Japan

**YAMADA, ESTHER V,** BIOCHEMISTRY. *Current Pos:* lectr, 59-60, from asst prof to prof, 60-94, EMER PROF BIOCHEM, FAC MED, UNIV MAN, 95- *Personal Data:* b London, Ont, July 19, 23; m 53; c Catherine Ruth. *Educ:* Univ Western Ont, BSc, 45, PhD(biochem), 51; McGill Univ, MSc, 47. *Prof Exp:* Nat Cancer Inst fel, Univ Western Ont, 52-55; res assoc, Karolinska Inst, Sweden, 55-57; res fel, NIH, 57-59. *Mem:* AAAS; Can Biochem Soc; Am Soc Biol Chemists; NY Acad Sci. *Res:* Transcription and translation; skeletal muscle metabolism; bioenergetics; membrane; bound enzymes; heart metabolism. *Mailing Add:* Dept Biochem Univ Man Fac Med 770 Bannatyne Ave Winnipeg MB R3E 0W3 Can. *Fax:* 204-783-0864

**YAMADA, KENNETH MANAO,** EXTRA-CELLULAR MATRIX, CELL ADHESION. *Current Pos:* CHIEF, LAB DEVELOP BIOL, NAT INST DENT RES, 91- *Personal Data:* Minneapolis, Minnesota, 44; m. *Educ:* Stanford Univ, PhD(biol sci), 71, MD, 72. *Prof Exp:* Chief, Membrane & Biochem Sect, Nat Cancer Inst, NIH, 80-91. *Mailing Add:* NIDR NIH Bldg 30 Rm 421 30 Convent Dr MSC 4370 Bethesda MD 20892-4370

**YAMADA, MASAAKI,** PLASMA PHYSICS. *Current Pos:* res assoc, Princeton Univ, 73-75, res staff, 75-78, res physicist plasma physics, Plasma Physics Lab, 78-82, PRIN RES PHYSICIST, PRINCETON UNIV, 82- *Personal Data:* b Japan, Aug 9, 42; m 71, JoAnn Nojiri; c Masahiro & Hideki. *Educ:* Univ Tokyo, Japan, BS, 66, MS, 68; Univ Ill, PhD(physics), 73. *Prof Exp:* Res asst physics, Univ Ill, 69-73. *Concurrent Pos:* Head, Magnetic Reconnection Exp Prog. *Mem:* Fel Am Phys Soc; Phys Soc Japan. *Res:* Experimental studies of plasma physics, including spheromak physics, general magnetohydrodynamics and micro-instabilities and transport properties of plasmas; magnetic reconnection. *Mailing Add:* Plasma Physics Lab Princeton Univ PO Box 451 Princeton NJ 08543. *Fax:* 609-243-2160

**YAMADA, RYUJI,** SUPERCONDUCTING MAGNETS, ACCELERATOR. *Current Pos:* accelerator consult, 67, PHYSICIST HIGH ENERGY PHYSICS, FERMI NAT ACCELERATOR LAB, 68- *Personal Data:* b Hiroshima City, Japan, Jan 3, 32; m 60, Nanako Narita; c Seiji & Kouji. *Educ:* Hiroshima Univ, Japan, BS, 54; Univ Tokyo, Japan, MS, 56, PhD(physics), 62. *Prof Exp:* Res assoc high energy physics, Inst Nuclear Study, Univ Tokyo, Japan, 56-68; res assoc, high energy physics, Brookhaven Nat Lab, 63-65; res assoc accelerator physics, Cornell Univ, 65-66. *Mem:* Am Phys Soc. *Res:* Development of super conducting magnets for energy doubler project and colliding detectors; high energy experiments using tevatron collider; construction of accelerators, including 16 inch cyclotron, 1 GeV INS electron synchrotron, 10 GeV cornell electron synchrotron, and NAL 500 GeV proton synchrotron. *Mailing Add:* MS 357 Fermilab Batavia IL 60510. *Fax:* 630-357-9713; *E-Mail:* Bitnet: yamada@fnalv

**YAMADA, SYLVIA BEHRENS,** POPULATION ECOLOGY. *Current Pos:* adj prof, Sch Oceanog, 81-83, res assoc fisheries, wildlife & zool, 83-84, RES ASSOC ZOOL, ORE STATE UNIV, 84- *Personal Data:* b Hamburg, Ger, May 7, 46; m 75; c 2. *Educ:* Univ BC, BSc, 68, MSc, 71; Univ Ore, PhD(marine ecol), 74. *Prof Exp:* Biologist fisheries, Pac Biol Sta Fisheries & Marine Serv, Dept Environ Can, 74-79; asst prof, Wellesley Col, Mass, 80-81. *Concurrent Pos:* Course coordr, Marine Ecol, Marine Biol Lab, Woods Hole, Mass, 80; lectr, Biol Dept, Univ Manitoba, 73, dept zool & fisheries & wildlife, Ore State Univ, 82- *Mem:* Ecol Soc Am; Western Soc Naturalists; Sigma Xi. *Res:* Chemical marking of salmon; incorporation and retention of trace elements in salmon tissue; ecology of intertidal mollusks, (Littorina sitkana, L scutulata, L planaxis, L littorea, L saxatilis, Batillaria attramentatia, Mytilus californianus and M edulis); molluskan aquaculture. *Mailing Add:* 3035 NW Taft Ave Corvallis OR 97330

**YAMADA, TADATAKA,** GASTROENTEROLOGY. *Current Pos:* PRES HEALTHCARE SERVS, SMITHKLINE BEECHAM, 96- *Personal Data:* b Tokyo, Japan. *Educ:* NY Univ, MD. *Prof Exp:* John G Searle prof & chmn, Dept Internal Med, Univ Mich, 90-96. *Mem:* Inst Med-Nat Acad Sci; Cent Soc Clin Res; Am Gastroenterol Asn (pres-elect, 96); Endocrine Soc. *Mailing Add:* SmithKline Beecham Corp 1 Franklin Plaza Philadelphia PA 19101

**YAMADA, TETSUJI,** METEOROLOGY, ENVIRONMENTAL SCIENCES. *Current Pos:* PRES, YAMADA SCI & ART CORP, 90- *Personal Data:* b Osaka, Japan, May 9, 42; US citizen; m 67; c 2. *Educ:* Osaka Univ, BE, 65, ME, 67; Colo State Univ, PhD(civil eng), 71. *Honors & Awards:* Soc Award, Meteorol Soc Japan, 84. *Prof Exp:* Fel civil eng, Colo State Univ, 71-72; mem res staff meteorol, Princeton Univ, 72-76; meteorologist, Argonne Nat Lab, 76-81; mem staff, Los Alamos Nat Lab, 81-90. *Mem:* Am Meteorol Soc; Meteorol Soc Japan; Sigma Xi. *Res:* Turbulence theory; numerical modelling of mountain flows, sea breeze and air pollution. *Mailing Add:* 147 Monte Rey Dr S Los Alamos NM 87544

**YAMADA, YOSHIKAZU,** ORGANIC CHEMISTRY. *Current Pos:* RETIRED. *Personal Data:* b Honokaa, Hawaii, May 20, 15; m 50; c 4. *Educ:* Univ Hawaii, BS, 37; Univ Mich, MS, 38; Purdue Univ, PhD(chem), 50. *Prof Exp:* Res chemist, Davidson Corp, Ill, 50-53; from sr proj engr to res engr, Mergenthaler Linotype Co, NY, 53-59; sr res chemist, Bell & Howell Co, Ill, 59-60, prin res chemist, Res Labs, Calif, 60-72; pres, Yamada-Graphics Corp, Irvine, 72-73. *Mem:* AAAS; Am Chem Soc; Sigma Xi. *Res:* Photosensitive systems; graphic media. *Mailing Add:* 6151 Sierra Bravo Rd Irvine CA 92612

**YAMAGISHI, FREDERICK GEORGE,** CONDUCTIVE POLYMERS. *Current Pos:* MEM TECH STAFF ORG CHEM, HUGHES RES LAB, HUGHES AIRCRAFT CO, 74-, STAFF CHEMIST, 85-, SR RES STAFF CHEMIST, 91-, SR RES SCIENTIST, 94- *Personal Data:* b Reno, Nev, Sept 14, 43; m 68, Joyce Ichinotsubo; c Wendy & Mark. *Educ:* Univ Calif, Los Angeles, BS, 65, PhD(org chem), 72; Calif State Col, MS, 67. *Prof Exp:* Fel, Dept Physics, Univ Pa, 72-73, res assoc org chem, 73-74. *Mem:* Am Chem Soc; Mat Res Soc; Electrochem Soc. *Res:* Organic conductors; one-dimensional materials; conducting polymers; liquid crystals; plasma polymerized thin films; nonlinear optical polymers; chemical sensors. *Mailing Add:* Sensors & Mats 3011 Malibu Canyon Rd Malibu CA 90265. *Fax:* 310-317-5484; *E-Mail:* fyamagishi@msmail4.hac.comM

**YAMAGUCHI, GARY T,** BIOMEDICAL ENGINEERING, BIOMECHANICS. *Current Pos:* ASST PROF, BIOMED ENG PROG, ARIZ STATE UNIV, 89- *Educ:* Calif Inst Technol, Pasadena, BS, 79; Mass Inst Technol, SMME, 81; Stanford Univ, PhD(mech eng), 89. *Honors & Awards:* Young Invest Award, NSF, 92. *Prof Exp:* Res asst, Biomech, & Human Rehab Lab, Mass Inst Technol, 79-81; syst integration engr, Lawrence Livermore Nat Lab, 81-84; biomed engr, Rehab Res & Develop Ctr, Vet Admin Med Ctr, 85-89. *Concurrent Pos:* Consult, Biomech Res & Consult Inc, 92-94, Biomechanix Inc, 94; prin investr, NSF, 89-91, 92-94, Nat Ins Disability Rehab Res Innovation Grants, 89-90, Barrow Neurol Inst, 90-91, 91-93 & 93-94, NIH, 89-91 & 92-, Nat Inst Chiropractic Res, 91-92 & Kimble Found, 91-94, SW Craniofacial Ctr, 91-92, Whitaker Found, 91-94 & 94-, Robert S Flinn Found, 93- *Mem:* Am Soc Biomech; Am Soc Mech Engrs; Biomed Eng Soc; Rehab Eng Soc NAm; Sigma Xi. *Res:* Optimal control and dynamic simulation of multiarticular movement, joint mechanics, computational modeling of muscle, tendon, and joints, coordinations, FNS. *Mailing Add:* 2517 E Rocky Slope Dr Tempe AZ 85048-9039. *Fax:* 602-965-0037

**YAMAGUCHI, MASATOSHI,** PLANT PHYSIOLOGY, BIOCHEMISTRY. *Current Pos:* Prin lab technician, Univ Calif, Davis, 41 & 46-50, instr, 50-52, from asst olericulturist to assoc olericulturist, 50-64, lectr, 64-73, prof veg crops, 73-81, olericulturist, 64-81, EMER PROF, UNIV CALIF, DAVIS, 81- *Personal Data:* b San Leandro, Calif, Mar 12, 18; m 42; c 3. *Educ:* Univ Calif, BS, 40, PhD(agr chem), 50. *Honors & Awards:* Japan Nat Sci Found Award, 79. *Concurrent Pos:* Fulbright res scholar, 59-60; vis prof, Univ Man, 67-68; consult veg crops, Sao Paulo & Parana, Brazil, 75-76, Beijing Veg Res Ctr, Beijing, China, 88. *Mem:* Am Chem Soc; Am Soc Hort. *Res:* Chemical constituents and quality of vegetables; physiological disorders of vegetable crops; biochemistry and physiology of vegetable fruit development and ripening; author of one book. *Mailing Add:* Dept Veg Crops Univ Calif Davis CA 95616

**YAMAGUCHI, TADANORI,** METAL OXIDE SEMICONDUCTOR. *Current Pos:* DIR RES & DEVELOP, MAXIM INTEGRATED PROD INC, 94- *Personal Data:* b Miyazaki, Japan, Jan 17, 49; m 78, Taeko Naito; c Lisa & Leo. *Educ:* Miyakonojyo Tech Col, BSEE, 69. *Prof Exp:* Res engr, Semiconnductor Div, Sony Corp, Japan, 69-77; prof proj mgr, Tektronix Inc, 78-85, prog mgr, 86-90, Tecktronix fel, 91-94,. *Mem:* Inst Elec & Electronics Engrs. *Res:* Device and technology development for advanced metaloxide semiconductor-large scale integration-very large scale integrations, including state-of-the-art device structure, also new device structure in n-channel metal oxide semiconductor, complementary metal oxide semiconductor, high-voltage metal oxide semiconductor, and advanced bipolar semiconductor integrated circuits; investigation of metal oxide semiconductor device physics and modeling. *Mailing Add:* 12757 NW Hartford St Portland OR 97229. *Fax:* 503-627-5560; *E-Mail:* tady@ernie.ico.tek.com

**YAMAKAWA, KAZUO ALAN,** solid state physics, for more information see previous edition

**YAMAMOTO, DIANE M,** medicinal chemistry, organic chemistry; deceased, see previous edition for last biography

**YAMAMOTO, HARRY Y,** PLANT BIOCHEMISTRY. *Current Pos:* from asst prof to assoc prof plant physiol, Univ Hawaii, Manoa, 61-70, actg assoc dean res, 80-82, dept chmn, 82-88, dir, Hawaii Inst Trop Agr & Human Resource, 93-96, PROF PLANT PHYSIOL, UNIV HAWAII, MANOA, 70- *Personal Data:* b Honolulu, Hawaii, Nov 26, 33; m 57, Millie Y Wakugawa; c Craig A & Joanne V. *Educ:* Univ Hawaii, BS, 55; Univ Ill, MS, 58; Univ Calif, Davis, PhD(biochem), 62. *Honors & Awards:* Samuel Cate Prescott Award, Inst Food Technologists, 69. *Concurrent Pos:* USPHS spec fel, Charles F Kettering Res Lab, 68-69; vis scientist, Inst Animal Physiol, Babraham, Cambridge, Eng, 76. *Mem:* Am Chem Soc; Am Soc Plant Physiol; Inst Food Technologists; AAAS. *Res:* Carotenoid function; photosynthesis; food biotechnology; xanthophyll-cycle in plant adaptation to light environment. *Mailing Add:* Hawaii Inst Trop Agr & Human Resource Univ Hawaii Honolulu HI 96822. *Fax:* 808-956-9105; *E-Mail:* yamamoto@hawaii.edu

**YAMAMOTO, HIROSHI,** IMMUNOLOGY. *Current Pos:* HEAD IMMUNOL, NAT INST NEUROSCI, NAT CTR NEUROL & PSYCHIAT, TOKYO, 90- *Personal Data:* b Osaka, Japan, Aug 23, 46; m 76; c 1. *Educ:* Osaka Univ, BS, 70, MS, 73, PhD(immunol) & DMS, 77. *Prof Exp:* Postdoctoral immunol, Scripps Clin Res Found, 77-78, res assoc, 78-79; assoc prof, Kochi Med Sch, Japan, 80-90. *Concurrent Pos:* Lectr, Kochi Med Sch, Japan, 90- *Mem:* Am Asn Immunologists. *Res:* Cell surface molecules that govern communications in immunology and neurology. *Mailing Add:* Dept Immunol Nat Ctr Neurol & Psychiat Ogawahigashi 4-1-1 Kodaira Tokyo 187 Japan. *Fax:* 81-423-46-1753

**YAMAMOTO, HIROTAKA,** MOLECULAR GLYCOBIOLOGY OF BRAIN TUMORS, MOLECULAR BIOLOGY OF NEURONAL PLASTICITY. *Current Pos:* CHIEF MOLECULAR NEUROBIOL LAB, CHICAGO INST NEUROSURG & NEURORES, 92- *Personal Data:* b Akita, Japan, Apr 27, 58; m 92; c 1. *Educ:* Tohoku Univ, MS, 84, PhD(neurosci), 88. *Prof Exp:* Instr, Tohoku Univ Hosp, Japan, 84-86; res scientist, Nihon Kayaku Co, Japan, 86-88; fel, Univ BC, Can, 88-89; res assoc, Northwestern Univ, 89-92. *Mem:* Am Asn Cancer Res; Soc Neurosci; Am Soc Cell Biol; AAAS. *Res:* Molecular biology of brain tumor-associate glycosyltransferases and glycosidases; molecular biology of NMDA receptors. *Mailing Add:* Chicago Inst Neurosurg & Neuroses 2515 N Clark St Chicago IL 60614. *Fax:* 773-935-2132

**YAMAMOTO, JOE,** PSYCHIATRY. *Current Pos:* dir, Adult Ambulatory Serv, 77-78, PROF PSYCHIAT, UNIV CALIF, LOS ANGELES, 77- *Personal Data:* b Los Angeles, Calif, Apr 18, 24; m 47; c 2. *Educ:* Univ Minn, BS, 46, MB, 48, MD, 49. *Prof Exp:* Asst prof psychiat, Sch Med, Univ Okla, 55-58, asst prof, 58-61; from asst prof to assoc prof psychiat, Sch Med, Univ Southern Calif, Sch Med, 58-66, mem fac, Psychoanal Inst, 66-69, prof psychiat, 69-77. *Concurrent Pos:* Clin dir, Adult Outpatient Psychiat Clin, Los Angeles County-Univ Southern Calif Med Ctr, 58-77; mem comt psychopath, NIH, 84-86. *Mem:* Fel Am Acad Psychoanal (pres, 78); fel Am Psychiat Asn; emer fel Am Col Psychiatrists; fel Am Asn Soc Psychiat (vpres 84-86); fel Am Orthopsychiat Asn (pres elect, 93). *Res:* Clinical and preventive psychiatry; social class factors, Asian/Pacific factors. *Mailing Add:* UCLA Neuropsy Inst 760 Westwood Plaza Los Angeles CA 90024-1759

**YAMAMOTO, KEITH ROBERT,** MOLECULAR BIOLOGY. *Current Pos:* fel biochem, Lab Gordon M Tomkins, Univ Calif, San Francisco, 73-75, from asst prof to assoc prof, 76-83, vchmn Dept Biochem & Biophys, 85-94, PROF BIOCHEM, UNIV CALIF, SAN FRANCISCO, 83-, DIR, BIOCHEM & MOLECULAR BIOL PROG, 88-, PROF & CHMN, DEPT CELLULAR & MOLECULAR PHARMACOL, 94- *Personal Data:* b Des Moines, Iowa, Feb 4, 46. *Educ:* Iowa State Univ, BSc, 68; Princeton Univ, PhD(biochem sci), 73. *Honors & Awards:* Swerling Lectr & Markey Lectr, Harvard Med Sch, 82; Rudin Lectr, Columbia Univ, 83; Weissberger Lectr, Univ Rochester, 83; Bernard Axelrod Lectr, Purdue Univ, 88; Lindner Lectr, Weizmann Inst, 90; Greg Pincus Medal, 90; Steenbock Lectr, Univ Wis, 92; Matrone Lectr, NC State Univ, 93; Sadler Lectr, Univ Colo, 95; duVigneaud Lectr, Cornell Univ, 95; Kosuge Lectr, Univ Calif, 95; Harvey Lectr, Rockefeller Univ, 95; Monsanto Lectr, Ohio State Univ, 96; Ochoa Lectr, NY Univ, 96. *Prof Exp:* Res asst biochem, Dept Biochem & Biophys, Iowa State Univ, 67-68; NIH trainee biochem sci, Princeton Univ, 68-73. *Concurrent Pos:* Fel, Helen Hay Whitney Found, 73-76; fel consult, Found Res Hereditary Dis, 74; mem sci adv comt, Dam Runyon-Walt Winchell Cancer Found, 77-81; res career develop award, NIH, 77-82, mem, Molecular Biol Study Sect, 86-90 & chmn, 87-90, dir, Subcomt Intramural Res Prog Rev Process, 89 & Nat Adv Coun Human Genome Res, 90-92; Dreyfus teacher scholar award, 82-86; mem, Genetics Biol Rev Panel, NSF, 84-87; assoc ed, J Molecular Biol, 88- & Cell Regulation, 88-; mem, Panel Sci Responsibility/Conduct Res, 90-91; ed, Molecular Biol Cell, 91-; fac res lectr, Univ Calif, San Francisco, 97. *Mem:* Nat Acad Sci; Am Soc Biol Chemists; Am Soc Develop Biol; Am Soc Microbiol; AAAS; Am Soc Biochem & Molecular Biol; Am Soc Cell Biol; fel Am Acad Arts & Sci; fel Am Acad Microbiol; Endocrine Soc; Genetics Soc Am. *Res:* Mechanisms of steroid receptor action; regulation of eukaryotic transcription; regulation and maintenance of chromosome structure. *Mailing Add:* Dept Cellular & Molecular Pharmacol Univ Calif Box 0450 513 Parnassus Ave Rm 51210 San Francisco CA 94143-0450. *Fax:* 415-476-6129; *E-Mail:* yamamoto@socrates.ucsf.edu

**YAMAMOTO, MITSUYOSHI,** SUPERCONDUCTIVE APPLICATION TO ELECTRICAL MACHINES. *Current Pos:* PROF ELEC MACH, TOKUSHOKU UNIV, 88- *Personal Data:* b Tokyo, Japan, Jan, 1923. *Educ:* Tokyo Univ, Bachelor, 44, Dr Eng, 61. *Prof Exp:* Dir, Heavy Apparatus Eng Lab, Toshiba Co, Ltd, 78-83; prof elec mach, Saitemca Univ, 84-88. *Mem:* Fel Inst Elec & Electronics Engrs. *Res:* Superconductive application to electrical machines; control technique electrical machines. *Mailing Add:* Mech Syst Eng Takushoku Univ 815-1 Tate-Machi Hachioji-Shi 193 Japan

**YAMAMOTO, NOBUTO,** MICROBIOLOGY, BIOPHYSICS. *Current Pos:* SR INVESTR, CANCER CTR & CHIEF, LAB CANCER IMMUNOL & MOLECULAR BIOL, EINSTEIN MED CTR, 93- *Personal Data:* b Nagawa City, Japan, Apr 25, 25; m 54; c 3. *Educ:* Kurume Inst Technol, BS, 47; Kyushi Univ, MS, 53; Nagoya Univ, PhD(bact), 58. *Prof Exp:* Asst prof, Sch Med, Gifu Univ, 58-62; vis scientist molecular biol, NIH, 62-63; from asst prof to assoc prof microbiol, Fels Res Inst & Sch Med, Temple Univ, 63-71, prof, 71-80; mem fac, Dept Microbiol, Hahnemann Med Ctr, 80-90; prof, Dept Biochem, Temple Univ, 90-93. *Concurrent Pos:* Vis researcher virol, Inst Cancer Res, Philadelphia, 59-61; vis scientist, Dept Bact, Ind Univ, 61-62. *Mem:* Am Soc Microbiol; Am Asn Cancer Res. *Res:* Virology; genetics; cancer research; molecular biology. *Mailing Add:* 1040 66th Ave Philadelphia PA 19126

**YAMAMOTO, RICHARD,** VETERINARY MICROBIOLOGY, MYCOPLASMOLOGY. *Current Pos:* asst microbiologist, Univ Calif, Davis, 62-64, lectr, 64-67, assoc microbiologist, 64-70, PROF & MICROBIOLOGIST, UNIV CALIF, DAVIS, 70-, DIR, MASTER PREV VET MED PROG, SCH VET MED, 90- *Personal Data:* b Wapato, Wash, May 27, 27; m 50; c 7. *Educ:* Univ Wash, BS, 52; Univ Calif, MA, 55, PhD(microbiol), 57. *Honors & Awards:* Tom Newman Int Award, 67; Nat Turkey Fedn Res Award, 70. *Prof Exp:* Asst specialist vet pub health, Univ Calif, 57-58, asst res microbiologist, 59; asst prof vet serol & asst vet serologist, Ore State Univ, 59-61. *Concurrent Pos:* Assoc ed, Poultry Sci, 67-72 & 80-86 & Avian Dis J, 75-88. *Mem:* Am Soc Microbiol; Poultry Sci Asn; Am Asn Avian Path; US Animal Health Asn; World Poultry Sci Asn; Int Orgn Mycoplasmology; Am Asn Vet Lab Diag. *Res:* Host parasite interactions (infection, immunity, epidemiology) with reference to avian species; mycoplasmas and viruses; development of rapid diagnostic terts for avian diseases. *Mailing Add:* 1013 Radcliffe Dr Davis CA 95616-8735

**YAMAMOTO, RICHARD KUMEO,** PHYSICS. *Current Pos:* Res staff physics, 63-64, from instr to assoc prof, 64-75, PROF PHYSICS, MASS INST TECHNOL, 75- *Personal Data:* b Honolulu, Hawaii, June 29, 35; m 61; c 3. *Educ:* Mass Inst Technol, SB, 57, PhD(physics), 63. *Mem:* Fel Am Phys Soc; AAAS; NY Acad Sci. *Res:* High energy nuclear physics; spectrometer techniques; study of lepton and quark interactions; electronic detectors. *Mailing Add:* Dept Physics Rm 24-043 Mass Inst Technol Cambridge MA 02139

**YAMAMOTO, RICHARD SUSUMU,** BIOCHEMISTRY. *Current Pos:* SR SCI ADV, TECH RESOURCES, INC, 84- *Personal Data:* b Honolulu, Hawaii, May 15, 20; m 46; c 1. *Educ:* Univ Hawaii, AB, 46; George Washington Univ, AM, 49; Johns Hopkins Univ, ScD, 54. *Prof Exp:* Res assoc biochem, Johns Hopkins Univ, 54-55; biochemist, Lab Nutrit & Endocrinol, Nat Inst Arthritis & Metab Dis, 55-62; biochemist biol, 62-70, biochemist etiology, Exp Path Br, 70-76, biochemist, Carcinogen Metab & Toxicol Br, Nat Cancer Inst, 76-84. *Concurrent Pos:* Vis scientist, Dept Molecular Oncol, Univ Tokyo & Div Biochem, Japanese Nat Cancer Ctr. *Mem:* AAAS; Am Inst Nutrit; Soc Exp Biol & Med; Am Asn Cancer Res; Am Asn Clin Chemists; Sigma Xi; Soc Toxicol. *Res:* Vitamin B12; nutritional obesity; lipid metabolism; chemical carcinogenesis; nutrition and endocrines in carcinogenesis. *Mailing Add:* 11109 Jolly Way Kensington MD 20895-1127

**YAMAMOTO, SACHIO,** MARINE CHEMISTRY, PHYSICAL CHEMISTRY. *Current Pos:* SR SCIENTIST, RDT & E DIV, NAVAL COMMAND CONTROL & OCEAN SURVEILLANCE CTR, 93- *Personal Data:* b Petaluma, Calif, Dec 12, 32; m 58, Irene Otamura; c Susan, Steven & Robert. *Educ:* Univ Calif, Berkeley, BS, 55; Iowa State Univ, PhD(phys chem), 59. *Prof Exp:* Res chemist, Calif Res Corp, 59-63; res chemist, US Naval Radiol Defense Lab, 63-69, Naval Undersea Ctr, 69-71; res & develop mgr, Naval Ocean Systs Ctr, 71-90; dir, Asian Off, Off Naval Res, 82-84 & 90-93. *Mem:* Am Chem Soc; Royal Soc Chem. *Res:* Environmental sciences; trace metal analysis; gas solubility; x-ray fluorescence analysis. *Mailing Add:* 3725 Notre Dame Ave San Diego CA 92122. *E-Mail:* yamamoto@nosc.mil

**YAMAMOTO, TATSUZO,** VIROLOGY. *Current Pos:* RETIRED. *Personal Data:* b Hardieville, Alta, Feb 8, 28. *Educ:* Univ Alta, BSc, 52, MSc, 55; Yale Univ, PhD(virol), 61. *Prof Exp:* Fel microbiol, Univ Toronto, 61-62; from asst prof to assoc prof virol, Univ Alta, 62-74, prof microbiol, 74-91. *Concurrent Pos:* Consult, Govt Can, 72-; sabbatical res assoc award, Can Int Develop Res Ctr, 79-80. *Mem:* Am Soc Microbiol; Am Fisheries Soc; Nat Geog Soc; Can Nat Geog Soc; Wildlife Dis Asn. *Res:* Replication and structure of animal viruses; viral diseases of fish; infectious pancreatic necrosis; dermal hyperplastics. *Mailing Add:* RR 7 Site 12A Comp A-1 Vernon BC V1T 7Z3 Can

**YAMAMOTO, TOSHIAKI,** DEVELOPMENT OF TURBULENCE MODEL FOR PERSONAL COMPUTER, NONTHERMAL PLASMA TECHNOLOGY FOR ENVIRONMENTAL APPLICATION. *Current Pos:* SR RES ENGR, RES TRIANGLE INST, 84- *Personal Data:* m, Toshiko Sakai; c Satoko & Riichi. *Educ:* Sophia Univ, BS, 67, MS, 69; Univ Ill, MS, 72; Ohio State Univ, PhD(electrohydrodyn), 79. *Prof Exp:* Res engr, United McGill Corp, 72-81; res engr & adj prof, Univ Denver, 81-84. *Concurrent Pos:* Tech comt, air pollution control div, Am Soc Mech Engrs, 84-92. *Mem:* Sigma Xi; Am Asn Aerosol Res; Am Soc Mech Engrs; Inst Electrostatics Japan; Japan Asn Aerosol Sci & Technol. *Res:* Application of atmospheric pressure plasma technologies; indoor air quality research-development of user friendly ventilation model, new computational scheme of K-E turbulence and particle transport models for personal computers; microcontamination program-evaluation of particle control technology due to electrostatics, thermophoresis and photophoresis at subatmospheric pressures. *Mailing Add:* 3212 Whitfield Rd Chapel Hill NC 27514. *Fax:* 919-541-6936

**YAMAMOTO, WILLIAM SHIGERU,** PHYSIOLOGY, COMPUTER SCIENCE. *Current Pos:* PROF COMPUT MED & CHMN DEPT, SCH MED, GEORGE WASHINGTON UNIV, 71- *Personal Data:* b Cleveland, Ohio, Sept 22, 24; m 65; c 3. *Educ:* Park Col, AB, 45; Univ Pa, MD, 49. *Hon Degrees:* MS, Univ Pa, 71. *Prof Exp:* Instr physiol, Sch Med, Univ Pa, 52-53, assoc, 55-57, instr biostatist & asst prof physiol, 57-66, prof physiol, 66-70; prof physiol & biomath, Sch Med, Univ Calif, 70-71. *Concurrent Pos:* Mem study sect, NIH, 63-65, mem Nat Adv Coun Res Resources, 71-75; consult, Health Care Tech Div, Nat Ctr Health Serv Res & Develop, 68-80 & Am Col Prev Med, 80- *Mem:* AAAS; Am Physiol Soc; Asn Comput Mach; Biomed Eng Soc; Am Col Prev Med; Am Col Med Informatics. *Res:* Computer applications in health services; physiology of respiratory regulation by carbon dioxide homeostasis. *Mailing Add:* Dept Comp Med George Washington Univ Med Ctr 2300 K St NW Washington DC 20037-1700

**YAMAMOTO, Y LUCAS,** NEUROSURGERY, NUCLEAR MEDICINE. *Current Pos:* res assoc neurosurg res, 61-68, from asst prof to assoc prof, 68-80, PROF NEUROL & NEUROSURG, MONTREAL NEUROL INST, MCGILL UNIV, 80- *Personal Data:* b Hokkaido, Japan, Jan 19, 28; Can citizen; m 58; c 3. *Educ:* Hokkaido Univ, BSc, 48, MD, 52; Yokohama Nat Univ, PhD(radiobiol), 61. *Prof Exp:* Intern med, Int Cath Hosp, Tokyo, Japan, 53; resident neurosurg, Med Ctr, Georgetown Univ, 54-58; res assoc nuclear med & radiobiol, Med Dept, Brookhaven Nat Lab, 58-61. *Concurrent Pos:* Mem, Am Bd Nuclear Med, 73- *Mem:* Soc Nuclear Med; Can Asn Nuclear Med; Am Col Nuclear Physicians; Can Neurosurg Soc. *Res:* Neurological science; cerebral circulation. *Mailing Add:* Montreal Neurol Inst 3801 Univ St Rm 688 Montreal PQ H3A 2B4 Can

**YAMAMOTO, Y STEPHEN,** ORGANIC CHEMISTRY, PHOTOGRAPHIC CHEMISTRY. *Current Pos:* info specialist, Du Pont Cent Res & Develop Exp Sta, 88-90, patent liaison, 90-92, tech ed, 92-96, INFO DEVELOPER, DUPONT CO, 96- *Personal Data:* b Topaz, Utah, Aug 6, 43; div; c Michael K. *Educ:* Univ Wis, BS, 65; Pa State Univ, PhD(org chem), 71. *Prof Exp:* Sr res chemist, Eastman Kodak Co Res Labs, 71-78; assoc prof chem, Rochester Inst Technol, 78-83; sr ed, Ullmann's Encycl Indust Chem, 83-88. *Concurrent Pos:* Coordr experimental learning, Rochester Inst Technol, 78-81. *Mem:* Am Chem Soc. *Mailing Add:* DuPont Co PO Box 80016 Wilmington DE 19880-0016. *Fax:* 302-992-3342; *E-Mail:* yamamoto@esvax.dnet.dupont.com

**YAMAMURA, HENRY ICHIRO,** NEUROCHEMISTRY, NEUROPHARMACOLOGY. *Current Pos:* asst prof, 75-77, ASSOC PROF, DEPT PHARMACOL, COL MED, UNIV ARIZ, 77- *Personal Data:* b Seattle, Wash, June 25, 40; m 64; c 1. *Educ:* Univ Wash, BS, 64, MS, 66, PhD(pharmacol), 69. *Prof Exp:* Pharm intern, Seattle, Wash, 60-64; staff pharmacist, 64-66; spec lectr pharmacol, Seattle Pac Col, 66-67. *Concurrent Pos:* NIMH spec fel pharmacol, Sch Med, Johns Hopkins Univ, 72-75; NIMH res scientist develop awardee, 75- *Mem:* AAAS; Soc Neurosci; Am Soc Neurochem; Am Soc Pharmacol & Exp Therapeut. *Res:* Release and uptake of brain neurohumoral transmitters; demonstration of brain neurotransmitter receptors and their alterations in neuropsychiatric disorders. *Mailing Add:* Dept Pharmacol & Biochem Univ Ariz Health Sci Ctr Rm 5122 Hiy 1501 N Campbell Ave Tucson AZ 85724-0001. *Fax:* 520-626-2204

**YAMANAKA, WILLIAM KIYOSHI,** NUTRITION, COMMUNITY HEALTH. *Current Pos:* RETIRED. *Personal Data:* b Kauai, Hawaii, Mar 19, 31; m 58; c 3. *Educ:* Univ Hawaii, BS, 55; Univ Calif, PhD(nutrit), 69. *Prof Exp:* Res assoc nutrit, Childrens Hosp East Bay, Oakland, Calif, 59-64; res asst, Univ Calif, Berkeley, 64-69; assoc prof nutrit, Univ Mo, Columbia, 69-75; mem fac, Univ Wash, 75-97. *Concurrent Pos:* Nutrit adv, Delta Area Head Start, Mo, 69-74. *Mem:* Am Dietetic Asn; Soc Nutrit Educ; Am Soc Clin Path; Am Home Econ Asn; Am Pub Health Asn. *Res:* Role of lipids in cardiovascular disease; effect of protein malnutrition of growing mammalian organisms; applied nutrition programs in developing countries; nutrition for cancer patients. *Mailing Add:* 6533 31st Ave NE Seattle WA 98115

**YAMANE, GEORGE M,** ORAL MEDICINE, ORAL PATHOLOGY. *Current Pos:* asst dean res & postdoc prog, NJ Dent Sch, Univ Med & Dent NJ, 77-80, prof oral med & radiol & chmn dept, 70-83, prof biodent sci, 83-88, dir & prof, Div Oral & Pathobiol, Dept Oral Pathol, Biol & Diag Sci, 88-92, EMER PROF BIODENT SCI, NJ DENT SCH, UNIV MED & DENT NJ, 92- *Personal Data:* b Honolulu, Hawaii, Aug 9, 24; m 51, Alice M Nemoto; c Wende Michiko, Linda Keiki & David Kiyoshi. *Educ:* Haverford Col, AB, 46; Univ Minn, Minneapolis, DDS, 50, PhD(oral path), 63. *Prof Exp:* Asst chem & zool, Univ Hawaii, 43-44; asst oral path & diag, Univ Minn, Minneapolis, 51-53; asst prof oral path, Univ Ill, Chicago, 57-59; asst prof oral path, Univ Wash, 59-63; dir tissue lab, 60-63; prof oral diag, med & roentgenol & chmn div, Univ Minn, Minneapolis, 63-70. *Concurrent Pos:* Consult, Children Orthop Hosp & Med Ctr, Seattle, 60-63; Vet Admin Hosps, American Lake, Wash, 62-63 & Minneapolis, 64-70 & div dent health, Wyo State Bd Health, 66-70; vis scientist, Armed Forces Inst Pathol, 82; vis prof, NY Univ Col Dent, 82, adj prof, 84- *Mem:* Fel AAAS; fel Am Acad Oral Path; fel Int Col Dent; Int Asn Dent Res; fel Am Col Dent; Sigma Xi. *Res:* Bone tissue formation; radiobiology; magnesium metabolism; psychosomatic etiology of oral lesions. *Mailing Add:* 168 E Sixth St St Paul MN 55101

**YAMANOUCHI, TAIJI,** PHYSICS. *Current Pos:* PHYSICIST, FERMI NAT ACCELERATOR LAB, 69- *Personal Data:* b Tokyo, Japan, Aug 16, 31; m 61; c 2. *Educ:* Tokyo Univ Ed, BS, 53, MS, 55; Univ Rochester, PhD(physics), 60. *Prof Exp:* Res assoc physics, Univ Rochester, 60-65, sr res assoc, 65-69. *Mem:* Am Phys Soc. *Res:* Experimental particle physics. *Mailing Add:* Fermilab PO Box 500 Batavia IL 60510

**YAMARTINO, ROBERT J,** COMPLEX TERRAIN-GEOMETRY FLOW TURBULENCE, POLLUTANT MODELING OXIDANT & ACID RAIN MODEL DEVELOPMENT. *Current Pos:* PRIN SCIENTIST, SIGMA RES CORP, 85- *Personal Data:* b Waltham, Mass, Nov 17, 44. *Educ:* Tufts Univ, BS, 66; Stanford Univ, PhD(physics), 74. *Prof Exp:* Res asst-assoc, Stanford Linear Accelerator Ctr Nat Lab, 67-72; fel, Purdue Univ, 72-74; scientist, Argonne Nat Lab, 74-80; sr scientist, Geomet GmbH, West Berlin, 80-81, Enfiron Res & Technol Inc, 81-85. *Concurrent Pos:* Consult, Geos GmbH & Geomet GmbH, 79-; adv, Environ Protection Agency Ger, 79-; reviewer & contribr, Var World Meteorol Orgns, Europ Monitoring Eval Prog, 83- & Dutch-Ger Phoxa Prog Rev & Workshops; mem, Comt on Meteorol Aspects of Air Pollution, Am Meteorol Soc, 91- *Mem:* Sigma Xi; Am Meteorol Soc; Am Phys Soc; Air & Waste Mgt Asn; Union Concerned Scientists. *Res:* Atmospheric dispersion modeling based on kinematic simulation of atmospheric turbulence; numerical methods employed in photochemical models; street canyon turbulence and dispersion models. *Mailing Add:* 36 Orchard Rd Bedford MA 01730. *E-Mail:* rjy@src.com

**YAMASHIRO, STANLEY MOTOHIRO,** BIOMEDICAL ENGINEERING. *Current Pos:* res assoc, 70-71, asst prof, 71-74, ASSOC PROF BIOMED ENG, UNIV SOUTHERN CALIF, 74- *Personal Data:* b Honolulu, Hawaii, Nov 26, 41; m 64; c 2. *Educ:* Univ Southern Calif, BS, 64, MS, 66, PhD(elec eng), 70. *Prof Exp:* Mem tech staff elec eng, Hughes Aircraft Co, 64-70. *Mem:* Fedn Am Socs Exp Biol. *Res:* Cardiopulmonary physiology; application of control theory and computer technology to biological systems. *Mailing Add:* Dept Biomed Eng Univ Southern Calif Los Angeles CA 90089-1451. *Fax:* 213-740-0343

**YAMASHIROYA, HERBERT MITSUGI,** MICROBIOLOGY, VIROLOGY. *Current Pos:* asst prof, 71-76, HEAD VIROL LAB, UNIV ILL HOSP, 71-, ASSOC PROF PATH, COL MED, 76-, DIR GRAD STUDIES PATH, 81- *Personal Data:* b Honolulu, Hawaii, Sept 14, 30; m 57, Kiyoka Jyone; c Gail, Eliot, Eric & Gary. *Educ:* Univ Hawaii, BA, 53; Univ Ill, Chicago, MS, 62, PhD(microbiol), 65; Registry Technologists, cert, 53. *Honors & Awards:* Tanner Shaughnessy Award, Microbiol, 82. *Prof Exp:* Supvr clin lab, Atomic Bomb Casualty Comn, Nat Acad Sci-Nat Res Coun, Hiroshima, Japan, 56-58; assoc scientist, IIT Res Inst, 64-65, res scientist, 65-68, sr scientist, 68-71. *Concurrent Pos:* Mem adv bd, Clin Lab & Blood Bank, State Ill, 79-92; lectr microbiol, Cook County Grad Sch Med, 77-82; lectr, Ill Col Podiatric Med, 81-90; lectr & consult med virol, Vet Admin West Side Hosp, 82- *Mem:* Am Soc Microbiol; Am Soc Clin Path; Sigma Xi; Am Soc Invest Pathol. *Res:* Tissue culture and its application to viruses and rickettsiae; viral pathogenesis; immunologic techniques and the immune mechanism; diagnostic procedures in microbiology and immunology. *Mailing Add:* 6521 N Maplewood Chicago IL 60645

**YAMASHITA, AYAKO,** PHARMACEUTICAL SCIENCE. *Current Pos:* SR RES SCIENTIST, WYETH-AYERST RES, AM HOME PRODUCTS CO, 91- *Educ:* Kyushu Univ, BS, 68, PhD(pharmaceut sci), 73. *Prof Exp:* Postdoctoral assoc, Chem Dept, Cornell Univ, 73-74, Med Sch, Harvard Univ, 74-76; res staff, Cornell Univ, 76-78 & Princeton Univ, 78-80; sr scientist, Upjohn Co, 80-89, DuPont-Merk Co, 89-91 & Am Cyanamid Co, 91-94. *Concurrent Pos:* Scholar, Japanese Sci Prom Sci, 71-73. *Mem:* Am

Chem Soc. *Res:* Exploration of synthetic methodology and transition chemistry in the context of the synthesis of novel structures in the cancer area. *Mailing Add:* 52 Dwight Pl No F Englewood NJ 07631. *Fax:* 9147-732-5561; *E-Mail:* yamasha@war.wyeth.com

**YAMAUCHI, HIROSHI,** NUCLEAR SCATTERING. *Current Pos:* RETIRED. *Personal Data:* b Honolulu, Hawaii, Mar 26, 23; wid; c Jody, Lois & Ann. *Educ:* Univ Hawaii, BS, 47; Harvard Univ, MA, 48, PhD(physics), 50. *Prof Exp:* From instr to asst prof physics, Colby Col, 50-54; theoret physicist, Nuclear Develop Assoc, Inc, NY, 54-55; from asst prof to assoc prof math, Univ Hawaii, 55-65; from assoc prof to prof math & physics, Chaminade Univ, Honolulu, 66-88. *Mem:* Am Phys Soc. *Res:* Elementary particle theory. *Mailing Add:* 1149 15th Ave Honolulu HI 96816

**YAMAUCHI, MASANOBU,** INORGANIC CHEMISTRY. *Current Pos:* from asst prof to assoc prof, 65-74, PROF CHEM, EASTERN MICH UNIV, 74- *Personal Data:* b Maui, Hawaii, Mar 3, 31; m 58; c 2. *Educ:* Univ Hawaii, BA, 53; Univ Mich, MS, 58, PhD(chem), 61. *Prof Exp:* Asst prof chem, Univ NMex, 60-65. *Mem:* Am Chem Soc. *Res:* Chemistry of boron hydrides and related compounds. *Mailing Add:* 2225 Steeplechase DR Ann Arbor MI 48103

**YAMAUCHI, TOSHIO,** MEDICAL GENETICS, PEDIATRICS. *Current Pos:* STAFF, FIRST COLONY PEDIAT. *Personal Data:* b Newell, Calif, Feb 13, 45; m; c 2. *Educ:* Northwestern Univ, BA, 66, PhD(biol sci), 72; Univ Tex Med Sch, MD, 79. *Prof Exp:* Fel med genetics, Univ Tex Syst Cancer Ctr, M D Anderson Hosp & Tumor Inst, 72-74, res assoc med genetics, 74-77, mem staff, Univ Tex Med Sch, 76-79. *Concurrent Pos:* Resident pediat, Hermann Hosp, 79-82. *Mem:* AMA; Am Acad Pediat. *Res:* Study of enzymes which are involved in the metabolism and activation of chemical carcinogens and the development of systems to study these enzymes in the human population. *Mailing Add:* First Colony Pediat 3425 Hwy 6 Suite 107 Sugar Land TX 77478-4439

**YAMAZAKI, HIROSHI,** BIOCHEMISTRY. *Current Pos:* from asst prof to assoc prof, 67-77, PROF BIOL, CARLETON UNIV, 77- *Personal Data:* b Hokkaido, Japan, Sept 5, 31; m 61, Toshiko Kasajima; c Christine, Ken & Amy. *Educ:* Hokkaido Univ, BS, 54, MS, 56; Univ Wis, PhD(biochem), 60. *Prof Exp:* Proj assoc biochem, Univ Wis, 61-63, res assoc, 63-65; res officer biol, Atomic Energy Can Ltd, 65-67. *Res:* Industrial biochemistry-enzyme immunoassay for detection of pathogens, toxins and pollutants; immobilization of polypeptides for production of immunoreagents and biotechnological products. *Mailing Add:* Dept Biol Carleton Univ Ottawa ON K1S 5B6 Can. *Fax:* 613-788-4497

**YAMAZAKI, RUSSELL KAZUO,** BIOCHEMICAL PHARMACOLOGY. *Current Pos:* ASSOC PROF PHARMACOL, WAYNE STATE UNIV, 78- *Personal Data:* b Topaz, Utah, Nov 23, 42; m 66, Jane Welton. *Educ:* Col Wooster, BA, 64; Mich State Univ, PhD(biochem), 69. *Prof Exp:* Res assoc biochem, Case Western Res Univ, 69-71; vis asst prof pharmacol, Univ Va, 71-73, asst prof, 73-78. *Mem:* Am Soc Biol Chemists; Am Chem Soc; Am Soc Plant Physiologists; AAAS. *Res:* Actions of hormones on the metabolism of mitochondria, peroxisomes and lysosomes; ubiquitin metabolism. *Mailing Add:* Dept Pharmacol Sch Med Wayne State Univ Detroit MI 48201-3421. *Fax:* 313-577-6739

**YAMAZAKI, WILLIAM TOSHI,** CEREAL CHEMISTRY. *Current Pos:* CHEMIST IN CHG SOFT WHEAT QUAL LAB, AGR RES SERV, USDA, OHIO AGR RES & DEVELOP CTR, 63- *Personal Data:* b San Francisco, Calif, May 10, 17; m 42; c 3. *Educ:* Univ Calif, BS, 39, MS, 41; Ohio State Univ, PhD(agr chem), 50. *Concurrent Pos:* Adj prof agron, Ohio State Univ & Ohio Agr Res & Develop Ctr, 57- *Mem:* AAAS; Am Asn Cereal Chem; Am Chem Soc. *Res:* Chemical and physical basis for processing quality in soft wheat and soft wheat flour. *Mailing Add:* 748 Hamilton Ave Wooster OH 44691-2712

**YAMBERT, PAUL ABT,** CONSERVATION. *Current Pos:* RETIRED. *Personal Data:* b Toledo, Ohio, May 15, 28; m 50; c 5. *Educ:* Univ Mich, BS, 50, MS, 51, MA, 55, PhD(conserv), 60. *Prof Exp:* Field scout exec, Boy Scouts of Am, 51-52; teacher, Ann Arbor High Sch, Mich, 53-57; prof natural resources, Wis State Univ, Stevens Point, 57-69; dean outdoor labs, Southern Ill Univ, Carbondale, 69-74, prof forestry dept, 74-87. *Concurrent Pos:* Vis prof, Univ Mich, 63. *Res:* Environmental attitude and knowledge; interpretation for the handicapped; outdoor recreation. *Mailing Add:* RR 5 Murray KY 42071

**YAMDAGNI, RAGHAVENDRA,** MASS SPECTROMETRY, NUCLEAR MAGNETIC RESONANCE SPECTROSCOPY. *Current Pos:* prof assoc, 75-78, SR INSTR, DEPT CHEM, UNIV CALGARY, 78- *Personal Data:* b Aligarh, India, June 30, 41; m 71, Vijay L Sharma; c Ravi & Sameer. *Educ:* Allahabad Univ, BSc, 57, MSc, 59, PhD, 65. *Prof Exp:* Res assoc, Cornell Univ, 65-68; res assoc mass spectrum, Univ Alta, 68-75. *Mem:* Am Soc Mass Spectrom; Chem Inst Can; Asn Off Anal Chemists. *Res:* Ion molecule reactions; thermodynamic and reaction kinetics studies; nuclear magnetic resonance spectroscopy; mass spectrometry. *Mailing Add:* Dept Chem Univ Calgary Calgary AB T2N 1N4 Can

**YAMIN, SAMUEL PETER,** PARTICLE PHYSICS. *Current Pos:* assoc physicist, 75-78, PHYSICIST, BROOKHAVEN NAT LAB, 78- *Personal Data:* b New York, NY, July 26, 38; div; c Eli & Ariana. *Educ:* Mass Inst Technol, SB, 60; Univ Pa, MS, 61, PhD(physics), 66. *Prof Exp:* Res assoc physics, Brookhaven Nat Lab, 66-69; asst prof physics, Rutgers Univ, New Brunswick, 69-75. *Mem:* Am Phys Soc. *Res:* Experimental elementary particle physics; particle beam optics; musical acoustics. *Mailing Add:* Bldg 510F Brookhaven Nat Lab Box 5000 Upton NY 11973-5000. *E-Mail:* yamin@bnl.gov

**YAMINI, SOHRAB,** GASTROENTEROLOGY. *Current Pos:* Resident surg, 82-85, fel gastroenterol, 86-87, ASST PROF GASTROENTEROL, KING-DREW MED CTR, UNIV CALIF, LOS ANGELES, 87-, ASSOC INVESTR, DIGESTIVE DIS RES CTR, 88- *Personal Data:* b Iran, Aug 11, 53; m 86. *Educ:* Nat Univ Iran, MD, 78. *Concurrent Pos:* Clin investr, Digestive Dis Res Ctr, 87; dir endoscopy, King-Drew Med Ctr, 87- *Res:* Multiple studies regarding effect of alcohol on gastrointestinal system; treatment of peptic ulcer disease and prevention of recurrence of ulcer. *Mailing Add:* 10128 Baywood Ct Los Angeles CA 90077

**YAMINS, J(ACOB) L(OUIS),** FOOD SCIENCE. *Current Pos:* VIS PROF FOOD SCI, RUTGERS UNIV, NEW BRUNSWICK, 67-; CONSULT, 69- *Personal Data:* b Fall River, Mass, Jan 8, 14; m 48; c 1. *Prof Exp:* Res assoc, Res Lab Org Chem, Mass Inst Technol, 39-42; sr chemist, Nat Fireworks, Inc, Mass, 43-46; sr chemist, Biochem Div, Interchem Corp, NJ, 47-48; res chemist & proj leader, Res Labs Div, Nat Dairy Prod Corp, 48-49, asst to vpres & dir res, 50-54, asst to pres, 54-58; dept head fundamental studies, Res & Develop Div, Am Sugar Co, NY, 58-65, dir sci develop, 65-67. *Concurrent Pos:* Adv chem dept, Adelphi Col, 50-; abstractor, Chem Abstrs. *Mem:* Fel AAAS; Am Chem Soc; Sigma Xi; Soc Chem Indust; fel NY Acad Sci; Inst Food Technologists. *Res:* Protein hydrolysis and isolation of amino acids; vitamin syntheses; preparation of primary explosives; tall oil; sterol isolation and syntheses; tocopherols; flavors; syntheses of long chain surface active agents and bactericides; antioxidants; baked products; carbohydrates; food product development; nutrition; single cell proteins; packaging. *Mailing Add:* PO Box 456 Sunderland MA 01375

**YAN, GUOCHEN,** TUMOR CELL BIOLOGY & HUMAN CANCER, GROW FACTOR & RECEPTOR SIGNAL TRANDUCTION. *Current Pos:* RES SCIENTIST, SUGEN INC, 95- *Personal Data:* b China; m 86, Guohong Zhang; c David. *Educ:* Jilin Univ, China, BS, 84; W Alton Jones Cell Sci Ctr, PhD(molecular cell biol), 93. *Prof Exp:* Postdoctoral fel, Howard Hughes Med Inst, 93-95. *Res:* Growth factor and receptors in tumor growth and development; developed several in vitro and in vivo tumor model studies. *Mailing Add:* 515 Galveston Dr Redwood City CA 94063. *Fax:* 650-369-0679; *E-Mail:* guocheny@sugen.sf.ca.us

**YAN, JOHNSON FAA,** PHYSICAL CHEMISTRY. *Current Pos:* SCI SPECIALIST, WEYERHAEUSER CORP, 77- *Personal Data:* b Amoy, China, May 21, 34; m 70. *Educ:* Nat Taiwan Univ, BS, 59; Kent State Univ, MS, 65, PhD(chem), 67. *Prof Exp:* Chief lab, Hwa Ming Pulp & Paper Manufactory, Chu-nan, Taiwan, 59-62; res assoc & fel, Cornell Univ, 67-69; develop assoc pulp & paper, Bowaters Carolina Corp, 69-77. *Mem:* AAAS; Am Chem Soc. *Res:* Physical chemistry, surface and colloid; polymers; biopolymers; pulp and paper. *Mailing Add:* 3801 SW 326th St Federal Way WA 98023-2611

**YAN, MAN FEI,** CERAMIC SCIENCE, PHYSICAL METALLURGY & OPTICAL FIBER PROCESSING. *Current Pos:* Mem tech staff, 76-87, supvr, 87-92, DISTINGUISHED MEM TECH STAFF, AT&T BELL LABS, 87-, TECH MGR, 92- *Personal Data:* b Kwang Tung, China, Dec 26, 48; m 77, Su-Su Goon; c Victor H, Leo H, Oscar H & Chrystal H. *Educ:* Mass Inst Technol, BS, 70, ScD, 76; Univ Calif, Berkeley, MS, 71. *Honors & Awards:* Ross Coffin Purdy Award, Am Ceramic Soc, 80; Fulrath Award, Univ Calif, Berkeley, 92. *Mem:* Am Ceramics Soc; Am Soc Metals; Am Optical Soc. *Res:* Sintering of solids; fiber optics; grain boundaries; grain boundary migration; glass fiber processing; electronic ceramics; magnetic ferrites; varistors; ceramic capacitor; metal-ceramic interfaces; super conductors. *Mailing Add:* Lucent Technol Bell Labs Rm 7F-224 600 Mountain Ave Murray Hill NJ 07974-2070. *Fax:* 908-582-2913; *E-Mail:* mfy@lucent.com

**YAN, SAU-CHI BETTY,** BIOTECHNOLOGY, CARBOHYDRATE BIOCHEMISTRY. *Current Pos:* sr biochemist biotechnol, 85-88, sr scientist cardiovasc, 89-93, SR RES SCIENTIST CARDIOVASC, ELI LILLY & CO, 94- *Personal Data:* b Hong Kong, Nov 25, 54; US citizen; c 1. *Educ:* Cent Mo State Univ, BS, 75; Iowa State Univ, PhD(biochem), 80. *Prof Exp:* Fel biochem, St Paul Ramsey Med Ctr, 80-82 & Univ Tex Med Sch, 82-85. *Concurrent Pos:* Grant reviewer, NSF, 90; chmn travel awards, Protein Soc, 90. *Mem:* Am Soc Biochem & Molecular Biol; Protein Soc; AAAS; Soc Chinese Bioscientists Am. *Res:* Using expertise in protein chemistry and carbohydrate analytical chemistry to discover new therapeutics for cardiovascular diseases. *Mailing Add:* Cardiovasc Dept Eli Lilly & Co Bldg 88-4 307 E McCarty St Indianapolis IN 46285

**YAN, TSOUNG-YUAN,** CHEMICAL PROCESS ENGINEERING, FUEL TECHNOLOGY & ENVIRONMENTAL ENGINEERING. *Current Pos:* from res engr to sr engr, Mobil Oil Corp, 62-70, from res assoc to sr res assoc, 78-82, res scientist, 82-91, SR RES CONSULT, MOBIL RES & DEVELOP CORP, 91- *Personal Data:* b Tainan, Taiwan, Sept 17, 33; m 61, Chiou-shuang Jou; c Kay & Roy. *Educ:* Nat Taiwan Univ, BS, 59; Purdue Univ, MS, 62, PhD(chem eng), 63. *Prof Exp:* Teacher, Tainan Sch, 52-55. *Concurrent Pos:*

Adv, Indust Tech Res Inst, Taiwan, 88-; assoc ed, Energy, 88- Mem: Am Chem Soc; Sigma Xi. Res: Catalysis, petroleum refining; coal upgrading and utilization; uranium in-situ leaching and refining processes; biomass conversion; lube oil processing, environmental control; process evaluation; fuel combustion; petrochemicals; natural gas processing; waste minimization. Mailing Add: 2427 Fairmount Ave Philadelphia PA 19130. Fax: 609-737-5217; E-Mail: tyyan@crl.mobil.com

**YAN, TUNG-MOW,** HIGH ENERGY PHYSICS. Current Pos: from asst to assoc prof, 70-81, PROF PHYSICS, CORNELL UNIV, 81- Personal Data: b Keelung, Taiwan, Nov 27, 36; m 64, Ren-Heui Lu; c Thomas K & Anthony K. Educ: Nat Taiwan Univ, BS, 60; Nat Tsinghua Univ, Taiwan, MS, 62; Harvard Univ, PhD(physics), 68. Prof Exp: Res assoc physics, Stanford Linear Accelerator Ctr, 68-70, vis scientist, 73-74. Concurrent Pos: Alfred P Sloan Found fel, 74-78. Mem: Fel Am Phys Soc. Res: Structure of elementary particles; properties of quantum field theories. Mailing Add: Newman Lab Nuclear Studies Cornell Univ Ithaca NY 14853. E-Mail: yan@mail.lns.cornell.edu

**YAN, WEN-BIN,** SOLID STATE PHYSICS, DIODE & TUNABLE SOLID STATE LASERS. Current Pos: SR SCIENTIST, LIGHT AGE INC, 95- Personal Data: b Inner Mongolia, China, May 20, 54; m 82, Xiao-Juan Guan; c Jia & James. Educ: Peking Univ, BS, 82; Rice Univ, MA, 86, PhD(phys chem), 87. Prof Exp: Postdoctoral res assoc, Princeton Univ, 87-89; res assoc, Nat Res Coun, Can, 89-91; physicist, Hughes Leitz Optical Technols, 92-93; sr scientist, M L Energia Inc, 93-95. Mem: Am Chem Soc. Res: Research and develoment of diode-pumped, solid state lasers for scientific, medical and industrial applications. Mailing Add: 67 Kinglet Dr S Cranbury NJ 08512. Fax: 732-563-1671

**YANABU, SATORU,** ELECTRICAL ENGINEERING, VACUUM CIRCUIT BREAKER. Current Pos: Mgr, High Power Lab, 76-85, sr mgr, High Voltage & High Power Lab, 85-90, SR MGR, POWER TRANSMISSION & SUBSTA ENG, TOSHIBA COOP, 90- Personal Data: b Japan, July 15, 41; m 65; c 3. Educ: Univ Tokyo, BEng, 64, Dr Eng, 90; Univ Liverpool, PhD(elec eng), 71. Concurrent Pos: Mem, Int Conf Large High Voltage Elec Systs, 81- Mem: Fel Inst Elec & Electronics Engrs. Res: Gas circuit breakers and vacuum circuit breakers. Mailing Add: Keihin Oper 2-4 Suehiro-Cho Yokohama 230 Japan

**YANAGIHARA, RICHARD,** VIRAL PATHOGENESIS, NEUROVIROLOGY. Current Pos: DIR, RETRO VIROL RES LAB, LEAHI HOSP. Personal Data: b Honolulu, Hawaii, Aug 3, 46; m; c 2. Educ: Univ Hawaii, Honolulu, BA, 68; Univ Cincinnati, MD, 72; Johns Hopkins Univ, MPH, 85. Prof Exp: Intern pediat, Health Sci Ctr, Univ Colo, Denver, 72-73, resident, 73-74, teaching fel infectious dis, 77-79; res assoc, NIH, Bethesda, Md, 74-76; resident pediat, Univ Calif, San Francisco, 76-77; res physician, NIH, Guam, 79-82, spec expert, 82-84, med officer, Nat Inst Neurol & commun dis & Stroke, 85- Mem: Infectious Dis Soc Am; Am Soc Virol; Am Soc Trop Med & Hyg; Soc Pediat Res. Res: Epidemiology and epizootiology of vector-borne viral zoonoses, particularly those involving nonarthropod vectors; pathogenesis of persistent viral infections using animal models; role of heavy metals and essential minerals in neurodegenerative diseases occurring in high incidence in the western Pacific region; human retroviruses. Mailing Add: Leahi Hosp Atherton Bldg 2nd Floor 3675 Kilauea Ave Honolulu HI 96816

**YANAGIMACHI, RYUZO,** REPRODUCTIVE BIOLOGY. Current Pos: from asst prof to assoc prof, 66-73, PROF ANAT, SCH MED, UNIV HAWAII, 73- Personal Data: b Sapporo, Japan, Aug 27, 28; m 60. Educ: Hokkaido Univ, BSc, 53, DSc, 60. Prof Exp: Res scientist, Worcester Found Exp Biol, 60-64; lectr biol, Hokkaido Univ, 64-66. Mem: Soc Study Reproduction; Am Asn Anat; Am Soc Cell Biol; Brit Soc Study Fertil. Res: Biology of reproduction, particularly biology and physiology of gametes and early development of mammals. Mailing Add: Dept Anat Univ Hawaii Burns Med Sch 1960 East-West Rd Honolulu HI 96822-2319

**YANAGISAWA, SAMUEL T,** ELECTRICAL ENGINEERING, ELECTRON TUBES & NIGHT VISION DEVICES. Current Pos: RETIRED. Personal Data: b Berkeley, Calif, Feb 18, 22; m 52, Fern; c Shane, Steven & Ian. Educ: Univ Calif, Berkeley, BSEE Hons, 42. Prof Exp: Qual control engr, Machlett Labs, Inc, 43-45, develop engr, 46-48, sr develop engr, 48-55, sect head spec prod eng, 55-57, chief engr display & storage tubes, 57-60, prod line mgr, 60-63; vpres eng & mfg, Warnecke Electron Tubes, Ill, 63-67; mgr, Imaging Sensors Div, Varo Inc, 67-68, gen mgr, Electron Devices Div, 68-72, vpres, 71-72, exec vpres & dir, 72-74, pres & chief exec officer, 74-76, chmn bd & chief exec officer, 76-78, chmn bd, pres & chief exec officer, 78-87, pres & dir, Electron Devices Div, 72-87. Concurrent Pos: Mem, eng adv coun, Univ Tex, Dallas, SMU; mem sci bd, US Army, 86-90; mem, chmn bd visitor, Univ Tex, McDonald Observ; pres, US Night Vision Mfr Asn, 80-87; dir, Dallas Coun Corld Affairs. Mem: Inst Elec & Electronics Engrs; Am Vacuum Soc; Sigma Xi; AAAS. Res: Management; design, development and production engineering of high power transmitting and microwave tubes; circuitry; vacuum switches; storage and display tubes; supervoltage electron accelerators; image converters and intensifiers; crossed field tubes; design development and production of image intensified and night vision systems. Mailing Add: 7708 Chalkstone Dr Dallas TX 75248

**YANAI, HIDEYASU STEVE,** ANALYTICAL CHEMISTRY, PHYSICAL CHEMISTRY. Current Pos: RETIRED. Personal Data: b Tokyo, Japan, Feb 26, 28; nat US; m 56; c Ruth D & Nina J. Educ: Tokyo Agr Col, BS, 47; Calif State Polytech Col, BS, 53; Univ Minn, PhD(phys chem), 58. Prof Exp: Sr scientist, Rohm & Haas Co, 58-69, analytical lab head, Res Div, 69-73, analytical res proj leader, Res Div, 73-79, proj leader, Plastics Res Dept, 79-81, res sect mgr plastics, 81-88, plastics bus mgr, 89-91, Pac region mgr, Japan, 91-92. Res: Plastics, polymer chemistry or polymers. Mailing Add: 302 Kenwood Dr Moorestown PA 08057

**YANARI, SAM SATOMI,** IMMUNOLOGY, BIOCHEMISTRY. Current Pos: RETIRED. Personal Data: b Gilcrest, Colo, May 27, 23; m 51; c 3. Educ: Univ Chicago, BS, 48, PhD, 52. Prof Exp: Res assoc, Univ Chicago, 52-53; res assoc, Armour & Co, 53-56; res assoc, Minn Mining & Mfg Co, 56-64; head, Biochem Dept, Armour Pharmaceut Co, Ill, 65-69; res dir & vpres, Wilson Labs, 69-72; dir res lab, Div Allergy & Clin Immunol, Henry Ford Hosp, Detroit, Mich, 72-89; chief res officer, Covalent Tech Corp. Mem: Am Chem Soc; Am Fedn Clin Res; Am Asn Clin Chem; Am Acad Allergy. Res: Mechanism of enzyme action; protein chemistry and structure; proteolytic enzymes; absorption and fluorescence spectroscopy; hormones; immunology. Mailing Add: 13328 Wales Huntington Woods MI 48070

**YANCEY, ASA G, SR,** GENERAL SURGERY, MEDICAL ADMINISTRATION. Current Pos: prof surg & assoc dean, 72-89, EMER PROF SURG, EMORY UNIV SCH MED, 89- Personal Data: b Atlanta, Ga, 1916; m 44, Carolyn E Dunbar; c Arthur, Carolyn L, Caren L & Asa Jr. Educ: Morehouse Col, BS; Mich Univ, MD, 41. Hon Degrees: DSc, Howard Univ & Morehouse Col. Honors & Awards: Avencap Award, Morehouse Sch Med. Prof Exp: Intern, City Hosp, Cleveland, 41-42; chief surg, Tuskagee Vet Admin Hosp, 48-58; med dir, Grady Mem Hosp, Atlanta, 72-89. Concurrent Pos: Mem, Fulton-Dekalb Hosp Authority, 89-93; prof surg, Morehouse Sch Med. Mem: Inst Med-Nat Acad Sci; Am Surg Asn; Nat Med Asn; Am Col Surgeons; AMA; Southern Surg Asn. Res: Designed and performed a modification of the Swenson technique for Hirsehsprings Disease. Mailing Add: 2845 Engle Rd NW Atlanta GA 30318-7216

**YANCEY, PAUL HERBERT,** ENVIRONMENTAL PHYSIOLOGY, COMPARATIVE BIOCHEMISTRY. Current Pos: from asst prof to assoc prof, 81-93, chair, 88-91, PROF BIOL, WHITMAN COL, 93- Personal Data: b Whittier, Calif, July 4, 51; m 78, C Susan Weiler; c 1. Educ: Calif Inst Technol, BS, 73; Scripps Inst Oceanog, Univ Calif, PhD(marine biol), 78. Prof Exp: NATO fel physiol, Univ St Andrews, Scotland, 78-80. Concurrent Pos: Res Corp grant, 86; vis scientist, NIH, 87-88; PEW fel, Mt Desert I Biol Lab, 90. Mem: AAAS; Soc Develop Biol; Am Inst Biol Sci; Coun Undergrad Res. Res: Biochemical and physiological adaptations in muscle proteins of fishes to temperature, pressure and salinity; properties of osmoregulatory compounds in laboratory mammals and desert mammals. Mailing Add: Biol Dept Whitman Col Walla Walla WA 99362

**YANCEY, ROBERT JOHN, JR,** VETERINARY MICROBIOLOGY, MICROBIAL PATHOGENESIS. Current Pos: SR SCIENTIST, UPJOHN CO, 80- Personal Data: b Austin, Tex, Sept 17, 48; m 69, Elizabeth Putnam; c Kimberley M. Educ: Univ Tex, Austin, BA, 71, PhD(microbiol), 77. Prof Exp: Instr med & gen microbiol, Univ Tex, Austin, 76-77, res assoc, Dept Microbiol, 77-78; fel, Dept Microbiol & Immunol, Univ Tex Health Sci Ctr Dallas, 78-79 & Sch Med, Univ Mo, 79-80. Concurrent Pos: Coordr microbiol teaching labs, Univ Tex, Austin, 76-77; conf group leader med microbiol, Univ Tex Health Sci Ctr Dallas & bacteriol lab instr, 78-79; bacteriol lab lectr, Sch Med, Univ Mo, 79-80. Mem: Sigma Xi; Am Soc Microbiol; AAAS; NY Acad Sci; Am Dairy Sci Asn. Res: Molecular mechanisms of bacterial pathogenesis; disease pathogenesis of slaphylococcal mastitis; antibiotic killing of intracellular pathogens; bacterial vaccine discovery; use of attenuated salmonella soluble protein preparation as heterologotes antigen expression vectors. Mailing Add: Central Res Pfizer Inc 601 W Cornhusker Way Lincoln NE 68521. Fax: 616-384-2347

**YANCEY, THOMAS ERWIN,** PALEONTOLOGY, SEDIMENTARY PETROLOGY. Current Pos: MEM STAFF, DEPT GEOL, TEX A&M UNIV, 80- Personal Data: b Lowville, NY, July 24, 41; m 71; c 3. Educ: Univ Calif, Berkeley, BA, 66, MA, 69, PhD(paleont), 71. Prof Exp: Lectr, Univ Malaya, 71-75; prof geol, Idaho State Univ, 75-80. Concurrent Pos: Consult. Mem: Geol Soc Am; Soc Econ Paleontologists & Mineralogists; Am Asn Petrol Geologists; Paleont Soc; Paleont Asn. Res: Paleoecology and systematics of Upper Paleozoic invertebrates, primarily molluscs and brachipods; studies of molluscs of all ages. Mailing Add: 1411 Caudill St College Station TX 77840

**YANCHICK, VICTOR A,** PHARMACY. Current Pos: DEAN PHARM, COL PHARM, UNIV OKLA, 85- Personal Data: b Joliet, Ill, Dec 3, 40; m 63; c 3. Educ: Univ Iowa, BS, 62, MS, 66; Purdue Univ, PhD(pharm), 68. Honors & Awards: Parenteral Drug Asn Res Awards, 66 & 68. Prof Exp: Instr pharm, Purdue Univ, 66-68; from asst prof to prof pharm, Univ Tex, Austin, 68-85, actg asst dean, 72-74, asst dean acad affairs, Col Pharm, 74-81, assoc dean, 81. Mem: Am Pharmaceut Asn; Am Soc Hosp Pharmacists; Acad Pharmaceut Sci; Am Asn Cols Pharm. Res: Parenteral drugs, primarily inactivation by other agents; drug interactions and incompatibilities; drug-nutrient interactions; geriatric pharmacotherapeutics. Mailing Add: Dean Pharm Col Pharm Box 26901 Univ Okla Health Ctr 941 S L Young Blvd Oklahoma City OK 73190-0001

**YANCIK, JOSEPH J,** MINING ENGINEERING. *Current Pos:* asst dir mining, 72-77, CHIEF DIV MINING RES, US BUR MINES, US DEPT INTERIOR, WASHINGTON, DC, 70- *Personal Data:* b Mt Olive, Ill, Dec 1, 30; m 55, Rosemary Panich; c Geri A & Ellen M. *Educ:* Univ Ill, Urbana-Champaign, BS, 54; Mo Sch Mines, MS, 56; Univ Mo-Rolla, PhD(mining eng), 60. *Prof Exp:* Mining engr, St Joseph Lead Co, 55-58, res assoc mining, Mo Sch Mines, 58-60; mgr res & develop explosives, Monsanto Co, 60-70. *Concurrent Pos:* Mem, Emergency Minerals Admin, US Dept Interior, 71-; vpres res & tech servs, Nat Coal Asn, 77-; chmn bd, Bituminous Coal Res, Inc, 77-79, vchmn bd & pres, 79-81; dir, Off Energy, Int Trade Admin, US Dept Com. *Mem:* Am Inst Mining, Metall & Petrol Engrs. *Res:* Mining research in areas of operations research in areas of operations, health and safety; explosives in areas of utilization, thermochemical and hydrodynamic properties; coal utilization. *Mailing Add:* 1703 James Payne Circle McLean VA 22101

**YANCOPOULOS, GEORGE D,** MOLECULAR BIOLOGY, NEUROSCIENCE. *Current Pos:* VPRES DISCOVERY, REGENERON PHARMACEUT INC, NY, 89- *Educ:* Columbia Univ, PhD(biochem & molecular biophys), 86, MD, 87. *Mailing Add:* Regeneron Pharmaceut Inc 777 Old Saw Mill River Rd Tarrytown NY 10591-6707

**YANDERS, ARMON FREDERICK,** ENVIRONMENTAL TOXICOLOGY. *Current Pos:* dean, Col Arts & Sci, 69-82, dir, Environ Trace Substances Res Ctr & Sinclair Comp Med Res Farm, 83-94, EMER PROF, UNIV MO, 94- *Personal Data:* b Lincoln, Nebr, Apr 12, 28; m 48, Evelyn Gatz; c Mark F & Kent M. *Educ:* Nebr State Col, AB, 48; Univ Nebr, PhD(zool), 53. *Prof Exp:* Res assoc genetics, Oak Ridge Nat Lab & Northwestern Univ, 53-54; biophysicist, US Naval Radiol Defense Lab, 55-58; assoc geneticist, Argonne Nat Lab, 58-59; assoc prof zool, Mich State Univ, 59-65, prof & asst dean, Col Natural Sci, 65-69. *Concurrent Pos:* Vis scientist, Commonwealth Sci & Indust Res Orgn, Canberra, Australia, 66; mem bd dir & consult, Assoc Midwestern Univs, 66-68; chmn bd & pres, Argonne Univs Asn, 70-77; mem, Mo Dioxin Adv Comt, 84- & adv comt environ hazards, US Vet Admin, 85-, chmn, 90- *Mem:* Fel AAAS; Environ Mutagen Soc; Soc Environ Toxicol & Chem; Radiation Res Soc; Sigma Xi; Genetics Soc Am. *Res:* Environmental toxicology. *Mailing Add:* 2405 Ridgefield Rd Columbia MO 65203-1531

**YANDL, ANDRE,** MATHEMATICS. *Personal Data:* b Algeria, NAfrica, Mar 28, 31. *Educ:* Univ Wash, BS, 56, PhD(math), 65. *Mem:* Am Math Soc; Math Asn Am. *Res:* Mathematics. *Mailing Add:* Dept Math Seattle Univ Seattle WA 98122

**YANEY, PERRY PAPPAS,** LASER RAMAN SPECTROSCOPY. *Current Pos:* assoc res physicist, Res Inst, 63-65, from asst prof to assoc prof physics, 65-77, PROF PHYSICS & ELECTRO-OPTICS, UNIV DAYTON, 77- *Personal Data:* b Columbus, Ohio, July 28, 31; m 61, Mary; c Anastasia, Felicia & Alexander. *Educ:* Univ Cincinnati, EE, 54, MS, 57, PhD(physics), 63. *Prof Exp:* Design engr, Baldwin Piano Co, Ohio, 54-55; res physicist, St Eloi Corp, 55-59; physicist, Electronics & Ord Div, Avco Corp, 59-62; Univ Cincinnati res fel, Wright-Patterson AFB, 62-63. *Concurrent Pos:* Consult, Univ Dayton Res Inst, 84-, Aero Propulsion & Power Dir, Wright-Patterson AFB, 81-; consult & vis scientist, Univ Southern Calif, 75. *Mem:* Am Phys Soc; Optical Soc Am; Inst Elec & Electronics Engrs; Am Inst Aeronaut & Astronaut; Am Asn Physics Teachers; Sigma Xi. *Res:* Coherent anti-Stokes Raman spectroscopy in gas discharges and plasmas; Raman microprobe spectroscopy on solids; laser probe measurements in combustion and flowing gases; lasers and their applications; electro-optical instrumentation techniques. *Mailing Add:* 4424 Renwood Dr Dayton OH 45429-5531. *Fax:* 513-229-2180; *E-Mail:* Bitnet: yaney@dayton

**YANG, AN TZU,** DYNAMICS. *Current Pos:* from asst prof to assoc prof eng, 64-71, NSF res grant, 66-69, PROF ENG, UNIV CALIF, DAVIS, 71- *Personal Data:* b Shanghai, China, Oct 5, 23; US citizen; m 52; c 2. *Educ:* Northwestern Col Eng, China, BS, 46; Ohio State Univ, MS, 50; Columbia Univ, DEngSc, 63. *Prof Exp:* Res engr, Columbia Univ, 55-56; vis prof, Inst Math, Univ Rio Grande do Sul, Brazil, 59-60; sr engr, Res & Develop Div, Am Mach & Foundry Co, 60-64. *Concurrent Pos:* NSF res grant, Stanford Univ, 70-71. *Mem:* Am Soc Mech Engrs. *Res:* Kinematic analysis and synthesis of mechanisms; dynamics of mechanical systems. *Mailing Add:* Dept Mech Eng Univ Calif Davis CA 95616

**YANG, ARTHUR JING-MIN,** STRUCTURE PROPERTY RELATIONSHIP OF A COMPOSITE, RUBBER ELASTICITY. *Current Pos:* PRES, INDUST SCI TECH NETWORK, 97- *Personal Data:* b Nanjing, Jiang-Hsu, Nov 28, 47; c 2. *Educ:* Fu Jen Univ, Taiwan, BS, 70; Brown Univ, PhD(chem), 75. *Prof Exp:* Assoc prof chem, Chem Dept, Fu Jen Univ, 75-80; sr res scientist, Amherst Col, Mass, 80-84; sr res scientist chem & physics, Res & Develop, Armstrong World Industs Inc, 84-97. *Concurrent Pos:* Vis prof, Brown Univ, 77-78. *Res:* Structure property relationship in a composite; macroscopic material properties from the microscopic interaction; viscoelasticity of a polymer material. *Mailing Add:* 916 Dorsea Rd Lancaster PA 17601

**YANG, BINGZHI,** AUTOIMMUNE DISEASES, TUMOR IMMUNOLOGY. *Current Pos:* researcher, 89-93, SCI ADV, WEIFANG MED COL, 90- *Personal Data:* b Wendeng, Shandong Prov, Feb 24, 63; m 86, Shudjia Li; c Kaite. *Educ:* Weifang Med Col, MD, 85; Shandong Acad Med Sci, MS, 88; Johns Hopkins Univ, PhD(immunol), 93. *Prof Exp:* Res asst, Weifang Med Col, 86-88; res assoc, Med Univ SC, 88-89. *Mem:* AAAS. *Res:* Applying molecular biology and immunology techniques to the discovery of the causes of autoimmune diseases and subsequently treating these patients with specific immunotherapy and gene therapy. *Mailing Add:* 2245 Chapel Valley Ln Timonium MD 21093. *Fax:* 410-955-1961

**YANG, C(HENG) Y(I),** STRUCTURAL DYNAMICS. *Current Pos:* assoc prof, 66-, EMER PROF, DEPT CIVIL ENG, UNIV DEL. *Personal Data:* b Tientsin, China, Dec 17, 30; m 61. *Educ:* Nat Taiwan Univ, BS, 53; Purdue Univ, MS, 58; Mass Inst Technol, DSc(civil eng), 62. *Prof Exp:* Asst civil eng, Nat Taiwan Univ, 54-56, Purdue Univ, 56-58 & Mass Inst Technol, 58-61, res engr, 61-62; asst prof, Univ Ill, 62-66. *Mem:* Assoc mem Am Soc Civil Engrs; Am Astronaut Soc; Am Soc Eng Educ; Soc Exp Stress Anal. *Res:* Wave propagation in solids investigated by method of characteristics; behavior of structural systems under deterministic and probabilistic loads; structural safety studies. *Mailing Add:* Dept Civil Eng Univ Del Newark DE 19716-0001

**YANG, CHAO-CHIH,** COMPUTER SCIENCE. *Current Pos:* PROF COMPUT SCI, UNIV NTEX, 85- *Personal Data:* b Changsha, China, Dec 17, 28; m 57; c 1. *Educ:* Chinese Naval Col Technol, BS, 53; Nat Chiao Tung Univ, MS, 62; Northwestern Univ, MS, 64, PhD(elec eng), 66. *Prof Exp:* Asst prof elec eng & info sci, Wash State Univ, 66-67; prof comput sci, Nat Chiao Tung Univ, 67-71; scientist, Int Bus Mach, San Jose Res Lab, 71-72; assoc prof info sci, Univ Ala, Birmingham, 72-79, prof comput & info sci, 79-85. *Mem:* Inst Elec & Electronics Engrs; Asn Comput Mach; Sigma Xi. *Res:* Design, implementation and analysis of computer algorithms related to theory of computation, operating systems principles. *Mailing Add:* Dept Comput Sci Univ NTex PO Box 13886 Denton TX 76203

**YANG, CHAO-HUI,** MATHEMATICS. *Current Pos:* PROF MATH, STATE UNIV NY COL ONEONTA. *Personal Data:* b Taichung, Taiwan, Aug 20, 28; m 63; c 2. *Educ:* Nat Taiwan Univ, BS, 51; Univ Mich, MA, 55; Univ Cincinnati, PhD(math), 58. *Prof Exp:* Res fel, Inst Math Sci, NY Univ, 58-59, assoc res scientist, 59-61; lectr math, Rutgers Univ, 61-64. *Mem:* Am Math Soc; Math Asn Am. *Res:* Maximal binary matrices; integral equations; integrability of trigonometric series; combinatorial and functional analyses. *Mailing Add:* 1929 Rockingham St McLean VA 22101-4923

**YANG, CHEN NING,** PHYSICS. *Current Pos:* ALBERT EINSTEIN PROF PHYSICS & DIR, INST THEORET PHYSICS, STATE UNIV NY, STONY BROOK, 66- *Personal Data:* b Hefei, Anhui, China, Sept 22, 22; US citizen; m 50; c 3. *Educ:* SW Assoc Univ, China, BSc, 42; Univ Chicago, PhD(physics), 48. *Hon Degrees:* DSc, Princeton Univ, 58, Polytech Inst Brooklyn, 65, Univ Wroclaw, 74, Gustavus Adolphus Col, Minn, 75, Univ Md, 79, Univ Durham, Eng, 79, Fudan Univ, China, 84, Eidg Technische Hochschule, Switz, 87, Moscow State Univ, 92, Drexel Univ, 95, TsingHua Univ, Taiwan, 96 & Chiao Tung Univ, 96. *Honors & Awards:* Nobel Prize in Physics, 57; Albert Einstein Commemorative Award, 57; Rumford Prize, 80; Nat Medal Sci, 86; Liberty Award, 86; Benjamin Franklin Medal, 93; Bower Prize, 94; N Bogollubov Prize, 96. *Prof Exp:* Instr physics, Univ Chicago, 48-49; mem, Inst Advan Study, Princeton, 49-66, prof, 55-66. *Concurrent Pos:* Bd trustees, Woods Hole Oceanog Inst, 62-78, Rockefeller Univ, 70-76, Salk Inst, 78-79 & Ben Gurion Univ, 81-; mem, Governing Coun, Courant Inst Math Sci, 63- & Sci Adv Comt, IBM, 66-71; chmn, Panel Theoret Physics, Physics Surv Comt, Nat Acad Sci, 65, Div Particles & Fields, Am Phys Soc, 70-71, Int Union Pure & Appl Physics, 72-76 & Fachbeirat, Max Planck Inst Physics, Munich, 80-83; bd dirs, AAAS, 75-79, Neurosci Inst, 83-88 & Sci Am, Inc, 83-90; hon prof, numerous univs, China; distinguished prof-at-large, Chinese Univ Hong Kong, 86- *Mem:* Nat Acad Sci; Am Philos Soc; Venezuelan Acad Sci; Korean Acad Sci & Technol; Royal Spanish Acad Sci; Polish Acad Sci; Royal Soc London; US Acad Sci; Chinese Acad Sci; Russ Acad Sci; Brazilian Acad Sci. *Res:* Theoretical physics. *Mailing Add:* Inst Theoret Physics State Univ NY Stony Brook NY 11794-3840

**YANG, CHIA HSIUNG,** NUCLEAR PHYSICS. *Current Pos:* From asst prof to assoc prof, 71-80, PROF PHYSICS, SOUTHERN UNIV, 80-, CHMN, 87- *Personal Data:* b Peikang, Taiwan, Sept 24, 40; US citizen; m 69; c 3. *Educ:* Tunghai Univ, Taiwan, BSc, 62; Tsing Hua Univ, Taiwan, MSc, 65; Washington Univ, MA, 67, PhD(physics), 71. *Concurrent Pos:* NASA res grant, 72-79. *Mem:* Sigma Xi; Am Phys Soc. *Res:* Microscopic study of isotropic superfluidity of neutron star matter by Yang and Clark method which combines Bardeen-Cooper-Schrieffer and correlated basis function theories. *Mailing Add:* 1062 Stoneliegh Dr Baton Rouge LA 70808-5767

**YANG, CHIH TED,** MORPHOLOGY, HYDROLOGY. *Current Pos:* tech rev staff, 79-88, int & spec projs coordr, 88-94, MGR SEDIMENTATION & RIVER HYDRAUL, US BUR RECLAMATION, 94- *Personal Data:* b Chung King, China, Jan 23, 40; m 68, Eveline Liu; c Michael & David. *Educ:* Cheng Kung Univ, Taiwan, BS, 62; Colo State Univ, MS, 65, PhD, 68. *Honors & Awards:* Robert E Horton Award, Am Geophys Union, 72; Walter L Hurber Res Prize, Am Soc Civil Engrs, 73; J C Stevens Award, 80; Cong Gold Medal, Pakistan Eng Cong, 86. *Prof Exp:* Assoc prof scientist, Ill State Water Surv, 68-74; hydraul engr, US Army Corp Engrs, 74-78. *Concurrent Pos:* Adj prof, Univ Colo, Denver, 82- *Mem:* Am Geophys Union; Am Soc Civil Engrs; Int Asn Hydraul Res. *Res:* Hydraulics, hydrology, morphology, sedimentation, hydraulic structure design. *Mailing Add:* US Bur Reclamation Code D8540 PO Box 25007 Denver CO 80225

**YANG, CHUI-HSU (TRACY)**, RADIATION BIOPHYSICS. *Current Pos:* RADIATION HEALTH OFFICER, JOHNSON SPACE CTR, NASA, 90- *Personal Data:* b Hunan, China, Nov 19, 38; US citizen; m 64; c 2. *Educ:* Tunghai Univ, BS, 59; North Tex State Univ, MS, 64; Univ Ill, PhD(biophys), 67. *Prof Exp:* Appointee biol, Argonne Nat Lab, 67-69; biophysicist, Lawrence Berkeley Lab, Univ Calif, 69-90. *Mem:* Cancer Res Asn; Biophys Soc; Radiation Res Soc; Am Soc Therapeut Radiol & Oncol; Tissue Cult Asn. *Res:* Effects of radiation on membrane, development and longevity; mechanisms and kinetics of recovery; space biology; responses of cultured mammalian cells to heavy ions and other environmental factors; mechanisms of cell transformation in vitro by radiation; somatic mutation by radiation. *Mailing Add:* SD2 NASA Johnson Space Ctr Houston TX 77058. *Fax:* 713-483-3058; *E-Mail:* tyang@sdmail.jsc.nasa.gov

**YANG, CHUN CHUAN**, MECHANICAL ENGINEERING, FLUID DYNAMICS. *Current Pos:* ROCKETDYNE DIV, BOEING N AM INC, 88- *Personal Data:* b Taichung, Jan 25, 36; m 66; c 2. *Educ:* Cheng-Kung Univ, BS, Taiwan, 59; Univ RI, MS, 65; Yale Univ, PhD(eng), 69. *Prof Exp:* Jr engr, Taiwan Mach Mfg Corp, 61-63; res asst heat transfer, Univ RI, 63-65; mem res staff geophys fluid dynamics, Yale Univ, 69-72; res scientist, Xonics, Inc, 72-74; res engr, Heat Transfer Res, Inc, 74-88. *Mem:* Am Soc Mech Engrs; Sigma Xi. *Res:* Heat transfer and fluid mechanics in two-phase flow; computational fluid dynamics. *Mailing Add:* Boeing NAm Inc Rocketdyne Div 6633 Canoga Ave PO Box 7922 Canoga Park CA 91309-7922

**YANG, CHUNG CHING**, SOLID STATE PHYSICS, QUANTUM ELECTRONICS. *Current Pos:* ENGR MGR, HEWLETT PACKARD, 85- *Personal Data:* b Peking, China, Sept 13, 38; US citizen; m 62; c 2. *Educ:* Univ Calif, Los Angeles, BS, 66; Harvard Univ, MS, 67, PhD(solid state physics), 72. *Prof Exp:* Mem sci staff, Xerox Corp, 72-78, res mgr, 78-80, tech res mgr, 80-85. *Mem:* Am Phys Soc. *Res:* Quantum optics; phase transition; transport across materials interfaces. *Mailing Add:* 19550 Braemar Ct Saratoga CA 95070

**YANG, CHUNG SHU**, BIOCHEMISTRY. *Current Pos:* asst prof, Rutgers Univ, 71-75, assoc prof, 75-79, prof biochem, 79-87, PROF & ASSOC CHAIR, DEPT CHEM BIOL, RUTGERS UNIV, 88- *Personal Data:* b Peking, China, Aug 8, 41; m 66; c 2. *Educ:* Nat Taiwan Univ, BS, 62; Cornell Univ, PhD(biochem), 67. *Honors & Awards:* Fac Res Award, Am Cancer Soc; Merit Award, Nat Cancer Inst; Distinguished Res Award, NJ Asn Biomed Res. *Prof Exp:* Fel biochem, Scripps Clin & Res Found, 67-69; res assoc, Yale Univ, 69-71. *Concurrent Pos:* Leader, Carcinogenesis & Prev Prog, Cancer Inst NJ. *Mem:* Am Soc Biochemists; Am Soc Molecular Biol; Am Soc Pharmacol; Am Inst Nutrit; Am Asn Cancer Res. *Res:* Mechanisms of biological oxygenation and carcinogen activation; etiology and mechanisms; prevention of carcinogenesis. *Mailing Add:* Lab Cancer Res Rutgers Univ Col Pharm Piscataway NJ 08855. *Fax:* 732-932-5767

**YANG, CHUNG-CHUN**, PURE MATHEMATICS, APPLIED MATHEMATICS. *Current Pos:* RES MATHEMATICIAN, NAVAL RES LAB, 70- *Personal Data:* b Kiang-su, China, Nov 21, 42; m 67; c 3. *Educ:* Nat Taiwan Univ, BS, 64; Univ Wis-Madison, MS, 66, PhD(math), 69. *Prof Exp:* Res assoc math, Mich State Univ, 69-70. *Concurrent Pos:* Comt mem Chinese translation comt, Am Math Soc; vis prof, Elec Eng & Comput Sci Dept, IIT, 83-84. *Mem:* Am Math Soc; Japanese Math Soc. *Res:* Factorization theory in the function theory of one complex variable; applications of theory of meromorphic functions to some physical and engineering problems; pattern recognition and image processing in computer science area. *Mailing Add:* Hong Kong Univ Sci & Tech Clearwater Bay Kowloon Hong Kong People's Republic of China

**YANG, CHUNG-TAO**, MATHEMATICS. *Current Pos:* from asst prof to assoc prof, 56-61, chmn dept, 78-83, PROF MATH, UNIV PA, 61- *Personal Data:* b Pingyang, China, May 4, 23; m 57; c 3. *Educ:* Chekiang Univ, BS, 46; Tulane Univ, PhD, 52. *Prof Exp:* Asst math, Chekiang Univ, 46-48; asst, Nat Acad Sci, China, 48-49; instr, Nat Taiwan Univ, 49-50; res assoc, Univ Ill, 52-54; mem staff, Inst Advan Study, 54-56. *Mem:* Am Math Soc; Math Asn Am; Sigma Xi. *Res:* General and algebraic topology; topological and differential transformation groups. *Mailing Add:* Dept Math Univ Pa Philadelphia PA 19104

**YANG, DA-PING (DAVID)**, GENETICS, CELL BIOLOGY. *Current Pos:* PRIN SCIENTIST, VACCINE PRECLIN DEVELOP DIV, WYETH-AYERST RES, INC, 88- *Personal Data:* b Peiping, China, Oct 5, 33; US citizen; m 67, Augustina Wan; c Yvonne & Victor. *Educ:* Nat Taiwan Univ, BSc, 56; Ottawa Univ, Can, MSc, 64, PhD(genetics), 69. *Prof Exp:* Agronomist, Rice Res Inst, Taiwan; instr, Ottawa Univ, Can, 64-68; fel biol, Nat Res Coun, Can, 68-70; sr res scientist & supvr, Cytol Lab, 71-82, supvr, Exp Biol & Immunol, Monoclonal Antibody Unit, 83-85. *Concurrent Pos:* Prin investr, Food & Drug Admin, 71-74, NIH, 72-74. *Mem:* Int Asn Biol Stand; Tissue Cult Asn. *Res:* Mammalian cell culture and cytogenetics; genetic toxicology; virology; somatic cell genetics; monoclonal antibody and hybridoma research. *Mailing Add:* Wyeth-Ayerst Res Inc PO Box 8299 Philadelphia PA 19101-8299. *Fax:* 215-989-4588

**YANG, DARCHUN BILLY**, POLYMER CHEMISTRY, HETEROGENEOUS & HOMOGENEOUS CATALYSIS. *Current Pos:* STAFF CONSULT, STANLEY WORKS, 88-; SR SCIENTIST, LOCTITE CORP. *Personal Data:* b Taipei, Taiwan, July 17, 45; m 71; c 2. *Educ:* Tamkang Univ, Taiwan, BS, 69; Furman Univ, MS, 73; Univ Ga, PhD(inorg

chem), 77. *Prof Exp:* Anal technician, Alpha Lab, Can, 74-75; fel, Univ Ga, 78-80; sr chemist, 80-86, staff chemist, Exxon Res & Eng Co, 87-88. *Concurrent Pos:* Chem teacher, Mil Acad Taiwan & Shulin High Sch, 69-71. *Mem:* Am Chem Soc; Sigma Xi. *Res:* Expert in adhesive and sealant research, especially in structure and instant adhesives; anaerobic, photo and thermal cure chemistries; thermal stability; polymerization kinetic by real time FTIR; surface chemistries; primers for low energy plastics and metal surfaces; structure-property relationships; coating, adhesive, and medical applications of polymers; thermal analysis of polymers; homogeneous and heterogeneous catalysis; new and improved catalysts; catalyst performance evaluation; physical characterization of catalyst and carrier; waste treatments. *Mailing Add:* 48 Lostbrook Rd West Hartford CT 06117-1928

**YANG, DAVID CHIH-HSIN**, BIOCHEMISTRY. *Current Pos:* from asst prof to assoc prof, 75-90, PROF CHEM, GEORGETOWN UNIV, 90- *Personal Data:* b Hsinchiang, China, Jan 8, 47; m 71. *Educ:* Nat Taiwan Univ, BSc, 68; Yale Univ, PhD(biochem), 73. *Prof Exp:* Res assoc, Rockefeller Univ, 73-75. *Mem:* Am Chem Soc; AAAS; Am Asn Univ Professors; Am Soc Biol Chemists; NY Acad Sci. *Res:* Structure of amino acyl-tRNA synthetases; conformational analysis of protein and nucleic acid; fluorescence spectroscopy; chemical modification of nucleic acid; animal lectins. *Mailing Add:* Dept Chem Georgetown Univ 37th & 0 Sts NW Washington DC 20057-0001. *Fax:* 202-687-6209; *E-Mail:* Bitnet: jnet%"dyang"@guvax

**YANG, DIFEI**, NON-INVASIVE DIAGNOSTICS. *Current Pos:* SR RES SCIENTIST, SPECTRX, INC, 96- *Personal Data:* b Jangsu, China, Nov 24, 69; m 94, Tony D Zheng. *Educ:* Peking Univ, BSc, 91; Univ Calif, Los Angeles, PhD(chem), 96. *Mem:* Am Chem Soc; Biophys Soc; Int Soc Optical Eng. *Res:* Developing minimally or non-invasive medical diagnostic devices through optical, analytical chemistry method; developing devices to improve health care of diabetic patients. *Mailing Add:* 6000 A Unity Dr Norcross GA 30071. *Fax:* 770-248-0922; *E-Mail:* dyang@spectrx.com

**YANG, DOMINIC TSUNG-CHE**, ORGANIC CHEMISTRY. *Current Pos:* from asst prof to assoc prof, 70-79, PROF ORG CHEM, UNIV ARK, LITTLE ROCK, 79- *Personal Data:* b Tainan, Taiwan, Oct 9, 33; US citizen; c Michael & Erik. *Educ:* St Benedict's Col, Kans, BS, 59; Univ Ga, PhD(org chem), 69. *Prof Exp:* Chemist, Nalco Chem Co, Ill, 59-64; instr toxicol & NIH res grant, Vanderbilt Univ, 68-70. *Mem:* Am Chem Soc; Sigma Xi. *Res:* Organic synthesis of polycyclic aromatic hydrocarbons; ultrasound accelerated organic reactions. *Mailing Add:* Dept Chem Univ Ark Little Rock AR 72204. *Fax:* 501-569-8838; *E-Mail:* dtyang@ualr.edu

**YANG, DOROTHY CHUAN-YING**, pediatrics, neurology, for more information see previous edition

**YANG, EDWARD S**, ELECTRONICS. *Current Pos:* from asst prof to assoc prof, 65-75, chmn dept, 87-89, & 93-96 PROF ELEC ENG, COLUMBIA UNIV, 75-; PROF MICROELECTRONICS, UNIV HONG KONG, 97- *Personal Data:* b Nanking, China, Oct 16, 37; US citizen; m 61, Ruth Chu; c 2. *Educ:* Cheng Kung Univ, Taiwan, BS, 57; Okla State Univ, MS, 61; Yale Univ, PhD(eng & appl sci), 66. *Prof Exp:* Jr engr, IBM Corp, 61-62, assoc engr, 62-63; asst electronics, Yale Univ, 63-65. *Concurrent Pos:* Dir, NSF res grant & prin investr, 67-81, NASA res grant, 67-69; contracts, Dept Energy, 77-82, Dept Defense, 77- & IBM Corp, 85-93. *Mem:* Fel Inst Elec & Electronics Engrs; Am Phys Soc; Mat Res Soc; Int Soc Optical Eng. *Res:* High-speed heterojunction bipolar transistors; highelectron-mobility transmittors (HMTs); integrated HBT/HEMTs; power microwave transistors; SiGe Mostransitors; high-temperature superconducors for MRI applications. *Mailing Add:* Dept Elec Eng Columbia Univ New York NY 10027

**YANG, FUNNEI**, MOLECULAR BIOLOGY, HUMAN GENETICS. *Current Pos:* ASST PROF HUMAN GENETICS, UNIV TEX, 82- *Educ:* Univ Wash, PhD(microbiol & immunol), 80. *Mailing Add:* Dept Cellular & Struct Biol Univ Tex Health Sci Ctr 7703 Floyd Curl Dr San Antonio TX 78284-7700

**YANG, GENE CHING-HUA**, MICROBIOLOGY, INFECTIOUS DISEASE. *Current Pos:* ASSOC PROF MICROBIOL & DIR MED TECHNOL PROG, SAGINAW VALLEY STATE COL, 76- *Personal Data:* b Kaohsuing, Taiwan, Feb 26, 38; US citizen; m 70; c 1. *Educ:* Tunghai Univ, BS, 60; Northwestern Univ, MS, 66; Mich State Univ, PhD(microbiol), 70. *Prof Exp:* Asst prof, Med Ctr, Univ Tenn, 71-76. *Concurrent Pos:* Mem bd, Dr Sun Yet Sen Inst, 77-; consult, St Luke's Hosp, Saginaw, 77- *Mem:* AAAS; Am Soc Med Technol; Am Soc Microbiol; Sigma Xi. *Res:* Pathogenic mechanism of enteric infection. *Mailing Add:* Dept Eng & Sci Saginaw Valley State Univ 7400 Bay Rd University Center MI 48710-0001

**YANG, GRACE L**, STATISTICS. *Current Pos:* From asst prof to assoc prof, 73-78, PROF STATIST, UNIV MD, COLLEGE PARK, 78- *Personal Data:* b Queichow, China; m 64; c 2. *Educ:* Univ Calif, Berkeley, MA, 63, PhD(statist), 66. *Mem:* Am Statist Asn; Inst Math Statist. *Res:* Mathematical statistics; biostatistics. *Mailing Add:* Dept Math Univ Md College Park MD 20742-0001

**YANG, H(SUN) T(IAO),** AEROSPACE ENGINEERING. *Current Pos:* res scientist, Eng Ctr, 58-63, assoc prof, 68-90, EMER PROF AERONAUT ENG, UNIV SOUTHERN CALIF, 90- *Personal Data:* b Hangchow, China, May 19, 24; m 65; c 3. *Educ:* Univ Wash, MS, 50; Calif Inst Technol, PhD(aeronaut, math), 55. *Prof Exp:* Res fel, Calif Inst Technol, 55-56; res assoc, Inst Fluid Dynamics, Univ Md, 56-58. *Concurrent Pos:* Fulbright-Hays lectr, 64-65; consult var indust concerns. *Mem:* Am Phys Soc; Am Inst Aeronaut & Astronaut. *Res:* Fluid dynamics; aerodynamics. *Mailing Add:* Dept Aerospace Eng 0651 Univ Southern Calif Los Angeles CA 90089-1191

**YANG, HEECHUNG,** BIOPHARMACEUTICALS, RATIONAL DRUG DESIGN. *Current Pos:* HEAD RES & INVESTMENT, YANGFARM PARTNERS, 96- *Personal Data:* b Seoul, Korea, Feb 15, 57; US Citizen. *Educ:* Seoul Nat Univ, BS, 78; Univ Wis-Madison, PhD(biochem), 85. *Prof Exp:* Scientist, Angenics, Inc, 86-87; sr res biochemist, Abbott Labs, 87-92; mgr mucosal res, ALZA Corp, 92-94; founder & chief scientist, Biophilies Technol, Inc, 94-96. *Concurrent Pos:* Vis scientist, Brookhaven Nat Lab, 84-85; fel, Brandeis Univ, 85-86. *Mem:* Am Soc Biochem & Molecular Biol; Am Chem Soc; AAAS; Controlled Release Soc; Am Asn Pharmaceut Scientists. *Res:* Mechanistic and applied research in enzymology, protein chemistry, immunodiagnostics, active site and receptor targeted drug designing; non-parenteral drug delivery and particle technology. *Mailing Add:* Yangfarm Partners PO Box 60970 Palo Alto CA 94306-0970. *E-Mail:* yangfarm@ix.netcom.com

**YANG, HENRY T Y,** ENGINEERING EDUCATION, COMPUTATIONAL METHODS. *Current Pos:* CHANCELLOR, UNIV CALIF, SANTA BARBARA, 94- *Personal Data:* b Chungking, China, Nov 29, 40; US citizen; m 67; c 2. *Educ:* Nat Taiwan Univ, BS, 62; WVa Univ, MS, 65; Cornell Univ, PhD, 68. *Prof Exp:* Struct engr, Gilbert Assocs, 68-69; from asst prof to prof aeronaut & astronaut, Purdue Univ, 69-94, sch head, 79-84, dean eng, 84-94. *Concurrent Pos:* Vis scientist, Air Force Flight Dynamics Lab, 76; Neil A Armstrong distinguished prof, Purdue Univ, 88. *Mem:* Nat Acad Eng; fel Am Inst Aeronaut & Astronaut; Am Soc Eng Educ; Am Soc Mech Engrs; Am Soc Civil Engrs. *Res:* Aeroelasticity; finite elements; structural dynamics; manufacturing; engineering education. *Mailing Add:* Off Chancellor Univ Calif Santa Barbara CA 93106. *Fax:* 805-893-8717

**YANG, HONG-YI,** IMMUNOLOGY. *Current Pos:* from asst prof to assoc prof, 68-83, PROF PATH, JOHN A BURNS SCH MED, UNIV HAWAII, MANOA, 83- *Personal Data:* b Tientsin, China, Mar 26, 33; US citizen; m 65; c 3. *Educ:* Nat Taiwan Univ, MD, 61; Univ Chicago, PhD(path), 67; Am Bd Path, cert, 69. *Prof Exp:* Res & teaching asst path, Univ Chicago, 63-67. *Concurrent Pos:* Assoc path, St Francis Hosp, 73-; consult pathologist, Castle Mem Hosp, 79- *Mem:* AMA; Am Asn Pathologists; Am Soc Exp Path; Am Soc Clin Pathologists. *Res:* Cellular immunity and macrophage functions; ultrastructural study of soft tissue tumors; immunopathology of renal disease. *Mailing Add:* Dept Path Biomed Sci Bldg Univ Hawaii 1960 East-West Rd Honolulu HI 96822-2319

**YANG, HOYA Y,** FOOD TECHNOLOGY. *Current Pos:* From asst prof to prof, 43-77, EMER PROF FOOD SCI, ORE STATE UNIV, 77- *Personal Data:* b Amoy, China, June 3, 12; nat US; m 46; c 2. *Educ:* Nanking Univ, BS, 36; Ore State Col, MS, 40, PhD(food technol), 44. *Concurrent Pos:* Consult, Food Industries. *Mem:* Am Chem Soc; Am Soc Enol; Inst Food Technologists; Am Soc Microbiol; Sigma Xi. *Res:* Food fermentation; food additives; food enzymes; food and food product analysis. *Mailing Add:* 1020 NW 30th St Corvallis OR 97330-4442

**YANG, IN CHE,** HYDROCHEMISTRY, INORGANIC CHEMISTRY. *Current Pos:* radiochemist isotope hydrol, 78-80, radiochem sect chief, Denver Cent Lab, Water Resource Div, 80-84, PROJ CHIEF HYDROCHEM, HYDROLOGIC INVEST PROG, US GEOL SURV, 84- *Personal Data:* b Taiwan, Feb 7, 34; US citizen; m 66, Lih H Sheu; c 3. *Educ:* Nat Taiwan Univ, BSc, 56; Carleton Univ, MSc, 66; Univ Wash, PhD(nuclear & inorg chem), 71. *Prof Exp:* Radiochemist radiation ecol, Univ Wash, 72, res assoc isotope geol, 72-75, res asst prof, 75-78. *Concurrent Pos:* Task mem, Stand Method Comt, Stand Method, 80-; New Zeland travel grant, NSF, 76. *Mem:* Am Geophys Union. *Res:* Applications of radioactive and stable isotopes to geology and hydrology; geochronology using carbon-14; tritium and potassium-argon dating; stable isotope ratios in hydrology using oxygen-18/oxygen-16, carbon-13/carbon-12 and deuterium/hydrogen ratios. *Mailing Add:* US Geol Surv MS 421 Denver Fed Ctr Box 25046 Denver CO 80225. *Fax:* 303-236-5047

**YANG, JEN TSI,** biophysical chemistry; deceased, see previous edition for last biography

**YANG, JENN-MING,** HIGH TEMPERATURE COMPOSITE MATERIALS, PROCESSING & MECHANICAL BEHAVIOR. *Current Pos:* PROF MAT SCI ENG, UNIV CALIF, LOS ANGELES, 86- *Personal Data:* b Hsin-Chu, Taiwan, Dec 20, 57; m 84, Su-Jen Ting; c Adrian T & Pauline T. *Educ:* Nat Tsing-Hua Univ, Taiwan, BS, 79; Univ Del, PhD(mat sci eng), 86. *Honors & Awards:* NSF Presidential Young Investr Award, 90. *Prof Exp:* Engr, Tex Instruments, Taiwan, 81-82. *Mem:* Mat Res Soc; Am Ceramic Soc; Metall Soc. *Res:* Processing and mechanical behavior of metal; intermetallic, ceramic and carbon matrix composites; aerospace structural and propulsional materials; high temperature deformation and fracture. *Mailing Add:* Dept Mat Sci & Eng Univ Calif Los Angeles CA 90024. *Fax:* 310-206-7353; *E-Mail:* jyang@seas.ucla.edu

**YANG, JEONG SHENG,** topology; deceased, see previous edition for last biography

**YANG, JOHN YUN-WEN,** ENVIRONMENTAL CHEMISTRY. *Current Pos:* SR CHEMIST, LINDE DIV, UNION CARBIDE CORP, 76- *Personal Data:* b Changsha, China, May 19, 30; US citizen; m 58; c 3. *Educ:* St Benedict's Col, Kans, BS, 52; Univ Kans, PhD(chem), 57. *Prof Exp:* Res assoc recoil carbon-14, Brookhaven Nat Lab, 57-59; sr chemist, US Naval Radiol Defense Lab, Calif, 59-60; res specialist, Atomics Int Div, NAm Aviation, Inc, 60-62, mem tech staff, Sci Ctr, 62-67; sr res scientist, Western NY Nuclear Res Ctr, 67-72; prin chemist, Environ Systs Dept, Calspan Corp, 72-76. *Concurrent Pos:* Adj assoc prof, State Univ NY, Buffalo, 70-76. *Mem:* Am Chem Soc; Am Nuclear Soc; NY Acad Sci. *Res:* Environmental air and water chemistry; physiocochemical methods of wastewater treatment; air pollution technology; radiation and isotope applications; water treatment and corrosion protection; radiation photochemistry; electrochemical processes. *Mailing Add:* 121 Ranch Trail Buffalo NY 14221

**YANG, JULIE CHI-SUN,** ANALYTICAL INORGANIC CHEMISTRY. *Current Pos:* RETIRED. *Personal Data:* b Beijing, China, June 10, 28. *Educ:* Tsing Hua Univ, China, BS, 49; Ind Univ, MA, 52; Univ Ill, PhD, 55. *Prof Exp:* Asst chem, Ind Univ, 50-52; res chemist, Res Ctr, Johns-Manville Corp, 55-59, sr res chemist, 59-67, res assoc, 67-72; sr group leader, W R Grace & Co, 72-74, res mgr, Construct Prod Div, 75-96. *Concurrent Pos:* Mem, Hwy Res Bd, Nat Acad Sci-Nat Res Coun. *Mem:* Am Chem Soc; Am Ceramic Soc; Clay Minerals Soc. *Res:* Inorganic silicate and cement chemistry; synthesis; properties; structures; material research; analytical instrumentation. *Mailing Add:* W R Grace & Co 62 Whittemore Ave Cambridge MA 02140-1623

**YANG, KEI-HSIUNG,** QUANTUM OPTICS, MEDICAL PHYSICS. *Current Pos:* MEM RES STAFF, T J WATSON RES CTR, IBM CORP, YORKTOWN HEIGHTS, NY, 79- *Personal Data:* b Taiwan, Dec 10, 40; US citizen; m 71; c 2. *Educ:* Nat Taiwan Univ, BS, 64; Univ Notre Dame, MS, 67; Univ Calif, Berkeley, PhD(physics), 74. *Prof Exp:* Teaching asst, Univ Notre Dame, 65-67, Univ Calif, Berkeley, 67-69; mem tech staff res, Bell Tel Labs, Murray Hill, NJ, 69; res asst, Lawrence Berkeley Lab, 69-73; mem staff, Res & Develop Ctr, Gen Elec Corp, 73-79. *Mem:* Am Phys Soc; Soc Info Display. *Res:* Continuous tunable coherent vacuum ultraviolet source; medical x-ray devices; liquid crystal displays. *Mailing Add:* T J Watson Res Ctr IBM Corp PO Box 218 Yorktown Heights NY 10598. *Fax:* 914-945-3030; *E-Mail:* kyang@watson.ibm.com

**YANG, KWANG-TZU,** MECHANICAL ENGINEERING. *Current Pos:* From asst prof to assoc prof, Univ Notre Dame, 56-62, chmn dept, 68-69, chmn dept aerospace & mech eng, 69-78, PROF MECH ENG, UNIV NOTRE DAME, 62-, VIOLA D HANK PROF ENG, 85- *Personal Data:* b China, Nov 12, 28; nat US; m 53, Heather Hsu; c Ginger, Eugene, Sara, Irene & Benson. *Educ:* Ill Inst Technol, BS, 51, MS, 52, PhD(heat transfer), 55. *Honors & Awards:* Heat Transfer Mem Award, Am Soc Mech Engrs. *Concurrent Pos:* Consult, Dodge Mfg Corp, 56-, Tyler Refrig Corp & Nuclear Regulatory Comn; NSF res grants, 56-; Off Naval Res grant, 61-64, Navy, 85- *Mem:* AAAS; fel Am Soc Mech Engrs; Am Soc Eng Educ; Am Inst Aeronaut & Astronaut. *Res:* Boundary-layer theory; nonlinear methods; forced and free convection; hydrodynamic stability; thermal radiation; food processing; manufacturing processes. *Mailing Add:* PO Box 309 Notre Dame IN 46556-0309. *Fax:* 219-631-8341; *E-Mail:* kwang-tzu.yang.1@nd.edu

**YANG, MAN-CHIU,** BIOCHEMISTRY. *Current Pos:* RES ASSOC, STATE UNIV NY, BUFFALO, 74- *Personal Data:* b Hankow, China, Aug 16, 46; m 71; c 1. *Educ:* Chinese Univ Hong Kong, BSc, 70; Univ Nebr, PhD(chem), 74. *Mem:* Biophys Soc; Am Chem Soc. *Res:* Study of the intermediates and enzymic systems in oxidative phosphorylation and photophosphorylation. *Mailing Add:* 25 Tanbark Circle Don Mills ON M3B 1N7 Can

**YANG, MARK CHAO-KUEN,** STATISTICS. *Current Pos:* From asst prof to assoc prof, 70-92, PROF STATIST, UNIV FLA, 92- *Personal Data:* b Tsuchuan, China, Dec 14, 42; m 68, Sharon; c 4. *Educ:* Nat Taiwan Univ, BS, 64; Univ Wis, MS, 67, PhD(statist), 70. *Concurrent Pos:* Consult, Redstone Arsenal, US Army Command, Ala, 72-73, Offshore Power Co, Fla, 73-74, Bell Lab, 83 & Logicon RDA, 86- *Mem:* Am Statist Asn; Inst Math Statist; AAAS. *Res:* Applied probability; stochastic processes; time series analysis; statistical genetics. *Mailing Add:* Dept Statist Univ Fla 225 Griffin Hall Gainesville FL 32611-2002. *Fax:* 352-392-5175; *E-Mail:* yang@stet.ufl.edu

**YANG, MEILING T,** INSTRUMENT MODIFICATION & FABRICATION. *Current Pos:* RETIRED. *Personal Data:* b Taiwan, Apr 21, 31; US citizen; m 60. *Educ:* Chung Kung Univ, BS, 54; Tex Tech Univ, MS, 58; Purdue Univ, PhD(chem), 62. *Prof Exp:* Teaching res fel, Purdue Univ, 62; vis asst prof res, La State Univ, 63-64; res chemist, Ethyl Corp, 64-70; asst soil chemist lab supvr, Agr Ext Serv, Tex A&M Univ, 71-81; res scientist, Anal Procedure Develop, Tex Tech Univ, 85-88. *Concurrent Pos:* Consult chemist, anal procedure develop, 81-85. *Mem:* Am Chem Soc. *Res:* Analytical methodology development; evaluation and comparison of analytical methods for trace mineral determination and enzyme assays; synthesis of specialty chemicals; spectroscopy, chromatography and polarography. *Mailing Add:* 956 Mesa Rd Nipomo CA 93444

**YANG, NIEN-CHU,** CHEMISTRY. *Current Pos:* from asst prof to prof chem, 56-92, GUSTAVUS F & ANN M SWIFT DISTINGUISHED SERV PROF, UNIV CHICAGO, 92- *Personal Data:* b Shanghai, China, May 1, 28; nat US; m 54, Ding-Djung Hwang; c 3. *Educ:* St John's Univ, China, BS, 48; Univ Chicago, PhD, 52. *Honors & Awards:* Gregory & Freda Jalpern Award, NY Acad Sci, 81. *Prof Exp:* Res assoc, Mass Inst Technol, 52-55; res fel, Harvard Univ, 55-56. *Concurrent Pos:* Alfred P Sloan fel, 60-64; res prof, Academia

Sinica, Beijing & Shanghai, 78-; mem, Academia Sinica, Taipei, 82- *Mem:* Fel AAAS; Am Chem Soc; Royal Soc Chem; Sigma Xi; fel Inter-Am Photochem Soc. *Res:* Photochemistry; organic synthesis; bio-organic chemistry. *Mailing Add:* Dept Chem Univ Chicago SCL-429 5733 Ellis Ave Chicago IL 60637. *Fax:* 773-702-0805

**YANG, OVID Y H,** PATHOLOGY, IMMUNOLOGY. *Current Pos:* DIR CLIN LAB, TITUS COUNTY MEM HOSP, MT PLEASANT, TEX, 76- *Personal Data:* b Korea; US citizen. *Educ:* Yonsei Univ, Korea, MD, 50; Univ Ottawa, PhD, 62. *Prof Exp:* Dir clin lab, Park Place Hosp, Port Arthur, Tex, 69-76. *Mem:* Am Soc Exp Path; Int Acad Path; Am Soc Clin Path; Col Am Path; AMA. *Res:* Chemical carcinogenesis; cancer immunology. *Mailing Add:* 3107 Fareway Mt Pleasant TX 75455-6731

**YANG, PAUL WANG,** SPECTROSCOPIC DATA PROCESSING. *Current Pos:* SCIENTIST, LAB SERV BR, ONT MINISTRY ENVIRON, 88- *Personal Data:* b Taichung, Taiwan, Oct 14, 53; m 83; c 1. *Educ:* Nat Chung Hsing Univ, BS, 75; Ohio Univ, PhD(anal chem), 83. *Prof Exp:* Res asst org anal, Union Indust Lab, Indust Res Inst, 77-79; res asst chem, Univ Calif, Riverside, 82-83; res assoc bioanal, Div Chem, Nat Res Coun, 83-88. *Concurrent Pos:* Consult, Bomem Inc, 86- *Mem:* Chem Inst Can. *Res:* Development of spectroscopic techniques and signal processing algorithms to facilitate the observation, interpretation of fundamental properties of lipid surfactant molecules and spectroscopic chromatographic data. *Mailing Add:* 5967 Talismen Ct Mississauga ON L5M 6A1 Can

**YANG, PHILIP YUNG-CHIN,** POLYMERS DEVELOPMENT, STRUCTURE PROPERTY RELATIONSHIPS. *Current Pos:* Advan chemist, B F Goodrich Co, 82-85, sr chemist, geon vinyl, 85-86, sr chemist, Div Elastomers & Latex, 87-89, RES & DEVELOP ASSOC, SPECIALTY POLYMERS & CHEMICALS DIV, B F GOODRICH CO, 89- *Personal Data:* b Pin-ton, Taiwan, Nov 20, 54; US citizen; m 86; c 1. *Educ:* Fen Chia Univ, BE, 76; Cleveland State Univ, MS, 79, Univ Ill, PhD(polymer sci & eng), 82. *Mem:* Am Chem Soc; Am Phys Soc; Am Inst Chem Engr; Soc Plastic Engr. *Res:* Research on polymeric materials, polymerization process and products development, structure property relationship; synthetic latexex development. *Mailing Add:* 1067 Treeline Dr Allentown PA 18103

**YANG, RALPH TZU-BOW,** CHEMICAL ENGINEERING, PHYSICAL CHEMISTRY. *Current Pos:* PROF & CHMN, DEPT CHEM ENG, UNIV MICH, 95- *Personal Data:* b Chungking, China, Sept 18, 42; US citizen; m 72, Frances H Chang; c Michael & Robert. *Educ:* Nat Taiwan Univ, BS, 64; Yale Univ, MS, 68, PhD(chem eng), 71. *Honors & Awards:* William H Walker Award, Am Inst Chem Eng; Inst Award Excellence in Indust Gases Tech, Am Inst Chem Eng. *Prof Exp:* Res assoc, NY Univ, 71-72 & Argonne Nat Lab, 72-73; scientist, Alcoa Lab, Aluminum Co Am, 73-74; group leader, Brookhaven Nat Lab, 74-78; from assoc prof to prof, State Univ NY, Buffalo, 78-93, dept chmn, 90-95, Praxair prof chem eng, 93-95. *Concurrent Pos:* Mem adv bd, Am Carbon Soc, 85-; program dir, NSF, 87-88; mem, adv bd, Ind Eng Chem Res, 91-93, Adsorption Sci Tech, 90-; series ed, Chem Eng Series, Imp Col Press, 96- *Mem:* Am Inst Chem Engrs; Am Chem Soc; Am Carbon Soc; Am Soc Eng Educ. *Res:* Heterogeneous kinetics; surface chemistry; diffusion; carbon; gas separation; adsorption processes; separations. *Mailing Add:* Dept Chem Eng Univ Mich Ann Arbor MI 48109-2136. *Fax:* 313-763-0459; *E-Mail:* yang@umich.edu

**YANG, RONG-CAI,** QUANTITATIVE & POPULATION GENETICS OF PLANT SPECIES, PLANT GENETICS RESOURCES MANAGEMENT & PLANT BREEDING. *Current Pos:* res assoc, 90-95, RES ASST PROF, UNIV ALTA, 95- *Personal Data:* b Jiangsu, China, Sept 29, 60; m 88, Xiao-Yan Mao; c Kevin. *Educ:* Nanjing Agr Univ, BSc, 82; Univ Sask, MSc, 86, PhD(plant genetics), 89. *Prof Exp:* Fel, Univ Sask, 89-90. *Mem:* Can Inst Forestry. *Res:* Quantitative and population genetics of plant species; analysis of genetic structure in natural and breeding populations of forest trees using RAPDs, isozymes and quantitative data; genetic consequences of conservation; molecular population genetics of Chinese fir. *Mailing Add:* Dept Renewable Resources Univ Alta Edmonton AB T6G 2H1 Can. *Fax:* 403-492-4323; *E-Mail:* ryang@gpu.srv.ualberta.ca

**YANG, SEN-LIAN,** OBSTETRICS & GYNECOLOGY. *Current Pos:* from instr to asst prof, 73-80, ASSOC PROF OBSTET & GYNEC, UNIV CHICAGO, 80- *Personal Data:* b Taipei, Taiwan, Jan 10, 38; Chinese citizen; m 66; c 2. *Educ:* Nat Taiwan Univ, MD, 63. *Prof Exp:* Resident obstet & gynec, Nat Taiwan Univ Hosp, 64-68; res fel immunol, US Naval Res Unit 2, 68-70; Ford Found fel reproductive biol & immunobiol, Dept Obstet & Gynec, Univ Pa, 70-71; resident obstet & gynec, Chicago Lying-in Hosp, Univ Chicago, 72-73. *Concurrent Pos:* Vis staff obstet & gynec, Nat Taiwan Univ Hosp, 68-70; fel reproductive biol & immunobiol, Chicago Lying-in Hosp, Univ Chicago, 73-74. *Mem:* Int Fedn Gynec & Obstet; Am Fertil Soc; Soc Study Reproduction; Am Col Obstetricians & Gynecologists; Asn Obstet & Gynec Repub China. *Res:* Immunobiology of reproductive medicine. *Mailing Add:* Chicago Lying-In Hosp-OG 5841 S Maryland Ave Chicago IL 60637-1463

**YANG, SHANG FA,** PLANT PHYSIOLOGY. *Current Pos:* from asst biochemist to assoc biochemist, 66-74, prof veg crops & biochemist, 74-94, EMER PROF, UNIV CALIF, DAVIS, 94-; VPRES, ACAD SINICA, TAIPEI, 97- *Personal Data:* b Tainan, Taiwan, Nov 10, 32; m 65; c 2. *Educ:* Nat Taiwan Univ, BS, 56, MS, 58; Utah State Univ, PhD(plant biochem), 62. *Honors & Awards:* Campbell Award, Am Inst Biol Sci, 69; Res Award, Int Plant Growth Substances Asn, 85; Wolf Prize in Agr, 91; Outstanding Res Award, Am Soc Hort Sci, 92. *Prof Exp:* Res fel, Univ Calif, Davis, 62-63; res assoc biochem, NY Univ Med Ctr, 63-64 & Univ Calif, San Diego, 64-66. *Concurrent Pos:* NSF res grant, 67-; vis prof, Univ Konstanz, 74, Nat Taiwan Univ, 83, Univ Cambridge, 83; Guggenheim fel, 82; prof, Hong Kong Univ Sci & Technol, 94-96. *Mem:* Nat Acad Sci; AAAS; Am Soc Biol Chemists; Am Soc Plant Physiol; Am Soc Hort Sci; Academia Sinica. *Res:* Biosynthesis and hormonal action of ethylene; postharvest biochemistry of fruits and vegetables; biochemical effects of sulfur dioxide on vegetation. *Mailing Add:* Acad Sinica Nanking-11529 Rep China Taipei Taiwan

**YANG, SHANG-TIAN,** BIOCHEMICAL ENGINEERING, BIOPROCESSING & BIOREACTOR ENGINEERING. *Current Pos:* PROF CHEM ENG, OHIO STATE UNIV, 85- *Personal Data:* b Taipei, Taiwan, Jan 15, 54; US citizen; m 78, I-Ching Tang; c Kevin, Grant & Hopen. *Educ:* Nat Taiwan Univ, BS, 76; Purdue Univ, MSE, 80, PhD(biochem eng), 84. *Prof Exp:* Res engr, Bio-Process Innovation, Inc, 84-85. *Concurrent Pos:* Postdoctoral res assoc, Purdue Univ, 84-85; dir, Ohio Bioprocessing Res Consortium, 96-; founder & res & develop dir, Bioprocessing Innovation Co, Inc, 96- *Mem:* Am Inst Chem Engrs; Am Chem Soc; Inst Food Technologists; Am Soc Microbiol. *Res:* Novel bioprocesses and bioreactors for biochemicals from agricultural commodities and food processing wastes; fermentation, enzyme technology, animal cell cultures, metabolic engineering, tissue engineering and biremediation. *Mailing Add:* Dept Chem Eng Ohio State Univ 140 W 19th Ave Columbus OH 43210. *Fax:* 614-292-3769; *E-Mail:* yang.15@osu.edu

**YANG, SHEN KWEI,** PHYSICAL & PHARMACEUTICAL CHEMISTRY, BIOCHEMISTRY. *Current Pos:* assoc prof, 77-81, PROF PHARMACOL, SCH MED, UNIFORMED SERV UNIV HEALTH SCI, 81- *Personal Data:* b Chung-King, China, May 4, 41; US citizen; m 68; c 1. *Educ:* Nat Taiwan Univ, BS, 64; Wesleyan Univ, MA, 69; Yale Univ, MPh, 70, PhD(phys chem), 72. *Honors & Awards:* Sci Achievement Award, Chinese Med & Health Asn, 78. *Prof Exp:* Fel biochem, Yale Univ, 72-73; res fel chem, Calif Inst Technol, 73-75; sr staff fel, Nat Cancer Inst, NIH, 75-77. *Concurrent Pos:* USPHS traineeship, Yale Univ, 72. *Mem:* Am Soc Pharmacol & Exp Therapeut; Am Asn Cancer Res; Am Soc Biol Chemists; Int Soc Study Xenobiotics. *Res:* Environmental toxicology, drug metabolism and chemical carcinogenesis. *Mailing Add:* Dept Pharmacol Uniformed Serv Univ Health 4301 Jones Bridge Rd Bethesda MD 20814-4799. *Fax:* 301-295-3220; *E-Mail:* Bitnet: yang@usuhs

**YANG, SHIANG-PING,** NUTRITION. *Current Pos:* chmn dept, 69-76, PROF FOOD & NUTRIT, TEX TECH UNIV, 69- *Personal Data:* b Hankow, China, Mar 5, 19; nat US; m 60. *Educ:* Nat Cent Univ, China, BS, 42; Iowa State Univ, MS, 49, PhD(nutrit), 56. *Prof Exp:* Animal husbandman, Nan-An Dairy Farms, China, 42-45; tech trainee, USDA, 45-46; sr animal husbandman, Chinese Nat Relief & Rehab Admin, 46-47; res assoc nutrit, Iowa State Univ, 49-56; chemist, Mead Johnson Res Ctr, 56-57; asst prof food & nutrit, Purdue Univ, 57-62; assoc prof, Va Polytech Inst, 62; prof, La State Univ, Baton Rouge, 63-69. *Concurrent Pos:* Fulbright lectr & vis prof, Nat Taiwan Univ, 59-60. *Mem:* Int Asn Bioinorg Scientists; Soc Environ Geochem & Health; Am Inst Nutrit. *Res:* Diets and carcinogenesis; protein metabolism; nutritional improvement of dietary proteins; factors influencing the qualities of food. *Mailing Add:* PO Box 768 Nipomo CA 93444-0768

**YANG, SHIOW-SHONG,** MICROBIOL PHYSIOLOGY, ENZYMOLOGY. *Current Pos:* SR RES BIOCHEMIST, SEPRACOR, INC, 92- *Personal Data:* b Taipei, Taiwan, Sept 17, 40; US citizen; m, Fei-o Chou; c Zsu-Yao & Zsu-Sun. *Educ:* Taipei Med Col, Taiwan, BS, 64; Nat Taiwan Univ, MS, 67; Univ Ga, Athens, PhD(biochem), 77. *Prof Exp:* Lectr biochem, Taipei Univ Med Col, 67-72; res assoc, Univ Ga, 77-79; res fel, Kettering Res Lab, 79-81; researcher, CPC Int, Inc, 81-87; sr res scientist, Henkel Res Corp, 87-91. *Mem:* AAAS; Am Soc Microbiol; Am Chem Soc; Protein Soc; Soc Indust Microbiol. *Res:* Screen, characterize and apply enzymes as biocatalyst in the manufacture of chiral pharmaceuticals; protein biochemistry; enzyme purification and characterization; kinetics; fermentation; biotransformation and biocatalysis. *Mailing Add:* 111 Locke Dr Marlborough MA 01752-7214. *Fax:* 508-481-7683; *E-Mail:* syang@sepracor.com

**YANG, SHUNG-JUN,** CELL BIOLOGY, RADIATION BIOLOGY. *Current Pos:* RADIATION BIOLOGIST, METHODIST HOSP, BROOKLYN, NY, 74- *Personal Data:* b Tientsin, China, Jan 13, 34; US citizen; m 64; c 3. *Educ:* Taiwan Univ, BS, 55; Univ Toronto, MS, 58; NC State Col, PhD(genetics), 62. *Prof Exp:* Fel cytogenetics, Baylor Col Med, 62-63, res instr, 63-64; res assoc radiation biol, Sch Med, Stanford Univ, 64-68; res assoc cell biol, Albert Einstein Col Med, 73-74. *Mem:* NY Acad Sci; Tissue Cult Asn; AAAS; Radiation Res Soc; Int Soc Anal Cytol; Am Asn Cancer Res. *Res:* Proliferation kinetics of mammalian cells in culture; cellular effects of anti-tumor agents; immune response in cancer patients; flow cytometry. *Mailing Add:* Dept Radiation Oncol Methodist Hosp 506 Sixth St Brooklyn NY 11215. *Fax:* 718-780-3688

**YANG, SONG-YU,** MOLECULAR BIOLOGY, BIOCHEMISTRY. *Current Pos:* HEAD, MED BIOCHEM LAB, INST BASIC RES DEVELOP DISABILITIES, 94- *Personal Data:* b Wu-Xi, China, Oct 27, 38; US citizen; m 65; c 2. *Educ:* Peking Med Col, China, MD, 60; City Univ NY, MA, 83, PhD(biochem), 84. *Prof Exp:* Instr biochem, Peking Med Col, 60-75; asst prof cancer immunol, Shanghai Inst Cell Biol, Academia Sinica, 75-81; res assoc biochem, City Col, City Univ NY, 84-88, res scientist, 88-94. *Concurrent Pos:* Investr, Am Heart Asn, 91-94, Wall Street Run Fel, 91. *Mem:* Am Soc Biochem & Molecular Biol; Am Chem Soc; AAAS; Sigma Xi. *Res:* Structure and expression of genes of fatty acid degradation; metabolism of saturated and unsaturated fatty acids; kinetics of coupled enzyme reactions; structure and function of multienzyme complex. *Mailing Add:* Dept Pharm Inst Basic Res Develop Disabilities 1050 Forest Hill Rd Staten Island NY 10314

**YANG, TAH TEH,** FLUID MECHANICS IN GAS TURBINES. *Current Pos:* from asst prof to prof, 62-93, EMER PROF FLUIDS, CLEMSON UNIV, 93- *Personal Data:* b Shanghai, China, Aug 15, 27; m 63; c 2. *Educ:* Shanghai Inst Technol, BS, 48; Okla State Univ, MS, 57; Cornell Univ, PhD(mech eng), 61. *Prof Exp:* Engr, Kaohsiung Harbor Bur, Taiwan, 49-55; proj engr, Wright Aeronaut Div, Curtiss Wright Corp, 60-62. *Concurrent Pos:* Prin investr, NSF grant, 63-64; US Army res grant, 63-66, res contract, 70-73; NASA grant, 69-72 & 84-85; res grants, USAF, 75-76, Singer Co, 77-79, USN, 80-82 & SC Energy Res & Develop Ctr, 85-86, United Technol, 87-89 & Morgantown Energy Technol Ctr, Dept Energy, 89-93; consult, Singer Co, 76- & Avco Corp, 77- *Mem:* Life fel Am Soc Mech Engrs; Am Inst Aeronaut & Astronaut. *Res:* Gas turbines for power generation; fluid mechanics with combustion; three dimensional flows. *Mailing Add:* 205 Mountaindale Rd Central SC 29630

**YANG, TA-LUN,** MEASUREMENT & TESTING, REAL-TIME ANALYSIS SYSTEMS. *Current Pos:* CHIEF ENGR & VPRES, ENSCO INC, 72- *Personal Data:* b Tien Tsin, China, Sept 20, 37; Taiwan citizen; m 64; c 2. *Educ:* Nat Taiwan Univ, BS, 60; Univ Calif, Berkeley, MS, 63, PhD(appl mech), 67. *Prof Exp:* Mem tech staff, Bellcomm Inc, 68-72. *Mem:* Am Soc Mech Engrs; Inst Elec & Electronics Engrs; Am Railway Eng Asn; Transp Res Bd. *Res:* Development of measurement technology and data processing techniques for dynamic testing and evaluation of rail, highway equipment and guideways. *Mailing Add:* Ensco Inc 5400 Port Royal Rd Springfield VA 22151

**YANG, TIEN-FANG,** physics, for more information see previous edition

**YANG, TSANYEN,** MICROBIAL PHYSIOLOGY & ENZYMOLOGY, PROTEIN CHEMISTRY. *Current Pos:* CONSULT, 87- *Personal Data:* b Ping-tung, Taiwan, Oct 22, 49; m 80; c 1. *Educ:* Tunghai Univ, Taiwan, BS, 70; McNeese State Univ, La, MS, 74; Univ Houston, PhD(microbiol), 78. *Prof Exp:* Res fel biochem, Sch Med, Univ Pa, 78-79; res assoc molecular biol, Sloan-Kettering Inst, NY, 79-81; asst prof biol & biol sci, Bowling Green State Univ, 81-87. *Mem:* AAAS; Am Soc Microbiol; NY Acad Sci. *Res:* Bacterial cytochrome oxidases, dehydrogenases and mutagenesis; properties, purification and characterization, and kinetic studies of enzymes; genetic alterations leading to changes in enzymes and proteins proper. *Mailing Add:* 8563 Royal Lythan Lane Holland OH 43528-9012

**YANG, TSU-JU (THOMAS),** PATHOBIOLOGY, IMMUNOBIOLOGY. *Current Pos:* assoc prof, 75-78, PROF PATHOBIOL, UNIV CONN, STORRS, 78-, ASST HEAD, 88-, JOINT APPOINTMENT, CELL & MOLECULAR BIOL, 89-, ACTG HEAD, 94- *Personal Data:* b Fengshang, Taiwan, Repub China, Aug 14, 32; m 61, Sue N Chou; c Kai H, Andrew T & Michael B. *Educ:* Nat Taiwan Univ, BVM, 55; Ministry Exam, Taipei, Taiwan, DVM, 59; McGill Univ, PhD(immunol), 71. *Honors & Awards:* Ralston Purina Small Animal Res Award, Am Vet Med Asn, 88. *Prof Exp:* Assoc mem immunol, Academia Sinica Inst Zool, 61-64; res assoc cytogenetics, Dept Animal Biol, Univ Pa, 64-66; res fel immunol, Dept Microbiol, Univ Minn, 66-67; demonstr immunol, McGill Univ, 68-71; asst prof immunol, Univ Tenn Mem Res Ctr, 71-75. *Concurrent Pos:* Vis fel, Walter & Eliza Hall Inst Med Res, Melbourne, Australia, 83; vis prof, Nat Taiwan Univ, Taipei, 90. *Mem:* Am Asn Cancer Res; Am Asn Immunologists; Am Soc Microbiol; AAAS; Am Asn Vet Immunologists. *Res:* Spontaneous regression of tumors; canine immunology; bovine immunology; mode of action of membrane reactive agents: antibodies and lectins; monoclonal antibodies; cytokines. *Mailing Add:* Dept Pathobiol U-89 Univ Conn Storrs CT 06269-3089. *Fax:* 860-486-2794; *E-Mail:* tyang@uconnvm.uconn.edu

**YANG, TSUTE,** electrical engineering, computer science, for more information see previous edition

**YANG, VICTOR CHI-MIN,** BIO-REACTORS, BIO-SENSORS & DIAGNOSTIC ASSAYS, TARGETED DRUG DELIVERY SYSTEMS. *Current Pos:* asst prof, 86-90, ASSOC PROF, SCH PHARM, UNIV MICH, 91- *Personal Data:* b Shanghai, Kiangsu, China, July 2, 49; US citizen; m, Iris S; c Joseph L & Emily S. *Educ:* Tamkang Col, Taiwan, BS, 72; ETex State Univ, MS, 77; Brown Univ, PhD(phys biochem), 83. *Honors & Awards:* Arthur Doolittle Award, Am Chem Soc, 90. *Prof Exp:* Res asst, ETex State Univ, 75-77; teaching-res asst, Brown Univ, 78-82; fel, Mass Inst Technol, 83-85. *Concurrent Pos:* Co-lectr pharmaceut eng, Mass Inst Technol, 84; prin investr, NIH, 87-91 & 93-, Whitaker Found Biomed Eng, 88-91; mem, Small Bus Innovation Res Prog, NIH, 90 & 93- *Mem:* Am Chem Soc; Biomed Eng Soc; Am Asn Pharmaceut Scientist; Am Soc Artificial Internal Organs; AAAS; Am Asn Col Pharm. *Res:* Development of bioreactors for extra corporeal blood detoxification; development of biosensors and diagnostic assays; development of site specific drug delivery systems; biomaterials biocompatibility. *Mailing Add:* Col Pharm Univ Mich Ann Arbor MI 48109-1065. *Fax:* 313-763-2022; *E-Mail:* victorcyang@um.cc.umich.edu

**YANG, WEI-HSUIN,** MECHANICS, APPLIED MATHEMATICS. *Current Pos:* from asst prof to assoc prof eng mech, 65-77, PROF APPL MECH, UNIV MICH, ANN ARBOR, 77- *Personal Data:* b Apr 1, 36; m 64; c 2. *Educ:* Cheng Kung Univ, Taiwan, BS, 58; Univ Wash, MS, 62; Stanford Univ, PhD(mech), 65. *Prof Exp:* Res engr, Boeing Co, 62; res fel, Calif Inst Technol, 64-65. *Concurrent Pos:* Ed consult, Math Rev, 66-67; consult, Gen Motors Corp, 67- *Res:* Solid mechanics including elasticity, plasticity and viscoelasticity; large deformation and numerical analysis. *Mailing Add:* Dept Mech Eng & Appl Mech Univ Mich Main Campus 2350 Hayward Ann Arbor MI 48109-2125

**YANG, WEITAO,** ELECTRONIC STRUCTURE THEORY, CHEMICAL DYNAMICS. *Current Pos:* ASST PROF, DUKE UNIV, DURHAM, 89- *Personal Data:* b Chaozhou, Guangdong, Mar 31, 61; m 93, Helen Wen Zhang. *Educ:* Beijing Univ, BS, 82; Univ NC, Chapel Hill, PhD(chem), 86. *Prof Exp:* Res assoc, Univ NC, Chapel Hill, 86-87 & Univ Calif, Berkeley, 88-89. *Concurrent Pos:* Sloan res fel, 93-95; vis assoc prof, Dept Chem, Hong Kong Univ Sci & Technol. *Mem:* Am Phys Soc; Am Chem Soc; Sigma Xi. *Res:* Development and application of the density-functional theory of atoms and molecules; ab initio theory for large molecules; structure and reactivity of large molecules; chemical dynamics and molecular spectroscopy. *Mailing Add:* Dept Chem Duke Univ Durham NC 27708-0346. *E-Mail:* yang@chem.duke.edu

**YANG, WEN JEI,** HEAT TRANSFER, BIOENGINEERING & FLUID DYNAMICS. *Current Pos:* lectr mech eng, 61-62, from asst prof to assoc prof, 62-70, PROF MECH ENG, UNIV MICH, ANN ARBOR, 70- *Personal Data:* b Taiwan, China, Oct 14, 31; m 60, Shu Yuan; c Ling H, Mimi L & Paul P. *Educ:* Nat Taiwan Univ, BS, 54; Univ Mich, MS, 56, PhD(mech eng), 60. *Honors & Awards:* Heat Transfer Mem Award, Am Soc Mech Engrs, 84; C Strouhal Award in Fluid Visualization, 89; Thermal Eng Mem Award, Japan Soc Mech Engrs, 92; Res Excellence Award, Am Soc Mech Engrs/Japan Soc Mech Engrs, 87. *Prof Exp:* Res engr, Sci Lab, Ford Motor Co, 57-58; res engr, Inst Indust Sci, Tokyo Univ, 60-61. *Concurrent Pos:* Consult, Tamano Works, Mitsui Shipbldg Co, Japan, 60-61, Tecumseh Prod Res Lab, 66-67, Atomic Power Div, Westinghouse Elec Corp, 67-68, Borg-Warner Mach, 68-71 & Environ Protection Agency, 70-72; ed-in-chief, Int J Biomed Eng, 71-73; invited vis prof, Inst Space & Aeronaut Sci, Univ Tokyo, 75; guest prof, Inst Tech Chem Eng, Tech Univ, Berlin, 75-76; consult, Ex-Cell-O, 76-80, Energy Develop Assocs, 79-80, Panasonic, 79-, Bendix Corp, 79-80, KMMCO, 81-, Sarns, 82 & Japan Life Int, 84-; fel, Japan Soc Prom Sci, 83; Ital Nat Res Coun fel, 86; hon vis prof, Tsinghua Univ, Beijing, China, 88; Deutsche Forschungsgemeinschaft fel, 88; J W Fulbright award, 91-92; co-ed-in-chief, J Flow Visualization & Image Processing, 93-; ed-in-chief, Int J Rotating Mach; Monbusho foreign spec vis prof, Tokyo Univ Agr & Technol, 96. *Mem:* Japan Soc Flow Visualization; fel Am Soc Mech Engrs; Sigma Xi; AAAS; Nat Soc Prof Engrs; NY Acad Sci; hon mem Chinese Soc Theoret & Appl Mech; corresp mem Ital Acad Med & Surg; assoc fel Am Inst Aeronaut & Astronaut; hon invited mem Heat Transfer Soc Japan. *Res:* Heat exchangers; heat transfer enhancement; flow visualization; thermograph and digital image processing; thermal physiology; cardiovascular fluid mechanics; hyperthermia; natural convection; applied optics; transport phenomena in materials processing; gas turbine blades cooling; fouri heat conduction. *Mailing Add:* Dept Mech Eng Univ Mich Ann Arbor MI 48109-2125

**YANG, WEN-CHING,** FLUIDIZATION & FLUID PARTICLE SYSTEMS, ENVIRONMENTAL TECHNOLOGIES. *Current Pos:* Sr engr, 68-76, fel engr, 76-92, ADV ENGR, WESTINGHOUSE ELEC CORP, PITTSBURGH, 93- *Personal Data:* b Taipei, China, Nov 11, 39; US citizen; m 68, Rae Tien; c Evonne & Peter. *Educ:* Nat Taiwan Univ, BS, 62; Univ Calif, Berkeley, MS, 65; Carnegie-Mellon Univ, PhD(chem eng), 68. *Honors & Awards:* Fluidized Processes Recognition Award, Particle Technol Forum, Am Inst Chem Engrs, 93. *Concurrent Pos:* Lectr, Univ Pittsburgh, 80 & 83; mem, PhD Adv Comt, Lehigh Univ, 82-84; vchmn, Prog Comt, Group 3b, Am Inst Chem Engrs, 83-85 & chmn, 86-87, vchmn, Prog Comt, Group 3c, 91-, chair, Prog Comt, Group 3, 93-94, secy, Particle Technol Forum, 93- *Mem:* Fel Am Inst Chem Engrs; Am Chem Soc; Chinese Chem Soc. *Res:* Mass transfer; thermodynamics; chemical vapor deposition and high temperature technology; fluidized bed technology; fluidized bed coal gasification and combustion; pneumatic transport; environmental technologies; power generation cycle analysis. *Mailing Add:* 236 Mt Vernon Ave Export PA 15632. *Fax:* 412-256-1222; *E-Mail:* wcyang@chem01.pgh.wec.com

**YANG, WEN-KUANG,** biochemistry, medicine, for more information see previous edition

**YANG, WILLIAM C T,** ANTI-MICROBIAL DRUGS, ANTI-ARRHYTHMIC DRUGS. *Current Pos:* EMER PROF PHARMACOL, SCII MED, UNIV SOUTHERN CALIF, 89- *Personal Data:* m, Ben-yi Chen. *Educ:* Univ Southern Calif, PhD(zool), 56. *Res:* Functions of cardiac mitochondria and liver microsomes. *Mailing Add:* Dept Cell & Neurobiol Univ Southern Calif BMT-401 1333 San Pablo St Los Angeles CA 90033

**YANG, XIAOWEI,** COMMUNICATIONS NETWORKS, BIOMEDICAL SIGNAL PROCESSING & DATA COMPRESSION. *Current Pos:* teaching asst elec eng, 84-86, res asst, 86-89, POSTDOCTORAL RES ASSOC BIOMED ENG, UNIV MD, 89-; PRES BIOMED ENG, MULTICHANNEL CONCEPTS, INC, 91-; SR PRIN ENGR, RMS INFO SYSTS, INC, 94- *Personal Data:* b Shanghai, China, July 19, 54; m 83; c 2. *Educ:* Wuhan Univ, China, BS, 78; EChina Normal Univ, MS, 82; Univ Md, MS, 88, PhD(elec eng), 89. *Prof Exp:* Asst researcher electrophysics, Wuhan Univ, 78-79; lectr electronics, EChina Normal Univ, 82-83; sr systs engr, Cambridge Res Assocs, Inc, 93-94. *Concurrent Pos:* Vis engr biomed eng, Micro Probe, Inc, 89-90; prin investr, Nat Inst Neurol Disorders & Stroke, NIH, 91- *Mem:* Inst Elec & Electronics Engrs; Inst Elec & Electronics Engrs Biomed Eng Soc; Inst Elec & Electronics Engrs Signal Processing Soc; Inst Elec & Electronics Engrs Pattern Analysis & Mach Intel; Inst Elec & Electronics Engrs Info Theory Soc; Inst Elec & Electronics Engrs Commun Soc. *Res:* Auditory representation of acoustic signals; speech recognition; speech data compression; neural signal discrimination; synaptic connectivity identification in neural networks; mathematical modeling of biological systems; biomedical instrumentation; modeling and simulation for communications networks. *Mailing Add:* 13740 Valley Oak Circle Rockville MD 20850

**YANG, XIAS-BING,** PLANT EPIDEMIOLOGY & DISEASE RISK ASSESSMENT, PLANT DISEASE CONTROL. *Current Pos:* ASST PROF PLANT PATH, IOWA STATE UNIV, 93- *Personal Data:* b Gaungzhou, China, Mar 12, 58; m 85, YiLin Bian; c Louis, Felix & Iris. *Educ:* Beijing Agr Univ, BA, 82, MS, 85; La State Univ, PhD(plant path), 89. *Prof Exp:* Res asst, La State Univ, 86-89; fel, USDA-Agr Res Sta, 89-90, Univ Ark, 90-93. *Concurrent Pos:* Mem, Epidemiol Comt, Am Phytopath Soc, 92-95, Dis Loss Comt, 93-96 & Soil Mycobiol Comt, 94-97; rep, NCR-137 Comt, USDA, 93- *Mem:* Am Phytopath Soc. *Res:* Use of statistical and mathematical model to predict plant disease epidemics to access the risk of biotechnology and to manage soybean diseases in midwest agricultural system; assessing impact of no-till farming practice on soybean disease over north central regions. *Mailing Add:* Dept Plant Path Iowa State Univ Ames IA 50011. *Fax:* 515-294-9420; *E-Mail:* xbyang@iastate.edu

**YANG, YAN-BO,** SEPARATION SCIENCE, SURFACE COATING & MODIFICATION CHEMISTRY. *Current Pos:* sr res chemist, 90-94, DIR RES, SEPARATIONS GROUP, INC, 94- *Personal Data:* b Chengde, Hebei Prov, China, March 30, 59; M 86, Bing Wang; c Qian-Zhou & Kai-Zhou. *Educ:* Beijing Inst Technol, BS, 82; State Univ Ghent, PhD(org chem), 87. *Prof Exp:* Fel, Purdue Univ, 87-90. *Mem:* Am Chem Soc; AAAS. *Res:* Column technology for high performance liquid chromatography; theories and practices in separation science; method development for the separation of a wide variety compounds, both small and large molecules. *Mailing Add:* Separation Group Inc 17434 Mojave St Hesperia CA 92345. *Fax:* 760-244-1984

**YANICK, NICHOLAS SAMUEL,** physical chemistry; deceased, see previous edition for last biography

**YANIV, SHLOMO STEFAN,** RADIOLOGICAL RISK ASSESSMENT, HEALTH EFFECTS OF RADIATION. *Current Pos:* sr health physicist, Prod Stand Br, Directorate Regulatory Stand, US Atomic Energy Comn, 72-75, tech asst to dir, Div Safeguards Fuel Cycle & Environ Res, 75-79, sr health physicist/radiation physics & health effects specialist, Radiation Protection & Health Effects Br, 79-93, SR TECH ADV HEALTH EFFECTS, OFF NUCLEAR REGULATORY COMN, WASHINGTON, DC, 93- *Personal Data:* b Poznan, Poland, Sept 11, 31; US citizen; div; c Orlie & Elan. *Educ:* Israel Inst Technol, BS, 54, Ingenieur, 55; Univ Pittsburgh, MS, 65, DSc(radiation health), 69; Am Bd Health Physics, cert, 66, recert, 81, 85, 89 & 93. *Prof Exp:* Radiation protection engr, Israel AEC, 58-62; univ health physicist, Grad Sch Pub Health, Univ Pittsburgh, 63-67, asst prof health physics & radiol, Sch Med, 69-72. *Concurrent Pos:* Am Cancer Soc grant, Univ Pittsburgh, 71-72; radiol physicist, Montefiore Hosp, 67-72; consult, radiol & health physics, several hosps, insts, & com co, Pittsburgh, 64-72 & Interagency Sci Review Group, 79-80; mem subcomt, Nuclear Measurements Stand, Am Nat Stand Inst, 76-82, sci work group, Interagency Task Force Health Effects Ionizing Radiation, 78-79, adv group, Harvard Univ Sch Pub Health, sci subpanel Inoizing Radiation Risk Assessment, 82-92, Comt Interagency Radiation Res & Policy Coord, 87-; adv, World Health Orgn, 81. *Mem:* Health Physics Soc. *Res:* Radiological risk assessment; environmental aspects of radionuclides use; radiation dosimetry; health effects of population exposure to ionizing radiation. *Mailing Add:* 18 Cedarwood Ct Rockville MD 20852. *Fax:* 301-492-3866

**YANIV, SIMONE LILIANE,** BUILDING ACOUSTICS, FORCE MEASUREMENTS. *Current Pos:* GROUP LEADER FORCE GROUP, NAT INST STAND & TECHNOL, 86- *Personal Data:* b France, May 17, 38; US citizen; c 2. *Educ:* Univ Pittsburgh, BS, 66, MS, 68, PhD(noise control), 72. *Prof Exp:* Noise pollution consult, Allegheny Co Health Dept, 72-73; bioacoust scientist effects noise on people, US Environ Protection Agency, Noise Abatement & Control Off, 73-74. *Mem:* Am Soc Testing & Mat. *Res:* Force metrology; sound absorption, propagation and isolation; acoustic measurements. *Mailing Add:* 9948 Lake Landing Rd Gaithersburg MD 20879

**YANIV, ZVI,** LIQUID CRYSTAL DEVICES, ACTIVE MATRIX. *Current Pos:* PRES, ADVAN TECHNOL INCUBATOR INC, 92-, SYNMATIX & KENT DISPLAY SYSTS, 93- *Personal Data:* b Botoshan, Romania, Apr 11, 46; US citizen; m, Monica Hartopahu; c Dan, Esther & Taly. *Educ:* Hebrew Univ, Jerusalem, BS, 70, MSc, 72; Kent State Univ, PhD(liquid crystals), 82. *Prof Exp:* Head, Electrooptics Dept & vpres, Practical Eng Col, Ben-Gurion Univ, 72-79; sr researcher, Kent State Univ, 79-82; pres, Optical Imaging Systs, 82-91. *Mem:* Inst Elec & Electronics Engrs; fel Soc Info Displays; Int Liquid Crystal Soc. *Res:* Microelectronics on glass; liquid crystals; active matrix liquid crystal devices; thin films; flat panel displays; avionic displays; high resolution large area sensors. *Mailing Add:* S I Diamond Technol Inc 12100 Technology Blvd Austin TX 78727. *Fax:* 248-737-9341

**YANKAUER, ALFRED,** PUBLIC HEALTH. *Current Pos:* PROF COMMUNITY MED & PEDIAT, MED SCH, UNIV MASS, WORCESTER, 73- *Personal Data:* b New York, NY, Oct 12, 13; m 48; c 2. *Educ:* Dartmouth Col, BA, 34; Harvard Univ, MD, 38; Columbia Univ, MPH, 47. *Honors & Awards:* Job Lewis Smith Award, Am Acad Pediat, 79; Excellence Award, Am PUb Health Asn, 90. *Prof Exp:* Dist health officer, New York City Dept Health, 48-50; asst prof prev med & pub health, Med Col, Cornell Univ, 48-50 & Sch Med, Univ Rochester, 50-52; dir, Bur Maternal & Child Health, NY State Dept Health, 52-61; regional adv maternal & child health, Pan-Am Health Orgn, WHO, 61-66; sr lectr maternal & child health, Sch Pub Health, Harvard Univ, 66-70, sr lectr health serv admin, 70-73. *Concurrent Pos:* Dir, Maternal & Child Health Serv, Health Bur, Rochester, NY, 50-52; lectr, Albany Med Col, 52-61; WHO vis prof, Madras Med Col, India, 57-59; ed, Am J Pub Health, 75-90. *Mem:* Fel Am Pub Health Asn; fel Am Acad Pediat. *Res:* Maternal and child health; school health; social medicine; health care. *Mailing Add:* Dept Community & Family Med Univ Mass Med Sch Worcester MA 01655

**YANKEE, ERNEST WARREN,** ORGANIC CHEMISTRY, MEDICINAL CHEMISTRY. *Current Pos:* RES ASSOC ORG CHEM, UPJOHN CO, 70- *Personal Data:* b Hayward, Calif, Nov 18, 43; m 65; c 2. *Educ:* La Sierra Col, BA, 65; Univ Calif, Los Angeles, PhD(org chem), 70. *Mem:* Am Chem Soc. *Res:* Synthesis and structure-activity relationships of prostaglandins. *Mailing Add:* 9033 W R Ave Kalamazoo MI 49001

**YANKEE, RONALD AUGUST,** MEDICINE. *Current Pos:* MED DIR, RI BLOOD CTR, 79-; PROF, BROWN UNIV, 79- *Personal Data:* b Franklin, Mass, May 24, 34. *Educ:* Tufts Univ, BS, 56; Yale Univ, MD, 60. *Prof Exp:* Intern med, Univ Va, 60-61; resident, Univ Mich, 62-63; sr investr, Nat Cancer Inst, 63-75; assoc prof, Sidney Farber Cancer Inst, Harvard Med Sch, 73-79. *Mem:* Transplantation Soc; Am Soc Hemat; Am Asn Blood Banks; Int Soc Exp Hemat. *Res:* Bone marrow transplantation; histocompatibility; platelet transfusion therapy; cancer chemotherapy. *Mailing Add:* RI Blood Ctr PO Box 9427 Providence RI 02940

**YANKELL, SAMUEL L,** DENTISTRY, TOXICOLOGY. *Current Pos:* RES PROF, SCH DENT MED, UNIV PA, 74- *Personal Data:* b Bridgeton, NJ, July 4, 35; m 58; c 3. *Educ:* Ursinus Col, BS, 56; Rutgers Univ, MS, 57, PhD, 60; Univ Pa, Sch Dent Med, RDH, 81. *Prof Exp:* Instr, Georgian Court Col, 60; sr res biochemist, Colgate-Palmolive Co, 60-63; head dept biochem & pharmacol, Smith, Miller & Patch, 63-65; sr pharmacologist, Menley & James Res Labs, 66-67; sect head biol labs, Smith Kline & French Inter-Am Corp, 67-69; head dept biol sci, Menley & James Labs, 69-74. *Mem:* Am Chem Soc; NY Acad Sci; Int Asn Dent Res; Am Soc Pharmacol & Exp Therapeut; Sigma Xi. *Res:* Nutrition; dermatology; dental research. *Mailing Add:* Univ Pa Sch Dent Med 4001 Spruce St Philadelphia PA 19104. *Fax:* 609-778-4375

**YANKO, WILLIAM HARRY,** RADIOCHEMISTRY, ORGANIC CHEMISTRY. *Current Pos:* RETIRED. *Personal Data:* b Manessen, Pa, Jan 6, 19; m 42, Thelma Atkinson; c Richard A & Pamela A (Yust). *Educ:* Geneva Col, BS, 40; Pa State Univ, MS, 41, PhD(org chem), 44. *Prof Exp:* Org res chemist, Cent Res Lab, Monsanto Chem Co, 43-46; org res chemist, Clinton Labs, Tenn, 46-47; radiochem res group leader, Cent Res Lab, Monsanto Chem Co, 47-60, group leader, 61-78, sr chemist, 78-82. *Mem:* Am Chem Soc; AAAS. *Res:* Synthetic antimalarials; anticancer drugs; radioisotopic synthesis. *Mailing Add:* 5612 Royalwood Dr Centerville OH 45429-6136

**YANKOV, LUBEN KRASTANOV,** NATURAL TAXANE ANALOGUES, SYNTHETIC & NATURAL BIOLOGICALLY ACTIVE PRODUCTS. *Current Pos:* DISTINGUISHED SR SCIENTIST, XECHEM, INC, 93- *Personal Data:* b Sofia, Bulgaria, Apr 5, 30; m 55, Maria Yankova-Bostanova; c Christian Lubenov. *Educ:* Higher Inst Chem Technol, Sofia, Bulgaria, MS, 54, PhD(natural prod), 64. *Honors & Awards:* Gold Medal, Nat Assembly Bulgaria, 80. *Prof Exp:* Head, Dept Sci Invest & Develop, State Corp, Bulgaria, 56-59; asst prof & lectr org chem, Higher Inst Chem Technol, 62-72, assoc prof & lectr, 72-80, prof & lectr, 80-93. *Concurrent Pos:* Mem, Fac Coun, Higher Inst Chem Technol, 72-93, mem & pres, sci coun, 76-92, head, Dept Org Chem, 82-93, vpres sci & develop, 85-89, mem, Acad Coun, 85-89; vpres heavy chem indust, State Corp Bulgaria, 72-76, pres, Bd Mgrs Verila, 87-92; pres, Cent Sci Inst Chem Technol, Bulgaria, 72-79; mem, Sci Coun, Bulgarian Acad Sci, Sophia, 72-89; sci adv, State Ministry Chem Indust, Bulgaria, 79-81. *Mem:* Union Bulgarian Chemists; Union Sci Workers; Am Chem Soc; Am Soc Pharmacognosy. *Res:* General organic chemistry, organic synthesis and natural products; isolation, purification and structural investigation of synthetic and natural biologically active products, using classical, modern physical and chemical techniques. *Mailing Add:* Xechem Inc 100 Jersey Ave Bldg B Suite 310 New Brunswick NJ 08901

**YANKWICH, PETER EWALD,** PHYSICAL CHEMISTRY, SCIENCE EDUCATION. *Current Pos:* exec officer, 85-91, SR STAFF ASSOC, DIRECTORATE EDUC & HUMAN RESOURCES, NSF, 91- *Personal Data:* b Los Angeles, Calif, Oct 20, 23; m 45, Elizabeth Ingram; c Alexandra, Leon II & Richard. *Educ:* Univ Calif, BS, 43, PhD(chem), 45. *Prof Exp:* Res chemist, Radiation Lab, Univ Calif, 44-46; instr chem, 47-48; from asst prof to assoc prof, Univ Ill, Urbana, 48-57, prof chem, 57-88. *Concurrent Pos:* NSF fel, Calif Inst Technol & Brookhaven Nat Lab, 60-61; vpres acad affairs, 77-82. *Mem:* Fel AAAS; Sigma Xi; Am Chem Soc; fel Am Phys Soc. *Res:* Chemical kinetics; isotope effects. *Mailing Add:* EHR Rm 835 NSF Arlington VA 22230. *Fax:* 703-306-0445; *E-Mail:* pyankwic@usf.gov

**YANNAS, IOANNIS VASSILIOS,** BIOMATERIALS, TISSUE REGENERATION. *Current Pos:* asst prof mech eng, Mass Inst Technol, 66-68, Du Pont asst prof, 68-69, assoc prof, 69-78, PROF POLYMER SCI & ENG, MASS INST TECHNOL, 78- *Personal Data:* b Athens, Greece, Apr 14, 35; div, Stamatia Frondistou; c Tania & Alexis. *Educ:* Harvard Col, AB, 57; Mass Inst Technol, MS, 59; Princeton Univ, MA, 65, PhD(phys chem), 66. *Honors & Awards:* Fred O Conley Award, Soc Plastics Engrs, 82; Founders Award, Soc Biomat, 82, Clemson Award, 92; Doolittle Award, Am Chem Soc, 88. *Prof Exp:* Res phys chemist, W R Grace & Co, 59-63. *Concurrent Pos:* Polymer consult; ed, J Biomed Mat Res, J Mat Sci, Mat Med. *Mem:* Inst Med-Nat Acad Sci; Am Chem Soc; NY Acad Sci; fel Am Inst Chemists; Am Soc Cell Biol; Soc Neurosci; fel Am Inst Med & Biol Eng; fel Biomatic Sci & Eng Soc. *Res:* Natural and synthetic polymers; analogs of extracellular matrix have been synthesized and used to induce regeneration of skin (dermis and epidermis) in humans and rodents (artificial skin);; peripheral nerve has been regenerated in rodents using analogs of extracellular matrix. *Mailing Add:* Dept Mech Eng Rm 3-332 Mass Inst Technol Cambridge MA 02139. *Fax:* 617-258-5802

**YANNI, JOHN MICHAEL,** DRUG DISCOVERY-HYPERSENSITIVITY & INFLAMMATION. *Current Pos:* asst dir inflammation res, 90-92, dir res, 92-94, SR DIR OPHTHAL PROGS, ALCON LABS INC, 94- *Personal Data:* b St Mary's, Pa, Nov 3, 52; m 79, Nancy Reedy; c Susan, Jennifer & Steven. *Educ:* Allegheny Col, BS, 74; Med Col Va, MS, 79, PhD(immunopathol), 82. *Prof Exp:* Res assoc, A H Robins Co, 80-88; group leader, Life Sci Res Labs, Eastman Kodak, 88-90. *Mem:* Am Soc Pharm & Exp Therapeut; NY Acad Sci; Soc Leukocyte Biol; Asn Res Vision & Ophthalmol; Inflammation Res Asn; Int Soc Immunopharmacol. *Res:* Pharmacological intervention in ocular allergic and inflammatory diseases. *Mailing Add:* Alcon Labs Inc 6201 South Freeway Fort Worth TX 76134-2099. *Fax:* 817-551-4584

**YANNITELL, DANIEL W,** MECHANICS, APPLIED MATHEMATICS. *Current Pos:* asst prof eng mech, 67-72, assoc prof eng sci, 72-77, ASSOC PROF MECH ENG, LA STATE UNIV, BATON ROUGE, 77- *Personal Data:* b Johnson City, NY, Sept 26, 41; m 70; c 2. *Educ:* Webb Inst Technol, BS, 62; Cornell Univ, PhD(mech), 67. *Prof Exp:* Res assoc & instr mech, Cornell Univ, 67. *Concurrent Pos:* Rocket Propulsion Lab, USAF, 81-82 & 86. *Mem:* Am Acad Mech. *Res:* Fluid mechanics; analytical and computational fluid dynamics. *Mailing Add:* 3330 Belmont Ave Baton Rouge LA 70808

**YANNONI, COSTANTINO SHELDON,** STRUCTURAL CHEMISTRY. *Current Pos:* res staff mem, Watson Res Ctr, 67-71, RES STAFF MEM, RES LAB, IBM CORP, 71- *Personal Data:* b Boston, Mass, May 20, 35; div; c 5. *Educ:* Harvard Col, AB, 57; Columbia Univ, MA, 60, PhD(chem), 67. *Prof Exp:* Res chemist, Union Carbide Res Inst, 66-67. *Concurrent Pos:* Chmn, Exp Nuclear Magnetic Resonance Conf, 81-82 & Gordon Conf on Magnetic Resonance, 87. *Mem:* Am Chem Soc. *Res:* Structure and dynamics of reactive intermediates; structure of molecules at interfaces. *Mailing Add:* 4073 Vistamont Dr San Jose CA 95118-1845

**YANNONI, NICHOLAS,** PHYSICAL CHEMISTRY. *Current Pos:* physicist, Rome Air Develop Ctr, 61-64, chief, Energetics Br, 64-73, chief, Opto-Electronic Physics Br, Air Force Cambridge Res Labs, 74-79, chief, Signal Processing & Timing Devices, Rome Air Develop Ctr, 80-90, CHIEF, INFRARED SURVEILANCE, ROME LAB, 90- *Personal Data:* b Boston, Mass, Aug 3, 27; m 55; c 4. *Educ:* Boston Univ, BA, 54, PhD(chem), 61; Boston Col, MBA, 80. *Honors & Awards:* Am Inst Chemists Medal, 54. *Prof Exp:* Res fel chem, Mellon Inst, 54-55; staff scientist, Device Develop Corp, 60-61. *Mem:* Sigma Xi; Am Crystallog Asn; Am Chem Soc; Am Phys Soc. *Res:* Crystal structure analysis; optics; atomic frequency/time standards; quartz oscillators. *Mailing Add:* 23 James Rd Needham MA 02194-1519

**YANO, FLEUR BELLE,** THEORETICAL PHYSICS. *Current Pos:* From asst prof to assoc prof, Calif State Univ, 64-73, assoc dean instruction, Sch Letters & Sci, 78-79, resident dir int prog Sweden & Denmark, 84-85, PROF PHYSICS, CALIF STATE UNIV, LOS ANGELES, 73- *Personal Data:* US citizen; m 59, Alva; c Robert. *Educ:* Columbia Univ, BS, 54; Univ Southern Calif, MA, 58; Univ Rochester, PhD(physics), 60. *Concurrent Pos:* Res Corp grant, Calif State Univ, Los Angeles & State Univ Groningen, 72-73, Calif Inst Technol, 77-78 & Uppsala Univ, 84-85. *Mem:* Am Phys Soc; AAAS. *Res:* Theoretical nuclear physics; intermediato energy physics; radiative muon capture by complex nuclei; pion correlations (pion interferometry Brown-Hanbury-Twiss Effect) in heavy ion collision. *Mailing Add:* 2128 Via Pacheco Palos Verdes Estates CA 90274. *Fax:* 213-343-2497; *E-Mail:* yano@mercury.calstatela.edu

**YANOFSKY, CHARLES,** MOLECULAR BIOLOGY. *Current Pos:* assoc prof biol, 58-61, PROF BIOL, STANFORD UNIV, 61- *Personal Data:* b New York, NY, Apr 17, 25; m 49; c 3. *Educ:* City Col New York, BS, 48; Yale Univ, MS, 50, PhD(microbiol), 51. *Hon Degrees:* DSc, Univ Chicago, 80 & Yale Univ, 81. *Honors & Awards:* Eli Lilly Award, 59; US Steel Found Award, 64; Howard Taylor Ricketts Award, 66; Lasker Med Res Award, 71; Waksman Award, Nat Acad Sci, 72; Louisa Gross Horwitz Prize, 76; Genetics Soc Am Medal, 83; Gairdner Found Int Award, 85; Thomas Hunt Morgan Medal, Genetics Soc Am, 90; Passano Award, 92; William C Rose Award, Am Soc Biochem & Molecular Biol, 97. *Prof Exp:* Res asst microbiol, Yale Univ, 51-54; asst prof, Sch Med, Western Res Univ, 54-58. *Concurrent Pos:* Lederle med fac award, 55-57; Am Heart Asn career investr, 69-95. *Mem:* Nat Acad Sci; AAAS; Am Acad Arts & Sci; Am Soc Microbiol; Genetics Soc Am; foreign mem Royal Soc; Leopold Ger Acad Naturalists. *Res:* Regulation of gene expression in bacteria with emphasis on transcriptional attenuation; evolution of protein structure; developmental regulation of sporulation in fungi. *Mailing Add:* Dept Biol Sci Stanford Univ Stanford CA 94305-5020

**YANOW, GILBERT,** PHYSICS, SOLAR ENERGY. *Current Pos:* staff mem physics, HEAD EDUC OUTREACH, JET PROPULSION LAB, CALIF INST TECHNOL, 74- *Personal Data:* b Los Angeles, Calif, Oct 15, 35; m 63; c 3. *Educ:* Univ Calif, Los Angeles, BA, 59; Univ Queensland, MS, 65; Australian Nat Univ, PhD(physics), 71. *Prof Exp:* Res specialist space sci, Douglas Aircraft Co, 56-63; lab instr physics, Univ Queensland, 64-65; sr lab instr, Australian Nat Univ, 65-71; sr engr, Martin Marietta, 71-72; res specialist, McDonnell Douglas Aircraft Co, 72-74. *Mem:* Am Radio Relay League; Sigma Xi. *Res:* Solar energy utilization; high speed gas dynamics; teaching methods; science education. *Mailing Add:* 23356 Wagontrail Rd Diamond Bar CA 91765-2045

**YANOWITCH, MICHAEL,** APPLIED MATHEMATICS. *Current Pos:* RETIRED. *Personal Data:* b Minsk, Russia, Feb 1, 23; nat US; wid; c Gail & Paul. *Educ:* Cooper Union, BEE, 43; NY Univ, MS, 50, PhD(math), 53. *Prof Exp:* Elec engr, Philco Corp, 43-46; instr elec eng, Polytech Inst Brooklyn, 48-49; asst, Inst Math Sci, NY Univ, 50-52, assoc res scientist, 57-58; sr mathematician, Reeves Instrument Corp, 52-57; assoc prof math, Adelphi Univ, 58-62, prof, 62-93. *Concurrent Pos:* Consult, Surv Bur Corp, 59-60 & Grumman Aircraft Eng Corp, 61-63; vis scientist, Nat Ctr Atmospheric Res, 65-66. *Mem:* Am Math Soc; Soc Indust & Appl Math; Math Asn Am. *Res:* Asymptotics; wave motion; atmospheric waves. *Mailing Add:* Dept Math & Comput Sci Adelphi Univ Garden City NY 11530

**YANTIS, PHILLIP ALEXANDER,** AUDIOLOGY. *Current Pos:* assoc prof, 65-69, prog dir speech path & audiol, 68-74, PROF AUDIOL, UNIV WASH, 69- *Personal Data:* b Portland, Ore, Mar 30, 28; m 54, Elna Mattila; c Stephen, Michael & Jeffrey. *Educ:* Univ Wash, BA, 50; Univ Mich, MA, 52, PhD(audiol), 55. *Prof Exp:* Res assoc physiol acoust, Univ Mich, 55-58, instr audiol, 57-60; from asst prof to assoc prof, Case Western Res Univ, 60-65. *Concurrent Pos:* Dir, Dept Audiol, Cleveland Hearing & Speech Ctr, 60-65; mem rev panel, Neurol & Sensory Dis Proj, USPHS, 67-69; field reader, Bur Educ Handicapped, HEW, 72-73, mem rev panel, Speech & Hearing Training, Rehab Serv Admin, 77-78; chmn, Coun Prof Stand Speech-Lang Path & Audiol, 82-84. *Mem:* Fel Am Acad Audiol; hon fel, Am Speech, Lang & Hearing Asn (vpres, 69-71, pres, 75); Am Auditory Soc. *Res:* Detection of aural harmonics; bone conduction audiometry; speech audiometry; middle ear immittance. *Mailing Add:* 1434 NW 204th Pl Seattle WA 98177. *Fax:* 206-543-1093; *E-Mail:* pay@u.washington.edu

**YANTIS, RICHARD P,** MATHEMATICS, OPERATIONS RESEARCH. *Current Pos:* PROF MATH, OTTERBEIN COL, 76- *Personal Data:* b Westerville, Ohio, July 1, 32; m 59, Jane McAllister; c John P & James T. *Educ:* US Naval Acad, BS, 54; Univ NC, MA, 62; Ohio State Univ, PhD(indust eng), 66. *Prof Exp:* USAF, 54-74, intel officer, 54-56, instr navig, 56-60, from instr to assoc prof math, USAF Acad, 62-70, assoc prof opers res, USAF Inst Technol, 71-74; teacher, Columbus Acad, 75-76. *Concurrent Pos:* Proj leader underground coal mining proj, Battelle Mem Inst, 74-75. *Mem:* Nat Coun Teachers Math. *Res:* Linear programming; integer linear programming. *Mailing Add:* 265 Storington Rd Westerville OH 43081

**YANUSHKA, ARTHUR,** MATHEMATICS. *Current Pos:* asst prof, 77-80, ASSOC PROF MATH & COMPUT SCI, CHRISTIAN BROS COL, 80- *Personal Data:* b NY, Dec 2, 48. *Educ:* Fordham Univ, BA, 70; Univ Ill, MS & PhD(math), 74. *Prof Exp:* Asst prof math, Univ Mich, 74-76 & Kans State Univ, 76-77. *Concurrent Pos:* Prin investr, Math Sci Sect, NSF, 78, 79. *Mem:* Math Asn Am. *Res:* Finite geometry and combinatorics. *Mailing Add:* Christian Bros Univ 650 E Pkwy S Memphis TN 38104-5581

**YAO, ALICE C,** NEONATAL-PRENATAL MEDICINE, PEDIATRIC CARDIOLOGY. *Current Pos:* from asst prof to assoc prof, 68-77, PROF PEDIAT, HEALTH SCI CTR, STATE UNIV NY, BROOKLYN, 77- *Personal Data:* b Philippines; US citizen. *Educ:* Far Eastern Univ, Manila, AA, 53, MD, 58. *Prof Exp:* Internship & residency pediat, Bellevue New York Univ Med Ctr, 59-61; fel pediat cardiol, NY Heart Asn, State Univ NY Downstate Med Ctr, 61-62, Johns Hopkins Hosp, 62-63; res fel neonatal physiol, Karolinska Hosp & Inst, Sweden, 65-68. *Concurrent Pos:* Attend physician, Univ Hosp Brooklyn, Childrens Med Ctr, Brooklyn, 69-; vis pediat, Kings County Hosp, Brooklyn, 69-; vis res scientist, Dept Pediat & Clin Pharmacol, Karolinska Hosp, Stockholm, Sweden, 74-75 & 82-83, Univ Hosp, Trondheim, Norway, 90-; vis res fel, Brown Univ Prog Med, Women & Infant Hosp, RI, 75 & 82. *Mem:* Soc Pediat Res; Am Pediat Soc; Am Physiol Soc; Am Acad Pediat; Sigma Xi; Am Col Cardiol. *Res:* Factors influencing postnatal maturation of the neonatal circulation; placental transfusion; blood volume and blood flows; hemorrhage; hypoxia; special interest on the splanchnic, peripheral circulations in relation to the systemic circulation. *Mailing Add:* State Univ NY Health Sci Ctr 450 Clarkson Ave Box 49 Brooklyn NY 11203

**YAO, DAVID D,** QUEUEING NETWORKS, DISCRETE-EVENT SYSTEMS. *Current Pos:* asst prof, 83-86, PROF, COLUMBIA UNIV, 88-, THOMAS ALVA EDISON PROF, 92- *Personal Data:* b Shanghai, China, July 14, 50; m 79, Helen Chen; c Henry & John. *Educ:* Univ Toronto, MASc, 81, PhD, 83. *Prof Exp:* Assoc prof, Harvard Univ, 86-88. *Concurrent Pos:* Pres young investr award, NSF, 87-92; acad vis, IBM TJ Watson Res Ctr, 89-; Guggenheim Found fel, 91-92; adj prof, Hong Kong Univ Sci Technol, 96-; vis prof, Yale Univ, 91-92; adj prof, Hong Kong Univ Sci Technol, 96- *Mem:* Inst Elec & Electronics Engrs; Opers Res Soc Am; Soc Indust & Appl Math. *Res:* Optimization and control of discrete event stochastic systems focusing on queueing networks and their applications in communication systems and computer integrated manufacturing systems; stochastic optimization techniques in such systems. *Mailing Add:* IEOR Dept Columbia Univ New York NY 10027-6699. *Fax:* 212-854-8103

**YAO, JAMES T-P,** STRUCTURAL ENGINEERING, ENGINEERING MECHANICS. *Current Pos:* head dept, 88-93, PROF CIVIL ENG, TEX A&M UNIV, 88-, CAROLYN SR & TOMMIE E LOHMAN PROFESSORSHIP ENG EDUC, 96- *Personal Data:* b Shanghai, China, July 7, 33; m 58, Anna L; c Tina L, Timothy H & Shana L. *Educ:* Univ Ill, Urbana, BS, 57, MS, 58, PhD(civil eng), 61. *Honors & Awards:* A M Freudenthal Medal, Am Soc Civil Engrs, 90, Richard R Torrens Award, 92, Pres Medal, 95; Max Planck Res Award, Alexander von Humboldt Found & Max Planck Soc, 90; Centennial Medallion, Am Soc Eng Educ, 93. *Prof Exp:* From asst prof to prof civil eng, Univ NMex, Albuquerque, 61-71; postdoctoral preceptor eng mech, Columbia Univ, NY, 64-65; prof civil eng, Purdue Univ, West Lafayette, Ind, 71-88, asst head, 83-88. *Concurrent Pos:* Asst dean grad sch, Purdue Univ, West Lafayette, Ind, 84-87; ed, J Struct Eng, Am Soc Civil Engrs, 90-92, vchmn, Struct Div Exec Comt, 90-91, chmn, 91-92. *Mem:* Am Soc Civil Engrs; Am Concrete Inst; Am Soc Eng Educ; Am Asn Univ Professors; Earthquake Eng Res Inst; NAm Fuzzy Info Processing Soc (pres, 85-88). *Res:* Structural fatigue; earthquake engineering; structural safety, control, and reliability; civil engineering education; engineering education. *Mailing Add:* Dept Civil Eng Tex A&M Univ College Station TX 77843-3136. *Fax:* 409-845-6554; *E-Mail:* jty0735@acs.tamu.educ

**YAO, JASON,** telecommunication, digital signal processing, for more information see previous edition

**YAO, JERRY SHI KUANG,** PHOTOGRAPHIC CHEMISTRY. *Current Pos:* PRES, EMPIRE STATE SCI, INC, 82- *Personal Data:* b Peiping, China, Oct 12, 25; m 46; c 2. *Educ:* Peking Univ, BS, 46; Mont State Col, PhD, 60. *Prof Exp:* Fel biochem, Mont State Col, 60-61; asst prof org & gen chem, Wis State Col, Stevens Point, 61-62; assoc prof, Dubuque, 62-63; res chemist, Gaf Corp, 63-66, tech specialist, Photo & Reproduction Div, 66-76, group leader res & develop, 76-82. *Mem:* Soc Photog Sci & Eng; Am Chem Soc. *Res:* Heterocyclic chemistry in relation to photography; silver halide emulsions. *Mailing Add:* PO Box 300 Mendon NY 14506-0300

**YAO, JOE,** WOOD SCIENCE, WOOD CHEMISTRY. *Current Pos:* RETIRED. *Personal Data:* b Antung, China, Feb 11, 30; m 68. *Educ:* Chung Hsing Univ, Taiwan, BS, 54; Mont State Univ, MS, 58; NC State Univ, PhD(wood sci, wood technol), 65. *Prof Exp:* Assoc wood technologist, Miss Forest Prod Utilization Lab, 70-79; asst prof, Wood Sci & Technol, Miss State Univ, 63-70, assoc prof, 70-79. *Concurrent Pos:* Asst forester, Miss Agr Exp Sta, 63-67; Forest Prod Utilization Lab, 67-70, assoc wood technologist, 70-79; vis prof, Nat Chung Hsing Univ, Taiwan, 73-74. *Mem:* AAAS; Soc Wood Sci & Technol; Forest Prod Res Soc; Am Inst Chemists; NY Acad Sci. *Res:* Wood particleboard properties; wood capillary structure; water diffusion in wood; shrinkage and related properties; low grade hardwood utilization; utilization of recycled wood fiber material. *Mailing Add:* 4115 Baynard Dr Houston TX 77072

**YAO, KUAN MU,** civil engineering, for more information see previous edition

**YAO, KUNG,** COMMUNICATIONS, SYSTEMS ENGINEERING. *Current Pos:* asst prof commun eng, 66-72, assoc prof, 72-78, PROF COMMUN ENG, UNIV CALIF, LOS ANGELES, 78- *Personal Data:* b Hong Kong, Nov 24, 38; US citizen; m 69. *Educ:* Princeton Univ, BSE, 61, MA, 63, PhD(elec eng), 65. *Prof Exp:* Res asst commun eng, Princeton Univ, 63-65; Nat Acad Sci-Nat Res Coun res fel syst eng, Univ Calif, Berkeley, 65-66. *Concurrent Pos:* Prin investr, NSF initiation grant, 68-71 & Off Naval Res, 72-. *Mem:* AAAS; Inst Elec & Electronics Engrs; Am Math Soc. *Res:* Research, teaching and consulting in communications theory and signal processing. *Mailing Add:* Dept Elec Eng Univ Calif 405 Hilgard Ave Los Angeles CA 90095-1594

**YAO, MENG-CHAO,** CHROMOSOME STRUCTURE, GENE REARRANGEMENT. *Current Pos:* MEM STAFF GENETICS, FRED HUTCHINSON CANCER RES CTR, 86- *Personal Data:* b Taipei, Taiwan, Mar 21, 49; US citizen; m 74; c Kairu Yao. *Educ:* Nat Taiwan Univ, BS, 71; Univ Rochester, MS, 74, PhD(biol), 75. *Prof Exp:* Postdoctoral fel cell biol, Yale Univ, 75-78; from asst prof to assoc prof develop biol, Wash Univ, St Louis, 78-86. *Concurrent Pos:* NIH res career develop award, 84; vis scholar, Univ Wash, 85-86, affil prof, Dept Zool, 88-; mem, Genetics Study Sect, NIH, 87-89. *Mem:* Am Soc Cell Biol; AAAS. *Res:* Various types of DNA rearrangements during development and growth of cells, primarily in the ciliated protozoan tetrahymena; gene amplification; telomere formation; chromosome breakage; DNA deletion; palindrome formation and DNA elimination; ribosomal RNA structure and function. *Mailing Add:* 3724 Cascadia Ave S Seattle WA 98144. *Fax:* 206-667-6526; *E-Mail:* mcyao@fred.fhcrc.org

**YAO, NENG-PING,** ADVANCED BATTERIES & FUEL CELLS, ELECTROCHEMISTRY. *Current Pos:* PRES, YAO INT INC, 85- *Personal Data:* b Shanghai, China, Oct 13, 38; m 67; c 1. *Educ:* Univ Calif, Los Angeles, BS, 63, MS, 65, PhD(chem eng), 69; Univ Chicago, MBA, 79. *Prof Exp:* Res engr, Univ Calif, Los Angeles, 63-69; mem tech staff chem technol, Atomics Int Div, N Am Rockwell Corp, 69-71; sect head electrochem technol, Heliotek Div, Textron Inc, 71-72; mem staff, Chem Eng Div, 72-76, assoc dir energy storage prog, 76-77, dir, off electrochem projs, Argonne Nat Lab, 77-85. *Concurrent Pos:* Adj prof, Purdue Univ, 80-; vis prof, Helsinki Univ Technol, Finland, 86-90. *Mem:* AAAS; Electrochem Soc; Am Chem Soc; Sigma Xi. *Res:* Electrochemical energy conversion systems; batteries and fuel cells; air and water pollution control systems. *Mailing Add:* 350 Meadow Ct Clarendon Hills IL 60514-2441

**YAO, RONG,** R-GLUTAMYL HYDROLASE, POTENTIAL TOOLS FOR BREAST CANCER SCREENING. *Current Pos:* RES SCIENTIST, WADSWORTH CTR, NY STATE DEPT HEALTH, 96- *Personal Data:* b Chengdu, China, Apr 27, 61; m, Jianguo Wang; c Richard & Angela. *Educ:* Sichuan Univ, China, Bs, 82; State Univ NY, Albany, PhD(molecular biol), 92. *Honors & Awards:* Travel Award, Chinese Acad Sci, 93; Upjohn/Pharmacia travel award, 96. *Prof Exp:* Res affil, Health Res Inc, 92-96. *Mem:* Am Asn Cancer Res. *Res:* Studies of the gene of r-glutamyl hydrolase and its role in acquired drug resistance and as a serum marker for breast cancer progression and metastasis; glutamly hydrolase transfection to examine overexpression of glutamyl hydrolase on methotrexate resistance status; glutamyl hydrolase protein structure evaluation. *Mailing Add:* Wadsworth Ctr Empire State Plaza Albany NY 12201-0509. *Fax:* 518-473-2900; *E-Mail:* yaor@wadsworth.org

**YAO, SHANG JEONG,** CHEMICAL PHYSICS, BIOMEDICAL SCIENCES. *Current Pos:* asst prof neurosurg & chem, Sch Med, Univ Pittsburgh, 71-79, res assoc prof, 79-87, res prof neurol surg, 87-92, RES PROF SURG & RES CHEMIST, SCH MED, UNIV PITTSBURGH, 92- *Personal Data:* b Canton, China, June 6, 34; US citizen; m 66, Huei Y Sun; c Gene J. *Educ:* Univ Ore, MA, 61; Univ Minn, Minneapolis, PhD chem, 66. *Prof Exp:* Asst prof phys sci, Wilbur Wright Col, Chicago City Col, 68-69; assoc surg res, Michael Reese Hosp & Med Ctr, Chicago, 69-71. *Concurrent Pos:* Robert A Welch Found fel theoret chem, Tex A&M Univ, 66-67; fel, Northwestern Univ, Evanston, 67-68; instr, Univ Chicago, 70-71; sr res scientist, Montefiore Univ Hosp, Pittsburgh, Pa, 71-94; prin investr, John A Hartford Found grant, 77-80 & NIH, 79-89 & 96-, Juv Diabetes Found Int, 89-91; mem var study sect, NIH, 87; distinguished lect & Lingan prof chem, Sun Yatsen Univ, China, 88; vis prof chem, Peking Univ, Beijing, China, 85, Nanjing Univ, China, 88, Fudan Univ, Shanghai, China, 88. *Mem:* Am Phys Soc; Am Soc Artificial Internal Organs; Soc Neurosci; Sigma Xi. *Res:* Irreversible thermodynamics; bioenergetics; quantum theory of enzyme specificity and theory of catalyst facilitated tunneling; implantable energy sources; electrochemical urea removal for hemodialysis; electrochemical sensors; biochemistry of the aging process. *Mailing Add:* 1695 Hastings Mill Rd Pittsburgh PA 15241

**YAO, SHI CHUNE,** HEAT TRANSFER, NUCLEAR ENGINEERING. *Current Pos:* from asst prof to assoc prof, 77-83, PROF MECH ENG, CARNEGIE-MELLON UNIV, 83- *Personal Data:* b Taiwan, Dec 31, 46; c 2. *Educ:* Nat Tsing Univ, Taiwan, BS, 68; Univ Calif, Berkeley, MS, 71, PhD(nuclear eng), 74. *Prof Exp:* Engr, Argonne Nat Lab, 74-77. *Concurrent Pos:* Consult, Nuclear Ctr & Steam Turbine Div, Westinghouse Elec Co, 78-, Cooling of Electronic Equip, IT&T, 85-86, USX, 87-88, Alcoa, 90-91, Dept Energy, 92-93 & USC, 93-95. *Mem:* Fel Am Soc Mech Engrs; Combustion Inst; Am Inst Chem Engrs. *Res:* Two phase flow and heat transfer; droplet flow; particle flow; cooling of electronic equipment; nuclear reactor thermal hydraulics; rod bundles; spray combustion; continuous castings. *Mailing Add:* Dept Mech Eng Carnegie-Mellon Univ Pittsburgh PA 15213. *Fax:* 412-268-3348; *E-Mail:* scyao@cmu.edu

**YAO, YORK-PENG EDWARD,** THEORETICAL HIGH ENERGY PHYSICS. *Current Pos:* asst prof physics, 66-72, assoc prof, 72-78, PROF PHYSICS, UNIV MICH, ANN ARBOR, 78- *Personal Data:* b Canton, China, Sept 11, 37; m 65; c 4. *Educ:* Univ Calif, Berkeley, BS, 60; Harvard Univ, MA, 63, PhD(physics), 64. *Prof Exp:* Assoc mem natural sci, Inst Advan Study, 64-66. *Mem:* Fel Am Phys Soc. *Res:* Quantum field theory; elementary particle physics. *Mailing Add:* Dept Physics Univ Mich Ann Arbor MI 48109

**YAO, ZEMIN,** LIPOPROTEIN METABOLISM & DISORDERS, PROTEIN FOLDING & ASSEMBLY. *Current Pos:* asst prof, 94-95, STAFF SCIENTIST, HEART INST, UNIV OTTAWA, 94-, ASSOC PROF, 95- *Personal Data:* b Shanghai, Aug 9, 52; Can citizen; m 83, Youjun Wang; c Edmund L. *Educ:* E China Normal Univ, BSc, 82; Univ BC, MSc, 85, PhD(biochem), 88. *Honors & Awards:* Irvine H Page Award, Am Heart Asn, 93. *Prof Exp:* Postdoctoral fel, Univ Alta, 88, asst prof, 91-94; postdoctoral fel, Univ Calif, San Francisco, 88-91. *Concurrent Pos:* Staff res investr, Gladstone Inst, Univ Calif, San Francisco, 91; McDonald scholar, Heart & Stroke Found Can, 93. *Mem:* AAAS; Am Soc Biochem & Molecular Biol; Am Heart Asn; Can Soc Biochem & Molecular Biol. *Res:* Pathological and physiological aspects of human lipoprotein metabolism; biosynthesis and catabolism of lipoproteins and their interaction with cell surface receptors. *Mailing Add:* Lipoprotein & Atherosclerosis Res Group Ottawa Heart Inst 1053 Carling Ave Ottawa ON K1Y 4E9 Can. *Fax:* 613-761-5281; *E-Mail:* zyao@heartinst.on.ca

**YAP, FUNG YEN,** ATMOSPHERIC SCIENCE, MARINE SCIENCE. *Current Pos:* mem tech staff, Comput Sci Corp, 76-77, sr mem, 77-78, tech mgr, 78-80, SR SCIENTIST, COMPUT SCI CORP, 80- *Personal Data:* b Jamaica, WI, Oct 12, 33. *Educ:* Brandeis Univ, BA, 58; Johns Hopkins Univ, PhD(physics), 67. *Prof Exp:* Asst prof physics, Wilson Col, 66-74, chmn dept, 72-74; sr digital programmer, Comput Sci Technicolor Assocs, 74-76. *Concurrent Pos:* Proj dir, NSF Award for Purchase of Instnl Sci Equip for Physics Dept, Wilson Col, 68-70. *Mem:* Sigma Xi; Am Phys Soc; Am Asn Physics Teachers. *Res:* Satellite navigation and remote sensing; atmospheric modelling; ozone modelling; solar ultraviolet flux determination by satellites; determination of temperature and humidity for storm prediction from satellite sounding measurements; determination of nuclear decay schemes; environmental pollution; artificial satellite image navigation; satellite remote sensing of ocean color. *Mailing Add:* 11032 Firethorn Dr Cupertino CA 95014-0444

**YAP, WILLIAM TAN,** PHYSICAL CHEMISTRY. *Current Pos:* RES CHEMIST, NAT INST STANDARDS & TECHNOL, 72- *Personal Data:* b Amoy, China, Aug 10, 34; US citizen; m 69; Lun Chiao; c Elizabeth & Priscilla. *Educ:* Mass Inst Technol, BS, 56, MS, 58, PhD(phys chem), 64. *Prof Exp:* Res chemist, Res Ctr, Hercules, Inc, 64-69; vis assoc biophys chem, NIH, 69-71. *Res:* Biophysical chemistry; solution properties of proteins and other macromolecules; electroanalytical chemistry. *Mailing Add:* 6204 Mori St McLean VA 22101

**YAPA, POOJITHA DAHANAYAKE,** CIVIL & ENVIRONMENTAL ENGINEERING. *Current Pos:* Res asst civil & environ eng, Clarkson Univ, 80-83, res asst prof, 83-86, asst prof, 86-92, ASSOC PROF CIVIL & ENVIRON ENG, CLARKSON UNIV, 92- *Personal Data:* b Colombo, Sri Lanka, Dec 10, 52; US citizen. *Educ:* Univ Sri Lanka, BEng (Hon), 76; Asian Inst Technol, MEng, 79; Clarkson Univ, PhD(fluid mech-civil eng), 83. *Concurrent Pos:* Chair, Task Comt & Oil Spill Modelling, Hydraulics Div, Am Soc Civil Engrs, 91-94, Environ Hydraul Comt; vis scientist, Nat Inst Resources & Environ, 92; vis res prof, Sci Univ Tokyo, 92-93. *Mem:* Am Soc Civil Engrs; Can Soc Civil Engrs; Int Asn Hydraul Res. *Res:* Mathematical modeling of oil and chemical spills; fundamentals of oil spreading phenomena; transport processes; computer graphics. *Mailing Add:* Civil & Environ Eng Clarkson Univ Potsdam NY 13699-5710. *Fax:* 315-268-7985; *E-Mail:* pdy@sun.soe.clarkson.edu

**YAPEL, ANTHONY FRANCIS, JR,** DRUG DELIVERY SYSTEMS, BIOMATERIALS. *Current Pos:* Sr res chemist, Minn Mining & Mfg Co, 66-71, res specialist, 71-75, sr res specialist, 75-78, mgr biokinetics res, 78-81, mgr, 81-86, lab mgr, biomat res, 86-88, LAB MGR, DRUG DELIVERY/EXPLORATORY RES, MINN MINING & MFG CO, 88- *Personal Data:* b Soudan, Minn, Aug 14, 37; m 60; c 3. *Educ:* St John's Univ, Minn, BA, 59; Univ Minn, Minneapolis, PhD(phys chem), 67. *Concurrent Pos:* Mem bd dir, Univ Minn Inst Technol Alumni Asn, 75-, vpres, 77-78, pres, 78-79; mem bd dir, St John's Univ Alumni Asn, 78-81, vpres, 80-81. *Mem:* Am Chem Soc; AAAS. *Res:* Fast reaction, temperature-jump relaxation and enzyme kinetics; physical chemistry of membranes; reverse osmosis phenomena; structure-activity correlations on biological systems; column chromatography; drug delivery systems; wound management studies; biomaterials; transdermal drug delivery; pulmonary-aerosol drug delivery. *Mailing Add:* 1935 Hythe St St Paul MN 55113-5336

**YAQUB, ADIL MOHAMED,** ALGEBRA. *Current Pos:* assoc prof, 60-67, PROF MATH, UNIV CALIF, SANTA BARBARA, 67- *Personal Data:* b Jordan, Jan 19, 28; nat US; m 51, Nancy Shiddell; c Charles & Hanah. *Educ:* Univ Calif, AB, 50, MA, 51, PhD(math), 55. *Prof Exp:* from instr to asst prof math, Purdue Univ, 55-60. *Mem:* Am Math Soc; Math Asn Am. *Res:* Algebraic structures; ring theory; number theory. *Mailing Add:* Dept Math Univ Calif Santa Barbara CA 93106. *Fax:* 805-893-2385

**YAQUB, JILL COURTANEY DONALDSON SPENCER,** GEOMETRY. *Current Pos:* RETIRED. *Personal Data:* b Almondsbury, Eng, Dec 17, 31; m 59. *Educ:* Oxford Univ, BA, 53, MA, 57, PhD(math), 60. *Prof Exp:* Asst lectr math, Royal Holloway Col, Univ London, 56-59; instr, Wash Univ, 60-61; asst prof, Tufts Univ, 61-63; from asst to prof math, Ohio State Univ, 75-83. *Concurrent Pos:* Alexander von Humboldt fel, 70-71 & 80-81. *Mem:* Am Math Soc. *Res:* Non-Desarguesian planes, inversive planes and their automorphism groups. *Mailing Add:* 4922 Olentangy Blvd Columbus OH 43214-2046

**YARAMANOGLU, MELIH,** MATHEMATICAL WATERSHED MODELING. *Current Pos:* DEPT HEAD & PROJ ENGR, TRANSP SYSTS DIV, ENG & ECON RES INC, 84- *Personal Data:* b Istanbul, Turkey, July 20, 47; m 73. *Educ:* Middle East Tech Univ, BS, 71, MS, 73; Univ Md, PhD(agr eng), 78. *Prof Exp:* Res assoc, Dept Agr Eng, Univ Md, 78-80, asst prof hydrol, 80-84. *Concurrent Pos:* Consult, Photovoltaic Systs Simulation & Design. *Mem:* Am Soc Agr Eng; Soc Comput Simulation. *Res:* Mathematical modeling of watersheds; hydrology; water quality; structured systems analysis; air traffic control software design. *Mailing Add:* 9200 Edwards Way Hyattsville MD 20783

**YARAR, BAKI,** HYDROMETALLURGY, PLASTICS RECYCLING. *Current Pos:* assoc prof, 80-86, PROF METALL ENG, COLO SCH MINES, 86- *Personal Data:* b Adana, Turkey, Feb 28, 41; US citizen; m 71; c 2. *Educ:* Mid E Tech Univ, Ankara, BSc, 65, MSc, 66; Univ London, Eng, PhD(phys chem) & DIC, 69. *Honors & Awards:* Cert Recognition, Metall Soc, 86; Serv Recognition Cert, Eng Found, 82 & 84; Recognition Cert Outstanding Contrib NATO Advan Study Inst, 84; Cert Outstanding Serv, Int Precious Metals Inst, 93. *Prof Exp:* From instr to assoc prof chem, Mid E Tech Univ, Ankara, 70-79; vis prof mineral technol, Univ BC, Vancouver, 79-80. *Concurrent Pos:* Consult, nat & int govt & indust, 80-; vis prof, Concepcion Univ & La Serena Univ, Chile, 85-; chmn, MPD Fundamentals Comt, Soc Mining Engrs, 89-90. *Mem:* Am Chem Soc; Soc Mining Engrs; Mat Res Soc; Sigma Xi. *Res:* Applied surface chemistry; extractive metallurgy; flotation; flocculation and gold processing; high temperature superconductor processing; author of over 120 technical publications and co-author or editor of 4 books; mineral processing; materials science; awarded one patent. *Mailing Add:* 13260 Braun Rd Colo Sch Mines Golden CO 80401-1643. *Fax:* 303-273-3795

**YARBOROUGH, LYMAN,** PHASE EQUILBRIA, NATURAL GAS PROCESSING. *Current Pos:* mgr process develop, Amoco Can Petrol Co, Calgary, 88-92, RES DIR, AMOCO PROD CO, TULSA, 92- *Personal Data:* b Cushing, Okla, Feb 13, 37; m 61, Peggy J Hammer; c Alan J. *Educ:* Okla State Univ, BS, 59, MS, 61, PhD(chem eng), 64. *Prof Exp:* Staff res engr, Amoco Prod Co, Chicago, 64-76, res supvr, Tulsa, 76-78, plant eng supvr, 78-81, mgr process eng, Chicago, 81-82 & Houston, 82-88. *Mem:* Am Inst Chem Engrs; Am Chem Soc; Soc Petrol Engrs. *Res:* Thermodynamics and phase behavior of fluids; hydrocarbons and mixtures of hydrocarbons; natural gas processing plant design. *Mailing Add:* 3158 E 38th Pl Tulsa OK 74105

**YARBOROUGH, WILLIAM WALTER, JR,** PLASMA PHYSICS. *Current Pos:* From asst to assoc prof, 74-88, chmn dept, 79-92, PROF PHYSICS, PRESBY COL, 88-, COORDR ACAD COMPUT, 94- *Personal Data:* b Tylertown, Miss, Jan 6, 45; m 68. *Educ:* Univ Chattanooga, AB, 67; Vanderbilt Univ, PhD(physics), 74. *Mem:* Am Asn Physics Teachers; Am Inst Physics. *Res:* Low energy theta pinch devices, particularly losses from such devices. *Mailing Add:* 300 Calvert Ave Clinton SC 29325. *E-Mail:* blyarb@cs1.presby.edu

**YARBRO, CLAUDE LEE, JR,** ECOLOGY. *Current Pos:* biologist, Biol Br, Res & Develop Div, US AEC, US Dept Energy, 60-67, biol scientist, Res Contracts Br, Lab & Univ Div, 67-72, biol scientist, Res & Develop Admin, 72-76, life scientist, Oak Ridge Opers, 76-84, SCIENTIST II, OAK RIDGE ASSOC UNIVS, 87- *Personal Data:* b Jackson, Tenn, Sept 26, 22; m 51, Mary C Frazier; c Laura, Elizabeth & David. *Educ:* Lambuth Col, BA, 43; Univ NC, PhD(biochem), 54. *Prof Exp:* Actg prof math & physics, Lambuth Col, 46-47; instr physics, Union Col, Tenn, 48; instr biochem, Vanderbilt Univ, 49-51; asst, Univ NC, 51-54, res assoc, 54-57, instr, 54-60. *Concurrent Pos:* Consult, Environ Sci, Waste Mgt, Educ & Training, 84- *Mem:* Ecol Soc Am; AAAS; fel Am Inst Chemists; Sigma Xi; Am Forestry Asn. *Res:* Phospholipid chemistry and metabolism; mechanism of renal calculus; formation and physical chemistry of calcium phosphate; ecological succession on sandstone bluffs. *Mailing Add:* 147 Alger Rd Oak Ridge TN 37830

**YARBRO, JOHN WILLIAMSON,** INTERNAL MEDICINE, MEDICAL ONCOLOGY. *Current Pos:* PROF MED, UNIV MO, 75- *Personal Data:* b Chattanooga, Tenn, Sept 15, 31; m 79. *Educ:* Univ Louisville, BA, 52, MD, 56; Univ Minn, PhD(biochem), 65. *Prof Exp:* Asst prof med, Univ Minn, 65-68; assoc prof, Univ Ky, 68-70, Univ Pa, 70-73; dir cancer ctrs prog, Nat Cancer Inst, 73-75. *Mem:* Am Col Physicians; Am Soc Hemat; Asn Community Cancer Ctrs (pres, 85-86); Am Soc Clin Oncol (secy-treas, 88). *Res:* Efficacy and mechanisms of drugs used in the treatment of malignant diseases. *Mailing Add:* 2604 Luan Ct Columbia MO 65203-1425

**YARBROUGH, CHARLES GERALD,** ZOOLOGY. *Current Pos:* VPRES ACAD AFFAIRS, PEACE COL, 93- *Personal Data:* b Lumberton, NC, Oct 13, 39; m 60; c 2. *Educ:* Wake Forest Univ, BS, 61, MA, 63; Univ Fla, PhD(zool), 70. *Prof Exp:* From instr to asst prof biol, Campbell Col, 64-75, assoc prof, 75-80; prof biol & chmn, Div Sci & Math, Wingate Col, 80-85, asst dean & prof biol, 85-91. *Concurrent Pos:* Chapman res grant, Am Mus Natural Hist, 64; AEC proj ecol researcher, Battelle Mem Inst, 68; prin investr, NC Bd Sci & Technol, 71-72 & US Dept Interior Endangered Species Prog, 78-82; vis grad prof, Univ Va, 75. *Mem:* Am Ornith Union; Cooper Ornith Soc; Sigma Xi; Ecol Soc Am. *Res:* Influence of physical factors, nutrients and heavy metals on biotic communities; metabolism and temperature regulation in vertebrates; ecological implications of energetics in animals. *Mailing Add:* Acad Affairs Peace Col 15 E Peace St Raleigh NC 27604-1176

**YARBROUGH, DAVID WYLIE,** THERMODYNAMICS & HEAT TRANSFER, THERMAL INSULATION. *Current Pos:* From asst prof to assoc prof, Tenn Technol Univ, 68-76, assoc dean, Grad Studies & Res, 76-79, prof chem eng, 76-87, PROF CHEM ENG & CHMN, TENN TECHNOL UNIV, 87- *Personal Data:* b Long Beach, Calif, May, 7, 37. *Educ:* Ga Inst Technol, BChE, 60, MS, 61, PhD(chem eng), 66. *Honors & Awards:* Univ Res Award, 86; Award of Appreciation, Am Soc Testing & Mats, 92. *Prof Exp:* 1st Lt & Capt, Active Duty US Army Sig Corp, 66-68. *Concurrent Pos:* Mem res staff, Oak Ridge Nat Lab, 79-80, adj res participant, 80-; gov bd, Int Thermal Conductivity Conf; fel, Int Thermal Conductivity Conf, 87, chmn 19th Conf, 86. *Mem:* Am Inst Chem Engrs; Sigma Xi; Am Soc Testing & Mats; NY Acad Sci. *Res:* Thermodynamics; physical properties; applied mathematics; energy conservation. *Mailing Add:* Tenn Technol Univ Stadium Dr Prescott Hall Rm 214 Cookeville TN 38505. *Fax:* 615-372-6172

**YARBROUGH, GEORGE GIBBS,** NEUROPHARMACOLOGY, PHARMACOLOGY. *Current Pos:* vpres, 84-86, SR VPRES, PHARMACOL DIV, PANLABS, INC, 86- *Personal Data:* b Houston, Tex, Jan 20, 43; m 64; c 2. *Educ:* Univ Houston, BS, 68; Vanderbilt Univ, PhD(pharmacol), 72. *Prof Exp:* Fel physiol, Univ Man, 72-73; from lectr to asst prof, Univ Sask, 73-75; res fel, Merck Inst Therapeut Res, 75-80, sr res fel neuropsychopharmacol, 80-83, sr res fel, 83-84. *Concurrent Pos:* Med Res Coun Can scholar, Univ Sask, 74-75. *Mem:* Am Soc Pharmacol & Exp Therapeut; Soc Neurosci; Am Chem Soc. *Res:* Physiology and pharmacology of synaptic transmission in the mammalian central nervous system. *Mailing Add:* 11804 N Creek Pkwy S Bothell WA 98011-8890. *Fax:* 425-487-3787

**YARBROUGH, JAMES DAVID,** ANIMAL PHYSIOLOGY, TOXICOLOGY. *Current Pos:* DEAN, COL ARTS & SCI, UNIV ALA, 89- *Personal Data:* b Stockton, Mo, Jan 15, 33; m 54, Donjett; c 3. *Educ:* Huntingdon Col, AB, 60; Univ Ala, MS, 61, PhD(biol), 64. *Prof Exp:* Asst prof biol, Univ Ala, 64-68; from assoc to prof zool, Miss State Univ, 68-78, head, Dept Biol Sci, 78-84, distinguished prof biol sci, 78-87; prof & head physiol, Univ Mo-Kansas City 87-89. *Mem:* Am Physiol Soc; Am Soc Pharmacol & Exp Therapeut; Am Soc Cell Biol; Sigma Xi; Am Soc Biochem & Molecular Biol. *Res:* Cytotoxcity of insecticides, mechanisms of vertebrate insecticide resistance, adaptive liver growth as induced by xenobiotics. *Mailing Add:* Col Arts & Sci Univ Ala Tuscaloosa AL 35487-0268

**YARBROUGH, KAREN MARGUERITE,** GENETICS, MICROBIOLOGY. *Current Pos:* Asst prof biol, Univ Southern Miss, 67-70, assoc prof microbiol, 70-81, prof & actg vpres acad affairs, 81-82, dir, Inst Genetics, 72-82, vpres, Res & Extended Serv, 82-90, PROF BIOL SCI, UNIV SOUTHERN MISS, 76-, VPRES RES & PLANNING, 90- *Personal Data:* b Memphis, Tenn, Mar 4, 38. *Educ:* Miss State Univ, BS, 61, MS, 63; NC State Univ, PhD(genetics), 67. *Concurrent Pos:* Assoc prof biol, Univ Southern Miss, 70-71, asst dean & res coordr, Col Sci & Technol, 76-81. *Mem:* Genetics Soc Am; Am Genetic Asn; Sigma Xi; NY Acad Sci; Am Soc Human Genetics; Am Dermatoglyphic Asn. *Res:* Population genetics; human genetics; dermatoglyphics; zoology. *Mailing Add:* PO Box 5116 Univ Southern Miss Hattiesburg MS 39406-0002

**YARBROUGH, LYNN DOUGLAS,** computer science, for more information see previous edition

**YARBROUGH, LYNWOOD R,** BIOCHEMISTRY, BIOPHYSICS. *Personal Data:* b Cherokee, Ala, July 26, 40; m 75. *Educ:* Univ Northwestern Ala, BS, 65; Purdue Univ, PhD(biochem, molecular biol), 71. *Prof Exp:* Res assoc molecular biol, Albert Einstein Col Med, 71-73, res assoc biophys, 73-75; from asst prof to prof biochem, Med Ctr, Univ Kans, 75-93. *Concurrent Pos:* Damon Runyon Found res fel, 72-74. *Mem:* Biophys Soc; Am Chem Soc; Sigma Xi; Am Soc Cell Biol; Am Soc Biochem & Molecular Biol; Am Soc Microbiol. *Res:* Tubulin structure and function; assembly of subunit proteins; cardiac stress responses and aging. *Mailing Add:* Dept Biochem & Molecular Biol Univ Kans Med Ctr 39th & Rainbow Blvd Kansas City KS 66160-7421

**YARCHOAN, ROBERT,** ACQUIRED IMMUNE DEFICIENCY SYNDROME, RETROVIRUSES. *Current Pos:* clin assoc, Metab Br, Nat Cancer Inst, NIH, 78-81, investr, 81-84, investr, Clin Oncol Prog, 84-88, sr investr, 88-89, chief, Retroviral Dis Sect, Med Br, 90-96, CHIEF, HIV & AIDS MALIGNANCY BR, NAT CANCER INST, NIH, 96- *Personal Data:* b New York, NY, July 21, 50; m 81, Giovanna Tosato; c Mark & John. *Educ:* Amherst Col, BA, 71; Univ Pa, MD, 75. *Honors & Awards:* Inventor's Award, US Dept Com, 86 & 87; Pub Health Serv Commendation Medal, 89, 92. *Prof Exp:* Resident med, Univ Minn Hosps, 75-78. *Concurrent Pos:* Assoc ed, J Immunol, 86-89, Acquired Immune Deficiency Syndrome Res & Human Retroviruses, 87-, Acquired Immune Deficiency Sydrome, 90- *Mem:* Am Asn Immunol; Am Fedn Clin Res; fel AAAS; Clin Immunol Soc; Am Soc Clin Invest; Int Aquired Immune Deficiency Sydrome Soc. *Res:* Immunodeficiency diseases, particularly AIDS; interactions between viruses & the immune system; AIDS-related malignancies. *Mailing Add:* Bldg 10 Rm 12N226 NIH Bethesda MD 20892. *Fax:* 301-402-3645; *E-Mail:* yarchoan@helix.nih.gov

**YARD, ALLAN STANLEY,** PHARMACOLOGY. *Current Pos:* DIR, DRUG REGULATORY AFFAIRS, BERLEX LABS INC, 84- *Personal Data:* b Rocktown, NJ, Nov 18, 27; m 57; c 2. *Educ:* Rutgers Univ, BS, 52; Med Col Va, PhD(pharmacol, biochem), 56. *Prof Exp:* Asst prof pharmacol, Rutgers Univ, 55-56; asst prof, Med Col Va, 56-60; sr scientist, Ortho Res Found, 60-63, Ortho res fel, 63-67; group chief, Hoffmann-LaRoche, 67-73, dir acad & govt liaison, 73-75, asst dir, Drug Regulatory Affairs, 75-84. *Concurrent Pos:* Mem co-adj fac, Rutgers Univ, 63- *Mem:* AAAS; Am Soc Pharmacol & Exp Therapeut; Soc Study Reproduction; Am Chem Soc; NY Acad Sci. *Res:* Drug metabolism; effect of drugs on liver metabolism; synthesis of hydrazino compounds; biochemistry and pharmacology of the oviduct, uterus and fertility control agents. *Mailing Add:* Med & Regulatory Affairs 324 Moss Creek Dr Hilton Head SC 29926

**YARDLEY, DARRELL GENE,** POPULATION GENETICS. *Current Pos:* Asst prof, 75-80, ASSOC PROF ZOOL, CLEMSON UNIV, 80- *Personal Data:* b Gorman, Tex, Apr 15, 48; m 72; c 3. *Educ:* Univ Tex, Austin, BA, 71, MA, 72; Univ Ga, PhD(zool), 75. *Concurrent Pos:* Vis assoc prof cell biol, Baylor Col Med, Houston, Tex. *Mem:* Genetics Soc Am; Soc Study Evolution. *Res:* Molecular and biochemical evolutionary genetics of fishes. *Mailing Add:* Dept Biol Sci Clemson Univ Clemson SC 29634-0001

**YARDLEY, DONALD H,** MINING ENGINEERING. *Current Pos:* RETIRED. *Personal Data:* b Estevan, Sask, Sept 9, 17; m 42. *Educ:* Queen's Univ, Ont, BSc, 41 & 46, MSc, 47; Univ Minn, PhD(geol), 51. *Prof Exp:* Asst to chief engr, Hardrock Gold Mines, 41-42; field engr, Andowan Mines, 45-46; party chief, Can Geol Surv, 47-48; asst mining, Univ Minn, St Paul, 47-49, from instr to assoc prof, 49-77; prof civil & mining eng, Univ Minn, Minneapolis, 77- *Res:* Geochemical exploration; heavy metals; geological engineering; economic geology. *Mailing Add:* 2107 Fairways Lane St Paul MN 55113

**YARDLEY, JAMES THOMAS, III,** PHYSICAL CHEMISTRY. *Current Pos:* sr chem physicist, Allied Corp, 77-80, sr res assoc, 80-82, res mgr, 82-85, ASSOC DIR, ALLIED CORP, 85-, TECH DIR, 96- *Personal Data:* b Taft, Calif, May 15, 42; m 66, 76, Anne Bagnall; c William, Margaret & Jonathan. *Educ:* Rice Univ, BA, 64; Univ Calif, Berkeley, PhD(chem), 67. *Prof Exp:* From asst prof to assoc prof chem, Univ Ill, Urbana, 67-77. *Concurrent Pos:* Dreyfus Found teacher-scholar award, 70-75; Alfred P Sloan fel, 72-73. *Mem:* Am Phys Soc; Am Chem Soc. *Res:* Molecular spectroscopy; vibrational energy transfer; molecular lasers; molecular dynamics. *Mailing Add:* Engineered Mat Res PO Box 1021R Morristown NJ 07960-4695

**YARDLEY, JOHN FINLEY,** AERONAUTICAL ENGINEERING. *Current Pos:* RETIRED. *Personal Data:* b St Louis, Mo, Feb 1, 25; m 46, Phyllis Steele; c Kathryn, Robert, Susan, Mary & Elizabeth. *Educ:* Iowa State Univ, BS, 44; Wash Univ, MS, 50. *Honors & Awards:* Inst Aerospace Sci Achievement Award, 61; John J Montgomery Award, 63; Spirit of St Louis Award, Am Soc Mech Engrs, 73; Am Astronaut Space Flight Award, 78; Goddard Award Trophy, 83; Elmer A Sperry Award, 86; Von Karman Astronaut Lectureship Award, 88. *Prof Exp:* Stress analyst aircraft design, McDonnell Aircraft Corp, 46-48, strength group engr, 48-51, proj stress engr, 51-54, chief strength engr, 54-58, proj engr Mercury capsule design, 58-60, base mgr spacecraft flight testing, Cape Canaveral, 60-64, Gemini Prog tech dir, 64-66, tech dir, 66-68, vpres & dep gen mgr, Eastern Div, McDonnell-Douglas Astronaut Co, 68-72, gen mgr, Eastern Div, 73-74; assoc adminr, Manned Space Flight, NASA, 74-76, Space Flight, 76-78, Space Transp Syst, 78-81; pres, McDonnell-Douglas Astronaut, 81-88, sr corp vpres, 88-89. *Mem:* Nat Acad Eng; Am Inst Aeronaut & Astronaut; Am Astronaut Soc; Int Acad Astronaut. *Res:* Applied mechanics; integration of advanced systems into space vehicles. *Mailing Add:* 14319 Cross Timbers Ct Chesterfield MO 63017-5718. *Fax:* 314-878-4319; *E-Mail:* jfyardley@aol.com

**YARDLEY, JOHN HOWARD,** PATHOLOGY. *Current Pos:* from instr to assoc prof, 54-72, assoc dean acad affairs, 77-84, PROF PATH, SCH MED, JOHNS HOPKINS UNIV, 72- *Personal Data:* b Columbia, SC, June 7, 26; m 52; c 3. *Educ:* Birmingham-Southern Col, AB, 49; Johns Hopkins Univ, MD, 53; Am Bd Path, dipl, 59. *Prof Exp:* Intern internal med, Vanderbilt Univ Hosp, 53-54. *Concurrent Pos:* From asst resident to resident, Johns Hopkins Hosp, 54-58. *Mem:* Am Asn Path & Bact; Int Acad Path; Am Soc Exp Path; Am Gastroenterol Asn. *Res:* Gastrointestinal diseases; electron microscopy. *Mailing Add:* Dept Path Johns Hopkins Hosp 632 Ross Res Bldg 720 Rutland Ave Baltimore MD 21205-2196. *Fax:* 410-614-0671

**YARGER, DOUGLAS NEAL,** ATMOSPHERIC PHYSICS, METEOROLOGY. *Current Pos:* Asst prof, 67-71, assoc prof meteorol & climatol, 71-80, PROF METEOROL & AGRON, IOWA STATE UNIV, 80- *Personal Data:* b Omaha, Nebr, July 13, 37; m 60; c 4. *Educ:* Iowa State Univ, BS, 59; Univ Ariz, MS, 62, PhD(meteorol), 67. *Mem:* Am Meteorol Soc; Optical Soc Am. *Res:* Radiative transfer in the atmosphere; physical meteorology. *Mailing Add:* 1612 Woodhaven Circle Ames IA 50010

**YARGER, FREDERICK LYNN,** PHYSICS OF HIGH PRESSURES, LASER ELECTRO OPTICS. *Current Pos:* from assoc prof to prof, 66-87, EMER PROF PHYSICS, NMEX HIGHLANDS UNIV, 87- *Personal Data:* b Lindsey, Ohio, Mar 8, 25; m 48, Mary Petersen; c Frederick D & Peter D. *Educ:* Capital Univ, BSc, 50; Ohio State Univ, MSc, 53, PhD(physics), 60. *Prof Exp:* Res asst physics, Los Alamos Sci Lab, 52, mem staff, 53-55 & 56; sr engr, Columbus Div, NAm Aviation Inc, Ohio, 56-58; res asst physics, Ohio State Univ, 58-60; supvry physicist, Nat Bur Stand, Colo, 60-64; sci specialist, Edgerton, Germeshausen & Grier, Inc, Nev, 64-65; sr res physicist, Falcon Res & Develop Co, Colo, 65-66. *Concurrent Pos:* Vis staff mem, Los Alamos Sci Lab, 74-92; vis prof, Nat Univ Mex, 68- *Mem:* Am Phys Soc; Optical Soc Am; Sigma Xi; Mex Phys Soc. *Res:* High pressure equations of state of liquids and solids using X-ray diffraction and spectroscopic techniques; biomedical instrumentation development; shock compression of materials; equations of state. *Mailing Add:* Dept Physics NMex Highlands Univ Las Vegas NM 87701. *Fax:* 505-454-3103

**YARGER, HAROLD LEE,** EXPLORATION GEOPHYSICS. *Current Pos:* STAFF GEOPHYS, CHEVRON, 86- *Personal Data:* b Ypsilanti, Mich, Mar 15, 40; m 65, Linda Bleeker; c 3. *Educ:* Antioch Col, BS, 62; State Univ NY Stony Brook, MA, 65, PhD(physics), 68. *Prof Exp:* Instr physics, State Univ NY Stony Brook, 67-68; res assoc, Northwestern Univ, 68-69; res assoc, Kans Geol Surv, Univ Kans, 69-70, res assoc geophys, 70-77, assoc scientist, 77-84, adj assoc prof physics & geol, 78-86, sr geophys scientist, 84-86, adj prof physics & geol, 84-86. *Concurrent Pos:* Res contracts, NASA, 72-74 & 73-75, US Geol Surv, 74-76, 78-79 & 83-85, Ark Geol Comn, 79-81 & 3D Gravity, Inc, 83-84. *Mem:* Am Asn Petrol Geologists; Am Geophys Union; Soc Explor Geophys. *Res:* Gravity and magnetics; remote sensing; airplane and satellite imagery for exploration and management of earth resources; high energy physics; bubble chamber work. *Mailing Add:* Chevron 1301 McKinney Houston TX 77010. *Fax:* 713-754-2016; *E-Mail:* hhlya@chovron.com

**YARGER, JAMES G,** GENETIC & METABOLIC ENGINEERING, FOOD & DRUG ADMINISTRATION PETITIONS. *Current Pos:* regulatory affairs officer, 93-95, DIR QUAL CONTROL & REGULATORY AFFAIRS, CAMBRIDGE CHEM, 96; PRES & FOUNDER CEDARBURG LABS, 97- *Personal Data:* b Waverly, Iowa, Sept 15, 51; m 74, Jeannie VanVickle; c 2. *Educ:* Univ Iowa, BA, 74; Brandeis Univ, PhD(biol), 81. *Prof Exp:* Fel, Harvard Univ, 81-83; res scientist, Miles Inc, 83-85, sr res scientist, 85-87; staff scientist, Amoco Technol Co, 87-92, task force leader, 91- *Mem:* Am Soc Qual Control; Sigma Xi; Regulatory Affairs Prof Soc; Japan Soc Biosci, Biotechnol & Agrochem. *Res:* Eukaryotic metabolic engineering; cloning and homologous-heterologous expression of genes in E coli and fungi; classical yeast genetics; industrial strain development; commercial product development; Food and Drug Administration product petition filings. *Mailing Add:* PO Box 111 Cedarburg WI 53012. *Fax:* 630-420-4897

**YARGER, WILLIAM E,** NEPHROLOGY. *Current Pos:* chief nephrology, 78-82, CHIEF MED, DURHAM VET ADMIN MED CTR, NC, 82- *Personal Data:* b Houston, Tex, Apr 1, 37; m 63; c 3. *Educ:* Tex Christian Univ, BA, 59; Baylor Univ, MD, 63. *Prof Exp:* Intern internal med, St Luke's

Hosp, NY, 63-64; resident, Baylor Affil Hosps, Houston, Tex, 64-67; lieutenant commander environ physiol, Naval Med Field Res Lab, NC, 67-69; NIH spec fel renal physiol, NY Univ, 69-71; from asst prof to assoc prof med, Duke Univ, 71-78. *Concurrent Pos:* Vchmn, Dept Med, Duke Univ, 85- *Mem:* Am Soc Clin Invest; Am Soc Nephrology; Am Phys Soc; Int Soc Nephrology. *Res:* Renal pathophysiology with particular interest in renal prostaglandins and thromboxan. *Mailing Add:* Durham Vet Admin Hosp 508 Fulton St Durham NC 27705-3897

**YARIAN, DEAN ROBERT,** ORGANIC CHEMISTRY. *Current Pos:* sr chemist, Cent Res Lab, 3M Co, St Paul, 60-65, Paper Prod Div, 65-70, chemist specialist, 70-78, mgr carbonless paper develop, Paper Prod Lab, 78-81, prod develop mgr, Telecommun Prod Div, 81-85, TECH MGR, ELEC SPECIALTIES DIV, 3M CO, AUSTIN, 85- *Personal Data:* b Warsaw, Ind, Oct 12, 33; m 54; c 7. *Educ:* DePauw Univ, BA, 55; Univ Wash, PhD(chem), 60. *Prof Exp:* Asst lectr, Univ Wash, 58-59. *Mem:* Am Chem Soc. *Res:* Organic synthesis; imaging chemistry; colloids; paper chemistry; statistics. *Mailing Add:* 106 El Reno Cove Lakeway TX 78734

**YARINGTON, CHARLES THOMAS, JR,** OTORHINOLARYNGOLOGY. *Current Pos:* head & neck surgeon & chief, Dept Otolaryngol, 78-88, chief, Dept Surg, 88-91, BD GOVS, MASON CLIN, 85-; CLIN PROF OTOLARYNGOL, UNIV WASH, 74- *Personal Data:* b Sayre, Pa, Apr 26, 34; m 63, Barbara Johnson; c 3. *Educ:* Princeton Univ, AB, 56; Hahnemann Med Col, MD, 60; Am Bd Otolaryngol, dipl, 65. *Honors & Awards:* Prof Doctor Ignacio Barraquer Mem Award, 68; Honor Award, Am Acad Ophthal & Otolaryngol, 74; Sir Henry Wellcome Prize, 84. *Prof Exp:* Rotating intern, Rochester Gen Hosp, 60-61; res gen surg, Dartmouth Med Sch Affil Hosps, 61-62; asst otolaryngol, Sch Med, Univ Rochester, 62-63, instr, 63-65; chief, Eye, Ear, Nose & Throat Serv, US Army Hosp, Ft Carson, Colo, 65-67; asst prof, Sch Med WVa Univ, 67-68; from assoc prof to prof otorhinolaryngol & chmn dept, Col Med, Univ Nebr, Omaha, 68-74. *Concurrent Pos:* Res otolaryngol, Sch Med, Univ Rochester, 62-65; consult, Colo State Hosp, 65-67 & Vet Admin Hosp, WVa, 67-68; chief, Vet Admin Hosp, Omaha & Univ Nebr Hosp, Omaha, 68-74; chief ear, nose & throat, Mason Clin & Va Mason Hosp, 74-89; consult, Surgeon Gen, USAF, 76-; bd gov, Am Acad Otolaryngol & Head & Neck Surg; clin prof surg, Uniformed Serv Univ, Bethesda, 86-; retired brig gen, USAF. *Mem:* Fel Am Col Surgeons; Am Soc Head & Neck Surgeons; Am Laryngol, Rhinol & Otol Soc; Am Laryngol Asn; Am Acad Otolaryngol; Am Broncho-Esophagolog Asn (pres, 87-88); Pac Coast Otol-Ophthal Soc (pres, 87-88). *Res:* Pathology and therapy of congenital and neoplastic defects in the head and neck; research and writing on health care reform. *Mailing Add:* Mason Clin 1100 Ninth Ave Seattle WA 98101

**YARINSKY, ALLEN,** PARASITOLOGY, CHEMOTHERAPY. *Current Pos:* CONSULT, 89- *Personal Data:* b Brooklyn, NY, May 6, 29; m 52; c 3. *Educ:* City Col New York, BS, 51; Columbia Univ, MS, 53; Univ NC, MS, 57, PhD, 61. *Prof Exp:* Med bacteriologist, Ft Detrick, Md, 54-56; res scientist, New York Dept Health, 61-65; res biologist, Sterling-Winthrop Res Inst, 66-69, head, Parasitol Dept, 69-79, dir Qual Assurance Dept, 79-89. *Concurrent Pos:* Lectr, Mem Inst Rev Bd, 89. *Mem:* Regulatory Affairs Prof Soc; Drug Info Asn. *Res:* Research on Clostridium botulinum type E toxin; immunological relationships of experimental Trichinella spirals infections; laboratory diagnosis of Protozoan and helminth infections; chemotherapy of parasitic infections; quality assurance; good clinical practices. *Mailing Add:* 53 Paxwood Rd Delmar NY 12054

**YARIS, ROBERT,** PHYSICAL CHEMISTRY. *Current Pos:* from asst prof to assoc prof chem, 64-70, PROF CHEM, WASHINGTON UNIV, 70- *Personal Data:* b New York, NY, Oct 16, 35; m 64. *Educ:* Univ Calif, Los Angeles, BS, 58; Univ Wash, PhD(phys chem), 62. *Prof Exp:* Res assoc phys chem, Univ Minn, 62-64. *Concurrent Pos:* Alfred P Sloan fel, 66- *Mem:* Am Phys Soc. *Res:* Theoretical and quantum chemistry; time-dependent perturbation theory; many body theory. *Mailing Add:* 7246 Pershing Ave No 1W St Louis MO 63130

**YARIV, A(MNON),** SEMICONDUCTOR LASERS, INTEGRATED OPTICS. *Current Pos:* prof elec eng, 66-82, Thomas G Myers prof elec eng & appl physics, 82-96, MARTIN ELAINE SUMMERFIELD PROF APPL PHYSICS & ELEC ENG, CALIF INST TECHNOL, 96- *Personal Data:* b Tel Aviv, Israel, Apr 13, 30; nat US; m 54; c 3. *Educ:* Univ Calif, Berkeley, BS, 54, MS, 56, PhD(elec eng), 59. *Honors & Awards:* Quantum Electronics Award, Inst Elec & Electronics Engrs, 80; Pender Award, 85; Ives Medal, Optical Soc Am, 86; Harvey Prize, Technion, Israel, 91. *Prof Exp:* Asst, Univ Calif, Berkeley, 55-58, res assoc, 58-59; mem tech staff, Bell Tel Labs, 59-66. *Concurrent Pos:* Indust consult; chmn bd & co-founder, Ortel Corp, Alhambra, Calif; co-founder, Accuwave Corp, Santa Monica, Calif & Arithmos Corp, Santa Clara, Calif. *Mem:* Nat Acad Sci; fel Nat Acad Eng; fel Am Optical Soc; Am Phys Soc; fel Inst Elec & Electronics Engrs; Am Asn Arts & Sci. *Res:* Lasers; nonlinear optics; optical communication; holographic optical data storage; quantum optics. *Mailing Add:* 2257 Homet Rd San Marino CA 91108-1327. *E-Mail:* ayariv@cco.caltech.edu

**YARKONY, DAVID R,** CHEMICAL PHYSICS. *Current Pos:* ASST PROF CHEM, JOHNS HOPKINS UNIV, 77- *Personal Data:* b Bronx, NY, Jan 28, 49. *Educ:* State Univ NY, Stony Brook, BA, 71; Univ Calif, Berkeley, PhD(chem), 75. *Prof Exp:* Res asst, Mass Inst Technol, 75-77. *Concurrent Pos:* Consult, Inst Comput Appln Sci & Eng, 78-79. *Mem:* Am Chem Soc. *Res:* Electronic structure theory; energy transport in solids. *Mailing Add:* Chem Dept Johns Hopkins Univ Baltimore MD 21218

**YARLAGADDA, RADHA KRISHNA RAO,** ELECTRICAL ENGINEERING. *Current Pos:* From asst prof to assoc prof, 66-78, PROF ELEC ENG, OKLA STATE UNIV, 78- *Personal Data:* b Velpucherla, India, Apr 1, 38; m 66; c 3. *Educ:* Univ Mysore, BE, 59; SDak State Univ, MS, 61; Mich State Univ, PhD(elec eng), 64. *Honors & Awards:* Premium Award, Brit Inst Elec Engrs, 66. *Concurrent Pos:* NSF res grant, 67-69; Air Force res grant, 81- *Mem:* Inst Elec & Electronics Engrs; Sigma Xi. *Res:* Digital signal processing; communication theory. *Mailing Add:* Sch Elec Eng Okla State Univ Stillwater OK 74075

**YARMOLINSKY, ADAM,** SCIENCE POLICY. *Current Pos:* prof policy sci, health care policy, nat security, 85-86, provost & vpres acad affairs, 87-93, REGENTS PROF PUB POLICY, UNIV MD, 93- *Personal Data:* b New York, NY, Nov 17, 22; m 90, Sarah Ames Ellis; c 4. *Educ:* Harvard Univ, AB, 43; Yale Univ, LLB, 48. *Prof Exp:* Prin dep asst secy defense, Dept Defense, 65-66; prof law & mem, Inst Polit, J F Kennedy Sch, Harvard Univ, 66-72; Ralph Waldo Emerson Univ prof, Univ Mass, 72-77; mem, Coun US Arms Control & Disarmament 77-79; pvt pract law, Kominers, Fort, Schlefer & Boyer, Washington, DC, 79-85. *Concurrent Pos:* Consult, Off Secy Defense, 66-68; Regional Med Prog, Mass, NH, RI, 68-70; Off Technol Assessment, 72-77; US Arms Control & Disarmament Agency, 79-80; chmn, Comt Sci & Law, Asn Bar, NY, 84-87; mem, Coun Foreign Relations, Am Law Inst. *Mem:* Inst Med-Nat Acad Sci; AAAS; Int Inst Strategic Studies; Am Law Inst; fel Am Acad Arts & Sci. *Res:* Large organization functioning; national security policy; arms control; author of numerous publications. *Mailing Add:* Univ Md 1000 Hilltop Circle Baltimore MD 21250. *Fax:* 410-455-1095

**YARMOLINSKY, MICHAEL BEZALEL,** MOLECULAR BIOLOGY. *Current Pos:* chief develop biochem & genetics sect, 84-88, CHIEF MICROBIAL GENETICS & BIOCHEM SECT, LAB BIOCHEM, NAT CANCER INST, NIH, BETHESDA, MD, 88- *Personal Data:* b New York, NY, Jan 18, 29; m 62; c 1. *Educ:* Harvard Univ, AB, 50; Johns Hopkins Univ, PhD(biol), 54. *Prof Exp:* Instr pharmacol, Col Med, NY Univ, 54-55; res assoc, McCollum-Pratt Inst, Johns Hopkins Univ, 58-61, asst prof, 61-63; res chemist, NIH, 64-70; dir res, CNRS Rech Biol Molec, Paris, 70-76; dir molecular genetics sect, Cancer Biol Prog, Frederick Cancer Res Fac, Md, 76-84. *Concurrent Pos:* NSF fel, Pasteur Inst, Paris, 63-64. *Mem:* Am Soc Biol Chemists; Am Soc Microbiol; fel AAAS. *Res:* Protein biosynthesis and its regulation; interactions between temperate bacteriophage and its host; replication control and partition of plasmids in bacteria. *Mailing Add:* Lab Biochem Nat Cancer Inst NIH Bldg 37 4D-15 Bethesda MD 20892

**YARMUSH, DAVID LEON,** APPLIED MATHEMATICS. *Current Pos:* RETIRED. *Personal Data:* b New York, NY, June 10, 28. *Educ:* Harvard Univ, BA, 49; Princeton Univ, PhD(math), 59. *Prof Exp:* Mathematician Chem & Radiation Labs, Army Chem Ctr, Md, 52-54; asst math, Princeton Univ, 54-56; mathematician, Tech Res Group, Inc, 56-67; res scientist, Courant Inst, NY Univ, 65-76; res assoc, Columbia Univ, 76-83, assoc res scientist, Dept Biol, 84-90. *Mem:* Am Math Soc. *Res:* Dynamic theory of games; radiation transport theory; structural vibrations and sound radiation; computer programming of deduction procedures; computer study of conformation of proteins. *Mailing Add:* 333 E 14th St New York NY 10003-4214

**YARMUSH, MARTIN LEON,** APPLIED IMMUNOLOGY, BIOSEPARATIONS. *Current Pos:* PROF & DEP CHMN, DEPT BIOCHEM ENG & BIOCHEM, CTR ADVAN BIOTECHNOL & MED, RUTGERS UNIV, 88- *Personal Data:* b Brooklyn, NY, Oct 8, 52; m 78, Deborah Weisfogel; c Rubin, Gabriel & Joshua. *Educ:* Yeshiva Univ, BA, 75; Rockefeller Univ, PhD(biochem & immunol), 79; Yale Univ, MD, 84. *Honors & Awards:* Pres Young Investr Award; Lucille D Markey Scholar Award; NIH Nat Res Serv Award; Hoechst-Celanese Innovative Res Award. *Prof Exp:* Res chemist biochem, NIH, 78-79; prin res assoc chem eng, Mass Inst Technol, 84-88. *Concurrent Pos:* Consult, NIH, Sepracor, Inc, Cabot Corp, Delta Biotechnol Ltd, Valio Finnish Dairy Cooperatives, E I Dupont de Nemours & Co, Inc, Ortho Diag, Union Carbide; adj asst prof, Sch Vet Med, Univ Pa, 80-83, adj assoc prof, 83-86. *Mem:* Am Chem Soc; Am Inst Chem Engrs; Am Asn Immunologists; fel Am Soc Artificial Internal Organs; AMA; fel Am Inst Med & Biol Engrs. *Res:* Applied immunology; molecular and cellular bioengineering; bioseparations; artificial organs. *Mailing Add:* Shriners Res Ctr 1 Kendall Sq Bldg 1400 Cambridge MA 02139

**YARNALL, JOHN LEE,** INVERTEBRATE ZOOLOGY, BIOLOGY. *Current Pos:* Asst prof, 69-72, assoc prof, 72-78, PROF BIOL, HUMBOLDT STATE UNIV, 78- *Personal Data:* b Elizabeth, NJ, Jan 27, 32; m 53; c 3. *Educ:* Univ Mont, BS, 53, MA, 62; Stanford Univ, PhD(biol), 72. *Mem:* AAAS; Am Soc Zoologists. *Res:* Invertebrate functional morphology and behavior, especially locomotion and feeding. *Mailing Add:* 154 Grange Rd Eureka CA 95503

**YARNELL, JOHN LEONARD,** SOLID STATE PHYSICS, NUCLEAR ENGINEERING. *Current Pos:* CONSULT, 81- *Personal Data:* b Topeka, Kans, Mar 1, 22; m 52; c 4. *Educ:* Univ Kans, AB, 47, AM, 49; Univ Minn, PhD(physics), 52. *Prof Exp:* Asst instr physics & math, Univ Kans, 47-49; asst, Univ Minn, 49-51; staff mem, Physics Div, Los Alamos Sci Lab, 52-65, group leader, Physics Div, 65-81. *Mem:* Fel Am Phys Soc. *Res:* Lattice dynamics; neutron diffraction; reactors; cryogenics; solid state physics. *Mailing Add:* 205 El Conejo St Los Alamos NM 87544

**YARNELL, RICHARD ASA,** ANTHROPOLOGY, ETHNOBOTANY. *Current Pos:* assoc prof anthrop, Univ NC, Chapel Hill, 71-75, assoc chmn dept, 73-75, prof, 74-94, EMER PROF ANTHROP, UNIV NC, CHAPEL HILL, 94- *Personal Data:* b Boston, Mass, May 11, 29; m, M Jean Black; c 4. *Educ:* Duke Univ, BS, 50; Univ NMex, MA, 58; Univ Mich, PhD(anthrop), 63. *Honors & Awards:* Fryxell Award, Soc Am Archaeol. *Prof Exp:* From instr to assoc prof anthrop, Emory Univ, 62-71. *Mem:* Fel AAAS; Soc Econ Bot; Soc Ethnobiol. *Res:* Analysis of archaeological plant remains; evolution of plant domestication; aboriginal plant utilization; cultural ecology; economic botany. *Mailing Add:* 417 Ridgefield Rd Chapel Hill NC 27514

**YARNS, DALE A,** ANIMAL PHYSIOLOGY. *Current Pos:* asst prof, 66-72, ASSOC PROF PHYSIOL & CHMN DEPT BIOL, WAGNER COL, 72- *Personal Data:* b Jackson, Minn, July 9, 30; m 54; c 2. *Educ:* Univ Minn, BS, 56; SDak State Col, MS, 58; Univ Md, PhD(animal sci), 64. *Prof Exp:* Res asst dairy husb, SDak State Univ, 56-58; lab technician animal sci, Univ Calif, Davis, 58-61; animal husbandryman, Beef Cattle Br, USDA, 61-64; assoc res physiol, Animal Med Ctr, 64-66. *Res:* Comparative cardiac and ruminant physiology. *Mailing Add:* 271 Bement Ave Staten Island NY 10310

**YAROSEWICK, STANLEY J,** ATOMIC PHYSICS, SPECTROSCOPY. *Current Pos:* PRES, KEENE STATE COL. *Personal Data:* b Epping, NH, Sept 10, 39; m 64; c 2. *Educ:* Univ NH, BS, 61; Clarkson Col Technol, MS, 63, PhD(physics), 66. *Prof Exp:* Asst prof physics, Clarkson Col Technol, 66-69; assoc prof, West Chester State Col, 69-74, prof, 74- *Mem:* Am Asn Physics Teachers. *Res:* Atomic emission spectra. *Mailing Add:* Keene State Col Hale Bldg 229 Main St Keene NH 03431-4183

**YARRINGTON, ROBERT M,** chemical engineering, for more information see previous edition

**YARROW, MARIAN RADKE,** PSYCHOPATHOLOGY. *Current Pos:* EMER SCIENTIST, LAB PSYCHOL & PSYCHOPATH, NIMH, NIH, 95- *Personal Data:* b Horicon, Wis, Mar 2, 18. *Educ:* Univ Wis-Madison, BA, 39; Univ Minn, MA, 42, PhD(child psychol), 44. *Honors & Awards:* G Stanley Hall Award, Am Psychol Asn, 87; Distinguished Scientist Award, Soc Res & Child Develop, 93. *Mem:* Am Psychol Asn; Soc Res & Child Develop. *Mailing Add:* NIMH NIH Clin Ctr Bldg 10 9000 Rockville Pike Rm 4N 206B Bethesda MD 20892. *Fax:* 301-402-2570

**YARUS, MICHAEL J,** MOLECULAR BIOLOGY, BIOCHEMISTRY. *Current Pos:* from asst prof to assoc prof, 67-79, PROF MOLECULAR, CELLULAR & DEVELOP BIOL, UNIV COLO, BOULDER, 79- *Personal Data:* b Pikeville, Ky, Mar 2, 40; m 62, 85; c 3. *Educ:* Johns Hopkins Univ, BA, 60; Calif Inst Technol, PhD(biophys), 66. *Prof Exp:* USPHS & NIH fels biochem, Stanford Univ, 65-67. *Concurrent Pos:* USPHS & NIH grant, 68- *Mem:* AAAS; Fedn Am Soc Exp Biol. *Res:* Minute viruses; transfer RNA; mammalian embryogeny; control of translation, origin of the code. *Mailing Add:* Dept Molecular Cellular & Develop Biol Campus Box 347 Univ Colo Boulder CO 80309-0347

**YASAR, TUGRUL,** MAGNETIC RECORDING, THIN FILM TECHNOLOGY. *Current Pos:* VPRES & GEN MGR, MAGNETO-OPTICS DIV, MRC, 90- *Personal Data:* b Ankara, Turkey, Sept 23, 41; US citizen; m 85; c 3. *Educ:* Robert Col, Istanbul, BS, 63; Princeton Univ, MA, 67, PhD(elec eng in solid state sci), 68. *Prof Exp:* Res engr photoelectronics, Bendix Res Labs, 67-73; chief eng, Gen Instruments, 73-76; dir eng, Nat Micronetics, Inc, 76-79, opers mgr, 79-81, vpres, 81-90. *Concurrent Pos:* Mem affil fac, Col Eng, Wayne State Univ, 68-69; mem adv coun, Ulster Community Col, 79- *Mem:* Inst Elec & Electronics Engrs; Int Soc Hybrid Microelectronics; Am Vacuum Soc; Sigma Xi; Am Ceramics Soc. *Res:* Photoemission from semiconductors; photoelectronic devices; imaging devices; amorphous semiconductors; ultrasonics; thin film technology; magnetic devices; semiconductor manufacturing technology; magneto-optics. *Mailing Add:* PO Box 94 West Hurley NY 12491

**YASBIN, RONALD ELIOTT,** INDUSTRIAL MICROBIOLOGY. *Current Pos:* from asst prof to assoc prof microbiol, 81-88, PROF BIOL SCIS, UNIV ROCHESTER, 88-, CO-DIR MOLECULAR & CELL BIOL , 88- *Personal Data:* b Brooklyn, NY, Apr 27, 47; m 72; Sherrill C Elkin; c Lorne I, Todd I, Spencer L. *Educ:* Pa State Univ, BS, 68; Cornell Univ, MS, 70; Univ Rochester, PhD(microbiol), 74. *Prof Exp:* Asst prof microbiol & molecular genetics, Pa State Univ, 76-81. *Concurrent Pos:* Dir biotechnol, Univ Rochester, 82-88, assoc prof dental res, 83-88, chair biol scis, 88-93, adj prof dental res, 88- *Mem:* Am Soc Microbiol; Environ Mutagen Soc; Genetics Soc; Sigma Xi. *Res:* The role of DNA repair systems in the production of mutations and carcinogenesis events; use of recombinant DNA technology to explore pathogenesis and secondary metabolites. *Mailing Add:* 6314 Dry Stone Gate Columbia MD 21045. *Fax:* 410-455-3668; *E-Mail:* yasbin@umbc.edu

**YASHON, DAVID,** NEUROSURGERY. *Current Pos:* from assoc prof to prof, 69-89, EMER PROF NEUROSURG, OHIO STATE UNIV, 89- *Personal Data:* b Chicago, Ill, May 13, 35; c Jaclyn, Lisa & Steven. *Educ:* Univ Ill, BSM, 58, MD, 60; FRCS(C), 69. *Prof Exp:* Instr neurosurg, Univ Chicago, 65-66; asst prof, Case Western Res Univ, 66-69. *Mem:* Cong Neurol Surg; Am Asn Neurol Surg; Soc Univ Surg; Am Acad Neurol; Asn Acad Surg; Am Asn Surg Trauma. *Res:* Cerebral physiology and metabolism during circulatory deficiency; spinal cord injury and metabolic effects. *Mailing Add:* 1492 E Broad St Apt 1201 Columbus OH 43205-1546

**YASKO, RICHARD N,** NUCLEAR PHYSICS. *Current Pos:* QUAL ASSURANCE LAB DIR, EMD, BENCHMARK ELECTRONICS ASSOCS, 91- *Personal Data:* b Conemaugh, Pa, Aug 29, 35; m 64; Janice M Strebe; c Greg & Tom. *Educ:* Pa State Univ, BS, 57, MS, 61, PhD(physics), 63. *Prof Exp:* Fel nuclear physics, Argonne Nat Lab, 63-64; asst prof physics, Villanova Univ, 64-67; adv physicist, IBM Corp, Endicott, 68-77; prod assurance mgr, Avco Syst Div, Avco Corp, 78-83; sr engr, Norden Systs, United Technol, Merrimack, NH, 83-86; assoc prof physics, Winona State Univ, 89-91. *Mem:* Am Phys Soc; Int Soc Testing & Failure Anal; Am Soc Metals; Electron Micros Soc Am; Int Soc Hybrid Microelectronics; Inst Elec & Electronics Engrs. *Res:* Surface physics; semiconductor device physics; ion implantation, spreading resistance diffusion profiling and capacitance; voltage testing of MOS devices; failure analysis; component failure analysis surface mount processes. *Mailing Add:* 1317 W Wincrest Dr Winona MN 55987. *Fax:* 507-453-4960; *E-Mail:* ryasko@luminet.net

**YASMINEH, WALID GABRIEL,** BIOCHEMISTRY. *Current Pos:* From jr scientist to assoc scientist pediat, 59-65, asst prof lab med, 67-72, ASSOC PROF LAB MED, SCH MED, UNIV MINN, MINNEAPOLIS, 72- *Personal Data:* b Amman, Jordan, Jan 21, 31; US citizen; m 60; c 3. *Educ:* Am Univ Cairo, BSc, 53; Univ Minn, Minneapolis, MSc, 63, PhD(biochem), 66. *Concurrent Pos:* Grad Sch grant, Sch Med, Univ Minn, Minneapolis, 68- *Mem:* Am Chem Soc. *Res:* Mammalian constitutive heterochromatin and repetitive DNA, nature, origin, function and relation to disease. *Mailing Add:* 2735 Mackubin No 10 St Paul MN 55113-2362

**YASSO, WARREN E,** GEOLOGY, GEOMORPHOLOGY. *Current Pos:* ASSOC PROF SCI EDUC, TEACHERS COL, COLUMBIA UNIV, 66- *Personal Data:* b New York, NY, Oct 19, 30; m 57; c 2. *Educ:* Brooklyn Col, BS, 57; Columbia Univ, MA, 61, PhD(geomorphol), 64. *Prof Exp:* Instr earth sci, Adelphi Univ, 61-64; asst prof geol, Va Polytech Inst, 64-66. *Concurrent Pos:* Prog dir educ, Nat Sea Grant Prog, Nat Oceanic & Atmospheric Admin, 78-79; dir, Microcomput Software Sci Proj, NY Power Authority, 84-86. *Mem:* AAAS; fel Geol Soc Am; Int Asn Sedimentol; Nat Asn Geol Teachers; Nat Sci Teachers Asn. *Res:* Coastal and continental shelf geological processes; curriculum research in earth sciences. *Mailing Add:* 528 Franklin Turnpike Ridgewood NJ 07450-1912

**YASUDA, HIROTSUGU,** POLYMER CHEMISTRY, PHYSICAL CHEMISTRY. *Current Pos:* prof chem eng, Univ Mo-Rolla, 78-88, sr investr, Mat Res Ctr, 78-88, dir, Thin Film Inst, 85-88, chmn, chem eng, Univ Mo, Columbia, 88-90, DIR, CTR SURFACE SCI & PLASMIC TECHNOL, UNIV MO, COLUMBIA, 90- *Personal Data:* b Kyoto, Japan, Mar 24, 30; m 68; Gerda L Schmidtke; c Ken Eric, Werner Akira & Lisbeth Kay. *Educ:* Kyoto Univ, BS, 53; State Univ NY Col Environ Sci & Forestry, MS, 59, PhD(polymer & phys chem), 61. *Prof Exp:* Fel, State Univ NY Col Environ Sci & Forestry, Syracuse, 61; chemist, Camille Dreyfus Lab, Res Triangle Inst, 61-63; res assoc, Ophthalmic Plastic Lab, Mass Eye & Ear Infirmary, 63-64 & Cedars-Sinai Med Ctr, 64-65; guest scientist, Royal Inst Technol, Sweden, 65-66; head membrane & med polymer sect, Camille Dreyfus Lab, Res Triangle Inst, 66-75, mgr polymer dept, 75-77. *Mem:* Am Chem Soc; AAAS. *Res:* Preparation and characterization of polymers; transport phenomena through polymer membrane; biomedical application of polymers, membrane technology, plasma polymerization and surface modifications; vacuum deposition of polymers. *Mailing Add:* W2009 Eng Bldg E Univ Mo Columbia MO 65211-0002

**YASUDA, STANLEY K,** ANALYTICAL CHEMISTRY. *Current Pos:* MEM STAFF, LOS ALAMOS NAT LAB, 57- *Personal Data:* b Pahoa, Hawaii, Jan 7, 31; m 55; c 3. *Educ:* Park Col, BA, 53; Kans State Univ, MS, 55, PhD(anal chem), 57. *Concurrent Pos:* Sr analyst, Chemagro Corp, 64. *Mem:* Fel Am Inst Chemists; Am Chem Soc; Sigma Xi. *Res:* Microanalytical methods for analysis of explosive and non-explosive materials, utilizing wet and instrumental techniques. *Mailing Add:* 75 San Juan Los Alamos NM 87544-2631

**YASUI, GEORGE,** CHEMICAL ENGINEERING. *Current Pos:* RETIRED. *Personal Data:* b Olympia, Wash, May 7, 22; m 50; c 4. *Educ:* Univ Denver, BS, 44; Univ Mich, MS, 48; Univ Wash, PhD(chem eng), 57. *Prof Exp:* Chem engr, Varnish Lab, Sherwin-Williams Co, 44-45 & Chem Eng Div, Argonne Nat Lab, 48-54; res scientist, Lockheed Missiles & Space Co, 56-60, staff scientist, 60-62, mgr res & develop staff, 62-63, asst mgr nuclear eng, 63-64, sr staff engr, 64-71; proj engr, Environ Qual Eng, Inc, 71-72; staff engr, Lockheed Missiles & Space Co, 72-90. *Mem:* Am Inst Chem Engrs; Sigma Xi. *Res:* Development of nosetips and heating shields for reentry vehicles; Analyses and testing of materials exposed to nuclear weapons; lasers; space environments. *Mailing Add:* 113 Demurrage Way Folsom CA 95630

**YASUKAWA, KEN,** ECOLOGY, ANIMAL BEHAVIOR. *Current Pos:* from asst prof to assoc prof, 80-90, PROF, DEPT BIOL, BELOIT COL, 90- *Personal Data:* b New York, NY, Sept 7, 49; m 72; c 2. *Educ:* State Univ NY, Stony Brook, BS, 71; Ind Univ, MS, 75, PhD(zool), 77. *Prof Exp:* Fel animal behav, Field Res Ctr, Rockefeller Univ, 77-80. *Concurrent Pos:* Prin investr, NSF, 84, 87-89, 90-93 & 94-; ed, Asn Field Ornithologists, 90-; vis prof, Dept Zool, Univ Wis-Madison, 91- *Mem:* Soc Am Naturalists; Animal Behav Soc; Ecol Soc Am; fel Am Ornithologists Union; Sigma Xi. *Res:* Avian behavioral ecology; evolution of mating systems; territoriality; population regulation; dominance hierarchies; communication behavior; function of avian vocal behavior; parental behavior. *Mailing Add:* Dept Biol Beloit Col 700 College St Beloit WI 53511-5595. *Fax:* 608-363-2718; *E-Mail:* yasukawa@beloit.edu

**YASUMURA, SEIICHI,** ENDOCRINOLOGY. *Current Pos:* Instr, 64-66, from asst prof to assoc prof, 66-91, PROF PHYSIOL, STATE UNIV NY DOWNSTATE MED CTR, 91- *Personal Data:* b New York, NY, Sept 28, 32; m 63; c 2. *Educ:* Occidental Col, AB, 58; Univ Cincinnati, PhD(anat), 62. *Concurrent Pos:* Fel, State Univ Groningen, 62-63; NSF fel, State Univ NY Downstate Med Ctr, 63-64; res collabr, Brookhaven Nat Lab, 75-; consult, Nat Inst Environ Health Sci, 80-82; Fulbright fel, 92. *Mem:* Endocrine Soc; Am Physiol Soc; Am Soc Clin Nutrit; Am Soc Bone & Mineral Res. *Mailing Add:* Dept Physiol Brookhaven Nat Lab Upton NY 11973-9999. *Fax:* 516-282-5311; *E-Mail:* yasumura@bnl.gov

**YASUNOBU, KERRY T,** BIOCHEMISTRY. *Current Pos:* asst prof chem, 58-62, assoc prof biochem, 62-64, PROF BIOCHEM, UNIV HAWAII, MANOA, 64- *Personal Data:* b Seattle, Wash, Nov 21, 25; m 52; c 1. *Educ:* Univ Wash, PhD(biochem), 54. *Prof Exp:* Res scientist, Univ Tex, 54-55; res assoc, Med Sch, Univ Ore, 55-58. *Concurrent Pos:* NSF sr fel, 63-64; NIH sr fel, 71-72. *Mem:* Am Chem Soc; Am Soc Biol Chemists; Sigma Xi. *Res:* Enzymology, especially oxidative, heme-enzymes and proteolytic enzymes. *Mailing Add:* 3270 Melemele Pl Honolulu HI 96822

**YATES, ALBERT CARL,** THEORETICAL PHYSICAL CHEMISTRY. *Current Pos:* PRES, COLO STATE UNIV, 90- *Personal Data:* b Memphis, Tenn, Sept 29, 41; m 62; c 2. *Educ:* Memphis State Univ, BS, 65; Ind Univ, Bloomington, PhD(chem physics), 68. *Prof Exp:* Res assoc chem, Univ Southern Calif, 68-69; from asst prof to assoc prof, Ind Univ, Bloomington, 69-74; assoc prof chem & assoc univ dean grad educ & res, Univ Cincinnati, 74-76, prof chem & univ dean grad educ & res, 76-; provost, Wash State Univ. *Mem:* Am Phys Soc; Am Chem Soc. *Res:* Collisions of charged particles with atomic and molecular systems; heavy-particle collisions; photo-absorption processes. *Mailing Add:* Colo State Univ 102 Administration Blvd Ft Collins CO 80523-0100. *Fax:* 970-491-0501

**YATES, ALLAN JAMES,** NEUROPATHOLOGY, NEUROCHEMISTRY. *Current Pos:* From asst prof to assoc prof, 75-84, PROF NEUROPATH, OHIO STATE UNIV, 84-, HEAD, NEUROPATH, 82- *Personal Data:* b Calgary, Alta, May 23, 43; m 68; c 2. *Educ:* Univ Alta, MD, 67; Univ Toronto, PhD(neurochem), 72; FRCP(C). *Mem:* Am Asn Neuropath; Am Soc Neurochem; Am Soc Path; Int Soc Neurochem; Int Soc Neuropath. *Res:* Physiological and biochemical aspects of glycolipids and their roles in diseases of the nervous system, with special reference to nerve degeneration, regeneration and gliomas. *Mailing Add:* Dept Path 4166 Graves Hall Ohio State Univ 333 W Tenth Ave Columbus OH 43210-1252. *Fax:* 614-293-8223

**YATES, ANN MARIE,** X-RAY ANALYSIS, METEORITES. *Current Pos:* mem chem fac, 77-78, RES SPECIALIST, ARIZ STATE UNIV, 78- *Personal Data:* b Ogdensburg, NY, Sept 29, 40. *Educ:* St Lawrence Univ, BS, 62; Ariz State Univ, PhD(chem), 66. *Prof Exp:* Asst prof anal chem, Ariz State Univ, 66-67; NIH res assoc inorg chem, Univ Pittsburgh, 67-68; dir labs, Chemalytics Inc, 68-74; mem chem fac, Maricopa County Community Col Dist, 76-77. *Mem:* Am Chem Soc; Sigma Xi; Meteoritical Soc. *Res:* Microanalytical techniques; x-ray diffraction; meteorite analysis. *Mailing Add:* 1627 E Wesleyan Dr Tempe AZ 85282-2763

**YATES, CHARLIE LEE,** FLUID MECHANICS, AEROCHEMISTRY. *Current Pos:* assoc prof, Mech Eng Dept, 79-83, ASSOC PROF, AEROSPACE & OCEAN ENG DEPT, VA POLYTECH INST & STATE UNIV, 87- *Personal Data:* b Harrellsville, NC, Apr 8, 36; c 3. *Educ:* Va Polytech Inst & State Univ, BS, 58; Calif Inst Technol, MS, 59; Johns Hopkins Univ, PhD, 78. *Prof Exp:* Aerospace engr, Westinghouse Elec Corp, 59-60; assoc engr, Appl Physics Lab, Johns Hopkins Univ, 60-64, sr engr, 64-79; Dept Chem Eng, Hampton Univ, 83-86. *Mem:* Am Inst Aeronaut & Astronaut; Am Soc Eng Educ; Sigma Xi. *Res:* Surface gravity wave physics; wave-wave interactions. *Mailing Add:* Aerospace & Ocean Eng Va Polytech Inst Blacksburg VA 24061-0203

**YATES, EDWARD CARSON, JR,** AEROELASTICITY, UNSTEADY AERODYNAMICS. *Current Pos:* RETIRED. *Personal Data:* b Raleigh, NC, Nov 3, 26; m 52, Carleen Wells; c Barry W. *Educ:* NC State Univ, BS, 48, MS, 49; Univ Va, MS, 53; Va Polytech Inst & State Univ, PhD(eng mech), 59. *Prof Exp:* Aerospace engr, Langley Res Ctr, NASA, 49-87, chief scientist, Loads & Aeroelasticity Div, 82-86, sr aerospace engr, Interdisciplinary Res Off, 87-92. *Concurrent Pos:* Lectr physics, Va Polytech Inst & State Univ, 59-67; adj assoc prof, NC State Univ, 64-75; prof, George Washington Univ, 68-92; assoc ed, J Aircraft, 72-78; vis prof, Univ Rome, La Sapienza, 90; mem, Sci Comt, Int Asn Boundary Element Methods, 90-92. *Mem:* Assoc fel Am Inst Aeronaut & Astronaut. *Res:* Subsonic, transonic and supersonic aerodynamics; unsteady aerodynamics; aeroelasticity; structural dynamics. *Mailing Add:* 3800 Chesapeake Ave Hampton VA 23669-4612

**YATES, FRANCIS EUGENE,** PHYSIOLOGY. *Current Pos:* PROF BIOMED ENG, DEPT BIOMED ENG, UNIV SOUTHERN CALIF, 69-, DIR, BIOMED ENG CTR, 77-; PROF CHEM ENG, MED & PHYSIOL, RALPH & MARJORIE CRUMP PROF MED ENG & DIR, CRUMP INST MED ENG, UNIV CALIF, LOS ANGELES, 80- *Personal Data:* b Pasadena, Calif, Feb 26, 27; m 49; c 5. *Educ:* Stanford Univ, BA, 47, MD, 51. *Honors & Awards:* Upjohn Award, Endocrine Soc, 62. *Prof Exp:* Intern, Philadelphia Gen Hosp, 50-51; instr physiol, Harvard Med Sch, 55-57, assoc, 57-59, asst prof, 59-60; from assoc prof to prof, Stanford Univ, 60-69, actg exec head dept physiol, 64-69. *Concurrent Pos:* Res fel physiol, Harvard Univ, 53-55; Markle scholar med sci, Harvard Med Sch, 59; mem, physiol training comt, Nat Inst Gen Med Sci, 64-70, mem med scientist training prog comt, 71-73; vis prof,

Stanford Univ, 69-; sect ed endocrinol & metab, Am J Physiol, 69-74; managing ed, Annals Biomed Eng, 71-74; consult prin scientist, Alza Corp; mem sci info prog adv comt, Nat Inst Neurol & Communicative Dis & Stroke, 76-; managing ed, Am J Physiol, Regulatory Integrative & Comp Physiol, 76-; mem, Space Biol Panel, NASA, 79-80; mem, Panel Basic Biomed Sci, Human Resources Comn, Nat Res Coun, 79-; mem adv bd biol, Harvey Mudd Col, 79- *Mem:* AAAS; Biomed Eng Soc (pres, 74-75); Am Physiol Soc; Endocrine Soc; NY Acad Sci; Sigma Xi. *Res:* Metabolism and inactivation of adrenal cortical hormones; analysis of endocrine feedback systems. *Mailing Add:* Dept Med Univ Calif-Los Angeles Med Monitoring Unit 1950 Sawtelle Blvd Suite 330 Los Angeles CA 90025-7014. *Fax:* 310-312-0551

**YATES, GEORGE KENNETH,** SPACE PHYSICS. *Current Pos:* ADJ PROF PHYSICS & ASTRON, CLEMSON UNIV, 94- *Personal Data:* b Chicago, Ill, Sept 24, 25; m 84, Gale S Pemberton; c George, Charles, John, James & Deborah. *Educ:* Harvard Univ, AB, 50; Univ Chicago, MS, 55, PhD(physics), 64; Suffolk Univ, JD, 80. *Prof Exp:* Physicist, Eng Res & Develop Lab, Ft Belvoir, Va, 50-53; res physicist, Air Force Geophys Lab, 64-89. *Res:* Physics of the near space environment. *Mailing Add:* 20 Fair Wind Dr Salem SC 29676-4303

**YATES, HARRIS OLIVER,** BIOLOGY. *Current Pos:* Instr, David Lipscomb Col, 57-59, from asst prof to assoc prof, 63-68, prof biol & chmn dept, 68-94, DISTINGUISHED PROF BIOL, DAVID LIPSCOMB COL, 94- *Personal Data:* b Paducah, Ky, Apr 14, 34; m 54; c 3. *Educ:* David Lipscomb Col, BA, 56; George Peabody Col, MA, 57; Vanderbilt Univ, PhD(biol), 65. *Res:* Experimental plant taxonomy. *Mailing Add:* Dept Biol David Lipscomb Univ 3901 Granny White Nashville TN 37204-3903

**YATES, JAMES T,** GERIATRICS, DIAGNOSTIC AUDIOLOGY. *Current Pos:* PROF & CHMN AUDIOL, SCH MED, UNIV HAWAII, 78-; PVT PRACT, 89- *Personal Data:* b Forney, Tex, June 8, 40; m 61; c Scott W & Jennifer A. *Educ:* Tex Tech Univ, BA(psychol) & BA(audiol), 65, MA, 66; Univ Denver, PhD(audiol), 70. *Prof Exp:* Teaching asst commun, Tex Tech Univ, 65-66; lab instr anat, Univ Denver, 66-69; dir audiol, Tex Tech Univ, 70-78; pvt pract, Denver, Colo, 66-69. *Concurrent Pos:* Consult, 70-78; prin investr grants & contracts, 70-; consult audiologist, Lubbock State Sch Ment Retardation, 72-75, WTex Rehab Ctr, 75-78; consult mgr, Kuakini Hosp, Honolulu, 90-92; exec dir, Scottish Rite Children's Ctr, Hawaii, 94-; assoc prof & dir audiol, Tex Tech Univ. *Mem:* Fel Am Speech & Hearing Asn; Acoust Soc Am; Acad Rehab Audiol; fel Am Acad Audiol. *Res:* Geriatric audiology; central auditory processing: development, deteriation and diagnosis of disorders of processing in children and adults. *Mailing Add:* SPA-Med 1410 Lower Campus Dr Univ Hawaii Honolulu HI 96822. *E-Mail:* jyates@hawaii.edu

**YATES, JEROME DOUGLAS,** POULTRY NUTRITION. *Current Pos:* res assoc nutrit & food sci, Campbell Soup Co, 64-68, res scientist, 69-85, prin scientist, 86-90, sr res prog mgr, 90-92, POULTRY NUTRIT, CAMPBELL SOUP CO, 92- *Personal Data:* b Center Point, Ark, Jan 5, 35; m 69; c 4. *Educ:* Univ Ark, BSA, 58, MS, 59; Mich State Univ, PhD(poultry nutrit), 64. *Prof Exp:* Nutrit technician, Mich State Univ, 59-63. *Mem:* Poultry Sci Asn; World Poultry Sci Asn. *Res:* Poultry nutrition emphasizing the influence of nutrients and other dietary components on quality of poultry meat; mineral and amino acid nutrition. *Mailing Add:* 805 Dinsmore Trail Fayetteville AR 72704

**YATES, JEROME WILLIAM,** ONCOLOGY, EPIDEMIOLOGY. *Current Pos:* VPRES CLIN AFFAIRS, ROSWELL PARK MEM INST, 87-; PROF MED ONCOL, MED SCH, STATE UNIV NY, BUFFALO, 87- *Personal Data:* b Rockford, Ill, Nov 9, 36; m 79, Mary McAuley; c Elizabeth & Sarah. *Educ:* Lawrence Univ, AB, 61; Univ Ill, MD, 65; Harvard Sch Pub Health, MPH, 81. *Prof Exp:* Prof med, Univ Vt Col Med, 78-82; assoc dir, Nat Cancer Inst, 82-87. *Concurrent Pos:* Ed, J Psychol Oncol, Nat Cancer Inst, 83-, J Nat Cancer Inst, 82-87; consult, Health Care Financing Admn, 81-82; World Health Orgn, 84, Nat Cancer Inst, 87-; res adv, Alta Cancer Bd, 86-94 & 97-; Am Cancer Soc Rev, 92-97. *Mem:* Am Asn Cancer Res; Am Soc Clin Oncol; Am Pub Health Asn; Am Soc Prev Oncol; Am Asn Cancer Inst. *Res:* Leukemia management; cancer in elderly; health care delivery issues and supportive care. *Mailing Add:* Vpres Clin Affairs Roswell Park Mem Inst Elm St Buffalo NY 14263. *Fax:* 716-845-3565; *E-Mail:* jyates@3103sc.buffalo.med.edu

**YATES, JOHN T, JR,** PHYSICAL CHEMISTRY, SURFACE CHEMISTRY. *Current Pos:* R K Mellon prof chem, 81, DIR, PITTSBURGH SURFACE SCI CTR, UNIV PITTSBURGH, 81- *Personal Data:* b Winchester, Va, Aug 3, 35; m 58, Kevin N; c Geoffrey W & Nathan A. *Educ:* Juniata Col, BS, 56; Mass Inst Technol, PhD, 60. *Honors & Awards:* Silver Medal, US Dept Com, 73, Gold Medal, 82; Samuel Wesley Stratton Award, Nat Bur Standards, 78; Kendall Award, Am Chem Soc; E W Morley Medal, Am Chem Soc, 90; Welch Award, Am Vacuum Soc, 94. *Prof Exp:* Res assoc chem, Mass Inst Technol, 60; instr & asst prof, Antioch Col, 60-63; Nat Res Coun-Nat Bur Standards res assoc, 63-65; staff mem, Phys Chem Div, Nat Bur Standards, 65-74, chief, Surface Processes & Catalysis Sect, 74-78. *Concurrent Pos:* Sr vis fel, Univ EAnglia, 70-71 & 72; trustee, Am Vacuum Soc, 74; mem bd dirs, Catalysis Soc, 76-81; Sherman Fairchild scholar, Calif Inst Technol, 77-78; chmn, Div Colloid & Surface Chem, Am Chem Soc, 80; distinguished vis lectr, Univ Tex, Austin, 78; vchmn & chmn, Gordon Conf on Molecular Dynamics of Surfaces, 79 & 82; mem vis comt, Div Chem & Chem Eng, Caltech, 86, comt, US Army Basic Sci Res, NRC, 87; chmn rev panel, Chem & Laser Sci Div, Los Alamos Nat Lab, 87; rev panel, Sci & Technol Ctrs, NSF, 88; adv bd, Petrol Res Found, 88; chmn, div chem, Am

Phys Soc, 89; A von Humboldt Sr Award, 95. *Mem:* Nat Acad Sci; fel Am Phys Soc; fel Am Vacuum Soc; Am Chem Soc. *Res:* Spectra of adsorbed molecules; heterogeneous catalysis; kinetics of adsorption and desorption; electron impact studies of adsorbed species; electronic properties of the chemisorbed layer; semiconductor surface chemistry; tribology and surface chemistry. *Mailing Add:* 2788 Shamrock St Allison Park PA 15101

**YATES, JON ARTHUR,** FILARIASIS, PARASITE IMMUNOLOGY. *Current Pos:* asst prof, 86-92, ASSOC PROF BIOL PARASITOL IMMUNOL, OAKLAND UNIV, ROCHESTER HILLS, 92- *Personal Data:* b Independence, Mo, Dec 14, 47. *Educ:* Univ Mo, BS, 73; Tulane Univ, MS, 76, PhD(parasitol), 81. *Prof Exp:* Res assoc, Tulane Univ, Colciencias Int Ctr Med Res, Cali & El Porvenir, Columbia, 77-80; res scholar immunol, Dept Epidemiol, Sch Pub Health, Univ Mich, 81-84, sr res fel epidemiol, 84-86. *Concurrent Pos:* Dir, Field Parasitol Lab, El Porvenir, Columbia, 78-79; scientist, Indo-US Res Initiative, Rajamundry, India, 85; guest lectr, Nat Inst Commun Dis, Delhi, India, 85; adj asst prof epidemiol, Sch Pub Health, Univ Mich, 86-, vis lectr, Grad Summer Session Epidemiol, 89; mem, Sci Working Group Filariasis, WHO, 87 & Trop Med Deleg Peoples Repub China, 88. *Mem:* Am Soc Trop Med & Hyg; Am Soc Parasitologists; Royal Soc Trop Med & Hyg; Am Soc Trop Vet Med. *Res:* Biology and immunology of parasitic nematode infections; vaccine models; chemotherapy; immunopathologic mechanisms in parasitic diseases; vector biology host-parasite interactions; filariasis. *Mailing Add:* Dept Biol Sci Oakland Univ Rochester MI 48309-4401

**YATES, KEITH,** PHYSICAL ORGANIC CHEMISTRY. *Current Pos:* RETIRED. *Personal Data:* b Preston, Eng, Oct, 22, 28; Can citizen; m 53; c 3. *Educ:* Univ BC, BA, 56, MSc, 57, PhD(org chem), 59; Oxford Univ, DPhil(phys chem), 61. *Honors & Awards:* Syntex Award, Chem Inst Can. *Prof Exp:* From asst prof to prof chem, Univ Toronto, 61-93, asst dean, Sch Grad Studies, 67-70, chmn dept, 74-85. *Mem:* Chem Inst Can; fel Royal Soc Can. *Res:* Physical and theoretical organic chemistry; acidity functions and reaction mechanisms. *Mailing Add:* 536 Arbutus Dr Mayne Island BC V0N 2J0 Can

**YATES, LELAND MARSHALL,** PHYSICAL CHEMISTRY. *Current Pos:* from instr to prof, 51-78, EMER PROF CHEM, UNIV MONT, 78- *Personal Data:* b Stevensville, Mont, Feb 11, 15; c 4. *Educ:* Mont State Univ, BA, 38, MA, 40; Wash State Univ, PhD(chem), 55. *Prof Exp:* Instr chem & physics, Custer Co Jr Col, 40-42 & 45-47; instr chem, Univ Mont, 47-49; asst, Wash State Univ, 49-51. *Mem:* Am Chem Soc. *Res:* Equilibrium constants and thermodynamics of complex ions; analysis for small concentration of ions. *Mailing Add:* 610 Hastings Ave Missoula MT 59801

**YATES, MARY ANNE,** nuclear chemistry, for more information see previous edition

**YATES, RICHARD ALAN,** BIOCHEMISTRY, MICROBIOLOGY. *Current Pos:* RETIRED. *Personal Data:* b Oakland, Calif, July 14, 30; m 58; c 1. *Educ:* Univ Calif, Berkeley, BA, 52, PhD(biochem), 56. *Prof Exp:* Res biochemist, Cent Res & Develop Dept, E I Du Pont de Nemours & Co Inc, 56-92, fermentation develop, DuPont Merck Pharamacol, 92-94. *Mem:* Am Soc Microbiol; Inst Food Technologists; AAAS; NY Acad Sci. *Res:* Biochemical control mechanisms; microbial genetic alterations; production of feedstock chemicals from renewable sources; single cell protein production and adaptation for human foods. *Mailing Add:* 233 Prospect Dr Wilmington DE 19803

**YATES, RICHARD LEE,** MATHEMATICS. *Current Pos:* assoc prof & chmn math sect, Purdue Univ, 67-70, prof & acad dean, 70-75, exec asst to chancellor, 75-80, prof, 80-93, EMER PROF MATH, PURDUE UNIV, 93- *Personal Data:* b Red Oak, Iowa, June 15, 31; m 61; c 2. *Educ:* Fla Southern Col, BS, 52; Univ Fla, MS, 54, PhD(math), 57. *Prof Exp:* Asst, Univ Fla, 52-56; asst prof, Univ Houston, 57-60; from asst prof to assoc prof, Kans State Univ, 60-67. *Mem:* Math Asn Am. *Res:* Classical number theory; modern algebra; lattice theory. *Mailing Add:* Dept Math Purdue Univ Calumet Campus Hammond IN 46323-2094

**YATES, ROBERT DOYLE,** CYTOLOGY. *Current Pos:* PROF ANAT & CHMN DEPT, SCH MED, TULANE UNIV, LA, 72- *Personal Data:* b Birmingham, Ala, Feb 28, 31; m 55; c 2. *Educ:* Univ Ala, BS, 54, MS, 56, PhD(anat), 60. *Honors & Awards:* Golden Apple Award, SAMA. *Prof Exp:* Instr gross anat & neuroanat, Univ Tex Med Br, Galveston, 61-64, from asst prof to prof microanat, 64-70. *Concurrent Pos:* Fel, Med Ctr, Univ Ala, 61-62; NIH career res develop award, 64. *Mem:* AAAS; Am Soc Cell Biol; Am Asn Anat; Am Soc Neuropath; Fedn Am Soc Exp Biol. *Res:* Electron microscopic studies of reversible alterations in the organelles and inclusions of cells subjected to experimentally induced stresses. *Mailing Add:* Dept Anat Sch Med Tulane Univ 1430 Tulane Ave New Orleans LA 70112-2699. *Fax:* 504-584-1687

**YATES, ROBERT EDMUNDS,** PHYSICAL CHEMISTRY. *Current Pos:* RETIRED. *Personal Data:* b Bisbee, Ariz, Aug 15, 26; m 47; c 4. *Educ:* Univ Ariz, BS, 48, MS 49; Mich State Univ, PhD(phys chem), 52. *Prof Exp:* Asst chem, Mich State Univ, 49-51; res engr, Dow Chem Co, 52-58; res chemist, Aerojet-Gen Corp, 58-61 & Rocket Power, Inc, 61-65; res chemist, Aerojet-Gen Corp, Calif, 66-67; chem specialist, 67-71; physicist, McClellan AFB, Sacramento, 71-90. *Mem:* Am Chem Soc. *Res:* Boron, fluorine and high temperature chemistry; thermodynamics and spectroscopy. *Mailing Add:* 7313 Pine Grove Way Folsom CA 95630-1923

**YATES, SCOTT RAYMOND,** soil physics, contaminant transport, for more information see previous edition

**YATES, SHELLY GENE,** CHEMISTRY, NATURAL PRODUCTS. *Current Pos:* RETIRED. *Personal Data:* b Altus, Okla, Feb 29, 32; m 54; c 4. *Educ:* Southwestern State Col, Okla, BS, 56; Okla State Univ, MS, 58. *Prof Exp:* Org chemist, Northern Regional Res Ctr, Agr Res Serv, USDA, 58-88. *Mem:* Am Chem Soc. *Res:* Natural products; isolation, characterization and analysis. *Mailing Add:* 5619 N Plaza Dr Peoria IL 61614

**YATES, STEVEN WINFIELD,** RADIOCHEMISTRY, NUCLEAR STRUCTURE. *Current Pos:* from asst prof to assoc prof, 75-85, PROF CHEM, UNIV KY, 85- *Personal Data:* b Memphis, Mo, Apr 19, 46; m 75, Linda Petrosky; c Michelle. *Educ:* Univ Mo, Columbia, BS, 68; Purdue Univ, Lafayette, PhD(chem), 73. *Honors & Awards:* Sturgill Award, 94. *Prof Exp:* Res asst chem, Purdue Univ, Lafayette, 71-73; fel, Argonne Nat Lab, 73-75. *Concurrent Pos:* Proctor & Gamble fel, 72; dir gen chem, 85-87; univ res prof, 92; distinguished prof, Col Arts & Sci, 93. *Mem:* Am Chem Soc; Am Phys Soc; Sigma Xi. *Res:* Level structures of transitional and deformed nuclei; inelastic scattering and transfer reactions; nuclear isomerism and high-spin phenomena; neutron induced reactions; neutron scattering; nuclear spectroscopy; nuclear lifetime measurements. *Mailing Add:* Dept Chem Univ Ky Lexington KY 40506-0055. *E-Mail:* yates@pop.uky.edu

**YATES, VANCE JOSEPH,** VETERINARY VIROLOGY. *Current Pos:* RETIRED. *Personal Data:* b Smithville, Ohio, Oct 25, 17; m 42; c 4. *Educ:* Ohio State Univ, BSc, 40, DVM, 49; Univ Wis, PhD, 60. *Prof Exp:* Instr high sch, Ohio, 40-41; asst prof animal path, Univ RI, 49-50, assoc prof & assoc res prof, 51-55, head dept, 51-79, prof animal path & res prof, 55-83. *Concurrent Pos:* Mem temp staff, Rockefeller Found, 63-64; vis prof dept exp biol, Baylor Col Med, 71-72. *Mem:* Am Vet Med Asn; Am Asn Avian Path. *Res:* Avian virology and pathology; oncogenicity of avian adenoviruses. *Mailing Add:* 40 Spring Hill Rd Kingston RI 02881

**YATES, WILLARD F, JR,** PLANT TAXONOMY, CYTOGENETICS. *Current Pos:* assoc prof, 67-78, prof, 78-96, EMER PROF BOT, BUTLER UNIV, 96- *Personal Data:* b Findlay, Ohio, June 20, 30; m 65; c 2. *Educ:* Eastern Ill Univ, BS, 58; Ind Univ, MA, 60, PhD(bot), 67. *Prof Exp:* Instr biol, Cumberland Col, 60-62; asst prof, Ball State Univ, 65-67. *Mem:* Tissue Cult Asn; Bot Soc Am; Am Soc Plant Taxon; Plant Molecular Biol Asn. *Res:* Plant cytotaxonomy; phytochemistry; plant tissue culture. *Mailing Add:* Dept Biol Sci Butler Univ 4600 Sunset Ave Indianapolis IN 46208-3443

**YATES-PARKER, NANCY L,** PESTICIDE REGISTRATION. *Current Pos:* Intern, Prod Develop Div, Monsanto Agr Co, St Louis, Mo, 80- 81, prod develop rep, Omaha, Nebr, 84-85, Kansas City, Mo, 85-86, prod develop assoc, St Paul, Minn, 86-88, sr registration specialist, St Louis, Mo, 88-89, MGR REGISTRATION, ENVIRON & PUB AFFAIRS, MONSANTO AGR CO, ST LOUIS, MO, 89- *Personal Data:* b Jackson, Miss, Nov 14, 56; m 84; c 1. *Educ:* Miss State Univ, BS, 78; Univ Mo, MS, 80; NC State Univ, PhD(hort), 84. *Mem:* Weed Sci Soc Am. *Res:* Development of pesticides; residue analysis of food commodities for pesticide residue. *Mailing Add:* Monsanto Agr Co B2NG 800 N Lindbergh Blvd St Louis MO 63167

**YATSU, FRANK MICHIO,** NEUROLOGY. *Current Pos:* PROF NEUROL & CHMN DEPT, UNIV TEX HEALTH SCI CTR, HOUSTON, 82- *Personal Data:* b Los Angeles, Calif, Nov 28, 32; m 55; c 1. *Educ:* Brown Univ, AB, 55; Case Western Res Univ, MD, 59. *Prof Exp:* From asst prof to assoc prof neurol, Univ Calif Med Ctr, San Francisco, 67-75, vchmn dept, 73-75; prof & chmn dept, Univ Ore Health Sci Ctr, 75-82. *Concurrent Pos:* Chief neurol serv, San Francisco Gen Hosp, 69-75; mem cardiovasc A res study comt, Am Heart Asn, 74-77; mem neurol disorders prog, Proj A Rev Comt, Nat Inst Neurol & Commun Disorders & Stroke, NIH, 75-79; mem adv coun, Epilepsy Ctr of Ore, 75- *Mem:* Am Acad Neurol; Am Neurol Asn; Am Soc Neurochem; Int Soc Neurochem. *Res:* Brain ischemia and atherosclerosis. *Mailing Add:* Dept Neurol Univ Tex Health Sci Ctr 6431 Fannin St Suite 7044-MSMB Houston TX 77030

**YATSU, LAWRENCE Y,** PLANT PHYSIOLOGY. *Current Pos:* plant physiologist, Field Lab Tung Invest, USDA, 60-61, RES CHEMIST, SOUTHERN REGIONAL RES CTR, USDA, 61- *Personal Data:* b Pasadena, Calif, Aug 2, 25; m 54; c 2. *Educ:* Mich State Univ, BS, 49; Univ Calif, MS, 50; Cornell Univ, PhD, 60. *Prof Exp:* Chemist, Strong, Cobb & Co, 54-55; res assoc, Cornell Univ, 55-60. *Concurrent Pos:* Adj assoc prof biol, Tulane Univ, 73- *Mem:* AAAS; Am Chem Soc; Bot Soc Am; Am Soc Plant Physiol; Am Inst Biol Scientists; Sigma Xi. *Res:* Cell biology; biochemistry. *Mailing Add:* 7611 Dalewood Rd New Orleans LA 70126-1837

**YATVIN, MILTON B,** PHYSIOLOGY, RADIOBIOLOGY. *Current Pos:* PROF RADIATION ONCOL, DEPT BIOSCI & MOLECULAR BIOL, SCH MED, ORE HEALTH SCI UNIV, 88- *Personal Data:* b New Brunswick, NJ, Nov 12, 30; m 52; c 3. *Educ:* Rutgers Univ, BS, 52, MS, 54, PhD(endocrinol, reproductive physiol), 62. *Prof Exp:* Instr dairy sci, Rutgers Univ, 55-56; lectr reproductive physiol, Univ PR, 57-59; from instr to assoc prof, Univ Wis-Madison, 63-71, prof radiobiol, Med Sch, 71-88, prof human oncol, 77-88. *Concurrent Pos:* NIH fel endocrinol, Rutgers Univ, 62-63. *Mem:* Biophys Soc; Radiation Res Soc; Soc Exp Biol & Med; Am Physiol Soc; Sigma Xi. *Res:* Cell damage and repair after exposure to ionizing radiation; nucleic acid-membrane relationships in cells. *Mailing Add:* Dept Radiation Oncol & Biochem & Molecular Biol Oregon Health Sci Univ 3181 SW Sam Jackson Park Rd Portland OR 97201-3098. *Fax:* 503-494-5447

**YAU, CHEUK CHUNG,** POLYESTERS. *Current Pos:* Develop chemist res & develop, Tenn Eastman Co, 79-83, res chemist, Eastman Chem Div, 83-84, sr chemist Res & Develop, 84-89, PRIN RES CHEMIST, EASTMAN CHEM DIV, EASTMAN KODAK CO, 89- *Personal Data:* b Hong Kong, Apr 21, 50; US citizen; m 77; c 2. *Educ:* Univ Hawaii, BS, 74; Ga Inst Technol, PhD(chem), 79. *Concurrent Pos:* Reviewer, J Org Chem, Am Chem Soc, 83- *Mem:* Am Chem Soc. *Res:* Understanding of polyester systems to improve their performance; predicting formulations of polyesters to meet property specifications. *Mailing Add:* 313 Highridge Rd Kingsport TN 37660

**YAU, CHIOU CHING,** FIBER & POLYMER SCIENCE. *Current Pos:* PROG CHEMIST, GILLETTE CO, 81- *Personal Data:* b Taiwan, Dec 31, 34; US citizen; m 66, Katherine Lee; c James & Jean. *Educ:* Nat Cheng Kung Univ, Taiwan, BS, 58; Ga Inst Technol, MS, 66; NC State Univ, PhD(fiber & polymer sci), 72. *Prof Exp:* Chem engr, Chinese Petrol Corp, 60-65; res chemist, Am Enka Corp, Akzona, Inc, 66-69; mem tech staff, Emery Indust Inc, 72-77; res scientist, Kimberly-Clark Corp, 77-79; sr res chemist, Kendall Co, 79-81. *Mem:* Am Chem Soc; Soc Plastics Engrs; Fedn Soc Coatings Technol. *Res:* Polymer synthesis; polymer characterization by thermal analysis; structure and property relationships of polymers; fiber chemistry; flame retardants for fibers and plastics; nonwovens, polymer emulsions and coatings; correction fluid technology. *Mailing Add:* 2008 West St Wrentham MA 02093. *Fax:* 617-463-2680

**YAU, KING-WAI,** NEUROPHYSIOLOGY, VISION. *Current Pos:* INVESTR, HOWARD HUGHES MED INST & PROF, SCH MED, JOHNS HOPKINS UNIV, 86- *Personal Data:* b China, Oct 27, 48; m 75; c 2. *Educ:* Princeton Univ, AB, 71; Harvard Univ, PhD(neurobiol), 76. *Honors & Awards:* Rank Prize, Eng, 80; Friedenwald Award, Asn Res Vision & Ophthal, 93; Alcon Res Inst Award, 94; Magnes Prize, Hebrew Univ Jerusalem, 96. *Prof Exp:* Res fel neurobiol, Sch Med, Stanford Univ, 76-79, physiol, Univ Cambridge, Eng, 79-80; from asst prof to assoc prof, Med Br, Univ Tex, 80-85, prof physiol & biophys, 85-86. *Concurrent Pos:* Vis fel, Trinity Col, Univ Cambridge, 80-81. *Mem:* Biophys Soc; Soc Neurosci; Asn Res Vision & Ophthal; Soc Gen Physiologists; Physiol Soc Eng; fel Am Acad Arts & Sci. *Res:* Retinal physiology; visual and olfactory transduction; ion channels. *Mailing Add:* Dept Neurosci Johns Hopkins Univ Med Sch 725 N Wolfe St Baltimore MD 21205

**YAU, LEOPOLDO D,** SEMICONDUCTOR PROCESS TECHNOLOGY, MOS DEVICE PHYSICS. *Current Pos:* sr scientist, 78-84, prin engr, 84-86, FEL, INTEL, 86- *Personal Data:* b Surigao, Philippines, Aug 15, 40; US citizen; m 71, Bella Tan; c Cedric Yau. *Educ:* Univ San Carlos, BS, 62; Univ Minn, MS, 65; Univ Ill, PhD(elec eng), 69. *Honors & Awards:* Globe Award for Advan Technol Res, State of Ore, 91; Intel Achievement Award for Dielectric Planarization, 92. *Prof Exp:* Asst prof elec eng, Univ Phillipines, 70-71, Univ Ill, 71-73; staff, Bell Telephone Labs, 73-78. *Concurrent Pos:* Semiconductor Res Corp mentor, Yale Univ & Univ Fla. *Mem:* Fel Inst Elec & Electronics Engrs. *Res:* Deep level impurities in silicon; short-channel device model ofmos-transistors; applications of electron-beam lithography; dynamic random access memory technology; ultra-thin dielectrics; low pressure CVD; plasma enhanced CVD; chemical-mechanical planarization. *Mailing Add:* 3539 NW Brunson Crest Loop Portland OR 97229

**YAU, SHING-TUNG,** MATHEMATICS. *Current Pos:* PROF MATH, HARVARD UNIV, 87- *Personal Data:* b Kwuntung, China, Apr 4, 49; m; c 2. *Educ:* Univ Calif, Berkeley, PhD(math), 71. *Hon Degrees:* PhD, Harvard Univ, 87. *Honors & Awards:* Veblen Prize, Am Mat Soc, 81; Certy Prize, Nat Acad Sci, 81; Field's Medal, 82; Humboldt Found Sr Scientist Award, 82; Crafoord Prize, Swed Acad Sci, 94; Nat Medal of Sci, 97. *Prof Exp:* Fel, Inst Advan Study, Princeton Univ, 71-72; asst prof math, State Univ NY, Stony Brook, 72-73; vis asst prof, Stanford Univ, 73-74; from asst prof to prof, 74-80; prof, Inst Advan Study, Princeton, 80-83; prof math, Univ Calif, San Diego, 83-87. *Concurrent Pos:* Distinguished vis prof, State Univ New York, Stony Brook, 90; Fairchild distinguished scholar, Calif Inst Technol, 90; MacArthur fel, 85; mem bd, Math Sci, Nat Acad Sci. *Mem:* Nat Acad Sci; NY Acad Sci; Acad Arts & Sci; Am Phys Soc; Soc Indust & Appl Math; AAAS; Am Math Soc. *Res:* Differential geometry. *Mailing Add:* Dept Math Harvard Univ Cambridge MA 02138

**YAU, STEPHEN S,** SOFTWARE ENGINEERING, PARALLEL & DISTRIBUTED COMPUTING SYSTEMS. *Current Pos:* PROF & CHMN COMPUT & INFO SCI, UNIV FLA, 88- *Personal Data:* b Wusei, Kiangsu, China, Aug 6, 35; m 64, Vickie Liu; c Andrew & Philip. *Educ:* Nat Taiwan Univ, BS, 58; Univ Ill, Urbana, MS, 59, PhD(elec eng), 61. *Honors & Awards:* Levy Medal, Franklin Inst, 63; Golden Plate Award, Am Acad Achievement, 64; Richard E Merwin Award, Inst Elec & Electronics Engrs, 81, Centennial Medal, 84, Extraordinary Achievement Award, 85. *Prof Exp:* Res asst elec eng, Univ Ill, Urbana, 59-61; from asst prof to prof elec eng, Northwestern Univ, 61-88, dir comput sci, 70-88, chmn, Comput Sci Dept, 72-77, Elec Eng & Comput Sci Dept, 77-88, Walter P Murphy prof elec eng & comput sci, 86-88. *Concurrent Pos:* Consult, Battelle Columbus Lab, 76-77 & Syst Develop Corp, 77; ed, Inst Elec & Electronics Engrs Transactions on Software Eng, 88-91. *Mem:* Fel AAAS; Am Soc Eng Educ; fel Inst Elec & Electronics Engrs; Asn Comput Mach; Soc Indust & Appl Math; Sigma Xi. *Res:* Development and maintenance methodologies of large-scale software systems; quality assurance; software metrics; parallel processing and distributed computing systems; fault-tolerant software. *Mailing Add:* Dept Comput Sci & Eng Ariz State Univ Box 875406 Tempe AZ 85287. *Fax:* 904-392-1220; *E-Mail:* yau@cis.ufl.edu

**YAU, STEPHEN SHING-TOUNG,** COMPLEX GEOMETRY & ALGEBRA, THEORY. *Current Pos:* assoc prof, 80-84, Univ Senate, admin, 86-89, PROF MATH, UNIV ILL, CHICAGO, 84-, DIR CONTROL & INFO LAB, 93- *Personal Data:* b Hong Kong, China, Apr 12, 52; c Andrew. *Educ:* State Univ NY, Stony Brook MA, 74, PhD(math), 76. *Prof Exp:* Mem res, Inst Advan Study, 76-77 & 81-82; asst prof math, Harvard Univ, 77-80. *Concurrent Pos:* Sloan res fel, Alfred Sloan Res Found, 80-84; co-prin investr, NSF, 80-84, prin investr, 84-88 & 89-91; vis prof, math, Princeton Univ, 81; vis assoc prof, Univ Southern Calif, 83-84; vis prof, Yale Univ, 84-85, Inst Mittag-Leffier, Royal Swedish Acad of Sci, 87, Johns Hopkins Univ, 89-90; univ scholar, Univ Ill, 88-91; prin investr, Army Res Off, 89-92; managing ed, J Algebraic Geom, 91- *Mem:* Am Math Soc; sr mem Inst Elec & Electronics Engrs; Soc Indust & Appl Math. *Res:* Structure theory and classification of weakly elliptic singularities; complex Plateau problems for strongly psuedoconvex manifolds; lie algebra and complex structures of hupersurface singularities; non linear filtering and control wavelet and signal processing; image database; algebraic geometry coding. *Mailing Add:* Dept Math Statist & Comput Sci Univ Ill Chicago M/C 249 Chicago IL 60607-7045. *Fax:* 312-996-1491; *E-Mail:* u32790@uic.edu

**YAU, WALLACE WEN-CHUAN,** analytical chemistry, polymer physics, for more information see previous edition

**YAU, WEN-FOO,** ENGINEERING MECHANICS, APPLIED MATHEMATICS. *Current Pos:* res engr, Eastern Lab, E I Du Pont de Nemours & Co, Inc, 69-72, staff engr, 72-78, res staff engr, 78-81, RES ASSOC, SAVANNAH RIVER LAB, E I DU PONT DE NEMOURS & CO, INC, 81- *Personal Data:* b Shanghai, China, June 11, 35; US citizen; m 62. *Educ:* Nat Taiwan Univ, BS, 58; Univ Mass, MS, 61; Princeton Univ, PhD, 65. *Prof Exp:* Instr civil eng, Univ Mass, 61-63; res assoc eng mech, Univ Ky, 65-66, asst prof, 66-69. *Mem:* Am Soc Mech Engrs. *Res:* Operation and safety considerations of the Savannah River Plant for production of nuclear materials. *Mailing Add:* 2103 Maple Dr N North Augusta SC 29841

**YAU-YOUNG, ANNIE O,** BIOCHEMISTRY & IMMUNOLOGY, CELL BIOLOGY. *Educ:* Boston Univ, PhD(biochem), 78. *Prof Exp:* Sr scientist, Liposome Technol Inc, 84-89; licensing assoc, Off Technol Licensing, Univ Calif, Berkeley, 89-93; Systemix, 93-95. *Mailing Add:* 4162 Crosby Pl Palo Alto CA 94306

**YAVERBAUM, SIDNEY,** MEDICAL MICROBIOLOGY, IMMUNOCHEMISTRY. *Current Pos:* RETIRED. *Personal Data:* b New York, NY, Jan 28, 23; m 67; c 2. *Educ:* Univ Pa, PhD(med microbiol), 52. *Prof Exp:* Asst, Univ Pa, 51-52, res assoc, 52-53; fel microbiol, Boyce Thompson Inst Plant Res, 54-55; res med bacteriologist, Bio-Detection Br, Phys Defense Div, US Dept Army, Ft Detrick, 55-70; sr res biologist, Corning Glass Works, 70-76; mem staff, Wampole Div, Carter Wallace Inc, 76-80; mem staff, Technion, 80; pres, Aries Biomed Assocs, 80-85; US Army Med Res Inst Chem Defense, 85-91. *Mem:* AAAS; Am Soc Microbiol; Am Chem Soc; Sigma Xi; NY Acad Sci. *Res:* Cytology of yeasts, fungi and bacteria; genetics and nutrition of bacteria; assay of fungicides; physiology of aerobic sporeforming bacteria; biochemical composition of microorganisms; radioactive antibodies; solid-phase radioimmunoassay; immobilized enzyme research; automated instrumentation for microbiology. *Mailing Add:* 1306 Liriope Ct Apt 104 Belcamp MD 21017-1366

**YAVORSKY, JAMES A,** CHEMISTRY OF POLYMERS, ADHESIVES & URETHANE CHEMISTRY. *Current Pos:* Develop chemist, 84-89, supvr & proj leader, 90-92, SR DEVELOP ASSOC, ICI POLYURETHANE, 93- *Personal Data:* b Beaver Falls, Pa, Feb 29, 56. *Educ:* Wake Forest Univ, BS, 78; Clemson Univ, PhD(chem), 84. *Mem:* Am Chem Soc; Forest Prods Soc. *Res:* Product development within polyurethanes such as automotive fascia, crash pads, bowling balls and specialty adhesives for wood products. *Mailing Add:* 391 Megan Dr Mickleton NJ 08056

**YAVORSKY, JOHN MICHAEL,** WOOD SCIENCE & TECHNOLOGY, WOOD PRODUCTS UTILIZATION. *Current Pos:* prof forestry, 67-84, dean, Sch Continuing Educ, 73-84, EMER DEAN SCH CONTINUING EDUC, STATE UNIV NY COL ENVIRON SCI & FORESTRY, SYRACUSE, 84- *Personal Data:* b Renovo, Pa, June 11, 19; m 42, Jane Stellman; c John, Laurence, Michael, Susan, Karen & Piera. *Educ:* State Univ NY, BS, 42, MS, 47, PhD(wood eng), 55. *Prof Exp:* Res assoc & assoc prof wood utilization, State Univ NY Col Forestry, Syracuse, 48-56; chief wood utilization sect, Forestry Div, Food & Agr Orgn, UN, Rome, Italy, 57-63, proj mgr forestry proj, Lima, Peru, 63-67, sr proj officer, UN Spec Fund, NY, 67. *Mem:* Forest Prod Res Soc; Soc Am Foresters; Soc Wood Sci & Technol; Int Soc Trop Foresters. *Res:* Planning and supervision of continuing education activities in forestry and forest products technology; world forestry aspects of forest industries development. *Mailing Add:* 124 SW 14th St Boynton Beach FL 33426. *E-Mail:* yavo1@aol.com

**YAVROUIAN, ANDRE,** FLIGHT HARDWARE MATERIALS ANALYSIS. *Current Pos:* MEM TECH STAFF, JET PROPULSION LAB, 79- *Personal Data:* b Shoumen, Bulgaria, Feb 28, 43; US citizen; m, Assia; c Robert & Janet. *Educ:* Sofia State Univ, MS, 68. *Prof Exp:* Res chemist, CalBio Chem, 69-78. *Concurrent Pos:* Pvt consult, Optical Radiation Corp, 80-81, Contex Corp, 80- & Ioptex Corp, 83- *Res:* Polymer characterization organic chemistry; contamination analysis; space environmental effects on materials; space flight material and hardware analysis; chemical consultation; propellent analysis and evaluation; materials evaluation and characterization. *Mailing Add:* 1476 Sunshine Dr Glendale CA 91208

**YAWS, CARL LLOYD,** CHEMICAL ENGINEERING, CHEMISTRY. *Current Pos:* ASSOC PROF CHEM ENG, LAMAR UNIV, 77- *Personal Data:* b Yoakum, Tex, Oct 1, 38; m 58; c 4. *Educ:* Tex A&I Col, BS, 60; Univ Houston, MS, 63, PhD(chem eng), 65. *Prof Exp:* Res chem engr, Baytown Labs, Esso Res & Eng Co, Tex, 63-65; process develop engr, Res & Develop Dept, Ethyl Corp, La, 65-68; sr engr & mem tech staff, Chem Mat Div, Tex Instruments, Inc, 68-77. *Mem:* Am Inst Chem Engrs; Am Chem Soc. *Res:* Chemicals; petrochemicals; petroleum refining; pollution control; solvent extractions; distillation; chlorination; fluorination; hydrogenation; desulfurization; catalytic reactions; chemical vapor deposition; fluorocarbons; chlorocarbons; specialty hydrocarbons; lubricants; gasolines; ultra purity silicon; carbides; nitrides. *Mailing Add:* 685 Birchwood Dr Port Neches TX 77651

**YAYANOS, A ARISTIDES,** BIOPHYSICS, DEEP-SEA BIOLOGY. *Current Pos:* Fel, Univ Calif, 67-68, asst res physiologist, 68-78, assoc res biophysicist, 78-83, RES BIOPHYSICIST & SR LECTR, SCRIPPS INST OCEANOG, UNIV CALIF, SAN DIEGO, 83-, PROF BIOPHYS. *Personal Data:* b Buffalo, NY, Jan 31, 40; m 66, Sandra Morall; c Meredith. *Educ:* Univ Buffalo, BA, 61; Pa State Univ, MS, 65, PhD(biophysics), 67. *Concurrent Pos:* NIH res career develop award, 70-75. *Mem:* Am Chem Soc; Math Asn Am; Am Soc Microbiol; AAAS; Radiation Res Soc. *Res:* Physiology of deep-sea invertebrates; deep-sea microbiology; physics and biology at high pressures; radiation biology. *Mailing Add:* PO Box 7220 Rancho Santa Fe CA 92067. *E-Mail:* ayayanos@ucsd.edu

**YAZ, EDWIN ENGIN,** CONTROL SYSTEMS, SIGNAL PROCESSING. *Current Pos:* from asst prof to assoc prof, 85-91, PROF ELEC ENG, UNIV ARK, 91- *Personal Data:* b Istanbul, Turkey, May 11, 54; m 80, Yvonne I Durak. *Educ:* Bosphorus Univ, BS, 76, MS, 79, PhD(elec eng), 82. *Honors & Awards:* Halliburton Found Award, 87 & 91. *Prof Exp:* Teaching asst elec eng, Bosphorus Univ, Turkey, 76-79; eng consult, Sun Electronics Co, Turkey, 78; instr elec eng, Yildiz Univ, Turkey, 79-82; researcher control systs, Marmara Res Inst & Res Inst Basic Sci, 82-84. *Concurrent Pos:* Res fel, Coord Sci Lab, Univ Ill, Urbana-Champaign, 84; vis prof, Space Systs Control Lab, Purdue Univ, W Lafayette, 92; assoc ed, Trans Automatic Control, Inst Elect & Electronics Engrs, Control Sys Soc Conf; Am Assoc Univ Prof(s) & Turkish Chamber Elec Engs. *Mem:* sr mem Inst Elec & Electronics Engrs; Am Soc Eng Educ; Am Asn Univ Prof. *Res:* Non-linear and stochastic control and estimation; stability theory with applications to robotics; statistical signal processing with applications to power systems. *Mailing Add:* Elec Eng Dept BEC 3217 Univ Ark Fayetteville AR 72701. *E-Mail:* ey1@engr.uark.edu

**YAZULLA, STEPHEN,** VISUAL SYSTEM, RETINA. *Current Pos:* from asst prof to assoc prof, 74-86, PROF NEUROBIOL, STATE UNIV NY, STONY BROOK, 86- *Personal Data:* b Jersey City, NJ, Sept 3, 45; m 67, 83, Margaret A Stanley; c Lisa, Debra, Caroline & Marie. *Educ:* Univ Scranton, BS, 67; Univ Del, MA, 69, PhD(psychol), 71. *Prof Exp:* Fel biol, Univ Del, 71-72; neurobiol, Harvard Univ, 72-74. *Concurrent Pos:* NIH res grant, prin investr, State Univ NY, Stony Brook, 76-; adj mem, NIH-Nat Eye Inst Vis A Study Sect, Div Res Grants, 85, mem, 86-90, Reviewers Reserve, 90-95; NSF grant, 90-92; assoc ed, Visual Neurosci, 93-97, J Neurocytol, 92-; vis prof, Univ Tex, Houston, 93. *Mem:* Sigma Xi; Asn Res Vision & Ophthal; Soc Neurosci; Int Brain Res Orgn. *Res:* Cellular mechanisms and anatomical organization underlying information processing in the vertebrate retina; light and electron microscopic autoradiography; immunocytochemistry; electrophysiology; pharmacology; biochemistry; cellular basis of visual processing. *Mailing Add:* Dept Neurobiol & Behav State Univ NY Stony Brook NY 11794-5230. *Fax:* 516-632-6661; *E-Mail:* yazulla@life.bio.sunysb.edu

**YCAS, MARTYNAS,** BIOLOGY, COMPUTER APPLICATIONS. *Current Pos:* from asst prof to prof, 56-88, EMER PROF MICROBIOL, SCH MED, STATE UNIV NY UPSTATE MED CTR, 88- *Personal Data:* b Voronezh, Russia, Dec 10, 17; nat US; m 45, Mary K Warren; c 3. *Educ:* Univ Wis, BA, 47; Calif Inst Technol, PhD(embryol), 50. *Hon Degrees:* Dr, Univ Vilnius, Lithuania, 92. *Prof Exp:* Instr, Univ Wash, 50-51; biologist pioneering res labs, Corps, US Dept Army, 51-56. *Res:* Biochemical evolution. *Mailing Add:* 109 Croyden Rd Syracuse NY 13224

**YE, GUANGNING,** genomic mapping, for more information see previous edition

**YE, JIAN,** CARDIOVASCULAR SURGERY, CARDIOLOGY. *Current Pos:* surg res asst, 92-96, RES COUN OFFICER-3, NAT RES COUN CAN, 96-; ADJ PROF SURG, UNIV MAN, 97- *Personal Data:* b Shangyu, China, Mar 28, 61; Can citizen. *Educ:* Wenzhou Med Col, China, MD, 83; Fujian Med Col, China, MSc, 88. *Prof Exp:* Clin resident surg, Wenzhou Med Col, 83-85, clin fel cardiovasc surg, 88-89, attending surgeon & asst prof, 89-90; cardiovasc res fel, Case Western Res Univ, 90-92. *Concurrent Pos:* Int scholar & vis surgeon, Cleveland Clin Found, 90. *Mem:* Chinese Med Asn. *Res:* Mechanism of myocardial ischemic/reperfusion injury and of brain ischemic injury during open heart surgery requiring circulatory arrest; optimizing and developing techniques of brain and heart perfusion to minimize or avoid ischemic/reperfusion injury during open heart surgery. *Mailing Add:* 768 Waverley St Winnipeg MB R3M 3C7 Can. *Fax:* 204-983-3154; *E-Mail:* ye@ibd.nrc.ca

**YE, QIZHUANG,** RATIONAL DRUG DESIGN, MECHANISTIC STUDIES. *Current Pos:* sr scientist, 90-94, RES ASSOC, PARKE-DAVIS PHARMACEUT RES, WARNER-LAMBERT CO, 94- *Personal Data:* b Aug 9, 57; m 87, Liqun Xiao; c Karen & Brian. *Educ:* Nanjing Col Pharm, BS, 82; Univ Kans, MS, 84, PhD(med chem), 88. *Prof Exp:* Res fel, Harvard Med Sch, 88-90. *Mem:* Am Soc Biochem & Molecular Biol; Am Chem Soc. *Res:* Structure and mechanism of human matrix metalloproteinases cloning and over-expression of human enzymes in E coli, protein purification and characterization; protein structure-function studies; mutagenisis studies; enzyme inhibitor development. *Mailing Add:* Dept Biochem Parke Davis Pharmaceut Res 2800 Plymouth Rd Ann Arbor MI 48105-2430. *Fax:* 313-996-1355; *E-Mail:* yeq@aa.wl.com

**YE, XIANG DONG,** SEMIGROUP ABSTRACT ALGEBRA. *Current Pos:* From asst prof to assoc prof, 87-91, PROF MATH, CALVIN COL, 91- *Personal Data:* m 72, Sh Xian Li; c Wei & Alice. *Educ:* Univ Iowa, MS, 83, PhD(math), 87. *Mem:* Am Math Soc; Math Assc Am. *Res:* Semigroup structure; abstract algebra. *Mailing Add:* Math Dept Calvin Col Grand Rapids MI 49546

**YE, ZHEN,** OCEAN PHYSICS, UNDERWATER ACOUSTICS. *Current Pos:* PROF PHYSICS, NAT CENT UNIV, TAIWAN, CHINA, 97- *Personal Data:* b Peking, China, Jan 22, 63; Can citizen; m 88, Wendy Yao; c Maggie. *Educ:* Peking Univ, BSc, 84; Univ Alta, PhD(physics), 91. *Prof Exp:* Postdoctoral fel, Univ Ottawa, 91-92; res scientist, Inst Ocean Sci, Can, 93-97. *Concurrent Pos:* Vis scientist, Univ Alta, 94, Japan Nat Res Inst Fisheries, Eng, 94, Nat Inst Water & Atmosphere Res, NZ, 96. *Mem:* Acoust Soc Am. *Res:* Superconductivity and transport theory; wave propagation in random media; scattering theory. *Mailing Add:* Dept Physics Nat Cent Univ Chung-Li Taiwan. *Fax:* 886-3-4251175; *E-Mail:* zhen@joule.phy.ncu.edu.tw

**YEADON, DAVID ALLOU,** CHEMISTRY. *Current Pos:* res chemist, Oilseed Crops Lab, 53-65, RES CHEMIST, COTTON FINISHES LAB, SOUTHERN REGIONAL RES LAB, USDA, 65- *Personal Data:* b New Orleans, La, Nov 10, 20; m 49; c 2. *Educ:* Loyola Univ, La, BS, 40; Univ Detroit, MS, 42. *Prof Exp:* Asst & lab instr, Univ Detroit, 40-42; chemist, Gelatin Prod Corp, Mich, 42-43; chemist, Esso Standard Oil Co, La, res chemist, Esso Labs, 43-50; res chemist, Southern Regional Res Lab, Naval Store Div, USDA, 50; res chemist, Alpine Corp, Miss, 50-53. *Mem:* Am Chem Soc; Sigma Xi; Am Asn Textile Chemists & Colorists. *Res:* Synthetic rubber; hydrocarbons; polymers, resins and coatings; chemistry, synthesis and applications of fats and oils; modifications to improve utilization of cotton; fire retardant cotton textiles. *Mailing Add:* 1460 Pressburg St New Orleans LA 70122-2046

**YEAGER, CHARLES ELWOOD (CHUCK),** AEROSPACE SCIENCE. *Current Pos:* RETIRED. *Personal Data:* b Myra, WVa, Feb 13, 23; m 45, Gennis F Dickhouse; c Sharon (Flick), Susan F, Donald C & Michael D. *Hon Degrees:* DSc, WVa Univ, 48, Marshall Univ, 69; DAeroSci, Salem Col, 75. *Honors & Awards:* Presidential Medal of Freedom, 85. *Prof Exp:* Var positions, USAF, 41-75. *Concurrent Pos:* US defense rep, Pakistan, 71-73; spec asst to comdr, Air Force Inspection & Safety Ctr, Norton AFB, Calif, 73, dir aerospace safety, 73-75. *Res:* First man to fly faster than the speed of sound. *Mailing Add:* PO Box 128 Cedar Ridge CA 95924-0128

**YEAGER, ERNEST BILL,** ELECTROCHEMISTRY. *Current Pos:* Asst physics & phys chem, Case Western Reserve Univ, 45-47, from instr to assoc prof chem, 48-58, actg chmn dept, 64-65, chmn dept, 69-72, chmn fac senate, 72-73, PROF CHEM, CASE WESTERN RESERVE UNIV, 58-, DIR CASE CTR ELECTROCHEM SCI, 76-, FRANK HOVORKA CHAIR CHEM, 83-, PROF CHEM ENG, 84-, FRANK HOVORKA EMER PROF CHEM, 90- *Personal Data:* b Orange, NJ, Sept 26, 24. *Educ:* Montclair State Col, BA, 45; Western Reserve Univ, MS, 46, PhD(phys chem), 48. *Hon Degrees:* Dr, Montclair State Col, 83. *Honors & Awards:* Acoust Soc Am Award, 56; Cert of Commendation, US Navy, 73; Acheson Medal, Electrochem Soc, 80. *Concurrent Pos:* Consult, Union Carbide Corp, 55- & Gen Motors Corp, 70; vis prof & NATO fel, Univ Southampton, 68; mem comt undersea warfare, Nat Acad Sci-Nat Res Coun, 63-73; rep mem, phys sci div, Nat Res Coun, 69-73, mem, comt Battery Mat & Fuel Cells for Vehicular Appln, Nat Mat Adv Bd, Nat Res Coun, 79-81 & comt Electrochem Aspects Energy Conserv & Prod, Nat Mat Adv Bd, 85-87; mem comn electrochem, Int Union Pure & Appl Chem, 69-75; mem underwater sound adv group, Off Naval Res, 72-74; mem, vis comt, Brookhaven Nat Lab & Montclair State Col, NJ, 78-80; mem, adv comt on USSR & Eastern Europe, Comn Int Relations, Nat Acad Sci, 80-; mem, electrolysis technol adv comt, US Dept Energy, 82-83 & advan fuel cell working group, 84-85; mem, rev comt chem technol div, Argonne Nat Lab, 84- *Mem:* Fel AAAS; fel Acoust Soc Am (vpres, 67-68); Am Chem Soc; Int Soc Electrochem (vpres, 67-68, pres, 70-71); Electrochem Soc (vpres, 62-64, pres, 64-65). *Res:* Ultrasonics; electrode kinetics; electrolytes; relaxation spectroscopy; electrocatalysis. *Mailing Add:* Dept Chem Case Western Reserve Univ Cleveland OH 44106

**YEAGER, HENRY, JR,** PULMONARY DISEASE. *Current Pos:* Assoc prof, 77-90, PROF MED, DIV PULMONARY & CRITICAL CARE MED, MED CTR, GEORGETOWN UNIV, 90- *Personal Data:* b Dallas, Tex, Sept 13, 33; m 76; c 1. *Educ:* Johns Hopkins Univ, MD, 57. *Mem:* Am Col Physicians; Am Thoracic Soc; Am Asn Immunologists; Am Fedn Clin Res; AMA; Am Col Chest Physicians; Am Physiol Soc; Soc Leukocyte Biol. *Res:* Pulmonary macrophage physiology; mycobacterial disease. *Mailing Add:* Med Ctr Georgetown Univ 3800 Reservoir Rd Washington DC 20007-2197

**YEAGER, HOWARD LANE,** MEMBRANE SCIENCE, ION EXCHANGE. *Current Pos:* from asst prof to assoc prof, 70-83, dept head, 88-93, PROF CHEM, UNIV CALGARY, 83- *Personal Data:* b Pittsburgh, Pa, Dec 24, 43. *Educ:* Univ Pittsburgh, BS, 65; Univ Wis-Madison, MS, 67; Univ Alta,

PhD(chem), 69. *Prof Exp:* Lectr anal chem, Univ Wis, 69-70. *Concurrent Pos:* Vis scientist, Nat Res Coun Can, 78-79. *Mem:* Am Chem Soc; Electrochem Soc; Chem Inst Can; AAAS; Sigma Xi; NAm Membrane Soc. *Res:* Transport in ion exchange membranes, ion exchange thermodynamics and synthetic membrane technology. *Mailing Add:* Dept Chem 2500 Univ Dr NW Univ Calgary Calgary AB T2N 1N4 Can. *Fax:* 403-289-9488

**YEAGER, PAUL RAY,** PHYSICS, INSTRUMENT ENGINEERING. *Current Pos:* PRES, DGR INC, 82- *Personal Data:* b Sherman, Tex, Feb 7, 31; m 56; c 2. *Educ:* Austin Col, BA, 52; George Wash Univ, MS, 70. *Prof Exp:* Engr instrumentation, Nat Adv Comt Aeronaut, 52-55, sr proj engr, 55-59; leader vacuum measurements group, NASA, 59-63, head vacuum measurements sect, 63-69, head environ measurements sect, 69-74, Head, Gen Res Instrumentation Br, 74-87. *Mem:* Am Vacuum Soc. *Res:* Mass spectrometry; vacuum instrumentation; thermal measurements. *Mailing Add:* 115 Paradise Point Rd Grafton VA 23692

**YEAGER, SANDRA ANN,** ORGANIC CHEMISTRY, BIOCHEMISTRY. *Current Pos:* ASSOC PROF ORG & BIOCHEM, MILLERSVILLE UNIV, 74- *Personal Data:* b Philadelphia, Pa, Jan 4, 39. *Educ:* Thiel Col, AB, 60; Univ NH, MS, 63, PhD(org chem), 68. *Prof Exp:* Asst prof chem, Hudson Valley Community Col, NY, 62-64; res asst, Children's Cancer Res Found, Boston, Mass, 68-69; asst prof chem, Pa State Univ, Mont Alto, 69-73; asst prof org & biochem, Wilson Col, 73-74. *Concurrent Pos:* Res assoc, Southwest Res Inst, San Antonio, Tex, 81; vis fac, Lehigh Univ, 85-86, Univ NH, 87. *Mem:* Am Chem Soc; World Future Soc; Sigma Xi; Asn Women Sci. *Res:* Analysis of biochemically important substances using varied chromatographic and electrophoretic techniques; synthesis of possible cancer chemotherapeutics; nuclear magnetic resonance in vitro and in vivo of metalloporphyrins. *Mailing Add:* Chem Dept Roddy Sci Ctr Millersville Univ Millersville PA 17551-0302

**YEAGER, VERNON LEROY,** GROSS ANATOMY. *Current Pos:* PROF ANAT, ST LOUIS UNIV, 71- *Personal Data:* b Williston, NDak, Nov 20, 26; m 47, Grethe Spoklie; c Thomas A, Donna J (Schuh), Susan E & Robin V. *Educ:* Minot State Col, BS, 49; Univ NDak, PhD(anat), 55. *Honors & Awards:* Hektoen Gold Medal, AMA, 78. *Prof Exp:* Teacher sci, Garrison High Sch, 49-51; prof anat, Univ NDak, 55-67; assoc prof, St Louis Univ, 67-68; Rockefeller Found vis prof, Mahidol Univ, Thailand, 68-71. *Concurrent Pos:* NSF fel, Northwestern Univ, Chicago, 60. *Mem:* Sigma Xi; Asn Clin Anatomists. *Res:* Pathology of connective tissues; cancer of the larynx; medical education. *Mailing Add:* Dept Anat St Louis Univ Sch Med St Louis MO 63104. *Fax:* 314-268-5127

**YEAGLE, PHILIP L,** BIOLOGICAL MEMBRANES. *Current Pos:* from asst prof to assoc prof, 78-91, PROF BIOCHEM, STATE UNIV NY, BUFFALO, 91- *Personal Data:* b 1949; US citizen; c 2. *Educ:* St Olaf Col, BA, 71; Duke Univ, PhD(chem), 74. *Honors & Awards:* Res Career Develop Award, NIH. *Prof Exp:* Fel, Univ Va, 74-78. *Mem:* Am Chem Soc; Am Soc Biochem & Molecular Biol; Biophys Soc; Asn Res Vision & Opthal; Am Soc Cell Biol. *Res:* Structure of cell membranes and relations of structure to function, including membrane fusion, photoreceptor function, and cholesterol protein interactions in membranes using biochemical and biophysical techniques. *Mailing Add:* Dept Biochem 140 Farber Hall State Univ NY Health Sci Ctr 3435 Main St Buffalo NY 14214. *Fax:* 716-829-2725; *E-Mail:* yeagle@acsu. buffalo.edu

**YEAKEY, ERNEST LEON,** ORGANIC CHEMISTRY. *Current Pos:* Res chemist, Texaco Chem Co, 60-67, supvr explor res, Jefferson Chem Co, 67-76, mgr res, 76-80, MGR NEW PROD DEVELOP, TEXACO CHEM CO, 80- *Personal Data:* b Sikeston, Mo, Aug 5, 34; m 61; c 2. *Educ:* Southeast Mo State Col, BS, 56; State Univ, Iowa, PhD(org chem), 60. *Mem:* Am Chem Soc. *Res:* Hydrogenation of nitriles to amines; reductive amination of alcohols to amines; synthetic routes to alpha olefins; catalytic synthesis of ethyleneamines; synthesis of heterocyclic amines. *Mailing Add:* 6316 Gato Path Austin TX 78731

**YEARGAN, JERRY REESE,** MICROELECTRONICS. *Current Pos:* from asst prof to assoc prof elec eng, 67-77, head dept, 77-82, PROF ELEC ENG, UNIV ARK, FAYETTEVILLE, 77-, UNIV PROF, 85- *Personal Data:* b Kirby, Ark, Jan 31, 40; m 59, Jane Evans; c Leigh A & W Brooks. *Educ:* Univ Ark, BSEE, 61, MSEE, 65; Univ Tex, Austin, PhD(elec eng), 67. *Prof Exp:* From asst engr to assoc engr, Tex Instruments, Inc, 61-63; res engr, Univ Tex, 66-67. *Mem:* Fel Inst Elec & Electronics Engrs; Am Phys Soc; Am Soc Eng Educ. *Res:* Analog and mixed-signal microelectronics; device modeling and circuit simulation. *Mailing Add:* Dept Elec Eng Bell 3217 Univ Ark Fayetteville AR 72701

**YEARGAN, KENNETH VERNON,** ENTOMOLOGY, ECOLOGY. *Current Pos:* From asst prof to assoc prof, 74-84, PROF ENTOMOL, UNIV KY, 84- *Personal Data:* b Clanton, Ala, Feb 12, 47; m 72; c 1. *Educ:* Auburn Univ, BS, 69; Univ Calif, Davis, PhD(entom), 74. *Mem:* Entom Soc Am; Int Orgn Biol Control; Sigma Xi. *Res:* Biological control of insect pests of soybeans and forage crops; theory and practice of population sampling; integrated pest management; ecology and behavior of insects and spiders. *Mailing Add:* Dept Entom Univ Ky 500 S Limestone St Lexington KY 40506-0001

**YEARGERS, EDWARD KLINGENSMITH,** BIOPHYSICS. *Current Pos:* asst prof, 68-70, assoc prof, 70-94, PROF BIOL, GA INST TECHNOL, 94- *Personal Data:* b Houma, La, Apr 27, 38; m 93; c 2. *Educ:* Ga Inst Technol, BS, 60; Emory Univ, MS, 62; Mich State Univ, PhD(biophys), 66. *Prof Exp:* US AEC res fel radiation physics, Oak Ridge Nat Lab, 66-67; NIH res fel theoret chem, Czech Acad Sci, 67. *Concurrent Pos:* Vis scientist plant physiol, Hebrew Univ, 85. *Mem:* Biophys Soc; Am Inst Biol Sci. *Res:* Molecular biophysics; protein structure; molecular aspects of aging. *Mailing Add:* Sch Biol Ga Inst Technol 225 N Ave NW Atlanta GA 30332. *Fax:* 404-894-0519; *E-Mail:* bigraey@acme.gatech.edu

**YEARIAN, MASON RUSSELL,** NUCLEAR PHYSICS, HIGH ENERGY PHYSICS. *Current Pos:* from asst prof to assoc prof, 61-71, PROF PHYSICS, STANFORD UNIV, 71-, DIR, HIGH ENERGY PHYSICS LAB, 73- *Personal Data:* b Lafayette, Ind, July 5, 32; m 56, 65; c 3. *Educ:* Purdue Univ, BS, 54; Stanford Univ, MS, 56, PhD(physics), 61. *Prof Exp:* Res assoc physics, Univ Pa, 59-61. *Res:* Electron scattering from nuclei and nucleons; nucleon form factors; charge distribution in nuclei; high energy particle physics. *Mailing Add:* 921 Cottrell Way Palo Alto CA 94305-4060

**YEARIAN, WILLIAM C,** ENTOMOLOGY. *Current Pos:* From asst prof to assoc prof, 65-74, PROF ENTOM, UNIV ARK, FAYETTEVILLE, 74- *Personal Data:* b Lake Village, Ark, May 20, 37; m 60; c 1. *Educ:* Univ Ark, Fayetteville, BS, 60, MS, 61; Univ Fla, PhD(entom), 66. *Mem:* Soc Invert Path; Entom Soc Am. *Res:* Forest entomology; applied insect pathology. *Mailing Add:* 1648 N Starr Dr Fayetteville AR 72701

**YEARICK, ELISABETH STELLE,** NUTRITION, BIOCHEMISTRY. *Current Pos:* prof, 66-79, EMER PROF NUTRIT & FOODS, ORE STATE UNIV, 79- *Personal Data:* b Spokane, Wash, July 1, 13. *Educ:* Univ Wis, BS, 34, MS, 35; Univ Iowa, PhD(nutrit), 60; Am Bd Nutrit, cert human nutrit, 65. *Prof Exp:* Asst dir dietetics, Duke Hosp, 48-53, asst prof, Duke Univ, 53; assoc prof nutrit, Univ Iowa, 53-57; assoc prof, WVa Univ, 60-66. *Mem:* Am Inst Nutrit; Am Dietetic Asn. *Mailing Add:* 145 W 16th Apt 406 Corvallis OR 97330-5762

**YEARY, ROGER A,** TOXICOLOGY, ENVIRONMENTAL HEALTH. *Current Pos:* exten vet toxicologist, Coop Exten Serv, Ohio State Univ, 65-67, from assoc prof to prof vet physiol & pharmacol, 67-84, adj prof, 84-90, EMER PROF VET PHYSIOL & PHARMACOL, COL VET MED, OHIO STATE UNIV, 90-; VPRES, HEALTH, SAFETY & ENVIRON, SERV MASTER CONSUMER SERV & TRUGREEN-CHEMLAWN, 92- *Personal Data:* b Cleveland, Ohio, Apr 26, 32; div; c 4. *Educ:* Ohio State Univ, DVM, 56; Am Bd Vet Toxicol, dipl; Am Bd Toxicol, dipl. *Prof Exp:* Staff sr toxicologist, Charles Pfizer & Co, Inc, Conn, 60-61; chief, Toxicol Sect, Lakeside Labs Div, Colgate-Palmolive Co, Wis, 61-65. *Concurrent Pos:* Toxicol consult, Lakeside Labs Div, Colgate-Palmolive Co, 65-67 & Minn Mining & Mfg Co, 67-77; NIH res grants, toxicol study sect, 73-77; consult, Chemlawn Corp, 77-81 & O M Scott & Sons, 78-81; dir, Employee & Environ Health, Chemlawn Corp, 81-86, vpres health & safety, 86-; corp safety officer, Ecolab, Inc, 88-90; vpres Health, Safety & Environ Affairs, Ecolab, Inc & Chemlawn Serv Corp, 90-92. *Mem:* AAAS; Am Soc Pharmacol & Exp Therapeut; Am Vet Med Asn; Soc Toxicol; Am Asn Clin Chemists; Am Conf Govt Indust Hygienists. *Res:* Environmental and occupational health. *Mailing Add:* Trugreen-Chemlawn 135 Winter Rd Delaware OH 43015-8903. *Fax:* 614-548-4860; *E-Mail:* ryeary@postbox.acs.ohio-state.edu

**YEATES, DONOVAN B,** MUCOCILIARY TRANSPORT, AEROSOL DEPOSITION & CLEARANCE. *Current Pos:* assoc dir environ med, Univ Ill, 78-87, actg dir, Great Lakes Ctr Occup Safety & Health, 87-88, assoc chief, Sect Environ Occup, 87-89, dir, Occup Safety & Health Ctr, 88-90, RES PROF MED, UNIV ILL, CHICAGO, 89-, PROF, PROG BIOENG, COL ENG, 92-; ASSOC RES CAREER SCIENTIST & RES PHYSIOLOGIST GM-15, VET ADMIN CTR, WEST SIDE CHICAGO, 92- *Personal Data:* b Cottesloe, Western Australia, Aug 24, 43. *Educ:* Univ Surrey, Eng, MS, 69; Univ Toronto, PhD(biophys), 75. *Prof Exp:* Fel, Can Cystic Fibrosis Found, 72-74; res physiologist, GS-13, Vet Admin West Side Med Ctr, 78-81, GS-14, 81-92. *Concurrent Pos:* Prin investr, Vet Admin, 90-, NIH, 90-, Vet Affairs, 92-; co-investr, Whitaker Found, 92-; collabr cellular regulation respiratory, Nat Heart Lung & Blood Inst, NIH, 92-, mechanisms lung edema & clearance, Am Lung Asn, 92- *Mem:* Am Thoracic Soc; Cent Soc Clin Res; Am Physiol Soc; AAAS; Am Soc Aerosol Med. *Res:* Airway pharmacology; ciliary activity; mucus rheology; lung defense mechanisms; neural regulation of airway function; biomedical instrumentation; effects of pollutants on the lungs. *Mailing Add:* Univ Ill 1940 W Taylor St Rm 212 Chicago IL 60612-7353. *Fax:* 312-996-1286

**YEATMAN, CHRISTOPHER WILLIAM,** FOREST GENETIC DIVERSITY & CONSERVATION. *Current Pos:* CONSULT, 91- *Personal Data:* b Port Pirie, Australia, Aug 6, 27; m 54, Norma L Kihl; c Christopher, Mignon, Dorothea & Sarah. *Educ:* Univ Adelaide, BSc, 51; Australian Sch Forestry, Canberra, dipl, 51; Yale Univ, MF, 57; PhD(forest genetics), 66. *Prof Exp:* Forester, Dept Woods & Forests, SAustralia, 51; forest officer, Forestry Comn Gt Brit, 51-53; asst, Petawawa Forest Exp Sta, 53-54, res forest officer, 54-66, res scientist, 66-89; Can proj mgr, Can Forest Tree Seed Ctr, Asn Southeast Asian Nations, Thailand, 89-91. *Concurrent Pos:* Mem & secy, Comt Forest Tree Breeding Can, 55-66, exec secy, 66-80; forest comt expert, Gen Resources, 78-88; comt, Experts Plant Genc Resources, Can, 82-89. *Mem:* Can Inst Forestry; Sigma Xi. *Res:* Silviculture; plantation establishment; tree breeding and forest genetics; genecology. *Mailing Add:* PO Box 721 Deep River ON K0J 1P0 Can. *Fax:* 613-584-1416

**YEATMAN, HARRY CLAY,** ZOOLOGY. *Current Pos:* From asst prof to assoc prof biol, Univ South, 50-59, chmn dept, 71-76, prof, 59-80, KENAN PROF BIOL, UNIV SOUTH 80-, ELDER HOSTEL PROF, 87- *Personal Data:* b Ashwood, Tenn, June 22, 16; m 49; c 2. *Educ:* Univ NC, AB, 39, MA, 42, PhD(zool), 53. *Concurrent Pos:* Consult, US Nat Mus, 48-, Woods Hole Oceanog Inst, 60- & SEATO, US Army, Thailand, 66-; vis prof marine biol, VA Inst Marine Sci, Gloucester Point, VA, 67; consult, Univ Tehran, Iran, 72- & WHO, 76-; Brown Found fel, Univ South, 84. *Mem:* AAAS; Soc Syst Zool; Am Soc Limnol & Oceanog; Am Soc Ichthyologists & Herpetologists; Am Ornith Union. *Res:* Limnology; taxonomy and ecology of freshwater and marine copepods. *Mailing Add:* PO Box 356 Jumpoff Rd Sewanee TN 37375-0356

**YEATMAN, JOHN NEWTON,** FOOD SCIENCE. *Current Pos:* CONSULT FOOD STANDS-QUAL EVAL, 75- *Personal Data:* b Washington, DC, Apr 30, 20; m 54; c 2. *Educ:* Univ Md, BS, 44; Univ Calif, Los Angeles, MS, 48. *Prof Exp:* Plant physiologist, USDA, 44-47; plant physiologist, Chem Corps, US Dept Army, Ft Detrick, 48-53; res food technol & leader, Qual Eval Invest, Agr Res Serv, USDA, 54-68, dir color res lab, Mkt Qual Res Div, 68-71; res food technol, Bur Foods, Div Food Technol, Food & Drug Admin, 71-75. *Mem:* Inst Food Technol; Inter-Soc Color Coun; Sigma Xi. *Res:* Research and development of methods for standards improvement by objectively measuring by physical and chemical means identity and quality factors in processed fruits and vegetables and their products; food standards and quality evaluation; instruments and inspection lighting. *Mailing Add:* 11106 Cherry Hill Rd Hyattsville MD 20783

**YEATS, FREDERICK TINSLEY,** BOTANY. *Current Pos:* PROF BIOL, HIGH POINT COL, 69- *Personal Data:* b Gadsden, Ala, Apr 4, 42; m 69; c 2. *Educ:* Miss Col, BS, 64; Univ Miss, MS, 67; Univ SC, PhD(biol), 71. *Mem:* Sigma Xi; Am Inst Biol Sci. *Res:* Developmental morphology in fern gametophytes; embryology in the genus Smilax. *Mailing Add:* Dept Biol High Point Univ 933 Montlieu Ave High Point NC 27262-3555

**YEATS, ROBERT SHEPPARD,** EARTHQUAKE HAZARDS. *Current Pos:* chmn dept, 77-85, PROF GEOL, ORE STATE UNIV, 77- *Personal Data:* b Miami, Fla, Mar 30, 31; m 93, Angela Brisland; c Robert, David, Stephen, Kenneth & Sara. *Educ:* Univ Fla, AB, 52; Univ Wash, MS & PhD(geol), 58. *Honors & Awards:* Richard Johns Distinguished Lectr Eng Geol, 95-96. *Prof Exp:* Exploitation engr, Shell Oil Co, 58-62, sr prod geologist, 62-64, sr geologist, 64-67; from assoc prof to prof geol, Ohio Univ, 67-77. *Concurrent Pos:* Consult, F Beach Leighton & Assocs, Calif & Energy Resources Br, US Geol Surv, 75; co-chief scientist, Deep Sea Drilling Proj, 73-74, 78; chmn, Structural Geol & Tectonics Div, Geol Soc Am, 84-85, Cordilleran sect, Geol Soc Am, 88-89, working group 1, Int Lithosphere Prog, 87-90, task group, Holocene earthquakes, 90-97. *Mem:* Fel AAAS; fel Geol Soc Am; Am Geophys Union; Seismol Soc Am; Am Asn Petrol Geol; Europ Union Geosci. *Res:* Structural evolution of Pacific continental margin of Americas and the Himalaya; application of plate tectonics to petroleum accumulation; active folds and faults, particularly in contractile continental areas. *Mailing Add:* Dept Geosci Ore State Univ Corvallis OR 97331-5506. *Fax:* 541-737-1200; *E-Mail:* yeatsr@bcc.orst.edu

**YEATS, RONALD BRADSHAW,** MICROCOMPUTER APPLICATIONS, CHEMICAL INFORMATION RETRIEVAL. *Current Pos:* asst prof, 68-74, assoc prof, 74-80, PROF ORG CHEM, BISHOPS UNIV, QUE, CAN, 80-, CHMN, DEPT CHEM, 90- *Personal Data:* b Newcastle-upon-Tyne, Eng, Mar 17, 41; Can citizen; m 62, Jacqueline M Kissock; c Ashley B & Caroline J. *Educ:* Univ Durham, BSc, 62, PhD(org chem), 65. *Prof Exp:* Mayo fel, Univ Western Ont, 65-67; lectr org chem, 67-68; asst researcher, Univ Hosp Ctr, Univ Sherbrooke, 70-71. *Concurrent Pos:* Hon prof chem, Univ Western Ont, 87- *Mem:* Royal Soc Chem; Chem Inst Can. *Res:* Natural products and synthesis; synthetic methods of organic chemistry; mechanism of solvolysis reactions. *Mailing Add:* Dept Chem Bishop's Univ Lennoxville PQ J1M 1Z7 Can. *Fax:* 819-822-9661

**YEATTS, FRANK RICHARD,** THEORETICAL PHYSICS. *Current Pos:* From asst prof to assoc prof, 64-81, PROF PHYSICS, COLO SCH MINES, 82- *Personal Data:* b Altoona, Pa, Mar 5, 36; m 60; c 2. *Educ:* Pa State Univ, BS, 58; Univ Ariz, MS, 63, PhD(physics), 64. *Mem:* Am Geophys Union; Am Phys Soc; Am Asn Physics Teachers. *Res:* Mathematical physics. *Mailing Add:* 1395 Nile St Golden CO 80401

**YECK, ROBERT GILBERT,** AGRICULTURAL ENGINEERING. *Current Pos:* vis prof, 80-89, CONSULT, AGR ENG, UNIV MD, 89- *Personal Data:* b La Valle, Wis, Dec 6, 20; m 44, Louise Latotzko; c William A & Alan F. *Educ:* Univ Wis, BS, 48; Univ Mo, MS, 53, PhD(agr eng), 60. *Prof Exp:* Proj leader environ & animals, Agr Eng Div, USDA, 48-51, lab leader bioclimatic studies, 51-58, invests leader animal environ, 58-60, br chief livestock eng & rural housing, 70-72, staff scientist, waste mgt & microbiol, 72-75, staff scientist farmstead eng & rural housing, agr res, USDA, 75-80. *Concurrent Pos:* Mem Agr bd, Nat Acad Sci, 71-74; consult, Food & Agr Orgn, UN, Italy, 64-67 & Agr Eng Grad Prog, Agrarian Univ, Peru, UN develop proj, 67-70; chmn, Int Symp Livestock Wastes, 71 & USDA Task Force Recycled Animal Wastes, 74; mem, President's Solar Domestic Pol Rev Group, 78; consult, Grain Storage World Bank, 84-86. *Mem:* Fel Am Soc Agr Engrs; Sigma Xi. *Res:* Farmstead engineering; rural housing; waste management; solar energy; anaerobic fermentation processes; livestock shelters; environmental stress bioclimatic studies; renewable energy sources. *Mailing Add:* 14301 Northwyn Dr Silver Spring MD 20904. *E-Mail:* rgyeck@aol.com

**YEDINAK, PETER DEMERTON,** theoretical physics, computer science theory; deceased, see previous edition for last biography

**YEE, ALBERT FAN,** POLYMER MATERIALS, MECHANICAL BEHAVIOR. *Current Pos:* PROF, MAT SCI, UNIV MICH, ANN ARBOR, 85- *Personal Data:* b Canton, China, Nov 1, 45; US Citizen; m 87; c 1. *Educ:* Univ Calif, Berkeley, BS, 67, PhD(chem), 71. *Prof Exp:* Staff, Gen Elec Corp R&D, 71-85. *Mem:* Fel Am Phys Soc; Am Chem Soc; Plastics & Rubber Instit, London; Soc Rheology; Mat Res Soc. *Res:* Mechanical behavior of polymeric materials & composites; physics of polymers; nature and origins of molecular relaxations in polymer glasses; toughening of polymer alloys and composites; nonliner viscoelasticity. *Mailing Add:* 4904 N Maple Rd Ann Arbor MI 48105-9614

**YEE, ALFRED A,** ENGINEERING, STRUCTURAL ENGINEERING. *Current Pos:* PRES, APPL TECHNOL CORP, 84- *Personal Data:* b Aug 5, 25; US citizen; m 75, Elizabeth Wong; c Mark K, Eric K, Malcolm K, Ian K, Suling V, Trevor K, I'Ling N & Lailan Fell. *Educ:* Rose-Hulman Inst Technol, BSCE, 48; Yale Univ, ME, 49. *Hon Degrees:* DE, Rose-Hulman Inst Technol, 76. *Honors & Awards:* Martin P Korn Award, Prestressed Concrete Inst, 65, Robert J Lyman Award, 84. *Prof Exp:* Pres, Alfred A Yee & Assocs, Inc, 53-82, tech vpres, Alfred A Yee Div, Leo A Daly, 82-89. *Concurrent Pos:* Consult mem offshore concrete structures, comt 357, Am Concrete Inst; comt mem, Coun Tall Buildings & Urban Habitat; task force proposed PCI design code of practice, Precast/Prestressed Concrete Inst. *Mem:* Nat Acad Eng; hon mem & fel Am Concrete Inst; hon mem & fel Am Soc Civil Engrs; fel Precast Prestressed Concrete Inst; Soc Naval Architects & Marine Engrs; Earthquake Eng Res Inst; Int Asn Bridge & Struct Eng; Nat Soc Prof Engrs. *Res:* Offshore and oceangoing vessels; reinforcing steel bar splices and concrete framing systems for high rise buildings; precast prestressed concrete construction; granted several patents; author of various publications. *Mailing Add:* Appl Technol Corp 1441 Kapiolani Blvd Suite 810 Honolulu HI 96814. *Fax:* 808-973-1808; *E-Mail:* atc@lava.net

**YEE, JOHN ALAN,** BONE BIOLOGY, CELL BIOLOGY. *Current Pos:* PROF BIOMED SCI, CREIGHTON UNIV. *Personal Data:* b Salt Lake City, Utah, Feb 11, 47; m 68; c 3. *Prof Exp:* Asst prof anat, Health Sci Ctr, Tex Tech Univ, 74-80, assoc prof, 80- *Mem:* Am Asn Anatomists; Am Soc Bone & Mineral Res; AAAS. *Res:* Elucidating the factors which regulate bone cell functions and how cell function changes with age. *Mailing Add:* Dept Anat Creighton Univ Sch Med 2500 California St Omaha NE 68178-0001

**YEE, KANE SHEE-GONG,** applied mathematics, for more information see previous edition

**YEE, RENA,** POLYMER-PHYSICAL CHEMISTRY. *Current Pos:* RES CHEMIST POLYMER PHYS CHEM, RES DEPT, NAVAL WEAPONS CTR, CHINA LAKE, CALIF, 73- *Personal Data:* b Hong Kong, June 1,36; US citizen; m 68; c 1. *Educ:* Chung Chi Col, Hong Kong, BS, 59; Univ NDak, Grand Fork, MS, 61; Univ Mass, Amherst, PhD(polymer phys chem), 67. *Prof Exp:* Res chemist polymer chem, Hercules Res Ctr, Wilmington, Del, 67-71; res assoc biochem, Univ Pa, 71-72. *Mem:* Am Chem Soc; Sigma Xi. *Res:* Polymer structural characterizations of polyolefin and collagen with x-ray diffraction, small light scattering refractive index-birefringence measurements and tritium exchange methods; surface chemistry of nitramines. *Mailing Add:* 908 Sylvia Ave Ridgecrest CA 93555-3155

**YEE, SINCLAIR SHEE-SING,** BIOENGINEERING, MICROELECTRONICS. *Current Pos:* from asst prof to prof elec eng, Univ Wash, 66-77, dir microtechnol lab, 74-77 CONSULT, 77- *Personal Data:* b China, Jan 20, 37; US citizen; m 61; c 2. *Educ:* Univ Calif, Berkeley, BS, 59, MS, 61, PhD(elec eng), 65. *Prof Exp:* Res engr, Lawrence Livermore Lab, 64-66. *Concurrent Pos:* Consult, Lawrence Livermore Lab, 66-75, Beckman Instruments, 77- & Tektronics Inc, 77-78; NIH spec res fels, Case Western Reserve Univ, 72-73 & Bioeng Ctr, Univ Wash, 73-74. *Mem:* Am Phys Soc; fel Inst Elec & Electronics Engrs. *Res:* Semiconductor physics and devices; bioinstrumentation; microelectronic devices; microsensors. *Mailing Add:* Dept Elec Eng FT-10 Univ Wash Seattle WA 98195-0001

**YEE, TIN BOO,** CHEMISTRY, CERAMICS. *Current Pos:* RES CHEMIST, REDSTONE ARSENAL, 55- *Personal Data:* b Canton, China, Feb 25, 15; US citizen; m 74. *Educ:* Ark State Col, BS, 38; Univ Ark, MS, 40; Univ Ill, AM, 50, PhD(chem), 54. *Prof Exp:* Chemist, Chem Warfare Serv, Huntsville Arsenal, Ala, 42-45; asst chemist, State Geol Surv, Ill, 45-55. *Concurrent Pos:* Instr, Exten, Univ Ala, 60; vis res scientist, Union Indust Res Inst, Taiwan, 70-71. *Mem:* Am Chem Soc; Am Ceramic Soc; AAAS. *Res:* Sol-gel process for making optical ceramics; develop durable rubberized material for repairing worn out sole and heel of shoes; mutations in flowers and plants by radiations; material research in microelectronics. *Mailing Add:* 719 Erskine St NW Huntsville AL 35805-2556

**YEE, TUCKER TEW,** ORGANIC CHEMISTRY, PHYSICAL ORGANIC CHEMISTRY. *Current Pos:* RES CHEMIST, NAVAL WEAPONS CTR, CHINA LAKE, CALIF, 72- *Personal Data:* b Toyshun, Canton, China, Mar 9, 36; US citizen; m 68; c 1. *Educ:* Knox Col, Ill, BA, 60; Univ Mass, PhD(org chem), 64. *Prof Exp:* Res assoc, Princeton Univ, 64-65; res chemist, Eastern Lab, E I du Pont de Nemours & Co, Inc, 65-67; sr res chemist, Arco Chem Co Div, Atlantic Richfield Co, Pa, 67-72. *Mem:* Sigma Xi; Am Chem Soc. *Res:* Chemistry of nitrogen containing heterocycles; radiochemical tracer technique; general organic syntheses; organic polymer syntheses and polymer applications. *Mailing Add:* Air Warfare Weapons Div 1 Administration Circle 4734-D Bldg 10630 China Lake CA 93555-6100

**YEE, WILLIAM C,** CHEMICAL & ENVIRONMENTAL ENGINEERING. *Current Pos:* chemist, 52-59, chem engr, 59-72, GROUP LEADER, OAK RIDGE NAT LAB, 72- *Personal Data:* b Boston, Mass, Sept 23, 28; m 54; c 3. *Educ:* Tufts Univ, BS, 48; Univ Tenn, MS, 59. *Prof Exp:* Chemist, Allied Chem & Dye Corp, 48-52. *Concurrent Pos:* Session chmn, Gordon Conf on Water, 66. *Mem:* Sigma Xi; Am Inst Chem Engrs; Am Chem Soc. *Res:* Environmental impact statement preparation; aquaculture; waste heat utilization; nutrition economics; nuclear desalination; agro-industrial complexes; waste and water treatment; ion exchange; radiation effects on metals; corrosion of nuclear materials; synthetic detergent technology. *Mailing Add:* 113 Westover Dr Oak Ridge TN 37830-4898

**YEEND, WARREN ERNEST,** GEOLOGY. *Current Pos:* RETIRED. *Personal Data:* b Colfax, Wash, May 14, 36; m 64, 85, Elissa Hirsh; c Erica. *Educ:* Wash State Univ, BS, 58; Univ Colo, MS, 61; Univ Wis, PhD(geol), 65. *Honors & Awards:* Spec Achievement Award, US Geol Surv, 75. *Prof Exp:* Geologist, US Geol Surv, 65-95. *Res:* Surficial geology in an area of oil shade interest in western Colorado; geomorphology; gold bearing gravels of the Sierra Nevada; economic geology; engineering geology along the Trans-Alaska pipeline; mapping and copper resource evaluation in southern Arizona; placer gold in Alaska; surficial geology in Alaska. *Mailing Add:* US Geol Surv 345 Middlefield Rd Menlo Park CA 94025

**YEGULALP, TUNCEL MUSTAFA,** MINING ENGINEERING, OPERATIONS RESEARCH. *Current Pos:* from asst prof to assoc prof, 72-85, PROF MINING, COLUMBIA UNIV, 85- *Personal Data:* b Konya, Turkey, Nov 5, 37; m 63; c Ali & Serdar. *Educ:* Tech Univ Istanbul, MS, 61; Columbia Univ, DEngSc(mining), 68. *Prof Exp:* Mining engr, Mineral Res & Explor Inst, Turkey, 61-63; res engr, Mobil Res & Develop Corp, 67-69; prog mgr, Mineral Res & Explor Inst, Turkey, 71-72. *Concurrent Pos:* Dir, NY Mining & Mineral Resources Res Inst, 87- *Mem:* Am Inst Mining, Metall & Petrol Engrs; Inst Mgt Sci; Opers Res Soc Am. *Res:* Mineral economics; hydraulic transport of coal in underground mines; earthquake forecasting; statistical methods in geomechanics; queueing models for open-pit mining; open pit limit algorithms. *Mailing Add:* Henry Krumb Sch Mines Columbia Univ New York NY 10027. *Fax:* 212-854-8362; *E-Mail:* yegulalp@columbia.edu

**YEH, BILLY KUO-JIUN,** INTERNAL MEDICINE, CARDIOVASCULAR DISEASES. *Current Pos:* asst prof med, Univ Miami, 70-73, asst prof pharmacol, 72-73, clin asst prof, 73-76, CLIN ASSOC PROF MED, SCH MED, UNIV MIAMI, 76- *Personal Data:* b Foochow, China, Aug 28, 37; m 65, Lydia Ou; c Elizabeth, Brian & William. *Educ:* Nat Taiwan Univ, MD, 61; Univ Okla, MS, 63; Columbia Univ, PhD(pharmacol), 67; Am Bd Internal Med, dipl & cert cardiovasc dis. *Prof Exp:* Intern med, Nat Taiwan Univ Hosp, 60-61; resident path, Med Ctr, Univ Okla, 63; teaching asst, Col Physicians & Surgeons, Columbia Univ, 64-67; asst resident, Emory Univ Affil Hosps, 68-69; staff cardiologist & chief sect clin pharmacol, Div Cardiol, Mt Sinai Med Ctr, Miami Beach, 69-71; co-actg chief, Heart Sta, Jackson Mem Hosp, 72-73; assoc dir, Div Clin Investr, Miami Heart Inst, Miami Beach, 73-76. *Concurrent Pos:* Fel, Univ Okla, 62-63; fel pharmacol, Col Physicians & Surgeons, Columbia Univ, 63-64; fel med, Sch Med, Emory Univ & Grady Mem Hosp, 67-68; fel Coun Clin Cardiol, Am Heart Asn. *Mem:* Fel Am Col Physicians; fel Am Col Cardiol; Am Soc Pharmacol & Exp Therapeut; Am Physiol Soc. *Res:* Clinical pharmacology; clinical cardiovascular disease. *Mailing Add:* 315 Palermo Ave Coral Gables FL 33134-6607. *Fax:* 305-445-6167

**YEH, CAVOUR W,** MICROWAVES, FIBER OPTICS. *Current Pos:* CONSULT, 92- *Personal Data:* b Nanking, China, Aug 11, 36; US citizen; m 60, Evelyn; c Vivian & John. *Educ:* Calif Inst Technol, BS, 57, MS, 58, PhD(elec eng), 62. *Prof Exp:* Res asst elec eng, Calif Inst Technol, 58-62; from asst prof to assoc prof, Univ Southern Calif, 62-67; from assoc prof to prof elec eng, Univ Calif, Los Angeles, 67-92. *Concurrent Pos:* Consult, Jet Propulsion Lab, 62-, Hughes Res Lab, 74-80. *Mem:* Fel Inst Elec & Electronics Engrs; fel Optical Soc Am; Int Union Radio Sci. *Res:* Theoretical & experimental aspect of electromagnetic waves: low-loss mm/sub-mm waveguides, ultra high speed fiber optics local network area, intergrated fiber optics structures; scattering & diffraction of wave by arbitrarily shape dielectric objects, moving medium, microwave antenna, multiple scattering effects & moving particle; nonlinear fiber optics. *Mailing Add:* 2432 Nalin Dr Los Angeles CA 90077

**YEH, CHAI,** electronics; deceased, see previous edition for last biography

**YEH, EDWARD H Y,** ELEMENTARY PARTICLE PHYSICS, FLUIDS. *Current Pos:* RETIRED. *Personal Data:* b Hsin-Chu, Taiwan, Jan 1, 30; US citizen; m 67, Gretchen; c Henry T & Daniel N. *Educ:* Nat Taiwan Univ, BS, 52; Kyushu Univ, Fukuoka, Japan, MS, 57; Univ NC, Chapel Hill, PhD(physics), 60. *Prof Exp:* Lectr physics, Nat Taiwan Univ, Taipei, 53-55; res staff, Dept Nuclear Physics, Col Gen Educ, Tokyo Univ, Meguroku, Japan, 57-58; res physicist, Nuclear Data Group, Nat Acad Sci-Nat Res Coun, Wash, DC 60-61; sr physicist, Res Electro Magnetic Waves, Germeshausen & Grier, Inc, Boston, 61-63; res scholar theoret physics, Dublin Inst Adv Scis, 63-66; prof physics & astron, Moorhead State Univ, Minn, 66-87; physicist, res infrared microwaves, Naval Air Warfare Ctr, China Lake, 84-94. *Concurrent Pos:* Vis prof, Fairfield Univ, Conn, 73-74. *Mem:* NY Acad Sci. *Res:* Infrared electrooptics; computer simulation; elemen particle physics; group theory; atomic and molecular physics; theoretical physics; electromagnetism; author of over thirty publications on the above research areas. *Mailing Add:* 15082 Columbia Lane Huntington Beach CA 92647

**YEH, FRANCIS CHO-HAO,** QUANTITATIVE GENETICS, POPULATION GENETICS. *Current Pos:* PROF GENETICS & BIOTECHNOL, UNIV ALTA, 86- *Personal Data:* b Hankow, China, Dec 20, 45; m 69; c 1. *Educ:* Univ Calgary, BSc, 70, PhD(genetics), 74. *Prof Exp:* Geneticist quantitative genetics, 74-80, tech adv genetics, 80-86. *Concurrent Pos:* Adj assoc prof, Dept Forest Sci, Univ Alta, 80- *Mem:* NAm Quantitative Forest Genetics Group; Int Union Forestry Res Orgn; Can Tree Improvement Asn; Genetics Soc Can; Genetics Soc Am. *Res:* Genetic structure of forest trees and breeding theories. *Mailing Add:* Dept Renewable Res Univ Alberta Rm 751 Gen Serv Bldg Edmonton AB T6G 2H1 Can

**YEH, GEORGE CHIAYOU,** PHYSICAL CHEMISTRY, CHEMICAL ENGINEERING. *Current Pos:* from assoc prof to prof, 61-91, dir res & patent affairs, 73-79, EMER PROF ENG, VILLANOVA UNIV, 79- *Personal Data:* b Kagi, Taiwan, Oct 3, 26; US citizen; m 57, Lillian R How; c Bryan V, Katheryne A, Christine J & Maximilliam S. *Educ:* Taiwan Univ, BSc, 50; Univ Tokyo, DEng, 53; Univ Toronto, MSc, 55, PhD(chem engr), 57. *Honors & Awards:* Am Inst Chem Award. *Prof Exp:* Lectr, Japanese Engrs Union, Tokyo, 51-53; assoc prof chem eng, Auburn Univ, 57-61; pres, Thermodyne Corp & Hommo Inc. *Concurrent Pos:* Prin investr res grants, Petrol Res Fund, 63-65 & NASA, 65-69; independent researcher, Thermodyne Co, 70-81. *Mem:* Fel Am Inst Chemists; AAAS; Am Inst Chem Engrs; Am Chem Soc; Japanese Soc Chem Eng. *Res:* Reactions at interfaces; interfacial phenomena; catalysis; quantum mechanics; solid state chemistry; electrochemical analysis; liquids separation; gas separation; energy conversion; vapor engine; water and wastewater; biomedical engineering; US and foreign patents. *Mailing Add:* 2 Smedley Dr Newton Square PA 19073-1012

**YEH, GOUR-TSYH,** HYDROSCIENCES, NUMERICAL MODELING. *Current Pos:* PROF CIVIL ENG, PA STATE UNIV, 89- *Personal Data:* b Lunhoutsun, Taiwan, Dec 5, 40; US citizen; m 71, Shu-Shen Kuo; c Apollo & Adam. *Educ:* Nat Taiwan Univ, BS, 64; Syracuse Univ, MS, 67; Cornell Univ, PhD(hydrol), 69. *Prof Exp:* Res assoc atmospheric diffusion, Cornell Univ, 69-71; vis res scientist air-sea interaction, NASA, Houston, 71-72; sr environ engr thermal hydraul, Ebasio Serv Inc, 72-73; sr hydraul-environ engr fluid mech, Stone & Webster Eng Corp, 73-77; res scientist hydrol, Oak Ridge Nat Lab, 77-82, sr res scientist, 82-89. *Concurrent Pos:* Adj prof, Northeastern Univ, 74-75. *Mem:* AAAS; Am Soc Civil Engrs; Am Geophys Union; Am Meteorol Soc; Nat Soc Prof Engrs. *Res:* Groundwater hydrology; computational fluid dynamics; environmental transport; numerical modeling; geochemical modeling. *Mailing Add:* Dept Civil Eng Pa State Univ 212 Sackett Bldg University Park PA 16802-1408. *Fax:* 814-863-7304; *E-Mail:* gty@darcy.psu.edu

**YEH, GREGORY SOH-YU,** POLYMER PHYSICS, ELECTRON MICROSCOPY. *Current Pos:* asst prof chem & metall eng, 67-69, assoc prof, 69-72, PROF MAT & METALL & CHEM ENG, UNIV MICH, ANN ARBOR, 72- *Personal Data:* b Shanghai, China, Apr 11, 33; US citizen; m 59; c 2. *Educ:* Holy Cross Col, BS, 57; Cornell Univ, MS, 60; Case Inst Technol, PhD(polymer physics), 66. *Prof Exp:* Res physicist, Goodyear Res Ctr, 60-61; sr res physicist, Gen Res Ctr, 61-64; res fel, Case Inst Technol, 66-67. *Concurrent Pos:* Fulbright fel, 73 & 83; Humboldt fel, 74, 76 & 77. *Mem:* Am Phys Soc; Electron Micros Soc Am; Am Chem Soc. *Res:* Polymer structure and properties; morphology and crystal structure; mechanical properties of polymers; electron diffraction. *Mailing Add:* Chem Eng Univ Mich Dow Bldg 3042 2300 Hayward St Ann Arbor MI 48109. *Fax:* 313-764-9236

**YEH, HARRY CHIANG,** STRUCTURAL CERAMICS. *Personal Data:* b Nanking, China, June 27, 35; m 65, Joyce Wu; c Bing & May. *Educ:* Nat Taiwan Univ, BS, 58; Brown Univ, MS, 63; Ill Inst Technol, PhD, 66. *Prof Exp:* Sr metallurgist, Res & Develop Lab, Corning Glass Works, 66-69; from asst prof to assoc prof metall eng, Cleveland State Univ, 69-80, actg chmn dept, 76-77, prof mat sci, Chem Eng Dept, 80-83; prog mgr, Allied Signal Ceramic Components, Allied Signal Inc, 83-97. *Mem:* Metall Soc; Am Ceramic Soc. *Res:* Processing and characterization of structural ceramics for heat engine applications. *Mailing Add:* 7024 Hedgewood Dr Rancho Palos Verdes CA 90275

**YEH, HEN-GEUL,** DIGITAL SIGNAL PROCESSING, SATELLITE COMMUNICATION SYSTEMS. *Current Pos:* PROF, DIGITAL SIGNAL PROCESSING, CALIF STATE UNIV, LONG BEACH, 83-; MEM TECH STAFF, JET PROPULSION LAB, CALIF INST TECH, 92- *Personal Data:* b Taiwan, China; US citizen; m, Chia-Ho Lee. *Educ:* Univ Calif, Irvine, PhD(control & digital signal processing), 82. *Honors & Awards:* New Technol Award, NASA, 87. *Prof Exp:* Mem tech staff, Parker-Hannifin Corp, 79-81; scientist, Magnavox Govt & Indust Electronics Co, 87-91. *Concurrent Pos:* Vis prof, Telecom Paris Univ, Paris, France, 88-89. *Mem:* Sr mem Inst Elec & Electronics Engrs. *Res:* Digital signal processing; satellite communication; digital demodulator; digital modem; systolic arrays. *Mailing Add:* Dept Elec Eng Calif State Univ Long Beach CA 90840

**YEH, HERMAN JIA-CHAIN,** PHYSICAL CHEMISTRY. *Current Pos:* vis fel, Lab Chem, Nat Inst Arthritis, Metabolism & Digestive Dis, 70-71, staff fel, 72-74, sr staff fel, 74-76, RES CHEMIST, NAT INST ARTHRITIS, METABOLISM & DIGESTIVE DIS, 76- *Personal Data:* b Taipei, Taiwan, Nov 15, 39. *Educ:* Cheng-Kung Univ, Taiwan, BS, 63; Univ Mass, Amherst, PhD(chem), 68. *Prof Exp:* Fel chem, Univ Mass, 68-69. *Mem:* AAAS; Am Chem Soc. *Res:* Nuclear magnetic resonance spectroscopy. *Mailing Add:* 9309 Bells Mill Rd Potomac MD 20854-2218

**YEH, HSIANG-YUEH,** MECHANICS. *Current Pos:* ASSOC PROF CIVIL ENG, PRAIRIE VIEW AGR & MECH COL, 69- *Personal Data:* b Tainan Hsien, Taiwan, Apr 1, 40; m 69; c 2. *Educ:* Cheng King Univ, Taiwan, BSE, 62; Univ NMex, MSCE, 67, PhD(civil eng), 69. *Prof Exp:* Jr engr, Taiwan Pub Works Bur, 63-65. *Mem:* Am Soc Civil Engrs; Am Soc Eng Educ. *Res:* Reliability analysis, random vibration and fatigue damage of structural systems. *Mailing Add:* PO Box 2244 Prairie View A&M Univ Prairie View TX 77446-2244

**YEH, HSI-HAN,** ELECTRICAL ENGINEERING, CONTROL SYSTEMS. *Current Pos:* ELEC ENGR, WRIGHT LAB, WRIGHT-PATTERSON AFB, 85- *Personal Data:* b Shanghai, China, Nov 10, 35; m 66, Lily Y Bao; c Anita & Sharon. *Educ:* Nat Taiwan Univ, BSc, 56; Chiao Tung Univ, MSc, 61; Univ NB, MSc, 63; Ohio State Univ, PhD(elec eng), 67. *Honors & Awards:* Gen Foulois Award, USAF, 88. *Prof Exp:* Asst engr, Taiwan Power Co, 58-60; res assoc elec eng, Ohio State Univ, 66-67; from asst prof to assoc prof elec eng, Univ Ky, 67-85. *Concurrent Pos:* Fac res, NASA, 73-74 & Air Force Off Sci Res, 81; vis prof, Nat Chiao Tung Univ, 75-76. *Mem:* Inst Elec & Electronics Engrs; Sigma Xi. *Res:* Distributed-parameter systems; computer-controlled systems; learning and adaptive control systems; robust control theory; US patents. *Mailing Add:* 1181 Mint Springs Dr Fairborn OH 45324-5728. *Fax:* 937-476-4000; *E-Mail:* yeh@falcon.flight.wpafb.af.mil

**YEH, HSU-CHI,** MECHANICAL ENGINEERING, INDUSTRIAL HYGIENE. *Current Pos:* RETIRED. *Personal Data:* b Taipei, Taiwan, Sept 30, 40; US citizen; m 66; c 2. *Educ:* Nat Taiwan Univ, BS, 63; Univ Minn, MS, 67, PhD(mech eng), 72. *Prof Exp:* Teaching asst mech eng, Univ Minn, 64-65, res asst mech eng & aerosol physics, 65-72; res assoc, Lovelace Biomed & Environ Res Inst, 72-73, res scientist aerosol physics, Inhalation Toxicol Res Inst, 73-97, aerosol sci group supvr, 82-97. *Concurrent Pos:* Mem, Sci Comt, 57, Task Group 2 Lung Dosimetry Model, Nat Coun Radiation Protection & Measurements, 84, bd dirs, Am Asn Aerosol Res, 89-; assoc ed, Aerosol Sci & Technol, 93-; clin prof, Col Pharm, Univ NMex. *Mem:* Health Physics Soc; Am Indust Hyg Asn; Ger Soc Aerosol Res; Air & Waste Mgt Asn; Am Asn Aerosol Res; Chinese Asn Aerosol Res. *Res:* Aerosol science and technology; inhalation toxicity associated with inhaled aerosols and the particle deposition in mammalian lungs including mammalian airway morphometry. *Mailing Add:* 9600 La Playa St NE Albuquerque NM 87111

**YEH, JAMES JUI-TIN,** MATHEMATICS. *Current Pos:* assoc prof, 65-68, PROF MATH, UNIV CALIF, IRVINE, 68-, CHMN DEPT. *Personal Data:* b Tainan, Formosa, Apr 26, 27; US citizen. *Educ:* Taiwan Univ, BS, 50; Univ Minn, MA, 54, PhD(math), 57. *Prof Exp:* Instr math inst technol, Univ Minn, 57-58 & Mass Inst Technol, 58-60; asst prof, Univ Rochester, 60-64; vis mem, Courant Inst Math Sci, NY Univ, 64-65. *Mem:* Am Math Soc. *Res:* Integration in function spaces; functional analysis; stochastic processes. *Mailing Add:* Dept Math Univ Calif Irvine CA 92697-0001

**YEH, K(UNG) C(HIE),** ELECTRICAL ENGINEERING. *Current Pos:* dean Eng Col, 92-95, PROF, DEPT ELEC ENG, NAT SUN YAT-SEN UNIV, TAIWAN, 92- *Personal Data:* b Hangchow, China, Aug 4, 30; m 57, Margaret Yung; c Joanna, Lisa, David & Richard. *Educ:* Univ Ill, BS, 53; Stanford Univ, MS, 54, PhD(elec eng), 58. *Honors & Awards:* Cert of Achievement Award, Inst Elec & Electronics Engrs Antennas & Propagation Group, 68; Sci Achievement Award, NATO, 92. *Prof Exp:* Asst, Electronics Lab, Stanford Univ, 54-58; res assoc elec eng, Univ Ill, Urbana-Champaign, 58-59, from asst prof to prof elec eng, 59-92, assoc, Ctr Advan Study, 73-74. *Concurrent Pos:* Mem, US Comn G, Int Sci Radio Union, vice-chmn, 81-84, chmn, 85-87; assoc ed, Radio Sci J, 79-81, ed, 83-86; US Panel mem, Electromagnetic Wave-Propogation Panel, Adv Group Aerospace Res & Develop, 84; prog chmn, Adv Group for Aerospace Res & Develop Panel Symp on Scattering & Propagation in Random Media, 87. *Mem:* Fel Inst Elec & Electronics Engrs; Am Geophys Union; Am Phys Soc. *Res:* Propagation, ionosphere and plasma; radio propagation; ionospheric dynamics. *Mailing Add:* Dept Elec Eng Nat Sun Yat-sen Univ Kaohsiung Taiwan. *Fax:* 886-7-525-4163; *E-Mail:* kcyeh@mail.nsysu.edu.tw

**YEH, KWAN-NAN,** POLYMER CHEMISTRY. *Current Pos:* from asst prof to prof textiles & consumer econ, 73-92, PROF MAT SCI & ENG, UNIV MD, COLLEGE PARK, 92- *Personal Data:* b Taichung, Taiwan, Feb 27, 38; m 65, Linda Lin; c Kenneth B & Frances M. *Educ:* Nat Taiwan Univ, BS, 61; Tulane Univ, La, MS, 65; Univ Ga, PhD(chem), 70. *Prof Exp:* Cotton Found res assoc fel, Nat Bur Stand, 70-72, res chemist, 72-73. *Mem:* Am Chem Soc; Am Asn Textile Chemists & Colorists; Textile Inst; Fiber Soc; Mat Res Soc. *Res:* Thermodynamics; thermochemistry; textile and polymer flammability; polymer characterization; polymer fiber evaluation. *Mailing Add:* Mat Eng Dept Univ Md 2100 Marie Mount College Park MD 20742-7531. *Fax:* 301-314-9601

**YEH, KWO-YIH,** CELL CULTURE. *Current Pos:* ASSOC PROF, DEPT MED, LA STATE UNIV MED CTR, 92- *Personal Data:* b Tao-yuan, Taiwan, Jan 20, 42; m 71. *Educ:* Taiwan Normal Univ, BS, 65; Washington Univ, St Louis, PhD(biol), 75. *Prof Exp:* Instr biol, Chung-Li High Sch, Taiwan, 65-66; teaching asst develop biol, Taiwan Normal Univ, 67-71; res asst, Washington Univ, St Louis, 71-75, res assoc, 75-77, res asst prof, 77-78; sr res scientist cell biol, Southern Res Inst, 78-83; assoc res scientist, Columbia Univ, 83-92. *Mem:* AAAS; Am Soc Cell Biol; Am Soc Zoologists; Soc Develop Biol; Am Gastroenterol Asn. *Res:* Developmental biology in vertebrates; structural and enzymic development of intestine; developmental endocrinology; cell proliferation and differentiation. *Mailing Add:* Dept Med La State Univ Med Ctr 1501 Kings Hwy Shreveport LA 71130

**YEH, LAI-SU LEE,** ENZYMOLOGY. *Current Pos:* RES SCIENTIST BIOCHEM, NAT BIOMED RES FOUND, 80- *Personal Data:* b Hunan, China, June 24, 42; US citizen; m 72; c 2. *Educ:* Taiwan Normal Univ, BS, 65; Sacramento State Univ, MS, 69; Univ Calif, Davis, PhD(agr chem), 79. *Prof Exp:* Res assoc enzym, Dept Biochem, Univ Utah, 75-77, res specialist clin biochem, Dept Pediat, 77-78. *Mem:* Am Chem Soc. *Mailing Add:* Nat Biomed Res Found 3900 Reservoir Rd NW Rm LR3 Washington DC 20007

**YEH, LEE-CHUAN CAROLINE,** BIOCHEMISTRY. *Current Pos:* Postdoctoral fel pharmacol, 84-85 & biochem, 85-90, RES INSTR BIOCHEM, UNIV TEX HEALTH SCI CTR, 90- *Personal Data:* b Jan 3, 54; US citizen. *Educ:* Fu-Jen Cath Univ, BS, 76; Univ Ga, MS, 79; Ore State Univ, PhD(nutrit), 84. *Mem:* Am Soc Biochem & Molecular Biol. *Res:* Higher-order structure, function, and interactions of RNAs and proteins. *Mailing Add:* Dept Biochem Univ Tex Health Sci Ctr 7703 Floyd Curl Dr San Antonio TX 78284-7760. *Fax:* 210-567-6595

**YEH, NAI-CHANG,** CONDENSED MATTER PHYSICS. *Current Pos:* ASST PROF PHYSICS, CALIF INST TECHNOL, 89- *Personal Data:* b Taiwan, Repub China, Dec 15, 61. *Educ:* Nat Taiwan Univ, Bachelor, 83; Mass Inst Technol, PhD(physics), 88. *Concurrent Pos:* Vis scientist, Thomas J Watson Res Ctr, Int Bus Mach Corp, 89-; Alfred P Sloan Found res fel, 90; David & Lucile Packard fel sci & eng, 92. *Mem:* Am Phys Soc; Mat Res Soc; AAAS. *Res:* Physical properties of conventional and high-temperature superconductors; electrical transport; magnetic and microwave experimental studies of vortex phases; vortex dynamics; phase transitions; dissipation in type-II superconductors. *Mailing Add:* Dept Physics 114-36 Calif Inst Technol Pasadena CA 91125. *Fax:* 626-683-9060

**YEH, NAI-SHYONG,** DEVELOP MATHEMATICAL MODELS FOR PRESSURE TESTS, DEVELOP & APPLY NEW ANALYSIS TECHNIQUES FOR WELL TEST IN PETROLEUM ENGINEERING. *Current Pos:* res engr, 86-89, SR RES ENGR, AMOCO PROD CO, TULSA RES CTR, 89- *Personal Data:* b Taipei, Taiwan, July 26, 55; US citizen; m 91, Jerry Shau; c Kathleen & Roger C. *Educ:* Nat Chung Kung Univ, Taiwan, BS, 78; Tulsa Univ, MS, 83, PhD(petrol eng), 86. *Res:* Develop advanced mathematical models and analysis techniques for well testing; conduct high-level analysis for the test from complex reservoir and well systems to characterize the underground hydrocarbon reservoir used for optimum oil-gas production. *Mailing Add:* Amoco Prod Co PO Box 3385 Tulsa OK 74102. *Fax:* 918-660-4163

**YEH, NOEL KUEI-ENG,** PARTICLE PHYSICS, MEDICAL PHYSICS. *Current Pos:* from asst prof to assoc prof, 69-80, chmn dept physics, appl physics & astron, 81-87, PROF PHYSICS, STATE UNIV NY, BINGHAMTON, 80- *Personal Data:* b Malacca, Malaysia, Dec 15, 37; m 65; c 2. *Educ:* Williams Col, BA, 61; Yale Univ, MS, 62, PhD(physics), 66. *Prof Exp:* Res assoc physics, Nevis Labs, Columbia Univ, 66-68; instr univ, 68-69. *Concurrent Pos:* Vis prof, Max-Planck Inst Physics & Astrophys, Munich, WGer, 76-77; vis physicist, Brookhaven Nat Lab, 63-74, Stanford Linear Accelerator Ctr, 70-73. *Mem:* Am Phys Soc. *Res:* Elementary particles; medical physics; radiation physics; particle interaction in solid state physics; radiation in environment. *Mailing Add:* Dept Physics State Univ NY PO Box 6000 Binghamton NY 13902-6000

**YEH, PAUL PAO,** ELECTRICAL & ELECTRONICS ENGINEERING, AVIONICS. *Current Pos:* CHIEF SCIENTIST, ADVAN SYSTS RES INC, 89- *Personal Data:* b Sun-Yang, China, Mar 25, 27; US citizen; m 53, Beverley Pamela Eng; c J Elaine (Gault), Paul E, Richard A & Ronald T. *Educ:* Univ Toronto, BASc, 51; Univ Pa, MS, 60, PhD(elec eng), 66. *Honors & Awards:* Achievement Award, Lockheed-Calif Co. *Prof Exp:* Design engr, James R Kearny Corp Can Ltd, 51 & Can Gen Elec Co, 51-56; asst prof elec technol, Broome Technol Community Col-State Univ NY, Binghamton, 56-57; sr design engr, H K Porter Co, Inc, Pa, 57; transformer engr, I-T-E Circuit Breaker Co, 57-58 & Kuhlman Elec Co, Mich, 58-59; sr design engr, Fed Pac Elec Co, NJ, 59-61; chief engr, Eisler Transformer Co, 61; assoc prof elec eng, Newark Col Eng, 61-67; supvr performance anal, Autonetics Div, NAm Rockwell Corp, 67-70; advan systs engr, S3-A Avionics, Lockheed-Calif Co, 70-72; supvr module commun systs, Site Defense Prog, McDonnell Douglas Corp, Huntington Beach, 72-73; mem tech staff, Aerospace Corp, Lockheed-Martin Corp, 73-78, sr res develop engr, Advan Develop Proj, 78-89. *Concurrent Pos:* Consult, Eisler Transformer Co, NJ, 61-62, Stand Transformer Co, Ohio, 62, H K Porter Co, Inc, Va, 62-65, Consol Edison Co NY, Inc & Niagara Transformer Co, NY, 63-64 & Pub Serv Elec & Gas Co, NJ, 66; lectr, Calif State Univ, Long Beach, 67-73; vis prof, Chung Shan Inst Sci & Technol, 89-92, Tsinghua Univ, 93-, Southeast Univ, 94-, Zhejiang Univ 94-; consult prof, Northwestern Poly Univ, 93-, Shanghai Univ, 94-; hon prof, Beijing Univ Aerosci & Aeronauts, 93-, Zhejzang Univ Sci Technol, 94- *Mem:* sr life mem Inst Elec & Electronics Engrs; Armed Forces Commun & Electronics Asn; Am Defense Preparedness Asn; Nat Sec Indust Asn. *Res:* Weapon delivery computer mechanization; air-to-air missile launch control problems; magnetic anomaly detection in antisubmarine warfare systems; communication and systems readiness verification as applied to antiballistic missile programs; cruise missile launch and control; stealth weapon systems technology; electronics warfare; nuclear hardening; information warfare. *Mailing Add:* 5555 Via De Campo Yorba Linda CA 92887-4916. *Fax:* 714-692-3153, 818-564-8540; *E-Mail:* drpaulpyeh@worldnet.att.net

**YEH, POCHI ALBERT,** OPTICS OF LAYERED MEDIA. *Current Pos:* PROF, UNIV CALIF, SANTA BARBARA, 89- *Personal Data:* b 1948; c 2. *Educ:* Nat Taiwan Univ, BS, 71; Caltech, MS, 75, PhD(physics), 77. *Honors & Awards:* Rudolf Kingslake Medal & Prize, 89. *Prof Exp:* Mem tech staff,

Rockwell Sci Ctr, 77-85, principle scientist, optics, 85-90. *Concurrent Pos:* Vis prof, Nat Taiwan Univ, 83-87. *Mem:* Fel Inst Elec & Electronics Engrs; fel Optical Soc Am. *Res:* Nonlinear optics and optical phase conjugation. *Mailing Add:* Dept Elec Eng Univ Calif 552 University Ave Santa Barbara CA 93106-0001

**YEH, PU-SEN,** AEROTHERMODYNAMICS, HEAT TRANSFER. *Current Pos:* PROF ENG, JACKSONVILLE STATE UNIV, 67-, HEAD DEPT, 83- *Personal Data:* b Hualien, Taiwan, July 7, 35; m 64; c 3. *Educ:* Nat Taiwan Univ, BSME, 58; Univ Ill, MS, 62; Rutgers Univ, PhD(mech eng), 67. *Mem:* Am Soc Eng Educ; Am Soc Mech Engrs. *Res:* Ignition and combustion of liquid fuel droplets; heat transfer problem of underground residential transformer; acoustic sootblower; computer-aided drafting and design. *Mailing Add:* Dept Eng Jacksonville State Univ Jacksonville AL 36265-1573

**YEH, RAYMOND T,** COMPUTER SCIENCE. *Current Pos:* at INT SOFTWARE SYSTS. *Personal Data:* b Hunan, China, Nov 5, 37; m 66; c 1. *Educ:* Univ Ill, BS, 61, MA, 63, PhD(math), 66. *Prof Exp:* Asst prof comput sci, Pa State Univ, 66-69; assoc prof comput sci & elec eng, Univ Tex, Austin, 69-74, prof, 74-, chmn dept comput sci, 75- *Concurrent Pos:* Ed transactions software eng, Inst Elec & Electronics Engrs. *Mem:* Am Math Soc; Asn Comput Mach; Inst Elec & Electronics Eng. *Res:* Software engineering; data base management. *Mailing Add:* Int Software Inc 9430 Res Blvd Echelon III Suite 250 Austin TX 78759

**YEH, SAMUEL D J,** BIOCHEMISTRY, MEDICAL SCIENCES. *Current Pos:* asst attend physician, 69-70 & 72-75, assoc attend physician, 75-83, ATTEND PHYSICIAN, MEM HOSP, NEW YORK CITY, 83-; ASSOC PROF MED, MED COL, CORNELL UNIV, 84- *Personal Data:* b Kunming, China, Apr 23, 26; US citizen; m 59, Marian Huang; c Vivian & Phoebe. *Educ:* Nat Defense Med Ctr, Shanghai, MD, 48; Johns Hopkins Univ, ScD(biochem), 60. *Prof Exp:* Instr med, Nat Defense Med Ctr, 48-53; asst resident, Lutheran Hosp, Md, 53-54; fel med, 54-57, from instr to asst prof biochem, Sch Hyg & Pub Health, Johns Hopkins Univ, 60-63; from instr to asst prof med, Med Col, Cornell Univ, 63-76, assoc prof clin med, 76-84. *Concurrent Pos:* Assoc prof clin med, Med Col Cornell Univ, 76-84, assoc prof med, 84- *Mem:* AAAS; Am Chem Soc; Am Inst Nutrit; Soc Nuclear Med; Am Col Nuclear Physicians. *Res:* Interrelationship between nutrients; intestinal absorption and marginal deficiencies; role of protein synthesis on metabolic functions; tumor localizing radionuclides. *Mailing Add:* Dept Radiol Sloan Kettering Cancer Ctr 1275 York Ave New York NY 10021. *Fax:* 212-717-3263

**YEH, SHU-YUAN,** PHARMACEUTICAL CHEMISTRY, PHARMACOLOGY. *Current Pos:* PHARMACOLOGIST, ADDICTION RES CTR, NAT INST DRUG ABUSE, 72- *Personal Data:* b Kwangtung, China, June 26, 26; US citizen; m 57; c 2. *Educ:* Nat Defense Med Ctr, Taiwan, BS, 51; Univ Iowa, MS, 57, PhD(pharmaceut chem), 59. *Prof Exp:* Pharmacist, Army, Navy & Air Force Hosp, Taiwan, 51-52; clin, Off of President, Taiwan, 53-55; res asst pharm, Univ Iowa, 55-59, res assoc med, 59-63, from res instr to res asst prof drug metab, Col Med, 63-70; asst prof, Univ Ky, 71. *Mem:* AAAS; Am Pharmaceut Asn; Acad Pharmaceut Sci; Am Soc Pharmacol & Exp Med; NY Acad Sci. *Res:* Development of methods for detection, isolation and identification of drug and its metabolites in the biological fluids. *Mailing Add:* Addiction Res Ctr Nat Inst Drug Abuse PO Box 5180 Baltimore MD 21224-0180. *Fax:* 410-550-1438

**YEH, TSYH TYAN,** FLUID DYNAMICS, FLOW METERING. *Current Pos:* MECH ENGR, FLOW METERING, NAT INST STAND & TECHNOL, 80- *Personal Data:* b Taiwan, Sept 11, 41; m, Shwu-Mei Chen; c Jeffrey & Kevin. *Educ:* Nat Taiwan Univ, BS, 54; Univ Calif, San Diego, MS, 68, PhD(eng sci), 71. *Prof Exp:* Res engr, Univ Calif, 71-74; mech engr, Argonne Nat Lab, 74-80. *Mem:* Am Phys Soc. *Mailing Add:* 7701 Rydal Terr Rockville MD 20855. *Fax:* 301-258-9201; *E-Mail:* ttyeh@enh.nist.gov

**YEH, WEI JIANG,** MAGNETIC & ELECTRICAL PROPERTIES OF HIGH TEMPERATURE SUPERCONDUCTORS. *Current Pos:* assoc prof, 90-95, PROF PHYSICS, UNIV IDAHO, 95- *Personal Data:* b Sichuan, China, Dec 5, 43; m, Boling Sun; c Carrie C. *Educ:* Chinese Univ Sci & Technol, BS, 68; State Univ NY, Stony Brook, MS, 81, PhD(physics), 84. *Prof Exp:* Engr, Shenyan Vacuum Technol Inst, 74-78; res assoc, Inst Physics, Beijing, China, 85-86, assoc prof, 87-90; instr physics, Univ Utah, 88-90. *Concurrent Pos:* Prin investr, NSF, 92-95 & 96- *Mem:* Am Phys Soc. *Res:* Static and dynamic behaviors of magnetic vortices in high temperature superconductors at various temperatures and magnetic fields. *Mailing Add:* Physics Dept Univ Idaho Moscow ID 83844-0903

**YEH, WILLIAM WEN-GONG,** WATER RESOURCES, HYDROLOGY. *Current Pos:* asst res engr eng syst, Univ Calif, Los Angeles, 67-69, from asst prof to prof eng syst, 69-83, chmn civil eng, 85-88, PROF CIVIL ENG, UNIV CALIF, LOS ANGELES, 83- *Personal Data:* b Szechwan, China, Dec 5, 38; m 67, Jennie Pao; c Michael W & Robert W. *Educ:* Cheng-Kung Univ, BS, 61; NMex State Univ, MS, 64; Stanford Univ, PhD(civil eng), 67. *Honors & Awards:* Robert E Horton Award, Am Geophys Union, 89. *Prof Exp:* Actg asst prof civil eng, Stanford Univ, 67. *Concurrent Pos:* Asst res engr, Dry-Lands Res Inst, Univ Calif, Riverside, 72-73; lectureship, Nat Coun Sci & Technol, Mexico, 73; Nat Polytech Inst, Mexico 81; expert water resources, Div Hydrol, Unesco, 74; Eng Found Fel Award, Eng Found, 81. *Mem:* Am Soc Civil Engrs; fel Am Geophys Union; Am Water Resources Asn. *Res:* Hydrology; water resources; optimization of large-scale water resources systems. *Mailing Add:* 5532B Boelter Hall Univ Calif Los Angeles CA 90095. *Fax:* 310-206-2222

**YEH, YEA-CHUAN MILTON,** PHOTOVOLTAIC DEVICE, SOLAR CELL. *Current Pos:* DIR, TECSTAR INC/APPL SOLAR ENERGY CORP, 82- *Personal Data:* b Szu-Chuan, China, Apr 16, 43; m 69, Grace C Shen; c Caroline L & Christopher S. *Educ:* Nat Taiwan Univ, BS, 65; Univ Calif, Los Angeles, MS, 69, PhD(elec eng), 73. *Honors & Awards:* Maj Monetary Award, NASA, 77. *Prof Exp:* Head, Radio Multiplex Relay Sta, Pen-Ho, Taiwan, 65-66; asst instr, Nat Taiwan Univ, 66-67; mem tech staff, Jet Propulsion Lab, 72-82. *Concurrent Pos:* Pres, Myk Technol, Inc, 83-92. *Mem:* Inst Elec & Electronics Engrs; Sigma Xi; Int Solar Energy Soc. *Res:* Initiated and developed the technology of the world's first large-scale production-line in manufacturing high-efficiency gallium arsenide and multi-junction solar cell on gallium arsenide or germanium substrates; granted three patents. *Mailing Add:* 1454 Princeton St Santa Monica CA 90404

**YEH, YIN,** QUANTUM ELECTRONICS, CHEMICAL PHYSICS. *Current Pos:* assoc prof, 72-78, PROF APPL SCI, UNIV CALIF, DAVIS, 78- *Personal Data:* b Chungking, China, Nov 1, 38; US citizen; m 61; c 2. *Educ:* Mass Inst Technol, BS, 60; Columbia Univ, PhD(physics), 65. *Prof Exp:* Res assoc physics, Columbia Radiation Lab, Columbia Univ, 65-66; Lawrence Radiation Lab fel, Lawrence Livermore Lab, 66-67, sr physicist, 67-72. *Concurrent Pos:* Lectr, St Mary's Col, Calif, 67-68; lectr, Univ Calif, Davis, 71-72; consult, Lawrence Livermore Lab, 72- *Mem:* AAAS; Sigma Xi; Biophys Soc; Am Phys Soc. *Res:* Application of laser spectroscopy to study dynamic phenomena in chemical physics, biophysics and solid state physics. *Mailing Add:* Dept Appl Sci & Eng Univ Calif Davis CA 95616. *Fax:* 530-752-2444; *E-Mail:* yyyeh@ucdavis.edu

**YEH, YUNCHI,** GROWTH FACTORS & CANCER, GENETICS. *Current Pos:* PROF BIOCHEM, UNIV ARK MED SCI, 79- *Personal Data:* b Oct 16, 30; m, Hsing-Wu Cheng; c John, I-Tien, Evan & Ann. *Educ:* Univ Calif, San Francisco, PhD(biochem & biophys), 64. *Mem:* Am Soc Biochem & Molecular Biol. *Res:* Virus inhibitors; growth factors and cancer. *Mailing Add:* Dept Biochem & Molecular Biol Univ Ark Med Sch 4301 W Markham St Slot 516 Little Rock AR 72205. *Fax:* 501-686-8169; *E-Mail:* ycyeh@life.uams.edu

**YEIN, FREDRICK SHU-CHUNG,** CLINICAL CHEMISTRY, PHARMACEUTICAL DEVELOPMENT. *Current Pos:* PROJ SCIENTIST, BECKMAN INSTRUMENTS INC, 91- *Personal Data:* m 74, Alice Mia-Ming Chen; c Kevin & James. *Educ:* Taiwan Chung-Hsing Univ, BS, 67; Univ Mo, MA, 72; Western Mich Univ, PhD(chem), 87. *Prof Exp:* Res specialist, Dalton Res Ctr, Univ Mo, 72-78; sr res scientist, Upjohn Co, 78-91. *Concurrent Pos:* Sr chemist, Syva, 87-88. *Mem:* Am Chem Soc; Am Asn Clin Chem; fel Am Inst Chemists; Am Soc Qual Control. *Res:* Clinical medicine and pharmaceutical research and development; clinical chemistry development; oxygen free radical mediated toxicity research. *Mailing Add:* 200 S Kraemer W366 Brea CA 92821-6228

**YEISER, JIMMIE LYNN,** VEGETATION MANAGEMENT, FOREST REGENERATION. *Current Pos:* From asst prof to assoc prof, 80-90, PROF FORESTRY, UNIV ARK, MONTICELLO, 91- *Personal Data:* b Owensboro, Ky, Feb 12, 52; m 79, Linda Love; c Kevin & Kristen. *Educ:* Univ Ky, BS, 74, MS, 76; Tex A&M Univ, PhD(forestry), 80. *Mem:* Soc Am Foresters; Weed Sci Soc Am. *Res:* Impact of competition from undesired herbaceous and woody species on crop forest species; management and manipulation of the undesired species with herbicides and forest litter for increased survival and growth. *Mailing Add:* Sch Forest Resources Univ Ark PO Box 3468 Monticello AR 71656. *Fax:* 870-460-1092; *E-Mail:* yeiser@uamont.edu

**YELENOSKY, GEORGE,** PLANT PHYSIOLOGY. *Current Pos:* SUPVRY PLANT PHYSIOLOGIST, CITRUS INVESTS, USDA, 64- *Personal Data:* b Vintondale, Pa, July 20, 29; m 63; c 3. *Educ:* Pa State Univ, BS, 55, MS, 58; Duke Univ, DF, 63. *Prof Exp:* Res forester, Northeastern Forest Exp Sta, US Forest Serv, 55-56 & 58-61; Int Shade Tree Conf res fel, 63-64. *Concurrent Pos:* Mem, Coun Agr Sci & Technol. *Mem:* Am Soc Plant Physiol; Am Soc Hort Sci. *Res:* Forestry; soil aeration and tree growth; cold hardiness of citrus trees; cryobiology membership; improve survival, growth and production of citrus; low temperature stress; identifying, characterizing and manipulating stress avoidance; tolerance systems that have evolved in citrus germplasm. *Mailing Add:* 1714 Hickorywood Lane Orlando FL 32818

**YELICH, MICHAEL RALPH,** CIRCULATORY SHOCK, METABOLISM. *Current Pos:* Res assoc, Dept Pediat, Loyola Univ, Chicago, 75-77, res assoc & instr, Dept Physiol, 77-81, adj instr, 81-82, asst prof, Stritch Sch Med, 83-90, clin asst prof, Dept Physiol & Pharmacol, Sch Dent, 90-93, res asst prof, Dept Physiol/Surg, Stritch Sch Med & Shock-Trauma Inst, 93-94, res grang coordr, Dept Physiol, 95-96, RES COORDR, DEPT PATH, LOYOLA UNIV, CHICAGO, 96- *Personal Data:* b Chicago Ill, June 26, 48; wid. *Educ:* Northwestern Univ, BA, 70, Univ Ark, MS, 73, PhD(physiol), 75. *Concurrent Pos:* Dir res, Dept Anesthesiol, Mt Sinai Hosp, Chicago, 81-83; asst prof, Depts Physiol & Anesthesiol, Rush Med Col, Chicago, 81-83; NIH prin investr, 86-88; independent consult, 93- *Mem:* Am Physiol Soc; Sigma Xi; AAAS; Shock Soc. *Res:* Study of pancreatic islet dysfunction during endotoxic and septic shock in relationship to the role of cytokines (IL1, TNF etc) on the glucose dyshomeostasis which occurs during circulatory shock. *Mailing Add:* Dept Path Loyola Univ Med Ctr Stritch Sch Med 2160 S First Ave Maywood IL 60153-5594. *Fax:* 630-216-8482

**YELLE, ROGER V,** PLANETARY ATMOSPHERES, RADIATIVE TRANSFER. *Current Pos:* ASSOC PROF, CTR SPACE PHYSICS, BOSTON UNIV, 93- *Personal Data:* b Taunton, Mass, July 19, 57. *Educ:* Worcester Polytech Inst, BS, 78; Univ Wis-Madison, MS, 80, PhD(physics), 84. *Prof Exp:* Teaching asst, Univ Wis-Madison, 78-79, res asst, 79-80 & 82-84; mem prof staff, Plasma Physics Lab, Princeton Univ, 80-82; res assoc, Univ Ariz, 84-88, sr res assoc, 88-89, asst res scientist, Lunar & Planetary Lab, 89-93. *Concurrent Pos:* Prin investr, NSF, 85-87 & NASA, 87- *Mem:* Am Geophys Union; Am Astron Soc. *Res:* Physical and chemical processes in planetary atmospheres; role of radiation in the initiation of chemical cycles and in the thermal balance in planetary atmospheres. *Mailing Add:* Ctr Space Physics Boston Univ 725 Commonwealth Ave Boston MA 02215

**YELLEN, GARY,** ION CHANNEL STRUCTURE FUNCTION, ELECTROPHYSIOLOGY. *Current Pos:* ASSOC PROF, NEUROBIOL, HARVARD MED SCH, MASS GEN HOSP, 92- *Personal Data:* b Belleville, NJ, Nov 20, 58. *Educ:* Harvard Col, AB, 79; Yale Univ, MPh, 81, PhD(physiol), 84. *Prof Exp:* Fel, Brandeis Univ, 84-86; asst prof neurosci, Johns Hopkins Univ, Sch Med, 86-92. *Concurrent Pos:* Asst investr, Howard Hughes Med Inst, 86-92; joint appointment biophys, Johns Hopkins Univ, Sch Med, 88-92. *Mem:* Soc Gen Physiologists; Biophys Soc; Soc Neurosci. *Res:* Ion channels control electrical activity in brain, heart and muscle tissue and are important targets for therapeutic drugs; study the structural basis of ion channel function through genetic manipulation and biophysical analysis of cloned channels. *Mailing Add:* Mass Gen Hosp Wellman 340A Boston MA 02114. *Fax:* 617-726-5748; *E-Mail:* yellen@helix.mgh.harvard.edu

**YELLEN, JAY,** ALGEBRA. *Current Pos:* ASST PROF MATH, STATE UNIV NY COL, FREDONIA, 76- *Personal Data:* b New York, NY, Dec 17, 48; m 71; c 1. *Educ:* Polytech Inst Brooklyn, BS, 69, MS, 71; Colo State Univ, PhD(math), 75. *Prof Exp:* Teaching asst math, Polytech Inst Brooklyn, 69-71; teaching asst, Colo State Univ, 71-75; asst prof, Allegheny Col, 75-76. *Mem:* Am Math Soc. *Res:* Group representation theory, particularly groups of central type; algebraic coding theory. *Mailing Add:* Fla Inst Technol 150 W University Ave Melbourne FL 32901

**YELLIN, ABSALOM MOSES,** PSYCHOPHYSIOLOGY, CHILD PSYCHIATRY. *Current Pos:* CHILD PSYCHIATRIST, PARK NICOLLET MED CTR, MINNEAPOLIS, MINN, 88- *Personal Data:* b Tel-Aviv, Israel, July 25, 36; US citizen; m 65; c 2. *Educ:* Univ Del, BA, 65, MA, 68, PhD(psychol), 70. *Prof Exp:* Scholar, Neuropsychiat Inst, Univ Calif, Los Angeles Sch Med, 69-71; asst prof res, Neuropsychiat Inst, Univ Calif, Los Angeles, 71-72; asst prof, Dept Psychiat, Univ Calif, Davis, 72-74; asst prof, Univ Minn, 74-80, dir, Clin Studies Unit, 74-83, dir res, Div Child Adolescent Psychiat, 74-87, assoc prof, Dept Psychiat, 80-87, dir, Lab Neurosci, 83-87, assoc dir, Child Psychiat Inpatient Unit, 85-87. *Concurrent Pos:* Consult pychologist, Minn. *Mem:* Am Psychol Asn; fel Int Soc Pychophysiol; NY Acad Sci; Soc Psychophysiol Res; Int Soc Develop Psychobiol; Sigma Xi. *Res:* Attention and information processing; attention deficit disorders and other disorders involving attentional deficits, chronobiology, mental retardation, psychophysiology; child psychology and psychiatry; psychopharmacology; voluntary control of autonomic functions. *Mailing Add:* 3800 Park Nicollet Blvd Minneapolis MN 55416-2699

**YELLIN, EDWARD L,** CARDIAC PHYSIOLOGY, BIOENGINEERING. *Current Pos:* Res assoc surg, Albert Einstein Col Med, 65-66, assoc surg & physiol, 66-68, asst prof, 68-72, assoc prof surg & physiol, 72-79, prof surg & physiol & biophys, 79-96, EMER PROF PHYSIOL & BIOPHYS, ALBERT EINSTEIN COL MED, 96- *Personal Data:* b Brooklyn, NY, July 2, 27; m 48; c 3. *Educ:* Colo State Univ, BS, 59; Univ Ill, MS, 61, PhD(mech eng), 64. *Concurrent Pos:* NIH sr fel cardiovasc tech, Univ Wash, 64-65. *Mem:* Am Physiol Soc; Biomed Eng Soc; Cardiovasc Syst Dynamics Soc. *Res:* Cardiac dynamics, particularly left ventricular filling and mitral valve dynamics; diastolic function of the heart; natural and artificial heart valves. *Mailing Add:* Dept Physiol & Biophysics Albert Einstein Col Med 1300 Morris Park Ave Rm 721 I Bronx NY 10461-1924. *Fax:* 718-430-8769; *E-Mail:* yellin@aecom.yu.edu

**YELLIN, HERBERT,** HEALTH SCIENCES, EXPERIMENTAL NEUROLOGY. *Current Pos:* RETIRED. *Personal Data:* b New York, NY, May 27, 35; m 63; c 5. *Educ:* City Col New York, BA, 56; Univ Calif, Los Angeles, PhD(anat & neurophysiol), 66. *Prof Exp:* Cytologist, Div Labs, Cedars of Lebanon Hosp, Los Angeles, 57-58; cytologist radiation path, Armed Forces Inst Path, US Army, 58-60; staff fel exp neurol, Nat Inst Neurol Dis & Blindness, NIH, 66-68; res physiologist trophic nerve functions, Nat Inst Neurol Dis & Stroke, NIH, 68-73; res physiologist neuronal develop & regeneration, Nat Inst Neurol & Communicative Dis & Stroke, NIH, 73-76; grants assoc sci admin, div res grants, NIH, 76-77, prog dir, Nat Eye Inst, 77-78, health scientist admin, Nat Inst Neurol & Commun Dis & Stroke, 78-, exec secy, Respiratory & Appl Physiol Study Sect. *Concurrent Pos:* Lectr anat, Sch Med & Dent, Georgetown Univ, 67-75; councilman assembly scientists, Nat Inst Neurolog & Communicative Dis & Stroke, NIH, 73-75. *Mem:* Am Asn Anatomists; Am Physiol Soc; Soc Neurosci; NY Acad Sci. *Res:* Sensorimotor characteristics of posture and locomotion; interrelationships of neurons and skeletal muscle. *Mailing Add:* PO Box 1358 Edmonds WA 98020-1358

**YELLIN, JOSEPH,** PHYSICS, ARCHAEOLOGY. *Current Pos:* co-dir, Archaeometry Lab, 73-86, ASSOC PROF PHYSICS & ARCHAEOL, HEBREW UNIV, JERUSALEM, ISRAEL, 73-, DIR, ARCHAEOMETRY UNIT, 86- *Personal Data:* b Tel Aviv, Israel, Apr 21, 38; US citizen; m 68; Ett Melamed; c Irit, Efrat & Tamar. *Educ:* Univ Del, BS & BA, 60; Univ Calif, Berkeley, PhD(physics), 65. *Prof Exp:* Teaching asst physics, Univ Calif, Berkeley, 60-62, res asst, 62-65, res physicist, Lawrence Berkeley Lab, 65-73. *Concurrent Pos:* Vis sr lectr, Hebrew Univ, 70-71; vis assoc prof, Univ Calif, Los Angeles, 78-79; sr res assoc, Nat Res Coun, Jet Propulsion Lab, Pasadena, Calif, 80-82; vis scholar, Harvard Univ. *Mem:* Am Phys Soc; NY Acad Sci; AAAS; Soc Appl Spectros. *Res:* Gamma-ray spectroscopy with application to element analysis; provenance of ancient ceramics obsidian and flint through chemical fingerprinting employing gamma-ray spectroscopy; neutron activation analysis. *Mailing Add:* Inst Archaeol Hebrew Univ Jerusalem Israel

**YELLIN, STEVEN JOSEPH,** EXPERIMENTAL HIGH ENERGY PHYSICS. *Current Pos:* asst prof & asst res physicist, 73-80, assoc prof residence & assoc res physicist, 80-88, PROF RESIDENCE & RES PHYS, UNIV CALIF, SANTA BARBARA, 88- *Personal Data:* b San Francisco, Calif, Dec 27, 41. *Educ:* Calif Inst Technol, BS, 63, PhD(physics), 71. *Prof Exp:* Physicist, German Electron Synchrotron, 71-73. *Res:* Electromagnetic interactions in elementary particle physics. *Mailing Add:* Dept Physics Univ Calif Santa Barbara CA 93106

**YELLIN, TOBIAS O,** BIOCHEMISTRY, PHARMACOLOGY. *Current Pos:* RES DIR BIOPROD OPER, BECKMAN INSTRUMENTS, INC, PALO ALTO, CALIF, 81- *Personal Data:* b Tel Aviv, Israel, Aug 22, 34; US citizen; m 66; c 3. *Educ:* Philadelphia Col Pharm, BS, 59, MS, 62; Univ Del, PhD(chem), 66. *Prof Exp:* Sr scientist, Abbott Labs, Ill, 66-71; sr pharmacologist, Smith Kline & French Labs, Pa, 71-73; head, Gastroenterol Sect, Rorer Res Labs, Pa, 73-75; mgr gastrointestinal pharmacol, ICI Americas Inc, Wilmington, Del, 75-81. *Concurrent Pos:* Vis instr pharmacol, Med Col Pa, 73-81. *Mem:* AAAS; Am Chem Soc; Am Soc Pharmacol & Exp Therapeut. *Res:* Gastrointestinal pharmacology and biochemistry; histamine and histamine antagonists; biology and chemistry of peptides. *Mailing Add:* L412 SB Pharmaceut PO Box 1539 King of Prussia PA 19406-0939

**YELLIN, WILBUR,** PHYSICAL MEASUREMENTS, SPECTROSCOPY. *Current Pos:* CONSULT ANALYTICAL CHEM, 90- *Personal Data:* b Passaic, NJ, Nov 1, 32; m 77, Carole Skurow; c Pamela, Claudia & David. *Educ:* Rutgers Univ, BSc, 54; Cornell Univ, PhD, 62. *Prof Exp:* Chemist, Nat Starch Corp, 54; asst chem, Cornell Univ, 54-58, res asst, 58-59; sr res chemist, Ozalid Div, Gen Aniline & Film Corp, 59-62; res chemist, Procter & Gamble Co, 62-70, sect head, Phys Sci, 70-82, sect head, Analytical Chem, 82-90. *Mem:* AAAS; Soc Appl Spectros; Coblentz Soc; Am Chem Soc. *Res:* Application of spectroscopic, analytical and physical measurement techniques to chemical problems, structure determinations and analyte measurement structure and physical properties of stratum corneum; metal ion complexes, photochemistry; Raman, infrared, uvvis and mass spectrometry. *Mailing Add:* 373 Compton Rd Cincinnati OH 45215-4145. *E-Mail:* yellin.wc@msn.com

**YELON, ARTHUR MICHAEL,** SOLID STATE PHYSICS. *Current Pos:* assoc prof, 72-74, dir, thin film res group, 84-90, chmn eng physics, 93-97, PROF ENG PHYSICS, ECOLE POLYTECH, UNIV MONTREAL, 74- *Personal Data:* b New York, NY, Apr 15, 34; m 58, Judith Liporosky; c Michael & Cindy. *Educ:* Cornell Univ, BA, 55; Case Inst Technol, MS, 59, PhD(physics), 61. *Prof Exp:* Asst physics, Case Inst Technol, 55-57, instr, 57-61; assoc mem res staff, Res Ctr, Int Bus Mach Corp, 61-62, mem res staff, 62-63; mem res staff, Lab Electrostatics & Metal Phys, Grenoble, France, 63-66; assoc prof appl sci, Yale Univ, 66-72. *Mem:* Am Phys Soc; Am Vacuum Soc; Am Asn Physics Teachers; Inst Elec & Electronics Engrs; Can Asn Physicists; Mat Res Soc. *Res:* Surface physics; amorphous silicon; magnetotransport, Meyer-Neltel rule (compensation law); high energy ion implantation. *Mailing Add:* Dept Eng Physics PO Box 6079 Sta Centre Ville Montreal PQ H3C 3A7 Can

**YELON, WILLIAM B,** EXPERIMENTAL SOLID STATE PHYSICS, NEUTRON & GAMMA RAY SCATTERING. *Current Pos:* assoc prof, 75-84, PROF PHYSICS, UNIV MO, COLUMBIA, 84-, SR RES SCIENTIST, LEADER NEUTRON SCATTERING, UNIV RES REACTOR, 75-, ADJ PROF, UNIV MO-ROLLA. *Personal Data:* b Brooklyn, NY, Aug 23, 44; m 66, Harriet Most; c Joshua, Rachel, Sasha (deceased) & Jessica. *Educ:* Haverford Col, BA, 65; Carnegie Mellon Univ, MS, 67, PhD(physics), 70. *Honors & Awards:* Sigma Xi Res Award, 85; Chancellors Award Outstanding Res, 86. *Prof Exp:* Fel physics, Brookhaven Nat Lab, 70-72; res physicist, Inst Laue-Langevin, 72-75. *Concurrent Pos:* Mem, Neutron Diffraction Comn, Int Union Crystalography, 77-82; ed, Neutron Diffraction Newsletter, 77-82; pub chmn, Conf Magnetism & Magnetic Mat, 88-94, treas, 95-98. *Mem:* Am Phys Soc; Mat Res Soc. *Res:* Neutron scattering; studies of phase transitions; gamma ray diffraction; crystallography; Mossbauer scattering; structure property relationships in permanent magnet phases and high Tc superconductors; magnetism. *Mailing Add:* Univ Mo Res Reactor Res Park Columbia MO 65211. *Fax:* 573-882-3443; *E-Mail:* yelon@reactor.murr.missouri.edu

**YELTON, DAVID BAETZ,** MICROBIOLOGY. *Current Pos:* asst prof, 73-80, ASSOC PROF MICROBIOL, WVA UNIV MED CTR, 80- *Personal Data:* b Cincinnati, Ohio, Jan 16, 45. *Educ:* Mass Inst Technol, BS, 66; Univ Mass, Amherst, MS, 69, PhD(microbiol), 71. *Prof Exp:* Instr cell biol, Med Sch, Univ Md, 72-73. *Mem:* Am Soc Microbiol; AAAS. *Res:* Genetics; molecular biology. *Mailing Add:* Dept Microbiol Univ WVa Med Ctr 2095 HSN Morgantown WV 26506-0002

**YEMMA, JOHN JOSEPH,** CYTOCHEMISTRY, CELL BIOLOGY. *Current Pos:* assoc prof, 71-80, PROF CELL BIOL, YOUNGSTOWN STATE UNIV, 80- *Personal Data:* b Youngstown, Ohio, July 14, 33; m 78; c 7. *Educ:* Youngstown State Univ, BS, 61; George Peabody Col, MA, 65; Pa State Univ, PhD(cytochem), 71. *Prof Exp:* Instr biol, Pa State Univ, 65-71. *Concurrent Pos:* Youngstown State Univ res grant, 72-79, 81-86; NIH trainee, 75. *Mem:* AAAS; Am Bot Soc; Am Inst Biol Sci; Sigma Xi. *Res:* Developmental biochemistry of biomembranes during stages of the cell cycle. *Mailing Add:* Dean Technol Youngstown State Univ 410 Wick Ave Youngstown OH 44555-0001

**YEN, ANDREW,** CANCER BIOLOGY, REGULATORY BIOLOGY. *Current Pos:* PROF PATH & DIR GRAD STUDIES ENVIRON TOXICOL, CORNELL UNIV, 88- *Personal Data:* b New York, NY, Mar 4, 48; m 75; c 3. *Educ:* Haverford Col, BA, 69; Univ Wash, MS, 70; Cornell Univ, PhD(biophys), 76. *Prof Exp:* Res fel, Harvard Univ, 76-78; mem staff, Sloan-Kettering Inst, 78-81; fac dir, assoc prof flow cytometry & internal med, Sch Med, Univ Iowa, 81-88. *Concurrent Pos:* Woodrow Wilson fel; Leukemia Soc Am fel. *Mem:* Am Asn Cancer Res; Am Soc Cell Biol; Soc Anal Cytol; Biophys Soc. *Res:* Cellular and molecular mechanisms regulating cell growth and differentiation in normal and neoplastic cells. *Mailing Add:* Dept Path Vet Col Cornell Univ T4017 Vet Res Tower Ithaca NY 14853-0001. *Fax:* 607-253-3317; *E-Mail:* ay13@cornell.edu

**YEN, BELINDA R S,** IMMUNOLOGY. *Current Pos:* res fel, 74-77, proj scientist, 77-, STAFF MICROBIOLOGIST, CLEVELAND CLIN FOUND. *Personal Data:* b Szechuen, China, Sept 2, 42; US citizen; c 2. *Educ:* Southern Ill Univ, Carbondale, BS, 62; Univ Ark, Fayetteville, MS, 66, PhD(immunol), 71. *Prof Exp:* Am Heart Asn fel, 71-72, Arthritis Found res fel, 72-73; res assoc clin immunol, Sch Med, Case Western Res Univ, 73-74. *Mem:* AAAS; NY Acad Sci; Am Soc Microbiol; Sigma Xi. *Res:* Clinical immunology; regulation of immune response; tumor immunology; clinical virology. *Mailing Add:* Cleveland Clin Found Sect Microbiol Lab Med 9500 Euclid Ave Cleveland OH 44195-5140

**YEN, BEN CHIE,** HYDRAULICS, FLUID MECHANICS. *Current Pos:* from asst prof to assoc prof hydraul, 67-76, PROF CIVIL ENG, UNIV ILL, URBANA, 76- *Personal Data:* b Canton, China, Apr 14, 35; m 93, Ruth H Chao. *Educ:* Nat Taiwan Univ, BS, 56; Univ Iowa, MS, 59, PhD(mech & hydraul), 65. *Honors & Awards:* Fulbright Distinguished Sr Lectr Award, 88; Best Tech Note Award, Am Soc Civil Engrs Hydraul Div, 94; V T Chow Mem Lect Award, Int Water Resources Asn, 96. *Prof Exp:* Civil engr, Army Engrs Br, Taiwan, 57-58; jr engr, Water Resources Planning & Develop Comn, Taiwan, 58; res assoc, Inst Hydraul Res, Univ Iowa, 60-64 & Princeton Univ, 64-66; prof civil eng & mem Ctr Advan Studies, Univ Va, 88-91. *Concurrent Pos:* Vis prof, Univ Karlsruhe, Ger, 74-75, Fed Sch Polytech, Lausanne, Switz, 82, Vrije Univ, Brussels, Belg, 83, Nat Taiwan Univ, Taipei, 83 & 91, Univ Stuttgart, Ger, 83 & 84, Univ New SWales, 85, Hong Kong Univ Sci & Tech, 95-96; dir, Second Int Conf Urban Storm Drainage, 81, Fourth Int Symp Stochastic Hydraul, 84, Int Conf Channel Flow & Catchment Runoff, 89; pres, Joint Comt Urban Drainage, Int Asn Hydraul Res & Int Asn Water Qual, 82-86; ed, Advan Hydrosci, 85-; assoc ed, J Hydraul Eng, 88-, J Hydraul Res, 85- *Mem:* Chinese Am Water Resouces Asn (pres, 93-95); Am Geophys Union; Int Asn Hydraul Res; Am Soc Civil Engrs; Int Water Resources Asn; Sigma Xi; Int Asn Hydrol Sci. *Res:* Open-channel hydraulics; sediment transport; surface hydrology; risk and reliability analysis; floods; urban drainage; infiltration. *Mailing Add:* Dept Civil Eng Univ Ill Urbana IL 61801. *Fax:* 217-333-0687

**YEN, BEN-TSENG,** CIVIL ENGINEERING. *Current Pos:* Res asst civil eng, Fritz Lab, Lehigh Univ, 57-60, res assoc, 60-64, from asst prof to assoc prof, 64-77, PROF CIVIL ENG, LEHIGH UNIV, 77- *Personal Data:* b Canton, China, Jan 19, 32; m 65; c 2. *Educ:* Nat Taiwan Univ, BS, 55; Lehigh Univ, MS, 59, PhD(struct eng), 63. *Concurrent Pos:* Consult industs, 61- *Mem:* Am Soc Civil Engrs; Struct Stability Res Coun (secy, 66-69); Sigma Xi. *Res:* Mechanical properties of materials; behavior and strength of civil engineering structures; fatigue and fracture of materials and structures. *Mailing Add:* Dept Civil Eng Fritz Lab 13 Lehigh Univ Bethlehem PA 18015

**YEN, BING CHENG,** CIVIL ENGINEERING, SOIL MECHANICS. *Current Pos:* from asst prof to assoc prof, 64-78, PROF CIVIL ENG, CALIF STATE UNIV, LONG BEACH, 78- *Personal Data:* b Shantung Province, China, June 13, 34; m 64; c 3. *Educ:* Nat Taiwan Univ, BS, 56; Univ Utah, PhD(civil eng), 63. *Prof Exp:* Found engr, Utah State Hwy Dept, 62-63; asst prof civil eng, Univ Utah, 63-64. *Concurrent Pos:* Consult, Dept Engrs, Los Angeles Co, 65-70 & Woodward-Clyde Consults, 72-78; Geotech consult. *Mem:* Am Soc Civil Engrs. *Res:* Soil mechanics and foundation engineering; i slope stability; earthquake effects on soil engineering; marine geomechanics; rock mechanics. *Mailing Add:* 31132 Ceanothus Dr Laguna Niguel CA 92677

**YEN, CHEN-WAN LIU,** aerospace science, for more information see previous edition

**YEN, DAVID HSIEN-YAO,** APPLIED MATHEMATICS, ENGINEERING MECHANICS. *Current Pos:* from asst prof to prof, 65-96, EMER PROF MATH, MICH STATE UNIV, 96- *Personal Data:* b Tsingtao, Shantung, Apr 18, 34; m 64, Lorraine C C; c Alex, Earl & Sarah. *Educ:* Nat Taiwan Univ, BS, 56; Mich State Univ, MS, 61; NY Univ, PhD(math), 66. *Prof Exp:* Asst prof civil eng & mech, Bradley Univ, 61-62. *Concurrent Pos:* Vis scientist, Inst Comp Appln Sci & Eng, NASA Langley Res Ctr, 74. *Mem:* Am Math Soc; Soc Indust Appl Math. *Res:* Mathematical mechanics; methods of applied mathematics. *Mailing Add:* Dept Math Mich State Univ East Lansing MI 48824-1027

**YEN, I-KUEN,** ENVIRONMENTAL ENGINEERING. *Current Pos:* PRIN, IKE YEN ASSOCS, 83- *Personal Data:* b Singapore, May 29, 30; US citizen; m 58; c 2. *Educ:* Nat Taiwan Univ, BS, 54; Mass Inst Technol, SM, 56, ScD(chem eng), 60. *Prof Exp:* Chem engr, Crucible Steel Co, 59-61; res scientist pollution control, Am Standard Corp, 61-64; group leader eng, C F Braun & Co, 64-68; dir contract res, Occidental Res Corp, 68-78, dir health, safety & environ, 78-83. *Concurrent Pos:* Adj prof, Newark Col Eng, 61-62, Stevens Inst Technol, 63-64, Harvey Mudd Col, 85-86 & USC, 87-88. *Mem:* Am Inst Chem Engrs; Am Chem Soc; NY Acad Sci. *Res:* Inorganic chemicals processing; health and safety; pollution control; process development; environmental engineering; research management. *Mailing Add:* 867 Marymount Lane Claremont CA 91711-1513

**YEN, JONG-TSENG,** ANIMAL SCIENCES & NUTRITION. *Current Pos:* RES ANIMAL SCI, AGR RES SERV, USDA, 78- *Personal Data:* b Tainan, Taiwan, Feb 12, 42; US citizen; m 70, Lei-Hwa Wang; c Joyce & James. *Educ:* Nat Taiwan Univ, BS, 64; Univ Ill, MS, 70, PhD(animal nutrit), 75. *Honors & Awards:* Nonruminant Nutrit Res Award, Am Soc Animal Sci, 93. *Prof Exp:* Teaching asst animal sci, Animal Sci Dept, Nat Taiwan Univ, 65-68; res asst swine nutrit, Animal Sci Dept, Univ Ill, 68-74, res assoc, 75; res assoc, Biochem Dept, Univ Mo, 75-77, res assoc, Animal Sci Dept, 77-78. *Concurrent Pos:* Swine consult, US Feed Grains Coun, 82; adj prof animal sci, Univ Nebr, 82-; wine consult, Am Soybean Asn, 94. *Mem:* Am Soc Animal Sci; Am Inst Nutrit. *Res:* Mechanism of growth stimulation by antibiotics; hepatic portal absorption of nutrients and gut metabolites; vitamin C in swine nutrition; post weaning stress in relation to nutrition; growth repartitioning agents for pigs. *Mailing Add:* US Meat Animal Res Ctr PO Box 166 Clay Center NE 68933. *Fax:* 402-762-4148

**YEN, MICHAEL R T,** PULMONARY CIRCULATION, BIOMECHANICS. *Current Pos:* PROF BIOMED ENG, MEMPHIS STATE UNIV, 87- *Personal Data:* b Chai-i, Taiwan, China, June 18, 40; US citizen; m, Min-Chu Chan; c Morris C & Eric C. *Educ:* Nat Taiwan Univ, BS, 62; Univ Calif, San Diego, PhD(bioeng), 73. *Prof Exp:* Fel bioeng, Univ Calif, San Diego, 73-75, from asst res prof to assoc res prof bioeng, 75-87. *Concurrent Pos:* Res Career Develop Award, NIH, 80-85; lectr bioeng, Univ Calif, San Diego, 83-86; consult lung injury & lung mech, Jaycor, 85-87; featured engr, Memphis Joint Eng Coun, 90. *Mem:* Biomed Eng Soc; fel Am Inst Med & Biol Eng; Am Soc Mech Engrs; Am Physiol Soc; Soc Chinese Bioscientists Am. *Res:* Pulmonary circulation to better understand the mechanical basis of blood flow in the human lung; pulmonary mechanics to study the mechanics of injury due to automobile collision; physically model the lung for application in the study of inhalation toxicology; biomechanics, heart mechanics, hypertension. *Mailing Add:* Dept Biomed Eng Memphis Univ Memphis TN 38152-0001. *Fax:* 901-678-4180

**YEN, NAI-CHYUAN,** SIGNAL & INFORMATION PROCESSING. *Current Pos:* RES PHYSICIST, NAVAL RES LAB, 82- *Personal Data:* b Shaoxing, China, Apr 12, 36; US citizen; m 67, Molly Kao; c Adelina, Beatrice & Clarette. *Educ:* Cheng Kung Univ, BS, 57; Univ RI, MS, 62; Harvard Univ, PhD(appl physics), 71. *Honors & Awards:* Alan Berman Res Publ Award, 89. *Prof Exp:* Elec engr electronics, Bendix Corp, 62-66; res physicist acoust, Naval Underwater Systs Ctr, 72-79; ocean engr, US Coast Guard Res & Develop Ctr, 79-82. *Concurrent Pos:* Vis fel, Yale Univ, 93-94. *Mem:* Acoust Soc Am; Inst Elec & Electronics Engrs; AAAS; Asn Comput Mach. *Res:* Radiation, transmission and reception of underwater acoustic waves; noise generation mechanisms and control; non-linear phenomena and oscillations; signal processing; electronic and electro-optics instrumentation; image processing and pattern recognition. *Mailing Add:* Naval Res Lab 4555 Overlook Ave SW Washington DC 20375-0002. *Fax:* 202-404-7420; *E-Mail:* yen@acoustics.nrl.navy.mil

**YEN, S C YEN,** REPRODUCTIVE ENDOCRINOLOGY. *Current Pos:* chmn dept, 72-87, PROF OBSTET & GYNEC, UNIV CALIF 70-, PROF REPRODUCTIVE MED & W R PERSONS CHAIR, 87- *Personal Data:* b Peking, China, Feb 22, 27; m 58; c 3. *Educ:* Chee-Loo Univ, China, BS, 49; Univ Hong Kong, MD, 54, DSc, 80; Am Bd Obstet & Gynec, dipl, 66; Am Bd Reprod Endocrinol, cert, 73. *Prof Exp:* Intern med, Queen Mary Hosp, Hong Kong, 54-55; resident obstet & gynec, Johns Hopkins Hosp, 56-60; instr, Johns Hopkins Univ, 58-60; chicf dcpt, Guam Mcm Hosp, 60-62; from asst prof to assoc prof reproductive biol, Sch Med, Case Western Res Univ, 62-70; assoc dir obstet, Univ Hosps, Cleveland, 68-70. *Concurrent Pos:* Teaching & res fels, Harvard Med Sch, 62. *Mem:* Inst Med-Nat Acad Sci; Am Diabetes Asn; Am Soc Gynec Invest (pres, 81); fel Am Col Obstet & Gynec; Asn Am Physicians; Endocrine Soc. *Res:* Obstetrics and gynecology. *Mailing Add:* Dept Reproductive Med Univ Calif Sch Med La Jolla CA 92093

**YEN, TEH FU,** ENERGY & ENVIRONMENT, SUBSURFACE MICROBIOL TECHNOLOGY. *Current Pos:* assoc prof, Dept Med, Dept Chem Eng & Environ Eng, 69-80, PROF, DEPT CIVIL & ENVIRON ENG, UNIV SOUTHERN CALIF, 80- *Personal Data:* b Kunming, China, Jan 9, 27; US citizen; m 59, Shaio P Siao. *Educ:* Cent China Univ, BS, 47; WVa Univ, MS, 53; Va Polytech Inst, PhD(org chem & biochem), 56. *Hon Degrees:* DSc, Pepperdine Univ, 82. *Honors & Awards:* Imper Crown Gold Medal, Iran, 77; Petrol Chem Award, Am Chem Soc, 93. *Prof Exp:* Asst, Cent China Univ, 47-48, Yunnan Univ, 48-49 & WVa Univ, 50-53; sr res chemist, Res Div, Goodyear Tire & Rubber Co, 55-59; fel petrol chem, Mellon Inst, 59-65, sr fel, Carnegie-Mellon Univ, 65-67; assoc prof chem, Calif State Univ, Los Angeles, 68-69. *Concurrent Pos:* Vis prof chem & chem eng, Nat Taiwan Univ, 67-68. *Mem:* Sr mem Am Chem Soc; Inst Petrol; Am Inst Chem Engrs; Am Soc Petrol Engrs; fel Royal Chem Soc; fel Inst Petrol UK; Chinese Am Chem Soc. *Res:* Technology and science to achieve clean energy in fossil fuels; microbiological processess applied to natural resources and waste recovery; membrane-mimetic chemistry applied to environmental engineering, wastewater decontamination and biotreatment. *Mailing Add:* 3620 S Vermont Ave Los Angeles CA 90089-2531. *Fax:* 213-744-1426

**YEN, TERENCE TSIN TSU,** BIOCHEMISTRY, GENETICS. *Current Pos:* RETIRED. *Personal Data:* b Shanghai, China, May 2, 37; m 64; c 3. *Educ:* Nat Taiwan Univ, BS, 58; Univ NC, PhD(biochem, genetics), 66. *Prof Exp:* Res scientist, res labs, Eli Lilly & Co, 65-93. *Concurrent Pos:* Adj prof, Ind Univ Sch Med; consult, pharmaceut discovery & develop. *Mem:* AAAS; Sigma Xi; Am Soc Biochem & Molecular Biol; Am Diabetes Asn; NAm Asn Study Obesity. *Res:* Biochemical defects and treatment of metabolic diseases in higher organisms; obesity; diabetes. *Mailing Add:* 8704 Hunting Trail Indianapolis IN 46217. *Fax:* 317-881-7340

**YEN, TIEN-SZE BENEDICT,** HEPATITIS B VIRUS, REGULATION OF GENE EXPRESSION. *Current Pos:* Asst prof, 85-91, ASSOC PROF PATH, UNIV CALIF, SAN FRANCISCO, 91- *Personal Data:* b Taipei, Taiwan, Oct 15, 53; US citizen; m 83, Maria He; c Cecilia & Brian. *Educ:* Stanford Univ, BS, 73; Duke Univ, MD, 82, PhD(biochem), 82. *Honors & Awards:* Cathay Hepatitis Award, SCBA, 90. *Concurrent Pos:* Chief anat path, San Francisco, Vet Admin Med Ctr, 96- *Mem:* Fel Am Soc Clin Path; Am Soc Cell Biol; Am Soc Investigative Path; US Can Acad Path. *Res:* How cellular and viral factors regulate hepatitis B virus gene expression in an effort to devise novel means of controlling viral replication in people with chronic hepatitis B virus infection. *Mailing Add:* Anatomic Path 113B 4150 Clement St San Francisco CA 94121. *Fax:* 415-750-6947; *E-Mail:* yen@sanfrancisco.va.gov

**YEN, TIM J,** BIOCHEMISTRY, MOLECULAR BIOLOGY. *Current Pos:* ASSOC MEM, INST CANCER RES, FOX CHASE CANCER CTR, 90- *Personal Data:* b Apr 3, 57; m, Joyce D Liporace; c Michael. *Educ:* Univ Calif, Santa Barbara, BA, 80, MA, 81, PhD(biochem), 85. *Honors & Awards:* Young Investr Award, Johns Hopkins Univ Sch Med, 88. *Prof Exp:* Fel, Johns Hopkins Univ Sch Med, 86-90. *Concurrent Pos:* Fel, Am Cancer Soc, 85-88; Lucille P Markey scholar, 89; adj prof, Dept Genetics, Univ Pa, 91. *Res:* Investigating the structure and function of a kinetochore associated microtubule-based motor protein in human cells; author of several publications. *Mailing Add:* Fox Chase Cancer Ctr 7701 Burholme Ave Philadelphia PA 19111-2497

**YEN, WILLIAM MAOSHUNG,** LASER SPECTROSCOPY. *Current Pos:* GRAHAM PURDUE PROF PHYSICS, UNIV GA, ATHENS, 86- *Personal Data:* b Nanking, China, Apr 5, 35; US citizen; m 78, Laurel F Curtis; c Jane L. *Educ:* Univ Redlands, Calif, BS, 56; Washington Univ, St Louis, PhD(physics), 62. *Prof Exp:* Res assoc physics, Washington Univ, St Louis, 62 & Stanford Univ, 62-65; from asst prof to prof, Univ Wis-Madison, 65-90. *Concurrent Pos:* Vis prof, Univ Tokyo, 72, Univ Paris, Orsay, France, 76 & J Goethe Univ, Frankfurt, Ger, 85; consult, Lawrence Livermore Nat Lab, 75-86, Argonne Nat Lab, 77-82, Fla State Univ Bd Regents, 88- & Rosemont Corp, St Paul, Minn, 89-; J S Guggenheim fel, 79-80; hon prof, Univ San Antonio de Abad de Cuzco, Peru, 82; Alexander von Humboldt Found sr US scientist award, 85 & 90; vchair, Luminescence & Display Sect, Electrochem Soc, 90-; Fulbright sr scholar, 95. *Mem:* Fel Am Phys Soc; fel Optical Soc Am; fel AAAS; Electrochem Soc; Sigma Xi. *Res:* Laser spectroscopic techniques for study of optical properties of solids specially the dynamical properties, transfer and relaxation, of optically excited states of light emitting materials. *Mailing Add:* Dept Physics Univ Ga Athens GA 30602-9986. *Fax:* 706-542-2492; *E-Mail:* wmyen@uoa.cc.uga.edu

**YEN, YIN-CHAO,** ENGINEERING PHYSICS, EARTH SCIENCES. *Current Pos:* RETIRED. *Personal Data:* b China, 27; US citizen; m 60, Grace Chui; c Stephanie P, Tina W & Michael H. *Educ:* Nat Taiwan Univ, BS, 51; Kans State Univ, MS, 56; Northwestern Univ, PhD(chem eng), 60. *Honors & Awards:* Civilian Qual Increase Award, US Army Cold Regions Res & Eng Lab, 64, 65 & 71, Civilian Spec Act Award, 65, Meritorious Performance Award, 65, Outstanding Performance Award, 71. *Prof Exp:* Chem engr, US Army Cold Regions Res & Eng Lab, 60-62, res chem engr, 62-67, res phys scientist, 67-68, supvry res phys scientist, 68-82, res phys scientist, 82-95. *Concurrent Pos:* From adj asst prof to adj assoc prof, Univ NH, 65-71 & vis prof, 71-74; invited lectr, Academia Sinica, China, 85. *Mem:* AAAS; Sigma Xi; Am Inst Chem Engrs. *Res:* Thermophysical properties of snow and ice; effect of density inversion and thermal instability phenomena associated with the ice-water systems and heat transfer characteristics in snow and ice involving phase change; atmospheric stability and turbulent heat exchange. *Mailing Add:* 4 Willow Spring Lane Hanover NH 03755

**YENCHA, ANDREW JOSEPH,** PHYSICAL CHEMISTRY, CHEMICAL PHYSICS. *Current Pos:* from asst prof to assoc prof, 70-89, PROF, STATE UNIV NY, ALBANY, 89- *Personal Data:* b Pa, July 3, 38; m 67, Mary F Patti. *Educ:* Univ Calif, Berkeley, BS, 63, Univ Calif, Los Angeles, PhD(chem), 68. *Prof Exp:* Res asst chem, Dow Chem Co, Calif, 60-62; res asst, Univ Calif, Berkeley, 62-63, teaching asst, Los Angeles, 64-65, res asst, 65-68; fel, Yale Univ, 68-70. *Mem:* Am Inst Physics; Am Chem Soc; Int Am Photochem Soc. *Res:* Molecular beam, molecular spectroscopy, Penning ionization electron spectroscopy, photoionization and threshold photoelectron spectroscopy. *Mailing Add:* Dept Chem State Univ NY Albany NY 12222. *E-Mail:* ajy26@cnsvax.albany.edu

**YENDOL, WILLIAM G,** entomology; deceased, see previous edition for last biography

**YENER, YAMAN,** THERMOFLUIDS ENGINEERING, RADIATIVE TRANSFER. *Current Pos:* assoc prof mech eng, 82-89, actg chmn dept, 89-91, PROF MECH ENG, NORTHEASTERN UNIV, 89-, ASSOC DEAN ENG, 93- *Personal Data:* b Ankara, Turkey, Oct 18, 46; m 76, Demet Alper; c Zeynep. *Educ:* Mid East Tech Univ, Ankara, BS, 68, MS, 70; NC

State Univ, Raleigh, PhD(mech eng), 73. *Prof Exp:* From asst prof to assoc prof mech eng, Mid East Tech Univ, 74-82, chmn dept, 78-80. *Concurrent Pos:* Actg chmn, Heat Tech & Energy Res Unit, Sci & Tech Res Coun Turkey, 78-80. *Mem:* Assoc mem Sigma Xi; Am Soc Mech Engrs; Am Soc Engr Sci. *Res:* Simultaneous radiation and convection in radiatively participating media; radiating aerosols; stability of natural convection in enclosed spaces; spectral methods as a numerical simulation technique in heat transfer problems. *Mailing Add:* Mech Eng Dept Northeastern Univ 360 Huntington Ave Boston MA 02115-5096. *E-Mail:* yaman@neu.edu

**YENISCAVICH, WILLIAM,** nuclear engineering, for more information see previous edition

**YEN-KOO, HELEN C,** DRUG SIDE EFFECTS, MECHANISM OF DRUG ADDICTION. *Current Pos:* GROUP LEADER & ACTG CHIEF PSYCHOPHARMACOL & TOXICOL, DIV DRUG BIOL, FOOD & DRUG ADMIN, 66- *Personal Data:* b Shanghai, China, May 8, 25; US citizen; m 58; c 1. *Educ:* Franco-Chinese Univ, BS, 46; Ohio State Univ, MS, 51; George Washington Univ, PhD(pharmacol), 55. *Prof Exp:* Lab asst pharmacog, Franco-Chinese Univ, 42-48; mgr manufacture, Nat Biol Prod, 46-49; teaching asst pharm, Ohio State Univ, 50-51 & pharmacol, George Washington Univ, 51-55; res assoc cancer, Med Lab, Roswell Park Res Inst, 55-56; res assoc pharmacol, Ortho Res Inst, Johnson & Johnson, 56-60; res assoc psychopharmacol, Geigy Pharmaceut Co, 60-64; group leader, Endo Lab, Du Pont Chem Co, 64-66. *Concurrent Pos:* Vis scientist, Naking Med Sch, People's Repub China, 86. *Mem:* NY Acad Sci; Am Soc Pharmacol & Therapeut; Am Soc Toxicol; Sigma Xi; Chinese Health & Med Asn (vpres, 78-80, pres, 80). *Res:* Drug effects on animal behavior, memory and learning activities. *Mailing Add:* 5310 Danbury Rd Bethesda MD 20814-2871

**YENSEN, ARTHUR ERIC,** ECOLOGY. *Current Pos:* DEPT BIOL, ALBERTSON COL. *Personal Data:* b Nampa, Idaho, Oct 13, 44; m 66, 86, Teresa Tarifa; c 3. *Educ:* Col Idaho, BS, 66; Ore State Univ, MA, 71; Univ Ariz, PhD(zool), 73. *Prof Exp:* asst prof biol, Millsaps Col, 73-78; asst prof biol, Boise State Univ, 78- *Concurrent Pos:* Ed, Murrelet, 83-87. *Mem:* Ecol Soc Am; Am Soc Mammalogists; Br Ecol Soc; Sigma Xi; Soc Conserv Biol. *Res:* Ecology and biosystematics of mammals; conservation biology. *Mailing Add:* Dept Biol Albertson Col Caldwell ID 83605

**YENSEN, RICHARD,** PSYCHOLOGY & PSYCHOTHERAPY. *Current Pos:* DIR, ORENDA INST, BALTIMORE, MD, 88-; PVT PRACT, BALTIMORE, MD, 88- *Personal Data:* b Washington, DC, Aug 28, 49. *Educ:* Univ Calif, Irvine, BA, 71, PhD(psychol), 75. *Prof Exp:* Res psychotherapist, Clin Sci Div, Md Psychiat Res Ctr, 72-74, clin consult, 74-75, res fel, 75-76 & 76-77; pvt pract, Baltimore, Md, 77-86 & Cambridge, Mass, 86-88. *Concurrent Pos:* Clin consult, Brotherhood Man Drug Coun Ctr, Md, Friends Med Sci Res & Clin Sci Div, Md Psychiat Res Ctr, 76-77, Oldfield's Sch Girls & Ctr Vaccine Develop, Univ Md Hosp, Baltimore, 79-82; dir, Inst Human Develop, Baltimore, Md & Cambridge, Mass, 80-88; systs integration consult, Directorate Civil Works, Progs Div, Army Corp Engrs, 81-83; clin supvr, Latino Ment Health Clin, Cambridge City Hosp, 87-88. *Mem:* Am Psychol Asn; AAAS; NY Acad Sci; Int Soc Study Subtle Energy Med; Inst Noetic Sci. *Res:* Application of digital computers to psychology and the process of psychotherapy; developing new tools for psychological assessment via multimedia environments and physiological monitoring; computer management of sensory overload; innovative psychotherapeutic techniques; pharmacognosy; placebo effects. *Mailing Add:* 2403 Talbot Rd Baltimore MD 21216

**YENTSCH, CHARLES SAMUEL,** MARINE BIOLOGY. *Current Pos:* EXEC DIR, BIGELOW LAB OCEAN SCI, BOOTHBAY HARBOR, 77- *Personal Data:* b Louisville, Ky, Sept 13, 27. *Educ:* Univ Louisville, BS, 50; Fla State Univ, MS, 53. *Prof Exp:* Asst marine biol, Fla State Univ, 52-53; asst biol oceanog, Univ Wash, 53-55; res assoc marine ecol, Woods Hole Oceanog Inst, 55-67; assoc prof oceanog, Nova Univ, 67-69, assoc prof marine biol, 69-71; prof marine sci & dir marine sta, Univ Mass, Amherst, 71-77. *Mem:* Am Soc Limnol & Oceanog; Phycol Soc Am. *Res:* Marine phytoplankton ecology. *Mailing Add:* Samoset Trail Boothbay ME 04537

**YENTSCH, CLARICE M,** TOXIC MICROALGAE BLOOMS, CYTOCHEMISTRY. *Current Pos:* RES SCIENTIST & EDUCATOR, BIGELOW LAB OCEAN SCI, 74-; EDUCATOR, EDUC DEVELOP CTR, NEWTON, MAINE, 93- *Personal Data:* b Wausau, Wis, Oct 10, 42; m, Charles S; c Colin C & Carlton R. *Educ:* Univ Wis-Madison, BS, 64, MAT, 65; Nova Univ, PhD(biol oceanog), 70. *Prof Exp:* Fel, Univ Mass Marine Sta, 70-72, researcher, 72-74. *Concurrent Pos:* Vis prof, Bowdoin Col Chem, 87-88 & 92-93, Boston Univ, 91, Marine Maritime Acad, 93; vis scientist, Scripps Inst Oceanog, 88. *Mem:* Am Chem Soc; Am Soc Limnol & Oceanog; Oceanog Soc; Int Soc Anal Cytol. *Res:* Red tides; toxic blooms; analytical cytology; flow cytometry/cell sorting. *Mailing Add:* Bigelow Labs McKowen Pt Rd West Boothbay Harbor ME 04575

**YEO, YUNG KEE,** SEMI CONDUCTOR PHYSICS, LOW-TEMPERATURE PHYSICS. *Current Pos:* from asst prof to assoc prof, 87-90, PROF, AIR FORCE INST TECHNOL, 90- *Personal Data:* b Kyungbuk, Korea, Apr 24, 38; US citizen; m 64, Young O Chang; c Songmi & Lami. *Educ:* Seoul Nat Univ, BS, 61; Univ Southern Calif, PhD(physics), 72. *Prof Exp:* Res asst, 69-72, res assoc, Univ Southern Calif, 72; physicist, Develco Inc, 73-74; res assoc, Univ Ore, 74-77; resident scientist, Avionics Lab, Wright-Patterson AFB, 77-78; sr physicist, Systs Res Lab, 78-80; res scientist, Universal Energy Systs, 80-84. *Concurrent Pos:* Adj lectr, Air Force

Inst Technol, 81. *Mem:* Am Phys Soc; Korean Scientists & Engrs Asn Am; Asn Korean Physicist Am. *Res:* Ion-implantation techniques used for fabrication of electronic devices and/or opto-electronic applications; electrical and optical properties of various compound semiconductors such as gallium arsenide and alluminum gallium arsenide. *Mailing Add:* Afit/Eng 2950 PST Wright Patterson AFB Dayton OH 45433. *Fax:* 937-255-2921; *E-Mail:* yyeo@afit.af.mil

**YEOMAN, LYNN CHALMERS,** MEDICAL EDUCATION & CURRICULUM. *Current Pos:* from instr to assoc prof, 72-84, PROF PHARMACOL, BAYLOR COL MED, 84-, DIR, CURRIC DATABASE PROG, OFF CURRIC, 95- *Personal Data:* b Evanston, Ill, May 17, 43; m 96, Carol S Moore; c Caroline, Christopher & Sarah. *Educ:* DePauw Univ, BA, 65; Univ Ill, Champaign, PhD(biochem), 70. *Prof Exp:* Assoc dir cell & molecular biol, Bristol-Myers Squibb Co, 88-90. *Concurrent Pos:* NIH training grant & univ fel, Baylor Col Med, 70-72; prin investr, Cancer Prog Proj grant, 73-; consult, Colon Cancer Working Group, M D Anderson Hosp & Tumor Inst, 85, Bristol Labs, 86, Oncos Ltd, 86-87; fac assoc, Huffington Ctr Aging, 95-98. *Mem:* Am Asn Cancer Res; Am Soc Biol Chemists; Am Chem Soc; Am Asn Immunologists; Am Soc Cell Biol; Soc Exp Biol & Med. *Res:* Studies on colon cell autocrine receptors, redifferentiating drugs and peptides, and anticancer drug resistance; tumor markers, tumor antigens and monoclonal antibodies. *Mailing Add:* Dept Pharmacol Baylor Col Med Houston TX 77030-3498. *Fax:* 713-798-3145; *E-Mail:* lyeoman@bcm.tmc.edu; 71227.3613@compuserve.com

**YEOMANS, DONALD KEITH,** FUNDAMENTAL ASTRONOMY. *Current Pos:* ASTRON TECH SUPVR, JET PROPULSION LAB, 76- *Personal Data:* b Rochester, NY, May 3, 42; m 70, Laurie R Ernst; c Sara K & Keith A. *Educ:* Middlebury Col, BS, 64; Univ Md, MS, 67, PhD(astron), 70. *Honors & Awards:* Asteroid 2956 Yeomans Award. *Prof Exp:* Supvr, Comput Sci Corp, 73-75. *Concurrent Pos:* Deleg, Interagency Working Group, NASA, 82-86, discipline specialist, Int Halley Watch, 82-89, prin investr comet rendezvous mission, 86-91; mem, NASA Comets & Asteroids Sci Working Group, 74-85, Discovery Prog Working Group, 90-92, Small Bodies Working Group, 92-95; prin investr, Near-Earth Asteroid Rendezvous Mission; mem, Div Dynamical Astron & Planetary Sci, Am Aston Soc. *Mem:* Int Astron Union; Am Astron Soc; Hist Sci Soc. *Res:* Comet and asteroid motions; future spacecraft mission studies; history of science; fundamental astronomy. *Mailing Add:* 833 Chehalem Rd La Canada CA 91011. *Fax:* 818-393-1159; *E-Mail:* donald.k.yeomans@jpl.nasa.gov

**YEOWELL, DAVID ARTHUR,** DRUGS. *Current Pos:* sr org chemist, Wellcome Res Labs, Burroughs Wellcome Co, 64-68, sr develop chemist, Chem Develop Labs, 68-71, head develop res, 71-73, mgr chem develop labs, 73-81, dir develop labs, 81-86, VPRES TECH DEVELOP, BURROUGHS WELLCOME CO, 86- *Personal Data:* b London, Eng, Jan 3, 37; m 64; c 3. *Educ:* Bristol Univ, BSc, 58, PhD, 61. *Prof Exp:* Swiss Nat Fund fel org chem, Univ Zurich, 61-62; Imp Chem Indust res fel biogenetics, Univ Liverpool, 62-64. *Mem:* Am Chem Soc; Royal Soc Chem. *Res:* Application of organic, physical and analytical chemical knowledge to devising economic and practical chemical and dosage form production scale processes for pharmaceuticals and their quality assurance. *Mailing Add:* 608 Concordia Ct Chapel Hill NC 27514

**YERAZUNIS, STEPHEN,** CHEMICAL ENGINEERING. *Current Pos:* RETIRED. *Personal Data:* b Pittsfield, Mass, Aug 21, 22; m 54, Mary Morris; c William & Elizabeth. *Educ:* Rensselaer Polytech Inst, BChE, 47, MChE, 48, DChE, 52. *Prof Exp:* Engr, Manhattan Proj, Oak Ridge, Tenn, 43-46 & Gen Elec Co, Mass, 47; from instr to assoc prof chem eng, Rensselaer Polytech Inst, 48-63, assoc dean, Sch Eng, 66-79, prof chem eng, 63- *Concurrent Pos:* Consult, Knolls Atomic Power Lab, NY, 56-72, NY State Dept Ment Hyg, 68-72 & Jet Propulsion Lab, 77-78. *Mem:* Fel Am Inst Chem Engrs; Am Soc Eng Educ. *Res:* Mass and heat transfer; vapor-liquid equilibrium; activation of radio-nuclides and their transport; appraisal of electrical energy alternatives; guidance of an autonomous planetary rover. *Mailing Add:* 32 Markay Ct Rochester NY 14618

**YERBY, ALONZO SMYTHE,** preventive medicine administration; deceased, see previous edition for last biography

**YERG, DONALD G,** METEOROLOGY. *Current Pos:* assoc prof, 55-60, PROF PHYSICS & DEAN GRAD SCH, MICH TECHNOL UNIV, 60- *Personal Data:* b Lewistown, Pa, Mar 4, 25; m 48; c 3. *Educ:* Pa State Univ, BS, 46, MS, 47, PhD(meteorol), 53. *Prof Exp:* Asst agr eng, Univ Calif, 47-48; instr math, Univ Alaska, 48-50; consult, Tech Info Div, Libr Cong, 51-52; asst ionosphere res, Pa State Univ, 52-53; lectr physics, Univ PR, 53-55. *Mem:* AAAS; Am Meteorol Soc; Int Soc Biometeorol; Am Geophys Union; Sigma Xi. *Res:* Meteorology of ionospheric regions; micrometeorology; biometeorology. *Mailing Add:* 1112 E Seventh Ave Houghton MI 49931

**YERG, RAYMOND A,** AEROSPACE MEDICINE, OCCUPATIONAL MEDICINE. *Current Pos:* RETIRED. *Personal Data:* b Jersey City, NJ, Apr 4, 17; m 46; c 3. *Educ:* Seton Hall Col, BS, 38; Georgetown Univ, MD, 42; Harvard Univ, MPH, 55. *Honors & Awards:* AMA Spec Aerospace Med Citation, 62; Air Force Asn Meritorious Award Support Mgt, 64. *Prof Exp:* Comdr, 1st Missile Div, Vandenberg AFB, US Air Force, Calif, 59-61, dep bioastronaut Air Force Eastern Test Range, 61-65, comdr, Aerospace Med Res Lab, Wright-Patterson AFB, Ohio, 65-68, chief sci & tech div, Hq US Air Force, The Pentagon, 68-72; corp med dir, Perlcin-Elmer Corp, 78-80 & 82-87 corp med dir, Am Can Co, 72. *Concurrent Pos:* Consult Occup Med. *Mem:* Fel Aerospace Med Asn; fel Am Col Prev Med; NY Acad Sci; fel Am Acad Occup Med; fel Am Occup Med Asn; fel Am Col Physicians. *Mailing Add:* 11808 Beekman Pl Potomac MD 20854

**YERGANIAN, GEORGE,** biology, for more information see previous edition

**YERGER, RALPH WILLIAM,** SYSTEMATIC ICHTHYOLOGY. *Current Pos:* RETIRED. *Personal Data:* b Reading, Pa, July 31, 22; m 54, Francis I Winterle; c Paula M, Rachelle A, Loreen K & Ralph W Jr. *Educ:* Pa State Univ, BS, 43, MS, 47; Cornell Univ, PhD(zool), 50. *Prof Exp:* Teacher high sch, Pa, 43; instr biol, Pa State Univ, Altoona Ctr, 47-48; instr nature study, Reading Mus, 48; from asst prof to assoc prof zool, Fla State Univ, 50-61, actg head dept, 52-54, assoc chmn undergrad studies, 75-77, assoc dean, Col Arts & Sci, 77-78 & 79-83, actg dean, Col Arts & Sci, 78-79, prof biol, 61- 82, univ serv prof, 83-88. *Res:* Taxonomy, ecology and distribution of fresh and salt water fishes of the southeastern United States, Central America and the Caribbean. *Mailing Add:* 2917 Woodside Dr Tallahassee FL 32312-2830

**YERGEY, ALFRED L, III,** ANALYTICAL CHEMISTRY, CHEMICAL KINETICS. *Current Pos:* res chemist, 77-85, SECT CHIEF, NAT INST CHILD HEALTH & HUMAN DEVELOP, NIH, 85- *Personal Data:* b Philadelphia, Pa, Sept 17, 41; m 63, 91; c 3. *Educ:* Muhlenberg Col, BS, 63; Pa State Univ, PhD(chem), 67. *Prof Exp:* Res fel chem, Rice Univ, 67-69; chemist, Esso Res & Eng Co, NJ, 69-71; sr scientist, Sci Res Instruments Corp, 71-77. *Mem:* Am Chem Soc; Am Soc Bone Mineral Res; Am Inst Nutrit. *Res:* Calcium kinetics of skeleton; applications of mass spectrometry; stable isotope applications to clinical problems; quadrupole mass spectrometry. *Mailing Add:* 10359 Lancelot Lane Columbia MD 21044. *Fax:* 301-402-0263; *E-Mail:* aly@helix.nih.gov

**YERGIN, PAUL FLOHR,** NUCLEAR PHYSICS. *Current Pos:* from asst prof to prof, 56-93, EMER PROF PHYSICS, RENSSELLAER POLYTECH INST, 93- *Personal Data:* b New York, NY, Apr 21, 23; m 47; c 2. *Educ:* Union Univ, NY, BS, 44; Columbia Univ, MA, 49, PhD, 53. *Prof Exp:* Asst electronics res, Gen Elec Co, NY, 42; asst, Gen Physics Lab, Union Univ, NY, 42-43; physicist, Radiation Lab, Columbia Univ, 44-45, mem sci staff, 45-52; from instr to asst prof, Univ Pa, 52-56. *Concurrent Pos:* Res affil, Lab Nuclear Sci, Mass Inst Technol, 80-82. *Res:* Photonuclear reactions; photopion reactions. *Mailing Add:* 2950 N Alvernon Way Apt 2103 Tucson AZ 85712-1432

**YERICK, ROGER EUGENE,** ANALYTICAL CHEMISTRY. *Current Pos:* from asst prof to assoc prof, 58-65, PROF CHEM, LAMAR UNIV, 65-, DEAN COL SCI, 74- *Personal Data:* b Kingsville, Tex, July 6, 32. *Educ:* Tex Col Arts & Indust, BS, 53. *Prof Exp:* Res asst analytical chem, Iowa State Univ, 53-57; asst prof chem, Tex Col Arts & Indust, 57-58. *Concurrent Pos:* Educ consult, Spec Training Div, Oak Ridge Assoc Univs, 62- *Mem:* AAAS; Am Chem Soc; Sigma Xi. *Res:* Analytical chemistry of chelates; analytical radiochemistry; analytical applications of liquid scintillation counting techniques. *Mailing Add:* 124 Rosine St Beaumont TX 77707

**YERKES, WILLIAM D(ILWORTH), JR,** ENVIRONMENTAL SCIENCES. *Current Pos:* RETIRED. *Personal Data:* b Wilkes Barre, Pa, May 29, 22; m 47; c 3. *Educ:* State Col Wash, BS, 48, PhD(plant path), 52. *Prof Exp:* Asst, State Col Wash, 48-52; asst plant pathologist, Mex Agr Prog, Rockefeller Found, 52-56, assoc plant pathologist, 56-60; microbiologist, Pioneering Res Lab, Kimberly-Clark Corp, 60-72; chmn, Dept Environ Sci, Grand Valley State Col, 72-79, mem staff, Sch Health Sci, 80-87. *Mem:* Am Soc Civil Engrs; Water Pollution Control Fedn; Nat Environ Health Asn; Sigma Xi. *Res:* Ecology of water pollution; effects of pollutants on aquatic biota; solid and hazardous waste management; food sanitation; biochemistry and biophysics of photosynthesis. *Mailing Add:* 3679 Blackfoot Ct Grandville MI 49418-1721

**YERRAM, NAGENDER RAO,** hematology, photochemistry, for more information see previous edition

**YERRAPRAGGADA, VENKAT,** FOOD SERVICE MANAGEMENT, NUTRITION EDUCATION. *Current Pos:* NUTRIT EDUC & MARKETING, CADDO PARISH SCH BD, 91- *Personal Data:* m 91, Sreedevi. *Educ:* Nat Dairy Res Inst, MS, 84; Univ Nebr, Lincoln, MS, 88, PhD(human nutrit), 91. *Honors & Awards:* Indian Coun Agr, Indian Coun Agr, 84. *Prof Exp:* Res asst, Univ Nebr, Lincoln, 87-91. *Mem:* Am Dietetic Asn; Am Sch Food Serv Asn; Am Soc Exp Biol. *Res:* Comparison of blood lipids between tropical oils like coconut oil or palm oil and other oils like soy bean oil. *Mailing Add:* 6003 Inglewood Ct Bossier City LA 71111-5665. *Fax:* 318-632-5341

**YESAIR, DAVID WAYNE,** BIOCHEMISTRY. *Current Pos:* PRES & CHIEF EXEC OFFICER, BIOMOLECULAR PROD INC, 84- *Personal Data:* b Newbury, Mass, Sept 9, 32; m 54, Ruth Avery; c Catherine, Karen & Peter. *Educ:* Univ Mass, BS, 54; Cornell Univ, PhD(biochem), 58. *Prof Exp:* Asst biochem, Cornell Univ, 55-57, res assoc, 58; res biochemist, Lederle Labs Div, Am Cyanimid, 59-61; NSF fel, Reading Univ, Eng, 61-62; sr scientist, biochem group, Arthur D. Little, Inc, 62-66, head, biochem and pharmacol group, 66-71 & 72-77, mgr, biomed sci sect, 77-82, vpres, 78-84. *Concurrent Pos:* Nat Cancer Inst spec res award, Inst Org Chem, Paris, France, 71-72; lectr, Mass Inst Technol, 72-82; biotechnol adv bd, Univ Conn, 86- *Mem:* Am Chem Soc; NY Acad Sci; Am Asn Cancer Res; Am Soc Pharmacol & Exp Therapeut; fel Am Inst Chemists; AAAS; Am Soc Toxicol; Sigma Xi; Int Soc Studying Xenobiotics (secy, 90-91); Am Asn Pharmaceut Scientist; fel Leukemia Soc Am. *Res:* Lipid biochemistry; cancer, obesity and diabetes; metabolism and mode of action of drugs affecting lipid metabolism; isolation, characterization and metabolic action of biologically active agents; development of drug delivery systems; drug delivery; lipid nutrition products. *Mailing Add:* BioMolecular Prod Inc PO Box 347 Byfield MA 01922

**YESINOWSKI, JAMES PAUL,** SOLID-STATE NUCLEAR MAGNETIC RESONANCE SPECTROSCOPY. *Current Pos:* SUPVRY RES CHEMIST, NAVAL RES LAB, WASHINGTON, DC, 91- *Personal Data:* b LaSalle, Ill, Mar 22, 50. *Educ:* Univ Ill, Urbana, BS, 71; Univ Cambridge, PhD(chem), 74. *Prof Exp:* Res assoc phys chem, Mass Inst Technol, 74-76; staff scientist, Miami Valley Labs, Procter & Gamble Co, 76-84; mem prof staff, Calif Inst Technol, 84-88; adj assoc prof chem & dir, Max T Rogers Nuclear Magnetic Resonance Fac, Mich State Univ, 88-91. *Concurrent Pos:* Am Cancer Soc fel, 76. *Res:* Nuclear magnetic resonance spectroscopy of solids, theory & applications; multiple-quantum nuclear magnetic resonance; optically-polarized surface nuclear magnetic resonance; 14N nuclear magnetic resonance and nuclear quadrupole resonance techniques. *Mailing Add:* Code 6120 Naval Res Lab Washington DC 20375-5342. *Fax:* 202-767-0594; *E-Mail:* yesinowski@nre.navy.mil

**YESNER, RAYMOND,** PATHOLOGY. *Current Pos:* from asst clin prof to assoc clin prof, Med Sch, Yale Univ, 49-64, assoc prof, 64-72, prof, 72-84, dir, Autopsy Serv, 87-93, EMER PROF PATH, MED SCH, YALE UNIV, 82-, SR RES SCIENTIST, 87- *Personal Data:* b Columbus, Ga, Apr 18, 14; m 47, Bernice Lieberman; c David, Donna & Steven. *Educ:* Harvard Univ, AB, 35; Tufts Col, MD, 41; Yale Univ, MA, 72. *Hon Degrees:* DHL, Quinnipiac Col, 92. *Honors & Awards:* Health Mem Award, Univ Tex, 84. *Prof Exp:* Intern & res, Beth Israel Hosp, Boston, Mass, 41-44; pathologist & chief, Lab Serv, Vet Admin Hosp, Newington, 47-53. *Concurrent Pos:* Pathologist & chief, Lab Serv, Vet Admin Hosp, West Haven, 53-74, chief staff, 69-74, chief pathologist, 74-77, dir anat path, 77-87; consult pathologist, Coop Study of Prostate, Vet Admin, chmn, Path Panel, Lung Cancer Chemother Study Group, 58-, mem, Path Res Eval Comt, sr physician, 71-74, Radiation Ther Oncol Group, 82-; chmn, WHO Lung Cancer Comt, Geneva, 77; path panel, Int Asn Study Lung Cancer, 82- *Mem:* Emer mem AMA; emer mem Am Asn Path & Bact; emer mem Col Am Path; emer mem Int Acad Path; Int Asn Study Lung Cancer. *Res:* Changes in blood viscosity; liver, lung and gastrointestinal disease; carcinoma of lung and prostate and bladder. *Mailing Add:* Path Dept Yale Med Sch 310 Cedar St New Haven CT 06510. *Fax:* 203-785-3348

**YESSIK, MICHAEL JOHN,** SOLID STATE PHYSICS. *Current Pos:* PRES, SURFACE SCI LABS, 89- *Personal Data:* b Webster, Mass, Nov 22, 41; m 70. *Educ:* Williams Col, BA, 62; Syracuse Univ, PhD(solid state sci), 66; Univ Cambridge, MA, 67. *Prof Exp:* NATO fel, Cavendish Lab, Univ Cambridge, 66-67, NSF fel, 67-68; sr res scientist physics, Sci Res Staff, Ford Motor Co, 68-75; mgr process develop, Photon Sources, Inc, 75-77, mgr new prod develop, 77-80, dir res & develop, 80-83; vpres res & develop, Bausch & Lomb Ophthal Inst, 83-85; eng mgr, Spectrophysics Inc, 85-89. *Mem:* Optical Soc Am; Sigma Xi; AAAS; Am Phys Soc; Inst Elec & Electronics Engrs. *Res:* Electronic and magnetic properties of metals and alloys; physical properties of high temperature ceramics; high-power gas laser development; materials processing using high-power lasers. *Mailing Add:* 925 Capuchino Ave Burlingame CA 94010

**YETT, FOWLER REDFORD,** APPLIED MATHEMATICS. *Current Pos:* RETIRED. *Personal Data:* b Johnson City, Tex, Oct 18, 19; m 45, Mary S Lytle; c Jane M, Rebecca (Root) & Mary (Coutts). *Educ:* Univ Tex, Austin, BS, 43, MA, 52; Iowa State Univ, PhD(appl math), 55. *Prof Exp:* Res chemist & chem engr, Manhattan Proj, 43-45; owner, Camera Supply Co, 46-49; teaching fel, Univ Tex, 49-52; instr math, Iowa State Univ, 52-55; asst prof, Long Beach State Col, 55-56 & Univ Tex, 56-65; chmn, Dept Math, Univ SAla, 65-68, prof math, 65-89. *Concurrent Pos:* Sr res engr, NAm Aviation, Inc, Downey, CA, 56-57 & 59; fac res assoc, Boeing Co, Seattle, Wash. *Mem:* Am Math Soc; Math Asn Am. *Res:* Nonlinear differential equations. *Mailing Add:* 660 Merritt Dr Mobile AL 36609

**YEUNG, DAVID LAWRENCE,** INFANT NUTRITION, INTERNATIONAL NUTRITION. *Current Pos:* infant nutritionist, H J Heinz Co, 76-82, mgr, Dept Nutrit Res, 82-84, coordr corp nutrit, 82-90, DIR CORP NUTRIT, H J HEINZ CO, 90-; ASSOC PROF NUTRIT, DEPT NUTRIT SCI, FAC MED, UNIV TORONTO, 82- *Personal Data:* b Hong Kong, Dec 18, 39; Can citizen; m 66, Elizabeth A Gerrie; c Kathryn E & Robert A. *Educ:* Univ Toronto, BA, 63, MA, 66, PhD(nutrit), 70. *Prof Exp:* From asst prof to assoc prof nutrit, Univ Guelph, 70-76. *Concurrent Pos:* Coordr food & nutrit sci, Inst Study & Appln Integrated Develop, 76-89; consult, Can Pediat Soc, 78- & ed nutrit res, 82-85; ed, Infant Nutrit Inst, 82-; vis assoc prof, Sun Yet Sen Univ Med Sci, Guangzhou, China, 85-92, W China Univ Med Sci, Chengdu, China, 87-91 & Zhejiang Med Univ, 90-92; adj prof, Ryerson Polytechnic Inst, Toronto, 90-92; pres, Heinz Inst Nutrit Sci, Inc, 95- *Mem:* Can Soc Nutrit; Can Pub Health Asn; Am Inst Nutrit; Can Inst Food Sci & Technol; Can Pediat Soc. *Res:* Infant nutrition, feeding and growth; food habits, nutritional status and requirement of the elderly; maternal and infant nutrition in China, the Far East and Eastern Europe; functional foods. *Mailing Add:* Dept R & D H J Heinz Co,Can Ltd 5700 Yonge St Suite 2100 North York ON M2M 4K6 Can. *Fax:* 416-226-5064

**YEUNG, EDWARD SZESHING,** ANALYTICAL CHEMISTRY, PHYSICAL CHEMISTRY. *Current Pos:* From instr to assoc prof, 72-81, PROF CHEM, IOWA STATE UNIV, 81- *Personal Data:* b Hong Kong, Feb 17, 48; m 71; c 2. *Educ:* Cornell Univ, AB, 68; Univ Calif, Berkeley, PhD(chem), 72. *Honors & Awards:* Chem Instrumentation Award, Am Chem Soc, 87, Anal Chem Award, 94. *Concurrent Pos:* Sloan Found fel, 74; ed, Progress Anal Spectros & Anal Chem. *Mem:* Am Chem Soc; NAm Photochem Soc; fel AAAS. *Res:* Pollution monitoring; high resolution spectroscopy; photochemistry; lasers; bioanalysis; DNA sequencing. *Mailing Add:* Dept Chem Iowa State Univ Ames IA 50011

**YEUNG, KATHERINE LU,** CANCER, PHARMACOLOGY. *Current Pos:* Res asst, 68-75, res assoc, 75-80, ASST PHARMACOLOGIST, CANCER CHEMOTHER, SYST CANCER CTR, UNIV TEX, 80- *Personal Data:* b Shanghai, China, July 28, 43; US citizen; m 68; c 2. *Educ:* Univ Houston, BS, 65, MS, 68. *Mem:* Sigma Xi; NY Acad Sci; Am Soc Pharm & Exp Therapeut; Am Asn Cancer Res. *Res:* Cancer chemotherapy; metabolism and distribution of antitumor agents in patients and experimental animals. *Mailing Add:* 1102 Stoney Hill Dr Houston TX 77077

**YEUNG, KING-WAH WALTER,** ULTRASOUND MEDICAL IMAGING, INTEGRATED ELECTRONICS FOR MEDICINE & BIOMECHANICAL ENGINEERING. *Current Pos:* Mem tech staff, Comput Syst Div, Hewlett-Packard Co, 78-83, Printing Technol Dept, 83-91, MEM TECH STAFF, MED DEPT, HEWLETT-PACKARD LABS, HEWLETT-PACKARD CO, 91- *Personal Data:* b Hong Kong, Mar 19, 54; US citizen; m 80, Wei-Wei V Ren; c Serena Y & Angela Y. *Educ:* Calif Inst Technol, BS, 78; Stanford Univ, MS, 83 & 96, PhD(elec eng), 88. *Mem:* Eng Med & Biol Soc; sr mem Inst Elec & Electronics Engrs. *Res:* Thermal ink jet technology; ultrasound imaging for diagnosing cardiac diseases; biomechanical engineering. *Mailing Add:* 10129 Mello Pl Cupertino CA 95014

**YEUNG, KWOK KAM,** CANCER MARKERS, DEVELOP IMMUNOASSAYS. *Current Pos:* res fel, 76-78, dir res, Molecular Diag, 88-92, DIR RES, MILES DIAGNOSTICS, MILES INC, 92- *Personal Data:* b Hong Kong, July 3, 49; US citizen; m 75, Rosita Tsou; c David & Alyssa. *Educ:* Calif State Univ, Fresno, BS, 72; Univ Notre Dame, MS, 74; Univ RI, PD(biochem & biophys), 78. *Honors & Awards:* Inventor Award, Allied Corp, 85. *Prof Exp:* Sr res scientist, Fisher Sci, 80-85; mgr res & develop, Cooper Biomed, 85-86; Fisher Diag, 86-88. *Concurrent Pos:* Vis scientist, Univ RI, 82. *Mem:* Am Soc Biol Chem & Molecular Biol; Am Asn Clin Chem. *Res:* Identify novel markers for in vitro diagnosis of human disease, primarily in the areas of cancer, diabetes and bone and cartilage diseases; conduct clinical trials with human specimens; develop rapid testing methods for these markers in automated analyzers. *Mailing Add:* 511 Benedict Ave Tarrytown NY 10591. *Fax:* 914-524-2458

**YEUNG, PATRICK PUI-HANG,** organic chemistry, textile chemistry, for more information see previous edition

**YEUNG, REGINALD SZE-CHIT,** CHEMICAL ENGINEERING, CHEMISTRY. *Current Pos:* ENGR, SHELL OIL CO, HOUSTON, 64- *Personal Data:* b Hong Kong, Apr 30, 32; US citizen; m 66; c 1. *Educ:* Univ London, BSc, 54; Mass Inst Technol, SM, 59, ScD(chem eng), 61. *Prof Exp:* Engr, Cabot Corp, 61-63. *Mem:* Am Chem Soc; Am Inst Chem Engrs. *Res:* Process development and design; reactor design; flame reactor design; insecticide production. *Mailing Add:* 10607 Creektree Dr Houston TX 77070

**YEUNG, RONALD WAI-CHUN,** FREE-SURFACE MECHANICS, SHIP & OFFSHORE DYNAMICS. *Current Pos:* PROF HYDROMECH, DEPT NAVAL ARCHIT & OFFSHORE ENG, UNIV CALIF, BERKELEY, 82-, DEPT CHAIR, 89- *Personal Data:* b Hong Kong, July 19, 45; US citizen; m 70, Grace Y Chow; c Brian H. *Educ:* Univ Calif, Berkeley, BS, 68, MS, 70, PhD(eng), 73. *Honors & Awards:* US Distinguished Scientist, Alexander von Humboldt Found, 88. *Prof Exp:* Naval architect, Advan Marine Technol, Litton Ship Systs, 70-71; res assoc hydrodyn, Dept Ocean Eng, Mass Inst Technol, 73-74, from asst prof to assoc prof naval archit, 74-82. *Concurrent Pos:* Instr, Long Beach Naval Shipyard, Univ Calif, Los Angeles, 71; prin investr, NSF, 75-83, fluid dynamics, Off Naval Res, 77-; consult, Maritech Inc, 74-77, Hydronautics Inc, 79-80, Ecodynamics, 86-88, Chevron Oil, 88-90, USCG, 88, Amoco Oil, 92- & Exxon PRC, 93-; rep, US-Japan Sci exchange shallow-water probs, 79-80; assoc ed, J Ship Res, 80-, Comput & Fluids, 84- & J Eng Math, 86-; Fulbright-Hayes sr fes, Dept Appl Math, Univ Adelaide, SAustralia, 81; vis distinguished scientist, Alexander von Humboldt Found, Univ Hamburg, WGer, 88-89. *Mem:* Soc Naval Architects & Marine Engrs; Am Soc Eng Educ; Int Soc Offshore & Polar Eng. *Res:* Theory of surface gravity waves; wave-ship or wave-structure interaction; theory of ship-ship interaction hydrodynamics; numerical methods in free-surface flows; non-linear breaking wave modeling; wave-viscosity interaction physics; highly separated flows. *Mailing Add:* 27 Indian Wells St Moraga CA 94556. *Fax:* 510-642-6128; *E-Mail:* rwyeung@garnet.berkeley.edu

**YEUNG, TIN-CHUEN,** TECHNOLOGY DEVELOPMENT & EVALUATION, TECHNOLOGY LICENSING & TRANSFER. *Current Pos:* DIR STRATEGIC DEVELOP, BAXTER HEALTHCARE CORP, 91- *Personal Data:* m, Bik K Tam; c Louise & Helen. *Educ:* State Univ NY, Stony Brook, BS, 75; State Univ NY, Downstate Med Ctr, PhD(pharmacol), 80; Northwestern Univ, MMgt, 87. *Prof Exp:* Res fel, Harvard Med Sch, 80-83; res investr, G D Searle & Co, 83-85; sr res investr & res scientist, NutraSweet Div, Monsanto Co, 86-88, mgr, Bus Ventures, 88-91, mgr, Exteernam Technol, 91. *Concurrent Pos:* Teaching asst, Downstate Med Ctr, State Univ NY, 75-80; res fel, Damon Runyon-Walter Winchell Cancer Found, 81-83. *Mem:* Asn Univ Technol Mgr; AAAS; Am Chem Soc. *Res:* Mechanism of action and toxicity of anti-cancer agents and anti-microbial agents. *Mailing Add:* 3550 Riverfalls Dr Northbrook IL 60062

**YEVICH, JOSEPH PAUL,** NEUROSCIENCES. *Current Pos:* sr scientist, Bristol-Myers Squibb, 69-74, sr investr, 74- 76, sr res assoc, 76-80, sr res scientist, 80-82,. assoc dir, 82- 86, DIR, BRISTOL-MYERS SQUIBB, 86- *Personal Data:* b McKees Rocks, Pa, Sept 20, 40; m 64, Mary Piemme; c Paul & Eileen. *Educ:* Carnegie-Mellon Univ, BS, 62, MS, 67, PhD(org chem), 69.

Prof Exp: Chemist, Gulf Res & Develop Corp, 62-65. Mem: AAAS; Am Chem Soc; Sigma Xi; Soc Neurosci; Int Cong Heterocyclic Chem; NY Acad Sci. Res: Design and synthesis of potential medicinal agents; design and synthesis of anti-inflammatory agents, bronchodilators and mediator-release inhibitors; CNS area on anxiolytics, antipsychotics, antidepressants and cognition enhancers, neuroprotective agents and antimigraine agents. Mailing Add: 115 Crest Rd Southington CT 06489-2807

**YEVICK, DAVID OWEN,** PHYSICS OPTICAL COMMUNICATIONS, OPTO-ELECTRONIC DEVICE PHYSICS. Current Pos: RES SOLID STATE PHYSICS, UNIV LUND, SWEDEN, 83-; PROF ELEC ENG, QUEEN'S UNIV, KINGSTON, 89- Personal Data: b New York City, May 3, 54; m 84; c 3. Educ: Harvard Univ, AB, 73; Princeton Univ, MS, 75, PhD(physics), 77. Prof Exp: Res asst physics, State Univ NY, Stony Brook, 77-79; researcher optics, Inst Optical Res, Stockholm 79-83. Concurrent Pos: Consult, Xerox Parc, 83-84; Bell Commun Res, 87, Amoco Technol Co & Corning Glass, 89; docent, Univ Lund, 84; assoc prof elec eng, Pa State Univ, 86-89. Mem: Fel Sr mem Inst Elec & Electronics Engrs; fel Optical Soc Am; fel Am Phys Soc; Acoust Soc Am; Soc Indust & Appl Math. Res: Numerical simulations of guided-wave and semiconductor opto-electronic devices, basic physics of opto-electronic devices; optical and electron transport processes in semiconductors. Mailing Add: Dept Elec Eng Queen's Univ Kingston ON K7L 3N6 Can. Fax: 613-545-6774; E-Mail: Yevick@qucdnee.ll.gueensu.ca

**YEVICK, GEORGE JOHANNUS,** PHYSICS. Current Pos: RETIRED. Personal Data: b Berwick, Pa, Apr 24, 22; m 45. Educ: Mass Inst Technol, BSc, 42, DSc(physics), 47. Hon Degrees: MEng, Stevens Inst Technol, 58. Prof Exp: Staff mem, Radiation Lab, Mass Inst Technol, 44-46; from asst prof to assoc prof, Stevens Inst Technol, 48-57, prof physics, 57-, prof eng physics, 77. Mem: Am Phys Soc; Soc Photo-Optical Instrument Engr; NY Acad Sci. Res: Theory of elementary particles; dynamical theory of many interacting particles; causal theory of quantum mechanics; control of thermonuclear fusion. Mailing Add: 536 Nordhoff Dr Leonia NJ 07605

**YEWDELL, JONATHAN WILSON,** ANTIGEN PROCESSING, VIRAL IMMUNOLOGY. Current Pos: sr investr, 87-93, CHIEF, CELLULAR BIOL SECT, VIRAL DIS LAB, NAT INST ALLERGY & INFECTIOUS DIS, NIH, 93- Personal Data: b Mt Vernon, NY, Dec 10, 53; m 82, Margaret Delaney; c Alison, W Theodore, Andrew & Alexander. Educ: Princeton Univ, AB, 75; Univ Pa, MD & PhD(immunol), 81. Prof Exp: Asst prof, Wistar Inst, 83-87. Res: How the cellular elements of the immune systems can determine whether a cell is harboring a pathogen; defining the molecular mechanisms of antigen presentation. Mailing Add: 1619 Nordic Hill Circle Silver Spring MD 20906. Fax: 301-402-7362; E-Mail: jon—yewdell@d4.niaid.pc.niaid.nih.gov

**YEZ, MARTIN S(IMON),** MECHANICAL ENGINEERING, AERONAUTICAL ENGINEERING. Current Pos: PROF ENG, EL CAMINO COL, 54- Personal Data: b Chicago, Ill, Apr 25, 20; m 46; c 1. Educ: Ill Inst Technol, BSME, 46; DePaul Univ, MA, 51. Prof Exp: Eng draftsman, Pullman Stand Car Mfg Co, 46; chief power engr, Commonwealth Edison Co, 47-49; prof eng, Wright Br, Chicago City Jr Col, 50-51; eng designer, Northrop Aircraft Co, 51-54. Mem: Am Cong Surv & Mapping. Res: Drafting room practices; surveying; geology; plant propagation. Mailing Add: 4029 Via Larga Vis Palos Verdes Peninsula CA 90274

**YGUERABIDE, JUAN,** BIOCHEMISTRY, BIOPHYSICS. Current Pos: ASSOC PROF BIOL, UNIV CALIF, SAN DIEGO, 72- Personal Data: b Laredo, Tex, Oct 9, 35; m 56; c 4. Educ: St Mary's Univ, Tex, BS, 57; Univ Notre Dame, PhD(phys chem), 62. Prof Exp: Res assoc, Radiation Lab, Univ Notre Dame, 61-63; mem res staff, Sandia Corp, NMex, 63-68; res assoc biochem, Stanford Univ, 68-69; lectr & res assoc biochem & biophys, Yale Univ, 69-72. Concurrent Pos: Fel, Radiation Lab, Univ Notre Dame, 62-63; consult prof chem, Univ NMex, 66-68; sci consult, Sandia Corp, NMex, 68-69. Mem: AAAS; Biophys Soc; Sigma Xi. Res: Structure, conformation and function of proteins and biological membranes; nanosecond fluorescence spectroscopy; mathematical physics. Mailing Add: Dept Biol C-0116 Univ Calif San Diego La Jolla CA 92093. Fax: 619-450-0635

**YIAMOUYIANNIS, JOHN ANDREW,** BIOCHEMISTRY, STATISTICS. Current Pos: CONSULT, 75- Personal Data: b Hartford, Conn, Sept 25, 42; div; c Ormen, Zeus, Athena, Lurleen, Portia & Apollo. Educ: Univ Chicago, SB, 63; Univ RI, PhD(biochem), 67. Honors & Awards: Humanitarian Award, Cancer Control Soc, 95. Prof Exp: Fel develop biol, Western Res Univ Sch Med, 67-68; assoc ed, Chem Abst Serv, 68-72; sci dir, Nat Health Fedn, 74-80; exec dir, Health Action, 80-84. Concurrent Pos: Co-ed, Fluoride, 72-81; pres, Safe Water Found, 79- Mem: Int Soc Fluoride Res. Res: Ganglioside biosynthesis; biochemical differentiation; subcellular particles; RNA synthesis in isolated nuclei; biological effects of inorganic fluoride; epidemiological ramifications of toxic substances; science and politics; high performance health; AIDS. Mailing Add: 6439 Taggart Rd Delaware OH 43015

**YIANNOS, PETER N,** PHYSICAL CHEMISTRY, ENGINEERING. Current Pos: RETIRED. Personal Data: b Olympia, Greece, Nov 27, 32; US citizen; m 62; c 3. Educ: Univ Mo-Rolla, BS, 56; Lawrence Univ, MS, 58, PhD(phys chem), 60. Honors & Awards: Albert Award, Tech Asn Pulp & Paper Indust. Prof Exp: From res group leader to sr res group leader, Scott Paper Co, 60-65, sect head, 65-66, mgr pioneering res, 66-67, tech consult, 67-69, mgr paper res, 69-73, dir paper res, 73-76, vpres prod develop, 76-79, vpres consumer res & develop, 79-81, vpres int res & develop, 81-83, vpres

fiber technol, 83-94. Concurrent Pos: Instr tech develop prog, Scott Paper Training Course, 64-69; lectr eng, Eve Div, PMC Cols, 66-67; assoc prof eng, Widener Col, 67-69, adj prof, 72-74. Mem: Am Chem Soc; Am Inst Chem Eng; Tech Asn Pulp & Paper Indust. Res: Molecular forces and surface phenomena; fibers and fiber bonding; wood technology and pulping; mechanical properties of fibers and sheet assemblies; technical management; materials science. Mailing Add: 2304 Empire Dr Wilmington DE 19810

**YIELDING, K LEMONE,** MOLECULAR BIOLOGY, MEDICINE. Current Pos: CHMN & PROF ANAT MED, UNIV S ALA, MOBILE, 80- Personal Data: b Auburn, Ala, Mar 25, 31; m 73; c 5. Educ: Ala Polytech Inst, BS, 49; Univ Ala, MS, 52, MD, 54. Prof Exp: Intern, Med Ctr, Univ Ala, 54-55; clin assoc, NIH, 55-57; resident, USPHS Hosp, 57-58; sr investr, Nat Inst Arthritis & Metab Dis, 58-64; prof biochem, assoc prof med & chief lab molecular biol, Med Ctr, Univ Ala, Birmingham, 64-80. Concurrent Pos: Asst prof med, Georgetown Univ, 58-64; consult, USPHS, 64- Mem: AAAS; Am Soc Pharmacol & Exp Therapeut; Soc Exp Biol & Med; Am Soc Biol Chem; Am Asn Anatomists; Am Asn Pathologists. Res: Molecular basis for biological regulation, including both genetic mechanisms and control of enzyme activity; elucidation of disease mechanisms and drug action in molecular terms. Mailing Add: 511 Woodland Dr Tuscumbia AL 35674. Fax: 409-765-9852

**YIH, CHIA-SHUN,** MECHANICS, APPLIED MATHEMATICS. Current Pos: from assoc prof to prof eng mech, 56-68, Stephan P Timoshenko Univ prof, 68-88, EMER PROF FLUID MECH, UNIV MICH, ANN ARBOR, 88-; EMER PROF ENG SCI, UNIV FLA, 90- Personal Data: b Kweiyang, China, July 25, 18; nat US; m 49; c 3. Educ: Nat Cent Univ, China, BS, 42; Univ Iowa, MS, 47, PhD(fluid mech), 48. Honors & Awards: Henry Russel lectr, Univ Mich, 74; Theodore Von Karman Medal, Am Soc Civil Engrs, 81; Fluid Dynamics Prize, Am Phys Soc, 85, Otto Laporte Award, 89. Prof Exp: Asst, Nat Bur Hydraul Res, China, 42-43; jr bridge engr, Nat Bur Bridge Design, 43-45; instr, Nat Kweichow Univ, 45; instr math, Univ Wis, 48-49; lectr, Univ BC, 49-50; assoc prof civil eng, Colo State Univ, 50-52; asst prof fluid mech & res engr, Univ Iowa, 52-54, assoc prof, 54-56. Concurrent Pos: Res assoc, Nat Ctr Sci Res, Univ Nancy, France, 51-52; NSF sr fel, Cambridge Univ, 59-60; consult, Huyck Felt Co, 60-64; Guggenheim fel, 64; vis prof, Univ Paris & Univ Grenoble, 70-71, Univ Karlsruhe, 77-78; von Humboldt award, 77-78; mem academia sinica, US Nat Acad Eng; ed, Adv Appl Mech, 71-82; grad res prof, Univ Fla, 86-90; hon prof, Univ Hong Kong, 96- Mem: Nat Acad Eng; fel Am Phys Soc; Academia Sinica. Res: Fluid mechanics, especially flows of nonhomogeneous fluids, geophysical fluid mechanics, waves and hydrodynamic stability; author 3 books and over 120 articles on fluid mechanics and applied mathematics. Mailing Add: 3530 W Huron River Dr Ann Arbor MI 48103

**YIH, ROY YANGMING,** AGRICULTURAL CHEMISTRY. Current Pos: Sr scientist, Rohm & Haas Co, 62-71, lab head, 72-73, proj leader, 73-81, res dept mgr, 82-94, RES DIR CHINA, ROHM & HAAS CO, SPRINGHOUSE, 95- Personal Data: b Changsha, China, Oct 5, 31; nat US; m 60, Madeline Wu; c Ann, Jean & John. Educ: Nat Taiwan Normal Univ, BS, 56; Univ SC, MS, 59; Rutgers Univ, PhD(plant physiol, biochem), 63. Mem: Am Chem Soc; Weed Sci Soc Am. Res: Agricultural products (herbicides, fungicides, and insecticides) development worldwide. Mailing Add: 94 Windover Lane Doylestown PA 18901. Fax: 215-619-1614

**YII, ROLAND,** ELECTRICAL ENGINEERING. Current Pos: RETIRED. Personal Data: b Chengtu, China, Aug 11, 19; m 54; c 3. Educ: Nanking Univ, BS, 45; Brown Univ, MS, 53; Univ Pa, PhD(elec eng), 65. Prof Exp: Mgr, Printing Dept, Sprague Elec Co, 52-54; prog & dept mgr, Burroughs Corp, 55-65; prof elec eng, Villanova Univ, 65-68; prof, Univ Fla, 68-77, res scientist, 77-84. Res: Solid state electronic and magnetic circuits; computer logic and variable radix computer. Mailing Add: 254 W Mitchell Ave Santa Rosa Beach FL 32459

**YILDIZ, ALAETTIN,** AERO ASTRONAUTICS, CARDIOLOGY. Current Pos: FLUID MECH & HEAT TRANSFER CONSULT, LA JOLLA, CALIF, 83- Personal Data: b Surmene, Turkey, Jan 5, 22; US citizen. Educ: Tech Univ West Berlin, MS, 56, PhD(fluid mech & heat transfer), 65. Prof Exp: Res eng aerodynamics, Res Lab, Siemens, Berlin, 60-62; asst prof & res assoc mech eng, Tech Univ West Berlin, 62-65; res scientist aeronaut & astronaut, Edcliff Instruments contractor NASA, 67-69; med scientist cardiol, City Hope Nat Med Ctr, Calif, 67-69, res, Univ Hosp, Vakifgureba, Turkey, 76-79; dir biomed eng, Nat Med Enterprises, Los Angeles, Calif, 79-80, scientist comn team, Fac Med, King Faisal Univ, 80-81, scientist med sci, Royal Al Hada Hosp, Saudi Arabia, 81-82. Concurrent Pos: Fel aeronaut sci, Calif Inst Technol, Pasadena, 69; sci advisor, Prog Data Co, Calif & Univ Calif, Los Angeles, 71-76. Mem: Am Inst Aeronaut & Astronaut; Ger Engrs Asn; Turkish Engrs Asn; Am Soc Mech Engrs. Res: Resistance coefficient of intimal surface on normal and pathological human aortas with special emphasis on development of atherosclerosis and stenosis of vessels; potential role of hydro-dynamics of the structures of blood vessels; implantation of electronic systems in human encephalon for self cerebellum stimulation; ballistics of spinning projectiles; establishing the dimensionless Yildiz-number related to aero-astronautics. Mailing Add: PO Box 2605 La Jolla CA 92038

**YIM, GEORGE KWOCK WAH,** HYPNOTHERAPY. Current Pos: from asst prof to prof pharmacol, 56-94, dept head, 83-90, HYPNOTHER INSTR, PURDUE UNIV, WEST LAFAYETTE, 95- Personal Data: b Honolulu, Hawaii, Jan 7, 30; m 52, Ramona Lew; c 5. Educ: Univ Iowa, BS, 52, MS, 54, PhD(pharmacol), 56. Prof Exp: Instr pharmacol, Univ Iowa, 55-56. Concurrent Pos: USPHS career develop award, 61-66; NIH spec fel, 66-67.

*Mem:* AAAS; Am Asn Col Pharm; Am Soc Pharmacol & Exp Therapeut; Soc Toxicol; Soc Neurosci; Nat Guild Hypnotists. *Res:* Pharmacological control of appetite; stress and endorphins; biochemical mechanisms of cancer cachexia and anorexia; chakras and mind/body dysfunction; healing approaches with hypnosis. *Mailing Add:* Hypno-Discovery 724 Essex St West Lafayette IN 47906

**YIM, MOON BIN,** FREE RADICALS IN BIOLOGY & MEDICINE, ELECTRON PARAMAGNETIC RESONANCE SPECTROSCOPY. *Current Pos:* sr staff fel, Lab Biochem, 88-94, RES CHEMIST, LAB BIOCHEM, NAT HEART, LUNG & BLOOD INST, NIH, 95- *Personal Data:* b Seoul, Korea, Apr 15, 40; US citizen; m 66, Sung Hye; c Gloria & Cynthia. *Educ:* Seoul Nat Univ, BS, 65; Univ Conn, PhD(phys chem), 74. *Prof Exp:* Instr & teaching postdoctoral fel phys chem, Univ Conn, 74-77; postdoctoral res assoc, Univ Tenn, 77-78; asst prof phys chem, Hamilton Col, 79; sr res assoc, Univ Chicago, 80-87. *Mem:* Am Soc Biochem & Molecular Biol; Am Chem Soc; Int EPR Soc. *Res:* Involvement of free radicals in biology and medicine, in disease and in aging; metalloenzymes and antioxidant enzymes. *Mailing Add:* Lab Biochem Nat Heart Lung & Blood Inst NIH Bldg 3 Rm 202 Bethesda MD 20892-0340. *Fax:* 301-496-0599

**YIN, CHIH-MING,** INSECT PHYSIOLOGY, INVERTEBRATE ENDOCRINOLOGY. *Current Pos:* asst prof, 78-82, ASSOC PROF ENTOM, UNIV MASS, 82- *Personal Data:* b Szechwan, China, July 2, 43; m 68; c 3. *Educ:* Taiwan Nat Univ, BSc, 66; Univ Sask, PhD(biol), 72. *Prof Exp:* Fel entom, Univ Mo-Columbia, 72-74, res assoc, 74-78; assoc, Cornell Univ, 78. *Mem:* Entom Soc Am; Sigma Xi; AAAS. *Res:* Hormonal control of growth, development and diapause in insects. *Mailing Add:* Dept Entom Univ Mass Fernald Hall Amherst MA 01003-0002

**YIN, FAY HOH,** VIROLOGY. *Current Pos:* RETIRED. *Personal Data:* b Peking, China, Mar 10, 32; US citizen; m 59; c 2. *Educ:* Univ Wis-Madison, BA, 54, MS, 55, PhD(biochem), 60. *Prof Exp:* Res asst biochem, Univ Wis-Madison, 60; res assoc virol, Dept Path, Univ Pa, 63-65; res chemist, Cent Res Dept, E I DuPont De Nemours & Co Inc, 66-86. *Mem:* Am Soc Microbiol; Am Soc Virol. *Res:* Biochemical studies of arbovirus and picornavirus replication. *Mailing Add:* 1804 Bellewood Rd Wilmington DE 19803

**YIN, FRANK CHI-PONG,** BIOMECHANICS, HEMODYNAMICS. *Current Pos:* fel cardiol, Johns Hopkins Med Inst, 77-78, asst prof med & physiol, 78-83, assoc prof, 83-88, PROF MED & BIOMED ENG, JOHNS HOPKINS MED INST, 88- *Personal Data:* b Kunming, Yunnan, China, June 21, 43; US citizen; m 75, Grace Chen; c Gregory & Jeffrey. *Educ:* Mass Inst Technol, BS, 65, MS, 67; Univ Calif, San Diego, PhD(bioeng), 70, MD, 73. *Prof Exp:* Res asst bioeng, Dept Appl Mech, Univ Calif, San Diego, 67-70, intern med, Univ Hosp, 73-74, asst resident, 74-75; clin assoc cardiovasc, Nat Inst Aging, NIH, 75-77. *Concurrent Pos:* Mem Cardiovasc Pulmonary Study Sect, Nat Heart, Lung & Blood Inst, NIH, 83-86; Estab investr, Am Heart Asn, 83-88. *Mem:* Am Heart Asn; fel Am Physiol Soc; Biomed Eng Soc; Am Soc Clin Invest; Biophys Soc; Am Soc Mech Eng; Am Inst Med Biol Eng. *Res:* Application of engineering principles and techniques to ventricular function, muscle mechanics, cell mechanics and hemodynamics; determination of mechanical properties of biological tissue under multiaxial loading conditions. *Mailing Add:* Cardiol Div 530 Carnegie Bldg Johns Hopkins Hosp 600 N Wolfe St Baltimore MD 21287. *Fax:* 410-614-1417; *E-Mail:* yin@yinmed.jhu.edu

**YIN, HELEN LU,** CELL MOTILITY. *Current Pos:* ASSOC PROF MED, SCH MED, HARVARD UNIV & MEM STAFF, MASS GEN HOSP, 78- *Educ:* Harvard Univ, PhD(physiol), 76. *Mailing Add:* Dept Physiol Univ Tex Southwest Med Ctr 5323 Harry Hines Blvd Dallas TX 75235-9040. *Fax:* 214-688-8685

**YIN, JOHN,** CHEMICAL ENGINEERING, MOLECULAR VIROLOGY & BIOCHEMICAL KINETICS. *Current Pos:* ASST PROF, THAYER SCH ENG, DARTMOUTH COL, 92- *Personal Data:* b Boston, Mass, Jan 6, 60. *Educ:* Columbia Col, BA, 82, BS, 83; Univ Calif, Berkeley, PhD(chem eng), 88. *Prof Exp:* Res fel, Max Plank Inst Biophys Chem, Gottingen, Ger, 88-92. *Concurrent Pos:* Res fel, Alexander von Humboldt Found, Ger, 88; young investr award, NSF, 94; Presidential early career award sci & eng, NSF, 96; adj prof chem, Dartmouth Col, 96-, adj prof molecular & cellular biol, 97- *Mem:* Alexander von Humboldt Asn Am; AAAS; Am Chem Soc; Am Inst Chem Engrs; Am Soc Microbiol. *Res:* Development of experimental and theoretical tools to study the growth and evolution of viruses; design of anti-viral strategies and improving live-vaccine production; engineering of nano-scale processes, bioinformatics and evolutionary design. *Mailing Add:* Thayer Sch Eng Dartmouth Col 8000 Cummings Hanover NH 03755-8000. *Fax:* 603-646-2277; *E-Mail:* jyin@dartmouth.edu

**YIN, JUN-JIE,** TIME DOMAIN ELECTRON SPIN RESONANCE SPECTROSCOPY, MEMBRANE BIOPHYSICS. *Current Pos:* staff fel, 94-96, RES BIOPHYSICIST, INSTR & BIOPHYSICS BR, CFSAN, FOOD & DRUG ADMIN, 96- *Personal Data:* b Anging, China, Mar 26, 44; m, Fang Bao; c Jodie. *Educ:* Univ Sci & Technol, China, BS, 68; Chinese Acad Sci Inst Biophys, MS, 81; Med Col Wis, PhD(biophys), 87. *Prof Exp:* Electronic engr, Huhhot Electronic Co, 68-78; res assoc, Inst Biophys, Chinese Acad Sci, 81-82; fel, Nat Biomed Electron Spin Resonance Ctr, Med Col Wis, 87-90, res scientist, 90-94. *Mem:* AAAS; Biophys Soc; Int Electron Spin Resonance Soc. *Res:* Structure and function in biological system; study of membrane dynamics; oxygen transport membranes; electron spin-relaxation mechanism in liquid phase; development of methodology which uses oxygen as a probe in pulse electron spin resonance to study membrane proteins; studies of interaction between drug and cell membranes; free radical and lipid peroxidation; natural antioxidants, the molecular mechanisms and the health benefits of natural products. *Mailing Add:* FDA HFS 717 200 C St NW Washington DC 20204. *E-Mail:* jyin@vax8.cfsan.fda.gov

**YIN, LO I,** PHYSICS. *Current Pos:* RETIRED. *Personal Data:* b Wuchang, China, Apr 19, 30; US citizen; m 58; c 2. *Educ:* Cent China Univ, BA, 49; Carleton Col, BA, 51; Univ Rochester, MA, 52, BS, 56; Univ Mich, MS, 59, PhD(physics), 63. *Honors & Awards:* IR-100 Award, 79; NASA Inventor of the Year, 80. *Prof Exp:* Res physicist, Bendix Res Lab, Bendix Corp, 64-67; aerospace technologist, NASA Goddard Space Flight Ctr, 67-90. *Concurrent Pos:* Vis prof chem, Univ Md, 72-76, adj prof, 77-90. *Mem:* Am Phys Soc; AAAS; Am Nuclear Soc; Soc Photo-Optical Instrumentation Engrs. *Res:* Atomic and nuclear physics; x-ray spectroscopy; x-ray and gamma-ray spectroscopy; x-ray and gamma-ray imaging; lixiscope, low intensity x-ray imaging scope. *Mailing Add:* 1207 Downs Dr Silver Spring MD 20904

**YIN, TOM CHI TIEN,** NEUROPHYSIOLOGY, BIOENGINEERING. *Current Pos:* from asst prof to assoc prof, 77-89, PROF NEURO PHYSIOL, UNIV WIS-MADISON, 89- *Personal Data:* b Kunming, China, Jan 7, 45; US citizen; m 72. *Educ:* Princeton Univ, BSE, 66; Univ Mich, PhD(elec eng), 73. *Prof Exp:* Fel neurophysiol, State Univ NY, Buffalo, 74; fel physiol, Johns Hopkins Univ, 74-77. *Concurrent Pos:* mem, Biopsychol Study Sect, NIH, 84-88, Hearing Res Study Sect, 92-; vis prof, Univ Queensland, Australia, 91. *Mem:* Soc Neurosci; Sigma Xi; Inst Elec & Electronics Engrs. *Res:* Neurophysiology of sensory and motor systems. *Mailing Add:* Dept Neurophys 283 B Med Sci Univ Wis 1300 University Ave Madison WI 53706-1585

**YIN, ZHIPING,** THIN FILM DEPOSITION & CHARACTERIZATION, CHEMICAL VAPOR DEPOSITION. *Current Pos:* PROCESS DEVELOP ENGR, MICRON TECHNOL INC, 97- *Personal Data:* b Shanghai, China, Oct 21, 58; m, Youngsheng Ma; c Lina Ma. *Educ:* Lanzhou Univ, China, BS, 82; City Univ NY, PhD(physics), 91. *Prof Exp:* Physicist, Solar Physics, NY, 91-92; res fel, Sch Elec & Electronics Eng Nanjang Technol Univ, Singapore, 92-95; res assoc, City Col NY, City Univ NY, 95-96. *Res:* Effects of chemical vapor deposition process on the optical properties of thin films; modeling the response of film optical properties with their microstructure and surface roughness. *Mailing Add:* 8000 S Federal Way PO Box 6 Boise ID 83707-0006. *Fax:* 208-368-2540; *E-Mail:* zyin@micron.com

**YING, KUANG LIN,** GENETICS, CYTOGENETICS. *Current Pos:* RETIRED. *Personal Data:* b Kiangsu, China, June 12, 27; Can citizen; m 55, Sun Chyi; c May, Bonni & Edward. *Educ:* Nat Taiwan Univ, BSc, 52; Univ Sask, PhD(cytol, genetics), 61. *Prof Exp:* Sr specialist plant breeding & genetics, Sino-Am Joint Comn Rural Reconstruct, 61-64; Med Res Coun Can res assoc, Univ Sask, 64-67, from asst prof human cytogenetics to assoc prof, Dept Pediat, 73-78; dir cytogenetics & prenatal detection lab, Valley Children's Hosp & Guidance Clin, Fresno, Calif, 78-81; head sect cytogenetics, Div Med Genetics, Children's Hosp, Los Angeles, Calif, 81-93; assoc clin prof, Dept Pediat, Sch Med, Univ Southern Calif, Los Angeles, 81-93. *Concurrent Pos:* Assoc prof, Grad Sch, Nat Taiwan Univ, 62-63. *Mem:* Genetics Soc Can; Am Soc Human Genetics; Tissue Cult Asn. *Res:* Human cytogenetics; prenatal detection of genetic disorders. *Mailing Add:* 4840 Elder Ave Seal Beach CA 90740

**YING, RAMONA YUN-CHING,** ELECTROCHEMISTRY, BATTERY. *Current Pos:* STAFF RES SCIENTIST PHYS CHEM, GEN MOTORS RES LABS, 83- *Personal Data:* b Taiwan, July 2, 57; US citizen; m 84; c 1. *Educ:* Univ Calif, Los Angeles, BS, 79; Univ Mich, Ann Arbor, PhD(chem eng), 85. *Mem:* Electrochem Soc. *Res:* Electroless plating, alloy plating; electrocatalysis, fuel cell; lead acid battery, corrosion. *Mailing Add:* 1863 Washington Rd Rochester Hills MI 48306

**YING, SEE CHEN,** SOLID STATE PHYSICS. *Current Pos:* from asst prof to assoc prof, 71-80, PROF PHYSICS, BROWN UNIV, 80- *Personal Data:* b Shanghai, China, Apr 4, 41; m 82. *Educ:* Univ Hong Kong, BSc, 63 & 64; Brown Univ, PhD(physics), 68. *Prof Exp:* Res assoc physics, Brown Univ, 68-69; res scientist, Univ Calif, San Diego, 69-71. *Concurrent Pos:* Res fel, A P Sloan Found, 72; Alexander von Humboldt Found US sr scientist award, 76. *Res:* Theoretical solid state physics; electronic properties of surfaces and interfaces; phase transitions on surfaces and low dimensional systems. *Mailing Add:* Dept Physics Brown Univ Providence RI 02912

**YING, WILLIAM H,** CIVIL ENGINEERING. *Current Pos:* asst prof mech math, 64-67, assoc prof civil eng, 67-72, PROF CIVIL ENG, CALIF STATE UNIV, LONG BEACH, 72- *Personal Data:* b Shanghai, China, July 1, 35; m 64. *Educ:* Cheng Kung Univ, Taiwan, BS, 57; Univ Mo-Rolla, MS, 61; Okla State Univ, PhD(civil eng), 65. *Prof Exp:* Engr, Chau & Lee Archit & Civil Engrs, Hong Kong, 57-58 & Pan-Ocean, Ltd, Okinawa, 58-60. *Mem:* Am Soc Civil Engrs; Am Soc Eng Educ; Am Inst Aeronaut & Astronaut. *Res:* Solid mechanics, including plates and shells, elasticity and dynamics of structures. *Mailing Add:* Dept Civil Eng Calif State Univ 1250 Bellflower Blvd Long Beach CA 90840-0001

**YING, ZHIQIANG CHARLES,** SURFACE SCIENCE, MATERIALS PHYSICS. *Current Pos:* ASST PROF, NMEX STATE UNIV, 96- *Personal Data:* b Shanghai, Sept 29, 60; m, Jane G Zhu; c Victor A. *Educ:* Peking Univ, BS, 83; Cornell Univ, MS, 87, PhD(physics), 90. *Prof Exp:* Res assoc, Univ Pa, 90-93; res staff, Oak Ridge Nat Lab, 93-96. *Mem:* Am Phys Soc; Am Vacuum Soc; Mat Res Soc. *Res:* Laser processing of materials, particularly those involving solid surface and molecular clusters; study of physical and chemical properties of these materials using nonlinear optical techniques. *Mailing Add:* 2721 Custer Way Las Cruces NM 88011. *E-Mail:* yingzc@nmsu.edu

**YIP, CECIL CHEUNG-CHING,** BIOCHEMISTRY, ENDOCRINOLOGY. *Current Pos:* from asst prof to assoc prof, 64-74, chmn, 90-95, PROF, BANTING & BEST DEPT MED RES, C H BEST INST, UNIV TORONTO, 74-, CHARLES H BEST PROF, 87-, VDEAN RES, FAC MED, 93- *Personal Data:* b Hong Kong, June 11, 37; m 60; c 2. *Educ:* McMaster Univ, BSc, 59; Rockefeller Univ, PhD(biochem, endocrinol), 63. *Honors & Awards:* Charles H Best Prize, 72. *Prof Exp:* Res assoc endocrinol, Rockefeller Univ, 63-64. *Concurrent Pos:* Med Res Coun Can med res scholar, 67-71. *Mem:* AAAS; Am Soc Biol Chem; Can Biochem Soc. *Res:* Insulin receptor structure and function; hormone-receptor interaction. *Mailing Add:* C H Best Inst Univ Toronto Toronto ON M5G 1L6 Can. *Fax:* 416-978-8528; *E-Mail:* cecil.yip@utoronto.ca

**YIP, GEORGE,** BIOCHEMISTRY, FOOD TECHNOLOGY. *Current Pos:* RETIRED. *Personal Data:* b Oakland, Calif, Nov 14, 26; m 53, Marion Gan; c Matthew G. *Educ:* Univ Calif, Berkeley, BS, 51; Georgetown Univ, MS, 59. *Prof Exp:* Chemist, Nat Canners Asn, Calif, 51-52; chemist, Div Food Chem, Food & Drug Admin, 55-56, res chemist pesticides, 56-63, sect chief herbicides & plant growth regulators, 63-71, chief, Biochem Technol Br, 71-72, chief, Indust Chem Contaminant Br, Div Chem Technol, 72-83, res anal chem, 84-87. *Mem:* Emer mem Am Chem Soc; fel Asn Off Anal Chem. *Res:* Methods of analysis for industrial chemical contaminants in foods; identification of unknown contaminants including degradation products. *Mailing Add:* 5211 Kipling St Springfield VA 22151-2928

**YIP, JOSEPH W,** DEVELOPMENTAL NEUROBIOLOGY. *Current Pos:* ASSOC PROF NEUROBIOL, SCH MED, UNIV PITTSBURGH, 81- *Personal Data:* b Hong Kong, Sept 17, 48; m 77; c 2. *Educ:* Wash State Univ, BS, 71; Univ Calif, San Francisco, PhD(physiol), 77. *Prof Exp:* Fel, Washington Univ, St Louis, 77-80. *Mem:* Soc Neurosci. *Res:* Specificity of synapse formation. *Mailing Add:* Dept Physiol Univ Pittsburgh Sch Med Pittsburgh PA 15261-0001

**YIP, KWOK LEUNG,** MEDICAL IMAGING, DIGITAL RADIOGRAPHY. *Current Pos:* SR STAFF RES SCIENTIST PHYSICS, RES LABS, EASTMAN KODAK CO, 84- *Personal Data:* b Canton, China, Sept 23, 44; m 72, Gee Ying Chao; c Nora L & Dana T. *Educ:* Chung Chi Col, Chinese Univ Hong Kong, BS, 65, dipl educ, 66; Providence Col, MS, 70; Lehigh Univ, PhD(physics), 73. *Prof Exp:* Teacher physics, King's Col, Hong Kong, 66-68; res fel physics, Univ Ill, Urbana, 73-75; sr tech specialist physics, Wilson Ctr Technol, Xerox Corp, 75-84. *Mem:* Am Phys Soc; Int Soc Optical Eng; Soc Imaging Sci & Technol. *Res:* Electronic printing; image processing; display and digitizer technologies; laser beam scanning and recording systems; medical imaging; digital radiography; systems modeling and analysis. *Mailing Add:* Eastman Kodak Co Res Labs 901 Elmgrove Rd Rochester NY 14653-5740. *Fax:* 716-726-2049; *E-Mail:* kwokyip@kodak.com

**YIP, RICK KA SUN,** CELL BIOLOGY, NEUROANATOMY. *Current Pos:* FEL CELL BIOL, UNIV TEX, 84- *Personal Data:* b 1952. *Educ:* Med Col Wis, PhD(anat), 85. *Mailing Add:* Dept Basic Sci Nova Southeastern Univ Terry Bldg Rm 1331 1750 NE 167th St Miami FL 33162-3017. *Fax:* 215-843-9082

**YIP, SIDNEY,** NUCLEAR ENGINEERING. *Current Pos:* from asst prof to assoc prof, 65-73, PROF NUCLEAR ENG, MASS INST TECHNOL, 73- *Personal Data:* b Peking, China, Jan 28, 36; US citizen; m 58. *Educ:* Univ Mich, BS, 58, MS, 59, PhD(nuclear eng), 62. *Prof Exp:* Res fel, Inst Sci Technol, Univ Mich, 62-63; res assoc eng physics, Cornell Univ, 63-65. *Concurrent Pos:* John Simon Guggenheim fel; Alexander von Humboldt found sr scientist award, Ger. *Mem:* Fel Am Phys Soc; Am Nuclear Soc. *Res:* Atomistic simulation of materials properties and behavior; statistical mechanics of dense fluids; molecular dynamics studies of atomic and polymeric glasses, interfacial phenomena and fracture. *Mailing Add:* Dept Nuclear Eng 24-208 Mass Inst Technol Cambridge MA 02139

**YIP, YUM KEUNG,** protein chemistry, hemoglobin, for more information see previous edition

**YIRAK, JACK J(UNIOR),** CHEMICAL ENGINEERING. *Current Pos:* RETIRED. *Personal Data:* b Omaha, Nebr, Oct 10, 18; m 45; c 2. *Educ:* Iowa State Col, BS, 40; Lawrence Col, MS, 42, PhD, 44. *Prof Exp:* Chem engr, Union Bag & Paper Corp, 44-48, group leader, 48-51, proj engr, Semi-Chem Pulp Mill, 51-54, asst pulp mill supt, 54-55; pulp mill proj engr, Bleached Div, Union Camp Corp, 55-60, construct proj engr, 60-64, asst construct engr, 64-66, construct proj mgr, 66-81, asst to proj dir, 81-89. *Mem:* Tech Asn Pulp & Paper Indust. *Res:* Pulp, paper and related products; tall oil. *Mailing Add:* 27 Sulgrave Rd Savannah GA 31406

**YNGVESSON, K SIGFRID,** MICROWAVES & SUBMILLIMETER WAVES, LOW-NOISE RECEIVERS. *Current Pos:* assoc prof, 70-78, PROF ELEC ENG, UNIV MASS, 78- *Personal Data:* b Lidko, Sweden, Mar 23, 36; m 65, Barbara Belton; c 2. *Educ:* Chalmers Univ Technol, Sweden, Civ ing, 58, Tekn Lic, 65, Tekn Dr, 68. *Honors & Awards:* Wallin Prize, Royal Acad Sci, 69. *Prof Exp:* Res asst electron physics, Chalmers Univ Technol, 59-64, res assoc, 66-68; res scholar physics, Univ Calif, Berkeley, 64-66, postdoctoral res asst, 68-70. *Concurrent Pos:* Vis prof, Chalmers Univ Technol, 77 & 85; Jubileums prof, Chalmers Univ, 92. *Mem:* Inst Elec & Electronics Engrs; Am Phys Soc. *Res:* Low noise receivers, especially for sub-millimeter waves; focal plane arrays for millimeter wave imaging. *Mailing Add:* Dept Elec & Comput Eng Univ Mass Amherst MA 01003. *Fax:* 413-545-4611; *E-Mail:* yngvesson@ecs.umass.edu

**YNTEMA, JAN LAMBERTUS,** PHYSICS. *Current Pos:* assoc physicist, 55-68, SR PHYSICIST, ARGONNE NAT LAB, 68- *Personal Data:* b Neth, Oct 5, 20; m 48; c 4. *Educ:* Free Univ, Amsterdam, NatPhilDrs, 48, DrPhysics, 52. *Prof Exp:* Res assoc physics, Princeton Univ, 49-52; asst prof, Univ Pittsburgh, 52-55. *Mem:* Am Phys Soc. *Res:* Radioactivity; gases at high temperatures; nuclear physics. *Mailing Add:* 5125 Grand Ave Western Springs IL 60558

**YNTEMA, MARY KATHERINE,** MATHEMATICS. *Current Pos:* RETIRED. *Personal Data:* b Urbana, Ill, Jan 20, 28. *Educ:* Swarthmore Col, BA, 50; Univ Ill, AM, 61, PhD(math), 65. *Prof Exp:* Teacher, Am Col Girls, Istanbul, 50-54 & Columbus Sch Girls, Ohio, 54-57; programmer, Lincoln Lab, Mass Inst Technol, 57-58; teacher high sch, Mont, 59-60; asst prof math, Univ Ill, Chicago, 65-67; asst prof comput sci, Pa State Univ, 67-71; assoc prof, Sangamon State Univ, 71-81, coordr math systs prog, 75-77, 80-81 & 84-86, chmn fac senate, 77-78, prof math, 81-92, coordr math syst prog, 88-92, div math & comput sect, 89-92. *Res:* Automata; context-free languages. *Mailing Add:* 22 Dean Park Dr Springfield IL 62707

**YOAKUM, ANNA MARGARET,** ANALYTICAL CHEMISTRY, PHYSICAL METALLURGY. *Current Pos:* EXEC VPRES & LAB DIR, STEWART LABS, INC, 67- *Personal Data:* b Loudon, Tenn, Jan 13, 33. *Educ:* Maryville Col, AB, 54; Univ Fla, MS, 56, PhD(anal chem), 60. *Prof Exp:* Supvr control lab, Greenback Indust, Inc, 56-59; sr res chemist, Chemstrand Res Ctr, Inc, 60-64; mem res staff, Oak Ridge Nat Lab, 64-69. *Mem:* Am Chem Soc; Soc Appl Spectros; NY Acad Sci; Am Soc Test & Mat; fel Am Inst Chem; Sigma Xi. *Res:* Analytical chemistry and trace analysis; research and method development in emission, flame, atomic absorption, x-ray fluorescence and infrared spectroscopy. *Mailing Add:* Twin Coves Lenoir City TN 37771-9060

**YOBURN, BYRON CROCKER,** PHARMACOLOGY. *Current Pos:* from asst prof to assoc prof, 87-94, PROF, COL PHARM, ST JOHN'S UNIV, 94, ASST DEAN, GRAD PHARM, 96- *Personal Data:* b Danbury, Conn, Nov 26, 50; m 76; c 2. *Educ:* Boston Univ, BA, 73; Hollins Col, MA, 76; Northeastern Univ, PhD(exp psychol), 79. *Prof Exp:* Fel neurobehav sci, Col Physicians & Surgeons, Columbia Univ, 79-81,; res scientist, NY State Psychiat Inst, 81-82; res assoc, Med Col, Cornell Univ, 82-83, instr pharmacol, 83-87. *Mem:* Soc Neurosci; NY Acad Sci; Am Soc Pharmacol & Exp Therapeut; Sigma Xi. *Res:* Basic mechanisms in opioid pharmacology, especially tolerance and dependence; opioid receptor plasticity. *Mailing Add:* Dept Pharmaceut Sci Col Pharm St John's Univ Grand Central & Utopia Pkwys Queens NY 11439. *Fax:* 718-990-6036

**YOCCA, FRANK D,** RECEPTOR PHARMACOLOGY, SEROTONIN. *Current Pos:* postdoctoral fel, Bristol-Myers Co, 84-85, res scientist, 85-87, sr res scientist, 87-89, assoc dir, 89-91, group leader, 91-, DIR NEUROSCI DRUG DISCOVERY, BRISTOL-MYERS SQUIBB CO. *Personal Data:* b Brooklyn, NY, July 22, 55. *Educ:* Manhattan Col, BS, 77; St John's Univ, MS, 81; NY Univ, PhD(pharmacol), 83. *Prof Exp:* Postdoctoral fel, Mt Sinai Sch Med, 83-84. *Concurrent Pos:* Adj asst prof, Dept Anesthesiol, Mt Sinai Sch Med, 89- *Mem:* Soc Neurosci; Am Soc Pharmacol & Exp Therapeut; NY Acad Sci; Am Chem Soc; Sigma Xi. *Res:* Delineation and classification of 5-HT, -like receptors in brain and periphery; 5-HTip receptors, specifically their regulation and possible heterogeneity; neuropsychopharmacology. *Mailing Add:* Bristol Myers Squibb 5 Res Pkwy Dept 401 Wallingford CT 06492

**YOCCOZ, JEAN-CHRISTOPHE,** MATHEMATICS. *Current Pos:* PROF MATH, UNIV PARIS-SUD, ORSAY. *Honors & Awards:* Fields Medal, Int Math Union, 94. *Concurrent Pos:* Mem, Res Inst, Univ France; assoc, Topology & Dynamics, Ctr Nat Sci Res. *Mailing Add:* Univ Paris-Sud Place Marechal Lattre Tassigny 75775 Paris 16 France

**YOCH, DUANE CHARLES,** MICROBIOLOGY, BIOCHEMISTRY. *Current Pos:* from asst prof to assoc prof biol, 78-85, PROF BIOL, UNIV SC, COLUMBIA, 85- *Personal Data:* b Parkston, SDak, Nov 4, 40; m 64; c 2. *Educ:* SDak State Univ, BS, 63, MS, 65; Pa State Univ, PhD(microbiol), 68. *Prof Exp:* Asst res microbiologist, Agr Exp Sta, Dept Cell Physiol, Univ Calif, Berkeley, 68-69, res specialist, 70-78. *Mem:* Am Soc Microbiol. *Res:* Biochemistry and molecular biology of nitrogen; iron-sulfur proteins; methylotrophic N2 fixation. *Mailing Add:* Dept Biol Univ SC Columbia SC 29208-0001

**YOCHELSON, ELLIS LEON,** INVERTEBRATE PALEONTOLOGY. *Current Pos:* RES ASSOC, SMITHSONIAN INST, 64- *Personal Data:* b Washington, DC, Nov 14, 28; m 50, Sally Watt; c Jeffrey, Abby & Chalres. *Educ:* Univ Kans, BS, 49, MS, 50; Columbia Univ, PhD, 55. *Honors & Awards:* Erasmus Haworth Award, Dept Geol, Univ Kans. *Prof Exp:* Asst, Univ Kans & Columbia Univ, 50-52; paleontologist-geologist, US Geol Surv, 52-85, Univ Md, 86-87. *Concurrent Pos:* Mem, Nat Res Coun, 57-71; treas, Int Paleont Asn, 71-75; organizer, NAm Paleontol Conv, 69, ed proceedings, 70-71; secy-gen, Ninth Int Cong Carboniferous Stratig & Geol, 79; Centennial Comt, US Geol Surv, 75-79. *Mem:* Sigma Xi; Paleont Soc (pres, 76); Hist Earth Sci Soc (secy-treas, 81-84, secy, 85-88, pres, 89). *Res:* Systematics and evolution of Paleozoic gastropods; phylogeny of Mollusca, especially early Paleozoic major taxa; enigmatic Paleozoic fossils; paleontology; stratigraphy-sedimentation; history of science; taxonomy; evolution. *Mailing Add:* Dept Paleobiol Nat Mus Natural Hist Washington DC 20560. *Fax:* 202-786-2832; *E-Mail:* yochelson.ellis@scmnh.si.edu

**YOCHIM, JEROME M,** ENDOCRINOLOGY, PHYSIOLOGY. *Current Pos:* from asst prof to assoc prof physiol, 62-70, PROF PHYSIOL, UNIV KANS, 71- *Personal Data:* b Chicago, Ill, Feb 23, 33; m 57; c 2. *Educ:* Univ Ill, BS, 55, MS, 57; Purdue Univ, PhD(biol sci), 60. *Prof Exp:* NIH fel anat, Col Med, Univ Ill, 60-62. *Concurrent Pos:* NIH career develop award, 71-76. *Mem:* AAAS; Am Asn Anatomists; Am Physiol Soc; Soc Study Reprod; Endocrine Soc; Sigma Xi. *Res:* Physiology of reproduction. *Mailing Add:* Dept Physiol & Cell Biol Univ Kans Lawrence KS 66045-0001

**YOCKEY, HUBERT PALMER,** THEORETICAL BIOLOGY, MOLECULAR BIOLOGY. *Current Pos:* RETIRED. *Personal Data:* b Alexandria, Minn, Apr 15, 16; m 46, Mary A Leach; c Franklin W, Cynthia A & Eric M. *Educ:* Univ Calif, Berkeley, AB, 38, PhD(physics), 42. *Prof Exp:* Jr physicist, Nat Defense Res Comt, Calif, 41-42; physicist radiation lab, Univ Calif, 42-44; sr physicist, Tenn Eastman Corp, 44-46; group leader irradiation physics, NAm Aviation, Inc, 46-52; chief nuclear physics, Convair Div, Gen Dynamics Corp, Tex, 52-53; asst dir health & physics div, Oak Ridge Nat Lab, Tenn, 53-59; mgr res & develop div, Aerojet-Gen Nucleonics Corp, 59-62 & Hughes Res Labs, 63-64; chief, Reactor Br, Combat Systs Test Activ Aberdeen Proving Ground, 64-80, chief Army Pulse Radiation Div, 80-85, dir, Nuclear Effects Directorate, 85-87. *Mem:* Fel Am Phys Soc; Am Nuclear Soc; AAAS; Health Phys Soc; fel Explorers Club. *Res:* Application of information theory to origin of life, genetic code, calculated information content of cytochrome c aging and radiation effects; established fast pulsed reactor facility; radiation effects in ferroelectrics; solid state physics; pulsed reactors. *Mailing Add:* 1507 Balmoral Dr Bel Air MD 21014-5638. *E-Mail:* yockey@aol.com

**YOCOM, PERRY NIEL,** INORGANIC CHEMISTRY. *Current Pos:* Mem tech staff, 57-70, RES GROUP HEAD, DAVID SARNOFF RES CTR, SUBSID SRI INT, 70- *Personal Data:* b Auburn, Maine, Sept 27, 30; m 62; c 3. *Educ:* Pa State Univ, BS, 54; Univ Ill, PhD, 58. *Honors & Awards:* David Sarnoff Award, Sci, 70. *Concurrent Pos:* Lectr, Advan Study Inst, NATO, 72. *Mem:* AAAS; Am Chem Soc; Electrochem Soc; Sigma Xi; Mineral Soc Am. *Res:* Chemistry of fused salts; crystal growth; defects in solids; rare earth phase chemistry; luminescence. *Mailing Add:* David Sarnoff Res Ctr CN 5300 201 Washington Rd Princeton NJ 08543-5300

**YOCUM, CHARLES FREDRICK,** BIOCHEMISTRY. *Current Pos:* from asst prof to assoc prof biol, 73-81, chmn biol, 85-91, PROF BIOL & CHEM, UNIV MICH, 82- *Personal Data:* b Storm Lake, Iowa, Oct 31, 41; m 82; c 1. *Educ:* Iowa State Univ, BS, 63; Ind Univ, PhD(biochem), 71. *Prof Exp:* Biochemist protein chem, ITT Res Inst, 63-68; NIH fel biochem, Cornell Univ, 71-73. *Concurrent Pos:* Mem, Adv Panel Metabolic Biol, NSF, 82-85, Adv Panel Chem Life Processes, 86, Adv Panel Plant Sci Ctrs, 88-89, Adv Panel USDA Photosynthesis Prog, 89; res grants, NSF & USDA. *Mem:* Am Chem Soc; Am Soc Plant Physiologists; AAAS; Biophys Soc; Am Soc Biol Chemists; Am Soc Photobiol. *Res:* Mechanisms of photosynthetic oxygen evolution and energy transduction in chloroplasts and blue-green algae. *Mailing Add:* Dept Biol Univ Mich Ann Arbor MI 48109-1048. *Fax:* 313-647-0884

**YOCUM, CONRAD SCHATTE,** PLANT PHYSIOLOGY. *Current Pos:* RETIRED. *Personal Data:* b Swarthmore, Pa, Mar 29, 19; m 46; c 3. *Educ:* Col William & Mary, BS, 40; Univ Md, MS, 47; Stanford Univ, PhD, 52. *Prof Exp:* Asst marine biol, Va Fisheries Lab, 46-47; asst plant physiol, Hopkins Marine Sta, 47-48; instr plant physiol, Harvard Univ, 52-55; asst prof, Cornell Univ, 55-61; from assoc prof to prof plant physiol, Univ Mich, Ann Arbor, 61-88. *Mem:* Am Soc Plant Physiol; Sigma Xi. *Res:* Photosynthesis; respiration; tropisms; nitrogen fixation. *Mailing Add:* 2080 Newport Rd Ann Arbor MI 48103-2330

**YOCUM, GEORGE DAVID,** ENVIRONMENTAL PHYSIOLOGY. *Current Pos:* RESEARCHER, OHIO STATE UNIV, 92- *Personal Data:* b Dayton, Ohio, Sept 21, 56. *Educ:* Ohio State Univ, BS, 84, MS, 87, PhD(entom), 92. *Mem:* AAAS; Am Soc Zool; Entom Soc Am; Sigma Xi. *Res:* Biochemistry and molecular biology of thermotolerance, thermosensitivity and cold shock in insects. *Mailing Add:* 31 Pacemont Rd Columbus OH 43202-1009. *Fax:* 614-292-2180; *E-Mail:* gyocum@magnvs.acs.ohio-state.edu

**YOCUM, RONALD HARRIS,** CHEMISTRY. *Current Pos:* MEM STAFF, QUANTUM CHEM CORP, 87- *Personal Data:* b Darby, Pa, June 2, 39. *Educ:* Gettysburg Col, BA, 61; Univ Pa, PhD(org chem), 65. *Prof Exp:* Dir res, Latin Am, 73-77, Designed Prod Dept, 77-78, dir prod res, 78-80, dir res, Mich Div, Dow Chem USA, 80-; mem staff, Norchem, Inc, 60. *Mem:* Am Chem Soc. *Mailing Add:* 571 Chaswil Ct 11500 Northlake Dr Cincinnati OH 45255-5602

**YODAIKEN, RALPH EMILE,** PATHOLOGY, OCCUPATIONAL HEALTH. *Current Pos:* SR MED OFFICER & CHMN SR ADV STAFF, NAT INST OCCUP SAFETY & HEALTH, 77- *Personal Data:* b Johannesburg, SAfrica, Aug 25, 28; US citizen. *Educ:* Univ Witwatersrand, MB & BCh, 56; Johns Hopkins Univ, MPH, 76. *Prof Exp:* Lectr path, Univ Witwatersrand, 58-63; assoc pathologist, Buffalo Gen Hosp, NY, 63-67; assoc prof path, Sch Med, Univ Cincinnati, 68-71; prof path & assoc prof med, Sch Med, Emory Univ, 71-77; asst researcher, Johns Hopkins Univ, 76-76. *Concurrent Pos:* Chief ultra structure res, Vet Admin Hosp, 71-76. *Mem:* Fel Am Col Preventive Med; Soc Occup & Environ Health; fel Am Col Path; fel Collegium Ramazzini; Am Occup Med Assoc; Acad Occup Med; Acad Prev Med; Am Pub Health Assoc. *Res:* Vascular pathology with special reference to diabetes. *Mailing Add:* 7100 Oak Forest Lane Bethesda MD 20817

**YODER, CHARLES FINNEY,** CELESTIAL MECHANICS, PLANETOLOGY. *Current Pos:* MEM TECH STAFF, JET PROPULSION LAB, 76- *Personal Data:* b Cincinnati, Ohio, July 18, 43; m 70; c 2. *Educ:* Univ Calif, Santa Barbara, BA, 68, PhD(physics), 73. *Prof Exp:* Fel, Dept Earth & Space Sci, Univ Calif, Los Angeles, 73-76. *Mem:* Am Geophys Union; Am Astron Soc. *Res:* Effect of tidal friction and gravitational resonances on planetary satellites; rotational dynamics; core mantle coupling mechanisms. *Mailing Add:* 9836 Burnet Ave North Hills CA 91343

**YODER, CLAUDE H,** INORGANIC CHEMISTRY. *Current Pos:* From asst prof to assoc prof, 66-80, chmn dept, 74-82, PROF CHEM, FRANKLIN & MARSHALL COL, 80-, DANA PROF CHEM, 86- *Personal Data:* b West Reading, Pa, Mar 16, 40; m 66; c 2. *Educ:* Franklin & Marshall Col, BA, 62; Cornell Univ, PhD(chem), 66. *Concurrent Pos:* Dreyfus Found teacher scholar, 71. *Mem:* AAAS; Am Chem Soc. *Res:* Bonding in organometallic compounds. *Mailing Add:* 2946 Kings Lane Lancaster PA 17601-1617

**YODER, DAVID LEE,** PLANT PATHOLOGY, SOIL MICROBIOLOGY. *Current Pos:* PLANT BREEDER, GILROY FOODS, INC, 78- *Personal Data:* b Bellefontaine, Ohio, June 23, 36; m 61; c 3. *Educ:* Goshen Col, BA, 60; Mich State Univ, MS, 68, PhD(plant path), 71. *Prof Exp:* Plant pathologist, Hunt-Wesson Foods, Inc, 71-78. *Mem:* AAAS; Am Soc Hort Sci; Am Plant Selections. *Res:* Soil-borne plant diseases; disease of tomatoes; soil fungistasis; onion genetics, pepper genetics and diseases of onion, garlic and pepper; tissue culture. *Mailing Add:* Gilroy Foods 1350 Pachenko Pass Hwy Gilroy CA 95020

**YODER, DONALD MAURICE,** agricultural chemistry, for more information see previous edition

**YODER, ELMON EUGENE,** AGRICULTURAL ENGINEERING, CIVIL ENGINEERING. *Current Pos:* AGR ENGR RES, USDA, LEXINGTON, 62- *Personal Data:* b Wolford, NDak, Oct 10, 21; m 47; c 4. *Educ:* Ore State Univ, BS, 47 & 54, MS, 61. *Prof Exp:* Civil engr design, Consumers Power Inc, 48-54; agr engr, Khon Trup Agr Univ, Thailand, 54-56; civil engr, Ore State Univ, 57-61. *Concurrent Pos:* Agr engr, Univ Ky, 65-66 & 76-78. *Mem:* Am Soc Agr Engrs; Tobacco Workers; Sigma Xi. *Res:* Tobacco mechanization and processing; improvement of tobacco combustion in health-related research. *Mailing Add:* 808 Surrey Lane Lexington KY 40503

**YODER, HATTEN SCHUYLER, JR,** EXPERIMENTAL PETROLOGY. *Current Pos:* petrologist, 48-71, dir, 71-86, EMER DIR, CARNEGIE INST WASH GEOPHYS LAB, 86- *Personal Data:* b Cleveland, Ohio, Mar 20, 21; m 59, Elizabeth M Bruffey; c Hatten S III & Karen M. *Educ:* Univ Chicago, SB, 41, cert(meteorol), 42 & 46; Mass Inst Technol, PhD(petrol), 48, Colo Sch Mines, 95. *Hon Degrees:* Dr, Univ Paris, 81; Colo Sch Mines, 95. *Honors & Awards:* Mineral Soc Am Award, 54; Day Medal, Geol Soc Am, 62; Arthur L Day Prize, Nat Acad Sci, 72; A G Werner Medal, Ger Mineral Soc, 72; Wollaston Medal, Geol Soc London, 79-; Roebling Medal, Mineral Soc Am, 92. *Prof Exp:* Aerologist, USNR, 42-46. *Concurrent Pos:* Vis prof, Calif Inst Technol, 58, Univ Tex, 64, Univ Colo, 66 & Univ Cape Town, 67; lectr, Nat Acad Sci, 72; consult, Los Alamos Nat Lab, 72-; independent trustee, Cutler Trust, 92- *Mem:* Nat Acad Sci; Mineral Soc Am (pres, 72); Geol Soc Am; Am Geophys Union; Geochem Soc; Am Chem Soc. *Res:* Experimental petrology; phase equilibria in mineral systems; properties of minerals at high pressure and high temperature; hydrothermal mineral synthesis; experimental heat transfer in silicates; history of petrology. *Mailing Add:* 6709 Melody Ln Bethesda MD 20817-3152. *Fax:* 202-686-2419; *E-Mail:* yoder@gl.ciw.edu

**YODER, JOHN MENLY,** ENDOCRINOLOGY, IMMUNOCHEMISTRY. *Current Pos:* RETIRED. *Personal Data:* b Ft Wayne, Ind, Oct 4, 31; m 60, Lois Baker; c 2. *Educ:* Purdue Univ, BS, 53, PhD(animal physiol), 61. *Prof Exp:* Res biochemist, Ames Co Div, Miles Labs, Inc, 61-72, sr res scientist, 72-92. *Mem:* Am Chem Soc. *Res:* Plant and animal physiology; silage fermentation; protein purification; characterization of proteins and polysaccharides by immunochemistry; gonadotropins; hepatitis antigen; antibody production; factor VIII; thyroxine assay; hemoglobin AIC; toxoplasmosis. *Mailing Add:* 26221 Bell Elkhart IN 46514

**YODER, LEVON LEE,** MUSICAL ACOUSTICS. *Current Pos:* assoc prof, 65-71, chmn dept, 65-76, PROF PHYSICS, ADRIAN COL, 71-, CHMN DEPT, 79- *Personal Data:* b Middlebury, Ind, June 22, 36; m 60, Anita Hoffman; c Teryl. *Educ:* Goshen Col, BA, 58; Univ Mich, MA, 61, PhD, 63. *Prof Exp:* Asst prof physics & chmn dept, Millikin Univ, 63-65. *Mem:* Catgut Acoust Soc; Am Asn Physics Teachers; Acoust Soc Am. *Res:* Acoustical properties of violins and trumpets. *Mailing Add:* 2499 Sword Hwy Adrian MI 49221

**YODER, NEIL RICHARD,** PARTICLE PHYSICS. *Current Pos:* at CYCLOTRON FACIL, IND UNIV. *Personal Data:* b Wichita, Kans, Mar 27, 37; m 68. *Educ:* Kans State Teachers Col, BA, 59; Pa State Univ, PhD(physics), 69. *Prof Exp:* Instr physics, Mich State Univ, 65-67; sr res assoc, Univ Md, College Park, 67- *Mem:* Am Phys Soc; Sigma Xi. *Res:* Phenomenological analysis of moderate energy nucleon-nucleon data; application of computers to on-line analysis of nuclear physics experimental data. *Mailing Add:* Ind Univ 2401 Milo B Sampson Lane Bloomington IN 47408. *Fax:* 812-855-6645

**YODER, OLEN CURTIS,** PLANT PATHOLOGY. *Current Pos:* From asst prof to assoc prof, 71-83, PROF PLANT PATH, CORNELL UNIV, 83- *Personal Data:* b Fairview, Mich, Jan 26, 42; m 67; c Brandon. *Educ:* Goshen Col, BA, 64; Mich State Univ, MS, 68, PhD(plant path), 71. *Concurrent Pos:* USDA res grant, 72-75 & 78-; Rockefeller Found res grant, 74 & 77-; sabbatical, Stanford Univ, 78-79; study leave, Mass Int Technol, 83-84; prog mgr, USDA/Competitive Res Grants, 85-97. *Mem:* AAAS; Am Phytopath Soc; Am Soc Microbiol; Sigma Xi; Int Soc Plant-Microbe InteraCTION. *Res:* Genetics and molecular biology of fungal pathogenicity to plants. *Mailing Add:* Dept Plant Path Cornell Univ Ithaca NY 14853

**YODER, PAUL RUFUS, JR,** OPTICS. *Current Pos:* CONSULT OPTICAL ENG, 85- *Personal Data:* b Huntingdon, Pa, Feb 6, 27; m 48, Sara E White; c David L, Martha A, Carol S & Alan D. *Educ:* Juniata Col, BS, 47; Pa State Univ, MS, 50. *Prof Exp:* Assoc prof physics & math, Bridgewater Col, 50-51; optical physicist, US Army Frankford Arsenal, 51-61; proj engr, 61-67, eng dept mgr, 67-82, asst to dir res, Perkin-Elmer Corp, 82-86; sr scientist, Taunton Technologies Inc, 86-91. *Concurrent Pos:* Lectr geometric optics, Univ Conn Exten, 77-86. *Mem:* Fel Optical Soc Am; fel Int Soc Optical Engr; Sigma Xi. *Res:* Design, development, fabrication and test of specialized optical instrumentation; author of two books, chapters in two additional books and more than 50 articles in field of optics. *Mailing Add:* 1220 Foxboro Dr Norwalk CT 06851-1152. *Fax:* 203-847-8244

**YODER, ROBERT E,** health physics, industrial hygiene, for more information see previous edition

**YODER, WAYNE ALVA,** INVERTEBRATE ZOOLOGY, ENTOMOLOGY. *Current Pos:* From asst prof to assoc prof, 72-85, PROF BIOL, FROSTBURG STATE UNIV, MD, 85- *Personal Data:* b Grantsville, Md, July 6, 43; m 67, Roveen Townsend; c Derek W & Kristin R. *Educ:* Goshen Col, BA, 65; Mich State Univ, MS, 71, PhD(zool), 72. *Mem:* Am Inst Biol Sci; Am Soc Zoologists; Entom Soc Am; Sigma Xi. *Res:* Systematic and ecological studies of the mites associated with silphid beetles. *Mailing Add:* Biol-Frostburg State Univ Frostburg MD 21532. *Fax:* 301-689-4737

**YODER WISE, PATRICIA S,** MANAGEMENT & MARKETING, GERONTICS. *Current Pos:* prof & exec assoc dean, 79-94, PROF & DEAN, TEX TECH UNIV, HEALTH SCI CTR, 94- *Personal Data:* b Wadsworth, Ohio, July 2, 41; m 73; c 2. *Educ:* Ohio State Univ, BSN, 63; Wayne State Univ, MSN, 68; Tex Tech Univ, EdD, 84. *Prof Exp:* Spec assignment nurse, Univ Hosp, 63-64; instr, Med Surg Nursing, Aultman Hosp, 65-66; res asst, Nursing Process, Wayne State Univ, 68; educ dir, Ohio Nurses' Asn, 68-72; asst dir nursing, Mt Clemons Hosp, 72-73; clin instr nursing, West Shore Community Col, 74-75; assoc prof & head nursing, Ferris State Col, 75-77; from asst prof to assoc prof & dir, Univ Colo, 77-79. *Concurrent Pos:* Vchair & chair, Mich Nurses' Asn, 72-76; consult, self employed, 73-; vchair & mem, Mich Bd Nursing, 77; coun continuing educ, Am Nurses' Asn, 78-82 & 82-85; acad adv panel, Hosp Satellite Network, 83- *Mem:* Am Nurses' Asn Coun (secy, 78-82). *Res:* Management, continuing education, marketing and teaching as they relate to nursing; gerontics nursing, especially involving pets. *Mailing Add:* Sch Nursing Tex Tech Univ Health Sci Ctr Lubbock TX 79430

**YODH, GAURANG BHASKAR,** PHYSICS. *Current Pos:* PROF PHYSICS, UNIV CALIF, IRVINE, 88- *Personal Data:* b Ahmedabad, India, Nov 24, 28; nat US; m 54; c 3. *Educ:* Univ Bombay, BSc, 48; Univ Chicago, MS, 51, PhD(physics), 55. *Prof Exp:* Instr physics, Stanford Univ, 54-56; res fel, Tata Inst Fundamental Res, India, 57-58; res physicist, Carnegie Inst Technol, 58-59, asst prof physics, 59-61; prof physics, Univ Md, College Park, 65-88. *Concurrent Pos:* Consult, US Naval Res Lab, DC, 65-69 & Argonne Nat Lab, 66-70; vis prof, Univ Ariz, 66-67; vis scientist, Goddard Space Flight Ctr, NASA, 76-77; prog officer elementary particle physics, NSF, 78-80. *Mem:* Fel Am Phys Soc. *Res:* Experimental and phenomenological study of high energy interactions of elementary particles and cosmic rays; gamma ray astronomy. *Mailing Add:* Dept Physics Univ Calif Irvine CA 92717. *Fax:* 714-856-7478

**YOERGER, ROGER R,** AGRICULTURAL ENGINEERING. *Current Pos:* prof, 58-78, head, Dept Agr Eng, 78-85, EMER PROF AGR ENG, UNIV ILL, URBANA, 85- *Personal Data:* b LeMars, Iowa, Feb 17, 29; wid; c Karen, Anita (Smith), Linda (Canull) & Daniel Summitt. *Educ:* Iowa State Univ, BS, 49, MS, 51, PhD(agr eng), 57. *Honors & Awards:* Massey Ferguson Medal, Am Soc Agr Engrs, 89. *Prof Exp:* Instr & asst prof agr eng, Iowa State Univ, 49-56; assoc prof, Pa State Univ, 56-58. *Concurrent Pos:* Consult engr, MESAC Enterprises, 56- *Mem:* Fel Am Soc Agr Engrs; Am Soc Eng Educ; Sigma Xi. *Res:* Off-road vehicles; noise reduction; vibration and operator comfort; field crop production equipment. *Mailing Add:* 107 W Holmes St Urbana IL 61801

**YOESTING, CLARENCE C,** PHYSICS, SCIENCE EDUCATION. *Current Pos:* RETIRED. *Personal Data:* b Apr 5, 12; US citizen; m 40; c 2. *Educ:* Cent State Col, Okla, BS, 36; Univ Okla, MEd, 47, EdD(sci educ), 65. *Prof Exp:* Teacher sci, Lacy Schs, Okla, 36-38, Loyal Schs, 38-40, Newkirk, Okla, 41-42 & Ponca Mil Acad, 45-47; prin & teacher, Tonkawa, Okla, 47-51; counr & teacher, Northeast High Sch, Oklahoma City, 51-61; prof physics, Cent State Univ Okla, 61-77. *Mem:* Nat Sci Teachers Asn; Am Inst Physics; Am Asn Physics Teachers. *Mailing Add:* 1716 S Rankin St Edmond OK 73013

**YOFFA, ELLEN JUNE,** VERY LARGE SCALE INTEGRATION DESIGN. *Current Pos:* Fel, 78-80, RES STAFF MEM, THOMAS J WATSON RES CTR, IBM, 80- *Personal Data:* b Boston, Mass, Aug 18, 51. *Educ:* Mass Inst Technol, BS, 73, PhD(physics), 78. *Mem:* Am Phys Soc; Sigma Xi. *Res:* Creating tools for very large scale integration design automation, and construction of interactive systems for large scale circuit design, wiring, and data interchange standards. *Mailing Add:* IBM Rm 33-109 PO Box 218 Yorktown Heights NY 10598-0218

**YOGANANDAN, NARAYAN,** BIOMECHANICS, SAFETY ENGINEERING. *Current Pos:* Vis prof, 86-87, asst prof, 87-91, ASSOC PROF, DEPT NEUROSURG, MED COL WIS, 91-; PROF NEUROSCI, DEPT VET AFFAIRS MED CTR, MILWAUKEE, 95- *Personal Data:* b India; US citizen. *Educ:* Mysore Univ, India, BS, 73, BSCE, 77; Indian Inst Sci, MSCE, 79; Marquette Univ, PhD(biomed eng), 85. *Concurrent Pos:* Adj asst prof biomed eng, Marquette Univ, 86-91, adj assoc prof, 91-; coherent prof mech eng, State Univ Fla, Miami, 88-; fac, Biophys Grad Prog, Med Col Wis, 90-; mem, Spinal Devices Comt, Am Soc Testing & Mat, 91-; asst chief, Neurosci Lab Res Serv, Dept Vet Affairs Med Ctr, Milwaukee, 91-95. *Mem:* Am Asn Automotive Med; assoc mem Am Asn Neurol Surgeons; Am Pub Health Asn; Am Soc Biomech; Am Soc Mech Engrs; Am Soc Testing & Mat; Biomed Eng Soc; Cervical Spine Res Soc; Eng Med & Biol Soc; Soc Automotive Engrs; Soc Eng Sci. *Res:* Biomedical aspects of the human body; biomechanics; mathematical modeling; crashworthiness; safety engineering; systems design; clinical trauma. *Mailing Add:* Dept Neurosurg 9200 W Wisconsin Ave Milwaukee WI 53226. *Fax:* 414-382-5374

**YOGANATHAN, AJIT PRITHIVIRAJ,** CHEMICAL ENGINEERING, BIOENGINEERING. *Current Pos:* from asst prof to assoc prof, 79-88, PROF CHEM ENG, GA INST TECHNOL, 88-, PROF MECH ENG, 89-, DIR, BIOENG CTR, 89-, CO-DIR EMORY/GEORGIATECH BIOMED TECHNOL CTR, 92-, ASSOC DIR INST BIOENG & BIOSCI, 95- *Personal Data:* b Colombo, Sri Lanka, Dec 6, 51. *Educ:* Univ Co, Univ London, Eng, BSc, 73; Calif Inst Technol, Pasadena, PhD(chem eng), 78. *Honors & Awards:* Goldsmid Medal, Univ Col, Univ London, 73; Edwin Walker Award, Brit Inst Mech Eng, 89. *Prof Exp:* Fel chem eng, Calif Inst Technol, 77-79. *Concurrent Pos:* Alexander von Humbolt fel, Humboldt Found, WGer, 85; mem, Int Stand Orgn sub comt prosthetic heartvalves, 85-; adj prof, Div Cardiovascular Med, Univ Ala Med Sch, 87-; mem, Surg & Bioeng Study Sect, NIH, 88-92; co-dir, Bioeng Ctr, Ga Inst Technol, 89-; vis prof, Danish Res Acad, 92. *Mem:* Fel Am Inst Med & Biol Eng; Am Inst Chem Engrs; Am Soc Echocardiography; Sigma Xi; Am Soc Eng Educ; Am Heart Asn; Am Soc Mech Eng. *Res:* Physics of blood flow in the human heart and its large vessels; non-invasive Doppler techniques; magnetic resonance imaging; computational fluid dynamics. *Mailing Add:* Sch Chem Eng Ga Inst Tech Atlanta GA 30332-0100. *Fax:* 404-894-2291

**YOGORE, MARIANO G, JR,** PARASITOLOGY, PUBLIC HEALTH. *Current Pos:* RETIRED. *Personal Data:* b Iloilo City, Philippines, Dec 29, 21; m 45; c 7. *Educ:* Univ Philippines, MD, 45; Johns Hopkins Univ, MPH, 48, DrPH, 57; Philippine Bd Prev Med & Pub Health, dipl, 56. *Prof Exp:* From instr to prof parasitol, Univ Philippines, 45-67; res assoc & assoc prof, Univ Chicago, 67-69, res assoc & prof parasitol, 69-86. *Concurrent Pos:* USPHS res fel, Dept Microbiol, Univ Chicago, 59-61; mem, Nat Res Coun Philippines, 57-73. *Mem:* Am Soc Trop Med & Hyg. *Res:* Immunity to parasitic diseases with special interest in schistosomiasis. *Mailing Add:* RR 2 Brighton IL 62012

**YOH, JOHN K,** PHYSICS. *Current Pos:* SCIENTIST RES & ADMIN, FERMI NAT ACCELERATOR LAB, 80- *Personal Data:* b Shanghai, China, Oct 9, 44; US citizen; m 84, Hua Zheng; c Kathryn. *Educ:* Cornell Univ, BA, 64; Calif Inst Technol, MS, 66, PhD(physics), 70. *Prof Exp:* Res asst high energy physics, Calif Inst Technol, 67-70; res assoc, Rutgers Univ, 70; NATO fel, Cern Europ Orgn Nuclear Res, 70-71, vis scientist, 71-73; res assoc, Columbia Univ, 73-77, asst prof, 77-80. *Res:* Colliding anti-proton proton project; experimental dileptons and high energy physics; co-discoverer of the b quark and t quark. *Mailing Add:* MS 318 Fermi Nat Accelerator Lab PO Box 500 Batavia IL 60510. *E-Mail:* johny@fnal.gov

**YOHE, CLEON RUSSELL,** ALGEBRA. *Current Pos:* Asst prof, 66-71, ASSOC PROF MATH, WASHINGTON UNIV, 71- *Personal Data:* b New York, NY, July 8, 41; m 66; c 1. *Educ:* Univ Pa, AB, 62; Univ Chicago, MS, 63, PhD(math), 66. *Mem:* AAAS; Am Math Soc. *Res:* Structure theory of rings. *Mailing Add:* Dept Math Washington Univ Box 1146 St Louis MO 63130-4899

**YOHE, JAMES MICHAEL,** COMPUTER SCIENCE, MATHEMATICS. *Current Pos:* DIR, INFO SYSTS & COMPUT SERVS, UNIV NORTHERN IOWA, 89- *Personal Data:* b Delaware, Ohio, June 8, 36; m 61; c 3. *Educ:* DePauw Univ, BA, 57; Univ Wis-Madison, MS, 62, PhD(math), 67. *Prof Exp:* Asst prof math, Math Res Ctr, Univ Wis-Madison, 67-68; asst prof, Pa State Univ, 68-69; proj assoc, Math Res Ctr, Univ Wis-Madison, 69-71, asst dir, 71-75, assoc dir, 75-78; dir acad comput, Univ Wis-Eau Claire, 79-86; dir, computing servs, Bradley Univ, 86-89. *Concurrent Pos:* Lectr, Univ Wis, 71-72, asst prof comput sci, 73-74. *Mem:* Am Math Soc; Math Asn Am; Asn Comput Mach. *Res:* Computer arithmetic; interval arithmetic; computer systems programming; graph theory. *Mailing Add:* Info Systs & Comput Servs Valparaiso Univ Kretzmann Hall Valparaiso IN 46383-6493

**YOHE, THOMAS LESTER,** PROCESS DESIGN, ANALYTIC CHEMISTRY. *Current Pos:* dir res, Philadelphia Suburban Water Co, 81-84, dir res & environ affairs, 84-89, sr mgr, 89-96, VPRES WATER QUAL, PHILADELPHIA SUBURBAN WATER CO, 96- *Personal Data:* b Bryn Mawr, Pa, Oct 30, 47; m 83, Maria Iglesias; c Kathryn. *Educ:* Slippery Rock State Col, BA, 74; Drexel Univ, MS, 76, PhD(environ sci), 82. *Prof Exp:* Teaching asst environ eng, Drexel Univ, 76-77, res asst, 77- 78, res assoc, 78-79; consult water quality, self employed, 79-81. *Concurrent Pos:* Mem, Res Adv Coun, Am Water Works Assoc, 88-91; chmn, Water Utility Coun, Pa Sect, Am Water Works Asn, 91-94; bd dirs, Pa Chap-Nat asn Water Cos, 93-; chmn, PENSERDEL Water Supply Comt, 94-; bd gov, Environ Tech Acad Philadelphia High Sch Acad. *Mem:* Am Chem Soc; Am Water Works Asn; Sigma Xi. *Res:* Optimize existing methods of drinking water treatment and analyses; develop new treatment and analysis methods. *Mailing Add:* 1406 Morstein Rd West Chester PA 19380. *E-Mail:* h2odol@aol.com

**YOHEM, KARIN HUMMELL,** cancer research, human malignant melanoma, for more information see previous edition

**YOHN, DAVID STEWART,** MICROBIOLOGY, VIRAL ONCOLOGY. *Current Pos:* dir, Comprehensive Cancer Ctr, 73-88, PROF VIROL, OHIO STATE UNIV, 69-, DEP DIR, COMPREHENSIVE CANCER CTR, 88- *Personal Data:* b Shelby, Ohio, June 7, 29; m 50, Olivetta K McCoy; c Linda, Kathleen, Joseph, David M & Kristine. *Educ:* Otterbein Col, BS, 51; Ohio State Univ, MS, 53, PhD, 57; Univ Pittsburgh, MPH, 60. *Honors & Awards:* Leadership Award, Leukemia Soc, 85. *Prof Exp:* Res assoc, Univ Pittsburgh, 56-60, asst res prof microbiol, Grad Sch Pub Health, 60-62; res prof, State Univ NY Buffalo, 62-71; assoc cancer res scientist, Roswell Park Mem Inst, 62-69. *Concurrent Pos:* Consult, Nat Cancer Inst, 70-; mem med & sci adv bd & bd trustees, Leukemia Soc Am, 71-; secy gen, Int Asn Comp Res Leukemia & Related Dis, 74-; pres, Ohio Cancer Res Assocs, 81- *Mem:* Am Soc Virol; Am Soc Microbiol; Am Asn Cancer Res; Am Asn Immunol. *Res:* Mammalian and oncogenic viruses; virus host-cell relationships; tumor immunology. *Mailing Add:* 1237 Norwell Dr Columbus OH 43220. *Fax:* 614-293-3333

**YOHO, CLAYTON W,** ORGANIC CHEMISTRY. *Current Pos:* CONSULT, 88- *Personal Data:* b Glen Dale, WVa, Dec 4, 24; m 49, 88, Judith A Clayton; c 3. *Educ:* W Liberty State Col, BSc, 49; Univ Pittsburgh, MSc, 51, PhD(org chem), 57. *Prof Exp:* Jr fel org res, Mellon Inst Indust Res, 51-54; process develop chemist, Merck & Co, Inc, 57-60; res supvr org res, Johnson Wax, 65-71, staff res supvr, 71-88, sr chemist, 60-88, tech investr, 76-88, sci assoc, 82-88, mgr new technol, 83-88. *Mem:* AAAS; Am Chem Soc. *Res:* Process development work involving vitamins B-1, B-12, and gibrel; organic synthesis work in the areas of adhesives, insect repellents, insect attractants and insecticides; product development of oral hygiene products. *Mailing Add:* 1232 Pleasant Valley Dr Baltimore MD 21228-2649

**YOHO, TIMOTHY PRICE,** DEVELOPMENTAL BIOLOGY, ENTOMOLOGY. *Current Pos:* asst prof, 74-77, ASSOC PROF BIOL, LOCK HAVEN COL, 77-, PROF BIOL SCI. *Personal Data:* b Nov 8, 41. *Educ:* West Liberty State Col, BS, 67; WVa Univ, PhD(develop biol & entomol), 72. *Prof Exp:* Fel res, WVa Univ, 72-74. *Concurrent Pos:* Liaison dir, Pa Comt Correspon Creation Evolution Controversy, 80- *Mem:* Sigma Xi; Entom Soc Am; Am Inst Biol Sci. *Res:* Electron microscopy; biochemistry; electrophysiology to study the photodynamic effect of light on dye-fed insects; death in visible light-exposed insects caused by food, drug and cosmetic dyes; danger to consumer and new insecticide development. *Mailing Add:* Dept Biol Lock Haven Univ 401 N Fairview St Lock Haven PA 17745-2390

**YOKE, JOHN THOMAS,** SYNTHETIC INORGANIC & ORGANOMETALLIC CHEMISTRY. *Current Pos:* assoc prof, 64-70, PROF CHEM, ORE STATE UNIV, 70- *Personal Data:* b New York, NY, Feb 27, 28; m 56; c 3. *Educ:* Yale Univ, BS, 48; Univ Mich, MS, 50, PhD(chem), 54. *Prof Exp:* Res chemist, US Army Chem Corp, 54-56, Univ Chicago, 55-56, Procter & Gamble Co, 56-58; instr chem, Univ NC, 58-59; asst prof, Univ Ariz, 59-64. *Concurrent Pos:* Minn Mining & Mfg Co fel, Univ Mich. *Mem:* Am Chem Soc. *Res:* Inorganic synthesis; coordination chemistry; group V compounds; fused salt electrochemistry; oxidation of ligands; catalysis. *Mailing Add:* 13 NW Edgewood Dr Corvallis OR 97330-2305

**YOKEL, FELIX Y,** GEOTECHNICAL ENGINEERING, STRUCTURAL ENGINEERING. *Current Pos:* CONSULT, 93- *Personal Data:* b Vienna, Austria, July 13, 22; US citizen; m 46, Susanne M Braun; c Uri, Yail & Benjamin. *Educ:* Univ Conn, BS, 59, MS, 61, PhD(civil eng), 63. *Honors & Awards:* Silver Medal, Dept Com, 76. *Prof Exp:* Tech dir, Hazbani River Diversion Proj, 50-56; design engr, Griswold Eng, 56-60; chief found engr, John Clarkeson, Consult Engr, 60-63; sr partner, Clarkeson, Clough & Yokel, Consult Engrs, 63-68; res engr, Nat Bur Stand, 68-78, chief geotech eng, 78-85, sr res engr, 85-93. *Concurrent Pos:* Chmn masonry comt, Am Nat Standards Inst; chmn comt found & excavation standards, Am Soc Civil Engrs. *Mem:* Am Soc Civil Engrs. *Mailing Add:* 8208 Fenway Rd Bethesda MD 20817-2731

**YOKEL, ROBERT ALLEN,** NEUROBEHAVIORAL TOXICOLOGY. *Current Pos:* from asst prof to assoc prof, 79-93, PROF PHARMACOL & TOXICOL, COL PHARM, UNIV KY, 93- *Personal Data:* b Rockford, Ill, June 22, 45; m 69, Susan J Brown; c Erich M & Kimberly A. *Educ:* Univ Wis-Madison, BS, 68; Univ Minn, Minneapolis, PhD(pharmacol), 73. *Prof Exp:* Res fel drug abuse, Ctr Res Drug Dependence, Dept Psychol, Concordia Univ, 73-75; asst prof pharmacol, Drug & Poison Info Ctr, Dept Pharmacol, Univ Cincinnati, 75-78, vis asst prof, Col Pharm, 78-79. *Concurrent Pos:* Prin investr, NIH res grants, 80-; NIH res career develop award. *Mem:* Behav Pharmacol Soc; Soc Neurosci; AAAS; Am Soc Pharmacol & Exp Therapeut; Behav Toxicol Soc; Soc Toxicol. *Res:* Toxicology of aluminum; neurobehavioral, pharmacokinetic and other factors defining and contributing to aluminum toxicity; identification of drugs useful in the treatment of aluminum-induced toxicity. *Mailing Add:* Pharm Bldg Univ Ky Med Ctr 907 Rose St Lexington KY 40536-0082. *Fax:* 606-257-7564; *E-Mail:* yokelr@uklans.uky.edu

**YOKELSON, BERNARD J(ULIUS),** ELECTRICAL ENGINEERING, TELEPHONE COMMUNICATIONS. *Current Pos:* CONSULT, 88- *Personal Data:* b Brooklyn, NY, Sept 14, 24; m 46; c 2. *Educ:* Columbia Univ, BS, 48; Polytech Inst Brooklyn, MEE, 54. *Prof Exp:* Mem tech staff transmission & switching, AT&T Bell Labs, 48-54, supvr switching syst & circuit develop, 54-59, head network & syst develop, 59-66, dir, Oper Systs Lab, 66-74, Electronic Power Systs Lab, 74-76, Local Switching Systs Lab, 76-80, Toll Digital Switching Lab, 80-88. *Concurrent Pos:* Dist Mgr, Ga, Serv Corps Retired Execs, 89- *Mem:* Fel Inst Elec & Electronics Engrs; Sigma Xi. *Res:* Telephone communications; electronic switching systems; automation of telephone operator services; digital computers. *Mailing Add:* 2535 The Fifth Fairway Roswell GA 30076. *E-Mail:* berney@mindspring.com

**YOKELSON, HOWARD BRUCE,** SYNTHETIC INORGANIC & ORGANOMETALLIC CHEMISTRY, POLYMER CHEMISTRY. *Current Pos:* res chemist, 87-92, staff chemist, 93-95, RES CHEMIST, AMOCO CHEM CO, 96- *Personal Data:* b Elizabeth, NJ, July 29, 56. *Educ:* Univ Del, BS, 78; Univ Wis-Madison, MS, 80, PhD(chem), 87. *Prof Exp:* Teaching asst, Dept Chem, Univ Wis-Madison, 78-80, rest asst, 83-87; res chemist, Teva Pharmaceut Co, Jerusalem, 81-82. *Concurrent Pos:* Vis lectr chem, N Cent Col, Naperville, Ill, 93- *Mem:* Am Chem Soc; Sigma Xi; AAAS. *Res:* Organosilicon, physical organic and polymer chemistry. *Mailing Add:* Amoco Chem Co PO Box 3011 Naperville IL 60566-7011

**YOKELSON, M(ARSHALL) V(ICTOR),** METALLURGICAL ENGINEERING. *Current Pos:* METALLURGICAL CONSULT, 85- *Personal Data:* b Brooklyn, NY, Nov 18, 18; m 53, Beatrice Eickler; c Joan & Howard. *Educ:* City Col New York, BChE, 38; Polytech Inst Brooklyn, MMetE, 51. *Prof Exp:* Metallurgist, Chance Vought Corp, 47-48; res metallurgist, Gen Cable Corp, 48-56, res supvr, 56-57, chief metallurgist, 57-67, chief metall engr, 67-85. *Concurrent Pos:* Metall consult, 85- *Mem:* Am Soc Metals Int; Am Inst Mining, Metall & Petrol Engrs; Wire Asn Int; fel Am Soc Testing & Mat. *Res:* Work-hardening and annealing characteristics of copper; fabricating methods; laboratory evaluation and service behavior of metallic components of power and communications cables. *Mailing Add:* 65 Sandy Hill Rd Westfield NJ 07090-2826

**YOKLEY, PAUL, JR,** MALACOLOGY. *Current Pos:* Instr biol, 50-53, from asst prof to prof biol, 53-93, EMER PROF ZOOL, UNIV N ALA, 93- *Personal Data:* b Mitchellville, Tenn, Aug 3, 23; m 46; c David & Mary-Jane. *Educ:* George Peabody Col, BS, 49, MA, 50; Ohio State Univ, PhD(zool), 68. *Honors & Awards:* Res Award, Asn Southeastern Biologists, 70; State Conserv Educr Year, Ala Wildlife Fedn, 72. *Concurrent Pos:* Sci consult, Colbert Co Schs, 67-68; Tenn Game & Fish Comn res grant, 69-72; fisheries scientist, Am Fisheries Soc; Am Fisheries res scientist fel; consult, Tenn Valley Authority, 71-; res grants, USDA, 73, 77, 78 & Corps of Engrs, 76, 78, 80, 81, 84, Tenn Wildlife Resources Agency, 87, & numerous others. *Mem:* Soc Syst Zool; Am Malacol Union. *Res:* Life history and ecology of freshwater mussels; ecology of the freshwater mussels in the Tennessee River. *Mailing Add:* 3698 Chisholm Rd Florence AL 35630

**YOKOSAWA, AKIHIKO,** HIGH ENERGY PHYSICS. *Current Pos:* physicist, 59-70, SR PHYSICIST, ARGONNE NAT LAB, 70- *Personal Data:* b Kofu, Japan, Nov 19, 27; US citizen; m 57; c 3. *Educ:* Tohoku Univ, Japan, BS, 51; Univ Cincinnati, MS, 53; Ohio State Univ, PhD(physics), 57. *Prof Exp:* Assoc prof physics, Ill State Univ, 57-59. *Mem:* Fel Am Phys Soc. *Res:* Elementary particle physics; experimental physics on polarization effects. *Mailing Add:* Argonne Nat Lab 9700 S Cass Ave Argonne IL 60439. *E-Mail:* ay@hep.anl.gov

**YOKOYAMA, MELVIN T,** NUTRITION, MICROBIOLOGY. *Current Pos:* asst prof, 75-80, ASSOC PROF ANIMAL NUTRIT, MICH STATE UNIV, 80- *Personal Data:* b Honolulu, Hawaii, Jan 22, 43. *Educ:* Univ Hawaii, BS, 66; Univ Ill, MS, 69, PhD(nutrit sci), 71. *Prof Exp:* Res asst dairy nutrit, Univ Ill, 66-69 & Nutrit Sci Prog, 66-71; res assoc nutrit biochem, Wash State Univ, 71-75. *Mem:* Am Soc Animal Sci; AAAS; Am Inst Nutrit; Sigma Xi. *Res:* Nutrition-microbiology. *Mailing Add:* Dept Animal Sci Mich State Univ 113 Anthony Hall East Lansing MI 48824-1225. *Fax:* 517-353-1699

**YOKOYAMA, SHOZO,** population genetics, molecular evolution, for more information see previous edition

**YOLDAS, BULENT ERTURK,** CERAMICS, GLASS TECHNOLOGY. *Current Pos:* FEL SCIENTIST MAT SCI, GLASS RES CTR, PPG INDUST, INC, 84- *Personal Data:* b Turkey, Feb 19, 38; US citizen; m; c 2. *Educ:* Ohio State Univ, BCerE, 63, MS, 64, PhD(glass & refractory), 66. *Honors & Awards:* George Westinghouse Award, 84. *Prof Exp:* Sr engr mat sci, Owens-Ill Tech Ctr, 66-74; fel scientist mat sci, Westinghouse Res Labs, 74-84. *Mem:* Fel Am Ceramic Soc; Sigma Xi. *Res:* Coating technology for electronic and consumer products; formation of glass and ceramic materials by chemical polymerization; high surface area; catalytic materials; porous ceramic, metal-organic compounds; optics. *Mailing Add:* 1605 Jamestown Pl Pittsburgh PA 15235

**YOLE, RAYMOND WILLIAM,** PETROLEUM GEOLOGY, CORDILLERAN GEOLOGY. *Current Pos:* from asst prof to assoc prof geol, Carleton Univ, 63-82, chmn dept, 67-70, prof, 82-92, ADJ PROF EARTH SCI, CARLETON UNIV, 92- *Personal Data:* b Middlesbrough, Eng, Feb 21, 27; Can citizen; m 57; c 4. *Educ:* Univ NB, BSc, 47; Johns Hopkins Univ, MA, 58; Univ BC, PhD(geol), 65. *Prof Exp:* Geologist, Calif Stand Co, Alta, 47-51, asst to vpres explor, 51-53, dist stratigr, 53-56. *Concurrent Pos:* Vis res geologist, Univ Reading, 70-71; assoc ed, Can Soc Petrol Geol, 74-77; vis prof, Fed Univ Pernambuco, Recife, Brazil, 76, Victoria Univ Wellington, NZ, 95. *Mem:* Can Soc Petrol Geol; fel Geol Asn Can; Am Asn Petrol Geol; Int Asn Sedimentologists. *Res:* Petroleum geology of Canadian offshore basins; stratigraphy and tectonic history of Canadian cordillera; Paleozoic stratigraphy and sedimentology. *Mailing Add:* Carleton Univ Dept Earth Sci 1125 Colonel By Dr Ottawa ON K1S 5B6 Can. *Fax:* 613-520-4490; *E-Mail:* rwyole@klutu.ca

**YOLKEN, HOWARD THOMAS,** MATERIALS PROCESSING, NONDESTRUCTIVE EVALUATION & NUCLEAR WASTE MGMT. *Current Pos:* GUEST RES, NAT INST STAND & TECHNOL, 96- *Personal Data:* b Birmingham, Ala, Jan 29, 38; m 67, Joan Pursell; c Lauren E (Dell). *Educ:* Univ Md, BS, 60, PhD(mat sci), 70. *Honors & Awards:* Bronze Medal, US Dept of Com, 81; Stichter Technol Award, Nat Inst Stand & Technol, 93. *Prof Exp:* Res metallurgist, Nat Inst Stand & Technol, 60-70, dept chief, Off Stand Ref Mat, 71-75, chief, Off Measurements Nuclear Technol, 76-81, chief, Off Nondestructive Eval, 82-89, chief, Off Intelligent Processing Mat, 89-93; mgr, Mat Processing Prog, Sci Appln Int Corp, 94-95. *Concurrent Pos:* Mem, Nat Mat Adv Bd Comts, Life Cycle Eng, Nat Res Coun, 68-88 & Indust Energy Conserv, 87-; mem tech adv comt nuclear safeguards, Int Atomic Energy Asn, 78 & 79; founding chmn, Gordon Res Conf Nondestructive Eval, 83; sci fel, US Cong, 84-85; chmn, Working Group Intel Processing Mat, White House Off Sci & Technol Policy, 85-93; founding ed-in-chief Res Nondestructive Eval, J Am Soc Nondestructive Testing, 88-93; bd dir & exec comt & chmn res coun, Am Soc Nondestructive Eval, 93-94; trustee, Fed Mat Soc, 94-96. *Res:* Fostered, at the national level, the concept and pursuit of intelligent processing of materials; directed major research effort on nondestructive evaluation for real-time materials process control; pioneered research in the application of ellipsometry to clean surfaces in ultrahigh vacuum. *Mailing Add:* 15400 Edward's Ferry Rd Poolesville MD 20837

**YOLLES, STANLEY FAUSST,** MEDICINE, PSYCHIATRY. *Current Pos:* prof & chmn dept, 71-81, psychiatrist in chief, Univ Hosp, 80-81, EMER PROF PSYCHIAT & BEHAV SCI, STATE UNIV NY, STONYBROOK, 81- *Personal Data:* b New York, NY, Apr 19, 19; m 42; c 2. *Educ:* Brooklyn Col, AB, 39; Harvard Univ, AM, 40; NY Univ, MD, 50; Johns Hopkins Univ, MPH, 57. *Prof Exp:* Parasitologist, Sector Malaria Lab, US Dept Army, 41-42, assoc dir, 42-44; intern, USPHS Hosp, Staten Island, NY, 50-51, resident psychiat, Lexington, Ky, 51-54; staff psychiatrist, Ment Health Study Ctr, NIMH, 54-55, from assoc dir to dir, 55-60, from assoc dir to dep dir extramural progs, 60-63, from dep dir to dir, NIMH, 63-70, assoc adminr for ment health, US Dept Health, Educ & Welfare, 68-70. *Concurrent Pos:* Clin prof psychiat, George Washington Univ, 67-71; spec consult, NY City Bd Educ; mem, Prof Adv Bd, Int Comt Against Ment Illness, 68-, Nat Adv Panel, Am Jewish Comt, 69-72, Expert Adv Panel Ment Health, WHO, 69-81, Med Adv Comt, Am Joint Distribution Comt, 70-; trustee, NY Sch Psychiat; sr consult, Southside Hosp, Bay Shore, South Oaks Hosp, Amityville & Nassau County Med Ctr, NY. *Mem:* AAAS; fel Am Psychiat Asn; fel Am Pub Health Asn; fel Am Col Psychiat; fel NY Acad Sci. *Res:* Community mental health; mental health administration; epidemiology of mental health. *Mailing Add:* Two Soundview Ct Stony Brook NY 11790

**YOLLICK, BERNARD LAWRENCE,** ANATOMY & SURGERY CANCER, HEAD & NECK GROSS ANATOMY & OTOLARYNGOLOY. *Current Pos:* ASST PROF OTOLARYNGOL, UNIV TEX HEALTH SCI CTR DALLAS, 67- *Personal Data:* b Toronto, Ont, Mar 24, 22; nat US; m 4, Liny L Pajgin; c 2. *Educ:* Univ Toronto, MD, 45; Am Bd Surg, dipl, 57; Am Bd Otolaryngol, dipl, 67. *Prof Exp:* Instr anat, Col Med, Univ Sask, 47-49; clin asst prof, Col Med, Baylor Univ, Houston, 54-60; clin asst prof otolaryngol, SW Med Sch, 64. *Concurrent Pos:* Fel surg, Am Cancer Soc, 53-54; consult, Houston Pulmonary Cytol Proj, 59 & Vet Admin Hosp, Dallas; asst prof, Dent Sch, Univ Tex, Houston, 54-60; adj assoc prof anat, Baylor Col Dent, Dallas, 89- *Mem:* Soc Human Genetics; Am Asn Anat; AMA; fel Am Col Surg; Soc Head & Neck Surgeons. *Res:* Induction of bone tumors in animals using heavy metals; experimental surgery in animals. *Mailing Add:* 4229 Bobbitt Dr Dallas TX 75229-4136

**YON, E(UGENE) T,** ELECTRICAL ENGINEERING, SOLID STATE ELECTRONICS. *Current Pos:* PRES & CHIEF OPER OFFICER, BAILEY CONTROLS INC, 91-; GROUP VPRES, ELSAG BAILEY INC, 93- *Personal Data:* b Mt Hope, WVa, Dec 29, 36; m 60; c 2. *Educ:* Univ Cincinnati, EE, 60; Case Western Reserve Univ, MS, 62, PhD, 65. *Prof Exp:* Sr staff engr, Electronics Div, Avco Corp, 65-67; asst prof elec eng, Case Western Reserve Univ, 67-70, assoc dir solid state electronics labs, 67-77, assoc prof, 70-77; vpres, Combustion Eng, Inc, 84-88; vpres, Booz, Allen & Hamilton, Inc, 78-83 & 88-91. *Concurrent Pos:* Consult, Avco Corp, 64-65 & 67-68, Babcock & Wilcox Corp, 67-, Am Radiation Res, Inc, 67-, Keithley Instruments, Inc, 68- & Solon Assocs, Inc, 68- *Mem:* Inst Elec & Electronics Engrs. *Res:* Semiconductor devices; biomedical engineering; technology, assessment and forecasting; process control. *Mailing Add:* Bailey Control Co 29801 Euclid Ave Wickliffe OH 44092

**YONAN, EDWARD E,** ORGANIC SYNTHESIS. *Current Pos:* RES ASSOC, G D SEARLE & CO, 86- *Personal Data:* b Beirut, Lebanon, Apr 15, 43; US citizen; m 72; c 2. *Educ:* Univ Wis, BS, 70. *Prof Exp:* Chemist, Hodag Chem Corp, 72-73 & Velsicol Chem Corp, 73-76; sr chemist, PPG Industs, Inc, 76-80; consult, 80-86. *Mem:* Am Chem Soc; Fire Retardant Chem Asn. *Res:* Organic synthesis and process development of agricultural chemicals such as herbicides, pesticides, phosgene, and related chemistry, carbonates, chloroformates, isocyanutes, and fire retardant additives. *Mailing Add:* 1369 New London Ct Carol Stream IL 60188-3393

**YONAS, GEROLD,** PULSED POWER, INERTIAL FUSION. *Current Pos:* div supvr, Sandia Labs, 72-73, dept mgr fusion res, 73-78, dir pulsed energy progs, 78-89, DIR LAB DEVELOP, SANDIA LABS, 89- *Personal Data:* b Cleveland, Ohio, Dec 8, 39; m 61; c 2. *Educ:* Cornell Univ, BS, 62; Calif Inst Technol, PhD(eng sci), 66. *Prof Exp:* Physicist & mgr electron beam res dept, Physics Int Co, 67-72. *Concurrent Pos:* Mem adv bd, Am for Energy Independence; assoc ed, J Fusion Energy. *Mem:* Am Phys Soc; Am Nuclear Soc; Sigma Xi. *Res:* Fusion; intense electron and ion beams; pulsed high voltage technology; inertial confinement fusion; laser technology; plasma physics; high pressure physics. *Mailing Add:* 5005 Rio Grande Lane NW Albuquerque NM 87107

**YONCE, LLOYD ROBERT,** PHYSIOLOGY. *Current Pos:* from asst prof to assoc prof, 57-85, PROF PHYSIOL, SCH MED, UNIV NC, CHAPEL HILL, 85- *Personal Data:* b Roscoe, Mont, Sept 27, 24; m 48, Mae F Knebel; c Kathleen & Mark. *Educ:* Mont State Col, BS, 49; Oregon State Univ, MS, 52; Univ Mich, PhD(physiol), 55. *Prof Exp:* Instr physiol, Ore State Univ, 51-52; instr, Med Sch, Univ Mich, 55-56. *Concurrent Pos:* Fel, Med Col Ga, 56-57; USPHS spec fel physiol, Univ Gothenburg. *Mem:* Fedn Am Soc Exp Biol; Am Microcirculation Soc. *Res:* Cardiovascular physiology; neurophysiology; physiology of diving animals. *Mailing Add:* 118 Hunters Ridge Rd Chapel Hill NC 27514. *E-Mail:* yonce@med.unc.edu

**YONDA, ALFRED WILLIAM,** MATHEMATICS. *Current Pos:* SOFTWARE SYSTS ENG, YONDA SOFTWARE SYSTS CONSULT, 91- *Personal Data:* b Cambridge, Mass, Aug 10, 19; m 49, 75, Peggy A Terrel; c Nancy, Kathryn, Elizabeth & John. *Educ:* Univ Ala, BS, 52, MA, 54. *Prof Exp:* Mathematician, Rocket Res, Redstone Arsenal, Ala, 53 & US Army Ballistic Res Labs, Aberdeen Proving Ground, Md, 54-56; instr math, Temple Univ, 56-57; assoc scientist, Res & Adv Develop Div, Avco Corp, 57-59; sr proj mem tech staff, Radio Corp Am, 59-66; mgr, Comput Anal & Prog Dept, Raytheon Corp, Bedford, 66-70, prin engr, Missile Systs Div, 70-73; mgr, Systs Anal & Prog Dept, Eastern Div, GTE Sylvania, Needham, Mass, 73-76, software eng, Atlantic Oper, 77-82, sr mem tech staff, Commun Systs Div, 83-87, sr mem tech staff, C3 Sector, Govt Systs Corp, 87-91. *Concurrent Pos:* Hon fel, Advan Level Telecom Training Ctr, Ghaziabad, India. *Mem:* AAAS; Inst Elec & Electronics Engrs Comput Soc; Math Asn Am; NY Acad Sci. *Res:* Computer systems analysis; simulation; communications systems analysis; software systems design; numerical analysis; telecommunications systems design. *Mailing Add:* 12 Sunset Dr Medway MA 02053

**YONEDA, KOKICHI,** ELECTROMICROSCOPY, CELL BIOLOGY. *Current Pos:* PROF PATH, UNIV KY, 86- *Educ:* Mara Med Col, Japan, MD, 68. *Mailing Add:* Lab Serv 113CD Vet Admin Med Ctr Lexington KY 40511-1093

**YONETANI, TAKASHI,** BIOCHEMISTRY, BIOPHYSICS. *Current Pos:* from asst prof to assoc prof phys biochem, 64-68, PROF PHYS BIOCHEM, DEPT BIOCHEM & BIOPHYS, UNIV PA, 68- *Personal Data:* b Kagawa-ken, Japan, Aug 6, 30; US citizen; m 58; c 1. *Educ:* Osaka Univ, BA, 53, PhD(biochem), 60. *Hon Degrees:* MD, Univ Umea, Sweden, 84. *Prof Exp:* Res fel biochem, Johnson Found, Univ Pa, 58-61; Swedish Med Res Coun res fel, Nobel Med Inst, Stockholm, 62-64. *Concurrent Pos:* USPHS career develop award, 67-72. *Mem:* AAAS; Am Soc Biol Chemists; Am Chem Soc; Biophys Soc. *Res:* Purification, crystallization and characterization of cytochrome oxidase, alcohol dehydrogenase and cytochrome c peroxidase; determination of structure and function of these enzymes by spectrophotometry, electron spin resonance and x-ray diffraction techniques; heart disease; artificial hemoglobin; metalloporphyrin synthesis. *Mailing Add:* Dept Biochem & Biophys Univ Pa C601 Richards Bldg Philadelphia PA 19104-6089. *Fax:* 215-898-8559

**YONG, RAYMOND N,** ENVIRONMENT & GEOTECHNICAL ENGINEERING, WASTE MANAGEMENT. *Current Pos:* From asst prof to assoc prof civil eng, 59-65, prof civil eng & appl mech, 65-73, WILLIAM SCOTT PROF CIVIL ENG & APPL MECH, MCGILL UNIV, 73-, DIR,

GEOTECH RES CTR, 76- *Personal Data:* b Singapore, Apr 10, 29; Can citizen; m 61, Florence Lechensky; c Raymond T & Christopher T. *Educ:* Washington & Jefferson Col, BA, 50; Mass Inst Technol, BSc, 52; Purdue Univ, MSc, 54; McGill Univ, MEng, 58, PhD(soil mech), 60. *Honors & Awards:* Izaak Walton Killam Mem Prize, Can Coun, 85; Chevalier de l'ordre nat du Quebec, 85; Charles B Dudley Prize, Am Soc Testing & Mat; R F Legget Award, Can Geotech Soc, 93. *Concurrent Pos:* Adj prof civil eng, Univ Fla, Gainesville, 84; assoc mem, Ctr Med, Ethics & Law, McGill Univ, 90; adj res prof civil eng, Carleton Univ, Ottawa, Ont, Can, 90. *Mem:* Am Soc Civil Engrs; Brit Inst Civil Engrs; Am Soc Testing & Mat; Soc Rheol; Int Soc Terrain-Vehicle Systs (pres, 93); fel Engr Inst Can; fel Royal Soc Can; fel Can Soc Civil Eng. *Res:* Soil mechanics; soil physics; nonlinear mechanics; plasticity; geo-environmental research technology. *Mailing Add:* McGill Univ Geotech Res Ctr 817 Sherbrooke St W Montreal PQ H3A 2K6 Can

**YONG, YAN,** STOCHASTIC EARTHQUAKE MODELING, WAVE PROPAGATION IN STRUCTURAL NETWORKS. *Current Pos:* res assoc, 87-88, asst prof, 88-92, ASSOC PROF, FLA ATLANTIC UNIV, 92- *Personal Data:* b Wuhan, China, July 23, 55; m 87. *Educ:* Wuhan Inst Bldg Mat, dipl eng mech, 82; Univ Ill, Urbana-Champaign, MS, 83, PhD (aerospace eng), 87. *Prof Exp:* Res asst, Univ Ill, 82-84. *Concurrent Pos:* NSF presidential young investr award, 90; vis scientist, Wright-Patterson AFB, 90. *Mem:* Am Soc Civil Eng; Am Inst Aeronaut & Astronaut; Acoust Soc Am. *Res:* Dynamics and control of large-scale complex structures; stochastic modeling of earthquake ground motions; dynamic response and control of civil structures under earthquake and wind excitations; random vibration; earthquake eng; author of nine publications. *Mailing Add:* Dept Ocean Eng Fla Atlantic Univ Boca Raton FL 33431-6498

**YONGE, KEITH A,** PSYCHIATRY. *Current Pos:* prof & head dept, 55-75, EMER PROF PSYCHIAT, UNIV ALTA, 75- *Personal Data:* b London, Eng, June 22, 10; m 47, Jane Beatty; c 4. *Educ:* McGill Univ, MD, CM, 48; Univ London, dipl psychol med, 52. *Prof Exp:* Mem staff psychiat, Med Res Coun, Eng, 51-52; dir, Ment Health Clin, Can, 52-54; from asst prof to assoc prof psychiat, Univ Sask, 55-57, clin dir, Univ Hosp, 55-57. *Concurrent Pos:* Can Coun leave fel, 71-72. *Mem:* Psychiat Asn; Can Med Asn; Can Psychiat Asn; Can Ment Health Asn. *Res:* Basic and clinical psychiatry; phenomenology of depression; cognitive effects of cannabis; nature of human aggression. *Mailing Add:* 4345 Kingscote Rd RR 3 Cobble Hill BC V0R 1L0 Can

**YONGUE, WILLIAM HENRY,** PROTOZOOLOGY, AQUATIC ECOLOGY. *Current Pos:* from instr to asst prof, 70-73, assoc prof, 73-85, ADJ PROF ZOOL, VA POLYTECH INST & STATE UNIV, 86- *Personal Data:* b Charlotte, NC, Aug 21, 26; m 48; c 1. *Educ:* Johnson C Smith Univ, BS, 49; Univ Mich, MS, 62; Va Polytech Inst & State Univ, PhD(zool), 72. *Prof Exp:* Head dept sci, West Charlotte High Sch, 59-70. *Concurrent Pos:* Res assoc & proj scientist, Univ Mich Biol Sta, 69-75; regional sci coordr, NC State Dept Pub Inst. *Mem:* Soc Protozoologists; Nat Sci Teachers Asn; Sigma Xi; fel AAAS; Am Micros Soc. *Res:* The ecology of freshwater protozoans using polyurethane foam substrates for sampling and as microhabitats; lentic plankton dynamics; effects of heat and toxicants on protists; intracellular parasitism effects in blood of water snakes; science education. *Mailing Add:* 6101 Vernedale Rd Charlotte NC 28212

**YONKE, THOMAS RICHARD,** ENTOMOLOGY, SYSTEMATICS. *Current Pos:* from asst prof to assoc prof, 67-77, PROF ENTOM, UNIV MO-COLUMBIA, 77-, DIR, ENTOM RES MUS, 78-, CHMN DEPT, 80- *Personal Data:* b Kankakee, Ill, Nov 30, 39; m 63; c 3. *Educ:* Loras Col, BS, 62; Univ Wis, Madison, MS, 64, PhD(entom), 67. *Prof Exp:* Instr entom, Univ Wis, Madison, 66-67. *Concurrent Pos:* Pres grad fac senate, Univ Mo-Columbia, 80-81. *Mem:* Entom Soc Am; Soc Syst Zool; AAAS; Sigma Xi. *Res:* Biology and systematics of Hemiptera; taxonomy of immature Heteroptera; biology of Cicadellidae; taxonomy of Coreidae. *Mailing Add:* 400 Longfellow Lane Columbia MO 65203

**YONKERS, ANTHONY J,** SURGERY, OTORHINOLARYNGOLOGY. *Current Pos:* From instr to assoc prof otorhinolaryngol, 68-72, vchmn dept, 72-74, 72-76, PROF OTOLARYNGOL & MAXILLOFACIAL SURG, UNIV NEBR MED CTR, 76-, CHMN DEPT, 74- *Personal Data:* b Muskegon, Mich, June 17, 38; c 4. *Educ:* Univ Mich, MD, 63. *Concurrent Pos:* Guest ed, Ear, Nose & Throat J, 81; prin investr, Univ Nebr Med Ctr, 83-84 & 85-; comdr, Mil & Hosp Order St Lazarus, Jerusalem, 84-; mil consult to surg gen, 84-, colonel flight surgeon, Med Corps, US Air Force & Dept Nebr Reserve Officers Asn US, 85. *Mem:* Am Acad Otolaryngol; fel Am Col Surg; Am Acad Facial Plastic & Reconstructive Surg; Am Acad Otolaryngic Allergy; Am Broncho-Esophagological Asn; Am Asn Cosmetic Surgeons; Triological Soc; Aerospace Med Asn; AMA. *Res:* Study of interferon in the treatment of juvenile papillomatosis; evaluation of new methods of management of children with clefts of the lip and palate; recognition and management of sleep apnea. *Mailing Add:* Dept Otolaryngol Univ Nebr Med Sch Oto-HNS 600 S 42nd Omaha NE 68198-1225

**YONUSCHOT, GENE R,** NUTRITION. *Current Pos:* ASSOC DEAN BASIC SCI, NEW ENG COL OSTEOP MED, 78- *Personal Data:* b Brooklyn, NY, Oct 29, 36; m 66; c 3. *Educ:* Calif Polytech Inst, BS, 63; Univ Mo-Columbia, PhD(biochem), 69. *Prof Exp:* Instr biochem, Univ NC, 69-71; asst prof biochem, George Mason Univ, 71-76; chmn, Biochem Dept, WVa Sch Osteop Med, 76-78. *Res:* Acidic chromosomal proteins and t-RNA in relation to the control of cell division and differentiation; medical school curriculum; lanthanide series elements in biology. *Mailing Add:* Dept Biochem & Nutrit New Eng Col Osteop Med 605 Pool Rd Biddeford ME 04005-9524

**YOO, BONG YUL,** PLANT PHYSIOLOGY, CELL BIOLOGY. *Current Pos:* from asst prof to assoc prof, 66-77, PROF BIOL, UNIV NB, FREDERICTON, 77- *Personal Data:* b Pusan, Korea, June 30, 35; Can citizen. *Educ:* Seoul Nat Univ, BSc, 58; Okla State Univ, MSc, 61; Univ Calif, Berkeley, PhD(bot), 65. *Prof Exp:* Nat Res Coun Can fel, 65-66. *Mem:* Am Soc Cell Biol; Am Soc Plant Physiol; Bot Soc Am; Can Soc Cell Biol; Sigma Xi. *Res:* Biogenesis of plant cell organelles. *Mailing Add:* Dept Biol Univ NB Fredericton NB E3B 6E1 Can. *Fax:* 506-453-3583

**YOO, MAN HYONG,** SOLID STATE PHYSICS, APPLIED MECHANICS. *Current Pos:* res staff scientist, Metals & Ceramics Div, SR RES STAFF & TASK LEADER, OAK RIDGE NAT LAB, 79- *Personal Data:* b Seoul, Korea, June 27, 35; m 60, Sung J Choo; c Phillip, Terry & Christopher. *Educ:* Mich State Univ, BS, 60, MS, 62, PhD(phys metall), 66. *Honors & Awards:* Dept Energy/Basic Energy Sci Award, 91; Humboldt Res Award, 93. *Prof Exp:* Res assoc, mech metall, Mich State Univ, 66-67. *Concurrent Pos:* Guest scientist, Nuclear Res Ctr, Julich, WGer, 84-85; vis prof, Tohoku Univ, Sendai, Japan, 88-89, Max-Planck Inst, Dusseldorf, Ger & Tech Univ, Hamburg, WGer. *Mem:* Mineral, Metals & Mat Soc; fel Am Soc Metals Int; Mat Res Soc; Sigma Xi; Am Asn Advan Sci. *Res:* Mechanical properties of materials; dislocation theory of plastic deformation and fracture; kinetic theory of lattice defects and irradiation effects; small angle neutron scattering; high-temperature intermetallic ordered alloys. *Mailing Add:* Oak Ridge Nat Lab PO Box 2008 Oak Ridge TN 37831-6115. *Fax:* 423-574-7659; *E-Mail:* oo@ornl.gov

**YOO, SEUNG HYUN,** BIOCHEMISTRY, MOLECULAR BIOLOGY. *Current Pos:* INVESTR, LAB CELLULAR BIOL, NIH, 91- *Personal Data:* b Busan, Korea, Nov 15, 50; US citizen; m 77, H Sue; c Donald, Timothy & Stephen. *Educ:* Seoul Nat Univ, BS, 73, MS, 75; Univ Tex, Austin, PhD(biochem), 80. *Prof Exp:* Res assoc, Clayton Found Biochem Inst, Univ Tex, Austin, 80-82; assoc prof, Dept Biochem, Hang Yang Univ, 84-87. *Mem:* Am Soc Biochem & Molecular Biol; Biophys Soc; AAAS. *Res:* Biochemistry of calcium storage protein chromogranin; calcium mobilization mechanism of inositol, 1,4,5 - trisphosphate sensitive calcium store. *Mailing Add:* NIDCD NIH 5 Res Ctr Rm 2A37 Rockville MD 20850-3227. *Fax:* 301-480-3242; *E-Mail:* seanhy@helix.nih.gov

**YOO, TAI-JUNE,** IMMUNOLOGY, INTERNAL MEDICINE. *Current Pos:* at DEPT MED, DIV ALLERGY & IMMUNOL, UNIV TENN HEALTH SCI CTR. *Personal Data:* b Seoul, Korea, Mar 7, 35; US citizen; m 63; c 3. *Educ:* Seoul Nat Univ, MD, 59; Univ Calif, Berkeley, PhD(med physics), 63. *Prof Exp:* Teaching asst biophys, Div Med Physics, Univ Calif, Berkeley, 60-61, res asst, Lawrence Radiation Lab, 61-63; asst in med, Sch Med, Wash Univ, 63-66; sr cancer res scientist, Roswell Park Mem Inst, 66-68; res prof biol, Niagara Univ, 68-69; asst prof med, Col Med, Univ Iowa, 72-75, assoc prof, 75-80. *Concurrent Pos:* NIH fel immunol, Wash Univ, 65-66; from intern to asst resident, Barnes Hosp, St Louis, Mo, 63-65; assoc resident, Sch Med, NY Univ, 68-69; clin investr, Vet Admin Hosp, Iowa City, Iowa, 72-75. *Mem:* AAAS; Biophys Soc; Am Asn Immunol; NY Acad Sci; Am Fedn Clin Res. *Res:* Molecular and cellular biology of immune phenomena; immunologic and allergic disorders; mechanism of autoimmunity of cochlea and hearing loss. *Mailing Add:* Dept Med Microbiol Immunol Univ Tenn Med Gp 956 Court Ave Rm H300 Memphis TN 38163. *Fax:* 901-528-5854

**YOOD, BERTRAM,** MATHEMATICAL ANALYSIS. *Current Pos:* prof, 72-82, EMER PROF MATH, PA STATE UNIV, 82- *Personal Data:* b Bayonne, NJ, Jan 6, 17; m 44; c Robert, Janet & Arthur. *Educ:* Yale Univ, BS, 38, PhD(math), 47; Calif Inst Technol, MS, 39. *Prof Exp:* From instr to asst prof math, Cornell Univ, 47-53; from asst prof to prof, Univ Ore, 53-72. *Concurrent Pos:* Vis assoc prof, Univ Calif, 56-57; vis res assoc, Yale Univ, 58-59; mem, Inst Adv Study, 61-62; vis prof, Univ Edinburgh, 69-70, Weizmann Inst, Israel, 78-79, Kans State Univ, 84-85, Reed Col, 85-86, Univ Ottawa, 87. *Mem:* Am Math Soc; Sigma Xi. *Res:* Banach algebra; Banach spaces; analysis. *Mailing Add:* 326 McAllister Pa State Univ University Park PA 16802

**YOON, DO YEUNG,** POLYMER CHEMISTRY. *Current Pos:* RES SCIENTIST POLYMER MAT, RES LAB, IBM CORP, 75- *Personal Data:* b Inchon, Korea, Jan 22, 47; m 71; c 3. *Educ:* Seoul Nat Univ, BS, 69; Univ Mass, MS, 71, PhD(polymer sci), 73. *Prof Exp:* Res assoc chem, Stanford Univ, 73-75. *Mem:* Am Chem Soc; Am Phys Soc. *Res:* Conformational statistics and conformation-dependent properties of polymers; morphology and properties of polymers. *Mailing Add:* IBM Almaden Res Ctr E1/080 650 Harry Rd San Jose CA 95120. *Fax:* 408-927-3310

**YOON, HYO SUB,** BIOENGINEERING, BIOMEDICAL ENGINEERING. *Current Pos:* NIH trainee biophysics, 71-74, SR RES ASSOC, DEPT BIOMED ENG, RENSSELAER POLYTECH INST, 74- *Personal Data:* b Kyungbook, Korea, Apr 17, 35; US citizen; m 72. *Educ:* Seoul Nat Univ, BS, 59; Univ Cincinnati, MS, 65; Pa State Univ, PhD(solid state sci), 71. *Prof Exp:* Res metallurgist, Sci Res Inst, Ministry Nat Defense, Korea, 59-62; res fel metall eng, Univ Cincinnati, 62-66; res asst solid state sci, Pa State Univ, 66-71. *Mem:* Am Soc Metals; Am Ceramic Soc; Inst Elec & Electronics Engrs; Am Crystallog Asn; Am Phys Soc; Sigma Xi. *Res:* Biomedical ultrasonics; bone biomechanics; crystal physics; biomaterials; dental materials; nondestructive testing; elasticity; calcified tissues; animal ultrasound. *Mailing Add:* Va Med Ctr Biomed Eng 79 Middleville Rd Northport NY 11768

**YOON, JI-WON,** DIABETES MELLITUS, VIRUS-INDUCED DISEASES. *Current Pos:* staff fel, 74-76, sr staff fel, 76-78, SR INVESTR VIROL, NIH, MD, 78- *Personal Data:* b Kangjin, Korea, Mar 28, 39; US citizen; m 68; c 2. *Educ:* Chosun Univ, Korea, BS, 59, MS, 61; Univ Conn, Storrs, MS, 71, PhD(path), 73. *Prof Exp:* Asst prof cell biol, Chosun Univ, 65-67, assoc prof microbiol, Med Sch, 67-69; teaching asst, Univ Conn, Storrs, 69-73; res fel pathobiol, Sloan-Kettering Cancer Inst, 73-74. *Concurrent Pos:* Adj fac, Med Sch, Howard Univ, 79-82. *Mem:* Am Soc Microbiol; Genetics Soc Am; Tissue Culture Asn Am; NY Acad Sci; AAAS. *Res:* Role of viruses and autoantibodies in the pathogenesis of insulin dependent diabetes mellitus; cultivation and characterization of human, non-human primate and murine pancreatic beta cell cultures in microculture system; virus and cell interaction in the disease process in human and animal. *Mailing Add:* Diabetes Res Ctr Fac Med Univ Calgary 3330 Hosp Dr NW Calgary AB T2N 4N1 Can

**YOON, JONG SIK,** GENETICS, EVOLUTION. *Current Pos:* assoc prof, 78-82, PROF BIOL SCI, BOWLING GREEN STATE UNIV, 82- *Personal Data:* b Suwon, Korea, Jan 25, 37; US citizen; m 62; c 3. *Educ:* Yonsei Univ, Korea, BS, 61; Univ Tex, Austin, MA, 64, PhD(genetics), 65. *Honors & Awards:* Young Scientist Award, Int Union Against Cancer, 70. *Prof Exp:* Res scientist assoc IV, Univ Tex, Austin, 62-65; res assoc oncol, M D Anderson Hosp, Univ Tex, 66-68; asst prof genetics & cytol, Yonsei Univ, Korea, 68-71; res scientist IV & V genetics, 71-74, instr cell biol, 74-75, res scientist genetics, Univ Tex, Austin, 75-78. *Concurrent Pos:* Dir, Nat Drosophila Species Resource Ctr, 82- *Mem:* Genetics Soc Am; Soc Study Evolution; AAAS; Sigma Xi; Am Genetic Asn; Environ Mutagen Soc; Am Soc Naturalists. *Res:* Cytogenetics; mutation; oncogenetics; radiation genetics; genome organization, speciation and evolution of Drosophila and other species; genic balance between euchromatin and heterochromatin of chromosomes; sister chromatid exchange of mammalian and human chromosomes. *Mailing Add:* Dept Biol Sci Bowling Green State Univ 1001 E Wooster St Bowling Green OH 43403-0001

**YOON, KWANGSUN PAUL,** MULTIPLE CRITERIA DECISION ANALYSIS. *Current Pos:* From asst prof to assoc prof, 80-92, PROF DECISION SCI, FAIRLEIGH DICKINSON UNIV, 93-, CHAIRPERSON, DEPT MGT & MKT, COL BUS ADMIN, 95- *Personal Data:* b Seoul, Korea, July 19, 47; US citizen; m 76, Soon Y Park; c Justin & Mark. *Educ:* Seoul Nat Univ, BS, 71; Kans State Univ, MS, 77, PhD(opers res), 80. *Concurrent Pos:* Vis assoc prof, Kans State Univ, 86-87; dep chmn, Dept Information Systs, Col Bus, 90-93. *Mem:* Sr mem Inst Indust Engrs; Prod & Opers Mgr Soc. *Res:* Multiple criteria decision making and its applications to service and production systems; author of three books from sage and springer-verlag. *Mailing Add:* 645 Fairview Pl Wyckoff NJ 07481. *Fax:* 201-692-7219; *E-Mail:* yoon@alpha.fdu.edu

**YOON, KYONGGEUN,** NUCLEIC ACID CHEMISTRY, TRANSUPTION. *Current Pos:* ASSOC DIR, APOLLON INC, 92- *Personal Data:* b Seoul, Korea, Mar 18, 48; US citizen; m, Bruce Johnson; c Carolyn & Sarah. *Educ:* Seoul Univ, BS, 70; Univ Utah, MS, 72; Univ Calif, Berkeley, PhD(chem), 76. *Prof Exp:* Res asst prof, Univ Pa, 82-86; res fel, Merck Sharp & Dohme, 86-89; prin res investr, Sterling, 89-92, res fel, 92. *Concurrent Pos:* Adj res prof, Univ Pa, 86- *Mem:* Am Soc Biochem & Molecular Biol. *Res:* Application of nucleic acid as therapeutic agents using multidisciplinary approach of nucleic acid chemistry, molecular and cell biology. *Mailing Add:* Dept Dermatol Jefferson Med Col 233 S 10th St Blumele Bldg Rm 450 Philadelphia PA 19107. *Fax:* 215-647-9732

**YOON, PETER HAESUNG,** SPACE PHYSICS. *Current Pos:* asst res scientist, 89-93, ASSOC RES SCIENTIST, INST PHYS SCI & TECHNOL, UNIV MD, 94- *Personal Data:* b Seoul, Korea, April 3, 58; m 87, Aeseun Loh; c Elias & Kate. *Educ:* Yonsei Univ, Seoul, Korea, BS, 80; Mass Inst Technol, PhD(plasma physics), 87. *Prof Exp:* Postdoctoral assoc space plasma physics, Ctr Space Res, Mass Inst Technol, Cambridge, Ma, 87-89. *Mem:* Sigma Xi; Am Phys Soc; Am Geophys Union. *Res:* Space and astrophysical plasma; radio emission process; plasma turbulence; nonlinear processes and kinetic and transport theory. *Mailing Add:* Inst Phys Sci & Technol Univ Md College Park MD 20742

**YOON, POKSYN SONG,** PROTEIN CHEMISTRY, HUMAN NEUTROPHIL IMMUNOLOGY. *Current Pos:* DIR LEARNING CTR, ROGER WILLIAMS UNIV, 96- *Personal Data:* b Howell, Mich, June 25, 48; div. *Educ:* Univ Mich, BS, 72; Univ Wis-Madison, PhD(biochem), 79. *Honors & Awards:* Fulbright-Hays lectr, Fulbright Comn, 82. *Prof Exp:* Res asst, Univ Wis, 73-80; res assoc, Univ Mich, 83-88; staff chemist, Boston Univ, 88-91; res fel, Brown Univ, 92-94. *Concurrent Pos:* Mem, Coun Thrombosis, Am Heart Asn. *Mem:* AAAS; Am Soc Biochem & Molecular Biol; Am Heart Asn; Sigma Xi. *Res:* Mechanisms of blood cell responses to vasoactive nitric acid; both human neutrophil and natural killer cell reactivities to exogenous stimuli are markedly depressed when cells are simultaneously exposed to nitric oxide; exploring the mechanisms of this immunosuppression. *Mailing Add:* 27 Jastram St Providence RI 02908. *Fax:* 401-831-0502

**YOON, RICK J,** GLASS-TO-METAL BONDING, CERAMIC-TO-METAL JOINING. *Current Pos:* PRES, IJ RES, 88- *Personal Data:* b Korea, Oct 5, 43; US citizen; m 71; c 2. *Educ:* Han Yang Univ, Seoul, Korea, BS, 69; Iowa State Univ, Ames, MS, 72, PhD(ceramic eng), 77. *Prof Exp:* Mat scientist, Anchor Hocking Corp, 78-79; res scientist, Kerr Div, Sybron Corp, 79-81; chief scientist, Rauland Div, Zenith Corp, 81-82; eng mgr, SPTC, Inc, 82-84; proj mgr, Bourns Instruments Inc, 84-88. *Concurrent Pos:* Consult, Smar Equip Industs, Brazil, 90, Daeha Co, Korea, 91 & Teltek Serv. *Mem:* Am Ceramic Soc; Nat Inst Ceramic Engrs; Am Soc Metals; Int Soc Hybrid Microelectronics; Int Electronics Packaging Soc; Sigma Xi. *Res:* Glass-to-metal seal/bonding for commercial applications; ceramic-to-metal bonding including titanium and molybdenum seal to glass or ceramic materials. *Mailing Add:* IJ Res 1965 Blair Ave Santa Ana CA 92705

**YOPP, JOHN HERMAN,** PLANT GROWTH REGULATORS & PHYCOLOGY. *Current Pos:* assoc prof, 74-79, assoc dean, Col Sci, 84-86, PROF BOT, SOUTHERN ILL UNIV, 79-, DEAN GRAD SCH, 86-, ASSOC VPRES RES, 86- *Personal Data:* b Paducah, Ky, Nov 13, 40; m 65, Donna M Denton; c John M, Joseph P & Anne M. *Educ:* Georgetown Univ, BS, 62; Univ Louisville, PhD(biol), 69. *Honors & Awards:* Kaplan Award, Sigma Xi. *Prof Exp:* Lectr human physiol, Catherine Spalding Col, 64-65; asst biol, NASA, 65-67; lectr, Univ Louisville, 68, researcher radioisotopes, AEC, 68-69; res fel plant physiol, Nat Res Coun, NASA, 69-70. *Concurrent Pos:* Prin investr, Environ Protection Agency, Ill, 73-74, NASA-NGR, 73-77, Ill Soybean Prog Operating Bd, 75-86, Nat Marine Fisheries Bd, 76-78, NASA, 77-79 & 82-86, Fisheries Bd, 76-78, NASA, 77-79 & 82-86, NIH Biomed Res Prog; lectr, Sigma Xi, 82-85; consult, Int Corn Prod Corp & Abbott Labs, 85-88; mem, Bd Nat Resources & Conserv, Ill, 87-, Exec Comt Grad Deans, African-Am Inst; chmn, Coun Res Policy & Grad Educ, Nat Asn State Univs & Land Grant Col; mem, Govs Rural Affairs Coun Ill, 92-; mem, GRE bd, 93-97; mem, TOEFL Pol Bd, 93-, chmn, 95-96; chmn, Nat Liaison Coun, 95-97. *Mem:* Int Soc Study Origin Life; Sigma Xi; Soc Res Admin. *Res:* Mechanisms of adaptation of plants to extreme environments, particularly hypersalinity and drought; soybean, cyanobacteria and aquatic plants; newly discovered plant hormones, the brassinosteroids; physiological mechanisms of adaptation to stress in plants. *Mailing Add:* Plant Biol Dept Southern Ill Univ Carbondale IL 62901. *Fax:* 618-453-4562; *E-Mail:* jyopp@siu.edu

**YORDY, JOHN DAVID,** ORGANIC CHEMISTRY. *Current Pos:* chair, Div Natural Sci, 81-87, PROF CHEM, GOSHEN COL, 77-, CHAIR, DEPT CHEM, 90- *Personal Data:* b St John's, Mich, Sept 17, 42; m 66; c 3. *Educ:* Goshen Col, BA, 67; Mich State Univ, PhD(org chem), 74. *Prof Exp:* Teacher chem & math, Wesley High Sch, Oturkpo, Nigeria, 67-70; res scientist, Lubrizol Corp, 74-77. *Concurrent Pos:* Vis prof chem, Univ Nairobi, 87-88. *Mem:* Am Chem Soc. *Res:* Lubrication chemistry; synthesis and transformations of cyclopropanol derivatives; natural products isolation, identification and syntheses; heterocyclic chemistry. *Mailing Add:* 2110 S Main St Goshen IN 46526-4795. *Fax:* 219-535-7509

**YORE, EUGENE ELLIOTT,** CONTROL SYSTEMS, MECHANICAL ENGINEERING. *Current Pos:* VPRES, MARINE SYSTS WEST, ALLIANT TECH SYSTS INC, 91- *Personal Data:* b Columbus, Ohio, Mar 6, 39; c Charlotte & Steven. *Educ:* Ohio State Univ, BSME, 62; Univ Calif, Berkeley, MS, 63, PhD(mech eng), 66. *Prof Exp:* Sr prin res scientist, Honeywell Inc, 66-70, sect chief, 70-73, mgr, 73-76, dir res, 76-78; dep sci & technol, asst secy of Army, 78-81; corp dir, Eng & Mfg Prod, Honeywell Inc, 81-83, vpres, Precision Weapons Opers, 84-89, vpres & gen mgr, Marine Systs Div, 89-91. *Concurrent Pos:* NASA trainee, Univ Calif, Berkeley, 64-66; proj mgr, res & develop team, President's Pvt Sector Surv on Govt Cost Control, Grove Comn, 83-84. *Mem:* Inst Elec & Electronics Engrs; Am Soc Mech Engrs; Am Inst Aeronaut & Astronaut; Am Defense Preparedness Asn. *Res:* Identification of dynamic systems and component parameter identification; optimal control of aerospace vehicles. *Mailing Add:* 2621 Second Ave No 1903 Seattle WA 98121

**YORIO, THOMAS,** MEMBRANE PHYSIOLOGY, OCULAR & RENAL PHARMACOLOGY. *Current Pos:* from asst prof to assoc prof, 77-91, PROF, DEPT PHARMACOL, UNIV TEX HEALTH SCI CTR, 91, DEAN, 93- *Personal Data:* b New York, NY, Aug 27, 48; m 70, Elena Ilijer; c Jennifer & Jeffrey. *Educ:* Herbert H Lehman Col, BA, 71; City Univ NY, PhD(pharmacol), 75. *Prof Exp:* Res asst, Dept Ophthal, Mt Sinai Sch Med, NY, 74-75, fel, 75-77. *Concurrent Pos:* Prin investr, Nat Kidney Found, 77-78, Am Heart Asn, 78-81, Nat Inst Arthritis, Metab & Digestive Dis, NIH, 79-82, minority hypertension res develop grant, Nat Heart, Lung & Blood Inst, 80-90, 87-92, 90-98, Tex Heart Asn, 88-90, Dept Defense, 92- & Nat Inst Gen Med Sci, 93-; fel, NSF, 75-77 & Nat Kidney Found fel, 77. *Mem:* Sigma Xi; NY Acad Sci; Asn Res Vision & Ophthal; Am Soc Pharmacol & Exp Therapeut; Europ Membrane Club; Am Heart Asn, Kidney Cardiovasc Dis; Soc Exp Biol & Med; Int Soc Eye Res; AAAS; Asn Ocular Pharmacol & Therapeut. *Res:* Hormonal regulation of epithelial transport of ions and water; role of lipid metabolism and prostaglandins in the response to aldosterone and antidiuretic hormone; regulation of intraocular pressure and control of aqueous humor formation and outflor; glaucoma research. *Mailing Add:* Grad Sch Biomed Sci Univ NTex Health Sci Ctr Ft Worth TX 76107-2644. *E-Mail:* yoriot@hsc.unt.edu

**YORK, ALAN CLARENCE,** WEED SCIENCE, COTTON PRODUCTION. *Current Pos:* Cotton specialist, 79-83, WEED SPECIALIST, NC STATE UNIV, 83- *Personal Data:* b Asheboro, NC, Jan 24, 52; m 73; c 2. *Educ:* NC State Univ, BS, 74, MS, 76; Univ Ill PhD(agron), 79. *Honors & Awards:* Outstanding Young Weed Scientist Award, Southern Weed Sci Soc, 91; Cotton Exten Educ Award, Cotton Found, 92; Outstanding Exten Award, Weed Sci Soc Am, 97. *Mem:* Weed Sci Soc Am; Am Peanut Res & Educ Soc; Coun Agr Sci Technol. *Res:* Development of weed management systems for agronomic crops, emphases on product performance, application technology, pesticide interactions, rotational crop responses, and integration of weed management programs into total production systems; extension and PGR evaluations. *Mailing Add:* NC State Univ Box 7620 Raleigh NC 27695-7620. *E-Mail:* alon__york@ncsu.edu

**YORK, CARL MONROE, JR,** PHYSICS. *Current Pos:* CONSULT, 88- *Personal Data:* b Macon, Ga, July 2, 25; m 69, Lewis; c Christopher, Paul, Leila & Diane. *Educ:* Univ Calif, Berkeley, AB, 46, MA, 50, PhD(physics), 51. *Prof Exp:* Fulbright fel physics, Univ Manchester, 51-52; res fel, Calif Inst Technol, 52-54; asst prof, Univ Chicago, 54-59; Ford Found & Guggenheim Found fel, Europ Orgn Nuclear Res, Geneva, 59-60; from assoc prof to prof, Univ Calif, Los Angeles, 60-69, asst chancellor res, 65-69, assoc dean grad div, 63-65; tech asst basic sci, Off Sci & Technol, Exec Off of the Pres, 69-72; vchancellor acad affairs, Univ Denver, 72-74; consult, 74-77; staff scientist, Lawrence Berkeley Lab, 77-81; consult, 81-84; dir, Syst Develop Found, 84-88. *Concurrent Pos:* Consult, Argonne Nat Lab, 57-61; TRW Systs, Calif, 61-69; Film Assocs, Calif, 62-65; Lawrence Radiation Lab, 66, NSF, 72-76, Fedn Rocky Mountain States, 74-75; Colo Energy Res Inst, 75-76; Calif Energy Resource, Conserv & Develop Comn, 75-76; Pac Gas & Elec Co, 77-84 & Lawrence Livermore Nat Lab, 81-83; bd dir, Ctr Theol & Natural Scis, 89- *Mem:* AAAS; Am Phys Soc. *Res:* Cosmic rays; elementary particles; positive sigma hyperon; high energy accelerator design; pion-nucleon scattering and production; muon decay and interactions; photo-production of pions; regional and state energy policies and plans; federal budgets for basic science and national science policy; validation of energy data bases and models; basic research in information science. *Mailing Add:* 26 Schooner Hill Oakland CA 94618

**YORK, CHARLES JAMES,** VIROLOGY, BACTERIOLOGY. *Current Pos:* ASSOC PROF COMP PATH, MED SCH, UNIV CALIF, SAN DIEGO, 67- *Personal Data:* b Calif, Sept 28, 19; m 44; c 4. *Educ:* Univ Calif, AB, 43; Ohio State Univ, DVM, 48; Cornell Univ, PhD(virol, bact), 50. *Prof Exp:* Asst bact, Univ Calif, 41-43, bacteriologist, Vet Sci Dept, 43-44; sr bacteriologist, Med Res Dept, Ohio State Univ, 44-46, bacteriologist, Vet Col, 46; res assoc, Vet Virus Inst, Cornell Univ, 48-52; dir virus res lab, Pitman-Moore Co, Ind, 52-63; prof vet sci & head dept vet res lab, Mont State Univ, 63-65; dir inst comp biol, Zool Soc San Diego, 65-70. *Concurrent Pos:* Mem WHO. *Mem:* Soc Exp Biol & Med; Am Vet Med Asn; Tissue Cult Asn; US Animal Health Asn; Am Pub Health Asn. *Res:* Virus diseases of man and animals; comparative medicine for animal research models. *Mailing Add:* 2510 Boatman Ave West Sacramento CA 95691

**YORK, DAVID ANTHONY,** ANIMAL PHYSIOLOGY, NUTRITION. *Current Pos:* Prof, 90-95, CHIEF, PHYSIOL & OBESITY RES, PENNINGTON BIOMED RES CTR, LA STATE UNIV, 90-, HIBERNIA-SCHLEIDER PROF, 95- *Personal Data:* b Birmingham, Eng, Mar 29, 45; m 67; c 2. *Educ:* Southampton Univ, UK, BSc, 66, PhD(physiol), 69. *Prof Exp:* Res assoc obesity, New Eng Med Ctr Hosp, 69-70; res assoc, Sch Med, Univ Calif, Los Angeles, 70-71; lectr nutrit, Dept Nutrit, Univ Southampton, 71-82; sr lectr, Dept Human Nutrit, 82-88, reader, fac med, 88-89. *Concurrent Pos:* Mem, UK Nat Comt Nutrit & Food Sci, 87-89; prof, Dept Physiol, Med Ctr, La State Univ, 90- *Mem:* Am Inst Nutrit; Biochem Soc UK; British Asn Study Obesity; Am Asn Study Obesity; Am Physiol Soc. *Res:* Control of food intake and energy expenditure; metabolic and endocrine basis for development of obesity in experimental models; role of the autonomic nervous system in control of energy balance. *Mailing Add:* Pennington Biomed Ctr 6400 Perkins Rd Baton Rouge LA 70808. *Fax:* 504-765-2525

**YORK, DEREK H,** GEOPHYSICS. *Current Pos:* lectr, 60-62, from asst prof to assoc prof, 62-74, PROF PHYSICS, UNIV TORONTO, 74- *Personal Data:* b Yorkshire, Eng, Aug 12, 36; m 61; c 1. *Educ:* Oxford Univ, BA, 57, DPhil(physics), 60. *Concurrent Pos:* Chmn, Subcomt Isotope Geophys & mem, Comt Geod & Geophys, Nat Res Coun Can, 67; staff mem, Lab Geol & Geochem, Univ Nice, France. *Mem:* Am Geophys Union; Can Asn Physicists. *Res:* Isotopic geophysics; temporal evolution of continents; reversals of earth's magnetic field. *Mailing Add:* Physics Dept McLennan Lab Univ Toronto 60 St George St Toronto ON M5S 1A1 Can

**YORK, DONALD GILBERT,** INTERSTELLAR MATTER, OBSERVATIONAL COSMOLOGY. *Current Pos:* assoc prof, 82-85, prof, 85-92, HORACE B HORTON PROF, ASTRON & ASTROPHYS CTR, UNIV CHICAGO, 92- *Personal Data:* b Shelbyville, Ill, Oct 28, 44; m 66; Anna; c Sean, Maurice, Chandler & Jeremy. *Educ:* Mass Inst Technol, BA, 66; Univ Chicago, PhD(astrophysics), 70. *Honors & Awards:* Distinguished Serv Award, NASA, 75. *Prof Exp:* From res asst to res assoc, Princeton Univ, 70-72, res staff astrophysics, 72-82. *Concurrent Pos:* Dir, Apache Point Observ, Sunspot, NMex, 84-, Sloan Digital Sky Surv. *Mem:* Int Astron Union; Am Astron Soc. *Res:* Determination physical properties of interstellar gas and dust, using ultraviolet and visual spectroscopic techniques, in our own galaxy as well as distant galactic systems. *Mailing Add:* Astron & Astrophys Ctr Univ Chicago 5640 S Ellis Ave Chicago IL 60637-1433

**YORK, DONALD HAROLD,** NEUROPHYSIOLOGY, NEUROSCIENCE. *Current Pos:* DIR, DEPT NEUROSCI, ST JOHN'S MERCY MED CTR, 94- *Personal Data:* b Moose Jaw, Sask, Jan 30, 44; m 66; c 3. *Educ:* Univ BC, BSc, 65, MSc, 66; Monash Univ, Australia, PhD(neurophysiol), 69. *Prof Exp:* Asst prof physiol, Queen's Univ, Ont, 68-75; from assoc prof to prof physiol, Sch Med, Univ Mo, Columbia, 82-93. *Concurrent Pos:* Med Res Coun Can grant, Queen's Univ, Ont, 69-72; scholar, Med Res Coun Can, 70-75; vis fel, Australian Nat Univ, 83-84; Adv Bd Nat Hydrocephalus Found, 87-; exec coun, Am Soc Neuromonitoring, 88- *Mem:* Sigma Xi; Can Physiol Soc; Am Physiol Soc; Soc Neurosci; Pharmacol Soc Can; Inst Elec & Electronics Engrs. *Res:* Motor control; evoked potentials and movement; synaptic transmission in central nervous system. *Mailing Add:* Dept Neurosci/St John's Mercy Med Ctr 615 S New Ballas Rd St Louis MO 63141-8221. *Fax:* 314-995-4111

**YORK, GEORGE KENNETH, II,** MICROBIOLOGY. *Current Pos:* actg asst prof, Univ Calif, Davis, 58-60, asst prof, 60-66, exten microbiologist, 66-96, EMER PROF FOOD SCI & TECHNOL, UNIV CALIF, DAVIS, 96- *Personal Data:* b Tucson, Ariz, July 1, 25; m 47; c 5. *Educ:* Stanford Univ, AB, 50; Univ Calif, PhD(microbiol), 60. *Prof Exp:* Asst bacteriologist, Nat Canners Asn, 51-53. *Mem:* NY Acad Sci; Am Soc Microbiol; Inst Food Technol. *Res:* Food microbiology; food-borne infections and intoxications; thermomicrobiology; modes of inhibition of microbes by chemicals; treatment and disposal of waste. *Mailing Add:* Dept Food Sci & Technol Univ Calif Davis CA 95616. *Fax:* 530-752-4759

**YORK, GEORGE WILLIAM,** LASERS. *Current Pos:* MEM STAFF PHYSICS, LOS ALAMOS SCI LAB, 74- *Personal Data:* b St Louis, Mo, Sept 26, 45; m 68; c 2. *Educ:* St Louis Univ, BS, 67; Univ Mo, Rolla, MS, 69, PhD(physics), 71. *Prof Exp:* Res assoc physics, Joint Inst Lab Astrophys, 72-74. *Mem:* Am Phys Soc; Laser Inst Am. *Res:* Development of high power gas lasers utilizing preionized electrical discharges in metal vapor system. *Mailing Add:* Los Alamos Nat Lab PO Box 1663 MS-P915 Los Alamos NM 87545

**YORK, HERBERT FRANK,** PHYSICS, SCIENCE POLICY. *Current Pos:* chancellor, 61-64 & 70-72, grad dean, 69-70, PROF PHYSICS,UNIV CALIF, SAN DIEGO, 65-; DIR EMER, INST GLOBAL CONFLICT & COOP, 89- *Personal Data:* b Rochester, NY, Nov 24, 21; m 47, Sybil Dunford; c Cynthia, Rachel & David. *Educ:* Univ Rochester, AB, 42, MS, 43; Univ Calif, PhD, 49. *Hon Degrees:* DSc, Case Western Reserve Univ, 60; LLD, Univ San Diego, 64; DrHumL, Claremont Grad Sch, 74. *Honors & Awards:* E O Lawrence Award, 84; Leo Szilard Award, 94. *Prof Exp:* Asst physics, Univ Rochester, 42-43; physicist, Radiation Lab, Univ Calif, 43-54, assoc dir, 54-58, dir, Lawrence Livermore Lab, 52-58, asst prof physics, 51-54; dir, Advan Res Projs Div, Inst Defense Anal & chief scientist, Advan Res Projs Agency, US Dept Defense, 58, dir defense res & eng, Off Secy Defense, 58-61; dir, Inst Global Conflict & Coop, 83-88. *Concurrent Pos:* Mem, Sci Adv Bd, USAF, 53-57, ballistic missile adv comt, Secy Defense, 55-58& Sci Adv Panel, US Army, 56-58; mem, President's Sci Adv Comt, 57-58 & 64-67, vchmn, 65-67; mem gen adv comt, US Arms Control & Disarmament Agency, 61-69; Guggenheim fel, 72-73; mem continuing comt, Conf Sci & World Affairs, 73-76; sr consult, Off Secy Defense, 77-81; mem, Defense Sci Bd, 78-81; US Ambassador, Comp Test Ban Talks, Geneva, 79-81. *Mem:* Am Phys Soc; Am Acad Arts & Sci; Am Inst Aeronaut & Astronaut; Inst Elec & Electronics Engrs; Int Acad Astronaut. *Res:* Science and public affairs; nuclear weapons and nuclear disamament problems. *Mailing Add:* 6110 Camino de la Costa La Jolla CA 92037. *Fax:* 619-459-9418; *E-Mail:* hyork@ucsd.edu

**YORK, J(ESSE) LOUIS,** AIR POLLUTION CONTROL, ENVIRONMENTAL SITE ASSESSMENTS. *Current Pos:* CONSULT, 83- *Personal Data:* b Plains, Tex, May 1, 18; m 45, 75, Ruth Robinson; c Terrell (Hemingway) & Kathleen (Carson). *Educ:* Univ NMex, BSE, 38; Univ Mich, MS, 40, PhD(chem eng), 50. *Prof Exp:* From instr to prof chem & metall eng, Univ Mich, 42-70, proj dir, Res Inst, 42-70; environ scientist, Stearns-Roger Corp, 70-72, chief environ scientist, 72-83. *Concurrent Pos:* Mem bd, Colo Sch Mines Found, 73-94. *Mem:* Am Chem Soc; Am Soc Mech Engrs; Air & Waste Mgt Asn; Am Inst Chem Engrs; Am Acad Environ Engrs. *Res:* Suspensions of fine particles; sprays; nozzles; combustion; air and water pollution control; entrainment; desalination; filtration; environmental studies and analyses. *Mailing Add:* 3557 S Ivanhoe St Denver CO 80237

**YORK, JAMES LESTER,** GERONTOLOGY, EPIDEMIOLOGY. *Current Pos:* RES SCIENTIST, NY STATE RES INST ADDICTIONS, BUFFALO, 74- *Personal Data:* b Peoria, Ill, Nov 12, 42; m 70, Patricia Stanton; c Benjamin & Nora. *Educ:* Bradley Univ, AB, 65; Univ Ill, PhD(pharmacol), 72. *Prof Exp:* Postdoctoral pharmacol, State Univ NY-Buffalo, 72-74. *Concurrent Pos:* Prin investr, NIH res grants, 76-78 & 87-93; referee-prof journals, Psychopharmacol, 78-90, Pharmacol, Biochem, Behav, 79-93, Alcohol, 84-90, J Studies on Alcohol, Physiol & Behav, 85-89, Alcoholism, 89-92; res assoc prof, Dept Psychol, State Univ NY-Buffalo, 81- *Mem:* Fedn Am Soc Exp Biol; Res Soc Alcoholism; Int Soc Biomed Res Alcoholism; Soc Stimulus Properties Drugs; Geront Soc. *Res:* Age-related changes in psychomotor performance and physiological function; tolerance to alcohol and other drugs; age-related changes in response to alcohol; chronic alcohol toxicity on motor/muscle and cardiovascular systems. *Mailing Add:* 783 Chestnuthill Rd East Aurora NY 14052. *Fax:* 716-887-2510; *E-Mail:* york@ria.org

**YORK, JAMES WESLEY, JR,** THEORETICAL PHYSICS, GRAVITATION. *Current Pos:* from assoc prof to prof, 73-88, dir, Inst Field Physics, 84-90, AGNEW H BAHNSON JR PROF PHYSICS, 89- *Personal Data:* b Raleigh, NC, July 3, 39; m 61, Betty Mattern; c Virginia (Setzer) & Guilford M. *Educ:* NC State Univ, BS, 62, PhD(physics), 66. *Honors & Awards:* Third Prize, Gravity Res Found, Mass, 75; Alfred Schild Mem lectr, Univ Tex, 79. *Prof Exp:* Asst prof physics, NC State Univ, Raleigh, 65-68; res assoc physics, Princeton Univ, 68-69, lectr, 69-70, asst prof, 70-73. *Concurrent Pos:* Vis asst prof, Univ Md, 72; prin investr, NSF, 74-; vis prof, Univ Paris, 76 & Univ Tex, 79, 87; vis scientist, Harvard-Smithsonian Ctr Astrophys, 77; mem, Int Soc Gen Relativity & Gravitation, 80- *Mem:* Fel Am Phys Soc; AAAS. *Res:* Gravitation and relativity; mathematical, astrophysical statistical and quantum theoretic aspects. *Mailing Add:* Dept Physics & Astron Univ NC Chapel Hill NC 27599-3255. *Fax:* 919-962-0480; *E-Mail:* york@physics.unc.edu

**YORK, JOHN LYNDAL,** BIOCHEMISTRY, PHYSICAL ORGANIC CHEMISTRY. *Current Pos:* assoc prof, 68-77, PROF BIOCHEM, SCH MED, UNIV ARK, LITTLE ROCK, 77- *Personal Data:* b Morton, Tex, Aug 14, 36; m 58; c 2. *Educ:* Harding Col, BS, 58; Johns Hopkins Univ, PhD(biochem), 62. *Prof Exp:* NIH trainee, 62-64; biochemist, Stanford Res Inst, 64-65; asst prof biochem, Med Units, Univ Tenn, Memphis, 65-68. *Concurrent Pos:* Vis prof, Karolinska Inst, Stockholm, 74-75; fel, Swedish Med Res Coun, 75. *Mem:* Am Soc Biol Chem; Am Chem Soc; Sigma Xi; AAAS. *Res:* Nature of the active site and mechanisms of action of non-heme iron proteins; Mossbauer effect; mechanisms of oxidation and oxygenation; structure and function of fibrinogen; mechanism of detoxicification by glutathione transferases. *Mailing Add:* Dept Biochem No 516 Univ Ark Med Col Little Rock AR 72205

**YORK, OWEN, JR,** ORGANIC CHEMISTRY. *Current Pos:* RETIRED. *Personal Data:* b Evansville, Ind, Oct 18, 27; m 48; c 3. *Educ:* Evansville Col, BA, 48; Univ Ill, MA, 50, PhD(org chem), 52. *Prof Exp:* Asst, Univ Ill, 48-52; res chemist, Hercules Powder Co, 52-56; head, Dept Chem, Ill Wesleyan Univ, 56-60; res supvr, W R Grace & Co, 60-61; from assoc prof to prof chem, Kenyon Col, 61-93, chmn dept, 64-73, reader & table leader, 64-72, chief reader, Advan Placement Chem, 72-76, assoc dir, Reading-Advan Placement Prog Educ Testing Serv, 79-84. *Concurrent Pos:* NSF fel, Stanford Univ, 68-69. *Mem:* AAAS; Am Chem Soc; NY Acad Sci. *Res:* Grignard reaction; oxidation; electrophilic substitution; isomerization of aromatic acids; synthetic photochemistry; catalysis; biomass; macromolecules. *Mailing Add:* PO Box 385 Gambier OH 43022-0385

**YORK, RAYMOND A,** INTERNATIONAL TECHNOLOGY TRANSFER. *Current Pos:* DEVELOPER REAL ESTATE SUBDIV, 88- *Personal Data:* b Baldwin, Kans, May 15, 17; c 3. *Educ:* Univ Kans, BSEE, 41. *Prof Exp:* Mgr, Gen Elec, Syracuse, NY, 50-69, gen mgr, International Lic Div, New York City, 69-82; consult, 82-88. *Concurrent Pos:* Indust Standard Domestic & Intl. *Mem:* Fel Inst Elec & Electronics Engrs. *Res:* Working with equipment for the measurement of the amount of nuclear exposure and for metal detection. *Mailing Add:* 1214 James St Syracuse NY 13203

**YORK, SHELDON STAFFORD,** BIOPHYSICAL CHEMISTRY. *Current Pos:* ASST PROF CHEM, UNIV DENVER, 72- *Personal Data:* b New Haven, Conn, Oct 29, 43; m 68; c 2. *Educ:* Bates Col, BS, 65; Stanford Univ, PhD(biochem), 71. *Prof Exp:* Am Cancer Soc res fel chem, Calif Inst Technol, 70-72. *Mem:* Am Chem Soc. *Res:* Protein-DNA recognition processes, specifically the conformational changes within the lac repressor protein which affect its ability to bind to the lac operator. *Mailing Add:* Dept Chem Univ Denver Denver CO 80208-0001

**YORKE, JAMES ALAN,** APPLIED MATHEMATICS, BIOMATHEMATICS. *Current Pos:* From res assoc to res assoc prof, 66-72, RES PROF MATH, INST PHYS SCI & TECHNOL, UNIV MD, COLLEGE PARK, 72-, DIR, 88- *Personal Data:* b Peking, China, Aug 3, 41; US citizen; m 63; c 8. *Educ:* Columbia Univ, AB, 63; Univ Md, College Park, PhD(math), 66. *Concurrent Pos:* Guggenheim fel, 80-81. *Mem:* AAAS; Am Math Soc; Math Asn Am; Soc Indust & Appl Math. *Res:* Qualitative ordinary differential equations; applications in epidemiology. *Mailing Add:* Inst Phys Sci & Technol Univ Md College Park MD 20742-2431

**YORKE, THOMAS H,** FLOOD, SURFACE WATER & SEDIMENT TRANSPORT. *Current Pos:* CHIEF, OFF SURFACE WATER, 96- *Personal Data:* b Abbington, Pa, Sept, 10, 42. *Educ:* Pa State Univ, BS, 64, MS, 67. *Mem:* Am Geophys Union; Am Water Resources Asn; Am Inst Hydrol. *Mailing Add:* Office Surface Water Nat Ctr MS 415 Reston VA 20192. *Fax:* 703-648-5295

**YORKS, TERENCE PRESTON,** SYSTEM MODELLING. *Current Pos:* INDEPENDENT CONSULT, 87- *Personal Data:* b Syracuse, NY, Apr 29, 47; m 87, Kathleen M Capels. *Educ:* Colo State Univ, BS, 69; NMex Highlands Univ, MS, 71; Tex A&M Univ, PhD(food sci), 76. *Prof Exp:* Res assoc animal sci, Colo State Univ, 76-78, res assoc modelling, natural resource ecol lab, 80-82; opers res analyst, Forest Serv, USDA, 79; consult modelling, Poudre Valley Res Inst, 82-83; sr tech info specialist chem, Environ Protection Agency, 83-84; staff officer admin, Nat Acad Sci, 84-85; systs scientist & asst prof range mgt, Univ Wyo, 85-87. *Concurrent Pos:* Postdoctorate animal sci, Colo State Univ, 76-78; vis asst prof, Range Sci Dept, Utah State Univ, 82-83, postdoctorate ecol, 89-90. *Mem:* Soc Range Mgt; Soc Conserv Biol. *Res:* Elucidation and monitoring of ecosystem-level interactions that can affect long-term human food and fiber supplies; computer-based natural resource, energy-flow and risk analyses; microbiological and chemical toxicology. *Mailing Add:* 1251 Mountain View Dr Smithfield UT 84335

**YOS, DAVID ALBERT,** BOTANY, INFORMATION SCIENCE. *Current Pos:* SCI LIBRN, ILL STATE UNIV, NORMAL, 82- *Personal Data:* b Trenton, NJ, Apr 24, 23; m 46; c 2. *Educ:* NY Univ, AB, 48; Univ Mo, MA, 52, MLS, 81; Univ Iowa, PhD(bot, plant anat), 60. *Prof Exp:* Instr biol, Burlington Col, 52-59; asst prof bot, Univ Wis-Green Bay, 60-62; teacher, High Sch, NJ, 63; from asst prof to prof biol, Eastern NMex Univ, 63-81, adj prof & sci librn, 81-82. *Mem:* Sigma Xi; AAAS. *Res:* Fluorescence microscopy of plant tissues; development of periderm; microtechnique; history of microscopy and photomicrography. *Mailing Add:* 116 N Parkside Rd Normal IL 61761

**YOS, JERROLD MOORE,** RE-ENTRY PHYSICS. *Current Pos:* SR SCIENTIST, SYSTS DIV, AVCO CORP, 57- *Personal Data:* b Clinton, Iowa, Jan 1, 30; m 60; c 3. *Educ:* Univ Nebr, AB, 52, MS, 54, PhD(physics), 56. *Mem:* Am Phys Soc. *Res:* Electromagnetics; gas physics; kinetic theory of gases; electrical discharges. *Mailing Add:* 1001 Main St 34 Woburn MA 01801-1253

**YOSEF, REUVEN,** habitat suitability & quality, avian migration, for more information see previous edition

**YOSHIDA, AKIRA,** BIOCHEMISTRY, GENETICS. *Current Pos:* DIR, DEPT BIOCHEM GENETICS, CITY HOPE MED CTR, 72- *Personal Data:* b Okayama, Japan, May 10, 24; m 54, Michiko; c Emmy. *Educ:* Univ Tokyo, MS, 47, DSc, 54. *Honors & Awards:* Japanese Human Genetics Am Soc Award, 81; Merit Award, NIH, 87. *Prof Exp:* From instr to asst prof chem, Univ Tokyo, 51-54, assoc prof chem & biochem, 54-60; res assoc biochem, Univ Pa, 61-63; res chemist, NIH, 63-65; res prof med genetics, Univ Wash, 64-72. *Concurrent Pos:* Int scholar & grant award, Rockefeller Found, 55-58. *Mem:* AAAS; Am Soc Biol Chem; Soc Hemat; Soc Human Genetics; Res Soc Alocholism; Japanese Soc Biol Chem; NY Acad Sci. *Res:* Human genetic abnormalities at the molecular level. *Mailing Add:* Dept Biochem Genetics City Hope Med Ctr 1500 Duarte Rd Duarte CA 91010. *Fax:* 626-357-1929

**YOSHIDA, FUMITAKE,** BIOENGINEERING & BIOMEDICAL ENGINEERING. *Current Pos:* from asst prof to prof, 46-76, EMER PROF CHEM ENG, KYOTO UNIV, 76- *Personal Data:* b Saitama, Japan, Mar 20, 13; m 41, Kazuko Yamagishi; c Hajime & Akiko (Nakane). *Educ:* Kyoto Univ, BEng, 37, DEng, 51. *Hon Degrees:* Dr, Univ Dortmund, Ger, 92. *Prof Exp:* Engr, Chem Eng Plant Design, Hitachi Ltd, 37-45. *Concurrent Pos:* Lectr, Kyoto Univ, 40-45; vis fel, Yale Univ, 52-53; res assoc, Univ Wis-Madison, 59; vis prof, Univ Calif, Berkeley, 63, Univ Pa, 70; guest prof, Univ Dortmund, Ger, 87; ed, Chem Eng Sci, 87-96. *Mem:* Nat Acad Eng; Soc Chem Engrs Japan (vpres, 67-69); Am Inst Chem Engrs; Am Chem Soc; Japanese Soc Artificial Organs; Am Soc Artificial Interal Organs. *Res:* Mass transfer operations in chemical engineering, such as gas absorption, distillation; applications of chemical engineering in medicine and bio process industries. *Mailing Add:* 2 Matsugasaki-Yobikaeshicho Sakyoku Kyoto 606 Japan. *Fax:* 81-75-791-2328

**YOSHIDA, TAKESHI,** IMMUNOPATHOLOGY. *Current Pos:* CLIN PROF, TOKYTO INST IMMUNOPHARMACOL, 84- DIR, 87- *Personal Data:* b Fukuoka, Japan, July 24, 38; m 64; c 2. *Educ:* Univ Tokyo, MD, 63, Dr Med Sci, 70. *Prof Exp:* Res mem immunol, Dept Tuberc, NIH, Tokyo, 64-71; asst prof, Dept Path, State Univ NY Buffalo, 71-74; from asst prof to assoc prof path, Univ Conn Health Ctr, 74-82, prof, 82-84. *Concurrent Pos:* Res assoc, Dept Path, NY Univ Med Ctr, 67-68; vis assoc, Lab Immunol, Nat Inst Allergy & Infectious Dis, Bethesda, 68-69, vis scientist, 71; Buswell fel, State Univ NY, Buffalo, 71-74, asst dir, Ctr Immunol, 73-74; Nat Inst Allergy & Infectious Dis res career develop award, 75-80. *Mem:* Am Asn Immunologists; Am Asn Pathologists; Am Asn Univ Pathologists; Reticuloendothelial Soc; NY Acad Sci. *Res:* Mechanisms of cell-mediated immunity, biological and physicochemical characterizations of effector molecules produced in vitro by stimulated lymphocytes, and in vivo activities of lymphokines. *Mailing Add:* CHUGA Res Inst Molecular Med 153-2 Nagai-Nihani-mura-Nihari-gun Ibaraki 30041 Japan. *Fax:* 81-3-3984-7874

**YOSHIKAMI, DOJU,** NEUROBIOLOGY, NEUROSCIENCE. *Current Pos:* from asst prof to assoc prof, 78-86, PROF BIOL, UNIV UTAH, 86- *Personal Data:* b Heart Mountain, Wyo. *Educ:* Reed Col, BA, 65; Cornell Univ, PhD(biochem & molecular biol), 70. *Prof Exp:* NIH fel appl physics, Cornell Univ, 70-71; NSF fel neurobiol, Harvard Univ Sch Med, 71-73, instr, 73-76, prin res assoc, 76-78. *Res:* Cellular and molecular neurobiology; structure and function of synapses. *Mailing Add:* 1074 E 600 S Salt Lake City UT 84102

**YOSHIKAWA, HERBERT HIROSHI,** NUCLEAR ENGINEERING, SOLID STATE PHYSICS. *Current Pos:* RETIRED. *Personal Data:* b South Dos Palos, Calif, May 13, 29; m 60, Helen Sadataki. *Educ:* Univ Chicago, PhB, 48, MS, 51; Univ Pa, PhD(physics), 58. *Prof Exp:* Sr engr physics, Hanford Labs, Gen Elec Co, 58-65; mgr graphite res & develop radiation effects, Pac Northwest Lab, Battelle-Northwest Lab, 65-70; mgr mat eng, Westinghouse Hanford Co, 70-78, mgr technol, Hanford Eng Develop Lab, 78-87, mgr strategic planning, 88-94. *Mem:* Am Nuclear Soc; AAAS; Sigma Xi. *Res:* Technology of fast breeder, light water and fusion reactors; materials development, irradiation testing and reactor environment characterization. *Mailing Add:* 2712 W Klamath Kennewick WA 99336

**YOSHIKAWA, SHOICHI,** NUCLEAR ENGINEERING. *Current Pos:* LECTR, ASTROPHYS SCI DEPT, PRINCETON UNIV, 61-, PRIN RES PHYSICIST, PLASMA PHYSICS LAB, 67- *Personal Data:* b Apr 9, 35. *Educ:* Univ Tokyo, BS, 58; Mass Inst Tech, MS, 60, PhD(nuclear eng), 61. *Concurrent Pos:* Vis prof, Cornell Univ, 72-73; prof, Dept Physics, Univ Tokyo, 73-76; spec res fel, Res Inst Fiscal & Monetary Policy, Japan, 85, Gakujuku-shinko-kai, Kyoto Univ, 88. *Res:* Published several books. *Mailing Add:* 302 Hartley Ave Princeton NJ 08540

**YOSHIKAWA, THOMAS T,** MEDICINE. *Current Pos:* MEM STAFF, MED CTR, GEORGE WASHINGTON UNIV. *Personal Data:* b Los Angeles, Calif, Feb 26, 41. *Educ:* Univ Mich, Md, 66; Am Bd Internal Med, dipl. *Honors & Awards:* Milo D Leavitt Mem Lectr Award, Am Geriat Soc, 94. *Prof Exp:* Intern, Harbor Gen Hosp, Torrance, Calif, 66-67, resident, 67-70, fel infectious dis, 72. *Concurrent Pos:* Adj prof health care sci, George Washington Univ. *Mem:* Am Col Physicians; Am Gynec Soc; Genetics Soc Am. *Mailing Add:* ACMD Geriat & Extended Care (114) Dept Vet Affairs 810 Vermont Ave NW Washington DC 20420

**YOSHIMOTO, CARL MASARU,** ENTOMOLOGY. *Current Pos:* HON RES ASSOC, CENTRE LAND & BIOL RESOURCES RES, AGR CAN, OTTAWA, 88- *Personal Data:* b Honolulu, Hawaii, Apr 27, 22; m 57, Ruth R Nishimura; c Carol K & Marie E. *Educ:* Iowa Wesleyan Col, BA, 50; Kans State Univ, MS, 52; Cornell Univ, PhD(entom), 55. *Prof Exp:* Entomologist, Entom Res Div, USDA, 55-57 & BP Bishop Mus, 58-69; sr res scientist, Dept Agr, Can Forestry Serv, 69-87. *Concurrent Pos:* Affil fac, Grad Sch, Univ Hawaii, 64-69; NSF grant, Brit Mus, London, Eng, 67-68; vis prof, Univ Calif, Riverside, 81-82. *Mem:* Entom Soc Am; Entom Soc Can; Sigma Xi. *Res:* Taxonomy of Hymenoptera; insect behavior and dispersal; zoogeography; biological control. *Mailing Add:* 6 Charing Rd Nepean ON K2G 0Z5 Can

**YOSHINAGA, KOJI,** ENDOCRINOLOGY. *Current Pos:* HEALTH SCIENTIST ADMINR, REPRODUCTION SCI BR, POP RES, NAT INST CHILD HEALTH & HUMAN DEVELOP, NIH, 78- *Personal Data:* b Yokohama, Japan, Mar 20, 32; m 61. *Educ:* Univ Tokyo, BSc, 55, MSc, 57, PhD(agr), 60. *Prof Exp:* Trainee physiol reproduction, Worcester Found Exp Biol, 61-64; vis scientist, Agr Res Coun Unit Reproduction Physiol & Biochem, Cambridge, 64-66; staff scientist, Worcester Found Exp Biol, 66-69; res assoc anat, Harvard Med Sch, 69, asst prof, 69-72, assoc prof, 72-79. *Concurrent Pos:* Pop Coun fel, Worcester Found Exp Biol, 62-63 & Agr Res Coun Unit Reproduction Physiol & Biochem, Cambridge, 64-65, Lalor Found fel, 65-66; adj prof, Georgetown Univ Sch Med, 84- *Mem:* Am Asn Anat; Endocrine Soc; Soc Study Reproduction; Am Physiol Soc; Soc Study Fertil. *Res:* Endocrinology and physiology of reproduction in female animals, especially the mechanisms involved in ovo-implantation, ovarian function and relationship between the egg development and hormone action. *Mailing Add:* 5706 Glenwood Rd Bethesda MD 20817. *Fax:* 301-496-0962

**YOSHINO, KOUICHI,** CHEMICAL PHYSICS, MOLECULAR SPECTROSCOPY. *Current Pos:* RES ASSOC, HARVARD-SMITHSONIAN CTR ASTROPHYS, 76- *Personal Data:* b Matsuyama, Japan, Jan 1, 31. *Educ:* Tokyo Univ Educ, BS, 53, MS, 55, PhD(physics), 72. *Prof Exp:* Physicist, Indust Res Inst Kanagawa, Japan, 54-58 & Govt Indust Res Inst, Tokyo, 58-65; res physicist, Air Force Cambridge Res Lab, 65-76. *Concurrent Pos:* Res physicist, Wentworth Inst, 61-63. *Mem:* Phys Soc Japan; Spectros Soc Japan; Optical Soc Am. *Res:* Determination of properties of ground and excited electronic states of molecules or atoms by high resolution vacuum ultraviolet spectroscopy such as nitrogen, oxygen, carbon monoxide and rare gases. *Mailing Add:* 11 Bellflower St Lexington MA 02173

**YOSHINO, TIMOTHY PHILLIP,** PARASITOLOGY, IMMUNOBIOLOGY. *Current Pos:* assoc prof, 88-91, PROF PATHOBIOL, UNIV WIS-MADISON, 91-, DIR CELLULAR & MOLECULAR PARISITOL TRAINING PROG, 92- *Personal Data:* b Turlock, Calif, Apr 5, 48; m 75; c 2. *Educ:* Univ Calif, Santa Barbara, BA, 70, MA, 71, PhD(biol), 75. *Honors & Awards:* Res Career Develop Award, Nat Inst Allergy & Infectious Dis, 84; Henry Baldwin Ward Medal, Amer Soc Parasitologists, 94. *Prof Exp:* Res assoc parasitol, Univ Calif, Santa Barbara, 71-73; res assoc invert immunol, Lehigh Univ, 75-77; from asst prof to assoc prof zool, Univ Okla, 78-88. *Concurrent Pos:* USPHS res fel, Nat Inst Allergy & Infectious Dis, 75. *Mem:* Am Soc Parasitologists; Soc Invert Path; AAAS; Am Soc Trop Med Hyg; Int Soc Develop Comp Immunol. *Res:* Humoral and cellular mechanisms of internal defense in bivalve and gastropod molluscs; immunobiology of schistosome-mollusc interactions; parasitic castration in molluscs; neurobiology of molluscan vectors of schistosomiasis. *Mailing Add:* Dept Pathobiol Sci Rm 4468 Vet Med Univ Wis-Madison 2015 Linden Dr W Madison WI 53706. *E-Mail:* yoshinot@svm.vetmed.wisc.edu

**YOSHIZUMI, SHOZO,** LOW TEMPERATURE PHYSICS. *Current Pos:* SR PHYSICIST, BIOMAGNETIC TECH INC, 92- *Personal Data:* b Japan, 1954. *Educ:* Stanford Univ, PhD(nat sci), 86. *Mem:* Am Phys Soc. *Mailing Add:* Biomagnetic Tech Inc 9727 Pacific Heights Blvd San Diego CA 92121

**YOSS, KENNETH M,** ASTRONOMY. *Current Pos:* prof, 64-93, EMER PROF ASTRON, UNIV ILL, URBANA, 93- *Personal Data:* b Hudson, Iowa, Jan 13, 26; m 55, Norma Henkel; c Roberta, Barbara & Ann. *Educ:* Univ Mich, BS, 48, MS, 50, PhD(astron), 53. *Prof Exp:* Asst prof astron & physics, Wilson Col, 52-53; from asst prof to assoc prof, La State Univ, 53-59; assoc prof astron, Mt Holyoke Col, 59-64. *Mem:* Am Astron Soc; Int Astron Union. *Res:* Spectrophotometry of objective prism and slit spectra; spectral and luminosity classification; radial velocities; galactic structure. *Mailing Add:* 9 Shuman Circle Urbana IL 61801. *Fax:* 217-244-7638; *E-Mail:* yoss@uhx.cso.uiuc.edu

**YOSS, ROBERT EUGENE,** NEUROANATOMY, NEUROLOGY. *Current Pos:* from asst prof to prof neurol, Mayo Grad Sch Med, Univ Minn, 57-82, CONSULT, MAYO CLIN, 57-, EMER PROF NEUROL, 82- *Personal Data:* b Spooner, Wis, Nov 28, 24; m 47; c 3. *Educ:* Univ Tenn, MD, 48; Univ Mich, MS & PhD(neuroanat), 52. *Prof Exp:* From instr to asst prof anat, Med Sch, Univ Mich, 49-54. *Concurrent Pos:* Fel neurol, Mayo Grad Sch Med, Univ Minn, 55-57. *Mem:* Am Asn Anat. *Res:* Anatomy of spinal cord; narcolepsy. *Mailing Add:* Rte 1 Box 258E Zumbro Falls MN 55991-9768

**YOST, FREDERICK GORDON,** METALLURGY. *Current Pos:* MEM TECH STAFF, SANDIA LABS, 72- *Personal Data:* b Norwalk, Conn, Aug 29, 40; m 63; c 2. *Educ:* Polytech Inst Brooklyn, BSMetE, 66; Iowa State Univ, PhD(metall), 72. *Mem:* Am Soc Metals; Am Inst Mining, Metall & Petrol Engrs; Mat Res Soc. *Res:* Kinetics of solid state phase transformations in metals and alloys, especially those in microelectronics. *Mailing Add:* MS 0340 Orgn 1831 Bldg 806 Rm 286 Sandia Labs Albuquerque NM 87185

**YOST, GAROLD STEVEN,** DRUG METABOLISM, MEDICINAL CHEMISTRY. *Current Pos:* ASST PROF, COL PHARM, WASH STATE UNIV, 81- *Personal Data:* b Denver, Colo, Sept 8, 49; m 78. *Educ:* Bethel Col, BS, 71; Univ Hawaii, MS, 74; Colo State Univ, PhD(chem), 77. *Prof Exp:* Fel pharmaceut chem, Univ Calif, San Francisco, 77-78; instr chem, Towson State Univ, 78-81. *Concurrent Pos:* Vis lectr, Dept Pharmacol, Johns Hopkins Univ, 79-81. *Mem:* Am Chem Soc; Int Soc Study Xenobiotics; Sigma Xi. *Res:* Marine and terrestrial natural products including poisonous feedstocks; suicidal inhibitors of cytochrome P-450 and other enzymes; stereoselective drug metabolism involving cytochrome P-450 and glucuronyltransferase. *Mailing Add:* Dept Pharm & Toxicol Univ Utah 112 Skaggs Hall Salt Lake City UT 84112-1107. *Fax:* 801-585-3945

**YOST, JOHN FRANKLIN,** organic chemistry; deceased, see previous edition for last biography

**YOST, JOHN R(OBARTS), JR,** CHEMICAL ENGINEERING. *Current Pos:* PRES, CHEM SOURCES, 93- *Personal Data:* b Phoenixville, Pa, July 10, 23; m 47; c 2. *Educ:* Ursinus Col, BS, 44; Univ Pa, MS, 49. *Prof Exp:* Process develop engr, Res Labs, Sharples Corp, 49-51; process develop engr, Merck & Co, 51-54; sect head, Process Eng, E R Squibb & Sons Div, Olin Mathieson Chem Corp, 54-61, head chem pilot plant, 61-67; vpres mfg, Ott Chem Co, 67-70, exec vpres, 70-73; pres, Muskegon Chem Co, 74- *Mem:* Am Chem Soc; Am Inst Chem Engrs. *Res:* Pharmaceutical compounds; unit processes leading to synthetic organic compounds; distillation and solvent extraction. *Mailing Add:* 806 Ruddiman Ave North Muskegon MI 49445-2928

**YOST, RICHARD A,** MASS SPECTROMETRY, INSTRUMENTATION. *Current Pos:* from asst prof to assoc prof, 79-89, PROF CHEM, UNIV FLA, 89- *Personal Data:* b Martins Ferry, Ohio, May 31, 53; m 79, Katherine S Fitzgerald; c Sarah E, Michael P & Matthew J. *Educ:* Univ Ariz, BS, 74; Mich State Univ, PhD(anal chem), 79. *Honors & Awards:* Distinguished Contrib to Mass Spectrometry Award, Am Soc Mass Spectrometry, 93. *Prof Exp:* Fel, NSF, 75-79 & Am Chem Soc Anal Div, 77-78. *Concurrent Pos:* Vis scientist, LaTrobe Univ, Victoria, Australia, 77; consult, Lawrence Livermore Nat Lab, 80-84, Finnigan MAT, 80-, Bristol-Myers Squibb, 89-; Chem rev bd, Livermore Nat Lab, 95- *Mem:* Am Chem Soc; Am Soc Mass Spectrometry; Int Chemometrics Soc. *Res:* Development of new analytical chemistry techniques using modern instrumentation and digital computers; application of new techniques in areas such as environmental, clinical and forensic chemistry. *Mailing Add:* Dept Chem Univ Fla Gainesville FL 32611. *Fax:* 904-392-4651; *E-Mail:* ryost@chem.ufl.edu

**YOST, ROBERT STANLEY,** ORGANIC CHEMISTRY. *Current Pos:* RETIRED. *Personal Data:* b Pottsville, Pa, Jan 24, 21; m 43, Sybil McNair; c James E & Robert S Jr. *Educ:* Pa State Univ, BS, 42; Duke Univ, PhD(org chem), 48. *Prof Exp:* Chemist, Hercules Powder Co, 42-43; lab instr chem, Duke Univ, 43-44; chemist, Res Labs, Rohm & Haas Co, 44-46, 47-59 & 68-89, head process res group, Redstone Res Labs, 59-68. *Mem:* Am Chem Soc. *Res:* Organic synthesis including synthetic resins and explosives; process research. *Mailing Add:* 4542 Holiday Heights Dr Oakwood GA 30566

**YOST, WILLIAM A,** PSYCHOACOUSTICS, PSYCHOPHYSICS. *Current Pos:* assoc prof, 77-78, PROF HEARING SCI, PSYCHOL & OTOLARYNGOL, LOYOLA UNIV, CHICAGO, 79- *Personal Data:* b Dallas, Tex, Sept 21, 44; m 69, Lee Prater; c 2. *Educ:* Colo Col, BA, 66; Ind Univ, Bloomington, PhD(psychol), 70. *Hon Degrees:* DSc, Colo Col, 97. *Prof Exp:* NSF fel, Univ Calif, San Diego, 70-71; asst prof speech psychol, Univ Fla, 71-74, assoc prof psychol, 74-77. *Concurrent Pos:* Mem & chmn, Comt Acoust Stand, 72-75; prog officer, Nat Sci Found, 82-84; adv panel, NSF, 80-86; assoc ed, J Acoust Soc Am, 87-; chair, Acoust Soc Am, 91-94, Nat Acad Sci, 93- *Mem:* Fel Acoust Soc Am; Am Psychol Asn; Sigma Xi; Int Audiol Soc; fel AAAS; Asn Res Otolaryngol (secy-treas, 85-87, pres, 89); Am Psychol Soc; fel Am Speech Hearing Lang Asn. *Res:* Binaural hearing; pitch perception; speech perception; auditory sensitivity and discrimination; noise pollution; complex sound processing. *Mailing Add:* Parmly Hearing Inst Loyola Univ Chicago 6525 N Sheridan Rd Chicago IL 60626. *Fax:* 773-508-2719; *E-Mail:* wyost@luc.edu

**YOTIS, WILLIAM WILLIAM,** MICROBIOLOGY. *Current Pos:* from instr to assoc prof, 60-72, interim chmn, 64-65, PROF MICROBIOL, MED SCH, LOYOLA UNIV CHICAGO, 73- *Personal Data:* b Almyros, Greece, Jan 17, 30; US citizen; m 57; c 3. *Educ:* Wayne State Univ, BS, 54, MS, 56; Northwestern Univ, PhD(microbiol), 60. *Prof Exp:* Asst microbiol, Wayne State Univ, 54-56; clin bacteriologist, Univ Hosp, Univ Mich, 56-57. *Concurrent Pos:* Res grants, NIH, 60-89, Eli Lilly Res Labs, 65-66, Syntex Res Labs, 66-68, Upjohn Co, 66-67, Off Naval Res grant, 89-92; consult, Am Type Cult Collection, 66-; vis scientist, Argonne Nat Lab, 77-88. *Mem:* AAAS; Am Med Asn; Am Soc Microbiol; Am Asn Dent Res; NY Acad Sci. *Res:* Investigations on mechanisms of microbial pathogenicity; nonspecific host defense mechanisms; bactericidal activity of body fluids; staphylococcal host-parasite relationship; hormonal influence on infection; bacterial physiology; isotachophoresis and scanning isoelectric focusing of medically important proteins; cariostasis by fluoride; oral microbiology with emphasis on potential periodonto pathogens. *Mailing Add:* 100 N La Salle St Chicago IL 60602

**YOU, KWAN-SA,** enzymology, cell biology, for more information see previous edition

**YOU, LI,** QUANTUM OPTICS, ATOM OPTICS. *Current Pos:* ASST PROF PHYSICS, GA INST TECHNOL, 96- *Personal Data:* m 88, Yongmei Wang. *Educ:* Univ Colo, Boulder, PhD(physics), 93. *Prof Exp:* NSF postdoctoral fel, Harvard Univ, 93-96. *Concurrent Pos:* NSF career Award, Ga Inst Technol, 97- & Off Naval Res Young Investr Award, 97- *Mem:* Am Phys Soc; Overseas Chinese Physicists Asn. *Res:* Theoretical processes involving light/matter interaction. *Mailing Add:* 1406F Druid Valley Dr Atlanta GA 30329. *E-Mail:* li.you@physics.gatech.edu

**YOUD, THOMAS LESLIE,** SOIL MECHANICS, EARTHQUAKE ENGINEERING. *Current Pos:* PROF CIVIL ENG, BRIGHAM YOUNG UNIV, PROVO, UTAH, 84- *Personal Data:* b Spanish Fork, Utah, Apr 2, 38; m 62, Denice; c Verlin, Lance, Melinda, Thomas & Emily. *Educ:* Brigham Young Univ, BES, 64; Iowa State Univ, PhD(civil eng), 67. *Prof Exp:* Res & civil engr, US Geol Surv, Menlo Park, 67-84. *Mem:* Am Soc Civil Engrs; Int Soc Soil Mech & Found Engrs; Earthquake Eng Res Inst. *Res:* Liquefaction of soils caused by earthquakes. *Mailing Add:* 1132 E 1010 N Orem UT 84057-4306

**YOUDELIS, W(ILLIAM) V(INCENT),** PHYSICAL METALLURGY. *Current Pos:* from assoc prof to prof, 65-96, head, Dept Eng Mat, 72-85, grad coordr, Mat Prog, Dept Mech Eng, 85-96, EMER PROF PHYS METALL, UNIV WINDSOR, 96-; PRES, YOUDELIS ASSOCS INC, 77-; PRES, INDISPERSE INDUST INC, WINDSOR, ONT, 85- *Personal Data:* b Edmonton, Alta, Aug 1, 31; div; c Grant & Blair. *Educ:* Univ Alta, BSc, 52; McGill Univ, MEng, 56, PhD(metall eng), 58. *Honors & Awards:* Hollenback Mem Prize, 93. *Prof Exp:* Mine engr, Steep Rock Iron Mines, Ont, 52-54; from asst prof to assoc prof phys metall, Univ Alta, 58-65. *Mem:* AAAS; Am Soc Metals; Am Inst Mining, Metall & Petrol Engrs; Can Inst Mining & Metall; Metals Soc; Inst Mat; Am Fenadryman's Soc; Asn Prof Engr Ont. *Res:* Solidification; thermodynamics and kinetics of phase transformations; aluminum alloys dental alloys; electronic materials. *Mailing Add:* Dept Mech & Mat Eng Univ Windsor Windsor ON N9B 3P4 Can

**YOUKER, JAMES EDWARD,** RADIOLOGY. *Current Pos:* PROF RADIOL & CHMN DEPT, MILWAUKEE COUNTY GEN HOSP, WIS, 68- *Personal Data:* b Cooperstown, NY, Nov 13, 28; div; c 2. *Educ:* Colgate Univ, AB, 50; Univ Buffalo, MD, 54; Am Bd Radiol, dipl, 60. *Prof Exp:* Asst prof radiol, Med Col Va, 61-63; from asst prof to assoc prof, Univ Calif, San Francisco, 64-68. *Concurrent Pos:* NIH res fel, Allmanna Sjukhuset, Malmo, Sweden, 62 & 63; attend radiologist, Proj HOPE, Indonesia, 58; USPHS grant dir, Training Radiologist & Technician Teams in Mammography, & co-dir, Training Prog Cardiovasc Radiol, 65-68. *Mem:* Radiol Soc NAm; Am Col Radiol; Asn Univ Radiol; Int Soc Lymphology. *Res:* Pulmonary function changes with lymphographic contrast media; pathology of congenital heart disease; chylous ascites and the spectrum of the disease. *Mailing Add:* Dept Radiol Med Col Wis Froedtert Meml Lutheran Hosp 9200 W Wisconsin Ave Milwaukee WI 53226-3212

**YOUKER, JOHN,** PHYSICAL CHEMISTRY, ANALYTICAL CHEMISTRY. *Current Pos:* from asst prof to assoc prof, 69-81, PROF CHEM, HUDSON VALLEY COMMUNITY COL, 81-, DEPT CHAIR, 89- *Personal Data:* b Auburn, NY, Sept 7, 43; m 67, Sandra Matera; c 4. *Educ:* Rensselaer Polytech Inst, BS, 65, PhD(phys chem), 69. *Prof Exp:* Chemist, Coated Abrasive & Tape Div, Norton Co, 68-69. *Concurrent Pos:* Hazardous mat coordr, Rensselaer Co. *Mem:* Am Chem Soc; Sigma Xi. *Res:* Spectroscopy; analytical chemistry; environmental science. *Mailing Add:* 203 Winter St Exten Troy NY 12180. *E-Mail:* youkejoh@office.hvcc.edu

**YOULA, DANTE C,** ELECTRICAL ENGINEERING, MICROWAVE ENGINEERING. *Current Pos:* PROF ELEC ENG & COMPUT SCI, POLYTECH UNIV, 55- *Personal Data:* b Brooklyn, NY, Oct 17, 25. *Educ:* City Col New York, BEE, 47; NY Univ, MS, 50. *Honors & Awards:* Baker Award, Inst Elec & Electronics Engrs, 64, 100th Yr Commemorative Medal for Contrib to Circuit Theory & Systs, 84, Field Award in Systs Sci & Eng, 88; Guillemin-Cauer Circuit Theory Award, 73; Tech Achievement Award, Circuit & Systs Soc, Inst Elec & Electronics Engrs, 91. *Prof Exp:* Engr, Jet Propulsion Labs, Calif Inst Technol, Pasadena, 51-54. *Concurrent Pos:* Ed, Trans on Circuit Theory, Inst Elec & Electronics Engrs, 65-67. *Mem:* Nat Acad Eng; fel Inst Elec & Electronics Engrs; Sigma Xi; NY Acad Sci. *Res:* Network theory and synthesis-linear and nonlinear; stability problem of time-varying structures; statistical communication theory; noise in linear and nonlinear systems; radar detection estimation and coding; feedback system theory. *Mailing Add:* Dept Elec Eng & Comput Sci Polytech Univ Long Island Ctr Farmingdale NY 11735

**YOULE, RICHARD JAMES,** PROTEIN TOXINS, RIBONUCLEASES. *Current Pos:* Staff fel, NIMH, NIH, 78-80, sr staff fel, lab neurochem, 81-84, sr investr, 84-88, SECT CHIEF, SURG NEUROL BR, NAT INST NEUROL & COMMUN DIS & STROKE, NIH, 88- *Personal Data:* b Concord, Calif, Sept 20, 51; m 81; c 3. *Educ:* Albion Col, AB, 74; Univ SC, PhD(biol), 77. *Res:* The mechanism of protein toxins (ricin and diptheria and

ribonucleases), inhibition of protein synthesis and how they can be linked to cell surface binding species, such as monoclonal antibodies, to create cell-type-specific toxins; physiological role of cell death and the mechanism of apoptosis. *Mailing Add:* Nat Inst Neurol & Commun Dis & Stroke NIH Bldg 10 Rm 5D-37 Bethesda MD 20205. *Fax:* 301-402-0380; *E-Mail:* youle@helix.nih.gov

**YOUMANS, HUBERT LAFAY,** ANALYTICAL CHEMISTRY. *Current Pos:* RETIRED. *Personal Data:* b Lexsy, Ga, Aug 2, 25; m 51; c 1. *Educ:* Emory Univ, AB, 49, MS, 50; La State Univ, PhD(anal chem), 61. *Prof Exp:* Chemist, Savannah River Plant, E I du Pont de Nemours & Co, SC, 52-57; develop chemist, Sucrochem Div, Colonial Sugars Co, Lab, 57-58; asst prof chem, Ft Hays Kans State Col, 61-64; res chemist, Atlas Chem Indust, Inc, Del, 64-67; from assoc prof to prof chem, Western Carolina Univ, 67-89. *Mem:* Am Chem Soc. *Res:* Absorptiometry; analytical separations; communications for chemistry students. *Mailing Add:* Speedwell Acres Cullowhee NC 28723

**YOUMANS, JULIAN RAY,** NEUROSURGERY. *Current Pos:* PROF NEUROSURG & CHIEF DEPT, SCH MED, UNIV CALIF, DAVIS, 67- *Personal Data:* b Baxley, Ga, Jan 2, 28; m 54; c 3. *Educ:* Emory Univ, BS, 49, MD, 52; Univ Mich, MS, 55, PhD(neuroanat), 57; Am Bd Neurol Surg, dipl, 60. *Prof Exp:* From asst prof to assoc prof neurosurg, Sch Med, Univ Miss, 59-63; from assoc prof to prof, Med Col SC, 63-67, chief div, 63-67. *Mem:* AMA; Am Acad Neurol; Am Asn Surg of Trauma; Am Col Surg; Am Asn Automotive Med. *Res:* Physiology of cerebral blood flow. *Mailing Add:* Dept Neurol Surg Univ Calif Davis Sch Med 2516 Stockton Blvd Sacramento CA 95817-2208

**YOUMANS, WILLIAM BARTON,** PHYSIOLOGY, AUTONOMIC NERVOUS SYSTEM & PHARMACOLOGY. *Current Pos:* chmn dept, 52-71, prof, 52-76, EMER PROF PHYSIOL, SCH MED, UNIV WIS-MADISON, 76- *Personal Data:* b Cincinnati, Ohio, Feb 3, 10; m 32, Cynthia Holbrook; c 3. *Educ:* Western Ky State Col, BS, 32, MA, 33; Univ Wis, PhD(med physiol), 38; Univ Ore, MD, 44. *Prof Exp:* Instr biol, Western Ky State Col, 32-35; from asst to instr physiol, Univ Wis, 35-38; from instr to prof, Med Sch, Univ Ore, 38-52, head dept, 45-52. *Concurrent Pos:* USPHS spec fel, 61-62; intern, Henry Ford Hosp, 44-45; mem, Physiol Study Sect, USPHS, 52-56 & Physiol Training Comt, 58-62. *Mem:* Am Physiol Soc. *Res:* Innervation of intestine; gastrointestinal motility; visceral reflexes; cardiac innervation, neurohormones; angiotensin; pharmacology. *Mailing Add:* 118 Klahanie View Lane Port Angeles WA 98362

**YOUNATHAN, EZZAT SAAD,** BIOCHEMISTRY, SYNTHETIC ORGANIC & NATURAL PRODUCTS CHEMISTRY. *Current Pos:* PROF BIOCHEM, LA STATE UNIV, BATON ROUGE, 68- *Personal Data:* b Deirut, Egypt, Aug 25, 22; nat US; m 58, Margaret J Tims; c Nadya & Carol Miriam (Younathan). *Educ:* Univ Cairo, BSc, 44; Fla State Univ, MA, 53, PhD, 55. *Prof Exp:* Chemist, Govt Labs, Egypt, 44-50; Seagrams' Int Training Prog fel, 50-51; res asst, Fla State Univ, 51-55, asst prof, 58-59; res assoc, Col Med, Univ Ill, 55-57; from asst prof to assoc prof biochem, Sch Med, Univ Ark, Little Rock, 59-66, actg head dept, 63-66; NIH spec fel & vis prof, Inst Enzyme Res, Univ Wis, 66-67. *Concurrent Pos:* Vis prof, Dept Biochem, Univ Calif, Berkeley, 78. *Mem:* Am Soc Biochem & Molecular Biol; Am Chem Soc; Soc Exp Biol & Med; AMA. *Res:* Mechanism of enzyme action; protein chemistry; control of carbohydrate metabolism; experimental diabetes. *Mailing Add:* Dept Biochem La State Univ 322 Choppin Hall Baton Rouge LA 70803-1806. *Fax:* 504-388-5321

**YOUNATHAN, MARGARET TIMS,** FOOD SCIENCE, NUTRITION. *Current Pos:* from assoc prof to prof, 71-93, EMER PROF HUMAN FOOD & NUTRIT, LA STATE UNIV, BATON ROUGE, 94- *Personal Data:* b Clinton, Miss, Apr 25, 26; m 58, Ezzat S; c Janet N & Carol M. *Educ:* Univ Southern Miss, BA, 46, BS, 50; Univ Tenn, MS, 51; Fla State Univ, PhD(food & nutrit), 58. *Prof Exp:* Instr food & nutrit, Ore State Univ, 51-55; res fel, Qm Food & Container Inst, Fla State Univ, 58-59; instr pediat, Sch Med, Univ Ark, Little Rock, 62-65, asst prof, 65-68. *Concurrent Pos:* Consult, Ark State Health Dept, 62-68; consult, USAID, Sierra Leone, WAfrica, 84 & Jamaica, WI, 87. *Mem:* Inst Food Technol; Am Home Econ Asn; Am Dietetic Asn; Am Meat Sci Asn; Am Inst Nutrit. *Res:* Heme pigments; antioxidants; lipid oxidation; infant and child nutrition; effects of products of lipid oxidation on biological tissue. *Mailing Add:* Human Nutrit & Food Sch Human Ecol La State Univ Baton Rouge LA 70806-6023. *Fax:* 504-388-2697

**YOUNES, MAGDY K,** EXERCISE PHYSIOLOGY, RESPIRATION. *Current Pos:* PROF MED, HEALTH SCI CTR, MAN UNIV, 82- *Personal Data:* b Damanhur, Egypt, July 13, 39. *Educ:* Alexandria Univ, Egypt, MD, 62; McGill Univ, Montreal, PhD(pulmonary physiol), 73; FRCP(C). *Mem:* Am Thoracic Soc; Am Physiol Soc; Am Col Chest Physicians. *Mailing Add:* Dept Int Med Univ Man Resp Hosp Rm RS-307 810 Sherbrook St Winnipeg MB R3A 1R8 Can. *Fax:* 204-787-2420

**YOUNES, USAMA E,** POLYMER COMPOSITES, POLYURETHANE ELASTOMERS. *Current Pos:* RES ADV, ARCO CHEM CO, 80- *Personal Data:* b Haifa, Israel, Sept 6, 49; US citizen; m 86, Najla Akkawi; c Camilia & Emile. *Educ:* Warren Wilson Col, BA, 71; Western Carolina Univ, MS, 73; Univ New Orleans, PhD(org chem), 78. *Prof Exp:* Fel polymer chem, Carnegie-Mellon Univ, 78-80. *Mem:* Soc Petrol Engrs; Footwear Indust Am; Am Chem Soc. *Res:* Syntheses and manufacturing of advanced composite materials through structural reaction injection moldings; syntheses of polyurethanes and polystyrenes as well as inherently flame retardant polymers; granted 30 patents; author of eleven publications. *Mailing Add:* 127 Bantery Rd West Chester PA 19380. *Fax:* 610-359-5552

**YOUNG, AINSLIE THOMAS, JR,** POLYMER CHEMISTRY. *Current Pos:* PROJ MGR, LOS ALAMOS NAT LAB, 89- *Personal Data:* b Norman, Okla, Mar 3, 43; m 68. *Educ:* Memphis State Univ, BS, 66, MS, 68; Univ Ky, PhD(phys chem), 71. *Prof Exp:* Fel, Univ Calif, Berkeley, 71-73 & La State Univ, Baton Rouge, 73-74; res chemist polymer chem, Ctr Res Lab, Mead Corp, 74-80; res chemist polymer chem, Los Alamos Nat Lab, 80-82, sect leader polymer chem, 82-85, proj mgr fusion prog, 85; consult, 85-88. *Mem:* Am Chem Soc; Sigma Xi; AAAS. *Res:* Applied polymer science. *Mailing Add:* 242 Rio Bravo Los Alamos NM 87544-3847

**YOUNG, ALLEN MARCUS,** ECOLOGY. *Current Pos:* cur & head, Dept Invertebrate Zool, 75-90, CUR ZOOL, MILWAUKEE PUB MUS, 91-, VPRES COLLECTION RES & PUB PROG, 94- *Personal Data:* b Ossining, NY, Feb 23, 42; div. *Educ:* State Univ NY New Platz, BA, 64; Univ Chicago, PhD(zool), 68. *Prof Exp:* Orgn Trop Studies, Inc fel for study in Costa Rica, Univ Chicago, 68-70; asst prof biol, Lawrence Univ, Appleton, Wis, 70-75. *Concurrent Pos:* NSF fel for study in Costa Rica, Lawrence Univ, 71-74; NSF res grant, 75-; res assoc, Nat Mus Costa Rica, 75-; Am Cocoa Res Inst grant, 78- *Mem:* AAAS; Ecol Soc Am; Lepidop Soc; Asn Trop Biol. *Res:* Population biology and behavior of neotropical Lepidoptera and Cicadidae; ecology of laboratory populations of Tribolium; insect pollination of cocoa. *Mailing Add:* 7461 N Lombardi Rd Milwaukee WI 53217

**YOUNG, ALVIN L,** PESTICIDE CHEMISTRY & TOXICOLOGY, BIOTECHNOLOGY SCIENCE & SCIENCE POLICY. *Current Pos:* DIR OFF AGR BIOTECHNOL, USDA, WASHINGTON, DC, 87- *Personal Data:* b Laramie, Wyo, Aug 3, 42; m 66, Gaela M Foss; c Kristian L & Anna M. *Educ:* Univ Wyo, BS, 64, MS, 65; Kans State Univ, PhD(agron), 68. *Honors & Awards:* Woodroof Lectr, 91. *Prof Exp:* Proj scientist environ res, Armament Lab, AFB, USAF, 68-71, environ sci consult, Occup & Environ Health Lab, Brooks AFB, San Antonio, 77-79, Sch Aerospace Med Epidemiol Div, 79-81; asst prof life sci, Dept Life Sci, USAF Acad, Colo, 71-74, assoc prof biol sci, Dept Chem & Biol Sci, 74-77, dir res, 75-77; spec asst environ sci, Dept Med & Surg, Vet Admin, Washington, DC, 81-83; sr policy analyst life sci, Off Sci & Technol Policy, Exec Off of the Pres, Washington, DC, 84-87. *Concurrent Pos:* Vis assoc prof, Univ Colo, Colorado Springs, 75-77; adv environ toxicol, Seveso Authority, Milan, Italy, 77-85, Australian Dept Vet Affairs, Woden Act, 83-85; mem, Whitehouse Agent Orange Working Groups, Washington, DC, 81-86, Joint Coun Food & Agr Sci, USDA, 84-87; chmn, Comt Interagency Radiation Res & Policy Coord, Off Sci & Technol Policy, 84-94. *Mem:* Sigma Xi; Am Soc Agron; Weed Sci Soc Am; Am Chem Soc; AAAS; Soc Environ Toxicol & Chem. *Res:* Environmental fate, toxicology and human risks of the tetrachlorodibenzo-p-dioxins; ecological impact and toxicity of the pesticides used in Vietnam; science policy of risk assessment/risk management applied to environmental issues. *Mailing Add:* 8209 Seven Pines Lane Waldorf MD 20603. *Fax:* 703-325-4429

**YOUNG, ANDREW TIPTON,** ASTRONOMICAL PHOTOMETRY, PLANETARY ASTRONOMY & ATMOSPHERIC OPTICS. *Current Pos:* ADJ ASSOC PROF ASTRON, SAN DIEGO STATE UNIV, 81- *Personal Data:* b Canton, Ohio, Apr 4, 35; m 54, 63, 68, Louise Gray; c 2. *Educ:* Oberlin Col, BA, 55; Harvard Univ, MA, 57, PhD(astron), 62. *Prof Exp:* Res fel, Observ, Harvard Univ, 60-65, lectr astron, 62-65; asst prof, Univ Tex, 65-67; mem tech staff, Aerospace Corp, 67-68 & Jet Propulsion Lab, 68-73; res scientist, Tex A&M Univ, 73-75, vis asst prof physics, 75-78, res scientist, 78-80. *Concurrent Pos:* Co-investr TV experiments, Mariner Mars, 69 & 71; consult, NASA & Texas A&M Univ, 94-97; assoc ed, ICARUS, 77-91; guest prof, Europ Southern Observ, 92-93. *Mem:* Fel AAAS; Am Astron Soc; fel Royal Astron Soc; fel Optical Soc Am; Int Astron Union. *Res:* Observational astronomy; astronomical photometry and instrumentation; photomultipliers; scintillation; planetary physics; atmospheric refraction. *Mailing Add:* Dept Astron San Diego State Univ San Diego CA 92182-1221. *Fax:* 619-594-1413; *E-Mail:* aty@mintaka.sdsu.edu

**YOUNG, ANNE B,** NEUROLOGY. *Current Pos:* JULIEANNE DORN PROF NEUROL, HARVARD MED SCH, 91-; CHIEF, NEUROLOGY SERV, MASS GEN HOSP, 91- *Educ:* Vassar Col, AB, 69; Johns Hopkins Univ, MD, 73, PhD(pharmacol), 74. *Honors & Awards:* Milton Wexler Award for Huntington's Dis Res, Huntington's Dis Soc Am, 89; Weinstein-Goldenson Award, United Cerebral Palsy Asn Inc, 90; David Seegal vis prof, Columbia Univ, 96; Presidential Lectr, Am Acad Neurol, 96. *Prof Exp:* From asst prof to prof chem, Dept Neurol, Univ Mich, 78-91. *Concurrent Pos:* Fel, Scottish Rite Found, Lexington, 73; med intern, Mt Zion Hosp & Med Ctr, San Francisco; neurol residency, Dept Neurol, Univ Calif, San Francisco; teacher-investr develop award, NIH, 79-84; fac develop award, Merck, 87-89. *Mem:* Inst Med-Nat Acad Sci. *Res:* Contributed numerous articles to professional journals. *Mailing Add:* Dept Neurol Mass Gen Hosp 14 Fruit St Boston MA 02114-2620

**YOUNG, ARTHUR,** ASTRONOMY. *Current Pos:* From asst prof to assoc prof, 67-74, PROF ASTRON, SAN DIEGO STATE UNIV, 74- *Personal Data:* b New York, NY, Jan 4, 40; m 60; c 2. *Educ:* Allegheny Col, BS, 60; Ind Univ, MA, 65, PhD(astron), 67. *Concurrent Pos:* Acad consult, Spitz Labs, 63-; vis staff scientist, High Altitude Observ, 81-82. *Mem:* Int Astron Union; Am Astron Soc. *Res:* Spectroscopy of cool stars; chromospheres and stellar magnetic activity; binary stars; hot pulsating stars. *Mailing Add:* Dept Astron San Diego State Univ San Diego CA 92182-0002. *E-Mail:* young@mintaka.sdsu.edu

**YOUNG, AUSTIN HARRY,** RADIATION CHEMISTRY, PHYSICAL TESTING OF PLASTICS. *Current Pos:* RETIRED. *Personal Data:* b Brighton, Mass, Oct 25, 28; m 58, Elizabeth Frank; c Katherine Anne (Schiffman) & Diane Elizabeth (Brown). *Educ:* Tufts Univ, BS, 50; Univ Wis, PhD(chem), 59. *Honors & Awards:* IR-100 Award, 78. *Prof Exp:* Develop chemist, Fabrics & Finishes Dept, EI du Pont de Nemours & Co, 50-51, supvr, Explosives Dept, 51-52; res asst, Army Chem Ctr, Edgewood, Md, 53-54; from res chemist to sr res chemist, A E Staley Mfg Co, 58-69, res assoc, 69-78, sr scientist, 78-83, mgr, Technol Group Polymerizable Prod Dept, 84-85, sr res scientist, 85-87, consult, 87 & 91-93; consult, Archer Daniels Midland Co, 87-90. *Mem:* AAAS; Am Chem Soc; Am Asn Cereal Chem; Sigma Xi. *Res:* Starch, colloid, polymer and radiation chemistry; kinetics; polymer synthesis and characterization; coatings; chromatography; thermal analysis; rheology; radiotracer techniques; graphic arts; health physics; microscopy; computer science; degradable plastics; environmental science; plastics technology; elementary particle physics; physics. *Mailing Add:* 151 Point Bluff Decatur IL 62521-5505

**YOUNG, BERNARD THEODORE,** PHYSICS. *Current Pos:* RETIRED. *Personal Data:* b Tarentum, Pa, Apr 13, 30; m 55; c 5. *Educ:* Slippery Rock State Univ, BS, 52; Tex A&M Univ, MS, 61, PhD(physics), 64; Angelo State Univ, BS, 87. *Prof Exp:* Res & develop engr, Tex Div, Dow Chem Co, 56-59; res asst physics, Tex A&M Univ, 60-63; from assoc prof to prof, Sam Houston State Univ, 63-68, dir, 65-68; assoc dean, Angelo State Univ, 68-70, prof physics & dean grad sch, 70-88, vpres acad affairs, 88-96. *Concurrent Pos:* Mem elem transparency proj, Tex Educ Agency, 66-67. *Mem:* Am Phys Soc; Am Asn Physics Teachers. *Res:* Molecular spectroscopy; atomic structure. *Mailing Add:* Off Acad Affairs Angelo State Univ 2601 W Ave N San Angelo TX 76909

**YOUNG, BING-LIN,** HIGH ENERGY PHYSICS. *Current Pos:* from asst prof to assoc prof, 70-79, PROF PHYSICS, IOWA STATE UNIV, 79- *Personal Data:* b Honan, China, Feb 3, 37; m 64, Theresa F Chen; c Rowena Y. *Educ:* Nat Taiwan Univ, BS, 59; Univ Minn, PhD(physics), 66. *Prof Exp:* Res assoc physics, Ind Univ, 66-68 & Brookhaven Nat Lab, 68-70. *Concurrent Pos:* Assoc physicist, Ames Lab, US AEC, 70-74, physicist, 74-79, sr physicist, 79-93; hon prof, Zhengzhon Univ, Henan Univ, Henan Normal Univ; guest prof, Jilin Univ, Dalian Univ Technol, Tongji Univ & Zhejion Univ, China; dir, Henan Fundamental & Appl Sci Res Inst, Henan, China, 90-; chair, Overseas Chinese Physics Asn, 93-94. *Mem:* Am Phys Soc; Overseas Chinese Physics Asn. *Res:* Theoretical physics of the elementary particles. *Mailing Add:* Dept Physics & Astron Iowa State Univ Ames IA 50011. *Fax:* 515-294-3747; *E-Mail:* young@alisuvax

**YOUNG, BRUCE ARTHUR,** AGRICULTURE, ANIMAL SCIENCE. *Current Pos:* PROF ANIMAL SCI, UNIV QUEENSLAND, AUSTRALIA. *Personal Data:* b Sydney, Australia, Jan 16, 39; m 95, June Scott; c Steven & Michael. *Educ:* Univ New Eng, Australia, BRurSc, 62, MRurSc, 65, PhD(physiol), 69. *Honors & Awards:* Excellence Res Award, Can Soc Animal Sci; Award Excellence Physiol, Can Asn Animal Breeders. *Prof Exp:* From asst prof to prof animal physiol, Univ Alta, 68-91. *Concurrent Pos:* Pres, World Conf Animal Prod, 88-93; int consult, animal prod. *Mem:* Am Soc Animal Sci; Can Soc Animal Sci; Agr Inst Can; Australian Soc Animal Prod. *Res:* Environmental physiology of animals; adaptation to physical environment; livestock production and energy metabolism in harsh environments. *Mailing Add:* Animal Prod Univ Queensland Gatton College Qld 4345 Australia. *Fax:* 61-754601444; *E-Mail:* bay@warigel.uqg.uq.edu.au

**YOUNG, C(HARLES), JR,** electronics, mechanical engineering, for more information see previous edition

**YOUNG, C(LARENCE) B(ERNARD) F(EHRLER),** chemistry, electrometallurgy; deceased, see previous edition for last biography

**YOUNG, C(HARLES) GILBERT,** ELECTROOPTICS, SYSTEMS ENGINEERING. *Current Pos:* tech dir infra red search & track, Martin Marietta, 87-88, mgr electro-optical eng, 88-90, mgr air defense initiatives, 90-91, mgr display systs, 91-93, STAFF SYSTS ENGR, MARTIN MARIETTA, 94-, SR ENGR, IBM, 93- *Personal Data:* b Pa, Feb 25, 30; m 59, Louise MacKeen; c Douglas, Steven & David. *Educ:* Elizabethtown Col, BA, 52; Univ Conn, MS, 56, PhD(physics), 61. *Prof Exp:* Physicist, Brookhaven Nat Lab, 56 & Navy Electronics Lab, Calif, 57; instr physics, Conn Col, 57-59; from res asst to instr, Univ Conn, 59-62; consult, Am Optical Co, 61-62, sr physicist, 62-65, mgr systs res dept, 65-70, gen mgr laser prod dept, 70-73, dir prod develop, 73-77; dir eng, Kollmorgen Corp, 77-79; asst tech mgr, New Eng Res Appln Ctr, Univ Conn, 79-80, dir tech develop combustion eng, 80-86; pres, Instaread Corp, 86-87. *Concurrent Pos:* Adj instr, Grad Sch Bus, Univ Conn, 80. *Mem:* Sr mem Inst Elec & Electronics Engrs; Optical Soc Am; Am Phys Soc; Int Soc Optical Eng. *Res:* Development and design of electro-optic sensor and tracker systems; design and evaluation of visual display devices for use in simulation and training devices; granted 18 patents and published over 80 articles. *Mailing Add:* 1331 College Pt Winter Park FL 32789. *Fax:* 407-306-3718; *E-Mail:* young_gil@ccmail.orl.mmc.com

**YOUNG, CHARLES ALBERT,** INDUSTRIAL ORGANIC CHEMISTRY. *Current Pos:* RETIRED. *Personal Data:* b Dodge Center, Minn, Oct 11, 11; m 50; c 2. *Educ:* Purdue Univ, BS, 33; Univ Notre Dame, MS, 34, PhD(org chem), 36. *Prof Exp:* Asst chem, Univ Notre Dame, 33-36; staff chemist, Jackson Lab, E I du Pont de Nemours & Co, Inc, 36-60, staff chemist, Exp Sta, 60-76. *Mem:* Am Chem Soc. *Res:* Synthetic rubber; organic water repellants; adhesives; dye synthesis and application; industrial and automotive finishes. *Mailing Add:* 726 Loveville Rd Apt 30 Hockessin DE 19707

**YOUNG, CHARLES STUART HAMISH,** ANIMAL VIRUS GENETICS. *Current Pos:* asst prof, 74-82, res scientist, 82-85, ASSOC PROF VIROL & GENETICS, DEPT MICROBIOL, COLUMBIA UNIV, 85- *Personal Data:* b Plymouth, UK, Feb 2, 44; m 70, Frances V Holden; c Charles A. *Educ:* Oxford Univ, BA, 66, DPhil(genetics), 69. *Prof Exp:* Lectr genetics, Biol Dept, Princeton Univ, 70-71; sci officer, Virol Inst Med Res Coun, 71-74. *Mem:* Am Soc Microbiol; Am Soc Virol. *Res:* Mechanisms of genetic recombination and gene expression in eukaryotic cells using DNA-containing animal viruses as model systems. *Mailing Add:* Dept Microbiol Columbia Univ Col Physicians & Surgeons 630 W 168th St New York NY 10032-3702. *Fax:* 212-305-4179

**YOUNG, CHARLES WESLEY,** DAIRY BREEDING & MANAGEMENT. *Current Pos:* RETIRED. *Personal Data:* b Enid, Okla, Dec 2, 29; m 52; c 3. *Educ:* Okla State Univ, BS, 56; NC State Univ, MS, 58, PhD(animal indust), 61. *Prof Exp:* From asst prof to prof animal sci, Univ Minn, St Paul, 60-93. *Concurrent Pos:* Columnist, Hoard's Dairyman, 76-82. *Mem:* Am Dairy Sci Asn. *Res:* Systems of breeding in dairy cattle; relationship between size and production in dairy cattle; economics of selection for milk yield in dairy cattle; milk pricing and component differentials. *Mailing Add:* 8644 Callahan Trail Inver Grove Heights MN 55076

**YOUNG, CHARLES WILLIAM,** INTERNAL MEDICINE, CANCER. *Current Pos:* from res assoc to assoc, 62-71, ASSOC MEM, SLOAN-KETTERING INST CANCER RES, 71-, ASSOC PROF MED, MED COL, CORNELL UNIV, 76- *Personal Data:* b Denver, Colo, Nov 19, 30; m 63; c 3. *Educ:* Columbia Univ, AB, 52; Harvard Univ, MD, 56. *Prof Exp:* Intern med, Second Med Div, Bellevue Hosp, New York, 56-57, resident, Second Med Div, Bellevue Hosp & Mem Hosp, 57-59; asst prof med, Med Col, Cornell Univ, 66-76. *Concurrent Pos:* Asst prof med, Med Col, Cornell Univ, 66-76; attend physician, Mem Hosp, 78- *Mem:* AAAS; Am Asn Cancer Res; Am Soc Clin Oncol; Am Fedn Clin Res; NY Acad Sci. *Res:* Oncology; biochemical pharmacology; embryology. *Mailing Add:* Mem Sloan-Kettering Cancer Ctr 1275 York Ave Rm H1017 New York NY 10021-6007. *Fax:* 212-639-5850

**YOUNG, CLIFTON A,** inorganic chemistry; deceased, see previous edition for last biography

**YOUNG, CLYDE THOMAS,** FOOD SCIENCE. *Current Pos:* assoc prof, 76-80, PROF, NC STATE UNIV, 80- *Personal Data:* b Durham, NC, Aug 22, 30; m 55; c 5. *Educ:* NC State Univ, BS, 52, MS, 55; Okla State Univ, PhD(food sci), 70. *Prof Exp:* Instr chem & math, NC State Univ, 54-56; asst head claims dept, Anderson-Clayton & Co, Ga, 58-59; res chemist, Ga Inst Technol, 59-60; asst res chemist, Ga Sta, Univ Ga, 60-76. *Mem:* Am Peanut Res & Educ Soc; Inst Food Technologists. *Res:* Major investigations in changes and variations in biochemical constituents of peanuts-factors affecting aroma, flavor, color, maturation and protein during development, harvesting, curing, storage, roasting and processing. *Mailing Add:* Dept Food Sci NC State Univ Box 7624 Raleigh NC 27695-0001

**YOUNG, CRAIG MARDEN,** LARVAL ECOLOGY OF MARINE INVERTEBRATES, DEEP SEA BIOLOGY. *Current Pos:* asst scientist, 85-88, assoc scientist, 88-92, SR SCIENTIST, HARBOR BR OCEANOG INST, 92- *Personal Data:* m 76, Robyn L Boyle; c April, Andrew & Stephanie. *Educ:* Brigham Young Univ, BS, 75, MS, 78; Univ Alberta, PhD(zool), 82. *Prof Exp:* Assoc res biol, Fla State Univ, 82-85. *Concurrent Pos:* Vis instr, Bamfield Marine Sta, Can, 84, 85, Marine Biol Lab Woodshole, 88; vis prof, Kristineberg Marine Biol Sta, Sweden, Darling Marine Ctr, Univ Maine, 93; adj prof, Fla Inst Technol, 91-, Fla Atlantic Univ, 91-; prin investr, NSF, NATO. *Mem:* Am Soc Zoologists; Ecol Soc Am; Am Soc Limnol & Oceanog. *Res:* Reproduction and larval biology of benthic marine invertebrates; more than 60 publications in national and international journals. *Mailing Add:* Harbor Br Oceanog Inst 5600 US Hwy 1 N Ft Pierce FL 34946. *Fax:* 561-468-0757, 465-2446

**YOUNG, DANA,** mechanical engineering; deceased, see previous edition for last biography

**YOUNG, DAVID A,** PHYSICAL CHEMISTRY. *Current Pos:* PHYSICIST, LAWRENCE LIVERMORE LAB, 67- *Personal Data:* b Carmel, Calif, Sept 26, 42. *Educ:* Pomona Col, BA, 64; Univ Chicago, PhD(chem), 67. *Mem:* Am Phys Soc. *Res:* Statistical mechanics of gases, liquids and solids. *Mailing Add:* 1874 Peary Way Livermore CA 94550. *E-Mail:* young5@llnl.gov

**YOUNG, DAVID A(NTHONY),** CHEMICAL ENGINEERING, POLYMER CHEMISTRY. *Current Pos:* CONSULT, TELTECH COMMUN. *Personal Data:* b Pittsburgh, Pa, Jan 6, 21; m 45, Margaret E Dooley; c 5. *Educ:* Pa State Univ, BS, 42. *Prof Exp:* Chem engr, Sun Oil Co, 42-47 & Warwick Wax Co, 47-48; group leader, Chem Eng Process Develop Dept, Spencer Chem Co, 48-59; chief engr, Eng Sci Div, Am Metal Prod Co, 59-62; sect head solution polymerization, Gen Tire & Rubber Co, Ohio, 62-70; sr process engr, J F Pritchard & Co, Kansas City, 70-76; staff engr, Kansas City Div, Allied Signal Aerospace, 76-84. *Concurrent Pos:* Instr, Kans State Teachers Col, 59. *Mem:* Am Inst Chem Engrs. *Res:* Design, construction and start-up of new chemical plants; hydrogen sulfide and sulphur dioxide recovery from stack gases; evaporation and burning of pulp mill waste liquors; equipment design and procurement for new polymer facilities; pilot plant production of new polymers including polyethylenes, nylon, specialized poly BD's, propyleneoxide rubber and polyimides;

treatment to detoxify chemical wastewater streams; developed 3 equations describing process variables of HF Alkylation Plant that resulted in a substantial increase in aviation gasoline production during WWII. *Mailing Add:* 9501 Meadow Lane Leawood KS 66206

**YOUNG, DAVID ALLEN,** BOTANY, BIOCHEMICAL SYSTEMATICS. *Current Pos:* at DEPT BOT, CORNELL UNIV. *Personal Data:* b Pomona, Calif, July 31, 46; c 2. *Educ:* Calif State Univ, Fullerton, BA, 71, MA, 72; Claremont Grad Sch & Univ Ctr, PhD(bot), 75. *Prof Exp:* Lab instr & instr bot, Calif State Univ, Fullerton, 70-72; res asst, Rancho Santa Ana Bot Garden, Claremont, Calif, 72-75; asst prof, Union Col, 75-76; asst prof, 76-80, prof, Univ Ill, Urbana, 80- *Mem:* Bot Soc Am; Am Asn Plant Taxonomists; Int Asn Plant Taxonomists; Soc Study Evolution; Am Soc Naturalists. *Res:* Biochemical systematics of the angiosperms; angiosperm phylogeny; cladistics. *Mailing Add:* Dean Provost Acad Col State Univ 108 Space Administration Ft Collins CO 80323

**YOUNG, DAVID BRUCE,** PHYSIOLOGY. *Current Pos:* From instr to asst prof, 72-77, assoc prof, 77-81, PROF PHYSIOL, SCH MED, UNIV MISS, 81- *Personal Data:* b Pittsburgh, Pa, Mar 13, 45; m 65; c 3. *Educ:* Univ Colo, BA, 67; Ind Univ, PhD(physiol), 72. *Concurrent Pos:* NIH trainee, Sch Med, Univ Miss, 72-74. *Mem:* Fedn Am Soc Exp Biol. *Res:* Fluid and electrolyte balance control mechanisms; hypertension. *Mailing Add:* Dept Physiol Univ Miss Med Ctr 2500 N State St Jackson MS 39216-4505

**YOUNG, DAVID CALDWELL,** ORGANIC CHEMISTRY. *Current Pos:* RETIRED. *Personal Data:* b Memphis, Tenn, June 18, 24; m 55, Laura Fries; c Thomas Caldwell, David Bruce & Patricia Carol. *Educ:* Davidson Col, BS, 46; Univ Fla, MS, 48, PhD(chem), 50. *Prof Exp:* Chemist, Edgar C Britton Res Lab, Dow Chem Co, 50-53, group leader, 53-62, patents coordr, 62-65, asst to dir, 65-70, asst to dir chem biol res, 70-74, asst to dir pharmaceut res & develop, 74-76, sr res specialist, Hydrocarbons & Energy Res, 77-80, sr environ specialist, Environ Serv Dept, 81-86. *Concurrent Pos:* Mem bd dirs, Am Chem Soc, 84-89, exec comt, 87-89. *Mem:* Am Chem Soc. *Res:* Leuckart reaction; phthalaldehydic acid; organic research and process development; chemical patents; environmental regulations. *Mailing Add:* 1223 Holyrood St Midland MI 48640

**YOUNG, DAVID MARSHALL,** PATHOLOGY, VETERINARY MEDICINE. *Current Pos:* prof vet sci & head dept, 77-85, PROF COMP PATH, DEPT VET SCI, MONT STATE UNIV, 77-, COORDR BIOMED RES PROG, 86-, DIR, MONT OFF RURAL HEALTH, 95- *Personal Data:* b Minot, ND, Aug 26, 42; m 87, Carole Johnson; c 4. *Educ:* Colo State Univ, DVM, 66; Ohio State Univ, MS, 67, PhD(comp path), 70. *Honors & Awards:* Maurice Shahan Res Award, 66; C L Davis Jour Award, C L Davis Found Advan Vet Path, 73. *Prof Exp:* Comp pathologist, Lab Toxicol, Nat Cancer Inst, 70-77, head, Comp Path Sect, DCT, NIH, 73-77. *Concurrent Pos:* Sr staff fel, NIH, 70-73; consult pathologist, Statutory Adv Comt, Food & Drug Admin, Dept Health, Educ & Welfare, 71; mem fac, Found Advan Educ Sci, NIH, 72-77; prof, Wash, Alaska, Mont, Idaho Med Prog, Mont State Univ, 78-85, dir, Am Indian Res Opportunities Prog, 84- *Mem:* AAAS; Int Acad Path; Am Asn Path; Am Vet Med Asn; Soc Pharmacol & Environ Path; Am Asn Cancer Res; Sigma Xi; Orthop Res Soc. *Res:* Comparative pathology; endocrine pathology; cancer; mineral metabolism; orthopedic pathology; animal models of human disease; toxicology; other medical and health sciences. *Mailing Add:* Mont Off Rural Health 304 Culbertson Hall Mont State Univ Bozeman MT 59717. *Fax:* 406-994-5559; *E-Mail:* aaidy@quest. oscs.montana.edu

**YOUNG, DAVID MATHESON,** ENVIRONMENTAL CHEMISTRY. *Current Pos:* RETIRED. *Personal Data:* b London, Eng, Apr 19, 28; m 53; c 6. *Educ:* Univ London, BSc, 48, PhD(chem), 49. *Prof Exp:* Asst lectr phys chem, St Andrews Univ, 49-51; res assoc, Amherst Col, 51-52; res fel, Nat Res Coun Can, 52-53; Royal Mil Col, Can, 53-54 & 55-56; Humboldt scholar, Phys Chem Inst, Munich, 54-55; res chemist, Dow Chem Can, Inc, 56-58, supvr, Res & Develop Lab, 58-65, asst res mgr, 65-72, mgr chem res & develop, 72-75, mgr environ affairs, 75-82, mgr sci affairs, 82-93. *Mem:* Chem Inst Can. *Res:* Physical adsorption of gases; boron chemistry; gas chromatography; heterogeneous catalysis; photochemistry. *Mailing Add:* 1619 Lancaster Ave Sarnia ON N7V 3S7 Can

**YOUNG, DAVID MICHAEL,** MEDICINE. *Current Pos:* chmn, dept biochem & molecular biol, 79-81, PROF BIOCHEM, DEPT BIOCHEM & MOLECULAR BIOL, COL MED, UNIV FLA, 79-, PROF MED, 79-, PROF PEDIAT, 85- *Personal Data:* b Bluffton, Ind, Oct 11, 35; m 72; c 4. *Educ:* Duke Univ, BS, 57, MD, 59. *Prof Exp:* Staff scientist, Lab Cellular Physics & Metab, Nat Heart Inst, NIH, 60-62; asst prof biol, dept biol, McCollum-Pratt Inst, NIH, 60-62; from asst prof to assoc prof biol chem, Sch Med, Harvard Univ, 65-79, chmn PhD prog cell biol 72-76; chief, Lab Phys Biochem, Mass Gen Hosp, 65-79. *Concurrent Pos:* Vis scientist, McCollum-Pratt Inst, Johns Hopkins Univ, 62-63; mem res allocations comt, Am Heart Asn, 76-79; cell biol study sect, NIH, 77-81 & cell physiol study sect, 78-82, chmn, 80-; ed-in-chief, J Molecular & Cellular Biochem, 83- *Mem:* Am Soc Biol Chem; fel AAAS; Biophys Soc; Am Soc Clin Invest; Am Soc Cell Biol; NY Acad Sci. *Res:* Studies of the structure and function of cellular growth factors, particularly as they relate to cancer research and abnormal growth of cells; studies on nerve growth factor as it relates both to the development of the nervous system and its potential role in promoting wound healing; biochemical and cell biology approaches aimed at understanding the control of cell growth. *Mailing Add:* Dept Biochem Univ Fla Box J-245 Gainesville FL 32610

**YOUNG, DAVID MONAGHAN, JR,** MATHEMATICS. *Current Pos:* prof math & dir comput ctr, 58-70, PROF MATH & COMPUT SCI & DIR CTR NUMERICAL ANALYSIS, UNIV TEX, AUSTIN, 70- *Personal Data:* b Boston, Mass, Oct 20, 23; m 49; c 3. *Educ:* Webb Inst Naval Archit, BS, 44; Harvard Univ, MA, 47, PhD(math), 50. *Prof Exp:* Instr & res assoc math, Harvard Univ, 50-51; mathematician, Aberdeen Proving Ground, 51-52; assoc prof math, Univ Md, 52-55; mgr math anal dept, Ramo-Wooldridge Corp, 55-58. *Mem:* Am Math Soc; Soc Indust & Appl Math; Math Asn Am; Asn Comput Mach. *Res:* Numerical analysis, especially the numerical solution of partial differential equations by finite difference methods; high-speed computing. *Mailing Add:* 3406 Monte Vista Dr Austin TX 78731-5723

**YOUNG, DAVID THAD,** SPACE PHYSICS. *Current Pos:* INST SCIENTIST, SOUTHWEST RES INST, SAN ANTONIO, TEX, 88- *Personal Data:* b Port of Spain, Trinidad, Apr 18, 43; US citizen; m 66, 90; c 6. *Educ:* Univ Southwestern La, BS, 64; Rice Univ, MS, 67, PhD(space physics), 70. *Hon Degrees:* Venia Docendi, Univ Bern, 80. *Prof Exp:* Grad fel, Dept Space Physics & Astron, Rice Univ, 64-70, res assoc, 70-71; sr res assoc, Physikalisches Inst, Univ Bern, 72-81; mem staff, Space Plasma Physics Group, Los Alamos Nat Lab, 81-87. *Concurrent Pos:* Consult, Europ Space Agency, NASA; vis scientist, Div Plasma Physics, Royal Inst Technol, Stockholm, 72- *Mem:* Am Geophys Union; Europ Geophys Soc. *Res:* Magnetospheric plasma physics, particularly the development of ion mass spectrometers for space flight and the analysis and application of this data. *Mailing Add:* Southwest Res Inst PO Drawer 28510 San Antonio TX 78284

**YOUNG, DAVID W,** HYDROCARBON BLENDING TO FORM IMPROVED PRODUCTS. *Current Pos:* RETIRED. *Personal Data:* b Oblong, Ill, Aug 16, 09. *Educ:* Univ Ky, BS, 31, MS, 35. *Hon Degrees:* DSc, Transylvania Univ, 35 & Queens Col, 68. *Honors & Awards:* Pioneering Award, Am Inst Chem, 67. *Prof Exp:* Res chemist, Ky Agr Exp Sta, 31-35, Laurel Hill Res Lab, Gen Chem Co, 36-40; sr res chemist, Esso Res & Eng Co, 40-55 & Sinclair Res Inc, 55-65; res assoc, Atlantic Richfield Co, 65-71; vpres, Compino Labs, 71-72; partner, R B MacMullin Assoc, 72-73; pres, David W Young & Assoc, 75-87; consult, 87-88. *Concurrent Pos:* Consult, US Army, US Armed Forces, 59-62; lectr, Sigma Xi, 63-67, Purdue Univ, 68-70 & Am Chem Soc Speakers Bur, 70-88; mem bd dirs, Asn Consult Chemists & Chem Engrs. *Mem:* Nat Acad Sci; Am Inst Chemists (pres, 71-73); Nat Asn Corrosion Eng; Am Chem Soc; AAAS. *Res:* Consulting on use of polymerization catalysts to form high polymers from hydrocarbon olefins. *Mailing Add:* 18508 Clyde Ave Homewood IL 60430

**YOUNG, DAVIS ALAN,** PETROLOGY, MINERALOGY & HISTORY OF IGNEOUS PETROLOGY. *Current Pos:* assoc prof, 78-83, PROF GEOL, CALVIN COL, 83- *Personal Data:* b Abington, Pa, Mar 5, 41; m 65, Dorothy Cairns; c Daniel, Timothy & Teresa. *Educ:* Princeton Univ, BSE, 62; Pa State Univ, MS, 65; Brown Univ, PhD(geol), 69. *Prof Exp:* Asst prof geol, NY Univ, 68-73; assoc prof geol, Univ NC, Wilmington, 73-78. *Mem:* Mineral Soc Am; Geol Soc Am; Sigma Xi; Am Sci Affil; Nat Asn Geol Teachers. *Res:* Precambrian igneous and metamorphic geology of New Jersey and southeastern Pennsylvania; petrology of syenites; history of geology in relation to Christianity. *Mailing Add:* Dept Geol Geog & Environ Studies Calvin Col Grand Rapids MI 49546. *Fax:* 616-957-6501; *E-Mail:* youn@legacy.calvin.edu

**YOUNG, DELANO VICTOR,** RECOMBINANT PROTEIN MANUFACTURING, NITRE OXIDE REGULATION OF CELL FUNCTION & GROWTH. *Current Pos:* sr scientist, Damon Biotech, 86-88, dir, 88-90, HEAD, CELL BIOL DEPT, ABBOTT BIOTECH, 90- *Personal Data:* b Honolulu, Hawaii, Nov 17, 45; m 70; c 1. *Educ:* Stanford Univ, BS, 67; Columbia Univ, PhD(biochem), 73. *Prof Exp:* Fel cell biol, Salk Inst Biol Studies, 73-75; asst prof chem, Boston Univ, 75-84; Bioassay Syst Corp, 84-86. *Concurrent Pos:* Vis scientist, Dept Biochem, Harvard Univ, 82-83; prin investr, NIH grants, 76-79, 81-84. *Mem:* AAAS; Sigma Xi; Am Soc Microbiol; Am Soc Biochem & Molecular Biol. *Res:* Large scale mammalian cell manufacturing, including characterization of cells and maximization of genetic expressions; cell growth control and signal transduction, especially as related to lymphokine, cytokine and growth factor action. *Mailing Add:* NitroMed Inc 801 Albany St Boston MA 02118-2394. *Fax:* 781-449-4010

**YOUNG, DENNIS LEE,** MATHEMATICAL STATISTICS, APPLIED STATISTICS. *Current Pos:* assoc prof, 75-84, PROF STATIST, ARIZ STATE UNIV, 84- *Personal Data:* b St Louis, Mo, Jan 22, 44; m 78; c 2. *Educ:* St Louis Univ, BS, 65; Purdue Univ, MS, 67, PhD(statist), 70. *Prof Exp:* Asst prof statist, NMex State Univ, 70-75. *Concurrent Pos:* Consult, Motorola Inc, 83-; expert witness, Ariz Atty Gen Off, 86. *Mem:* AAAS; Inst Math Statist; Am Statist Asn; Am Soc Qual Control. *Res:* Multivariate statistical analysis; applications of statistical methods to science and industry. *Mailing Add:* Dept Math Ariz State Univ Tempe AZ 85287-1804. *Fax:* 602-965-8119; *E-Mail:* dennis.young@asu.edu

**YOUNG, DONALD ALCOE,** GENETICS, PLANT BREEDING. *Current Pos:* POTATO CONSULT. *Personal Data:* b Fredericton, NB, Oct 21, 29; m 55; c 3. *Educ:* McGill Univ, BSc, 52; Univ Wis, MS, 54, PhD(genetics), 57. *Prof Exp:* Res off, Can Dept Agr, 57-66, sect head potato breeding, 66-73, prog mgr, 73-86. *Concurrent Pos:* Mem, Work Planning Comt Potato Breeding, 59-; chmn, Work Planning Comt Potato Texture, 64- *Mem:* Potato Asn Am; Can Soc Hort Sci; Genetics Soc Can. *Res:* Potato breeding; sample selection as related to potato quality; disease resistance. *Mailing Add:* 1289 Lincoln Rd Fredericton NB E3B 8J5 Can. *Fax:* 506-457-0170; *E-Mail:* youngd@nb.sympatico.ca

**YOUNG, DONALD C,** INORGANIC CHEMISTRY, AGRICULTURAL CHEMISTRY. *Current Pos:* VPRES RES & DEVELOP, INTEGRATED AGR RESOURCES, 97-; PVT CONSULT. *Personal Data:* b Paducah, Ky, Feb 25, 33; m 51; c 4. *Educ:* Univ Calif, Riverside, BA, 61, PhD(inorg chem), 66. *Prof Exp:* from res asst petrochem to sr res chemist, Unocal, 53-69, from res assoc to sr res assoc fertilizer chem, 69-78, staff consult, Union Oil Co, 78-89, sr staff consult, Sci & Technol Div, 89-95. *Concurrent Pos:* Res scholar, Univ Calif, Riverside, 66-68. *Mem:* Am Chem Soc. *Res:* Chemistry and technology of polyphosphoric acid; transition-metal complexes in homogeneous catalysis; carborane chemistry; transition metal complexes of dicarbollide ion; fertilizer and soil chemistry; herbicide and plant growth regulator chemistry. *Mailing Add:* 245 Altura Dr Fullerton CA 92835-1301

**YOUNG, DONALD CHARLES,** ANALYTICAL CHEMISTRY. *Current Pos:* sr res chemist, 85-89, res assoc, 89-90, ANALYTICAL COORDR, CHEVRON RES CO, 91- *Personal Data:* b Fremont, Ohio, June 29, 44; m 91, Shari O'Neal; c 3. *Educ:* Harvard Univ, AB, 66; Univ NC, Chapel Hill, PhD(anal chem), 71. *Prof Exp:* Res assoc chem, Purdue Univ, 71-72; asst prof chem, Oakland Univ, 72-78; proj chemist, Gulf Oil Corp, 78-84, sr res chemist, 84. *Mem:* Am Chem Soc; Sigma Xi; Soc Appl Spectros. *Res:* Nuclear magnetic resonance methods of analysis; infrared spectroscopy; process analysis; petroleum, petroleum products, and petrochemical analysis. *Mailing Add:* Chevron Res & Technol Co PO Box 1627 Richmond CA 94802-0627. *Fax:* 510-242-1792; *E-Mail:* dcyo@chevron.com

**YOUNG, DONALD EDWARD,** HIGH ENERGY PHYSICS, PHYSICS OF BEAMS. *Current Pos:* physicist, 67-90, EMER SCIENTIST, FERMI NAT ACCELERATOR LAB, 90- *Personal Data:* b Lake Zurich, Ill, June 13, 22; m 47, Bille Hooper; c Lynda J, Patricia A & Phillip E. *Educ:* Ripon Col, BA, 46; Univ Minn, MS, 51, PhD(nucleon scattering), 59. *Prof Exp:* Asst physics, Univ Minn, 49-53; physicist, Labs, Gen Mills Co, 53-60; head, Physics Div, Midwestern Univs Res Asn, 60-67; prof physics, Univ Wis, 67. *Concurrent Pos:* Pres, Particle Accelerator Corp, 90- *Mem:* Fel Am Phys Soc; Sigma Xi; AAAS. *Res:* Proton linear accelerator design; high energy particle accelerators design and operation; magnetic field measurements; nuclear physics and radioactivity; proton-proton scattering; dosimetry; radiation damage; antiproton production and collection. *Mailing Add:* 4513 Cornell Ave Downers Grove IL 60515-2609

**YOUNG, DONALD F(REDRICK),** ENGINEERING MECHANICS, BIOMEDICAL FLUID ENGINEERING. *Current Pos:* Res assoc, Iowa State Univ, 52-53, from instr to assoc prof eng mech, 52-61, prof eng sci & mech, 61-74, DISTINGUISHED PROF ENG, IOWA STATE UNIV, 74- *Personal Data:* b Joplin, Mo, Apr 27, 28; m 50, Ann Cooper; c Michael, Pamela, Susan, Christopher & David. *Educ:* Iowa State Univ, BS, 51, MS, 52, PhD(eng mech), 56. *Mem:* Am Soc Eng Educ; fel Am Soc Mech Engrs. *Res:* Fluid mechanics; biomechanics. *Mailing Add:* Dept Aerospace Eng & Eng Mech Iowa State Univ Ames IA 50011. *Fax:* 515-294-8584; *E-Mail:* dfyoung@iastate.edu

**YOUNG, DONALD RAYMOND,** PHYSIOLOGICAL PLANT ECOLOGY, COMPUTER MODELING. *Current Pos:* asst prof, 84-90, ASSOC PROF BIOL, VA COMMONWEALTH UNIV, 90- *Personal Data:* b Beaver Falls, Pa, May 11, 54; m 76, Debra Belle; c Zachary J & Ellen A. *Educ:* Clarion Univ Pa, BS, 75; Univ Wyo, MS, 79, PhD(bot), 82. *Prof Exp:* Asst prof bot, Univ Wyo, 82-83; res scholar phys ecol, Univ Calif, Los Angeles, 83-84. *Mem:* Ecol Soc Am; Bot Soc Am; Sigma Xi. *Res:* Effects of microclimate, crown architecture and leaf display on the water relations, photosynthesis and small-scale distribution patterns of understory plants; physiological ecology of Paulownia tomentosa as related to use in reclamation. *Mailing Add:* Dept Biol Va Commonwealth Univ Box 2012 Richmond VA 23284-9004. *Fax:* 804-367-0503; *E-Mail:* dyoung@cabell.vcu.edu

**YOUNG, DONALD REEDER,** PHYSICS. *Current Pos:* PROF PHYSICS, LEHIGH UNIV, 86- *Personal Data:* b Logan, Utah, July 21, 21; m 46; c 4. *Educ:* Utah State Agr Col, BA, 42; Mass Inst Technol, PhD(physics), 49. *Prof Exp:* Mem staff, Radiation Lab, Mass Inst Technol, 42-45, asst, Insulation Lab, 45-49; tech engr, 49-52, proj engr, 52-61, sr engr & mgr device & mat characterization, 61-71, res staff mem, IBM Corp, 71-86. *Concurrent Pos:* Alexander von Humboldt US sr scientist award, 80-81; mgr interface physics, IBM Corp, 77-86. *Mem:* Fel Am Phys Soc; fel Inst Elec & Electronics Engrs. *Res:* Electrical breakdown; ferroelectric materials; superconductors; semiconductors. *Mailing Add:* Fairchild Lab Lehigh Univ Bethlehem PA 18015

**YOUNG, DONALD STIRLING,** CLINICAL PATHOLOGY. *Current Pos:* PROF, DEPT PATH & LAB MED, UNIV PA, 84-, VCHAIR, LAB MED, 94- *Personal Data:* b Belfast, Northern Ireland, Dec 17, 33; c 3. *Educ:* Aberdeen Univ, MB & ChB, 57; Univ London, PhD(chem path), 62. *Honors & Awards:* J H Roe Award, Am Asn Clin Chemists, 73, Ames Award, 77, Bernard Gerulat Award, 77, Van Slyke Award, 85; Gerard B Lambert Award, Gerard B Lambert Awards Orgn, 75; W Roman Lectr, Australian Asn Clin Biochem, 79; Gerald T Evans Award, Acad Clin Lab Physicians & Scientists, 81; Corning Lectr, Asn Clin Biochem, 85. *Prof Exp:* Lectr mat med, Aberdeen Univ, 58-59; resident chem path, Royal Postgrad Med Sch London, 62-64; vis scientist, NIH, 65-67, chief clin chem, 67-77; head, Mayo Clin, 77-84. *Concurrent Pos:* Chmn bd ed, Clin Chem, Am Asn Clin Chemists, 73-78 & 85-87, pres, 80. *Mem:* Brit Asn Clin Biochem; Am Asn Clin Chemists (pres, 80); Acad Clin Lab Physicians & Scientists; Int Fedn Clin Chem (vpres, 82-85, pres, 85-90). *Res:* Clinical chemistry; development and application of high resolution analytical techniques in the clinical laboratory; optimized use of the clinical laboratory. *Mailing Add:* Dept Path Univ Pa Sch Med Philadelphia PA 19104-4283

**YOUNG, EARLE F(RANCIS), JR,** ENVIRONMENTAL CONTROL, PROCESS METALLURGY. *Current Pos:* RETIRED. *Personal Data:* b Pittsburgh, Pa, Aug 27; wid; c 3. *Educ:* Carnegie Inst Technol, BS, 49. *Prof Exp:* Res engr chem eng, Babcock & Wilcox Co, 49-51; res engr, Olin Mathieson Chem Corp, 51-54, proj group leader, 54-56; process engr, Jones & Laughlin Steel Corp, 56-57, sr develop engr, 57-58, res supvr, 58-61, supvr ore res, 61-65, asst dir chem & raw mat serv, Tech Serv Div, 65-69, dir environ control, 69-72, gen mgr, 73-76; dir environ affairs, Am Iron & Steel Inst, 76-78, asst vpres, 78-80, vpres energy & environ, 80-85, environ, 80-87, environ & energy, 87-89. *Concurrent Pos:* Instr, Carnegie Inst Technol, 57-58; vol environ consult, Indust Exec Serv Corp, 93-94, World Environ Ctr, 92-96 & US Asia Environ Partnership, 96. *Mem:* Am Chem Soc; Am Inst Chem Engrs; Soc Mining Engrs; Am Iron & Steel Inst. *Res:* Upgrading of iron ores; fluid dynamics of steelmaking; air and stream pollution. *Mailing Add:* 1600 N Oak St N0720 Arlington VA 22209-2764. *Fax:* 703-525-7434; *E-Mail:* efyir@aol.com

**YOUNG, EDMOND GROVE,** FLUORINE CHEMISTRY. *Current Pos:* CONSULT, 82- *Personal Data:* b Govans, Md, Oct 29, 17; m 46, Jean Auwetter; c Stephen, Janet, Russell & Timothy. *Educ:* Univ Md, BS, 38, PhD(org chem), 43. *Prof Exp:* Asst chem, Univ Md, 38-43; chemist, Sharples Chem, Inc, Mich, 43-44; res chemist, E I du Pont de Nemours & Co, Inc, 44-48; tech sales, Kinetics Chem, Inc, 48-49, sales mgr aerosol propellants, 49-50; sales develop, Kinetic Chem Div, E I Du Pont de Nemours & Co, Inc, 50-52, mgr kinetic chem div, 52-57, mgr develop conf, 57-68, mgr develop conf & govt liaison, Develop Dept, 68-73, mgr bus develop, Cent Res & Develop Dept, 73-82. *Concurrent Pos:* Mem, Franklin Inst; consult, NASA, 82-83, Jet Propulsion Lab, 84-88; fed liaison, Univ Del, 88- *Mem:* AAAS; Am Chem Soc; Com Develop Asn. *Res:* Reaction of metallo-organics; chemistry of fluorinated compounds; commercial chemical development and marketing. *Mailing Add:* PO Box 67 Mickleton NJ 08056-0067

**YOUNG, EDWARD JOSEPH,** geochemistry, mineralogy, for more information see previous edition

**YOUNG, EDWIN H(AROLD),** CHEMICAL ENGINEERING, METALLURGICAL ENGINEERING. *Current Pos:* from instr to prof, 47-89, EMER PROF CHEM & METALL ENG, UNIV MICH, ANN ARBOR, 89-; CONSULT ENGR, 47- *Personal Data:* b Detroit, Mich, Nov 4, 18; m 44, Signe Soma; c David & Barbara. *Educ:* Univ Detroit, BChE, 42; Univ Mich, MSE, 49 & 51. *Honors & Awards:* Award, Nat Soc Prof Engrs, 77; Donald Q Kern Award, Am Inst Chem Engrs, 79. *Prof Exp:* Jr chem engr, Wright Air Develop Ctr, 42-43; instr chem eng, Univ Detroit, 46-47. *Mem:* Am Chem Soc; fel Am Soc Mech Engrs; fel Am Inst Chem Engrs; fel Am Inst Chemists; Nat Soc Prof Engr (pres, 68-69); fel Am Soc Heating Refrig & Air Conditioning Engrs. *Res:* Heat transfer; process design; design of process equipment; forensic engineer; technical expert on explosions and fires. *Mailing Add:* Dept Chem & Metall Eng Univ Mich Ann Arbor MI 48109-2136

**YOUNG, ELEANOR ANNE,** NUTRITION. *Current Pos:* assoc prof, 77-87, PROF MED, DEPT MED, UNIV TEX HEALTH SCI CTR, SAN ANTONIO, 87-; ASSOC PROF FOODS & NUTRIT, INCARNATE WORD COL, 72- *Personal Data:* b Houston, Tex, Oct 8, 25. *Educ:* Incarnate World Col, BA, 47; St Louis Univ, MEd, 55; Univ Wis, PhD(nutrit), 68. *Prof Exp:* Asst prof foods & Nutrit, Incarnate World Col, 53-63 & 68-72; sr res assoc, Univ Tex Health Sci Ctr, Dept Med, 68-72, asst prof med, 72-77. *Concurrent Pos:* Consult, Audie Murphy Vet Admin Hosp, San Antonio, 73-, Med Ctr Hosp, 73- *Mem:* Am Inst Nutrit; Am Bd Human Nutrit; Am Soc Clin Nutrit; Am Dietetic Asn; Am Pub Health Asn. *Res:* Metabolic response and feeding-fasting intervals in man; metabolism of intravenously infused maltose; lactose intolerance; nutritional adaptations after partial small bowel resections; effect of semistarvation diets on the gastrointestinal tract and heart; effect of gastric stapling on the gastrointestinal tract; nutrition, health and aging. *Mailing Add:* Dept Med 110 Laurel Heights Pl San Antonio TX 77812-5216. *Fax:* 210-567-4654

**YOUNG, ELIZABETH BELL,** SPEECH PATHOLOGY, AUDIOLOGY. *Current Pos:* CONSULT & LECTR, LOCAL NAT AGENCIES & ORGN, 83- *Personal Data:* b Franklinton, NC, July 2, 29. *Educ:* NC Col Durham, AB, 48, MA, 50; Ohio State Univ, PhD(speech sci, speech & hearing ther), 59. *Prof Exp:* Chmn dept English, Barber-Scotia Col, 48-53; chmn dept speech, Talladega Col, 53-55; asst prof, Va State Col, 56-57; prof speech correction & dir speech clin, Fla A&M Univ, 59; chmn dept English & speech, Fayetteville State Col, 59-63; asst prof speech path, Col Dent, Howard Univ, 63-64; chmn dept English & lang, Md State Col, 65-66; prof speech path, undergrad & grad prog & supvr speech & audiol training clin prog, Cath Univ Am, 66-79; supvr speech clin, 69-79; staff aide, US House Rep, 80-82; prof commun, Univ DC, 82-83. *Concurrent Pos:* Consult, nat orgns, mgt firms, etc, 83- *Mem:* Fel Am Speech & Hearing Asn. *Res:* Pathology of speech and hearing mechanism and speech science; observations in the field of speech and hearing pathology and science. *Mailing Add:* 8104 W Beach Dr NW Washington DC 20012

**YOUNG, ELTON THEODORE,** MOLECULAR BIOLOGY. *Current Pos:* from asst prof to assoc prof, 69-81, PROF BIOCHEM & GENETICS, UNIV WASH, 81- *Personal Data:* b Brush, Colo, May 1, 40; m 62; c 3. *Educ:* Univ Colo, BA, 62; Calif Inst Technol, PhD(biophys), 67. *Prof Exp:* Fel molecular biol, Univ Geneva, 67-69. *Mem:* Fedn Am Soc Exp Biol. *Res:* Regulation of gene expression and protein transport in yeast. *Mailing Add:* Dept Biochem Univ Wash Sch Med 3900 7th Ave NE Seattle WA 98195-0001

**YOUNG, ERIC D,** BIOMEDICAL ENGINEERING. *Current Pos:* from asst prof to assoc prof, Dept Biomed Eng, Sch Med, Johns Hopkins Univ, 75-87, assoc prof, Dept Neurosci, 81-87 & Dept Otolaryngol, 85-87, PROF, DEPTS BIOMED ENG, NEUROSCI & OTOLARYNGOL, SCH MED, JOHNS HOPKINS UNIV, 87- *Personal Data:* b Elko, Nev, July 9, 45; m; c 2. *Educ:* Calif Inst Technol, BS, 67; Johns Hopkins Univ, PhD(biomed eng), 72. *Prof Exp:* Postdoctoral fel, Dept Pharmacol & Physiol Sci, Univ Chicago, 72-74, res assoc, 74-75. *Concurrent Pos:* NIH postdoctoral fel, 72-74, res career develop award, 79-83; coordr, Undergrad Prog Biomed Eng, Whiting Sch Eng, Johns Hopkins Univ, 81-; mem, tech comt Physiol & Psychol Acoust, Acoust Soc Am, 77-80, Commun Dis Rev Comt, Nat Inst Neurol Commun Dis & Stroke; ad hoc mem, Commun Sci Study Sect, NIH, 80, Hearing Sci Study Sect, 83; ad hoc grant reviewer, Whittaker Found, 87-90; ad hoc manuscript reviewer, J Neurophysiol, Hearing Res, J Acoust Soc Am; consult, Res Triangle Inst, 90. *Mem:* Sr mem Biomed Eng Soc; fel Acoust Soc Am; Asn Res Otolaryngol; Soc Neurosci; AAAS; Sigma Xi. *Res:* Biomedical engineering; neuroscience; otolaryngology/head and neck surgery. *Mailing Add:* Dept Biomed Eng Johns Hopkins Sch Med 720 Rutland Dr Baltimore MD 21205-2109

**YOUNG, EUTIQUIO CHUA,** MATHEMATICAL ANALYSIS. *Current Pos:* from asst prof math to assoc prof, 65-74, PROF MATH, FLA STATE UNIV, 74- *Personal Data:* b Del Gallego, Philippines, July 17, 32; m 61; c 3. *Educ:* Far Eastern Univ, Manila, BS, 54; Univ Md, MA, 60, PhD(math), 62. *Prof Exp:* Asst prof math, Univ Conn, 61-62; head dept math, Far Eastern Univ, Manila, 62-64; assoc prof, De la Salle Col, Manila, 64-65. *Mem:* Math Asn Am; Am Math Soc. *Res:* Cauchy problems, uniqueness of solutions of boundary value problems and comparison theorems for partial differential equations. *Mailing Add:* Dept Math Fla State Univ Tallahassee FL 32306-1037

**YOUNG, FRANCIS ALLAN,** EYE VISION & PRIMATOLOGY. *Current Pos:* From instr to prof, 48-88, DIR, PRIMATE RES CTR, WASH STATE UNIV, 57-, EMER PROF PSYCHOL, 88- *Personal Data:* b Utica, NY, Dec 29, 18; m 45; c Francis A III & Thomas R. *Educ:* Tampa Univ, Fla, BS, 41; Case Western Res Univ, MA, 45; Ohio State Univ, PhD(psychol), 49. *Honors & Awards:* Apollo Award, Am Optom Asn, 80. *Concurrent Pos:* Consult, Ment Health Res Inst, Wash, 54-67, Vet Admin Blind Rehab Ctr, Palo Alto, Calif, 74-84, Nat Inst Neurol, Commun Dis & Stroke, 76-84; vis res prof, Sch Med, Univ Ore, 63-64, Med Sch, Univ Uppsala, Sweden, 71 & Optom Sch, Univ Houston, 79-81; actg asst dir, Regional Primate Res Ctr, Univ Wash, 66-68; chmn, Gov't Comt Sexual Psychopath, Wash, 66-68; mem, res adv comt, Dept Insts, Wash, 69-70. *Mem:* AAAS; fel Am Psychol Asn; Am Acad Optom; Neaurosci Soc; Optical Soc Am. *Res:* Role of genetics and environment in the development of visual refractive errors including myopia in humans and sub-human primates, with emphasis on the role of accommodation; mechanisms of accommodation; video display terminal syndrome; role of vision in motion sickness. *Mailing Add:* Primate Res Ctr Wash State Univ Pullman WA 99164-1170

**YOUNG, FRANK COLEMAN,** EXPERIMENTAL PLASMA PHYSICS, NUCLEAR DIAGNOSTICS. *Current Pos:* RES PHYSICIST, US NAVAL RES LAB, 72- *Personal Data:* b Roanoke, Va, June 10, 35; m 59; c 3. *Educ:* Johns Hopkins Univ, BA, 57; Univ Md, PhD(nuclear physics), 62. *Prof Exp:* NSF res fel, US Naval Res Lab, 62-63; from asst prof to assoc prof physics, Univ Md, 63-72. *Concurrent Pos:* Vis scientist, Sandia Nat Lab, 86-87; chmn, Int Conf Plasma Sci, Inst Elec & Electronic Engrs, 87, exec comt Plasma Sci & Applns comt, 91- *Mem:* Am Phys Soc; Inst Elec & Electronics Engrs; Nuclear & Plasma Sci Soc. *Res:* Experimental nuclear physics; application of nuclear techniques to studies of hot dense plasmas; plasmas for x-ray lasers. *Mailing Add:* 100 Mel Mara Dr Oxon Hill MD 20745

**YOUNG, FRANK E,** BIOTECHNOLOGY, MICROBIOLOGY. *Current Pos:* RETIRED. *Personal Data:* b Mineola, NY, Sept 1, 31; m 56; c 5. *Educ:* State Univ NY, MD, 56; Western Reserve Univ, PhD(microbiol), 62. *Hon Degrees:* DSc, Roberts Wesleyan Col, Rochester, 83 & Houghton Col, Houghton, 84, State Univ NY, 86, Long Island Univ, 86, Western Baptist Col, 88. *Honors & Awards:* Edward Mott Moore Award, 85. *Prof Exp:* From intern to resident path, Univ Hosps, Cleveland, Ohio, 56-60; from instr to asst prof, Western Res Univ, 62-65; from assoc mem to mem, Depts Microbiol & Exp Path, Scripps Clin & Res Found, 65-70; prof microbiol, path, radiation biol & biophys & chmn, Dept Microbiol, Sch Med & Dent, Univ Rochester, 70-79, dean, 79-84, vpres health affairs, 81-84; comnr, Food & Drug Admin, 84-89; dep asst secy health, sci & environ, Dept Health & Human Servs, 89-93; dir, Off Emergency Preparedness, 93-95. *Concurrent Pos:* Am Cancer Soc res grant, 62-; fac res assoc, Am Cancer Soc, 62-70; NIH res grants, 65-, training grant, 70-; NSF res grant, 70-72; assoc prof, Univ Calif, San Diego, 67-70; dir, Clin Microbiol Labs, Strong Mem Hosp, 70-79, microbiologist-in-chief, 76-79; dir, Health Dept Labs, Monroe Co, 70-79, mem bd, Am Asn Med Cols. *Mem:* Inst Med-Nat Acad Sci; Am Soc Microbiol; AAAS; Am Acad Microbiol; Sigma Xi. *Res:* Mechanism of deoxyribonucleic and mediated transformation of bacterial and animal cells; regulation of bacterial cell surface; pathobiology of Neisseria gonorrhea. *Mailing Add:* 8508 Woodhaven Blvd Bethesda MD 20817

**YOUNG, FRANK GLYNN,** CHEMISTRY, CATALYSIS. *Current Pos:* RETIRED. *Personal Data:* b New York, NY, Dec 29, 16; m 41. *Educ:* Dartmouth Col, AB, 37; Columbia Univ, PhD(org chem), 41. *Prof Exp:* Asst chem, Columbia Univ, 37-41; res chemist, Union Carbide Corp, 41-55, group leader radiation & isotope chem, 55-60, chem physics, Parma Res Labs, 60-63, sr res scientist, 63-83; consult & pres, Catalysis, Inc, 85-87. *Concurrent Pos:* Lectr Catalysis, Ctr Prof Advan, 75-84 & McGraw-Hill, 77-81. *Mem:* Emer mem Am Chem Soc; Int Cong Catalysis. *Res:* Mechanisms of catalytic processes; isotopic tracer studies; heterogeneous catalysis and surfaces. *Mailing Add:* 3913 Butternut Ct Brandon FL 33511-7961

**YOUNG, FRANK HOOD,** COMPUTER SCIENCE EDUCATION, SOFTWARE ENGINEERING. *Current Pos:* PROF COMPUT SCI & HEAD DEPT, ROSE-HULMAN INST TECHNOL, IND, 87- *Personal Data:* b Baltimore, Md, Dec 31, 39; m 61, Julie Nevius; c 4. *Educ:* Haverford Col, BA, 61; Univ Pa, MA, 63, PhD(math), 68. *Prof Exp:* Instr math, Temple Univ, 65-68; from asst prof to prof, Knox Col, Ill, 68-87, chmn dept, 76-81. *Concurrent Pos:* Vis res asst prof, Dept Comput Sci, Univ Ill, 73; Fulbright vis sr lectr, Dept Comput Sci, Univ Lagos, Nigeria, 75-76; vis assoc prof, Dept Comput Sci, Univ Iowa, 81-82. *Mem:* Asn Comput Mach; Math Asn Am. *Res:* Software engineering; reusable design schemes; analysis of algorithms; computer science education. *Mailing Add:* Dept Comput Sci Rose-Hulman Inst Technol 5500 Wabash Ave Terre Haute IN 47803

**YOUNG, FRANK NELSON, JR,** BIOLOGY, MEDICAL ENTOMOLOGY. *Current Pos:* from asst prof to prof, 49-85, EMER PROF ZOOL, IND UNIV, BLOOMINGTON, 85- *Personal Data:* b Oneonta, Ala, Nov 2, 15; m 43, Frances Norman; c Frances E (Vonlterrmann) & Frank N III. *Educ:* Univ Fla, BS, 38, MS, 40, PhD(biol), 42. *Prof Exp:* Asst prof biol, Univ Fla, 46-49. *Concurrent Pos:* E S George fel, Univ Mich, 51; Guggenheim fel, 60-61; fel, La State Univ, 63; res assoc, Fla Dept Agr, 72, US Nat Mus Natural Hist, 90. *Mem:* Am Soc Zool; Soc Study Evolution. *Res:* Taxonomy and ecology of aquatic Coleoptera; medical entomology; speciation and extinction of animals; land snails of genus Liguus. *Mailing Add:* 1121 Linden Dr Bloomington IN 47408

**YOUNG, FRANKLIN,** NUTRITION, BIOCHEMISTRY. *Current Pos:* prof & chair health, 85-87, PROF NUTRIT-INTRODUCTORY, APPL & ADVAN, WEST CHESTER UNIV, PA, 88- *Personal Data:* b Beijing, China, Feb 1, 28; nat US; m 82, Kathlina Patanella. *Educ:* Mercer Univ, AB, 51; Univ Fla, BSA, 52, MAgr, 54, PhD(nutrit), 60. *Prof Exp:* Asst vet sci, Univ Fla, 54-60, fel biochem, 60-61; res assoc, Bowman Gray Sch Med, 61-65, res instr prev med & assoc biochem, 65-66; assoc prof food & nutrit sci, nutrit-introductory, advan & grad, Univ Hawaii, 66-83; prof & chair foods & nutrit, Univ Utah, 83-85. *Concurrent Pos:* Prin investr, Univ Hawaii, 66-83. *Mem:* Am Inst Nutrit; Am Chem Soc; Sigma Xi. *Res:* Atherosclerosis, lipid metabolism, hypertension and human nutrition. *Mailing Add:* Dept Health West Chester Univ West Chester PA 19383

**YOUNG, FRANKLIN ALDEN, JR,** MATERIALS SCIENCE. *Current Pos:* assoc prof, 70-75, PROF DENT MAT & CHMN DEPT, COL DENT MED, MED UNIV SC, 75- *Personal Data:* b Harrisburg, Pa, Mar 14, 38; m 59, 73, Caroyn Herron; c 3. *Educ:* Univ Fla, BIE, 60, MSE, 63; Univ Va, DSc(mat sci), 68. *Honors & Awards:* Isaih Lew Award, Am Acad Implant Dent, 91. *Prof Exp:* Instr metall, Clemson Univ, 63-65, asst prof mat eng, 68-70. *Concurrent Pos:* J ed, Dent Mat, 83-; pres, Implant Res Group, Int Asn Dental Res, 87-88; Rcs Career Award, NIH, 72-77. *Mem:* Am Soc Metals; Int Asn Dent Res; Sigma Xi; fel Acad Dent Mat; Mats Res Soc; Int Asn Dent Res. *Res:* Materials of medicine and dentistry; titanium alloy surfaces and their effects on dental and orthopaedic implants; CAD-CAM applications to dental and orthopaedic prosthesis. *Mailing Add:* Dept Mat Sci Med Univ SC 171 Ashley Ave Charleston SC 29425

**YOUNG, FRED M(ICHAEL),** HEAT TRANSFER, FLUID MECHANICS. *Current Pos:* DEAN ENG, LAMAR UNIV, 79- *Personal Data:* b Dallas, Tex, Aug 29, 40; m 63; c 2. *Educ:* Southern Methodist Univ, BSME, 63, MSME, 65, PhD(mech eng), 67. *Prof Exp:* Propulsion engr, Gen Dynamics/Ft Worth, 63-64; from asst prof to assoc prof mech eng, Lamar Univ, 67-74, dir grad eng studies, 72-74; head eng & appl sci, Portland State Univ, 74-79. *Concurrent Pos:* Consult, Mobil Oil, Bethlehem Steel & Beaumont Yard. *Mem:* Am Soc Mech Engrs; Am Soc Eng Educ. *Res:* Two phase heat transfer; unsteady fluid flow; transient boiling; compter-aided design. *Mailing Add:* Box 10057 Lamar Univ Beaumont TX 77710. *Fax:* 409-880-8121; *E-Mail:* fred@lub001.lamar.edu

**YOUNG, FREDERICK GRIFFIN,** PETROLEUM GEOLOGY, STRAT-SEDIMENT. *Current Pos:* VPRES EXPLOR, TARGET ENERGY INC, 97. *Personal Data:* b Niagara Falls, Ont, Nov 7, 40; m 63, Pat Miller; c 2. *Educ:* Queen's Univ, Ont, BSc, 63; McGill Univ, MSc, 64, PhD(geol), 70. *Prof Exp:* Geologist, Hudson's Bay Oil & Gas Co, 64-66; res scientist stratig, Inst Sedimentary & Petrol Geol, Geol Surv Can, 69-78; sr staff geol, Home Oil Co, 78-80, chief geol, 80-83, mgr, Frontiers Explor, 83-87, sr explor, 87-91, geol adv, 91-95; independent geologist, 96. *Mem:* Am Asn Petrol Geologists; Soc Econ Paleont & Mineral; Can Soc Petrol Geologists (pres, 94); Sigma Xi. *Res:* Physical stratigraphy; lithofacies analyses; geology of Upper Precambrian and Cambrian; clastic sedimentation; trace fossils; Mesozoic and Cenozoic geology of Mackenzie Delta area; petroleum geology. *Mailing Add:* Target Energy Inc 2600 700 Ninth Ave SW Calgary AB T2P 3V4 Can. *E-Mail:* youngr@cal,sybersurf.net

**YOUNG, FREDERICK J(OHN),** ELECTRICAL ENGINEERING. *Current Pos:* LSI CONSULT, 74- *Personal Data:* b Buffalo, NY, May 19, 31; m 54, Beverly Hall; c John F, James R & Jeffrey K. *Educ:* Carnegie Inst Technol, BS, 53, MS, 54, PhD(elec eng), 56. *Honors & Awards:* Young Elect Engr Award, 63. *Prof Exp:* From instr to prof elec eng, Carnegie-Mellon Univ, 55-71; res engr, Labs, Westinghouse Elec Corp, 57-63, consult engr, 63-71, adv engr, 71-73. *Concurrent Pos:* Consult, Westinghouse Air Brake Co, 56, Union Switch & Signal Div, 57 & 60, Cornell Aeronaut Lab, Inc & Concrete Accessories Corp, 59, Oak Ridge Nat Labs, 74-, Westinghouse Res, 74-, Allied Chem Corp, 76-, TRW, Inc, 77-, ERDA, 77-, Mech Res, Inc, 77- & Berg Elec, Inc, 84-; ed, Proceedings of Inst Elec & Electronics Engrs, 68; reviewer, Zent Br Math, EGer Acad Sci, 70-; secy bd, Erebus Ltd, Eng, 75-; pres, Frontier Timber Co, 75- *Mem:* Inst Elec & Electronics Engrs; Sigma Xi.

*Res:* Acoustical horns; electromagnetic field theory in ferrous media; magnetodydrodynamics; plasmadynamics; magneto-oceanography; magneto-mechanical devices; coupled transmission lines in VLSI. *Mailing Add:* 800 Minard Run Rd Bradford PA 16701-3718. *Fax:* 814-368-6685

**YOUNG, FREDERICK WALTER, JR,** PHYSICAL CHEMISTRY. *Current Pos:* RETIRED. *Personal Data:* b Hebron, Va, Sept 13, 24; m 50; c 2. *Educ:* Hampden-Sydney Col, BS, 44; Univ Va, PhD(chem), 50. *Prof Exp:* Instr, Hampden-Sydney Col, 44-46; res assoc, Oak Ridge Nat Lab, 50-51, chemist, Solid State Div, 56-69, assoc dir, 69-87, dir, 87-91. *Concurrent Pos:* Res assoc, Univ Va, 51-56. *Mem:* Fel AAAS; Am Crystallog Asn; fel Am Phys Soc; Am Asn Crystal Growth; Mat Res Soc. *Res:* Chemical properties of metal surfaces; observations of dislocations in metals; radiation damage in metals. *Mailing Add:* 2900 W Gallaher Ferry Rd Knoxville TN 37932

**YOUNG, GEORGE ANTHONY,** METEOROLOGY, EXPLOSION PHENOMENA. *Current Pos:* RETIRED. *Personal Data:* b New York, NY, Nov 8, 19; m 49, Hazel Chafey; c Paul, Jeffrey, Kenneth & Gary. *Educ:* NY Univ, BS, 48, MS, 49, PhD(meteorol), 65. *Prof Exp:* Res asst meteorol, NY Univ, 49-50; res assoc, Naval Surface Warfare Ctr, 50-93; sr scientist, Epoch Eng Inc, 93-94. *Mem:* Am Meteorol Soc. *Res:* Micrometeorology; hydrodynamics; turbulence; underwater explosions; environmental effects; effects of conventional and nuclear explosions in air and water, including military damage and environmental impact. *Mailing Add:* 3611 Janet Rd Silver Spring MD 20906-4353

**YOUNG, GEORGE JAMISON,** physical chemistry; deceased, see previous edition for last biography

**YOUNG, GEORGE ROBERT,** BIOLOGICAL CHEMISTRY, NUTRITION. *Current Pos:* RETIRED. *Personal Data:* b Monmouth, Ill, Mar 9, 25; m 46; c 4. *Educ:* Univ Ind, BS, 49, PhD(biol chem), 56; Northwestern Univ, MS, 52. *Prof Exp:* Fel biol chem, Univ Ind, 55-56; instr, Dent Br, Univ Tex, 56-57, asst prof, 57-62; from assoc prof to prof biochem & nutrit, Sch Dent, Univ Mo, Kans City, 62-84, coord grad studies, 67-72, prof med, Sch Med, 73-84, pro biochem & nutrit, Sch Basic Life, 85-86, chmn dept, Sch Dent, 62-86. *Mem:* Am Chem Soc; Int Asn Dent Res; Sigma Xi. *Res:* Collagen and collagenase; invasiveness of cells; solubility of tooth enamel; nutrition and periodontal metabolism. *Mailing Add:* 10999 Bradshaw Overland Park KS 66210

**YOUNG, GERALD A,** NEUROPSYCHOPHARMACOLOGY. *Current Pos:* PHARMACOLOGIST, FOOD & DRUG ADMIN, 93- *Personal Data:* b Plainwell, Mich, Jan 9, 36; m 76; c 3. *Educ:* Colo Col, BA, 58; Western Mich Univ, MA, 68; McMaster Univ, PhD(psychol), 73. *Prof Exp:* Res psychol, Kalamazoo State Hosp, 72-73; asst prof, Western Mich Univ, 73-74; res assoc, Univ Md, Baltimore, 74-81, sr res assoc, 81-93. *Concurrent Pos:* Adj asst prof pharmacol, Univ Md, Baltimore, 78-79, adj assoc prof, 79- *Mem:* Am Soc Pharmacol & Exp Therapeut; Soc Neurosci. *Res:* Neuropsychopharmacology of psychoactive drugs; electroencephalogram spectral analysis; self-administration of drugs of abuse by experimental animals; behavioral pharmacology. *Mailing Add:* Health & Human Serv Food & Drug Admin 5600 Fisher Lane Rockville MD 20857

**YOUNG, GILBERT FLOWERS, JR,** NEUROLOGY, PEDIATRICS. *Current Pos:* from asst prof to assoc prof pediat, 57-71, from asst prof to assoc prof neurol, 60-71, PROF NEUROL & PEDIAT, MED UNIV SC, 71- *Personal Data:* b Mayesville, SC, Sept 23, 22. *Educ:* Col Charleston, BA, 42; Univ NC, MA, 46, Med Col SC, MD, 47; Am Bd Pediat, dipl, 58; Am Bd Psychiat & Neurol, dipl, 66, cert neurol with spec competence child neurol, 69. *Prof Exp:* Intern, Med Col Va Hosp, 47-48; instr pharmacol, Univ NC, 48-49; resident pediat, Roper Hosp, Charleston, SC, 51-53; pvt pract, 53-56; resident child develop, Children's Hosp, Columbus, Ohio, 56-57. *Concurrent Pos:* Resident, Mass Gen Hosp, 60-63; consult, Med Univ SC Hosp & Roper Hosp, Charleston. *Mem:* AMA; Am Acad Pediat; Am Acad Neurol; Sigma Xi. *Res:* Child neurology and development; congenital encephalopathies. *Mailing Add:* 1057 S Shem Dr Mt Pleasant SC 29464

**YOUNG, GLENN REID,** NUCLEAR PHYSICS, HIGH ENERGY HEAVY ION REACTIONS. *Current Pos:* fel nuclear physics, 78-80, mem res staff, 80-87, GROUP LEADER, OAK RIDGE NAT LAB, 87- *Personal Data:* b Kingsport, Tenn, Aug 22, 51; m 80, Katherine A Geoffroy; c Meredith E & Lianne R. *Educ:* Univ Tenn, BA, 73; Mass Inst Technol, PhD(physics), 77. *Prof Exp:* Fel Mass Inst Technol, 77-78. *Mem:* Sigma Xi; fel Am Phys Soc. *Res:* Heavy ion reactions; ultra relativistic heavy ion reactions; high energy proton-nucleus reactions. *Mailing Add:* Physics Div Bldg 6003 PO Box 2008 Oak Ridge Nat Lab Oak Ridge TN 37831-6372. *Fax:* 423-576-2822; *E-Mail:* young@orph01.phy.ornl.gov

**YOUNG, GRANT MCADAM,** STRATIGRAPHY, SEDIMENTOLOGY. *Current Pos:* from lectr to assoc prof, 63-78, PROF GEOL, UNIV WESTERN ONT, 78- *Personal Data:* b Glasgow, Scotland, Aug 23, 37; m 60; c 3. *Educ:* Glasgow Univ, BSc, 60, PhD(geol), 67. *Prof Exp:* Res demonstr geol, Univ Wales, 62-63. *Concurrent Pos:* Nat Res Coun Can & Geol Surv Can grants, Univ Western Ont, 65-; co-leader Int Geol Correlation Prog Projs, 72- *Mem:* Soc Econ Paleont & Mineral; Geol Soc Am; Geol Asn Can. *Res:* Paleoclimatology glacigenic rocks in global correlation; Huronian rocks of Ontario; Upper Precambrian rocks of Arctic Canada, Canadian Cordillera and South Australia; geochemistry of sedimentary rocks. *Mailing Add:* Dept Earth Sci Univ Western Ont London ON N6A 5B7 Can. *Fax:* 519-661-3198

**YOUNG, H(ENRY) BEN, JR,** technical management, mechanical engineering; deceased, see previous edition for last biography

**YOUNG, HAROLD EDLE,** FORESTRY. *Current Pos:* BIOMASS MGR, JAMES W SEWALL CO, 82- *Personal Data:* b Arlington, Mass, Sept 4, 17; m 43, Audrey London; c Marjorie L, Susan M, Emily J & Michael P. *Educ:* Univ Maine, BS, 37; Duke Univ, MF, 46, PhD(tree physiol), 48. *Honors & Awards:* Hitchcock Award, Forest Prod Res Soc Am, 74; Burckhart-Medaille, Fac Forestery, Univ Gottingen, 80. *Prof Exp:* Field asst, US Forest Serv, 37-40; from instr to prof forestry, Univ Maine, 48-82. *Concurrent Pos:* Fulbright res scholar, Norway, 63-64; vis appointment, Dept Forestry, Australian Nat Univ, 68-69; consult, Off Opers Anal, US Air Force, 51-59. *Mem:* Fel AAAS; Soc Am Foresters; corresp mem Soc Forestry Finland. *Res:* Soils; biomass studies within complete forest concept. *Mailing Add:* 77 Forest Ave Orono ME 04473-1414

**YOUNG, HAROLD HENRY,** ANALYTICAL CHEMISTRY. *Current Pos:* RETIRED. *Personal Data:* b Malone, NY, Sept 11, 27; m 51; c 5. *Educ:* St Michael's Col, Vt, BS, 51. *Prof Exp:* Chem tech, Works Lab, Gen Elec Co, 51-52; shift supvr, Ind Ord Works, E I du Pont de Nemours & Co, Inc, Ind, 52-54, lab supvr, Savannah River Plant, SC, 54-57; tech reviewer, Div Civilian Appln, US Dept Energy, Oak Ridge, Tenn, 57-58, non-destructive testing specialist, Div Isotopes Develop, Washington, DC, 58-59; isotopes training specialist, 59-62, nuclear educ & training specialist, 62-73, educ & training specialist, Div Biomed & Environ Res, 73-75, sr training coordr, Div Univ & Manpower Develop Progs, US AEC, 75-77, chief, Instnl Prog Br, Educ Progs Div, 77-85, chief, Lab Prog Br, Univ & Ind Prog Div, Off Energy Res, US Dept Energy, Washington, DC, 82-99. *Mem:* Am Nuclear Soc; AAAS. *Res:* Quality control of nitrocellulose, plutonium and special nuclear materials; radioisotope and radiation applications. *Mailing Add:* 10 Holly Gaithersburg MD 20545

**YOUNG, HAROLD WILLIAM, JR,** HETEROGENOUS CATALYSIS, ZEIGLER-NAITA CATALYSIS. *Current Pos:* SR SCIENTIST, DSM COPOLYMER INC, 88- *Personal Data:* b Moscow, Idaho, Nov 4, 46. *Educ:* Univ Fla, BS, 66, PhD((chem), 73. *Prof Exp:* Researcher, Dow Chem Co, 74-88. *Concurrent Pos:* Adj prof, La State Univ, 91-92. *Mem:* Am Chem Soc. *Res:* Catalysts for chemical processes, including ethylene oxide, unsaturated nitriles, polyethylene and ethylene-propylene rubber. *Mailing Add:* PO Box 2591 Baton Rouge LA 70821

**YOUNG, HARRISON HURST, JR,** PHYSICAL CHEMISTRY. *Current Pos:* RETIRED. *Personal Data:* b Drumright, Okla, Sept 24, 19; m 42; c 2. *Educ:* Princeton Univ, AB, 40; Columbia Univ, PhD(chem), 50; Fordham Univ, JD, 74. *Prof Exp:* Asst, Nat Defense Res Comt, 41-45; instr chem, Williams Col, Mass, 47-50; res group leader, Wesvaco Div, Food Mach & Chem Corp, FMC Corp, 50-52, res sect mgr, 52-56, asst to dir res, Westvaco Mineral Prod Div, 56-58, mgr detergent applns res, Inorg Res & Develop Dept, 59-62, tech recruitment mgr, Chem Div, 62-70, mem staff, Chem Group, Patent & Licensing Dept, 70-85, patent atty, 75-85. *Mem:* Am Chem Soc. *Res:* Reaction kinetics; industrial inorganic chemicals; detergent applications; agricultrual pesticides. *Mailing Add:* 529 Custis Rd Glenside PA 19038-2011

**YOUNG, HENRY EDWARD,** USE OF STEM CELLS FOR TISSUE REPAIR & GENE THERAPIES, HISTOLOGY EMBRYOLOGY & ANATOMY. *Current Pos:* ASST PROF ANAT & SURG, MERCER UNIV SCH MED, 88- *Personal Data:* b Dayton, Ohio, Dec 5, 51; m 76, Valerie E Achorn; c Katherine E. *Educ:* Ohio State Univ, BS, 74; Univ Ark, MS, 77; Tex Tech Univ, PhD(anat), 83. *Prof Exp:* Muscular Dystrophy Asn, fel Biochem, Case Western Res Univ, 83-85, NIH fel, 85-87; instr biochem, Rush-Presby-St Lukes Med Ctr, 87-88. *Mem:* Am Soc Cell Biol; Tissue Cult Asn. *Res:* Harvesting and use of vertebrate pluripotent mesenchymal stem cells as a source for tissue transplantation and as a vehicle for gene therapies. *Mailing Add:* Mercer Univ Med Sch Macon GA 31207. *Fax:* 912-752-4038

**YOUNG, HEWITT H,** INDUSTRIAL & HUMAN FACTORS ENGINEERING. *Current Pos:* chmn indust eng fac, 67-76, prof, 67-88, EMER PROF ENG, ARIZ STATE UNIV, 88- *Personal Data:* b Willoughby, Ohio, May 16, 23; m 45, Beatrice; c David, William, Gary, John, Brian & Russell. *Educ:* Case Inst Technol, BSME, 44, MSIE, 50; Ariz State Univ, PhD, 66. *Prof Exp:* Engr, Lamp Develop Lab, Gen Elec Co, Ohio, 46-48; instr graphics, Case Inst Technol, 48-50; indust engr jet engines, Tapco Div, Thompson Prod, Inc, Ohio, 50-53; prof indust eng, Purdue Univ, 53-67. *Concurrent Pos:* Chmn, Col-Indust Comt Mat Handling Educ, 66-68 & Nat Coun Indust Eng Acad Dept Heads, 71-72; NASA/Am Soc Eng Educ fel, 67 & USAF/Am Soc Eng Educ fel, 70. *Mem:* Am Soc Eng Educ; fel Am Inst Indust Engrs (vpres, 72-75, 77-79). *Res:* Large-scale systems analysis; performance analysis; human engineering. *Mailing Add:* Dept Indust Eng Ariz State Univ Tempe AZ 85287-5906

**YOUNG, HO LEE,** environment sciences, for more information see previous edition

**YOUNG, HOBART PEYTON,** ECONOMICS, OPERATIONS RESEARCH. *Current Pos:* PROF ECONS & PUB POLICY, UNIV MD, 81- *Personal Data:* b Evanston, Ill, Mar 9, 45; m 82, Fernanda; c Patrick & Benjamin. *Educ:* Harvard Univ, BA, 66; Univ Mich, PhD(math), 70. *Honors & Awards:* Lester R Ford Award, Math Asn Am, 76. *Prof Exp:* Economist, Nat Water Comn, 71; assoc prof math, Grad Sch, City Univ New York, 71-75; res scholar & dept chmn, Int Inst Appl Systs Anal, 76-81. *Concurrent Pos:* Vis prof, Univ Bonn, 78, Univ Paris, 81 & Univ Chicago, 87; consult, numerous govt agencies; dir grants, US Army Res Off, 73-74, NSF, 75-86, 90-91, Off Naval Res, 86-89 & Russel Sage Found, 89-92; guest scholar,

Brookings Inst, 88-89, 94; Erskine fel, NZ, 90; inst scholar, Int Inst Appl Systs Anal, 94. *Mem:* Economet Soc; Am Polit Sci Asn; Opers Res Soc Am; Am Econ Asn. *Res:* Voting and representation; public economics, game theory, group decision theory; negotiation. *Mailing Add:* Dept Econ Johns Hopkins Univ 3400 N Charles St Baltimore MD 21218. *Fax:* 301-403-4675; *E-Mail:* pyoung@puafmail.umd.edu

**YOUNG, HONG YIP,** AGRICULTURAL CHEMISTRY. *Current Pos:* RETIRED. *Personal Data:* b Wailuku, Hawaii, Nov 27, 10; m 37; c 3. *Educ:* Univ Hawaii, BS, 32, MS, 33. *Prof Exp:* Sci aide, Pineapple Res Inst, 33-40, from jr chemist to chemist, 40-67; from assoc agronomist to agronomist, Agr Exp Sta, Col Trop Agr, Univ Hawaii, 67-75, emer agronomist, 75-84. *Concurrent Pos:* Vis scientist, Int Rice Res Inst, 65-66; consult, Indian Agr Res Inst, 68. *Mem:* Am Chem Soc; Sigma Xi. *Res:* Plant, soil, hormone and pesticide residue analysis; mineral nutrition of plants. *Mailing Add:* 676 Hakaka St Honolulu HI 96816-4765

**YOUNG, HOWARD ALAN,** MOLECULAR IMMUNOLOGY. *Current Pos:* staff scientist, 81-83 & 83-88, HEAD, CELLULAR & MOLECULAR IMMUNOL SECT, NAT CANCER INST, FREDERICK CANCER RES & DEVELOP CTR, 88- *Personal Data:* b Ossining, NY, Jan 29, 48; m 78, Helga Steigerwald; c Lauren. *Educ:* Univ Mass, BS, 69; Univ Wash, MS, 72, PhD(microbiol), 74. *Prof Exp:* Postdoctoral fel, Nat Cancer Inst, 74-76, staff fel, 76-79; head, Tech Serv, Bethesda Res Labs, 81-83. *Mem:* Am Soc Microbiol; Int Interferon Soc; AAAS; Am Asn Immunologists; Cytokine Soc. *Res:* Investigation of gene regulation in the immune system with special emphasis on interferon gamma; gene regulation and large granular lymphocyte specific gene expression. *Mailing Add:* Cellular & Molecular Immunol Sect Nat Cancer Inst FCRDC Lab Exp Immunol Bldg 560 Rm 31-23 PO Box B Frederick MD 21702-1201. *Fax:* 301-846-1673; *E-Mail:* youngh@ncifcrf.gov

**YOUNG, HOWARD FREDERICK,** zoology; deceased, see previous edition for last biography

**YOUNG, HOWARD SETH,** PHYSICAL CHEMISTRY. *Current Pos:* RETIRED. *Personal Data:* b Birmingham, Ala, July 7, 24; m 45; c Alice M, Glenn R, Margaret R, George M, Ralph H, Elizabeth A & Joan M. *Educ:* Birmingham Southern Col, BS, 42; Brown Univ, PhD(chem), 48. *Prof Exp:* Chemist, Eastman Kodak Co, 44-46 & 48-51, sr res chemist, 51-62, from res assoc to sr res assoc, 63-70, head, Eng Res Div, 70-75, head, Phys & Anal Chem Res Div, 75-84, asst dir, 84-85, dir res labs, Eastman Chem Div, 85-89. *Mem:* Sigma Xi; Am Chem Soc. *Res:* Inorganic chemistry; catalysis. *Mailing Add:* 1909 E Sevier Ave Kingsport TN 37664

**YOUNG, HUGH DAVID,** SCIENCE EDUCATION. *Current Pos:* From instr to assoc prof, 56-76, head, Dept Natural Sci, 62-74, PROF PHYSICS, CARNEGIE-MELLON UNIV, 76- *Personal Data:* b Ames, Iowa, Nov 3, 30; m 60, Alice Carroll; c Gretchen & Rebecca. *Educ:* Carnegie Inst Technol, BS, 52, MS, 53, PhD(physics), 59, Carnegie-Mellon Univ, BFA, 72. *Mem:* Am Phys Soc; Am Asn Physics Teachers. *Res:* Physics textbook writing; new teaching materials for introductory college physics courses. *Mailing Add:* Dept Physics Carnegie-Mellon Univ Pittsburgh PA 15213. *Fax:* 412-681-0648; *E-Mail:* hdy+@andrew.cmu.edu

**YOUNG, IAN THEODORE,** ELECTRICAL ENGINEERING, ANALYTICAL CYTOLOGY. *Current Pos:* PROF APPL PHYSICS, TECH UNIV DELFT, NETH, 81- *Personal Data:* b Chicago, Ill, Dec 15, 43; m 77; c 3. *Educ:* Mass Inst Technol, SB & SM, 66, PhD(elec eng), 69. *Honors & Awards:* Res Prize, Schlumberger Found, 90. *Prof Exp:* From instr to assoc prof elec eng, Mass Inst Technol, 67-79; group leader, Lawrence Livermore Lab, 78-81. *Concurrent Pos:* Vincent Hayes fel, Mass Inst Technol, 69-71; consult, Lincoln Labs, 72-78 & Coulter Biomed Res Corp, 75-78; fel, Neth Orgn Res, 75-77; guest prof, Tech Univ Neth, 75-76, Tech Univ Sweden, 76 & Tech Univ Lausanne, Switz, 80; mem, Cytol Automation Comn, Nat Cancer Inst, NIH, 77-81; ed, Bio Imaging. *Mem:* Inst Elec & Electronics Engrs; Med & Biol Soc; Soc Anal Cytol; fel Royal Microscopal Soc. *Res:* Quantitative microscopy; image processing; pattern recognition; signal processing. *Mailing Add:* Dept Appl Physics Loreutzweg 1 Tech Univ Delft Delft 2628 Netherlands

**YOUNG, IN MIN,** audiology, psychoacoustics, for more information see previous edition

**YOUNG, IRVING,** MEDICINE, PATHOLOGY. *Current Pos:* assoc dir labs, Div Path, 52-71, CHMN DIV LABS, ALBERT EINSTEIN MED CTR, 71-; CLIN PROF PATH, SCH MED, TEMPLE UNIV, 75- *Personal Data:* b New York, NY, Aug 15, 22; m 48; c 3. *Educ:* Johns Hopkins Univ, AB, 43, MD, 46. *Prof Exp:* Asst pathologist, Kings County Hosp, Brooklyn, NY, 49-51. *Mem:* AMA; Fedn Am Soc Exp Biol. *Res:* Immunomorphologic correlation; histochemistry of chromosomes; surgical pathology. *Mailing Add:* 681 Meetinghouse Rd Elkins Park PA 19027

**YOUNG, IRVING GUSTAV,** ANALYTICAL CHEMISTRY, PHYSICAL CHEMISTRY. *Current Pos:* RETIRED. *Personal Data:* b Brooklyn, NY, Dec 10, 19; m 41, Rosalyn Shanken; c Arlene L (Alyehs) & Jeffrey M. *Educ:* City Col New York, BS, 39; Polytech Inst Brooklyn, MS, 50; Temple Univ, PhD, 67. *Prof Exp:* Res asst, Bellevue Hosp, Columbia Univ, 39-42; asst chemist, Picatinny Arsenal, 42-44; battery technologist, US Elec Mfg Corp, 44-51; sr res chemist, Int Resistance Co, 51-56, sr res scientist, 59-64; chief chemist, Transition Metals & Chem Co, 56-57; asst res scientist, Leeds & Northrup Co, 57-59; res fel, Temple Univ, 64-65; chemist, Advan Technol Staff, Indust Div, Honeywell, Inc, 65-74, develop supvr, Honeywell Power Sources Ctr, 74-76; mgr, Energy Progs, Am Nat Standards Inst, 76-83; lectr chem, Ogontz Campus, Pa State, 83-89. *Mem:* Am Chem Soc; Instrument Soc Am; Air Pollution Control Asn; Water Pollution Control Fedn; Am Soc Test & Mat; Inst Elec & Electronics Engrs. *Res:* Electrochemistry; process analyzers; air and water pollution; standards coordination. *Mailing Add:* 22 Four Leaf Rd Levittown PA 19056-1923

**YOUNG, J LOWELL,** SOIL BIOCHEMISTRY & BIOLOGY, SOIL CLAY MINERALOGY. *Current Pos:* from asst prof to prof soil sci, 57-88, COURTESY PROF SOIL SCI, ORE STATE UNIV, 88- *Personal Data:* b Perry, Utah, Dec 13, 25; m 50, Ruth Ann Jones; c Gordon R, LoAnn, Colene & Kathryn. *Educ:* Brigham Young Univ, BS, 53; Ohio State Univ, PhD(soils), 56. *Prof Exp:* Asst agron, Agr Exp Sta, Ohio State Univ, 53-56, fel agr biochem, Univ, 56-57. *Concurrent Pos:* From chemist to supvry res chemist, Agr Res Serv, USDA, 57-88, collabr, 88-91; assoc ed, Soil Sci Soc Am J, 75-80. *Mem:* Am Soc Agron; Soil Sci Soc Am; Int Soc Soil Sci; Int Humic Substances Soc; Sigma Xi; Inst Alternative Agri. *Res:* Enzymes in cotyledons of germinating seeds; amino acids of soils, humic substances, root exudates; D-amino acids uptake and metabolism by higher plants; nitrogen and soil particulates as nonpoint-source pollutants eroded from agricultural lands; soil properties affecting beneficial root-fungus symbioses (endomycorrhiza); forms of nitrogen in soil; anhydrous $NH_3$ and $NH_4$ reactions with soils; clay-size and colloidal organic-minerals as primary feeder surfaces for soil microbes and plant roots. *Mailing Add:* Dept Crops & Soil Sci Ore State Univ Corvallis OR 97331

**YOUNG, JACK PHILLIP,** APPLICATION OF LASERS TO ANALYTICAL CHEMISTRY. *Current Pos:* Chemist, 55-82, sr staff mem, 82-88, SR STAFF MEM II, OAK RIDGE NAT LAB, 88- *Personal Data:* b Ind, Oct 28, 29; m 55, Jean Kennedy; c James, Mark, David, Timothy & Karen. *Educ:* Ball State Teachers Col, BS, 50; Univ Ind, PhD(chem), 55. *Honors & Awards:* I R 100 Award for Single Atom Detection. *Mem:* Fel AAAS; Am Chem Soc; Sigma Xi. *Res:* Actinide chemistry; spectroscopy of solutions, molten salts, solid state compounds; laser spectroscopy; photoionization studies; applications of lasers to chemical analysis; fiber optics. *Mailing Add:* 100 Westlook Circle Oak Ridge TN 37830. *Fax:* 423-574-8363; *E-Mail:* qyp@ornl.gov

**YOUNG, JAMES ALBERT,** RANGE ECOLOGY, SEED & SEED BED ECOLOGY. *Current Pos:* RANGE SCIENTIST, AGR RES SERV, USDA, 65- *Personal Data:* b Yreka, Calif, Aug 19, 37; m 58, Cheryl G Smith; c Theresa, Patrick & Nancy. *Educ:* Chico State Univ, BS, 60; NDak State Univ, MS, 62; Ore State Univ, PhD(range sci). *Honors & Awards:* Chapline Res Award, Soc Range Mgt, 90. *Mem:* Fel Soc Range Mgt; fel Weed Sci Soc Am; Agron Soc; Sigma Xi. *Res:* Ecology of temperate desert rangelands in western North America. *Mailing Add:* 110 Riverhaven Pl Reno NV 89509-2152. *Fax:* 702-784-1712

**YOUNG, JAMES ARTHUR, JR,** PHYSICS, ELECTRICAL ENGINEERING. *Current Pos:* proj mgr UNDP Brazil, Int Telecommunications Union, 75-78, affil prof elec engr, Univ Wash, 78-, adj prof, 82-87, dean eng sci, 85-87, EMER PROF, COGSWELL COL NORTH, 88- *Personal Data:* b Tacoma, Wash, Feb 12, 21; m 43, Janet Barton; c James III & Margaret (Hansche). *Educ:* Calif Inst Technol, BS, 43; Univ Wash, PhD(physics), 53. *Prof Exp:* Radar officer, US Army Signal Corps, 43-46; res engr rocket instrumentation, Jet Propulsion Lab, Calif Inst Technol, 46-47; teaching fel physics, Univ Wash, 47-53; co-dir, Radio Res Lab, Bell Tel Labs, Holmdel, 53-76. *Mem:* Inst Elec & Electronics Engrs; Am Phys Soc. *Res:* Communications research; encoding, modulation transmission and switching of information signals, particularly for high radio frequency and optical media. *Mailing Add:* 13921 Silven Ave NE Bainbridge Island WA 98110

**YOUNG, JAMES CHRISTOPHER F,** HEALTH & SAFETY, ANALYTICAL CHEMISTRY & MYCOTOXINS. *Current Pos:* RES SCIENTIST, ECORC, AGR CAN, 72- *Personal Data:* b Charlottetown, PEI, Apr 1, 40; m 66, Judy Reid; c Scott, Rebecca & Stacey. *Educ:* Mt Allison Univ, BSc, 60; McMaster Univ, MSc, 62; Mass Inst Technol, PhD(org chem), 71. *Honors & Awards:* Agcellence Award, Agr & Agrifood Can Res Excellence, 93. *Prof Exp:* Teacher sci, Kitchener-Waterloo Col & Voc Sch, 62-64; lectr chem, Sir Wilfred Laurier Univ, 64-66. *Concurrent Pos:* Rockefeller Found fel, NY Col Forestry, Syracuse Univ, 71-72; fel, Mass Spectrometry Res Unit, Univ Col Swausee, UK, 91-92. *Mem:* AAAS; Chem Inst Can; Am Chem Soc. *Res:* Natural product chemistry; organic chemistry analytical methodology; mycotoxins; ergot alkaloids; chemicals used in animal communication; insect pheromones; mass spectrometry. *Mailing Add:* Agr Can ECORC Ottawa ON K1A 0C6 Can. *E-Mail:* youngjc@em.agr.ca

**YOUNG, JAMES FORREST,** LASER PHYSICS, ENGINEERING. *Current Pos:* PROF ELEC ENG, RICE UNIV, 90- *Personal Data:* b Meadville, Pa, June 22, 43; m 71. *Educ:* Mass Inst Technol, BS, 65, MS, 66; Stanford Univ, PhD(elec eng), 70. *Prof Exp:* Res assoc, E L Ginzton Lab, Stanford Univ, 70-75, res prof elec eng, 75-90. *Concurrent Pos:* Consult, Coherent, Inc, 70-75, Spectra-Physics Inc, 76- & Bell Tel Labs, 77- *Mem:* Am Inst Physics; fel Optical Soc Am; Inst Elec & Electronics Engrs. *Res:* Quantum electronics; nonlinear optics; experimental techniques and instruction. *Mailing Add:* Rice Univ MS 366 PO Box 1892 Houston TX 77251

**YOUNG, JAMES GEORGE,** INDUSTRIAL PHARMACY. *Current Pos:* DIR DEVELOP, PHARMAQUEST CORP, 86- *Personal Data:* b Milwaukee, Wis, July 18, 26; m 54; c 3. *Educ:* Univ Wis, BS, 48, MS, 49; Univ NC, PhD(pharm), 52. *Prof Exp:* Asst prof pharmaceut chem, Med Col Va, 51-54 & Univ Tenn, 56-58; sr chemist, Riker Labs, Inc, 58-60, dir prod develop, 60-72; dir develop, G D Searle & Co, 72-86. *Mem:* AAAS; Am Chem Soc; Am Pharmaceut Asn; NY Acad Sci. *Res:* Pharmaceutical aerosol formulation; drug stabilization; general pharmaceutical development. *Mailing Add:* 731 Ambria Dr Mundelein IL 60060-4814

**YOUNG, JAMES H,** AGRICULTURAL ENGINEERING. *Current Pos:* From asst prof to assoc prof, 66-76, PROF BIOL & AGR ENG, NC STATE UNIV, 76- *Personal Data:* b LaFayette, Ky, Mar 19, 41; m 63, Lou Scott; c Leigh A (Sanders) & James S. *Educ:* Univ Ky, BSAE, 62, MSAE, 64; Okla State Univ, PhD(eng), 66. *Concurrent Pos:* Bd dirs, Am Soc Agr Engrs, 82-84, 88-90. *Mem:* Fel Am Soc Agr Engrs; Am Soc Eng Educ; Am Peanut Res Educ Soc; Am Soc Heating, Refrigerating & Air-Conditioning Engrs. *Res:* Heat and mass transfer in biological materials including tobacco, wheat and peanuts; growth simulation of peanuts as affected by environment; automatic monitoring of weather parameters affecting crop production. *Mailing Add:* NC State Univ Campus Box 7625 Raleigh NC 27695-7625. *Fax:* 919-515-7760; *E-Mail:* Jim__Young@ncsu.edu

**YOUNG, JAMES HOWARD,** mathematics, for more information see previous edition

**YOUNG, JAMES ROGER,** PHYSICS. *Current Pos:* RETIRED. *Personal Data:* b Fordland, Mo, June 14, 23; m 45; c 3. *Educ:* Park Col, AB, 46; Univ Mo, BA, 49, PhD(physics), 52. *Prof Exp:* Res physicist, Res Lab, Gen Elec Co, Schenectady, 51-63, mgr advan develop vacuum prod, 63-64, mgr eng, 64-66, mgr plasma light sources, Res & Develop Ctr, 74-85. *Mem:* Am Vacuum Soc (treas, 73-83); Am Phys Soc; Am Inst Physics. *Res:* Vacuum physics; physical electronics. *Mailing Add:* 34 Nott St Rexford NY 12148

**YOUNG, JANIS DILLAHA,** BIOCHEMISTRY. *Current Pos:* assoc biochemist, Lowell Labs, McLean Hosp, Belmont, Mass, 79-82, RES ASSOC, DIV INFECTIOUS DIS CHILDREN'S HOSP MED CTR, 82-; DIR, PEPTIDE SYNTHESIS FACIL, DEPT BIOL CHEM, UNIV CALIF, LOS ANGELES, 85- *Personal Data:* b Little Rock, Ark, July 12, 27; m 56; c 2. *Educ:* Hendrix Col, BA, 49; Univ Okla, MS, 51; Univ Calif, Berkeley, PhD(biochem), 60. *Honors & Awards:* Alexander von Humboldt Sr Scientist Award. *Prof Exp:* Biochemist, Armour Labs, Chicago, Ill, 51-54; instr chem, Colby Col, 54-55; NIH trainee virol, Univ Calif, Berkeley, 59-61; assoc res scientist, Lab Med Entom, Kaiser Found Res Inst, 61-70; assoc res biochemist, Space Sci Lab & Adj Assoc Prof Immunol, Dept Bact & Immunol, Univ Calif, Berkeley, 71-79; res assoc, dept biol chem, Harvard Med Sch, 79-85. *Mem:* Am Chem Soc; Am Soc Biol Chemists. *Res:* Solid phase peptide synthesis. *Mailing Add:* Skyline Peptides 6039 Skyline Blvd No A Oakland CA 94611-1034. *Fax:* 510-748-0698

**YOUNG, JAY ALFRED,** CHEMICAL SAFETY, HAZARDOUS CHEMICALS LABELING. *Current Pos:* CHEM SAFETY CONSULT, 80- *Personal Data:* b Huntington, Ind, Sept 8, 20; m 42, 62; c 18. *Educ:* Univ Ind, BS, 39; Oberlin Col, AM, 40; Univ Notre Dame, PhD, 50. *Honors & Awards:* Chem Health & Safety Award, Am Chem Soc, 91. *Prof Exp:* Chief chemist, Asbestos Mfg Co, Ind, 40-42; ord engr, US War Dept, DC, 42-44; from instr to prof chem, King's Col, Pa, 49-69; vis prof, Carleton Univ, 69-70; Hudson Prof Chem, Auburn Univ, 70-75; vis prof chem, Fla State Univ, 75-77; mgr tech publ, Chem Mfrs Asn, DC, 77-80. *Concurrent Pos:* Ed, Int J Chem Health & Safety, 80-83; expert witness & tech consult in labeling hazardous chem & prod liability, 79- *Mem:* Fel AAAS; Am Chem Soc. *Res:* Safe use, handling, precautionary labeling and disposal of chemicals; application of chemical reactions to manufacturing processes and to consumer uses and concomitant prevention of injury, property damage and loss. *Mailing Add:* 12916 Allerton Lane Silver Spring MD 20904

**YOUNG, JAY MAITLAND,** IMMUNOASSAYS, PHYSIOLOGICAL DIAGNOSTICS & CANCER MARKERS. *Current Pos:* res biochemist & proj mgr, Abbott Labs, 77-82, int clin specialist, 82-85, clin proj mgr, 85-90, qual & sci support mgr, 90-95, PROD QUAL ASSURANCE MGR, ABBOTT LABS, 95- *Personal Data:* b Louisville, Ky, Nov 26, 44. *Educ:* Vanderbilt Univ, BA, 66; Yale Univ, MS, 67, MPh, 68, PhD(chem), 71. *Prof Exp:* Asst prof chem, Bryn Mawr Col, 70-76. *Concurrent Pos:* NIH fel, Oxford Univ, 71-72; vis scientist, Inst Cancer Res, Philadelphia, Pa, 75-76. *Mem:* AAAS; Am Med Writers Asn. *Res:* Immuno assays in areas of endocrinology including ferti fertility, pregnancy, thyroid hormones, cardiovascular status, metabolic function and of neurodiagnostics and cancer markers; corresponding instrument systems. *Mailing Add:* Abbott Diag Div D-9FK AP31 200 Abbott Park Rd Abbott Park IL 60064-3537. *Fax:* 847-937-0317

**YOUNG, JEFF,** PHYSICS. *Current Pos:* PROF PHYSICS, UNIV BC, VANCOUVER. *Personal Data:* b Nov 3, 56. *Educ:* Univ BC, BASc, 79; Univ Toronto, MSc, 81, PhD, 83. *Honors & Awards:* Gerhard Herzberg Medal, Can Asn Physicists, 94. *Prof Exp:* Res officer, Nat Res Coun, Ont, 83-93. *Mem:* Am Phys Soc; Can Asn Physicists. *Res:* Optoelectronics; semiconductor dynamics; photonic bond structure materials; coherent spectroscopy. *Mailing Add:* Dept Physics Univ BC Vancouver BC V6T 1Z1 Can. *Fax:* 604-822-4750; *E-Mail:* young@physics.ubc.ca

**YOUNG, JERRY H,** ENTOMOLOGY. *Current Pos:* RETIRED. *Personal Data:* b Fitzhugh, Okla, Aug 4, 31; m 52; c 1. *Educ:* Okla State Univ, BS, 55, MS, 56; Univ Calif, Berkeley, PhD(parasitol), 59. *Prof Exp:* Prof entom, Okla State Univ, 59- *Mem:* Entom Soc Am; Entom Soc Can. *Res:* Cotton insect control; mite morphology; Hymenoptera taxonomy; integrated and biological control of cotton insects. *Mailing Add:* 2421 S 78th St Lincoln NE 68506

**YOUNG, JERRY WESLEY,** ANIMAL NUTRITION. *Current Pos:* asst prof animal nutrit, 65-70, assoc prof animal sci & biochem, 70-74, PROF ANIMAL SCI & BIOCHEM, IOWA STATE UNIV, 74- *Personal Data:* b Mulberry, Tenn, Aug 19, 34; m 59; c 2. *Educ:* Berry Col, BS, 57; NC State Univ, MS, 59, PhD(animal nutrit), 63. *Honors & Awards:* Am Feed Indust Award, Outstanding Res Dairy Nutrit, Am Dairy Sci Asn, 87. *Prof Exp:* Res asst animal nutrit, NC State Univ, 57-63; USPHS fel biochem, Inst Enzyme Res, Univ Wis, 63-65. *Mem:* Am Chem Soc; Am Dairy Sci Asn; Am Inst Nutrit; Am Soc Animal Sci; Sigma Xi. *Res:* Ketosis and fatty liver lactating dairy cows; volatile fatty acid metabolism in ruminants; gluconeogenesis and glucose metabolism in ruminants, in vivo kinetics of glucose; effects of nutrition upon reproduction; effects of animal products on cholesterol and lipoprotein metabolism; effects of niacin in dairy nutrition. *Mailing Add:* Dept Animal Sci Iowa State Univ 313 Kildee Hall Ames IA 50011-0001. *Fax:* 515-294-6445

**YOUNG, JOHN A,** ATMOSPHERIC SCIENCE DYNAMICS. *Current Pos:* from asst prof to assoc prof, 66-69, chmn, 84-87, PROF METEOROL, UNIV WIS-MADISON, 75- *Personal Data:* b Washington, DC, July 4, 39; m 88, Gail Snowden; c Annie & Madeline. *Educ:* Miami Univ, BA, 61; Mass Inst Technol, PhD(meteorol), 66. *Prof Exp:* NSF fel, Univ Oslo, 66. *Concurrent Pos:* NSF res grant, 71-; vis assoc prof, Mass Inst Technol, 73-74; mem Global Atmospheric Res Prog, Nat Acad Sci, 73-78, 80-86; vis scientist, Oxford Univ, 87, Nat Meteorol Ctr, 88. *Mem:* Fel Am Meteorol Soc. *Res:* Dynamic meteorology and oceanography; monsoons; numerical modeling; planetary boundary layers. *Mailing Add:* Dept Atmospheric & Oceanic Sci Univ Wis Madison WI 53706. *Fax:* 608-262-0166; *E-Mail:* young@meteor.wisc.edu

**YOUNG, JOHN ALAN,** ELECTRICAL ENGINEERING. *Current Pos:* RETIRED. *Personal Data:* b Nampa, Idaho, Apr 24, 32; m 54, Rosemary Murray; c Gregory, Peter & Diana. *Educ:* Ore State Univ, BSEE, 53; Stanford Univ, MBA, 58. *Prof Exp:* Various mkt & financial pos, Hewlett Packard Co Inc, Palo Alto, Calif, 58-63, gen mgr microwave div, 63-68, vpres elec prod group, 68-74, exec vpres, 74-77, chief operating officer, 77-78, pres, 77-92, chief exec officer, 78-92. *Mem:* Nat Acad Eng. *Mailing Add:* 3200 Hillview Ave Palo Alto CA 94304-1201

**YOUNG, JOHN COLEMAN,** STATISTICS. *Current Pos:* from asst prof to assoc prof, 71-77, PROF MATH, MCNEESE STATE UNIV, 77- *Personal Data:* b Leesville, La, July 13, 42; m 64; c 1. *Educ:* Northwestern State Univ, BA, 64, MS, 65; Southern Methodist Univ, PhD(statist), 71. *Prof Exp:* Asst instr math, Northwestern State Univ, 64-65; asst prof, McNeese State Univ, 67-69; instr statist, Southern Methodist Univ, 69-71. *Mem:* Am Statist Asn. *Res:* Multivariate analysis; discrimination, analysis of variance and goodness of Fit test for multivariate populations. *Mailing Add:* Dept Math McNeese State Univ PO Box 92340 Lake Charles LA 70609-2340

**YOUNG, JOHN DING-E,** tumor immunology, membrane biochemistry, for more information see previous edition

**YOUNG, JOHN FALKNER,** PHARMACODYNAMICS, RISK ASSESSMENT. *Current Pos:* SUPVRY RES BIOLOGIST, NAT CTR TOXICOL RES, 73- *Personal Data:* b Tyler, Tex, Apr 3, 40; m 77, Victoria Molter; c Christopher B & Matthew A. *Educ:* NTex State Univ, BA, 63; Univ Houston, BS, 66; Univ Fla, MS, 69, PhD(pharmaceut res), 73. *Concurrent Pos:* Exec secy, Agent Orange Working Group Sci Panel, 86-89; adj appointments, Col Pharm, Dept Pharmacol & Interdisciplinary Toxicol, Univ Ark Med Sci. *Mem:* Am Pharmaceut Asn; Soc Appl Spectros; Sigma Xi; Teratology Soc; Soc Comput Simulation. *Res:* Application of the principles of pharmacokinetics to teratogenic research; development of analytical procedures used to quantitate chemicals from biological fluids and tissues; simulation of data on hybrid computer; investigation of the utility of pharmacokinetics and pharmacodynamics in risk assessment. *Mailing Add:* Div Biometry & Risk Assessment Nat Ctr Toxicol Res Jefferson AR 72079. *Fax:* 870-543-7720; *E-Mail:* jyoung@nctr.fda.gov

**YOUNG, JOHN H,** PHYSICS. *Current Pos:* asst prof, 70-77, ASSOC PROF PHYSICS, UNIV ALA, BIRMINGHAM, 77- *Personal Data:* b Shamokin, Pa, Aug 16, 40. *Educ:* Gettysburg Col, BA, 62; Univ NH, MS, 64; Clark Univ, PhD, 69. *Prof Exp:* Asst physics, Clark Univ, 64-66. *Mem:* Am Phys Soc. *Res:* Description of the gravitational field of a rotating mass in the general theory by exact means; two body problem in general relativity; three body nucleon problem. *Mailing Add:* 3945 Wakefield Dr Colorado Springs CO 80906-4322

**YOUNG, JOHN KARL,** NEUROENDOCRINOLOGY. *Current Pos:* CONSULT, 86- *Personal Data:* b Minneapolis, Minn, Aug 15, 51; m 77, Paula Jean Spesock; c Michael & Matthew. *Educ:* Cornell Univ, BS, 72; Univ Calif, Los Angeles, PhD(anat), 77. *Prof Exp:* Teaching fel anat, dept anat, Univ Minn, 77-79; asst prof anat, Howard Univ, 79-86. *Concurrent Pos:* Prin investr, NIH res grant, Howard Univ, 80-83. *Mem:* Am Asn Anatomists; Am Physiol Soc. *Res:* Possible neuroendocrine basis of anorexia nervosa; specialized glial cells that may mediate effects of glucose upon hypothalamic regulation of feeding. *Mailing Add:* Dept Anat Howard Univ 520 W St NW Washington DC 20059

**YOUNG, JOHN W(ATTS),** ASTRONAUTICS, AERONAUTICAL ENGINEERING. *Current Pos:* Pilot on first manned Gemini flight, NASA, 65, backup pilot for Gemini 6, command pilot, Gemini 10 mission, 66, backup command module pilot for Apollo 7, command module pilot for Apollo 10, 69, backup spacecraft comdr for Apollo, 13, spacecraft comdr of Apollo 16, 72, backup spacecraft comdr for Apollo 17, 72, ASTRONAUT, NASA, 62-, ASSOC DIR TECH, JOHNSON SPACE CTR, 96- *Personal Data:* b San Francisco, Calif, Sept 24, 30; c 2. *Educ:* Ga Inst Technol, BSAE, 52. *Hon Degrees:* LLD, Western State Univ Col Law, 69; DrApplSci, Fla Technol Univ, 70. *Honors & Awards:* Ivan C Kinchloe Award, Soc Exp Test Pilots, 72. *Mem:* Fel Am Astronaut Soc; assoc fel Soc Exp Test Pilots; Am Inst Aeronaut & Astronaut. *Mailing Add:* NASA-Johnson Space Ctr Mail Code ACS Houston TX 77058

**YOUNG, JOHN W(ESLEY), JR,** COMPUTER SCIENCE. *Current Pos:* SR CONSULT ANALYST, SYSTS ENG, SCRIPPS RANCH, NCR CORP, 57- *Personal Data:* b Baltimore, Md, June 16, 24; m 50; c 1. *Educ:* Albright Col, AB, 45; Harvard Univ, MS, 55. *Prof Exp:* Supvry analyst data processing, US Dept Defense, Washington, DC, 49-56. *Concurrent Pos:* Guest lectr, Univ Calif, Los Angeles, 66- *Mem:* Asn Comput Mach; Inst Elec & Electronics Engrs; Asn Comput Ling; Sigma Xi. *Res:* Design, application and programming of digital computers, especially problem formulation languages, simulation, artificial intelligence and operating systems; data base systems; query languages. *Mailing Add:* 460 Ferne Ave Palo Alto CA 94306-4620

**YOUNG, JOHN WILLIAM,** MATHEMATICS, COMPUTER SCIENCE. *Current Pos:* RETIRED. *Personal Data:* b Toronto, Ont, Nov 16, 12; nat US; m 39; c 1. *Educ:* Univ Fla, AB, 34, BS, 37, MA, 40, PhD(math), 52. *Prof Exp:* Prin & sch teacher, Fla, 34-42; instr math, Univ Fla, 46-54; appl sci rep, Int Bus Mach Corp, Ga, 54-55; mathematician & comput prog consult, IBM Res Comput Ctr, NY, 55-57; mathematician & comput prog consult, Missile Test Ctr, Radio Corp Am, 57-58; head anal & info processing, Res Div, Radiation, Inc, 59-60, head eng comput serv, 61-68, mem serv staff, 68-71; mem sr specialist staff, Data Systs Div, Martin Marietta Corp, Fla, 72-75; vis assoc prof comput sci, Fla Technol Univ, 75-76; mem sr tech staff, Educ Comput Corp, Orlando, 76-81. *Concurrent Pos:* Consult, Sci Systs Serv, Melbourne, 76; comput consult, 81- *Mem:* Nat Coun Teachers Math; Math Asn Am; Asn Comput Mach. *Res:* Applications of electronic digital computers; computer performance measurement and evaluation; simulation of computer systems. *Mailing Add:* 304 Broadview Ave Altamonte Springs FL 32701-6233

**YOUNG, JOSEPH HARDIE,** BIOLOGY. *Current Pos:* from asst prof to assoc prof biol, 59-65, chmn dept, 66-80, PROF BIOL, SAN JOSE STATE UNIV, 65- *Personal Data:* b Salt Lake City, Utah, Aug 11, 18; m 66; c 1. *Educ:* Stanford Univ, PhD(biol), 54. *Prof Exp:* From instr to asst prof zool, Tulane Univ, 54-59. *Mem:* AAAS; Entom Soc Am; Am Soc Zool; Sigma Xi. *Res:* Insect embryology; arthropod morphology; marine biology. *Mailing Add:* 6888 Goldpine Ct San Jose CA 95120

**YOUNG, JOSEPH MARVIN,** PATHOLOGY, ANATOMY. *Current Pos:* resident surg, 46-51, resident path, 51-54, CHIEF LAB SERV, VET ADMIN HOSP, 54-; PROF PATH, UNIV TENN MED UNITS, MEMPHIS, 62- *Personal Data:* b Marshall, Tex, Oct 16, 19; m 42; c 4. *Educ:* Harvard Univ, BS, 43; Johns Hopkins Univ, MD, 45. *Prof Exp:* Intern surg, Johns Hopkins Hosp, 45-46. *Mem:* AAAS; Col Am Path; Am Asn Path & Bact; Am Soc Exp Path; Sigma Xi. *Res:* Joint reactions and spread of cancer. *Mailing Add:* 1145 Oak Ridge Dr Memphis TN 38111

**YOUNG, KEITH PRESTON,** PALEONTOLOGY, STRATIGRAPHY. *Current Pos:* From asst prof to prof, 48-88, EMER J NALLE GREGORY PROF GEOL, UNIV TEX, AUSTIN, 88- *Personal Data:* b Buffalo, Wyo, Aug 18, 18; m 49; c 3. *Educ:* Univ Wyo, BA, 40, MA, 42; Univ Wis, PhD(stratig), 48. *Mem:* Paleont Soc; Geol Soc Am; Soc Econ Paleont & Mineral; Am Asn Petrol Geol; Am Inst Prof Geologists; Sigma Xi. *Res:* Cretaceous stratigraphy and paleontology of southwestern North America; Cephalopods and rudists. *Mailing Add:* 5919 Highland Hills Dr Austin TX 78731

**YOUNG, KENNETH CHRISTIE,** self learning systems, weather forecasting, for more information see previous edition

**YOUNG, KENNETH KONG,** HIGH ENERGY PHYSICS, PARTICLE ASTROPHYSICS. *Current Pos:* from asst prof to assoc prof, 67-77, PROF PHYSICS, UNIV WASH, 77- *Personal Data:* b Vancouver, BC, Mar 19, 37; m 67. *Educ:* Univ Wash, BSc, 59; Univ Pa, PhD(physics), 65. *Prof Exp:* Res assoc physics, Univ Mich, 65-67. *Concurrent Pos:* Assoc, Europ Orgn Nuclear Res. *Mem:* Am Phys Soc. *Res:* Accelerator experiments; test standard model, search for evidence of supersymmetry; neutrino astronomy; proton-decoy; neutrino oscillations. *Mailing Add:* Dept Physics PO Box 35160 Univ Wash Seattle WA 98195-1560

**YOUNG, KONRAD KWANG-LEEI,** integrated circuit technology, semiconductor devices, for more information see previous edition

**YOUNG, LAI-SANG,** MATHEMATICS. *Current Pos:* PROF MATH, UNIV CALIF, LOS ANGELES. *Honors & Awards:* Ruth Lyttle Math Prize, Am Math Soc, 93. *Mailing Add:* Dept Math Univ Calif 405 Hilgard Ave Los Angeles CA 90024-1301

**YOUNG, LARRY DALE,** PSYCHOPHYSIOLOGY, MEDICAL PSYCHOLOGY. *Current Pos:* asst prof, 80-88, assoc prof psychol, 88-96, PROF ANESTHESIA, BOWMAN GRAY SCH MED, 96- *Personal Data:* b Fountain Head, Tenn, Dec 13, 48; m 70; c 2. *Educ:* David Lipscomb Col, BA, 70; Univ Ga, MS, 72; Harvard Univ, PhD(psychol), 79. *Prof Exp:* Asst prof psychol, Univ Miss, 78-80. *Concurrent Pos:* Consult, Comn Accreditation Rehab Facil, 84-; consult ed, Annals Behav Med, 91-94. *Mem:* Soc Psychophysiol Res; Soc Behav Med; Asn Advan Behav Ther; Am Psychol Asn; Int Asn Study Pain; Asn Appl Psychophysiol & Biofeedback. *Res:* Application of behavioral principles to management of stress and pain associated with chronic illness or with stress related medical disorders; disease prevention and health promotion. *Mailing Add:* Pain Control Ctr Bowman Gray Sch Med Winston-Salem NC 27157. *Fax:* 910-716-5537

**YOUNG, LAURENCE RETMAN,** BIOENGINEERING, INSTRUMENTATION. *Current Pos:* payload specialist, 92-93, APOLLO PROG PROF ASTON, JOHNSON SPACE CTR, NASA, 95- *Personal Data:* b New York, NY, Dec 19, 35; m 60, Jody Fisher; c Eliot F, Leslie A & Robert R. *Educ:* Amherst Col, AB, 55; Mass Inst Technol, BS, 57, MS, 59, ScD(instrumentation), 62; Univ Paris, cert, 58. *Honors & Awards:* Dryden Lectr, Am Inst Aeronaut & Astronaut, 82; Franklin V Taylor Award, Human Factors, Inst Elec & Electronics Engrs, 83; Alza Lectr, Biomed Eng Soc, 84. *Prof Exp:* Engr, Instrumentation Lab, Mass Inst Technol, 56 & 58-60 & Sperry Gyroscope Co, 57; res asst, Sch Med, Univ PR, 60-61; from asst prof to prof aeronaut & astronaut, Mass Inst Technol, 62-95. *Concurrent Pos:* Consult to var indust & govt orgns, 62-; mem exec comt, Conf Eng Med & Biol, 67; mem, Eng Biol & Med Training Comt, NIH, 70-73; vis prof, Swiss Fed Inst Technol, 72-73 & Univ Zurich, 72-73; mem staff, Conserv Nat Arts Metiers, France, 72-73; mem eng & clin care subcomt, Nat Acad Eng; mem, cardiovasc panel, Nat Acad Sci & Comt Space Biol & Med, Space Sci Bd, Nat Res Coun, 74-; chmn, Vestibular Panel, Nat Acad Sci, 77; CHABA Coun, 82-85; Aeronaut & Space Engr Bd, Nat Res Coun, 82-; Airforce Studies Bd, 82-87; vis prof elec eng, Stanford Univ, 87-88; vis scientist, Ames Res Ctr, NASA, 87-88; prof, Baylor Col Med, 91- *Mem:* Nat Acad Eng; Inst Med-Nat Acad Sci; Biomed Eng Soc (pres, 79); Int Acad Astronautics; fel Inst Elec & Electronics Engrs. *Res:* Application of control theory to man-vehicle problems, especially orientation; flight simulators; space laboratory experimentation on vestibular function; effect of space travel on humans. *Mailing Add:* Man-Vehicle Lab Rm 37-207 Mass Inst Technol Cambridge MA 02139-4307. *E-Mail:* lry@mit.edu

**YOUNG, LAWRENCE,** ELECTRICAL ENGINEERING MATERIALS & DEVICES. *Current Pos:* from assoc prof to prof, 63-90, EMER PROF, DEPT ELEC ENG, UNIV BC, 90- *Personal Data:* b Hull, Eng, July 5, 25; Brit & Can citizen; m 51, Margaret EJ Carr. *Educ:* Cambridge Univ, BA, 46, PhD(natural sci), 50, ScD, 63. *Honors & Awards:* Callinan Award, Electrochem Soc, Can Electrochem Award, 90. *Prof Exp:* Jr Harwell res fel, Atomic Energy Res Est, Harwell, 49-51; fel, Nat Res Can, Ottawa, 51-52; asst lectr chem, Imp Col, London, 52-55; res staff, BC Res Coun, Vancouver, 55-63. *Concurrent Pos:* Assoc ed, Electrochem Soc, 67-83. *Mem:* Fel Royal Soc Can; fel Inst Elec & Electronics Engrs; Electrochem Soc. *Res:* Anodic oxide films; ellipsometry; semiconductor devices; thin films plasma and thermal oxidation of silicon; photo refractive effect in lithium niobate integrated optic devices. *Mailing Add:* 3226 W 51st Ave Vancouver BC V6N 3V7 Can

**YOUNG, LAWRENCE DALE,** ANIMAL SCIENCE, ANIMAL BREEDING. *Current Pos:* RES GENETICIST, US MEAT ANIMAL RES CTR, USDA, 76- *Personal Data:* b Lafayette, Ind, Sept 13, 50; m 72, Deborah Cook; c 3. *Educ:* Purdue Univ, BS, 72; Okla State Univ, MS, 73, PhD(animal breeding), 75. *Prof Exp:* Res asst, Okla State Univ, 72-75. *Concurrent Pos:* NDEA fel, Okla State Univ, 74-75. *Mem:* Am Soc Animal Sci; Coun Advan Sci & Technol. *Res:* Animal genetics; physiological genetics. *Mailing Add:* US Meat Animal Res Ctr PO Box 166 Clay Center NE 68933

**YOUNG, LAWRENCE DALE,** NEMATOLOGY, PLANT BREEDING. *Current Pos:* from adj asst prof to adj assoc prof, 80-91, ADJ PROF, UNIV TENN, 91-; PLANT PATHOLOGIST, AGR RES SERV, USDA, 79- *Personal Data:* b Hartford, Ky, Apr 18, 51; m 71; c 2. *Educ:* Univ Ky, BS, 73; NC State Univ, MS, 75, PhD(plant path), 78. *Prof Exp:* Plant breeder, Pfizer Genetics, 78-79. *Mem:* Am Phytopath Soc; Crop Sci Am; Soc Nematologist. *Res:* Practical control measures for nematodes that reduce yield of soybeans by developing resistant cultivars and nongenetical methods such as crop rotation. *Mailing Add:* 71 Stratford Lane Jackson TN 38305-9457. *Fax:* 901-425-4729

**YOUNG, LAWRENCE EUGENE,** medicine, hematology; deceased, see previous edition for last biography

**YOUNG, LEO,** ELECTRONICS. *Current Pos:* DIR, RES & LAB MGT, DEPT DEFENSE, 81- *Personal Data:* b Vienna, Austria, Aug 18, 26; US citizen; m 83, Ruth; c Philip, Sarah & Joseph. *Educ:* Cambridge Univ, BA(math), 45, BA(physics), 47, MA, 50; Johns Hopkins Univ, MS, 56, DrEng, 59. *Hon Degrees:* DHL, Johns Hopkins Univ, 89. *Honors & Awards:* Microwave Prize, Inst Elec & Electronics Engrs, 63, Microwave Career Award, 88. *Prof Exp:* Lectr physics, Bradford Technol Col, 47-48; engr, A C Cossor, Ltd, 48-51; head, Microwave & Antenna Lab, Decca Radar, Ltd, 51-53; adv engr, Westinghouse Elec Corp, 53-60; head microwave tech prog, Stanford Res Inst, 60-73; staff consult & assoc supt, Naval Res Lab, 73-81. *Concurrent Pos:* Consult, Westinghouse Elec Corp, Stanford Linear Accelerator Ctr, Varian & TRW Systs, 60-; lectr, Stanford Univ, 63; mem, US Comn A, Int Union Radio Sci, 65-, mem, US Nat Comn, 78-; vis prof, Univ

Leeds, 66, Israel Inst Technol, 70-71 & Univ Bologna, 71; Tech Prog Comt chmn, Inst Elec & Electronics Engrs Microwave Soc, 65, pres, 69; mem bd dir, Inst Elec & Electronics Engrs, 71-74 & 79-82, vpres, 79; distinguished lectr summer sch, Eng, 75; chmn eng adv bd, NSF, 79-81; mem US Nat Comt, Int Union Radio Sci, 78-84; assoc mem, Govt Univ Indust Res Roundtable, 82-85; exec secy, Dept Defense, Univ Forum, 82-86; Adv Group Aeorospace Res & Develop lectr, Italy, 71. *Mem:* Fel AAAS; fel Inst Elec & Electronics Engrs (pres, 80); Sigma Xi. *Res:* Microwaves; optics; radar; filters; antennas; design and manufacturing. *Mailing Add:* 6407 Maiden Lane Bethesda MD 20817-5611

**YOUNG, LEONA GRAFF,** PHYSIOLOGY. *Current Pos:* Instr physiol, Emory Univ, 67-68, USPHS fel biochem, 69-71, instr physiol, 71-72, asst prof, 72-76, ASSOC PROF PHYSIOL, SCH MED, EMORY UNIV, 76- *Personal Data:* b New York, NY, Dec 22, 36; m 58; c 3. *Educ:* Bryn Mawr Col, BA, 58; Univ SC, MS, 60; Emory Univ, PhD(physiol), 67. *Concurrent Pos:* USPHS res grant, 72- *Mem:* Biophys Soc; Am Physiol Soc; AAAS; Am Soc Cell Biol. *Res:* Mammalian spermatozoan motility; fertility; immunological infertility; contraception; contractile proteins. *Mailing Add:* Dept Physiol Emory Univ 1440 Clifton Rd NE Atlanta GA 30307-1053

**YOUNG, LEONARD M,** GEOLOGY. *Current Pos:* Asst prof, 67-74, ASSOC PROF GEOL, NORTHEAST LA UNIV, 74- *Personal Data:* b Dallas, Tex, Oct 20, 35. *Educ:* Rice Univ, BA, 57; Univ Okla, MS, 60; Univ Tex, Austin, PhD(geol), 68. *Mem:* Soc Econ Paleontologists & Mineralogists; Nat Asn Geol Teachers. *Res:* Carbonate and terrigenous sedimentary petrology; sedimentary processes; textural parameters; sedimentary structures; fluid inclusion paleotemperatures. *Mailing Add:* Dept Geosci Northeast La Univ 700 University Ave Monroe LA 71209-0550

**YOUNG, LEWIS BREWSTER,** catalysis, petrochemicals, for more information see previous edition

**YOUNG, LI,** DESIGN AUTOMATION, AUTOMATED MANUFACTURING. *Current Pos:* MECH TECH STAFF, LUCENT TECHNOL, 95- *Personal Data:* b Taipei, Taiwan. *Educ:* Tunghai Univ, Taiwan, BS, 79; Univ Fla, ME, 85, PhD(mech eng), 86. *Prof Exp:* Res assoc, Univ Fla, 83-86, fel, 86-87; instr robot geom, 87; mech tech staff, AT&T Bell Labs, 87-95. *Mem:* Am Soc Mech Engrs. *Res:* Design theory, methodology, and technique of mechanical system; automated manufacturing; robotics; mechanism and machine design and analysis. *Mailing Add:* 553 Stony Brook Dr Bridgewater NJ 08807

**YOUNG, LINDA,** laser spectroscopy, for more information see previous edition

**YOUNG, LIONEL WESLEY,** PEDIATRICS, RADIOLOGY. *Current Pos:* PROF RADIOL & PEDIAT, HEALTH CTR, UNIV PITTSBURGH, 75- *Personal Data:* b New Orleans, La, Mar 14, 32; m 57; c 3. *Educ:* St Benedict's Col, Kans, BS, 53; Howard Univ, MD, 57. *Honors & Awards:* John Caffey Award; Gold Cert, Nat Med Asn, 70. *Prof Exp:* From sr instr to asst prof radiol, Med Ctr, Univ Rochester, 65-69, asst prof pediat, 66-69, assoc prof radiol & pediat, 69-75. *Concurrent Pos:* Nat Cancer Inst traineeship grant radiation ther, Med Sch, Univ Rochester, 59-60; Children's Bur, Dept HEW fel pediat radiol, Sch Med, Univ Cincinnati, 63-65; abstractor radiol, Am J Roentgenol & Radium Ther & Nuclear Med, 65-; clin consult, NY State Dept Health, 67-75; mem radiol training comt, Nat Inst Gen Med Sci, NIH, 71-73; pediat radiol consult, Comt Prof Self-Eval & Continuing Educ, Am Col Radiol, 72-82. *Mem:* Radiol Soc NAm; Am Roentgen Ray Soc; Soc Pediat Radiol (pres, 84-85); fel Am Col Radiol; Asn Univ Radiologists; fel Am Acad Pediat. *Res:* Magnification radiography and tomography in pediatric radiology; radiology of renal hypoplasias and dysplasias; duodenal, pancreatic and renal injury from blunt trauma; skeletal dysplasias and metabolic bone disease in childhood. *Mailing Add:* Loma Linda Univ Med Ctr 11234 Anderson St Loma Linda CA 92354-2870

**YOUNG, LLOYD MARTIN,** ACCELERATOR PHYSICS. *Current Pos:* PROJ LEADER, LOS ALAMOS NAT LAB, 79- *Personal Data:* b Merricourt, NDak, Nov 9, 42; m 66; c 2. *Educ:* Univ NDak, BS, 65, MS, 66; Univ Ill, PhD(physics), 72. *Prof Exp:* Res Assoc, Univ Ill, 72-74, asst prof physics, 74-79, sr res physicist, 77-79. *Mem:* Am Phys Soc. *Res:* Development of an electron accelerator having a 100% duty factor using a superconducting linac through which the beam is recirculated several times. *Mailing Add:* 6 Karen Circle Los Alamos NM 87544

**YOUNG, LOUIS LEE,** FOOD SCIENCE. *Current Pos:* RES FOOD TECHNOLOGIST, POULTRY PROD TECHNOL, RUSSELL RES CTR, AGR RES SERV, USDA, 71- *Personal Data:* b El Paso, Tex, Nov 22, 41. *Educ:* Tex A&M Univ, BS, 64, MS, 67, PhD(poultry prod technol), 70. *Prof Exp:* Res asst poultry nutrit, Tex Agr Exp Sta, 64-67; res fel poultry prod technol, Tex A&M Univ, 67-68; res assoc, Tex Agr Exp Sta, 68-71. *Mem:* AAAS; Poultry Sci Asn; Inst Food Technol; Sigma Xi. *Res:* Food chemistry and microbiology; poultry processing; recovery and utilization of protein from food processing waste; muscle chemistry. *Mailing Add:* 550 Congress Pkwy Lawrenceville GA 30244

**YOUNG, LOUISE GRAY,** PLANETARY ATMOSPHERES, MOLECULAR SPECTROSCOPY. *Current Pos:* RETIRED. *Personal Data:* b Los Angeles, Calif, Oct 4, 35; m 53, 68, Andrew; c Gregory & Elizabeth. *Educ:* Univ Calif, Los Angeles, BS, 58, MS, 59; Calif Inst Technol, PhD(eng), 63. *Prof Exp:* Consult engr, Douglas Aircraft, 62-63; scientist, Joint Prog, Jet Propulsion Lab, Calif Inst Technol & NASA, 63-65; res astron, 66-73; res assoc physics, Tex A&M Univ, 73-79; res assoc atmospheric physics, Geophys Lab, USAF, 79-80; res assoc astron, San Diego State Univ, 80-86. *Concurrent Pos:* Asst prof eng, Univ Calif, Los Angeles, 65-66; assoc ed, J Quant Spectros & Radiative Transfer, 66-78; res assoc astron, Univ Tex, Austin, 67; vis astronr, Nat Acad Sci Exchange Prog, Nicholas Copernicus Univ, Torun, Poland, 72 & Inst Space Res, USSR, 80. *Mem:* Int Astron Union; Optical Soc Am; Am Meterol Soc; Am Astron Soc. *Res:* Calculation of molecular spectra; application of spectroscopic data to the transmission of radiation in planetary atmospheres. *Mailing Add:* 4906 63rd St San Diego CA 92115-2506. *E-Mail:* molspec%@y386@mintaka.sdsu.edu

**YOUNG, LYLE E(UGENE),** ENGINEERING MECHANICS. *Current Pos:* RETIRED. *Personal Data:* b Branford, NDak, Oct 16, 19; m 42, Marguerite Swenson; c Lois, Crystal, Tom & Nancy. *Educ:* Univ Minn, BA, 41, MS, 49. *Prof Exp:* Asst supvr track, Pa, RR, 41-42; instr graphics & surv, Univ Minn, 45-53; prof eng mech, Univ Nebr, Lincoln, 53-84, asst dean, Col Eng, 66-70, assoc dean, Col Eng & Technol, 70-84, interim dean, Col Eng & Technol, 79-81. *Mem:* Am Soc Eng Educ; Nat Soc Prof Engrs. *Res:* Mechanics of materials; concrete. *Mailing Add:* 3120 N 75 St Ct Lincoln NE 68507

**YOUNG, M(ILTON) G(ABRIEL),** ELECTRONICS ENGINEERING, MATERIALS SCIENCE. *Current Pos:* RETIRED. *Personal Data:* b Coopersburg, Pa, Nov 29, 11; m 37; c 3. *Educ:* Lehigh Univ, BS, 32; Harvard Univ, MS, 33. *Prof Exp:* Elec engr, Saucon Hosiery Mills, 33-34; asst chemist, Devoe & Raynolds Corp, 34-35; res engr, Hamilton Watch Co, 35-36; sr mfg engr, Western Elec Co, 36-40; instr elec eng, Univ Del, 40-42, from asst prof to prof & chmn dept, 42-73, actg dean, Sch Eng, 51-52, dir, Nema-Univ Res Lab, 58-77, exec officer elec eng, 73-74, emer prof elec eng, 74- *Concurrent Pos:* Consult, Triumph Explosives Co, 40-44, Bio-Chem Res Found, Franklin Inst, 42-45 & Gen Develop Corp, 50-; guest prof, Birla Eng Col, India, 57-58. *Mem:* Sr mem Inst Elec & Electronics Engrs; Sigma Xi. *Res:* Industrial electronics; ultrasonics. *Mailing Add:* Univ Del Newark DE 19711

**YOUNG, MARGARET CLAIRE,** anatomy, physiology, for more information see previous edition

**YOUNG, MARTIN DUNAWAY,** PARASITOLOGY, MALARIOLOGY. *Current Pos:* RES PROF PARASITOL, COL VET MED & DEPT IMMUNOL MED MICROBIOL & DEPT MED, COL MED, UNIV FLA, 74- *Personal Data:* b Moreland, Ga, July 4, 09; m 38, GeDelle Brabham; c Martin B & Margaret Y (Anderson). *Educ:* Emory Univ, BS, 31, MS, 32; Johns Hopkins Univ, ScD(parasitol), 37. *Hon Degrees:* DSc, Emory Univ, 63, Mich State Univ, 75 & Univ Fla, 85. *Honors & Awards:* Rockefeller Pub Serv Award, 53; Darling Medal & Prize, WHO, 63; Order of Manuel Amador Guerrero, Govt Panama, 74; Gorgas Medal, Asn Mil Surgeons US, 74; Cert Merit, Gorgas Mem Inst, 74; LePrince Award, Am Soc Trop Med & Hyg, 76 & Craig lectr, 84. *Prof Exp:* Jr zoologist, NIH, 37-40, dir, Malaria Res Lab, 41-50, in charge imported malaria studies, 43-46, dir, Malaria Sur Liberia, 48, sanitarian, 44-48, sr scientist, 48-50, scientist dir, 50-64, head sect epidemiol, Nat Inst Allergy & Infectious Dis, Lab Trop Dis, 50-61, asst chief lab parasite chemother, 61-62, assoc dir, Extramural Prog, 62-64; dir, Gorgas Mem Lab, 64-74, dir res, Gorgas Mem Inst, 72-74. *Concurrent Pos:* Vis prof, ETenn State Teachers Col, 39, Ala Med Ctr, 65-74 & Mem Univ, St Johns, NFL, 77; coun, AAAS, 47-48 & 52-56; mem expert adv panel malaria, WHO, 50-84; mem malaria adv panel, Pan Am Health Orgn, 57-68; consult, Int Coop Admin, India, 57, WHO, Rumania, 61, CZ Dept, 64-74 & US AID, Africa, 80, PAHO, Jamaica; ed pro team, Am J Trop Med Hyg, 59; lectr, Meharry Med Sch, 60 & Med Sch, Univ Panama, 64-69; mem, Bd Health, Columbia, SC, 60-61; mem, Nat Res Cou, 62-65; mem malaria & parasitic dis comns, Armed Forces Epidemiol Bd, Dept Defense, 65-73; hon res assoc, Smithsonian Inst, 66-74; clin prof, Sch Med, La State Univ, 67-76; res assoc, Gorgas Mem Lab, 74-77; mem bd dirs, Gorgas Mem Inst, 77-83; prin investr, Effects Insect Pathogens on the Ability of Mosquitoes to transmit Malaria grant, USAID, 81-85. *Mem:* Fel AAAS; Am Soc Parasitol (pres, 65); Am Soc Trop Med & Hyg (pres, 52); Royal Soc Trop Med & Hyg; AMA; emer mem Am Mosquito Control Asn. *Res:* Malaria parasitology, epidemiology and treatment; parasitic protozoa, helminths; parasitic diseases, especially biology, epidemiology and treatment; parasitic protozoa, mainly human and animal malaria and helminths, with emphasis on life cycles; host parasite relationships; epidemiology; treatment and control. *Mailing Add:* 610 NW 89th St Gainesville FL 32607-1453

**YOUNG, MATT,** OPTICS. *Current Pos:* PHYSICIST, OPTOELECTRONICS DIV, NAT INST STAND & TECHNOL, 76- *Personal Data:* b Brooklyn, NY, Jan 30, 41; m 64, Deanna Clair; c David & Rachel. *Educ:* Univ Rochester, BS, 62, PhD(optics), 67. *Honors & Awards:* Newton Award, 62; Silver Medal, Dept Com, 83, Gold Medal, 94. *Prof Exp:* Res assoc optics, Univ Rochester, 67; asst prof physics, Univ Waterloo, 67-70; asst prof electrophys, Rensselaer Polytech Inst, 70-74; assoc prof natural sci, Verrazzano Col, 74-75. *Concurrent Pos:* Optics res corresp, Physics Teacher J, 73-76; tech ed, Optical Spectra, 74; consult, Holobeam, Inc, 74, Res & Develop Ctr, Gen Elec Co, 74-75 & NY State Energy Comn, 75; assoc ed, J Optical Soc Am, 74-79; vis scientist, Weizmann Inst Sci, Israel, 84, ed rev bd, Nat Inst Stand & Technol, Boulder, 83-; adj prof elec & comput eng, Univ Colo, 87- *Mem:* Optical Soc Am; AAAS; Fedn Am Scientists; Int Soc Optical Eng. *Res:* Optical fiber measurements; optical processing and holography; lasers and coherent optics; measurement technology; solar energy; laser produced plasmas. *Mailing Add:* Optoelectronics Div Nat Inst Stand & Technol 325 Broadway Boulder CO 80303

**YOUNG, MAURICE ISAAC,** mechanical & aerospace engineering, for more information see previous edition

**YOUNG, MICHAEL DAVID,** pharmaceutical chemistry, for more information see previous edition

**YOUNG, MORRIS NATHAN,** OPHTHALMOLOGY. *Current Pos:* EMER DIR, NY DOWNTOWN HOSP, 81- *Personal Data:* b Lawrence, Mass, July 20, 09; m 48, Chesle V Barnes; c Cheryl L (Deknatel) & Charles C. *Educ:* Mass Inst Technol, BS, 30; Harvard Univ, MA, 31; Columbia Univ, MD, 35; Am Bd Ophthal, dipl. *Prof Exp:* Intern, Queen's Gen Hosp, NY, 35-37; resident ophthal, Harlem Eye & Ear Hosp, 38-40; asst flight surgeon, Maxwell Field, Ala, 41-42; sr eye, ear, nose & throat officer, Walter Reed Gen Hosp, Washington, DC, 42, chief, eye, ear, nose & throat serv, 69th Ata Hosp, 42-44, 235th Gen Hosp, 44-45, med officer & mem staff, 301st Logistical Support Brigade, 66, dep comdr, 343rd Gen Hosp, 66-67, dep comr & chieff prof serv, 307th Gen Hosp, 67-69, staff med officer, 818th Hosp Ctr, 69; dir ophthal & attend, Beekman Downtown Hosp, NY City, 69-80, emer dir ophthal, 71-80. *Concurrent Pos:* Ophthalmologist & auth, 45-; attend & prof, Fr & Polyclin Med Sch & Health Ctr, 63-77; med adv, Dir Selective Serv, NY Dist, 65-; consult ophthalmologist, Beth Israel Med Ctr, NY, 72- & St Vincent's Hosp & Med Ctr, 77- *Mem:* AMA; Pan-Am Med Asn; Contact Lens Asn Ophthal; Am Acad Ophthal; Acad Comp Med; NY Acad Med. *Res:* Medicine; mnemonics and art of memory; science exhibits; illusion practices. *Mailing Add:* 2 Fifth Ave Apt 16M New York NY 10011

**YOUNG, MYRON H(WAI-HSI),** NUCLEAR ENGINEERING, MATHEMATICAL MODELING. *Current Pos:* from asst prof to prof mech eng, 63-77, PROF MARINE SCI & NUCLEAR ENG, LA STATE UNIV, BATON ROUGE, 80- *Personal Data:* b Shanghai, China, July 3, 29; US citizen; m 59; c 5. *Educ:* La State Univ, BS, 53, MS, 57; NC State Col, PhD(nuclear eng), 63. *Prof Exp:* From instr to asst prof eng mech, La State Univ, 56-62; supvry nuclear engr, Air Force Flight Dynamics Lab, Wright-Patterson AFB, 63. *Concurrent Pos:* Consult, Eng Physics Lab, Wright Air Develop Ctr, Wright-Patterson AFB, 59-60 & Air Force Flight Dynamics Lab, 64-65; consult, Systs Res Lab, Inc, 66- *Mem:* Am Nuclear Soc; Am Soc Eng Educ; Sigma Xi; Int Asn Math Modeling. *Res:* Estuarine hydrodynamic modeling; cumulative impact study on wet land environment; data management systems. *Mailing Add:* 645 Sunset Blvd Baton Rouge LA 70808

**YOUNG, NELSON FORSAITH,** BIOCHEMISTRY. *Current Pos:* RETIRED. *Personal Data:* b Everett, Wash, Oct 17, 14; m 42; c 4. *Educ:* Univ Wash, BS, 36; NY Univ, PhD(biochem), 45. *Prof Exp:* Res chemist, Mem Hosp, 40-43; asst, Sloan-Kettering Inst, 45-48; from asst prof to prof clin path, Med Col Va, 58-78, lectr biochem, 70-78. *Mem:* Am Soc Clin Path; Am Chem Soc. *Res:* Renal function; protein metabolism; radiation effects. *Mailing Add:* 1600 Westwood Ave Richmond VA 23227

**YOUNG, PATRICK HENRY,** TRIBOLOGY. *Current Pos:* Res chemist, 84-88, staff res chemist, 88-92, SR RES CHEMIST, E I DU PONT DE NEMOURS & CO, INC, 92- *Personal Data:* b Lancaster, Ohio, July 29, 58; m 90, Susan Rossiter; c Alana. *Educ:* Univ Rio Grande, BS, 80; Ohio Univ, PhD(chem), 84. *Mem:* Am Chem Soc; Soc Appl Spectros. *Res:* New product development of polyester films using state of the art dispersion and compounding technology; understanding the tribology of surfaces as to develop products that are easily engineered. *Mailing Add:* E I Du Pont de Nemours & Co Inc PO Box 89 Circleville OH 43113

**YOUNG, PAUL ANDREW,** NEUROANATOMY. *Current Pos:* from asst prof to assoc prof, 57-72, actg chmn dept, 69-73, PROF ANAT, SCH MED, ST LOUIS UNIV, 72-, CHMN DEPT, 73- *Personal Data:* b St Louis, Mo, Oct 3, 26; m 49, Catherine Hofmeister; c Paul, Robert, David, Ann (Rottler), Carol (Hamel), Richard, James, Steven, Kevin & Michael. *Educ:* St Louis Univ, BS, 47, MS, 53; Univ Buffalo, PhD(anat), 57. *Honors & Awards:* AOA Honor Med Soc, 72, Golden Apple, 74, Acad Sci, St Louis, 93. *Prof Exp:* From asst to instr anat, Univ Buffalo, 53-57. *Mem:* Am Asn Anat; Soc Neurosci; Sigma Xi; Am Asn Clin Anat. *Res:* Neuroanatomy, human and experimental. *Mailing Add:* St Louis Univ Med Sch 1402 S Grand Blvd St Louis MO 63104-1028. *Fax:* 314-268-5127

**YOUNG, PAUL GARY,** CELL CYCLE, TRANSPORT. *Current Pos:* PROF BIOL, QUEENS UNIV, 74- *Personal Data:* b Victoria, BC, Sept, 1947. *Educ:* Univ Victoria, BSc(Hon), 68; Univ Toronto, PhD(zool), 72. *Prof Exp:* Fel, Calif Inst Technol, 72-74. *Concurrent Pos:* Vis prof, Univ Edinburgh, 80-81, Cold Spring Harbor Labs, 87-88. *Mem:* AAAS; Genetics Soc Am; Genetics Soc Can; Can Soc Cell & Molecular Biol. *Res:* Regulation of the cell cycle. *Mailing Add:* Dept Biol Queens Univ Kingston ON K7L 3N6 Can. *Fax:* 613-545-6617

**YOUNG, PAUL MCCLURE,** MATHEMATICS. *Current Pos:* prof math & vpres univ develop, 70-86, EMER PROF, KANS STATE UNIV, 86- *Personal Data:* b Seaman, Ohio, Feb 13, 16; m 42, Edna Schroeder; c 2. *Educ:* Miami Univ, AB, 37; Ohio State Univ, MA, 39, PhD(math), 41. *Prof Exp:* From instr to asst prof math, Miami Univ, 41-47; from assoc prof to prof, Kans State Univ, 47-62, assoc dean, Sch Arts & Sci, 56-62; vpres acad affairs, Univ Ark, 62-66; exec dir, Mid-Am State Univs Asn, 66-78. *Mem:* AAAS; Am Math Soc; Math Asn Am. *Res:* Analysis; approximation of functions by integral means; characterization of integral means. *Mailing Add:* Kans State Univ 2023 Arthur Dr Manhattan KS 66502-3918

**YOUNG, PAUL RUEL,** COMPUTER SCIENCES, MATHEMATICAL LOGIC. *Current Pos:* chmn, Dept Comput Sci, 83-88, assoc dean eng, 91-94, PROF COMPUT SCI, UNIV WASH, 88- *Personal Data:* b St Marys, Ohio, Mar 16, 36; c Lisa R & Neal E. *Educ:* Antioch Col, BS, 59; Mass Inst Technol, PhD(math), 63. *Prof Exp:* Asst prof math, Reed Col, 63-66; from asst prof to prof comput sci & math, Purdue Univ, Lafayette, 66-83; prof comput info sci & math & chmn, Dept Comput Info Sci, Univ NMex, 78-79; asst dir comput & info sci & eng, NSF, 94-96. *Concurrent Pos:* NSF fel, Stanford Univ, 65-66; vis prof, Univ Calif, Berkeley, 72-73 & 82-83; mem, Advan Comt Comput Sci, NSF, 77-80, chmn, 79-80; Woodrow Wilson fel; NSF fel; Brittingham vis prof, Univ Wis, 88-89; chair, Comput Res Asn, 88-91; vis prof comput sci, Univ Wis, 96-97. *Mem:* Asn Comput Mach; Inst Elec & Electronics Engrs. *Res:* Theoretical computer science, with an emphasis on questions of computational complexity and on connections with mathematical logic. *Mailing Add:* Dept Comput Sci FR-35 Univ Wash Seattle WA 98195

**YOUNG, PETER CHUN MAN,** BIOCHEMISTRY & ENDOCRINOLOGY. *Current Pos:* asst prof, Sch Med, Ind Univ, Indianapolis, 71-77, dir, Lab Human Tumor Stem Cell Cloning, 82-87, Lab Human In Vitro Fertilization & Embryo Transfer (IVF-ET), 83-85, DIR, ENDOCRINE LAB, SCH MED, IND UNIV, INDIANAPOLIS, 71-, ASSOC PROF OBSTET & GYNEC, 77-, DIR, ANDROLOGY LAB, 92- *Personal Data:* b Hong Kong, Dec 19, 36; Can citizen; m 67, Deanna Abellera; c Tippy & Terrence. *Educ:* McGill Univ, BS, 61, MS, 63, PhD(biochem), 67. *Honors & Awards:* Prize Award, Cent Asn Obstetricians & Gynecologists, 79. *Prof Exp:* Res assoc endocrinol, St Michael's Hosp, 67-71. *Res:* Biochemistry of steroid hormones; reproductive endocrinology; biology of cancer. *Mailing Add:* Dept Obstet & Gynec Ind Univ Med Ctr MF 102B Indianapolis IN 46202-5196. *Fax:* 317-278-2884

**YOUNG, PETER RONALD,** CYTOKINES & GROWTH FACTORS, SIGNAL TRANSDUCTION. *Current Pos:* from assoc sr investr to sr investr & asst dir, 83-86, FEL, SMITHKLINE BEECHAM PHARMACEUT, 83- *Personal Data:* b London, Eng, Feb 27, 53; US citizen; m 76, Helen Berman; c Jason A. *Educ:* Oxford Univ, BA, 75, MA, 79; Univ Pa, PhD(molecular biol), 80. *Prof Exp:* Fel, Fox Chase Cancer Ctr, 80-83. *Mem:* Am Soc Biochem & Molecular Biol. *Res:* Focus on the biology and molecular biology of cytokines including IL-1, TNF, erythroprotein and IL-5; studies examine production and activity on target cells and mechanisms for regulation therapeutically. *Mailing Add:* SmithKline Beecham Pharmaceut UE 0548 PO Box 1539 King of Prussia PA 19406-0939. *Fax:* 215-270-7962; *E-Mail:* youngp%phvax.dnet@smithkline.com

**YOUNG, PHILLIP GAFFNEY,** NUCLEAR PHYSICS. *Current Pos:* res fel, Los Alamos Nat Lab, 66-68, mem staff nuclear cross sect eval, 68-75, group leader nuclear cross sect eval, 75-81, STAFF MEM, LOS ALAMOS NAT LAB, 81- *Personal Data:* b Beeville, Tex, July 21, 37; m 60; c 3. *Educ:* Univ Tex, Austin, BS, 61, MA, 62; Australian Nat Univ, PhD(nuclear physics), 65. *Prof Exp:* Res fel nuclear physics, Australian Nat Univ, 65-66. *Mem:* Am Phys Soc; Am Nuclear Soc. *Res:* Low energy nuclear physics; neutron-particle and charged-particle cross sections and polarization. *Mailing Add:* T2 B243 Los Alamos Nat Lab PO Box 1663 Los Alamos NM 87545

**YOUNG, RALPH ALDEN,** SOIL FERTILITY. *Current Pos:* chmn, Dept Agr Biochem & Soil Sci, Nev Agr Exp Sta, Univ Nev, Reno, 63-65, chmn, Div Plant Soil & Water Sci, 65-75, prof soil sci & soil scientist, 63-75, assoc dir, 75-82, EMER PROF SOIL SCI, UNIV NEV, 84- *Personal Data:* b Arickaree, Colo, July 14, 20; m 42; c 2. *Educ:* Colo State Univ, BS, 42; Kans State Univ, MS, 47; Cornell Univ, PhD(agron), 53. *Prof Exp:* Instr soils, Kans State Univ, 47-48; asst prof soils, NDak State Univ, Univ & asst soil scientist, Exp Sta, 48-50 & 53-55, from assoc prof & assoc soil scientist to prof soils & soil scientist, 55-62; vis prof, Univ Calif, Davis, 62-63. *Mem:* Fel AAAS; Soil Sci Soc Am; Am Soc Agron; Soils Conserv Soc Am; Sigma Xi. *Res:* Fertilizer-water interactions; soil as a waste treatment system. *Mailing Add:* 2229 Stagecoach Rd Grand Junction CO 81503

**YOUNG, RALPH HOWARD,** CHEMICAL PHYSICS, SOLID STATE PHYSICS. *Current Pos:* RES ASSOC, COPY PRODS RES & DEVELOP, EASTMAN KODAK CO, 71- *Personal Data:* b Berkeley, Calif, Mar 22, 42; m 68, Milly Gan; c Cedric J. *Educ:* Calif Inst Technol, BS, 64; Stanford Univ, PhD(chem physics), 68. *Prof Exp:* Lectr chem, Stanford Univ, 68; asst prof, Jackson State Col, 68-70; lectr, Univ Calif, Riverside, 70. *Mem:* Sigma Xi. *Res:* Photoconduction in organic solids triboelectricity; quantum chemistry; quantum axiomatics; electron-transfer photophysics. *Mailing Add:* 270 Cobb Terr Rochester NY 14620

**YOUNG, RAYMOND A,** WOOD CHEMISTRY. *Current Pos:* PROF FORESTRY, UNIV WIS-MADISON, 75- *Personal Data:* b Buffalo, NY, Mar 14, 45; m 62; c 2. *Educ:* State Univ NY, BS, 66, MS, 68; Univ Wash, PhD(wood chem), 73. *Prof Exp:* Process supvr paper prod, Kimberly-Clark Corp, 68-69; Textile Res Inst fel, Princeton Univ, 73-74, staff scientist textiles,. *Concurrent Pos:* Vis scientist, Swed Forest Prods Lab, Stockholm, 72-73; Sr Fulbright res scholar, Aristotelian Univ, Thessalonike, Greece, 89. *Mem:* Tech Asn Pulp & Paper Indust; Fiber Soc; Am Chem Soc. *Res:* Solvent pulping of wood; chemical modification of cellulose and high yield pulp fibers; lignocellulosic based composites. *Mailing Add:* Dept Forestry Univ Wis Madison WI 53706-1089

**YOUNG, RAYMOND H(YKES),** ELECTRICAL ENGINEERING. *Current Pos:* RETIRED. *Personal Data:* b Bellefonte, Pa, June 23, 21. *Educ:* Bucknell Univ, BS, 43; Northwestern Univ, MS, 51, PhD(elec eng), 57. *Prof Exp:* Test engr, Gen Elec Co, 43-46; instr elec eng, Bucknell Univ, 47-50, from asst prof to assoc prof, 53-70, prof, 70-83. *Mem:* Inst Elec & Electronics Engrs. *Res:* Switching theory; relation of electrical engineering to medical and biological sciences. *Mailing Add:* 320 N Ninth St Sunbury PA 17801

**YOUNG, RAYMOND HINCHCLIFFE, JR,** CALCINATION OF KAOLIN, BENEFICATION OF MINERALS. *Current Pos:* res assoc, 85-89, DEVELOP ASSOC, ENGELHARD CORP, NJ, 89- *Personal Data:* b Pennsauken, NJ, Nov 22, 28; m 53; c 4. *Educ:* Pa Mil Col, BS, 53; Univ Maine, MS, 55, PhD(org chem), 61. *Honors & Awards:* A K Doolittle Award, Am Chem Soc, 72. *Prof Exp:* Res chemist, Monsanto Co, 60-70, Freeport Kaolin Co, 70-85. *Mem:* AAAS; Am Chem Soc; Soc Mineral Eng; Tech Asn Pulp & Paper Indust. *Res:* Device and direct basic research projects related to kaolin clay. *Mailing Add:* Engelhard Corp PO Box 337 Gordon GA 31031. *Fax:* 912-628-5827

**YOUNG, REGINALD H F,** SANITARY & CIVIL ENGINEERING. *Current Pos:* res asst pub health, Univ Hawaii, 63, asst prof environ health & sanit eng, 66-69, assoc prof civil eng, 69-74, asst dir, Water Resources Res Ctr, 73-78, prof civil eng, 74-95, assoc dean, Col Eng, 79-89 & 94-95, interim dean, 80-81 & 89-94, EMER PROF CIVIL ENG, UNIV HAWAII, 95- *Personal Data:* b Honolulu, Hawaii, May 17, 37; m 59; c 2. *Educ:* Univ Hawaii, BS, 59, MS, 65; Wash Univ, DSc(environ & sanit eng), 67. *Prof Exp:* Jr engr, Paul Low Eng, 59; jr engr, Sunn, Low, Tom & Hara, Inc, 59, asst proj engr, 62-63. *Mem:* Am Acad Environ Engrs; Am Soc Civil Engrs; Water Environ Fedn; Am Water Works Asn; Sigma Xi; Asn Environ Eng Professors. *Res:* Water quality management and pollution control; water and sewage treatment; industrial waste treatment; solid wastes management and control. *Mailing Add:* Col Eng Univ Hawaii Manoa 2540 Dole St Honolulu HI 96822

**YOUNG, REUBEN B,** MEDICINE, PEDIATRICS. *Current Pos:* from asst prof to assoc prof, 63-71, dir med staff hosp & exec assoc dean, Sch Med, 77-79, PROF PEDIAT, MED COL VA, 71-, PROF GENETICS, 75-, ASSOC DEAN CONTINUING MED EDUC, 79- *Personal Data:* b Wilmington, NC, Apr 2, 30; m 53; c 3. *Educ:* Med Col Va, BS, 53, MD, 57. *Prof Exp:* Instr pediat, Univ Pa, 61-63. *Mem:* Am Acad Pediat; Endocrine Soc; Am Diabetes Asn. *Res:* Pediatric endocrinology and diabetology; catecholamine metabolism in children; hypoglycemia in children. *Mailing Add:* 1223 E Marshall St Box 6 Richmond VA 23219

**YOUNG, RICHARD A,** GEOLOGY. *Current Pos:* Asst prof earth sci, State Univ NY Col, Geneseo, 66-72, assoc prof, 72-79, chmn dept, 77-86, PROF GEOL SCI, STATE UNIV NY COL, GENESEO, 79- *Personal Data:* b Providence, RI, Aug 5, 40; m 64; c 2. *Educ:* Cornell Univ, BA, 62; Wash Univ, PhD(geol), 66. *Honors & Awards:* Cole Mem Res Award, Geol Soc Am, 88. *Concurrent Pos:* Prin investr geol mapping proj using Apollo Mission photog, NASA Contract, 72-75; vis fac mem, Univ Canterbury, 72; hydrologist, US Geol Surv, 76-; Environ Protection Agency grant, 79-82. *Mem:* AAAS; Geol Soc Am; Sigma Xi. *Res:* Cenozoic geology, including sedimentation, geomorphology, glacial geology and vulcanism; lunar geology. *Mailing Add:* 43 Oak Geneseo NY 14454

**YOUNG, RICHARD ALLEN,** MOLECULAR BIOLOGY. *Current Pos:* PROF BIOL, MASS INST TECHNOL, 84- *Personal Data:* b Pittsburgh, Pa, Mar 12, 54. *Educ:* Ind Univ, BS, 75; Yale Univ, PhD(molecular biol & biochem), 79. *Honors & Awards:* Molecular Parasitol Award, Burroughs Wellcome Co, 87; Chiron Corp Biotechnol Award, Am Soc Microbiol, 94. *Prof Exp:* Postdoctoral fel, Swiss Inst Exp Cancer Res, Lausanne, Switz, 79-80, Stanford Univ, Calif, 81-84. *Concurrent Pos:* Mem, Whitehead Inst Biomed Res, Cambridge, 84-; grantee, WHO, NIH, 84-91. *Mem:* Am Soc Microbiol; Genetics Soc Am; AAAS; Am Acad Microbiol; Molecular Med Soc. *Mailing Add:* Whitehead Inst Biomed Res 9 Cambridge Ctr Cambridge MA 02142-1401

**YOUNG, RICHARD D,** PHYSICS, ELECTRICAL ENGINEERING. *Current Pos:* RETIRED. *Personal Data:* b New York, NY, Mar 16, 24; m 50, Ragna B Bertelsen; c Nina & John. *Educ:* Princeton Univ, AB, 45; Calif Inst Technol, MS, 47, PhD(physics), 52. *Prof Exp:* Teaching asst, Calif Inst Technol, 48-50; mem tech staff, Hughes Aircraft Co, 50-54; mem sr staff, Ramo-Wooldridge Corp, TRW Space Technol Labs & Bunker-Ramo Corp, 54-64 & Informatics, Inc, 64-67; asst prog dir, Tracor, Inc, 67-68; dir systs eng, Digilinc Systs Corp, 68-69; mem sr staff, Synergetic Sci, Inc, 69-70; sr sci specialist, Data Systs Div, Litton Industs, Inc, Van Nuys, 70-87; consult, 87-90. *Mem:* Sigma Xi. *Res:* Advanced systems engineering and systems analysis of military command and control systems, electronic countermeasures and radar; theoretical nuclear physics. *Mailing Add:* 54 Saddlebow Rd Bell Canyon CA 91307

**YOUNG, RICHARD EDWARD,** BIOLOGICAL OCEANOGRAPHY. *Current Pos:* from asst prof to assoc prof, 69-82, PROF OCEANOG, UNIV HAWAII, MANOA, 82- *Personal Data:* b Los Angeles, Calif, Aug 20, 38; m 63; c 2. *Educ:* Pomona Col, BA, 60; Univ Southern Calif, MS, 64; Univ Miami, PhD(oceanog), 68. *Prof Exp:* Res asst oceanog, Inst Marine Sci, Univ Miami, 65-68, res scientist, 68; asst prof zool, Ohio Wesleyan Univ, 68-69. *Concurrent Pos:* Mem, Cephalopod Int Adv Coun. *Res:* Cephalopod, deep-sea and invertebrate biology. *Mailing Add:* 122 Alhoni St Kailua HI 96734

**YOUNG, RICHARD L,** ORGANIC CHEMISTRY. *Current Pos:* MGR, QUAL SYSTS & NEW TECHNOL, DUPONT, NEN PROD, 66- *Personal Data:* b Rushville, Ill, Nov 22, 32; m 53; c 3. *Educ:* Univ Ill, BSc, 54; Brown Univ, PhD(org chem), 59; Boston Univ, MBA, 85. *Prof Exp:* Res chemist, Res Inst Med & Chem, 58-61; res assoc biochem, Col Agr, Univ Wis, 61-63; asst prof agr biochem, Univ Hawaii, 64-66. *Mem:* Am Chem Soc; Sigma Xi. *Res:* Peptide synthesis; tritium and carbon-14 radiochemicals. *Mailing Add:* 880 Chestnut St Newton MA 02168

**YOUNG, RICHARD WAIN,** ANATOMY. *Current Pos:* From asst prof to assoc prof, 60-68, PROF ANAT, SCH MED, UNIV CALIF, LOS ANGELES, 68- *Personal Data:* b Albany, NY, Dec 15, 29; m 55; c 4. *Educ:* Antioch Col, BA, 56; Columbia Univ, PhD(anat), 59. *Hon Degrees:* Dr Sci, Univ Chicago, 80. *Honors & Awards:* Fight for Sight Res Citation, 69; Friedenwald Award, Asn Res in Vision & Ophthalmol, 76. *Concurrent Pos:* NSF fel anat, Univ Bari & Caroline Inst, Sweden, 59-60; Markle scholar med sci, 62-67; guest investr anat, Dept Biol, Saclay Nuclear Res Ctr, France, 66-67; mem, Jules Stein Eye Inst, Univ Calif, Los Angeles. *Mem:* Am Asn Anat; Am Soc Cell Biol; Asn Res Vision & Ophthal. *Res:* Cell biology; radioisotope studies of ocular tissues. *Mailing Add:* Dept Anat UCLA Sch Med Los Angeles CA 90024

**YOUNG, ROBERT A,** PHYSICS, PHYSICAL CHEMISTRY. *Current Pos:* RETIRED. *Personal Data:* b New York, NY, June 8, 29; m 51, 57, 69; c Carol A (Narrity). *Educ:* Univ Wash, BS, 51, PhD(physics), 59. *Prof Exp:* Res asst, Univ Wash, 53-59; engr, Boeing Airplane Co, 59-60; from physicist to sr physicist, Stanford Res Inst, 60-67, chmn, Atmospheric Chem Physics Dept, 67-68; prof physics, York Univ, 68-75; dir res, Xonics, Inc, 75-79; chmn & pres, Quantatec Int, Inc, 79-85; sr scientist, Rocketdyne, Inc, 85-90. *Concurrent Pos:* Consult, Dept Physics, Univ Wash, 59-60; vis fel, Joint Inst Lab Astrophys, Univ Colo, 66-67 & Lab Astrophys & Space Physics, 74-75; chmn & pres, Intra-Space Int, 72-75; prin investr, approx 20 res contracts. *Mem:* AAAS; Am Phys Soc; Am Geophys Union. *Res:* Energy transfer; atomic and molecular processes and spectra; rocket experimentation; balloon, aircraft stratospheric measurements; short wavelength chemical lasers. *Mailing Add:* 330 Leisure World Mesa AZ 85206-3144

**YOUNG, ROBERT ALAN,** SOLID STATE PHYSICS, CRYSTALLOGRAPHY. *Current Pos:* res assoc prof physics & head, Diffraction Lab, Ga Inst Technol, 57-63, prof physics & head crystal physics br, 64-82, prof, 82-87, EMER PROF PHYSICS, GA INST TECHNOL, 88- *Personal Data:* b St Cloud, Minn, Jan 24, 21; m 48, 77; c 3. *Educ:* Polytech Inst Brooklyn, PhD(physics), 59. *Hon Degrees:* Dr, Univ Toulouse, France, 79. *Prof Exp:* Res asst prof & res physicist, Ga Inst Technol, 51-53; instr physics, Polytech Inst Brooklyn, 53-57. *Concurrent Pos:* Co-ed, J Appl Crystallog, 67-69, ed, 70-78; mem, US Nat Comt Crystallog, 69-74 & 76-78, chmn, 79-81; comn, powder diffraction, Int Union Crystallog, 87- *Mem:* Fel Brit Inst Physics; French Soc Mineral & Crystallog; fel Am Phys Soc; Am Crystallog Asn (treas, 68-71, vpres, 72, pres, 73). *Res:* Crystal physics; x-ray, neutron and electron diffraction theory and applications; structural locations and roles of minor impurities; atomic scale mechanisms; apatites; tooth enamel; extension of methods for greater detail; thermally stimulated current studies. *Mailing Add:* Sch Physics Ga Inst Technol Atlanta GA 30332. *Fax:* 404-853-9958

**YOUNG, ROBERT B, JR,** AERONAUTICAL & ASTRONOMICAL ENGINEERING. *Current Pos:* PRES, LOCKHEED ENG & SCI CO, HOUSTON. *Honors & Awards:* Leadership Qual Mgmt Award, Am Inst Aeronaut & Astronaut, 92. *Mailing Add:* Lockheed Eng & Sci Co PO Box 58561 Houston TX 77258

**YOUNG, ROBERT HAYWARD,** PHOTOCHEMISTRY, ORGANIC POLYMER CHEMISTRY. *Current Pos:* MEM STAFF, WEYERHAEUSER CO, 80- *Personal Data:* b Andover, NB, Mar 18, 40; m 65; c 2. *Educ:* Mt Allison Univ, BSc, 62, MSc, 63; Mich State Univ, PhD(org chem), 67. *Prof Exp:* Asst prof org chem, Georgetown Univ, 67-73; group leader, Union Carbide Corp, 73-80. *Mem:* Am Chem Soc; Chem Inst Can. *Res:* Organic chemistry and photochemistry of singlet oxygen; polymer chemistry, adhesive bonding fundamentals; phenolic resin chemistry; wood chemistry; material science. *Mailing Add:* Weyerhaeuser Co WTC Tacoma WA 98477. *Fax:* 253-927-6324; *E-Mail:* young3@wdni.com

**YOUNG, ROBERT JOHN,** ANIMAL NUTRITION. *Current Pos:* MEM STAFF, INST HEALTH PROM, CHARLOTTE. *Personal Data:* b Calgary, Alta, Feb 10, 23; m 50; c 2. *Educ:* Univ BC, BSA, 50; Cornell Univ, PhD(animal nutrit), 53. *Prof Exp:* Asst poultry nutrit, Cornell Univ, 50-53; res assoc, Banting & Best Dept Med Res, Univ Toronto, 53-56; res biochemist, Int Minerals & Chem Corp, Ill, 56-58 & Procter & Gamble Co, Ohio, 58-60; assoc prof animal nutrit & poultry husb, 60-65, head, Dept Poultry Sci, 65-76, prof animal nutrit, NY State Col Agr & Life Sci, Cornell Univ, 65-, chmn, Dept Animal Sci, 76- *Mem:* Poultry Sci Asn; Am Inst Nutrit. *Res:* Mineral metabolism; energy value of fats and fatty acids; nutrition and metabolism of protein and amino acids. *Mailing Add:* Corp Health Servs Inc 4400 Park Rd No 330 Charlotte NC 28209-3130

**YOUNG, ROBERT L(YLE),** MECHANICAL ENGINEERING, AEROSPACE ENGINEERING. *Current Pos:* from assoc prof to prof, Univ Tenn, 57-64, dir, Arnold Eng Develop Ctr Grad Prog, 57-64, assoc dean, Space Inst, 64-79, PROF MECH & AEROSPACE ENG, SPACE INST, UNIV TENN, 64- *Personal Data:* b Neoga, Ill, Apr 3, 25; m 46, 69; c 3. *Educ:* Northwestern Univ, BS, 46, MS, 48, PhD(eng), 53. *Prof Exp:* Instr mech eng,

Northwestern Univ, 48-53, asst prof, 53-57. *Concurrent Pos:* Consult, USAF, 57- *Mem:* Am Soc Mech Engrs; Am Inst Aeronaut & Astronaut; Am Soc Eng Educ; Nat Soc Prof Engrs; Sigma Xi. *Res:* Heat transfer and fluid mechanics with current emphasis on solidification in near zero g environments. *Mailing Add:* 110 Park Circle Tullahoma TN 37388

**YOUNG, ROBERT LEE,** ELECTRICAL ENGINEERING. *Current Pos:* prof elec eng & asst to dean col eng, 77-91, ADJ PROF ELEC ENG, UNIV SOUTHWESTERN LA, 91- *Personal Data:* b Houston, Tex, Apr 10, 34; m 56; c 5. *Educ:* La State Univ, Baton Rouge, BS, 56, MS, 58; Tex A&M Univ, PhD(elec eng), 66. *Prof Exp:* Instr elec eng, La State Univ, 58-59; from asst prof to assoc prof, Southwestern La Univ, 59-68; prof & chmn dept, Northern Ariz Univ, 68-71, asst dean, Col Eng, 70-71; prof eng, Nicholls State Univ, 71-77. *Mem:* Inst Elec & Electronics Engrs; Am Soc Eng Educ. *Res:* Multivariable control systems; electronic systems. *Mailing Add:* 138 Robichaux Lane Broussard LA 70518

**YOUNG, ROBERT M,** biochemistry, biology; deceased, see previous edition for last biography

**YOUNG, ROBERT NORMAN,** MEDICAL CHEMISTRY. *Current Pos:* Sr res chemist, Merck Frosst, res fel, from assoc dir to exec dir, 92-94, ASSOC HEAD RES & VPRES, MERCK FROSST CTR THERAPEUT RES, MERCK FROSST CAN INC, 94- *Personal Data:* m 70, Vivien Blundell; c Colin N & Alexander N. *Educ:* Univ Victoria, BS, 67; Univ BC, PhD(chem), 71; Imperial Col Sci Tech, DIC, 74. *Concurrent Pos:* Adj prof chem, Univ BC, 93- *Mem:* Can Soc Chem; Am Chem Soc. *Res:* Novel drugs affecting the arachidonic acid cascade; cyclooxygenase inhibitors; synthesis of pharmaceuticals and natural products. *Mailing Add:* Merck Frosst Can Inc PO Box 1005 Pointe Claire-Dorval PQ H9R 4P8 Can. *Fax:* 514-428-2624

**YOUNG, ROBERT RICE,** NEUROLOGY, NEUROPHYSIOLOGY. *Current Pos:* PROF NEUROL, UNIV CALIF, 92- *Personal Data:* b Washington, Pa, Aug 26, 34; m 59; c 3. *Educ:* Yale Univ, SB, 56; Harvard Med Sch, MD, 61. *Prof Exp:* Intern, Peter Bent Brigham Hosp, Boston, 61-62; resident neurol, Mass Gen Hosp, 62-65; NIH spec fel neurophysiol, Oxford Univ, 65-67; dir, clin neurophysiol lab, Harvard Med Sch & Mass Gen Hosp, Boston, 68-87; prof neurol, Harvard Med Sch, 86-92; chief spinal cord injury serv, Vet Admin Med Ctr, 87-92. *Concurrent Pos:* Vis scientist clin neurophys, Swedish Med Res Coun, Uppsala Univ, 79; Josiah Macy Jr Found fac scholar award, 79; ed, J Spinal Cord Med. *Mem:* Am Acad Neurol; Am Neurol Asn; Am Asn Electromyog & Electrodiag; Soc Neurosci; Am Paraplegia Soc (pres). *Res:* Discharge properties of spinal motoneurones, (1) their synchronization to produce tremor, the role played by muscle spindle primary afferent discharge in that synchronization and (2) their abnormalities in spastic paresis including alterations in reflex circuits underlying spasticity; neuro rehabilitation-restorative neurology. *Mailing Add:* Dept Neurol Univ Calif 105 Irvine Hall Irvine CA 92697-4275. *Fax:* 714-824-2076; *E-Mail:* rryoung@uci.edu

**YOUNG, ROBERT WILLIAM,** MUSICAL ACOUSTICS, ENVIRONMENTAL NOISE. *Current Pos:* CONSULT ARCHIT ACOUST & COMMUN NOISE, 55- *Personal Data:* b Mansfield, Ohio, May 11, 08; m 47, Evelyn S Cross; c Conrad W, Theodore L & Elizabeth F. *Educ:* Ohio Univ, BS, 30; Univ Wash, PhD(physics), 34. *Prof Exp:* Physicist, C G Conn, Ltd, 34-42; physicist, Div War Res, Univ Calif, 42-46, res assoc, Marine Phys Lab, 46; physicist, USN Electronics Lab, 46-67, consult acoust, Naval Undersea Ctr, 67-74, Naval Ocean Systs Ctr, 74-87. *Mem:* AAAS; fel Acoust Soc Am (vpres, 53-54, pres, 60-61). *Res:* Acoustics of wind musical instruments; piano strings and tuning; underwater ambient and ship noise and sound propagation; acoustical standards; techniques for analyzing sonic booms; architectural acoustics; community noise measurement and description. *Mailing Add:* 1696 Los Altos Rd San Diego CA 92109. *Fax:* 619-273-8732

**YOUNG, ROGER GRIERSON,** comparative biochemistry; deceased, see previous edition for last biography

**YOUNG, RONALD JEROME,** REPRODUCTIVE BIOCHEMISTRY, REPRODUCTIVE TOXICOLOGY. *Current Pos:* CONSULT, 80- *Personal Data:* b Hong Kong, Aug 10, 32; m 62; c 2. *Educ:* Univ Sydney, BSc, 54; Univ NSW, PhD, 58. *Prof Exp:* Fel, Univ Wis, 58-62; lectr biochem, Monash Univ, 63-67; fel, Univ Calif, 67-70; assoc prof reproductive biol, Med Ctr, Cornell Univ, 70-80. *Mem:* Am Soc Biochem & Molecular Biol. *Res:* Biochemistry of fertilization; reproductive biology. *Mailing Add:* Toxicol Div Chem Physiol & Toxicol Br Chem R&D Eng Ctr Aberdeen Proving Ground MD 21010-5423

**YOUNG, ROY ALTON,** BOTANY, PLANT PATHOLOGY. *Current Pos:* RETIRED. *Personal Data:* b McAlister, NMex, Mar 1, 21; m 50, Marilyn R Sandman; c Janet E & Randall O. *Educ:* NMex A&M Col, BS, 41; Iowa State Univ, MS, 42, PhD, 48. *Hon Degrees:* LLD, NMex State Univ, 78. *Prof Exp:* From asst prof to prof, Ore State Univ, 48-76, head, Dept Bot & Plant Path, 58-66, dean res, 66-70, actg pres, 69-70, vpres res & grad studies, 70-76; chancellor, Univ Nebr, Lincoln, 76-80; managing dir & pres, Boyce Thompson Inst Plant Res, Cornell Univ, 80-86. *Concurrent Pos:* Mem, Comn Undergrad Educ Biol Sci, 63-68; Gov's sci Coun, 87-90; chmn, Subcomt Plant Pathogens, Agr Bd, Nat Acad Sci-Nat Res Coun, 65-68; mem, US Comt Man & Biosphere, UNESCO, 73-82; chmn, Standing Comt Environ & Energy, Nat Asn State Univs & Land-Grant Cols, 74-82, Comt Environ, 84-86; chancellor,

Univ Nebr, Lincoln, 76-80; managing dir & pres, Boyce Thompson Inst Plant Res, Cornell Univ, 80-86. *Mem:* Fel AAAS; Am Phytopath Soc; Nat Asn State Univs & Land-Grant Cols; Sigma Xi. *Res:* Biological science; plant pathogens. *Mailing Add:* 3605 NW Van Buren Ave Corvallis OR 97330-4950

**YOUNG, RUSSELL DAWSON,** OPTICS, SURFACE SCIENCE. *Current Pos:* PRES, R D YOUNG CONSULTS INC, 88- *Personal Data:* b Huntington, NY, Aug 17, 23; m 54, Carol Vaughn Jones; c Bessmarie, Gale, Janet & Shari. *Educ:* Rensselaer Polytech Inst, BS, 53; Pa State Univ, MS, 56, PhD(physics), 59. *Honors & Awards:* Nobel Prize Citation, 86; Presidential Citation, 86. *Prof Exp:* Res assoc, Pa State Univ, 59-61; mem staff, Nat Bur Stand, 61-73, chief, Mech Processes Div, 75-80, Ind Syst Div & Mech Prod Div, 80-81. *Concurrent Pos:* Guest worker, Nat Inst Stand & Technol, 81. *Mem:* Am Phys Soc; Optical Soc Am. *Res:* Physical characterization of surfaces; micrometrology; field electron emission; field emission; electron tunneling; electron energy distribution scanning tunneling microscopy. *Mailing Add:* R D Young Consults Inc 852 Riverside Dr Pasadena MD 21122

**YOUNG, RYLAND F,** BACTERIOPHAGE, EXOTOXINS. *Current Pos:* From asst prof to assoc prof, Dept Med Biochem & Genetics, 78-86, PROF, DEPT BIOCHEM & BIOPHYS, TEX A&M UNIV, 86- *Personal Data:* b Bloomington, Ind, Aug 24, 46; m 75, Virginia C; c Jennifer, Ryland, Campbell & Sarah. *Educ:* Rice Univ, AB, 68; Univ Tex, PhD(molecular biol), 75. *Mem:* AAAS; Am Soc Metals; Fedn Am Socs Exp Biol. *Res:* Molecular genetics of bacteriophage lysis; genetics of bacterial exotoxins; nucleolar function in fission yeast. *Mailing Add:* Dept Biochem & Biophys Tex A&M Univ College Station TX 77843

**YOUNG, SANFORD TYLER,** ORGANIC CHEMISTRY. *Current Pos:* RETIRED. *Personal Data:* b Chicago, Ill, Apr 14, 36; m 61; c 2. *Educ:* Univ Ill, BS, 58; Univ Rochester, PhD(org chem), 63. *Prof Exp:* From res chemist to sr res chemist, FMC Corp, 62-74, res assoc, 74-81, supvr, Agr Chem Div, 82-96. *Mem:* Am Chem Soc. *Res:* Process research; high pressure reactions; laboratory safety. *Mailing Add:* 24700 Deepwater Pt Dr #15 St Michaels MD 21663

**YOUNG, SETH YARBROUGH, III,** ENTOMOLOGY, VIROLOGY. *Current Pos:* from asst prof to assoc prof, 67-76, PROF ENTOM, UNIV ARK, FAYETTEVILLE, 76- *Personal Data:* b Victoria, Miss, June 8, 41; m 61; c 3. *Educ:* Miss State Univ, BS, 63; Auburn Univ, PhD(entom), 67. *Prof Exp:* Res entomologist, Stored Prod Res Lab, Mkt Qual Res Div, USDA, Ga, 66-67. *Mem:* Entom Soc Am; Soc Invert Path. *Res:* Insect virology. *Mailing Add:* Agriculture Bldg 321 Univ Ariz Fayetteville AR 72701

**YOUNG, SHARON CLAIRENE,** ZOOLOGY, ANATOMY. *Current Pos:* From asst prof to assoc prof, 68-73, PROF BIOL, SOUTHERN NAZARENE UNIV, 73- *Personal Data:* b Elk City, Okla, Aug 3, 42. *Educ:* Bethany Nazarene Col, BS, 64; Okla State Univ, MS, 65, PhD(zool), 69. *Concurrent Pos:* Rec secy, chmn biol sci sect, Okla Acad Sci. *Mem:* Nat Asn Biol Teachers; AAAS; Sigma Xi. *Res:* Thrips resistance in peanuts; behavior of Mongolian gerbil; very low density lipoproteins. *Mailing Add:* Dept Biol Southern Nazarene Univ 6729 NW 39th Expressway Bethany OK 73008-2605

**YOUNG, SIMON N,** NEUROSCIENCES. *Current Pos:* fel, 71-75, from asst prof to assoc prof, 75-86, PROF NEUROCHEM, DEPT PSYCHIAT, MCGILL UNIV, 87-, PROF, SCH DIETETICS & HUMAN NUTRIT, 90- *Personal Data:* b Godalming, Eng, Feb 6, 45; m, Naomi Kogan; c Anthony & Emily. *Educ:* Oxford Univ, BA, 67; London Univ, MS, 68, PhD(biochem), 71. *Honors & Awards:* Borden Award, Can Soc Nutrit Sci, 89; Heinz Lehmann Award, Can Col Neuropsychopharmacol, 90. *Prof Exp:* Res asst biochem, Inst Neurol, London Univ, 68-71. *Mem:* Soc Neurosci; Can Col Neuropsychophamacol; Can Soc Nutrit Sci. *Res:* Investigation of brain biogenic amine synthesis and function in experimental animals and in man; the effects of diet on brain metabolism and behavior. *Mailing Add:* Dept Psychiat McGill Univ 1033 Pine Ave W Montreal PQ H3A 1A1 Can. *Fax:* 514-398-4370; *E-Mail:* mc51@musica.mcgill.ca

**YOUNG, STUART,** VETERINARY PATHOLOGY. *Current Pos:* assoc prof path, Colo State Univ, 64-72, dir, NIH Grad Training Prog, 65-72, dir, NIH Vision Res Training Prog, 79-82, prof, 72-87, EMER PROF PATH, COL VET MED & BIOMED SCI, COLO STATE UNIV, 87- *Personal Data:* b Haslington, Eng, Dec 30, 25; nat US; m 53, Irene J Bremner. *Educ:* Royal Vet Col, Univ London, MRCVS, 48; Royal Dick Sch Vet Studies, Univ Edinburgh, DVSM, 51; Mich State Univ, MS, 54; Univ Calif, Davis, PhD(path), 63. *Prof Exp:* Asst vet invest officer, Vet Invest Lab, NScotland Col Agr, 49-55; from asst pathologist to assoc pathologist, Vet Res Lab, Mont State Univ, 55-61; assoc prof path, Univ Minn, 63-64. *Concurrent Pos:* NIH spec res fel, Cambridge Univ, 59 & Univ Bern, Switz, 70-71; vis scientist, Univ Bern, Switz, 77. *Mem:* Teratol Soc; Asn Res Vision Ophthal; Am Asn Neuropath; AAAS; Am Vet Med Asn; Conf Res Workers Animal Dis; hon mem Am Col Vet Ophthal. *Res:* Infectious, metabolic and developmental disorders of central nervous system; pathology of chronic, progressive pneumonopathies; pathogenesis of nutritional myopathies; retinal developmental disorders; comparative ophthalmic pathology. *Mailing Add:* Dept Path Colo State Univ Ft Collins CO 80523

**YOUNG, SUE ELLEN,** OPHTHALMOLOGY. *Current Pos:* chief, Ophthal Serv, 75-81, ASST PROF OPHTHAL, UNIV TEX CANCER SYST, 74- *Personal Data:* b Port Arthur, Tex, Nov 28, 39; wid. *Educ:* Univ Tex, BA, 61; Univ Tex, Galveston, MD, 69. *Honors & Awards:* Honor Award, Am Acad Ophthal, 90. *Prof Exp:* From intern to resident ophthal, Univ Tex, Houston, 69-73; fel neuro ophthal, Johns Hopkins Hosp, 73-74. *Concurrent Pos:* Fel, Columbia Presby Hosp, 74; asst prof, Univ Tex Med Br, Houston, 74-81; mem Practicing Ophthalmologist Adv Comt, Am Acad Ophthal; pvt pract, 81- *Mem:* Am Acad Ophthal; Am Asn Ophthal; AMA. *Res:* Breast carcinoma metastatic to the choroid its value as a prognosic indicator and its management. *Mailing Add:* Brackenridge Hosp 1313 Red River No 206 Austin TX 78701-1900

**YOUNG, SYDNEY SZE YIH,** QUANTITATIVE GENETICS, POPULATION GENETICS. *Current Pos:* PROF GENETICS, OHIO STATE UNIV, 67- *Personal Data:* b Fukien, China, Nov 8, 24; m 54; c 1. *Educ:* Nantung Univ, BAgrSc, 47; Sydney Tech Col, FSTC, 51; Univ NSW, MSc, 56, DSc(genetics), 66; Univ Sydney, PhD(genetics), 59. *Prof Exp:* From res scientist to prin res scientist, Div Animal Genetics, Commonwealth Sci & Indust Res Orgn, 59-67. *Concurrent Pos:* Commonwealth Sci & Indust Res Orgn overseas fel, 63-64. *Mem:* Biomet Soc; Genetics Soc Am; AAAS. *Res:* Theoretical and experimental quantitative and population genetics; animal breeding; biostatistics. *Mailing Add:* 430 Monaco Dr Punta Gorda FL 33950

**YOUNG, THOMAS EDWARD,** NUCLEAR PHYSICS. *Current Pos:* RETIRED. *Personal Data:* b Chaves Co, NMex, June 15, 28; m 60; c 2. *Educ:* Rice Univ, PhD(physics), 58. *Prof Exp:* Asst prof physics, Pac Col, Calif, 58-60 & Trinity Univ, Tex, 60-61; physicist, Aerojet Nuclear Co, 61-81, EG&G, Idaho, 81- *Mem:* Am Asn Physics Teachers. *Res:* Neutron reactions and low energy charged particle reactions; radiation shielding. *Mailing Add:* 1184 Atlantic St Idaho Falls ID 83404

**YOUNG, TZAY Y,** COMPUTER VISION, IMAGE PROCESSING. *Current Pos:* PROF ELEC & COMPUT ENG, UNIV MIAMI, 74-, CHMN DEPT, 88- *Personal Data:* b Shanghai, China, Jan 11, 33; m 65, Lily Liu; c Debbie C & Arthur C. *Educ:* Nat Taiwan Univ, BS, 55; Univ Vt, MS, 59; Johns Hopkins Univ, DrEng, 62. *Prof Exp:* Res assoc, Carlyle Barton Lab, Johns Hopkins Univ, 62-63; mem tech staff, Bell Tel Lab, Holmdel, NJ, 63-64; asst prof elec eng, Carnegie-Mellon Univ, 64-68, assoc prof, 68-74. *Concurrent Pos:* Assoc ed, Inst Elec & Electronics Engrs Trans Comput, 74-76, Ed Comt, Inst Elec & Electronics Engrs Trans, Pattern Analysis & Mach Intel, 79-84, Adv Bd, 84-90. *Mem:* Fel Inst Elec & Electronics Engrs. *Res:* Computer vision and image processing; signal and information theory; pattern recognition; computer processing of biological data. *Mailing Add:* Dept Elec & Comput Eng Univ Miami Coral Gables FL 33124

**YOUNG, VERNON ROBERT,** NUTRITION, BIOCHEMISTRY. *Current Pos:* Lectr nutrit biochem, Mass Inst Technol, 65-66, asst prof physiol chem, 66-70, assoc prof nutrit biochem, 70-77, PROF NUTRIT BIOCHEM, MASS INST TECHNOL, 77-; BIOCHEMIST, DEPT SURG, MASS GEN HOSP & HARVARD MED SCH, 87-; DIR MASS SPECTROMETRY FACIL, SHRINERS BURN INST, BOSTON, 91- *Personal Data:* b Rhyl, Wales, Nov 15, 37; US & Brit citizen; m 66, Janice Maria Harrington; c 5. *Educ:* Univ Reading, BSc, 59; Cambridge Univ, dipl agr, 60; Univ Calif, Davis, PhD(nutrit), 65; Am Bd Nutrit, dipl. *Hon Degrees:* DSc, Univ Reading, Eng, 86; MD, Univ Uppsala, Sweden, 97. *Honors & Awards:* Mead Johnson Award, Am Inst Nutrit, 73; Borden Award, 83; Vickers Lectr, Brit Neonatal Soc, 86; McCollum Award, Am Soc Clin Nutrit, 87; Mank Prize Nutrit, 89; Burns Lectr, Royal Col Physicians & Surgeons, 90; Gold Medal Nutrit Soc India, 91; Res Award, Bristol-Myers, Squibb, 95; Roger J Williams Award, 96; Brackenridge Lectr, Univ Tex, 96; E Bruce & Virginia Street Lectr, Univ NTex, 96. *Concurrent Pos:* Prog mgt human nutrit, Competitive Res Grants Prog, USDA, 80-81; assoc prog dir, Mass Inst Technol Clin Res Ctr, Cambridge, Mass, 85-87; dir res, Shriner's Burn Inst, 87-90; biochemist, Dept Surg, Mass Gen Hosp & Harvard Med Sch, Boston, 87-; vis prof, Sch Med, Case Western Res Univ, 88, Dartmouth Med Sch, 88-; sr vis scientist, Human Nutrit Ctr Aging, Tufts Univ, 88-; vis scholoar, Health Sci Ctr, Univ Tex, 96. *Mem:* Nat Acad Sci; Am Inst Nutrit (pres, 91-92); Nutrit Soc Eng; Am Soc Clin Nutrit; Geront Soc Am; Am Chem Soc. *Res:* Human nutrient requirements; protein and amino acids metabolism in human subjects; regulation of skeletal muscle protein metabolism; nutrition and aging with reference to humans; nutrient bioavailability-use of stable isotopes. *Mailing Add:* Dept Nutrit Biochem Bldg E18 Rm 613 Mass Inst Technol 50 Ames St Cambridge MA 02139

**YOUNG, VIOLA MAE (HORVATH),** MEDICAL MICROBIOLOGY. *Current Pos:* RETIRED. *Personal Data:* b Allegan, Mich, Oct 9, 15; c 2. *Educ:* Mich State Col, BS, 36; Univ Ill, MS, 43; Loyola Univ, Ill, PhD, 53. *Prof Exp:* Technician, Ill Res & Educ Hosp, Chicago, 37-43; instr bact, Univ Chicago Med Sch, 43-45; bacteriologist & parasitologist, Mt Sinai Hosp & Res Found, Chicago, 45-47; res assoc, Sch Trop Med, PR, 47-48; parasitologist, Hektoen Inst, Cook Co Hosp, Ill, 48-54; supvry bacteriologist, Dept Bact, Walter Reed Army Inst Res, 54-61; chief, Microbiol Serv, Clin Path Dept, Clin Ctr, NIH, 61-68; head, Res Microbiol Sect, Baltimore Cancer Res Ctr, Clin Br, Nat Cancer Inst, 68-80; consult microbiol & pub health, 80- *Concurrent Pos:* Asst supv bacteriologist, State Hosp Serv, Ill, 43-45; dir lab, Presby Hosp, San Juan, PR, 47-48; lectr, Loyola Univ, Ill, 49-54; mem fac, Rackham Grad Sch, Univ Mich, 69-; mem, Am Bd Microbiol; consult microbiol & pub health, 81-; microbiologist, Off-Drinking Water, Environ Protection Agency, 88- *Mem:* Hon mem Am Soc Microbiol; Am Acad Microbiol; AAAS. *Res:* All infectious agents causing diarrhea; ecology of intestinal tract; Pseudomonas aeruginosa; host-parasite relationships; normal antibodies and immunological response; infection prevention in cancer patients; interrelationships among microorganisms; opportunistic infections; normal flora. *Mailing Add:* 5203 Bangor Dr Kensington MD 20895. *E-Mail:* fopw@dgs.dgsys.com

**YOUNG, WARREN MELVIN,** ASTRONOMY. *Current Pos:* Assoc prof astron & planetarium dir, 62-80, PROF & CHMN, DEPT PHYSICS & ASTRON, YOUNGSTOWN STATE UNIV, 80- *Personal Data:* b Massillon, Ohio, Dec 30, 37; m 60; c 2. *Educ:* Case Inst Technol, BS, 60; Ohio State Univ, MS, 61, PhD(astron), 71. *Mem:* Am Astron Soc; Int Planetarium Soc. *Res:* Spectrum binary stars; photometry; satellites of giant planets particularly Iapetus. *Mailing Add:* Dept Physics & Astron Youngstown State Univ Youngstown OH 44555. *Fax:* 330-742-3121; *E-Mail:* amphys02@ysub.ysu. edu

**YOUNG, WILLIAM ALLEN,** petroleum geochemistry, for more information see previous edition

**YOUNG, WILLIAM ANTHONY,** PHYSICAL CHEMISTRY, ENGINEERING MANAGEMENT. *Current Pos:* LAB SUPVR, CHEMIST LAB, 84- *Personal Data:* b Cleveland, Ohio, Feb 10, 23; m 54; c 2. *Educ:* Univ Wash, Seattle, BS, 49, MS, 53. *Prof Exp:* Res chemist, Am Marietta Co, 53-54; chemist, Thermodyn Sect, Nat Bur Stand, 54-55; test engr, Douglas Aircraft Co, 55-56; res engr, Atomics Int Div, NAm Rockwell Corp, 56-57, sr res chemist, 57-68, mem tech staff, 68-71; mgr analytical develop & testing lab, Nuclear Energy Div, 72-74, mgr analytical technol develop, 74-81, mgr lab automation, Wilmington Mfg Dept, Gen Elec Co, 81-84. *Mem:* Am Chem Soc; Am Phys Soc; Am Nuclear Soc; Sigma Xi; fel Am Inst Chem; Am Soc Qual Control; Soc Appl Spectros. *Res:* Metal hydrides; solid state chemistry; high temperature heterogeneous reactions; diffusion in solids; reaction kinetics; thermophysical properties; molecular structure; analytical chemistry; computer applications; environmental sciences; chemical safety; lab automation. *Mailing Add:* 6309 Pintail Ct Wilmington NC 28403-1929

**YOUNG, WILLIAM BEN,** PHYSICAL METALLURGY, THERMAL SPRAY COATINGS. *Current Pos:* RETIRED. *Personal Data:* b Camden, Mich, Oct 29, 34; m 59, Elaine; c Scott & Michelle. *Educ:* Cent Mich Univ, BS, 56; Mich State Univ, BS, 61. *Prof Exp:* Teacher math & sci, Port Austin High Sch, 56-59; staff metallurgist, Linde Div, Union Carbide Corp, 61-67; eng mgr, Mat Sci Dept, Perfect Circle Prods Div, Dana Corp, 67-97. *Mem:* Fel Am Soc Metals Int; Am Ceramic Soc; Soc Automotive Engrs. *Res:* Metallurgical development of wear resistant coatings applied by metallizing processes; plasma, flame spray and detonation gun processes. *Mailing Add:* 599 Baker Rd Hagerstown IN 47346

**YOUNG, WILLIAM DONALD, JR,** BACTERIOLOGY, SYSTEMATICS. *Current Pos:* ARTIST-BLACKSMITH, CUSTOM STEEL FORGINGS, W D YOUNG, JR, 77- *Personal Data:* b Glen Ridge, NJ, Nov 2, 38. *Educ:* Fairleigh Dickinson Univ, BS, 60, MS, 74. *Prof Exp:* Res asst parasitol, NY Med Col, 61-62; sci asst clin chem, Walter Reed Army Inst Res, 62-64; scientist bact, Warner Lambert Res Inst, Morris Plains, 64-77. *Mem:* Nat Acad Eng; Am Soc Metals; NY Acad Sci; Am Soc Microbiol. *Res:* Development of rapid biochemical tests for use in diagnostic bacteriology; use of computer technology in the identification of bacterial cultures. *Mailing Add:* RR 1 Box 61 Franklin NY 13775

**YOUNG, WILLIAM GLENN, JR,** THORACIC SURGERY. *Current Pos:* from asst prof to assoc prof, 57-63, PROF SURG, MED CTR, DUKE UNIV, 63- *Personal Data:* b Washington, DC, Feb 26, 25; m 52; c 4. *Educ:* Duke Univ, MD, 48; Am Bd Surg, dipl, 58; Am Bd Thoracic Surg, dipl, 58. *Prof Exp:* Resident surg, Duke Hosp, 56-57. *Concurrent Pos:* Mem sr surg staff, Duke Hosp, 57-; attend surgeon, Vet Admin Hosp, Durham, NC, 57-; consult, Watts Hosp, Durham, 58- & Womack Army Hosp, Ft Bragg, 59- *Mem:* Soc Vascular Surg; Soc Univ Surg; AMA; Am Asn Thoracic Surg; fel Am Col Surg. *Res:* Cardiovascular surgery, application of moderate and profound hypothermia in cardiovascular surgery. *Mailing Add:* Dept Surg Duke Hosp Box 3617 Durham NC 27702-3617

**YOUNG, WILLIAM H,** NUCLEAR ENGINEERING. *Current Pos:* MGT CONSULT, WILLIAM H YOUNG & ASSOCS, INC, 85- *Personal Data:* b Ilion, NY; m, Betty; c Deborah (Streeton), William & Elizabeth. *Educ:* Webb Inst Naval Archit, BS; Georgre Washington Univ, MS. *Prof Exp:* Various pos, Div Naval Reactors, AEC, 62-71, assoc dir submarines, 68-71; staff mem, Burns & Roe, Inc, 71-76, vpres, Breeder Reactor Div & head corp strategic planning, 76-83, vpres proj opers, 84-85; asst secy nuclear energy, Dept Energy, 89-93. *Concurrent Pos:* Chmn, Advan Reactor Subcomt & Nuclear Eng Comt, Am Soc Mech Engrs. *Mem:* Am Nuclear Soc; Soc Naval Archit & Marine Engrs. *Mailing Add:* William H Young & Assocs 1442 Sequoia Circle Toms River NJ 08753-2864

**YOUNG, WILLIAM JOHNSON, II,** GENETICS, ANATOMY. *Current Pos:* RETIRED. *Personal Data:* b Lynn, Mass, Dec 10, 25; m 50; c 2. *Educ:* Amherst Col, BA, 50, MA, 52; Johns Hopkins Univ, PhD(biol), 56. *Prof Exp:* Res assoc biol, Johns Hopkins Univ, 56-57, from asst prof to assoc prof anat, Sch Med, 57-66, assoc prof biophys, 66-68; prof anat & chmn dept, Col Med, Univ Vt, 68- *Mem:* Genetics Soc Am; Am Soc Human Genetics; Am Genetic Asn; Am Asn Anat; Sigma Xi. *Res:* Drosophila biochemical genetics; cytogenetics. *Mailing Add:* Univ Vermont Col Med Burlington VT 05403

**YOUNG, WILLIAM PAUL,** SURGERY. *Current Pos:* RETIRED. *Personal Data:* b Spokane, Wash, Oct 11, 13; m 42; c 3. *Educ:* Univ Wis, BS, 37, MS, 39, MD, 41. *Prof Exp:* Intern, Res Hosp, Kansas City, Mo, 41-42; res surg, Univ Wis Hosps, 46-49, instr surg, Univ, 50; chief surg serv, Southeast Fla State Tuberc Hosp, Lantana, 51; chief surg serv, Vet Admin Hosp, Madison, Wis, 52; from asst prof to assoc prof, 53-56, prof surg, Cardiovasc Surg Sect, Med Sch, Univ Wis-Madison, 56-88. *Concurrent Pos:* USPHS trainee, Univ Wis Hosps, 49-50; consult, Vet Admin. *Mem:* AMA; Am Heart Asn; Am Col Surg; Am Asn Thoracic Surg. *Res:* Cardiovascular surgery; pulmonary hypertension associated with congenital heart disease; homografts; myocardial revascularization and studies of anticoagulation techniques. *Mailing Add:* 600 Highland Ave Madison WI 53792-0001

**YOUNG, WILLIAM RAE,** ELECTRICAL ENGINEERING, MOBILE RADIO COMMUNICATIONS. *Current Pos:* RETIRED. *Personal Data:* b Lawton, Mich, Oct 30, 15; wid; c Roy, Susan & Barbara. *Educ:* Univ Mich, Ann Arbor, BSEE, 37. *Prof Exp:* Mem tech staff, Bell Tel Labs, 37-50, supvr classified mil systs, 50-52, supvr switching syst studies, 52-54, supvr data systs planning, 54-56, head dept, 56-61, head, Dept Switching Systs Studies, 61-70, head, Dept Mobile Systs Eng, 70-79. *Mem:* Fel Inst Elec & Electronics Engrs. *Res:* Mobile radio, propagation studies and system planning for vehicular and portable communications. *Mailing Add:* 1137 Applewood Dr Freehold NJ 07748-3982

**YOUNG, WILLIAM W, JR,** glycosphingolipid biology, immunology, for more information see previous edition

**YOUNGBERG, CHESTER THEODORE,** FOREST SOILS. *Current Pos:* RETIRED. *Personal Data:* b Seattle, Wash, Mar 26, 17; m 41; c 4. *Educ:* Wheaton Col, BS, 41; Univ Mich, MF, 47; Univ Wis, PhD(soils), 51. *Prof Exp:* Asst soils, Univ Wis, 47-51, forest soils specialist, Weyerhaeuser Timber Co, 51-52; assoc prof soils, Ore State Univ, 52-57; forestry specialist, Monsanto Chem Co, 57-58; prof forest soils, Ore State Univ, 58-82; consult forest soils, 82-92. *Concurrent Pos:* Exchange prof, NC State Univ, 69-70. *Mem:* Soc Am Foresters; fel Am Soc Agron; Soil Sci Soc Am; Sigma Xi. *Res:* Soil-vegetation relationships; forest humus; symbiotic nitrogen fixation in non-leguminous plants; tree nutrition; slope-stability. *Mailing Add:* 1963 Manorview Lane NW Salem OR 97304

**YOUNGBLOM, JANEY HEG-JOUNG,** CYTOGENETICS. *Personal Data:* b Seoul, SKorea, Oct 28, 55; US citizen; m 84, James; c Emily & Reuben. *Educ:* Rutgers Univ, BS, 77, MS, 78, PhD(genetics & cell biol), 87. *Prof Exp:* Fel, Univ Calif, San Fransisco, 78-89; genetic dis specialist, Calif State Health Dept, 89-90. *Mem:* Am Soc Human Genetics; Genetics Soc Am. *Res:* Sub-telomeric regions of human chromosomes and comparing these DNA segments' distribution in the genome of closely related nonhuman primate species; investigation of mitochondrial DNA and function in Leber's hereditary optic neuropathy disease. *Mailing Add:* 1083 El Paseo Turlock CA 95382. *E-Mail:* jyoungb@koko.csustan.edu

**YOUNGBLOOD, BETTYE SUE,** ORGANIC CHEMISTRY. *Current Pos:* asst prof, 62-65, PROF CHEM, JACKSONVILLE STATE UNIV, 65- *Personal Data:* b Powhatan, Ala, Dec 6, 26. *Educ:* Auburn Univ, BS, 46; Univ Ala, MS, 49, PhD(chem), 57. *Prof Exp:* High sch teacher, Ala, 46-50; instr chem, Univ Miss, 50-52; high sch teacher, Ala, 56-57; asst ed chem nomenclature, Chem Abstr Serv, 57-59, assoc ed, 59-62. *Mem:* Int Union Pure & Appl Chem; Am Chem Soc; fel Am Inst Chemists; Sigma Xi; Nat Sci Teacher's Asn. *Res:* Reaction mechanisms of aliphatic sulfonyl chlorides and derivatives; organic nomenclature of steroids and alkaloids. *Mailing Add:* 602 12th St NE Jacksonville AL 36265

**YOUNGBLOOD, DAVE HARPER,** PHYSICS. *Current Pos:* assoc prof physics, 67-77, dir, Cyclotron Inst, 78-91, PROF PHYSICS, TEX A&M UNIV, 77- *Personal Data:* b Waco, Tex, Oct 30, 39. *Educ:* Baylor Univ, BS, 61; Rice Univ, MA, 63, PhD(physics), 65. *Prof Exp:* Fel, Argonne Nat Lab, 65-67. *Mem:* Fel Am Phys Soc. *Res:* Nuclear spectroscopy and reaction theory; nuclear physics; giant resonances. *Mailing Add:* Cyclotron Inst Tex A&M Univ College Station TX 77843-3366

**YOUNGDAHL, CARL KERR,** APPLIED MECHANICS, REACTOR ENGINEERING. *Current Pos:* Mathematician, 60-74, SR MATHEMATICIAN, ARGONNE NAT LAB, 74- *Personal Data:* b Chicago, Ill, Aug 14, 34; m 63, Marilyn Lapalio; c Carl, Andrew & David. *Educ:* Univ Chicago, AB, 53; Ill Inst Technol, BS, 56, MS, 57; Brown Univ, PhD(appl math), 60. *Concurrent Pos:* Vis lectr, Ill Inst Technol, 63-64. *Mem:* Sigma Xi; Am Soc Mech Engrs; Am Acad Mech; Soc Eng Sci. *Res:* Pressure transients in reactor piping systems; dynamic plastic deformation of reactor components; thermoelasticity; fusion reactor structural analysis; approximation methods in dynamic plasticity; computational methods in reactor analysis. *Mailing Add:* Reactor Eng Div Argonne Nat Lab Argonne IL 60439. *Fax:* 630-252-3361; *E-Mail:* ck_youngdahl@qmgate.anl.gov

**YOUNGDAHL, PAUL F,** MECHANICAL ENGINEERING. *Current Pos:* CONSULT MECH ENGR, 74- *Personal Data:* b Brockway, Pa, Oct 8, 21; m 43, Elinor L Jensen; c Mark E, Marcia L & Melinda L. *Educ:* Univ Mich, BSE, 42, MSE, 49, PhD(mech eng), 61. *Prof Exp:* Asst sr engr, E I du Pont de Nemours & Co, 42-43 & 46-48; teaching fel & instr, Univ Mich, 48-53; dir res, Mech Handling Systs, Mich, 53-62; from assoc prof to prof mech eng, Univ Mich, Ann Arbor, 62-74. *Concurrent Pos:* Staff consult, Mech Handling Systs, 62-70; design consult, Liquid Drive Corp, 62-; patent & prod liability law suit consult & expert witness; sr lectr mech eng, San Jose State Univ, 77- *Mem:* AAAS; Am Soc Mech Engrs; Am Soc Eng Educ; Nat Soc Prof Engrs. *Res:* System design criteria, specifically directed at automation of mass manufacturing chemical process equipment. *Mailing Add:* 501 Forest Ave Penthouse Four Palo Alto CA 94301

**YOUNGDALE, GILBERT ARTHUR,** ORGANIC CHEMISTRY. *Current Pos:* RETIRED. *Personal Data:* b Detroit, Mich, Jan 15, 29; m 56; c 5. *Educ:* Univ Detroit, BS, 54, MS, 56; Wayne State Univ, PhD(org chem), 59. *Prof Exp:* Res assoc med chem, Upjohn Co, 59-90. *Mem:* Am Hypoglycemic Agents; Am Chem Soc. *Mailing Add:* 1702 Greenbriar Dr Portage MI 49024

**YOUNGER, DANIEL H,** COMBINATORIAL MATHEMATICS. *Current Pos:* assoc prof, 68-75, chmn, Dept Combinatorics & Optimization, 78-79, PROF MATH, UNIV WATERLOO, 75- *Personal Data:* b Flushing, NY, Sept 30, 36; m 65, Phyllis Koch; c Kirsten, Meredith & Benjamin. *Educ:* Columbia Univ, AB, 57, BS, 58, MS, 59, PhD(elec eng), 63. *Prof Exp:* Sloan fel, Princeton Univ, 63-64; res engr, Res & Develop Ctr, Gen Elec Co, NY, 64-67. *Concurrent Pos:* Managing ed, J Combinatorial Theory, 68-75; vis scholar, Mass Inst Technol, 81-82. *Mem:* Sigma Xi; Am Math Soc; Can Math Soc. *Res:* Graph theory, especially minimax theory of directed graphs; algorithms. *Mailing Add:* 130 Dunbar Rd Waterloo ON N2L 2E9 Can

**YOUNGER, MARY SUE,** APPLIED STATISTICS, STATISTICAL PROCESS CONTROL. *Current Pos:* asst prof, 74-76, ASSOC PROF STATIST, UNIV TENN, 76- *Personal Data:* b Roanoke, Va, Aug 28, 44. *Educ:* Hollins Col, BA, 66; Va Polytech Inst & State Univ, MS, 69, PhD(statist), 72. *Prof Exp:* Asst prof statist, Va Polytech Inst & State Univ, 72-74. *Concurrent Pos:* Consult, Elec Consumers Coun, 80-81, St Mary's Hosp, Knoxville, 81-82, Saturn Corp, 90-91; assoc dean, Grad Bus Studies, Univ Tenn, Knoxville, 85-86. *Mem:* Am Statist Asn; Decision Sci Inst. *Res:* Applied statistics; applications of statistical process control; author of books on linear regression and publications in medicine, sociology, psychology. *Mailing Add:* Dept Statist Univ Tenn Knoxville TN 37996-0532

**YOUNGER, STEPHEN MICHAEL,** ATOMIC PHYSICS, THEORETICAL PHYSICS. *Current Pos:* physics prog mgr, 89-95, dir, Ctr Int Security Affairs, 95-96. *Personal Data:* b Baltimore, Md, Nov 2, 51; m 74, Maryellen Mahler; c James & Joel. *Educ:* Cath Univ Am, BA, 73; Univ Md, MS, 76, PhD(physics), 78. *Prof Exp:* Physicist physics, Nat Bur Stand, 74-82; physicist, Lawrence Livermore Nat Lab, 82-89. *Concurrent Pos:* Res assoc, Nat Res Coun/Nat Bur Stand, 78-79. *Mem:* Fel Am Phys Soc. *Res:* Theory of atomic structure; atomic process in dense plasmas; nuclear weapons design; high energy density physics. *Mailing Add:* Los Alamos Nat Lab MS A105 PO Box 1663 Los Alamos NM 87545. *Fax:* 505-665-3283; *E-Mail:* smyounger@ lanl.gov

**YOUNGGREN, NEWELL A,** BIOLOGY. *Current Pos:* RETIRED. *Personal Data:* b River Falls, Wis, Mar 15, 15; m 41; c 2. *Educ:* River Falls State Col, BE, 37; Univ Wis, MPh, 40; Univ Colo, PhD, 56. *Prof Exp:* Asst prof biol, Northland Col, 46-48; asst prof, Bradley Univ, 48-55; asst prof, Univ Colo, 55-60, chmn dept, 58-60; head, Dept Biol Sci, Univ Ariz, 68-74, prof biol sci, 61-83. *Concurrent Pos:* Inst dir, NSF, 58-60. *Mem:* Fel AAAS; Am Inst Biol Sci; Nat Asn Biol Teachers. *Res:* Cellular biology; biology education; slime mold physiology. *Mailing Add:* 5750 Vista Val Verde Tucson AZ 85727

**YOUNGKEN, HEBER WILKINSON, JR,** PHARMACOLOGY. *Current Pos:* RETIRED. *Personal Data:* b Philadelphia, Pa, Aug 13, 13; m 42; c 2. *Educ:* Bucknell Univ, AB, 35; Mass Col Pharm, BS, 38; Univ Minn, MS, 40, PhD, 42. *Hon Degrees:* DSc, Univ RI, 72. *Honors & Awards:* E L Newcomb Res Award, 53; Am Soc Pharmacog Award, 70; Egyptian Pharm Award, 77. *Prof Exp:* Asst biol & pharmacog, Mass Col Pharm, 35-39; asst pharmacog, Col Pharm, Univ Minn, 39-42; from instr to prof, Univ Wash, 42-57; prof pharmacog & dean, Col Pharm, Univ RI, 57-81, provost, Health Sci Affairs, 69-81. *Concurrent Pos:* Chmn, Plant Sci Seminar, 51; Nat Adv Coun Ed Health prof, 64-68; pres, Univ RI Found, 84-87. *Mem:* Fel AAAS; Am Pharmaceut Asn; Soc Exp Biol Med; NY Acad Sci; Sigma Xi; Am Soc Hosp Pharm; Am Soc Pharmacog (pres, 70). *Res:* Plant chemistry and pharmacology of plant constituents; biosynthesis of drug plant glycosides and alkaloids; drugs from the sea. *Mailing Add:* 188 Oakwoods Dr Peace Dale RI 02883

**YOUNGLAI, EDWARD VICTOR,** BIOCHEMISTRY, REPRODUCTIVE PHYSIOLOGY. *Current Pos:* from asst prof to assoc prof, 70-82, PROF OBSTET & GYNEC, MCMASTER UNIV, 82- *Personal Data:* b Trinidad, WI, July 15, 40; Can citizen; m 70, Jeanette Wong-Sing; c Marlene R & Natalie S. *Educ:* McGill Univ, BSc, 64, PhD(biochem), 67. *Prof Exp:* Res asst biochem, McGill Univ, 64-67. *Concurrent Pos:* Fel exp med, McGill Univ, 67-68; Med Res Coun Can fel vet clin studies, Cambridge Univ, 68-70; Med Res Coun Can scholar, 70-75 & res grants, McMaster Univ, 70- *Mem:* Brit Soc Endocrinol; Am Fertil Soc; Am Soc Andrology. *Res:* Control of gonadal function; gonadal steroid biosynthesis and metabolism; secretion of hormones; gonadal growth factors. *Mailing Add:* Dept Obstet & Gynec McMaster Univ Health Sci Ctr Hamilton ON L8N 3Z5 Can. *Fax:* 905-524-2911; *E-Mail:* younglai@fhs.csu.mcmaster.ca

**YOUNGLOVE, JAMES NEWTON,** MATHEMATICS. *Current Pos:* assoc prof, 65-71, PROF MATH, UNIV HOUSTON, 71- *Personal Data:* b Coleman, Tex, Dec 16, 27; m 49; c 3. *Educ:* Univ Tex, BA, 51, PhD(math), 58. *Prof Exp:* Instr math, Univ Tex, 52-58; asst prof, Univ Mo, 58-65. *Mem:* Am Math Soc; Math Asn Am. *Res:* Point set topology. *Mailing Add:* Dept Math Univ Houston Univ Park 4614 Rockwood Dr Houston TX 77004

**YOUNGMAN, ARTHUR L,** BOTANY. *Current Pos:* ASST PROF BIOL, WICHITA STATE UNIV, 65- *Personal Data:* b Chicago, Ill, Oct 24, 37; m 63; c 2. *Educ:* Univ Mont, BA, 59; Western Res Univ, MS, 61; Univ Tex, PhD(bot), 65. *Mem:* Ecol Soc Am. *Res:* Physiological ecology of vascular plants; environmental impact of industrial activity on terrestrial ecosystems. *Mailing Add:* Dept Biol Sci Wichita State Univ 1845 Fairmont St Wichita KS 67260-0001

**YOUNGMAN, EDWARD AUGUST,** organic chemistry, polymer chemistry, for more information see previous edition

**YOUNGMAN, PHILIP JOHN,** REGULATION OF GENE EXPRESSION, SPORULATION. *Current Pos:* ASSOC PROF GENETICS, UNIV GA, 91- *Personal Data:* b Middletown, NY, Mar 6, 51. *Educ:* Harvard Univ, BA, 73; Mass Inst Technol, PhD(biochem), 79. *Prof Exp:* Fel, Harvard Univ, 80-83, res assoc, 83-85; from asst prof to assoc prof, Univ Pa, 85-91. *Mem:* Genetics Soc Am; Am Soc Microbiol. *Res:* Regulation of developmental gene expression in bacteria; signal transduction; control of growth-related metabolism and physiology; RNA polymerase-promoter interaction; novel methods for genetic manipulation of bacteria. *Mailing Add:* Dept Genetics Univ Ga 1180 E Broad St Athens GA 30601-3040. *E-Mail:* youngman@bscr.uga.edu

**YOUNGMAN, VERN E,** AGRONOMY. *Current Pos:* ASSOC PROF AGRON, COLO STATE UNIV, 67- *Personal Data:* b Valley, Nebr, Sept 11, 28; m 54. *Educ:* Univ Nebr, BS, 55, MS, 57; Wash State Univ, PhD(agron), 62. *Prof Exp:* Instr agron, Univ Nebr, 56-58; from instr to asst prof, Wash State Univ, 58-67. *Mem:* Am Soc Agron; Soc Econ Bot; Asn Off Seed Analysts; Nat Asn Cols & Teachers Agr. *Res:* Physiology, ecology and management of crop plants. *Mailing Add:* 1320 Parkwood Dr Ft Collins CO 80525

**YOUNGNER, JULIUS STUART,** MEDICAL MICROBIOLOGY. *Current Pos:* asst res prof virol & bact, Sch Med, Univ Pittsburgh, 49-56, from assoc prof to prof microbiol, 56-89, chmn dept, 66-85, chmn, Dept Microbiol, Biochem & Molecular Biol, 85-89, DISTINGUISHED SERV PROF MICROBIOL, UNIV PITTSBURGH, 90- *Personal Data:* b New York, NY, Oct 24, 20; m 43, 64, Rina C Balter; c Lisa & Stuart. *Educ:* NY Univ, AB, 39; Univ Mich, MS, 41, ScD(bact), 44; Am Bd Med Microbiol, dipl. *Honors & Awards:* Lippard Mem lectr, Col Physicians & Surgeons, Columbia Univ, 80. *Prof Exp:* From asst to instr bact, Univ Mich, 41-44; asst path, Manhattan Proj, Univ Rochester, 45-46; instr, Univ Mich, 46-47; sr asst scientist, Nat Cancer Inst, 47-49. *Concurrent Pos:* Vis prof, Nat Univ Athens, 63; mem virol & rickettsial study sect, NIH, 66-70; mem comn influenza, Armed Forces Epidemiol Bd, 70-73; mem bd sci counr, Nat Inst Allergy & Infectious Dis, 70-74; nat lectr, Found Microbiol, 72-73; mem study group, Immunol & Infectious Dis, Health Res & Serv Found, 79, Chmn, 78-79; mem clin A fel study sect, NIH, 79-80; mem, Microbiol & Virol Study Group, Am Cancer Soc, 81-85, chmn, 84-85; James W McLaughlin vis prof, Med Br, Univ Tex, Galveston, 84; chmn, Comt Ethical Pract, Am Soc Microbiol, 97- *Mem:* AAAS; Am Acad Microbiol; Am Soc Microbiol; Infectious Dis Soc Am; Am Soc Virol (pres, 86-); hon mem Int Soc Interferon Res; Am Soc Immunol; elect hon mem Int Soc Interferon & Cytokine Res. *Res:* Replication and properties of animal viruses; cellular and host resistance to virus infection; persistent viral infections. *Mailing Add:* Dept Molecular Genetics & Biochem E1254 Biomed Sci Tower Univ Pittsburgh Sch Med Pittsburgh PA 15261-0001. *Fax:* 412-624-1401; *E-Mail:* julius@hoffman.mqen.pitt.edu

**YOUNGQUIST, R(UDOLPH) WILLIAM,** FOOD BIOCHEMISTRY. *Current Pos:* RES BIOCHEMIST, PROCTER & GAMBLE CO, 62- *Personal Data:* b Minneapolis, Minn, Aug 10, 35; m 59; c 3. *Educ:* Univ Minn, BChem, 57; Iowa State Univ, MS, 60, PhD(biochem), 62. *Mem:* Am Chem Soc; Am Asn Cereal Chemists. *Res:* Starch and carbohydrate food biochemistry. *Mailing Add:* 470 Stonehurst Cincinnati OH 45231-2714

**YOUNGQUIST, WALTER,** GEOLOGY, PALEONTOLOGY. *Current Pos:* CONSULT PETROL GEOLOGIST. *Personal Data:* b Minneapolis, Minn, May 5, 21; m 43; c John, Karen, Louise & Robert. *Educ:* Gustavus Adolphus Col, BA, 42; Univ Iowa, MS, 43, PhD(geol), 48. *Prof Exp:* Jr geologist, Groundwater Div, US Geol Surv, Iowa, Va & La, 43-44; asst prof geol, Univ Idaho, 48-51; geologist, Int Petrol Co, Peru, 51-52, sr geologist, 52-53, chief, Spec Studies Sect, 53-54; prof geol, Univ Kans, 54-57; prof, Univ Ore, 57-66; consult, Minerals Dept, Humble Oil & Refining Co, 66-73, Exxon Minerals, 74-78; geothermal resources consult, Eugene Water & Elec Bd, 73-91. *Mem:* Fel AAAS; Geol Soc Am; Am Asn Petrol Geologists; Geothermal Resources Coun; NW Energy Asn; NY Acad Sci. *Res:* Geology and economics of mineral resources; petroleum geology; geothermal resources. *Mailing Add:* PO Box 5501 Eugene OR 97405

**YOUNGS, CLARENCE GEORGE,** FOOD PROCESSING. *Current Pos:* RETIRED. *Personal Data:* b Didsbury, Alta, Oct 23, 26; m 51; c 3. *Educ:* Univ Alta, BSc, 48; Univ Sask, MSc, 53, PhD(chem), 57. *Honors & Awards:* Res Award, Glycerine Producers Asn, 57 & 62. *Prof Exp:* Res officer crop utilization, Prairie Regional Lab, Nat Res Coun, Can, 48-81. *Concurrent Pos:* Consult, Studies Int Develop Res Centre, Food & Agr Orgn, Junta Del Acuerdo de Cartagena, Canola Coun Can, Govt Sask & Univ Sask; Can Comt Fats & Oils, Expert Comt Grain Qual; Selection Panel Strategic grants, Food & Agr. *Mem:* Hon mem Agr Inst Can; emer mem Can Inst Food Sci & Technol. *Res:* Utilization of prairie crops for food and feed, particularly oilseeds and legumes. *Mailing Add:* 821 Wilson Crescent Saskatoon SK S7J 2M3 Can

**YOUNGS, ROBERT LELAND,** FORESTRY, INTERNATIONAL DEVELOPMENT. *Current Pos:* prof, Dept Forest Prod, 85-95, EMER PROF, VA POLYTECH INST & STATE UNIV, 95- *Personal Data:* b Pittsfield, Mass, Feb 10, 24; m 49, Esther L Stevenson; c 5. *Educ:* State Univ NY, BS, 48; Univ Mich, MWT, 50; Yale Univ, PhD(forestry), 57. *Honors & Awards:* Wood Award, Forest Prod Res Soc, 57; Presidential Rank Award, Sr Exec Serv, 81 & 84; Distinguished Serv Award, Soc Wood Sci & Technol, 90. *Prof Exp:* Forest prod technologist, Forest Prod Lab, US Forest Serv, 51-66, proj leader fundamental properties, 58-64, chief, Div Solid Wood Prod Res, 64-66, dir, Div Forest Prod & Eng Res, 67-70, dir, Southern Forest Exp Sta, 70-72, assoc dep chief res, 72-75, dir, Forest Prod Lab, 75-85. *Concurrent Pos:* Foresty consult, 85-; coordr, Forest Prods Div, Int Union Forestry Res Orgns, 83-90. *Mem:* Soc Am Foresters; Soc Wood Sci & Technol (secy-treas, 58-59, vpres, 60-61, pres, 62-63); Forest Prod Res Soc; Int Soc Trop Foresters; Sigma Xi; hon mem Int Union Forestry Res Orgns. *Res:* Basic physical and mechanical properties of wood and related factors. *Mailing Add:* Dept Forest Prod Brooks Forest Prod Ctr Va Polytech Inst & State Univ Blacksburg VA 24061-0503. *Fax:* 540-231-3330; *E-Mail:* youngs@vtvmi

**YOUNGS, WILEY JAY,** METALLOCYCLYNES, CONDUCTING POLYMERS. *Current Pos:* assoc prof, 90-93, PROF INORG CHEM, UNIV AKRON, OHIO, 93- *Personal Data:* b Gouverneur, NY, July 5, 49; m 78, Claire A Tessier; c Jessica & Kelly. *Educ:* State Univ NY, Albany, BA, 72; State Univ NY, Buffalo, PhD(chem), 80. *Prof Exp:* Fel, Northwestern Univ, Evanston, Ill, 80-83; from asst prof to assoc prof inorg chem, Case Western Res Univ, Cleveland, Ohio, 83-90. *Concurrent Pos:* Collateral fac mem, Ohio Aerospace Inst, Cleveland, Ohio, 90-; fac res assoc, Maurice Morton Inst Polymer Sci. *Mem:* Am Chem Soc; Am Crystallog Asn; AAAS; Am Asn Univ Professors. *Res:* Synthesis of organometallic molecular conductors and conducting polymers; synthesis of high temperature polymers; synthesis of organometallic compounds with antitumor activity; mechanistic investigation of lithium induced alkyne cyclization reactions; x-ray structural characterization of inorganic, organic and organometallic compounds; synthesis and characterization of discotic mesophase liquid crystals. *Mailing Add:* Dept Chem Univ Akron Akron OH 44325-3601. *Fax:* 330-972-7370; *E-Mail:* youngs@atlas.chemistry.uakron.edu

**YOUNGSTROM, RICHARD EARL,** CHROMATOGRAPHY, RADIOCHEMISTRY. *Current Pos:* SR GROUP LEADER, LEMMON CO, 93- *Personal Data:* b Durham, NC, Sept 11, 43; m 69, 82, Janine E Tretinik; c 2. *Educ:* Duke Univ, BS, 65; Wash Univ, MA, 69. *Prof Exp:* Asst scientist steroid chem, Schering Corp, 69-70, assoc scientist, 70-71, scientist radiochem, 71-73, sr scientist, 73-77, res sect leader, 77-85; midwest mgr, YML, Inc, 86-90; sect head, Pharmaceut Analysis, Southern Testing & Res, 91-93. *Mem:* Am Soc Testing & Mat; Am Chem Soc; Am Asn Pharmaceut Sci. *Res:* Chromatography solvent theory; optimization methods; approaches to standardized performance testing of sorbents, radiochromatography, liquid scintillation and flow systems; writing training programs in chromatography & radiochemistry. *Mailing Add:* TEVA Pharm USA 8-10 Gloria Lane Fairfield NJ 07004

**YOUNKIN, LARRY MYRLE,** CIVIL ENGINEERING. *Current Pos:* from asst prof to assoc prof, 66-81, PROF CIVIL ENG, BUCKNELL UNIV, 81- *Personal Data:* b Markleton, Pa, Oct 16, 36; m 69; c 1. *Educ:* Geneva Col, BS, 56; Univ Pittsburgh, BSCE, 59, MSCE, 62; Va Polytech Inst & State Univ, PhD(civil eng), 71. *Prof Exp:* Instr civil eng, Univ Pittsburgh, 56-59; asst prof, Geneva Col, 59-62; instr, Univ NMex, 62-64. *Concurrent Pos:* Consult engr, Pa Dept Transp, 71-77 & USDA Soil Conserv Serv, 82- *Mem:* Am Soc Civil Engrs; Am Geophys Union; Am Water Resources Asn. *Res:* Open channel flow; hydraulic structures; sediment transport and yield from construction; surface water hydrology. *Mailing Add:* Four Hilltop Rd Lewisburg PA 17837

**YOUNKIN, STUART G,** PLANT PATHOLOGY. *Current Pos:* RETIRED. *Personal Data:* b US, Jan 16, 12; m 43; c 5. *Educ:* Iowa State Univ, BS, 36, MS, 39; Cornell Univ, PhD, 43. *Prof Exp:* From asst plant pathologist & geneticist to plant pathologist & geneticist, Campbell Soup Co, 43-52, asst to dir res, 52-53, dir agr res, 53-62, vpres agr res, 62-77, pres, Campbell Inst Agr Res, 66-77. *Concurrent Pos:* Mem agr bd, Nat Acad Sci-Nat Res Coun, 62-68, pres, Agr Res Inst, 64-65; mem panel world food supply, President's Sci Adv Comt, 66-67. *Mem:* Soc Econ Botanists; Am Soc Hort Sci; Am Phytopath Soc. *Res:* Virus diseases of potatoes; vegetable disease control; breeding of tomatoes and peppers. *Mailing Add:* 309 Bridgeboro Rd Apt 3337 Moorestown NJ 08057

**YOUNOSZAI, RAFI,** ANATOMY. *Current Pos:* assoc prof, 79-85, PROF ANAT, COL OSTEOPATH MED PAC, 86- *Personal Data:* b Kabul, Afghanistan, June 13, 30; m 64; c 2. *Educ:* Univ Calif, Berkeley, BSc, 57; Univ Minn, PhD(anat), 71. *Prof Exp:* From instr to asst prof, Dept Anat, Univ Minn, 71-78. *Concurrent Pos:* Res coordr, Res Orgn Comt, Am Osteop Asn, Nat Osteop Found, 80-82, dir, Off Int Progs. *Mem:* Am Asn Clin Anatomists; Am Diabetes Asn; Nat Coun Int Health. *Res:* Interacellular transport and release of insulin; effect of a low protein and high carbohydrate diet on insulin release; insulin release patterns of induced islet adenomas; electromyographic studies on patients with somatic dysfunctions before and subsequent to manipulative therapy; ossification of cranial sutures. *Mailing Add:* Dept Anat Col Osteop Med Pac 309 E College Plaza Pomona CA 91766-1899

**YOUNSZAI, M KABIR,** GASTROENTEROLOGY. *Current Pos:* PROF & CHAIR, DEPT PEDIAT, UNIV LOUISVILLE, 88- *Personal Data:* b Kabul, Afghanistan, Oct 2, 32. *Educ:* Am Univ Beirut, MD, 62. *Prof Exp:* From pediat, Univ Iowa Hosp, 79-88. *Mem:* Soc Pediat Res; Am Soc Clin Nutrit; Am Gastroenterol Asn. *Mailing Add:* Dept Pediat Univ Louisville Sch Med 2301 S Third St Louisville KY 40292-2001

**YOUNT, DAVID EUGENE,** ELEMENTARY PARTICLE PHYSICS, DIVING PHYSIOLOGY. *Current Pos:* assoc prof physics, Univ Hawaii, Honolulu, 69-72, chmn, Dept Physics & Astron, 79-85, actg asst vpres acad affairs, 85, vpres res & grad educ, 86-95, PROF PHYSICS, UNIV HAWAII, HONOLULU, 72- *Personal Data:* b Prescott, Ariz, June 5, 35; m 62, 75, Christel M Notz; c Christine, Gregory, Steffen & Sonja. *Educ:* Calif Inst Technol, BS, 57; Stanford Univ, MS, 59, PhD(physics), 63. *Honors & Awards:* Stover-Link Award, 87. *Prof Exp:* From instr to asst prof physics, Princeton Univ, 62-64; NSF fel, Linear Accelerator Lab, Orsay, France, 64-65; res assoc, Stanford Linear Accelerator Ctr, 65-69. *Concurrent Pos:* 3M Co fel, Princeton Univ, 63; dir, Hawaii Topical Conf Particle Physics, 71. *Mem:* Am Chem Soc; Am Phys Soc; Undersea & Hyperbaric Med Soc; Sigma Xi. *Res:* Positron scattering, leptonic K-meson decay, hadronic photon absorption, photoproduction of mesons, positron-electron colliding beams, bubble nucleation, and decompression sickness; instrumentation for particle beams and beam monitors, spark chambers, streamer chambers and multiwire proportional chambers. *Mailing Add:* Dept Physics & Astron Univ Hawaii 2505 Correa Rd Honolulu HI 96822. *Fax:* 808-956-2930; *E-Mail:* in%dey@uhhepg.phys.hawaii.edu

**YOUNT, ERNEST H,** MEDICINE. *Current Pos:* from instr to prof med, 48-84, chmn dept, 52-72, EMER PROF MED, BOWMAN GRAY SCH MED, 84- *Personal Data:* b Lincolnton, NC, Feb 23, 19; m 42, Betty Shuford; c Ernest H III, Peter S & Martha (Yates). *Educ:* Univ NC, BA, 40; Vanderbilt Univ, MD, 43. *Prof Exp:* Asst med, Univ Chicago, 45-48. *Concurrent Pos:* Consult, Oak Ridge Inst Nuclear Studies, 50-58; mem dean's comt, Vet Admin Hosp, Salisbury, 54-63; mem, Nat Bd Med Exam, 58-61, chmn, 61. *Mem:* Am Fedn Clin Res; Am Soc Internal Med; Am Col Physicians; Am Diabetes Asn; Asn Prof Med. *Res:* Malaria; adrenal and thyroid function; diabetes. *Mailing Add:* 2800 Greenwich Rd Winston-Salem NC 27104

**YOUNT, RALPH GRANVILLE,** BIOCHEMISTRY. *Current Pos:* from asst prof chem & asst chemist to assoc prof & assoc chemist, 60-72, chmn, Biochem-Biophys Prog, 73-78, PROF BIOCHEM & CHEM, WASH STATE UNIV, 72- *Personal Data:* b Indianapolis, Ind, Mar 25, 32; m 57, Valerie A Piefho; c Jonathan, Andrea & Alison. *Educ:* Wabash Col, AB, 54; Iowa State Univ, PhD, 58. *Honors & Awards:* MERIT Award, NIH, 86. *Prof Exp:* Res assoc enzym, Brookhaven Nat Lab, 58-60. *Concurrent Pos:* NIH spec fel, Sch Med, Univ Pa & vis prof, Johnson Found, 69-70; mem, biochem/biophysics panel, NSF, 82-85; mem, Comt A & NHLBI, 86-90, chmn fel comt, MDA, 86-91; vpres, MDA, 87-92. *Mem:* Fel AAAS; Am Soc Biochem & Molecular Biol; Am Chem Soc; Protein Soc; Biophys Soc (pres, 94-); Fed Am Soc Exp Biol (pres, 97-98). *Res:* Mechanism of enzyme action as it applies to contractile proteins; synthesis of small molecules of biological interest. *Mailing Add:* Dept Biochem & Biophys Wash State Univ Pullman WA 99164-4660

**YOUNT, WILLIAM J,** ALLERGY, IMMUNOLOGY. *Current Pos:* PROF MED, MICROBIOL & IMMUNOL, SCH MED, UNIV NC, 70- *Personal Data:* b Menominee, Mich, Aug 24, 36; div; c 3. *Educ:* Univ Wis-Madison, MD, 60. *Concurrent Pos:* Vis prof, Clin Res Centre, London, 78-79; vis Kenan prof, Cambridge Univ, 87-88. *Mem:* Am Soc Clin Invest; Fedn Am Soc Exp Biol. *Res:* Humoral immunodeficiency; IgG subclass immunobiology; systemic lupus erythematosus; rheumatic diseases. *Mailing Add:* Dept Med Univ NC Sch Med 3033 TARC CB 7280 Chapel Hill NC 27599-7280. *Fax:* 919-966-1739; *E-Mail:* uncwjy@uncmvs.oit.unc.edu

**YOUNTS, SANFORD EUGENE,** SOIL SCIENCE, AGRONOMY. *Current Pos:* assoc dean, Col Agr & Dir Rural Develop Ctr, 69-72, VPRES SERV, UNIV GA, 72-, PROF AGRON, 69- *Personal Data:* b Lexington, NC, Aug 29, 30; m 54; c 1. *Educ:* NC State Univ, BS, 52, MS, 55; Cornell Univ, PhD(agron), 57. *Prof Exp:* Asst prof soils, Univ Md, 57-58; agronomist, Am Potash Inst, 58-60; assoc prof soils, NC State Col, 60-64; regional dir, Am Potash Inst, 64-67, vpres, 67-69. *Mem:* AAAS; fel Am Soc Agron; Int Soc Soil Sci; fel Soil Sci Soc Am. *Res:* Soil fertility and crop physiology; root growth of field crops as influenced by fertilizer and lime placement; chloride nutrition of corn; potash requirements of forage crops; nitrogen sources for turf; copper nutrition of wheat, corn and soybeans. *Mailing Add:* 121 Thornhill Dr Athens GA 30607

**YOURTEE, JOHN BOTELER,** CHEMICAL ENGINEERING, POLYMER CHEMISTRY. *Current Pos:* SECT LEADER, HOECHST CELANESE CORP, NJ, 85- *Personal Data:* b Fredericksburg, Va, Dec 2, 46; m 68; c 2. *Educ:* Univ Del, BS, 68; Mass Inst Technol, SM, 69; Univ Wis, PhD(chem eng), 73. *Prof Exp:* Res engr, Union Carbide Corp, 73-75; sr res engr plastics, 75-77; sr group leader, Merck & Co, Pittsburgh, 77-81; staff engr, Exxon Chem Co, 81-85. *Mem:* Sigma Xi; Soc Plastics Engrs; Am Ceramic Soc; Am Inst Chem Engrs. *Res:* Product and process development of thermoplastic polymers and water-soluble polymers with current emphasis on engineering plastics. *Mailing Add:* Three Jefferson Dr Flanders NJ 07836

**YOURTEE, LAWRENCE KARN,** ORGANIC CHEMISTRY. *Current Pos:* assoc prof, 48-57, chmn dept, 57-71, Childs prof, 58-80, McEwen prof, 80-82, EMER MCEWEN PROF CHEM, HAMILTON COL, 82- *Personal Data:* b Brunswick, Md, Mar 6, 17; m 41, Mildred Conkle; c Edward. *Educ:* Wash Col, Md, BS, 37; Ga Inst Technol, MS, 39; Univ Tex, PhD(chem), 48. *Prof Exp:* Instr chem, Ga Inst Technol, 40-42 & Univ Tex, 46-47; asst prof, Univ Tenn, 47-48. *Mem:* Am Chem Soc; Sigma Xi. *Res:* Synthesis and properties of heterocyclic nitrogen compounds; Pfitzinger reaction; use of ion-exchange resins in organic synthesis and separations. *Mailing Add:* 188 Winding Pond Rd Londonderry NH 03053

**YOUSE, BEVAN K,** MATHEMATICAL ANALYSIS. *Current Pos:* asst prof, 54-67, ASSOC PROF MATH, EMORY UNIV, 67- *Personal Data:* b Markle, Ind, Apr 5, 27; m 58; c 1. *Educ:* Auburn Univ, BS, 49; Univ Ga, MS, 52. *Prof Exp:* Instr math, Memphis State Univ, 52-53 & Univ Ga, 53-54. *Concurrent Pos:* NSF fac fel, 60-61. *Mem:* AAAS; Am Math Soc; Math Asn Am; Sigma Xi. *Res:* Mathematical analysis. *Mailing Add:* Dept Math Emory Univ 1746 Alderbrook Rd NE Atlanta GA 30345

**YOUSE, HOWARD RAY,** BOTANY. *Current Pos:* RETIRED. *Personal Data:* b Bryant, Ind, May 22, 15; m 42. *Educ:* DePauw Univ, BA, 37; Ore State Col, MS, 42; Purdue Univ, PhD(bot), 51. *Prof Exp:* From instr to prof bot, DePauw Univ, 40-80, head, Dept Bot & Bact, 73-78, chmn dept, 78-80. *Mem:* AAAS; Bot Soc Am. *Res:* Pollen grains; seed germination. *Mailing Add:* Seminary St Greencastle IN 46135

**YOUSEF, IBRAHIM MOHMOUD,** biochemistry & clinical biochemistry, for more information see previous edition

**YOUSEF, MOHAMED KHALIL,** ENVIRONMENTAL PHYSIOLOGY. *Current Pos:* from asst prof to assoc prof, 70-74, COORDR HEALTH PREPROF PROG, UNIV NEV, LAS VEGAS, 73-, DISTINGUISHED PROF BIOL & PHYSIOL, 74-, DIR, DESERT BIOL RES CTR, 80- *Personal Data:* b Cairo, Egypt, Aug 19, 35; US citizen; m 63, Annetta McCommis; c Laila F & Omar M. *Educ:* Ain Shams Univ, Cairo, BSc, 59; Univ Mo, Columbia, MS, 63, PhD(environ physiol), 66. *Honors & Awards:* W F Peterson Found Award, Animal Biometeorol, Neth; Japan Soc, Prom Sci Award. *Prof Exp:* Res assoc environ physiol, Univ Mo, Columbia, 66-67; vis asst prof, Inst Arctic Biol, Univ Alaska, 67-68; asst prof, Lab Environ Path-physiol, Desert Res Inst, Univ Nev, 68-70. *Concurrent Pos:* Dean, Col Sci, United Arab Emirates, 90-93. *Mem:* Int Soc Biometeorol; Am Physiol Soc; Soc Exp Biol & Med; Endocrine Soc. *Res:* Physiological adaptations to desert, mountain and arctic environments; role of the respiratory, cardiovascular and endocrine systems in adaptation; comparative thermoregulation during rest and exercise under different environments; comparative adaptations of organisms to various stressful environments; emphasis is on the role of cardiovascular, respiratory and endocrine systems. *Mailing Add:* Dept Biol Univ Nev 4505 Maryland Pkwy Box 454004 Las Vegas NV 89154-4004. *Fax:* 702-895-3956

**YOUSEM, DAVID MARK,** RADIOLOGY, NEURORADIOLOGY. *Current Pos:* asst prof, Dept Radiol, 90-93, ASST PROF, DEPT OTORHINOLARYNGOL, UNIV PA, 91-, ASSOC PROF, DEPT RADIOL, 93- *Personal Data:* b Baltimore, Md, Aug 5, 59; m, Marilyn S Zeligman; c Ilyssa J & Mitchell B. *Educ:* Univ Mich, BS, 80, MD, 83; Am Bd Radiol, cert, 87. *Prof Exp:* Intern, Dept Internal Med, Union Mem Hosp, Baltimore, 83-84; resident diag radiol, Johns Hopkins Hosp, 86-87, fel gen radiol & neuroradiol, 87-88; fel, Neuroradiol Sect, Hosp Univ Pa, 88-90. *Concurrent Pos:* Prin investr, Radiol Soc NAm, 90-91, Berlex Industs, 92 & 93-94; mem, Radiographics Imaging Panel, Radiol Soc NAm, 92-96, vchmn, 94-96; vis prof, Univ SFla, 92, Maine Med Ctr, Portland, 92, Brown Cancer Ctr, Louisville, Ky, 92, Mass Eye & Ear Infirmary, Boston, 94 & Emory Univ, 96. *Mem:* Radiol Soc NAm; Am Roentgen Ray Soc; Am Soc Head & Neck Radiol; sr mem Am Soc Neuroradiol; Soc Magnetic Resonance Imaging; Asn Chemoreception Sci; Am Col Radiol; Am Asn Acad Chief Residents Radiol; Int Soc Magnetic Resonance Med. *Res:* Requisite of neuroradiology; author of numerous publications. *Mailing Add:* 538 Hamilton Rd Merion PA 19066. *Fax:* 215-662-3283; *E-Mail:* yousem@oasis.rad.upenn.edu

**YOUSIF, SALAH MOHAMMAD,** ELECTRICAL ENGINEERING. *Current Pos:* from asst prof to assoc prof, 69-80, PROF ELEC ENG, CALIF STATE UNIV, SACRAMENTO, 80- *Personal Data:* b Burin, Palestine, Nov 15, 38; m 68; c 3. *Educ:* Univ Alexandria, BSEE, 62; Mid East Tech Univ, Ankara, MSEE, 64; Ore State Univ, PhD(elec eng), 69. *Prof Exp:* Elec engr, Jordan Broadcasting Serv, 62-63 & Kuwait Broadcasting Serv, 64-65; instr elec eng, Mich State Univ, 66-68 & Ore State Univ, 68-69. *Mem:* Inst Elec & Electronics Engrs; Soc Indust & Appl Math; Pattern Recognition Soc. *Res:* Control, information and power systems; pattern recognition. *Mailing Add:* Dept Elec Eng Calif State Univ 6000 J St Sacramento CA 95819-2605

**YOUSON, JOHN HAROLD,** CELL ULTRASTRUCTURE, ENDOCRINOLOGY. *Current Pos:* PROF ZOOL, UNIV TORONTO, 69- *Educ:* Univ Western Ont, PhD(zool), 69. *Mailing Add:* Dept Anat & Zool Scarborough Col Univ Toronto Toronto ON M1C 1A4 Can. *Fax:* 416-287-7642; *E-Mail:* youson@macpost.scar.utoronto.ca

**YOUSSEF, MARY NAGUIB,** COMPUTER SCIENCES. *Current Pos:* PROF COMPUT SCI, WESTERN CONN STATE UNIV, 90- *Personal Data:* US citizen; c 1. *Educ:* Univ Cairo, BS, 58; Columbia Univ, MA, 64; Stanford Univ, MS, 67; Ore State Univ, PhD(statist), 70. *Honors & Awards:* Centennial Medal, Inst Elec & Electronics Engrs, 84. *Prof Exp:* Instr celestial mech, Cairo Univ, 58-61; Ford Found fel, 62-63 & 65-67; mem tech staff & researcher, Oper Res Ctr, Inst Nat Planning, Cairo, 63-65; mem tech staff syst analysis, Bell Tel Labs, 70-81; assoc prof, City Univ New York, 81-83; adv engr, IBM, 83-85; sr fac mem, SRI-IBM, 85- *Concurrent Pos:* Assoc prof oper res & comput info systs, Baruch Col, City Univ New York, 81-82. *Mem:* Sigma Xi; sr mem Inst Elec & Electronics Engrs; Asn Comput Mach. *Res:* Modeling and analyzing queuing systems; data communications and protocols; methods for projecting telecommunication traffic in a special environment; economic and time series forecasting. *Mailing Add:* 3 Ivy Lane Monroe CT 06460

**YOUSSEF, NABIL NAGUIB,** MORPHOLOGY, CELL BIOLOGY. *Current Pos:* from res asst to res assoc, Utah State Univ, 64-68, asst prof, 68-75, assoc prof zool, 75-82, PROF BIOL, UTAH STATE UNIV, 82- *Personal Data:* b Cairo, Egypt, Oct 19, 37; US citizen; m 63; c Nameer, Nadeer & Naguib. *Educ:* Ain Shams Univ, Cairo, BSc, 58; Utah State Univ, MS, 64, PhD(zool), 66. *Prof Exp:* Asst instr entom & zool, Ain Shams Univ, Cairo, 58-60. *Concurrent Pos:* USDA grant, 66-68; dir, Electron Micros Facil; pres, Pan Agro. *Mem:* Sigma Xi; AAAS; fel Royal Entom Soc London; Entom Soc Am; Soc Protozoologists. *Res:* Fine structure of Protozoa and Insecta with special emphasis on morphogeneses of normal and abnormal tissues induced by drugs or pathogens; host-parasite (protozoa and fungi) relationships. *Mailing Add:* Dept Biol Utah State Univ Logan UT 84322-0001. *Fax:* 435-750-1575

**YOUSTEN, ALLAN A,** MICROBIAL PHYSIOLOGY, MICROBIAL INSECTICIDES. *Current Pos:* from asst prof to assoc prof, 71-86, PROF MICROBIOL, VA POLYTECH INST & STATE UNIV, 86- *Personal Data:* b Racine, Wis, Nov 9, 36; c 2. *Educ:* Univ Wis, BS, 58; Cornell Univ, MS, 60, PhD, 63. *Prof Exp:* Microbial biochemist, Int Minerals & Chem Corp, 65-69; NIH spec fel, Univ Wis, 69-71. *Concurrent Pos:* Fulbright-Hays fel, Pasteur Inst, 80; vis prof, Ariz State Univ, 87, Heriot-Watt Univ, Edinburgh, Scotland, 94. *Mem:* AAAS; Am Soc Microbiol; Soc Indust Microbiol; Soc Invert Path. *Res:* Physiology and structure of microorganisms; bacterial spore formation and germination; bacterial insect pathogens; physiology, metabolism, structure, and taxonomy of spore-forming bacteria used as microbial insecticides; fate of these bacteria in the environment, their fermentative production and genetic manipulation. *Mailing Add:* Dept Biol Va Polytech Inst & State Univ Blacksburg VA 24061. *Fax:* 540-231-9307; *E-Mail:* yousten@vtvm1.cc.vt.edu

**YOUTCHEFF, JOHN SHELDON,** ASTROPHYSICS. *Current Pos:* PROG DIR, US POSTAL SERV HQ, WASHINGTON, DC, 73- *Personal Data:* b Newark, NJ, Apr 16, 25; m 50, Elsie Koerner; c Karen J, John S Jr, Mark A, Heidi M & Lisa E. *Educ:* Columbia Univ, AB & BS, 50; Univ Calif, Los Angeles, PhD, 54. *Prof Exp:* Dir test staff, US Naval Air Missile Test Ctr, 50-53; opers analyst, Advan Electronics Ctr, Gen Elec Co, 53-56, functional engr, Missile & Space Div, 56-60, consult engr, 60-63, mgr advan reliability concepts oper, 63-72; mgr reliability & maintainability, Litton Industs, 72-73. *Mem:* Fel AAAS; sr mem Inst Elec & Electronics Engrs; assoc fel Am Inst Aeronaut & Astronaut; Am Soc Mech Engrs; sr mem Am Astron Soc. *Res:* Operations analysis; advanced systems planning; aerospace and environmental systems. *Mailing Add:* 1400 S Joyce St Apt 540 Arlington VA 22202

**YOUTSEY, KARL JOHN,** PHYSICS. *Current Pos:* Physicist, Physics Dept, UOP Inc, 61-64, physicist, Mat Sci Lab, 68-73, dir mat sci, Corp Res, 73-75, dir prod & process develop, Wolverine Div, 75-79, vpres & gen mgr, Automotive Prod Div, 79-85, GEN MGR, ENVIRON CONTROL & MGT SYSTS, UOP INC, 85- *Personal Data:* b Chicago, Ill, May 6, 39; m 69; c 4. *Educ:* Loyola Univ, Chicago, BS, 61; Ill Inst Technol, MS, 65, PhD(physics), 68. *Mem:* Sigma Xi; Am Phys Soc; Am Soc Metals. *Res:* Electronic and physical properties of ceramics; fuel cell technology; solar thermal energy systems; thin film technology; laboratory and industrial automation systems and design; hazardous waste treatment. *Mailing Add:* 1647 Riverside Ct Glenview IL 60025-2033

**YOUTZ, BYRON LEROY,** nuclear physics, energy studies; deceased, see previous edition for last biography

**YOVANOVITCH, DRASKO D,** HIGH ENERGY PHYSICS. *Current Pos:* PHYSICIST, NAT ACCELERATOR LAB, 72-, CHMN, PHYS DEPT, 79- *Personal Data:* b Belgrade, Yugoslavia, May 24, 30; US citizen; m 54; c 2. *Educ:* Belgrade Univ, BSc, 52; Univ Chicago, MSc, 56, PhD(physics), 59. *Prof Exp:* Res assoc physics, Enrico Fermi Inst, Univ Chicago, 59-60; asst physicist, Univ Calif, San Diego, 60-62; assoc physicist, High Energy Physics Div, Argonne Nat Lab, 62-72. *Mem:* Fel Am Phys Soc. *Mailing Add:* Fermi Nat Accelerator Lab PO Box 500 Batavia IL 60510

**YOVICICH-JONES, GEORGE S,** CIVIL ENGINEERING, ENVIRONMENTAL ENGINEERING. *Current Pos:* prof engr & gen mgr, 56-70, BD CHMN, ARCADIA ENG INT, INC, 70-, PRES & CHIEF EXEC OFFICER, 87- *Personal Data:* b Belgrade, Yugoslavia, June 2, 27; m 60, Sofia Sekulic; c Steven. *Educ:* Northwestern Univ, BSCE, 51, MSCE, 56, PhD(bus admin), 58. *Hon Degrees:* Dr, Univ Fla, 72; PhD, Hamilton State Univ. *Prof Exp:* Overseas & domestic projs, US Corps Engrs, 51-54; civil engr, Hollabird & Root, Chicago, 56-57. *Concurrent Pos:* Prof struct eng, Northwestern Univ; chmn econs, Univ Ill; bd chmn, Oakton Col; pres, Hamilton State Univ; pres, Tetrakear & Assocs, Inc. *Mem:* Am Soc Civil Engrs; Prof Engrs Soc Am. *Mailing Add:* Arcadia Int & Co Inc PO Box 712 Skokie IL 60076. *Fax:* 847-480-0493

**YOVITS, MARSHALL CLINTON,** RELATING INFORMATION TO DECISION MAKING. *Current Pos:* dean, Purdue Sch Sci, 80-88, prof comput & info sci, 80-93, EMER PROF, IND UNIV-PURDUE UNIV, INDIANAPOLIS, 93-, CHMN SR ACAD, 94- *Personal Data:* b Brooklyn, NY, May 16, 23; m 52, Anita; c Bruce, Mara & Steven. *Educ:* Union Col, BS, 44, MS, 48; Yale Univ, MS, 50, PhD(physics), 51. *Honors & Awards:* Comp Pioneer, Inst Elec & Electronics Engrs, 90. *Prof Exp:* Physicist, Nat Adv Comt for Aeronaut, Langley Field, Va, 44-46; instr physics, Union Col, 46-48; instr, Yale Univ, 48-50; sr physicist, Appl Physics Lab, Johns Hopkins Univ, 51-56; physicist, Off Naval Res, 56, head, Info Systs Br, 56-62, dir, Naval Anal Group, 62-66; prof comput & info sci & chmn dept, Ohio State Univ,

66-79. *Concurrent Pos:* AEC fel, 50-51; ed, Adv Comput, 70-; chmn comput sci conf, Columbus, Ohio, 73 & Indianapolis, Ind, 82; mem biomed comt study sect, NIH, 70-74; chmn Comp Res Asn, 73-75; Indianapolis Ctr Adv Res fel, 88-89; bd gov, Inst Elec & Electronics Engrs Comput Soc, 88-89. *Mem:* Fel Inst Elec & Electronics Engrs; fel Asn Comput Mach; fel AAAS; Sigma Xi; Inst Elec & Electronics Engrs Comput Soc. *Res:* Information systems; management information; self-organizing systems; information science; development of a generalized theory of information flow analysis; relating information to its use in decision-making. *Mailing Add:* 9016 Dewberry Ct Indianapolis IN 46260. *Fax:* 317-274-9742; *E-Mail:* imcy100@indyvax.iupui.edu

**YOW, MARTHA DUKES,** PEDIATRICS. *Current Pos:* Instr bact, Baylor Col Med, 49-50, instr pediat, 50-52, from instr to asst assoc prof, 55-69, dir, Pediat Infectious Dis Sect, 64-82, PROF PEDIAT, BAYLOR COL MED, 69- *Personal Data:* b Talbotton, Ga, Jan 15, 22; m 44; c 3. *Educ:* Univ SC, BS, 40, MD, 43; Am Bd Pediat, dipl. *Concurrent Pos:* Res fel pediat, Baylor Col Med, 50-52, Jones fel, 55-; NIH grant; mem bd sci coun, Nat Inst Allergy & Infectious Dis. *Mem:* Am Fedn Clin Res; Am Soc Microbiol; Soc Pediat Res; Infectious Dis Soc Am; Am Acad Pediat; Am Pediat Soc. *Res:* Infectious diseases; applied virology. *Mailing Add:* 2502 Underwood St Houston TX 77030

**YOZAWITZ, ALLAN,** CLINICAL NEUROPSYCHOLOGY. *Current Pos:* DIR, CLIN NEUROPSYCHOL UNIT, HUTCHINGS PSYCHIAT CTR, SYRACUSE, NY, 77- *Personal Data:* b Brooklyn, NY, Jan 8, 49; m 73, Arlene Susan Greenfield; c Elissa, Justin & Lyanne. *Educ:* Polytech Inst Brooklyn, BS, 70; Queens Col, MA, 73; City Univ New York, PhD(neuropsychol), 77; Am Bd Prof Psychol & Am Bd Clin Neuropsychol, dipl, 84. *Prof Exp:* Res asst, Audition Lab Biomet Res, NY State Psychiat Inst, 70-73, res scientist, 73-77. *Concurrent Pos:* Co-investr, NIMH grant, Biomet Res, NY State Psychiat Inst, 74-77, consult, Geront Sect, 75-76; co-dir, NIMH Training Prog Clin Neuropsychol, Cornell Univ, Ithaca, 79-83; consult clin neuropsychol, Syracuse Develop Ctr, 79-83 & Benjamin Rush Ctr, Syracuse, 80-88; asst prof, Dept Psychiat, Col Med, State Univ NY, Health Sci Ctr, Syracuse, 79-89, assoc prof, 89-; adj asst prof, Dept Psychol, Syracuse Univ, 79-89, adj assoc prof, 89-; consult ed, J Clin & Exp Neuropsychol, 83-95; dir continuing educ, Int Neuropsychol Soc, 85-94; consult, NY State Bd Psychol, 87-88; mem, NY State Bd Psychol, 88-; consult ed, The Clin Neuropsychologist, 91-94; chair, NY State Bd Psychol, 93-94. *Mem:* Int Neuropsychol Soc; Am Psychol Asn; NY Acad Sci; Soc Neurosci; NY State Psychol Asn; Int Brain Res Orgn. *Res:* Neuropsychological mediation of psychiatric disorder involving the effects of nondominant hemispheric processes on affective states; clinical practice of neuropsychology with psychiatric patients; neuropsychological rehabilitation of psychiatric vulnerability. *Mailing Add:* 5170 Winterton Dr Fayetteville NY 13066

**YOZWIAK, BERNARD JAMES,** MATHEMATICS. *Current Pos:* RETIRED. *Personal Data:* b Youngstown, Ohio, July 5, 19; m 43, Helen A Mika; c Ruth (Lewis), John B, Mark S & Bernard P. *Educ:* Marietta Col, AB, 40; Univ Pittsburgh, MS, 51, PhD(math), 61. *Hon Degrees:* LLD, Youngstown State Univ, 92. *Prof Exp:* Clerk, Youngstown Sheet & Tube Co, 40-41; high sch prin & teacher, Ohio, 41-42; civilian instr, US Army Air Forces Tech Training Command, Ill & Wis, 42-44; clerk, Youngstown Sheet & Tube Co, 44-45; high sch prin & teacher, Ohio, 45-47; from asst prof to prof math, Youngstown State Univ, 47-92, chmn dept, 66-71, dean, Col Arts & Sci, 71-92, emer dean, 92. *Mem:* Math Asn Am; Sigma Xi. *Res:* Summability methods. *Mailing Add:* 2080 S Schenley Ave Youngstown OH 44511

**YPHANTIS, DAVID ANDREW,** BIOPHYSICS, BIOCHEMISTRY. *Current Pos:* PROF BIOL, UNIV CONN, 68- *Personal Data:* b Boston, Mass, July 14, 30; m 53; c 5. *Educ:* Harvard Univ, AB, 52; Mass Inst Technol, PhD(biophys), 55. *Prof Exp:* Am Cancer Soc fel, Mass Inst Technol, 55-56; from asst biophysicist to assoc biophysicist, Argonne Nat Lab, 56-58; from asst prof to assoc prof biochem, Rockefeller Univ, 58-65; prof biol, State Univ NY Buffalo, 65-68; prof biophys & chmn, Dept Biol, 67-68. *Concurrent Pos:* Consult, Argonne Nat Lab, 58-62 & NIH, 67- *Mem:* AAAS; Am Chem Soc; Biophys Soc; Am Soc Biol Chem; Sigma Xi. *Res:* Physical biochemistry; protein physical chemistry; ultracentrifugation. *Mailing Add:* Dept Molec & Cell Biol Univ Conn U-125 Storrs CT 06269-3125

**YU, A TOBEY,** ENGINEERING. *Current Pos:* RETIRED. *Personal Data:* b Chekiang, China, Jan 6, 21. *Educ:* Mass Inst Technol, MA, 46; Lehigh Univ, PhD(civil eng), 49; Columbia Univ, MBA, 72. *Honors & Awards:* Outstanding Eng Achievement, Am Soc Civil Engrs, 77, Am Literal Engrs, 78 & Chinese Inst, 78; Mater Handling Award, Am Soc Mech Engrs, 87; Richards Awards, Am Inst Mining Engrs, 87. *Prof Exp:* Design engr, Hewitt Robins Inc, 51-59, vpres opers, Div Litton Indust, Hewitt Robins, 67-71; tech div eng, Compania Minera Santa Fe, 59-67; pres & chmn, Orba Corp, 72-86. *Mem:* Nat Acad Eng; Am Inst Mining Engrs; Soc Mining Explor & Metall; Nat Soc Prof Engrs. *Mailing Add:* 962 Gullane Dr Cypress Run Tarpon Springs FL 34689. *Fax:* 813-789-3620

**YU, ANDREW B C,** PHARMACEUTICS, BIOPHARMACEUTICS. *Current Pos:* SR RES PHARMACIST, STERLING WINTHROP RES INST, 79- *Personal Data:* b Nov 24, 45; US citizen. *Educ:* Albany Col Pharm, BS, 71; Univ Conn, PhD(pharmaceut sci), 76. *Prof Exp:* Asst prof pharm, Northeastern Univ, 76-80. *Concurrent Pos:* Investr, NIH biomed res support grant, 77-78; co-investr res contract, Dooner Labs, 78-79; monograph writer, Am Pharmaceut Asn, Pharmaceut Excipient Codex Comt, 78-79. *Mem:* Am Asn Pharmaceut Scientists; NY Acad Sci. *Res:* Pharmacokinetics of drugs in renal diseased patients; use of antibiotics in the treatment of bacterial endocarditis. *Mailing Add:* 134 Berkshire Blvd Albany NY 12203

**YU, ANTHONY WOONCHIU,** LASER PHYSICS, QUANTUM OPTICS. *Current Pos:* prin scientist, 91-93, CHIEF SCIENTIST, HUGHES STX CORP, 93- *Personal Data:* b Hong Kong, May 30, 60; US citizen; m, Cecilia Ho. *Educ:* Univ Cent Fla, BS, 82; Ga Inst Technol, MS, 84, PhD(physics), 88. *Honors & Awards:* Cert of Recognition, NASA, 93. *Prof Exp:* Mem tech staff, GTE Labs Inc, 88-91. *Mem:* Optical Soc Am; Am Phys Soc; Inst Elec & Electronics Engrs. *Res:* Advance laser transmitter research for application in free space intersatellite laser communications, laser ranging and remote sensing; semiconductor lasers, mater oscillator and power amplifier lasers, solid state lasers and ultrafast phenomena; fiber optics communications, quantum optics and nonlinear dynamics. *Mailing Add:* Hughes STX Corp Rm 301D 7701 Greenbelt Rd Greenbelt MD 20770. *Fax:* 301-286-1750; *E-Mail:* Anthony_yu@ccmail.gsfc.nasa.gov

**YU, BIN,** STATISTICAL METHODOLOGIES, STOCHASTIC MODELING OF PROBLEMS FROM IMAGE COMPRESSION & REMOTE SENSING. *Current Pos:* asst prof, 92-97, ASSOC PROF STATIST, UNIV CALIF, BERKELEY, 97- *Personal Data:* b Harbin, China, Mar 18, 63; m 87, Ke-ning Shen. *Educ:* Peking Univ, BS, 84; Univ Calif, Berkeley, MA, 87, PhD(statist), 90. *Prof Exp:* Asst prof statist, Univ Wis-Madison, 90-93. *Concurrent Pos:* NSF postdoctoral fel, Math Sci Res Inst, Berkeley, 91; vis asst prof statist, Yale Univ, 92. *Mem:* Am Statist Asn; Inst Math Statist; Royal Statist Soc; Inst Elec & Electronics Engrs; Biomet Soc. *Res:* Statistical inference; applied probability and information theory; problems from image compression; remote sensing and clone mapping of chromosomes. *Mailing Add:* 609 San Miguel Ave Berkeley CA 94707

**YU, BYUNG PAL,** BIOCHEMISTRY, CELL PHYSIOLOGY. *Current Pos:* assoc prof, 73-78, PROF PHYSIOL, UNIV TEX HEALTH SCI CTR, SAN ANTONIO, 78- *Personal Data:* b Ham Hung, Korea, June 27, 31; US citizen; m 59; c 1. *Educ:* Mo State Univ, BS, 60; Univ Ill, PhD, 65. *Honors & Awards:* Henry L Moss Award, Am Diabetes Asn, Res & Career Develop Award. *Prof Exp:* From res instr to res asst prof, Med Col Pa, 65-68, from asst prof to assoc prof, 68-73. *Concurrent Pos:* Pres, Am Aging Asn; chair biol sci, Geront Soc Am; mem nutrit study sect, NIH; assoc ed, J Geront. *Mem:* Am Physiol Soc; fel Geront Soc Am; Oxygen Soc. *Res:* Biological membrane structure; biological aspects of aging; free radicals. *Mailing Add:* Dept Physiol Univ Tex Health Sci Ctr San Antonio TX 78284-7756. *Fax:* 210-567-4410

**YU, CHANG-AN,** BIOCHEMISTRY. *Current Pos:* from assoc prof to prof, 81-85, REGENTS PROF BIOCHEM, OKLA STATE UNIV, 85- *Personal Data:* b Taiwan, Oct 19, 37; US citizen; m 68; c 2. *Educ:* Nat Taiwan Univ, BS, 61, MS, 64; Univ Ill, PhD(biochem), 69. *Prof Exp:* Fel biochem, Univ Ill, 69-70; vis asst prof chem, State Univ NY, 70-75, res assoc prof, 76-80. *Mem:* Am Soc Biol Chemists; Am Chem Soc; Biophys Soc; AAAS. *Res:* Membrane bioenergetic; biological oxidation; ubiquinone; protein interaction; photosynthesis. *Mailing Add:* Dept Biochem Okla State Univ NRC-246 Stillwater OK 74078-0454. *Fax:* 405-744-6612; *E-Mail:* cayuq@kway.okstate.edu

**YU, CHIA-NIEN,** organic chemistry, for more information see previous edition

**YU, CHYANG JOHN,** solid state physics, inorganic chemistry, for more information see previous edition

**YU, CLEMENT TAK,** DATA BASE MANAGEMENT, MULTIMEDIA RETRIEVAL. *Current Pos:* assoc prof, 78-84, PROF COMPUT SCI, UNIV ILL, CHICAGO, 84- *Personal Data:* b Hong Kong, Aug 31, 48; US citizen; m 75, Teresa Chan; c Victor & Christine. *Educ:* Columbia Univ, BSc, 70; Cornell Univ, MSc, 72, PhD(comput sci), 73. *Prof Exp:* From asst prof to assoc prof comput sci, Univ Alta, Edmonton, 73-78. *Concurrent Pos:* Consult, Syst Develop Corp, Santa Monica, Calif, 82-86, Microelectronics Comput Corp, Austin, Tex & various other corp; mem, adv comt, NSF; chmn, ACM Spec Interest Group on Info Retrieval, 85-87; grantee, NSF, 79-98; mem ed bd, assoc ed, Inst Elec & Electronics Engrs Trans on Knowledge & Data Eng, J Distrub & Parallel Databases, Int J Knowledge & Software Eng. *Mem:* Asn Comput Mach; Inst Elec & Electronics Engrs. *Res:* Date base management; multimedia retrieval; query processing in different types of database systems. *Mailing Add:* Dept Elec Eng & Comput Sci Univ Ill Chicago IL 60607-7053. *Fax:* 312-413-0024; *E-Mail:* yu@dbis.eecs.uic.edu

**YU, DAVID TAK YAN,** RHEUMATOLOGY. *Current Pos:* fel rheumatology, 71-74, asst prof med, 74-80, ASSOC PROF RHEUMATOLOGY, UNIV CALIF, LOS ANGELES, 81- *Personal Data:* b Hong Kong, Feb 20, 43; m 67; c 1. *Educ:* Univ Hong Kong, BS & MB, 66. *Prof Exp:* Intern med, Univ Hong Kong, 66-67 & Long Island Col Hosp, NY, 68-69; pathologist, Hong Kong Govt Inst Path, 67-68; resident, Montefiore Hosp, NY, 69-71. *Concurrent Pos:* Guest investr immunol, Rockefeller Univ, New York, 78-79, asst prof, 79-80. *Mem:* Am Asn Immunol; Am Fedn Clin Res; Am Rheumatism Asn; Am Asn Microbiol. *Res:* Cause and mechanisms of the rheumatic diseases; the arthritis conditions Reiter's syndrome and ankylosing spondylitis. *Mailing Add:* Dept Med Rm 35-40 Rehab Ctr Univ Calif 1000 Veteran Ave Los Angeles CA 90024-1670. *Fax:* 310-206-8606

**YU, DAVID U L,** NUCLEAR PHYSICS, STRUCTURAL MECHANICS. *Current Pos:* PRES, DULY CONSULTS, 83- *Personal Data:* b Hong Kong, Aug 27, 40; nat US; m 65; c 2. *Educ:* Seattle Pac Col, BSc, 61; Univ Wash, PhD(theoret physics), 64. *Prof Exp:* Res assoc prof theoret physics, Stanford Univ, 64-66; Brit Sci Res Coun fel physics, Univ Surrey, 66-67; from asst prof to assoc prof, Seattle Pac Col, 67-73; mgr, Comput Sci Corp, Richland,

Washington & El Segundo, Calif, 73-75; exec vpres & dir, Basic Technol, Inc, 75-83. *Concurrent Pos:* Vpres, Int Inst Technol, 77-; fel, Ford Found, 62-63, NASA Jet Propulsion Lab, 69-70 & NSF fel, Ill Inst Tech, 72. *Mem:* Am Phys Soc; Am Asn Physics Teachers; Am Soc Mech Engrs. *Res:* Nuclear structure and reactions; elementary particle physics. *Mailing Add:* 1912 MacArthur St Rancho Palos Verdes CA 90732. *Fax:* 310-548-6094

**YU, FANG XIN,** STOCHASTIC PROCESS MODELING, GROUNDWATER CONTAMINATION MODELING. *Current Pos:* RES ASSOC IV, LA STATE UNIV, 91- *Personal Data:* b Hai-Yang, Shandong, China, Dec 25, 54; m 84, Wei-hua Li; c Lily. *Educ:* Xinjiang August-First Agr Col, China, BS, 76; La State Univ, MS, 88, PhD(civil eng), 92. *Prof Exp:* Instr fluid mech & soil mech, Xinjang Kashi Agr Col China, 76-78; instr theoret mech, Xinjiang August-First Agr Col, China, 78-79, asst prof, 79-85. *Concurrent Pos:* Prin investr, La Transp Res Ctr, 93-; vis scholar, La State Univ. *Res:* Groundwater solute transport modeling, rainfall-run off modeling, stochastic process modeling, parameter estimation, model evaluation, optimization algorithms, irrigation and infiltration process modeling, surface and subsurface hydrology and hydraulics, river mechanics, sedimentation and saltwater intrusion modeling. *Mailing Add:* 4042 Stoneleigh Dr Baton Rouge LA 70808. *Fax:* 504-767-9156; *E-Mail:* tpfang@lsuvm.sncc.lsu.edu

**YU, FRANCIS T S,** ELECTRICAL ENGINEERING. *Current Pos:* PROF ELEC ENG, PA STATE UNIV, 80-, EVAN PUGH PROF, 85- *Personal Data:* b Amoy City, China, Nov 12, 32; US citizen; m 62, Lucy Cha; c 3. *Educ:* Mapua Inst Technol, BSEE, 56; Univ Mich, MSE, 58, PhD(elec eng), 64. *Prof Exp:* Res asst, Commun Sci Lab, Univ Mich, 58-64, res assoc engr, 64-66, instr elec eng, 60-64, lectr, 64-65; from asst prof to prof, Wayne State Univ, 66-80. *Mem:* Fel Inst Elec & Electronics Engrs; fel Optical Soc Am; fel Soc Photo-Optical Instrumentation Engrs; fel Photonics Soc Chinese-Am. *Res:* Optical communication and filtering; optical information processing; holography; information theory; optical computing; neural networks; fiber sensors; photonefractive optis. *Mailing Add:* Dept Elec Eng Pa State Univ University Park PA 16802. *Fax:* 814-865-7065; *E-Mail:* ftyece@engr.psu.edu

**YU, FU-LI,** CHEMICAL CARCINOGENESIS. *Current Pos:* from asst to assoc prof, 79-85, PROF BIOCHEM, COL MED, UNIV ILL, 85-, HEAD, DEPT BIOMED SCI, 90- *Personal Data:* b Peking, China, May 2, 34; US citizen; m 80, Jie Feng; c Chan-Ching & Chan M. *Educ:* Taiwan Chung-Shing Univ, BS, 56; Univ Ala, MS, 62; Univ Calif, San Francisco, PhD(biochem), 65. *Prof Exp:* Instr biochem, Univ NMex, 65-66; fel trainee, Inst Cancer Res, Columbia Univ, 66-69, res assoc, 69-73; asst prof, Jefferson Med Col, 73-79. *Concurrent Pos:* Res grantee, NIH & Am Cancer Soc; prin investr, Nat Cancer Inst, 74-90, Am Cancer Soc, 78-81. *Mem:* Am Soc Biol Chemists; Am Asn Cancer Res; Am Chem Soc; Harvey Soc; Soc Chinese Bio Scientists Am. *Res:* Chemical carcinogenesis; hormone action; nucleic acid metabolism; RNA polymerase; gene regulation in mammalian cells; mechanisms of action of chemical carcinogens, particularly aflatoxin B1, at the transcriptional level. *Mailing Add:* Dept Biomed Sci Univ Ill Col Med 1601 Parkview Ave Rockford IL 61107. *Fax:* 815-395-5666

**YU, GRACE WEI-CHI HU,** BIOLOGY, MOLECULAR BIOLOGY. *Current Pos:* ASST PROF PLANT PHYSIOL, DEPT BIOL., CALIF STATE UNIV, DOMINGUEZ HILLS, 78- *Personal Data:* b Feb 10, 37; US citizen; m 62; c 2. *Educ:* Nat Taiwan Univ, BS, 59; Wash State Univ, MS, 63; Duke Univ, PhD(plant physiol), 67. *Prof Exp:* Res assoc plant physiol, Duke Univ, 66-68; lectr bot, Sch Med, Univ Calif, Los Angeles, 68, res assoc plant physiol, 68-71, asst res biologist, Neuropsychiat Inst, 71-72, ment health training prog fel, Brain Res Inst, 72-78, res assoc hemat & oncol, Dept Pediat, 75-78. *Concurrent Pos:* Comput prog cert, Control Data Inst, 82; instr biol, bot, human anat & physiol, Los Angeles Commun Col & Compton Commun Col, 78- *Mem:* AAAS; Am Soc Plant Physiologists; Sigma Xi. *Res:* Plant physiology, especially ion transport; developmental biology; software quality engineering. *Mailing Add:* 30303 Via Borica Rancho Palos Verdes CA 90274

**YU, GRETA,** physics, operations research, for more information see previous edition

**YU, HAO KENT,** BIOSENSOR DEVELOPMENT & CLINICAL INSTRUMENTATION, IMAGING ANALYSIS. *Current Pos:* SR SCIENTIST & PRIN INVESTR, CALSPAN SRL CORP, 95- *Personal Data:* b Beijing, May 18, 59, US citizen; m 90, Mary R; c Anna R. *Educ:* Beijing Polytech Univ, BS, 82; State Univ NY, Buffalo, MS, 90, PhD(biophysics), 92. *Honors & Awards:* Second Prize New Sci & Technol Develop, Dept Health, Gout China, 86. *Prof Exp:* Res asst, Roswell Park Cancer Inst, 78-92; chief engr, Beijing-ERMC Biochem Instruments, 82-87; postdoctoral fel, Georgetwon Univ, 92-94; res scientist, Oper Technol, Tex, 94-95. *Concurrent Pos:* US Army grant, US Army, Biol & Mat Command, Ft Detrict, Md, 96. *Mem:* Biophys Soc. *Res:* Biosensor development and clinical diagnostic instrumentation; immuno and nucleic acid-assay development for infectious diseases agent identification and sensitive detection; fluorescence imaging and spectroscopy studies on lipid monu layers. *Mailing Add:* Bldg E3549 Aberdeen Proving Ground MD 21010. *Fax:* 410-671-5807; *E-Mail:* khyu@ cml.apgea.army.mil

**YU, HWA NIEN,** ELECTRICAL ENGINEERING. *Current Pos:* Assoc engr, Res Lab, IBM Corp, 57-59, staff engr, Adv Systs Develop Div, 59-62, res staff mem semiconductor develop, Res Ctr, 62-80, mgr device & circuit technol, 80-93, EMER MEM, T J WATSON RES CTR, IBM CORP, 93- *Personal Data:* b Shanghai, China, Jan 17, 29; m 55; c 3. *Educ:* Univ Ill, BS, 53, MS, 54, PhD(elec eng), 58. *Mem:* Sigma Xi. *Res:* Computer design; semiconductor devices; electronic computers; semiconductors. *Mailing Add:* 2849 Hickory St Yorktown Heights NY 10598

**YU, HYUK,** PHYSICAL CHEMISTRY, BIOPHYSICS. *Current Pos:* from asst prof to assoc prof, 67-77, PROF CHEM, UNIV WIS-MADISON, 78- *Personal Data:* b Kapsan, Korea, Jan 20, 33; m 64; c 3. *Educ:* Seoul Nat Univ, BS, 55; Univ Southern Calif, MS, 58; Princeton Univ, PhD(phys chem), 62. *Honors & Awards:* Fulbright-Hays lectr Korea, 72; Fulbright lectr, 72. *Prof Exp:* Res chemist, Nat Bur Stand, 63-67. *Concurrent Pos:* Res assoc, Dartmouth Col, 62-63; consult, Nat Bur Standards, DC, Eastman Kodak Co, NY & Tenn Eastman Co; John Simon Guggenheim Fel, 84-85. *Mem:* Am Chem Soc; Am Phys Soc; NY Acad Sci; Biophys Soc; Mat Res Soc. *Res:* Structure and dynamics of biomembranes; polymer solution characterizations; syntheses of macromolecules; polymer dynamics in bulk and concentrated solutions; interfacial phenomena of polymers. *Mailing Add:* Dept Chem Univ Wis Madison WI 53706

**YU, JAMES CHUN-YING,** ACOUSTICS, FLUID DYNAMICS. *Current Pos:* AEROSPACE TECHNOLOGIST ACOUST, NASA LANGLEY RES CTR, 77- *Personal Data:* b Hunan, China, Oct 14, 40; US citizen; m 65; c 2. *Educ:* Nat Taiwan Univ, BSc, 62; Syracuse Univ, MSc, 68, PhD(mech eng), 71. *Prof Exp:* Instr mech eng, Syracuse Univ, 70-71; asst res prof, George Washington Univ, 71-75, assoc res prof, 75-76, assoc prof, 76-77. *Concurrent Pos:* NASA res grant, Langley Res Ctr, 71- *Mem:* Am Inst Aeronaut & Astronaut; Acoust Soc Am. *Res:* Sound generation from fluid flows; acoustic measurements and instrumentation; turbulent flows. *Mailing Add:* 105 Hoy Ct MS 235 Hampton VA 23681-0001

**YU, JASON C,** TRANSPORTATION ENGINEERING, CIVIL ENGINEERING. *Current Pos:* CONSULT, 88- *Personal Data:* b Hupei, China, Feb 5, 36; m 65; c 3. *Educ:* Univ Taiwan, BS, 57; Ga Inst Technol, MS, 63; Univ WVa, PhD(civil eng), 67. *Prof Exp:* Traffic engr, WVa State Rd Comn, 64-65; res assoc civil eng, Univ WVa, 66-67; res specialist transp eng, Univ Pa, 67-68; from asst prof to assoc prof civil eng, Va Polytech Inst & State Univ, 68-74; prof civil eng, Univ Utah, 74-88. *Concurrent Pos:* Mem tech comt parking & traffic control devices, Transp Res Bd, Nat Acad Sci-Nat Res Coun, 69-; ed, External Transp, Int Joint Comt Tall Bldg, 73- *Mem:* Am Soc Civil Engrs; Inst Traffic Engrs; Am Soc Eng Educ. *Res:* Transportation energy conservation strategies; urban transit system optimization; transportation system planning, design and operation; effects of transportation on land use development. *Mailing Add:* 4845 Bronbreck St Salt Lake City UT 84117

**YU, JEN,** PHYSICAL MEDICINE & REHABILITATION. *Current Pos:* PROF PHYS MED & REHAB, COL MED, UNIV CALIF, IRVINE, 81-, CHAIR DEPT, 82- *Personal Data:* b Taipei, Taiwan, Jan 23, 43; US citizen; m 73, Janet Chen; c Benjamin & Christopher. *Educ:* Nat Taiwan Univ, MD, 68; Univ Pa, PhD(physiol), 72. *Prof Exp:* Asst prof phys med & rehab, Sch Med, Univ Pa, 75-76; from asst prof to assoc prof, Univ Tex, Health Sci Ctr, San Antonio, 76-81. *Mem:* Am Acad Phys Med & Rehab; Am Cong Rehab Med; Am Asn Anatomists; Soc Neurosci; Asn Acad Physiatrists. *Res:* Neurobiological basis of rehabilitation medicine, including neurobiological studies on learning and memory, control of movement, and recovery after injury. *Mailing Add:* Dept Phys Med & Rehab Univ Calif Irvine Med Ctr 101 The City Dr Orange CA 92868. *Fax:* 714-456-6557

**YU, KAI FUN,** STATISTICS, MATHEMATICS. *Current Pos:* MATH STATISTICIAN, NIH, 90- *Personal Data:* b Guangzhou, China, July 19, 50; m 78. *Educ:* Dartmouth Col, AB, 73; Columbia Univ, PhD(statist), 78. *Prof Exp:* Asst prof statist, Yale Univ, 78-83; assoc prof, Univ SC, 84-90. *Mem:* Inst Math Statist; Sigma Xi. *Mailing Add:* NIH Bldg 6100 Rm 7B13 Bethesda MD 20892

**YU, KAI-BOR,** SIGNAL PROCESSING, COMMUNICATION. *Current Pos:* TECH STAFF, GEN ELEC RES & DEVELOP CTR, 88- *Personal Data:* b Canton, China, Apr 20, 53; US citizen; m 82, Wen L Fan; c Christina & Anna. *Educ:* Yale Univ, BS, 77; Brown Univ, MS, 79; Purdue Univ, PhD(elec eng), 82. *Prof Exp:* Asst prof elec eng, Va Polytech Inst & State Univ, 82-88. *Concurrent Pos:* Adj prof, Rensselaer Polytech Inst. *Mem:* Sr mem Inst Elec & Electronics Engrs. *Res:* Signal processing; image processing; pattern recognition; communication and radar. *Mailing Add:* Gen Elec Co KWC-1317A PO Box 8 Schenectady NY 12301. *Fax:* 518-387-7332; *E-Mail:* yu@crd.ge.com

**YU, KARL KA-CHUNG,** SOLID STATE ELECTRONICS, MATERIALS SCIENCE. *Current Pos:* SR STAFF PHYSICIST, HUGHES AIRCRAFT CO, 79- *Personal Data:* b Shanghai, China, Aug 31, 36; m 62; c 2. *Educ:* Carnegie-Mellon Univ, BS, 57, MS, 59, PhD(elec eng, mat sci), 66. *Prof Exp:* Assoc engr, Westinghouse Elec Corp, 59-61, sr engr, 66-78; prin staff engr, McDonnell Douglas Corp, 78-79. *Mem:* Inst Elec & Electronics Engrs. *Res:* Research and development in the area of solid state semiconductor device physics with emphasis on memory devices. *Mailing Add:* Torrance Res Ctr Hughes Aircraft Co 3100 W Lomita Blvd Torrance CA 90509

**YU, LEEPO CHENG,** BIOPHYSICS. *Current Pos:* staff fel, 73-75, sr staff fel, 76-77, RES PHYSICIST MUSCLE X-RAY DIFFRACTION, NAT INST ARTHRITIS, MUSCULO-SKELETAL & SKIN, 77- *Personal Data:* b Shanghai, China, June 25, 39; m 65; c 1. *Educ:* Brown Univ, BS, 63; Univ Md, PhD(physics), 69. *Prof Exp:* Res assoc muscle physiol, Brown Univ, 69-72. *Concurrent Pos:* Mem ed bd, Biophys J, 86-89. *Mem:* Am Phys Soc; Biophys Soc. *Res:* X-ray diffraction of striated vertebrate muscle; theoretical modelling of force generation. *Mailing Add:* NIH Bldg 6 Rm 111 Bethesda MD 20892. *Fax:* 301-402-0009; *E-Mail:* lcyu@helix.nih.gov

**YU, LINDA,** BIOENERGETICS. *Current Pos:* assoc res biochemist, 81-84, res prof, 84-86, ASSOC PROF, DEPT CHEM, OKLA STATE UNIV, STILLWATER, 86- *Personal Data:* b Taiwan, China, Feb 7, 43; m 68; c 2. *Educ:* Nat Taiwan Norm Univ, Taipei, BS, 66; Univ Ill, Urbana, MS, 68, PhD(microbiol), 70. *Prof Exp:* Res assoc, Dept Chem, State Univ NY, Albany, 70-74, res asst prof, lab bioenergetics, 74-79, dept chem, 79-81. *Concurrent Pos:* Vis instr, Dept Chem, State Univ NY, Albany, 70-74; grants, NIH & Okla Dept Com, 87-88, USDA, 87- *Mem:* Am Soc Biochem & Molecular Biol. *Res:* Membrane bioenergetic, membrane enzymes and phospholipid-protein interaction. *Mailing Add:* Dept Biochem Okla State Univ Stillwater OK 74078-0001

**YU, LUCY CHA,** PSYCHOLOGICAL STRESS OF ELDERLY, HEALTH STATUS. *Current Pos:* assoc prof, 85-91, PROF HEALTH POLICY & ADMIN, PA STATE UNIV, 91- *Personal Data:* b Champaign, Ill, Aug 10, 37; m 62, Francis T S; c Peter, Ann & Edward. *Educ:* Univ Mich, BS, 62, MAls, 72, PhD(educ-gerontol), 81. *Prof Exp:* Dir, Pub Health Libr, Univ Mich, 73-81. *Concurrent Pos:* Sr res assoc, Inst Policy Res & Eval, Penn State Univ, 82-91, sr res scientist, 91-; vis scientist, Nat Ctr Health Stats, 91; vis prof, Johns Hopkins Univ, 91; dir, PhD Prog, Pa State Univ, 92-94. *Mem:* Am Pub Health Asn; Gerontol Soc Am. *Res:* Disease patterns of elderly, cognitive impairment, depression, functional status of intergenerational transfer of resources and cultural factors and their influence on health status. *Mailing Add:* Pa State Univ Dept Health Policy & Admin 115 Henderson Bldg University Park PA 16802

**YU, MANG,** MOLECULAR BIOLOGY, BIOTECHNOLOGY. *Current Pos:* SCI CO-FOUNDER, IMMUSOL INC, 92-, DIR HIV GENE THER, 94- *Personal Data:* b July 14, 56; m 95, Fang Fang; c Charles F. *Educ:* Fudan Univ, BS, 82; Shanghai Med Univ, MS, 85; Ind Univ, PhD(molecular biol), 92. *Prof Exp:* Instr biochem, Shanghai Med Univ, 85; proj group leader, Gene Ther Team, Univ Calif, San Diego, 93-94. *Concurrent Pos:* Exec vpres, Int Soc Ind Univ & Purdue Univ, 89-90; pres & founder, Bioventure Bus Asn, 92-; consult, Univ Alberta, Can, 94- *Mem:* AAAS; Soc Chinese Bioscientists Am. *Res:* Ribozyme clinical human trial for HIV infection with scientists and physicians; Ribozyme gene therapy for HBV & HCV infection. *Mailing Add:* 7155B Calaforia Ct San Diego CA 92122. *Fax:* 619-677-0587; *E-Mail:* yu@immusol.com

**YU, MANG CHUNG,** ANATOMY, NEUROANATOMY. *Current Pos:* ASST PROF ANAT, COL MED & DENT NJ, 72- *Personal Data:* b Hong Kong, Mar 4, 39; US citizen; m 66. *Educ:* St Edward's Univ, BS, 63, MS, 66, PhD(anat), 70. *Prof Exp:* Fels, State Univ NY, Buffalo, 70-72. *Concurrent Pos:* Consult neuroanat, Vet Admin Hosp, East Orange, NJ, 72- *Mem:* Am Physiol Soc; Am Soc Neurosci; AAAS; Am Asn Anat. *Res:* Neurobiology; neuropathology. *Mailing Add:* Dept Anat UMDMJ NJ Med Sch 185 S Orange Ave Newark NJ 07103

**YU, MASON K,** MECHANICAL ENGINEERING. *Current Pos:* RETIRED. *Personal Data:* b Canton, China, Aug 2, 26; US citizen; m 50; c 5. *Educ:* Univ Mich, BSME, 50, MSME, 51. *Prof Exp:* Engr, Borg-Warner Corp, 51-53; res engr, Continental Aviation Eng Corp, 53-55; sr res engr, Emissions Res Dept, Gen Motors Res Labs, 55-88. *Mem:* Am Soc Mech Engrs; Sigma Xi. *Res:* Computer application to gas turbine thermodynamic turbomachinery research and development. *Mailing Add:* 550 W Brown Birmingham MI 48009

**YU, MEI-YING WONG,** MOLECULAR VIROLOGY & CHARACTERIZATION, VIRAL SAFETY OF PLASTIC DERIVATIVES. *Current Pos:* sr staff res fel, 80-81, SR RES CHEM, CTR BIOLOGICS EVAL RES, FOOD & DRUG ADMIN, 81- *Personal Data:* b Tainan, Taiwan, Repub China; US citizen; c 1. *Educ:* Kachsiung Med Col, Taiwan, Repub China, BS, 64; Univ Ala, Birmingham, MS, 68, PhD(pharmacol), 70. *Prof Exp:* Postdoctoral res fel, Dept Pharmacol, Baylor Sch Med, Houston, Tex, 70-71; res assoc, Dept Zool, Univ Tex, Austin, 71-74; sr staff res fel, Lab Develop Neurobiol, NICHD, NIH, 74-80. *Mem:* Am Soc Pharmacol & Exp Therapeut; Fedn Am Soc Exp Biol. *Res:* Charactcrization and efficacy of plasma derived therapeutic products; characterization of recombinant derived hepatitis B and C viral antigens and their immunoreactivity; viral safety of plasma derived products using PCR methodology. *Mailing Add:* Div Hemat CBER/FDA 1401 Rockville Pike Rockville MD 20852-1448. *Fax:* 301-402-2780

**YU, MING LUN,** SOLID STATE PHYSICS. *Current Pos:* mgr analytical res, 84-93, sr mgr mat analytical, 90-91, RES STAFF MEM, T J WATSON RES CTR, IBM CORP, 78- *Personal Data:* b Hong Kong, Aug 21, 45; US citizen; m 78, Lynne A Latham; c Joyce G & Elaine L. *Educ:* Hong Kong Univ, BSc, 67; Calif Inst Technol, MSc, 71, PhD(physics), 74. *Prof Exp:* Res assoc, Brookhaven Nat Lab, 73-74; asst physicist, 74-76; assoc physicist, 76-78. *Concurrent Pos:* Vis scientist, Physics Dept, State Univ NY, Stony Brook, 76-79. *Mem:* Fel Am Phys Soc; Am Vacuum Soc. *Res:* Superconductivity; Josephson devices; secondary ion mass spectrometry; surface physics; chemistry. *Mailing Add:* IBM Res Div T J Watson Res Ctr PO Box 218 Yorktown Heights NY 10598. *Fax:* 914-945-2141; *E-Mail:* myu@watson.ibm.com

**YU, MING-HO,** ENVIRONMENTAL HEALTH, NUTRITION. *Current Pos:* vis asst prof plant biochem, Huxley Col, Western Wash Univ, 69-70, lectr environ biol, 70-71, from asst prof to assoc prof, 71-79, PROF ENVIRON BIOL, HUXLEY COL, WESTERN WASH UNIV, 79- *Personal Data:* b Kaohsiung, Taiwan, May 22, 28; m 56; c 3. *Educ:* Nat Taiwan Univ, BS, 53; Utah State Univ, MS, 64, PhD(plant nutrit & biochem), 67. *Prof Exp:* Res asst agr chem, Taiwan Agr Res Inst, 54-55; asst res fel chem, Inst Chem Acad Sinica, 59-62; fel, Utah State Univ, 67 & Univ Alta, 67-68. *Concurrent Pos:* Fulbright Travel Grant, 62; vpres, Int Soc Fluoride Res, 88-; vis prof, Iwate Med Univ, Japan, 89-90; ed, Environ Sci, 90- *Mem:* AAAS; Int Soc Fluoride Res; NY Acad Sci; Am Chem Soc; Am Inst Nutrit. *Res:* Fluoride effects on the physiology and biochemistry of animals and plants; effects of pollutants on health; vitamin C metabolism. *Mailing Add:* Huxley Col Western Wash Univ Bellingham WA 98225-9181. *Fax:* 360-650-7284

**YU, NAI-TENG,** BIOPHYSICAL CHEMISTRY. *Current Pos:* from asst to assoc prof, 70-80, PROF CHEM, GA INST TECHNOL, 80- *Personal Data:* b Pingtung, Formosa, Aug 19, 39; m 66. *Educ:* Nat Taiwan Univ, BS, 63; NMex Highlands Univ, MS, 66; Mass Inst Technol, PhD(phys chem), 69. *Honors & Awards:* Sustained Res Award, Sigma Xi, 86. *Prof Exp:* Res chemist, Arthur D Little, Mass, 66; res assoc chem, Mass Inst Technol, 69-70. *Concurrent Pos:* Res Corp res grant, Ga Inst Technol, 71-72, USPHS res grants, 71-; res career develop award, NIH, 76-81; adj prof ophthal, Emory Univ, 82- *Mem:* AAAS; Am Chem Soc; Biophys Soc; Asn Res Vision & Ophthal. *Res:* Laser Raman spectroscopy of biopolymers; metalloporphyrins and hemoproteins; mechanisms of cataract lens formation; development of biomedical instrumentation. *Mailing Add:* Dept Chem Hong Kong Univ Sci & Technol Clearwater Bay Kowloon Hong Kong People's Republic of China. *Fax:* 404-894-4031

**YU, OLIVER SHUKIANG,** PROBABILITY & STATISTICS, ENERGY & UTILITY SYSTEMS. *Current Pos:* DIR, ENERGY & UTILITY SYST, SRI INT, 89- *Personal Data:* b Chentu, China, July 8, 39; m 62, 85, Joanna Chu; c Amy, Christopher & Hamilton. *Educ:* Nat Taiwan Univ, BSEE, 59; Ga Inst Technol, MSEE, 62; Stanford Univ, MS, 67, PhD(opers res), 72. *Prof Exp:* Res assoc civil defense study, Merrimack Col, 63-64; opers analyst, Opers Analysis Dept, Stanford Res Inst, 64-68, res engr, Systs Eval Dept, 68-70, sr res engr, 70-74; planning specialist, Commonwealth Edison Co, 77; proj mgr, Elec Power Res Inst, 74-77, tech asst to mgr, Res & Develop Planning & Assessment Dept, 78, tech mgr, Energy Study Ctr, 78-79, mgr planning anal, 79-89. *Concurrent Pos:* Consult systs analysis, SRI Int, 75; adj prof, Univ Calif, Berkeley, 80-85, Santa Clara Univ, 75-81, Calif State Univ, Hayward, 75-79 & San Jose State Univ, 79-81; Fulbright fel, 61-62; consult prof, Stanford Univ, 83-85. *Mem:* Sigma Xi; Inst Elec & Electronics Engrs; Opers Res Soc Am; Int Asn Energy Economists. *Res:* Planning, analysis and evaluation of energy and utility systems strategy and operations. *Mailing Add:* SRI Int 333 Ravenswood Ave Menlo Park CA 94025. *Fax:* 650-859-5134; *E-Mail:* oliver_yu@qm.sri.com

**YU, PAUL KIT-LAI,** PHOTONICS FOR COMMUNICATIONS. *Current Pos:* From asst prof to assoc prof, 83-93, PROF ELEC & COMPUT ENG, UNIV CALIF, SAN DIEGO, 93- *Personal Data:* b Hong Kong, July 12, 57; US citizen; m 86, Duang De; c Lea, Elton & Stephen. *Educ:* Calif Inst Technol, BSc & MSc, 79, PhD(appl physics), 83. *Concurrent Pos:* Vis assoc, Calif Inst Technol, 83-84; ed, Electron Device Soc Newslett, Inst Elec & Electronics Engrs, 94- *Mem:* Sr mem Inst Elec & Electronics Engrs; Optical Soc Am. *Res:* Solid state semiconductor device and materials; optoelectronics; secure optical communication; photonic band structures; photonics for analog signal transmissions; high speed photonics devices such as modulator, photo detectors, lasers and optical switches. *Mailing Add:* Dept Elec & Comput Eng Univ Calif San Diego La Jolla CA 92093-0407. *Fax:* 619-534-0556; *E-Mail:* yu@ece.ucsd.edu

**YU, PAUL N,** internal medicine, cardiology; deceased, see previous edition for last biography

**YU, PETER HAO,** NEUROCHEMISTRY, NEUROPSYCHOPHARMACOLOGY. *Current Pos:* SR RES SCIENTIST, PSYCHIAT RES DIV, CAN DEPT HEALTH, 75- *Personal Data:* b Liaoning, China, May 26, 42; Can citizen; m 70; c 3. *Educ:* Nat Taiwan Univ, BSc, 64, MSc, 67; Univ Gottingen, DSc(agr biol), 71. *Prof Exp:* Res scientist, Asn Molecular Biol Res, Ger, 71-73; assoc prof, Nat Taiwan Univ, 73-75. *Concurrent Pos:* Consult, Res Prog Directorate, Health & Welfare, Can, 77-; res assoc, Dept Psychiat, Univ Sask, 78- *Mem:* Int Soc Neurochem. *Res:* Regulation of metabolism of catecholamine and the possible relationship to mental disorder. *Mailing Add:* Neuropsychiat Res Div Rm A102 Med Res Bldg Univ Sask Saskatoon SK S7N 5E4 Can

**YU, PETER YOUND,** EXPERIMENTAL SOLID STATE PHYSICS, SEMICONDUCTORS. *Current Pos:* assoc prof, 79-81, PROF PHYSICS, UNIV CALIF, BERKELEY, 81- *Personal Data:* b Shanghai, China, Sept 8, 44; m 71; c 2. *Educ:* Univ Hong Kong, BSc, 66 & 67; Brown Univ, PhD(physics), 72. *Prof Exp:* Fel, Univ Calif, Berkeley, 71-72; res staff mem, Thomas J Watson Res Ctr, IBM Corp, 73-79. *Mem:* Fel Am Phys Soc; AAAS. *Res:* Optical properties and light scattering of semiconductors; picosecond laser spectroscopy; high pressure physics; defects in semiconductors. *Mailing Add:* Physics Dept Univ Calif Berkeley CA 94720. *Fax:* 510-643-8497; *E-Mail:* pyyu@lbl.gov

**YU, ROBERT KUAN-JEN,** BIOCHEMISTRY, NEUROCHEMISTRY. *Current Pos:* PROF & CHMN, MED COL VA, RICHMOND, VA, 88- *Personal Data:* b China, Jan 27, 38; m 72, Helen C; c David S & Jennifer S. *Educ:* Tunghai Univ, Taiwan, BS, 60; Univ Ill, Urbana, PhD(chem), 67. *Hon Degrees:* ScD, Toyko Univ, 80; MA, Yale Univ, 86. *Honors & Awards:* Kitasato Medal; Jacob Javits Neurosci Investr Award; Alexander von Humboldt Stiftung Sr Investr Award. *Prof Exp:* Res assoc neurol biochem,

Albert Einstein Col Med, 68-69; from instr to assoc prof, Yale Univ Med Sch, 69-82, prof neurol biochem, 83-88. *Concurrent Pos:* NIH fel, Albert Einstein Col Med, 67-68; Mary Fulton fel, William Randolph Hearst Found; Josiah Macy Found fel. *Mem:* AAAS; Am Chem Soc; Am Soc Neurochem; NY Acad Sci; Int Soc Neurochem; Soc Neurosci; Sigma Xi; Am Soc Biol Chemists. *Res:* Chemistry and metabolism of sphingolipids; sphingolipidosis; properties of lipids in solution and membrane; complex carbohydrates; membrane synthesis and assembly. *Mailing Add:* Dept Biochem & Molecular Biophys Med Col Va Va Commonwealth Univ Richmond VA 23298. *Fax:* 804-828-1473; *E-Mail:* rkyu@gems.vcu.edu

**YU, RUEY JIIN,** SKIN PHARMACOLOGY, ACUPUNCTURE. *Current Pos:* LIC ACUPUNCTURIST. *Personal Data:* b Hsin-chu, Taiwan, Mar 23, 32; m 59; c 3. *Educ:* Nat Taiwan Univ, BSc, 56, MSc, 60; Univ Ottawa, PhD(org chem), 65; Sch Int Asn Acupuncture, dipl, 84; Samra Univ, OMD, 86. *Prof Exp:* Lectr chem, Nat Univ Taiwan, 61-62; Nat Res Coun Can fel, 65-67; asst prof, Temple Univ, 67-73, assoc prof dermat & consult, Skin & Cancer Hosp, 73-83. *Concurrent Pos:* Clin pract, traditional Chinese acupuncture, dipl, Nat Comn Cert Acupuncture. *Mem:* Am Asn Acupuncture & Oriental Med; Am Acad Dermat. *Res:* Dermatopharmacology for skin disorders, such as age spots and wrinkles; pain control with Chinese acupuncture. *Mailing Add:* 4 Lindenwold Ave Ambler PA 19002

**YU, SHARON S M,** BIOCHEMISTRY. *Current Pos:* ADJ PROF, CALIF STATE UNIV, FRESNO, 86- *Personal Data:* b Taiwan; US citizen. *Educ:* City Univ New York, PhD(biochem), 75. *Prof Exp:* Res assoc, New York Blood Ctr, Lindsley F Kimball Res Inst, 75-85. *Mem:* Fedn Am Soc Exp Biol. *Res:* Biosynthesis of plasma proteins. *Mailing Add:* 8 Norton St Santa Ana CA 92612

**YU, SHIH-AN,** BOTANY. *Current Pos:* from asst prof to assoc prof, 67-75, PROF BIOL, EASTERN MICH UNIV, 75- *Personal Data:* b Hupei, China, May 10, 27; m 55. *Educ:* Nat Taiwan Univ, BS, 50; Univ NH, MS, 56, PhD(hort), 59. *Prof Exp:* Res assoc forage breeding, Mich State Univ, 59-64; lectr bot, Univ Mich, 65-66, res assoc, 66-67. *Mem:* Sigma Xi. *Res:* Fungal genetics and molecular genetics. *Mailing Add:* Dept Biol Eastern Mich Univ 316 Mark Jefferson Ypsilanti MI 48197-2211

**YU, SHIU YEH,** biochemistry, organic chemistry, for more information see previous edition

**YU, SHUDONG,** STRUCTURAL DYNAMICS, MODELING & ANALYSIS OF NUCLEAR FUEL. *Current Pos:* ASST PROF SOLID MECH, RYERSON POLYTECH UNIV, 97- *Personal Data:* b Wendeng, China, Mar 14, 62; Can citizen; m 86, Zhiying J Ding; c Daniel & Brian. *Educ:* SChina Metall Inst, BEng, 82; Northeastern Univ, China, MASc, 84; Univ Toronto, PhD(mech eng), 95. *Prof Exp:* Asst lectr, Northeastern Univ, 84-88; res assoc, Univ Ottawa, 88-89; fuel design engr, Atomic Energy Can Ltd, 94-97. *Mem:* Am Soc Mech Engrs. *Res:* Linear, non-linear and random vibrations; modelling and analysis of nuclear fuels under various operating conditions; finite element analysis of stresses, strains and temperatures in structures; dynamics of beams, mates and shells; kineto-elastodynamics of mechanisms. *Mailing Add:* 350 Victoria St Toronto ON M5B 2K3 Can. *Fax:* 416-979-5265; *E-Mail:* syu@acs.ryerson.ca

**YU, SIMON SHIN-LUN,** PHYSICS. *Current Pos:* PHYSICIST, LAWRENCE BERKELEY LAB, UNIV CALIF, 90- *Personal Data:* b Hong Kong, Mar 24, 45; US citizen; m 70. *Educ:* Seattle Pac Univ, BSc, 67; Univ Wash, Seattle, MS & PhD(physics), 70. *Prof Exp:* Res asst physics, Seattle Pac Univ, 64-67; fel, Univ Wash, 70-73; res assoc, Univ Pittsburgh, 73-77; physicist, Lawrence Livermore Lab, 77-90. *Mem:* Am Phys Soc. *Res:* Theoretical physics. *Mailing Add:* Lawrence Berkeley Lab Univ Calif MS-47-112 Berkeley CA 94720

**YU, SIMON SHYI-JIAN,** BIOCHEMICAL TOXICOLOGY, INSECTICIDE TOXICOLOGY. *Current Pos:* from asst prof to assoc prof, 80-86, PROF, UNIV FLA, 86- *Personal Data:* b Lotung, Taiwan, Sept 11, 35; US citizen; m 67, Rachel R Yeh; c Robert & Edmund. *Educ:* Nat Taiwan Univ, BS, 59; McGill Univ, MS, 65, PhD(entom), 68. *Prof Exp:* Res entomologist, Taiwan Sugar Co, 61-62; res asst toxicol, McGill Univ, 63-68; fel toxicol, Cornell Univ, 68-69; res assoc toxicol, Ore State Univ, 69-74, asst prof, 74-79. *Concurrent Pos:* Prin investr, Univ Fla, 81- *Mem:* Entom Soc Am; AAAS; Am Chem Soc; Sigma Xi. *Res:* Biochemical toxicology of insects and related species, including detoxication mechanisms, enzyme induction, insecticide metabolism, insecticide resistance, insect-host plant interactions and purification of detoxifying enzymes. *Mailing Add:* Dept Entom & Nematol Univ Fla Gainesville FL 32611. *Fax:* 352-392-0190

**YU, STEPHEN KIN-CHEUN,** PROCESS ENGINEERING, PROCESS RESEARCH & DEVELOPMENT. *Current Pos:* SR PROCESS ENGR, ORTHO-MCNEIL PHARMACEUT CORP, 89- *Personal Data:* b Canton, China, Feb 14, 51; US citizen; m, Mei Wu; c Diane, Jason & Melissa. *Educ:* NY Univ BS, 74. *Prof Exp:* Sr process develop engr, Maxwell House-Gen Food Corp, 74-81; sr process engr, Engelhard Indus, 81-82, Pepsi Co, 82-85, Dary McKee, 85-87; sr proj engr, Ortho Diagnostic Systs Inc, Johnson & Johnson Co, 87-89. *Mem:* Int Soc Pharmaceut Engrs; Chinese Am Chem Soc. *Res:* Apply statistical technique to analyze and improve pharmaceutical solid dosage manufacturing process; analyze pharmaceutical technology transfer process to improve new product development efficiency and manufacturing. *Mailing Add:* 2000 Sims Pl South Plainfield NJ 07080. *Fax:* 908-218-1268

**YU, THOMAS HUEI-CHUNG,** HALOGEN LAMP CHEMISTRY, VACUUM TECHNOLOGY. *Current Pos:* Develop engr, Gen Elec Lighting, 86-88, advan engr, 88-91, sr advance engr, 91-92, TEAM LEADER, GEN ELEC LIGHTING, 92- *Personal Data:* b Taipei, Taiwan, Mar 20, 57; m, Bang-Huei Yen; c Frank & Alice. *Educ:* Nat Taiwan Univ, BS, 80; Univ Rochester, PhD(chem eng), 86. *Concurrent Pos:* Vprin, Chinese Acad Cleveland, 91-92, dir, 92- *Mem:* Am Inst Chem Engrs. *Res:* High temperature transport phenomenon; kinetics; gas-solid reactions; high temperature lamp chemistry; thermodynamics; Getter chemistry for lamp application; mass spectroscopy; lamp design and process. *Mailing Add:* Gen Elec Nela Park Bldg 323 East Cleveland OH 44112

**YU, TS'AI-FAN,** MEDICINE, METABOLISM. *Current Pos:* assoc prof, 66-73, res prof, 73-82, EMER PROF RES, MT SINAI SCH MED, 82- *Personal Data:* b Shanghai, China, Oct 24, 11; nat US. *Educ:* Ginling Col, China, BA, 32; Peking Union Med Col, China, MD, 36. *Honors & Awards:* Woman Med Award, 83. *Prof Exp:* From intern to chief resident med, Peiping Union Med Col, 35-40; instr med, Col Physicians & Surgeons, Columbia Univ, 50-56, assoc, 56-59, asst prof, 60-66. *Mem:* Am Physiol Soc; Am Soc Pharmacol & Exp Therapeut; Harvey Soc; Am Soc Nephrol; Am Rheumatism Asn; Int Soc Nephrol. *Res:* Calcium and phosphorous metabolism in osteomalacia; purine metabolism and gout. *Mailing Add:* Gout Res Unit Mt Sinai Med Ctr One Gustave L Levy Pl New York NY 10029-6574

**YU, WEI WEN,** STRUCTURAL ENGINEERING. *Current Pos:* from assoc prof to prof civil eng, 72-82, curators prof, 82-92, EMER CURATORS PROF CIVIL ENG, UNIV MO, ROLLA, 92- *Personal Data:* b Shantung, China, July 10, 24; US citizen; m 53; c 3. *Educ:* Taiwan Norm Technol, BS, 50; Okla State Univ, MS, 55; Cornell Univ, PhD(struct eng), 60. *Prof Exp:* Teaching asst civil eng, Taiwan Norm Technol, 50-54; struct designer, T H McKaig & Assocs, NY, 55-56 & 59-60; res asst struct, Cornell Univ, 57-59; engr, Am Iron & Steel Inst, 60-67; staff engr, TRW, Inc, 67-68. *Concurrent Pos:* Lectr, City Col New York, 64-65. *Mem:* Fel Am Soc Civil Engrs; Am Concrete Inst. *Res:* Cold-formed steel structures; semi-rigid connection of steel framing; deflection of reinforced concrete beams; steel structures. *Mailing Add:* Dept Civil Eng Univ Mo Rolla MO 65409

**YU, WEN-SHI,** CHEMICAL ENGINEERING. *Current Pos:* ENGR, BROOKHAVEN NAT LAB, 61- *Personal Data:* b Shanghai, China, Nov 17, 34; US citizen. *Educ:* Nat Taiwan Univ, BS, 56; Pratt Inst, MS, 58; Polytech Inst Brooklyn, PhD(chem eng), 64. *Mem:* Women Engrs; Sigma Xi. *Res:* Heat-transfer of forced-convection with liquid metals in the nuclear and space fields; heat transfer of single-phase and two-phase (boiling) flow; computer coding in applied science field; research development of hydrogen storage systems; thermal storage study and safety studies in the controlled thermal reactor program. *Mailing Add:* 108 81st Ave Kew Gardens NY 11415

**YU, YAO NAN,** ELECTRICAL ENGINEERING. *Current Pos:* PROF ELEC ENG, UNIV BC, VANCOUVER, 60- *Personal Data:* b China, Oct 21, 09. *Educ:* Toyoko Inst Technol, BS, 36, PhD(elec eng), 63. *Prof Exp:* Prof & dept head elec eng, Nat Taiwan Univ, 55-60. *Mem:* China Soc Elec Eng; Power Eng Soc. *Mailing Add:* Dept Eng Univ BC 4234 W 14th Ave Vancouver BC V6R 2X8 Can

**YU, YI-YUAN,** ENGINEERING MECHANICS, AEROSPACE ENGINEERING. *Current Pos:* dean, Newark Col Eng, 81-85, prof, 81-93, EMER PROF MECH ENG, NJ INST TECHNOL, 93- *Personal Data:* b China, Jan 29, 23; nat US; m 52, Eileen Wu; c Yolanda & Lisa. *Educ:* Univ Tientsin, China, BS, 44; Northwestern Univ, MS, 50, PhD(eng mech), 51. *Prof Exp:* Res assoc, Northwestern Univ, 51; asst prof appl mech, Wash Univ, St Louis, 51-54; assoc prof mech eng, Syracuse Univ, 54-57; prof mech eng, Polytech Inst Brooklyn, 57-66; consult engr, Gen Elec Co, 66-71; distinguished prof aeronaut eng, Wichita State Univ, 72-75; mgr eng, Rocketdyne Div, Rockwell Int, 75-79, exec eng, Energy Systs Group, 79-81. *Concurrent Pos:* Guggenheim fel, 59-60; consult, US Naval Appl Sci Lab, 63-69; lectr, Gen Elec Mod Eng Course, 63-73; adv, Mid East Tech Univ, Turkey, 66; mem, Ad Hoc Comt Dynamic Shock anal, USN, 67-68; chmn, Grad Studies Div, Am Soc Eng Educ, 85-86, Curtis W McGraw Res Award Comt, 91-92, Comt Mech Educ, Am Acad Mech, 93-94. *Mem:* Assoc fel Am Inst Aeronaut & Astronaut; fel Am Soc Mech Engrs; Am Soc Eng Educ; Am Soc Composites; Am Acad Mech. *Res:* Stress and vibration analysis; theory of elasticity; theory of plates and shells; dynamics and control of structural and mechanical systems; vibrations of plates and shells; piezoelectricity. *Mailing Add:* NJ Inst Technol 323 High St Newark NJ 07102. *Fax:* 973-643-0674; *E-Mail:* yu@admini.njit.edu

**YU, YONG MING,** STABLE ISOTOPE TRACER TECHNIQUE, PROTEIN & AMINO ACID METABOLISM. *Current Pos:* asst biochemist, 88-93, ASSOC BIOCHEMIST, DEPT SURGERY, MASS GEN HOSP, 94-; ASST BIOCHEMIST, DEPT SURGERY, SHRINERS BURN INST, 89- *Personal Data:* b Beijing, China, June 20, 45; m 71, Bei-Lei Ling; c Yi-Qian Y. *Educ:* Peking Univ, BS, 67; Peking Union Med Col, MD, 70; Mass Inst Technol, PhD(nutritional biochem), 87. *Prof Exp:* Res fel surge trauma serv, Mass Gen Hosp & Shriners Burn Inst, 80-87. *Concurrent Pos:* Res fel surgery, Harvard Univ, 80-90, instr, 92-; vis scientist, Mass Inst Technol, 92; vis lectr, Dept Surgery, Univ Hosp, Univ Alberta, 94. *Mem:* Am Burn Asn; Sigma Xi; Am Inst Nutrition; NY Acad Sci. *Res:* Study of protein and energy metabolism in healthy subjects and in severely injured leg burn injury and sepsis patients using stable isotope and short-term radioactive isotope. *Mailing Add:* Shriner Burn Inst 51 Blossom St Rm 216 Boston MA 02114

**YU, YUN-SHENG,** FLUID MECHANICS, WATER RESOURCES. *Current Pos:* assoc prof, 60-64, PROF FLUID MECH, UNIV KANS, 64- *Personal Data:* b I-Hsing, Kiangsu, China, Nov 21, 26; US citizen; m 60; c 4. *Educ:* Nat Taiwan Univ, BS, 53; Univ Iowa, MS, 56; Mass Inst Technol, ScD(civil eng), 60. *Honors & Awards:* Li-Found Fel. *Prof Exp:* Res assoc hydraul, Iowa Inst Hydraul Res, 56-57; res assoc Hydrodyn Lab, Mass Inst Technol, 59-60. *Concurrent Pos:* Consult, US Army Tank-Automotive Ctr, 66; vis prof, Univ Mich, 67; vis prof, Qinghua Univ, Beijing, China, 80-81; tech adv, Inst Water Resources & Environ Res, Bur Environ Protection, Beijing, China, 87-; hon prof, Hehai Univ, Nanjing, China. *Mem:* Math Asn Am; Int Water Resources Asn; Am Geophys Union; Am Water Resources Asn; Am Soc Civil Engrs. *Res:* Theoretical and applied hydrodynamics; water pollution; water resources systems analysis. *Mailing Add:* 2501 Harvard Rd Lawrence KS 66049-2618

**YUAN, FAN,** MICROCIRCULATION, BIOTRANSPORT PROCESS. *Current Pos:* INSTR, HARVARD MED SCH, 91- *Personal Data:* b Beijing, China, Oct 11, 60; m 91, Hui Li. *Educ:* Beijieng Univ, BS, 83, MS, 85; City Univ NY, PhD(bioeng), 90. *Honors & Awards:* IPM Innovative Instrumentation Award, Microcirculatory Soc, 93 & 94. *Prof Exp:* Res asst, City Univ NY, 86-90, adj lectr thermodyn, 88-89; fel, Carnegie Mellon Univ, 90-91. *Mem:* AAAS; Biomed Eng Soc; Radiation Res Soc. *Res:* Transport of molecules across microvessel wall and in interstitial space; microcirculation; delivery of novel therapeutic agents in tumors; tissue oxygen tension; biomechanics. *Mailing Add:* Dept Biomed Eng Duke Univ Box 90281 Durham NC 27708. *Fax:* 617-726-3603; *E-Mail:* fyuen@bullwinkle.mgh.harvard.edu

**YUAN, JIAN-MIN,** CHEMICAL & LASER PHYSICS, NONLINEAR DYNAMICS. *Current Pos:* from asst prof to assoc prof, 78-91, PROF PHYSICS, DEPT PHYSICS & ATMOSPHERIC SCI, DREXEL UNIV, 91- *Personal Data:* b Chungking, China, Aug 31, 44; m 71, Barbara O-Ching; c 2. *Educ:* Nat Taiwan Univ, BS, 66, MS, 68; Univ Chicago, PhD(chem physics), 73. *Prof Exp:* Fel scattering theory, Quantum Theory Proj, Univ Fla, 73-75; instr & res assoc laser interaction, Dept Chem, Univ Rochester, 75-78. *Mem:* Am Phys Soc; Am Chem Soc; Sigma Xi. *Res:* Interaction of atomic and molecular dynamics with an intense laser field; nonlinear dynamics; molecular scattering theories; semiclassical approach; surface physics; quantum chaos; chaotic scattering. *Mailing Add:* Dept Physics & Atmospheric Sci Drexel Univ Philadelphia PA 19104. *Fax:* 215-895-5934

**YUAN, JIANN-SHIUN,** SEMICONDUCTOR DEVICE MODELING & SIMULATION, ANALOG & DIGITAL INTEGRATED CIRCUIT DESIGN. *Current Pos:* asst prof, 90-95, ASSOC PROF MICROELECTRONICS, UNIV CENT FLA, 95- *Personal Data:* m 83, Hui-li Yao; c Michael J & Jerry G. *Educ:* Nat Univ Marine Sci & Technol, BS, 80; Univ Fla, MS, 84, PhD(elec eng), 88. *Prof Exp:* Res asst, Univ Fla, 85-88; design engr, Tex Instruments Inc, 88-89. *Concurrent Pos:* Vis scientist, Motorola, 91. *Mem:* Sr mem Inst Elec & Electronics Engrs. *Res:* Electrical engineering; author 60 journals and 40 conferences publications. *Mailing Add:* Dept Elec & Comput Eng Univ Cent Fla Orlando FL 32816. *Fax:* 407-823-5836; *E-Mail:* jsy@engr.ucf.edu

**YUAN, JUN,** APPLIED CLAY MINERALOGY, INDUSTRIAL MINERALS & ROCKS. *Current Pos:* sr res scientist, 93-96, LEADER CRUDE RES, ENGLISH CHINA CLAYS PLC, 96- *Personal Data:* b Zhuji, China, Oct 27, 65; m 89, Xujia Weng; c 2. *Educ:* Zhejiang Univ, BS, 84, Ind Univ, MS, 91, PhD(geol), 95. *Prof Exp:* Asst geologist, Tianjin Geol Acad, 84-86. *Mem:* Soc Mining Metall & Eng; Clay Minerals Soc; Micros Soc Am. *Res:* Geology, mineralogy and industrial applications of Kaolin Clays from USA, UK and China; mechanism of benefication technologies for industrial minerals such as flotation, magnetic separation and flocculation. *Mailing Add:* PO Box 471 618 Kaolin Rd Sandersville GA 31082. *Fax:* 912-553-5797; *E-Mail:* jun_yuan@ecc.com

**YUAN, LUKE CHIA LIU,** PHYSICS. *Current Pos:* CHMN BD DIRS, SYNCHROTRON RADIATION RES CTR, TAIWAN, 83- *Personal Data:* b Changtchfu, China, Apr 5, 12; US citizen; m 42, Chien-Shiung Wu; c Vincent. *Educ:* Yenching Univ, BS, 32, MS, 34; Calif Inst Technol, PhD(physics), 40. *Hon Degrees:* DSc, Nanking Univ People's Repub China, 86. *Honors & Awards:* Sci Achievement Medal, Repub China, 59, Pres Medal, 94; Achievement Award, Chinese Inst Elec Eng, 62. *Prof Exp:* Asst physics, Yenching Univ, 32-34; asst, Calif Inst Technol, 37-40, fel, 40-42; res physicist, RCA Labs, 42-46; res assoc, Princeton Univ, 46-49; sr physicist, Brookhaven Nat Lab, Upton, 49-82, consult, 82-87. *Concurrent Pos:* Guggenheim fel, 58; vis prof, Europ Orgn Nuclear Res, 72-76, Ctr d'Etude Nucleare de Saclay, France, 72-76; bd dir, Adelphi Univ Energy Res Ctr, 79-87; vis prof, Inst High Energy Physics, USSR, 79, Univ Paris, France, 82; hon adv, Sci & Technol Workers' Asn, Chinese Acad Sci, People's Repub China; hon prof, Chinese Univ Sci & Tech, Hefei, Anhwei Prov, Nankai Univ, Tientsin, Honan Univ, Southeastern Univ, Nanjing, People's Repub China. *Mem:* Fel Am Phys Soc; Acad Sinica; NY Acad Sci. *Res:* High energy physics; super energy accelerator and particle detection systems; cosmic rays; radio direction finding; frequency modulation radar systems. *Mailing Add:* 15 Claremont Ave New York NY 10027. *Fax:* 212-316-0698

**YUAN, ROBERT,** MOLECULAR BIOLOGY. *Current Pos:* PROF MICROBIOL, UNIV MD, 85- *Personal Data:* b Paris, France, Oct 9, 38; m 92, Yuan Lin; c Nicole. *Educ:* Antioch Univ, BS; Albert Einstein Inst Col Med, PhD(molecular biol), 66. *Honors & Awards:* Helen Hay Award. *Prof Exp:* Sect chief molecular biol, Nat Inst Cancer, 75-85. *Concurrent Pos:* Res fel, Harvard Univ, 66-71; vis lect, Univ Edinburgh, 70-71; assoc prof, Univ Basel, 71-77; 1st Secy, US Embassy, London, 85-86. *Mem:* AAAS; Am Soc Biochem & Molecular Biol; Chinese Biosci Am. *Res:* Biology curriculum development; biotechnology assessment. *Mailing Add:* Dept Microbiol Univ Md College Park MD 20742-0001. *Fax:* 301-314-9491; *E-Mail:* robert_yuan@umail.umd.edu

**YUAN, ROBERT L,** ENGINEERING, STRUCTURAL CONCRETE MATERIALS. *Current Pos:* from asst prof to assoc prof, 68-81, PROF CIVIL ENG, UNIV TEX, ARLINGTON, 81- *Personal Data:* b Nanking, China, 1937; US citizen; m 68; c 2. *Educ:* Cheng Kung Univ, Taiwan, BS, 60; Univ Ill, Urbana, MS, 64, PhD(theoret & appl mech), 68. *Prof Exp:* Res assoc concrete res, Univ Ill, 67-68. *Mem:* Am Concrete Inst; Soc Exp Stress Analysis; Am Soc Civil Eng. *Res:* Concrete and new building material research. *Mailing Add:* 1817 Elm Crest Dr Arlington TX 76012

**YUAN, SHAO-YUEN,** CHEMICAL ENGINEERING. *Current Pos:* from res engr to sr res engr, Chevron Res Co, 56-66, supvr prod develop & tech serv, Chevron Chem Co, 66-69, sr proj engr, 69-75, staff engr, 75-78, sr staff engr, 78-81, REGIONAL EXEC, CHEVRON RES CO, STANDARD OIL CALIF, 81- *Personal Data:* b Shanghai, China, July 30, 29; US citizen; m 49; c 2. *Educ:* Ill Inst Technol, BS, 50; Univ Louisville, MS, 51. *Prof Exp:* Res engr, E I du Pont de Nemours, 51-56. *Mem:* Am Inst Chem Engrs; Am Chem Soc. *Mailing Add:* 70 Heritage Rd San Rafael CA 94901-8308

**YUAN, SIDNEY WEI KWUN,** cryogenics, thermodynamics, for more information see previous edition

**YUAN, TZU-LIANG,** soils, for more information see previous edition

**YUCEOGLU, YUSUF ZIYA,** internal medicine, cardiology, for more information see previous edition

**YUDELSON, JOSEPH SAMUEL,** POLYMER CHEMISTRY, PHOTOCHEMISTRY. *Current Pos:* RETIRED. *Personal Data:* b Philadelphia, Pa, July 20, 25; m 52, Tanya; c Aline, Michael, Leslie & Margot. *Educ:* Univ Pittsburgh, BS, 50; Ill Inst Technol, PhD(chem), 55. *Honors & Awards:* IR100 Award, 84. *Prof Exp:* Res chemist, Eastman Kodak Res Lab, 54-57, sr res chemist, 57-60, res assoc phys chem, 60-70, sr lab head, 70-80, sr res assoc, Magnetic Media Lab, 80-90; contractor, Sterling-Winthrop Res Group, 90-93. *Mem:* Assoc Am Chem Soc; Sigma Xi. *Res:* Physical chemistry of hydrophilic polymers; photographic chemistry; nonaqueous solvents; inorganic photochemistry; magnetic media; developing ultra fine magnetic particles for chemical separations; investigating new magnetic media for high density information storage; contrast agents for ultrasound and magnetic resonance imaging. *Mailing Add:* 77 Calumet St Rochester NY 14610

**YUDKOWSKY, ELIAS B,** EDUCATIONAL ADMINISTRATION, DENTISTRY. *Current Pos:* ASSOC PROF ANAT, SCH MED & PROF & DIR, DIV DENT PROGS, UNIV NMEX, 82- *Personal Data:* b Brooklyn, NY, June 3, 32. *Educ:* Northwestern Univ Dent Sch, DDS, 57; Univ Calif, San Francisco, PhD(endocrinol), 68. *Prof Exp:* Dent pract, Chicago, Ill, 58-61; instr oral diag, Northwestern Univ Dent Sch, 59-61; asst secy coun dent res, Am Dent Asn, 67-69; asst dean, Harvard Sch Dent Med, 69-70; asst prof anat, Med Univ SC Col Med, 70-78, assoc prof oral path, 70-78, asst chmn, 74-78; prof & chmn, Dept Dent Hyg, ETenn State Univ, 78-82. *Concurrent Pos:* Consult, Am Dent Asn, 70-75; task force cardiovasc & hypertensive dis, SC Dent Asn, 75-78, Tenn Higher Educ Comt, 79-82, regional dent educ planning, 82-83, col health related profs, Idaho State Univ, 84-85, Prof Sem Consults, Inc, 85- & Col Health, Univ Cent Fla, 86-; assoc ed, Head & Neck Cancer Abstr, 83-84; dir dent progs & mem bd dirs, Prof Seminar Consults, Inc, 82- *Mem:* Am Dent Asn; Am Asn Dent Sch; fel AAAS; Am Asn Univ Prof. *Res:* Nucleic acid levels in rat uterus; normal-abnormal head and neck development; forensic odontology. *Mailing Add:* 1033 W Vernon Park Pl Chicago IL 60607

**YUE, A(LFRED) S(HUI-CHOH),** ELECTRONIC MATERIALS ENGINEERING. *Current Pos:* PROF MAT SCI, UNIV CALIF, LOS ANGELES, 69- *Personal Data:* b Canton, China, Nov 12, 20; m 44, Virginia Tang; c Mary, John & David. *Educ:* Chao-Tung Univ, China, BS, 42; Ill Inst Technol, MS, 50; Purdue Univ, PhD(metall eng), 57. *Honors & Awards:* Apollo-Soyuz Award, NASA; Skylab Award, NASA. *Prof Exp:* Instr metall eng, Purdue Univ, 52-56; res metallurgist, Dow Chem Co, 56-62; res scientist, Lockheed Palo Alto Res Lab, 62-63, staff scientist, 63-66, sr mem, 66-69. *Concurrent Pos:* Chair prof, Tsing Hua Univ, Taiwan, Repub China, 75; hon prof, Xian Jiao-Tong Univ, China, 80. *Mem:* Am Inst Mining, Metall & Petrol Eng; Am Soc Metals. *Res:* High Tc superconductor films, multilayered structures by MBE and MOCVD techniques for devices applications; preparation of p-n homo- and heterojunctions via the liquid-phase-epitaxial, chemical vapor deposition, close-space-vapor-transport and the directional solidification techniques. *Mailing Add:* 6532 Boelter Hall Univ Calif Los Angeles CA 90095-1595. *Fax:* 310-206-7353

**YUE, ON-CHING,** ELECTRICAL ENGINEERING. *Current Pos:* SUPVR, BELL LABS, 77- *Personal Data:* b Macao, Apr 9, 47; US citizen; m 73; c 2. *Educ:* Cooper Union, BEE, 68; Rochester Inst Technol, MSEE, 71; Univ Calif, San Diego, PhD(info sci), 77. *Prof Exp:* Sr engr, Electronics Div, Gen Dynamics Corp, 68-77. *Mem:* Inst Elec & Electronics Engrs. *Res:* Communication theory; computer performance analysis. *Mailing Add:* AT&T Bell Labs Rm Ho-3M-366 101 Crawfords Corner Rd Holmdel NJ 07733

**YUE, ROBERT HON-SANG,** BIOCHEMISTRY. *Current Pos:* DIR QUAL ASSURANCE, CLIN RES ASSOC, 94- *Personal Data:* b Canton, China, Sept 9, 37; US citizen; m 70, Noel S Liang; c Jennifer A, Alana F & Sylvia I. *Educ:* ETex Baptist Col, BS, 61; Univ Utah, PhD(biol chem), 68. *Prof Exp:* Res assoc biochem, Lab Study Hereditary & Metab Dis, Univ Utah, 68-70; assoc res scientist, Inst Rehab Med, NY Univ Med Ctr, 70-72, res scientist, 72-73, res asst prof, 73-76, res assoc prof rehab med, 76-81; res biochemist, Revlon Health Care Group, 81-85; dir prod develop, Enzon, Inc, 85-90, sr dir, 90-93. *Mem:* Am Chem Soc; AAAS; NY Acad Sci; Am Heart Asn; Parenteral Drug Asn. *Res:* Physical chemistry of the isolated proteins; mechanism of enzyme action; blood coagulation. *Mailing Add:* 259-15 86th Ave Floral Park New York NY 11001. *E-Mail:* 74133.777@compuserve.com

**YUEN, DAVID ALEXANDER,** GEOPHYSICS, FLUID DYNAMICS & LARGE SCALE COMPUTATIONS. *Current Pos:* assoc prof, 85-89, PROF GEOPHYS, UNIV MINN, 89- *Personal Data:* b Hong Kong, June 14, 48; US citizen. *Educ:* Calif Inst Technol, BS, 69; Scripps Inst Oceanog, Univ Calif, San Diego, MS, 73; Univ Calif, Los Angeles, PhD(geophys), 78. *Prof Exp:* Res geophysicist, Univ Calif, Los Angeles, 74-77; NSF fel geophys, Univ Toronto, 78-79; from asst prof to assoc prof geophys, Ariz State Univ, 80-85; assoc prof, Univ Colo, 85. *Concurrent Pos:* NATO fel, Univ Toronto, 79-80; assoc ed, J Geophys Res, 83-86. *Mem:* Am Geophys Union; Am Chem Soc; Am Phys Soc; Soc Indust & Appl Math. *Res:* Earth's mantle; different time scales of instability mechanisms; rheology of the mantle; seismic attenuation processes in elastic-gravitational free oscillations; rotational dynamics; ice ages; magna chamber processes; mantle convection. *Mailing Add:* 1530 S Sixth St Minneapolis MN 55454

**YUEN, MAN-CHUEN,** FLUID DYNAMICS, HEAT TRANSFER. *Current Pos:* From asst prof to assoc prof mech eng & astronaut sci, 64-75, PROF MECH ENG, NORTHWESTERN UNIV, 75- *Personal Data:* b Hong Kong, Aug 5, 33; nat US; m 58; c 3. *Educ:* Purdue Univ, BS, 56; Mass Inst Technol, MS, 58; Harvard Univ Univ, PhD(eng), 65. *Concurrent Pos:* Chmn, Mech Eng & Astronaut Sci Dept, Northwestern Univ, 78-79. *Mem:* Am Soc Mech Engrs. *Res:* Multiphase and multicomponent fluid mechanics and heat transfer. *Mailing Add:* Dept Mech Eng Northwestern Univ Evanston IL 60201-2970

**YUEN, PAUL C(HAN),** ELECTRICAL ENGINEERING. *Current Pos:* assoc prof elec eng, Univ Hawaii, Manoa, 61-65, actg dean, Col Eng, 69 & 77-78, assoc dean, 70-79, asst to chancellor, 71-72, actg dir, Ctr Eng Res, 76-77, dir, Hawaii Natural Energy Inst, 77-81, PROF ELEC ENG, UNIV HAWAII, MANOA, 65-, DEAN, COL ENG, 81-; ACTG PRES, PAC INT CTR HIGH TECHNOL RES, 83- *Personal Data:* b Hilo, Hawaii, June 7, 28; m 52; c 2. *Educ:* Univ Chicago, BS, 52; Ill Inst Technol, MS, 55, PhD(elec eng), 60. *Honors & Awards:* Centennial Medal, Inst Elec & Electronics Engrs, 84. *Prof Exp:* Cyclotron technician, Univ Chicago, 50-52; engr, Standard Coil Prod, 53-54; assoc res engr, Armour Res Found, 54-57; res engr, Ill Inst Technol, 57-60, asst prof elec eng, 60-61. *Concurrent Pos:* Mem, Geothermal Resources Coun. *Mem:* Am Geophys Union; Am Soc Eng Educ; Inst Elec & Electronics Engrs; Int Union Radio Sci; Sigma Xi. *Res:* Radio wave propagation; satellite communications; ionospheric physics; renewable energy resources. *Mailing Add:* Col Eng Univ Hawaii Honolulu HI 96822

**YUEN, TED GIM HING,** EXPERIMENTAL PATHOLOGY. *Current Pos:* RES ASSOC NEUROPATH, HUNTINGTON MED RES INST, 72- *Personal Data:* b Canora, Sask, Dec 21, 33; m 58, Dorene Zachary; c Marc, Nancy, Phillip & Linda. *Educ:* Andrews Univ, BA, 56; Univ Southern Calif, PhD(exp path), 69. *Prof Exp:* Fel exp path, Univ Southern Calif, 69-71. *Concurrent Pos:* Res assoc, Dept Path, Univ Southern Calif, 75-76. *Mem:* Am Asn Pathologists; Soc Biomat; Int Soc Histotechnol. *Res:* Ultrastructural study of the effects of electrical stimulation of the brain and peripheral nerves; biocompatibility of neural implants. *Mailing Add:* Dept Neurol Res Huntington Med Res Inst 734 Fairmount Ave Pasadena CA 91105

**YUEN, WING,** breakthrough dehydration, for more information see previous edition

**YUH, HUOY-JEN,** SOLID STATE PHYSICS, PHYSICAL CHEMISTRY. *Current Pos:* mem res staff, Photoconductor Res, 83-, proj mgr, 90-, PRIN SCIENTIST SCIENTIST, XEROX CORP, 96- *Personal Data:* b Taiwan, China; US citizen; m 77, Shey-Shing Sheu; c Gloria & Jessica. *Educ:* Nat Tsing-Hwa Univ, Taiwan, China, BS, 75; Univ Chicago, PhD(chem), 81. *Prof Exp:* Fel chem, Johns Hopkins Univ, 81-83. *Mem:* Mat Res Soc. *Res:* Photoconductor material research; fundamental study of charge-transport material properties. *Mailing Add:* 31 Fall Meadow Dr Pittsford NY 14534-9513

**YUHAS, JOSEPH GEORGE,** animal behavior, zoology, for more information see previous edition

**YUI, KATSUYUKI,** t cell tolerance, t cell development, for more information see previous edition

**YUILL, THOMAS MACKAY,** VIROLOGY, ECOLOGY. *Current Pos:* from asst prof to assoc prof, Univ Wis-Madison, 68-76, chmn, Dept Vet Sci, 78-82, asst dir, Agr Exp Sta & assoc dean res & grad training, 82-93, PROF VET SCI & WILDLIFE ECOL, UNIV WIS-MADISON, 76-, PROF PATHOBIOL, 82-, DIR, INST ENVIRON STUDIES, 93- *Personal Data:* b Berkeley, Calif, June 14, 37; m 60, Ann Warnes; c Eileen & Gwen. *Educ:* Utah State Univ, BS, 59; Univ Wis, MS, 62, PhD(vet sci), 64. *Honors & Awards:* Distinguished Serv Award, Wildlife Dis Asn. *Prof Exp:* Lab officer virol, Walter Reed Army Inst Res, 64-66, med biologist, SEATO Med Res Lab, 66-68. *Concurrent Pos:* Consult, NIH & Environ Protection Agency, 77-; pres, Orgn Trop Studies, 80-85; hon prof vet microbiol, Univ Antioquia Fac Vet Med, Colombia, SAm; consult, US Agency Int Dev, 87- *Mem:* Am Soc Microbiol; Wildlife Soc; Wildlife Dis Asn (treas, 80-85, pres, 85-87); Am Soc Trop Med & Hyg; Royal Soc Trop Med & Hyg; Am Inst Biol Sci. *Res:* Arbovirus epizootiology; wildlife diseases, especially arthropod-borne; virus ecology; effects of non-lethal infections and intoxications on wildlife. *Mailing Add:* Inst Environ Studies 1007 WARF Univ Wis 610 Walnut St Madison WI 53705. *Fax:* 608-262-0014; *E-Mail:* tomyuill@macc.wisc.edu

**YUILLE, ALAN,** VISION THEORETICAL NEUROSCIENCES. *Current Pos:* SR RES SCIENTIST, SMITH KETTLEWELL EYE RES INST, CALIF, 95- *Personal Data:* b London, Eng, May 7, 55. *Educ:* Cambridge Univ, BA, 76, MA, 79, PhD(appl math & theoret physics), 86. *Prof Exp:* Postdoctoral fel, Univ Tex & Univ Calif, Santa Barbara, 81-82; vis scientist, Mass Inst Technol, 82-83; res assoc, Harvard Univ, 86-88, from asst prof to assoc prof, 88-96. *Concurrent Pos:* Lectr, Harvard Univ, 86-87; affil, Mass Inst Technol, 86-88; Fesler-Lambert vis prof, Univ Minn, 92; vis scientist, Isaac Newton Inst Math, Eng, 93; ed, J Math Imaging & Vision. *Res:* Quantum gravity; Bayesian decision theory and psychophysics; neural information processing systems. *Mailing Add:* Smith-Kettlewell Eye Res Inst 2232 Webster St San Francisco CA 94115-1821. *Fax:* 415-561-1610; *E-Mail:* yuille@sheri.shi.org

**YUKAWA, S(UMIO),** MECHANICAL METALLURGY. *Current Pos:* metallurgist, 54-86, CONSULT, GEN ELEC CO, 86- *Personal Data:* b Seattle, Wash, Apr 25, 25; m 51; c 1. *Educ:* Univ Mich, BSE(chem eng) & BSE(metall eng), 51, MSE, 52, PhD(metall eng), 55. *Prof Exp:* Res assoc metall eng, Univ Mich, 53-54, instr, 54. *Mem:* Fel Am Soc Metals; Am Inst Mining, Metall & Petrol Engrs; fel Am Soc Mech Engrs; Am Soc Testing & Mat; Sigma Xi. *Res:* Mechanical properties and engineering design criteria of metallic materials especially on deformation, fracture and fatigue behavior in power generation applications including steam and gas turbines, electrical generators and nuclear power equipment. *Mailing Add:* 4925 Valkyrie Dr Boulder CO 80301-4360

**YUKICH, JOSEPH E,** MATHEMATICAL STATISTICS. *Current Pos:* assoc prof, 85-95, FULL PROF MATH, LEHIGH UNIV, 95- *Personal Data:* b Cleveland, Ohio. *Educ:* Oberlin Col, BA, 78; Mass Inst Technol, PhD(math), 83. *Honors & Awards:* Fulbright Jr Lectr Award, France, 83 & 84, Sr Lectr Award, 90. *Prof Exp:* Vis prof, Univ Strasburg, France, 83-85 & 90. *Mem:* Inst Math Statist. *Res:* Probability theory and combinatorial optimization; empirical processes. *Mailing Add:* Dept Math Lehigh Univ Bethlehem PA 18015

**YUKON, STANFORD P,** PHYSICS. *Current Pos:* RES PHYSICIST, ROME LAB, 82- *Personal Data:* b Kansas City, Mo, Mar 20, 39; m 73. *Educ:* Mass Inst Technol, BS, 61; Brandeis Univ, PhD(physics), 68. *Mem:* Am Phys Soc; AAAS. *Res:* Superconducting electronics. *Mailing Add:* 34 Cliff Rd Wellesley MA 02181-3024

**YULE, HERBERT PHILLIP,** INFORMATION SCIENCE & SYSTEMS, OTHER COMPUTER SCIENCES. *Current Pos:* mgr spec proj, Chem Div, 85-88, software engr, 89-92, GROUP LEADER RADIOACTIVE WASTE CHARACTERIZATION, ARGONNE NAT LAB, 92- *Personal Data:* b Chicago, Ill, Apr 17, 31; m 61; c 2. *Educ:* Univ Chicago, PhD(nuclear chem), 60. *Prof Exp:* Res chemist, Calif Res Corp, 57-61; staff mem, Gen Atomic Div, Gen Dynamics Corp, Calif, 62-66; assoc prof activation analysis, Tex A&M Univ, 66-69, assoc prof comput sci, 67-69; res chemist, Nat Bur Stand, 69-72; staff consult, NUS Corp, 72-74, mgr comput serv, 74-78, dir info processing, 78-85. *Concurrent Pos:* Adj assoc prof biochem, Baylor Col Med, 67-69; plenary lectr, Nat Bur Stand, 68 & NATO, 70; consult, Nat Bur Stand, 74- *Mem:* Sigma Xi. *Res:* Activation analysis, especially computer techniques; numerical analysis of data; computer and system programming; gamma-ray spectrometry. *Mailing Add:* 8360 Parkview Dr Darien IL 60561-1707. *Fax:* 630-252-5657

**YUM, SU IL,** CHEMICAL ENGINEERING, BIOMEDICAL ENGINEERING. *Current Pos:* develop engr, Alza Corp, 71-72, co-proj leader, 72-74, proj leader, 74-75, area dir eng, 75-78, OTS prog dir, 78-81, TTS PROD RES DIR, ALZA RES, ALZA CORP, 81- *Personal Data:* b Seoul, Korea, June 25, 39; US citizen; m 68; c 2. *Educ:* Yonsei Univ, BS, 62; Univ Minn, MS, 67, PhD(chem eng), 70. *Prof Exp:* Res assoc biomat, Univ Utah, 69-71. *Mem:* Am Chem Soc; Am Inst Chem Engrs. *Res:* Hydrodynamics of two-phase flow; diffusion in liquids and polymeric membranes; design of medical devices; stress analysis in plastic products; transdermal mass transfer. *Mailing Add:* 950 Pagemill Rd Palo Alto CA 94304

**YUN, KWANG-SIK,** PHYSICAL CHEMISTRY. *Current Pos:* ASSOC PROF CHEM, UNIV MISS, 67- *Personal Data:* b Seoul, Korea, July 27, 29; m 60; c 1. *Educ:* Seoul Nat Univ, BS, 52; Univ Cincinnati, PhD(chem), 61. *Prof Exp:* Res assoc, Inst Molecular Physics, Univ Md, 60-63; Nat Res Coun Can fel, 63-65; scientist, Nat Ctr Atmospheric Res, Colo, 65-67. *Mem:* Am Chem Soc; Sigma Xi. *Res:* Kinetic theory of gases and liquids; gas phase chemical kinetics and chemical reactions of atmospheric gases. *Mailing Add:* Dept Chem Univ Miss University MS 38677

**YUN, SEUNG SOO,** ACOUSTICS, PHYSICAL ACOUSTICS. *Current Pos:* from asst prof to assoc prof, 67-86, PROF PHYSICS, OHIO UNIV, 87- *Personal Data:* b Korea, Mar 1, 31; US citizen; m 57; c 3. *Educ:* Clark Univ, AB, 57; Brown Univ, MSc, 61, PhD(physics), 64. *Prof Exp:* Asst physicist, Ore Regional Primate Res Ctr, 63-65; res physicist, IIT Res Inst, 65-67. *Concurrent Pos:* Vis scientist, Air Force Mats Lab, ADD, Seoul, Korea, 73-74, 77-80; vis prof, Chubu Univ, Kasugai, Japan, 87. *Mem:* Acoust Soc Am; Mats Res Soc; Am Phys Soc; AAAS. *Res:* Physical acoustics and ultrasonics; absorption and dispersion of ultrasound in liquid and solid; critical phenomena; internal frictions, structure and mechanical properties of solids. *Mailing Add:* Dept Physics Ohio Univ 251B Clippinger Athens OH 45701-2979

**YUN, SUK KOO,** theoretical high energy physics; deceased, see previous edition for last biography

**YUN, YOUNG MOK,** ENTOMOLOGY, PHYTOPATHOLOGY. *Current Pos:* sr entomologist, 87-89, QUAL CONTROL MGR, HILLESHOG MONO-HY, INC, 89- *Personal Data:* b Chung Song Co, Korea, Sept 22, 31; m 66; c 2. *Educ:* Wash State Univ, BS, 61; Ore State Univ, BS, 62; Mich State Univ, MS, 64, PhD(entom), 67. *Prof Exp:* Entomologist, Agr Res Ctr, Great Western Sugar Co, 67-85; sr entomologist, Mono-HY Sugar Beet Seed, Inc, 85-87. *Mem:* Entom Soc Am; Am Soc Sugar Beet Technologists; Am Phytopath Soc. *Res:* Biology, ecology, and control of insects, nematodes, and diseases affecting sugar beets. *Mailing Add:* 1142 Winslow Circle Longmont CO 80501

**YUND, E WILLIAM,** EXPERIMENTAL PSYCHOLOGY & PSYCHOACOUSTICS, VISION. *Current Pos:* RES PSYCHOLOGIST, DEPT VET AFFAIRS MED CTR, MARTINEZ, CALIF, 73-, DIR, RES COMPUT FACIL, 79- *Personal Data:* b Pittsburgh, Pa, Feb 15, 44; m 66, Mary A Stallard. *Educ:* Knox Col, BA, 65; Harvard Univ, MA, 67; Northeastern Univ, PhD(psychol), 70. *Concurrent Pos:* Res assoc psychol, Univ Calif, Berkeley, 72-80; adj assoc prof neurol, Sch Med, Univ Calif, Davis, 78-82. *Mem:* Acoust Soc Am; Asn Res Vision & Ophthal; Am Psychol Soc; AAAS; Am speech-lang-hearing Asn. *Res:* Binaural phenomena; pitch perception; auditory neurophysiology hearing aids; color vision; spatial effects; visual search; event-related potentials. *Mailing Add:* 723 Woodhaven Rd Berkeley CA 94708. *Fax:* 510-228-5738; *E-Mail:* yund@ebire.org

**YUND, MARY ALICE,** DEVELOPMENTAL BIOLOGY, TECHNOLOGY ASSESSMENT. *Current Pos:* CONSULT BIOTECHNOL, GRANT PREP, PROJ MGT, 88- *Personal Data:* b Xenia, Ohio, Feb 12, 43; m 66, R William. *Educ:* Knox Col, BA, 65; Harvard Univ, MA, 67, PhD(biol), 70. *Prof Exp:* NIH fel, Univ Calif, Berkeley, 70-72, trainee, 72-73, res geneticist, 73; asst prof biol, Wayne State Univ, 74-75; asst res geneticist, Univ Calif, Berkeley, 75-88. *Concurrent Pos:* Res grants, NSF, 75 & NIH, 77; Adv Panel Develop Biol, NSF, 84-88; lectr, genetics, 86- *Mem:* Sigma Xi; Soc Develop Biol; Genetics Soc Am; Soc Comp & Integrative Biol; AAAS; Soc Indust Microbiol; Asn Women Sci. *Res:* Hormonal control of gene activity in differentiation of imaginal discs of Drosophila melanogaster; mechanism of steroid hormone action. *Mailing Add:* 723 Woodhaven Rd Berkeley CA 94708. *Fax:* 510-525-1715; *E-Mail:* yund@worldnet.att.net

**YUND, RICHARD ALLEN,** MINERALOGY, GEOCHEMISTRY. *Current Pos:* from asst prof to assoc prof, 61-68, PROF GEOL, BROWN UNIV, 68- *Personal Data:* b Ill, Dec 14, 33; m 57; c 2. *Educ:* Univ Ill, PhD(geol), 60. *Honors & Awards:* Sr Scientist Award, WGer Gov, 78; Award of Volcanology, Geochem & Petrol Sect, Am Geophys Union, 81. *Prof Exp:* Fel, Geophys Lab, Carnegie Inst, 60-61. *Concurrent Pos:* Vis prof, Monash Univ, Melbourne, Australia, 73-; Fulbright sr res award, 73-74. *Mem:* Mineral Soc Am; Geochem Soc; Am Geophys Union. *Res:* Experimental study of diffusion in minerals; kinetics and mechanisms of mineralogical reactions and transformations; ductile deformation of minerals; interaction of these processes. *Mailing Add:* Dept Geol Sci Brown Univ Providence RI 02912-1846

**YUNE, HEUN YUNG,** RADIOLOGY, SURGERY. *Current Pos:* PROF RADIOL, IND UNIV, INDIANAPOLIS, 71-, JOHN A CAMPBELL PROF RADIOL, SCH MED, 91-, PROF OTOLARYNGOL, HEAD & NECK SURG, 93- *Personal Data:* b Seoul, Korea, Feb 1, 29; US citizen; m 56, Kay Kim; c Jeanny (Wildi), Helen (Bolles) & Marc E. *Educ:* Severance Union Med Col, MD, 56; Am Bd Radiol, dipl, 64; Korean Bd Radiol, dipl, 65. *Honors & Awards:* Silver Medal, Am Roentgen Ray Soc, 71, Bronze Medal, 75. *Prof Exp:* Resident gen surg, Presby Med Ctr, Korea, 56-60; resident radiol, Vanderbilt Univ Hosp, 60-63, instr, Univ, 62-64; chief radiologist, Presby Med Ctr, Korea, 64-66; from asst prof to assoc prof radiol, Vanderbilt Univ, 66-71. *Concurrent Pos:* Staff radiologist, Indianapolis Vet Admin Hosp, 71 & Wishard Mem Hosp, Indianapolis, 75- *Mem:* Radiol Soc NAm; Am Roentgen Ray Soc; Asn Univ Radiol; Am Soc Head & Neck Radiol; fel Am Col Radiol. *Res:* Vascular radiology; tumor angiography, angiography in trauma, angiography in endocrine disorder and lymphangiography; eye, ear, nose and throat radiology; head and neck tomography and contrast radiography in head and neck. *Mailing Add:* 8932 Spicewood Ct Indianapolis IN 46260. *Fax:* 317-274-1848

**YUNG, W K ALFRED,** NEUROLOGY, NEURO-ONCOLOGY. *Current Pos:* Asst prof neuro-oncol, Univ Tex, 81-86, asst prof tumor biol, 85-86, assoc prof neuro-oncol & tumor biol, 86-92, FAC MEM BIOMED, GRAD SCH BIOMED SCI, UNIV TEX, 83-, PROF NEUROL & TUMOR BIOL, DEPT NEURO-ONCOL, MD ANDERSON CANCER CTR, 92- *Personal Data:* b Hong Kong, Apr 8, 48; c 3. *Educ:* Univ Minn, BSc, 71; Univ Chicago, MD, 75. *Honors & Awards:* PHS Nat Res Serv Award, USPHS. *Concurrent Pos:* Franklin McLean res award, Univ Chicago, 75; cancer chemotherapy training grant, 79-81; asst neurologist, M D Anderson Cancer Ctr, Univ Tex, 81-83, assoc neurologist, 83-, dept chmn, 84-; mem, Path A Study Sect, NIH, 90-95. *Mem:* NY Acad Sci; fel Am Acad Neurol (treas); Am Soc Cell Biol; AAAS; Am Asn Cancer Res; Soc Neurosci. *Res:* Chemotherapy and biologic therapy for primary brain tumor, growth regulation and autocrine growth factor expression in primary brain tumors. *Mailing Add:* Dept Neuro-oncol M D Anderson Cancer Ctr Univ Tex 1515 Holcombe Blvd Box 100 Houston TX 77030-4095. *Fax:* 713-794-4999

**YUNGBLUTH, THOMAS ALAN,** GENETICS, PLANT BREEDING. *Current Pos:* From asst prof to assoc prof, 66-80, PROF BIOL, WESTERN KY UNIV, 80- *Personal Data:* b Warren, Ill, Dec 12, 34. *Educ:* Univ Ill, BS, 56; Univ Minn, PhD(genetics), 66. *Mem:* Am Soc Agron; Crop Sci Soc Am; AAAS. *Mailing Add:* Dept Biol Western Ky Univ 1 Big Red Way St Bowling Green KY 42101-3576

**YUNGEN, JOHN A,** SOILS & SOILS SCIENCE, HORTICULTURE. *Current Pos:* from asst prof to prof, 59-88, EMER PROF AGRON, S ORE EXP STA, ORE STATE UNIV, 88- *Personal Data:* b Independence, Ore, Dec 30, 21; m 53; c 3. *Educ:* Ore State Univ, BS, 50, MS, 59. *Prof Exp:* Res asst soil fertil, Ore Agr Exp Sta & USDA, 50-53 & crops-soils, SOre Exp Sta, Ore State Univ, 54-59. *Concurrent Pos:* Supt, SOre Exp Sta, Ore State Univ, 81-88. *Mem:* Am Soc Agron. *Res:* Agronomic crops and vegetable crops; crops production; weed control; soil fertility; seed production. *Mailing Add:* 1875 Niedermeyer Dr Central Point OR 97502

**YUNGHANS, WAYNE N,** CYTOLOGY. *Current Pos:* asst prof, 74-80, ASSOC PROF CYTOL, STATE UNIV NY COL FREDONIA, 80- *Personal Data:* b Lakewood, Ohio, Dec 10, 45; m 69; c 2. *Educ:* Heidelberg Col, BS, 67; Purdue Univ, MS, 69, PhD(cytol), 74. *Honors & Awards:* State Univ NY Res Found Award, 75; NSF Award, 78. *Prof Exp:* Res asst microbiol, US Army, 69-71. *Mem:* AAAS; Sigma Xi. *Res:* Isolation and purification of cellular membranes including plasma membranes, Golgi apparatus and endoplasmic reticulum; membranes characterized for enzyme activities and protein kinases and phosphoproteins. *Mailing Add:* Dept Biol State Univ NY Fredonia NY 14063-1198

**YUNICK, ROBERT P,** ORGANIC POLYMER CHEMISTRY. *Current Pos:* mgr, Henry/Howard Wright Res Ctr, Schenectady Int, Inc, 63-72, dir res, 72-76, vpres res, 76-80, VPRES CORP TECH, HENRY/HOWARD WRIGHT RES CTR, SCHENECTADY INT, INC, 80- *Personal Data:* b Schenectady, NY, Oct 27, 35; m 59; c 3. *Educ:* Union Col, NY, BS, 57; Rensselaer Polytech Inst, PhD(org chem), 61. *Prof Exp:* Res chemist, Olefins Div, Union Carbide Chem Corp, 61-63. *Mem:* Am Chem Soc; Am Ornithologists Union; Sigma Xi. *Res:* Organic synthesis of intermediates for resin synthesis; synthesis of phenolic, hydrocarbon, resorcinolic, polyester and polyesterimide resins; synthesis of high-temperature polymers. *Mailing Add:* Schenectady Chem Inc 2750 Balltown Rd Schenectady NY 12309. *Fax:* 518-382-8129

**YUNIS, ADEL A,** INTERNAL MEDICINE. *Current Pos:* from asst prof to assoc prof & dir hemat, 64-68, PROF MED & BIOCHEM, SCH MED, UNIV MIAMI, 68-, DIR DIV HEMAT, HOWARD HUGHES LABS HEMAT RES, 68- *Personal Data:* b Rahbeh, Lebanon, Mar 17, 30; m 59; c 3. *Educ:* Am Univ Beirut, BA, 50, MD, 54. *Prof Exp:* Clin fel hemat, Washington Univ, 57-58, res fel, 58-59, res assoc biochem, 59-61, from instr to asst prof med, Med Sch, 61-64. *Concurrent Pos:* Am Leukemia Soc scholar, 61-66; USPHS res career develop award, 66-71. *Mem:* Am Fedn Clin Res; Am Soc Hemat; Am Soc Exp Path; Asn Am Physicians; Am Soc Biol Chemists. *Res:* Colony stimulating factor and modulators of granulopoiesis; mechanism of action of bone marrow toxins and the pathogenesis of chloramphenicol-induced blood dyscrasias. *Mailing Add:* Dept Biochem R-38 Univ Miami Sch Med PO Box 016960 Miami FL 33101-6960

**YUNIS, EDMOND J,** MEDICINE, PATHOLOGY. *Current Pos:* CHIEF, DIV IMMUNOGENETICS, DANA-FARBER CANCER INST & PROF PATH, HARVARD MED SCH, 76-; DIR HLA LAB, NORTHEAST REGIONAL RED CROSS BLOOD PROG, 76- *Personal Data:* b Sincelejo, Colombia, Aug 8, 29; US citizen; m 65; c 4. *Educ:* Nat Univ Colombia, MD, 54. *Prof Exp:* Resident anat path, Univ Kans, 55-57; resident clin path, Univ Hosps, Univ Minn, Minneapolis, 57-59, from instr to prof lab med, 60-71, dir blood bank, 61-68, dir div immunol, 66-76, prof lab med & path, 71-76. *Concurrent Pos:* Sr assoc, Ctr Blood Res, 85- *Mem:* Am Soc Exp Path; Am Asn Immunol; Transplantation Soc; Am Asn Pathologists; Am Soc Histocompatibility & Immunogenetics. *Res:* Antigenicity in cells and animals; immunological capacity in animals related to thymus; transplantation immunology and immunogenetics. *Mailing Add:* Dept Path Dana Farber Cancer Inst 44 Binney St Boston MA 02115-6084. *Fax:* 617-632-4466

**YUNIS, JORGE J,** GENETICS, PATHOLOGY. *Current Pos:* DIR, CANCER BIOL DIV & PROF PATH & MICROBIOL, THOMAS JEFFERSON UNIV, 93- *Personal Data:* b Sincelejo, Colombia, Oct 5, 33; US citizen. *Educ:* Inst Simon Araujo, Colombia, BS, 51; Cent Univ Madrid, MD, 56, PhD, 57. *Honors & Awards:* Clin Prof Year, Harvard Med Sch, 87; honoree, Columbian Parliament, Bogata, Columbia, 86. *Prof Exp:* Intern, Prov Hosp, Barranquilla, Colombia, 57-58, resident internal med, 58-59; resident clin & anat path, Univ Minn, Minneapolis, 59-62, from instr to assoc prof lab med, 62-69, head, Div Med Genetics, 62-77, dir grad studies lab med

& path, 69-74, prof lab med & path, 69-89; vchmn, Dept Neoplastic Dis, Hahnemann Univ Hosp, 89-93. *Concurrent Pos:* Fel lab med, Univ Minn, Minneapolis, 62-63, chmn, Human Genetics Comt Health Sci, 72-77; mem bd trustees, Leukemia Soc Am. *Mem:* Am Soc Human Genetics; Am Soc Cell Biol; Am Asn Path & Bact; Acad Clin Lab Physicians & Sci; Am Soc Hemat; Columbian Acad Med; Leukemia Soc Am. *Res:* Fine structure and molecular organization of human chromosomes; chromosome defects in human cancer. *Mailing Add:* 911 Summit Rd Narbeth PA 19072

**YUNKER, MARK BERNARD,** MARINE CHEMISTRY ORGANICS & METALS. *Current Pos:* mem staff, 80-86, RES SCIENTIST, DEPT FISHERIES & OCEANS, 86- *Personal Data:* b Toronto, Ont, Dec, 48; c 1. *Educ:* Univ Waterloo, BSc, 71, PhD(chem), 75. *Prof Exp:* Res assoc chem, Univ Hawaii, 75-77; lectr chem, Univ Victoria, 77-79. *Concurrent Pos:* Nat Res Coun Can fel, 75-77; mem, Comt Marine Analytical Chem, Nat Res Coun Can, 84-; vis scientist, dept chem, Univ Victoria, 84-86. *Mem:* Am Chem Soc; Chem Inst Can. *Res:* Synthetic chemistry of bioactive compounds; isolation and structure determination of marine natural products; fundamental studies in marine chemistry, both organics and metals; statistical analysis and interpretation of marine environmental data; determination of the fate and transport of metals and organics in marine and freshwater environments; organic geochemistry. *Mailing Add:* 7137 Wallace Dr RR 1 Brentwood Bay BC V0S 1A0 Can

**YUNKER, MARTIN HENRY,** PHARMACY. *Current Pos:* RETIRED. *Personal Data:* b Milton Junction, Wis, Dec 28, 28; m 53; c 2. *Educ:* Univ Wis, BS, 51, MS, 53, PhD(phys pharm), 57. *Prof Exp:* Res asst to mgr pharmaceut prod, Merck, Sharp & Dohme Div, Merck, Inc, 57-58, supvr, Granulation Dept, 58-59, supvr qual control, 59-61, res assoc pharmaceut res, 61-63; sr res pharmacist, Abbott Labs, 63-91. *Mem:* Am Pharmaceut Asn; Acad Pharmaceut Sci; Sigma Xi; Am Asn Pharmaceut Scientists. *Res:* Pharmaceutical research, including tablet formulations; biopharmaceutics; in vitro drug dissolution; preformulation characterization of drugs; parenteral formulations. *Mailing Add:* 3035 Burris St Waukegan IL 60087

**YUNKER, WAYNE HARRY,** LIQUID SODIUM COOLANT TECHNOLOGY. *Current Pos:* RETIRED. *Personal Data:* b Corvallis, Ore, Jan 8, 36; c 3. *Educ:* Ore State Col, BS, 57; Univ Wash, PhD(chem), 61. *Prof Exp:* Res scientist chem, Gen Elec Co, 63-65; sr res scientist, Battelle Mem Inst, 65-70; sr res scientist chem, Westinghouse Hanford Co, 71-77, fel scientist chem, 78-94. *Mem:* Am Chem Soc; Sigma Xi. *Res:* Physical chemistry of materials interactions. *Mailing Add:* 1422 Potter Richland WA 99352

**YUNUS, MUHAMMAD BASHARAT,** INTERNAL MEDICINE, RHEUMATOLOGY. *Current Pos:* sr fel rheumatology, Univ Ill Col Med, 78-79, asst prof med, 79-85, assoc prof med, 85-93, PROF MED, UNIV ILL COL MED, PEORIA, ILL, 93- *Personal Data:* b Barisal, Bangladesh, March 1, 42; US citizen; m 81; c Omar, Deeba & Murad. *Educ:* Brojomohun Col, ISC, 59; Chittagong Med Col, MBBS, 64; Am Bd Internal Med, dipl, 79, Am Bd Internal Med, Rheumatology, dipl, 82; FRCP(E), 90. *Prof Exp:* Fel gastroenterol, Hull Royal Infirmary, Eng, 74-75; sr med registr, St Marys Hosp, Kettering, Eng, 75-76; resident med, Worcester City Hosp, Mass, 76-77, fel rheumatology, 77-78. *Concurrent Pos:* Reviewer, N Eng J Med, J Rheumatology, 81-, Clin Exp Rheumatology, 86- & Pain, 86-; grant reviewer, NIH, 87, Arthritis Soc Can, 87; chmn Nonarticular Rheumatism Study Group, Am Rheumatism Asn, 88. *Mem:* Fel Am Col Physicians; fel Am Rheumatism Asn; Int Asn Study Pain; fel Am Col Rhemotology; Bangladesh Med Asn NAm. *Res:* Completed the first detailed controlled clinical study of a rheumatologic conditon called fibromyalgia syndrome with many other original articles in this field subsequently; first genetic study in fibromyalgia syndrome; fibromyalgia syndrome research. *Mailing Add:* Dept Med Univ Ill Col Med 1 Illini Dr Peoria IL 61605-2576. *E-Mail:* yunus@uic.edu

**YURA, HAROLD THOMAS,** OPTICAL SIGNALS. *Current Pos:* SR SCIENTIST PHYSICS, AEROSPACE CORP, 70- *Personal Data:* b Buffalo, NY, Nov 20, 37; m 59; c 2. *Educ:* Calif Inst Technol, BS, 59, PhD(physics), 62. *Prof Exp:* Staff scientist physics, Rand Corp, 62-70. *Concurrent Pos:* Adj prof, Univ Calif, Los Angeles, 75- *Mem:* Fel Optical Soc Am. *Res:* Wave propagation in random media and laser propagation phenomenology; strong optical scintellation effects; extension of the Huygens Fresnel principle to random media. *Mailing Add:* PO Box 92957 Aerospace Corp M2-246 Los Angeles CA 90009

**YURA, JOSEPH ANDREW,** CIVIL & STRUCTURAL ENGINEERING. *Current Pos:* from asst prof to prof, 66-82, WARREN BELLOWS PROF, UNIV TEX, AUSTIN, 82- *Personal Data:* b Hazelton, Pa, Apr 11, 38; m 64, Joan M Seman; c Thomas, Christine, Paul & Elizabeth. *Educ:* Duke Univ, BS, 59; Cornell Univ, MS, 61; Lehigh Univ, PhD, 65. *Honors & Awards:* T R Higgins Lectr, Am Inst Steel Construct, 74; Raymond C Reese Res Prize, Am Soc Civil Engrs, 91. *Prof Exp:* Asst prof, Lehigh Univ, 65-66. *Concurrent Pos:* Hussein M Alharthy Centennial prof, Univ Tex, Austin, 87. *Mem:* Am Soc Civil Engrs; Struct Stability Res Coun; Res Coun Struct Connections; Am Soc Eng Educ. *Res:* Civil engineering; structural engineering. *Mailing Add:* 5308 Bull Run Austin TX 78727

**YURCHAK, SERGEI,** CHEMICAL ENGINEERING. *Current Pos:* Res chem engr, 69-72, sr res engr, 72-77, assoc engr, 76-80, res assoc, 80-83, sr res assoc, 83-87, scientist, 87-88, MGR, LIGHT GAS UPGRADING/PETROCHEM GROUP, MOBIL RES & DEVELOP CORP, 88- *Personal Data:* b Butler Twp, Pa, Feb 11, 43. *Educ:* Pa State Univ, BS, 64; Univ Wis, PhD(chem eng), 68. *Mem:* Am Inst Chem Engrs; Am Chem Soc; Sigma Xi. *Res:* Reaction kinetics and reactor design; process development; synthetic fuels. *Mailing Add:* 209 Nassau Ave Paulsboro NJ 08066

**YURCHENCO, JOHN ALFONSO,** MEDICAL MICROBIOLOGY. *Current Pos:* RETIRED. *Personal Data:* b San Juan, Arg, Feb 22, 15; nat US; m 44; c 4. *Educ:* Albion Col, BA, 41; Johns Hopkins Univ, ScD(bact), 49. *Prof Exp:* Chief, Div Microbiol, Eaton Labs, Inc, 48-55; head, Dept Chemother, Squibb Inst Med Res, 55-56; sr res scientist, Wyeth Labs, Inc, 56-82. *Res:* Chemotherapy bacterial infections; bacterial pathogenicity and virulence; low temperature stability of infectious bacterial pools; immunology. *Mailing Add:* 24 Pond Lane Bryn Mawr PA 19010

**YURETICH, RICHARD FRANCIS,** SEDIMENTOLOGY, GEOCHEMISTRY. *Current Pos:* asst prof, 80-85, ASSOC PROF, DEPT GEOSCI, UNIV MASS, 85- *Personal Data:* b Brooklyn, NY, Aug 30, 50; m 74. *Educ:* New York Univ, BA, 71; Princeton Univ, MA, 76, PhD(geol), 76. *Prof Exp:* Res geologist, Gulf Res & Develop, Gulf Oil Corp, 76-77; asst prof geol, State Univ NY Col Oneonta, 77-80. *Mem:* Geol Soc Am; Soc Econ Paleontologists & Mineralogists; Clay Minerals Soc; Am Asn Petrol Geologists; Am Geophys Union. *Res:* Lacustrine deposits; surface waters; rift valleys; clay minerals. *Mailing Add:* Geosci Dept Univ Mass PO Box 35820 Amherst MA 01003-5820

**YUREWICZ, EDWARD CHARLES,** GLYCOPROTEINS, FERTILIZATION. *Current Pos:* asst prof, 75-85, ASSOC PROF GYNEC & OBSTET, SCH MED, WAYNE STATE UNIV, 85- *Personal Data:* b Philadelphia, Pa, Feb 10, 45; m 67; c 2. *Educ:* Univ Del, BA, 66; Sch Med, Johns Hopkins Univ, PhD(physiol chem), 71. *Prof Exp:* Fel biochem, Univ Calif, Davis, 71-74; sr res biochemist, Merck Inst Therapeut Res, 74-75. *Mem:* AAAS; Am Soc Cell Biol; Am Soc Biochem & Molecular Biol; Soc Study Reprod; Soc glycobiol. *Res:* Structural characterization of cervical mucus glycoproteins; biochemical and immunochemical analysis of glycoprotein antigens in mammalian oocyte zona pellucida; biochemistry of sperm-egg interaction; immunocontraception. *Mailing Add:* Dept Gynec & Obstet Sch Med Wayne State Univ CS Mott Ctr Detroit MI 48201. *Fax:* 313-577-8554

**YURKE, BERNARD,** NONCLASSICAL STATES OF LIGHT. *Current Pos:* MEM TECH STAFF, AT&T BELL LABS, 83- *Personal Data:* b Wittenberg, Ger, Nov 28, 51; US citizen; m 83. *Educ:* Univ Tex, Austin, BS, 75, MA, 76; Cornell Univ, PhD(physics), 83. *Mem:* Am Phys Soc; Optical Soc Am. *Res:* Quantum optics and electronics; the generation and detection of nonclassical states of the electromagnetic field called squeezed states. *Mailing Add:* 1011 Edgewood Ave Plainfield NJ 07060

**YURKIEWICZ, WILLIAM J,** INSECT PHYSIOLOGY, BIOCHEMISTRY. *Current Pos:* PROF BIOL, MILLERSVILLE STATE COL, 66- *Personal Data:* b Bloomsburg, Pa, Sept 21, 39; m 65; c 2. *Educ:* Bloomsburg State Col, BS, 60; Bucknell Univ, MS, 62; Pa State Univ, PhD(entom), 65. *Prof Exp:* Asst entom, Pa State Univ, 63-65; res entomologist, USDA, Ga, 65-66. *Mem:* Entom Soc Am. *Res:* Insect flight physiology; neutral lipid and phospholipid composition and metabolism in insects; neural control of insect flight. *Mailing Add:* Dept Biol Millersville Univ Millersville PA 17551

**YURKOWSKI, MICHAEL,** BIOCHEMISTRY, NUTRITION. *Current Pos:* RETIRED. *Personal Data:* b Sask, Can, Sept 1, 28; m 57; c 3. *Educ:* Univ Sask, BSA, 51, MSc, 59; Univ Guelph, PhD(nutrit), 68. *Prof Exp:* Analytical chemist, Western Potash Corp Ltd, Sask, 51-52; indust chemist, Cereal & Oilseed Processing, Sask Wheat Pool, Can, 52-56; anal chemist, Plant Prod Div, Can Dept Agr, Ont, 59-60; food & drug directorate, Can Dept Nat Health & Welfare, Man, 60-62; res scientist marine lipid biochem, Halifax Lab, Freshwater Inst, 62-65, appl & basic nutrit fish & freshwater organisms, 68-84, res scientist nutrit lipid biochem, Dept Fisheries & Oceans, Can, Artic Mgt Sect, 84-91. *Mem:* Am Oil Chemists' Soc; Can Inst Food Sci & Technol. *Res:* Nutrition and metabolism of arctic marine animals; lipid biochemistry of arctic marine animals; odors in freshwater and freshwater fish. *Mailing Add:* 6 Celtic Bay Winnipeg MB R3T 2W9 Can

**YUROW, HARVEY WARREN,** ANALYTICAL CHEMISTRY. *Current Pos:* RETIRED. *Personal Data:* b New York, NY, Feb 14, 32; m 56, Marion Kaplan; c Jared, Marshall & Rona. *Educ:* Queens Col (NY), BS, 54; Pa State Univ, PhD(anal chem), 60. *Prof Exp:* Dept Defense fel, Rutgers Univ, 59-60; res chemist, Edgewood Arsenal, 60-88. *Mem:* Am Chem Soc; Sigma Xi. *Res:* Trace analysis of organic compounds via chromogen formation; structure-activity relationships for physiologically active compounds; organic analysis via chemiluminescence. *Mailing Add:* 3801 Maryland Ave Abingdon MD 21009

**YUSHOK, WASLEY DONALD,** BIOCHEMISTRY, CANCER. *Current Pos:* ASSOC MEM DIV BIOCHEM, INST CANCER RES, 66- *Personal Data:* b Woodbine, NJ, Mar 11, 20; m 50. *Educ:* Rutgers Univ, BS, 41, MS, 43; Cornell Univ, PhD(chem embryol), 50. *Prof Exp:* Asst, Rutgers Univ, 44-43 & Cornell Univ, 46-49; asst to ed handbk biol data, Nat Res Coun, 50; res assoc, Univ Tex Med Br, 50-52; res biochemist, Biochem Res Found, 52-59, head, Div Cancer Biochem, 59-66. *Mem:* AAAS; Am Chem Soc; Am Asn Cancer Res; NY Acad Sci. *Res:* Regulation of metabolism and enzymes in cancer cells; nucleotide, protein and carbohydrate metabolism; intracellular energy-dependent protein degradation. *Mailing Add:* 7610 Dorcas St Philadelphia PA 19111-3324

**YUSKA, HENRY,** ORGANIC CHEMISTRY. *Current Pos:* prof 66-85, EMER PROF CHEM, BROOKLYN COL, 85- *Personal Data:* b Brooklyn, NY, Nov 7, 14; wid; c Kenneth & Reynold. *Educ:* City Col New York, BS, 35; Polytech Inst Brooklyn, MS, 39; Univ Ill, PhD(org chem), 42. *Prof Exp:* Res chemist, Jewish Hosp, Brooklyn, NY, 35-39; asst chem, Univ Ill, 41; res org chemist, Barrett Div, Allied Chem & Dye Corp, 42-43; resin group leader, Interchem Corp, 43-60, dir, Dept Org Chem, Cent Res Labs, 60-63; tech dir, Sun Chem Corp, 63-66. *Concurrent Pos:* Instr, Eve Div, Hunter Col, 43-46. *Mem:* Am Chem Soc. *Res:* Synthetic resins; organic synthesis of monomers; biochemistry. *Mailing Add:* 113-09 107th Ave Richmond Hill NY 11419

**YUSPA, STUART HOWARD,** CANCER. *Current Pos:* SR INVESTR CANCER, NAT CANCER INST, 72-, CHIEF, LAB CELLULAR CARCINOGENESIS & TUMOR PROM, DIV CANCER ETIOLOGY, 81- *Personal Data:* b Baltimore, Md, July 19, 41; m 65; c 2. *Educ:* Johns Hopkins Univ, BS, 62; Univ Md, MD, 66; Am Bd Internal Med, dipl, 72. *Honors & Awards:* Montagna lectr, 88; Lila Gruber Cancer Res Award, 89; Elizabeth Miller Mem Lectr, 90; G H A Clowes Award, 93. *Prof Exp:* Intern internal med, Hosp Univ Pa, 66-67; res assoc cancer, Nat Cancer Inst, 67-70; resident internal med, Hosp Univ Pa, 70-72. *Concurrent Pos:* Mem biol models segment, Carcinogenesis Prog, Nat Cancer Inst, 72-78, Ed-in-chief, Molecular Carcinogenesis. *Mem:* Am Asn Cancer Res; AAAS; Amer Soc Cell Biol; Soc Invest Dermat. *Res:* Determine mechanisms whereby chemicals initiate or promote malignant transformation of epithelial cells. *Mailing Add:* Div Basic Sci Bldg 37 Rm 3B25 Nat Cancer Inst NIH Bethesda MD 20892

**YUST, CHARLES S(IMON),** PHYSICAL METALLURGY. *Current Pos:* METALLURGIST, METALS & CERAMICS DIV, OAK RIDGE NAT LAB, 60- *Personal Data:* b Newark, NJ, Jan 21, 31; m 55; c 3. *Educ:* Newark Col Eng, BS, 52; Univ Tenn, MS, 60. *Prof Exp:* Metall engr, Oak Ridge Gaseous Diffusion Plant, 52-60. *Mem:* Am Ceramic Soc; Sigma Xi. *Res:* Theory of solid state sintering; deformation mechanisms in ceramics. *Mailing Add:* 106 Newcrest Lane Oak Ridge TN 37830

**YUTRZENKA, GERALD J,** NEUROPHARMACOLOGY. *Current Pos:* ASSOC PROF PHYSIOL & PHARMACOL, SCH MED, UNIV SDAK, 84-, DIR ADMIS, 91- *Personal Data:* b Crookston, Minn, Jan 27, 53; m 79, Barbara Arneson; c Christopher & David. *Educ:* Moorhead State Univ, BS, 74; Univ NDak, MS, 77, PhD(physiol), 79. *Concurrent Pos:* Res assoc, Dept Biochem, Baylor Col Med, 79; fel, Dept Pharmacol, Med Col Va, 80-84. *Mem:* Am Soc Pharmacol & Exp Therapeut; Int Soc Neurochem; Sigma Xi; Am Soc Exp Biol & Med; Indian Acad Neurosci. *Res:* Neuropharmacology and neurochemical mechanisms underlying establishment of physical dependence on central nervous system depressant drugs. *Mailing Add:* Dept Physiol & Pharmacol Sch Med Univ SDak Vermillion SD 57069. *E-Mail:* gyutrzen@sunbird.usd.edu

**YUVARAJAN, SUBBARAYA,** POWER ELECTRONICS, MOTOR CONTROL. *Current Pos:* ASSOC PROF ELECTRONICS, NDAK STATE UNIV, FARGO, 83- *Personal Data:* b Sowdhapuram, India, Sept 15, 41; m 73; c 2. *Educ:* Madras Univ, India, BS, 61, BE, 66; Indian Inst Technol, India, MTech, 69, PhD(elec eng), 81. *Prof Exp:* Lectr elec eng, PSG Col Tech, Coimbatore, 69-74; lectr & asst prof elec eng, Indian Inst Technol, Madras, 74-83. *Mem:* Inst Elec & Electronics Engrs; Am Soc Eng Educ; Sigma Xi. *Res:* Analyzed a complete variable speed induction motor drive using digital computer simulation; application of new power semiconductor devices for the conversion of electrical power from one form to another. *Mailing Add:* Dept Elec Eng NDak State Univ Fargo ND 58105

**YUWILER, ARTHUR,** NEUROSCIENCES. *Current Pos:* from asst prof to assoc prof biochem, 70-76, PROF PSYCHIAT, UNIV CALIF, LOS ANGELES, 76-; CHIEF NEUROBIOCHEM RES, VET ADMIN BRENTWOOD HOSP, 62- *Personal Data:* b Mansfield, Ohio, Apr 4, 27; m 50; c 3. *Educ:* Univ Calif, Los Angeles, BS, 50, PhD(biochem), 56. *Prof Exp:* Asst chem, Univ Calif, Los Angeles, 50-51, asst physiol chem, 52-54, asst chem, 54-56, res biochemist, 57-59; res neurobiochemist, Vet Admin, Calif, 56-57; res assoc & dir labs & biochem sect, Schizophrenia & Psychopharmacol Res Proj, Ypsilanti State Hosp & Univ Mich, 59-62. *Concurrent Pos:* Res biochemist, Ment Health Res Inst, Univ Mich, 59-62; mem, Brain Res Inst, Univ Calif, Los Angeles, 65-; mem, Basic Sci Res Comt, Vet Admin, 66-69, Career Develop Award Comt, NIMH, 70-76, Calif State Ment Health Adv Comt, 70-71 & Sci Adv Comt, Dystonia Found, 77-83 & 85-88; chair, Career Develop Award Comt, NIMH, 82-83. *Mem:* Am Soc Neurochem; Int Soc Neurochem; Am Col Neuropsychopharmacol; Soc Biol Psychiat; Am Soc Biol Chemists; Sigma Xi; Soc Neurosci. *Res:* Aromatic amino acids; enzymes; biochemistry of mental disease; intermediary metabolism of monoamines; stress; childhood autism; pineal gland. *Mailing Add:* Neurobiochem Lab T-85 Va Med Ctr Wilshire/Sawtelle Blvd Los Angeles CA 90073

**YUZVINSKY, SERGEY,** MATHEMATICS. *Current Pos:* PROF MATH, UNIV ORE, 80- *Personal Data:* b Lennengrad, Russia, Aug 27,36. *Educ:* Lennengrad State Univ, PhD(math), 66. *Mem:* Am Math Soc. *Res:* Mathematics. *Mailing Add:* 4758 Manzonita St Eugene OR 97405

# Z

**ZABARA, JACOB,** PHYSIOLOGY, NEUROPHYSIOLOGY. *Current Pos:* asst prof, 67-72, ASSOC PROF PHYSIOL, GRAD SCH, TEMPLE UNIV, 72- *Personal Data:* b Philadelphia, Pa, May 8, 32; m 70; c 2. *Educ:* Johns Hopkins Univ, BS, 53; Univ Pa, MS, 58, PhD(physiol), 59. *Prof Exp:* USPHS fel, Univ Pa, 59-60; instr pharmacol, Dartmouth Col, 60-61; instr, Univ Pa, 61-63; USPHS spec fel biomath, 63-64; instr physiol, Univ Pa, 64-65, assoc pharmacol, 65-67, assoc physiol, 65-67. *Concurrent Pos:* Vis prof, Hadassah Med Sch, Hebrew Univ, Stanford Univ. *Mem:* Soc Neurosci; Biophys Soc; Undersea Med Soc; Am Asn Anat; Am Physiol Soc; Am Epilepsy Soc. *Res:* Neurophysiology and cybernetics; epilepsy. *Mailing Add:* Dept Physiol & Biophys Temple Univ Sch Med 3223 N Broad St Philadelphia PA 19140-5007

**ZABEL, HARTMUT,** SOLID STATE PHYSICS. *Current Pos:* chmn dept, 93-96, PROF PHYSICS, RUHR UNIV BOCHUM, 89- *Personal Data:* b Radolfzell, WGer, Mar 21, 46; m 73, Rosemarie Havers; c Cordula, Astrid & Julia. *Educ:* Univ Bonn, Vordipl, 69; Tech Univ Munich, Hauptdipl, 73; Univ Munich, PhD(physics), 78. *Prof Exp:* Fel physics, Univ Houston, 78-79; from asst prof to prof, Univ Ill, Urbana-Champaign, 79-89. *Concurrent Pos:* Beckman fel, Ctr Advan Studies, Univ Ill, 82; guest scientist, Brookhaven Nat Lab, 85, 88, Risoe Nat Lab, Denmark, 86 & Nat Inst Stand & Technol, Md, 93; dir, Solid State Sci Prog, Mat Res Lab, Dept Energy, 86-89; adj prof physics, Univ Ill, Urbana-Champaign, 89- *Mem:* Ger Phys Soc; fel Am Phys Soc; Mat Res Soc; Europ Phys Soc. *Res:* X-ray and thermal neutron scattering studies of structural, thermal, magnetic, lattice dynamical properties of condensed matter systems, hydrogen in metals, intercalated graphite, semiconductor and metal superlattices, quasicrystals; magnetic thin films and superlattices; oxidation and oxicle layers; x-ray supermirrors. *Mailing Add:* Exp Physics IV Ruhr Univ Bochum Universitatsstr 150 44780 Bochum Germany. *Fax:* 49-234-7094173; *E-Mail:* hartmut.zabel@.rz.ruhr__uni__biochum.de

**ZABEL, ROBERT ALGER,** FOREST PATHOLOGY. *Current Pos:* RETIRED. *Personal Data:* b Boyceville, Wis, Mar 11, 17; m 44; c 5. *Educ:* Univ Minn, BS, 38; State Univ NY, MS, 41, PhD(bot), 48. *Prof Exp:* Lab aide, Lake States Forest Exp Sta, US Forest Serv, 40; from asst prof to assoc prof forest path, State Univ NY Col Environ Sci & Forestry, 47-53, head, Dept Bot & Forest Path, 53-54, assoc dean biol sci & undergrad instr, 64-69, vpres acad affairs, 70-73, prof, 53-85. *Mem:* AAAS; fel Soc Am Foresters; Am Soc Microbiol; Am Phytopath Soc. *Res:* Forest products deterioration; wood decays; lumber stains; evaluation of preservatives; root and heart rots; toxicants and fungicides. *Mailing Add:* 4563 Broad Rd Syracuse NY 13215-2403

**ZABIELSKI, CHESTER V,** METALLURGY. *Current Pos:* SR PHYS METALLURGIST, US ARMY MAT RES AGENCY, 67- *Personal Data:* b Schenectady, NY, July 19, 23. *Educ:* Union Univ, NY, BS, 47; Columbia Univ, BS, 49; Rensselaer Polytech Inst, MS, 54 & 56; Univ Pittsburgh, PhD(metall), 65. *Honors & Awards:* Res & Develop Award, US Dept Defense, 87. *Prof Exp:* Chemist, Gen Aniline & Film Corp, 50-52; Olin Mathieson res asst, Rensselaer Polytech Inst, 52-54; metall engr, Westinghouse Elec Corp, Pa, 57-58; asst prof metall, Univ Pittsburgh, 58-67. *Concurrent Pos:* Ford Found res grant, Univ Pittsburgh. *Mem:* Am Soc Metals; Am Inst Mining, Metall & Petrol Engrs; Am Inst Chem Engrs; Am Chem Soc; Nat Asn Corrosion Engrs; Am Electrochem Soc. *Res:* Physical metallurgy; corrosion; metallurgy of uranium, steel, zirconium, titanium, copper and stainless steels; high temperature alloys; molten salt reactions; kinetics; thermodynamics; optical and x-ray spectroscopy. *Mailing Add:* Box 380369 Cambridge MA 02238

**ZABIK, JOSEPH,** behavioral pharmacology, for more information see previous edition

**ZABIK, MARY ELLEN,** FOOD SCIENCE. *Current Pos:* Instr food res, 61-68 & 69-70, from asst prof to prof food chem, 70-90, ASSOC DEAN ACAD AFFAIRS, MICH STATE UNIV, 88-, DISTINGUISHED UNIV PROF, 90- *Personal Data:* b Kendallville, Ind, Jan 20, 37; m 58, Matthew John; c John M. *Educ:* Purdue Univ, BS, 59; Mich State Univ, MS, 61, PhD(food sci), 70. *Honors & Awards:* Borden Award, Am Home Econ Asn, 83. *Mem:* Fel Inst Food Technologists; Am Oil Chemists Soc; Am Asn Cereal Chemists; Poultry Sci Asn; Am Home Econ Asn; Am Chem Soc. *Res:* Food chemistry and rheology; functionality of carbohydrates and proteins in food systems; reduction of environmental contamination from food systems. *Mailing Add:* 5 Col Human Ecol Mich State Univ East Lansing MI 48824-1030. *Fax:* 517-432-3646; *E-Mail:* mezabik@msu.edu

**ZABIK, MATTHEW JOHN,** CHEMISTRY, TOXICOLOGY. *Current Pos:* From asst prof to assoc prof, 65-72, PROF ENTOM & ASSOC DIR PESTICIDE RES CTR, MICH STATE UNIV, 72- *Personal Data:* b South Bend, Ind, Aug 22, 37; m 58; c 1. *Educ:* Purdue Univ, Lafayette, BS, 59; Mich State Univ, MS, 62, PhD(org chem), 65. *Mem:* Am Chem Soc; Soc Environ Toxicol & Chem. *Res:* Photochemistry; environmental toxicology of xenobiotics. *Mailing Add:* 5300 Barton Rd PO Box 326 Williamston MI 48895-0326

**ZABIN, BURTON ALLEN,** INORGANIC CHEMISTRY, ANALYTICAL CHEMISTRY. *Current Pos:* dir res, 63-72, DIV MGR CHEM, BIO-RAD LABS, 72- *Personal Data:* b Chicago, Ill, Mar 18, 36; m 72. *Educ:* Univ Ill, BS, 57; Purdue Univ, PhD(inorg chem), 62. *Prof Exp:* Res assoc chem, Stanford Univ, 62-63. *Mem:* Am Chem Soc. *Res:* Separations chemistry, including ion exchange resins, gel filtration materials and other column chromatographic materials. *Mailing Add:* Bio-Rad Lab 2000 Alfred Nobel Dr Hercules CA 94547-1801

**ZABIN, IRVING,** BIOCHEMISTRY, MOLECULAR BIOLOGY. *Current Pos:* res assoc biol chem, 50-51, from lectr to assoc prof, 51-64, PROF BIOL CHEM, SCH MED, UNIV CALIF, LOS ANGELES, 64- *Personal Data:* b Chicago, Ill, Nov 13, 19; m 42, Esther Marshall; c Lee, Fred & Carol. *Educ:* Univ Ill, BS, 40; Univ Chicago, PhD(biochem), 49. *Prof Exp:* Res assoc biochem, Univ Chicago, 49-50. *Concurrent Pos:* Nat Multiple Sclerosis Soc scholar, 59-60; Guggenheim fel, 67-68; NATO sr fel sci, 75; vis prof, Pasteur Inst, Paris, 59-60 & 67-68 & Imp Col London, 75. *Mem:* AAAS; Am Soc Biol Chem; Am Soc Microbiol. *Res:* Protein structure, synthesis and control. *Mailing Add:* Dept Biol Chem Univ Calif Sch Med Los Angeles CA 90095-1737

**ZABINSKI, MICHAEL PETER,** SOLID MECHANICS, BIOMECHANICS. *Current Pos:* PROF ENG & PHYSICS, FAIRFIELD UNIV, 69- *Personal Data:* b Haifa, Israel, May 30, 41; US citizen; m 64; c 1. *Educ:* Univ Conn, BS, 62, MS, 63; Yale Univ, MS, 66, MPhil, 68, PhD(eng & appl sci), 69; Univ New Haven, MS, 77. *Prof Exp:* Sr engr, Olin Corp, 63-66. *Concurrent Pos:* Res grant, Fairfield Univ, 69-72; NIH grant internal med, Sch Med, Yale Univ, 72-76. *Mem:* Am Soc Mech Engrs; Am Soc Eng Educ; Am Chem Soc. *Res:* Digital computing; computers in public school education; physical principles of peristaltic phenomena; mechanical properties of tissue. *Mailing Add:* 382 Hitching Post Dr Orange CT 06477

**ZABLOCKA-ESPLIN, BARBARA,** NEUROPHARMACOLOGY, NEUROPHYSIOLOGY. *Current Pos:* asst prof, 68-77, ASSOC PROF PHARMACOL & THERAPEUT, MCGILL UNIV, 77- *Personal Data:* b Warsaw, Poland, Jan 5, 25; m 64; c 4. *Educ:* Med Acad, Warsaw, dipl, 52, MD, 61. *Prof Exp:* Asst prof pharmacol, Med Acad, Warsaw, 52-55, sr asst prof, 55-61; Riker Int fel, Col Med, Univ Utah, 61-62, res assoc, 62-65, asst res prof, 65-68. *Mem:* Am Soc Pharmacol & Exp Therapeut; Can Pharmaceut Asn. *Res:* Central excitatory and depressant drugs; central transmitter substances. *Mailing Add:* 428 Claremont Ave Montreal PQ H3Y 2N2 Can

**ZABLOW, LEONARD,** CARDIAC ELECTROPHYSIOLOGY, NEUROPHYSIOLOGY. *Current Pos:* res asst neurol, Columbia Univ, 52-60, res assoc, 60-73, sr staff assoc, 73-85, sr staff assoc, Pharmacol Col Physicians & Surgeons, 85-90, SCI PROGRAMMER, HOWARD HUGHES MED INST, COLUMBIA UNIV, 90- *Personal Data:* b New York, NY, Sept 3, 27; m 50, Ellen Soswow; c Joel & Lori. *Educ:* Calif Inst Technol, BSc, 48; Columbia Univ, MA, 50. *Prof Exp:* Res worker biochem, Worcester Found Exp Biol, 51-52. *Concurrent Pos:* Lectr, Polytech Inst Brooklyn, 59-66. *Mem:* Fel AAAS; Biophys Soc; Am Phys Soc. *Res:* Focal generator size in clinical and experimental epilepsy; source distributions in electroencephalography; computer analysis of the electroencephalogram and electromyogram; models in cardiac electrophysiology; measurement and modelling of calcium intracellular distributions. *Mailing Add:* 5610 Post Rd Bronx NY 10471. *Fax:* 212-795-7997; *E-Mail:* zablowl@cpmc3.cpmc.columbia.edu

**ZABORSKY, OSKAR RUDOLF,** BIOTECHNOLOGY, BIOLOGICAL CHEMISTRY. *Current Pos:* DIR BD BIOL, NAT RES COUN, 89- *Personal Data:* b Neuwalddorf, Czech, Oct 6, 41; US citizen; m 68; c 2. *Educ:* Philadelphia Col Pharm & Sci, BSc, 64; Univ Chicago, PhD(chem), 68. *Prof Exp:* NIH fel, Harvard Univ, 68-69; sr res chemist, Corp Res Labs, Exxon Res & Eng Co, Linden, NJ, 69-74; prog dir, NSF, 74-83; pres & chief exec officer, OMEC Int Inc, 84-88; pres, Ozcom Int Inc, 88-89. *Concurrent Pos:* Chmn, Comt Biotechnol Nomenclature & Info Orgn, NAS, 85-86, mem, Marine Biotechnol Comt, 83-85, chmn bioexpo, 85 & 86. *Mem:* AAAS; Am Chem Soc; Am Inst Chem Engr; Am Soc Microbiol; Soc Indust Microbiol. *Res:* Biotechnology; enzyme technology; renewable resources; biocatalysis; biomass chemicals and fuels; biochemical engineering; biomaterials; marine biotechnology; information science; environmental technology; bioinformatics; technology transfer. *Mailing Add:* Univ Hawaii Nat Energy Inst Honolulu HI 96822

**ZABORSZKY, JOHN,** ELECTRICAL ENGINEERING. *Current Pos:* chmn, Automatic Control Area, Washington Univ, 59-65, rotating chmn, Dept Systs Mech & Aerospace Eng, 65-68, chmn, Control Systs Sci & Eng, 68-74, chmn, Dept Systs Sci & Math, 74-89, PROF ENG, WASHINGTON UNIV, 56- *Personal Data:* b Budapest, Hungary, May 13, 14; nat US; div. *Educ:* Josef Nador Royal Hungarian Tech Univ, Budapest, dipl, 37, DSc, 42. *Honors & Awards:* Centennial Medal, Inst Elec & Electronics Engrs, 84; Richard E Bellman Control Heritage Award, Am Automatic Control Coun, 86. *Prof Exp:* Chief engr in charge power syst eng, Munic Elec Works, Budapest, 44-48; from asst prof to prof eng, Univ Mo, 48-56. *Concurrent Pos:* Docens, Royal Hungarian Tech Univ, 46-47; consult, Westinghouse Elec Co, E Pittsburg, Pa, 50-51, McDonnell Douglas Corp, St Louis, Mo, 55-75, Emerson Elec Co, St Louis, 62-67, Hi-Voltage Equip Co, Cleveland, Ohio, 57-72; mem, Working Group for Stand on Static Capacitor Switching, Power Eng Soc, 57-58, Power Syst Eng Comt, Subcomt Systs, 77-; mem bd dirs, Inst Elec & Electronics Engrs, 74-75, dir, Div I, 74-75. *Mem:* Nat Acad Eng; Soc Indust & Appl Math; fel Inst Elec & Electronics Engrs; Am Soc Mech Engrs; hon mem Hungarian Acad Sci; Sigma Xi. *Res:* Control theory; optimal control; functional analysis approaches; identification adaptive control;

estimation and filtering bilinear systems; controllability and observability; power systems dynamics, stability and control; switching phenomena; high voltage direct current; author of 2 books and numerous publications. *Mailing Add:* Sch Eng & Appl Sci Washington Univ PO Box 1040 St Louis MO 63130. *Fax:* 314-935-6121

**ZABRANSKY, RONALD JOSEPH,** CLINICAL MICROBIOLOGY, CLINICAL BACTERIOLOGY. *Current Pos:* DEPT PATH, UNIV TEX, GALVESTON, 91- *Personal Data:* b Little Ferry, NJ, Mar 18, 35; m 58; c 3. *Educ:* Rutgers Univ, BS, 56; Ohio State Univ, MS, 61, PhD(microbiol), 63; Am Bd Med Microbiol, dipl, 69. *Prof Exp:* Microbiologist, Battelle Mem Inst, 59-60; teaching asst med microbiol bact, Ohio State Univ, 60-61, res asst, 61-63; assoc consult microbiol, Mayo Clin, 63-64, consult, 64-69; dir div microbiol, Mt Sinai Med Ctr, Milwaukee, 69-91. *Concurrent Pos:* Asst clin prof, Dept Microbiol, Med Col Wis, 70-74, assoc adj prof microbiol, 75-84, adj prof, 84-; chmn, Nat Registry Microbiologists, 74-79; mem bd gov, Am Acad Microbiol, 74-79; assoc clin prof allied health, Univ Wis-Milwaukee, 78-84, prof, 84-; mem, Nat Comt Clin Lab Stand, 80-; consult, Microbiol Device Panel, Food & Drug Admin, 81-; prof path & lab med, Med Sch, Univ Wis, Milwaukee Clin Campus, 83-; ed, Clin Microbiol Newsletter, 85- *Mem:* Fel Am Acad Microbiol; Am Pub Health Asn; Am Soc Microbiol. *Res:* Isolation and identification of anaerobic bacteria; invitro evaluation of antibiotics; antibiotic testing of anaerobic bacteria. *Mailing Add:* Univ Tex Med Br 301 University Blvd Galveston TX 77555-2708

**ZABRECKY, JAMES R,** CANCER INVASION & METASTASIS, IMMUNODIAGNOSTIC DEVELOPMENT. *Current Pos:* PROG MGR, ONCOGENE SCI INC, 89- *Personal Data:* b Whiting, Ind, Aug 2, 55. *Educ:* Ind Univ, BS, 77; Univ Calif, PhD(biochem), 81. *Mem:* AAAS; Am Soc Biochem & Molecular Biol. *Res:* Development of immunoreagents and assays for the detection and treatment of cancer. *Mailing Add:* 80 Rogers St Cambridge MA 02142-1168

**ZABRISKIE, FRANKLIN ROBERT,** ASTRONOMY. *Current Pos:* PRES, ASTRO COMPUT CONTROLS, INC, 80- *Personal Data:* b New York, NY, Dec 21, 33; m. *Educ:* Princeton Univ, BSE, 55, MSE, 57, PhD(astron), 60. *Prof Exp:* Asst prof astron, Wesleyan Univ, 60-66; assoc prof astron, Pa State Univ, University Park, 66-79. *Mem:* Am Astron Soc; Int Astron Union; Am Geophys Union. *Res:* Design of instruments for optical telescopes; photoelectric stellar classification; studies of long period variable stars. *Mailing Add:* Harpsa Birsah Orkney KW17 2ND Scotland

**ZABRISKIE, JOHN LANSING, JR,** organic chemistry, for more information see previous edition

**ZABRONSKY, HERMAN,** RELIABILITY, QUEUEING THEORY. *Current Pos:* SR STATISTICIAN, AM SYSTS CORP, 79- *Personal Data:* b Brooklyn, NY, Apr 5, 27; m 57; c 2. *Educ:* City Univ New York, BS, 48; Univ Pa, MA, 51. *Prof Exp:* Assoc mathematician, Oak Ridge, 51-53; sr engr, Ford Instrument Co, 53-58 & RCA, 58-67; staff scientist, Comput Sci Corp, 67-73, Calculon, 78-79. *Concurrent Pos:* Lectr math, Stevens Inst Technol, 59-65; consult econ, Int Bus Serv, 80-81. *Mem:* Math Asn Am. *Res:* Applied probability queueing reliability; econometrics; statistical theory of communications; partial differential equations; boundary value problems related to heat and mass transfer; reactors. *Mailing Add:* 10857 Bucknell Dr Silver Spring MD 20902

**ZABUSKY, NORMAN J,** COMPUTATIONAL FLUID DYNAMICS, VISIOMETRICS & MODELING. *Current Pos:* STATE NJ PROF COMPUTATIONAL FLUID DYNAMICS, RUTGERS UNIV, 88- *Personal Data:* b NY, Jan 4, 29; m 54, Charlotte Fox; c Stacia E, Erica F & Alexander N. *Educ:* Col City New York, BEE, 51; Mass Inst Technol, MS, 53; Calif Inst Technol, PhD(physics), 59. *Honors & Awards:* Potts Medal, Franklin Inst, 86; Kiev Nonlinear Conf Medal, 89. *Prof Exp:* Tech staff analog simulation, Raytheon Missile & Radar Div, 53-55; vis assoc plasma physics, Princeton Plasma Physics Lab, 60-61; tech staff reentry physics, Bell Labs, 61-63, supvr plasma physics, 63-68, head, Dept Computational Physics, 68-74, Dept Models & Systs, 74-75; prof math, Univ Pittsburgh, 76-88. *Concurrent Pos:* Dir, Int Sch Nonlinear Math & Physics, Max Planck Inst, Munich, 66; consult, Geophys Plasma Dynamics Br, Naval Res Lab, 76-91, Los Alamos Nat Lab, 84-91. *Mem:* Fel Am Phys Soc; fel AAAS. *Res:* Vortex dynamics and turbulence in two and three dimensions; contour and filament dynamics for inviscid flows; nonlinear dynamical systems; data visualization, quantification and scientific modeling. *Mailing Add:* 30 S Adelaide Ave Apt 8D Highland Park NJ 08904. *Fax:* 732-445-5313; *E-Mail:* nzabusky@caip.rutgers.edu

**ZACCARIA, ROBERT ANTHONY,** DEVELOPMENTAL BIOLOGY, VERTEBRATE ENDOCRINOLOGY. *Current Pos:* Asst prof, 73-80, ASSOC PROF BIOL, LYCOMING COL, 80- *Personal Data:* b Philadelphia, Pa, May 29, 43; m 64; c 3. *Educ:* Bridgewater Col, BA, 65; Univ Va, PhD(biol), 73. *Mem:* Soc Integ & Comp Biol; AAAS; Am Inst Biol Sci; Sigma Xi. *Res:* Interaction among chromatophores in development of pigmentation in amphibians; limb regeneration in urodeles. *Mailing Add:* Dept Biol Lycoming Col Williamsport PA 17701

**ZACCHEI, ANTHONY GABRIEL,** DRUG METABOLISM, BIOCHEMICAL TOXICOLOGY. *Current Pos:* RETIRED. *Personal Data:* b Philadelphia, Pa, Mar 31, 40; m 63; c 3. *Educ:* Villanova Univ, BS, 61, MS, 65; Univ Minn, Minneapolis, PhD(biochem), 68. *Prof Exp:* Res assoc pharmacol, Merck Sharp & Dohme Res Labs, 61-64, sr res pharmacologist, 68-70, res fel, 70-73, sr res fel drug metabolism, 73-78, dir human drug metabolism, 78-85, sr investr, 85-90, dir, biochem toxicol, 90-95. *Concurrent Pos:* Vis asst prof, Inst Lipid Res, Baylor Col Med, 72; adj asst prof med, Jefferson Med Col, 79-85; mem spec study sect, Nat Inst Gen Med Sci, NIH, 78-87. *Mem:* Am Soc Pharmacol & Exp Therapeut; Am Chem Soc; Am Soc Mass Spectrometry. *Res:* Investigations into the physiological disposition of new drug products including absorption, excretion and metabolic studies; investigate mechanism of drug toxicity. *Mailing Add:* 1836 Webster Lane Ambler PA 19002-2428

**ZACH, RETO,** ZOOLOGY, ECOLOGY. *Current Pos:* researcher ecol, 78-84, MGR ENVIRON SCI BR, ATOMIC ENERGY CAN, LTD, 85- *Personal Data:* b Davos-Platz, Switz, Dec 27, 40; Can citizen; m 66; c 1. *Educ:* Univ Alta, Edmonton, BSc, 72; Univ Toronto, PhD(zool), 77. *Prof Exp:* Fel zool, Univ BC, Vancouver, 77-78. *Mem:* Ecol Soc Am; Cooper Ornith Soc. *Res:* Environmental impact of nuclear energy; ecological modelling; animal behavior; birds. *Mailing Add:* Atomic Energy Can Ltd Environ Sci Br Pinawa MB R0E 1L0 Can

**ZACHARIAS, DAVID EDWARD,** X-RAY CRYSTALLOGRAPHY, ORGANIC CHEMISTRY. *Current Pos:* RETIRED. *Personal Data:* b Philadelphia, Pa, May 16, 26; m 68; c 3. *Educ:* Temple Univ, AB, 53, AM, 54; Univ Pittsburgh, PhD(x-ray crystallog), 69. *Prof Exp:* From jr chemist to sr chemist, Smith Kline & Fr Labs, Pa, 54-71; res assoc, Molecular Struct Lab, Inst Cancer Res, 71-83, sr res assoc, 83- *Concurrent Pos:* Ed consult, Int Cancer Res Data Bank, 81-89. *Mem:* Am Crystallog Asn; Am Chem Soc. *Res:* Synthesis of heterocyclic compounds; single crystal x-ray structure determination of organic and biologically important compounds; x-ray powder diffraction. *Mailing Add:* 421 W Charlotte St Lancaster PA 17603. *Fax:* 215-728-3574; *E-Mail:* zacharias@fccc.edu

**ZACHARIASEN, FREDRIK,** THEORETICAL PHYSICS. *Current Pos:* from asst prof to assoc prof, 60-65, PROF PHYSICS, CALIF INST TECHNOL, 65- *Personal Data:* b Chicago, Ill, June 14, 31; m 57, Nancy Walker; c Kerry & Judith. *Educ:* Univ Chicago, PhB, 50, BS, 51; Calif Inst Technol, PhD(physics), 56. *Prof Exp:* Instr physics, Mass Inst Technol, 55-56, jr res physicist, Univ Calif, 56-57; res assoc physics, Stanford Univ, 57-58, asst prof, 58-60. *Concurrent Pos:* Consult, Rand Corp, 56-; Sloan Found fel, 60-64; consult, Los Alamos Sci Lab, 61-; Inst Defense Analysis, 61-; Guggenheim Found fel, 70-71; Mitre Corp, 78-; assoc dir, Los Alamos Nat Lab, 82-83. *Res:* High energy particle physics. *Mailing Add:* Dept Physics Calif Inst Technol Pasadena CA 91109

**ZACHARIASEN, K(ARSTEN) A(NDREAS),** chemical engineering, for more information see previous edition

**ZACHARIUS, ROBERT MARVIN,** PLANT CELL TISSUE CULTURE, PLANT-PARASITE INTERACTIONS. *Current Pos:* CONSULT, R M ZACHARIUS & ASSOC. *Personal Data:* b New York, NY, Mar 21, 20; m 44, Esther Zimmerman; c Leslie-Ann (McAulay), Susan L (Fretz), Jeffrey D & Erica J (Daharsh). *Educ:* NY Univ, BA, 43; Univ Colo, MA, 48; Univ Rochester, PhD(plant physiol), 53. *Prof Exp:* Asst chem, Univ Colo, 47-48; asst bot, Cornell Univ, 51-52; res chemist, Gen Cigar Co, Inc, Pa, 52-54; biochemist, Eastern Utilization Res Br, USDA, 54-57, res chemist, Eastern Utilization Res & Develop Div Pa, 57-71, res chemist, Plant Prod Lab, Eastern Regional Res Ctr, Agr Res Ctr, 71-74, res chemist, 74-84, res chemist, Beltsville Agr Res Ctr, 84-89. *Concurrent Pos:* Adj lectr biochem, St Joseph's Col, Pa, 67-68. *Mem:* Phytochem Soc NAm; Biochem Soc; Am Chem Soc; Am Soc Plant Physiol; Sigma Xi. *Res:* Non-protein nitrogen compounds of plants; plant proteins; Nicotiana alkaloids; ion-exchange and chromatographic methods; electrophoresis; antimetabolites; plant metabolism; proteolytic inhibitors; plant-parasite interactions, stress physiology and phytoalexin induction; plant cell tissue culture. *Mailing Add:* 6567 River Clyde Dr Highland MD 20777

**ZACHARUK, R Y,** INSECT MORPHOLOGY, INSECT PATHOLOGY. *Current Pos:* assoc prof, Univ Regina, 63-65, chmn dept, 65-67, prof, 67-93, EMER PROF BIOL, UNIV REGINA, 93- *Personal Data:* b Yorkton, Sask, May 1, 28; m 52; c Gaylene & Glenn. *Educ:* Univ Sask, BSA, 50, MSc, 55; Univ Glasgow, PhD(histochem, physiol), 61. *Prof Exp:* Res officer entom, Res Sta, Can Dept Agr, 50-63. *Concurrent Pos:* Agr Inst Can fel, 59-61. *Mem:* AAAS; Entom Soc Am; Asn Chemoreception Sci; Can Soc Entom; Can Soc Zool. *Res:* Sense organ ultrastructure; neurophysiology; entomophagous fungi; histochemistry. *Mailing Add:* 55 Dale Crescent Univ Regina Regina SK S4N 5J6 Can. *Fax:* 306-585-4894

**ZACHARY, JAMES F,** NEUROPATHOLOGY, ULTRASOUND. *Current Pos:* Asst prof, 83-89, ASSOC PROF PATH, UNIV ILL, 89- *Personal Data:* b Elgin, Ill, May 22, 50. *Educ:* Northern Ill Univ, BS, 72; Univ Ill, DVM, 77, PhD(path), 83; Am Col Vet Path, dipl, 83. *Concurrent Pos:* Ed-in-chief, Vet Path, 94. *Mem:* Am Col Vet Pathologists; Am Inst Ultrasound Med; Am Soc Investigative Path; Soc Neurosci; Am Vet Med Asn. *Res:* Neurodegenerative diseases; bioeffects of pulse wave and diagnostic ultrasound. *Mailing Add:* 2001 S Lincoln Ave Urbana IL 61802. *Fax:* 217-244-6629; *E-Mail:* zacharyj@ux1.cso.uiuc.edu

**ZACHARY, LOREN WILLIAM,** ENGINEERING. *Current Pos:* asst prof, 76-80, ASSOC PROF ENG MECH, IOWA STATE UNIV, 80- *Personal Data:* b Colfax, Iowa, Apr 26, 43; m 63; c 2. *Educ:* Iowa State Univ, BS, 66, MS, 74, PhD(eng mech), 76. *Prof Exp:* Asst eng, Aerospace Div, Martin Marietta Corp, 66-72. *Mem:* Soc Exp Mech. *Res:* Experimental stress analysis; non-destructive testing. *Mailing Add:* 4305 Ross Rd Ames IA 50014

**ZACHARY, NORMAN,** COMPUTER SCIENCE, SYSTEMS ANALYSIS. *Current Pos:* EXEC VPRES & DIR, DATA ARCHITECTS, INC, 71- *Personal Data:* b New York, NY, Sept 14, 26; m 54; c 3. *Educ:* NY Univ, AB, 47; Harvard Univ, PhD, 52. *Prof Exp:* Asst prof math, Univ Md, 51-52; mem, Inst Advan Study, 52-54; mem tech staff, Hughes Aircraft Co, 54-55; sect head, Sylvania Elec Prod, Inc, 55-57, lab mgr, Electronic Systs Div, 58-60; staff consult, Otis Elevator Co, 57-58; vpres, Gen Tel Co, Calif, Gen Tel & Electronics Corp, 60-63; dir commun & data systs, NAm Aviation, Inc, 63-64; dir, Harvard Comput Ctr, Mass, 64-71. *Concurrent Pos:* Consult, banking, ins & financial industs. *Mem:* Am Math Soc; Asn Comput Mach. *Res:* Computers and systems analysis with application to the solution of engineering, administrative and management problems; real time systems; integrated business data processing. *Mailing Add:* 257 Prince St West Newton MA 02165

**ZACHMANOGLOU, ELEFTHERIOS CHARALAMBOS,** PARTIAL DIFFERENTIAL EQUATIONS. *Current Pos:* From asst prof to assoc prof, 62-70, assoc head dept, 81-93, PROF MATH, PURDUE UNIV, LAFAYETTE, 70- *Personal Data:* b Thessaloniki, Greece, Mar 19, 34; US citizen; c 4. *Educ:* Rensselaer Polytech Inst, BAeroE, 56, MS, 57; Univ Calif, Berkeley, PhD(appl math), 62. *Concurrent Pos:* Fulbright res grant, Univ Rome, 65-66. *Mem:* Am Math Soc. *Res:* Partial differential equations; wave propagation. *Mailing Add:* Dept Math Purdue Univ West Lafayette IN 47907-1395. *E-Mail:* ecz@math.purdue.edu

**ZACHOS, COSMAS K,** THEORETICAL PARTICLE PHYSICS. *Current Pos:* asst physicist, 83-86, PHYSICIST, ARGONNE NAT LAB, 86- *Personal Data:* b Athens, Greece, Sept 8, 51; m 88, Sue Leurgans; c Evangelie & Timothy. *Educ:* Princeton Univ, AB, 74; Calif Inst Technol, PhD(physics), 79. *Prof Exp:* Res fel, Calif Inst Technol, 79; res assoc, Univ Wis-Madison, 79-81; res assoc, Fermi Nat Accelerator Lab, 81-83. *Mem:* Sigma Xi; Am Phys Soc; Math Asn Am. *Res:* Supergravity, sigma models and superstrings; theoretical high energy physics; infinite dimensional and quantum algebras; duality. *Mailing Add:* HEP 362 Argonne Nat Lab Argonne IL 60439-4815. *E-Mail:* zachos@hep.anl.gov

**ZACK, NEIL RICHARD,** INORGANIC CHEMISTRY, FLUORINE CHEMISTRY. *Current Pos:* SR TECH STAFF MEM, LOS ALAMOS NAT LAB, 90- *Personal Data:* b Canton, Ohio, Apr 26, 47; m 78, Jean Lucille Harten. *Educ:* Rensselaer Polytech Inst, BS, 69; Marshall Univ, MS, 70; Univ Idaho, PhD(chem), 74. *Prof Exp:* Fel chem, Utah State Univ, 74-75; fel, Univ Idaho, 75-76; sr chemist, Allied Chem Corp, 76-79; group leader, Exxon Nuclear Idaho Co, 79-80. *Concurrent Pos:* Consult hazardous chem safety; nuclear safeguards & security; nuclear materials; section mgr, sr tech sci, Westinghouse Idaho Nuclear Co, Inc, 81- *Mem:* Am Chem Soc; Sigma Xi. *Res:* Inorganic heterocyclics; fluorine containing derivatives of catenated sulfur compounds. *Mailing Add:* Los Alamos Nat Lab PO Box 1663 MSNO E541 Los Alamos NM 87545-0001. *Fax:* 55-667-7626; *E-Mail:* nzack@lanl.gov

**ZACKAY, VICTOR FRANCIS,** PHYSICAL METALLURGY. *Current Pos:* RETIRED. *Personal Data:* b San Francisco, Calif, May 2, 20. *Educ:* Univ Calif, BS, 47, MS, 48, PhD(metall), 52. *Honors & Awards:* Howe Award, Am Soc Metals, 60, Albert Sauveur Achievement Award, 71. *Prof Exp:* Instr phys metall, Univ Calif, 51-52; asst prof, Pa State Univ, 52-54; res scientist, Sci Lab, Ford Motor Co, 54-57, supvr metall, 58-59, asst mgr metall, 60-62; lectr metall, Univ Calif, Berkeley, 62-66, asst dir, Inorg Mat Res Div, Lawrence Berkeley Lab, 64-75, from prof to assoc dean eng, 66-74; pres, Mat & Methods Inc, 80-89. *Mem:* Fel Am Soc Metals; fel Am Inst Mining, Metall & Petrol Engrs. *Res:* Advanced materials science; engineering, technology and manufacturing for engines; energy conversion and storage; electronics, medical, dental and environmental systems. *Mailing Add:* 1014 West Rd New Canaan CT 06840

**ZACKROFF, ROBERT V,** INTERMEDIATE FILAMENTS, MICROTUBULES. *Current Pos:* ASST PROF, MASS COL PHARM, 92- *Personal Data:* b Philadelphia, Pa, Sept 14, 51. *Educ:* Temple Univ, AB, 73, MA, 75, PhD(biol), 79. *Prof Exp:* Res asst, Temple Univ, 73-75; fel, Carnegie-Mellon Univ, 79-81; sr res assoc, Med Sch, Northwestern Univ, 81-82, asst prof, 83-84; prin investr, Marine Biol Lab, Woods Hole, Mass, 84-85; adj prof, Univ RI, 86-92. *Concurrent Pos:* Lectr biol, Bryant Col, 88- *Mem:* Soc Protozool; Soc Evolutionary Protistol. *Res:* Actin; biochemistry of the cytoskeleton; ciliate motility; microtubules and intermediate filaments. *Mailing Add:* Dept Biol Mass Col Pharm 179 Longwood Ave Boston MA 02115-5896

**ZACKS, JAMES LEE,** VISON RESEARCH, NEUROSCIENCE. *Current Pos:* assoc prof, 72-77, PROF PSYCHOL, MICH STATE UNIV, 77- *Personal Data:* b Iron Mountain, Mich, Mar 23, 41; m 66; c 2. *Educ:* Harvard Univ, BA, 63; Univ Calif, Berkeley, MS & PhD(psychol), 67. *Prof Exp:* Asst prof psychol, Univ Pa, 67-71. *Concurrent Pos:* Prog dir, USPHS training grant, 70-76; prin investr, NSF res grant, 70-75; adj prof zool, Mich State Univ, 76-, adj prof radiol, 85-; vis prof, Dept Psychol, Northwestern Univ, 79-80; prin investr, NIH Res Grant, 88- *Mem:* Fel Optical Soc Am; Psychonomic Soc; Asn Res Vision & Ophthal. *Res:* Basic visual capacities and peripheral visual mechanisms which might determine them; visual perceptual changes on aging. *Mailing Add:* 1755 Sashabaw Dr Okemos MI 48864-3842

**ZACKS, SHELEMYAHU,** MATHEMATICAL STATISTICS, STATISTICAL ANALYSIS. *Current Pos:* chmn, 80-83, PROF MATH & STATIST, STATE UNIV NY, BINGHAMTON, 80- *Personal Data:* b Tel Aviv, Israel, Oct 15, 32; m 55; c 2. *Educ:* Hebrew Univ, Israel, BA, 55; Israel Inst Technol, MSc, 60; Columbia Univ, PhD(indust eng), 62. *Prof Exp:* Sr lectr statist, Israel Inst Technol, 63-65; prof, Kans State Univ, 65-68; prof, Univ NMex, 68-70; prof math & statist, Case Western Res Univ, 70-79, chmn dept, 74-79; prof, Va Poly Tech, 79-80. *Concurrent Pos:* Fel statist, Stanford Univ, 62-63; consult, Inst Mgt Sci & Eng, George Washington Univ, 67-87. *Mem:* Fel Am Statist Asn; fel Inst Math Statist; Int Statist Inst; fel AAAS; Oper Res Soc Am. *Res:* Optimal design of sequential experiments; statistical adaptive processes; stochastic control; charge point detection. *Mailing Add:* Dept Math Sci State Univ NY Binghamton NY 13902-6000. *Fax:* 607-777-2450

**ZACKS, SUMNER IRWIN,** PATHOLOGY. *Current Pos:* RETIRED. *Personal Data:* b Boston, Mass, June 29, 29; m 53; c 3. *Educ:* Harvard Univ, BA, 51, MD, 55; Am Bd Path, dipl, 61. *Hon Degrees:* MA, Univ Pa & Brown Univ. *Honors & Awards:* Hektoen Bronze Medal, AMA, 61. *Prof Exp:* From intern to asst resident path, Mass Gen Hosp, Boston, 55-58; from asst prof to prof path, Sch Med, Univ Pa, 62-76; prof path & chmn dept, Sch Med, Brown Univ, 76-82. *Concurrent Pos:* Neuropathologist, Pa Hosp, 61-76, assoc dir, Ayer Lab, 64-76; pathologist-in-chief, Miriam Hosp, 76- *Mem:* Histochem Soc (secy, 65-69); Am Soc Exp Path; Am Soc Cell Biol; Am Asn Neuropath; fel Col Am Path. *Res:* Fine structure of neuromuscular junctions, normal and in disease; fine structure pathology of muscle; molecular pathology of endotoxins; muscle regeneration. *Mailing Add:* Miriam Hosp Providence RI 02906

**ZACZEK, NORBERT MARION,** ORGANIC CHEMISTRY. *Current Pos:* From instr to assoc prof, 62-71, PROF CHEM, LOYOLA COL MD, 71- *Personal Data:* b Baltimore, Md, Aug 15, 36; m 73; c 1. *Educ:* Loyola Col, Md, BS, 58; Carnegie-Mellon Univ, PhD(org chem), 62. *Mem:* AAAS; Am Chem Soc; Royal Soc Chem. *Mailing Add:* Dept Chem Loyola Col 4501 N Charles St Baltimore MD 21210-2600

**ZACZEPINSKI, SIOMA,** hydroprocessing, research management, for more information see previous edition

**ZADEH, L(OTFI) A,** ARTIFICIAL INTELLIGENCE EXPERT SYSTEMS. *Current Pos:* chmn dept, 63-68, PROF ELEC ENG, UNIV CALIF, BERKELEY, 59-, DIR BERKELEY INITIATIVE IN SOFT COMPUT, 97- *Personal Data:* b Baku, Russia, Feb 4, 21; nat US; m 46; c 2. *Educ:* Teheran Univ, BS, 42; Mass Inst Technol, MS, 46; Columbia Univ, PhD(elec eng), 49. *Hon Degrees:* Dr, Paul-Sabatier Univ, Toulouse, France, 86 & State Univ NY, 89. *Honors & Awards:* Educ Medal, Inst Elec & Electronics Engrs, 73, Centennial Medal, 84; Eringen Medal, Soc Eng Sci Lectr Award, 75; Honda Prize, Honda Found, Japan, 89. *Prof Exp:* From instr to prof elec eng, Columbia Univ, 46-59. *Concurrent Pos:* Chmn US comn, Int Union Radio Sci; ed, Int J Fuzzy Sets & Systs, J Math Anal & Appln & J Comput & Syst Sci; mem, Int Advan Study, Princeton, NJ, 56, bd trustees, Int Asn Knowledge Engrs; sr fel, NSF, 56-57 & 62-63; vis prof elec eng, Mass Inst Technol, 62 & 68; Guggenheim Found fel, 67-68; vis scientist, Res Lab, IBM, San Jose, Calif, 68, 73 & 77; vis scholar, Artificial Intel Ctr, SRI Int, Menlo Park, Calif, 81; vis mem, Ctr Study Lang & Info, Stanford Univ, 88. *Mem:* Nat Acad Eng; Am Math Soc; Asn Comput Mach; fel Inst Elec & Electronics Engrs; fel AAAS; Int Fuzzy Syst Asn; Soc Eng Sci; Am Asn Artificial Intel; fel World Coun Cybernetics. *Res:* System theory; information processing; theory of fuzziness; artificial intelligence; expert systems; natural language understanding; knowledge representation; theory of evidence; expert systems; author of various publications. *Mailing Add:* Dept Elec Eng & Comput Sci Sada Hall Univ Calif Berkeley CA 94720

**ZADNIK, VALENTINE EDWARD,** GEOLOGY, ENGINEERING GEOLOGY. *Current Pos:* staff geologist contracts & grants, 84-97, STAFF GEOLOGIST, OFF ENERGY RESOURCES, US GEOL SURV, 74-; LIAISON GEOLOGIST, NAT PETROL RES ALASKA, 77- 84- *Personal Data:* b Cleveland, Ohio, Feb 13, 34; m 58, Donna; c Anthony, Janelle, Jerome & Rudolph. *Educ:* Western Res Univ, BA, 57; Univ Ill, MS, 58, PhD(geol, civil eng), 60. *Prof Exp:* Res geologist, Jersey Prod Res Co, 64-65; sr res geologist, Esso Prod Res Co, 65-66; res geologist, US Army Res Off, 66-74. *Concurrent Pos:* Fel int affairs, Princeton Univ, 70-71; mem, Comt Rock Mech & Comt Seismol, Nat Acad Sci. *Mem:* Asn Eng Geol; Sigma Xi. *Res:* Petroleum exploration; carbonate rock petrography; solid-earth geophysics, particularly seismology, gravity, geomagnetism and geodesy. *Mailing Add:* 105 S Park Dr Arlington VA 22204

**ZADOFF, LEON NATHAN,** PHYSICS. *Current Pos:* CHIEF SCIENTIST, EMS DEVELOP CORP, FARMINGDALE, 72- *Personal Data:* b Passaic, NJ, Aug 6, 23; m 44; c 2. *Educ:* Cooper Union, BChE, 48; NY Univ, PhD(physics), 58. *Prof Exp:* Chem engr, Flintkote Co, 48; petrol chemist, Paragon Oil Co, 48-49; protein chemist, Botany Mills, Inc, 49; jr chem engr, City Fire Dept, New York, 49-52; physicist, NY Naval Shipyard, 52-54; proj supvr reactor physics, Ford Instrument Co, 54-58; assoc scientist, Repub Aviation Corp, 58-64; specialist physicist, Repub Aviation Div, Fairchild-Hiller Corp, NY, 64-72. *Concurrent Pos:* Lectr, Adelphi Col, 58-; adj assoc prof, NY Inst Technol, 72- *Mem:* AAAS; Am Phys Soc; NY Acad Sci. *Res:* Theoretical, plasma and reactor physics; electromagnetic wave propagation; quantum mechanics. *Mailing Add:* 17 Spruce St Merrick NY 11566

**ZADUNAISKY, JOSE ATILIO,** PHYSIOLOGY, MARINE BIOLOGY & OPHTHAMOLOGY. *Current Pos:* PROF, DIV MARINE BIOL, ROSENSTEIL SCH MARINE ATMOSPHERE SCI, UNIV MIAMI, 96- *Personal Data:* b Rosario, Arg, July 15, 32; m 54; c 2. *Educ:* Univ Buenos Aires, MD, 56 & 58. *Honors & Awards:* Alcon Award Outstanding Contrib Vision Res, Alcon Inst, Tex, 84. *Prof Exp:* Instr, Inst Physiol, Med Sch, Univ Buenos Aires, 52-56; Arg Nat Res Coun estab investr, Dept Biophys, Med Sch, Univ Buenos Aires, 60-63; assoc prof physiol & dir res, Dept Ophthal, Sch Med, Univ Louisville, 64-67; assoc prof ophthal & physiol, Sch Med, Yale Univ, 67-73; prof physiol & exp ophthal, Med Sch, NY Univ, 73-96, dir, Sackler Inst, 81-96. *Concurrent Pos:* Arg Res Coun fel biochem, Univ Col, Dublin, 58-59 & Inst Biol Chem, Copenhagen, 59-60; USPHS grants, 62-; exec ed, Exp Eye Res, 70-92; investr, Mount Desert Island Biol Lab, Maine, 75-; consult, Visual Sci A Study Sect, USPHS, 76-80; ed, Current Topics Eye Res, 80- & Chloride Transport in Biol Membranes, 82- *Mem:* Fel NY Acad Sci; Biophys Soc; Asn Res Vision & Ophthal; Am Physiol Soc; Int Soc Eye Res (secy, 78-81, secy, 80-84, pres, 84-88). *Res:* Transport and permeability of biological membranes, especially epithelial tissues. *Mailing Add:* Div Marine Biol Univ Miami 4600 Richemacker Expressway Miami FL 33129. *Fax:* 212-263-5886

**ZAEHRINGER, MARY VERONICA,** FOODS. *Current Pos:* RETIRED. *Personal Data:* b Philadelphia, Pa, May 27, 11. *Educ:* Temple Univ, BS, 46; Cornell Univ, MS, 48, PhD(foods), 53. *Prof Exp:* Asst food res, Cornell Univ, 46-48, 51-53; from instr to asst prof home econ res, Mont State Col, 48-50; res prof home econ, Univ Idaho, 53-72, res prof food sci, 72-73, res prof bact & biochem, Agr Exp Sta, 73-76. *Concurrent Pos:* Res fel, Inst Storage & Processing Agr Produce, State Agr Univ, Wageningen, Holland, 67-68. *Mem:* Am Asn Cereal Chem; Inst Food Technol; Potato Asn Am. *Res:* Potato texture; quality of food products. *Mailing Add:* 614 Ash St Moscow ID 83843

**ZAERR, JOE BENJAMIN,** FOREST PHYSIOLOGY, GROWTH HORMONES. *Current Pos:* from asst prof to prof forestry, 65-95, asst dean, Grad Sch, 77-80, EMER PROF FORESTRY, ORE STATE UNIV, 95- *Personal Data:* b Los Angeles, Calif, Sept 9, 32; m 54, Lois M Bingham; c Linda M, Laura S & Jon B. *Educ:* Univ Calif, Berkeley, BS, 54, PhD(plant physiol), 64. *Prof Exp:* Res assoc, Crops Res Div, Agr Res Serv, USDA, Md, 64-65; vpres, PMS Instrument Co, Corvallis, 67-86. *Concurrent Pos:* Vis res prof, Agr Univ, Warsaw, Poland, 73-74; Univ Munich, WGer, 89-90; Fulbright res scholar, WGer, 81-82, Ger, 94-95. *Mem:* AAAS; Am Soc Plant Physiol; Soc Am Foresters; Scand Soc Plant Physiol. *Res:* Plant growth regulators; forest regeneration; root growth; plant water relations. *Mailing Add:* Forestry Sch Ore State Univ Corvallis OR 97331-5705. *E-Mail:* zaerrj@ccmail.orst.edu

**ZAFFARANO, DANIEL JOSEPH,** NUCLEAR PHYSICS. *Current Pos:* RETIRED. *Personal Data:* b Cleveland, Ohio, Dec 16, 17; m 46; c 6. *Educ:* Case Inst Technol, BS, 39; Ind Univ, MS, 48, PhD(physics), 49. *Prof Exp:* Tech liaison, Nat Carbon Co, 40-45; contract liaison, Appl Physics Lab, Johns Hopkins Univ, 45-46; from assoc prof to prof physics, Iowa State Univ, 49-67, chmn dept, 61-71, distinguished prof, 67-88, vpres res & grad dean, 71-88. *Concurrent Pos:* Sci liaison officer, US Off Naval Res, London, 57-58. *Mem:* Fel Am Phys Soc; Sigma Xi. *Res:* Experimental nuclear physics. *Mailing Add:* 3108 Ross Rd Ames IA 50014

**ZAFFARONI, ALEJANDRO,** BIOCHEMISTRY. *Current Pos:* pres & dir res, 68-80, chief exec officer, 80-88, FOUNDER & CO-CHMN, ALZA CORP, 88- *Personal Data:* b Montevideo, Uruguay, Feb 27, 23; m 46; c 2. *Educ:* Univ Montevideo, BS, 41; Univ Rochester, PhD(biochem), 49. *Hon Degrees:* DSc, Univ Rochester, 72; Dr, Univ Repub, Montevideo, Uruguay, 83. *Honors & Awards:* President's Award, Weizmann Inst, Israel, 78; Pioneer Award, Am Inst Chemists, 79; Nat Medal of Technol, 95. *Prof Exp:* Dir biol res, Syntex SA, Mex, 51-54, dir res & develop, 54-56, vpres, 56-61, pres, Syntex Labs, Inc, exec vpres, Syntex Corp & pres, Syntex Res Ctr, Calif, 61-68. *Concurrent Pos:* Hon prof, Univ Montevideo, 59; pres, Dynapol, 72-83; consult prof pharmacol, Med Sch, Stanford Univ, 78-; founder & chmn, Dynax Res Inst Molecular & Cellular Biol, 80-82. *Mem:* Nat Acad Eng; Am Chem Soc; Soc Exp Biol & Med; Endocrine Soc; Am Soc Biol Chemists; Am Soc Microbiol; Inst Med-Nat Acad Sci. *Res:* Biochemistry and drug delivery devices. *Mailing Add:* Alza Corp 950 Page Mill Rd Palo Alto CA 94304. *Fax:* 415-496-8104; *E-Mail:* alex.zaffaroni@alza.com

**ZAFIRATOS, CHRIS DAN,** NUCLEAR PHYSICS. *Current Pos:* from asst prof to assoc prof, 68-72, chmn dept, 78-82, PROF PHYSICS, UNIV COLO, 72- *Personal Data:* b Portland, Ore, Nov 18, 31. *Educ:* Lewis & Clark Col, BS, 57; Univ Wash, PhD(physics), 62. *Prof Exp:* Res instr nuclear physics, Univ Wash, 62; staff mem, Los Alamos Sci Lab, 62-64; asst prof physics, Ore State Univ, 64-68. *Concurrent Pos:* Chmn, Nuclear Physics Lab, Univ Colo, 74-76 & 85-86, assoc vchancellor, 86-92, vpres, Acad Affairs & Res, 92-, dean, Syst Wide Grad Sch, 92- *Mem:* Fel Am Phys Soc; fel Japan Soc Prom Sci. *Res:* Nuclear reactions; neutron and nuclear structure physics. *Mailing Add:* Dept Physics Univ Colo CB390 Boulder CO 80302. *Fax:* 303-492-6616

**ZAFIRIOU, EVANGHELOS,** PROCESS CONTROL & OPTIMIZATION, SEMICONDUCTOR MANUFACTURING. *Current Pos:* Asst prof, 87-91, ASSOC PROF CHEM ENG, UNIV MD, COL PARK, 91- *Personal Data:* b Athens, Greece, Nov 15, 59. *Educ:* Nat Tech Univ Athens, dipl, 83; Calif Inst Technol, PhD(chem eng), 87. *Concurrent Pos:* NSF Presidential Young Investr award, 90-95. *Mem:* Am Inst Chem Eng; Inst Elec & Electronics Engrs; Am Chem Soc; Soc Indus & Appl Math. *Res:* Control system design, in particular robust control, model predictive control, batch control; optimal operation of chemical processes; process resiliency; semiconductor manufacturing. *Mailing Add:* Inst Systs Res Univ Md College Park MD 20742. *Fax:* 301-314-9920; *E-Mail:* zafiriou@isr.umd.edu

**ZAGAR, WALTER T,** PHYSICAL CHEMISTRY, POLYMER CHEMISTRY. *Current Pos:* RETIRED. *Personal Data:* b Brooklyn, NY, Oct 15, 28; m 51; c 4. *Educ:* Manhattan Col, BS, 50; Fordham Univ, MS, 55, PhD(phys chem), 58. *Prof Exp:* Chemist, Dextran Corp, 52-53; instr chem, Notre Dame Col, NY, 55-56; instr, Manhattan Col, 56-57; sr scientist, Polymer Chem Div, W R Grace & Co, 57-66; mgr, Plastics Div, Allied Chem Corp, 66; mgr polymer develop, Chemplex Corp, 66-67; sr res chemist, Plastics Div, Allied Chem Corp, NJ, 67-72, La, 72-73, tech supvr, 73-94. *Mem:* Soc Plastics Engrs; Am Chem Soc; NY Acad Sci. *Res:* Polymer development in area of polyethylene blends and additive systems for polymers, especially antioxidants, antistats and ultraviolet absorbers. *Mailing Add:* 5013 Parkhurst Dr Baton Rouge LA 70816

**ZAGATA, MICHAEL DEFOREST,** NATURAL RESOURCES POLICY, ENVIRONMENTAL REGULATION. *Current Pos:* DIR ENVIRON & SAFETY, TENNECO OIL CO, 86- *Personal Data:* b Oneonta, NY, May 28, 42. *Educ:* State Univ NY, Oneonta, BS, 64, MS, 68; Iowa State Univ, PhD(wildlife ecol), 72. *Prof Exp:* Teacher biol, Oneonta Consolidated Sch & Southampton Pub Schs, 64-69; asst prof wildlife ecol, Sch Forest Resources, Univ Maine, 72-75; field dir, Wildlife Soc, 76-77; dir fed rel, Nat Audubon Soc, 77-79; prog develop off, Bd Agr & Nat Resources, Nat Acad Sci, 79-80; mgr ecol sci, Tenneco, Inc, 80-86. *Concurrent Pos:* Prin investr, US Forest Serv, 73-75; co-chmn, Pub Lands Task Force, Nat Asn Mfrs; exec bd, Nat Resources Coun Am; mem, Waterfowl Feeding Adv Comt, US Fish & Wildlife Serv, 77-79; chmn, Conserv Affairs Comt, Wildlife Soc, 79-; mem, Nat Adv Comt Regional Plan Asn, 78 & Nat Comt Fish & Wildlife Res, 78- *Mem:* Wildlife Soc; Soc Petrol Indust Biologists; NY Acad Sci; Am Fisheries Soc; Soc Wetland Scientists. *Res:* Impact of man-induced perturbations on fish and wildlife habitats and on the populations which occupy those habitats, natural resource policy. *Mailing Add:* 11618 Peacan Creek Dr Houston TX 77043-4510

**ZAGER, RONALD,** AROMA CHEMICAL MANUFACTURE, ORGANIC FLUOROCARBONS. *Current Pos:* CONSULT, RONALD ZAGER ASSOCS, 88- *Personal Data:* b New York, NY, Dec 27, 34; m 95, Anne C Chase; c Scott L & Joseph D. *Educ:* Brooklyn Col, BS, 55; Stevens Inst Technol, MS, 69. *Prof Exp:* Res chemist, Charles Pfizer, 56-58; res & develop chemist, Halocarbon Prod Corp, 58-66; develop chemist, Tenneco Chem Corp, 66-71; sr develop chemist, Giuaudan Corp, 71-77; tech dir, Int Flavors & Fragrances, 77-88. *Mem:* Asn Consult Chemists & Chem Engrs (pres, 91-92); Am Chem Soc. *Res:* Aroma chemicals; fluorocarbons; medical devices, prostetics; pharmaceutical inhalents; management and general research; manufacturing problem solving; experimental design; project management. *Mailing Add:* 85 Glen Ledge Rd Box 1200 Glen NH 03838. *E-Mail:* rzager@moose.ncia.net

**ZAGER, STANLEY E(DWARD),** CHEMICAL ENGINEERING. *Current Pos:* assoc prof, 77-83, PROF CHEM ENG, YOUNGSTOWN STATE UNIV, 83- *Personal Data:* b Sheldon, Iowa, Mar 6, 21; m 49; c 2. *Educ:* Iowa State Univ, BS, 43; Purdue Univ, PhD(chem eng), 50. *Prof Exp:* Jr chemist, Shell Develop Co, 43-46; res engr, Johns-Manville Corp, 50-57; sr res engr, Res Ctr, B F Goodrich Co, 57-60; sect leader, 60-63, corp task force sccy, 64-65, mgr mgt & comput sci, 66-76; mgr process develop & licensing, H K Ferguson Co, 76-77. *Mem:* Am Chem Soc; Am Inst Chem Engrs; Asn Comput Mach; Sigma Xi. *Res:* Application of computers and mathematics to scientific and business problems; process development, design, economics; improving energy recovery from fossil fuels, process and product development; heterogeneous catalysis; polymer processing. *Mailing Add:* 1001 Hickory Grove Medina OH 44256-1658

**ZAGHLOUL, MONA ELWAKKAD,** INTEGRATED CIRCUITS DESIGN WITH APPLICATIONS TO HIGH FREQUENCY, ANALOG & DIGITAL DESIGN. *Current Pos:* from asst prof to assoc prof, 80-89, PROF, DEPT ELEC ENG & COMPUT SCI, GEORGE WASHINGTON UNIV, 89-, CHAIR, 94- *Personal Data:* m 68, Amir; c Kareem & Norann. *Educ:* Univ Waterloo, MASc, 70, MMath, 71, PhD(elec eng), 75. *Prof Exp:* Sr mem tech staff, Comput Sci Corp, 78-80. *Concurrent Pos:* Electronic engr, Nat Inst Stand & Technol, 84- *Mem:* Fel Inst Elec & Electronics Engrs Circuits & Systs Soc; Int Neural Network Soc. *Res:* Design and application of integrated circuits in analog systems and high frequency; microelectromechanical systems with applications to sensors; neural systems algorithms and their hardware implementation. *Mailing Add:* Dept Elec Eng & Comput Sci George Washington Univ Washington DC 20052. *E-Mail:* zaghloul@seasigwv.edu

**ZAGON, IAN STUART,** ONCOLOGY, DEVELOPMENTAL NEUROBIOLOGY. *Current Pos:* from asst prof to prof anat, 74-91, PROF GENETICS, PA STATE UNIV, 75-, PROF CELL & MOLECULAR BIOL & NEUROSCI, 84-, PROF NEUROSCI & ANAT, 91- *Personal Data:* b New York, NY, Mar 28, 43; m 64, Eileen Kostel. *Educ:* Univ Wis-Madison, BS, 65; Univ Ill, Urbana, MS, 69; Univ Colo, Denver, PhD(anat), 72. *Prof Exp:* Asst prof biol struct, Med Sch, Univ Miami, 72-74. *Concurrent Pos:* Biol Stain Comn fel, 68 & 71; grantee, Am Cancer Soc, Am Heart Asn, NIH, Nat Inst Drug Abuse & Pa Res Corp; consult, Nat Inst Drug Abuse, Rockville, Md, 80-; prin investr, NIH grants; consult & reviewer, NIH, Bethesda, Md, 84-; grant reviewer, Am Heart Asn, Pa, 85-95, mem, Res Comt, 88-96, bd dirs, 92-96, vpres, 93-96. *Mem:* Soc Neurosci; Am Asn Anat; AAAS; Int Soc Develop Neurosci; Asn Res Vision & Ophthal; Am Soc Cell Biol. *Res:* Developmental neurobiology, focusing on normal and abnormal brain development; relationship of endogenous opioid systems to brain development; biological influences of opioids and opioid receptors in cancer; editor and author of two books. *Mailing Add:* Dept Neurosci & Anat Col Med Hershey Med Ctr Pa State Univ PO Box 850 Hershey PA 17033-0850

**ZAGZEBSKI, JAMES ANTHONY,** MEDICAL PHYSICS, MEDICAL IMAGING. *Current Pos:* Res assoc, Univ Wis-Madison, 72-75, adj asst prof, Dept Oncol & Radiol, 75-77, asst prof, 77-81, PROF, DEPTS MED PHYSICS, RADIOL & HUMAN ONCOL, UNIV WIS-MADISON, 86- *Personal Data:* b Stevens Point, Wis, Aug 5, 44; m 66; c 2. *Educ:* St Mary's Col, BS, 66; Univ Wis, Madison, MS, 68, PhD(radiol sci), 72. *Mem:* Am Asn Physicists Med; Am Inst Ultrasound Med; Inst Elec & Electronics Engrs Ultrasonic & Frequency Control Soc. *Res:* Diagnostic ultrasound imaging and tissue characterization; development of methods for assessing medical ultrasound equipment performance; application of ultrasound in speech research; ultrasound hypothermia. *Mailing Add:* 522 Dunning St Madison WI 53704

**ZAHALSKY, ARTHUR C,** BIOCHEMISTRY, TOXICOLOGY. *Current Pos:* PROF IMMUNOL, SOUTHERN ILL UNIV, EDWARDSVILLE, 71- *Personal Data:* b New York, NY, Oct 31, 30; div. *Educ:* McGill Univ, BSc, 52; NY Univ, PhD(microbiol), 63. *Prof Exp:* Res assoc, Haskins Labs, 58-66; res collabr, Brookhaven Nat Labs, 68-74; asst prof microbiol, Queens Col, NY, 66-69; assoc prof biochem, Doctoral Prog, City Univ NY, 69-71. *Concurrent Pos:* Consult immunotoxicol, Immunox Res. *Mem:* AAAS; Am Soc Parasitol; Am Soc Microbiol; Am Acad Clin Toxicol; Sigma Xi. *Res:* Immune response to environmental toxicants; immune disorders from halogenated hydrocarbons; host immune response to parasites. *Mailing Add:* Dept Biol Sci 132 N Kansas St Edwardsville IL 62025

**ZAHARIA, ERIC STAFFORD,** DEVELOPMENTAL DISABILITIES. *Current Pos:* CONSULT, PARK CITY, UTAH, 95- *Personal Data:* b Pomona, Calif, Aug 24, 48; m 67, Caryle Koentz; c Tye W & Tieg A. *Educ:* Pomona Col, BA, 70; Univ Ariz, Tucson, MEd, 73; George Peabody Col, PhD, 78. *Prof Exp:* Ment retardation worker, Ariz Training Prog, 70-71, unit dir, 71-73; dir, Residential Serv, Willmar State Hosp, Minn, 73-76; res asst, Inst Ment Retardation & Intellectual Develop Nashville, 76-78; dir, Dept Ment Health/Ment Retardation, State Tenn, 78-79, Caswell Ctr, 79-86; prog adminr, Colo Div, Develop Disabilities, 86-90; dir, Utah Div, Serv People Disabilities, 90-95. *Concurrent Pos:* Adj fac mem, E Carolina Univ, Greenville, 79-86. *Mem:* Am Asn Ment Retardation. *Res:* Development disabilities; mental retardation. *Mailing Add:* 8010 Juniper Dr Park City UT 84060-5370

**ZAHARKO, DANIEL SAMUEL,** PHARMACOLOGY, PHYSIOLOGY. *Current Pos:* CONSULT PHARMACOL, 92- *Personal Data:* b New Westminster, BC, Nov 3, 30; US citizen; m 59, Nancy Wilder; c Konrad, Mark & Anni. *Educ:* Univ BC, BPE, 53, dipl educ, 54; Univ Ill, MS, 55, PhD(physiol), 63. *Honors & Awards:* Co-winner, Ebert Prize, Am Pharmaceut Asn, 72. *Prof Exp:* Instr, Univ Sask, 55-57 & Univ Ill, 57-59; instr to asst prof pharmacol, Ind Univ, Bloomington, 63-68; USPHS res fel, Nat Cancer Inst, 68-70, pharmacologist, Lab Chem Pharmacol, 70-84, pharmacologist, Pharmacol Br, Develop Therapeut Prog, 85-92. *Mem:* Am Asn Cancer Res; AAAS; Am Soc Pharmacol & Exp Therapeut. *Res:* Environmental physiology; biochemical pharmacology; cancer chemotherapy; pharmacokinetics; drug development. *Mailing Add:* 5308 Trailway Dr Rockville MD 20853

**ZAHED, HYDER ALI,** science communications, for more information see previous edition

**ZAHED, ISMAIL,** MANY-BODY PHYSICS. *Current Pos:* res asst, 84-87, asst prof, 87-90, ASSOC PROF PHYSICS, STATE UNIV NY, STONY BROOK, 90- *Personal Data:* b Algeria. *Educ:* Mass Inst Technol, MSc, 81, PhD(physics), 83. *Prof Exp:* Res asst physics, Niels Bohr Inst, 83-84. *Mem:* Am Phys Soc. *Res:* Role of hadronic constituents in nuclear physics; behavior of hadronic matter at high temperature and density. *Mailing Add:* 12 Coraway Rd East Setauket NY 11733

**ZAHLER, RAPHAEL,** CARDIAC MOLECULAR BIOLOGY, CLINICAL CARDIOVASCULAR MEDICINE. *Current Pos:* asst prof, 86-92, ASSOC RES PROF, SCH MED, YALE UNIV, 92- *Personal Data:* b New York, NY, June 14, 45; m 86, Mary Gatter; c 4. *Educ:* Yale Univ, MD, 80; Univ Chicago, PhD(math), 70. *Honors & Awards:* Henry Christian Award, Am Fedn Clin Res, 92. *Prof Exp:* Lectr math, Univ Calif, Berkeley, 70-72; assoc prof, Rutgers Univ, 75-78. *Concurrent Pos:* Mem, Coun Basic Sci, Am Heart Asn. *Mem:* Fel Am Col Cardiol; Am Fedn Clin Res; Am Heart Asn; Am Physiol Soc. *Res:* A molecular biology of the isoforms of the sodium pump as they relate to cardiac function; applications of mathematics to medicine; applied mathematics. *Mailing Add:* 333 Cedar St 3 FMP New Haven CT 08510-8017. *Fax:* 203-785-7144

**ZAHLER, STANLEY ARNOLD,** MICROBIOL GENETICS. *Current Pos:* from asst prof to assoc prof, 59-79, assoc dir, Div Biol Sci, 75-78, PROF MICROBIOL GENETICS, CORNELL UNIV, 79-, CHAIRPERSON, GENETICS & DEVELOP, 90- *Personal Data:* b New York, NY, May 28, 26; m 52; c 3. *Educ:* NY Univ, AB, 48; Univ Chicago, MS, 49, PhD, 52. *Prof Exp:* Instr gen bact, Northern Ill Col Optom, 51; USPHS fel bact, Univ Ill, 52-54; instr microbiol, Univ Wash, 54-57, asst prof, 57-58; asst prof, Med Ctr, WVa Univ, 59. *Concurrent Pos:* Consult, Gen Elec Corp, 63-69, Sandoz, Inc, 80-82, Dow Chem, 81-84, Eastman Kodak Co, 85-88; USPHS spec fel, Scripps Clin & Res Found, 66-67. *Mem:* AAAS; Am Soc Microbiol; Genetics Soc Am; Brit Soc Gen Microbiol. *Res:* Bacteriophages; microbial genetics; metabolic controls; genetics of Bacillus subtilis and other bacilli. *Mailing Add:* 217 Cornell St Ithaca NY 14850. *Fax:* 607-255-2428

**ZAHLER, WARREN LEIGH,** BIOCHEMISTRY. *Current Pos:* asst prof, 72-77, ASSOC PROF BIOCHEM, UNIV MO, COLUMBIA, 77- *Personal Data:* b Springville, NY, June 28, 41; m 68, Lucy Perez; c Maya & Lara. *Educ:* Alfred Univ, BA, 63; Univ Wis-Madison, MS, 66, PhD(biochem), 68. *Prof Exp:* NIH fel molecular biol, Vanderbilt Univ, 67-71, res assoc, 71-72. *Mem:* AAAS; Am Chem Soc; Am Soc Biochem & Molecular Biol; Sigma Xi. *Res:* Characterization of the kinetics and mechanism of enzyme catalysis. *Mailing Add:* Dept Biochem Univ Mo 117 Schweitzer Hall Columbia MO 65211. *Fax:* 573-882-5635; *E-Mail:* bcwarren@muccmail.missouri.edu

**ZAHN, JOHN J,** ELASTIC STABILITY, STRUCTURAL DESIGN. *Current Pos:* ENGR, FOREST PROD LAB, FOREST SERV, USDA, 64- *Personal Data:* b Beaver Dam, Wis, May 8, 32; div; c 3. *Educ:* Univ Wis, BS, 54, MS, 59, PhD(mech). 64. *Honors & Awards:* L J Markwardt Award, Forest Prod Res Soc, 78; Raymond C Reese Res Prize, Am Soc Civil Engrs, 88. *Prof Exp:* Instr eng mech, Univ Wis, 59-62, lectr, 62-64. *Mem:* Am Soc Civil Engrs; Fedn Am Scientists. *Res:* Theory of elasticity; elastic stability; applied mathematics; probability. *Mailing Add:* 2648 Van Hise Ave Madison WI 53705-3740

**ZAHND, HUGO,** BIOCHEMISTRY. *Current Pos:* Tutor chem, 28-34, from instr to prof, 34-72, EMER PROF CHEM, BROOKLYN COL, 72- *Personal Data:* b Berne, Switz, May 16, 02; nat US; m 26, 68; c 2. *Educ:* NY Univ, BS, 26; Columbia Univ, AM, 29, PhD(biochem), 33. *Concurrent Pos:* Contrib, Chem & Technol Food & Food Prod, Intersci Publ, Inc, New York, NY, 44, & Acad Am Encycl, Arete Publ Co, Princeton, NJ, 80. *Mem:* Fel AAAS; Am Chem Soc; Hist Sci Soc; fel Am Inst Chem; NY Acad Sci. *Res:* Labile sulfur in proteins; quantitative inorganic and organic analysis; history of chemistry; chromatography as applied to the fields of alkaloids, amino acids and proteins. *Mailing Add:* 42 Herbert Ave Port Washington NY 11050

**ZAHNLEY, JAMES CURRY,** BIOCHEMISTRY. *Current Pos:* RES CHEMIST, WESTERN REGIONAL RES CTR, AGR RES SERV, USDA, 66- *Personal Data:* b Manhattan, Kans, Apr 16, 38; div; c Timothy & Paul. *Educ:* Kans State Univ, BS, 58; Purdue Univ, MS, 62, PhD(biochem), 63. *Prof Exp:* Res assoc enzym, Syntex Inst Molecular Biol, Calif, 63-64, assoc biochem, 64-65; asst res biochemist, NIH grant, 65-66. *Mem:* AAAS; Am Soc Biochem & Molecular Biol; Am Chem Soc; Protein Soc. *Res:* Enzymology; protein chemistry; food proteins. *Mailing Add:* Western Regional Res Ctr USDA 800 Buchanan St Albany CA 94710

**ZAHN-WAXLER, CAROLYN,** PSYCHOLOGY. *Current Pos:* staff fel, Lab Socio-environ Studies, NIMH, 66-69, res psychologist, 70-94, sect chief, Child Behav Dis, 86-95, RES PSYCHOLOGIST, LAB DEVELOP PSYCHOL & SECT CHIEF, CHILD BEHAV DIS, NIMH, 95- *Personal Data:* b Sturgeon Bay, Wis, Apr 5, 40. *Educ:* Univ Wis, BA, 62; Univ Minn, MA, 64, PhD, 67. *Prof Exp:* Res asst, Dept Educ Psychol, Univ Minn, 62-63. *Concurrent Pos:* Res & teaching asst, Inst Child Develop, Univ Minn, 64-, instr psychol, 65-; instr, Psychol Dept, Macalester Col, 66-; assoc ed, Develop Psychol, 88-92, ed, 92-; Harris vis prof, Harris Ctr Develop Studies, Univ Chicago, 92. *Mem:* Fel Am Psychol Soc; fel Am Asn App & Prev Psychol; AAAS; Soc Res Child Develop; Am Orthopsychiat Asn; Int Soc Study Behav Develop; Int Soc Res Emotion; Soc Life Hist Res Psychopath; Soc Res Child & Adolescent Psychopath; fel Am Psychol Asn. *Res:* Social development and affect regulation; developmental psychopathology and adaptation; etiology of disruptive behavior disorders; comorbidity of externalizing and internalizing problems; socialization, risk and protective factors; assessment of problem behaviors in preschool children. *Mailing Add:* Sect Develop Psychopath NIMH Bldg 15-K Rm 104 15 North Dr MSC2668 Bethesda MD 20892-2668. *Fax:* 301-402-1218

**ZAHORIAN, STEPHEN A,** ELECTRICAL ENGINEERING. *Current Pos:* from asst prof to assoc prof elec eng, 79-94, prof, 94-96, CHMN, DEPT ELEC & COMPUT ENG, OLD DOMINION UNIV, 96- *Personal Data:* b Nov 20, 47. *Educ:* Univ Rochester, BS, 69; Syracuse Univ, MS, 73, PhD(elec eng), 78. *Prof Exp:* Engr, RCA Corp, 69-71; instr & res engr elec & comput eng, Syracuse Univ, 77-79. *Mem:* Inst Elec & Electronics Engrs; assoc Acoust Soc Am. *Res:* Author of several published articles. *Mailing Add:* Dept Elec & Comput Eng Old Dominion Univ Kaufman/Duckworth Hall 231 Norfolk VA 23529-0246

**ZAHRADKA, PETER,** CARDIOVASCULAR MOLECULAR BIOLOGY, CELL GROWTH REGULATION. *Current Pos:* ASST PROF, UNIV MAN, 91- *Personal Data:* b Sudbury, Ont, Nov 30, 55; m 80, Catherine L Blair; c Jennifer L & Erin D. *Educ:* Univ Western Ont, BSc, 78, PhD(biochem), 84. *Prof Exp:* Fel, Stanford Univ, 84-85; fel, Univ Guelph, 85-89, asst prof, 89-91. *Concurrent Pos:* Weisman mem res fel, Juv Diabetes Found Int, 87-89; asst ed, Molecular Cell Biochem. *Mem:* Can Biochem Soc; Am Soc Cell Biol; Int Soc Heart Res; Am Heart Asn. *Res:* Analysis of the signalling systems and gene activation mechanisms associated with angiotensin II-dependent growth stimulation and cholesterol metabolism in vascular smooth muscle. *Mailing Add:* Inst Cardiovascular Sci St Boniface Res Ctr 351 Tache Ave Winnipeg MB R2H 2A6 Can. *Fax:* 204-233-6723

**ZAHRADNIK, RAYMOND LOUIS,** CHEMICAL ENGINEERING, ENERGY SCIENCE. *Current Pos:* CONSULT & PRES MOUNTAIN BAY ASSOCS, 92. *Personal Data:* b Ford City, Pa, Sept 18, 36; m 60; c 3. *Educ:* Carnegie Inst Technol, BS, 59, MS, 61, PhD(chem eng). 63. *Prof Exp:* Sr engr res labs, Westinghouse Elec Corp, 61-65, fel engr, 65-66; from assoc prof to prof chem eng, Carnegie-Mellon Univ, 67-74; dir, Div Coal Conversion & Utilization, ERDA, 75-76; pres, Ray Zahradnik Consult, Inc, 76-77; dir

energy res, Occidental Oil & Gas, Div Occidental Petrol Corp, 77-82; pres, Occidental Oil Shale Inc, 82-92. *Concurrent Pos:* Prog mgr energy res & technol, NSF, 72-74; mem res coord panel, Gas Res Inst, 77- *Res:* Energy research. *Mailing Add:* PO Box 771814 Steamboat Springs CO 80477

**ZAIA, JOHN ANTHONY,** hematology, for more information see previous edition

**ZAIDEL, ERAN,** NEUROPSYCHOLOGY. *Current Pos:* Res fel psychobiol, 73-76, sr res fel, 76-80, VIS ASSOC, DEPT BIOL, CALIF INST TECHNOL, 80- *Personal Data:* b Kibbutz Yagur, Israel, Jan 23, 44; US citizen; m 65; c 2. *Educ:* Columbia Univ, AB, 67; Calif Inst Technol, MSc, 68, PhD(psychobiol), 73. *Mem:* Soc Res Child Develop; Int Neuropsychol Soc; Acad Aphasia. *Res:* Neurolinguistics and psycholinguistics; cognitive and developmental psychology; epistemology and the philosophy of science, of mind and of language. *Mailing Add:* Dept Psychol Univ Calif 405 Hilgard Ave Los Angeles CA 90024-1301

**ZAIDER, MARCO A,** nuclear physics, radiological physics, for more information see previous edition

**ZAIDI, IQBAL MEHDI,** GLYCOBIOLOGY & GLYCOTECHNOLOGY, CARBOHYDRATE CONSUMABLES KITS-DEVELOPMENT. *Current Pos:* SCIENTIST, PERKIN ELMER APPL BIOSYST DIV, 91- *Personal Data:* b Bijnor, India, June 30, 57; US citizen; m 93, Nuzhat. *Educ:* Aligarh Univ, India, Premed Cert, 74, BS, 76, MS, 78, PhD(biochem), 84; NY State Health Dept, radiation safety cert, 89. *Prof Exp:* Res fel, Indust Toxicol Res Ctr, 79-93; res affil, NY State Health Dept, 84-91. *Mem:* Am Chem Soc; AAAS; NY Acad Sci. *Mailing Add:* 850 Lincoln Ctr Dr Foster City CA 94404

**ZAIDI, SYED AMIR ALI,** NUCLEAR PHYSICS. *Current Pos:* asst prof, 66-68, ASSOC PROF PHYSICS, UNIV TEX, AUSTIN, 68-, ASSOC DIR, CTR NUCLEAR STUDIES, 67- *Personal Data:* b Lahore, Pakistan, Apr 15, 35; m 62. *Educ:* Punjab Univ, BSc, 56; Univ Gottingen, 57-58; Univ Heidelberg, dipl physics, 60, PhD(physics), 64. *Prof Exp:* Vis res scientist, Max Planck Inst Nuclear Physics, 64-66. *Mem:* Fel Am Phys Soc. *Res:* Isobaric analogue resonances; nuclear structure studies using shell model description of reaction theory; heavy ion induced reactions; elementary particle physics. *Mailing Add:* Dept Physics Univ Tex Austin TX 78712

**ZAIDINS, CLYDE,** ASTROPHYSICS, GAMMA RAY ASTRONOMY. *Current Pos:* PROF PHYSICS, UNIV COLO, DENVER, 71- *Personal Data:* b Apr 30, 39; c Paul M & Sandra L (Lilja). *Educ:* Calif Inst Technol, BS, 61, MS, 63, PhD(physics), 67. *Mem:* Sigma Xi; Brit; Nat Sci Technol Authority; Asn Appl Sci; Am Asn Physics Technol; Am Phys Soc. *Res:* Astrophysics, nuclear astrophysics; nucleaosynthesis gamma ray astronomy. *Mailing Add:* Dept Physics Univ Colo-Denver Campus Box 157 PO Box 173364 Denver CO 80217-3364

**ZAIDMAN, SAMUEL,** ABSTRACT & PARTIAL DIFFERENTIAL EQUATIONS, PSEUDODIFFERENTIAL OPERATORS. *Current Pos:* PROF MATH, UNIV MONTREAL, 64- *Personal Data:* b Bucharest, Romania, Sept 4, 33; Can citizen; m 62, Janne Fiorani; c Marina, Anna-Maria, Cristina & Enrichetta. *Educ:* Univ Bucharest, Lic, 55; Univ Paris, Dr d'Etat, 70. *Prof Exp:* Asst math, Univ Bucharest, 55-59; vis prof, CNR Italy, 61-64. *Concurrent Pos:* Vis prof, Univ Geneva, 66-68, Univ Padova CNR Italy, 79-80. *Mem:* Am Math Soc. *Res:* Abstract differential equations; pseudo-differential operators; almost-periodic equations; partial differential equations; almost-periodic functions; theory of distributions; abstract analysis. *Mailing Add:* Dept Math Univ Montreal 2900 Edward Montpetit Montreal PQ H3C 3J7 Can. *Fax:* 514-343-5700

**ZAIKA, LAURA LARYSA,** FOOD CHEMISTRY. *Current Pos:* RES CHEMIST FOOD SAFETY, SCI & EDUC ADMIN-AGR RES, USDA, 64- *Personal Data:* b Kharkow, Ukraine, June 23, 38; US citizen. *Educ:* Drexel Inst Tech, BS, 60; Univ Pa, PhD(org chem), 64. *Mem:* Am Chem Soc; Inst Food Technologists; Asn Off Analytical Chemists. *Res:* 2-aryl benzimidazoles; 1, 2, 3-benzotriazines; meat flavor investigations; chromatography; microbial metabolites; fermented meat products; spices. *Mailing Add:* 40 Johns Rd Cheltenham PA 19012-1420

**ZAIM, SEMIH,** SYNTHETIC RUBBER, RHEOLOGY OF POLYMERS. *Current Pos:* PRES, ZAIM ASSOCS CONSULT, 93- *Personal Data:* b Bursa, Turkey, Mar 1, 26; US citizen; m 51, Ismet Agirbas; c Sina, Bulent & Beyhan. *Educ:* Univ Istanbul, Turkey, BS, 47, MS, 49. *Prof Exp:* Chem engr aviation fuels & lubricant qual control res develop, Arge Res Labs, Ankara, Turkey, 49-61; NATO res fel aviation fuels res & develop, Carde Res Labs, Que, Can, 61-62; res chemist polymer, Res & Develop Div, Polysar Corp, Sarnia, Ont, Can, 62-69 & Tex US Res Ctr, Parsippany, NJ, 69-76; res supvr adhesives, Essex Chem Corp, Sayreville, NJ, 76-81; vpres res & develop specialty chem, Chessco-Process Res Prod, Trenton, NJ, 81-93. *Concurrent Pos:* Consult, UN Develop Prog, 79-81. *Res:* Metal working lubricants, specialty chemicals for quartz and silicon wafer and bearing ball manufacturing; adhesives and sealants; granted two us patents. *Mailing Add:* 3 Lowel Ave Mountain Lakes NJ 07046. *Fax:* 973-335-6360; *E-Mail:* zaimsemih@worldnet.att.net

**ZAININGER, KARL HEINZ,** SOLID STATE PHYSICS, PHYSICAL ELECTRONICS. *Current Pos:* RETIRED. *Personal Data:* b Endorf, Ger, Aug 3, 29; US citizen; m 52; c 3. *Educ:* City Col New York, BSEE, 59; Princeton Univ, MSE, 61, MA, 62, PhD(elec eng), 64. *Honors & Awards:* RCA Labs Achievement Award, 65. *Prof Exp:* Mem tech staff, David Sarnoff Res Ctr, 59-68, group head solid state device technol group RCA Labs, 68-77; dir commercialization, Solar Energy Res Inst, 77-78; dir microelectronics, Electronic Devices & Technol Lab, US Army, 78-80; exec vpres, Siemens Corp Res & Support, Siemens Res & Technol Lab, Princeton, NJ, 80-86, pres & res dir, 86-91. *Concurrent Pos:* David Sarnoff fel, doctoral studies prog, 62; mem orgn & tech prog comt, Mos Interface Specialist Conf, Las Vegas, 64-68; gen chmn & chmn, Bd Dir Inst Elec & Electronics Engrs Nat Reliability Physics Symp, 71; chmn, Electronics Physics Dept, LaSalle Univ, 73-76; mem conf bd, Adv Panel Radiation Device Technol, 89; ed, Inst Elec & Electronics Engrs trans, electron devices; mem, Nat Res Coun Mat Adv Bd; chmn, Pub Serv Elec & Gas Corp, Res & Develop Strategy Comt; mem, Res & Develop Coun NJ; mem, Inst Elec & Electronics Engrs Standards Bd; very large scale integration technol sci coordr, UCLA; UN specialist, Intergrated Circuit Technol, Jerusalem, Isreal. *Mem:* Fel Inst Elec & Electronics Engrs; Am Phys Soc. *Res:* Semiconductor devices; thin film physics; plasmas in solids; physical and electrical properties of SiO2; oxidation and optical properties of Si and GaAs; physics and technology of metal-insulator-semiconductor devices; radiation effects of metal-insulator-semiconductor structures. *Mailing Add:* 9 E Shore Dr Princeton NJ 08540

**ZAISER, JAMES NORMAN,** MECHANICAL ENGINEERING. *Current Pos:* asst prof, 65-76, ASSOC PROF MECH ENG, BUCKNELL UNIV, 76- *Personal Data:* b Salem, NJ, Jan 23, 34; m 57; c 3. *Educ:* Univ Del, PhD(appl sci), 64. *Prof Exp:* Instr mech eng, Univ Del, 58-63; res engr, Exp Sta, E I du Pont de Nemours & Co, 63. *Concurrent Pos:* NSF grant, Bucknell Univ, 66-67. *Mem:* Am Soc Mech Engrs; Am Soc Eng Educ. *Res:* Nonlinear analysis and dynamics of particles and rigid bodies; nonlinear analysis of systems described by ordinary and partial differential equations. *Mailing Add:* c/o Mech Eng Dept Bucknell Univ Lewisburg PA 17837

**ZAITLIN, MILTON,** PLANT VIROLOGY. *Current Pos:* assoc dir, biotechnol prog, dir, Biotechnol Prog, 83-91, PROF PLANT PATH, CORNELL UNIV, 73-, ASSOC DIR, 91-, EMER PROF, 97- *Personal Data:* b Mt Vernon, NY, Apr 2, 27; m 51; c 4. *Educ:* Univ Calif, BS, 49; Univ Calif, Los Angeles, PhD(plant physiol), 54. *Prof Exp:* Res officer, Commonwealth Sci & Indust Res Orgn, Canberra, Australia, 54-58; asst prof hort, Univ Mo, 58-60; asst agr biochem, Univ Ariz, 60-62, from assoc prof to prof agr biochem & plant path, 66-73. *Concurrent Pos:* Guggenheim & Fulbright fels, 66-67; assoc ed, Virol, 66-71, 82-84, ed, 72-81; bd dir Int Soc Plant Mol Biol, 85-89; sr ed, Molecular Plant-Microbe Interactions, 87-90. *Mem:* Soc Gen Microbiol; fel Am Phytopath Soc; Am Soc Plant Physiologists; Am Soc Virol; Int Soc Plant Molecular Biol; fel AAAS. *Res:* Plant viruses; molecular biology of plant virus disease; molecular basis of plant-virus infections; generation of virus disease-resistant plants by transformation with viral genes. *Mailing Add:* Dept Plant Path Cornell Univ Ithaca NY 14853. Fax: 607-255-7824; *E-Mail:* m211@cornell.edu

**ZAJAC, ALFRED,** PHYSICS. *Current Pos:* From instr to assoc prof, 55-74, PROF PHYSICS & CHMN DEPT, ADELPHI UNIV, 74- *Personal Data:* b Vienna, Austria, Feb 18, 17; US citizen; m 50; c 2. *Educ:* Univ St Andrews, BSc, 46, Hons, 48; NY Univ, MS, 52; Polytech Inst Brooklyn, PhD(physics), 57. *Concurrent Pos:* NSF res grant, 62-64; adj prof physics, Hofstra Univ. *Mem:* Am Phys Soc; Am Asn Physics Teachers; Am Crystallog Asn. *Res:* Crystal perfection, thermal motion and anomalous transmission of x-rays. *Mailing Add:* Dept Physics 133 Hofstra Univ Weed Hall 207 Hempstead NY 11550

**ZAJAC, BARBARA ANN,** INTERNAL MEDICINE, INFECTIOUS DISEASES. *Current Pos:* sr dir immunol & infectious dis, 92-95, ASST VPRES, WYETH-AYERST LABS, 95- *Personal Data:* b Fountain Springs, Pa, Mar 15, 37; m 57, Ihor; c Andre J. *Educ:* Univ Pa, BA, 58, PhD(microbiol), 67; Med Col Pa, MD, 79. *Prof Exp:* Assoc pediat/virol, Univ Pa, 69-70; from asst prof to assoc prof microbiol, Med Col Pa, 70-76; resident internal med, Abington Mem Hosp, 79-82; fel infectious dis, Hosp Univ Pa, 82-84; dir clin res, Merck Sharp & Dohme Res Labs, 84-88; group dir immunol & infectious dis, Du Pont Merck Pharmaceut Co, 88-92. *Concurrent Pos:* NIH fel, Div Virus Res, Children's Hosp Philadelphia, Pa, 67-69; grants, Res Corp & Anna Fuller Fund, 72-73, Damon Runyon Mem Fund, 73-75 & Nat Cancer Inst, 73-76; affil staff physician, Abington Mem Hosp, 86- *Mem:* AMA; Am Col Physicians; Infectious Dis Soc Am; Am Soc Transplant Physicians. *Res:* DNA viruses (EBV, VZV, Hepatitis B) host-parasite relationships and immune responses; clinical investigation, immunology and infectious diseases. *Mailing Add:* PO Box 940 Hockessin DE 19707-9993. *Fax:* 610-989-4578

**ZAJAC, FELIX EDWARD, III,** NEUROPHYSIOLOGY, BIOMEDICAL ENGINEERING. *Current Pos:* MEM FAC, DEPT MECH ENG, STANFORD UNIV, CALIF. *Personal Data:* b Baltimore, Md, Dec 4, 41; m 62; c 2. *Educ:* Rensselaer Polytech Inst, BEE, 62; Stanford Univ, MS, 65, PhD(neurosci), 68. *Prof Exp:* Staff assoc, Lab Neural Control, Nat Inst Neurol Dis & Stroke, 68-70; asst prof elec eng, Univ Md, College Park, 70-73, assoc prof, 73-80, dir, Biomed Res Lab, 71-80; Eng Res & Develop Ctr, Vet Admin Med Ctr, Palo Alto, Calif, 80- *Mem:* AAAS; Am Physiol Soc; Soc Neurosci; Inst Elec & Electronics Engrs. *Res:* Neural control and biomechanics of animal movement with emphasis on cat locomotion and jumping. *Mailing Add:* 4138 Willmar Dr Palo Alto CA 94306

**ZAJAC, IHOR,** MEDICAL MICROBIOLOGY, VIROLOGY. *Current Pos:* res assoc, E I Du Pont, 83-90, RES ASSOC, DU PONT MERCK PHARMACOL CO, 90- *Personal Data:* b Lwiw, Ukraine, May 26, 31; US citizen; m 57; c 1. *Educ:* Univ Pa, BA, 58; Hahnemann Med Col, MS, 60, PhD(microbiol), 64. *Prof Exp:* Asst microbiol, Hahnemann Med Col, 64-65, instr, 65; asst prof, Jefferson Med Col, 65-71; assoc sr investr, 71-75, sr investr, Smith Kline & French Labs, 75-83. *Concurrent Pos:* Vis lectr, Med Col Pa, 72-78; vis assoc prof, Hahnemann Med Col, 81-; adj assoc prof, Jefferson Med Col, 81-85. *Mem:* Am Soc Microbiol; Soc Exp Biol & Med; Sigma Xi. *Res:* Enteroviruses; cell-virus interactions; cell membrane; interferon; bacterial and viral chemotherapy; anaerobic bacteria; bacterial receptors; neoplastic chemotherapy; drug metabolism and disposition and interaction; pharmacokinetics. *Mailing Add:* PO Box 940 Hockessin DE 19707

**ZAJAC, WALTER WILLIAM, JR,** ORGANIC CHEMISTRY, CHEMISTRY. *Current Pos:* From asst prof to assoc prof, 59-72, PROF CHEM, VILLANOVA UNIV, 72- *Personal Data:* b Central Falls, RI, July 19, 34; m 59, Mary S Nilan; c Marita, Walter III, Amy, Robert, Jenny & John. *Educ:* Providence Col, BS, 55; Va Polytech Inst, MS, 57, PhD(chem), 60. *Concurrent Pos:* Fel, Univ Alta, 65-66. *Mem:* Am Chem Soc; Sigma Xi. *Res:* Reduction and oxidation of organic compounds; synthesis, reactions and comformation of carbocyclic and heterocyclic systems; chemistry of nitro compounds; carbohydrates. *Mailing Add:* Dept Chem Villanova Univ Villanova PA 19085. *E-Mail:* zajac@rsgchem.vill.edu

**ZAJACEK, JOHN GEORGE,** ORGANIC CHEMISTRY. *Current Pos:* MGR OXYGENATED PROD RES, ARCO CHEM CO, 62- *Personal Data:* b Allentown, Pa, May 8, 36; m 64; c 3. *Educ:* Lehigh Univ, BA, 58; Cornell Univ, PhD(org chem), 62. *Mem:* Am Chem Soc. *Res:* Oxidation of hydrocarbons; epoxidation of olefins; reactions of carbon monoxide; reduction of aromatic nitro compounds; metal catalyzed reactions; chemistry of selenium reactions; isocyanates; polyols. *Mailing Add:* 669 Clovelly Lane Devon PA 19333-1846

**ZAJONC, ARTHUR GUY,** LASER PHYSICS, ATOMIC PHYSICS. *Current Pos:* asst prof, 78-84, ASSOC PROF PHYSICS, AMHERST COL, 84- *Personal Data:* b Boston, Mass, Oct 11, 49; m 74; c 2. *Educ:* Univ Mich, Ann Arbor, BSE, 71, MS, 73, PhD(physics), 76. *Prof Exp:* Fel atomic physics, Joint Inst Lab Astrophys, Nat Bur Stand & Univ Colo, 76-78. *Concurrent Pos:* Vis scientist, Ecole Normale Superieure, 81-82, Max Planck Inst Quantum Optics, 84 & Univ Hanover, Inst Quantum Optics, 86. *Mem:* Am Phys Soc; Am Asn Physics Teachers; Hist Sci Soc; Optic Soc Am; fel Lindisarne Asn. *Res:* Experimental foundations of physics; laser spectroscopy; radiative transfer; electron-atom collisions. *Mailing Add:* Dept Physics Amherst Col 100 Boltwood Ave Amherst MA 01002-5000

**ZAJTCHUK, RUSS,** MEDICAL SCIENCE. *Current Pos:* COMMANDING GEN, US MED RES & MAT COMMAND, ASST TO ASST SECY DEF, BIOL & CHEM DEF, CHIEF OPER OFF, DEPT DEF TELEMEDICINE TESTBED, 94- *Personal Data:* b Ukraine, 1940; m, Joan T. *Hon Degrees:* Dr, Russian Mil Acad Med. *Prof Exp:* Asst prof, Dept Surg, Univ Chicago; chair & prog dir, Walter Reed Army Med Ctr, Nat Naval Med Ctr; prof, Uniformed Serv Univ Health Sci, George Washington Univ. *Concurrent Pos:* Dir, Task Force Aesculapius. *Mem:* Russ Acad Sci. *Mailing Add:* US Army Med Res & Mat Command MCMR-2A Ft Detrick MD 21702-5012. *Fax:* 301-619-2982

**ZAK, BENNIE,** SPECTROSCOPY, ELECTROPHORESIS. *Current Pos:* From asst prof to prof, 57-90, EMER PROF CLIN CHEM, WAYNE STATE UNIV, 90- *Personal Data:* b Detroit, Mich, Sept 29, 19; m 46; c 3. *Educ:* Wayne State Univ, BS, 48, PhD(chem), 52. *Honors & Awards:* Ames Award, Am Asn Clin Chem, 74, Gen Diagnostics Lectr, 81; Benedetti-Pichler Award, Am Microchem Soc, 84. *Concurrent Pos:* Res technician, Detroit Receiving Hosp, 50-51, med lab analyst & jr assoc chem, 51-57, head clin chem, 80-; consult, Sinai Hosp, Detroit, Mich, 53-, St John's Hosp, 60-91, Vet Admin Hosp, Allen Park, 61-, Holy Cross Hosp, 62-91 & William Beaumont Hosp, Royal Oak, 65-91; fac res award, Sigma Xi, 73. *Mem:* Am Chem Soc; Am Asn Clin Chem. *Res:* Spectrophotometric procedures in clinical chemistry on trace metals; peroxidase-coupled indicator reactions; problems involved with hyperlipidemia-hyperproteinemia measurements; problems in electrophoresis. *Mailing Add:* Wayne State Univ Sch Med 540 E Canfield Detroit MI 48021

**ZAK, RADOVAN HYNEK,** BIOCHEMISTRY, PHYSIOLOGY. *Current Pos:* fel biochem, Univ Chicago, 63-65, instr, 65-67, from asst prof to assoc prof, 67-79, PROF, DEPT MED, UNIV CHICAGO, 79- *Personal Data:* b C Budejovice, Czech, June 15, 31; US citizen; m 63; c 2. *Educ:* Prague Univ, Czech, BS, 52, Dr Nat Sci, 54; Czech Acad Sci, Prague, PhD(biomed sci), 61. *Honors & Awards:* Nat Award, Czech Acad Sci, 58. *Prof Exp:* Instr org chem, Med Sch, Prague Univ, 51-53; res scientist physiol, Inst Physiol, Czech Acad Sci, 57-61; res fel physiol chem, Dept Med, Northwestern Univ, Chicago, 61-63. *Mem:* AAAS; Am Physiol Soc; Int Soc Heart Res; Am Soc Cell Biol. *Res:* Cardiac hypertrophy; protein synthesis and degradation; proliferation of cardiac myocytes; muscle proteins. *Mailing Add:* Dept Med Casdiovascular Univ Chicago Pritcke Sch Med 5841 Maryland Ave Chicago IL 60637-1463

**ZAKAIB, DANIEL D,** PETROLEUM CHEMISTRY, ANALYTICAL CHEMISTRY. *Current Pos:* CONSULT, D D ZAKAIB & ASSOC, 85- *Personal Data:* b Montreal, Que, Apr 1, 25; m 48, Phyllis; c Gary & Geoffrey. *Educ:* Montreal Tech Inst, dipl chem, 46; Sir George Williams Univ, BSc, 53.

*Prof Exp:* Supvr, Montreal Refinery Lab, Brit Am Oil Co, 48-55, asst refinery chemist, 55-58, analysis technologist, Head Off Toronto, 58-63, coordr, Analytical Res Labs, Brit Am Res & Develop Co, 63-66; mgr analytical & chem res, Res & Develop Dept, Gulf Oil Can, Ltd, 66-69, supvr petrol chem sect, Phys Sci Div, Gulf Res & Develop Co, 69-71, dir tech opers, Res & Develop Dept, Gulf Can, Ltd, 71-85. *Concurrent Pos:* Consult all fascets of res & develop function, 86- *Mem:* Am Chem Soc; Am Soc Testing & Mat; Can Asn Appl Spectros; fel Chem Inst Can. *Res:* Technical administration of industrial research facility. *Mailing Add:* 2 Confederation Way Thornhill ON L3T 5R5 Can

**ZAKHARI, SAMIR,** PHARMACY, PHARMACOLOGY. *Current Pos:* CHIEF, BIOMED RES BR, NAT INST ALCOHOLIC ABUSE & ALCOHOLISM, 90- *Personal Data:* b Egypt, Dec 24, 44. *Educ:* Cairo Univ, BS, 65, MS, 69; Chekoslovak Acad Sci, PhD(pharmacol), 75. *Prof Exp:* Asst prof, Univ Pa Sch Med, 75-77; sr toxicologist, Allied Chem Corp, 77-79; dir physiol, Borriston Res Lab, 81-85. *Mailing Add:* Biomed Res Br Nat Inst Alcoholic Abuse & Alcoholism 6000 Executive Blvd Suite 402 Bethesda MD 20892. *Fax:* 301-594-0673; *E-Mail:* s.zakhari@wilko.niaaa.ndh.gov

**ZAKHARY, RIZKALLA,** HUMAN ANATOMY. *Current Pos:* asst prof anat, 67-70, ASSOC PROF ANAT, SCH DENT, UNIV SOUTHERN CALIF, 70- *Personal Data:* b Assiut, Egypt, Sept 5, 24; m 66; c 2. *Educ:* Cairo Univ, BS, 49, MS, 54; Tulane Univ, PhD(anat), 64. *Prof Exp:* Technician & res asst biochem, US Naval Med Res Unit 3, Cairo, Egypt, 50-56; instr biol chem & gen sci, Am Univ Cairo, 57-60; asst prof anat & physiol, Sch Dent, Loyola Univ, La, 64-67. *Concurrent Pos:* NIH grant, Tulane Univ, 65-67. *Mem:* AAAS; Am Asn Anatomists; Am Asn Univ Profs. *Res:* Hypothermia, academic and applied aspects; cryobiology; stress and hypothermia; vascular casting. *Mailing Add:* Dept BKN & PT Univ Southern Calif 1540 Alczar St CHP 155 Los Angeles CA 90033

**ZAKI, ABD EL-MONEIM EMAM,** HISTOLOGY, ORAL BIOLOGY. *Current Pos:* res assoc, Col Dent, Univ Ill, 67-70, asst prof histol, Col Dent & lectr, Col Med, 70-72, assoc prof histol, Col Dent & Sch Basic Med Sci, Med Ctr, 72-75, PROF HISTOL, COL DENT, UNIV ILL, 75- *Personal Data:* b Cairo, Egypt, Dec 18, 33; US citizen. *Educ:* Cairo Univ, BChD, 55, DDR, 58; Ind Univ, MSD, 62; Univ Ill, PhD(anat), 69. *Prof Exp:* Dent surgeon, Demonstration & Training Ctr, Qualyub, UAR, 55-59; teaching asst, Ind Univ Sch Dent, 60-61; from instr to asst prof, Fac Dent, Cairo Univ, 62-67. *Concurrent Pos:* UAR govt spec mission mem grad study, US, 59-62. *Mem:* AAAS; Am Asn Anat; Electron Micros Soc Am; Int Asn Dent Res; Sigma Xi. *Res:* Cellular control of mineralization using a rodent odontogenic model; cytological and cytochemical aspects of odontogenesis; dental pulp tissue response to therapeutic agents. *Mailing Add:* Dept Oral Biol MC 690 801 S Paulina St Chicago IL 60612-7213

**ZAKI, MAHFOU H,** environmental medicine, public health, for more information see previous edition

**ZAKIAN, VIRGINIA ARAXIE,** CHROMOSOME STRUCTURE, CELL CYCLE CONTROL. *Current Pos:* PROF, DEPT MOLECULAR BIOL, PRINCETON UNIV, 95- *Personal Data:* b Philadelphia, Pa, Feb 10, 48; m 73, Robert N Sandberg; c Megan & Eric. *Educ:* Cornell Univ, AB, 70; Yale Univ, PhD(biol), 75. *Honors & Awards:* Sr Woman Award Women in Cell Biol, Am Soc Cell Biol, 95. *Prof Exp:* NIH fel, Princeton Univ, 75-76; fel, Univ Wash, 76-78; from asst mem to assoc mem, Fred Hutchinson Cancer Res Ctr, 79-87, mem basic sci, 87-95. *Concurrent Pos:* Affil prof, Univ Wash, 79-95; prin investr, NIH & Am Cancer Soc, 79-; mem, Study Sect Microbiol & Virol, Am Cancer Soc, 85-89; mem, Nat Yeast Comt, 85-89; ed, Plasmid, 86-90, Chromosoma, 90-, Trends in Cell Biol, 91-, J Exp Zool, 91-, Molecular & Cellular Biol, 92; mem, Microbiol Genetics Study Sect, NIH, 91-; consult, Geran Corp, 93- *Mem:* Am Soc Cell Biol; Am Women Sci; Genetics Soc Am; fel AAAS; fel Am Acad Microbiol. *Res:* To determine the cis and transacting components that ensure the faithful maintenance of eukaryotic chromosomes and specifically to determine the role of telomeres, the physical ends of eukaryotic chromosomes, in chromosome stability and behavior. *Mailing Add:* Dept Molecular Biol Princeton Univ Princeton NJ 08544. *Fax:* 206-667-6726

**ZAKIM, DAVID,** BIOCHEMISTRY. *Current Pos:* VINCENT ASTOR DISTINGUISHED PROF MED, CORNELL UNIV MED COL, 83-, PROF BIOCHEM, GRAD SCH MED SCI, 83- *Personal Data:* b Paterson, NJ, July 10, 35; m 57, 78, Dagmar A Stanke; c Michael, Eric, Thomas, Tamara & Robert. *Educ:* Cornell Univ, AB, 56; State Univ NY, Brooklyn, MD, 61; Am Bd Internal Med, dipl. *Prof Exp:* Intern, NY Hosp, 61-62, asst resident, 62-63, fel, 63-65; from asst prof to prof med & pharmacol, Univ Calif, San Francisco, 68-83. *Mem:* Am Asn Physicians; Am Soc Biol Chemists. *Res:* Fusion of proteins with lipid vesicles; demonstration of the lipid-dependence of uridine diphosphate-glucuronology transferace; elucidation of mechanism for uptake of fatty acids and bilirubin into cells. *Mailing Add:* Dept Med-Gastroenterol Cornell Univ Med Col 1300 York Ave New York NY 10021-4805

**ZAKIN, JACQUES L(OUIS),** CHEMICAL ENGINEERING. *Current Pos:* prof chem eng & chmn dept, 77-94, HELEN C KURTZ PROF, OHIO STATE UNIV, 94- *Personal Data:* b New York, NY, Jan 28, 27; m 50; c Richard J, David F, Barbara E, Emily A & Susan B. *Educ:* Cornell Univ, BChem Eng, 49; Columbia Univ, MSc, 50; NY Univ, DEng Sc, 59. *Honors & Awards:* Tech Person of the Year, Columbus Tech Coun, 87; Josef Hlavka Medal, Inst Hydrodynamics, Czech Acad Sci, 92. *Prof Exp:* Chem engr res labs, Flintkote Co, 50-51; from res technologist to supvry technologist, Res

Dept, Socony Mobil Oil Co, 51-56 & 58-62; from assoc prof to prof chem eng, Univ Mo, Rolla, 62-77. *Concurrent Pos:* Adj asst prof, Hofstra Col, 59-60 & 62; Am Chem Soc-Petrol Res Fund Int fel & vis prof, Israel Inst Technol, 68-69, vis prof, 94-95; vis scientist, Naval Res Lab, Washington, DC, 75-76; vis prof, Casali Inst, Hebrew Univ, 87; sr Fulbright res fel, Technion, Israel, 94-95. *Mem:* Fel Am Inst Chem Engrs; Am Chem Soc; Rheology Soc; Am Soc Eng Educ; Sigma Xi. *Res:* Surfactant drag reduction in turbulent flow; structure of surfactant micelles; detailed structure of liquid turbulence; transport of viscous crudes as concentrated oil-in-water emulsions; rheology of polymer and surfactant solutions. *Mailing Add:* Dept Chem Eng Ohio State Univ Columbus OH 43210

**ZAKKAY, VICTOR,** FLUID MECHANICS, COMBUSTION. *Current Pos:* assoc prof aerospace eng, NY Univ, 64-65, prof aeronaut & astronaut, 65-73, asst dir, Aerospace Lab, 70-76, from actg chmn to chmn, Dept Appl Sci, 76-84, prof appl sci, 73-, dir, Antonio Ferri Aerospace & Energetics Labs, 76-90, VINCENT ASTOR PROF AEROSPACE, NY UNIV, 90- *Personal Data:* b Baghdad, Iraq, Sept 8, 27; US citizen; m 52; c 2. *Educ:* Polytech Inst Brooklyn, BAeroE, 52, MS, 53, PhD(aeronaut), 59. *Prof Exp:* Res asst, Polytech Inst Brooklyn, 52-55, res assoc, 55-58, res group leader, 58-59, from res asst prof to res assoc prof, 59-64. *Mem:* Am Inst Aeronaut & Astronaut. *Res:* Hypersonic and viscous compressible flow; heat transfer; experimental aerodynamics; combustion; turbulent mixing; fuel combustion fluidized bed coal combustion; hypersonic aerodynamics; wind tunnel technology; solar energy. *Mailing Add:* NY Univ 34 Stuyvesant St New York NY 10003

**ZAKRISKI, PAUL MICHAEL,** ANALYTICAL CHEMISTRY. *Current Pos:* Sr res chemist, 66-74, SECT LEADER, RES DIV, B F GOODRICH CO, BRECKSVILLE, 74- *Personal Data:* b Amsterdam, NY, July 12, 40; m 64; c 3. *Educ:* Univ Rochester, AB, 62; Univ Cincinnati, PhD(org chem), 67. *Mem:* Am Chem Soc; Am Soc Mass Spectrometry. *Res:* Mass spectrometry for structure elucidation; high speed chromatography. *Mailing Add:* 8329 Wyatt Rd Cleveland OH 44147

**ZAKRZEWSKI, RICHARD JEROME,** VERTEBRATE PALEONTOLOGY. *Current Pos:* from asst prof to assoc prof earth sci, 69-78, PROF GEOL, FT HAYS STATE UNIV, 78-, DIR, STERNBERG MEM MUS, 73- *Personal Data:* b Hamtramck, Mich, Nov 5, 40; m 66; c 2. *Educ:* Wayne State Univ, BS, 63; Univ Mich, MS, 65, PhD(vert paleont), 68. *Prof Exp:* NSF fel geol, Idaho State Univ-Los Angeles Co Mus, 68-69. *Mem:* Soc Vert Paleont; Paleont Soc; Am Soc Mammal; Soc Syst Zool; Am Quaternary Asn. *Res:* Fossil mammals, particularly rodents; late Cenozoic stratigraphy. *Mailing Add:* 509 W 31st St Hays KS 67601

**ZAKRZEWSKI, SIGMUND FELIX,** BIOCHEMISTRY, ENVIRONMENTAL SCIENCES. *Current Pos:* RETIRED. *Personal Data:* b Buenos Aires, Arg, Sept 15, 19; m 56; c Kristina Harff. *Educ:* Univ Hamburg, MS, 52, PhD(biochem), 54. *Prof Exp:* Res asst, Sch Med, Western Res Univ, 52-53; Yale Univ, 53-56; sr cancer res scientist, Roswell Park Mem Inst, 56-61, assoc cancer res scientist, 61-71, prin cancer res scientist, Dept Exp Therapeut, 71-76, prin cancer res scientist, Dept Clin Pharm & Therapeut, 78-87, consult, Dept Exp Ther, 87-93. *Concurrent Pos:* Emer prof, Dept Pharmacol, State Univ NY Buffalo, Roswell Park Div; vis prof, Buffalo State Col, Tech Univ, Gdansk, Poland. *Mem:* AAAS. *Res:* Cancer chemotherapy; metabolism of folic acid and folic acid antagonist; pharmacokinetics of anticancer drugs in man. *Mailing Add:* 260 Lakewood Pkwy Buffalo NY 14226. *E-Mail:* sigzak@ubrms.cc.buffalo.edu

**ZAKRZEWSKI, THOMAS MICHAEL,** AEROSPACE SCIENCES, CHEMISTRY. *Current Pos:* GROUP VPRES, MID-ATLANTIC REGION, NICHOLS RES GROUP, 83- *Personal Data:* b Jackson, Mich, Mar 13, 43; m 68; c 3. *Educ:* Univ Mich, BS, 63. *Prof Exp:* Tech staff mem EO & IR sensors, Willow Run Labs, Inst Sci & Technol, Univ Mich, 63-69; tech staff mem IR sensors & systs, Gen Res Corp, 69-73; dir Washington opers IR systs & simulations, Mission Res Corp, 73-74; tech staff mem, Inst Res & Active Optics, 74-75, dir, Space Systs Dept, Gen Res Corp, 75-81, dir, Washington Opers, Flow Gen, Inc, 78-81, dir, Eastern Opers, Technol Appln Group & Space Systs Dept, 81-83. *Concurrent Pos:* Chmn, Comt Optical Measurements for Missile Tests, Air Force Studies Bd, Nat Res Coun, 86-90. *Mem:* AAAS; Sigma Xi; Am Inst Aeronaut & Astronaut; Am Chem Soc; Nat Space Inst; Am Soc Naval Engrs. *Res:* Electro-optical and infrared sensors, target signatures, and phenomenology; advanced offensive and defensive strategic systems; advanced space systems technology. *Mailing Add:* 10917 Howland Dr Reston VA 22091-4903

**ZALANI, SUNITA,** VIROLOGY, GENE REGULATION. *Current Pos:* Fel, Dept Biochem, 88-91, RES ASSOC, LINEBERGER COMP CANCER CTR, UNIV NC, CHAPEL HILL, 91- *Personal Data:* b Baroda, Gujari, India, June 27, 61; m 85, Suresh Siddhanti; c Samir. *Educ:* MS Univ, India, BS, 80, MS, 82, PhD(biochem), 89. *Mem:* assoc mem, Am Soc Biochem & Molecular Biol. *Res:* Gene regulation of Epstein-Barr Virus (EBV) promoters, we have examined whether disruption of EBV latency can be mediated through cellular SPI and 21F-268 transcription factors. *Mailing Add:* Lilly Corp Ctr Eli Lilly & Co Indianapolis IN 46285. *Fax:* 919-966-3015

**ZALAY, ANDREW W(ILLIAM),** ORGANIC CHEMISTRY. *Current Pos:* SR RES CHEMIST, STERLING-WINTHROP RES INST, 58- *Personal Data:* b Budapest, Hungary, May 20, 18; m 46, Ethel; c 3. *Educ:* Budapest Tech Univ, dipl, 40, EMe, 42. *Prof Exp:* Chem engr, 36-40, Dr Chem Eng, Budapest Tech Univ, 36-42; Pharmacist, Pasmany Peter Univ Sci; Res lab leader org chem, Chinoin Pharmaceut Works, Budapest, 51-56; res chemist, Textile Res Inst, NJ, 57-58. *Mem:* Am Chem Soc. *Res:* Pharmaceuticals. *Mailing Add:* 416 Robbins Ave PO Box 5938 Trenton NJ 08638-3724

**ZALAY, ETHEL SUZANNE,** ORGANIC CHEMISTRY. *Current Pos:* res chemist, 58-69, assoc res chemist, 69-77, RES CHEMIST, STERLING-WINTHROP RES INST, STERLING DRUG, INC, 77- *Personal Data:* b Budapest, Hungary, Sept 1, 19; m 46; c 3. *Educ:* Univ Sci Budapest, Hungary, PhD, 44. *Prof Exp:* Owner, Dr Somody Lab, 45-51; org chemist, Fine Chem Producing Union, 51-54; owner, Dr Somody Lab, 54-56; org chemist, Textile Res Inst, 57; res chemist, Biol Res Lab, Philadelphia Gen Hosp, 57-58. *Mem:* Am Chem Soc. *Res:* Fine organic chemicals; phospholipids; pharmaceuticals; heterocyclic chemistry. *Mailing Add:* 905 Myrtle Ave Albany NY 12208-2219

**ZALESAK, JOSEPH FRANCIS,** UNDERWATER ACOUSTICS, TRANSDUCTION. *Personal Data:* b Fountain Hill, Pa, Jan 2, 42; m 85, Carol McFall; c Jennifer, Judith, Matthew, Robert & Bradford. *Educ:* LaSalle Col, BA, 63; Lehigh Univ, MS, 67, PhD(solid state physics), 72. *Prof Exp:* Physicist, Naval Res Lab, 63-66, res physicist, 72-95. *Concurrent Pos:* Assoc prof, Univ Cent Fla, 80-81. *Mem:* Acoust Soc Am; Am Inst Physics. *Res:* Underwater acoustic calibration techniques and development of calibration systems which implement the above techniques; acoustic radiation from vibrating structures; develop specialized underwater acoustic transducers. *Mailing Add:* Naval Undersea Warfare Ctr-USRD PO Box 568337 Orlando FL 32856-8337. *Fax:* 407-857-5259; *E-Mail:* jzalesak@usro.nuwc.navy.mil

**ZALESKI, HALINA MARIA,** SWINE PRODUCTION & MANAGEMENT, REPRODUCTIVE PHYSIOLOGY. *Current Pos:* EXTEN SWINE SPECIALIST, UNIV HAWAII, 93- *Personal Data:* b Marlborough, Gt Brit, June 24, 50; Can citizen; m 73, Christopher E Mewhort; c Celka Z & Lisa Z. *Educ:* Univ Sask, BSc, 74; Univ Guelph, PhD(animal sci), 92. *Prof Exp:* Owner/mgr, Self-Reliance & Hard Struggle Coop Farm, 73-85; res asst, Univ Sask, 74-75, lab instr chem, 75-76; field rep, Swine Improv Serv Coop, 80; mgr farrowing & breeding, V & V Livestock Ltd, 85-89; res assoc, Univ Ill, 92-93. *Concurrent Pos:* Training coordr swine prod, Farm Start, 81-85, Sask Indian Agr Prog, 81-85 & Manpower Indust Training Prog, 81-85; instr swine prod, Wascana Inst, 88-89. *Mem:* Am Soc Animal Sci; Soc Study Reproduction; Agr Inst Can. *Res:* Identification of problems in the passage of piglets through the reproductive tract at parturition; livestock waste management; swine production management. *Mailing Add:* Dept Animal Sci Univ Hawaii 1800 East-West Rd Honolulu HI 96822. *Fax:* 808-956-4883; *E-Mail:* halina@hawaii.edu

**ZALESKI, JAN F,** REGULATION OF METABOLISM IN FRESHLY ISOLATED & CRYOPRESERVED HEPATOCYTES, CHEMICAL CARCINOGENISIS. *Current Pos:* RES ASSOC PROF, DEPT PHARMACOL & TOXICOL, RUTGERS STATE UNIV, NJ, 89- *Personal Data:* b Bytom, Poland, Feb 3, 49; US citizen; m 71, Margaret Toczkowska; c Marta & Monika. *Educ:* Univ Warsaw, MS, 71, PhD(biochem), 78. *Honors & Awards:* Award for Res Excellence, Ministry Sci & Higher Educ, Poland, 78. *Prof Exp:* From res assoc to assoc prof biochem, Inst Biochem, Univ Warsaw, Poland, 71-82; assoc scientist, Cardiovasc Res Prog, Okla Med Res Found, 82-85; res assoc, Dept Biochem & Biophys, Univ Pa, 85-88. *Concurrent Pos:* Vis scientist, Dept Exp Therapeut, Roswell Park Mem Inst, Buffalo, 79-82, Great Lakes Lab, State Univ NY, Buffalo, 88; mem, Nat Inst Environ Health Sci Ctr Excellence, Piscataway, 89- *Mem:* Am Soc Biochem & Molecular Biol; Int Soc Study Xenobiotics. *Res:* Regulation and integration of cellular metabolism; metabolism of xenobiotics; cellular toxicology; chemical carcinogenesis; isolation and cryopreservation of hepatocytes; regulation of membrane-bound enzymes; experimental diabetes; bioartificial liver devices. *Mailing Add:* 843 Bryn Mawr Ave Narberth PA 19072-1515. *Fax:* 732-445-6905; *E-Mail:* jzaleski@eohsi.rutgers.edu

**ZALESKI, MAREK BOHDAN,** immunogenetics, transplantation; deceased, see previous edition for last biography

**ZALESKI, WITOLD ANDREW,** CHILD & ADOLESCENCE PSYCHIATRY. *Current Pos:* assoc prof, 67-73, prof pediat & assoc prof psychiat, 73-87, dir, Alvin Buckwold Ctr, Univ Hosp, 67-87, EMER PROF, UNIV SASK, 87- *Personal Data:* b Pyzdry, Poland, Apr 4, 20; Can citizen; m 48; c 4. *Educ:* Univ Edinburgh, MB, ChB, 46; Royal Col Physicians & Surgeons, Ireland, dipl psychol med, 52; Royal Col Physicians & Surgeons Can, cert psychiat, 62; Univ Sask, MD, adeundem, 64; FRCP(C), 72; Royal Col Psychiat, cert, 73. *Prof Exp:* Dep supt & consult psychiatrist, Ment Retardation Insts, Regional Hosp Bd Eng, Birmingham, 54-58; clin dir, Sask Training Sch, Moose Jaw, Can, 58-67. *Concurrent Pos:* Vis consult psychiat, Univ Sask Hosp, 62-67, vis consult, St Paul's Hosp & City Hosp, Saskatoon; hon consult, Univ Hosp, Saskatoon, 87-; hon prof psychiatry, Univ BC, 88. *Mem:* Fel Can Pediat Soc; fel Can Acad of Child Psychiat; Can Med Asn; Can Psychiat Asn. *Res:* Etiology and prevention of mental retardation; inborn errors of metabolism; behavioral programs for the retarded; delivery of services in mental retardation. *Mailing Add:* 4195 Rockridge Rd West Vancouver BC V7W 1A3 Can

**ZALEWSKI, EDMUND JOSEPH,** ORGANIC POLYMER CHEMISTRY. *Current Pos:* From technician polyester to group leader polymer, 50-67, mgr polymer, 67-69, MGR RES, SCHENECTADY CHEM, INC, 69- *Personal Data:* b Schenectady, NY, July 23, 31; m 58; c 5. *Educ:* Union Col, BS, 64. *Mem:* Am Chem Soc; Soc Plastics Engrs. *Res:* Development of organic and heterocyclic polymers exhibiting excellent mechanical properties coupled with chemical and thermal resistance for use as electrical insulation. *Mailing Add:* 2761 Maida Lane Schenectady NY 12306

**ZALIK, RICHARD ALBERT,** APPROXIMATION THEORY, ROTORDYNAMICS. *Current Pos:* from asst prof to assoc prof, 78-85, PROF MATH, AUBURN UNIV, 85- *Personal Data:* b Buenos Aires, Arg, Nov 20, 43; nat US; m 70; c Daniel & David. *Educ:* Univ Buenos Aires, Licenciate, 68; Technion, Israel Inst Technol, DSc(math), 73. *Prof Exp:* Lectr math, Ben Gurion Univ Negev, Israel, 74-77; vis asst prof, Univ Rhode Island, 77-78. *Concurrent Pos:* Prin invest, Cray Res Inc, 88, NASA, 89; NASA & Am Soc Eng Educ fac fel, Marshall Space Flight Ctr, 87 & 88. *Mem:* Am Math Soc; Math Assn Am; Soc Ind & Appl Math. *Mailing Add:* Dept Math Auburn Univ Auburn AL 36849-5310. *Fax:* 334-844-6555; *E-Mail:* zalik@mail.auburn.edu

**ZALIK, SARA E,** DEVELOPMENTAL BIOLOGY, CELL BIOLOGY. *Current Pos:* from asst prof to assoc prof, 66-78, PROF ZOOL, UNIV ALTA, 78- *Personal Data:* b Mex, May 23, 39; m 66; c 2. *Educ:* Nat Univ Mex, BS, 59; Univ Ill, PhD(anat), 63. *Prof Exp:* NIH int fel, Biol Div, Oak Ridge Nat Lab, 63-64; asst prof cell biol, Ctr Res & Advan Studies, Nat Polytech Inst, Mex, 64-66. *Mem:* AAAS; Can Soc Cell Biol; Am Soc Zool; Soc Develop Biol; Am Soc Cell Biol; Sigma Xi. *Res:* Cell differentiation and metaplasia; cell surface and its role in differentiation and early embryogenesis. *Mailing Add:* Dept Zool Univ Alta Edmonton AB T6G 2E9 Can

**ZALIK, SAUL,** PLANT PHYSIOLOGY, BIOCHEMISTRY. *Current Pos:* from asst prof to prof, plant physiol & biochem, 52-86, EMER PROF PLANT PHYSIOL & BIOCHEM, UNIV ALTA, 86- *Personal Data:* b Ratcliffe, Sask, May 11, 21; m 66; c 2. *Educ:* Univ Man, BSA, 43, MSc, 48; Purdue Univ, PhD(plant physiol), 52. *Prof Exp:* Lectr plant sci, Univ Man, 48-49. *Mem:* AAAS; Am Soc Plant Physiol; Can Biochem Soc. *Res:* Metabolism of lipids; nucleic acids and proteins in relation to plant differentiation and development. *Mailing Add:* Univ Alta 13019 66th Ave Edmonton AB T6H 1Y6 Can

**ZALIPSKY, JEROME JAROSLAW,** ANALYTICAL CHEMISTRY. *Current Pos:* from sr scientist to group leader phys chem, 70-74, SECT HEAD PHYS & MICROANALYTICAL CHEM, WILLIAM H RORER INC, 74- *Personal Data:* b Ukraine; US citizen; c 2. *Educ:* St Joseph's Col, BS, 58, MS, 62; Univ Pa, PhD(analytical chem), 70. *Prof Exp:* From chemist to group leader analytical chem, Nat Drug Co, Richardson-Merrill Inc, 58-70. *Mem:* Am Chem Soc. *Res:* Chemical structure elucidation of new drug substance; kinetics; characterization of hydrolysis products; analytical and physical profile of drug substance. *Mailing Add:* 7600 Woodlawn Ave Philadelphia PA 19138

**ZALISKO, EDWARD JOHN,** FUNCTIONAL MORPHOLOGY, HISTOLOGY & HISTOCHEMISTRY. *Current Pos:* PROF BIOL ZOOL, BLACKBURN COL, 89- *Personal Data:* b Peoria, Ill, Jan 8, 58; m 82; c 2. *Educ:* Southern Ill Univ, Carbondale, BA, 80, MA, 82; Wash State Univ, PhD(zool), 87. *Prof Exp:* Asst prof zool, Southeast Mo State Univ, 87-89. *Mem:* Sigma Xi; AAAS; Am Soc Ichthyologists & Herpetologists; Am Soc Zoologists; Soc Study Amphibians & Reptiles. *Res:* Functional morphology of amphibian reproductive systems and snake oral glands using light and electron microscopy and histochemistry. *Mailing Add:* 19 Ridge Dr Carlinville IL 62626-1831

**ZALKIN, HOWARD,** BIOCHEMISTRY. *Current Pos:* from asst prof to assoc prof, 66-72, PROF BIOCHEM, PURDUE UNIV, LAFAYETTE, 72- *Personal Data:* b New York, NY, Dec 31, 34; m 66; c 3. *Educ:* Univ Calif, Davis, BS, 56, MS, 59, PhD(biochem), 61. *Prof Exp:* Res assoc chem, Harvard Univ, 61-62; res assoc biochem, Pub Health Res Inst New York, 62-64; res assoc, Col Physicians & Surgeons, Columbia Univ, 64-66. *Concurrent Pos:* Fels, NSF, 61-63, USPHS, 63-64 & USPHS fel biol sci, Stanford Univ, 72-73; vis scholar, Stanford Univ, 80-81; mem, Biochem Study Sect, NIH, 87-91. *Mem:* Am Soc Biochem & Molecular Biol; Am Soc Microbiol. *Res:* Structure, function and regulation of glutamine amidotranferase genes-enzymes; transcriptional and translational regulation of purine nucleotide synthesis. *Mailing Add:* Dept Biochem Purdue Univ West Lafayette IN 47907-1968. *Fax:* 765-494-7897

**ZALKOW, LEON HARRY,** ORGANIC CHEMISTRY. *Current Pos:* assoc prof, 65-69, PROF CHEM, GA INST TECHNOL, 69- *Personal Data:* b Millen, Ga, Nov 27, 29; m 71; c 1. *Educ:* Ga Inst Technol, BCE, 52, PhD(chem), 56. *Prof Exp:* Res fel, Wayne State Univ, 55-56, 57-59; res chemist, E I du Pont de Nemours & Co, 56-57; asst prof chem, Okla State Univ, 59-62, assoc prof, 62-65. *Concurrent Pos:* Prof & head dept chem, Univ of the Negev, 70-72. *Mem:* AAAS; Am Chem Soc; Royal Soc Chem. *Res:* Natural products; conformational analysis; chemistry of bicyclic azides. *Mailing Add:* Sch Chem & Biochem Ga Inst Technol Atlanta GA 30312

**ZALL, LINDA S,** GEOLOGY, CIVIL ENGINEERING & ENVIRONMENTAL SCIENCES. *Current Pos:* WITH US GOVT, 85- *Personal Data:* b Nov 15, 50; US citizen. *Educ:* Cornell Univ, BS, 72, MS, 74, PhD(civil & environ eng), 76. *Prof Exp:* Instr photo-geol, Cornell Univ, 71-75; consult environ & eng remote sensing, Earth Satellite Corp, 75-85. *Concurrent Pos:* Eng geologist, Trans Alaska Oil Pipeline Proj, 73. *Mem:* Sigma Xi. *Res:* Photo-geology; various remote sensing techniques. *Mailing Add:* 6812 Wilson Lane Bethesda MD 20817

**ZALL, ROBERT ROUBEN,** FOOD SCIENCE, DAIRY SCIENCE. *Current Pos:* from assoc prof to prof, 71-92, EMER PROF FOOD SCI, CORNELL UNIV, 92- *Personal Data:* b Lowell, Mass, Dec 6, 25; m 49, Hollie L Wiseblood; c Judy (Kusek), Linda & Jonathan. *Educ:* Univ Mass, BS, 49, MS, 50; Cornell Univ, PhD(food sci), 68. *Honors & Awards:* Howard Marlatt Award Lab Technol, NY State Sanitarians, 79. *Prof Exp:* Lab dir dairy prod, Grandview Dairies, Inc, NY, 50-51, mgr, Butter & Cheese Div, 51-53, mgr, Condensed Milks & Powder Div, 53-57, gen mgr corp, 57-66; dir res & prod, Crowley Food Co, 68-71. *Concurrent Pos:* Environ Protection Agency pollution abatement demonstration grant, Whey Fractionation Plant, Crowley Foods Co, 69-72, proj dir, 71-; proj dir, farm ultrafiltration, Dairy Res Inc, 84-85. *Mem:* Inst Food Technologists; Am Soc Agr Engrs; Int Asn Milk, Food & Environ Sanitarians; Int Dairy Fedn. *Res:* Detergents as inhibitors in food; reusing cleaning fluids to reduce consumption of energy and chemicals; reclamation and renovation of food wastes; membrane filtration processing; utilization of whey fractions in foods; on farm ultrafiltration. *Mailing Add:* Dept Food Sci Stocking Hall Cornell Univ Ithaca NY 14853. *E-Mail:* rrzi@cornell.edu

**ZALLEN, EUGENIA MALONE,** FOOD SCIENCE, RESEARCH DESIGN & MANAGEMENT. *Current Pos:* EXEC VPRES, MALONE GROUP INT CONSULT, 90- *Personal Data:* b Camp Hill, Ala, July 18, 32; m 59, Harold. *Educ:* Auburn Univ, BS, 53; Purdue Univ, MS, 60; Univ Tenn, PhD(food sci), 74. *Prof Exp:* Dietetic intern, Med Ctr, Duke Univ, 53-54, assoc dietitian, 54-57; asst chief dietary, Univ Hosp, Emory Univ, 57-58; from instr to asst prof food & nutrit, Auburn Univ, 62-66; asst prof food, nutrit & inst admin, Univ Md, 67-72; researcher dairy sci, Okla State Univ, 72-73; researcher, Univ Tenn, 73-74; assoc prof & dir, Sch Home Econ, Univ Okla, 74-80; dean, ECarolina Univ, NC, 80-84, prof, 80-90. *Concurrent Pos:* Consult, Head Start Day Care Ctrs, Ala, 65-66; field reader, Bur Res, HEW, DC, 66-; consult, Univ Consult, Inc, Ala, 68 & Optimal Systs, Inc, Ga, 69-; pres, Acad World, Inc, Consults, 75-86; vis prof, Univ Hawaii, 89. *Mem:* Am Dietetic Asn; Inst Food Technologists; Sigma Xi. *Res:* Quality factors in quantity food production; analysis of changes in food habits; refrigerated foods; home canning of fish for year round source of Omega 3FA; sensory perceptions of elderly. *Mailing Add:* PO Box 8767 Columbus GA 31908-8767

**ZALLEN, RICHARD,** CONDENSED MATTER PHYSICS, OPTICAL PROPERTIES OF SOLIDS. *Current Pos:* PROF PHYSICS, VA TECH, 83- *Personal Data:* b New York, NY, Jan 1, 37; m 64, Doris Teichler; c Jennifer A & Avram A. *Educ:* Rensselaer Polytech Inst, BS, 57; Harvard Univ, AM, 59, PhD(solid state physics), 64. *Prof Exp:* Res asst solid state physics, Harvard Univ, 59-64, res fel, 64-65; staff mem, Xerox Res Labs, 65-83. *Concurrent Pos:* Vis assoc prof, Technion, 71-72; vis fel, Imperial Col, 90-91. *Mem:* Fel Am Phys Soc; Mat Res Soc. *Res:* Experimental studies of optical properties of solids; vibrational and electronic structure of molecular solids, layer crystals, semiconductors, and amorphous solids; Raman scattering; optical effects in solids at high pressure; percolation theory; nanocrystalline solids; solid state theory. *Mailing Add:* Dept Physics Va Tech Blacksburg VA 24061. *Fax:* 540-231-7511; *E-Mail:* rzallen@vt.edu

**ZALMAN, LEORA S,** CELL BIOLOGY, IMMUNOLOGY. *Current Pos:* SR SCIENTIST, AGOURON PHARMACEUT, 93- *Educ:* Univ Calif, Berkeley, PhD(microbiol), 72. *Mailing Add:* Pharm Dept Agouron Pharm 3565 General Atomics Ct San Diego CA 92121. *E-Mail:* zalman@agouron.com

**ZALOM, FRANK G,** INTEGRATED PEST MANAGEMENT, HORTICULTURAL CROPS ENTOMOLOGY. *Current Pos:* LECTR, EXTEN ENTOMOLOGIST & AES ENTOMOLOGIST, UNIV CALIF, 80-; DIR, UNIV CALIF STATEWIDE INTEGRATED PEST MGT PROJ, 87- *Personal Data:* b Chicago, Ill, Mar 3, 52; m 79, Janet Smilanick; c Martina & Nicholas. *Educ:* Ariz State Univ, BS, 73, MS, 75; Univ Calif, Davis, PhD(entom), 79. *Honors & Awards:* Excellence Entomol Award, Am Registry Prof Entomolgists, 90; Outstanding Achievement in Extension, Entomol Soc Am, 92. *Prof Exp:* Asst prof, Univ Minn, 79-80. *Concurrent Pos:* Lectr, Int Agr Develop, 80-; Fulbright sr res fel, Spain, 92-93; assoc ed, Calif Agr Magazine, 93-, Entom Probs, 94-; mem, Gov Exotic Pest Eradication Task Force, 95-96. *Mem:* Entom Soc Am; AAAS; Czechoslovak Soc Arts & Sci; Asn Appl Insect Ecologists. *Res:* On the management of insect pests of horticultural crops and vegetables using chemical and nonchemical approaches; overwintering and springtime emergence of insects in subtropical areas. *Mailing Add:* Statewide Integrated Pest Mgt Univ Calif Davis CA 95616. *Fax:* 530-752-6004; *E-Mail:* fgzalom@ucdavis.edu

**ZALOSH, ROBERT GEOFFREY,** FIRE PROTECTION ENGINEERING, HAZARD ANALYSIS. *Current Pos:* PROF FIRE PROTECTION ENG, WORCESTER POLYTECH INST, 90- *Personal Data:* b New York, NY, Oct 10, 44; m 65, Gloria Katz; c Michael & Matthew. *Educ:* Cooper Union, BE, 65; Univ Rochester, MS, 66; Northeastern Univ, PhD(mech eng), 70. *Prof Exp:* Assoc scientist, Space Systs Div, Avco Corp, 66-67; sr scientist, Mt Auburn Res Assocs, Inc, 70-75; sr res scientist, Factory Mutual Res Corp, 75-78, mgr Explosion & Energetics Sect, 78-84, asst mgr appl res, 84-87, mgr, 88-90. *Concurrent Pos:* Consult. *Mem:* Am Soc Mech Engrs; Combustion Inst; Soc Fire Protection Engrs; Nat Fire Protection Asn. *Res:* Fire and explosion protection; explosion venting; vapor cloud dispersal; blast wave phenomena; advanced battery hazards; fire suppression; explosion research. *Mailing Add:* 20 Rockland Wellesley MA 02181. *E-Mail:* bzalosh@wpi.wpi.edu

**ZALUBAS, ROMUALD,** ASTROPHYSICS. *Current Pos:* RETIRED. *Personal Data:* b Pandelys, Lithuania, July 20, 11; nat US; m 39; c 1. *Educ:* Kaunas State Univ, MA, 36; Georgetown Univ, PhD(astrophys), 55. *Prof Exp:* Asst astron, Vilnius State Univ, 40-44; dir sec sch, Ger, 45-49; instr math, Nazareth Col (NY), 49-51; instr, Georgetown Univ, 52-57; physicist, Nat Bur Standards, 55-87. *Mem:* AAAS; Am Astron Soc; Sigma Xi; Optical Soc Am. *Res:* Description and analysis of atomic spectra; thorium wavelength standards; atomic energy levels of the rare earth elements; critical compilation of energy level data of the first thirty elements (hydrogen through zinc). *Mailing Add:* 908 Roswell Dr Silver Spring MD 20901-2128

**ZALUCKY, THEODORE B,** pharmacy, pharmaceutical chemistry; deceased, see previous edition for last biography

**ZALUSKY, RALPH,** INTERNAL MEDICINE, HEMATOLOGY. *Current Pos:* from asst prof to assoc prof, 66-77, PROF MED, MT SINAI SCH MED, 77-; CHIEF DIV HEMAT-ONCOL, BETH ISRAEL MED CTR, 76- *Personal Data:* b Pawtucket, RI, Oct 11, 31; m 58; c 3. *Educ:* Brown Univ, AB, 53; Boston Univ, MD, 57; Am Bd Internal Med, dipl, 64, hemat, 72. *Prof Exp:* From intern to sr resident med, Duke Univ Hosp, 57-62. *Concurrent Pos:* USPHS fel, Thorndike Mem Lab, Harvard Univ, 59-61; res assoc med, Mt Sinai Hosp, 64-65; asst attend hematologist, 65-66, actg chief hemat, 72-76, attend hematologist, 77- *Mem:* Am Fedn Clin Res; Am Soc Clin Nutrit; Am Soc Hemat. *Res:* Interrelationships between vitamin B-twelve and folic acid metabolism; sodium and potassium membrane transport; abnormal hemoglobins; erythropoietin physiology. *Mailing Add:* Dept Med Div Hemat-Oncol Mt Sinai Sch Med Beth Israel Med Ctr 10 Nathan Dr Perlman Pl New York NY 10003-3896. *Fax:* 212-420-4498

**ZAM, STEPHEN G, III,** PARASITOLOGY. *Current Pos:* from asst prof parasitol to assoc prof zool, 66-77, ASSOC PROF MICROBIOL & CELL SCI, UNIV FLA, 77- *Personal Data:* b Toledo, Ohio, Nov 3, 32. *Educ:* Georgetown Univ, BS, 54; Catholic Univ, MS, 56; Univ Southern Calif, PhD(biol sci), 66. *Prof Exp:* Asst prof biol, Loyola Univ (Calif), 66. *Concurrent Pos:* Consult, Marineland, 67- *Mem:* Am Soc Parasitol; Am Soc Trop Med & Hyg; Int Soc Parasitol. *Res:* Nematode physiology including biochemistry of nematode egg hatching and larval molting; immunology to helminth infections. *Mailing Add:* 5050 NW 39th Ave Gainesville FL 32606

**ZAMAN, KHAIRUL B M Q,** AEROSPACE SCIENCES. *Current Pos:* res assoc, NASA Langley Res Ctr Va, 82-85, AEROSPACE ENGR, NASA LEWIS RES CTR, 86- *Personal Data:* b Dhaka, Bangladesh, Aug 31, 47; US citizen; m 73, Afroz Jahan; c Sarah H & Sophie J. *Educ:* Univ Bangladesh, BS, 69, MS, 73; Univ Houston, PhD(mech eng), 78. *Prof Exp:* Lectr, Univ Bangladesh, 70-73; res scientist, Univ Houston, 78-82. *Mem:* Am Phys Soc; Am Inst Aeronaut & Astronaut. *Res:* Turbulent shear flows; separated flows; flow control. *Mailing Add:* NASA Lewis Res Ctr 21000 Brookpark Rd Cleveland OH 44135. *Fax:* 216-433-3000

**ZAMANZADEH, MEHROOZ,** CORROSION & METALLURGICAL ENGINEERING, FAILURE ANALYSIS. *Current Pos:* PRES MATCO ASSOC, 92- *Personal Data:* b Tehran, Iran, Mar 12, 50; m 83; c 1. *Educ:* San Jose State Univ, BS, 74, MS, 75; Pa State Univ, PhD(metall), 80. *Prof Exp:* Sr metallurgist corrosion, Buehler-NIOC, 80-85; fel corrosion, Carnegie-Mellon Univ, 85-87; mgr, Metall Div, Prof Serv Indust, Pittsburgh Testing Lab Div, 87-92. *Concurrent Pos:* Lectr, Carnegie-Mellon Univ, 88-90. *Mem:* Nat Asn Corrosion Engrs; Am Soc Metals; Am Inst Chem Engrs. *Res:* Division management; research and development; technical responsibilities; teaching; conducted and reviewed thousands of metallurgical failure analysis and on site investigations in materials science and engineering; author of 37 publications in materials science and corrosion engineering journals. *Mailing Add:* 4640 Campbells Run Rd Pittsburgh PA 15205. *E-Mail:* mehrooz@aol.com

**ZAMBERNARD, JOSEPH,** CYTOLOGY. *Current Pos:* prof, 75-77, CHMN DEPT ANAT, SCH MED, WRIGHT STATE UNIV, 77- *Personal Data:* b Sept 5, 33; US citizen. *Educ:* Univ Ala, AB, 53, MS, 56; Tulane Univ, PhD(cytol), 64. *Prof Exp:* Fel virol & immunol, Sch Med, Univ Colo, Denver, 64-66, asst prof anat, 66-72; assoc prof, Albany Med Col, 72-75. *Mem:* Electron Micros Soc Am; Am Soc Cell Biol; Am Asn Anatomists; Tissue Cult Asn. *Res:* Virology and immunology; ultrastructure. *Mailing Add:* Dept Anat Wright State Univ Sch Med Dayton OH 45435

**ZAMBITO, ARTHUR JOSEPH,** ORGANIC CHEMISTRY. *Current Pos:* RETIRED. *Personal Data:* b Rochester, NY, Sept 7, 14; m 42, Kathryn Terrill; c 7. *Educ:* Univ Mich, BS, 40, MS, 41, PhD(org chem), 47. *Prof Exp:* From res chemist to sr res chemist, Merck & Co Inc, 41-64, sect leader, Res & Develop Lab, 64-75, sr res fel, 75-84. *Mem:* Am Chem Soc. *Res:* Synthesis of pharmaceuticals; synthesis and isolation of amino acids; preparation of parenteral solutions and emulsions; synthesis of anticancer agents; antibiotics. *Mailing Add:* 75 Hillcrest Dr Clark NJ 07066-2936

**ZAMBONI, LUCIANO,** PATHOLOGY, ELECTRON MICROSCOPY. *Current Pos:* from asst prof to prof path, Univ Calif, Los Angeles, 65-91, chief dept path & head electron micros, Los Angeles Co Harbor-Univ Calif Los Angeles Med Ctr, 65-91, EMER PROF PATH & LAB MED, UNIV CALIF, LOS ANGELES, 91- *Personal Data:* b San Dona di Piave, Italy, Sept 6, 29; m 57; c 2. *Educ:* Univ Rome, MD, 55, dipl gastroenterol, 58. *Prof Exp:* Instr path, Univ Rome, 55-59; asst resident anat, Univ Calif, Los Angeles, 59-60; instr, McGill Univ, 60-61; asst resident path, Karolinska Inst, Sweden, 61-63.

*Mem:* Electron Micros Soc Am; Am Soc Cell Biol; Am Fertil Soc; Soc Study Reproduction; Ital Med Asn. *Res:* Reproductive biology; ultrastructural studies on embryogenesis, early reproduction and fertilization. *Mailing Add:* Dept Path Univ Calif Los Angeles Med Ctr 1000 W Carson St Torrance CA 90509

**ZAMBRASKI, EDWARD K,** kidney physiology, for more information see previous edition

**ZAME, ALAN,** MATHEMATICS, COMPUTER SCIENCE. *Current Pos:* Assoc prof, 65-76, PROF MATH, UNIV MIAMI, 76-, CHMN, MATH & COMPUT SCI, 89- *Personal Data:* b New York, NY, Aug 16, 41; m 89. *Educ:* Calif Inst Technol, BS, 62; Univ Calif, Berkeley, PhD(math), 65. *Mem:* Am Math Soc; Am Math Asn. *Res:* Number theory; functional and combinatorial analysis. *Mailing Add:* Dept Math-Comput Sci Univ Miami Coral Gables FL 33124

**ZAME, WILLIAM ROBIN,** ANALYSIS & FUNCTIONAL ANALYSIS. *Current Pos:* from asst prof to assoc prof, 72-81, PROF MATH, STATE UNIV NY, BUFFALO, 81- *Personal Data:* b Long Beach, NY, Nov 4, 45; m 90. *Educ:* Calif Inst Technol, BS, 65; Tulane Univ, MS, 67, PhD(math), 70. *Prof Exp:* Evans instr math, Rice Univ, 70-72; assoc prof, Tulane Univ, 75-78. *Mem:* Am Math Soc; Am Soc Econometric. *Res:* Several complex variables; Banach algebras, C-algebras; mathmatical economics. *Mailing Add:* Dept Econ Univ Calif 405 Hilgard Ave Los Angeles CA 90024-1477

**ZAMECNIK, PAUL CHARLES,** MEDICINE. *Current Pos:* from instr to assoc prof, Harvard Univ, 42-56, Collis P Huntington prof, 56-79, dir, J C Warren Labs, 56-79, EMER PROF ONCOL MED, SCH MED, HARVARD UNIV, 79-; PRIN SCIENTIST, WORCESTER FOUND EXP BIOL, 79- *Personal Data:* b Cleveland, Ohio, Nov 22, 12; m 36; c 3. *Educ:* Dartmouth Col, AB, 33; Harvard Univ, MD, 36. *Hon Degrees:* Dr, Univ Utrecht, 66; DSc, Columbia Univ, 71, Harvard Univ, 82, Roger Williams Col, 83, Dartmouth Col, 88 & Univ Mass. *Honors & Awards:* Nat Medal of Sci, 91; John Collins Warren Triennial Prize, 46 & 50; James Ewing Award, 63; Borden Award, 65; Am Cancer Soc Nat Award, 68; Passano Award, 70; Merck Award, Am Soc Biol Chem, 97. *Prof Exp:* Resident med, C P Huntington Mem Hosp, Boston, 36-37; intern, Univ Hosps, Cleveland, 38-39; Moseley traveling fel from Harvard Univ, Carlsberg Lab, Copenhagen, 39-40; Finney-Howell fel, Rockefeller Inst, 41-42. *Concurrent Pos:* Physician, Mass Gen Hosp, 56-79, sr physician, 79-, hon physician, 79- *Mem:* Nat Acad Sci; Asn Am Physicians; Am Acad Arts & Sci; Am Soc Biol Chemists; Am Asn Cancer Res (pres, 64-65). *Res:* Protein synthesis; cancer; nucleic acid metabolism; virology. *Mailing Add:* Worcester Found Exp Biol 222 Maple Ave Shrewsbury MA 01545

**ZAMEL, NOE,** RESPIRATORY PHYSIOLOGY. *Current Pos:* assoc prof, 72-80, PROF MED, FAC MED & DIR RESPIRATORY PHYSIOL, TRIHOSP RESPIRATORY SERV, UNIV TORONTO, CAN, 80- *Personal Data:* b Rio Grande, Brazil, Apr 2, 35; m 59; c 3. *Educ:* Col Med, Fed Univ Rio Grande do Sul, Brazil, MD, 58. *Honors & Awards:* Miguel Couto Award, Col Med, Fed Univ Rio Grande do Sul, 58; Cecile Lehman Mayer Award, Am Col Chest Physicians, 69. *Prof Exp:* From instr to assoc prof med, Col Med, Fed Univ Rio Grande do Sul, Brazil, 62-70; assoc prof med & dir respiratory physiol, Col Med, Univ Nebr, Omaha, 70-72. *Concurrent Pos:* Res fel respiratory physiol, Cardiovasc Res Inst, Univ Calif, San Francisco, 69. *Mem:* Am Col Chest Physicians; Am Thoracic Soc; Am Fedn Clin Res; Can Soc Clin Invest; Am Physiol Soc. *Res:* Lung mechanics; asthma. *Mailing Add:* Dept Med Univ Toronto Mt Sinai Hosp 600 University Ave Rm 656 Toronto ON M5G 1X5 Can. *Fax:* 416-586-8558

**ZAMENHOF, PATRICE JOY,** MOLECULAR GENETICS. *Current Pos:* asst prof, 64-71, ASSOC PROF BIOL CHEM, SCH MED, UNIV CALIF, LOS ANGELES, 71- *Personal Data:* b Santa Rosa, Calif, Apr 2, 34; m 61. *Educ:* Univ Calif, Berkeley, AB, 56, PhD(microbiol), 62. *Prof Exp:* Res assoc biochem, Col Physicians & Surgeons, Columbia Univ, 62-64. *Concurrent Pos:* USPHS res grants, Univ Calif, Los Angeles, 65-68 & 70-, career develop award, Nat Inst Gen Med Sci, 67, mem cancer ctr, 75- *Mem:* Am Soc Microbiol; Genetics Soc Am; Am Soc Biol Chemists; Sigma Xi. *Res:* Mutagenic mechanisms; genetic instability in microorganisms; mutator genes; repair of genetic damage; functional interactions of inactive mutant proteins. *Mailing Add:* Dept Biol Chem Univ Calif-Los Angeles Sch Med Los Angeles CA 90024

**ZAMENHOF, ROBERT G A,** MEDICAL PHYSICS. *Current Pos:* HEAD, IMAGING PHYSICS SECT, MED PHYSICS DIV, NEW ENG MED CTR HOSP, 82-, PROF MED PHYSICS, DEPT RADIATION ONCOL, 89- *Personal Data:* b Kidugala, EAfrica, 1946. *Educ:* Polytech N London, BS, 69; Univ Strathclyde, MS, 71; Mass Inst Technol, PhD(appl radiation physics), 77. *Mem:* Am Asn Physics Med; Biomed Eng Soc; Am Col Radiol. *Mailing Add:* Dept Radiol Deaconess Hosp Harvard Med Sch 1 Deaconess Rd Boston MA 02215

**ZAMENHOF, STEPHEN,** NEUROCHEMISTRY. *Current Pos:* PROF MICROBIAL GENETICS & BIOL CHEM, SCH MED, UNIV CALIF, LOS ANGELES, 64- *Personal Data:* b Warsaw, Poland, June 12, 11; US citizen; m 61, Patrice J Driskell. *Educ:* Warsaw Polytech Sch, Dr Tech Sci, 36; Columbia Univ, PhD(biochem), 49. *Prof Exp:* From asst prof to assoc prof biochem, Columbia Univ, 49-64. *Concurrent Pos:* Guggenheim fel, 58-59. *Mem:* Am Soc Biol Chem; Am Inst Nutrit; Soc Neurosci; Am Asn Anatomists; Int Soc Develop Neurosci; Sigma Xi. *Res:* Microbial genetics; nucleic acids; prenatal brain development. *Mailing Add:* Dept Micro & Immunol Univ Calif Sch Med Los Angeles CA 90024

**ZAMES, GEORGE,** MATHEMATICAL SYSTEMS THEORY. *Current Pos:* prof, 74-83, MACDONALD PROF ELEC ENG, MCGILL UNIV, 83-; SR FEL, CAN INST ADVAN RES, 84- *Personal Data:* b Lodz, Poland, Jan 7, 34; m 64; c 2. *Educ:* McGill Univ, BEng, 54; Imp Col, London Univ, dipl, 60; Mass Inst Technol, ScD(elec eng), 60. *Honors & Awards:* Field Award Sci & Eng, Inst Elec & Electronics Engrs, 85; Izaak Walton Killam Mem Prize, Can Coun, 95; Rufus Oldenburger Medal, Am Soc Mech Engrs, 96. *Prof Exp:* Res assoc elec eng, Mass Inst Technol, 54-61, asst prof, 61- 62, 63-65; res fel appl physics, Harvard Univ, 62-63; asst prof elec eng, Mass Inst Technol, 63-65; Nat Acad Sci res fel, Electronic Res Ctr, NASA, 65-68; sr scientist, Electronic Res Ctr, NASA, 68-72; vis prof elec eng, Technion, Haifa, 72-74. *Concurrent Pos:* Athlone fel, Imp Col, London Univ, 54-56; RR Associateship, Nat Acad Sci, 66-67; assoc ed, Soc Indust Appl Math J Control, 67-84, Systems & Control Lett, 80-84, Indust Math Asn J Math Control & Info, 83; Guggenheim fel, 67-68; Killiam fel, 84-86; assoc ed, Math Control, Signals & Systs, 88-91; consult ed, J Robust Control, 91- *Mem:* Fel Inst Elec & Electronics Engrs; Sigma Xi; fel Royal Soc Can; sr fel Can Inst Advan Res. *Res:* Nonlinear systems; feedback organizations; control system theory; communication system theory; functional analysis. *Mailing Add:* Dept Elec Eng 3480 University St Montreal PQ H3A 2A7 Can

**ZAMICK, LARRY,** THEORETICAL NUCLEAR PHYSICS. *Current Pos:* assoc prof, 66-70, PROF PHYSICS, RUTGERS UNIV, 70- *Personal Data:* b Winnipeg, Man, Mar 15, 35; m 66, Mona Monis; c Deborah L & Jonathan. *Educ:* Univ Man, BSc, 57; Mass Inst Technol, PhD(physics), 61. *Honors & Awards:* Sr US Scientist Alexander Von Humboldt Award, 86; Collab Res Award, NATO, 87. *Prof Exp:* Instr physics, Princeton Univ, 62-65, res assoc, 65-66. *Concurrent Pos:* Vis prof, Princeton Univ, 78, Weizmann Inst, 81. *Mem:* Fel Am Phys Soc. *Res:* Nuclear structure theory-effective interaction of nucleons in anucleus; superdeformed states. *Mailing Add:* Seven Meredith Pl E Piscataway NJ 08854. *Fax:* 732-932-4343; *E-Mail:* zamick@ruthep. rutgers.edu

**ZAMIKOFF, IRVING IRA,** DENTISTRY, PROSTHODONTICS. *Current Pos:* ASSOC PROF PROSTHODONT, SCH DENT, LA STATE UNIV, NEW ORLEANS, 70- *Personal Data:* b Toronto, Ont, Feb 13, 43; m 67; c 2. *Educ:* Univ Toronto, DDS, 67; Univ Mich, MS, 70; Am Bd Prosthodont, dipl, 72. *Concurrent Pos:* Vis dentist, Charity Hosp, New Orleans, 70- *Mem:* Am Dent Asn; Int Asn Dent Res; Can Dent Asn; Am Col Prosthodont. *Mailing Add:* 2103 59th St W Bradenton FL 34209

**ZAMIR, LOLITA ORA,** BIO-ORGANIC CHEMISTRY, ORGANIC CHEMISTRY. *Current Pos:* assoc prof, 82-84, PROF, INST ARMAND FRAPPIER, APPL MICROBIOL DEPT, UNIV QUEBEC, 84- *Personal Data:* b Cairo, Egypt; Israeli & US citizen; m 85; c Cedric. *Educ:* Israel Inst Technol, MSc, 66; Yale Univ, PhD(bio-org chem), 73. *Prof Exp:* Teaching asst chem, Yale Univ, 68-73; res fel biochem, Harvard Univ, 73-74; sr res chemist, Merck Inst, 74-75; from asst prof to assoc prof chem & assoc mem, Ctr Biochem Res, State Univ NY, Binghamton, 75-82. *Concurrent Pos:* auxillary prof, Chem Dept, McGill Univ, 82- *Mem:* Am Chem Soc; Am Asn Women Sci; Am Asn Univ Prof. *Res:* Biosynthesis; natural products; plants of microorganisms origin. *Mailing Add:* Univ Que Inst Armand Frappier Ctr Bact 531 Blvd Des Prairies Montreal PQ H7N 4Z3 Can

**ZAMORA, ANTONIO,** computer science, chemistry, for more information see previous edition.

**ZAMORA, CESARIO SIASOCO,** VETERINARY HISTOLOGY, VETERINARY GROSS ANATOMY. *Current Pos:* asst prof, Wash State Uniiv, 72-76, assoc prof, 76-81, head anat div, Dept Vet & Comp Anat, Pharmacol & Physiol, Col Vet Med, 81-82, PROF ANAT, WASH STATE UNIV, 81- *Personal Data:* b Marikina, Philippines, Nov 1, 38; US citizen; m 66, Marynella Cruz; c Pauline & M Jennifer. *Educ:* Univ Philippines, DVM, 59; Univ Minn, MS, 64; Univ Wis-Madison, PhD(vet sci), 72. *Prof Exp:* Instr vet anat, Univ Philippines, 59-62; res asst, Univ Minn, 62-64; instr to asst prof vet anat, Univ Philippines, 64-69; res asst, Univ Wis, 69-72. *Concurrent Pos:* Pvt vet pract (part-time), 59-62, 64-69. *Mem:* Am Vet Med Asn; Am Asn Vet Anatomists; World Asn Vet Anatomists; Asn Am Vet Med Col; Am Asn Anatomists. *Res:* Structure and function of the gastrointestinal tract of pigs; pathophysiology of gastric ulcers and enteric diseases of swine; structure and function of endocrine and reproductive organs of domestic animals. *Mailing Add:* Col Vet Med Wash State Univ Pullman WA 99164-6520. *Fax:* 509-335-4650

**ZAMORA, PAUL O,** carcinogenesis, for more information see previous edition

**ZAMORANO, LUCIA JOPEHINA,** NEUROSURGERY, STEREOTAXIS. *Current Pos:* ASSOC PROF NEUROSURG, WAYNE STATE UNIV, 91- *Personal Data:* b Santiago, Chile, Oct 23, 58; Chilean citizen. *Educ:* Cath Univ Med Sch, MD, 80; Freie Univ, West Berlin, Ger, PhD, 86. *Prof Exp:* Asst, Freie Univ, West Berlin, 83-86; attend neurosurgeon, Henry Ford Hosp, 86-91. *Res:* Instrumentation and software to perform computer guided surgery. *Mailing Add:* Neurosurg 6e UHCD MC Wayne State Univ Sch Med 540 E Canfield St Detroit MI 48324. *Fax:* 313-745-4099

**ZAMOST, BRUCE LEE,** MICROBIAL PHYSIOLOGY, DOWN STREAM PROCESSING. *Current Pos:* SCIENTIST, PROTEIN EXPRESSION TECHNOL, ZYMO GENETICS INC, SEATTLE, 94- *Personal Data:* b Chicago, Ill, Aug 19, 56. *Educ:* Southern Ill Univ, BA, 81, MS, 83. *Prof Exp:* Assoc researcher, Novo Labs Inc, 83-85, researcher, 85-87, staff research,

Novo Nordisk Bioindust, 87-90, staff researcher Bioprocessing Group, Novo Nordisk Entotech, 90-94. *Mem:* Soc Indust Microbiol; Am Chem Soc. *Res:* expression of recombinant fusion proteins in E Coli and physiological studies governing expression in Pichia Methanolica. *Mailing Add:* 2817 34th Ave W Seattle WA 98199. *Fax:* 206-442-6608; *E-Mail:* zamostb@zg1.com

**ZAMRIK, SAM YUSUF,** ENGINEERING MECHANICS. *Current Pos:* from instr to assoc prof, 60-75, PROF ENG MECH, PA STATE UNIV, UNIVERSITY PARK, 75- *Personal Data:* b Damascus, Syria, Dec 11, 32; US citizen; m 54; c 4. *Educ:* Univ Tex, BA, 56, BS, 57; Pa State Univ, MS, 61, PhD(eng mech), 65. *Prof Exp:* Design engr, Tex Pipe Line Co, 57-58; proj engr & consult, Gen Petrol Authority, 58-60. *Concurrent Pos:* Consult, Nat Forge Co, 68-72 & Gen Elec Co; fels, NASA & Ford Found; tech reviewer, NSF, NASA, Am Soc Mech Engrs & Soc Exp Stress Anal. *Mem:* Am Soc Testing & Mat; Am Soc Mech Engrs; Soc Exp Stress Anal; Sigma Xi. *Res:* Radiation effects on structural materials; fatigue and fracture mechanics; biaxial creep-fatigue interaction. *Mailing Add:* 457 Nimitz Ave State College PA 16801

**ZANAKIS, STELIOS (STEVE) H,** MANAGEMENT SCIENCE, APPLIED STATISTICS. *Current Pos:* from assoc prof to prof & chmn decision sci & info syst, Col Bus Admin, 80-86, PROF, FLA INT UNIV, 86- *Personal Data:* b Athens, Greece, Nov 16, 40; c 3. *Educ:* Nat Tech Univ, Athens, Dipl, 64; Pa State Univ, MBA, 70, MA, 72, PhD(mgt sci), 73. *Prof Exp:* Engr aerodyn, Greek Res Ctr Nat Defense, 65-66; indust engr mgt consult, Greek Prod Ctr, 67-68; asst prof indust eng & systs anal, WVa Col Grad Studies, 72-76, prog dir, 73-80, assoc prof, 76-80. *Concurrent Pos:* Consult, Ashland Oil, 73, Union Carbide Corp, 75-76, WVa Dept Hwy, 76-77 & Charleston Area Med Ctr, 78-79; mem, WVa State Comprehensive Health Plan Comt, 73-74; prin, Mgt Decision Syst Consults, 76-; guest ed, Mgt Sci, 83, Europ J Oper Res, 86; vis res prof, Tech Univ Crete, Greece, 94; adj prof, Mgt Info Syst, Univ West Indies, 95-96. *Mem:* Decision Sci Inst; Inst Opers Res & Mgt Sci; Hellenic Oper Res Soc. *Res:* Statistics and operations management software development for microcomputers, applications of operations research/management science techniques to solve real management problems; production, inventory, distribution management; hospital management engineering; conflict resolution via elicitation of opinions for program evaluation and consensus building; simulation and computer applications; prog evaluation and fund allocation under conflicting goals and qualitative or quantitative criteria; forecasting and statistical analysis. *Mailing Add:* Sch Bus Admin Dept Decision Sci & Info Syst Fla Int Univ Miami FL 33199

**ZAND, ROBERT,** BIOPHYSICAL CHEMISTRY, POLYMER CHEMISTRY & NEUROCHEMISTRY. *Current Pos:* assoc res biophysicist, 63-73, from asst prof to assoc prof, 68-86, PROF BIOCHEM & RES SCI, UNIV MICH, ANN ARBOR, 86-, PROF MACROMOLECULAR SCI & ENG, 92- *Personal Data:* b New York, NY, Jan 7, 30; m 52; c 3. *Educ:* Univ Mo, BS, 51; Polytech Inst Brooklyn, MS, 54; Brandeis Univ, PhD(chem), 61. *Prof Exp:* Res chemist, Irvington Varnish & Insulator, 53. *Concurrent Pos:* NIH fel, Harvard Med Sch, 61-63; fel, Brandeis Univ, 61-63; ODOL Found lectr, Univ Buenos Aires, 72; vis prof, Escola Paulista de Med, Sao Paulo, Brazil, 76; Inst Venezolano de Investigaciones Cientificas, Caracas Venezuela, 79; consult, Recreational Innovations-Med Prods Div, AISIN Seiki Co, Ltd; proj display prod opers, Gen Elec, 89-91. *Mem:* Am Chem Soc; Biophys Soc; Am Soc Neurochem; Am Soc Biol Chem; Int Soc Neurochem; Sigma Xi; Protein Soc. *Res:* Conformation of proteins, synthetic macromolecules and small molecules by spectroscopic methods; synthesis, physical and biological properties of nucleic acid analogs, polymers; synthesis and properties of conducting and electro-optic polymers. *Mailing Add:* Biophys Res Div Univ Mich Inst Sci & Technol 930 N University Ann Arbor MI 48109-1055

**ZANDER, ANDREW THOMAS,** SPECTROSCOPY. *Current Pos:* DIR MEAS LAB, VARIAN RES CTR, 87- *Personal Data:* b Chicago, Ill, Oct 27, 45; m 77; c 3. *Educ:* Univ Ill, Urbana, BS, 68; Univ Md, PhD(analytical chem), 76. *Prof Exp:* Chemist, Chicago Bridge & Iron Co, 66; asst chemist analytical chem, Stand Oil Co, Ind, 68-69; res assoc, Dept Chem, Ind Univ, 76-77; asst prof analytical chem, Cleveland State Univ, 77-79; staff scientist, Spectra Metrics, Inc, 79-84; sr staff engr, Perkins-Elmer Inc, 84-87. *Mem:* Am Chem Soc; Soc Appl Spectros; Sigma Xi; Optical Soc Am; fel Am Inst Chemists; Inst Elec & Electronics Engrs. *Res:* Design and development of single- and multi-element methods of atomic spectrometric analysis for trace metals; high resolution studies of spectral features in atomic spectroscopy; instrument systems. *Mailing Add:* 10380 Imperial Ave Cupertino CA 95014

**ZANDER, ARLEN RAY,** NUCLEAR PHYSICS, ATOMIC PHYSICS. *Current Pos:* PROVOST/VPRES ACAD AFFAIRS, NE LA UNIV, 89- *Personal Data:* b Shiner, Tex, Dec 12, 40; m 64, Dorothy Mayer; c Melanie, Aaron & Bryan. *Educ:* Univ Tex, Austin, BS, 64; Fla State Univ, PhD(nuclear physics), 70. *Prof Exp:* Res physicist, Phillips Petrol Co, 64-65; from asst prof to assoc prof, ETex State Univ, 70-79, external grants coordr, 74-77, prof physics, 79-89, from asst dean to dean arts & sci, 82-89. *Mem:* Am Asn Univ Adminrs; Am Asn Physics Teachers; Am Asn Higher Educ; Sigma Xi. *Res:* Direct nuclear reaction mechanisms; experimental fast neutron activation studies; x-ray fluorescence studies utilizing charged particle accelerators; atomic collisions. *Mailing Add:* Off Acad Affairs Northeast La Univ Monroe LA 71209-0700. *Fax:* 318-342-1034; *E-Mail:* zander@alpha.nlu.edu

**ZANDER, DONALD VICTOR,** AVIAN PATHOLOGY, POULTRY NUTRITION & HUSBANDRY. *Current Pos:* RETIRED. *Personal Data:* b Bellingham, Wash, Feb 15, 16; m 45; c 3. *Educ:* Univ Calif, Berkeley, BS, 41; Col State Univ, MS, 45, DVM, 50; Univ Calif, Davis, PhD(comp path), 53.

*Honors & Awards:* C A B Bottorff Serv Award, Am Asn Avian Path, 90. *Prof Exp:* Asst specialist & lectr vet med, Univ Calif, Davis, 50-53, asst prof, 53-55; lab instr bact, Colo State Univ, 48; dir poultry health res & serv, H & N Int, 55-89. *Concurrent Pos:* Pres, Western Poultry Dis Conf, 57; dir, Western Dist, Am Asn Avian Path, 84-88. *Mem:* Poultry Sci Asn; Am Vet Med Asn; Am Asn Avian Path (pres, 65-66); World Poultry Sci Asn; World Poultry Vet Asn. *Res:* Avian diseases; pathology, diagnosis and epizootiology; poultry husbandry and nutrition; pathogen-free poultry. *Mailing Add:* 18340 160th Ave NE Woodinville WA 98072

**ZANDER, VERNON EMIL,** MATHEMATICS. *Current Pos:* PRES, INTERCOASTAL DATA CORP, 82- *Personal Data:* b Toledo, Wash, Feb 3, 39; m 66; c 4. *Educ:* Univ Wash, BS, 61; Cath Univ, MS, 65, PhD(math), 69. *Prof Exp:* Mathematician, NIH, 61-66; from asst prof to assoc prof math, West Ga Col, 68-82. *Mem:* Am Math Soc; Math Asn Am. *Mailing Add:* 129 Bankhead Ave Carrollton GA 30117

**ZANDI, IRAJ,** CIVIL ENGINEERING. *Current Pos:* from assoc prof to prof, 66-80, actg dir, Nat Ctr Energy Mgt & Power, 72-77, NAT CTR PROF CIVIL ENG, UNIV PA, 80- *Personal Data:* b Teheran, Iran, June 30, 31; m 58; c 5. *Educ:* Univ Teheran, BS, 52; Univ Okla, MS, 57; Ga Inst Technol, PhD, 59. *Hon Degrees:* MA, Univ Pa, 71. *Honors & Awards:* Sigma Xi Ferst Award, Ga Inst Technol, 61. *Prof Exp:* Dir, Dept Environ Sanit, Ministry of Health, Govt Iran, 59-61; assoc prof eng, Abadan Inst Technol, Iran, 61-62; asst prof civil eng, Univ Del, 62-66. *Concurrent Pos:* Ed, J Pipeline, Am Soc Civil Engrs, 66-70, Elsevie Sci Publ Co, 79-; ed & publ, J Resource Mgt Technol, 81- *Mem:* Am Soc Eng Educ; Am Soc Civil Engrs; Am Inst Chem Engrs. *Res:* Pipeline engineering; resource recovery; resources and energy systems. *Mailing Add:* Dept Systs Eng Rm 229C Towne Bldg Univ Pa 220 S 33rd St Philadelphia PA 19104

**ZANDLER, MELVIN E,** THEORETICAL CHEMISTRY. *Current Pos:* Asst prof, 66-75, ASSOC PROF CHEM, WICHITA STATE UNIV, 75- *Personal Data:* b Wichita, Kans, Nov 28, 37; m 59; c 4. *Educ:* Friends Univ, BA, 60; Univ Wichita, MS, 63; Ariz State Univ, PhD(phys chem), 66. *Concurrent Pos:* Fel, Univ Utah, 66; Petrol Res Fund res grant, 68-70; vis prof, Univ Calif, Berkeley, 78; NSF grant microcomput, 81-83; res fel, Air Force Acad, 87; Air Force Off Sci Res Initiation Grant, 88; sabbatical, Okla State Univ, 90. *Mem:* Am Chem Soc; Sigma Xi. *Res:* Theory of liquids and liquid mixtures; statistical thermodynamics; semi-empirical and ab-initio molecular orbital calculations; generation and optimization of reactive potential energy surfaces; educational use of microcomputer and workstations. *Mailing Add:* Chem Dept Wichita State Univ Wichita KS 67260-0051

**ZANDY, HASSAN F,** PHYSICS, X-RAY ABSORPTION. *Current Pos:* PROF PHYSICS, UNIV BRIDGEPORT, 54- *Personal Data:* b Tehran, Iran, Mar 11, 12; US citizen; m 43; c Tyrone, Doreen & Shora. *Educ:* Univ Birmingham, BSc, 35, MSc, 49; Univ Teheran, PhD(physics), 53. *Hon Degrees:* PhD, Univ Teheran, 52, Univ Leicester, 53. *Prof Exp:* Instr physics, Univ Teheran, 37-46, asst prof, 50-53; lectr, Univ Leicester, 47-50; Fulbright fel, Brooklyn Polytech Inst, 53-54. *Concurrent Pos:* Mem, Vis Scientist Prog Physics, NSF, 59-; NSF fac fel, 63-64; res grant plasma res, Univ Bridgeport, 72-73; chair, Sci & Math Depts, Milford Acad. *Mem:* Am Asn Physics Teachers; Sigma Xi; Am Inst Physics. *Res:* High vacuum technique; measurement of temperature of hot plasmas by x-ray spectroscopy. *Mailing Add:* 34 Rosellen Dr Trumbull CT 06611

**ZANER, KEN SCOTT,** RHEOLOGY, NUCLEAR MAGNETIC RESONANCE. *Current Pos:* ASSOC PROF MED, SCH MED, BOSTON UNIV, 89- *Educ:* State Univ NY, Downstate Med Ctr, MD & PhD(biophys), 75. *Prof Exp:* Asst prof med-hemat, Mass Gen Hosp, 78-89. *Mailing Add:* Hemat-Oncol Serv Boston Univ Sch Med 80 E Concord St South Bldg Rm 304 Boston MA 02118-2394. *Fax:* 617-541-5636

**ZANETTI, NINA CLARE,** CELL DIFFERENTIATION, CELL BIOLOGY. *Current Pos:* asst prof biol, develop biol & histol, ASSOC PROF BIOL, SIENA COL, 91- *Personal Data:* b Passaic, NJ, May 31, 55; m 89, John B Davis. *Educ:* Muhlenberg Col, BS, 77; Syracuse Univ, PhD(biol), 82. *Prof Exp:* NIH fel develop biol, Univ Iowa, 82-85. *Mem:* AAAS; Am Soc Cell Biol; Soc Develop Biol; Sigma Xi. *Res:* Cell differentiation and histogenesis in embryonic development of the vertebrate limb; the role of extracellular matrix, cell shape, cytoskelton, and epithelial-mesenchymal interactions in regulation of cartilage differentiation. *Mailing Add:* Dept Biol Siena Col Loudonville NY 12211. *Fax:* 518-783-2986

**ZANEVELD, JACQUES RONALD VICTOR,** OCEANOGRAPHY. *Current Pos:* PROF OCEANOG, ORE STATE UNIV, 71- *Personal Data:* b Leiderdorp, Neth, July 12, 44; US citizen; m 80; c 2. *Educ:* Old Dom Univ, BS, 64; Mass Inst Technol, SM, 66; Ore State Univ, PhD(oceanog), 71. *Concurrent Pos:* Dir res, Sea Tech, Inc, 79-91. *Mem:* Am Geophys Union; Optical Soc Am; Am Soc Limnol & Oceanog. *Res:* Theory of radiative transfer, visibility, relationship of inherent and apparent optical properties; relationship of particulate and inherent optical properties; optical oceanography instrumentation. *Mailing Add:* 2265 NW Estaview Circle Corvallis OR 97330

**ZANEVELD, LOURENS JAN DIRK,** REPRODUCTIVE PHYSIOLOGY. *Current Pos:* PROF OBSTET, GYNEC & BIOCHEM, RUSH MED CTR, RUSH UNIV, 83- *Personal Data:* b The Hague, Neth, Mar 22, 42; US citizen; div; c 1. *Educ:* Old Dom Col, BSc, 63; Univ Ga, DVM, 67, MS, 68,

PhD(biochem), 70. *Honors & Awards:* Young Andrologist Award, Am Soc Andrology. *Prof Exp:* Res assoc biochem, Univ Ga, 69-71; asst prof obstet & gynec, Univ Chicago, 71-74; sci adv & chief, Pop Res Ctr, IIT Res Inst, 74-75; from assoc prof to prof physiol, obstet & gynec, Univ Ill Med Ctr, 75-83, actg head, Dept Physiol & Biophys, 79-83. *Concurrent Pos:* Endowed chair, Boysen prof, Rush Univ. *Mem:* Am Soc Andrology; Soc Study Reproduction; Am Vet Med Asn. *Res:* Reproduction; biochemistry and physiology of male and female genital tract secretions, spermatozoa and fertilization; infertility; contraception; reproductive toxicology. *Mailing Add:* Obstet/Gynec Res Rush Med Ctr 600 S Paulina St Chicago IL 60612-3832

**ZANGER, MURRAY,** PHYSICAL ORGANIC CHEMISTRY. *Current Pos:* from asst prof to assoc prof org chem, 64-72, PROF CHEM, PHILADELPHIA COL PHARM & SCI, 72- *Personal Data:* b New York, NY, May 5, 32; m 62; c 2. *Educ:* City Col New York, BS, 53; Univ Kans, PhD(org chem), 59. *Prof Exp:* Fel chem, Univ Wis, 59-60; res chemist, Marshall Lab, E I du Pont de Nemours & Co, 60-64. *Concurrent Pos:* USPHS res grant phenothiazine chem, 66-69; consult, Sadtler Res Labs, 68- *Mem:* Am Chem Soc. *Res:* Organophosphorus compounds; benzothiazoles; daunomycinone synthesis; sulfa drugs; organic mechanisms; nuclear magnetic resonance spectroscopy; anti-AIDS compounds. *Mailing Add:* Philadelphia Col Pharm Sci 43rd St & Kingsessing Ave Philadelphia PA 19104-4495. *Fax:* 215-895-1100; *E-Mail:* mizanger@pcps.edu

**ZANGWILL, ANDREW,** THEORETICAL CONDENSED MATTER PHYSICS. *Current Pos:* assoc prof, 85-92, PROF PHYSICS, GA INST TECHNOL, 92- *Personal Data:* b Cleveland, Ohio, Sept 27, 54. *Educ:* Carnegie-Mellon Univ, BS, 76; Univ Pa, PhD(physics), 81. *Prof Exp:* Res scientist, Brookhaven Nat Lab, 81-83; asst prof physics, Polytech Inst NY, 83-85. *Mem:* Am Phys Soc; Am Vacuum Soc; Mat Res Soc. *Res:* Theoretical problems in condensed matter and statistical physics, with particular emphasis on epitaxial phenomena. *Mailing Add:* Sch Physics Ga Inst Technol Atlanta GA 30332. *Fax:* 404-853-9958; *E-Mail:* zangwill@zang1.gatech.edu

**ZANINI-FISHER, MARGHERITA,** SOLID STATE PHYSICS, ELECTROCHEMISTRY. *Current Pos:* PRIN RES SCIENTIST ASSOC, SENSORS & PROCESS DEPT, SCI RES LAB, FORD MOTOR CO, 77- *Personal Data:* b Como, Italy, Jan 5, 47; m 76; c 1. *Educ:* Univ Rome, PhD(physics), 71. *Prof Exp:* Res assoc physics, Italian Nat Res Coun, 71-74; staff scientist, 74-76; res assoc, Moore Sch Elec Eng, Univ Pa, 76-77. *Concurrent Pos:* Res assoc, Div Eng, Brown Univ, 74-76. *Mem:* Am Phys Soc. *Res:* New materials used for energy storage; electrochemistry; transport properties of solids; soild state sensors. *Mailing Add:* Ford Res Labs MS 3028 PO Box 2053 Dearborn MI 48121

**ZANJANI, ESMAIL DABAGHCHIAN,** HEMATOLOGY, PHYSIOLOGY. *Current Pos:* CHIEF RES, VET ADMIN MED CTR, 87- *Personal Data:* b Resht, Iran, Dec 23, 38; m 63; c 3. *Educ:* NY Univ, BA, 64, MS, 66, PhD(hemat), 69. *Prof Exp:* From asst to res assoc exp hemat, NY Univ, 65-70; asst prof med & physiol, Mt Sinai Sch Med, 70-74, assoc prof physiol, 74-77; prof med & physiol, Sch Med, Univ Minn, 77-87. *Mem:* AAAS; Harvey Soc; Am Soc Hemat; Am Soc Zool; NY Acad Sci. *Res:* Experimental hematology; hemopoietic stimulating factor; mechanisms of blood cell production and release; renal involvement in erythropoiesis; erythropoiesis in submammalian species; fetal erythropoiesis. *Mailing Add:* Vet Admin Med Ctr Attn Res 151B 1000 Locust St Reno NV 89520

**ZANKEL, KENNETH L,** ATMOSPHERIC SCIENCES. *Current Pos:* scientist, Res Inst Advan Studies, 69-75, MEM STAFF, MARTIN MARIETTA ENVIRONMENTAL SYSTS, VERSAR, INC, 75- *Personal Data:* b New York, NY, Mar 29, 30; m 84, Sally A Campbell; c Anne E. *Educ:* Rutgers Univ, BS, 51; Fla State Univ, MS, 55; Mich State Univ, PhD(physics), 58. *Prof Exp:* Asst res prof physics, Mich State Univ, 58-59; asst prof, Univ Ore, 59-63; Fulbright fel, Univ Heidelberg, 63-64; sr fel, Calif Inst Technol, 64-66; sr res fel, Sect Genetics Develop & Physiol, Cornell Univ, 66-69. *Mem:* Air Pollution Control Asn; fel Acoust Soc Am. *Res:* Environmental sciences; source emissions; receptor modeling; measurements methods. *Mailing Add:* 861 Terry Creek Rd Traveler's Rest SC 29690

**ZANNIS, MARIA,** BIOCHEMISTRY. *Current Pos:* Fel med, 79-83, asst prof med, 83-89, ASSOC PROF MED & BIOCHEM, MCGILL UNIV, 89- *Personal Data:* b Athens, Greece, June 2, 48. *Educ:* McGill Univ, BS, 73, MS, 75, PhD(molecular biol/immunol), 79. *Honors & Awards:* Res Award, Can Govt, 83; Scientist Award, Can Med Coun, 88. *Mem:* Am Molecular Biol Soc; Am Cell Biol Soc. *Mailing Add:* McGill Cancer Ctr Box 710 McGill Univ 3655 Drummond St Montreal PQ H3G 1Y6 Can

**ZANNIS, VASSILIS I,** MOLECULAR GENETICS. *Current Pos:* assoc prof med & biochem, 84-87, PROF MED & BIOCHEM, BOSTON UNIV MED SCH, 87- *Personal Data:* b Kourounia Chios, Greece, Nov 18, 40; m 72; c 2. *Educ:* Univ Athen, Greece, BS, 68; Univ Calif, Berkeley, PhD(biochem), 75. *Prof Exp:* Fel, Univ Calif, San Francisco, 75-77; res assoc, Mass Inst Technol, 77-88; res assoc, Harvard Med Sch, 79-82, asst prof pediat, Harvard Med Sch, 82-84. *Concurrent Pos:* Adj asst mem, Mem Sloan Kettering Cancer Ctr, 82-84; instr, Dept Oral Biol, Harvard Med Sch, 84-; prof biochem, Univ Crete, 86-; mem, Coun Arteriosclerosis, Am Heart Asn. *Mem:* Biophys Soc; Am Chem Soc; Am Heart Asn; Am Inst Nutrition; Am Soc Biol Chem. *Res:* Utilization of biochemical cell and molecular biological approaches to investigate the molecular basis of human diseases associated with structural alterations in apolioprotein genes and the regulation of expression of these genes; author of 60 scientific publications. *Mailing Add:* Dept Med Sect Molecular Genetics R420 Boston Univ Med Ctr 700 Albany St W 509 Boston MA 02118-2394. *Fax:* 617-638-5141

**ZANNONI, VINCENT G,** BIOCHEMISTRY, PHARMACOLOGY. *Current Pos:* PROF PHARMACOL, MED SCH, UNIV MICH, ANN ARBOR, 74- *Personal Data:* b New York, NY, June 12, 28. *Educ:* City Col New York, BS, 51; George Washington Univ, MS, 56, PhD(biochem), 59. *Prof Exp:* Biochemist, Goldwater Mem Hosp, New York, 51-54 & Nat Heart Inst, 54-56; res chemist, Nat Inst Arthritis & Metab Dis, 57-63; from asst prof to prof biochem pharmacol, Sch Med, NY Univ, 63-74. *Mem:* AAAS; Am Soc Biol Chemists; Am Soc Pharmacol & Exp Therapeut; NY Acad Sci. *Res:* Inborn errors of metabolism; mechanisms of reactions; amino acid metabolism; enzymology; biochemical pharmacology. *Mailing Add:* Dept Pharmacol Univ Mich Med Sch A22OD-MSRB111 Ann Arbor MI 48109-0001

**ZANONI, ALPHONSE E(LIGIUS),** ENGINEERING. *Current Pos:* instr civil eng, Marquette Univ, 60-61, from asst prof to assoc prof, 64-76, chmn dept, 70-72, PROF CIVIL ENG, COL ENG, MARQUETTE UNIV, 76- *Personal Data:* b Melrose Park, Ill, July 24, 34; m 60; c 6. *Educ:* Marquette Univ, BCE, 56; Univ Minn, MS, 60, PhD(civil eng), 64. *Prof Exp:* Consult engr, Toltz, King, Duvall, Anderson, Inc, Minn, 58-60. *Concurrent Pos:* Consult water & waste water probs indust & munic. *Mem:* Am Soc Civil Engrs; Am Water Works Asn; Water Pollution Control Fedn; Sigma Xi; Asn Environ Eng Prof. *Res:* Water supply and pollution control. *Mailing Add:* Col Eng Marquette Univ PO Box 1881 Milwaukee WI 53201-1881

**ZANOWIAK, PAUL,** PHARMACEUTICS, CONTINUING PHARMACEUTICAL EDUCATION. *Current Pos:* chmn dept, 71-85, actg dean, 72-74, PROF PHARMACEUT, TEMPLE UNIV, 71-, DIR, DIV CONTINUING PHARMACEUT EDUC, 81- *Personal Data:* b Little Falls, NJ, July 11, 33; m 57; c Matthew G, Jennifer A, Tamara J & Patricia E. *Educ:* Rutgers Univ, BS, 54, MS, 57; Univ Fla, PhD(pharm), 59. *Prof Exp:* Instr pharm, Col Pharm, Univ Fla, 58-59; res & develop chemist, Noxell Corp, Md, 59-64; from asst prof to assoc prof pharmaceut, Sch Pharm, WVa Univ, 64-71. *Concurrent Pos:* Am Found Pharm Educ fel. *Mem:* Am Pharmaceut Asn; Acad Pharmaceut Res & Sci; Am Asn Col Pharm; Am Inst Hist Pharm; Am Asn Pharmaceut Scientists; Sigma Xi. *Res:* Design and evaluation of dosage forms. *Mailing Add:* 225 Summit Ave Jenkintown PA 19046

**ZANZUCCHI, PETER JOHN,** ANALYTICAL CHEMISTRY. *Current Pos:* SR STAFF CHEMIST, DAVID SARNOFF RES CTR, RCA CORP, 67- *Personal Data:* b Syracuse, NY, Apr 21, 41; m 67. *Educ:* Le Moyne Col, NY, BS, 63; Univ Ill, Urbana, MS, 65, PhD(chem), 67. *Mem:* Electrochem Soc; Optical Soc Am. *Res:* Measurement of the optical properties of inorganic materials, particularly semiconductor materials in the wavelength range 0.2 to 200 micrometers. *Mailing Add:* 13 Jill Dr Lawrenceville NJ 08648

**ZAPATA, PATRICIO,** NEUROPHYSIOLOGY, SENSORY PHYSIOLOGY. *Current Pos:* PROF NEUROBIOL, FAC SCI, CATH UNIV CHILE, 73-, PROF PHYSIOL, FAC MED, 77- *Personal Data:* b Santiago, Chile, Oct 26, 37; m 64, Carolina Larrain; c Patricio, Rodrigo, Carolina & Gonzalo. *Educ:* Cath Univ Chile, Bachellor, 59, Licentiate, 62; Univ Chile, MD, 63. *Prof Exp:* Fel neurophysiol, Nat Comn Med Fac, Chile, 63-64; postdoctoral fel physiol, Univ Utah, 65-66 & neurol, 67. *Concurrent Pos:* Vis assoc prof physiol, Univ Utah, 73-74, vis prof, 81-82; assoc ed, Arch Biol Med Exp, 88-92, ed, Biol Res 92-; Regional rep, Int Soc Arterial Chemoreception, 88- *Mem:* Am Physiol Soc; Soc Neurosci; Roy Soc Med; NY Acad Sci; Int Soc Arterial Chemoreception (pres, 93-96). *Res:* Mechanisms of chemoreception and reflex control of respiratory and cardiovascular functions. *Mailing Add:* Lab Neurobiol Cath Univ Chile Dept Physiol Sci PO Box 114-D Santiago 1 Chile. *Fax:* 56-2-222-5515; *E-Mail:* pzapata@genes.bio.puc.cl

**ZAPFFE, CARL ANDREW,** metallurgy, space sciences; deceased, see previous edition for last biography

**ZAPHYR, PETER ANTHONY,** STATISTICS, MANAGEMENT INFORMATION SYSTEMS. *Current Pos:* CONSULT, EXEC SERV CORPS, 91- *Personal Data:* b Wheeling, WVa, Sept 4, 26; m 56, Sophya Digenis; c Mary K & Anthony J. *Educ:* Bethany Col, WVa, BS, 48; Univ WVa, MS, 49; Univ Pittsburgh, PhD(math), 57. *Prof Exp:* Instr math, Univ WVa, 49-50; asst, Ill Inst Technol, 50-51 & Univ Pittsburgh, 51-52; analyst, Westinghouse Elec Corp, Pittsburgh, 52-61, mgr, Digital Anal & Comput Sect, 61-65, asst to dir, Anal Dept, 65-69, mgr, Eng Comput Systs, Nuclear Energy Systs, 69-73, mgr, Eng Comput Serv, 73-80, dir, Power Systs Comput Ctr, 80-87, dir, Comput Serv, 87-91. *Concurrent Pos:* Mem & officer bd trustees, H C Frick Community Hosp, Mt Pleasant, Pa. *Mem:* Asn Comput Mach. *Res:* Administration of industrial computing services and advanced applications of computers in engineering, science, manufacturing and management. *Mailing Add:* 150 Morrison Ave Greensburg PA 15601

**ZAPISEK, WILLIAM FRANCIS,** BIOCHEMISTRY, DEVELOPMENTAL BIOLOGY. *Current Pos:* from asst prof to assoc prof, 68-77, PROF BIOCHEM, CANISIUS COL, 77- *Personal Data:* b Morris, NY, Mar 29, 35; m 59, Claudia Buck; c Cynthia, Felicia & Kristen. *Educ:* Syracuse Univ, BA, 60; Univ Conn, MS, 65, PhD(biochem), 67. *Prof Exp:* Fel biochem, Los Alamos Sci Lab, 67-68. *Concurrent Pos:* J Williams Fulbright prof, Dept Biol & Pharm Sci, Aston Univ, Birmingham, Eng, 95-96. *Mem:* AAAS; Am Chem Soc; Soc Develop Biol. *Res:* Modeling of terotogenesis; dietary induction of cancer, DNA hypomethylation. *Mailing Add:* Dept Chem Canisius Col Buffalo NY 14208. *Fax:* 716-888-3112; *E-Mail:* wzapisek@canisius.bitnet

**ZAPOL, WARREN MYRON,** MEDICINE. *Current Pos:* PROF ANESTHESIA, HARVARD MED SCH, 85-, REGINALD JENNEY PROF, 91-, HENRY ISAIIH DORR PROF, 93-; ANESTHETIST-IN-CHIEF, MASS GEN HOSP, 93- *Personal Data:* b New York, NY, Mar 16, 42; m 68, Nikki J Kaplan; c David & Elisabeth. *Educ:* Mass Inst Technol, BS, 62; Univ Rochester, MD, 66. *Hon Degrees:* MA, Harvard Univ, 90. *Honors & Awards:* Antarctic Serv Medal. *Prof Exp:* Res assoc, Nat Heart Inst, Bethesda, Md, 67-70; resident, Harvard Univ, 70-72, asst prof anesthesia, 72-78, assoc prof & dir, Spec Ctr Res Adult Respiratory Failure, 78-88. *Concurrent Pos:* Investr, US Antarctic Prog, 76-78, 82-83, 86, 92 & 93. *Mem:* Am Physiol Soc; Am Soc Anesthesiologists; Am Soc Artificial Internal Organs. *Res:* Pulmonary circulation in animal models and man with acute lung injury; novel drug therapy in acute respiratory failure; diving seals in Antarctica. *Mailing Add:* Dept Anesthesia Mass Gen Hosp Fruit St Boston MA 02114. *E-Mail:* zapol@hetix.mgh.harvard.edu

**ZAPOLSKY, HAROLD SAUL,** THEORETICAL PHYSICS. *Current Pos:* chmn, Dept Physics & Astron, 73-79, PROF PHYSICS, RUTGERS UNIV, 73- *Personal Data:* b Chicago, Ill, Dec 24, 35; m 62, Lois Steff; c Sarah & David. *Educ:* Shimer Col, AB, 54; Cornell Univ, PhD(physics), 62. *Prof Exp:* Nat Acad Sci-Nat Res Coun res assoc physics, Goddard Inst Space Studies, NY, 62-63; res assoc, Univ Md, College Park, 63-65, asst prof, 65-70; from assoc prog dir to prog dir theoret physics, NSF, 70-73. *Concurrent Pos:* Sr vis scientist, Dept Appl Math & Theoret Physics, Univ Cambridge, 79-80. *Mem:* Am Phys Soc; Am Astron Soc; NY Acad Sci. *Res:* Quantum electrodynamics; astrophysics; general relativity; non-linear systems. *Mailing Add:* Dept Physics Rutgers Univ New Brunswick NJ 08903. *Fax:* 732-445-4343

**ZAPSALIS, CHARLES,** FOOD SCIENCE, CHEMISTRY. *Current Pos:* from asst prof to assoc prof, 65, PROF CHEM, FRAMINGHAM STATE COL, 65-, CHMN DEPT, 66- *Personal Data:* b Lowell, Mass, Sept 22, 22; m 48. *Educ:* Springfield Col, BS, 52; Univ Mass, PhD(food sci, chem), 63. *Prof Exp:* Teacher, Jr High Sch, Mass, 52-53 & high, NY, 54-55; head sci dept high sch, Mass, 56-60; instrumental chemist, Beechnut Life Savers, Inc, 63, res mgr, 63-65. *Mem:* Am Chem Soc; Inst Food Technol; Sigma Xi. *Res:* Anthocyanins, chemical identification; pesticide methodology and characterization of tea components by gas chromatography; characterization of amino acids and polypeptides. *Mailing Add:* 265 Singletary Lane Framingham MA 01702

**ZAR, JERROLD HOWARD,** ECOLOGY, PHYSIOLOGY. *Current Pos:* from asst prof to assoc prof, 71-78, chmn dept, 78-84, PROF BIOL SCI, NORTHERN ILL UNIV, 78-, ASSOC PROVOST GRAD STUDIES & RES & DEAN GRAD SCH, 84- *Personal Data:* b Chicago, Ill, June 28, 41; m 67, Carol Bachenheimer; c David M & Adam J. *Educ:* Northern Ill Univ, BS, 62; Univ Ill, Urbana, MS, 64, PhD(zool), 67. *Prof Exp:* Res assoc physiol ccol, Univ Ill, Urbana, 67-68. *Concurrent Pos:* Res assoc, Dept Zool, Univ Ill, Urbana, 67-68; staff consult, Argonne Nat Lab, 73-77, vis scientist, Div Radiol & Environ Res, 74; staff consult, US Environ Protection Agency, 74-84; mem comt to rev methods ecotoxicol, Environ Studies Bd, Nat Res Coun, 79-81; vis ecologist, Biol Sta, Univ Mich, 86; adj prof statist, Northern Ill Univ, 89-91. *Mem:* Fel AAAS; Ecol Soc Am; Am Physiol Soc; Am Statist Asn; Biomet Soc; Am Soc Zool; Sigma Xi. *Res:* Ecology; ecological animal physiology; statistical data processing environmental assessment; biostatistical analysis. *Mailing Add:* Grad Sch Northern Ill Univ De Kalb IL 60115-2864. *E-Mail:* jhzar@niu.edu

**ZARAFONETIS, CHRIS JOHN DIMITER,** internal medicine; deceased, see previous edition for last biography

**ZARCARO, ROBERT MICHAEL,** GENETICS, DEVELOPMENTAL BIOLOGY. *Current Pos:* Asst prof, 66-75, ASSOC PROF BIOL, PROVIDENCE COL, 75- *Personal Data:* b Springfield, Mass, Mar 4, 42; m 64; c 3. *Educ:* Providence Col, BA, 64, MS, 66; Brown Univ, PhD(biol), 71. *Mem:* AAAS. *Res:* Role of sulfhydryl compounds in mammalian pigmentation; genetic regulation of the multiple molecular forms of tyrosinase; role of protyrosinase in regulating melanogenesis. *Mailing Add:* Dept Biol Providence Col 549 River Ave & Eaton St Providence RI 02918-0001. *Fax:* 401-865-2057

**ZARCO, ROMEO MORALES,** immunochemistry, public health, for more information see previous edition

**ZARDECKI, ANDREW,** OPTICS, RELATIVITY. *Current Pos:* STAFF MEM, LOS ALAMOS NAT LAB, 81- *Personal Data:* b Warsaw, Poland, Aug 26, 42; m 66; c 1. *Educ:* Univ Warsaw, BSc, 64, MSc, 64; Polish Acad Sci, DSc, 68. *Prof Exp:* From asst to asst prof physics, Warsaw Tech Univ, 64-73; asst prof physics, Laval Univ, 73-79. *Concurrent Pos:* Fel, Laval Univ, 70-72. *Mem:* Am Phys Soc. *Res:* Functional techniques in the optical coherence theory; radiation theories, transport processes; atmospheric optics; pulse propagation in laser media; light scattering; cosmology; computer modeling and simulation; relativity. *Mailing Add:* Los Alamos Nat Lab MS E541 PO Box 1663 Los Alamos NM 87545. *E-Mail:* azz@lanl.gov

**ZARDENETA, GUSTAVO,** BIOCHEMISTRY. *Current Pos:* asst instr biochem, 89-95, ASST PROF ORAL MAXILLOFACIAL SURG, UNIV TEX HEALTH SCI CTR, 95- *Personal Data:* b Matamoros, Mex, Aug 24, 57. *Educ:* Univ Tex, Austin, BS, 79, MS, 84, PhD(biochem), 87. *Prof Exp:* Fel chem, Univ Tex, Austin, 87-89. *Mem:* Am Soc Biochem & Molecular Biol; AAAS; Soc Advan Chicanos & Native Am Sci; Hispanic Fac Asn. *Res:* Biochemistry; protein folding; biochemistry of temporomandibular joint disorders; free radicals in biology. *Mailing Add:* Dept Oral & Maxillofacial Surg Univ Tex Health Sci Ctr 7703 Floyd Curl Dr San Antonio TX 78284-0001. *Fax:* 210-567-2995; *E-Mail:* zardeneta@vthscsa.edu

**ZARDINI, ELSA MATILDE,** FLORA OF PARAGUAY, TAXONOMY OF ASTERACEAE & ONAGRACEAE. *Current Pos:* res assoc, 84, asst cur, 85-91, ASSOC CUR, MO BOT GARDEN, 91- *Personal Data:* b La Plata, Buenos Aires, Arg, June 9, 49; m 84, Alwyn H Gentry; c Maria L. *Educ:* Nat Univ La Plata, Arg, MS, 73, PhD(bot), 74. *Prof Exp:* Asst prof bot, Univ Buenos Aires, Arg, 75-76; hon res fel ethnobot, Harvard Univ, 76-77; asst prof, Nat Univ La Plata, Arg, 78, prof, 78-84. *Concurrent Pos:* Guggenheim fel, Guggenheim Found, 76-77; investr, Nat Coun of invests, Sci & Technol, Arg, 78-84; chief vascular plants, Mus of La Plata, Arg, 81-82; vis prof bot, Univ Buenos Aires, 82; chmn bot, Nat Univ La Plata, Arg, 82-84; Nat Geog Soc Grants, 88-99. *Mem:* Asn Trop Biol (secy-treas, 85-87); Org Flora Neotropica; Am Soc Plant Taxonomists; Nat Geog Soc; Soc Econ Bot. *Res:* Flora of Paraguay: program of plant collecting to document the vascular plants as a basis to produce a computerized checklist of Paraguay; taxonomy of Asteraceae of Paraguay and Ludwigia (Onagraceae). *Mailing Add:* Missouri Bot Garden PO Box 299 St Louis MO 63166. *E-Mail:* zardini@mobot.org

**ZARE, RICHARD NEIL,** CHEMICAL PHYSICS, ANALYTICAL CHEMISTRY. *Current Pos:* prof chem, 77-80, Shell distinguished prof, 80-85, MARGUERITE BLAKE WILBUR PROF CHEM, STANFORD UNIV, 88- *Personal Data:* b Cleveland, Ohio, Nov 19, 39; m 63; c 3. *Educ:* Harvard Univ, BA, 61, PhD(chem physics), 64. *Honors & Awards:* Michael Polanyi Medal, 79; Earle K Plyler Prize, Am Phys Soc, 81, Irving Langmuir Prize, 85; Nat Medal Sci, 83; Gibbs Medal, Am Chem Soc, 90, Debye Award, 91. *Prof Exp:* Fel, Harvard, 64; res assoc & fel, Joint Inst Lab Astrophys, Univ Colo, 64-65; asst prof chem, Mass Inst Technol, 65-66; asst prof physics, Univ Colo, 66-67, from asst prof to assoc prof physics & chem, 67-69; prof chem, Columbia Univ, 69-77. *Concurrent Pos:* Mem, Joint Inst Lab Astrophys, Univ Colo, 66-67, fel, 67-69, non-resident fel, 69; Alfred P Sloan res fel, 67-69; consult, Aeronomy Lab, Nat Oceanic & Atmospheric Admin, Radio Stand Physics Div, Nat Bur Stand, 68-77; Higgins prof nat sci, Columbia Univ, 75-77; Bing fel, 96; chmn, Nat Acad Sci, 96. *Mem:* Nat Acad Sci; AAAS; fel Am Phys Soc; Am Chem Soc; Am Acad Arts & Sci; Royal Chem Soc. *Res:* Problems associated with molecular photodissociation, molecular fluorescence and molecular chemiluminescence; application of lasers to chemical problems. *Mailing Add:* Dept Chem Stanford Univ Stanford CA 94305-5080

**ZAREM, ABE MORDECAI,** STRATEGIC PLANNING & BUSINESS DEVELOPMENT, MULTIMEDIA & ADVANCED TELECOMMUNICATIONS. *Current Pos:* CHMN, PRES & OWNER, ABE M ZAREM & CO, 81- *Personal Data:* b Chicago, Ill, Mar 7, 17; m 41, Esther Moss; c Janet, David & Mark. *Educ:* Ill Inst Technol, BS, 39; Calif Inst Technol, MS, 40, PhD(elec eng, phys, math), 44. *Hon Degrees:* LLD, Univ Calif, Santa Cruz, 67 & Ill Inst Technol, 68. *Honors & Awards:* Albert F Sperry Medal, Instrument Soc Am, 69; Eng '70 Merit Award, Inst Advan Eng, 70. *Prof Exp:* Group mgr elec eng, US Naval Ord Test Sta, 45-48; assoc dir & mgr, Stanford Res Inst, 48-56; founder, pres & chmn bd, Electro-Optical Systs, Inc, 56-67; vpres, Xerox Corp, 63-67, sr vpres, dir corp develop & mem bd dirs, 67-69; consult mgt & eng, 69-75; chmn & chief exec officer, Xerox Develop Corp, 76-81. *Concurrent Pos:* Lectr, Solar & Unconventional Energy Sources, Univ Calif, 56-61; mem, Adv Coun, Sch Eng, Stanford Univ, 66-78; trustee, City of Hope, 66-; mem, eng adv bd & bd dir, Harvey Mudd Col, 67-69; mem adv comt, Div Eng & Appl Sci, Calif Inst Technol, 69-77, Adv Comt Competitive Technol, Dept Com, State Calif, 88-91; founder & managing dir, Frontier Asn, 80-; mem, Competitive Technol Adv Comt, State Calif, 89-91; mem, Calif Coun Sci & Technol, 89- *Mem:* Nat Acad Eng; fel Inst Elec & Electronics Engrs; Solar Energy Soc; fel Am Inst Elec Eng; fel Am Inst Aeronaut & Astronaut; fel Inst Radio Engrs. *Res:* Technoeconomic planning and strategic business development for many organizations and institutions; education and the impact of science and technology on economic development; consultation on multimedia and advanced telecommunication opportunities; author of one book; inventor. *Mailing Add:* 9640 Lomitas Ave Beverly Hills CA 90210

**ZAREM, HARVEY A,** PLASTIC SURGERY. *Current Pos:* prof surg & chief, Div Plastic Surg, Med Sch, 73-87, EMER PROF, UNIV CALIF, LOS ANGELES, 87- *Personal Data:* b Savannah, Ga, Feb 13, 32; m 58; c 3. *Educ:* Yale Univ, BA, 53; Columbia Univ, MD, 57. *Prof Exp:* Assoc prof surg, Univ Chicago, 66-73. *Concurrent Pos:* Markle scholar, Markle Found, 68. *Mem:* Plastic Surg Res Coun; Soc Univ Surgeons; Am Cleft Palate Asn; Soc Head & Neck Surgeons; Microcirc Soc. *Res:* Microvasculature; microsurgery. *Mailing Add:* 1301 20th St Suite 470 Santa Monica CA 90404

**ZAREMSKY, BARUCH,** ORGANOMETALLIC CHEMISTRY, PLASTICS CHEMISTRY. *Current Pos:* RES CHEMIST, FERRO CHEM DIV, FERRO CORP, BEDFORD, 53- *Personal Data:* b Cleveland, Ohio, Sept 21, 26; m 51; c 3. *Educ:* Western Res Univ, BS, 48, MS, 50, PhD(org chem), 54. *Mem:* Am Chem Soc. *Res:* Additives for polyvinyl chloride polypropylene, polycarbonates and polyesters; specialist in synthesis of organotens. *Mailing Add:* 3701 Mayfield Rd Apt 215 Cleveland OH 44121-1750

**ZARET, BARRY L,** NUCLEAR CARDIOLOGY, CARDIAC RESEARCH. *Current Pos:* from asst prof to prof, 73-84, BERLINER PROF INTERNAL MED, YALE UNIV, 84-, CHIEF CARDIOL, 78- *Personal Data:* b New York, NY, Oct 3, 40; m 63; c 3. *Educ:* Queens Col, NY, BS, 62; NY Univ,

MD, 66; Yale Univ, MA, 82. *Honors & Awards:* Blumgart Award, Soc Nuclear Med, New Eng Chap. *Prof Exp:* Intern & resident internal med, NY Univ-Bellevue Hosp Med Ctr, 66-69; res fel cardiol, Johns Hopkins Sch Med, 69-71; major, USAF Marine Corps, Travis AFB, 71-73. *Concurrent Pos:* Assoc ed, Yearbk Nuclear Med, 80-95; ed-in-chief, J Nuclear Cardiol, 93. *Mem:* Am Physiol Soc; fel Am Col Cardiol; fel Am Heart Asn; Asn Univ Cardiologists; Am Soc Clin Invest; NAm Soc Cardiac Radiol; Asn Prof Cardiol (pres elect). *Res:* Nuclear cardiology; myocardial metabolism; cardiac imaging; studies of acute myocardial infarction and thrombolysis. *Mailing Add:* Dept Med Cardiol Yale Univ Sch Med 333 Cedar St 3 FMP New Haven CT 06520-8017. *Fax:* 203-785-7144

**ZARING, WILSON MILES,** MATHEMATICS. *Current Pos:* RETIRED. *Personal Data:* b Shelbyville, Ky, Nov 9, 26; m 50; c 2. *Educ:* Ky Wesleyan Col, AB, 50; Univ Ky, MA, 52, PhD(math), 55. *Honors & Awards:* Max Beberman Award, Ill Coun Teachers Math, 76. *Prof Exp:* From instr to asst prof math, Univ Ill, Urbana, 55-63, grad adv, 79-82, assoc prof, 63-81, dir grad studies, 82-91. *Concurrent Pos:* Consult, CSMP, 74-78. *Mem:* Am Math Soc; Math Asn Am; Sigma Xi. *Res:* Analysis; number theory. *Mailing Add:* 2208 Meadow Valley Rd Champaign IL 61821. *E-Mail:* zaring@uiuc.edu

**ZARKOWER, ARIAN,** VETERINARY MEDICINE, IMMUNOLOGY. *Current Pos:* from asst prof to prof, 65-95, MEM STAFF, CTR AIR ENVIRON STUDY, PA STATE UNIV, 70-, EMER PROF VET SCI, 95- *Personal Data:* b Tarnopol, Poland, Oct 10, 29; US citizen; m 60; c 2. *Educ:* Ont Vet Col, DVM, 56; Univ Maine, MS, 60; Cornell Univ, PhD(immunochem), 65. *Prof Exp:* Dist vet, NB Prov Vet Serv, 56-57; vet pvt pract, 57-58; res asst animal path, Univ Maine, 58-70; res officer, Animal Dis Res Inst, Can Dept Agr, 60-62; res asst immunochem, Cornell Univ, 62-65. *Res:* Experimental pathology; immune response and resistance in animals to infections; inflammatory responses. *Mailing Add:* Dept Vet Sci Pa State Univ 115 Henning Bldg University Park PA 16802-0001. *Fax:* 814-863-6140

**ZARLING, JOHN P,** ARCTIC ENGINEERING, HEAT TRANSFER. *Current Pos:* assoc prof, 76-80, PROF MECH ENG, UNIV ALASKA, FAIRBANKS, 80- *Personal Data:* b Elmhurst, Ill, Mar 15, 42; m 65; c 3. *Educ:* Mich Tech Univ, BS, 64, MS, 66, PhD(eng mech), 71. *Prof Exp:* Instr eng, Univ Wis-Madison, 66-68, from asst prof to assoc prof, Univ Wis-Parkside, 71-76. *Concurrent Pos:* Asst vchancellor, Univ Wis-Parkside, 74-76; dir, Inst Northern Eng, Univ Alaska, Fairbanks, 86-91, assoc dean eng, 86-91. *Mem:* Am Soc Eng Educ; Am Soc Mech Engrs; Am Soc Heating, Ventillating & Air Conditioning Engrs. *Res:* Heat transfer problems associated with an arctic climate including perma frost, frost heave, building design etc. *Mailing Add:* 58 Raven Dr Fairbanks AK 99709

**ZARNOCH, STANLEY JOSEPH,** TREEGROWTH MODELING, MATHEMATICAL ECOLOGY. *Current Pos:* math statistician, USDA Forest Serv, 76-77 & 80-85, res forester, 85, forest modeler, 85-88, MATH STATISTICIAN, USDA FOREST SERV, 88- *Personal Data:* b Newark, NJ, Jan 5, 50; m 75, Deborah L Herbert; c Melissa & Richard. *Educ:* Rutgers Univ, BS, 71; Pa State Univ, MS, 73; Va Polytech Inst & State Univ, PhD(forest biometrics), 76. *Prof Exp:* Asst prof fish & wildlife statist math ecol & nonparametrics, Mich State Univ, 77-80. *Concurrent Pos:* Consult, Consumer Power Co, Jackson, Mich, 78-80; mem math comt, Soc Am Foresters, 83. *Mem:* Biomet Soc. *Res:* Effects of global climate change on loblolly pine growth by using mathematical models that are based on physiological growth processes; forest health monitoring and assessment research. *Mailing Add:* Southern Res Sta USDA Forest Serv PO Box 2680 Ashville NC 28802. *Fax:* 704-257-4840

**ZARNSTORFF, MARK EDWARD,** INTEGRATED PEST MANAGEMENT, FORAGES-CROPPING SYSTEMS. *Current Pos:* EXTEN ASSOC INTEGRATED PEST MGT, NC STATE UNIV, 92- *Personal Data:* b Elkhorn, Wis, Oct 25, 57; m 82, Sara Wade; c Natasha A. *Educ:* Univ Wis, BS, 80; NC State Univ, MS, 86, PhD(crop sci), 90. *Prof Exp:* Field agronomist, Midland-Land O'Lakes Coop, 81-82; agron ctr mgr, Kewaunee Coop, 82-84. *Mem:* Am Soc Agron; Am Forage & Grassland Coun. *Res:* Ecological and agronomic aspects of no-till establishment of forage legumes and grasses; physiologic aspects of switchgrass seed dormancy. *Mailing Add:* NDak State Univ N Cent Res Exten Ctr Rte 3 Box 174 Minot ND 58701. *Fax:* 919-515-7959; *E-Mail:* m__zarnstorff@ncsu.edu

**ZARNSTORFF, MICHAEL CHARLES,** PLASMA PHYSICS. *Current Pos:* RES STAFF PHYSICIST, PLASMA PHYSICS LAB, PRINCETON UNIV, 84- *Personal Data:* b Denver, Colo, Aug 8, 54. *Educ:* Univ Wis, BS, 76, PhD(physics), 84. *Prof Exp:* Staff physicist, Lawrence Livermore Nat Lab, 76-77. *Concurrent Pos:* Distinguished lab fel, 95. *Mem:* Fel Am Phys Soc. *Res:* Plasma transport phenomena; experiment on tokamak devices. *Mailing Add:* Plasma Physics Lab Princeton Univ PO Box 451 Princeton NJ 08544. *Fax:* 609-243-2874; *E-Mail:* zarnstorff@pppl.gov

**ZAROBILA, CLARENCE JOSEPH,** interferometic fiber optic sensors, fiber optic intensity sensors, for more information see previous edition

**ZAROSLINSKI, JOHN F,** PHARMACOLOGY, BIOCHEMISTRY. *Current Pos:* RETIRED. *Personal Data:* b Chicago, Ill, Sept 12, 25; m 51; c 2. *Educ:* Univ Chicago, PhB, 49; Loyola Univ, Ill, PhD(pharmacol), 65. *Prof Exp:* Chemist, Armour Pharmaccut Co, 51-53; from pharmacologist to sr pharmacologist, Baxter Lab Inc, 53-58; sci dir, Arnar-Stone Labs, Inc, Div Am Hosp Supply Corp, 58-65, vpres res & develop, 65-75, vpres sci planning,

75-78. *Concurrent Pos:* Adj prof, Stritch Sch Med, Loyola Univ, Chicago, 65-88; res consult, US Vet Hosp, Hines, Ill. *Mem:* Brit Pharmacol Soc; Am Chem Soc; NY Acad Sci; Am Soc Pharmacol & Exp Therapeut. *Res:* Pharmaceutical development; biochemical pharmacology; protein binding of drugs; evaluation of hypnotic drugs; pharmaceutical development and introduction of Intropin (dopamine) into therapy for treatment of shock in humans; supervised scientific and clinical studies leading to approval for use of dopamine in the treatment of shock. *Mailing Add:* 1202 Norman Lane Deerfield IL 60015-3116

**ZARTMAN, DAVID LESTER,** CYTOGENETICS, REPRODUCTION. *Current Pos:* chmn & prof, Dept Dairy Sci, 84-94, CHMN & PROF, DEPT ANIMAL SCI, OHIO STATE UNIV, COLUMBUS, 94- *Personal Data:* b Albuquerque, NMex, July 6, 40; m 63, Micheal A Plemmons; c Kami R & Dalan L. *Educ:* NMex State Univ, BS, 62; Ohio State Univ, MS, 66, PhD(cytogenetics), 68. *Prof Exp:* From asst prof to prof animal & range sci, NMex State Univ, 68-84. *Concurrent Pos:* NIH fel, 73; Fulbright-Hays fel, 76; pres, Mary K Zartman Inc, 78-84; consult, Bio-Med Electronics Inc, 84-92. *Mem:* Fel AAAS; Am Dairy Sci Asn; Sigma Xi; Am Soc Animal Sci; Poultry Sci Asn Inc; Am Registry Prof Animal Scientists. *Res:* Sex and fertility control; reproduction; animal breeding; radio-telemetry of body temperature; new dairy farm management systems. *Mailing Add:* Ohio State Univ Animal Sci 2029 Fyffe Columbus OH 43210-1094. *Fax:* 614-292-2929; *E-Mail:* zartman.3@osu.edu

**ZARTMAN, ROBERT EUGENE,** GEOCHRONOLOGY, ISOTOPE GEOCHEMISTRY. *Current Pos:* chief, 81-85, GEOLOGIST, ISOTOPE GEOL BR, US GEOL SURV, 62- *Personal Data:* b Lancaster, Pa, May 19, 36; m 75; c 7. *Educ:* Pa State Univ, BS, 57; Calif Inst Technol, MS, 59, PhD(geol), 63. *Honors & Awards:* Meritorious Serv Award, US Dept Interior, 86. *Prof Exp:* Fel geol, Calif Inst Technol, 62. *Concurrent Pos:* Vis assoc, Calif Inst Technol, 71-72; chmn working group on radiogenic isotopes, Int Asn Volcanology & Chem Earth's Interior, 73-81; mem Lunar Sample Rev Panel, 73-76, working group Precambrian of US & Mex, 76-82, US Geodynamics Comt, 81-84 & Crustal Genesis Rev Panel, 83-84; vis scholar, Univ Chicago, 88. *Mem:* Fel Geol Soc Am; fel Mineral Soc Am; Am Geophys Union; Geochem Soc. *Res:* Determination of geologic age by the potassium-argon, rubidium-strontium and uranium-thorium-lead radiometric methods; study of geological processes and crustal/mantle structure by use of natural isotopic tracer systems. *Mailing Add:* 10077 W Tufts Pl Littleton CO 80127

**ZARUCKI, TANYA Z,** ENDOCRINOLOGY, STEROID RECEPTORS. *Educ:* Columbia Univ, PhD(human genetics & develop), 79. *Prof Exp:* Asst prof cell biol, Baylor Col Med, 83-86; staff researcher, Syntex, 86-92. *Res:* Molecular biology. *Mailing Add:* 735 Torreya Ct Palo Alto CA 94303

**ZARWYN, B(ERTHOLD),** electronics engineering, operations research, for more information see previous edition

**ZARY, KEITH WILFRED,** PLANT BREEDING, GENETICS. *Current Pos:* res dir, 85-95, VPRES RES, BEAR CREEK GARDENS INC, 96- *Personal Data:* b Sask, Nov 28, 48; m 80, Gloria Dyok; c Jessica & Ryan. *Educ:* Univ Sask, BS, 71; Tex A&M Univ, MS, 78, PhD(hort), 80. *Prof Exp:* Res asst, Tex A&M Univ, 77-79; plant breeder, Sun Seeds/Agrigenetics Corp, 80-85. *Mem:* Am Soc Hort Sci; AAAS; Sigma Xi. *Res:* Development of novel varieties of roses (Rosa hybrida) for commercial and home gardening use. *Mailing Add:* Bear Creek Gardens Inc PO Box 1329 6500 Donlon Rd Somis CA 93066

**ZARZECKI, PETER,** PHYSIOLOGY, NEUROPHYSIOLOGY. *Current Pos:* from assoc prof to assoc prof, 77-96, EMER PROF PHYSIOL, QUEEN'S UNIV, ONT, 96- *Personal Data:* b Boston, Mass, Aug 29, 45. *Educ:* Univ Miami, BS, 68; Duke Univ, PhD(physiol & pharmacol), 74. *Prof Exp:* Res assoc neurophysiol, Rockefeller Univ, 74-77. *Concurrent Pos:* Vis scientist physiol, Gothenburg Univ, 77; Med Res Coun Can res grant, 78-89, res develop award, 78-88. *Mem:* Soc Neurosci; Can Physiol Soc; Can Asn Neurosci. *Res:* Electrophysiological investigations into the control of the mammalian cerebral motor cortex. *Mailing Add:* Dept Physiol Queen's Univ Kingston ON K7L 3N6 Can

**ZASADA, ZIGMOND ANTHONY,** FORESTRY. *Current Pos:* RETIRED. *Personal Data:* b Schenectady, NY, May 1, 09; m 37, Marie Anderson; c John. *Educ:* State Univ NY, BS, 31. *Prof Exp:* Forester, Chippewa Nat Forest, US Forest Serv, 33-45, proj leader, Lake States Forest Exp Sta, 45-51, res ctr leader, 51-61, res forester, DC, 61-63, asst dir, NCent Forest Exp Sta, Minn, 63-67; res assoc, Cloquet Forestry Ctr, Col Forestry, Univ Minn, 67-76. *Concurrent Pos:* Forestry consult, 76- *Mem:* Fel Soc Am Foresters; Sigma Xi. *Res:* Economics of forest management and utilization; silviculture; mechanized timber harvesting. *Mailing Add:* 1015 Third Ave NW Grand Rapids MN 55744

**ZASK, ARIE,** BONE METABOLISM & OSTEOPOROSIS, PEPTIDOMIMETICS. *Current Pos:* sr scientist, 84-88, res scientist, 88-91, PRIN SCIENTIST, WYETH-AYERST RES, 91- *Personal Data:* b Tel Aviv, Israel, Dec 20, 56. *Educ:* State Univ NY, Stony Brook, BS, 77; Princeton Univ, PhD(chem), 82. *Prof Exp:* Fel, Columbia Univ, 82-84. *Mem:* Am Chem Soc; AAAS. *Res:* Drug discovery for diseases of bone metabolism, osteoporosis and diabetes; petidomimetic research; dcvclopmcnt of organic synthesis methodology; organometallic chemistry. *Mailing Add:* Wyeth-Ayerst Res 401 N Middletown Rd Pearl River NY 10965

**ZASKE, DARWIN ERHARD,** CLINICAL PHARMACOLOGY. *Current Pos:* asst prof pharmacol, 75-80, MEM FAC, DEPT ADMIN & SOCIAL PHARMACOL, UNIV MINN, 80-, ASST HEAD PHARM PRACT. *Personal Data:* b Wadena, Minn, Mar 20, 49. *Educ:* Univ Minn, BS, 72, PharmD, 73. *Prof Exp:* Clin pharmacologist, St Paul-Ramsey Hosp & Med Ctr, 73-80. *Concurrent Pos:* Instr pharmacol, Univ Minn, 73-74. *Mem:* Am Burn Asn; Am Soc Hosp Pharm. *Res:* Clinical application of drug-kinetic principles with the goal being patient individualization of drug therapy to provide more optimal patient therapy. *Mailing Add:* Pharm 5-130 Univ Minn 308 Harvard St SE St Paul MN 55455-0353

**ZASLAVSKY, THOMAS,** MATROID THEORY, GRAPH THEORY. *Current Pos:* assoc prof, 85-88, PROF MATH, STATE UNIV NY, BINGHAMTON, 88- *Personal Data:* b Brooklyn, NY, Jan 16, 44; m 85; c 3. *Educ:* City Col NY, BS, 65; Mass Inst Technol, PhD(math), 74. *Prof Exp:* Instr math, Mass Inst Technol, 75-77; asst prof, Ohio State Univ, 77-84. *Concurrent Pos:* Vis researcher, Univ Evansville, 84-85. *Mem:* Am Math Soc; Math Asn Am. *Res:* Matroids, especially invariants; arrangements of hyperplanes; signed and biased graphs, including matroids, coloring and topological signed graph theory. *Mailing Add:* Math Sci Dept State Univ NY Binghamton NY 13902-6000

**ZATKO, DAVID A,** INORGANIC CHEMISTRY. *Current Pos:* MEM STAFF, UNIVAC DIV, SPERRY CORP, 80- *Personal Data:* b North Tonawanda, NY, Nov 12, 40; m 66; c 1. *Educ:* Colgate Univ, BA, 62; Univ Wis, PhD(chem), 66. *Prof Exp:* Asst prof chem, Univ Ala, 67-74, assoc prof, 74-80. *Mem:* Am Chem Soc. *Res:* Analytic inorganic chemistry; coordination chemistry of silver II and silver III, palladium II, substituted ferrocenes; photoelectron spectroscopy; free radical ligands; oxidation-reductions in nonaqueous solvents. *Mailing Add:* 434 Sailmaker Way Lansdale PA 19446

**ZATUCHNI, GERALD IRVING,** OBSTETRICS & GYNECOLOGY. *Current Pos:* PROF, DEPT OBSTET & GYNEC, NORTHWESTERN UNIV, 77-, DIR, PROG APPL RES FERTIL REGULATION, 77- *Personal Data:* b Philadelphia, Pa, Oct 5, 35; m 58; c 3. *Educ:* Temple Univ, AB, 54, MD, 58, MSc, 65. *Prof Exp:* Instr obstet & gynec, Med Sch, Temple Univ, 65-66; dir family planning, Pop Coun, Inc, 66-69; adv, Govt of India, 69-71; Pop Coun, Inc consult family planning & obstet, WHO, 71-73; adv, Govt Iran, 73-75. *Mem:* AAAS; Am Fedn Clin Res; Am Fertil Soc; Am Col Obstet & Gynec. *Res:* Human reproductive research; contraceptive development; family planning; population study and research; high risk obstetrics. *Mailing Add:* 680 N Lake Shore Dr Suite 1000 Chicago IL 60611

**ZATUCHNI, JACOB,** INTERNAL MEDICINE, CARDIOVASCULAR DISEASE. *Current Pos:* from instr to assoc prof, 50-61, clin prof, 62-66, prof, 66-87, EMER PROF MED, TEMPLE UNIV SCH MED, 87-; SR DIAGNOSTICIAN & DIR CLIN SERV, SECT CARDIOVASC DIS, PA HOSP, 87-; CLIN PROF MED, SCH MED, UNIV PA, 88- *Personal Data:* b Philadelphia, Pa, Oct 8, 20; m 45, Evelyn Schwartz; c Stephen, Dory (Blau), Beth (Waldor) & Michael. *Educ:* Temple Univ, AB, 41, MD, 44, MS, 50; Am Bd Internal Med, cert, 52; Am Bd Internal Med Cardiovasc Dis, cert, 58. *Honors & Awards:* George L Steele Mem lectr, Mass Heart Asn, 67; Distinguished Achievement Award, Am Heart Asn, 85. *Prof Exp:* Chief, Sect Cardiol, Episcopal Hosp, Philadelphia, 69-82. *Concurrent Pos:* Teaching chief med, Episcopal Hosp, 58-67, head, Sect Cardiovasc Dis, 67-82, dir, Dept Med, 74-82, head, Heart Sta, 82-87 & attend physician, 82-87; fel coun clin cardiol, Am Heart Asn, 63-; mem, bd dirs, Am Heart Asn, Southeasten Pa, 90-91. *Mem:* AAAS; Am Thoracic Soc; AMA; fel Am Col Physicians; Sigma Xi; fel Am Col Cardiol; fel Am Col Chest Physicians; Am Fed Clin Res; Am Heart Asn; Am Soc Echocardiography; NY Acad Sci. *Res:* Cardiovascular diseases; 147 articles published. *Mailing Add:* Eighth & Spruce St Pa Hosp Philadelphia PA 19107

**ZATZ, JOEL L,** PHARMACEUTICS. *Current Pos:* From asst prof to assoc prof, 68-79, PROF PHARMACEUT, RUTGERS UNIV, 79- *Personal Data:* US citizen. *Educ:* Long Island Univ, BS, 56; St John's Univ, MS, 65; Columbia Univ, PhD(pharmaceut sci), 68. *Concurrent Pos:* Consult, var pharmaceut co; chair-elect, NY Chap, Soc Cosmetic Chemists, 97. *Mem:* Am Pharmaceut Asn; fel Soc Cosmetic Chemists; Am Asn Pharmaceut Scientists; Am Chem Soc; Am Asn Col Pharm. *Res:* Factors that influence transport of drugs through skin, including the physical chemistry of disperse systems and applications to pharmaceutical and cosmetic products. *Mailing Add:* 77 Woodside Ave Metuchen NJ 08840. *Fax:* 732-445-3134

**ZATZ, LESLIE M,** RADIOLOGY. *Current Pos:* from instr radiol to assoc prof, 59-72, actg dir diag radiol, 66-67, PROF RADIOL, SCH MED, STANFORD UNIV, 72- *Personal Data:* b Schenectady, NY, Nov 2, 28; m 53; c 3. *Educ:* Union Col, NY, BS, 48; Albany Med Col, MD, 52; Univ Pa, MMS, 59. *Prof Exp:* Intern, Univ Chicago Clins, 52-53; resident radiol, Hosp Univ Pa, 55-58. *Concurrent Pos:* NIH spec res fel, Postgrad Med Sch, Univ London, 65-66; consult, Vet Admin Hosp, Palo Alto, Calif, 60-72, chief radiol, 72- *Mem:* Am Col Radiol; Asn Univ Radiol; AMA; Am Soc Neuroradiol. *Res:* New diagnostic radiologic methods. *Mailing Add:* Stanford Univ Sch Rm S-072 Stanford CA 94305

**ZATZ, MARION M,** IMMUNOLOGY. *Current Pos:* PROG ADMINR, CELLULAR & MOLECULAR BASIS DIS DIV, NAT INST GEN MED SCI, NIH, 84- *Personal Data:* b New York, NY, Feb 10, 45. *Educ:* Barnard Col, BA, 65; Cornell Univ, PhD(immunol & microbiol), 70. *Prof Exp:* Fel immunol, Hosp Spec Surg, 70-71; Damon Runyon fel biochem, Albert Einstein Col Med, 71-72; instr microbiol, Sch Med, Yale Univ, 72-73, asst prof microbiol & path, 73-77, dir, Tissue Typing Lab, 72-74; guest worker, Immunol Br, Nat Cancer Inst, 74-79; assoc res prof biochem, Sch Med, George Washington Univ, 78-84. *Concurrent Pos:* Asst clin prof med, Sch Med, Georgetown Univ, 78-81. *Mem:* Am Asn Immunologists. *Res:* Investigation of spontaneous leukemogenesis in AKR-J mice; investigation of genetic basis of resistance to growth of lymphoma; T-cell differentiation; thymic hormones. *Mailing Add:* Nat Inst Gen Med Sci/NIH 5333 Westbard Ave Bethesda MD 20892

**ZATZ, MARTIN,** PHARMACOLOGY, PSYCHIATRY. *Current Pos:* res assoc, 74-76, staff fel, 76-78, MED OFFICER RES, SECT PHARMACOL, LAB CLIN SCI, NIMH, 78- *Personal Data:* b 1944; US citizen. *Educ:* Albert Einstein Col Med, PhD(pharmacol), 70, MD, 72. *Prof Exp:* Resident psychiat, Sch Med, Yale Univ, 72-74. *Res:* Circadian rhythms; cyclic nucleotides; regulation of receptor sensitivity; pineal gland. *Mailing Add:* Lab Cellular Biol NIMH NIH 9000 Rockville Pike Bldg 36 Rm 2A17 Bethesda MD 20892-4068. *Fax:* 301-496-4103

**ZATZKIS, HENRY,** THEORETICAL PHYSICS, APPLIED MATHEMATICS. *Current Pos:* from asst prof to prof, Newark Col, 53-71, from actg chmn to chmn dept, 59-85, distinguished prof math, 71-85, EMER CHMN DEPT, NEWARK COL, 85- *Personal Data:* b Holzminden, Ger, Apr 7, 15; nat US; m 51, Natalie Serlin; c Mark & David. *Educ:* Ohio State Univ, BS, 42; Ind Univ, MS, 44; Syracuse Univ, PhD(physics), 50. *Prof Exp:* Instr physics, Ind Univ, 42-44; instr, Univ NC, 44-46; instr math, Syracuse Univ, 46-51; instr, Univ Conn, 51-53. *Mem:* Sigma Xi. *Res:* Theory of relativity; heat conduction; acoustics; history of mathematics, probability. *Mailing Add:* 5 Elliott Pl West Orange NJ 07052

**ZATZMAN, MARVIN LEON,** PHYSIOLOGY. *Current Pos:* from asst prof to assoc prof, 56-73, PROF PHYSIOL, MED CTR, UNIV MO, COLUMBIA, 73- *Personal Data:* b Philadelphia, Pa, Aug 6, 27; m 51; c Allen & Robin. *Educ:* City Col New York, BS, 50; Ohio State Univ, MS, 52, PhD(physiol), 55. *Prof Exp:* Asst prof physiol, Ohio State Univ, 55-56. *Mem:* AAAS; Biophys Soc; Int Soc Nephrology; Am Physiol Soc. *Res:* Renal, cardiovascular, hibernation. *Mailing Add:* Dept Physiol Univ Mo Med Ctr Columbia MO 65212

**ZAUDER, HOWARD L,** ANESTHESIOLOGY. *Current Pos:* prof anesthesiol & chmn dept, 78-89, prof pharmacol, 78-89, EMER PROF ANESTHESIOL & PHARMACOL, STATE UNIV NY UPSTATE MED CTR, 89- *Personal Data:* b New York, NY, Sept 13, 23; m 53; c 2. *Educ:* Univ Vt, AB, 47, MS, 49; Duke Univ, PhD(physiol, pharmacol), 52; NY Univ, MD, 55. *Prof Exp:* Res assoc pharmacol, Univ Vt, 51-53; from asst prof to assoc prof anesthesiol, Albert Einstein Col Med, Yeshiva Univ, 58-67; prof anesthesiol & chmn dept, Med Sch, Univ Tex, San Antonio & prof pharmacol, Health Sci Ctr, 68-78, assoc dean prof affairs, Univ, 77-78. *Mem:* AAAS; Am Soc Pharmacol & Exp Therapeut; fel Am Col Anesthesiol. *Res:* Pharmacology of anesthetic agents; effects of radiation on response to anesthesia; pulmonary physiology; clinical application of gas chromatography. *Mailing Add:* 30600 N Pima Rd Scottsdale AZ 85262

**ZAUDERER, BERT,** COAL TECHNOLOGY, ENERGY CONVERSION. *Current Pos:* PRES, COAL TECH CORP, 81- *Personal Data:* b Vienna, Austria, Mar 8, 37; US citizen; m 61; c 5. *Educ:* City Col New York, BME, 58; Mass Inst Technol, SM, 60, ScD(mech eng), 62. *Prof Exp:* Res engr, Gen Elec Co, 61-67, group leader, 67-70; mgr magnetohydrodyn progs, Space Sci Lab, 70-79 & Energy Dept, 80-81. *Mem:* Assoc fel Am Inst Aeronaut & Astronaut; Am Phys Soc; Am Soc Mech Engrs. *Res:* Coal technology; advanced energy conversion; magnetohydrodynamic power. *Mailing Add:* c/o Coal Tech Corp PO Box 154 Merion PA 19066-0154

**ZAUDERER, MAURICE,** IMMUNE RESPONSES, T LYMPHOCYTE SPECIFICITY. *Current Pos:* ASSOC PROF ONCOL, MICROBIOL & IMMUNOL, UNIV ROCHESTER, 84- *Educ:* Mass Inst Technol, PhD(cellular biol), 72. *Res:* Regulation of immune responses; cellular immunology. *Mailing Add:* Cancer Ctr Univ Rochester 601 Elmwood Ave Box 704 Rochester NY 14642-0001. *Fax:* 716-271-7277

**ZAUGG, HAROLD ELMER,** ORGANIC CHEMISTRY. *Current Pos:* RETIRED. *Personal Data:* b Chicago, Ill, Feb 27, 16; m 40; c 3. *Educ:* Oberlin Col, AB, 37; Univ Minn, PhD(org chem), 41. *Prof Exp:* Asst org chem, Univ Minn, 38-40; res chemist, Abbott Labs, 41-56, res scientist, 56-59, res fel, 59-72, sr res fel, 72-80. *Concurrent Pos:* Fel, Purdue Univ, 58; chmn, Gordon Conf Org Reactions & Processes, 61; mem med study sect, NIH, 64-68; vis prof, Univ Southern Calif, 66; mem med chem study group, Walter Reed Army Inst Res, 77-81. *Mem:* Am Chem Soc. *Res:* Central nervous system drugs; organic syntheses and reaction mechanisms; solvent effects; chemistry of delocalized anions; amidoalkylations; medicinal chemistry of the cannabinoids. *Mailing Add:* 270 E Park Ave Lake Forest IL 60045-1339

**ZAUGG, WALDO S,** BIOCHEMISTRY. *Current Pos:* RETIRED. *Personal Data:* b LaGrande, Ore, Dec 13, 30; m 53; c 4. *Educ:* Brigham Young Univ, BA, 58, PhD(biochem), 61. *Prof Exp:* Fel, Enzyme Inst, Univ Wis, 61-62; fel, Charles F Kettering Res Lab, 62-63, staff scientist, 63-65; biochemist, Western Fish Nutrit Lab, US Fish & Wildlife Serv, 65-76; operator, Mill-A Chem Lab, 76-78; biochemist, Nat Marine Fisheries Serv, Cook Field Sta, 78-92. *Concurrent Pos:* Asst prof, Antioch Col, 63-65; USPHS grant, 64-65. *Mem:* Am Soc Biol Chemists. *Res:* Oxidation-reduction reactions and bioenergetics in photosynthetic bacteria, plants, mammals and poikilotherms; physiology and biochemistry of anadromous fishes. *Mailing Add:* 1031 Jessup Rd Cook WA 98605

**ZAUKELIES, DAVID AARON,** POLYMER, FIBER & FABRIC PHYSICS. *Current Pos:* CONSULT, 86- *Personal Data:* b Detroit, Mich, May 22, 25; m 56; c 2. *Educ:* Mich State Univ, BS, 46; Northwestern Univ, PhD(phys chem), 50. *Prof Exp:* Asst, Northwestern Univ, 46-49, res assoc phys chem, 49-50; res physicist, Dow Chem Co, 51-54; prof chem, Lee Col (Tenn), 54-55; res physicist, Chemstrand Corp, 55-60, Chemstrand Res Ctr, Inc, NC, 60-61, from assoc scientist to scientist, 61-70; scientist, 70-71, sci fel, Tech Ctr, 71-81, sr Monsanto fel, Monsanto Textiles Co, 81-85. *Mem:* Am Chem Soc; Am Phys Soc. *Res:* Soiling of fibers and fabrics; spinning of nylon yarns; continuous measurement of spun yarn properties and frequency analysis; measurement of fabric color variations and measurement of fabric hand; polyaromatic fibers, cords and composites; carpet, fabrics and fibers; optical properties of yarns and fabrics; statistical analysis of data. *Mailing Add:* PO Box 388 Cantonment FL 32533-0388

**ZAUNER, CHRISTIAN WALTER,** EXERCISE PHYSIOLOGY, PULMONARY PHYSIOLOGY. *Current Pos:* DEAN, SCH HEALTH & HUMAN PERFORMANCE, E CAROLINA UNIV, GREENVILLE, NC. *Personal Data:* b July 21, 30; m 57; c 3. *Educ:* West Chester State Col, BS, 56; Syracuse Univ, MS, 57; Southern Ill Univ, PhD(phys educ), 63. *Prof Exp:* Asst prof exercise physiol & res, Temple Univ, 63-65; assoc prof exercise physiol & res, Univ Fla, 65-71, assoc prof med, 70-71, prof exercise physiol, res & med, 71-84; dir, Sports Med Inst, Mt Sinai Med Ctr, Miami Beach, Fla, 84-87; chair, Dept Exercise Sport Sci, Ore State Univ. *Concurrent Pos:* Univ Fla fac develop grant & Thordgray Mem Fund, Dept Clin Physiol, Malmo Gen Hosp, Sweden, 71-72 & 78; consult cardiac rehab, Hosp Corp Am; Nat Acad Sci exchange scientist, Czechoslovakia, 86, 88 & 90. *Mem:* Am Physiol Soc; Am Asn Health, Phys Educ & Recreation; Am Col Sports Med; Sigma Xi. *Res:* Lipid metabolism; exercise and training effects on lipids, work capacity, pulmonary and respiratory function; child athletes; exercise and training effects on circulation; placticity of human skeletal muscle fibers. *Mailing Add:* Sch Health & Human Performance E Carolina Univ Greenville NC 27858

**ZAUSTINSKY, EUGENE MICHAEL,** geometry, computer applications to geometry & mathematics education; deceased, see previous edition for last biography

**ZAVADA, MICHAEL STEPHAN,** PALEOECOLOGY, PLANT TAXONOMY. *Current Pos:* asst prof, 94-96, ASSOC PROF BOT & CHMN BIOL, PROVIDENCE COL, 96- *Personal Data:* b Bridgeport, Conn, Aug 25, 52; m 90, Jeanne E Ledford; c Erin, Justin, Michael, Yolanda, Becky & Sarah. *Educ:* Ariz State Univ, BS, 74, MS, 76; Univ Conn, BA, 82, PhD(evolutionary biol), 82. *Prof Exp:* Res assoc paleobot, Ind Univ, 82-84, Ohio State Univ, 84-85; lectr bot & paleobot, Univ Witwatersrand, S Africa, 85-87; from asst prof to assoc prof bot, Univ Southwestern La, Lafayette 88-94. *Concurrent Pos:* Adj res assoc, Mo Bot Garden, 87-88. *Mem:* Am Asn Stratig Palynologists; Bot Soc Am; Int Orgn Paleobotanists; Soc Study Evolution; Am Asn Teachers Slavic & E Europ Lang. *Res:* Investigate the origin and diversification of flowering plants; reproductive biology of flowering plants and plant-animal interactions. *Mailing Add:* 416 Eaton St Providence RI 02908

**ZAVALA, MARIA ELENA,** PLANT DEVELOPMENT. *Current Pos:* STAFF, DEPT BIOL, YALE UNIV. *Personal Data:* b Pomona, Calif, Jan 9, 50. *Educ:* Pomona Col, BA, 72; Univ Calif, Berkeley, PhD(bot), 78. *Prof Exp:* Res assoc, Dept Biol, Ind Univ, 78-80; plant res physiologist, USDA, 80- *Concurrent Pos:* Lectr, Dept Bot, Univ Calif, Berkeley, 78. *Mem:* Bot Soc Am; Am Soc Cell Biol; Am Soc Plant Taxonomists; AAAS; Soc Advan Chinese & Native Americans Sci. *Res:* Plant anatomy and cell biology; development of pollen; cryogenic storage of plant cells; high resolution localization of plant compounds in situ. *Mailing Add:* Dept Biol Calif State Univ Northridge CA 91330-0001

**ZAVARIN, EUGENE,** BIOCHEMICAL SYSTEMATICS, SURFACE CHEMISTRY OF LIGNOCELLULOSICS. *Current Pos:* Asst, Univ Calif, Berkeley, 52-53, sr lab technician, Forest Prod Lab, Univ Calif, 52-54, asst specialist, 54-56, asst forest prod chemist, 56-62, assoc chemist, 62-68, prof forestry & forest prod chemist, 68-91, EMER PROF FORESTRY & FOREST PROD CHEMIST, FOREST PROD LAB, UNIV CALIF, 91- *Personal Data:* b Sombor, Yugoslavia, Feb 21, 24; US citizen; m 56, Valentina Kuzubov; c Ksenya, Sergey, Michael, Nina & Mavrik. *Educ:* Univ Gottingen, dipl, 49; Univ Calif, Berkeley, PhD(org chem), 54. *Concurrent Pos:* NIH fel, Inst Org Chem, Gif-sur-Yvette, France, 63. *Mem:* Am Chem Soc; Int Acad Wood Sci. *Res:* Chemosystematics; chemistry of natural products; polymer chemistry of lignocellulosics; use of terpenoid composition in chemosystematics and genetics of Coniferae; determination of biosynthesis of terpenoids by computer-assisted statistics; thermal analysis of lignocellulosics; reactions of furylic polymers and model compounds; surface chemistry of wood. *Mailing Add:* Forest Prod Lab Univ Calif 1301 S 46th St Richmond CA 94804. *Fax:* 510-215-4299; *E-Mail:* zavarin@nature.berkeley.edu

**ZAVECZ, JAMES HENRY,** PHARMACOLOGY. *Current Pos:* ASST PROF, DEPT PHARMACOL, EASTERN VA MED SCH, 80- *Personal Data:* b Bethlehem, Pa, Dec 15, 46. *Educ:* LaSalle Col, BA, 68; Ohio State Univ, PhD(pharmacol), 74. *Prof Exp:* Fel pharmacol, Med Col, Cornell Univ, 74-76, instr, 76-77; res pharmacologist, ICI Americas, Inc, 78-80. *Mem:* NY Acad Sci; AAAS; Sigma Xi. *Res:* Effects of histamine on the heart; mechanism of action of cardiac glycosides. *Mailing Add:* Dept Pharmacol La State Univ Sch Med 1501 Kings Hwy PO Box 33932 Shreveport LA 71130-3932

**ZAVISZA, DANIEL MAXMILLIAN,** POLYMER CHEMISTRY, COATINGS. *Current Pos:* SR POLYMER CHEMIST, POLYMER LATEX, 94- *Personal Data:* b Hazardville, Conn, Nov 28, 38; m, Jean Engel. *Educ:* Col Holy Cross, BS, 60; Clark Univ, PhD(phys org chem), 66. *Prof Exp:* Res chemist, Am Cyanamid Co, 66-74, sr res chemist, 74-82; proj leader, Hercules Inc, 82-91; tech dir, Raffi & Swanson Inc, Wilmington, Mass, 91-94. *Mem:* Am Chem Soc; Am Soc Testing & Mat; Am Asn Textile Chemists & Colorists. *Res:* Organic polymer research and development; protein chemistry; condensation polymers; polyurethane and acrylic coatings for textiles, wood, paper and film. *Mailing Add:* Polymer Latex 83 Authority Dr Fitchburg MA 01420

**ZAVITSAS, ANDREAS ATHANASIOS,** PHYSICAL ORGANIC CHEMISTRY. *Current Pos:* from asst prof to assoc prof, 67-73, grad dean, 75-79, PROF CHEM, BROOKLYN CTR, LONG ISLAND UNIV, 73- *Personal Data:* b Athens, Greece, July 14, 37; US citizen; m 59, Lourdes Romanacce; c Athanasios. *Educ:* City Col New York, BS, 59; Columbia Univ, MA, 61, PhD(chem), 62. *Prof Exp:* Res assoc chem, Brookhaven Nat Lab, 62-64; res chemist, Monsanto Co, Mass, 64-67. *Concurrent Pos:* Lectr, New Sch Soc Res, 61-64. *Mem:* Am Chem Soc; NY Acad Sci. *Res:* Organic free-radical chemistry; phenolic resin; electrochemical sensors. *Mailing Add:* Dept Chem Long Island Univ University Plaza Brooklyn NY 11201. *Fax:* 718-488-1465; *E-Mail:* zavitsas@aurora.liunet.edu

**ZAVODNEY, LAWRENCE DENNIS,** NONLINEAR STRUCTURAL DYNAMICS, VISCO-ELASTIC DAMPING. *Current Pos:* ASSOC PROF & CHAIR, CEDARVILLE COL, 92- *Personal Data:* b Akron, Ohio, June 24, 51; m 76; c 4. *Educ:* Univ Akron, BSME, 74, MSME, 77; Va Polytech Inst & State Univ, PhD(eng mech), 88. *Prof Exp:* Res asst vibrations & acoust, Dept Mech Eng, Univ Akron, 74-77; sr engr, Babcock & Wilcox Res & Develop Div, J Ray McDermott Inc, 77-79; instr mech, Dept Eng Sci & Mech, Va Polytech Inst & State Univ, 79-80, instr & res asst, 82-87; asst prof vibrations & mech, Dept Eng Mech, Ohio State Univ, 88-92. *Concurrent Pos:* Lectr mech, Dept Mech Eng, Yarmouk Univ, 80-82; asst prof, Ohio Aerospace Inst, 90-92. *Mem:* Am Soc Mech Engrs; Am Acad Mech. *Res:* Theoretical and experimental analysis of linear and nonlinear vibrations of multidegree-of-freedom systems; nonlinear system identification; modal analysis; instrumentation; random vibration of nonlinear systems; experimental mechanics. *Mailing Add:* Dept Eng Cedarville Col PO Box 601 Cedarville OH 45314

**ZAVODNI, JOHN J,** PHYSIOLOGY. *Current Pos:* asst prof, 68-75, ASSOC PROF ZOOL & CHMN DEPT SCI, PA STATE UNIV, MCKEESPORT CAMPUS, 75- *Personal Data:* b Gallitzin, Pa, June 17, 43; m 65. *Educ:* St Francis Col, Pa, BS, 64; Pa State Univ, PhD(physiol), 68. *Prof Exp:* Instr biol, St Francis Col, Pa, 64-65. *Mem:* NY Acad Sci; Am Asn Sex Educ & Coun; Sex Educ & Info Coun US. *Res:* Effects of exposure to increased oxygen tensions on the endocrine system; enforcement of water pollution. *Mailing Add:* Dept Biol/Chem Pa State Univ University Dr McKeesport PA 15132-7698

**ZAVODNI, ZAVIS MARIAN,** ROCK MECHANICS, GEOLOGICAL ENGINEERING. *Current Pos:* MGR GEOTECH ENG, KENNECOTT, 87- *Personal Data:* b Prague, Czech, Aug 17, 41; US citizen; m 81, Cathy L Gradt; c Zachary J & Suzanne M. *Educ:* Princeton Univ, BSE, 64; Univ Ariz, MS, 69, PhD(geol eng), 71. *Honors & Awards:* Appl Res Award, US Nat Comt Rock Mech, 79. *Prof Exp:* Instr math, Univ Sch, 64-66 & Am Sch Paris, 66-67; asst prof geol, Brooklyn Col, 71-74; mining engr, Kennecott Copper Corp, 74-83, chief geotech engr, Kennecott Minerals Co, 83-87. *Concurrent Pos:* Geotech engr, Pincock, Allen & Holt, Inc, Tucson, Ariz, 72-74. *Mem:* Asn Eng Geologists; Can Inst Mining & Metall; Am Inst Mining, Metall & Petrol Engrs; Int Soc Rock Mech. *Res:* Slope stability; geomechanics; slope failure kinematics; mine waste dump design; tailings embankment design. *Mailing Add:* 535 12th Ave Salt Lake City UT 84103

**ZAVON, MITCHELL RALPH,** PESTICIDE TOXICOLOGY, INDUSTRIAL HYGIENE. *Current Pos:* PRES, AGATHA CORP, 68- *Personal Data:* b Woodhaven, NY, May 9, 23; m 47, Betty Benthold; c Peter, Dan, Julie & Barbara. *Educ:* Boston Univ, MD, 49. *Prof Exp:* From asst prof to clin prof indust med, Kettering Lab, Col Med, Univ Cincinnati, 55-71; assoc dir, Huntington Res Ctr, 71-74; med dir, Ethyl Corp, 74-76; health dir, Occidental Chem Corp, 76-86. *Concurrent Pos:* Dir occup health serv, Cincinnati Health Dept, 55-61, asst health comnr, 61-74; consult, USPHS, 57-59, 66-69, Joint Congressional Comt Atomic Energy, 58-59, Louisville-Jefferson County Health Dept, 59-60 & USDA, 63-69; exec coordr, Miami Valley Proj, Ohio, 68-71; mem staff, St Mary's & Niagara Falls Mem Hosp, Sci Adv Bd, Int Joint Comt, 77-80. *Mem:* AAAS; Am Med Asn; Am Indust Hyg Asn; fel Am Pub Health Asn; fel Am Col Occup & Environ Med. *Res:* Radiation protection; biological effects of agricultural chemicals; occupational health; toxicology. *Mailing Add:* 4497 Lower River Rd Lewiston NY 14092. *Fax:* 716-754-7422

**ZAVORTINK, THOMAS JAMES,** ENTOMOLOGY, BIOLOGY. *Current Pos:* MEM FAC, DEPT BIOL, UNIV SAN FRANCISCO, 84- *Personal Data:* b Ravenna, Ohio, May 27, 39; c 2. *Educ:* Kent State Univ, BS, 61; Univ Calif, Los Angeles, MA, 63, PhD(zool), 67. *Honors & Awards:* John N Belkin Mem Award. *Prof Exp:* Asst res zoologist entom, Univ Calif, Los Angeles, 68-74; asst cur entom, Calif Acad Sci, San Francisco, 74-75; mem fac, dept biol, Univ San Francisco, 75-82; res entom, Walter Reed Army Inst Res, Washington, DC, 82-84. *Concurrent Pos:* Consult, Southeast Asia Mosquito Proj, Smithsonian Inst, 68-71; lectr, Int Ctr Pub Health Res, Univ SC, 85. *Mem:* Am Mosquito Control Asn; Pac Coast Entom Soc (pres, 90); Soc Syst Biol. *Res:* Systematics and biology of mosquitoes and bees. *Mailing Add:* Dept Biol Univ San Francisco San Francisco CA 94117. *Fax:* 415-422-2346; *E-Mail:* zavortinkt@usfla.edu

**ZAWACKI, BRUCE EDWIN,** BURN SURGERY, BIOETHICS. *Current Pos:* asst prof, 71-74, ASSOC PROF SURG, SCH MED, UNIV SOUTHERN CALIF, 75-, PROF MED & RELIG, 93-, HEAD PHYSICIAN BURN WARD, LOS ANGELES CO-UNIV SOUTHERN CALIF MED CTR, 71- *Personal Data:* b Northampton, Mass, Dec 6, 35; m 61; c 3. *Educ:* Col Holy Cross, BS, 57; Harvard Med Sch, MD, 61; Univ Southern Calif, MA, 86. *Prof Exp:* Chief trauma study, US Army Inst Surg Res, 67-69; surgeon, Southern Calif Permanente Med Group, 69-71. *Concurrent Pos:* Consult, State Calif Comt Orgn & Delivery Burn Care, 78- *Mem:* Am Burn Asn. *Res:* Inhalation injury; doctor-patient relationship in life-threatening illnesses; burn depth. *Mailing Add:* 1200 N State St Rm 12650 Los Angeles CA 90033-4525

**ZAWADA, EDWARD T, JR,** NEPHROLOGY, NUTRITION. *Current Pos:* assoc prof med, 83-87, PROF MED, PHYSIOL & PHARMACOL, SCH MED, UNIV SDAK, 87-, FREEMAN PROF & CHMN, DEPT INTERNAL MED, 87- *Personal Data:* b Chicago, Ill, Oct 3, 47; m 77; c 3. *Educ:* Loyola Univ, Chicago, BS, 69, Maywood, MD, 73; Am Col Physicians, cert internal med, 76, cert nephrol, 78, cert nutrit, 87, cert critical care, 87, cert geriat, 88. *Prof Exp:* Asst prof med, Sch Med, Univ Calif, Los Angeles, 78-79, Univ Utah, 79-81; assoc prof, Med Col Va, 81-83. *Concurrent Pos:* Prin investr, Va Merit Rev, 82-; chmn, Dept Int Med, Royal C Johnson Va Med Ctr, Sch Med Univ SDak, 87-; reviewer, Nephrology & Geriat Journals, 83- *Mem:* Fel Am Col Physicians; fel Am Col Chest Physicians; fel Am Col Nutrit; Am Soc Pharmacol & Exp Therapeut; Int Soc Nephrology; Am Soc Magnesium Res. *Res:* Role of divalent ions (calcium, magnesium, and phosphate) in blood pressure regulation; geriatric renal-urinary diseases; critical care; geriatrics. *Mailing Add:* Dept Internal Med Univ SDak 2501 W 22nd St Sioux Falls SD 57117-1570

**ZAWADZKI, JOSEPH FRANCIS,** ORGANIC CHEMISTRY. *Current Pos:* RES INVESTR CHEM PROCESS RES, SEARLE LABS, 64- *Personal Data:* b Withee, Wis, May 30, 35; m 70; c 3. *Educ:* Northland Col, BA, 57; Loyola Univ (Ill), MS, 60, PhD(org chem), 62. *Prof Exp:* Res assoc org chem, Univ Chicago, 62-64. *Mem:* Am Chem Soc; Sigma Xi. *Res:* Synthetic organic chemistry; reaction mechanisms; molecular rearrangements. *Mailing Add:* 7 Edgewater Dr Rouses Point NY 12979-1611

**ZAWADZKI, ZBIGNIEW APOLINARY,** medicine; deceased, see previous edition for last biography

**ZAWESKI, EDWARD F,** ORGANIC CHEMISTRY. *Current Pos:* SR RES ASSOC, TECH CTR, ETHYL CORP, BATON ROUGE, 83- *Personal Data:* b Jamesport, NY, Nov 2, 33; m 65; c 4. *Educ:* Fordham Univ, BS, 55; Iowa State Univ, PhD(org chem), 59. *Prof Exp:* Chemist, Res Labs, Ethyl Corp, 59-79; mgr lubricant crankcase develop & technol, Edwin Cooper Inc, 79-83. *Mem:* Am Chem Soc; Soc Automotive Engrs; Am Oil Chem Soc. *Res:* Synthesis of new components for lubricants including crankcase, industrial, gears, hydraulic oils and fuels; formulation of lubricant blends for crankcase applications and the synthesis of new components for crankcase oils. *Mailing Add:* Amoco Chem MC B-1 150 W Warrenville Rd Naperville IL 60563-8400

**ZAWISZA, JULIE ANNE A,** TECHNICAL MANAGEMENT, MEDICAL SCIENCES. *Current Pos:* dir, Technol & Regulatory Affairs, 92-94, MGR BIOMED TECH PROGS, HEALTH INDUST MFG ASN, 90- *Personal Data:* b Niles, Mich, Jan 30, 56. *Educ:* Ind Univ Northwest, cert, 76; Univ Mich, BS, 84; George Washington Univ, MA, 91. *Prof Exp:* Med technologist, NIH, 84-86; George Washington Med Ctr, 86-90. *Mem:* AAAS; Am Soc Med Technologists; Am Soc Clin Path; Am Asn Clin Chem; Nat Comt Clin Lab Standards. *Res:* Biomedical and technology related projects and programs representing the medical device industry; compilation of comments on legislative or regulatory proposals; technical discussions on device related issues; stategic planning and policy development. *Mailing Add:* 8503 Bershire Dr Ypsilanti MI 48198. *Fax:* 202-783-8750

**ZBAR, BERTON,** IMMUNOBIOLOGY. *Current Pos:* clin assoc, Med Br, Nat Cancer Inst, NIH, 65-66, surgeon, Biol Br, 66-70, head, Cellular Immunity Sect, Biol Br, 70-76, sr surgeon, Cellular Immunity Sect, Lab Immunobiol, 76-80, CHIEF, CELLULAR IMMUNITY SECT, LAB IMMUNOBIOL, NAT CANCER INST, NIH, 80-, CHIEF, LAB IMMUNOBIOL, 88- *Personal Data:* b Brooklyn, NY, May 22, 38; c 1. *Educ:* Brooklyn Col, BS, 59; State Univ NY, MD, 63; Am Bd Internal Med, dipl, 83, dipl oncol, 85. *Prof Exp:* Internship & residency, Internal Med, Univ Utah Sch Med, 63-65. *Concurrent Pos:* USPHS Comn Corps, 65-; assoc ed J Nat Cancer Inst, 71-80. *Mem:* Am Asn Cancer Res; Am Soc Human Genetics. *Res:* Recessive oncogenes in human renal cell carcinoma and small lung carcinoma; inherited forms of human cancer; Von Hippel-Lindau disease. *Mailing Add:* Nat Cancer Inst Lab Immunobiol Bldg 560 Rm 12-71 Frederick MD 21702

**ZBARSKY, SIDNEY HOWARD,** BIOCHEMISTRY. *Current Pos:* RETIRED. *Personal Data:* b Vonda, Sask, Feb 19, 20; m 44, Miriam Frankel; c Ralph, Jonathan & Deborah. *Educ:* Univ Sask, BA, 40; Univ Toronto, MA, 42, PhD(biochem), 46. *Prof Exp:* Res officer, Biol & Med Res Br, Atomic Energy Proj, 46-48; asst prof physiol chem, Univ Minn, 48-49; from assoc prof to prof biochem, Univ BC, 49-85. *Concurrent Pos:* Killam sr fel, Univ BC, 72-73. *Mem:* AAAS; Am Chem Soc; Can Physiol Soc; Can Biochem Soc (vpres, 66-67, pres, 67-68); Am Soc Biol Chemists. *Res:* Detoxication mechanisms; metabolism of British anti-lewisite, purines and pyrimidines; nucleases and nucleic acid enzymes in the intestinal mucosa. *Mailing Add:* 1420 W 49th Ave Vancouver BC V6M 2R5 Can

**ZBORALSKE, F FRANK,** RADIOLOGY. *Current Pos:* assoc prof radiol, Sch Med, Stanford Univ, 67-72, dir, Div Diag Radiol, 67-75, prof radiol, 72-, EMER PROF, STANFORD UNIV. *Personal Data:* b Fall Creek, Wis, Aug 2, 32; m 58; c 4. *Educ:* Marquette Univ, MD, 58. *Prof Exp:* Intern, St Joseph's Hosp, Milwaukee, 58-59; resident, Milwaukee Co Gen Hosp, 59-62; from instr to asst prof radiol, Sch Med, Marquette Univ, 62-65; actg asst prof, Med Ctr, Univ Calif, San Francisco, 64, from asst prof to assoc prof radiol & dir, Exp Radiol Lab, 65-67, chief, Sect Gastrointestinal Radiol, 66-67. *Concurrent Pos:* Radiologist, Milwaukee Co Gen Hosp, 62-65; James Picker Found scholar radiol, 62-65; attend physician & consult, Vet Admin Hosp, Wood, Wis, 65; co-dir NIH res training grants diag radiol, Med Ctr, Univ Calif, San Francisco, 65-67 & dir res training grant, Sch Med, Stanford Univ, 67-76; consult, Vet Admin Hosp, Palo Alto, Calif, 68 & Santa Clara Valley Med Ctr, San Jose, 68- *Mem:* Asn Univ Radiologists; Asn Am Gastroenterol Asn. *Res:* Esophageal motility; esophageal epithelial cell kinetics. *Mailing Add:* 120 Patricia Lane Sutter Creek CA 95685

**ZBOROWSKI, ANDREW,** OCEAN ENGINEERING, NAVAL ARCHITECTURE. *Current Pos:* prof naval archit, 83-85, CHMN, OCEAN ENGR PROG, FLA INST TECHNOL, 92- *Personal Data:* b Broniszewice, Poland, May 12, 36; US citizen; m 61; c 2. *Educ:* Gdansk Univ Technol, Poland, BSc, 57, MSc, 59, PhD(ship hydrodyn), 68, DSc, 73. *Prof Exp:* Res asst ship hydrodyn, Inst Fluid Flow Mach, Polish Acad Sci, 60-64; res officer, Danish Hydro & Aerodynamic Lab, 64-65 & Inst Fluid Flow Mach, 66-69; from asst prof to assoc prof naval archit, Gdansk Univ Technol, 70-78; prof, Univ Basrah, Iraq, 78-81; eng consult offshore vehicles design, Broun & Root, Inc, Houston, 82-83. *Concurrent Pos:* Navy Summer Res Prog, David Taylor Res Ctr, 90. *Mem:* Soc Naval Architects & Marine Engrs. *Res:* Ship hydrodynamics with particular emphasis on ship motions and stability in a seaway; application to offshore vehicles design and enhancement of their efficiency and safety; design of high speed small craft. *Mailing Add:* 3356 Mazur Dr Melbourne FL 32901

**ZBUZEK, VLASTA KMENTOVA,** ENDOCRINOLOGY, PHYSIOLOGY. *Current Pos:* adj asst prof, 80-85, ASSOC PROF NEUROENDOCRINOL, DEPT ANESTHESIOL, UNIV MED & DENT NJ, 85-, DEPT PHARMACOL, 94- *Personal Data:* b Velka Losenice, Czech, Sept 6, 33; US citizen; div. *Educ:* Charles Univ, MS, 63, Can Sci, 69, Dr rer nat(physiol), 69. *Prof Exp:* Res assoc exp endocrinol, Lab Endocrinol & Metab, Prague, 56-69; res fel reprod physiol, Pop Coun, Rockefeller Univ, 69-71; assoc res scientist physiol & endocrinol, Dept Path, NY Univ, 71-75, res scientist neuroendocrinol, Dept Anesthesiol, 75-78; res physiologist, Vet Admin Med Ctr, NY, 78-80. *Mem:* Endocrine Soc; Geront Soc; NY Acad Sci; Int Soc Neuroendocrinol. *Res:* Isolation and identification of TRH; gonado-thyroidal relationships; the effects of hormones on cholesterol metabolism; pathophysiology of vasopressin; vasopressin and aging; neuropeptides and aging; the effect of nicotine on vasopressin system; nicotine and pain perception. *Mailing Add:* 100 Manhattan Ave Apt 1314 Union City NJ 07087-5246. *Fax:* 973-982-4172

**ZBUZEK, VRATISLAV,** BIOCHEMISTRY, ENDOCRINOLOGY. *Current Pos:* RETIRED. *Personal Data:* b Prague, Czech, Mar 13, 30; US citizen; m 93, Jitka Martinkova. *Educ:* Charles Univ, Czech, cert, 53, Cand Sci, 65, Dr rer nat, 67. *Prof Exp:* Res assoc biochem & physiol, Phys Cult Res Inst, Czech, 53-64; res assoc biochem & endocrinol, Lab Endocrinol & Metab, Charles Univ, 64-68; res assoc biochem & endocrinol, Rockefeller Univ, 70-75, asst prof biochem & cell biol, 75-77; asst prof biochem & neuroendocrinol, Univ Med & Dent NJ, 80-93. *Concurrent Pos:* Lectr, Fac Phys Cult & Sports, Charles Univ, 56-62; res fel physiol & endocrinol, Pop Coun, NY, 68-70; adj assoc prof, Col Staten Island, City Univ NY, 78-81; adj fac, St Peters Col, NJ, 87-88. *Mem:* Harvey Soc; Am Chem Soc; NY Acad Sci; Int Soc Neuroendocrinol. *Res:* Biochemistry and physiology of muscular activity; pituitary-thyrotropic function; ultrastructure of C-cells and bone cells; biochemistry of cytotoxic T-lymphocytes; neuropeptides and aging; the effect of nicotine on vasopressin system. *Mailing Add:* Na Brezince 20 15000 Prague 5 Czech Republic

**ZDAN, WILLIAM,** SYSTEMS & ELECTRONICS ENGINEERING. *Current Pos:* BUS COUNR, US SMALL BUS ADMIN, 87-; ENG CONSULT; REG DIR, SERV CORPS RETIRED EXECS, 88-, CHMN, 89- *Personal Data:* b New York, NY, June 9, 19; m 49; c 2. *Educ:* Cooper Union, BEE, 42; Polytech Inst Brooklyn, MEE, 55. *Prof Exp:* Proj engr, Western Elec Co, 41-51; proj mgr airborne naval guid control & display systs, Sperry Gyroscope Co, 51-59; sr engr for design of the Atlas ballistic missile guid & control syst, Arma Div, Am Bosch Arma Corp, 59-62; from mgr guid & control space vehicles to head systs analysis deep submergence prog, Sperry Gyroscope Co, 62-67; sr res sect head, Sperry Systs Mgt Div, Great Neck, 67-71, prog mgr & tech dir ship res simulators, vessel traffic mgt systs, vehicle maneuvering trainers, comput generated images, display systs & artificial intel, Sperry Div, Sperry Corp, 71-84; mgr res & develop, Expert & Artificial Intel Systs, Systs Mgt Group, Unisys Corp, 84-87. *Concurrent Pos:* Eng consult, B Z Consults, 87-; regional dir Automatic Data Processing. *Mem:* Am Asn Artificial Intel; Inst Elec & Electronics Engrs Comput Soc; Asn Comput Mach. *Res:* Digital computer analysis and evaluation of large real-time military systems; design and development of vehicle simulators and ship handling trainers; system synthesis and design of vessel traffic management systems, real-time computer-generated image display systems and artificial intelligence systems. *Mailing Add:* 30 Appletree Lane East Hills NY 11576

**ZDANIS, RICHARD ALBERT,** PHYSICS. *Current Pos:* PROVOST & UNIV VPRES, CASE WESTERN RES UNIV, 88-, PROF PHYSICS, 88- *Personal Data:* b Baltimore, Md, July 15, 35; m 55, Barbara Rosenberger; c Michael R & Carole L (Cavanagh). *Educ:* Johns Hopkins Univ, AB, 57, PhD(physics),

60. *Prof Exp:* Res assoc physics, Princeton Univ, 60-61, instr, 61-62; from asst prof to assoc prof, Johns Hopkins Univ, 62-69, prof physics, 69-88, assoc provost, 75-79, vpres admin serv, 77-79, vprovost, 79-88. *Concurrent Pos:* Consult, Naval Ord Lab, 67-68, 69-74; bd trustees/dirs, Assoc Univs, Inc, 76-, Univ Corp Atmospheric Res, 78-81, Johns Hopkins Prog Int Educ Gynec & Obstets, 81-89, Asn Univs Res Astron, Inc, 82-, Coun Govt Reel, 83-89, Cleveland Educ Fund, 90-96, Am Red Cross, Greater Cleveland Chap, 91-, Great Lakes Mus Sci, Environ & Technol, 92- *Mem:* Am Phys Soc; AAAS; NY Acad Sci. *Res:* Experimental elementary particle research. *Mailing Add:* Provost's Off Case Western Res Univ 10900 Euclid Ave Cleveland OH 44106-7004

**ZDERIC, JOHN ANTHONY,** PHARMACEUTICAL CHEMISTRY. *Current Pos:* RETIRED. *Personal Data:* b San Jose, Calif, Jan 5, 24; m 49, Marie A Lobrovich; c 1. *Educ:* San Jose State Col, AB, 50; Stanford Univ, MS, 52, PhD(org chem), 55. *Prof Exp:* Squibb fel, Wayne State Univ, 55-56; res chemist, Syntex Corp, 56-59, asst dir chem res, 59-61, dir labs, Syntex Inst Molecular Biol, 61-62, dir corp planning div, 64-66, vpres com develop, Syntex, Int, Mex, 66-70, asst corp vpres, Syntex Corp, 67-70, vpres, Syntex Labs Inc, Calif, 70-73, vpres admin & tech affairs, Syntex Res, 73-93. *Concurrent Pos:* Mem staff, Swiss Fed Inst Technol, 62-64; mem bd govs, Syva, 74-77; mem, Bd Dir, Japan Soc Northern Calif. *Mem:* Am Chem Soc. *Res:* Raney nickel catalyzed hydrogenolyses; macrocylic antibiotics; steroidal hormones; nucleosides and nucleotides. *Mailing Add:* 2369 Sharon Oaks Dr Menlo Park CA 94025

**ZDRAVKOVICH, VERA,** HARZARDOUS WASTE TECHNOLOGIES. *Current Pos:* from asst prof to assoc prof, 67-77, PROF CHEM, PRINCE GEORGE'S COMMUNITY COL, 77- *Personal Data:* b Subotica, Yugoslavia, Dec 19, 39; US citizen; m 62; c 2. *Educ:* Univ Belgrade, BS, 62; Univ Novi Sad, MS, 66; George Washington Univ, PhD(org chem), 79. *Prof Exp:* Teaching asst org chem, Univ Novi Sad, 63-66; res asst chem, George Washington Univ, 66-67. *Concurrent Pos:* Lectr, George Washington Univ, 82; consult, Gattys Chem Co, 86. *Mem:* Am Chem Soc; Nat Sci Teachers Asn; AAAS; Soc Col Sci Teaching. *Res:* Organic and general chemistry; acid rain-receptor mitigation technologies; written laboratory manuals regarding organic, general and biochemistry. *Mailing Add:* 16309 Marlboro Pike Upper Marlboro MD 20772-7785

**ZEALEY, MARION EDWARD,** BIOCHEMISTRY, MICROBIOLOGY. *Current Pos:* RETIRED. *Personal Data:* b Augusta, Ga, Mar 26, 13; m 48; c 4. *Educ:* Paine Col, AB, 34; Atlanta Univ, MS, 40; Univ Minn, PhD, 60. *Prof Exp:* Instr chem, Miles Col, 36-43; assoc prof, Paine Col, 43-44; assoc prof biochem, Meharry Med Col, 48-59, USPHS fel, 63-65, prof microbiol, 65-81. *Mem:* AAAS; Am Chem Soc; Sigma Xi. *Res:* Protein denaturation; x-ray effects; nucleic acids; cell biology. *Mailing Add:* 4201 Voctory Pkwy No 410 Cincinnati OH 45229-1661

**ZEAMER, RICHARD JERE,** SYSTEMS DESIGN & SYSTEMS SCIENCE, HISTORY & PHILOSOPHY OF SCIENCE. *Current Pos:* PRES & MGR, APPL SCI ASSOCS, SALT LAKE CITY, UTAH, 89- *Personal Data:* b Orange, NJ, May 13, 21; m 44, 69; c 5. *Educ:* Mass Inst Technol, BS, 43, MS, 48; Univ Utah, PhD(mech eng), 75. *Prof Exp:* Prof engr, Morton C Tuttle Co, Boston, Mass, 49-53; process engr, Nekoosa-Edwards Paper Co, Port Edwards, Wis, 53-55; process engr & group leader, WVa Pulp & Paper Co, Luke, Md, 55-60; engr supvr, Allegany Ballistics Lab, Rocket Center, WVa, 60-65; rocket eng supvr, Hercules Powder Co, Magna, Utah, 65-69; sr tech specialist, Hercules Rocket Plant, Hercules Inc, Magna, Utah, 69-83, proj eng mgr, Hercules Aerospace Div, 83-89. *Mem:* Assoc fel Am Inst Aeronaut & Astronaut. *Res:* Mechanics; structures; flow; aerodynamics; acoustics; aeroballistics; combustion; detonation; heat transfer; improved material refining, heating, drying; process control; rocket design for greater thrust and reliability; lighter weight; aerodynamics for improved steering; rocket vibration prediction; jet signature prediction; computer calculation of phenomena. *Mailing Add:* 843 13th Ave Salt Lake City UT 84103

**ZEBIB, ABDELFATTAH M G,** COMPUTATIONAL FLUID MECHANICS, HYDRODYNAMIC STABILITY. *Current Pos:* From asst prof to prof, 77-95, DISTINGUISHED PROF & CHMN MECH AEROSPACE ENG, RUTGERS UNIV, 95- *Personal Data:* b Cairo, Egypt, Sept 11, 46; US citizen; m 74, Jean A Adamson; c Adam, Neil & Tarik. *Educ:* Cairo Univ, BS, 67; Univ Colo Boulder, MS, 71 & PhD(mech eng), 75. *Prof Exp:* Instr mech power eng, Cairo Univ, 67-70; fel, Univ Colo Boulder, 75-76. *Concurrent Pos:* Res assoc, Univ Calif, San Diego, 73; res geophysicist, Univ Calif, Los Angeles, 78; vis scholar & res assoc, Stanford Univ, 83-84; consult, IT&T Advan Technol Ctr, 86, IBM Sci Res Ctr, Palo Alto, 84-85 & AT&T Bells, 85- *Mem:* Fel Am Phys Soc; Soc Indust & Appl Math; Am Soc Mech Engrs. *Res:* Computational fluid mechanics which include heat transfer and hydrodynamic instabilities; cooling of microelectronics; material processing; flow control; geophysics. *Mailing Add:* Dept Mech & Aerospace Eng Rutgers Univ New Brunswick NJ 08903. *Fax:* 732-932-3124; *E-Mail:* zebib@jove.rutgers.edu

**ZEBOLSKY, DONALD MICHAEL,** PHYSICAL CHEMISTRY. *Current Pos:* asst prof, 64-68, ASSOC PROF PHYS CHEM, CREIGHTON UNIV, 68- *Personal Data:* b Chicago, Ill, Aug 20, 33; m 57; c 8. *Educ:* Northwestern Univ, BA, 56; Kans State Univ, PhD(phys chem), 63. *Prof Exp:* Chemist, Baxter Labs, 56-57; asst prof phys chem, Northern Ill Univ, 63-64. *Mem:* Am Chem Soc; NY Acad Sci; Calorimetry Conf. *Res:* Thermodynamics, kinetics and polarography of ionpairs and of transition metal-ion chelate formation; computer modeling of mixing heats in the critical region from equations of state. *Mailing Add:* Dept Chem Creighton Univ Omaha NE 68178-0104. *Fax:* 402-280-5737; *E-Mail:* zeb@creighton.edu

**ZEBOUNI, NADIM H,** SOLID STATE PHYSICS. *Current Pos:* teaching asst, 57-58, asst prof, 60-65, ASSOC PROF PHYSICS, LA STATE UNIV, BATON ROUGE, 65-, PROF ASTRON, 74- *Personal Data:* b Beirut, Lebanon, Apr 14, 28; c 2. *Educ:* Univ Paris, BS, 53; Nat Sch Advan Telecommun, France, MS, 55; La State Univ, PhD(physics), 61. *Prof Exp:* Eng del to Mid East, Co Gen TSF, 55-57. *Mem:* Am Phys Soc. *Mailing Add:* Dept Physics La State Univ Baton Rouge LA 70803

**ZEBOVITZ, EUGENE,** VIROLOGY. *Current Pos:* RETIRED. *Personal Data:* b Chicago, Ill, Feb 24, 26; m 51; c 7. *Educ:* Roosevelt Univ, BS, 49; Univ Chicago, MS, 52, PhD(microbiol), 55. *Prof Exp:* Microbiologist, US Army Biol Labs, Ft Detrick, Md, 55-58; microbiologist, Universal Foods Corp, Wis, 58-62; microbiologist, US Army Biol Labs, 62-70; microbiologist, Naval Med Res Inst, Nat Naval Med Ctr, 70-74; health scientist adminr biol sci, Div Res Grants, NIH 74-84, asst chief for referral, 84-89. *Mem:* AAAS; Am Soc Microbiol; Sigma Xi; Soc Exp Biol & Med. *Res:* Mechanism of virus replication; molecular biology; viral genetics; health science administration. *Mailing Add:* 1413 W 12th St Frederick MD 21702

**ZEBROSKI, EDWIN L,** DECISION ANALYSIS, FORENSIC ANALYSIS. *Current Pos:* prin engr, 88-90, DIR SAFETY & RISK MGT, APTECH, 90- *Personal Data:* b Chicago, Ill, Apr 1, 21; m 69, Gisela K Rudolph; c Lars, Zoe, Susan & Margaret. *Educ:* Univ Chicago, BS, 41; Univ Calif, Berkeley, PhD(phys chem), 47. *Honors & Awards:* Chas A Coffin Award. *Prof Exp:* Vis prof nuclear eng, Purdue Univ, 76-77; dir, Nuclear Safety Anal Ctr, 79-81; vpres & dir, Eng Div, Inst Nuclear Opers, 81-83; chief nuclear scientist, Elec Power Res Inst, 83-87. *Concurrent Pos:* Proj engr, Submarine Advan Reactor, Triton; mgr develop engr, Gen Elec Co; consult, Energy Res Adv Bd, 85-86; dir syst & mats, Elec Power Res Inst; mem, Nat Res Coun Panels; consult, Elec de France, Tokyo Elec Power Co, Kojima Corp, Julich Lab, Ger, Oak Ridge Nat Lab & Energoexport, Moscow. *Mem:* Nat Acad Eng; fel Am Nuclear Soc; fel AAAS; Am Phys Soc; fel Am Inst Chemists; Sigma Xi; Soc Risk Anal. *Res:* Heavy elements; extraction processes; reactor design and analysis; safety analysis; risk management; management information systems; safeguards and accountability of weapons materials; energy systems materials and corrosion; radiochemistry; probabilistic risk analysis; physical chemistry; nuclear chemistry; computer applications; decision analysis. *Mailing Add:* 1546 Plateau Ave Los Altos CA 94024-5320. *Fax:* 650-948-3841; *E-Mail:* edzebroski@worldnet.att.net

**ZEBROWITZ, LESLIE ANN,** PSYCHOLOGY. *Current Pos:* From asst prof to assoc prof, 70-82, chmn dept, 86-91, PROF PSYCHOL, BRANDEIS UNIV, 82-, MANUEL YELLEN PROF SOCIAL RELS, 89- *Personal Data:* b Detroit, Mich, Nov 8, 44; div; c Caleb J McArthur & Loren Z McArthur. *Educ:* Univ Wis, BA, 66; Yale Univ, MS, 68, PhD, 70. *Concurrent Pos:* Ford Found fac fel, 73-74; res grantee, NIMH, 75-81 & 87-; vis scholar, Seoul Nat Univ, 85, Henry Murray Res Ctr, Radcliffe Col, 91-92; prog dir social psychol, NSF, 94-95; vis Erskine fel, Univ Canterbury, NZ, 96. *Mem:* Fel Am Psychol Asn; Am Psychol Soc; Soc Exp Social Psychol. *Res:* Social perception. *Mailing Add:* Dept Psychol Brandeis Univ Waltham MA 02254. *Fax:* 781-736-3291; *E-Mail:* zebrowitz@binah.cc.brandeis.edu

**ZEBROWITZ, S(TANLEY),** ELECTRICAL ENGINEERING, COMMUNICATIONS. *Current Pos:* RETIRED. *Personal Data:* b New York, NY, Nov 28, 27; m 53; c 2. *Educ:* City Col New York, BEE, 49; Univ Pa, MS, 54; Temple Univ, MBA, 81. *Prof Exp:* Engr, Res Div, Philco Corp, 49-61, mgr tech staff, 62-65, mgr systs eng, 65-72, mgr design eng, Commun & Eng Div, Ford Aerospace & Commun, 72-81; pres, Stelcom Int Inc, 81-87. *Concurrent Pos:* Consult, Rome Air Develop Ctr, USAF, 62-; mem US comt for study group IX, Consult Comt on Int Radio, 66-72; exec comt, Int Solid Circuits Conf, 66-76. *Mem:* Fel Inst Elec & Electronics Engrs. *Res:* Communication systems; microwave and troposcatter propagation and system design; signal processing; integrated communication and computer networks. *Mailing Add:* 1914 Lantern Lane Oreland PA 19075

**ZECHIEL, LEON NORRIS,** ASTROPHYSICS, OPTICS. *Current Pos:* RETIRED. *Personal Data:* b Wilmington, Del, Sept 23, 23; m 46, Dorothy Jane Fawcett; c Barbara Jane (Barnes), Robert Norris, Janet Christine (Dib) & Margaret Ann (Roberts). *Educ:* DePauw Univ, AB, 48; Ohio State Univ, MA, 51. *Prof Exp:* Res assoc, Res Found, Ohio State Univ, 53-58, assoc supvr & asst to dir, 58-59; sect head, GPL Div, Gen Precision, Inc, NY, 59-63, prin scientist, 63-68; mgr data mgt systs, Sanders Assocs, Inc, NH, 68-72; sr systs engr, NCR-Postal Systs Div, SC, 72-74; prog mgr, Dayton Res Div, Hobart Corp, 74-75, mgr proj planning, 76-86. *Res:* Reentry and space vehicle guidance and navigation; aeronautical charting; optical and infrared instrumentation; stellar photography; air navigation; reconnaissance and surveillance techniques; computerized data management systems; postal systems automation; automated weighing and package labelling systems. *Mailing Add:* 103 Heather Lane Mauldin SC 29662-2015

**ZECHMAN, FREDERICK WILLIAM, JR,** PHYSIOLOGY. *Current Pos:* from asst prof to assoc prof, Med Ctr, Univ Ky, 61-68, prof physiol & chmn, Dept Physiol & Biophys, 68-80, assoc dean res & grad studies, 82-87, vchancellor, 87-89, PROF PHYSIOL, MED CTR, UNIV KY, 89- *Personal Data:* b Mar 16, 28; m 50; c 2. *Educ:* Otterbein Col, BS, 49; Univ Md, MS, 51; Duke Univ, PhD, 56. *Prof Exp:* Asst zool, Univ Md, 49-51; biologist & asst to head biol br, US Off Naval Res, 51-53; instr physiol, Duke Univ, 53-57; from asst prof to assoc prof, Miami Univ, 57-61. *Concurrent Pos:* Consult biophys br, Aerospace Med Lab, Wright-Patterson AFB, 60-61; vis prof, Univ Hawaii, 71-72. *Mem:* AAAS; Am Physiol Soc; Aerospace Med Asn; Soc Exp Biol & Med. *Res:* Respiratory regulation and mechanics; prolonged and periodic acceleration; effects of lower body negative pressure and posture change; mechanical, reflex and subjective responses to added airflow resistance; bedrest; exercise. *Mailing Add:* PO Box 1252 Wrightsville Beach NC 28480

**ZECHMANN, ALBERT W,** MATHEMATICS. *Current Pos:* ASST PROF MATH, UNIV NEBR, LINCOLN, 61- *Personal Data:* b Sioux City, Iowa, Aug 21, 34; m 65; c 1. *Educ:* Iowa State Univ, BS, 56, MS, 59, PhD(appl math), 61. *Mem:* Math Asn Am. *Res:* Solution of visco-elastic problems; unification of the theory of partial differential equations; study of Cauchy problem for elliptic equations. *Mailing Add:* 6710 Everett St Lincoln NE 68506

**ZEDECK, MORRIS SAMUEL,** PHARMACOLOGY, TOXICOLOGY. *Current Pos:* PRES, ZEDECK ADV GROUP INC, 88-; ADJ ASSOC PROF, JOHN JAY COL CRIMINAL JUSTICE, 90- *Personal Data:* b Brooklyn, NY, Jan 25, 40; m 89, Ellen L Seplow; c Sharon, Beth & Deborah. *Educ:* Long Island Univ, BS, 61; Univ Mich, PhD(pharmacol), 65; City Univ NY, MBA, 87. *Prof Exp:* Asst prof pharmacol, Sch Med, Yale Univ, 67-68; asst mem, Sloan-Kettering Inst Cancer Res, 68-76; from asst prof to assoc prof pharmacol, Grad Sch Med Sci, Sloan-Kettering Div, Cornell Univ, 76-83; assoc mem, Sloan-Kettering Inst Cancer Res, 76-83, vpres opers, Edward Blank Assoc, Inc, 83-88. *Concurrent Pos:* Fel pharmacol, Sch Med, Yale Univ, 65-67. *Mem:* Am Asn Cancer Res; Am Soc Pharmacol & Exp Therapeut; Soc Toxicol; Am Col Toxicol; Am Col Forensic Examrs. *Res:* Consultant and expert witness in drug and chemical related matters; mechanism of action studies and preclinical toxicology studies of cancer chemotherapeutic agents; chemical carcinogenesis. *Mailing Add:* 245 E 80th St New York NY 10021

**ZEDEK, MISHAEL,** MATHEMATICS. *Current Pos:* from asst prof to assoc prof, 58-67, PROF MATH, UNIV MD, COLLEGE PARK, 68- *Personal Data:* b Kaunas, Lithuania, July 16, 26; m 56, Meira E Oschinsky; c Daniel & Thalia. *Educ:* Hebrew Univ, Israel, MSc, 52; Harvard Univ, PhD(math), 56. *Prof Exp:* Asst, Hebrew Univ, Israel, 52-53; asst, Harvard Univ, 53-55; instr math, Univ Calif, Berkeley, 56-58. *Mem:* Am Math Soc; London Math Soc. *Res:* Mathematical analysis; complex analysis; interpolation and approximation. *Mailing Add:* Dept Math Univ Md College Park MD 20742-0001. *Fax:* 301-314-0827; *E-Mail:* mnz@mary.umd.edu

**ZEDLER, EMPRESS YOUNG,** SPEECH PATHOLOGY, PSYCHOLOGY. *Current Pos:* RETIRED. *Personal Data:* b Abilene, Tex, Nov 9, 08; m 28. *Educ:* Univ Tex, Austin, BA, 28, MA, 48, PhD(speech path), 52. *Prof Exp:* Prof spec educ, Hearing & Lang Clin, SW Tex State Univ, 48-77, chmn dept, 64-77, prof & dir, 77-80; pvt pract, psychol & lang-learning disabilities, 81- *Mem:* Fel Am Speech & Hearing Asn; Am Psychol Asn; Acad Aphasia; fel Am Cong Rehab Med. *Res:* Language; learning disabilities; special research in diagnosis and treatment of dyslexia and related disabilities. *Mailing Add:* 1100 S Laurel Ave Luling TX 78648-3507

**ZEDLER, JOY BUSWELL,** WETLAND ECOLOGY, ECOSYSTEM RESTORATION. *Current Pos:* lectr, 69-72, from asst prof to assoc prof, 72-80, PROF BIOL, SAN DIEGO STATE UNIV, 80-, DIR, PAC ESTUARINE RES LAB, 86- *Personal Data:* b Sioux Falls, SDak, Oct 15, 43; m 65, Paul H; c Emily & Sarah. *Educ:* Augustana Col (SDak), BS, 64; Univ Wis, Madison, MS, 66, PhD(bot), 68. *Honors & Awards:* Theodora Sperry Award, Soc Ecol Restoration. *Prof Exp:* Asst bot, Univ Wis-Madison, 64-66, fel, 66-67, res asst, 67-68; instr, Univ Mo, Columbia, 68-69. *Concurrent Pos:* Mem, Water Sci & Technol Bd, Nat Res Coun, 91. *Mem:* Am Soc Limnol & Oceanog; Ecol Soc Am; Estuarine Res Fedn; Soc Wetland Scientists; Soc Ecol Restoration. *Res:* Coastal wetland structure and functioning, especially salt marsh ecology; restoration of wetland ecosystems. *Mailing Add:* Dept Biol San Diego State Univ San Diego CA 92182-4625. *Fax:* 619-594-2035; *E-Mail:* jzedler@surstrolae.sdsu.edu

**ZEDLER, PAUL H(UGO),** ECOLOGY, PLANT ECOLOGY. *Current Pos:* from asst to assoc prof, 69-78, PROF BIOL, SAN DIEGO STATE UNIV, 78-, DIR BIOL FIELD STAS. *Personal Data:* b Milwaukee, Wis, June 22, 41; m 65; c 2. *Educ:* Univ Wis-Milwaukee, BS, 63; Univ Wis-Madison, MS, 66, PhD(bot), 68. *Prof Exp:* Arboretum botanist, Univ Wis, 64-68; fel forestry, Univ Mo, Columbia, 68-69. *Concurrent Pos:* Vis scholar, Univ Col NWales, Bangor, 80; chmn, Ecol Prog Area, San Diego State Univ, 85-86; vis scientist, Western Australia Wildlife Res Ctr, Woodvale WAustralia, 86. *Mem:* AAAS; Brit Ecol Soc; Ecol Soc Am; Ecol Soc Australia. *Res:* Plant population ecology, fire ecology, successional studies, plant-substrate relationships; temporary wetlands. *Mailing Add:* Dept Biol San Diego State Univ San Diego CA 92182-0002

**ZEE, ANTHONY,** THEORETICAL HIGH ENERGY PHYSICS. *Current Pos:* PROF PHYSICS, UNIV CALIF, SANTA BARBARA, 85- *Personal Data:* b China; m 71. *Educ:* Princeton Univ, AB, 66; Harvard Univ, AM, 68, PhD(physics), 70. *Prof Exp:* Mem physics, Inst Advan Study, 70-72; asst prof, Rockefeller Univ, 72-73; asst prof physics, Princeton Univ, 73-78; assoc prof physics, Univ Pa, 78-80; prof physics, Univ Wash, 80-85. *Concurrent Pos:* A P Sloan Found fel, 73-78; mem, Inst Theoret Physics, Santa Barbara, 85- *Res:* Unification of fundamental interactions; aspects of cosmology and gravity. *Mailing Add:* Inst Theoret Physics Univ Calif Santa Barbara CA 93106-4030

**ZEE, DAVID SAMUEL,** NEUROLOGY, NEUROPHYSIOLOGY. *Current Pos:* from asst prof to assoc prof, 75-84, PROF NEUROL, JOHNS HOPKINS UNIV, 85- *Personal Data:* b Chicago, Ill, Aug 14, 44; c 2. *Educ:* Northwestern Univ, BA, 65; Johns Hopkins Univ, MD, 69. *Prof Exp:* Clin assoc neurol, NIH, 73-75. *Concurrent Pos:* Nat Inst Neurol Dis & Stroke grant, 75-80, Nat Eye Inst res grant, 80-85; NIH res grant, 76-97. *Mem:* Asn Res Vision & Ophthal; Soc Neurosci; Am Acad Neurol; Am Neurol Asn. *Res:* Ocular motor disorders; ocular motor physiology; computer modelling; vestibular disorders. *Mailing Add:* 12229 Carroll Mill Ellicott City MD 21042

**ZEE, PAULUS,** PEDIATRICS, BIOCHEMISTRY. *Current Pos:* PEDIATRICIAN, SWEETWATER HOSP, 85- *Personal Data:* b Amsterdam, Neth, July 2, 28; US citizen; m 57; c 4. *Educ:* Univ Amsterdam, MD, 54; Tulane Univ, PhD(biochem), 65. *Prof Exp:* Resident pediat, Children's Mercy Hosp, Kansas City, Mo, 56-58; asst prof, Univ Tenn, 64-68, assoc prof pediat & physiol, 68-85. *Concurrent Pos:* Mem, St Jude Children's Res Hosp, 64-85. *Mem:* Am Oil Chem Soc; AMA; Am Acad Pediat; Am Inst Nutrit; Am Soc Clin Nutrit. *Res:* Lipid metabolism of the newborn; pediatric nutrition. *Mailing Add:* Sweetwater Med Clin 202 Church St Sweetwater TN 37874-2821. *Fax:* 423-213-8598

**ZEE, YUAN CHUNG,** VIROLOGY. *Current Pos:* Res bacteriologist, Virol Div, Naval Biol Lab, Univ Calif, Berkeley, 63-66, from asst prof to assoc prof, 66-74, PROF VET MICROBIOL & CHMN DEPT, UNIV CALIF, DAVIS, 74- *Personal Data:* b Shanghai, China, Aug 29, 35; m 66. *Educ:* Univ Calif, Berkeley, AB, 57, MA, 59, PhD(comp path), 66, Univ Calif, Davis, DVM, 63. *Mem:* Am Vet Med Asn; Am Soc Microbiol. *Res:* Biological properties of animal viruses; mechanisms of virus replication and electron microscopy. *Mailing Add:* 1015 Kent Dr Davis CA 95616

**ZEE-CHENG, ROBERT KWANG-YUEN,** ORGANIC CHEMISTRY, MEDICINAL CHEMISTRY. *Current Pos:* RETIRED. *Personal Data:* b Kashan, Chekiang, China, Sept 2, 25; US citizen; m 49; c Chi-Lui, Chi-Sung, Chi-Feng & Chi-Wa. *Educ:* China Tech Inst, BS, 45; NMex Highlands Univ, MS, 57; Univ Tex, Austin, PhD(org chem), 63. *Honors & Awards:* Award for Outstanding Contrib to Achievement of Sci Knowledge in Cancer Chemother, Coun Prin Scientists Midwest Res Inst, 73. *Prof Exp:* Res chemist & chem engr, Taiwan Pulp & Paper Corp, 46-56; asst org chem, NMex Highlands Univ, 56-57; res scientist & teaching asst, Univ Tex, Austin, 57-59; assoc chemist, Midwest Res Inst, 59-61; Welch Found fel, Univ Tex, Austin, 61-62; sr chemist, Celanese Corp Am, Tex, 62-65; sr chemist, Biol Sci Div, Midwest Res Inst, 65-71, prin chemist, 71-80; asst dir drug develop lab, Univ Kans Med Ctr, 80-, res prof, Dept Pharmacol, Toxicol & Therapeut, 83-92. *Concurrent Pos:* Contrib ed, Drugs of the Future, 83-, Sci Adv Bd, Drug News & Perspectives, 89-; vis prof, Shanghai Med Univ, 89; consult, Shanghai 12th Pharm Factory, 89- *Mem:* Am Chem Soc; Sigma Xi; AAAS; NY Acad Sci; Am Asn Cancer Res. *Res:* Physical chemistry; chemical engineering; synthesis; identification; reaction mechanism of organic compounds; heterocyclic chemistry; cancer chemotherapy; pharmacology. *Mailing Add:* 6 Montrouge Ct Manchester MO 63011-4127

**ZEEMAN, MAURICE GEORGE,** TOXOCOLOGIST, ENVIRONMENTAL SCIENCES. *Current Pos:* chief, Toxicol Sect, Off Toxic Substances, 88-89, SUPVRY BIOLOGIST & CHIEF ENVIRON EFFECTS BR, OFF POLLUTION PREV & TOXICS, US ENVIRON PROTECTION AGENCY, 89- *Personal Data:* b Rockland, Mass, Dec 1, 42; m 86, Dianne Bradley. *Educ:* Calif State Univ, Northridge, BA, 69; Univ Calif, Los Angeles, MA, 72; Utah State Univ, PhD(zool), 80. *Prof Exp:* Teaching asst biol, Dept Zool, Univ Calif, Los Angeles, 69-70 & 71-72; res asst, Dept Biol, Utah State Univ, 75-80; toxicologist, Ctr Vet Med, Food & Drug Admin, 80-88. *Concurrent Pos:* Adj prof environ toxicol, NIH, Grad Sch, Dept Pharmacol & Toxicol, 82- *Mem:* Fel AAAS; Am Col Toxicol; Asn Govt Toxicologists; Soc Environ Toxicol Chem; Sigma Xi; NY Acad Sci. *Res:* Environmental toxicology effects of toxic agents on fish immune system; aquatic toxicology; pesticide effects of fish immunology and hematology; ecological risk assessment; structure-activity relationships. *Mailing Add:* US EPA OPPT HERD 7403 401 M St SW Washington DC 20460

**ZEEVAART, JAN ADRIAAN DINGENIS,** PLANT PHYSIOLOGY, BIOCHEMISTRY. *Current Pos:* assoc prof, 65-70, PROF PLANT PHYSIOL, MICH STATE UNIV, 70- *Personal Data:* b Baarland, Neth, Jan 5, 30; m 56; c 1. *Educ:* State Agr Univ Wageningen, BSc, 53, MSc, 55, PhD(plant physiol), 58. *Honors & Awards:* Medal, Int Plant Growth Substance Asn, 91. *Prof Exp:* Asst plant physiol, State Agr Univ Wageningen, 55-58; res fel, Calif Inst Technol, 60-63; assoc prof, McMaster Univ, 63-65. *Concurrent Pos:* Guggenheim fel, Milstead Lab Chem Enzymol, Sittingbourne Res Ctr, 73-74. *Mem:* Am Inst Biol Sci; Am Soc Plant Physiol; corresp mem Royal Dutch Acad Sci; AAAS; Int Plant Growth Substance Asn. *Res:* Physiology of flower formation; plant development as regulated by growth substances; gibberellins and abscisic acid; environmental physiology. *Mailing Add:* Dept Bot S-218 Mich State Univ 166 Plant Biol East Lansing MI 48824-1312. *Fax:* 517-353-9168; *E-Mail:* 22900mgr@msu.edu

**ZEEVI, ADRIANA,** IMMUNOLOGY. *Current Pos:* asst prof path, 84-85, ASSOC PROF PATH & SURG, UNIV PITTSBURGH, 89-; INVESTR, CENT BLOOD BANK PITTSBURGH, 85- *Personal Data:* b Cluj, Romania, May 11, 48; US citizen. *Educ:* Bar-Ilan Univ, Israel, BA, 72, MSH, 73, PhD(immunol), 79. *Honors & Awards:* Young Investr Award, Am Soc Histocompatibility & Immunogenetics. *Prof Exp:* Res fel, Blood Ctr S Eastern Wis, 79-82, assoc investr, 82-83, investr, 83-85. *Concurrent Pos:* New investr award, NIH, 82-85; adj asst prof, Med Col Wis, 83-85; councellor, Am Soc Histocompatibility & Immunogenetics, 90- *Mem:* Am Soc Histocompatibility & Immunogenetics. *Res:* Immunology; author of over 150 publications. *Mailing Add:* Dept Transplant Path Biomed Sci Tower Univ Pittsburgh Pittsburgh PA 15261-2583

**ZEFFREN, EUGENE,** BIO-ORGANIC CHEMISTRY, GENERAL MANAGEMENT. *Current Pos:* vpres res & develop, Helene Curtis, Inc, 79-95, pres, 95-96, CORP SR VPRES, HELEN CURTIS USA, 96- *Personal Data:* b St Louis, Mo, Nov 21, 41; m 64; c 2. *Educ:* Washington Univ, AB, 63; Univ Chicago, MS, 65, PhD(org chem), 67. *Prof Exp:* Res chemist enzym, Procter & Gamble Co, 67-71, group leader, 71-74, sect head, 74-77, assoc dir, toilet goods div, Winton Hill Tech Ctr, 77-79. *Concurrent Pos:* Vchmn sci adv comt, Cosmetic Toiletry & Fragrance Asn, 84-88, chmn, 88-90, bd dir, 96- *Mem:* Am Chem Soc; Soc Cosmetic Chemists; AAAS. *Res:* Mechanism of enzyme action; model systems for enzymic catalysis; chemistry of hair keratins; protein structure. *Mailing Add:* 325 N Wells St Helene Curtis Chicago IL 60610

**ZEGARELLI, EDWARD VICTOR,** DENTISTRY. *Current Pos:* RETIRED. *Personal Data:* b Utica, NY, Sept 9, 12; m 39, Irene Ceconi; c Edward Jr, David J, Philip E & Peter J. *Educ:* Columbia Univ, AB, 34, DDS, 37; Univ Chicago, MS, 42; Am Bd Oral Med, dipl, 56. *Hon Degrees:* DSc, Columbia Univ, 83. *Honors & Awards:* Austin Sniffin Medal Honor, Dent Soc, NY, 61, Jarvie-Burkhardt Medal Honor, 70; Samuel J Miller Medal, Am Acad Oral Med, 76; Henry Spenaded Award, Dent Soc NY, 79; William J Gies Medal, Am Col Dentists, 81. *Prof Exp:* Asst dent, 37-38, from instr to asst prof, 38-47, head diag & roentgenol, 47-57, prof, 57-58, dir, Div Stomatol, 58-77, Edwin S Robinson prof dent, Sch Dent & Oral Surg, 58-78, dean, 74-78; dir dent serv, Columbia-Presby Med Ctr, 74-78; emer prof dent & emer dean, Sch Dent & Oral Surg, Columbia Univ, 74-78. *Concurrent Pos:* Dent alumni res award, Columbia Univ, 63; mem univ coun, Columbia Univ, 59-62, cancer coordr & chmn comt dent res, Sch Dent & Oral Surg; mem coun dent therapeut, Am Dent Asn, 63-69, vchmn, 68-69, consult, 69-, consult, coun dent mat & devices, 70-; mem, NY Bd Dent Exam, 63-71, pres, 70-71; attend dent surgeon & dir dent serv, Columbia-Presby Med Ctr & Delafield Inst Cancer Res; cent off consult & dentist in residence, Vet Admin, DC; police surgeon, New York Police Dept; chmn comt exam, NE Regional Bd Dent Examr, 69-91 & joint panel drugs in dent, Nat Acad Sci-Nat Res Coun-Food & Drug Admin; consult, EORange, Kingsbridge & Montrose Vet Admin Hosps, Grasslands, Phelps Mem & Vassar Bros Hosps & USPHS; dir dent serv, Columbia-Presby Med Ctr, 74-78; mem, NY State Health Res Coun, 75-80; Consult dent, Columbia-Presby Med Ctr, 78. *Mem:* AAAS; Am Cancer Soc; fel Am Col Dentists; hon mem Dent Soc Guatemala; Am Dent Asn; Nat Acad Pract. *Res:* Diseases of the mouth and jaws, especially diagnosis; pharmacotherapeutics of oral diseases. *Mailing Add:* 120 Gory Brook Rd Sleepy Hollow NY 10591

**ZEGEL, WILLIAM CASE,** ENVIRONMENTAL ENGINEERING, PROJECT MANAGEMENT. *Current Pos:* PRES, WATER & AIR RES INC, 79- *Personal Data:* b Port Jefferson, NY, Aug 4, 40; m 62; c 2. *Educ:* Stevens Inst Technol, ME, 61, MS, 62, DSc, 65; Environ Eng Intersoc, dipl, 76. *Prof Exp:* Instr chem, Newark Col Eng, 61-64; sr res engr, Allied Chem Corp, 64-68; develop mgr, Scott Res Labs, 68-72; sr res assoc, Ryckman, Edgerly, Tomlinson & Assocs, 72-75; vpres opers, Environ Sci & Eng Inc, 75-79; pres, Strategic Planning & Res Group, 83-86. *Concurrent Pos:* Vis lectr, Stevens Inst Technol, 65-68; tech consult, Environ Protection Agency Regional Air Pollution Study, 74-75; dir, Air Pollution Control Asn, 83-86; coun chair, Commun & Mkt, Air & Waste Mgt Asn, 88-91. *Mem:* Am Inst Chem Engrs; fel Air & Waste Mgt Asn (vpres, 85-86); AAAS; Nat Soc Prof Engrs. *Res:* Atmospheric chemistry; water chemistry; pollution control technology; environmental impact assessment; process analysis; project management. *Mailing Add:* 11011 NW 12th Pl Gainesville FL 32607

**ZEGURA, STEPHEN LUKE,** HUMAN BIOLOGY, BIOLOGICAL ANTHROPOLOGY. *Current Pos:* from asst prof to assoc prof anthrop, 72-92, assoc prof genetics, 77-88, PROF ANTHROP, UNIV ARIZ, 92- *Personal Data:* b San Francisco, Calif, July 2, 43; m 83, Elizabeth Chesney; c Daniel & Krista. *Educ:* Stanford Univ, BA, 65; Univ Wis, Madison, MS, 69, PhD(human biol), 71. *Prof Exp:* Asst prof anthrop, NY Univ, 71-72. *Concurrent Pos:* NY Univ career develop grant, Smithsonian Inst, 72, Irex, 88, Nat Res Coun, 90. *Mem:* AAAS; Am Asn Phys Anthrop; Classification Soc; Am Anthrop Asn; Soc Study Human Biol. *Res:* Multivariate statistics; biological distance; Eskimology; population genetics; evolutionary theory; Adriatic population structure. *Mailing Add:* Dept Anthrop Univ Ariz Tucson AZ 85721. *Fax:* 520-621-2088; *E-Mail:* zeguras@ccit.arizona.edu

**ZEHEB, EZRA,** THEORY & DESIGN OF ROBUSTLY STABLE SYSTEMS. *Current Pos:* sr lectr, 68-70, PROF ELEC ENG, TECHNION-ISRAEL INST TECHNOL, 88- *Personal Data:* b Haifa, Israel. *Educ:* Technion-Israel Inst Technol, BSc, 58, MSc, 62, DSc, 66. *Prof Exp:* Mem tech staff, Bell Tel Labs, 68; dir electronics, Appl Res & Develop Ctr, Israel, 70-72; prof elec eng, Tel-Aviv Univ, 85-82. *Concurrent Pos:* Vis prof, Stevens Inst Technol & Univ Mo, Columbia, 67 & Univ Calif, Davis, 76; consult, Ministry Indust & Com, Israel, 72-80; chmn, Working Group Robust Control, Int Fedn Automatic Control, 87- *Mem:* Fel Inst Elec & Electronics Engrs; Am Math Soc; Sigma Xi. *Res:* Theory and design of robustly stable systems; multidimensional systems theory; signal processing; filter theory. *Mailing Add:* 13 Holland St Haifa 34987 Israel. *E-Mail:* zeheb@ee.technion.ac.il

**ZEHNER, DAVID MURRAY,** SURFACE PHYSICS. *Personal Data:* b Philadelphia, Pa, Aug 7, 43; m 67. *Educ:* Drexel Inst Technol, BS, 66; Brown Univ, PhD(physics), 71. *Prof Exp:* Res asst physics, Brown Univ, 67-71; res physicist surface physics, Oak Ridge Nat Labs, 71-80. *Mem:* Sigma Xi; Am Phys Soc; Am Vacuum Soc. *Res:* Investigation of surface properties of solids using surface sensitive spectroscopic techniques employing electrons, photons and ions as scattering probes; surface damage, chemisorption and catalytic phenomena. *Mailing Add:* 4619 Brandywine Dr Lenoir City TN 37771-6851

**ZEHNER, LEE RANDALL,** CARBOHYDRATE CHEMISTRY & METABOLISM. *Current Pos:* DIR BIOTECH PROGS, BIOSPHERICS INC, 85-, VPRES SCI SERV, 91- *Personal Data:* b Lansdowne, Pa, Mar 15, 47; m 73, Susan Hovland; c Adam & Erica. *Educ:* Univ Pa, BS, 68; Univ Minn,

PhD(org chem), 73. *Prof Exp:* Res chemist org chem, Arco Chem Co, 73-75, sr res chemist, 75-78; group leader process develop, Ashland Chem Co, 78-82; mgr org process res, W R Grace & Co, 82-85. *Mem:* Am Chem Soc; Am Inst Chem Engrs; Inst Food Technol; NY Acad Sci; Am Mgt Asn. *Res:* Specialty chemical and petrochemical processes; carbohydrate chemistry; heterogeneous catalysis; metabolism of carbohydrate derivatives; design novel food ingredients. *Mailing Add:* 131 Brinkwood Rd Brookeville MD 20833. *Fax:* 301-210-4908; *E-Mail:* zehner@erols.com

**ZEHR, ELDON IRVIN,** BACTERIOLOGY, PLANT NEMATOLOGY. *Current Pos:* From asst prof to assoc prof, 69-73, PROF PLANT PATH, CLEMSON UNIV, 78- *Personal Data:* b Manson, Iowa, June 25, 35; m 57, Rosa Waidelich; c Jeffrey, Darrell, Russell, Ann, Tammy, Marie & Judy. *Educ:* Goshen Col, BA, 60; Cornell Univ, MS, 65, PhD(plant path), 69. *Honors & Awards:* Godley-Snell Award, 92; Carroll R Miller Award, Nat Peach Coun, 94. *Mem:* Am Phytopath Soc; AAAS. *Res:* Diseases of apples and peaches; biocontrol of nematodes. *Mailing Add:* Dept Plant Path & Physiol Clemson Univ Clemson SC 29634-0377. *Fax:* 864-656-0274; *E-Mail:* ezehr@clemson.edu

**ZEHR, FLOYD JOSEPH,** EXPERIMENTAL PHYSICS. *Current Pos:* from asst prof to assoc prof, 65-82, head dept, 69-71, PROF PHYSICS, WESTMINSTER COL, PA, 82- *Personal Data:* b Lowville, NY, June 28, 29; m 57, Pearl Bauman; c David M, Kenton J, Bonnie M & Mary A. *Educ:* Eastern Mennonite Col, BS, 54; Goshen Col, BA, 57; Syracuse Univ, MS, 61 & 63, PhD(physics), 67. *Prof Exp:* Teacher jr high sch, PR, 54-56 & sr high sch, NY, 57-59. *Concurrent Pos:* Researcher, Argonne Nat Lab, 71-72 & Oak Ridge Nat Lab, 79-80; prof physics, Malaysia, 88-89 & 91-93, area coordr, 91-93. *Mem:* Am Asn Physics Teachers; Am Solar Energy Soc. *Res:* Measurement of interatomic potential between lithium ions and helium atoms and lithium ions and hydrogen atoms; nuclear decay studies of LU-174 and Tm-174; neutron capture-gamma ray decay studies; residential solar space heating analyses; energy efficient residential thermal envelope analyses; world food and energy resources. *Mailing Add:* Dept Physics Westminster Col New Wilmington PA 16172. *Fax:* 412-946-7146; *E-Mail:* fzchr@westminster.edu

**ZEHR, JOHN E,** HYPERTENSION, RENIN-ANGIOTENSIN. *Current Pos:* RETIRED. *Personal Data:* b Foosland, Ill, Dec 29, 29; m 51; c 4. *Educ:* Eureka Col, BS, 64; Ind Univ, PhD(physiol), 68. *Prof Exp:* Res assoc physiol, Mayo Grad Sch Med, 68-70; res scientist physiol, Univ Wash, 70-72; prof, Bethel Col, 72-95. *Concurrent Pos:* Mem study sect, NIH, 78-80; vis prof, Jicin Med Sch, Japan, 80-81. *Mem:* Am Physiol Soc; Sigma Xi; Am Heart Asn; Int Soc Hypertension. *Res:* Neural control of the circulation in normal and hypertensive models. *Mailing Add:* 306 W Burkwood Ct Urbana IL 61801

**ZEHR, MARTIN DALE,** NEUROPSYCHOLOGY. *Current Pos:* RESEARCHER, MED CTR, KANSAS CITY, MO, 88- *Personal Data:* b Carthage, NY, Sept 30, 50. *Educ:* State Univ NY, Binghamton, BA, 72; Memphis State Univ, MS, 75, PhD(clin psychol), 79; Univ Mo, Kansas City, JD, 85. *Prof Exp:* Grant coordr victimization, Correctional Res & Eval Ctr, 77-78; psychol intern, Vet Admin Med Ctr, Topeka, Kans, 78-79; neuropsychologist, Vet Admin Med Ctr, Kansas City, Mo, 79-82; atty at law, Benson & McKay, Kansas City, Mo, 85-88. *Concurrent Pos:* Adj asst prof, Dept Psychiat, Sch Med, Kans Univ, 80- *Mem:* Am Psychol Asn; Nat Acad Neuropsychologists; NY Acad Sci. *Res:* Relationship between structural or systemic damage to cortical tissues and disruption of behavioral and cognitive-intellectual functions. *Mailing Add:* 5607 Rockhill Rd Kansas City MO 64110

**ZEHRT, WILLIAM H(AROLD),** CIVIL ENGINEERING. *Current Pos:* PROF CIVIL ENG & CHMN DEPT, UNIV S ALA, 66- *Personal Data:* b Racine, Wis, June 9, 22; m 55; c 3. *Educ:* Univ Wis, BS, 44, MSCE, 58, PhD(civil eng), 62. *Prof Exp:* Gen engr, Gen Eng Co, Wis, 47-48; bridge engr, Wis State Hwy Comn, 48-51; regional bridge engr, US Forest Serv, 51-55; br mgr bldg & related struct, Pub Works Off, Ninth Naval Dist, Ill, 55-57; instr civil eng struct, Univ Wis, 57-61; prof civil eng, Miss State Univ, 61-63; prof, Univ Ala, 63-66. *Mem:* Sigma Xi. *Res:* Engineering structures; basic properties of wood as a structural material. *Mailing Add:* 1318 Dauphin St Mobile AL 36604-2122

**ZEI, DINO,** EXPERIMENTAL PHYSICS, HISTORY OF SCIENCE. *Current Pos:* prof physics, Ripon Col, 57-78, chmn, Dept Physics, 57-88, William Harley Barber distinguished prof, 78-92, EMER WILLIAM HARLEY BARBER DISTINGUISHED PROF, RIPON COL, 92- *Personal Data:* b Chicago, Ill, Aug 20, 27; m 49; c 2. *Educ:* Beloit Col, BS, 50; Univ Wis, MS, 52, PhD, 57, MA, 72. *Prof Exp:* Physicist, Nat Bur Stand, 50; instr physics, Beloit Col, 52-53; asst prof, Milton Col, 53-54; assoc prof, St Cloud State Col, 55-57. *Mem:* Am Asn Univ Profs; Am Asn Physics Teachers; Am Phys Soc; Hist Sci Soc. *Res:* Atomic spectroscopy with lasers. *Mailing Add:* 674 E Jackson St Ripon WI 54971

**ZEICHNER-DAVID, MARGARITA,** MOLECULAR & DEVELOPMENTAL BIOLOGY. *Current Pos:* RES ASSOC PROF BIOL, SCH DENT, UNIV SOUTHERN CALIF, 81- *Personal Data:* b Mako, Hungary, July 20, 46; m 79; c 2. *Educ:* Polytech Inst, Mexico City, PhD(cell biol), 74. *Mem:* Sigma Xi; AAAS; Am Soc Cell Biol; Am Asn Dent Res; Am Soc Zoologists; NY Acad Sci. *Res:* Molecular genetics of tooth development. *Mailing Add:* Ctr Craniofacial Biol Univ Southern Calif Dent Sch 2250 Alcazar St CSA Rm 106 Los Angeles CA 90033. *Fax:* 213-342-2981

**ZEIDE, BORIS,** GROWTH & YIELD STUDY, FOREST MENSURATION. *Current Pos:* assoc prof, 80-86, PROF FORESTRY, UNIV ARK, 86- *Personal Data:* b Moscow, USSR, Mar 30, 37; US citizen; m 81; c 2. *Educ:* Moscow Col Forestry, USSR, MSc, 59; All-Union Inst Standards, USSR, PhD(forestry), 70. *Prof Exp:* Forester, Kalmuck Forest Mgt Dist, 59-60; res scientist forestry, All-Union Inst Standards, 66-68, head lab, 68-73; sr lectr ecol, Hebrew Univ, Israel, 74-76; res fel forestry, Harvard Univ, 76-77; asst prof forestry, Rutgers Univ, 77-80. *Concurrent Pos:* Vis prof, Univ Joensuu, Finland, 88, Clemson Univ, 89, Inst Global Climate, USSR, 90 & Madrid Univ, Spain, 91. *Mem:* Soc Am Foresters. *Res:* Fractal geometry of tree crowns structure and dynamics of forest stands methodology of ecological modeling; silviculture; biometry. *Mailing Add:* Univ Ark Sch Forestry RR 4 Monticello AR 71656

**ZEIDENBERGS, GIRTS,** ELECTRICAL ENGINEERING, SOLID STATE PHYSICS. *Current Pos:* develop engr, Systs Prod Assurance, 74-77, adv engr, Biomed Systs, 77-80, prod safety prog mgr, Info Records Div, 80-81, PROG MGR PROD SAFETY PROGS, IBM CORP, 81- *Personal Data:* b Tukums, Latvia, Apr 5, 34; US citizen; m 55; c 3. *Educ:* Univ Conn, BS, 57; Syracuse Univ, MEE, 59, PhD(elec eng), 66. *Prof Exp:* Prog engr, Gen Elec Co, 57-59, engr, 59-63; res engr, Syracuse Univ, 63-67. *Mem:* Inst Elec & Electronics Engrs. *Res:* Network and circuit design; semiconductor devices; heterojunction; biomedical systems. *Mailing Add:* IBM Corp 10/644 2000 Purchase St Purchase NY 10577

**ZEIDERS, KENNETH EUGENE,** MICROBIOLOGY, AGRONOMY. *Current Pos:* RETIRED. *Personal Data:* b Sunbury, Pa, Aug 21, 20. *Educ:* Pa State Univ, BS, 55, MS, 58. *Prof Exp:* Tech asst plant path, US Regional Pasture Res Lab, Agr Res Serv, USDA, 57-59, plant pathologist, 59-75, res plant pathologist, 75-89. *Concurrent Pos:* Plant pathologist, Dept Plant Path, Pa State Univ, 60-89. *Mem:* Am Phytopath Soc; Sigma Xi; Am Soc Agron. *Res:* Diseases of forage grasses and legumes; inoculation methods; screening for disease resistance; environmental plant pathology; role of diseases in modeling of forage crop production systems. *Mailing Add:* 60 Mountain View Dr Reedsville PA 17084

**ZEIDLER, JAMES ROBERT,** SIGNAL PROCESSING, SOLID STATE ELECTRONICS & COMMUNICATIONS SYSTEMS. *Current Pos:* SCIENTIST, COMMUN DEPT NRAD, 90- *Personal Data:* b Carlinville, Ill, Dec 1, 44; m 68, Wanda Butler; c Brandon J & Kevin A. *Educ:* MacMurray Col, BA, 66; Mich State Univ, MS, 68; Univ Nebr, Lincoln, PhD(physics), 72. *Prof Exp:* Asst physics, Mich State Univ, 66-68; asst, Univ Nebr, Lincoln, 68-73, res assoc & instr optics, 73-74; physicist, Signal Processing Underwater Commun, Naval Undersea Ctr, 74-77, supvry physicist, Naval Ocean Systs Ctr, San Diego, 77-83, tech adv res, eng & systs, asst secy Navy, Washington, DC, 83-84, scientist, Space Systs & Technol Div, Naval Ocean Systs Ctr, 84-90. *Concurrent Pos:* Adj prof, Dept Elec & Comput Eng, Univ Calif, San Diego, 89- *Mem:* Fel Inst Elec & Electronics Engrs,; Inst Elec & Electronics Engrs Commun Soc; Inst Elec & Electronics Engrs Signal Processing Soc; Inst Elec & Electronics Engrs Electron Soc. *Res:* Adaptive signal processing techniques; image processing; wireless communications systems; solid state devices. *Mailing Add:* Dept Elec & Comput Eng Mail Code 407 Univ Calif San Diego La Jolla CA 92093-0407. *Fax:* 619-553-1718; *E-Mail:* zeidler@ nosc.mil

**ZEIDMAN, BENJAMIN,** NUCLEAR PHYSICS. *Current Pos:* SR PHYSICIST, ARGONNE NAT LAB, 57- *Personal Data:* b New York, NY, Oct 6, 31; m 56, 72, Anne; c Michael, William & Kate. *Educ:* City Col New York, BS, 52; Washington Univ, PhD, 57. *Honors & Awards:* Sr Scientist Award Alexander Von Humboldt Found, 75. *Concurrent Pos:* Ford Found fel, Niels Bohr Inst, Copenhagen, Denmark, 63-64; vis prof, State Univ NY, Stonybrook, 72 & Max Plank Inst, Heidelberg, Ger, 75-76. *Mem:* AAAS; fel Am Phys Soc; Sigma Xi. *Res:* Intermediate energy; electron; nuclear reactions, scattering, spectroscopy and structure. *Mailing Add:* Argonne Nat Lab Bldg 203 Argonne IL 60439. *Fax:* 630-252-3903; *E-Mail:* zeidman@anl. gov

**ZEIDMAN, IRVING,** PATHOLOGY. *Current Pos:* RETIRED. *Personal Data:* b Camden, NJ, Mar 17, 18; m 53; c 2. *Educ:* Univ Pa, AB, 37, MD, 41. *Prof Exp:* From instr to prof path, Sch Med, Univ Pa, 46-83. *Res:* Cancer; chemical factors in cell adhesiveness; method of measuring surface area; effect of hyaluronidase on spread of tumors; transpulmonary passage of tumor cells; spread of cancer in lymphatic system. *Mailing Add:* PO Box 3 Barnegat Light NJ 08006

**ZEIGEL, ROBERT FRANCIS,** VIROLOGY, CYTOLOGY. *Current Pos:* RETIRED. *Personal Data:* b Washington, DC, June 22, 31; m 57, 77, Deanna Meigs; c Robin D, Jennifer L & Lisa A. *Educ:* Eastern Ill Univ, BS, 53; Harvard Univ, AM, 55, PhD(biol), 59. *Prof Exp:* Res biologist, Nat Cancer Inst, 59-66; assoc prof microbiol, Roswell Park Mem Inst, State Univ NY, Buffalo, 68-83, div rep, Dept Microbiol, 70-72, rep, App & Prom Comt, 76-78, coordr, Electron Micros Facil, Cancer Cell Ctr, 80-86, assoc cancer res scientist, assoc prof exp path, 83-91. *Concurrent Pos:* Consult, Nat Cancer Inst, 69-70; mem, Coun Asn Scientists, Roswell Park Mem Inst, 74-76. *Mem:* AAAS; Am Soc Cell Biol; Electron Micros Soc Am; Am Soc Zool. *Res:* Fine structural studies of mode of synthesis of oncogenic viral agents; search for viral agents and their association with human neoplasia; ultrastructure of picean tumors with possible environmental etiology; surface topography of maxillofacial prostheses with relation to their ability to be adapted to various bio-environments; ultrastructure of problems in metastasis; identification of occult viral agents from patients with AIDS or pre-AIDS syndrome. *Mailing Add:* S 4498 Woodchuck Rd East Aurora NY 14092

**ZEIGER, ERROL,** ENVIRONMENTAL MUTAGENESIS, MICROBIOLOGY. *Current Pos:* res microbiologist & head microbiol genetics sect, 76-78, res microbiologist & head environ mutagenesis group, Cellular & Genetic Toxicol Br, 78-91, HEAD, ENVIRON TOXICOL PROG, NAT INST ENVIRON HEALTH SCI, 91- *Personal Data:* b New York, NY, Dec 11, 39; m 63; c 3. *Educ:* City Col New York, BS, 60; George Washington Univ, MS, 69, PhD(microbiol), 73; NC Cent Univ, JD, 91. *Prof Exp:* Lab sci asst, Walter Reed Army Inst Res, 63-65; biologist, Lab Parasitic Dis, NIH, 65-66; fel, Dept Microbiol, George Washington Univ, 66-69; res microbiologist, Genetic Toxicol Br, Food & Drug Admin, 69-76. *Concurrent Pos:* Ed-in-chief, Environ & Molecular Mutagenesis. *Mem:* AAAS; Environ Mutagen Soc; Genotox & Environ Mutagen Soc; Genetic Toxicol Asn. *Res:* Microbial systems for the detection of environmental mutagens; development and validation of short-term predictive tests; use of short-term test systems in evaluating the genetic toxicology of chemicals; relationships between genetic toxicity and carcinogenicity. *Mailing Add:* 1504 Lamont Ct Chapel Hill NC 27514-2537. *Fax:* 919-541-2483; *E-Mail:* zeiger@niehs.nih.gov

**ZEIGER, H PAUL,** COMPUTER SCIENCE. *Current Pos:* asst prof aerospace eng, 66-71, ASSOC PROF COMPUT SCI, UNIV COLO, BOULDER, 71-, CHMN DEPT, 78- *Personal Data:* b Niagara Falls, NY, Nov 12, 36; m 59; c 3. *Educ:* Mass Inst Technol, SB, 58, SM, 60, PhD(elec eng), 64. *Prof Exp:* Ford Found fel elec eng, Mass Inst Technol, 64-65; asst prof elec eng, Univ BC, 65-66. *Mem:* Sigma Xi. *Res:* Processing and transmission of information; automatic control; applied abstract algebra; art of computer programming; software engineering; formal methods for programmers. *Mailing Add:* 604 Tenth St Boulder CO 80302-7507

**ZEIGER, HERBERT J,** THEORETICAL PHYSICS, SOLID STATE PHYSICS. *Current Pos:* RETIRED. *Personal Data:* b Bronx, NY, Mar 16, 25; m 54, Hanna Bloom; c Joel, Susan & Judith. *Educ:* City Col New York, BS, 44; Columbia Univ, MA, 48, PhD, 52. *Honors & Awards:* Townes Medal, Optical Soc Am, 81. *Prof Exp:* Union Carbide & Carbon Corp fel, Columbia Univ, 52-53; res physicist, Lincoln Lab, Mass Inst Technol, 53-90. *Concurrent Pos:* Vis scientist, Mass Inst Technol. *Mem:* Fel Am Phys Soc. *Res:* Solid state and molecular physics; masers and lasers; semiconductor physics. *Mailing Add:* 167 Pond Brook Rd Chestnut Hill MA 02167

**ZEIGER, WILLIAM NATHANIEL,** NATURAL PRODUCTS CHEMISTRY. *Current Pos:* STAFF, MCCORMICK & CO INC. *Personal Data:* b Highland Park, Mich, Sept 7, 46; m 73. *Educ:* Wayne State Univ, BA, 69; Univ Pa, PhD(chem), 72. *Prof Exp:* NIH trainee, 72-74, asst mem, Monell Chem Senses Ctr, 72- *Mem:* Am Chem Soc. *Res:* Food and flavor chemistry. *Mailing Add:* McCormick Wild Inc 226 Schilling Circle Hunt Valley MD 21031

**ZEIGHAMI, ELAINE ANN,** DATA BASE MANAGEMENT. *Current Pos:* res staff mem, Oak Ridge Nat Lab, 79-83, group leader, Health Safety Res Div, 83-88, res staff mem, Measurements Appln & Develop Group, 88- & ENVIRON REGUL & REMEDIAL GROUP, OAK RIDGE NAT LAB, 96- *Personal Data:* b Perry, Okla, Nov 13, 44. *Educ:* Okla State Univ, BS, 67, MS, 69; Univ Okla, PhD(epidemiol-biostatist), 74. *Prof Exp:* Asst math, Okla State Univ, 68-70 & Dept Math, Univ Okla, 71-72; instr, Northwestern State Col, 70-71; asst prof epidemiol, Dept Community Med, Sch Med, Pahlavi Univ, 74-77; res asst prof epidemiol, Dept Res Med, Univ Pa, 77-79. *Concurrent Pos:* Vis assoc prof, Dept Community Med, Pahlavi Univ, 78-79. *Mem:* Soc Epidemiol Res. *Res:* Health effects of drinking water contaminants and minerals; applications of statistical techniques and computer techniques to human health effects data; biomonitoring applications to human populations. *Mailing Add:* Oak Ridge Nat Lab X-10 Area 1060 Commerce Pl Oak Ridge TN 37830

**ZEIGLER, A(LFRED) G(EYER),** INORGANIC CHEMISTRY, CHEMICAL ENGINEERING. *Current Pos:* CONSULT, 86-; CONSULT, ENVIRON PROTECTION AGENCY, 92- *Personal Data:* b Chambersburg, Pa, Nov 12, 23; m 50, Betty J Keiser; c Mary E & Donald. *Educ:* Bucknell Univ, BSChE, 44; Pa State Univ, cert, 50. *Prof Exp:* Chief chem engr, Cochrane Corp, 46-52; tech dir, Am Water Softener Co, 52-63, gen mgr, 58-63, pres, 60-63, mgr, Water Conditioning Div, Envirex, Inc, 63-78, mgr, Indust Group, 78-83, mgr, Mkt Develop, 83-86. *Concurrent Pos:* Consult, Elec Boat Div, Gen Dynamics Corp, tech comt, People's Rebub China. *Mem:* Am Soc Testing & Mat; Am Chem Soc; Nat Asn Corrosion Engrs. *Res:* Industrial water conditioning; industrial waste treatment; decontamination of radioactive wastes; remediation contaminated aquifers. *Mailing Add:* 4243 Howell Rd Malvern PA 19355

**ZEIGLER, BERNARD PHILIP,** MODELLING & SIMULATION, KNOWLEDGE-BASED SYSTEMS. *Current Pos:* PROF ELEC & COMPUT ENG, UNIV ARIZ, 85- *Personal Data:* US citizen; c 3. *Educ:* McGill Univ, BEng, 62; Mass Inst Technol, MS, 64; Univ Mich, PhD(comput sci), 69. *Prof Exp:* From asst prof to assoc prof comput sci, Univ Mich, 69-75; vis prof, Weizmann Inst Sci, Israel, 76-80; prof, Wayne State Univ, 81-84. *Concurrent Pos:* Vis prof IBM Chair, Univ Ghent, Belg, 78, Nat Acad Sci, Shanghai Univ, Peoples Repub China, 85. *Mem:* Inst Elec & Electronics Engrs Comput Soc; fel Inst Elec & Electronics Engrs. *Res:* Methodology and software design for modelling and simulation of discrete event systems; applied artificial intelligence. *Mailing Add:* Dept Elec & Comput Eng Univ Ariz Tucson AZ 85721. *E-Mail:* zeiglereece.arizona.edu

**ZEIGLER, DAVID WAYNE,** CARDIOVASCULAR PHYSIOLOGY, ENDOCRINOLOGY. *Current Pos:* asst prof, 84-91, ASSOC PROF PHYSIOL, DEPT PHYSIOL & PHARMACOL, SCH MED, UNIV SDAK, 91- *Personal Data:* b Forest City, Iowa, Jan 30, 49; m 73; c 4. *Educ:* Iowa State Univ, BS, 71, MS, 73; Univ Mo, PhD(physiol), 83. *Prof Exp:* Retinal tech opthal, Wills Eye Hosp, Philadelphia, 74-77; res fel physiol, Univ Mo, Columbia, 77-82; fel pharmacol, Univ Minn, Minneapolis, 82-84. *Concurrent Pos:* Chair res comt, Am Heart Asn, Dakota affil, 90-; mem, High Blood Pressure Coun, Am Heart Asn. *Mem:* Am Physiol Soc; Sigma Xi. *Res:* Hormonal factors involved in the development of hypertension; the role of the renin-angiotension system in causing increased vascular reactivity. *Mailing Add:* 404 N Yellowstone Dr Brandon SD 57005-1563

**ZEIGLER, JOHN MARTIN,** ORGANOSILICON CHEMISTRY, PHYSICAL ORGANIC CHEMISTRY. *Current Pos:* PRES, SILCHEMY INC, 89- *Personal Data:* b Greensburg, Ind, Dec 5, 51. *Educ:* Wabash Col, BA, 74; Univ Ill, Urbana, PhD(org chem), 79. *Honors & Awards:* IR-100 Award, Res & Develop Mag, 85. *Prof Exp:* Res chemist, Am Cyanamid Co, 79-81; mem tech staff, Sandia Nat Labs, 81-85, supvr Polymers Div, 85-89. *Concurrent Pos:* Consult silicon-based mats & polymers; expert witness. *Mem:* Am Chem Soc; Sigma Xi; AAAS; Soc Photo Optical Instrumentation Engrs; Am Phys Soc. *Res:* Synthesis, characterization and physical and electronic properties of organopolysilanes and other organic electronic materials; organometallic and synthetic organic chemistry; physical chemistry. *Mailing Add:* Silchemy Inc 338 Nicklaus Dr SE Rio Rancho NM 87112. *Fax:* 505-294-0098

**ZEIGLER, ROYAL KEITH,** mathematics, applied statistics; deceased, see previous edition for last biography

**ZEIKUS, J GREGORY,** MICROBIOLOGY. *Current Pos:* FAC, MICH BIOTECHNOL INST. *Personal Data:* b Rahway, NJ, Oct 2, 45; m 67; c 2. *Educ:* Univ SFla, BA, 67; Ind Univ, Bloomington, MA, 68, PhD(microbiol), 70. *Prof Exp:* NIH fel microbiol, Univ Ill, Champaign, 70-72; from asst prof to assoc prof, Univ Wis-Madison, 72-80, prof bact, 80- *Concurrent Pos:* Vis scientist & fel, Univ Marburg, Ger, 76-77 & Inst Pasteur, France, 81-82. *Mem:* Sigma Xi; Am Soc Microbiol; AAAS. *Res:* Microbial physiology and ecology; anaerobic bacterial metabolism; microbial methance formation; industrial fermentations. *Mailing Add:* Mich Biotechnol Inst 3900 Collins Rd PO Box 27609 Lansing MI 48909-0609. *Fax:* 517-337-2122

**ZEILER, FREDERICK,** FINITE ELEMENT METHOD, COMPUTER IMPLEMENTATION OF NUMERICAL METHOD. *Current Pos:* RETIRED. *Personal Data:* b Berndorf, Austria, June 28, 21; Can citizen; m 53; c 3. *Educ:* Univ Man, BSc, 45; Univ Alta, MSc, 47; Univ Minn, MA, 55, PhD(math), 67. *Prof Exp:* From lectr to prof math, Univ Man, 67-90. *Concurrent Pos:* Fel, Nat Res Coun, 45 & 46, NSF, 66. *Mem:* Can Math Cong; Can Appl Math Soc; Math Asn Am. *Res:* Numerical analysis; ordinary differential equation; partial differential equation. *Mailing Add:* Group 160 Box 11 RR 1 Vermette MB R0G 2W0 Can

**ZEILER, KATHRYN GAIL,** algal molecular biology & biochemistry, lipid biotechnology, for more information see previous edition

**ZEILER, MICHAEL DONALD,** BEHAVIOR-ETHOLOGY. *Current Pos:* assoc prof, 69-72, CANDLER PROF PSYCHOL, EMORY UNIV, 72- *Personal Data:* b New York, NY, Oct 9, 33; m 54, Marlene Strum; c Douglas, Thomas, Jean & Diana. *Educ:* Stanford Univ, AB, 54; New Sch Soc Res, MA, 60, PhD(psychol), 62. *Prof Exp:* Asst prof psychol, Wellesley Col, 62-67; assoc prof child behav & develop, Univ Iowa, 67-69. *Mem:* Fel Am Psychol Asn; fel Am Psychol Soc; Psychonomics Soc; Animal Behav Soc. *Res:* Evolution of learning and the role of learning in evolution. *Mailing Add:* Dept Psychol Emory Univ Atlanta GA 30322. *E-Mail:* psymdz@unix.cc.emory.edu

**ZEILIK, MICHAEL,** BINARY STARS, INNOVATION IN ASTRONOMY EDUCATION. *Current Pos:* from asst prof to assoc prof, 75-85, dir, Ctr Grad Studies, 88-91, PROF ASTRON, UNIV NMEX, 85- *Personal Data:* b Bridgeport, Conn, Sept 26, 46; m 85, Kimberly Lesser; c Zachary A & Jeremy A. *Educ:* Princeton Univ, BA, 68; Harvard Univ, MA, 69, PhD(astron), 75. *Honors & Awards:* Harlow Shapley lectr, Am Astron Soc, 76-85. *Prof Exp:* Instr astron, Southern Conn State Col, 69-72 & Harvard Univ, 74-75. *Concurrent Pos:* Vis assoc prof astron, Univ Calif, Berkeley, 80; prin investr, grant Res Corp & educ grant NSF, 80-85 & 93-97, res grant NSF & NASA, 89-92. *Mem:* Int Astron Union; Am Astron Soc; Am Asn Physics Teachers; Am Asn Astron Educ. *Res:* Multiwavelength observations of active binary star systems; ethnoastronomy and archaeoastronomy of the US southwest; learning astronomy by novices. *Mailing Add:* Dept Physics & Astron Univ NMex Albuquerque NM 87131-1156. *Fax:* 505-277-1520; *E-Mail:* zeilik@chicoma.la.unm.edu

**ZEINER, FREDERICK NEYER,** ZOOLOGY. *Current Pos:* from asst prof to prof, 46-74, EMER PROF ZOOL, UNIV DENVER, 74- *Personal Data:* b Finley, NDak, Mar 20, 17; m 42. *Educ:* Univ Denver, BS, 38; Ind Univ, PhD(zool), 42. *Prof Exp:* Asst zool, Ind Univ, 38-40. *Concurrent Pos:* Res consult, Martin Co, 59 & 61; mem gov bd, Am Inst Biol Sci, 67-71. *Mem:* AAAS; Am Inst Biol Sci; Sigma Xi. *Res:* Pituitary-ovarian relationships during pregnancy; space physiology. *Mailing Add:* 1417 S Elizabeth St Denver CO 80210

**ZEISS, CHESTER RAYMOND,** ALLERGY, OCCUPATIONAL MEDICINE. *Current Pos:* Asst prof, 74-86, PROF MED & ALLERGY-IMMUNOL, MED SCH, NORTHWESTERN UNIV, CHICAGO, 86-; ASSOC CHIEF STAFF, VET ADMIN LAKESIDE MED CTR, CHICAGO, 81- *Personal Data:* b Evergreen Park, Ill, Jan 4, 41; m 64; c 3. *Educ:* Northwestern Univ, Evanston, BA, 63; Med Sch, Northwestern Univ, Chicago, MD, 67. *Honors & Awards:* Clin Investr Award, Vet Admin Med Res Serv, 81. *Concurrent Pos:* Prof med, Med Sch, Northwestern Univ, 84- *Mem:* Am Acad Allergy & Clin Immunol; Am Asn Immunologists; Am Col Physicians. *Res:* Immunology of occupational lung disease and IgE mediated hypersensitivity. *Mailing Add:* Vet Admin Lakeside Med Ctr 333 E Huron Chicago IL 60611. *Fax:* 312-642-6348

**ZEITLIN, BRUCE ALLEN,** ASTRONOMY. *Current Pos:* VPRES, IGC/ADVAN SUPERCONDUCTORS & INTERMAGNETICS GEN CORP, 86-; CORP VPRES, IGC & GEN MGR, APD CRYOGENICS, 96- *Personal Data:* b New York, NY, July 31, 43; m 65, Amy J Kozan; c Laurence, Jessica & Andrea. *Educ:* Rensselaer Polytech Inst, BS, 65; Stevens Inst Technol, MS, 68. *Prof Exp:* Scientist, Airco Cent Res Lab, 65-70; tech dir, Magnetic Corp Am, 70-72. *Mem:* Am Phys Soc. *Res:* Superconducting material technology. *Mailing Add:* APD Cryogenics 1833 Vultee St Allentown PA 18103. *E-Mail:* bzeit@apdcryogenics.com

**ZEITLIN, JOEL LOEB,** MATHEMATICS. *Current Pos:* assoc prof, 73-80, PROF MATH, CALIF STATE UNIV, NORTHRIDGE, 80- *Personal Data:* b Los Angeles, Calif, July 9, 42; m 72. *Educ:* Univ Calif, Los Angeles, BA, 63, MA, 66, PhD(math), 69. *Prof Exp:* Asst prof math, Wash Univ, 69-72; prof, Univ Valparaiso, 72-73. *Concurrent Pos:* Fulbright Hays scholar, 72-73. *Mem:* Math Asn Am; Am Math Soc. *Res:* Lie groups; representation theory; special functions; geometry. *Mailing Add:* Dept Math Calif State Univ 18111 Nordhoff St Northridge CA 91330-8313

**ZEITZ, LOUIS,** BIOPHYSICS, PHYSICS. *Current Pos:* RETIRED. *Personal Data:* b Lakewood, NJ, Jan 22, 22; m 46, Pearl Glaser; c Catherine & Jan. *Educ:* Univ Calif, Berkeley, AB, 48; Stanford Univ, PhD(biophys), 62. *Prof Exp:* Res asst x-ray instrumentation, Appl Res Labs, Montrose, Calif, 51-52, res physicist, 52-56; res assoc physics, Univ Redlands, 56-58; res assoc, Biophys Lab, Stanford Univ, 58-59; res assoc, Sloan-Kettering Inst, 62-63, assoc mem, Biophys Div, 69-89; assoc prof, Sloan-Kettering Div, Grad Sch Med, Cornell Univ, 69-89. *Concurrent Pos:* Nat Inst Child Health & Develop res grant, Sloan-Kettering Inst, 65-67; Dept Energy & NIH-Nat Cancer Inst grants. *Mem:* AAAS; Biophys Soc; Radiation Res Soc; NY Acad Sci. *Res:* X-ray spectrochemical analysis; trace elements in living systems; mechanisms of radiation effects on cell development; in vivo bone mineral content measurement; radiological physics. *Mailing Add:* 131 W 80th St New York NY 10024

**ZEIZEL, A(RTHUR) J(OHN),** ENVIRONMENTAL SCIENCE, NATURAL HAZARDS MITIGATION. *Current Pos:* prog mgr water hazard, 79-82, POLICY MGR EARTHQUAKES & NATURAL HAZARDS, FED EMERGENCY MGT AGENCY, 82- *Personal Data:* b Waterbury, Conn, Aug 17, 33; m 70, Joan Hanson; c Edward, Mark & Jeffrey. *Educ:* Univ Conn, BA, 56; Univ Ill, MS, 59, PhD(geol), 60. *Prof Exp:* Planning requirements officer, Off Metrop Develop, Dept Housing & Urban Develop, 67-68, dir, Water Resources Res, 68-72, environ scientist, Off Asst Secy for Res & Technol, 72-79. *Concurrent Pos:* Mem comt water resources res, Fed Coun Sci & Technol; sci adv new town construct, US-France Coop, 72-73; liaison, US Decade Natural Disaster Reduction, Nat Acad Sci; proj leader, earthquake loss reduction, NATO, 78-80; tech negotiator US-Mexico agreement for coop in natural disasters, 82-84; vis expert, UN Ctr Regional Develop, Japan, 88; liaison, Subcomt Natural Disasters, Off Sci & Technol Policy, White House. *Mem:* AAAS; fel Geol Soc Am. *Res:* Urban environmental planning; natural hazard reduction; water resources management; hydrogeology. *Mailing Add:* Mitigation Directorate Fed Emergency Mgt Agency 500 C St SW Washington DC 20472

**ZELAC, RONALD EDWARD,** RADIOLOGICAL HEALTH, RADIOLOGICAL PHYSICS. *Current Pos:* RES SCIENTIST, LANDAUER INC, 92- *Personal Data:* b Chicago, Ill, Jan 22, 41; m 61; c 2. *Educ:* Univ Ill, Urbana, BS, 62, MS, 64; Univ Mich, Ann Arbor, MS, 65; Univ Fla, PhD(environ sci), 70; Am Bd Health Physics, cert, 71, recert, 81, 85, 89, 93; Am Bd Med Physics, cert, 90. *Prof Exp:* Res asst solid state physics, Coord Sci Lab, Univ Ill, Urbana, 63-64; chief health physicist, IIT Res Inst, 65-68; asst prof radiation biol, Temple Univ, 70-80, dir radiol health, Biohazards Control & Chem Right to Know, 70-92, assoc prof radiol, Temple Univ, 80-92. *Concurrent Pos:* Radiation physicist, Mercy Med Ctr, Chicago, 67-68; consult, Wyeth Labs, Pa, 71-, Presby-Univ Pa Med Ctr, 74-86, Mobil Res & Develop Corp, NJ, 77-, Metropolitan Hosp, Philadelphia, 77-86, Smith Kline & French lab, 79-86, Rorer Group Inc, Pa, 86-92, DuPont & Co, 86-87 & Johnson Matthey, Pa, 86-90; chmn, Campus Radiation Safety Officer's Conf, 72-74, Am Bd Health Physics Panel Examr, 88-92; adj assoc prof radiol, Univ Pa, 80-86; assoc vprovost environ health & safety, Temple Univ, 87-, adj prof radiol, 92-; adj prof environ health, Northwestern Univ, 91-; mem, Radiation Protection Subcomt, Am Asn Physicists Med, 96- *Mem:* Health Physics Soc; Am Asn Physicists in Med; Sigma Xi; Am Acad Health Physics; Am Col Med Physics. *Res:* Radiation dosimetry and radiological safety in research and health sciences. *Mailing Add:* 860 N DeWitt Pl No 1307 Chicago IL 60611-1722

**ZELAZNY, LUCIAN WALTER,** SOIL MINERALOGY, CHEMISTRY. *Current Pos:* assoc prof, 76-82, PROF SOIL MINERAL, VA POLYTECH INST & STATE UNIV, 82-, THOMAS B HUTCHESON JR PROF, 93- *Personal Data:* b Bristol, Conn, May 8, 42; m 62, Layel Parker; c Laura, Lisa, Lesley, Lucian M & Lloyd. *Educ:* Univ Vt, BS, 64, MS, 66; Va Polytech Inst, PhD(soil chem), 70. *Prof Exp:* From asst prof to assoc prof soils, Univ Fla, 70-75. *Concurrent Pos:* Nat Acad Sci-Nat Res Coun grant; vis scholar, Fla Inst Phosphate Res, 82, Univ Del, 84, Rutgers Univ, 85, Univ Ky, 85, Oak Ridge Nat Lab, 88 & NS State Univ, 93; bd dirs, Soil Sci Soc Am, 82-93. *Mem:* Fel Am Soc Agron; Clay Mineral Soc; Sigma Xi; fel Soil Sci Soc Am; Minerals Soc Am; Int Soc Soil Sci. *Res:* Research interests are soil acidity; phosphorus, potassium, and aluminum chemistry; relationships among chemical, physical and mineralogical properties of soils; techniques of quantitative mineralogical analysis. *Mailing Add:* Crop & Soil Sci Va Polytech Inst CSES 0404 Blacksburg VA 24061-0404. *Fax:* 540-231-3431; *E-Mail:* mountain@vtvm1.cc.vt.edu

**ZELAZO, NATHANIEL KACHOREK,** ROBOTICS, SUPERCOMPUTERS. *Current Pos:* CHIEF EXEC OFFICER, ASTRONAUT CORP AM, 59-; CHMN BD, KEARFOTT GUID & NAVIG CO, 88- *Personal Data:* b Lomza, Poland, Sept, 28, 18; US citizen; m 43; c 2. *Educ:* City Col NY, BS, 40; Univ Wis, MS, 59. *Hon Degrees:* PhD, Milwaukee Sch Eng, 83, Univ Wis, 86. *Honors & Awards:* Albert Einstein Award, Am Technion Soc, 82; Centennial Medal, Inst Elec & Electronics Engrs, 84; Billy Mitchell Award, Air Force Asn. *Prof Exp:* Engr, Dept Defense, 41-52; vpres, Norden Ketay Div, United Technologies, 52-55; dir res & develop, Avionics Div, John Oster Co, 55-59. *Concurrent Pos:* Geschaftsf06hrer, Astronaut GmbH; dir, Astronaut C A Ltd, 70-; vpres, Astronaut Foreign Sales Corp, 84- *Mem:* Inst Elec & Electronics Engrs; Nat Soc Prof Engrs; Am Soc Naval Engrs; Am Inst Aeronaut & Astronaut. *Res:* Avionics; cryogenics; navigation. *Mailing Add:* 4115 N Teutonia Ave PO Box 523 Milwaukee WI 53209

**ZELBY, LEON W,** ELECTRICAL ENGINEERING, PHYSICS. *Current Pos:* PROF ELEC ENG, UNIV OKLA, 67- *Personal Data:* b Sosnowiec, Poland, Mar 26, 25; US citizen; m 54, Rachel Kupfermintz; c Laurie S & Andrew S. *Educ:* Univ Pa, BS, 56, PhD(elec eng & physics), 61; Calif Inst Technol, MS, 57. *Prof Exp:* Res engr physics, RCA, NJ, 59-61; mem fac, Univ Pa, 61-67. *Concurrent Pos:* Consol Electrodyn Corp fel, Calif Inst Technol, 56-57; Minn-Honeywell Regulator Co fel, Univ Pa, 57-58, Harrison fel, 58-59; consult, RCA, 61-67 & Moore Sch Elec Eng, Univ Pa, 62-67; chief scientist energy analysis, Inst energy Analysis, Oak Ridge, 75-76; NASA fac fel, Lewis Res Ctr, Cleveland, 82, 83, & 85; ed, Inst Elec & Electronics Engrs & Soc Mag, 90- *Mem:* Franklin Inst; Inst Elec & Electronics Engrs. *Res:* Energy analysis and policy; biomedical instrumentation; electromagnetic wave propagation; plasma diagnostics; effects of microwaves on organisms. *Mailing Add:* 1009 Whispering Pines Norman OK 73072. *E-Mail:* zelby@mailhost.ecn.uoknor.edu

**ZELDES, HENRY,** physical chemistry; deceased, see previous edition for last biography

**ZELDIN, MARTEL,** POLYMER CHEMISTRY, INORGANIC CHEMISTRY. *Current Pos:* CONSULT, 72-; DEAN SCI & TECHNOL, COL STATEN ISLAND, CITY UNIV NEW YORK, 93- *Personal Data:* b New York, NY, Aug 11, 37; m 58, Carol Parish; c 4. *Educ:* Queens Col, NY, BS, 59; Brooklyn Col, MA, 62; Pa State Univ, PhD(chem), 66. *Prof Exp:* Chemist, Interchem Corp, 60-62; proj scientist, Union Carbide Corp, 66-68; from asst prof to assoc prof chem, Polytech Inst Brooklyn, 68-80; prof chem & chmn dept, Ind Univ & Purdue Univ, 81-84. *Concurrent Pos:* Ed, J Inorg & Organometallic Polymers; vis scientist, IBM, Yorktown Heights, 74. *Mem:* Am Chem Soc. *Res:* Inorganic and organometallic polymers. *Mailing Add:* Off Dean Sci & Technol Col Staten Island City Univ NY 2800 Victory Blvd Bldg 1A Rm 313 Staten Island NY 10314

**ZELDIN, MICHAEL HERMEN,** CELL BIOLOGY, VISUAL PHYSIOLOGY. *Current Pos:* SR RES FEL, HARVARD UNIV, 74- *Personal Data:* b Philadelphia, Pa, Mar 25, 38; m 61; c 3. *Educ:* Franklin & Marshall Col, BS, 59; Temple Univ, MA, 61, PhD(biol), 65. *Prof Exp:* Res assoc biol, Brandeis Univ, 65-67; asst prof, Tufts Univ, 67-74. *Concurrent Pos:* NIH fel, 65-67. *Mem:* AAAS; Am Chem Soc; Asn Res Vision & Ophthal. *Res:* Biochemistry and electrophysiology of the vertebrate retina; neurophysiology, structure and function of membranes. *Mailing Add:* 2 Chilton St Cambridge MA 02138

**ZELDIS, JEROME B,** LIVER DISEASES. *Current Pos:* ASSOC PHYSICIAN, BETH ISRAEL HOSP, 85-; ASST PROF MED, HARVARD MED SCH, 87- *Personal Data:* b Waterbury, Conn, Apr 6, 50; m; c 2. *Educ:* Yale Univ, MD & PhD(molecular, biophysics & biochem), 78. *Prof Exp:* Res & clin fel med, Mass Gen Hosp, 81-85; instr med, Harvard Med Sch, 85-87. *Mem:* Am Asn Immunologists; Am Gastroenterol Soc; Am Asn Liver; Am Col Physicians. *Res:* viral hepatitis. *Mailing Add:* Celgene Corp 7 Powder Horn Dr Warren NJ 07059

**ZELEN, MARVIN,** BIOSTATISTICS. *Current Pos:* chmn, Dept Biostatist, 81-90, PROF STATIST SCI, SCH PUB HEALTH, HARVARD UNIV, 77-; CHAIR, DEPT BIOSTAT, DANA-FARBER CANCER INST, 77- *Personal Data:* b New York, NY, June 21, 27; m 50, Thelma Geier; c 2. *Educ:* City Col New York, BS, 49; Univ NC, MA, 51; Am Univ, PhD(statist), 57. *Hon Degrees:* AM, Harvard Univ, 77. *Prof Exp:* Mathematician, Nat Bur Stand, 52-61; head math statist & appl math sect, Nat Cancer Inst, 63-67; prof statist,

State Univ NY, Buffalo, 67-77, dir statist lab, 71-77. *Concurrent Pos:* Vis assoc prof, Univ Calif, Berkeley, 58; assoc prof math, Univ Md, 60-61; permanent mem math res ctr, Univ Wis, 61-72; sr Fulbright scholar, Imp Col & Sch Hyg & Trop Med, Univ London, 65-66; pres, Frontier Sci & Technol Res Found. *Mem:* Biomet Soc; fel Am Statist Asn; fel Inst Math Statist; Royal Statist Soc; fel Am Acad Arts & Sci; fel AAAS. *Res:* Model building in biomedical sciences; statistical planning of scientific experiments; clinical trials in cancer; probability and mathematical statistics. *Mailing Add:* Harvard Sch Pub Health 677 Huntington Ave Boston MA 02115. *Fax:* 617-632-2444; *E-Mail:* zelen@jimmy.harvard.edu

**ZELENKA, JERRY STEPHEN,** ELECTRONICS ENGINEERING, OPTICS. *Current Pos:* vpres, 86-88, CORP VPRES, SCI APPLN INT CORP, 88- *Personal Data:* b Cleveland, Ohio, Jan 27, 36; m 58; c 3. *Educ:* Univ Mich, Ann Arbor, BS, 58, MS, 59, PhD(elec eng), 66. *Honors & Awards:* M Barry Carlton Award, Sigma Xi. *Prof Exp:* Engr, Res Div, Bendix Corp, 59-61; res engr radar & optics, Univ Mich, Ann Arbor, 61-72; res engr, Environ Res Inst Mich, 72-76; sr scientist, 76-80, asst vpres, Sci Appln Inc, 80-85. *Concurrent Pos:* Lab instr, Univ Mich, Ann Arbor, 58-59, lectr, 72; consult, Westinghouse Elec Corp, 69-72, Gen Motors Corp & IBM Corp, 71-76. *Mem:* Inst Elec & Electronics Engrs; Optical Soc Am. *Res:* Systems analysis pertaining to coherent radars and to coherent optical processors. *Mailing Add:* Loral Defense Syst PO Box 895 Litchfield Park AZ 85340

**ZELENKA, PEGGY SUE,** DEVELOPMENTAL BIOLOGY. *Current Pos:* sr staff fel develop biol, 75-77, GENETICIST, NAT EYE INST, 77- *Personal Data:* b Joplin, Mo, Oct 4, 42; m 66. *Educ:* Rice Univ, BA, 64; Johns Hopkins Univ, PhD(biophys), 71. *Prof Exp:* Fel pediat, Johns Hopkins Sch Med, 71-72; staff fel develop biol, Nat Inst Child Health & Human Develop, 72-75. *Mem:* Asn Res Vision & Ophthal; AAAS; Am Soc Cell Biol. *Res:* Biochemical mechanisms of cellular differentiation during embryonic development; specifically those changes occurring in membranes of developing embryonic chick lenses. *Mailing Add:* Nat Eye Inst NIH Bldg 6 Rm 214 Bethesda MD 20892-2730. *Fax:* 301-496-1759

**ZELENY, LAWRENCE,** AGRICULTURAL CHEMISTRY, ORNITHOLOGY. *Current Pos:* RETIRED. *Personal Data:* b Minneapolis, Minn, Apr 30, 04; m 30; c 2. *Educ:* Univ Minn, BA, 25, MS, 27, PhD(agr biochem), 30. *Honors & Awards:* Patuxent Conserv Award, 77; Paul Bartsch Award, Audubon Naturalist Soc, 88. *Prof Exp:* Asst farm hort, Univ Minn, 28-29, agr biochem, 29, guest fel, 30; agent, US Forest Serv, 31-32; chief chemist, Visual Display, Inc, 33-35; assoc chemist, USDA, 35-41, grain technologist, 41-42, sr grain technologist & chief standardization res sect, grain, feed & seed br, agr mkt serv, 42-43, prin grain technologist & chief standardization & testing br, grain div, 53-66, consult, 67-72. *Mem:* AAAS; Am Chem Soc; Am Oil Chem Soc; Asn Off Anal Chem; Am Asn Cereal Chem (pres, 56-57); NAm Bluebird Soc; Sigma Xi. *Res:* Chemistry of fats and oils; cereal chemistry; biochemistry; chemical compositon of truck crops; quality evaluation of oilseeds, cereal grains and their products; population restoration of eastern bluebird. *Mailing Add:* 4312 Van Buren St Hyattsville MD 20782-1189

**ZELENY, WILLIAM BARDWELL,** PHYSICS EDUCATION. *Current Pos:* asst prof, 62-65, ASSOC PROF PHYSICS, NAVAL POSTGRAD SCH, 65- *Personal Data:* b Minneapolis, Minn, Mar 14, 34; m 60, 88, Mayra Portillo; c Thomas & Indira. *Educ:* Univ Md, BS, 56; Syracuse Univ, MS, 58, PhD(physics), 60. *Prof Exp:* Lectr physics, Univ Sydney, 60-62. *Concurrent Pos:* Consult, Data Dynamics, Inc, 65-67. *Res:* Quantum field theory; electrodynamics. *Mailing Add:* Dept Physics Naval Postgrad Sch Monterey CA 93943. *Fax:* 408-656-2834

**ZELEZNICK, LOWELL D,** IMMUNOLOGY, ALLERGY. *Current Pos:* GEN MGR, ALLERGAN, 91- *Personal Data:* b Milwaukee, Wis, Feb 1, 35; m 61; c 2. *Educ:* Univ Ill, Chicago, BS, 56, PhD(biochem), 61. *Prof Exp:* Res assoc biochem, Upjohn Co, 64-68; head biochem sect, 68-72, dir allergy dept, Alcon Labs Inc, 72-77; vpres sci & technol, Aerwey Labs, Inc, 77-78; vpres, Licensing Bus Develop, Allergan, 78-91. *Concurrent Pos:* Ciba fel microbiol, Ciba Pharmaceut Co, 61-63; fel molecular biol, Albert Einstein Col Med, 63-64; USPHS fel, 64-65; adj prof, Tex Christian Univ, 68. *Mem:* AAAS; Am Chem Soc; Am Soc Biol Chem; Am Acad Allergy & Clin Immunol. *Res:* Drug metabolism; biosynthesis and structure of lipopolysaccharides and bacterial cell walls; immunology-allergy research; quality control and product development. *Mailing Add:* Licensing Investment Mgt Assocs 26 Lakeview Irvine CA 92604-3681. *Fax:* 714-651-9312; *E-Mail:* drz211935@aol.com

**ZELEZNY, WILLIAM FRANCIS,** PHYSICAL CHEMISTRY. *Current Pos:* RETIRED. *Personal Data:* b Rollins, Mont, Sept 5, 18; m 49, Virginia Scarcliff. *Educ:* Mont State Col, BS, 40; Mont Sch Mines, MS, 41; Univ Iowa, PhD(phys chem), 51. *Prof Exp:* Chemist, Anaconda Copper Mining Co, 41-44; instr metall & phys chem, Univ Iowa, 48-49; aeronaut res scientist, Nat Adv Comt Aeronaut, 51-54; asst metallurgist, Div Indust Res, State Col Wash, 54-57; sr scientist, Atomic Energy Div, Phillips Petrol Co, Idaho, 57-66; asst metallurgist, Idaho Nuclear Corp, 66-70; mem staff, Los Alamos Sci Lab, 70-80. *Mem:* Am Chem Soc; Am Soc Metals; Am Inst Mining, Metall & Petrol Eng. *Res:* Kinetics of reaction at high temperatures; x-ray diffraction and spectroscopy; crystal structure; microprobe analysis of irradiated nuclear fuels. *Mailing Add:* PO Box 37 Rollins MT 59931

**ZELIGMAN, ISRAEL,** dermatology; deceased, see previous edition for last biography

**ZELINSKI, ROBERT PAUL,** POLYMER CHEMISTRY, RUBBER CHEMISTRY. *Current Pos:* RETIRED. *Personal Data:* b Chicago, Ill, Jan 13, 20; m 45; c 4. *Educ:* DePaul Univ, BS, 41; Northwestern Univ, PhD(org chem), 45. *Prof Exp:* Asst, Northwestern Univ, 41-42; from instr to prof chem & chmn dept, DePaul Univ, 43-55; group leader, Rubber Synthesis Br, Phillips Petrol Co, 55-61, from sect mgr to mgr, 61-75, mgr, Eng Plastics Br, Res Div, 75-84. *Concurrent Pos:* Asst, Northwestern Univ, 43-44. *Mem:* Am Chem Soc; Sigma Xi; Soc Plastics Engrs. *Res:* Synthesis of plastics and rubbers. *Mailing Add:* Rte 1 Box 517A Bartlesville OK 74006-9801

**ZELINSKI, TERESA A,** PEDIATRICS. *Current Pos:* Res assoc, Dept Pediat & Child Health, Fac Med, Univ Man, 84-85, fel, 85-86, asst prof, 87-92, ASSOC PROF, RH LAB, DEPT PEDIAT & CHILD HEALTH, FAC MED, UNIV MAN, 92-, DEPT HUMAN GENETICS, 93-; SCI DIR, SECT BLOOD GROUP SEROLOGY, DEPT PEDIAT & CHILD HEALTH, HEALTH SCI CTR, WINNIPEG, 93- *Educ:* Univ Man, BSc, 78, MSc, 81, PhD, 84. *Concurrent Pos:* Fac fund fel, Univ Man, 85-86, Sydney Israels fel, Childrens Hosp Winnipeg Res Found, 86-87; comt mem, Dept Coun, Dept Pediat, Fac Med, 87-, Continuing Educ, 88-, fac coun grad studies, 94-; prof, Childrens Hosp Winnipeg Res Found, Inc, 92- *Mem:* Can Biochem Soc; Am Soc Biol Chemists; Am Soc Human Genetics; Genetics Soc Can; Int Soc Blood Transfusion; Am Asn Blood Banks. *Res:* Pediatrics and child health. *Mailing Add:* RH Lab 735 Notre Dame Ave Winnipeg MB R3E 0L8 Can

**ZELINSKY, DANIEL,** ALGEBRA. *Current Pos:* from asst prof to prof, 49-93, chmn dept, 75-78, EMER PROF MATH, NORTHWESTERN UNIV, EVANSTON, 93- *Personal Data:* b Chicago, Ill, Nov 22, 22; m 45, Zelda Oser; c Mara (Sachs), Paul & David. *Educ:* Univ Chicago, SB, 41, SM, 43, PhD(math), 46. *Prof Exp:* Instr math, Univ Chicago, 43-44; asst, Appl Math Group, Columbia Univ, 44-45; Nat Res Coun fel, Univ Chicago, 46, instr math, 46-47; Nat Res Coun fel, Inst Advan Study, 47-49. *Concurrent Pos:* Mem exec comt, Nat Res Coun, 66-67; ed jour, Am Math Soc, 61-64, 83-87; chmn, Sect A, AAAS, 84-87. *Mem:* AAAS; Am Math Soc; Math Asn Am. *Res:* Rings; homological algebra. *Mailing Add:* Dept Math Northwestern Univ Evanston IL 60208

**ZELIS, ROBERT FELIX,** CARDIOVASCULAR PHYSIOLOGY, CIRCULATION-CONTROL. *Current Pos:* PROF MED, COL MED, PA STATE UNIV, 74-, DIR CARDIOL RES, 84- *Personal Data:* b Perth Amboy, NJ, Aug 5, 39; m 60, Gail A Heelon; c Robert, Kathleen, Karen & David. *Educ:* Univ Mass, BS, 60; Univ Chicago, MD, 64. *Prof Exp:* Resident, Harvard Univ, Beth Israel Hosp, 66; clin assoc cardiol, Nat Heart Inst, NIH, 66-68; from asst prof to assoc prof med, Univ Calif, Davis, 68-74. *Concurrent Pos:* Chief cardiol div, M S Hershey Med Ctr, 74-84; vis scientist, Pharmacol Inst, Univ Freiburg, WGer, 81-82; vis prof, Univ Lausanne, Switz, 89-90; Fogarty sr int fel, 89-90. *Mem:* Am Physiol Soc; Am Soc Pharmacol & Exp Therapeut; Asn Am Physicians; Am Soc Clin Invest (vpres, 84-85); Am Fedn Clin Res (pres, 77-78); Am Heart Asn. *Res:* Local and neurohumoral mechanisms controlling regional blood flow, how they alter with congestive heart failure and resulting local and systematic metabolic consequences; heart failure. *Mailing Add:* M S Hershey Med Ctr Pa State Univ Col Med PO Box 850 Hershey PA 17033. *Fax:* 717-531-1793; *E-Mail:* rzelis@med.hme.psu.edu

**ZELITCH, ISRAEL,** BIOCHEMISTRY, PLANT PHYSIOLOGY. *Current Pos:* asst biochemist, Conn Agr Exp Sta, 52-54, assoc biochemist, 54-60, biochemist, 60-74, head, Dept Biochem & Genetics, 63-94, S W Johnson distinguished scientist, 74-94, EMER S W JOHNSON DISTINGUISHED SCIENTIST, CONN AGR STA, 94- *Personal Data:* b Philadelphia, Pa, June 18, 24; m 46, Ruth H Goldman; c Helen, Bernard & Deborah. *Educ:* Pa State Univ, BS, 47, MS, 48; Univ Wis, PhD(biochem), 51. *Prof Exp:* Nat Res Coun fel, Col Med, NY Univ, Bellevue Med Ctr, 51-52. *Concurrent Pos:* Adj prof, Yale Univ, 58-; Guggenheim fel, Oxford Univ, 60; panel mem, NSF, 62-64 & Physiol Chem Study Sect, NIH, 66-70; Regents lectr, Univ Calif, Riverside, 71; Fulbright distinguished prof, Yugoslavia, 81. *Mem:* Am Chem Soc; fel AAAS; Am Soc Plant Physiol (pres, 77-78); fel Am Acad Arts & Sci; Am Soc Biochem & Molecular Biol. *Res:* Plant biochemistry; photosynthesis; respiration; plant productivity. *Mailing Add:* Dept Biochem & Genetics Conn Agr Exp Sta PO Box 1106 New Haven CT 06504

**ZELKOWITZ, MARVIN VICTOR,** SOFTWARE ENGINEERING, PROGRAM MEASUREMENT. *Current Pos:* from asst prof to assoc prof, 71-90, PROF COMPUT SCI, UNIV MD, 90-; FAC APPOINTEE, NAT INST STAND & TECHNOL, 76- *Personal Data:* b Brooklyn, NY, Aug 7, 45; m 70; c 2. *Educ:* Rensselaer Polytech Inst, 67; Cornell Univ, MS, 69, PhD(comput sci), 71. *Prof Exp:* Instr computer sci, Ithaca Col, 70-71. *Concurrent Pos:* Chair, Spec Interest Group Software Eng, Asn Comput Mach, 79-81, Tech Comt Software Eng, Inst Elec & Electronics Engrs, Computer Soc, 84-86; ser ed, Ablex Ser Software Eng, 85-, Acad Press Advances Comput, 94- *Mem:* Asn Comput Mach; fel Inst Elec & Electronics Engrs Comput Soc. *Res:* Complexity, understanding and development of computer environments including tools, interfaces and measurement of the underlying development processes. *Mailing Add:* Dept Comput Sci Univ Md College Park MD 20742. *Fax:* 301-405-6707; *E-Mail:* mvz@cs.umd.edu

**ZELL, BLAIR PAUL,** DIGITAL & ANALOGUE PROCESS CONTROL, FLUID DYNAMICS OF CENTRIFUGAL PUMPS. *Current Pos:* SR ELEC ENGR, PETERS MACHINERY CO, 96- *Personal Data:* b Waterloo, Iowa, Mar 11, 42; m 61, Elizabeth Stenzel; c Jeffrey & Deborah. *Educ:* Roosevelt Univ, BS, 70. *Prof Exp:* Electronics technician, US Navy, 62-70; indust eng assoc, Western Elec, 70-71; field serv engr, Teledyne Pines, 71-72; electronics technician, Chicago Circuit Drilling, 73-74; systs engr, Aurora Pump, Gen signal, 74-76, mgr systs eng, 76-84, dir systs res & develop, 84-91, sr res & develop systs, 92-93; automation engr, Tetrapak Processing Syst, 93-96. *Concurrent Pos:* Chmn tech comt, Am Soc Heating, Refrig & Air Conditioning Engrs, 85-87. *Mem:* Instrument Soc Am; Indust Comput Soc; Am Soc Bakery Engrs. *Res:* Fluid dynamics of centrifugal pumps and fans. *Mailing Add:* ON 735 Lea Dr Geneva IL 60134. *Fax:* 414-947-7252

**ZELL, HOWARD CHARLES,** ORGANIC CHEMISTRY. *Current Pos:* RETIRED. *Personal Data:* b Philadelphia, Pa, Feb 11, 22; m 52, Tatiana E Kopal. *Educ:* St Joseph's Univ, BS, 43; Univ Del, MS, 51; Univ Pa, PhD(org chem), 64. *Prof Exp:* Chemist, Publicker Industs, Inc, 43-47; res assoc org chem, Merck Sharp & Dohme Res Lab, 48-65; assoc scientist, Ethicon, Inc, 65-67, sr scientist, 67-69, prin scientist, 69-74; chemist, Food & Drug Admin, 74-81, supvy chemist, 81-87; dir regulatory affairs, Marsam Pharmaceut Inc, 88-96. *Mem:* AAAS; Am Chem Soc; Sigma Xi. *Res:* Medicinal and polymer chemistry. *Mailing Add:* 504 Montgomery Rd Ambler PA 19002

**ZELLER, ALBERT FONTENOT,** NUCLEAR PHYSICS, APPLIED SUPERCONDUCTIVITY. *Current Pos:* staff physicist, 79-92, SR PHYSICIST & HEAD RES FACIL DEPT, NAT SUPERCONDUCTING CYCLOTRON LAB, MICH STATE UNIV, 92- *Personal Data:* b Oakland, Calif, Jan 10, 47; m 72, Pat Gainey; c Fiona & Rebecca. *Educ:* Univ Wash, BA, 71; Fla State Univ, MS, 73, PhD(nuclear chem), 74. *Prof Exp:* Res assoc nuclear physics, Fla State Univ, 74-75; res fel, Dept Nuclear Physics, Australian Nat Univ, 75-78; res assoc nuclear physics, Cyclotron Inst, Tex A&M Univ, 78-79. *Concurrent Pos:* Vis asst prof physics, Tex A&M Univ, 79; bd dir, Appl Superconductivity Conf, 92-, Cryog Eng Conf, 95- *Mem:* Am Phys Soc; sr mem Inst Elec & Electronics Engrs. *Res:* Constructing superconducting magnets and equipment for nuclear physics research. *Mailing Add:* Cyclotron Lab Mich State Univ East Lansing MI 48824-1321. *Fax:* 517-353-5967; *E-Mail:* zeller@nscl.msu.edu

**ZELLER, EDWARD JACOB,** geochemistry; deceased, see previous edition for last biography

**ZELLER, FRANK JACOB,** REPRODUCTIVE ENDOCRINOLOGY. *Current Pos:* asst, 53-56, res assoc, 56-57, from instr to assoc prof, 57-76, PROF ZOOL, IND UNIV, BLOOMINGTON, 76- *Personal Data:* b Chicago, Ill, Dec 6, 27; m 52; c 3. *Educ:* Univ Ill, BS, 51, MS, 52; Ind Univ, PhD(zool), 57. *Prof Exp:* Instr zool, Bryan Col, 52-53. *Mem:* Endocrine Soc; Soc Study Reproduction. *Res:* Reproduction in birds; effects of gonadotropins and sex hormones on the anterior pituitary gland and gonads. *Mailing Add:* 1040 S Manor Dr Bloomington IN 47401

**ZELLER, KURT ALAN,** MYCOLOGY, FUNGAL GENETICS. *Current Pos:* RES ASSOC, DEPT PLANT PATH, KANS STATE UNIV, 95- *Personal Data:* b LaPorte, Ind, Apr 12, 65. *Educ:* Ind Univ, BS, 87; Purdue Univ, PhD(biol), 94. *Prof Exp:* Postdoctoral res assoc, Purdue Univ, 95, instr DNA fingerprinting & genetic anal, 95. *Mem:* Mycol Soc Am; Soc Study Evolution. *Res:* How and why self/non-self recognition mechanisms and host specialization influence fungal speciation and evolution processes. *Mailing Add:* Throckmorton Hall Dept Plant Path Kans State Univ Manhattan KS 66506. *E-Mail:* kzeller@plantpath.ksu.edu

**ZELLER, MICHAEL EDWARD,** HIGH ENERGY PHYSICS. *Current Pos:* from instr to assoc prof, 69-82, PROF PHYSICS, YALE UNIV, 83-, HENRY FORD II PROF, 96- *Personal Data:* b San Francisco, Calif, Oct 8, 39; m 60; c 2. *Educ:* Stanford Univ, BS, 61; Univ Calif, Los Angeles, MS, 63, PhD(physics), 68. *Prof Exp:* Res asst physics, Univ Calif, Los Angeles, 63-68, res fel, 68-69. *Mem:* NY Acad Sci; fel Am Phys Soc. *Res:* Polarization phenomena in the kaon-nucleon interaction; high energy, strong and weak interaction polarization phenomena; collider physics; weak interactions-decays. *Mailing Add:* Dept Physics Yale Univ PO Box 6666 New Haven CT 06511

**ZELLEY, WALTER GAUNTT,** ELECTROCHEMISTRY. *Current Pos:* RETIRED. *Personal Data:* b Camden, NJ, Oct 1, 21; m 46; c 3. *Educ:* Univ Pa, BS, 42. *Prof Exp:* Chemist, Lake Ont Ord Works, 42-43; chemist, Burlington Reduction Works, Aluminum Co Am, 43-44, res engr, Res Lab, 44-65, sr scientist, 65-67, eng assoc, 67-71, sect head, Alcoa Tech Ctr, 71-79, tech mgr, 80-84. *Mem:* Am Electroplaters Soc; Sigma Xi; Tech Asn Graphic Arts. *Res:* Chemical and electrochemical surface finishing of aluminum; application of aluminum in the graphic arts and packaging; organic coatings for aluminum. *Mailing Add:* 620 Frank St New Kensington PA 15068

**ZELLMER, DAVID LOUIS,** ANALYTICAL CHEMISTRY. *Current Pos:* From asst prof to assoc prof, 69-77, PROF CHEM, CALIF STATE UNIV, FRESNO, 77- *Personal Data:* b Portland, Ore, June 12, 42; m 67; c 1. *Educ:* Univ Mich, BSChem, 64; Univ Ill, MS, 66, PhD(analytical chem), 69. *Mem:* Am Chem Soc; Meteoritical Soc. *Res:* Application of radiochemical and electrochemical techniques to the study of semiconducting electrode materials; analysis of extraterrestrial materials; instrumentation automation; computer assisted instruction. *Mailing Add:* Dept Chem Sch Nat Sci Calif State Univ M/S 70 Fresno CA 93740

**ZELLNER, BENJAMIN HOLMES,** astronomy, for more information see previous edition

**ZELLWEGER, ANDRES G,** AERONAUTICAL & ASTRONAUTICAL ENGINEERING. *Current Pos:* dep assoc adminr advan design & mgt control, Fed Aviation Admin, 89-90, dir, Res & Develop Serv, 90, dir, Opers Res Serv, 90-95, DIR AVIATION RES, FED AVIATION ADMIN, 95- *Personal Data:* b Apr 27, 41. *Educ:* Univ Iowa, BA, 63; Harvard Univ, PhD(comput sci), 71. *Prof Exp:* Res asst, Harvard Univ, 67-71; comput specialist, Transp Systs Ctr, US Dept Transp, 71-73, Off Res & Develop, 73-74, comput scientist, Advan Concepts & Technol Div, Off Systs Eng Mgt, Fed Aviation Admin, 74-77, asst chief, 77-80, chief, 80-81, comput scientist, Advan Automation Prog Off, 81-85, mgr, Syst Eng Div, 85-88; vpres & dir technol, CTA Inc, 88-89. *Concurrent Pos:* Mem, Software Tech Comt, Am Inst Aeronaut & Astronaut, 82-90. *Mem:* Asn Comput Mach; Inst Elec & Electronics Engrs Comput Soc; Am Inst Aeronaut & Astronaut. *Mailing Add:* US Dept Transp Rm 302 800 Independence Ave SW Washington DC 20591

**ZELMAN, ALLEN,** BIOPHYSICS, BIOENGINEERING. *Current Pos:* from asst prof to assoc prof biophys & biomed eng, 75-82, PROF BIOMED ENG, RENSSELAER POLYTECH INST, 83- *Personal Data:* b Los Angeles, Calif, Feb 12, 38; m 71, Adala M Stearns; c Bil Chad & Adala Suzette. *Educ:* Univ Calif, Berkeley, BA, 64, PhD(biophys), 71. *Prof Exp:* Asst prof biophys, Meharry Med Col, 72-75. *Mem:* Am Soc Eng Educ. *Res:* Theoretical and experimental nonequilibrium thermodynamics. *Mailing Add:* Dept Biomed Eng Rensselaer Polytech Inst 110 Eighth St Troy NY 12180-3522

**ZELMANOV, EFIM ISAAKOVICH,** MATHEMATICS. *Current Pos:* PROF MATH, YALE UNIV, 95- *Educ:* Novofibirsky Univ, Russia, PhD(math), 80; Leningrad Univ, St Petersburg, Doctoral Scientist, 85. *Honors & Awards:* Fields Medal, 94. *Prof Exp:* Prof math, Univ Wis, 90-94, Univ Chicago, 94-95. *Mailing Add:* Dept Math Yale Univ 10 Hillhouse Ave New Haven CT 06520-8283

**ZELMANOWITZ, JULIUS MARTIN,** MATHEMATICS, ALGEBRA. *Current Pos:* from asst prof to assoc prof, 66-77, assoc vchancellor acad affairs, 85-87, PROF MATH, UNIV CALIF, SANTA BARBARA, 77-, ASSOC VCHANCELLOR ACAD PERSONNEL, 88- *Personal Data:* b New York, NY, Feb 20, 41; m 62, Joan Troubel; c Dawn Michele. *Educ:* Harvard Univ, AB, 62; Univ Wis-Madison, MS, 63, PhD(math), 66. *Prof Exp:* Instr math, Univ Wis-Madison, 66. *Concurrent Pos:* Vis asst prof, Univ Calif, Los Angeles, 69-70, vis assoc prof, 73-74; assoc prof, Carnegie-Mellon Univ, 70-71; vis prof, Univ Rome, 77, The Technion, 79, McGill Univ, 82, Univ Munich, 83, McGill Univ, 87 & Univ Munich, 88. *Mem:* Math Asn Am; Am Math Soc. *Res:* Algebra, rings and modules; endomorphism rings. *Mailing Add:* Dept Math Univ Calif 552 University Ave Santa Barbara CA 93106-0001. *Fax:* 805-893-7712; *E-Mail:* julius@math.ucsb.edu

**ZELNIK, MELVIN,** DEMOGRAPHY. *Current Pos:* assoc prof, 66-69, PROF DEMOGRAPHY, JOHNS HOPKINS UNIV, 69- *Personal Data:* b New York, NY, Sept 22, 28; m 62; c 2. *Educ:* Miami Univ, BA, 55; Princeton Univ, PhD(sociol), 59. *Honors & Awards:* Carl S Schultz Award, Am Pub Health Asn, 81. *Prof Exp:* Instr sociol, Pa State Univ, 58-59; demographic statistician, Pop Div, US Bur Census, 59-61 & 64-66; res assoc, Off Pop Res, Princeton Univ, 61-62; asst prof sociol, Ohio State Univ, 62-64. *Concurrent Pos:* Ford Found adv, Nat Inst Public Health, Indonesia, 72-73; Fulbright sr res fel, Univ Philippines, 86-87. *Mem:* Pop Asn Am; Int Union Sci Study Pop. *Res:* Premarital sexual activity, use or nonuse of contraception, and reproductive behavior of adolescent females and males. *Mailing Add:* 304 Gailridge Rd Lutherville Timonium MD 21093

**ZELSON, PHILIP RICHARD,** BIOCHEMISTRY. *Current Pos:* asst prof oral med, 74-77, clin asst prof oral med, 78-87, CLIN ASST PROF ORAL MED, SCH DENT MED, UNIV PA, 97- *Personal Data:* b Long Beach, Calif, Sept 3, 45; m 67; c 2. *Educ:* Northwestern Univ, DDS, 70; Univ Rochester, PhD(biochem), 75. *Concurrent Pos:* Res assoc biochem taste, Monell Chem Senses Ctr, 74-75, asst mem, 75-; res assoc biochem taste, Vet Admin, 75-78, staff dentist & researcher, 78- *Mem:* AAAS. *Res:* Etiologic and diagnostic factors in periodontal disease. *Mailing Add:* 213 N Morgan Ave Havertown PA 19083-5009

**ZELTERMAN, DANIEL,** BIOSTATISTICS, MEDICINE. *Current Pos:* PROF EPIDEMIOL, YALE UNIV. *Personal Data:* b New York, NY; m 80. *Educ:* State Univ NY, Buffalo, BA(statist) & BA(comput sci), 75; Yale Univ, PhD(statist), 83. *Prof Exp:* Asst prof math, State Univ NY, Albany, 80-88; prof biostatist, Univ Minn, 88- *Concurrent Pos:* Co-prin investr, NIH, 86-; assoc ed, Comput Statist & Data Analysis, 90-; chief exec officer, STEP Int. *Mem:* Am Statist Asn; Biomet Soc; Inst Math Statist. *Res:* Develop statistical methodology for applications in medical, biological and social sciences; estimating the limits of longevity and models of survival for cancer and acquired immunodeficiency syndrome patients. *Mailing Add:* Dept Epidemiol Yale Sta 60th College St Sch Med Yale Univ PO Box 208034 New Haven CT 06520-8034. *Fax:* 612-626-0660; *E-Mail:* dan@muskie.biostat.umn.edu

**ZELTMANN, ALFRED HOWARD,** PHYSICAL CHEMISTRY. *Current Pos:* RETIRED. *Personal Data:* b Brooklyn, NY, Dec 25, 21; m 51; c 3. *Educ:* State Col Wash, BS, 48; Univ NMex, PhD(chem), 52, MS, 61. *Prof Exp:* Staff mem phys chem, Los Alamos Sci Lab, Univ Calif, 46-84. *Mem:* Am Chem Soc. *Res:* Chemical kinetics; radiation chemistry; high vacuum; preparation and chemistry of gaseous hydrides; nuclear magnetic resonance; complex ions; laser spectroscopy; laser isotope separation. *Mailing Add:* 100 La Cueva St Los Alamos NM 87544-2521

**ZELTMANN, EUGENE W,** PHYSICAL CHEMISTRY. *Current Pos:* mgr environ planning, Gas Turbine Div, Gen Elec Co, 72-80, mgr opers planning, 80-84, Mkt Support & Prog Develop, 84-88, MGR, MKT DEVELOP COMMUN, GEN ELEC CO, 88- *Personal Data:* b Chicago, Ill, June 26, 40; m 74; c 2. *Educ:* Beloit Col, BA, 62; Johns Hopkins Univ, MA, 64, PhD(chem), 67. *Prof Exp:* Nuclear chemist, Knolls Atomic Power Lab, Gen Elec Co, NY, 67-70; Alfred E Smith fel in NY State, 70-71; asst to dir power div, NY State Pub Serv Comn, 71-72. *Mem:* Am Chem Soc; Sigma Xi. *Res:* Chemical kinetics; fission track imaging analyses for purpose of determining presence of minute amounts of fissionable materials. *Mailing Add:* NY Pub Serv Empire State Plaza Albany NY 12200

**ZEMACH, CHARLES,** ELEMENTARY PARTICLE PHYSICS, FLUID DYNAMICS. *Current Pos:* RETIRED. *Personal Data:* b Los Angeles, Calif, Sept 15, 30; m 58, Mary St John; c Arthur M, Dorothy E & Kenneth D. *Educ:* Harvard Univ, BA, 51, PhD(physics), 55. *Prof Exp:* Nat Sci fel, 55-56; instr physics, Univ Pa, 56-57; res assoc, Univ Calif, Berkeley, 57-58, from asst prof to prof, 58-71; officer & spec asst for technol, US Arms Control & Disarmament Agency, State Dept, 70-74, mem policy planning staff, 74-76; dep div leader, Los Alamos Nat Lab, 82-86, staff mem, 76-81 & 87-93. *Concurrent Pos:* Alfred P Sloan Found fel, 59-63; Guggenheim Found fel, 66-67. *Mem:* Am Phys Soc. *Res:* Thermal neutron diffraction; quantum electrodynamics; strong interactions of elementary particles; fluid dynamics; turbulence; turbulence spectral modeling. *Mailing Add:* 740 Canyon Rd Los Alamos NM 87544. *Fax:* 505-665-5926; *E-Mail:* zemach@ni.net

**ZEMACH, RITA,** STATISTICS, PUBLIC HEALTH. *Current Pos:* RETIRED. *Personal Data:* b Paterson, NJ, Apr 3, 26; m 47; c 2. *Educ:* Barnard Col, BA, 47; Mich State Univ, MS, 61, PhD(statist, probability), 65. *Prof Exp:* Instr statist & probability, Mich State Univ, 65-66, asst prof systs sci, 66-72; assoc prof biostatist, Univ Mich, Ann Arbor, 72-73; chief prog anal, Mich Dept Pub Health, 73-88, biometric specialist, 88-92. *Concurrent Pos:* Mem, Health Care Technol Study Sect, HEW, 72-76; adj instr, Col Human Med, Mich State Univ, 77-89. *Mem:* AAAS; fel Am Statist Asn; Am Pub Health Asn; Biomet Soc. *Res:* Analysis of health effects of environmental contamination. *Mailing Add:* 381 Kelburn Rd No 213 Deerfield IL 60015-4322

**ZEMAITIS, MICHAEL ALAN,** BIOCHEMICAL PHARMACOLOGY, TOXICOLOGY. *Current Pos:* Instr, 75-76, asst prof, 76-80, ASSOC PROF PHARMACOL, UNIV PITTSBURGH, 80- *Personal Data:* b York, Pa, Aug 21, 46; div; c 2. *Educ:* Univ Pittsburgh, BS, 69; Pa State Univ, PhD(pharmacol), 75. *Mem:* Am Soc Pharmacol & Exp Therapeut; Soc Toxicol; NY Acad Sci. *Res:* Pathways of drug metabolism in man and laboratory animals; identification of metabolites of drugs and environmental chemicals. *Mailing Add:* 532 Salk Hall Univ Pittsburgh Sch Dent Med Pittsburgh PA 15261-0001

**ZEMAN, FRANCES JANE,** NUTRITION. *Current Pos:* from asst prof to assoc prof, 64-74, PROF NUTRIT, UNIV CALIF, DAVIS, 74- *Personal Data:* b Cleveland, Ohio, Mar 5, 25. *Educ:* Western Res Univ, BS, 46, MS, 57; Ohio State Univ, PhD(nutrit), 63. *Prof Exp:* Dietitian, Cleveland City Hosp, Ohio, 49-51, teaching dietitian, Sch Nursing, 51-57; asst prof home econ, Kent State Univ, 57-64. *Mem:* AAAS; Am Physiol Soc; Am Inst Nutrit; Sigma Xi. *Res:* Nutrition in reproduction. *Mailing Add:* 1102 Colby Dr Davis CA 95616

**ZEMANEK, JOSEPH, JR,** ACOUSTICS. *Current Pos:* RETIRED. *Personal Data:* b Blessing, Tex, Jan 1, 28; m 50; c 2. *Educ:* Univ Tex, BS, 49; Southern Methodist Univ, MS, 57; Univ Calif, Los Angeles, PhD(physics), 62. *Honors & Awards:* Kauffman Gold Medal, Soc Explor Geophysicists, 71; Gold Medal for Tech Achievement, Soc Prof Well Log Analysts, 90. *Prof Exp:* Test engr, Gen Elec Co, 49-50; jr technologist, Field Res Lab, Magnolia Petrol Co, Mobil Res & Develop Corp, 51-53, from res technologist to sr res technologist, 53-58, sr res technologist, 61-67, res assoc acoustic well logging, 67-81, sr scientist, Petrol Well Log Interpretation, 81-90. *Mem:* Sigma Xi; Soc Petrol Engrs; Soc Prof Well Log Analysts. *Res:* Acoustic wave propagation in isotropic media, attenuation and velocity measurements; acoustic well logging, development of instrumentation and methods; wave propagation in boreholes. *Mailing Add:* 1007 Greenbriar Lane Duncanville TX 75137

**ZEMANIAN, ARMEN HUMPARTSOUM,** CIRCUIT THEORY, TRANSFINITE GRAPHS. *Current Pos:* chmn dept, 67-68 & 71-74, LEADING PROF ENG, STATE UNIV NY, STONY BROOK, 62- *Personal Data:* b Bridgewater, Mass, Apr 16, 25; m 58, Edna Williamson; c Peter, Thomas, Lewis & Susan. *Educ:* City Col New York, BEE, 47; NY Univ, MEE, 49, Eng ScD, 53. *Honors & Awards:* Sci Award, Armenian Students Asn, 82; Kapitsa Gold Medal Honor, Russ Acad Nat Sci, 96. *Prof Exp:* Tutor elec eng, City Col New York, 47-48; engr, Maintenance Co, 48-52; from instr to assoc prof elec eng, NY Univ, 52-62. *Concurrent Pos:* Vis prof math inst, Univ Edinburgh, 68-69; consult, All-Tronics, Inc & Anaesthesia Assocs, NY; managing ed, Siam Rev, Soc Indust & Appl Math, 69-71, ed-in-chief publs, 70-74, vpres publ, 74-75; vis scholar, Food Res Inst, Stanford Univ, 75-76; NSF fac fel sci, 75-76; co-founder & co-ed jour, Circuits Systs & Signal Processing; co-founder biennial conf, Int Symposia Math Theory Networks & Systs; prof honoris causa, Dubna Int Univ, Dubna, Russ, 96. *Mem:* Fel Inst Elec & Electronics Engrs; Am Math Soc; Sigma Xi; foreign mem Armenian Acad Sci; Armenian Acad Eng; Russ Acad Nat Sci. *Res:* Mathematical systems theory; distribution theory; integral transforms; electrical network theory; periodic marketing systems; computational methods; graph theory; infinite networks. *Mailing Add:* Dept Elec Eng State Univ NY Stony Brook NY 11794-2350. *Fax:* 516-632-8494; *E-Mail:* zeman@sbee.sunysb.edu

**ZEMBRODT, ANTHONY RAYMOND,** TECHNOLOGY TRANSFER, GLOBAL CONSULTANT. *Current Pos:* CONSULT, ZEMBRODT & ASSOCS, 93- *Personal Data:* b Covington, Ky, Jan 2, 43; m 66, Geraldine Schneider; c Anthony Jr, Melanie & Jennifer. *Educ:* Thomas More Col, BA, 65; Ohio Univ, PhD(phys chem), 70. *Prof Exp:* Scientist, Bristol Myers Co, Cincinnati, 69-78, sect mgr, 79-85, dir, Global Technol Acquisitions, 85-93. *Concurrent Pos:* Lectr, NKy State Univ, 71-76 & Thomas More Col, 78. *Mem:* Chem Specialties Mfrs Asn; NAm Thermal Anal Soc; Am Chem Soc; Am Oil Chem Soc; Licensing Exec Soc; Asn Consult Chemists & Chem Engrs. *Res:* Company will complement existing manufacturing and marketing businesses for rapid and focused technology and product execution using the newest domestic, european and asian resources. *Mailing Add:* 1004 Park Lane Covington KY 41011. *Fax:* 606-431-5148; *E-Mail:* zembrodt@lx.netcom.com

**ZEMEL, JAY N(ORMAN),** ENERGY & MASS TRANSPORT IN MESOSCALE SYSTEMS, INFORMATION ACQUISITION. *Current Pos:* chmn, Elec Eng & Sci Dept, Univ Pa, 72-77, dir, Ctr Chem Electronics, 79-85, dir, Ctr Sensor Technol, 85-90, RCA prof solid state electronics, 66-93, RAMSEY PROF SENSOR TECHNOL, MOORE SCH ELEC ENG, UNIV PA, 93- *Personal Data:* b New York, NY; m 50; c 3. *Educ:* Syracuse Univ, AB, 49, MS, 53, PhD, 56. *Hon Degrees:* MA, Univ Pa, 71. *Prof Exp:* Physicist, Naval Ord Lab, 54-58, chief surface & film group, Solid State Div, 58-66. *Concurrent Pos:* Vis scientist, Zenith Radio Res Lab, Ltd, London, 64; coord ed, Thin Solid Films, 70-72, ed-in-chief, 72; vis prof, Ctr Invest & Advan Studies, Nat Polytech Inst, Mex, 71; mem comt predictive testing for mat performance, Nat Mat Adv Bd, 71-72; mem adv comt solidification metals & semiconductors, Univ Space Res Asn, 72-77; chmn, Gordon Conf on MIS Structures, 76; vis prof elec eng, Univ Tokyo, 78; dir, NATO Advan Study Inst on Non-Destructive Eval of Semiconductor Mat & Devices, 78 & NATO Advan Study Inst Chem Sensitive Elec Develop, 80. *Mem:* Am Phys Soc; Inst Elec & Electronics Engrs; Instrument Soc Am; Electrochem Soc. *Res:* Study of and applications mass transport in micron and submicron structures; flow and pressure sensing. *Mailing Add:* Dept Elec Eng Univ Pa 200 S 33rd St Philadelphia PA 19104. *Fax:* 215-573-2068; *E-Mail:* zemel@ee.upenn.edu

**ZEMEL, MICHAEL BARRY,** CARDIOVASCULAR PHYSIOLOGY, HYPERTENSION. *Current Pos:* DEPT HEAD NUTRIT & PROF NUTRIT, PHYSIOL & MED, UNIV TENN, 90- *Personal Data:* b Newark, NJ, Apr 6, 54; m 76, Paula Carney; c Abigail L & Rachel E. *Educ:* Univ Wis-Madison, BS, 76, MS, 78, PhD(nutrit sci), 80. *Prof Exp:* Asst prof nutrit, Wayne State Univ, 80-85, assoc prof nutrit & endocrinol, 85-90. *Concurrent Pos:* Res endocrinologist, Vet Admin Med Ctr, 87-91; mem, Coun High Blood Pressure Res, Am Heart Asn. *Mem:* Fel Am Heart Asn; Am Inst Nutrit; Am Soc Clin Nutrit; Am Soc Hypertension; Endocrine Soc. *Res:* Role of intracellular calcium in insulin sensitivity and lipogenesis; mechanisms of agouti gene-induced obesity; role of insulin resistance in hypertension. *Mailing Add:* Dept Nutrit Univ Tenn 1215 W Cumberland Ave Rm 229 Knoxville TN 37996-1900. *Fax:* 423-974-3491; *E-Mail:* mzemel@utk.edu

**ZEMKE, WARREN T,** SPECTROSCOPY, THEORETICAL CHEMISTRY. *Current Pos:* From instr to assoc prof, 66-80, PROF CHEM, WARTBURG COL, 80- *Personal Data:* b Fairmont, Minn, Oct 9, 39; m 68, Barbara Belk; c Wayne, Caroline & Mark. *Educ:* St Olaf Col, BA, 61; Ill Inst Technol, PhD(chem), 69. *Concurrent Pos:* Vis assoc prof, Univ Iowa, 78-79. *Mem:* Sigma Xi; AAAS; Am Chem Soc; Am Phys Soc. *Res:* Molecular electronic wave functions; molecular spectroscopy and structure. *Mailing Add:* Dept Chem Wartburg Col Waverly IA 50677

**ZEMLICKA, JIRI,** ORGANIC & MEDICINAL CHEMISTRY, BIOCHEMISTRY. *Current Pos:* vis scientist, Mich Cancer Found, Karmanos Cancer Inst, 68-69, res scientist, 70-80, chief, Bio-Org Chem Lab, Dept Chem 72-90, assoc mem, 80-83, MEM, MICH CANCER FOUND, KARMANOS CANCER INST, 83-, CHMN, DEPT CHEM, 91-; PROF BIOCHEM, SCH MED, WAYNE STATE UNIV, 85- *Personal Data:* b Prague, Czech, July 31, 33; m 61, Helena Zvarova; c 2. *Educ:* Charles Univ, Prague, MS, 56, RNDr, 66; Czech Acad Sci, PhD(org chem), 59. *Prof Exp:* Res asst anal biochem, Inst Food Technol, Prague, 56; res scientist, Inst Org Chem & Biochem, Czech Acad Sci, 59-68; assoc prof, Wayne State Univ, 71-85. *Concurrent Pos:* Ad hoc mem, med chem study sect A, NIH, 79, spec reviewer, bio-org & natural prod chem rev group, 80, 87 & 91. *Mem:* Am Chem Soc; Czech Soc Arts & Sci Am; NY Acad Sci. *Res:* Chemistry of nucleic acids; protein biosynthesis; cancer and viral chemotherapy. *Mailing Add:* Karmanos Cancer Inst 110 E Warren Ave Detroit MI 48201-1379. *Fax:* 313-831-8714; *E-Mail:* jiriz@mcf.roc.wayne.edu

**ZEMLIN, WILLARD R,** SPEECH & HEARING SCIENCES. *Current Pos:* Dir speech & hearing res lab, 61-76, PROF SPEECH & HEARING SCI, UNIV ILL, URBANA-CHAMPAIGN, 76- *Personal Data:* b Two Harbors, Minn, July 20, 20; m 54; c 2. *Educ:* Univ Minn, BA, 57, MS, 60, PhD(speech), 61. *Concurrent Pos:* Consult, Lincoln State Sch, 65-67. *Mem:* Am Speech & Hearing Asn; Acoust Soc Am. *Res:* Anatomy and physiology of normal and pathological speech and hearing mechanisms. *Mailing Add:* 1519 W Park Ave Champaign IL 61821

**ZEMMER, JOSEPH LAWRENCE, JR,** ALGEBRA. *Current Pos:* From asst prof to prof, 50-87, chmn dept, 67-70 & 73-76, EMER PROF MATH, UNIV MO, COLUMBIA, 87- *Personal Data:* b Biloxi, Miss, Feb 23, 22; m 50, Joan Kornfield; c Joel A, Rachel L & Judith L. *Educ:* Tulane Univ, BS, 43, MS, 47; Univ Wis, PhD(math), 50. *Honors & Awards:* Fulbright lectr, Osmania Univ, India, 63-64. *Mem:* Am Math Soc; Math Asn Am; Can Math Soc. *Res:* Near-rings, near-fields and semi-fields. *Mailing Add:* Dept Math Univ Mo Columbia MO 65211. *E-Mail:* mathjlz7@showme.missouri.edu

**ZEMON, STANLEY ALAN,** PHYSICS. *Current Pos:* MEM TECH STAFF, GTE LABS, INC, 65- *Personal Data:* b Detroit, Mich, June 16, 30; m 67. *Educ:* Harvard Univ, AB, 52; Columbia Univ, AM, 58, PhD(physics), 64. *Prof Exp:* Res asst physics, Columbia Univ, 58-62, res scientist, 63-64, res assoc, 64-65. *Mem:* Am Phys Soc; Inst Elec & Electronics Engrs; Sigma Xi. *Res:* Superconductivity; low temperature physics; microwaves; acoustoelectric effect; ultrasonics; semiconductors; Brillouin scattering; lasers; acoustic surface waves; nonlinear acoustics; optical guided waves; nonlinear optics. *Mailing Add:* GTE Labs Inc 40 Sylvan Rd Waltham MA 02254

**ZEN, E-AN,** GEOLOGY, PETROLOGY. *Current Pos:* ADJ PROF, UNIV MD, 90- *Personal Data:* b Peking, China, May 31, 28; nat US. *Educ:* Cornell Univ, BA, 51; Harvard Univ, AM, 52, PhD(geol), 55. *Honors & Awards:* Arthur L Day Medal, Geol Soc Am; Roebling Medal, Mineral Soc Am; Distinguished Serv Medal, US Dept Int; Major John Coke Medal, Geol Soc London, 92; Thomas Jefferson Award, Va Mus Natural Hist, 96; Award for Distinguished Contrib Pub Understanding Geol, Am Geol Inst, 94. *Prof Exp:* Res fel, Oceanog Inst, Woods Hole, 55-56, res assoc, 56-58; vis asst prof, Univ NC, 58-59; res geologist, US Geol Surv, 59-89. *Concurrent Pos:* Vis assoc prof, Calif Inst Technol, 62; Crosby vis prof, Mass Int Technol, 72; pres, Geol Soc Wash, 72 & Mineral Soc Am, 76; Harry Hess sr vis fel, Princeton, 81; counr, Geol Soc Am, 85-88; emer scientist, US Geol Surv. *Mem:* Nat Acad Sci; fel AAAS; Geol Soc Am (vpres, 90-91, pres, 92); fel Mineral Soc Am (pres, 76); Mineral Asn Can; fel Am Acad Arts & Sci. *Res:* Phase equilibrium of sedimentary and metamorphic rocks; stratigraphy and structure of Northern Appalachians and Northern Rockies; igneous petrology. *Mailing Add:* Dept Geol Univ Md College Park MD 20742

**ZENCHELSKY, SEYMOUR THEODORE,** analytical chemistry; deceased, see previous edition for last biography

**ZENDER, MICHAEL J,** NUCLEAR PHYSICS. *Current Pos:* From asst prof to assoc prof & chmn dept, 66-72, PROF PHYSICS, CALIF STATE UNIV, FRESNO, 73- *Personal Data:* b Austin, Minn, Feb 27, 39. *Educ:* St John's Univ, Minn, BA, 61; Vanderbilt Univ, PhD(physics), 66. *Mem:* Am Asn Physics Teachers; AAAS; Health Physics Soc; Am Asn Physicists Med. *Res:* Low energy nuclear, beta and gamma-ray spectroscopy; study of the Auger effect by using a post acceleration Geiger counter in conjunction with very thin counter windows; radiation safety; x-ray fluorescence analysis. *Mailing Add:* 1523 W Robinwood Lane Fresno CA 93711

**ZENG, SHENGKE,** OCCUPATIONAL SAFETY, ULTRASONIC HEARING. *Current Pos:* NAT RES COUN RES ASSOC, DIV SAFETY RES, NAT INST OCCUP SAFETY & HEALTH, 94- *Personal Data:* b Tianjin, People Repub China, Dec 22, 49; m 85, Shiyi Wang; c Laura. *Educ:* Guangxi Univ, China, Bachelor Eng, 82; Drexel Univ, MS, 90, PhD(biomed eng), 93. *Prof Exp:* Fac mem elec eng, Dept Physics, Guangxi Univ, 82-86. *Concurrent Pos:* Adj vis res asst prof, Drexel Univ, Biomed & Sci Inst, 93-94. *Mem:* Inst Elec & Electronics Engrs; Acoust Soc Am; Sigma Xi. *Res:* Ultrasonic hearing research, the role of parametric demodulation and the quadratic property in human amplitude-modulated ultrasonic hearing; occupational safety research, hydration cancellation in protective barrier testing. *Mailing Add:* Div Safety Res Nat Inst 1095 Willowdale Rd Morgantown WV 26505-2819. *Fax:* 304-284-5877; *E-Mail:* saz0@niosr1.em.cdc.gov

**ZENG, ZHAO-BANG,** QUANTITATIVE GENETICS, STATISTICAL GENETICS. *Current Pos:* res assoc, NC State Univ, 86-90, vis asst prof statist & genetics, 90-91, res asst prof, 92-94, RES ASSOC PROF STATIST & GENETICS, NC STATE UNIV, 94- *Personal Data:* b Wuhan, China, Dec 8, 57; m 83, Jia Ma; c Jiemin. *Educ:* Huazhong Agr Univ, China, BSc, 81; Univ Edinburgh, PhD(genetics), 86. *Prof Exp:* Asst lectr animal genetics, Huazhong Agr Univ, China, 82-83. *Concurrent Pos:* Vis prof, China Agr Univ, China, 95; adj prof, Huuzhong Agr Univ China, 95- *Mem:* Am Soc Genetics; Soc Study Evolution; Biometric Soc; Sigma Xi. *Res:* Develop theoretical and statistical concepts, models and methods for analyzing genetic variation of quantitative characters of organisms in artificial and natural populations, including advancing statistical methods for mapping quantitative trait genes. *Mailing Add:* Dept Statist NC State Univ Raleigh NC 27695-8203. *Fax:* 919-515-7315; *E-Mail:* zeng@stat.ncsu.edu

**ZENGEL, JANET ELAINE,** NEUROPHYSIOLOGY. *Current Pos:* RES BIOLOGIST, VET ADMIN MED CTR, GAINESVILLE, 80-; ASSOC PROF NEUROSCI & NEUROSURG, COL MED, UNIV FLA, 80- *Personal Data:* b Baltimore, Md, Feb 21, 48; m 74; c 1. *Educ:* Western Md Col, BA, 70; Univ Miami, PhD(physiol & biophysics), 73. *Prof Exp:* Res instr physiol & biophysics, Sch Med, Univ Miami, 74-78, res asst prof, 78-79; sr assoc anat, Sch Med, Emory Univ, 79-80. *Mem:* Biophys Soc; Soc Neurosci; AAAS. *Res:* Neurophysiology; synaptic and neuromuscular transmission; role of calcium 2 in transmitter release; mechanisms of changes in efficacy; spinal cord physiology and anatomy. *Mailing Add:* 7710 SE County Rd Micanopy FL 32667

**ZENGEL, JANICE MARIE,** MOLECULAR GENETICS, BACTERIAL PHYSIOLOGY. *Current Pos:* RES ASSOC MOLECULAR GENETICS, BIOL DEPT, UNIV ROCHESTER, 79- *Personal Data:* b Baltimore, Md, Feb 21, 48; m 74; c 3. *Educ:* Western Md Col, BA, 70; Univ Wis, PhD(genetics), 76. *Prof Exp:* Fel molecular genetics, Pharmacol Dept, Stanford Univ, 76-78, Neurol Dept, Baylor Col Med, 78-79. *Mem:* Am Soc Microbiol. *Res:* E coli molecular basis for the regulation of ribosome synthesis in E coli, using biochemical, genetic and recombinant DNA techniques. *Mailing Add:* Biol Sci Dept Univ Md Catonsville MD 21228

**ZENGER, DONALD HENRY,** GEOLOGY. *Current Pos:* From instr to assoc prof, 62-73, chmn, Geol Dept, 84-92, PROF GEOL, POMONA COL, 73-, MINNIE B CAIRNS CHAIR GEOL, 90- *Personal Data:* b Little Falls, NY, July 27, 32; m 57, Ann Reardon; c David W & Susan A. *Educ:* Union Col, NY, BS, 54; Dartmouth Col, MA, 59; Cornell Univ, PhD(geol), 62. *Concurrent Pos:* Grants, Geol Soc Am, 63 & Am Chem Soc, 66-74; vis geologist, Unocal Res, 84-95; assoc ed, J Sedimentary Petrol, 82-88, Corbonates & Evaporides, 86- *Mem:* Geol Soc Am; Int Asn Sedimentologists; Am Asn Petrol Geologists; Nat Asn Geol Teachers; Soc Econ Paleont & Mineral. *Res:* Silurian and Devonian stratigraphy, paleontology and carbonate petrology, particularly dolomitization, New York, Wyoming and California. *Mailing Add:* Dept Geol Pomona Col 609 N College Ave Claremont CA 91711

**ZENISEK, CYRIL JAMES,** zoology, for more information see previous edition

**ZENITZ, BERNARD LEON,** MEDICINAL CHEMISTRY. *Current Pos:* RETIRED. *Personal Data:* b Baltimore, Md, Mar 26, 17; m 56, Joan Richea; c Seth & Paula. *Educ:* Univ Md, BS, 37, PhD(pharmaceut chem), 43. *Honors & Awards:* Col Medal Gen Excellence & Pharmacog Prize, 37. *Prof Exp:* Teaching asst, Univ Md, 41; fel, Northwestern Univ, 43-44; sr res chemist, Frederic Stearns & Co, Mich, 44-47; sr res chemist & lab head, Sterling-Winthrop Res Inst, 47-81. *Mem:* Am Chem Soc; Sigma Xi. *Res:* Thymus gland extracts; sympathomimetic amines; quartenary ammonium salts; synthetic detergents; sterols; preparation of B-cyclohexylakylamines; halogen ring substituted propadrines; coronary dilators; local anesthetics; tranquilizers; antioxidants; antiinflammatory agents; antiobesity drugs; bronchodilators; analgesics. *Mailing Add:* N Oaks Apt 620 725 Mt Wilson Lane Baltimore MD 21208

**ZENK, MEINHART HANS CHRISTIAN,** ENZYMOLOGY, HEAVY METAL METABOLISM. *Current Pos:* asst, Dept Bot, 59-67, PROF & DEPT CHAIR PHARMACEUT BIOL, UNIV MUNICH, 80- *Personal Data:* b Donauworth, Ger, Feb 4, 33; m 64, 89, Toni M Kutchan; c Annabelle & Isabelle. *Educ:* Purdue Univ, MS, 58; Univ Munich, PhD(plant physiol), 59. *Hon Degrees:* PhD, Purdue Univ, 91. *Honors & Awards:* Tate & Lyle Award, Phytochem Soc Eng, 76; Liebig Denkmunze Award, Soc Ger Chemists, 89; Green Rosette Award & Mentorat for Prom of Europ Sci, Korber Found, 89; Order of Merit, Fed Repub Ger, 90; Pergamon Prize & Medaille, Phytochem Soc, 91. *Prof Exp:* Prof & dept chair, Ruhr Univ, Bochum, Ger, 68-80, dean, Dept Biol, 72-73. *Concurrent Pos:* Senate mem, Ger Nat Sci Found, 77-83; co-ed, Phytochem. *Mem:* Foreign assoc Nat Acad Sci; Europ Acad Arts & Sci; Ger Acad Nat Sci; Bavarian Acad Sci; Acad Europea; foreign assoc Acad Sci Ukraine. *Res:* Enzymology of alkaloid biosynthesis (benzophen anthridine, berberine, morphine) in intact plants, plant cell suspension cultures and animal tissue; heavy metal metabolism in metal-tolerant, sensitive and hyper accumulating plants. *Mailing Add:* Pharmaceut Biol Univ Munich Karlstr 29 80333 Munich Germany

**ZENKER, NICOLAS,** PHARMACEUTICAL CHEMISTRY. *Current Pos:* RETIRED. *Personal Data:* b Paris, France, Dec 3, 21; nat US; m 52; c 4. *Educ:* Cath Univ Louvain, Cand, 48; Univ Calif, MA, 53, PhD(pharmaceut chem), 58. *Prof Exp:* Biochemist, Mt Zion Hosp, San Francisco, 58-60; asst prof pharmaceut chem, Univ Md, Baltimore, 60-63, assoc prof, 63-69, head dept, 69-79, prof med chem, 69-89. *Mem:* Am Chem Soc. *Res:* Synthesis and mode of action of metabolic analogues; thyroadrenergic relationships. *Mailing Add:* 812 Jamieson Rd Longford MD 21093

**ZENSER, TERRY VERNON,** BIOCHEMISTRY, PHARMACOLOGY. *Current Pos:* asst prof biochem & med, St Louis Univ, 76-80, assoc prof med, 80-85, assoc prof biochem, 80-86, PROF MED, SCH MED, ST LOUIS UNIV, 85-, PROF BIOCHEM, 86- *Personal Data:* b Port Clinton, Ohio, Aug 1, 45; m 68; c 2. *Educ:* Ohio State Univ, BS, 67; Univ Mo, Columbia, PhD(biochem), 71. *Prof Exp:* Captain, US Army Med Res Inst Infectious Dis, 71-75; lectr, Hood Col, Frederick, Md, 74-75. *Concurrent Pos:* Adj asst prof biochem & med, Univ Pittsburgh, 75-76. *Mem:* Geront Soc; Am Asn Cancer Res; Am Soc Biol Chemists; Am Soc Pharmacol & Exp Therapeut; Sigma Xi; Am Fedn Clin Res. *Res:* Drug metabolism; biology of aging; mechanism of initiation of toxic and carcinogenic effects of chemicals. *Mailing Add:* Dept Med & Biochem St Louis Univ GRECC (11G-JB) Vet Admin Med Ctr St Louis MO 63125. *Fax:* 573-894-6614

**ZENTILLI, MARCOS,** METALLOGENY, GEOCHRONOLOGY. *Current Pos:* from asst prof to assoc prof, 73-86, chmn dept, 84-86, PROF GEOL, DALHOUSIE UNIV, 86- *Personal Data:* b Santiago, Chile, May 31, 40; m 63, Armgard Raczynski; c Francisca, Veronica & Patricia. *Educ:* Univ De Chile, BS, 63; Queen's Univ, PhD(geol), 74. *Prof Exp:* Geologist mineral deposit, Inst Invest Geologicas, 63-68, explor, Geophys Eng, Ltd, Toronto, 72. *Concurrent Pos:* Assoc dir, Lester Pearson Inst Int Develop, 85-86; vpres, Cuesta Res Ltd, NS, Can. *Mem:* Fel Geol Asn Can; fel Soc Econ Geologists; Can Inst Mining & Metall; Asn Geoscientists Int Develop; Int Asn Genesis Ore Deposits; Geol Soc Chile. *Res:* Regional metallogenic evolution of the Central Andes; fission track thermochronology applied to basin analysis, tectonics and ore deposits. *Mailing Add:* Dept Earth Sci Dalhousie Univ Halifax NS B3H 3J5 Can. *Fax:* 902-494-6889; *E-Mail:* zentilli@ac.dal.ca

**ZENTMYER, GEORGE AUBREY, JR,** PHYTOPATHOLOGY. *Current Pos:* asst pathologist, Univ Calif, Riverside, 44-48, assoc plant pathologist, 48-55, fac res lectr, 64, chmn, Dept Plant Path, 68-73, prof, 63-81, PLANT PATHOLOGIST, UNIV CALIF, RIVERSIDE, 55-, EMER PROF PLANT PATH, 81- *Personal Data:* b North Platte, Nebr, Aug 9, 13; m 41, Dorothy Dudley; c Elizabeth (Dossa), Jane (Fernald) & Susan. *Educ:* Univ Calif, Los Angeles, AB, 35; Univ Calif, MS, 36, PhD(plant path), 38. *Honors & Awards:* Award Distinction, Am Phytopath Soc, 83. *Prof Exp:* Asst plant path, Univ Calif, 36-37; asst pathologist, Div Forest Path, Bur Plant Indust, USDA, 37-40 & Conn Exp Sta, 40-44. *Concurrent Pos:* Consult, Pineapple Res Inst, 61, Trust Territory, Pac Islands, 64 & 66, Rockefeller Found, Colombia, 67, Australian Govt, 68, US Agency Int Develop, Ghana & Nigeria, 69, NSF Panel, 71-, SAfrican Govt & avacado growers, 80, Israel & avacado growers & Western Australian Govt, 83, Ministry Agr, Univ Cordoba, Spain, 89 & Costa Rican govt, 93; Guggenheim fel, 64-65; mem, Nat Res Coun, 68-73; NATO sr sci fel, Eng, 71; mem var comts, Nat Acad Sci-Nat Res Coun; assoc ed, Annual Rev Phytopath, 70-; pres, Pac Div, AAAS, 74-75; counr, Int Soc Plant Path, 78-83; Bellagio scholar, Rockefeller Found, 85. *Mem:* Nat Acad Sci; fel Am Phytopath Soc (secy, 59-62, pres, 65-66); Int Soc Plant Path; Mycol Soc Am; Asn Trop Biol; Sigma Xi; Indian Phytopath Soc; Phillipine Phytopath Soc; Brit Mycol Soc; AAAS. *Res:* Biology and physiology of root pathogens, especially Phytophthora; chemotaxis; chemotherapy; fungicides; diseases of avocado, cacao, other tropicals and subtropicals. *Mailing Add:* Dept Plant Path Univ Calif Riverside CA 92521-0122. *Fax:* 909-787-4294

**ZENTNER, THOMAS GLENN,** PULP CHEMISTRY, PAPER CHEMISTRY. *Current Pos:* vpres res & develop, Olinkraft, Inc, La, 66-68, rep, Forest Prod Div, Olin Corp, West Monroe, 68-75, vpres res, Olinkraft, Inc, 74-79, VPRES RES, MANVILLE FOREST PROD, INC, 80- *Personal Data:* b Rowena, Tex, Aug 6, 26; m 52; c 5. *Educ:* Tex A&M Univ, BS, 48; Inst Paper Chem, MS, 50, Lawrence Col, PhD(chem), 52. *Prof Exp:* Mem staff, Gardner Div, Diamond Nat Corp, 52-59, dir res & develop, 59-60; dir forest prod oper, Olin Mathieson Chem Corp, 60-66. *Mem:* Am Chem Soc; corp mem Tech Asn Pulp & Paper Indust. *Res:* Paperboard manufacture; coating; converting for packaging; graphic arts. *Mailing Add:* 7116 Whites Ferry Rd West Monroe LA 71291

**ZENZ, CARL,** OCCUPATIONAL MEDICINE. *Current Pos:* CONSULT, 80- *Personal Data:* b Vienna, Austria, Feb 1, 23; US citizen; m 47; c 3. *Educ:* Jefferson Med Col, MD, 49; Univ Cincinnati, ScD, 57. *Prof Exp:* Intern, Ausbury Hosp, Minneapolis, Minn, 49-50; gen pract, Minn & Wis, 50-52; resident occup med, Allis-Chalmers Corp, 56-57, chief clin serv, 57-62, chief physician, 62-63, med dir, 63-65, dir med & hyg serv, 65-70, dir med serv, 70-80. *Mem:* AAAS; Am Occup Med Asn; Am Indust Hyg Asn; fel Am Pub Health Asn; fel Am Acad Occup Med (past pres). *Mailing Add:* 2418 S Root River Pkwy West Allis WI 53227-1846

**ZENZ, DAVID R,** MUNICIPAL SLUDGE MANAGEMENT, MUNICIPAL SLUDGE PROCESSING. *Current Pos:* Coordr res, 68-90, MGR RES & TECH SERV, METROP WATER RECLAMATION, DIST GREATER CHICAGO, 90- *Personal Data:* b Chicago, Ill, Sept 17, 43; m 68; c 1. *Educ:* Ill Inst Technol, BS, 65, MS, 66, PhD(environ eng), 68. *Concurrent Pos:* Adj prof, Ill Inst Technol, 68-72 & 91-; chmn, Sludge Mgt Comt, Water Pollution Control Fedn; pres, Ill Water Pollution Control Asn, 90-91. *Mem:* Water Pollution Control Fedn; Am Acad Environ Engrs. *Res:* Published papers on municipal sludge management, municipal sludge processing, advanced wastewater treatment and wastewater nutrification. *Mailing Add:* 2347 Bayside Ct Lisle IL 60532

**ZENZ, FREDERICK A(NTON),** CHEMICAL ENGINEERING. *Current Pos:* PRES, FREDRICK A ZENZ INC, 88- *Personal Data:* b New York, NY, Aug 1, 22; m 49; c 4. *Educ:* Queens Col, BS, 42; NY Univ, MChE, 50; Polytech Inst Brooklyn, DChE, 61. *Honors & Awards:* Tyler Award, Am Inst Chem Engrs, 58. *Prof Exp:* Chem engr, M W Kellogg Co, 42-44 & 46, develop engr, 53-56; chem engr, Kellex Corp, 44-45; res engr, Carbide & Carbon Chem Corp, Tenn, 45-46; process engr, Hydrocarbon Res, Inc, 46-53; mgr, Process Dept, Assoc Nucleonics, Inc, 56-62; prof eng, Manhattan Col, 69-87; dir, Process Equip Modelling & Mfg Co, 74-88. *Concurrent Pos:* Lectr, NY Univ, 51-52; adj prof, Polytech Inst Brooklyn, 59-; consult, 62-; tech dir, Particulate Solid Res, Inc, 70-; vpres, Ducon Co, 75-81; emer prof eng, Manhattan Col, 87-; consult. *Mem:* Am Chem Soc; Am Nuclear Soc; Sigma Xi; fel Am Inst Chem Engrs. *Res:* Fluidization; two-phase flow; tower design; distillation; particle filtration; gas-solid reactions; nuclear power reactors; isotope separation; air fractionation; petroleum refining; ammonia. *Mailing Add:* PO Box 241 Garrison NY 10542

**ZEOLI, G(ENE) W(ESLEY),** ELECTRICAL ENGINEERING. *Current Pos:* PRES, GENE W ZEOLI, INC, 81- *Personal Data:* b Los Angeles, Calif, Nov 9, 26; m 56; c 2. *Educ:* Univ Calif, Berkeley, BS, 48, MS, 49; Univ Calif, Los Angeles, PhD, 71. *Prof Exp:* Lectr elec eng, Univ Calif, 48-49; asst, Mass Inst Technol, 49-50, 51-52; mem tech staff radar systs res, Hughes Aircraft Co, 52-54, group head sensor syst anal, 54-57, sr scientist & head info processing staff, Signal Processing & Display Lab, 57-68, sr scientist, Staff Radar Systs & Signal Processing Lab, 68-76, chief scientist, Advan Progs Div, 76-81. *Concurrent Pos:* Lectr, Univ Calif, Los Angeles, 54-55 & Loyola Univ, 71-72. *Res:* Radar systems design and performance studies. *Mailing Add:* 1405 Granvia Altamira Palos Verdes Estates CA 90274

**ZEPF, THOMAS HERMAN,** SURFACE PHYSICS, QUANTUM OPTICS. *Current Pos:* From asst prof to assoc prof, Creighton Univ, 62-75, from actg chmn dept to chmn dept, 63-73 & 81-93, PROF PHYSICS, CREIGHTON UNIV, 75- *Personal Data:* b Cincinnati, Ohio, Feb 13, 35. *Educ:* Xavier Univ, Ohio, BS, 57; St Louis Univ, MS, 60, PhD(physics), 63. *Concurrent Pos:* Consult physicist, Omaha Vet Admin Hosp, 66-71; vis prof physics, St Louis Univ, 73-74. *Mem:* AAAS; Am Phys Soc; Am Asn Physics Teachers; Sigma Xi; Sci Res Soc. *Res:* Surface barrier analysis of metals and semiconductors;

laser-induced desorption; diagnostics of laser-generated plasmas; laser propagation and particulate interaction; methods of x-ray diffraction; unltra-high vacuum techniques. *Mailing Add:* Dept Physics Creighton Univ Omaha NE 68178-0114. *E-Mail:* thzepf@creighton.edu

**ZEPP, EDWIN ANDREW,** ENDOCRINOLOGY, LIPID METABOLISM. *Current Pos:* Res assoc, 76-78, asst prof, 70-84, ASSOC PROF BIOCHEM, KIRKSVILLE COL OSTEOPATH MED, 84- *Personal Data:* b Orange, Calif, Sept 15, 45; m 79; c 2. *Educ:* WVa Univ, AB, 67, MS, 72, PhD(pharmacol), 76. *Concurrent Pos:* Prin investr, Nat Cancer Inst, NIH, 78-; adj asst prof, Northeast Mo State Univ, 81- *Mem:* Endocrine Soc; Am Diabetes Asn. *Res:* Hormonal control of lipid metabolism and alterations by tumor-bearing and under conditions of dietary manipulation. *Mailing Add:* 30 Craig Martin Ct St Peters MO 63376

**ZEPP, RICHARD GARDNER,** ENVIRONMENTAL CHEMISTRY, BIOGEOCHEMISTRY. *Current Pos:* RES CHEMIST, US ENVIRON PROTECTION AGENCY, 71- *Personal Data:* b Brooklyn, NY, Nov 20, 41; m 68; c 1. *Educ:* Furman Univ, BS, 63; Fla State Univ, PhD(chem), 68. *Honors & Awards:* Environ Protection Agency Sci & Tech Achievement Award, 83, 85, 86, 89, 92, 93 & 95; Distinguished Serv Award, Environ Chem Div, Am Chem Soc, 92. *Prof Exp:* Res assoc photochem, Mich State Univ, 69-70. *Concurrent Pos:* Adj prof, Univ Miami & State Univ NY. *Mem:* Am Chem Soc; Sigma Xi; Am Soc Limnol & Oceanog; AAAS; Soc Environ Toxicol & Chem; Am Geophys Union. *Res:* Biogeochemical processes in soil and water; environmental photochemistry; ecological effects of solar ultraviolet radiation. *Mailing Add:* US Environ Protection Agency 960 College Station Rd Athens GA 30605-2700

**ZEPPA, ROBERT,** THORACIC SURGERY. *Current Pos:* co-chmn dept, 66-71, CHMN, DEPT SURG, SCH MED, 71-, PROF SURG & PHARMACOL, UNIV MIAMI, 65- *Personal Data:* b New York, NY, Sept 17, 24; m 52; c 2. *Educ:* Columbia Univ, AB, 48; Yale Univ, MD, 52. *Prof Exp:* Intern, Med Ctr, Univ Pittsburgh, 52-53; asst resident surg, Sch Med, Univ NC, 53-56, thoracic resident, 56-57, instr thoracic surg, 58-60, from asst prof surg to assoc prof, 60-65. *Concurrent Pos:* USPHS career trainee, Sch Med, Wash Univ, 56-58; Markle scholar med sci, 59-64; assoc dir clin res unit, NC Mem Hosp, 61-65; chief surg serv, Vet Admin Hosp, Miami, Fla, 65-72. *Mem:* Am Col Surg; Am Surg Asn; Soc Surg Alimentary Tract; Soc Univ Surg. *Res:* Biologically active amines; portal hypertension; gastrointestinal physiology. *Mailing Add:* Dept Surg Univ Miami Rm 310 1600 NW Tenth Ave Miami FL 33136-1015

**ZERBE, JOHN IRWIN,** WOOD SCIENCE, WOOD TECHNOLOGY. *Current Pos:* VOL, 94- *Personal Data:* b Hegins, Pa, June 4, 26; m 51, Ruby Deitrich; c Lynne D (Durst), Eric A & Donna L (Barker). *Educ:* Pa State Univ, BS, 51; State Univ NY, MS, 53, PhD(wood technol), 56. *Prof Exp:* Asst wood technol, State Univ NY, 51-56; res asst prof housing res, Univ Ill, 56-58; mgr, Govt Specifications & Stand Dept, Nat Forest Prod Asn, 58-59, asst vpres, Tech Serv, 59-70; dir forest prod & eng res, Forest Serv, USDA, 70-76, mgr energy res, develop & application, 76-94. *Mem:* Forest Prod Soc; Soc Wood Sci & Technol; Soc Am Foresters; Am Soc Testing & Mat; Biomass Energy Res Asn. *Res:* Mechanical properties of wood, conversion of wood to solid and liquid fuel, energy from biomass; energy conservation. *Mailing Add:* 3310 Heatherdell Lane Madison WI 53713-3446. *Fax:* 608-231-9592

**ZERBY, CLAYTON DONALD,** QUALITY IMPROVEMENT. *Current Pos:* CONSULT QUALITY IMPROV, 88- *Personal Data:* b Cleveland, Ohio, Jan 27, 24; m 49; c 3. *Educ:* Case Western Res Univ, BS, 50; Univ Tenn, MS, 56, PhD(physics), 60. *Prof Exp:* Engr, Oak Ridge Nat Lab, 50-54, group leader physics, 54-63, mgr physics & eng, Defense & Space Systs Dept, 63-66, mgr dept, 66-67, gen mgr, Korad Laser Dept, 67-71, pres, Ocean Systs, Inc, 71-73, Domsea Farms, Inc, 72-74, tech serv mgr, Nuclear Div, 74-76, dir off waste isolation, 76-78; plant mgr, Paducah Gaseous Diffusion Plant, Union Carbide Corp, 78-84; dir mgt syst compliance, Martin Marietta Energy Syst, 84-88. *Concurrent Pos:* Lectr, Univ Tenn, 61-63 & Univ Ky, 80-81. *Mem:* Am Phys Soc; Am Nuclear Soc; Sigma Xi. *Res:* Theory of electromagnetic interactions; Monte Carlo methods; nuclear weapons effects; space vehicle radiation shielding; shielding against high energy particles; interaction of high energy particles with complex nuclei; nuclear waste terminal storage; quality improvement techniques. *Mailing Add:* 1102 W Outer Dr Oak Ridge TN 37830

**ZERELLA, PAUL J,** CONTINUOUS CRYSTALLIZATION. *Current Pos:* from res engr to prin res engr, US Borax Inc, 81-91, pilot plant mgr, 91-93, mgr new bus develop, 93-95, technol mgr, Borax Europe, UK, 96, VPRES TECHNOL & QUAL DIR, US BORAX INC, 97- *Personal Data:* b Youngstown, Ohio, Mar 1, 51; m 93, Martha R Jones. *Educ:* Ohio State Univ, BS, 73; Univ Ariz, MS, 78, PhD(chem eng). 81. *Prof Exp:* Process engr, Diamond Shamrock, 73-76; chem eng instr, Univ Ariz, 80-81. *Res:* Laboratory, pilot and full scale development of industrial crystallization; systems process simulation and process development. *Mailing Add:* 26877 Tourney Rd Valencia CA 91355-1847. *Fax:* 805-287-5455

**ZEREN, RICHARD WILLIAM,** MECHANICAL ENGINEERING, ENERGY. *Current Pos:* CORP ENG & OPERS, PROVEN ALTERNATIVES, INC, 91- *Personal Data:* b Baltimore, Md, June 3, 42; m 65, Rebecca Morelock; c Mark, Gregory & Seth. *Educ:* Duke Univ, BSME, 64; Stanford Univ, MS, 65, PhD(eng), 70. *Prof Exp:* Actg asst prof mech eng, Stanford Univ, 69; asst prof, Mich State Univ, 70-74; asst to dir, Fossil Fuel & Advan Systs Div, Elec Power Res Inst, 74-77, mgr prog integration & eval,

78-79; sr assoc, Booz-Allen & Hamilton, Inc, 80; dir res & develop planning & eval, Elec Power Res Inst, 80-81, Planning & Eval Div, 81-89, mem div, 89-90, Spec Proj, 90-91. *Concurrent Pos:* NSF trainee, 64-68; mem, Planning Forum. *Mem:* Am Soc Mech Engrs. *Res:* Engineering and operations policy for energy efficiency corporation; energy technology policy. *Mailing Add:* 150 Corona Way Portola Valley CA 94028. *Fax:* 415-285-5805

**ZEREZ, CHARLES RAYMOND,** HEMATOLOGY, RED BLOOD CELL METABOLISM. *Current Pos:* INTERNAL MED CLIN PRACT, 85- *Personal Data:* b Aleppo, Syria, July 24, 56; US citizen; m 91, Aileen M K Yee; c Megan. *Educ:* Univ Calif, Los Angeles, BS, 78, CPhil, 82, PhD(biochem), 85, MD, 92; Calif State Univ, MS, 81. *Honors & Awards:* Upjohn Award, 92. *Prof Exp:* Res asst, Dept Chem & Biochem, Univ Calif, Sch Med, Los Angeles, 80-81 & 81-84, teaching assoc, Dept Chem & Biochem, 81-82, asst biochemist, Dept Med, 86-95; res assoc, Dept Med, Harbor-Univ Calif Med Ctr, 84-85. *Concurrent Pos:* Prin investr, Res & Educ Inst, Harbor-Univ Calif, Med Ctr, 86-, asst dir, Hemat Res Lab, 87-95; resident physician, St Mary Med Ctr, Long Beach, Calif, 92-93 & 94-, Univ Calif, Los Angeles Med Ctr, 93-94. *Mem:* Am Chem Soc; Am Med Asn; Am Soc Hemat; Am Col Physicians. *Res:* Red blood cell metabolism in hemolytic anemias; sickle cell disease, thalassemia and enzyme deficiency anemias; the mechanisms of red cell hemolysis in these disorders. *Mailing Add:* 17 Sylvan Oak Way Baltimore MD 21236. *Fax:* 310-320-6515

**ZERILLI, FRANK J,** THEORETICAL PHYSICS. *Current Pos:* RES PHYSICIST, NAVAL SURFACE WARFARE CTR, 79- *Personal Data:* b Brooklyn, NY, Dec 25, 42. *Educ:* Princeton Univ, PhD(theoret physics), 69. *Prof Exp:* Res assoc, Univ NC, 69-72; asst prof physics, Wash State Univ, 72-75 & Mich State Univ, 75-79. *Mem:* Am Phys Soc; Sigma Xi. *Res:* Strength and fracture of materials; equilibrium of reacting energetic materials. *Mailing Add:* Detonation Phys Div Naval Surface Weapons Ctr Silver Spring MD 20903-5640. *Fax:* 301-394-4634

**ZERLA, FREDRIC JAMES,** HISTORY OF MATHEMATICS. *Current Pos:* Asst prof, 63-72, from asst chmn dept to actg chmn dept, 69-74, ASSOC PROF MATH, UNIV SFLA, 72-, UNDERGRAD ADV, DEPT MATH, 74- *Personal Data:* b Wheeling, WVa, Feb 23, 37; m 66, Helga Merz; c 6. *Educ:* Col Steubenville, BA, 58; Fla State Univ, MS, 60, PhD(math), 67. *Mem:* Math Asn Am. *Res:* Derivations in algebraic fields; field theory; history of mathematics. *Mailing Add:* Dept Math Univ SFla 4202 Fowler Ave Tampa FL 33620. *Fax:* 813-974-2700; *E-Mail:* dtyaxaa@cfrvm.cfr.usf.edu

**ZERLIN, STANLEY,** PSYCHOPHYSIOLOGY, ELECTROPHYSIOLOGY. *Current Pos:* ASSOC PROF & RES ASSOC AUDITORY PROCESSES, OTOLARYNGOL LABS, UNIV CHICAGO, 67- *Personal Data:* b New York, NY, Sept 15, 29; m 59; c 2. *Educ:* City Col New York, BS, 51; Columbia Univ, MA, 53; Western Res Univ, PhD(audition), 59. *Prof Exp:* Asst proj dir, Cleveland Hearing & Speech Ctr, 57-58; proj dir, Auditory Res Lab, Vet Admin, 59-63, res scientist, 59-62, res dir, 62-63; res assoc auditory processes, Cent Inst for Deaf, 63-65; res assoc auditory evoked responses, Houston Speech & Hearing Ctr, 65-67. *Mem:* Soc Neurosci; Acoust Soc Am; Am Speech & Hearing Asn; Int Soc Audiol. *Res:* Auditory electrophysiology, evoked response; cochlear processes; binaural interaction. *Mailing Add:* 1457 E 55th Pl Chicago IL 60637

**ZERNER, MICHAEL CHARLES,** CHEMISTRY, MOLECULAR ELECTRONIC STRUCTURE. *Current Pos:* PROF CHEM & PHYSICS, QUANTUM THEORY PROD, UNIV FLA, GAINESVILLE, 81-, CHAIR CHEM, 88- *Personal Data:* b Boston, Mass, Jan 31, 40; m 66, Anna G Fujerstam; c Erik & Emma. *Educ:* Carnegie-Mellon Univ, BSc, 61; Harvard Univ, MA, 62, PhD, 66. *Honors & Awards:* Int Soc Quantum Biol & Pharmacol Award, 86; Humboldt Prize Sr US Scientist, Ger, 93. *Prof Exp:* NIH fel, Univ Uppsala, Sweden, 68-70; from asst prof to assoc prof chem, Univ Guelph, Can, 70-80; prof chem, Univ Guelph, 80-82. *Concurrent Pos:* Vis scientist, Univ NC, 75, Stanford Univ, 76; consult, Eastman Kodak, 78-; vis prof quantum chem, Univ Uppsala, 78-79; vis prof, Potificaia Univ, Brazil, 80, Tech Univ, Munich, Ger, 86, Max Planck Inst Physics & Astrophysics, 88, 89, 91 & 93, Wilhelm-Westfalliche Univ, Munster, Ger, 92 & Tech Univ Munchen, 92; mem bd dirs, Quantum Chem Prog Exchange, Ind Univ, 80-87; vis prof chem, Univ Fla, Gainesville, 81, assoc dir, Quantum Theory proj, 82-; adj prof, Univ Guelph, 82-86; assoc ed, Int J Quantum Chem, 82-; Fulbright distinguished prof, Ruder Boskovic Inst, Zagreb, 87; ed, Advan Quantum Chem, 88-; vis sr scientist, Brookhaven Nat Lab, 90. *Mem:* Am Inst Physics; Int Soc Quantum Biol; AAAS; Am Chem Soc; NY Acad Sci. *Res:* Molecular electronic structure; molecular bonding, structure, reactivity and spectroscopy predicted from the concepts of theoretical chemistry and physics. *Mailing Add:* Univ Fla 362 Williamson Hall Gainesville FL 32611. *Fax:* 352-392-8758; *E-Mail:* zerner@qtp.ufl.edu

**ZERNIK, JOSEPH,** BONE BIOLOGY, EUKARYOTIC GENE EXPRESSION. *Current Pos:* ASSOC PROF ORTHOD, UNIV SOUTHERN CALIF, 91- *Personal Data:* b Jerusalem, Israel, Oct 24, 55; m 83; c 2. *Educ:* Univ Tel-Aviv, DMD, 83; Univ Conn, PhD(biomed sci), 88. *Prof Exp:* Asst prof orthod, Univ Conn, 88-91. *Mem:* Am Soc Bone & Mineral Res; Am Asn Dent Res; AAAS. *Res:* Cloned and characterized rat gene for bone alkaline phosphatase and studied the function of its promoters; developmental regulation of alkaline phosphatase expression. *Mailing Add:* 9110 Gregory Way Beverly Hills CA 90211

**ZERNOW, LOUIS,** HIGH STRAIN RATE MATERIAL BEHAVIOR. *Current Pos:* PRES, ZERNOW TECH SERV INC, 81- *Personal Data:* b Brooklyn, NY, Dec 27, 16; m 40, Edith H Weinstein; c Lenore R, Elaine, Melvin R & Richard H. *Educ:* Cooper Union, BChE, 38; Johns Hopkins Univ, PhD(physics), 53. *Honors & Awards:* Outstanding Leadership Award, Am Defense Preparedness Asn, 87. *Prof Exp:* Mem staff, Ballistic Res Labs, Aberdeen Proving Ground, Ord Dept, US Dept Army, 40-51, chief, Rocket & Ammunition Br, 51-53 & Detonation Physics Br, 53-55; dir res & mgr ord res div, Aerojet-Gen Corp, 55-63; pres, Shock Hydrodynamics, Div Whittaker Corp, 63-81. *Concurrent Pos:* Consult, US Dept Army, Gould Inc, Gen Dynamics, Bendix, Aerojet & USAF, Rockwell Int; mem, Int Ballistics Comt, 93. *Mem:* Am Inst Aeronaut & Astronaut; Am Inst Mining, Metall & Petrol Eng; Am Soc Metals; Am Phys Soc; Acoust Soc Am; NY Acad Sci; Sigma Xi. *Res:* Detonation and aerosol physics; explosives; high strain-rate behavior of materials; shock waves in solids; effects of super pressure on solids; ordnance systems and explosive metal forming; shaped charge design; armor systems; undersea defense systems. *Mailing Add:* 1103 E Mountain View Ave Glendora CA 91741-3165. *Fax:* 909-592-4002

**ZERO, DOMENICK THOMAS,** DENTAL CARIES RESEARCH. *Current Pos:* res & clin assoc, 85-90, SR RES & CLIN ASSOC, EASTMAN DENT CTR, 90- *Personal Data:* b Brooklyn, NY, Sept 24, 49. *Educ:* St Johns Univ, BS, 71; Georgetown Univ, DDS, 75; Univ Rochester, MS, 80. *Honors & Awards:* Michael G Buonocore Prize, Am Asn Dent Res; Int Col Dent Award. *Prof Exp:* Res asst, Eastman Dent Ctr, 77-78, res assoc, 79-81; asst prof, Va Commonwealth Univ, 81-85. *Concurrent Pos:* Prin investr, NIH/NIDR grants. *Mem:* Int Asn Dent Res; Europ Orgn Caries Res. *Res:* Development of intra-oral models for the study of dental caries; study of microbial virulence related to the development of dental caries; oral retention of topical fluoride products and its relationship to the clinical effectiveness of fluoride products. *Mailing Add:* 10 Broken Hill Rd Pittsford NY 14534

**ZEROKA, DANIEL,** THEORETICAL PHYSICAL CHEMISTRY. *Current Pos:* from asst prof to assoc prof, 67-90, PROF CHEM, LEHIGH UNIV, 90- *Personal Data:* b Plymouth, Pa, June 22, 41; m 67, Alexandra S Kotulak; c Daniel M & Andrea M. *Educ:* Wilkes Col, BS, 63; Univ Pa, PhD(theoret chem), 66. *Prof Exp:* NSF fel statist mech, Yale Univ, 66-67. *Concurrent Pos:* Vis res scientist, DuPont, 84; sabbatical, Cornell, 85; US Army fac, Edgewood Area Aberdeen Proving Ground, 89-93. *Mem:* Am Chem Soc; Am Phys Soc; Sigma Xi. *Res:* Quantum chemistry; statistical mechanics; magnetic resonance; electronic structure of solids. *Mailing Add:* Dept Chem Lehigh Univ 6 E Packer Ave Bethlehem PA 18015-3172. *Fax:* 610-758-6536; *E-Mail:* dzoo@lehigh.edu

**ZERONIAN, SARKIS HAIG,** CELLULOSE CHEMISTRY. *Current Pos:* from asst prof to prof textile sci, Univ Calif, Davis, 68-94, chmn, Div Textile & Clothing, 78-86, prof mech eng & mat sci, 83-94, EMER PROF TEXTILE SCI, UNIV CALIF, DAVIS, 94-, EMER PROF MECH ENG & MAT SCI, 94- *Personal Data:* b Manchester, Eng, June 30, 32; US citizen; m 70, Irene Bulnevis. *Educ:* Univ Manchester, BScTech, 53, MScTech, 55, PhD(cellulose chem), 62, DSc(polymer & fiber sci), 83. *Honors & Awards:* Div Fel Award, Cellulose Paper & Textile Div, Am Chem Soc, 93, Anselme Payen Award, 96. *Prof Exp:* Res officer cellulose chem, Brit Cotton Indust Res Asn, Manchester, Eng, 58-60; res fel, Inst Paper Chem, 62-63; sr res fel nonwoven fabrics, Univ Manchester Inst Sci Technol, 63-66; res assoc cellulose chem, Columbia Cellulose Co, BC, Can, 66-68. *Concurrent Pos:* Chmn, Cellulose, Paper & Textile Div, Am Chem Soc, 83; Fiber Soc lectr, 87-88; counr, Am Chem Soc, 90-93. *Mem:* Am Chem Soc; Am Asn Textile Chem & Colorists; fel Brit Textile Inst; Fiber Soc. *Res:* Chemical and physical properties of natural and man-made fibers; properties of textile finishes; cellulose chemistry. *Mailing Add:* Div Textiles & Clothing Univ Calif Davis CA 95616-8422. *Fax:* 530-752-7584; *E-Mail:* shzeronian@ucdavis.edu

**ZERVAS, NICHOLAS THEMISTOCLES,** NEUROSURGERY. *Current Pos:* resident neurosurg, 58-62, CHIEF NEUROSURG SERV, MASS GEN HOSP, 77-; HIGGINS PROF NEUROSURG, HARVARD UNIV, 86- *Personal Data:* b Lynn, Mass, Mar 9, 29; m 59, Thalia Poleway; c T Nicholas, Christopher L & Rhea. *Educ:* Harvard Univ, AB, 50; Univ Chicago, MD, 54. *Hon Degrees:* DSc, Curry Col, 87. *Prof Exp:* Intern, NY Hosp, 54-55; resident neurol, Montreal Neurol Inst, 55-56; fel sterotaxic cerebral surg, Univ Paris, 60-61; asst attend surgeon & assoc neurosurg, Jefferson Med Col, Philadelphia, 62-66, asst prof surg, 66-67; chief neurosurg serv, Beth Israel Hosp, Boston, 67-77; from asst prof to prof surg, Harvard Univ, 67-86. *Concurrent Pos:* Vis lectr, Dept Nutrit & Food Sci, Mass Inst Technol, 73-86; chmn, Mass Coun Arts & Humanities, 83-91, Am Bd Neurol Surg, 90-91. *Mem:* Inst Med-Nat Acad Sci; Am Acad Neurol Surgeons (treas, 84-87, secy, 87-90, pres, 90-91); Am Asn Neurol Surgeons; Soc Neurol Surgeons; Am Neurol Asn; Am Bd Neurol Surg; Sigma Xi; Am Acad Arts & Sci; AMA; Am Col Surgeons; AAAS; Res Soc Neurol Surgeons; hon mem Soc Neurosurg France; Soc Neurosci. *Mailing Add:* Dept Neurosurg Serv Mass Gen Hosp 32 Fruit St Boston MA 02114-2698. *Fax:* 617-726-6789

**ZERWEKH, CHARLES EZRA, JR,** organic chemistry; deceased, see previous edition for last biography

**ZERWEKH, ROBERT PAUL,** ENGINEERING MANAGEMENT, MANAGEMENT OF INNOVATION. *Current Pos:* from asst prof to prof mech eng, 70-91, ASSOC VCHANCELLOR, UNIV KANS, 87-, PROF ENG MGT, 91-, DIR TECHNOL TRANSFER, 96- *Personal Data:* b Peoria, Ill, Feb 25, 39; m 74, Marilyn Bevan; c Robert, Richard & Michael. *Educ:* Univ Mo, Rolla, BS, 61; Univ Ill, Urbana, MS, 63; Iowa State Univ, PhD(metall), 70. *Prof Exp:* Sr engr mat, Elec Boat Div, Gen Dynamics Corp,

65-67. *Concurrent Pos:* Fac res fel, NASA-Am Soc Eng Educ, 75; sci grant, NASA/Langley Res Ctr, 76-78 & Gulf & Western Energy Prod Group, 79-83; assoc dean eng, Univ Kans, 80-87. *Mem:* Am Soc Eng Mgt; Sigma Xi. *Res:* Technology transfer; management of innovation; strategy. *Mailing Add:* Res & Pub Serv Univ Kans Lawrence KS 66045

**ZETIK, DONALD FRANK,** RESERVOIR ENGINEERING, COMPUTER SIMULATOR DEVELOPMENT. *Current Pos:* SR COMPUT SCIENTIST, DOWELL-SCHLUMBERGER, 85- *Personal Data:* b Brenham, Tex, Nov 28, 38; m 69; c 2. *Educ:* Tex A&M Univ, BS, 61; Univ Tex, Austin, PhD(phys chem), 70. *Prof Exp:* Engr petrol prod, Prod Res Lab, Humble Oil Co, 61-63; res assoc chem physics, Wash State Univ, 68-70; sr engr assoc reservoir mgt, Cities Serv Oil & Gas Corp, 70-85. *Concurrent Pos:* Adj prof, Univ Tulsa, 76-77. *Mem:* Soc Petrol Engrs. *Res:* Numerical simulation of fluid flow in porous media; development of new simulation techniques. *Mailing Add:* 9124 E 67th Pl S Tulsa OK 74133-2211

**ZETLMEISL, MICHAEL JOSEPH,** ELECTROCHEMISTRY & NONAQUEOUS ELECTROLYTES, APPLIED STATISTICS & EXPERIMENTAL DESIGN. *Current Pos:* RES CHEMIST & PROJ LEADER CORROSION & ELECTROCHEM, PETROLITE CORP, 71-, FEL ELECTROCHEM, 85-, FEL INDUST APPLNS, 89- *Personal Data:* b Baltimore, Md, Feb 26, 42; m 71; c 5. *Educ:* Spring Hill Col, BS, 66; Marquette Univ, MS, 67; St Louis Univ, PhD(chem), 71. *Mem:* Am Chem Soc; Sigma Xi. *Res:* Electrochemistry of high temperature melts as related to corrosion of metals in gas turbines and boilers; refinery corrosion problems. *Mailing Add:* 7237 Maryland Ave St Louis MO 63130-4419

**ZETTEL, LARRY JOSEPH,** COMPUTER SCIENCE EDUCATION. *Current Pos:* assoc prof, 80-85, PROF COMPUT SCI, LORAS COL, 85- *Personal Data:* b Detroit, Mich, Sept 12, 44. *Educ:* Univ Detroit, BS, 65; Mich State Univ, MS, 66, PhD(math), 70; Univ NMex, MS, 77. *Prof Exp:* Asst prof & chmn dept, Muskingum Col, 69-77, assoc prof math, 77-80. *Mem:* Math Asn Am; Asn Comput Mach; Inst Elec & Electronics Engrs Comput Soc. *Res:* Non-associative algebras; computer usage in undergraduate instruction. *Mailing Add:* Dept Math & Comput Sci Loras Col 1450 Alta Vista Dubuque IA 52001

**ZETTER, BRUCE ROBERT,** CELL & TUMOR BIOLOGY, VASCULARIZATION. *Current Pos:* from asst prof to assoc prof, 78-93, PROF, HARVARD MED SCH, 93- *Personal Data:* b Providence, RI, Dec 23, 46; m 85, Sally Ourieff; c Olivia & Gabriel. *Educ:* Brandeis Univ, BA, 68; Univ RI, PhD(biol), 74. *Hon Degrees:* MS, Harvard Univ, 93. *Honors & Awards:* Fac Res Award, Am Cancer Soc, 83; Merit Award, NIH, 88. *Prof Exp:* Fel, Mass Inst Technol, 74-76; fel, Salk Inst, 76-77; asst res biochemist, Univ Calif Med Ctr, San Francisco, 77-78. *Concurrent Pos:* Res assoc, Children's Hosp Med Ctr, Boston, Mass, 78- *Mem:* Am Soc Cell Biol; Am Asn Cancer Res. *Res:* Biology of the cells that comprise the vasculature, the vascular smooth muscle and endothelial cells; interactions of blood vessels with growing tumors with a special interest in the migration of endothelial cells and tumor cells; mechanisms of tumor metastasis including cell adhesion and cell migration; development of diagnostic and progressive cancer tests. *Mailing Add:* Dept Surg Harvard Med Sch Children's Hosp 300 Longwood Ave Boston MA 02115. *Fax:* 617-735-7403

**ZETTL, ANTON,** MATHEMATICS. *Current Pos:* assoc prof, 69-73, PROF MATH, NORTHERN ILL UNIV, 73- *Personal Data:* b Gakovo, Yugoslavia, Apr 25, 35; US citizen; m 64; c 2. *Educ:* Ill Inst Technol, BS, 59; Univ Tenn, MA, 62, PhD(math), 64. *Prof Exp:* From asst to assoc prof math, La State Univ, Baton Rouge, 64-69. *Concurrent Pos:* NASA res grants, 65-67; res mem, Math Res Ctr, Univ Wis, 67-68; vis res fel, Univ Dundee, Scotland, 74-75; Brit Sci Res Coun res grant, 74-75; NSF res grants, 74-75, 75-76 & 76-77; vis res scientist, appl math div, Argonne Nat Lab, 81-82 & 86-87, spec term app consult, 82-86 & 87-88; chmn, Math Northern Ill Univ, 83-86. *Mem:* Am Math Soc; Soc Indust & Appl Math; Math Asn Am; Ger Asn Appl Math & Mech. *Res:* Differential equations; differential operators; norm inequalities for derivatives and differences. *Mailing Add:* Dept Math Northern Ill Univ De Kalb IL 60115

**ZETTLER, FRANCIS WILLIAM,** PLANT PATHOLOGY, ENTOMOLOGY. *Current Pos:* From asst prof to assoc prof, 66-75, PROF, UNIV FLA, 75- *Personal Data:* b Easton, Pa, Aug 13, 38; m 61; c 2. *Educ:* Pa State Univ, BS, 61; Cornell Univ, MS, 64, PhD(plant path), 66. *Mem:* Am Phytopath Soc. *Res:* Transmission of plant viruses. identification, characterization and control of plant viruses; virus diseases of ornamental plants; research involving edible root crops in the family Araceae. *Mailing Add:* Dept Plant Path Univ Fla PO Box 110680 Gainesville FL 32611-2002

**ZETTNER, ALFRED,** CLINICAL PATHOLOGY. *Current Pos:* PROF PATH & HEAD, DIV CLIN PATH, UNIV CALIF, SAN DIEGO, 68- *Personal Data:* b Laibach, Yugoslavia, Nov 21, 28; US citizen; m 59; c 2. *Educ:* Graz Univ, MD, 54. *Honors & Awards:* Gerald T Evans Award, 79. *Prof Exp:* Asst prof path & clin path, Yale Univ, 63-67, assoc prof clin path, 67-68, dir dept clin micros, 63-68. *Concurrent Pos:* NIH trainee clin path, Yale Univ, 61-63. *Mem:* AAAS; Am Soc Clin Path; Am Fedn Clin Res; Acad Clin Lab Physicians & Sci; Am Asn Clin Chem. *Res:* Competitive binding assays; folates in human serum. *Mailing Add:* 6011 Beaumont Ave La Jolla CA 92037-6705

**ZEVNIK, FRANCIS C(LAIR),** CHEMICAL ENGINEERING. *Current Pos:* PRES, ZEVNIK ASSOCS, 87- *Personal Data:* b Joliet, Ill, Jan 1, 22; m 45; c 5. *Educ:* Univ Wis, BS, 43, MS, 47. *Prof Exp:* Chem engr, Sharples Chem, 43-44; chem supvr, E I du Pont de Nemours & Co, Inc, 47-53; sr engr, C F Braun & Co, 53-56; consult, E I du Pont de Nemours & Co, Inc, 56-65, sr res supvr, 65-69, sr design consult, 70-72; dir res eng, Kendall Co, 72-80, Fibre Prod Lab, 80-85, corp tech dir, 85-87. *Mem:* Am Inst Chem Engrs; Am Chem Soc; Tech Asn Pulp & Paper Indust. *Res:* Micro-porous structures and complex multi-component structures employing micro-porous materials; chemical engineering design; engineering evaluations and economics; nonwoven and spunbonded textile sheet structures. *Mailing Add:* 6327 Hobbton Hwy Clinton NC 28328-9533. *Fax:* 910-592-3024

**ZEVOS, NICHOLAS,** PHYSICAL CHEMISTRY. *Current Pos:* from asst prof to assoc prof, 69-82, chmn, Dept Chem, 78-90, PROF, STATE UNIV NY, POTSDAM, 82- *Personal Data:* b Manchester, NH, June 24, 32; m 66, Denise; c 2. *Educ:* St Anselm's Col, BA, 54; Univ NH, PhD(chem), 63. *Prof Exp:* Instr chem, Univ NH, 63-64; res fel radiation chem, Sloan Kettering Inst, 64-66; fel, Cornell Univ, 66-68. *Concurrent Pos:* Res assoc, Danish Nat Labs, Roskilde, Denmark, Radiation Lab, Univ Notre Dame & Chem Dept, Brookhaven Nat Labs. *Mem:* AAAS; Am Chem Soc; Sigma Xi; InterAm Photochem Soc. *Res:* Chemical kinetics; radiation chemistry, pulse radiolysis; laser photochemistry. *Mailing Add:* 183 Blanchard Rd Potsdam NY 13676

**ZEWAIL, AHMED H,** LASERS, SOLAR ENERGY. *Current Pos:* from asst prof to prof, 76-89, LINUS PAULING PROF CHEM & PROF PHYSICS, CALIF INST TECHNOL, 90-; DIR, LAB MOLECULAR SCI, NSF. *Personal Data:* b Egypt, Feb 26, 46; m; c Maha, Amani & Nabeel. *Educ:* Univ Alexandria, Egypt, BS, 67, MS, 69; Univ Pa, PhD(chem), 74. *Hon Degrees:* MA, Oxford Univ, 91; DSche, Am Univ, Cairo, 93. *Honors & Awards:* Buck-Whitney Medal, Am Chem Soc, 85, Harrison Howe Award, 89, Nobel Laureate Signature Award, 92; W Albert Noyes Jr Mem Lectr, Univ Rochester, 87; Jean Day Lectr, Rutgers Univ, 88; Francis E Blacet Lectr, Univ Calif, Los Angeles, 88; Eyring Lectr, Ariz State Univ, 88 & 89; Harry Emmett Gunning Lectr, Univ Alta, 89; King Faisal Int Prize in Sci, 89; Earnest C Watson Lectr, Calif Inst Technol, 90; Am Chem Soc Max T Rogers Lectr, Mich State Univ, 90; Reilly Lectr, Univ Notre Dame, 90; Hoechst Prize, 90; Flygare Mem Lectr, Univ Ill, 90; Sir Cyril Hinshelwood Chair Lectr, Oxford, 91; Jacob Bigeleisen Endowed Lectr, Stony Brook, 91; Richard B Bernstein Mem Lectr, Univ Calif, Los Angeles, 91; Carl Zeiss Int Award Ger, 92; Earl K Plyler Prize, Am Phys Soc, 93; Wolf Prize Chem, 93; Medal, Royal Neth Acad Arts & Sci, 93. *Prof Exp:* Instr & researcher chem, Univ Alexandria, 67-69; res fel chem physics, Univ Calif, Berkeley, 74-75, IBM res fel, 75-76. *Concurrent Pos:* Distinguished vis lectr, Univ Tex, Austin, 77 & Am Chem Soc, Wayne State Univ, 85; chmn, Conf Advan Laser Spectros, San Diego, 77, 29th Ann Conf Mod Spectros, Calif, 82 & Int Conf Photochem & Photobiol, Egypt, 83; Alfred P Sloan Found fel, 78-82; mem, Panel US-France Coop Sci Prog, 79, Comt Infrared & Raman Spectros, Int Union Pure & Appl Chem, 81-, Int Sci Comt Conf Recent Advan Molecular Reaction Dynamics, 85, Phys Chem Workshop, NSF, 87 & Tech Prog Comt, Int Quantum Electronics Conf, 90; John van Geuns vis prof, Univ Amsterdam, Neth, 79; Camille & Henry Dreyfus teacher-scholar award, 79-85; ed, Laser Chem Int J, 80-85, J Phys Chem, 86, 88 & 91, Chem Physics Lett, 90 & 91-; vis prof, Univ Bordeaux, France, 81, Ecole Normale Superieure, France, 83 & Am Univ Cairo, 88; Alexander von Humboldt sr US scientist award, 83; NSF award, 84-86 & 88-90; John S Guggenheim Mem Found fel, 87; Rolf Sammet vis prof, Johann Wolfgang Coethe-Univ, Ger, 90; Christensen prof fel, St Catherine's Col, Oxford, 91; vis prof, Tex A&M Univ, 92 & Univ Iowa, 92. *Mem:* Nat Acad Sci; Am Inst Physics; Inter Am Photochem Soc; Am Chem Soc; fel Am Phys Soc; Soc Photo-Optical Instrumentation Engrs; Optical Soc Am; Int Soc Magnetic Resonance; Europ Photochem Asn; Sigma Xi; Am Acad Arts & Sci; Europ Acad Arts, Sci & Humanities. *Res:* Nonlinear laser spectroscopy; radiationless processes in molecules; energy transfer in solids; picosecond spectroscopy; solar photovoltaic conversion and laser-induced chemistry; ultrafast lasers and electrons and applications in chemistry and biology; author of 10 publications; awarded one US patent. *Mailing Add:* Dept Chem Arthur Amos Noyes Lab Chem Physics Calif Inst Technol Mail Code 127-72 Pasadena CA 91125. *Fax:* 626-792-8456

**ZEY, EDWARD G,** PHARMACEUTICAL, PROCESS DEVELOPMENT OPERATIONS SUPPORT. *Current Pos:* res assoc, 89-92, SR RES ASSOC, HOECHST CELANESE CORP, 92- *Personal Data:* b McAllen, Tex, Sept 25, 38; m 62, Dorothy K Duderstadt; c Edward B & Kathryn M. *Educ:* Tex A&M Univ, BS, 61; Univ Kans, PhD(org chem), 68. *Prof Exp:* Res chemist, Celanese Corp, 68-79, staff chemist, 79-89. *Mem:* Am Chem Soc. *Res:* Process development and plant support on commodity and bulk pharmaceutical intermediate chemicals; working on vapor phase and liquid phase technologies. *Mailing Add:* 522 Evergreen Dr PO Box 9077 Corpus Christi TX 78469-9077. *Fax:* 512-242-4122

**ZEY, ROBERT L,** ORGANIC CHEMISTRY. *Current Pos:* from asst prof to assoc prof, 65-72, PROF CHEM, CENT MO STATE UNIV, 72- *Personal Data:* b California, Mo, Sept 19, 32; m 60, Janet Ingalls; c Kenneth R & Robert D. *Educ:* Cent Methodist Col, AB, 54; Univ Nebr, MS, 59, PhD(chem), 61. *Prof Exp:* Res chemist, Mallinckrodt Chem Works, 61-65. *Mem:* Am Chem Soc. *Res:* Nitrogen heterocycles; nuclear magnetic resonance; mass spectrometry. *Mailing Add:* 77 S Main Warrensburg MO 64093-9801

**ZEYEN, RICHARD JOHN,** PLANT PATHOLOGY, HOST-PARASITE INTERACTIONS. *Current Pos:* acad fel, Univ Minn, St Paul, 67-70, res assoc, 70-73, from asst prof to assoc prof, 73-82, PROF, DEPT PLANT PATH, UNIV MINN, ST PAUL, 82- *Personal Data:* b Mankato, Minn, Jan 17, 43; m 84. *Educ:* Mankato State Univ, BS, 65, MS, 67; Univ Minn, St Paul,

PhD(plant path & physiol), 70. *Prof Exp:* Asst gen biol, Mankato State Univ, 65-67. *Concurrent Pos:* Underwood fel, Agr, Food Res Coun, UK, 93. *Mem:* Am Inst Biol Sci; Am Phytopath Soc; AAAS; Sigma Xi; Micros Soc Am. *Res:* Host-parasite relationships, physiology, in situ microanalysis of plant cell responses to fungal parasite attack; electron optical facility director; plant resistance to fungal paresites. *Mailing Add:* 2206 Hoyt Ave W St Paul MN 55108

**ZFASS, ALVIN MARTIN,** GASTROENTEROLOGY, HEPATOLOGY. *Current Pos:* from instr to assoc prof med, 63-77, DIR ENDOSCOPY, VA COMMONWEALTH UNIV, MED COL, VA, 63-, PROF MED, 77- *Personal Data:* b Norfolk, Va, Mar 30, 31; m 63; c 1. *Educ:* Univ Va, BA, 53; Med Col Va, MD, 57. *Honors & Awards:* Am Cancer Soc Prof Educ Award. *Prof Exp:* Intern med, Bellevue-Cornell Med Ctr, 57-58; resident, Manhattan Vet Hosp, 58-60; mem, Sloan-Kettering Cancer Ctr, 60-61. *Concurrent Pos:* Fel gastroenterol, Manhattan Vet Hosp, 61-63; sabbatical, Sloan-Kettering Cancer Clin, 81-82. *Mem:* Am Gastroenterol Asn; Am Soc Gastroenterol Endoscopy; fel Am Col Physicians; fel Am Col Gastroenterol. *Res:* Smooth muscle physiology of the esophagus; gastrointestinal hormones; biliary endoscopy; laser therapy. *Mailing Add:* Dept Med-Gastroenterol MCV Box 43 Richmond VA 23298

**ZGANJAR, EDWARD F,** NUCLEAR PHYSICS. *Current Pos:* from asst prof to assoc prof, 70-75, PROF PHYSICS, LA STATE UNIV, BATON ROUGE, 75- *Personal Data:* b Virginia, Minn, July 31, 38; m 60; c 4. *Educ:* St John's Univ, Minn, BS, 60; Vanderbilt Univ, MS, 63, PhD(physics), 66. *Prof Exp:* AEC fel, Vanderbilt Univ, 60-62 & 64-65, Nat Reactor Testing Sta, 65-66. *Concurrent Pos:* Sabbatical leave, Oak Ridge Nat Lab, 73-74; chmn, Exec Comt, UNISOR, 73-75 & 79-80; mem, Syst Nuclear Energy Comt & Radiation Safety Comt, La State Univ, 75-; mem, Exec Comt, Hollifield Heavy Iron Res Facil Users Groups; invited vis scientist, Brookhaven Nat Lab, 76 & 77 & GSI, Darmstadt, WGer, 81-82. *Mem:* Fel Am Phys Soc; Sigma Xi; Am Chem Soc. *Res:* Low energy nuclear spectroscopy; experimental nuclear structure. *Mailing Add:* 435 Kenilworth Pkwy Baton Rouge LA 70808. *Fax:* 504-388-5983

**ZHANG, BING-RONG,** CHEMICAL VAPOR DEPOSITION, DIELECTRIC THIN FILM. *Current Pos:* DIR & MGR RES & DEVELOP, FAITH INT CORP USA, 90-; INSTR PHYSICS, FRONT RANGE COMMUNITY COL, 91- *Personal Data:* b Shanghai, China, Apr 15, 44; m 70; c 2. *Educ:* Nanjing Univ, China, MS, 82; Colo State Univ, MS, 87. *Prof Exp:* Engr, Nanjing Commun Works, 78-79; grad res asst & teaching asst elec eng, Colo State Univ, 84-90. *Concurrent Pos:* Consult, Faith Int Corp, Saudi Arabia & Kuwait, 91- *Mem:* Am Physics Soc. *Res:* Chemical vapor deposition of dielectric thin films and diagnostics for semiconductors; magnetism and magnetic materials; infrared measurement system. *Mailing Add:* PO Box 755 Broomfield CO 80038-0755

**ZHANG, CUN-QUAN,** GRAPH & NETWORK THEORY. *Current Pos:* from asst prof to assoc prof, 87-96, PROF MATH, WVA UNIV, 96- *Personal Data:* b Shanghai, China, Aug, 1952; US citizen; m 82, Hui-Min Yang; c Jennifer. *Educ:* Simon Fraser Univ, PhD(math), 86. *Prof Exp:* Asst prof, Simon Fraser Univ, 86-87. *Mem:* Am Math Soc. *Res:* Connectivity of graph network, coloring, cycles, paths in graphs; flows in network algorithms. *Mailing Add:* 117 Diamond Ct Morgantown WV 26505. *E-Mail:* cqzhang@math.wva.edu

**ZHANG, DACHUN,** STABLE ISOTOPE GEOCHEMISTRY. *Current Pos:* STABLE ISOTOPE LAB MGR, GLOBAL GEOCHEM CORP, 89- *Personal Data:* b Nanyang, Henan, China, Aug 15, 46; m 72, Xiurong Duan; c Jean & Yi. *Educ:* Peking Univ, BS, 70, MS, 82; Univ Chicago, PhD(geochem), 88. *Mem:* Am Geophys Union. *Res:* Geochemistry of stable isotopes; application of stable isotopes into geological problems such as granite genesis and water-rock interactions. *Mailing Add:* 6919 Eton Ave Canoga Park CA 91303. *E-Mail:* ay991@lafn.org

**ZHANG, DONG ER,** MEDICAL RESEARCH. *Current Pos:* res assoc, Dept Med, Gastroenterol Div, 91-92, Hemat/Oncol Div, 92-93, STAFF PHD, DEPT MED, HEMAT/ONCOL DIV, BETH ISRAEL HOSP, 93-; ASST PROF MED, HARVARD MED SCH, 95- *Personal Data:* b Beijing, China, Oct 15, 59; m 83, Dongxian; c Yannan C & Phillip Y. *Educ:* Beijing Univ, China, BS, 83; Univ Houston, PhD, 87. *Honors & Awards:* First Award, NIH, 94. *Prof Exp:* Res fel human biochem & genetics, Univ Tex Med Br, 88-89, instr, 90-91; instr med, Harvard Med Sch, 91-95. *Concurrent Pos:* Sigma Xi res award, 87; asst prof, Univ Tex Med Br, 95- *Mem:* Am Soc Biochem & Molecular Biol; Am Soc Hemat. *Res:* Hematopoietic gene expression and related protein characterization; author of 31 publications. *Mailing Add:* Harvard Inst Med Rm 953 77 Ave Louis Pasteur Boston MA 02115. *Fax:* 617-667-3299

**ZHANG, DUAN ZHONG,** MULTIPHASE FLOW, GRANULAR FLOW. *Current Pos:* POSTDOCTORAL RES ASSOC, THEORET DIV, FLUID DYNAMICS GROUP, LOS ALAMOS NAT LAB, 95- *Personal Data:* b Fuzhou, China, Oct 18, 62; m 88, Dali Yang; c Horace Yang. *Educ:* EChina Tech Univ Water Resources, BS, 82; Chinese Acad Sci, MS, 86; Johns Hopkins Univ, PhD(mech eng), 93. *Prof Exp:* Lectr fluid mech & solid mech, Col Yangtze Transp, 82-84; res scientist, Inst Mech, Chinese Acad Sci, 86-88; postdoctoral fel, Dept Mech Eng, Johns Hopkins Univ, 94-95. *Concurrent Pos:* Vis scholar, Dept Appl Math & Theoret Physics, Cambridge Col, 94. *Mem:* Am Soc Mech Eng; Soc Rheology; Am Physics Soc. *Res:* Modeling and computer simulation of multiphase and granular flows; computational fluid dynamics; macroscopic model from the statistical physics principles for particulate materials. *Mailing Add:* Los Alamos Nat Lab T-3/B216 Los Alamos NM 87545. *Fax:* 505-665-5926; *E-Mail:* dzhang@lanl.gov

**ZHANG, FAMING,** X-RAY CRYSTALLOGRAPHY, STRUCTURE BASED DRUG DESIGN. *Current Pos:* SR SCIENTIST, ELI LILLY & CO, 94- *Personal Data:* m 85, Susan Cai; c Samuel & David. *Educ:* Wuhan Univ, MS, 84, PhD(biochem), 90. *Prof Exp:* Postdoctoral fel, Southwestern Med Ctr, Univ Tex, Dallas, 90-94, res instr, 92-94. *Mem:* Am Crystallog Asn. *Res:* Macromolecular structure research; using three-dimensional structure of proteins to design pharmaceuticals. *Mailing Add:* Lilly Corp Ctr Indianapolis IN 46285. *Fax:* 317-276-9722; *E-Mail:* zfm@lilly.com

**ZHANG, HONG,** NUMERICAL ALGORITHM DESIGN & DEVELOPMENT, PARALLEL ALGORITHM & NUMERICAL LINEAR ALGEBRA. *Current Pos:* Asst prof, 89-96, ASSOC PROF, DEPT MATH SCI, CLEMSON UNIV, 96- *Personal Data:* b Beijing, China, Dec, 1956; US citizen; m 83; c 2. *Educ:* Beijing Normal Univ, BS, 82; Mich State Univ, MS, 85, PhD(appl math), 89. *Concurrent Pos:* Lectr, Capital Univ Econ & Bus, Beijing, 82-83; vis asst prof, Dept Math, Iowa State Univ, 91; vis scientist, Inst Comput Appl Sci & Eng, Langley Res Ctr, NASA, 92-94, 95 & 96; vis prof for women award, NSF, Dept Math, La State Univ, 96- *Mem:* Soc Indust & Appl Math; Am Math Soc. *Res:* Mathematical modeling and computer simulation; sequential and parallel numerical algorithm analysis and development for large scale applications; designing parallel algorithms for fundamental linear algebraic systems, such as eigen value problems and linear systems; parallel multi-objective optimization and time parallel algorithm for differential equations; chemical polymerization; iterative algebraic solution process. *Mailing Add:* Dept Math Sci Clemson Univ Clemson SC 29634. *E-Mail:* zhang@math.lsu.edu

**ZHANG, JIANPING,** INTELLIGENT EDUCATIONAL SOFTWARE, MACHINE LEARNING. *Current Pos:* Asst prof, 90-96, ASSOC PROF COMPUT SCI, UTAH STATE UNIV, 96- *Personal Data:* b Wuhan, China, Mar 18, 56; m 83, Yilin Weng; c Lorna L & Edwin M. *Educ:* Wuhan Univ, BS, 82; Univ Ill, PhD(comput sci), 90. *Concurrent Pos:* Guest assoc prof, SE Univ, China. *Mem:* Inst Elec & Electronics Engrs; Am Asn Artificial Intel; Asn Advan Comput Educ; Asn Comput Mach. *Res:* Investigate methods for creating intelligent, interactive, and adaptive computer based instructional systems; develop computer systems with learning capabilities. *Mailing Add:* 1287 Eastridge Dr Logan UT 84321. *Fax:* 435-797-3265; *E-Mail:* jianping@zhang.cs.usu.edu

**ZHANG, JOHN YONGXING,** APPLIED BIOMECHANICS. *Current Pos:* SR ENGR & SCIENTIST, GUIDANT CORP-CARDIAC PACEMAKERS INC, 94- *Personal Data:* b Wubu, China, Oct 15, 56; m 82, Yen Wang; c Jiaxiao, Jessica & Jeffrey. *Educ:* Xian Sci & Tech Univ, BS, 82; Mich Tech Univ, MS, 86; Old Dominion Univ, PhD(eng), 91. *Prof Exp:* Instr & engr, NW Univ Agr, China, 82-84; res assoc, Old Dominion Univ, 91-92, res asst prof, Ctr Biotechnol, 92-94. *Mem:* Am Soc Mech Engrs; Am Soc Biomat; Am Soc Biomech. *Res:* Bioengineering and biomechanics research and applications in clinical field; medical device development, design and testing. *Mailing Add:* 3036 Valento Lane St Paul MN 55117-1273. *E-Mail:* john.zhang@guidant.com

**ZHANG, JOHN ZENG HUI,** GAS-PHASE CHEMICAL REACTION, GAS-SURFACE INTERACTIONS. *Current Pos:* asst prof chem, 90-94, ASSOC PROF, CHEM DEPT, NY UNIV, 94- *Personal Data:* b Shanghai, China, Feb 15, 61. *Educ:* EChina Normal Univ, BS, 82; Univ Houston, PhD(chem physics), 87. *Prof Exp:* Fel chem physics, Univ Calif, Berkeley, 87-90. *Concurrent Pos:* Camille & Henry Dreyfus Found new fac award, 90; pres fac fel, NSF, 94; A P Sloan res fel, 95. *Mem:* Am Chem Soc; Am Phys Soc. *Res:* Chemical reaction dynamics; molecular collision dynamics; molecule-surface interactions; chemical reaction on metal surfaces; catalysis. *Mailing Add:* Dept Chem NY Univ 4 Washington Pl Rm 514 New York NY 10003-6621

**ZHANG, JONATHAN,** PHYSICAL CHEMISTRY. *Current Pos:* SR SCIENTIST, LIGHTWAVE MICROSYSTS CORP, 95- *Personal Data:* m 86, Kathy Song; c Tracy S & Jeffrey B. *Educ:* Peking Univ, BS, 83; Tsinghua Univ, MS, 86; State Univ NY, PhD(chem), 92. *Prof Exp:* Asst prof physics, Tsinghua Univ, 86-88; res chemist, Laserphotonics Techol, 92-95. *Mem:* Am Chem Soc; Optical Soc Am. *Res:* Organic nonlinear optical materials; photorefractive polymers and organics for light emitting diodes; optical interconnects, optical switches and telecom systems. *Mailing Add:* 2950 Scott Blvd Santa Clara CA 95050

**ZHANG, JUN,** OCEAN WAVE MECHANICS, OCEAN ENGINEERING. *Current Pos:* asst prof, 87-93, ASSOC PROF CIVIL & OCEAN ENG, TEX A&M UNIV, 93- *Personal Data:* m; c Xin Yi & Franklin M. *Educ:* Shanghai Jiao Tong Univ, BS, 68; Mass Inst Technol, MS, 84, ScD, 87. *Prof Exp:* Naval architect, Hunan Shipping Co, 70-78. *Concurrent Pos:* Prin investr, Offshore Technol Res Ctr, 88- *Mem:* Assoc mem Am Soc Chem Engr; Am Geophys Union. *Res:* Nonlinear surface gravity ocean waves; non-linear wave; wave interaction in ocean waves and their applications in offshore and coastal engineering. *Mailing Add:* 1311 Austin Ave College Station TX 77845. *Fax:* 409-862-8162; *E-Mail:* j-zahang@tamu.edu

**ZHANG, KER,** TELECOMMUNICATIONS, WIRELESS LOCAL AREA NETWORKS. *Current Pos:* VPRES, MICROTEK LAB INC, 96- *Personal Data:* m; c Alex. *Educ:* Jinan Univ, China, BS, 82; Univ Mass, MS, 85; Worcester Polytech Inst, PhD(elec eng), 90. *Prof Exp:* Lead engr, Motorola, Inc, 90-91; group leader, Rockwell Int, 91-96. *Mem:* Sr mem Inst Elec & Electronics Engrs. *Res:* Wireless communication with emphasis on wireless Linked Access Network and digital receiver algorithm. *Mailing Add:* 1000 Park Newport No 311 Newport Beach CA 92660

**ZHANG, NAN,** FIBER OPTICS, TELECOMMUNICATIONS. *Current Pos:* OPTICAL ENG SPECIALIST, ADC TELECOMMUN INC, 96- *Personal Data:* b Jinan, Shandong, June 3, 66; Can citizen; m; c Mengyou & Mengya. *Educ:* Shandong Univ, BEE, 85, MS, 88; Univ Montreal, PhD(semiconductor device), 96. *Honors & Awards:* Golden Medal, Chinese Govt, 96. *Prof Exp:* Asst prof & engr, Nat Lab Crystal Mats, Shandong Univ, 88-93. *Mem:* Optical Soc Am; Optical Soc China. *Res:* Fiberoptical components including connectors, switches and electronic differential analyzers, as well as network design, nonlinear optics, single crystal growth, semiconductor processing, ion implantation and semiconductor device characterizations; optical and optomechanical design, laser system diagnosis, alignment and testing. *Mailing Add:* 5900 Clearwater Dr No 204 Minnetonka MN 55343. *Fax:* 612-946-3910; *E-Mail:* nan__zhang@adc.com

**ZHANG, QIMING,** ELECTRICAL ENGINEERING, MATERIALS SCIENCE ENGINEERING. *Current Pos:* from asst prof to assoc prof mat, 91-96, ASSSOC PROF ELEC ENG, MAT RES LAB, PA STATE UNIV, 96- *Personal Data:* b Shaoxin, Zhejiang, China, Jan 14, 57; m 86, Ailan Cheng; c Andrew. *Educ:* Nanjing Univ, BS, 81; Pa State Univ, PhD(physics), 86. *Mem:* Am Phys Soc; Inst Elec & Electronics Engrs; Mat Res Soc Am; Am Ceramic Soc. *Res:* Interface phenomena; ferroelectric phase transitions and their applications; actuator, sensor and transducer based on electromechanical effects in ceramic, polymer, and thin films; electro-optics and non-linear optical materials. *Mailing Add:* Mat Res Lab Pa State Univ University Park PA 16802. *E-Mail:* qxz1@psuvm.psu.edu

**ZHANG, QING,** STOCHASTIC CONTROL, APPPLIED PROBABILITY. *Current Pos:* ASSOC PROF MATH, UNIV GA, 94- *Personal Data:* b Baoding, China, Oct 20, 59; m 87, Qian Fang; c Sheena & Sean. *Educ:* Nankai Univ, China, BSc, 83; Brown Univ, MSc, 85, PhD(appl math), 88. *Prof Exp:* Postdoctoral fel, Univ BC, Can, 88-89, Univ Toronto, 89-91; asst prof math, Univ Ky, 91-93; vis res prof, Univ Toronto, 93-94. *Concurrent Pos:* Prin investr, Off Naval Res, 96- *Mem:* Soc Indust & Appl Math. *Res:* Applied mathematics; applied probability; stochastic optimal control; singular perturbation; nonlinear filtering; manufacturing systems; hierarchical control. *Mailing Add:* 130 Buckeye Br Athens GA 30605. *Fax:* 706-542-2573; *E-Mail:* qingz@math.uga.edu

**ZHANG, RENDUO,** FLOW TRANSPORT IN VADOSE ZONE & GROUNDWATER SYSTEMS. *Current Pos:* ASST PROF SOIL PHYSICS, UNIV WYO, 93- *Personal Data:* b Bijie, Guizhom, China, Oct 15, 50; m 77, Guangling Xia; c Jiao & Jesse. *Educ:* Wuhan Univ Hydraul & Elec Eng, BS, 82; Univ Ariz, MS, 86, PhD(soil physics), 90. *Prof Exp:* Teaching asst soil physics lab, Univ Ariz, 85-86, res assoc, 86-90; fel, US Salinity Lab, USDA, 90-93. *Mem:* Am Geophys Union; Soil Sci Soc Am. *Res:* Study of physical processes occuring in soil and environment; model water movement, solute transport and heat flow in variably saturated porous media; simulate soil water and groundwater stochastic processes; describe soil spatial variability and heterogeneity. *Mailing Add:* 1975 N 17th St Laramie WY 82070-1907. *Fax:* 307-766-5549; *E-Mail:* renduo@uwyo.edu

**ZHANG, SHOUYU,** PHYSICS. *Current Pos:* PHYSICIST, HEP, 89- *Personal Data:* b Kaifeng, Dec 12, 62; m 89, Xueging Tang; c Frank. *Educ:* Univ Sci & Technol, China, BS, 82, MS, 85; Academia Sinica, PhD(physics), 89. *Concurrent Pos:* Res fel, Univ Mich, 89-93. *Mem:* Am Physics Soc. *Res:* History of science. *Mailing Add:* 1808 Arabian Ave Naperville IL 60565. *E-Mail:* zhangsy@fnalv.gov

**ZHANG, XIAO,** ELECTRON MICROSCOPY & MICROANALYSIS. *Current Pos:* ADVAN MAT SCIENTIST, GEN ELEC CO, 93- *Personal Data:* b Shanghai, China, Sept 25, 61; m 86, Yiqun Pan; c Margaret. *Educ:* Shanghai Univ Technol, China, BS, 84; Univ Tenn, Knoxville, MS, 89, PhD(metall eng), 92. *Prof Exp:* Asst lectr, Shanghai Jiao Tong Univ, Br, China, 84-87; res teaching asst, Univ Tenn, Knoxville, 87-92, res assoc, Oak Ridge Nat Lab, 92-93. *Mem:* Micros Soc Am; Mat Res Soc; Am Soc Mat; Minerals, Metals & Mat Soc; Microbeam Anal Soc. *Res:* Electron holography and its application to materials science; field emission electron microscopy; characterization of ferroelectric domain walls; polymer microscopy; structure-property relationship of polymer blends; Monte-Carlo simulation of electron-solid interactions; microwave sintering of ceramic composites; characterization of Schottky barrier devices. *Mailing Add:* Gen Elec Plastics 1 Nory Lane Selkirk NY 12158. *Fax:* 304-863-7108; *E-Mail:* po16418%pbgvm1.gesninet@ge1vm.schdy.ge.com

**ZHANG, XUMU,** CHEMISTRY. *Current Pos:* ASST PROF, DEPT CHEM, PA STATE UNIV, 94- *Personal Data:* b East Zhou City, Hubei, China, Oct 30, 61; m 86, Liping Xiong; c Isadora Y. *Educ:* Wuhan Univ, BS, 82; Chinese Acad Sci, Fuzhou, MS, 85; Stanford Univ, PhD, 92. *Honors & Awards:* Young Investr Award, Off Naval Res, 96. *Prof Exp:* Staff researcher, Chinese Acad Sci, 82-85; postgrad/staff, Univ Calif, 85-87; fel, Stanford Univ, 92-94; postdoctoral fel, Stanford Univ, 92-94. *Concurrent Pos:* Franklin Veatch fel, 91; consult, Adelphi Tech Inc, 93-94; grantee, Camille & Henry Dreyfus Found, 94. *Mem:* Am Chem Soc. *Res:* Transition metal catalyzed asymmetric synthesis for chiral drugs. *Mailing Add:* Pa State Univ 276 Camelort Dr State College PA 16803

**ZHANG, YINGBO,** MAGNETIC THIN FILM PROCESS & CHARACTERIZATION. *Current Pos:* MAT SCIENTIST, APPL MAGNETICS CORP, 96- *Personal Data:* m 90, Yu. *Educ:* Tsinghua Univ, BSEE, 86, MS, 89; Univ Nebr, PhD(physics), 95. *Prof Exp:* Postdoctoral res scientist, CVC Prod Inc, 95-96. *Mem:* Mat Res Soc; Am Phys Soc. *Res:* Sputtered cobalt/nickle multilayer material system; magnetic recording; magnetoresistance/giant magnetoresistance recording. *Mailing Add:* 340 Rutherford St No 94 Goleta CA 93117

**ZHANG, YOUXUE,** VOLCANOLOGY, KINETICS OF GEOLOGICAL PROCESSES. *Current Pos:* asst prof, 91-97, ASSOC PROF GEOL, UNIV MICH, 97- *Personal Data:* b Hunan, China, Sept 17, 57; m 82, Zhengjiu Xu; c Dan & Ray. *Educ:* Peking Univ, BS, 82; Columbia Univ, MA, 85, MPhil, 87, PhD(geol), 89. *Honors & Awards:* F W Clarke Award, Geochem Soc, 93; Nat Young Investr Award, NSF, 94. *Prof Exp:* Postdoctoral fel, Calif Inst Technol, 89-91. *Concurrent Pos:* Prin investr, NSF, 91- *Mem:* Am Geophys Union; Geochem Soc; Mineral Soc Am; AAAS. *Res:* Gas-driven volcanic and lake eruptions; kinetics and dynamics of geological processes; experimental petrology, volatiles; geochemical evolution of the earth and planets; kimberlites, mantle xenoliths, diamond and thermodynamics. *Mailing Add:* Geol Sci Dept Univ Mich Ann Arbor MI 48109-1063. *Fax:* 313-763-4690; *E-Mail:* youxue@umich.edu

**ZHANG, ZHI-QIANG,** population ecology, acarology, for more information see previous edition

**ZHANG, ZIYANG,** FISH OTOLITH MICROSTRUCTURE & CHEMISTRY, FISH OTOLITH IMAGE DIGITIZING & PROCESSING. *Current Pos:* FEL, GOVT CAN FISHERIES & OCEANS, PAC BIOL STA, 91- *Personal Data:* b Shanghai, China, Feb 1, 60; m 88, Minwen Ye; c Luke. *Educ:* Qingdao Ocean Univ, China, BSc, 82; Univ Wales, MSc, 88, PhD(fish otolith growth & appln), 91. *Prof Exp:* Teacher ichthyol & oceanog, Shanghai Fisheries Sch, China, 82-85; fel, Inst Mar Res, Flodevigen Marine Res Sta, Norway, 91. *Res:* Fish otolith microstructure and otolith growth; effect of various ecological and physiological factors on otolith growth and utilize otolith microstructure to study the past events experienced by individual fish such as growth rate, migration route; way to use otolith to seperate wild salmon from hatchery-released ones. *Mailing Add:* Pac Biol Sta Nanaimo BC V9R 5K6 Can. *Fax:* 250-756-7053

**ZHAO, WEIGUANG,** BONE BIOLOGY, LIMB REGENERATION. *Current Pos:* RES FEL, HARVARD MED SCH, MASS GEN HOSP, 95- *Personal Data:* b Shanghai, China, Aug 13, 58. *Educ:* Beijing Sec Med Sch, MD, 83; Univ SDak, PhD(anat). *Honors & Awards:* Young Investr Award, Am Soc Bone & Mineral Res, 96. *Prof Exp:* Resident, Dept Surg, Beijing Jishuitan Hosp, 83-85; chief resident, Dept Surg, Beijing Emergency Med Ctr, 85-86; res asst, Univ SDak, 90-94, teaching asst, 91-93. *Concurrent Pos:* Res fel, Arthritis Res, Harvard Med Sch, Mass Gen Hosp, 95- *Mem:* Am Asn Anatomists. *Res:* Bone remodeling in transgenic mouse in which a mutation has been targeted to the Col1a-1 gene in type I collagen that results in resistance to collagenase digestion. *Mailing Add:* Arthritis Res 149 Navy Yard 13th St MGH-E Charlestown MA 02129

**ZHAO, YUGI,** HIV PATHOGENESIS & DRUG RESISTANCE IN FISSION YEAST MODEL SYSTEM, DIAGNOSTIC SERVICES FOR HIV & OTHER INFECTIONS. *Current Pos:* ASST PROF PEDIAT, BIOTECHNOL & MICROBIOL-IMMUNOL, MED SCH, NORTHWESTERN UNIV, 94-; DIR, MOLECULAR DIAG LAB, CHILDRENS MEM HOSP, CHICAGO, 94- *Personal Data:* b Qingdao, China, May 20, 57; m Sharon C; c Jennie, Andrew & Adam. *Educ:* Shandong Col, BS, 81; Ore State Univ, MS, 85, PhD(microbial genetics), 91. *Honors & Awards:* Res Award, Am Cancer Soc, 94. *Prof Exp:* Res asst prof, Col Physicians & Surgeons, Columbia Univ, 92-94. *Concurrent Pos:* Ed biol sci, Sci Press, New York Ltd, 95-; prin investr, NIH, 97- *Mem:* AAAS; Am Soc Microbiologists; Am Radiation Res Soc; Am Pediat Infectious Dis Soc; Nat AIDS Clin Trials Groups. *Res:* Use of fission yeast model system to study HIV vpr gene; pathogenesis and drug resistance of HIV in infected patients. *Mailing Add:* 1550 E Castle Ct Palatine IL 60067. *Fax:* 773-880-6609; *E-Mail:* yzhao@nwu.edu

**ZHAO, YUNXIN,** SIGNAL PROCESSING, PATTERN RECOGNITION. *Current Pos:* ASST PROF, DEPT ELEC & COMPUT ENG, UNIV ILL, URBANA-CHAMPAIGN, 94-, RES ASST PROF, BECKMAN INST & COORD SCI LAB, 94- *Personal Data:* b Feb 27, 57; m, Xinhua Zhuang; c Michelle Y. *Educ:* Beijing Inst Posts & Telecommun, BS, 82; Univ Wash, MSEE, 84, PhD(elec eng), 88. *Honors & Awards:* NSF Career Award, 95. *Prof Exp:* Sr res staff & proj leader, Speech Technol Lab, Panasonic Technol Inc, 88-94. *Concurrent Pos:* Assoc ed, Trans Speech & Audio Processing, Inst Elec & Electronics Engrs; prin investr robust automatic speech recognition, NSF & speech processing for hearing aid design, Whitaker Found Biomed Prog. *Mem:* Sr mem Inst Elec & Electronics Engrs; assoc mem Acoust Soc Am. *Res:* Speech processing and recognition, signal processing and pattern recognition; human-computer intelligent interaction; signal procesing algorithms for hearing aid design; granted five US patents. *Mailing Add:* Beckman Inst Univ Ill 405 N Mathews Ave Urbana IL 61801. *Fax:* 217-244-8371

**ZHENG, SHUMING,** ORGANIC CHEMISTRY. *Current Pos:* RES ASSOC, ILL INST TECHNOL, 90-; INSTR PHYS PHARM & ORG CHEM, UNIV ILL, 93- *Personal Data:* b Nanjing, Jiangsu, China, Dec 20, 49. *Educ:* Nanjing Inst Chem Technol, BS, 82, MS, 85, PhD(chem-biomed eng). *Prof Exp:* Instr chem, Nanjing Inst Educ, China, 82-86. *Mem:* Am Chem Soc; Sco Am Mech Eng; Am Inst Chem Engrs. *Mailing Add:* 5201 W 121st Pl Alsip IL 60558

**ZHENG, XIAO LU,** FLAT PANEL INFORMATION DISPLAYS, GALLIUM ARSENIDE DEVICE. *Current Pos:* PRES, ELITE INSTRUMENTS CORP, 95- *Personal Data:* b Shanghai, China, July 2, 51. *Educ:* Univ Mich, MS, 82; Mass Inst Technol, PhD(semiconductor physics), 89. *Honors & Awards:* Res Initiation Award, NSF, 93. *Prof Exp:* Asst prof physics, State Univ NY, Albany, 90-93; sr staff, Kopin Co, 93-95. *Mem:* Am Phys Soc; Soc Info Display; Mat Res Soc. *Res:* Gallium arsenide semiconductor materials and devices; mechanism of light emitting porous silicon; liquid crystal flat panel displays; spectroscopy methods for semiconductors; author of over 30 publications. *Mailing Add:* PO Box 594 Mansfield MA 02048. *Fax:* 508-753-9001; *E-Mail:* zheng@worldnet.att.net

**ZHENG, XIAOCI,** IMPROVEMENT OF WEAR RESISTANCE, IMPROVEMENT OF CORROSION RESISTANCE. *Current Pos:* ASSOC SCIENTIST, UNITED TECHNOLOGIES, 91- *Personal Data:* b Shanghai, China, Apr 21, 49; m 81; c 1. *Educ:* Qufu Norm Univ, China, BS, 81; Univ Sci & Technol, China, MS, 84; Univ Wis-Madison, PhD(mat sci), 91. *Prof Exp:* Res asst, Inst Elec Eng, Acad Sinica, 82-84; lectr, Dept Appl Physics, Tsinghua Univ China, 84-86; res asst, Ctr Plasma Aided Mfg, Univ Wis-Madison, 86-91. *Mem:* Am Phys Soc; Am Soc Metals; Mat Res Soc. *Res:* Surface modification of materials by coating and ion beam techniques; high vacuum; microscopy; surface analysis. *Mailing Add:* 804 Eagle Heights Apt C Madison WI 53705

**ZHENG, YUAN FANG,** ROBOTICS & AUTOMATION, MULTI-SENSOR INTEGRATION. *Current Pos:* assoc prof, 89-92, PROF COMPUT & ROBOTICS, OHIO STATE UNIV, 92- *Personal Data:* b Shanghai, China, July 2, 46; m 76, Yu-Lu Zhang; c Julia R. *Educ:* Tsinghua Univ, BS, 70; Ohio State Univ, MS, 80, PhD(elec eng), 84. *Prof Exp:* From asst prof to assoc prof comput & robotics, Clemson Univ, 84-89. *Concurrent Pos:* Prin investr, Savannah River Lab, 85-88, NSF, 88- & Off Naval Res, 90-; NSF presidential young investr award, 87. *Mem:* Sr mem Inst Elec & Electronics Engrs. *Res:* Sensor integrated robotics system for advanced manufacturing; computer network for real-time applications; neural computing for intelligent mobile robots; non-contact sensing for surface measurement and inspection. *Mailing Add:* Dept Elec Eng Ohio State Univ Columbus OH 43210-1272. *Fax:* 614-292-7596; *E-Mail:* zheng@ee.eng.ohio_state.edu

**ZHONG, PEI,** medical physics, for more information see previous edition

**ZHONG, YAOKUN,** IMAGE COMPRESSION BY WAVELET TRANSFER, APPLICATIONS OF NEURAL NETWORKS. *Current Pos:* software engr, 91-95, SR SCIENTIST, NETROLOGIC INC, 95- *Personal Data:* b, Guangdong, China, May 13, 40; m 68, Zhenyi Yang; c Wenli & Wenjie. *Educ:* Peking Univ, dipl, 65; Int Educ Eval, PhD, 90. *Prof Exp:* Asst, Peking Univ, China, 68-79, engr & lectr, 80-85, sr engr & assoc prof, 85-90. *Concurrent Pos:* Chinese expert, Mutsushita Elec, Japan, 85-87; vis prof & res assoc, Univ Calif, Santa Barbara, 88-90; consult, Neural Net Res & Develop Assoc, 94; Cubic Defense Systs, 96; Horizons Technol Inc, 97. *Res:* Application software and applied computer systems including image compression, neural networking, natural language processing, multi-media techniques, Chinese/English compatible computer systems and Chinese processing. *Mailing Add:* 8385 Westmore Rd No 14 San Diego CA 92126

**ZHONG, YUANZHEN,** POLYMER SYNTHESIS, POLYMER CHARACTERIZATION. *Current Pos:* res chemist, 90-92, sr res chemist, 92-96, RES SCIENTIST, GAP CHEM CORP, INT SPECIALTY PROD, 96- *Personal Data:* b Guangzhou, China, May 2, 47; nat US; m 72, Susan Siying Chen; c Xin & Xun. *Educ:* Jinan Univ, China, BS, 70; Zhongshan Univ, China, MS, 82; Rutgers Univ, PhD(polymer chem), 90. *Prof Exp:* Res staff, Res Inst Chem Eng, China, 70-73 & 75-78; res asst, Zhongshan Univ, China, 79-82 & Rutgers Univ, 84-90; res lectr, Southern China Normal Univ, 82-84; res chemist, GAF Chem Corp, 90-92. *Mem:* Am Chem Soc. *Res:* Polymer synthesis, characterization and application, including solution and precipitation polymerization, co-polymer composition control; water soluble polymers, polyelectrolytes, cross linked polymers, hydrogels, biodegradable polymers; physical chemistry properties of polymer solutions, light scattering and luminescence quenching. *Mailing Add:* Int Specialty Prods 1361 Alps Rd Wayne NJ 07470. *Fax:* 973-628-3886; *E-Mail:* yzhong@ispcorp.com

**ZHONGCHI, LIU,** DEVELOPMENTAL GENETICS, FLOWER DEVELOPMENT. *Current Pos:* ASST PROF, UNIV MD, COLLEGE PARK, 95- *Personal Data:* b Canton, Peoples Repub China, Nov 10, 61; div. *Educ:* Wuhan Univ, Peoples Repub China, BS, 82; Harvard Univ, MA, 88, PhD(biol), 90. *Prof Exp:* Postdoctoral fel, Calif Inst Technol, 91-95. *Concurrent Pos:* Postdoctoral fel, Damon Runyon-Walter Winchell Cancer Res Found, 91 & Life Sci Res Found, 92-94. *Mem:* Am Soc Plant Physiologists; Soc Chinese Bioscientists Am. *Res:* Investigate the genetic and cellular basis of higher plant development; isolation of two genes (Leunig and TSO1), which are essential regulators of flower development in Arabidopsis thaliana. *Mailing Add:* Dept Plant Biol 3236 H J Patterson Hall College Park MD 20742. *Fax:* 301-314-9082; *E-Mail:* zl17@umail.umd.edu

**ZHOU, HUA WEI,** EARTHQUAKE & EXPLORATION SEISMOLOGY, DATA PROCESSING. *Current Pos:* asst prof, 89-95, ASSOC PROF GEOPHYS, UNIV HOUSTON, 95- *Personal Data:* b Beijing, China, Aug 2, 57; m 82; c 2. *Educ:* China Univ Geosci, Wuhan, BS, 80; Calif State Univ, Long Beach, MS, 84; Calif Inst Technol, PhD(geophys), 89. *Prof Exp:* Lectr math, China Univ Geosci, Wuhan, 80-82; res asst, Calif Inst Technol, 84-89. *Mem:* Am Geophys Union; Soc Explor Geophys. *Res:* Earthquake seismology, seismo-tectonics and exploration geophysics; digital data processing, inverse theory, seismic wave propagation and computer graphics. *Mailing Add:* 13530 La Concha Lane Houston TX 77083. *Fax:* 713-748-7906; *E-Mail:* hzhou@uh.edu

**ZHOU, KEMIN,** SYSTEM THEORY & CONTROL. *Current Pos:* asst prof, 90-96, ASSOC PROF, DEPT ELEC & COMPUT ENG, LA STATE UNIV, 96- *Personal Data:* b Wuhu, China, May 7, 62; m 91, Jing Shi; c Eric Kaige. *Educ:* Beijing Univ Aeronaut & Astronaut, BS, 82; Univ Minn, MS, 86, PhD(control sci & dynamical systs), 88. *Prof Exp:* Postdoctoral fel, Calif Inst Technol, 88-90. *Concurrent Pos:* Lectr, Calif Inst Technol, 89-90; prin investr, NSF, 92-, Army Res Off, 96-, Air Force Off Sci Res, 97-; consult, Eveready Battery Co, 96; assoc ed, Trans Automatic Controls, Inst Elec & Electronics Engrs, 96- *Mem:* Inst Elec & Electronics Engrs; Inst Elec & Electronics Engrs Control Syst Soc. *Res:* Robust control; model approximation and system identification. *Mailing Add:* Dept Elec & Comput Eng La State Univ Baton Rouge LA 70803. *E-Mail:* kemin@ee.lsu.edu

**ZHOU, QIAN,** combustion, air pollution control & computational fluid dynamics, for more information see previous edition

**ZHOU, SIMON ZHENG,** GAS LASER, PHOTOCHEMISTRY. *Current Pos:* SR SCIENTIST, CALIF DIGITAL LASER SYST, 88- *Personal Data:* b Shanghai, China, Jan 31, 42; US citizen. *Educ:* Shanghai Univ Sci & Technol, Bachelor, 65, Master, 67. *Prof Exp:* Scientist, Shanghai Inst Laser Technol, 74-87. *Mem:* Soc Photo-Optical Instrumentation Engrs. *Res:* Patent for first compact sealed off excimer laser with long gas lifetime for industry and scientific application; laser induced metal deposition technology and system for semiconductor industry applications. *Mailing Add:* Calif Digital Laser Systs 17000 Figueroa St Gardena CA 90248

**ZHOU, ZHEN-HONG,** SEMICONDUCTOR MANUFACTURING, PROCESS INTEGRATION & MACHINE AUTOMATION. *Current Pos:* HEAD CONSULT, ACT RES CORP, 91-; AT&T BELL LABS FEL, 91- *Personal Data:* b JiAn City, Jiang Xi Province, Oct 16, 68; US citizen. *Educ:* Polytech Univ, BS, 90; Mass Inst Technol, MS, 91, PhD, 94. *Prof Exp:* Res asst, IBM TJ Watson Res Ctr, 87-89; res fel, Mass Inst Technol, 89-93. *Mem:* Inst Elec & Electronics Engrs; guest mem Sigma Xi. *Res:* Design, characterize, control, model, optimize and automate process and equipment for integrated circuits manufacturing; develop new processes and sensors for semiconductor materials processing. *Mailing Add:* 3102 Sands Pl Bronx NY 10461. *Fax:* 407-345-6904; *E-Mail:* zhou@mtl.mit.edu

**ZHU, CHENG,** BIOENGINEERING. *Current Pos:* ASST PROF MECH ENG, GA INST TECHNOL, 90- *Personal Data:* b Guangzhou, China, Feb 10, 57. *Educ:* Zhejiang Univ, BS, 82; Columbia Univ, MS, 85, PhD(eng mech), 88. *Honors & Awards:* Harold Lamport Award, Biomed Eng Soc, 91; Y C Fung Young Investr Award, Am Soc Mech Engrs, 92. *Prof Exp:* Res fel bioeng, Univ Calif, San Diego, 88-90. *Concurrent Pos:* Pres fac fel, NSF, 93. *Mem:* Am Soc Mech Engrs; Biomed Eng Soc. *Mailing Add:* George W Woodruff Sch Mech Eng Ga Inst Technol Atlanta GA 30332-0405

**ZHU, DONG,** tribology, machine design, for more information see previous edition

**ZHU, JACK JINGQUAN,** AUTOMATIC CONTROL SYSTEM DESIGN & DEVELOPMENT, MEDICAL ELECTRONICS. *Current Pos:* SR CONTROL SYST ENGR & ELECTRONICS PROJ ENGR, QUICKIE DESIGNS, SUNRISE MED, 95- *Personal Data:* b Shanghai, China, Jan 26, 38; m 66, Chongshan Sun; c Frank Liang. *Educ:* Tsinghua Univ, Beijing, BS, 60. *Hon Degrees:* MS, Tsinghua Univ, Beijing, 62 & Univ Minn, 90. *Prof Exp:* Proj res engr, Res Inst Automation, China Acad Sci, 62-80; vis res fel, Dept Elec Eng, 3M Advan Res Ctr, Univ Minn, 80-82; proj & design res engr, Beijing Res Inst Control Eng, 82-83 & Beijing Comput Control & Measurement Co, 83-88; proj res engr, Beijing Green Field Sci & Technol Co, 88-89; control syst engr, Krishnamurti Found Am & Keltac Eng Inc, Minn, 90-91; sr control syst engr, Spectrum Eng Inc, Minn, 91-92 & Innovex Eng Inc, Minn, 92-95. *Concurrent Pos:* Lectr, Dept Automatic Control, China Univ Sci & Technol, 63-64, & Dept Elec Eng, Univ Minn, 89-90; process engr & tech consult, AG West Int, Calif, 87-89; tech consult, China Nat Mach Import & Export Co, Beijing, 87-89. *Mem:* Inst Elect & Electroniics Engrs Automatic Control Soc. *Res:* Aerospace altitude control simulator; adaptive controller-expert system; real time computer control; supervisor telecommunication aerospace system; micro inch accuracy thin film grinding machine; electronics specialty controller for wheelchair. *Mailing Add:* 4843 N Doon Way Fresno CA 93726-0236

**ZHU, LONG DE,** III-V & II-IV-V NITRIDE MATERIALS & DEVICES, SEMICONDUCTOR EPITAXY & OPTOELECTRONICS DEVICES. *Current Pos:* SR STAFF SCIENTIST, NZ APPL TECHNOL, 93- *Personal Data:* b Jilin, China, Sept 14, 41; US citizen; m 68, Jinlong Cui; c Haiyan, Min & Yingyi. *Educ:* Peking Univ, PhD(solid state physics & devices), 63. *Prof Exp:* Asst researcher, Chinese Acad Sci, 63-76, from assoc res prof to res prof, 76-94. *Concurrent Pos:* Vis scientist, Cornell Univ, 83-86; vis prof, Rutgers Univ, 91-93, Cornell Univ, 93-94. *Mem:* Phys Soc China; Optical Soc China; Electronics Soc China. *Res:* Gallium arsenide/gallium aluminum arsenide and indium gallium arsenide phosphorous/indium phosphorous heterojunction; lasers and electro-absorption modulators; fabricated ledge wave guide Grinsch QV lasers and phased array lasers; world's first ternary II-IV-V2 nitrides crystalline films. *Mailing Add:* 8A Gill St Woburn MA 01801. *Fax:* 781-935-2188

**ZHU, XIAORONG,** AEROSOLS. *Current Pos:* RESEARCHER, UNIV MIAMI, 92- *Educ:* Beijing Univ, BS, 82; Chinese Acad Geol Sci, MS, 85; Univ Miami, PhD(marine & atmospheric chem), 92. *Honors & Awards:* F G Walton Prize, Univ Miami, 93. *Mem:* Am Geophys Union. *Res:* Atmospheric chemistry, geochemical cycles, trace metals, aerosols including their physical and chemical characteristics and long distance transportation. *Mailing Add:* 7803 N Kendall Dr Miami FL 33156. *Fax:* 305-361-4891; *E-Mail:* xzhu@rsmas.miami.edu

**ZHU, XIAOYANG,** CHEMISTRY, PHYSICAL CHEMISTRY. *Current Pos:* ASST PROF CHEM, UNIV MINN, MINNEAPOLIS, 97- *Personal Data:* b Suzhou, China, Dec 17, 63. *Educ:* Fudan Univ, China, BS, 84; Univ Tex, PhD(chem), 89. *Honors & Awards:* Cottrell Scholar Award, 96. *Prof Exp:* Res scientist, Ctr Mat Chem, Univ Tex, Austin, 90-92; Alexander von Humboldt postdoctoral fel, Ger, 92-93; asst prof chem, Southern Ill Univ, Carbondale, 93-97. *Mem:* Am Chem Soc; Am Vacuum Soc; Mat Res Soc; Sigma Xi. *Res:* Nonthermal growth of wide band gap compound semiconductors; gallium arsenide surface passivation; chemical beam epitaxy; atomic layer epitaxy; state-resolved dynamics of monolayer surface reactions; surface photochemistry; nonresonant vacuum ultraviolet single photon ionization time-of-flight mass spectroscopy; author of numerous publications. *Mailing Add:* Dept Chem Univ Minn Minneapolis MN 55455. *E-Mail:* zhu@chem.umn.edu

**ZIA, PAUL Z,** STRUCTURAL ENGINEERING. *Current Pos:* assoc head dept, NC State Univ, 67-79, prof, 65-88, head dept, 79-88, distinguished univ prof, 88-96, EMER DISTINGUISHED UNIV PROF CIVIL ENG, NC STATE UNIV, 96- *Personal Data:* b Changchow, China, May 13, 26; US citizen; m 51; c 2. *Educ:* Nat Chiao Tung Univ, BSCE, 49; Univ Wash, MSCE, 52; Univ Fla, PhD, 60. *Honors & Awards:* Martin P Korn Award, Prestressed Concrete Inst, 74; T Y Lin Award, Am Soc Civil Engrs, 75, Raymond C Reese Award, 76 & A J Boase Award, 92; Western Elec Fund Award, Am Soc Eng Educ, 76, Lamme Award, 86; Joe W Kelly Award, Am Concrete Inst, 84. *Prof Exp:* Struct designer, Lakeland Eng Assocs, Inc, 51-53, proj engr, 53-54, secy & chief struct engr, 54-55, vpres, 55; from instr to asst prof civil eng, Univ Fla, 55-61; assoc prof, NC State Univ, 61-64; vis assoc prof, Univ Calif, Berkeley, 64-65. *Concurrent Pos:* Vchmn, Concrete & Struct Adv Comt, Strategic Hwy Res Prog, Nat Res Coun, 87-89; mem, Exec Comt, Transp Res Bd, 88-91. *Mem:* Nat Acad Eng; fel Am Soc Civil Engrs; Prestressed Concrete Inst; Am Soc Eng Educ; fel Am Concrete Inst (vpres, 87-89, pres, 89-90); Nat Soc Prof Engrs. *Res:* Mechanical properties of high performance concrete and prestressed concrete structures. *Mailing Add:* Dept Civil Eng NC State Univ Campus Box 7908 Raleigh NC 27695-7908

**ZIA, ROYCE K P,** THEORETICAL PHYSICS. *Current Pos:* from asst prof to assoc prof, 76-83, PROF, DEPT PHYSICS, VA POLYTECH INST & STATE UNIV, 83- *Personal Data:* b Shaoyang, China, Dec 1, 43; US citizen; m 71. *Educ:* Princeton Univ, AB, 64; Mass Inst Technol, PhD(physics), 68. *Prof Exp:* NATO fel physics, Europ Orgn Nuclear Res, Switz, 68-69; res fels, Univ Birmingham, Eng, 69-72, Rutherford High Energy Lab, 72-73 & Univ Southampton, 73-76. *Concurrent Pos:* Danforth assoc; Alexander von Humboldt fel. *Mem:* Sigma Xi. *Res:* Statistical and high energy physics; phase transitions and critical phenomena; applications of renormalization group analysis to interfacial properties and non-equilibrium steady state systems. *Mailing Add:* Dept Physics Va Polytech Inst Blacksburg VA 24061. *Fax:* 540-231-7511

**ZIBOH, VINCENT AZUBIKE,** BIOCHEMISTRY. *Current Pos:* FAC, DEPT DERMAT, SCH MED, UNIV CALIF, DAVIS. *Personal Data:* b Warri, Nigeria, Apr 21, 32; m 62; c 3. *Educ:* Doane Col, AB, 58; St Louis Univ, PhD(biochem), 62. *Prof Exp:* Res fel neurochem, Ill State Psychiat Inst, Chicago, 62-64; lectr chem path, Med Sch, Univ Ibadan, 64-67; res assoc dermat, Sch Med, Univ Miami, 67-69; asst prof dermat & biochem, 69- *Concurrent Pos:* WHO fel clin chem, Bispebjerg Hosp, Copenhagen, Denmark, 66. *Mem:* AAAS; Brit Biochem Soc; Am Chem Soc; Soc Invest Dermat. *Res:* Biochemistry of lipids and steroids; regulation of lipogenesis from glucose in skin; biosynthesis and biochemical basis of prostaglandin action in the skin. *Mailing Add:* Dept Dermat TB 192 Sch Med Univ Calif Davis CA 95616-5224

**ZICKEL, JOHN,** MACHINE DESIGN. *Current Pos:* RETIRED. *Personal Data:* b Munich, Ger, Feb 9, 19; US citizen; m 42; c 2. *Educ:* Lehigh Univ, BS, 48, MS, 49; Brown Univ, PhD(appl math), 53. *Honors & Awards:* Teeter Award, Soc Automotive Engrs, 78. *Prof Exp:* Specialist struct anal nuclear reactors, Knolls Atomic Power Lab, 52-55, Gen Elec Atomic Power Dept, 55-58; mgr, Struct Res Rocket Dept, Aerojet Gen Corp, 58-67; prof mech eng, Calif State Univ, 67-81, chmn, Mech Eng Dept, 81-91. *Concurrent Pos:* Expert witness litigations. *Mem:* Fel Am Soc Mech Engrs; Soc Exp Mech; Sigma Xi; Am Soc Eng Educ; Soc Automotive Engrs. *Res:* Automobile collisions; probabilistic design; product liability. *Mailing Add:* 6063 Ranger Way Carmichael CA 95608

**ZICKER, ELDON LOUIS,** soil science; deceased, see previous edition for last biography

**ZIDEK, JAMES VICTOR,** STATISTICS. *Current Pos:* from asst prof to assoc prof probability & statist, 67-76, head dept, 84-89, PROF STATIST, UNIV BC, 76- *Personal Data:* b Acme, Alta, Sept 26, 39; m 61, Patricia L Donald. *Educ:* Univ Alta, BSc, 61, MSc, 63; Stanford Univ, PhD(math statist), 67. *Prof Exp:* Lectr probability & statist, Univ Alta, 62-63. *Concurrent Pos:* Hon res fel, Univ Col London, 71-82; vis sr res scientist, Commonwealth Sci &

Indust Orgn, Australia, 76-77; mem, Statist Grant Selection Comt, NSERC, 78-81; sr assoc ed, Can J Statist, 80-83; prof statist, Univ Wa, 83-84; vis prof, Imp Col London, 83-84; vis scientist, Coun Sci & Indust Res, 83; mem, Adv Comt Methodology, Statist Can, 85-88; Izaak Walton Killam Mem fel, 89-90, 92-94. *Mem:* Fel Inst Math Statist; Stat Soc Can (pres-elect 86, pres, 87); Royal Statist Soc; fel Am Statist Asn; Int Statist Inst; Int Asn Survey Statist. *Res:* Statistical decision theory; environmetrics. *Mailing Add:* Dept Statist 6356 Agriculture Rd Univ BC Vancouver BC V6T 1Z2 Can. *Fax:* 604-822-6960; *E-Mail:* jim@stat.ubc.ca

**ZIDULKA, ARNOLD,** RESPIRATORY RESEARCH. *Current Pos:* asst prof, 72-77, ASSOC PROF MED, MCGILL UNIV, 77- *Personal Data:* b Montreal, Que, July 9, 41. *Educ:* McGill Univ, BSc, 62 & MD, 66; Sir George Williams Univ, BA, 64; FRCP(C), 71; Am Bd Internal Med, dipl, 72; dipl respiratory dis, 74. *Hon Degrees:* FCCP, Am Col Chest Physicians, 79. *Prof Exp:* Res dir respiratory, Meakins-Christie Labs, 82-93. *Concurrent Pos:* Internist, pulmonary consult, Queen Mary Vet Hosp, 72-77; Montreal Chest Hosp & Royal Victoria Hosp, 72- & Montreal Gen Hosp, 77-; dir, Respiratory Technol, Montreal Gen Hosp, 82- & Montreal Chest Hosp, 83- *Mem:* Can Soc Clin Invest; Am Physiol Soc; Royal Col Physicians & Surgeons Can; Am Thoracic Soc; Am Col Chest Physicians; Can Lung Asn. *Res:* Pleural pressure measurements; lung chest-wall interdependence; cardiopulmonary resuscitation; attaining ventilation by high-frequency chest wall compression; chest physiotherapy by high frequency chest wall compression; atelectasis induced by chest physiotherapy; negative pressure ventilation; pulmonary wedge pressure; mechanics and gas exchange; obstructive sleep apnea. *Mailing Add:* Montreal Gen Hosp 1650 Cedar Ave Rm D7-177 Montreal PQ H3G 1A4 Can

**ZIEBARTH, TIMOTHY DEAN,** ORGANIC CHEMISTRY, PHYSICAL ORGANIC CHEMISTRY. *Current Pos:* CHIEF CHEMIST, HAUSER LABS, 74- *Personal Data:* b Glendive, Mont, June 10, 46; m 66; c 2. *Educ:* Mont State Univ, BS, 69; Ore State Univ, PhD(org chem), 73. *Prof Exp:* Fel org chem, Univ Colo, 72-74. *Mem:* Am Chem Soc. *Res:* Photochemistry of allylic amines; novel methods of polymer analysis; forensic chemistry. *Mailing Add:* 4641 Huey Circle Boulder CO 80303

**ZIEBUR, ALLEN DOUGLAS,** MATHEMATICS. *Current Pos:* RETIRED. *Personal Data:* b Shawano, Wis, May 1, 23; m 49; c 2. *Educ:* Univ Wis, PhD, 50. *Prof Exp:* From instr to assoc prof math, Ohio State Univ, 51-61; assoc prof, State Univ NY, Binghamton, 61-63; prof math, 63-88. *Mem:* Am Math Soc; Math Asn Am; Soc Indust & Appl Math. *Res:* Differential equations. *Mailing Add:* 48 Kendall Ave Binghamton NY 13903-1556

**ZIEG, ROGER GRANT,** PARASITOLOGY, PROTOZOOLOGY. *Current Pos:* RES SCIENTIST, PETO SEED INC, 84- *Personal Data:* b McCooke, Nebr, Aug 16, 39; m 70; c 2. *Educ:* Univ Nebr, BS, 61, MS, 63; Iowa State Univ, PhD(develop biol), 81. *Prof Exp:* In-charge res asst, Tissue Cult Collection, Am Type Cult Collection, 66-68, Protozoan Collection, 68-75; teaching asst biol & phys biochem, Iowa State Univ, 75-80; res fel cell biol, Univ Minn, 80-84. *Res:* Corn and soybean tissue culture; morphogenesis in plant cell cultures; isolation of secondary products from plant tissue cultures; protoplast isolation and fusion. *Mailing Add:* 560 College St Woodland CA 95695

**ZIEGER, HERMAN ERNST,** ORGANIC CHEMISTRY. *Current Pos:* from instr to assoc prof, 61-73, PROF CHEM, BROOKLYN COL, 73- *Personal Data:* b Philadelphia, Pa, May 17, 35; m 60, Nancy Jones; c Elaine Ruth (Hayes), Richard Martin & Susan Marjorie. *Educ:* Muhlenberg Col, BS, 56; Pa State Univ, PhD(org chem), 61. *Prof Exp:* Fulbright scholar, Univ Heidelberg, 60-61. *Concurrent Pos:* Vis assoc, Calif Inst Technol, 67-68; Alexander von Humboldt Found fel, 74-75; mem doctoral fac, City Univ New York. *Mem:* Am Chem Soc; Sigma Xi. *Res:* Organolithium chemistry; aryne chemistry; radical anion processes; kinetics and stereochemistry of carbanion coupling processes; fourier transform nuclear magnetic resonance spectroscopy in organic structure determination. *Mailing Add:* Dept Chem Brooklyn Col Brooklyn NY 11210. *Fax:* 718-951-4607; *E-Mail:* hezbc@cunyvm.cuny.edu

**ZIEGLER, ALFRED M,** PALEONTOLOGY, STRATIGRAPHY. *Current Pos:* asst prof, 66-72, ASSOC PROF PALEONT, UNIV CHICAGO, 72-, PROF STRATIG, 76- *Personal Data:* b Boston, Mass, Apr 23, 38; m 64, 86, Barbara Waggoner; c Allan & Jessica. *Educ:* Bates Col, BSc, 59; Oxford Univ, DPhil, 64. *Prof Exp:* Fel paleont, Calif Inst Technol, 64-66. *Concurrent Pos:* NSF grant, 72-74 & 87. *Mem:* Geol Soc Am; Brit Palaeontol Asn; Sigma Xi. *Res:* Paleontology, paleoecology and stratigraphy of the Silurian age deposits of the British Isles, Norway and eastern North America and world paleogeography. *Mailing Add:* 5492 E Everett Ave Apt 1 Chicago IL 60615-5923

**ZIEGLER, CAROLE L,** EARTHQUAKE DISASTER PREPAREDNESS. *Current Pos:* RES ASSOC, UNIV CALIF, SAN DIEGO, 80-; CONSULT, INST HIGH BLOOD PRESSURE RES, 82- *Personal Data:* b Chicago, Ill, Sept 12, 46; m 70, Michael G; c Barbara & Matthew. *Educ:* Mundelein Col, BS, 68; George Washington Univ, MS, 79. *Prof Exp:* Qual control chemist, Witco Chem Co, 69-70; chemist, Midwest Res Inst, 71-73; res assoc, Univ Tex Med Br, 80. *Concurrent Pos:* Lectr environ geol, Univ San Diego, 87-; mem & consult, Off Disaster Preparedness, San Diego County-Earthquake Awareness Comt, 90- *Mem:* Grad Women in Sci; Am Women Sci. *Res:* Mineralogy of sediments; trace element analysis using atomic absorption in weathered rock sequences; concentrations of PCBs in the environment using gas-chromatograph techniques. *Mailing Add:* Marine & Environ Studies Prog Univ San Diego 5998 Alcala Park San Diego CA 92110-2429

**ZIEGLER, DANIEL,** BIOCHEMISTRY. *Current Pos:* assoc prof, 61-68, MEM STAFF, CLAYTON FOUND BIOCHEM INST, 61-; PROF CHEM, UNIV TEX, AUSTIN, 68- *Personal Data:* b Quinter, Kans, July 6, 27; m 52, Mary Alice Weir; c Daniel L, Paul W, Mary C & James M. *Educ:* St Benedict's Col, Kans, BS, 49; Loyola Univ, Ill, PhD(biochem), 55. *Honors & Awards:* Bernard B Brodie Award, Am Soc Pharmacol, 90; Alexander von Humboldt Award, Ger, 91. *Prof Exp:* Fel enzyme chem, Inst Enzyme Res, Univ Wis, 55-59, asst prof, 59-61. *Concurrent Pos:* Estab investr, Am Heart Asn, 60-65; career develop award, USPHS, 65-75; ed, J Biol Chem, 78- *Mem:* AAAS; Am Chem Soc; Am Soc Biol Chem; Sigma Xi; Am Soc Pharmacol & Exp Therapeut; NY Acad Sci. *Res:* Synthesis of protein hormones; mammalian mixed-function drug oxidases; flavoproteins of the electron transport system. *Mailing Add:* Biochem Inst Dept Chem Univ Tex Austin TX 78712

**ZIEGLER, DEWEY KIPER,** NEUROLOGY. *Current Pos:* assoc prof neurol, Univ Kans Med Ctr, 58-63, chmn dept, 73-85, prof, 63-85, EMER PROF NEUROL, UNIV KANS MED CTR, KANSAS CITY, 86- *Personal Data:* b Omaha, Nebr, May 31, 20; m 54; c 3. *Educ:* Harvard Univ, BA, 41, MD, 45. *Prof Exp:* Assoc neurol, Col Physicians & Surgeons, Columbia Univ, 53-55; asst prof, Med Sch, Univ Minn, 55-56. *Concurrent Pos:* Consult, US Fed Hosp, Springfield, Mo & Vet Admin Hosp, Kansas City, Mo, 64-; clin prof neurol, Med Sch, Univ Mo-Kansas City; dir, Am Bd Psychiat & Neurol, 74-; mem comt stroke coun, Am Heart Asn, 81-83, mem exec comt. *Mem:* AMA; Soc Neurosci; Am Neurol Asn; fel Am Col Physicians; Am Epilepsy Soc; Am Acad Neurol, (pres, 79-81). *Res:* Epidemiology and natural history of cerebrovascular disease; neurophysiological and biochemical basis of migraine. *Mailing Add:* Dept Neurol Univ Kans Med Ctr Kansas City KS 66103

**ZIEGLER, EDWARD N,** CHEMICAL ENGINEERING, ENVIRONMENTAL ENGINEERING. *Current Pos:* asst prof, 65-72, ASSOC PROF CHEM ENG, POLYTECH UNIV, 72- *Personal Data:* b Bronx, NY, Aug 15, 38; m 74, Phyllis M Dean; c Kenneth & Kaitlin. *Educ:* City Col New York, BChE, 60; Northwestern Univ, MS, 62, PhD(chem eng), 64. *Honors & Awards:* William H White Award. *Prof Exp:* Res assoc transport phenomena in fluidized solid systs, Argonne Nat Lab, 62-63; process res engr, Esso Res & Eng Co, 64-65. *Concurrent Pos:* Ed, Encycl Environ Sci & Eng, 2nd Ed, 83, & Advan Series Environ Sci & Eng, 79-80; consult, Brookhaven Nat Lab, 74-80; proj consult, Consol Edison Co, 80-94; consult, Environ Protection Agency, 95- *Mem:* Am Inst Chem Engrs; Sigma Xi; Air & Waste Mgt Asn. *Res:* Applied reaction kinetics; air pollution control; coal conversion; fluidization. *Mailing Add:* Dept Chem Eng Polytech Univ 6 Metrotech Ctr Brooklyn NY 11201. *Fax:* 718-260-3776; *E-Mail:* eziegler@duke.poly.edu

**ZIEGLER, EKHARD E,** PEDIATRICS, NEONATOLOGY. *Current Pos:* from asst prof to assoc prof, 73-81, PROF PEDIAT, UNIV IOWA, 81- *Personal Data:* b Saalfelden, Austria, Apr, 12, 40; div; c Stefan, Gabriele & Lena. *Educ:* Univ Innsbruck, Austria, MD, 64. *Honors & Awards:* Nutrit Award, Am Acad Pediat, 88. *Prof Exp:* Asst, Dept Pediat, Univ Innsbruck, Austria, 71-73. *Concurrent Pos:* Mem, Nutrit Study Sect, NIH, 88-92. *Mem:* Am Acad Pediat; Soc Pediat Res; Am Soc Clin Nutrit; Soc Exp Biol & Med; Nutrit Soc; Am Pediat Soc. *Res:* Pediatric nutrition; mineral metabolism; energy metabolism; growth and body composition; nutrition of the premature infant. *Mailing Add:* Dept Pediat Univ Hosp Iowa City IA 52242. *Fax:* 319-356-8669

**ZIEGLER, FREDERICK DIXON,** biochemistry, physiology, for more information see previous edition

**ZIEGLER, FREDERICK EDWARD,** ORGANIC CHEMISTRY. *Current Pos:* from asst prof to assoc prof, 65-78, PROF CHEM, YALE UNIV, 78- *Personal Data:* b Teaneck, NJ, Mar 29, 38; m 62; c 2. *Educ:* Fairleigh Dickinson Univ, BS, 60; Columbia Univ, MA, 61, PhD(chem), 64. *Prof Exp:* Eugene Higgins fel, Columbia Univ, 60-61; NIH fel, 61-64; NSF fel, Mass Inst Technol, 64-65. *Concurrent Pos:* Res career develop award, NIH, 73-78. *Mem:* Am Chem Soc; Royal Soc Chem. *Res:* Organic synthetic methods and natural products synthesis. *Mailing Add:* Sterling Chem Labs Yale Univ 225 Propect St PO Box 208107 New Haven CT 06520-8107

**ZIEGLER, GEORGE WILLIAM, JR,** physical chemistry; deceased, see previous edition for last biography

**ZIEGLER, HANS K(ONRAD),** ELECTRONICS ENGINEERING. *Current Pos:* RETIRED. *Personal Data:* b Munich, Ger, Mar 1, 11; nat US; m 37, Friederika Groenbold; c Frederica (Meindl), Hans P & Christine (Griffith). *Educ:* Munich Tech Univ, BS, 32, MS, 34, PhD(electronic eng), 36. *Honors & Awards:* Meritorious Civil Serv Awards, 62 & 87; Antarctica Medal, 64; Gold Commendation Medal, Armed Forces Commun & Electronics Asn, 74. *Prof Exp:* Asst prof elec eng, Munich Tech Univ, 34-36; chief res & develop dept, Rosenthal Isolatoren, Inc, 36-47; sci consult, US Army Signal Res & Develop Lab, 47-56, asst dir res, 56-58, dir astroelectronics div, 58-59, chief scientist, 59-66, tech dir, 63-66, dep for sci & chief scientist, US Army Electronics Command, 66-71, dir, US Army Electronics Technol & Devices Lab, 71-76. *Concurrent Pos:* Consult, Kohler Co, Wis, 51-55; consult, 76- *Mem:* Fel Am Astronaut Soc; fel Inst Elec & Electronics Engrs; distinguished mem Armed Forces Commun & Electronics Asn. *Res:* Military electronics; communications; space science and technology; energy sources, conversion and transmission; solar energy; geophysics; meteorology; research management. *Mailing Add:* Neptune Conva-Ctr 101 Walnut St Colts Neck NJ 07753

**ZIEGLER, HARRY KIRK,** MACROPHAGE FUNCTION, IMMUNE RESPONSE GENE CONTROL. *Current Pos:* asst prof, 81-87, ASSOC PROF IMMUNOL, EMORY MED SCH, 87- *Personal Data:* b Greensburg, Pa, Mar 25, 51; m 85. *Educ:* Johns Hopkins Univ, BA, 73, PhD(microbiol), 78. *Prof Exp:* Teaching fel immunol, Med Sch, Harvard Univ, 78-80, instr, 80-81. *Mem:* Am Asn Immunologists. *Res:* Mechanism of lymphocyte and macrophage function related to the regulation of immune responses. *Mailing Add:* Dept Microbiol & Immunol Emory Med Sch 3170 Rollins Bldg 1510 Clifton Atlanta GA 30322-1100. *Fax:* 404-727-3659

**ZIEGLER, JAMES FRANCIS,** NUCLEAR PHYSICS. *Current Pos:* Mem res staff, 67-69, DIR, HIGH ENERGY ACCELERATOR LAB, RES CTR, IBM CORP, 69- *Personal Data:* b Apr 20, 39; US citizen; m 69. *Educ:* Yale Univ, BS, 57, MS, 65, PhD(nuclear physics), 67. *Mem:* Am Phys Soc. *Res:* Solid state analysis using nuclear physics techniques; ion-induced x-rays; nuclear backscattering; nuclear channeling; ion-implantation; optical microcircuits. *Mailing Add:* IBM T J Watson Res Ctr 28-0 PO Box 218 Yorktown Heights NY 10598

**ZIEGLER, JOHN BENJAMIN,** LEPIDOPTERA, SYSTEMATICS. *Current Pos:* RETIRED. *Personal Data:* b Rochester, NY, Jan 2, 17; wid; c Katherine L, Jeffrey B & Conrad L. *Educ:* Univ Rochester, BS, 39; Univ Ill, MS, 40, PhD(org chem), 46. *Prof Exp:* Jr chemist, Merck & Co, Inc, NJ, 40-43; spec res asst, Univ Ill, 43-46; res chemist, J T Baker Chem Co, NJ, 46-48; assoc chemist, Develop Div, Ciba Pharmaceut Co, 48-52; supvr develop res labs, 52-62, mgr process res, 62-70, dir chem develop, Pharmaceut Div, Ciba-Geigy Corp, 70-75, dir process res, Pharmaceut Div, 75, sr staff scientist, 76-80; lab & bus admin, Depts Biol & Chem Physics, Seton Hall Univ, 80-82. *Concurrent Pos:* Exec coun mem-at-large, Lepidopterists Soc, 93-95; vchmn exec coun, Int Sci Collectors Asn, 93-; exec dir, Int Sci Collectors Asn, 96- *Mem:* Am Chem Soc; Sigma Xi; Lepidopterists Soc (treas, 50-53); Lepidoptera Res Found; Int Sci Collectors Asn; Asn Trop Lepidoptera. *Res:* Lepidoptera (especially Lycaenidae, Theclinae, Eumaeini); zoogeography, taxonomy, systematics, life history, host plants. *Mailing Add:* 64 Canoe Brook Pkwy Summit NJ 07901-1434

**ZIEGLER, JOHN HENRY, JR,** MEAT SCIENCE, ANIMAL SCIENCE. *Current Pos:* from instr animal indust to prof meat sci, 54-87, EMER PROF MEAT SCI, PA STATE UNIV, 87- *Personal Data:* b Altoona, Pa, Nov 10, 24; m 49, Dorothy Jane Shockey; c Stephen John, Gregory Ray & Timothy Martin. *Educ:* Pa State Univ, BS, 50, MS, 52, PhD(animal indust), 65. *Honors & Awards:* Signal Serv Award, Am Meat Sci Asn, 88. *Prof Exp:* Soil conservationist, USDA, 49; asst animal husb, Pa State Univ, 50-52; nutritionist, Near's Food Co, NY, 52-54. *Mem:* Am Meat Sci Asn; Am Soc Animal Sci; Inst Food Technologists; Sigma Xi. *Res:* Meat animal carcass evaluation and utilization; basic adipose tissue anatomy and physiology; meat product development. *Mailing Add:* 200 W Whitehall Rd State College PA 16801

**ZIEGLER, MICHAEL GREGORY,** PHARMACOLOGY, MEDICINE. *Current Pos:* assoc prof, 80-93, actg dir, 92-93, DIR, CLIN RES CTR, UNIVV CALIF, SAN DIEGO, 93-, PROF MED, 93- *Personal Data:* b Chicago, Ill, May 12, 46; m; c Barbara & Matthew. *Educ:* Loyola Univ, Chicago, BS, 67; Med Sch, Univ Chicago, MD, 71. *Prof Exp:* Residency med, Med Sch, Univ Kans, 73; pharmacol res assoc, NIMH, 73-75, pharmacologist, 75-76; attend physician med & consult, NIH, 74-76; asst prof med & pharmacol, Univ Tex Med Br Galveston, 76-80. *Mem:* Am Fedn Clin Res; Am Soc Nephrology; Am Soc Hypertension; Am Heart Asn; Am Soc Clin Invest. *Res:* Clinical pharmacology; hypertension; sympathetic nervous system; neurotransmitters; catecholamines. *Mailing Add:* Univ Calif San Diego Med Ctr 200 W Arbor Dr No 8341 San Diego CA 92103. *Fax:* 619-543-7717; *E-Mail:* mziegler@ucsd.edu

**ZIEGLER, MICHAEL ROBERT,** MATHEMATICAL ANALYSIS. *Current Pos:* ASSOC PROF MATH, MARQUETTE UNIV, 71- *Personal Data:* b York, Pa, Oct 31, 42; m 64; c 4. *Educ:* Shippensburg State Col, BS, 64; Univ Del, MS, 67, PhD(math), 70. *Prof Exp:* Instr math, Univ Del, Georgetown Exten, 69-70; fel, Univ Ky, 70-71. *Mem:* Am Math Soc; Math Asn Am. *Res:* Complex analysis; geometric function theory; univalent functions. *Mailing Add:* 509 W Dean Ct Milwaukee WI 53217-2640

**ZIEGLER, MIRIAM MARY,** PROTEIN CHEMISTRY, ENZYMOLOGY. *Current Pos:* LECTR & RES SCIENTIST, DEPT BIOCHEM & BIOPHYS, TEX A&M UNIV, COLLEGE STATION, 81- *Personal Data:* b Gainesville, Fla, Dec 15, 45; m 78, Thomas O Baldwin; c Rebecca J & Ruth E. *Educ:* Bucknell Univ, BS, 67; Harvard Univ, MA, 70, PhD(biochem), 72. *Prof Exp:* Res fel biol, Harvard Univ, 72-73, lectr, 73-75, res fel, 75-76; res fel biochem, Univ Ill, Urbana, 76-78, vis asst prof, 78-81. *Mem:* Biophys Soc; Am Soc Microbiol. *Res:* Enzymatic mechanism, structure, and subunit function of bacterial luciferase; protein folding and assembly. *Mailing Add:* Dept Biochem & Biophys Tex A&M Univ College Station TX 77843-2128. *Fax:* 409-845-4946; *E-Mail:* mziegler@bioch.tamu.edu

**ZIEGLER, PAUL FOUT,** CHEMISTRY. *Current Pos:* RETIRED. *Personal Data:* b Baltimore, Md, Dec 3, 16; m 45; c 2. *Educ:* Otterbein Col, BS, 39; Univ Cincinnati, MS, 47, PhD(chem), 63. *Prof Exp:* Analyst, Am Rolling Mills, Ohio, 39-40, chemist, 40-46; Auburn Univ, 49-82. *Concurrent Pos:* Vis prof, Univ PR, Mayaguez, 82-83. *Mem:* Am Chem Soc; Sigma Xi. *Res:* Analytical and organic chemistry; synthesis and rearrangement. *Mailing Add:* 573 Homewood Dr Auburn AL 36830-5584

**ZIEGLER, PETER,** ORGANIC CHEMISTRY, BIOCHEMISTRY. *Current Pos:* RETIRED. *Personal Data:* b Vienna, Austria, Mar 26, 22; m 48, Frances McConnell. *Educ:* Sir Geo Williams Col, BSc, 44; McGill Univ, PhD(biochem), 51. *Prof Exp:* Chemist, Frank W Horner, Ltd, 44-48; asst, McGill Univ, 48-51; group leader, Can Packers Ltd, 51-65, asst dir res, 66-83. *Mem:* Am Chem Soc; fel Chem Inst Can. *Res:* Fine chemicals; pharmaceuticals. *Mailing Add:* 330 Spadina Rd Apt 702 Toronto ON M5R 2V9 Can

**ZIEGLER, RICHARD JAMES,** VIROLOGY. *Current Pos:* asst prof microbiol, 71-77, assoc prof med microbiol & immunol, 77-89, PROF, MED SCH, UNIV MINN, DULUTH, 89-, ASST DEAN ADMIS, 89-, EXEC DEAN, MED SCH, 91- *Personal Data:* b Norristown, Pa, May 30, 43. *Educ:* Muhlenberg Col, BS, 65; Temple Univ, PhD(microbiol), 70. *Prof Exp:* Instr microbiol, Med Sch, Temple Univ, 69; res assoc genetics, Rockefeller Univ, 70-71. *Concurrent Pos:* Fel, Swed Med Res Coun, 81. *Mem:* AAAS; Am Soc Virol; Am Soc Microbiol; Asn Am Med Cols; Am Soc Neurochem; Soc Neurosci. *Res:* Effects of neurotropic viral multiplication on central nervous system function; acquired immunodeficiency syndrome virus effects on neural function. *Mailing Add:* Dept Microbiol Med & Immunol Univ Minn Sch Med Duluth MN 55812. *Fax:* 218-726-6235

**ZIEGLER, ROBERT C(HARLES),** PHYSICS, ENVIRONMENTAL SCIENCES. *Current Pos:* CONSULT, 81- *Personal Data:* b Buffalo, NY, Dec 11, 27. *Educ:* Univ Buffalo, BA, 50, PhD(physics), 57. *Prof Exp:* Lectr physics, Univ Buffalo, 55-56; proj engr, Nucleonics Dept, Bell Aircraft Corp, 56-57; mem staff, Cornell Aeronaut Lab, Inc, 57-66, head remote sensing sect, 66-71, head environ sci sect, 71-73; tech staff environ sci dept, Calspan Corp, 75-81. *Concurrent Pos:* Consult, 74-75. *Mem:* Am Phys Soc; Nat Soc Prof Engrs. *Res:* Geometrical and physical optics; nuclear physics; aerial remote sensing; environmental research. *Mailing Add:* 26 High Park Blvd Buffalo NY 14226-4209

**ZIEGLER, ROBERT G,** INORGANIC CHEMISTRY. *Current Pos:* from asst prof to prof, Lincoln Mem Univ, 57-92, head dept, 69-74, chmn, Div Natural Sci, 80-86, EMER PROF CHEM, LINCOLN MEM UNIV, 93- *Personal Data:* b The Dalles, Ore, Apr 24, 24; m 53, Martha Brindley; c David C, Ruth J (Russell) & Robbie A. *Educ:* Ore State Univ, BA, 48, MS, 51; Univ Tenn, PhD, 69. *Prof Exp:* Control chemist, Barium Prod Ltd, 48-49; res chemist, Nitrogen Div, Allied Chem Corp, 52-57. *Mem:* Am Chem Soc; Am Sci Affil; Sigma Xi; Am Asn Physics Teachers. *Res:* Analytical and coordination chemistry; fertilizer technology. *Mailing Add:* 144 Kirby St Harrogate TN 37752. *E-Mail:* rgziegler@centuryinter.nct

**ZIEGLER, THERESA FRANCES,** CHEMISTRY, APPLICATION OF RADIO ISOTOPES IN INDUSTRIAL RESEARCH. *Current Pos:* CONSULT, 85- *Personal Data:* b Budapest, Hungary; nat US; wid; c 1. *Educ:* Eotvos Lorand Univ, Budapest, BS, 46, PhD(phys chem), 49. *Prof Exp:* Res engr, State Biochem Res Inst, Hungary, 49-50; chemist, Steel Plant Lab, 53-56; radiochemist, Nat Health & Labor Inst, 56-57; radiochemist, radiation safety officer, Stamford Res Labs, Am Cyanamid Co, 57-85. *Mem:* Am Chem Soc; Am Nuclear Soc; NY Acad Sci. *Res:* Radiosyntheses and radio-tracerwork in the following fields-agricultural and industrial chemicals, herbicides, pesticides and insecticides; pharmaceuticals; catalysts; technology of plastics, fibers and papers; surface coatings; biological membranes; industrial hygiene, toxicity studies; autoradiography, experience with sealed sources; radioactive semi-micro and micro syntheses. *Mailing Add:* 1452 Riverbank Rd Stamford CT 06903-2015

**ZIEGLER, WILLIAM ARTHUR,** INORGANIC CHEMISTRY. *Current Pos:* mgr, Analysis Lab, 80, MGR SUPPORT GROUP, ADVAN MAT DIV, MAT RES CORP, 81- *Personal Data:* b St Louis, Mo, Feb 10, 24; m 51; c 2. *Educ:* Univ Ill, AB, 48, MS, 49, PhD(analytical chem), 52. *Prof Exp:* Teaching asst, Univ Ill, 48-52; chemist, Mallinckrodt Chem Works, 52, supvr, 52-55, asst mgr anal dept, Uranium Div, 55-60, mgr analysis dept, 60-66, tech asst to dir qual control, 66-67; tech specialist, Nuclear Div, Kerr-McGee Corp, 67-69, mgr qual assurance, 69-70; mgr analytical sect, Eastern Res Ctr, Stauffer Chem Co, 71-79. *Mem:* Am Chem Soc. *Res:* Sampling; uranium chemistry. *Mailing Add:* 61 Pocconock Trail New Canaan CT 06840

**ZIEGRA, SUMNER ROOT,** PEDIATRICS. *Current Pos:* RETIRED. *Personal Data:* b Deep River, Conn, Feb 13, 23; m 45; c 2. *Educ:* Univ Vt, BS, 45; Yale Univ, MD, 47; Am Bd Pediat, dipl, 57. *Prof Exp:* Fel pediat, Sch Med, NY Univ, 49-51; asst prof pediat, State Univ NY Downstate Med Ctr, 56-60; assoc prof, Jefferson Med Col, 60-63; from assoc prof to prof, Hahnemann Med Col, 63-70; prof, Col Med, Thomas Jefferson Univ, 70-72; prof pediat, Med Col Pa, 73-81, chmn dept, 75-81. *Concurrent Pos:* Dir div B, Dept Pediat, Philadelphia Gen Hosp, 63-70, coordr, Hahnemann Div, 66-67; dir dept pediat, Lankenau Hosp, 70-72. *Res:* Infectious diseases. *Mailing Add:* 776 Hilview Rd Malvern PA 19355-3428

**ZIELEN, ALBIN JOHN,** SYSTEMS ANALYSIS, PHYSICAL CHEMISTRY. *Current Pos:* RETIRED. *Personal Data:* b Chicago, Ill, Dec 22, 25; m 92, Laura Harris. *Educ:* Miami Univ, BA, 50; Univ Calif, PhD(chem), 53. *Prof Exp:* Asst chem, Univ Calif, 51-52; chemist, Radiation Lab, Univ Calif, 52-53; assoc chemist, Argonne Nat Lab, 53-87. *Mem:* Am Chem Soc. *Res:* Computer programming; neptunium solution chemistry; electrochemistry; reaction kinetics; complex ions. *Mailing Add:* 14673 Yosemite Dr Sun City West AZ 85375. *Fax:* 602-546-0073

**ZIELEZNY, MARIA ANNA,** BIOSTATISTICS. *Current Pos:* clin asst prof, 71-73, asst prof, 74-80, ASSOC PROF BIOSTATIST, DEPT SOCIAL & PREV MED, SCH MED, STATE UNIV NY, BUFFALO, 80- *Personal Data:* b Kaczkowizna, Poland, Sept 20, 39; US citizen; m 69. *Educ:* Univ Warsaw, MS, 62; Univ Calif, Los Angeles, PhD(biostatist), 71. *Prof Exp:* Res asst statist, Math Inst, Polish Acad Sci, Warsaw, 62-65. *Mem:* Am Statist Asn; Am Pub Health Asn; Biomet Soc. *Res:* Statistical applications in particular to medicine, development of statistical methods in evaluation, discriminant analysis, measures of association, techniques for qualitative data. *Mailing Add:* Dept Sociol & Prev Med State Univ NY Health Ctr 3435 Main St Buffalo NY 14214-3001

**ZIELEZNY, ZBIGNIEW HENRYK,** MATHEMATICAL ANALYSIS. *Current Pos:* assoc prof, 70-71, PROF MATH, STATE UNIV NY, BUFFALO, 71- *Personal Data:* b Knurow, Poland, Jan 11, 30; m 69, Maria Glinska. *Educ:* Wroclaw Univ, Masters, 54, PhD(math), 59; Polish Acad Sci, docent, 64. *Prof Exp:* Adj math, Wroclaw Tech Univ, 58-61; adj, Polish Acad Sci, 61-64, docent, 64-69; vis prof, Univ Kiel, 69-70. *Concurrent Pos:* Vis prof, Univ Kiel, WGer, 79 & 82. *Mem:* Am Math Soc. *Res:* Analysis, functional analysis; differential equations; existence and regularity of solutions of convolution equations in various spaces of distributions. *Mailing Add:* Dept Math Rm 106 Diefendorf Hall State Univ NY Buffalo NY 14214-3093

**ZIELINSKA PFABE, MALGORZATA,** HEAVY ION PHYSICS, REACTION MECHANISM. *Current Pos:* from asst prof to prof, 82-89, SOPHIA SMITH PROF PHYSICS, SMITH COL, 91- *Personal Data:* b Bielsuo, Poland, Nov 7, 38; US citizen; m 62, Jerzy W; c Renata & Hubert. *Educ:* Univ Warsaw, Poland, MSc, 61; Inst Nuclear Res, Poland, PhD(theoret physics), 69. *Honors & Awards:* Maria Sklodowska-Curie Medal, Pilsudski Inst Am. *Prof Exp:* Res assoc, Inst Nuclear Res, Poland, 61-69, asst prof, 69-71 & 73-78; res fel, Tech Univ, Munich, Ger, 71-72; vis asst prof, Rensselaer Polytech Inst, 78-82; res fel heavy ions accelerator, Ganil, 87, Australian Nat Univ, 90. *Concurrent Pos:* Adj prof physics, Rensselaer Polytech Inst, 83-91; chair, New Eng Sect, Am Phys Soc, 91-92, sect rep, Nat Coun, 93-94. *Mem:* Fel Am Phys Soc; Sigma Xi; Am Asn Physics Teachers. *Res:* Microscopic and macroscopic descriptions of the dynamics of collisions between heavy ions; studies of mechanisms of the energy dissipation in fission, fusion and deep inelastic collisions; emission of eight particles during fission and heavy ion reactions. *Mailing Add:* Dept Physics Smith Col Northampton MA 01063. *Fax:* 413-585-3786; *E-Mail:* mpfabe@smith.smith.edu

**ZIELINSKI, ADAM,** ELECTRICAL ENGINEERING, OCEAN ENGINEERING. *Current Pos:* ASSOC PROF, UNIV VICTORIA, 85- *Personal Data:* b Jaroslaw, Poland, Oct 2, 43; Can citizen; m 75; c 2. *Educ:* Wroclaw Tech Univ, BEE & MEE, 67, PhD(elec eng), 72. *Prof Exp:* Res assoc, Wroclaw Tech Univ, 67-68, asst prof, 68-72; res fel, Tokyo Inst Technol, 72-74 & Univ NB, 74-75; asst prof, 75-80, assoc prof elec eng, Mem Univ Nfld, 80- *Concurrent Pos:* Investr, Nat Res Coun Can operating grants, 76-77 & 78-92, Natural Sci & Eng Res Coun Can strategic grant ocean eng, 78-81 & PRAI grant, 81-82. *Mem:* Sr mem Inst Elec & Electronics Engrs. *Res:* Applied underwater acoustics; acoustic communication; specialized sonar systems; electronic instrumentation and signal processing. *Mailing Add:* Dept Elec Eng Univ Victoria PO Box 3055 Victoria BC V8W 3P6 Can

**ZIELINSKI, PIOTR ANDRZEJ,** SURFACE SCIENCE, CATALYSIS. *Current Pos:* SR SURFACE SCIENTIST, COMINCO RES, 93- *Personal Data:* b Lodz, Poland, Jan 10, 54; Can citizen; m 88, Joanna Papierska; c Michael & Arthur. *Educ:* Tech Univ Lodz, MSc, 77, PhD(chem eng), 82. *Honors & Awards:* Award, Polish Min Educ, 83 & 85. *Prof Exp:* Asst prof catalysis, Tech Univ Lodz, 82-88; postdoctoral fel, Univ Alta, 88-92; res assoc, Univ Laval, 92-93. *Concurrent Pos:* Postdoctoral fel, Univ Louis Pasteur, 84-85. *Mem:* Am Chem Soc; Can Inst Mining. *Res:* Investigations of solid surfaces; active surface sites; heterogenous catalysis; new catalytic materials; kinetics and mechanism of catalytic reactions; adsorption and absorption; carbon deposit; temperature programmed techniques in surface studies; surface phenomena in flotation. *Mailing Add:* 2416 11th Ave Castzegar BC V1N 3A9 Can. *E-Mail:* piotr.zielinski@cominco.com

**ZIELINSKI, THERESA JULIA,** THEORETICAL CHEMISTRY. *Current Pos:* PROF CHEM, NIAGARA UNIV, NY, 80- *Personal Data:* b Brooklyn, NY. *Educ:* Fordham Univ, BS, 63, MS, 68, PhD(chem), 73. *Prof Exp:* Asst prof chem, Col Mt St Vincent, 72-79. *Mem:* Am Chem Soc. *Res:* Theoretical chemical study of purines and pyrimidines. *Mailing Add:* 24 Tiffany Pl East Amherst NY 14051-1839

**ZIELKE, H RONALD,** NEUROCHEMISTRY, CELL BIOLOGY. *Current Pos:* asst prof, 73-81, res assoc prof, 81-89, ASSOC PROF PEDIAT, SCH MED, UNIV MD, 89- *Personal Data:* b Pscinno, Poland, June 7, 42; US citizen; m 67; c 2. *Educ:* Univ Ill, BS, 64; Mich State Univ, PhD(biochem), 68. *Prof Exp:* Res assoc, AEC Plant Res Lab, Mich State Univ, 68-71; res fel, Genetics Unit, Mass Gen Hosp, 71-73. *Concurrent Pos:* Monsanto fel, 69; dir, Am Type Cult Collection, 81-87. *Mem:* Am Soc Neurochem; Am Soc Biochem & Molecular Biol. *Res:* Metabolism and enzymology of brain and cultured mammalian cells; adenosine receptors. *Mailing Add:* Dept Pediat Res Sch Med Univ Md Baltimore MD 21201-1509

**ZIEMAN, JOSEPH CROWE, JR,** MARINE ECOLOGY, BIOLOGICAL OCEANOGRAPHY & SEAGRASS ECOSYSTEMS. *Current Pos:* from asst prof to assoc prof, 71-89, PROF ENVIRON SCI, UNIV VA, 89- *Personal Data:* b Mobile, Ala, June 9, 43; m 67, Rita Tinnell. *Educ:* Tulane Univ, BS,

65; Univ Miami, MS, 68, PhD(marine sci), 70. *Honors & Awards:* George Barley Award, Everglades Conserv, 96. *Prof Exp:* Res asst thermal pollution, Inst Marine Sci, Univ Miami, 68-70; fel syst ecol, Inst Ecol, Univ Ga, 70-71. *Concurrent Pos:* Mem, Tech Adv Panel, Fla Keys Nat Marine Sanctuary, 93- *Mem:* Ecol Soc Am; Am Soc Limnol & Oceanog; Sigma Xi; AAAS; Estuarine Res Fedn; Asn Caribbean Marine Labs. *Res:* Comparative studies of tropical and temperate interface zones, seagrasses, coral reefs, mangroves and salt marshes; production, colonization, succession and recovery from disturbances; simulation modeling of growth and succession; marine biogeochemistry. *Mailing Add:* Dept Environ Sci Clark Hall Univ Va Charlottesville VA 22903. *E-Mail:* jcz@virginia.edu

**ZIEMBA, W T,** MATHEMATICS. *Current Pos:* FAC MEM, DEPT MANAGERIAL SCI, UNIV BC. *Mailing Add:* Dept Managerial Sci Univ BC 2053 Main Mall Vancouver BC V6T 1Z2 Can

**ZIEMER, PAUL L,** HEALTH PHYSICS. *Current Pos:* ASST SECY ENERGY ENVIRON SAFETY & HEALTH, US DEPT ENERGY, 90- *Personal Data:* b Toledo, Ohio, June 28, 35; m 58; c 4. *Educ:* Wheaton Col, BS, 57; Vanderbilt Univ, MS, 59; Purdue Univ, PhD(bionucleonics), 62; Am Bd Health Physics, dipl, 65. *Honors & Awards:* Lederle Pharm Fac Award, 64; Elda E Anderson Award, Health Physics Soc, 71. *Prof Exp:* Physicist, US Naval Res Lab, Wash, 57; health physicist, Oak Ridge Nat Lab, 59; radiol control officer, Purdue Univ, 59-82, assoc head bionucleonics, 71-81; from asst prof to prof health physics, Purdue Univ, West Lafayette, 62-90, head, Sch Health Sci, 83-90. *Concurrent Pos:* Consult, Harrison Steel Castings Co, Ind, 62-66, satellite div, Union Carbide Corp, 66-67, Calif Nuclear, Inc, 66-68, Breed Radium Inst, 68-70, Detroit Diesel Allison Div, Gen Motors Corp, 69 & 77- Mobil Field Res Labs, 70- & Midwest Radiation Protection, Inc, 71-88; mem panel examr, Am Bd Health Physics, 69-71; mem, Sci Comt Oper Health Physics, Nat Coun Radiation Protection, 46-90, Int Standards Orgn, Working Group 6, Sci Comt Radiation Protection, 76-81; ed, Health Physics J, 79-84; vchmn comt N-13 radiation protection standards, Am Nat Standards, 81-82, chmn, 82-89; mem, US Dept Energy, Adv Comt Nuclear Sci, Energy & Health Physics Fels, 81-83; mem, Nat Prog Rev Comt Low-Level Radioactive Waste Mgt, US Dept Energy, 80-87, chmn, 80-83; mem, Bd Dir, N Prk Col, 81-86, chmn, 84-86; mem, Tech Adv Comt, Ill Dept Nuclear Safety, 85-90; mem, Spec Task Force on Bioassay, Oak Ridge Assoc Univs & Nat Cancer Inst, 86-87. *Mem:* Health Physics Soc (pres, 75); Int Radiation Protection Asn; AAAS; Am Acad Health Physics (pres, 87). *Res:* Radon emanation rates; radiation dosimetry. *Mailing Add:* 920 Southernview Dr N West Lafayette IN 47905-3798

**ZIEMER, ROBERT RUHL,** WATERSHED MANAGEMENT, WILDLAND HYDROLOGY. *Current Pos:* res forester, 60-77, RES HYDROLOGIST, PAC SOUTHWEST RES STA, USDA FOREST SERV, 77- *Personal Data:* b Oklahoma City, Okla, Oct 25, 37. *Educ:* Univ Calif, Berkeley, BS, 59, MS, 63; Colo State Univ, PhD(earth resources), 78. *Prof Exp:* Teaching asst forestry, Univ Calif, Berkeley, 59-60. *Concurrent Pos:* Intel officer, Nev Air Nat Guard, 60-67; adj prof, Humboldt State Univ, 72-; prof forestry, State Calif, 75-; chmn, Tech Comt Evaporation & Transpiration, Am Geophys Union, 76-81 & Watershed Mgt, Int Union Forestry Res Orgn, 88-; res fel, East-West Ctr, 85-; dir, Redwood Sci Lab, 86- *Mem:* Am Geophys Union; Int Union Geod & Geophys; Int Union Forestry Res Orgn. *Res:* Effects of forest management on hillslope processes, fishery resources, and stream environments; risk of landslides and erosion; timing and routing of sediment in relation to cumulative effects and anadromous and resident fish habitat. *Mailing Add:* 1700 Bayview Dr Arcata CA 95521. *Fax:* 707-825-2901

**ZIEMER, RODGER EDMUND,** ELECTRICAL ENGINEERING, COMMUNICATIONS THEORY. *Current Pos:* chmn dept, 84-93, PROF, DEPT ELEC ENG, UNIV COLO, COLORADO SPRINGS, 84- *Personal Data:* b Sargeant, Minn, Aug 22, 37; m 62, Sandra L Person; c Mark E, Amy L, Norma I & Sandra L. *Educ:* Univ Minn, BS, 60, MS, 62, PhD(elec eng), 65. *Hon Degrees:* Dr, Tech Univ, Iasi, Romania, 96. *Prof Exp:* From asst prof to prof elec eng, Univ Mo, Rolla, 68-88, grad coordr dept, 78-80. *Concurrent Pos:* Consult, Electronics & Space Div, Emerson Elec Co, St Louis, 74-85, govt electronics div, Motorola Inc, Scottsdale, Ariz, 80-84; on leave, Motorola Inc, Scottsdale, Ariz, 80-81 & 91. *Mem:* Fel Inst Elec & Electronics Engrs; Am Soc Eng Educ; Sigma Xi; Armed Forces Electronics Asn. *Res:* Statistical communication theory environments; personal communications systems; spread spectrum communication techniques; digital signal processing. *Mailing Add:* 8315 Pilot Ct Colorado Springs CO 80920. *E-Mail:* ziemer@signal.uccs.edu

**ZIEMER, WILLIAM P,** MATHEMATICS. *Current Pos:* Assoc prof, 61-77, PROF MATH, IND UNIV, BLOOMINGTON, 77- *Personal Data:* b Manitowoc, Wis, Mar 26, 34; m 57; c 3. *Educ:* Univ Wis, BS, 56, MS, 57; Brown Univ, PhD(math), 61. *Mem:* Am Math Soc; Math Asn Am. *Res:* Geometric analysis; area theory; surface theory; differential geometry. *Mailing Add:* Dept Math Ind Univ Bloomington IN 47405-4301

**ZIEMNIAK, STEPHEN ERIC,** TRANSITION METAL OXIDE SOLUBILITY BEHAVIOR, NUCLEAR REACTOR COOLANT TECHNOLOGY. *Current Pos:* LEAD ENGR, KNOLLS ATOMIC POWER LAB, LOCKHEED MARTIN CO, 70- *Personal Data:* b Rochester, NY, Mar 6, 42; m 70, Virginia M Strang; c Brian & Jason. *Educ:* Rensselaer Polytech Inst, BChE, 64, PhD(chem eng), 68. *Prof Exp:* Fel, Los Alamos Sci Lab, 68-69. *Concurrent Pos:* Adj fac, Rensselaer Polytech Inst, 77-79. *Res:* Establish principles of corrosion product transport in pressurized water reactor coolants, including thermodynamics of metal oxide solubility behavior; hydrothermal crystallization mechanisms; fluid mechanics and numerical turbulence models. *Mailing Add:* 3 Crystal Lane Latham NY 12110

**ZIEN, TSE-FOU,** INFORMATION SCIENCE & SYSTEMS. *Current Pos:* res aeronaut engr, 70-80, BR HEAD, NAVAL SURFACE WARFARE CTR, 80- *Personal Data:* b Shanghai, China, Sept 13, 37; US citizen; m 62, Suzy Shen; c Livia & Conroy. *Educ:* Nat Taiwan Univ, BSc, 58; Brown Univ, MSc, 63; Calif Inst Technol, PhD(aeronaut), 67. *Prof Exp:* Engr, Third Shipyard Chinese Navy, 58-60; res fel aeronaut, Calif Inst Technol, 67; res assoc fluid sci, Case Western Res Univ, 67-70. *Concurrent Pos:* Prof lectr, George Washington Univ, 75-85; mem, Fluid Dynamics Tech Comt, Am Inst Aeronaut & Astronaut, 79-82, Thermophys Tech Comt, 82-85 & Appl Aerodyn Tech Comt, 90-93; chmn, Heat Transfer Panel, Naval Aeroballistics Comn, 81-84; vis prof, Nat Cheng-Kung Univ, 87 & 88; adj prof, Cath Univ Am, 88- *Mem:* Assoc fel Am Inst Aeronaut & Astronaut; Am Phys Soc; Soc Indust & Appl Math. *Res:* Hypersonic flows; holographic interferometry; viscous flow and heat transfer; aerodynamic heating and ablation modelling; bio-fluid dynamics; measurement of viscosity of gases. *Mailing Add:* Naval Surface Warfare Ctr Code B40 Dahlgren VA 22448

**ZIENIUS, RAYMOND HENRY,** ANALYTICAL CHEMISTRY. *Current Pos:* asst prof, 67-72, ASSOC PROF CHEM, SIR GEORGE WILLIAMS CAMPUS, CONCORDIA UNIV, 72-, DIR, CHEM & BIOCHEM COOP PROGS, 86- *Personal Data:* b Montreal, Que, Nov 8, 34; m 70, Heather Florence; c Charles & Stephen. *Educ:* McGill Univ, BSc, 56, PhD, 59. *Prof Exp:* Asst chemist, Dom Tar & Chem Co, Ltd, 55; res chemist, Cent Res Lab, Can Industs Ltd, 59-67. *Mem:* Fel Chem Inst Can. *Res:* Gas chromatography. *Mailing Add:* Dept Chem Sir George Williams Campus Concordia Univ Montreal PQ H3G 1M8 Can

**ZIENTY, FERDINAND B,** CHEMISTRY. *Current Pos:* CONSULT, 83- *Personal Data:* b Chicago, Ill, Mar 21, 15; wid; c Kathleen (deceased), Jane & Donald. *Educ:* Univ Ill, BS, 35; Univ Mich, MS, 36, PhD(pharmaceut chem), 38. *Prof Exp:* Res chemist, Monsanto Co, 38-40, res group leader, 40-47, from asst dir res to dir res, 47-60, adv org chem res, Org Chem Div, 60-64, mgr res & develop, food, feed & fine chem, 64-79, dir res & develop, Health Care Develop, 79-83. *Concurrent Pos:* Vpres res, George Lueders & Co, Subsid Monsanto Co, 68-70. *Mem:* Fel AAAS; Am Chem Soc; Am Pharmaceut Asn; Am Inst Chem Eng; fel NY Acad Sci; Inst Food Technol. *Res:* Antispasmodics; sulfa drugs; ethylenediamine derivatives; organic heterocycles, including imidazole and thiophene chemistry; organic acids and anhydrides; nucleophilic substitutions; nucleophilicity of thiols; catalytic oxidations; flavors. *Mailing Add:* 850 Rampart Dr St Louis MO 63122-1644

**ZIERDT, CHARLES HENRY,** MEDICAL MICROBIOLOGY, EPIDEMIOLOGY. *Current Pos:* RETIRED. *Personal Data:* b Pittsburgh, Pa, Apr 24, 22; m 42, Margaret M Wise; c Charles Jr, Carolyn, Douglas & Richard. *Educ:* Pa State Univ, BS, 43; Univ Mich, MS, 45; George Washington Univ, PhD(microbiol), 67. *Prof Exp:* Res asst pharmaceut, Parke Davis Pharmaceut, 45-48; bacteriologist clin microbiol, Henry Ford Hosp, 48-53; staff microbiologist, Health & Human Serv, NIH, 53-94. *Concurrent Pos:* Instr gen microbiol, Found Adv Educ Sci, NIH; scientist sponsor, Univ Md. *Mem:* Am Soc Microbiol; Sigma Xi; fel Am Acad Microbiol. *Res:* Taxonomy of anaerobic Corynebacterium; Pseudomonas aeruginosa pathogenicity and typing; Staphylococcus aureus typing and hospital epidemiology; Blastocystis hominis classification ultrastructure, antigenicity, culture and pathogenicity; cultivation of Mycobacterium leprae; microsporidium diagnosis in human infections; author of 120 manuscripts, contributor and patentee. *Mailing Add:* 4100 Norbeck Rd Rockville MD 20853-1869

**ZIERING, LANCE K,** CHEMICAL ENGINEERING. *Current Pos:* PRES, SPECIALTY USA, 89- *Personal Data:* b New York, NY, May 17, 39; m 61; c 2. *Educ:* City Col New York, BScChE, 62; Columbia Univ, MScChE, 63; Univ Conn, MBA, 69. *Prof Exp:* Chem engr, Am Cyanamid Co, 63-65, res chem engr, 65-67, group leader supvr, 67-69; asst prod mgr, ICI Am Inc, 69-71, tech sales rep, 71-72, prod mgr films, 72-74, asst to vpres plastics, 74-76, tech serv mgr, 76-79, mkt mgr, 79-80, dir mkt, 80-81, vpres & gen mgr rubicon, 81-89. *Res:* Process and product development of fuel cell and battery electrodes and components; cost estimating. *Mailing Add:* 17 Tullamore Dr West Chester PA 19382

**ZIERLER, KENNETH,** MEDICINE, PHYSIOLOGY. *Current Pos:* PROF PHYSIOL & MED, SCH MED, JOHNS HOPKINS UNIV & PHYSICIAN, JOHNS HOPKINS HOSP, 73- *Personal Data:* b Baltimore, Md, Sept 5, 17; m 41, Margery Shapiro; c Peggy (Rosenthal), Linda (Jucovy), Sally, Amy & Michael. *Educ:* Johns Hopkins Univ, AB, 36; Univ Md, MD, 41. *Prof Exp:* Fel med, Sch Med, Johns Hopkins Univ, 46-48, from instr to prof med, 48-72, prof physiol, 69-72; dir, Inst Muscle Dis, Inc, 72-73. *Concurrent Pos:* Asst physician, Outpatient Dept, Johns Hopkins Hosp, 46-53, physician, 53-55, physician-in-charge, Phys Ther Dept, 50-57, chemist, 57-68, physician, 53-72, assoc prof environ med, Sch Hyg & Pub Health, Johns Hopkins Univ, 54-59; mem, Ed Bd, J Clin Invest, 59-64; adj prof, Rockefeller Univ, 72-73 & Med Sch, Cornell Univ, 72-73; assoc ed, Med, 63-72, Circulation Res, 68-74 & ed, 66-68; chmn, Adv Comt Physiol, Off Naval Res, 64-72. *Mem:* Am Physiol Soc; Am Soc Clin Invest; Asn Am Physicians; Endocrine Soc. *Res:* Muscle metabolism and function; hormonal action; biomembranes; circulation; tracer kinetics; insulin, water and electrolytes. *Mailing Add:* Blalock Bldg Rm 904 Johns Hopkins Univ Sch Med 600 N Wolfe St Baltimore MD 21287-4904

**ZIERLER, NEAL,** CRYPTOLOGY. *Current Pos:* RETIRED. *Personal Data:* b Baltimore, Md, Sept 17, 26; c R Eugene, Joan M & Ann M. *Educ:* Johns Hopkins Univ, AB, 46; Harvard Univ, AM, 49, PhD(math), 59. *Prof Exp:* Mathematician-physicist, Ballistic Res Labs, Aberdeen Proving Ground, Md,

51-52; mem staff, Instrumentation Lab, Mass Inst Technol, 52-54 & Lincoln Lab, 54-60; res group supvr, Jet Propulsion Lab, Calif Inst Technol, 60-61; sr scientist, Arcon Corp, Mass, 61-62; mem staff, Lincoln Lab, Mass Inst Technol, 62; sub-dept head, Mitre Corp, Mass, 62-65; mem staff, Ctr Commun Res, Inst Defense Anal, 65-96. *Mem:* Am Math Soc; Math Asn Am; fel Inst Elec & Electronics Engrs. *Res:* Algebra; mathematical foundations of quantum mechanics; coding and decoding of information; computer applications. *Mailing Add:* 126 Leabrook Lane Princeton NJ 08540

**ZIESKE, JAMES DAVID,** EPITHELIAL PROTEIN SYNTHESIS. *Current Pos:* ASST SCIENTIST, DEPT CORNEA RES, EYE RES INST, 84- *Educ:* Univ Mich, PhD(biochem), 81. *Res:* Epithelial protein synthesis during wound repair. *Mailing Add:* Dept Cornea Res Schepens Eye Res Inst Retina Found 20 Staniford St Boston MA 02114-2500

**ZIETLOW, JAMES PHILIP,** PHYSICS. *Current Pos:* assoc dean, 68-78, prof physics, 65-86, EMER PROF PHYSICS, COL ARTS & SCI, WESTERN MICH UNIV, 86- *Personal Data:* b Chicago, Ill, Dec 15, 21; m 52; c 3. *Educ:* De Paul Univ, BS, 48; Ill Inst Technol, MS, 49, PhD(physics), 55. *Prof Exp:* Sr res physicist, Res & Develop Labs, Pure Oil Co, 51-56; prof physics & math, NMex Highlands Univ, 56-65, head, Dept Physics & Math, 56-63 & 64-65, grad dean, 63-64. *Mem:* Am Phys Soc; Coblentz Soc. *Res:* Infrared, Raman, ultraviolet and mass spectroscopies. *Mailing Add:* 2515 Carlyle Dr Kalamazoo MI 49008

**ZIETZ, JOSEPH R, JR,** ORGANOMETALLIC CHEMISTRY. *Current Pos:* ASSOC DIR RES & DEVELOP, ETHYL CORP, 52- *Personal Data:* b Menominee, Mich, May 12, 25; m 49; c 4. *Educ:* Spring Hill Col, BS, 47; Marquette Univ, MS, 49; Tulane Univ, PhD(org chem), 52. *Prof Exp:* Chemist, Warren Petrol Co, 49-50. *Mem:* Am Chem Soc. *Res:* Organic synthesis; synthesis and chemistry of main group metal-organic compounds. *Mailing Add:* 7836 Rue Cachet Ct Baton Rouge LA 70808

**ZIEVE, GARY W,** CELL FRACTIONATION, RIBONUCLEOPROTEIN ASSEMBLY. *Current Pos:* asst prof, 82-91, ASSOC PROF, DEPT PATH, STATE UNIV NY, STONY BROOK, 91- *Personal Data:* b Milwaukee, Wis, Apr 23, 51; m; c Alex & Sarah. *Educ:* Calif Inst Technol, BS, 73; Mass Inst Technol, PhD(cell biol), 77. *Prof Exp:* Res assoc, Mass Inst Technol, 79-82. *Mem:* Am Soc Cell Biol; Sigma Xi. *Res:* Synthesis, assembly and intracellular transport of the small nuclear ribonucleoprotein particles in eukaryotic cells. *Mailing Add:* 59 June Ave Northport NY 11768. *Fax:* 516-444-3424; *E-Mail:* gzieve@path.som.sunysb.edu

**ZIEVE, LESLIE,** MEDICINE. *Current Pos:* EMER DISTINGUISHED PHYSICIAN, VET ADMIN HOSP, MINNEAPOLIS, 85- *Personal Data:* b Minneapolis, Minn, Aug 6, 15; m 41; c 1. *Educ:* Univ Minn, MA, 39, MD, 43, PhD(med), 52; Am Bd Internal Med, dipl, 51. *Honors & Awards:* Middleton Award, 62. *Prof Exp:* Resident med, Med Sch, Univ Minn, Minneapolis, 46-49, from instr to prof, 49-62; dir spec cancer lab, Vet Admin Hosp, Minneapolis, 61-72, staff physician, 49-77, assoc chief staff for res, 61-77; dir res, dept med, Hennepin County Med Ctr, 77-85. *Concurrent Pos:* Chief nuclear med, Vet Admin Hosp, Minneapolis, 50-72; mem exec comt, Grad Sch, Univ Minn, Minneapolis, 65-68; ed, J Lab & Clin Med, 67-70. *Mem:* Am Col Physicians. *Res:* Diseases of the liver and pancreas. *Mailing Add:* PO Box 287 Spring Park MN 55384-0287

**ZIFF, MORRIS,** INTERNAL MEDICINE, RHEUMATOLOGY. *Current Pos:* prof, 58-87, EMER ASHBEL SMITH PROF INTERNAL MED, SOUTHWEST MED CTR, UNIV TEX HEALTH SCI CTR, DALLAS, 88-, EMER MORRIS ZIFF PROF RHEUMATOLOGY, 88- *Personal Data:* b New York, NY, Nov 19, 13; m 40, 78, Jacqueline Miller; c Edward & David. *Educ:* NY Univ, BS, 34, PhD(chem), 37, MD, 48. *Honors & Awards:* Carol Nachman Prize, 74; Bunim Medal, Am Col Rheumat, 82, First Gold Medal, 88. *Prof Exp:* Asst chem, NY Univ, 34-39; asst biochem, Col Physicians & Surgeons, Columbia Univ, 39-41, vis scholar, 41-44; instr & lectr, NY Univ, 44, adj asst prof, 48-50, from asst prof med to assoc prof, 54-58; prof internal med, Southwest Med Ctr, Health Sci Ctr, Univ Tex, Dallas, 58-87. *Concurrent Pos:* Instr, City Col NY, 41-44; from intern to asst resident, Bellevue Hosp, 48-50, chmn, Clin Res Sect Study Group Rheumatic Dis, 52-58; consult, USPHS, 55-63; founding dir, H C Simmons Arthritis Res Ctr, 83-84. *Mem:* Am Chem Soc; Harvey Soc; Am Soc Clin Invest; Am Col Rheumatology; Am Col Physicians; Asn Am Physicians. *Res:* Chemistry of connective tissue; rheumatic diseases; immunology; chronic inflamation in rheumatoid arthritis, particulary the role of the endothelial cell in the facilitation of emigration of lymphocytes and macrophages into perivascular space. *Mailing Add:* Dept Internal Med Univ Tex Southwestern Med Ctr 5323 Harry Hines Blvd Dallas TX 75235-9030. *Fax:* 214-648-9100; *E-Mail:* ziffo1@swmed.edu

**ZIFFER, HERMAN,** ORGANIC CHEMISTRY. *Current Pos:* RES CHEMIST, NIH, 59- *Personal Data:* b New York, NY, Feb 22, 30; m 55; c 3. *Educ:* City Col New York, BS, 51; Ind Univ, MA, 53; Univ Ore, PhD(chem), 55. *Prof Exp:* Res chemist, Nat Aniline Div, Allied Chem Corp, 55-59. *Concurrent Pos:* Sabbatical, Stanford Univ, 69-70, Univ Groningen, Neth, 85. *Mem:* Am Chem Soc; Royal Soc Chem. *Res:* Photochemistry; asymmetric synthesis and the use of optical rotatory dispersion and other physical measurements for structure determination; biotransformations by enzymes and micro-organisms. *Mailing Add:* Bldg 5-B1-31 NIH Bethesda MD 20892-0510

**ZIGLER, EDWARD,** PSYCHOLOGY. *Current Pos:* from asst prof to prof psychol, 59-76, chmn, Dept Psychol, 73-74, HEAD, PSYCHOL SECT, CHILD STUDY CTR, YALE UNIV, 67-, STERLING PROF PSYCHOL, 76-, DIR, BUSH CTR CHILD DEVELOP & SOCIAL POLICY, 77- *Personal Data:* b Mar 1, 30. *Educ:* Univ Mo, BS, 54; Univ Tex, PhD, 58. *Hon Degrees:* MA, Yale Univ, 67; Dr, Boston Col, 85, Univ Mo, 93, City Univ NY, 95; LHD, Bank St Col Educ, 89, Univ New Haven, 91, St Joseph Col, West Hartford, 91; LLD, Gonzaga Univ, 95. *Honors & Awards:* Dale Richmond Mem Award, Am Acad Pediat, 76, C Anderson Aldrich Award, 85; G Stanley Hall Award, Am Psychol Asn, 79, Nicholas Hobbs Award, 85, Edgar A Doll Award, 86, Award for Distinguished Prof Contrib to Knowledge, 86, Award for Distinguished Contrib to Community Psychol & Community Ment Health, 89; Nat Achievement Award, Asn Advan Psychol, 85; Blanche F Ittleson Mem Lectr Award, Am Orthopsychiat Asn, 89; Distinguished Achievement Award Res, Int Asn Sci Study Ment Deficiency, 92; Kurt Lewin Award, Soc Psychol Study Social Issues, 95. *Prof Exp:* Staff psychologist, Child Guidance Clin, Tex Univ, Austin, 56-57; intern psychol, Worcester State Univ, Mass, 57-59. *Concurrent Pos:* Asst prof, Univ Mo, Columbia, 58-59, dir, Child Diag Ctr, 58-59; dir, Child Develop Prog, Dept Psychol, Yale Univ, 61-76, Inst Social & Policy Studies, 75-, Sch Med, Psychol & Child Study Ctr, 82-; dir, Off Child Develop & chief, Children's Bur, HEW, 70-72; consult, Dept Health & Human Serv, Carnegie Corp, Ford Found, Found Child Develop & others; mem numerous comts, adv bds & panels; consult ed, J Exp Psychol & J Exp Res Personality. *Mem:* Inst Med-Nat Acad Sci; hon mem Am Acad Child & Adolescent Psychiat. *Res:* Cognitive and social-emotional development in children, particularly those who are mentally retarded or from lower-income families; effects of early childhood intervention and supplemental child care. *Mailing Add:* Dept Psychol Yale Univ PO Box 208205 New Haven CT 06520. *Fax:* 203-432-7147

**ZIGMAN, SEYMOUR,** BIOCHEMISTRY. *Current Pos:* from instr to asst prof, 62-70, PROF OPHTHAL & BIOCHEM, SCH MED & DENT, UNIV ROCHESTER, 75- *Personal Data:* b Far Rockaway, NY, Nov 21, 32; m 54; c 1. *Educ:* Cornell Univ, BA, 54; Rutgers Univ, MS, 56, PhD(biochem), 59. *Hon Degrees:* DSc, Univ Repub, Montevideo, Uruguay. *Prof Exp:* Fel biochem of the eye, Mass Eye & Ear Infirmary, 59-61, res assoc, 61-62. *Concurrent Pos:* Corp & investr, Marine Biol Lab, Woods Hole, Mass; res assoc, Mote Marine Lab, Sarasota, Fla; biol consult, Eastman Kodak Co. *Mem:* Am Chem Geront; Am Soc Biol Chemists; Am Soc Photobiol; Asn Res Vision & Ophthal. *Res:* Photobiology of the lens and retina; role of cataract and retinal degeneration of near-ultraviolet radiation; lens pigments to enhance vision. *Mailing Add:* Dept Ophthal Res Univ Rochester Sch Med 601 Elmwood Ave PO Box 314 Rochester NY 14642-0001

**ZIGMOND, MICHAEL JONATHAN,** NEUROCHEMISTRY, NEUROPLASTICITY. *Current Pos:* from asst prof to prof biol & psychol, 78-86, PROF BEHAV NEUROSCI & PSYCHIAT, UNIV PITTSBURGH, 86-, DIR TRAINING CTR NEUROSCI, 86- *Personal Data:* b Waterbury, Conn, Sept 1, 41; m 66; c 2. *Educ:* Carnegie-Mellon Univ, BS, 63; Univ Chicago, PhD(biopsychol), 68. *Honors & Awards:* Res Scientist Award, NIMH, 86; Merit Award, NIMH, 93. *Prof Exp:* Teaching asst psychol, Carnegie-Mellon Univ, 62-63; res assoc, Mass Inst Technol, 67-69, instr, 69-70. *Concurrent Pos:* NIMH & Nat Inst Neurol & Commun Dis & Stroke grantee, Univ Pittsburgh, 70-; mem, Neuropsychol Res Rev Comt, NIMH, 74-78, res career develop awards, 75-; assoc dir basic res, Clin Res Ctr; assoc ed, J Neurosci, 80- & consult ed, Physiol Psychol, 81- *Mem:* AAAS; Am Soc Neurochem; Soc Neurosci; Am Soc Pharmacol & Exp Therapeut; Sigma Xi; NY Acad Sci. *Res:* Interactions between brain neurochemistry, behavior and environment; control of biogenic amine metabolism; neuroplasticity; biological basis of recovery of function following brain damage; animal model of Parkinsonism, biogenic amines and stress. *Mailing Add:* Dept Neurosci Univ Pittsburgh 570 Crawford Hall Pittsburgh PA 15260-0001. *Fax:* 412-624-7327; *E-Mail:* zigmond@bns.pitt.edu

**ZIGMOND, RICHARD ERIC,** NEUROPHARMACOLOGY, NEUROBIOLOGY. *Current Pos:* PROF, CASE WESTERN RES UNIV, 89- *Personal Data:* b Willimantic, Conn, May 9, 44. *Educ:* Harvard Col, BA, 66; Rockefeller Univ, PhD(neurobiol), 71. *Honors & Awards:* Javits Neuro Invest Award; Res Scientist Award, NIMH. *Prof Exp:* Fel physiol psychol, Rockefeller Univ, 71-72; fel neurochem, Univ Cambridge, 72-75; from asst prof to assoc prof, Harvard Med Sch, 75-89. *Concurrent Pos:* Tutor biochem sci, Harvard Col, 75-76; lectr neurobiol course, Marine Biol Lab, 81-84; lectr neurobiol & behav course, Cold Spring Harbor Lab, 79-; lectr, rev & update neurosurgeons, Woods Hole, Mass, 84, 86, 88; chmn, Gordon Conf Neuronal Plasticity, 91. *Mem:* Soc Neurosci; Brit Pharmacol Soc; Am Soc Pharmacol & Exp Therapeut; AAAS; Endocrine Soc. *Res:* Regulation of the levels of enzymes involved in the synthesis of neurotransmitters; recovery of function after neural damage; functional anatomy of the sympathetic nervous system; neurochemistry. *Mailing Add:* Dept Neurosci Case Western Res Univ 10900 Euclid Ave Cleveland OH 44106-4975. *Fax:* 216-368-4560

**ZIGMOND, SALLY H,** CHEMOTAXIS, CELL LOCOMOTION. *Current Pos:* From asst prof to assoc prof, 76-87, PROF BIOL, UNIV PA, 87- *Personal Data:* b Kalamazoo, Mich, Feb 5, 44. *Educ:* Wellesley Col, BA, 66; Rockefeller Univ, PhD(biol), 72. *Concurrent Pos:* Mem, cell biol study sect, NIH, 82-84; asst ed, J Cell Biol, 86- *Mem:* Am Soc Cell Biol. *Res:* The motile activities of polymorphonuclear leukocytes including chemotaxis, locomotion and pinocytosis; correlation of cell behavior with biochemical events. *Mailing Add:* Dept Biol Univ Pa Philadelphia PA 19104-6018

**ZIGRANG, DENIS JOSEPH,** SYSTEM DESIGN ENGINEERING, DESIGN ENGINEERING. *Current Pos:* RETIRED. *Personal Data:* b Livermore, Iowa, May 11, 26; m 48; c 5. *Educ:* Iowa State Col, BS, 49 & 50; Univ Tulsa, MS, 70, PhD(chem eng), 76. *Prof Exp:* Supvr qual, Minn Mining & Mfg Co, 50-52; nuclear res engr, NAm Aviation, 52-55, sr res engr aerospace, 55-58; engr specialist, Martin Co, 58-62; chief mech engr, Bendix Corp, 63-66; engr specialist systs, Rockwell Int, 66-78; assoc prof mech eng, Univ Tulsa, 78-90. *Concurrent Pos:* Vis lectr, Univ Colo, 59-61. *Mem:* AAAS; Am Soc Eng Educ; Am Soc Mech Engrs; Am Inst Aeronaut & Astronaut. *Res:* Diffusion of moisture or solvents with composite materials; application of probability in engineering design; corrosion of oil-gas field materials; computational methods, particularly replacement of nomographs with explicit solution approximations. *Mailing Add:* 1502 S Boulder Ave Apt 16A Tulsa OK 74119

**ZIHLMAN, ADRIENNE LOUELLA,** PHYSICAL ANTHROPOLOGY. *Current Pos:* From asst prof to assoc prof, 67-79, chmn dept, 75-77, PROF ANTHROP, OAKES COL, UNIV CALIF, SANTA CRUZ, 79- *Personal Data:* b Chicago, Ill, Dec 29, 40. *Educ:* Univ Colo, Boulder, BA, 62; Univ Calif, Berkeley, PhD(anthrop), 67. *Concurrent Pos:* Wenner-Gren Found Anthrop Res grants, Transvaal Mus, Pretoria, SAfrica, Univ Witwatersrand, Anthrop Inst, Zurich & Med Sch, Makerere Univ, Uganda, 69, Nat Mus Kenya, Nairobi & Transvaal Mus, 74, Transvaal Mus, Univ Witwatersrand, 79. *Mem:* AAAS; Am Asn Phys Anthrop; Am Anthrop Asn; Am Soc Mammal; Int Primatol Soc. *Res:* Locomotor behavior and anatomy of primates; reconstruction of behavior and anatomy of fossil hominoids; ape evolution and human origins; women in evolution. *Mailing Add:* Soc Sci 1 Univ Calif Santa Cruz CA 95064

**ZIKAKIS, JOHN PHILIP,** BIOLOGICAL SCIENCES, BIOCHEMISTRY. *Current Pos:* res assoc biochem genetics, Univ Del, 68-70, from asst prof to assoc prof, 70-81, prof agr biochem, Col Agr, 81-89, prof marine biol & biochem, Col Marine Sci, 81-89, prof food sci, Col Human Resources, 87-89, EMER PROF, UNIV DEL, 89- *Personal Data:* b Piraeus, Greece, Sept 16, 33; US citizen; m 58, Kiki Matrozos; c Salome. *Educ:* Univ Del, BA, 65, MS, 67, PhD(biol, biochem), 70. *Honors & Awards:* Cert & Gold Medal, Univ Patra, Greece, 73; Distinguished Serv Award, Am Chem Soc, 91. *Prof Exp:* Res asst nutrit, Stine Lab, E I du Pont de Nemours & Co, Inc, 59-61. *Concurrent Pos:* Sci consult, Fedn Am Socs Exp Biol, 75; trustee, Riverside Hosp, 77-84; Nat Oceanic & Atmospheric Admin grants, 77-84; vis prof & Fulbright scholar, Univ Panama, 84-85, sci adv, 85-87; adv to pres, Univ Panama, 85-89; acad & indust consult; vpres & dir res & technol, United Chitotechnol, Newark, Del, 89-93. *Mem:* Am Chem Soc; Am Dairy Sci Asn; Am Inst Biol Sci; AAAS; NY Acad Sci; Inst Food Technologists; Sigma Xi; Am Chitosci Soc. *Res:* Various studies with xanthine oxidase as it relates to atherosclerosis; immunological and nutritional studies with xanthine oxidase; biochemical genetic studies on milk and blood protein; polymorphisms; animal product and by-product biochemistry; mammary metabolism and enzymology; marine by-products in nutrition, pharmaceuticals and biotechnology; chitin and chitosan specialists; patentee in field; contributor of over 125 articles in professional journals and author of two books; conducted pioneering research in enzymology which led to the discovery, isolation and purification of human colostral xanthine oxidase; nutritional studies using chitin and whey resulted in the alleviation of lactose intolerance; for the first time, isolated and purified chitinase from soy-bean seeds. *Mailing Add:* 3430 Galt Ocean Dr Suite 1402 Ft Lauderdale FL 33308

**ZILBER, JOSEPH ABRAHAM,** MATHEMATICS. *Current Pos:* from asst prof to assoc prof, 62-92, EMER ASSOC PROF MATH, OHIO STATE UNIV, 92- *Personal Data:* b Boston, Mass, July 27, 23; m 54, Judith Levine; c Jay, Jonathan & Jeremy. *Educ:* Harvard Univ, AB, 43, MA, 46, PhD, 63. *Prof Exp:* Instr math, Columbia Univ, 48-50 & Johns Hopkins Univ, 50-55; asst prof, Univ Ill, 55-56; lectr, Northwestern Univ, 56-57; res assoc, Brown Univ, 57-62, Yale Univ, 62. *Mem:* AAAS; Am Math Soc; Math Asn Am. *Res:* Algebraic topology; category theory. *Mailing Add:* Dept Math Ohio State Univ Columbus OH 43210-1174. *E-Mail:* zilber@math.ohio-state.edu

**ZILCH, KARL T,** ORGANIC CHEMISTRY. *Personal Data:* b St Louis, Mo, Nov 14, 21; m 50; c 7. *Educ:* Univ Mo, AB, 43, MA, 47, PhD(chem), 49. *Prof Exp:* Asst chem, Univ Mo, 47-49; res chemist, Northern Utilization Res Br, USDA, 49-55; res chemist & group leader, Henkle Corp-Emory Group, 55-59, res sect head, 59-61, dir new technol research, 61-89. *Concurrent Pos:* Instr chem, Bradley Univ, 50-51. *Mem:* Am Chem Soc; Am Oil Chem Soc; Swiss Chem Soc. *Res:* Synthesis and processing carboxylic acids; reactions and end use application of carboxylic acids. *Mailing Add:* 4195 Lake Knoll Dr Mason OH 45040

**ZILCZER, JANET ANN,** CRYSTALLOGRAPHY, EDUCATION. *Current Pos:* instrnl asst, Northern Va Community Col, 84-87, mgt analyst, 88-93, sr mgt analyst, 93-95, LECTR, NORTHERN VA COMMUNITY COL, 83-, MGT LEAD ANALYST, 95- *Personal Data:* b New York, NY, Apr 30, 55. *Educ:* George Washington Univ, BA, 76, MPhil, 79, PhD(geol), 81. *Prof Exp:* Teaching fel geol, George Washington Univ, 76-79; Smithsonian fel, Nat Mus Natural Hist, 79-81; lectr, George Mason Univ, 81-82. *Concurrent Pos:* Vis researcher, Nat Mus Natural Hist, Smithsonian Inst, 78; vis asst prof, George Washington Univ, 82-83; asst prof lectr, 83-84; abstractor, Am Mineralogist, 83-85 & Mineral Abstr, 83- *Mem:* Mineral Soc Am; Geol Soc Am; Int Asn Math Geol. *Res:* Feldspar mineralogy; optical mineralogy; crystal physics and chemistry. *Mailing Add:* 2351 N Quantico St Arlington VA 22205

**ZILE, MAIJA HELENE,** BIOCHEMISTRY. *Current Pos:* asst prof, 81-85, ASSOC PROF, MICH STATE UNIV, 85- *Personal Data:* b Latvia, Aug 3, 29; nat US; div; c 3. *Educ:* Univ Md, BS, 54; Univ Wis, MS, 56, PhD(biochem), 59. *Prof Exp:* Res fel biochem, Univ Wis, 59 & Harvard Univ, 59-61; res assoc biochem, Univ Wis-Madison, 61-76, assoc scientist, 76-81. *Mem:* Sigma Xi; Am Inst Nutrit; Soc Exp Biol & Med; NY Acad Sci; Am Asn Cancer Res. *Res:* Metabolism and function of vitamin A; function of vitamin A in cell proliferation and differentiation; anticarcinogenic properties of vitamin A; nutrition and cancer. *Mailing Add:* Dept Food Sci & Human Nutrit Mich State Univ 236 Food Sci Bldg East Lansing MI 48824-0001. *Fax:* 517-353-8963

**ZILINSKAS, BARBARA ANN,** PLANT MOLECULAR BIOLOGY. *Current Pos:* asst prof, 75-80, assoc prof, 80-86, PROF BIOCHEM, COOK COL, RUTGERS UNIV, 86- *Personal Data:* b Waltham, Mass, Sept 21, 47. *Educ:* Framingham State Col, BA, 69; Univ Ill, Urbana, MS, 70, PhD(biol), 75. *Prof Exp:* Lab technician biol, Univ Mass Environ Exp Sta, 68-69; NASA fel, Univ Ill, Urbana, 69-72, res & teaching asst, 73-74; fel, Smithsonian Radiation Biol Lab, 75. *Concurrent Pos:* Vis scholar, Harvard Univ, 82-83. *Mem:* Am Soc Plant Physiologists; Plant Molecular Biol Soc; Am Soc Photobiol; AAAS; Sigma Xi. *Res:* Plant response to environmental stress; biochemistry and biophysics of the photosynthetic light reactions; plant molecular biology. *Mailing Add:* Dept Plant Sci Rutgers Univ New Brunswick NJ 08903. *Fax:* 732-932-8899

**ZILKE, SAMUEL,** AGRONOMY, ECOLOGY. *Current Pos:* AGR CONSULT, 72- *Personal Data:* b Chatfield, Man, Nov 4, 14. *Educ:* Univ Sask, BA, 48, BSEd, 49, BSAgr, 53, MS, 54; SDak State Univ, PhD(agron), 67. *Prof Exp:* Res officer & res asst plant ecol, Univ Sask, 50-55; res asst bot, SDak State Univ, 57-59 & agron & weed sci, 59-61; instr agr, Exten & Col Div, Alta Agr Col, 66-70; agr consult, 70-71; technician, Can Wildlife Serv, 71-72. *Concurrent Pos:* Lectr, Col Agr, Univ Sask, 52-55, consult fertilizers & herbicides, 66-71. *Mem:* Agr Inst Can; Ecol Soc Am; Can Soc Soil Sci; Am Inst Biol Sci; Agron Soc Am. *Res:* Ecological life histories of plants and their physiology under field conditions; effect of variable soil moisture and temperature on seeds; response of field and grass crops to fertilizer and herbicides; effect of aeration of soil on nitrification in late May and June; improvement of habitat for browsers such as Virginia deer, porcupine and rabbits; investigation into the effects of minimum tillage on yields of field crops. *Mailing Add:* PO Box 147 Springside SK S0A 3V0 Can

**ZILKEY, BRYAN FREDERICK,** PLANT SCIENCE, BIOCHEMISTRY. *Current Pos:* RES SCIENTIST TOBACCO, RES BR, CAN DEPT AGR, 69- *Personal Data:* b Manitou, Man, Apr 14, 41; m 64; c 3. *Educ:* Univ Man, BSA, 62, MSc, 63; Purdue Univ, PhD(plant physiol), 69. *Mem:* Can Soc Plant Physiol; Am Soc Plant Physiol; Can Fedn Biol Sci; Agr Inst Can; Weed Sci Soc Am. *Res:* Lipid and carbohydrate metabolism and biosynthesis in germinating and developing castor bean endosperm; biochemistry and physiology of tobacco growth; tobacco smoke chemistry and biological properties; weed control in tobacco, ginseng, sweet potatoes; winter cereals; ginseng. *Mailing Add:* 154 Colborne St N Simcoe ON N3Y 3V3 Can

**ZILL, LEONARD PETER,** biochemistry; deceased, see previous edition for last biography

**ZILLER, STEPHEN A, JR,** TOXICOLOGY, REGULATORY AFFAIRS. *Current Pos:* VPRES SCI & TECH AFFAIRS, GROCERY MFG AM, 94- *Personal Data:* b Kansas City, Mo, Nov 2, 38; m 61; c 4. *Educ:* Rockhurst Col, BA, 61; St Louis Univ, PhD(biochem), 67. *Prof Exp:* Res biochemist, Res Div, Procter & Gamble Co, 67-69, res nutritionist, 69-70, nutritionist, Food Prod Develop Div, 71-74, sect head food safety & nutrit, Food Prod Develop Div, 74-77, assoc dir, Indust Food Prod Develop, 77-81, assoc dir prof & regulatory serv, Beverage Prod Develop Div, 81-86, Food Prod Develop, 86-89, assoc dir prof & regulatory serv, Food & Beverage Prod, Res & Develop, 89-94. *Concurrent Pos:* Chmn, Tech Comt, Inst Shortening & Edible Oils, 89-, Sci Res Comt, Nat Food Processors Asn, 90- *Mem:* Am Chem Soc; Sigma Xi. *Res:* Metabolism of sterols and bile acids; drug metabolism; protein nutrition; food, beverage safety and nutrition. *Mailing Add:* 1808 Old Meadow Rd Apt 513 McLean VA 22102

**ZILVERSMIT, DONALD BERTHOLD,** NUTRITIONAL BIOCHEMISTRY. *Current Pos:* prof, 66-90, EMER PROF, DIV NUTRIT SCI & SECT BIOCHEM, MOLECULAR & CELL BIOL, DIV BIOL SCI, CORNELL UNIV, 90- *Personal Data:* b Hengelo, Holland, July 11, 19; nat US; m 45, Kitty Fonteyn; c 3. *Educ:* Univ Calif, BS, 40, PhD(physiol), 48. *Hon Degrees:* Dr, Univ Utrecht, Neth, 80. *Honors & Awards:* Borden Award, Am Inst Nutrit, 76; George Lyman Duff Mem lectr, 78; Bristol Myers Squibb/Mead Johnson Award, 90. *Prof Exp:* Clin demonstr, Dent Sch, Univ Calif, 46-48; from instr to prof physiol, Med Units, Univ Tenn, 48-66. *Concurrent Pos:* Consult, NIH, 55-; ed, J Lipid Res, 59-61; Am Heart Asn career investr, 59-; guest prof, State Univ Leiden, 61-62; vis fel exp path, Australian Nat Univ, 66; ed, Biochimica & Biophysica Acta, 69-80; NIH, Nat Heart, Lung & Blood Inst task forces arteriosclerosis, 70-71, 78-79, 80-82; vis prof biochem, Mass Inst Technol, 72-73; ed, Proceedings Soc Exp Biol & Med, 75- & adv bd, 77-; mem coun arteriosclerosis, Am Heart Asn. *Mem:* Nat Acad Sci; Am Physiol Soc; Soc Exp Biol & Med; Am Soc Biol Chemists; Am Inst Nutrit; Philos Soc Asn; AAAS. *Res:* Lipid metabolism; lipoproteins; membrane biochemistry; endocytosis; arteriosclerosis; use of isotopes in metabolic work. *Mailing Add:* Div Nutrit Sci Cornell Univ Ithaca NY 14853. *Fax:* 607-255-1033; *E-Mail:* d213@cornell.edu

**ZILZ, MELVIN LEONARD,** CELL BIOLOGY, BIOCHEMISTRY. *Current Pos:* asst prof biol, Concordia Sr Col, 65-72, chmn dept natural sci, 71-72, assoc prof biol & registr admis, 72-77, asst pres & assoc acad dean, 76-78, assoc prof ministry, 76-79, dean admin, 78-83, dir planning & budget admin, 83-85, PROF PASTORAL MINISTRY, CONCORDIA THEOL SEM, 79- *Personal Data:* b Detroit, Mich, Apr 15, 32; m 57; c 3. *Educ:* Concordia Teachers Col, Ill, BS, 53; Univ Mich, Ann Arbor, MS & MA, 64; Wayne State Univ, PhD(biol), 70; Concordia Theol Sem, Ft Wayne, colloquy dipl, 78. *Prof Exp:* Tutor pvt sch, Ill, 53-57; instr high sch, Mich, 57-65, chmn dept sci, 58-65. *Concurrent Pos:* Instr, Mich Lutheran Col, 62-63; ordained clergyman, 78- *Res:* Cellular research, especially cell division and the anaphase movement of chromosomes; biomedical ethics. *Mailing Add:* 1704 Frenchman's Xing Ft Wayne IN 46825

**ZIMAR, FRANK,** CHEMISTRY, CERAMICS. *Current Pos:* res chemist, Corning Glass Works, 45-51, res assoc, 51-56, res supvr, 56-70, res assoc, 70-75, SR RES SCIENTIST, CORNING GLASS WORKS, 75- *Personal Data:* b Berlin, Wis, Apr 5, 18; m 43, 57, Delores R Sonner; c 7. *Educ:* Univ Wis, BS, 41; Univ Rochester, PhD(phys chem), 45. *Prof Exp:* Asst, Off Sci Res & Develop, Univ Rochester, 41-45. *Mem:* Am Ceramic Soc; Brit Soc Glass Technol; Sigma Xi. *Res:* Kinetics of heterogeneous reactions; surface chemistry of glass; thermal setting solder glass; glass redraw; application of films to glass; glass fiber technology; fiber optic waveguides; catalyst support ceramics. *Mailing Add:* 106 Lake St Hammondsport NY 14840

**ZIMBELMAN, JAMES RAY,** PLANETARY GEOLOGY, REMOTE SENSING. *Current Pos:* GEOLOGIST, CEPS/NASM, SMITHSONIAN INST, 88- *Personal Data:* b Jamestown, NDak, Sept 10, 54; m 76, Cheryl A Hughes. *Educ:* Northwest Nazarene Col, BA, 76; Univ Calif, Los Angeles, MS, 78; Ariz State Univ, PhD(geol), 84. *Prof Exp:* Fel, Lunar & Planetary Inst, 84-86, staff scientist, 86-88. *Concurrent Pos:* Lectr, Univ Houston, Clear Lake, 86-88; prin investr, Grants Planetary Geol & Geophys, NASA, 86-; dir, Regional Planetary Image Facil, 89- *Mem:* Am Geophys Union; Geol Soc Am. *Res:* Geologic mapping of Mars and Venus, examining opperant geologic processes; sand transport and deposition in the Mojave Desert of California, as a possible indicator of recent climatic change. *Mailing Add:* CEPS/NASM MRC 315 Smithsonian Inst Washington DC 20560. *Fax:* 202-786-2566; *E-Mail:* jrz@ceps.nasm.edu

**ZIMBELMAN, ROBERT GEORGE,** REPRODUCTIVE ENDOCRINOLOGY, ANIMAL HEALTH. *Current Pos:* EXEC VPRES, AM SOC ANIMAL SCI, 87- *Personal Data:* b Keenesburg, Colo, Sept 4, 30; m 52, 87; c 4. *Educ:* Colo State Univ, BS, 52; Univ Wis, MS, 57, PhD(endocrinol), 60. *Prof Exp:* Instr genetics, Univ Wis, 57-60; res assoc, Upjohn Co, 60-64, head reproduction & physiol res, Agr Prod Div, 65-71, res mgr reproduction & physiol res, 71-76, exp agr sci, 77-83, dir reproduction & growth physiol res, 83-86, sci affairs, 86-87. *Mem:* Am Soc Animal Sci; Am Inst Biol Sci; Soc Study Reproduction; fel AAAS; Am Dairy Sci Asn. *Res:* Improving fertility and preciseness of breeding time in cattle with synchronization of estrus, improved mammary development and milk production by dairy cattle, endocrinology of growth of farm animals, new approaches to inhibition of estrus in pets, molecular biology in animals. *Mailing Add:* 15608 Yellowhorn Ct Rockville MD 20853. *Fax:* 301-571-1837

**ZIMBRICK, JOHN DAVID,** RADIATION BIOPHYSICS, RADIATION CHEMISTRY. *Current Pos:* MGR, BIOL & CHEM DEPT, BATTELLE PAC NORTHWEST LAB, 89-; PROF RADIOL SCI & MEM GRAD FAC, WASH STATE UNIV, 90- *Personal Data:* b Dickinson, NDak, Sept 18, 38; m 62; c 2. *Educ:* Carleton Col, BA, 60; Univ Kans, MS, 62, PhD(radiation biophys), 67. *Prof Exp:* Asst physicist, IIT Res Inst, 62-64; chief, Environ Studies Sect, Health Serv Lab, US AEC, Idaho, 67-68; Nat Inst Gen Med Sci fel, Lab Nuclear Med & Radiation Biol, Univ Calif, Los Angeles, 68, US AEC fel, 68-69; from asst prof to assoc prof, Univ Kans, 69-77, prof radiation biophys, 77-84, chmn, Radiation Biophys, 82-84; exec secy, Radiation Study Sect, NIH, 84-89. *Concurrent Pos:* Consult mem, Radiation Study Sect, NIH, 78-82, chmn, 80-82; prog mgr radiobiol, US Dept Energy, 81-82; assoc ed, Radiation Res J, 84-88; NSF fac sci fel, Los Alamos Nat Lab, 76-77. *Mem:* Health Physics Soc; Radiation Res Soc (pres, 90-91); Biophys Soc; Sigma Xi; AAAS. *Res:* In vivo studies on DNA base damage induced by gamma radiation; electron spin resonance spectroscopy of radicals produced in biomolecules by radiation; application of electron spin resonance to cancer detection and treatment. *Mailing Add:* BD Radiation Effects Res 342 NAS 2101 Constitution Ave Washington DC 20418. *Fax:* 509-376-9449

**ZIMDAHL, ROBERT LAWRENCE,** AGRONOMY, WEED SCIENCE. *Current Pos:* from asst prof to assoc prof, 68-77, PROF WEED SCI, COLO STATE UNIV, 77- *Personal Data:* b Buffalo, NY, Feb 28, 35; m 56, 93, Pamela J McLean; c 4. *Educ:* Cornell Univ, BS, 56, MS, 66; Ore State Univ, PhD(agron), 68. *Prof Exp:* Res assoc agron, Cornell Univ, 63-64. *Concurrent Pos:* Vis prof, Univ Bologna, Italy, 76; vis scientist, Int Rice Res Inst, Philippines, 84-85; tech adv, USAID, Morocco, 89-90. *Mem:* Fel Weed Sci Soc Am; Am Soc Agron; AAAS. *Res:* Herbicide degradation in soil; environmental pollution by pesticides; ethics in weed science/agriculture; weed management in crops. *Mailing Add:* Weed Res Lab Colo State Univ Ft Collins CO 80523. *Fax:* 970-491-3862; *E-Mail:* rzimdahl@cerss.agsci.colostate.edu

**ZIMERING, SHIMSHON,** mathematical analysis; deceased, see previous edition for last biography

**ZIMET, CARL NORMAN,** psychology, for more information see previous edition

**ZIMM, BRUNO HASBROUCK,** BIOPHYSICAL CHEMISTRY, POLYMER CHEMISTRY. *Current Pos:* PROF CHEM, UNIV CALIF, SAN DIEGO, 60- *Personal Data:* b Kingston, NY, Oct 31, 20; m 44; c 2. *Educ:* Columbia Univ, AB, 41, MS, 43, PhD(chem), 44. *Honors & Awards:* Leo Hendrik Baekland Award, Am Chem Soc, 57; Bingham Medal, Soc Rheol, 60; High Polymer Physics Prize, Am Phys Soc, 63; Chem Sci Award, Nat Acad Sci, 81; Kirkwood Medal, Yale Univ, 82. *Prof Exp:* Asst chem, Columbia Univ, 41-44; res assoc & instr, Polytech Inst Brooklyn, 44-46; from instr to assoc prof, Univ Calif, 46-52; res assoc, Gen Elec Co, 51-60. *Concurrent Pos:* Vis lectr, Harvard Univ, 50-51; vis prof, Yale Univ, 60. *Mem:* Nat Acad Sci; Am Chem Soc; Am Phys Soc; Soc Rheol; Am Soc Biol Chemists; Biophys Soc; Am Acad Arts & Sci. *Res:* Theory of macromolecular solutions; properties and structure of high polymers and biological macromolecules. *Mailing Add:* 2522 Horizon Way La Jolla CA 92037-1122

**ZIMM, CARL B,** MAGNETIC MATERIALS, CRYOGENICS. *Current Pos:* STAFF SCIENTIST, ASTRON CORP, 85- *Personal Data:* b Schenectady, NY, Mar 31, 54. *Educ:* Univ Calif, Santa Cruz, BA, 75; Cornell Univ, PhD (physics), 82. *Prof Exp:* Postdoctoral, Los Alamos Nat Lab, 83. *Mem:* Am Phys Soc; Cryog Soc Am. *Res:* Thermal and magnetic properties of materials used in development of magnetic refrigeration; design of magnetic refrigeration devices. *Mailing Add:* Astronaut Tech Ctr 5800 Cottage Grove Rd Madison WI 53716-1387. *E-Mail:* zimm%astroatc.uucp@cs.wisc.edu

**ZIMM, GEORGIANNA GREVATT,** DROSOPHILA. *Current Pos:* bibliogr genetics, 68-75, res assoc biol, 75-85, specialist genetics, 85-92, RESEARCHER, UNIV CALIF, SAN DIEGO, 92- *Personal Data:* b Jersey City, NJ, Nov 5, 17; m 44; Bruno H; c Louis H & Carl B. *Educ:* Columbia Univ, BA, 40; Univ Pa, MA, 42; Univ Calif, Berkeley, PhD(zool), 50. *Prof Exp:* Teaching asst biol, Univ Del, 40-42; teaching asst zool, Barnard Col, Columbia Univ, 43-45, lectr, 45-46; teaching asst, Univ Calif, Berkeley, 46-50. *Mem:* AAAS; Genetics Soc Am. *Res:* Writing and research on the genome of Drosophila melanogaster, especially mutants and cytological and molecular rearrangements; research on Y-chromosome male-sterility mutants in Drosophila. *Mailing Add:* Dept Biol 0322 Univ Calif San Diego La Jolla CA 92093. *Fax:* 619-534-0053; *E-Mail:* gzimm@ucsd.edu

**ZIMMACK, HAROLD LINCOLN,** INSECT PATHOLOGY, COMPARATIVE ANIMAL PHYSIOLOGY. *Current Pos:* RETIRED. *Personal Data:* b Chicago, Ill, Feb 12, 25; m 56, Barbara J Keen; c Cinda L, John M & Lissa C. *Educ:* Eastern Ill Univ, BS, 51; Iowa State Univ, MS, 53, PhD(entom), 56. *Prof Exp:* Asst, Iowa State Univ, 51-56; prof biol, Eastern Ky Univ, 56-63; prof zool, Ball State Univ, 63-90. *Concurrent Pos:* Sigma Xi & Ind Acad Sci res grants-in-aid, 67-68. *Mem:* Am Soc Zoologists; Entom Soc Am; AAAS; Soc Invert Path. *Res:* Rapid screening of potential insect pathogen through physiological studies. *Mailing Add:* 5101 N County Rd 450 W Muncie IN 47304

**ZIMMER, ARTHUR JAMES,** PHARMACEUTICAL CHEMISTRY. *Current Pos:* RETIRED. *Personal Data:* b St Louis, Mo, May 12, 14; m 40; c 1. *Educ:* St Louis Col Pharm, BS, 40; Wash Univ, MS, 43, PhD(chem), 46. *Prof Exp:* From instr to prof, St Louis Col Pharm, 41-78, Charles E Caspari prof chem, 78-80. *Concurrent Pos:* Biochemist, Snodgras Lab, City Hosp, 60-; mem, US Pharmacopeial Conv, 70. *Mem:* Am Chem Soc; Am Pharmaceut Asn. *Res:* Instrumental analysis of pharmaceutical compounds. *Mailing Add:* 3401 McAdams Pkwy Godfrey IL 62035-1225

**ZIMMER, CARL R(ICHARD),** ELECTRICAL ENGINEERING. *Current Pos:* from asst prof to assoc prof, 59-91, EMER PROF ENG, ARIZ STATE UNIV, 91- *Personal Data:* b Syracuse, NY, July 10, 27; m 65. *Educ:* Cornell Univ, BEE, 49; Syracuse Univ, MEE, 50, PhD(elec eng), 58. *Prof Exp:* Res assoc elec eng, Syracuse Univ, 53-56, instr, 56-59. *Concurrent Pos:* Consult, Motorola Aerospace Ctr, 65-67. *Mem:* Inst Elec & Electronics Engrs. *Res:* Solid state devices; active networks. *Mailing Add:* 733 East Geneva Dr Tempe AZ 85282

**ZIMMER, DAVID E,** PLANT PATHOLOGY, PLANT BREEDING. *Current Pos:* STAFF, RICHARD B RUSSELL AGR RES CTR. *Personal Data:* b Neoga, Ill, Sept 25, 35; m 56; c 2. *Educ:* Eastern Ill Univ, BS, 57; Purdue Univ, MS, 59, PhD(plant path), 61. *Prof Exp:* Res plant pathologist, USDA, NDak State Univ, 61-, adj prof plant path, res leader & tech adv, 77-88. *Mem:* AAAS; Am Phytopath Soc; Crop Sci Soc Am. *Res:* Genetics of parasitism with special emphasis on obligate parasites; inheritance and nature of disease resistance in oilseed crops and the improvement of oil-seed crops through disease resistance breeding. *Mailing Add:* 190 Mc Duffie Dr Athens GA 30605

**ZIMMER, ELIZABETH ANNE,** MOLECULAR EVOLUTION, MOLECULAR GENETICS. *Current Pos:* from asst prof to assoc prof, 84-90, ADJ ASSOC PROF BIOCHEM & BOT, LA STATE UNIV, BATON ROUGE, 90-; PRIN INVESTR & BOTANIST, LAB MOLECULAR SYSTEMATICS, SMITHSONIAN, 90- *Personal Data:* b Rochester, NY, Dec 19, 51. *Educ:* Cornell Univ, BS, 73; Univ Calif, Berkeley, PhD(biochem), 81. *Honors & Awards:* Dobzhansky Prize, Soc Study Evolution, 82. *Prof Exp:* Fel biol, Stanford Univ, 81-82 & Wash Univ, 83-84. *Concurrent Pos:* Prin investr, NSF grant, Spec Creativity Ext, 87-91; distinguished lectr, Enhance Visibility Women & Minorities in Sci, Univ Calif, Irvine, 90; assoc ed, J Heredity, 90-96 & Molecular Biol & Evolution, 91-93; lectr, Class 54, Univ NH, 91; ed, Methods Enzymol Vol 224, 93 Molecular Evolution, Molecular Phylogenetics & Evolution, 91-; USDA panelist, Plant Genome Initiative, 91; adj assoc prof bot, Duke Univ, 91-, genetics, George Washington Univ, 91-;

NSF vis prof for women, Calif Inst Technol, 93-96; coun mem, Am Genetics Asn, 94-; Mellon vis scholar, Rancho Santa Ana Bot Gardens, 94, res assoc, 94-; coun, Space Sci Bd, 96- *Mem:* Soc Study Evolution; Am Soc Biochem & Molecular Biol; Am Soc Plant Taxonomists; Soc Syst Biol; AAAS; Asn Women Sci. *Res:* Plant molecular evolution; ribosomal gene evolution; correlations between molecular and organismal characters for tracing evolution of flowering plants; multigene family differentiation; science education; conservation genetics. *Mailing Add:* Lab Molecular Systematics MSC NMNH Smithsonian Inst Washington DC 20560. *E-Mail:* zimmer@onyx.si.edu

**ZIMMER, G(EORGE) A(RTHUR),** mechanical engineering, for more information see previous edition

**ZIMMER, HANS,** ORGANIC CHEMISTRY. *Current Pos:* From asst prof to assoc prof, 54-61, PROF CHEM, UNIV CINCINNATI, 61- *Personal Data:* b Berlin, Ger, Feb 5, 21; m 46, Marlies H Wunsch; c Hans M. *Educ:* Tech Univ, Berlin, Cand, 47, Dipl, 49, DrIng, 50. *Honors & Awards:* Rieveschl Award, 90. *Concurrent Pos:* Vis prof, Univ Mainz, 66-67, Univ Bonn, 67, Univ Bern, 71 & Univ Stuttgart, 83; ed, Methodicum Chemicum; consult, Marion Merrell Dow, 60, Morton Int, 86; ed, Ann Reports Inorg & Gen Syntheses, 72-78. *Mem:* Fel AAAS; Am Chem Soc; Ger Chem Soc; fel Humboldt Soc. *Res:* Synthetic and metal organic chemistry; organophosphoros chemistry; environmental chemistry. *Mailing Add:* Dept Chem Univ Cincinnati Cincinnati OH 45221-0001

**ZIMMER, JAMES GRIFFITH,** PREVENTIVE MEDICINE, COMMUNITY HEALTH. *Current Pos:* from sr instr to asst prof prev med & community health, 63-67, actg chmn dept prev med, 68-69, ASSOC PROF PREV MED & COMMUNITY HEALTH, SCH MED & DENT, UNIV ROCHESTER, 68- *Personal Data:* b Lynbrook, NY, Apr 10, 32; m 93, Susan B Price; c 3. *Educ:* Cornell Univ, BA, 53; Yale Univ, MD, 57; London Sch Hyg & Trop Med, dipl trop pub health, 66; Am Bd Internal Med, dipl, 65. *Honors & Awards:* Key Award, Am Pub Health Asn, 90. *Prof Exp:* Intern internal med, Grace-New Haven Community Hosp, Conn, 57-58; resident, Strong Mem Hosp, Rochester, NY, 58-60; asst chief dermat, Walter Reed Army Inst Res, 61-63. *Concurrent Pos:* Milbank fac fel, Univ Rochester, 64-71; pres, exec dir, Med Serv Int, Inc, 68-70; pres, Genesee Valley Med Found, 70-79; med dir, Regional Utilization & Med Rev Proj, 71- *Mem:* Am Fedn Clin Res; Am Pub Health Asn; Int Epidemiol Asn; fel Am Col Prev Med; Royal Soc Trop Med & Hyg; assoc Am Col Epidemiol. *Res:* Community health; medical care research, especially in areas of utilization and quality of care review and care of chronically ill and aged. *Mailing Add:* Dept Community & Prev Med Univ Rochester Med Ctr Rochester NY 14642. *Fax:* 716-461-4532; *E-Mail:* zimmer@prevmed.rochester.edu

**ZIMMER, LOUIS GEORGE,** GEOLOGY. *Current Pos:* partner, 62-84, OWNER, MAGAW & ZIMMER, 84- *Personal Data:* b Marseilles, Ill, Nov 30, 26; m 48; c 2. *Educ:* Augustana Col, BA, 50; Univ Iowa, MS, 52. *Prof Exp:* Subsurface geologist, Ohio Oil Co, 52-57; dist geologist, J M Huber Corp, 57-62. *Mem:* Am Asn Petrol Geologists; Soc Independent Prof Earth Scientists. *Res:* Petroleum geology. *Mailing Add:* 2904 Ridgewood Dr Edmond OK 73013-8031

**ZIMMER, MARTIN F,** THERMODYNAMICS, EXPLOSIVES. *Current Pos:* RETIRED. *Personal Data:* b Metz, France, Apr 25, 29; US citizen; m; c 3. *Educ:* Univ Munich, BS, 55, MS, 58; Munich Tech Univ, PhD(chem technol), 61. *Prof Exp:* Head, Fuel Res Lab, Ger Aeronaut Res Inst, Munich, 60-62; chemist, Naval Ord Sta, 62, head, Thermodyn Br, 62-70; dir, High Explosive Res & Develop Lab, Eglin AFB, Fla, 70-76; res prog mgr conventional munition, Air Force Off Sci Res, Bolling AFB, Washington, DC, 76-78; tech dir, Munitions Div, Air Force Armament Lab, Eglin AFB, Fla, 80-88, syst prog dir, Int Modular Standoff Weapon (5 nations), MSD, 88-90, tech dir, Wright Lab Armament Directorat, 90-95. *Mem:* Combustion Inst. *Res:* Thermodynamics and combustion characteristics of energetic materials; detonation physics and explosive related phenomena; scientific and administrative management. *Mailing Add:* 124 Bayou Dr Niceville FL 32578

**ZIMMER, RUSSEL LEONARD,** INVERTEBRATE BIOLOGY. *Current Pos:* Instr, Univ Southern Calif, 60-63, vis asst prof, 63-64, asst prof, 64-68, resident dir, Santa Catalina Marine Biol Lab, 68-76, ASSOC PROF BIOL SCI, UNIV SOUTHERN CALIF, 68- *Personal Data:* b Springfield, Ill, Nov 7, 31; m; c 2. *Educ:* Blackburn Col, AB, 53; Univ Wash, MS, 56, PhD(zool), 64. *Mem:* AAAS; Am Soc Zool; Soc Syst Zool; Marine Biol Asn UK. *Res:* Reproductive biology; larval development, metamorphosis and systematics of minor invertebrate phyla, especially Phoronida and Bryozoa. *Mailing Add:* Dept Biol Sci Univ Southern Calif 3616 Trousdale Pkwy Los Angeles CA 90089-0015

**ZIMMER, STEPHEN GEORGE,** VIROLOGY, MOLECULAR BIOLOGY. *Current Pos:* asst prof path, 76-83, ASSOC PROF, UNIV KY, 83- *Personal Data:* b Trenton, NJ, Oct 26, 42; m 67, Constance James; c Stephen & Courtney. *Educ:* Rutgers Univ, AB, 64, MS, 66; Univ Colo, PhD(exp path), 73. *Prof Exp:* Fel molecular biol virol, Washington Univ, 74-76. *Mem:* Am Soc Microbiol; AAAS; Am Asn Cancer Res. *Res:* Regulation of viral gene expression; molecular mechanisms of viral transformation; mechanisms of invasion and metastasis; cancer research. *Mailing Add:* Dept Microbiol Univ Ky Med Sch 800 Rose St Lexington KY 40536-0001

**ZIMMER, WILLIAM FREDERICK, JR,** ORGANIC POLYMER CHEMISTRY. *Current Pos:* RETIRED. *Personal Data:* b Glouster, Ohio, June 4, 23; m 44, Califern M Volp; c William F III, Thomas John, Robert Todd, Kathryn Lynn (Arslen), Patricia Ann & Elizabeth C (Caruso). *Educ:* Ohio State Univ, BSc, 48, MSc, 49, PhD(chem), 52. *Prof Exp:* Org chemist, Res Lab, Durez Plastics & Chems, Inc, 52-55; res supvr, Hooker Chem Corp, 55-59, mgr polymer res, 59-62; mgr fiber res, Behr-Manning Div, Norton Co, 63-64, group leader chem appln res & develop, 64-68, asst dir res, Grinding Wheel Div, 68-74, res assoc, 74-86. *Concurrent Pos:* Consult, 86-88. *Mem:* Am Chem Soc. *Res:* Organofluorine chemistry; plastics and polymer chemistry and applications; fiber technology; abrasive systems and materials research; new product research and development. *Mailing Add:* 23053 Westchester Blvd Apt G-301 Port Charlotte FL 33980

**ZIMMERBERG, HYMAN JOSEPH,** MATHEMATICS. *Current Pos:* from instr to prof math, 46-92, EMER PROF MATH, RUTGERS UNIV, NEW BRUNSWICK, 92- *Personal Data:* b New York, NY, Sept 7, 21; m 43, Helen Yarmush; c Sharon (deceased), Betty, Joshua Jay & Morris Arthur. *Educ:* Brooklyn Col, BA, 41; Univ Chicago, MS, 42, PhD(math), 45. *Prof Exp:* Instr math, Univ Chicago, 42-45 & NC State Col, 45-46. *Concurrent Pos:* Vis prof, Univ Ore, 61 & Drew Univ, 62 & 63; dir, Undergrad Res Participation, NSF, Rutgers Univ, 62-69, 71-73 & 77; consult, NSF Student & Coop Prog, 67-70. *Mem:* Am Math Soc; Math Asn Am; Sigma Xi; Am Asn Univ Prof. *Res:* Boundary value problems; linear integro-differential-boundary-parameter problems; self-adjoint systems. *Mailing Add:* 345 Becker St Highland Park NJ 08904-2522. *E-Mail:* zimmerbe@math.rutgers.edu

**ZIMMERER, ROBERT P,** PLANT PHYSIOLOGY, MICROBIOLOGY. *Current Pos:* from instr to assoc prof biol, Juniata Col, 61-74, chmn dept, 74-77 & 87-93, Dana prof & emer prof, 74-93, PROF BIOL, JUNIATA COL, 74- *Personal Data:* b Sheboygan, Wis, Dec 7, 29; m 56, Mary McLean; c Kay, Carolyn & Bill. *Educ:* Univ Wis, BS, 54; Cornell Univ, MS, 61; Pa State Univ, PhD(bot), 66. *Prof Exp:* Asst to sales mgr, Stauffer Chem Co, 55-56; asst plant mgr, Hopkins Agr Chem Co, 56-57; chemist, Marathon Div, Am Can Co, 57-59; asst bot, Cornell Univ, 59-61. *Concurrent Pos:* Res assoc, Hershey Med Ctr, Pa State Univ, 70; vis prof, Univ Maine, 71; consult, USDA, 72-74 & J C Blair Mem Hosp, 74-80; World Environ Technol Inc, 97- *Mem:* Sigma Xi; Am Soc Microbiol. *Res:* Variation of the immune response in hosts to pathogens. *Mailing Add:* Dept Biol Juniata Col Huntingdon PA 16652

**ZIMMERER, ROBERT W,** EXPERIMENTAL PHYSICS, INSTRUMENTATION. *Current Pos:* CONSULT, 81- *Personal Data:* b Brooklyn, NY, May 21, 29; m 60; c 2. *Educ:* Worcester Polytech Inst, BS, 51; NY Univ, MS, 55; Univ Colo, PhD(physics), 60. *Prof Exp:* Design engr, Hazeltine Electronics Corp, 51-55; asst physics, Univ Colo, 55-57, res assoc, 57-60; physicist, Nat Bur Stand, 60-66; chief scientist, Wm Ainsworth & Sons, Inc, Colo, 66-69; pres, Scientech, Inc, 69-72, vpres, 72-81. *Concurrent Pos:* Dept Com sci fel, 65-66; phys sci consult, US Army Fitzsimons Gen Hosp, 69-85; res assoc, Univ Colo, 94- *Mem:* Fel Instrument Soc Am; Am Phys Soc; AAAS; Sigma Xi. *Res:* Microwave spectroscopy of gases; microwave generation and propagation at very short wavelengths; microwave power measurement; mass measurement by new methods; lung physiology; microcomputer modeling and use in classroom teaching. *Mailing Add:* 2035 Longs Peak Ave Longmont CO 80501

**ZIMMERING, STANLEY,** GENETICS. *Current Pos:* from assoc prof to prof, 62-90, EMER PROF BIOL, BROWN UNIV, 90- *Personal Data:* b New York, NY, Apr 14, 24; m 51; c 3. *Educ:* Brooklyn Col, AB, 47; Columbia Univ, AM, 49; Univ Mo, PhD(zool), 53. *Prof Exp:* Lectr biol & res assoc, Univ Rochester, 53-55; asst prof, Trinity Col, Conn, 55-59; res exec zool, Ind Univ, 59-62. *Res:* Segregation mechanisms; radiation genetics; chemical mutagenesis. *Mailing Add:* 12 Chapin Rd Barrington RI 02806

**ZIMMERMAN, ARTHUR MAURICE,** PHYSIOLOGY, CELL BIOLOGY. *Current Pos:* prof, Dept Zool, Univ Toronto, 64-94, grad secy, 70-75, assoc chmn grad affairs, 75-78, assoc dean, Div IV, Sch Grad Studies, 78-81, actg dir, Inst Immunol, 80-81, EMER PROF ZOOL, UNIV TORONTO, 94- *Personal Data:* b New York, NY, May 24, 29; m 53, Selma Blau; c Susan, Beth & Robert. *Educ:* NY Univ, BA, 50, MS, 54, PhD(cell physiol), 56. *Prof Exp:* Technician, NY Univ, 51-52; res assoc, NY Univ & Marine Biol Lab, Woods Hole, 55-56; Lalor res fel, Marine Biol Lab, Woods Hole, 56; res fel, Nat Cancer Inst, Univ Calif, 56-58; from instr to asst prof pharmacol, Col Med, Downstate Med Ctr, State Univ NY, 58-64. *Concurrent Pos:* Mem corp, Marine Biol Lab, Woods Hole; ed, Cell Biol Series, Acad Press, 78-; assoc ed, Can J Biochem, 80-85; vis prof anat, Univ Tex Health Sci Ctr, San Antonio; vis scientist, Weizmann Inst Sci, 82; vis prof, Univ Fla, Gainesville, 83; ed, Biochem & Cell Biol, 85-93 & Exp Cell Res, 83-93, Cell Biol Int, Western Hemisphere, 85-94. *Mem:* Am Soc Cell Biol (treas, 74-78); Can Soc Cell Biol (pres, 76); Int Fedn Cell Biol (secy-gen, 85-93, pres, 96-); Int Cell Cycle Soc (pres, 86-88); fel AAAS. *Res:* Cell division; mechanism of cytokinesis and karyokinesis; nuclear-cytoplasmic interrelations; physiological effects of temperature and pressure; amoeboid movement; physicochemical aspects of protoplasmic gels; cell cycle studies and drug action on cells. *Mailing Add:* Dept Zool Univ Toronto Toronto ON M5S 1A1 Can

**ZIMMERMAN, BARRY,** ORGANIC POLYMER & GENERAL CHEMISTRY. *Current Pos:* bus mgr urethane prods, 78-80, dir res & develop & mkt, 81-83, VPRES PROD MGT & TECH SERV, GEN FELT INDUST, INC, SADDLE BROOK, NJ, 86-; SR VPRES & MANAGING DIR, TRACE INT HOLDINGS INC, NY, 87- *Personal Data:* b New York, NY, Jan 14, 38; m 62, Barbara Nachimson; c Debra, Jill & Hope. *Educ:* Brooklyn Col, BSc, 59, AM, 61; Fordham Univ, PhD(org chem), 67. *Prof Exp:* Lectr

chem, Brooklyn Col, 59-61; instr, Bronx Community Col, 62-66; proj leader chem & plastics, Union Carbide Corp, NY, 62-72, mkt area sales mgr, Urethane Intermediates, 76-78. *Concurrent Pos:* Vpres, Foam Prod Group Inc, 87, dir, 88; chmn & chief exec officer, Foamex Latin Am, 93-; dir, Gen Felt Indust, Inc, 93-; exec vpres, Fuamet Int Inc, 96- *Mem:* Am Chem Soc; fel Royal Soc Chem; NY Acad Sci; fel Am Inst Chemists. *Res:* Synthesis and application of new chemical species in rubber processing; cure accelerators; silanes; inorganic bonding in elastomer matricies; insecticide synthesis; microencapsulation; physiochemical properties of polyelectrolytes and other colloids; polyurethane synthesis and catalysis; general environmental sciences. *Mailing Add:* 710 Park Ave New York NY 10021. *Fax:* 212-593-1363

**ZIMMERMAN, BARRY,** IMMUNOLOGY. *Current Pos:* ASSOC PROF PEDIAT, UNIV TORONTO, 84-, HEAD, DIV ALLERGY, HOSP SICK CHILDREN, 84- *Personal Data:* b Toronto, Ont, Nov 6, 41; m 64; c 2. *Educ:* Univ Toronto, MD, 65; FRCP(Can), 80; Am Bd Pediat, dipl, 81. *Prof Exp:* Asst prof pediat & mem staff, Inst Immunol, Univ Toronto, 72-80; assoc prof pediat, Dept Pediat & mem staff, Host Resistance Prog, McMaster Univ, 81-83. *Concurrent Pos:* Mem staff immunol, Hosp Sick Children & scientist, Res Inst, 71-80; grants, Med Res Coun Can, 71- & Nat Cancer Inst Can, 76-78; Med Res Coun Can scholar, 74-79; sr scientist, Res Inst, Hosp Sick Children, 84- *Mem:* Am Asn Immunol; Am Asn Immunologists; Can Soc Immunol; Am Acad Allergy & Clin Immunol. *Res:* Immunochemistry of lymphocyte surface antigens and receptors; transplantation; homograft prolongation by antilymphocyte and enhancing sera; characterization of leukemic lymphocytes; cellular regulation of IgE antibody production; investigation of asthma. *Mailing Add:* 45 A Alvin Ave Toronto ON M4T 2A7 Can

**ZIMMERMAN, BEN GEORGE,** PHARMACOLOGY. *Current Pos:* from asst prof to assoc prof, 63-72, PROF PHARMACOL, UNIV MINN, MINNEAPOLIS, 72- *Personal Data:* b Newark, NJ, July 1, 34; m 60; c 2. *Educ:* Columbia Univ, BS, 56; Univ Mich, PhD(pharmacol), 60. *Prof Exp:* Pharmacologist, Lederle Labs, Am Cyanamid Co, 60-61; res fel, Cardiovasc Labs, Col Med, Univ Iowa, 61-63. *Concurrent Pos:* Mem, Coun High Blood Pressure Res, Coun Circulation & Coun Basic Sci, Am Heart Asn. *Mem:* Am Soc Pharmacol & Exp Therapeut; Soc Exp Biol & Med. *Res:* Vascular effects of angiotensin and other pressor agents; influence of the sympathetic nervous system on various vascular beds; vascular role of prostaglandins. *Mailing Add:* Dept Pharmacol 3-249 Millard Hall Univ Minn 435 Delaware St SE Minneapolis MN 55455-0347

**ZIMMERMAN, C DUANE,** COMPUTER SCIENCE. *Current Pos:* SR TECH ADV, HEALTH DATA SCI CORP, 83- *Personal Data:* b Mayville, Wis, Oct 23, 35. *Educ:* Andrews Univ, BA, 57; Univ Minn, Minneapolis, MS, 60, PhD(comput sci), 69. *Prof Exp:* Instr math, Southern Missionary Col, 61-63; mathematician, Control Data Corp, 64-66; asst prof comput sci, Univ Minn, Minneapolis, 69-70; asst prof biomath, Loma Linda Univ, 70-80; dir syst develop, HBO & Co, 80-83. *Mem:* Asn Comput Mach; Inst Elec & Electronics Engrs Comput Soc. *Res:* Computer-medical applications. *Mailing Add:* Health Data Sci Corp 268 W Hospitality Lane San Bernardino CA 92408

**ZIMMERMAN, CARLE CLARK, JR,** CHEMICAL ENGINEERING. *Current Pos:* Res engr process develop, Marathon Oil Co, 63-64, advan res engr, 64-70, sr res engr, 70-74, mgr analysis dept, 74-77, mgr petrol chem dept, 77-81, mgr oil shale proj group, 81-83, MGR INSTRUMENTATION & ENG DEPT, DENVER RES CTR, MARATHON OIL CO, 83- *Personal Data:* b Winchester, Mass, Apr 25, 34; m 60; c 2. *Educ:* Bucknell Univ, BS, 56; Cornell Univ, PhD(chem eng), 63. *Mem:* Am Inst Chem Engrs; Sigma Xi. *Res:* Development and design of new chemical processes. *Mailing Add:* 2539 W Ridge Ct Littleton CO 80120-3029

**ZIMMERMAN, CAROL JEAN,** ENGINEERING GEOPHYSICS. *Current Pos:* EXPLORATION GEOPHYICIST, EXXON EXPLOR CO, 91- *Personal Data:* b Pittsburgh, Pa, Aug 21, 51; m 83; c 2. *Educ:* Rensselaer Polytech Inst, BS, 73; Univ Wis, MS, 76, PhD(oceanog), 80. *Prof Exp:* Res asst, Univ Wis-Madison, 74-80; res specialist, Exxon Prod Res Co, 80-91. *Concurrent Pos:* Teaching asst, Univ Wis-Madison, 76-77. *Mem:* Soc Explor Geophysicists; Am Geophys Union; Marine Technol Soc; Sigma Xi. *Res:* Evaluation and design of seismic source and receiver arrays for offshore oil exploration; development of exploration techniques and strategies for offshore placer exploration; design of exploration strategy for vertical seismic profiling; seismic interpretation; processing for direct hydrocarbon indicators. *Mailing Add:* Exxon Explor Co 233 Benmar Houston TX 77060-2598

**ZIMMERMAN, CHERYL LEA,** PHARMACOKINETICS. *Current Pos:* Asst prof, 83-90, ASSOC PROF PHARMACEUT, UNIV MINN, MINNEAPOLIS, 90- *Personal Data:* b Chippewa Falls, Wis, May 2, 53; m 83, Rory P Remmel. *Educ:* Univ Wis-Madison, BS, 76; Univ Wash, PhD(pharmaceut), 83. *Mem:* Am Asn Pharmaceut Scientists; AAAS; Int Soc Study Xenobiotics. *Res:* Development of in vivo and in situ models for the study of first-pass removal of orally administered drugs. *Mailing Add:* 2374 Bourne Ave St Paul MN 55108. *E-Mail:* zimme005@maroon.tc.umn.edu

**ZIMMERMAN, CRAIG ARTHUR,** PHYSIOLOGICAL ECOLOGY, ANIMAL BEHAVIOR. *Current Pos:* assoc prof, 75-80, chmn dept, 75-87, PROF BIOL, AURORA UNIV, 80- *Personal Data:* b Painesville, Ohio, Mar 22, 37; m 62; c 2. *Educ:* Baldwin-Wallace Col, BS, 60; Univ Mich, MS, 62 & 64, PhD(bot), 69. *Prof Exp:* From instr to asst prof biol, Centre Col Ky, 67-74;

environ specialist, Spindletop Res, Inc, 74-75. *Concurrent Pos:* Consult, Kane Co Govt & Morton Arboretum; chmn, Acca Bot Prog, Morton Arboretum, 90-; chmn, Biol Div, Assoc Cols Chicago Area, 80-81 & 91-92. *Mem:* Am Inst Biol Sci; AAAS; Ecol Soc Am; Sigma Xi. *Res:* Causes, characteristics, and evolution of weed plants; comparing the biology of the weed with that of related cultivars and narrow endemics; biological indicators of stream pollution; behavior of pheasants and quail. *Mailing Add:* Dept Math & Sci Aurora Univ 347 S Gladstone Ave Aurora IL 60506-4877

**ZIMMERMAN, DALE A,** ORNITHOLOGY, ECOLOGY & BOTANY. *Current Pos:* From asst prof to prof, 57-88, chmn dept, 77-88, EMER PROF BIOL, WESTERN NMEX UNIV, 88- *Personal Data:* b Imlay City, Mich, June 7, 28; m 50; c 1. *Educ:* Univ Mich, BS, 50, MS, 51, PhD, 56. *Concurrent Pos:* Mem expeds, Africa, 61, 63, 65 & 66. *Mem:* Am Ornith Union; Wilson Ornith Soc; Cooper Ornith Soc; Brit Ornith Union. *Res:* Taxonomy and ecology of birds and plants. *Mailing Add:* 1011 W Florence Silver City NM 88061

**ZIMMERMAN, DANIEL HILL,** BIOCHEMISTRY, IMMUNOLOGY. *Current Pos:* VPRES RES & DEVELOP, CELL MED, INC, 87- *Personal Data:* b Los Angeles, Calif, June 3, 41; m 63; c 3. *Educ:* Emory & Henry Col, BS, 63; Univ Fla, MS, 66, PhD(biochem), 69. *Prof Exp:* Jr staff fel biochem, Nat Inst Arthritis, Metab & Digestive Dis, 69-71, sr staff fel, 71-73; cellular immunologist, Electro Nucleonics Labs Inc, 73-77, sr res scientist, Res & Develop Dept, 77-80, prog mgr cell immunol, 81-87. *Mem:* Am Asn Immunol. *Res:* Synthesis and secretion of proteins; differentiation of antibody producing cells. *Mailing Add:* 66 Canal Ctr Plaza Suite 510 Alexandria VA 22314

**ZIMMERMAN, DEAN R,** ANIMAL NUTRITION. *Current Pos:* assoc prof, 67-73, PROF ANIMAL SCI, IOWA STATE UNIV, 73- *Personal Data:* b Compton, Ill, July 2, 32; m 53; c 2. *Educ:* Iowa State Univ, BS, 54, PhD(swine nutrit), 60. *Prof Exp:* Res assoc nutrit, Univ Notre Dame, 60-62; asst prof biol, Wartburg Col, 62-65; assoc prof animal sci, Purdue Univ, 65-67. *Mem:* Am Soc Animal Sci; Am Inst Nutrit; Sigma Xi. *Res:* Nutrition research, especially compensatory growth and development; nutrition-disease interrelationships; bioavailability of amino acids; amino acid interrelationships. *Mailing Add:* Dept Animal Sci Rm 337 Kildee Hall Iowa State Univ Ames IA 50011-0001

**ZIMMERMAN, DON CHARLES,** BIOLOGICAL CHEMISTRY, PLANT PHYSIOLOGY. *Current Pos:* RES CHEMIST, SCI & EDUC ADMIN-AGR RES, USDA, 59-, CTR DIR, AGR RES SERV, 88-; ADJ PROF BIOCHEM, NDAK STATE UNIV, 69- *Personal Data:* b Fargo, NDak, Feb 27, 34; m 58; c 1. *Educ:* NDak State Univ, BS, 55, MS, 59, PhD(biochem), 64. *Concurrent Pos:* Asst prof, NDak State Univ, 64-69. *Mem:* AAAS; Am Chem Soc; Am Soc Plant Physiol. *Res:* Metabolism of unsaturated fatty acids; their oxidation by lipoxygenase and other enzymes during early plant growth. *Mailing Add:* Northern Crop Sci Lab Univ Sta Box 5677 Fargo ND 58105

**ZIMMERMAN, DONALD NATHAN,** physical inorganic chemistry, for more information see previous edition

**ZIMMERMAN, EARL ABRAM,** NEUROLOGY, NEUROENDOCRINOLOGY. *Current Pos:* PROF & CHMN NEUROL, ORE HEALTH SCI UNIV, 85- *Personal Data:* b Harrisburg, Pa, May 5, 37; m 67, 82, 91, Jody Hall; c David A. *Educ:* Franklin & Marshall Univ, BS, 59; Univ Pa, MD, 63. *Honors & Awards:* Wartenburg lectr, Am Acad Neurol, 85. *Prof Exp:* Resident & intern med, Presby Hosp, 63-65; resident neurol, Neurol Inst, NY, 65-68; fel endocrinol, Columbia Univ, 70-72, from asst prof to assoc prof, 72-81, prof neurol, Col Physicians & Surgeons, 81-85. *Concurrent Pos:* Asst attend physician neurol, Presby Hosp, 72-77, assoc attend physician, 78-81, attend physician, 81-; Lucy Moses Basic Res Prize neurol, Columbia Univ, 74. *Mem:* Am Neurol Asn; Am Acad Neurol; Endocrine Soc; Soc Neurosci; Histochem Soc. *Res:* Organization and evaluation of neuropeptide pathways in mammalian brain with an emphasis on hypothalmic systems; Alzheimer's and other degenerative neurological diseases. *Mailing Add:* Dept Neurol Ore Health Sci Univ Sch Med 3181 SW S Jackson Portland OR 97201-3098. *Fax:* 503-494-7242; *E-Mail:* zimmerme@ohsu.edu

**ZIMMERMAN, EARL GRAVES,** ECOLOGICAL GENETICS, POPULATION GENETICS. *Current Pos:* asst prof, NTex State Univ, 70-75, fac res grant, 70-72, assoc prof pop genetics, 75-77, assoc prof biol sci, 77-81, PROF POP GENETICS, N TEX STATE UNIV, 81- *Personal Data:* b Detroit, Mich, Feb 15, 43; m 75; c 2. *Educ:* Ind State Univ, Terre Haute, BS, 65; Univ Ill, Urbana, MS, 67, PhD(zool), 70. *Honors & Awards:* Jackson Award, Am Soc Mammal, 70. *Prof Exp:* Asst mammal comp anat, Univ Ill, Urbana, 65-69, asst cytogenetics, 69-70. *Mem:* Am Soc Mammal; Genetics Soc Am; Soc Study Evolution. *Res:* Population genetics, biochemical variation and evolution of vertebrates. *Mailing Add:* Dept Biol NTex State Univ Box 5218 Denton TX 76203-0218

**ZIMMERMAN, EDWARD JOHN,** THEORETICAL PHYSICS, PHILOSOPHY OF SCIENCE. *Current Pos:* from asst prof to prof, 51-89, chmn dept, 62-66, EMER PROF PHYSICS, UNIV NEBR, LINCOLN, 89- *Personal Data:* b Waynetown, Ind, July 12, 24; m 45, Dorothy Wynne; c Ann W & Mary A. *Educ:* Univ Kans, AB, 45; Univ Ill, MS, 47, PhD(physics), 51. *Prof Exp:* Res assoc nuclear physics, Univ Ill, 50-51. *Concurrent Pos:* Vis prof, Hamburg Univ, 57-58; NSF sci fac fel philos sci, Cambridge Univ, 66-67. *Mem:* Fel Am Phys Soc. *Res:* Foundations of physics; quantum mechanics. *Mailing Add:* 601 Marshall Ave Lincoln NE 68510

**ZIMMERMAN, ELMER LEROY,** PHYSICS. *Current Pos:* RETIRED. *Personal Data:* b Washington Co, Pa, Feb 5, 21; m 45; c 4. *Educ:* Washington & Jefferson Col, AB, 42; Syracuse Univ, MA, 44; Ohio State Univ, PhD(physics), 50. *Prof Exp:* Physicist, Tenn Eastman Corp, 44-45, Oak Ridge Nat Lab, 50-55 & Nuclear Develop Corp Am, 55-58; supvr critical exp unit, Atomics Int Div, NAm Aviation, Inc, 58-60; vpres & tech dir, Solid State Radiations, Inc, 60-62; group leader radiation effects & reactor opers, Atomics Int Div, NAm Aviation, Inc, 62-64; asst mgr, Weapons Effects Dept, Solid State Physics Lab, TRW Systs, 64-67, mgr, Electronic & Electro-magnetic Effects Dept, Vulnerability & Hardness Lab, 67-69, mem staff, Opers Res Dept, 69-77; nuclear survivability mgt, Guid & Control Div, Litton Industs, Inc, 77-88. *Mem:* Am Phys Soc; Inst Elec & Electronics Engrs; Am Nuclear Soc. *Res:* Nuclear spectroscopy and resonance; reactor physics and instrumentation; critical experiments; semiconductor radiation detectors; radiation effects and transport; ballistic and cruise missile systems engineering. *Mailing Add:* 22650 MacFarlane Dr Woodland Hills CA 91364

**ZIMMERMAN, EMERY GILROY,** anatomy, medicine; deceased, see previous edition for last biography

**ZIMMERMAN, ERNEST FREDERICK,** TERATOLOGY, DEVELOPMENTAL BIOLOGY. *Current Pos:* assoc prof res pediat, 68-71, dir, Grad Prog Develop Biol, 71-85, ASSOC PROF RES PHARMACOL, UNIV CINCINNATI, 68-, DIR DIV CELL BIOL, INST DEVELOP RES, CHILDREN'S HOSP RES FOUND, 68-, PROF PEDIAT, COL MED, 71- *Personal Data:* b New York, NY, June 2, 33; m 57; c 3. *Educ:* George Washington Univ, BS, 56, MS, 58, PhD(pharmacol), 61. *Prof Exp:* Res asst pharmacol, George Washington Univ, 56-58; fel biol, Mass Inst Technol, 60-62; from instr to asst prof, Sch Med, Stanford Univ, 62-68. *Mem:* AAAS; Am Soc Biol Chemists; Teratol Soc (pres, 89-90); Soc Cell Biol; Am Soc Pharmacol & Exp Therapeut. *Res:* Role of neurotransmitters in development and differentiation; mechanisms of action of teratogenic drugs. *Mailing Add:* Dept Ped Children's Hosp Res Found 3333 Burnet Ave Cincinnati OH 45229-3039. *Fax:* 513-559-4317

**ZIMMERMAN, EUGENE MUNRO,** HEALTH SCIENCE ADMINISTRATION, VIROLOGY. *Current Pos:* grants assoc, NIH, 76-77, asst prog dir carcinogenesis, Nat Cancer Inst, 77-78, exec secy, Review Br, 78-81, EXEC SECY, ALLERGY & IMMUNOL STUDY SECT, DIV RES GRANTS, NIH, 82- *Personal Data:* b New Haven, Conn, June 27, 40. *Educ:* Yale Univ, BA, 60; Wesleyan Univ, MA, 62; Univ Md, College Park, PhD(microbiol), 68. *Prof Exp:* Microbiologist, Ft Detrick, Md, 69-70; asst proj dir, Microbiol Assocs Inc, Md, 70-73; sr scientist, Litton-Bionetics Inc, 73-76. *Concurrent Pos:* Consult, Mt Sinai Sch Med, 75-76. *Mem:* AAAS; Tissue Cult Asn; Am Soc Microbiol; Sigma Xi. *Res:* Grant and contract review; biology of oncogenic herpesviruses and oncarnaviruses; treatment and prophylaxis of leukemia in animal models. *Mailing Add:* 33 Brighton Dr Gaithersburg MD 20877

**ZIMMERMAN, GARY ALAN,** CLINICAL CHEMISTRY. *Current Pos:* PROVOST, ANTIOCH UNIV, SEATTLE, WASH, 88- *Personal Data:* b Seattle, Wash, Oct 19, 38; m 60, 88; c 2. *Educ:* Calif Inst Technol, BS, 60; Univ Wis, PhD(org chem), 65. *Prof Exp:* From asst prof to prof chem, Seattle Univ, 64-76, dir clin chem, 68-83, dean, Sch Sci & Eng, 73-80, vpres acad affairs, 80-81, exec vpres, 81-87. *Concurrent Pos:* Lectr, Univ Wash, 65 & vis sci prog, Pac Sci Ctr, Seattle, 66-68; consult, Gordon Res Conf, 66-70 & Swed Hosp & Med Ctr, Seattle, 68-83; vis prof chem, Univ Idaho, 73. *Mem:* Fel AAAS; Am Chem Soc; Am Asn Clin Chemists (treas, 80-81, pres elect, 82, pres, 83). *Res:* Clinical applications of enzymatic assays; trace metal analyses. *Mailing Add:* 4818-102 Lane NE Antioch Univ 2607 Second Ave Kirkland WA 98033-7642

**ZIMMERMAN, GEORGE B,** COMPUTATIONAL, ATOMIC & PLASMA PHYSICS. *Current Pos:* staff mem, A Div, Lawrence Livermore Nat Lab, 70-80, assoc div leader, X Div, 80-84, computational physics div leader, 84-87, chief scientist, 87-92, group leader, P Div, 92-94, GROUP LEADER, X DIV, LAWRENCE LIVERMORE NAT LAB, 94- *Personal Data:* b Schenectady, NY, Dec 21, 46; m 80, Sarah A Cook; c Shandy (Cole) & Nieves. *Educ:* Harvey Mudd Col, BS, 69; Univ Calif, Berkeley, MA, 71. *Honors & Awards:* Ernest O Lawrence Award, Dept Energy, 83. *Prof Exp:* Mass spectrometer design analyst, Perkin-Elmer Corp, 67-69. *Mem:* Fel Am Phys Soc. *Res:* Develop computational methods and tools, such as the LASNEX code, to simulate inertial confinement fusion, astrophysics and national security applications. *Mailing Add:* Lawrence Livermore Nat Lab L472 PO Box 808 Livermore CA 94550. *Fax:* 510-423-9969; *E-Mail:* gzimmerman@llnl.gov

**ZIMMERMAN, GEORGE LANDIS,** PHYSICAL CHEMISTRY. *Current Pos:* asst prof, 51-55, assoc prof, 55, PROF CHEM, BRYN MAWR COL, 55- *Personal Data:* b Hershey, Pa, Aug 27, 20; m 53. *Educ:* Swarthmore Col, AB, 41; Univ Chicago, PhD, 49. *Prof Exp:* Res chemist sam labs, Manhattan Dist Proj, Columbia, 42-46; instr, Mass Inst Technol, 49-51. *Mem:* Am Chem Soc. *Res:* Molecular spectroscopy. *Mailing Add:* 125 Kennedy Lane Bryn Mawr PA 19010

**ZIMMERMAN, GEORGE OGUREK,** LOW TEMPERATURE PHYSICS, SUPERCONDUCTIVITY. *Current Pos:* From asst prof to assoc prof physics, Boston Univ, 63-73, from assoc chmn to chmn dept, 72-83, chmn fac coun, 85-86, PROF PHYSICS, BOSTON UNIV, 73- *Personal Data:* b Katowice, Poland, Oct 20, 35; US citizen; m 64, Isa Kaftal. *Educ:* Yale Univ, BS, 58, MS, 59, PhD(physics), 63. *Concurrent Pos:* Vis scientist, Nat Magnet Lab, Mass

Inst Technol, 65-85; assoc physicist, Univ Calif, San Diego, 73; vis physicist, Brookhaven Nat Lab, 80; vis scholar, Harvard Univ, 88, Kamerling-Onnes Lab, Leiden, Neth, 88; grantee, NSF & AFOSR; pres, Zerres Corp, 91-97. *Mem:* AAAS; NY Acad Sci; Am Phys Soc; Sigma Xi; Mat Res Soc. *Res:* Low temperature phenomena, cryogenics, specifically pertaining to liquid and solid helium three; investigation of paramagnetic phenomena; investigation of phase transitions; two-dimensional magnetism; superconductivity; research grants, patents; cooperative John-Teller effect. *Mailing Add:* Dept Physics Boston Univ 590 Commonwealth Ave Boston MA 02215. *Fax:* 617-353-9393; *E-Mail:* goz@buphy.bu.edu

**ZIMMERMAN, HARRY MARTIN,** pathology; deceased, see previous edition for last biography

**ZIMMERMAN, HOWARD ELLIOT,** CHEMISTRY & PHOTOCHEMISTRY, QUANTUM MECHANICS & ORGANIC SYNTHESIS. *Current Pos:* assoc prof, 60-61, PROF CHEM, UNIV WIS-MADISON, 61-, ARTHUR C COPE CHAIR CHEM, 75-, HILLDALE CHAIR CHEM, 90- *Personal Data:* b New York, NY, July 5, 26; wid; c 3. *Educ:* Yale Univ, BS, 50, PhD(chem), 53. *Honors & Awards:* Photochem Award, Am Chem Soc, 75 & James Flack Norris Award Phys-Org Chem, 76; Halpen Award, NY Acad Sci, 79; Chem Pioneering Award, Am Inst Chemists, 86; Hilldale Award in Phys Sci, Univ Wis, 90. *Prof Exp:* Nat Res Coun postdoctoral fel chem, Harvard Univ, 53-54; from instr to asst prof, Northwestern Univ, 54-60. *Concurrent Pos:* Mem grants comt, Res Corp, 66-72; chmn, 4th Int Union Pure & Appl Chem, Int Photochem Symp, Baden-Baden, Ger, 72; co-chmn org div, Inter Am Photchem Soc, 76-81, mem exec comt, 81-86; fel, Japan Soc Prom Sci; Sr Humboldt fel, 88; Cope scholar award, Am Chem Soc, 90. *Mem:* Nat Acad Sci; Royal Soc Chem; Ger Chem Soc; Am Chem Soc. *Res:* Organic, physical-organic, synthetic organic chemistry; photochemistry; theoretical organic chemistry; photobiology; reaction mechanisms; stereochemistry; unusual organic phenomena and species. *Mailing Add:* Dept Chem Univ Wis Madison WI 53706

**ZIMMERMAN, HYMAN JOSEPH,** MEDICINE, HEPATOLOGY. *Current Pos:* prof, 65-90, EMER PROF MED, GEORGE WASHINGTON UNIV, 90- *Personal Data:* b Rochester, NY, July 14, 14; m 43; c 4. *Educ:* Univ Rochester, AB, 36; Stanford Univ, MA, 38, MD, 43. *Honors & Awards:* Distinguished Achievement Award, Am Asn Study Liver Dis, 86; Gold Medal, Can Liver Found, 89. *Prof Exp:* Intern, Stanford Univ Hosp, 42-43; resident med, Gallinger Munic Hosp & Med Div, George Washington Univ, 46-48, clin instr, Sch Med, 48-51; asst prof, Col Med, Univ Nebr, 51; chief med serv, Vet Admin Hosp, Omaha, 51-53; clin assoc prof med, Col Med, Univ Ill, 53-57; prof & chmn dept, Chicago Med Sch, 57-65. *Concurrent Pos:* Asst chief med serv, Vet Admin Hosp, DC, 48-49, dir liver & metab res lab, 65-68; chief med serv, Vet Admin West Side Hosp, Chicago, 53-65; chmn, Dept Med, Mt Sinai Hosp, 57-65; prof, Sch Med, Boston Univ, 68-71; lectr, Sch Med, Tufts Univ, 68-71; clin prof med, Sch Med, Sch Med, Howard Univ, Georgetown Univ & Uniformed Serv Univ Health Sci; chief med serv, Vet Admin Hosp, DC, 68-78, distinguished physician, 84-89; distinguished scientist, Armed Forces Inst Path, 89-90, vis scientist, 91- *Mem:* Am Soc Clin Invest; Am Asn Study Liver Disease; Am Diabetes Asn; Am Fedn Clin Res; master Am Col Physicians; Am Gastroenterol Asn. *Res:* Physiology of the liver; toxicology; effect of drugs on the liver; hepatotoxicity. *Mailing Add:* 7913 Charleston Ct Bethesda MD 20817-1421. *Fax:* 202-782-4694

**ZIMMERMAN, IRWIN DAVID,** neurophysiology, biophysics, for more information see previous edition

**ZIMMERMAN, IVAN HAROLD,** CHEMICAL PHYSICS. *Current Pos:* CODE PHYSICIST, LAWRENCE LIVERMORE NAT LAB, 84- *Personal Data:* b Orland, Calif, Nov 21, 43; m 75; c 1. *Educ:* Ore State Univ, BS, 66; Univ Wash, PhD(physics), 72. *Prof Exp:* Fel chem, Univ Rochester, 72-76, res assoc, 77-78; asst prof physics, Clarkson Col, 78-83. *Mem:* Am Phys Soc; Am Chem Soc; NY Acad Sci; AAAS. *Res:* Atomic and molecular collisions; effects of intense laser radiation on molecular processes; ion-surface encounters; molecules near solid surfaces; strong-shock hydrodynamics. *Mailing Add:* 3727 Crofters Ct Pleasanton CA 94588

**ZIMMERMAN, JACK MCKAY,** SURGERY. *Current Pos:* ASSOC PROF SURG, JOHNS HOPKINS UNIV, 65- *Personal Data:* b New York, NY, Feb 4, 27; m 53, Doris Perkinson; c Anne Z (Morgan) & John S W. *Educ:* Princeton Univ, AB, 49; Johns Hopkins Univ, MD, 53; Univ Kansas City, MA, 63. *Honors & Awards:* Heritage Award, Johns Hopkins Univ; James H Jackson Award, Jackson-Newman Found. *Prof Exp:* From intern to resident surg, Johns Hopkins Hosp, 53-59; assoc prof, Sch Med, Univ Kans, 59-65. *Concurrent Pos:* Asst, Johns Hopkins Univ, 54-59, surgeon, 65-, Halsted fel surg path, Univ, 55-56, instr, 58-59; staff surgeon, Vet Admin Hosp, Kansas City, 59-60, chief surg serv, 60-65; consult, Sch Dent, Univ Kans, 60 & Vet Admin Hosp, Baltimore; chief surg, Church Home & Hosp, 65- *Mem:* Am Col Surg; Soc Univ Surg; Acad Hospice Physicians; Soc Surg Alimentary Tract; Soc Med Consult Armed Forces. *Res:* Thoracic surgery; wound healing and infections; care of advanced malignancy; medical education; care of terminal illness. *Mailing Add:* 100 N Broadway Baltimore MD 21231. *Fax:* 410-562-6230

**ZIMMERMAN, JAMES KENNETH,** BIOCHEMISTRY. *Current Pos:* from asst prof to assoc prof, Clemson Univ, 71-83, assoc head biol sci, 89-93, actg head, 93-95, PROF BIOCHEM, CLEMSON UNIV, 83-, CHAIR BIOL SCI, 95- *Personal Data:* b Nelson, Nebr, Aug 23, 43. *Educ:* Univ Nebr, Lincoln,

BS, 65; Northwestern Univ, Evanston, PhD(biochem), 69. *Prof Exp:* NIH fel, Univ Va, 69-71. *Mem:* AAAS; Am Chem Soc; Am Soc Biochem & Molecular Biol; Biochem Soc Gt Brit. *Res:* Associating protein systems, complement interactions; analytical gel chromatography by direct scanning; analytical ultracentrifugation; computer simulations. *Mailing Add:* Dept Biol Sci Clemson Univ Clemson SC 29634-1903. *E-Mail:* jkzmm@clemson.edu

**ZIMMERMAN, JAMES ROSCOE,** ZOOLOGY, ENTOMOLOGY. *Current Pos:* RETIRED. *Personal Data:* b Norwood, Ohio, July 12, 28; m 50; c 3. *Educ:* Hanover Col, AB, 53; Ind Univ, MA, 55, PhD(zool), 57. *Prof Exp:* Asst prof zool, Univ Wichita, 57-58; assoc prof biol, Ind Cent Col, 58-61, actg chmn dept, 59-61; from asst prof to prof biol, NMex State Univ, 61-88, head dept, 74-78. *Concurrent Pos:* Vis prof, Escuela Sup De Agric'Herm Escob CD Juarez, 78-81. *Mem:* AAAS; Am Soc Zool; Entom Soc Am; Soc Systs Zool; Am Entom Soc; Sigma Xi. *Res:* Taxonomy of dytiscidae; parasitic hymenoptera. *Mailing Add:* 141 N Sawtelle Ave Tucson AZ 85716-4722

**ZIMMERMAN, JAY ALAN,** MAMMALIAN PHYSIOLOGY, GERONTOLOGY. *Current Pos:* ASSOC PROF BIOL, ST JOHN'S UNIV, NY, 75- *Personal Data:* b Philadelphia, Pa, Mar 1, 45; m 72; c 2. *Educ:* Franklin & Marshall Col, AB, 67; Rutgers Univ, PhD(zool), 75. *Concurrent Pos:* Vis scientist, Orentreich Found Advan Sci; pres, Multisciences Assocs. *Mem:* Sigma Xi; Geront Soc; Soc Study Reproduction; AAAS. *Res:* Adaptive mechanisms of organ-system function and biochemistry during aging; chemical carcinogenesis and oncogene expression in senescence; alcohol absorption and physiology. *Mailing Add:* Dept Biol St John's Univ 8000 Utopia Pkwy Jamaica NY 11439. *Fax:* 718-990-5958; *E-Mail:* ypjzbio@sjmusic.stjohns.edu

**ZIMMERMAN, JOHN F,** ANALYTICAL CHEMISTRY, SCIENCE EDUCATION. *Current Pos:* From asst prof to assoc prof, 63-79, PROF CHEM, WABASH COL, 79- *Personal Data:* b Monticello, Iowa, June 22, 37; m 59; c 3. *Educ:* Univ Iowa, BS, 59; Univ Kans, PhD(chem), 64. *Res:* Use of personal computers in the chemistry lecture and teaching laboratory; development of instrumentation for undergraduate laboratory instruction; multimedia instruction. *Mailing Add:* Dept Chem Wabash Col Crawfordsville IN 47933

**ZIMMERMAN, JOHN GORDON,** PHYSICAL CHEMISTRY, INORGANIC CHEMISTRY. *Current Pos:* RETIRED. *Personal Data:* b Brooklyn, NY, May 31, 16; m 39, Ruth Truitt; c 4. *Educ:* Univ Pa, BS, 37, MS, 39; Georgetown Univ, PhD(chem), 71. *Prof Exp:* Instr gen sci, Monmouth Jr Col, 38-42; shift supvr org chem prod, Ala Ord Works, 42-43; instr chem, Drexel Inst, 43-44; develop chemist org chem, Publicker Industs, Inc, 44-47; chmn sci div, St Helena Exten, Col William & Mary, 47-48; asst prof, gen & phys chem, Westminster Col, 48-51; from asst prof to prof chem, US Naval Acad, 51-82. *Mem:* Am Chem Soc. *Res:* Kinetics of substitution reactions of transition metal complexes. *Mailing Add:* 1708 Old Generals Hwy Annapolis MD 21401

**ZIMMERMAN, JOHN HARVEY,** medical entomology, for more information see previous edition

**ZIMMERMAN, JOHN LESTER,** ECOLOGY. *Current Pos:* Asst prof zool, 63-68, assoc prof biol, 68-76, PROF BIOL, KANS STATE UNIV, 76- *Personal Data:* b Hamilton, Ont, Feb 17, 33; US citizen; m 55; c 3. *Educ:* Mich State Univ, BS, 53, MS, 59; Univ Ill, PhD(zool), 63. *Concurrent Pos:* Sci adv environ protection, Atlantic-Richfield Co, Calif, 74-75. *Mem:* Am Ornith Union; Wilson Ornith Soc; Cooper Ornith Soc. *Res:* Birds, physiological ecology; habitat relection in grassland community ecology. *Mailing Add:* Dept Biol Kans State Univ 232 Ackert Hall Manhattan KS 66506-4901

**ZIMMERMAN, JOHN R(ICHARD),** MECHANICAL ENGINEERING. *Current Pos:* prof, 76-88, EMER PROF MECH & AEROSPACE ENG, UNIV DEL, 88- *Personal Data:* b Allentown, Pa, July 25, 25; m 54; c 2. *Educ:* Yale Univ, BE, 46; Boston Univ, STB, 52; Lehigh Univ, MS, 60, PhD, 66. *Prof Exp:* Assoc prof mech eng, Pa State Univ, 66-71; prof, Clarkson Col Technol, 71-74; vis prof, Cornell Univ, 74-76. *Mem:* Am Soc Mech Engrs; Am Soc Eng Educ; Am Asn Univ Prof; Sigma Xi; Am Soc Automotive Engrs. *Res:* Mechanical design; computer simulation; random vibrations; land transportation. *Mailing Add:* 922 Quail Lane Newark DE 19711

**ZIMMERMAN, JOSEPH,** PHYSICAL CHEMISTRY, POLYMER CHEMISTRY. *Current Pos:* CONSULT, 85- *Personal Data:* b New York, NY, Aug 9, 21; m 48, Marion E; c Neil, Donna (Herbert) & Steven. *Educ:* City Col New York, BS, 42; Columbia Univ, AM, 47, PhD(chem), 50. *Honors & Awards:* LaVoisier Award Tech Achievement, DuPont, 96. *Prof Exp:* Res chemist, Carothers Res Lab, E I du Pont de Nemours & Co, Inc, 50-53, res assoc, 53-62, res fel, 62-64, res mgr, Carothers Res Lab, 64-71, res mgr, Indust Fibers Div, 71-78, from res mgr to sr res fel, Textile Fibers Dept, Pioneering Res Div, 78-84. *Mem:* Am Chem Soc; Sigma Xi; AAAS; Fiber Soc. *Res:* Polymer and fiber research, especially polyamides, polyesters and aramids. *Mailing Add:* 906 Barley Dr PO Box 4042 Wilmington DE 19807

**ZIMMERMAN, LEONARD NORMAN,** BACTERIOLOGY. *Current Pos:* from asst prof to prof, Pa State Univ, University Park, 51-89, head, Dept Microbiol & Cell Biol, 73-78, assoc dean res, Col Sci, 78-89, dean, 88-89, EMER DEAN & EMER PROF BACT, PA STATE UNIV, UNIVERSITY PARK, 89- *Personal Data:* b Brooklyn, NY, Sept 13, 23; m 46, Rima

Grossman; c Erik E, Raul L & Leda E. *Educ:* Cornell Univ, BS, 48, MS, 49, PhD(bact), 51. *Prof Exp:* Asst, Cornell Univ, 48-51. *Mem:* AAAS; Am Soc Microbiol. *Res:* Bacterial genetics and regulatory mechanisms. *Mailing Add:* 306 Frear Lab Pa State Univ University Park PA 16802. *E-Mail:* lnz1@psuvm.psu.edu

**ZIMMERMAN, LESTER J,** agronomy, mathematics; deceased, see previous edition for last biography

**ZIMMERMAN, LORENZ EUGENE,** PATHOLOGY. *Current Pos:* PROF PATH & OPHTHAL, GEORGETOWN UNIV SCH MED, 83- *Personal Data:* b Washington, DC, Nov 15, 20; m 45, 59; c 6. *Educ:* George Washington Univ, AB, 43, MD, 45; Am Bd Path, dipl, 52. *Hon Degrees:* DSc, Univ Ill, 81. *Honors & Awards:* Ernst Jung Prize, Ernst Jung Found, Hamburg, Ger, 76; F C Donders Medal, Neth Opthal Soc, Groningen, 78; Estelle Doheny mem lectr, Estelle Doheny Eye Found, Los Angeles, 78; Sir William Bowman lectr, Ophthal Soc UK, London, 80; Medalla de Oro, Barraquer Inst, Barcelona, Spain, 69; Leslie Dana Gold Medal, St Louis Soc Blind, 82; Jules Stein Award, Res Prevent Blindness, Inc, 85; Medalla de Oro Jorge Malbran, Fundacion Oftalmologica Arg, Buenos Aires, 86; John Milton McLean Medal, NY Hosp-Cornell Med Ctr, New York, NY, 88; Mericos H Whittier Award, Mericos Eye Ctr-Scripps Mem Hosp, La Jolla, Calif, 89; Lighthouse Pisart Vision Award, New York, NY, 90. *Prof Exp:* Chief ophthal path, Armed Forces Inst Path, 53-83. *Concurrent Pos:* Assoc prof, Sch Med, George Washington Univ, 54-83, clin prof ophthal path, 63-; lectr, Johns Hopkins Univ, 59-; head, WHO Int Ref Ctr Tumors Eye & Ocular Adnexa, 72-; consult ophthal path, Wash Hosp Ctr, 75-; clin prof path, Uniformed Serv Univ Health Sci, 76- *Mem:* Verhoeff Soc; Pan-Am Asn Ophthal; Asn Res Vision & Ophthal; Am Acad Ophthal & Otolaryngol. *Res:* Pathology of diseases of the eye and ocular adnexa. *Mailing Add:* Dept Path Armed Forces Inst Path Washington DC 20306-0002

**ZIMMERMAN, MARY PRISLOPSKI,** SYNTHETIC ORGANIC CHEMISTRY. *Current Pos:* RES ASSOC, DEPT CHEM, PROTOTEK, DUBLIN, CALIF, 91- *Personal Data:* b Bath, NY, Dec 3, 47; m 75. *Educ:* State Univ NY Albany, BS, 70; Wesleyan Univ, MA, 73; Univ Rochester, MS, 74, PhD(org chem), 77. *Prof Exp:* Fel, Univ Rochester, 76-78, instr, 76-78; adj asst prof org chem, Clarkson Inst Technol, 78-84; res assoc, Dept Chem, Stanford Univ, 84-91. *Mem:* Am Chem Soc; Sigma Xi. *Res:* Synthesis of natural products; synthetic methods; synthesis of morphinans; sterol biosynthesis. *Mailing Add:* 6497 Sierra Lane Dublin CA 94568-2617

**ZIMMERMAN, MICHAEL RAYMOND,** CLINICAL PATHOLOGY, PALEOPATHOLOGY. *Current Pos:* PROF PATH, HAHNEMANN UNIV, 87- *Personal Data:* b Newark, NJ, Dec 26, 37; m 60; c 2. *Educ:* Wash & Jefferson Col, BA, 59; NY Univ, MD, 63; Univ Pa, PhD(anthrop), 76. *Prof Exp:* Major, Walter Reed Army Hosp, US Army, 68-70; pathologist, Lankenau Hosp, 70-72; asst prof path, Univ Pa, 72-77; pathologist, Wayne County Gen Hosp, 77-80; assoc prof path, Hahnemann Univ, 80-82; pathologist, Jeanes Hosp, 82-85; dir clin labs, Coney Island Hosp, 85-87. *Concurrent Pos:* Assoc prof, Univ Mich, 77-80; adj assoc prof, Univ Pa, 80-87, adj prof, 86-; clin prof, State Univ NY, Brooklyn, 86-87. *Mem:* Col Am Pathologists; Paleopath Asn; US-Can Acad Path; Am Soc Clin Pathologists; Am Asn Phys Anthrobiologists; Asn Clin Scientists. *Res:* Paleopathology, the study of the diseases of ancient peoples; studies of mummies from Alaska and Egypt have provided information on the evolution of various diseases, including atherosclerosis and cancer. *Mailing Add:* Dept Path 1 Gustavel Levy Pl PO Box 1032 New York NY 10029

**ZIMMERMAN, NEIL J,** INDOOR AIR QUALITY, VENTILATION. *Current Pos:* ASST PROF INDUST HYG, PURDUE UNIV, 81- *Personal Data:* b Cincinnati, Ohio, June 29, 48; m 71, Marilyn Cember; c Leah F C, Hannah B & Aaron S. *Educ:* Northwestern Univ, BS, 71; Univ NC, MS, 76, PhD(air & indust hyg), 80. *Prof Exp:* Sr design engr, P & W Engrs, Chicago, 71-74; res asst, Pres Coun Environ Qual, 76. *Mem:* Am Indust Hyg Asn; Int Occup Health Asn; Am Acad Indust Hyg; Am Conf Govt Indust Hygienists. *Res:* Investigate various aspects of occupational exposures to toxic agents, including exposure assessment, evaluation and design of controlling ventilation systems, and specifically, the problems resulting from indoor air quality problems; industrial hygiene. *Mailing Add:* Sch HSCI-Civil Purdue Univ West Lafayette IN 47907-1338. *Fax:* 765-496-1377

**ZIMMERMAN, NEIL M,** SINGLE-ELECTRON TUNNELING, LOW-FREQUENCY ELECTRICAL NOISE. *Current Pos:* RES PHYSICIST, NAT INST STAND & TECHNOL, 94- *Personal Data:* b Long Island, NY, 1960. *Educ:* Rensselaer Polytech Inst, BS, 82; Cornell Univ, MS, 85, PhD(physics), 89. *Prof Exp:* Postdoctoral mem staff, AT&T Bell Labs, 89-92; res physicist, Naval Res Lab, 92-94. *Res:* Standards applications of single-electron tunneling devices, including a direct current standard, a capacitance standard and a high-accuracy measurement of the fine-structure constant alpha; noise and charge offset in single-electron tunneling devices. *Mailing Add:* Bldg 220 Rm B258 Nat Inst Stand & Technol Gaithersburg MD 20899. *E-Mail:* neilz@eeel.nist.gov

**ZIMMERMAN, PETER DAVID,** ARMS CONTROL & VERIFICATION, EXPORT CONTROL & NUCLEAR NON-PROLIFERATION. *Current Pos:* PRIN, ZIMMERMAN ASSOC; ADJ RES STAFF MEM, INST DEFENSE ANALYSIS. *Personal Data:* b June 15, 41; US citizen; m 67, Eva Daniels; c Eric D & S Rebecca. *Educ:* Stanford Univ, BS, 63, PhD(physics), 69; Lund Univ, Sweden, Filosofie Licentiat, 67. *Prof Exp:* Res fel physics, Ger Electron Synchrotron, 69-71; adj asst prof physics & planetary sci, Univ Calif, Los Angeles, 71-73; res assoc physics, Fermi Nat Accelerator Lab, 73-74; from asst prof to prof, La State Univ, 74-86; sr assoc, Carnegie Endowment Int Peace, 86-89; distinguished vis prof, George Washington Univ, 90-91; sr fel, Ctr Strategic & Int Studies, 91-94. *Concurrent Pos:* Res affil, Mass Inst Technol, 75-86; vis assoc res physicist, Univ Calif, San Diego, 81; consult, Var Defense Related Firms; William C Foster fel, US Arms Control & Disarmament Agency, 84-86; mem, US Start Deleg, 85-86. *Mem:* Fel Am Phys Soc; Sigma Xi; AAAS; Coun Foreign Rels; Int Inst Strategic Studies. *Res:* Arms control, especially ballistic missile defense, nuclear proliferation and new verification technologies; electron scattering experiments from nuclei, principally at large energy loss. *Mailing Add:* 10125 Nedra Dr Great Falls VA 22066. *Fax:* 703-931-7792; *E-Mail:* peterz@erols.com

**ZIMMERMAN, RICHARD HALE,** HORTICULTURE, PLANT PHYSIOLOGY. *Current Pos:* PLANT PHYSIOLOGIST, AGR RES CTR, USDA, 65- *Personal Data:* b Bowling Green, Ohio, Apr 11, 34; m 66; c 2. *Educ:* Mich State Univ, BS, 56; Rutgers Univ, MS, 59, PhD(hort), 62. *Honors & Awards:* J H Gourley Award, Am Soc Hort Sci, 72, Stark Award, 78 & 82, Darrow Award, 82; Norman Jay Colman Award, Am Asn Nurserymen, 84. *Prof Exp:* Silviculturist, Tex Forest Serv, 62-64. *Mem:* Int Soc Hort Sci; Int Plant Propagators Soc; AAAS; fel Am Soc Hort Sci; Int Asn Plant Tissue Cult; Tissue Cult Asn. *Res:* Tissue culture; juvenility and flower initiation in fruit trees and other woody plants; effects of growth regulators on plant growth and development. *Mailing Add:* Fruit Lab Agr Res USDA 10300 Baltimore Ave Rm 329 Bg010A Barc-W Beltsville MD 20705-2350. *Fax:* 301-504-5062

**ZIMMERMAN, ROBERT ALLAN,** RADIOLOGY. *Current Pos:* from asst prof to assoc prof, Hosp Univ Pa, 72-81, chief, Sect Neuroradiol, 79-85, PROF RADIOL, SCH MED, HOSP UNIV PA, 81-; CHIEF PEDIAT NEURORADIOL, CHILDREN'S HOSP PHILADELPHIA, 88- *Personal Data:* b Philadelphia, Pa, June 23, 38; m 60; c 2. *Educ:* Temple Univ, BA, 60; Georgetown Univ Sch Med, MD, 64. *Prof Exp:* Intern, Georgetown Univ Hosp, 64-65; physician resident fel, Hosp Univ Pa, 65-69; radiologist, US Army, Europe, 69-72. *Concurrent Pos:* Assoc ed, J Comput Tomography, 77-82. *Mem:* Am Soc Neuroradiol; Radiol Soc NAm; Asn Univ Radiologists; Am Soc Head & Neck Radiol; Soc Pediat Radiol; Europ Soc Neuroradiol. *Res:* Medical imaging of central nervous system trauma, using medical imaging in the diagnosis and management of pediatric brain tumors. *Mailing Add:* Dept Radiol Children's Hosp Philadelphia 34th St & Civic Center Blvd Philadelphia PA 19104. *Fax:* 215-590-4127

**ZIMMERMAN, ROBERT LYMAN,** PHYSICS. *Current Pos:* asst prof, 66-74, PROF PHYSICS, PHYSICS DEPT & INST THEORET SCI, UNIV ORE, 74- *Personal Data:* b La Grande, Ore, Dec 30, 35; m 57; c 5. *Educ:* Univ Ore, BA, 58; Univ Wash, PhD(physics), 63. *Prof Exp:* Physicist, Lawrence Radiation Lab, Univ Calif, Berkeley, 64-66. *Concurrent Pos:* Res assoc, Univ Ore, 70-74. *Mem:* Am Phys Soc; Sigma Xi. *Res:* Quantum field theory; elementary particle physics; gravitation; astrophysics; general relativity; cosmology; investigation of properties of exact solutions in general relativity, properties of the Big Bang and production of gravitational radiation by energetic astrophysical events. *Mailing Add:* 528 Kingswood Ave Eugene OR 97405

**ZIMMERMAN, ROGER M,** CIVIL ENGINEERING, STRUCTURAL MECHANICS. *Current Pos:* sr mem tech staff, 80-90, DISTINGUISHED MEM TECH STAFF, SANDIA NAT LABS, 90- *Personal Data:* b Rehoboth, NMex, May 15, 36; m 56, Mary E Nielsen; c Paul E & Michael L. *Educ:* Univ Colo, BS, 59, MS, 61, PhD(civil eng), 65. *Prof Exp:* Instr civil eng, Univ Colo, 59-63, res assoc, 63-64; from asst prof to assoc prof civil eng, NMex State Univ, 64-70, asst dean eng, 67-72, prof, 70-80, assoc dean, 72-74, actg dean, 74-75. *Concurrent Pos:* Sr engr, Phys Sci Lab, NMex State Univ, 75-79; vis scientist, Rockwell Int Sci Ctr, 79-80; comnr, Eng Accreditation Comn, Accreditation Bd Eng & Technol. *Mem:* Am Soc Civil Engrs; Nat Soc Prof Engrs. *Res:* Multiaxial strength properties of plain concrete; deterioration of plain concrete; biomechanical aspects of simulated side and rear automobile impacts; safety aspects of school bus seats; evaluation of structures for seismic response; applications of ultrasonics to predict space shuttle tiles properties; rock mechnics field testing to evaluate tuff for storage medium for high-level radioactive wastes; transient shock testing of electronic components for launchings, payload ejections and stage separations. *Mailing Add:* Sandia Nat Labs MS 0309 Albuquerque NM 87185-5800

**ZIMMERMAN, ROGER PAUL,** NEUROBIOLOGY, VISUAL PHYSIOLOGY. *Current Pos:* patent agt, 94-96, PATENT ATTY BIOL & CHEM, OLSON & HIERL LAW FIRM, 96- *Personal Data:* b Oak Park, Ill, Sept 29, 46; m 74; c 2. *Educ:* Univ Ill, Chicago, BS, 68; Yale Univ, MPhil, 69, PhD(biol), 77. *Prof Exp:* Res asst paleobot, Dept Biol Sci, Univ Ill, Chicago, 65-68; teaching asst, Dept Biol, Yale Univ, 60 & 73; res fel, Biol Lab, Harvard Univ, 76-78; asst prof neurolsci, Rush-Presby-St Lukes Med Ctr, Rush Med Col, 78-84, physiol, 79-89, assoc prof neurol sci, 84-94, assoc prof physiol, 89-94. *Concurrent Pos:* Participant, NSF Summer Res Prog, Univ Ill, Chicago, 68; NSF fel, Yale Univ, 68-73; res asst, Walter Reed Army Inst Res, US Army, 70-72; NIH fel, Harvard Univ, 76-78, teaching fel, Dept Biol, 78; course dir med neurobiol, Rush Med Col, 81-; STEPS fel, Marine Biol Lab, Woods Hole, MA, 82; lectr, Dept Anat & Cell Biol, Univ Ill, Chicago, 86-; actg dir, Div Cell Biol, Rush Univ, 90-; course dir, molecular cell biol, 90-, vis scientist, cellular, molecular & struct biol, Northwestern Univ, 89-90; adj assoc prof, Med Col, Univ Ill, Chicago, 87- *Mem:* Asn Res Vision & Ophthal; Soc Neurosci; AAAS; Sigma Xi. *Res:* Neurobiology of vision, including the physiology, development and ultrastructure of synaptic interactions in the vertebrate retina; physiology and pharmacology of glial cells; control of gene expression in the adult and developing nervous system. *Mailing Add:* Olson & Hierl Ltd 20 N Wacker Dr 36th Floor Chicago IL 60606. *Fax:* 312-633-1564; *E-Mail:* u22379@uicvm.uic.edu

**ZIMMERMAN, SARAH E,** IMMUNOLOGY, MICROBIOLOGY & MOLECULAR BIOLOGY. *Current Pos:* res assoc microbiol, 71-73, immunologist, Dept Path, 73-95, SUPVR MOLECULAR DIAG, DEPT PATH, SCH MED, IND UNIV, INDIANAPOLIS, 95- *Personal Data:* b Indianapolis, Ind, Oct 29, 37. *Educ:* Ind Univ, AB, 59, MA, 61; Wayne State Univ, PhD(biochem), 69. *Prof Exp:* Res asst biochem, Sch Med, Wayne State Univ, 68-69; res assoc chem, Ind Univ, Bloomington, 69-71. *Mem:* Sigma Xi; Am Soc Microbiol; Am Asn Immunologists; Am Chem Soc. *Res:* Diagnosis of viral and bacterial infections and genetic defects by molecular biology methods; immunological diagnosis of viral, bacterial and fungal infections. *Mailing Add:* 29 Kendal Dr Kennett Square PA 19348-2323. *Fax:* 317-278-0643

**ZIMMERMAN, SARAH LIPPINCOTT,** ASTROMETRY. *Current Pos:* Res asst astron, Swarthmore Col, 42-51, res assoc, 52-72, lectr, 61-76, dir, 72-81, prof, 77-81, EMER PROF ASTRON & EMER DIR, SPROUL OBSERV, SWARTHMORE COL, 81- *Personal Data:* b Philadelphia, Pa, Oct 26, 20; wid. *Educ:* Univ Pa, BA, 42; Swarthmore Col, MA, 50. *Hon Degrees:* DSc, Villanova Univ, 73. *Concurrent Pos:* Vis assoc astronr, Lick Observ, 49 & Calif Inst Technol, 78; Fulbright fel, France, 53-54; mem, Fr Solar Eclipse Exped to Oland, Sweden, 54; partic, Vis Prof Prog, Am Astron Soc, 61-; vpres, Comn 26, Int Astron Union, 70-73, pres, 73-76; nat lectr, Sigma Xi, 72. *Mem:* Am Astron Soc; Int Astron Union; Sigma Xi. *Res:* Parallaxes of nearby stars; double stars; search for planetary companions to nearby stars; stellar masses; chromosphere studies; spicules. *Mailing Add:* 306 Bell Rd Cinnaminson NJ 08077-2916

**ZIMMERMAN, SELMA BLAU,** EMBRYOLOGY, CELL BIOLOGY. *Current Pos:* asst prof, York Univ, 74-75, assoc prof, 74-87, coordr, 77-79, 81-82 & 85-86, PROF NATURAL SCI, GLENDON COL, YORK UNIV, 87- *Personal Data:* b New York, NY, Apr 1, 30; m 53, Arthur M; c Susan, Beth & Robert. *Educ:* Hunter Col, BA, 50; NY Univ, MS, 54, PhD, 58. *Prof Exp:* Res asst, NY Univ, 53-55; res assoc pharmacol, Col Med, State Univ NY Downstate Med Ctr, 60-61; instr biol, Hunter Col, 61-64 & York Univ, Ont, 65-66; res assoc zool, Univ Toronto, 66-69. *Concurrent Pos:* Assoc ed, Biochem & Cell Biol. *Mem:* AAAS; Can Soc Cell & Molecular Biol; Can Asn Women Sci; Sigma Xi. *Res:* Pigment cell physiology; mechanisms of cell division; cell cycle studies drug action on cells, hydrostatic pressure effects on sytoskeleton and effects of cannabis on fertilization. *Mailing Add:* Natural Sci Div 2275 Bayview Ave Toronto ON M4N 3M6 Can

**ZIMMERMAN, SHELDON BERNARD,** MICROBIOLOGY. *Current Pos:* sect head pharmaceut, 63-83, ASSOC DIR BASIC MICROBIOL, MERCK INST THERAPEUT RES, 83- *Personal Data:* b New York, NY, Nov 7, 26; m 50; c 1. *Educ:* City Col New York, BS, 48; Long Island Univ, MS, 65; NY Univ, PhD(biol), 71. *Prof Exp:* Chemist pharmaceut, Vitamin Corp Am, 49-51; develop microbiologist pharmaceut, Schering Corp, 51-63. *Mem:* Am Soc Microbiol; NY Acad Sci. *Res:* Discovery and mode of action of antibiotics; microbial physiology; microbial ecology; structure-activity relationships of antibiotics; automated microbiological assays; microbial chemotherapeutics. *Mailing Add:* 30 Hemlock Terr Springfield NJ 07081

**ZIMMERMAN, STANLEY WILLIAM,** ELECTRICAL ENGINEERING. *Current Pos:* in charge high voltage res lab, 45-58, prof, 45-76, EMER PROF ELEC ENG, SCH ELEC ENG, CORNELL UNIV, 76- *Personal Data:* b Detroit, Mich, July 30, 07; m 32; c 4. *Educ:* Univ Mich, BS & MS, 30. *Prof Exp:* Asst, Res Dept, Detroit Edison Co, 29-30; test man, Gen Elec Co, NY & Mass, 30-32, test man, Pittsfield Works Lab, 32-34, res & develop engr, Lightning Arrester Dept, 35-45. *Concurrent Pos:* Mem staff, Eng Dept, Westinghouse Elec Corp, Pa, 52-, Ramo-Wooldridge, Inc, 59-60 & Lawrence Radiation Lab, Univ Calif, 61 & 66-67; mem, Int Conf Large Elec High Tension Systs; consult. *Mem:* Am Soc Eng Educ; sr mem Inst Elec & Electronics Engrs; Brit Inst Elec Engrs. *Res:* Circuit interruption and protection devices; lightning studies; single transient oscillography; wide band transformers; heavy machinery; electrical measurements and insulation; extra-high voltage apparatus design; ionization, pulsed radiation and partial discharge measurements; sulphur hexafluoride power transmission systems; dielectric stress analysis. *Mailing Add:* 102 Valley Rd Ithaca NY 14850

**ZIMMERMAN, STEPHEN WILLIAM,** NEPHROLOGY, MEDICINE. *Current Pos:* fel, Univ Wis, 69-70, fel nephropath, 72-74, from asst prof to assoc prof, 74-87, PROF MED, UNIV WIS, 87- *Personal Data:* b Ironton, Mo, Dec 27, 41; 78; c 5. *Educ:* Univ Wis, BS, 63, MD, 66. *Prof Exp:* Chief nephrology, Fitzsimmons Army Hosp, 70-72. *Concurrent Pos:* NIH grant, 77-80. *Mem:* Am Soc Nephrology; Int Soc Nephrology; Am Fedn Clin Res; Nat Kidney Found; Int Soc Peritoneal Dialysis. *Res:* Effects of environmental toxins on the kidney; pathogenesis of renal disease; peritoneal dialysis. *Mailing Add:* Dept Med Nephrology 600 Highland Ave Madison WI 53792-0001

**ZIMMERMAN, STEVEN B,** BIOCHEMISTRY. *Current Pos:* RES CHEMIST, NAT INST DIABETES, DIGESTIVE & KIDNEY DIS, 64- *Personal Data:* b Chicago, Ill, June 5, 34; m 56; c 2. *Educ:* Univ Ill, BS, 56, MS, 57; Stanford Univ, PhD(biochem), 61. *Prof Exp:* Nat Found res fel, 61-62. *Mem:* Am Soc Biochem & Molecular Biol. *Res:* Nucleic acid synthesis and structure; mechanism of enzyme action; macromolecular crowding effects. *Mailing Add:* Nat Inst Diabetes Digestive & Kidney Dis Bldg 5 Rm 328W Bethesda MD 20892

**ZIMMERMAN, STUART O,** MATHEMATICAL BIOLOGY. *Current Pos:* assoc prof biomath, M D Anderson Hosp & Tumor Inst, Univ Tex, 68-72, head, Div Biomed Info Resources, 81-84, exec dir info systs, 85-86, Kathryn O'Conner res prof, 86-88, PROF BIOMATH & BIOMATHEMATICIAN, DENT SCI INST, UNIV TEX, HOUSTON, 72-, MATTIE ALLEN FAIR RES CHAIR, 88- *Personal Data:* b Chicago, Ill, July 27, 35; m 59; c 1. *Educ:* Univ Chicago, BA, 54, PhD(math biol), 64. *Prof Exp:* Res assoc, Univ Chicago, 63-65, from instr to asst prof math biol, 65-67. *Concurrent Pos:* Consult, Ill State Dent Soc, 61- & Am Dent Asn, 66-; assoc prof biomath & assoc mem, Dent Sci Inst, Univ Tex, Houston, 67-, assoc mem, Grad Sch Biomed Sci, 68-70, mem, 70, actg dir, Common Res Comput Facil, M D Anderson Hosp & Tumor Inst Houston, 68-73, chmn exec bd, Houston Educ & Res Comput Ctr, 73-86, head, Dept Biomath, 88- *Mem:* AAAS; Am Statist Asn; Asn Comput Mach; Soc Math Biol. *Res:* Biomedical computing; mathematical modeling; image processing; computer karyotyping; information management systems; design and analysis of cancer and dental clinical trials. *Mailing Add:* 9906 Bob White Dr Houston TX 77096

**ZIMMERMAN, THOM J,** OPHTHALMOLOGY, OCULAR PHARMACOLOGY. *Current Pos:* actg chmn, Dept Ophthal, 77, assoc prof, 77-79, PROF OPHTHAL, PHARMACOL & EXP THERAPEUT & CHMN, DEPT OPHTHAL, OSCHNER CLIN, LA STATE UNIV MED CTR, 79- *Personal Data:* b Lincoln, Ill, Oct 5, 42; m 70; c Jessica. *Educ:* Univ Ill, Champaign-Urbana, BS, 64, MD, 68; Univ Fla, PhD(pharmacol), 76. *Prof Exp:* Intern, Presby St Lukes Hosp, Chicago, 68-69; resident, Dept Ophthal, Col Med, Univ Fla, 71-74, corneal fel, 74-75; glaucoma fel, Dept Ophthal, Washington Univ, St Louis, 76-77. *Concurrent Pos:* Heed Ophthalmic Found fel, 76-77; ophthalmic consult glaucoma, US Pub Health Hosp, New Orleans, 77-82; Robert E McCormick scholar, Res Prevent Blindness, Inc, 78; consult, Eye Adv Coun, Food & Drug Admin, 79, Nat Eye Adv Coun & Nat Eye Inst, 83 & Handicapped Children's Serv Prog, Off Prev & Pub Health Serv, 85; res career develop award, Nat Eye Inst, 78-; fight for sight dept award, Oschner Clin, 80-81. *Mem:* Fel Am Col Clin Pharmacol; AMA; Asn Res Vision & Ophthal; Am Soc Clin Pharmacol; Am Soc Contemp Ophthal. *Res:* Ocular pharmacology; pharmacology of the glaucoma drugs; clinical care of glaucoma medical and surgical. *Mailing Add:* Dept Ophthal Univ Louisville Sch Med Louisville KY 40202. *Fax:* 502-852-7298

**ZIMMERMAN, THOMAS PAUL,** IMMUNOPHARMACOLOGY, DRUG TRANSPORT. *Current Pos:* assoc div dir, 88-92, RES BIOCHEMIST, WELLCOME RES LABS, BURROUGHS WELLCOME & CO, USA, INC, 71-, PRIN SCIENTIST, 84-, DIV DIR, 92- *Personal Data:* b Plainfield, NJ, Sept 3, 42; m 91; c 2. *Educ:* Providence Col, BS, 64; Brown Univ, PhD(biochem), 69. *Prof Exp:* Res fel biol & med sci, Nat Inst Neurol Dis & Stroke, Brown Univ, 69-71. *Concurrent Pos:* Mem, Adv Comt on Chemother & Hemat, Am Cancer Soc, 83-87, chair, 87. *Mem:* Am Soc Pharmacol & Exp Therapeut; Am Asn Cancer Res; Int Soc Immunopharmacology; Int Soc Antiviral Res. *Res:* Purine metabolism and the mode of action of purine antimetabolites; cyclic nucleotide metabolism; biological methylation reactions; immunosuppression; metabolic studies of purine and pyrimidine antimetabolites; determination of mechanisms by which pharmacological agents modulate immune and inflammatory cell function; nucleoside and drug transport; antiviral chemotherapy. *Mailing Add:* Bayer Corp 8368 US 70 W PO Box 507 Clayton NC 27520. *Fax:* 919-315-8579

**ZIMMERMAN, TOMMY LYNN,** SOIL & WATER CONSERVATION. *Current Pos:* ASSOC PROF & TECH COORDR SOIL & WATER CONSERV & MGT TECHNOL, AGR TECH INST, OHIO STATE UNIV, 75- *Personal Data:* b Lima, Ohio, July 23, 43; m 67, Susan Hover; c Cheryl (Botkin) & Craig. *Educ:* Ohio State Univ, BS, 66; Pa State Univ, MS, 69, PhD(agron), 73. *Prof Exp:* From instr to asst prof agron, Delaware Valley Col, 71-75. *Concurrent Pos:* Consult soil scientist, 73-75 & 95-; cert prof soil scientists, ARCPACS, 80- *Mem:* Am Soc Agron; Soil & Water Conserv Soc; Coun Agr Sci Technol; Am Soc Agr Engrs. *Res:* Use of constructed wetlands for wastewater disposal. *Mailing Add:* Agr Tech Inst Ohio State Univ 1328 Dover Rd Wooster OH 44691-4000. *Fax:* 330-262-7634; *E-Mail:* zimmerman.4@osu.edu

**ZIMMERMAN, WALTER BRUCE,** SOLID STATE PHYSICS. *Current Pos:* ASSOC PROF PHYSICS, IND UNIV, SOUTH BEND, 69-, CHMN, DEPT PHYSICS, 74- *Personal Data:* b Evergreen Park, Ill, Nov 27, 33; m 55; c 3. *Educ:* Andrews Univ, BA, 55; Mich State Univ, MS, 57, PhD(physics), 60. *Prof Exp:* Asst physics, Mich State Univ, 58-60; sr physicist solar energy conversion, Gen Dynamics Astronaut, 60-62; from asst prof to assoc prof physics, Andrews Univ, 62-69. *Mem:* Am Phys Soc; Am Asn Physics Teachers; Am Vacuum Soc; Sigma Xi. *Res:* Changes that occur in infrared absorption spectrum and lattice constant of lithium hydride as its isotopic composition is varied; magnetic effect in biological processes; agglutination of red blood cells in a magnetic field; solar energy conversion by cadmium sulfide films. *Mailing Add:* Dept Phys Ind Univ PO Box 7111 South Bend IN 46634

**ZIMMERMAN, WILLIAM FREDERICK,** CELL BIOLOGY. *Current Pos:* asst prof, 66-72, ASSOC PROF BIOL, AMHERST COL, 72- *Personal Data:* b Chicago, Ill, July 7, 38; m 64; c 2. *Educ:* Princeton Univ, BA, 60, PhD(biol), 66. *Hon Degrees:* MA, Amherst Col, 80. *Prof Exp:* Instr biol, Princeton Univ, 64-66. *Concurrent Pos:* NSF res grants, 66-70; NIH spec fel, 69-70; Nat Eye Inst res grants, 70-83; vis res fel, Univ Nijmegen, 73-74 & Cambridge Univ, 79-80. *Mem:* AAAS; Asn Res Vision & Ophthal. *Res:* Entrainment of circadian rhythms in insects; action spectra, carotenoid metabolism; cellular biochemistry of visual cycles, photoreceptor cell renewal and retinal pigment epithelium. *Mailing Add:* Dept Biol Amherst Col Amherst MA 01002-5002

**ZIMMERMANN, CHARLES EDWARD,** plant physiology, for more information see previous edition

**ZIMMERMANN, F(RANCIS) J(OHN),** CRYOGENIC ENGINEERING. *Current Pos:* prof, 62-86, dir res & contract progs, 64-68, EMER PROF MECH ENG, LAFAYETTE COL, 86- *Personal Data:* b Jersey City, NJ, Apr 21, 24; m 50, Margaret M Stephens; c Stephen R & Marcy J. *Educ:* Yale Univ, BE, 48; Mass Inst Technol, SM, 50, ME, 51, ScD, 53. *Prof Exp:* Staff engr, Arthur D Little, Inc, 52-55; from asst prof to assoc prof mech eng, Yale Univ, 55-62. *Concurrent Pos:* Consult, Arthur D Little, Inc, 55-61 & Air Prod & Chem, Inc, 63-73; asst prog dir eng prog, NSF, 61-62. *Mem:* Am Soc Mech Engrs; Am Soc Eng Educ; Cryogenic Soc Am. *Res:* Thermodynamics; heat transfer; cryogenic engineering. *Mailing Add:* Dept Mech Eng Lafayette Col Easton PA 18042

**ZIMMERMANN, H(ENRY) J(OSEPH),** ELECTRICAL ENGINEERING, ELECTRONICS. *Current Pos:* from instr to prof, 40-78, assoc dir res lab electronics, 52-61, dir, 61-76, EMER PROF ELEC ENG, MASS INST TECHNOL, 78- *Personal Data:* b St Louis, Mo, May 11, 16; m 45; c 4. *Educ:* Wash Univ, BS, 38; Mass Inst Technol, SM, 42. *Prof Exp:* Instr, Wash Univ, 38-40. *Mem:* Fel Inst Elec & Electronics Engrs. *Res:* Electronic circuits; signal processing and perception. *Mailing Add:* Elec Eng Dept Mass Inst Technol 77 Massachusetts Ave Cambridge MA 02139

**ZIMMERMANN, MARK EDWARD,** PHYSICS, COMPUTER SCIENCE. *Current Pos:* PHYSICIST, US GOVT, 81- *Personal Data:* b Weimar, Tex, Sept 29, 52; m 78; c 3. *Educ:* Rice Univ, BA, 74; Calif Inst Technol, MS, 76, PhD(physics), 80. *Prof Exp:* Physicist, Inst Defense Analyses, 79-81. *Mem:* Am Phys Soc. *Res:* Studies of developments in the physical sciences and information technologies; computer software development. *Mailing Add:* 9511 Gwyndale Dr Silver Spring MD 20910

**ZIMMERMANN, R ERIK,** ASTROPHYSICS, SCIENCE EDUCATION. *Current Pos:* DIR, ROBERT J NOVINS PLANETARIUM, OCEAN COUNTY COL, 74-; LECTR ASTRON, OCEAN CO COL, 74- *Personal Data:* b Newark, NJ, Oct 29, 41; m 71, Gayle M Stephens; c Bradley L, Brendan L, R Stephen & J Erik. *Educ:* Pomona Col, BA, 63; Univ Calif, Los Angeles, MA, 66, PhD(astron), 70. *Prof Exp:* Asst prof astron, Mich State Univ, 68-71; assoc prof astron, Kean Col, NJ, 71-74. *Mem:* Int Planetarium Soc; Royal Astron Soc Can; Sigma Xi; Mid Atlantic Planetarium Soc. *Res:* Stellar structure and evolution. *Mailing Add:* Robert J Novins Planetarium Ocean County Col CN 2001 Toms River NJ 08754-2001. *E-Mail:* zimmermann@monmouth.com

**ZIMMERMANN, ROBERT ALAN,** PROTEIN SYNTHESIS, PROTEIN-RNA INTERACTION. *Current Pos:* assoc prof microbiol & biochem, Univ Mass, Amherst, 73-77, head, biochem, dept, 79-86, actg dir, Grad Prog Molecular & Cell Biol, 85-88, PROF BIOCHEM, UNIV MASS, AMHERST, 77- *Personal Data:* b Philadelphia, Pa, July 17, 37; m 87, Athleen Kammerer; c Hannah K. *Educ:* Amherst Col, BA, 59; Mass Inst Technol, PhD(biophys), 64. *Prof Exp:* Vis scientist biochem, Acad Sci USSR, 65-66; res fel microbiol, Med Sch, Harvard Univ, 66-69; res assoc molecular biol, Univ Geneva, 70-73. *Concurrent Pos:* Helen Hay Whitney Found fel, 68; sr fel, Europ Molecular Biol Orgn, 72; adv, WHO, 75-78; NIH res career develop award, 75; mem, Molecular Biol Study Sect, NIH, 78-82 & Molecular Biochem Panel, NSF, 94-97. *Mem:* Am Chem Soc; Am Soc Biochem & Molecular Biol; AAAS; Am Soc Microbiol; Sigma Xi. *Res:* Structure and function of the ribosome in protein biosynthesis, including topography of tRNA binding sites, protein-tRNA interactions in assembly, and properties of mutationally altered ribosomes and their protein and RNA components. *Mailing Add:* Dept Biochem & Molecular Biol Univ Mass Amherst MA 01003

**ZIMMERMANN, WILLIAM, JR,** LOW TEMPERATURE PHYSICS. *Current Pos:* lectr, 59-61, from asst prof to assoc prof, 61-70, PROF PHYSICS, UNIV MINN, MINNEAPOLIS, 70- *Personal Data:* b Philadelphia, Pa, Oct 28, 30; m 62, Elizabeth Strout; c Michael S, Sarah L & Christopher L. *Educ:* Amherst Col, AB, 52; Calif Inst Technol, PhD(physics), 58. *Prof Exp:* Fulbright fel, Neth, 58-59. *Concurrent Pos:* NSF sr fel, Finland, 67-68; vis scientist, Finland, 75-76. *Mem:* Am Phys Soc; Am Asn Physics Teachers; AAAS. *Res:* Low temperature physics; superfluid helium; liquid helium-3/helium-4 mixtures. *Mailing Add:* Sch Physics & Astron Univ Minn 116 Church St SE Minneapolis MN 55455. *Fax:* 612-624-4578; *E-Mail:* zimmermann@physics.spa.umn.edu

**ZIMMIE, THOMAS FRANK,** GEOTECHNICAL ENGINEERING, ENVIRONMENTAL GEOTECHNOLOGY. *Current Pos:* PROF CIVIL ENG, RENSSELAER POLYTECH INST, 73-, OWNER & CHIEF EXEC OFFICER, CIVROTECH ENG, PC, 93- *Personal Data:* b Scranton, Pa, Jan 24, 39; m 89, Judith Spain; c David, Amy Braden & James Braden. *Educ:* Worcester Polytech Inst, BS, 60; Univ Conn, MS, 62, PhD(geotech eng), 72. *Honors & Awards:* Spec Serv Award, Am Soc Testing & Mat, 80, Charles B Dudley Award, 84. *Prof Exp:* Civil engr, USN Oceanog Off, 61; staff engr, Linde Div, Union Carbide Corp, 64-67; consult, T F Zimmie, PE, 67-72; fel, Norweg Geotech Inst, 72-73. *Concurrent Pos:* Eng partner, Wang & Zimmie Consult Engrs, 73-80; geotech engr, NY State Dept Environ Conserv, 83-85; town engr, Town North Greenbush, 85-88; prog mgr geomech, NSF, 88-90. *Mem:* Am Soc Civil Engrs; Am Soc Testing & Mat; Asn Ground Water Scientists & Engrs; Asn Soil & Found Engrs; Transp Res Bd; Am Geophys Union. *Res:* Environmental geotechnology-landfill siting and design, freeze/thaw effects on soil, hydraulic conductivity of soil; geotechnical engineering-laboratory testing, soil dynamics, earthquake engineering; centrifuge modeling; ground water; contaminant transport. *Mailing Add:* Civil Eng Dept Rensselaer Polytech Inst Troy NY 12180-3590. *Fax:* 518-276-4833; *E-Mail:* zimmit@rpi.edu

**ZIMMON, DAVID SAMUEL,** GASTROENTEROLOGY, LIVER DISEASE. *Current Pos:* instr med, Med Col, 65, asst prof, 66-72, assoc prof, 72-79, PROF CLIN MED, SCH MED, NY UNIV, 79- *Personal Data:* b Brooklyn, NY, Dec 2, 33; m 62; c 3. *Educ:* Harvard Univ, MD, 58; Am Bd Internal Med, dipl, 66 & 68. *Prof Exp:* From intern to sr asst resident med, 2nd Med Div, Bellevue Hosp & Mem Ctr Cancer, 58-61; fel gastroenterol, 2nd Med Div, Bellevue Hosp, 61-62; res asst liver dis, Royal Free Hosp, London, 62-64. *Concurrent Pos:* Chief, Gastroenterol Sect, NY Vet Admin Med Ctr, 65; asst vis physician, Bellevue Hosp, 69. *Mem:* Med Res Soc; Am Fedn Clin Res; Am Asn Study Liver Dis; Am Gastroenterol Asn; Am Soc Gastrointestinal Endoscopy. *Res:* Liver disease; hypertension; biliary and pancreatic disease; endoscopy; endoscopic surgery. *Mailing Add:* 7 Farmview Rd Port Washington NY 11050

**ZIMMT, WERNER SIEGFRIED,** polymer chemistry, museum conservation, for more information see previous edition

**ZIMNISKI, STEPHEN JOSEPH,** ONCOLOGY, HORMONE-DEPENDENT CANCERS. *Current Pos:* SR SCIENTIST & ASSOC PROF OBSTET, WOMEN'S RES INST, UNIV KANS, 90- *Personal Data:* b Biddeford, Maine, Oct 9, 48; m 92, Suzanne Gagnon; c Kristen. *Educ:* Univ Maine, BS, 70; Univ Mo, MA, 73; Boston Univ, PhD(physiol), 80. *Prof Exp:* Instr & lectr biol, Univ Mo, 70-74; instr, Univ Maine, 75-77; lectr allied health, Northeastern Univ, 79-81; from asst prof to assoc prof biochem, Univ Miami, 84-90. *Mem:* Am Asn Cancer Res; Am Soc Biochem & Molecular Biol; Endocrine Soc; Soc Study Reproduction; AAAS; Int Asn Breast Cancer Res. *Res:* Actions and effects of estrogens and antiestrogens on breast cancer, induction, differentiation and growth. *Mailing Add:* Women's Res Inst 2903 E Central Wichita KS 67214-4716. *Fax:* 316-687-5231

**ZIMNY, MARILYN LUCILE,** ANATOMY. *Current Pos:* from asst prof to assoc prof, 54-64, actg head dept, 75-76, head dept, 76-90, PROF ANAT, LA STATE UNIV MED CTR, NEW ORLEANS, 64-, VCHANCELLOR ACAD AFFAIRS & DEAN SCH GRAD STUDIES, 90- *Personal Data:* b Chicago, Ill, Dec 12, 27. *Educ:* Univ Ill, BA, 48; Loyola Univ, Ill, MS, 51, PhD(anat), 54. *Prof Exp:* Asst anat, Med Sch, Loyola Univ, Ill, 51-53. *Concurrent Pos:* Vis prof, Sch Med, Univ Costa Rica, 61 & 62; mem, Inst Arctic Biol, Univ Alaska, 66. *Mem:* Am Asn Anat (pres, 83); Am Physiol Soc; Micros Soc Am; Am Asn Dent Sch. *Res:* Light microscopy and transmission/scanning electron microscopy of joint related tissues such as ligaments and articular cartilage in health and disease. *Mailing Add:* La State Univ Med Ctr 433 Bolivar St New Orleans LA 70112-2223. *Fax:* 504-568-5588

**ZIMRING, LOIS JACOBS,** SCIENCE FOR THE NON-SCIENCE MAJOR, CHANGING COSMOLOGICAL CONCEPTS. *Current Pos:* from asst prof to prof, 66-90, EMER PROF NATURAL SCI, MICH STATE UNIV, 91- *Personal Data:* b Chicago, Ill, Nov 19, 23; div; c 1. *Educ:* Univ Chicago, BS, 45, MS, 49, PhD(phys chem), 64. *Prof Exp:* Trainee microbiol, Morgan Park Jr Col, 49-51; lectr phys sci, Univ Chicago, 59-61, instr, 61-64; asst prof chem, Univ Minn, 64-66. *Mem:* Sigma Xi. *Res:* Ultraviolet spectra of conjugated systems; crystal spectra of transition metal halides; solid state mixed alum systems; chirality of prebiotic molecules; changing cosmological views. *Mailing Add:* 1123 Abbott Rd East Lansing MI 48823

**ZINDER, NORTON DAVID,** MOLECULAR GENETICS. *Current Pos:* Asst, Rockefeller Univ, 52-58, from assoc prof to prof, 58-76, dean post grad & grad educ, 93-96, JOHN D ROCKEFELLER JR PROF MICROBIAL GENETICS, ROCKEFELLER UNIV, 76- *Personal Data:* b New York, NY, Nov 7, 28; m 49, Marilyn; c Stephen Henry & Michael Ira. *Educ:* Columbia Univ, AB, 47; Univ Wis, MS, 49, PhD(med microbiol), 52. *Hon Degrees:* DSc, Univ Wis, 90. *Honors & Awards:* Eli Lilly Award Microbiol, 62; US Steel Found Award Molecular Biol, Nat Acad Sci, 66; Sci Freedom & Responsibility Award, AAAS, 82. *Concurrent Pos:* Scholar, Am Cancer Soc, 55-58; assoc ed, Virol, 65-90; mem, Div Comt Biol & Med Sci, NSF, 69-72; sect ed, Intervirol, 73-82; consult, Off Technol Assessment, US Cong, Washington, DC, 79-81; chmn, Sect Genetics, Nat Acad Sci, 79-82, mem, Bd Army Sci & Technol, 82-88, coun mem, 88-91; coun mem, Am Acad Arts & Sci, 84-87. *Mem:* Nat Acad Sci; fel AAAS; Genetics Soc Am; Am Soc Microbiol; Am Soc Biol Chemists; Sigma Xi; Am Acad Arts & Sci; Am Soc Virol. *Res:* Virology; protein biosynthesis; genetics. *Mailing Add:* Rockefeller Univ 1230 York Ave New York NY 10021-6399. *E-Mail:* zinder@rockvax.rockefeller.edu

**ZINDER, STEPHEN HENRY,** ANAEROBIC MICROORGANISMS, ENVIRONMENTAL MICROBIOLOGY. *Current Pos:* asst prof, 80-86, ASSOC PROF MICROBIOL, CORNELL UNIV, 86- *Personal Data:* b Madison, Wis, Oct 22, 50; m 76; c 3. *Educ:* Kenyon Col, BA, 72; Colo State Univ, MS, 74; Univ Wis, PhD(bact), 77. *Prof Exp:* Instr chem, Colo State Univ, 72-74; res asst bact, Univ Wis, 74-77; scholar pub health, Univ Calif, Los Angeles, 77-79. *Mem:* Am Soc Microbiol; AAAS; Sigma Xi. *Res:* Physiology and ecology of methanogenic and other anaerobic bacteria. *Mailing Add:* Dept Microbiol 307 Stocking Hall Cornell Univ Ithaca NY 14853-7201

**ZINDLER, ALAN,** GEOCHEMISTRY. *Current Pos:* From asst prof to prof geol sci, 80-93, ADJ SR RES SCIENTIST, LAMONT-DOHERTY EARTH OBSERV, COLUMBIA UNIV, 94-; CHMN & PROF GEOL, FLA STATE UNIV, 94- *Personal Data:* b Tampa, Fla, June 9, 53. *Educ:* Fla State Univ, BS, 76; Mass Inst Technol, PhD(geochem), 80. *Concurrent Pos:* Dir geochem, Nat High Magnetic Field Lab, Fla State Univ, 94- *Res:* Isotope geology applied to the study of the differentiation and evolution of the earth; global change and the environment. *Mailing Add:* 1800 E Paul Dirac Dr Tallahassee FL 32306-4005

**ZINDLER, RICHARD EUGENE,** MATHEMATICS, OPERATIONS RESEARCH. *Current Pos:* from asst prof to assoc prof, 52-63, PROF ENG RES, PA STATE UNIV, 63- *Personal Data:* b Benton Harbor, Mich, Mar 5, 27; m 58; c 2. *Educ:* Mich State Univ, BS & MS, 49, PhD(math), 56. *Prof Exp:* Asst math, Mich State Univ, 49-52. *Mem:* AAAS; Am Math Soc; Acoust Soc Am; Opers Res Soc Am; Asn Comput Mach. *Res:* Weapon system analysis and synthesis; primate behavior. *Mailing Add:* 639 Stoneledge Rd State College PA 16803

**ZINGARO, JOSEPH S,** SCIENCE EDUCATION, CHEMISTRY. *Current Pos:* RETIRED. *Personal Data:* b Mt Morris, NY, Mar 5, 28; m 52; c 4. *Educ:* State Univ NY Col Geneseo, BS, 51; Syracuse Univ, MS, 55 & 62, PhD, 66. *Prof Exp:* Teacher & chmn dept sci, Vernon-Verona-Sherrill Cent Sch, 51-58; prof chem & chmn dept, State Univ NY, Buffalo, 58-89. *Concurrent Pos:* NSF inst grants, 66-81. *Mem:* AAAS; Am Chem Soc. *Res:* Science teaching, especially chemistry teaching; electrical conductance and thermodynamic functions as they relate to solutions. *Mailing Add:* 7 Towhee Ct East Amherst NY 14051

**ZINGARO, RALPH ANTHONY,** SYNTHETIC INORGANIC & ORGANOMETALLIC CHEMISTRY. *Current Pos:* from asst prof to assoc prof, 54-64, PROF CHEM, TEX A&M UNIV, 64- *Personal Data:* b Brooklyn, NY, Oct 27, 25; m 50, Mary J Waterstradt; c 2. *Educ:* City Col New York, BS, 46; Univ Kans, MS, 49, PhD, 50. *Prof Exp:* Sr res chemist, Eastman Kodak Co, 50-52; asst prof, Univ Ark, 52-53; res chemist, Am Cyanamid Co, 53-54. *Concurrent Pos:* NIH spec fel, 68-; Fulbright lectr, Univ Buenos Aires, 72. *Mem:* Am Chem Soc; NY Acad Sci; Sigma Xi; fel AAAS. *Res:* Chemistry and biochemistry of selenium, tellurium and arsenic; trace elements in fossil fuels; chemically deposited semiconducting thin films. *Mailing Add:* Dept Chem Tex A&M Univ College Station TX 77843. *Fax:* 409-845-4719; *E-Mail:* zingaro@chemvx.tamu.edu

**ZINGESER, MAURICE ROY,** ANATOMY, ORTHODONTICS. *Current Pos:* RES PROF ANAT, DENT SCH, ORE HEALTH SCI UNIV, 80- *Personal Data:* b Birmingham, Ala, Mar 17, 21; m 47; c 3. *Educ:* New York Univ, AB, 42; Columbia Univ, DDS, 46; Tufts Univ, MS, 50; Am Bd Orthod, dipl, 63. *Prof Exp:* Intern surg, New York Polyclin Hosp, 46-48; clin assoc orthod, Tufts Univ, 48-50; dent surgeon, USPHS, 50-52. *Concurrent Pos:* Guest lectr, Tufts, Boston & Georgetown Univs, 60-69; vis scientist anthrop & path, Ore Regional Primate Res Ctr, 63-80; contrib, Int Cong Anthrop & Ethnol Sci, 68; chmn crainiofacial biol sect, Int Cong Primatol, 72; guest lectr, Hebrew Univ & Univ London, 72. *Mem:* AAAS; Am Dent Asn; Am Asn Orthod; Am Asn Anat; Am Asn Phys Anthrop. *Res:* Primate odontology, craniofacial embryology and craniology. *Mailing Add:* 2460 SW Winchester Ave Portland OR 97225-4432

**ZINGESSER, LAWRENCE H,** RADIOLOGY, NEURORADIOLOGY. *Current Pos:* CHIEF NEURORADIOL & ATTEND PHYSICIAN, ST VINCENT'S HOSP, NY, 77- *Personal Data:* b Portchester, NY, Dec 27, 30; m 82, Mary McLarnen; c Jessica N, Suzanne, Jennifer & Eliza. *Educ:* Syracuse Univ, AB, 51; Chicago Med Sch, MD, 55. *Prof Exp:* From intern med to resident, Grad Hosp, Univ Pa, 55-57; resident radiol, Grace-New Haven Hosp, Yale Univ, 59-62; from asst prof to prof radiol, Albert Einstein Col Med, 73-77. *Concurrent Pos:* NIH spec fel neuroradiol, Albert Einstein Col Med, 62-64; Nat Inst Neurol Dis & Stroke grant cerebral blood flow, 66-69, clin prof radiol, 77-79 asst attend, Bronx Munic Hosp Ctr, NY, 63-65; clin prof radiol, NY Med Col, 80- *Mem:* Am Soc Neuroradiol; Radiol Soc NAm; Am Col Radiol; Fr Soc Neuroradiol. *Res:* Regional cerebral blood flow in neurologic disease states; neuroradiology. *Mailing Add:* St Vincents Hosp 153 W 11th St New York NY 10011-8305

**ZINGG, WALTER,** SURGERY, BIOMEDICAL ENGINEERING. *Current Pos:* RETIRED. *Personal Data:* b Kloten, Switz, Mar 29, 24; Can citizen; wid; c 4. *Educ:* Univ Zurich, MD, 50; Univ Man, MSc, 52; FRCS(C), 58. *Hon Degrees:* DSc, Univ Laval, 86. *Prof Exp:* Lectr physiol, Univ Man, 56-57, lectr surg, 57-61, asst prof, 61-64; from asst prof to assoc prof, Univ Toronto, 64-78, mem inst biomed eng, 72-75, prof & assoc dir, 75-83, prof surg & hon prof dent, 78-89, dir inst biomed eng, 83-89. *Concurrent Pos:* Assoc scientist, Hosp Sick Children, 64-68, sr scientist, 68-80, head, Div Surg Res, 64-88; consult, Ont Crippled Children's Ctr, Toronto, 65-90 & Ont Vet Col, Univ Guelph, 70-79. *Mem:* Can Physiol Soc; Can Biomat Soc (pres, 78-80); fel Am Col Surg; fel Am Col Cardiol; Can Med Biol Eng Soc (pres, 84-88); Wound Healing Soc. *Res:* Biomaterials. *Mailing Add:* Inst Biomed Eng Toronto ON M5S 1A4 Can. *Fax:* 905-382-2165; *E-Mail:* wzingg@vaxxine.com

**ZINGMARK, RICHARD G,** PHYCOLOGY, ALGOLOGY. *Current Pos:* RES ASSOC MARINE SCI, BELLE W BARUCH COASTAL RES INST, UNIV SC, 70-, PROF BIOL & MARINE SCI, 76- *Personal Data:* b San Francisco, Calif, July 4, 41; m 62; c 6. *Educ:* Humboldt State Col, BA, 64, MA, 65; Univ Calif, Santa Barbara, PhD(biol), 69. *Prof Exp:* NSF fel, Marine Lab, Duke Univ, 69-70. *Concurrent Pos:* Consult, James H Carr & Assoc, 76-; sr Fulbright res award, 89-90. *Mem:* Phycol Soc Am; Int Phycol Soc; Estaurine Res Fedn. *Res:* Physiological ecology of marine algae; biomass, productivity and photosynthesis of phytoplankton, benthic microalgae and macroalgae; red tide research; coastal management. *Mailing Add:* Dept Biol Sci Univ SC Coker Life Sci Bldg Rm 401 Columbia SC 29208. *Fax:* 803-777-4002; *E-Mail:* zingmark@biol.scarolina.edu

**ZINGULA, RICHARD PAUL,** PALEONTOLOGY. *Current Pos:* CONSULT GEOLOGIST, 86- *Personal Data:* b Cedar Rapids, Iowa, May 31, 29; m 53; c 2. *Educ:* Iowa State Univ, BS, 51; La State Univ, MS, 53, PhD(geol), 58. *Prof Exp:* Assoc geologist, Humble Oil & Refining Co, 54-60, supvry paleontologist, 60-69, sr prof geologist, 69-72; res paleontologist, Imp Oil Ltd, 72-74; sr prof geologist, Exxon Co USA, 74-76, sr explor geologist, 76-82, geol assoc, 82-86. *Mem:* Paleont Soc Am. *Res:* Micropaleontology; stratigraphy. *Mailing Add:* 5134 Lymbar Houston TX 77096-5318

**ZINK, GILBERT LEROY,** IMMUNOGENETICS. *Current Pos:* res assoc lectr dept biol sci, 72-75, asst prof, 75-80, ASSOC PROF BIOL SCI, PHILADELPHIA COL PHARM & SCI, 80-, CHAIRPERSON, DEPT BIOL SCI, 83- *Personal Data:* b Wheeling, WVa, Aug 14, 42; m 63; c 4. *Educ:* Ohio State Univ, BSc, 65, MSc, 67, PhD(immunogenetics), 71. *Prof Exp:* Res assoc, Ohio State Univ, 67-71, res assoc immunogenetics lab, Dept Dairy Sci, 72. *Concurrent Pos:* Co-investr, NIH res grant, 77-80. *Res:* Genetics. *Mailing Add:* 1410 Spackmans Lane West Chester PA 19380-1061

**ZINK, JEFFREY IRVE,** INORGANIC CHEMISTRY, PHOTOCHEMISTRY. *Current Pos:* from asst prof to assoc prof, 70-82, PROF CHEM, UNIV CALIF, LOS ANGELES, 82- *Personal Data:* b Milwaukee, Wis, Jan 8, 45; m 68. *Educ:* Univ Wis, BS, 66; Univ Ill, PhD(chem), 70. *Honors & Awards:* Alexander von Humboldt Award, 78; John Simon Guggenheim fel, 88. *Prof Exp:* Teaching asst chem, 66-67, Univ Ill, 66-67, res asst chem, 67-68. *Concurrent Pos:* Camille & Henry Dreyfus teacher-scholar, 74-79. *Mem:* Am Chem Soc; Interam Photochem Soc; Nat Audubon Soc. *Res:* Photochemistry, tribroluminescence; solar energy conversion and storage; structure and bonding transition metal compounds. *Mailing Add:* Dept Chem Univ Calif Los Angeles CA 90024-4199

**ZINK, ROBERT EDWIN,** MATHEMATICS. *Current Pos:* from asst prof to assoc prof math, 56-66, asst head dept, 65-69, asst dean grad sch, 69-72, PROF MATH, PURDUE UNIV, LAFAYETTE, 66- *Personal Data:* b Minneapolis, Minn, Nov 16, 28; m 50, Gloria M Brownell; c David M, Richard J & William T. *Educ:* Univ Minn, BA, 49, MA, 51, PhD(math), 53. *Prof Exp:* Asst math, Univ Minn, 49-53; instr, Purdue Univ, 53-54; lectr, George Washington Univ, 55-56. *Concurrent Pos:* Vis prof, Wabash Col, 61-62 & dept math, Univ Calif, Irvine, 68-69. *Mem:* Am Math Soc; Math Asn Am; Sigma Xi. *Res:* Theory of measure and integration; theory of functions of a real variable; Schauder bases for Banach function spaces; several articles in a variety of journals. *Mailing Add:* Dept Math Purdue Univ Lafayette IN 47907

**ZINK, SANDRA,** physics, computer science, for more information see previous edition

**ZINKE, OTTO HENRY,** PHYSICS. *Current Pos:* RETIRED. *Personal Data:* b Webster Groves, Mo, Aug 13, 26; m 55; c 3. *Educ:* Wash Univ, AB, 50, AM, 53, PhD, 56. *Prof Exp:* Salesman, Nuclear Consults Corp, 52-53; mem res staff, Linde Co Union Carbide Corp, 56-57; asst prof physics, Univ Mo, 57-59; from asst prof to assoc prof physics, Univ Ark, Fayetteville, 59-69, prof, 69-80. *Res:* Transient phenomena in plasmas and metals. *Mailing Add:* 817 N Jackson Fayetteville AR 72701-2234

**ZINKE, PAUL JOSEPH,** FORESTRY, SOIL SCIENCE. *Current Pos:* PROF FORESTRY & SOIL SCI, UNIV CALIF, BERKELEY, 57- *Personal Data:* b Los Angeles, Calif, Nov 10, 20; m 47; c 2. *Educ:* Univ Calif, BS, 42, MS, 52, PhD(soil sci), 56. *Prof Exp:* Forester, Tongass Nat Forest, US Forest Serv, 42-43, res forester, Calif Forest & Range Exp Sta, 46-56. *Concurrent Pos:* In charge, Calif Soil Veg Surv, USDA-US Forest Serv, 59-61; adv, Appl Sci Res Corp Thailand, 67-; adv, Radar Nat Resource Inventory Amazon Basin, Brazil, 71-; mem comt study defoliation effects in SE Asia, Nat Acad Sci, 71- *Mem:* AAAS; Soc Am Foresters; Soil Sci Soc Am; Soil Conserv Soc Am; Soc Range Mgt; Sigma Xi. *Res:* Forest influences and environment; forest soils; soil morphology; soil-vegetation relationships; plant ecology. *Mailing Add:* 145 Mulford Hall Univ Calif Berkeley CA 94720-3114

**ZINKEL, DUANE FORST,** NATURAL PRODUCTS & NAVAL STORES CHEMISTRY. *Current Pos:* RETIRED. *Personal Data:* b Manitowoc, Wis, Aug 11, 34; m 61, Loretta S Schweiger; c Susan, Joseph, Mary, Robert & Catherine. *Educ:* Univ Wis, BS, 56, PhD(biochem), 61. *Prof Exp:* Res chemist, Forest Prod Lab, US Forest Serv, 61-91. *Mem:* Am Chem Soc. *Res:* Softwood extractives and derived products; structure determination; analytical development and analysis; biosynthesis; specialist in navel stores chemistry (softwood extractives, rosin, turpentine, fatty acids); development of analytical methods, isolation and structure elucidation, chemotoxonomy. *Mailing Add:* 2323 Hollister Ave Madison WI 53705-5315

**ZINKERNAGEL, ROLF MARTIN,** IMMUNOLOGY. *Current Pos:* assoc prof, Div Exp Path, 79-88, prof, Dept Path, 88-92, HEAD, INST EXP IMMUNOL, UNIV ZURICH, 92- *Personal Data:* b Basel, Switz, Jan 6, 44; m 68, Kathrin G Ludin; c Christine, Annelies & Martin. *Educ:* Univ Basel, MD, 68; Australian Nat Univ, PhD, 75. *Hon Degrees:* Dr, Univ Liege & Univ Canberra, 96. *Honors & Awards:* Co-recipient Nobel Prize in Med, 96; Kinyoun Lectr, NIH, 79; Campbell Mem Lectr, 82; A V Graefe Lectr, Berlin, 83; Armauer Hansen Mem Lectr, Addis Abeba, 83; Peter Gorer Lectr, Brit Soc Immunol, 86; Grabar Lectr, Fr Soc Immunol, 93; Harvey Lectr, 94; Albert Lasker Award Basic Med Res, 95. *Prof Exp:* Intern surg, Clara-Spital, 68-69; postdoctoral fel, Lab Electron Micros, Inst Anat, Univ Basel, 69-70; postdoctoral fel, Inst Biochem, Univ Lausanne, 71-73; vis fel, Dept Microbiol,

John Curtin Sch Med Res, Australian Nat Univ, 73-75; assoc prof, Dept Immunopath, Scripps Univ, 76-79, prof, 79. *Concurrent Pos:* Adj assoc prof, Dept Path, Univ Calif, San Diego, 77-79; mem, Study Sect Virol, NIH, 79-80, Task Force Immunol, 80; minister res, Indust Action Regulation Immunol & Immunopath. *Mem:* Foreign assoc Nat Acad Sci; Am Asn Pathologists; Swiss Soc Allergy & Immunol; hon mem Fr Soc Immunol; hon mem Scand Soc Immunol; Swiss Soc Path; Swiss Soc Microbiol; Swiss Soc Cell & Molecular Biol; fel Am Acad Microbiol; Academia Europea; Ger Soc Immunol; Int Soc Antiviral Res; Am Asn Immunologists. *Res:* MHC-restricted t-cell recognition; tymus role in determining MHC-restricted t-cell specificity; NK-cell activity in virus infections; t-cell epitope escape virus mutants; tolerances to viruses; role of virus-specific t-cells in causing immunopathology. *Mailing Add:* Dept Path Univ Hosp Inst Exp Immunol Zurich CH-8091 Switzerland. *Fax:* 41-1-2554420

**ZINKHAM, ROBERT EDWARD,** MECHANICAL METALLURGY. *Current Pos:* RETIRED. *Personal Data:* b Rochester, Pa, Jan 19, 23; m 56; c 3. *Educ:* Geneva Col, BS, 49; Carnegie-Mellon Univ, BSME, 49; Univ Pittsburgh, MS, 56. *Prof Exp:* Develop engr, Jones & Laughlin Steel Corp, 49-57; supvr mech testing, Allegheny Ludlum Steel Corp, 57-60; res engr drilling methods, Gulf Res & Develop Co, 60-63; res scientist mech metall, Reynolds Metals Co, 63-68, dir, 68-86. *Concurrent Pos:* Chmn subcomt fracture toughness, Metal Prop Coun, Inc, 72- *Mem:* Am Soc Mech Engrs; fel Am Soc Metals; Am Soc Testing & Mat. *Res:* Mechanical metallurgy, specializing in fracture mechanics, fatigue, mechanical testing and residual stresses involving aluminum. *Mailing Add:* 9204 Westmoor Dr Richmond VA 23229

**ZINKHAM, WILLIAM HOWARD,** PEDIATRICS. *Current Pos:* From instr to prof, 56-77, DISTINGUISHED SERV PROF PEDIAT, SCH MED, JOHNS HOPKINS UNIV, 77- *Personal Data:* b Uniontown, Md, May 23, 24; m 52; c 2. *Educ:* Johns Hopkins Univ, AB, 44, MD, 47; Am Bd Pediat, cert pediat, 56, cert hemat-oncol, 74. *Mem:* Am Pediat Soc; Soc Clin Invest; Soc Pediat Res. *Res:* Hematology; metabolism of normal and abnormal erythrocytes. *Mailing Add:* Dept Pediat & Oncol Johns Hopkins Univ Baltimore MD 21205

**ZINKL, JOSEPH GRANDJEAN,** CYTOLOGY, TOXICOLOGY. *Current Pos:* PROF CLIN PATH, SCH VET MED, UNIV CALIF, DAVIS, 76- *Personal Data:* b Albuquerque, NMex, Aug 30, 39; m 69; c 2. *Educ:* Univ Calif, Davis, BS, 64, DVM, 66, PhD(comparative path), 71. *Prof Exp:* Sr fel, Nat Inst Environ Health, 71-74; pathologist, US Fish & Wildlife Res, 74-76. *Mem:* Am Col Vet Pathologists; Wildlife Dis Asn; Am Soc Vet Clin Path. *Res:* Brain cholinesterase activity in forest birds after aerial application of insecticides; phagocytic, bactericidal and chemotactic ability of neutrophils of domestic animals; clinical cytology of diseases of domestic animals; effects of anticholinescerase insecticides on wild mammals, birds and fish. *Mailing Add:* 2731 Blackburn Dr Davis CA 95616

**ZINMAN, WALTER GEORGE,** CHEMISTRY. *Current Pos:* RETIRED. *Personal Data:* b New York, NY, Nov 9, 29; m 55; c 2. *Educ:* Rensselaer Polytech Inst, BChE, 51; Harvard Univ, PhD(chem), 55. *Prof Exp:* Res chemist missile & space vehicle div, Gen Elec Co, 56-59; prin res & develop engr, Repub Aviation Corp, 59-65; res group leader, Polytech Inst Brooklyn, 65-66; propulsion engr, Grumman Aerospace Eng Corp, 66-70, consult, 70-72; asst to dir res, Surface Activation Corp, NY, 72-73; chem consult, 73-97. *Mem:* Am Chem Soc; Am Phys Soc; Sigma Xi. *Res:* Reaction of dissociated gases with solids; gaseous detonations; homogeneous kinetics; fluid mechanics and reacting flows; foundations thermodynamics. *Mailing Add:* 8 Conventry Rd Syosset NY 11791

**ZINN, BEN T,** COMBUSTION, FLUID MECHANICS. *Current Pos:* from asst prof to prof, 65-74, REGENTS PROF, GA INST TECHNOL, 74-, DAVID S LEWIS JR CHAIR, 92- *Personal Data:* b Tel-Aviv, Israel, Apr 21, 37; US citizen; c 2. *Educ:* NY Univ, BS, 61; Stanford Univ, MS, 62; Princeton Univ, MA, 63, PhD(aerospace & mech sci), 66. *Honors & Awards:* Sustained Res Award, Sigma Xi, 76. *Prof Exp:* Asst res combustion instability, Princeton Univ, 64-65. *Concurrent Pos:* Consult, Lockheed Ga Res Labs, Naval Weapons Ctr, Calif & adv group aerospace res & develop, NATO; consult, Brazilian Space Res Inst, 77-; ed measurements in combustion systs, Am Inst Aeronaut & Astronaut Progress in Aeronaut & Astronaut J, 77-78; mem bd vis, Nat Acad Fire Prevention & Control, 78-80; assoc ed, Am Inst Aeronaut & Astronaut. *Mem:* Nat Acad Eng; Combustion Inst; Assoc fel Am Inst Aeronaut & Astronaut. *Res:* Combustion in energy and propulsion generating devices; fire safety; acoustics. *Mailing Add:* 3656 Paces Valley Rd NW Atlanta GA 30327

**ZINN, DALE WENDEL,** ANIMAL HUSBANDRY. *Current Pos:* DEAN COL AGR & FORESTRY & DIR AGR & FORESTRY EXP STA, WVA UNIV, 75- *Personal Data:* b Parkersburg, WVa; m 54; c 2. *Educ:* WVa Univ, MS, 56; Univ Mo, PhD, 53. *Prof Exp:* Asst prof animal husb, NMex State Univ, 57-61; from assoc prof to prof animal sci, Tex Tech Univ, 61-75, chmn dept, 69-74, asst dean, Col Agr Sci & dir div agr serv, 74-75. *Mem:* Am Soc Animal Sci; Am Meat Sci Asn; Sigma Xi. *Res:* Production and quality factors affecting quantity and quality of meat and meat products. *Mailing Add:* 37 Harewood Manor Morgantown WV 26505

**ZINN, DONALD JOSEPH,** invertebrate zoology; deceased, see previous edition for last biography

**ZINN, JOHN,** APPLIED PHYSICS. *Current Pos:* assoc chem, 55-56, MEM STAFF, LOS ALAMOS SCI LAB, UNIV CALIF, 57- *Personal Data:* b Brooklyn, NY, Feb 28, 28; m 54; c 3. *Educ:* Cornell Univ, AB, 49; Univ Calif, Berkeley, PhD(phys chem), 58. *Prof Exp:* Chemist, Catalin Corp Am, 49-50 & M W Kellogg Co, 52-54. *Concurrent Pos:* Asst prof, Dept Aeronaut Eng, Univ Colo, 67-68. *Mem:* Am Phys Soc; AAAS; Am Geophys Union. *Res:* Theoretical research in atmospheric physics and chemistry; atmospheric effects of nuclear explosions. *Mailing Add:* 249 Rio Bravo Dr Los Alamos NM 87544

**ZINN, ROBERT JAMES,** ASTRONOMY. *Current Pos:* asst prof, 79-82, assoc prof, 82-87, PROF ASTRON, YALE UNIV OBSERV, 87- *Personal Data:* b Chicago, Ill, Aug 4, 46; m 79; c 3. *Educ:* Case Inst Technol, BS, 68; Yale Univ, PhD(astron), 74. *Prof Exp:* Fel astron, Hale Observs, Carnegie Inst Washington, 74-79. *Mem:* Am Astron Soc; Int Astron Union. *Res:* Stellar evolution; the chemical compositions of globular cluster stars, variable stars, and the stellar populations of the galaxies of the Local Group. *Mailing Add:* Yale Univ Dept Astron PO Box 208101 260 Whitney Ave New Haven CT 06520-8101

**ZINN, WALTER HENRY,** PHYSICS. *Current Pos:* RETIRED. *Personal Data:* b Kitchener, Ont, Dec 10, 06; nat US; m 33, 56; c 2. *Educ:* Queen's Univ, Ont, BA, 27, MA, 29; Columbia Univ, PhD(physics), 34. *Hon Degrees:* DSc, Queen's Univ, Ont, 57. *Honors & Awards:* Enrico Fermi Award, 69. *Prof Exp:* Asst physics, Queen's Univ, Ont, 27-28; asst, Columbia Univ, 31-32; from instr to asst prof, City Col New York, 32-41; physicist, Metall Lab, Manhattan Dist, Univ Chicago, 42-46; dir, Argonne Nat Lab, 45-56; vpres, Combustion Eng, Inc, 59-71. *Concurrent Pos:* Spec consult, Joint Cong Comt Atomic Energy, 56; spec mem, President's Sci Adv Comt; pres, Gen Nuclear Eng Corp, 56-64. *Mem:* Nat Acad Sci; Nat Acad Eng; AAAS; fel Am Phys Soc; Am Nuclear Soc (pres, 55). *Res:* Nuclear physics and reactor development. *Mailing Add:* 2940 Bay Meadow Ct Clearwater FL 34621

**ZINNER, ERNST K,** PHYSICS. *Current Pos:* res assoc, 72-74, sr res scientist, 74-89, RES PROF PHYSICS, WASHINGTON UNIV, ST LOUIS, 89- *Personal Data:* b Steyr, Austria, Jan 30, 37. *Educ:* Tech Univ, Vienna, MS, 60; Washington Univ, Mo, PhD(physics), 72. *Prof Exp:* Instr physics, Col Vet Med, Vienna, 63-64; prog & calculation magnetic field distrib, Brown-Boveri Co, Switz, 64-65. *Concurrent Pos:* Vis scientist, Max-Planck Inst Physics, Ger, 80, Max-Planck Inst Chem, Ger, 80, Univ Pavia, Italy, 89. *Mem:* Fel Am Phys Soc; fel Meteoritical Soc; AAAS; Am Geophys Union; Sigma Xi. *Res:* High energy physics; effects of the interplanetary environment on the moon and meteoritic parent bodies; ion microprobe isotopic and trace element studies of meteorites and interplanetary dust with implications for early solar system chronology; nucleosynthesis of elements in stars and the history of presolar material; discovery of interstellar grains in meteorites. *Mailing Add:* Campus Box 1105 St Louis MO 63130

**ZINNER, STEPHEN HARVEY,** INFECTIOUS DISEASES, EPIDEMIOLOGY. *Current Pos:* asst prof biol & med sci, 72-76, assoc prof, 76-81, PROF MED, MED SECT, BROWN UNIV, 81- *Personal Data:* b New York, NY, Apr 29, 39; m 66; c 2. *Educ:* Northwestern Univ, BA, 61; Sch Med, Univ Pa, MD, 65; Am Bd Internal Med, cert internal med, 72, cert infectious dis, 74. *Prof Exp:* Res fel bact & immunol, Channing Lab, Med Sch, Harvard Univ, 67-68, res assoc med, 68-69, res fel, Thorndike Lab, 61-71, instr med, Med Sch, 71-72. *Concurrent Pos:* Field officer, Nat Heart Dis Control, USPHS, 67-69; clin instr med, Med Sch, Harvard Univ, 72-; consult infectious dis, RI Hosp, Women & Infants Hosp & Vet Admin Hosp, 72-, Miriam Hosp, Providence, 76-; head, Div Infectious Dis, Roger Williams Med Ctr & Brown Univ, 72-, Hosp, 89- *Mem:* Infectious Dis Soc Am; Am Soc Microbiol; Am Fedn Clin Res; Soc Epidemiol Res; Sigma Xi; Am Soc Clin Invest. *Res:* Epidemiology of blood pressure in infants and children; infections in the immunosuppressed patient; antibiotic combinations; new methods for in vitro antibiotic activity determinations; reactive antibodies to Gram-negative infecting organisms. *Mailing Add:* Roger Williams Gen Hosp 825 Chalkstone Ave Providence RI 02908-4728

**ZINNES, HAROLD,** ORGANIC CHEMISTRY. *Current Pos:* scientist, Warner-Lambert Res Inst, 58-63, sr scientist, 63-68, sr res assoc, 68-77, DIR PHARMACEUT TECH DEVELOP, WARNER-LAMBERT INT, 77- *Personal Data:* b New York, NY, Apr 7, 29; m 53; c 3. *Educ:* Rutgers Univ, BS, 51; Univ Mich, MS, 52, PhD, 55. *Prof Exp:* Res assoc, E R Squibb & Co, 56-58. *Mem:* Am Chem Soc; Am Pharmaceut Asn. *Res:* Medicinals; natural products; antibiotics; heterocycles; indoles; benzothiazines; anti-inflammatory agents; international pharmaceutical development. *Mailing Add:* 4566 Carlton Golf Dr Lake Worth FL 33467-8128

**ZINS, GERALD RAYMOND,** pharmacology; deceased, see previous edition for last biography

**ZINSER, EDWARD JOHN,** CHEMICAL INDUSTRY INFRASTRUCTURE DEVELOPMENT. *Current Pos:* PRIN CONSULT, BPD&R INC, 94- *Personal Data:* b Toronto, Ont, Mar 13, 41; m 66, Dana Jarnel; c Bradley, Emily & Gregory. *Educ:* Univ Toronto, BSc, 65, PhD(anal & inorg chem), 69. *Prof Exp:* Asst, Univ Toronto, 65-68; fel, Queen's Univ, Ont, 69-70; res chemist, Marshall Lab, E I du Pont de Nemours & Co Inc, 70-71 & Exp Sta, Wilmington, 72, sr prod specialist, 72-73, tech objectives mgr, Finishes Div, 73-74, res supvr, Marshall Res & Develop Lab, 74-75, prod mgr, Finishes Div, 76-77, nat mkt mgr, Maintenance Finishes, 78-79, worldwide mkt & prod planning mgr, 79-80, worldwide bus mgr, Packaging Finishes, 80-82, mgr, Health Prod, Cent Res Dept, 82-84, planning mgr, Latin

Am Int Dept, 84-88, bus mgr, Eng Serv, 88-93. *Concurrent Pos:* Nat Res Coun Can scholar, Univ Toronto, 68-70. *Mem:* Am Chem Soc; Chem Inst Can; Fedn Soc Coatings Technol; Nat Asn Corrosion Engrs. *Res:* Environmental analytical chemistry; electrochemistry; spectroscopy; organic coatings; fluorocarbon coatings; specialty chemical production in developing countries. *Mailing Add:* BPD&R Inc PO Box 531 Newtown Square PA 19073. *E-Mail:* ejz531@bellatlantic.net

**ZINSMEISTER, GEORGE EMIL,** MECHANICAL ENGINEERING, HEAT TRANSFER. *Current Pos:* asst prof, 66-69, ASSOC PROF MECH ENG, UNIV MASS, AMHERST, 69- *Personal Data:* b Huntington, NY, Dec 27, 39; m 65. *Educ:* Rensselaer Polytech Inst, BME, 61; Purdue Univ, MSME, 63, PhD(mech eng), 65. *Prof Exp:* Res engr, E I du Pont de Nemours & Co, Inc, Del, 65-66. *Concurrent Pos:* NSF res grants, 67-70 & 72-73. *Mem:* Am Soc Mech Engrs. *Res:* Heat transfer in composite materials; prediction of thermal processing conditions in foods; engineering education. *Mailing Add:* Dept Mech & Indust Eng Univ Mass PO Box 32210 Amherst MA 01003-2210

**ZINSMEISTER, PHILIP PRICE,** DEVELOPMENTAL BIOLOGY. *Current Pos:* assoc prof & chmn div sci & math, 73-80, PROF BIOL, OGLETHORPE UNIV, 80- *Personal Data:* b Columbus, Ohio, May 15, 40; m 68; c 1. *Educ:* Wittenberg Univ, BS, 62; Univ Ill, MS, 66, PhD(zool), 69. *Prof Exp:* Master biol, US Peace Corps, Ghana, 62-64; asst prof biol, Northeast Mo State Col, 70; lectr, Univ Sci & Technol, Kumasi, Ghana, 70-72; vis asst prof, Univ Ill, 72-73. *Concurrent Pos:* Res assoc, Emory Univ, 80-81 & 87-88; Fulbright fel, Belize, 93-94. *Mem:* Am Inst Biol Sci; Soc Develop Biol; AAAS. *Res:* Insect oogenesis and development; nerve cell development. *Mailing Add:* Dept Math Sci Oglethorpe Univ 4484 Peachtree Rd NE Atlanta GA 30319-2797. *E-Mail:* pzinsmei@oglethorpe.edu

**ZINSMEISTER, WILLIAM JOHN,** BIOGEOGRAPHY, EVOLUTION. *Current Pos:* res assoc geol, 84-90, PROF, PURDUE UNIV, 90- *Personal Data:* b Nogales, Ariz, May 6, 43; m 66; c 2. *Educ:* Calif State Col, Long Beach, BS, 69; Univ Calif, Riverside, MS, 73, PhD(geol), 74. *Honors & Awards:* Antarctic Serv Medal, NSF, 83. *Prof Exp:* Res assoc paleontol, Inst Polar Studies, 75-80, sr res assoc, 80-85. *Concurrent Pos:* NSF grant, 74-76 & 77-; Nat Geog Soc grant, 76-77; adv, Earth Sci Adv Comt, Brit Antarctic Surv, Nat Environ Res Coun, UK, 81, Int Comn Cretaceous Climates, 83- *Mem:* Paleont Soc; Int Paleont Union; Sigma Xi; AAAS. *Res:* Changes in the distribution of shallow-water marine faunas in the southern hemisphere in response to the final fragmentation of Gondwanaland during the late Cretaceous and early Tertiary; role polar regions played in the evolution of modern marine fauna. *Mailing Add:* 2101 Edgewood Dr West Lafayette IN 47906. *E-Mail:* zinsmoll@omni.cc.purdue.edu

**ZINSSER, HARRY FREDERICK,** CARDIOLOGY. *Current Pos:* fel, Univ Pa, 47-48, from asst instr to assoc, 48-51, asst prof clin med, 51-53, asst prof med, 53-55, assoc prof clin med, 55-58, assoc prof med, 58-68, prof cardiol, Div Grad Med, 63-68, dir cardiol, Grad Hosp, 63-78, chmn, Dept Med, 70-79, prof, 68-85, EMER PROF MED, SCH MED, UNIV PA, 85- *Personal Data:* b Pittsburgh, Pa, May 1, 18; m 43, Patricia Wonderling; c Michael H, Daniel F, Kendall R & Sally A. *Educ:* Univ Pittsburgh, BS, 37, MD, 39. *Hon Degrees:* LLD, Univ Pa, 71. *Prof Exp:* Teaching fel internal med, Sch Med, Univ Pittsburgh, 40-42, asst instr, 46-47. *Concurrent Pos:* Secy, Subspecialty Bd Cardiovasc Dis, 79-81; vpres, Am Heart Asn, 79-80. *Mem:* Am Fedn Clin Res; Am Soc Clin Invest; Am Clin & Climat Asn; Asn Univ Cardiol; AAAS. *Res:* Cardiovascular diseases. *Mailing Add:* 1112 Woodmont Rd Gladwyne PA 19035

**ZIOCK, KLAUS OTTO H,** EXPERIMENTAL PHYSICS. *Current Pos:* from assoc prof to prof, 60-95, actg dir, Va Assoc Res Ctr, 62-64, EMER PROF PHYSICS, UNIV VA, 95- *Personal Data:* b Herchen, Ger, Feb 4, 25; nat US; m 52; c 4. *Educ:* Univ Bonn, Dipl, 49, Dr rer nat, 56. *Honors & Awards:* Alexander von Humboldt Award, 77. *Prof Exp:* Physicist, E Leybold's Nachfolger, Ger, 50-55; res assoc, Univ Bonn, 56-58; res assoc physics, Yale Univ, 58-60, asst prof, 60-62. *Concurrent Pos:* Vis scientist, Europ Orgn Nuclear Res, 69-70. *Mem:* Am Phys Soc. *Res:* Nuclear physics; physics of elementary particles; atomic physics. *Mailing Add:* Dept Physics Univ Va Charlottesville VA 22901

**ZIOLKOWSKI, RICHARD WALTER,** ELECTROMAGNETICS, NUMERICAL MODELING. *Current Pos:* ASSOC PROF ELEC ENG, DEPT ELEC & COMPUT ENG, UNIV ARIZ, 90- *Personal Data:* b Warsaw, NY, Nov 22, 52; m 81; c 2. *Educ:* Brown Univ, ScB, 74; Univ Ill, MS, 75, PhD(physics), 80. *Prof Exp:* Engr, Lawrence Livermore Nat Lab, 81-84, computational electronics & electromagnetics thrust area leader, 84-90. *Concurrent Pos:* Vchmn, Int Inst Elec & Electronics Engrs AP-S, Symp & Nat Radio Sci, 89-; mem, Union Radio Sci Int, Comn B, Tech Activ Comt, 89- *Mem:* Inst Elec & Electronics Engrs; Int Union Radio Sci; Am Phys Soc; Acoust Soc Am. *Res:* Application of new mathematical methods to linear and nonlinear problems dealing with the interaction of acoustic and electromagnetic waves with scattering objects, plasmas and dielectric materials. *Mailing Add:* Univ Ariz Tucson AZ 85721

**ZIOLO, RONALD F,** CHEMISTRY. *Current Pos:* assoc scientist, 73, scientist, 74-78, SR SCIENTIST, XEROX CORP, 78- *Personal Data:* b Philadelphia, Pa, Aug 16, 44; m 67; c 3. *Educ:* Univ Calif, Los Angeles, BS, 66; Temple Univ, PhD(chem), 70. *Prof Exp:* Res fel chem, Calif Inst Technol, 71-72. *Concurrent Pos:* Vis distinguished prof, Dept Fundamental Physics, Univ Barcelona, 97-; co-dir, Rank Xerox-Univ, Barcelona Magnetics Lab, 97-

*Mem:* AAAS; Am Chem Soc; Am Crystallog Asn; Mat Res Soc; Am Phys Soc; Inst Elec & Electronics Engrs Magnetics Soc. *Res:* Quantum magnetic effects in mesoscopic and manostructured materials and clusters; novel magnetic, optical, electrical, thermal and mechanical properties; synthesis and structure; high stability aqueous magnetic colloids; ferrofluids. *Mailing Add:* Wilson Ctr Res & Technol 0144-39D Xerox Corp 800 Phillips Rd Webster NY 14580. *Fax:* 716-422-1035; *E-Mail:* vziolo@wb.xerox.com

**ZIOMEK, CAROL A,** TRANSGENIC EXPRESSION, EMBRYO CULTURE. *Current Pos:* PRIN SCIENTIST, GENZYME CORP, 90- *Personal Data:* b Wilkes-Barre, Pa, Sept 26, 50. *Educ:* Wilkes Col, Wilkes-Barre, Pa, BS, 72; Johns Hopkins Univ, PhD(biol), 78. *Prof Exp:* Fel embryol, Dept Anat, Univ Cambridge, Eng, 78-82; staff scientist cell biol, Worcester Found Exp Biol, 82-90. *Mem:* Am Soc Cell Biol; AAAS; Soc Develop Biol; Soc Study Reprod. *Mailing Add:* 17 Shadowbrook Lane Milford MA 01757. *Fax:* 508-872-9080

**ZIONY, JOSEPH ISRAEL,** ENGINEERING GEOLOGY. *Current Pos:* RETIRED. *Personal Data:* b Los Angeles, Calif, Apr 6, 35; m 61, Denise Pourroy; c David, Daniel & Sarah. *Educ:* Univ Calif, Los Angeles, AB, 56, MA, 59, PhD(geol), 66. *Honors & Awards:* E B Burwell Award Eng Geol, Geol Soc Am, 87. *Prof Exp:* Geologist, Mil Geol Br, US Geol Surv, DC, 57-59, Fuels Br, Calif, 59-60, Southwestern Br, 65-69 & Eng Geol Br, 69-73, dep chief, Off Earthquake Studies, Reston, Va, 73-76, Earthquake Hazards Br, Menlo Park, 76-77, asst chief geologist, Western Region, 77-81, Eng Seismol & Geol Br, Menlo Park, Calif, 81-86; asst dir mining & geol, Calif Dept Conserv, Sacramento, Calif, 88-91. *Mem:* Geol Soc Am; Seismol Soc Am; Asn Eng Geol. *Res:* Earthquake hazards assessment; delineation of active faults in southern California; evaluation of their relative activity using late Quaternary slip histories; estimation of their earthquake potential. *Mailing Add:* 1640 Escobita Ave Palo Alto CA 94306

**ZIPES, DOUGLAS PETER,** MEDICINE. *Current Pos:* from asst prof to assoc prof, 70-76, PROF MED, SCH MED, IND UNIV, 76-; DISTINGUISHED PROF MED, PHARMACOL & TOXICOL, KRAUNERT INST CARDIOL, 94-, DIR, DIV CARDIOL & KRAUNERT INST CARDIOL, 95- *Personal Data:* b White Plains, NY, Feb 27, 39; m 61; c 3. *Educ:* Dartmouth Col, BA, 61; Dartmouth Med Sch, BMed Sci, 62; Harvard Med Sch, MD, 64. *Honors & Awards:* Distinguished Achievement Award, Am Heart Asn, 89; Distinguished Scientist Award, NAm Soc Pacing & Electrophysiol, 95. *Prof Exp:* Intern & resident med, Duke Univ Med Ctr, 64-66, fel cardiol, 66-68; vis prof electrophysiol, Masonic Res Lab, 70-71. *Concurrent Pos:* Chmn, Cardiovasc Bds, Am Bd Internal Med, Data Safety Monitoring Bd, NHLBI Study Affirm, Steering & Exec Comt, NHLBI Study AVID, Develop Comt, Am Col Cardiol; bd dirs, Am Col Cardiol, Am Bd Internal Med & NAm Soc Pacing & Electrophysiol; ed-in-chief, J Cardiovasc Electrophysiol. *Mem:* Fel Am Col Cardiol; Am Heart Asn; Am Soc Clin Invest; Asn Univ Cardiologists (pres, 95); Asn Am Physicians; NAm Asn Pacing & Electrophysiol (pres, 89). *Res:* Clinical and animal investigations into mechanisms responsible for cardiac arrhythmias with special emphasis on the roll of autonomic nervous system. *Mailing Add:* Krannert Inst Cardiol 1111 W Tenth St Indianapolis IN 46202

**ZIPF, ELIZABETH M(ARGARET),** BIOLOGY, INFORMATION SCIENCE. *Current Pos:* RETIRED. *Personal Data:* b Barrington, NJ, Nov 17, 27. *Educ:* Univ Va, BA, 50, PhD(biol), 59; Univ Pa, MA, 52. *Prof Exp:* Res biologist cancer res, Med Sch, Univ Va, 55; res asst biol, Princeton Univ, 56-57; assoc ed, Biosci Info Serv, 57-62, sr assoc ed, 62-63, actg supvry ed, biol & bio-med subj, Biol Abstracts, 63-64, suvry ed, 64-71, head, Ed Dept, 71-80, actg dir, Sci Div, 80-81, tech consult to pres, 81- *Concurrent Pos:* Fel, Univ Pa, 62-63; consult in prep Water Resources Thesaurus, Off Water Resources Res, US Dept Interior, 66; mem, Z-39 Comt, Am Stand Asn, 66-67 & Nat Fed Sci Abstracting & Indexing Serv. *Mem:* Fel AAAS; Am Inst Biol Sci; Coun Biol Ed; Am Soc Zool. *Res:* Biological research in invertebrate and vertebrate embryology; teratoma formation in salamanders; information science in biology and biomedical fields. *Mailing Add:* PO Box 127 Barrington NJ 08007

**ZIPFEL, CHRISTIE LEWIS,** LIGHTWAVE DEVICES RELIABILITY. *Current Pos:* RES PHYSICS, SUMMIT APPL RES, 96- *Personal Data:* b Detroit, Mich, Oct 2, 41; m 64; c 1. *Educ:* Vassar Col, AB, 63; Univ Mich, MS, 65, PhD(physics), 69. *Prof Exp:* Instr physics, State Univ NY, Stony Brook, 69-72; asst prof, Towson State Col, 72-74; res assoc, Bell Labs, Murray Hill, 71-76, mem tech staff, 76-96. *Res:* LED reliability. *Mailing Add:* Summit Appl Res 164 Canoebrook Pkwy Summit NJ 07901

**ZIPFEL, GEORGE G, JR,** acoustics, transducer technology, for more information see previous edition

**ZIPFEL, WARREN ROGER,** LASER SPECTROSCOPY, COMPUTER MODELLING. *Current Pos:* Res asst, Boyce Thompson Inst, 84-87, res assoc plant biol, 92-93, RES ASSOC APPL PHYSICS, CORNELL UNIV, 93- *Personal Data:* b Montclair, NJ, Nov 17, 55; m; c 5. *Educ:* Cornell Univ, BS, 87, PhD(biophys), 93. *Mem:* AAAS; Biophys Soc. *Res:* Energy transfer in photosynthesis; two photon fluorescence in biological imaging, especially in neurobiology. *Mailing Add:* Cornell Univ Clark Hall Rm 212 Ithaca NY 14853. *Fax:* 607-255-7658; *E-Mail:* wrz2@cornell.edu

**ZIPP, ARDEN PETER,** PHYSICAL INORGANIC CHEMISTRY. *Current Pos:* from asst prof to assoc prof, 68-73, DISTINGUISHED TEACHING PROF CHEM, STATE UNIV NY COL CORTLAND, 85- *Personal Data:* b Dolgeville, NY, July 14, 38; m 89, Kathryn Buxton Vernay; c 2. *Educ:* Colgate Univ, AB, 60; Univ Pa, PhD, 64. *Honors & Awards:* Nat Catalyst Award, 91 Manufacturing Chemists Assoc. *Prof Exp:* Asst prof chem, Drew Univ, 64-66. *Concurrent Pos:* Chief Exam Chem Int Baccalaureate Orgn. *Mem:* Am Chem Soc; Sigma Xi; Nat Sci Teachers Asn. *Res:* Photochemistry of transition metal complexes; oxidation reduction reactions of transition metal ions. *Mailing Add:* Dept Chem State Univ NY Col Cortland NY 13045. *E-Mail:* zipp@snycorva.cortland.edu

**ZIPPIN, CALVIN,** BIOSTATISTICS, EPIDEMIOLOGY. *Current Pos:* instr, Sch Pub Health, Univ Calif, Berkeley, 53-55, from asst res biostatistician to res biostatistician, Cancer Res Inst, 55-67, asst prof prev med, 58-60, lectr, 60-67, lectr path, 61-67, prof epidemiol, Cancer Res Inst, Dept Epidemiol & Int Health & Dept Path, 67-91, EMER PROF EPIDEMIOL, SCH MED, UNIV CALIF, SAN FRANCISCO, 91- *Personal Data:* b Albany, NY, July 17, 26; m 64, Patricia Schubert; c David B & Jennifer D. *Educ:* State Univ NY, AB, 47. *Hon Degrees:* DSc, John Hopkins Univ, 53. *Prof Exp:* Res asst statist, Sterling-Winthrop Res Inst, 47-50; res asst biostatist, Johns Hopkins Univ, 50-53. *Concurrent Pos:* Consult, US Naval Biol Lab, 55-66; Letterman Gen Hosp, 58-75, WHO, 69- & Am Joint Comt Cancer, 69-89; vis assoc prof, Stanford Univ, 62; NIH spec fel, London Sch.Hyg & Trop Med, 64-65; temp adv, WHO, 69, 72 & 74; Eleanor Roosevelt Int Cancer fel, Univ London, 75; vis res worker, Middlesex Hosp Med Sch, London, 75; fac adv, Regional Cancer Ctr, Trivandrum, India, 83- *Mem:* AAAS; fel Am Statist Asn; Biomet Soc; fel Royal Statist Soc; hon mem Int Asn Cancer Registries. *Res:* Identification of environmental and other factors associated with the risk of cancer as well as study of patient and disease characteristics which influence pattern of survival following diagnosis of a malignancy; biometry and epidemiology in cancer research. *Mailing Add:* 4 Warren Ct Belvedere Tiburon CA 94920. *Fax:* 415-476-0524; *E-Mail:* czippin@itsa.ucsf.edu

**ZIPRIN, RICHARD LEWIS,** MICROBIAL PATHOGENICITY, RESISTANCE MECHANISMS. *Current Pos:* MICROBIOLOGIST, AGR RES SERV, USDA, 75- *Personal Data:* b New York, NY, Feb 25, 43; m 73, Yolanda Acacio; c Brian A. *Educ:* Fairleigh Dickinson Univ, BS, 64; Long Island Univ, MS, 67; Iowa State Univ, PhD(bacteriol), 70. *Prof Exp:* Res assoc food technol, Iowa State Univ, 70-71, vis asst prof genetics, 73-74, res assoc, Vet Med Res Inst, 74-75; Univ postdoctoral fel, Ohio State Univ, 71-72; master, Conestoga Col, 72-73. *Mem:* Am Soc Microbiol; Poultry Sci Asn. *Res:* Food technology; salmonellosis; listeriosis. *Mailing Add:* 2905 Arryo Court S College Station TX 77845

**ZIPSER, DAVID,** MOLECULAR GENETICS. *Current Pos:* PROF, DEPT COGNITIVE SCI, UNIV CALIF, SAN DIEGO, 82- *Personal Data:* b New York, NY, May 31, 37; m 65; c 2. *Educ:* Cornell Univ, BS, 58; Harvard Univ, PhD(biochem), 63. *Prof Exp:* Prof biol, Columbia Univ, 65-69; investr genetics, Cold Spring Harbor Lab, 70-82. *Res:* Lactose operon function in bacteria. *Mailing Add:* 1851 Nester St Philadelphia PA 19115

**ZIRAKZADEH, ABOULGHASSEM,** mathematics; deceased, see previous edition for last biography

**ZIRIN, HAROLD,** ASTRONOMY. *Current Pos:* PROF ASTROPHYS, CALIF INST TECHNOL, 64- *Personal Data:* b Boston, Mass, Oct 7, 29; m 57; c 2. *Educ:* Harvard Univ, AB, 50, MA, 51, PhD(astrophys), 53. *Prof Exp:* Physicist, Rand Corp, 52-53; instr astron, Harvard Univ, 53-55; mem sr res staff, High Altitude Observ, Univ Colo, 55-64. *Concurrent Pos:* Sloane fel, 58-60; Guggenheim fel, 61; dir, Big Bear Solar Observ, 69-; mem staff, Hale Observ, 64-80; dir, Aura, 78-83. *Mem:* Am Astron Soc. *Res:* Solar physics; stellar spectroscopy; interstellar matter; geophysics. *Mailing Add:* 1178 Sonoma Dr Altadena CA 91001-3150

**ZIRKER, JACK BERNARD,** SOLAR PHYSICS. *Current Pos:* dir, 76-84, astronr, 76-96, EMER ASTRONOMER, NAT SOLAR OBSERV, 97- *Personal Data:* b New York, NY, July 19, 27; m 51, Lorette Zuckerman; c 3. *Educ:* City Col NY, BME, 49; Harvard Univ, PhD(astron), 56. *Prof Exp:* Mech eng labs, Radio Corp Am, 49-53, astrophysicist, Sacramento Peak Observ, 56-64; astrophysicist & prof physics, Univ Hawaii, 64-76. *Concurrent Pos:* Consult, NASA, 68-; mem, Astron Adv Panel, NSF, 73-76 & mem comt, Solar-Terrestrial Res, Nat Res Coun, 81-82. *Mem:* Am Astron Soc; Int Astron Union. *Res:* Physics of the outer atmosphere of the sun; physics of corona, solar wind, prominences; analysis of spectroscopic, polarimetric solar observations. *Mailing Add:* Sacramento Peak Observ Sunspot NM 88349. *Fax:* 505-434-7029; *E-Mail:* jzirker@noao.edu

**ZIRKIN, BARRY RONALD,** CELL BIOLOGY, REPRODUCTIVE BIOLOGY. *Current Pos:* from asst prof to assoc prof, 74-81, PROF REPRODUCTIVE BIOL, JOHNS HOPKINS UNIV, 81-, HEAD DEPT, 84- *Personal Data:* b Bronx, NY, May 17, 42; m 65; c 2. *Educ:* State Univ NY, Binghamton, BA, 63; Univ Rochester, MS, 65, PhD(cell biol), 69. *Prof Exp:* Asst cell biol, Univ Calif, Davis, 69-71; asst prof biol, Ill Inst Technol, 71-74. *Concurrent Pos:* Asst ed, Biol Reproduction J, 81-85; mem, Clin 3 Study Sect, NIH, 80-84, Reproductive Biol Study Sect, 84-88. *Mem:* Soc Study Reproduction (treas, 85-88); Am Soc Cell Biol; Am Asn Anatomists; Soc Study Reproduction; Am Soc Andrology. *Res:* Hormonal regulation of spermatogenesis; quantitative relationship between cell structure and function. *Mailing Add:* Dept Pop Dynamics Sch Pub Health Johns Hopkins Univ 615 N Wolfe St Baltimore MD 21205-2103. *Fax:* 410-955-0792

**ZIRKIND, RALPH,** PHYSICS. *Current Pos:* PROF PHYSICS, UNIV RI, 73- *Personal Data:* b New York, NY, Oct 20, 18; m 40, Ann Goldman; c Sheila, Elaine & Edward. *Educ:* City Col New York, BS, 40; Ill Inst Technol, MS, 46; Univ Md, College Park, PhD(physics), 59. *Hon Degrees:* DSc, Univ RI, 68. *Prof Exp:* Tech asst metall, Naval Inspector Ord, US Dept Navy, 41-42, physicist, 42-45, physicist, Bur Aeronaut, 45-52, chief physicist, 52-60; physicist, Advan Res Projs Agency, US Dept Defense, 60-64; prof aerospace eng, Polytech Inst Brooklyn, 64-70; prof elec eng, Univ RI, 70-72; physicist, Advan Projs Res Agency, US Dept Defense, 72-74; prin scientist, Gen Res Corp, McLean, Va, 74-81. *Concurrent Pos:* Consult, Jet Propulsion Lab, 64-76; consult, 81- *Mem:* Am Phys Soc; Sigma Xi. *Res:* Optical and radiation physics; atmospheric sciences; optical physics; lasers, atmospheric physics. *Mailing Add:* 820 Hillsboro Dr Silver Spring MD 20902-3202

**ZIRKLE, LARRY DON,** MECHANICAL ENGINEERING. *Current Pos:* asst prof, 70-74, assoc prof, 74-87, DIR STUDENT SERV, ENG, TECHNOL & ARCHIT, OKLA STATE UNIV, 77-, PROF MECH ENG, 87- *Personal Data:* b Wheeler, Tex, Nov 11, 36; m 57; c 3. *Educ:* Okla State Univ, BS, 59, MS, 60; Univ Tex, Austin, PhD(eng mech), 69. *Prof Exp:* Assoc engr, Tex Instruments Inc, 60-61; asst prof eng mech, Univ Tex, Austin, 69-70. *Mem:* Am Soc Mech Engrs; Am Soc Eng Educ; Nat Soc Prof Engrs. *Res:* Random vibrations with particular interest in nonlinear systems; application of engineering to biomedical problems; control theory; nonlinear analysis; dynamics; student counseling and advisement, academic student affairs; co-op education; accident reconstruction. *Mailing Add:* 8 N Pecan Dr Stillwater OK 74075

**ZISCHKE, JAMES ALBERT,** INVERTEBRATE ZOOLOGY, AQUATIC ECOLOGY. *Current Pos:* RETIRED. *Personal Data:* b Sioux Falls, SDak, Sept 18, 34; m 61, Deloris F Palmquist; c Paula A. *Educ:* Univ Wis, BS, 57; Univ SDak, MA, 60; Tulane Univ, PhD(parasitol), 66. *Prof Exp:* Instr, St Olaf Col, 63-65, from asst prof to prof biol, 66-97. *Concurrent Pos:* Partic, AEC Res Prog, PR Nuclear Ctr, 67; Duke Univ res fel, Cent Univ Venezuela, 67-68; NSF fac fel, Univ Miami, 71-72 & Argonne Nat Lab, 76; aquatic biologist, US Environ Protection Agency, 76-80 & Oak Ridge Nat Lab, 78-79; prin investr, US Environ Protection Agency, 82-85 & US Fish & Wildlife Serv, 85-87, Minn Pollution Control Agency, 89- *Mem:* Am Soc Zool; Ecol Soc Am. *Res:* Lake restoration and management; stream ecology; aquatic toxicology. *Mailing Add:* 18316 Captive Lake Rd Garrison MN 56450. *Fax:* 507-646-3104

**ZISK, STANLEY HARRIS,** RADAR ASTRONOMY, SEAFLOOR IMAGING. *Current Pos:* res prof, 88-90, PROF, DEPT GEOL & GEOPHYS, INST GEOPHYS, UNIV HAWAII, 90- *Personal Data:* b Boston, Mass; c 3. *Educ:* Mass Inst Technol, SB & SM, 53; Stanford Univ, PhD(elec eng & radio astron), 65. *Prof Exp:* Res assoc elec eng, Mass Inst Technol, 65-68, mem sci staff, Haystack Observ, 68-88. *Concurrent Pos:* Prin investr, Haystack Observ, 69-; vis scientist, Ltapetinga Radio Observ, Brazil, 74-84, Brown Univ, 80, Univ Hawaii, 79-88. *Mem:* Acoust Soc Am; Am Geophys Union; Union Radio Int Sci; Inst Elec & Electronics Engrs. *Res:* Planetary surfaces research, geological history and current physical/geochemical state; analysis of planetary radar data: Earth, Moon, Mars and Venus; analysis of sea floor acoustic imaging data. *Mailing Add:* Sch Ocean & Earth Sci Univ Hawaii 2525 Correa Rd Honolulu HI 96822. *E-Mail:* shz@soest.hawaii.edu

**ZISKIN, MARVIN CARL,** BIOMEDICAL ENGINEERING. *Current Pos:* from asst prof to assoc prof radiol & med physics, 68-76, PROF RADIOL & MED PHYSICS, MED SCH, TEMPLE UNIV, 76-, CHMN COMT BIOPHYS & BIOENG, 74- *Personal Data:* b Philadelphia, Pa, Oct 1, 36; m 60; c 3. *Educ:* Temple Univ, AB, 58, MD, 62; Drexel Inst, MSBmE, 65. *Prof Exp:* Intern, West Jersey Hosp, Camden, 62-63; NIH fel, Drexel Inst, 63-65; NASA fel theoret biophys, 65; instr radiol & res assoc diag ultrasonics, Hahnemann Med Col, 65-66. *Concurrent Pos:* Lectr biomed eng, Drexel Univ, 65-71; adj assoc prof, 71-; NSF fel analog & digital electronics, 72; mem comt on sci & arts, Franklin Inst, 72-; mem bd dirs, Inst Ultrasonics in Med. *Mem:* Am Inst Ultrasound in Med (pres, 82-84); Am Heart Asn; Inst Elec & Electronics Engrs; Soc Photo-Optical Instrument Eng; NY Acad Sci. *Res:* Biomathematics; diagnostic ultrasonics; thermography; image processing; vision; hearing; information processing in the nervous system. *Mailing Add:* 900 Abington Rd Cherry Hill NJ 08034-3902

**ZISSIS, GEORGE JOHN,** INFRARED-EO TECHNOLOGY & SYSTEMS. *Current Pos:* chief scientist, Infrared & Optics Div, 73-89, EMER SR RES PHYSICIST, ENVIRON RES INST MICH, 89- *Personal Data:* b Lebanon, Ind, Dec 31, 22; m 54, Wanda Evans; c John, Christopher, Maida (Laird) & Maria (Doyle). *Educ:* Purdue Univ, BS, 46, MS, 50, PhD(physics), 54. *Honors & Awards:* Pub Serv Award, US Dept Interior, 72. *Prof Exp:* Instr eng physics, Purdue Univ, 46-50, 52-54; assoc scientist, Atomic Power Div, Westinghouse Elec Corp, 54-55; mem spec air defense study, Off Naval Res, 57; alt head infrared lab, Willow Run Labs, Inst Sci & Technol, 55-64, head lab, 64-69, chief scientist, Infrared & Optics Div, 69-73. *Concurrent Pos:* Vis lectr, Univ Mich, 61-62; lectr, Dept Elec Eng, 70-72; adj prof elec & comput eng, 73-; mem staff, Res Eng, Support Div, Inst Defense Anal, DC, 62-64, consult, 64-72; consult, Army Res Off, 64-72; mem comt space prog earth observ, Nat Res Coun-Nat Acad Sci, chmn, 69-72; adv, Div Earth Sci, US Geol Surv; ed-in-chief, J Remote Sensing of the Environ, 71-78; consult, Infrared Technol, 89-93. *Mem:* Fel AAAS; fel Optical Soc Am; Sigma Xi; fel Int Soc Optical Eng. *Res:* High resolution spectroscopy; infrared; radiometry; optical radiation physics; precision measurements. *Mailing Add:* 1549 Stonehaven Rd Ann Arbor MI 48104-4149

**ZITARELLI, DAVID EARL,** MATHEMATICS, HISTORY OF MATHEMATICS. *Current Pos:* Asst prof, 70-77, ASSOC PROF MATH, TEMPLE UNIV, 77- *Personal Data:* b Chester, Pa, Aug 12, 41; m 66, Anita Paul; c Paul & Nicole. *Educ:* Temple Univ, BA, 63, MA, 65; Pa State Univ, PhD(math), 70. *Concurrent Pos:* Vis prof, Vanderbilt Univ, 76. *Mem:* Am Math Soc; Math Asn Am; Can Soc Hist & Philos Math; Nat Coun Teachers Math. *Res:* History of mathematics; algebraic theory of semigroups. *Mailing Add:* Dept Math Temple Univ Philadelphia PA 19122. *Fax:* 215-204-6433; *E-Mail:* davidz@euclid.temple.edu

**ZITNAK, AMBROSE,** PLANT BIOCHEMISTRY, FOOD TECHNOLOGY. *Current Pos:* RETIRED. *Personal Data:* b Bratislava, Czech, Dec 30, 22; nat Can; m 50; c 3. *Educ:* Slovak Inst Tech, Czech, BSA, 46; Univ Alta, MSc, 53, PhD, 55. *Prof Exp:* Res officer, Agr Res Inst, Czech, 46-47; asst forage chem, Agr Exp Sta, Swiss Fed Inst Technol, 47-48; asst plant biochem, Univ Alta, 51-55, chief analyst feed & soil chem, 55-57; assoc prof hort biochem, Univ Guelph, 57-88. *Mem:* Can Inst Food Technol; Can Soc Plant Physiol; Can Soc Hort Sci; Can Geog Soc; Agr Inst Can. *Res:* Solanaceous glycoalkaloids; plant growth substances; technology of fruit and vegetable preservation; heat-browning of potato products; physiology of the potato tuber; cyanogenic glucosides. *Mailing Add:* 47 Walnut Dr Guelph ON N1G 2W1 Can

**ZITNEY, STEPHEN EDWARD,** SUPERCOMPUTING, PARALLEL PROCESSING. *Current Pos:* sr chem engr, 89-93, GROUP LEADER, PROCESS SIMULATION PROJ, CRAY RES, INC, 94- *Personal Data:* b Homestead, Pa, Aug 2, 61; m 88, Donna Green; c David, Matthew & Sarah. *Educ:* Carnegie-Mellon Univ, BS, 83; Univ Ill, Urbana-Champaign, MS, 86, PhD(chem eng), 89. *Concurrent Pos:* Consult, Univ Ill, 87. *Mem:* Am Inst Chem Engrs; Soc Indust & Appl Math; Instrument Soc Am. *Res:* Chemical process synthesis, design, optimization, and control; supercomputing strategies for chemical process engineering; applied mathematics, especially sparse matrix methods. *Mailing Add:* Cray Res Inc 655E Lone Oak Dr Eagan MN 55121-1560. *Fax:* 612-683-3099; *E-Mail:* sez@cray.com

**ZITOMER, RICHARD STEPHEN,** MOLECULAR BIOLOGY. *Current Pos:* from asst prof to assoc prof, 76-89, PROF GENETICS, DEPT BIOL SCI, STATE UNIV NY, 89- *Personal Data:* b New York, NY, Sept 29, 46; m 69, Marjorie Schneller; c Joseph, Joshua, Rachel & Peter. *Educ:* Univ Pa, BA, 68, PhD(biol), 72. *Prof Exp:* Fel, Dept Biochem, Univ Pa, 72-73 & Dept Genetics, Univ Wash, 73-75. *Concurrent Pos:* Res career develop award, NIH, 81-86; Alexander von Humbolt fel, 81-82; mem, Genetics Study Sect, NIH, 89-92 & 95-98. *Mem:* Am Soc Microbiol; Genetics Soc Am. *Res:* Regulation of the expression of oxygen regulated genes of yeast. *Mailing Add:* Dept Biol Sci State Univ NY 1400 Washington Ave Albany NY 12222. *Fax:* 518-442-4767; *E-Mail:* rz144@albnyvms

**ZITRIN, ARTHUR,** PSYCHIATRY. *Current Pos:* from clin asst to clin instr psychiat, 49-54, from asst clin prof to assoc prof, 54-67, PROF PSYCHIAT, SCH MED, NY UNIV, 67- *Personal Data:* b NY, Apr 10, 18; m 42; c 2. *Educ:* City Col New York, BS, 38; NY Univ, MS, 41, MD, 45. *Prof Exp:* Instr physiol, Hunter Col, 48-49. *Concurrent Pos:* Pvt pract; sr psychiatrist, Bellevue Hosp, 50-, asst dir psychiat div, 54-55, dir, 55-69. *Mem:* Am Psychiat Asn; Am Psychoanal Asn; Asn Res Nerv & Ment Dis. *Res:* Physiological psychology; psychoanalysis; clinical psychiatry. *Mailing Add:* 56 Ruxton Rd Great Neck NY 11023-1529

**ZITRIN, CHARLOTTE MARKER,** PHOBIC DISORDER, PANIC DISORDER. *Current Pos:* ASSOC PROF PSYCHIAT, ALBERT EINSTEIN COL MED, 89- *Personal Data:* b New York, NY, Sept 30, 18; m 43, Arthur; c Richard & Elizabeth. *Educ:* New York Univ, BA, 39, MD, 43. *Prof Exp:* Intern, Kings County Hosp, 43-44; resident pediat, Bellevue Hosp, 44-45; asst pediat, NY Univ Bellevue Med Ctr, 45-46, res fel, 48-49, instr pediat, 49-54, asst prof, 54-58, asst clin prof pediat, NY Univ Med Ctr, 58-60; resident psychiat, Hillside Hosp, 60-63, clin asst, 64-65; supv psychiatrist, Hillside Hosp, Div Long Island Jewish Med Ctr, 65-93, dir, Behav Ther Clin, 70-89, dir, Phobia Clin, 70-89. *Concurrent Pos:* Attend physician pediat, Long Island Jewish Hosp, 58-60; dir, Phobia Clin, Hillside Hosp, Div Long Island Jewis Med Ctr, 72-; asst prof clin psychiat, State Univ NY, Stony Brook, 73-81, clin assoc prof psychiat, 82-89; assoc prof psychiat, Albert Einstein Col Med, 89- *Mem:* Fel Am Psychopath Asn; NY Acad Sci; fel Am Psychiat Asn; ΛΛΛS; Asn Advan Behav Ther. *Res:* Therapy of panic and phobic disorders; prevalance of mitral valve prolapse in panic disorder; prevalance of thyroid disorder and irritable bowel syndrome in panic disorder; risk factors in children of agorophobic parents. *Mailing Add:* 56 Ruxton Rd Great Neck NY 11023

**ZITTER, ROBERT NATHAN,** SOLID STATE PHYSICS, QUANTUM ELECTRONICS. *Current Pos:* PROF PHYSICS, SOUTHERN ILL UNIV, CARBONDALE, 67- *Personal Data:* b New York, NY, Oct 3, 28; m 64. *Educ:* Univ Chicago, BA, 50, MS, 52 & 60, PhD(physics), 62. *Prof Exp:* Mathematician, US Naval Proving Grounds, 52; res physicist, Chicago Midway Labs, 52-60; mem tech staff, Bell Tel Labs, 62-67. *Mem:* Am Phys Soc. *Res:* Semiconductors and semimetals; photoconductivity; gaseous lasers; infrared detection. *Mailing Add:* 155 Hawthorn Hollow Rd Carbondale IL 62901. *Fax:* 618-453-3000

**ZITTER, THOMAS ANDREW,** PLANT VIROLOGY. *Current Pos:* mem staff & assoc prof, 79-92, PROF, DEPT PLANT PATH, CORNELL UNIV, 92- *Personal Data:* b Saginaw, Mich, Dec 30, 41; m 66; c Timothy, Daniel & Julie. *Educ:* Mich State Univ, BS, 63, PhD(plant path), 68. *Prof Exp:* Asst prof & asst plant pathologist, Agr Res & Educ Ctr, Univ Fla, 68-74, assoc prof, 74-79. *Mem:* Am Phytopath Soc; Entom Soc Am; Asn Appl Biologists. *Res:* Isolation and identification of vegetable viruses; establishment of plant-vector-virus relationships; determination of epidemiology and control of virus diseases; vegetable diseases. *Mailing Add:* Dept Plant Path Cornell Univ Ithaca NY 14853. *E-Mail:* taz1@cornell.edu

**ZITZEWITZ, PAUL WILLIAM,** EXPERIMENTAL ATOMIC PHYSICS. *Current Pos:* from asst prof to assoc prof, 73-83, PROF PHYSICS, UNIV MICH, DEARBORN, 83-, ASSOC DEAN, COL ARTS, SCI & LETTERS, 88- *Personal Data:* b Chicago, Ill, June 5, 42; m 66, Barbara Shaw; c Eric & Karin. *Educ:* Carleton Col, BA, 64; Harvard Univ, AM, 65, PhD(physics), 70. *Prof Exp:* Scholar physics, Univ Western Ont, 70-72; res fel & sr physicist, Corning Glass Works, 72-73. *Concurrent Pos:* Alexander von Humboldt fel, 79-80. *Mem:* Am Phys Soc; Am Asn Physics Teachers; Sigma Xi; Nat Sci Teachers Asn. *Res:* Positrons; positron interactions in solids; positronium; teaching and learning of physics; computer enhancement of teaching and learning improving K-12 science education; fundamental constants. *Mailing Add:* Dept Nat Sci Univ Mich Dearborn 4901 Evergreen Rd Dearborn MI 48128. *E-Mail:* pwz@mich.edu

**ZIVI, SAMUEL M(EISNER),** OPTICAL ENGINEERING, NUCLEAR ENGINEERING. *Current Pos:* RETIRED. *Personal Data:* b St Louis, Mo, June 4, 25; m 49, Irene Bettman; c 3. *Educ:* Iowa State Univ, BSME, 46; Wash Univ, MSME, 48. *Prof Exp:* Mech engr, Kennard Corp, 48-52; sr mech engr, Midwest Res Inst, 52-55, sect head, 55-56; staff engr, Atomic Energy Div, Am-Standard Corp, 56-57; develop engr, Kennard Div, Am Air Filter Co, Inc, 57-58; Singer Librascope, 81-83; mem tech staff, TRW Inc, 58-71 & 84-89. *Concurrent Pos:* Lectr, Kjeller, Norway, 62. *Mem:* Am Soc Mech Engrs; Sigma Xi. *Res:* Thermodynamics; heat transfer; optical engineering; fluid mechanics. *Mailing Add:* 2016 Euclid-4 Santa Monica CA 90405. *Fax:* 310-452-0500; *E-Mail:* szivi@netvip.com

**ZLATKIS, ALBERT,** GAS CHROMATOGRAPHY. *Current Pos:* from instr to assoc prof chem, 54-63, chmn dept, 58-62, PROF CHEM, UNIV HOUSTON, 63- *Personal Data:* b Pomorzany, Poland, Mar 27, 24; nat US; m 47, Esther Shessel; c Debra (Peck), Lori (Jordan) & Robert M. *Educ:* Univ Toronto, BASc, 47, MASc, 48; Wayne State Univ, PhD(chem), 52. *Honors & Awards:* Chromatog Award, Am Chem Soc, 73; Technol Award, NASA, 75 & 80, Patent Award, 78; Chromatog Commemorative Medal, 80; Tswett Mem Medal, USSR Acad Sci, 80; Waters Award, 90. *Prof Exp:* Demonstr chem eng, Univ Toronto, 47-48; instr, Wayne State Univ, 49-52, res assoc, 52-53; res chemist, Shell Oil Co, Tex, 53-55. *Concurrent Pos:* Lectr, Am Chem Soc, 61, 63 & 66; chmn, Int Symp Advan Chromatography, 63-; adj prof chem, Baylor Col Med, 75- *Mem:* Am Chem Soc; Sigma Xi. *Res:* Development of clinical analyses such as cholesterol; use of capillary columns and ionization in environmental analysis; concentration techniques for water analysis; flavor analysis; water purification; author of various publications. *Mailing Add:* 3350 McCue Rd Apt 601 Houston TX 77056. *Fax:* 713-784-1152

**ZLETZ, ALEX,** PHYSICAL CHEMISTRY, ORGANIC CHEMISTRY. *Current Pos:* RETIRED. *Personal Data:* b Detroit, Mich, Mar 28, 19; m 48; c Elyu M (Koentopp), Marc H, Adam L & Robin K (Manus). *Educ:* Wayne Univ, BS, 40, MS, 48; Purdue Univ, PhD(chem), 50. *Prof Exp:* Electroplating chemist, Auto City Plating Co, 41; res chemist, Stand Oil Co, 50-54, group leader, 54-61; group leader, Am Oil Co, 61-79; mem staff, Amoco Chem Corp, 79-84. *Concurrent Pos:* Guest scientist, Free Radicals Proj, Nat Bur Stand, 57. *Mem:* Am Chem Soc; Royal Soc Chem; AAAS; Sigma Xi. *Res:* High vacuum; extreme pressure; aryl borons; polyolefins; liquid rocket fuels; free radical and hydrocarbon chemistry; catalysis; fluids and lubricants; greases; railway diesel lubricating oil; hydrocarbon oxidation; homogeneous and heterogeneous oxidation of hydrocarbons to chemical intermediates. *Mailing Add:* 1004 Mill St Apt 106 Naperville IL 60563-2529

**ZLOBEC, SANJO,** APPLIED MATHEMATICS. *Current Pos:* Nat Res Coun Can grants, 70-91, from asst prof to assoc prof, 70-84, PROF MATH, MCGILL UNIV, 84- *Personal Data:* b Brezicani, Yugoslavia, Nov 16, 40; m 65; c 2. *Educ:* Univ Zagreb, BEng, 63, MSc, 67; Northwestern Univ, PhD(appl math), 70. *Prof Exp:* Res engr, Northwestern Univ, 68-69, lectr math, 69-70. *Concurrent Pos:* Vis asst prof, Univ Zagreb, 71-72; vis prof, Univ Del, 78 & Univ Witwatersrand, Johannesburg, 85-86; vis scientist, Coun Sci Indust Res, Pretoria, 78-79 & 85-86. *Mem:* Am Math Soc. *Res:* Optimization theory and applications; applied functional analysis; numerical analysis; mathematics of operations research. *Mailing Add:* Dept Math & Statist Burnside Hall Rm 1005 McGill Univ 805 Sherbrooke St W Montreal PQ H3A 2K6 Can

**ZLOT, WILLIAM LEONARD,** mathematics, for more information see previous edition

**ZLOTNICK, MARTIN,** TECHNOLOGY DEVELOPMENT, TECHNOLOGY OF DECISION MAKING. *Current Pos:* TECH STAFF, NICHOLS RES CORP, 85- *Personal Data:* b New York, NY, Feb 16, 28; m 82; c 4. *Educ:* NY Univ, BAeroE, 48; Univ Va, MAeroE, 51. *Prof Exp:* Aeronaut res scientist, Nat Adv Comt Aeronaut, Va, 48-53; prin aerodynamicist, Repub Aviation Corp, NY, 53-55; prin staff scientist, Avco Res & Adv Develop, Mass, 55-62; mem prof staff, Hudson Inst, NY, 62-65; prin res scientist, Heliodyne Corp, Calif, 65-66 & Avco Everett Res Lab, Mass, 66-68; phys scientist, US Army Advan Ballistic Missile Defense Agency, 68-75; proj officer, Dept Energy, 75-80, br chief advan concepts,

81-82. *Concurrent Pos:* Consult, Hudson Inst, 66-68, 82-85, Technol Develop, 94- *Mem:* Am Inst Aeronaut & Astronaut; Sigma Xi. *Res:* Role-playing games; technology of decision making. *Mailing Add:* 2500 Que St NW Apt 413 Washington DC 20007. *E-Mail:* mzlotnick@aol.com

**ZLOTNIK, ALBERT,** T CELL ONTOGENY, CYTOKINE BIOLOGY. *Current Pos:* staff scientist, 84-88, SR STAFF SCIENTIST, DNAX RES INST, 89- *Personal Data:* b Mex, Nov 29, 54; US citizen; m 82; c 3. *Educ:* Univ Colo, PhD(immunol), 81. *Prof Exp:* Postdoctoral fel immunol, Nat Jewish Hosp, Denver, 82-83. *Concurrent Pos:* Assoc ed, J Immunol, 87- *Mem:* Soc Leukocyte Biol; Am Asn Immunologists; AAAS. *Res:* Identification of novel cytokines and chemokines; role of cytokines in T cell ontogeny. *Mailing Add:* 507 Alger Dr Palo Alto CA 94306. *Fax:* 650-496-1200; *E-Mail:* zlotnik@dnax.org

**ZMIJEWSKI, CHESTER MICHAEL,** IMMUNOLOGY. *Current Pos:* assoc prof, 75-84, PROF PATH, SCH MED, UNIV PA, 84-; ASSOC DIR, WILLIAM PEPPER LAB, UNIV PA HOSP, 83- *Personal Data:* b Buffalo, NY, June 3, 32; m 54, Helen E Borkowski; c Michael, Christopher, Robert & David. *Educ:* Univ Buffalo, BA, 55, MA, 57, PhD(immunol), 60; Millard Fillmore Hosp, cert med tech, 55. *Hon Degrees:* MA, Univ Pa, 78. *Prof Exp:* Asst bact & immunol, Sch Med, Univ Buffalo, 55-58, instr & res fel, 60-61; asst prof clin path & dir blood bank, Med Col Va, 61-63; from asst prof immunol to assoc prof, Sch Med, Duke Univ, 63-70; dir transplantation immunol, Ortho Res Found, 70-73. *Concurrent Pos:* Lectr, Approved Sch Med Technol, 59-61; consult blood bank & serol labs, Millard Fillmore Hosp, Buffalo, 60-61; mem ad hoc subcomt stand adv panel collab res in transplantation & immunol, NIH, 64; immunologist, Yerkes Regional Primate Res Ctr, 65; assoc res prof, Sch Med, State Univ NY, Buffalo; dir clin immunol, 73- *Mem:* Affil Royal Soc Med; Am Asn Immunol; NY Acad Sci; Am Asn Blood Banks. *Res:* Immunohematology; immunogenetics; histocompatibility testing for human allo-transplantation; cancer research and tissue culture. *Mailing Add:* William Pepper Lab Hosp Univ Pa Philadelphia PA 19104-4283

**ZMOLA, PAUL C(ARL),** ENGINEERING. *Current Pos:* CONSULT, 81- *Personal Data:* b Chicago, Ill, Nov 21, 23; wid; c 1. *Educ:* Purdue Univ, BS, 44, MS, 47, PhD(eng), 50. *Prof Exp:* Mfg engr, Western Elec Co, 44-45; instr mech eng, Purdue Univ, 45-48; sr develop engr, Oak Ridge Nat Lab, 50-55; mgr reactor eng, Small Submarine Reactor Proj, Combustion Eng, Inc, 56-59, mgr adv develop, Combustion Div, 59-66, mgr thermal design, 67-71, mgr res & develop prod sales, Power Systs Group, 72-76, dir, Tech Liaison Corp, Group, 77-80. *Mem:* AAAS; Am Soc Mech Engrs; Am Nuclear Soc. *Res:* Nuclear reactor design and development; heat transfer; thermodynamics; fluid mechanics. *Mailing Add:* 5409 Newington Rd Bethesda MD 20816-3317

**ZMOLEK, WILLIAM G,** ANIMAL SCIENCE. *Current Pos:* RETIRED. *Personal Data:* b Toledo, Iowa, July 3, 21; m 45; c 5. *Educ:* Iowa State Col, BS, 44, MS, 51. *Honors & Awards:* Outstanding Educ Accomplishments Extension Award, Am Animal Sci Asn, 78. *Prof Exp:* County exten dir, Iowa State Univ, 44-47, Extent Livestock Specialist, 48-84, prof animal sci, agr exten serv, 63-84. *Concurrent Pos:* Agr rep, Newton Nat Bank, 48. *Mem:* Am Soc Animal Sci. *Mailing Add:* 2022 McCarthy Rd Ames IA 50014

**ZOBACK, MARK D,** GEOPHYSICS. *Current Pos:* PROF GEOPHYS, STANFORD UNIV, 84- *Personal Data:* b Brooklyn, New York, 48. *Educ:* Univ Ariz, BS, 69; Stanford Univ, MS, 73, PhD(geophys), 75. *Prof Exp:* Res assoc, Nat Res Coun, 75-76; geophysicist, US Geol Surv, 76-84. *Concurrent Pos:* Assoc ed, J Geophys Res, 81-84. *Mem:* Fel Geol Soc Am. *Res:* Author of numerous technical publications. *Mailing Add:* 716 Garland Dr Palo Alto CA 94303

**ZOBACK, MARY LOU CHETLAIN,** TECTONICS. *Current Pos:* Nat Res Coun fel, 78-79, GEOPHYSICIST, US GEOL SURV, 79- *Personal Data:* b Sanford, Fla, July 5, 52; m 73, Mark D; c Eli & Megan. *Educ:* Stanford Univ, BS, 74, MS, 75, PhD(geophys), 78. *Honors & Awards:* Macelwane Award, Am Geophys Union, 87. *Concurrent Pos:* Mem, US Geodynamics Comt, Nat Res Coun, 85-89; chmn, World Stress Map Proj, Inter-Union Comn Lithosphere, 86-90; Gilbert fel, US Geol Surv, 90-91; mem, Panel Coupled Hydrol & Tectonic Processes, Yuca Mountain, Nev, 90-92. *Mem:* Nat Acad Sci; fel Geol Soc Am; Fel Am Geophys Union. *Res:* Pattern and sources of the in situ stress field; structural style and tectonism in extensional regimes, particularly the Basin and Range province. *Mailing Add:* US Geol Surv MS 977 345 Middlefield Rd Menlo Park CA 94025. *Fax:* 650-329-5163; *E-Mail:* zoback@andreas.wr.usss.gov

**ZOBEL, ALICJA MARIA,** HISTOCHEMISTRY & CYTOCHEMISTRY OF CELLS PRODUCING PHENOLIC COMPOUNDS, SECONDARY METABOLITES AS DEFENSE COMPOUNDS OF THE PLANT CELLS. *Current Pos:* res assoc chem, 86-90, CONJUNCT ASSOC PROF BIOCHEM, TRENT UNIV, 90- *Personal Data:* b Warszawa, Poland, Jan 4, 48; Can citizen; m 86, Stewart Brown; c Aleksandra & Maigozata. *Educ:* Warsaw Univ, Master Degree, 71, PhD(plant cytophysiol), 79. *Prof Exp:* Res assoc, Dept Pharmacog, Med Acad, Krakow, Poland, 77. *Concurrent Pos:* Vis scientist food sci, Cornell Univ, 86-87; course instr biochem & hon thesis supvr chem, Trent Univ, 91- *Mem:* Phytochem Soc NAm (secy, 93). *Res:* Localization of phenolic compounds in different cells of a plant and extruded to plant surface, as a defense system; immunogold labelling of enzymes in secondary and primary metabolism; phytoalexius produced by plants under biotic and abiotic shens. *Mailing Add:* Trent Univ Peterborough ON K9J 7B8 Can

**ZOBEL, BRUCE JOHN,** FOREST GENETICS. *Current Pos:* from assoc prof to prof forest genetics, 56-62, Edwin F Conger distinguished prof forestry, 62-80, EMER PROF & CONSULT, NC STATE UNIV, 80-; ASSOC, ZOBEL FORESTRY ASSN. *Personal Data:* b Calif, Feb 11, 20; m 41, Barbara Lemon; c Donald, Kathleen, Lois & Julie. *Educ:* Univ Calif, BS, 43, MF, 49, PhD(forest genetics), 51. *Hon Degrees:* DSc, NY State Univ, Syracuse, 86. *Honors & Awards:* Biol Res Award, Am Soc Foresters, 68; Res Award, Tech Asn Pulp & Paper Asn, 73, Gold Medal, 75; Oliver Max Gardner Award, 72; Outstanding Exten Serv Award, NC State Univ, 73 & Forest Farmer Award, 78. *Prof Exp:* Asst to logging engr, Pac Lumber Co, 43-44; sr lab asst, Univ Calif, 46-49; silviculturist, Tex Forest Serv, 51-56. *Mem:* Fel Am Soc Foresters; fel Tech Asn Pulp & Paper Asn; fel Int Acad Wood Sci. *Res:* Silviculture. *Mailing Add:* Col Forest Resources NC State Univ Box 8002 Raleigh NC 27650-8022. *Fax:* 919-467-0329

**ZOBEL, C(ARL) RICHARD,** MOLECULAR BIOPHYSICS, BIOPHYSICAL CHEMISTRY. *Current Pos:* asst prof, 62-68, ASSOC PROF BIOPHYS SCI, SCH MED, STATE UNIV NY, BUFFALO, 68- *Personal Data:* b Pittsburgh, Pa, Aug 29, 28; m 55; c 2. *Educ:* Purdue Univ, BS, 51; Univ Rochester, PhD(phys chem), 54. *Prof Exp:* Res assoc physics, Univ Mich, 54-56; asst prof chem, Am Univ Beirut, 56-59; res assoc biophys, Johns Hopkins Univ, 59-62. *Concurrent Pos:* Du Pont fel infrared spectros, 55-56. *Mem:* AAAS; Electron Micros Soc Am; Biophys Soc; Am Soc Cell Biol. *Res:* Electron microscopy, particularly of macromolecules and ordered complexes of macromolecules; development of staining methods for electron microscopy; ultra structure and function of motile systems, particularly platelets; cell adhesion. *Mailing Add:* Dept Biophys Sci State Univ 112 Cary Hall Buffalo NY 14215-4028

**ZOBEL, DONALD BRUCE,** PLANT ECOLOGY. *Current Pos:* From asst prof to assoc prof, 68-82, PROF BOT, ORE STATE UNIV, 82- *Personal Data:* b Salinas, Calif, July 17, 42; m 66, Priscilla F Matthews; c Cheryl & Gregory. *Educ:* NC State Univ, BS, 64; Duke Univ, MA, 66, PhD(bot), 68. *Concurrent Pos:* Prin investr, NSF grants, 74-77, 81-84 & 94-; vis scientist, Taiwan Forestry Res Inst, Taipei, 76-77; lectr, Fulbright Prog, Nepal, 84-85; Indo Am fel, Naini Tal, India, 91. *Mem:* Ecol Soc Am; AAAS; Brit Ecol Soc; Nat Inst Ecol India. *Res:* Forest ecology; autecology of conifers; ecology of forest understory plants; plant water relations. *Mailing Add:* Dept Bot & Plant Path Ore State Univ Corvallis OR 97331-2902. *E-Mail:* zobeld@bcc.orst.edu

**ZOBEL, HENRY FREEMAN,** STARCH STRUCTURE & PROPERTIES. *Current Pos:* RETIRED. *Personal Data:* b Ft Scott, Kans, Mar 13, 22; m 44, Bernadine Sefton; c Nancy (Koch), Sherry (Millington) & Debbie (Schirmer). *Educ:* Univ Ill, Champaign, BS, 50, MS, 51. *Honors & Awards:* Plenary lectr, Starch Conf, Detmold, Ger, 86; E A Day Mem Lectr, Pa State Univ, University Park, Pa. *Prof Exp:* Chemist, Northern Regional Lab, Ill, 51-67; sr res scientist, Moffett Tech Ctr, CPC Int Inc, 67-86. *Concurrent Pos:* Corn Industs res fel, Northern Regional Lab, Ill, 65-67; mem sci adv comt, Am Inst Baking; consult, US Feed Grains Coun & consult Starch Struct, properties, utilization & bread staling. *Mem:* Am Asn Cereal Chem. *Res:* Physical properties and structure of natural polymers such as granular starches, starch derived products and synthetic polymers; writer, major subject-starch; x-ray diffraction and differential scanning calorimeter analysis. *Mailing Add:* ABCV Starch 1105 Bel Air Dr Darien IL 60561

**ZOBRIST, GEORGE W(INSTON),** ELECTRICAL ENGINEERING, COMPUTER SIMULATION. *Current Pos:* prof comput sci, Grad Eng Ctr, St Louis, 82-85, PROF COMPUT SCI, UNIV MO, ROLLA, 85-, CHMN COMPUT SCI, 94- *Personal Data:* b Highland, Ill, Feb 13, 34; m 55, Freida G Rich; c Barbara, George & Jean. *Educ:* Univ Mo, BSEE, 58, PhD(elec eng), 65; Wichita State Univ, MSEE, 61. *Prof Exp:* Electronic scientist, US Naval Ord Test Sta, Calif, 58-59; assoc engr, Boeing Co, Kans, 59-60; res assoc radar, Res Dept, Wichita State Univ, 60-61; from instr to assoc prof elec eng, Univ Mo, Columbia, 61-69, undergrad prog dir, 68-69; assoc prof elec & electronic systs, Univ SFla, 69-70; prof elec eng & chmn dept, Univ Miami, 70-71; prof elec & electronic systs, Univ SFla, 71-76; prof elec eng & chmn dept, Univ Toledo, 76-79; dir comput sci & eng, Sanborn, Steketee, Otis & Evans, 79-82. *Concurrent Pos:* Lectr, Stevens Inst Technol, 67; NASA res grant, 67-68; sr vis res fel, Univ Edinburgh, 72-73; elec engr & consult, US Naval Ord Test Sta, Calif, 65; consult, Wilcox Elec, Mo, 66-69, M Jones Assoc, Calif, 67-68, Med Serv Bur, Fla, 69-73, Defense Commun Agency, 71-72, US Naval Res Lab, 71-72, NASA Kennedy Space Ctr, Fla, 73-76, 88, 89 & 93-94, Prestolite Co, Toledo, 77-79, IBM, Lexington, Ky, 84-86, Wright Patterson AFB, Ohio, 86, Patrick AFB, 87 & Oak Ridge Nat Lab, 92. *Mem:* Inst Elec & Electronics Engrs; Soc Comput Simulation. *Res:* Topological analysis of networks; electrical engineering education; computer-aided circuit design; software engineering 661 computer science education; computer simulation; software metrice; computer networks. *Mailing Add:* Dept Comput Sci Univ Mo Rolla MO 65409. *Fax:* 573-341-4501; *E-Mail:* zobrist@.umr.edu

**ZOCHOLL, STANLEY E,** ELECTRICAL POWER SYSTEMS, MICRO-PROCESSOR TECHNOLOGY. *Current Pos:* DIR PROTECTION TECHNOL, ABB ASEA-BROWN BOVERI INC, 47- *Personal Data:* b Philadelphia, Pa, July 23, 29; m; c 3. *Educ:* Drexel Univ, BS, 58, MS, 73. *Mem:* Fel Inst Elec & Electronics Engrs. *Mailing Add:* 71 E Rambler Dr Southampton PA 18966

**ZODROW, ERWIN LORENZ,** MATHEMATICAL GEOLOGY, COAL-SULFATE MINERALOGY. *Current Pos:* assoc prof, 78-87, PROF GEOL, UNIV COL CAPE BRETON, 87- *Personal Data:* b Deutsch Krone, Ger, Jan 5, 34; Can citizen; m 63; c Tanya M. *Educ:* St Francis Xavier Univ, BSc, 62; Pa State Univ, MSc, 67; Univ Western Ont, PhD(geol), 73. *Prof Exp:*

Asst party chief geol, Que Cartier Mining Co, 61; field engr, Algoma Ore Properties, 62-63; mem staff mine & develop, Iron Ore Co Can, 64-68; lectr & asst prof, Xavier Col, 70-78. *Concurrent Pos:* Res assoc, NS Mus, 77-; cur fossil plants, Univ Col Cape Breton, 83; invited scientist, Smithsonian Inst, 87, Polish Geol Surv, 89, Wroclaw Univ, 88, US Geol Surv, 94; paleontol inspector, Prov NS, 90-92; res scientist, US Geol Surv, Dept Interior, 93-95. *Mem:* Systs Asn; Paleont Soc Am; Can Inst Mining & Metall; fel Geol Asn Can. *Res:* Upper Carboniferous phytostratigraphy and paleobiology of eastern Canada and European correlation; trace-elemental stratigraphy of Sydney Coalfield (Upper Carboniferous), Nova Scotia Canada; mathematical geology, distributions and factor analysis (applied), secondary sulfate mineralogy and pyrite oxidation products in coals; trace elements in coal. *Mailing Add:* Dept Geol Univ Col Cape Breton Sydney NS B1P 6L2 Can. *Fax:* 902-562-0119; *E-Mail:* ezodrow@sparc.uccb.ns.ca

**ZOELLER, GILBERT NORBERT,** DENTISTRY. *Current Pos:* assoc prof & dir clin, Dent Fac, 74-76, PROF & DIR GEN PROG DENT, SCH DENT MED, SOUTHERN ILL UNIV, 78-; HOSP STAFF DENT, ST ANTHONY'S MED CTR, 75-; PVT PRACT GEN DENT, ST LOUIS, 57- *Personal Data:* b St Louis, Mo, Sept 30, 31; m 53; c 3. *Educ:* St Louis Univ, BS, 53, DDS, 57. *Prof Exp:* Instr pedodont, St Louis Univ, Sch Dent, 57-62, assoc prof prosthodont, 66-70. *Concurrent Pos:* Several USPHS grants, 68-70. *Mem:* Int Asn Dent Res; Sigma Xi. *Res:* Dental materials; in vitro penetration of acid etchant into dentin; biomedical bases for dental therapy; effect of x-rays upon fetal rat calvarial bone cells. *Mailing Add:* 12010 Theiss Rd St Louis MO 63128

**ZOELLER, JOSEPH ROBERT,** HOMOGENEOUS CATALYSIS, INDUSTRIAL & ENGINEERING CHEMISTRY. *Current Pos:* res chemist, Eastman Chem Div, 81-87, sr res chemist, 87-91, prin res chemist, 91, RES ASSOC, EASTMAN CHEM CO, 92- *Personal Data:* b New York, NY, Nov 23, 53; m 82, Elaine C Graves; c Andrew B & Elizabeth L. *Educ:* Hofstra Univ, BS, 75; Purdue Univ, MS, 78; Va Polytech Inst & State Univ, PhD(org chem), 81. *Mem:* Am Chem Soc; Sigma Xi. *Res:* Generation of industrial chemical intermediates from synthesis gas using homogeneous catalysis. *Mailing Add:* 2421 Rivermont Dr Kingsport TN 37660-2367. *Fax:* 423-229-4558; *E-Mail:* usechwlg@ibmmail.com

**ZOELLNER, JOHN ARTHUR,** STATISTICS. *Current Pos:* DEP & TECH DIR, ELECTROMAGNETIC COMPATIBILITY ANALYSIS CTR, DEPT DEFENSE, 76- *Personal Data:* b Ames, Iowa, July 27, 27; m 51; c 3. *Educ:* Iowa State Col, BS, 51, MS, 53. *Prof Exp:* Mgr statist methods, Gen Elec Co, 56-61; supvr anal & prog, IIT Res Inst, 61-63, mgr opers dept, 63-66, asst dir opers, 66-69, dep dir opers, 69-75. *Mem:* Inst Elec & Electronics Engrs; Asn Comput Mach; Opers Res Soc Am. *Res:* Analytical engineering; operational and statistical analysis. *Mailing Add:* 5 Chase Rd Annapolis MD 21401

**ZOGG, CARL A,** MEDICAL PHYSIOLOGY, NUTRITION. *Current Pos:* asst prof physiol, 63-71, assoc prof physiol & pharmacol, 71-78, PROF PHYSIOL, SCH MED, UNIV NDAK, 78- *Personal Data:* b Belleville, Ill, Feb 9, 27; m 52; c 6. *Educ:* Univ Ill, BS, 49, MS, 60, PhD(nutrit in dairy sci), 62. *Prof Exp:* Milk sanitarian, Dressel Young Dairy, 49-58; asst dairy sci, Univ Ill. 58-62, res assoc physiol reprod, 62-63. *Mem:* Am Physiol Soc; Am Mil Soc. *Res:* Ruminant nutrition and physiology; male reproductive physiology; physiology of lactation of simple stomached animals; hyperbaric physiology, nutrition and microbiology; nutritional studies conducted on subjects exposed to hyperbaric helium-molecular oxygen environmental conditions; cecal function in monogastric animals and gastrointestinal motility. *Mailing Add:* 2602 Eighth Ave Grand Forks ND 58203

**ZOGLIO, MICHAEL ANTHONY,** pharmaceutical chemistry, for more information see previous edition

**ZOGORSKI, JOHN STEWARD,** ENVIRONMENTAL SCIENCE, WATER RESOURCES. *Current Pos:* ASSOC PROF ENVIRON SCI, IND UNIV, 77-, DIR, ENVIRON SYSTS APPLN CTR, 79- *Personal Data:* b Trenton, NJ, Mar 5, 46; c 4. *Educ:* Drexel Univ, BS, 69; Rutgers Univ, MS, 72, PhD(environ sci), 75. *Prof Exp:* Hydrologist, Water Resources Div, US Geol Surv, 65-79; proj mgr, Rice Univ, 73-74; asst prof civil & environ eng, Univ Louisville, 74-77. *Concurrent Pos:* Co-prin investr, NJ Water Resources Res Inst, Rutgers Univ, 72-73 & Clark Maritime Proj, Sverdrup & Parcel & Assocs, Univ Louisville, 74-75; proj dir & prin investr, Colgate-Palmolive, Inc, 75; proj dir & prin investr, Louisville Water Co, 74-77 & Ky Water Resources Res Inst, 77-78; co-prin investr, Ohio State Univ & Ind Univ, 77-78, Indianapolis Water Co, 78-80, Ind State Bd Health, 78-80, Ind Dept Natural Resources, 78-79 & 80-81, US Geol Surv, 80-81 & City Columbus, Ind, 80-81; prin investr, US Environ Protection Agency, 81-82; consult, Union Carbide Corp, 80 & US Environ Protection Agency, 81. *Mem:* Am Water Works Asn; Water Pollution Control Fedn; Int Asn Water Pollution Res; Am Water Resources Asn; Int Water Resources Asn. *Res:* Environmental sciences and environmental engineering with emphasis on water resources and water quality assessment; applied hydrology; management of river basins; water and wastewater treatment; aquatic chemistry; impacts of surface mining; removal of trace organics from drinking water. *Mailing Add:* 7508 Junco Lane Black Hawk SD 57718

**ZOGRAFI, GEORGE,** PHARMACEUTICAL CHEMISTRY, SURFACE CHEMISTRY. *Current Pos:* dean, 75-80, PROF PHARM, UNIV WIS-MADISON, 72- *Personal Data:* b New York, NY, Mar 13, 36; m 57; c 4. *Educ:* Columbia Univ, BS, 56; Univ Mich, MS, 58, PhD(pharmaceut chem), 60. *Hon Degrees:* DSc, Columbia Univ, 76. *Honors & Awards:* Ebert Prize, Am Pharmaceut Asn, 84; Res Achievement Award for Simulation of Res, 88; Dale E Wurster Res Award Pharmaceut, Am Asn Pharmaceut Scientists, 90, Distinguished Pharmaceut Scientist Award, 95; Ernest Volwiler Award Res Achievement, Am Asn Col Pharm, 96; Nat Rho Chi Lectr, Rho Chi Hon Soc, 97. *Prof Exp:* Asst prof pharm, Columbia Univ, 60-64; from asst prof to assoc prof, Univ Mich, 64-72. *Concurrent Pos:* Am Found Pharmaceut Educ Pfeiffer Mem res fel, Utrecht Univ, 70-71; vis scientist, Merck Sharp & Dohme Res Labs, 80, Merck Frosst Can, 88. *Mem:* Inst Med-Nat Acad Sci; Am Pharmaceut Asn; fel Am Acad Pharmaceut Sci; Am Chem Soc; Sigma Xi; fel Am Asn Pharmaceut Scientists; Int Pharmaceut Fedn; Int Asn Colloid & Interface Scientists; Am Inst Hist Pharm; fel AAAS; Am Asn Cols Pharm. *Res:* Physical chemical basis for therapeutic activity of drugs; interfacial activity of drugs; lipids and proteins emphasizing structure and function of biological membranes. *Mailing Add:* Sch Pharm Univ Wis 425 N Charter St Madison WI 53706. *Fax:* 608-262-3397

**ZOIS, CONSTANTINE NICHOLAS,** URBAN METEOROLOGY, AIR-SEA INTERACTIONS. *Current Pos:* PROF METEOROL, KEAN COL, NJ, 67- *Personal Data:* b Newark, NJ, Feb 21, 38; m 71, Elyse Stein; c Jennifer & Jonathan. *Educ:* Rutgers Univ, BA, 61, PhD(geophys fluid dynamics), 80; Fla State Univ, MS, 65. *Prof Exp:* Instr math, Rutgers Univ, 61-62; instr meteorol, Fla State Univ, 62-65; res meteorologist, Nat Weather Serv, 65-67. *Concurrent Pos:* Adj prof math, Essex County Col, 69-72; consult, Connell, Foley & Geiser, 83-86; chair atmospheric sci, NY Acad Sci, 86-87. *Mem:* NY Acad Sci. *Res:* Dynamical, thermodynamical and morphological features of urban heat islands, with emphasis on energy transfers between the urban fabric and the atmosphere. *Mailing Add:* 2798 Carol Rd Union NJ 07083

**ZOLBER, KATHLEEN KEEN,** NUTRITION. *Current Pos:* RETIRED. *Personal Data:* b Walla Walla, Wash, Dec 9, 16; m; m 37. *Educ:* Walla Walla Col, BS, 41; Wash State Univ, MA, 61; Univ Wis, PhD(food systs admin), 68. *Prof Exp:* Food serv dir, Walla Walla Col, 41-50, mgr col store, 51-59, from asst prof to assoc prof foods & nutrit, 59-64; dir dietetic internship, Loma Linda Univ, 67-71, dir dietetic educ, 71-84, dir nutrit serv, 72-84, prof nutrit, Med Ctr, 64-92, prog dir nutrit, Sch Pub Health, 84-92. *Concurrent Pos:* Mead Johnson fel, Am Dietetic Asn. *Mem:* Am Dietetic Asn (pres-elect, 81-82, pres, 82-83); Am Mgt Asn; Am Pub Health Asn; Am Home Econ Asn; AAAS. *Res:* Productivity in food service systems; role of technicians in health care professions; health and nutrition. *Mailing Add:* PO Box 981 Loma Linda CA 92354

**ZOLLA-PAZNER, SUSAN BETH,** IMMUNOLOGY. *Current Pos:* NIH fel, 67-69, asst prof, 69-78, ASSOC PROF PATH, MED SCH, NY UNIV, 78-; RES MICROBIOLOGIST, MANHATTAN VET ADMIN HOSP, 69-, CHIEF CLIN IMMUNOL, 79-, CO-DIR, ACQUIRED IMMUNE DEFICIENCY SYNDROME CTR, 83- *Personal Data:* b Chicago, Ill, Feb 25, 42. *Educ:* Stanford Univ, BA, 63; Univ Calif, San Francisco, PhD(microbiol), 67. *Mem:* AAAS; Am Asn Immunol. *Res:* Regulation of the immune response; effects of malignancies on immune function. *Mailing Add:* 18124N Vet Admin Hosp 423 E 23rd St New York NY 10010-5050. *Fax:* 212-951-3468

**ZOLLARS, RICHARD LEE,** INTERFACIAL PHENOMENA, HETEROPHASE REACTOR DESIGN. *Current Pos:* from asst prof to assoc prof, 78-89, actg assoc dean eng, 92-93, PROF CHEM ENG, WASH STATE UNIV, 89-, DEPT CHAIR, 93- *Personal Data:* b Minneapolis, Minn, Nov 9, 46; m 68, Diane M Dillner; c Melanie & Andrew. *Educ:* Univ Minn, BChe, 68; Univ Colo, MS, 72, PhD(chem eng), 74. *Prof Exp:* Sr engr, Union Carbide Corp, 74-77; asst prof chem eng, Univ Colo, 77-78; prog dir, NSF, 83-84. *Mem:* Am Inst Chem Engrs; Am Chem Soc; Am Soc Eng Educ; AAAS; Sigma Xi. *Res:* Fundamental aspects of hetero phase reactions; interfacial phenomenon; stability analysis; particulate systems; adsorption from the liquid phase. *Mailing Add:* Dept Chem Eng Wash State Univ Pullman WA 99164-0001. *Fax:* 509-335-9608; *E-Mail:* scef0002@wsuvm1

**ZOLLER, PAUL,** POLYMER PHYSICS. *Current Pos:* PROF, DEPT MECH ENG, UNIV COLO, 86- *Personal Data:* b Lucerne, Switz, Nov 23, 39; nat US; m 67; c 2. *Educ:* Swiss Fed Inst Technol, dipl phys, 65; Univ Wis-Madison, MSc, 67, PhD(physics), 68. *Prof Exp:* Res assoc physics, Univ Wis, 68-69; res physicist polymers, Film Dept, E I du Pont de Nemours & Co, 69-72; prof polymer sci, Neu-Technikum Buchs, Switz, 72-77; mem staff polymer sci, Cent Res & Develop Dept, E I Du Pont de Nemours & Co, Inc, 77-86. *Mem:* Fel Am Phys Soc. *Res:* Pressure, volume and temperature relationships of polymers; polymer rheology; characterization and low-temperature properties of polymers; polymer processing. *Mailing Add:* Dept Mech Eng Univ Colo CB 427 Boulder CO 80309

**ZOLLER, WILLIAM H,** NUCLEAR CHEMISTRY. *Current Pos:* FAC, DEPT CHEM, UNIV WASH, SEATTLE. *Personal Data:* b Cedar Rapids, Iowa, Mar 3, 43; m 69; c 4. *Educ:* Univ Alaska, BS, 65; Mass Inst Technol, PhD(nuclear chem), 69. *Prof Exp:* Tech asst, Inst Geophys, Univ Hawaii, 65; res asst, Arthur A Noyes Nuclear Chem Ctr, Mass Inst Technol, 65-69, res assoc, 69; res assoc, Inst Geophys, Univ Hawaii, 69-70; from asst prof to assoc prof nuclear & environ chem, Univ Md, College Park, 70-79, prof nuclear & analytical chem, 79- *Mem:* AAAS; Am Phys Soc; Am Meteorol Soc; Am Chem Soc; Am Geophys Union. *Res:* Nuclear phenomenon and environmental chemical problems, especially with respect to air and water pollution; instrumental neutron and photon activation analysis of air pollutants; atmospheric chemical studies in Antarctica the Arctic and Hawaii. *Mailing Add:* Dept Chem BG10 Univ Wash Box 351700 Seattle WA 98195

**ZOLLINGER, JOSEPH LAMAR,** ORGANIC CHEMISTRY. *Current Pos:* res specialist, 3M Co, 57-77, sr res specialist, 77-79, sr patent liaison, 79-85, DIV SCIENTIST, INTELLECTUAL PROPERTY, 3M CO, 85- *Personal Data:* b Salt Lake City, Utah, July 9, 27; m 52; c 7. *Educ:* Univ Utah, BS, 51, PhD(chem), 54. *Prof Exp:* Res org chemist, M W Kellogg Co, 54-57. *Mem:* Am Chem Soc. *Res:* Organic fluorine compounds; elastomers; fluoronitrogen compounds; polymers; silicon compounds; abrasion resistant coatings. *Mailing Add:* 2138 Greenbrier St 3M Ctr Bldg 236-1B-133 St Paul MN 55117-2236

**ZOLLMAN, DEAN ALVIN,** PHYSICS EDUCATION. *Current Pos:* assoc prof, 77-81, distinguished univ teaching scholar, 96-97, PROF PHYSICS, KANS STATE UNIV, 81- *Personal Data:* b Kendallville, Ind, Oct 13, 41; m 74, Jacqueline D Spears; c 2. *Educ:* Ind Univ, BS, 64, MS, 65; Univ Md, PhD(physics), 70. *Honors & Awards:* Distinguished Serv Award, Am Asn Physics Teachers, Robert A Millikan Medal. *Prof Exp:* Asst prof physics, Kans State Univ, 70-75; staff physicist, Am Asn Physics Teachers, 75-77. *Concurrent Pos:* Film repository ed, Am Asn Physics Teachers, 76-81; vis assoc prof physics, Univ Utah, 81-82; guest prof, Univ Munich, 89. *Mem:* Am Asn Physics Teachers; Nat Sci Teachers Asn; Am Phys Soc; Int Asn Comput Educ; Nat Asn Res Sci Teaching. *Res:* Applications of multi-medic, interactive video and computer technologies to physics instruction. *Mailing Add:* Dept Physics 116 Cardwell Hall Kans State Univ Manhattan KS 66506-2601. *Fax:* 785-532-7167; *E-Mail:* dzollman@phys.ksu.edu

**ZOLLO, RONALD FRANCIS,** CIVIL ENGINEERING, MATERIALS SCIENCE. *Current Pos:* assoc prof, 72-83, PROF, DEPT CIVIL ARCHIT & ENVIRON ENG, UNIV MIAMI, 83- *Personal Data:* b Brooklyn, NY, Sept 13, 41. *Educ:* Carnegie Inst Technol, BS, 63, MS, 66; Carnegie-Mellon Univ, PhD(civil eng), 71. *Prof Exp:* Lectr civil eng, City Col New York, 69, asst prof, 70-72. *Concurrent Pos:* Consult, Roman Stone Construct Co, Inc, 71-76; res fel, Battelle Mem Inst, 72-76; NSF res grant, City Col New York & Battelle Mem Inst, 72-76; consult prof engr. *Mem:* Am Soc Civil Engrs; Am Soc Eng Educ; Am Concrete Inst. *Res:* Hybrid computer techniques applied to civil engineering problems; structural and solid mechanics; fiber reinforced concrete; ferro cement. *Mailing Add:* Dept Civil Eng Univ Miami PO Box 248294 Coral Gables FL 33124-6630

**ZOLLWEG, JOHN ALLMAN,** PHYSICAL CHEMISTRY. *Current Pos:* sr res assoc, 82-86, ASSOC PROF CHEM ENG, CORNELL UNIV, 86- *Personal Data:* b Rochester, NY, July 3, 42; m 67; c 2. *Educ:* Oberlin Col, AB, 64; Cornell Univ, PhD(phys chem), 69. *Prof Exp:* NSF fel, Mass Inst Technol, 68-70; from asst prof to assoc prof chem, Univ Maine, Orono, 70-82. *Concurrent Pos:* Vis res fel, Cornell Univ, 80-81. *Res:* Experimental and theoretical study of fluids, including excess enthalpies of mixtures at cryogenic temperatures, vapor-liquid equilibrium, supercritical extraction, sound speed and surface tension; simulation of two dimensional systems on a digital computer. *Mailing Add:* 643 Frnk H T Rhodes Hall Cornell Univ Ithaca NY 14853

**ZOLLWEG, ROBERT JOHN,** EXPERIMENTAL PHYSICS. *Current Pos:* RETIRED. *Personal Data:* b Medina, NY, Aug 1, 24; m 46, Aileen Boules; c Lynn F & Vicky Z (Dunteman). *Educ:* Northwestern Univ, BS, 49, MS, 50; Cornell Univ, PhD(physics), 55. *Prof Exp:* Asst, Cornell Univ, 50-54; sr physicist, Res Labs, Westinghouse Elec Corp, 54-68, adv physicist, 68-80, consult physicist, 80-89. *Mem:* Am Phys Soc. *Res:* Solid state optics; photoemission and optical absorption; electron reflection from metal surfaces; optical properties of plasmas; thermionic energy conversions; arc discharges; thermodynamics and material properties. *Mailing Add:* 4560 Bulltown Rd Murrysville PA 15668

**ZOLMAN, JAMES F,** NEUROPSYCHOLOGY, PSYCHOPHARMACOLOGY. *Current Pos:* asst prof, 64-69, assoc prof, 69-79, PROF PHYSIOL & BIOPHYS, MED CTR, UNIV KY, 79- *Personal Data:* b Dayton, Ohio, Aug 1, 36; m 56; c 2. *Educ:* Denison Univ, BS, 58; Univ Calif, Berkeley, PhD(psychol), 63. *Prof Exp:* NIMH fel, Dept Psychiat & Brain Res Inst, Univ Calif, Los Angeles, 62-64. *Concurrent Pos:* Found Fund fel res psychiat, Inst Psychiat, London, Eng, 71-72; Fogarty sr int fel, Dept Animal Behaviour, Cambridge, Eng, 79-80; vis prof, Dept Psychol, Latrobe Univ, Bundoora, Victoria, Australia, 87. *Mem:* AAAS; Am Psychol Asn; Psychonomic Soc; Soc Neurosci; Int Soc Develop Psychobiol. *Res:* Developmental psychopharmacology. *Mailing Add:* Dept Physiol Univ Ky Med Sch 800 Rose St Lexington KY 40536-0001

**ZOLNOWSKI, DENNIS RONALD,** nuclear physics, for more information see previous edition

**ZOLOTOROFE, DONALD LEE,** CHEMICAL ENGINEERING, POLYMER CHEMISTRY. *Current Pos:* Chem engr, 71-76, sr engr, 76-82, RES FEL, ROHM & HAAS CO, 82- *Personal Data:* b Bronx, NY, Sept 5, 46; m 88, Eileen T Fetter. *Educ:* Cornell Univ, BS, 67, MS, 69, PhD(chem eng), 71. *Res:* Physical properties of polymeric systems; bulk, solution, and emulsion polymerization processes (product and process development); high pressure process development; monomer process engineering. *Mailing Add:* Rohm & Haas Co 727 Norristown Rd Spring House PA 19477

**ZOLTAI, TIBOR,** MINERALOGY, CRYSTALLOGRAPHY. *Current Pos:* RETIRED. *Personal Data:* b Gyor, Hungary, Oct 17, 25; m 50; c 3. *Educ:* Univ Toronto, BASc, 55; Mass Inst Technol, PhD(mineral), 59. *Hon Degrees:* Dr, Tech Univ Heavy Indust, Miskolc, Hungary, 89. *Prof Exp:* From asst prof

to assoc prof mineral, Univ Minn, Minneapolis, 59-62, chmn, dept geol & geophys, 63-71, prof, 64-92. *Concurrent Pos:* Consult, US Bur Mines, Ft Snelling, Minn, 59-90; vis prof, Univ Saarlandes, Saarborucken, Ger, 68; vis prof, Univ Cent Venezuela, Caracas, 78-79; vis prof, Univ Chem Indust, Veszprem, Hungary, 89; consult & mem, NAS/NRC Geochem Div, Comt Fibrous Mat as Health Hazards, 80-83; mem, NAS/NRC Life Sci Div, Comt Non-Occup Health Risks Asbestiform Fibers, 82-84; mem, rev panel NIH res grant, Mt Sinai Sch Med, NY, 83; mem, range studies adv panel, Minn Dept Health, 85. *Mem:* Geol Soc Am; Mineral Soc Am; Am Crystallog Asn; Mineral Asn Can; Hungarian Acad Sci. *Res:* Crystal structures and crystal chemistry of minerals; mineralogy and physical properties of asbestos. *Mailing Add:* 476 Summit Ave St Paul MN 55102

**ZOLTAN, BART JOSEPH,** INSTRUMENTATION, ELECTRO-OPTICS. *Current Pos:* PRIN RES SCIENTIST, MED RES DIV, AM CYANAMID, 77- *Personal Data:* b Dec 26, 46; US citizen; m 80, Constance Kohler; c Andrew, Adam & Laura. *Educ:* Fairleigh Dickinson Univ, BS, 69, MS, 73. *Prof Exp:* Sr engr, Kearfott Div, Singer Co, 69-77. *Mem:* Inst Elec & Electronics Engrs; Instrument Soc Am; AAAS. *Res:* Development of instrumentation in support of biomedical and pharmacological research; use of electro-optical techniques for measurements or analysis; design of biomedical devices. *Mailing Add:* 152 De Wolf Rd Westwood NJ 07675. *Fax:* 914-732-5581; *E-Mail:* zoltanbj@pr.cyanamid.com

**ZOLTEWICZ, JOHN A,** ORGANIC CHEMISTRY. *Current Pos:* from asst prof to assoc prof chem, 63-73, PROF CHEM, UNIV FLA, 73- *Personal Data:* b Nanticoke, Pa, Dec 5, 35; m 65; c 3. *Educ:* Princeton Univ, AB, 57, PhD(org chem), 60. *Prof Exp:* NATO fel, Univ Munich, 60-61; Shell Corp Fund fel, Brown Univ, 61-62, NIH fel, 62-63. *Mem:* Am Chem Soc. *Res:* Heterocyclic chemistry; kinetics; rates and mechanism of hydrogen-deuterium exchange in heterocycles; radical-anion heteroaromatic nucleophilic substitution; thiamine model studies; covalent amination. *Mailing Add:* Chem Dept Univ Fla Gainesville FL 32611-7200

**ZOLTON, RAYMOND PETER,** HEMATOLOGY. *Current Pos:* SR SCIENTIST COAGULATION, ORTHO DIAG INC, 74- *Personal Data:* b Jersey City, NJ, May 21, 39; m 60; c 3. *Educ:* Newark Col Eng, BS, 63; Univ Del, MS, 67; Purdue Univ, PhD(biochem), 72. *Prof Exp:* Engr dyes, E I du Pont de Nemours & Co, Inc, 63-68; res assoc, Wayne State Univ, 72-74. *Concurrent Pos:* Mem thrombosis coun, Am Heart Asn. *Mem:* Am Soc Coagulation; Am Chem Soc. *Res:* Development of diagnostic test for coagulation and fibrinolysis parameters. *Mailing Add:* Austin Rd Bethlehem NH 03574-0062

**ZOMBECK, MARTIN VINCENT,** PHYSICS, X-RAY ASTRONOMY. *Current Pos:* PHYSICIST, SMITHSONIAN ASTROPHYS OBSERV, 78- *Personal Data:* b Peekskill, NY, Aug 14, 36; m 63, Monique Lagoathe; c Yann & Richard. *Educ:* Mass Inst Technol, BS, 57, PhD(physics), 69. *Prof Exp:* Observer, Smithsonian Astrophys Observ, 61-64; res asst physics, Mass Inst Technol, 64-69; proj scientist, Am Sci & Eng, Inc, 69-73; head physics & instrumentation, Damon Corp, 73-74; res assoc, Harvard Col Observ, 74-78. *Concurrent Pos:* Fulbright scholar, WGer. *Mem:* Am Astron Soc; Int Astron Union. *Res:* Solar and stellar x-ray astronomy from rockets and space observatories; x-ray imaging instrumentation; x-ray optics; x-ray spectroscopy. *Mailing Add:* 42 Fletcher St Winchester MA 01890

**ZOMPA, LEVERETT JOSEPH,** INORGANIC CHEMISTRY. *Current Pos:* from asst prof to assoc prof, Univ Mass, Boston, 66-71, chmn dept, 73-83, dir grad prog, 84-88, vchancellor acad affairs & provost, 88-91, PROF CHEM, UNIV MASS, BOSTON, 77-, CHMN DEPT, 95- *Personal Data:* b Lawrence, Mass, May 31, 38; m 66; c 6. *Educ:* Merrimack Col, BS, 59; Col Holy Cross, MS, 60; Boston Col, PhD(inorg chem), 64. *Prof Exp:* Asst prof chem, Boston Col, 64-65; fel, Mich State Univ, 65-66. *Mem:* Am Chem Soc; Sigma Xi. *Res:* Transition metal complexes of stereorestrictive amines and amino acids; complexes of anions-structure, bonding and selectivity. *Mailing Add:* 6 Kathleen Dr Andover MA 01810. *Fax:* 617-265-7173; *E-Mail:* zumpz@umbsky.cc.edu

**ZOMZELY-NEURATH, CLAIRE ELEANORE,** neurobiology, for more information see previous edition

**ZON, GERALD,** ORGANIC CHEMISTRY. *Current Pos:* SCIENTIST, DIV BIOCHEM & BIOPHYS, FOOD & DRUG ADMIN. *Personal Data:* b Buffalo, NY, Apr 3, 45. *Educ:* Canisius Col, BS, 67; Princeton Univ, PhD(org chem), 71. *Prof Exp:* Res assoc chem, Ohio State Univ, 71-72, NIH fel, 72-73; assoc prof chem, Cath Univ Am, 73- *Concurrent Pos:* Sr res assoc, Andrulis Res Corp, 75- *Mem:* Am Chem Soc; Fedn Am Supporting Sci & Technol. *Res:* Synthesis, stereochemistry and mechanism of anticancer drugs; novel reactions of organometalloid systems. *Mailing Add:* Lynx Therapeut 3832 Bay Center Pl Hayward CA 94545

**ZONEREICH, SAMUEL,** EARLY DETECTION OF CORONARY HEART DISEASE, PROPHYLAXIS OF HYPERTENSION CARDIOVASCULAR DISEASE. *Current Pos:* PROF MED, EINSTEIN MED COL, 88-; DIR RES & CARDIAC EDUC, FLUSHING MED CTR, 90- *Personal Data:* b Mihaileni, Nov 4, 20; US citizen; m, Olga. *Educ:* State Univ NY, MD, 66. *Prof Exp:* Lectr cardiol, Iassy, 51-59; fel cardiol, Sorbonne, Paris, 62; dir non-invasive cardiol, Queens Hosp, 66-90, assoc dir med, 68-79, dir cardiol, 70-80; assoc prof med, State Univ NY, Stony Brook, 71-78, prof, 78-89. *Concurrent Pos:* Attending & consult cardiol, 68-; fel, Clin

Coun, Am Heart Asn, 74-; vis prof, Univ Tokyo, Japan, 90. *Mem:* Emer fel Am Col Cardiol; Am Heart Asn; Soc Echocardiography; Am Soc Hypertension; fel Am Col Angiol. *Res:* Non-invasive cardiology; diabetes and the heart; hypertension and diabetes prophylaxis and epidemiology. *Mailing Add:* Albert Einstein Col Med 1300 Morris Park Ave Bronx NY 10461-1926. *Fax:* 718-670-4510

**ZONIS, IRWIN S(AMUEL),** CHEMICAL ENGINEERING. *Current Pos:* plant mgr, Essex Chem Corp, 62-63, opers mgr, 63-64, vpres opers, Chem Div, 64-69, GEN MGR CHEM DIV & VPRES, ESSEX CHEM CORP, 69- *Personal Data:* b Boston, Mass, June 22, 30; m 55; c 3. *Educ:* Rensselaer Polytech Inst, BChE, 50; Mass Inst Technol, MS, 52. *Prof Exp:* Proj mgr, Nat Res Corp, 51-57; chief process engr, Columbia-Nat Corp, 57-59; supvr chem eng, Dixon Chem & Res Inc, 59-62. *Concurrent Pos:* Mem, NJ State Air Pollution Control Comn, 66-67 & NJ State Clean Air Coun, 68, vchmn, 70, 71, chmn, 72- *Mem:* AAAS; Am Chem Soc; Am Inst Chem Engrs; Air Pollution Control Asn; Sigma Xi. *Res:* Heavy inorganic chemicals; production management; air quality control; extractive metallurgy. *Mailing Add:* 71 Crestmont Rd West Orange NJ 07052-1626

**ZOOK, ALMA CLAIRE,** SPECTROSCOPY OF DIATOMIC MOLECULES, NONLINEAR OPTICS. *Current Pos:* asst prof, 82-87, ASSOC PROF PHYSICS, POMONA COL, 87- *Personal Data:* b Los Angeles, Calif, June 27, 50. *Educ:* Pomona Col, Calif, BA, 72; Univ Calif, Berkeley, PhD(astron), 79. *Prof Exp:* Asst prof physics, Hamilton Col, 78-82. *Mem:* Am Astron Soc; Astron Soc Pac; Optical Soc Am; Am Women Sci; AAAS; Sigma Xi. *Res:* Laboratory spectroscopy of astronomically interesting molecules; optical phase conjugation in barium titanate. *Mailing Add:* Physics Pomona Col Claremont CA 91711

**ZOOK, BERNARD CHARLES,** RADIATION PATHOLOGY, CONGENITAL HEART DISEASE. *Current Pos:* from asst prof to assoc prof, 69-83, DIR, ANIMAL RES FACIL, MED CTR, GEORGE WASHINGTON UNIV, 72-, PROF PATH, 83- *Personal Data:* b Beach, NDak, Nov 1, 35; m 55, Elinore A Schillo; c Bernita E (Leonard), Melinda S & Andrew K. *Educ:* Colo State Univ, BS, 62, DVM, 63; Am Col Vet Pathologists, cert, 68. *Prof Exp:* Res fel path, Med Sch, Harvard Univ, 63-67, asst pathologist, Sch Pub Health, 67-68, res fel electron micros, Sch Pub Health, 67-69. *Concurrent Pos:* Res fel path, Angell Mem Hosp, 63-67, assoc pathologist, 67-69; res assoc, Smithsonian Inst, 69-; mem bd dirs, Nat Soc Med Res, 82-85; consult, Litton Bionetics, 74-80, Pop Coun, 81-86 & Fraunhofer Inst, 85-86; adj prof path, Am Univ, 88-91. *Mem:* Am Vet Med Asn; Am Col Vet Pathologists; Radiation Res Soc; Am Asn Pathologists; Soc Tox Pathologists; Am Asn Lab Animal Sci; Sigma Xi. *Res:* Tissue effects of ionizing and non-ionizing radiation (ultrasound, radio frequency) radiation. *Mailing Add:* Med Ctr George Washington Univ 2300 Eye St NW Washington DC 20037

**ZOOK, HARRY DAVID,** ORGANIC CHEMISTRY, ACADEMIC ADMINISTRATION. *Current Pos:* asst chem, Pa State Univ, 39-41, from instr to assoc prof, 41-60, asst to vpres res, 65-70, prof chem, 60-81, asst vpres res & assoc dean grad sch, 70-81, EMER PROF, PA STATE UNIV, UNIVERSITY PARK, 81- *Personal Data:* b Milroy, Pa, Feb 8, 16; m 37; c 2. *Educ:* Pa State Univ, BS, 38, PhD(org chem), 42; Northwestern Univ, MS, 39. *Prof Exp:* Asst org chem, Northwestern Univ, 38-39. *Concurrent Pos:* Vis lectr, Stanford Univ, 62. *Mem:* Am Chem Soc. *Res:* Kinetics and mechanism of organic reactions. *Mailing Add:* 110 Village Lane Winter Park FL 32792-3412

**ZOOK, HERBERT ALLEN,** OPTICAL DETECTION OF SMALL BODIES IN SPACE, PLANETARY RINGS. *Current Pos:* SPACE SCIENTIST, SOLAR SYST EXPLOR DIV, NASA-JOHNSON SPACE CTR, 74- *Personal Data:* b Laurel, Mont, Apr 21, 32; m 69; c Pamela. *Educ:* Mont State Col, BS, 58, MS, 60. *Mem:* Meteoritical Soc; Planetary Soc; Am Geophys Union; Nat Space Soc. *Res:* Origin and evolution of meteoroids and meteorites and their relationships to comets and asteroids; orbital and collisional evolution of meteoroids are theoretically studied and experimental spacecraft impact data are evaluated. *Mailing Add:* 1703 Bowline Rd Houston TX 77062

**ZOON, KATHRYN C,** HUMAN INTERACTIONS, CYTOKINE BIOLOGY. *Current Pos:* supvr chemist, 83-89, dir, Div Cytokine Biol, 89-92, DIR, CTR BIOLOGICS EVAL & RES, FOOD & DRUG ADMIN, 80- *Educ:* Rensselaer Polytech Inst, BS, 70; Johns Hopkins Univ, PhD(biochem), 75. *Prof Exp:* Fel, NIH, 75-77, staff fel & sr staff fel, 77-83. *Concurrent Pos:* Ed, J Inteferon Res. *Mem:* Am Soc Biol Chemists. *Res:* Regulatory issues related to biologics and biotech products; interferon purification, characterization and interferon receptors; author numerous scientific papers. *Mailing Add:* FDA HF M-1 1401 Rockville Pike Suite 200 N Rockville MD 20852

**ZOPF, DAVID ARNOLD,** IMMUNOCHEMISTRY, CARBOHYDRATE ANTIGENS. *Current Pos:* VPRES & CHIEF OPERATING OFFICER, BIOCARB INC, 88- *Personal Data:* b St Louis, Mo; m; c 4. *Educ:* Washington Univ, St Louis, MD, 69. *Prof Exp:* Chief, Sect Biochem Path, Path Lab, Nat Cancer Inst, 79-88. *Mem:* Asn Am Physician; Am Soc Biochem & Molecular Biol. *Res:* Biochemistry and immunochemistry of complex carbohydrates. *Mailing Add:* Drug Develop Neose Pharmaceut 102 Witmer Rd Horsham PA 19044. *Fax:* 215-688-2640

**ZORDAN, THOMAS ANTHONY,** PHYSICAL CHEMISTRY. *Current Pos:* ENGR, ZORDAN ASSOCS, 88- *Personal Data:* b Rockford, Ill, Nov 21, 43. *Educ:* Northern Ill Univ, BS, 65; Univ Louisville, PhD(phys chem), 69. *Prof Exp:* Res chemist, Gulf Res & Develop Co, 69-72; sr engr, Nuclear Ctr, Westinghouse Elec Corp, 72-74, mgr safeguards eval, 74-77, mgr reliability & safety, 77-78, mgr standard plant eng, 78-80; proj mgr, D'Appolonia Consult Engrs, 80-88. *Mem:* Am Chem Soc; AAAS; Am Inst Chem Engrs. *Res:* Thermodynamics of solutions and pure substances; theory of the liquid state; calorimetry of chemical reactions; nuclear power reactor safety; nuclear power plant design. *Mailing Add:* 3807 Edinburg Dr Murrysville PA 15668

**ZORN, GUS TOM,** HIGH ENERGY PHYSICS. *Current Pos:* assoc prof physics, 62-72, PROF PHYSICS, UNIV MD, COLLEGE PARK, 72- *Personal Data:* b Ada, Okla, June 18, 24; wid. *Educ:* Okla State Univ, BS, 48; Univ NMex, MS, 52; Univ Padua, PhD(physics), 54. *Prof Exp:* Res assoc physics, Brookhaven Nat Lab, 54-56, assoc physicist, 56-62. *Concurrent Pos:* Vis scientist, Max Planck Inst Physics, 58; vis physicist, Frascat Nat Lab, Italy, 67-68, 76-77 & DESY Lab, Hamburg, WGer, 84. *Mem:* Fel Am Phys Soc; Ital Phys Soc; NY Acad Sci. *Res:* Experimental high energy and elementary particle physics, using nuclear emulsions, bubble chambers, counters, spark chambers, and streamer and proportional wire chambers. *Mailing Add:* Dept Physics Univ Md Rm 4310 Bldg 082 College Park MD 20742. *Fax:* 301-699-9195

**ZORN, JENS CHRISTIAN,** ATOMIC PHYSICS, HISTORY & SCIENCE. *Current Pos:* from asst prof to assoc prof, Univ Mich, Ann Arbor, 62-69, dir, Residential Col, 72-74, assoc dean, Col Arts & Sci, 80-82, PROF PHYSICS, UNIV MICH, ANN ARBOR, 70- *Personal Data:* b Halle, Ger, June 19, 31; US citizen; m 54, Frances Barnhart; c Eric & Karen. *Educ:* Miami Univ, AB, 55; Yale Univ, MS, 57, PhD(physics), 61. *Prof Exp:* Engr, Sarkes Tarzian, Inc, Ind, 53-54; res asst physics, Univ Tubingen, 55-56; consult, Yale Univ, Sch Med, 59-61, instr, 61-62. *Concurrent Pos:* Vis prof, Univ Puebla, 64-65; Phoenix fac fel, Univ Mich, 65-66, Ombudsman, 82-90. *Mem:* Fel Am Phys Soc; Am Asn Physics Teachers. *Res:* Atomic and molecular structure; atomic beams; microwave spectroscopy; laboratory astrophysics; space physics; scientific manpower administration. *Mailing Add:* 1409 Randall Lab Physics Univ Mich 500 E University Ave Ann Arbor MI 48109-1120. *Fax:* 313-662-0683; *E-Mail:* jenszorn@umich.edu

**ZORNETZER, STEVEN F,** NEUROBIOLOGY, SCIENCE MANAGEMENT. *Current Pos:* PERSONNEL OPTIMIZATION & BIOMOLECULAR SCI & TECH DEPT, OFF NAVAL RES, 82- *Personal Data:* b New York, NY, Jan 21, 45; m 69; c 1. *Educ:* State Univ NY, Stony Brook, BA, 66; Univ Wis-Madison, MA, 67; Univ Calif, Irvine, PhD(biol), 71. *Honors & Awards:* William P Beck Sci Res Award, Interstate Postgrad Med Asn, 74. *Prof Exp:* From asst prof to assoc prof neurosci, Col Med, Univ Fla, 71-80; assoc prof pharmacol, Univ Calif, Irvine, 80-82. *Concurrent Pos:* Sloan res fel, 75; adj prof psychiat, Uniformed Serv Univ Health Sci, 85- *Mem:* AAAS; Soc Neurosci; NY Acad Sci; Int Brain Res Orgn. *Res:* Neural information processing; memory; synaptic plasticity; neural changes during aging. *Mailing Add:* 7735 Rocton Ct Chevy Chase MD 20815

**ZORNIG, JOHN GRANT,** communications engineering, digital systems, for more information see previous edition

**ZOROWSKI, CARL F(RANK),** MECHANICAL ENGINEERING, MECHANICAL DESIGN & MANUFACTURING. *Current Pos:* from assoc prof to prof, NC State Univ, 62-69, assoc head dept, 66-72, head dept, 72-79 & 92, assoc dean, Sch Eng, 79-85 & 93, R J REYNOLDS PROF MECH ENG & AEROSPACE ENG, NC STATE UNIV, 69- *Personal Data:* b Pittsburgh, Pa, July 14, 30; m 85, Louise P Lockwood; c Kathleen, Karl & Kristine. *Educ:* Carnegie Inst Technol, BS, 52, MS, 53, PhD(mech eng), 56. *Honors & Awards:* Western Elec Award, Am Soc Eng Educ, 68; Fiber Soc Res Award, 70; Charles Russ Richards Award, Am Soc Mech Engrs, 75. *Prof Exp:* From instr to assoc prof mech eng, Carnegie Inst Technol, 54-62. *Concurrent Pos:* Orgn Europ Econ Coop sr vis fel, Brit Iron & Steel Res Asn, Sheffield, Eng, 62; consult, Army Res Off, Durham, 71 & Monsanto Co, 63-80, engr, Int Bus Mach, 85-92; dir, Div Succeed Proj, Inst Mfg Systs Eng, 93- *Mem:* Am Soc Mech Engrs (vpres, 80-83); Am Soc Eng Educ; Fiber Soc. *Res:* Design for manufacturability; computer aided design for automated manufacturing; applied mechanics and mechanical design with emphasis on fibers, textile and composite property characterization and deformation mechanics; metal forming mechanics; mechanical system and component design and dynamic response analysis. *Mailing Add:* 103 Windyrush Lane Cary NC 27511. *Fax:* 919-515-7685; *E-Mail:* carl_zorowski@ncsu.edu

**ZORY, PETER S, JR,** LASERS. *Current Pos:* PROF ELEC ENG, UNIV FLA, GAINESVILLE, 88- *Personal Data:* b Syracuse, NY, Oct 9, 36; m 61, Barbara Futterer; c Michael & Brian. *Educ:* Syracuse Univ, BS, 58; Carnegie-Mellon Univ, PhD(physics), 64. *Prof Exp:* Physicist, Gyroscope Div, Sperry Rand Corp, 64-66, sr physicist, 66-68; res staff mem, T J Watson Res Ctr, IBM Corp, 68-78; sr scientist, Optical Info Systs Inc, 78-83; McDonnell-Douglas Astronaut, Opto-Electronics Ctr, Elmsford, NY, 83-86; mgr, Laser Technol, Gen Elec Electronics Lab, Syracuse, NY, 86-88. *Mem:* Inst Elec & Electronics Engrs; Optical Soc Am. *Res:* Laser research. *Mailing Add:* Dept Elec Eng Univ Fla 129 Larsen Hall PO Box 116200 Gainesville FL 32611

**ZORZOLI, ANITA,** biochemistry, physiology; deceased, see previous edition for last biography

**ZOSS, ABRAHAM OSCAR,** INTERNATIONAL TECHNOLOGY TRANSFER, PETROCHEMICALS. *Current Pos:* PRES, BUS DEVELOP INT, 84- *Personal Data:* b South Bend, Ind, Feb 17, 17; m 39, 78, Magda Szanto; c Roger, Joel & Hope (Schladen). *Educ:* Univ Notre Dame, BSChE, 38, MS, 39, PhD(org chem), 41. *Honors & Awards:* Centennial of Sci Award, Univ Notre Dame, 65. *Prof Exp:* Asst, Univ Notre Dame, 39-41; res chemist, Gen Aniline & Film Corp, NJ, 41-43, Pa, 43-47, dept chemist, NJ, 47-49, area supt, 49-51, prod mgr, 51-54, tech mgr, 54-55, plant mgr, 55-57; mgr mfg admin, Chem Div, Minn Mining & Mfg Co, 57-58, div prod mgr, 58-60; vpres, Photek, Inc, 60-62; asst corp tech dir, Celanese Corp, 62-65, corp tech dir, 65-66, corp dir com develop, 66-69; vpres, Tenneco Chem, Inc, NY, 69-71; vpres corp dev, Universal Oil Prod Co, 71-72; group vpres, Engelhard Minerals & Chem Corp, 72-75, vpres bus develop, 75-77; vpres corp develop, CPS Chem Co, Inc, 77-84. *Concurrent Pos:* Mem field info agency, Off Tech Serv, US Dept Com, Ger, 46; consult, 84- *Mem:* Fel AAAS; Am Chem Soc; Am Inst Chem Engrs; fel Am Inst Chemists; NY Acad Sci; Am Sect Societe de Chimie Industrielle (pres, 91-). *Res:* Acetylene and high polymer chemistry; petrochemicals; synthetic fibers; plastics; technology transfer; coatings; commercial development; catalytic chemistry; specialty monomers and polymers. *Mailing Add:* 45 East End Ave Suite 11D New York NY 10028-7982. *Fax:* 212-650-1689; *E-Mail:* zoss@aol.com

**ZOSS, LESLIE M(ILTON),** MECHANICAL ENGINEERING, MEASUREMENT & CONTROL SYSTEMS. *Current Pos:* CONSULT, 58- *Personal Data:* b Lockport, NY, Nov 23, 26; m 49, Carolyn B Luers; c David L, Cynthia C (Giles), Judith E (Meister) & Lisa M (Haley). *Educ:* Purdue Univ, BS, 49, MS, 50, PhD(mech eng), 52. *Honors & Awards:* Donald P Eckman Educ Award, Instrument Soc Am, 68. *Prof Exp:* Instr, Mech Eng Lab, Purdue Univ, 49-50; res engr, Taylor Instrument Co, 52-55, tech training dir, 55-58; from asst prof to prof, Valpraiso Univ, 58-66, head dept, 65-76, res prof mech eng, 66-86. *Concurrent Pos:* Consult, Esso Res & Eng Co, 59-65, Am Oil Co, 66-68, Shell Chem Co, 69-70 & Eli Lilly & Co, 71- *Mem:* Am Soc Mech Engrs; fel Instrument Soc Am; hon mem Int Soc Measurement & Control. *Res:* Instrumentation for automatic control; special interest in system start up and trouble shooting. *Mailing Add:* 2990 Horse Hill Dr E Indianapolis IN 46214

**ZOTOS, JOHN,** MATERIALS SCIENCE, METALLURGY. *Current Pos:* from asst prof to prof, 60-92, EMER PROF MECH ENG, NORTHEASTERN UNIV, 92- *Personal Data:* b Brockton, Mass, Jan 12, 32; m 58; c 3. *Educ:* Northeastern Univ, BSChE, 54; Mass Inst Technol, MSMet, 56, Metall Engr, 67. *Honors & Awards:* Adams Mem Award, Am Welding Soc, 72. *Prof Exp:* Eng asst metall, Raytheon Mfg Co, 54; proj metallurgist, Watertown Arsenal's Rodman Lab, 55-56, asst chief exp foundry br, 56-60. *Concurrent Pos:* Mat & metall consult & lectr to indust, 60-; consult & mem bd dir, Indust Magnetics, Inc, Mass, 63-70; NSF sci fac fel, 63-70; Welding Res Coun study grant, 69; consult & mem tech adv bd, Thermo Magnetics, Inc, Mass, 70-73. *Mem:* Am Foundrymen's Soc; Am Defense Preparedness Asn; Am Inst Mining, Metall & Petrol Engrs; Am Inst Chem Engrs; Am Soc Metals; Am Powder Metall Inst. *Res:* Development of mathematical models which describe the chemical, mechanical and physical properties of both ferrous and non-ferrous casting alloys; use of electromagnetic solid state joining for bonding similar and dissimilar metals and alloys; the role and responsibilities of the professional person in his civic and religious communities. *Mailing Add:* 28 Old Coach Rd Cohasset MA 02025

**ZOTTOLA, EDMUND ANTHONY,** FOOD SCIENCE. *Current Pos:* assoc prof food sci & industs, 66-72, exten food microbiologist, 66-84, PROF FOOD SCI & NUTRIT, UNIV MINN, ST PAUL, 72- *Personal Data:* b Gilroy, Calif, June 25, 32; m 60, Marsha Olson; c Joseph, Sarah, Joshua & Theresa. *Educ:* Ore State Univ, BS, 54, MS, 58; Univ Minn, St Paul, PhD(dairy tech), 64. *Honors & Awards:* Educr Award, Int Asn Milk, Food & Environ Sanitarians, 88, Sherman Award, 89. *Prof Exp:* Res asst food sci, Ore State Univ, 56-58; res fel food sci & industs, Univ Minn, St Paul, 58-64; bacteriologist, Nat Dairy Prod Corp, Ill, 64-65; microbiologist, Nodaway Valley Foods, Iowa, 65-66. *Mem:* Fel Inst Food Technologists; Am Dairy Sci Asn; Int Asn Milk, Food & Environ Sanitarians. *Res:* Spoilage and pathogenic microorganisms in food; thermal destruction of microorganisms; airborne microorganisms; food plant and equipment sanitation; detection of microorganisms in raw and processed foods; attachment of microorganisms to food and food contact surfaces; microorganisms involved in cheese manufacturing and the technology of cheese manufacture; membrane processing liquid foods, UF/RO/MF. *Mailing Add:* Dept Food Sci & Nutrit Univ Minn 1334 Eckles Ave St Paul MN 55108-1040. *Fax:* 612-625-5272

**ZOTTOLI, ROBERT,** INVERTEBRATE ZOOLOGY. *Current Pos:* From asst prof to assoc prof, 65-75, PROF BIOL, FITCHBURG STATE COL, 75- *Personal Data:* b Boston, Mass, Apr 17, 39; m; c 3. *Educ:* Bowdoin Col, BA, 60; Univ NH, MS, 63, PhD(zool), 66. *Mem:* AAAS; Sigma Xi; Am Soc Limnol & Oceanog; Am Soc Zool. *Res:* Natural history of polychaetous annelid worms; polychaete family amphareitidae. *Mailing Add:* Biol Dept Fitchburg State Col Fitchburg MA 01420-2697

**ZOTTOLI, STEVEN JAYNES,** NEUROBIOLOGY. *Current Pos:* from asst prof to assoc prof, 87-93, PROF BIOL, WILLIAMS COL, WILLIAMSTOWN, MASS, 93-, SCHOW PROF BIOL, 94- *Personal Data:* b Boston, Mass, Aug 28, 47; c 4. *Educ:* Bowdoin Col, BA, 69; Univ Mass, Amherst, MS, 72, PhD(zool), 76. *Prof Exp:* Lectr cell physiol, Col Our Lady of the Elms, 73-74; Nat Inst Neurol, Commun Dis & Stroke fel, Res Inst Alcoholism, Buffalo, NY, 75-77, res scientist II, 77-78; asst prof physiol, State Univ NY, Buffalo, 78-80. *Concurrent Pos:* Grass fel, 78; trustee, Grass Found, 87-90, 94-98, vpres, 94- *Mem:* Soc Neurosci; Am Soc Zoologists; Sigma Xi; AAAS. *Res:* Neurophysiological, morphological and behavioral studies of Mauthner cell function in teleosts. *Mailing Add:* Dept Biol Williams Col Williamstown MA 01267

**ZOU, HUNG BIN,** RADIO FREQUENCY NOISE MODELING, NASA LARGE GAP SUSPENSION MODEL. *Current Pos:* syst engr, 87-89, comput engr, 89-91, SR SCIENTIST, INTERMAGNETICS GEN CORP, 91- *Personal Data:* b Fuzhou, China, Aug 5, 37; US citizen; m Jin Yang; c Thomas Thieu & Andrea Yucho. *Educ:* Peking Normal Univ, BS, 60; Peking Univ, MS, 63; Western Mich Univ, PhD(comput sci & graph theory), 86. *Prof Exp:* Asst prof, State Univ NY, Fredonia, 86-87. *Concurrent Pos:* Co-investr, NASA, 89-93, Dept Transp, 94-95; prin investr, Dept Transp, 94-95. *Mem:* Math Asn Am; Int Soc Magnetic Resonance Med; Inst Elec & Electronics Engrs. *Res:* Developed new systems and new theories. *Mailing Add:* 649 Plank Rd Troy NY 12182

**ZOU, XINGYU,** OPTICAL COMMUNICATION. *Current Pos:* MEM TECH STAFF, HARMONIC LIGHTWAVES, 95- *Personal Data:* b Suzhou, China, Sept 25, 64; m 91, Zhongmin Yao; c Alex M. *Educ:* Univ Sci & Technol, China, BA, 87; Univ Rochester, MA, 89, PhD(physics), 93. *Prof Exp:* Res assoc, Optical Commun Lab, Univ Southern Calif, 93-95. *Concurrent Pos:* Mem, Optical Commun Comt, Inst Elec & Electronics Engrs, 96- *Mem:* Inst Elec & Electronics Engrs; Optical Soc Am. *Res:* Analog optical communication systems specifically for ultra-long distance CATV supertrunk link; digital optical communication system including optical amplifier and wavelength-division multiplexing optical systems and networks. *Mailing Add:* 549 Baltic Way Sunnyvale CA 94089. *Fax:* 408-542-2512; *E-Mail:* xingyu.zou@harmonic-lightwaves.com

**ZOUROS, ELEFTHERIOS,** POPULATION GENETICS. *Current Pos:* PROF BIOL, DALHOUSIE UNIV, 73- & UNIV CRETE, 83- *Personal Data:* b Lesbos, Greece, Aug 31, 39; m 68; c 2. *Educ:* Agr Col Athens, BSc, 63, PhD(biol), 68; Univ Chicago, PhD(biol), 72. *Prof Exp:* Res assoc biol, Agr Col Athens, 65-68; fel pop biol, Univ Chicago, 69-73. *Concurrent Pos:* Scholar, Greek Nat Found Scholars, 66; Ford Found fel, 69. *Mem:* Genetics Soc Am; Am Soc Naturalists; Genetics Soc Can; Soc Study Evolution. *Res:* Genetic basis of the evolutionary process. *Mailing Add:* Dept Biol Sci Dalhousie Univ Halifax NS B3H 4J1 Can

**ZRAKET, CHARLES ANTHONY,** ELECTRICAL & SYSTEMS ENGINEERING. *Current Pos:* RETIRED. *Personal Data:* b Lawrence, Mass, Jan 9, 24; m 61; c 4. *Educ:* Northeastern Univ, BS, 51; Mass Inst Technol, SM, 53. *Hon Degrees:* DEng, Northeastern Univ, 88. *Prof Exp:* Tech staff mem, Digital Comput Lab, Mass Inst Technol, 51-53 & Lincoln Labs, 53-54, sect leader, 54-56, group leader, 56-58; dept head systs design, Mitre Corp, 58-61, tech dir, Systs Planning & Res Div, 61-67, vpres & tech dir, 67-69, vpres, 69-74, sr vpres, 75-78, exec vpres, 78-86, pres & chief exec officer, 86-90. *Concurrent Pos:* Consult, Dept Defense. *Mem:* Nat Acad Eng; fel Inst Elec & Electronics Engrs; Am Mgt Asn; Am Inst Aeronaut & Astronaut; NY Acad Sci; fel Am Acad Arts & Sci; fel AAAS. *Res:* Digital computers; digital computer programming; electronic control systems for large-scale, real-time use; information systems; communications systems; transportation systems; environmental control; energy; educational technology; law enforcement. *Mailing Add:* 71 Sylvan Lane Weston MA 02193

**ZRUDSKY, DONALD RICHARD,** SOLID STATE PHYSICS, ELECTRICAL ENGINEERING. *Current Pos:* PRES & OWNER, OPTIMUM SCI INC. *Personal Data:* b Cedar Rapids, Iowa, Apr 4, 34; div; c 2. *Educ:* Iowa State Univ, BS, 56, MS, 59; Univ Iowa, PhD(physics), 68. *Prof Exp:* Asst engr, Rockwell Corp, 56-57; res helper physics, Ames Lab, 57-59; res staff, Rockwell Corp, 59-62, assoc engr, 62-65; NASA trainee physics, Univ Iowa, 65-68; from asst prof to assoc prof elec eng, Univ Toledo, 68-80. *Concurrent Pos:* Dir NSF grant, 70-71; consult, Keithley Instruments Corp, 73 & Los Alamos Sci Lab, 78. *Mem:* Am Phys Soc; Inst Elec & Electronics Engrs. *Res:* Solid state materials, specifically, magnetic alloys, magnetic compounds and semiconductors; solid state devices; integrated circuits; field effect devices; stirling cycle magnetic heat engines; electronic circuits; instrumentation. *Mailing Add:* 719 River Rd Liberty Hill TX 78642

**ZSCHEILE, FREDERICK PAUL, JR,** plant physiology, phytopathology; deceased, see previous edition for last biography

**ZSIGMOND, ELEMER K,** PHARMACOLOGY, BIOCHEMISTRY. *Current Pos:* EMER PROF ANESTHESIOL, MED CTR, UNIV ILL, 79- *Personal Data:* b Budapest, Hungary, May 16, 30; US citizen; m 63, Kathryn Fogarasi; c Zoltan & William. *Educ:* Univ Budapest, MD, 55. *Honors & Awards:* Pro Sanitate Award, 94. *Prof Exp:* Intern med, Clins, Med Sch, Univ Budapest, 54-55; resident internal med, Sztalinvarosi Korhaz, Hungary, 55-56; cardiol res, Balatonfured, Hungary, 56-57; intern, Allegheny Gen Hosp, Pittsburgh, Pa, 60-61, resident anesthesiol, 61-63, dir anesthesiol res lab, 66-68; prof anesthesiol, Med Ctr, Univ Mich, Ann Arbor, 68-79. *Concurrent Pos:* Res asst/assoc, Anesthesiol Lab, Mercy Hosp, Pittsburgh, Pa, 57-59. *Mem:* Am Soc Anesthesiol; Int Anesthesia Res Soc; NY Acad Sci; Am Soc Clin Pharmacol; AMA; Asn Univ Anesthesiol. *Res:* Plasmacholinesterase studies to determine susceptibility to drugs used in anesthesia; malignant hyperpyrexia determinations; intravenous anesthetics on cardio-respiratory system; muscle relaxants and reversing drugs; jet-anesthesia studies. *Mailing Add:* Dept Anesthesiol M-C 515 Univ Ill Col Med Chicago IL 60612. *Fax:* 312-996-4019

**ZSIGRAY, ROBERT MICHAEL,** MICROBIOLOGY. *Current Pos:* asst prof, 70-76, ASSOC PROF MICROBIOL, UNIV NH, 76- *Personal Data:* b Glen Rogers, WVa, Mar 22, 39; m 70; c 4. *Educ:* Miami Univ, AB, 61; Georgetown Univ, MS, 67, PhD(biol), 69. *Prof Exp:* Microbiologist, Wis State Lab Hyg,

61; res technologist genetics, US Army Biol Lab, Ft Detrick, 62-64, Nat Res Coun res assoc, 68-70. *Mem:* AAAS; Am Soc Microbiol. *Res:* Entry of exogenous DNA into cells. *Mailing Add:* Dept Microbiol Spaulbing Hall Univ NH Durham NH 03824-4724

**ZSOTER, THOMAS,** INTERNAL MEDICINE. *Current Pos:* PRACT INT MED, 94- *Personal Data:* b Budapest, Hungary, Dec 27, 22; m 53; c 2. *Educ:* Univ Budapest, MD, 47; FRCP(C). *Prof Exp:* Resident med, Univ Budapest, 47-49, instr internal med, 49-51; from asst prof to assoc prof med, Univ Szeged, 50-57; head circulation lab, Ayerst, McKenna & Harrison, Ltd, 57-60; assoc prof pharmacol, Univ Toronto, 66-, assoc prof med, 68- *Concurrent Pos:* Fr Govt fel, Paris, 48-49; staff mem, Div Internal Med, Toronto Western Hosp, Ont, 66-, dir, 73-75. *Mem:* Fel Am Col Physicians; Can Pharmacol Soc; Can Fedn Biol Soc; fel Royal Col Can; Can Cardiovasc Soc; Can Soc Clin Invest. *Res:* Circulation; pathophysiology; congestive heart failure; hemodynamics in experimental valvular defects; microscopic circulation; cardiovascular pharmacology; hypertension; calcium antagonistic drugs; catecholemines. *Mailing Add:* 27 Otter Cresent Toronto ON M5M 2W3 Can

**ZUBAL, I GEORGE,** MEDICAL IMAGING, THERAPY PLANNING. *Current Pos:* ASST PROF, STATE UNIV NY, 81-; STAFF MEM, YALE UNIV, NEW HAVEN, CONN. *Personal Data:* b Lorain, Ohio, July 9, 50. *Educ:* Ohio State Univ, BS, 72, MS, 74; Univ des Saarlandes, WGer, PhD(biophys), 81. *Concurrent Pos:* Fel, Brookhaven Nat Lab, 81- *Mem:* Inst Elec & Electronics Engrs. *Res:* Development of software programs for analyzing medical patient pictures and application of these results to the radio therapy planning with nonconventional radiation. *Mailing Add:* 296 Lawrence St New Haven CT 06511-2310

**ZUBALY, ROBERT B(ARNES),** NAVAL ARCHITECTURE, MECHANICAL ENGINEERING. *Current Pos:* From instr to assoc prof, 55-66, PROF ENG, STATE NY MARITIME COL, 66- *Personal Data:* b Philadelphia, Pa, Apr 20, 33; m 56, Mary L Rabe; c 3. *Educ:* Webb Inst Naval Archit, BS, 55; Columbia Univ, MS, 59. *Concurrent Pos:* Res engr, Davidson Lab, Stevens Inst Technol, 57-61; res assoc, Webb Inst Naval Archit, 61- *Mem:* Soc Naval Archit & Marine Engrs; Am Soc Eng Educ. *Res:* Ship design; ship response to sea; ocean transportation; naval architecture, hydrodynamics. *Mailing Add:* 194 Huntington Bay Rd Huntington NY 11743

**ZUBAY, GEOFFREY,** BIOLOGY. *Current Pos:* assoc prof, 63-71, PROF MOLECULAR BIOL, COLUMBIA UNIV, 72- *Personal Data:* b Chicago, Ill, Nov 15, 31. *Educ:* Univ Chicago, PhB, 49, MS, 52; Harvard Univ, PhD(phys chem), 57. *Prof Exp:* NSF res fel molecular biol, King's Col, Univ London, 57-59, NIH fel, 59-60; res assoc, Rockefeller Inst, 60-61; asst biochemist, Brookhaven Nat Lab, 61-63. *Res:* Molecular biology of gene regulation; reactions leading to the origin of life. *Mailing Add:* Dept Biol Sci Fairchild Ctr Columbia Univ 2960 Broadway New York NY 10027-6902

**ZUBECK, ROBERT BRUCE,** RECORDING PHYSICS, MATERIALS SCIENCE TRIBOLOGY. *Current Pos:* VPRES DISK PROCESS DEVELOP. *Personal Data:* b Minneapolis, Minn, Oct 12, 44; m 69, Irene Vidaurri; c Stella Eleanor. *Educ:* Univ Minn, BPhys, 66; Stanford Univ, MS, 68, PhD(appl physics), 73. *Prof Exp:* Consult, Stanford Res Inst, 69-70, res assoc appl physics, Stanford Univ, 73-77; adv engr, IBM, 77-81; sr engr mgr, Sperry Magnetic Peripherals; mgr, Sputtering Process Tech, 82-84; Domain Technol, 84-90; dir, Adv Prod Develop, Conner Peripherals, 90-94. *Mem:* Am Phys Soc; Am Vacuum Soc. *Res:* magnetic flux pinning in high field superconductors; electronbeam co-deposition techniques; sputtering of thin films, magnetic recording disk and head process development; synthesis of new superconductors; thin film magnetics; process reliability. *Mailing Add:* 1102 Lisa Lane Los Altos CA 94024. *Fax:* 650-988-7147; *E-Mail:* blochwall@aol.com

**ZUBER, B(ERT) L,** BIOENGINEERING. *Current Pos:* From asst prof to assoc prof bioeng & physiol, Univ Ill, Chicago, 65-73, actg head bioeng prog, 70-71, prof physiol, Med Ctr, 73-78, PROF BIOENG, UNIV ILL, CHICAGO, 73- *Personal Data:* b Houston, Tex, Oct 27, 38; m 92, Rebecca Friedman; c 3. *Educ:* Univ Pa, BA, 60, BS, 61; Mass Inst Technol, MS, 63, PhD(bioeng), 65. *Concurrent Pos:* Consult, Biosysts, Inc, Mass, 65-66, Aerospace Med Res Lab, Wright-Patterson AFB, Ohio, 71, Pollution Monitors, Inc, Chicago, 71, Dept Psychiat, Univ Chicago, 76-77, Manteno Ment Health Ctr, Ill, 77-79 & Eng Design Assocs, San Francisco, 76-79; asst attend, Presby-St Luke's Hosp, 65-69, assoc attend, 69-76; dir, Biomed Eng Consult Serv, 66-67; USPHS res grant, 68-73; NSF res grant, 74-76; mem bd dir, Nat Asn Bioengrs, 72-75; vis scientist, Bell Labs, NJ, 75; consult, Chicago Habits Clin, Ltd, Evanston, Ill, 79 & Rehab Eng Res & Design Ctr, Hines Vet Admin Hosp, Hines, Ill, 80-85; lectr, Dept Orthopedics, Stritch Sch Med, Loyola Univ, Maywood, Ill, 80-; mem comt, Biomed Eng Soc, 82-84; organizer, OMS Int Res Conf on the Oculomotor Syst, 82; sci prog co-chair, 38th Annual Conf on Engr in Med & Biol, 85; mem publ bd, Biomed Eng Soc, 86-90, chmn publ bd, 87-90, mem, bd dirs, 87-90; vis scientist, Univ de Provence, Marseille, France, 90. *Mem:* Am Physiol Soc; Inst Elec & Electronics Engrs; Biomed Eng Soc; Int Brain Res Orgn. *Res:* Physiological control systems; neurophysiological and control systems aspects of visual and oculo-motor function; bioinstrumentation; bioengineering education; information processing in reading; reading aids for the blind. *Mailing Add:* Dept Bioeng 851 S Morgan St Univ Ill Chicago Chicago IL 60607-7052. *E-Mail:* u08215@uicvm.edu

**ZUBER, MARCUS STANLEY,** AGRONOMY. *Current Pos:* prof, 56-82, EMER PROF AGRON, UNIV MO, COLUMBIA, 82- *Personal Data:* b Gettysburg, SDak, Jan 10, 12; m 41; c 1. *Educ:* SDak State Univ, BS, 37; Iowa State Univ, MS, 40, PhD(plant breeding), 50. *Hon Degrees:* DSc, SDak State Univ, 83. *Prof Exp:* Agent corn invests, Div Cereal Crops & Dis, Mo Agr Exp Sta, USDA, 37-42, assoc agronomist & in charge corn breeding, Div Cereal Crops, 46-50, res agronomist & in charge, 50-73, res leader, Corn Breeding, Div Cereal Crops, 73-76. *Mem:* Fel AAAS; fel Am Soc Agron. *Res:* Corn breeding and genetics; physiology; insect and disease resistance; cereal chemistry. *Mailing Add:* 1408 Bus Loop 70 W Columbia MO 65202

**ZUBER, MARIA T,** GEOPHYSICS. *Current Pos:* Nat Res Coun res assoc, Goddard Space Flight Ctr, NASA, 85-86, geophysicist, 86-92, adj res scientist, 93, SR RES SCIENTIST, LAB TERRESTRIAL PHYSICS, GODDARD SPACE FLIGHT CTR, NASA, 94-; PROF GEOPHYSICS & PLANETARY SCI, MASS INST TECHNOL, 95- *Educ:* Univ Pa, BA, 80; Brown Univ, ScM, 83, PhD(geophys), 86. *Concurrent Pos:* Assoc res prof geophysics, John Hopkins Univ, 91-92, sec decade soc assoc prof, 93-95, prof, 95; guest investr, Woods Hole Oceanog Inst, 96 & 97. *Mem:* Am Geophys Union; AAAS; Am Astron Soc. *Res:* Theoretical modeling of geophysical processes; analysis of altimetry, gravity and tectonics to determine structure and dynamics of the earth and solid planets. *Mailing Add:* Dept Earth Atmospheric & Planetary Sci Mass Inst Technol Bldg 54 Rm 520 Cambridge MA 02139-4307. *Fax:* 617-258-9697; *E-Mail:* zuber@mit.edu

**ZUBER, NOVAK,** ENGINEERING. *Current Pos:* SR REACTOR ANALYST REACTOR SAFETY RES, NUCLEAR REGULATORY COMN, 77- *Personal Data:* b Belgrade, Yugoslavia, Dec 4, 22; nat US; m 58. *Educ:* Univ Calif, Los Angeles, BS, 51, MSc, 54, PhD(eng), 59. *Honors & Awards:* Mem Award, Am Soc Mech Engrs, 62. *Prof Exp:* From asst res engr to assoc res engr, Univ Calif, Los Angeles, 51-58; mem tech staff, Res Lab, Ramo-Wooldridge Corp, 58-60; thermal engr, Gen Eng Lab, Gen Elec Co, 60-62, sr thermal engr, Adv Tech Labs, 62-65, consult engr, Res & Develop Ctr, 65-67; prof mech eng, NY Univ, 67-69; Fuller E Callaway prof, Ga Inst Technol, 69-77. *Concurrent Pos:* Consult, Mech Div, Off Sci Res, USAF, 63 & Los Alamos Sci Lab, 67. *Mem:* Am Inst Aeronaut & Astronaut; Am Inst Chem Engrs; Am Soc Mech Engrs; Sigma Xi. *Res:* Heat transfer; fluid dynamics; thermodynamics; transport phenomena in multi-phase systems. *Mailing Add:* 703 New Mark Esplanade Rockville MD 20850-2739

**ZUBER, WILLIAM HENRY, JR,** PHYSICAL CHEMISTRY. *Current Pos:* asst prof, 66-70, ASSOC PROF CHEM, MEMPHIS STATE UNIV, 70- *Personal Data:* b Memphis, Tenn, Sept 26, 37; m 59; c 3. *Educ:* Memphis State Univ, BS, 60; Univ Ky, PhD(phys chem), 64. *Prof Exp:* Asst prof chem, Murray State Univ, 64-66. *Mem:* Am Chem Soc. *Res:* Nonaqueous solution chemistry. *Mailing Add:* Dept Chem Memphis State Univ Memphis TN 38152-0001

**ZUBERER, DAVID ALAN,** SOIL MICROBIOLOGY, MICROBIAL ECOLOGY. *Current Pos:* from asst prof to assoc prof, 78-90, PROF MICROBIOL, TEX A&M UNIV, 90- *Personal Data:* b Paterson, NJ, Feb 9, 47; m 68; c 1. *Educ:* WVa Univ, AB, 69, MS, 71; Univ SFla, PhD(biol), 76. *Prof Exp:* Res scientist microbiol, Univ Fla, 76-78. *Mem:* Am Soc Microbiol; Am Soc Agron; Soil Sci Soc Am; AAAS; Soc Indust Microbiol. *Res:* Biological nitrogen fixation, including associative N2-fixation in grasses and N2-fixation by legumes; use of beneficial microorganisms to enhance plant nutrient uptake; mycorrhizae and reclamation microbiology. *Mailing Add:* Dept Soil & Crop Sci Tex A&M Univ College Station TX 77843-2474

**ZUBIETA, JON ANDONI,** INORGANIC CHEMISTRY. *Current Pos:* asst prof, 73-80, ASSOC PROF CHEM, STATE UNIV NY, ALBANY, 80- *Personal Data:* b New York, June 16, 45; m 69; c 2. *Educ:* Fordham Univ, BS, 66; Columbia Univ, PhD(chem), 71. *Prof Exp:* Res assoc chem, Univ Sussex, 71-73. *Concurrent Pos:* NIH fel, 72-73; NATO travelling fel, 81-82. *Mem:* Am Chem Soc. *Res:* Inorganic models for molybdoenzymes; electroanalytical chemistry; structure and reactivity of cluster compounds. *Mailing Add:* Dept Chem Syracuse Univ Syracuse NY 13244-0002

**ZUBKO, L(EONARD) M(ARTIN),** MECHANICAL ENGINEERING. *Current Pos:* RETIRED. *Personal Data:* b Bridgeport, Conn, July 8, 20; m 41; c 1. *Educ:* Rutgers Univ, BSME, 42; Rensselaer Polytech Inst, MME, 49. *Prof Exp:* Instr mech eng, Rensselaer Polytech Inst, 46-49; assoc prof, Univ Ill, 49-51 & 52-55; proj engr, Sverdrup Parcel Consult Engrs, 51-52; mgr propulsion appl res, Flight Propulsion Lab Dept, Gen Elec Co, 55-60, mgr adv eng, 60-73, mgr USSR progs, 73-85. *Concurrent Pos:* Mem subcomt combustion, NASA, 56-58; adj assoc prof, Univ Vt, 64-71. *Mem:* Am Soc Mech Engrs; Am Inst Aeronaut & Astronaut; Am Ord Asn; Nat Soc Prof Engrs; Sigma Xi. *Res:* Gas dynamics; fluid mechanics; heat transfer; combustion; mechanisms. *Mailing Add:* 3130 Laurel Dr Mt Dora FL 32757

**ZUBKOFF, MICHAEL,** MEDICINE. *Current Pos:* PROF & CHMN, DEPT COMMUN & FAMILY MED, DARTMOUTH MED SCH, 75- *Personal Data:* b June 2, 44; c 3. *Educ:* Am Int Col, BA, 65; Columbia Univ, MA, 66, PhD(econ), 69. *Prof Exp:* Instr econ, Columbia Univ, 67-69; Woodrow Wilson teaching fel, Meharry Med Col & Fisk Univ, 69-70; from asst prof to assoc prof health econ, Meharry Med Col & Vanderbilt Univ, 70-75. *Concurrent Pos:* Deleg & health spokesman, White House Summit Inflation, Washington, DC, 74; prof health econ & mgt, Amos Tuck Sch Bus Admin & adj prof econ & policy studies, Dartmouth Col, 75-; consult, Domestic Coun, White House, 76-80, Nat Ctr Health Serv Res, Health Care Financing Admin, House Subcomt Health & Environ, Senate Subcomt Health, Off Secy Health

& Human Serv & Geriat Assessment & Planning Prog, South Shore Hosp & Med Ctr, Miami, 80-; mem var med & educ comts, Inst Med-Nat Acad Sci, 77- Mem: Inst Med-Nat Acad Sci. Res: Health economics and management; author of numerous technical publications. Mailing Add: Dept Community & Family Med Prog Dartmouth Med Sch Hanover NH 03755

**ZUBKOFF, PAUL L(EON)**, BIOCHEMISTRY, ENVIRONMENTAL SCIENCES. Current Pos: PRES & SR CONSULT, MICRO SCI CONSULT, 83-; CHEMIST, SURFACE WATER HYDROL, US ENVIRON PROTECTION AGENCY, 89- Personal Data: b Niagara Falls, NY, Nov 24, 34; m 60; c 2. Educ: Univ Buffalo, BA, 56; George Washington Univ, MS, 58; Cornell Univ, PhD(biochem), 62. Prof Exp: Res asst biochem, George Washington Univ, 56-58; res asst, Cornell Univ, 58-61; res biol chemist, Univ Calif, Los Angeles, 61-63; NIH trainee & res assoc biophys, Mass Inst Technol, 63-66; asst prof biochem, Ohio State Univ, 66-70; sr marine scientist & head environ physiol, Va Inst Marine Sci, 70- 82; assoc prof marine sci, Col William & Mary & Univ Va, 70-83. Concurrent Pos: Adj prof marine sci, Va Inst Marine Sci-Col William & Mary, 83-; vis fel, Dept Agron, Cornell Univ, Ithaca, NY, 88-89. Mem: Atlantic Estuarine Res Soc; Am Chem Soc; Am Nuclear Soc; Am Soc Limnol & Oceanog; Sigma Xi; Estuarine Res Fedn; Marine Biol Asn UK. Res: Dynamics of aquatic ecosystems; comparative biochemistry of macromolecules; metabolism of marine invertebrates; influences of terrestrial environments on surface and ground water hydrodynamics. Mailing Add: 2000 S Eads St Arlington VA 22202-3167

**ZUBLENA, JOSEPH PETER**, PRODUCTION COUNSELING, AGENT & GROWER TRAINING. Current Pos: assoc prof agron & soils, 79-87, prof agron & soils, 87-88, PROF & EXTEN SPECIALIST IN-CHARGE SOIL SCI, CLEMSON UNIV, 88- Personal Data: b Englewood, NJ, Nov 26, 51; m 78, Lisette Stabenau; c Ailis & Jonathan. Educ: Rutgers Univ, BS, 73, MS, 76, PhD(agron), 79. Prof Exp: Teaching asst crops & soils, Rutgers Univ, 73-74, res assoc, 75-77, res intern, 77-79. Concurrent Pos: Lectr, Clemson Univ, 83; assoc state prog leader, Natural Resources & Community & Rural Develop, 94-96; asst dir, Exten Co Oper, 96- Mem: Agron Soc Am; Soil Sci Soc Am; Crop Sci Soc Am. Res: Land application of waste products as fertilizer, lime or amendment sources; improved corn fertilizer efficiencies through placement, timing and source and rate selections; herbicide accelerated degradation phenomena; cultivar testing; aflatoxin as affected by production practices; agronomic utilization of by-products. Mailing Add: NC State Univ PO Box 7602 Raleigh NC 27695-7602. Fax: 919-515-3135; E-Mail: joseph_zublena@ncsu.edu

**ZUBLER, EDWARD GEORGE**, INORGANIC CHEMISTRY. Current Pos: LAMP CHEM CONSULT, TELTECH RESOURCES NETWORK, 92- Personal Data: b Lackawanna, NY, Mar 12, 25; m 50, Marybelle Browning; c Karen, Kurt & Rena. Educ: Canisius Col, BS, 49; Univ Notre Dame, PhD(phys chem), 53. Honors & Awards: Elenbaas Award, Philip's Gloeilampenfabrieken-Neth, 81; Steinmetz Award, Gen Elec, 73. Prof Exp: Res phys chemist, Gen Elec Co, 53-65, tech leader, 65-72, res adv, 72-87; consult, Lamp Chem, 87-91. Concurrent Pos: Lectr, Fenn Col, 60-65 & Cleveland State Univ, 65-66; exec comt, High & Temperature Mat Div, Electrochem Soc, 84- Mem: Am Chem Soc; Electrochem Soc. Res: High temperature gas-metal reactions; chemical transport processes; mass spectrometry; high vacuum and high purity gas techniques; microbalance techniques; computer themodynamic calculations. Mailing Add: 28430 Hidden Valley Dr Chagrin Falls OH 44022. E-Mail: edzubler@worldnet.att.net

**ZUBRISKI, JOSEPH CAZIMER**, SOIL SCIENCE. Current Pos: From asst prof to assoc prof, 51-63, PROF SOILS, NDAK STATE UNIV, 63- Personal Data: b Goodman, Wis, July 7, 19; m 46; c 3. Educ: Univ Wis, BS, 47, MS, 48, PhD(soils), 51. Mem: Soil Sci Soc Am; Am Soc Agron. Res: Soil fertility; effect of plant population and fertilizers on yield and quality of sunflower seeds; soil phosphorus; fertilizer and water management of irrigated crops. Mailing Add: 302 30th Ave N No 11 Fargo ND 58102

**ZUBROD, CHARLES GORDON**, CANCER. Current Pos: RETIRED. Personal Data: b New York, NY, Jan 22, 14; m 40; c 5. Educ: Col of the Holy Cross, AB, 36; Columbia Univ, MD, 40. Hon Degrees: DSc, Col of the Holy Cross, 69. Honors & Awards: Lasker Award, 72. Prof Exp: Intern, Cent Islip State Hosp, NJ, 40-41 & Jersey City Hosp, NY, 41-42; intern & asst resident med, Presby Hosp, New York, 42-43; instr med, Sch Med, Johns Hopkins Univ, 46-49, asst prof med & pharmacol, 49-53; assoc prof med & dir res, Dept Med, St Louis Univ, 53-54; chief gen med br, Nat Cancer Inst, 54-55, clin dir, 55-61, chmn med bd, 57-58, dir int res, 61-65, sci dir chemother, 65-72, dir div cancer treatment, 72-74; prof oncol & chmn dept, prof med & dir, Comprehensive Cancer Ctr, Sch Med, Univ Miami, 74-88. Concurrent Pos: Roche res fel chemother bact dis, Johns Hopkins Hosp, 46-49; mem, Mt Desert Island Biol Lab; mem & mem exec comt, Lerner Marine Lab, Bimini. Mem: Am Soc Clin Invest; Am Soc Pharmacol & Exp Therapeut; Am Asn Cancer Res (pres, 77); Am Asn Cancer Insts (pres, 78); Asn Am Physicians. Res: Pharmacology, especially of cancer chemotherapeutic agents; marine biology. Mailing Add: 8100 Conn Ave Apt 801 Chevy Chase MD 20815-2815

**ZUBRZYCKI, LEONARD JOSEPH**, MEDICAL MICROBIOLOGY. Current Pos: PROF MICROBIOL, TEMPLE UNIV, SCH MED, 61- Personal Data: b Camden, NJ, Feb 25, 32; m 54; c 1. Educ: Temple Univ, AB, 53, PhD(med microbiol), 58. Prof Exp: Sr scientist, Wyeth, Inc, 58-61. Mem: AAAS; Am Soc Microbiol; Am Venereal Dis Soc. Res: Bacterial genetics; diagnostic bacteriology. Mailing Add: Dept Microbiol Temple Univ Sch Med 3400 N Broad St Philadelphia PA 19140-5196

**ZUCCA, RICARDO**, SEMICONDUCTOR TECHNOLOGY, SEMICONDUCTOR DEVICES. Current Pos: MEM TECH STAFF, ROCKWELL SCI CTR, 72- Personal Data: b Trieste, Italy, Feb 7, 36; US citizen; m 58, Olga Fongi; c Gerry, Silvana, Rudy & Fernando. Educ: Univ Rosario, Arg, MA, 60; Univ Calif, Berkeley, PhD(physics), 71. Prof Exp: Prof physics, Univ Rosario, Arg, 69-72. Mem: Am Phys Soc; sr mem Inst Elec & Electronics Engrs. Res: Semiconductor physics and semiconductor devices; gallium arsenide digital high-speed technology; infrared semiconductor mercury cadmium tellurium and its applications to infrared devices; power semiconductor. Mailing Add: Rockwell Sci Ctr 1049 Camino Dos Rios Thousand Oaks CA 91360. E-Mail: rzucca@scimail.risc.rockwell.com

**ZUCCARELLI, ANTHONY JOSEPH**, MOLECULAR BIOLOGY, MOLECULAR GENETICS. Current Pos: asst prof biol, 76-80, assoc prof microbiol, 80-91, PROF MICROBIOL & BIOCHEM, LOMA LINDA UNIV, 91- Personal Data: b New York, NY, Aug 11, 44; m 68, Sharron A Ames; c Cara N & A Alexander. Educ: Cornell Univ, BS, 66; Loma Linda Univ, MS, 68; Calif Inst Technol, PhD(biophys), 74. Prof Exp: Fel molecular biol, Am Cancer Soc, 74-76. Concurrent Pos: Roberts scholar, Cornell Univ, 64-65; NSF grad fel, 68-71; assoc fac, Biol Dept, Loma Linda Univ, 80-, Biochem Dept, 85- Mem: Am Soc Microbiol; AAAS; Sigma Xi; NY Acad Sci; Am Chem Soc. Res: Genetic polymorphism of Staphylococus aureus; investigation of functions of prokaryotic genes using recombinant DNA technology; determinants of bacterial virulence; DNA sequencing instrumentation; molecular typing of pathogenic organisms; fidelity of enzymatic DNA polymerization; molecular genetics of bacteriophages. Mailing Add: Dept Microbiol & Molecular Genetics AH115 Loma Linda Univ Loma Linda CA 92350. Fax: 909-824-4035; E-Mail: azuccarelli@ccmail.llu.edu

**ZUCCHETTO, JAMES JOHN**, SYSTEMS ECOLOGY, ENVIRONMENTAL SCIENCE. Current Pos: DIR, BD ENERGY & ENVIRON SYSTS, NAT ACAD SCI, 85- Personal Data: b Brooklyn, NY, Mar 11, 46; m 78; c Jason & Tim. Educ: Polytech Inst Brooklyn, BS, 66; NY Univ, MS, 69; Univ Fla, PhD(syst ecol), 75. Prof Exp: Mem tech staff, Bell Tel Labs, Inc, 68-71; asst syst ecol, Univ Fla, 72-75, assoc eng energy in transp, 75-76; guest researcher environ, Univ Stockholm, 76-78; asst prof regional sci, Univ Pa, 78-85. Concurrent Pos: Researcher, Rockefeller Found, 77 & Univ Pa, 78-79; consult, US Nat Res Coun, 76 & Fed Energy Admin, 75. Mem: Int Soc Ecol Modeling; Soc Ecol Econs. Res: Ecological models; regional energy-ecological-economic interactions; energy analysis; general systems; environmental impact evaluation; systems analysis, energy technology and policy. Mailing Add: Nat Acad Sci HA270 2101 Constitution Ave NW Washington DC 20418. Fax: 202-334-3370

**ZUCHELLI, ARTLEY JOSEPH**, PHYSICS. Current Pos: assoc prof, 63-67, PROF PHYSICS, GEORGE WASHINGTON UNIV, 67- Personal Data: b Alexandria, Va, Nov 3, 34. Educ: Univ Va, BA, 55, PhD(physics), 58. Prof Exp: NSF fel, Univ Birmingham, 58-59; assoc prof physics, Univ Miss, 59-63. Res: Theoretical, classical and quantum fields. Mailing Add: George Washington Univ 725 21st St NW Rm 105 Washington DC 20052-4211

**ZUCK, DONALD ANTON**, PHARMACEUTICAL CHEMISTRY. Current Pos: RETIRED. Personal Data: b Hafford, Sask, Dec 27, 18; m 57, Julie Louise Elma Kelly; c 3. Educ: Univ Alta, BSc, 48; Univ Wis, MS, 50, PhD(pharm), 52. Prof Exp: Lectr, Sch Pharm, Univ BC, 50-52; from pharmaceut chemist to sr pharmaceut chemist, Eli Lilly & Co, 52-65; prof pharm, Col Pharm, Univ Sask, 65-86. Concurrent Pos: Examr, Pharm Exam Bd Can, 72-77; sci ed, Can J Pharmaceut Sci, 72-82; mem, Drug Qual Assessment Comt, 74- Mem: Am Pharmaceut Asn; fel Am Found Pharm Educ; Can Pharm Asn; Am Asn Cols Pharm; Asn Fac Pharm Can. Res: Physical chemistry as applied to pharmaceutical problems. Mailing Add: 103 Baldwin Crescent Saskatoon SK S7H 3M5 Can

**ZUCK, ROBERT KARL**, botany; deceased, see previous edition for last biography

**ZUCKER, ALEXANDER**, NUCLEAR PHYSICS, ACCELERATORS. Current Pos: PROF, UNIV TENN. Personal Data: b Zagreb, Yugoslavia, Aug 1, 24; nat US; m 53, Joan-Ellen; c Rebecca, Claire & Susannah. Educ: Univ Vt, BA, 47; Yale Univ, MS, 48, PhD(physics), 50. Prof Exp: Res asst physics, Yale Univ, 48-50; physicist, Oak Ridge Nat Lab, 50-53, sr physicist, 53-70, assoc dir, Electronuclear Div, 60-70, dir, Heavy Ion Proj, 72-74, assoc dir phys sci, 73-88, actg dir, 88, assoc dir nuclear technologies, 89-93; exec dir, Environ Studies Bd, Nat Acad Sci-Nat Acad Eng, 70-72. Concurrent Pos: Guggenheim fel & Fulbright res scholar, 66-67; Ford prof physics, Univ Tenn, 68-72; mem, Comt Nuclear Sci & Nuclear Physics Panel, Physics Surv, Nat Res Coun; US del peaceful uses of atomic energy, USSR; mem-at-large, US Nat Comt, Int Union Pure & Appl Physics, 76-78; mem, res coordr coun, Gas Res Inst, 78-85; mem, Nuclear Physics Deleg to People's Repub China, Nat Acad Sci, 79; ed, Nuclear Sci Applns, 80; mem, Adv Panel Technologies to Reduce US Mat Import Vulnerability, Off Technol Assessment, 82-85; mem, Comt Manpower, Nat Res Coun, 82-83; mem, Coun Energy Eng Res, Dept Energy, 83-; mem, White House Steel Indust/Nat Labs Initiative, 84-86; mem, Am Phys Soc, Panel Pub Affairs, 86-, Subpanel Int Sci Affairs, 88-; chmn, Am Soc Mech Engrs Nat Lab Technol Transfer Comt, 87- Mem: Fel AAAS; fel Am Phys Soc; fel Sigma Xi; Am Soc Metals. Res: Nuclear reactions with heavy ions; medium energy nuclear physics, including scattering and polarization of protons; few-nucleon interactions; high-current electronuclear machines; AVF and heavy ion cyclotrons; environment and public policy; managing physical research programs related to energy. Mailing Add: 103 Orange Lane Oak Ridge TN 37830. E-Mail: zuckeraje@aol.com

**ZUCKER, GORDON L(ESLIE)**, mineral processing engineering, for more information see previous edition

**ZUCKER, IRVING,** BIOLOGICAL RHYTHMS, NEUROENDOCRINOLOGY. *Current Pos:* from asst prof to assoc prof, 66-74, PROF PSYCHOL, UNIV CALIF, BERKELEY, 74- *Personal Data:* b Montreal, Que, Oct 2, 40; m 63; c 2. *Educ:* McGill Univ, BSc, 61; Univ Chicago, PhD(biopsychol), 64. *Prof Exp:* Res assoc reprod physiol, Ore Regional Primate Res Ctr, 64-65; vis scientist, Sch Med, Univ Wis, 65; res assoc reprod physiol, Ore Regional Primate Res Ctr, 66. *Mem:* AAAS; Animal Behav Soc; Am Soc Mammalogists; Neurosci Soc; Soc Study Biol Rhythms. *Res:* Seasonal reproductive cycles; Circadian clocks; behavioral endocrinology; hibernation; circannual rhythms. *Mailing Add:* Dept Psychol Univ Calif 345 Mulford Hall Berkeley CA 94720-0001

**ZUCKER, IRVING H,** PHYSIOLOGY, HEART FAILURE & REFLEX CONTROL. *Current Pos:* USPHS fel, Univ Nebr Med Ctr, Omaha, 72-73, asst prof, 73-76, assoc prof, 76-83, PROF PHYSIOL, UNIV NEBR MED CTR, OMAHA, 83-, CHMN PHYSIOL & BIOPHYS, 89- *Personal Data:* b Bronx, NY, July 13, 42; m 70, Judith F Silver; c Sherri, Dana & Lauren. *Educ:* City Col New York, BS, 65; Univ Mo, Kansas City, MS, 67; New York Med Col, PhD(physiol), 72. *Concurrent Pos:* Merit award, NIH, 92- *Mem:* Am Physiol Soc; Am Heart Asn; Soc Exp Biol & Med; Sigma Xi. *Res:* Cardiovascular receptors and the neural control of blood volume; regulation of autonomic control in heart failure; role of nitric oxide and angiotension II. *Mailing Add:* Dept Physiol & Biophys Univ Nebr Med Ctr 600 S 42nd St Omaha NE 68198-4575. *Fax:* 402-559-4438; *E-Mail:* izucker@mail.unml.edu

**ZUCKER, JOSEPH,** solid state physics, for more information see previous edition

**ZUCKER, MARJORIE BASS,** PHYSIOLOGY, HEMATOLOGY. *Current Pos:* assoc prof path, 63-71, PROF PATH, SCH MED, NY UNIV, 71- *Personal Data:* b New York, NY, June 10, 19; m 38; c 4. *Educ:* Vassar Col, AB, 39; Columbia Univ, PhD(physiol), 44. *Prof Exp:* Instr physiol, Col Physicians & Surgeons, Columbia Univ, 42-44, res asst, 45-49; from asst prof to assoc prof, Col Dent, NY Univ, 49-55; assoc mem, Sloan-Kettering Inst Cancer Res, 55-63. *Concurrent Pos:* Asst res dir, Eastern Div Res Lab, Am Nat Red Cross, 63-70; mem, Hemat Study Sect, NIH, 70-74, Int Comt Haemostasis & Thrombosis, 70-76 & review comt B, Nat Heart, Lung & Blood Inst, 76-80. *Mem:* Am Physiol Soc; Soc Exp Biol & Med; Am Soc Hemat; Int Soc Hemat; Int Soc Thrombosis & Haemostasis. *Res:* Platelets and blood coagulation. *Mailing Add:* Dept Path NY Univ Med Ctr 550 First Ave New York NY 10016-6402

**ZUCKER, MARTIN SAMUEL,** PLASMA PHYSICS, RADIATION PHYSICS. *Current Pos:* RETIRED. *Personal Data:* b New York, NY, Mar 15, 30; m 58; c 3. *Educ:* Cornell Univ, BEngPhys, 52; Univ Wis, MSc, 53, PhD(nuclear physics), 61. *Prof Exp:* Asst physicist, Brookhaven Nat Lab, 58-62, consult, Radiation Div, Nuclear Eng Dept, 61-63, assoc physicist, 63-96. *Mem:* AA.\S; Am Phys Soc; Am Asn Physics Teachers; Am Nuclear Soc; Sigma Xi. *Res:* Fast neutron polarization; electrical effects of nuclear radiations on matter; direct conversion of energy to electricity; statistical mechanics; chemical physics; accelerator development; scientific applications of computers. *Mailing Add:* PO Box 96 East Moriches NY 11940

**ZUCKER, MELVIN JOSEPH,** SOLID STATE PHYSICS. *Current Pos:* chmn, Dept Math & Physics, 69-77, ASSOC PROF, MERCER COUNTY COMMUNITY COL, NJ, 69- *Personal Data:* b Charleston, SC, May 6, 29; div; c 2. *Educ:* Brooklyn Col, BS, 51; Rutgers Univ, PhD(physics), 57. *Prof Exp:* Physicist, Airborne Instruments Lab, Cutler-Hammer, Inc, 57-59; mem tech staff, Semiconductor Div, Hughes Aircraft Co, 58-62; mem tech staff, Am-Standard Corp, NJ, 62-68. *Concurrent Pos:* Consult, Off Promoting Tech Innovation, State NJ. *Mem:* Am Phys Soc. *Res:* Impurities in superconductors; semiconductor devices; paramagnetic resonance; peizoresitivity studies in semiconductors. *Mailing Add:* Dept Tech Mercer County Community Col PO Box B Trenton NJ 08690

**ZUCKER, OVED SHLOMO FRANK,** ELECTRICAL ENGINEERING, PLASMA PHYSICS. *Current Pos:* STAFF PHYSICIST, PHYSICS INT CO, 78-; PRES, ENERGY COMPRESSION RES CORP. *Personal Data:* b Jerusalem, Israel, June 24, 39; US citizen; m 60; c 3. *Educ:* City Univ NY, BEE, 65. *Prof Exp:* Mem tech staff elec eng, Lawrence Livermore Lab, 65-78. *Concurrent Pos:* Ed, Energy Storage Compression & Switching Conf & Proceedings, 74; consult physics, Lawrence Livermore Lab, 78-79 & La Jolla Inst, 79. *Mem:* Am Phys Soc; Inst Elec & Electronics Engrs. *Res:* Relativistic electron beam; space-time energy compression; solid state physics; laser electronics; pulsed power. *Mailing Add:* Energy Compression Res Corp 6355 Nancy Ridge Dr San Diego CA 92121

**ZUCKER, PAUL ALAN,** PHYSICS, THEORETICAL PHYSICS. *Current Pos:* SR PHYSICIST, APPL PHYSICS LAB, JOHNS HOPKINS UNIV, 75- *Personal Data:* b New York, NY, Nov 20, 44; m 91; c 3. *Educ:* Univ Chicago, BS, 66; Stanford Univ, MS, 67, PhD(physics), 71. *Prof Exp:* Res assoc physics, Univ Ore, 70-72 & Univ Minn, 72-75. *Mem:* Am Phys Soc; AAAS; Inst Elec & Electronics Engrs; Sigma Xi. *Res:* Electroproduction and weak production of nucleon resonances; signal processing; Kalman filtering; system identification; estimation; model validation; gravity models; geodesy. *Mailing Add:* 12813 Huntsman Way Pontiac MD 20854-2311

**ZUCKER, ROBERT ALPERT,** CLINICAL PSYCHOLOGY, SUBSTANCE ABUSE & DEVELOPMENTAL PSYCHOPATHOLOGY. *Current Pos:* from asst prof to assoc prof, Univ Mich, 68-75, prof clin psychol, 75-94, co-dir clin training, 82-94, PROF PSYCHOL, DEPT PSYCHIAT & PSYCHOL & DIR, ALCOHOL CTR, DIR DIV SUBSTANCE ABUSE, DEPT PSYCHIAT, FAC ASSOC, RES CTR GROUP DYNAMICS, INST SOCIAL RES, UNIV MICH. *Personal Data:* b New York, NY, Dec 9, 35; m 79, Kristine Freeark; c Lisa, Alex, Eleanor & Katherine. *Educ:* City Col New York, BCE, 56; Harvard Univ, PhD(clin psychol), 66. *Prof Exp:* Asst prof psychol, Rutgers Univ, 63-68. *Concurrent Pos:* Consult ed, J Studies Alcohol, 64-84; prin investr grants adolescent drinking, NIMH, 66-71, study alcoholism & antisocial behav, Nat Inst Alcohol Abuse & Alcoholism, 87-; consult, Vet Admin Hosp, Battle Creek, Mich, 74-76; vis prof, Univ Tex, Austin, 76; bd dir, Nat Coun Alcoholism, 78-81; vis scholar alcohol problems, Nat Inst Alcohol Abuse & Alcoholism, 80-81; lectr, Nebr Symp Motivation, 86, Vanderbilt Alcohol Symp, 88; mem psychol rev comt, Nat Inst Alcohol Abuse & Acoholism, 88-; vis prof, Univ Mich, 90-91; fel, Inst Children Youth & Families, Mich State Univ, 92. *Mem:* Fel Am Psychol Asn (pres elect); fel Am Orthopsychiat Asn; Soc Life Hist Res Psychopath. *Res:* Longitudinal development of psychopathology with special interest in alcohol and drug abuse; personality influences on behavior; behavior change. *Mailing Add:* Univ Mich Alcohol Res Ctr 401 E Eishenhower Pkwy Suite 2A Ann Arbor MI 48108-3318. *Fax:* 313-998-7994; *E-Mail:* zuckerra@umich.edu

**ZUCKER, ROBERT MARTIN,** BIOPHYSICS, BIOLOGY. *Current Pos:* SR SCIENTIST, MANTECH ENVIRON SCI, 85- *Personal Data:* b New York, NY, May 13, 43; m. *Educ:* Univ Calif, Los Angeles, BS, 65, MS, 66, PhD(biophys), 70. *Prof Exp:* Res scientist hemat, Univ Calif, Los Angeles, 66-70; res, Max Planck Inst Protein & Leather Res, 70-72; sr scientist biophys & biol, Papanicolaou Cancer Res Inst, 72-84. *Concurrent Pos:* Assoc prof med, Univ Miami, 74-84. *Mem:* Am Chem Soc; Am Soc Cell Biol; NY Acad Sci; Am Asn Cancer Res. *Res:* Cellular biophysics; flow cytometry; image analysis. *Mailing Add:* US EPA NHEERI MD 67 Research Triangle Park NC 27771. *Fax:* 919-549-4665

**ZUCKER, ROBERT STEPHEN,** NEUROPHYSIOLOGY. *Current Pos:* From asst prof to assoc prof, 73-85, PROF NEUROBIOL, UNIV CALIF, BERKELEY, 85- *Personal Data:* b Philadelphia, Pa, Apr 18, 45; m 83, Susan Schwartz; c David, Mark & Ariel. *Educ:* Mass Inst Technol, SB, 66; Stanford Univ, PhD(neurol sci), 71. *Concurrent Pos:* Hon asst res assoc, dept biophys, Univ Col, Univ London, Eng, 71-73; temp investr, Cellular Neurobiol Lab, Nat Ctr Sci Res, France, 73-74; res fel, Alfred P Sloan Found, 76-80; prin investr, NSF & NIH res grants, 77-; sr investr, Marine Biol Lab, Woods Hole, Mass, 80 & 81; Javit neurosci investr award, NIH, 87-94. *Mem:* Soc Neurosci; AAAS; Biophys Soc; Sigma Xi; Fed Am Scientists; Union Concerned Scientists. *Res:* Synaptic transmission; synaptic plasticity; excitable membrane biophysics; neurophysiological basis of behavior; neuronal calcium metabolism; egg fertilization and activation. *Mailing Add:* Univ Calif Dept Molecular & Cell Biol Box 111 Life Sci Addn Berkeley CA 94720. *Fax:* 510-643-6791; *E-Mail:* zucker@garnet.berkeley.edu

**ZUCKER, STEVEN MARK,** MATHEMATICS. *Current Pos:* PROF, DEPT MATH, JOHNS HOPKINS UNIV, 84- *Personal Data:* b New York, NY, Sept 12, 49. *Educ:* Brown Univ, ScB, 70; Princeton Univ, PhD(math), 74. *Prof Exp:* Asst prof math, Rutgers Univ, 74-80; assoc prof math, Ind Univ, 81-84. *Concurrent Pos:* NSF grant, 76- *Mem:* Am Math Soc. *Res:* Analytic methods in algebraic geometry; Hodge theory and the cohomology of projective varieties; differential geometry. *Mailing Add:* Dept Math Johns Hopkins Univ Baltimore MD 21218-2689

**ZUCKER, STEVEN WARREN,** COMPUTER VISION, ROBOTICS. *Current Pos:* Fel, Univ Md, 74-76, asst prof elec eng, 76-80, assoc prof, 80-84, PROF, MCGILL UNIV, 85- *Personal Data:* b Philadelphia, Pa, Apr 20, 48; m 74; c 2. *Educ:* Carnegie-Mellon Univ, BS, 69; Drexel Univ, MEGN, 72 & PhD(biomed eng), 75. *Concurrent Pos:* Prin, Lognicom Corp. *Mem:* Fel Can Inst Advan Res; fel Inst Elec & Electronics Engrs. *Res:* Computational vision and biological perception. *Mailing Add:* Dept Elec Eng McGill Univ 3480 University St Montreal PQ H3A 2A7 Can

**ZUCKERBERG, HYAM L,** MATHEMATICS. *Current Pos:* PROF MATH, LONG ISLAND UNIV, 80- *Personal Data:* b New York, NY, Dec 5, 37; m 64; c 1. *Educ:* Yeshiva Univ, BA & BHL, 59, MA, 61, PhD(math), 63. *Prof Exp:* Res mathematician, Davidson Lab, Stevens Inst Technol, 63-80. *Mem:* Am Math Soc. *Res:* Conformal mapping; potential theory; Hilbert spaces; topology; Bergman kernel function. *Mailing Add:* Dept Math Long Island Univ 1 University Plaza Brooklyn NY 11201-5320

**ZUCKERBROD, DAVID,** ELECTROCHEMISTRY, BATTERIES & FUEL CELLS. *Current Pos:* ELECTROCHEM TECHNOLOGIST, W L GORE & ASSOCS, 94- *Personal Data:* b Brooklyn, NY, Aug 27, 54; m 79. *Educ:* Rensselaer Polytech Inst, BS, 75, PhD(inorg chem), 82. *Prof Exp:* Sr engr, Westinghouse Elec Corp, 80-88; sr res chemist, W R Grace & Co, Columbia, Md, 88-94. *Mem:* Am Chem Soc; Electrochem Soc. *Res:* Development of electrodes and separators for fuel cells, rechargeable batteries and primary batteries. *Mailing Add:* 2705 Copperfield Ct Baltimore MD 21209-2533

**ZUCKER-FRANKLIN, DOROTHEA,** CELL BIOLOGY. *Current Pos:* USPHS res fel electron micros, 61-63, from asst prof to assoc prof, 63-74, PROF MED, SCH MED, NY UNIV, 74- *Personal Data:* b Berlin, Ger, Aug 9, 29; US citizen; m 56; c 1. *Educ:* Hunter Col, BA, 52; NY Med Col, MD, 56; Am Bd Internal Med, dipl, 53. *Prof Exp:* Intern med, Philadelphia Gen

Hosp, Pa, 56-57; resident, Montefiore Hosp, NY, 57-59, USPHS res fel hemat, 59-61. *Concurrent Pos:* Assoc ed, Blood, 64-75 & 81, J Reticuloendothelial Soc, 65-73; Am J Path, 78-, Am J Med & J Hemat Oncol; USPHS res career scientist award, 66-76; assoc attend physician, Univ Hosp, NY, 68-74, attend physician, 74-; spec consult, Path Training Comt, Nat Inst Gen Med Sci; assoc attend physician, Univ Hosp, NY, 68-74, attend physician, 74-; mem, Blood Prod Comt, Food & Drug Admin, 81. *Mem:* Inst Med-Nat Acad Sci; Am Soc Hemat (pres, 94-95); Am Soc Exp Path; Am Soc Clin Invest; Am Asn Physicians; fel NY Acad Sci; Am Fedn Clin Res; Am Soc Psysiol; Am Asn Immunologists; Am Soc Cell Biol; Reticuloendothelial Soc (pres, 84-85); fel AAAS; Am Soc Exp Path; Int Soc Hemat; Int Retroviol Asn. *Res:* Hematology, including white blood cells, coagulation of blood and platelets; immunology; electron microscopy. *Mailing Add:* Dept Med UH 445 NY Univ Med Ctr 550 First Ave New York NY 10016-6451. *Fax:* 212-263-8230; *E-Mail:* dorthea.zucker_franklin@ccmail.med.nyu.edu

**ZUCKERKANDL, EMILE,** MOLECULAR EVOLUTION, REPETITIVE SEQUENCE FAMILIES. *Current Pos:* PRES, INST MOLECULAR MED SCI, 92- *Personal Data:* b Vienna, Austria, July 4, 22; Fr citizen; m 50, Jane G Metz. *Educ:* Univ Ill, Urbana, MS, 47; Univ Sorbonne, PhD(biochem), 59. *Honors & Awards:* Order of Merit, Govt. *Prof Exp:* Fel, Calif Inst Technol, 59-64; res dir, Nat Sci Res Ctr, Montpellier, France, 67-80; dir, Ctr Macromolecular Biochem, 65-75; res dir, Nat Ctr Sci Res, Montpellier, France, 67-80; pres, Linus Pauling Inst, 80-92. *Concurrent Pos:* Consult genetics, Stanford Univ, 63, vis prof, 64; vis prof biol, Univ Del, 76; ed-in-chief, J Molecular Evolution, 71-; appointee, Molecular Biol Comn, DGRST, Paris, 67-70, Med Biochem Nat Inst Health & Med Res, Paris, 68-74, comt consult, Univ Paris. *Mem:* Fel AAAS; Soc Study Origins Life; Int Soc Molecular Evolution. *Res:* Molecular evolution: relation to organismal evolution; evolution of gene-gene interaction; issue of the molecular clock; questions of functions in non-coding DNA; interaction of the environment with genetic systems. *Mailing Add:* Inst Molecular Med Sci 460 Page Mill Rd Palo Alto CA 94306. *Fax:* 650-322-3009

**ZUCKERMAN, BENJAMIN MICHAEL,** ASTRONOMY. *Current Pos:* PROF ASTRON, UNIV CALIF, LOS ANGELES, 82- *Personal Data:* b New York, NY, Aug 16, 43. *Educ:* Mass Inst Technol, SB & SM, 63; Harvard Univ, PhD(astron), 68. *Honors & Awards:* Helen B Warner Prize, Am Astron Soc, 75; Muhlmann Prize, Astron Soc Pac, 86. *Prof Exp:* From asst prof to prof physics & astron, Univ Md, College Park, 68-83. *Concurrent Pos:* Alfred P Sloan res fel, 72-74; consult, Jet Propulsion Lab; Guggenheim Found fel, 77. *Mem:* Int Astron Union; Int Union Radio Sci; Am Astron Soc. *Res:* Infrared and radio astronomy. *Mailing Add:* Dept Physics & Astron Univ Calif 405 Hilgard Ave Los Angeles CA 90095

**ZUCKERMAN, ISRAEL,** mathematics, for more information see previous edition

**ZUCKERMAN, LEO,** LABORATORY MEDICINE, TECHNICAL MANAGEMENT. *Current Pos:* RETIRED. *Personal Data:* b Brooklyn, NY, July 3, 17; m 42, Anne Bernstein; c Barry, Elliot & Diana. *Educ:* Brooklyn Col, BA, 42. *Prof Exp:* Foreman blood fractionation, E R Squibb & Sons, 42-44, res assoc group leader, 44-52; res assoc, Ortho Res Found, 52-58, supvr blood prod & biol mfg, Ortho Pharmaceut Corp, 58-62, mgr fractionation dept, Ortho Diag, 62-72, mfg dir biochem prod, 72-73, mfg dir serol prod, 73-76, dir mfg serv int, 76-78, dir tech serv int, 78-82, dir regulatory compliance, Ortho Diag Systs, 82-84. *Concurrent Pos:* Consult, 84- *Mem:* Am Chem Soc; Am Inst Chem; Am Asn Clin Chem; Soc Cryobiol; NY Acad Sci; Am Asn Blood Banks. *Res:* Coagulation; immunology; serology; chromatography; electrophoresis; lyophilization; protein isolation and characterization; clinical chemistry; cryobiology; blood fractionation. *Mailing Add:* 1983 Holland Brk Rd W Somerville NJ 08876-3845

**ZUCKERMAN, MARTIN MICHAEL,** MATHEMATICAL LOGIC. *Current Pos:* asst prof, 68-72, ASSOC PROF MATH, CITY COL NEW YORK, 72- *Personal Data:* b Brooklyn, NY, June 27, 34; m 60. *Educ:* Brandeis Univ, BA, 55; Brown Univ, MA, 60; Yeshiva Univ, PhD(math), 67. *Prof Exp:* Mathematician, Int Elec Co, 61-63; instr math, NY Univ, 63-66; asst prof, Hunter Col, 67-68. *Mem:* Am Math Soc; Asn Symbolic Logic; Math Asn Am. *Res:* Set theory. *Mailing Add:* Dept Math City Col NY Convent Ave & 138th St New York NY 10031-9100

**ZUCKERMAN, MARVIN,** PERSONALITY, PSYCHOPATHOLOGY. *Current Pos:* assoc prof, 69-71, PROF PSYCHOL, UNIV DEL, 71- *Personal Data:* b Chicago, Ill, Mar 21, 28; c Steven H & April (Schanoes). *Educ:* NY Univ, PhD(psychol), 54. *Prof Exp:* Clin psychologist, Norwich State Hosp, Conn, 53-54 & Larve D Carter Mem Hosp, Ind, 54-56; res assoc & asst prof psychiat, Inst Psychiat Res, Ind Univ Med Ctr, 56-60; asst prof psychol, Brooklyn Col, 60-62; assoc prof, Adelphi Univ, 62-63; res assoc, Endocrinol Res Labs, Albert Einstein Med Ctr, Philadelphia, Pa, 63-69. *Concurrent Pos:* Vis prof, Dept Psychol, Inst Psychiat, London, Eng, 75-76 & Dept Exp Psychol, Oxford Univ, Eng, 83-84; bd mem, Int Soc Study Individual Differences, 81-89. *Mem:* Fel Am Psychol Asn; fel Am Psychol Soc; Int Soc Study Individual Differences (pres, 85-87). *Res:* Personality theory research and assessment; psychobiology of personality; personality trait of sensation seeking. *Mailing Add:* Dept Psychol Univ Del Newark DE 19716-2577. *Fax:* 302-831-3645; *E-Mail:* zuckerma@udel.edu

**ZUCKERMAN, SAMUEL,** ORGANIC CHEMISTRY, COLORANT CHEMISTRY. *Current Pos:* CONSULT, 81- *Personal Data:* b New York, NY, Oct 22, 15; m 38, Beatrice Forman; c Roy & Andrew. *Educ:* City Col, BS, 37; Polytech Inst Brooklyn, MS, 42, PhD, 50. *Honors & Awards:* Medal Award, Soc Cosmetic Chem, 70. *Prof Exp:* Chemist, H Kohnstamm & Co, 36-50, tech dir & plant mgr, Brooklyn Div, 50-60, vpres & dir, 59-84. *Mem:* Am Chem Soc; Soc Cosmetic Chem. *Res:* Organic synthesis of dyestuffs; chemical microscopy; cosmetic colors for camouflage; certified food, drug and cosmetic colors. *Mailing Add:* 8611 Timber Hill Lane Potomac MD 20854-4240

**ZUCKERMAN, STEVEN H,** SOMATIC CELL GENETICS, MICROPHAGE BIOLOGY. *Current Pos:* SR SCIENTIST, ELI LILLY & CO, 83- *Educ:* Univ Minn, PhD(microbiol & immunol), 77. *Mailing Add:* Eli Lilly & Co Lilly Corp Ctr Drop Code 0434 Indianapolis IN 46285

**ZUCKERMANN, MARTIN JULIUS,** PHYSICS. *Current Pos:* assoc prof, 69-80, PROF PHYSICS, MCGILL UNIV, 80- *Personal Data:* b Berlin, Ger, July 7, 36; m 60; c 4. *Educ:* Oxford Univ, BA, 60, PhD(phyiscs), 64. *Prof Exp:* Fel, Univ Chicago, 64-65; asst prof physics, Univ Va, 65-67; lectr, Imp Col, Univ London, 67-69. *Mem:* Am Inst Physics. *Res:* Theoretical solid state physics; investigation into superconductivity and magnetism in disordered systems; weather physics. *Mailing Add:* Dept Physics McGill Univ Sherbrooke St W Montreal PQ H3A 2M5 Can. *Fax:* 514-398-8434

**ZUCLICH, JOSEPH A,** LASER BIOEFFECTS, OPTICAL BIOPSY. *Current Pos:* sr mem tech staff, 93-97, SECT MGR OPTICAL RADIATION, TASC, 97- *Personal Data:* b New York, NY, July 25, 42; m 81, Carol Homburg. *Educ:* Stevens Inst Technol, BS, 64; Yale Univ, MS, 66; Columbia Univ, PhD(chem physics), 69. *Prof Exp:* Res fel, Univ Hawaii, 69-79; NIH fel, Univ Calif, Riverside, 70-73; prin res scientist, Krug Int, 73-92. *Concurrent Pos:* Adj asst prof physics, Univ Tex, San Antonio, 75-76; adj assoc prof, Health Sci Ctr, Univ Tex, 76-78; guest scientist, Los Alamos Nat Lab, 91. *Mem:* AAAS; Laser Inst Am; Am Soc Photobiol; Int Soc Optical Eng. *Res:* Ocular effects of laser radiation and medical diagnostic applications of lasers; emphasis on laser safety and UV and IR radiation effect on ocular tissues. *Mailing Add:* TASC 4241 Woodcock Dr Suite B-100 San Antonio TX 78228-1330. *Fax:* 210-534-0420; *E-Mail:* joe.zuclich@platinum.brooks.af.mil

**ZUDKEVITCH, DAVID,** CHEMICAL ENGINEERING, SEPARATION & THERMODYNAMICS. *Current Pos:* ADJ PROF, DEPT CHEM ENG, COLUMBIA UNIV, 79- *Personal Data:* b Hadera, Israel, Jan 15, 30; US citizen; c 1. *Educ:* Israel Inst Technol, BSc, 53, Dipl Ing, 54; Polytech Inst Brooklyn, MChE, 58, PhD(chem eng), 59. *Prof Exp:* Plant engr, Fertilizers & Chem Co, Israel, 53; lab dir, Alliance Tire & Rubber Co, 53-55; engr, Exxon Res & Eng Co, 59-62, eng assoc & consult thermodyn, 62-75; sr eng assoc, Allied Chem Corp, 75-85. *Concurrent Pos:* Adj prof, Columbia Univ. *Mem:* Am Chem Soc; Am Inst Chem Engrs; Am Petrol Inst; Gas Processors Asn; Comt Data Sci & Technol. *Res:* Development of correlations for physical and thermodynamic properties, especially phase equilibria; evaluation and development of separation and transport processes; evaluation and design of pollution abatement processes and energy utilization. *Mailing Add:* PO Box 327 Cedar Knolls NJ 07927. *Fax:* 973-627-6291

**ZUECH, ERNEST A,** ORGANIC CHEMISTRY. *Current Pos:* RETIRED. *Personal Data:* b Frontenac, Kans, Nov 17, 34; m 56; c 3. *Educ:* Kans State Col, Pittsburg, BS, 55, MS, 56; Iowa State Univ, PhD(org chem), 60. *Prof Exp:* Asst org chem, Ohio State Univ, 60-61; chemist, Phillips Petrol Co, 61-68, sect mgr, 68-78, br mgr, 78-80, dir petrol res, 80-91; proj mgr, Dept Energy, 92-96. *Mem:* Am Chem Soc. *Res:* Organometallic chemistry. *Mailing Add:* 3000 Shore Dr Grove OK 74344

**ZUEHLKE, CARL WILLIAM,** ANALYTICAL CHEMISTRY. *Current Pos:* RETIRED. *Personal Data:* b Bonduel, Wis, Oct 28, 16; m 44, 77, 88, Hildegard Pfeffer; c Stephen & David. *Educ:* Univ Wis, BS, 38; Univ Mich, MS, 40, PhD(analytical chem), 42. *Prof Exp:* Chief chemist, Methods Lab, Gen Chem Div, Allied Chem & Dye Corp, 42-45, E St Louis Works, 45-46, asst mgr, Chem Control Div, 46-48; res assoc, Eastman Kodak Co, 48-61, asst head, Chem Div, Res Labs, 61-68, head, Analytical Sci Div, Res Labs, 68-79. *Concurrent Pos:* Chmn, Gordon Res Conf Analytical Chem, 67. *Mem:* Am Chem Soc. *Res:* Analytical chemistry of germanium; analysis for micro amounts of mercury. *Mailing Add:* 92 Skyview Lane Rochester NY 14625

**ZUEHLKE, RICHARD WILLIAM,** CONFERENCE MANAGEMENT. *Current Pos:* assoc marine scientist, Grad Sch Oceanog, 80-85, ASST TO DIR, GORDON RES CONFERENCES, GORDON RES CTR, UNIV RI, 90- *Personal Data:* b Milwaukee, Wis, June 17, 33; m 55, Carol Yates; c Kenneth R, William W & Deanne E. *Educ:* Lawrence Col, BS, 55; Univ Minn, PhD(chem), 60. *Prof Exp:* From instr to asst prof chem, Lawrence Univ, 58-68; chmn dept chem, Univ Bridgeport, 68-73, acad liaison officer, 73-74, Remington prof, 68-80. *Concurrent Pos:* Consult, Kimberly-Clark Corp, 60-62; NSF fac fel, Univ Pittsburgh, 66-67; consult, United Illum Co, 69-71 & Wooster Davis & Cifelli Chem Specialties Corp, 70-73; consult, Oxford Univ Press, 74-76 & Sperry Remington Co, 76-77; vis prof oceanog, Univ RI, 76-77; pres, TRC Consults, 85-90. *Mem:* AAAS; Am Chem Soc; fel Am Inst Chem. *Res:* Computer simulation and modeling; instrument design; laboratory automation; information management software. *Mailing Add:* 1410 South Rd Wakefield RI 02879. *Fax:* 401-783-7644; *E-Mail:* rzuehlke@uriacc.uri.edu

**ZUG, GEORGE R,** HERPETOLOGY, MORPHOLOGY. *Current Pos:* asst cur herpet, 69-73, chmn, Dept Vert Zool, 77-83, CUR HERPET, MUS NATURAL HIST, SMITHSONIAN INST, 73- *Personal Data:* b Carlisle, Pa, Nov 16, 38; m 60, Patricia A Brehm; c Jon R & Erin E. *Educ:* Albright Col, BS, 60; Univ Fla, MS, 63; Univ Mich, PhD(zool), 68. *Prof Exp:* Instr zool, Univ Mich, 68. *Concurrent Pos:* Affil prof biol, George Mason Univ, 93-; vis res prof, Univ Kent, Durrell Inst, Conserv & Ecol, 94- *Mem:* Soc Study Amphibians & Reptiles; Soc Syst Biol; Herpetologists League; Soc Conserv Biol; Sigma Xi. *Res:* Systematics and evolution of reptiles and amphibians, particularly chelonians; morphology of reptiles and amphibians and functional relationships; evolution and biogeography of Pacific lizards. *Mailing Add:* Div Amphibians & Reptiles MRC-162 Nat Mus Natural Hist Smithsonian Inst Washington DC 20560

**ZUGIBE, FREDERICK T,** FORENSIC PATHOLOGY, CARDIOVASCULAR DISEASES. *Current Pos:* CHIEF MED EXAMR, ROCKLAND COUNTY, NY, 69- *Personal Data:* b Garnerville, NY, May 28, 28; m 51; c Fred, Thomas, Cathryn, Theresa, Mary, Matthew & Kevin. *Educ:* St Francis Col, BS, 52; Univ Chicago, MS, 59, PhD(anat), 60; WVa Univ, MD, 68; Cert Family Practice, 78, anat path, 80 & forensic path, 82. *Honors & Awards:* Physicians Recognition Award, AMA, 71-74, 74-77, 77-80 & 81-84, 85-88; Shields Law Enforcement Award, 73; Distinguished Serv Award, Rockland County & Am Legion Award for Serv in Nicaragua During Earthquake, 73; Am Heart Asn Serv Recognition Award, 74; Law Enforcement Award, Police Chiefs Asn, 80. *Prof Exp:* Res histologist, Lederle Labs, Am Cyanamid Co, 50-52, chemist, 53-55; res asst ophthal, Col Physicians & Surgeons, Columbia Univ, 55; res histochemist in chg atherosclerosis sect, Vet Admin Hosp, Downey, Ill, 56-60; dir cardiovasc res, Vet Admin Hosp, Pittsburgh, 61-69. *Concurrent Pos:* Adj prof, Duquesne Univ; asst res prof, Univ Pittsburgh, Sch Med, 61-69; asst prof pathol, Columbia Univ, Col Physicians & Surgeons, 69-75, adj assoc prof path, 75-; consult path, ABC Labs, 72-79; consult, comt connective tissue, skeletal & muscle, Vet Admin & sci res technol, 74-77, dir, Angelus Path Lab, 72-82 & Acad Labs, 76-78; consult path & physician, Police Surgeon Fire, Surgeon & Ambulance Corp Physician; fel, Coun Arteriosclerosis, Am Heart Asn; continuing educ award path, Am Soc Clin Path & Am Col Path, 75-77, 77-80, 81-84 & 85-88; vis prof, Dept Path, Univ Wis, Med Sch, 86-95; res grants, NIH, Am Heart Asn & Am Cancer Soc. *Mem:* Histochem Soc; fel Am Heart Asn; NY Acad Sci; fel Am Acad Forensic Sci; fel Am Col Cardiol; fel Col Am Pathologists; Nat Asn Med Examr; assoc Scientists & Scholars Int (pres); AAAS; Sigma Xi. *Res:* Atherosclerosis and aging research; carbohydrate, lipid and enzyme histochemistry; ultramicrohistochemistry; cardiovascular research; forensic pathology research; Shroud of Turin research; crucifixion research; numerous publications in medical and scientific journals & several book chapters in medical and scientific books one textbook and 3 non-fiction books; Zuyibe-Gilbert Syndrome (glycoprotein storage disease). *Mailing Add:* 1 Angelus Dr Garnerville NY 10923. *Fax:* 914-364-2896

**ZUHR, RAYMOND ARTHUR,** SURFACE PHYSICS, THIN FILM DEPOSITION. *Current Pos:* MEM STAFF, OAK RIDGE NAT LAB, 77- *Personal Data:* b New York, NY, May 20, 40; m 82; c 3. *Educ:* Rensselaer Polytech Inst, BME, 62, MS, 72, PhD(physics), 74. *Prof Exp:* Assoc, Rensselaer Polytech Inst, 74-76; res assoc, State Univ NY, Albany, 76-77. *Mem:* Am Phys Soc; Am Vacuum Soc; Mat Res Soc. *Res:* Solid state physics and formation of thin films; study of single crystal surfaces using Rutherford backscattering and electron spectroscopy; plasma-wall interactions in magnetic confinement fusion devices using Rutherford backscattering and nuclear reaction analysis. *Mailing Add:* Oak Ridge Nat Lab Bldg 3137 MS 6057 PO Box 2008 Oak Ridge TN 37831-6057

**ZUICHES, JAMES J,** DEMOGRAPHY, RURAL SOCIOLOGY. *Current Pos:* DEAN, COL AGR & HOME ECON, 95-; DIR, AGR RES CTR, 95-; DIR, COOP EXTEN, 95- *Personal Data:* b Eau Claire, Wis, Mar 24, 43; m 67, Carol Kurilo; c J Daniel & Joseph K. *Educ:* Univ Portland, BA, 67; Univ Wis, Madison, MS, 69, PhD(sociol), 73. *Honors & Awards:* Sustained Super Performance Award, NSF, 82. *Prof Exp:* From asst prof to prof sociol, Mich State Univ, 71-82; assoc dir & prof rural sociol, Cornell Univ Ag Exp Sta & Off for Res Rural Sociol, 82-86; dir, Agr Res Ctr & assoc dean, Col Agr & Home Econ, 86-94, prof, Dept Rural Sociol, 86-94; prog dir, Food Syst & Rural Develop, W K Kellogg Found, 94-95. *Concurrent Pos:* Vis prof sociol, Univ Surrey, Guildford, 78-79; from assoc prog dir to prog dir, NSF, 79-82; consult, Univ Ga, 81- & Univ Minn, 85-86. *Mem:* Fel AAAS; Rural Sociol Soc (pres, 92-93); Pop Asn Am; Coun Agr Sci & Technol; Am Sociol Asn. *Res:* Migration and population changes in urban and rural areas, indirect cost policies, patent and licensing policies and the administration of research. *Mailing Add:* 815 SE Meadow Vale Dr Pullman WA 99163. *Fax:* 509-335-1065; *E-Mail:* zuiches@wsu.edu

**ZUIDEMA, GEORGE DALE,** GENERAL SURGERY. *Current Pos:* RETIRED. *Personal Data:* b Holland, Mich, Mar 8, 28; m 53; c 4. *Educ:* Hope Col, AB, 49; Johns Hopkins Univ, MD, 53; Am Bd Surg, dipl, 60. *Hon Degrees:* DSc, Hope Col, 69. *Honors & Awards:* Russel Award, Univ Mich, 63; hon fel, Royal Col Surg, Ireland, 72. *Prof Exp:* Intern surg, Mass Gen Hosp, 53-54, asst resident, 54 & 57-58, chief resident, 59; from asst prof to prof, Univ Mich, 60-64, prof surg, Med Sch & vprovost med affairs, 84-94; surgeon-in-chief, Johns Hopkins Hosp, 64-84, prof surg & dir dept, Sch Med, Johns Hopkins Univ, 64-84. *Concurrent Pos:* Fel, Harvard Med Sch, 59; attend surgeon, Ann Arbor Vet Admin Hosp, 60-64; USPHS sr res fel, 61, career develop award, 63; Markle scholar acad med, 61-66; asst ed, J Surg Res, 60, ed, 66-; consult, Walter Reed Army Med Ctr, Sinai & Baltimore City Hosps & Clin Ctr, NIH; co-ed-in-chief, Surg, 75-87. *Mem:* Inst Med-Nat Acad Sci; fel Am Col Surgeons; Asn Am Med Cols; Soc Univ Surgeons; Am Surg Asn; Am Soc Clin Surg. *Res:* Cardiovascular and acceleration physiology; space medicine; gastrointestinal and hepatic physiology. *Mailing Add:* Med Sci 1 Bldg M3246 Univ Mich Ann Arbor MI 48109

**ZUK, MARLENE,** BEHAVIORAL ECOLOGY. *Current Pos:* ASST PROF BIOL, UNIV CALIF, RIVERSIDE, 89- *Personal Data:* b Philadelphia, Pa, May 20, 56; m 86. *Educ:* Univ Calif, Santa Barbara, BA, 77; Univ Mich, MS, 83, PhD(zool), 86. *Honors & Awards:* Outstanding Young Investr, Am Soc Naturalists, 88. *Prof Exp:* Postdoctoral, Univ NMex, 87-89. *Mem:* Soc Study Evolution; Animal Behav Soc. *Res:* Evolution of sexual behavior, especially the effect of parasites on host sexual selection; mate choice; insect song. *Mailing Add:* Dept Biol Univ Calif University Dr Riverside CA 92521

**ZUK, WILLIAM,** structural engineering, for more information see previous edition

**ZUKAS, EUGENE G,** ALLOYS. *Current Pos:* RETIRED. *Personal Data:* b Armstrong, Pa, Dec 19, 21. *Educ:* Univ Pittsburgh, BS, 43, MS, 50; Lehigh Univ, PhD(metall), 52. *Prof Exp:* Staff mem, Los Alamos Sci Lab, 52-86. *Mem:* Fel Am Soc Metals Int. *Mailing Add:* 1847 W Camino Urbano Green Valley AZ 85614

**ZUKER, CHARLES S,** SIGNAL TRANSDUCTION IN THE DROSOPHILA MELANOGASTER VISUAL SYSTEM. *Current Pos:* asst prof, Dept Biol, Univ Calif, 86-89, assoc prof, Dept Biol & Neurosci, Sch Med, 89-93, PROF, DEPT BIOL & NEUROSCI, UNIV CALIF, SAN DIEGO, 93-; INVESTR, HOWARD HUGHES MED INST, 93- *Personal Data:* b Arica, Chile, June 27, 57. *Educ:* Univ Catolica de Valparaiso, Chile, BSc, 77; Mass Inst Technol, PhD(biol), 83. *Honors & Awards:* Alfred P Sloan Award, Sloan Found, 88; Basil O'Connor Award, March of Dimes, 89. *Prof Exp:* Fel, Dept Biochem, Univ Calif, Berkeley, 83-86; res fel, Jane Coffin Childs Mem Fund Med Res, 84-86. *Concurrent Pos:* Prin investr, Univ Calif, San Diego, 86-; assoc investr, Howard Hughes Med inst, 89-93. *Res:* To characterize molecularly and biochemically mechanisms utilized for signal transduction in the visual system in Drosophila; we have isolated a set of photoeceptor cell-specific genes that encode components of this sensory transduction pathway and have used them as molecular tools to study their function interactions and regulation. *Mailing Add:* 0649 Univ Calif San Diego La Jolla CA 92093-0649

**ZUKER, MICHAEL,** biomathematics, for more information see previous edition

**ZUKIN, STEPHEN R,** PSYCHIATRY, NEUROSCIENCE. *Current Pos:* assoc prof psychiat, 82-87, assoc prof neurosci, 84-87, PROF PSYCHIAT & NEUROSCI, ALBERT EINSTEIN COL MED, YESHIVA UNIV, 87- *Personal Data:* b Philadelphia, Pa, Aug 19, 48; c 2. *Educ:* Haverford Col, BA, 70; Johns Hopkins Univ, Baltimore, MD, 74. *Honors & Awards:* Citation Classic, Inst Sci Info, 92; Kempf Fund Award, Res Develop In Psychobiological Psychiat, 92. *Prof Exp:* Asst prof psychiat, State Univ NY, 77-79 & Mt Sinai Sch Med, 79-82. *Concurrent Pos:* Dir res, Bronx Psychiat Ctr, 83- *Mem:* Am Col Neuropsychopharmacol; Am Soc Pharmacol & Exp Therapeut; Soc Neurosci; Am Psychiat Asn. *Res:* Function and regulation of brain NMDA receptors; molecular mechanisms of psychotic illness; mechanisms of action of psychotomimetic drugs; development of NMDA-related treatments of neuropsychiatric diseases. *Mailing Add:* Albert Einstein Col Med 1300 Morris Park Ave F111 Bronx NY 10461-1924

**ZUKOSKI, CHARLES FREDERICK,** SURGERY. *Current Pos:* PROF SURG, COL MED, UNIV ARIZ, 69- *Personal Data:* b St Louis, Mo, Jan 26, 26; m 53; c 3. *Educ:* Univ NC, AB, 47; Harvard Med Sch, MD, 51. *Prof Exp:* From intern surg to resident, Roosevelt Hosp, New York, 51-52; resident, Univ Ala Hosp, 55-58, instr, Univ, 58-59; res fel, Med Col Va, 59-61; from asst prof to assoc prof, Sch Med, Vanderbilt Univ, 61-68; assoc prof, Univ NC, Chapel Hill, 68-69. *Concurrent Pos:* Nat Inst Neurol Dis & Blindness spec trainee, 59-61; Nat Inst Allergy & Infectious Dis spec fel, 66-67; Josiah Macy Jr sr fac fel, 76-77. *Mem:* Am Col Surg; Soc Univ Surg; Am Surg Asn; Am Soc Exp Path; Transplantation Soc. *Res:* Homotransplantation; renal allografts; experimental and clinical research. *Mailing Add:* Dept Surg Serv Vet Admin Med Ctr 3601 S Sixth Ave Tucson AZ 85723-0001

**ZUKOSKI, EDWARD EDOM,** FLUID MECHANICS, COMBUSTION. *Current Pos:* Sr res engr, Jet Propulsion Lab, 54-57, from asst prof to assoc prof eng, 57-66, PROF JET PROPULSION & MECH ENG, CALIF INST TECHNOL, 66- *Personal Data:* b Birmingham, Ala, June 29, 27; m 60; c 3. *Educ:* Harvard Univ, BS, 50; Calif Inst Technol, MS, 51, PhD(aeronaut), 54. *Concurrent Pos:* Mem fire res comt, Nat Acad Sci, 65-71. *Mem:* Fel Am Inst Aeronaut & Astronaut; Int Combustion Inst. *Res:* Combustion of air-fuel mixtures; interaction of transverse jets with supersonic flows; separation of turbulent boundary layers; electrical phenomena in high density seeded plasma; uncontrolled fires in buildings. *Mailing Add:* 3815 Fairmeade Rd Pasadena CA 91107

**ZUKOTYNSKI, STEFAN,** SOLID STATE PHYSICS, ELECTRICAL ENGINEERING. *Current Pos:* from asst prof to assoc prof, 68-81, PROF ELEC & COMPUT ENG, UNIV TORONTO, 81- *Personal Data:* b Warsaw, Poland, Feb 26, 39; m 68; c 1. *Educ:* Univ Warsaw, Mag, 61, PhD(physics), 66. *Prof Exp:* Nat Res Coun Can fel, Univ Alta, 66-68. *Concurrent Pos:* Consult, Elec Eng Consociates Ltd, 71-; resident vis, Bell Labs, 77-78; pres, Torion Plasma Corp. *Mem:* Can Asn Physicists; Am Phys Soc; Inst Elec & Electronics Engrs. *Res:* Electrical and optical properties of semiconductors and semiconductor devices. *Mailing Add:* Dept Elec & Comput Eng Univ Toronto Toronto ON M5S 3G4 Can

**ZUKOWSKI, CHARLES ALBERT,** INTEGRATED CIRCUIT DESIGN CIRCUIT SIMULATION. *Current Pos:* asst prof, 85-90, ASSOC PROF ELEC ENG, COLUMBIA UNIV, 90- *Personal Data:* b Buffalo, NY, Aug 17, 59; m 83; c 2. *Educ:* Mass Inst Technol, BS & MS, 82, PhD(elec eng), 85. *Prof Exp:* Res assoc elec eng, Mass Inst Technol, 85. *Concurrent Pos:* NSF presidential young investr, 87; mem, Tech Comt, Int Conf Comput Design, 88-91 & Custom Integrated Circuits Conf, 90-93; consult, Int Bus Mach Corp, 89- *Mem:* Inst Elec & Electronics Engrs. *Res:* Design of high-performance digital integrated circuits, especially for the application of telecommunications; computer-aided design challenges such as circuit simulation, optimization and timing analysis. *Mailing Add:* Dept Elec Eng Columbia Univ 1311 SW Mudd Bldg New York NY 10027-6699. *E-Mail:* c9z@columbia.edu

**ZULALIAN, JACK,** METABOLISM. *Current Pos:* SR RES CHEMIST METAB, AGR DIV, AM CYANAMID CO, 66- *Personal Data:* b New York, NY, Apr 21, 36. *Educ:* Queens Col, NY, BS, 57; Purdue Univ, Lafayette, PhD(chem), 62. *Prof Exp:* Res assoc natural prod biosynthesis, Korman Res Labs, Albert Einstein Med Ctr, Philadelphia, 62-66. *Mem:* Am Chem Soc. *Res:* Organic synthesis; metabolism of organic compounds designed for use in agriculture as herbicides; pesticides and animal health; radiotracter synthesis. *Mailing Add:* Am Cyanamid Co PO Box 400 Princeton NJ 08540

**ZULEEG, RAINER,** RADIATION EFFECTS IN SEMICONDUCTORS, THIN-FILM FERROELECTRIC MATERIALS. *Current Pos:* CONSULT SEMICONDUCTORS, 90-; ADJ PROF CHEM, UNIV CALIF, IRVINE, 92- *Personal Data:* b Erlangen, Ger, Sept 23, 27; US citizen; m 58; c 2. *Educ:* Tohoku Univ, Japan, PhD(solid state physics), 72. *Prof Exp:* Staff dir, McDonnell Douglas, 67-90. *Concurrent Pos:* Lectr, Univ Calif, Irvine, 72-89; guest prof, Royal Melbourne Inst Technol, 75 & 82 & Univ Davisburg, Ger, 87; sr fel, McDonnell Douglas, 86; adj prof, Univ Colo, 90- *Mem:* Am Phys Soc; Inst Elec & Electronics Engrs; Electrochem Soc. *Res:* Semiconductor devices and integrated circuits; radiation effects of microelectronic components and thin-film ferroelectric materials. *Mailing Add:* 33571 Avenida Calita San Juan Capistrano CA 92675

**ZULL, JAMES E,** BIOCHEMISTRY, CELLULAR BIOLOGY. *Current Pos:* from asst prof to assoc prof, 66-72, PROF BIOL, CASE WESTERN RES UNIV, 77- *Personal Data:* b North Branch, Mich, Sept 29, 39; m 61, 68; c 3. *Educ:* Houghton Col, BA, 61; Univ Wis, MS, 63, PhD(biochem), 66. *Prof Exp:* Fel biochem, Univ Wis, 65-66. *Concurrent Pos:* NIH career develop award, 71-76; vis prof biochem, Inst Pathophysiol, Bern, Switz, 74-75. *Mem:* Am Soc Bone Mineral Res; Am Soc Biol Chemists; AAAS; Protein Soc. *Res:* Membrane-hormone interactions; hormone mechanisms; peptide structure; lysosome function; calcium wet abolisms; molecular biology of peptide hormone receptors. *Mailing Add:* Dept Biol Case Western Res Univ Cleveland OH 44106

**ZULLO, VICTOR AUGUST,** invertebrate paleontology, zoology; deceased, see previous edition for last biography

**ZUMAN, PETR,** ELECTROCHEMISTRY, PHYSICAL ORGANIC CHEMISTRY. *Current Pos:* PROF CHEM, CLARKSON UNIV, 70- *Personal Data:* b Prague, Czech, Jan 13, 26; m 51, H Radmila Dobiasova; c John & Daniela. *Educ:* Charles Univ, Prague, RNDr(chem), 50; Czech Acad Sci, DrSc, 62; Univ Birmingham, DSc, 68. *Hon Degrees:* Dr, Univ Bologna, 96. *Honors & Awards:* Heyrovsky Medal, Czech Acad Sci, 60 & 90; Coover lectr, Am Chem Soc, 73; Theophilus Redwood lectr, The Chem Soc, 75; Benedetti-Pichler Award, Am Microchem Soc, 75; Gold Medal Award, Am Electroplaters Soc, 76; Medal Pharm, Res Inst, Warsaw, Poland, 95. *Prof Exp:* Head, Org Polarography Div, J Heyrovsky Inst Polarography, Czech Acad Sci, Prague, 50-68. *Concurrent Pos:* Sr vis fel, Univ Birmingham, 66-70; distinguished vis prof, Brooklyn Polytech Inst, 67; consult, Xerox Corp, 72-76, Technicon, 74-, IBM Corp, 75-76 & 81 & Texaco, 85-; vis prof, Univ Amsterdam, 77, Free Univ Brussels, 77, Univ Utrecht, 79 & 81, Tech Univ Lyngby, 83, Univ Linz, 83, Deakin Univ, Australia, 87, Univ Bologna, 87, 88, 89, 91, 93, 95 & 96. *Mem:* Am Chem Soc; Sigma Xi; fel Royal Soc Chem; fel Electrochem Soc; Int Soc Electrochem; fel Chem Inst Can; Int Union Pure & Appl Chem. *Res:* Use of polarography and other electrochemical and optical methods for study of reactivity, equilibria, kinetics and mechanisms of reactions of organic compounds. *Mailing Add:* Dept Chem Clarkson Univ Box 5810 Potsdam NY 13699-5810. *Fax:* 315-268-6610

**ZUMBERGE, JAMES FREDERICK,** GEODESY. *Current Pos:* MEM TECH STAFF, JET PROPULSION LAB, 90- *Personal Data:* b Ann Arbor, Mich, Jan 26, 53; m 84, Cinthia Franklin; c J Franklin & Thomas. *Educ:* Univ Mich, BS, 74; Calif Inst Technol, PhD(physics), 81. *Prof Exp:* Mem tech staff, MDH Industs, Inc, 81-82, appl sci mgr, 82-86, dir, 86-85, vpres, 88-90. *Mem:* Am Geophys Union. *Res:* Applications of the global positioning system to geodesy. *Mailing Add:* Jet Propulsion Lab 238-600 4800 Oak Grove Dr Pasadena CA 91109. *E-Mail:* jfz@cobra.jpl.nasa.gov

**ZUMBRO, MARTHA VAUGHAN,** NUCLEAR PHYSICS, NUCLEAR CHEMISTRY. *Current Pos:* Staff mem, 78-, GROUP LEADER MESON PHYSICS, LOS ALAMOS NAT LAB, UNIV CALIF. *Personal Data:* b Lubbock, Tex, Jan 8, 51; m 73. *Educ:* Hardin-Simmons Univ, BS, 72; Auburn Univ, MS, 74; Fla State Univ, PhD(nuclear chem), 77. *Mem:* Am Phys Soc. *Res:* Nuclear structure; nuclear moments; mesic x-ray studies. *Mailing Add:* Los Alamos Nat Labs PO Box 1663 Lansce-6 MSH 812 Los Alamos NM 87545

**ZUMBRUNNEN, CHARLES EDWARD,** DENTISTRY *Current Pos:* RETIRED. *Personal Data:* b Grafton, WVa, Oct 29, 21; m 85; c 2. *Educ:* WVa Wesleyan Col, BS, 43; Northwestern Univ, Chicago, DDS, 45; Univ NC, Chapel Hill, MPH, 64. *Prof Exp:* Pvt dent pract, Huntington, WVa, 48-51 & 54-63; dir, Bur Dent Pub Health, NH Dept Health & Welfare, 64-90. *Concurrent Pos:* Instr, Sch Dent Med, Tufts Univ, 69-; prof, NH Tech Inst, Concord, 70-71 & 80-; exec secy, NIH Bd Dent Examrs, 78- *Mem:* Asn State & Territorial Dent Dirs; Am Col Dent; Am Dent Asn; Am Asn Pub Health Dentists. *Res:* Dental health education methodology in elementary schools. *Mailing Add:* 6 Riverhill Rd Concord NH 03303

**ZUMBRUNNEN, DAVID ARNOLD,** MATERIALS PROCESSING, THERMAL SYSTEMS. *Current Pos:* ASSOC PROF MECH ENG, CLEMSON UNIV, 88- *Personal Data:* b Salt Lake City, Utah, Sept 3, 55; m 83, Elizabeth Buck. *Educ:* Univ Minn, BME, 77; Purdue Univ, MS, 84, PhD(mech eng), 88. *Prof Exp:* US Naval officer, Nuclear Submarine Propulsion Prog, 77-82; assoc engr, MPR Assocs, Inc, 83-85. *Concurrent Pos:* Presidential fac fel, White House/NSF, 92-97. *Mem:* Am Soc Mech Engrs; Am Inst Aeronaut & Astronaut; Am Soc Mfg Engrs; Soc Plastics Engrs; AAAS. *Res:* Novel methods for production of composite materials and polymer blends; nonlinear dynamical effects in thermal and fluidic systems; explore areas where important advances can be made of relevance to industry. *Mailing Add:* 2560 Scenic Circle Seneca SC 29672. *Fax:* 864-656-4435

**ZUMINO, BRUNO,** GENERAL RELATIVITY, PARTICLE PHYSICS. *Current Pos:* PROF PHYSICS, UNIV CALIF, BERKELEY, 81- *Personal Data:* b Rome, Italy, Apr 28, 23; div. *Educ:* Res assoc physics, New York Univ, 51-53, from asst prof to prof, 53-68. *Honors & Awards:* Dirac Medal, Int Centre Theoret Physics, Trieste, Italy, 87; Heineman Prize Math Physics, Am Phys Soc, 88; Max-Planck Medal, Ger Phys Soc, 89; Wigner Medal, Found Group Therapy, 92. *Prof Exp:* Sr researcher, Europ Orgn Nuclear Res, 68-81. *Mem:* Nat Acad Sci; fel Am Acad Arts & Sci; fel Am Phys Soc; Ital Phys Soc. *Res:* Relativity and gravitation; particle physics. *Mailing Add:* Dept Physics Univ Calif Berkeley CA 94720

**ZUMOFF, BARNETT,** MEDICINE, MEDICAL RESEARCH. *Current Pos:* ATTEND PHYSICIAN & CHIEF, DIV ENDOCRINOL & METAB, BETH ISRAEL MED CTR, 81-; PROF MED, ALBERT EINSTEIN COL MED, 77- *Personal Data:* b Brooklyn, NY, June 1, 26; m 51, Selma Silver; c Janine, Francine D & Linda I. *Educ:* Columbia Univ, AB, 45; Long Island Col Med, MD, 49. *Prof Exp:* Res fel, Sloan-Kettering Inst, 55-57, from asst to assoc, 57-61. *Concurrent Pos:* Asst dir, Clin Res Ctr, Montefiore Hosp, 61-76, dir, 76-81 & attend med & oncol, 61-82. *Mem:* Am Soc Clin Invest; Am Diabetes Asn; Aerospace Med Asn; Asn Mil Surg US; Am Fedn Clin Res; Endocrine Soc. *Res:* Human steroid metabolism; cholesterol metabolism and atherosclerosis; radioisotope tracer studies in man; hormones in breast and prostate cancer; obesity; reproductive biology; hormonal chronobiology; diabetes mellitus; psycho endocrinology; hormones in coronary artery disease. *Mailing Add:* Div Endocrinol & Metab Dept Med Beth Israel Med Ctr New York NY 10003. *Fax:* 212-420-2224; *E-Mail:* bzumoff@bethisraelny.org

**ZUMSTEG, FREDRICK C, JR,** EXPERIMENTAL SOLID STATE PHYSICS. *Current Pos:* RES PHYSICIST, E I DU PONT DE NEMOURS & CO, INC, 73- *Personal Data:* b Mansfield, Ohio, Apr 24, 43; m 86, Helen Metzger; c Eric. *Educ:* Univ Ill, BS, 64; Univ Rochester, PhD(physics), 72. *Prof Exp:* Res assoc, Cornell Univ, 71-73. *Mem:* Am Phys Soc. *Res:* Development and characterization of new electrooptic and nonlinear optic materials. *Mailing Add:* 2715 Silverside Rd Wilmington DE 19810

**ZUMWALT, GLEN W(ALLACE),** AERONAUTICAL ENGINEERING. *Current Pos:* DISTINGUISHED PROF AEROSPACE ENG, WICHITA STATE UNIV, 68- *Personal Data:* b Vinita, Okla, Apr 21, 26; m 52; c 5. *Educ:* Univ Tex, BS, 48 & 49, MS, 53; Univ Ill, PhD(mech & aeronaut eng), 59. *Prof Exp:* Instr eng mech, Univ Tex, 53-55; res assoc mech eng, Univ Ill, 55-59; from asst prof to prof aeronaut eng, Okla State Univ, 59-68. *Concurrent Pos:* Fel, Inst Aerophys, Univ Toronto, 62; consult var industs. *Mem:* Assoc fel Am Inst Aeronaut & Astronaut; Am Soc Eng Educ. *Res:* Gas dynamics; aerodynamics; wind tunnel test and design; aircraft icing protection. *Mailing Add:* 1702 S Georgetown St Wichita KS 67218

**ZUMWALT, LLOYD ROBERT,** PHYSICAL CHEMISTRY, NUCLEAR CHEMISTRY. *Current Pos:* prof, 67-80, EMER PROF NUCLEAR ENG, NC STATE UNIV, 80- *Personal Data:* b Richmond, Calif, Sept 4, 14; m 41, 60, Doreen Spiller; c Scott & Alicia. *Educ:* Univ Calif, BS, 36; Calif Inst Technol, PhD(phys chem), 39. *Prof Exp:* Asst, Calif Inst Technol, 36-39, Noyes fel, 39-41; res chemist, Shell Develop Co, 41-42; officer, Manhattan Proj, US Army, 42-46; sr chemist, Oak Ridge Nat Lab, 46-48; dir, Western Div, Tracerlab, Inc, 48-56; vpres, Nuclear Sci & Eng Corp, 56-57; res staff mem, Gen Atomic Div, Gen Dynamics Corp, 57-60; sr res adv, 60-67. *Concurrent Pos:* Consult, Gen Atomic Co, 67-79, Los Alamos Sci Lab & Brookhaven Nat Lab, 73-78, Oak Ridge Nat Lab, 81, US Nuclear Regulatory Comn, 82-84, EG&G, Idaho Nat Eng Lab, 90. *Mem:* Am Chem Soc; fel Am Nuclear Soc; Sigma Xi. *Res:* Fission product and tritium diffusion and sorption in materials; high temperature and nuclear reactor chemistry; effect of radiaiton on materials; nuclear fuel recycle; HTGR nuclear fuel. *Mailing Add:* 10 Dixie Trail Raleigh NC 27607

**ZUND, JOSEPH D(AVID),** GEOMETRY, GEODESY. *Current Pos:* assoc prof math sci, 70-71, PROF MATH & MATH SCI, NMEX STATE UNIV, 72- *Personal Data:* b Ft Worth, Tex, Apr 27, 39. *Educ:* Agr & Mech Col Tex, BA & MS, 61; Univ Tex, Austin, PhD(math), 64. *Prof Exp:* Res assoc, Southwest Ctr, Advan Studies, Tex, 64 & 65; from asst prof to assoc prof math, NC State Univ, 65-69; assoc prof, Va Polytech Inst, 69-70. *Concurrent Pos:* Res assoc, Inst Field Physics, Univ NC, Chapel Hill, 64-65; vis lectr, Dept Math, 65; vis prof, Cambridge Univ, 68-70. *Mem:* Tensor Soc; Am Meteorol Soc; Am Geophys Union; fel Royal Astron Soc; fel Int Asn Geodesy. *Res:* Differential and projective geometry; general relativity; electromagnetic theory; differential geodesy; history of science and technology. *Mailing Add:* Dept Math Sci NMex State Univ Las Cruces NM 88003. *Fax:* 505-646-1064; *E-Mail:* jzund@umsu.edu

**ZUNDE, PRANAS,** INFORMATION MEASURES, SYSTEMS THEORY & COMPUTER VISION. *Current Pos:* sr res scientist, 65-68, assoc prof info sci & indust eng, 68-72, PROF INFO SCI, GA INST TECHNOL, 72- *Personal Data:* b Kaunas, Lithuania, Nov 26, 23; US citizen; wid; c Alge, Audronis, Aurelia, Aidis & Gytis. *Educ:* Hannover Tech Univ, MS, 47; George Washington Univ, MS, 65; Ga Inst Technol, PhD(indust eng), 68. *Honors & Awards:* Lead Award, Soc Man Eng, 86. *Prof Exp:* Consult info systs, Europe, 47-61; syst analyst, Document Inc, Washington, DC, 61-63; proj mgr info systs, 63-64, dep head mgt systs, 64-65. *Concurrent Pos:* Consult, Document, Inc, 65-66, Lockheed-Ga Co, 66-67, Ga State Govt, 71 & Nat Inst Technol, Quito, Ecuador, 72; prin investr, HEW, 69-71 & NSF, 72-; Fulbright prof, Nat Acad Sci, Univ Vienna, Austria; vis prof, Univ Simon Bolivar, Caracas, Venezuela, 78, J Kepler Univ, Linz, Austria, 81 & Riso Nat Lab, Roskilde, Denmark, 83; consult, NY State Educ Dept, 93. *Mem:* Sigma Xi; Am Soc Info Sci; Semiotic Soc Am. *Res:* Design of information and communication systems; human factors in systems design; control and socioeconomic systems; operations research; systems theory; design of educational systems; foundations of information science. *Mailing Add:* Col Comput Ga Inst Technol 225 North Ave Atlanta GA 30332. *Fax:* 404-894-9846; *E-Mail:* zunde@gatech.edu

**ZUNIGA, MARTHA C,** IMMUNOLOGY. *Current Pos:* ASST PROF BIOL, UNIV CALIF, SANTA CRUZ, 90- *Personal Data:* b Lorado, Tex, Dec 28, 50. *Educ:* Univ Tex, Austin, BS, 71; Yale Univ, MS, 75, PhD(biol), 77. *Honors & Awards:* Presidential Investr Award, NSF. *Prof Exp:* Sr investr microbiol, Univ Tex, Austin, 80-86, asst prof, 86-90. *Mem:* Am Soc Cell Biol; Am Asn Immunol; Sigma Xi; Nat Inst Sci. *Res:* Immunology. *Mailing Add:* Dept Biol Linsheimer Lab Univ Calif Santa Cruz CA 95064

**ZUNKER, HEINZ OTTO HERMANN,** PATHOLOGY. *Current Pos:* ASSOC PATHOLOGIST, ST ELIZABETH HOSP, BEAUMONT, TEX, 86- *Personal Data:* b Berlin, Ger, May 27, 24; m 63; c 2. *Educ:* Free Univ Berlin, MD, 54; Am Bd Path, cert, 66. *Prof Exp:* From intern to resident internal med, Free Univ Berlin, 54-56; head pharmacol res, Pharmaceut Co, 57-59; res assoc pharmacol, Columbia Univ, 60-61, assoc path, Col Physicians & Surgeons, 65-68, asst prof, 68; chief path & dir labs, Deaconess Hosp, Evansville, Ind, 68-73; assoc prof path & dir clin path, Col Med, Univ S Fla, 74-75; chief pathologist & dir labs, Beaumont Med Surg Hosp, Beaumont, 75-82. *Concurrent Pos:* Vis fel path, Columbia-Presby Med Ctr, 62-65; asst attend pathologist, Presby Hosp & consult pathologist, Harlem Hosp, New York, 66-68; assoc prof allied health sci, Univ Evansville & Ind State Univ, Evansville, 72-73; consult, surg path. *Mem:* Col Am Path; Am Soc Clin Path; NY Acad Sci. *Res:* Pharmacology; experimental pathology; electron microscopy; clinical chemistry. *Mailing Add:* 6840 Hialeah St Beaumont TX 77706-5447

**ZUO, FULIN,** SOLID STATE PHYSICS, SUPERCONDUCTORS. *Current Pos:* asst prof, 90-96, ASSOC PROF, DEPT PHYSICS, UNIV MIAMI, 96- *Personal Data:* b Yang Zhong, China, Dec 5, 62. *Educ:* Nanjing Inst Technol, BS, 83; Ohio State Univ, MS, 85, PhD(condensed matter physics), 88. *Prof Exp:* Postdoctoral, Univ Ill, Urbana-Champaign, 88-90. *Mem:* Am Phys Soc. *Res:* Magnetic and transport properties in superconductor, including oxide and organic superconductors. *Mailing Add:* Dept Physics Univ Miami Coral Gables FL 33146. *Fax:* 305-284-4222; *E-Mail:* zuo@physics.miami.edu

**ZUO, YUEGANG,** BIOGEOCHEMISTRY, PHOTOCHEMISTRY. *Current Pos:* res fel, Drinking Water Res Ctr, 92-93, RES SCIENTIST, SE ENVIRON RES PROG, FLA INT UNIV, 93- *Personal Data:* b Hubei, China, Sept 17, 58; m, Yiwei Deng; c RuiXiao & Ruiting. *Educ:* Wuhan Univ, BS, 82; Inst Environ Chem Acad Sinica, MS, 84; Swiss Fed Inst Technol, PhD(environ sci), 92. *Prof Exp:* Res asst, Inst Environ Chem, Acad Sinica, Beijing, 84-86, res assoc/head eco-effect lab, Res Ctr Eco-Environ Sci, 86-88; res asst, Swiss Fed Inst Water Resources & Pollution Control, 88-92. *Mem:* AAAS; Am Chem Soc; Am Geophys Union; Europ Photochem Asn; Chinese Chem Soc; Chinese Environ Sci Soc. *Res:* Environmental chemistry with emphasis on the production of photooxidants, decomposition of organic pollutants in atmospheric liquids and the formation of acid rain; photochemical and microbiological cycling of dissolved organic substances in the oceans; marine chemistry. *Mailing Add:* SE Environ Res Prog VH-Rm 317 Fla Int Univ Miami FL 33199. *Fax:* 305-348-3894; *E-Mail:* zuoy@servax.fiu.edu

**ZUPERKU, EDWARD JOHN,** BREATHING CONTROL, RESPIRATORY NEURONS. *Current Pos:* From asst prof to assoc prof, 74-89, PROF BIOMED ENG, MED COL WIS, 89-; BIOMED ENGR, VET ADMIN MED CTR, MILWAUKEE, 75- *Personal Data:* b Chicago, Ill, Sept 14, 42; m 75, Brenda Seale; c David, Christina, Daniel & James. *Educ:* Marquette Univ, BEE, 65, MS, 67, PhD(biomed eng), 70. *Concurrent Pos:* Prin investr, Vet Admin Med Ctr, 78- *Mem:* Am Physiol Asn; Am Thoracic Soc; Am Heart Asn; Neurosci Soc; Biomed Eng Soc. *Res:* Mathematical modeling of neural circuits; processing of afferent input patterns by the central nervous system; neurotransmitters of respiratory neurons. *Mailing Add:* Res Serv 151 Zablocki Vet Admin Med Ctr Milwaukee WI 53295. *Fax:* 414-645-6550

**ZURAWSKI, VINCENT RICHARD, JR,** BIOCHEMISTRY, IMMUNOLOGY. *Current Pos:* PRES & CHIEF EXEC OFFICER, APOLLON, INC, 92- *Personal Data:* b Irvington, NJ, June 10, 46; m 68, Mary R Stanziola; c Daniel V & John A. *Educ:* Montclair State Col, BA, 68; Purdue Univ, PhD(chem), 73. *Prof Exp:* Res assoc biochem, Purdue Univ, 74; res fel med virol, immunochem & cell biol, Harvard Med Sch, 75-78, instr path, 78-79; co-founder & vpres, Centocor 79-82, sr vpres, 82-83, exec vpres, 83-87, tech dir, 79-82, corp secy, 81-86, sr vpres & chief sci officer, 87-93. *Concurrent Pos:* Res fel med virol, immunochem & cell biol, Cardiac Biochem Lab, Mass Gen Hosp, Boston, 75-78, res fel, Cell & Molecular Res Lab, 78-79, NIH, 76-78 & Med Found, 78-79; lectr, Dept Obstet & Gynec, Harvard Med Sch, 85-; prin investr, Nat Cancer Inst res grant; NIH grant, 85-90; mem, Adv Comt Develop Res Cancer Diag, Nat Cancer Inst, 88-89, Biotech Adv Comt, Philadelphia Tech Coun, 92-; mem bd dirs, Pa Biotech Asn, 93- *Mem:* AAAS; Am Chem Soc; Am Soc Microbiol; Am Asn Immunologists; Tissue Cult Asn; Soc Nuclear Med; Am Asn Cancer Res; Am Soc Biochem & Molecular Biol. *Res:* Immunochemical and immunobiological research aimed at producing monoclonal antibodies of predetermined specificity both in vivo and in vitro for structural studies; diagnostic and therapeutic applications and applications to cellular immunology; cell biological and molecular genetics studies with particular emphasis on problems associated with ovarian cancer. *Mailing Add:* Apollon One Great Valley Pkwy Malvern PA 19355. *Fax:* 610-647-9732

**ZUREK, WOJCIECH HUBERT,** COSMOLOGY & GALAXY FORMATION, PHYSICS OF INFORMATION & QUANTUM MEASUREMENTS. *Current Pos:* J R Oppenheimer fel, 84-87, staff mem, 87-90, THEORET ASTROPHYS GROUP LEADER, LOS ALAMOS NAT LAB, 91- *Personal Data:* b Bielsko-Biala, Silesia, Poland, Dec 19, 51; US citizen; m 77, Anna K Debogorska; c Agnes A & Maximilian F. *Educ:* S Staszic Tech Univ, Poland, MSc, 74; Univ Tex, Austin, PhD(physics), 79. *Prof Exp:* Res fel, Dept Physics, Univ Tex, Austin, 79-81; Tolman res fel, Calif Inst Technol, 81-83. *Concurrent Pos:* Vis fel, Astrophys Univ Oxford, 81; assoc prof, Santa Fe Inst, 88- *Res:* Decoherence and the transition from quantum to classical; cosmology and galaxy formation; physics of information, exitropy and complexity; Maxwellian demonology; relativistic astrophysics. *Mailing Add:* T-6 B288 LANL Box 1663 Los Alamos NM 87545

**ZURIER, ROBERT B,** CELL BIOLOGY. *Current Pos:* PROF MED & CHIEF RHEUMATOLOGY SECT, SCH MED, UNIV PA, 80- *Personal Data:* b Passaic, NJ, Feb 19, 34; m 62; c 1. *Educ:* Rutgers Univ, BS, 55; Southwestern Med Sch, Univ Tex, MD, 62; Univ Pa, MA, 82. *Prof Exp:* From asst prof to prof, Sch Med, Univ Conn, 73-80. *Concurrent Pos:* Guggenheim Found fel, 86-87. *Mem:* Am Soc Clin Invest; Am Rheumatism Asn; Am Asn Immunologists; AAAS. *Res:* Role of prostaglandins and fatty acids in immune responses and inflammatory reactions. *Mailing Add:* Div Rheumatology Univ Mass Med Ctr 55 Lake Ave N Worcester MA 01655-0335. *Fax:* 508-856-1983

**ZUR LOYE, HANS-CONRAD,** CHEMISTRY. *Current Pos:* ASSOC PROF, DEPT CHEM, MASS INST TECHNOL, 89- *Educ:* Brown Univ, BSc, 83; Univ Calif, Berkeley, PhD(chem), 88. *Prof Exp:* Postdoctoral fel, Dept Chem, Northwestern Univ, Evanston, Ill, 88-89. *Concurrent Pos:* Exxon fac fel, Am Chem Soc, 94. *Mailing Add:* Dept Chem Mass Inst Technol 77 Massachusetts Ave Cambridge MA 02139-4307

**ZURMUHLE, ROBERT W,** NUCLEAR PHYSICS. *Current Pos:* Res assoc, 61-63, from asst prof to assoc prof, 63-76, PROF PHYSICS, UNIV PA, 76- *Personal Data:* b Lucerne, Switz, Nov 27, 33; US citizen. *Educ:* Univ Zurich, PhD(physics), 60. *Mem:* Fel Am Phys Soc. *Res:* Nuclear structure and nuclear reactions. *Mailing Add:* Dept Physics Univ Pa Philadelphia PA 19104. *Fax:* 215-898-2010

**ZUSMAN, FRED SELWYN,** MATHEMATICS. *Current Pos:* EXEC SCIENTIST & DIR COMPUT SCI, ARC PSG, INC, 72- *Personal Data:* b Boston, Mass, July 24, 31; m 54; c 2. *Educ:* Harvard Univ, AB, 52, MA, 55. *Prof Exp:* Analyst, Nat Security Agency, 52-54; sr mathematician appl physics lab, Johns Hopkins Univ, 55-61; sr scientist, Opers Res Inc, 62; dir comput lab, Nat Biomed Res Found, 63; dir comput ctr, Opers Res Inc, 63-67, sr scientist, 67-69; vpres, Sci Mgt Systs, Inc, 69-72. *Concurrent Pos:* Lectr, Sch Hyg & Pub Health, Johns Hopkins Univ, 60-63. *Mem:* Asn Comput Mach; Opers Res Soc Am. *Res:* Operations research; computer technology; system simulation; computer sciences. *Mailing Add:* 200 E Indian Spring Dr Silver Spring MD 20901

**ZUSMAN, JACK,** PSYCHIATRY, PUBLIC HEALTH. *Current Pos:* RETIRED. *Personal Data:* b Brooklyn, NY, Jan 6, 34; m 55; c 4. *Educ:* Columbia Univ, AB, 55, MPH, 66; Ind Univ, MA, 56; Albert Einstein Col Med, MD, 60. *Prof Exp:* Intern, USPHS Hosp, New Orleans, La, 60-61; epidemic intel serv officer, Communicable Dis Ctr, 61-62, ment health career develop officer, NIMH, 62-66, staff psychiatrist, Epidemiol Studies Br, 66-67, chief, Ctr Epidemiol Studies, 67-68; assoc prof psychiat, State Univ NY, Buffalo, 68-71, dir div community psychiat, 69-74, prof, 71-75; prof psychiat,

Univ Southern Calif, 75- *Concurrent Pos:* Trainee community psychiat, Columbia Univ, 64-66; adj prof law & psychiat, 74-75 & Univ Southern Calif, 79- *Mem:* AMA; Am Acad Psychiat & Law; Am Psychiat Asn. *Res:* Social factors which influence the course of mental illness and methods of their control; interaction of law and psychiatry; methods of organizing and providing medical care. *Mailing Add:* Dept Psychiat Univ SFla Col Med 13301 N 30th St Tampa FL 33612-3807

**ZUSPAN, FREDERICK PAUL,** OBSTETRICS & GYNECOLOGY. *Current Pos:* chmn, Dept Obstet & Gynec, 74-87, PROF & R L MEILING CHAIR OBSTET & GYNEC, OHIO STATE UNIV, 88- *Personal Data:* b Richwood, Ohio, Jan 20, 22; m 43; c 3. *Educ:* Ohio State Univ, BA, 47, MD, 51. *Prof Exp:* Chief, Dept Obstet & Gynec, McDowell Mem Hosp, Ky, 56-58, chief clin serv, 57-58; asst prof obstet & gynec, Sch Med, Western Res Univ, 59-60; prof & chmn dept, Med Col Ga, 60-66; Joseph Bolivar DeLee prof & chmn dept, Univ Chicago, 66-74. *Concurrent Pos:* Oglebay fel obstet & gynec, Sch Med, Western Res Univ, 58-60; assoc examr & dir, Am Bd Obstet & Gynec, 65-80; gynecologist-in-chief, Chicago Lying-In Hosp, 66-74; pres, Barren Found, 74-76; founding ed, J Reprod Med; ed, Am J Obstet & Gynec & Current Concepts in Obstet & Gynec; consult ed, Acta Cytologica, Exerpta Medica, Obstet & Gynec Surv, Hypertension, J Obstet & Gynec (Mex) & J Reprod Med. *Res:* Human reproductive physiology; epinephrine and norephinephrine in the obstetric patient; maternal-fetal medicine. *Mailing Add:* Ohio State Univ Hosp 1654 Upham Dr Columbus OH 43210-1250

**ZUSPAN, G WILLIAM,** METALLURGICAL ENGINEERING. *Current Pos:* RETIRED. *Personal Data:* b Richwood, Ohio, Mar 24, 26; m 48; c 5. *Educ:* Ohio State Univ, BMetE & MS, 51. *Prof Exp:* Plant metallurgist, E I du Pont de Nemours & Co, 51-53; res metallurgist, Battelle Mem Inst, 53-54; asst prof metall eng, Drexel Univ, 54-67, assoc prof eng, 67, dean freshman, 67-80, asst vpres student affairs, 72-91. *Mem:* Am Soc Metals; Am Soc Eng Educ; Nat Asn Corrosion Engrs. *Res:* Chemical metallurgy and corrosion. *Mailing Add:* 13559 Calderon Rd San Diego CA 92129

**ZUSSMAN, MELVIN PAUL,** POLYMER CHEMISTRY. *Current Pos:* RES CHEMIST, EXP STA, E I DU PONT DE NEMOURS & CO, 87- *Personal Data:* b Boston, Mass Aug 6, 56; m 80; c 2. *Educ:* Haverford Col, BA, 78; Carnegie-Mellon Univ, PhD(chem), 82. *Prof Exp:* Res chemist, US Steel Res Ctr, 82-83; sr engr, Res & Develop Labs, Westinghouse Elec Corp, 84-87. *Concurrent Pos:* Sr lectr, chem dept, Carnegie-Mellon Univ, 84. *Mem:* Am Chem Soc; AAAS; Sigma Xi. *Res:* Development of new or modified polymers for electronics applications; effects of high energy particles on polymeric materials; preparation and characterization of ordered organic films. *Mailing Add:* 2627 Epping Rd Wilmington DE 19810-1166

**ZUSY, DENNIS,** ECOLOGY, PHILOSOPHY OF SCIENCE. *Current Pos:* PROF PHILOS & RELIG, AQUINAS INST THEOL, 67- *Personal Data:* b Milwaukee, Wis, Dec 21, 28. *Educ:* Aquinas Inst, MA, 52 & 56; Northwestern Univ, MS, 64, PhD(biol), 67. *Prof Exp:* Asst prof philos, St Xavier Col, Ill, 56-62; from asst prof to prof biol, Clarke Col, 71-81. *Concurrent Pos:* Vis asst prof biol, Concordia Teachers Col, Ill, 67-71. *Mem:* Sigma Xi. *Res:* Biological rhythms; freshwater ecology; philosophical implications and history of scientific concepts. *Mailing Add:* St Pius Priory 1909 S Ashland Ave Chicago IL 60608-2994

**ZUXON, SUN,** PHYSICS. *Current Pos:* Res asst & group leader, China Inst Atomic Energy, 65-78, assoc prof & sect leader, 78-82, prof, 86, PRES, CHINA INST ATOMIC ENERGY, 85- *Personal Data:* b Wuhan, China, Nov 15, 37; wid; c Qian. *Educ:* Tsing Hua Univ, BS, 61, PhD, 65. *Concurrent Pos:* Vis scientist, Dept Physics, Munich Univ, 78-80, Los Alamos Nat Lab, 82-83; ed-in-chief, Chinese J Sci & Technol Atomic Energy, 87-, Chinese J Nuclear Physics, 88- *Mem:* Chinese Nuclear Soc; Chinese Phys Soc; Chinese Nuclear Physics Soc (vpres, pres 87-). *Res:* Contributed articles on body reactions, low energy polarization reactions and high energy polarization reactions; development of first on-line particle identification and multi-parameter data acquisition system in China; discovery of low-energy quasi-free scattering; measurement of the longitudinal components of spin-rotation parameters of p-d for the first time. *Mailing Add:* China Inst Atomic Energy PO Box 275 Beijing 102413 China

**ZUZACK, JOHN W,** ORGANIC CHEMISTRY. *Current Pos:* from asst prof to assoc prof, 66-89, PROF MED CHEM, ST LOUIS COL PHARM, 90- *Personal Data:* b St Louis, Mo, Sept 24, 38; m 62; c 3. *Educ:* St Louis Univ, BS, 61, MS, 64, PhD(org chem), 67. *Prof Exp:* Lab instr freshman & org chem, St Louis Univ, 61-65, res asst med chem, 65-66. *Mem:* Am Chem Soc. *Res:* Leukemia chemotherapy; structure activity relationships in rickettsiostatic pyrrolidine analgesic agents and the diels alder reaction. *Mailing Add:* Dept Med Chem St Louis Col Pharm 4588 Parkview Pl St Louis MO 63110-1089

**ZUZOLO, RALPH C,** CELL PHYSIOLOGY, CELLULAR MICROSURGERY & MICROINJECTION. *Current Pos:* supvr, Dept Biol, Sch Gen Studies, City Col New York, 68-92, instr, Robert Chambers Lab Cellular Microsurg, 74-80, assoc prof biol, 75-90, CO-DIR, ROBERT CHAMBERS LAB, SCH GEN STUDIES, CITY COL NEW YORK, 80-, PROF, 90-, CHMN MASTER PROG, 93-, DEP CHMN, DEPT BIOL, 96- *Personal Data:* b Italy, Sept 5, 29; US citizen; m 72, Betty Ann Fong. *Educ:* NY Univ, BA, 56, MS, 60, PhD(biol), 65. *Prof Exp:* Res fel, Dept Path Lab, Univ Tex, 66-67; res scientist, Guggenheim Inst Dent Res, NY Univ, 78-80. *Concurrent Pos:* Grants, NASA, NY Univ, 66, Biomed Support, City Col New York, 71, Ellis Phillips Found, 81 & Olympus Corp Am, 83, 85 & 96; consult cellular microsurg & microinjection, 72-; from adj asst prof to adj assoc prof, NY Univ, 74-80; vis scientist, Boyce Thompson Inst Plant Res, 77-78; dir Course & Standings, SGS, City Col New York, 84-92. *Mem:* AAAS; Am Inst Physics; Soc Appl Spectros; Sigma Xi; NY Acad Sci; Soc In Vitro Biol. *Res:* Microsurgery, the application of the laser as a microsurgical tool and the effect of lasers irradiation on cells; effect of chemical carcinogens and bisulfite on nucleic acid in living cells; the effect and detection of insect nuclear polyhedrosis virus after microinjection into early vertebrate embryos; design and construction of instruments for cellular microsurgery and microinjection; development of techniques and methods for single cell manipulation and analysis; image analysis as applied to protozoa; cellular micromanipulation and microinjection; culturing and evaluation of abnormal giant Amoeba Protens. *Mailing Add:* 131 Valentine St Mt Vernon NY 10550. *Fax:* 212-650-8585; *E-Mail:* zuzolo@scisun.sci.ccny

**ZVAIFLER, NATHAN J,** MEDICINE, IMMUNOLOGY. *Current Pos:* PROF RHEUMAT, UNIV CALIF, SAN DIEGO, 70- *Personal Data:* b Newark, NJ, Nov 26, 27; m 52, 83; c 4. *Educ:* Haverford Col, BS, 48; Jefferson Med Col, MD, 52. *Prof Exp:* Resident med, Univ Mich, 55-58, instr, Med Sch, 58-59; from instr to prof, Georgetown Univ, 60-70. *Concurrent Pos:* NIH fel arthritis, Univ Mich, 58-60; Macy Found Scholar, 76-77; vis prof, Rockefeller Univ, 83- *Res:* Arthritis. *Mailing Add:* Dept Med 8417 Univ Calif San Diego Med Ctr 9500 Gilman Dr La Jolla CA 92093-0664. *Fax:* 619-297-8204

**ZVEJNIEKS, ANDREJS,** ORGANIC CHEMISTRY. *Current Pos:* RETIRED. *Personal Data:* b Rauna, Latvia, Jan 6, 22; m 51. *Educ:* Latvia Univ, BS, 43, MS, 44; Royal Inst Technol, Sweden, PhD, 55. *Prof Exp:* Res engr, Liljeholmens Stearinfabriks, AB, Sweden, 45-48, sect leader, 48-56; qual control supvr, Conn Adamant Plaster Co, 56; tech adv to plant mgr, Chem Div, Gen Mills, Inc, 57-58, tech dir, Petrol Chem Dept, 58-60, dir appln res, 60-62, sr scientist, 62; pres, AZ Prod, Inc, Fla, 62-72; pres & chief exec officer, AZS Corp, 72-84. *Concurrent Pos:* Mem, Hwy Res Bd, Nat Acad Sci-Nat Res Coun, 59- *Mem:* Am Chem Soc. *Res:* Organic ammonium compounds; ore flotation reagents; petroleum chemicals. *Mailing Add:* 2337 Christopher Walk Atlanta GA 30327

**ZVENGROWSKI, PETER DANIEL,** MATHEMATICS. *Current Pos:* from asst prof to assoc prof 70-85, chmn div pure math, 72-74, PROF MATH, UNIV CALGARY, 85- *Personal Data:* b New York, NY, Sept 8, 39; m 84; c 2. *Educ:* Rensselaer Polytech Inst, BS, 59; Univ Chicago, MS, 60, PhD(math), 65. *Prof Exp:* Asst prof math, Univ Ill, Urbana, 64-70. *Mem:* Can Math Soc. *Res:* Algebraic topology and homotopy theory; G-invariant homotopy theory; span of differentiable manifolds, in particular flag manifolds, Grassmann manifolds, projective Stiefel manifolds; applications in quantum field theory. *Mailing Add:* Dept Math & Statist Univ Calgary Calgary AB T2N 1N4 Can. *E-Mail:* zvengrow@acs.ucalgary.ca

**ZVONAR, ZORAN,** WIRELESS COMMUNICATIONS, MULTIUSER DETECTION. *Current Pos:* SYST DESIGN ENGR, COMMUN DIV, ANALOG DEVICES INC, 94- *Personal Data:* b Belgrade, Yugoslavia, Apr 5, 62; m 91, Milica Stojanovic; c Ivan & Vanya. *Educ:* Univ Belgrade, dipl, 86, MSEE, 89; Northeastern Univ, PhD(elec eng), 93. *Prof Exp:* Postdoctoral res engr, Woods Hole Oceanog Inst, 93-94. *Concurrent Pos:* Adj prof, Northeastern Univ, 95- *Mem:* Inst Elec & Electronics Engrs. *Res:* Implementation of wireless communications systems; multiuser detection in fading channels; wireless multiple-access; radio reception; radio receiver design. *Mailing Add:* Commun Div Analog Devices Inc 804 Woburn St Wilmington MA 02118. *Fax:* 781-937-1051; *E-Mail:* zoran.zvonar@analog.com

**ZWAAN, JOHAN THOMAS,** PEDIATRIC OPHTHALMOLOGY, HUMAN EMBRYOLOGY. *Current Pos:* PROF OPHTHAL, PEDIAT & CELLULAR STRUCTURAL BIOL, UNIV TEX HEALTH SCI CTR, 89- *Personal Data:* b Gorinchem, Neth, Sept 28, 34; m 60, 89; c 4. *Educ:* Univ Amsterdam, MedDrs, 60, Dr(embryol), 63. *Prof Exp:* From asst anat to head asst, Lab Anat & Embryol, Univ Amsterdam, 58-63; fel pediat, Sch Med, Johns Hopkins Univ, 63-64; from asst prof to assoc prof, Sch Med, Univ Va, 64-71; assoc prof anat, Harvard Med Sch, 71-78, from asst prof to assoc prof ophthal, 78-89. *Concurrent Pos:* Lectr, Acad Phys Educ, Amsterdam, 62-63; res assoc ophthal, Children's Hosp Med Ctr, Boston, 71-75; assoc prof anat & resident ophthal, Albany Med Col, 75-78; asst ophthal, Mass Eye & Ear Infirmary, 78-83, dir pediat & ocular motility serv, 81-89, asst surg, 83-89; res assoc, Mass Inst Technol, 81-87. *Mem:* AAAS; Soc Develop Biol; Asn Res Vision & Ophthal; Am Acad Ophthal. *Res:* Chemical and morphological changes in differentiation of vertebrate cells (model system eye lens); developmental genetics; ophthalmic genetics; teratology; normal and abnormal development of the visual system. *Mailing Add:* Univ Tex Health Sci Ctr 7703 Floyd Curl Dr San Antonio TX 78284-6230. *Fax:* 210-567-8413

**ZWADYK, PETER, JR,** MICROBIOLOGY. *Current Pos:* asst prof path, 71-75, asst prof microbiol, 71-76, ASSOC PROF PATH, DUKE UNIV, 75-, ASSOC PROF MICROBIOL, 76-; CHIEF MICROBIOL, VET ADMIN HOSP, DURHAM, 71- *Personal Data:* b Kansas City, Kans, Apr 3, 41; m 63; c 4. *Educ:* Univ Kans, BS, 62; Univ Iowa, MS, 66, PhD(microbiol), 71. *Prof Exp:* Microbiologist, Sci Assocs, 62-63; scientist microbiol, Mead Johnson & Co, 66-69. *Mem:* Am Soc Microbiol; Sigma Xi; Southeastern Asn Clin Microbiol; Am Acad Microbiol. *Res:* DNA probes; antibiotics; general clinical microbiology. *Mailing Add:* Dept Path Duke Univ Sch Med Durham NC 27710-7599

**ZWAIN, ISMAIL HASSAN,** MOLECULAR ENDOCRINOLOGY, REPRODUCTIVE PHYSIOLOGY. *Current Pos:* MOLECULAR ENDOCRINOLOGIST, SCH MED, UNIV CALIF, SAN DIEGO, 94- *Personal Data:* b Kufa, Iraq, July 1, 51. *Educ:* Univ Baghdad, Iraq, DVM, 73; Univ Bordeaux, France, MSc, 80; Univ Caen, France, PhD(reproductive endocrinol), 83, DSc(reproductive biol), 88. *Prof Exp:* Reproductive endocrinologist, Univ Baghdad, 73-79; fel, Univ Caen, France, 83-87; res scientist, Pop Coun, Ctr Biomed Res, 88-94. *Mem:* AAAS; Am Soc Andrology; Endocrine Soc; Soc Study Reproduction; Am Fertil Soc; Am Soc Cell Biol. *Res:* Investigation of endocrine and paracrine regulation of testicular function; cell-cell interactions within testis; determine mechanism of cell death (apoptosis) in mammalian. *Mailing Add:* Dept Reproductive Med Sch Med Univ Calif San Diego BSB-5045 9500 Gilman Dr La Jolla CA 92093-0633

**ZWANZIG, FRANCES RYDER,** CHEMISTRY. *Current Pos:* RETIRED. *Personal Data:* b South Amboy, NJ, Oct 22, 29; m 53, Robert W; c Elizabeth Z & Carl P. *Educ:* Columbia Univ, BA, 51; Yale Univ, MS, 53, PhD(chem), 56. *Prof Exp:* Res asst physiol chem, Sch Med, Johns Hopkins Univ, 55-58; asst ed, Rev Mod Physics, Am Phys Soc, Washington, DC, 69-73; asst ed, Transp Res Bd, Nat Acad Sci Washington DC, 77-80, staff officer, Off Chem & Chem Technol, 79-81, assoc ed proc, 80-83, managing ed proc, 83-96. *Mem:* Am Chem Soc; Coun Biol Ed. *Mailing Add:* 5314 Sangamore Rd Bethesda MD 20816

**ZWANZIG, ROBERT WALTER,** CHEMICAL PHYSICS. *Current Pos:* RESEARCHER BIOPHYS, NIH, 88- *Personal Data:* b Brooklyn, NY, Apr 9, 28; m 53; c 2. *Educ:* Polytech Inst Brooklyn, BS, 48; Univ Southern Calif, MS, 50; Calif Inst Technol, PhD(chem), 52. *Honors & Awards:* Peter Debye Award Phys Chem, Am Chem Soc, 76, Irving Langmuir Award, Chem Physics, 85, Joel H Hildebrand Award, 94. *Prof Exp:* Res fel theoret chem, Yale Univ, 51-54; asst prof chem, Johns Hopkins Univ, 54-58; phys chemist, Nat Bur Stand, 58-66; res prof, Inst Phys Sci & Technol, Univ Md, Col Park, 66-79, distinguished prof, 79-88. *Concurrent Pos:* Sherman Fairchild scholar, Calif Inst Technol, 74-75; Fogarty scholar, residences, NIH, 87-88. *Mem:* Nat Acad Sci; Am Chem Soc; Am Phys Soc; Am Acad Arts & Sci. *Res:* Theoretical chemical physics; statistical mechanics; theory of liquids, gases and biophysics. *Mailing Add:* 5314 Sangamore Rd Bethesda MD 20816-2355. *Fax:* 301-496-0825

**ZWANZIGER, DANIEL,** THEORETICAL PHYSICS. *Current Pos:* vis scientist, 65-67, assoc prof, 67-70, PROF PHYSICS, NY UNIV, 70- *Personal Data:* b New York, NY, May 20, 35; m 77, Dana Levor; c Jenny & Emily. *Educ:* Columbia Univ, BA, 55, PhD(physics), 60. *Prof Exp:* NSF fel physics, Univ Calif, Berkeley, 60-61, lectr, 61-62; scientist, Univ Rome, 62-63; vis, Saclay Ctr Nuclear Studies, France, 63-65. *Concurrent Pos:* Assoc, Europ Ctr Nuclear Res, Switz, 80; vis prof, Ecole Normale Superieure, France, 81; vis mem, Inst Avan Study, 84. *Mem:* Am Phys Soc; Fedn Am Scientists. *Res:* Quantum field theory; mathematical physics; elementary particle physics. *Mailing Add:* Dept Physics NY Univ Grad Sch Arts & Sci 4 Washington Pl New York NY 10003. *E-Mail:* zwanzige@acf2.nyu.edu

**ZWART, JOHN W,** SOLID STATE PHYSICS. *Current Pos:* PROF PHYSICS, DORDT COL, 83- *Personal Data:* b Chicago, Ill, Aug 23, 55; m 75, Laurey Wyma; c Kathryn & Mark. *Educ:* Calvin Col, BA, 77; Mich State Univ, MS, 79, PhD(physics), 85. *Concurrent Pos:* Vis assoc prof physics, Calvin Col, 91-92. *Mem:* Am Phys Soc; Am Asn Physics Teachers; Am Sci Affil; Am Soc Eng Educ. *Res:* Science and physics education. *Mailing Add:* Dordt Col 498 Fourth Ave NE Sioux Center IA 51250. *E-Mail:* zwart@dordt.edu

**ZWARUN, ANDREW ALEXANDER,** MEDICAL DEVICE DEVELOPMENT, STERILIZATION. *Current Pos:* DIR RES, PROPPER MFG CO, 77- *Personal Data:* b Pidvolochyska, Ukraine, Feb 9, 43; US citizen; m 67; c 2. *Educ:* Ohio State Univ, BSc, 65, MSc, 67; Univ Ky, PhD(soil microbiol), 70. *Prof Exp:* Asst prof agron, Univ Md, Eastern Shore, 70-71; chief microbiologist, Johnston Labs, Inc, 71-74; res microbiologist, Betz Labs, Inc, 74-76. *Mem:* Am Soc Microbiol; Health Indust Mfg Asn; Sigma Xi. *Res:* Automation of microbial and biochemical procedures; trace metal toxicities; microbial activity in soils and water; industrial water treatment. *Mailing Add:* 10 Schoolhouse Lane Roslyn Heights NY 11577

**ZWASS, VLADIMIR,** MANAGEMENT INFORMATION SYSTEMS. *Current Pos:* from asst prof to assoc prof, 75-84, PROF COMPUT SCI, FAIRLEIGH DICKINSON UNIV, 84- *Personal Data:* b Lvov, USSR, Feb 3, 46; US citizen; m 77, Alicia Kogut; c Joshua. *Educ:* Moscow Inst Energetics, MS, 69; Columbia Univ, MPh & PhD(comput sci), 75. *Prof Exp:* Mem prof staff, Int Atomic Energy Agency, 70. *Concurrent Pos:* Consult, Metrop Life Ins Co, Diebold Group & Citicorp; NSF grant, 82-83; co-prin investr, USN, 85-86; ed-in-chief, J Mgt Info Systs, 84- *Mem:* Inst Elec & Electronic Engrs; Asn Comput Mach; Sigma Xi. *Res:* Management information systems; software engineering; operating systems; management information systems and computer science as scientific disciplines. *Mailing Add:* 19 Warewood Rd Saddle River NJ 07458

**ZWEBEN, CARL HENRY,** COMPOSITE MATERIALS & STRUCTURES, ELECTRONIC PACKAGING. *Current Pos:* ADVAN TECHNOL MGR, SPACE DIV, GEN ELEC, MARTIN MARIETTA CO, LOCKHEED MARTIN, 78- *Personal Data:* b Albany, NY. *Educ:* Cooper Union, BCE, 60; Columbia Univ, MS, 61; Polytech Inst, Brooklyn, PhD(appl mech), 66. *Honors & Awards:* Tech Brief Award, NASA, 72. *Prof Exp:* Res engr, Space Sci Lab, Gen Elec Co, 66-69; sr res engr, Jet Propulsion Lab, 69-70; prog mgr, Mat Sci Corp, 70-72; res assoc, E I du Pont de Nemours & Co, Inc, 72-78. *Concurrent Pos:* Consult, Nat Mat Adv Bd, Nat Acad Sci, 69 & 81-82 & Ctr Composite Mat, Univ Del, 78-; lectr, Univ Calif, Los Angeles, 73- & Univ Cambridge, Eng, 79-; consult, Metal Matrix Composites Info Anal Ctr, US Dept Defense, Congress Off Technol Assessment. *Mem:* Am Soc Testing & Mat; fel Am Soc Mech Engrs; Am Soc Civil Engrs; fel Soc Advan Mat & Process Eng; assoc Am Inst Aeronaut & Astronaut. *Res:* Properties and application of polymer, metal and ceramic matrix composite materials, including, design analysis, development, test methods, micromechanics, fatigue, fracture, impact, failure mechanics, material development structural test electronic packaging. *Mailing Add:* Lockheed Martin Missiles & Space-Valley Forge PO Box 8555 Philadelphia PA 19101

**ZWEBEN, STUART HARVEY,** SOFTWARE ENGINEERING. *Current Pos:* from asst prof to assoc prof, 74-92, actg chmn dept, 83-84, PROF COMPUT & INFO SCI, OHIO STATE UNIV, 92-, CHMN COMPUT & INFO SCI, 94- *Personal Data:* b New York, NY, Apr 21, 48; m 71, Rochelle Small; c Naomi. *Educ:* City Col New York, BS, 68; Purdue Univ, MS, 71, PhD(comput sci), 74. *Prof Exp:* Syst analyst comput sci, IBM Corp, 69-70; instr, Purdue Univ, 74. *Concurrent Pos:* Prin investr res grant, Ohio State Univ, 75, Dow Chem Co, 78-79, US Army Res Off, 80-83, NSF, 81-83, 88-90, 91-94 & 93-96, Dept Educ, 82-85, AT&T, 84, 86-88 & Appl Info Tech Res Ctr, 89-90; grant coordr grants, HEW, 77-79; secy-treas, Comput Sci Accred Bd, 86-87, vpres, 87-89, pres, 89-91; assoc ed, Inst Elec & Electronics Engrs Trans Software Eng, 90-; bd dirs, Comput Res Asn, 97-98. *Mem:* Asn Comput Mach (vpres, 92-94, pres, 94-96); Inst Elec & Electronics Engrs; Am Asn Univ Prof. *Res:* Software engineering; programming methodology; software testing; software reuse. *Mailing Add:* Dept Comput & Info Sci 2036 Neil Ave Mall Columbus OH 43210. *Fax:* 614-292-2911; *E-Mail:* zweben@cis.ohio-state.edu

**ZWEIBEL, ELLEN GOULD,** THEORETICAL ASTROPHYSICS. *Current Pos:* STAFF MEM SOLAR PHYSICS, HIGH ALTITUDE OBSERV, NAT CTR ATMOSPHERIC RES, 78- *Personal Data:* b New York, NY, Dec 20, 52. *Educ:* Univ Chicago, BA, 73; Princeton Univ, PhD(astrophys sci), 77. *Prof Exp:* Vis mem, Inst Advan Study, 77-78. *Mem:* Am Astron Soc. *Res:* Plasma astrophysics, especially cosmic rays and solar and interplanetary physics. *Mailing Add:* Joint Inst Lab Astrophys Univ Colo CB 440 Boulder CO 80309. *Fax:* 303-492-0642

**ZWEIDLER, ALFRED,** CHROMOSOMES, NUCLEAR PROTEINS. *Current Pos:* MEM, INST CANCER RES, 71- *Personal Data:* b Switz; m; c 3. *Educ:* Univ Zurich, PhD(cell biol), 66. *Concurrent Pos:* Adj assoc prof biochem, Univ Pa, 85- *Mem:* AAAS; Am Soc Cell Biol; Protein Soc; Swiss Genetic Soc; Sigma Xi. *Res:* chromosome structure and function. *Mailing Add:* 304 Ashbourne Rd Cheltenham PA 19012

**ZWEIFACH, BENJAMIN WILLIAM,** physiology, bioengineering; deceased, see previous edition for last biography

**ZWEIFEL, GEORGE,** ORGANIC CHEMISTRY. *Current Pos:* assoc prof chem, 63-72, PROF CHEM, UNIV CALIF, DAVIS, 72- *Personal Data:* b Rapperswil, Switz, Oct 2, 26; m 53; c 2. *Educ:* Swiss Fed Inst Technol, Dr sc tech, 55. *Prof Exp:* Res asst carbohydrate chem, Univ Edinburgh, 55-56; res fel, Univ Birmingham, 56-58; res assoc boron chem, Purdue Univ, 58-63. *Mem:* Am Chem Soc; Sigma Xi. *Res:* Chemistry of natural products; utilization of organoboranes and organoalanes in organic syntheses. *Mailing Add:* Dept Chem Univ Calif Davis CA 95616

**ZWEIFEL, PAUL FREDERICK,** MATHEMATICAL PHYSICS, NUCLEAR SCIENCE. *Current Pos:* from prof to univ prof, 68-75, DISTINGUISHED UNIV PROF PHYSICS & NUCLEAR ENG, VA POLYTECH INST & STATE UNIV, 75- *Personal Data:* b New York, NY, June 21, 29; m 60, 67; c 4. *Educ:* Carnegie Inst Technol, BS, 48; Duke Univ, PhD, 54. *Honors & Awards:* E O Lawrence Award, 72. *Prof Exp:* Asst physicist, Chem Lab, Am Brake Shoe Co, 48; teacher, Malcom Gordon Sch, NY, 48-49; asst, Duke Univ, 50-52; res assoc, Knolls Atomic Power Lab, Gen Elec Co, 53-56; mgr theoret physics, 56-57; consult physicist, 57-58; assoc prof nuclear eng, Univ Mich, Ann Arbor, 58-60, prof, 60-68. *Concurrent Pos:* Fel, Duke Univ, 52-53; mem adv comt reactor physics, Atomic Energy Comn, 57-64; vis prof, Middle East Tech Univ, Ankara, 64-65; consult, indust orgns & govt labs; vis prof, Rockefeller Univ, 73, 74-75; fel, J S Guggenheim Mem Found, 74-75; vis prof, Univ Florence, 75, 81-83, 85, vis prof, Univ Ulm, WGer, 78, Univ Milan, 78; consult, Los Alamos Sci Lab, 75- & Nuclear Regulatory Comn, 76. *Mem:* Am Phys Soc; Am Nuclear Soc; Fedn Am Sci (secy, 57-58); Am Math Soc; Int Asn Math Physics. *Res:* Mathematical physics; neutron transport theory and nuclear energy; foundations of quantum mechanics. *Mailing Add:* Ctr Transp Theoret & Math Physics Va Polytech Inst & State Univ 212A Rodeson Hall Blacksburg VA 24061-0435. *Fax:* 540-231-7511

**ZWEIFEL, RICHARD GEORGE,** HERPETOLOGY. *Current Pos:* From asst cur to assoc cur, Am Mus Natural Hist, 54-65, chmn dept, 68-80, cur herpet, 65-89, EMER CUR, AM MUS NATURAL HIST, 89- *Personal Data:* b Los Angeles, Calif, Nov 5, 26; m 56, Frances Wimsatt; c Matthew, Kenneth & Ellen (James). *Educ:* Univ Calif, Los Angeles, BA, 50; Univ Calif, Berkeley, PhD(zool), 54. *Prof Exp:* Sci Attach, Gondwana, 74-75. *Mem:* Am Soc Ichthyol & Herpet; Soc Study Evolution; Soc Study Amphibians & Reptiles; Herpet League. *Res:* Ecology and systematics of amphibians and reptiles. *Mailing Add:* Box 354 Portal AZ 85632. *Fax:* 520-558-2243

**ZWEIFLER, ANDREW J,** INTERNAL MEDICINE. *Current Pos:* resident internal med, 57-60, Nat Heart & Lung Inst fel, 60-63, from instr to assoc prof, 60-72, PROF INTERNAL MED, MED CTR, UNIV MICH, ANN ARBOR, 72- *Personal Data:* b Newark, NJ, Feb 2, 30; m 54; c 5. *Educ:* Haverford Col, AB, 50; Jefferson Med Col, MD, 54. *Prof Exp:* Intern, Mt Sinai Hosp, NY, 54-55. *Concurrent Pos:* Vis prof, Meharry Med Col, 67-68; fel coun arteriosclerosis & coun thrombosis, Am Heart Asn. *Mem:* Am Fedn Clin Res. *Res:* Thrombosis; vascular disease; hypertension. *Mailing Add:* Div Hypertension Dept Int Med Univ Hosp 3918 Taubman Ctr Ann Arbor MI 48109-0356

**ZWEIG, FELIX,** ELECTRICAL ENGINEERING. *Current Pos:* From asst prof to assoc prof, 43-55, chmn dept, 61-66, PROF ENG & APPL SCI, YALE UNIV, 66- *Personal Data:* b Ft Wayne, Ind, Sept 25, 16; m 45; c 3. *Educ:* Yale Univ, BE, 38, PhD(elec eng), 41. *Concurrent Pos:* Res assoc, Mass Inst Technol, 46; consult, Gen Elec Co, 46-48, Gen Precision, Inc, 51-59, Burroughs Corp, 53, Bristol Co, 60-61 & Autonetics Div, NAm Aviation, Inc, 61. *Mem:* Inst Elec & Electronics Engrs; Sigma Xi. *Res:* Feedback control systems and inertial navigation. *Mailing Add:* 23283 Costa Del Sol Blvd Boca Raton FL 33433

**ZWEIG, GEORGE,** HIGH ENERGY PHYSICS, NEUROSCIENCES. *Current Pos:* FOUNDER & PRES, SIGNITION INC, 85- *Personal Data:* b Moscow, USSR, May 20, 37; US citizen; c 2. *Educ:* Univ Mich, BS, 59; Calif Inst Technol, PhD(physics), 63. *Prof Exp:* Nat Acad Sci-Nat Res Coun fel high energy physics, Europ Orgn Nuclear Res, Geneva, Switz, 63-64; from asst prof to prof physics, Calif Inst Technol, 64-83. *Concurrent Pos:* Sloan Found fel, 66-78; vis prof physics, Univ Wis-Madison, 67-68; MacArthur fel, 81; mem staff, Los Alamos Nat Lab, 81-85; vis assoc, Calif Inst Technol, 83- *Mem:* Nat Acad Sci; Am Phys Soc; Inst Elec & Electronics Engrs; AAAS; Am Math Soc; Asn Res Otolaryngol; Int Soc Optical Eng; Soc Indust & Appl Math. *Mailing Add:* Los Alamos Nat Lab MS B276 PO Box 1663 Los Alamos NM 87545-0001

**ZWEIG, GILBERT,** ENGINEERING PHYSICS, PHOTO-OPTICS. *Current Pos:* PRES, GLENBROOK TECHNOLOGIES, 83- *Personal Data:* b New York, NY, Apr 5, 38; c 3. *Educ:* NY Univ, BA & BME, 60, MS, 65. *Prof Exp:* Res staff mem, IBM, T J Watson Res Ctr, 61-63; supvr advan res, Pitney-Bowes, Inc, 63-73; vpres & cofounder, Imtex, Inc, 73-74; dep tech dir, TWT Labs Inc, Div Arkwright Inc, 74-78, dir tech bus develop, 78-81; vpres, MCI Optonix Inc, Subsid Mitsubishi Chem Industs Am, 81-83. *Mem:* Sigma Xi; Soc Photog Sci & Eng; Am Asn Physicists Med. *Res:* Imaging systems of non-silver classification; including electrophotographic diazo and radioluminescent image technologies; x-ray luminescent imaging. *Mailing Add:* 24 Stiles Ave Morris Plains NJ 07950

**ZWEIG, JOHN E,** MECHANICAL ENGINEERING. *Current Pos:* mech engr, Watervliet Arsenal, 60-64, chief, Exp Mech & Thermodyn Lab, 64-71, chief, Appl Math & Mech Div, 71-77, CHIEF DEVELOP ENGR, WATERVLIET ARSENAL, 77- *Personal Data:* b Poestenkill, NY, June 24, 36; m 66; c 3. *Educ:* Rensselaer Polytech Inst, BME, 57, MSE, 60, PhD(mech eng), 70. *Prof Exp:* Instr mech eng, Rensselaer Polytech Inst, 57-59. *Mem:* Am Soc Mech Engrs; Soc Exp Stress Anal; Sigma Xi. *Res:* Fluid dynamics; heat transfer; experimental mechanics. *Mailing Add:* 56 Zweig Way Poestenkill NY 12140-1704

**ZWEIMAN, BURTON,** INTERNAL MEDICINE. *Current Pos:* Assoc med, Univ Pa, Sch Med, 63-67, from asst prof to assoc prof, 67-75, co-chief allergy & immunol, 69-74, CHIEF, ALLERGY & IMMUNOL SECT, UNIV PA, SCH MED, 74-, PROF NEUROL, 80- *Personal Data:* b New York, NY, June 7, 31; m 62, Claire Traig; c Amy B & Diane S. *Educ:* Univ Pa, AB, 52, MD, 56. *Honors & Awards:* Lindback Award, 67. *Concurrent Pos:* Mem bd dirs, Am Bd Allergy & Immunol, co-chmn, 79-80; ed, J Allergy & Clin Immunol, 88-93. *Mem:* Am Acad Allergy (pres-elect, 93-94); Am Asn Immunol; Am Col Physicians; Am Fedn Clin Res. *Res:* Cellular inflammatory reactions in allergic diseases; immunologic mechanisms in neurologic disease and systemic lupus erythematosus. *Mailing Add:* Univ Pa Sch Med 36th & Hamilton Walk Philadelphia PA 19104

**ZWEMER, THOMAS J,** ORTHODONTICS. *Current Pos:* prof dent & assoc dean clin sci, Sch Dent, 66-84, VPRES ACAD AFFAIRS, MED COL GA, 84- *Personal Data:* b Mishawaka, Ind, Mar 23, 25; m 49; c 3. *Educ:* Univ Ill, DDS, 50; Northwestern Univ, MSD, 54. *Prof Exp:* Instr pedodont, Marquette Univ, 50-52, from asst prof to assoc prof oral rehab, 52-58; from asst prof to assoc prof orthod, Sch Dent, Loma Linda Univ, 58-66, chmn dept, 60-66. *Concurrent Pos:* Mem attend staff, Wood's Vet Admin Hosp, 54-56; consult, Cerebral Palsy Clin, 54-58; chief dent serv, Milwaukee Children's Hosp, 55-58. *Mem:* Am Asn Orthod; Am Dent Asn; Am Col Dent; Int Asn Dent Res; Sigma Xi. *Res:* Health care delivery systems; physical anthropology. *Mailing Add:* 3138 Natalie Circle Augusta GA 30909

**ZWERDLING, SOLOMON,** SOLID STATE PHYSICS, PHYSICAL CHEMISTRY. *Current Pos:* SUPVR ADVAN PHOTOVOLTAIC DEVELOP GROUP, JET PROPULSION LAB, 79- *Personal Data:* b New York, NY, Jan 31, 22; m 44; c 3. *Educ:* Drew Univ, BA, 43; Johns Hopkins Univ, MA, 44; Columbia Univ, MA, 47, PhD(chem), 52. *Prof Exp:* Instr chem, Johns Hopkins Univ, 43-44; asst prof naval sci & tactics, Columbia Univ, 46, asst chem, 46-49; sr res chemist, Lever Bros Co, 51-52; asst group leader & div staff physicist, Lincoln Lab, Mass Inst Technol, 52-63, staff physicist, Div Sponsored Res, Ctr Mat Sci & Eng, 63-68; res scientist, Douglas Advan Res Labs, Calif, 68-70, mgr res, Solid State Sci Dept,

McDonnell Douglas Res Labs, 70-74; dir solar energy prog, Argonne Nat Lab, 75-77; mgr res & develop, Northeast Solar Energy Ctr, 77-79. *Concurrent Pos:* Mem bd dir, A D Jones Optical Co Inc, Burlington, Mass. *Mem:* Fel Optical Soc Am; Int Solar Energy Soc; sr mem Inst Elec & Electronics Engrs; Am Phys Soc. *Res:* Infrared absorption of solids; infrared magneto-optical effects in semiconductors at liquid helium temperature; physics of semiconductor electronic energy band structure; excitons in semiconductors; far infrared spectroscopy and detectors; metal physics, strength and corrosion; general solar energy conversion; photovoltaic solar cells; chemical vapor deposition technology for thin film electronic devices. *Mailing Add:* 1339 Riviera Dr Pasadena CA 91107

**ZWICK, DAAN MARSH,** PHOTOGRAPHIC CHEMISTRY, PHYSICS. *Current Pos:* RETIRED. *Personal Data:* b New York, NY, July 28, 22; m 48; c 3. *Educ:* Univ Vt, BSChem, 43. *Honors & Awards:* Kalmus Gold Medal, Soc Motion Picture & TV Engrs, 72, Agfa-Gevaert Gold Medal, 75, Progress Medal, 81. *Prof Exp:* Instr physics, Univ Vt, 43-44; res chemist photog chem, Eastman Kodak Co Res Labs, 44-56, res assoc photog sci, 56-73, sr lab head color physics, 73-78, sr res assoc, 78-86. *Mem:* Fel Soc Motion Picture & TV Engrs; fel Soc Photog Scientists & Engrs; hon fel Brit Kinematograph Sound & TV Soc. *Res:* Physics of color photography, with emphasis on image structure and the psychophysics of imaging. *Mailing Add:* 15 Nunda Blvd Rochester NY 14610

**ZWICK, EARL J,** MATHEMATICS. *Current Pos:* assoc prof, 63-72, PROF MATH, IND STATE UNIV, TERRE HAUTE, 72- *Personal Data:* b Canton, Ohio, May 20, 31. *Educ:* Kent State Univ, BS, 53, MS, 57; Ohio State Univ, PhD(math ed), 64. *Prof Exp:* Teacher pub sch, Ohio, 53-61; instr math, Ohio State Univ, 62-63. *Mem:* Nat Coun Teachers Math. *Res:* Teaching methods. *Mailing Add:* 30 Chickadee Lane Terre Haute IN 47803

**ZWICKEL, FRED CHARLES,** WILDLIFE ECOLOGY, ORNITHOLOGY. *Current Pos:* from asst prof to prof, 67-85, EMER PROF ZOOL, UNIV ALTA, 85- *Personal Data:* b Seattle, Wash, Dec 18, 26; m 51, Ruth M Kocher; c Jeffry G, Heidi L & Wendy J. *Educ:* Wash State Univ, BSc, 50, MSc, 58; Univ BC, PhD(zool), 65. *Honors & Awards:* Roberts Award, Cooper Ornith Soc, 65. *Prof Exp:* Biologist, State Dept Game, Wash, 50-61; asst prof wildlife ecol, Ore State Univ, 66-67. *Concurrent Pos:* Nat Res Coun Can-NATO overseas res fel natural hist, Aberdeen Univ, 65-66; sabbatical study, Inst Appl Zool, Univ Hokkaido, Sapporo, Japan, 73-74, Wau Ecol Inst, Papua, New Guinea, 80-81 & Colo Div Wildlife, Ft Collins, 84. *Mem:* Am Ornith Union; Cooper Ornith Soc; Wildlife Soc; Am Soc Mammal. *Res:* Population ecology; general biology of gallinaceous birds and land mammals. *Mailing Add:* Dept Zool Univ Alta Box 81 Mansons Landing BC V0P 1K0 Can

**ZWICKER, BENJAMIN M G,** CHEMISTRY. *Current Pos:* RETIRED. *Personal Data:* b Pendleton, Ore, July 11, 15; m 42; c 2. *Educ:* Whitman Col, AB, 35; Univ Wash, MS, 38, PhD(phys chem), 40. *Prof Exp:* Res chemist, B F Goodrich Chem Co, 40-43, mgr, Akron Exp Sta, 43-50, dir new prod planning, 50-60, dir planning, 60-78, in-charge environ sci, 58-78; res assoc, Scripps Inst Oceanog, Univ Calif, San Diego, 79-85. *Concurrent Pos:* Mem tech & res comts, Off Rubber Reserve, 43-50; consult indust chem & toxicol, 78- *Mem:* Am Chem Soc; Soc Chem Indust; Am Inst Chem Eng; Asn Indust Hygienists Am. *Res:* Analytical, physical and organic chemistry; academic oceanography; geology; microscopy; polymer chemistry; industrial chemistry and economics; research, development and business management toxicology, biodegradation; industrial hygiene. *Mailing Add:* 5851 Tulane St San Diego CA 92122-3221

**ZWICKER, GARY M,** VETERINARY PATHOLOGY, TOXICOLOGIC PATHOLOGY. *Current Pos:* assoc scientist, Toxicol Dept, 87-91, res scientist, Dept Drug Safety, 91-93, RES ASSOC, DEPT HEALTH & ENVIRON SERVS, DOW CHEM CO, 94- *Personal Data:* b Lewiston, Idaho, June 20, 37; m 62, Geraldine J Newby; c Randy, Tom, Karen & Debra. *Educ:* Wash State Univ, BS, 61, DVM, 62; Purdue Univ, MS, 72, PhD(vet path), 73. *Prof Exp:* Vet pathologist & capt, US Army Chem Res & Develop Lab, Edgewood Arsenal, Md, 62-64; Haskell Lab Toxicol & Indust Med, E I Du Pont de Nemours, 64-67; sr res scientist vet pathologist, Squibb Inst Med Res, ER Squibb & Sons, 67-70; grad instr, Sch Vet Sci & Med, Purdue Univ, 70-72; Nat Cancer Inst spec fel, 72-74; sr res scientist, Biol Dept, Batelle-Pac Northwest Labs, Richland, Wash, 74-75, res assoc II, 75-78; mgr vet path & gen toxicol, Environ Health Ctr, Stauffer Chem Co, 78-85, prin pathologist, Cheesebrough-Pond's Inc, Stauffer Chem Group, 86-87. *Mem:* Am Col Vet Pathologists; Sigma Xi; Soc Toxicol; Soc Toxicol Pathologists. *Res:* Interdisciplinary preclinical studies designed toward development of safe effective new drugs for pulmonary, inflammatory, and neurologic disorders in humans; toxicologic-pathology mechanistic studies designed to better understand drug-effects. *Mailing Add:* 9447 Promontory Circle Indianapolis IN 46236. *Fax:* 317-873-7341

**ZWICKER, WALTER KARL,** SOLID STATE CHEMISTRY. *Current Pos:* PVT CONSULT, 91- *Personal Data:* b Vienna, Austria, Sept 5, 23; US citizen; m 56. *Educ:* Univ Vienna, PhD(mineral chem), 54. *Prof Exp:* Res fel chem, Harvard Univ, 54-55; res chemist, Metals Res Labs, Union Carbide Corp, 55-59, & Res Ctr, Union Carbide Nuclear Co, 59-64; sr res chemist, Thiokol Chem Corp, 64-65; sr proj leader, Philips Labs, NAm Philips Corp, 65-90. *Mem:* Emer mem Electro Chem Soc; fel Am Mineral Soc. *Res:* Solid state and materials science; crystal growth; mineral synthesis and phase equilibria; thin films; semiconductors and dielectrics. *Mailing Add:* 76 River Rd Scarborough Briarcliff Manor NY 10510-2412

**ZWIEP, DONALD N,** MECHANICAL ENGINEERING. *Current Pos:* prof mech eng & head dept, 57-88, actg provost & vpres acad affairs, 88-90, EMER PROF & DEPT HEAD, WORCESTER POLYTECH INST, 90- *Personal Data:* b Hull, Iowa, Mar 18, 24; m 48, Marcia Hubers; c 4. *Educ:* Iowa State Univ, BS, 48, MS, 51. *Hon Degrees:* DE, Worcester Polytech Inst, 65. *Honors & Awards:* Dedicated Serv Medal, Am Soc Mech Engrs, Centennial Medal; Centennial Medal, Am Soc Eng Educ. *Prof Exp:* From asst prof to assoc prof mech eng, Colo State Univ, 51-57. *Concurrent Pos:* Chief consult, Aviation Div, Forney Mfg Co, 56-57; chmn trustees, James F Lincoln Arc Welding Found, 76- *Mem:* Am Soc Mech Engrs (pres, 79-80); Am Soc Eng Educ; Am Welding Soc; Sigma Xi; Soc Mfg Engrs. *Res:* Design and mechanics. *Mailing Add:* 47 Birchwood Dr Holden MA 05120

**ZWIER, PAUL J,** MATHEMATICS. *Current Pos:* from asst prof to assoc prof, 60-74, chmn dept, 77-80, PROF MATH, CALVIN COL, 74- *Personal Data:* b Denver, Colo, Oct 24, 27; m 51; c 6. *Educ:* Calvin Col, AB, 50; Univ Mich, MA, 51; Purdue Univ, PhD(math), 60. *Prof Exp:* Instr math, Purdue Univ, 58-60. *Mem:* Math Asn Am; Am Math Soc. *Res:* Non-associative rings. *Mailing Add:* 2075 Nathan Dr SE Grand Rapids MI 49508-1578

**ZWILLING, BRUCE STEPHEN,** IMMUNOBIOLOGY. *Current Pos:* from asst prof to assoc prof, 74-88, PROF MICROBIOL, COL BIOL SCI, OHIO STATE UNIV, 88- *Personal Data:* b Brooklyn, NY, Jan 16, 43; m 67; c 2. *Educ:* Fairleigh Dickinson Univ, BS, 65; NY Univ, MS, 68; Univ Mo, PhD(microbiol), 71. *Prof Exp:* Guest worker immunol, Biol Br, Nat Cancer Inst, 72-73. *Concurrent Pos:* Chmn, Div E, Am Soc Microbiol; gov coun, Soc Leukemia Biol; dir flow cytometer, Monoclonal Antibody Facil. *Mem:* AAAS; Am Soc Microbiol; Am Asn Cancer Res; Am Asn Immunol; Sigma Xi; Soc Leukemia Biol. *Res:* Regulation of MHC Class II expression; macrophage activating interferongamma mediated second signal generation. *Mailing Add:* Dept Microbiol Ohio State Univ 484 W 12th Ave Columbus OH 43210-1292. *Fax:* 614-292-1538

**ZWILSKY, KLAUS M(AX),** METALLURGY, MATERIALS SCIENCE. *Current Pos:* PRES, WASHINGTON TECHNOL CONNECTION, 93- *Personal Data:* b Berlin, Ger, Aug 16, 32; US citizen; m 56, Roberta Allen; c Mark & Ellen. *Educ:* Mass Inst Technol, BS, 54, MS, 55, ScD, 59. *Honors & Awards:* Nat Mat Advan Award, Fedn Mat Socs, 90. *Prof Exp:* Dir metall res, New Eng Mat Lab, Inc, 59-62; sr res assoc metall, Pratt & Whitney Aircraft Div, United Aircraft Corp, 62-63; sr scientist solid state, Melpar, Inc, Westinghouse Air Brake Co, 63-64; head alloy develop br, David Taylor Res Ctr, Annapolis, Md, 64-67; phys metallurgist, AEC, Dept Energy, 67-73, chief, Mat & Radiation Effects Br, Off Fusion Energy, 73-81; exec dir, Nat Mat Adv Bd, Nat Acad Sci, 81-93. *Concurrent Pos:* Trustee, Advan Semiconductor Mat Int, 84-87, 88-89, pres, 90. *Mem:* Fel Advan Semiconductor Mat Int; Minerals, Metals & Mat Soc; Sigma Xi. *Res:* Physical and nuclear metallurgy including high temperature, composite, and powder metallurgy; nuclear materials for fission reactors and materials for fusion reactors; strategic materials; materials science, engineering, science and technology policy, technical peer review. *Mailing Add:* 11422 Dorchester Lane Rockville MD 20852. *Fax:* 301-984-6125

**ZWISLOCKI, JOZEF JOHN,** AUDITORY BIOPHYSICS, PSYCHOPHYSICS. *Current Pos:* res assoc prof audiol, Syracuse Univ, 57-62, from assoc prof to prof elec eng, 60-74, founding dir, Lab Sensory Commun, 63-74, & Inst Sensory Res, 74-84, prof neurosci, 84-88, distinguished prof neurosci, 88-92, DISTINGUISHED RES PROF, INST SENSORY RES, SYRACUSE UNIV, 92- *Personal Data:* b Lwow, Poland, Mar 19, 22; nat US; m 54, 92. *Educ:* Swiss Fed Tech Inst, EE, 44, ScD, 48. *Hon Degrees:* Dr, Adam Mickiewicz Univ, Poznan, Poland, 91. *Honors & Awards:* Sigma Xi Fac Res Award, 73; Amplifon Prize, Int Res & Study, Milan, Italy, 76; Javits Neurosci Investigators Award, 84; First Berkesy Medal, Acoust Soc Am, 85; Award of Merit, Asn Res Otolaryngol, 88; Medal Acoust Soc, Poland, 91; Medal Med Acad, Poznan, Poland, 91; Hugh Knowles Prize, 92; Carhart Mem lect, Am Auditory Soc, 92. *Prof Exp:* Res asst & head, Electroacoust Lab, Dept Otolaryngol, Univ Basel, 45-51; res fel, Psychoacoust Lab, Harvard Univ, 51-57. *Concurrent Pos:* Assoc res prof, State Univ NY Upstate Med Ctr, 61-67, res prof, 67-; mem comt hearing, bio-acoust & biomech, Nat Res Coun, 53-92, chmn, 67-68, mem exec coun, 61-68; mem rev panel commun sci, NIH, 66-70, chmn, 69-70, mem communicative disorders rev comt, 71-75; Acoust Soc Am, mem tech coun, Tech Comt Psychol & Physiol Acoust, chmn, 62 & 63, mem exec coun, 82-85, mem, long Range Planning Comt, 82-86, chmn, 83-86; chmn bd sci adv, Univ Wis Health Sci Ctr, 75-78; mem adv bd, Univ Fla Inst Advan Study Communiocative Processes, 76; mem, Comn Auditory Physiol, Int Union Physiol Sci, 82-; assoc mem, Int Comn Acoust, Int Union Pure & Appl Physics, 82. *Mem:* Nat Acad Sci; fel Acoust Soc Am; Int Soc Audiol; NY Acad Sci; Asn Res Otolaryngol; fel Am Speech & Hearing Asn; assoc mem Am Otol Soc; AAAS. *Res:* Sound transmission in middle and inner ear; psychoacoustics; mathematical analysis of auditory system; audiological diagnostic methods; acoustic instruments. *Mailing Add:* Inst Sensory Res Syracuse Univ Syracuse NY 13244-5290. *Fax:* 315-443-1184; *E-Mail:* joe_ zwislocki@isr.smr.edu

**ZWOLENIK, JAMES J,** CHEMISTRY, ADMINISTRATION. *Current Pos:* prog officer, chem dynamics & chem thermodyn progs, Chem Sect, NSF, 67-70, policy analyst, Off Policy Studies, 70-71, Spec Anal Sect, Div Sci Resources Studies, 71-74, off div dir, Div Sci Resources Studies, 74-75, staff dir & exec secy, Comt Eighth Nat Sci Bd, 75-76, spec asst, Nat Sci Bd, 76-79, head, oversight sect, Off Audit & Oversight, 79-89, ASST INSPECTOR GEN OVERSIGHT, OFF INSPECTOR GEN, NSF, 89- *Personal Data:* b Cleveland, Ohio, Dec 31, 33. *Educ:* Western Res Univ, AB, 56; Yale Univ, PhD(phys chem), 61; Univ Cambridge, PhD(phys chem), 64. *Honors &*

*Awards:* Ethics Award, Am Inst Chemists, 91. *Prof Exp:* NSF fel, Queens Col, Univ Cambridge, 60-62; res chemist, Fundamental Res Group, Chevron Res Co, 63-67. *Concurrent Pos:* Instr, Exten Div, Univ Calif, Berkeley, 65-67; collabr, Smithsonian Radiation Biol Lab, 68-70; vpres, Higher Educ Group, Washington, DC, 76-77, pres, 77-78. *Mem:* Am Chem Soc; Am Phys Soc; AAAS; Cosmos Club; Sigma Xi; fel Am Inst Chemists. *Res:* Photochemistry; kinetic spectroscopy; science policy; higher education; ethics in scholarship. *Mailing Add:* NSF 4201 Wilson Blvd Arlington VA 22230. *E-Mail:* jzwoleni@nsf.gov

**ZWOLINSKI, BRUNO JOHN,** PHYSICAL CHEMISTRY. *Current Pos:* dir, Thermodyn Res Ctr, 61-78, PROF CHEM, TEX A&M UNIV, 61- *Personal Data:* b Buffalo, NY, Nov 4, 19; m 52; c 3. *Educ:* Canisius Col, BS, 41; Purdue Univ, MS, 43; Princeton Univ, AM, 44, PhD(phys chem), 47. *Honors & Awards:* US Calorimetry Award; Crane-Patterson Award. *Prof Exp:* Instr chem eng, sci & mgt war training, Purdue Univ, 42; asst, Princeton Univ, 43-44; res scientist, Manhattan Proj, Columbia Univ, 44-45; Am Chem Soc fel, Univ Utah, 47-48, asst prof chem, 48-53; sr physicist, Stanford Res Inst, 53-57; prin res chemist & dir res projs chem & petrol res lab & lectr chem, Carnegie Inst Technol, 57-61. *Concurrent Pos:* Asst dir chem prog, NSF, 54-57; mem adv bd off critical tables, Nat Res Coun. *Mem:* Fel NY Acad Sci; fel Am Inst Chemists; fel AAAS. *Res:* Compilation of selected values of physical, thermodynamic and spectral data of chemical compounds; dynamic properties of liquids; charge or electron transfer phenomena in chemical kinetics; statistical thermodynamics. *Mailing Add:* Chem Dept Tex A&M Univ College Station TX 77840

**ZWOLINSKI, MALCOLM JOHN,** FIRE ECOLOGY, NATURAL RESOURCE MANAGEMENT. *Current Pos:* Res assoc watershed mgt, 64-65, from asst prof to assoc prof, 66-72, PROF WATERSHED MGT, UNIV ARIZ, 72-, ASSOC DIR, SCH RENEWABLE NATURAL RESOURCES, 75- *Personal Data:* b Winchester, NH, Oct 23, 37; m 59; c 2. *Educ:* Univ NH, BS, 59; Yale Univ, MF, 61; Univ Ariz, PhD(watershed mgt), 66. *Mem:* Fel AAAS; Soc Am Foresters; Soc Range Mgt. *Res:* Fire ecology; effects of fire on natural ecosystems, including vegetation, soils and water; prescribed burning and fire management; watershed hydrology; watershed management including vegetation and soil influences. *Mailing Add:* Sch Renewable Natural Resources Col Agr Univ Ariz Tucson AZ 85721-0043

**ZWOYER, EUGENE,** STRUCTURAL ENGINEERING. *Current Pos:* PRIN, EUGENE ZWOYER CONSULT ENG, 92- *Personal Data:* b Plainfield, NJ, Sept 8, 26; m 46, Dorothy Seward; c Gregory, Jeffrey & Douglas. *Educ:* Univ NMex, BS, 47; Ill Inst Technol, MS, 49; Univ Ill, PhD(eng), 53. *Honors & Awards:* Can-Am Civil Eng Amity Award, Am Soc Civil Engrs, 88. *Prof Exp:* Assoc prof civil eng, Univ NMex, 48-61, res prof civil eng & dir, Eric H Wang Civil Eng Facil, 61-71; exec dir & secy, Am Soc Civil Engrs, 72-82; pres, Am Eng Soc, 82-84; pres, T Y Lin Int, 84-89; chief operating officer, Polar Molecular Corp, 90, mgt consult to pres, 91. *Concurrent Pos:* Res assoc, Univ Ill, 51-53, consult engr, Eugene Zwoyer & Assocs, 53-72, 90-; mem, Interprof Coun Environ Design, 72-82, secy, 72 & 78; trustee, People-to-People Int, 74-86 & Small Bus Res Corp, 76-79; mem, Engr Joint Coun Int Comn, 75-79, Cert Comn, 75-79 & Finance Comt, 75-79, dir Coun, 77-79, chmn, Sub-Comt 1979 UN Conf Sci & Technol Develop, 78-80; dir, Eng Socs Comn Energy, 77-82, secy, treas & mem exec comt, 78; vpres, World Fedn Eng Orgn, 82-88. *Mem:* Fel AAAS; fel Am Soc Civil Engrs; Nat Soc Prof Engrs; Am Concrete Inst; Am Soc Eng Educ. *Res:* Ultimate strength of structures, particularly on structures to resist effects of nuclear weapons. *Mailing Add:* 6363 Christie Ave No 1326 Emeryville CA 94608. *Fax:* 510-526-6940

**ZYCH, ALLEN DALE,** ASTROPHYSICS. *Current Pos:* from asst prof to assoc prof, 70-82, PROF PHYSICS, UNIV CALIF, RIVERSIDE, 82- *Personal Data:* b Cleveland, Ohio, Apr 8, 38; m 75; c 2. *Educ:* Case Inst Technol, BS, 61, MS, 65; Case Western Res Univ, PhD(physics), 68. *Prof Exp:* Fel physics, Case Western Res Univ, 68-70. *Mem:* Am Phys Soc; Am Geophys Union; Am Astron Soc; Inst Elec & Electronics Engrs. *Res:* Experimental high energy astrophysics. *Mailing Add:* Inst Geophys-Planetary Physics Univ Calif Riverside CA 92502

**ZYGMONT, ANTHONY J,** SYSTEMS ENGINEERING. *Current Pos:* ASSOC PROF ELEC ENG SYSTS, VILLANOVA UNIV, 63- *Personal Data:* b Philadelphia, Pa, Sept 16, 37. *Educ:* Villanova Univ, BEE, 59; Drexel Univ, MSEE, 63; Univ Pa, PhD(elec eng), 71. *Prof Exp:* Jr engr commun systs, Philco Corp, 59-62; cngr, Radio Corp Am, 62-63; sr cngr radar systs, Philco Corp, 63. *Concurrent Pos:* Educ consult, Philadelphia Elec Co, 70- *Mem:* Inst Elec & Electronics Engrs; Instrument Soc Am; Am Soc Eng Educ. *Res:* Application of systems engineering to large scale problems, especially the problems of identification and optimization. *Mailing Add:* 56 Wellfleet Lane Wayne PA 19087-5848

**ZYGMUNT, WALTER A,** MICROBIOLOGY, BIOCHEMISTRY. *Current Pos:* RETIRED. *Personal Data:* b Calumet City, Ill, Mar 24, 24; m 52; c 2. *Educ:* Univ Ill, BS, 47, MS, 48, PhD(bact), 50. *Prof Exp:* Res microbiologist res labs, Merck & Co, Inc, 50-53; res microbiologist & biochemist, Mead Johnson Res Ctr, 53-75, assoc dir biol res, 75-78, assoc dir drug regulatory affairs, 78-87. *Mem:* Fel AAAS; Am Chem Soc; Am Soc Microbiol; fel Am Acad Microbiol; Soc Indust Microbiol. *Res:* Microbial chemistry; chemotherapy; amino acid antagonists; immunology; pulmonary biochemistry; metabolic diseases. *Mailing Add:* 8118 Larch Lane Evansville IN 47710

**ZYSKIND, JUDITH W,** BIOLOGY. *Current Pos:* assoc prof, 82-86, PROF DEPT BIOL, SAN DIEGO STATE UNIV, 86- *Personal Data:* b Cincinnati, Ohio, July 2, 39; m 75, Douglas W Smith; c Aviva D & Joy E. *Educ:* Univ Dayton, BS, 61; Iowa State Univ, MS, 64, PhD(biol), 68. *Prof Exp:* Fel, Dept Genetics, Iowa State Univ, 69-70, lectr, 70-72, fel, Dept Biochem, 72-74; fel, Dept Biol, Univ Calif, San Diego, 74-77, asst res biologist, 77-82. *Concurrent Pos:* Fel, NIH, 75-77; co-dir, Cert Prog Rocombinant DNA Technol, San Diego State Univ, coordr, Macromolecular Structural Analysis Resource Ctr, assoc dir, Molecular Biol Inst, dir, Microchem Core Facil; prin investr, NSF, 83-98; co-prin investr, NIH, 91-98. *Mem:* Am Soc Biochem & Molecular Biol; Am Soc Microbiol; AAAS; Asn Women Sci; Sigma Xi. *Res:* Biology; mechanisms coordinating rate of initiation of DNA replication with growth rate; control of expression of DNA initiator protein; antisense RNA delivery to analyze global control and identify essential genes. *Mailing Add:* Dept Biol San Diego State Univ San Diego CA 92182-0057. *Fax:* 619-594-5676; *E-Mail:* jzyskind@sunstroke.sdsu.edu

**ZYTNER, RICHARD G,** REMEDIATION OF CONTAMINATED SOIL *Current Pos:* asst prof, 91-97, ASSOC PROF ENVIRON ENG, UNIV GUELPH, 97- *Personal Data:* b Leamington, Ont, Sept 18, 58; m 88, Linda Brefka. *Educ:* Univ Windsor, Ont, BASc, 82, MASc, 84, PhD(civil eng), 88. *Prof Exp:* Res asst, Univ Windsor, 82-84 & 85-88; res assoc, Univ Stuttgart, Ger, 84-85; indust res fel, Clayton Environ Consult, 88-90, proj mgr, 90-91. *Concurrent Pos:* Lectr, Dept Civil Eng, Univ Windsor, 90. *Mem:* Water Environ Fedn; Int Water Qual Asn; Can Soc Civil Engrs. *Res:* Investigation into various soil remediation technology, including soil vapour extraction; For volatile and semivolatile chemicals, develop a better understanding of chemical behavior in soil. *Mailing Add:* Univ Guelph Sch Eng Guelph ON N1G 2W1 Can. *Fax:* 519-836-0227; *E-Mail:* zytner@net2.eos.uoguelph.ca